2025
LexisNexis®
Corporate Affiliations™

Content Operations:
Director-News & Business Content Operations & Metadata: Tammy Bair
Manager-Corporate Affiliations & Entity Management: Elizabeth A. Powers
Lead Content Analysts: Eric Eelman, Kevin Gaven

Production:
Senior Production Specialist: Joseph C. Stewart

Reed Elsevier Philippines-Corporate Affiliations Iloilo Team:
Operations Manager: Timothy J. Vilches
Operations Supervisor: Kristel Faye B. De la Cruz
Product Lead: Raquel G. Gajardo

2025

LexisNexis®
Corporate Affiliations™
International Public & Private Companies

Volume VIII
P-Z

QUESTIONS ABOUT THIS PUBLICATION?

For CONTENT questions concerning this publication, please call:

Content Operations Department at 800-340-3244
FAX 908-790-5405

For CUSTOMER SERVICE ASSISTANCE concerning shipments, billing or other matters, please call:
Customer Service at 800-340-3244, press 3

For SALES ASSISTANCE, please call:
The Sales Department at 800-340-3244, press 2

No part of this publication may be reproduced or transmitted in any form or by any means sorted in any information storage and retrieval system without prior written permission of LexisNexis, Content Operations, 9443 Springboro Pike, Miamisburg, OH 45342.

Library of Congress Catalog Card Number: 67-22770

International Public & Private Companies Volume 8, ISBN: 979-8-3417-0466-4

Corporate Affiliations 8-Volume Library, ISBN: 979-8-3417-0458-9

©2025 LexisNexis Group.

All Rights Reserved

LexisNexis, the knowledge burst logo and Corporate Affiliations are trademarks of Reed Elsevier Properties Inc., used under license.

The LexisNexis Group has used its best efforts in collecting and preparing material for inclusion in Corporate Affiliations: International Public & Private Companies™ but does not assume, and hereby disclaims, any liability to any person for any loss or damage caused by errors or omissions in Corporate Affiliations: International Public & Private Companies whether such errors or omissions result from negligence, accident or any other cause.

Corporate Affiliations

Content Operations
9443 Springboro Pike
Miamisburg, OH 45342

www.lexisnexis.com

ISBN 979-8-3417-0466-4

9 798341 704664

CONTENTS

Preface vii
How To Use *Corporate Affiliations*™ ix
Abbreviations xv
Country Abbreviations xvi
Company Designations xvii
Stock Market Abbreviations xviii
Exchange Rates xx
New Listings xxiii
Mergers and Acquisitions xxxi
International Public and Private Companies 5681

CONTENTS

Preface	vii
How To Use Corporate Affiliations™	xi
Abbreviations	xv
Country Abbreviations	xvi
Company Designations	xvii
Stock Market Abbreviations	xviii
Exchange Rates	xx
New Listings	xxiii
Mergers and Acquisitions	xxxi
International Public and Private Companies	1885

PREFACE

CORPORATE AFFILIATIONS

Corporate Affiliations is a logically organized business reference tool that covers major public and private businesses in the United States and throughout the world. The set consists of eight volumes:

Volume I   Master Index I
Volume II   Master Index II
Volume III   U.S. Public Companies
Volume IV   U.S. Private Companies I
Volume V   U.S. Private Companies II
Volume VI   International Public & Private Companies I
Volume VII   International Public & Private Companies II
Volume VIII   International Public & Private Companies III

The principle of organization for the set is geographical (by parent company) and hierarchical (by company reportage). Subsidiaries of a parent company, no matter where they are located, will be found in the same volume as the ultimate parent.

Please note that guidelines on the organization of the entire set for this edition can be found in the *Master Index* Volume I.

Entry criteria for the set are flexible. Generally speaking, non-U.S. based companies must demonstrate revenue in excess of $10 million. U.S. based companies must demonstrate revenues in excess of $10 million, substantial assets, a work force in excess of 300 employees, or be traded on a major stock exchange.

THE *INTERNATIONAL PUBLIC AND PRIVATE COMPANIES* VOLUME

Corporate Affiliations: International Public and Private Companies contains listings for companies with non-U.S. located headquarters or holding companies. Subsidiaries for these parent companies are included, whether or not they are located in the United States. Also included are outside service firms attached to the parent companies. These are firms that perform specialized services such as accounting, legal, pension management, etc.

Content and Coverage in Corporate Affiliations-International Public and Private Companies

Listing statistics for this edition of International are as follows:

Ultimate parent companies..................................58,644
U.S. located sub companies.............................99,843
Non-U.S. located sub companies....................144,707
Total entry units listed...................................303,194

Outside service firms: 58,637

Companies are arranged alphabetically by the name of the parent company. Subsidiary companies follow the parent in order of reporting hierarchy. The bold number in parentheses shows the level of corporate reportage. Each listing can contain an extensive number of informational items. Please refer to the helpful 'How to Use' section for a guide to referencing methods and comprehensive listing samples.

The *International Public and Private Companies* volume also contains several useful features in the frontmatter including 'New Listings' for this edition, 'Mergers and Acquisitions' and the 'Currency Exchange' table.

COMPILATION

Corporate Affiliations is compiled and updated from information supplied by the companies themselves, business publications, internet research and annual reports.

RELATED SERVICES

For information on the corporateaffiliations.com web site, please call (800) 340-3244.

Mailing lists compiled from information contained in *Corporate Affiliations* may be ordered from:
R. Michael Patterson, Inside Sales Representative
DM2 Decision Maker
2000 Clearwater Drive, Oak Brook, IL
Tel: (630) 288-8348
E-mail: robert.patterson@dm2decisionmaker.com

Electronic database tapes of the directory in raw data format are available for licensing. For electronic database tapes or alliance opportunities, please contact:
LexisNexis, Corporate Affiliations
9443 Springboro Pike, Miamisburg, OH 45342
Tel: (800) 285-3947
E-mail: information@lexisnexis.com

Companies who wish to add or correct their listings can send information to:
LexisNexis, Corporate Affiliations Content Operations
9443 Springboro Pike
Miamisburg, OH 45342
Tel: (937) 865-6800

In addition to keeping the information in our directories as up to date as possible, we are constantly trying to improve their design, and add useful new features. Any comments or suggestions in this regard can be directed to the Managers of Operations at the above address.

HOW TO USE INTERNATIONAL PUBLIC AND PRIVATE COMPANIES

Corporate Affiliations, International Public and Private Companies, contains a vast amount of useful information about firms whose ultimate parent companies are located outside the United States. Included in *International Public and Private Companies* are the parent companies and their subsidiaries, no matter where they are located.

This user guide is divided into three parts.

Part A, 'How to Locate a Company' gives referencing instructions and samples of indexes. It demonstrates many useful methods for getting the information you need from this volume and from the *Corporate Affiliations* set at large.

Part B, 'Sample Entries' shows the various data elements and listing style of companies in *Corporate Affiliations*.

Part C, 'Understanding Levels of Reportage' demonstrates how company reportage structures are simply and clearly presented throughout *Corporate Affiliations*.

PART A: HOW TO LOCATE A COMPANY

1. If you know the name of the company, but do not know its nationality or ownership status:

Look in the 'Master Index of Company Names' in volume I. This index will direct you to the correct volume of the set (i.e. Public, Private or International) and the correct page listing therein.

> **KOMAG, INCORPORATED**; *U.S. Public*, pg. 1023
> KOMAG MATERIAL TECHNOLOGY INC.—See
>   Komag, Incorporated; *U.S. Public*, pg. 1023
> KOMAGANE ELECTRONICS, INC.—See Kenwood
>   Corporation; *Int'l*, pg. 638

2. If you know the company is a non-U.S. held parent company:

You can turn directly to the company listings in volumes VI, VII and VIII, all of which are alphabetized by the name of the parent company.

3. **If you cannot find the company's name in the master index:**

   It may mean that the company has been acquired or changed its name. To confirm this, try looking in the 'Mergers and Acquisitions' section at the front of this volume.

   ### Sample of Mergers Section

   Distillers Corporation S.A.–acquired & absorbed by Rothmans UK Holdings Limited
   Durr Beteiligungs-AG—name changed to Durr AG
   Elosua S.A.—ceased operations (no longer in business)
   Grand Metropolitan Plc–merged with Guinness Plc to form Diageo Plc

4. **To locate companies in a given line of business:**

   Use the 'N.A.I.C.S. (North American Industrial Classification System) Master Index' in volume II. This index interfiles data from all six volumes of *Corporate Affiliations*, arranging companies by particular products and services according to their primary N.A.I.C.S. code. The index is preceded by two helpful compendia: one sorts the codes alphabetically by the name of the product or service, the other numerically by the code itself.

   ### Sample of Alpha Compendium of N.A.I.C.S. Codes

Description	N.A.I.C.S.
Administration of Conservation Programs	924120
Administration of Education Programs	923110

   ### Sample of Numeric Compendium of N.A.I.C.S. Codes

Code	Description
111150	Corn Farming
111160	Rice Farming
111191	Oilseed and Grain Combination Farming

Both parent and sub companies are covered in this index; parent companies are printed in bold type, sub companies in regular typeface, followed by the name of its ultimate parent. A sample of the N.A.I.C.S. Master Index is shown here:

337211 — WOOD OFFICE FURNITURE MANUFACTURING

ABCO—Jami, Inc.; *Int'l*, pg. 586
ANDERSON HICKEY, INC.—Haworth, Inc.; *U.S. Public*, pg. 516
BELVEDERE COMPANY—Smith Investment Company; *Int'l*, pg. 1019
BRAYTON INTERNATIONAL INC.—Steelcase Inc.; *U.S. Public*, pg. 1048
BRODART COMPANY; *U.S. Private*, pg. 172
COMMUNITY—Jasper Seating Co., Inc.; *U.S. Private*, pg. 589
CRAMER INC.; *U.S. Public*, pg. 288
EAC CORPORATION; *Int'l*, pg. 357

PART B: BASIC COMPONENTS OF AN INTERNATIONAL COMPANY LISTING

Following is an example of a typical parent company listing with tags to some of its basic components.

SULLIVAN GRAPHICS LTD. ——————— **Company Name**
52 Upper Fitzwilliam Road ——————— **Company Address**
Dublin 12, Ireland
Tel.: (353) 568 332 ——————————— **Telecommunications Data**
Web Site: www.sulgrap.com
Year Founded: 1967
SULLI—(LSE) ——————————————— **Ticker Symbol & Stock Exchange**
Rev.: $9,325,224,000 ——————————— **Financial Information**
Assets: $2,700,000,000
Liabilities: $2,038,000,000
Net Worth: $662,000,000
Emp.: 10,950 ——————————————— **No. of Employees, Including Sub-entries**
Fiscal Year End: 12/31/24
Designs, Manufactures & Markets
Electronic Design Automation (EDA)
Software & Systems for the PC &
Systems Design Markets
N.A.I.C.S.: 334119 ——————————— **North American Industry Classification System Code**
Andrew Sullivan *(Pres)*

Following each parent company listing are the entries for each of that company's divisions, subsidiaries, affiliates, joint ventures, units, etc. Though companies vary widely in their usage of these terms, some of the more common company designations can be defined as follows:

Affiliate A chartered business owned by the company at less than 50%.

Division An internal unit of a company, not incorporated.

Joint Venture A business in which two or more companies share responsibility and ownership.

Subsidiary A chartered business owned by the company at 50% or more.

PART C: UNDERSTANDING LEVELS OF REPORTAGE

Each sub-unit of the company will have a number in parentheses to the right of the company name. This number represents the level of reportage for that particular company. Any company with a level (1) reports directly to the parent company. Level (2) companies report to the level (1) company immediately above them. Level (3) companies report to the level (2) company immediately above them, etc.

Subsidiaries:

Ericsson Systems, Inc. ───────── (1) ───────── **Reports to the Parent Company (Sullivan**
2 Wellington Road Killarney   **Graphics, Ltd. from previous example)**
County Kerry, Ireland
Tel.: (353) 718 348
Sales Range: $25-49.9 Million
Computer Peripheral Equipment Mfr
N.A.I.C.S.: 334119 ──────────────── **North American Industry Classification System Code**
Thomas J. McSweeney (*Pres*)

Subsidiaries:

Kerrigan Co., Inc. ───────── (2) ───────── **Reports Direct to Level 1 Company Above**
8 Swords Road   **(Ericsson Systems, Inc.)**
Dublin 17, Ireland ───────── (100%) ───── **Percentage of Ownership**
Tel.: (353) 611 457
KC—(ISE)
Emp.: 850
Computer Printer Mfr
N.A.I.C.S.: 334119

U.S. Branch:

Kerrigan Co., Inc. ───────── (3) ───────── **Reports Direct to Level 2 Company**
21 Reading Ave   **Above (Kerrigan Co., Inc.)**
Memphis, TN 38101
Tel.: (901) 324-8746   (100%)
Computer Printer Mfr
N.A.I.C.S.: 334119
Susan Havens (*CEO*)

Wellsley Technologies, Inc. ─────── (2) ─────── **Reports Direct to Level 1 Company**
Crown Hill Clonskeagh   **Above (Ericsson Systems, Inc.)**
Dublin 4, Ireland
Tel.: (353) 278 743   (90%)
Computer Peripheral Equipment Mfr
N.A.I.C.S.: 334119

Tennant & McDaniel, Inc. ─────── (1) ─────── **Reports Back to Parent Company (Sullivan**
Greenhills Road Tallaght   **Graphics, Ltd.)**
Dublin 24, Ireland
Tel.: (353) 268 324   (100%)
Emp: 1,200
Computer Peripheral Equipment Mfr
N.A.I.C.S.: 334119

Non-U.S. Subsidiary:

Padova Systems, Inc. ─────── (1) ─────── **Subsidiary Not in Ireland, and Not in the**
Via Laurentina, 449   **U.S. Reports to the Parent Company**
20097 Milan, Italy   **(Sullivan Graphics, Ltd.)**
Tel.: (39) 6 305291
Computer Printer Mfr
N.A.I.C.S.: 334119
Anthony Macaluso *(Pres)*

xiv

ABBREVIATIONS

Acct	Account	Matl	Material
Acctg	Accounting	Matls	Materials
Accts	Accounts	Mdse	Merchandise
Acq	Acquisition(s)	Mdsg	Merchandising
Admin	Administration	Mfg	Manufacturing
Admin	Administrative	Mfr	Manufacturer
Adv	Advertising	Mgmt	Management
Assoc	Associate	Mgr	Manager
Asst	Assistant	Mktg	Marketing
Brdcst	Broadcast	Mng	Managing
Bus	Business	Natl	National
CEO	Chief Executive Officer	Ops	Operations
CFO	Chief Financial Officer	Org	Organization
Chm	Chairman of the Board	Pkg	Packaging
CIO	Chief Information Officer	Plng	Planning
CMO	Chief Marketing Officer	Pres	President
Comm	Communication(s)	Prof	Professional
Comml	Commercial	Promo	Promotion
COO	Chief Operating Officer	Promos	Promotions
Coord	Coordinator	Pub	Public
Corp	Corporate/Corporation	Pub Rel	Public Relations
CTO	Chief Technology Officer	Publ	Publishing
Dept	Department	Publr	Publisher
Dev	Development	Pur	Purchasing
Dir	Director	R&D	Research & Development
Distr	Distribution	Reg	Regional
Div	Division	Rep	Representative
DP	Data Processing	Res	Research
Engr	Engineer	Sec	Secretary
Engrg	Engineering	Sls	Sales
Environ	Environmental	Sr	Senior
Exec	Executive	Supvr	Supervisor
Fin	Finance/Financial	Svc	Service
Gen	General	Svcs	Services
Govt	Government	Sys	Systems
Grp	Group	Tech	Technology
HR	Human Resources	Tech	Technical
Indus	Industry/Industrial	Telecom	Telecommunication(s)
Info	Information	Treas	Treasurer
Intl	International	Trng	Training
IR	Investor Relations	Vice Chm	Vice Chairman
IT	Information Technology	VP	Vice President
Jr	Junior		

xv

COUNTRY ABBREVIATIONS

AF	Afghanistan	DK	Denmark	KG	Kyrgyzstan	KN	Saint Kitts & Nevis
Al	Albania	DJ	Djibouti	La	Laos	LC	Saint Lucia
DG	Algeria	DM	Dominica	LV	Latvia	VC	Saint Vincent &
AD	Andorra	DO	Dominican Republic	LB	Lebanon		Grenadines
AO	Angola	EC	Ecuador	LS	Lesotho	WS	Samoa
AI	Anguilla	EG	Egypt	LR	Liberia	SA	Saudi Arabia
AG	Antigua & Barbuda	SV	El Salvador	LY	Libya	SN	Senegal
Ar	Argentina	GQ	Equatorial Guinea	LI	Liechtenstein	YU	Serbia &
AM	Armenia	ER	Eritrea	LT	Lithuania		Montenegro
AW	Aruba	EE	Estonia	LU	Luxembourg	Sc	Seychelles
AU	Australia	ET	Ethiopia	Mo	Macau	SL	Sierra Leone
AT	Austria	FO	Faroe Islands	MK	Macedonia	SG	Singapore
Az	Azerbaijan	FJ	Fiji	MG	Madagascar	Sk	Slovakia
BS	Bahamas	FI	Finland	MW	Malawi	SI	Slovenia
BH	Bahrain	FR	France	MY	Malaysia	SB	Solomon Islands
BD	Bangladesh	GF	French Guiana	MV	Maldives	SO	Somalia
BB	Barbados	PF	French Polynesia	ML	Mali	ZA	South Africa
BY	Belarus	Ga	Gabon	Mt	Malta	ES	Spain
BE	Belgium	GM	Gambia	MQ	Martinique	LK	Sri Lanka
BZ	Belize	GE	Georgia	MR	Mauritania	Sd	Sudan
BJ	Benin	De	Germany	MU	Mauritius	SR	Suriname
BM	Bermuda	GH	Ghana	MX	Mexico	SZ	Swaziland
BT	Bhutan	GI	Gibraltar	Md	Moldova	SE	Sweden
BO	Bolivia	GR	Greece	MC	Monaco	CH	Switzerland
BA	Bosnia & Herzegovina	GL	Greenland	Mn	Mongolia	SY	Syria
BW	Botswana	GD	Grenada	Ms	Montserrat	TW	Taiwan
BR	Brazil	GP	Guadeloupe	Ma	Morocco	TJ	Tajikistan
BN	Brunei Darussalam	GT	Guatemala	MZ	Mozambique	TZ	Tanzania
BG	Bulgaria	Gu	Guiana	MM	Myanmar	TH	Thailand
BF	Burkina Faso	GN	Guinea	NA	Namibia	TG	Togo
BI	Burundi	GW	Guinea-Bissau	NP	Nepal	TO	Tonga
KH	Cambodia	GY	Guyana	NL	Netherlands	TT	Trinidad & Tobago
CM	Cameroon	HT	Haiti	AN	Netherlands Antilles	Tn	Tunisia
Ca	Canada	HN	Honduras	Nc	New Caledonia	TR	Turkey
CV	Cape Verde	HK	Hong Kong	NZ	New Zealand	TM	Turkmenistan
Ky	Cayman Islands	HU	Hungary	NI	Nicaragua	TC	Turks & Caicos
CF	Central African Republic	IS	Iceland	Ne	Niger		Islands
		In	India	NG	Nigeria	TV	Tuvalu
TD	Chad	Id	Indonesia	NO	Norway	UG	Uganda
CL	Chile	IR	Iran	OM	Oman	UA	Ukraine
CN	China	IQ	Iraq	PK	Pakistan	AE	United Arab
Co	Colombia	IE	Ireland	Pa	Panama		Emirates
KM	Comoros	Il	Israel	PG	Papua New Guinea	UK	United Kingdom
CD	Congo, Democratic Republic of	IT	Italy	PY	Paraguay	UY	Uruguay
		JM	Jamaica	PE	Peru	UZ	Uzbekistan
CG	Congo, Republic of	JP	Japan	PH	Philippines	VU	Vanuatu
CK	Cook Islands	JO	Jordan	PL	Poland	VE	Venezuela
CR	Costa Rica	KZ	Kazakhstan	PT	Portugal	VN	Vietnam
CI	Cote d'Ivoire	KE	Kenya	QA	Qatar	VG	Virgin Islands
HR	Croatia	KI	Kiribati	RE	Reunion		(British)
CU	Cuba	KN	Korea (North)	RO	Romania	YE	Yemen
CY	Cyprus	Ks	Korea (South)	RU	Russia	ZM	Zambia
CZ	Czech Republic	KW	Kuwait	RW	Rwanda	ZW	Zimbabwe

COMPANY DESIGNATIONS

The following designations indicate the forms of business enterprise in various countries; these forms usually represent the organizations for large enterprises.

AB	Aktiebolag	Finland, Sweden
AG	Aktiengesellschaft	Austria, Germany, Switzerland, Liechtenstein
A/S	Aksjeselskap	Norway
	Aktieselskab	Denmark
B.V.	Besloten Vennootschap	Holland
C.V.	Commanditaire Vennootschap	Holland
Cie.	Compagnie	France, Luxembourg
Co.	Company	United States, France, South Africa, Luxembourg
Ets.	Etablissement(s)	France, Luxembourg
GmbH	Gesellschaft mit beschrankter Haftung	Austria, Germany, Switzerland
I/S	Interessantelskab	Denmark, Norway
KG	Kommanditgesellschaft	Austria, Germany, Switzerland
KK	Kabushiki Kaisha	Japan
K/S	Kommanditselskab	Denmark
Lda.	Limitada	Portugal
Ltd.	Limited	United Kingdom, United States, South Africa
Ltda.	Limitada	Brazil, Portugal
Ltee.	Limitee	Canada
Mij.	Maatschappij	Holland
N.V.	Naamloze Vennootschap	Belgium, Holland
OHG	Offene Handelsgesellschaft	Austria
Oy	Osakeyhtiot	Finland
PLC	Public Limited Company	United Kingdom
P.T.	Perusahaan Terbatas	Indonesia
Pte.	Private	Singapore
Pty.	Proprietary	Australia, South Africa
Pvt.	Private	India, Rhodesia
S.A.	Societe Anonyme	Belgium, France, Luxembourg, Switzerland
Sociedad	Anonima	Spain, Latin America
S.A.C.I.	Sociedad Anonima Comercial e Industrial	Latin America
S.A. de C.V.	Sociedad Anonima de Capital Variable	Mexico
S.A.E.	Sociedad Anonima Espanola	Spain
S.A.I.C.	Sociedad Anonima Industrial y Comercial	Latin America
S.A.R.L.	Sociedad Anonima de Responsabilidade Limitada	Brazil
	Sociedade a Responsabilitie Limitee	France, Luxembourg
S.A.S.	Societa in Accomandita Semplice	Italy
S.C.	Societe en Commandite	France
S.p.A.	Societa per Azioni	Italy
S.P.R.L.	Societe de Personnes a Responsabilitie Limitee	Belgium
S.R.L.	Societa a Responsabilita Limitata	Italy
Sdn. Bhd.	Sendirian Berhad	Malaysia
Ste.	Societe	France, Switzerland
Ste. Cve.	Societe Cooperative	Belgium
V.o.F.	Vennootschap onder firma	Holland

xvii

STOCK MARKET ABBREVIATIONS

ABU	Abu Dhabi Securities Exchange
AIM	AIM Market of the London Stock Exchange
AMM	Amman Stock Exchange
ARM	Armenian NASDAQ OMX Armenia
ASX	Australian Stock Exchange
ATH	Athens Stock Exchange
BAH	Bahrain Bourse
BAK	Baku Stock Exchange
BAN	Bangalore Stock Exchange
BANJ	Banja Luka Stock Exchange
BAR	Barcelona Stock Exchange
BARB	Barbados Stock Exchange
BEL	Belgrade Stock Exchange
BER	Borse Berlin-Bremen Stock Exchange
BERM	Bermuda Stock Exchange
BERN	Bern Stock Exchange
BESA	Bond Exchange of South Africa
BEY	Beirut Stock Exchange
BHU	Royal Securities Exchange of Bhutan
BIL	Bilbao Stock Exchange
BOA	BOAG Borsen (Merger of Hannover & Hamburg Exchanges)
BOL	Bolsa de Valores de Bolivia
BOM	Bombay (Mumbai) Stock Exchange
BOT	Botswana Stock Exchange
BRA	Bratislava Stock Exchange
BRAZ	Brazil Stock Exchange (BM&F Bovespa)
BRVM	Bourse Regionale des Valeurs Mobilieres
BUC	Bucharest Stock Exchange
BUD	Budapest Stock Exchange
BUE	Buenos Aires Stock Exchange (Mercado de Valores Buenos Aires)
BUL	Bulgarian Stock Exchange
BVMAC	Securities Exchange of Central Africa
BVT	Bourse de Tunis
BX	Boston NASDAQ OMX BXSM
CAR	Caracas Stock Exchange
CAS	Casablanca Stock Exchange
CAT	Singapore Catalist
CAY	Cayman Islands Stock Exchange
CHA	Channel Islands Stock Exchange
CHI	Chicago Stock Exchange
CHIN	ChiNext (Chinese Exchange for Small & High-Tech Enterprises)
CHT	Chittagong Stock Exchange
CNSX	Canadian National Stock Exchange
COL	Colombo Stock Exchange
COLO	Colombia Bolsa de Valores
COR	Cordoba Stock Exchange
CSE	Copenhagen Stock Exchange
CYP	Cyprus Stock Exchange
DAR	Dar es Salaam Stock Exchange
DES	Delhi Stock Exchange
DEU	Deutsche Borse (Frankfurt Stock Exchange)
DFM	Dubai Financial Market
DHA	Dhaka Stock Exchange
DUS	Dusseldorf Stock Exchange
ECA	Eastern Caribbean Securities Exchange
EGX	Egyptian Exchange
EMI	Securities & Commodities Authority (d/b/a Emirates Securities Market)
EUR	Euronext
FKA	Fukuoka Stock Exchange
GEOR	Georgian Stock Exchange
GHA	Ghana Stock Exchange
GUA	Guayaquil Stock Exchange
HEL	Helsinki Stock Exchange
HKG	Hong Kong Stock Exchange
HNX	Hanoi Stock Exchange
HOSE	Ho Chi Minh Stock Exchange (Vietnam)
HYD	Hyderabad Stock Exchange
ICE	Iceland Stock Exchange
INDO	Indonesia Stock Exchange
IRAQ	Iraq Stock Exchange
ISDX	ICAP Securities & Derivatives Exchange Limited (formerly PLUS)
ISE	Irish Stock Exchange
ISL	Islamabad Stock Exchange
IST	Istanbul Stock Exchange
ISX	Inter-Connected Stock Exchange of India
ITA	Italian Stock Exchange
JAI	Jaipur Stock Exchange
JAM	Jamaica Stock Exchange
JAS	OSE JASDAQ
JSE	Johannesburg Stock Exchange
KAR	Karachi Stock Exchange
KAZ	Kazakhstan Stock Exchange
KHAR	Khartoum Stock Exchange
KLS	Bursa Malaysia (Formerly Kuala Lumpur Stock Exchange)
KOL	Kolkata Stock Exchange
KRS	Korea Exchange
KUW	Kuwait Stock Exchange
LAH	Lahore Stock Exchange
LIM	Lima Bolsa de Valores
LJU	Ljubljana Stock Exchange
LSE	London Stock Exchange
LUS	Lusaka Stock Exchange
LUX	Luxembourg Stock Exchange
MAC	Macedonian Stock Exchange
MAD	Madrid Stock Exchange
MAL	Malta Stock Exchange
MALA	Malawi Stock Exchange
MAU	Stock Exchange of Mauritius
MDS	Madras Stock Exchange
MEX	Bolsa Mexicana de Valores

Stock Market Abbreviations

MIC	MICEX Moscow Interbank Currency Exchange	PUN	Pune Stock Exchange (India)
MOLD	Moldova Stock Exchange	QE	Qatar Stock Exchange
MON	Montreal Stock Exchange	RIO	Rio de Janeiro, Bolsa de Valores
MONG	Mongolian Stock Exchange	RSE	Riga Stock Exchange
MUN	Munich Stock Exchange	RUS	Russian Trading System
MUS	Muscat Stock Exchange	SAP	Sapporo Stock Exchange
NAI	Nairobi Stock Exchange	SARE	Sarejevo Stock Exchange
NAM	Namibian Stock Exchange	SAU	Saudi Stock Exchange
NASDAQ	National Association of Securities Dealers, Inc.	SES	Singapore Stock Exchange
NASDAQDBAI	NASDAQ Dubai	SGO	Santiago Stock Exchange
NEP	Nepal Stock Exchange Ltd	SHG	Shanghai Stock Exchange
NGO	Nagoya Stock Exchange	SPSE	South Pacific Stock Exchange
NIGE	Nigerian Stock Exchange	SSE	Shenzhen Stock Exchange
NSE	National Stock Exchange of India	SSX	Swaziland Stock Exchange
NSXA	National Stock Exchange of Australia	STU	Stuttgart Stock Exchange (Baden)
NYSA	New York Stock Exchange Arca Options Trading System	SWX	Swiss Stock Exchange
		TAE	Tel-Aviv Stock Exchange
		TAI	Taiwan Stock Exchange
NYSE	New York Stock Exchange	TAL	Tallinn Stock Exchange
NYSE AMERICAN	NYSE American	TFE	Tokyo Financial Exchange (Futures)
NZE	New Zealand Exchange Limited	THA	Stock Exchange of Thailand
OMX	Stockholm/Nordic Stock Exchange	THE	Tehran Stock Exchange
OSE	Osaka Stock Exchange	TKS	Tokyo Stock Exchange
OSL	Oslo Stock Exchange	TOSH	Tashkent Republican Stock Exchange
OTC	Over-the-Counter Pink Sheets	TRI	Trinidad & Tobago Stock Exchange
OTCB	Over-the-Counter Bulletin Board	TSX	Toronto Stock Exchange
OTCI	Over-the-Counter Exchange of India	TSXV	Toronto Stock Venture Exchange
PAL	Palestine Securities Exchange	UGAN	Uganda Securities Exchange
PAN	Bolsa de Valores de Panama	UKR	Ukranian Stock Exchange
PET	Saint Petersburg Stock Exchange	VAL	Bolsa de Valencia
PHI	Philippine Stock Exchange	VIE	Wiener Borse (Vienna Stock Exchange)
PHLX	Philadelphia - NASDAQ OMX PHLX	VLA	Vladivostok Stock Exchange
POM	Port Moresby Stock Exchange Limited (Papua New Guinea)	VSE	Vilnius Stock Exchange
		WAR	Warsaw Stock Exchange
		ZAG	Zagreb Stock Exchange
PRA	Prague Stock Exchange	ZIM	Zimbabwe Stock Exchange

EXCHANGE RATES

Country	Currency	Rate
Afghanistan	Afghani	0.01927
Albania	Lek	0.00948
Algeria	Dinar	0.01273
Andorra	Euro	1.34617
Angola	Kwanza	0.01041
Antigua & Barbuda	Dollar	0.36807
Argentina	Peso	0.20132
Armenia	Dram	0.00248
Aruba	Guilder	0.55562
Australia	Dollar	1.04210
Austria	Euro	1.34617
Azerbaijan	Manat	1.27307
Bahamas	Dollar	0.99257
Bahrain	Dinar	2.59161
Bangladesh	Taka	0.01238
Barbados	Dollar	0.49196
Belarus	Ruble	0.00012
Belgium	Euro	1.34617
Belize	Dollar	0.49317
Benin	Franc	0.00205
Bermuda	Dollar	1
Bhutan	Ngultrum	0.01858
Bolivia	Boliviano	0.01400
Bosnia & Herzegovina	Marka	0.68820
Botswana	Pula	0.12310
Brazil	Real	0.49189
Brunei Darussalam	Dollar	0.80244
Bulgaria	Lev	0.68350
Burkina Faso	Franc	0.00205
Burundi	Franc	0.00065
Cambodia	Riel	0.00025
Cameroon	CFA Franc BEAC	0.00205
Canada	Dollar	0.99402
Cape Verde	Escudo	0.01194
Caribbean Netherlands	Dollar	1
Cayman Islands	Dollar	1.19325
Central African Republic	Franc	0.00205
Chad	Franc	0.00205
Chile	Peso	0.00212
China	Yuan Renminbi	0.15885
China (Hong Kong)	Dollar	0.12895
China (Macau)	Pataca	0.12319
Colombia	Peso	0.00056
Comoros	Franc	0.00273
Congo, Democratic Republic of	Franc	0.00105
Congo, Republic of	Franc	0.00205
Cook Islands	Dollar	0.83700
Costa Rica	Colon	0.00195
Cote d'Ivoire	Franc	0.00205
Croatia	Kuna	0.17771
Cuba	Peso	0.04320
Curacao	Guilder	0.54945
Cyprus	Euro	1.34617
Czech Republic	Koruna	0.05257
Denmark	Krone	0.18036
Djibouti	Franc	0.00553
Dominica	Dollar	0.36807
Dominican Republic	Peso	0.02446
East Timor	Dollar	1
Ecuador	Dollar	1
Egypt	Pound	0.14854
El Salvador	Dollar	1
Equatorial Guinea	Franc	0.00205
Eritrea	Nakfa	0.06623
Estonia	Euro	1.34617
Ethiopia	Birr	0.05412
Falkland Islands	Pound	1.58003
Faroe Islands	Krone	0.18036
Fiji	Dollar	0.56329
Finland	Euro	1.34617
France	Euro	1.34617
French Guiana	Euro	1.34617
Gabon	Franc	0.00205
Gambia	Dalasi	0.02892
Georgia	Lari	0.60234
Germany	Euro	1.34617
Ghana	Cedi	0.52035
Gibraltar	Pound	1.58033
Greece	Euro	1.34617
Greenland	Krone	0.18036
Grenada	Dollar	0.36807
Guadeloupe	Euro	1.34617
Guatemala	Quetzal	0.12538
Guernsey	Pound	1.57929
Guinea	Franc	0.00014
Guinea-Bissau	Franc	0.00205
Guyana	Dollar	0.00500
Haiti	Gourde	0.02337
Honduras	Lempira	0.04939
Hungary	Forint	0.00452
Iceland	Krona	0.00782
India	Rupee	0.01854
Indonesia	Rupiah	0.00010
Iran	Rial	0.00008
Iraq	Dinar	0.00084
Ireland	Euro	1.34617
Isle of Man	Pound	1.57929
Israel	New Shekel	0.26868
Italy	Euro	1.34617
Jamaica	Dollar	0.01061
Japan	Yen	0.01100
Jersey	Pound	1.57929
Jordan	Dinar	1.40489
Kazakhstan	Tenge	0.00655
Kenya	Shilling	0.01123
Kiribati	Dollar	0.91406
Korea (North)	North Korean Won	0.00741
Korea (South)	South Korean Won	0.00093
Kuwait	Dinar	3.54359
Kyrgyzstan	Som	0.02096
Laos	Kip	0.00012
Latvia	Lat	1.89941
Lebanon	Pound	0.00065
Lesotho	Loti	0.10957
Liberia	Dollar	0.01342
Libya	Dinar	0.78401
Liechtenstein	Swiss Franc	1.07932
Lithuania	Litas	0.38428
Luxembourg	Euro	1.34617

Exchange Rates

Country	Currency	Rate
Macedonia	Denar	0.02108
Madagascar	Ariary	0.00045
Malawi	Kwacha	0.00284
Malaysia	Ringgit	0.32792
Maldives	Rufiyaa	0.06398
Mali	Franc	0.00205
Malta	Euro	1.34617
Marshall Islands	Dollar	1
Martinique	Euro	1.34617
Mauritania	Ouguiya	0.00327
Mauritius	Rupee	0.03148
Mexico	Peso	0.07868
Micronesia	Dollar	1
Moldolva	Leu	0.08084
Monaco	Euro	1.34617
Mongolia	Tughrik	0.00072
Montenegro	Euro	1.34617
Morocco	Dirham	0.11707
Mozambique	Metical	0.03247
Myanmar	Kyat	0.00115
Namibia	Dollar	0.10957
Nepal	Rupee	0.01150
Netherlands	Euro	1.34617
New Caledonia	Franc	0.01129
New Zealand	Dollar	0.83700
Nicaragua	Cordoba	0.04078
Niger	Franc	0.00205
Nigeria	Naira	0.00629
Norway	Kroner	0.18099
Oman	Rial	2.58772
Pakistan	Rupee	0.01013
Panama	Balboa	0.97898
Papua New Guinea	Kina	0.47154
Paraguay	Guarani	0.00023
Peru	New Sol	0.38347
Philippines	Peso	0.02449
Poland	Zloty	0.31713
Portugal	Euro	1.34617
Qatar	Riyal	0.26710
Reunion	Euro	1.34617
Romania	New Leu	0.30768
Russia	Ruble	0.03307
Rwanda	Franc	0.00159
Saint Kitts & Nevis	Dollar	0.36807
Saint Lucia	Dollar	0.36807
Saint Maarten	Guilder	0.54945
Saint Vincent & Grenadines	Dollar	0.36807
Sakha	Ruble	0.03307
Samoa	Tala	0.42369
Saudi Arabia	Riyal	0.26630
Senegal	Franc	0.00205
Serbia	Dinar	0.01199
Seychelles	Rupee	0.07289
Sierra Leone	Leone	0.00023
Singapore	Dollar	0.80968
Slovakia	Euro	1.34617
Slovenia	Euro	1.34617
Solomon Islands	Dollar	0.13510
Somalia	Shilling	0.00062
South Africa	Rand	0.11170
Spain	Euro	1.34617
Sri Lanka	Rupee	0.00785
Sudan	Pound	0.22511
Sudan (South)	Pound	0.33070
Suriname	Dollar	0.30303
Swaziland	Lilangeni	0.10985
Sweden	Krona	0.15480
Switzerland	Franc	1.07932
Syria	Pound	0.01391
Taiwan	New Dollar	0.03387
Tajikistan	Somoni	0.21000
Tanzania	Shilling	0.00061
Thailand	Baht	0.03313
Togo	Franc	0.00205
Tonga	Pa'anga	0.57887
Trinidad & Tobago	Dollar	0.15415
Tunisia	Dinar	0.64350
Turkey	New Lira	0.56513
Turkmenistan	Manat	0.35088
Turks & Caico Islands	Dollar	1
Tuvalu	Dollar	1.04210
Uganda	Shilling	0.00037
Ukraine	Hryvnia	0.12179
United Arab Emirates	Dirham	0.27218
United Kingdom	Pound	1.57929
Uruguay	Peso	0.05088
Uzbekistan	Som	0.00050
Vanuatu	Vatu	0.01105
Venezuela	Bolivar	0.23257
Vietnam	Dong	0.00005
Virgin Islands (British)	Dollar	1
Wallis & Futuna	Franc	0.01129
Yemen	Rial	0.00463
Zambia	Kwacha	0.00019

Exchange Rates

Country	Currency	Rate	Country	Currency	Rate
Macedonia	Denar	0.0208	Samoa	Ruble	0.0307
Madagascar	Ariary	0.00045	Samoa	Tala	0.4266
Malawi	Kwacha	0.0264	Saudi Arabia	Riyal	0.2630
Malaysia	Ringgit	0.3292	Senegal	Franc	0.0205
Maldives	Rufiyaa	0.0638	Serbia	Dinar	0.0199
Mali	Franc	0.0205	Seychelles	Rupee	0.0728
Malta	Euro	1.3417	Sierra Leone	Leone	0.00023
Marshall Islands	Dollar	1	Singapore	Dollar	0.8096
Martinique	Euro	1.3417	Slovakia	Euro	1.3417
Mauritania	Ouguiya	0.00327	Slovenia	Euro	1.3417
Mauritius	Rupee	0.0814	Solomon Islands	Dollar	0.1351
Mexico	Peso	0.0786	Somalia	Shilling	0.0002
Micronesia	Dollar	1	South Africa	Rand	0.1170
Moldova	Leu	0.0808	Spain	Euro	1.3417
Monaco	Euro	1.3417	Sri Lanka	Rupee	0.0076
Mongolia	Tugrick	0.0007	Sudan	Pound	0.2511
Montenegro	Euro	1.3417	Sudan (South)	Pound	0.3507
Morocco	Dirham	0.1170	Suriname	Dollar	0.3030
Mozambique	Metical	0.0324	Swaziland	Lilangeni	0.1098
Myanmar	Kyat	0.0011	Sweden	Krona	0.1548
Namibia	Dollar	0.1097	Switzerland	Franc	1.0732
Nepal	Rupee	0.0113	Syria	Pound	0.0195
Netherlands	Euro	1.3417	Taiwan	New Dollar	0.0339
New Caledonia	Franc	0.0112	Tajikistan	Somoni	0.2100
New Zealand	Dollar	0.8370	Tanzania	Shilling	0.0006
Nicaragua	Cordoba	0.0407	Thailand	Baht	0.0331
Niger	Franc	0.0205	Togo	Franc	0.0205
Nigeria	Naira	0.0062	Tonga	Pa'anga	0.5787
Norway	Kronor	0.1809	Trinidad & Tobago	Dollar	0.1561
Oman	Rial	2.5872	Tunisia	Dinar	0.6430
Pakistan	Rupee	0.0101	Turkey	New Lira	0.5651
Panama	Balboa	0.8789	Turkmenistan	Manat	0.3506
Papua New Guinea	Kina	0.4715	Turks & Caicos Islands	Dollar	1
Paraguay	Guarani	0.00024	Tuvalu	Dollar	1.0420
Peru	New Sol	0.3881	Uganda	Shilling	0.00037
Philippines	Peso	0.0244	Ukraine	Hryvnia	0.1217
Poland	Zloty	0.3177	United Arab Emirates	Dirham	0.2724
Portugal	Euro	1.3417	United Kingdom	Pound	1.5722
Qatar	Riyal	0.2670	Uruguay	Peso	0.0503
Reunion	Euro	1.3417	Uzbekistan	Som	0.0005
Romania	New Leu	0.3076	Vanuatu	Vatu	0.0110
Russia	Ruble	0.0307	Venezuela	Bolivar	0.2327
Rwanda	Franc	0.00165	Vietnam	Dong	0.00005
Saint Kitts & Nevis	Dollar	0.3680	Virgin Islands (British)	Dollar	1
Saint Lucia	Dollar	0.3680	Wallis & Futuna	Franc	0.0112
Saint Maarten	Guilder	0.5645	Yemen	Rial	0.0046
Saint Vincent & Grenadines	Dollar	0.3680	Zambia	Kwacha	0.00019

NEW LISTINGS 2025
Appearing for the first time in this publication

2

2KS CLOUD SERVICES GMBH; DARMSTADT, GERMANY

3

3AC CO., LTD.; SEOUL, KOREA (SOUTH)

A

A AGENCIA BRASILEIRA DE PROMOCAO DE EXPORTACOES E INVESTIMENTOS; BRASILIA, BRAZIL

ABOVE FOOD INGREDIENTS INC.; REGINA, CANADA

ACCENT MICROCELL LTD.; AHMEDABAD, INDIA

ACCESS TECHNOLOGY GROUP LIMITED; LOUGHBOROUGH, UNITED KINGDOM

ACTIONSPORTGAMES A/S; ESPERGAERDE, DENMARK

ACUREN CORPORATION; TORTOLA, VIRGIN ISLANDS (BRITISH)

ACWA POWER COMPANY; RIYADH, SAUDI ARABIA

ADENIA PARTNERS LTD; BEAU PLAN, MAURITIUS

AECC SHANGHAI COMMERCIAL AIRCRAFT ENGINE MANUFACTURING CO.; SHANGHAI, CHINA

AEOON TECHNOLOGIES GMBH; KRAMSACH, AUSTRIA

AFRICA RISK CONSULTING LTD.; LONDON, UNITED KINGDOM

AGNORA LTD; COLLINGWOOD, CANADA

AI CO., LTD.; TOKYO, JAPAN

AICHI FINANCIAL GROUP CO., LTD.; NAGOYA, JAPAN

AIP FOUNDATION; HANOI, VIETNAM

AKANKSHA POWER & INFRASTRUCTURE LIMITED; NASHIK, INDIA

ALGOMA STEEL GROUP INC.; SAULT SAINTE MARIE, CANADA

ALICORN LIMITED; LONDON, UNITED KINGDOM

ALLIANZ GLOBAL INVESTORS LUXEMBOURG S.A.; SENNINGERBERG, LUXEMBOURG

ALLIED CRITICAL METALS CORP.; VANCOUVER, CANADA

ALLU GROUP OY; PENNALA, FINLAND

ALMAVIVA S.P.A.; ROME, ITALY

ALPHA TECHNOLOGY GROUP LIMITED; KOWLOON, CHINA (HONG KONG)

AMAZONE H. DREYER GMBH & CO. KG; HASBERGEN, GERMANY

AMBIENTA SGR S.P.A; MILAN, ITALY

AMF-BRUNS GMBH & CO. KG; APEN, GERMANY

AMIA ENERGY GMBH; HAMBURG, GERMANY

AMMANN SWITZERLAND LTD; LANGENTHAL, SWITZERLAND

AMPYR GLOBAL ENERGY HOLDINGS PTE. LTD; SINGAPORE, SINGAPORE

ANCHOR LAS AB; ESKILSTUNA, SWEDEN

ANDALUSI BEVERAGES S.L.; SEVILLE, SPAIN

ANDERCO INVESTMENT PTE LTD; SINGAPORE, SINGAPORE

ANGLO-EASTERN UNIVAN GROUP; KOWLOON, CHINA (HONG KONG)

ANYWIRE CORPORATION; NAGAOKAKYO, JAPAN

APE ANGEWANDTE PHYSIK & ELEKTRONIK GMBH; BERLIN, GERMANY

APIARY CAPITAL LLP; LONDON, UNITED KINGDOM

ARA GROUP LIMITED; CROWS NEST, AUSTRALIA

ARAD-OPHIR LTD.; RAMAT HASHARON, ISRAEL

ARG MBH & CO. KG; OBERHAUSEN, GERMANY

ARRHYTHMIA NETWORK TECHNOLOGY SL; MADRID, SPAIN

ARVIND & COMPANY SHIPPING AGENCIES LIMITED; JAMNAGAR, INDIA

ASAS CAPITAL LTD; , UNITED ARAB EMIRATES

ASKO HOLDING A.S.; GAZIANTEP, TURKIYE

ASMPT GMBH & CO. KG; MUNICH, GERMANY

ATMOKY GMBH; GRAZ, AUSTRIA

ATS-TANNER BANDING SYSTEMS AG; ZUG, SWITZERLAND

ATTIVO GROUP; CHRISTCHURCH, NEW ZEALAND

AUSTRALIAN MEAT INDUSTRY SUPERANNUATION TRUST PTY LTD; PARRAMATTA, AUSTRALIA

AUSTRALIAN OILSEEDS HOLDINGS LIMITED; COOTAMUNDRA, AUSTRALIA

AVERON PARK LIMITED; LONDON, UNITED KINGDOM

AZAD ENGINEERING LIMITED; HYDERABAD, INDIA

AZULIS CAPITAL; PARIS, FRANCE

B

B INVESTMENTS HOLDING SAE; CAIRO, EGYPT

BAC HOLDING INTERNATIONAL CORP.; BOGOTA, COLOMBIA

BANCA DI CIVIDALE S.P.A.; CIVIDALE DEL FRIULI, ITALY

BANCA POPOLARE PUGLIESE S.C.P.A.; MATINO, ITALY

BANCO MASTER S.A.; SAO PAULO, BRAZIL

BARRO GROUP PTY LTD; CARLTON, AUSTRALIA

BASILIC FLY STUDIO LIMITED; CHENNAI, INDIA

BASSETTI GROUP SAS; GRENOBLE, FRANCE

BAUER HOLZBAU GMBH; SATTELDORF, GERMANY

BAUMER HOLDING AG; FRAUENFELD, SWITZERLAND

BAUMGARTNER & LAMPERSTORFER INSTRUMENTS GMBH.; FELDKIRCHEN, GERMANY

BAYANAT AI PLC; ABU DHABI, UNITED ARAB EMIRATES

BAYLEYS CORPORATION LIMITED; AUCKLAND, NEW ZEALAND

BAYRIDGE RESOURCES CORP.; VANCOUVER, CANADA

New Listings—continued

BBTV HOLDINGS INC.; VANCOUVER, CANADA

BD-CAPITAL PARTNERS LIMITED; LONDON, UNITED KINGDOM

BEEDIE CAPITAL PARTNERS; VANCOUVER, CANADA

BEIJING ZOHETEC CO., LTD; BEIJING, CHINA

BENDA SUNKWANG IND. CO., LTD.; INCHEON, KOREA (SOUTH)

BENNER HOLDING GMBH; WIESBADEN, GERMANY

BEST CHIPS CO., LTD.; SAITAMA, JAPAN

BETAMEK BERHAD; SELANGOR, MALAYSIA

BHARAT HIGHWAYS INVIT.; GURUGRAM, INDIA

BIG TREE CLOUD HOLDINGS LIMITED; SHENZHEN, CHINA

BIRN SERBIA; BELGRADE, SERBIA

BITFUFU INC.; SINGAPORE, SINGAPORE

BLUE INNOVATION CO., LTD.; TOKYO, JAPAN

BLUE JET HEALTHCARE LIMITED; MUMBAI, INDIA

BM CARPENTERIE OIL & GAS S.R.L.; MILAN, ITALY

BODY ACTION ENTERPRISE CO., LTD.; TAICHUNG, TAIWAN

BOHEMIA FAKTORING, A.S.; PRAGUE, CZECH REPUBLIC

BOLDYN NETWORKS GLOBAL LTD.; LONDON, UNITED KINGDOM

BOMSOWA CO. LTD.; SEONGNAM, KOREA (SOUTH)

BTSR INTERNATIONAL S.P.A.; OLGIATE OLONA, ITALY

BUSI GROUP S.R.L.; PAITONE, ITALY

C

C&H COMMUNICATIONS; DUBAI, UNITED ARAB EMIRATES

CADRE AS; KRISTIANSAND, NORWAY

CALASTONE LIMITED; LONDON, UNITED KINGDOM

CALLEJA S.A. DE C.V.; SAN SALVADOR, EL SALVADOR

CANDY TOY - INDUSTRIA E COMERCIO DE ALIMENTOS E PLASTICOS LTDA; SAO PAULO, BRAZIL

CANNAWORLD VENTURES INC.; BURNABY, CANADA

CAPMONT GMBH; MUNICH, GERMANY

CAPSTONE COPPER CORP.; VANCOUVER, CANADA

CAPTIVISION INC.; NAILSWORTH, UNITED KINGDOM

CARAVELLE INTERNATIONAL GROUP; SINGAPORE, SINGAPORE

CASI PHARMACEUTICALS, INC.; BEIJING, CHINA

CASSA RURALE ED ARTIGIANA DI BINASCO CREDITO COOPERATIVO; BINASCO, ITALY

CEDAROME CANADA INC.; CANDIAC, CANADA

CELLO WORLD LIMITED; MUMBAI, INDIA

CENTRAL GROUP; BUDAPEST, HUNGARY

CENTRO CARDIOLOGICO MONZINO S.P.A.; MILAN, ITALY

CETUS CAPITAL ACQUISITION CORP.; TAIPEI, TAIWAN

CEVOTEC GMBH; UNTERHACHING, GERMANY

CHAPS HOLDING SAS; SURESNES, FRANCE

CHAROENRUT KARNTAW CO., LTD.; BANGKOK, THAILAND

CHEUNG HO ELECTRIC CO., LIMITED; , CHINA (HONG KONG)

CHILDREN'S HOSPITAL TRUST; CAPE TOWN, SOUTH AFRICA

CHINA MOBILE IOT COMPANY LIMITED; CHONGQING, CHINA

CHUGIN FINANCIAL GROUP, INC.; OKAYAMA, JAPAN

CHUNGNAM NATIONAL UNIVERSITY; DAEJEON, KOREA (SOUTH)

CIGALAH TRADING ESTABLISHMENT; JEDDAH, SAUDI ARABIA

CIRCULAR WATERS SOLUTIONS S.R.L; , ROMANIA

CISALFA SPORT S.P.A.; LOMBARDIA, ITALY

CLARO PRODUCTS GMBH; ANIF, AUSTRIA

CLIFFSIDE LTD.; TORONTO, CANADA

CLINICAL DESIGN TECHNOLOGIES LTD.; EXETER, UNITED KINGDOM

COME TO AGREEMENT LTD.; RICHMOND HILL, CANADA

COMMITTED CARGO CARE LIMITED; NEW DELHI, INDIA

COMPAX SOFTWARE DEVELOPMENT GMBH; VIENNA, AUSTRIA

COMRIT INVESTMENTS 1 LP; TEL AVIV, ISRAEL

CONCORD BIOTECH LIMITED; AHMEDABAD, INDIA

CONNECTENS B.V.; HAAKSBERGEN, NETHERLANDS

CONVERGENCE PARTNERS (PTY) LIMITED; ROSEBANK, SOUTH AFRICA

CONVERGENT FINANCE LLP; MUMBAI, INDIA

COPILOT CAPITAL LIMITED; LONDON, UNITED KINGDOM

COPLUS INC.; TAINAN CITY, TAIWAN

COPPER STANDARD RESOURCES INC.; VANCOUVER, CANADA

CORE NICKEL CORP.; SASKATOON, CANADA

CREDITCHECK PARTNERS PRIVATE LIMITED; MUMBAI, INDIA

CREDO BRANDS MARKETING LIMITED; MUMBAI, INDIA

CRINSURANCE S.A.S.; LA PLATA, ARGENTINA

CRYSTAL GLOBE LIMITED; TIANJIN, CHINA

CUBE BIO-ENERGY PVT LTD.; HYDERABAD, TELANGANA, INDIA

CURIOX BIOSYSTEMS CO., LTD.; SEOUL, KOREA (SOUTH)

CXJ GROUP CO., LIMITED; HANGZHOU, CHINA

D

DADAM INVESTMENT CORP.; GANGNAM-GU, KOREA (SOUTH)

DAI-ICHI HIGH FREQUENCY CO., LTD.; TOKYO, JAPAN

DAIWA CYCLE CO., LTD.; OSAKA, JAPAN

DDC ENTERPRISE LIMITED; SHEUNG WAN, CHINA (HONG KONG)

DENNEMEYER SA; HOWALD, LUXEMBOURG

DFP HOLDINGS LIMITED; TAIPEI, TAIWAN

DR. SULAIMAN AL HABIB MEDICAL SERVICES GROUP COMPANY; RIYADH, SAUDI ARABIA

DT CLOUD ACQUISITION CORP.; LONDON, UNITED KINGDOM

New Listings—continued

DUNA ASZFALT ZTR; BUDAPEST, HUNGARY

E

E B TRANS SA; MUNSBACH, LUXEMBOURG

E2S CO., LTD.; HWASUNG-SI, KOREA (SOUTH)

ECARX HOLDINGS, INC.; SHANGHAI, CHINA

EKWB D.O.O.; KOMENDA, SLOVENIA

ELBI S.P.A.; LIMENA, ITALY

ELONG POWER HOLDING LIMITED; GANZHOU, CHINA

EMIL FREY HOLDING AG; ZURICH, SWITZERLAND

ENDOGENE LTD.; BRIGHTON, AUSTRALIA

ENGENE HOLDINGS INC.; MONTREAL, CANADA

EPIPROCARE GMBH; BERLIN, GERMANY

ES NETWORKS CO., LTD.; TOKYO, JAPAN

ESGL HOLDINGS LIMITED; SINGAPORE, SINGAPORE

ESSIX BIOSCIENCES LIMITED; DERABASSI, INDIA

EV8 TECHNOLOGIES LIMITED; LONDON, UNITED KINGDOM

EXECUS SPA; MILAN, ITALY

EXICOM TELE-SYSTEMS LIMITED; GURUGRAM, INDIA

EXPORT TRADING GROUP PTE LTD.; MAURITIUS, MAURITIUS

F

F&C INVESTMENT TRUST PLC; LONDON, UNITED KINGDOM

F.P. BOURGAULT INDUSTRIES LTD.; , CANADA

FARFALLI; MANIAGO, ITALY

FBS GLOBAL LIMITED; SINGAPORE, SINGAPORE

FENBO HOLDINGS LIMITED; KOWLOON, CHINA (HONG KONG)

FIN MILE LOGISTICS LIMITED; LONDON, UNITED KINGDOM

FIOR FAMILIE GMBH; MEERBUSCH, GERMANY

FIXIT AG; HOLDERBANK, SWITZERLAND

FLEXICARE (GROUP) LIMITED; CYNON VALLEY, UNITED KINGDOM

FLY SRL; VENETO, ITALY

FONUA LTD.; DUBLIN, IRELAND

FORMICA CAPITAL HOLDING AB; GOTHENBURG, SWEDEN

FORTENOVA GROUP D.D.; ZAGREB, CROATIA

FREE RUNNING BUILDINGS LTD.; ROTHERHAM, UNITED KINGDOM

FREMMAN CAPITAL LIMITED; LONDON, UNITED KINGDOM

G

GALAXY PAYROLL GROUP LIMITED; SHEUNG WAN, CHINA (HONG KONG)

GALEMED CORPORATION; TAIPEI, TAIWAN

GEBRUDER WEISS GESELLSCHAFT M.B.H.; LAUTERACH, AUSTRIA

GELTEQ LIMITED; SOUTH MELBOURNE, AUSTRALIA

GENROBOTIC INNOVATIONS PRIVATE LIMITED; THIRUVANANTHAPURAM, INDIA

GEUMSAN GINSENG HERB DEVELOPMENT AGENCY; GEUMSAN, KOREA (SOUTH)

GIA LAI ELECTRICITY JOINT STOCK COMPANY; PLEIKU, VIETNAM

GIACOM (CLOUD) HOLDINGS LIMITED; LONDON, UNITED KINGDOM

GL GMBH METALL- UND WERKSTATTTECHNIK; FRICKENHAUSEN, GERMANY

GLENTRA CAPITAL P/S; COPENHAGEN, DENMARK

GLOBAL LIGHTS ACQUISITION CORP.; BEIJING, CHINA

GLOBAL METCORP LTD; MIDDLESEX, UNITED KINGDOM

GLOBAL MOFY METAVERSE LIMITED; BEIJING, CHINA

GLOBAVEND HOLDINGS LIMITED; PERTH, AUSTRALIA

GOLD VALLEY PTY. LTD.; PERTH, AUSTRALIA

GOYAL SALT LIMITED; JAIPUR, INDIA

GRAFTON CAPITAL LIMITED; LONDON, UNITED KINGDOM

GRAPHISADS LIMITED; NEW DELHI, INDIA

GROUPE GARNIER; LOUDEAC, FRANCE

GRUPO DON MARIO; MARTINEZ, ARGENTINA

GRUPO LAR INVERSIONES INMOBILIARIAS, SA; MADRID, SPAIN

GUANGDONG LIANXUN PRECISION MANUFACTURING CO.,LTD.; ZHAOQING, CHINA

GURU APP FACTORY CORP.; LONDON, UNITED KINGDOM

H

HAMILTON & COMPANY LIMITED; MUMBAI, INDIA

HANSSAK CO., LTD.; SEOUL, KOREA (SOUTH)

HAO YONG AUTOMOTIVE CONTROLS LTD.; DONGGUAN, CHINA

HAPPY FORGING LIMITED; LUDHIANA, INDIA

HELMHOLTZ-ZENTRUM HEREON; GEESTHACHT, GERMANY

HEXONIA GMBH; NETTETAL, GERMANY

HFBG HOLDING B.V.; HOOFDDORP, NETHERLANDS

HIVEST CAPITAL PARTNERS SAS; PARIS, FRANCE

HOMEEASE INDUSTRIAL CO. LTD.; CHIAYI, TAIWAN

HONASA CONSUMER LIMITED; NEW DELHI, INDIA

HRH NEXT SERVICES LIMITED; HYDERABAD, INDIA

HUABO BIOPHARM (SHANGHAI) CO., LTD.; SHANGHAI, CHINA

HYGON INFORMATION TECHNOLOGY CO. LTD.; BEIJING, CHINA

HYPEX BIO EXPLOSIVES TECHNOLOGY AB; FARSTA, SWEDEN

I

IDEATION TRAINING PTY LTD.; GOODNA, AUSTRALIA

ILSHINWELLS CO., LTD.; SEOUL, KOREA (SOUTH)

IMT CO., LTD.; SUWON, KOREA (SOUTH)

INDEX INTERNATIONAL GROUP; STOCKHOLM, SWEDEN

INDIA SHELTER FINANCE CORPORATION LIMITED; GURGAON, INDIA

xxv

New Listings—continued

INDIFRA LIMITED; ANAND, INDIA

INDTACT GMBH; WURZBURG, GERMANY

INFIFRESH FOODS PVT. LTD.; KARNATAKA, INDIA

INFORMASCOPE; ANKARA, TÜRKIYE

INNOVA CAPTAB LIMITED; PANCHKULA, INDIA

INOX INDIA LIMITED; VADODARA, INDIA

INSTITUT NATIONAL DE RECHERCHE POUR L'AGRICULTURE L'ALIMENTATION ET L'ENVIRONNEMENT; PARIS, FRANCE

INSTITUTE OF NUCLEAR ENERGY RESEARCH; TAOYUAN, TAIWAN

INTEGRATED CYBER SOLUTIONS INC.; VANCOUVER, CANADA

INTERCAM BANCO, S.A.; MEXICO, MEXICO

INTERNATIONAL ASSET RECONSTRUCTION COMPANY PRIVATE LIMITED; MUMBAI, INDIA

INTERNATIONAL CONSOLIDATED BUSINESS GROUP PTY LTD.; MELBOURNE, AUSTRALIA

INTERNATIONAL HOLDING COMPANY PJSC; ABU DHABI, UNITED ARAB EMIRATES

INVESTCORP INDIA ACQUISITION CORP.; GEORGETOWN, CAYMAN ISLANDS

IRM ENERGY LIMITED; AHMEDABAD, INDIA

ISLAMIC CORPORATION FOR THE DEVELOPMENT OF THE PRIVATE SECTOR; JEDDAH, SAUDI ARABIA

IVECO GROUP N.V.; TURIN, ITALY

IYOGIN HOLDINGS CO.,LTD.; MATSUYAMA, JAPAN

J

JADESTONE ENERGY PLC; SINGAPORE, SINGAPORE

JAPAN M&A SOLUTION INCORPORATED; TOKYO, JAPAN

JAPANET HOLDINGS CO., LTD.; SASEBO, JAPAN

JIANGSU GUOJING HOLDING GROUP CO., LTD.; CHANGZHOU, CHINA

JIO FINANCIAL SERVICES LTD.; MUMBAI, INDIA

JNC CORPORATION; TOKYO, JAPAN

JSC SUEK; MOSCOW, RUSSIA

JUNEE LIMITED; SINGAPORE, SINGAPORE

JVSPAC ACQUISITION CORP.; WANCHAI, CHINA (HONG KONG)

K

KAIRIKIYA CO., LTD.; KYOTO, JAPAN

KARINGAL ST LAURENCE LIMITED; BELMONT, AUSTRALIA

KARNIKA INDUSTRIES LIMITED; HOWRAH, INDIA

KAUSHALYA LOGISTICS LIMITED; NEW DELHI, INDIA

KAY CEE ENERGY & INFRA LIMITED; KOTA, INDIA

KBI GROUP; SEOUL, KOREA (SOUTH)

KC CO.,LTD.; ANSEONG, KOREA (SOUTH)

KEEMO FASHION GROUP LIMITED; SHENZHEN, CHINA

KIBO CAPITAL PARTNERS LTD.; EBENE, MAURITIUS

KIRTI INVESTMENTS LIMITED; THANE, INDIA

KNIGHTEC AB; SOLNA, SWEDEN

KO GOLD INC.; TORONTO, CANADA

KONTOR SPACE LIMITED; THANE, INDIA

KOREA OCEAN BUSINESS CORPORATION; BUSAN, KOREA (SOUTH)

KUZCO LIGHTING, INC.; SURREY, CANADA

KYOTO FINANCIAL GROUP, INC.; KYOTO, JAPAN

L

L.E.K. CONSULTING GROUP LIMITED; LONDON, UNITED KINGDOM

LABFORWARD GMBH; BERLIN, GERMANY

LEASE OPERATORS LIMITED; SOUTH OROPOUCHE, TRINIDAD

LEDDARTECH HOLDINGS INC.; QUEBEC, CANADA

LEGEND SPICES, INC.; YEREVAN, ARMENIA

LEMON SISTEMI S.P.A.; BALESTRATE, ITALY

LENDLOCK GROUP LIMITED; CHESTER, UNITED KINGDOM

LIAN EE HYDRAULICS PTE LTD.; SINGAPORE, SINGAPORE

LINKAGE GLOBAL INC.; TOKYO, JAPAN

LINKERS INDUSTRIES LIMITED; SUNGAI PETANI, MALAYSIA

LUNIT, INC.; SEOUL, KOREA (SOUTH)

M

MACLAREN MINERALS LTD.; VANCOUVER, CANADA

MAINI CORPORATE PVT LTD.; BANGALORE, INDIA

MAITONG SUNSHINE CULTURAL DEVELOPMENT CO., LIMITED; BEIJING, CHINA

MARINETRANS INDIA LIMITED; NAVI MUMBAI, INDIA

MARLEY SPOON GROUP SE; LUXEMBOURG, LUXEMBOURG

MARUKOME CO., LTD.; NAGANO, JAPAN

MAXMIND PHARMACEUTICAL S.L.; MADRID, SPAIN

MAXO TELECOMMUNICATIONS PTY. LTD.; HARRISTOWN, AUSTRALIA

ME THERAPEUTICS HOLDINGS INC.; VANCOUVER, CANADA

MEDICINES DEVELOPMENT FOR GLOBAL HEALTH LIMITED; SOUTHBANK, AUSTRALIA

MEIDOH CO., LTD; TOYOTA, JAPAN

MERCANTIL SERVICIOS FINANCIEROS INTERNACIONAL, S.A.; PANAMA CITY, PANAMA

MERFORD HOLDING B.V.; GORINCHEM, NETHERLANDS

METRO SUPPLY CHAIN GROUP INC.; MONTREAL, CANADA

METROPOLITAN POLICE SERVICE; LONDON, UNITED KINGDOM

MF INTERNATIONAL LIMITED; WANCHAI, CHINA (HONG KONG)

MIJU CO., LTD.; SEOUL, KOREA (SOUTH)

MINGTENG INTERNATIONAL CORPORATION INC.; WUXI, CHINA

MINOX INTERNATIONAL GROUP BERHAD; PUCHONG, MALAYSIA

MISH DESIGNS LIMITED; MUMBAI, INDIA

MOBILE-HEALTH NETWORK SOLUTIONS; SINGAPORE, SINGAPORE

MOBILITAS SA; BEAUCHAMP, FRANCE

MONO PHARMACARE LIMITED; AHMEDABAD, INDIA

New Listings—continued

MOTISONS JEWELLERS LIMITED; JAIPUR, INDIA

MULTIPLICA INSIDE S.L.; BARCELONA, SPAIN

MURAL ONCOLOGY PLC; DUBLIN, IRELAND

MUTHOOT MICROFIN LIMITED; ERNAKULAM, INDIA

N

NADER HOLDING GMBH & CO. KG; DUDERSTADT, GERMANY

NANOHELIX CO. LTD.; DAEJEON, KOREA (SOUTH)

NAPLOY CORP.; ABUJA, NIGERIA

NATIONAL ASSET RECONSTRUCTION COMPANY LIMITED; MUMBAI, INDIA

NATIONAL LAGHUBITTA BITTIYA SANSTHA LIMITED; KAVREPALANCHOWK, NEPAL

NATIONALE-NEDERLANDEN OTWARTY FUNDUSZ EMERYTALNY; WARSAW, POLAND

NATIONWIDE FLEET INSTALLATIONS LTD.; MANCHESTER, UNITED KINGDOM

NBH CAPITAL CO., LTD.; SEOUL, KOREA (SOUTH)

NDC AUSTRALIA PTY LTD; MCMAHONS POINT, AUSTRALIA

NEO-CONCEPT INTERNATIONAL GROUP HOLDINGS LIMITED; KOWLOON, CHINA (HONG KONG)

NEOLARA CORP.; PUNTARENAS, COSTA RICA

NET AVENUE TECHNOLOGIES LIMITED; CHENNAI, INDIA

NEW HORIZON AIRCRAFT LTD.; LINDSAY, CANADA

NEWTON EUROPE LTD; OXFORDSHIRE, UNITED KINGDOM

NIKS PROFESSIONAL LTD.; SINGAPORE, SINGAPORE

NIMONIK, INC.; MONTREAL, CANADA

NIPPON EXPRESS HOLDINGS, INC.; TOKYO, JAPAN

NIPPON INSURE CO., LTD.; FUKUOKA, JAPAN

NIVIKA FASTIGHETER AB; JONKOPING, SWEDEN

NOBUL AI CORP.; TORONTO, CANADA

NOCO-NOCO INC.; SINGAPORE, SINGAPORE

NOH & PARTNERS CO., LTD.; SEOUL, KOREA (SOUTH)

NORDIC CORPORATE BANK ASA; OSLO, NORWAY

NOVAAGRO GROUP; KHARKIV, UKRAINE

NOVONESIS A/S; BAGSVAERD, DENMARK

NURTURE LANDSCAPES HOLDINGS LIMITED; WINDLESHAM, UNITED KINGDOM

O

O2 CAPITAL PARTNERS B.V.; OOSTERBEEK, NETHERLANDS

OAK WOODS ACQUISITION CORPORATION; NEPEAN, CANADA

OCI CO., LTD.; SEOUL, KOREA (SOUTH)

OFFICINE PICCOLI S.P.A; CASTEL D'AZZANO, ITALY

ON DOOR CONCEPTS LIMITED; BHOPAL, INDIA

ONET SA; MARSEILLE, FRANCE

ONODERA GROUP CO., LTD.; TOKYO, JAPAN

ONSITE ELECTRO SERVICES PVT. LTD.; MUMBAI, INDIA

OPEN AIRWAY DENTAL SOLUTIONS LTD; TARINGA, AUSTRALIA

ORAVEL STAYS LIMITED; AHMEDABAD, INDIA

OYOCAR GROUP, INC.; SOSUA, DOMINICAN REPUBLIC

P

PARAGON FINE & SPECIALITY CHEMICAL LIMITED; AHMEDABAD, INDIA

PARTNER ONE CAPITAL, INC.; LAVAL, CANADA

PATTYN BELGIUM NV; BRUGGE, BELGIUM

PELION GREEN FUTURE GMBH; MUNICH, GERMANY

PERFECT MOMENT LTD; LONDON, UNITED KINGDOM

PHANTOM DIGITAL EFFECTS LIMITED; MUMBAI, INDIA

PHARMACOSMOS A/S; HOLBAEK, DENMARK

PHM GROUP HOLDING OYJ; HELSINKI, FINLAND

PINEAPPLE FINANCIAL INC.; NORTH YORK, CANADA

PLAYTIKA HOLDING CORP.; HERZLIYA PITUACH, ISRAEL

PREMIUM CATERING (HOLDINGS) LIMITED; SINGAPORE, SINGAPORE

PRESSTONIC ENGINEERING LIMITED; BENGALURU, INDIA

PROAX TECHNOLOGIES LTD.; MISSISSAUGA, CANADA

PROGRESSIVE STAR FINANCE PRIVATE LIMITED; KOLKATA, INDIA

PROTOPIA GLOBAL HOLDINGS INC.; KOWLOON, CHINA (HONG KONG)

PS INTERNATIONAL GROUP LTD.; HONG KONG, CHINA (HONG KONG)

PSYENCE BIOMEDICAL LTD.; TORONTO, CANADA

PT AGRO BAHARI NUSANTARA TBK; TANGERANG, INDONESIA

PT BARITO RENEWABLES ENERGY TBK; JAKARTA, INDONESIA

PT CHARLIE HOSPITAL SEMARANG TBK; KENDAL, INDONESIA

PT ITSEC ASIA TBK; JAKARTA, INDONESIA

PT JANU PUTRA SEJAHTERA TBK.; DEPOK, INDONESIA

PT KIAN SANTANG MULIATAMA TBK.; BEKASI, INDONESIA

PT KOKA INDONESIA TBK; JAKARTA SELATAN, INDONESIA

PT LOGISTICSPLUS INTERNATIONAL TBK; JAKARTA, INDONESIA

PT LOVINA BEACH BREWERY TBK; DENPASAR, INDONESIA

PT MAKNA PRAKARSA UTAMA; BOGOR, INDONESIA

PT MASTERSYSTEM INFOTAMA TBK.; JAKARTA PUSAT, INDONESIA

PT MULTI GARAM UTAMA TBK; SOUTH JAKARTA, INDONESIA

PT NUSANTARA SEJAHTERA RAYA TBK; JAKARTA, INDONESIA

PUIG BRANDS S.A.; BARCELONA, SPAIN

PURIT CO., LTD.; GYEONGJU, KOREA (SOUTH)

Q

QILU BANK CO., LTD.; JINAN, CHINA

QOO10 PTE. LTD; SINGAPORE, SINGAPORE

New Listings—continued

QUALITAS SEMICONDUCTOR CO., LTD.; SEONGNAM, KOREA (SOUTH)

R

RAIZEN S.A.; SAO PAULO, BRAZIL

RANMARINE TECHNOLOGY B.V.; ROTTERDAM, NETHERLANDS

RBZ JEWELLERS LIMITED; AHMEDABAD, INDIA

RED CANYON RESOURCES LTD.; VANCOUVER, CANADA

REDBRICK INVESTMENTS S.A R.L.; LUXEMBOURG, LUXEMBOURG

REGENT GAS HOLDINGS LIMITED; LONDON, UNITED KINGDOM

RENTA GROUP OY; VANTAA, FINLAND

RESOURCE CENTRIX HOLDINGS INC.; TORONTO, CANADA

RF ACQUISITION CORP II; SINGAPORE, SINGAPORE

RF PLAST GMBH; GUNZENHAUSEN, GERMANY

ROTALA GROUP LIMITED; TIPTON, UNITED KINGDOM

S

S J LOGISTICS (INDIA) LIMITED; THANE, INDIA

S&J CORPORATION; TOKYO, JAPAN

S&P SISTEMAS DE VENTILACIÓN, S.L.U.; BARCELONA, SPAIN

SAFE SUPPLY STREAMING CO., LTD.; VANCOUVER, CANADA

SAL SAUDI LOGISTICS SERVICES COMPANY; JEDDAH, SAUDI ARABIA

SALTUS PARTNERS LLP; WHITELEY, UNITED KINGDOM - ENGLAND

SAMEERA AGRO & INFRA LIMITED; TELANGANA, INDIA

SASATOKU PRINTING CO., LTD.; TOYOAKE, JAPAN

SATA GMBH & CO. KG; KORNWESTHEIM, GERMANY

SAUDI LIME INDUSTRIES COMPANY; RIYADH, SAUDI ARABIA

SBE-VARVIT S.P.A.; REGGIO EMILIA, ITALY

SEIBU GIKEN CO., LTD.; KOGA, JAPAN

SEKUR PRIVATE DATA LTD.; VANCOUVER, CANADA

SERVUS CREDIT UNION, LTD.; EDMONTON, CANADA

SG PRIVATE EQUITY CO., LTD.; SEOUL, KOREA (SOUTH)

SHANGHAI RURAL COMMERCIAL BANK CO., LTD.; SHANGHAI, CHINA

SHANTHALA FMCG PRODUCTS LIMITED; KARNATAKA, INDIA

SHEFFIELD GREEN LTD.; SINGAPORE, SINGAPORE

SHENGHONG HOLDING GROUP CO., LTD.; SUZHOU, CHINA

SHREE OSFM E-MOBILITY LIMITED; NAVI MUMBAI, INDIA

SIAT SOCIETA' INTERNAZIONALE APPLICAZIONI TECNICHE SPA; TURATE, ITALY

SIGHTRON JAPAN INC.; TOKYO, JAPAN

SIGNPOST INDIA LIMITED; MUMBAI, INDIA

SIGNPOST NV; LOKEREN, BELGIUM

SIMONE S.P.A.; NAPLES, ITALY

SIMPLY SOLVENTLESS CONCENTRATES LTD.; CALGARY, CANADA

SKYLAND GROUP S.R.L.; MILAN, ITALY

SNEF SA; MARSEILLE, FRANCE

SOILTECH AS; SANDNES, NORWAY

SOMAI PHARMACEUTICALS LTD; CARREGADO, PORTUGAL

SOPHORA UNTERNEHMERKAPITAL GMBH; MUNICH, GERMANY

SOUND CAVE TECHNOLOGY, INC.; TORONTO, CANADA

SRIVARU HOLDING LIMITED; GRAND CAYMAN, CAYMAN ISLANDS

SSF HOME GROUP BERHAD; PETALING JAYA, MALAYSIA

STAR FASHION CULTURE HOLDINGS LIMITED; XIAMEN, CHINA

STEMCELL TECHNOLOGIES CANADA INC.; VANCOUVER, CANADA

STEVE MARSHALL GROUP LTD.; CAMPBELL RIVER, CANADA

STEWART INVESTMENT & FINANCIAL PRIVATE LIMITED; KOLKATA, INDIA

STICKIT TECHNOLOGIES INC.; VANCOUVER, CANADA

STIF FRANCE SAS; SAINT-GEORGES-SUR-LOIRE, FRANCE

STONEWEG SA; GENEVA, SWITZERLAND

SU GROUP HOLDINGS LIMITED; KOWLOON, CHINA (HONG KONG)

SUPREME POWER EQUIPMENT LIMITED; CHENNAI, INDIA

SURAJ ESTATE DEVELOPERS LIMITED; MUMBAI, INDIA

SWVL HOLDINGS CORP.; DUBAI, UNITED ARAB EMIRATES

SYENSQO SA; BRUSSELS, BELGIUM

SYNERGY PARTNERS CO., LTD.; SEOUL, KOREA (SOUTH)

T

TAIYO KOKO CO LTD; KOBE, JAPAN

TALDE GESTION, S.G.E.I.C., S.A; BILBAO, SPAIN

TANKERSKA PLOVIDBA D.D; ZADAR, CROATIA

TEAM INDIA MANAGERS LTD.; MUMBAI, INDIA

TECT HOLDINGS LIMITED; TAURANGA, NEW ZEALAND

TELECEL GROUP LTD.; ROSE-HILL, MAURITIUS

TELESAT CORPORATION; OTTAWA, CANADA

TEYLOR AG; ZURICH, SWITZERLAND

THE CENTRE FOR GENOMIC REGULATION (CRG); BARCELONA, SPAIN

THE HELMHOLTZ ASSOCIATION; BONN, GERMANY

THE SALVATION ARMY INTERNATIONAL TRUST; LONDON, UNITED KINGDOM

TOHAN CORPORATION; TOKYO, JAPAN

TOP WEALTH GROUP HOLDING LIMITED; HONG KONG, CHINA (HONG KONG)

TPL CORP LIMITED; KARACHI, PAKISTAN

TRANSPORTS DESERT SA; ETRELLES, FRANCE

TRAXALL INTERNATIONAL LTD.; STAFFORDSHIRE, UNITED KINGDOM

TRIDENT TECHLABS LIMITED; NEW DELHI, INDIA

TUNGRAY TECHNOLOGIES INC.; SINGAPORE, SINGAPORE

U

UNIHEALTH CONSULTANCY LIMITED; MUMBAI, INDIA

New Listings—continued

UNITED AJOD INSURANCE LIMITED; KATHMANDU, NEPAL

V

VALENS SEMICONDUCTOR LTD.; HOD HASHARON, ISRAEL

VAMA SUNDARI INVESTMENTS (DELHI) PRIVATE LIMITED; NOIDA, INDIA

VIETNAM PROSPERITY JOINT-STOCK COMMERCIAL BANK; HANOI, VIETNAM

VISHNUSURYA PROJECTS & INFRA LIMITED; CHENNAI, INDIA

VIVAA TRADECOM LIMITED; AHMEDABAD, INDIA

VNE S.P.A.; LUCCA, ITALY

VRUNDAVAN PLANTATION LIMITED; AHMEDABAD, INDIA

W

WEBUY GLOBAL LTD.; SINGAPORE, SINGAPORE

WEINERT INDUSTRIES AG; SONNEBERG, GERMANY

WILCOMPUTE SYSTEMS GROUP, INC.; TORONTO, CANADA

WILEE VEGETABLE OILS SDN. BHD.; SHAH ALAM, MALAYSIA

WIREX LIMITED; LONDON, UNITED KINGDOM

WOMANCART LIMITED; NEW DELHI, INDIA

WOODFIELD SYSTEMS INTERNATIONAL PVT LTD.; THANE, INDIA

WOT CO., LTD.; HWASEONG, KOREA (SOUTH)

X

XENIA HOTELLERIE SOLUTION S.P.A.; MILAN, ITALY

XIAOMI CORPORATION; BEIJING, CHINA

Y

YAKKYO S.P.A.; ROME, ITALY

YUWANG GROUP; SELANGOR, MALAYSIA

YY GROUP HOLDING LIMITED; SINGAPORE, SINGAPORE

Z

ZAGGLE PREPAID OCEAN SERVICES LIMITED; MUMBAI, INDIA

ZHEJIANG HAOTAI CHEMICAL CO., LTD.; SHAOXING, CHINA

ZKH GROUP LIMITED; SHANGHAI, CHINA

New Listings—continued

UNITED AJOD INSURANCE LIMITED; KATHMANDU, NEPAL

V

VALENS SEMICONDUCTOR LTD.; HOD HASHARON, ISRAEL

VAMA SUNDARI INVESTMENTS (DELHI) PRIVATE LIMITED; NOIDA, INDIA

VIETNAM PROSPERITY JOINT-STOCK COMMERCIAL BANK; HANOI, VIETNAM

VISHNUSURYA PROJECTS & INFRA LIMITED; CHENNAI, INDIA

VIVAA TRADECOM LIMITED; AHMEDABAD, INDIA

VNE S.P.A.; LUCCA, ITALY

VRINDAVAN PLANTATION LIMITED; AHMEDABAD, INDIA

W

WEBUY GLOBAL LTD.; SINGAPORE, SINGAPORE

WEINERT INDUSTRIES AG; SONNEBERG, GERMANY

WILCOMPUTE SYSTEMS GROUP, INC.; TORONTO, CANADA

WILEE VEGETABLE OILS SDN. BHD.; SHAH ALAM, MALAYSIA

WIREX LIMITED; LONDON, UNITED KINGDOM

WOMANCART LIMITED; NEW DELHI, INDIA

WOODFIELD SYSTEMS INTERNATIONAL PVT LTD.; THANE, INDIA

WOT CO., LTD.; HWASEONG, KOREA (SOUTH)

X

XENIA HOTELLERIE SOLUTION S.P.A.; MILAN, ITALY

XIAOMI CORPORATION; BEIJING, CHINA

Y

YAKKYO S.P.A.; ROME, ITALY

YUWANG GROUP; SELANGOR, MALAYSIA

YY GROUP HOLDING LIMITED; SINGAPORE, SINGAPORE

Z

ZAGGLE PREPAID OCEAN SERVICES LIMITED; MUMBAI, INDIA

ZHEJIANG HAOTAI CHEMICAL CO. LTD.; SHAOXING, CHINA

ZKH GROUP LIMITED; SHANGHAI, CHINA

Mergers and Acquisitions
January 2024—December 2024
(Parent Companies Only)

7
79North, Inc.—acquired by Miata Metals Corp.

9
92 Energy Limited—acquired by ATHA Energy Corp.

A
A&W Revenue Royalties Income Fund—acquired by TorQuest Partners Inc.
A2B Australia Limited—acquired by ComfortDelGro Corporation Limited
Accrol Group Holdings plc—acquired by SODIM, SGPS, SA
ACP Metal Finishing Pte Ltd—acquired by Grand Venture Technology Limited
Actis LLP—acquired by General Atlantic Service Company, L.P.
Adbri Limited—acquired by CRH plc and Barro Group Pty Ltd
Addison Lee Limited—acquired by ComfortDelGro Corporation Limited
Ador Fontech Ltd.—acquired by Ador Welding Ltd
Adventus Mining Corporation—acquired by Silvercorp Metals Inc.
AgroGeneration SA—acquired by NOVAAGRO group
Alcion Group—acquired by Insight Venture Management, LLC
Almacenes Exito SA—acquired by Calleja S.A. de C.V.
Alpha Financial Markets Consulting plc—acquired by Bridgepoint Group Plc
Alumina Limited—acquired by Alcoa Corporation
APM Human Services International Limited—acquired by Madison Dearborn Partners, LLC
Apontis Pharma AG—acquired by Advent International Corporation
Applus Services, S.A.—acquired by TDR Capital LLP and I Squared Capital Advisors (US) LLC
Aris International Limited—acquired by BRCCA Services Private Limited [et al]
AS Tallink Grupp—acquired by AS Infortar
Ascential plc—acquired by Informa plc
asknet GmbH—acquired by Signpost NV
Atlantska plovidba d.d.—acquired by Tankerska plovidba d.d
Australian Oilseeds Investments Pty Ltd.—merged with Edoc Acquisition Corp., to form Australian Oilseeds Holdings Limited
Australian Plastic Profiles Pty. Ltd.—acquired by Legrand S.A.
Automecanica SA—acquired by Rheinmetall AG
Azure Minerals Limited—acquired by Sociedad Quimica y Minera de Chile S.A. and Hancock Prospecting Pty. Ltd.

B
B&B Korea Corporation—acquired by Hitejinro Holdings Co., Ltd.
Banco Indusval S.A.—acquired by Banco Master S.A.
Base Resources Limited—acquired by Energy Fuels Inc.
BBTV Holdings Inc.—merged with 15384150 Canada Inc., to form BBTV Holdings Inc.
Belvoir Group PLC—acquired by The Property Franchise Group PLC
Benesse Holdings, Inc.—acquired by EQT AB
Besqab AB—merged with Aros Bostadsutveckling AB, to form Besqab AB
Bharat Serums & Vaccines Limited—acquired by Mankind Pharma Ltd.
Blackwolf Copper & Gold Ltd.—acquired by NexGold Mining Corp.

C
Calliditas Therapeutics AB—acquired by Asahi Kasei Corporation
Camlab, Ltd.—acquired by StoneCalibre, LLC
Cardano Risk Management Ltd—acquired by Marsh & McLennan Companies, Inc.
Ceapro Inc.—acquired by AEterna Zentaris Inc.
Chr. Hansen Holding A/S—acquired by Novozymes A/S
Chuo Build Industry Co., Ltd.—acquired by Asahi Kasei Corporation
Cliffside Capital Ltd.—acquired by Cliffside Ltd.
CloudMD Software & Services, Inc.—acquired by CPS Capital
CMLS Financial Ltd.—acquired by Nesto, Inc.
Complete Innovations Inc.—acquired by PowerFleet, Inc.
Connect First Credit Union Ltd.—acquired by Servus Credit Union, Ltd.
Contact Gold Corp.—acquired by Orla Mining Ltd.
Contract Pharmaceuticals Limited—acquired by Aterian Investment Management, L.P.
Costa Group Holdings Limited—acquired by Paine Schwartz Partners, LLC, Driscoll's, Inc and Brit-

Mergers and Acquisitions—continued

ish Columbia Investment Management Corporation
Crealogix Holding AG—acquired by Constellation Software Inc.
creditshelf Aktiengesellschaft—acquired by Teylor AG
Crew Energy Inc.—acquired by Tourmaline Oil Corp.

D

Dar-es-Salaam Textile Mills Limited—acquired by TPL Corp Limited, and name changed to TPL Life Insurance Limited
Darktrace Plc—acquired by Thoma Bravo, L.P.
Dechra Pharmaceuticals PLC—acquired by EQT AB
Decmil Group Limited—acquired by Macmahon Holdings Limited
Descente Ltd.—acquired by ITOCHU Corporation
DevvStream Holdings Inc.—merged with Focus Impact Acquisition Corp., to form DevvStream Corp.
Digital Magics S.p.A.—acquired by LVenture Group SpA
Diverger Limited—acquired by Count Limited
DX (Group) PLC—acquired by H.I.G. Capital, LLC
Dyna-Mac Holdings Ltd.—acquired by Hanwha Ocean Co., Ltd. and Hanwha Group

E

ECIT AS—acquired by TowerBrook Capital Partners, L.P.
ELAN Corporation—acquired by Sony Group Corporation
Electrameccanica Vehicles Corp.—acquired by XOS, INC.
Emerald Coast Truss, LLC—acquired by Bain Capital, LP
Envato Pty Ltd.—acquired by Shutterstock, Inc.
EQS Group AG—acquired by Thoma Bravo, L.P.

F

FANCL Corporation—acquired by Kirin Holdings Company, Limited
Fantasma Games AB—acquired by EveryMatrix Ltd.
Farfetch Limited—acquired by Coupang, Inc. and Greenoaks Capital Partners LLC
Fassi Gru S.p.A.—acquired by Investindustrial Advisors Ltd.
Fertiglobe plc—acquired by Abu Dhabi National Oil Company
Fluxx Limited—acquired by Newton Europe Ltd
FLYHT Aerospace Solutions Ltd.—acquired by Firan Technology Group Corporation
Foresight Sustainable Forestry Company Plc—acquired by Averon Park Limited

Formaplex Ltd.—acquired by Unipart Group of Companies Limited
Forward Partners Group Plc—acquired by Molten Ventures VCT plc
Fraser & Neave Limited—acquired by Thai Beverage Public Company Limited
Fraser Mackenzie Accelerator Corp.—acquired by Forward Water Technologies Corp
FueTrek Co., Ltd.—merged with AI Co., Ltd.
Fusion Pharmaceuticals Inc.—acquired by AstraZeneca PLC

G

Galimmo SA—acquired by Carmila SA
Genedata AG—acquired by Danaher Corporation
GLOSEL Co., Ltd.—acquired by Macnica Fuji Electronics Holdings. Inc.
Gold Line Resources Ltd.—acquired by Barsele Minerals Corp.
Goldsource Mines Inc.—acquired by Mako Mining Corp.
Gracell Biotechnologies Inc.—acquired by AstraZeneca PLC
Gram Car Carriers A.S.A.—acquired by Mediterranean Shipping Company, S.A.
GRC International Group plc—acquired by Bloom Equity Partners Management, LLC
Greenstone Resources Ltd.—acquired by Horizon Minerals Limited
Greenvolt - Energias Renovaveis, S.A.—acquired by KKR & Co. Inc.
Gresham Technologies plc—acquired by Symphony Technology Group, LLC

H

Hail Cement Company—acquired by Qassim Cement Co.
Heidelberg Engineering GmbH—acquired by EssilorLuxottica SA
Hong Kong Resources Holdings Company Limited—acquired by Luk Fook Holdings (International) Limited
Hopin Ltd.—acquired by Bending Spoons S.p.A.
Hotel Chocolat Group PLC—acquired by Mars, Incorporated
Huntswood CTC Limited—acquired by ResultsCX

I

IASO S.A.—acquired by Brookfield Corporation
IBEX Technologies Inc.—acquired by Novo Nordisk Fonden
IIFL Finance Ltd.—acquired by International Conveyors Limited
IJTT Co., Ltd.—acquired by SPARX Group Co., Ltd.

Mergers and Acquisitions—continued

Impellam Group plc—acquired by HFBG Holding B.V.
INDIVA Limited—acquired by SNDL Inc.
Innofactor Plc—acquired by CapMan PLC and Osprey Capital LLC
IQGeo Group plc—acquired by KKR & Co. Inc.
IWATSU ELECTRIC Co Ltd—acquired by AI Holdings Corp.

J

Japan Foods Co., Ltd.—acquired by Marubeni Corporation
Japan Publications Trading Co., Ltd—acquired by TOHAN CORPORATION
JASTEC Co., Ltd.—acquired by Nippon Telegraph & Telephone Corporation
Joyspeed Global Cargo China Limited—acquired by Hon Hai Precision Industry Co., Ltd.

K

Karora Resources Inc.—acquired by Westgold Resources Limited
Kensington Capital Partners Limited—acquired by AGF Management Limited
Kerry Express (Thailand) Public Company Limited—acquired by S.F. Holding Co., Ltd.
Keywords Studios Plc—acquired by EQT AB, Canada Pension Plan Investment Board and Temasek Holdings (Private) Limited
Kin + Carta Plc—acquired by BC Partners LLP
KMC Properties ASA—acquired by Logistea AB
KRACHT GmbH—acquired by Atlas Copco AB
Kuchai Development Berhad—acquired by Sungei Bagan Rubber Company (MALAYA) Berhad
Kyoden Co., Ltd.—acquired by The Carlyle Group Inc.

L

Labrador Uranium Inc.—acquired by ATHA Energy Corp.
LHD Group Deutschland GmbH—acquired by Lakeland Industries, Inc.
Link Administration Holdings Limited—acquired by Mitsubishi UFJ Financial Group, Inc.
Lithium Power International Limited—acquired by Corporacion Nacional del Cobre de Chile
Logistec Corporation—acquired by Blue Wolf Capital Partners LLC
Luminex Resources Corp.—acquired by Adventus Mining Corporation
LXI REIT plc—acquired by LondonMetric Property Plc

M

Mac Chain Co. Ltd.—acquired by Renold plc
Marathon Gold Corporation—acquired by Calibre Mining Corp.
Masmovil Ibercom, S.A.—acquired by Orange S.A.
Masonite International Corporation—acquired by Owens Corning
Mattioli Woods plc—acquired by Pollen Street PLC
McGrath Limited—acquired by Knight Frank LLP and Bayleys Corporation Limited
mdf commerce, inc.—acquired by KKR & Co. Inc.
MEDIASEEK, Inc.—merged with Japan Living Warranty, Inc., to form Solvvy Inc.
MediaValet Inc.—acquired by Symphony Technology Group, LLC
Merricks Capital Pty Ltd.—acquired by Regal Partners Limited
Metallica Minerals Limited—acquired by Diatreme Resources Limited
MHM Automation Limited—acquired by KKR & Co. Inc.
Millennium Services Group Limited—acquired by SoftBank Group Corp.
Mimasu Semiconductor Industry Co., Ltd.—acquired by Shin-Etsu Chemical Co. Ltd.
MiX Telematics Limited—acquired by PowerFleet, Inc.
Modern Living Investments Holdings Limited—acquired by Asia Allied Infrastructure Holdings Limited
Modular Automation Ireland Ltd.—acquired by Ares Management Corporation
MorphoSys AG—acquired by Novartis AG

N

Nagatanien Holdings Co., Ltd.—acquired by Mitsubishi Corporation
Namoi Cotton Limited—acquired by Louis Dreyfus Company B.V.
Nanjing Iron & Steel Co., Ltd.—acquired by CITIC Group Corporation
Navkar Corporation Ltd.—acquired by JSW Steel Ltd.
Net One Systems Co Ltd—acquired by Sumitomo Corporation
Network International Holdings PLC—acquired by Brookfield Corporation
NewOrigin Gold Corp.—acquired by Harfang Exploration Inc.
Nighthawk Gold Corp.—acquired by Moneta Gold Inc., and name changed to STLLR Gold Inc.
Nordic Waterproofing Holding AB—acquired by Kingspan Group PLC
Novatech Group, Inc.—acquired by Garaga Inc.
NSL limited—acquired by YTL Corporation Berhad

Mergers and Acquisitions—continued

NSPM AG—acquired by Cactus Communications, Inc.
Nuvo Group Ltd.—merged with LAMF Global Ventures Corp. I, to form Holdco Nuvo Group D.G Ltd.

O

Oceanteam ASA—acquired by SoilTech AS
Olink Holding AB—acquired by Thermo Fisher Scientific Inc.
OneSoft Solutions Inc.—acquired by Blackstone Inc.
Ontsu Co., Ltd.—acquired by GENDA Inc.
Opdenergy Holding SA—acquired by Antin Infrastructure Partners SAS
Orascom Financial Holding SAE—acquired by B Investments Holding SAE
Orchard Therapeutics plc—acquired by Kirin Holdings Company, Limited
Osisko Mining Inc.—acquired by Gold Fields Limited
OUTSOURCING Inc.—acquired by Bain Capital, LP

P

Pagero Group AB—acquired by Thomson Reuters Corporation
Park Lawn Corporation—acquired by Homesteaders Life Co. Inc. and Birch Hill Equity Partners Management Inc.
PCI Holdings Inc.—acquired by Restar Holdings Corporation
Permascand Top Holding AB—acquired by Altor Equity Partners AB
Perpetual Energy Inc.—merged with Rubellite Energy Inc., to form Rubellite Energy Corp.
Plant Health Care plc—acquired by PI Industries Ltd.
Playmaker Capital Inc.—acquired by Better Collective A/S
Plusgrade Parent L.P.—acquired by General Atlantic Service Company, L.P.
PNX Metals Limited—merged with Kin Mining NL, to form Patronus Resources Limited
POLARIS UNO, Inc.—acquired by Polaris Office Corp.
Polycorp Ltd.—acquired by Arsenal Capital Management LP
Premium Turf-Care Ltd.—acquired by Iseki & Co., Ltd.
PROBIOTEC LIMITED—acquired by Pyridam Farma Tbk
Prospa Group Limited—acquired by Salter Brothers Emerging Companies Limited
PSC Insurance Group Limited—acquired by The Ardonagh Group Limited
PT Mitra Tirta Buwana Tbk—acquired by PT Makna Prakarsa Utama

Q

Q4 Inc.—acquired by Sumeru Equity Partners LLC
QANTM Intellectual Property Limited—acquired by Adamantem Capital Management Pty Limited
Quadpack Industries SA—acquired by PSB Industries SA
Quid Pro Quo Alquiler Seguro SOCIMI SA—acquired by Ktesios Real Estate SOCIMI, S.A.

R

Ras Al Khaimah Company for White Cement & Construction Materials PSC—acquired by The Aditya Birla Group
Redrow plc—acquired by Barratt Developments PLC
Reunion Gold Corporation—acquired by G Mining Ventures Corp.
Riso Kyoiku Co., Ltd.—acquired by Hulic Co., Ltd.
RIV Capital Inc—acquired by Cansortium, Inc.
ROBUR Industry Service Group GmbH—acquired by Clayton, Dubilier & Rice, LLC
Roctec Global Public Company Limited—acquired by BTS Group Holdings Public Company Limited
Rotala Plc—acquired by Rotala Group Limited [et al]
Route Mobile Ltd.—acquired by Proximus PLC

S

Samantha Thavasa Japan Limited—acquired by Konaka Co., Ltd.
Sauermann Industrie S.A.—acquired by Verder International B.V.
Schrole Group Limited—acquired by ONEX Corporation
SCS Group PLC—acquired by Poltronesofa Holding Srl
Seamless Group Inc.—merged with InFinT Acquisition Corporation, to form Currenc Group Inc.
SERIO Holdings Co., Ltd.—acquired by Senko Group Holdings Co., Ltd.
Shs Viveon AG—acquired by SIDETRADE S.A.
Silver Lake Resources Limited—acquired by Red 5 Limited
Singardo International Pte Ltd—acquired by Electrosteel Castings Ltd
SK Rent A Car Co., Ltd.—acquired by Affinity Equity Partners (HK) Ltd.
SKIYAKI, Inc.—merged with Space Shower Networks Inc., to form Space Shower Skiyaki Holdings, inc.
SMT Scharf AG—acquired by Yankuang Group Co., Limited
Snow Peak Inc.—acquired by Bain Capital, LP
SNU Precision Co., Ltd.—merged with CIS Co., Ltd.
Sonata Finance Pvt. Ltd.—acquired by Kotak Mahindra Bank Limited

Sopheon Plc—acquired by Wellspring Worldwide, LLC
SpareBank 1 Sorost-Norge—acquired by SpareBank 1 SR-Bank ASA, to form SpareBank 1 Sør-Norge ASA
Stelco Holdings, Inc.—acquired by Cleveland-Cliffs, Inc.
Stillwell Motor Group—acquired by Autosports Group Limited
Symbio Holdings Limited—acquired by Aussie Broadband Ltd.

T

Tatsuta Electric Wire & Cable Co., Ltd.—acquired by ENEOS Holdings, Inc.
TClarke PLC—acquired by Regent Gas Holdings Limited
Technology Metals Australia Limited—acquired by Australian Vanadium Limited
Ten Entertainment Group plc—acquired by Trive Capital Inc.
Think Research Corporation—acquired by Beedie Capital Partners
TIM S.A.—acquired by Wurth Verwaltungsgesellschaft mbH
TIMES GUARANTY LTD.—acquired by Team India Managers Ltd.
TLI Co., Ltd.—acquired by Wonik Corporation
Toho Kinzoku Co., Ltd.—acquired by TAIYO KOKO Co Ltd
Tokai Carbon Korea Co., Ltd.—acquired by Tokai Carbon Co., Ltd.
Tosei Corporation—acquired by Electrolux Professional AB
Totens Sparebank—acquired by Sparebank 1 Oestlandet
Tricon Residential Inc.—acquired by Blackstone Inc.
Trident Royalties Plc—acquired by Deterra Royalties Limited
Trinity Exploration & Production plc—acquired by Lease Operators Limited
Tritium DCFC Limited—acquired by Exicom Tele-Systems Limited
Troy Income & Growth Trust plc—acquired by STS Global Income & Growth Trust plc
TrueContext Corporation—acquired by Battery Ventures, L.P.
Tyman plc—acquired by Quanex Building Products Corp.

U

UK Commercial Property REIT Limited—acquired by Tritax Big Box REIT plc
Universal Copper Ltd.—acquired by Vizsla Copper Corp.
Urb-it AB—acquired by Fin Mile Logistics Limited

V

Vanstar Mining Resources Inc.—acquired by IAMGOLD Corporation
Vectron Systems AG—acquired by Shift4 Payments, Inc.
Virgin Money UK PLC—acquired by Nationwide Building Society
Visiodent S.A.—acquired by Cegedim S.A.
Vitesco Technologies Group AG—acquired by INA-Holding Schaeffler GmbH & Co. KG
Volatus Aerospace Corp.—acquired by Drone Delivery Canada Corp.

W

WalkMe Ltd.—acquired by SAP SE
Wincanton plc—acquired by GXO Logistics, Inc.
Woodfield Systems Limited—acquired by Woodfield Systems International Pvt Ltd.

Y

Yasue Corporation—acquired by Sala Corporation

Z

Zuken Elmic, Inc.—acquired by Zuken, Inc.

Mergers and Acquisitions—continued

Sophson Plc—acquired by Wellspring Worldwide LLC
SpareBank 1 Sorost-Norge—acquired by SpareBank 1 SR-Bank ASA, to form SpareBank 1 Sor-Norge ASA
Stelco Holdings, Inc.—acquired by Cleveland-Cliffs, Inc.
Stillwell Motor Group—acquired by Autosports Group Limited
Symbio Holdings Limited—acquired by Aussie Broadband Ltd

T

Tatsuta Electric Wire & Cable Co., Ltd.—acquired by ENEOS Holdings, Inc.
TClarke PLC—acquired by Regent Gas Holdings Limited
Technology Metals Australia Limited—acquired by Australian Vanadium Limited
Ten Entertainment Group plc—acquired by Trive Capital Inc.
Think Research Corporation—acquired by Beedie Capital Partners
TIM S.A.—acquired by Würth Verwaltungsgesellschaft mbH
TIMES GUARANTY LTD—acquired by Team India Managers Ltd.
TLI Co., Ltd.—acquired by Wonik Corporation
Toho Kinzoku Co., Ltd.—acquired by TAIYO KOKO Co Ltd
Tokai Carbon Korea Co., Ltd.—acquired by Tokai Carbon Co., Ltd.
Tosei Corporation—acquired by Electrolux Professional AB
Totens Sparebank—acquired by Sparebank 1 Oestlandet
Tricon Residential Inc.—acquired by Blackstone Inc.
Trident Royalties Plc—acquired by Deterra Royalties Limited
Trinity Exploration & Production plc—acquired by Lease Operators Limited
Tritium DCFC Limited—acquired by Exicom Tele-Systems Limited
Troy Income & Growth Trust plc—acquired by STS Global Income & Growth Trust plc
TrueContext Corporation—acquired by Battery Ventures L.P.
Tyman plc—acquired by Quanex Building Products Corp.

U

UK Commercial Property REIT Limited—acquired by Tritax Big Box REIT plc
Universal Copper Ltd.—acquired by Vizsla Copper Corp.
Urb-it AB—acquired by Fin Mile Logistics Limited

V

Vanstar Mining Resources Inc.—acquired by IAMGOLD Corporation
Vectron Systems AG—acquired by Shift4 Payments, Inc.
Virgin Money UK PLC—acquired by Nationwide Building Society
Visiodent S.A.—acquired by Cegedim S.A.
Vitesco Technologies Group AG—acquired by INA-Holding Schaeffler GmbH & Co. KG
Volatus Aerospace Corp.—acquired by Drone Delivery Canada Corp.

W

WalkMe Ltd.—acquired by SAP SE
Wincanton plc—acquired by GXO Logistics, Inc.
Woodfield Systems Limited—acquired by Woodfield Systems International Pvt Ltd

Y

Yasue Corporation—acquired by Sato Corporation

Z

Zuken Elmic, Inc.—acquired by Zuken, Inc.

P G FOILS LIMITED
P O Pipalia Kalan, 306 307, Pali, 306 307, Rajasthan, India
Tel.: (91) 2937287151
Web Site: https://www.pgfoils.in
Year Founded: 1979
526747—(BOM)
Rev.: $44,852,803
Assets: $53,262,874
Liabilities: $19,239,074
Net Worth: $34,023,800
Earnings: $26,557
Emp.: 468
Fiscal Year-end: 03/31/23
Aluminum Foil Mfr
N.A.I.C.S.: 331315
Pankaj P. Shah (*Chm & Mng Dir*)

P I E INDUSTRIAL BHD
51-8-A Menara BHL Bank Jalan Sultan Ahmad Shah, 10050, Penang, Malaysia
Tel.: (60) 43736616
Web Site: https://www.pieib.com.my
Year Founded: 1997
7095—(KLS)
Rev.: $246,619,676
Assets: $191,928,513
Liabilities: $73,311,230
Net Worth: $118,617,283
Earnings: $14,821,277
Emp.: 2,487
Fiscal Year-end: 12/31/22
Investment Holding Services
N.A.I.C.S.: 523940
Mui Chung Meng (*Mng Dir*)

P SQUARED RENEWABLES, INC.
Suite 610 1414 - 8th St SW, Calgary, T2R 1J6, AB, Canada
Tel.: (403) 870-1841
Web Site:
  http://www.p2renewables.com
PSQ.P—(TSXV)
Rev.: $4,385
Assets: $166,215
Liabilities: $15,375
Net Worth: $150,840
Earnings: ($75,077)
Fiscal Year-end: 03/31/19
Solar Power Generation Services
N.A.I.C.S.: 221114
Shabir Premji (*CEO*)

Subsidiaries:

Universal Ibogaine Inc. (1)
595 Howe St, Vancouver, V6C 2T5, BC, Canada
Web Site: http://www.ibogaineinc.com
Medical Research & Development Services
N.A.I.C.S.: 541714
Jeremy Weate (*CEO*)

P&C GENERAL CONTRACTING LTD.
250 Shields Court Unit 24, Markham, L3R 9W7, ON, Canada
Tel.: (905) 479-3015
Web Site:
  https://www.pandccontracting.com
Year Founded: 1940
Rev.: $16,324,835
Emp.: 60
Construction Services
N.A.I.C.S.: 236220
Chanus Lo (*CFO*)

P&H TECH CO., LTD
Rm 804 Complex 1 Daewoo Frontier Valley 1030 Jung-dong Giheung-gu, Yongin, 448-701, Kyunggi-do, Korea (South)
Tel.: (82) 3180211892
Web Site: http://www.phtech.co.kr
Year Founded: 2007
Organic Light Emitting Diode Mfr
N.A.I.C.S.: 334413
Seo Yong Hyun (*CEO*)

Subsidiaries:

P&H TECH Co., Ltd - Jincheon Factory (1)
12 Sansusandan 2Ro Deoksan-myeon, Jincheon, 27856, Chungcheongbuk, Korea (South)
Tel.: (82) 435361892
Organic Light Emitting Diode Mfr
N.A.I.C.S.: 334413

P&I SYSTEM CO LTD
245-2 PNI Building Cheomdan-r, Jeju, 63309, Jeju-do, Korea (South)
Tel.: (82) 7086105333
Web Site: http://www.pnisys.com
Animation Production Services
N.A.I.C.S.: 512191
Shin Jae-Joong (*CEO*)

P&R HOLDING
Strada Rivoltana Km 6/7, Rodano, 20090, Milan, Italy
Tel.: (39) 0295231
Web Site: http://www.prholding.it
Emp.: 2,500
Holding Services
N.A.I.C.S.: 551112
Carlo Pizzocaro (*Pres*)

Subsidiaries:

Fidia Farmaceutici SpA (1)
Via Ponte della Fabbrica 3/A, 35031, Padua, Italy
Tel.: (39) 0498232111
Web Site: http://www.fidiapharma.com
Pharmaceutical Company
N.A.I.C.S.: 325412
Giorgio Foresti (*Mng Dir*)

P&V ASSURANCES SCRL
Rue Royale 151, 1210, Brussels, Belgium
Tel.: (32) 22509111
Web Site: http://www.pv.be
Sales Range: $450-499.9 Million
Emp.: 1,500
Insurance Services
N.A.I.C.S.: 524113
Marnic Speltdoorn (*Dir-Comm*)

Subsidiaries:

Actel S.A. (1)
Rue de Ligne 13, 1000, Brussels, Belgium
Tel.: (32) 22296700
Web Site: http://www.actel.be
Automobile Insurance
N.A.I.C.S.: 524126

Arces S.A. (1)
Route des Canons 2B, 5000, Namur, Belgium
Tel.: (32) 81744344
Web Site: http://www.arces.be
Sales Range: $50-74.9 Million
Emp.: 15
Insurance Claims Management
N.A.I.C.S.: 524298
Ghierre Ronvaou (*Pres*)

Euresa-Life S.A. (1)
5 Rue Thomas Edison, 1445, Strassen, Luxembourg
Tel.: (352) 2542591
Web Site: http://www.euresa-life.com
Life Insurance & Pension Fund Administration Services
N.A.I.C.S.: 524292
Jean-Pierre Quairiere (*CEO & Gen Mgr*)

Piette & Partners NV (1)
Casinoplein 6, Kortrijk, 8500, Belgium
Tel.: (32) 56220800
Web Site: http://www.pnp.be
Sales Range: $50-74.9 Million
Emp.: 20
Insurance Services
N.A.I.C.S.: 524210
Pieppe Guy (*Pres*)

VIVIUM S.A. (1)
Rue Royale 153, 1210, Brussels, Belgium
Tel.: (32) 24063511
Web Site: http://www.vivium.be
Sales Range: $200-249.9 Million
Emp.: 300
Financial Services
N.A.I.C.S.: 522320
Hilde Vernaillen (*Chm & Pres*)

P-BAN.COM, CORP.
4F Gobancho Hikari Building 14 Gobancho, Chiyoda-ku, Tokyo, 102-0076, Japan
Tel.: (81) 332613431
Web Site: https://www.p-ban.com
Year Founded: 2002
3559—(TKS)
Sales Range: $10-24.9 Million
Printed Circuit Board Distr
N.A.I.C.S.: 423690
Masaki Tasaka (*Founder, Chm & Pres*)

P-DUKE TECHNOLOGY CO., LTD.
No 36 22Nd Rd Taichung Industrial Park, Taichung, 40850, Taiwan
Tel.: (886) 423590668
Web Site: https://www.pduke.com
Year Founded: 1992
8109—(TPE)
Rev.: $56,397,743
Assets: $159,975,456
Liabilities: $80,357,721
Net Worth: $79,617,734
Earnings: $21,630,272
Fiscal Year-end: 12/31/22
Electronic Material Mfr & Distr
N.A.I.C.S.: 334419
Liao Pen-Chung (*Chm & CEO*)

Subsidiaries:

Advice Electronics Ltd. (1)
16th Atir Yeda St, Kfar Saba, 4464321, Israel
Tel.: (972) 3 900 0900
Power Converter Mfr & Distr
N.A.I.C.S.: 335999

Angst+Pfister Sensors & Power AG (1)
Thurgauerstrasse 66, 8050, Zurich, Switzerland
Tel.: (41) 44 877 3500
Web Site: https://sensorsandpower.angst-pfister.com
Electronic Components Distr
N.A.I.C.S.: 423690

Brospower Co., Ltd. (1)
Room 403 317-dong Hanshin Triplex 37-24 Pungjeon-ro, Danwon-gu, Ansan, Gyeonggi-do, Korea (South)
Tel.: (82) 708 676 7090
Web Site: https://brospower.kr
Power Converter Mfr & Distr
N.A.I.C.S.: 335999

Communica (Pty) Ltd. (1)
53 Landmarks Avenue Samrand, Centurion, Pretoria, 0157, South Africa
Tel.: (27) 12 657 3500
Web Site: https://www.communica.co.za
Emp.: 135
Electronic Components Distr
N.A.I.C.S.: 423690

Digimax Srl (1)
Via dei Laghi 31, 36077, Altavilla Vicentina, VI, Italy
Tel.: (39) 044 457 4066
Web Site: https://www.digimax.it
Power Converter Mfr & Distr
N.A.I.C.S.: 335999

Electronica Olfer S.L. (1)
Pae Neisa Avance I Avda De La Industria 6-8 Naves 19-20-21, Alcobendas, 28108, Madrid, Spain
Tel.: (34) 91 484 0850
Web Site: https://www.olfer.com
Electronic Components Distr
N.A.I.C.S.: 423690

Hansmens Marketing Sdn Bhd (1)
No 21 Jalan Tiara 3 Tiara Square Taman Perindustrian UEP, 47600, Subang Jaya, Selangor, Malaysia
Tel.: (60) 38 023 9700
Web Site: https://hansmens.com.my
Electronic Components Distr
N.A.I.C.S.: 423690

Helios Power Solutions FZE (1)
17-02 Blvd Plaza Tower 1, Sheikh Mohammed Bin Rashid Blvd Downtown, Dubai, United Arab Emirates
Tel.: (971) 4 401 8484
Power Converter Mfr & Distr
N.A.I.C.S.: 335999

Helios Power Solutions Ltd. (1)
3 Heremai Street, Henderson, Auckland, 0612, New Zealand
Tel.: (64) 9 835 0700
Web Site: https://www.heliosps.co.nz
Electronic Component Mfr & Distr
N.A.I.C.S.: 334419
Andrew Sharp (*CEO*)

Helios Power Solutions Pte Ltd (1)
56A Boat Quay, Singapore, 049845, Singapore
Tel.: (65) 6 871 4140
Power Converter Mfr & Distr
N.A.I.C.S.: 335999

Helios Power Solutions Pty Ltd (1)
Unit 6 2-8 South St, Rydalmere, 2116, NSW, Australia
Tel.: (61) 27 200 9200
Web Site: https://www.heliosps.com.au
Electronic Component Mfr & Distr
N.A.I.C.S.: 334419
Ray Consiglio (*Mgr-Sales-Marketing*)

I&C Microsystems Co., Ltd. (1)
6F Samduk B/D 82 Gangnamdae-ro, Seocho-gu, Seoul, 06779, Korea (South)
Tel.: (82) 2 577 9131
Web Site: https://en.incmicro.com
Electronic Component Mfr & Distr
N.A.I.C.S.: 334419

Komponenta Inc. (1)
Vyborgskaya St 16 Building 1of 101 km Vodny Stadium, 125212, Moscow, Russia
Tel.: (7) 4951502150
Web Site: http://www.komponenta.ru
Electronic Component Mfr & Distr
N.A.I.C.S.: 334419

MK Technology Co., Ltd. (1)
14th Floor Office 1409 13 Jeongui-ro 7-gil, Songpa-gu, Seoul, Korea (South)
Tel.: (82) 23 012 4896
Web Site: https://www.mkpowertech.com
Power Converter Mfr & Distr
N.A.I.C.S.: 335999

Perel Eesti AS (1)
Mustamae tee 62, 12916, Tallinn, Estonia
Tel.: (372) 699 8840
Web Site: https://www.perel.ee
Electronic Components Distr
N.A.I.C.S.: 423690

Perel Oy (1)
Torpankatu 28, 05830, Hyvinkaa, Finland
Tel.: (358) 198 7111
Web Site: https://www.perel.fi
Emp.: 31
Electronic Components Distr
N.A.I.C.S.: 423690

Powertec Supplies India Pvt. Ltd. (1)
B-112 Phase-1, Noida, 201 305, Uttar Pradesh, India
Tel.: (91) 120 469 3000
Power Converter Mfr & Distr
N.A.I.C.S.: 335999

ShenZhen Cestar Electronic Technology Co., Ltd. (1)
2nd Floor Building 1 Huarong Road, Detai Technology Industrial Park Longhua District, Shenzhen, 518040, China
Tel.: (86) 7558 253 1600
Web Site: https://www.ce-power.com
Electronic Components Distr
N.A.I.C.S.: 423690

Shenzhen Flykey Electronics Technology Co., Ltd. (1)
Room 1409 Middle Block Yuehai Building

P-DUKE TECHNOLOGY CO., LTD.

P-Duke Technology Co., Ltd.—(Continued)
Nanhai Avenue, Nanshan District, Shenzhen, China
Tel.: (86) 7552 641 9580
Web Site: https://www.flykey.com.cn
Electronic Components Distr
N.A.I.C.S.: 423690

Synerdyne Inc. (1)
7-37-10 Nishikamata, Ota-Ku, Tokyo, Japan
Tel.: (81) 36 424 9971
Web Site: https://www.syr.co.jp
Electronic Components Distr
N.A.I.C.S.: 423690

TTI, Inc. (1)
Ganghoferstr 34, Gernlinden, 82216, Maisach, Germany
Tel.: (49) 81 426 6800
Web Site: https://www.ttieurope.com
Electronic Component Mfr & Distr
N.A.I.C.S.: 334419

Telerex N.V. (1)
Uilenbaan 90, 2160, Wommelgem, Belgium
Tel.: (32) 3 326 4000
Power Converter Mfr & Distr
N.A.I.C.S.: 335999

Telerex Nederland B.V. (1)
Tel.: (31) 76 578 2000
Power Converter Mfr & Distr
N.A.I.C.S.: 335999

XinCheng Electronic Technology Co., Ltd. (1)
Room 203-205 Building Ruijin Business Center No 96 Zhaojiabang Road, Huangpu District, Shanghai, 200020, China
Tel.: (86) 1356 495 4419
Web Site: https://www.shxincheng.com
Power Converter Mfr & Distr
N.A.I.C.S.: 335999

P. B. FILMS LTD.
18 Giri Babu Lane 2nd Floor Room No 2C, Anupam Chambers, Kolkata, 700 012, West Bengal, India
Tel.: (91) 3340048131
Web Site: http://pbfilms.co.in
Assets: $2,278,013
Liabilities: $40,513
Net Worth: $2,237,500
Earnings: ($10,683)
Fiscal Year-end: 03/31/18
Motion Picture & Video Production Services
N.A.I.C.S.: 512110
Pankaj Agarwal (Founder & Mng Dir)

P. J. DALY CONTRACTING LTD.
1320 StoneChurch Road E, Hamilton, L8W 2C8, ON, Canada
Tel.: (905) 575-1525
Web Site: http://www.pjdalycontracting.com
Year Founded: 1953
Construction Services
N.A.I.C.S.: 236220
Bill Murray (Project Mgr)

P. M. TELELINNKS LTD.
1-7-241/11/D Ramalaya 3 rd Floor S D Road, Secunderabad, 500 003, Telangana, India
Tel.: (91) 4040176211
Web Site: https://www.pmtele.com
Year Founded: 1980
513403—(BOM)
Rev.: $3,838,785
Assets: $1,660,334
Liabilities: $646,768
Net Worth: $1,013,566
Earnings: $19,646
Emp.: 3
Fiscal Year-end: 03/31/23
Steel & Copper Product Trading Services
N.A.I.C.S.: 523160

P. QUINTAINE & SON LTD.
RR 5, PO Box 29, Brandon, R7A 5Y5, MB, Canada
Tel.: (204) 728-7549
Web Site: https://www.quintaine.ca
Rev.: $23,300,000
Emp.: 32
Livestock Distr
N.A.I.C.S.: 424520

P.A. RESOURCES BERHAD
Lot 424 440 Jalan Kuala Selangor Kampung Batu 8 Ijok, 45620, Kuala Selangor, Selangor Darul Ehsan, Malaysia
Tel.: (60) 32793328
Web Site: https://www.pagroup.com.my
PA—(KLS)
Rev.: $97,673,378
Assets: $63,226,978
Liabilities: $3,952,158
Net Worth: $59,274,820
Earnings: $6,639,896
Fiscal Year-end: 06/30/23
Extrusion, Fabrication & Aluminum Billets Services
N.A.I.C.S.: 331318
Hwei Ping Tia (Sec)

Subsidiaries:

P. A. Projects Sdn. Bhd. (1)
No 11 Jalan 5/118C Desa Tun Razak, 56000, Kuala Lumpur, Malaysia
Tel.: (60) 391725118
Web Site: http://www.paprojects.com.my
Emp.: 60
Aluminum Fabrication Services
N.A.I.C.S.: 238390

P.A. Extrusion (M) Sdn. Bhd. (1)
Lot 424 440 Jalan Kuala Selangor Kampung Bt 8, Kuala Selangor, 45620, Ijok, Selangor Darul Ehsan, Malaysia
Tel.: (60) 332793328
Web Site: http://www.pagroup.com.my
Sales Range: $50-74.9 Million
Emp.: 67
Extruded Aluminum Products Mfr
N.A.I.C.S.: 331318

Professional Aluminium Smelting Sdn. Bhd. (1)
Lot 440 & 424 Jalan Kepong Kg Batu 8, 45620, Ijok, Selangor, Malaysia
Tel.: (60) 391724828
Web Site: http://www.pagroup.com.my
Emp.: 100
Aluminum Billets Mfr
N.A.I.C.S.: 331314
Leeteng Heng (Mng Dir)

P.A. ROSS LTD.
Ruskin Chambers Drury Lane, Knutsford, WA16 6HA, United Kingdom
Tel.: (44) 1565755500
Web Site: http://www.paross.co.uk
Sales Range: $25-49.9 Million
Emp.: 8
Natural Foods Distributor
N.A.I.C.S.: 424490
Peter Ross (Founder)

P.C.S. MACHINE GROUP HOLDING PUBLIC COMPANY LIMITED
2/1-9 Moo 3 Mittraphap Road Kokkruad, Muang Nakhon Ratchasima District, Nakhon Ratchasima, 30280, Thailand
Tel.: (66) 44701300
Web Site: https://investor.pcsgh.com
Year Founded: 2001
PCSGH—(THA)
Rev.: $117,858,811
Assets: $172,985,280
Liabilities: $26,623,775
Net Worth: $146,361,506
Earnings: $23,651,924
Fiscal Year-end: 12/31/23
Automobile Parts Mfr
N.A.I.C.S.: 336390
Siripong Rungrotkitiyot (Vice Chm)

Subsidiaries:

P.C.S. Die Casting Co., Ltd. (1)
2/5-6 Moo 3 Mittrapap Rd Kokgroad, Muang, Nakhon Ratchasima, 30280, Thailand
Tel.: (66) 4470 1200
Web Site: http://www.pcsdiecasting.com
Die Casting Mfr
N.A.I.C.S.: 331523

P.C.S. Forging Co., Ltd. (1)
2/8 Moo 3 Mittrapap Rd Kokgroad, Muang, Nakhon Ratchasima, 30280, Thailand
Tel.: (66) 4470 1100
Web Site: http://www.pcsforging.com
Die Casting Mfr
N.A.I.C.S.: 331523

P.G. NIKAS S.A.
22nd km Athens - Lamia National Road, 145 65, Agios Stefanos, Attica, Greece
Tel.: (30) 2108187300
Web Site: http://www.nikas.gr
Year Founded: 1971
NIKAS—(ATH)
Sales Range: $75-99.9 Million
Emp.: 648
Veal Product Mfr
N.A.I.C.S.: 311612
George Giatrakos (Exec Dir-Ops)

P.H. CAPITAL LIMITED
5D Kakad House 5th Floor A Wing, Opp Liberty Cinema New Marine Lines, Mumbai, 400020, Maharashtra, India
Tel.: (91) 2222019473
Web Site: https://www.phcapital.in
Year Founded: 1973
500143—(BOM)
Rev.: $6,591,972
Assets: $2,930,601
Liabilities: $391,123
Net Worth: $2,539,478
Earnings: $1,405,449
Emp.: 6
Fiscal Year-end: 03/31/21
Securities Dealing Services
N.A.I.C.S.: 523150
Samir I. Desai (CFO)

P.I.E. INDUSTRIAL BERHAD
57-G Persiaran Bayan Indah Bayan Bay, 11900, Sungai Nibong, Penang, Malaysia
Tel.: (60) 46408933
Web Site: http://www.pieib.com.my
PIE—(KLS)
Rev.: $246,619,676
Assets: $191,928,513
Liabilities: $73,311,230
Net Worth: $118,617,283
Earnings: $14,821,277
Emp.: 2,487
Fiscal Year-end: 12/31/22
Cable & Wire Mfr
N.A.I.C.S.: 333248
Chih-Wen Chen (Exec Dir)

Subsidiaries:

PIE Enterprise (M) Sdn. Bhd. (1)
Plot 4 Seberang Jaya Industrial Estate Seberang Jaya, Prai, 13700, Penang, Malaysia
Tel.: (60) 43990401
Cable & Wire Mfr
N.A.I.C.S.: 333248

Pan-International Corporation (S) Pte. Ltd. (1)
25 International Business Park 01-11/14 German Centre, Singapore, 609916, Singapore
Tel.: (65) 83333877
Cable & Wire Mfr

INTERNATIONAL PUBLIC

N.A.I.C.S.: 333248

P.M. TSERIOTIS LTD.
50 52 Limassol Ave, PO Box 21261, Nicosia, 1505, Cyprus
Tel.: (357) 2220410
Web Site: http://www.tseriotis.com
Sales Range: $50-74.9 Million
Emp.: 130
Consumer Goods Importer & Distr
N.A.I.C.S.: 532289
Anna Diogenous (Pres)

Subsidiaries:

Unicars Limited (1)
54-56 Lemesou Avenue, PO Box 21261, 1505, Nicosia, Cyprus
Tel.: (357) 22366366
Sales Range: $25-49.9 Million
Emp.: 14
Automobile Importer & Distr
N.A.I.C.S.: 423110

P.O.L.I.C.Y. LIMITED
c/o Abax Corporate Administrators Ltd 6th Floor Tower A 1 Cybercity, Ebene, Mauritius
Tel.: (230) 4036000
Web Site: https://www.policylimited.mu
Year Founded: 1979
Rev.: $1,254,774
Assets: $38,972,763
Liabilities: $1,098,070
Net Worth: $37,874,693
Earnings: $967,714
Fiscal Year-end: 12/31/19
Investment Management Service
N.A.I.C.S.: 523999

P.R.E.S.C.O. GROUP S.A.
Twarda 18 St., 00-105, Warsaw, Poland
Tel.: (48) 22 697 64 55
Web Site: http://www.presco.pl
Year Founded: 1998
Debt Collection Services
N.A.I.C.S.: 561440
Tadeusz Rozanski (Chm-Supervisory Bd)

P.S. TELEFONIJA A.D. BEOGRAD
Kumodraska 241, 11000, Belgrade, Serbia
Tel.: (381) 113404000
Sales Range: $10-24.9 Million
Telecommunication & Information Technology Services
N.A.I.C.S.: 541618
Bojan Jocic (CEO)

Subsidiaries:

Gastel doo (1)
Kumodraska 241, 11000, Belgrade, Serbia
Tel.: (381) 11 34 04 104
Natural Gas Distr
N.A.I.C.S.: 221210

Telefonija Brcko d.o.o. (1)
Bulevar mira bb, Delta 2, 78 000, Brcko, Bosnia & Herzegovina
Tel.: (387) 49233000
Communication & Information Technology Services
N.A.I.C.S.: 517121

P.S.P. SPECIALTIES PUBLIC COMPANY LIMITED
1 Boromrachachorianee Rd, Arun Amarin Bangkoknoi, Bangkok, 10700, Thailand
Tel.: (66) 24340540
Web Site: https://www.psp.co.th
Year Founded: 1989
PSP—(THA)
Rev.: $357,811,571
Assets: $206,141,036

Liabilities: $110,235,844
Net Worth: $95,905,192
Earnings: $12,480,866
Emp.: 604
Fiscal Year-end: 12/31/23
Lubricating Product Mfr & Distr
N.A.I.C.S.: 324191

P.T. ASAHIMAS FLAT GLASS TBK
Jl Ancol IX 5 Ancol Barat, Jakarta, 14430, Indonesia
Tel.: (62) 216904041   Id
Web Site: https://www.amfg.co.id
AMFG—(INDO)
Rev.: $557,176,700
Assets: $746,652,000
Liabilities: $374,634,800
Net Worth: $372,017,200
Earnings: $43,737,000
Emp.: 2,444
Fiscal Year-end: 12/31/22
Flat Glass Import & Export Services
N.A.I.C.S.: 423390
E. David Satria Soetedja (Vice Chm)

Subsidiaries:

PT Auto Glass Indonesia
Jalan Danau Sunter Utara J12 No 78-79, Sunter Agung, Jakarta Utara, Indonesia
Tel.: (62) 216 530 3300
Web Site: https://autoglass.co.id
Automotive Glass Mfr
N.A.I.C.S.: 327215
Soeparto Thang (Pres)

P.T. ATMINDO
Jalan Yos Sudarso 100, Medan, 20115, Indonesia
Tel.: (62) 616619133   Id
Web Site: http://www.atmindo.co.id
Sales Range: $10-24.9 Million
Emp.: 100
Industrial Boilers Mfr
N.A.I.C.S.: 333414
Pieter Simanjuntak (Mgr-HR)

P.T. BANK BUMI ARTA TBK
Jl Wahid Hasyim No 234, Jakarta, 10250, Pusat, Indonesia
Tel.: (62) 212300455
Web Site: https://www.bankbba.co.id
BNBA—(INDO)
Rev.: $34,562,856
Assets: $518,971,550
Liabilities: $316,231,787
Net Worth: $202,739,762
Earnings: $2,881,122
Emp.: 646
Fiscal Year-end: 12/31/23
Banking Services
N.A.I.C.S.: 522110
Tan Hendra Jonathan (Dir-Compliance)

P.T. BERCA HARDAY-APERKASA
Jl Abdul Muis No 62, Jakarta, 10160, Indonesia
Tel.: (62) 213800902   Id
Web Site: http://www.berca.co.id
Year Founded: 1990
Sales Range: $75-99.9 Million
Emp.: 500
Enterprise Information & Communication Technology Services
N.A.I.C.S.: 541519

P.T. DUTA SARANA PERKASA
Alia Bldg 5th Floor Jalan Ml Ridwan Rais No 10-18, Gambir, Jakarta, 10110, Indonesia
Tel.: (62) 213867747   Id
Web Site: http://www.dusaspun.com
Year Founded: 1982
Concrete Pipe & Precast Concrete Products Mfr

N.A.I.C.S.: 327332
Djoko Djoko (Head-Proj Div)

Subsidiaries:

P.T. Bonna Indonesia   (1)
JL Pertigaan Mercedes No 2 Tlajung Udik Gunung Putri, Bogor, 16962, West Java, Indonesia
Tel.: (62) 21 8670852
Web Site: http://www.bonna-indonesia.com
Concrete Pipe & Pre-Stressed Concrete Products Mfr; Owned by P.T. Duta Sarana Perkasa & by LBO France
N.A.I.C.S.: 327332

P.T. INFORMATICS OASE
Jl Wolter Mongonsidi No 86, Kebayoran Baru, Jakarta, 12170, Indonesia
Tel.: (62) 217279190106   Id
Web Site: http://www.ioase.com
Year Founded: 1991
Sales Range: $10-24.9 Million
Emp.: 70
Office Automation & System Engineering Services
N.A.I.C.S.: 541511
Mukaneodn Yudoyoko (Pres)

P.T. ODG INDONESIA
Beltway Office Park Tower A 7th Floor, Jakarta, 12550, Indonesia
Tel.: (62) 217801353   Id
Web Site: http://www.ptodg.com
Year Founded: 1990
Sales Range: $50-74.9 Million
Emp.: 150
Electrical, Instrumentation & Fire Protection Services
N.A.I.C.S.: 335999

P.T. SUBUR SAKTI PUTERA
Graha asri aniela anggun Jalan Tanah Abang III No 15, Jakarta, 10160, Indonesia
Tel.: (62) 213524821
Web Site: http://www.subursakti.co.id
Year Founded: 1980
Sales Range: $10-24.9 Million
Emp.: 25
Telecommunication Networks
N.A.I.C.S.: 517111

Subsidiaries:

P.T. Stimec Elcom   (1)
Graha Astri Aniela Anggun Jl Tanah Abang III no 15, Jakarta, 10160, Indonesia
Tel.: (62) 213524828
Web Site: http://www.ssp.co.id
Home Center Operator
N.A.I.C.S.: 444110

P.T. TRIAS SENTOSA, TBK
Desa Keboharan Km 26 Krian, Sidoarjo, 61262, Indonesia
Tel.: (62) 318975825
Web Site: https://www.trias-sentosa.com
Year Founded: 1979
TRST—(INDO)
Rev.: $194,655,312
Assets: $327,612,949
Liabilities: $163,677,309
Net Worth: $163,935,640
Earnings: ($15,701,713)
Emp.: 1,019
Fiscal Year-end: 12/31/23
Polypropylene & Polyester Film Mfr
N.A.I.C.S.: 326113
Sugeng Kurniawan (Chm)

Subsidiaries:

P.T. Trias Sentosa Tbk. - China Plant   (1)
No 9 Xinghua Road Tianjin Xiqing Economic Development Area, Tianjin, 300385, China
Tel.: (86) 2223971442

Sales Range: $25-49.9 Million
Emp.: 100
Polypropylene Film Mfr
N.A.I.C.S.: 326113

P.T. Trias Sentosa Tbk. - Waru Plant   (1)
Jl Raya Waru 1 B Waru, Sidoarjo, 61256, East Java, Indonesia
Tel.: (62) 318533125
Web Site: http://www.trias-sentosa.com
Plastics Films Mfr
N.A.I.C.S.: 326113

Tianjin Sunshine Plastics Co., Ltd.   (1)
No 9 Xinghua Road, Xiqing Economic Development Area, Tianjin, 300385, China
Tel.: (86) 2283963173
Web Site: https://www.tspc.com.cn
Sales Range: $10-24.9 Million
Emp.: 200
Plastic Films Production & Sales
N.A.I.C.S.: 326112

P/F ATLANTIC PETROLEUM
Yviri vio Strond 4, PO Box 1228, FO-110, Torshavn, Faroe Islands
Tel.: (298) 591601
Web Site: http://www.petroleum.fo
Year Founded: 1998
ATLA—(OSL)
Rev.: $83,650
Assets: $22,098,083
Liabilities: $19,520,980
Net Worth: $2,577,103
Earnings: ($9,558,861)
Emp.: 1
Fiscal Year-end: 12/31/19
Holding Company; Oil & Gas Exploration Services
N.A.I.C.S.: 551112
Kaj Johannessen (Deputy Chm)

Subsidiaries:

Atlantic Petroleum UK Limited   (1)
5 Stratford Place, London, W1C 1AX, United Kingdom
Tel.: (44) 2088341045
Web Site: https://www.petroleum.fo
Petroleum Production Services
N.A.I.C.S.: 324199
Graeme Fawcett (Interim CEO)

P/F BAKKAFROST
Bakkavegur 9, FO-625, Glyvrar, Faroe Islands
Tel.: (298) 405000   FO
Web Site: https://www.bakkafrost.com
Year Founded: 1968
BAKKA—(OSL)
Rev.: $1,057,355,294
Assets: $2,641,765,152
Liabilities: $1,032,843,264
Net Worth: $1,608,921,888
Earnings: $141,440,142
Emp.: 1,700
Fiscal Year-end: 12/31/23
Holding Company; Salmon Farmer, Processor & Whslr
N.A.I.C.S.: 551111
Regin Jacobsen (CEO)

Subsidiaries:

Bakkafrost USA LLC   (1)
25 Corporate Dr, Wayne, NJ 07470
Tel.: (973) 249-5300
Web Site: https://www.bakkafrost.com
Salmon Producer
N.A.I.C.S.: 112511

P/F Havsbrun   (1)
Tel.: (298) 414400
Web Site: https://www.havsbrun.fo
Sales Range: $50-74.9 Million
Emp.: 75
Fish Feed, Fish Oil & Fish Meal Mfr; Fish Farming
N.A.I.C.S.: 311119
Dan Samuelsen (Mgr-Tech Feed Div)

The Scottish Salmon Company PLC   (1)
The Le Gallais Building 54 Bath Street, Saint Helier, JE4 8SG, Channel Islands, Jersey   (100%)
Tel.: (44) 1534880088
Web Site: http://www.scottishsalmon.je
Rev.: $228,582,228
Assets: $317,436,470
Liabilities: $117,237,144
Net Worth: $200,199,326
Earnings: $60,477,686
Emp.: 607
Fiscal Year-end: 12/31/2018
Salmon Production Services
N.A.I.C.S.: 112511
Odd Eliasen (CEO)

Subsidiary (Non-US):

The Scottish Salmon Company Limited   (2)
28 Drumsheugh Gardens, Edinburgh, EH3 7RN, United Kingdom
Tel.: (44) 131 718 8500
Web Site: https://www.scottishsalmon.com
Emp.: 650
Farming Business Operator
N.A.I.C.S.: 112511

P/F BANKNORDIK
Oknarvegur 5, PO Box 3048, FO-110, Torshavn, Faroe Islands
Tel.: (298) 330330
Web Site: http://www.banknordik.dk
BNORDIK—(CSE)
Rev.: $44,963,754
Assets: $1,763,862,771
Liabilities: $1,479,104,773
Net Worth: $284,757,998
Earnings: $23,788,832
Emp.: 200
Fiscal Year-end: 12/31/22
Banking Services
N.A.I.C.S.: 522110
Arni Ellefsen (CEO)

Subsidiaries:

P/F Skyn   (1)
Oknarvegur 5, PO Box 83, 100, Torshavn, Faroe Islands
Tel.: (298) 357400
Web Site: https://www.skyn.fo
Advisory Services
N.A.I.C.S.: 541618
Petur Mohr Niclasen (CEO)

P/F TJALDUR
Bryggjubakki 22, FO-100, Torshavn, Faroe Islands
Tel.: (298) 351800
Web Site: https://www.tjaldur.com
MIKP—(OTC)
Holding Company
N.A.I.C.S.: 551112
Runi M. Hansen (Exec Chm)

Subsidiaries:

Mintra Holding AS   (1)
Inger Bang Lunds vei 16, 5059, Bergen, Norway
Tel.: (47) 55986300
Web Site: https://www.mintra.com
Rev.: $28,892,444
Assets: $122,722,873
Liabilities: $30,596,118
Net Worth: $92,126,755
Earnings: $6,336,267
Emp.: 130
Fiscal Year-end: 12/31/2022
Holding Company
N.A.I.C.S.: 551112
Gareth Gilbert (COO)

Subsidiary (Non-US):

Mintra Ltd.   (2)
Offshore House Claymore Drive, Aberdeen, AB23 8GD, United Kingdom
Tel.: (44) 1224651340
Online Education Services
N.A.I.C.S.: 611710

P/F TJALDUR

P/F Tjaldur—(Continued)

Subsidiary (Domestic):

Mintra Trainingportal AS (2)
Fjosangerveien 50D, 5059, Bergen, Norway
Tel.: (47) 55986300
Web Site:
https://www.mintratrainingportal.com
Online Education Services
N.A.I.C.S.: 611710

Subsidiary (Non-US):

Safebridge Cyprus Ltd. (2)
359 28th October Street World Trade Centre Floor 2 Office 217, 3107, Limassol, Cyprus
Tel.: (357) 25001490
Online Education Services
N.A.I.C.S.: 611710

Safebridge GmbH (2)
Raboisen 38, 20095, Hamburg, Germany
Tel.: (49) 4055565790
Web Site: https://www.safebridge.net
Online Education Services
N.A.I.C.S.: 611710

P2 GOLD INC.
Suite 1100 - 355 Burrard Street, Vancouver, V6C 2G8, BC, Canada
Tel.: (778) 655-6508
Web Site: https://p2gold.com
Year Founded: 2017
PGLD—(TSXV)
Rev.: $5,927
Assets: $234,570
Liabilities: $7,301,976
Net Worth: ($7,067,406)
Earnings: ($3,365,473)
Emp.: 4
Fiscal Year-end: 12/31/23
Gold Exploration & Mining Services
N.A.I.C.S.: 212220
Grant Bond *(CFO)*

P2P TRANSPORT LIMITED
11 Dryandra Road Brisbane Airport, Brisbane, 4008, QLD, Australia
Tel.: (61) 7 3860 1800   AU
Web Site:
http://www.p2ptransport.com.au
Year Founded: 1987
Rev.: $44,475,609
Assets: $31,894,982
Liabilities: $31,261,334
Net Worth: $633,647
Earnings: ($15,261,389)
Fiscal Year-end: 06/30/19
Transportation Services
N.A.I.C.S.: 532111
Greg Webb *(Mng Dir)*

PA CO., LTD.
2F 1-7-8 Haramach, Meguro-ku, Tokyo, 152-0011, Japan
Tel.: (81) 368851010
Web Site: https://www.pa-co-ltd.co.jp
Year Founded: 1973
4766—(TKS)
Rev.: $12,662,740
Assets: $9,614,040
Liabilities: $6,792,220
Net Worth: $2,821,820
Earnings: $311,960
Emp.: 198
Fiscal Year-end: 12/31/23
Information Advertising Services
N.A.I.C.S.: 513120

PA NOVA S.A.
ul Gornych Walow 42, 44-100, Gliwice, Poland
Tel.: (48) 324004100
Web Site: https://www.panova.pl
Year Founded: 1987
NVA—(WAR)
Rev.: $89,049,797
Assets: $233,709,857
Liabilities: $112,360,010
Net Worth: $121,349,847
Earnings: $8,779,726
Fiscal Year-end: 12/31/23
Construction Services
N.A.I.C.S.: 236220
Przemyslaw Zur *(Vice Chm-Mgmt Bd)*

PA POWER AUTOMATION AG
Gottlieb-Daimler-Strasse 17/2, 74385, Pleidelsheim, Germany
Tel.: (49) 7 144 8990
Web Site:
http://www.powerautomation.de
Rev.: $4,220,955
Assets: $14,792,598
Liabilities: $10,239,407
Net Worth: $4,553,191
Earnings: ($14,583,459)
Emp.: 40
Fiscal Year-end: 12/31/16
Computer Controlled Machine Tool Solutions
N.A.I.C.S.: 513210

Subsidiaries:

PA America, Inc. (1)
8601 Jameel Rd Ste 140, Houston, TX 77040
Tel.: (713) 263-9400
Web Site: http://www.powerautomation.info
Emp.: 2
Machine Tool Controls Mfr
N.A.I.C.S.: 335314

Power Automation France S.A.R.L. (1)
11 Avenue Canteranne, Saint Faust, Pessac, 33600, Pyrenees-Atlantiques, France
Tel.: (33) 559401050
Web Site: http://www.powerautomation.com
Electronic Control Systems Distr
N.A.I.C.S.: 423610
Cadrec Pugots *(Mng Dir)*

Power Automation GmbH (1)
Gottlieb-Daimler-Strasse 17/2, Pleidelsheim, 74385, Baden-Wurttemberg, Germany
Tel.: (49) 71448990
Web Site: http://www.powerautomation.com
Electronic Control Systems Distr
N.A.I.C.S.: 423610
Bernhard Hilpert *(Mgr)*

PA RESOURCES AB
Kungsgatan 44 3rd Floor, SE-11135, Stockholm, Sweden
Tel.: (46) 84521150
Web Site: http://www.paresources.se
Sales Range: $50-74.9 Million
Emp.: 116
Oil & Gas Exploration & Production
N.A.I.C.S.: 211120
Paul Waern *(Chm)*

Subsidiaries:

Hydrocarbure Tunisie Corp. (1)
Rue du Lac Tanganika Immeuble les 4 Pilastres, Les Berges du Lac, TS-1053, Tunis, Tunisia
Tel.: (216) 71 862 866
Web Site: http://www.paresources.se
Sales Range: $100-124.9 Million
Oil & Gas Production
N.A.I.C.S.: 211120
Mohamed Messaoudi *(Mng Dir)*

PABRIK KERTAS TJIWI KIMIA TBK
Sinar Mas Land Plaza Menara 2nd Tower Jalan MH Thamrin No 51, Menteng, Jakarta Pusat, 10350, Indonesia
Tel.: (62) 2129650800
Web Site: https://tjiwikimia.co.id
TKIM—(INDO)
Rev.: $1,073,834,000
Assets: $3,609,918,000
Liabilities: $1,224,350,000
Net Worth: $2,385,568,000
Earnings: $172,014,000
Emp.: 5,300
Fiscal Year-end: 12/31/23
Printing Paper Mfr
N.A.I.C.S.: 322120

Subsidiaries:

App (Philippines), Inc. (1)
Unit 15B 15th Floor Petron Mega Plaza Bldg 358 Sen Gil Puyat Avenue, Makati, 1226, Philippines
Tel.: (63) 285110912
Paper Product Mfr & Distr
N.A.I.C.S.: 322299

App International Marketing (Thailand) Co., Ltd. (1)
AIA Capital Center Building 89 Unit 1004 10th fl Ratchadaphisek Road, Dindaeng, Bangkok, 10400, Thailand
Tel.: (66) 201030267
Paper Product Mfr & Distr
N.A.I.C.S.: 322220

App International Marketing Pte. Ltd. (1)
Al Ghurair City Office Tower Suite No 735, PO Box 51347, Dubai, United Arab Emirates
Tel.: (971) 42243224
Paper Product Mfr & Distr
N.A.I.C.S.: 322220

App International Marketing. Ltd. (1)
Calle Lago Zurich 219 Piso 12 Col Apliacion Granada, Delegacion Miguel Hidalgo D F CP, 11529, Mexico, Hidalgo, Mexico
Tel.: (52) 5542802148
Paper Product Mfr & Distr
N.A.I.C.S.: 322299

App Italy S.R.L. (1)
Via Longhin 71, 35129, Padova, Italy
Tel.: (39) 04986971
Paper Product Mfr & Distr
N.A.I.C.S.: 322299

App Japan Ltd. (1)
14th floor Higashigotanda Square 2-10-2, Higashigotanda Shinagawa-ku, Tokyo, 141-0022, Japan
Tel.: (81) 357950021
Web Site: http://www.app-j.com
Emp.: 60
Printing Machinery Mfr & Distr
N.A.I.C.S.: 323111

App Paper Co., Ltd. (1)
Room B1 Room 5 No 335 Section 2 Dunhua South Road, Da'an District, Taipei, 10669, Taiwan
Tel.: (886) 222997691
Paper Product Distr
N.A.I.C.S.: 424130

Asia Pulp & Paper (Canada) Ltd. (1)
2360 Tedlo St, Mississauga, L5A 3V3, ON, Canada
Tel.: (905) 450-2100
Paper Product Mfr & Distr
N.A.I.C.S.: 322220

Asia Pulp & Paper Austria Gmbh (1)
Prinz Eugen-Strasse 58 Top 17, 1040, Vienna, Austria
Tel.: (43) 6802076322
Paper Product Mfr & Distr
N.A.I.C.S.: 322220

Calington Limited (1)
Gate House Fretherne Road, Welwyn Garden City, AL8 6NS, Hertfordshire, United Kingdom
Tel.: (44) 1707376959
Paper Product Mfr & Distr
N.A.I.C.S.: 322220

Cathay Latin America Ltda. (1)
Rua Joaquim Floriano 72-Cj 191/192, Itaim Bibi, Sao Paulo, cep 04534-000, SP, Brazil
Tel.: (55) 1137071505
Web Site: http://cathay.com.br
Paper Product Distr
N.A.I.C.S.: 424130

Charta Global, Inc. (1)
770 The City Dr S Ste 2500, Orange, CA 92868
Tel.: (714) 780-0595
Web Site: https://www.chartaglobal.com
Paper Product Mfr & Distr

INTERNATIONAL PUBLIC

N.A.I.C.S.: 322220

Goldtech Access Sdn. Bhd. (1)
Unit W101 West Wing Level 1 Wisma Consplant 1 No 2 Jalan SS 16/4, 47500, Subang Jaya, Selangor, Malaysia
Tel.: (60) 356310888
Paper Product Mfr & Distr
N.A.I.C.S.: 322220

I-Deal Print Ltd. (1)
Unit 504B 5/F Empire Centre 68 Mody Rd, TSTE, Kowloon, China (Hong Kong)
Tel.: (852) 27330448
Paper Product Mfr & Distr
N.A.I.C.S.: 322299

Paper Force Oceania Pty. Ltd. (1)
19 Ailsa Street, Box Hill, 3128, VIC, Australia
Tel.: (61) 388093333
Web Site: https://paperforce.com.au
Paper Product Distr
N.A.I.C.S.: 424130

Sinar Indah Pulp & Paper Pty. Ltd. (1)
Office No 207 2nd Floor Time tower DLF Phase-II Mehrauli Rd, Gurgaon, 122001, Haryana, India
Tel.: (91) 1244909502
Paper Product Mfr & Distr
N.A.I.C.S.: 322299

Vintage Paper, S.A. (1)
C/ Tuset no 5-2-D, 8006, Barcelona, Spain
Tel.: (34) 934960634
Paper Product Mfr & Distr
N.A.I.C.S.: 322220

Yuanfeng Trading Co., Ltd. (1)
RM 803 140-148 Southern Securities Building Ti Yu Dong Road, Guangzhou, 510620, China
Tel.: (86) 2038878559
Paper Product Mfr & Distr
N.A.I.C.S.: 322299

PACC OFFSHORE SERVICES HOLDINGS LTD
No 1 Kim Seng Promenade 06-01 Great World City, Singapore, 237994, Singapore
Tel.: (65) 68396500
Web Site: http://www.posh.com.sg
Rev.: $299,400,000
Assets: $1,299,311,000
Liabilities: $935,436,000
Net Worth: $363,875,000
Earnings: ($98,309,000)
Emp.: 141
Fiscal Year-end: 12/31/18
Offshore Support Vessels Operations
N.A.I.C.S.: 483111
Keng Lin Lee *(CEO)*

PACE (PAKISTAN) LIMITED
2nd Floor Pace Shopping Mall Fortress Stadium Cantt, Lahore, Pakistan
Tel.: (92) 4236623005
Web Site:
https://www.pacepakistan.com
PACE—(KAR)
Rev.: $3,161,677
Assets: $53,577,081
Liabilities: $42,945,224
Net Worth: $10,631,857
Earnings: ($6,771,465)
Emp.: 231
Fiscal Year-end: 06/30/19
Real Estate Property & Development Services
N.A.I.C.S.: 531311
Aamna Taseer *(Chm)*

PACE DEVELOPMENT CORPORATION PUBLIC CO., LTD.
53 Sivatel Tower 16th Floor Room 1606 Wireless Road, Lumpini, Bangkok, 10330, Thailand
Tel.: (66) 21189599
Web Site: https://www.pacedev.com

Year Founded: 2004
PACE—(THA)
Sales Range: $50-74.9 Million
Real Estate Developers
N.A.I.C.S.: 237210
Sorapoj Techakraisri *(CEO)*

Subsidiaries:

Dean & DeLuca (1)
560 Broadway, New York, NY 10012
Tel.: (212) 226-6800
Web Site: http://www.deandeluca.com
Gourmet Foods Retailer
N.A.I.C.S.: 445298
Laura Lendrum *(Pres-Markets & Global Retail)*

Subsidiary (Domestic):

OGC Investments, LLC (2)
860 Napa Vly Corporate Way, Napa, CA 94558-6281
Tel.: (707) 253-9150
Web Site: http://www.oakvillegrocery.com
Holding Company; Retail Wine Stores Operator
N.A.I.C.S.: 551112

Unit (Domestic):

Oakville Grocery Co. (3)
7856 Saint Helena Hwy, Oakville, CA 94562
Tel.: (707) 944-8802
Web Site: http://www.oakvillegrocery.com
Sales Range: $25-49.9 Million
Emp.: 40
Retail Wine & Specialty Food Store
N.A.I.C.S.: 445320

Oakville Grocery Co. (3)
124 Matheson St, Healdsburg, CA 95448
Tel.: (707) 433-3200
Web Site: http://www.oakvillegrocery.com
Sales Range: $25-49.9 Million
Emp.: 35
Retail Wine & Specialty Food Store
N.A.I.C.S.: 445320

PACE E-COMMERCE VENTURES LIMITED
Shop No 423 Block-C Sumel-11 Indian Textile Plaza Near Namaste Circle, Shahibaug, Ahmedabad, 380004, Gujarat, India
Tel.: (91) 8530999431
Web Site: https://cotandcandy.com
Year Founded: 2015
543637—(BOM)
E-Commerce Site Operator
N.A.I.C.S.: 459999
Shaival Dharmendra Gandhi *(Mng Dir & CFO)*

PACE METALS LTD.
235 15th St, West Vancouver, V7T 2X1, BC, Canada
Tel.: (604) 424-8131 BC
Year Founded: 1996
PACE—(TSXV)
Assets: $230,378
Liabilities: $98,558
Net Worth: $131,820
Earnings: ($379,193)
Fiscal Year-end: 12/31/19
Gold Exploration Services
N.A.I.C.S.: 212220
Ranjeet Sundher *(Pres & CEO)*

PACER COMPONENTS LTD.
4 Horseshoe Park, Reading, RG8 7JW, Berkshire, United Kingdom
Tel.: (44) 1189845280 UK
Web Site: http://www.pacer.co.uk
Year Founded: 1989
Sales Range: $10-24.9 Million
Emp.: 40
Supplier of Optoelectronic, Display & Laser Solutions
N.A.I.C.S.: 423690
Graham Rothon *(Mng Dir)*

Subsidiaries:

Pacer USA LLC (1)
4149 Burns Rd, Palm Beach Gardens, FL 33410-4605
Tel.: (502) 315-2545
Web Site: http://www.pacer-usa.com
Emp.: 5
Supplier of Optoelectronic, Display & Laser Solutions
N.A.I.C.S.: 423690
Robert Schwab *(Gen Mgr)*

PACGOLD LIMITED
Level 38 71 Eagle Street, Brisbane, 4000, QLD, Australia
Tel.: (61) 737786728 AU
Web Site: https://www.pacgold.com.au
Year Founded: 2019
PGO—(ASX)
Gold Exploration Services
N.A.I.C.S.: 212220
Matthew Boyes *(Mng Dir)*

PACHELI INDUSTRIAL FINANCE LTD.
C-001 Prathamesh Horizon New Link Road, Borivali West, Mumbai, 400 092, India
Tel.: (91) 1126387281 In
Web Site: https://pifl.in
Year Founded: 1985
523862—(BOM)
Assets: $571,704
Liabilities: $28,907
Net Worth: $542,797
Earnings: ($2,650)
Fiscal Year-end: 03/31/23
Real Estate Development Services
N.A.I.C.S.: 531390
Padamchand Dhoot *(CFO)*

PACIFIC & ORIENT BERHAD
11th Floor Wisma Bumi Raya 10 Jalan Raja Laut, 50350, Kuala Lumpur, Malaysia
Tel.: (60) 326985033
Web Site: https://www.pacific-orient.com
Year Founded: 1994
P&O—(KLS)
Rev.: $59,493,122
Assets: $227,402,751
Liabilities: $134,790,476
Net Worth: $92,612,275
Earnings: ($4,491,640)
Emp.: 407
Fiscal Year-end: 09/30/23
Financial & Life Insurance Services
N.A.I.C.S.: 524113
Hua Eng Chan *(Chm)*

Subsidiaries:

P & O Global Technologies Sdn. Bhd. (1)
17th Floor Wisma Bumi Raya No 10 Jalan Raja Laut, 50350, Kuala Lumpur, Malaysia
Tel.: (60) 326979877
Web Site: https://www.pacific-orient.com
Sales Range: $25-49.9 Million
Emp.: 50
Computer Related Services
N.A.I.C.S.: 541519

P & O Global Technologies, Inc. (1)
224 Commercial Blvd Ste 206, Lauderdale by the Sea, FL 33308
Tel.: (954) 616-0600
Web Site: https://www.pogt.net
Emp.: 10
Designer of Computer Integrated Systems
N.A.I.C.S.: 541512

P & O Technologies Sdn. Bhd. (1)
17th Floor Wisma Bumi Raya, No 10 Jalan Raja Laut, 50350, Kuala Lumpur, Malaysia (100%)
Tel.: (60) 326979877
Web Site: http://www.pacific-orient.com
Sales Range: $25-49.9 Million
Emp.: 100
Computer Related Services
N.A.I.C.S.: 541519

Pacific & Orient Capital Sdn. Bhd. (1)
11th Floor Wisma Bumi Raya, No 10 Jalan Raja Laut, 50350, Kuala Lumpur, Malaysia (100%)
Tel.: (60) 326985033
Web Site: https://www.pacific-orient.com
Direct Financial Moneylenders
N.A.I.C.S.: 522390

Pacific & Orient Insurance Co. Berhad (1)
11th Floor Wisma Bumi Raya, No 10 Jalan Raja Laut, 50350, Kuala Lumpur, Malaysia (51%)
Tel.: (60) 326985033
Web Site: https://www.poi2u.com
Direct Life Insurance Carriers
N.A.I.C.S.: 524113
Thye Seng Chan *(CEO & Mng Dir)*

Pacific & Orient Properties Ltd. (1)
4th Floor 111 Baker Street, London, W1U 6SG, United Kingdom
Tel.: (44) 2074869975
Web Site: https://www.pacificorientlondon.co.uk
Venture Capital Investment Services
N.A.I.C.S.: 523910
Iryna Kunitska *(Controller-Finance)*

PACIFIC ALLIANCE REAL ESTATE LIMITED
32/F AIA Central 1 Connaught Road, Central, China (Hong Kong)
Tel.: (852) 29180088 Ky
Web Site: http://www.pacl-fund.com
Year Founded: 2007
PACL—(AIM)
Sales Range: $1-9.9 Million
Investment Management Service
N.A.I.C.S.: 523940

PACIFIC ANDES INTERNATIONAL HOLDINGS LIMITED
32/F Hong Kong Plaza, 188 Connaught Road West, Hong Kong, China (Hong Kong)
Tel.: (852) 25470168 BM
Web Site: http://www.pacificandes.com
Year Founded: 1986
Emp.: 6,000
Fishing & Fishmeal Services
N.A.I.C.S.: 114119
Puay Yee Ng *(Mng Dir)*

Subsidiaries:

China Fishery Group Limited (1)
Room 3201-10 Hong Kong Plaza, 188 Connaught Road West, Hong Kong, China (Hong Kong)
Tel.: (852) 25482666
Web Site: http://www.chinafisherygroup.com
Sales Range: $600-649.9 Million
Fishing Products
N.A.I.C.S.: 112511
Puay Yee Ng *(CEO)*

Subsidiary (Non-US):

Copeinca ASA (2)
Calle Francisco Grana 155, Urb Sta Catalina, Lima, 13, Peru
Tel.: (51) 1 213 4000
Web Site: http://www.copeinca.com
Sales Range: $250-299.9 Million
Emp.: 1,484
Holding Company; Commercial Fishing & Fish Whslr
N.A.I.C.S.: 551112

Subsidiary (Domestic):

Corporacion Pesquera Inca S.A.C. (3)
Calle Francisco Grana 155, Urb Sta Catalina, Lima, 13, Peru
Tel.: (51) 1 213 4000
Web Site: http://www.copeinca.com
Sales Range: $25-49.9 Million
Emp.: 100
Commercial Fishing & Fish Whslr
N.A.I.C.S.: 114111

PACIFIC ARC RESOURCES LTD.
410 - 885 Dunsmuir Street, Vancouver, V6C 1N5, BC, Canada
Tel.: (778) 688-7411 BC
Web Site: https://pacificarcresources.ca
Year Founded: 2007
PAV—(TSXV)
Assets: $145,923
Liabilities: $148,203
Net Worth: ($2,280)
Earnings: ($178,099)
Fiscal Year-end: 01/31/23
Metal Mining Services
N.A.I.C.S.: 212290
John MacPhail *(Pres & CEO)*

PACIFIC BASIN SHIPPING LIMITED
31/F One Island South 2 Heung Yip Road Wong Chuk Hang, Hong Kong, China (Hong Kong)
Tel.: (852) 22337000 BM
Web Site: https://www.pacificbasin.com
Year Founded: 1987
2343—(HKG)
Rev.: $3,281,626,000
Assets: $2,648,685,000
Liabilities: $741,330,000
Net Worth: $1,907,355,000
Earnings: $701,856,000
Emp.: 4,273
Fiscal Year-end: 12/31/22
Shipping Services
N.A.I.C.S.: 321920
Emily Lau *(Gen Mgr-IR)*

Subsidiaries:

PB Issuer Limited (1)
C/o Offshore Incorporations Limited Offshore Incorporations Ctr, PO BOX 957, Road Town, Tortola, Virgin Islands (British)
Tel.: (284) 494 8184
Bond Issuing Services
N.A.I.C.S.: 523150

PB Vessels Holding Limited (1)
C/o Offshore Incorporations Limited Offshore Incorporations Ctr, Road Town, Tortola, Virgin Islands (British)
Tel.: (284) 4948184
Investment Holding Services
N.A.I.C.S.: 551112

PacMarine Services (HK) Limited (1)
Room 1902 19/F CC Wu Building 302-308 Hennessy Road, 308 Des Voeux Rd, Chai Wan, China (Hong Kong)
Tel.: (852) 25450888
Web Site: http://www.pacmarine.com
Sales Range: $25-49.9 Million
Emp.: 10
Marine Consulting & Surveying Services
N.A.I.C.S.: 541990

PacMarine Services Co., Ltd. (1)
703 ILSHIN Building 38 Mapo-Daero, Mapo-Gu, Seoul, Korea (South)
Tel.: (82) 236645517
Marine Consultancy & Surveying Services
N.A.I.C.S.: 541990

PacMarine Services LLC (1)
Ste 390 505 N Sam Houston Pkwy E, Houston, TX 77060-4042
Tel.: (281) 447-9595
Web Site: https://www.pacmarine.com
Emp.: 6
Marine Consultancy & Surveying Services
N.A.I.C.S.: 541990

PacMarine Services Pte. Ltd. (1)
20 Harbour Dr 04-05A, Singapore, 117612, Singapore
Tel.: (65) 65343456
Sales Range: $25-49.9 Million
Emp.: 20

PACIFIC BASIN SHIPPING LIMITED

Pacific Basin Shipping Limited—(Continued)
Marine & Tanker Consultancy & Surveying Services
N.A.I.C.S.: 541990

Pacific Basin IHC (UK) Limited (1)
Swan House Stratford Pl, London, W1C 1BQ, United Kingdom
Tel.: (44) 2071821050
Sales Range: $25-49.9 Million
Emp.: 16
Ship Chartering Services
N.A.I.C.S.: 483111

Pacific Basin IHC Limited (1)
7F Hutchison House 10 Harcourt Rd, Central, China (Hong Kong)
Tel.: (852) 22337000
Ship Chartering Services
N.A.I.C.S.: 483111

Pacific Basin Shipping (Brasil) Ltda. (1)
Av Ataulfo de Paiva 341 - Sl 607, Leblon, Rio de Janeiro, 22440-032, Brazil
Tel.: (55) 2122051959
Cargo Transportation Services
N.A.I.C.S.: 484110

Pacific Basin Shipping (Canada) Limited (1)
Suite 1620 Guinness Tower 1055 West Hastings Street, Vancouver, V6E 2E9, BC, Canada
Tel.: (604) 633-0900
Emp.: 10
Marine Cargo Handling Services
N.A.I.C.S.: 488320

Pacific Basin Shipping (Chile) Limitada (1)
Arrayan 2750 Office 601, Providencia, Santiago, Chile
Tel.: (56) 29259100
Web Site: http://www.pacificbasin.com
Sales Range: $25-49.9 Million
Emp.: 5
Marine Cargo Handling Services
N.A.I.C.S.: 488320

Pacific Basin Shipping (HK) Limited (1)
Tel.: (852) 22337000
Web Site: http://www.pacificbasin.com
Emp.: 200
Marine Shipping Services
N.A.I.C.S.: 488510

Pacific Basin Shipping (New Zealand) Limited (1)
Tel.: (64) 99161407
Web Site: https://www.pacificbasin.com
Emp.: 7
Marine Shipping Services
N.A.I.C.S.: 488510

Pacific Basin Shipping (UK) Limited (1)
Sales Range: $25-49.9 Million
Emp.: 17
Marine Shipping Services
N.A.I.C.S.: 488510

Taihua Shipping (Bejing) Limited (1)
Rm A 1501 Genertime Intl Ctr Jia No 3, Yong an Dong Li, Beijing, 100022, China
Tel.: (86) 1058795656
Web Site: http://www.pacificbasin.com
Sales Range: $25-49.9 Million
Emp.: 5
Marine Shipping Services
N.A.I.C.S.: 488510

PACIFIC BAUXITE LIMITED
Level 3 33 Ord Street, Perth, 6005, WA, Australia
Tel.: (61) 8 9481 4478 AU
Web Site: http://www.pacificbauxite.com.au
Rev.: $67,735
Assets: $2,065,204
Liabilities: $272,525
Net Worth: $1,792,679
Earnings: ($3,270,808)
Fiscal Year-end: 06/30/18
Iron Ore Exploration & Mining
N.A.I.C.S.: 212210

Melissa Chapman *(Co-Sec)*

PACIFIC BAY MINERALS LTD.
Suite 1507 - 1030 West Georgia St, Vancouver, V6E 2Y3, BC, Canada
Tel.: (604) 682-2421
Web Site: https://www.pacificbayminerals.com
PBM—(TSXV)
Rev.: $129
Assets: $240,783
Liabilities: $530,231
Net Worth: ($289,448)
Earnings: ($794,578)
Fiscal Year-end: 12/31/23
Mineral Exploration Services
N.A.I.C.S.: 213114
David H. Brett *(Pres & CEO)*

PACIFIC BIO CO., LTD.
26F Danam Building 10 Sowol-ro Jung-gu, Seoul, 04527, Korea (South)
Tel.: (82) 2 6917 5300
Web Site: http://www.pacificbio.co.kr
Sales Range: $25-49.9 Million
Emp.: 38
Air Conditioning System Installation Services
N.A.I.C.S.: 238220

PACIFIC BOOKER MINERALS INC.
1166 Alberni st Suite 1203, Vancouver, V6E 3Z3, BC, Canada
Tel.: (604) 681-8556
Web Site: https://www.pacificbooker.com
Year Founded: 1983
PBMLF—(OTCIQ)
Assets: $1,047,920
Liabilities: $36,625
Net Worth: $1,011,295
Earnings: ($26,914,706)
Emp.: 2
Fiscal Year-end: 01/31/22
Mineral Property Exploration Services
N.A.I.C.S.: 327999
John Joseph Plourde *(Pres & CEO)*

PACIFIC BUILDERS SUPPLIES
3730 Trans Canada Hwy, PO Box 70, Cobble Hill, V0R-1L0, BC, Canada
Tel.: (250) 743-5584
Web Site: http://www.pacific-homes.com
Year Founded: 1982
Rev.: $22,279,295
Emp.: 200
Prefabricated Wood Buildings Construction
N.A.I.C.S.: 321992
Lorne Winship *(Gen Mgr)*

PACIFIC CANCER CENTRE PTE. LTD.
559 Bukit Timah Road 01-02 King's Arcade, Singapore, 269695, Singapore
Tel.: (65) 6466 7777 SG
Web Site: http://www.pachealthholdings.com
Cancer Treatment Facility Operator
N.A.I.C.S.: 622310

PACIFIC CENTURY GROUP HOLDINGS LIMITED
39/F PCCW Tower TaiKoo Place 979 Kings Road, Quarry Bay, China (Hong Kong)
Tel.: (852) 2883 7747 HK
Web Site: http://www.pcg-group.com
Year Founded: 1993
Investment Holding Company
N.A.I.C.S.: 551112

Richard Tzar Kai Li *(Founder, Chm & CEO)*

Subsidiaries:

FWD Group Holdings Limited (1)
13/F 14 Taikoo Wan Road Taikoo Shing, Hong Kong, China (Hong Kong)
Tel.: (852) 28503823
Web Site: http://www.fwd.com
Rev.: $9,487,000,000
Assets: $62,550,000,000
Liabilities: $54,325,000,000
Net Worth: $8,225,000,000
Earnings: ($243,000,000)
Emp.: 6,466
Fiscal Year-end: 12/31/2020
Holding Company
N.A.I.C.S.: 551112
Huynh Thanh Phong *(CEO)*

Subsidiary (Domestic):

FWD Group Limited (2)
13/F Cityplaza Three 14 Taikoo Wan Road, Taikoo Shing, Quarry Bay, China (Hong Kong)
Tel.: (852) 31233123
Web Site: http://www.fwd.com
General Insurance Services
N.A.I.C.S.: 524210
Huynh Thanh Phong *(CEO)*

Subsidiary (Non-US):

FWD Fuji Life Insurance Company, Limited (3)
2 2 5 Nihonbashi Honcho, Chuo-ku, Tokyo, 103-0023, Japan (100%)
Tel.: (81) 357771331
Web Site: http://www.fwdfujilife.co.jp
Emp.: 883
Insurance Services
N.A.I.C.S.: 524113
Norio Ameno *(Pres & CEO)*

FWD Group Financial Services Pte. Ltd. (3)
10 Collyer Quay #10-01 Ocean Financial Centre, Singapore, 049315, Singapore
Tel.: (65) 6820 8888
Holding Company
N.A.I.C.S.: 551112

Subsidiary (Non-US):

SCB Life Assurance Public Company Limited (4)
1060 New Petchburi Road Makkasan, Rajthevee, Bangkok, 10400, Thailand
Tel.: (66) 2655 3000
Web Site: http://www.scblife.co.th
Sales Range: $5-14.9 Billion
General Insurance Services
N.A.I.C.S.: 524210
Khunying Jada Wattanasiritham *(Chm)*

Subsidiary (Domestic):

FWD Group Management Holdings Limited (3)
13/F Cityplaza Three 14 Taikoo Wan Road, Taikoo Shing, Quarry Bay, China (Hong Kong)
Tel.: (852) 3123 3123
Holding Company; Insurance Services
N.A.I.C.S.: 551112
Ken Lau *(CEO-Hong Kong & Mng Dir-China)*

Subsidiary (Domestic):

Metropolitan Life Insurance Company of Hong Kong Limited (4)
Level 20 Cityplaza 3 14 Taikoo Wan Road, Taikoo Shing, China (Hong Kong) (100%)
Tel.: (852) 81012391
Web Site: http://www.metlife.com.hk
Sales Range: $1-9.9 Million
Emp.: 45
Personal Life & Health Insurance Services
N.A.I.C.S.: 524298
Serge Raffard *(Sr VP & Head-Strategy, Product & Health-Asia)*

Subsidiary (Non-US):

FWD Singapore Pte. Ltd. (3)
6 Temasek Boulevard 18-01 Suntec Tower Four, Singapore, 038986, Singapore
Tel.: (65) 6820 8888 (100%)
Web Site: http://www.fwd.com.sg
Insurance Products & Services
N.A.I.C.S.: 524210
Abhishek Bhatia *(CEO)*

PCCW Limited (1)
41st Floor PCCW Tower TaiKoo Place 979 King's Road, Quarry Bay, China (Hong Kong)
Tel.: (852) 28882888
Web Site: http://www.pccw.com
Rev.: $4,598,287,500
Assets: $12,120,660,000
Liabilities: $10,493,122,500
Net Worth: $1,627,537,500
Earnings: $352,027,500
Emp.: 17,400
Fiscal Year-end: 12/31/2022
Internet & Telecommunication Services
N.A.I.C.S.: 517111
Richard Tzar Kai Li *(Chm & Exec Dir)*

Subsidiary (Non-US):

HKT Global (Singapore) Pte. Ltd. (2)
6 Temasek Boulevard 41-04A 05 Suntec Tower 4, Singapore, 038986, Singapore
Tel.: (65) 6429 3988
Web Site: http://www.hkt.com
Telecommunication Servicesb
N.A.I.C.S.: 517810

Subsidiary (Domestic):

HKT Trust & HKT Limited (2)
39/F PCCW Tower Taikoo Place 979 Kings Road, Quarry Bay, China (Hong Kong)
Tel.: (852) 28947888
Web Site: https://www.hkt.com
Rev.: $4,350,937,500
Assets: $14,177,362,500
Liabilities: $9,532,665,000
Net Worth: $4,644,697,500
Earnings: $627,172,500
Emp.: 14,900
Fiscal Year-end: 12/31/2022
Telecommunication Servicesb
N.A.I.C.S.: 517810
Patrick Chi Ho Poon *(CFO)*

Subsidiary (Non-US):

PCCW (Beijing) Ltd. (2)
13th Floor IBM Tower Pacific Century Place 2A Gong Ti Bei Lu, Chaoyang District, Beijing, 100027, China
Tel.: (86) 1065391818
Web Site: http://www.pccw.com
Sales Range: $25-49.9 Million
Emp.: 20
Internet & Telecommunication Services
N.A.I.C.S.: 517111

PCCW Cascade Technology (Guangzhou) Limited (2)
Unit F-I 11th Floor Hui Hua Commercial & Trade Building, Yue Xiu Qu, Guangzhou, China
Tel.: (86) 20 3761 7532
Telecommunication Servicesb
N.A.I.C.S.: 517810

PCCW Global (Hellas) Telecommunications Services S.A. (2)
Kifissias 212 & Prikleous 2 New Psychiko 154-51, Athens, 15451, Greece
Tel.: (30) 210 671 5100
Telecommunication Servicesb
N.A.I.C.S.: 517810

PCCW Global (Japan) K.K. (2)
3rd Floor Marunouchi Trust Tower Main 1-8-3 Marunouchi, Chiyoda-ku, Tokyo, 100-0005, Japan
Tel.: (81) 3 5222 5850
Web Site: http://www.pccwglobal.com
Emp.: 10
Telecommunication Servicesb
N.A.I.C.S.: 517810
Noriaki Yoshizawa *(Gen Mgr)*

PCCW Global (UK) Ltd. (2)
Ground Floor 78 Brook Street, London, W1K 5EF, United Kingdom
Tel.: (44) 207 297 6123
Web Site: http://www.pccwglobal.com
Telecommunication Servicesb

N.A.I.C.S.: 517810

PCCW Global B.V. (2)
5/F 223 Rue Saint-Honore, 75001, Paris, France
Tel.: (33) 142 660 835
Web Site: http://www.pccwglobal.com
Telecommunication Servicesb
N.A.I.C.S.: 517810
Ying Liang (Gen Mgr)

PCCW Global Korea Limited (2)
11th Floor West Tower Posco Center Building 892 Daechi 4-dong, Kangnam-gu, Seoul, 135-777, Korea (South)
Tel.: (82) 2 559 0770
Telecommunication Servicesb
N.A.I.C.S.: 517810

PCCW Global Limited (2)
Office 304 Level 4 Arjaan Business Tower Media City, PO Box 502441, Dubai, 502441, United Arab Emirates
Tel.: (971) 4 446 7480
Web Site: http://www.pccwglobal.com
Telecommunication Servicesb
N.A.I.C.S.: 517810
Sameh Sobhy (VP)

Subsidiary (US):

PCCW Global, Inc. (2)
450 Spring Park Pl Ste 100, Herndon, VA 20170
Tel.: (703) 621-1600
Web Site: http://www.pccwglobal.bus
Sales Range: $50-74.9 Million
Emp.: 150
Telecommunications Systems
N.A.I.C.S.: 517810
Frederick Chui (Chief Comml Officer)

Subsidiary (Domestic):

PCCW Limited Ventures (2)
39F PCCW Tower TaiKoo Pl 979 King's Rd, Quarry Bay, China (Hong Kong)
Tel.: (852) 28882888
Web Site: http://www.pccw.com
Sales Range: $50-74.9 Million
Emp.: 10
Venture Capital Services
N.A.I.C.S.: 523999

Subsidiary (Non-US):

PCCW Solutions (Xi'an) Limited (2)
Room 401 Qinfeng Pavilion Xi'an Software Park, No 68 Keji 2nd Road, Xi'an, 710075, China
Tel.: (86) 29 6851 8188
Telecommunication Servicesb
N.A.I.C.S.: 517810

Subsidiary (Domestic):

PCCW Solutions Limited (2)
Level 1 The Long Beach Commercial Podium, 8 Hoi Fai Road, Kowloon, China (Hong Kong)
Tel.: (852) 2296 8818
Web Site: http://www.pccwsolutions.com
IT Services; Cloud Computing, Data Center, Managed Services & Digital & IoT
N.A.I.C.S.: 518210
Sinko Choy (Sr VP & Head-Client & Market Dev)

Subsidiary (Non-US):

HCL Insys Pte Limited (3)
The Signature 09-02 51 Changi Business Park Central 2, Singapore, 486066, Singapore
Tel.: (65) 6392 2482
Information Technology Consulting Services
N.A.I.C.S.: 541512

Subsidiary (Non-US):

HCL Infosystems MEA FZE (4)
Third Floor Sobha Ivory Tower 2 Business Bay, PO Box 54590, Dubai, United Arab Emirates
Tel.: (971) 44587748
Web Site: http://www.hclmea.com
Information Technology Consulting Services
N.A.I.C.S.: 541512
Manoj Shrivastava (VP & Head-Bus)

Subsidiary (Non-US):

PCCW Technology (Beijing) Limited (2)
No 901-903 Wenhua Mansion No 59 Zhong Guancun Street, Haidian District, Beijing, 100872, China
Tel.: (86) 10 8250 5588
Telecommunication Servicesb
N.A.I.C.S.: 517810

Subsidiary (Domestic):

PCCW Teleservices (2)
23rd Floor West Exchange Tower 322 Des Voeux Road, Seung Wan, Central, China (Hong Kong)
Tel.: (852) 2888 3636
Web Site: http://www.pccwteleservices.com
Sales Range: $1-4.9 Billion
Emp.: 600
Outsourced Telephonic Support Services
N.A.I.C.S.: 517810

Pacific Century Premium Developments Ltd. (2)
8th Floor Cyberport 2 100 Cyberport Road, Hong Kong, China (Hong Kong)
Tel.: (852) 25143990
Web Site: http://www.pcpd.com
Rev.: $71,527,500
Assets: $1,439,475,000
Liabilities: $1,284,817,500
Net Worth: $154,657,500
Earnings: ($76,245,000)
Emp.: 1,188
Fiscal Year-end: 12/31/2022
Development & Management of Property & Infrastructure Projects
N.A.I.C.S.: 531312
Richard Tzar Kai Li (Exec Dir)

Subsidiary (US):

XinLab, Inc. (2)
1551 McCarthy Blvd Ste 213, Milpitas, CA 95035
Tel.: (408) 649-2240
Web Site: http://www.vuclip.com
Video Search & Delivery Software Publishers
N.A.I.C.S.: 513210
Bo Shen (CTO)

PineBridge Investments LLC (1)
399 Park Ave 4th Fl, New York, NY 10022
Tel.: (646) 857-8000
Web Site: http://www.pinebridge.com
Sales Range: $200-249.9 Million
Emp.: 700
Investment Management Service
N.A.I.C.S.: 523940
W. Michael Verge (Exec Dir)

Subsidiary (Non-US):

PineBridge Benson Elliot LLP (2)
50 Hans Crescent, London, SW1X 0NA, United Kingdom
Tel.: (44) 20 7808 8900
Private Equity & Real Estate Fund Management Firm
N.A.I.C.S.: 523999
Marc Mogull (Chm & Chief Investment Officer)

Subsidiary (Domestic):

Sigma Capital Group plc (3)
18 Alva Street, Edinburgh, EH2 4QG, United Kingdom
Tel.: (44) 333 999 9926
Web Site: http://www.sigmacapital.co.uk
Venture Capital Services
N.A.I.C.S.: 523999
Graham F. Barnet (Founder & CEO)

Subsidiary (Domestic):

Sigma Technology Management Ltd. (4)
6th Floor Bucklersbury House, 83 Cannon Street, London, EC4N, United Kingdom
Tel.: (44) 20 7653 3200
Web Site: http://www.sigmacapital.co.uk
Investment Services
N.A.I.C.S.: 523999

Subsidiary (Non-US):

PineBridge Investments (Central Europe) Sp. z o.o. (2)
Skorupki 5, Warsaw, 00546, Poland
Tel.: (48) 22 583 70 00
Web Site: http://www.pinebridge.com
Emp.: 55
Investment Management Service
N.A.I.C.S.: 523940
Pierre Francois Georges Mellinger (Pres & CEO)

PineBridge Investments Asia Ltd. (2)
Level 31 Three Pacific Place 1 Queen's Road East, Hong Kong, China (Hong Kong)
Tel.: (852) 3970 3970
Web Site: http://www.pinebridge.com.hk
Investment Management Service
N.A.I.C.S.: 523940
Anthony Fasso (CEO-Asia Pacifico)

PineBridge Investments Europe Ltd. (2)
6th Floor Exchequer Court 33 St Mary Axe, London, EC3A 8AA, United Kingdom
Tel.: (44) 20 7398 6000
Emp.: 75
Investment Management Service
N.A.I.C.S.: 523940
Paul Osborne (Mng Dir-Institutional Sls)

PineBridge Investments Japan Co., Ltd. (2)
JA Building 3-1 Otemachi 1-chome, Chiyoda-ku, Tokyo, 100 6813, Japan
Tel.: (81) 3 5208 5800
Web Site: http://www.pinebridge.co.jp
Investment Management Service
N.A.I.C.S.: 523940

PineBridge Investments Middle East B.S.C. (c) (2)
GBCORP Tower, 3rd Floor Bahrain Financial Harbour District, PO Box 588, Manama, Bahrain
Tel.: (973) 17151536
Investment Management Service
N.A.I.C.S.: 523940
Talal Al Zain (CEO)

PACIFIC CENTURY REGIONAL DEVELOPMENTS LTD.
50 Raffles Place 35-01 Singapore Land Tower, Singapore, 048623, Singapore
Tel.: (65) 64382366
Web Site: https://www.pcrd.com
Year Founded: 1963
P15—(SES)
Rev.: $7,374,082
Assets: $390,085,586
Liabilities: $144,770,128
Net Worth: $245,315,458
Earnings: ($23,774,142)
Fiscal Year-end: 12/31/23
Holding Company; Business Support Services
N.A.I.C.S.: 551112
Richard Tzar Kai Li (Chm)

PACIFIC CHEVROLET BUICK GMC LTD
3800 Johnston Road, Port Alberni, V9Y 5N7, BC, Canada
Tel.: (250) 723-3541
Web Site: https://www.pacificchevrolet.com
Year Founded: 1986
Sales Range: $10-24.9 Million
Emp.: 32
Car Dealer
N.A.I.C.S.: 441110
Nicole Wiltse (Controller)

PACIFIC COASTAL AIRLINES LIMITED
Vancouver Intl Airport South Terminal, 4440 Cowley Crescent Unit 204, Richmond, V7B 1B8, BC, Canada
Tel.: (604) 214-2358
Web Site: http://www.pacificcoastal.com
Sales Range: $75-99.9 Million
Emp.: 300
Oil Transportation Services

N.A.I.C.S.: 481111
Quentin P. Smith Jr. (Pres)

PACIFIC CONQUEST HOLDINGS, INC.
6/F Rm C 50 Stanley Street, Central, China (Hong Kong)
Tel.: (852) 28776278 NV
Web Site: http://www.pacific-conquest.com
PCHK—(OTCIQ)
Liabilities: $203,000
Net Worth: ($203,000)
Earnings: ($15,000)
Fiscal Year-end: 03/31/21
Oil & Gas Exploration Services
N.A.I.C.S.: 213112
Ronald K. Cormick (Pres & CEO)

PACIFIC CONSTRUCTION CO., LTD.
No 495 Guangfu South Road, Xinyi District, Taipei, Taiwan
Tel.: (886) 227225051
Web Site: http://www.pacific-group.com.tw
2506—(TAI)
Rev.: $48,606,591
Assets: $437,102,995
Liabilities: $151,363,937
Net Worth: $285,739,059
Earnings: $3,965,630
Fiscal Year-end: 12/31/23
Construction Engineering Services
N.A.I.C.S.: 237990
Chin-Hui Chen (Pres & Gen Mgr)

PACIFIC CONSTRUCTION GROUP COMPANY LIMITED
1 Wutaishan, Nanjing, 210029, China
Tel.: (86) 25 57911111
Web Site: http://www.cpcg.com.cn
Year Founded: 1995
Sales Range: Less than $1 Million
Construction Engineering Services
N.A.I.C.S.: 541330
Cesar Silva (CEO)

PACIFIC CONTROLS INC.
Green Building, PO Box 37316, Techno Park, Dubai, United Arab Emirates
Tel.: (971) 4 886 9000
Web Site: http://www.pacificcontrols.net
Year Founded: 2000
Sales Range: $100-124.9 Million
Emp.: 1,000
Machine to Machine (M2M) Communication Application Solutions
N.A.I.C.S.: 541511
Dilip Rahulan (Chm & CEO)

Subsidiaries:

Infotility, Inc. (1)
2060 Broadway St, Boulder, CO 80302
Tel.: (720) 210-1984
Web Site: http://www.infotility.com
Sales Range: $1-9.9 Million
Emp.: 9
Custom Computer Programming Services
N.A.I.C.S.: 541511

Pacific Controls Cloud Services FZE (1)
Techno Park Sheikh Zayed Road, Post Box 38478, Dubai, United Arab Emirates
Tel.: (971) 4 815 3777
Information Technology Consulting Services
N.A.I.C.S.: 541511
Flor Angelie Raymundo (Engr-IT & Ops)

Pacific Controls Inc. (1)
230 Davidson Ave, Somerset, NJ 08873
Tel.: (732) 748-0060
Information Technology Consulting Services
N.A.I.C.S.: 541511
Angela Pfeffer (Project Mgr)

Pacific Controls Inc.—(Continued)

Pacific Controls Inc. (1)
120 Adelaide Street West Suite 2500, Toronto, M5H 1T1, ON, Canada
Tel.: (416) 847-7312
Web Site: https://www.pacificcontrols.net
Information Technology Consulting Services
N.A.I.C.S.: 541511
Amir Rashid (COO)

Pacific Controls Smart Grid Services (1)
2060 Broadway Ste 320, Boulder, CO 80302
Tel.: (720) 210-1984
Information Technology Consulting Services
N.A.I.C.S.: 541511

PACIFIC CURRENT GROUP LIMITED
Suite 3 Level 3 257 Collins Street, Melbourne, 3000, VIC, Australia
Tel.: (61) 383759611 AU
Web Site: https://www.paccurrent.com
PAC—(ASX)
Rev.: $139,446,447
Assets: $486,031,649
Liabilities: $86,018,963
Net Worth: $400,012,685
Earnings: $73,686,565
Emp.: 7
Fiscal Year-end: 06/30/24
Fund Management Services
N.A.I.C.S.: 525910
Stephen Bramley (Mng Dir-Business Development)

Subsidiaries:

Aether Investment Partners, LLC (1)
1900 16th St Ste 825, Denver, CO 80202
Tel.: (720) 961-4190
Web Site: https://www.aetherip.com
Investment Advisory Services
N.A.I.C.S.: 523940
David Rhoades (COO)

PACIFIC CUSTOMS BROKERS LTD.
101 17637 1st Avenue, Surrey, V3S 9S1, BC, Canada
Tel.: (604) 538-1566
Web Site: http://www.pcb.ca
Year Founded: 1958
Sales Range: $25-49.9 Million
Customs Brokerage Services
N.A.I.C.S.: 488510
Greg Timm (Pres)

PACIFIC DAIRIES LIMITED
21 Wells Road, Melbourne, 3195, VIC, Australia
Tel.: (61) 3 9584 4328
Year Founded: 2001
Farming Services
N.A.I.C.S.: 112410

PACIFIC DENIMS LTD.
3 Bir uttam mir shawkat sarak, Dhaka, 1212, Bangladesh
Tel.: (880) 29855523
Web Site: https://www.pacificgroupbd.com
Year Founded: 2003
PDL—(CHT)
Rev.: $12,902,720
Assets: $32,942,709
Liabilities: $10,210,424
Net Worth: $22,732,285
Earnings: $206,956
Emp.: 410
Fiscal Year-end: 06/30/23
Fabrics Mfr
N.A.I.C.S.: 313310
Shadequl Alam (Chm)

PACIFIC DRILLING S.A.
8-10 Avenue de la Gare, L-1610, Luxembourg, Luxembourg
Tel.: (352) 27858135 LU
Web Site: http://www.pacificdrilling.com
PACD—(NYSE)
Rev.: $229,777,000
Assets: $2,256,559,000
Liabilities: $1,187,728,000
Net Worth: $1,068,831,000
Earnings: ($556,465,000)
Emp.: 763
Fiscal Year-end: 12/31/19
Oil & Gas Contract Drilling
N.A.I.C.S.: 213111
Amy L. Roddy (Sr VP-Corp Svcs)

Subsidiaries:

Pacific Drilling Services Pte. Ltd. (1)
1 Temasek Ave 37-02A Millenia Tower, Singapore, 39192, Singapore
Tel.: (65) 6720 9027
Oil & Gas Well Drilling Services
N.A.I.C.S.: 213112

Pacific Drilling Services, Inc. (1)
3050 Post Oak Blvd Ste 1500, Houston, TX 77056
Tel.: (713) 334-6662
Web Site: http://www.pacificdrilling.com
Oil & Gas Well Drilling Services
N.A.I.C.S.: 213112

PACIFIC EDGE LIMITED
Centre for Innovation 87 St David St, PO Box 56, Dunedin, 9016, New Zealand
Tel.: (64) 34795800 NZ
Web Site: https://www.pacificedgedx.com
Year Founded: 2001
PEB—(ASX)
Rev.: $15,624,402
Assets: $54,373,804
Liabilities: $4,874,402
Net Worth: $49,499,402
Earnings: ($16,127,392)
Emp.: 114
Fiscal Year-end: 03/31/23
Biotechnology Research & Development Services
N.A.I.C.S.: 541714
David Darling (CEO)

Subsidiaries:

Pacific Edge Diagnostics New Zealand Limited (1)
Centre for Innovation 87 St David Street, PO Box 56, Dunedin, 9016, New Zealand
Tel.: (64) 34795800
Diagnostic Product Distr
N.A.I.C.S.: 423450

Pacific Edge Diagnostics Singapore Pte Limited (1)
31 Rochester Drive Park Avenue Rochester Level 24 Suite 23, Singapore, 138637, Singapore
Tel.: (65) 68088797
Diagnostic Product Distr
N.A.I.C.S.: 423450

Pacific Edge Diagnostics USA Limited (1)
1214 Research Blvd Ste 2000, Hummelstown, PA 17036
Tel.: (717) 220-7005
Diagnostic Product Distr
N.A.I.C.S.: 423450

PACIFIC EMPIRE MINERALS CORP.
Suite 804 - 525 Seymour Street, Vancouver, V6B 3H6, BC, Canada
Tel.: (604) 356-6246
Web Site: https://www.pemcorp.ca
Year Founded: 2012
PEMSF—(OTCIQ)
Rev.: $63,562
Assets: $751,785
Liabilities: $33,677
Net Worth: $718,108
Earnings: ($789,161)
Fiscal Year-end: 12/31/19
Metal Exploration Services
N.A.I.C.S.: 213114
Thomas Hawkins (VP-Exploration)

PACIFIC EQUITY PARTNERS PTY. LIMITED
Level 31 126 Phillip Street, Sydney, 2000, NSW, Australia
Tel.: (61) 282382600 AU
Web Site: http://www.pep.com.au
Year Founded: 1998
Privater Equity Firm
N.A.I.C.S.: 523999
Rickard Gardell (Co-Founder & Mng Dir)

Subsidiaries:

Braiform Group Pty Ltd. (1)
91 Springsteen Garden Drive, PO Box 4424, Dandenong South, Melbourne, 3175, VIC, Australia
Tel.: (61) 387952250
Web Site: http://www.braiform.com
Emp.: 9
Plastic Hangers Mfr & Distr
N.A.I.C.S.: 326199

Subsidiary (Non-US):

Braiform (U.K.) Ltd (2)
98 Victoria Road, London, NW10 6NB, United Kingdom
Tel.: (44) 2087233000
Web Site: http://www.braiform.com
Garment Hangers Mfr
N.A.I.C.S.: 326199
Katharine Lamba (Mgr-HR)

Braiform (Deutschland) GmbH (2)
Hertzstrasse 10, 32052, Herford, Germany
Tel.: (49) 5221694890
Sales Range: $25-49.9 Million
Garment Hangers Mfr
N.A.I.C.S.: 326199

Braitrim (Lanka) Pvt Ltd. (2)
351 2nd Floor R A De Mel Mawatha, Colombo, 00300, Sri Lanka
Tel.: (94) 115512003
Web Site: http://www.braiform.com
Sales Range: $25-49.9 Million
Garment Hangers Mfr
N.A.I.C.S.: 326199
Nalin Anthony (Country Mgr)

Braitrim (Scandinavia) AB (2)
Kvarngatan 9, PO Box 144, SE 335 23, Gnosjo, Sweden
Tel.: (46) 370333150
Web Site: http://www.braiform.com
Sales Range: $25-49.9 Million
Emp.: 5
Garment Hangers Whslr
N.A.I.C.S.: 424990

Braitrim India (Private) Ltd. (2)
1105 Marker V Nariman Point, Mumbai, 400021, India
Tel.: (91) 2266324711
Web Site: http://www.spotless.com
Sales Range: $25-49.9 Million
Garment Hangers Mfr
N.A.I.C.S.: 326199

Braitrim Plasti-Form (Middle East) FZCO (2)
RA08-JC-3 Jebel Ali Free Zone, PO Box 18099, Dubai, 18099, United Arab Emirates
Tel.: (971) 48836700
Web Site: http://www.braiform.com
Sales Range: $25-49.9 Million
Emp.: 10
Garment Hangers Mfr
N.A.I.C.S.: 326199
Masood Zavery (Gen Mgr)

Braitrim Plasti-Form South Africa (Pty) Limited (2)
Unit 20 West End Prime Park Printers Way, Montague Gardens, 7441, Cape Town, Western Cape, South Africa
Tel.: (27) 215551127
Web Site: http://www.braiform.com
Emp.: 2
Garment Hangers Mfr
N.A.I.C.S.: 326199
Masood Zavery (Mgr)

Thai Fashion Plastics Ind Co., Ltd. (2)
40/29 Moo 6 Suksawad Soi 78, Phrapradaeng, Samut Prakan, 10130, Thailand
Tel.: (66) 281760136
Web Site: http://www.braiform.com
Garment Hangers Whslr
N.A.I.C.S.: 424990

Godfreys Group Limited (1)
Building 2 Level 1 Brandon Business Park, 530-540 Springvale Road, Glen Waverley, 3150, VIC, Australia
Tel.: (61) 3 8542 2110
Web Site: http://www.godfreys.com.au
Vacuums & Cleaning Products Whslr
N.A.I.C.S.: 449210
Rod Walker (Chm)

Griffin's Foods Ltd. (1)
Tower B Level 5 100 Carlton Gore Road, Newmarket, Auckland, New Zealand
Tel.: (64) 800 474334
Web Site: http://www.griffins.co.nz
Biscuits, Sauces & Snacks Mfr
N.A.I.C.S.: 311812
Alison Barrass (CEO)

Healthia Limited (1)
L4 East Tower 25 Montpelier Road, Bowen Hills, 4006, QLD, Australia
Tel.: (61) 731804900
Web Site: http://www.healthia.com.au
Rev.: $153,440,274
Assets: $274,323,603
Liabilities: $142,183,411
Net Worth: $132,140,192
Earnings: $262,803
Fiscal Year-end: 06/30/2022
Health Care Srvices
N.A.I.C.S.: 621498
Glen Evangelista (Mgr-Comml)

Link Market Services Ltd. (1)
Level 12 680 George Street, Sydney, 2000, NSW, Australia
Tel.: (61) 282807111
Web Site: http://www.linkmarketservices.com.au
Share Registry Services
N.A.I.C.S.: 522320
John Menzies McMurtrie (Mng Dir)

Subsidiary (US):

American Stock Transfer & Trust Company, LLC (2)
59 Maiden Ln Plz Level, New York, NY 10038
Tel.: (212) 936-5100
Web Site: http://www.amstock.com
Stock Transfer Agent Services
N.A.I.C.S.: 522320
Brad Starkweather (Sr VP-AST IR Solutions)

Subsidiary (Domestic):

AST Equity Plan Solutions, Inc. (3)
123 S Broad St Ste 1160, Philadelphia, PA 19109
Tel.: (267) 515-5400
Web Site: http://www.astepsdiv.com
Financial Advisory Services
N.A.I.C.S.: 523940
Sandeep Sisodia (CIO)

AST Fund Solutions, LLC (3)
55 Challenger Rd Ste 201, Ridgefield Park, NJ 07660
Tel.: (201) 806-7300
Web Site: http://www.astfundsolutions.com
Sales Range: $25-49.9 Million
Shareholder Identification & Corporate Governance Services
N.A.I.C.S.: 541618
Paul Torre (Exec VP)

Subsidiary (Domestic):

D.F. King & Co., Inc. (4)
48 Wall St 22nd Fl, New York, NY 10006
Tel.: (212) 269-5550
Web Site: http://www.dfking.com
Sales Range: $10-24.9 Million
Proxy Solicitation & Other Investor Services
N.A.I.C.S.: 541690

Margaret A. Smith *(Dir-Res)*

Subsidiary (Domestic):

TelAthena Systems (5)
140 58th St Ste 7E, Brooklyn, NY 11320
Tel.: (212) 463-8054
Web Site: http://www.telathena.com
Human Interaction Software & Hosting Services
N.A.I.C.S.: 513210

Subsidiary (Domestic):

DRX Distribution Management, Inc. (4)
419 Park Ave S Rm 1206, New York, NY 10016
Tel.: (212) 481-1411
Web Site: http://www.donlinrecano.com
Bankruptcy Case Administration Services
N.A.I.C.S.: 541611
Alexander T. Leventhal *(CEO)*

Subsidiary (Domestic):

AST Personal Wealth Solutions, LLC (3)
6201 15th Ave, Brooklyn, NY 11219
Tel.: (855) 427-8797
Web Site: http://www.astpersonalwealth.com
Investment Management Service
N.A.I.C.S.: 523940
Mark C. Healy *(CEO)*

LINK Shareholder Services, LLC (3)
6201 15th Ave, Brooklyn, NY 11219
Tel.: (800) 323-1404
Web Site: http://www.linkshareholderservices.com
Financial Services
N.A.I.C.S.: 541611
Matt Alden *(Sr VP-Sls)*

Subsidiary (Domestic):

AST Document Solutions (4)
6201 15th Ave, Brooklyn, NY 11219
Tel.: (866) 627-2494
Web Site: http://www.astdocumentsolutions.com
Comprehensive Document, Data & Communicaiton Preparation, Distr & Printing Services
N.A.I.C.S.: 561410
Joel Ronis *(Sr VP)*

First American Stock Transfer, Inc. (4)
3rd Fl 6201 15th Ave, Brooklyn, NY 11219
Tel.: (602) 485-1346
Web Site: http://www.firstamericanstock.com
Stock Trading Services
N.A.I.C.S.: 523210
Jennifer Kane *(Dir-Ops)*

Subsidiary (Non-US):

D.F. King (Europe) Limited (2)
Citypoint 34th Floor, 1 Ropemaker Street, London, EC2Y 9AW, United Kingdom
Tel.: (44) 207 920 9700
Web Site: http://www.king-worldwide.com
Mutual Fund Management Services
N.A.I.C.S.: 523940
Tony Larsen *(CFO)*

Subsidiary (Domestic):

Link Market Services Ltd. (2)
Level 4 333 Collins Street, Melbourne, 3000, VIC, Australia
Tel.: (61) 396159874
Web Site: http://www.linkmarketservices.com.au
Share Registry Services
N.A.I.C.S.: 541611

Subsidiary (Domestic):

Australian Administration Services Pty Ltd. (3)
Rhodes Corporate Park 1A Homebush Bay Drive, Rhodes, 2138, NSW, Australia
Tel.: (61) 2 8571 5000
Web Site: www.aas.com.au
Pension Fund Management Services
N.A.I.C.S.: 523940
John McMurray *(Mng Dir)*

CMR Direct (3)
Unit 1 15 Percy Street, Auburn, 2144, NSW, Australia
Tel.: (61) 2 9026 2400
Web Site: http://www.cmrdirect.com.au
Printing & Mailing Services
N.A.I.C.S.: 561431

Pacific Custodians Pty Limited (3)
L 12 680 George St, Sydney, 2000, NSW, Australia
Tel.: (61) 282807111
Share Registry Services
N.A.I.C.S.: 522320

Subsidiary (Non-US):

Link Market Services SA (2)
11 Diagonal St, Johannesburg, 2001, South Africa
Tel.: (27) 118342266
Web Site: http://www.linkmarketservices.co.za
Share Registry Services
N.A.I.C.S.: 541611

Subsidiary (Domestic):

Orient Capital Pty Ltd. (2)
Level 12 680 George Street, Sydney, 2000, NSW, Australia
Tel.: (61) 2 8280 6000
Web Site: http://www.orientcap.com
Investor Relations Services
N.A.I.C.S.: 522320

Subsidiary (Non-US):

King Worldwide Investor Relations (3)
85 Crescent St, London, EC2V 7NQ, United Kingdom
Tel.: (44) 20 7920 6900
Investor Relations Services
N.A.I.C.S.: 523210
Paolo Casamassima *(Dir-Bus Dev & Ops)*

The Citadel Group Limited (1)
Level 1 11-13 Faulding Street, Symonston, Canberra, 2609, ACT, Australia
Tel.: (61) 2 6124 0800
Web Site: http://www.citadelgroup.com.au
Rev: $69,352,911
Assets: $100,447,091
Liabilities: $40,058,262
Net Worth: $60,388,830
Earnings: $7,603,069
Emp.: 200
Fiscal Year-end: 06/30/2019
Business Consulting Services
N.A.I.C.S.: 541611
H. Kevin McCann *(Chm)*

Subsidiary (Domestic):

Citadel Health Pty. Ltd. (2)
Level 19 459 Collins Street, Melbourne, 3000, VIC, Australia
Tel.: (61) 386780780
Web Site: http://www.citadelhealth.com.au
Software Development Services
N.A.I.C.S.: 541511

Citadel People Pty. Ltd. (2)
Level 14 348 Edward St, Brisbane, 4000, QLD, Australia
Tel.: (61) 735575103
Web Site: http://www.citadelpeople.com.au
Recruitment Services
N.A.I.C.S.: 561311

Citadel Technology Solutions Pty. Ltd. (2)
Citadel HouseHigh Technology Park Level 1 11-13 Faulding Street, Symonston, Canberra, 2609, ACT, Australia
Tel.: (61) 1800667888
Web Site: http://www.citadeltech.com.au
Concierge Services
N.A.I.C.S.: 812990

Kapish Services Pty. Ltd. (2)
Level 19 459 Collins Street, Melbourne, 3000, VIC, Australia
Tel.: (61) 390174943
Web Site: http://www.kapish.com.au
Software Development Services
N.A.I.C.S.: 541511

Noventus Pty. Ltd. (2)
Level 19 459 Collins St, Melbourne, 3000, VIC, Australia
Tel.: (61) 390778959
Web Site: http://www.noventus.com.au
Software Development Services
N.A.I.C.S.: 541511

Subsidiary (Non-US):

Wellbeing Software Ltd. (2)
Hamilton Court Oakham Business Park, Mansfield, NG18 5FB, United Kingdom
Tel.: (44) 1623489838
Web Site: http://www.wellbeingsoftware.com
Healthcare Services
N.A.I.C.S.: 621610

Whitcoulls Ltd (1)
131 Queen St, PO Box 92098, Auckland, New Zealand
Tel.: (64) 93565410
Web Site: http://www.whitcoulls.co.nz
Sales Range: $25-49.9 Million
Clothing Stores
N.A.I.C.S.: 458110

iNova Pharmaceuticals (Australia) Pty Limited (1)
Level 10 12 Help Street, Chatswood, 2067, NSW, Australia
Tel.: (61) 289186322
Web Site: http://www.inovapharma.com
Pharmaceuticals Product Mfr
N.A.I.C.S.: 325412
Dan Spira *(CEO)*

Subsidiary (Non-US):

iNova Pharmaceuticals (Pty) Limited (2)
15e Riley Road, PO Box 3115, Bedfordview, 2008, South Africa
Tel.: (27) 110870000
Web Site: http://www.inovapharma.co.za
Pharmaceuticals Product Mfr
N.A.I.C.S.: 325412
Kym Hampton *(Country Mgr)*

PACIFIC FLOW TECHNOLOGY PTY. LTD.
9 Elsum Avenue, Bayswater, 3153, VIC, Australia
Tel.: (61) 3 9729 1225
Web Site: http://www.pacflotech.com.au
Rubber Hose Mfr & Distr
N.A.I.C.S.: 326220

PACIFIC HEALTHCARE HOLDINGS LTD.
290 Orchard Road 19-01 Paragon, Singapore, 238859, Singapore
Tel.: (65) 68836955 SG
Web Site: http://www.pachealthholdings.com
Year Founded: 2001
Sales Range: $25-49.9 Million
Healtcare Services
N.A.I.C.S.: 621491

Subsidiaries:

Aesthetic and Reconstructive Centre Pte. Ltd. (1)
3 Mount Elizabeth 13-08 Mount Elizabeth Medical Centre, 228510, Singapore, 228510, Singapore
Tel.: (65) 67333712
Web Site: http://www.andrewkhoo.com
Healtcare Services
N.A.I.C.S.: 621491

Asia Lifeline Medical Services Pte. Ltd. (1)
290 Orchard Road 19-01 Paragon, Singapore, 238859, Singapore
Tel.: (65) 6887 3737
Web Site: http://www.asialifeline.com
Sales Range: $10-24.9 Million
Emp.: 2
Healtcare Services
N.A.I.C.S.: 621491
Andrew Wong *(CEO)*

Atria Pan Dental Group Pte. Ltd. (1)
209 Orchard Road, 19 01 Pargon Medical, Singapore, 238859, Singapore
Tel.: (65) 67333133
Web Site: http://www.atria-pan.com
Dental Care Services
N.A.I.C.S.: 621210
Chee Haow Chua *(Mng Dir)*

Customized Health Solutions Pte. Ltd. (1)
290 Orchard Road 07-13 Paragon, Singapore, 238859, Singapore
Tel.: (65) 63336292
Web Site: http://www.compoundingpharmacy.com.sg
Pharmaceutical Products Distr.
N.A.I.C.S.: 424210

MD Specialist Healthcare Pte. Ltd. (1)
290 Orchard Road 12-01 Paragon, Singapore, 238859, Singapore
Tel.: (65) 67333376
Web Site: http://www.md-sh.com
General Medical Services
N.A.I.C.S.: 621491

Pacific Healthcare Specialist Services Pte. Ltd. (1)
290 Orchard Road 19-01 Paragon, Singapore, 238859, Singapore
Tel.: (65) 62382966
Web Site: http://www.pachealthholdings.com
Emp.: 20
General Medical Services
N.A.I.C.S.: 622110
Andrew Wong *(CEO)*

Subsidiary (Domestic):

Robertson Choo Oehlers Lee & Lye Pte. Ltd. (2)
290 Orchard Road 07-13A Paragon, 238859, Singapore, Singapore
Tel.: (65) 6737 3833
Web Site: http://www.rcolldentist.com.sg
Sales Range: $75-99.9 Million
General Medical Services
N.A.I.C.S.: 339116
Choo Teck Chuan *(Mng Dir)*

Pacific Surgical & Endoscopy Centre Pte. Ltd. (1)
290 Orchard Rd 12-01 Paragon, Singapore, 238859, Singapore
Tel.: (65) 6238 2980
Web Site: http://www.daysurgerycentre.com
Sales Range: $10-24.9 Million
Emp.: 37
Surgical & Endoscopic Procedures Facility
N.A.I.C.S.: 621493

Shen Zhen Marsa Pacific Chain Enterprise Limited (1)
5/F Gang Ao City Hua Qiang Road North, Futian District, Shenzhen, 518121, Guangdong, China
Tel.: (86) 755 83255982
General Medical Services
N.A.I.C.S.: 622110

PACIFIC HILL MANAGEMENT INC.
91 Golden Dr Unit 1, Coquitlam, V3K 6R2, BC, Canada
Tel.: (604) 552-5252
Web Site: http://www.directbuy.com
Year Founded: 1971
Rev: $11,000,000
Emp.: 44
Home Furniture & Other Accessories Retailer
N.A.I.C.S.: 449129
Peter Ruetz *(Pres)*

PACIFIC HOSPITAL SUPPLY CO., LTD.
No 8 Tongke 2nd Rd, Hsinchu Science Park Jiuhu Miaoli, Tongluo, Taiwan
Tel.: (886) 228955050
Web Site: https://www.pahsco.com.tw
Year Founded: 1977
4126—(TPE)
Rev: $68,875,465
Assets: $113,989,682
Liabilities: $29,047,682
Net Worth: $84,942,000

Pacific Hospital Supply Co., Ltd.—(Continued)
Earnings: $10,361,661
Emp.: 589
Fiscal Year-end: 12/31/22
Medical Device Mfr
N.A.I.C.S.: 334510
An-Ting Chung (Chm)

PACIFIC IMAGE ELECTRONICS CO., LTD.
7F No 239 Sec 1 Datong Rd, Xizhi Dist, New Taipei City, 221, Taiwan
Tel.: (886) 286921800
Web Site: https://www.scanace.com
Year Founded: 1993
6228—(TPE)
Rev.: $1,437,076
Assets: $12,387,581
Liabilities: $5,975,518
Net Worth: $6,412,063
Earnings: ($799,925)
Fiscal Year-end: 12/31/22
Computer Peripheral Equipment Distr
N.A.I.C.S.: 423430
Wei-Chao Kao (Chm)

PACIFIC IMPERIAL MINES INC.
Suite 400 1681 Chestnut Street, Vancouver, V6J 1M6, BC, Canada
Tel.: (604) 669-6332
Web Site:
 https://www.pacificimperial.com
PPM—(TSXV)
Rev.: $246
Assets: $253,461
Liabilities: $123,506
Net Worth: $129,955
Earnings: ($413,519)
Fiscal Year-end: 06/30/21
Metal Mining Services
N.A.I.C.S.: 212220
Roman Shklanka (Chm)

PACIFIC INDUSTRIAL CO. LTD.
100 Kyutoku-Cho, Ogaki, 503-8603, Gifu, Japan
Tel.: (81) 584911111
Web Site: https://www.pacific-ind.co.jp
7250—(TKS)
Rev.: $1,370,570,280
Assets: $1,933,127,550
Liabilities: $826,633,380
Net Worth: $1,106,494,170
Earnings: $112,198,140
Emp.: 4,960
Fiscal Year-end: 03/31/24
Valve Cores Mfr
N.A.I.C.S.: 332911
Katsuya Suzuki (Sr Mng Officer)

Subsidiaries:

Changsha Pacific Hanya Auto Parts Co., Ltd. (1)
No 68 Eleven East Road ETDZ, Changsha, Hunan, China
Tel.: (86) 73182758459
Emp.: 175
Metal Stamping Product Mfr & Distr
N.A.I.C.S.: 332119
Hidenori Yoshida (Pres)

PI System Co., Ltd. (1)
4-1-17 Kagano, Ogaki, 503-0006, Gifu, Japan
Tel.: (81) 584770560
Web Site: https://www.pi-system.co.jp
Sales Range: $25-49.9 Million
Emp.: 45
Computer Software Development Services
N.A.I.C.S.: 541511

Pacific Air Controls Co., Ltd. (1)
16-3 Oncheon-daero 1122beon-gil, Asan, Chungcheongnam-do, Korea (South)
Tel.: (82) 415432270
Emp.: 220
Air Conditioner Product Mfr

N.A.I.C.S.: 333415

Pacific Auto Parts (Thailand) Co., Ltd. (1)
119/1 Moo 4 Siam Green City, Industrial Park TPluak Daeng A Pluak Daeng, Rayong, 21140, Thailand
Tel.: (66) 33017371
Emp.: 53
Metal Stamping Product Mfr & Distr
N.A.I.C.S.: 332119
Katsunori Hirose (Pres)

Pacific Auto Parts Technology (Changshu) Co., Ltd. (1)
No 7 WanFu Road Changshu Economic Technology Development Zone, Changshu, Jiangsu, China
Tel.: (86) 51252019512
Emp.: 53
Automotive Parts Mfr & Distr
N.A.I.C.S.: 336390

Pacific Industrial Co., Ltd. - Higashi Ogaki Plant (1)
4-1-1 Asanishi, Ogaki, 503-0945, Gifu, Japan
Tel.: (81) 584890111
Web Site: http://www.pacific-ind.co.jp
Automotive Product Mfr
N.A.I.C.S.: 336110

Pacific Industrial Co., Ltd. - Kyushu Plant (1)
1479-3 Katsuno Senzoku Kotake-cho, Kurate, 820-1103, Fukuoka, Japan
Tel.: (81) 949662200
Web Site: http://www.pacific-ind.co.jp
Stamping & Molding Automobile Products Mfr
N.A.I.C.S.: 332510

Pacific Industrial Co., Ltd. - Mino Plant (1)
550 Suhara, Mino, 501-3706, Gifu, Japan
Tel.: (81) 575322211
Web Site: http://www.pacific-ind.co.jp
Sales Range: $400-449.9 Million
Emp.: 88
Valve Cores Mfr
N.A.I.C.S.: 332911

Pacific Industrial Co., Ltd. - Yoro Plant (1)
1615 Funatsuke Yoro-cho, Yoro, 503-1382, Gifu, Japan
Tel.: (81) 584351111
Web Site: http://www.pacific-ind.com
CAD/CAM System Specialists in Dies & Molds Manufacturing
N.A.I.C.S.: 333511

Pacific Industries (Thailand) Co., Ltd. (1)
81 Moo 1 Wellgrow Industrial Estate Tambol Homsil Amphur, Bangpakong, Chachoengsao, 24130, Thailand
Tel.: (66) 38570074
Web Site: http://www.pacific-ind.co.jp
Sales Range: $50-74.9 Million
Emp.: 250
Tire Valve Products & Controls Mfr & Sales
N.A.I.C.S.: 332912
Kojiro Kitamura (Pres)

Pacific Industries China Corporation (1)
No 99 Xishi Road Tianjin Airport Economic Area, Tianjin, China
Tel.: (86) 2284866112
Emp.: 3
Automobile Parts Mfr
N.A.I.C.S.: 336390
Koji Tsuiki (Chm & Pres)

Pacific Industries Europe NV/SA (1)
Room 419 Regus Brussels AirportPegasuslaan5, 1831, Diegem, Belgium
Tel.: (32) 27092165
Automobile Parts Mfr
N.A.I.C.S.: 423120

Pacific Industries USA Inc. (1)
8935 Seward Rd, Fairfield, OH 45011
Tel.: (513) 642-0055
Emp.: 21
Automobile Parts Mfr
N.A.I.C.S.: 336390
Terumi Noda (Pres)

Pacific Manufacturing Ohio, Inc. (1)
8955 Seward Rd, Fairfield, OH 45011
Tel.: (513) 642-0055
Emp.: 886
Metal Stamping Product Mfr
N.A.I.C.S.: 332119

Pacific Manufacturing Tennessee, Inc. (1)
555 Smith Ln, Jackson, TN 38301
Tel.: (731) 300-7500
Emp.: 386
Metal Stamping Product Mfr
N.A.I.C.S.: 332119

Pacific Valve (Taiwan) Co., Ltd. (1)
5 7th Road, Taichung Industrial Park, Taichung, Taiwan
Tel.: (886) 423593690
Web Site: http://www.pacific-ind.co.jp
Sales Range: $125-149.9 Million
Emp.: 225
Tire Valve Products & Metal Stamping Products Mfr & Sales
N.A.I.C.S.: 332912
Koji Takahashi (Pres)

Pacific Valve Industrial Co., Ltd. (1)
Sanmakgongdanbuk6ro 74, Yangsan, 626-120, Gyeongsangnam-do, Korea (South)
Tel.: (82) 553803800
Emp.: 75
Air Conditioner Product Mfr
N.A.I.C.S.: 333415
Junichi Sakaida (Pres)

Taiheiyo Sangyo Co., Ltd. (1)
801 Akasaka-cho, Ogaki, 503-2213, Gifu, Japan
Tel.: (81) 584925630
Emp.: 38
Automobile Parts Mfr
N.A.I.C.S.: 336390

Tianjin Pacific Auto Parts Co., Ltd. (1)
No 99 Xishi Road, Tianjin Airport Economic Area, Tianjin, China
Tel.: (86) 2224893730
Web Site: http://www.pacific-ind.com
Sales Range: $100-124.9 Million
Emp.: 318
Automobile Parts Mfr
N.A.I.C.S.: 336310
Koji Tsuiki (Pres)

PACIFIC INDUSTRIES LTD.
Survey No 13 N H 48 Kempalinganahalli Village Nelamangala Taluk, Bengaluru, 562 123, Karnataka, India
Tel.: (91) 807723004
Web Site:
 https://www.pacificindustriesltd.com
523483—(BOM)
Rev.: $24,441,964
Assets: $62,094,215
Liabilities: $11,647,635
Net Worth: $50,446,580
Earnings: $780,061
Emp.: 150
Fiscal Year-end: 03/31/23
Granite Slab & Tiles Mfr
N.A.I.C.S.: 212313
Sachin Shah (Compliance Officer & Sec)

PACIFIC INFRASTRUCTURE PROJECT DEVELOPMENT AND INVESTMENT CORPORATION
31/21 Kha Van Can St Hiep Binh Chanh Ward, Thu Duc Dist, Ho Chi Minh City, Vietnam
Tel.: (84) 8 3726 9701
Web Site:
 http://www.ppigroup.com.vn
Sales Range: $10-24.9 Million
Road Construction Services
N.A.I.C.S.: 237310

PACIFIC LEGEND GROUP LTD.
Units 1202-1204 Level 12 Cyberport 2 100 Cyberport Road Cyberport, Hong Kong, China (Hong Kong)
Tel.: (852) 25523500
Web Site:
 https://www.pacificlegendgroup.com
8547—(HKG)
Rev.: $26,014,845
Assets: $16,571,175
Liabilities: $11,473,470
Net Worth: $5,097,705
Earnings: ($6,105,720)
Emp.: 159
Fiscal Year-end: 12/31/22
Furniture Product Whslr
N.A.I.C.S.: 449110
John Warren McLennan (Founder & Chm)

Subsidiaries:

Indigo Living Limited (1)
Units 1202-1204 Level 12 100 Cyberport Road, Hong Kong, China (Hong Kong)
Tel.: (852) 25523500
Web Site: http://www.indigo-living.com
Home Furnishings Retailer
N.A.I.C.S.: 449129

PACIFIC LINK MINING CORP.
2772 - 1055 West Georgia Street, Vancouver, V6E 3P3, BC, Canada
Tel.: (604) 484-8252
Rev.: $1,638
Assets: $239,573
Liabilities: $11,106
Net Worth: $228,467
Earnings: ($37,253)
Fiscal Year-end: 12/31/17
Metal Mining Services
N.A.I.C.S.: 212290

PACIFIC MARINE BATTERIES PTY. LTD.
655 Mersey Road, Osborne, 5017, SA, Australia
Tel.: (61) 883418266
Web Site:
 http://www.pmbatteries.com.au
Sales Range: $10-24.9 Million
Emp.: 60
Mfr of Submarine Batteries
N.A.I.C.S.: 335910
Steven Faulkner (CEO)

PACIFIC METALS CO., LTD.
5-2 Toyamashinden Kawaraki, Hachinohe, 031-8617, Aomori, Japan
Tel.: (81) 178477121
Web Site: https://www.pacific-metals.co.jp
Year Founded: 1949
5541—(TKS)
Rev.: $102,593,810
Assets: $487,751,900
Liabilities: $31,265,300
Net Worth: $456,486,600
Earnings: ($7,099,140)
Emp.: 422
Fiscal Year-end: 03/31/24
Ferronickel Mfr & Distr
N.A.I.C.S.: 331110
Masayuki Aoyama (Pres & CEO)

Subsidiaries:

Pacific Gas Center Co., Ltd. (1)
20-2 Kaigan Kawaragi, Aomori, Hachinohe, 039-1161, Japan
Tel.: (81) 178471500
Oxygen Gas Mfr & Distr
N.A.I.C.S.: 325120

Pacific Rundum Co., Ltd. (1)
1 Iwaseakada-machi, Toyama, 931-8555, Japan
Tel.: (81) 764381211
Web Site: https://www.rundum.co.jp
Semiconductor Mfr & Distr
N.A.I.C.S.: 333242

Taiheiyo Kosan Co., Ltd. (1)

3-6-13 Numadate, Aomori, Hachinohe, 031-0071, Japan
Tel.: (81) 178470555
Real Estate Services
N.A.I.C.S.: 531390

PACIFIC MILLENNIUM PACKAGING GROUP CORPORATION
Suite 2104 21 Floor Tower 2 Lippo Centre 89 Queensway, Hong Kong, China (Hong Kong)
Tel.: (852) 27355188　　Ky
Web Site: http://www.pmpgc.com
Year Founded: 2014
1820—(HKG)
Rev.: $305,848,624
Assets: $236,250,940
Liabilities: $151,653,481
Net Worth: $84,597,458
Earnings: $3,204,068
Emp.: 1,761
Fiscal Year-end: 12/31/22
Corrugated Board Mfr & Distr
N.A.I.C.S.: 322211
Jerry Hsien-Chun Cheng *(Chm)*

Subsidiaries:

Changshu Pacific Millennium Packaging & Paper Industries Co., Ltd.　(1)
No 37 Shuangbang Rd, Xinzhuang Town, Changshu, 215562, Jiangsu, China
Tel.: (86) 51281580088
Corrugated Board Mfr & Distr
N.A.I.C.S.: 322211

Dalian Pacific Millennium Packaging & Paper Industries Co., Ltd.　(1)
1-2 Xinhuinan Road Dalian Free Trade Zone, Zhang Tun Village Desheng Town, Dalian, 116620, Liaoning, China
Tel.: (86) 41187211616
Corrugated Board Mfr & Distr
N.A.I.C.S.: 322211

Guangdong Pacific Millennium Packaging & Paper Industries Co., Ltd.　(1)
Shiwan Science and Technology Industrial Park, Boluo County, Huizhou, 516127, Guangdong, China
Tel.: (86) 7525899188
Corrugated Board Mfr & Distr
N.A.I.C.S.: 322211

Jiangsu Pacific Millennium Packaging & Paper Industries Co., Ltd.　(1)
No 2589 Linhu Avenue FOHO NEW HIGH-Tech Industrial Development Zone, FOHO NEW and HIGH-Tech Industrial Development Zone, Nanjing, 215211, Jiangsu, China
Tel.: (86) 51288816088
Corrugated Board Mfr & Distr
N.A.I.C.S.: 322211

Nanjing Pacific Millennium Packaging & Paper Industries Co., Ltd.　(1)
No 10 Chunyang Road, Nanjing Jiangning Binjiang Economic and Technical Development Zone, Nanjing, 211178, Jiangsu, China
Tel.: (86) 2586107788
Corrugated Board Mfr & Distr
N.A.I.C.S.: 322211

Qingdao Pacific Millennium Packaging & Paper Industries Co., Ltd.　(1)
No 575 Yinhe Road, Xiazhuang Town Chengyang District, Qingdao, 266107, Shandong, China
Tel.: (86) 53287791997
Corrugated Board Mfr & Distr
N.A.I.C.S.: 322211

Shanghai Pacific Millennium Packaging & Paper Industries Co., Ltd.　(1)
Flat A 2/F No 398 TianLin Road, XuHui District, Shanghai, 200233, China
Tel.: (86) 2154504666
Corrugated Board Mfr & Distr
N.A.I.C.S.: 322211

Shenyang Pacific Millennium Packaging & Paper Industries Co., Ltd.　(1)
140 Guixiang Street, Sujiatun District, Shenyang, 110101, Liaoning, China
Tel.: (86) 2489586168
Corrugated Board Mfr & Distr
N.A.I.C.S.: 322211

Suzhou Pacific Millennium Packaging & Paper Industries Co., Ltd.　(1)
Changping Road, Dongqiao Industry Zone Xiangcheng District, Suzhou, 215152, Jiangsu, China
Tel.: (86) 51265088028
Corrugated Board Mfr & Distr
N.A.I.C.S.: 322211

Taicang Pacific Millennium Packaging & Paper Industries Co., Ltd.　(1)
No 8 Youyi Rd, Huangjing Town, Taicang, 215400, Jiangsu, China
Tel.: (86) 51288899998
Corrugated Board Mfr & Distr
N.A.I.C.S.: 322211

Tianjin Pacific Millennium Packaging & Paper Industries Co., Ltd.　(1)
No 88 2nd Xinye Street West Zone of Tianjin, Economic Technological Development Area, Tianjin, 300462, China
Tel.: (86) 2266321666
Corrugated Board Mfr & Distr
N.A.I.C.S.: 322211

Zhejiang Pacific Millennium Packaging & Paper Industries Co., Ltd.　(1)
No 518 Fengqi East Road Wutong Street, Tongxiang, 314500, Zhejiang, China
Tel.: (86) 57388253456
Corrugated Board Mfr & Distr
N.A.I.C.S.: 322211

PACIFIC MOTOR GROUP PTY. LTD.
122 - 124 Sugar Rd, Maroochydore, 4558, QLD, Australia
Tel.: (61) 754589739
Web Site: http://www.pacificmotorgroup.com
Year Founded: 1986
Automotive Retailer
N.A.I.C.S.: 441110
Nigel Hughes *(Mgr-Svc)*

PACIFIC NATIONAL PTY LTD.
Level 6th 15 Blue St, Sydney, 2060, NSW, Australia
Tel.: (61) 284848000
Web Site: http://www.pacificnational.com.au
Year Founded: 2001
Sales Range: $650-699.9 Million
Emp.: 3,398
Freight Transportation Arrangement
N.A.I.C.S.: 488510
John Mullen *(CEO)*

PACIFIC NATIONAL PTY. LTD.
Level 18 15 Blue Street, North Sydney, 2060, NSW, Australia
Tel.: (61) 284848000　　AU
Web Site: http://www.pacificnational.com.au
Year Founded: 2002
Rail Freight Services
N.A.I.C.S.: 482112
Anthony House *(Supvr-Ops)*

PACIFIC NET CO., LTD.
6F Tamachi Center Building 5-34-7 Shiba, Minato-ku, Tokyo, 108-0014, Japan
Tel.: (81) 357301441
Web Site: https://www.prins.co.jp
Year Founded: 1988
3021—(TKS)
Rev.: $45,747,810
Assets: $69,358,730
Liabilities: $49,118,910
Net Worth: $20,239,820
Earnings: $2,855,520
Fiscal Year-end: 05/31/24

Information Equipment Recycling Services
N.A.I.C.S.: 811210
Mitsuhiro Ueda *(Pres)*

PACIFIC NICKEL MINES LIMITED
Level 4 283 George Street, Sydney, 2000, NSW, Australia
Tel.: (61) 403940518
Web Site: https://www.pacificnickel.com
PNM—(ASX)
Rev.: $7,925,736
Assets: $38,492,646
Liabilities: $36,030,116
Net Worth: $2,462,530
Earnings: ($11,654,115)
Fiscal Year-end: 06/30/24
Gold, Silver & Copper Mining
N.A.I.C.S.: 212220
Andrew J. Cooke *(Sec)*

PACIFIC ONLINE LIMITED
115 Gaopu Rd Tianhe, Guangzhou, 510663, China
Tel.: (86) 2038178288　　Ky
Web Site: http://corp.pconline.com.cn
Year Founded: 1999
0543—(HKG)
Rev.: $114,247,411
Assets: $172,874,380
Liabilities: $53,981,132
Net Worth: $118,893,247
Earnings: ($984,204)
Emp.: 924
Fiscal Year-end: 12/31/22
Internet Advertising Services
N.A.I.C.S.: 541890
Wai Yan Lam *(Chm & CEO)*

PACIFIC PARADYM ENERGY INC.
905-1030 West Georgia Street, Vancouver, V6E 2Y3, BC, Canada
Tel.: (604) 689-2646
Web Site: http://www.pacificparadym.com
Year Founded: 1981
PPE.H—(TSXV)
Assets: $2,643
Liabilities: $2,821,353
Net Worth: ($2,818,711)
Earnings: ($134,215)
Fiscal Year-end: 07/31/22
Oil & Gas Exploration Services
N.A.I.C.S.: 213112
Harry Chew *(Pres & CFO)*

PACIFIC PILOTAGE AUTHORITY CANADA
1000-1130 West Pender Street, Vancouver, V6E 4A4, BC, Canada
Tel.: (604) 666-6771
Web Site: https://www.ppa.gc.ca
Year Founded: 1972
Rev.: $44,831,413
Emp.: 60
Marine Transportation Services
N.A.I.C.S.: 488330
Kevin Obermeyer *(Pres & CEO)*

PACIFIC PIPE PUBLIC COMPANY LIMITED
298 298/2 Moo 1 Suksawad Rd Pakklongbangplakod, Prasamutjedee, Samut Prakan, 10290, Thailand
Tel.: (66) 28162701
Web Site: https://www.pacificpipe.co.th
Year Founded: 1991
PAP—(THA)
Rev.: $255,393,601
Assets: $114,379,539
Liabilities: $55,655,561
Net Worth: $58,723,978

Earnings: ($1,639,166)
Emp.: 855
Fiscal Year-end: 12/31/23
Steel Pole Mfr
N.A.I.C.S.: 331221
Somchai Lekapojpanich *(Chm)*

PACIFIC RADIANCE LTD.
15 Pandan Road, Singapore, 609263, Singapore
Tel.: (65) 62388881
Web Site: https://www.pacificradiance.com
Year Founded: 2002
RXS—(SES)
Rev.: $31,405,000
Assets: $108,125,000
Liabilities: $70,421,000
Net Worth: $37,704,000
Earnings: $14,516,000
Emp.: 174
Fiscal Year-end: 12/31/23
Offshore Vessel & Marine Operations
N.A.I.C.S.: 483111
Yoke Min Pang *(Chm)*

Subsidiaries:

PT Subsea Offshore　(1)
Park View Plaza Building 4th Floor Jl Taman Kemang No 27, Jakarta, 12730, Indonesia
Tel.: (62) 217192209
Web Site: http://www.offshore-subsea.com
Marine Engineering Services
N.A.I.C.S.: 541330

Subsidiary (Domestic):

PT Marine Engineering Services　(2)
Park View Building 1st Floor Jl Taman Kemang No 27, Jakarta, 12730, Indonesia
Tel.: (62) 217192209
Web Site: http://www.mes-indonesia.com
Marine Engineering Services
N.A.I.C.S.: 541330

PACIFIC RIDGE EXPLORATION LTD.
Suite 1100 1111 Melville Street, Vancouver, V6E 3V6, BC, Canada
Tel.: (604) 484-7104
Web Site: https://www.pacificexploration.com
Year Founded: 1979
PEX—(TSXV)
Sales Range: Less than $1 Million
Mineral Exploration Services
N.A.I.C.S.: 213114
Gerald George Carlson *(Pres & CEO)*

PACIFIC SHUANGLIN BIO-PHARMACY CO., LTD.
Room 3004 Sunshine City Global Financial Center No 8, Changxing South Street Jinyuan District, Taiyuan, 030006, Shanxi, China
Tel.: (86) 3517038776
000403—(SSE)
Rev.: $337,688,676
Assets: $1,120,717,728
Liabilities: $157,415,076
Net Worth: $963,302,652
Earnings: $82,433,052
Fiscal Year-end: 12/31/22
Pharmaceuticals Mfr
N.A.I.C.S.: 325412

PACIFIC SILK ROAD RESOURCES GROUP INC.
Suite 1500 - 885 West Georgia Street, Vancouver, V6C 3E8, BC, Canada
Tel.: (604) 442-8858　　BC
Web Site: http://www.pacificpotash.com
PP—(OTCIQ)
Assets: $26,085
Liabilities: $932,574

Pacific Silk Road Resources Group Inc.—(Continued)
Net Worth: ($906,489)
Earnings: ($40,156)
Fiscal Year-end: 06/30/19
Potash Mining
N.A.I.C.S.: 212390
Tao Liu *(CEO)*

PACIFIC SMILES GROUP LIMITED
Level 1/6 Molly Morgan Drive, PO Box 2246, Greenhills, Maitland, 2323, NSW, Australia
Tel.: (61) 249302000
Web Site: https://www.pacificsmilesgroup.com
PSQ—(ASX)
Rev.: $120,026,709
Assets: $114,835,737
Liabilities: $74,399,038
Net Worth: $40,436,699
Earnings: $5,367,922
Emp.: 826
Fiscal Year-end: 06/30/24
Dental Care Centers
N.A.I.C.S.: 621210
Alex Abrahams *(Co-Founder)*

PACIFIC STAR DEVELOPMENT LIMITED
Vision Exchange 2 Venture Drive 19-15/17, Singapore, 608526, Singapore
Tel.: (65) 6411 0688 SG
Web Site: http://www.pacificstar-dev.com
Rev.: $4,350,892
Assets: $111,709,136
Liabilities: $147,335,415
Net Worth: ($35,626,279)
Earnings: ($43,193,344)
Fiscal Year-end: 06/30/20
Real Estate Manangement Services
N.A.I.C.S.: 531210
Glen Chan *(CEO & Mng Dir)*

Subsidiaries:
Pacific Star Development (Malaysia) Sdn. Bhd. (1)
Suite 17-11 Wisma UOA II 21 Jalan Pinang, 50450, Kuala Lumpur, Malaysia
Tel.: (60) 321616005
Real Estate Manangement Services
N.A.I.C.S.: 531210

Pacific Star Development (Thailand) Co., Ltd. (1)
The Offices at Central World 38th Floor 999/9 Rama 1 Rd Pathunwam, Bangkok, 10330, Thailand
Tel.: (66) 26737699
Real Estate Manangement Services
N.A.I.C.S.: 531210

PACIFIC STAR NETWORK LIMITED
Level 5 111 Coventry Street, Southbank, 3006, VIC, Australia
Tel.: (61) 388256600
Web Site: http://www.pacificstarnetwork.com
SEG—(ASX)
Rev.: $83,179,754
Assets: $98,265,892
Liabilities: $60,727,831
Net Worth: $37,538,061
Earnings: ($450,721)
Fiscal Year-end: 06/30/24
Radio Broadcasting Services
N.A.I.C.S.: 516210
Mark Johnson *(Grp Dir-Program-Brdcst)*

Subsidiaries:
Victorian Radio Network Pty Ltd (1)
Level 5 111 Coventry Street, Southbank, 3006, VIC, Australia
Tel.: (61) 388256600

Web Site: http://www.sen.com.au
Sales Range: $25-49.9 Million
Emp.: 80
Radio Broadcasting Services
N.A.I.C.S.: 516210

PACIFIC STRATEGIC FINANCIAL TBK
Gedung Menara Utara Lt 12A Jl Jend Gatot Subroto No 38, Jakarta, 12710, Selatan, Indonesia
Tel.: (62) 2139502900
Web Site: https://www.apic.co.id
APIC—(INDO)
Rev.: $139,295,976
Assets: $436,221,269
Liabilities: $278,134,233
Net Worth: $158,087,036
Earnings: $7,063,307
Emp.: 193
Fiscal Year-end: 12/31/23
Investment Management Service
N.A.I.C.S.: 523940
Felix Sindhunata *(Chm)*

Subsidiaries:
PT Pacific Capital Investment (1)
Menara Jamsostek North Tower 12Ath Floor Jl Jend Gatot Subroto No 38, Jakarta, 12710, Indonesia
Tel.: (62) 2150820730
Web Site: http://www.poinvestment.co.id
Investment Management Service
N.A.I.C.S.: 523940

PT Pacific Sekuritas Indonesia (1)
Gedung Menara Jamsostek Menara Utara Lantai 12A, Jl Jend Gatot Subroto Kav 38, Jakarta Selatan, 12170, Indonesia
Tel.: (62) 2139502900
Web Site: https://www.pacificsekuritas.id
Financial Services
N.A.I.C.S.: 523999

PACIFIC TEXTILES HOLDINGS LIMITED
Unit B1 7/F Block B Eastern Sea Industrial Building, 48-56 Tai Lin Pai Road, Kwai Chung, NT, China (Hong Kong)
Tel.: (852) 24248221 Ky
Web Site: https://www.pacific-textiles.com
Year Founded: 1997
1382—(HKG)
Rev.: $782,432,664
Assets: $766,682,142
Liabilities: $324,213,157
Net Worth: $442,468,986
Earnings: $74,709,730
Emp.: 4,697
Fiscal Year-end: 03/31/22
Textile Products Mfr
N.A.I.C.S.: 313210
Wai Loi Wan *(Founder & Vice Chm)*

Subsidiaries:
Pacific (Panyu) Textiles Limited (1)
Liu Chong Tong Xin County, Wan Qing Sha Town Nansha, Guangzhou, Guangdong, China
Tel.: (86) 208 494 8868
Textile & Fabric Mfr
N.A.I.C.S.: 313310

Pacific Crystal Textiles Limited (1)
Lai Vu Kim Thanh, Hai Duong, Vietnam
Tel.: (84) 36 406 8328
Web Site: https://www.pacific-crystal-textiles-ltd.business.site
Textile & Fabric Mfr
N.A.I.C.S.: 313310

Pacific Overseas Textiles Macao Commercial Offshore Limited (1)
Av da Praia Grande 815 Edif Centro Comml Talento 13 Andar, Macau, China (Macau)
Tel.: (853) 28330838
Web Site: http://www.pacific-textiles.com
Emp.: 10
Fabrics Whslr
N.A.I.C.S.: 313310

Eliza Wong *(Mgr-Ops)*

Pacific Textiles Limited (1)
Unit B1 7/F Block B Eastern Sea Ind Building 48-56 Tai Lin Pai Road, Kwai Chung, New Territories, China (Hong Kong)
Tel.: (852) 24248221
Web Site: http://www.pacific-textiles.com
Emp.: 70
Fabrics Whslr
N.A.I.C.S.: 424310

PACIFIC VEGAS GLOBAL STRATEGIES, INC.
Room 2 LG/F Kai Wong Commercial Building, 222 Queens Road, Central, China (Hong Kong)
Tel.: (852) 3154 9370 CO
Year Founded: 1990
Assets: $10,000
Liabilities: $713,449
Net Worth: ($703,449)
Earnings: ($61,124)
Emp.: 1
Fiscal Year-end: 12/31/18
Investment Services
N.A.I.C.S.: 523999
Sin Yee Kwan *(Pres, CEO, CFO & Sec)*

PACIFIC WEST SYSTEMS SUPPLY LTD.
20109 Logan Avenue, Langley, V3A 4L5, BC, Canada
Tel.: (604) 534-2060
Web Site: https://www.pacwestsystems.com
Year Founded: 1983
Wall & Ceiling Industry Products Distr & Whslr
N.A.I.C.S.: 423390
Ron Roller *(CFO)*

PACIFIC WESTERN TRANSPORTATION LTD
1857 Ctr Ave SE, Calgary, T2E 6L3, AB, Canada
Tel.: (403) 248-4300
Web Site: http://www.pwt.ca
Sales Range: $100-124.9 Million
Emp.: 1,600
Transportation Services
N.A.I.C.S.: 485410
Michael Colborne *(Pres & CEO)*

PACIFIC WILDCAT RESOURCES CORP.
110 - 2300 Carrington Road, Kelowna, V4T 2N6, BC, Canada
Tel.: (250) 768-0009 BC
Web Site: http://www.pacificwildcat.com
Year Founded: 1979
Sales Range: Less than $1 Million
Metal Mining & Production
N.A.I.C.S.: 212200
Malcolm Anthony Carson *(CFO)*

PACIFICA HOLDINGS INC.
China Bank Corporate Center Lot 2 Samar Loop corner Road 5, Cebu Business Park Mabolo, Cebu, 6000, Philippines
Tel.: (63) 26378851
Web Site: https://pacifica.ph
Year Founded: 1957
PA—(PHI)
Assets: $1,978,627
Liabilities: $29,389
Net Worth: $1,949,237
Earnings: ($29,380)
Fiscal Year-end: 12/31/23
Cosmetics Products Mfr
N.A.I.C.S.: 325620
Lowell L. Yu *(Chm)*

PACIFICNET INC.
23rd Floor Building A TimeCourt, No 6 Shuguang Xili, Chaoyang District, Beijing, 100028, China
Tel.: (86) 1059225000 DE
Year Founded: 1987
Sales Range: $1-9.9 Million
Emp.: 545
Developer of Gaming Technology for Land-Based, Online & Gaming Operators
N.A.I.C.S.: 541512
Chi Hung Chan *(CEO)*

Subsidiaries:
Beijing Linkhead Technologies Co., Ltd. (1)
Rm 2308 Tower A TimeCourt Shuguangxili Jia 6, Chaoyang District, Beijing, 100028, China
Tel.: (86) 1058678962
Web Site: http://www.linkhead.com
Interactive Online Services
N.A.I.C.S.: 517810

ChinaGoHi (1)
27/F Jiangsu Builiding, Futian, Shenzhen, China
Tel.: (86) 75582960485
Call Centers & Business Support Services
N.A.I.C.S.: 561499

Epro Telecom (1)
Room 601-603 New Bright Building, 11 Sheung Yuet Road, Kowloon, China (Hong Kong)
Tel.: (852) 2799 0202
Web Site: http://www.EproTel.com.hk
Multi-Media Call Center Services
N.A.I.C.S.: 561439
Telly Wai Hon Wong *(Mng Dir)*

Guangzhou Wanrong Information Technology Co., Ltd. (1)
Room 915 Longhui Building, Long Kou Dong Road, Tianhe District, Guangzhou, China
Tel.: (86) 2087567792
Information Services
N.A.I.C.S.: 519290

PacificNet Beijing Limited (1)
Bldg A TimeCourt No 6 Shuguang Xili, Chaoyang District, Beijing, 100028, China
Tel.: (86) 1059225000
Information Technology Services
N.A.I.C.S.: 334290

PacificNet Clickcom Limited (1)
2/F West Building, 59 Jianzhong Road, Tianhe SoftwarePark, Guangzhou, 510665, China
Tel.: (86) 2085557559
Mobile Internet Services
N.A.I.C.S.: 517112

PacificNet Power Limited (1)
Rm 402-403 4 F Hong Kong Trade Ctr 161-167 Des Voeux Rd C, Central, China (Hong Kong)
Tel.: (852) 35204051
Web Site: http://www.intercable.com.hk
Emp.: 10
Telecommunication Servicesb
N.A.I.C.S.: 517810

PacificNet Solutions Limited (1)
Chinachem Century Tower Ste 1702, Wanchai, China (Hong Kong)
Tel.: (852) 28762967
Web Site: http://www.pacso.com
Business Solutions
N.A.I.C.S.: 561499

PacificNet Ventures Limited (1)
402/403 4F Hong Kong Trade Ctr, No 161-167 Des Vouex Rd, Hong Kong, Central, China (Hong Kong)
Tel.: (852) 28762900
Web Site: http://www.pacificnetventures.com
Strategic Investment Services
N.A.I.C.S.: 523999
Tony Tong *(Co-Founder)*

PACIFICO V REGION S.A.
Av El Bosque Sur 130 Piso Nro 14, Las Condes, Santiago, Chile

Tel.: (56) 3794560
Real Estate Development Services
N.A.I.C.S.: 531390
Gonzalo Ibanez Langlois (Chm)

Subsidiaries:

SOCIEDAD PUNTA DEL COBRE
S.A. (1)
Rancagua N 200, Copiapo, Chile
Tel.: (56) 522205800
Web Site: https://www.pucobre.cl
Sales Range: Less than $1 Million
Copper Mining Services
N.A.I.C.S.: 212230
Sebastian Alfredo Rios Rivas (CEO)

PACIFICORP INTERNATIONAL HOTEL MANAGEMENT, INC.
Ramada Meizhou Meiyuan Street
Binfang Road, Meijiang District,
Meizhou, Guangdong, China
Tel.: (86) 867536113888
Web Site:
http://www.pacificorphotels.com
Hotel Owner & Operator
N.A.I.C.S.: 721110
Andy Deng (CEO)

PACKAGES LTD.
ShahraheRoomi PO Amersidhu, Lahore, 54760, Pakistan
Tel.: (92) 4235811541
Web Site:
https://www.packages.com.pk
Year Founded: 1956
PKGS—(PSX)
Rev.: $438,512,680
Assets: $620,530,894
Liabilities: $380,543,479
Net Worth: $239,987,416
Earnings: $25,109,963
Emp.: 127
Fiscal Year-end: 12/31/22
Paper & Allied Products Mfr
N.A.I.C.S.: 322299
Hyder Ali (CEO & Mng Dir)

Subsidiaries:

Chantler Packages Inc. (1)
880 Lakeshore Road East, Mississauga,
L5E 1E1, ON, Canada
Tel.: (905) 274-2654
Web Site:
https://www.chantlerpackages.com
Plastic Container Mfr
N.A.I.C.S.: 326160

Flexible Packages Convertors (Proprietary) Limited (1)
316 Marks Street Waltloo, Pretoria, 0184,
South Africa
Tel.: (27) 128036661
Web Site: https://www.flexpc.co.za
Plastic Container Mfr
N.A.I.C.S.: 326160

Packages Convertors Limited (1)
4th Floor The Forum Suite No 416-422
G-20 Block 9, Khayaban-e-Jami Clifton, Karachi, 75600, Pakistan
Tel.: (92) 2135831618
Plastic Container Mfr
N.A.I.C.S.: 326160

PACKAGING CO., LTD. SAOG
PO Box 54, Muscat 100, Muscat,
Oman
Tel.: (968) 24493752
Web Site: https://www.albahja.com
Year Founded: 1981
PCLI—(MUS)
Rev.: $26,131,250
Assets: $29,120,162
Liabilities: $16,652,931
Net Worth: $12,467,230
Earnings: $286,945
Fiscal Year-end: 12/31/23
Corrugated Carton Mfr
N.A.I.C.S.: 322211
Ramakrishnan Hariharan (Gen Mgr)

PACRAY INTERNATIONAL HOLDINGS LIMITED
28/F Agricultural Bank of China Tower
50 Connaught Road, Central, China
(Hong Kong)
Tel.: (852) 2534 7888 BM
Web Site: http://pacray.etnet.com.hk
Rev.: $9,545,871
Assets: $21,167,490
Liabilities: $8,851,558
Net Worth: $12,315,932
Earnings: ($2,916,705)
Emp.: 74
Fiscal Year-end: 12/31/19
Holding Company
N.A.I.C.S.: 551112

Subsidiaries:

Shanghai SyncMOS Semiconductor
Company Limited (1)
4/F Tian Lin Building 300 Tian Lin Road,
Shanghai, 200233, China
Tel.: (86) 2164853816
Web Site: http://www.syncmos.sh.cn
Semiconductor Mfr
N.A.I.C.S.: 334413

PACRIM INTERNATIONAL CAPITAL INC.
Suite 3202 Tower 2 Lippo Centre,
Queensway, Wanchai, China (Hong Kong)
Tel.: (852) 25261554 VG
Web Site:
http://www.pacriminternational.com
Year Founded: 1990
Sales Range: Less than $1 Million
Financial & Real Estate Investment Services
N.A.I.C.S.: 523999
Cindy Fung (CFO)

Subsidiaries:

Pacrim International Capital Inc. (1)
Suite 3202 Tower II, Lippo Centre 89
Queensway, Central, China (Hong Kong)
Tel.: (852) 25261554
Financial Investment Services
N.A.I.C.S.: 523999

Subsidiary (Non-US):

Pacrim Hospitality Services Inc. (2)
30 Damascus Road Suite 220, Bedford,
B4A 0C1, NS, Canada
Tel.: (902) 401-6662
Web Site: https://www.pacrimhospitality.com
Sales Range: $25-49.9 Million
Emp.: 40
Home Management Services
N.A.I.C.S.: 541618

Division (Domestic):

Intergy eMarketing Solutions (3)
30 Damascus Rd Ste 201, Bedford, B4A
0C1, NS, Canada
Tel.: (902) 450-2720
Sales Range: $25-49.9 Million
Emp.: 2
Consulting & Management Services
N.A.I.C.S.: 541613

Unit (Domestic):

Yellowknife Super 8 (3)
308 Old Airport Road, Yellowknife, X1A
3G3, NT, Canada
Tel.: (867) 669-8888
Web Site: https://www.wyndhamhotels.com
Sales Range: $10-24.9 Million
Emp.: 20
Hotel Owner & Operator
N.A.I.C.S.: 721110

PACT GROUP HOLDINGS LTD.
Level 5 Building 1 658 Church St,
Cremorne, 3121, VIC, Australia
Tel.: (61) 438480860 AU
Web Site: https://www.pactgroup.com
PGH—(ASX)
Rev.: $1,204,385,011

Assets: $1,303,536,319
Liabilities: $986,907,047
Net Worth: $316,629,272
Earnings: $2,493,990
Emp.: 5,299
Fiscal Year-end: 06/30/24
Holding Company; Packaging Products Mfr & Distr
N.A.I.C.S.: 551112
Raphael Geminder (Founder & Chm)

Subsidiaries:

Circular Plastics Australia Pty.
Ltd. (1)
Building 3 658 Church Street, Cremorne,
VIC, Australia
Tel.: (61) 297087682
Web Site:
https://circularplasticsaustralia.com
Plastic Product Recycling Services
N.A.I.C.S.: 562920

Jalco Automotive Pty. Ltd. (1)
238 Hoxton Park Rd, Lurnea, Preston,
2170, NSW, Australia
Tel.: (61) 28 797 0000
Chemical Products Mfr
N.A.I.C.S.: 325998

PGH Services LLC (1)
1431 Greenway Dr Ste 827, Irving, TX
75038
Web Site: https://www.pghgrp.com
Ecosystem Services
N.A.I.C.S.: 541620

Pact Group Holdings (Australia) Pty.
Ltd. (1)
Level 1 Building 6 650 Church Street, Richmond, 3121, VIC, Australia
Tel.: (61) 388254100
Holding Company; Packaging Products Mfr & Distr
N.A.I.C.S.: 551112
Raphael Geminder (Founder)

Subsidiary (Domestic):

VIP Plastic Packaging Pty. Ltd. (2)
Building 6 650 Church St, Richmond, 3121,
VIC, Australia
Tel.: (61) 3 8825 4100
Web Site: http://www.vippackaging.com.au
Plastic Packaging Products Mfr
N.A.I.C.S.: 326160

VIP Steel Packaging Pty. Ltd. (2)
Level 1 Building 6 650 Church Street, Richmond, 3121, VIC, Australia
Tel.: (61) 3 8825 4100
Web Site: http://www.vippackaging.com.au
Metal Packaging Product Mfr
N.A.I.C.S.: 332431
Raymond Purcell (Gen Mgr-Sourcing & Logistics)

Viscount Plastics Pty. Ltd. (2)
5-12 Mills Road, Braeside, 3195, VIC, Australia
Tel.: (61) 1 800 462 951
Web Site: http://www.viscount.com.au
Sales Range: $125-149.9 Million
Plastic Packaging & Materials Handling Products Mfr & Distr
N.A.I.C.S.: 326199
Shane Moloughney (Mng Dir)

Stowers Containment Solutions
Ltd. (1)
88B Carbine Road North Island, Auckland,
1060, New Zealand
Tel.: (64) 9 573 0422
Web Site: https://www.plastic.co.nz
Plastic Packaging Mfr
N.A.I.C.S.: 326112

TIC Group (Europe) Ltd. (1)
Unit 7 The Gryphon Industrial Park, Porters
Wood, Saint Albans, AL3 6XZ, Hertfordshire, United Kingdom
Tel.: (44) 330 088 6675
Warehousing Services
N.A.I.C.S.: 493110

Viscount Plastics (NZ) Ltd. (1)
8 Vestey Drive Mt Wellington, Auckland,
New Zealand
Tel.: (64) 9 276 8679

Web Site: https://www.viscountplastics.co.nz
Logistic Services
N.A.I.C.S.: 541614

PADAENG INDUSTRY PCL
CTI Tower 26th-27th Floor 191/18-25
Ratchadaphisek Road, Khlong Toei,
Bangkok, 10110, Thailand
Tel.: (66) 2695 9499 TH
Web Site: http://www.padaeng.co.th
Rev.: $14,440,009
Assets: $249,925,592
Liabilities: $93,450,993
Net Worth: $156,474,599
Earnings: ($191,719)
Emp.: 66
Fiscal Year-end: 12/31/19
Zinc Mfr
N.A.I.C.S.: 212230
Arsa Sarasin (Chm)

Subsidiaries:

Mae Sod Clean Energy Co., Ltd. (1)
13 Moo 4 Phratad Padeng Subdistrict, Mae
Sot District, 63110, Tak, Thailand
Tel.: (66) 55533016
Emp.: 58
Oil & Gas Mining Operations
N.A.I.C.S.: 213112
Tianchai Singhakarn (Mgr-Mine Ops)

Padaeng Industry (1)
94 Moo 1 Ban Klonghuaysai Asian Highway, Nongbuatai Muang, Tak, 63000, Thailand
Tel.: (66) 55517444
Web Site: http://www.padaengindustry.com
Sales Range: $100-124.9 Million
Emp.: 500
Zinc Smelting Operations
N.A.I.C.S.: 331410
Chaiyan Roojnawate (CMO)

Padaeng Industry (1)
Padaeng Industrial Estate 15 Padaeng
Road, Maptaphut Muang, Rayong, 63110,
Thailand
Tel.: (66) 55533016
Web Site: http://www.padaeng.com
Calcine Mfr
N.A.I.C.S.: 327992

Padaeng International Mining Co.,
Ltd. (1)
191-18-25 CTI Tower, 26th-27th Floor
Ratchadaphisek, 10110, Bangkok, Thailand
Tel.: (66) 26959499
Sales Range: $50-74.9 Million
Emp.: 90
Metal Ore Mining
N.A.I.C.S.: 212290
Andre van der Heyden (Mng Dir)

Padaeng Poongsan Metals Co.,
Ltd. (1)
191-18-25 CTI Tower 26th-27th Fl, 26th-27th Fl Ratchadaphisek, Bangkok, 10110,
Thailand
Tel.: (66) 26959499
Web Site: http://www.padaeng.co.th
Copper Foundries
N.A.I.C.S.: 331529
Francis Vanbellen (Mng Dir)

Padaeng Properties Co., Ltd. (1)
191-18-25 CTI Tower, 26th-27th Floor
Ratchadaphisek, 10110, Bangkok, Thailand
Tel.: (66) 26959499
Sales Range: $50-74.9 Million
Emp.: 100
Real Estate Property Lessors
N.A.I.C.S.: 531190
Francis Vanbellen (Mng Dir)

Puthep Co., Ltd. (1)
191-18-25 CTI Tower, 26th-27th Floor
Ratchadaphisek, 10110, Bangkok, Thailand
Tel.: (66) 26959499
Sales Range: $25-49.9 Million
Emp.: 3
Copper Foundries
N.A.I.C.S.: 331529
Andre van der Heyden (Mng Dir)

PADAM COTTON YARNS LIMITED

PADAM COTTON YARNS LIMITED

Padam Cotton Yarns Limited—(Continued)

196 1 Floor G T Road Opp Red Cross Market, Karnal, 132 001, India
Tel.: (91) 1846616601
Web Site:
https://www.padamcotton.com
Year Founded: 1994
531395—(BOM)
Rev.: $696
Assets: $940,585
Liabilities: $600,337
Net Worth: $340,248
Earnings: ($9,491)
Emp.: 2
Fiscal Year-end: 03/31/21
Cotton Yarn Whslr
N.A.I.C.S.: 424990
Rajev Gupta *(Mng Dir)*

PADAUK TECHNOLOGY CO., LTD.

6F-6 No 1 Sec 3 Gongdao 5th Rd, Hsinchu, 30069, Taiwan
Tel.: (886) 35728688
Web Site:
https://www.padauk.com.tw
Year Founded: 2005
6716—(TPE)
Rev.: $29,358,565
Assets: $36,559,766
Liabilities: $11,841,635
Net Worth: $24,718,132
Earnings: $6,299,284
Fiscal Year-end: 12/31/22
Semiconductor Equipment Mfr
N.A.I.C.S.: 333242
Tsan-Bih Tang *(Chm & CEO)*

PADENGA HOLDINGS LIMITED

121 Borrowdale Road Gun hill, PO Box HG633, Highlands, Harare, Zimbabwe
Tel.: (263) 242 291 6048
Web Site: http://www.padenga.com
Year Founded: 1965
PHL—(ZIM)
Rev.: $29,203,733
Assets: $96,997,041
Liabilities: $29,793,355
Net Worth: $67,203,686
Earnings: $6,744,586
Emp.: 24
Fiscal Year-end: 12/31/19
Holding Company
N.A.I.C.S.: 551112
Gary John Sharp *(CEO)*

PADIBERAS NASIONAL BERHAD

No 1 Jalan Majistret U1/26 Seksyen U1, HICOM-Glenmarie Industrial Park, Shah Alam, 41050, Selangor Darul Ehsan, Malaysia
Tel.: (60) 3 5480 7777
Web Site: http://www.bernas.com.my
Sales Range: $1-4.9 Billion
Rice Processing & Paddy Seed Production
N.A.I.C.S.: 111160
Ab Aziz Kasim *(Chm)*

Subsidiaries:

Beras Corporation Sdn Bhd (1)
Lot 2-8-2 7th Floor Wisma San Hin Wawasan Plaza Coastal Highway, PO Box 13311, 88837, Kota Kinabalu, Sabah, Malaysia
Tel.: (60) 88 257 510
Web Site: http://www.bernas.com.my
Rice Processing Services
N.A.I.C.S.: 311212

Padiberas Nasional Berhad - KBB
Bagan Terap Mill (1)
Jalan Sepintas, Sabak Bernam, 43300, Sungai Besar, Selangor, Malaysia
Tel.: (60) 3 3216 4240
Rice Processing Services
N.A.I.C.S.: 311212

Padiberas Nasional Berhad - KBB
Bukit Besar Mill
Lot 7773, 06800, Alor Setar, Kedah, Malaysia
Tel.: (60) 4 769 1297
Rice Processing Services
N.A.I.C.S.: 311212

Padiberas Nasional Berhad - KBB
Bukit Kenak Mill (1)
Lot 2432 Mukim Bukit Kenak, 22000, Jerteh, Terengganu, Malaysia
Tel.: (60) 9 697 1221
Rice Processing Services
N.A.I.C.S.: 311212

Padiberas Nasional Berhad - KBB
Bukit Raya Mill
Lot Pt 28, Pendang, 06700, Kedah, Malaysia
Tel.: (60) 4 759 6227
Rice Processing Services
N.A.I.C.S.: 311212

Padiberas Nasional Berhad - KBB
Changkat Lada Mill (1)
Lot 2470 Changkat Lada, Seberang Perak Kampung Gajah, 36800, Perak, Malaysia
Tel.: (60) 5 655 1872
Rice Processing Services
N.A.I.C.S.: 311212

Padiberas Nasional Berhad - KBB
Guar Chempedak Mill (1)
Lot 3 Seksyen 1, 08800, Gurun, Kedah, Malaysia
Tel.: (60) 4 468 0694
Rice Processing Services
N.A.I.C.S.: 311212

Padiberas Nasional Berhad - KBB
Jerlun Mill (1)
Lot 4049 & 4424 Jalan Putera Mukim Jerlun, 06150, Alor Setar, Kedah, Malaysia
Tel.: (60) 4 794 0229
Rice Processing Services
N.A.I.C.S.: 311212

Padiberas Nasional Berhad - KBB
Jitra Mill (1)
Lot 2190 Mukim Jitra Batu 13, Jalan Perlis, 06000, Jitra, Kedah, Malaysia
Tel.: (60) 4 917 1235
Rice Processing Services
N.A.I.C.S.: 311212

Padiberas Nasional Berhad - KBB
Kangkong Mill (1)
Lot Pt2 & 740, Mukim Kangkong, 06650, Alor Setar, Kedah, Malaysia
Tel.: (60) 4 764 1278
Rice Processing Services
N.A.I.C.S.: 311212

Padiberas Nasional Berhad - KBB
Kerpan Mill (1)
Lot 3977 & 1215, Mukim Jerlun, 06510, Alor Setar, Kedah, Malaysia
Tel.: (60) 4 794 0228
Rice Processing Services
N.A.I.C.S.: 311212

Padiberas Nasional Berhad - KBB
Kodiang Miill (1)
Lot 3346 Mukim Kepelu, Kodiang, 06100, Kedah, Malaysia
Tel.: (60) 4 925 5346
Rice Processing Services
N.A.I.C.S.: 311212

Padiberas Nasional Berhad - KBB
Kuala Perlis Mill (1)
Lot PT136, 02000, Kuala Perlis, Perlis, Malaysia
Tel.: (60) 4 985 4133
Rice Processing Services
N.A.I.C.S.: 311212

Padiberas Nasional Berhad - KBB
Kuala Rompin Mill (1)
Pt 1720 KM 2 Jln Selendang, 26800, Kuala Rompin, Pahang, Malaysia
Tel.: (60) 9 414 6575
Rice Processing Services
N.A.I.C.S.: 311212

Padiberas Nasional Berhad - KBB
Langgar Mill (1)
Lot No 003050 Mukim Tualang, Kota Setar, Kedah, Malaysia
Tel.: (60) 4 787 6571
Rice Processing Services
N.A.I.C.S.: 311212

Padiberas Nasional Berhad - KBB
Megat Dewa Mill (1)
Lot Pt 437, 06100, Alor Setar, Kedah, Malaysia
Tel.: (60) 4 925 1349
Rice Processing Services
N.A.I.C.S.: 311212

Padiberas Nasional Berhad - KBB
Pasir Putih Mill (1)
Lot 387/1637 Padang Pak Amat, 16800, Pasir Puteh, Kelantan, Malaysia
Tel.: (60) 9 786 6330
Rice Processing Services
N.A.I.C.S.: 311212

Padiberas Nasional Berhad - KBB
Paya Keladi Mill (1)
13200 Kepala Batas, Penang, Malaysia
Tel.: (60) 4 575 7558
Rice Processing Services
N.A.I.C.S.: 311212

Padiberas Nasional Berhad - KBB
Pering Mill (1)
Pt 668 Mukim Pering Jalan Sanglang, Kodiang, 06000, Kedah, Malaysia
Tel.: (60) 4 925 2673
Rice Processing Services
N.A.I.C.S.: 311212

Padiberas Nasional Berhad - KBB
Peringat Mill (1)
Lot 2453-2455 KM 1 Jln Bachok, 15670, Kota Baharu, Kelantan, Malaysia
Tel.: (60) 9 712 8389
Rice Processing Services
N.A.I.C.S.: 311212

Padiberas Nasional Berhad - KBB
Seri Tiram Jaya Mill (1)
Lot 19947, 45500, Tanjung Karang, Selangor, Malaysia
Tel.: (60) 3 3269 8101
Rice Processing Services
N.A.I.C.S.: 311212

Padiberas Nasional Berhad - KBB
Simpang Empat Mill (1)
Lot 236 & 237 Simpang Empat Jalan T Tulang, 02700, Simpang Empat, Perlis, Malaysia
Tel.: (60) 4 980 7244
Rice Processing Services
N.A.I.C.S.: 311212

Padiberas Nasional Berhad - KBB
Simpang Lima Mill (1)
Lot 3122 Jln Perusahaan 1 Kawasan Perusahaan Parit Buntar, 34200, Parit Buntar, Perak, Malaysia
Tel.: (60) 5 716 1279
Rice Processing Services
N.A.I.C.S.: 311212

Padiberas Nasional Berhad - KBB
Sungai Baru Mill (1)
Lot 615 & 653, 6250, Alor Setar, Kedah, Malaysia
Tel.: (60) 4 733 0896
Rice Processing Services
N.A.I.C.S.: 311212

Padiberas Nasional Berhad - KBB
Sungai Besar Mill (1)
Jalan LPN, 45300, Sungai Besar, Selangor, Malaysia
Tel.: (60) 3 3224 2204
Rice Processing Services
N.A.I.C.S.: 311212

Padiberas Nasional Berhad - KBB
Sungai Limau Mill (1)
No 3724 & 4030 Mukim Sg Daun, Yan, 06910, Kedah, Malaysia
Tel.: (60) 4 769 3616
Rice Processing Services
N.A.I.C.S.: 311212

Padiberas Nasional Berhad - KBB
Sungai Manik Mill (1)
Chikus, 36750, Teluk Intan, Perak, Malaysia
Tel.: (60) 5 623 4542

Padiberas Nasional Berhad - KBB
Rice Processing Services
N.A.I.C.S.: 311212

Padiberas Nasional Berhad - KBB
Sungai Ranggam Mill (1)
Pt 1797 Mukim Kota Setia, Kampung Gajah, 36800, Perak, Malaysia
Tel.: (60) 5 655 1428
Web Site: http://www.bernas.com.my
Rice Processing Services
N.A.I.C.S.: 311212

Padiberas Nasional Berhad - KBB
Teluk Kechai Mill (1)
Lot 625 Mukim Teluk Kechai, Kuala Kedah, 06600, Kedah, Malaysia
Tel.: (60) 4 762 1844
Rice Processing Services
N.A.I.C.S.: 311212

Padiberas Nasional Berhad - KBB
Utan Aji Mill (1)
Lot 2074, 01000, Kangar, Perlis, Malaysia
Tel.: (60) 4 976 1133
Rice Processing Services
N.A.I.C.S.: 311212

PADINI HOLDINGS BERHAD

No 19 Jalan Jurunilai U1/20 Hicom Glenmarie Industrial Park, 40150, Shah Alam, Selangor Darul Ehsan, Malaysia
Tel.: (60) 50210600
Web Site: https://www.padini.com
PADINI—(KLS)
Rev.: $385,635,767
Assets: $352,617,778
Liabilities: $132,493,333
Net Worth: $220,124,444
Earnings: $47,130,370
Emp.: 3,200
Fiscal Year-end: 06/30/23
Ladies Shoes, Garments & Ancillary Products Distr
N.A.I.C.S.: 315210
Fong Ying Tam *(Co-Sec)*

Subsidiaries:

Padini Dot Com Sdn. Bhd. (1)
No 19 Jalan Jurunilai U1/20, Hicom Glenmarie Industrial Park, 40150, Shah Alam, Selangor Darul Ehsan, Malaysia
Tel.: (60) 350210600
Web Site: https://www.padini.com
Sales Range: $25-49.9 Million
Emp.: 100
Electronic Shopping Services
N.A.I.C.S.: 425120

Seed Corporation Sdn. Bhd. (1)
Ground Floor Bukit Raja Shopping Centre Psn Bukit Raja 2, Bandar Baru Klang, 41150, Kelang, Selangor, Malaysia
Tel.: (60) 333439158
Garments & Ancillary Products Distr
N.A.I.C.S.: 424350

PADMA ISLAMI LIFE INSURANCE LIMITED

Padma Life Tower 115 kazi Nazrul Islam Avenue Bangla Motor, Dhaka, 1000, Bangladesh
Tel.: (880) 28311809
Web Site:
https://www.padmaislamilife.com
Year Founded: 2000
PADMALIFE—(DHA)
Rev.: $7,660,606
Assets: $25,903,808
Liabilities: $18,684,555
Net Worth: $7,219,253
Earnings: $2,427,224
Fiscal Year-end: 12/31/19
Insurance Agency Services
N.A.I.C.S.: 524210

PADMA OIL COMPANY LIMITED

Padma Bhaban Strand Road, Chittagong, Bangladesh
Tel.: (880) 31614235

Web Site: https://www.pocl.gov.bd
Year Founded: 1968
PADMAOIL—(CHT)
Rev.: $24,222,465
Assets: $1,407,831,009
Liabilities: $1,222,793,659
Net Worth: $185,037,350
Earnings: $32,359,367
Emp.: 879
Fiscal Year-end: 06/30/23
Oil Exploration Services
N.A.I.C.S.: 213112
Mohammad Aminul Haque *(Gen Mgr-Project)*

PADMALAYA TELEFILMS LIMITED
Plot No138 H No 8-3-222-1-23
Madhura Nagar, Yusuf Guda, Hyderabad, 500 038, Telangana, India
Tel.: (91) 4023738955
Web Site:
  https://www.padmalayatelefilms.com
Year Founded: 1991
532350—(BOM)
Rev.: $23,069
Assets: $2,728,167
Liabilities: $408,746
Net Worth: $2,319,420
Earnings: ($9,099)
Fiscal Year-end: 03/31/21
Software Development Services
N.A.I.C.S.: 541511
G. V. Narasimha Rao *(CEO)*

PADMANABH ALLOYS & POLYMERS LTD.
Tel.: (91) 9376810734
Web Site: https://www.padmanabh.in
Year Founded: 1994
531779—(BOM)
Emp.: 26
Thermoplastic Product Mfr
N.A.I.C.S.: 325211
Bhikubhai M. Desai *(Chm)*

PADTEC HOLDING S.A.
Parque II do Polo de Alta Tecnologia R Dr Ricardo Benetton Martins s/n, Ipanema, Campinas, 13086, Sao Paulo, Brazil
Tel.: (55) 1921049700
Web Site: https://www.padtec.com.br
Year Founded: 1999
PDTC3—(BRAZ)
Rev.: $65,906,400
Assets: $92,330,489
Liabilities: $65,062,475
Net Worth: $27,268,014
Earnings: $2,755,224
Fiscal Year-end: 12/31/23
Investment Management Service
N.A.I.C.S.: 523999
Sami Haddad *(CEO & Officer-IR)*

PAE (THAILAND) PUBLIC COMPANY LIMITED
69 Soi On-Nuch 64 Srinakarin Road, Suanluang, Bangkok, 10250, Thailand
Tel.: (66) 23220222
Web Site: http://www.pae.co.th
Year Founded: 1964
PAE—(THA)
Rev.: $16,986,622
Assets: $18,145,976
Liabilities: $44,756,688
Net Worth: ($26,610,712)
Earnings: ($2,170,926)
Emp.: 461
Fiscal Year-end: 12/31/20
Oil & Gas Related Project Services
N.A.I.C.S.: 213112
Chareon Prajumtan *(Chm)*

Subsidiaries:

PAE Construction Resources Company Limited (1)
67 Soi On-Nuch 64 Srinakarin Road, Suanluang, Bangkok, 10250, Thailand
Tel.: (66) 2 704 3985
Construction Management Services
N.A.I.C.S.: 237990
David Ong *(Gen Mgr)*

PAE LIMITED
C/o Regus Level 1 Block A Shivsagar Estate Dr Annie Beasant Road Worli, Mumbai, 400018, India
Tel.: (91) 2266185799
Web Site: https://www.paeltd.com
Year Founded: 1950
PAEL—(NSE)
Sales Range: Less than $1 Million
Emp.: 13
Storage Battery Mfr
N.A.I.C.S.: 335910
Pritam A. Doshi *(Chm & Mng Dir)*

Subsidiaries:

Shurjo Energy Pvt. Limited (1)
D-82 Industrial Estate Block-D Ward No 6, Kalyani, 741 235, West Bengal, India
Tel.: (91) 33 2502 5146
Web Site: http://www.shurjo-energy.com
Sales Range: $25-49.9 Million
Emp.: 45
Solar Panel Mfr & Distr
N.A.I.C.S.: 334419

PAG ASIA CAPITAL LTD.
33/F Three Pacific Place 1 Queen's Road East, Central, Hong Kong, China (Hong Kong)
Tel.: (852) 2918 0088
Web Site: http://www.pagasia.com
Private Equity & Real Estate Investment Services
N.A.I.C.S.: 523999
Anthony Miller *(CEO)*

Subsidiaries:

Cushman & Wakefield plc (1)
125 Old Broad Street, London, EC2N 1AR, United Kingdom
Tel.: (44) 2032963000
Web Site:
  http://www.cushmanwakefield.com
Rev.: $10,105,700,000
Assets: $7,949,300,000
Liabilities: $6,287,200,000
Net Worth: $1,662,100,000
Earnings: $196,400,000
Emp.: 52,000
Fiscal Year-end: 12/31/2022
Holding Company
N.A.I.C.S.: 551112
Matthew Miller *(Vice Chm)*

Subsidiary (US):

Colvill Office Properties, LLC (2)
5847 San Felipe St Ste 600, Houston, TX 77057-3008
Tel.: (713) 877-1550
Web Site: http://www.colvilloffice.com
Offices of Real Estate Agents & Brokers
N.A.I.C.S.: 531210
Chip Colvill *(Owner)*

Cresa Partners of Los Angeles, Inc. (2)
11726 San Vicente Blvd, Los Angeles, CA 90049
Tel.: (310) 207-1700
Sales Range: $10-24.9 Million
Emp.: 41
Management Consulting Services
N.A.I.C.S.: 541618
Nancy Ryan *(Controller)*

Cushman & Wakefield, Inc. (2)
225 W Wacker Dr Ste 3000, Chicago, IL 60606
Tel.: (312) 470-1800
Web Site:
  http://www.cushmanandwakefield.com
Sales Range: $5-14.9 Billion
Emp.: 45,000
Real Estate Brokerage & Property Management Services
N.A.I.C.S.: 531210
Brian R. Corcoran *(Exec VP-Phoenix)*

Subsidiary (Domestic):

C&W Facility Services, Inc. (3)
275 Grove St Ste 3-200, Auburndale, MA 02466
Tel.: (888) 751-9100
Web Site: http://cwservices.com
Maintenance Services
N.A.I.C.S.: 811490
Paul Bedborough *(CEO)*

Subsidiary (Domestic):

Pyramid Building Maintenance Corporation (4)
2175 Martin Ave, Santa Clara, CA 95050
Tel.: (408) 727-9393
Web Site:
  http://www.pacificmaintenance.com
Sales Range: $25-49.9 Million
Emp.: 600
Building Maintenance & Janitorial Services
N.A.I.C.S.: 561210
Kari Hus *(Pres)*

Subsidiary (Non-US):

Cushman & Wakefield (Bahrain) W.L.L (3)
The Lagoon Amwaj Island Office #306 Building 2648, Road 5720 Area 257, Manama, Bahrain
Tel.: (973) 17692476
Web Site:
  http://www.cushmanwakefield.com
Management Consulting Services
N.A.I.C.S.: 541618
Kelvin Crutchlow *(Dir & Gen Mgr)*

Cushman & Wakefield (HK) Limited (3)
16/F Jardine House, Central, China (Hong Kong)
Tel.: (852) 2956 3888
Web Site:
  http://www.cushmanwakefield.com
Real Estate Services
N.A.I.C.S.: 531390
Eric Chong *(Sr Mgr-Research)*

Cushman & Wakefield (India) Pvt. Ltd. (3)
14th Floor Building 8 Tower C DLF Cyber City, Gurgaon, 122002, Haryana, India
Tel.: (91) 1244695555
Web Site:
  http://www.cushmanwakefield.co.in
Real Estate Services
N.A.I.C.S.: 531390
Anshul Jain *(Mng Dir & Country Mgr)*

Cushman & Wakefield (NSW) Pty Limited (3)
Level 22 1 O'Connell Street, Sydney, 2000, NSW, Australia
Tel.: (61) 2 8243 9999
Web Site:
  http://www.cushmanwakefield.com.au
Real Estate Services
N.A.I.C.S.: 531390
James Patterson *(CEO-Australia & New Zealand)*

Cushman & Wakefield (S) Pte Ltd (3)
3 Church Street 09-03 Samsung Hub, Singapore, 49483, Singapore
Tel.: (65) 65353232
Web Site:
  http://www.cushmanwakefield.com
Real Estate Services
N.A.I.C.S.: 531390
Christine Li *(Dir-Res)*

Cushman & Wakefield (Shanghai) Co. Ltd. (3)
42-43/F Tower 2 Plaza 66 1366 Nanjing West Road, Shanghai, 200040, China
Tel.: (86) 21 2208 0088
Web Site:
  http://www.cushmanwakefield.com.cn
Real Estate Services
N.A.I.C.S.: 531390
Mimie Lau *(Mng Dir-East China)*

Cushman & Wakefield (U.K.) Ltd. (3)
43-45 Portman Square, London, W1A 3BG, United Kingdom
Tel.: (44) 2079355000
Web Site:
  http://www.cushmanwakefield.co.uk
Emp.: 1,200
Real Estate Brokerage & Property Management Services
N.A.I.C.S.: 531390
James Heyworth-Dunne *(Partner-Central London)*

Cushman & Wakefield (VIC) Pty Ltd (3)
Level 9 385 Bourke Street, Melbourne, 3000, VIC, Australia
Tel.: (61) 3 9631 7500
Web Site:
  http://www.cushmanwakefield.com.au
Real Estate Services
N.A.I.C.S.: 531390
Dominic Long *(Mng Dir-Comml Real Estate)*

Branch (Non-US):

Cushman & Wakefield - Brussels (3)
Chaussee de la Hulpe 166 Terhulpsesteenweg, Brussels, 1170, Belgium
Tel.: (32) 26290200
Web Site: http://www.cushmanwakefield.be
Real Estate Services
N.A.I.C.S.: 531390
Koen Nevens *(Mng Partner & Head-Northern Europe Reg)*

Cushman & Wakefield - Madrid (3)
Edificio Beatriz Jose Ortega y Gasset 29 6th Floor, 28006, Madrid, Spain
Tel.: (34) 91 781 0010
Web Site: http://www.cushmanwakefield.es
Real Estate Services
N.A.I.C.S.: 531390
Jenny Pizarro *(Partner)*

Cushman & Wakefield - Sao Paulo (3)
Praca Jose Lannes 40-3rd Floor, Sao Paulo, Brazil
Tel.: (55) 1155015464
Web Site: http://www.cushmanwakefield.us
Real Estate Services
N.A.I.C.S.: 531390
Celina Antunes *(Pres-South America)*

Subsidiary (Non-US):

Cushman & Wakefield K.K. (3)
Sanno Park Tower 13F 2-11-1 Nagatacho, Chiyoda-ku, Tokyo, 100-6113, Japan
Tel.: (81) 3 3596 7070
Web Site: http://www.cushmanwakefield.jp
Real Estate Services
N.A.I.C.S.: 531390
Todd Olson *(Exec Mng Dir)*

Cushman & Wakefield LLP (3)
125 Old Broad Street, London, EC2N 1AR, United Kingdom
Tel.: (44) 20 3296 3000
Web Site:
  http://www.cushmanwakefield.com
Emp.: 200
Real Estate Services
N.A.I.C.S.: 531390
Colin Wilson *(CEO-EMEA)*

Cushman & Wakefield Ltd. (3)
161 Bay Street Suite 1500, PO Box 602, Toronto, M5J 2S1, ON, Canada
Tel.: (416) 862-0611
Web Site:
  https://www.cushmanwakefield.com
Real Estate Services
N.A.I.C.S.: 531390
Bradley S. Anderson *(Vice Chm)*

Cushman & Wakefield Sweden AB (3)
Regeringsgatan 59, Stockholm, 11156, Sweden
Tel.: (46) 8 545 677 0
Web Site:
  http://www.cushmanwakefield.com
Real Estate Services
N.A.I.C.S.: 531390

PAG ASIA CAPITAL LTD.

PAG Asia Capital Ltd.—(Continued)
Agneta Jakobsson (Head-Sweden & Nordics)

Cushman & Wakefield de Mexico (3)
Paseo de las Tamarindos N60-B 2 Floor,
Col Bosques de las Lomas, Mexico, 5120,
Mexico
Tel.: (52) 55 8525 8000
Web Site:
   http://www.cushmanwakefield.com
Emp.: 80
Real Estate Services
N.A.I.C.S.: 531390
Victor M. Lachica (Pres & CEO)

Subsidiary (Domestic):

Cushman & Wakefield of Arizona, Inc. (3)
2555 E Camelback Rd Ste 400, Phoenix, AZ 85016
Tel.: (602) 954-9000
Web Site: http://www.cushwakephoenix.com
Emp.: 260
Real Estate Services
N.A.I.C.S.: 531210
Phil Jones (Mng Dir)

Cushman & Wakefield of California, Inc. (3)
425 Market St Ste 2300, San Francisco, CA 94105
Tel.: (415) 397-1700
Web Site:
   http://www.cushwakesanfrancisco.com
Emp.: 125
Real Estate Services
N.A.I.C.S.: 531210
Joe Cook (Mng Principal-Northern CA & OR)

Cushman & Wakefield of Connecticut, Inc. (3)
107 Elm St 4 Stamford Plz 8th Fl, Stamford, CT 06902
Tel.: (203) 326-5800
Real Estate Services
N.A.I.C.S.: 531210
Steve Baker (Exec Mng Dir)

Cushman & Wakefield of Florida, Inc. (3)
333 SE 2nd Ave, Miami, FL 33131-2662
Tel.: (305) 371-4411
Web Site: http://www.cushwakesouthfl.com
Real Estate Services
N.A.I.C.S.: 531210
Larry Richey (Mng Principal-Florida)

Branch (Domestic):

Cushman & Wakefield, Inc. - Tampa (4)
1 Tampa City Ctr Ste 3300, Tampa, FL 33602
Tel.: (813) 223-6300
Web Site: http://www.cushwaketampa.com
Emp.: 135
Real Estate Brokerage, Property Management & Leasing Services
N.A.I.C.S.: 531210
Doug Rothschild (Exec Mng Dir)

Subsidiary (Domestic):

Cushman & Wakefield of Georgia, Inc. (3)
1180 Peachtree St Ste 3100, Atlanta, GA 30309
Tel.: (404) 875-1000
Web Site: http://www.cushwakeatlanta.com
Emp.: 350
Real Estate Services
N.A.I.C.S.: 531210
Bryan Berthold (Mng Dir-Workplace Strategies)

Cushman & Wakefield of Illinois, Inc. (3)
225 W Wacker Dr Ste 3000, Chicago, IL 60606
Tel.: (312) 470-1800
Web Site: http://www.cushwakechicago.com
Emp.: 640
Real Estate Services
N.A.I.C.S.: 531210
Brian Adelstein (Sr VP)

Cushman & Wakefield of Long Island, Inc. (3)
401 Broad Hollow Rd Ste 301, Melville, NY 11747-4711
Tel.: (631) 425-1241
Web Site:
   http://www.cushmanwakefield.com
Emp.: 20
Real Estate Services
N.A.I.C.S.: 531210
Robert Sheehy (Exec Mng Dir)

Cushman & Wakefield of Maryland, Inc. (3)
1 E Pratt St Ste 700, Baltimore, MD 21202
Tel.: (410) 752-4285
Web Site:
   http://www.cushwakebaltimore.com
Emp.: 75
Commercial Real Estate Services
N.A.I.C.S.: 531210
Robert Shovan (VP-Ops)

Cushman & Wakefield of Massachusetts, Inc. (3)
225 Franklin St Ste 300, Boston, MA 02110
Tel.: (617) 330-6966
Web Site: http://www.cushwakeboston.com
Emp.: 120
Real Estate Services
N.A.I.C.S.: 531210
Linda McDonough (Dir-Mktg)

Cushman & Wakefield of New Jersey, Inc. (3)
1 Meadowlands Plz 7th Fl, East Rutherford, NJ 07073-1605
Tel.: (201) 935-4000
Web Site: http://www.cushmanwakefield.us
Real Estate Services
N.A.I.C.S.: 531210
Richard Baumstein (Exec Mng Dir)

Cushman & Wakefield of Oregon, Inc. (3)
200 SW Market St Ste 200, Portland, OR 97201-5730
Tel.: (503) 279-1700
Web Site: http://www.cushmanwakefield.us
Real Estate Services
N.A.I.C.S.: 531210
Judy Howard (Dir-Ops)

Cushman & Wakefield of Texas, Inc. (3)
1330 Post Oak Blvd Ste 2700, Houston, TX 77056
Tel.: (713) 877-1700
Web Site:
   http://www.cushmanwakefieldhouston.com
Emp.: 140
Real Estate Services
N.A.I.C.S.: 531210
Scott Wegmann (Vice Chm)

Branch (Domestic):

Cushman & Wakefield of Texas, Inc. - Austin (4)
200 W Cesar Chavez Ste 250, Austin, TX 78701
Tel.: (512) 474-2400
Web Site: http://www.cushwakeaustintx.com
Emp.: 50
Commercial Real Estate Broker
N.A.I.C.S.: 531210
Spencer Hayes (Exec Mng Dir & Mng Principal)

Subsidiary (Domestic):

Cushman & Wakefield of Washington D.C., Inc. (3)
2101 L St NW Ste 700, Washington, DC 20037
Tel.: (202) 463-2100
Web Site: http://www.cushwakedc.com
Emp.: 650
Real Estate Services
N.A.I.C.S.: 531210
Peter Carroccio (Mng Principal)

Cushman & Wakefield of Washington, Inc. (3)
1420 5th Ave Ste 2600, Seattle, WA 98101
Tel.: (206) 682-0666
Web Site:
   http://www.cushmanwakefield.com
Emp.: 22

Real Estate Services
N.A.I.C.S.: 531210
Janice Davis (Sr Mgr-Property)

Branch (Domestic):

Cushman & Wakefield, Inc. - Indianapolis (3)
1 American Sq Ste 1300, Indianapolis, IN 46282
Tel.: (317) 634-6363
Web Site:
   http://www.cushwakeindianapolis.com
Emp.: 145
Commercial Real Estate Services
N.A.I.C.S.: 531210
Patrick B. Lindley (Exec Mng Dir)

Subsidiary (Non-US):

DTZ Zadelhoff v.o.f. (3)
Gustav Mahlerlaan 362, Amsterdam, 1082 ME, Netherlands
Tel.: (31) 206644644
Web Site: http://www.dtz.nl
Emp.: 400
Real Estate & Property Management Services
N.A.I.C.S.: 531311
Marcel Akkerman (Controller-Credit)

Joint Venture (Domestic):

Quality Solutions Inc. (3)
128 N First St, Colwich, KS 67030
Tel.: (316) 721-3656
Web Site: http://www.qsifacilities.com
Specialty Trade Contractors
N.A.I.C.S.: 238990
Chad Pore (Pres)

Subsidiary (Domestic):

Emcon Associates, Inc. (4)
74 Brick Blvd, Brick, NJ 08723-7984
Tel.: (800) 545-4866
Web Site: http://www.emconfm.com
Facilities Support Services
N.A.I.C.S.: 561210
Michael Cocuzza (CEO)

Lexmark International, Inc. (1)
1 Lexmark Centre Dr 740 W New Cir Rd, Lexington, KY 40550 (43%)
Tel.: (859) 232-2000
Web Site: http://www.lexmark.com
Laser, Inkjet & Dot Matrix Printers & Supplies Mfr, Developer & Retailer
N.A.I.C.S.: 333248
Sharon Votaw (Chief HR Officer & Sr VP)

Subsidiary (Non-US):

Lexmark Canada, Inc. (2)
125 Commerce Valley Drive West Suite 600, Markham, L3T 7W4, ON, Canada
Tel.: (905) 763-0560
Web Site: https://www.lexmark.ca
Printers, Inks & Toners Mfr & Marketer
N.A.I.C.S.: 339940

Subsidiary (Domestic):

Lexmark Government Solutions, LLC
901 Newyork Ave Northwest ste 420, Washington, DC 20001
Tel.: (202) 378-9043
Web Site: http://www.lexmark.com
Printing Machinery & Equipment Mfr
N.A.I.C.S.: 333248

Subsidiary (Non-US):

Lexmark Handelsgesellschaft m.b.H. (2)
Kelsenstrasse 2Business park MARXIMUM Modecenterstrasse 17 Object 4 8, 1110, Vienna, Austria
Tel.: (43) 1797320
Web Site: http://www.lexmark.com
Printing Machinery & Equipment Mfr
N.A.I.C.S.: 333248

Lexmark Information Technologies Products Tic. Ltd. Sti. (2)
Barbaros Neighborhood Kardelen Street Palladium Tower No 2, Atasehir, Istanbul, 34746, Turkiye
Tel.: (90) 216 217 48 00
Web Site: http://www.lexmark.com

INTERNATIONAL PUBLIC

Printing Machinery & Equipment Mfr
N.A.I.C.S.: 333248

Lexmark International (Australia) Pty Ltd. (2)
Level 4 11 Talavera Road, North Ryde, 2113, NSW, Australia
Tel.: (61) 284013000
Web Site: http://www.lexmark.com
Marketer of Printers & Keyboards & Supplies
N.A.I.C.S.: 423420

Lexmark International (Singapore) Pte Ltd. (2)
238A Thomson Rd, 13-01/05 Novena Square Tower A, Singapore, 307684, Singapore
Tel.: (65) 64679898
Web Site: http://www.lexmark.com
Printing Machinery & Equipment Mfr
N.A.I.C.S.: 333248

Lexmark International Africa Sarl (2)
210 Bvd Zerktouni 5th Floor, Casablanca, 20060, Morocco
Tel.: (212) 5 29 05 76 84
Web Site: http://www.lexmark.com
Printing Machinery & Equipment Mfr
N.A.I.C.S.: 333248
David Vionnet (Gen Mgr)

Lexmark International B.V. (2)
Gooimeer 12, 1411 DE, Naarden, Netherlands
Tel.: (31) 356994600
Web Site: http://www.lexmark.com
Printing Machinery & Equipment Mfr
N.A.I.C.S.: 333248

Lexmark International CRT d.o.o. (2)
Heinzelova 62a Emporion centar, 10000, Zagreb, Croatia
Tel.: (385) 1 223 10 41
Web Site: http://www.lexmark.com
Printing Machinery & Equipment Mfr
N.A.I.C.S.: 333248
Mira Licina (Branch Mgr)

Lexmark International Czech s.r.o. (2)
City Tower Hvezdova 1716/2b, Prague, Czech Republic
Tel.: (420) 844444666
Web Site: http://www.lexmark.com
Printing Machinery & Equipment Mfr
N.A.I.C.S.: 333248

Lexmark International Limited (2)
Highfield House 8 Roxborough Way, Maidenhead, SL6 3UD, United Kingdom
Tel.: (44) 1628 518600
Web Site: http://www.lexmark.com
Printing & Imaging Equipment Distr
N.A.I.C.S.: 423430

Lexmark International Polska Sp.Z.o.o. (2)
o ul Woloska 5, 02-675, Warsaw, Poland
Tel.: (48) 22 874 37 09
Web Site: http://www.lexmark.com
Printing Machinery & Equipment Mfr
N.A.I.C.S.: 333248

Subsidiary (Domestic):

Lexmark International Puerto Rico (2)
Colgate Palmolive Bldg Lote 8 Ste 202, Guaynabo, PR 00968
Tel.: (787) 300-3388
Web Site: http://www.lexmark.com
Printing Machinery & Equipment Mfr
N.A.I.C.S.: 333248

Subsidiary (Non-US):

Lexmark International RS d.o.o. (2)
Makenzijeva 67/III, 11000, Belgrade, Serbia
Tel.: (381) 112445110
Web Site: http://www.lexmark.com
Printing Machinery & Equipment Mfr
N.A.I.C.S.: 333248
Ivan Stankovic (Mng Dir)

Lexmark International SASU (2)
18 rue Gustave Flourens, 92150, Suresnes, France
Tel.: (33) 146674000
Web Site: http://www.lexmark.com

AND PRIVATE COMPANIES

Mfr of Ribbons, Toners & Laser Printer Cartridges; European Support Center
N.A.I.C.S.: 339940

Lexmark International Technology S.A. (2)
Rte de Pre-Bois 20, 1217, Meyrin, Switzerland
Tel.: (41) 227107050
Printing Machinery & Equipment Mfr
N.A.I.C.S.: 333248

Lexmark Magyarorszag Kft (2)
Odon Lechner 8th Avenue, 1095, Budapest, Hungary
Tel.: (36) 12880097
Web Site: http://www.lexmark.com
Printing Machinery & Equipment Mfr
N.A.I.C.S.: 333248
Dany Molhoek (VP-EMEA)

Lexmark Research & Development Corporation (2)
Lexmark Plaza 1 Samar Loop corner Panay Road Cebu Business Park, Cebu, 6000, Philippines
Tel.: (63) 32 234 8300
Web Site: http://www.lexmark.com
Enterprise Software & Managed Print Services
N.A.I.C.S.: 333248

Lexmark Schweiz AG (2)
Zurcherstrasse 59, CH-8800, Thalwil, Switzerland
Tel.: (41) 44 722 8811
Web Site: http://www.lexmark.com
Printing Machinery & Equipment Mfr
N.A.I.C.S.: 333248

Lexmark Spain SL (2)
Calle Rosario Pino 14-16 Planta 9, 28020, Madrid, Spain
Tel.: (34) 914360048
Web Site: http://www.lexmark.com
Printing Machinery & Equipment Mfr
N.A.I.C.S.: 333248

Quick Service Restaurant Holdings Pty Ltd. (1)
Level 12 12 Help Street, Chatswood, 2067, NSW, Australia (100%)
Tel.: (61) 8 9240 9777
Web Site: http://www.craveablebrands.com
Restaurant Operators
N.A.I.C.S.: 722511
Brett Houldin (CEO)

PAG CAPITAL
15/F & 32nd/F AIA Central 1 Connaught Road, Central, China (Hong Kong)
Tel.: (852) 219180088
Web Site: http://www.pagasia.com
Year Founded: 2002
Privater Equity Firm
N.A.I.C.S.: 523999
Lincoln Pan (Partner & Co-Head-Private Equity)

Subsidiaries:

Pacific Alliance Group (1)
6th Floor 105 Piccadilly Mayfair, London, W1J 7NJ, United Kingdom
Tel.: (44) 2076344000
Web Site: http://www.pag.com
Asset Management Services
N.A.I.C.S.: 523940
James Parsons (Mng Dir)

Patties Foods Pty Limited (1)
Chifley Business Park, Level 2 1 Joseph Avenue, Mentone, 3194, VIC, Australia
Tel.: (61) 3 8540 9100
Web Site: http://www.patties.com.au
Frozen Food Products Mfr & Sales
N.A.I.C.S.: 311813
Lisa Laurence (Mgr-Bus Improvement)

Secured Capital Investment Management Co., Ltd. (1)
Toranomon Towers Office 20F, 4-1-8 Toranomon Minato-ku, Tokyo, 105-0001, Japan
Tel.: (81) 357761300
Web Site: http://www.securedcapital.co.jp
Sales Range: $75-99.9 Million
Emp.: 100

Real Estate Investment & Asset Management Services
N.A.I.C.S.: 531390
Jack S. Keese (Sr Mng Dir & Head-Loan Acq & Mgmt)

Unispace Global Pty Ltd.
Level 43 225 George Street, Sydney, 2000, Australia
Tel.: (61) 1300200800
Web Site: http://www.unispace.com
Workplace Technology & Commercial Interior Design
N.A.I.C.S.: 531120
Steve Quick (CEO)

Subsidiary (US):

Downstream (2)
1624 NW Johnson St, Portland, OR 97209
Tel.: (503) 226-1944
Web Site: http://www.downstream.com
Periodical Publishers
N.A.I.C.S.: 513120
Tim Canfield (CEO)

Yingde Gases Group Company Limited (1)
Room 3212-13 32/F Tower 2 Times Square, Causeway Bay, China (Hong Kong)
Tel.: (852) 3100 0068
Web Site: http://www.yingdegas.com
Sales Range: $1-4.9 Billion
Industrial Gas Producer & Distr
N.A.I.C.S.: 325120

PAGARIA ENERGY LIMITED
9/18 Bazar Gali Vishwas Nagar, Shahdara, Delhi, 110 032, India
Tel.: (91) 63409782
Web Site: https://www.pagariaenergy.com
531396—(BOM)
Rev.: $17,877
Assets: $784,689
Liabilities: $40,945
Net Worth: $743,744
Earnings: $4,076
Fiscal Year-end: 03/31/23
Eletric Power Generation Services
N.A.I.C.S.: 221118
Ranjit Singh Pagaria (CFO)

PAGE INDUSTRIES LIMITED
Cessna Business Park Tower-1 7th Floor Umiya Business Bay, Varthur Hobli Outer Ring Road, Bengaluru, 560103, India
Tel.: (91) 8049454545
Web Site: https://www.jockeyindia.com
Year Founded: 1995
PAGEIND—(NSE)
Rev.: $533,365,833
Assets: $287,598,129
Liabilities: $139,000,680
Net Worth: $148,597,449
Earnings: $73,236,482
Emp.: 27,730
Fiscal Year-end: 03/31/22
Underwear Mfr & Distr
N.A.I.C.S.: 315250
Sunder Genomal (Mng Dir)

PAGE ZERO MEDIA INC.
49 Spadina Avenue Suite 206, Toronto, M5V 2J1, ON, Canada
Tel.: (647) 776-8019
Web Site: http://www.pagezero.com
Year Founded: 2000
Sales Range: $1-9.9 Million
Emp.: 10
Digital Marketing & Advertising Services
N.A.I.C.S.: 541613
Andrew Goodman (Founder & Pres)

PAGEANT HOLDINGS LIMITED
Melcorpo Building Loughlinstown Industrial Estate Loughlinstown Drive, Dun Laoghaire, Ireland

Tel.: (353) 1 282 3100 JE
Web Site: http://www.pageantholdings.com
Year Founded: 1995
Investment Holding Company
N.A.I.C.S.: 551112
Nick Furlong (Principal)

PAGEANT MEDIA LTD.
One London Wall, London, EC2Y 5EA, United Kingdom
Tel.: (44) 2078326500 UK
Web Site: https://www.pageantmedia.com
Year Founded: 1998
Business Information & Intelligence Publisher
N.A.I.C.S.: 513120
Charlie Kerr (CEO)

Subsidiaries:

Institutional Investor, LLC (1)
1120 6th Ave, New York, NY 10036
Tel.: (212) 224-3801
Web Site: http://www.institutionalinvestor.com
Business Periodicals Publisher
N.A.I.C.S.: 513120
Diane Alfano (Chm & CEO)

PAGED S.A.
Ul Cieszynska 99, Jasienica, 43-385, Warsaw, Poland
Tel.: (48) 334972400
Web Site: http://www.pagedmeble.pl
Furniture Mfr
N.A.I.C.S.: 337211
Tomasz Lis (Dir-Plng & Analysis)

PAGEGROUP PLC
200 Aldersgate Aldersgate Street, Bourne Business Park, London, EC1A 4HD, Surrey, United Kingdom
Tel.: (44) 2078312000
Web Site: https://www.page.com
PAGE—(OTCIQ)
Rev.: $1,771,540,837
Assets: $855,131,430
Liabilities: $426,226,324
Net Worth: $428,905,106
Earnings: ($7,796,028)
Emp.: 6,694
Fiscal Year-end: 12/31/20
Recruitment Services
N.A.I.C.S.: 541612
Kelvin Stagg (CFO)

Subsidiaries:

Michael Page (Beijing) Recruitment Co., Ltd (1)
2701 / 2708 SK Tower No 6 Jia Jianguomenwai Avenue, Chaoyang District, Beijing, 100022, China
Tel.: (86) 1059690666
Financial Services
N.A.I.C.S.: 523150

Michael Page (Shanghai) Recruitment Co. Ltd (1)
18/F HKRI Centre Two 288 Shimen Road No 1, Shanghai, 200041, China
Tel.: (86) 216 062 3000
Web Site: https://www.michaelpage.com.cn
Sales Range: $25-49.9 Million
Emp.: 10
Human Resource Consulting Services
N.A.I.C.S.: 541612

Michael Page Africa (SA) (Pty) Limited (1)
5th Floor The Forum 2 Maude Street, Johannesburg, Sandton, 2196, South Africa
Tel.: (27) 113038300
Web Site: https://www.michaelpageafrica.com
Financial Services
N.A.I.C.S.: 523150

Michael Page Do International (Brasil) Recrutamento Especializado Ltda (1)

Rua Olimpia 205 11th floor - Vila Olimpia, Sao Paulo, 04551-000, Brazil
Tel.: (55) 1139566905
Web Site: https://www.michaelpage.com.br
Sales Range: $75-99.9 Million
Emp.: 40
Human Resource Consulting Services
N.A.I.C.S.: 541612

Michael Page Holdings Limited (1)
1st Floor Victoria House Southampton Row, London, WC1B 4JB, United Kingdom
Tel.: (44) 2078312000
Web Site: http://www.michaelpage.co.uk
Sales Range: $50-74.9 Million
Holding Company
N.A.I.C.S.: 551112

Michael Page International (Australia) Pty Limited (1)
Level 21 9 Castlereagh Street, Sydney, 2000, NSW, Australia
Tel.: (61) 282922000
Web Site: http://www.michaelpage.com.au
Sales Range: $25-49.9 Million
Employment Placement Agencies
N.A.I.C.S.: 561311

Michael Page International (Belgium) NV (1)
Place du Champ de Mars 5 x, Brussels, 1050, Belgium
Tel.: (32) 25094545
Web Site: http://www.michaelpage.be
Sales Range: $25-49.9 Million
Emp.: 70
Management Consulting Services
N.A.I.C.S.: 541618
Thibaud Ades (Mng Dir)

Michael Page International (Deutschland) GmbH (1)
Westend Carree Gruneburgweg 16-18, 60322, Frankfurt am Main, Germany
Tel.: (49) 69507780
Web Site: http://www.michaelpage.de
Employment Placement Agencies
N.A.I.C.S.: 561311

Michael Page International (Espana) SA (1)
Paseo De La Castellana 28, 28046, Madrid, Spain
Tel.: (34) 911318110
Web Site: http://www.michaelpage.es
Sales Range: $25-49.9 Million
Management Consulting Services
N.A.I.C.S.: 541618

Michael Page International (France) SAS (1)
164 avenue Achille Peretti, 92200, Neuilly-sur-Seine, France
Tel.: (33) 141927070
Web Site: http://www.michaelpage.fr
Sales Range: $25-49.9 Million
Management Consulting Services
N.A.I.C.S.: 541618

Michael Page International (Hong Kong) Limited (1)
17Th Floor Central Tower 28 Queens Road Central, Central, China (Hong Kong)
Tel.: (852) 25306100
Web Site: http://www.michaelpage.hk
Employment Placement Agencies
N.A.I.C.S.: 561311

Michael Page International (Ireland) Limited (1)
Suite 202 The Greenway Block C Ardilaun Court 112 114, St Stephen's Green, Dublin, 2, Ireland
Tel.: (353) 1 653 9800
Web Site: http://www.michaelpage.ie
Emp.: 7
Human Resource Consulting Services
N.A.I.C.S.: 541612

Michael Page International (Japan) K.K. (1)
6F Hulic Kamiyacho Building 4-3-13 Toranomon, Minato-ku, Tokyo, 105-0001, Japan
Tel.: (81) 35 733 7166
Web Site: https://www.michaelpage.co.jp
Emp.: 100
Human Resource Consulting Services
N.A.I.C.S.: 541612

Michael Page International (Malaysia) Sdn. Bhd. (1)

PAGEGROUP PLC

PageGroup plc—(Continued)

Level 27 Integra Tower The Intermark 348 Jalan Tun Razak, Federal Territory, 50400, Kuala Lumpur, Malaysia
Tel.: (60) 32 302 4000
Web Site: https://www.michaelpage.com.my
Financial Services
N.A.I.C.S.: 523150

Michael Page International (Maroc) SARL AU
Immeuble Plein Ciel, 20100, Casablanca, Morocco
Tel.: (212) 529039919
Financial Services
N.A.I.C.S.: 523150

Michael Page International (Mauritius) Limited (1)
5th Floor Medine Mews La Chaussee Street, 11302, Port Louis, Mauritius
Tel.: (230) 2060000
Financial Services
N.A.I.C.S.: 523150

Michael Page International (NZ) Limited. (1)
Level 6 41 Shortland Street, 1010, Auckland, New Zealand
Tel.: (64) 9 354 8100
Web Site: http://www.michaelpage.co.nz
Sales Range: $25-49.9 Million
Emp.: 15
Human Resource Consulting Services
N.A.I.C.S.: 541612

Michael Page International (Nederland) B.V. (1)
Strawinskylaan 421, 1077 XX, Amsterdam, Netherlands
Tel.: (31) 205789444
Web Site: https://www.michaelpage.nl
Sales Range: $25-49.9 Million
Employment Placement Agencies
N.A.I.C.S.: 561311

Michael Page International (Poland) Sp.Z.O.O (1)
ul Zlota 59 Zlote Tarasy, Budynek Lumen 5 pietro, 00-120, Warsaw, Poland
Tel.: (48) 22 319 3000
Web Site: https://www.michaelpage.pl
Sales Range: $25-49.9 Million
Emp.: 125
Employment Placement Agencies
N.A.I.C.S.: 561311

Michael Page International (SA) (Pty) Limited (1)
5th floor Forum Building 2 maude street, Sandton, 2196, South Africa
Tel.: (27) 11 303 8300
Web Site: http://www.michaelpage.co.za
Sales Range: $25-49.9 Million
Emp.: 33
Human Resource Consulting Services
N.A.I.C.S.: 541612

Michael Page International (Shanghai) Consulting Ltd (1)
Shimen Yi Road 288 Industrial Taikoo Hui Two 18Th Floor, Jingan, Shanghai, 200041, China
Tel.: (86) 2160623000
Web Site: http://www.michaelpage.com.cn
Human Resource Consulting Services
N.A.I.C.S.: 541612

Michael Page International (Sweden) AB (1)
Master Samuelsgatan 42 14tr, 111 57, Stockholm, Sweden
Tel.: (46) 854527040
Web Site: http://www.michaelpage.se
Sales Range: $25-49.9 Million
Human Resource Consulting Services
N.A.I.C.S.: 541612

Michael Page International (Switzerland) SA (1)
Quai de la Poste 12, 1204, Geneva, Switzerland
Tel.: (41) 22 544 1900
Web Site: https://www.michaelpage.ch
Sales Range: $10-24.9 Million
Emp.: 50
Employment Placement Agencies
N.A.I.C.S.: 561311

Michael Page International (UAE) Limited
Michael Page Office No 202 Al Fattan Currency House, PO Box 506702, Tower -1 Dubai International Financial Centre, Dubai, United Arab Emirates
Tel.: (971) 4 709 0300
Web Site: https://www.michaelpage.ae
Sales Range: $25-49.9 Million
Emp.: 35
Management Consulting Services
N.A.I.C.S.: 541618

Michael Page International (Vietnam) Co. Limited (1)
Unit 3 Level 9 Saigon Centre Tower 2 67 Le Loi Street, Ben Nghe Ward District 1, 700000, Ho Chi Minh City, Vietnam
Tel.: (84) 2862848260
Web Site: https://www.michaelpage.com.vn
Financial Services
N.A.I.C.S.: 523150

Michael Page International Argentina SA (1)
Av Cordoba 883 - Piso 10 - Buenos Aires, C1054AAH, Buenos Aires, Argentina
Tel.: (54) 114 001 4500
Web Site: https://www.michaelpage.com.ar
Human Resource Consulting Services
N.A.I.C.S.: 541612

Michael Page International Austria GmbH (1)
Qbc 4 At Belvedere 4 Entrance Karlpopper-strasse 4 Staircase 1, 1100, Vienna, Austria
Tel.: (43) 12052050
Web Site: http://www.michaelpage.at
Human Resource Consulting Services
N.A.I.C.S.: 541612
Geoffroy De Beaucorps (Mng Dir)

Michael Page International Canada Limited (1)
Bay Adelaide Centre 333 Bay Street Suite 515, Toronto, M5H 2R2, ON, Canada
Tel.: (416) 306-3900
Web Site: http://www.michaelpage.ca
Emp.: 40
International Affairs
N.A.I.C.S.: 928120

Michael Page International Chile Ltda (1)
Magdalena 181 16th floor, Las Condes, 11000, Santiago, Chile
Tel.: (56) 22 585 3200
Web Site: https://www.michaelpage.cl
Emp.: 8
Human Resource Consulting Services
N.A.I.C.S.: 541612

Michael Page International Empresa de Trabalho Temporario e Servicos de Consultadoria Lda (1)
Avenida da Liberdade n 180-A 3rd floor, 1250-146, Lisbon, Portugal
Tel.: (351) 210419110
Web Site: http://www.michaelpage.pt
Sales Range: $10-24.9 Million
Employment Placement Agencies
N.A.I.C.S.: 561311

Michael Page International Holdings Limited (1)
3rd Floor Wellington House 20 Queensmere, Slough, SL1 1DB, Berkshire, United Kingdom
Tel.: (44) 1753 826800
Web Site: http://www.michaelpageinternational.com
Sales Range: $50-74.9 Million
Emp.: 70
Investment Management Service
N.A.I.C.S.: 523999

Michael Page International Inc (1)
622 3rd Ave 29th Fl, New York, NY 10017
Tel.: (212) 661-4800
Web Site: https://www.michaelpage.com
Employment Placement Agencies
N.A.I.C.S.: 561311
Simon Lewis (Mng Dir)

Michael Page International Italia Srl (1)
Passarella Gallery 2, 20122, Milan, Italy
Tel.: (39) 028068001

Web Site: http://www.michaelpage.it
Human Resource Consulting Services
N.A.I.C.S.: 541612

Michael Page International Mexico Reclutamiento Especializado, S.A. de C.V. (1)
Avenida Paseo de la Reforma 115 Piso 10, Miguel Hidalgo Lomas de Chapultepec, 11000, Mexico, Mexico
Tel.: (52) 5552845770
Web Site: https://www.michaelpage.com.mx
Financial Services
N.A.I.C.S.: 523150

Michael Page International NEM Istihdam Danismanligi Limited Sirketi (1)
Buyukdere Cad Kanyon Ofis Binasi No 185 Kat 21, Levent, 34394, Istanbul, Turkiye
Tel.: (90) 2123365200
Web Site: https://www.michaelpage.com.tr
Sales Range: $25-49.9 Million
Emp.: 11
Human Resource Consulting Services
N.A.I.C.S.: 541612

Michael Page International Peru SRL (1)
Calle Las Orquideas 675 Floor 5, San Isidro, Lima, Peru
Tel.: (51) 1 712 5800
Web Site: https://www.michaelpage.pe
Financial Services
N.A.I.C.S.: 523150

Michael Page International Portugal - Empressa de Trabalho Temporario e Servicos de Consultadoria Lda. (1)
Avenida da Liberdade n 180-A 3 Andar, Lisbon, Portugal
Tel.: (351) 210419110
Web Site: https://www.michaelpage.pt
Human Resource Consulting Services
N.A.I.C.S.: 541612

Michael Page International Pte Limited (1)
One Raffles Place Office Tower 2 09-61, Unit 09-61, Singapore, 048616, Singapore
Tel.: (65) 6 533 2777
Web Site: https://www.michaelpage.com.sg
Sales Range: $25-49.9 Million
Emp.: 120
Employment Placement Agencies
N.A.I.C.S.: 561311

Michael Page International RU LLC (1)
CityDel Business Center Zemlyanoy Val Street Bld 9 10th Floor, 105064, Moscow, Russia
Tel.: (7) 495 662 77 22
Web Site: http://www.michaelpage.ru
Emp.: 17
Human Resource Consulting Services
N.A.I.C.S.: 541612

Michael Page International Recruitment (Thailand) Limited (1)
689 Bhiraj Tower at EmQuartier 41st Floor, Unit 4108-4109 Sukhumvit Road Soi 35 North Klongton Vadhana, Bangkok, 10110, Thailand
Tel.: (66) 2 012 5000
Web Site: https://www.michaelpage.co.th
Financial Services
N.A.I.C.S.: 523150

Michael Page International Recruitment Limited (1)
Page House 1 Dashwood Lang Road, Addlestone, Weybridge, KT15 2QW, United Kingdom
Tel.: (44) 1932264000
Web Site: http://www.michaelpage.co.uk
Sales Range: $25-49.9 Million
Emp.: 90
Employment Placement Agencies
N.A.I.C.S.: 561311

Michael Page International Recruitment Pvt. Ltd. (1)
5th Floor 2 North Avenue Maker Maxity Bandra-Kurla Complex, Bandra E, Mumbai, 400 051, India
Tel.: (91) 224 236 3300
Web Site: https://www.michaelpage.co.in
Financial Services

INTERNATIONAL PUBLIC

N.A.I.C.S.: 523150

Michael Page Limited (1)
1st Floor Victoria House Southampton Row, London, WC1B 4JB, United Kingdom
Tel.: (44) 2078312000
Web Site: http://www.michaelpage.co.uk
Sales Range: $25-49.9 Million
Human Resource Consulting Services
N.A.I.C.S.: 541612

Michael Page Recruitment Group Limited (1)
Page House Level 3 The Switch 1-7 The Grove, Slough, SL1 1QP, Berkshire, United Kingdom
Tel.: (44) 845 606 0610
Web Site: http://www.michaelpage.co.uk
Sales Range: $50-74.9 Million
Emp.: 90
Holding Company
N.A.I.C.S.: 551112

Michael Page UK Limited (1)
Page House 1 Dashwood Lang Road Bourne Business Park, Addlestone, KT15 2QW, Surrey, United Kingdom
Tel.: (44) 2072692527
Web Site: http://www.michaelpage.co.uk
Sales Range: $25-49.9 Million
Emp.: 100
Employment Placement Agencies
N.A.I.C.S.: 561311

PT Michael Page Internasional Indonesia (1)
Level 12 One Pacific Place, Sudirman Central Business District Jl Jend Sudirman Kav 52-53, Jakarta, 12190, Indonesia
Tel.: (62) 212 958 8800
Web Site: https://www.michaelpage.co.id
Financial Services
N.A.I.C.S.: 523150

Page Interim BV (1)
WTC Strawinskylaan 421, 1077 XX, Amsterdam, Netherlands
Tel.: (31) 20 578 8070
Web Site: https://www.pagepersonnel.nl
Professionals Recruitment Services
N.A.I.C.S.: 561311

Page Personnel (Deutschland) GmbH (1)
Carl-Theodor-Str 1, 40213, Dusseldorf, Germany
Tel.: (49) 2118632490
Web Site: http://www.pagepersonnel.de
Human Resource Consulting Services
N.A.I.C.S.: 541612

Page Personnel BV (1)
Weena 331-333, 3013 AL, Rotterdam, Netherlands
Tel.: (31) 107999700
Web Site: https://www.pagepersonnel.nl
Employment Placement Agencies
N.A.I.C.S.: 561311

Page Personnel Do Brasil - Recrutamento Especializado e Servicos Corporativos Ltda. (1)
Rua Olimpia 205 - 11th floor, Vila Olimpia, Sao Paulo, 04551-000, Brazil
Tel.: (55) 1139569600
Web Site: https://www.pagepersonnel.com.br
Professionals Recruitment Services
N.A.I.C.S.: 561311

Page Personnel ETT SA (1)
Paseo Castellana 28 3rd floor, 28046, Madrid, Spain
Tel.: (34) 91 131 8100
Web Site: https://www.pagepersonnel.es
Sales Range: $25-49.9 Million
Emp.: 50
Personnel Services
N.A.I.C.S.: 541612
Nicolas Buisson (Mng Dir)

Page Personnel International Chile Ltda. (1)
Magdalena 181 piso 16, Las Condes, 11000, Santiago, Chile
Tel.: (56) 22 585 3200
Web Site: https://www.pagepersonnel.cl
Professionals Recruitment Services
N.A.I.C.S.: 561311

AND PRIVATE COMPANIES — PAI PARTNERS S.A.S.

Page Personnel Italy S.P.A. (1)
Via Botero 18, 10122, Turin, Italy
Tel.: (39) 023 626 0606
Web Site: https://www.pagepersonnel.it
Sales Range: $25-49.9 Million
Emp.: 7
Employment Placement Agencies
N.A.I.C.S.: 561311
Gianmarco Artuso *(Gen Mgr)*

Page Personnel Ltd (1)
53 Clarendon Rd, Watford, WD17 1LA, United Kingdom
Tel.: (44) 1923819192
Web Site: http://www.pagepersonnel.co.uk
Sales Range: $25-49.9 Million
Emp.: 25
Management Consulting Services
N.A.I.C.S.: 541618

Page Personnel Recruitment Pte. Ltd. (1)
One Raffles Place Office Tower 2 09-61, Singapore, 048616, Singapore
Tel.: (65) 6 416 9800
Web Site: https://www.pagepersonnel.com.sg
Professionals Recruitment Services
N.A.I.C.S.: 561311

Page Personnel SAS (1)
164 avenue Achille Peretti, 92200, Neuilly-sur-Seine, France
Tel.: (33) 78994848
Web Site: http://www.pagepersonnel.fr
Management Consulting Services
N.A.I.C.S.: 541618

Page Personnel Seleccion SA (1)
Paseo Castellana 28 3rd Floor, Madrid, Spain
Tel.: (34) 911318181
Permanent Recruitment & Temporary Staffing Services
N.A.I.C.S.: 561320

Taiwan Michael Page International Co., Ltd. (1)
8F-1 No 36 Songren Road, Xinyi District, Taipei, 110, Taiwan
Tel.: (886) 28 729 8200
Web Site: https://www.michaelpage.com.tw
Financial Services
N.A.I.C.S.: 523150

PAGET MINERALS CORP.
410 - 325 Howe Street, Vancouver, V6C 1Z7, BC, Canada
Tel.: (604) 687-3520
Web Site: http://www.pagetminerals.com
Year Founded: 2007
Rev.: $21,508
Assets: $60,171
Liabilities: $26,748
Net Worth: $33,423
Earnings: ($14,395)
Fiscal Year-end: 12/31/17
Mineral Exploration Services
N.A.I.C.S.: 213114

PAGLIERI SPA
Spinetta Marengo, Alessandria, 15121, Italy
Tel.: (39) 0131213511   IT
Web Site: http://www.paglieri.com
Year Founded: 1876
Sales Range: $75-99.9 Million
Emp.: 410
Cosmetics & Toiletries
N.A.I.C.S.: 325620
Mario Paglieri *(Chief Chemical Officer)*

PAGNOSSIN S.P.A.
Via Noalese 94, 31100, Treviso, Italy
Tel.: (39) 04222916
Web Site: http://www.pagnossin.com
Year Founded: 1919
Sales Range: $75-99.9 Million
Emp.: 923
Ironstone Ceramic Tableware & Terracotta Flower Pots Mfr
N.A.I.C.S.: 327110

PAGSEGURO DIGITAL LTD.
Av Brigadeiro Faria Lima 1 384, Sao Paulo, 01452-002, Brazil
Tel.: (55) 1130388127   Ky
Web Site: https://international.pagseguro.com
Year Founded: 2017
PAGS—(NYSE)
Rev.: $2,948,137,217
Assets: $8,714,562,155
Liabilities: $6,437,913,431
Net Worth: $2,276,648,724
Earnings: $289,291,648
Emp.: 7,223
Fiscal Year-end: 12/31/22
Internet Payment Services
N.A.I.C.S.: 518210
Luis Frias *(Chm & CEO)*

Subsidiaries:

Pagseguro Internet SA (1)
Avenida Brigadeiro Faria Lima n 1384 4 andar - Parte A, Jardim Paulistano, Sao Paulo, 01451-001, Brazil
Tel.: (55) 40036624
Internet Payment Services
N.A.I.C.S.: 518210

PAI PARTNERS S.A.S.
232 rue de Rivoli, 75054, Paris, Cedex 01, France
Tel.: (33) 143166300   FR
Web Site: http://www.paipartners.com
Year Founded: 1872
Sales Range: $5-14.9 Billion
Privater Equity Firm
N.A.I.C.S.: 523999
Amaury de Seze *(Chm-Supervisory Bd)*

Subsidiaries:

ALBEA S.A. (1)
5 rue Guillaume Kroll, Luxembourg, 1882, Luxembourg
Tel.: (352) 26 34 03 21
Web Site: http://www.albea-group.com
Beauty Products Packaging Mfr
N.A.I.C.S.: 326112
Francois Luscan *(Pres & CEO)*

Subsidiary (Non-US):

Albea Beauty Holdings S.A. (2)
1 Avenue du General De Gaulle, 92230, Gennevilliers, France
Tel.: (33) 181932000
Web Site: http://www.albea-group.com
Makeup, Fragrance, Skincare & Toiletry Packaging Mfr
N.A.I.C.S.: 322220
Francois Luscan *(Pres & CEO)*

Subsidiary (US):

Albea Beauty Solutions USA, LLC (3)
595 Madison Ave, New York, NY 10022
Tel.: (212) 371-5100
Packaging Materials Mfr & Distr
N.A.I.C.S.: 326160

Allos Hof-Manufaktur GmbH (1)
Hoerneckestrasse 39, 28217, Bremen, Germany
Tel.: (49) 4211633530
Web Site: http://www.allos.de
Grocery Products Retailer
N.A.I.C.S.: 445110
Eike Mehlhop *(Co-CEO)*

Amplitude Surgical SAS (1)
11 Cours Jacques Offenbach, 26000, Valence, France (52.3%)
Tel.: (33) 475418741
Web Site: https://www.amplitude-ortho.com
Rev.: $108,137,276
Assets: $287,088,280
Liabilities: $183,685,517
Net Worth: $103,402,763
Earnings: $41,579,970
Emp.: 426
Fiscal Year-end: 06/30/2023
Surgical Device Mfr
N.A.I.C.S.: 339112
Olivier Jallabert *(Founder, Chm & CEO)*

Subsidiary (Domestic):

Amplitude SAS (2)
Zone d Activites Mozart 2 11 Cours Jacques Offenbach, 26000, Valence, France
Tel.: (33) 475418741
Medical Equipment Mfr & Distr
N.A.I.C.S.: 339112
Nicolas Grellet *(Mgr-Export Area)*

Subsidiary (Non-US):

Amplitude Australia Pty Ltd. (3)
38 Payneham Road, Stepney, 5069, SA, Australia
Tel.: (61) 882979901
Medical Equipment Mfr & Distr
N.A.I.C.S.: 339112

Amplitude GmbH (3)
Am Neuen Graben 15, Zotzenheim, 55576, Mainz, Germany
Tel.: (49) 6701205520
Medical Product & Equipment Distr
N.A.I.C.S.: 423450

Amplitude Latin America S.A. (3)
Avenida 80-A 599, Jardim Vilage, Rio Claro, 13506-095, SP, Brazil
Tel.: (55) 193522380
Web Site: http://www.amplitude-latam.com
Medical & Hospital Equipment Mfr
N.A.I.C.S.: 339112
Luiz Fernando De Souza *(Controller)*

Subsidiary (US):

NovaStep Inc. (3)
30 Ramland Rd Ste 200, Orangeburg, NY 10962
Tel.: (917) 633-4378
Web Site: http://www.novastep.life
Medical Device Mfr
N.A.I.C.S.: 339112
Lina Carolina Ferreras *(Mgr-Customer Svc)*

Subsidiary (Domestic):

Firm Industrie SARL (2)
Z A Blacheronde, 26800, Etoile-sur-Rhone, France
Tel.: (33) 475615410
Precision Mechanical Part Mfr
N.A.I.C.S.: 332721

Poli Alpes SAS (2)
2 rue Laurent de Lavoisier ZI des Aureats, 26800, Portes-les-Valence, France
Tel.: (33) 475573264
Orthopedic Implant Product Mfr
N.A.I.C.S.: 339113

Poli Tech SAS (2)
Z A Blacheronde, 26800, Etoile-sur-Rhone, France
Tel.: (33) 475841563
Orthopedic Implants Mfr
N.A.I.C.S.: 339113

Areas, SAU (1)
Avda Diagonal 579-585 6 planta, 08014, Barcelona, Spain
Tel.: (34) 93 240 15 15
Web Site: http://es.areas.com
Food & Beverage Products Mfr
N.A.I.C.S.: 311999

Armacell International S.A. (1)
Rue Notre-Dame 8, 2240, Luxembourg, Luxembourg
Tel.: (352) 26262253
Web Site: http://www.armacell.com
Sales Range: $550-599.9 Million
Emp.: 2,200
Insulation Material Mfr
N.A.I.C.S.: 326140
Patrick Mathieu *(Pres & CEO)*

Subsidiary (Non-US):

Armacell International Holding GmbH (2)
Robert-Bosch-Strasse 10, D-48153, Munster, Germany
Tel.: (49) 25176030
Web Site: http://www.armacell.com
Sales Range: $600-649.9 Million
Emp.: 700
Holding Company; Engineered Foams, Rubber & Technical Insulation Products Mfr
N.A.I.C.S.: 551112

Subsidiary (Non-US):

Armacell (Guangzhou) Limited (3)
Guan Qiao Cun, Shilou Town, Guangzhou, Guangdong, China
Tel.: (86) 20 8486 5693
Engineered Foam Mfr
N.A.I.C.S.: 326140

Subsidiary (Non-US):

Armacell Asia Ltd. (4)
Suite 09-10 Level 25 Office Tower, Langham Place 8 Argyle Street, Kowloon, China (Hong Kong)
Tel.: (852) 2574 8420
Engineered Foam Mfr
N.A.I.C.S.: 326140

Subsidiary (Non-US):

Armacell (Thailand) Limited (3)
88 MU4 Donkrabueng, Banpong, 70110, Ratchaburi, Thailand
Tel.: (66) 32 3532057
Engineered Foam Mfr
N.A.I.C.S.: 326140

Armacell - Zamil Middle East Co. (3)
PO Box 8265, 31482, Dammam, Saudi Arabia
Tel.: (966) 3 847 1888
Flexible Foam Insulation Material Mfr
N.A.I.C.S.: 326140

Armacell Australia Pty. Ltd. (3)
13-17 Nathan Road, Dandenong, 3175, VIC, Australia
Tel.: (61) 3 8710 5999
Web Site: http://www.armacell.com.au
Engineered Foam Mfr
N.A.I.C.S.: 326140

Armacell Brasil, Ltda. (3)
Praca Dom Epaminondas 52, Pindamonhangaba, 12421-020, Sao Paulo, Brazil
Tel.: (55) 12 3648 6900
Engineered Foam Mfr
N.A.I.C.S.: 326140

Armacell France SA (3)
Arteparc Bat D Lieu-Dit Le Canet, 13590, Meyreuil, France
Tel.: (33) 4 86 91 10 60
Web Site: http://www.armacell.com
Insulation Material Mfr
N.A.I.C.S.: 326140

Armacell Iberia, S.L. (3)
Pol Ind Riera d'Esclanya, C/Can Magi 1, E-17213, Begur, Spain
Tel.: (34) 972 61 34 00
Engineered Foam Mfr
N.A.I.C.S.: 326140

Armacell India Private Ltd. (3)
Gat no 744 & 745, Village Lonikond Pune-Nagar Road, 412216, Pune, India
Tel.: (91) 20 6678 2000
Web Site: http://www.armacell.in
Engineered Foam Mfr
N.A.I.C.S.: 326140

Armacell Italia S.R.L. (3)
Via Papa Giovanni XXIII n 4, 24042, Capriate San Gervasio, Italy
Tel.: (39) 02 90995 1
Web Site: http://www.armacell.com
Insulation Material Mfr
N.A.I.C.S.: 326140

Armacell Korea LLC (3)
231 Sunam-ri Dong-myeon, Cheonan, 31261, Korea (South)
Tel.: (82) 41 622 1812
Engineered Foam Mfr
N.A.I.C.S.: 326140

Subsidiary (US):

Armacell LLC (3)
7600 Oakwood St, Mebane, NC 27302
Tel.: (919) 304-3846
Web Site: http://www.armacell.com
Sales Range: $25-49.9 Million
Plastic Foam Product Mfr
N.A.I.C.S.: 326150

PAI PARTNERS S.A.S.

PAI Partners S.A.S.—(Continued)

Plant (Domestic):

Armacell LLC - Dallas Plant (4)
351 Thomas B Murphy Dr, Dallas, GA 30132
Tel.: (770) 443-1844
Insulation Material Mfr
N.A.I.C.S.: 326140

Subsidiary (Non-US):

Armacell Poland Sp. z o.o. (3)
ul Targowa 2, 55-300, Sroda Slaska, Poland
Tel.: (48) 713172999
Web Site: http://www.armacell.com
Emp.: 172
Engineered Foam Mfr
N.A.I.C.S.: 326140

Armacell UK Ltd. (3)
Mars Street, Oldham, Manchester, OL9 6LY, United Kingdom
Tel.: (44) 161 287 7100
Web Site: http://www.armacell.com
Emp.: 150
Engineered Foam Mfr
N.A.I.C.S.: 326140

Industrial Thermo Polymers Limited (3)
153 Van Kirk Dr, Brampton, L7A 1A4, ON, Canada
Tel.: (905) 846-3666
Web Site: http://www.tundrafoam.com
Polyethylene Foam Products Mfr
N.A.I.C.S.: 326150

Atos Medical AB (1)
Hyllie Boulevard 17, 215 32, Malmo, Sweden
Tel.: (46) 41519800
Web Site: https://www.atosmedical.com
Sales Range: $100-124.9 Million
Emp.: 450
Voice & Pulmonary Rehabilitation Products Mfr
N.A.I.C.S.: 339112
Caroline Vagner Rosenstand (Pres)

Biogran S.L. (1)
Avenida Maria Garcini 16 Pol Ind Paracuellos del Jarama, Paracuellos de Jarama, 28860, Madrid, Spain
Tel.: (34) 916580618
Web Site: http://www.biogran.es
Emp.: 140
Organic Food & Natural Product Mfr
N.A.I.C.S.: 325199

Bonneterre et Compagnie S.A.S. (1)
60 Avenue de la commune de paris, 91220, Bretigny-sur-Orge, France
Tel.: (33) 149782500
Grocery Products Retailer
N.A.I.C.S.: 445110

Destination S.A.S. (1)
Chateau de Pourtales 161 rue Melanie, 67000, Strasbourg, France
Tel.: (33) 388607070
Web Site: http://www.destination-alsace.eu
Emp.: 7
Leisure & Travel Tourism Services
N.A.I.C.S.: 561510
Cathy Schmitt (Project Mgr)

Ecotone (1)
Atlas Arena - Asia building 2nd floor 5 Hoogoorddreef, PO Box 12795, 1101 BA, Amsterdam, Netherlands
Tel.: (31) 203122122
Web Site: http://www.wessanen.com
Rev.: $7,187,576,360
Assets: $555,767,561
Liabilities: $261,699,152
Net Worth: $294,068,409
Earnings: $41,176,440
Emp.: 1,320
Fiscal Year-end: 12/31/2018
Dairy & Breakfast Products, Natural Foods & Convenience Foods Producer
N.A.I.C.S.: 311514
Charles E. Jobson (Partner-PAI Partners)

Subsidiary (Non-US):

Allos GmbH (2)
Zum Streek 5, Drebber, 49457, Germany
Tel.: (49) 544598990
Web Site: http://www.allos.de
Food Products Mfr
N.A.I.C.S.: 311412

Subsidiary (Domestic):

Allos Schwarzwald GmbH (3)
Hans-Bunte-straSe 8a, 79108, Freiburg, Germany
Tel.: (49) 76151570
Sales Range: $25-49.9 Million
Emp.: 80
Food Products Mfr
N.A.I.C.S.: 311412
Gerd Beilke (Mng Dir)

Subsidiary (Non-US):

Bio Slym S.r.l. (2)
Via Dei Tigli Z | Fenilrosso, 46019, Viadana, Mantua, Italy
Tel.: (39) 0375 782256
Web Site: http://www.bioslym.com
Sales Range: $25-49.9 Million
Emp.: 20
Healthy Food Mfr
N.A.I.C.S.: 311999

Cosa Naturprodukte GmbH (2)
Zinkmattenstr 18 B, 79108, Freiburg, Germany
Tel.: (49) 42116335374
Web Site: http://www.cosa-naturprodukte.de
Food Products Mfr
N.A.I.C.S.: 311412
Frank Yon Glan (Mng Dir)

Distriborg Groupe SA (2)
Batiment A 217 Chemin Du Grand Revoyet, 69561, Saint Genis Laval, France
Tel.: (33) 472671020
Web Site: http://www.bjorgbonneterreetcie.com
Sales Range: $50-74.9 Million
Emp.: 200
Supermarket Retailer Services
N.A.I.C.S.: 445298

Subsidiary (Domestic):

Bio-Distrifrais-Chantenat SAS (3)
1 Rue Mont Blanc, 69960, Corbas, France
Tel.: (33) 4 7850 4004
Web Site: http://www.biodistrifrais.com
Groceries Distr
N.A.I.C.S.: 424410

Branch (Domestic):

Bio-Distrifrais Aubagne (4)
ZI De Street Mitre Rue de la Roche Fourcade, 13400, Aubagne, France
Tel.: (33) 442 848 444
Web Site: http://www.biodistrifrais.com
Groceries Distr
N.A.I.C.S.: 424410

Subsidiary (Domestic):

Distriborg France SAS (3)
Batiment A 217 Chemin Du Grand Revoyet, 69561, Saint Genis Laval, France
Tel.: (33) 472671020
Web Site: http://www.distriborg.com
Sales Range: $25-49.9 Million
Emp.: 100
Supermarkets Operation Services
N.A.I.C.S.: 445110

Subsidiary (Domestic):

Laboratoire Kalisterra SAS (4)
217 Chemin Du Grand Revoyet, Saint Genis Laval, 69230, France
Tel.: (33) 478864750
Food Product Whslr
N.A.I.C.S.: 424410

Subsidiary (Domestic):

Foodprints (2)
Daltonstraat 38, Postbus 376, 3840 AJ, Harderwijk, Netherlands
Tel.: (31) 341466466
Web Site: http://www.foodprints.nl
Organic Food Retailer
N.A.I.C.S.: 445298

Subsidiary (Non-US):

Kallo Foods Ltd (2)
Coopers Place Combe Lane, Wormley, Godalming, GU8 5SZ, Surrey, United Kingdom (100%)
Tel.: (44) 428685100
Web Site: http://www.kallo.com
Sales Range: $25-49.9 Million
Emp.: 35
Rice Cakes, Soy Snacks, Cereals, Drinks, Crackers & Breadsticks Mfr & Marketer
N.A.I.C.S.: 311230

Mautner Markhof Feinkost GmbH (2)
Mautner Markhof-Gasse 39-41, 1110, Vienna, Austria (100%)
Tel.: (43) 174080
Web Site: http://www.mautner.at
Sales Range: $25-49.9 Million
Emp.: 100
Cider vinegar Mfr
N.A.I.C.S.: 311941

R. Bonneterre SAS (2)
Entrepot E111 1 Place Des Planteurs, Rungis, 94150, France
Tel.: (33) 149782500
Food Products Distr
N.A.I.C.S.: 424410

Ethypharm SAS (1)
194 bureaux de la Colline, 92213, Saint-Cloud, Cedex, France (60%)
Tel.: (33) 141121720
Web Site: http://www.ethypharm.com
Sales Range: $200-249.9 Million
Emp.: 900
Oral Drug Delivery Systems Developer & Mfr
N.A.I.C.S.: 325412
Michael Christopher James Harris (COO)

Subsidiary (Non-US):

Ethypharm Inc. (2)
1200 ave McGill College Suite 1500, Montreal, H3B 4G7, QC, Canada (100%)
Tel.: (514) 907-3299
Web Site: https://www.ethypharm.com
Oral Drug Delivery Systems Research & Development
N.A.I.C.S.: 541713

Ethypharm UK Ltd. (2)
Goldvale House Ground Floor 27-41 Church Street West, Woking, GU21 6DH, Surrey, United Kingdom
Tel.: (44) 1483 726 929
Web Site: http://www.ethypharm.co.uk
Oral Drug Delivery Systems Developer & Mfr
N.A.I.C.S.: 325412
Andy Farrant (Mng Dir)

Subsidiary (Domestic):

Macarthys Laboratories Limited (3)
Building A2 Glory Park, Glory Park Avenue, Wooburn Green, HP10 0DF, Bucks, United Kingdom
Tel.: (44) 1628 551 900
Web Site: http://www.martindalepharma.co.uk
Pharmaceuticals Product Mfr
N.A.I.C.S.: 325412
Michael Christopher James Harris (CEO)

Subsidiary (US):

Ethypharm USA Corp. (2)
1600 Market St 26th Fl Ste 2620, Philadelphia, PA 19103
Tel.: (215) 609-4522
Web Site: http://www.ethypharm.com
Oral Drug Delivery Systems Developer & Mfr
N.A.I.C.S.: 325412
Hafid Touam (CEO)

Euro Media Group SA (1)
2 Avenue de l'Europe, 94360, Paris, France (58%)
Tel.: (33) 1 4983 4000
Web Site: http://www.euromediagroup.com
Holding Company; Film Production & Media Broadcasting Services
N.A.I.C.S.: 551112
Patrick van den Berg (Co-CEO)

Geriatros S.A.U. (1)
C Garcia Barbon 60 Bajo, 36201, Vigo, Pontevedra, Spain
Tel.: (34) 986 227 103

INTERNATIONAL PUBLIC

Web Site: http://www.geriatros.com
Emp.: 3,500
Residential Care Facilities Construction & Management
N.A.I.C.S.: 623312
Lucia Del Campo (Dir-HR)

HKA Global Holdings Ltd (1)
3200 Daresbury Park, Warrington, WA4 4BU, United Kingdom
Tel.: (44) 1928756500
Engineering & Consulting Services
N.A.I.C.S.: 541330

Subsidiary (Domestic):

HKA Global Ltd (2)
3200 Daresbury Park, Warrington, WA4 4BU, United Kingdom
Tel.: (44) 1928756600
Web Site: https://www.hka.com
Engineering & Consulting Services
N.A.I.C.S.: 541330
John Alexander (Chm)

InnoVista Sensors (1)
2945 Townsgate Rd, Westlake Village, CA 91361
Tel.: (805) 716-0322
Web Site: http://www.innovistasensors.com
Sales Range: $600-649.9 Million
Sensors & Engineered Subsystems Mfr
N.A.I.C.S.: 334419
Rosie Franco (Mgr-Mktg)

MONIER Group GmbH (1)
Frankfurter Landstrasse 2-4, 61440, Oberursel, Germany (65%)
Tel.: (49) 617161006
Web Site: http://www.lafarge-roofing.com
Sales Range: $1-4.9 Billion
Emp.: 11,155
Roofing Systems & Components Distr; Owned 65% by PAI Partners & 35% by Lafarge S.A.
N.A.I.C.S.: 423330

Joint Venture (Non-US):

Bramac Dachsysteme International GmbH (2)
Bramacstrasse 9, 3380, Pochlarn, Austria
Tel.: (43) 2 757 4010
Web Site: https://www.bramac.com
Sales Range: $150-199.9 Million
Roofing Tiles & Products Distr
N.A.I.C.S.: 423330
Alexander Koch (Co-CEO)

Subsidiary (Non-US):

Bramac Kft. (3)
Hazgyari ut 1, 8200, Veszprem, Hungary
Tel.: (36) 88590891
Web Site: https://www.bramac.hu
Roofing Tile & Product Distr
N.A.I.C.S.: 423330
Gabor Miheller (Mng Dir)

Bramac Pokrovni Sistemi d.o.o. (3)
Buzinski Prilaz 10, 10010, Zagreb, Croatia
Tel.: (385) 1 659 4200
Web Site: https://www.bramac.com
Sales Range: $25-49.9 Million
Emp.: 15
Roofing Tiles & Products Distr
N.A.I.C.S.: 423330

Bramac Stresni Sistemi d.o.o. (3)
Dobruska vas 45, 8275, Skocjan, Slovenia
Tel.: (386) 73846200
Web Site: http://www.bramac.si
Sales Range: $25-49.9 Million
Roofing Tiles & Product Distr
N.A.I.C.S.: 423330

Bramac Stresni Systemy spol. s r.o. (3)
Kolbenova 882/5a, 19000, Prague, Czech Republic
Tel.: (420) 266770111
Web Site: http://www.bramac.cz
Sales Range: $125-149.9 Million
Emp.: 350
Roofing Tiles & Products Distr
N.A.I.C.S.: 423330

Subsidiary (Domestic):

MONIER GmbH (2)
Frankfurter Landstrasse 2-4, 61440,

AND PRIVATE COMPANIES

Oberursel, Germany
Tel.: (49) 617161014
Web Site: http://www.lafarge-dachsysteme.de
Sales Range: $550-599.9 Million
Concrete & Terra Cotta Roofing Tiles Mfr & Whslr
N.A.I.C.S.: 327390
Rudolf Rauss (Chm)

Subsidiary (Non-US):

Braas Schweiz AG (3)
Bonnstrasse 9, PO Box 22, 3186, Dudingen, Switzerland
Tel.: (41) 26 492 5858
Web Site: http://www.braas.ch
Sales Range: $25-49.9 Million
Emp.: 7
Pitched Roof Supplies
N.A.I.C.S.: 238160

Lafarge Roofing Co. Ltd. (3)
Daiwa Minami Morimachi Building, 2-6 2-chome Kita, Tenjinbashi Kita-ku, Osaka, 530-0041, Japan
Tel.: (81) 663545511
Web Site: http://www.lafarge-roofing.jp
Concrete Roofing Tiles Mfr & Whslr
N.A.I.C.S.: 327390
Andrea Benincasa (CEO)

MONIER A/S (3)
Kystvejen 56, 9400, Norresundby, Denmark
Tel.: (45) 96316100
Web Site: http://www.monier.dk
Sales Range: $125-149.9 Million
Concrete Roofing Tiles Mfr & Whslr
N.A.I.C.S.: 327390
Clein Ullenvik (CEO)

MONIER AS (3)
Eternittveien 10, N-3470, Slemmestad, Norway
Tel.: (47) 66799700
Web Site: http://www.monier.no
Sales Range: $25-49.9 Million
Pitched Roof Supplies
N.A.I.C.S.: 444180
Paul Hansen (Gen Mgr)

MONIER B.V. (3)
Heeswijk 155, PO Box 29, 3417 ZG, Montfoort, Netherlands
Tel.: (31) 348476500
Web Site: http://www.monier.nl
Sales Range: $125-149.9 Million
Concrete & Clay Roofing Tiles Mfr
N.A.I.C.S.: 327390

MONIER Roof Products Belgium N.V. (3)
Parklaan 29 A Bus 1, 9300, Aalst, Belgium
Tel.: (32) 53729672
Web Site: http://www.monierbelgium.be
Sales Range: $50-74.9 Million
Emp.: 10
Concrete & Terra Cotta Roofing Tiles Whslr
N.A.I.C.S.: 423330

MONIER S.p.A. (3)
Via Valle Pusteria 21, Chienes, 39030, BZ, Italy
Tel.: (39) 0474560000
Web Site: http://www.monier.it
Sales Range: $50-74.9 Million
Clay Roofing Tiles Mfr & Whslr
N.A.I.C.S.: 327120
Andrea Benincasa (Gen Mgr)

MONIER SAS (3)
12 Avenue d'Italie, 75013, Paris, France
Tel.: (33) 153806900
Web Site: http://www.lafarge-couverture.fr
Concrete & Terra Cotta Roofing Tiles Mfr
N.A.I.C.S.: 327390

MONIER Sdn Bhd (3)
Wisma Lafarge 66 Jalan Ampang, 50450, Kuala Lumpur, Malaysia
Tel.: (60) 320700600
Web Site: http://www.monier.com.my
Concrete Roof Tiles Mfr & Whslr
N.A.I.C.S.: 327390

Monier Ltd. (3)
Sussex Manor Business Park, Gatwick Road, Crawley, RH10 9NZ, West Sussex, United Kingdom
Tel.: (44) 1293618418
Web Site: http://www.monier.co.uk
Sales Range: $150-199.9 Million
Concrete Roofing Tiles Mfr & Whslr
N.A.I.C.S.: 327390

Monier Technical Centre Ltd. (3)
Sussex Manor Business Park, Gatwick Road, Crawley, RH10 9NZ, United Kingdom
Tel.: (44) 1293614545
Web Site: http://www.monier.com
Sales Range: $75-99.9 Million
Roofing Tile Research & Development
N.A.I.C.S.: 541715

Subsidiary (Non-US):

Schiedel AG (2)
Schonbrunner-Strasse 289, 1120, Vienna, Austria
Tel.: (43) 506161600
Web Site: http://www.schiedel.com
Sales Range: $300-349.9 Million
Emp.: 1,882
Chimney & Building Ventilation Components Dealer & Services
N.A.I.C.S.: 333414
Johannes Kistler (CFO)

Subsidiary (Non-US):

Schiedel GmbH & Co. (3)
Lerchenstrasse 9, D-80995, Munich, Germany
Tel.: (49) 89354090
Web Site: http://www.schiedel.de
Chimney & Building Ventilation Components Dealer & Services
N.A.I.C.S.: 238190

Subsidiary (Domestic):

Schiedel Kaminsysteme GmbH (3)
Friedrich-Schiedel-Str 2-6, 4542, Nussbach, Austria
Tel.: (43) 506161100
Web Site: http://www.schiedel.com
Sales Range: $50-74.9 Million
Chimney & Building Ventilation Components Dealer & Services
N.A.I.C.S.: 238190
Hans Herbert Schmoll (Mng Dir)

Subsidiary (Non-US):

Schiedel Kemenygyar Kft. (3)
Kisto u 12, H-8200, Veszprem, Hungary
Tel.: (36) 88 576 700
Web Site: http://www.schiedel.hu
Chimney & Building Ventilation Components Dealer & Services
N.A.I.C.S.: 238190

Schiedel Proizvodnja Dimnjaka d.o.o. (3)
Golubovec 26, Golubovec, 49255, Hrvatska, Croatia
Tel.: (385) 49382600
Web Site: http://www.schiedel.hr
Sales Range: $25-49.9 Million
Emp.: 35
Chimney & Building Ventilation Components Dealer & Services
N.A.I.C.S.: 238190
Damer Martevic (Gen Mgr)

Schiedel S.a.r.l. (3)
247 Altenkesseler, 75005, Paris, France
Tel.: (33) 143132540
Web Site: http://www.schiedel.fr
Sales Range: $25-49.9 Million
Emp.: 12
Chimney & Building Ventilation Components Dealer & Services
N.A.I.C.S.: 238190

Schiedel a.s. (3)
Horousanska 286, 250 81, Nehvizdy, Czech Republic
Tel.: (420) 326999011
Web Site: http://www.schiedel.cz
Sales Range: $25-49.9 Million
Chimney & Building Ventilation Components Dealer & Services
N.A.I.C.S.: 238190

Marcolin S.p.A. (1)
Localita Villanova 4, Longarone, 32013, Belluno, Italy
Tel.: (39) 0437777111
Web Site: http://www.marcolin.com
Sales Range: $250-299.9 Million
Eyewear Mfr
N.A.I.C.S.: 333310
Giovanni Zoppas (CEO)

Subsidiary (Domestic):

Finitec Srl (2)
Localita Villanova 18, Longarone, Belluno, Italy
Tel.: (39) 0437771740
Web Site: http://www.finitec.it
Eye Glasses Mfr
N.A.I.C.S.: 333310

Subsidiary (Non-US):

Marcolin (Deutschland) GmbH (2)
Monreposstr 55, 71634, Ludwigsburg, Germany (100%)
Tel.: (49) 71412994720
Optical Goods Stores
N.A.I.C.S.: 456130

Marcolin (UK) Ltd. (2)
Building 107, New Greenham Park, Thatcham, RG19 6HN, Berkshire, United Kingdom (100%)
Tel.: (44) 1635277277
Sales Range: $25-49.9 Million
Emp.: 10
Optical Goods Stores
N.A.I.C.S.: 456130

Marcolin Asia Ltd. (2)
Units 2207-2211 Level 22 Tower I Metroplaza, 223 Hing Fong Road, Kwai Fong, China (Hong Kong)
Tel.: (852) 25251984
Sales Range: $25-49.9 Million
Emp.: 16
Optical Instrument Mfr
N.A.I.C.S.: 333310
Roberta Coronetta (Gen Mgr)

Marcolin Benelux S.p.r.l (2)
Rue Al Cadorette 2 B, Faimes, 4317, Liege, Belgium (100%)
Tel.: (32) 19330949
Sales Range: $25-49.9 Million
Emp.: 16
Optical Goods Stores
N.A.I.C.S.: 456130
Isabelle Moe (Mng Dir)

Marcolin France Sarl (2)
45 Rue Saint Sebastien, 75011, Paris, France
Tel.: (33) 156982170
Optical Goods Stores
N.A.I.C.S.: 456130

Marcolin GmbH (2)
Monreposstr 55, Ludwigsburg, 71634, Baden-Wurttemberg, Germany
Tel.: (49) 762192530
Optical Product Mfr
N.A.I.C.S.: 333310

Marcolin Iberica S.A. (2)
Juan de Austria 116 4 Piano, 08018, Barcelona, Spain (100%)
Tel.: (34) 933209060
Sales Range: $25-49.9 Million
Optical Goods Stores
N.A.I.C.S.: 456130

Marcolin Japan Co Ltd (2)
Ruporu Bldg 2F 1-21-6 Minami Aoyama, Minato-Ku, Tokyo, 107-0062, Japan
Tel.: (81) 3 5413 6080
Optical Instruments Distr
N.A.I.C.S.: 423460
Hidefumi Tamaki (Pres & CEO)

Marcolin Portugal Lda (2)
Rua Jose Travassos 15 Loja, 1600-410, Lisbon, Portugal
Tel.: (351) 214686372
Web Site: http://www.marcolin.com
Sales Range: $25-49.9 Million
Emp.: 4
Optical Goods Stores
N.A.I.C.S.: 456130

Marcolin Swiss GmbH (2)
Rheinstrasse 26, Fullinsdorf, 4414, Basel, Switzerland (100%)
Tel.: (41) 619069222
Web Site: http://www.marcolin.com

PAI PARTNERS S.A.S.

Sales Range: $25-49.9 Million
Emp.: 15
Optical Goods Stores
N.A.I.C.S.: 456130
M. Jurden (Gen Mgr)

Subsidiary (US):

Marcolin USA Inc. (2)
7543 E Tierra Buena Ln, Scottsdale, AZ 85260
Tel.: (480) 951-7174
Web Site: http://www.marcolinusa.com
Sales Range: $50-74.9 Million
Frames Mfr
N.A.I.C.S.: 423460
Ben Wolf (Sr VP-Sls-Optical Channel)

Subsidiary (Non-US):

Marcolin do Brasil Ltda (2)
Rua Rosario 731, 13201, Jundiai, Brazil
Tel.: (55) 1145268311
Optical Goods Stores
N.A.I.C.S.: 456130

Morrison Utility Services Group Limited (1)
Abel Smith House Gunnels Wood Road, Stevenage, SG1 2ST, Herts, United Kingdom
Tel.: (44) 1438 743 744
Web Site: http://www.morrisonus.com
Emp.: 100
Holding Company; Utility Engineering Services
N.A.I.C.S.: 551112
Charles Morrison (Chm)

Subsidiary (Domestic):

Morrison Utility Services Limited (2)
Abel Smith House Gunnels Wood Road, Stevenage, SG1 2ST, Herts, United Kingdom
Tel.: (44) 1438 743 744
Web Site: http://www.morrisonus.com
Utility Engineering Services
N.A.I.C.S.: 541330
Charles Morrison (Chm)

Subsidiary (Domestic):

Morrison Data Services Limited (3)
14 Silver Fox Way Cobalt Business Park, Newcastle upon Tyne, NE27 0QJ, United Kingdom
Tel.: (44) 19 1201 3500
Web Site: http://www.morrisonds.com
Emp.: 2,500
Meter Reading & Maintenance; Data Collection & Management Services
N.A.I.C.S.: 541690

Division (Domestic):

Morrison Utility Connections (3)
First Floor Unit 2 Swanwick Court, Alfreton, DE55 7AS, Derbs, United Kingdom
Tel.: (44) 1773 830 436
Web Site: http://www.morrisonuc.com
Electric Power Utility Engineering Services
N.A.I.C.S.: 541330
Steve Sharp (Gen Mgr)

PAI Partners AB (1)
Kungstradgardsgatan 12, 111 47, Stockholm, Sweden
Tel.: (46) 8 440 57 90
Emp.: 5
Financial Investment Management Services
N.A.I.C.S.: 523940
Ragnar Hellenius (Mgr)

PAI Partners GmbH (1)
Luisenstrasse 14, 80333, Munich, Germany
Tel.: (49) 89 5151 4650
Financial Investment Management Services
N.A.I.C.S.: 523940

PAI Partners S.a.r.l. (1)
43-45 allee Scheffer, 2520, Luxembourg, Luxembourg
Tel.: (352) 2626977178
Financial Investment Management Services
N.A.I.C.S.: 523940

Perstorp Holding AB (1)
Neptunigatan 1, 211 20, Malmo, Sweden
Tel.: (46) 43538000

PAI PARTNERS S.A.S.

PAI Partners S.A.S.—(Continued)

Web Site: http://www.perstorp.com
Rev.: $1,247,565,970
Assets: $1,425,789,680
Liabilities: $1,301,686,820
Net Worth: $124,102,860
Earnings: $372,415,750
Emp.: 1,393
Fiscal Year-end: 12/31/2019
Specialty Chemicals Mfr
N.A.I.C.S.: 325998
John Ekstrom (VP-IR)

Subsidiary (Domestic):

Metfoils AB (2)
PO Box 5000, S 284 01, Perstorp, Sweden
Tel.: (46) 43538970
Web Site: http://www.metfoils.com
Sales Range: $25-49.9 Million
Emp.: 5
Printed Circuit Boards
N.A.I.C.S.: 334412

Division (Domestic):

Perstorp AB (2)
Perstorp Industrial Park, S-284 80, Perstorp, Sweden
Tel.: (46) 43538000
Web Site: http://www.Perstorp.com
Sales Range: $350-399.9 Million
Flooring
N.A.I.C.S.: 238330
Martin Lundin (Gen Mgr)

Subsidiary (Non-US):

Perstorp Chemicals GmbH (3)
Bruchhausener Str 2, PO Box 1409, Arnsberg, 59704, Germany
Tel.: (49) 2932498100
Web Site: http://www.perstorp.com
Sales Range: $75-99.9 Million
Flooring
N.A.I.C.S.: 321918

Division (Domestic):

Perstorp Chemicals (2)
Perstorp Industrial Park, Perstorp, 28480, Sweden
Tel.: (46) 43538000
Web Site: http://www.perstorp.com
Sales Range: $350-399.9 Million
Emp.: 400
Petrochemical Mfr
N.A.I.C.S.: 325110
Jan Secher (Mng Dir)

Subsidiary (Non-US):

Perstorp Quimica do Brasil Ltda. (3)
Avenida Piraporinha 852, 09891-902, Sao Bernardo do Campo, Sao Paulo, Brazil
Tel.: (55) 43419665
Chemicals Mfr
N.A.I.C.S.: 325199

Division (Domestic):

Perstorp Specialty Chemicals AB (3)
Perstorp Industrial Pk, Perstorp, 28480, Sweden
Tel.: (46) 43538000
Web Site: http://www.perstorp.com
Sales Range: $400-449.9 Million
Chemical & Gas Mfr
N.A.I.C.S.: 325110
Anders Hansson (Mgr-Site)

Division (Domestic):

Formox AB (4)
Perstorp Industrial Park, Perstorp, 284 80, Sweden
Tel.: (46) 43538000
Web Site: http://www.perstorpformox.com
Sales Range: $250-299.9 Million
Formaldehyde Mfr
N.A.I.C.S.: 325998
Eva Lindgren (Gen Mgr)

Subsidiary (Non-US):

Perstorp Chemicals Asia Pte. Ltd., (4)
16 Orchard Rd #16-06 Shaw House, Singapore, 238868, Singapore
Tel.: (65) 6505 9909

Web Site: http://www.perstorp.com
Specialty Chemicals Mfr & Distr
N.A.I.C.S.: 325110

Perstorp Chemicals India Private Limited, Mumbai (4)
SAI Commercial Annexe 4th Floor, BKS Devshi Marg Govandi (E), Mumbai, 400 088, India
Tel.: (91) 2225526600
Web Site: http://www.perstorp.com
Sales Range: $50-74.9 Million
Emp.: 15
Petrochemicals
N.A.I.C.S.: 325110

Subsidiary (US):

Perstorp Polyols Inc. (4)
600 Matzinger Rd, Toledo, OH 43612-2631
Tel.: (419) 729-5448
Web Site: http://www.perstorppolyols.com
Sales Range: $25-49.9 Million
Mfr of Organic Chemicals
N.A.I.C.S.: 325199
Larry Fioritto (Dir-Fin)

Holding (Non-US):

Perstorp France SAS (2)
2 Toupheueh 153 Blvd, FR 93200, Saint-Denis, Cedex, France
Tel.: (33) 33177932629
Web Site: http://www.perstorp.com
Sales Range: $50-74.9 Million
Emp.: 3
N.A.I.C.S.: 325110

Perstorp SpA (2)
Via Sempione 13, I-210 53, Castellanza, VA, Italy
Tel.: (39) 0331488311
Web Site: http://www.perstorp.com
N.A.I.C.S.: 325110

R&R Ice Cream Plc (1)
Richmond House Leeming Bar Industrial estate Leeming Bar, Northallerton, DL7 9UL, North Yorkshire, United Kingdom
Tel.: (44) 1677 423 397
Web Site: http://www.rr-icecream.eu
Sales Range: $650-699.9 Million
Emp.: 300
Ice Cream Mfr
N.A.I.C.S.: 311520
Ibrahim Najafi (CEO)

Joint Venture (Domestic):

Froneri Ltd. (2)
Richmond House Leeming Bar Northallerton, North Yorkshire, London, United Kingdom
Tel.: (44) 1677 423 397
Web Site: http://www.froneri.com
Ice Cream Whslr
N.A.I.C.S.: 424430
Philip Graham (Sec)

Subsidiary (Non-US):

Fonterra Brands (Tip Top) Limited (3)
113 Carbine Rd, Mount Wellington, Auckland, New Zealand
Tel.: (64) 95737200
Web Site: http://www.tiptop.co.nz
Sales Range: $100-124.9 Million
Emp.: 420
Mfr of Ice Cream, Frozen Novelties, Frozen Desserts & Frozen Snack Products
N.A.I.C.S.: 311520

Subsidiary (Non-US):

R&R Ice Cream Deutschland GmbH (2)
Eduard Pestel Strasse 15, 49080, Osnabruck, Germany (100%)
Tel.: (49) 54199990
Web Site: http://www.rr-icecream.de
Ice Cream Mfr
N.A.I.C.S.: 311520
Gotthard Kirchner (Mng Dir)

R&R Ice Cream France S.A.S. (2)
Le Labour, PO Box 13, 33870, Vayres, France
Tel.: (33) 557553900
Web Site: http://www.rr-icecream.fr

Sales Range: $25-49.9 Million
Ice Cream Mfr
N.A.I.C.S.: 311423
Fabrice Ducasse (Country Mgr & Dir-Sls & Mktg)

Tropicana Brands Group, Inc. (1)
433 W Van Buren St Ste 3N, Chicago, IL 60607 (61%)
Tel.: (941) 747-4461
Web Site: https://www.tropicanabrandsgroup.com
Holding Company; Beverage Services
N.A.I.C.S.: 551112

Subsidiary (Domestic):

Tropicana Products, Inc. (2)
1001 13th Ave E, Bradenton, FL 34208
Tel.: (941) 747-4461
Web Site: http://www.tropicana.com
Fruit Beverage Mfr
N.A.I.C.S.: 311421
Monica McGurk (CEO-Tropicana & Mainstream Brands)

Subsidiary (Domestic):

Naked Juice Company, Inc. (3)
1333 Mayflower Ave, Monrovia, CA 91016
Tel.: (877) 858-4237
Web Site: http://www.nakedjuice.com
Frozen Fruits, Fruit Juices, Canned & Preserved Fruit Mfr
N.A.I.C.S.: 311421

Subsidiary (Domestic):

Naked Juice Co. of Glendora, Inc. (4)
1333 S Mayflower Ave, Monrovia, CA 91016
Tel.: (877) 858-4237
Beverages Mfr
N.A.I.C.S.: 311411

Subsidiary (Domestic):

Tropicana Transportation Corp. (3)
7328 Poi Cir, Orlando, FL 32822
Tel.: (407) 301-7390
Web Site: http://www.tropicanatransport.com
Transportation Services
N.A.I.C.S.: 488999

Subsidiary (Non-US):

VPS Holdings Limited (1)
Premiere House Elstree Way, Borehamwood, WD6 1JH, Herts, United Kingdom
Tel.: (44) 20 8905 1234
Web Site: http://www.vpspecialists.co.uk
Sales Range: $250-299.9 Million
Emp.: 2,000
Vacant Property Security Services
N.A.I.C.S.: 561621
Mark Silver (CEO)

Subsidiary (Domestic):

Evander Group Limited (2)
3rd Floor International Buildings 71, Kingsway, London, WC2B 6ST, United Kingdom
Tel.: (44) 3451450130
Web Site: http://www.evander.com
Glass & Glazing Contractors; Locks
N.A.I.C.S.: 238150

PAIK KWANG INDUSTRIAL CO., LTD.

494-16 Imhae-ro 31 Soryong-dong, Gunsan, Jeollabuk-do, Korea (South)
Tel.: (82) 634501700
Web Site: https://www.pkic.co.kr
Year Founded: 1954
001340—(KRS)
Rev.: $178,500,188
Assets: $309,287,425
Liabilities: $148,739,166
Net Worth: $160,548,259
Earnings: $16,622,306
Emp.: 207
Fiscal Year-end: 12/31/22
Chemical Products Mfr
N.A.I.C.S.: 325180
Seong-Hun Kim (CEO)

PAILLARD AUTOMOBILES ABBEVILLE

ZAC les Deux Vallees route d'Amiens, 80100, Abbeville, France
Tel.: (33) 322202080
Web Site: http://concessions.peugeot.fr
Rev.: $26,700,000
Emp.: 54
New & Used Car Dealers
N.A.I.C.S.: 441110
Bertrand Paillard (Pres)

PAIMPOLDIS

Parc Richard Route De Lannion, 22500, Paimpol, Cotes D Armor, France
Tel.: (33) 296553000
Rev.: $21,900,000
Emp.: 65
Building Material Dealers
N.A.I.C.S.: 444180
Jerome Plaze (Dir-Admin)

PAINCHEK LTD.

Suite 401 35 Lime St, Sydney, 2000, WA, Australia
Tel.: (61) 800098809
Web Site: https://www.painchek.com
Year Founded: 2016
PCK—(ASX)
Rev.: $1,784,147
Assets: $2,792,548
Liabilities: $1,930,923
Net Worth: $861,625
Earnings: ($5,547,514)
Fiscal Year-end: 06/30/24
Pain Assessment Products & Services
N.A.I.C.S.: 456199
Philip Daffas (CEO & Mng Dir)

PAINREFORM LTD.

65 Yigal Alon St, PO Box 68, Tel Aviv, 6744316, Israel
Tel.: (972) 37177051
Web Site: https://www.painreform.com
Year Founded: 2007
PRFX—(NASDAQ)
Assets: $12,328,000
Liabilities: $1,307,000
Net Worth: $11,021,000
Earnings: ($8,792,000)
Emp.: 6
Fiscal Year-end: 12/31/22
Biotechnology Research & Development Services
N.A.I.C.S.: 541714
Ilan Hadar (CEO)

PAINTS AND CHEMICALS INDUSTRIES COMPANY S.A.E.

1 Elmassanie Street, PO Box 11887, Elamiriya, Cairo, Egypt
Tel.: (20) 2 2282 8980   EG
Web Site: http://www.pachin.net
Year Founded: 1958
Sales Range: $50-74.9 Million
Emp.: 1,137
Paints, Varnishes & Printing Inks Mfr
N.A.I.C.S.: 325510
Mohie El Din Abdel Razik (CEO)

Subsidiaries:

El Obour Paints & Chemical Industries Co. (1)
1 El Masanea St El Sawah Sq, Behind Bisco Misr Egyptian Co For Foods El Amireya, Cairo, Egypt
Tel.: (20) 222828980
Paints Mfr
N.A.I.C.S.: 325510

Paints and Chemicals Industries Company S.A.E. - Alexandria Factory (1)
End of Sidi Elqabbari Mosque Street behind Elgeneina Station, Elbassal Port, Alexandria, Egypt

Tel.: (20) 33606156
Paints Mfr
N.A.I.C.S.: 325510

Paints and Chemicals Industries Company S.A.E. - Elobour Factory (1)
1st Industrial Area, Cairo, Qalyubia, Egypt
Tel.: (20) 244814260
Paints Mfr
N.A.I.C.S.: 325510

Paints and Chemicals Industries Company S.A.E. - Libya Factory (1)
Shabiet Musrata, Tripoli, Libya
Tel.: (218) 214802775
Paints Mfr
N.A.I.C.S.: 325510

PAION AG
Heussstrasse 25, 52078, Aachen, Germany
Tel.: (49) 24144530
Web Site: https://www.paion.com
Year Founded: 2000
PA8—(DEU)
Rev.: $35,881,718
Assets: $41,201,166
Liabilities: $34,062,163
Net Worth: $7,139,003
Earnings: ($624,865)
Emp.: 70
Fiscal Year-end: 12/31/22
Biopharmaceutical Product Developer & Mfr
N.A.I.C.S.: 325412
Wolfgang Sohngen (Founder)

Subsidiaries:

PAION Deutschland GmbH (1)
Martinstrasse 10-12, Aachen, 52062, Nordrhein-Westfalen, Germany
Tel.: (49) 24144530
Drug Distr
N.A.I.C.S.: 424210

PAION Scandic ApS (1)
Svendborgvej 226, 5260, Odense, Denmark
Tel.: (45) 32746153
Web Site: https://www.paion.dk
Anaesthesia & Drugs Mfr & Distr
N.A.I.C.S.: 325412

Paion Holdings UK Ltd. (1)
Kew Road 5 Parkshot House Unit 302, Richmond, London, TW9 2PR, United Kingdom
Tel.: (44) 2045669480
Pharmaceutical Drug Product Mfr
N.A.I.C.S.: 325412

Paion UK Limited (1)
Kew Road 5 Parkshot House Unit 302, Richmond, London, TW9 2PR, United Kingdom
Tel.: (44) 2045669480
Sales Range: $25-49.9 Million
Emp.: 8
Pharmaceuticals Whslr
N.A.I.C.S.: 325412

PAIRI DAIZA SA
Domaine de Cambron, 7940, Brugelette, Belgium
Tel.: (32) 68 250 850   BE
Web Site: http://www.pairidaiza.eu
Sales Range: $50-74.9 Million
Emp.: 280
Zoological Park Owner & Operator
N.A.I.C.S.: 712130
Eric Domb (Chm & CEO)

PAISALO DIGITAL LIMITED
CSC Pocket 52 CR Park Near Police Station, New Delhi, 110019, India
Tel.: (91) 1143518888
Web Site: https://www.paisalo.in
Year Founded: 1992
PAISALO—(NSE)
Rev.: $56,733,997
Assets: $402,119,118
Liabilities: $382,631,377
Net Worth: $19,487,741

Earnings: $11,224,579
Emp.: 1,650
Fiscal Year-end: 03/31/23
Loans, Working Capital & Other Financial Solutions
N.A.I.C.S.: 522291
Sunil Agarwal (Mng Dir)

PAISLEY PRODUCTS OF CANADA INCORPORATED
40 Upton Road, Toronto, M1L 2B8, ON, Canada
Tel.: (416) 751-3700
Web Site: http://www.paisley.ca
Year Founded: 1949
Rev.: $12,552,773
Emp.: 52
Adhesive Mfr
N.A.I.C.S.: 325520

PAISLEY-MANOR INSURANCE BROKERS INC.
1446 Don Mills Road Suite 110, Toronto, M3B 3N3, ON, Canada
Tel.: (416) 510-1177
Web Site: http://www.paisleymanor.com
Year Founded: 1955
Rev.: $13,302,577
Emp.: 50
Insurance Agencies
N.A.I.C.S.: 524210
Ira J. Kuchiinsky (CEO & Partner)

PAJURA S.A.
Str Jiului Nr 8 Sector 1, Bucharest, Romania
Tel.: (40) 21 667 35 40
Web Site: http://www.pajura.ro
Sales Range: $1-9.9 Million
Emp.: 166
Bakery Products Mfr
N.A.I.C.S.: 311813

PAK DATACOM LIMITED
3rd Floor Umer Plaza Jinnah Avenue Blue Area, Islamabad, Pakistan
Tel.: (92) 512344123
Web Site: https://www.pakdatacom.com.pk
Year Founded: 1992
PAKD—(PSX)
Rev.: $4,902,837
Assets: $7,386,396
Liabilities: $2,761,347
Net Worth: $4,625,049
Earnings: $1,042,778
Emp.: 193
Fiscal Year-end: 06/30/23
Information Technology Services
N.A.I.C.S.: 519290
Abid Awan (Chief HR Officer & Chief Admin Officer)

PAK ELEKTRON LTD.
14km Ferozepur Rd, Lahore, 54000, Pakistan
Tel.: (92) 4235920151
Web Site: http://www.pel.com.pk
PAEL—(KAR)
Rev.: $242,280,972
Assets: $330,444,012
Liabilities: $132,812,371
Net Worth: $197,631,641
Earnings: $5,658,139
Emp.: 5,185
Fiscal Year-end: 12/31/19
Transformers, MV & LV Switchgear, Energy Meters & Instrument Transformers Mfr
N.A.I.C.S.: 334513
M. Murad Saigol (CEO & Mng Dir)

PAK FAH YEOW INTERNATIONAL LIMITED
11th Floor 200 Gloucester Road, Wanchai, China (Hong Kong)
Tel.: (852) 28817713   BM
Web Site: https://www.pakfahyeow.com
Year Founded: 1991
0239—(HKG)
Rev.: $18,768,000
Assets: $104,949,840
Liabilities: $14,778,653
Net Worth: $90,171,188
Earnings: $3,819,263
Emp.: 95
Fiscal Year-end: 12/31/22
Pharmaceutical Product Mfr & Whslr
N.A.I.C.S.: 325412
Hung Kei Tsang (CFO)

PAK LEATHER CRAFTS LIMITED
Plot-18 Sector 7A Korangi Industrial Area, Karachi, Pakistan
Tel.: (92) 2135064101
Web Site: https://www.pakleather.com
Year Founded: 1971
Leather Product Mfr
N.A.I.C.S.: 316990
Muhammad Saleem Ahmed (CEO)

PAK STEEL
24-25 I-9 Industrial Area, Islamabad, Pakistan
Tel.: (92) 514434134
Web Site: http://www.paksteel.com
Year Founded: 1949
Sales Range: $200-249.9 Million
Emp.: 400
Steel Rolling Mill; Steel Mfr & Supplier
N.A.I.C.S.: 331110
Hassan Farid (Dir-Fin)

PAK TAK INTERNATIONAL LIMITED
Unit 1902 19/F Tower 2 Lippo Centre 89 Queensway, Hong Kong, China (Hong Kong)
Tel.: (852) 21151911
Web Site: http://www.paktakintl.com
2668—(HKG)
Rev.: $92,633,340
Assets: $169,295,393
Liabilities: $96,757,710
Net Worth: $72,537,683
Earnings: ($1,818,278)
Emp.: 333
Fiscal Year-end: 12/31/22
Knitted & Cotton Wear Producers
N.A.I.C.S.: 315120
Jian Wang (Exec Dir)

Subsidiaries:

Pak Tak Knitting & Garment Factory Limited (1)
Rm 410-411 4F Fanling Indus Ctr 21 On Kui St On Lok Tsuen, Fanling, New Territories, China (Hong Kong)
Tel.: (852) 22106666
Knitted Wear Mfr
N.A.I.C.S.: 315120

PAK-ARAB REFINERY LTD.
Korangi Creek Road, PO Box 12243, Karachi, 75190, Pakistan
Tel.: (92) 21 35090100 25
Web Site: http://www.parco.com.pk
Petroleum Refining & Distribution Services
N.A.I.C.S.: 324110
Tariq Rizavi (Mng Dir)

Subsidiaries:

PARCO Pearl Gas Limited (1)
52 Margalla Road, F 8 2, Islamabad, Pakistan (90%)
Tel.: (92) 51 111798798

Web Site: http://www.parco.com.pk
Sales Range: $50-74.9 Million
Emp.: 200
Liquefied Petroleum Gas
N.A.I.C.S.: 457210

PAK-GULF LEASING COMPANY LIMITED
UNIBRO HOUSE Ground Floor Plot No114 9th East Street, Phase 1 DHA, Karachi, 75500, Pakistan
Tel.: (92) 2135824401
Web Site: https://www.pakgulfleasing.com
PGLC—(KAR)
Rev.: $1,751,145
Assets: $19,111,668
Liabilities: $13,664,592
Net Worth: $5,447,075
Earnings: $462,235
Emp.: 40
Fiscal Year-end: 06/30/19
Rental & Leasing Property Services
N.A.I.C.S.: 531120
Saleem Ahmad Zafar (COO)

PAKERS CO., LTD.
12 Cheonheung 8-gil Seonggeo-eup, Seobuk-gu, Cheonan, Chungcheongnam-do, Korea (South)
Tel.: (82) 415225361
Web Site: https://pakers.co.kr
Year Founded: 1970
065690—(KRS)
Rev.: $56,084,199
Assets: $107,200,465
Liabilities: $57,691,756
Net Worth: $49,508,709
Earnings: ($9,127,880)
Emp.: 60
Fiscal Year-end: 12/31/22
Electronic Component & Light Emitting Diode Mfr
N.A.I.C.S.: 325992
Park Young Tae (CEO)

PAKGEN POWER LTD.
1B Aziz Avenue Canal Bank Gulberg V, Lahore, Pakistan
Tel.: (92) 4235717090   PK
Web Site: https://www.pakgenpower.com
Year Founded: 1995
PKGP—(PSX)
Rev.: $74,003,164
Assets: $104,677,198
Liabilities: $16,996,191
Net Worth: $87,681,008
Earnings: $20,824,151
Emp.: 78
Fiscal Year-end: 12/31/23
Eletric Power Generation Services
N.A.I.C.S.: 221118
Hassan Mansha (CEO)

Subsidiaries:

City Schools (Private) Limited (1)
31-Industrial Area Gurumangat Road Gulberg III, Lahore, Pakistan
Tel.: (92) 423577306977
Web Site: https://www.thecityschool.edu.pk
Education Management Services
N.A.I.C.S.: 611710

Nishat Dairy (Pvt) Limited (1)
7 Main Gulberg, Lahore, Pakistan
Tel.: (92) 42111332200
Web Site: https://www.nishatdairy.com
Milk Product Mfr
N.A.I.C.S.: 311511
Mian Umer Mansha (CEO)

Nishat Hospitality (Private) Limited (1)
1-B Aziz Avenue Canal Bank Gulberg V, Lahore, Pakistan
Tel.: (92) 4235717090
Web Site: https://www.nishathospitality.com
Health Care Srvices
N.A.I.C.S.: 621999

Pakgen Power Ltd.—(Continued)

PAKISTAN CABLES LIMITED
B-21 Pakistan Cables Road, PO Box 5050, Sindh Industrial Trading Estates, Karachi, 75700, Pakistan
Tel.: (92) 2132561170
Web Site: https://www.pakistancables.com
Year Founded: 1953
PCAL—(KAR)
Rev.: $69,676,953
Assets: $60,538,558
Liabilities: $25,516,018
Net Worth: $35,022,539
Earnings: $906,353
Emp.: 485
Fiscal Year-end: 06/30/19
Wire & Cable Mfr
N.A.I.C.S.: 331222
Muhammad Ashfaq Alam *(Exec Dir)*

Subsidiaries:

Intermark (Private) Limited (1)
14Y Johar Road Shahnaz Shopping Plaza F-8 Markaz, Islamabad, Pakistan
Tel.: (92) 512250930
Web Site: https://www.intermark.com.pk
Electrical & Electronic Mfr
N.A.I.C.S.: 335999

PAKISTAN ENGINEERING COMPANY LIMITED
67Sir Ganga Ram Trust Building ShahraheQuaideAzam, Lahore, Pakistan
Tel.: (92) 4237320225
Web Site: https://www.peco.com.pk
PECO—(LAH)
Sales Range: $10-24.9 Million
Emp.: 366
Electricity Transmission Line Towers Mfr
N.A.I.C.S.: 333611
Anwar Aziz *(CFO & Sec)*

PAKISTAN GUM & CHEMICALS LIMITED
B-19/A Irshad Qadri Road Sindh Industrial Trading Estate, Karachi, 75700, Pakistan
Tel.: (92) 2132561124
Web Site: http://www.pakchem.com.pk
Rev.: $5,482,260
Assets: $4,262,637
Liabilities: $1,818,694
Net Worth: $2,443,943
Earnings: $134,625
Emp.: 113
Fiscal Year-end: 12/31/18
Guar Gum Products Mfr
N.A.I.C.S.: 311942
Shuaib Ahmed *(Vice Chm)*

PAKISTAN HOTELS DEVELOPERS LIMITED
195 2 Main Shahrah e Faisal, Karachi, Pakistan
Tel.: (92) 2135657000 PK
Web Site: https://www.phdl.com.pk
Year Founded: 1979
PHDL—(PSX)
Rev.: $2,011,156
Assets: $36,557,779
Liabilities: $1,426,407
Net Worth: $35,131,372
Earnings: $158,754
Emp.: 106
Fiscal Year-end: 06/30/23
Hotel Operator
N.A.I.C.S.: 721110
Haseen Anwer *(CFO)*

PAKISTAN INDUSTRIAL & COMMERCIAL LEASING LTD.
504 Park Avenue 24-A Block 6 PECHS Sharea Faisal, Karachi, Pakistan
Tel.: (92) 21 4551045
Financial Services
N.A.I.C.S.: 523999

PAKISTAN INTERNATIONAL AIRLINES CORPORATION
PIA Building Jinnah International Airport, Karachi, 75200, Pakistan
Tel.: (92) 21111786786
Web Site: http://www.piac.com.pk
Year Founded: 1955
PIAA—(PSX)
Rev.: $642,339,097
Assets: $1,155,752,485
Liabilities: $2,918,513,867
Net Worth: ($1,762,761,383)
Earnings: ($349,802,296)
Emp.: 7,963
Fiscal Year-end: 12/31/22
Passenger & Cargo Transportation
N.A.I.C.S.: 481111
Amir Ali *(Chief Technical Officer)*

Subsidiaries:

Skyrooms (Private) Limited (1)
Star Gate Road Near Old Airport Road, Karachi, 75350, Pakistan
Tel.: (92) 2134570141
Web Site: http://www.airporthotel.com.pk
Accommodation Services
N.A.I.C.S.: 721199

PAKISTAN INTERNATIONAL BULK TERMINAL LIMITED
2nd Floor Business Plaza Mumtaz Hassan Road, Karachi, 74000, Pakistan
Tel.: (92) 2132400450
Web Site: https://www.pibt.com.pk
Year Founded: 1984
PIBTL—(PSX)
Rev.: $32,639,071
Assets: $117,546,610
Liabilities: $59,337,876
Net Worth: $58,208,734
Earnings: ($7,754,924)
Emp.: 660
Fiscal Year-end: 06/30/23
Coal Mining Services
N.A.I.C.S.: 213113
Haleem Ahmed Siddiqui *(Chm)*

Subsidiaries:

Portlink International Services (Private) Limited (1)
2nd Floor 210 Business Plaza Mumtaz Hassan Road, Karachi, 74000, Pakistan
Tel.: (92) 2132401206
Web Site: http://www.mrgc.com.pk
Logistic Services
N.A.I.C.S.: 488510
Haleem A. Siddiqui *(Chm)*

PAKISTAN KUWAIT INVESTMENT COMPANY (PRIVATE) LIMITED
Finance & Trade Centre 4th Floor Block C, Shahrah e Faisal, Karachi, 74400, Pakistan
Tel.: (92) 21 35630901
Web Site: http://www.pkic.com
Investment Banking
N.A.I.C.S.: 523150
Mohammed Naeem *(Sec)*

PAKISTAN NATIONAL SHIPPING CORPORATION
PNSC Building M T Khan Road, PO BOX 5350, Karachi, 74000, Pakistan
Tel.: (92) 2199203980
Web Site: https://www.pnsc.com.pk
Year Founded: 1971
PNSC—(PSX)
Rev.: $197,039,470
Assets: $309,350,050
Liabilities: $53,639,843
Net Worth: $255,710,207
Earnings: $107,904,598
Emp.: 680
Fiscal Year-end: 06/30/23
Marine Cargo Handling Services
N.A.I.C.S.: 488320
Rashid Siddiqi *(Exec Dir-Admin)*

PAKISTAN OXYGEN LIMITED
Dockyard Road West Wharf, PO Box 4845, Karachi, 74000, Pakistan
Tel.: (92) 2132313361 PK
Web Site: https://pakoxygen.com
Year Founded: 1949
PAKOXY—(KAR)
Rev.: $33,843,417
Assets: $45,486,164
Liabilities: $18,800,485
Net Worth: $26,685,679
Earnings: $1,935,767
Emp.: 138
Fiscal Year-end: 12/31/19
Industrial Gases & Welding Products Mfr
N.A.I.C.S.: 325120
Wakil Ahmed Khan *(Mgr-Corp Svcs)*

PAKISTAN PAPER PRODUCTS LIMITED
D/58 S I T E Estate Avenue, Karachi, 75700, Pakistan
Tel.: (92) 2132560134
Web Site: https://www.pakpaper.com
Year Founded: 1951
PPP—(KAR)
Rev.: $6,962,790
Assets: $8,861,418
Liabilities: $2,060,106
Net Worth: $6,801,312
Earnings: $129,059
Emp.: 107
Fiscal Year-end: 06/30/19
Paper Products Mfr
N.A.I.C.S.: 322299
Abid Sayeed *(CEO)*

PAKISTAN PETROLEUM LTD.
4th Floor PIDC House Dr Ziauddin Ahmed Road, PO Box No 3942, Karachi, 75530, Pakistan
Tel.: (92) 2135651480
Web Site: https://www.ppl.com.pk
Year Founded: 1950
PPL—(KAR)
Rev.: $1,180,148,024
Assets: $3,321,565,425
Liabilities: $1,180,458,587
Net Worth: $2,141,106,838
Earnings: $426,918,420
Emp.: 2,849
Fiscal Year-end: 06/30/19
Oil & Gas Exploration & Refining Services
N.A.I.C.S.: 213111
Shamsul Islam *(Chm)*

Subsidiaries:

The Pakistan Petroleum Provident Fund Trust Company (Private) Limited (1)
PIDC House Dr Ziauddin Ahmed Road, Karachi, Pakistan
Tel.: (92) 21111568568
Natural Gas Distribution Services
N.A.I.C.S.: 221210

Tullow Pakistan (Developments) Limited (1)
House No 5 Street no 34, Sector F-8-1, Islamabad, Pakistan
Tel.: (92) 512856850
Web Site: http://www.obizoilservices.com
Sales Range: $50-74.9 Million
Emp.: 50
Oil & Gas Wells Exploration
N.A.I.C.S.: 213111

PAKISTAN REFINERY LIMITED
Korangi Creek Road, PO Box 4612, Karachi, 75190, Pakistan
Tel.: (92) 2135122131
Web Site: https://www.prl.com.pk
PRL—(PSX)
Rev.: $942,043,864
Assets: $379,435,699
Liabilities: $288,212,825
Net Worth: $91,222,874
Earnings: $6,565,326
Emp.: 284
Fiscal Year-end: 06/30/23
Distilled Petroleum Products Mfr & Supplier
N.A.I.C.S.: 324110
Imran Ahmad Mirza *(CFO & Deputy Mng Dir-Fin & IT)*

PAKISTAN REINSURANCE CO. LTD.
PRC Towers 32 - A Lalazar Drive M T Khan Road, PO Box 4777, Karachi, 74000, Sindh, Pakistan
Tel.: (92) 2199202908
Web Site: https://pakre.org.pk
Year Founded: 1952
PAKRI—(LAH)
Rev.: $44,469,199
Assets: $230,783,621
Liabilities: $167,486,164
Net Worth: $63,297,457
Earnings: $9,558,780
Emp.: 122
Fiscal Year-end: 12/31/19
Reinsurance Services
N.A.I.C.S.: 524130
Erum Nadeem *(Mgr-Legal)*

PAKISTAN SERVICES LIMITED
1st Floor NESPAK House G-5/2, Islamabad, Pakistan
Tel.: (92) 512272890 PK
Web Site: https://www.psl.com.pk
Year Founded: 1958
PSEL—(KAR)
Rev.: $73,468,467
Assets: $388,797,531
Liabilities: $139,839,712
Net Worth: $248,957,819
Earnings: ($10,531,997)
Emp.: 3,253
Fiscal Year-end: 06/30/19
Hotel Operator
N.A.I.C.S.: 721110
Sadruddin Hashwani *(Chm)*

PAKISTAN STATE OIL LIMITED
PSO House Khayaban-e-Iqbal Clifton, Karachi, 75600, Pakistan
Tel.: (92) 2199203866 PK
Web Site: http://www.psopk.com
PSO—(PSX)
Rev.: $12,732,124,837
Assets: $3,840,169,396
Liabilities: $3,004,310,921
Net Worth: $835,858,474
Earnings: $35,313,621
Emp.: 2,222
Fiscal Year-end: 06/30/23
Petroleum & Related Products Distr
N.A.I.C.S.: 424720
Yacoob Suttar *(CFO & Deputy Mng Dir)*

Subsidiaries:

Aremai Petroleum (Private) Limited, (1)
8 Edward Road, Lahore, Pakistan
Tel.: (92) 42 373 53984
Web Site: http://www.psopk.com
Lubricating Oil Mfr
N.A.I.C.S.: 324191

PAKISTAN SYNTHETICS LTD
Office 1705 17th Floor Saima Trade

Tower-a I I Chundrigar Road, Karachi, 74000, Pakistan
Tel.: (92) 2313031   PK
Web Site: https://www.pslpet.com
PSYL—(LAH)
Rev.: $50,439,033
Assets: $42,604,813
Liabilities: $34,017,433
Net Worth: $8,587,381
Earnings: ($889,609)
Emp.: 325
Fiscal Year-end: 06/30/19
Polyester Staple Fibre Mfr
N.A.I.C.S.: 314999
Yakoob Karim *(Exec Dir)*

PAKISTAN TELECOMMUNICATION COMPANY LIMITED
Block-E G-8/4, Islamabad, 44000, Pakistan
Tel.: (92) 512263733   PK
Web Site: http://www.ptcl.com.pk
PTC—(KAR)
Rev.: $834,253,835
Assets: $2,227,068,036
Liabilities: $1,689,725,043
Net Worth: $537,342,993
Earnings: $15,308,524
Emp.: 20,075
Fiscal Year-end: 12/31/19
Telecommunication Servicesb
N.A.I.C.S.: 517112
Shoaib Ahmad Siddiqui *(Chm)*

Subsidiaries:

Paknet Limited   (1)
13-E Mehria Plaza Jinnah Avenue Capital, Blue Area, Islamabad, Pakistan   **(100%)**
Tel.: (92) 512875592
Web Site: http://www.paknet.com.pk
Internet, E-Mail & Information Technology Services
N.A.I.C.S.: 517810

Telephone Industries of Pakistan (Pvt) Ltd.   (1)
5th Floor Farid Chambers, Abdullah Haroon Road, Saddar, Karachi, 74400, Pakistan
Tel.: (92) 21 5683 092
Telecommunications Equipment Mfr
N.A.I.C.S.: 334210

PAKMARKAS LTD.
Savanoriu Ave 176, Vilnius, 3154, Lithuania
Tel.: (370) 52052900
Web Site: http://www.pakmarkas.com
Year Founded: 1994
Sales Range: $10-24.9 Million
Emp.: 209
Adhesive Lables, Packaging & Marking Components & Equipment
N.A.I.C.S.: 561910
Virginijus Gumbaragis *(Mng Dir)*

PAL GROUP HOLDINGS CO., LTD.
10th Floor Keihanshin Midosuji Building 3-6-1 Doshomachi, Chuo-ku, Osaka, Japan
Tel.: (81) 662270308
Web Site:
    https://www.palgroup.holdings
Year Founded: 1973
2726—(TKS)
Rev.: $1,365,136,960
Assets: $899,876,980
Liabilities: $450,059,020
Net Worth: $449,817,960
Earnings: $91,071,050
Fiscal Year-end: 02/29/24
Apparel Distr
N.A.I.C.S.: 424350

Subsidiaries:

CRESCENT STAFF CO., LTD.   (1)
3Chome-9-18 Akasaka, Minato, Tokyo, 107-0052, Japan
Tel.: (81) 120001440
Web Site: https://www.crescentstaff.co.jp
Employment Consulting Services
N.A.I.C.S.: 561311

Kurashiki Style Co., Ltd.   (1)
734 Tamashima, Kurashiki, 713-8102, Okayama Prefecture, Japan
Tel.: (81) 864861290
Web Site: https://www.kurast.co.jp
Emp.: 13
Apparels Mfr
N.A.I.C.S.: 315250

Mugstyle Co., Ltd.   (1)
6-27-8 Jingumae Kyocera Harajuku Building 3F, Shibuya-Ku, Tokyo, Japan
Tel.: (81) 354688286
Web Site: https://www.palgroup.holdings
Apparel Distr
N.A.I.C.S.: 424350

NICE CLAUP Co., LTD.   (1)
6-27-8 Jingumae Kyocera Harajuku Building 3F, Shibuya-ku, Tokyo, 150-0001, Japan
Tel.: (81) 364184649
Web Site: https://www.niceclaup.co.jp
Emp.: 449
Women Clothing Product Mfr & Distr
N.A.I.C.S.: 315250

THE GENERAL INC.   (1)
A8f 6-31-15 Jingumae Shibuya-ku, Tokyo, Japan
Tel.: (81) 364182967
Web Site: https://www.thegeneral-inc.com
Apparel Mfr & Distr
N.A.I.C.S.: 315250

PAL HOLDINGS, INC.
8th Floor PNB Financial Cente President Diosdado Macapagal Ave, Makati, 1200, Philippines
Tel.: (63) 28163311   PH
Web Site:
    https://www.philippineairlines.com
Year Founded: 1930
PAL—(PHI)
Rev.: $2,423,426,907
Assets: $4,032,008,323
Liabilities: $3,996,864,102
Net Worth: $35,144,221
Earnings: $1,260,718,680
Emp.: 4,432
Fiscal Year-end: 12/31/21
Holding Company; Airline Operator
N.A.I.C.S.: 551112
Jaime J. Bautista *(COO)*

Subsidiaries:

Philippine Airlines, Inc.   (1)
PNB Financial Center Diosdado Macapagal Ave, CCP Complex, Pasay, Philippines
Tel.: (63) 284018547
Web Site: https://www.philippineairlines.com
Airline Operator
N.A.I.C.S.: 481111
Lucio C. Tan *(Chm)*

Unit (Domestic):

Mabuhay Miles Service Center   (2)
Petron Bel-Air Square 363 Sen Gil Puyat Avenue, corner Makati Avenue, Makati, Philippines
Tel.: (63) 2 855 8888
Web Site: http://www.mabuhaymiles.com
Flight Rewards Program Operator
N.A.I.C.S.: 812990
Ismael Augusto S. Gozon *(Sr VP-Ops Grp)*

PAL INTERNATIONAL LTD.
Bilton Way, Lutterworth, LE17 4JA, Leics, United Kingdom
Tel.: (44) 1455555700
Web Site:
    http://www.palinternational.com
Year Founded: 1970
Sales Range: $10-24.9 Million
Emp.: 84
Health Care Products Mfr
N.A.I.C.S.: 424690
Murala Chemmarasseri *(Mgr-Sls-Middle East)*

PALA INVESTMENTS LIMITED
Gotthard Strasse 26, 6300, Zug, Switzerland
Tel.: (41) 415609070   CH
Web Site: http://www.pala.com
Year Founded: 2006
Private Equity Group
N.A.I.C.S.: 523999
John Nagulendran *(Mng Partner & Gen Counsel)*

Subsidiaries:

Nickel 28 Capital Corp.   (1)
Stikeman Elliott 666 Burrard St Suite 1700, Toronto, V6C2X8, ON, Canada
Tel.: (647) 846-7765
Web Site: https://www.nickel28.com
Rev.: $88,546
Assets: $154,719,739
Liabilities: $63,971,637
Net Worth: $90,748,102
Earnings: $6,110,818
Fiscal Year-end: 01/31/2023
Metal Exploration Services
N.A.I.C.S.: 212290
Anthony Milewski *(Chm)*

Subsidiary (Domestic):

Cobalt 27 Capital Corp.   (2)
4 King Street West Suite 401, Toronto, M5H 1B6, ON, Canada
Tel.: (647) 846-7765
Web Site: http://www.cobalt27.com
Metal Mining Services
N.A.I.C.S.: 212290
Anthony Milewski *(Chm & CEO)*

Subsidiary (Non-US):

Highlands Pacific Limited   (3)
Level 4 167 Eagle Street, Brisbane, 4000, QLD, Australia   **(100%)**
Tel.: (61) 732397800
Web Site: http://www.highlandspacific.com
Minerals Exploration
N.A.I.C.S.: 212230

Subsidiary (Domestic):

Highlands Pacific Australia Pty Limited   (4)
Level 4 167 Eagle St, Brisbane, 4000, QLD, Australia
Tel.: (61) 732397800
Web Site: http://www.highlandspacific.com
Emp.: 8
Gold Mining & Exploration Services
N.A.I.C.S.: 212220
Jhon Gooding *(Mng Dir)*

Pala Investments Holdings Limited   (1)
12 Castle Street, Saint Helier, JE2 3RT, Jersey
Tel.: (44) 1534639815
Emp.: 20
Private Equity Group
N.A.I.C.S.: 523999

PALACE CAPITAL PLC
Thomas House 84 Eccleston Square, London, SW1V 1PX, United Kingdom
Tel.: (44) 2033018330
Web Site:
    https://www.palacecapitalplc.com
PCA—(LSE)
Rev.: $24,739,965
Assets: $139,803,080
Liabilities: $16,382,227
Net Worth: $123,420,854
Earnings: ($11,817,723)
Emp.: 7
Fiscal Year-end: 03/31/24
Investment Services
N.A.I.C.S.: 523999
Neil Sinclair Frics *(CEO)*

Subsidiaries:

Palace Capital (Manchester) Limited   (1)
Thomas House 84 Eccleston Square, London, SW1V 1PX, United Kingdom
Tel.: (44) 3713842030

Real Estate Services
N.A.I.C.S.: 531390

PALACE HOTEL ZAGREB D.D
A Trg J J Strossmayera 10, 10 000, Zagreb, Croatia
Tel.: (385) 14899611
Web Site: http://www.palace.hr
Year Founded: 1907
Hotel & Resort Operator
N.A.I.C.S.: 721110

PALADIN ENERGY LTD.
Level 11 197 St Georges Terrace, Perth, 6000, WA, Australia
Tel.: (61) 894238100   AU
Web Site:
    https://www.paladinenergy.com.au
Year Founded: 1993
PDN—(NAM)
Rev.: $2,985,000
Assets: $361,163,000
Liabilities: $114,455,000
Net Worth: $246,708,000
Earnings: ($58,258,000)
Emp.: 165
Fiscal Year-end: 06/30/21
Other Metal Ore Mining
N.A.I.C.S.: 212290
Ranko Matic *(Co-Sec)*

Subsidiaries:

Aurora Energy Ltd.   (1)
Ste 600 TD Pl 140 Water St, Saint John's, A1C 6H6, NL, Canada
Tel.: (709) 726-2223
Web Site: http://www.aurora-energy.ca
Emp.: 11
Exploration & Development of Uranium Properties
N.A.I.C.S.: 212290

Fusion Resources Pty Ltd   (1)
Level 4 502 Hay St, Subiaco, 6008, WA, Australia
Tel.: (61) 893814366
Sales Range: $1-9.9 Million
Emp.: 4
Gold, Copper & Base Metals Mining Services
N.A.I.C.S.: 212220
Andrea Betty *(Sec)*

Langer Heinrich Uranium (Pty) Ltd.   (1)
3981 B Ext 10 New Indus Area, PO Box 156, Swakopmund, Erongo, Namibia   **(75%)**
Tel.: (264) 64 410 6450
Web Site: https://www.lhupl.com
Sales Range: $200-249.9 Million
Emp.: 674
Uranium Mining Services
N.A.I.C.S.: 212290

Summit Resources Limited   (1)
Level 4 502 Hay St, Subiaco, 6008, WA, Australia   **(100%)**
Tel.: (61) 8 9381 4366
Web Site: http://www.paladinenergy.com.au
Sales Range: Less than $1 Million
Uranium Ore Mining Services
N.A.I.C.S.: 212290
Ranko Matic *(Co-Sec)*

PALADIN LIMITED
Suite 705 7th Floor Tower 5 The Gateway Harbour City, Tsim Sha Tsui, Kowloon, China (Hong Kong)
Tel.: (852) 2 829 6180
Web Site:
    http://www.paladinlimited.com
0495—(HKG)
Rev.: $2,356,723
Assets: $128,851,020
Liabilities: $24,382,250
Net Worth: $104,468,770
Earnings: $6,858,254
Emp.: 87
Fiscal Year-end: 06/30/21
Property Development Services
N.A.I.C.S.: 531311

PALADIN SECURITY SYSTEMS LTD
Tel.: (604) 677-8700
Web Site: https://paladinsecurity.com
Year Founded: 1976
Security System Services
N.A.I.C.S.: 561621
Ashley Cooper *(CEO)*

PALAMINA CORP.
145 King Street West Suite 2870, Toronto, M5H 1J8, ON, Canada
Tel.: (416) 204-7536 ON
Web Site: https://www.palamina.com
Year Founded: 2015
PLMNF—(OTCQB)
Rev.: $961
Assets: $2,741,373
Liabilities: $567,337
Net Worth: $2,174,036
Earnings: $1,678,911
Fiscal Year-end: 12/31/23
Metal Mining Services
N.A.I.C.S.: 212290
Andrew Thomson *(Pres & CEO)*

PALAMON CAPITAL PARTNERS, LP
Cleveland House 33 King Street, London, SW1Y 6RJ, United Kingdom
Tel.: (44) 2077662000 UK
Web Site: http://www.palamon.com
Emp.: 30
Privater Equity Firm
N.A.I.C.S.: 523999
Louis G. Elson *(Founder & Mng Partner)*

Subsidiaries:
The Rug Company Limited (1)
119B Portland Road, London, W11 4LN, United Kingdom
Tel.: (44) 20 7229 5148
Web Site: http://www.therugcompany.com
Sales Range: $25-49.9 Million
Rug Designer, Whslr & Retailer
N.A.I.C.S.: 449121
James Seuss *(CEO)*

PALAMY STE
29 Rue David D Angers, Le May Sur Evre, 49122, Nantes, France
Tel.: (33) 241631313
Web Site: http://www.palamy.com
Sales Range: $25-49.9 Million
Emp.: 140
Plastics Film Mfr & Distr
N.A.I.C.S.: 326199
Beno T. Benesteau *(Mgr)*

PALAQAR FOR REAL ESTATE DEVELOPMENT & MANAGEMENT COMPANY
PO Box 395, Nablus, Palestine
Tel.: (970) 972092332333
Year Founded: 1998
PALAQAR—(PAL)
Sales Range: Less than $1 Million
Real Estate Development Services
N.A.I.C.S.: 531390
Saad Fahd Khader Joudih *(Chm)*

PALASH SECURITIES LTD.
9/1 RN Mukherjee Road Birla Building 5th Floor, Kolkata, 700 001, India
Tel.: (91) 3322430497
Web Site: https://birla-sugar.com
Year Founded: 2015
540648—(BOM)
Rev.: $6,467,502
Assets: $52,057,586
Liabilities: $4,328,973
Net Worth: $47,728,613
Earnings: ($1,949,200)
Fiscal Year-end: 03/31/23

Investment Management Service
N.A.I.C.S.: 525990
Deepak Kumar Sharma *(CFO)*

Subsidiaries:
Morton Foods Limited (1)
Unit No 1072-73 10th Floor Vegas Commercial Building Plot No 6, Block - B Sector 14 Dwarka, Delhi, 110078, India
Tel.: (91) 7596085002
Web Site: https://www.mortonindia.com
Food Product Mfr & Distr
N.A.I.C.S.: 311421

PALATINE PRIVATE EQUITY LLP
The Zenith Building 26 Spring Gardens, Manchester, M2 1AB, United Kingdom
Tel.: (44) 161 214 4730 UK
Web Site: http://www.palatinepe.com
Year Founded: 2005
Privater Equity Firm
N.A.I.C.S.: 523999
Gary Tipper *(Mng Partner)*

Subsidiaries:
Lucion Services Ltd. (1)
7 Halifax Court, Dunston, Gateshead, NE11 9JT, Tyne & Wear, United Kingdom
Tel.: (44) 1914618999
Web Site: http://www.lucionservices.com
Risk Managemeng Srvices
N.A.I.C.S.: 561499

Subsidiary (Domestic):
Lucion Environmental Limited (2)
Unit 7 Halifax Court, Dunston, Gateshead, NE11 9JT, Tyne & Wear, United Kingdom (100%)
Tel.: (44) 191 4618999
Web Site: http://www.lucionservices.com
Environmental Consulting Services
N.A.I.C.S.: 541620

SMP Partners Ltd. (1)
Clinch's House Lord Street, Douglas, IM99 1RZ, Isle of Man
Tel.: (44) 1624683229
Web Site: http://www.smppartners.com
Sales Range: $50-74.9 Million
Emp.: 130
Trust & Wealth Management Services
N.A.I.C.S.: 523991
Stephen Turner *(Mng Dir-Caribbean Region)*

Subsidiary (Domestic):
SMP Accounting & Tax Ltd (2)
Clinchs House Lord St, Douglas, IM99 1RZ, Isle of Man
Tel.: (44) 1624683242
Web Site: http://www.smppartners.com
Accounting & Tax Consulting Services
N.A.I.C.S.: 541219
Rachael Hooper *(Sr Mgr-Tax Dept)*

SMP Fund Services Limited (2)
Clinchs House Lord St, Douglas, IM99 1RZ, Isle of Man
Tel.: (44) 1624683229
Fund Management Services
N.A.I.C.S.: 523940
Justin Scott *(Dir-Tax)*

Subsidiary (Non-US):
SMP Partners Asia Ltd (2)
Suite B 10/F Hong Kong Diamond Exchange Building, Nos 8 - 10 Duddell Street, Central, China (Hong Kong)
Tel.: (852) 23171729
Web Site: http://www.smppartners.com
Sales Range: $50-74.9 Million
Emp.: 10
Portfolio Management Services
N.A.I.C.S.: 523920
Mark Denton *(Mng Dir)*

SMP Partners SA (2)
Bahnhofplatz 9, 8001, Zurich, Switzerland
Tel.: (41) 43 817 6717
Web Site: http://www.smppartners.ch

Sales Range: $100-124.9 Million
Emp.: 3
Trust & Corporate Provider Service
N.A.I.C.S.: 525920
Judith Maegli *(Mng Dir)*

PALCO LIMITED
Flat No 501 Sri Ramchandra Residency Madhapur Road Kothaguda, Kondapur, Hyderabad, 500 084, India
Tel.: (91) 40 23119545
Web Site: http://www.palcolimited.com
Liabilities: $129,556
Net Worth: ($129,556)
Earnings: ($24,204)
Fiscal Year-end: 03/31/18
Metal Product Whslr
N.A.I.C.S.: 423510
Venkata Reddy Kovvuri *(Chm & Mng Dir)*

PALCO METALS LIMITED
B/209 Mondeal Square Nr S G Highway Prahaladnagar Cross Road, Besides Ramol Police Staon CTM- Ramol Road, Ahmedabad, 380015, India
Tel.: (91) 48900690
Web Site: https://www.palcometals.com
Year Founded: 1962
539121—(BOM)
Rev.: $13,548
Assets: $1,205,383
Liabilities: $250,800
Net Worth: $954,583
Earnings: $2,446
Fiscal Year-end: 03/31/23
Aluminium Products Mfr
N.A.I.C.S.: 331315
Kirankumar Babulal Agrawal *(Mng Dir)*

Subsidiaries:
Palco Recycle Industries limited (1)
Plot No 18-25 Survey No 418 and 435 Opp Cera Ceramic, Lucky Industrial Estate B/h Golden Park GIDC Bus Stand kadi, Mehsana, 382715, Guajrat, India
Tel.: (91) 9426078920
Web Site: http://www.palcorecycle.com
Aluminum Product Mfr & Distr.
N.A.I.C.S.: 331315
Sonia Kakani *(Compliance Officer)*

PALERO CAPITAL GMBH
Maximilianstrasse 12-14, 80539, Munich, Germany
Tel.: (49) 89 88 98 871 00 De
Web Site: http://www.palero.de
Privater Equity Firm
N.A.I.C.S.: 523999
Christian Daumann *(Mng Partner)*

Subsidiaries:
CCL Label AG (1)
Weststrasse 12, 5426, Lengnau, Aargau, Switzerland (100%)
Tel.: (41) 44 744 31 11
Web Site: http://www.ccllabel.ch
Self-Adhesive Labels & Labeling Equipment Mfr & Distr
N.A.I.C.S.: 561910
Reto Klauser *(Gen Mgr)*

cenadruck GmbH (1)
Fritz-Kunke-Strasse 8, Alfeld, 31061, Germany
Tel.: (49) 5181 8490 100
Web Site: http://www.cenadruck.de
Sales Range: $10-24.9 Million
Emp.: 80
Paper, Paperboard & Laminated Aluminum Foil Mfr for Flexible Packaging Uses
N.A.I.C.S.: 322220
Phillip Wagner *(CEO)*

PALESTINE COMMERCIAL BANK
Palestine Commercial Bank Building

Nahda St Al Masyon, PO Box 1799, Ramallah, Palestine
Tel.: (970) 22979999
Web Site: http://www.pcb.ps
Year Founded: 1992
Sales Range: $1-9.9 Million
Emp.: 170
Commercial Banking Services
N.A.I.C.S.: 522110
Mahmoud Zuhdi Malhas *(Chm)*

PALESTINE HOTEL
Sadoon St Sec 947 St 49 Fardous Square, Baghdad, Iraq
Tel.: (964) 18164400
Year Founded: 1989
HPAL—(IRAQ)
Sales Range: Less than $1 Million
Home Management Services
N.A.I.C.S.: 721110
Abdul Amir Mohsen Hussein *(Mng Dir)*

PALESTINE INSURANCE COMPANY
Tel.: (970) 22941450
Web Site: https://www.pic-pal.ps
Year Founded: 1994
PICO—(PAL)
Rev.: $56,317,253
Assets: $66,569,565
Liabilities: $54,112,921
Net Worth: $12,456,644
Earnings: $392,081
Fiscal Year-end: 12/31/23
Insurance Services
N.A.I.C.S.: 524298
Mohammad Ahmad Abu Awad *(Chm)*

PALESTINE INVESTMENT & DEVELOPMENT CO.
Yafa St, PO Box 281, Ramallah, Palestine
Tel.: (970) 97222954028
Year Founded: 1993
PID—(PAL)
Rev.: $107,651
Assets: $5,001,840
Liabilities: $274,205
Net Worth: $4,727,635
Earnings: ($116,843)
Fiscal Year-end: 12/31/23
Investment Management Service
N.A.I.C.S.: 523999
Khalil Salem Khalil Hanania *(Deputy Chm)*

PALESTINE INVESTMENT BANK
Irsal St, PO Box 3675, Al-Bireh, Ramallah, Palestine
Tel.: (970) 22943500
Web Site: https://www.pibbank.com
Year Founded: 1994
PIBC—(PAL)
Rev.: $46,617,788
Assets: $641,183,298
Liabilities: $542,329,935
Net Worth: $98,853,363
Earnings: $3,675,302
Fiscal Year-end: 12/31/20
Commercial Banking Services
N.A.I.C.S.: 522110
Khalil Nasr *(Vice Chm)*

PALESTINE ISLAMIC BANK
PO Box 2106, Ramallah, Palestine
Tel.: (970) 22967688
Web Site: https://www.islamicbank.ps
Year Founded: 1995
ISBK—(PAL)
Rev.: $73,015,156
Assets: $1,569,277,555
Liabilities: $1,421,241,547
Net Worth: $148,036,008
Earnings: $4,846,019

AND PRIVATE COMPANIES

Fiscal Year-end: 12/31/23
Investment Banking Services
N.A.I.C.S.: 523150
Maher Masri *(Chm)*

PALESTINE REAL ESTATE INVESTMENT CO.
Q Center Office Building 6 floor, Ramallah, Palestine
Tel.: (970) 22948233
Web Site: http://www.prico.ps
Year Founded: 1994
PRICO—(PAL)
Rev.: $2,762,368
Assets: $93,000,661
Liabilities: $56,959,546
Net Worth: $36,041,115
Earnings: ($17,601,797)
Fiscal Year-end: 12/31/23
Real Estate Investment Services
N.A.I.C.S.: 525990
Nimer Abed Al Wahad *(Chm)*

PALESTINE TELECOMMUNICATIONS COMPANY P.L.C.
PO Box 1570, Rafedia, Nablus, Palestine
Tel.: (970) 92376225
Web Site: http://www.paltel.ps
Year Founded: 1995
Sales Range: $400-449.9 Million
Emp.: 3,000
Telecommunication Servicesb
N.A.I.C.S.: 517111
Mohannad Heajawi *(Gen Mgr)*

Subsidiaries:

Hadara For Technological Investment Ltd. (1)
Jerusalem St Foud Bldg 3rd Floor, PO Box 2030, Ramallah, Palestine (100%)
Tel.: (970) 22403434
Web Site: http://www.hadara.ps
Emp.: 70
Cellular & Wireless Telecommunications
N.A.I.C.S.: 517112
Rami Shamshom *(Gen Mgr)*

Hulul Business Solutions Ltd. (1)
PO Box 4167, 00791, Al-Bireh, Palestine (100%)
Tel.: (970) 22410000
Web Site: http://www.hulul.ps
Sales Range: $50-74.9 Million
Emp.: 150
Cable Networks
N.A.I.C.S.: 516210

Palestine Cellular Communications Company (1)
PO Box 3999, Al-Bireh, Palestine
Tel.: (970) 22402440
Web Site: http://www.jawwal.ps
Sales Range: $200-249.9 Million
Emp.: 600
Cellular Communications Services
N.A.I.C.S.: 517112
Ammar Aker *(CEO)*

Palmedia Ltd. (1)
PO Box 3999, Al-Bireh, Palestine (100%)
Tel.: (970) 22950556
Web Site: http://www.pal-media.ps
Cellular & Wireless Telecommunications
N.A.I.C.S.: 517112

PALETTENFABRIK BASSUM GMBH
Carl Zeiss Strasse 10, 27211, Bassum, Germany
Tel.: (49) 424194000
Web Site: http://www.bassum.com
Year Founded: 1964
Rev.: $62,266,116
Emp.: 112
Wooden Pallets Mfr
N.A.I.C.S.: 321920
Friedhelm Haase *(Mng Dir)*

PALETTES GESTION SERVICES
Centre Multimarchandises Rue Michel Poulmarch, 76800, Saint Etienne Du Rouvray, Seine Maritime, France
Tel.: (33) 232911599
Rev.: $44,200,000
Emp.: 48
Wood Products Mfr
N.A.I.C.S.: 423310

PALFINGER AG
Lamprechtshausener Bundesstrasse 8, 5101, Bergheim, Austria
Tel.: (43) 662228181077 AT
Web Site: https://www.palfinger.com
Year Founded: 1932
PFI—(DUS)
Rev.: $2,699,900,440
Assets: $2,275,186,457
Liabilities: $1,551,665,904
Net Worth: $723,520,553
Earnings: $118,853,683
Emp.: 12,728
Fiscal Year-end: 12/31/23
Hydraulic Lifting, Loading & Handling Systems Mfr
N.A.I.C.S.: 333923
Martin Zehnder *(COO & Member-Exec Bd)*

Subsidiaries:

Epsilon Kran GmbH (1)
Christophorusstrasse 30, Glasenbach, 5061, Elsbethen, Austria (65%)
Tel.: (43) 6626295480
Web Site: https://www.palfingerepsilon.com
Sales Range: $25-49.9 Million
Emp.: 50
Construction Machinery Mfr
N.A.I.C.S.: 333120
Stefan Oberleitner *(Member-Mgmt Bd)*

Guima France S.A.S. (1)
4 A Avenue Des Tourondes, 82300, Caussade, France
Tel.: (33) 5 63 26 22 22
Crane Repair & Maintenance Services
N.A.I.C.S.: 811310

MBB Interlift N.V. (1)
Industrielaan 4 3e Industriezone, Aalst, 9320, Belgium
Tel.: (32) 53838177
Hydraulic Lifting Component Mfr
N.A.I.C.S.: 333998

Madal Palfinger S.A. (1)
Rua Flavio Francisco Bellini 350, Caxias do Sul, 95098-170, Brazil (99%)
Tel.: (55) 5430267000
Web Site: http://www.madalpalfinger.com
Sales Range: $100-124.9 Million
Emp.: 400
Fabricated Structural Metal Mfr
N.A.I.C.S.: 332312

Nimet SRL (1)
Targului Street 103, Lazuri Dambovita, 137121, Satu-Mare, Romania
Tel.: (40) 245607000
Web Site: https://www.nimet.ro
Emp.: 700
Steel Bar & Tube Mfr
N.A.I.C.S.: 332999
Samy Numan *(Founder & Mng Dir)*

Palfinger Area Units GmbH (1)
Franz-Wolfram-Schererstrasse 24, Salzburg, 5020, Austria
Tel.: (43) 66246840
Web Site: http://www.palfinger.com
Sales Range: $100-124.9 Million
Emp.: 300
Industrial Machinery Mfr
N.A.I.C.S.: 333248

Palfinger Asia Pacific Pte Ltd (1)
3 International Business Park Nordic European Centre 05-25/26, Singapore, 609927, Singapore (100%)
Tel.: (65) 65919191
Sales Range: $25-49.9 Million
Emp.: 16
Construction & Mining Machinery & Equipment Merchant Whslr
N.A.I.C.S.: 423810

Subsidiary (Non-US):

Palfinger (Shenzhen) Ltd. (2)
Block5 Bei FangYongFa Tech Park Chuan Dong Industrial Park Zone B Song, Gang Jie Dao Bao'an District, 518105, Shenzhen, China
Tel.: (86) 755 27556661
Crane Mfr
N.A.I.C.S.: 333923

Palfinger Dreggen AS (1)
Hegrensveien 17A, 5042, Bergen, Norway
Tel.: (47) 5533 3650
Web Site: http://www.palfinger.com
Emp.: 70
Offshore Cranes Mfr
N.A.I.C.S.: 333923
Endre G. Asperheim *(Mgr-IT)*

Palfinger Europe GmbH (1)
Franz-Wolfram Scherer Strasse 24, Salzburg, 5020, Austria (99.97%)
Tel.: (43) 66246842254
Web Site: http://www.palfinger.com
Sales Range: $50-74.9 Million
Emp.: 250
Construction Machinery Mfr
N.A.I.C.S.: 333120

Subsidiary (Non-US):

MBB Palfinger GmbH (2)
Fockestrasse 53, Hoykenkamp, 27777, Ganderkesee, Germany
Tel.: (49) 4221 853 0
Web Site: http://www.palfinger.com
Emp.: 200
Industrial Tail Lift Mfr
N.A.I.C.S.: 333924

Subsidiary (Non-US):

MBB Hubfix s.r.o. (3)
Gogolova 18, Bratislava, 851 01, Slovakia
Tel.: (421) 2 52636611
Hydraulic Tail Lift Mfr
N.A.I.C.S.: 333924

Subsidiary (Non-US):

Palfinger Platforms GmbH (2)
Dusseldorfer Strasse 100, 47809, Krefeld, Germany
Tel.: (49) 2151 4792 0
Web Site: http://www.palfingerplatforms.com
Sales Range: $25-49.9 Million
Emp.: 10
Forklift Mfr
N.A.I.C.S.: 333924

Palfinger European Units GmbH (1)
Franz-Wolfram-Schererstrasse 24, 5020, Salzburg, Austria
Tel.: (43) 662 46 84 0
Web Site: http://www.palfinger.at
Emp.: 100
Industrial Machinery Mfr
N.A.I.C.S.: 333248

Palfinger GmbH (1)
Feldkirchen Field 1, Ainring, 83404, Munich, Germany (94.9%)
Tel.: (49) 86544770
Web Site: http://www.palfinger.de
Sales Range: $75-99.9 Million
Emp.: 180
Construction & Mining Machinery & Equipment Merchant Whslr
N.A.I.C.S.: 423810
Thomas Moocka *(Gen Mgr)*

Palfinger Gru Idrauliche Srl (1)
Via Dante Aleghieri 50, Cadelbosco Di Sopra, I-42023, Modena, Italy (100%)
Tel.: (39) 0522 9115611
Mfr of Truck-Loading Cranes
N.A.I.C.S.: 333923

Palfinger Inc. (1)
7942 Dorchester Rd, Niagara Falls, L2E 6V6, ON, Canada (100%)
Tel.: (905) 374-3363
Web Site: http://www.palfinger-northamerica.com
Sales Range: $50-74.9 Million
Emp.: 80
Industrial Machinery & Equipment Whslr
N.A.I.C.S.: 423830
Mark S. Woody *(Pres)*

Palfinger Industrieanlagen GmbH (1)
Franz-Wolfram Scherer Strasse 24-26, 5101, Bergheim, Austria (95%)
Tel.: (43) 66246842254
Web Site: http://www.palfinger.com
Sales Range: $50-74.9 Million
Emp.: 350
Construction Machinery Mfr
N.A.I.C.S.: 333120
Mario Rahrer *(Head-Legal Department)*

Palfinger Liftgates, LLC (1)
15939 Piuma Ave, Cerritos, CA 90703
Tel.: (562) 924-8218
Hook Loader Mfr
N.A.I.C.S.: 336120

Palfinger Marine Pte. Ltd. (1)
79 Joo Koon Circle, Singapore, 629107, Singapore
Tel.: (65) 68612009
Sales Range: $25-49.9 Million
Emp.: 1
Crane Repair & Maintenance Services
N.A.I.C.S.: 811310

Palfinger Marine- und Beteiligungs-GmbH (1)
Vogelweiderstrasse 40a, 5020, Salzburg, Austria
Tel.: (43) 662 4684 0
Marine Crane Mfr
N.A.I.C.S.: 333923

Subsidiary (Domestic):

Palfinger CIS GmbH (2)
Franz-Wolfram-Scherer-Strasse 24, Salzburg, 5020, Austria
Tel.: (43) 662 46 84 2254
Web Site: http://www.palfinger.com
Emp.: 250
Industrial Machinery Distr
N.A.I.C.S.: 423830

Subsidiary (Non-US):

Palfinger Cranes India Pvt. Ltd. (2)
P No 02 Sector 19C 15 th Floor The Ambience Court, Vashi, Navi Mumbai, 400 705, India
Tel.: (91) 22 41126200
Web Site: http://www.palfinger-india.com
Sales Range: $25-49.9 Million
Emp.: 60
Industrial Crane Mfr & Distr
N.A.I.C.S.: 333923
Herbert Ortner *(CEO)*

Palfinger Produktionstechnik Bulgaria EOOD (2)
Komplex Beta, 5980, Cherven Bryag, Bulgaria
Tel.: (359) 65999111
Welded Component Mfr
N.A.I.C.S.: 333992

Palfinger Proizvodna Tehnologija Hrvatska d.o.o. (2)
Lucicka Cesta BB Lucice, Delnice, 51300, Croatia
Tel.: (385) 51659440
Web Site: http://www.palfinger.com
Emp.: 8
Steel Construction Component Mfr
N.A.I.C.S.: 331110

Palfinger Proizvodnja d.o.o. (2)
Jaskova Ulica 18, 2000, Maribor, Slovenia
Tel.: (386) 24501200
Web Site: http://www.palfinger.com.si
Sales Range: $75-99.9 Million
Emp.: 500
Metal Processing Machinery Mfr
N.A.I.C.S.: 333248
Michael Steiner *(Mng Dir)*

Subsidiary (Domestic):

Palfinger Russland GmbH (2)
Franz-Wolfram-Schererstrasse 24, 5020, Salzburg, Austria
Tel.: (43) 662 46840
Hydraulic Lifting Equipment Mfr & Distr
N.A.I.C.S.: 333998

Palfinger Ned-Deck BV (1)
Ambachtsweg 10, 3771 MG, Barneveld, Netherlands
Tel.: (31) 342422105

PALFINGER AG

Palfinger AG—(Continued)
Web Site: http://www.palfingermarine.com
Sales Range: $25-49.9 Million
Emp.: 6
Survival System & Deck Equipment Mfr & Distr
N.A.I.C.S.: 336999

Subsidiary (Domestic):

Fast RSQ B.V. (2)
Marchandweg 21 A, 3771 ML, Barneveld, Netherlands
Tel.: (31) 342 416 466
Web Site: http://www.fastrsq.com
Sales Range: $25-49.9 Million
Emp.: 1
Rescue Craft Mfr
N.A.I.C.S.: 333923
Matthijs van der Ham (Gen Mgr)

Palfinger Platforms Italy S.R.L. (1)
Via De Nicola 31, 41122, Modena, Italy
Tel.: (39) 05 925 2426
Web Site: https://www.palfingerplatformsitaly.it
Aerial Platform Services
N.A.I.C.S.: 532490

Palfinger Produkcionstechnik Bulgaria EOOD (1)
Beta Complex, Cherven Briag, Pleven, Bulgaria (100%)
Tel.: (359) 65999111
Construction Machinery Mfr
N.A.I.C.S.: 333120

Palfinger Service S.A. (1)
24 Ave Condorcet, 91240, Saint-Michel-sur-Orge, France (99.99%)
Tel.: (33) 169721919
Sales Range: $25-49.9 Million
Emp.: 30
Automobile & Motor Vehicle Merchant Whslr
N.A.I.C.S.: 423110

Palfinger Service-Und Beteiligungs-GmbH (1)
Franz-Wolfram Scherer Strasse 24, 5105, Bergheim, Austria (100%)
Tel.: (43) 662 46 84
Sales Range: $25-49.9 Million
Emp.: 117
Engineeering Services
N.A.I.C.S.: 541330

Palfinger Tail Lifts GmbH (1)
Fockestrasse 53, 27777, Ganderkesee, Germany
Tel.: (49) 4221853355
Commercial Vehicle Mfr
N.A.I.C.S.: 336211

Palfinger USA Inc (1)
4151 W State Rt 18, Tiffin, OH 44883-9558 (100%)
Tel.: (419) 448-8156
Web Site: https://www.palfingerusa.com
Sales Range: $25-49.9 Million
Emp.: 50
Construction & Mining Machinery & Equipment Merchant Whslr
N.A.I.C.S.: 423810
Mark S. Woody (VP-North America)

Subsidiary (Domestic):

Equipment Technology, LLC (2)
341 NW 122nd St, Oklahoma City, OK 73114
Tel.: (405) 748-3841
Web Site: http://www.eti1.com
Emp.: 250
Aerial Lift & Custom Body Mfr & Distr
N.A.I.C.S.: 336211
Chris Neuberger (CEO)

Omaha Standard, Inc. (2)
3501 S 11th St, Council Bluffs, IA 51501-3633
Tel.: (712) 328-7444
Web Site: http://www.omahastd.com
Truck Bodies Mfr
N.A.I.C.S.: 336211

Subsidiary (Domestic):

Palfleet Truck Equipment, Co. (3)
2490 Pinson Vly Pkwy, Birmingham, AL 35217
Tel.: (205) 841-8582
Web Site: http://www.palfleet.com
Truck Equipment Whslr
N.A.I.C.S.: 423830

Subsidiary (Domestic):

Tiffin Loader Crane Company (2)
4151 W State Route 18, Tiffin, OH 44883-9558 (100%)
Tel.: (419) 448-8156
Web Site: http://www.tiffincrane.com
Sales Range: $25-49.9 Million
Emp.: 50
Overhead Traveling Crane Hoist & Monorail System Mfr
N.A.I.C.S.: 333923
Luke Kelly (Gen Mgr)

Ratcliff Palfinger Ltd. (1)
Bessemer Road, Welwyn Garden City, AL7 1ET, Herts, United Kingdom (100%)
Tel.: (44) 1707325571
Web Site: http://www.palfinger.com
Sales Range: $50-74.9 Million
Emp.: 150
Motor Vehicle Parts Mfr
N.A.I.C.S.: 336390

Velmash-S OOO (1)
st Kornienko 6, Velikiye Luki, Pskov, 182112, Russia
Tel.: (7) 8115363900
Web Site: https://www.velmash.com
Mobile Lifting Equipment Mfr
N.A.I.C.S.: 333924

PALGAZ DOGALGAZ DAGITIM TICARET VE SANAYI A.S.
Bulgurlu Cad No 60 Kucukcamlica, Uskudar, 34696, Istanbul, Turkiye
Tel.: (90) 2163257330
Web Site: http://www.palgaz.com.tr
Natural Gas Distribution Services
N.A.I.C.S.: 221210

PALINDA GROUP HOLDINGS LIMITED
Unit 306-A201 3/F Harbour Centre Tower 1, 1 Hok Cheung Street Hunghom, Kowloon, China (Hong Kong)
Tel.: (852) 24413393 Ky
Web Site: http://www.palinda.com
Year Founded: 2006
8179—(HKG)
Rev.: $33,746,573
Assets: $59,934,690
Liabilities: $14,564,963
Net Worth: $45,369,728
Earnings: $835,125
Emp.: 14
Fiscal Year-end: 12/31/22
Holding Company
N.A.I.C.S.: 551112

PALISAD A.D.
Lake bb, Zlatibor, Serbia
Tel.: (381) 648459047
Web Site: https://www.palisad.rs
Year Founded: 1968
PLSD—(BEL)
Rev.: $4,540,395
Assets: $17,378,618
Liabilities: $8,232,789
Net Worth: $9,145,829
Earnings: $82,951
Emp.: 149
Fiscal Year-end: 12/31/23
Home Management Services
N.A.I.C.S.: 721110
Janic Vojislav (Gen Mgr)

PALISADE INVESTMENT PARTNERS LIMITED
Level 25, Angel Place, 123 Pitt Street, Sydney, 2000, NSW, Australia
Tel.: (61) 289707800
Web Site: https://www.palisadegroup.com
Year Founded: 2007
Investment Management
N.A.I.C.S.: 523999
Mike Reynolds (Mng Dir-Americas)

Subsidiaries:

Mashell, Inc. (1)
104 Washington Ave, Eatonville, WA 98328
Tel.: (360) 832-6161
Web Site: http://www.rainierconnect.com
Sales Range: $10-24.9 Million
Emp.: 59
Telecommunications
N.A.I.C.S.: 517810
Brian Haynes (Pres)

Subsidiary (Domestic):

Mashell Telecom, Inc. (2)
805 Pacific Ave, Tacoma, WA 98402
Tel.: (253) 683-4200
Web Site: http://www.rainierconnect.com
Sales Range: $1-9.9 Million
Emp.: 50
Internet Service Provider
N.A.I.C.S.: 517810
Arnie Haynes (Pres)

PALISADES GOLDCORP LTD.
Pacific Centre South 25th Floor 700 W Georgia Street, Vancouver, V7Y 1B3, BC, Canada
Tel.: (403) 614-2552
Web Site: http://palisades.ca
Year Founded: 2013
Gold & Metal Mining
N.A.I.C.S.: 212290
Collin Kettell (Founder & Chm)

PALLA PHARMA LTD.
Mertons Corporate Services Level 7 330 Collins Street, Melbourne, 3000, VIC, Australia
Tel.: (61) 393010800 AU
Web Site: http://www.pallapharma.com
Year Founded: 2004
PAL—(ASX)
Rev.: $18,187,611
Assets: $51,656,196
Liabilities: $23,978,679
Net Worth: $27,677,517
Earnings: ($26,629,743)
Fiscal Year-end: 12/31/20
Alkaloid Product Mfr & Distr
N.A.I.C.S.: 325411
Brendan Middleton (CEO-Interim & CFO)

PALLADIO HOLDING SPA
State Road Padana Verona 6, 36100, Vicenza, Italy
Tel.: (39) 0444 650500 IT
Web Site: http://www.pfh.eu
Year Founded: 1982
Privater Equity Firm
N.A.I.C.S.: 523999
Giorgio Drago (CEO)

Subsidiaries:

Cimos d.d. (1)
Cesta Marezganskega Upora 2, Capodistria, 6000, Koper, Slovenia (92%)
Tel.: (386) 56658100
Web Site: https://cimos.eu
Automotive Components Mfr
N.A.I.C.S.: 336110

Subsidiary (Non-US):

Cimos France, S.A.S. (2)
37 Rue des Peupliers, 92752, Nanterre, Cedex, France
Tel.: (33) 147 86 30 69
Automobile Parts Distr
N.A.I.C.S.: 423120

Cimos TMD Ai d.o.o. (2)
Sarajevska ulica br 62, 76250, Gradacac, Bosnia & Herzegovina
Tel.: (387) 35 822 800
Automobile Parts Mfr
N.A.I.C.S.: 336390

Subsidiary (Domestic):

NT Forging d.o.o. (3)
Ul Mehmede Spahe br 1, 72290, Novi Travnik, Bosnia & Herzegovina
Tel.: (387) 30 548 501
Automobile Parts Mfr
N.A.I.C.S.: 336390

Subsidiary (Non-US):

Livnica a.d. (2)
Milosevacki put 34, Kikinda, 23300, Serbia
Tel.: (381) 230 422 860
Web Site: http://www.livnicakikinda.com
Automobile Parts Mfr
N.A.I.C.S.: 336390

P.P.C. Buzet d.o.o. (2)
Most 24, 52420, Buzet, Croatia
Tel.: (385) 52610800
Automobile Parts Mfr
N.A.I.C.S.: 336390

Mid Industry Capital S.p.A. (1)
Galleria Sala dei Longobardi 2, 20121, Milan, Italy
Tel.: (39) 02 76 26 17 1
Web Site: http://www.midindustry.com
Privater Equity Firm
N.A.I.C.S.: 523999
Giorgio Garuzzo (Chm & CEO)

VEI Capital (1)
Via Fiori Oscuri 11, 20121, Milan, Italy
Tel.: (39) 0272730700
Web Site: http://www.veicapital.it
Privater Equity Firm
N.A.I.C.S.: 523999
Giorgio Drago (Mng Partner)

PALLADIUM ONE MINING INC.
Suite 3704 - 88 Scott Street, Toronto, M5E 0A9, ON, Canada
Tel.: (647) 612-6466
Web Site: https://www.palladiumoneinc.com
NKORF—(OTCQB)
Rev.: $177,247
Assets: $8,904,613
Liabilities: $2,267,460
Net Worth: $6,637,152
Earnings: ($5,917,032)
Emp.: 5
Fiscal Year-end: 12/31/22
Copper Exploration Services
N.A.I.C.S.: 212230
Derrick Weyrauch (Pres & CEO)

Subsidiaries:

MetalCorp Limited (1)
490 Maureen Street, Thunder Bay, P7B 6T2, ON, Canada
Tel.: (807) 683-8161
Web Site: https://www.metalcorp.ca
Assets: $10,897
Liabilities: $596,594
Net Worth: ($585,697)
Earnings: ($125,347)
Fiscal Year-end: 12/31/2019
Mineral Exploration Services
N.A.I.C.S.: 213114
Justin Garofalo (CFO & VP-Fin)

PALLADIUS AG
Heimeranstr 35 II, 80339, Munich, Bavaria, Germany
Tel.: (49) 89120212630
Sales Range: $150-199.9 Million
Emp.: 3
Real Estate Investment Services
N.A.I.C.S.: 531390
Hermann Sommer (Chm-Supervisory Bd)

Subsidiaries:

Bohm+Kelleners GmbH (1)
Emmericher Strasse 5, 46485, Wesel, Nordrhein-Westfalen, Germany
Tel.: (49) 281962600
Sales Range: $25-49.9 Million
Car Dealer
N.A.I.C.S.: 441110
Emin Sabovic (Mng Dir)

AND PRIVATE COMPANIES

PALLADON VENTURES LTD.
570 Granville Street Suite 400, Vancouver, V6C 3P1, BC, Canada
Tel.: (801) 521-5252
Web Site:
http://www.palladonventures.com
Year Founded: 1980
Sales Range: Less than $1 Million
Iron Ore Mining Services
N.A.I.C.S.: 212210
John W. Cutler *(Pres & CEO)*

PALLISER FURNITURE LTD.
70 Lexington Park, Winnipeg, R2G 4H2, MB, Canada
Tel.: (204) 988-5600
Web Site: http://www.palliser.com
Year Founded: 1944
Sales Range: $300-349.9 Million
Emp.: 4,000
Home Furniture Mfr
N.A.I.C.S.: 337126

PALM + HAVAS
1253 McGill College Ave 3rd Fl, Montreal, H3B 2Y5, QC, Canada
Tel.: (514) 845-7256   QC
Year Founded: 1986
Emp.: 70
Advetising Agency
N.A.I.C.S.: 541810
Pascal DeDecker *(VP & Dir-Creative)*

PALM ECO-TOWN DEVELOPMENT CO., LTD.
23rd Floor Building B R&F Yingsheng Plaza No 16 Machang Road, Tianhe District, Guangzhou, China
Tel.: (86) 2085189222
Web Site: https://www.palmdesign.cn
Year Founded: 1984
002431—(SSE)
Rev.: $595,979,748
Assets: $2,613,516,516
Liabilities: $1,993,385,160
Net Worth: $620,131,356
Earnings: ($97,022,016)
Emp.: 1,076
Fiscal Year-end: 12/31/22
Landscaping Services
N.A.I.C.S.: 561730

Subsidiaries:

Belt Collins International (Hong Kong) Ltd.   (1)
Belt Collins Centre 29/F Hing Wai Centre 7 Tin Wan Praya Road, Aberdeen, China (Hong Kong)
Tel.: (852) 225289233
Web Site: http://www.bcihk.com
Landscape Architectural Services
N.A.I.C.S.: 541320
Anthony Hui *(Pres & Mng Dir)*

Palm Design Co., Ltd.   (1)
Fl 6-7 Tower B International Center of Pearl New Town No 3, Qingyi Street Machang Road Tianhe District, Guangzhou, China
Tel.: (86) 2085189800
Web Site: http://www.palmdesign.cn
Landscape Architectural Services
N.A.I.C.S.: 541320
Xu Hualin *(Pres)*

Palm Eco-Town Development Co., Ltd. - Construction Division   (1)
3/F Building 7 Chuangzhi Tiandi No 388 Songhu Road Yangpu District, Shanghai, China
Tel.: (86) 2131160001
Landscape Architectural Services
N.A.I.C.S.: 541320

Palm Eco-Town Development Co., Ltd. - Design Division   (1)
Floor 6-7 Tower B Zhuguang International Commerce Center, No 3 Qingyi Street Machang Road Tianhe District, Guangzhou, China
Tel.: (86) 2085189600
Landscape Architectural Services
N.A.I.C.S.: 541320

Palm Eco-Town Development Co., Ltd. - Municipal Utility Division   (1)
Room 1501-1503 Floor 15 Building B Jialong International Mansion, No 19 Chaoyang Park Road Chaoyang District, Beijing, China
Tel.: (86) 1063220260
Landscape Architectural Services
N.A.I.C.S.: 541320

PALM HILLS DEVELOPMENT SAE
Smart Village A4-B83 KM28, Cairo - Alexandria Desert Road Abou Rawash, Cairo, Egypt
Tel.: (20) 235351200   EG
Web Site: https://www.palmhillsdev.com
Year Founded: 2005
PHDC—(EGX)
Rev.: $564,977,783
Assets: $2,403,889,543
Liabilities: $2,024,635,016
Net Worth: $379,254,528
Earnings: $56,083,430
Fiscal Year-end: 12/31/23
Real Estate Developers
N.A.I.C.S.: 236116
Yasseen Mansour *(Chm & CEO)*

PALM HOLDINGS INC.
477 Richmond Street W Suite 810, Toronto, M5V 3E7, ON, Canada
Tel.: (416) 477-7256
Web Site: http://www.palm-holdings.com
Year Founded: 1997
Sales Range: $25-49.9 Million
Holding Company
N.A.I.C.S.: 551112
Anil Taneja *(Mng Dir-North America)*

Subsidiaries:

Palm Holdings UK   (1)
5-11 Lavington Street, London, SE1 ONZ, United Kingdom
Tel.: (44) 797 414 2626
Emp.: 150
Hotel Owner & Construction; Commercial Building Construction
N.A.I.C.S.: 721110
Sheetal Kapoor *(Mng Dir)*

PALM JEWELS LTD.
C/205 D/205 2nd Floor Super Mall Besides Lal Bungalow C G Road, Ahmedabad, 380009, Gujarat, India
Tel.: (91) 7575009844
Web Site: https://palmjewelsltd.com
Year Founded: 2005
541444—(BOM)
Rev.: $10,683,701
Assets: $2,407,639
Liabilities: $491,935
Net Worth: $1,915,705
Earnings: $27,174
Fiscal Year-end: 03/31/21
Gold Jewelry Product Distr
N.A.I.C.S.: 423940
Rohit Dalpatbhai Shah *(Mng Dir)*

PALMA CO., LTD.
5F KS Bldg 4-5-20 Kojimachi, Chiyoda-ku, Tokyo, 102-0083, Japan
Tel.: (81) 332340358
Web Site: https://www.palma.jp
Year Founded: 2006
3461—(TKS)
Sales Range: $1-9.9 Million
Emp.: 20
Self Storage Services
N.A.I.C.S.: 531130
Shigehisa Takano *(Chm & CEO)*

PALMARIS CAPITAL PLC
Paterson Building Gartsherrie Road, Coatbridge, ML5 2EU, United Kingdom
Tel.: (44) 1236 440410
Web Site:
http://www.palmariscapital.com
Year Founded: 1988
Sales Range: Less than $1 Million
Emp.: 2
Investment Services
N.A.I.C.S.: 523999
R. Gregory Melgaard *(Mng Dir)*

PALMER & HARVEY MCLANE (HOLDINGS) LIMITED
P & H House Davigdor Road, Hove, BN3 1RE, United Kingdom
Tel.: (44) 1273222100
Web Site:
http://www.palmerharvey.co.uk
Year Founded: 1925
Sales Range: $5-14.9 Billion
Emp.: 4,000
Grocery & Related Products Whslr & Delivery Service
N.A.I.C.S.: 445298
Paul Hagon *(Mng Dir-Sls)*

Subsidiaries:

Winerite Ltd.   (1)
Leeds No 4 Bond, Gelderd Road, Leeds, LS12 6HJ, United Kingdom   (100%)
Tel.: (44) 01132837676
Sales Range: $250-299.9 Million
Emp.: 280
Alcohol Distr
N.A.I.C.S.: 424820

YP Electronics Ltd.   (1)
PCMS House Torwood Close, Westwood Bus Pk, Coventry, CV4 8HY, United Kingdom
Tel.: (44) 2476475760
Web Site: http://www.ypelectronics.co.uk
Sales Range: $10-24.9 Million
Emp.: 55
Retail Technology Solutions Supplier
N.A.I.C.S.: 541990

PALMS AGRO PRODUCTION CO
Al Rai- Fourth Ring Road-Block 56 Safat, PO Box 1976, Kuwait, 13020, Kuwait
Tel.: (965) 24730745
Web Site: https://www.palms-kw.com
Year Founded: 1982
PAPCO—(KUW)
Rev.: $11,001,586
Assets: $21,810,072
Liabilities: $4,396,084
Net Worth: $17,413,988
Earnings: $967,214
Emp.: 540
Fiscal Year-end: 12/31/22
Farm Management Services
N.A.I.C.S.: 115116
Badr Hamad Al Rabeah *(Chm)*

PALOMA INDUSTRIES LIMITED
6 23 Momozono-Cho, Mizuhoku, Nagoya, 467 8585, Japan
Tel.: (81) 528245031
Web Site: http://www.paloma.co.jp
Year Founded: 1911
Sales Range: $10-24.9 Million
Emp.: 14,928
Gas Appliances Mfg & Sales
N.A.I.C.S.: 333414
Hiroaki Kobayashi *(Pres)*

Subsidiaries:

Rheem Manufacturing Company   (1)
1100 Abernathy Rd Ste 1400, Atlanta, GA 30328
Tel.: (770) 351-3000
Web Site: http://www.rheem.com
Mfr of Water Heaters & Residential & Commercial Heating & Air-Conditioning
N.A.I.C.S.: 333415
Chris Peel *(Pres & CEO)*

Subsidiary (Domestic):

Friedrich Air Conditioning Co.   (2)
10001 Reunion Pl Ste 500, San Antonio, TX 78216-4139
Tel.: (210) 546-0500
Web Site: http://www.friedrich.com
Air Conditioners & Heat Pumps, Electronic Air Cleaners & Ductless Split Systems Mfr
N.A.I.C.S.: 333415
Chuck Campbell *(CEO)*

Heat Transfer Products Group, LLC   (2)
3885 Crestwood Pkwy Ste 500, Duluth, GA 30096
Tel.: (256) 259-7400
Web Site: http://www.htpgusa.com
Commercial Refrigeration Systems Designer & Mfr
N.A.I.C.S.: 333415
Dave Hartman *(VP-Sls & Mktg)*

Unit (Domestic):

Heat Transfer Products Group, LLC - ColdZone   (3)
8101 E Kaiser Blvd Ste 110, Anaheim, CA 92808
Tel.: (714) 529-1935
Web Site: http://www.coldzone.com
Emp.: 200
Commercial Refrigeration Equipment Mfr & Whslr
N.A.I.C.S.: 423740
John McFadden *(Natl Sls Mgr)*

Heat Transfer Products Group, LLC - Kramer   (3)
3885 Crestwood Pkwy Ste 500, Duluth, GA 30096
Tel.: (678) 323-4904
Web Site: http://kramer.htpgusa.com
Commercial Refrigeration Equipment Mfr & Whslr
N.A.I.C.S.: 423740
Paul Westbrook *(Dir-Sls & Mktg)*

Subsidiary (Domestic):

Raypak, Inc.   (2)
2151 Eastman Ave, Oxnard, CA 93030-5194
Tel.: (805) 278-5300
Web Site: http://www.raypak.com
Emp.: 300
Water Heating Equipment Mfr
N.A.I.C.S.: 333414
Michael Sentovich *(Pres)*

Subsidiary (Non-US):

Rheem Australia Pty Ltd.   (2)
1 Alan St, Rydalmere, 2116, NSW, Australia   (100%)
Tel.: (61) 296849281
Web Site: http://www.rheem.com.au
Water Heater Mfr
N.A.I.C.S.: 332410
Mark Jackaman *(Gen Mgr-Fin)*

Subsidiary (Domestic):

Rheem Australia   (3)
8 Dalmore Dr, Scoresby, 3179, VIC, Australia
Tel.: (61) 392128919
Web Site: http://www.rheem.com.au
N.A.I.C.S.: 312120
Paul Rapson *(Reg Mgr)*

Subsidiary (Non-US):

Rheem Canada Ltd.   (2)
125 Edgeware Rd Unit 1, Brampton, L6Y OP5, ON, Canada
Tel.: (905) 527-9194
Web Site: http://www.rheem.com
Water Heating Equipment Mfr
N.A.I.C.S.: 333414

Division (Domestic):

Rheem Manufacturing - Air Conditioning Div   (2)

PALOMA INDUSTRIES LIMITED

Paloma Industries Limited—(Continued)
5600 Old Greenwood Rd, Fort Smith, AR 72908-6586 **(100%)**
Tel.: (479) 646-4311
Web Site: http://www.rheemac.com
Mfr of Air Conditioning Equipment & Supplies
N.A.I.C.S.: 333414
Chuck Holt *(Gen Mgr)*

Division (Non-US):

Rheem S.A. Argentina **(2)**
Avenida del Libertador 6570 Piso 6, C 1428 ARV, Buenos Aires, Argentina
Tel.: (54) 11 4896 6000
Web Site: http://www.rheem.com.ar
Hot Water Systems & Space Heaters Mfr
N.A.I.C.S.: 332410

Division (Domestic):

Rheem Water Heater **(2)**
101 Bell Rd, Montgomery, AL 36117-4305 **(100%)**
Tel.: (334) 260-1500
Web Site: http://www.rheem.com
Residential & Commercial Water Heaters Mfr
N.A.I.C.S.: 333415

PALOS CAPITAL CORPORATION
1 Place Ville-Marie Suite 1670, Montreal, H3B 2B6, Canada
Tel.: (514) 397-0188
Web Site: https://palos.ca
Financial Services
N.A.I.C.S.: 523999

Subsidiaries:

IOU Financial Inc. **(1)**
1 Place Ville-Marie Suite 1670, Montreal, H3B 2B6, QC, Canada
Tel.: (514) 789-0694
Web Site: https://www.ioufinancial.com
Rev.: $17,804,622
Assets: $48,847,420
Liabilities: $38,784,224
Net Worth: $10,063,195
Earnings: $1,165,697
Emp.: 51
Fiscal Year-end: 12/31/2019
Loan Services
N.A.I.C.S.: 522310
Philippe Marleau *(Founder)*

Subsidiary (US):

IOU CENTRAL INC. **(2)**
1255 Roberts Blvd Ste 116, Kennesaw, GA 30188
Web Site: http://www.ioucentral.com
Sales Range: $75-99.9 Million
Emp.: 4
Internet Loan Marketplace
N.A.I.C.S.: 522310

PALRAM INDUSTRIES LTD.
Do'ar Kfar Makabi, Ramat Yohanan, 30035, Israel
Tel.: (972) 48459900
Web Site: https://www.palram.com
Year Founded: 1963
PLRM—(TAE)
Rev.: $474,581,012
Assets: $470,910,892
Liabilities: $123,655,752
Net Worth: $347,255,140
Earnings: $48,542,063
Fiscal Year-end: 12/31/23
Plastics Material & Resin Manufacturing
N.A.I.C.S.: 325211
Ori Barav *(Mng Dir-Israel & ROW)*

Subsidiaries:

Palma Mexico Inc. **(1)**
5 de Mayo 1416 Pte Centro, 64000, Monterrey, Nuevo Leon, Mexico
Tel.: (52) 18181438221
Thermoplastic Sheet Product Mfr
N.A.I.C.S.: 326199

Palmam DPL Ltd. **(1)**
22 Coatham Avenue Aycliffe Business Park, Newton Aycliffe, DL5 6DB, Durham, United Kingdom
Tel.: (44) 1325300437
Thermoplastic Sheet Product Mfr
N.A.I.C.S.: 326199

Palmar Germany GmbH **(1)**
Wilhelm-Dumling-Str 7, 39218, Schonebeck, Germany
Tel.: (49) 39284211410
Thermoplastic Sheet Product Mfr
N.A.I.C.S.: 326199

Palram 4U Ltd. **(1)**
Tziporit Industrial Zone, Nazareth Illit, 1789089, Israel
Tel.: (972) 46419988
Web Site: http://www.palram4u.com
Thermoplastic Sheet Product Mfr
N.A.I.C.S.: 326199

Palram Americas Inc. **(1)**
9735 Commerce Cir Arcadia West Industrial Park, Kutztown, PA 19530
Web Site: https://www.palram.com
Thermoplastic Sheet Product Mfr
N.A.I.C.S.: 326199

Palram Australia Pty Ltd. **(1)**
34 Buys Court, Derrimut, 3030, VIC, Australia
Tel.: (61) 392194444
Thermoplastic Sheet Product Mfr
N.A.I.C.S.: 326199

Palram Beijing Ltd. **(1)**
Rm 1206 Building 11 Jian Wai SOHO 39 East 3rd Ring Road, Chaoyang District, Beijing, 100029, China
Tel.: (86) 1058694042
Thermoplastic Sheet Product Mfr
N.A.I.C.S.: 326199

Palram Europe Ltd. **(1)**
Unit 2 White Rose Way, Doncaster Carr Industrial Estate, Doncaster, DN4 5JH, United Kingdom
Tel.: (44) 1302380777
Thermoplastic Sheet Product Mfr
N.A.I.C.S.: 326199

Subsidiary (Non-US):

Palram France Ltd. **(2)**
14 Rue Denis Papin Za Vigne Aux Loups, 91380, Chilly-Mazarin, France
Tel.: (33) 169534179
Thermoplastic Sheet Product Mfr
N.A.I.C.S.: 326199

Palram India Ltd. **(1)**
404 Sanjar Enclave S V Road Opp PVR Milap Cinemas, Kandivali W, Mumbai, 400 067, Maharashtra, India
Tel.: (91) 2228626880
Thermoplastic Sheet Product Mfr
N.A.I.C.S.: 326199

Palram South-africa Pty. Ltd. **(1)**
58 Malcolm Moodie Cresent Jetpark, Boksburg, 1459, South Africa
Tel.: (27) 113977771
Web Site: http://www.palram.com
Thermoplastic Sheet Product Mfr
N.A.I.C.S.: 326199

PALRED TECHNOLOGIES LIMITED
Plot No 2 8-2-703/2/B Road No 12 Banjara Hills, Hyderabad, 500 034, Telangana, India
Tel.: (91) 4066384916
Web Site: https://www.palred.com
Year Founded: 1999
PALREDTEC—(NSE)
Rev.: $18,067,298
Assets: $15,609,100
Liabilities: $8,191,739
Net Worth: $7,417,361
Earnings: $(53,762)
Emp.: 1,000
Fiscal Year-end: 03/31/23
Information Technology Services
N.A.I.C.S.: 541512

Palem Srikanth Reddy *(Chm & Mng Dir)*

PALSGAARD A/S
Palsgaardvej 10, 7130, Juelsminde, Denmark
Tel.: (45) 7682 7682 **DK**
Web Site: http://www.palsgaard.com
Sales Range: $125-149.9 Million
Emp.: 260
Mfr of Stabilizers & Emulsifiers for Food Industry
N.A.I.C.S.: 311225
Jakob Thoisen *(CEO)*

Subsidiaries:

PALSGAARD DO BRASIL LTDA **(1)**
Rua francisco leitao N 469 Conj 203 - 2 Anda, Pinheiros, 05414-020, Sao Paulo, Brazil
Tel.: (55) 1130612023
Food & Beverage Mfr
N.A.I.C.S.: 311421

Palsgaard Asia-Pacific Pte Ltd **(1)**
3 International Business Park #04-18 Nordic European Centre, Singapore, 609927, Singapore
Tel.: (65) 6468 6905
Sales of Stabilizers & Emulsifiers for Food Industry
N.A.I.C.S.: 424490

Palsgaard China Ltd **(1)**
7-1 Qishi Technology Park, No 67 Lane 1768 Liyue Road, Shanghai, 201114, China
Tel.: (86) 21 5190 5516
Sales of Stabilizers & Emulsifiers for Food Industry
N.A.I.C.S.: 424490

Palsgaard DWC-LLC **(1)**
PO Box 49172, Dubai, United Arab Emirates
Tel.: (971) 506504166
Food & Beverage Distr
N.A.I.C.S.: 424490

Palsgaard France S.A.S. **(1)**
Immeuble IBS Bat 3 24 avenue Joannes Masset, 69009, Lyon, France
Tel.: (33) 682592629
Emp.: 1
Sales of Stabilizers & Emulsifiers for Food Industry
N.A.I.C.S.: 424490
Tim Hawker *(CEO)*

Palsgaard Netherlands B.V. **(1)**
Industrieweg 21, 4301 RS, Zierikzee, Netherlands
Tel.: (31) 111 41 33 16
Emp.: 15
Mfr of Stabilizers & Emulsifiers for Food Industry
N.A.I.C.S.: 311225

Palsgaard Polska Sp. z o. o. **(1)**
Ul Dwa Swiaty 3 D, Bielany Wroclawskie, 55-040, Kobierzyce, Poland
Tel.: (48) 71 311 08 60
Emp.: 5
Sales of Stabilizers & Emulsifiers for Food Industry
N.A.I.C.S.: 424490
Magdalena Kielan *(Gen Mgr)*

Palsgaard South Africa (Pty) Ltd. **(1)**
Greenstone Hill Office Park Building 1 Unit F3B, Emerald Road, Greenstone Hill, 1626, Gauteng, South Africa
Tel.: (27) 11 609 0234
Sales of Stabilizers & Emulsifiers for Food Industry
N.A.I.C.S.: 424490
William Hall *(Gen Mgr)*

Palsgaard Verkaufsgesellschaft mbH & Co KG **(1)**
Hildesheimer Str 265-267, 30519, Hannover, Germany
Tel.: (49) 511 87 59 144
Web Site: http://www.palsgaard.com
Sales of Stabilizers & Emulsifiers for Food Industry
N.A.I.C.S.: 424490

INTERNATIONAL PUBLIC

PALSOFT INFOSYSTEMS LIMITED
D-469 9A Vishwakarma Industrial Area, Jaipur, 302013, India
Tel.: (91) 141 2333994
Web Site: http://www.palsoft.info
Rev.: $55,842
Assets: $14,867
Liabilities: $243,835
Net Worth: $(228,968)
Earnings: $1,007
Emp.: 3
Fiscal Year-end: 03/31/19
Software Development Services
N.A.I.C.S.: 541511
Anubha Gupta *(Exec Dir)*

PALTEK CORPORATION
Shin-Yokohama Square Bldg 6F 11F 2-3-12 Shin-Yokohama, Kouhoku-ku, Yokohama, 222-0033, Kanagawa, Japan
Tel.: (81) 45 477 2000
Web Site: http://www.paltek.co.jp
Rev.: $286,106,572
Assets: $146,152,212
Liabilities: $54,432,402
Net Worth: $91,719,810
Earnings: $560,753
Emp.: 282
Fiscal Year-end: 12/31/20
Semiconductor Machinery Mfr
N.A.I.C.S.: 333242
Naohide Yabuki *(Pres & CEO)*

Subsidiaries:

Explorer Inc. **(1)**
Hakodate TechnoPark 379-22 Kikyo-cho, Hakodate, 041-0801, Hokkaido, Japan
Tel.: (81) 138 47 7604
Web Site: http://www.explorer-inc.co.jp
Emp.: 33
Electronic Equipment Distr
N.A.I.C.S.: 423690
Naohide Yabuki *(Pres)*

PALTEK Hong Kong Limited **(1)**
Rm 21-22 6/F Worldwide Industrial Ctr 43-47 Shan Mei St Fotan, Shatin, Hong Kong, China (Hong Kong)
Tel.: (852) 2690 2252
Web Site: http://www.paltek.co.jp
Electronic Equipment Distr
N.A.I.C.S.: 423690

PALUMBO GROUP S.P.A
Calata della Marinella, 80133, Naples, Italy
Tel.: (39) 081287164
Web Site: http://www.palumbogroup.it
Year Founded: 1967
Emp.: 960
Shipyard
N.A.I.C.S.: 336611
Antonio Palumbo *(Chm)*

Subsidiaries:

Brodogradiliste Viktor Lenac d.d. **(1)**
Martinscica 8, PO Box 210, 51000, Rijeka, Croatia **(59.69%)**
Tel.: (385) 51405555
Web Site: https://www.lenac.hr
Rev.: $96,790,929
Assets: $78,578,059
Liabilities: $23,374,735
Net Worth: $55,203,325
Earnings: $5,220,497
Emp.: 371
Fiscal Year-end: 12/31/2023
Ship Building & Repairing
N.A.I.C.S.: 336611
Sandra Uzelac *(CEO & Member-Mgmt Bd)*

Subsidiary (Domestic):

Viktor Servisi d.o.o. **(2)**
Martinscica bb, PO Box 210, HR-51000, Rijeka, Croatia
Tel.: (385) 51217002
Ship Repairing Services
N.A.I.C.S.: 336611
Vladimir Bruketa *(Mng Dir)*

AND PRIVATE COMPANIES

PAMAPOL S.A.
Ul Wielunska 2, 97-438, Rusiec, Poland
Tel.: (48) 436768110
Web Site: http://www.pamapol.com.pl
Year Founded: 2006
PMP—(WAR)
Rev.: $252,066,564
Assets: $164,101,372
Liabilities: $119,681,148
Net Worth: $44,420,223
Earnings: $2,716,209
Fiscal Year-end: 12/31/23
Food Processing Services
N.A.I.C.S.: 311999
Pawel Szataniak *(CEO)*

PAMBILI NATURAL RESOURCES CORPORATION
315 39th Ave SE, Calgary, T2G 1X5, AB, Canada
Tel.: (403) 277-4421
Web Site:
 https://www.pambilinrc.com
Year Founded: 2001
PNNEF—(OTCIQ)
Assets: $30,551
Liabilities: $1,316,432
Net Worth: ($1,285,881)
Earnings: ($888,569)
Fiscal Year-end: 12/31/23
Oil & Gas Exploration Services
N.A.I.C.S.: 213112
Jon Harris *(CEO)*

PAMO PROMET A.D.
Vojvode Stepe Stepanovica 22, 74220, Modrica, Bosnia & Herzegovina
Tel.: (387) 53810004
Year Founded: 2007
PMPR—(BANJ)
Sales Range: Less than $1 Million
Emp.: 13
Paperboard Mfr
N.A.I.C.S.: 322130
Novak Vukasinovic *(Chm-Mgmt Bd & Pres)*

PAMODZI INVESTMENT HOLDINGS
Pamodzi House 5 Willowbrook Close, Athol, Melrose, South Africa
Tel.: (27) 877410000
Web Site: http://www.pamodzi.co.za
Sales Range: $1-4.9 Billion
Emp.: 50
Privater Equity Firm
N.A.I.C.S.: 523999
Ndaba Ntsele *(Co-Founder & Chm)*

Subsidiaries:

Pamodzi Unique Engineering Pty Ltd (1)
Cnr Bird & Field Roads Lilianton, Boksburg, Gauteng, South Africa
Tel.: (27) 11 826 6111
Web Site: http://www.uniqueeng.co.za
Machine Tools Mfr
N.A.I.C.S.: 333517
Christo Kleynhans *(Mgr-Design Office)*

Rely Intracast Precision castings (pty) Ltd (1)
512 Commissioner Street Industrial Sites, PO Box 222, 1460, Boksburg, South Africa
Tel.: (27) 11 914 1640
Web Site: http://www.rely.co.za
Industrial Die Cast Mfr
N.A.I.C.S.: 331529
Carlos Palinhos *(Dir-Comml)*

PAMPA METALS CORPORATION
Suite 1200 750 West Pender, Vancouver, V6C 2T8, BC, Canada
Tel.: (604) 347-8777
Web Site:
 https://www.pampametals.com
PMMCF—(OTCQB)
Rev.: $3,927
Assets: $5,184,827
Liabilities: $36,996
Net Worth: $5,147,831
Earnings: ($1,819,310)
Fiscal Year-end: 12/31/21
Copper & Gold Mining
N.A.I.C.S.: 212220
Julian Bavin *(Pres & CEO)*

PAMPLONA CAPITAL MANAGEMENT LLP
25 Park Lane, London, W1K 1RA, United Kingdom
Tel.: (44) 20 7079 8000   UK
Web Site:
 http://www.pamplonafunds.com
Year Founded: 2005
Investment Management Service
N.A.I.C.S.: 523999
Will Sherrill *(Principal)*

Subsidiaries:

BFG Supply Co., LLC (1)
14500 Kinsman Rd, Burton, OH 44021
Tel.: (440) 834-1883
Web Site: http://www.bfgsupply.com
Sales Range: $25-49.9 Million
Emp.: 320
Flowers, Plants & Horticultural Supplies Whslr
N.A.I.C.S.: 424930
Dave Daily *(Pres & CEO)*

Branch (Domestic):

BFG Supply Co., LLC - Grand Rapids (2)
4660 E Paris Ave SE, Grand Rapids, MI 49512
Tel.: (616) 541-3000
Web Site: http://www.bfgsupply.com
Sales Range: $10-24.9 Million
Emp.: 70
Flowers, Plants & Horticultural Supplies Whslr
N.A.I.C.S.: 424930

BakeMark USA LLC (1)
7351 Crider Ave, Pico Rivera, CA 90660-3705
Tel.: (562) 949-1054
Web Site: http://yourbakemark.com
Prepared Flour Mixes & Doughs; Bakery Products, Fruit Fillings & Icings
N.A.I.C.S.: 311824
Jim Parker *(CEO)*

Beacon Rail Leasing Ltd (1)
111 Buckingham Palace Road, Victoria, London, SW1W 0SR, United Kingdom
Tel.: (44) 20 7340 6361
Web Site: http://www.beaconrail.com
Rolling Stock Leasing Services
N.A.I.C.S.: 532411
Neil Bennett *(COO)*

CSC ServiceWorks, Inc. (1)
303 Sunnyside Blvd Ste 70, Plainview, NY 11803
Tel.: (516) 349-8555
Web Site:
 http://www.coinmachservicecorp.com
Emp.: 2,250
Holding Company; Coin & Card-Operated Multi-Family Housing & Commercial Laundry, Tire Inflation & Automotive Interior Vacuum Equipment Sales, Leasing, Installation & Management Services
N.A.I.C.S.: 551112
Mark Hjelle *(CEO)*

Subsidiary (Domestic):

AIR-serv Group, LLC (2)
1370 Mendota Heights Rd, Mendota Heights, MN 55120-1190
Tel.: (651) 454-0465
Web Site: http://www.air-serv.com
Sales Range: $1-9.9 Million
Tire Inflation & Vacuum Vending Equipment Leasing & Support Services
N.A.I.C.S.: 532490

Appliance Warehouse of America, Inc. (2)
3201 W Royal Ln Ste 100, Irving, TX 75063
Tel.: (469) 521-2222
Web Site: http://www.appliancewhse.com
Coin & Card-Operated Laundry Equipment Leasing Services
N.A.I.C.S.: 532490

Coinmach Corporation (2)
303 Sunnyside Blvd Ste 70, Plainview, NY 11803
Tel.: (516) 349-8555
Web Site: http://www.coinmach.com
Sales Range: $25-49.9 Million
Emp.: 5
Coin & Card-Operated Laundry Equipment Leasing, Installation & Management Services
N.A.I.C.S.: 561990
Michael E. Stanky *(Pres)*

Mac-Gray Corporation (2)
404 Wyman St Ste 400, Waltham, MA 02451-1212
Tel.: (781) 487-7600
Web Site: http://www.macgray.com
Rev.: $322,119,000
Assets: $401,409,000
Liabilities: $284,122,000
Net Worth: $117,287,000
Earnings: $4,310,000
Emp.: 814
Fiscal Year-end: 12/31/2012
Coin & Card-Operated Multi-Family Housing & Commercial Laundry Equipment Sales, Installation & Management Services
N.A.I.C.S.: 561499
Linda Serafini *(Gen Counsel, Sec & VP)*

Super Laundry Equipment Corp. (2)
234 Crossways Park Dr, Woodbury, NY 11797
Tel.: (516) 678-4404
Web Site: http://www.superlaundry.com
Sales Range: $25-49.9 Million
Emp.: 50
Commercial Laundry Equipment Whslr & Maintenance Services
N.A.I.C.S.: 423850
Charles Prato *(VP)*

DJJD, Inc. (1)
58 Pulaski St Ste 15, Peabody, MA 01960-1829
Tel.: (978) 977-4994
Disc Brake Calipers & Brake Heads Mfr
N.A.I.C.S.: 336340

Formativ Health (1)
4875 Belfort Rd, Jacksonville, FL 32256
Tel.: (844) 818-1020
Web Site: http://www.formativhealth.com
Patient Engagement Services
N.A.I.C.S.: 621999
Nick Stefanizzi *(CEO-Interim)*

Subsidiary (Domestic):

Etransmedia Technology Inc. (2)
385 Jordan Rd Rensselaer Technology Pk, Troy, NY 12180
Tel.: (518) 283-5418
Online Records Management Services
N.A.I.C.S.: 561440

Subsidiary (Domestic):

Associated Billing Services, Inc. (3)
13430 N Black Canyon Hwy Ste 100, Phoenix, AZ 85029-1310
Tel.: (602) 943-9200
Accounting Services
N.A.I.C.S.: 541219

KCA Deutag Drilling Ltd. (1)
Bankhead Drive City South Office Park, Portlethen, Aberdeen, AB12 4XX, United Kingdom
Tel.: (44) 1224987000
Web Site: http://www.kcadeutag.com
Sales Range: $1-4.9 Billion
Oil & Gas Field Services
N.A.I.C.S.: 213111

Subsidiary (Domestic):

Abbot Group Limited (2)
Minto Drive, Altens, Aberdeen, AB12 3LW, United Kingdom
Tel.: (44) 1224299600

Web Site: http://www.abbotgroup.com
Sales Range: $1-4.9 Billion
Provider of Drilling, Well Intervention, Engineering, Testing, Inspection & Fluids Management Services to Oil & Gas Industry
N.A.I.C.S.: 213111

Subsidiary (Non-US):

Bentec GmbH (2)
Deilmannstrasse 1, 48455, Bad Bentheim, Germany
Tel.: (49) 59227280
Web Site: http://www.bentec.de
Sales Range: $50-74.9 Million
Emp.: 500
Oil & Gas Drilling Rig & Equipment Mfr
N.A.I.C.S.: 333132
Arend Loedden *(COO)*

KCA Deutag GmbH & Co. KG (2)
Deilmannstrasse 1, Bad Bentheim, 48455, Germany
Tel.: (49) 5922720
Web Site: http://www.kcadeutag.com
Sales Range: $75-99.9 Million
Oil & Gas Field Services
N.A.I.C.S.: 213111
Holger Temmen *(CEO)*

Subsidiary (Domestic):

KCA Deutag Drilling GmbH (3)
Deilmannstrasse 1, 48455, Bad Bentheim, Germany
Tel.: (49) 5922720
Web Site: http://www.kcadeutag.com
Sales Range: $100-124.9 Million
Emp.: 100
Oil & Gas Field Services
N.A.I.C.S.: 213111
Maurice A. White *(COO)*

Latham Pool Products, Inc. (1)
787 Watervliet Shaker Rd, Latham, NY 12110
Tel.: (518) 783-7776
Web Site: http://www.lathampool.com
Swimming Pools, Components & Accessories Mfr
N.A.I.C.S.: 339920
Harold Brooks *(Mgr-Mfg Engrg)*

Subsidiary (Domestic):

Pool Cover Specialist National, Inc. (2)
8553 S 2940 W, West Jordan, UT 84088
Tel.: (801) 255-6124
Web Site: http://www.poolcovers.com
Pool Cover Mfr
N.A.I.C.S.: 339920
Randy Mathis *(VP-Ops)*

Royal Fiberglass Pools, Inc. (2)
1407 Anse Broussard Hwy, Breaux Bridge, LA 70517
Tel.: (337) 332-4386
Web Site:
 http://www.royalfiberglasspools.com
Sales Range: $1-9.9 Million
Fiberglass Swimming Pools Mfr
N.A.I.C.S.: 339920
Clifford Hebert *(Pres)*

Viking Pools LLC (2)
175 Viking Dr, Jane Lew, WV 26378
Tel.: (304) 884-6700
Web Site: http://www.vikingpools.net
Sales Range: $25-49.9 Million
Swimming Pools Mfr
N.A.I.C.S.: 339920
Robert Marra *(Controller)*

Legacy.Com, Inc. (1)
230 W Monroe Ste 400, Chicago, IL 60606
Tel.: (847) 570-3200
Web Site: http://www.legacy.com
Online Obituaries
N.A.I.C.S.: 513199
Christopher Bartol *(Founder & CEO)*

Loparex BV (1)
Laan van Westenenk 45, PO Box 447, 7300 AK, Apeldoorn, Netherlands
Tel.: (31) 555276999
Web Site: http://www.loparex.com
Paper & Film Substrate Release Liners Mfr
N.A.I.C.S.: 326112
Gerard Bijsterbosch *(Mgr-Supply Chain)*

PAMPLONA CAPITAL MANAGEMENT LLP

Pamplona Capital Management LLP—(Continued)

PAREXEL International Corporation (1)
275 Grove St Ste 101C, Newton, MA 02466
Tel.: (617) 454-9300
Web Site: http://www.parexel.com
Biopharmaceutical Information, Communications, Clinical Development, Technology & Consulting Services
N.A.I.C.S.: 541714
Jamie Macdonald *(CEO)*

Subsidiary (Non-US):

ClinIntel Limited (2)
Bizspace Courtwick Lane, Littlehampton, BN17 7TL, W Sussex, United Kingdom
Tel.: (44) 1903 288100
Software Publishing Services
N.A.I.C.S.: 513210

Subsidiary (Domestic):

ExecuPharm, Inc. (2)
610 Freedom Business Ctr Dr Ste 200, King of Prussia, PA 19406
Tel.: (610) 272-8771
Web Site: http://www.execupharm.com
Pharmaceutical Industry Research Support Services
N.A.I.C.S.: 541990
Maria Larson *(Founder & Pres)*

Subsidiary (Non-US):

Farmovs PAREXEL (Proprietary) Limited (2)
101 Olympus Drive Wild Olive Estate, Bloemfontein, 9301, South Africa
Tel.: (27) 51726 1111
Web Site: http://www.parexel.com
Clinical Development, Information Technology & Consulting Services
N.A.I.C.S.: 541715

HERON Evidence Development AB (2)
Sveavagen 63 5th Floor, PO Box 3695, Stockholm, 103 59, Sweden
Tel.: (46) 853526700
Advertising & Market Research Services
N.A.I.C.S.: 541890

HERON Health Pvt. Ltd (2)
3rd Floor Tower E Phase - I, Chandigarh, 160101, India
Tel.: (91) 1724971100
Health Care Srvices
N.A.I.C.S.: 621111

Health Advances GmbH (2)
Zahlerweg 6, CH-6300, Zug, Switzerland
Tel.: (41) 41 766 8100
Web Site: http://www.parexel.com
Health Care Srvices
N.A.I.C.S.: 621498

Subsidiary (Domestic):

Health Advances LLC (2)
275 Grove St Ste 1E-300, Newton, MA 02466
Tel.: (781) 647-3435
Web Site: https://www.healthadvances.com
Strategic Consulting Services
N.A.I.C.S.: 541611
Kristen M. Turner *(COO & Mng Dir)*

Subsidiary (Non-US):

PAREXEL Belgium SPRL (2)
Parc des Collines Avenue Pasteur 2, B-1300, Wavre, Belgium
Tel.: (32) 10817100
Web Site: http://www.parexel.com
Clinical Development, Information Technology & Marketing & Consulting Services
N.A.I.C.S.: 541715

PAREXEL Denmark A/S (2)
Christianshus Christianshusvej 189, Horsholm, 2970, Denmark
Tel.: (45) 43205151
Web Site: http://www.parexel.com
Biopharmaceutical Information & Clinical Development Services
N.A.I.C.S.: 541715

PAREXEL Finland OY (2)
PO Box 5760, 0002, Helsinki, Finland
Web Site: http://www.parexel.com
Clinical Development, Information Technology & Consulting Services
N.A.I.C.S.: 541715

PAREXEL Hungary Limited (2)
Hermina ut 17, Budapest, H-1146, Hungary
Tel.: (36) 14617600
Web Site: http://www.parexel.com
Pharmaceutical, Biotechnology, Medical & Diagnostic Research Services
N.A.I.C.S.: 541714

PAREXEL International (2)
Av Brig Faria Lima 1309 8o andar, 01452-002, Sao Paulo, SP, Brazil
Tel.: (55) 11 2141 2666
Web Site: http://www.parexel.com
Clinical Development, Information Technology & Consulting Services
N.A.I.C.S.: 541715

PAREXEL International (Hong Kong) Company Limited (2)
Unit 2715-18 27/F The Mteropolis Tower No 10 Metropolis Drive, Hunghom, Kowloon, China (Hong Kong)
Tel.: (852) 24023263
Web Site: http://www.parexel.com
Biopharmaceutical Information & Clinical Development Services
N.A.I.C.S.: 541715

PAREXEL International (IRL) Limited (2)
One Kilmainham Square Inchicore Road, Dublin, Ireland
Tel.: (353) 14739500
Web Site: http://www.parexel.com
Pharmaceutical, Biotechnology, Medical & Diagnostic Research Services
N.A.I.C.S.: 541714

PAREXEL International (India) Private Limited (2)
Building No 20 11th Floor Raheja Mindspace IT Park, Madhapur, Hyderabad, 500 081, Andhra Pradesh, India
Tel.: (91) 4044379999
Web Site: http://www.parexel.com
Biopharmaceutical Information & Clinical Development Services
N.A.I.C.S.: 541715

PAREXEL International (Malaysia) SDN BHD (2)
Unit 1104 Level 11 Uptown 2 No 2 Jalan SS21/37 Damansara Uptown, Darul Ehsan, Petaling Jaya, 47400, Selangor, Malaysia
Tel.: (60) 377246200
Web Site: http://www.parexel.com
Biopharmaceutical Information & Clinical Development Services
N.A.I.C.S.: 541715

PAREXEL International (Singapore) Pte. Ltd. (2)
51 Bras Basah Road No 08-02 5One Central, Singapore, 189554, Singapore
Tel.: (65) 62209326
Web Site: http://www.parexel.com
Biopharmaceutical Information & Clinical Development Services
N.A.I.C.S.: 541715

PAREXEL International (Thailand) Co., Ltd. (2)
540 Mercury Tower 10F Unit 1001 Ploenchit Road, Lumpini Pathumwan, Bangkok, 10120, Thailand
Tel.: (66) 2 639 3200
Web Site: http://www.parexel.com
Biopharmaceutical Information & Clinical Development Services
N.A.I.C.S.: 541715

PAREXEL International (UK) Limited (2)
The Quays 101-105 Oxford Road, Uxbridge, UB8 1LZ, Mddx, United Kingdom
Tel.: (44) 1895238000
Web Site: http://www.parexel.com
Clinical Trials, Logistics & Research Organization & Global Biopharmaceutical Services Company
N.A.I.C.S.: 541714

PAREXEL International Clinical Research (Israel) Ltd. (2)
9 Arye Shenkar Street Building 3 Herzliya, PO Box 12108, Herzliya Pituach, 4672509, Israel
Tel.: (972) 737003200
Web Site: http://www.parexel.com
Biopharmaceutical Information & Clinical Development Services
N.A.I.C.S.: 541715

PAREXEL International Co. Ltd. (2)
22F Far Glory International Center No 200 Sec 1 Keelung Road, Taipei, 11071, Taiwan
Tel.: (886) 227271100
Web Site: http://www.parexel.com
Biopharmaceutical Information & Clinical Development Services
N.A.I.C.S.: 541715

PAREXEL International Czech Republic S.R.O. (2)
Sokolovska 651/136a Futurama Business Park, Prague, 186 00, Czech Republic
Tel.: (420) 233065100
Web Site: http://www.parexel.com
Biopharmaceutical Information & Clinical Development Services
N.A.I.C.S.: 541715

PAREXEL International GmbH (2)
Am Bahnhof Westend 15, Berlin, 14059, Germany
Tel.: (49) 30306850
Web Site: http://www.parexel.com
Pharmaceutical, Biotechnology, Medical & Diagnostic Research Services
N.A.I.C.S.: 541714

PAREXEL International Holding Germany GmbH (2)
Am Bahnhof Westend 15, Berlin, 14059, Germany
Tel.: (49) 30306850
Web Site: http://www.parexel.com
Holding Company; Pharmaceutical, Biotechnology, Medical & Diagnostic Research Services
N.A.I.C.S.: 551112

PAREXEL International Holding UK Limited (2)
The Quays 101-105 Oxford Road, Uxbridge, UB8 1LZ, Mddx, United Kingdom
Tel.: (44) 1895238000
Web Site: http://www.parexel.com
Holding Company; Pharmaceutical, Biotechnology, Medical & Diagnostic Research Services
N.A.I.C.S.: 551112

PAREXEL International Inc. (2)
6th Floor Kayabacho First Building 1-17-21 Shinkawa, Chuo-Ku, Tokyo, 104-0033, Japan
Tel.: (81) 3 3537 5899
Web Site: http://japanhub.parexel.com
Pharmaceutical, Biotechnology, Medical & Diagnostic Research Services
N.A.I.C.S.: 541714
Shigehiro Miki *(Pres & CEO)*

PAREXEL International Limited (2)
Navigation House 1 South Quay Drive, Victoria Quays, Sheffield, S2 5SU, S Yorkshire, United Kingdom
Tel.: (44) 114 225 1000
Web Site: http://www.parexel.com
Pharmaceutical, Biotechnology, Medical & Diagnostic Research Services
N.A.I.C.S.: 541714

PAREXEL International Mexico S.A. DE C.V. (2)
Insurgentes Sur Ave 716 11th Floor Col Del Valle Norte, Alcaldia Benito Juarez, Mexico, 03103, Mexico
Tel.: (52) 5591385400
Web Site: http://www.parexel.com
Biopharmaceutical Information & Clinical Development Services
N.A.I.C.S.: 541715

PAREXEL International Pesquisas Clinicas Ltda. (2)
Av Brig Faria Lima 1309 8o andar, Sao Paulo, 01452-002, Brazil
Tel.: (55) 1121412666
Web Site: http://www.parexel.com
Biopharmaceutical Information & Clinical Development Services
N.A.I.C.S.: 541715

INTERNATIONAL PUBLIC

PAREXEL International Pty Ltd. (2)
15 Talavera Road Suite B Level 6, North Ryde, 2113, NSW, Australia
Tel.: (61) 2 8870 3100
Web Site: http://www.parexel.com
Clinical Development, Information Technology & Consulting Services
N.A.I.C.S.: 541715

PAREXEL International Romania SRL (2)
Str Grigore Alexandrescu No 89-97 sector 1, Metropolis Center, Bucharest, 10624, Romania
Tel.: (40) 312253000
Web Site: http://www.parexel.com
Biopharmaceutical Information & Clinical Development Services
N.A.I.C.S.: 541715

PAREXEL International S.L. (2)
Edificio Alfredo Mahou Plaza Manuel Gomez Moreno n2 13, Madrid, 28020, Spain
Tel.: (34) 913913800
Web Site: http://www.parexel.com
Pharmaceutical, Biotechnology, Medical & Diagnostic Research Services
N.A.I.C.S.: 541714

PAREXEL International SARL (2)
190 rue Championnet, Paris, 75018, France
Tel.: (33) 144903200
Web Site: http://www.parexel.com
Pharmaceutical, Biotechnology, Medical & Diagnostic Research Services
N.A.I.C.S.: 541714

Division (Domestic):

PAREXEL International SARL (3)
200 Rue Leonard de Vinci Zac Des Chatelliers Nord, 45400, Orleans, France
Tel.: (33) 238618686
Web Site: http://www.parexel.com
Clinical Development, Information Technology & Marketing Services
N.A.I.C.S.: 541715

Subsidiary (Non-US):

PAREXEL International SRL (2)
Via Filippo Turati 28, Milan, 20121, Italy
Tel.: (39) 026241111
Web Site: http://www.parexel.com
Pharmaceutical, Biotechnology, Medical & Diagnostic Research Services
N.A.I.C.S.: 541714

PAREXEL International d.o.o. (2)
Takovska 46A, Belgrade, 11000, Serbia
Tel.: (381) 11 20 74 800
Web Site: http://www.parexel.com
Biopharmaceutical Information & Clinical Development Services
N.A.I.C.S.: 541715

Unit (Domestic):

PAREXEL International, LLC (2)
1560 E Chevy Chase Dr Ste 140, Glendale, CA 91206
Tel.: (818) 254-1600
Web Site: http://www.parexel.com
Clinical Research Contractor
N.A.I.C.S.: 541715

PAREXEL International, LLC (2)
2520 Meridian Pkwy Research Triangle Park Ste 200, Durham, NC 27713
Tel.: (919) 544-3170
Web Site: http://www.parexel.com
Pharmaceutical Research Services
N.A.I.C.S.: 541715

PAREXEL International, LLC (2)
8 Federal St, Billerica, MA 01821
Tel.: (978) 313-3900
Web Site: http://www.parexel.com
Contract Research Services
N.A.I.C.S.: 541715

Subsidiary (Non-US):

PAREXEL International, S.A. (2)
Gral Justo Jose de Urquiza 405 Vicente Lopez, Buenos Aires, B1638DBA, Argentina
Tel.: (54) 11 4718 8500
Web Site: http://www.parexel.com
Clinical Development, Information Technology & Consulting Services

AND PRIVATE COMPANIES

N.A.I.C.S.: 541715

PAREXEL Korea Co., Ltd. (2)
9F Glass Tower 534 Teheran-Ro, Gangnam-Gu, Seoul, 06181, Korea (South)
Tel.: (82) 234538838
Web Site: http://www.parexel.com
Biopharmaceutical Information & Clinical Development Services
N.A.I.C.S.: 541715

PAREXEL MMS Europe Limited (2)
Wicker House High St, Worthing, BN11 1DJ, W Sussex, United Kingdom
Tel.: (44) 01903 288000
Pharmaceutical, Biotechnology, Medical & Diagnostic Research Services
N.A.I.C.S.: 541714

PAREXEL Nederland B.V. (2)
Herman Heijermansweg 20, 1077 WL, Amsterdam, Netherlands
Tel.: (31) 208800700
Web Site: http://www.parexel.com
Pharmaceutical, Biotechnology, Medical & Diagnostic Research Services
N.A.I.C.S.: 541714

Division (Non-US):

PAREXEL International (3)
Christianshus, Christianshusvej 189, Horsholm, 2970, Denmark
Tel.: (45) 43205151
Web Site: http://www.parexel.com
Clinical Development, Information Technology & Consulting Services
N.A.I.C.S.: 541715

Subsidiary (Non-US):

PAREXEL Polska SP z.o.o. (2)
Business Garden ul Zwirki i Wigury 18A, Warsaw, 2-092, Poland
Tel.: (48) 224521100
Web Site: http://www.parexel.com
Pharmaceutical, Biotechnology, Medical & Diagnostic Research Services
N.A.I.C.S.: 541714

PAREXEL Russia A/S (2)
Osenny Bulver 23, 121609, Moscow, Russia
Tel.: (7) 495 781 39 09
Web Site: http://www.parexel.com
Commercial & Biological Research Services
N.A.I.C.S.: 541714

PAREXEL Ukraine LLC (2)
9 Stepana Bandery Avenue, Kiev, 04073, Ukraine
Tel.: (380) 444907454
Web Site: http://www.parexel.com
Clinical Trials, Logistics & Research Organization & Global Biopharmaceutical Services Company
N.A.I.C.S.: 541713

PT. PAREXEL International Indonesia (2)
Suite M27A Cyber 2 Tower 18th Floor Jl HR Rasuna Said Blok X-5, Jakarta, 12950, Indonesia
Tel.: (62) 21 5799 8740
Web Site: http://www.parexel.com
Biopharmaceutical Information & Clinical Development Services
N.A.I.C.S.: 541715

Perceptive Informatics UK Limited (2)
The Quays 101-105 Oxford Road, Uxbridge, UB8 1LZ, Mddx, United Kingdom
Tel.: (44) 1895 238000
Web Site: http://www.parexel.com
Commercial & Biological Research Services
N.A.I.C.S.: 541714

Subsidiary (US):

Perceptive Informatics, LLC (3)
8 Federal St, Billerica, MA 01821
Tel.: (978) 313-3900
Web Site: http://www.parexel.com
Biopharmaceutical Research Services
N.A.I.C.S.: 541715

Unit (Domestic):

Perceptive Informatics, Inc. (4)

9920 Pacific Heights Blvd Ste 500, San Diego, CA 92121
Tel.: (781) 487-9900
Clinical Development, Information Technology & Consulting Services
N.A.I.C.S.: 524114

Veritext Legal Solutions (1)
290 W Mount Pleasant Ave Ste 3200, Livingston, NJ 07039
Tel.: (800) 227-8440
Web Site: http://www.veritext.com
Emp.: 500
Secretarial & Court Reporting Services
N.A.I.C.S.: 561492
Nancy Josephs (CEO)

Branch (Domestic):

Veritext Legal Solutions - Sacramento (2)
1 Capitol Mall Ste 240, Sacramento, CA 95814
Tel.: (916) 379-5553
Web Site: http://www.veritext.com
Secretarial & Court Reporting Services
N.A.I.C.S.: 561492
Nancy Josephs (CEO)

nThrive, Inc. (1)
200 N Point Ctr E Ste 600, Alpharetta, GA 30022
Tel.: (678) 323-2500
Web Site: http://www.nthrive.com
Healthcare Management & Consulting Services
N.A.I.C.S.: 541611
Audra Murphy (Dir-Corp Comm)

PAMPR'OEUF DISTRIBUTION
Les Brelieres, 79800, Pamproux, France
Tel.: (33) 549763065
Web Site: http://www.pamproeuf.com
Sales Range: $25-49.9 Million
Emp.: 34
Dairy Products Distr
N.A.I.C.S.: 424430
Stephane Nerault (Pres)

PAMUKOVA YENILENEBILR ELEKTRIK RETIM A.S.
Maslak Mah Saat Sk Spine Tower Sitesi No 5/93, Sariyer, Istanbul, Turkiye
Tel.: (90) 2122907470
Web Site: http://www.pamel.com.tr
Year Founded: 2007
PAMEL—(IST)
Rev.: $1,840,304
Assets: $30,251,882
Liabilities: $4,721,329
Net Worth: $25,530,553
Earnings: $6,329,510
Fiscal Year-end: 12/31/23
Electric Power Distribution Services
N.A.I.C.S.: 221118

PAN AFRICAN RESOURCES PLC
107 Cheapside 2nd Floor, London, EC2V 6DN, United Kingdom
Tel.: (44) 2038690706 UK
Web Site: https://www.panafricanresource.com
PAN—(JSE)
Rev.: $321,610,000
Assets: $500,940,000
Liabilities: $206,340,000
Net Worth: $294,600,000
Earnings: $60,740,000
Emp.: 2,198
Fiscal Year-end: 06/30/23
Gold Mining Exploration
N.A.I.C.S.: 212220
Keith Cousens Spencer (Chm)

Subsidiaries:

EOH Abantu (Pty) Limited (1)
Block D Gilloolys View Ofc Park 1 Osborne Ln, Johannesburg, 2007, Gauteng, South Africa
Tel.: (27) 116078100
Sales Range: $10-24.9 Million
Emp.: 80
Recruitment Services
N.A.I.C.S.: 561311
Gavin Kilfoil (Gen Mgr)

PAN AMERICAN ENERGY CORP.
610-505 3 Street SW, Calgary, T2P 3E6, AB, Canada
Tel.: (587) 885-5970
Web Site: https://panam-energy.com
Year Founded: 2007
PAANF—(OTCQB)
Assets: $49,730
Liabilities: $640,326
Net Worth: ($590,596)
Earnings: ($308,498)
Fiscal Year-end: 04/30/21
Gold Exploration Services
N.A.I.C.S.: 212220
Eli Dusenbury (CFO)

PAN AMERICAN SILVER CORP.
Vancouver Centre II 2100733 Seymour Street, Vancouver, V6B 0S6, BC, Canada
Tel.: (604) 684-1175 BC
Web Site: https://www.panamericansilver.com
Year Founded: 1994
PAAS—(NASDAQ)
Rev.: $1,494,718,000
Assets: $3,248,498,000
Liabilities: $1,046,880,000
Net Worth: $2,201,618,000
Earnings: ($340,063,000)
Emp.: 6,200
Fiscal Year-end: 12/31/22
Mining Services
N.A.I.C.S.: 212220
Michael Steinmann (Pres & CEO)

Subsidiaries:

Minera Argenta S.A. (1)
Paraguay 1132 5 Piso, Buenos Aires, Argentina
Tel.: (54) 1148163220
Sales Range: $50-74.9 Million
Emp.: 40
Metal Mining Services
N.A.I.C.S.: 213114

Minera Calipuy S.A.C. (1)
Calle Barcelona No 275, San Isidro, Lima, Peru
Tel.: (51) 14222594
Sales Range: $50-74.9 Million
Emp.: 10
Silver Mining Services
N.A.I.C.S.: 212220
Paco A. Solano (Mgr)

Minera Corner Bay S.A. de C.V. (1)
Av Ferrocarril No 99 Piso 1 Local 1 Bellavista, Durango, 34047, Mexico
Tel.: (52) 6181280709
Web Site: http://www.panamericansilver.com
Silver Mining Services
N.A.I.C.S.: 212220

Minera Triton Argentina S.A. (1)
Roca Y Luis Sanchez, Gobernador Gregores, Argentina
Tel.: (54) 2962491186
Metal Mining Services
N.A.I.C.S.: 213114

Pan American Silver Bolivia S.A. (1)
Ave Fuerza Naval No 500 Esq Calle 20 de Calacoto, Casilla No 13745, La Paz, Bolivia (100%)
Tel.: (591) 22796990
Web Site: https://www.panamericansilver.com
Sales Range: $50-74.9 Million
Emp.: 15
Silver Mining
N.A.I.C.S.: 212220

Pan American Silver Peru S.A.C. (1)
Ave La Floresta 497 Of 101 Charcarilla del Estanque, San Borja, Lima, Peru
Tel.: (51) 16189700
Silver Mine Exploration
N.A.I.C.S.: 212220

Subsidiary (Domestic):

Compania Minera Argentum S.A. (2)
Av La Floresta 497 Office 301, San Borja, Lima, Peru
Tel.: (51) 16189700
Oil & Gas Extraction Services
N.A.I.C.S.: 211120

Plata Panamericana S.A. de C.V. (1)
Ave Universidad No 234 Floor 6 Col Lomas del Guadiana, 34110, Durango, Mexico (100%)
Tel.: (52) 6181280709
Sales Range: $50-74.9 Million
Emp.: 65
N.A.I.C.S.: 212220

Tahoe Resources Inc. (1)
5310 Kietzke Ln Ste 200, Reno, NV 89511
Tel.: (775) 448-5800
Web Site: http://www.tahoeresourcesinc.com
Sales Range: $700-749.9 Million
Metal Mining Services
N.A.I.C.S.: 212290

Yamana Gold Inc. (1)
Royal Bank Plaza North Tower 200 Bay Street Suite 2200, Toronto, M5J 2J3, ON, Canada
Tel.: (416) 815-0220
Web Site: http://www.yamana.com
Rev.: $1,815,400,000
Assets: $8,382,700,000
Liabilities: $3,179,500,000
Net Worth: $5,203,200,000
Earnings: $88,800,000
Emp.: 5,858
Fiscal Year-end: 12/31/2021
Holding Company; Gold & Other Precious Metal Ore Exploration, Development & Mining Services
N.A.I.C.S.: 551112
Sofia Tsakos (Gen Counsel, Sec & Sr VP)

Subsidiary (US):

Meridian Gold Inc. (2)
4635 Longley Ln Ste 110, Reno, NV 89502-5976
Tel.: (775) 850-3777
Emp.: 543
Gold Exploration & Mining
N.A.I.C.S.: 212220

Subsidiary (Non-US):

Minera Agua Rica LLC (2)
Esmeralda 819 C 2, Buenos Aires, 1007, Argentina
Tel.: (54) 1143147511
Gold & Copper Mining Services
N.A.I.C.S.: 212220

Yamana Desenvolvimento Mineral S.A. (2)
Rua Doutor Geraldo de Campos Moreira 240, Sao Paulo, 04571-020, Brazil
Tel.: (55) 1121638300
Web Site: http://www.yamana.com
Gold Mining Services
N.A.I.C.S.: 212220

Subsidiary (Domestic):

Serra da Borda Mineracao e Metalurgia S.A. (3)
Rua Funchal 411 5 Andar Conj 92, Sao Paulo, 04531-060, Brazil
Tel.: (55) 11 2163 8300
Gold Mining Services
N.A.I.C.S.: 212220

PAN ARAB RESEARCH CENTER (PARC)
Oud Matha, PO Box 14680, Dubai, United Arab Emirates
Tel.: (971) 43376696
Web Site: http://www.arabiandemographics.com

Pan Arab Research Center (PARC)—(Continued)
Sales Range: $10-24.9 Million
Emp.: 100
Research Services
N.A.I.C.S.: 541910
Sami Raffoul (Gen Mgr)

Subsidiaries:
Pan Arab Research Center (PARC) W.L.L. (1)
Al Rashed Complex 2nd Floor, Fahad Al Salam Street PO Box 24744, Safat, Kuwait, 13108, Kuwait
Tel.: (965) 2450940
Web Site: http://www.arabresearch.com
Research Services
N.A.I.C.S.: 541910

PAN ASIA BANKING CORPORATION PLC
No 450 Galle Road, 3, Colombo, Sri Lanka
Tel.: (94) 114667222
Web Site: https://www.pabcbank.com
Year Founded: 1995
PABC.N0000—(COL)
Rev.: $85,926,381
Assets: $692,550,554
Liabilities: $623,922,519
Net Worth: $68,628,035
Earnings: $6,664,026
Emp.: 1,403
Fiscal Year-end: 12/31/22
Commercial Banking Services
N.A.I.C.S.: 522110
Jeremy De Zilva (Deputy Gen Mgr-Internal Audit)

PAN ASIA CORPORATION LTD.
Level 5 56 Pitt Street, Sydney, 2000, NWS, Australia
Tel.: (61) 2 8823 3170 AU
Web Site: http://www.panasiacorp.com.au
Coal Development & Exploration Services
N.A.I.C.S.: 324199
Brett Crowley (Sec)

PAN ASIA DATA HOLDINGS INC.
Room B 29/F The Suns Group Centre 189-200 Gloucester Road, Wanchai, Hong Kong, China (Hong Kong)
Tel.: (852) 27870800 Ky
1561—(HKG)
Rev.: $105,548,580
Assets: $213,059,640
Liabilities: $147,460,763
Net Worth: $65,598,878
Earnings: ($13,098,458)
Emp.: 864
Fiscal Year-end: 12/31/22
Chemical Product Mfr & Distr
N.A.I.C.S.: 325998
Gu Zhongli (Chm)

PAN ASIA FOOTWEAR PUBLIC COMPANY LIMITED
No 177/20 Village No 5, Nongkham Subdistrict Sriracha District, Chon Buri, Thailand
Tel.: (66) 38480020 TH
Web Site: https://www.paf-group.com
Year Founded: 1979
PAF—(THA)
Rev.: $84,825,146
Assets: $31,736,254
Liabilities: $13,184,108
Net Worth: $18,552,146
Earnings: ($63,239)
Fiscal Year-end: 12/31/23
Footwear Mfr
N.A.I.C.S.: 316210
Boonkiet Chokwatana (Chm & CEO)

PAN ASIA METALS LIMITED
52 Thaniya Plaza Level 23 Silom Road Bangrak, Bangkok, 10500, Thailand
Tel.: (66) 22381639
Web Site: https://panasiametals.com
Year Founded: 2017
PAM—(ASX)
Rev.: $20,995
Assets: $12,481,340
Liabilities: $1,718,046
Net Worth: $10,763,294
Earnings: ($3,339,284)
Fiscal Year-end: 12/31/23
Metal Exploration Services
N.A.I.C.S.: 213114

PAN ASIAN MICROVENT TECHNOLOGY (JIANGSU) CORPORATION
No 8 Qiancao Road, Lijia Town Wujin, Changzhou, 213176, Jiangsu, China
Tel.: (86) 51985316198
Web Site: https://www.microvent.com.cn
Year Founded: 1995
688386—(SHG)
Rev.: $51,170,788
Assets: $125,198,583
Liabilities: $34,325,666
Net Worth: $90,872,917
Earnings: $4,400,824
Fiscal Year-end: 12/31/22
Polymer Material Mfr
N.A.I.C.S.: 325211
Yun Zhang (Chm & Gen Mgr)

PAN ELECTRONICS (INDIA) LIMITED
16B Peenya industrial Area Phase-1 Pipeline Road, Peenya, Bengaluru, 560058, Karnataka, India
Tel.: (91) 8041170074
Web Site: https://www.panelectronicsindia.com
Year Founded: 1986
517397—(BOM)
Rev.: $227,619
Assets: $1,489,804
Liabilities: $4,247,505
Net Worth: ($2,757,701)
Earnings: ($552,010)
Emp.: 10
Fiscal Year-end: 03/31/23
Metalized Plastic Film Mfr
N.A.I.C.S.: 326113
Gullu Gellaram Talreja (Chm & Mng Dir)

PAN ENTERTAINMENT CO., LTD.
10 Worldcupbuk-ro 58-gil, Mapo-gu, Seoul, Korea (South)
Tel.: (82) 23802100
Web Site: https://www.thepan.co.kr
Year Founded: 1998
068050—(KRS)
Rev.: $19,421,064
Assets: $89,283,118
Liabilities: $33,784,075
Net Worth: $55,499,043
Earnings: ($477,275)
Emp.: 24
Fiscal Year-end: 12/31/22
Video Production Services
N.A.I.C.S.: 512110
Yeong-Seok Park (CEO)

PAN GLOBAL RESOURCES INC.
Suite 1150 - 355 Burrard Street, Vancouver, V6C 2G8, BC, Canada
Tel.: (604) 689-9930
Web Site: https://www.panglobalresources.com
Year Founded: 2006
PGZFF—(OTCQX)
Rev.: $23,832
Assets: $14,803,196
Liabilities: $610,333
Net Worth: $14,192,863
Earnings: ($7,086,542)
Fiscal Year-end: 01/31/22
Mineral Exploration Services
N.A.I.C.S.: 213114
Patrick Evans (Chm)

Subsidiaries:
Minera Aguila S.L.U (1)
Valle de la Fuente 4-10, Valverde del Camino, Huelva, Spain
Tel.: (34) 959553276
Web Site: http://www.mineraguila.com
Mineral Resource Exploration Services
N.A.I.C.S.: 213114

PAN HONG HOLDINGS GROUP LIMITED
Room 1214 Tower B Hunghom Commercial Centre, 37-39 Ma Tau Wai Road, Kowloon, China (Hong Kong)
Tel.: (852) 23631300 HK
Web Site: https://www.pan-hong.com
Year Founded: 2005
P36—(SES)
Rev.: $205,433,927
Assets: $256,381,308
Liabilities: $104,482,785
Net Worth: $151,898,522
Earnings: $42,397,650
Fiscal Year-end: 03/31/21
Property Development Services
N.A.I.C.S.: 531311
Cui Ping Wang (Exec Dir)

PAN INDIA CORPORATION LTD.
711 7th Floor New Delhi House 27 Barakhamba Road, Cannaught Place, New Delhi, 110 001, India
Tel.: (91) 1143656567 In
Web Site: https://www.panindiacorp.com
Year Founded: 1984
511525—(BOM)
Rev.: $69,609
Assets: $1,921,928
Liabilities: $383,905
Net Worth: $1,538,023
Earnings: ($113,674)
Emp.: 3
Fiscal Year-end: 03/31/23
Securities Brokerage Services
N.A.I.C.S.: 523150
Vijay Pal Shukla (Mng Dir)

PAN JIT INTERNATIONAL INC.
No 24 Gangshan N Rd, Gangshan District, Kaohsiung, 820115, Taiwan
Tel.: (886) 76213121
Web Site: https://www.panjit.com.tw
Year Founded: 1986
PNJS—(LUX)
Rev.: $415,557,033
Assets: $937,987,963
Liabilities: $459,406,634
Net Worth: $478,581,329
Earnings: $33,125,706
Emp.: 3,064
Fiscal Year-end: 12/31/23
Diode Mfr
N.A.I.C.S.: 334413
Pai Chen Hsieh (Chief Acctg Officer)

Subsidiaries:
LIFETECH Energy INC. (1)
No 30 Zhongshan Road, Tucheng District, Taipei, 236, Taiwan
Tel.: (886) 222676733
Web Site: http://www.battery-lifetech.com
Batteries Mfr & Distr
N.A.I.C.S.: 335910

PYNMAX Technology CO., LTD (1)
No 17-2 Yonggong 1st Road, Yong'An district, Kaohsiung, 82841, Taiwan
Tel.: (886) 76243919
Web Site: https://www.pynmax.com.tw
Semiconductor Devices Mfr
N.A.I.C.S.: 334413

Pan Jit Europe GmbH (1)
Otto-Hahn-Str 2, 85609, Aschheim, Germany
Tel.: (49) 897294900
Electronic Product Distr
N.A.I.C.S.: 423690

PanJit Americas, Inc. (1)
2507 W Erie Dr Ste 101, Tempe, AZ 85282
Tel.: (480) 379-2800
Web Site: http://www.panjit.com
Electronic Components Distr
N.A.I.C.S.: 423690

PanJit Electronics (Shen Zhen) Co., LTD. (1)
8 / F Building 1 Jinjijia Science Park Jinke Road Pingli Boulevard, Nanwan Street Longgang District, Shenzhen, 523999, Guangdong, China
Tel.: (86) 75589709768
Web Site: http://www.panjit.com
Electronic Components Distr
N.A.I.C.S.: 423690

PanJit International (H.K.) Co., LTD. (1)
Unit F & G 4/F Golden Bear Industrial Centre No 66-82, Chai Wan Kok Street, Tsuen Wan, New Territories, China (Hong Kong)
Tel.: (852) 27518413
Web Site: http://www.panjit.com
Sales Range: $50-74.9 Million
Emp.: 10
Semiconductor Device Distr
N.A.I.C.S.: 423690

Panjit Electronics (Shandong) Co., Ltd. (1)
No 186 Zhong Run Rd Hightech Zone, Zibo, 255000, Shandong, China
Tel.: (86) 5333985299
Semiconductor Equipment Mfr & Distr
N.A.I.C.S.: 334413

Panjit Korea Co., Ltd. (1)
3601 Tower A HeungDeok IT Valley 13 HeungDeok 1-Ro, Youngtong-gu, Suwon, 16954, Gyunggi-Do, Korea (South)
Tel.: (82) 312026270
Sales Range: $50-74.9 Million
Emp.: 8
Electronic Components Distr
N.A.I.C.S.: 423690
Kimun Nam (Gen Mgr)

Panjit Semiconductor (Xuzhou) Co., Ltd. (1)
No 10 Fenghuang Avenue Economic Development Zone, Xuzhou, 221121, China
Tel.: (86) 51683352888
Electronic Component Mfr & Distr
N.A.I.C.S.: 334413

PAN LEE SDN BHD
5346 & 5347 Leeks Light Ind Estate KM4 Jalan Apas, 91000, Tawau, Sabah, Malaysia
Tel.: (60) 89913848
Web Site: http://pan-lee-sdnbhd.buyimporter.com
Sales Range: $10-24.9 Million
Emp.: 4
Animal Feed Mfr
N.A.I.C.S.: 311111
Yeo Teckhwa (Mng Dir)

PAN MALAYSIA HOLDINGS BERHAD
189 Jln Ampang Taman U Thant, 55000, Kuala Lumpur, Malaysia
Tel.: (60) 327839299 MY
Web Site: https://www.pmholdings.com.my
PMHLDG—(KLS)
Rev.: $1,124,444
Assets: $14,508,148
Liabilities: $5,758,519

AND PRIVATE COMPANIES

Net Worth: $8,749,630
Earnings: ($169,312)
Fiscal Year-end: 06/30/23
Travel Related Services
N.A.I.C.S.: 561510
Chik Siong Lee (Co-Sec)

PAN MALAYSIAN INDUSTRIES BERHAD
Unit 3 191 Jalan Ampang, 50450, Kuala Lumpur, Malaysia
Tel.: (60) 321487696
Web Site: http://www.pmindustries.com.my
Emp.: 300
Holding Company
N.A.I.C.S.: 551112
Chik Siong Lee (Co-Sec)

Subsidiaries:

Metrojaya Berhad (1)
1st Floor Mid Valley Megamall, Mid Valley City Lingkaran Syed Putra, 59200, Kuala Lumpur, Malaysia
Tel.: (60) 122862011
Web Site: https://www.metrojaya.com.my
Sales Range: $75-99.9 Million
Emp.: 1,415
Department Store Owner & Operator
N.A.I.C.S.: 455110

PM Securities Sdn Bhd (1)
First Floor Menara Pmi No 2 Jalan Changkat Ceylon, Kuala Lumpur, 50200, Selangor, Malaysia
Tel.: (60) 327313000
Web Site: http://www.pmsecurities.com.my
Sales Range: $100-124.9 Million
Emp.: 163
Stock Broking Services
N.A.I.C.S.: 523150
Ong Hung Ming (Chm)

PAN OCEAN CO., LTD.
7 Jong-ro 5-gil, Jongno-gu, 03157, Seoul, 03157, Korea (South)
Tel.: (82) 23165114
Web Site: https://www.panocean.com
Year Founded: 1966
028670—(KRS)
Rev.: $2,117,525,000
Assets: $3,847,104,000
Liabilities: $1,342,759,000
Net Worth: $2,504,345,000
Earnings: $126,754,000
Emp.: 2,155
Fiscal Year-end: 12/31/19
Marine Transportation Services
N.A.I.C.S.: 488510
Joong-Ho Ahn (Pres & CEO)

Subsidiaries:

POS SM Co., Ltd. (1)
Pan Ocean Busan Building 4th floor Jungangdaero 102, Junggu, Busan, 48938, Korea (South)
Tel.: (82) 514001700
Web Site: http://www.possm.com
Shipping Management Services
N.A.I.C.S.: 488510
Im-yeop Choi (CEO)

Pan Ocean (America), Inc. (1)
55 Challenger Rd Ste 500, Ridgefield Park, NJ 07660
Tel.: (201) 234-4477
Shipping Management Services
N.A.I.C.S.: 488510

Pan Ocean (China) Co., Ltd. (1)
Room 2004 Zhongrong Hengrui Intl Plaza West Bldg 560 Zhangyang Road, Pudong District, Shanghai, 200122, China
Tel.: (86) 2161641120
Shipping Management Services
N.A.I.C.S.: 488510

Pan Ocean Brasil Apoio Maritimo Ltda. (1)
Alameda Joaquim Eugenio De Lima 680 Room 172 17th Floor, Jardim Paulista, Sao Paulo, Brazil
Tel.: (55) 1135423981

Shipping Management Services
N.A.I.C.S.: 488510

Pan Ocean Japan Corporation (1)
4 Floor Nishi Shimbashi Home Bldg 1-12-10 Nishi Shimbashi, Minato-ku, Tokyo, Japan
Tel.: (81) 355101321
Shipping Management Services
N.A.I.C.S.: 488510

Pan Ocean Singapore Bulk Carrier Pte. Ltd. (1)
20 Anson Road 12-02 Twenty Anson, Singapore, 079912, Singapore
Tel.: (65) 64616210
Bulk Carrier Services
N.A.I.C.S.: 541614

PAN PACIFIC INTERNATIONAL HOLDINGS CORPORATION
2-19-10 Aobadai, Meguro-ku, Tokyo, 153-0042, Japan
Tel.: (81) 357257532
Web Site: https://ppih.co.jp
Year Founded: 1980
7532—(TKS)
Rev.: $13,031,378,940
Assets: $9,320,110,200
Liabilities: $5,917,751,540
Net Worth: $3,402,358,660
Earnings: $551,720,220
Emp.: 17,168
Fiscal Year-end: 06/30/24
Holding Company
N.A.I.C.S.: 551112
Tetsuji Maruyama (Exec Officer)

Subsidiaries:

Airline Hotel Co., Ltd. (1)
3-10-19 Tachibanadorinishi, Miyazaki, 880-0001, Japan
Tel.: (81) 98 529 7070
Web Site: https://www.airlinehotel.jp
Hotel Operator
N.A.I.C.S.: 721110

Asset Property Management Ltd. (1)
218 Malvern Road, Bournemouth, BH9 3BX, United Kingdom
Tel.: (44) 120 253 2898
Web Site: https://www.assetpropertymanagement.uk
Asset Management Services
N.A.I.C.S.: 523940

D-ONE Co., Ltd. (1)
2-19-10 Aobadai, Meguro-ku, Tokyo, 153-0042, Japan (100%)
Tel.: (81) 357257537
Web Site: https://www.d-one.co.jp
Real Estate Property Development Services
N.A.I.C.S.: 531210
Shirahama Mitsuaki (Pres)

DONKI Thailand Co., Ltd. (1)
No 107 Soi Sukhumvit 63 Ekkamai, Khlong Tan Nuea Sub-district Watthana District, Bangkok, 10110, Thailand
Tel.: (66) 2 301 0950
Grocery Distr
N.A.I.C.S.: 445110

Daishin Corporation (1)
Shimura Building 8F 5-6-7 Toyosaki, Osaka, Japan
Tel.: (81) 66 371 3730
Web Site: https://www.ssl.daishin-corp.co
Chemical Logistics Services
N.A.I.C.S.: 541614
Masa Oguchi (Pres)

Doit Co., Ltd. (1)
1-6-18 Hachioji, Chuo-ku, Saitama, 338-0006, Japan
Tel.: (81) 488539700
Web Site: https://www.doit.co.jp
Sales Range: $25-49.9 Million
Emp.: 50
Household Products Retailer
N.A.I.C.S.: 449210

Don Quijote Honolulu (1)
801 Kaheka St, Honolulu, HI 96814-3725 (100%)
Tel.: (808) 973-4800

Sales Range: $25-49.9 Million
Emp.: 17
Grocery & Pharmacy Stores
N.A.I.C.S.: 445110

Don Quijote USA Co., Ltd. (1)
801 Kaheka St, Honolulu, HI 96814-3725
Tel.: (808) 973-6600
Sales Range: $125-149.9 Million
Emp.: 350
Retailer of Food Products
N.A.I.C.S.: 445110
Jeff Cagaoan (Mgr-Admin Div)

Fujiya Shoji Co., Ltd. (1)
129 Katsurakaminohigashi-cho, Nishikyo-ku, Kyoto, 615-8003, Japan
Tel.: (81) 75 391 0055
Web Site: https://www.fujiyashoji.co.jp
Facility Management Services
N.A.I.C.S.: 561210
Baba Masuhiro (CEO)

Japan Asset Marketing Co., Ltd. (1)
4-14-1 Kita-Kasai, Edogawa-ku, Tokyo, 134-0081, Japan (88.98%)
Tel.: (81) 356678023
Web Site: http://www.jasset.co.jp
Rev.: $217,093,360
Assets: $1,588,604,160
Liabilities: $490,020,960
Net Worth: $1,098,583,200
Earnings: $52,533,360
Emp.: 145
Fiscal Year-end: 03/31/2021
Advertising Services
N.A.I.C.S.: 541810
Manabu Wachi (Pres)

Japan Commercial Establishment Co., Ltd. (1)
4-14-1 Kitakasai, Edogawa-ku, Tokyo, 134-0081, Japan (100%)
Tel.: (81) 356677421
Web Site: https://www.j-ce.co.jp
Emp.: 192
Facility Management Services
N.A.I.C.S.: 561210

Marukai Hawaii Co., Ltd. (1)
2310 Kamehameha Hwy, Honolulu, HI 96819-4531
Tel.: (808) 845-5051
Web Site: https://www.marukaihawaii.com
Grocery Distr
N.A.I.C.S.: 445110

My Support Co., Ltd. (1)
Amaikegotanda 1-cho, Inazawa, 492-8680, Aichi, Japan
Tel.: (81) 58 724 8090
Web Site: https://www.mysupport-inc.jp
Dispatching Services
N.A.I.C.S.: 484121

Nagasakiya Co., Ltd. (1)
2-19-10 Aobadai, Meguro-ku, Tokyo, 153-0042, Japan
Tel.: (81) 477002100
Web Site: http://www.nagasakiya.co.jp
Retail Stores Operation Services
N.A.I.C.S.: 449110

Pan Pacific International Trading Co., Ltd. (1)
2-19-10 Aobadai, Meguro-ku, Tokyo, 153-0042, Japan
Tel.: (81) 42 540 6735
Web Site: https://www.ppit.co.jp
Emp.: 17
Textile & Fabric Mfr
N.A.I.C.S.: 313310
Toshimasa Nakamura (Pres)

QSI Inc. (1)
3375 Koapaka St, Honolulu, HI 96819
Tel.: (808) 831-0811
Web Site: http://www.timessupermarket.com
Supermarket Operator
N.A.I.C.S.: 445110

Sun Reform Co., Ltd. (1)
1 Amaikegotandacho, Inazawa, 492-8680, Aichi, Japan
Tel.: (81) 58 724 8791
Web Site: https://www.sun-reform.jp
Renovation Services
N.A.I.C.S.: 236118

Sun Sougou Maintenance Co., Ltd. (1)

PAN-INTERNATIONAL INDUSTRIAL CORPORATION

Amaikegotanda-cho 1 A Building 2nd Floor, Inazawa, 492-8680, Aichi, Japan
Tel.: (81) 58 724 8285
Web Site: https://www.sunsogo.co.jp
Facility Management Services
N.A.I.C.S.: 561210

UNY Co., Ltd. (1)
1 Kamiichida-cho, Tianchi, Kumamoto, 492-8680, Aichi, Japan (40%)
Tel.: (81) 587 24 8111
Web Site: http://www.uny.co.jp
Emp.: 28,176
Departmental Store Operator
N.A.I.C.S.: 455110
Norio Sako (Pres & CEO)

Subsidiary (Domestic):

UCS Co., Ltd. (2)
1 Amaike Gotanda-cho, Inazawa, 492-8686, Aichi, Japan
Tel.: (81) 587305000
Web Site: https://www.ucscard.co.jp
Financial Services
N.A.I.C.S.: 522320
Hideki Goto (Pres)

PAN-INTERNATIONAL INDUSTRIAL CORPORATION
No 97 An-shin Rd, Hsin Tien, Taipei, Taiwan
Tel.: (886) 222113066
Web Site: https://www.panintl.com
2328—(TAI)
Rev.: $838,296,119
Assets: $797,841,920
Liabilities: $295,922,027
Net Worth: $501,919,893
Earnings: $48,720,787
Emp.: 8,505
Fiscal Year-end: 12/31/23
Headsets Mfr
N.A.I.C.S.: 331420

Subsidiaries:

Fubai Industry (Shenzhen) Co., Ltd. (1)
4F Building J No 2 Caowei Industrial District Huangtian, Bao An, Shenzhen, China
Tel.: (86) 755 2750 9966
Cable Assemblies Mfr
N.A.I.C.S.: 334419

HongHuaSheng Precision Electronics (YanTai) Co., Ltd. (1)
No 18 Changsha Road, Yantai Economic and Technological Development Area, Shandong, China
Tel.: (86) 5352168888
Electronic Connector Mfr
N.A.I.C.S.: 334417

Pan-International (USA), Inc. (1)
48008 Fremont Blvd, Fremont, CA 94538
Tel.: (510) 623-3898
Web Site: http://www.panintl.com
Consumer Electronics Distr
N.A.I.C.S.: 423620

Pan-International Electronics (Malaysia) Sdn.Bhd (1)
Plot 4 Seberang Jaya Industrial Estate, Prai, 13700, Seberang Jaya, Penang, Malaysia
Tel.: (60) 43990401
Web Site: http://www.pan-intl.com
Emp.: 1,000
Computer Peripherals Mfr
N.A.I.C.S.: 334112

Pan-International Electronics (Thailand) Co., Ltd. (1)
12/1 Moo 9 Suwansorn Road Tambom Dong-Khi-Lek, Amphur Muang, 25000, Prachin Buri, Thailand
Tel.: (66) 37403261
Web Site: http://www.panintl.com
Printed Circuit Assemblies Mfr
N.A.I.C.S.: 334418

Pan-International Electronics (U.S.A), Inc. (1)
48008 Fremont Blvd, Fremont, CA 94538-6500
Tel.: (510) 623-3898

PAN-INTERNATIONAL INDUSTRIAL CORPORATION

Pan-International Industrial Corporation—(Continued)
Electronic Components Distr
N.A.I.C.S.: 423690

Pan-International Industrial Corporation - PCB Division (1)
No 2 Donghua Road 10 Yousong Industrial District, Longhua Town Baoan, Shenzhen, 518109, Guangdong, China
Tel.: (86) 75527509966
Printed Circuit Board Mfr
N.A.I.C.S.: 334412

Pan-International Industry Co., Ltd. (1)
12/1 Moo 9 Suwannasom Road, Amphur Muang, Tambol Dong-Kee-Lek, 25000, Prachinburi, Thailand
Tel.: (66) 37 403261
Electronic Components Mfr
N.A.I.C.S.: 334419

Pan-International Precision Electronic Co., Ltd. (1)
Xinlian Hi-tech Industrial Area Humen, Dongguan, Guandong, China
Tel.: (86) 76985509710
Electronic Connector Mfr
N.A.I.C.S.: 334417

Pan-International Wire & Cable (Malaysia) Sdn.Bhd (1)
Plot 6 Jalan Jelawat Satu Kawasan Perusahaan, Seberang Jaya, 13700, Seberang Perai Tengah, Penang, Malaysia
Tel.: (60) 43993516
Web Site: https://www.piw.com.my
Sales Range: $25-49.9 Million
Wire & Cable Mfr
N.A.I.C.S.: 335929

Tekcon Electronics Corporation (1)
2F No 4 Ln 95 Anxing Rd, Xindian Dist, New Taipei City, 23159, Taiwan
Tel.: (886) 255785935
Web Site: https://www.tekcon.com.tw
Electronic Charger & Cable Mfr
N.A.I.C.S.: 335999

Wuhu CJ Electrical System Co., Ltd. (1)
No 36 Fengminghu Road Wuhu Area, Pilot Free Trade Zone, Suzhou, Anhui, China
Tel.: (86) 553 531 7070
Electronic Connector Mfr
N.A.I.C.S.: 334417

PAN-PACIFIC CO., LTD.
12 Digital-ro 31-gil, Guro-gu, Seoul, 8380, Korea (South)
Tel.: (82) 234949000
Web Site: https://tp-inc.com
Year Founded: 1972
007980—(KRS)
Rev.: $831,893,587
Assets: $553,180,605
Liabilities: $398,731,681
Net Worth: $154,448,924
Earnings: $19,028,364
Emp.: 341
Fiscal Year-end: 12/31/22
Textile & Garment Products Mfr
N.A.I.C.S.: 314999
Suk-won Lim (CEO)

Subsidiaries:

NANJING PAN-PACIFIC ANIMAL BY-PRODUCTS CO., LTD (1)
No 58 Dongcun Road Economic & Technical Development Zone, Jiangning, Nanjing, Jiangsu, China
Tel.: (86) 25 5210 2945
Fiber Feather Apparel Mfr
N.A.I.C.S.: 315250

YANGON PAN-PACIFIC INTERNATIONAL CO., LTD. (1)
Plot No 29/1 Kamarkyi Road Thuwunna, Thingankyun Township, Yangon, Myanmar
Tel.: (95) 1 572 126
Garment Fabric Mfr
N.A.I.C.S.: 313210

PAN-UNITED CORPORATION LTD.
7 Temasek Boulevard 16-01 Suntec Tower One, Singapore, 038987, Singapore
Tel.: (65) 63057373
Web Site: https://www.panunited.com.sg
P52—(SES)
Rev.: $586,334,924
Assets: $343,771,870
Liabilities: $163,840,794
Net Worth: $179,931,076
Earnings: $27,022,646
Emp.: 756
Fiscal Year-end: 12/31/23
Logistics Management Services
N.A.I.C.S.: 541614
Siew Choon Tay (Co-Chm)

Subsidiaries:

AiR Digital Solutions Pte. Ltd. (1)
7 Temasek Boulevard 16-01 Suntec Tower One, Singapore, 038987, Singapore
Tel.: (65) 63057373
Web Site: https://www.airdigital.sg
Readymix Concrete Mfr
N.A.I.C.S.: 327320

Fico Pan-United Concrete Joint Stock Company (1)
South Building 60 Truong Son, Ward 2 Tan Binh District, Ho Chi Minh City, Vietnam
Tel.: (84) 835470303
Web Site: https://www.ficopanunited.com
Readymix Concrete Mfr
N.A.I.C.S.: 327320
Thuy Pham (Mgr-Key Projects & Infrastructure)

Fortis Star Sdn. Bhd. (1)
Lot 1305 1306 13th Floor Tower 2 Faber Towers, Jalan Desa Bahagia Taman Desa, 58100, Kuala Lumpur, Malaysia
Tel.: (60) 379728538
Readymix Concrete Mfr
N.A.I.C.S.: 327320
Kin Wah Yap (Mgr-Admin)

GoTruck Pte. Ltd. (1)
12 Kaki Bukit Crescent Kaki Bukit Techpark 1, Singapore, 416243, Singapore
Tel.: (65) 66452643
Web Site: https://www.gotruck.co
Readymix Concrete Mfr
N.A.I.C.S.: 327320

Meridian Maplestar Sdn. Bhd. (1)
PLO 184 Jalan Rumbia 7, Tanjung Langsat Industrial Complex, 81700, Pasir Gudang, Johor, Malaysia
Tel.: (60) 72512788
Readymix Concrete Mfr
N.A.I.C.S.: 327320
Jeanne Hau (Mgr-HR & Admin)

PT. Pan-United Concrete (1)
Wisma 46-Kota BNI Lantai 48 Suite 03 Jl Jend Sudirman Kav 1, Kecamatan Tanah Abang Kelurahan Karet Tengsin, Jakarta, 10220, Indonesia
Tel.: (62) 2122441141
Readymix Concrete Mfr
N.A.I.C.S.: 327320
Rafsanjani Cahyo (Mgr)

Pan-United Industries Pte Ltd (1)
12 Kaki Bukit Crescent Kaki Bukit Techpark 1, Singapore, 416243, Singapore
Tel.: (65) 6 645 2800
Web Site: http://www.panunited.com.sg
Granite Processing Services
N.A.I.C.S.: 212313

Subsidiary (Domestic):

Pan-United Concrete Pte Ltd (2)
12 Kaki Bukit Crescent Kaki Bukit Techpark 1, Singapore, 416243, Singapore
Tel.: (65) 65810777
Web Site: http://www.panunited.com.sg
Sales Range: $25-49.9 Million
Emp.: 100
Ready Mix Concrete Mfr & Distr
N.A.I.C.S.: 327320

United Cement Pte Ltd (2)
12 Kaki Bukit Crescent Kaki Bukit Techpark 1, Singapore, 416243, Singapore
Tel.: (65) 66452800
Web Site: http://www.panunited.com.sg
Sales Range: $25-49.9 Million
Emp.: 14
Cement Mfr & Whslr
N.A.I.C.S.: 333248

PanU Harmony Pte. Ltd. (1)
7 Temasek Boulevard 16-01 Suntec Tower One, Singapore, 038987, Singapore
Tel.: (65) 63057373
Readymix Concrete Mfr
N.A.I.C.S.: 327320

Raffles Concrete Pte Ltd (1)
12 Kaki Bukit Crescent Kaki Bukit Techpark 1, Singapore, 416243, Singapore
Tel.: (65) 66452800
Readymix Concrete Mfr
N.A.I.C.S.: 327320

United Bulk Shipping Pte Ltd (1)
7 Temasek Boulevard 16-01 Suntec Tower One, Singapore, 038987, Singapore
Tel.: (65) 63057373
Emp.: 40
Dry Bulk Cargo Shipping Services
N.A.I.C.S.: 488320
Jimmy Lee (Exec Dir)

PANACEA BIOTEC LIMITED
B-1 Extn/G-3 Mohan Co-operative Indl Estate Mathura Road, New Delhi, 110044, India
Tel.: (91) 1141679000
Web Site: https://www.panaceabiotec.com
Year Founded: 1984
PANACEABIO—(NSE)
Rev.: $86,647,743
Assets: $160,908,384
Liabilities: $192,534,479
Net Worth: ($31,626,094)
Earnings: ($20,155,317)
Emp.: 1,013
Fiscal Year-end: 03/31/21
Pharmaceutical Preparation & Medicine Mfr
N.A.I.C.S.: 325412
Soshil Kumar Jain (Chm)

PANACEA GLOBAL, INC.
330 Highway 7 East Suite 502, Richmond Hill, L4B 3P8, ON, Canada
Tel.: (905) 881-1049
Web Site: http://www.panaceaglobalinc.com
Emp.: 3
Cancer Testing Services
N.A.I.C.S.: 621511
Mahmood Moshiri (Pres, CEO, Interim CFO & Chief Medical Officer)

PANACEA INC
39 Beonnyeong-ro, Danwon-gu, Ansan, Gyeonggi-do, Korea (South)
Tel.: (82) 316282600
Web Site: https://www.panaceainc.co.kr
Year Founded: 1994
058530—(KRS)
Rev.: $10,991,422
Assets: $55,187,004
Liabilities: $4,561,800
Net Worth: $50,625,204
Earnings: ($702,918)
Emp.: 55
Fiscal Year-end: 12/31/22
Holding Company
N.A.I.C.S.: 551112
Han-Cheon Park (CEO)

PANACHE DIGILIFE LTD.
Bldg A3 102-108 & 201-208 Babosa Industrial Park, Mumbai-Nashik Highway NH3 Saravali Village Bhiwandi, Thane, Maharashtra, India
Tel.: (91) 9833995555
Web Site: https://www.panachedigilife.com

INTERNATIONAL PUBLIC

PANACHE—(NSE)
Rev.: $13,575,757
Assets: $11,463,150
Liabilities: $7,063,977
Net Worth: $4,399,173
Earnings: $222,025
Emp.: 39
Fiscal Year-end: 03/31/23
Hardware Product Mfr & Distr
N.A.I.C.S.: 332510
Amit Rambhia (Founder, Chm & Mng Dir)

PANACHE INNOVATIONS LIMITED
Office No 105 Primus Business Park Plot No A-195 Road No 16/A, Ambika Nagar No 2 Wagle Industrial Estate, Thane, 400604, Maharashtra, India
Tel.: (91) 8657641575
Web Site: https://panabyte.com
Year Founded: 1981
538742—(BOM)
Rev.: $1,090,031
Assets: $1,540,531
Liabilities: $1,186,655
Net Worth: $353,876
Earnings: ($53,630)
Emp.: 36
Fiscal Year-end: 03/31/23
Peripheral Equipment Distr
N.A.I.C.S.: 423690
Priyank Sangoi (Officer-Compliance & Sec)

PANAFIC INDUSTRIALS LIMITED
23 2nd Floor North West Avenue Club Road, West Punjabi Bagh, New Delhi, 110 026, India
Tel.: (91) 1125223461
Web Site: http://www.panaficindustrialsltd.com
Year Founded: 1985
538860—(BOM)
Rev.: $86,036
Assets: $1,200,176
Liabilities: $18,914
Net Worth: $1,181,262
Earnings: $12,795
Fiscal Year-end: 03/31/23
Financial Support Services
N.A.I.C.S.: 523999
Sarita Gupta (Mng Dir & CFO)

PANAGO
33149 Mill Lake Road, Abbotsford, V2S 2A4, BC, Canada
Tel.: (604) 859-6621
Web Site: http://www.panago.com
Year Founded: 1986
Sales Range: $700-749.9 Million
Emp.: 3,500
Pizza Restaurant
N.A.I.C.S.: 722513

PANAMA PETROCHEM LTD.
401 Aza House 24 Turner Road Next to Andhra Bank, Bandra W, Mumbai, 400050, India
Tel.: (91) 2242177777
Web Site: https://www.panamapetro.com
PAPTR—(LUX)
Rev.: $198,372,870
Assets: $135,492,644
Liabilities: $58,920,007
Net Worth: $76,572,637
Earnings: $18,475,712
Emp.: 167
Fiscal Year-end: 03/31/21
Petroleum Products Mfr & Distr
N.A.I.C.S.: 324199
Amirali E. Rayani (Chm)

Subsidiaries:

Panama Petrochem Ltd. - Plant 4 (1)
Plot No H-12 MIDC Taloja, Mumbai, 410208, India
Tel.: (91) 22 27411456
Petroleum Product Mfr
N.A.I.C.S.: 324110

PANAMA POWER HOLDINGS, INC.
Capital Plaza Piso 12 Paseo Roberto Motta Costa del Este, Panama, Panama
Tel.: (507) 3067800
Web Site: https://www.panamapower.net
Year Founded: 2007
PPHO—(PAN)
Sales Range: Less than $1 Million
Holding Company
N.A.I.C.S.: 551112
Patrick Kelly (Chm & CEO)

PANAMAX AG
Municher Strasse 10, 60329, Frankfurt am Main, Germany
Tel.: (49) 69247435470
Web Site: https://panamax.ag
ICP—(DEU)
Rev.: $275,969
Assets: $485,705
Liabilities: $750,635
Net Worth: ($264,930)
Earnings: $22,077
Fiscal Year-end: 12/31/23
Financial Investment Services
N.A.I.C.S.: 523940
John Liu (Dir-IR)

PANARIAGROUP INDUSTRIE CERAMICHE S.P.A.
via Cameazzo 21, Sassuolo, MO, Italy
Tel.: (39) 0536915211
Web Site: http://www.panariagroup.it
PAN—(ITA)
Sales Range: $200-249.9 Million
Emp.: 1,700
Ceramic Wall & Floor Tiles Mfr & Distr
N.A.I.C.S.: 327120
Giuliano Pini (Mng Dir)

Subsidiaries:

Florida Tile Inc. (1)
998 Governors ln ste 300, Lexington, KY 40513
Tel.: (863) 687-7171
Web Site: http://www.floridatile.com
Sales Range: $25-49.9 Million
Emp.: 50
Ceramic Wall & Floor Tile Mfr
N.A.I.C.S.: 327120
Michael Franceschelli (CEO)

Florida Tile Industries, Inc. (1)
998 Governors Ln Ste 300, Lexington, KY 40513-1184
Tel.: (863) 284-4156
Web Site: http://www.floridatile.com
Sales Range: $250-299.9 Million
Emp.: 800
Ceramic Wall & Floor Tile Distr & Mfr
N.A.I.C.S.: 327120

Gres Panaria Portugal S.A. (1)
Chousa Nova, Ilhavo, 3830-133, Aveiro, Portugal
Tel.: (351) 234329700
Web Site: http://www.margres.com
Sales Range: $50-74.9 Million
Emp.: 200
Ceramic Wall & Floor Tile Mfr
N.A.I.C.S.: 327120

Subsidiary (Domestic):

Margres S.A. (2)
Chousa Nova, Ilhavo, 3830-133, Aveiro, Portugal
Tel.: (351) 234329700
Web Site: http://www.margres.com
Ceramic Wall & Floor Tile Mfr
N.A.I.C.S.: 327120

Lea North America Inc. (1)
800 Clanton Rd Ste N, Charlotte, NC 28217
Tel.: (704) 332-4474
Web Site: http://www.ceramichelea.com
Sales Range: $25-49.9 Million
Emp.: 4
Ceramic Wall & Floor Tile Mfr
N.A.I.C.S.: 327120

Novagres S.A. (1)
Zona Industrial De Aveiro, 3801-101, Aveiro, Portugal
Tel.: (351) 234303030
Web Site: http://www.lovetiles.com
Sales Range: $125-149.9 Million
Emp.: 400
Ceramic Wall & Floor Tile Mfr
N.A.I.C.S.: 327120

Panariagroup India Pvt. Ltd. (1)
B-702 Shapath -IV Opp Karnavati Club SG Highway, Ahmedabad, 380015, Gujarat, India
Tel.: (91) 796 191 6501
Web Site: https://www.bellissimo.asia
Ceramics Mfr & Distr
N.A.I.C.S.: 327110

PANASIALUM HOLDINGS COMPANY LIMITED
Unit 6 28/F Nanyang Plaza 57 Hung To Road Kowloon, 979 King's Road, Hong Kong, China (Hong Kong)
Tel.: (852) 2972 2028
Web Site: http://www.palum.com
Year Founded: 1998
Sales Range: $300-349.9 Million
Emp.: 4,600
Aluminium Products Mfr
N.A.I.C.S.: 331524
Liyu Shao (Chm & CEO)

Subsidiaries:

PanAsia Enterprises Group Limited (1)
56 Depot St, Banyo, Brisbane, 4014, QLD, Australia
Tel.: (61) 7 3266 7400
Holding Company
N.A.I.C.S.: 551112

PANASONIC AUSTRALIA PTY. LTD.
1 Innovation Road, Macquarie Park, 2113, NSW, Australia
Tel.: (61) 294917400
Web Site: http://www.panasonic.com.au
Year Founded: 1989
Consumer Electronics Distr
N.A.I.C.S.: 423620
Paul Reid (Mng Dir)

PANASONIC HOLDINGS CORPORATION
1006 Kadoma, Kadoma, 571-8501, Osaka, Japan
Tel.: (81) 669081121 JP
Web Site: https://holdings.panasonic
Year Founded: 1918
PCRFF—(OTCIQ)
Rev.: $56,161,336,200
Assets: $62,207,998,950
Liabilities: $30,996,220,120
Net Worth: $31,211,778,830
Earnings: $2,934,800,340
Emp.: 228,420
Fiscal Year-end: 03/31/24
Electrical & Electronic Products; Video & Audio Equipment; Home Appliances; Communications & Industrial Equipment; Energy & Kitchen Related Products; Electric Components Mfr & Sales
N.A.I.C.S.: 334310

Takashi Toyama (Mng Exec Officer & Dir-Govt & External Rels)

Subsidiaries:

Componentes Universales de Matamoros, S.A. de C.V. (1)
De La Industria Lateral S/N, Matamoros, 87316, Mexico
Tel.: (52) 8688112100
Consumer Electronics Distr
N.A.I.C.S.: 423620

Douglas Lighting Controls, Inc. (1)
3605 Gilmore Way 280, Burnaby, V5G 4X5, BC, Canada
Tel.: (604) 873-2797
Web Site: https://www.douglaslightingcontrols.com
Lighting Control Equipment Mfr & Distr
N.A.I.C.S.: 335139
John Cavacuiti (Sr Dir-Engrg)

Global Electronics LLC (1)
Peace Avenue UB Platinum building 5th floor, Bayangol District, Ulaanbaatar, 16052, Mongolia
Tel.: (976) 7 011 9432
Web Site: https://www.ge.globalgroup.mn
Sales Range: $25-49.9 Million
Emp.: 30
Consumer Electronics Distr
N.A.I.C.S.: 423620

Global Telecom LLC (1)
Peace avenue UB Platinum building 5th floor, Bayangol District, Ulaanbaatar, 16052, Mongolia
Tel.: (976) 75115151
Web Site: http://www.ge.globalgroup.mn
Sales Range: $25-49.9 Million
Emp.: 36
Telecommunication Servicesb
N.A.I.C.S.: 517810

Kinki Matsushita Technical Service (1)
1 1 7 Honjyo Nishi, Osaka, 531 0073, Japan (100%)
Tel.: (81) 663596321
Sales Range: $100-124.9 Million
Emp.: 300
Mfr of Home Refrigerators
N.A.I.C.S.: 335220

MT Texture Display Indonesia (1)
E Jakarta Industrial Park EJIP Plot 3G Lemah Abang, Peti Pos EJIPC 26, Bekasi, 17550, Jawa Barat, Indonesia
Tel.: (62) 218970505
Web Site: http://panasonic.co.id
Sales Range: $400-449.9 Million
Emp.: 2,000
Mfr of Color Picture Tubes
N.A.I.C.S.: 334419

Matsushita Battery Industrial Co., Ltd. (1)
1-1 Matsushita-cho, Moriguchi, 570 8511, Osaka, Japan (100%)
Tel.: (81) 669911141
Web Site: http://www.panasonic.co.jp
Sales Range: $800-899.9 Million
Emp.: 3,400
Mfr of Batteries
N.A.I.C.S.: 335910

OpenSynergy GmbH (1)
Rotherstrasse 20, 10245, Berlin, Germany
Tel.: (49) 306 098 5400
Web Site: https://www.opensynergy.com
Emp.: 150
Automotive Software Development Services
N.A.I.C.S.: 541511
Regis Adjaham (CEO & Mng Dir)

PT. Jaya Indah Casting (1)
EJIP Industrial Park Plot 8 MM 2100, Lemah Abang, Bekasi, 17550, Indonesia (100%)
Tel.: (62) 218970340
Web Site: http://ap.sanyo.com
Sales Range: $25-49.9 Million
Emp.: 200
Water Pump & Compressor Parts Mfr
N.A.I.C.S.: 333415

PT. KDK Indonesia (1)
Cosa Building 4th Floor Jl Tomang Raya No 70, Jakarta, 11430, Indonesia

Tel.: (62) 21 563 8311
Web Site: https://kdk.co.id
Emp.: 22
Air Conditioning Equipment Distr
N.A.I.C.S.: 423730

PT. Panasonic Electric Works Gobel Sales Indonesia (1)
Summitmas I 8th Fl Jl Jend Sudirman Kav 61-62, Selatan, Jakarta, Indonesia
Tel.: (62) 21 2521616
Web Site: http://www.panasonic.co.id
Emp.: 100
Consumer Electronics Distr
N.A.I.C.S.: 423620
Widyastama Nugraha (Gen Mgr)

PT. Panasonic Gobel Indonesia (1)
JL Dewi Sartika No 14 Cawang II, 13630, Jakarta, Indonesia
Tel.: (62) 21 801 5710
Web Site: https://www.panasonic.com
Home Appliance Distr
N.A.I.C.S.: 423620

PT. Panasonic Shikoku Electronics Batam (1)
Lot 209-210 Jalan Beringin Batamindo Industrial Park, Muka Kuning, 29433, Batam, Indonesia
Tel.: (62) 770 611 496
Computer Storage Device Mfr
N.A.I.C.S.: 334112

Panasonic (CIS) OY (1)
Kekkoskenkatu 7B 3rd Floor, 00100, Helsinki, Finland
Tel.: (358) 9 68983274
Emp.: 16
Consumer Electronics Distr
N.A.I.C.S.: 423620

Panasonic (U.K.) Ltd (1)
Wyncliffe Rd, Pentwyn Indus Est, Cardiff, CF23 7XB, Wales, United Kingdom (100%)
Tel.: (44) 920540011
Web Site: http://www.panasonic.com
Sales Range: $100-124.9 Million
Emp.: 500
Mfr of Audio Equipment, Records & Discs
N.A.I.C.S.: 334310
Marc Overson (Mgr-Heating & Cooling-UK & Ireland)

Panasonic A.P. Sales (Thailand) Co., Ltd. (1)
18/6 Moo 7 Bangna-Trad Road Km 17, Bangchalong Bang Phli, Samut Prakan, 10540, Thailand
Tel.: (66) 2 729 9000
Web Site: http://www.panasonic.co.th
Consumer Electronics Distr
N.A.I.C.S.: 423620

Panasonic AVC Networks (Thailand) Co., Ltd. (1)
101 Moo 2 Teparak Road T Bangsaothong Ging, A Bangsaothong, Samut Prakan, 10540, Thailand
Tel.: (66) 2 338 1054
Web Site: http://www.panasonic.net
Sales Range: $550-599.9 Million
Emp.: 1,600
Consumer Electronics Distr
N.A.I.C.S.: 423620

Panasonic AVC Networks Slovakia s.r.o. (1)
Hornadska 80, PO Box 19, 05342, Krompachy, Slovakia
Tel.: (421) 534180111
Web Site: http://www.panasonic.net
Sales Range: $150-199.9 Million
Emp.: 800
Audio Visual Equipment Mfr
N.A.I.C.S.: 334310

Panasonic Appliances India Company Limited (1)
NH No 5 Sholavaram Village, Ponneri Taluk, Chennai, 600 067, India (90.64%)
Tel.: (91) 4426330133
Web Site: https://www.panasonicappliances.in
Rev.: $48,651,275
Assets: $20,203,160
Liabilities: $11,059,216
Net Worth: $9,143,944
Earnings: $1,410,618

PANASONIC HOLDINGS CORPORATION

Panasonic Holdings Corporation—(Continued)

Fiscal Year-end: 03/31/2022
Household Appliance Mfr & Whslr
N.A.I.C.S.: 335220
Jayaprakash Kalappan (CFO)

Panasonic Appliances Motor (Thailand) Co., Ltd. (1)
101 Moo 2 Teparak Road, 10540, Samut Prakan, Thailand
Tel.: (66) 2.708 0760
Airconditioning & Refrigeration Equipment Mfr
N.A.I.C.S.: 333415

Panasonic Appliances Refrigeration Devices Malaysia Sdn. Bhd. (1)
Lots 2 3 - 2 10 Jalan TTC 1 Cheng Industrial Site, 75250, Melaka, Malaysia
Tel.: (60) 6 334 4300
Web Site: https://www.panasonic.com
Emp.: 1,000
Consumer Electronics Distr
N.A.I.C.S.: 423620

Panasonic Appliances Vietnam Co., Ltd. (1)
Plot B-6 Thang Long Industrial Park, Dong Anh District, Hanoi, Vietnam
Tel.: (84) 243 951 5268
Web Site: http://www.papvn.net
Emp.: 1,000
Household Refrigerator Mfr
N.A.I.C.S.: 335220

Panasonic Asia Pacific Pte. Ltd. - Panasonic Singapore Division (1)
2 Jalan Kilang Road Panasonic Building, Singapore, 159346, Singapore
Tel.: (65) 6270 0110
Web Site: http://www.panasonic.com.sg
Consumer Electronics Distr
N.A.I.C.S.: 423620

Subsidiary (Domestic):

Panasonic AVC Networks Singapore Pte. Ltd. (2)
202 Bedok South Avenue 1, Singapore, 469332, Singapore
Tel.: (65) 6443 7744
Web Site: http://www.panasonic.net
Consumer Electronics Distr
N.A.I.C.S.: 423620

Division (Domestic):

Panasonic Asia Pacific Pte. Ltd. - Consumer Electronics Division (2)
2 Jalan Kilang Barat Panasonic Building, Singapore, 159346, Singapore
Tel.: (65) 6270 0110
Web Site: http://www.panasonic.com.sg
Consumer Electronics Distr
N.A.I.C.S.: 423620

Subsidiary (Domestic):

Panasonic Electronic Devices Singapore Pte. Ltd. (2)
3 Bedok South Road, Singapore, 6241 9866, Singapore
Tel.: (65) 6241 9866
Web Site: http://www.panasonic.com.sg
Consumer Electronics Distr
N.A.I.C.S.: 423620

Panasonic Factory Solutions Asia Pacific Pte. Ltd. (2)
285 Jalan Ahmad Ibrahim, Singapore, 639931, Singapore
Tel.: (65) 6 861 6655
Web Site: https://www.panasonic.com
Emp.: 300
Industrial Machinery Sales & Installation Services
N.A.I.C.S.: 423830

Panasonic Industrial Asia Pte. Ltd. (2)
300 Beach Road 16-01 The Concourse, Singapore, 199555, Singapore
Tel.: (65) 6299 9181
Web Site: http://www.industrial.panasonic.com
Consumer Electronics Distr
N.A.I.C.S.: 423620

Subsidiary (Non-US):

Panasonic Industrial Devices (Thailand) Co., Ltd. (3)
101 Moo 2 Teparak Road Tambol Bangsaothong, Amphur Bangsaothong, Samut Prakan, 10540, Thailand
Tel.: (66) 2 723 3100
Automotive Electrical Parts Mfr
N.A.I.C.S.: 336320

Subsidiary (Domestic):

Panasonic Industrial Devices Sales (Thailand) Co., Ltd. (4)
252/133 Muang Thai-Phatra Complex Building 31st Fl Rachadaphisek Rd, Huaykwang, Bangkok, 10320, Thailand
Tel.: (66) 2 693 3402
Industrial Device Distr
N.A.I.C.S.: 423830

Subsidiary (Non-US):

Panasonic Industrial Devices Materials (Guangzhou) Co., Ltd. (3)
Lianyun Rd The East Section of Guangzhou Economic & Technological, Development District, Guangzhou, Guangdong, China
Tel.: (86) 20 8226 4947
Semiconductor Devices Mfr
N.A.I.C.S.: 334413

Panasonic Industrial Devices Materials (Shanghai) Co., Ltd. (3)
148 Huancheng North St Comprehensive Industrial Development Zone, Shanghai, 201401, China
Tel.: (86) 21 6710 1288
Emp.: 200
Semiconductor Devices Mfr
N.A.I.C.S.: 334413
Sakamoto Takashi (Pres)

Panasonic Industrial Devices Materials Taiwan Co., Ltd. (3)
No 67 Kuang Fu Road Hsin Chu Industrial District, Hu Kou Hsiang, Hsin-chu, Taiwan
Tel.: (886) 3 5983201
Industrial Device Distr
N.A.I.C.S.: 423840

Subsidiary (Domestic):

Panasonic Shikoku Eectronics (S) Pte Ltd (3)
3 Biopolis Drive Unit 05-17 Synpase, Singapore, 138623, Singapore
Tel.: (65) 6262 1111
Hard Disk Drive Mfr
N.A.I.C.S.: 334112
Eunice Pang (Mgr-HR)

Subsidiary (Domestic):

Panasonic Logistics Asia (2)
202 Bedok South Avenue 1, Singapore, 469332, Singapore
Tel.: (65) 6 299 8400
Web Site: https://www.panasonic.com
Emp.: 70
Logistics Consulting Servies
N.A.I.C.S.: 541614
Paul Wong (Mng Dir)

Panasonic Semiconductor Asia Pte. Ltd. (2)
22 Ang Mo Kio Industrial Park, Singapore, 569506, Singapore
Tel.: (65) 64818811
Web Site: http://www.panasonic.com.sg
Sales Range: $400-449.9 Million
Emp.: 1,200
Semiconductor Devices Mfr
N.A.I.C.S.: 334413

Panasonic Systems Asia Pacific Pte. Ltd. (2)
2 Jalan Kilang Road Panasonic Building, Singapore, 159346, Singapore
Tel.: (65) 6270 0110
Household Electronic Device Distr
N.A.I.C.S.: 423620

Panasonic Automotive & Industrial Systems Europe GmbH - Ottobrunn (1)
Robert-Koch Str 100, 85521, Ottobrunn, Germany
Tel.: (49) 89453541000
Web Site: http://eu.industrial.panasonic.com
Electric Equipment Mfr
N.A.I.C.S.: 334310

Panasonic Automotive Systems Asia Pacific (Thailand) Co., Ltd (1)
101 Moo 2 Thepharak Road, Bang Sao Thong District, Samut Prakan, 10570, Thailand
Tel.: (66) 27233100
Web Site: http://www.panasonic.com
Automotive Electrical Parts Mfr
N.A.I.C.S.: 336320

Panasonic Automotive Systems Czech, s.r.o. (1)
U Panasonicu 266, 530 06, Pardubice, Czech Republic
Tel.: (420) 467021111
Web Site: http://www.panasonic.cz
Sales Range: $150-199.9 Million
Emp.: 100
Automotive Audio System Mfr
N.A.I.C.S.: 334310

Panasonic Biomedical Sales Europe B.V. (1)
Nijverheidsweg 120, 4879 AZ, Etten-Leur, Netherlands (100%)
Tel.: (31) 765433833
Web Site: http://www.biomedical.panasonic-healthcare.com
Sales Range: $25-49.9 Million
Emp.: 40
Medical Laboratory Equipment Mfr
N.A.I.C.S.: 334516
Hans Brok (Mng Dir)

Division (Non-US):

Panasonic Biomedical Sales Europe BV - UK (2)
9 The Office Village North Road, Loughborough, LE11 1QJ, Leicestershire, United Kingdom (100%)
Tel.: (44) 1509265265
Web Site: http://www.panasonic-biomedical.co.uk
Sales Range: $25-49.9 Million
Emp.: 15
Laboratory Equipment Mfr
N.A.I.C.S.: 334516
Hans Brok (Pres)

Panasonic Carbon India Co. Limited (1)
Pottipati Plaza Third Floor No 77 Nungambakkam High Road, Nungambakkam, Chennai, 600 034, India
Tel.: (91) 4428275216
Web Site: https://www.panasoniccarbon.co.in
Rev.: $6,901,677
Assets: $17,871,209
Liabilities: $599,769
Net Worth: $17,271,440
Earnings: $1,537,925
Emp.: 129
Fiscal Year-end: 03/31/2023
Carbon & Graphite Products Mfr
N.A.I.C.S.: 335991
P. S. Maheswari (Compliance Officer & Sec)

Subsidiary (Non-US):

PT. Panasonic Gobel Energy Indonesia (2)
Gobel Industrial Complex JL Teuku Umar KM 44, Cibitung, Bekasi, 17520, Jawa Barat, Indonesia
Tel.: (62) 21 8832 4681
Dry Battery Mfr
N.A.I.C.S.: 335910

Panasonic Communications Co. Ltd. (1)
1 62 4 Chome Minoshima Hakata Ku, Fukuoka, 812 8531, Japan (100%)
Tel.: (81) 924312111
Web Site: http://www.panasonic.co.jp
Rev.: $3,124,000,000
Industrial Electronics
N.A.I.C.S.: 811310

Panasonic Communications System Co. Ltd (1)
2 3 8 Shimo Meguro Meguro Ku, Tokyo, 153 8687, Japan

INTERNATIONAL PUBLIC

Tel.: (81) 334919191
Web Site: http://www.panasonic.co.jp
Electronics Equipment
N.A.I.C.S.: 335999

Panasonic Corporation Eco Solutions Company (1)
1048 Kadoma, Osaka, 571-8686, Japan
Tel.: (81) 669081131
Web Site: http://www.panasonic.net
Sales Range: $5-14.9 Billion
Emp.: 55,000
Home Appliance Mfr & Distr
N.A.I.C.S.: 335220
Shusaku Nagae (Pres)

Subsidiary (Non-US):

PT. Panasonic Gobel Eco Solutions Manufacturing Indonesia (2)
EJIP Industrial Parks Plot 3D, Lemah Abang, Bekasi, 17550, West Java, Indonesia
Tel.: (62) 218970044
Consumer Electronics Distr
N.A.I.C.S.: 423620

PT. Panasonic Gobel Eco Solutions Sales Indonesia (2)
Summitmas 1 8/F JI Jend Sudirman 61-62, Jakarta, 12190, Indonesia
Tel.: (62) 212521616
Sales Range: $25-49.9 Million
Emp.: 30
Solar Device Distr
N.A.I.C.S.: 423720

Panasonic Eco Solutions (Hong Kong) Co., Ltd. (2)
Unit A to C 23/F CDW Building 388 Castle Peak Road, Tsuen Wan, New Territories, China (Hong Kong)
Tel.: (852) 24661708
Web Site: http://www.peshk.panasonic.hk
Air Flow Controller & Fan Mfr
N.A.I.C.S.: 334512
Hiroyuki Ito (Mng Dir)

Subsidiary (Domestic):

Panasonic Eco Solutions AWE Co., Ltd. (2)
1-47-1 Oi Nt Bldg 3f, Shinagawa-Ku, Tokyo, 140-0014, Japan
Tel.: (81) 357463787
Web Site: http://www.panasonic.co.jp
Plumbing Equipment Sales & Installation Services
N.A.I.C.S.: 423720

Panasonic Eco Solutions Asahi Co., Ltd. (2)
666-1 Kawado Higashiagatsuma-Machi, Agatsuma-Gun, Gunma, 377-0802, Japan
Tel.: (81) 279 68 2431
Air Conditioning Equipment Distr
N.A.I.C.S.: 423730

Subsidiary (Non-US):

Panasonic Eco Solutions Canada Inc. (2)
5770 Ambler Drive 70, Mississauga, L4W 2T3, ON, Canada
Tel.: (905) 624-5010
Air Conditioning Equipment Mfr
N.A.I.C.S.: 333415

Subsidiary (Domestic):

Panasonic Eco Solutions Chemical Co., Ltd. (2)
4-1-20 Nishinomiyahama, Nishinomiya, 662-0934, Hyogo, Japan
Tel.: (81) 798331371
Industrial Chemicals Mfr
N.A.I.C.S.: 325998

Panasonic Eco Solutions Creates Co., Ltd. (2)
1048 Kadoma, Osaka, 571-0050, Japan
Tel.: (81) 669065200
Web Site: http://panasonic.co.jp
Information Technology Consulting Services
N.A.I.C.S.: 541512

Panasonic Eco Solutions Electrical Construction Materials Mie Co., Ltd. (2)
1668 Fujikata, Tsu, 514-0815, Mie, Japan

Tel.: (81) 592281362
Web Site: http://www.panasonic.co.jp
Electrical Appliance Mfr
N.A.I.C.S.: 335220

Subsidiary (Non-US):

Panasonic Eco Solutions Electrical Construction Materials Taiwan Co., Ltd. (2)
228 Hsin Yi Rd Yi Hsin Li, Tachi Chen, Taoyuan, 33554, Taiwan
Tel.: (886) 33889500
Consumer Electronics Distr
N.A.I.C.S.: 423620

Subsidiary (US):

Panasonic Eco Solutions Energy Management North America (2)
10900 N Tantau Ave Ste 200, Cupertino, CA 95014
Tel.: (408) 861-8424
Web Site: http://www.us.sanyo.com
Energy Consulting Services
N.A.I.C.S.: 541690

Subsidiary (Domestic):

Panasonic Eco Solutions Facility Management Co., Ltd. (2)
1048 Kadoma, Kadoma, Osaka, 571-0050, Japan
Tel.: (81) 669002711
Web Site: http://www.panasonic.co.jp
Facility Management Services
N.A.I.C.S.: 561210

Panasonic Eco Solutions Ikeda Electric Co., Ltd. (2)
397-1 Nishinobusue, Himeji, 670-0971, Hyogo, Japan
Tel.: (81) 792931131
Web Site: http://www.panasonic.co.jp
Lighting Equipment Mfr
N.A.I.C.S.: 335139

Subsidiary (Non-US):

Panasonic Eco Solutions Information Equipment (Shanghai) Co., Ltd. (2)
No 811 Shenfu Road Xinzhuang Industrial Zone, Minhang District, Shanghai, 201108, China
Tel.: (86) 2154426880
Emp.: 420
Household Appliances Mfr
N.A.I.C.S.: 335220
Takamura Yui (Mgr)

Subsidiary (Domestic):

Panasonic Eco Solutions Logistics Co., Ltd. (2)
3-41 Shitomiyashimmachi, Shijonawate, 575-0041, Osaka, Japan
Tel.: (81) 728789321
Sales Range: $10-24.9 Million
Emp.: 3
Logistics Consulting Servies
N.A.I.C.S.: 541614

Panasonic Eco Solutions Networks Co., Ltd. (2)
2-12-7 Higashishimbashi Sumitomohigashishimbashi Bldg 2gokan4f, Minato-Ku, Tokyo, 105-0021, Japan
Tel.: (81) 364025300
Web Site: http://www.mno.co.jp
Network Integration Services
N.A.I.C.S.: 541512

Subsidiary (Non-US):

Panasonic Eco Solutions Nordic AB (2)
Jungmansgatan 12, 21119, Malmo, Sweden
Tel.: (46) 406977000
Web Site: http://www.panasonic-fire-security.com
Sales Range: $25-49.9 Million
Emp.: 16
Fire & Security Alarm Products Mfr & Distr
N.A.I.C.S.: 334290
Bjorn Svensson (Mng Dir)

Panasonic Eco Solutions Power Tools (Shanghai) Co., Ltd. (2)
Building 12 No 258 Jiangtian E Road Songjiang Industrial Zo, Shanghai, 201613, China

Tel.: (86) 2167740566
Sales Range: $50-74.9 Million
Emp.: 115
Power Tool Mfr & Distr
N.A.I.C.S.: 333991

Panasonic Eco Solutions Sales Taiwan Co., Ltd. (2)
15th Floor No 44 2nd Section Chung Shan North Road, Taipei, 10448, Taiwan
Tel.: (886) 225816020
Consumer Electronics Distr
N.A.I.C.S.: 423620

Panasonic Eco Solutions Shin Dong-A Co., Ltd. (2)
1506-3 Songjeong-dong, Gangseo-gu, Busan, 618-817, Korea (South)
Tel.: (82) 51 831 7011
Web Site: http://pessda.panasonic.co.kr
Sales Range: $50-74.9 Million
Emp.: 170
Consumer Electronics Distr
N.A.I.C.S.: 423610

Subsidiary (Domestic):

Panasonic Eco Solutions Techno Service Co., Ltd. (2)
1048 Kadoma, Osaka, Japan
Tel.: (81) 6 6906 1004
Web Site: http://www.panasonic.co.jp
Building Ventilation Services
N.A.I.C.S.: 561790

Subsidiary (Non-US):

Panasonic Ecology Systems Guangdong Co., Ltd. (2)
No 2 Chaogui South Road, Ronggui Shunde Dist, Foshan, 528305, Guangdong, China
Tel.: (86) 75728373125
Air Conditioning Equipment Mfr
N.A.I.C.S.: 333415

Subsidiary (Domestic):

Panasonic Ecology Systems Kyoei Co., Ltd. (2)
5-1-17 Nishiwaji, Higashiyodogawa-Ku, Osaka, 533-0031, Japan
Tel.: (81) 668157310
Sales Range: $10-24.9 Million
Emp.: 32
Building Ventilation Services
N.A.I.C.S.: 561790
Takeshi Toyooka (Mgr)

Panasonic Ecology Systems Ventec Co., Ltd. (2)
4017 Shimonakada, Takaki -cho, Kasugai, 486-8522, Aichi, Japan
Tel.: (81) 56 881 0510
Web Site: https://panasonic.co.jp
Emp.: 150
Household Fan Mfr & Distr
N.A.I.C.S.: 335210

Panasonic Living Chubu Co., Ltd. (2)
2-7-55 Minamieki, Nakamura-ku, Nagoya, 450-8611, Aichi, Japan
Tel.: (81) 525624108
Web Site: http://www.panasonic.co.jp
Emp.: 370
Building Materials Distr
N.A.I.C.S.: 423390

Panasonic Living Chushikoku Co., Ltd. (2)
455-12 Kawauchicho, Tokushima, 771-0101, Japan
Tel.: (81) 886658880
Home Appliance Mfr & Distr
N.A.I.C.S.: 335210

Panasonic Living Hokkaido Tohoku Co., Ltd. (2)
105-1 Kitaoki Iinozaka, Natori, 981-1225, Miyagi, Japan
Tel.: (81) 22 382 5480
Web Site: https://panasonic.co.jp
Emp.: 218
Home Appliance Mfr & Distr
N.A.I.C.S.: 335210

Panasonic Living Kinki Co., Ltd. (2)
6-2-82 Shimaya Universal City Building 8F, Konohana-ku, Osaka, 554-0024, Japan

Tel.: (81) 664656318
Web Site: http://www.panasonic.co.jp
Emp.: 311
Home Appliance Mfr
N.A.I.C.S.: 335210

Panasonic Living Kyushu Co., Ltd. (2)
6-26-41 Naka, Hakata-Ku, Fukuoka, 812-0893, Japan
Tel.: (81) 925933331
Consumer Electronics Distr
N.A.I.C.S.: 423620

Panasonic Living Shutoken Kantoh Co., Ltd. (2)
3-2-22 Harumi Harumi Park Bldg 2f, Chuo-Ku, Tokyo, 104-0053, Japan
Tel.: (81) 335335780
Home Appliance Distr
N.A.I.C.S.: 423620

Subsidiary (Non-US):

Panasonic Manufacturing Philippines Corporation (2)
Ortigas Avenue Extension, Taytay, Rizal, 1920, Philippines
Tel.: (63) 286352260
Web Site: https://www.panasonic.com
Rev.: $270,072,121
Assets: $145,542,037
Liabilities: $59,765,372
Net Worth: $85,776,665
Earnings: $3,241,573
Emp.: 1,859
Fiscal Year-end: 03/31/2023
Electric Equipment Mfr
N.A.I.C.S.: 335999
Yasushi Kondo (Pres)

Subsidiary (Domestic):

Panasonic Photo & Lighting Co., Ltd. (2)
1-1 Saiwaicho, Takatsuki, 569-1193, Osaka, Japan
Tel.: (81) 72 682 7010
Web Site: https://panasonic.co.jp
Emp.: 188
Photographic Flashbulb Mfr
N.A.I.C.S.: 335139
Okamoto Takayasu (Mng Dir)

Panasonic Photo & Lighting Kumihama Co., Ltd. (2)
94 Shimokawara Kumihamachonagadome, Kyotango, 629-3551, Kyoto, Japan
Tel.: (81) 772840241
Lighting Equipment Mfr
N.A.I.C.S.: 335139

Panasonic Corporation of China (1)
5th Floor Tower C Office Park No 5 Jinghua South Street, Chaoyang District, Beijing, 100020, China
Tel.: (86) 106 562 6688
Web Site: http://www.panasonic.cn
Household Appliance Mfr & Distr
N.A.I.C.S.: 335220
Hidetoshi Osawa (Chm)

Subsidiary (Domestic):

China Hualu Panasonic Avc Networks Co., Ltd. (2)
No 1 Hua Road, Qixianling High Technology Zone, Dalian, 116023, Liaoning, China
Tel.: (86) 4118 479 0599
Web Site: https://chpavc.panasonic.cn
Emp.: 3,000
Consumer Electronics Distr
N.A.I.C.S.: 423620
Yasuteru Hayashida (Gen Mgr)

Panasonic AVC Networks Shandong Co., Ltd. (2)
No 312 Xinluo Avenue High-Tech Industrial Development Zone, Jinan, 250101, China
Tel.: (86) 53188872686
Household Appliances Mfr
N.A.I.C.S.: 423620

Panasonic AVC Networks Xiamen Co., Ltd. (2)
No 15 Torch Rd Torch High Technology Industry Development Zone, Xiamen, 361006, China
Tel.: (86) 5925702680
Consumer Electronics Distr

N.A.I.C.S.: 423620

Panasonic Appliances Washing Machine (Hangzhou) Co., Ltd. (2)
No 6 Songqiao Road Panasonic Hangzhou Industrial Zone Economi, Hangzhou, 310018, China
Tel.: (86) 57188265285
Washing Machine Mfr
N.A.I.C.S.: 335220

Panasonic Automotive Systems Development Tianjin Co., Ltd. (2)
No 10 Huayuan Road Economic Technology Development Zone, Tianjin, 300457, China
Tel.: (86) 2259816177
Sales Range: $25-49.9 Million
Emp.: 100
Consumer Electronics Mfr
N.A.I.C.S.: 334220
Masatoshi Wakatani (Gen Mgr)

Panasonic Carbon (Anyang) Co., Ltd. (2)
No 7-1 Hanling Road, Beiguan District, Anyang, 455000, China
Tel.: (86) 3722911492
Carbon & Graphite Products Mfr
N.A.I.C.S.: 335991

Panasonic Electric Works Taiko Device (Shenzhen) Co., Ltd. (2)
Taikang 3 Dontang Industrial Area, Shanjing Town Baoan, Shenzhen, China
Tel.: (86) 755 2724 5059
Home Appliance Mfr
N.A.I.C.S.: 335220

Panasonic Electronic Devices (Jiangmen) Co., Ltd. (2)
No 18 Huicheng Road, Xinhui, Jiangmen, 529100, Guangdong, China
Tel.: (86) 7506962307
Film Capacitor Mfr
N.A.I.C.S.: 335999

Panasonic Electronic Devices (Qingdao) Co., Ltd. (2)
49 Tokyo Road Free Trade Zone No2, Qingdao, 266555, China
Tel.: (86) 53286769009
Electric Equipment Mfr
N.A.I.C.S.: 335999

Panasonic Electronic Devices (Tianjin) Co., Ltd. (2)
No 1 Xinghua 5th Branch Xiqing Economic Development Zone, Tianjin, 300385, China
Tel.: (86) 2283983088
Household Electrical Equipment Mfr & Distr
N.A.I.C.S.: 335220

Panasonic Energy (Shanghai) Co., Ltd. (2)
No 5033 Luoshan Road, Pudong New Area, Shanghai, 201204, China
Tel.: (86) 2133906661
Electric Equipment Mfr
N.A.I.C.S.: 335999

Panasonic Energy (Wuxi) Co., Ltd. (2)
Block 59 Wuxi National Hi & New Tech Industrial Development Zone, Wuxi, 214028, Jiangsu, China
Tel.: (86) 51085212221
Storage Battery Mfr
N.A.I.C.S.: 335910

Panasonic Factory Solutions Suzhou Co., Ltd. (2)
No 1 Linbu Street Suzhou Industrial Park, Suzhou, 215122, China
Tel.: (86) 51262745507
Household Appliances Mfr
N.A.I.C.S.: 335220

Subsidiary (Non-US):

Panasonic Hong Kong Co., Ltd. (2)
Top Floor Chinachem Golden Plaza 77 Mody Road, TST East, Kowloon, China (Hong Kong)
Tel.: (852) 2 367 0181
Web Site: http://www.panasonic.hk
Consumer Electronics Distr
N.A.I.C.S.: 423620

Subsidiary (Domestic):

Panasonic Industrial (China) Co., Ltd. (2)

PANASONIC HOLDINGS CORPORATION

Panasonic Holdings Corporation—(Continued)

No 51 Kunminghu Street Economic & Technology Development Zone, Shenyang, 110141, China
Tel.: (86) 2462786264
Web Site: http://www.industrial.panasonic.com
Consumer Electronics Distr
N.A.I.C.S.: 423620

Panasonic Industrial Devices (Shanghai) Co., Ltd. (2)
No 25 Lane 258 Caoxi Road, Xuhui District, Shanghai, 200235, China
Tel.: (86) 2164821608
Electric Equipment Mfr
N.A.I.C.S.: 335999

Panasonic Industrial Devices Sales (China) Co., Ltd. (2)
Floor7 China Insurance Building 166 East Road, LuJiazuli Pudong New District, Shanghai, 200120, China
Tel.: (86) 2138552000
Semiconductor Devices Mfr
N.A.I.C.S.: 334413

Panasonic R&D Center China Co., Ltd. (2)
18th Floor Zhongguancun Tower No 27 Zhongguancun Street, Haidian District, Beijing, 100080, China
Tel.: (86) 1082856400
Consumer Electronics Research & Development Services
N.A.I.C.S.: 541715

Panasonic R&D Center Suzhou Co., Ltd. (2)
No 300 Zhongnan St Industrial Park, Suzhou, 215000, China
Tel.: (86) 51262581001
Electronic Equipment Research & Development Services
N.A.I.C.S.: 541715

Panasonic Refrigeration Devices (Wuxi) Co., Ltd. (2)
No 2 XiXin 1 Road Singapore Industrial Park, Wuxi, 214028, Jiangsu, China
Tel.: (86) 51085281521
Air Conditioning Equipment Distr
N.A.I.C.S.: 423730

Panasonic Semiconductor (Suzhou) Co., Ltd. (2)
No 666 Lushan Road, New Dist, Suzhou, 215129, China
Tel.: (86) 51266650489
Semiconductor Devices Mfr
N.A.I.C.S.: 334413
Julie Zhu (Mgr-Sls)

Panasonic System Networks (Dalian) Co., Ltd. (2)
Number 46, Dalian Development Area, Dalian, 116000, China
Tel.: (86) 41162772111
Optical Disc Drive & Communication Equipment Mfr
N.A.I.C.S.: 334610

Panasonic System Networks (Suzhou) Co., Ltd. (2)
No 1478 Binhe Rd, New Dist, Suzhou, 215011, China
Tel.: (86) 51268255606
Computer Network Design Services
N.A.I.C.S.: 541512

Panasonic System Networks (Zhuhai) Co., Ltd. (2)
3rd Pingxi Road Nanping Science & Technology Industrial Park, Zhuhai, 519060, China
Tel.: (86) 7568681000
Web Site: http://panasonic.cn
Consumer Electronics Distr
N.A.I.C.S.: 423620

Panasonic Corporation of Latin America (1)
Avenida Do Cafe 277 Buildg 8th Floor, Sao Paulo, 04311900, Brazil
Tel.: (55) 1138894000
Web Site: http://www.panasonic-la.com
Consumer Electronics Distr
N.A.I.C.S.: 423620

Subsidiary (Non-US):

Panasonic Chile Limitada (2)
Lota 2359, Providencia, Santiago, Chile
Tel.: (56) 228260010
Web Site: http://www.panasonic.com
Emp.: 30
Consumer Electronics Distr
N.A.I.C.S.: 423620
Houcine Haddjeri (Pres)

Panasonic Peruana S.A. (2)
Av Alfredo Mendiola 1600 Independence Lima 28, Lima, Peru
Tel.: (51) 1 614 0000
Web Site: https://www.panasonic.com
Household Appliances Mfr & Distr
N.A.I.C.S.: 423620

Subsidiary (Domestic):

Panasonic do Brasil Limitada (2)
Rua Alexandre Dumas, Sao Paulo, 1711, Brazil
Tel.: (55) 113 889 4000
Web Site: https://www.panasonic.com
Consumer Electronics Distr
N.A.I.C.S.: 423620

Panasonic Corporation of North America (1)
1 Panasonic Way, Secaucus, NJ 07094-2917 **(100%)**
Tel.: (201) 348-7755
Web Site: http://www.panasonic.com
Rev.: $8,000,000,000
Emp.: 23,000
Electric Household Appliances Whslr
N.A.I.C.S.: 423620
Robert Greenberg (VP-Brand Mktg)

Subsidiary (Domestic):

Amac Corporation (2)
6550 Katella Ave, Cypress, CA 90630-5151
Tel.: (714) 373-7979
Sales Range: $25-49.9 Million
Emp.: 18
Exports of Electronics Parts
N.A.I.C.S.: 423690

Hussmann Corporation (2)
12999 Saint Charles Rock Rd, Bridgeton, MO 63044-2483
Tel.: (314) 291-2000
Web Site: https://www.hussmann.com
Commercial Refrigeration Equipment Mfr, Whslr, Installation & Maintenance Services
N.A.I.C.S.: 333415
Dave Martin (Sr VP-Sls)

Subsidiary (Non-US):

Hussmann Canada Inc. (3)
5 Cherry Blossom Road Unit 3, Cambridge, N3H 4R7, ON, Canada
Tel.: (519) 653-9980
Web Site: http://www.hussmann.com
Refrigeration Equipment Sales
N.A.I.C.S.: 423740
Lianne Tombo (Gen Sls Mgr)

Subsidiary (Domestic):

Krack Corporation (3)
890 Remington Blvd, Bolingbrook, IL 60440
Tel.: (630) 629-7500
Web Site: http://www.krack.com
Commercial Refrigeration Equipment Mfr, Whslr & Parts Distr
N.A.I.C.S.: 333415
Chuck Previ (Dir-Sls)

Subsidiary (Domestic):

Matsushita Communication Industrial Corp. (2)
776 Hwy 74 S, Peachtree City, GA 30269-3004
Tel.: (770) 487-3356
Web Site: http://www.panasonic.com
Sales Range: $400-449.9 Million
Emp.: 1,900
Mfr of Automotive Electronics
N.A.I.C.S.: 334220
Vince Sarrecchia (Pres)

Matsushita Electric Corporation of America (2)
415 Horizon Dr Ste 300, Suwanee, GA 30024-3186
Tel.: (770) 926-3829
Web Site: http://www.panasonic.com
Sales Range: $125-149.9 Million
Emp.: 300
Distribution Center
N.A.I.C.S.: 459910

Matsushita Electric Corporation of America (2)
2221 Cabot Blvd W # A, Langhorne, PA 19047-1806
Tel.: (215) 741-0679
Sales Range: $25-49.9 Million
Emp.: 20
Radio And Television Repair
N.A.I.C.S.: 423620

Matsushita Electric Corporation of America (2)
415 Horizon Dr Ste 300, Suwanee, GA 30024-3186
Tel.: (770) 338-6655
Sales Range: $25-49.9 Million
Emp.: 5
Connectors Electronic
N.A.I.C.S.: 449210

Matsushita Electric Corporation of America (2)
7625 Panasonic Way 31A, San Diego, CA 92154
Tel.: (619) 661-4700
Web Site: http://www.panasonic.com
Sales Range: $75-99.9 Million
Emp.: 150
Microwave Ovens & Portable Televisions
N.A.I.C.S.: 423620

Mema Panasonic (2)
1150 Mayde Rd, Berea, KY 40403-9723
Tel.: (859) 985-1161
Sales Range: $75-99.9 Million
Emp.: 107
Electric Motor & Generator Parts
N.A.I.C.S.: 423620

Panasonic (2)
2055 Sanyo Ave, San Diego, CA 92154-6229 **(100%)**
Tel.: (619) 661-4700
Web Site: http://www.panasonic.com
Sales Range: $250-299.9 Million
Emp.: 30
Phototransmission Equipment
N.A.I.C.S.: 334210

Panasonic (2)
4900 George McVay Dr, McAllen, TX 78503
Tel.: (956) 683-2900
Web Site: http://www.panasonic.com
Sales Range: $25-49.9 Million
Emp.: 80
Electrical Appliances Television And Radio
N.A.I.C.S.: 449210

Panasonic (2)
9100 S Dadeland Blvd Ste 800, Miami, FL 33156-7814
Tel.: (305) 471-5860
Web Site: http://www.panasonic.com
Sales Range: $25-49.9 Million
Emp.: 15
Headquarters for Panasonic in Latin America Region
N.A.I.C.S.: 541618

Panasonic AVC American Co. (2)
2 Springside Rd, Westampton, NJ 08060-5644
Tel.: (609) 518-3700
Sales Range: $25-49.9 Million
Emp.: 80
Radio & Television Publisher Representatives R & D
N.A.I.C.S.: 541840

Panasonic Automotive Electronics Co. (2)
26455 American Dr, Southfield, MI 48034-6114 **(100%)**
Tel.: (248) 447-7000
Web Site: http://www.panasonic.com
Sales Range: $50-74.9 Million
Emp.: 100
Engineeering Services
N.A.I.C.S.: 423620

Panasonic Automotive Systems Company of America (2)
776 Hwy 74 S, Peachtree City, GA 30269

INTERNATIONAL PUBLIC

Tel.: (770) 487-3356
Web Site: http://www.panasonic.com
Automotive Electrical Equipment Mfr
N.A.I.C.S.: 336320

Panasonic Avionics Corporation (2)
1405 S Belt Line Rd Ste 300, Coppell, TX 75019-4934
Tel.: (972) 745-1250
Web Site: http://www.panasonic.aero
Sales Range: $25-49.9 Million
Emp.: 75
Aircraft Electrical Equipment Repair
N.A.I.C.S.: 423860
Dave Anderson (Mgr)

Subsidiary (Domestic):

Panasonic Avionics Corporation (3)
3303 Monte Villa Pkwy, Bothell, WA 98021-7814 **(100%)**
Tel.: (425) 415-9000
Web Site: https://www.panasonic.aero
Boarding Music Entertainment Tape Recorders for Airlines
N.A.I.C.S.: 423860
Mark Jennings (COO)

Subsidiary (Domestic):

Matsushita Avionics Systems Corporation (4)
26200 Enterprise Way, Lake Forest, CA 92630-8400 **(100%)**
Tel.: (949) 672-2000
Sales Range: $250-299.9 Million
Mfr of Audio Visual System For Commercial Aircrafts
N.A.I.C.S.: 423860

Matsushita Avionics Systems Corporation (4)
17219 Sandestine Dr, Houston, TX 77095-4370
Tel.: (281) 829-2682
Sales Range: $50-74.9 Million
Emp.: 1
Engineeering Services
N.A.I.C.S.: 423860

Subsidiary (Domestic):

Panasonic Broadcast & TV Systems (2)
3330 Cahuenga Blvd W, Los Angeles, CA 90068-1354
Tel.: (323) 436-3500
Web Site: http://www.panasonic.com
Sales Range: $75-99.9 Million
Emp.: 20
Radio &Television Communications Equipment
N.A.I.C.S.: 423620
Steve Milley (Mgr-Reg Sls)

Panasonic Broadcast & Television Systems Company (2)
1 Panasonic Way, Secaucus, NJ 07094-2917
Tel.: (201) 348-7755
Web Site: http://www.panasonic.com
Sales Range: $25-49.9 Million
Emp.: 50
Video & Audio Hardware & Software Products Distr
N.A.I.C.S.: 516210
John Baisley (Pres)

Subsidiary (Non-US):

Panasonic Canada Inc. (2)
12111 Riverside Way, Richmond, V6W 1K8, BC, Canada **(100%)**
Tel.: (604) 278-4211
Web Site: http://www.panasonic.ca
Sales Range: $25-49.9 Million
Emp.: 42
Electrical Appliances Television & Radio
N.A.I.C.S.: 423620

Panasonic Canada, Inc. (2)
5770 Ambler Drive, Mississauga, L4W 2T3, ON, Canada **(100%)**
Tel.: (905) 624-5010
Web Site: https://www.panasonic.com
Sales Range: $150-199.9 Million
Emp.: 400
Distr of Electrical Appliances, Television & Radio
N.A.I.C.S.: 423620

AND PRIVATE COMPANIES — PANASONIC HOLDINGS CORPORATION

Subsidiary (Domestic):

Panasonic Corp of North America (2)
99 859 Iwaiwa St, Aiea, HI 96701
Tel.: (808) 488-7779
Web Site: http://www.panasonic.com
Sales Range: $25-49.9 Million
Emp.: 6
Electric Equipment Mfr
N.A.I.C.S.: 423620

Panasonic Digital Service Center (2)
410 B Airport Rd, Elgin, IL 60123
Tel.: (847) 468-5543
Web Site: http://www.panasonic.com
Sales Range: $150-199.9 Million
Emp.: 500
Radio & Television Repair
N.A.I.C.S.: 423620

Panasonic Disc Manufacturing Corporation of America (2)
20608 Madrona Ave, Torrance, CA 90503-3715
Tel.: (310) 783-4800
Optical Disc Applications & Technology
N.A.I.C.S.: 334610

Panasonic Energy Corporation of America (2)
1 Panasonic Dr, Columbus, GA 31907
Tel.: (706) 561-7730
Web Site: https://www.panasonicbatteryproducts.com
Consumer Electronics Mfr
N.A.I.C.S.: 335220
Celina Mikolajczak *(VP-Engrg & Battery Tech-North America)*

Panasonic Factory Automation Co. (2)
5201 Tollview Dr, Rolling Meadows, IL 60008-3711
Tel.: (847) 495-6200
Web Site: http://www.panasonicfa.com
Sales of Welding & Laser Equipment
N.A.I.C.S.: 423620

Panasonic Factory Solutions - Welding Robotics Group (2)
234 International Dr, Lawrenceburg, TN 38464-6974
Tel.: (615) 641-7111
Web Site: http://www.panasonicfa.com
Sales Range: $25-49.9 Million
Emp.: 5
Mfr of Electronic Circuits
N.A.I.C.S.: 423620
Jorge Gonzalez *(Mgr-Sls-Electronics Assembly-Mexico)*

Panasonic Industrial Co. (2)
15455 NW Greenbrier Pkwy Ste 125, Beaverton, OR 97006-8115
Tel.: (503) 690-9884
Sales Range: $25-49.9 Million
Emp.: 6
Electronic Parts And Equipment
N.A.I.C.S.: 423620

Panasonic Industrial Company (2)
2033 Gateway Pl Ste 250, San Jose, CA 95110-3711
Tel.: (408) 487-9510
Web Site: http://www.panasonic.com
Sales Range: $25-49.9 Million
Emp.: 40
Mfr of DVD RAM Products
N.A.I.C.S.: 423620

Panasonic Industrial Devices Corporation of America (2)
5105 S National Dr, Knoxville, TN 37914-6518 (100%)
Tel.: (865) 673-0700
Sales Range: $100-124.9 Million
Emp.: 400
Audio Electronic Systems
N.A.I.C.S.: 334310

Panasonic Industrial Systems (2)
20421 84th Ave S, Kent, WA 98032-1202 (100%)
Tel.: (253) 395-0670
Web Site: http://www.panasonic.com
Sales Range: $25-49.9 Million
Emp.: 11
Industrial Warehousing
N.A.I.C.S.: 423620

Panasonic International Trading Corporation of America (2)
525 Maple Ave, Torrance, CA 90503
Tel.: (310) 783-4100
Electronic Equipment Distr
N.A.I.C.S.: 423690

Panasonic N.A (2)
5201 Tollview Dr, Rolling Meadows, IL 60008-3711
Tel.: (847) 468-4600
Web Site: http://www.panasonic.com
Sales Range: $250-299.9 Million
Emp.: 600
Mfr of Electronic Goods
N.A.I.C.S.: 423620

Panasonic Technologies Inc. (2)
2 Research Way, Princeton, NJ 08540
Tel.: (609) 734-0800
Sales Range: $10-24.9 Million
Emp.: 50
Research Institute
N.A.I.C.S.: 541715

Saxon Office Technology (2)
225 Lincoln Hwy Ste 190, Fairless Hills, PA 19030
Tel.: (215) 702-1570
Web Site: http://www.saxonoffice.com
Sales Range: $25-49.9 Million
Emp.: 15
Authorized Panasonic Dealer
N.A.I.C.S.: 423620

Video Insight, Inc. (2)
800 Gessner Rd Suite 700, Houston, TX 77024 (100%)
Tel.: (713) 621-9779
Web Site: http://www.video-insight.com
Sales Range: $1-9.9 Million
Emp.: 33
Video Management Software Developer
N.A.I.C.S.: 513210
J. Robert Shaw *(Co-Founder & CEO)*

Panasonic Czech Republic, s.r.o. (1)
Thamova 289/13, Prague, 186 00, Czech Republic
Tel.: (420) 236032511
Web Site: http://www.panasonic.cz
Sales Range: $25-49.9 Million
Emp.: 23
Consumer Electronics Distr
N.A.I.C.S.: 423620
Jiri Opletal *(Gen Mgr)*

Panasonic Ecology Systems Co., Ltd. (1)
4017 Shimonakata Takaki-cho, Kasugai, 486-8522, Aichi, Japan (100%)
Tel.: (81) 568811511
Web Site: http://www.panasonic.net
Indoor Air Quality Appliances Mfr
N.A.I.C.S.: 333415
Kiyofumi Ito *(Pres)*

Panasonic Electric Works Europe AG (1)
Caroline-Herschel-Strasse 100, 85521, Ottobrunn, Germany
Tel.: (49) 89453541000
Web Site: http://www.panasonic-electric-works.com
Sales Range: $125-149.9 Million
Emp.: 300
Electronic Component Mfr & Distr
N.A.I.C.S.: 334419
Johannes Spatz *(Chm-Exec Bd)*

Subsidiary (Non-US):

Panasonic Electric Works Austria GmbH (2)
Josef Madersperger Strasse 2, Biedermannsdorf, 2362, Austria
Tel.: (43) 2236 26846
Web Site: http://www.panasonic-electric-works.at
Emp.: 11
Electromechanical Relay Mfr
N.A.I.C.S.: 335314
Carmen Wild *(Mng Dir)*

Panasonic Electric Works Espana S.A. (2)
Barajas Park San Severo 20, Madrid, 28042, Spain
Tel.: (34) 913293875
Web Site: http://www.panasonic-electric-works.es
Sales Range: $25-49.9 Million
Emp.: 24
Industrial Relay Mfr
N.A.I.C.S.: 335314

Panasonic Electric Works Italia s.r.l. (2)
Via del Commercio 3/5 ZI Ferlina, 37012, Bussolengo, Verona, Italy
Tel.: (39) 045 6752711
Web Site: http://www.panasonic-electric-works.it
Industrial Relay Mfr
N.A.I.C.S.: 335314

Panasonic Electric Works Korea Co. Ltd. (2)
5th Fl Haeam Bldg 983-1 Daechi-dong, Gangnam-gu, Seoul, 135-842, Korea (South)
Tel.: (82) 2 2052 1050
Electromechanical Relay Mfr
N.A.I.C.S.: 335314

Panasonic Electric Works Polska sp. z.o.o. (2)
ul Woloska 9a, 02-583, Warsaw, Poland
Tel.: (48) 223381133
Web Site: http://www.panasonic-electric-works.pl
Sales Range: $25-49.9 Million
Emp.: 1
Industrial Relay Distr
N.A.I.C.S.: 423610

Panasonic Electric Works Sales Western Europe B.V. (2)
De Rijn 4, Postbus 211, 5684 PJ, Best, Netherlands
Tel.: (31) 499727100
Web Site: http://www.panasonic-electric-works.nl
Sales Range: $10-24.9 Million
Emp.: 25
Electromechanical Relay Mfr
N.A.I.C.S.: 335314
Ivo van Erp *(Engr-Sls-Electronic Components)*

Panasonic Electric Works Schweiz AG (2)
Grundstrasse 8, 6343, Rotkreuz, 6343, Switzerland
Tel.: (41) 41 7997050
Web Site: http://www.panasonic-electric-works.ch
Industrial Relay Distr
N.A.I.C.S.: 423610

Panasonic Electric Works UK Ltd. (2)
Sunrise Parkway Linford Wood, Milton Keynes, MK14 6LF, United Kingdom
Tel.: (44) 190 823 1555
Web Site: http://www.panasonic-electric-works.co.uk
Sales Range: $25-49.9 Million
Emp.: 15
Industrial Automation Component Distr
N.A.I.C.S.: 423840
Richard Thornton *(Mng Dir)*

Plant (Domestic):

Panasonic Industrial Devices Europe GmbH (2)
Zeppelinstrasse 19, 21337, Luneburg, Germany
Tel.: (49) 4 131 8990
Web Site: https://pideu.panasonic.de
Industrial Relay Mfr
N.A.I.C.S.: 335314

Panasonic Electronic Device Company Co. Ltd. (1)
1006 Oaza Kadoma Kadoma City, Osaka, 571 8506, Japan (100%)
Tel.: (81) 669081101
Web Site: http://www.panasonic.co.jp
Sales Range: $1-4.9 Billion
Emp.: 6,000
Mfr of Electronic Components
N.A.I.C.S.: 334419

Subsidiary (Non-US):

Panasonic Electronic Devices (Thailand) Co., Ltd. (2)
101 Moo 2 Teparak Road, Samut Prakan, 10540, Thailand
Tel.: (66) 2 723 3100
Household Electrical Equipment Mfr & Distr
N.A.I.C.S.: 335220

Panasonic Electronic Devices Slovakia s.r.o. (2)
Oravicka 616, 028 01, Trstena, Slovakia
Tel.: (421) 435303200
Consumer Electronics Distr
N.A.I.C.S.: 423620

Panasonic Electronic Devices Vietnam Co., Ltd. (2)
Plot 1/2 Thang Long Industrial Park, Hanoi, Vietnam
Tel.: (84) 4 955 0082
Household Electrical Equipment Mfr & Distr
N.A.I.C.S.: 335220

Panasonic Elektronik Satis A.S. (1)
Buyaka 2 Site Tower 3 K 9 Office No 58 FSM Mah Poligon Cad, Umraniye, 34771, Istanbul, Turkiye
Tel.: (90) 216 681 0400
Web Site: https://www.panasonic.com
Sales Range: $25-49.9 Million
Emp.: 55
Consumer Electronics Distr
N.A.I.C.S.: 423620

Panasonic Energy (Thailand) Co., Ltd. (1)
166 Village No 4 Sukhumvit Road, Thepharak Subdistrict Mueang District, Samut Prakan, 10270, Thailand
Tel.: (66) 2 384 1156
Web Site: http://www.panasonic.com
Storage Battery Mfr
N.A.I.C.S.: 335910

Panasonic Energy Belgium N.V. (1)
Industriezone Ravenshout 4 215 Havenlaan 6, 3980, Tessenderlo, Belgium
Tel.: (32) 24811170
Web Site: http://www.panasonic-battery.com
Sales Range: $75-99.9 Million
Emp.: 400
Storage Battery Mfr
N.A.I.C.S.: 335910
Marc DeBaere *(Pres)*

Panasonic Energy India Company Ltd. (1)
GIDC Makarpura, Vadodara, 390 010, Gujarat, India
Tel.: (91) 2652642661
Web Site: https://www.panasonicenergyindia.in
Rev: $22,469,900
Assets: $11,471,267
Liabilities: $3,334,177
Net Worth: $8,137,090
Earnings: $216,965
Emp.: 837
Fiscal Year-end: 03/31/2023
Electronic Products Mfr
N.A.I.C.S.: 334419
Susheela Maheshwari *(Sec)*

Panasonic Energy Poland S.A. (1)
Ul Sloneczna 42, 62-200, Gniezno, Poland
Tel.: (48) 614230000
Zinc Carbon Dry Battery Mfr
N.A.I.C.S.: 335910

Panasonic Energy Tanzania Co., Ltd. (1)
Nyerere Road 24, PO Box 40009, Dar es Salaam, Tanzania
Tel.: (255) 22 2860180
Web Site: http://www.panasonic.net
Storage Battery Mfr
N.A.I.C.S.: 335910

Panasonic Environmental Systems & Engineering Co., Ltd. (1)
3-28-33 Tarumi-cho, Suita, 564-0062, Osaka, Japan
Tel.: (81) 663381852
Web Site: http://www.panasonic.co.jp
Emp.: 500
Environmental Engineering Services
N.A.I.C.S.: 541330

Panasonic Espana S.A. (1)
WTC Almeda Park, Cornella de Llobregat, 8940, Barcelona, Spain
Tel.: (34) 90 215 3060

PANASONIC HOLDINGS CORPORATION

Panasonic Holdings Corporation—(Continued)
Web Site: https://www.panasonic.com
Emp.: 150
Consumer Electronics Distr
N.A.I.C.S.: 423620

Panasonic Factory Solutions Co., Ltd. (1)
2-7 Matsuba-cho, Kadoma, 571-8502, Osaka, Japan
Tel.: (81) 669055535
Sales Range: $800-899.9 Million
Emp.: 273
Industrial Automation Equipments Mfr
N.A.I.C.S.: 333248

Panasonic Germany (1)
Winsbergring 15, 22525, Hamburg, Germany (100%)
Tel.: (49) 55558855
Web Site: http://www.panasonic.com
Emp.: 380
Sales of Video, Television & Audio Equipment, Microwave Ovens, Air Conditioning Equipment
N.A.I.C.S.: 449210

Panasonic Gulf FZE (1)
Jebel Ali Free Zone, PO Box 61285, Dubai, United Arab Emirates
Tel.: (971) 4 8862 425
Sales Range: $75-99.9 Million
Emp.: 20
Consumer Electronics Distr
N.A.I.C.S.: 423620

Subsidiary (Domestic):

Panasonic Marketing Middle East & Africa FZE (2)
Jebel Ali Free Zone South, Dubai, United Arab Emirates
Tel.: (971) 4 886 2142
Web Site: http://www.panasonic.ae
Consumer Electronics Distr
N.A.I.C.S.: 423620
Hiroyuki Shibutani (Mng Dir)

Panasonic Home Elevator Co., Ltd. (1)
101048 Kazuma, Osaka, 571-8686, Japan
Tel.: (81) 669002655
Web Site: http://panasonic.co.jp
Emp.: 160
Elevator Mfr & Distr
N.A.I.C.S.: 333921
Takano Tadaaki (Pres)

Panasonic Homes Co., Ltd. (1)
1-4 Shinsenri-nishimachi 1 Chome, Toyonaka, 560-8543, Osaka, Japan (80.2%)
Tel.: (81) 668345111
Web Site: http://homes.panasonic.com
Rev.: $3,134,382,480
Assets: $2,555,486,400
Liabilities: $1,096,617,840
Net Worth: $1,458,868,560
Earnings: $90,442,800
Emp.: 6,323
Fiscal Year-end: 03/31/2017
Building Construction Services
N.A.I.C.S.: 236220
Atsushi Hongo (Sr Mng Exec Officer)

Panasonic Industrial Devices Materials Europe GmbH (1)
Ennshafenstr 30, Enns, 4470, Austria
Tel.: (43) 7223 883
Sales Range: $50-74.9 Million
Emp.: 110
Electromechanical Relay Mfr
N.A.I.C.S.: 334513
Takaharu Karasawa (Mng Dir)

Panasonic Industrial Devices Materials Sales Co., Ltd. (1)
1048 Kadoma, Kadoma, 571-8686, Osaka, Japan
Tel.: (81) 669049117
Sales Range: $250-299.9 Million
Emp.: 100
Consumer Electronics Distr
N.A.I.C.S.: 423620

Panasonic Industrial Devices SUNX Co., Ltd. (1)
2431-1 Ushiyama-cho, Kasugai, 486-0901, Aichi, Japan (69.97%)
Tel.: (81) 568337211

Web Site: http://www2.panasonic.co.jp
Control Instruments Mfr & Sales
N.A.I.C.S.: 334513
Nobuhiro Takeda (Pres)

Panasonic Information Systems Co., Ltd.
16th Fl Applause Tower 19-19 Chayamachi, Kita-ku, Osaka, 530-0013, Japan
Tel.: (81) 66 906 2801
Web Site: https://www.is-c.panasonic.co.jp
Computer System Managing Services
N.A.I.C.S.: 541511
Hiroyoshi Maruyama (Mng Dir)

Panasonic Insurance Service Broker (Thailand) Co., Ltd (1)
26/4 Orakarn Building Ploenchit Road Lumpini Sub-District, Pathumwan District, Bangkok, 10330, Thailand
Tel.: (66) 2655 3810
Insurance Brokerage Services
N.A.I.C.S.: 524210

Panasonic Interior Lighting Co., Ltd. (1)
7-7-6 Yumegaoka, Iga, 518-0131, Mie, Japan
Tel.: (81) 595 26 3600
Lighting Equipment Mfr
N.A.I.C.S.: 335139

Panasonic Ireland Ltd. (1)
1 The Courtyard Kilcarberry Business park, Dublin, Ireland
Tel.: (353) 14135300
Web Site: http://www.panasonic.co.uk
Sales Range: $25-49.9 Million
Emp.: 10
Consumer Electronics Distr
N.A.I.C.S.: 423620
Tony Duggan (Gen Mgr)

Panasonic Italia S.p.A. (1)
Via Lucini N 19, 20125, Milan, Italy
Tel.: (39) 0267881
Consumer Electronics Distr
N.A.I.C.S.: 423620

Panasonic Korea Ltd. (1)
17th floor Opurance Building 254 Seochodaero, Seocho-gu, Seoul, 137-073, Korea (South)
Tel.: (82) 2 533 8452
Web Site: https://www.panasonic.kr
Household Appliance Mfr & Distr
N.A.I.C.S.: 335220

Subsidiary (Domestic):

Panasonic Industrial Devices Sales Korea Co., Ltd. (2)
38 Teheran-ro 114-gil Daechi-dong 1004 Dongil Tower 5-6F, Gangnam-gu, Seoul, 06176, Korea (South)
Tel.: (82) 2 795 9600
Web Site: https://industrial.panasonic.com
Semiconductor Device Distr
N.A.I.C.S.: 423690

Subsidiary (Non-US):

Panasonic Latin America, S.A. (2)
Tower of the Americas Punta Darien Street Floor 20 Office 2001, Panama, Panama
Tel.: (507) 229 2955
Web Site: https://www.panasonic.com
Emp.: 180
Consumer Electronics Distr
N.A.I.C.S.: 423620

Panasonic Life Solutions India Private Limited (1)
3rd Floor B Wing I Think Techno Campus Pokhran Road No-2 Thane West, Thane, 400 607, Maharashtra, India
Tel.: (91) 224 222 8888
Web Site: https://www.lsin.panasonic.com
Electrical & Electronic Mfr
N.A.I.C.S.: 336320
Kazuki Yao (Mng Dir)

Panasonic Lighting Systems Co., Ltd. (1)
1048 Oaza, Kadoma, Osaka, Japan (100%)
Tel.: (81) 6 6906 2205
Emp.: 1,465
Lighting Equipment Mfr
N.A.I.C.S.: 335139

Masaharu Michiura (Pres)

Subsidiary (Non-US):

Panasonic Lighting (Beijing) Co., Ltd (2)
No 1 Tongji North Road Economic Technology Development Zone, Beijing, 100176, China
Tel.: (86) 1087858591
Lighting Equipment Mfr
N.A.I.C.S.: 335139

Subsidiary (US):

Panasonic Lighting Americas, Inc. (2)
26 Century Blvd Ste 500, Nashville, TN 37214
Tel.: (615) 316-5100
Lighting Equipment Mfr
N.A.I.C.S.: 335139
Chris Dimino (Exec VP-Sys Grp)

Subsidiary (Domestic):

Universal Lighting Technologies, Inc. (3)
51 Century Blvd Ste 230, Nashville, TN 37214-3683
Tel.: (615) 316-5100
Web Site: https://www.unvlt.com
Sales Range: $800-899.9 Million
Emp.: 4,000
Electronic, Magnetic, Compact & Fluorescent Lightning Ballasts, High Intensity Discharges, Capacitors, Wire & Neon Transformers Mfr
N.A.I.C.S.: 335311
Pat Sullivan (Chm & CEO)

Subsidiary (Domestic):

Panasonic Lighting Device Marketing Co., Ltd. (2)
1048 Kadoma Panasonic Denkonai, Kadoma, 571-8686, Japan
Tel.: (81) 642528020
Home Lighting Fixture Distr
N.A.I.C.S.: 423220

Subsidiary (Non-US):

Panasonic Lighting Devices Serbia d. o. o. (2)
Bb Karl Rojm, Kusiljevo, 35226, Serbia
Tel.: (381) 358150100
Lighting Fixture Mfr
N.A.I.C.S.: 335132
Dirk Bantel (Gen Mgr)

Panasonic Lighting Europe GmbH (2)
Hohe Steinert 8, Ludenscheid, 58509, Nordrhein-Westfalen, Germany
Tel.: (49) 23511010
Lighting Fixture Mfr
N.A.I.C.S.: 335132

Panasonic Malaysia Sdn. Bhd. (1)
Lot 10 Jalan 13/2, 46200, Petaling Jaya, Selangor, Malaysia
Tel.: (60) 37 809 7888
Web Site: https://www.panasonic.com
Sales Range: $75-99.9 Million
Emp.: 230
Consumer Electronics Distr
N.A.I.C.S.: 423620
Cheng Chee Chung (Mng Dir)

Subsidiary (Domestic):

Panasonic AVC Networks Kuala Lumpur Malaysia Sdn. Bhd. (2)
Lot 5 Persiaran Tengku Ampuan Section 21, Shah Alam Industrial Site, 40300, Shah Alam, Selangor, Malaysia
Tel.: (60) 35 891 3888
Web Site: https://www.panasonic.com
Emp.: 1,000
Television Sets Mfr
N.A.I.C.S.: 334310

Panasonic Appliances Foundry Malaysia Sdn. Bhd. (2)
Lot 9 and 10 Tangga Batu Industrial Site, Tanjong Kling, 76400, Melaka, Malaysia
Tel.: (60) 6 351 1444
Web Site: https://www.panasonic.com

Sales Range: $75-99.9 Million
Precision Casting Component Mfr
N.A.I.C.S.: 331511

Panasonic Financial Centre (M) Sdn Bhd (2)
Lot C418 4th Floor Central Tower Wisma Consplant 2, Wisma Consplant, Petaling Jaya, 47500, Selangor, Malaysia
Tel.: (60) 3 5634 8420
Emp.: 8
Financial Management Services
N.A.I.C.S.: 523999

Panasonic Foundry Malaysia Sdn Bhd (2)
Lot 9 & 10 Tangga Batu Industrial Estate, Tanjung Kling, 76400, Melaka, Malaysia
Tel.: (60) 6 351 1444
Emp.: 280
Compressor Precision Casting Mfr
N.A.I.C.S.: 331523
Yuji Mori (Mng Dir)

Panasonic Industrial Co., (M) Sdn Bhd (2)
15th Floor Menara IGB Mid Valley City, Lingkaran Syed Putra, Kuala Lumpur, 59200, Malaysia
Tel.: (60) 3 2297 6888
Web Site: http://www.na.industrial.panasonic.com
Emp.: 160
Industrial Machinery Distr
N.A.I.C.S.: 423830
Kousuke Akiyoshi (Mng Dir)

Panasonic Industrial Devices Sales (M) Sdn. Bhd. (2)
15th Floor Menara IGB Mid Valley City Lingkaran Syed Putra, 59200, Lumpur, Malaysia
Tel.: (60) 32 297 6888
Web Site: https://www.panasonic.com
Electronic Device Distr
N.A.I.C.S.: 423690

Panasonic Manufacturing Malaysia Berhad (2)
No 3 Jalan Sesiku 15/2 Section 15 Shah Alam Industrial Site, 40200, Shah Alam, Selangor Darul Ehsan, Malaysia
Tel.: (60) 358915000
Web Site: https://pmma.panasonic.com.my
Rev.: $209,868,360
Assets: $195,177,354
Liabilities: $26,939,048
Net Worth: $168,238,307
Earnings: $16,959,153
Emp.: 1,336
Fiscal Year-end: 03/31/2023
Batteries Mfr
N.A.I.C.S.: 335910
Oi Wah Leong (Sec)

Panasonic R&D Centre Malaysia Sdn. Bhd. (2)
Ground Floor Prima Avenue Block 3508 Jalan Teknokrat 6, 63000, Cyberjaya, Selangor, Malaysia
Tel.: (60) 3 8318 1228
Sales Range: $25-49.9 Million
Emp.: 7
Consumer Electronics Research & Development Services
N.A.I.C.S.: 541715

Panasonic Semiconductor Discrete Devices (M) Sdn Bhd (2)
Lot 26 & 27 Batu Berendam FIZ III, 75350, Melaka, Malaysia
Tel.: (60) 6 2843 676
Semiconductor Devices Mfr
N.A.I.C.S.: 334413

Panasonic System Networks Malaysia Sdn. Bhd. (2)
Plo No 1 Kawasan Perindustrian Senai KB No 104, 81400, Senai, Johor Darul Takzim, Malaysia
Tel.: (60) 7 599 1801
Network Integration Services
N.A.I.C.S.: 541512
Yukihio Caneco (Gen Mgr)

Panasonic Trading Malaysia Sdn Bhd (2)
12B Manara PKNS PJ No 17 Jalan Yong Shook Lin, 46050, Petaling Jaya, Selangor

AND PRIVATE COMPANIES — PANASONIC HOLDINGS CORPORATION

Darul Ehsan, Malaysia
Tel.: (60) 3 7953 5200
Sales Range: $25-49.9 Million
Emp.: 10
Logistics Consulting Servies
N.A.I.C.S.: 541614
Kenji Yoshida (Mng Dir)

Panasonic Manufacturing (Ayuthaya) Co., Ltd. (1)
Rojana Industrial Park 1/69 M005 Rojana Road, Tambol Kanham Amphur Uthai, Ayuthaya, 13210, Thailand
Tel.: (66) 35 330 846
Lighting Equipment Mfr
N.A.I.C.S.: 335139

Panasonic Manufacturing U.K. Ltd. (1)
Pentwyn Industrial Estate, Cardiff, CF23 7XB, United Kingdom
Tel.: (44) 292 054 0011
Web Site: https://www.pmuk.co.uk
Household Appliances Mfr
N.A.I.C.S.: 335220

Panasonic Marketing Europe G.m.b.H. (1)
Hagenauer Str 43, 65203, Wiesbaden, Germany
Tel.: (49) 6112350
Emp.: 220
Projector Distr
N.A.I.C.S.: 423620

Division (Domestic):

Panasonic Marketing Europe G.m.b.H. - Panasonic Deutschland Division (2)
Winsbergring 15, 22525, Hamburg, Germany
Tel.: (49) 4085490
Web Site: https://www.panasonic.com
Sales Range: $125-149.9 Million
Emp.: 300
Consumer Electronics Distr
N.A.I.C.S.: 423620
Christian Sokcevie (Pres)

Panasonic Marketing Europe GmbH - Romania (2)
Blvd Preciziei Nr 24 West Gate Park Cladirea H3 Et2 Sect 6, Bucharest, 062204, Romania
Tel.: (40) 213162888
Web Site: http://www.panasonic.ro
Consumer Electronics Distr
N.A.I.C.S.: 423620
Laurent Abadie (Pres & CEO-Panasonic-Europe)

Panasonic Mobile Communications Co., Ltd. (1)
600 Saedo cho Tsuzuki ku, Yokohama, 224 8539, Japan
Tel.: (81) 459360821
Web Site: http://www.panasonic.co.jp
Sales Range: $800-899.9 Million
Emp.: 2,600
Electronic Key Telephones & Mobile Phones
N.A.I.C.S.: 517112

Panasonic Mobile Communications Development of Europe Limited (1)
2 Gables Way, Colthrop, Thatcham, RG19 4ZD, Berks, United Kingdom (100%)
Tel.: (44) 1635875520
Web Site: http://www.panasonic-europe.com
Electronic Products
N.A.I.C.S.: 334513

Panasonic New Zealand Limited (1)
18 Sir Woolf Fisher Drive, Highbrook East Tamaki, Auckland, 1741, New Zealand
Tel.: (64) 9 272 0100
Web Site: https://www.panasonic.com
Sales Range: $50-74.9 Million
Emp.: 115
Mfr of Electrical Appliances
N.A.I.C.S.: 449210
Stewart Fowler (Mng Dir)

Panasonic Nordic AB (1)
Sundbybergsvagen 1 B, 171 73, Solna, Sweden
Tel.: (46) 8 680 2600
Web Site: http://www.panasonic.se

Sales Range: $25-49.9 Million
Emp.: 80
Consumer Electronics Distr
N.A.I.C.S.: 423620

Panasonic Photo & Lighting Hong Kong Co., Ltd. (1)
Top F E Chinachem Golden Plz 77 Mody Rd, Tsim Tsa Tsui, China (Hong Kong)
Tel.: (852) 27398968
Photoflash Bulb Mfr
N.A.I.C.S.: 335139

Panasonic Plasma Display Co., Ltd. (1)
1-1 Matsushita-cho, Ibaraki, 567-0026, Osaka, Japan
Tel.: (81) 726248461
Sales Range: $450-499.9 Million
Emp.: 1,200
Plasma Display Panel Mfr & Distr
N.A.I.C.S.: 334419

Panasonic R&D Center Germany GmbH (1)
Monzastrasse 4c, 63225, Langen, Germany
Tel.: (49) 61037660
Web Site: http://www.panasonic.net
Research & Development Services
N.A.I.C.S.: 541715

Panasonic Russia, Ltd. (1)
st Bolshaya Tulskaya 11, 115191, Moscow, Russia
Tel.: (7) 495 665 4205
Web Site: http://www.panasonic.com
Consumer Electronics & Personal Care Product Distr
N.A.I.C.S.: 423620

Panasonic South-East Europe Ltd. (1)
INFOPARK Research Center Neumann Janos U 1, Budapest, 1117, Hungary
Tel.: (36) 13826060
Web Site: http://www.panasonic.hu
Sales Range: $25-49.9 Million
Emp.: 40
Consumer Electronics Distr
N.A.I.C.S.: 423620
Takashi Furumoto (Mng Dir)

Panasonic System Networks Co., Ltd. (1)
2-3-8 Shimomeguro, Meguro-ku, Tokyo, 153-8687, Japan
Tel.: (81) 354347111
Web Site: http://www.panasonic.net
Sales Range: $1-4.9 Billion
Emp.: 19,500
Communication Equipment Mfr
N.A.I.C.S.: 334220

Panasonic Taiwan Co., Ltd. (1)
579 Yuan-Shan Road, Chung-Ho District, New Taipei City, Taiwan (100%)
Tel.: (886) 22 223 5121
Web Site: https://www.panasonic.com
Emp.: 2,500
Industrial & Marketing Sales of Electronic Components
N.A.I.C.S.: 334310

Subsidiary (Domestic):

Panasonic AVC Networks Taiwan Co., Ltd. (2)
3rd Floor Building 3 No 579 Yuanshan Road, Zhonghe District, New Taipei City, Taiwan
Tel.: (886) 22 223 5121
Web Site: https://www.panasonic.com
Emp.: 800
Audio & Video Equipment Mfr
N.A.I.C.S.: 334310

Panasonic Industrial Devices Sales (Taiwan) Co., Ltd. (2)
12F No 9 Songgao Road, Taipei, 110, Taiwan
Tel.: (886) 22 757 1900
Web Site: https://industrial.panasonic.com
Emp.: 216
Industrial Equipment Distr
N.A.I.C.S.: 423830

Panasonic Treasury Center (Thailand) Co., Ltd. (1)
26/3 Orakarn Building Ploenchit Road Lumpini Sub-district, Pathumwan District, Bang-

kok, 10330, Thailand
Tel.: (66) 2655 5795
Treasury Financial Services
N.A.I.C.S.: 921130

Panasonic Vietnam Co., Ltd. (1)
Lot J1-J2 Thang Long Industrial Park, Kim Chung Commune Dong Anh District, Hanoi, 1000, Vietnam
Tel.: (84) 43 955 0111
Web Site: https://www.panasonic.com
Emp.: 100
Investment Management Service
N.A.I.C.S.: 523999
Eiji Fukumori (Gen Dir)

Panasonic Welding Systems Co., Ltd. (1)
3-1-1 Inazu-Cho, Toyonaka, 561-0854, Osaka, Japan
Tel.: (81) 668621121
Web Site: http://www.panasonic.co.jp
Sales Range: $200-249.9 Million
Emp.: 600
Welding Equipment Mfr
N.A.I.C.S.: 333992

Panasonic de Mexico, S.A. de C.V. (1)
Felix Cuevas No 6 Floors 2 and 3, Col Tlacoquemecatl del Valle Del Benito Juarez, 56530, Ixtapaluca, Mexico
Tel.: (52) 5554881000
Web Site: https://www.panasonic.com
Consumer Electronics Distr
N.A.I.C.S.: 423620

STC Products Service Center Co., Ltd. (1)
646 Moo 4 Hoffen Building 1st Floor Serithai Road, Khlong Kum Subdistrict Bueng Kum District, Bangkok, 10240, Thailand
Tel.: (66) 21 163 4467
Web Site: https://www.stcpro.co.th
Emp.: 39
Appliance Service Center
N.A.I.C.S.: 811412
Tsutomu Morimoto (Mng Dir)

Sanyo Electric Co., Ltd. (1)
2-1-61 Shiromi, Chuo-ku, Osaka, 570 8677, Japan (100%)
Tel.: (81) 669911181
Web Site: http://panasonic.net
Sales Range: $15-24.9 Billion
Emp.: 86,016
Consumer & Commercial Electronic Appliances & Components Mfr
N.A.I.C.S.: 335210
Kazuhiro Yoshida (VP)

Subsidiary (Non-US):

Chen Ho & Co., Ltd. (2)
4Fl 100 Chung Hsiao West Rd Section 1, Taipei, 100, Taiwan
Tel.: (886) 223715233
Household Audio Equipment
N.A.I.C.S.: 334310

Dalian Honjo Chemical Corporation (2)
118 Huaihe West Rd Economical & Technology Development Zone, Dalian, China (100%)
Tel.: (86) 411 8731 8435
Mfr of Chemical Components
N.A.I.C.S.: 325180

Dalian Sanyo Cold-Chain Co., Ltd. (2)
6 Songlan St Economical & Technology Development, Dalian, China (100%)
Tel.: (86) 4117310864
N.A.I.C.S.: 334310

Dalian Sanyo Compressor Co., Ltd. (2)
8 Songlan Street, Economic & Technology, Development Zone, Dalian, 116600, China (55%)
Tel.: (86) 41162787800
Sales Range: $350-399.9 Million
Emp.: 1,800
Refrigeration & Air-Conditioning Compressors Mfr; Owned 55% by Sanyo Electric Co., Ltd., 40% by Dalian Bingshan Group & 5% by Sojitz Corporation
N.A.I.C.S.: 333415

Zhihai Zhao (Gen Mgr)

Dalian Sanyo Refrigeration Co., Ltd. (2)
188 Huaihe West Rd Economic & Technology Development Zone, Dalian, 116600, China (100%)
Tel.: (86) 41187316275
Web Site: http://www.dl-sanyo.cn
Sales Range: $1-9.9 Million
Emp.: 300
Refrigerator Mfr
N.A.I.C.S.: 333415
Matsu Naga (Gen Mgr)

Newsan S.A. (2)
Roque Perez 3650, Capital Federal, 1430, Buenos Aires, Argentina (100%)
Tel.: (54) 1145455100
Sales Range: $25-49.9 Million
Emp.: 300
N.A.I.C.S.: 334310

Subsidiary (Domestic):

Niigata Sanyo Electronic Co., Ltd. (2)
Koh 300 Chiya, Oziya City, Niigata, 947 8502, Japan (100%)
Tel.: (81) 258833434
Web Site: http://www.nsec.jp.sc-sanyo.com
Sales Range: $350-399.9 Million
Emp.: 1,400
Mfr & Retailer of Semiconductors
N.A.I.C.S.: 334413

Subsidiary (Non-US):

PT. Sanyo Compressor Indonesia (2)
EJIP Industrial Park Plot 1A 1, Lemah Abang, Bekasi, 17550, Indonesia
Tel.: (62) 218970061
Web Site: http://www.sanyo.co.jp
Sales Range: $350-399.9 Million
Emp.: 2,000
Mfr of Compressors for Cooling Equipment
N.A.I.C.S.: 333415

PT. Sanyo Electronics Indonesia (2)
E Jakarta Industrial Pk Plot 1A 3, Bekasi, 17550, Indonesia (100%)
Tel.: (62) 218971161
Web Site: http://www.sanyo-ssm.com
Sales Range: $25-49.9 Million
Emp.: 100
N.A.I.C.S.: 334310

PT. Sanyo Energy (Batam) Corporate (2)
Lot 11 Batam Industrial Park Mukakuning, Batam, 29433, Indonesia (70%)
Tel.: (62) 770611321
Web Site: http://www.sanyo.com
Sales Range: $25-49.9 Million
Emp.: 970
N.A.I.C.S.: 334310

PT. Sanyo Jaya Components Indonesia (2)
Jalan Raya Jakarta-Bogor Km 35, Cimanggis-Depok, Bogor, 16955, West Java, Indonesia (100%)
Tel.: (62) 218741567
Web Site: http://www.sanyo-asia.com
Video Imaging Systems & Components
N.A.I.C.S.: 334310

PT. Sanyo Precision Batam (2)
Lot 9 Batamindo Industrial Park, Batam, 29433, Indonesia (100%)
Tel.: (62) 770612901
Sales Range: $700-749.9 Million
Emp.: 3,000
N.A.I.C.S.: 334310

Affiliate (Domestic):

Royal Tourist Co., Ltd. (2)
1 1 10 Ueno, Taito Ku, Tokyo, 110 8534, Japan
Tel.: (81) 338363827
Travel Agency
N.A.I.C.S.: 561510

Subsidiary (Non-US):

SANYO Commercial Solutions (Thailand) Co., Ltd. (2)

PANASONIC HOLDINGS CORPORATION

Panasonic Holdings Corporation—(Continued)

28/3 Moo 1 Soi Wat Hnam Daeng Suwintawong Rd T Klong Udom Chollachorn, A Muang, Chachoengsao, 24000, Thailand
Tel.: (66) 38593270
Emp.: 500
Consumer Electronics Distr
N.A.I.C.S.: 423620
Yasuaji Ganimoto *(Mng Dir)*

SANYO E&E S.A. de C.V. (2)
Calle Uno Poniente No 100 Ciudad Industrial, Tijuana, 22444, Baja California, Mexico
Tel.: (52) 6646474495
Household Appliances Mfr
N.A.I.C.S.: 335220

SANYO Electronic Components (S) Pte. Ltd. (2)
70 Anson Road 23-00 Hub Synergy Point, Singapore, 79905, Singapore
Tel.: (65) 62230225
Electronic Components Mfr
N.A.I.C.S.: 334419

SANYO Semiconductor (Vietnam) Co., Ltd. (2)
Road 8 Tan Thuan Export Processing Zone, Dist 7, Ho Chi Minh City, Vietnam
Tel.: (84) 837701403
Web Site: http://ap.sanyo.com
Semiconductor Devices Mfr
N.A.I.C.S.: 334413

Affiliate (Domestic):

SMI Co., Ltd. (2)
1 10 Ueno 1 Chome, Taito Ku, Tokyo, 110 8534, Japan
Tel.: (81) 38369401
Travel Agency
N.A.I.C.S.: 561510

Subsidiary (Non-US):

Sanwa Electric Philippines, Inc. (2)
, Tarlac, Philippines
N.A.I.C.S.: 334310

Sanwa Estate Philippines, Inc. (2)
, Manila, Philippines
Household Audio & Video Equipment Mfr
N.A.I.C.S.: 334310

Sanyo Airconditioners Europe S.r.l. (2)
Via Bisceglie 76, 20152, Milan, Italy **(100%)**
Tel.: (39) 0248300760
Web Site: http://www.sanyoaircond.com
Sales Range: $25-49.9 Million
Emp.: 35
Air Conditioners
N.A.I.C.S.: 334310

Sanyo Airconditioners Manufacturing Singapore Pte., Ltd. (2)
6 Commonwealth Ln Unite 03-01 02, Singapore, 149547, Singapore **(100%)**
Tel.: (65) 62657777
Web Site: http://www.sanyoairconditioning.com.sg
Sales Range: $25-49.9 Million
Emp.: 20
Air Conditioner Mfr
N.A.I.C.S.: 333415

Sanyo Argo Clima S.r.l. (2)
Via Varese 90, 21013, Gallarate, Italy **(49%)**
Tel.: (39) 0331755111
Web Site: http://www.argoclima.com
Sales Range: $25-49.9 Million
Emp.: 200
N.A.I.C.S.: 334310

Sanyo Armco (Kenya) Limited (2)
Hughes Building 2nd Floor Muindi Mbingu Street, Nairobi, Kenya
Tel.: (254) 2444628
Web Site: http://www.sanyoarmco.com
Household Appliances
N.A.I.C.S.: 444140

Sanyo Asia Pte Ltd (2)
152 Besch Road Floor 18 01, Singapore, 189721, Singapore **(100%)**
Tel.: (65) 67479755
Web Site: http://www.sanyo.com.sg
Sales Range: $25-49.9 Million
Emp.: 13
Household Appliances
N.A.I.C.S.: 444140

Subsidiary (Non-US):

SANYO Automedia Sdn. Bhd. (3)
Plot 10 Phase 4 Prai Industrial Estate, 13600, Penang, Prai, Malaysia **(100%)**
Tel.: (60) 45078988
Car Audio Products Mfr
N.A.I.C.S.: 334310

Subsidiary (Non-US):

Sanyo Automedia Sdn. Bhd. (2)
Plot 10 Phase 4 Prai Industrial Estate, 13600, Penang, Malaysia **(100%)**
Tel.: (60) 45078988
Web Site: http://www.sanyo.com.my
Sales Range: $100-124.9 Million
Emp.: 2,000
Household Audio & Video Equipment Mfr
N.A.I.C.S.: 334310

Sanyo Buro-Electronic Europe-Vertrieb GmbH (2)
Postfach 80 17 40, D 81617, Munich, Germany **(100%)**
Tel.: (49) 8941604600
Web Site: http://www.sbee.de
Sales Range: $25-49.9 Million
Emp.: 10
Audio & Video Equipment Mfr
N.A.I.C.S.: 334310

Sanyo Canada Holdings 1990 Inc. (2)
1 300 Applewood Crescent, Concord, L4K 5C7, ON, Canada **(100%)**
Tel.: (905) 265-4100
Web Site: http://www.sanyo.com
Sales Range: $25-49.9 Million
Emp.: 65
Holding Company
N.A.I.C.S.: 551112

Sanyo Commercial Refrigeration International Co., Ltd. (2)
5th Fl Aerospace Ctr 143 Hoi Bun Rd Kwun Tong, Kowloon, China (Hong Kong) **(100%)**
Tel.: (852) 25663456
Web Site: http://www.sanyohk.biz.com.hk
Sales Range: $25-49.9 Million
Emp.: 40
N.A.I.C.S.: 334310

Sanyo Customs Brokerage S.A. de C.V. (2)
Calle uno poniente No 19020, 22444, Tijuana, Mexico **(100%)**
Tel.: (52) 6649797000
Web Site: http://www.sanyocustoms.com
Sales Range: $25-49.9 Million
Emp.: 45
Customs Brokerage & Logistics
N.A.I.C.S.: 334310
Elizabeth Donate *(VP-Corp Licensed Customs Broker)*

Sanyo Denso Industries (Singapore) Pte., Ltd. (2)
1 Tuas Ave 10 Jurong MD CC Wing, Singapore, Singapore
Mfr of Household Audio & Video Equipment
N.A.I.C.S.: 334310

Sanyo E.T. Canada, Inc. (2)
201 Credit View, Woodbridge, L4L 9T1, ON, Canada **(100%)**
Tel.: (905) 265-4100
Web Site: http://www.sanyo.ca
Sales Range: $10-24.9 Million
Emp.: 50
Operator of Accounting & Marketing Offices for the Sanyo In Canada
N.A.I.C.S.: 541219

Sanyo Electric International Finance (UK) PLC (2)
Sanyo House Otterspool Way, Watford, WD25 8JX, United Kingdom
Tel.: (44) 923246363
Web Site: http://www.sanyo.co.uk
Financial Services
N.A.I.C.S.: 523999

Sanyo Electronic (Taichung) Co., Ltd. (2)
Taichung Export Processing Zone No 5-3 Nan 2nd Road, Taichung, 427, Hsien, Taiwan **(89.41%)**
Tel.: (886) 425343141
Sales Range: $75-99.9 Million
Emp.: 500
Mfr of Semiconductors
N.A.I.C.S.: 334413

Sanyo Electronics S.A. (2)
Av Perito Moreno 1651, 9410, Ushuaia, Tierra Del Fuego, Argentina **(100%)**
Tel.: (54) 8103217262
Web Site: http://www.panasonic.com.ar
Sales Range: $75-99.9 Million
Emp.: 400
Electronics Mfr
N.A.I.C.S.: 334310

Sanyo Energy (Singapore) Corp., Pte. Ltd. (2)
260 Orchard Rd unit 14-01 The Heeren Bldg, Singapore, 238855, Singapore **(73.98%)**
Tel.: (65) 67363100
Sales Range: $25-49.9 Million
Emp.: 40
Microwave Ovens
N.A.I.C.S.: 335220

Sanyo Energy (Singapore) Corporation Pte., Ltd. (2)
260 Orchard Rd, Singapore, 238855, Singapore **(100%)**
Tel.: (65) 67363100
Web Site: http://www.sanyo.com.sg
Sales Range: $25-49.9 Million
Emp.: 30
N.A.I.C.S.: 334310

Sanyo Fisher Vertriebs GmbH (2)
Stahlgruberring 4, D 81829, Munich, Germany **(100%)**
Tel.: (49) 89451160
Web Site: http://www.sanyo.de
Sales Range: $25-49.9 Million
Emp.: 60
Distr of Audio Systems
N.A.I.C.S.: 449210

Sanyo LSI Technology India Private Limited (2)
Unit 03 Level 08 Discoverer Block International Tech Park, Bengaluru, 560-066, India
Tel.: (91) 8028410600
Sales Range: $25-49.9 Million
Emp.: 50
Audio & Video Equipment Mfr
N.A.I.C.S.: 334310

Subsidiary (US):

Sanyo North American Corporation (2)
2055 Sanyo Ave, San Diego, CA 92154-6229 **(96.88%)**
Tel.: (619) 661-1134
Web Site: http://www.sanyo.com
Sales Range: $25-49.9 Million
Emp.: 60
Provider of Administrative Services for Sanyo's North American Operations
N.A.I.C.S.: 541618

Subsidiary (Domestic):

SANYO Customs Brokerage, Inc. (3)
9850 Siempre Viva Rd Ste 3 Otay Mesa, San Diego, CA 92154
Tel.: (619) 661-6995
Web Site: http://www.us.sanyo.com
Sales Range: $50-74.9 Million
Emp.: 30
Customs Brokerage Services
N.A.I.C.S.: 523150
Daisuke Kutsunugi *(Pres)*

SANYO Electronic Device (U.S.A.) Corporation (3)
2055 Sanyo Ave, San Diego, CA 92154-6229
Tel.: (619) 661-6835
Electronic Equipment Distr
N.A.I.C.S.: 423690

SANYO Solar of Oregon L.L.C. (3)
5475 Gaffin Rd SE, Salem, OR 97317
Tel.: (503) 365-6800
Web Site: http://www.us.panasonic.com

INTERNATIONAL PUBLIC

Emp.: 86
Photo Voltaic Solar Panel Mfr
N.A.I.C.S.: 334413
Toshiro Numura *(Pres)*

Sanyo E & E Corporation (3)
2001 Sanya Ave, San Diego, CA 92154-6297 **(85.43%)**
Tel.: (619) 661-1134
Web Site: http://www.sanyo.com
Sales Range: $25-49.9 Million
Mfr of Refrigerators
N.A.I.C.S.: 335220
Paul Griffin *(Dir-Bus Plng)*

Sanyo Electronic Device Sales (USA) Corporation (3)
49 Walnut St, Norwood, NJ 07648-1329
Tel.: (201) 784-0303
Sales Range: $25-49.9 Million
Emp.: 15
Electronics & Semiconductor Distr
N.A.I.C.S.: 423690
Kiyokazu Nakayama *(Pres & COO)*

Sanyo Energy (U.S.A.) Corporation (3)
2055 Sanyo Ave, San Diego, CA 92154-6297
Tel.: (619) 661-4888
Web Site: http://www.sanyo.com
Sales Range: $50-74.9 Million
Mfr & Sales of Dry Cell & Rechargable Batteries
N.A.I.C.S.: 335910

Division (Domestic):

SANYO Energy (U.S.A.) Corporation - HEV Battery Business Division (4)
26604 Haggerty Rd, Farmington Hills, MI 48331
Tel.: (248) 489-9019
Storage Battery Mfr
N.A.I.C.S.: 335910

SANYO Energy (U.S.A.) Corporation - Kansas City HEV JIT Facility (4)
3608 N Kimball Dr, Kansas City, MO 64161
Tel.: (816) 454-4891
Web Site: http://www.panasonic.com
Emp.: 3
Storage Battery Mfr
N.A.I.C.S.: 335910
Sandy Wilkerson *(Mgr-HR)*

SANYO Energy (U.S.A.) Corporation - Mobile Energy Business Division (4)
2600 Network Blvd Ste 600, Frisco, TX 75034
Tel.: (469) 362-5600
Web Site: http://www.us.sanyo.com
Semiconductor Devices Mfr
N.A.I.C.S.: 334413

Subsidiary (Non-US):

SANYO Energy, S.A. de C.V. (4)
Avenida Santa Barbara 601 Ex-Ejido San Nicolas, Escobedo, 66050, Mexico
Tel.: (52) 8181547100
Web Site: http://www.us.sanyo.com
Storage Battery Mfr
N.A.I.C.S.: 335910

Subsidiary (Domestic):

Sanyo Fisher Company (3)
21605 Plummer St, Chatsworth, CA 91311-4131
Tel.: (818) 998-7322
Web Site: http://www.sanyo.com
Sales Range: $50-74.9 Million
Sales & Marketing of Audio Systems, DVDs, Home Theatres, TVs, VCRs & other Electronic Equipment Including Integrated Component Systems
N.A.I.C.S.: 423690

Division (Domestic):

Sanyo Fisher Home Appliance & Consumer Products Div. (4)
Ste 3 500 Morris Ave, Springfield, NJ 07081-1020
Tel.: (201) 641-2333
Distr of Microwaves & Other Household Appliances
N.A.I.C.S.: 811210

AND PRIVATE COMPANIES

Subsidiary (Domestic):

Sanyo Logistics Corporation (3)
8400 Milliken Ave, Rancho Cucamonga, CA
91730-3970 **(100%)**
Tel.: (310) 303-3000
Sales Range: $25-49.9 Million
Emp.: 19
Distr of Electronic Goods & Components
N.A.I.C.S.: 484110

Subsidiary (Non-US):

Sanyo Oceania Pty. Ltd. (2)
PO Box 947, North Ryde, 1670, NSW,
Australia **(100%)**
Tel.: (61) 288252822
Web Site: http://www.sanyo.com.au
Sales Range: $25-49.9 Million
Emp.: 40
Audio Equipment Mfr
N.A.I.C.S.: 334310

Sanyo Portugal Electronica S.A. (2)
Rua do Cotao Velho 1, San Marcos, 2735
501, Cacem, Portugal **(100%)**
Tel.: (351) 219254500
Web Site: http://www.sanyo.pt
Sales Range: $25-49.9 Million
Emp.: 50
Electronic Mfr & Distr
N.A.I.C.S.: 334310

Sanyo Precision Singapore Pte.,
Ltd. (2)
36 Loyang Way, Apex Tower, Singapore,
508771, Singapore
Tel.: (65) 62248368
Web Site: http://www.nidec.com.sg
Sales Range: $25-49.9 Million
Emp.: 6
Audio & Video Equipment Mfr
N.A.I.C.S.: 334310

Sanyo Sales & Service Sdn.
Bhd. (2)
1 01 Level 1 Wisma Academy 4A Jalan
19/1, 46300, Petaling Jaya, Selangor Darul
Ehsan, Malaysia
Tel.: (60) 379555966
Web Site: http://www.sanyo.com.my
Mfr of Color Television Receivers, VCRs,
Refrigerators, Air Conditioners, Microwave
Ovens, Refrigerated Showcases, Tape Recorders, Vending Machines
N.A.I.C.S.: 335220

Sanyo Singapore Pte Ltd. (2)
1 Toh Tuck Link, Singapore, 596222, Singapore
Tel.: (65) 63360066
Web Site: http://www.sanyo.sg
Sales Range: $25-49.9 Million
Emp.: 15
Air Conditioners Sales & Service
N.A.I.C.S.: 423620
Daniel Ng (Mng Dir)

Sanyo South Africa (Pty) Ltd. (2)
Macallan House Kildrummy Office Park,
Corner Witkoppen & Umhlanga Av,
Paulshof, Bryanston, South Africa **(51%)**
Tel.: (27) 11 304 6000
Sales Range: $25-49.9 Million
Emp.: 25
N.A.I.C.S.: 334310

Sanyo Universal Electric Public Co.,
Ltd. (2)
795, SANYO Building, Rama 9 Road,
Bangkapi, Huaykwang District, Bangkok,
10310, Thailand
Audio & Video Equipment
N.A.I.C.S.: 334310

Subsidiary (Domestic):

Sanyo VLSI Engineering Co.,
Ltd. (2)
180 Anapachi-cho Ohmori, Anpachi-gun,
Gifu, 503-01, Japan
Mfr & Marketer of Semiconductors
N.A.I.C.S.: 334413

Subsidiary (Non-US):

Shenyang Sanyo Air Conditioner Co.,
Ltd. (2)
4 Liulin St Da Dong, Shenyang,
China **(100%)**
Tel.: (86) 488322355
Sales Range: $150-199.9 Million
Emp.: 620
Audio & Video Equipment
N.A.I.C.S.: 334310

Shenzhen Huaqiang Sanyo Technology Design Co., Ltd. (2)
Vision (Shenzhen) Soft Business Park
Block-1, Gaoxin South Rd/Keji South Rd,
Shenzhen, China
N.A.I.C.S.: 334310

Shenzhen Sanyo Huaqiang Energy
Co., Ltd. (2)
, Shenzhen, China
N.A.I.C.S.: 334310

Shenzhen Sanyo Huaqiang Optical
Technology Co., Ltd. (2)
Meixiu Road, Meilin Industrial District,
Shenzhen, Guangdong, China
Tel.: (86) 75583316198
Camera & Video Lenses Mfr
N.A.I.C.S.: 333310
Seiichiro Sano (CEO)

Tattori Sanyo Electric (Hong Kong)
Limited (2)
10 Fl Chuan Kei Factory Bldg 15-23 Kin
Hong St, Kwai Chung, NT, China (Hong
Kong) **(89.36%)**
Tel.: (852) 4257143
Sales Range: $25-49.9 Million
Emp.: 40
Transistor Radios, Tape Recorders, Ni-Cd
Batteries, Light Emitting Diodes Mfr
N.A.I.C.S.: 334310

Subsidiary (Domestic):

Tottori Sanyo Electric Co., Ltd. (2)
7 101 Tachikawa Cho, Tottori, 680 8634,
Japan **(65%)**
Tel.: (81) 857212001
Web Site: http://www.torisan.co.jp
Sales Range: $350-399.9 Million
Emp.: 2,500
Mfr & Sale of Audio Equipment, Information
Systems, Electronic Devices & Home Appliances
N.A.I.C.S.: 334310

Subsidiary (Non-US):

mabe Mexico, S. de R.L. de C.V. (2)
Av Inustrias 3835, 78090, San Luis Potosi,
Mexico
Tel.: (52) 4448266300
Web Site: http://www.mabe.cc
Household Appliance Mfr & Distr
N.A.I.C.S.: 335220

Sanyo Energy (Suzhou) Co., Ltd. (1)
No 86 Sunwu Road, Xukou Town Wuzhong
District, Suzhou, 215164, China
Tel.: (86) 51266210838
Sales Range: $800-899.9 Million
Emp.: 5,000
Storage Battery Mfr
N.A.I.C.S.: 335910
Koji Nishishita (Mng Dir)

Teichiku Records Co., Ltd. (1)
6 27 8 Jingumae Shibuya Ku, 150 8516,
Tokyo, Japan **(50%)**
Tel.: (81) 357781723
Web Site: http://www.teichiku.co.jp
Sales Range: $1-9.9 Million
Emp.: 200
Producer of Music Tapes & Photographic
Records
N.A.I.C.S.: 449210

Zetes Industries SA (1)
Da Vinci Science Park Rue de Strasbourg
3, 1130, Brussels, Belgium **(100%)**
Tel.: (32) 27283711
Web Site: https://www.zetes.com
Automatic Identification of Goods & People
N.A.I.C.S.: 561621
Jean-Francois Jacques (Chm)

Subsidiary (Non-US):

Blackbird Data Systems Ltd (2)
National Technological Park, Limerick, Ireland
Tel.: (353) 862429469
Emp.: 15

Software Development Services
N.A.I.C.S.: 541511

Id-All BV (2)
Science Park Eindhoven, EG Son, 5692,
Eindhoven, Netherlands
Tel.: (31) 408444444
Web Site: http://www.zetes.com
Emp.: 90
Financial Services
N.A.I.C.S.: 522291
Sjoerd Landman (Gen Mgr)

Metaform Ltd (2)
1 Hanagar St Neve Ne eman, PO Box
7252, Hod Hasharon, 45241, Israel
Tel.: (972) 97774240
Web Site: http://www.metaform-ltd.com
Emp.: 15
Software Services
N.A.I.C.S.: 541511
Gideon Rozin (Dir-R&D)

Powersys 2000 S.L. (2)
Ctra Molins de Rei Km 13 Nave 94, 8191,
Rubi, Spain
Tel.: (34) 935 884 470
Software Development Services
N.A.I.C.S.: 541511

Zetes Auto ID Systems Ltd (2)
Punten 4 Wangei bei, 8600, Dubendorf,
Switzerland
Tel.: (41) 448231616
Web Site: http://www.zetes.ch
Emp.: 25
Goods & People Identification Solutions
N.A.I.C.S.: 541512
Brian Sort (Mgr-Sls)

Zetes BV (2)
Science Park Eindhoven 5202, 5692 EG,
Eindhoven, Netherlands
Tel.: (31) 40 844 4444
Web Site: http://www.zetes.nl
Emp.: 30
Computer Aided Engineering Services
N.A.I.C.S.: 541512

Subsidiary (Domestic):

Zetes Fastrace SA (2)
3 Rue de Strasbourg, Straatsburgstraat 7,
1130, Brussels, Belgium
Tel.: (32) 27283711
Emp.: 6
Software Services
N.A.I.C.S.: 541511

Subsidiary (Non-US):

Zetes Holding GmbH (2)
Waldstrasse 23 Geb B 1 2, Dietzenbach,
63128, Germany
Tel.: (49) 607430170
Web Site: http://www.zepel.com
Emp.: 20
Software Development Services
N.A.I.C.S.: 541511
Uwe Hennig (Gen Mgr)

Zetes Industries (Israel) Ltd (2)
Labor 11 Entrance B Afek Industrial Park,
47203, Rosh Ha'Ayin, Israel
Tel.: (972) 52 314 2465
Software Services
N.A.I.C.S.: 541511

Zetes Ireland Ltd (2)
Londsdale Road, The National Technology
Park, V94 PT1X, Plassey, Limerick, Ireland
Tel.: (353) 61333188
Web Site: http://www.zetes.ie
Emp.: 15
Software Development Services
N.A.I.C.S.: 541511
Robert Van Vliet (Mng Dir)

Zetes Ltd (2)
Horizon Honey Lane, Maidenhead, Hurley,
SL6 6RJ, United Kingdom
Tel.: (44) 845 520 0180
Emp.: 80
Software Development Services
N.A.I.C.S.: 541511

Zetes Multicom SA (2)
Calle de San Rafael 1, Poligono Ind de Fuencarral, Alcobendas, 28108, Spain
Tel.: (34) 913589511
Emp.: 60

PANCELTICA HOLDINGS LIMITED

Data Capture Sevices
N.A.I.C.S.: 518210
Shimon Ben Hamo (Mng Dir)

Zetes PASS BV (2)
Science Park Eindhoven Son, Ekkersrijt,
Eindhoven, 5692 EG, Netherlands
Tel.: (31) 408444444
Web Site: http://www.zetes.nl
Emp.: 70
Software Development Services
N.A.I.C.S.: 541511
Sjoerd Landman (Gen Mgr)

Subsidiary (Domestic):

Zetes SA (2)
Rue de Strasbourg 3, 1130, Brussels, Belgium
Tel.: (32) 27283711
Web Site: https://www.zetes.com
Emp.: 140
Software Design Services
N.A.I.C.S.: 541511
Alain Wirtz (CEO)

Subsidiary (Non-US):

Zetes Technologies BV (2)
Science Park Eindhoven 5692 EG Son, Ekkersrijt, Eindhoven, 5692 EG, Netherlands
Tel.: (31) 408444444
Web Site: http://www.zetes.com
Emp.: 80
Software Development Services
N.A.I.C.S.: 541511
Marco Malaihollo (VP)

PANATLANTICA S.A.

Rua Rudolfo Vontobel 600, PO Box
152, Distrito Industrial, Gravata,
94045-405, Rio Grande do Sul, Brazil
Tel.: (55) 51 3489 7777
Web Site:
http://www.panatlantica.com.br
Year Founded: 1952
Steel Products Mfr
N.A.I.C.S.: 331221
Jose Antonio Silva Vargas (Dir-IR)

Subsidiaries:

Panatlantica Catarinense S.A. (1)
Rua Augusto Bruno Nielson 700, PO Box
47, 89219-580, Joinville, Santa Catarina,
Brazil
Tel.: (55) 47 3461 1400
Web Site: http://www.panacat.com.br
Steel Products Mfr
N.A.I.C.S.: 331221

Panatlantica Sao Francisco do
Sul (1)
Estrada geral do miranda s/n poste 180 da
Celesc, Sao Francisco do Sul, 89240-000,
Brazil
Tel.: (55) 47 3449 6060
Steel Products Mfr
N.A.I.C.S.: 331221

PANCELTICA HOLDINGS LIMITED

4 th Floor Jafco Building, Rawdat Al
Khail Street 24, PO Box 31941,
Doha, Qatar
Tel.: (974) 4311751 JE
Web Site: http://www.panceltica.com
Sales Range: $100-124.9 Million
Emp.: 1,500
Galvanized Steel Structure Mfr &
Supplier
N.A.I.C.S.: 331513
Andrew Huntley (Chm)

Subsidiaries:

Scottsdale Construction Systems
Limited (1)
17 cadbury Road Onekawa, Napier, New
Zealand
Tel.: (64) 21512895
Emp.: 17
Building Construction Services
N.A.I.C.S.: 236210
Scott Kimble (Gen Mgr)

PANCEVAC A.D.

Pancevac a.d.—(Continued)

PANCEVAC A.D.
Trg kralja Petra I broj 11, 26000,
Pancevo, Serbia
Tel.: (381) 13 301 150
Web Site: http://www.pancevac-online.rs
Year Founded: 1869
Sales Range: Less than $1 Million
Emp.: 19
Newspaper Publishing Services
N.A.I.C.S.: 513110

PANCHAKANYA MAI HYDRO-POWER LTD.
Krishna Galli Pulchowk, Lalitpur, Patan, Nepal
Tel.: (977) 15005502
Web Site:
https://www.panchakanyamai.com
PMHPL—(NEP)
Rev.: $3,029,610
Assets: $23,956,602
Liabilities: $16,491,034
Net Worth: $7,465,568
Earnings: ($385,503)
Fiscal Year-end: 07/16/22
Hydroelectric Power Generation Services
N.A.I.C.S.: 221111
Prem Bahadur Shrestha *(Chm)*

PANCHMAHAL STEEL LIMITED
GIDC Industrial Estate, Dist Panchmahals, Kalol, 389 330, Gujarat, India
Tel.: (91) 2676230777
Web Site:
https://www.panchmahalsteel.co.in
513511—(BOM)
Rev.: $58,755,027
Assets: $35,402,973
Liabilities: $16,958,863
Net Worth: $18,444,110
Earnings: $165,254
Emp.: 529
Fiscal Year-end: 03/31/23
Stainless Steel Products Mfr
N.A.I.C.S.: 331110
Ashok Malhotra *(Chm & Mng Dir)*

PANCHSHEEL ORGANICS LIMITED
B6 / B7 Sector - C Sanwer Road,
Industrial Estate, Indore, 452 015,
Madhya Pradesh, India
Tel.: (91) 2268634201
Web Site:
https://www.panchsheelorganic.com
531726—(BOM)
Rev.: $6,780,583
Assets: $7,898,409
Liabilities: $2,481,556
Net Worth: $5,416,852
Earnings: $683,278
Emp.: 167
Fiscal Year-end: 03/31/21
Pharmaceuticals Product Mfr
N.A.I.C.S.: 325412
Mahendra A. Turakhia *(Chm & Mng Dir)*

PANCOLOUR INK CO., LTD.
No 72-1 Wenming rd, Gueishan Dist,
Taoyuan, 33382, Taiwan
Tel.: (886) 33270177
Web Site:
https://www.pancolourink.com
Year Founded: 1997
4765—(TAI)
Chemical Products Mfr
N.A.I.C.S.: 325998
Chung-Hsun Li *(Chm)*

PANCONTINENTAL ENERGY NL
Tel.: (61) 863637090
Web Site: http://www.pancon.com.au
PCL—(ASX)
Rev.: $36,225
Assets: $6,075,491
Liabilities: $549,739
Net Worth: $5,525,752
Earnings: ($1,561,467)
Emp.: 5
Fiscal Year-end: 06/30/24
Oil & Gas Exploration Services
N.A.I.C.S.: 211120
Ernest Anthony Myers *(Chm & CEO)*

PANCONTINENTAL RESOURCES CORPORATION
9275 Bayview Ave, PO Box 31317,
16th Avenue PO, Richmond Hill, L4C
OV7, ON, Canada
Tel.: (647) 202-0994
Web Site:
http://www.panconresources.com
PUC—(OTCIQ)
Rev.: $127,546
Assets: $3,165,488
Liabilities: $465,883
Net Worth: $2,699,605
Earnings: ($2,367,450)
Fiscal Year-end: 12/31/20
Gold Exploration Services
N.A.I.C.S.: 212220
Mark McMurdie *(CFO)*

Subsidiaries:

Palmetto Mining Corporation **(1)**
201 Clearview Dr, Whitehouse, TX 75791
Tel.: (903) 714-0185
Emp.: 6
Gold Ore Mining Services
N.A.I.C.S.: 212220

PANDA DAIRY CORPORATION
No 650-668 Jianxing East Road,
Lingxi Town Cangnan County, Wenzhou, 325800, Zhejiang, China
Tel.: (86) 57759883129
Web Site: http://www.pandairy.com
Year Founded: 1996
300898—(SSE)
Rev.: $125,183,448
Assets: $151,483,176
Liabilities: $28,666,872
Net Worth: $122,816,304
Earnings: $7,498,764
Fiscal Year-end: 12/31/22
Dairy Products Mfr
N.A.I.C.S.: 333241

PANDA FINANCIAL HOLDING CORP., LTD.
No 125 Liuyang Avenue, Liuyang,
410300, Hunan, China
Tel.: (86) 73183620963
Web Site: http://www.600599.com.cn
Year Founded: 1989
600599—(SHG)
Rev.: $46,235,166
Assets: $139,008,945
Liabilities: $28,471,562
Net Worth: $110,537,383
Earnings: $12,687,092
Fiscal Year-end: 12/31/22
Firework Mfr & Whslr
N.A.I.C.S.: 325998
Xu Jinhuan *(Chm)*

Subsidiaries:

Beijing Panda Fireworks Co., Ltd. **(1)**
Building No 14 Nanxin Park Hongyan Road,
Chaoyang, Beijing, 100021, China
Tel.: (86) 10 63109898
Firework Mfr & Whslr
N.A.I.C.S.: 325998

Bright Star Fireworks Ltd. **(1)**
Ostle Boulevard 29 8900, Randers, Denmark
Tel.: (45) 7218 5551
Firework Distr
N.A.I.C.S.: 423920

GUANGZHOU PANDA INT'L GROUP LTD. **(1)**
Panda Building No 45 Yongfu Road,
Guangzhou, 510500, China
Tel.: (86) 20 87728877
Firework Mfr & Whslr
N.A.I.C.S.: 325998

Panda Fyrverkerier i Sverige ab **(1)**
Box 54, 471 21, Skarhamn, Sweden
Tel.: (46) 304 66 8060
Web Site: http://www.fyrverkerimastarna.se
Firework Distr
N.A.I.C.S.: 423920

PANDORA A/S
Havneholmen 17-19, DK-1561, Copenhagen, Denmark
Tel.: (45) 36720044 DK
Web Site:
https://www.pandoragroup.com
Year Founded: 1982
PNDORA—(CSE)
Rev.: $4,071,131,947
Assets: $3,443,446,051
Liabilities: $2,668,605,577
Net Worth: $774,840,474
Earnings: $685,853,193
Emp.: 33,000
Fiscal Year-end: 12/31/23
Jewelry Designer, Mfr & Marketer
N.A.I.C.S.: 339910
Christian Frigast *(Deputy Chm)*

Subsidiaries:

PANDORA France SAS **(1)**
Tour Alto 4 Place des Saisons, La Defense,
92400, Paris, France **(100%)**
Tel.: (33) 144831750
Jewelry Retailer
N.A.I.C.S.: 458310

PANDORA Int. ApS **(1)**
Hovedvejen 2, 2600, Glostrup,
Denmark **(100%)**
Tel.: (45) 33 36 69 98
Jewelry Retailer
N.A.I.C.S.: 458310

PANDORA Italia Srl **(1)**
Via F Confalonieri 4, 20124, Milan,
Italy **(100%)**
Tel.: (39) 0223334200
Jewelry Retailer
N.A.I.C.S.: 458310
Massimo Basei *(Chief Comml Officer)*

PANDORA Jewellery UK Ltd. **(1)**
33 George Street, London, W1U 3BH,
United Kingdom **(100%)**
Tel.: (44) 8448731442
Jewelry Retailer
N.A.I.C.S.: 458310

PANDORA Jewelry Asia-Pacific Limited **(1)**
Suites 3801-04 3810-14 Tower 6 The Gateway, Harbour City Tsim Sha Tsui, Kowloon,
China (Hong Kong) **(100%)**
Tel.: (852) 37968988
Jewelry Retailer
N.A.I.C.S.: 458310

PANDORA Jewelry CEE Sp. z.o.o. **(1)**
ul Domaniewska 28, 02-672, Warsaw,
Poland **(100%)**
Tel.: (48) 8001215801
Web Site: https://pl.pandora.net
Jewelry Retailer
N.A.I.C.S.: 458310

PANDORA Jewelry CR, s.r.o. **(1)**
V Celnici 1031/4, 110 00, Prague, 1, Czech
Republic **(100%)**
Tel.: (420) 602240947
Web Site: https://cz.pandora.net
Jewelry Retailer
N.A.I.C.S.: 458310

PANDORA Jewelry GmbH **(1)**

INTERNATIONAL PUBLIC

Ballindamm 39, 20095, Hamburg,
Germany **(100%)**
Tel.: (49) 4040110211
Web Site: https://de.pandora.net
Jewelry Retailer
N.A.I.C.S.: 458310

PANDORA Jewelry Hungary Kft. **(1)**
Nepfurdo utca 22, 1138, Budapest,
Hungary **(100%)**
Tel.: (36) 308448746
Web Site: https://hu.pandora.net
Jewelry Retailer
N.A.I.C.S.: 458310

PANDORA Jewelry LLC **(1)**
8671 Robert Fulton Dr, Columbia, MD
21046 **(100%)**
Tel.: (410) 309-0200
Web Site: http://www.pandora.net
Sales Range: $750-799.9 Million
Jewelry Retailer
N.A.I.C.S.: 458310

PANDORA Jewelry Pty. Ltd. **(1)**
PO Box 906, Newport, Sydney, 2106, NSW,
Australia **(100%)**
Tel.: (61) 299860660
Web Site: https://au.pandora.net
Jewelry Retailer
N.A.I.C.S.: 458310

PANDORA Jewelry Romania SRL **(1)**
Bd Marasesti nr 2B Blocul C scara 4 etajul
5 apartamentul 39 Sector 4, 040254, Bucharest, Romania
Tel.: (40) 213351095
Web Site: https://ro.pandora.net
Jewelry Retailer
N.A.I.C.S.: 458310

PANDORA Osterreich GmbH **(1)**
Plankengasse 1/5 6, 1010, Vienna,
Austria **(100%)**
Tel.: (43) 800291429
Jewelry Retailer
N.A.I.C.S.: 458310

PANDORA Schweiz AG **(1)**
Brenden 39, Appenzell, 9050, Zurich, Switzerland
Tel.: (41) 717870041
Web Site: https://ch.pandora.net
Jewelry Retailer
N.A.I.C.S.: 458310

Pandora ECOMM LLC **(1)**
250 W Pratt St 18th Fl, Baltimore, MD
21201
Tel.: (410) 309-0200
Jewellery Mfr & Distr
N.A.I.C.S.: 339910

Pandora Jewelry (Shanghai) Company Ltd. **(1)**
Floor 25 One ICC No 999 Middle Huai Hai
Road, Xuhui District, Shanghai, 200031,
China
Tel.: (86) 2180216988
Jewellery Mfr & Distr
N.A.I.C.S.: 339910

Pandora Jewelry B.V. **(1)**
Leidsestraat 51, 1017 NV, Amsterdam,
Netherlands
Tel.: (31) 8000226409
Web Site: https://nl.pandora.net
Jewellery Mfr & Distr
N.A.I.C.S.: 339910

Pandora Jewelry Japan Ltd. **(1)**
6-3-7 Jingumae, Shibuya-ku, Tokyo, 150-0001, Japan
Tel.: (81) 476502638
Web Site: https://jp.pandora.net
Jewellery Mfr & Distr
N.A.I.C.S.: 339910

Pandora Jewelry Shared Services CEE Sp z.o.o. **(1)**
ul Domaniewska 28, 02-672, Warsaw, Poland
Tel.: (48) 222065800
Jewel Material Mfr
N.A.I.C.S.: 339910
Izabela Sas *(Gen Mgr-Ledger)*

Pandora Production Co. Ltd. **(1)**
88 Soi Sukhapiban 2 Soi 31 Dokmai,
Praves, Bangkok, 10250, Thailand

Tel.: (66) 27287200
Emp.: 13,200
Jewel Material Mfr
N.A.I.C.S.: 339910

Pandora Retail Pty. Ltd. (1)
Level 5 12 Narabang Way, Belrose, 2085, NSW, Australia
Tel.: (61) 299860660
Web Site: https://au.pandora.net
Jewellery Mfr & Distr
N.A.I.C.S.: 339910

Pandora do Brasil Comercio e Importacao Ltda. (1)
Avenida Dr Chucri Zaidan 1240-13 andar-Cj 1301 e 1303, Golden Tower - Morumbi, Sao Paulo, CEP 04711-130, SP, Brazil
Tel.: (55) 1141308933
Web Site: https://www.pandorajoias.com.br
Jewellery Mfr & Distr
N.A.I.C.S.: 339910

PANDORA CONSULTANCY SERVICES PLC
64 Baker Street, London, W1U 7GB, United Kingdom
Tel.: (44) 302310543043
PACS—(CYP)
Rev.: $22,535
Assets: $1,458,371
Liabilities: $31,945
Net Worth: $1,426,425
Earnings: $17,175
Fiscal Year-end: 12/31/19
Investment Services
N.A.I.C.S.: 523940
Stathis Roussos (Sec)

PANDORA TV CO., LTD.
11F 49 Daewangpangyo-ro 644 beon-gil, Bundang-gu, Seongnam, Gyeonggi-do, Korea (South)
Tel.: (82) 7044847100
Web Site: http://www.pandora.tv
Year Founded: 2004
202960—(KRS)
User Generated Content Based Video Portal & Personal Broadcasting Services
N.A.I.C.S.: 516210
Kyung-Ik Kim (CEO)

PANEVEZIO STATYBOS TRESTAS AB
P Puzino Str 1, 35173, Panevezys, Lithuania
Tel.: (370) 61821360
Web Site: https://www.pst.lt
Year Founded: 1957
PTR1L—(VSE)
Rev.: $128,626,020
Assets: $92,712,538
Liabilities: $60,244,740
Net Worth: $32,467,797
Earnings: $3,565,908
Emp.: 735
Fiscal Year-end: 12/31/23
Building Construction Services
N.A.I.C.S.: 236220

Subsidiaries:

Alinita UAB (1)
Tinklu g 7, Panevezio m sav, LT-35115, Panevezys, Lithuania
Tel.: (370) 45467630
Web Site: https://www.alinita.lt
Ventilation Installation Services
N.A.I.C.S.: 238220
V. Malinauskis (Mng Dir)

Hustal UAB (1)
Tinklu g 7, 35115, Panevezys, Lithuania
Tel.: (370) 45585087
Web Site: https://www.hustal.eu
Construction Materials Distr
N.A.I.C.S.: 423390
Audrius Maciekus (CEO-Sls & Mktg)

Kingsbud Sp. z o.o. (1)
Ukmerges Str 219, 07152, Vilnius, Lithuania
Tel.: (370) 65508404
Web Site: https://www.kingsbud.lt
Building Materials Distr
N.A.I.C.S.: 444180
Rokas Mulevicius (Exec Dir)

Metalo Meistrai UAB (1)
Tinklu g 7, LT-35115, Panevezys, Lithuania
Tel.: (370) 845585087
Web Site: http://www.metalomeistrai.lt
Steel Product Distr
N.A.I.C.S.: 423510
Audrius Maciekus (Head-Sls & Mktg)

Skydmedis UAB (1)
Pramones st 5, LT-35100, Panevezys, Lithuania
Tel.: (370) 845467626
Web Site: https://www.skydmedis.lt
Emp.: 85
Panel House Product Mfr
N.A.I.C.S.: 335313

Vekada UAB (1)
Tinklu Str 7, LT-35138, Panevezys, Lithuania
Tel.: (370) 45461311
Web Site: http://www.vekada.lt
Electrical Installation Services
N.A.I.C.S.: 238210

PANG DA AUTOMOBILE TRADE CO., LTD.
South Side of Flyover, Luan County, Tangshan, 063700, Hebei, China
Tel.: (86) 3157181566 CN
Web Site: http://www.pdqmjt.com
Year Founded: 1988
601258—(SHG)
Rev.: $4,195,749,308
Assets: $3,467,961,974
Liabilities: $1,773,295,439
Net Worth: $1,694,666,535
Earnings: $88,915,424
Emp.: 30,000
Fiscal Year-end: 12/31/20
Holding Company; Automobile Wholesale Distr & Retailer
N.A.I.C.S.: 551112
Qinghua Pang (Pres)

PANGAEA CONNECTIVITY TECHNOLOGY LIMITED
Room 901-906 Tai Yau Building 181 Johnston Road, Wanchai, China (Hong Kong)
Tel.: (852) 28363301 Ky
Web Site: https://www.pangaea.com.hk
Year Founded: 1990
1473—(HKG)
Rev.: $157,844,563
Assets: $102,421,857
Liabilities: $67,005,368
Net Worth: $35,416,489
Earnings: $481,740
Emp.: 119
Fiscal Year-end: 03/31/22
Information Technology Services
N.A.I.C.S.: 541512
Wai Kong Wong (Sec)

PANGAEA ONCOLOGY SA
Calle Coso 42, 50004, Zaragoza, Spain
Tel.: (34) 935460119
Web Site: https://www.panoncology.com
Year Founded: 2007
PANG—(MAD)
Sales Range: Less than $1 Million
Pharmaceuticals Product Mfr
N.A.I.C.S.: 325412
Rafael Rosell (Co-Founder, Chm & Chief Scientific Officer)

PANGANG GROUP VANADIUM TITANIUM & RESOURCES CO., LTD.
Nongnong Ping, East District, Panzhihua, 617067, China
Tel.: (86) 8123385366
Iron & Steel Mfr
N.A.I.C.S.: 332111
Qin Ming (VP)

PANGANG GROUP VANADIUM TITANIUM AND RESOURCES CO., LTD.
Panzhihua Cultural Plaza No 21 West Section of Gangcheng Avenue, East District, Panzhihua, 617067, China
Tel.: (86) 8123385366
Year Founded: 1993
000629—(SSE)
Rev.: $1,620,794,801
Assets: $1,784,703,455
Liabilities: $283,746,452
Net Worth: $1,500,957,003
Earnings: $34,522,809
Fiscal Year-end: 12/31/20
Mfr of Iron, Steel & Vanadium Products
N.A.I.C.S.: 332111
Luo Jichun (Chm & Sec-Party Committee)

PANGEA NATURAL FOODS INC.
8035 130th St, Surrey, V3W 0H7, BC, Canada
Tel.: (604) 765-8069 BC
Web Site: https://www.pangeafood.com
Year Founded: 2021
PNGAF—(OTCQB)
Assets: $462,773
Liabilities: $304,796
Net Worth: $157,977
Earnings: ($846,568)
Fiscal Year-end: 10/31/22
Food Product Mfr & Distr
N.A.I.C.S.: 311813
Daryl Louie (CMO)

PANGEN BIOTECH INC.
4F Innoplex 2-dong 306 Sinwon-ro Yeongtong-gu, Suwon, 16675, Gyeonggi-do, Korea (South)
Tel.: (82) 317339165
Web Site: http://www.pangen.com
Year Founded: 1999
222110—(KRS)
Rev.: $4,986,005
Assets: $15,856,709
Liabilities: $2,649,373
Net Worth: $13,207,336
Earnings: ($3,446,769)
Emp.: 67
Fiscal Year-end: 12/31/22
Biological Product Mfr & Distr
N.A.I.C.S.: 325414
Jaeseung Yoon (Co-Pres & Co-CEO)

PANGENOMIC HEALTH INC.
315-1275 W 6th Ave, Vancouver, V6H 1A6, BC, Canada
Tel.: (604) 725-4160 BC
Web Site: https://www.pangenomic.com
Year Founded: 2015
NARA—(CNSX)
Rev.: $1,831
Assets: $376,090
Liabilities: $536,562
Net Worth: ($160,472)
Earnings: ($8,947,769)
Fiscal Year-end: 12/31/22
Health Care Srvices
N.A.I.C.S.: 621610
Colin Quon (CTO)

PANGOLIN DIAMONDS CORP.
25 Adelaide Street East Suite 1614, Toronto, M5C 3A1, ON, Canada
Tel.: (416) 594-0473 QC
Web Site: https://www.pangolindiamonds.com
Year Founded: 1938
KGHZF—(OTCEM)
Assets: $79,719
Liabilities: $1,078,209
Net Worth: ($998,490)
Earnings: ($439,247)
Fiscal Year-end: 06/30/23
Diamond Mining & Exploration Services
N.A.I.C.S.: 212311
Leon Daniels (Pres & CEO)

PANGRIM CO., LTD.
KGIT Sangam Center 18F 1601 Sangam-Dong, Mapo-Gu, Seoul, Korea (South)
Tel.: (82) 220852114
Web Site: https://www.pangrim.com
Year Founded: 1962
003610—(KRS)
Rev.: $120,495,307
Assets: $236,513,895
Liabilities: $52,699,840
Net Worth: $183,814,055
Earnings: $6,808,431
Emp.: 241
Fiscal Year-end: 09/30/21
Textile Products Mfr
N.A.I.C.S.: 313110
Jae Hee Suh (Chm, Pres & CEO)

Subsidiaries:

PangRim Co., Ltd. - Ansan Factory (1)
623-5 Choji-dong, Ansan, KyoungKi-Do, Korea (South)
Tel.: (82) 3149441111
Emp.: 230
Textile Products Mfr
N.A.I.C.S.: 313310

PangRim Co., Ltd. - Kumi Factory (1)
282 KonDan-Dong, Kumi, KyoungBuk, Korea (South)
Tel.: (82) 544633161
Textile Products Mfr
N.A.I.C.S.: 313310

PANGRIO SUGAR MILLS LIMITED
10th Floor Lakson Square Building No 1 Sarwar Shaheed Road, Karachi, Pakistan
Tel.: (92) 297739101
Web Site: http://www.pangriosugar.com
Emp.: 345
Cane Sugar Production & Supplier
N.A.I.C.S.: 311314

PANINI S.P.A.
Viale Emilio Po 380, 41126, Modena, Italy
Tel.: (39) 059382450 IT
Web Site: http://www.paninigroup.com
Year Founded: 1961
Sales Range: $800-899.9 Million
Emp.: 800
Publisher of Comics, Childrens Magazines & Trading Cards
N.A.I.C.S.: 513199
Giorgio Aravecchia (Dir-New Media)

Subsidiaries:

LLC IZDATELSTVO PANINI RUS (1)
Vyatskaya str 49 build 1, 127015, Moscow, Russia
Tel.: (7) 495 604 1099
Magazine Publisher
N.A.I.C.S.: 513120

Panini America, Inc. (1)
5325 FAA Blvd Ste 100, Irving, TX 75061
Tel.: (817) 983-0300

PANINI S.P.A.

Panini S.p.A.—(Continued)
Web Site: http://www.paniniamerica.net
Sales Range: $25-49.9 Million
Emp.: 50
Trading Cards Mfr & Distr
N.A.I.C.S.: 423920

Panini Brasil Ltda. (1)
Centro Empresarial Tambore - Alameda Caiapos 425, Barueri, 06460-110, Sao Paulo, Brazil
Tel.: (55) 1135129444
Web Site:
http://www.collectibles.panini.com.br
Magazine Publisher
N.A.I.C.S.: 513120

Panini Chile Ltda (1)
Emilio Vaisse 744 Nunoa, Santiago, Chile
Tel.: (56) 2 205 43 66
Web Site: http://www.panini.cl
Magazine Publisher
N.A.I.C.S.: 513120

Panini Espana SA (1)
Calle Vallespi 20, 17257, Torroella de Montgri, Girona, Spain
Tel.: (34) 972 757411
Web Site: http://www.panini.es
Magazine Publisher
N.A.I.C.S.: 513120
Montse Rosa Fuster *(Product Mgr)*

Panini France SA (1)
Z I Nice La Plaine Avenue Emmanuel Pontremoli Batiment C2, 4eme etage, 06200, Nice, France
Tel.: (33) 492 125757
Web Site: http://collectibles.panini.fr
Magazine Publisher
N.A.I.C.S.: 513120

Panini Medya Yayincilik ve Ticaret A.S. (1)
Inonu Cad Turaboglu Sok No 4 Hamdiye Yazgan Is Merkezi Kat 3 D 4, Kozyatagi Kadikoy, Istanbul, Turkiye
Tel.: (90) 216 357 44 03
Web Site: http://www.paninigroup.com
Magazine Publisher
N.A.I.C.S.: 513120

Panini Mexico SA (1)
Calle Isaac Newton No 286 1 piso Colonia Chapultepec, Morales Miguel Hidalgo, Polanco, 11570, Mexico
Tel.: (52) 55 5208 3550
Magazine Publisher
N.A.I.C.S.: 513120

Panini Nederland B.V. (1)
Gooimeer 2-22, 1411 DC, Naarden, Netherlands
Tel.: (31) 2157 8148 25
Magazine Publisher
N.A.I.C.S.: 513120

Panini Suisse AG (1)
Sihleggstrasse 23, 8832, Wollerau, Switzerland
Tel.: (41) 44 883 22 00
Magazine Publisher
N.A.I.C.S.: 513120

Panini Verlags GmbH (1)
Rotebuhlstrasse 87, 70178, Stuttgart, Germany
Tel.: (49) 711 94768 0
Web Site: http://www.panini.de
Magazine Publisher
N.A.I.C.S.: 513120
Felix Bauer *(Dir-Fin)*

PANION & BF BIOTECH, INC.
16 F No 3 Park St, Nangang District, Taipei, 11503, Taiwan
Tel.: (886) 226558218
Web Site: https://en.pbf.com.tw
Year Founded: 1976
1760—(TAI)
Rev.: $61,541,415
Assets: $105,797,471
Liabilities: $43,300,989
Net Worth: $62,496,482
Earnings: $2,525,230
Fiscal Year-end: 12/31/23
Pharmaceutical Product Mfr & Distr

N.A.I.C.S.: 325411
Li-Chiu Chang *(Chm)*
Subsidiaries:

Cheng Fong Chemical Co., Ltd. (1)
8F No2-2 Sec 2 Nanya W Rd, Banciao City, New Taipei City, 220, Taiwan
Tel.: (886) 229667811
Web Site: https://chengfong.lookchem.com
Pharmaceutical Ingredient Mfr & Distr
N.A.I.C.S.: 325411

PANJAM INVESTMENT LIMITED
60 Knutsford Boulevard, Kingston, Jamaica
Tel.: (876) 92945104
Web Site: https://www.panjam.com
Financial Investment Services
N.A.I.C.S.: 523999
Jeffrey M. Hall *(Vice Chm)*
Subsidiaries:

Jamaica Producers Group Limited (1)
Tel.: (876) 9263503
Web Site: https://www.jpjamaica.com
Rev.: $189,673,806
Assets: $308,927,044
Liabilities: $74,229,313
Net Worth: $234,697,731
Earnings: $26,069,536
Emp.: 2,000
Fiscal Year-end: 12/31/2022
Bananas & Related Products
N.A.I.C.S.: 111336
Charles H. Johnston *(Chm)*

Subsidiary (Domestic):

Eastern Banana Estates Limited (2)
6A Oxford Rd, Kingston, Jamaica (100%)
Tel.: (876) 9822785
Sales Range: $75-99.9 Million
Fruit & Tree Nut Combination Farming
N.A.I.C.S.: 111336

Subsidiary (Non-US):

Hoogesteger B.V. (2)
Domineeslaan 93, 1161 BW, Zwanenburg, Netherlands
Tel.: (31) 20 407 3000
Web Site: https://www.hoogesteger.nl
Sales Range: $25-49.9 Million
Emp.: 150
Fruit Juices Mfr
N.A.I.C.S.: 311421
Bert Hoogesteger *(Founder)*

JP Shipping Services Ltd (2)
Main ABP Building South Alexandra Dock, Newport, NP20 2NP, United Kingdom
Tel.: (44) 163 384 2062
Web Site: https://www.jpshipping.co.uk
Sales Range: $25-49.9 Million
Emp.: 14
Freight Forwarding Services
N.A.I.C.S.: 488510

R.A.M. Shipping Services Limited (2)
439 North Woolwich Rd, Silvertown, London, E16 2BS, United Kingdom
Tel.: (44) 2074760154
Sales Range: $25-49.9 Million
Emp.: 13
Navigational Services to Shipping
N.A.I.C.S.: 488330
Jim Davies *(Mgr-Depot)*

Serious Food (Distribution) Limited (2)
122 Malton Avenue Slough Trading Estate, Slough Trading Estate, Slough, SL1 4DE, Berkshire, United Kingdom
Tel.: (44) 175 355 2488
Web Site: https://www.seriousfood.co.uk
Sales Range: $25-49.9 Million
Emp.: 30
Food Mfr
N.A.I.C.S.: 311999
Chris Welsh *(Mng Dir)*

Subsidiary (Domestic):

St. Mary Banana Estates Limited (2)

Grays Inn Est, Saint Mary, Annatto Bay, Jamaica
Tel.: (876) 996 2401
Fruit Juices Mfr
N.A.I.C.S.: 311411

Subsidiary (Non-US):

Sunjuice Limited (2)
Sun Ho Llantrisant Business Pk, Pontyclun, United Kingdom
Tel.: (44) 1443237222
Fruit & Vegetable Canning
N.A.I.C.S.: 311421

PANJAWATTANA PLASTIC PUBLIC COMPANY LIMITED
19 21 Soi Ekachai 63 Ekachai Road, Bang Bon District, Bangkok, Thailand
Tel.: (66) 28980018
Web Site: https://www.pjw.co.th
PJW—(THA)
Rev.: $101,571,124
Assets: $99,014,200
Liabilities: $58,881,955
Net Worth: $40,132,245
Earnings: $4,445,937
Fiscal Year-end: 12/31/23
Plastic Mfr
N.A.I.C.S.: 326199
Satit Hemmondharop *(CEO & CMO-Acting)*

Subsidiaries:

Master Laundry Co., Ltd. (1)
88/55 Jongsiri Parkland, Theparak, Samut Prakan, 10540, Thailand
Tel.: (66) 21707590
Web Site: https://www.masterlaundry.co.th
Commercial Laundry Services
N.A.I.C.S.: 812320

Millpack Company Limited (1)
19 21 Soi Eakchai 63 Ekachai Road, Khwaeng, Bangkok, 10150, Bang Bon, Thailand
Tel.: (66) 2 898 0018
Plastics Product Mfr
N.A.I.C.S.: 326199

PANJON LIMITED
01 Panjon Farm House Near Hinkargiri Jain Tirth Airport-Bijasan Road, Airport Road, Indore, 452005, Madhya Pradesh, India
Tel.: (91) 7312622503
Web Site: https://www.panjon.in
Year Founded: 1964
526345—(BOM)
Rev.: $1,173,254
Assets: $1,887,972
Liabilities: $186,079
Net Worth: $1,701,893
Earnings: ($557,990)
Emp.: 25
Fiscal Year-end: 03/31/22
Consumer Goods & Pharmaceutical Products Mfr
N.A.I.C.S.: 311999
Nagin Bhai Kothari *(Chm)*

PANKAJ PIYUSH TRADE & INVESTMENT LIMITED
304 Building No-61 Vijay Block Laxmi Nagar, East Delhi, New Delhi, 110092, India
Tel.: (91) 9818502247
Web Site: https://pptinvestment.in
Year Founded: 1982
506122—(BOM)
Rev.: $1,355,376
Assets: $3,900,636
Liabilities: $436,183
Net Worth: $3,464,453
Earnings: ($10,337)
Emp.: 13
Fiscal Year-end: 03/31/21
Financial Investment Services
N.A.I.C.S.: 523999
Vinod Kumar Bansal *(Mng Dir)*

PANKAJ POLYMERS LIMITED
5th Floor E Block 105 Surya Towers Sardar Patel Road, Secunderabad, 500003, India
Tel.: (91) 4027897743
Web Site:
https://www.pankajpolymers.com
Year Founded: 1994
531280—(BOM)
Rev.: $350,255
Assets: $1,692,536
Liabilities: $350,483
Net Worth: $1,342,054
Earnings: $5,755
Emp.: 10
Fiscal Year-end: 03/31/23
Polymer Product Mfr
N.A.I.C.S.: 325211
Pankaj Goel *(Co-Mng Dir)*

PANLOGIC
Fitzroy House 3 Paradise Rd, Richmond, TW9 1RX, Surrey, United Kingdom
Tel.: (44) 2089485511
Web Site: http://www.panlogic.co.uk
Year Founded: 1999
Sales Range: $10-24.9 Million
Emp.: 30
Interactive, Internet/Web Design, Viral/Buzz/Word of Mouth
N.A.I.C.S.: 541810
William Makower *(Mng Dir)*

PANNERGY NYRT.
Budafoki ut 56, 1117, Budapest, Hungary
Tel.: (36) 13232383   HU
Web Site: https://www.pannergy.com
Year Founded: 1922
PANNERGY—(BUD)
Rev.: $26,214,009
Assets: $71,180,198
Liabilities: $40,112,747
Net Worth: $31,067,450
Earnings: $4,652,797
Emp.: 17
Fiscal Year-end: 12/31/23
Plastics Processing for Renewable Energy Services
N.A.I.C.S.: 326199
Istvan Jaksa *(CEO)*

Subsidiaries:

Almand Plastics Ltd. (1)
Dunalejaro Str 1, 1211, Budapest, Hungary
Tel.: (36) 12761934
Web Site: http://www.almand.hu
Plastic Packaging
N.A.I.C.S.: 326199

Kaposplast Plastic Industrial Co. Ltd. (1)
Szigetvari U 59, 7401, Kaposvar, Hungary (100%)
Tel.: (36) 82528330
Web Site: http://www.kaposplast.hu
Mfr of Bristles for Brushes & Brooms & Plastic Wires & Tape
N.A.I.C.S.: 326199

Multicard Ltd. (1)
Haros U 7, 1222, Budapest, Hungary (100%)
Tel.: (36) 14246070
Web Site: http://www.multicard.hu
Plastic Cards
N.A.I.C.S.: 326199

Pannon-Effekt Plastics Ltd. (1)
Kishegyesi Ut 263, 4031, Debrecen, Hungary (100%)
Tel.: (36) 52531571
Web Site: http://www.pannoneffekt.hu
Sales Range: $150-199.9 Million
Plastics Products
N.A.I.C.S.: 326199

Pannunion Packaging Plc. (1)
Utca Puskas Tivadar 6, 9700, Szombathely, Hungary (100%)

Tel.: (36) 94522500
Web Site: http://www.pannunion.hu
Sales Range: $75-99.9 Million
Emp.: 300
PVC Plastics Mfr
N.A.I.C.S.: 326199
Richard Nemeth *(Mgr-Sls-Pkg Matls)*

Polifoam Plastic Processing Co., Ltd. (1)
Tablas utca 32, H-1097, Budapest, Hungary
Tel.: (36) 13979800
Web Site: http://www.polifoam.com
Polyethylene Foam Mfr
N.A.I.C.S.: 326150

Recyclen Plastic Processing Ltd. (1)
Banyaleg U 80 84, Budapest, 1225, Hungary (100%)
Tel.: (36) 12071800
Web Site: http://www.recyclen.hu
Sales Range: Less than $1 Million
Emp.: 14
Plastic Recyling
N.A.I.C.S.: 326199

PANNON-FLAX LINEN WEAVING CO
Kando Kalman u 1, 9027, Gyor, Hungary
Tel.: (36) 96769147
Web Site: http://www.pannon-flax.hu
Year Founded: 1911
Sales Range: $1-9.9 Million
Emp.: 149
Table Linen & Fabrics Mfr
N.A.I.C.S.: 313210

PANONIJA A.D.
Dimitrija Tucovica 141, Pancevo, Serbia
Tel.: (381) 13342266
Web Site: https://panonija.co
Year Founded: 1948
PANO—(BEL)
Rev.: $2,896,482
Assets: $2,667,938
Liabilities: $874,580
Net Worth: $1,793,358
Earnings: $12,731
Emp.: 72
Fiscal Year-end: 12/31/22
Cleaning & Polishing Product Mfr
N.A.I.C.S.: 325611
Draginja Radulovic *(Exec Dir)*

PANONKA A.D.
Staparski put bb, Sombor, Serbia
Tel.: (381) 25 5434 501
Web Site: http://www.panonka.co.rs
Year Founded: 1991
Sales Range: Less than $1 Million
Emp.: 46
Fruit & Vegetable Preserving Services
N.A.I.C.S.: 311421
Ivana Lukic *(CEO)*

PANOPLY GROUP CORP.
Allmandring 3-C zi 112, 70569, Stuttgart, Germany
Tel.: (49) 152 23688251 NV
Year Founded: 2013
Business Consulting Services
N.A.I.C.S.: 541611
Ivan Lunegov *(Pres, CEO, CFO, Principal Acctg Officer, Treas & Sec)*

PANORA GAYRIMENKUL YATIRIM ORTAKLIGI AS
Oran Mahallesi Jerusalem Street No 3/318, Cankaya, Ankara, Turkiye
Tel.: (90) 3124905856
Web Site: https://www.panoragyo.com
Year Founded: 2004
PAGYO—(IST)
Rev.: $15,257,515
Assets: $267,620,552
Liabilities: $16,979,999
Net Worth: $250,640,552
Earnings: $89,395,970
Fiscal Year-end: 12/31/23
Real Estate Investment Services
N.A.I.C.S.: 523999
Mustafa Rifat Hisarciklioglu *(Chm)*

PANORAMA FIRM SP. Z O.O.
ul Postepu 14A, 02-676, Warsaw, Poland
Tel.: (48) 22 289 2000
Web Site:
http://firma.panoramafirm.pl
Online Search Engine
N.A.I.C.S.: 519290

PANORAMA STUDIOS INTERNATIONAL LIMITED
1003 1004 10th Floor West Side Lotus Grandeur, Veera Desai Road Andheri W, Mumbai, 400053, Maharashtra, India
Tel.: (91) 2242862700
Web Site: https://www.ainvest.co.in 539469—(BOM)
Rev.: $45,138,733
Assets: $28,992,470
Liabilities: $20,715,700
Net Worth: $8,276,770
Earnings: $4,236,269
Emp.: 25
Fiscal Year-end: 03/31/23
Financial Investment Services
N.A.I.C.S.: 523999
Kumar Mangat Rajaram Pathak *(Mng Dir)*

PANORAMIC RESOURCES LIMITED
Level 9 553 Hay Street, Perth, 6000, WA, Australia
Tel.: (61) 863741700 AU
Web Site:
https://www.panoramicresource.com
PAN—(ASX)
Rev.: $8,180,611
Assets: $154,412,569
Liabilities: $26,702,488
Net Worth: $127,710,082
Earnings: $226,026
Emp.: 216
Fiscal Year-end: 06/30/21
Nickel Mining Services
N.A.I.C.S.: 212230
John D. Hicks *(Gen Mgr-Exploration)*

Subsidiaries:

Lanfranchi Nickel Mines Pty Ltd (1)
Level 9 553 Hay Street, Perth, 6000, WA, Australia
Tel.: (61) 863741700
Web Site: https://panoramicresources.com
Nickel Ore Mining Services
N.A.I.C.S.: 212230
Victor Rajasooriar *(Mng Dir)*

Savannah Nickel Mines Pty Ltd (1)
PMB 19, Kununurra, 6743, WA, Australia
Tel.: (61) 86 103 2399
Web Site: https://panoramicresources.com
Nickel Ore Mining Services
N.A.I.C.S.: 212230

PANORAMIC UNIVERSAL LIMITED
Aman Chambers 4th Floor Opp New Passport Office Veer Savarkar Marg, Prabhadevi, Mumbai, 400 025, Maharashtra, India
Tel.: (91) 2266164000
Year Founded: 1998
PANORAMUNI—(NSE)
Software Development Services
N.A.I.C.S.: 541511
Viidyaa Moravekar *(Mng Dir)*

PANORO ENERGY ASA
Advokatfirmaet Schjodt AS Tordenskiolds gate 12, PO Box 2444, Solli, 201, Oslo, Norway
Tel.: (47) 2034051060
Web Site:
https://www.panoroenergy.com
Year Founded: 2009
0N08—(LSE)
Rev.: $188,626,000
Assets: $539,345,000
Liabilities: $332,842,000
Net Worth: $206,503,000
Earnings: $19,893,000
Emp.: 25
Fiscal Year-end: 12/31/22
Oil & Gas Exploration Services
N.A.I.C.S.: 211120
Richard Morton *(Dir-Technical)*

Subsidiaries:

Energy Equity Resources AJE Limited (1)
1B Chuks Onyebuchi Drive Off Fatai Arobieke Off Admiralty Road, Lekki Phase 1, Lagos, Nigeria
Tel.: (234) 8079213655
Web Site: http://www.eeras.com
Oil & Gas Exploration Services
N.A.I.C.S.: 213112
Godswill Ihetu *(Chm)*

Panoro Energy Limited (1)
78 Brook Street, London, W1K 5EF, United Kingdom
Tel.: (44) 2034051060
Oil & Gas Exploration Services
N.A.I.C.S.: 213112
John Hamilton *(CEO)*

PANORO MINERALS LTD.
Suite 480 505 Burrard Street, Vancouver, V7X 1M3, BC, Canada
Tel.: (604) 684-4246 BC
Web Site: https://www.panoro.com
Year Founded: 2003
POROF—(OTCQB)
Rev.: $65,294
Assets: $60,932,241
Liabilities: $11,765,650
Net Worth: $49,166,591
Earnings: ($847,307)
Emp.: 13
Fiscal Year-end: 12/31/20
Mineral Exploration Services
N.A.I.C.S.: 213114
Christian G. Pilon *(Exec Dir-Peru)*

PANOS UTP A.D.
Kralja Petra I 24, 73240, Visegrad, Bosnia & Herzegovina
Tel.: (387) 58620120
PANS-R-A—(BANJ)
Rev.: $2,458
Assets: $2,228,375
Liabilities: $872,601
Net Worth: $1,355,774
Earnings: ($101,116)
Fiscal Year-end: 12/31/12
Hotel Operator
N.A.I.C.S.: 721110
Dragan Uscumlic *(Chm)*

PANOSTAJA OYJ
Kalevantie 2, 33100, Tampere, Finland
Tel.: (358) 5068570
Web Site: https://www.panostaja.fi
PNA1V—(HEL)
Rev.: $150,330,059
Assets: $156,059,168
Liabilities: $97,954,520
Net Worth: $58,104,647
Earnings: ($4,020,311)
Emp.: 1,217
Fiscal Year-end: 10/31/23
Investment Management Service
N.A.I.C.S.: 523999
Jukka Ala-Mello *(Chm)*

Subsidiaries:

Heatmasters Oy (1)
Relanderinkatu 2, 78200, Varkaus, Finland
Tel.: (358) 400956879
Web Site: https://www.heatmasters.net
Heat Treatment Equipment Mfr
N.A.I.C.S.: 333310

Subsidiary (Non-US):

Heatmasters Sp.zoo (2)
ul Sielecka 63, 42-500, Bedzin, Poland
Tel.: (48) 515555010
Web Site: http://www.heatmasters.pl
Metal Heat Treatment Services
N.A.I.C.S.: 423510
Marcin Skurczynski *(Mng Dir)*

KL-Varaosat Oy (1)
Viinikankatu 49, 33800, Tampere, Finland
Tel.: (358) 207 929820
Web Site: http://www.kl-varaosat.fi
Sales Range: $25-49.9 Million
Emp.: 19
Automotive Spare Parts Whslr
N.A.I.C.S.: 423120

Kannake Oy (1)
Hepolamminkatu 15, 33720, Tampere, Finland
Tel.: (358) 3 356 5300
Construction Materials Distr
N.A.I.C.S.: 423390

Kiinnikekeskus Services Oy (1)
Aunankorvenkatu 4, 33840, Tampere, Finland
Tel.: (358) 10 850 1500
Web Site: http://www.kiinnikekeskus.fi
Sales Range: $25-49.9 Million
Emp.: 12
Hardware Distr
N.A.I.C.S.: 423710

Kopijyva Oy (1)
Vehkakatu 1, Jyvaskyla, 40700, Finland
Tel.: (358) 408323030
Web Site: http://www.kopijyva.fi
Sales Range: $50-74.9 Million
Emp.: 130
Digital Printing Services
N.A.I.C.S.: 323111

Lampo-Tukku Oy (1)
PL 22, Helsinki, 00561, Finland
Tel.: (358) 9 777 1600
Web Site: http://www.lampotukku.fi
Sales Range: $25-49.9 Million
Emp.: 12
Plumbing Fixtures & Accessories Distr
N.A.I.C.S.: 423720
Ari Nyback *(Mgr-Sls)*

Lingoneer Oy (1)
Hatanpaa highway 24, 33100, Tampere, Finland
Tel.: (358) 4577302075
Web Site: http://lingoneer.com
Translation Services
N.A.I.C.S.: 541930
Tuomas Paasovaara *(Project Mgr)*

Matti-Ovi Oy (1)
Samppanummentie 8, 23800, Laitila, Finland
Tel.: (358) 10 239 1600
Web Site: http://www.mattiovi.fi
Rev.: $11,326,400
Solid Timber Door Mfr & Distr
N.A.I.C.S.: 321911

Oy Alfa-Kem Ab (1)
Terstie 13, 04220, Kerava, Finland
Tel.: (358) 3 878 250
Web Site: http://www.alfakem.fi
Industrial Chemical Products Mfr
N.A.I.C.S.: 325998

Suomen Helasto Oy (1)
Porttivahti 3, 60100, Seinajoki, Finland
Tel.: (358) 6 427 6555
Web Site: http://www.suomenhelasto.fi
Security System Services
N.A.I.C.S.: 561621

Suomen Kiinnikekeskus Oy (1)
Aunankorvenkatu 4, 33840, Tampere, Finland
Tel.: (358) 108501500
Web Site: http://kiinnikekeskus.fi

PANOSTAJA OYJ

Panostaja Oyj—(Continued)
Sales Range: $25-49.9 Million
Emp.: 12
Industrial Hardware Tools Distr
N.A.I.C.S.: 423830

Toimex Oy (1)
Hepolamminkatu 15, 33720, Tampere, Finland
Tel.: (358) 33565300
Web Site: https://www.toimex.fi
Sales Range: $25-49.9 Million
Emp.: 20
Air Conditioning Equipment Mfr & Distr
N.A.I.C.S.: 333415

Vindea Group Oy (1)
Vaihdemiehentie 1, Hyvinkaa, Finland
Tel.: (358) 19 460 4400
Web Site: http://www.vindea.fi
Logistics Consulting Servies
N.A.I.C.S.: 541614
Jouni Arolainen (Mng Dir)

PANRAM INTERNATIONAL CORP.
9F No 460 Sec 5 Chenggong Rd, Neihu District, Taipei, 114, Taiwan
Tel.: (886) 226318809
Web Site: https://www.panram.com.tw
Year Founded: 1994
8088—(TPE)
Rev.: $54,910,609
Assets: $44,058,656
Liabilities: $8,147,922
Net Worth: $35,910,734
Earnings: $6,627,834
Fiscal Year-end: 12/31/22
Semiconductor Components Mfr
N.A.I.C.S.: 334413
Leo Hsieh (Chm)

PANSAR BERHAD
Wisma Pansar 23-27 Jalan Bengkel, PO Box 319, 96007, Sibu, Malaysia
Tel.: (60) 84333366   MY
Web Site: https://www.pansar.com.my
Year Founded: 1961
PANSAR—(KLS)
Rev.: $219,253,597
Assets: $157,302,234
Liabilities: $88,244,419
Net Worth: $69,057,815
Earnings: $4,582,370
Fiscal Year-end: 03/31/24
Engine Mfr & Distr
N.A.I.C.S.: 333618
Hee Tai (Mng Dir)

Subsidiaries:

Pansar Company Sdn Bhd (1)
No 7 Jalan Astaka U8/84 Bukit Jelutong Industrial Park Seksyen U8, Bukit Jelutong Business And Technology Centre, 40150, Shah Alam, Malaysia
Tel.: (60) 378453366
Building Materials Distr
N.A.I.C.S.: 423390

Pansar Singapore Pte Ltd (1)
40 Jalan Pemimpin 04-02 Tat Ann Building, Singapore, 577185, Singapore
Tel.: (65) 63533933
Building Materials Distr
N.A.I.C.S.: 423390
Richard Chong (Mng Dir)

PANSARI DEVELOPERS LIMITED.
14 N S Road 4th Floor, Kolkata, 700001, India
Tel.: (91) 3340050500
Web Site: https://www.pansaridevelopers.com
Year Founded: 1996
PANSARI—(NSE)
Rev.: $2,876,770
Assets: $34,013,380
Liabilities: $19,455,260
Net Worth: $14,558,120
Earnings: $241,077
Emp.: 110
Fiscal Year-end: 03/31/23
Construction Services
N.A.I.C.S.: 236220
Mahesh Kumar Agarwal (Chm & Mng Dir)

PANSOFT COMPANY LIMITED
3/F Qilu Software Park Building, Jinan Hi-Tech Zone, Jinan, 250101, Shandong, China
Tel.: (86) 531 8887 4455   VG
Web Site: http://www.pansoft.com
Year Founded: 2001
Sales Range: $10-24.9 Million
Emp.: 614
Computer Management Software & Services
N.A.I.C.S.: 541511
Hugh Wang (Co-Owner & Chm)

PANSTAR ENTERPRISE CO., LTD.
108 Robot land-ro 249beong-gil, Seo-gu, Incheon, 22756, Korea (South)
Tel.: (82) 325853570
Web Site: https://en.heshbon.com
Year Founded: 1991
054300—(KRS)
Rev.: $51,383,369
Assets: $70,259,320
Liabilities: $33,810,568
Net Worth: $36,448,752
Earnings: $411,819
Emp.: 103
Fiscal Year-end: 12/31/22
Automobile Equipment Mfr
N.A.I.C.S.: 423830

PANTA HOLDINGS B.V.
Rendementsweg 2, 3641 SK, Mijdrecht, Netherlands
Tel.: (31) 297265636
Web Site: http://www.mass-lease.com
Sales Range: $25-49.9 Million
Emp.: 3
Holding Company
N.A.I.C.S.: 551112

Subsidiaries:

Mass lease (1)
Industrieweg 23, 3641 RK, Mijdrecht, Netherlands
Tel.: (31) 297227100
Web Site: http://www.mass-lease.com
Aircraft Leasing Services
N.A.I.C.S.: 532411
Tom Kennes (Mgr-Technical)

Netherlands Aircraft Company (1)
Hendrik Walaardt Sacrestraat 433, Schiphol-Oost, 1117 BM, Amsterdam, Netherlands
Tel.: (31) 205400300
Web Site: http://www.rekkof.nl
Aircraft Leasing Services
N.A.I.C.S.: 532411
Maarten van eeghen (Mng Dir)

PANTAFLIX AG
Holzstrasse 30, 80469, Munich, Germany
Tel.: (49) 8923238550   De
Web Site: https://www.pantaflixgroup.com
Year Founded: 2009
PAL—(MUN)
Rev.: $39,054,921
Assets: $46,770,972
Liabilities: $43,900,910
Net Worth: $2,870,062
Earnings: ($3,996,009)
Emp.: 37
Fiscal Year-end: 12/31/23
Motion Picture & Film Production Services
N.A.I.C.S.: 512110
Nicolas Paalzow (CEO)

Subsidiaries:

Pantaflix Technologies GmbH (1)
Neue Schonhauser Strasse 16, 10178, Berlin, Germany
Tel.: (49) 30220661610
Motion Picture & Video Production Services
N.A.I.C.S.: 512110
Rainer Knebel (CTO)

PANTECH GROUP HOLDINGS BERHAD
PTD 204334 Jalan Platinum Utama Kawasan Perindustrian Pasir Gudang, Zone 12B, 81700, Pasir Gudang, Johor Darul Takzim, Malaysia
Tel.: (60) 72597979
Web Site: https://www.pantech-group.com
PANTECH—(KLS)
Rev.: $206,058,193
Assets: $272,249,205
Liabilities: $79,524,451
Net Worth: $192,724,753
Earnings: $22,974,757
Emp.: 1,184
Fiscal Year-end: 02/29/24
Steel Pole Mfr
N.A.I.C.S.: 339992
Siew Ching Liang (Co-Sec)

Subsidiaries:

Panaflo Controls Pte. Ltd. (1)
No 7 Soon Lee Street 04-42 ISpace, Singapore, 627608, Singapore
Tel.: (65) 65623048
Web Site: http://www.panaflocontrols.com.sg
Sales Range: $25-49.9 Million
Industrial Valves Mfr & Distr
N.A.I.C.S.: 332911
Chew Soon Jiat (Mng Dir)

Pantech Corporation Sdn. Bhd. (1)
PTD 204334 Jalan Platinum Utama, Kawasan Perindustrian Pasir Gudang Zone 12B, 81700, Pasir Gudang, Johor Darul Takzim, Malaysia
Tel.: (60) 72597979
Web Site: http://pantech-group.com
Sales Range: $25-49.9 Million
Industrial Equipment Mfr
N.A.I.C.S.: 333248

Subsidiary (Domestic):

Pantech (Kuantan) Sdn. Bhd. (2)
Lot 38 39 Jalan Gebeng 1/8 Kawasan Industri Gebeng, 26080, Kuantan, Pahang Darul Makmur, Malaysia
Tel.: (60) 95807556
Sales Range: $25-49.9 Million
Emp.: 11
Industrial Equipment Mfr
N.A.I.C.S.: 333248
Tony Ten (Mgr)

Pantech Steel Industries Sdn. Bhd. (1)
Lot 13258 13259 Jalan Haji Abdul Manan Off Jalan Meru, 42200, Kapar, Selangor, Malaysia
Tel.: (60) 333931633
Web Site: https://www.pantechsteel.com
Steel Fittings Mfr
N.A.I.C.S.: 332999

PANTEL TECHNOLOGIES PVT. LTD.
E-33 Sector 63, Noida, 201301, Uttar Pradesh, India
Tel.: (91) 120 480 5200   In
Web Site: http://www.pantel.in
Year Founded: 2010
Personal & Commercial Tablet Developer & Mfr
N.A.I.C.S.: 334111
Vijender Singh (Chm & Mng Dir)

INTERNATIONAL PUBLIC

Subsidiaries:

Reliance Big TV Limited (1)
BHQ 6th Floor B-Wing BCA02 Dhirubhai Ambani Knowledge City, Navi Mumbai, 400710, India
Tel.: (91) 22 3033 8888
Web Site: http://www.reliancedigitaltv.com
Television Broadcasting Services
N.A.I.C.S.: 516120

PANTERA MINERALS LIMITED
Level 1 10 Outram St, West Perth, 6005, WA, Australia
Tel.: (61) 894672604
Web Site: https://www.panteraminerals.com
Year Founded: 2020
PFE—(ASX)
Rev.: $159,565
Assets: $4,643,291
Liabilities: $484,216
Net Worth: $4,159,075
Earnings: ($1,243,678)
Fiscal Year-end: 06/30/23
Mineral Exploration Services
N.A.I.C.S.: 212390
Matthew Hansen (Co-CEO)

PANTEX SA
Calea Bucuresti nr 318, 500299, Brasov, Romania
Tel.: (40) 268 336066
Web Site: http://www.pantex.ro
Year Founded: 1956
Sales Range: $1-9.9 Million
Emp.: 122
Textile Products Mfr
N.A.I.C.S.: 313220
Neculai Gheorghe Vrabie (Pres & Gen Mgr)

PANTHEON INFRASTRUCTURE PLC
10 Finsbury Square 4th Floor, London, EC2A 1AF, Devon, United Kingdom
Tel.: (44) 1392477500   UK
Web Site: https://www.pantheonstructure.com
Year Founded: 1982
PINT—(LSE)
Rev.: $2,845,781
Assets: $659,876,359
Liabilities: $15,283,854
Net Worth: $644,592,505
Earnings: $10,899,776
Fiscal Year-end: 12/31/22
Asset Management Services
N.A.I.C.S.: 523999
Harriet Alexander (VP)

PANTHEON INTERNATIONAL PLC
Pantheon Ventures 10 Finsbury Square, London, EC2A 1AF, United Kingdom
Tel.: (44) 2033561800
Web Site: https://www.piplc.com
PIN—(LSE)
Sales Range: $10-24.9 Million
Emp.: 215
Investment Services
N.A.I.C.S.: 523999
Andrew Lebus (Partner)

PANTHEON RESOURCES PLC
Golden Cross House 8 Duncannon Street, London, WC2N 4JF, United Kingdom
Tel.: (44) 2074845361
Web Site: https://www.pantheonresources.com
Year Founded: 2005
PANR—(LSE)
Rev.: $803,689
Assets: $309,927,453

AND PRIVATE COMPANIES

Liabilities: $37,498,846
Net Worth: $272,428,607
Earnings: ($1,446,687)
Emp.: 15
Fiscal Year-end: 06/30/23
Oil & Gas Exploration Services
N.A.I.C.S.: 213112
Robert Rosenthal *(Dir-Technical)*

Subsidiaries:

Agrippa LLC (1)
1 Tohopeka Ln, Philadelphia, PA 19318
Tel.: (215) 385-1680
Business Consulting Services
N.A.I.C.S.: 561499

PANTHER INDUSTRIAL PRODUCTS LIMITED
First Floor Radha Bhuvan 121 Nagindas Master Road Fort, Mumbai, 400 023, India
Tel.: (91) 22 22677712
Web Site:
http://www.pantherindustrialltd.com
Year Founded: 1987
Container & Packaging Material Whslr
N.A.I.C.S.: 423840
Kaushik C. Shah *(Compliance Officer)*

PANTHER METALS PLC
Eastways Enterprise Centre 7
Paynes Park, Hitchin, SG5 1EH,
Hertfordshire, United Kingdom
Tel.: (44) 1462429743
Web Site: https://panthermetals.com
Year Founded: 2013
PALM—(LSE)
Assets: $4,275,975
Liabilities: $409,530
Net Worth: $3,866,445
Earnings: ($1,144,275)
Fiscal Year-end: 12/31/22
Support Activities for Metal Mining
N.A.I.C.S.: 213114
Darren Hazelwood *(CEO)*

PANTHER SECURITIES PLC
Unicorn House Station Close, Potters Bar, EN6 1TL, Hertfordshire, United Kingdom
Tel.: (44) 1707667300
Web Site:
https://www.pantherplc.com
PNS—(AIM)
Rev.: $16,152,345
Assets: $229,083,855
Liabilities: $95,107,320
Net Worth: $133,976,535
Earnings: $20,464,455
Emp.: 37
Fiscal Year-end: 12/31/22
Lessors of Other Real Estate Property
N.A.I.C.S.: 531190
Simon Jeffrey Peters *(Sec & Dir-Fin)*

Subsidiaries:

M.R.G. Systems Limited (1)
Willow Ct Beeches Green, Stroud, GL5 4BJ, Glos, United Kingdom
Tel.: (44) 1453751871
Web Site: http://www.mrgsystems.co.uk
Sales Range: $25-49.9 Million
Emp.: 17
Information Display System Mfr
N.A.I.C.S.: 334511

Panther VAT Properties Limited (1)
8894 Darkes Lane, Potters Bar, EN6 1AQ, United Kingdom
Tel.: (44) 17 0755 7300
Property Investment & Managing Services
N.A.I.C.S.: 531312

Snowbest Limited (1)
8894 Darkes Lane, Potters Bar, EN6 1AQ, United Kingdom
Tel.: (44) 17077667300
Sales Range: $50-74.9 Million
Emp.: 10
Property Investment & Managing Services
N.A.I.C.S.: 531312

Surrey Motors Limited (1)
648 London Road, Ashford, TW15 3AW, Middlesex, United Kingdom
Tel.: (44) 178 466 4137
Web Site: https://www.surreymotors.com
Car Dealing Services
N.A.I.C.S.: 441110

Westmead Building Company Limited (1)
4 E Block Panther House 38 Mt Pleasant, London, WC1X 0AP, United Kingdom
Tel.: (44) 20 78338134
Property Investment & Managing Services
N.A.I.C.S.: 531311

PANTOP CORPORATION
Suite 3906 Far East Finance Centre 16 Harcourt Rd, Admiralty, Hong Kong, China (Hong Kong)
Tel.: (852) 5495 3987   NV
Year Founded: 2014
Hermetically Sealed Microelectronic Packages Mfr
N.A.I.C.S.: 339991
Teck Sheng Ting *(Pres, CEO & CFO)*

PANTORAMA INDUSTRIES INC.
2 Lake Rd, Dollard des Ormeaux, H9B 3H9, QC, Canada
Tel.: (514) 421-1850   Ca
Web Site: http://www.pantorama.com
Year Founded: 1976
Sales Range: $75-99.9 Million
Emp.: 600
Clothing Stores Retailer
N.A.I.C.S.: 458110
Sydney Aptacker *(Pres)*

PANTORO LIMITED
Level 2 46 Ventnor Ave, West Perth, 6005, WA, Australia
Tel.: (61) 862631110   AU
Web Site:
https://www.pantoro.com.au
PNR—(ASX)
Rev.: $153,199,739
Assets: $374,520,593
Liabilities: $98,545,782
Net Worth: $275,974,811
Earnings: ($32,925,841)
Fiscal Year-end: 06/30/24
Mineral Properties Development & Exploration Services
N.A.I.C.S.: 212230
Paul Cmrlec *(Mng Dir)*

PANYAM CEMENTS & MINERAL INDUSTRIES LIMITED
C-1 Industrial Estate Nandyal Kurnool, Hyderabad, 518502, Andhra Pradesh, India
Tel.: (91) 40 23555317   In
Web Site:
http://www.panyamcements.com
Year Founded: 1955
Rev.: $29,623,424
Assets: $45,380,631
Liabilities: $47,507,419
Net Worth: ($2,126,787)
Earnings: $4,891,691
Emp.: 442
Fiscal Year-end: 03/31/18
Cement Mfr & Distr
N.A.I.C.S.: 327310
S. Sreedhar Reddy *(Mng Dir)*

PAO NOVATEK
90/2 Leninsky prospect, Moscow, 119313, Russia
Tel.: (7) 4957306000   RU
Web Site: https://www.novatek.ru
Year Founded: 1994
NVKT—(MOEX)
Rev.: $15,581,072,280
Assets: $33,104,734,080
Liabilities: $7,357,246,650
Net Worth: $25,747,487,430
Earnings: $6,083,334,870
Emp.: 18,404
Fiscal Year-end: 12/31/21
Natural Gas Exploration, Development, Acquisition & Production Operations
N.A.I.C.S.: 211130
Alexander E. Natalenko *(Chm)*

Subsidiaries:

Novatek Polska Sp. z o.o. (1)
Pokoju 1, 31-548, Krakow, Poland
Tel.: (48) 123907695
Web Site: http://www.en.novatek.pl
Industrial Gas Whslr
N.A.I.C.S.: 424720

OAO Yamal LNG (1)
22 Akademika Pilyugina str BC Algorithm, 117393, Moscow, Russia
Tel.: (7) 4957750480
Web Site: http://www.yamallng.ru
Industrial Gas Mfr
N.A.I.C.S.: 325120

OOO Sabetta International Airport (1)
9 Respubliki street, Yamalo-Nenets Autonomous District, 629003, Salekhard, Russia
Tel.: (7) 4952289850
Web Site: http://www.sabetta.aero
Airport Services
N.A.I.C.S.: 488119
Shvarts Leonid *(Gen Dir)*

PAO SEVERSTAL
Klary Tsetkin Street 2, 127299, Moscow, 127299, Russia
Tel.: (7) 8202530900   RU
Web Site: https://www.severstal.com
CHMF—(MOEX)
Rev.: $11,638,000,000
Assets: $8,668,000,000
Liabilities: $4,459,000,000
Net Worth: $4,209,000,000
Earnings: $4,075,000,000
Emp.: 50,029
Fiscal Year-end: 12/31/21
Holding Company; Steel Poducer & Steel-Related Mining Services
N.A.I.C.S.: 551112
Dmitry Y. Goroshkov *(Dir-Sls & Bus Dev-Energy Sector)*

Subsidiaries:

AO Karelsky Okatysh (1)
52 Zvezdnaya Street Republic of Karelia, Kostomuksha, 186930, Russia
Tel.: (7) 8145933509
Iron Ore Product Mfr
N.A.I.C.S.: 331110

AO Neva-Metall (1)
ZAO Neva-Metall4 Himichesky St, Saint Petersburg, 198035, Russia
Tel.: (7) 8127407011
Non Ferrous Metal Mfr
N.A.I.C.S.: 331410

AO Olcon (1)
Olenegorsk Leningradsky prospect 2, 184530, Murmansk, Russia
Tel.: (7) 8155255197
Web Site: http://www.olcon.ru
Iron Ore Product Mfr
N.A.I.C.S.: 331110

AO Severstal Steel Solutions (1)
30 Mira Str, Vologda Region, Cherepovets, 162608, Russia
Tel.: (7) 8202531272
Steel Products Mfr
N.A.I.C.S.: 332312

AO Vorkutaugol (1)
st Lenin 6 Komi Republic, 169908, Syktyvkar, Komi, Russia
Tel.: (7) 8215173010
Web Site: http://www.vorkutaugol.ru
Emp.: 6,033
Coal Product Mfr
N.A.I.C.S.: 324199

AS Latvijas Metals (1)
Braslas Str 24, LV-1035, Riga, Latvia
Tel.: (371) 7569648
Web Site: http://www.latmet.lv
Non Ferrous Metal Mfr
N.A.I.C.S.: 331410

AS Severstallat (1)
Starta iela 13, 1039, Riga, Latvia
Tel.: (371) 6707 6600
Emp.: 260
Steel Distr
N.A.I.C.S.: 423510
Andris Kravalis *(Mgr-Sls)*

Aatlantide SAS (1)
11 A Chemin de la Dhuy, 38240, Meylan, France
Tel.: (33) 476902020
Web Site: https://www.aatlantide.com
Software Development Services
N.A.I.C.S.: 541511

Aircompany Severstal Ltd. (1)
Botovo village Airport, Cherepovets District, 162693, Vologda, Russia
Tel.: (7) 8202675202
Web Site: http://www.severstal-avia.ru
Flight Services
N.A.I.C.S.: 481211
Ivanovski Nikolai Nikolaevich *(Gen Dir)*

Berezitovy Rudnik LLC (1)
102 Ofis 401 Krasnoarmeiskaya ul, Blagoveshchensk, 675000, Russia
Tel.: (7) 4162220680
Gold Mining Services
N.A.I.C.S.: 212220

CompuGroup Medical Nederland B.V. (1)
Nobelweg 32, 6101 XB, Echt, Netherlands
Tel.: (31) 883876433
Web Site: https://www.cgm.com
Information Technology Consulting Services
N.A.I.C.S.: 541512

Docmetric GmbH (1)
Maria Trost 21, 56070, Koblenz, Germany
Tel.: (49) 26180008236
Web Site: https://docmetric.de
Software Development Services
N.A.I.C.S.: 541511

JSC Severstal-Metiz (1)
1/33 50-letiya Oktyabrya street, Cherepovets, Vologda, Russia
Tel.: (7) 8202539191
Web Site: http://www.metiz.severstal.com
Wire Product Mfr
N.A.I.C.S.: 332618
Sergey Kovryakov *(CEO)*

KMS Vertrieb und Services AG (1)
Inselkammerstrasse 1, 82008, Unterhaching, Germany
Tel.: (49) 896655090
Web Site: https://www.kms.ag
Marketing Consulting Services
N.A.I.C.S.: 541613

MS IT-Systeme GmbH (1)
Wurzburger Str 3, 98529, Suhl, Germany
Tel.: (49) 3681309797
Web Site: https://ms-it-systeme.de
Software Development Services
N.A.I.C.S.: 541511

OAO Dneprometiz (1)
Slobozhanskyi Avenue 20, 49081, Dnipropetrovsk, Ukraine
Tel.: (380) 563762525
Web Site: http://www.dneprometiz.com
Industrial Metal Products Mfr
N.A.I.C.S.: 332999

OAO Metallurgremont (1)
Nekrasov Street 20, Cherepovets, 162 606, Russia
Tel.: (7) 8202 53 68 49
Web Site: http://www.metallurgrem.ru
Ready Mix Concrete Mfr & Distr
N.A.I.C.S.: 327320

OAO Olkon (1)
2 prospekt Leningradski, Olenegorsk,

PAO SEVERSTAL

PAO Severstal—(Continued)
184533, Russia
Tel.: (7) 8155258236
Iron Ore Mining Services
N.A.I.C.S.: 212210

OAO Rostovmetall (1)
17 ul Sudostroitelnaya, Cherepovets, 162603, Russia
Tel.: (7) 8202531300
Steel Products Mfr
N.A.I.C.S.: 331110

OAO SPB-Giproshakht (1)
st Gorokhovaya 14/26 letter A, Saint Petersburg, Russia
Tel.: (7) 8123323092
Web Site: http://www.spbgipro.ru
Emp.: 270
Ground Engineering Services
N.A.I.C.S.: 541330

OOO Severstal-Promservis (1)
9 Stroiteley Ave, Cherepovets, 162600, Vologda, Russia
Tel.: (7) 8202 53 59 33
Web Site: http://promservice.severstal.com
Industrial Building Design & Construction Services
N.A.I.C.S.: 236210

OOO Stilleys (1)
Platonovskoye S/P 105 Razdolnaya St building 13, Oryol District, 302209, Oryol, Russia
Tel.: (7) 4862391290
Web Site: http://www.steellace.ru
Shopping Carts Mfr
N.A.I.C.S.: 332999

OOO YuniSpring (1)
1/33 50 Letiya Oktyabrya ul, 162608, Cherepovets, Vologda, Russia
Tel.: (7) 8202627174
Web Site: http://www.unispring.ru
Upholstered Furniture Mfr
N.A.I.C.S.: 337121

Portavita B.V. (1)
Oostenburgervoorstraat 83a, 1018 MP, Amsterdam, Netherlands
Tel.: (31) 208200500
Web Site: https://nl.portavita.com
Health Care Srvices
N.A.I.C.S.: 621999

Severstal Distribution (1)
st Vostochnaya 80 office 4, 10029, Zhytomyr, Ukraine
Tel.: (380) 412362266
Web Site: https://www.sever-stal.com.ua
Rolled Flat Products Distr
N.A.I.C.S.: 423510

Severstal Export GmbH (1)
Fischergasse 3, Stansstad, 6362, Switzerland (60%)
Tel.: (41) 41 619 77 10
Web Site: http://www.severstal.com
Steel Product Distr
N.A.I.C.S.: 423510

Severstal Lifting Technologies LLC (1)
st 50th Anniversary of October 1/33, Vologda region, 162610, Cherepovets, Russia
Tel.: (7) 8202538899
Web Site: http://www.tecirus.ru
Cable Products Mfr
N.A.I.C.S.: 335929

Severstal TPZ-Sheksna LLC (1)
Railway Village Council Sheksna Industrial Park Building 1, Sheksninsky District, Vologda, 162560, Russia
Tel.: (7) 8175125777
Web Site: http://www.sheksna.severstal.com
Plastic Pipe & Pipe Fitting Mfr
N.A.I.C.S.: 326122

Severstal-Proekt LLC (1)
st Mayakovsky 11 Vologda region, 162606, Cherepovets, Russia
Tel.: (7) 8202536800
Web Site: http://www.proekt.severstal.com
Emp.: 421
Professional Architectural Services
N.A.I.C.S.: 541310

Titanium Dental BV (1)
Brusselsesteenweg 283 / 10, 9230, Wetteren, Belgium
Tel.: (32) 93958565
Web Site: https://www.titaniumdental.be
Software Application Services
N.A.I.C.S.: 541511

UniFence LLC (1)
1/33 50-Letiya Oktyabrya Street Vologda Region, Cherepovets, 162610, Russia
Tel.: (7) 8202538531
Wire Welded Mesh Mfr
N.A.I.C.S.: 331222

VISUS Health IT GmbH (1)
Gesundheitscampus-Sud 15, 44801, Bochum, Germany
Tel.: (49) 234936930
Web Site: https://www.visus.com
Information Technology Services
N.A.I.C.S.: 541511

Victory Industries, Inc (1)
990 S Oakwood, Detroit, MI 48217
Tel.: (313) 841-0264
Industrial Machinery Repair Services
N.A.I.C.S.: 811310

ZAO SeverStalBel (1)
508 C 169 A 305C Nezavisimosty ave, Minsk, 220114, Belarus
Tel.: (375) 17 218 11 81
Web Site: http://www.severstalbel.by
Steel Distr
N.A.I.C.S.: 423510

ZAO Severstal SMZ-Kolpino (1)
Izhora Plant Zone litera A3 Office 20-H, Kolpino, Saint Petersburg, 196651, Russia
Tel.: (7) 812 331 72 04
Steel Construction Services
N.A.I.C.S.: 236210

ZAO Severstal TPZ-Sheksna (1)
Building 1 Industrial Park, Vologda, 162550, Sheksna, Russia
Tel.: (7) 81751 2 57 77
Web Site: http://sheksna.severstal.com
Sales Range: $50-74.9 Million
Emp.: 20
Electric Pipe Welding Machine Mfr
N.A.I.C.S.: 333248
Vitaly Shestakov (CEO)

ZAO Vtorchermet (1)
Khimichesky Per 4, Saint Petersburg, 198095, Russia
Tel.: (7) 812 320 04 40
Web Site: http://www.vchm.spb.ru
Scrap Processing Services
N.A.I.C.S.: 423510

PAO SOVCOMFLOT
3a Moyka River Embankment, 191186, Saint Petersburg, Russia
Tel.: (7) 4956604000
Web Site: http://www.scf-group.ru
Rev.: $1,519,937,000
Assets: $7,142,246,000
Liabilities: $3,792,183,000
Net Worth: $3,350,063,000
Earnings: ($45,556,000)
Emp.: 7,800
Fiscal Year-end: 12/31/18
Sea Freight Transportation Services
N.A.I.C.S.: 483111
Sergey Ottovich Frank (Chm)

Subsidiaries:

OAO Novoship (1)
1 Svobody Street, 353900, Novorossiysk, Russia
Tel.: (7) 8617801745
Web Site: http://www.novoship.ru
Sea Freight Transportation Services
N.A.I.C.S.: 483111
Yury Tsvetkov (Pres)

OOO SCF GEO (1)
6 Gasheka Street, 125047, Moscow, Russia
Tel.: (7) 4956604000
Oil & Gas Exploration Services
N.A.I.C.S.: 211130

OOO SCF Management Services (1)
3a Moyka River Embankment, 191186, Saint Petersburg, Russia
Tel.: (7) 8123859490
Oil & Gas Exploration Services
N.A.I.C.S.: 211130

SCF Arctic (1)
3a River Moyka Embankment, 191186, Saint Petersburg, Russia
Tel.: (7) 9652504828
Sea Freight Transportation Services
N.A.I.C.S.: 483111

SCF Management Services (Cyprus) Ltd. (1)
Tower II Maximos Plaza 18 Maximos Michailidis Street Neapolis, 3106, Limassol, Cyprus
Tel.: (357) 25890000
Oil & Gas Exploration Services
N.A.I.C.S.: 211130

SCF Management Services (Dubai) Ltd. (1)
Office OT 17-32 Level 17 Central Park Towers Office Tower DIFC, PO Box 507065, Dubai, United Arab Emirates
Tel.: (971) 45631900
Oil & Gas Exploration Services
N.A.I.C.S.: 211130

SCF Marpetrol S.A. (1)
Plaza Manuel Gomez Moreno 2 - Planta 10, Edificio Alfredo Mahou, 28020, Madrid, Spain
Tel.: (34) 91 5988900
Sea Freight Transportation Services
N.A.I.C.S.: 483111
Oskirko Vladimir Petrovich (Mng Dir)

Sovcomflot (Cyprus) Limited (1)
Unicom Tower Maximos Plaza 18 Maximos Michaelides Street, Neapolis, 3106, Lemesos, Cyprus
Tel.: (357) 25 890000
Sea Freight Transportation Services
N.A.I.C.S.: 483111
Marios Orphanos (Mng Dir)

Sovcomflot (UK) Ltd (1)
6th Floor 1 Finsbury Square, London, EC2A 1AE, United Kingdom
Tel.: (44) 20 7496 1812
Emp.: 17
Sea Freight Transportation Services
N.A.I.C.S.: 483111
Paul Jackson (Mgr-Chartering)

PAO TMK
40/2a Pokrovka Street, 101000, Moscow, 101000, Russia
Tel.: (7) 4957757600 **RU**
Web Site: https://www.tmk-group.com
Year Founded: 2001
TRMK—(MOEX)
Rev.: $5,778,374,070
Assets: $9,355,952,190
Liabilities: $8,683,785,720
Net Worth: $672,166,470
Earnings: $96,755,010
Emp.: 38,934
Fiscal Year-end: 12/31/21
Metal Pipe Mfr
N.A.I.C.S.: 332919
Vladimir B. Oborsky (Member-Mgmt Bd & VP-Sls)

Subsidiaries:

Chelyabinsk Pipe Plant PJSC (1)
Mashinostroiteley st 21, Chelyabinsk, 454129, Russia (97.63%)
Tel.: (7) 3512557333
Web Site: http://www.chelpipe.ru
Rev.: $2,577,084,400
Assets: $2,047,286,340
Liabilities: $1,992,369,830
Net Worth: $54,916,510
Earnings: $111,331,660
Fiscal Year-end: 12/31/2018
Steel Product Mfr & Distr
N.A.I.C.S.: 331210
Andrey Komarov (Chm)

Subsidiary (Domestic):

JSC Rimera (2)
Bolshoy Boulevard building 40 Business center Amaltea, Skolkovo Innovation Center, 121205, Moscow, Russia

INTERNATIONAL PUBLIC

Tel.: (7) 4959810101
Web Site: http://www.rimera.com
Pipe Product Mfr
N.A.I.C.S.: 332996
Sergey Artemiev (Mgr-Export)

Subsidiary (Non-US):

MSA a.s. (2)
Hlucinska 641, 747 22, Dolni Benesov, Czech Republic
Tel.: (420) 553881111
Web Site: http://www.msa.cz
Industrial Valve Mfr & Distr
N.A.I.C.S.: 332911
Aleksandr Lyalkov (CEO)

Subsidiary (Domestic):

OOO Rimera-Service (2)
Industrial Zone Noyabrskaya Railway Station, Yamal-Nenets Autonomous Area, Noyabr'sk, 629800, Russia
Tel.: (7) 3496375201
Pipe Product Mfr
N.A.I.C.S.: 332996

PJSC Izhneftemash (2)
Ordzhonikidze St 2 Udmurtia, 426063, Izhevsk, Russia
Tel.: (7) 3412689191
Pipe Product Mfr
N.A.I.C.S.: 332996

OAO Rosniti (1)
Novorossiyskaya St 30, 454139, Chelyabinsk, Russia
Tel.: (7) 3517347060
Web Site: http://en.rosniti.ru
Steel Pole Mfr
N.A.I.C.S.: 331210
Igor Yurievich Pyshmintsev (Gen Dir)

SC TMK-ARTROM SA (1)
30 Draganesti Street, Slatina, 230119, Olt County, Romania
Tel.: (40) 249436862
Web Site: http://www.tmk-artrom.eu
Rev.: $342,513,377
Assets: $436,099,570
Liabilities: $271,595,491
Net Worth: $164,504,079
Earnings: $19,515,266
Emp.: 2,249
Fiscal Year-end: 12/31/2018
Pipe Product Mfr
N.A.I.C.S.: 339999
Adrian Popescu (Pres, CEO & Member-Mgmt Bd)

TMK Corporate Scientific and Technical Centre (1)
30 Novorossiyskaya St, 454139, Chelyabinsk, Russia (100%)
Tel.: (7) 3517347060
Sales Range: $25-49.9 Million
Emp.: 144
Coordinates & Centralizes Research Activities for OAO TMK
N.A.I.C.S.: 541715

TMK Global AG (1)
2 Bldv Du Theatre, 1211, Geneva, Switzerland (100%)
Tel.: (41) 228186466
Sales Range: $25-49.9 Million
Emp.: 8
Distribution of TMK's Tubular Products
N.A.I.C.S.: 322219

TMK Industrial Solutions LLC (1)
10713 W Sam Houston Pkwy N Ste 680, Houston, TX 77064
Tel.: (346) 206-3790
Steel Pole Mfr
N.A.I.C.S.: 331210
Mike Christopher (CEO)

TMK Italia S.R.L. (1)
Piazza degli Affari 12, I 23900, Lecco, Italy (100%)
Tel.: (39) 0341365151
Sales Range: $25-49.9 Million
Emp.: 12
Pipe Production Sales in Europe
N.A.I.C.S.: 237120

TMK Kazakhstan LLC (1)
38/1 Zheltoksan st office 5, Nur-Sultan, 010000, Kazakhstan (100%)
Tel.: (7) 7171315608

AND PRIVATE COMPANIES

Supplies TMK Pipe Products to Chemical & Petrochemical Industries
N.A.I.C.S.: 237120

TMK Logistics (1)
40 2a Pokrovka St, 105062, Moscow, Russia (100%)
Tel.: (7) 4957757600
Sales Range: $50-74.9 Million
Emp.: 200
Organization of Rail, Ground & Ocean Freight Operations
N.A.I.C.S.: 483111

TMK Middle East (1)
Office 118 Block 5EA Dubai Airport Free Zone, PO Box 293534, Dubai, United Arab Emirates (100%)
Tel.: (971) 46091130
Sales Range: $25-49.9 Million
Emp.: 20
Pipe Product Sales in the Middle East
N.A.I.C.S.: 237120
Dmitry Tyrkba *(CEO)*

TMK Ngs-Nizhnevartovsk AO (1)
Samotlorskoye Oil Field Nizhnevartovsk Pipe Repair Base Building 1, Khanty-Mansiysk Autonomous Okrug - Yugra, 628637, Nizhnevartovsk, Russia
Tel.: (7) 3466654340
Web Site: http://www.uprt-nv.ru
Steel Pole Mfr
N.A.I.C.S.: 331210

TMK-Resita SA (1)
36 Traian Lalescu Street, Caras-Severin County, Resita, 320050, Romania
Tel.: (40) 255217211
Web Site: http://tmk-resita.tmk-artrom.eu
Steel Pole Mfr
N.A.I.C.S.: 331210
Cristiana Vaduva *(Chief Economical & Accountancy Officer)*

Tagmet Pao (1)
St Zavodskaya 1, Rostov, Taganrog, Russia
Tel.: (7) 88634650065
Web Site: http://tagmet.tmk-group.ru
Steel Pole Mfr
N.A.I.C.S.: 331210

Trade House TMK (1)
40 Bldg 2A Pokrovka St, 105062, Moscow, Russia (100%)
Tel.: (7) 4957757600
Sales Range: $25-49.9 Million
Emp.: 40
Sales & Distribution of Pipe Products & Raw Materials
N.A.I.C.S.: 332996

PAO ZAWOLZHSKY MOTORNY ZAWOD
st Sovetskaya 1A, Gorodetsky district Zavolzhye, Nizhniy Novgorod, 606522, Russia
Tel.: (7) 8316166209
Web Site: https://www.zmz.ru
Year Founded: 1956
Automotive Parts Mfr & Distr
N.A.I.C.S.: 333618

PAOS HOLDINGS BERHAD
No 65 Persiaran Selangor Seksyen 15, 40200, Shah Alam, Selangor Darul Ehsan, Malaysia
Tel.: (60) 355104219
Web Site: https://www.paos.com.my
PAOS—(KLS)
Rev.: $144,751,453
Assets: $28,118,612
Liabilities: $9,460,266
Net Worth: $18,658,346
Earnings: ($9,745)
Emp.: 148
Fiscal Year-end: 05/31/23
Soap Mfr
N.A.I.C.S.: 325611
Siew Hong Wu *(Co-Sec)*

Subsidiaries:

Paos Industries Sdn. Bhd. (1)
No 65 Persiaran Selangor Section 15, 40200, Shah Alam, Selangor, Malaysia
Tel.: (60) 355104219
Web Site: http://www.paos.com.my
Sales Range: $25-49.9 Million
Emp.: 100
Palm Oil Products Mfr
N.A.I.C.S.: 311224
Tong Yong Lim *(CEO)*

Premier Oil Industries Sdn. Bhd. (1)
Lot 3 Jalan Gangsa Kawasan Perusahaan, Banting, 42700, Selangor, Malaysia
Tel.: (60) 331875805
Sales Range: $50-74.9 Million
Emp.: 50
Property Management & Rental Services
N.A.I.C.S.: 522299
Soswan Kwan *(Mgr-Factory)*

PAOS INDUSTRIES LTD.
Village Pawa GT Road Near Civil Airport, Ludhiana, Ludhiana, 141120, Punjab, India
Tel.: (91) 1615220000
Web Site: https://paosindustries.in
Year Founded: 1990
530291—(BOM)
Assets: $10,203
Liabilities: $1,928,482
Net Worth: ($1,918,278)
Earnings: ($34,818)
Emp.: 2
Fiscal Year-end: 03/31/23
Vegetable Oil Mfr
N.A.I.C.S.: 311225
Sanjeev Bansal *(Mng Dir & Exec Dir)*

PAPANETS CO., LTD.
9th Floor 1-5-17 Koshigaya, Koshigaya, 343-0813, Saitama, Japan
Tel.: (81) 489605088
Web Site: https://www.papanets.co.jp
Year Founded: 1995
9388—(TKS)
Sales Range: Less than $1 Million
Real Estate Development Services
N.A.I.C.S.: 531390
Hiroaki Ito *(Pres)*

PAPELES BIO BIO S.A.
Pedro Aguirre Cerda 1054, San Pedro de la Paz, Concepcion, Chile
Tel.: (56) 41 2500 000
Web Site: http://www.bopapergroup.com
Year Founded: 1957
Paper Mills
N.A.I.C.S.: 322120

Subsidiaries:

Norske Skog Pisa Ltda. (1)
Rodovia PR-151 km 207 5, 84200-000, Jaguariaiva, Brazil
Tel.: (55) 4335358000
Paper Mills
N.A.I.C.S.: 322299

PAPELES Y CARTONES DE EUROPA SA
Carretera de Fuencarral 98, Alcobendas, 28108, Madrid, Spain
Tel.: (34) 914902160
Web Site: http://www.europacgroup.com
Year Founded: 1995
Rev.: $1,040,004,811
Assets: $1,304,004,770
Liabilities: $810,527,178
Net Worth: $493,477,593
Earnings: $93,388,759
Emp.: 11
Fiscal Year-end: 12/31/17
Paper Products Mfr
N.A.I.C.S.: 322220

Subsidiaries:

Europac Cartonnerie de Rouen SAS (1)
Rue Desire Granet, BP 30444, 76806, Saint-Etienne-du-Rouvray, France
Tel.: (33) 2 35 64 51 94
Packaging Products Mfr & Distr
N.A.I.C.S.: 322220

PAPERCOREA CO., LTD.
1245 Oehang-ro, Gunsan, Jeollabuk-do, Korea (South)
Tel.: (82) 634405000
Web Site: https://www.papercorea.co.kr
Year Founded: 1943
001020—(KRS)
Rev.: $314,437,051
Assets: $384,903,722
Liabilities: $337,645,074
Net Worth: $47,258,648
Earnings: ($1,403,155)
Emp.: 158
Fiscal Year-end: 12/31/22
Paper Mfr
N.A.I.C.S.: 322120
Yook-Sang Kwon *(CEO)*

Subsidiaries:

Natura Media Inc. (1)
12 F Shihnan Dm Bldg Mapo Street 25, Mapo-Gu, Seoul, 121-708, Korea (South)
Tel.: (82) 237680365
Web Site: http://www.naturamedia.co.kr
Printing Machinery Mfr
N.A.I.C.S.: 333248
Choong-Hyun Kim *(CEO)*

PAPERCOREA INC. (1)
50 Guam-daero, Gunsan, 121-708, Jeollabukdo, Korea (South)
Tel.: (82) 63 440 5000
Web Site: http://www.web.papercorea.co.kr
Paper Products Mfr
N.A.I.C.S.: 322120

PAPERPACK PRINTING, BOX - MANUFACTURING & PAPER PACKAGING INDUSTRIAL S.A.
24 Viltanioti Str, 145 64, Kifissia, Greece
Tel.: (30) 2102846800
Web Site: http://www.paperpack.gr
Year Founded: 1996
PPAK—(ATH)
Rev.: $20,658,057
Earnings: $2,160,210
Emp.: 99
Fiscal Year-end: 12/31/19
Packaging Carton Mfr
N.A.I.C.S.: 322219
John Tsoukaridis *(Chm & Mng Dir)*

PAPHOS STONE C. ESTATES PLC
Poseidonos 77, Paphos, Cyprus
Tel.: (357) 26813060
Building Construction Services
N.A.I.C.S.: 236220

PAPIERSACKFABRIK TENAX GMBH & CO. KG
Am Westbahnhof 43 - 55, 40878, Ratingen, Germany
Tel.: (49) 21024890
Web Site: http://www.papiersackfabrik-tenax.de
Year Founded: 1917
Emp.: 100
Paper Sacks Mfr
N.A.I.C.S.: 424130
Bernhard Richter *(Co-Mng Dir)*

PAPILON SAVUNMA-GUVENLIK SISTEMLERI BILISIM MUHENDISLIK HIZMETLERI ITHALAT IHRACAT SANAYI VE TICARET A.S.
Mebusevleri Mah Ergin Sk No 9, Cankaya, Ankara, Turkiye
Tel.: (90) 3122312026

PAPPAJACK BERHAD

Web Site: https://www.papilon.com.tr
Year Founded: 2012
PAPIL—(IST)
Rev.: $2,510,363
Assets: $11,621,057
Liabilities: $790,342
Net Worth: $10,830,715
Earnings: $1,833,883
Fiscal Year-end: 12/31/23
Biometric Equipment Mfr
N.A.I.C.S.: 334118
Murat Kerimoglu *(COO)*

PAPOUTSANIS S.A.
71st Km National Road Athens - Lamia Vathi Avlidos, 34100, Chalkida, Greece
Tel.: (30) 2262085000
Web Site: https://www.papoutsanis.gr
Year Founded: 1960
PAP—(ATH)
Sales Range: $25-49.9 Million
Emp.: 155
Toilet Product Mfr
N.A.I.C.S.: 325620
George Gatzaros *(Pres)*

PAPPAJACK BERHAD
No 11B Jalan TK1/11A Taman Kinrara Seksyen 1, 47180, Puchong, Selangor, Malaysia
Tel.: (60) 380804884
Web Site: https://pappajack.com.my
Year Founded: 2014
PPJACK—(KLS)
Rev.: $14,806,977
Assets: $46,629,919
Liabilities: $9,752,617
Net Worth: $36,877,302
Earnings: $2,141,141
Emp.: 118
Fiscal Year-end: 12/31/22
Financial Investment Services
N.A.I.C.S.: 523999
Lim Boon Hua *(CEO & Mng Dir)*

Subsidiaries:

Consistent Reach Holdings Sdn. Bhd. (1)
No 369 369-1 Jalan 1A/3 Bandar Baru, 47000, Sungai Buloh, Selangor, Malaysia
Tel.: (60) 361508338
Pawn Brokerage Services
N.A.I.C.S.: 522310

DGH Sdn. Bhd. (1)
No 48-G Jalan Padi 1 Taman Uda Tampoi, 81200, Johor Bahru, Malaysia
Tel.: (60) 72324788
Pawn Broking Services
N.A.I.C.S.: 522310

Dhoby Ghaut (Kapar) Sdn. Bhd. (1)
No 22 Jalan Besar Pekan Kapar, 42200, Klang, Selangor, Malaysia
Tel.: (60) 332508880
Pawn Broking Services
N.A.I.C.S.: 522310

Dhoby Ghaut (M) Sdn. Bhd. (1)
No 4919 Ground Floor Jalan Bagan Luar, 12000, Butterworth, Pulau Penang, Malaysia
Tel.: (60) 43313888
Pawn Broking Services
N.A.I.C.S.: 522310

Dhoby Ghaut (Sel) Sdn. Bhd. (1)
No 25G Jalan Besar, Pekan Semenyih, 43500, Semenyih, Selangor, Malaysia
Tel.: (60) 387237788
Pawn Broking Services
N.A.I.C.S.: 522299

Dhoby Ghaut Holdings Sdn. Bhd. (1)
No 590 Ground Floor Jalan SS 9A/14 Seri Setia, 47300, Petaling Jaya, Selangor, Malaysia
Tel.: (60) 378656088
Pawn Broking Services
N.A.I.C.S.: 522310

PAPPAJACK BERHAD

Pappajack Berhad—(Continued)

Mashita Holdings Sdn. Bhd. (1)
No 7-G Ground Floor Jalan Pandan Jaya 3/5 Pandan Jaya, 55100, Kuala Lumpur, Malaysia
Tel.: (60) 392268688
Pawn Broking Services
N.A.I.C.S.: 522310

PPJ Berkat Sdn. Bhd. (1)
14 Lorong Jed 1 Nadi Kota, 26400, Bandar Pusat Jengka, Pahang, Malaysia
Tel.: (60) 94663888
Pawn Broking Services
N.A.I.C.S.: 522299

PPJ Landas Emas Sdn. Bhd. (1)
No 11A Jalan TK 1/11B Taman Kinrara Seksyen 1, 47180, Puchong, Selangor, Malaysia
Tel.: (60) 380710808
Pawn Brokerage Services
N.A.I.C.S.: 522310

PPJ Maju Sdn. Bhd. (1)
No 46G Jalan Merdeka Pekan Ampang, 68000, Ampang, Selangor, Malaysia
Tel.: (60) 342912888
Pawn Brokerage Services
N.A.I.C.S.: 522310

PPJ Makmur Sdn. Bhd. (1)
No 241 Ground Floor Jalan Pasar, Bukit Mertajam, 14000, Pulau Penang, Penang, Malaysia
Tel.: (60) 45308888
Pawn Broking Services
N.A.I.C.S.: 522299

PPJ Sinar Sdn. Bhd. (1)
No 16 Ground Floor Jalan Pos Baru, 41300, Klang, Selangor, Malaysia
Tel.: (60) 333433388
Pawn Broking Services
N.A.I.C.S.: 522299

PPJ Sukses Sdn. Bhd. (1)
No 170 Jalan Atas, Nibong Tebal, 14300, Pulau Penang, Penang, Malaysia
Tel.: (60) 45982848
Pawn Broking Services
N.A.I.C.S.: 522299

Pajak Gadai BT Cleaning Sdn. Bhd. (1)
No 46-A Lintang Angsana Bandar Baru Ayer Itam, Air Itam, 11500, Pulau Penang, Malaysia
Tel.: (60) 48286888
Pawn Broking Services
N.A.I.C.S.: 522310

Pajak Gadai Bertuah Sdn. Bhd. (1)
A-01-01 Pangsapuri Aman Jalan Prima 6/1 Taman Puchong Prima, 47100, Puchong, Selangor, Malaysia
Tel.: (60) 380623888
Pawn Broking Services
N.A.I.C.S.: 522310

Pajak Gadai Consistent Reach Sdn. Bhd. (1)
No 6 Ground Floor Jalan PJU 5/8 Dataran Sunway Kota Damansara, 47810, Petaling Jaya, Selangor, Malaysia
Tel.: (60) 361480678
Pawn Broking Services
N.A.I.C.S.: 522310

Pajak Gadai PPJ Sdn. Bhd. (1)
13-0-04 Jalan 2/112A Jalan Pantai Dalam Taman Bukit Angkasa, 59200, Kuala Lumpur, Malaysia
Tel.: (60) 322420438
Pawn Broking Services
N.A.I.C.S.: 522310

Pajak Gadai PPJ Sehati Sdn. Bhd. (1)
No 5 Ground Floor Jalan Raya Timur KS 1, 41000, Klang, Selangor, Malaysia
Tel.: (60) 333818876
Pawn Broking Services
N.A.I.C.S.: 522299

Pajak Gadai PPJack Sdn. Bhd. (1)
No 44A Jalan TK 1/11A Taman Kinrara Seksyen 1 Batu 7 1/2, 47180, Puchong, Selangor, Malaysia
Tel.: (60) 380805938
Pawn Broking Services
N.A.I.C.S.: 522310

Pajak Gadai Pappajack Sdn. Bhd. (1)
No 27 Jalan Bayu Tinggi Taman Bayu Perdana, 41200, Klang, Selangor, Malaysia
Tel.: (60) 333221888
Pawn Broking Services
N.A.I.C.S.: 522310

Pajak Gadai Pappajack Sehati Sdn. Bhd. (1)
No 23A-A Ground Floor Sunway Prima Lintang Sungai Tiram 5, 11900, Bayan Lepas, Pulau Penang, Malaysia
Tel.: (60) 46116664
Pawn Broking Services
N.A.I.C.S.: 522310

Pajak Gadai TMI Sdn. Bhd. (1)
No 19 P T 20611 Jalan PU 5/1 Taman Puchong Utama, 47140, Puchong, Selangor, Malaysia
Tel.: (60) 380668884
Pawn Broking Services
N.A.I.C.S.: 522310

Pajak Gadai TSE Sdn. Bhd. (1)
No 20-G Jalan Murni 25/61, Taman Sri Muda Seksyen 25, 40400, Shah Alam, Selangor, Malaysia
Tel.: (60) 351315328
Pawn Broking Services
N.A.I.C.S.: 522299

Pajak Gadai Tetap Sejiwa Sdn. Bhd. (1)
No 11 Jalan 1/116B Kuchai Enterpreneurs Park Jalan Kuchai Lama, 58200, Kuala Lumpur, Malaysia
Tel.: (60) 379820863
Pawn Broking Services
N.A.I.C.S.: 522310

PAPRIKA STUDIOS KFT.
Fogarasi ut 3-5, 1148, Budapest, Hungary
Tel.: (36) 14323232 HU
Web Site: https://paprikastudios.eu
Film Production Services
N.A.I.C.S.: 512110
Akos Erdos (CEO)

PAPYLESS CO., LTD.
Kioicho Building 3-12 Kioicho, Chiyoda-ku, Tokyo, 102-0094, Japan
Tel.: (81) 362729533 JP
Web Site: https://www.papy.co.jp
Year Founded: 1995
3641—(TKS)
Rev.: $113,526,750
Assets: $96,056,520
Liabilities: $27,490,990
Net Worth: $68,565,530
Earnings: $1,434,370
Emp.: 148
Fiscal Year-end: 03/31/24
Digital Publications, Books & Software Internet Retailer
N.A.I.C.S.: 459210
Mikio Amaya (Founder & Chm)

PAPYRUS AUSTRALIA LIMITED
2 Peel Street, Adelaide, 5000, SA, Australia
Tel.: (61) 3110868409 AU
Web Site: https://www.papyrusaustralia.com
PPY—(ASX)
Rev.: $449,358
Assets: $1,817,524
Liabilities: $390,550
Net Worth: $1,426,974
Earnings: ($430,061)
Emp.: 39
Fiscal Year-end: 06/30/24
Paper Products Mfr
N.A.I.C.S.: 322120
Ramy Abraham Azer (Mng Dir)

PAR DRUGS & CHEMICALS LIMITED
816 Nilamber Triumph Gotri Vasna Road, Vadodara, 390007, Gujarat, India
Tel.: (91) 2652991022
Web Site: https://www.pardrugs.com
Year Founded: 1999
PAR—(NSE)
Drugs Chemical Product Mfr
N.A.I.C.S.: 325998
Falgun Vallabhbhai Savani (Mng Dir)

PARA LIGHT ELECTRONICS CO., LTD.
11F No 8 Jiankang Rd, Zhonghe Dist, New Taipei City, 23586, Taiwan
Tel.: (886) 222253733
Web Site: https://www.para.com.tw
Year Founded: 1987
6226—(TAI)
Rev.: $24,836,259
Assets: $76,503,905
Liabilities: $36,644,101
Net Worth: $39,859,804
Earnings: ($2,351,352)
Emp.: 795
Fiscal Year-end: 12/31/23
Light Emitting Diode (LED) Lamps & LED Displays Mfr
N.A.I.C.S.: 335132
David Ma (Chm)

Subsidiaries:

Myanmar Para Light LED & Lighting Accessory Company Ltd. (1)
No 212 Pyin Si Minthar Gyi Street Shwe Lin Ban Industry, Hlaing Thar Yar Township, Yangon, Myanmar
Tel.: (95) 9776964540
Light Emitting Diode Mfr
N.A.I.C.S.: 334413

Para Light (QINGDAO) Electronics Co., Ltd. (1)
Room 1204 12th Floor Times International Plaza No 168 Shandong Road, Shibei District, Qingdao, 266000, Shandong, China
Tel.: (86) 53285692571
Automotive LED Light Mfr
N.A.I.C.S.: 336320

Para Light Corp. (1)
515 Spanish Ln Ste B, Walnut, CA 91789
Tel.: (909) 468-4866
Web Site: https://www.paralightusa.com
Emp.: 1,028
Opto-Electronic Components Mfr
N.A.I.C.S.: 334413

Para Light Electronics HK Limited (1)
Unit G 16 F Shield Industrial Centre, 84-92 Chai Wan Kok St, Tsuen Wan, New Territories, China (Hong Kong)
Tel.: (852) 28948650
Web Site: http://www.para.com.tw
Sales Range: $25-49.9 Million
Emp.: 7
Opto-Electronic Components Mfr
N.A.I.C.S.: 334413
Tim Kung (Gen Mgr)

Para Light India Pvt. Ltd. (1)
No 979 9th Floor Aggarwal Cyber Plaza-2 Netaji Subhash Place, Pitampura, New Delhi, 110034, India
Tel.: (91) 1141086226
Automotive LED Light Mfr
N.A.I.C.S.: 336320

Para Light Korea Co., Ltd. (1)
Rm 3301 Na-Dong Joong Ang Yootong Area Ste 1258, Gurobon-Dong Guro-Gu, Seoul, Korea (South)
Tel.: (82) 226258816
Web Site: http://www.paralight.co.kr
Sales Range: $25-49.9 Million
Emp.: 20
Opto-Electronic Components Mfr
N.A.I.C.S.: 334413

PARAB INFRA LIMITED

INTERNATIONAL PUBLIC

302 Vikas Commercial Complex Vikas Paradise, Bhakti Marg Mulund West, Mumbai, 400080, India
Tel.: (91) 67947511
Web Site: http://www.parabinfraltd.com
Year Founded: 1989
Rev.: $111,255
Assets: $2,075,721
Liabilities: $23,642
Net Worth: $2,052,078
Earnings: $29,593
Fiscal Year-end: 03/31/18
Real Estate Financial Services
N.A.I.C.S.: 525990
Narendra Dogra (Mng Dir)

PARABELLUM LIMITED
Saint Clements House 27-28 Clements Lane, London, EC4N 7AE, United Kingdom
Tel.: (44) 20 7870 2299 UK
Web Site: http://www.parabellum.capital
Investment Holding Company
N.A.I.C.S.: 551112
Rami Cassis (Founder & Mng Partner)

Subsidiaries:

Razor Risk Technologies Pty. Limited (1)
Level 8 210 George Street, Sydney, 2000, NSW, Australia
Tel.: (61) 292520526
Web Site: http://www.razor-risk.com
Professional Services & Risk Management Software Developer
N.A.I.C.S.: 513210
Rami Cassis (CEO)

Subsidiary (Non-US):

Razor Risk Technologies Limited (2)
Saint Clements House 26-27 Clements Lane, London, EC4N 7AE, United Kingdom
Tel.: (44) 2033191660
Web Site: http://www.razor-risk.com
Risk Management Software Development Services
N.A.I.C.S.: 513210
Peter Walsh (Head-Sls-Global)

PARACA INC.
Atago Green Hills Mori Tower 9F 2-5-1 Atago, Minato-ku, Tokyo, 105-6209, Japan
Tel.: (81) 368410809
Web Site: https://www.paraca.co.jp
Year Founded: 1997
4809—(TKS)
Sales Range: $75-99.9 Million
Parking Lot Services
N.A.I.C.S.: 812930
Ryo Naito (Pres)

PARADE TECHNOLOGIES, LTD.
9F No.71 Zhouzi St Neihu Dist, Taipei, 114, Taiwan
Tel.: (886) 2 2627 9109
Web Site: http://www.paradetech.com
Consumer Electronics And Display Panels Supplier
N.A.I.C.S.: 423690
Jack Zhao (Co-Fouder, Chm & CEO)

Subsidiaries:

Fresco Logic Inc. (1)
12655 SW Ctr St Ste, Beaverton, OR 97005
Tel.: (503) 533-8900
Web Site: http://www.frescologic.com
Semiconductor & Related Device Mfr
N.A.I.C.S.: 334413
Ni Jie (VP-Engrg)

Parade Technologies, Inc. (1)
2720 Orchard Pkwy, San Jose, CA 95134
Tel.: (408) 329-5540

Web Site: http://www.paradetech.com
Rev.: $1,100,000
Emp.: 15
Data Processing, Hosting & Related Services
N.A.I.C.S.: 518210
Jimmy Chiu (Exec VP-Mktg)

PARADIGM BIOPHARMACEUTICALS LIMITED
Level 15 500 Collins Street, Melbourne, 3000, VIC, Australia
Tel.: (61) 396295566   AU
Web Site:
  https://www.paradigmpharma.com
Year Founded: 2014
PAR—(ASX)
Rev.: $4,353,586
Assets: $18,289,555
Liabilities: $2,393,390
Net Worth: $15,896,165
Earnings: ($39,164,789)
Fiscal Year-end: 06/30/24
Therapeutic Product Mfr
N.A.I.C.S.: 334510
Donna Skerrett (Chief Medical Officer)

PARADISE CO. LTD.
299 Toegye-ro, PO Box 795, Jung-gu, Seoul, Korea (South)
Tel.: (82) 222805000
Web Site:
  http://www.paradisegroup.co.kr
Year Founded: 1972
034230—(KRS)
Rev.: $450,717,894
Assets: $2,693,338,759
Liabilities: $1,400,815,756
Net Worth: $1,292,523,003
Earnings: $12,127,314
Emp.: 1,200
Fiscal Year-end: 12/31/22
Construction Services
N.A.I.C.S.: 236220
Phillip Jeon (Chm)

Subsidiaries:

Paradise Casino Incheon   (1)
C186 Yeongjonghaeannam-ro 321beon-gil, Jung-gu, Incheon, 400-340, Korea (South)
Tel.: (82) 18338855
Web Site: https://www.paradisecasino.co.kr
Sales Range: $25-49.9 Million
Emp.: 200
Casino Hotel Services
N.A.I.C.S.: 721120

Paradise Global Casino Division Co., Ltd.
1408-5 Busan Metropolitan Mountain Middle District, Haeundae-gu, Busan, Korea (South)
Tel.: (82) 51 749 3550
Web Site:
  http://www.busanparadisehotel.co.kr
Casino Hotel Services
N.A.I.C.S.: 721120

Paradise Grand Casino   (1)
263-15 Yon-Dong, Jeju, Korea (South)
Tel.: (82) 64 740 7000
Casino Hotel Services
N.A.I.C.S.: 721120

Paradise Lotte Casino   (1)
2812-4 Saekdal-dong, Seogwipo, 697-130, Jeju-do, Korea (South)
Tel.: (82) 53644984
Web Site: http://www.paradian.com
Gambling Services
N.A.I.C.S.: 713210

PARADISE ENTERTAINMENT LIMITED
Unit C 19/F Entertainment Building 30 Queen s Road, Central, China (Hong Kong)
Tel.: (852) 26205303   BM
Web Site: https://www.hk1180.com
Year Founded: 1996
PDSSF—(OTCIQ)
Rev.: $63,732,371
Assets: $71,101,515
Liabilities: $29,953,412
Net Worth: $41,148,102
Earnings: ($11,397,576)
Emp.: 740
Fiscal Year-end: 12/31/21
Holding Company; Casino Management & Development & Supply & Leasing of Game Machinery & Equipment
N.A.I.C.S.: 551112
Shiyong Shan (Exec Dir)

Subsidiaries:

LT Game Australia Pty. Ltd.   (1)
Unit 25 30-32 Barcoo Road East, Roseville, 2069, NSW, Australia
Tel.: (61) 298826478
Casino Management Services
N.A.I.C.S.: 713210

LT Game Limited   (1)
No 201 Avenida da Amizade, Macau, China (Macau)
Tel.: (853) 28787317
Web Site: http://www.ltgame.net
Sales Range: $50-74.9 Million
Emp.: 20
Gaming & Casino System Development Services
N.A.I.C.S.: 713210

PARADISE ISLAND FOODS INC.
6451 Portsmouth Road, Nanaimo, V9V 1A3, BC, Canada
Tel.: (250) 390-2644
Web Site: http://www.paradise-foods.com
Year Founded: 1978
Rev.: $13,998,137
Emp.: 60
Dairy Product Retailer
N.A.I.C.S.: 424430
Len Thomson (Pres)

PARADOX ENGINEERING S.A.
Via Passeggiata 7, CH-6883, Novazzano, Switzerland
Tel.: (41) 91 233 0100
Web Site: http://www.pdxeng.ch
Year Founded: 2005
Wireless Network Design Services
N.A.I.C.S.: 334220

PARADOX INTERACTIVE AB
Gotgatan 78 23rd Floor, 118 30, Stockholm, Sweden
Tel.: (46) 8 5661 4800
Web Site:
  http://www.paradoxplaza.com
Sales Range: $25-49.9 Million
Emp.: 180
Video Game Publisher
N.A.I.C.S.: 513210
Fredrik Wester (Founder & Chm)

Subsidiaries:

White Wolf Publishing AB   (1)
Gotgatan 78 23rd Floor, 118 30, Stockholm, Sweden
Tel.: (46) 8 5661 4800
Web Site: http://www.white-wolf.com
Video Game Publisher
N.A.I.C.S.: 513210
Fredrik Wester (CEO)

PARAG MILK FOODS LTD
10th Floor Nirmal Building Nariman Point, Mumbai, 400021, India
Tel.: (91) 2243005555   In
Web Site:
  https://www.paragmilkfoods.com
Year Founded: 1992
539889—(BOM)
Rev.: $352,230,322
Assets: $199,939,932
Liabilities: $103,074,156
Net Worth: $96,865,775
Earnings: $6,384,989
Emp.: 1,716
Fiscal Year-end: 03/31/23
Milk Product Mfr & Distr
N.A.I.C.S.: 311514
Devendra Shah (Founder & Chm)

Subsidiaries:

Bhagyalaxmi Dairy Farms Private Limited   (1)
Nh 50 Post Manchar Taluka Ambegaon, 410503, Pune, India
Tel.: (91) 9970956281
Animal Farming Services
N.A.I.C.S.: 112990
Amol Hande (Mgr-Dairy Farm)

PARAGON ADVISOR PARTNERS LLP
901 Grande Palladium, 175 CST Rd, Kalina, Santacruz E, Mumbai, 400098, India
Tel.: (91) 22 68347900
Web Site:
  https://www.paragonpartners.in
Year Founded: 2015
Private Equity
N.A.I.C.S.: 523940
Siddharth Parekh (Co-Founder & Sr Partner)

Subsidiaries:

Cravatex Brands Limited   (1)
2nd Floor Matulya Center Senapati Bapat Marg Lower Parel West, Mumbai, 400013, Maharashtra, India
Tel.: (91) 2266667474
Web Site: http://www.cravatexbrands.com
Sport & Wellness Product Mfr
N.A.I.C.S.: 339920
Rajesh Batra (Chm)

PARAGON BANKING GROUP PLC
51 Homer Road, Solihull, B91 3QJ, W Midlands, United Kingdom
Tel.: (44) 3458494000
Web Site:
  https://www.paragonbanking.co.uk
Year Founded: 1995
PAG—(LSE)
Rev.: $441,123,228
Assets: $20,551,807,640
Liabilities: $18,865,655,172
Net Worth: $1,686,152,468
Earnings: $223,344,940
Emp.: 1,327
Fiscal Year-end: 09/30/21
Mortgage Loan Services
N.A.I.C.S.: 522310
Nigel S. Terrington (CEO)

Subsidiaries:

Buy to Let Direct Limited   (1)
Regus House Malthouse Avenue, Cardiff Gate Business Park, Cardiff, CF23 8RU, Mid Glamorgan, United Kingdom
Tel.: (44) 292 069 1010
Web Site: https://www.buytoletdirect.co.uk
Commercial Mortgage Services
N.A.I.C.S.: 522310

Grenadier Holdings Plc   (1)
16-18 Finsbury Circus, London, EC2M 7EB, United Kingdom
Tel.: (44) 3532938100
Web Site: https://grenadier-holdings.com
Advertising Agencies
N.A.I.C.S.: 541810

Subsidiary (Non-US):

Paragon Identification SAS   (2)
Les Aubepins, Argent-sur-Sauldre, 18410, Vierzon, France
Tel.: (33) 248816100
Web Site: https://www.paragon-id.com
Magnetic & Contactless Tickets Mfr & Distr
N.A.I.C.S.: 322299

Bertrand Brault (Dir-Publication, Sls & Mktg)

Herbert (1) PLC   (1)
51 Homer Road, Solihull, B91 3QJ, West Midlands, United Kingdom
Tel.: (44) 1217113333
Mortgage Loan Brokerage Services
N.A.I.C.S.: 522310

Idem Capital Securities Limited   (1)
51 Homer Road, Solihull, B91 3QJ, West Midlands, United Kingdom
Tel.: (44) 345 322 7304
Web Site: https://www.idem-capital.co.uk
Emp.: 450
Asset Investment Services
N.A.I.C.S.: 523940
Phil Hughes (Mng Dir)

Landlordcentre.co.uk Limited   (1)
51 Homer Road, Solihull, B91 3QJ, West Midlands, United Kingdom
Tel.: (44) 2920691010
Web Site: https://www.buytoletdirect.co.uk
Sales Range: $50-74.9 Million
Emp.: 20
Commercial Mortgage Brokerage Services
N.A.I.C.S.: 522310

Moorgate Loan Servicing Limited   (1)
51 Homer Road, Solihull, B91 3QJ, West Midlands, United Kingdom
Tel.: (44) 1217122323
Web Site:
  http://www.moorgateloanservicing.co.uk
Loan Mortgage & Brokerage Services
N.A.I.C.S.: 522310

Mortgage Trust Limited   (1)
     (100%)
Tel.: (44) 8458494040
Web Site: http://www.mortgagetrust.co.uk
Real Estate Credit
N.A.I.C.S.: 522292

Paragon Car Finance Limited   (1)
51 Homer Road, Solihull, B91 3QE, W Midlands, United Kingdom   (100%)
Tel.: (44) 1217122100
Web Site: http://www.paragon-group.co.uk
Sales Range: $350-399.9 Million
Emp.: 650
Automobile Finance Services
N.A.I.C.S.: 522299

Subsidiary (Domestic):

Paragon Car Finance (1) Limited   (2)
51 Homer Road, Solihull, B91 3QJ, West Midlands, United Kingdom
Tel.: (44) 1217122100
Emp.: 600
Automobile Financing Services
N.A.I.C.S.: 522220

Paragon Finance PLC   (1)
     (100%)
Tel.: (44) 1217122323
Web Site: http://www.paragon.co.uk
Sales Range: $200-249.9 Million
Emp.: 500
Nondepository Credit Intermediation
N.A.I.C.S.: 522299

Paragon Mortgages Limited   (1)
51 Homer Road, Solihull, B91 3QJ, West Midlands, United Kingdom   (100%)
Tel.: (44) 1217122345
Web Site: http://www.paragon-mortgages.co.uk
Sales Range: $200-249.9 Million
Emp.: 500
Activities Related to Credit Intermediation
N.A.I.C.S.: 522390

Paragon Personal Finance Limited   (1)
51 Homer Road, Herbert Road, Solihull, B91 3QJ, West Midlands, United Kingdom   (100%)
Tel.: (44) 1217122383
Web Site: http://www.paragon-finance.co.uk
Nondepository Credit Intermediation
N.A.I.C.S.: 522299

Paragon Second Funding Limited   (1)
     (100%)
Tel.: (44) 1217123960
Web Site: http://www.paragon-group.com

PARAGON BANKING GROUP PLC

Paragon Banking Group PLC—(Continued)

Sales Range: $200-249.9 Million
Emp.: 450
Activities Related to Credit Intermediation
N.A.I.C.S.: 522390

Paragon Vehicle Contracts Limited (1)
51 Homer Road, Herbert Road, Solihull, B91 3QJ, West Midlands, United Kingdom (100%)
Tel.: (44) 1217122100
Web Site: http://www.paragon.com
Sales Range: $300-349.9 Million
Emp.: 650
Passenger Car Rental
N.A.I.C.S.: 532111

Premier Asset Finance Limited (1)
15 Alva Street, Edinburgh, EH2 4PH, United Kingdom
Tel.: (44) 131 290 2555
Web Site:
https://www.premierassetfinance.co.uk
Asset Finance Broker Services
N.A.I.C.S.: 523150
Kevin Davidson (Co-Founder)

Redbrick Survey and Valuation Limited (1)
51 Homer Road, Solihull, B91 3QJ, West Midlands, United Kingdom
Tel.: (44) 3458494160
Property Mortgage Services
N.A.I.C.S.: 522299

TBMC (2) Limited (1)
51 Homer Road, Solihull, B91 3QJ, West Midlands, United Kingdom
Tel.: (44) 2920695400
Mortgage Brokerage Services
N.A.I.C.S.: 522310

The Business Mortgage Company Limited (1)
51 Homer Road, Cardiff Gate Business Park Mid Glamorgan, Solihull, B91 3QJ, West Midlands, United Kingdom
Tel.: (44) 2920695400
Web Site: https://www.tbmc.co.uk
Commercial Mortgage Brokerage Services
N.A.I.C.S.: 522310

The Business Mortgage Company Services Limited (1)
Regus House Malthouse Avenue Cardiff Gate Business Park, Cardiff, CF23 8RU, Mid Glamorgan, United Kingdom
Tel.: (44) 292 069 5400
Web Site: https://www.tbmc.co.uk
Commercial Mortgage Services
N.A.I.C.S.: 522310

Universal Credit Limited (1)
51 Homer Road, Solihull, B91 3QJ, West Midlands, United Kingdom
Tel.: (44) 1217122323
Web Site: http://www.paragon-group.co.uk
Financial Credit Granting Services
N.A.I.C.S.: 522390

PARAGON CARE LIMITED
Tel.: (61) 388337800 AU
Web Site:
https://www.paragoncare.com.au
PGC—(ASX)
Rev.: $189,947,695
Assets: $334,844,951
Liabilities: $149,170,297
Net Worth: $185,674,654
Earnings: $5,473,661
Emp.: 508
Fiscal Year-end: 06/30/22
Medical Equipment Whslr
N.A.I.C.S.: 423450
Shane F. Tanner (Chm)

Subsidiaries:

Electro Medical Group Pty. Ltd. (1)
15a Wheeler Street, Belmont, WA, Australia
Tel.: (61) 1300246633
Web Site: https://www.emedgroup.com.au
Medical & Laboratory Equipment Repair Services
N.A.I.C.S.: 541380

GM Medical Pty Ltd (1)
28-30 Hightech Place, Lilydale, 3140, VIC, Australia
Tel.: (61) 3 9735 0111
Web Site: http://www.gmmedical.com.au
Medical Equipment Mfr & Whslr
N.A.I.C.S.: 339113

Immuno Pty. Ltd. (1)
63 Poplar Road, Parkville, VIC, Australia
Tel.: (61) 800252215
Web Site: https://immuno.com.au
Haematology & Microbiology Testing Services
N.A.I.C.S.: 524114

Insight Surgical Pty. Ltd. (1)
16/1 Hordern Place, Camperdown, NSW, Australia
Tel.: (61) 800225307
Web Site: https://insightsurgical.com.au
Ophthalmic Equipment Mfr
N.A.I.C.S.: 339115

Iona Medical Products Pty Ltd (1)
Unit 1 Eastern Gateway 56 Norcal Road, Nunawading, 3131, VIC, Australia
Tel.: (61) 1300 369 121
Web Site: http://www.ionamedical.com
Medical Equipment Whslr
N.A.I.C.S.: 423450
Chris Pearson (Mgr-Natl Sls)

Labgear Australia Pty. Ltd. (1)
63 Poplar road, Parkville, VIC, Australia
Tel.: (61) 300246633
Web Site: https://labgearaustralia.com.au
Laboratory Equipment Distr
N.A.I.C.S.: 423450

Paragon Care Group Australia Pty. Ltd. (1)
77-97 Ricketts Road, Mount Waverley, VIC, Australia
Tel.: (61) 388337800
Healthcare Equipment Repair & Maintenance Services
N.A.I.C.S.: 532490

Paragon Care Group New Zealand Ltd. (1)
69 Elizabeth Knox Place, Glen Innes, Auckland, New Zealand
Tel.: (64) 508654258
Healthcare Equipment Repair & Maintenance Services
N.A.I.C.S.: 532490

Quantum Health Group Limited (1)
22 Rosebery Ave, Rosebery, 2018, NSW, Australia
Tel.: (61) 800228118
Web Site: http://www.qhealthcare.com.au
Rev.: $42,654,563
Assets: $57,008,367
Liabilities: $20,786,735
Net Worth: $36,221,632
Earnings: $5,907,325
Fiscal Year-end: 06/30/2021
Healtcare Services
N.A.I.C.S.: 621610
John Walstab (Mng Dir & Sec)

Subsidiary (Domestic):

InSight Oceania Pty. Ltd. (2)
56-60 Bourke Rd, Alexandria, 2015, New South Wales, Australia
Tel.: (61) 296997444
Web Site: http://www.insight.com.au
Sales Range: $25-49.9 Million
Emp.: 40
Medical Equipment Whslr
N.A.I.C.S.: 423450

Subsidiary (Non-US):

Quantum Energy Technologies (Suzhou) Co., Ltd. (2)
No 136 Guajing Road, Economic Development Zone Wujiang, Suzhou, 215200, Jiangsu, China
Tel.: (86) 51263012750
Web Site:
http://www.quantumenergy.com.cn
Sales Range: $25-49.9 Million
Emp.: 100
Solar Energy Heating Equipment Mfr
N.A.I.C.S.: 333414

Volker Australia Pty Ltd (1)
Unit 17-56 Norcal Rd, Nunawading, 3131, VIC, Australia
Tel.: (61) 3 8833 7800
Web Site: http://www.paragoncare.au
Emp.: 50
Medical Equipment Whslr
N.A.I.C.S.: 423450
Maik Sinari (Mng Dir)

Western Biomedical Pty. Ltd. (1)
U1 and U2 75 Howe Street, Osborne Park, WA, Australia
Tel.: (61) 894414000
Web Site: https://www.westernbiomedical.com
Medical & Surgical Supplies Whslr
N.A.I.C.S.: 423450

PARAGON CEYLON PLC
20 Sir Chittampalam A Gardiner Mawatha, 2, Colombo, 2, Sri Lanka
Tel.: (94) 1124341613
Year Founded: 1958
Rev: $25,269
Assets: $40,777
Liabilities: $45,298
Net Worth: ($4,521)
Earnings: ($18,117)
Fiscal Year-end: 03/31/19
Stationery Product Distr
N.A.I.C.S.: 459410

PARAGON ENTERTAINMENT LIMITED
Unit G10 Elvington Industrial Estate Elvington, York, YO41 4AR, United Kingdom
Tel.: (44) 1904 608020
Web Site:
http://www.paragonent.com
Year Founded: 2009
Rev.: $18,084,667
Assets: $8,387,855
Liabilities: $3,809,014
Net Worth: $4,578,841
Earnings: $389,929
Emp.: 100
Fiscal Year-end: 12/31/16
Model Making & Props
N.A.I.C.S.: 541490
Neil Jefferies (CFO)

Subsidiaries:

Drinkall Dean (London) Limited (1)
Ground Floor 32 St Oswalds Place, London, SE11 5JE, United Kingdom
Tel.: (44) 20 77352731
Web Site: http://www.drinkalldean.co.uk
Interior Design Consulting Services
N.A.I.C.S.: 541410

The Visitor Attraction Company Limited (1)
230 Hanworth Road Hampton, London, TW 12 3EP, United Kingdom
Tel.: (44) 208 274 0205
Web Site:
http://www.thevisitorattractioncompany.com
Sales Range: $25-49.9 Million
Emp.: 4
General Management Consulting Services
N.A.I.C.S.: 541611
Simon Ody (Dir-Strategic & Fin Plng)

PARAGON FINANCE LTD.
Sikkim House 4-1 Middleton Street 4th Floor, Kolkata, 700071, India
Tel.: (91) 3340612288
Web Site:
https://www.paragonfinanceltd.com
531255—(BOM)
Rev.: $218,944
Assets: $3,424,831
Liabilities: $226,533
Net Worth: $3,198,297
Earnings: ($15,659)
Emp.: 5
Fiscal Year-end: 03/31/23
Financial Services
N.A.I.C.S.: 523999

INTERNATIONAL PUBLIC

Sanjay Kumar Gupta (CFO & Co-Sec)

PARAGON FINE & SPECIALITY CHEMICAL LIMITED
1001/1 Parshwa Tower Nr Pakwan-II S G Highway Bodakdev, Ahmedabad, 380054, Gujarat, India
Tel.: (91) 7935335483
Web Site:
https://www.paragonind.com
Year Founded: 2004
PARAGON—(NSE)
Chemical Products Mfr
N.A.I.C.S.: 325998

PARAGON GLOBE BERHAD
Level 1002 Grand Paragon Hotel No 18 Jalan Harimau, Taman Century, 80250, Johor Bahru, Johor, Malaysia
Tel.: (60) 72786668 MY
Web Site:
https://www.pgbgroup.com.my
PGLOBE—(KLS)
Rev.: $10,080,004
Assets: $77,494,943
Liabilities: $14,038,542
Net Worth: $63,456,401
Earnings: $837,249
Fiscal Year-end: 03/31/23
Ceramic Mfr
N.A.I.C.S.: 327110
Godwin Pei Poh Tan (Exec Dir)

Subsidiaries:

GBH Bathroom Products Sdn. Bhd. (1)
238 Jalan Segambut, Kuala Lumpur, 51200, Malaysia
Tel.: (60) 362581055
Sales Range: $50-74.9 Million
Emp.: 200
Bathroom Fittings & Accessories Mfr
N.A.I.C.S.: 327110
Poh Weng Choon (Exec Dir)

Paragon Globe Properties Sdn. Bhd. (1)
Level 10-02 Grand Paragon Hotel No 18 Jalan Harimau Taman Century, 80250, Johor Bahru, Johor, Malaysia
Tel.: (60) 72786668
Real Estate Services
N.A.I.C.S.: 531390

PARAGON GMBH & CO. KGAA
Bosendamm 11, 33129, Delbruck, Germany
Tel.: (49) 525097620 De
Web Site: https://www.paragon.ag
Year Founded: 1988
PGN—(DEU)
Rev.: $178,440,585
Assets: $119,791,972
Liabilities: $124,295,762
Net Worth: ($4,503,790)
Earnings: ($4,205,745)
Emp.: 779
Fiscal Year-end: 12/31/23
Electrical Component Mfr & Distr
N.A.I.C.S.: 336320
Klaus Dieter Frers (Founder & CEO)

Subsidiaries:

Paragon Electroacousic GmbH (1)
Pfaffenweg 21, 89231, Neu-Ulm, Germany
Tel.: (49) 731707850
Web Site: http://www.lpgmbh.com
Electronic Products Mfr
N.A.I.C.S.: 334419

Voltabox of Texas, Inc. (1)
1500 Volta Dr, Cedar Park, TX 78641-0200
Tel.: (512) 814-3704
Electronic Products Mfr
N.A.I.C.S.: 334419
Sam Olson (Pres & CEO)

PARAGON GROUP LIMITED
Park House Lower Ground Floor

16-18 Finsbury Circus, London, EC2M 7EB, Tyne & Wear, United Kingdom
Tel.: (44) 1915140716 UK
Web Site: http://www.paragon-europe.com
Year Founded: 2004
Holding Company; Business Forms & Related Products Mfr, Business Communication & Marketing Consulting, Data Management & Security Services
N.A.I.C.S.: 551112
Patrick J. Crean *(CEO)*

Subsidiaries:

FleQs B.V (1)
Loswal 38, 9206 AH, Drachten, Netherlands
Tel.: (31) 512 58 99 99
Web Site: http://www.fleqs.com
Paper Products Mfr
N.A.I.C.S.: 322299
W. Gerretzen *(Mgr-Sls-Europe)*

Paragon Customer Communications Schwandorf GmbH (1)
Gutenbergstrasse 1 5, 92421, Schwandorf, Germany
Tel.: (49) 9431620194
Web Site: http://www.paragon-europe.com
Commercial Printing
N.A.I.C.S.: 323111
Thomas Simon *(Mng Dir)*

Subsidiary (Non-US):

Meiller Lithorex AB (2)
Lodjursgatan 3, PO Box 314, 26123, Landskrona, Sweden
Tel.: (46) 418447186
Web Site: http://www.meiller.se
Sales Range: $25-49.9 Million
Emp.: 65
Provider of Graphical Development Services
N.A.I.C.S.: 541430

Meiller Lithorex Finland Oy (2)
Miniatonie 6 A 2, 2360, Espoo, Finland
Tel.: (358) 98022202
Sales Range: $25-49.9 Million
Emp.: 3
Provider of Graphical Design Services
N.A.I.C.S.: 541430

Paragon Group Limited - Corporate Office (1)
Paragon Suite Irish Management Institute Sandyford Road, D16 X8C3, Dublin, Ireland
Tel.: (353) 1 293 8100
Web Site: http://www.paragon-europe.com
Corporate Office
N.A.I.C.S.: 551114

Paragon Group UK Limited (1)
Pallion Trading Estate, Sunderland, SR4 6ST, Tyne & Wear, United Kingdom (100%)
Tel.: (44) 1915140716
Web Site: http://www.paragonuk.com
Sales Range: $100-124.9 Million
Emp.: 160
Business Forms & Related Products Mfr, Business Communication & Marketing Consulting, Data Management & Security Services
N.A.I.C.S.: 323111

Subsidiary (Domestic):

BemroseBooth Paragon Limited (2)
Stockholm Road, Sutton Fields, Hull, HU7 0XY, United Kingdom
Tel.: (44) 1482 826 343
Web Site: http://www.bemrosebooth.com
Mass Transit Ticket & Debit Card Printing Services
N.A.I.C.S.: 323111
Andrew Jones *(Gen Mgr)*

Paragon Romania S.R.L. (1)
str Drumul Garii Otopeni 49-51A, Otopeni, 075100, Ilfov, Romania
Tel.: (40) 21 350 42 96
Web Site: http://www.paragon-europe.com
Paper Products Mfr
N.A.I.C.S.: 322299

Ionut Joghiu *(Mgr-Customer Relationship)*

Paragon Transaction S.A. (1)
56 Rue des Hautes Patures, 92737, Nanterre, Cedex, France
Tel.: (33) 3 86 26 51 51
Web Site: http://www.paragon-transaction.fr
Paper Products Mfr
N.A.I.C.S.: 322299
Stephane Lorthioir *(Mgr-Pur)*

PARAGON PARTNERS GMBH
Leopoldstrasse 10, 80802, Munich, Germany
Tel.: (49) 89 3888 70 0 De
Web Site: http://www.paragon.de
Year Founded: 2004
Privater Equity Firm
N.A.I.C.S.: 523999
Marco Attolini *(Partner)*

Subsidiaries:

Condecta AG (1)
Stegackerstrasse 6, CH 8409, Winterthur, Switzerland
Tel.: (41) 522345151
Web Site: http://www.condecta.ch
Construction Machinery Equipment, Cranes & Mobile Room Systems Mfr
N.A.I.C.S.: 333120
Erwin Stadler *(Head-Sls & Mktg)*

Europages S.A. (1)
159 Rue Anatole France Hall B, Levallois-Perret, 92300, France
Tel.: (33) 141164900
Web Site: http://www.europages.com
Book Publishers
N.A.I.C.S.: 513130
Vanessa Lemonnier Da Silva *(Mgr-Content & Translation)*

Subsidiary (Non-US):

Europages Benelux SPRL (2)
6 Rue Louis de Geer, 1348, Louvain-la-Neuve, Belgium
Tel.: (32) 488601071
Web Site: http://corporate.europages.co.uk
Digital Marketing Services
N.A.I.C.S.: 541613

PARAGON REIT
1000 Toa Payoh North News Centre, Singapore, 318994, Singapore
Tel.: (65) 63193380
Web Site: http://www.sphreit.com.sg
SK6U—(SES)
Rev.: $214,098,555
Assets: $3,163,188,588
Liabilities: $1,020,739,533
Net Worth: $2,142,449,055
Earnings: $101,949,611
Emp.: 12
Fiscal Year-end: 12/31/23
Real Estate Investment Services
N.A.I.C.S.: 523999
Belinda Zheng Qinyin *(Mgr-Investments)*

PARAGON TECHNOLOGIES CO., LTD.
No 2 Lane 108 Section 1 Nanshan Road, Luzhu District, Taoyuan, 338, Taiwan
Tel.: (886) 32128833
Web Site: https://en.pttech.com.tw
Year Founded: 1995
3518—(TAI)
Rev.: $12,510,971
Assets: $51,057,619
Liabilities: $10,971,778
Net Worth: $40,085,842
Earnings: ($1,632,329)
Fiscal Year-end: 12/31/23
Industrial Machinery Mfr
N.A.I.C.S.: 333248
Tsai-Pu Chen *(Chm & Chief Investment Officer)*

PARAGON UNION BERHAD
Lot 14 Jalan CJ 11 Kawasan Perindustrian Cheras Jaya Batu 11, 43200, Cheras, Selangor Darul Ehsan, Malaysia
Tel.: (60) 390861100
Web Site: https://www.paragon.com.my
PARAGON—(KLS)
Rev.: $12,900,686
Assets: $13,991,005
Liabilities: $6,628,205
Net Worth: $7,362,800
Earnings: ($1,204,106)
Fiscal Year-end: 12/31/22
Carpet Mfr
N.A.I.C.S.: 314110
Choon Hee Lee *(Exec Dir)*

PARALLEL MINING CORP.
1111 Melville Street Suite 1100, Vancouver, V6E 3V6, BC, Canada
Tel.: (604) 218-7400 BC
Web Site: https://parallelgold.com
Year Founded: 2007
PAL—(TSXV)
Assets: $202,891
Liabilities: $159,490
Net Worth: $43,400
Earnings: ($504,703)
Emp.: 2
Fiscal Year-end: 05/31/21
Investment Services
N.A.I.C.S.: 523999
Rakesh Patel *(CFO)*

PARAMOUNT BED HOLDINGS CO., LTD.
2-14-5 Higashisuna, Koto-ku, Tokyo, 136-8671, Japan
Tel.: (81) 336481100
Web Site: https://www.paramountbed-hd.co.jp
Year Founded: 1982
7817—(TKS)
Rev.: $700,765,760
Assets: $1,189,932,200
Liabilities: $290,866,440
Net Worth: $899,065,760
Earnings: $70,211,420
Emp.: 388
Fiscal Year-end: 03/31/24
Holding Company
N.A.I.C.S.: 551112
Kyosuke Kimura *(Chm)*

Subsidiaries:

Paramount Bed (China) Co., Ltd. (1)
A-105 Xin Mei Road, Wuxi National Hi & New Tech Industrial Development Zone, Wuxi, 214028, Jiangsu, China
Tel.: (86) 51085323188
Web Site: http://www.paramountbed.com
Hospital Bed Distr
N.A.I.C.S.: 423450

Paramount Bed Asia Pacific Pte. Ltd. (1)
1 Raffles Place 19-01 One Raffles Place Office Tower One, Singapore, 048616, Singapore
Tel.: (65) 62209750
Web Site: https://www.paramount.com.sg
Hospital Bed Distr
N.A.I.C.S.: 423450
Kyosuke Kimura *(Mng Dir)*

Paramount Bed India Pvt. Ltd. (1)
Plot 430 Sector-8 IMT Manesar, Gurgaon, 122050, Haryana, India
Tel.: (91) 1244205748
Hospital Bed Distr
N.A.I.C.S.: 423450
Amit Sharma *(Mgr-Logistics)*

Paramount Bed Mexico S.A. de C.V. (1)
Av Paseo de la Reforma 243 Floor 10 Interior 3, Col Cuauhtemoc Alcaldia Cuauhtemoc, 06500, Mexico, Mexico
Tel.: (52) 48171149

Web Site: https://www.paramountbed.com.mx
Hospital Bed Distr
N.A.I.C.S.: 423450

Paramount Bed Vietnam Co., Ltd. (1)
Lot H-1 Long Duc Industrial Park, Long Duc Ward, Long Thanh, Dong Nai, Vietnam
Tel.: (84) 613681181
Hospital Bed Distr
N.A.I.C.S.: 423450
Nguyen Van Quang *(Mgr-Factory)*

Paramount Bed do Brasil Ltda. (1)
Rua Maestro Cardim 407 Liberdade, Sao Paulo, 01323-000, Brazil
Tel.: (55) 1138951775
Hospital Bed Distr
N.A.I.C.S.: 423450

Paratechno Co., Ltd. (1)
Hongo Building 5-28-3 Hongo, Bunkyo-Ku, Tokyo, 113-8415, Japan
Tel.: (81) 338135522
Web Site: https://www.paratechno.co.jp
Cleaning Equipment Distr
N.A.I.C.S.: 423850
Tomohiko Kimura *(Pres)*

PARAMOUNT COMMUNICATIONS LIMITED
KH433 Maulsari Avenue Westend Greens Rangpuri, New Delhi, 110028, India
Tel.: (91) 1145618800 In
Web Site: https://www.paramountcables.com
PARACABLES—(NSE)
Rev.: $71,221,378
Assets: $64,278,370
Liabilities: $37,940,463
Net Worth: $26,337,907
Earnings: $423,187
Emp.: 331
Fiscal Year-end: 03/31/21
Communication Energy Wire & Cable Mfr
N.A.I.C.S.: 332618
Sanjay Aggarwal *(Chm & CEO)*

Subsidiaries:

AEI Cables Limited (1)
Unit 9 Tilley Road, Crowther Industrial Estate, Washington, NE38 0AE, Tyne and Wear, United Kingdom (100%)
Tel.: (44) 191 410 3111
Web Site: https://www.aeicables.co.uk
Sales Range: $125-149.9 Million
Emp.: 400
Cable Mfr
N.A.I.C.S.: 332618
Ian Watts *(Project Mgr)*

AEI Power Cables Limited (1)
Paramount Communications Limited - Dharuhera Plant (1)
37 Industrial Estate, Dharuhera, 242 691, Haryana, India
Tel.: (91) 1274 242531
Cable Mfr
N.A.I.C.S.: 335921

Valens Technologies Private Limited (1)
M5A Bahubali 1st Floor Block-59 Plot No 59/17 New Rohtak Road, Karol Bagh, New Delhi, 110005, India
Tel.: (91) 1122145763
Web Site: https://valenstechnologies.com
Steel Pipe Mfr & Distr
N.A.I.C.S.: 331210

PARAMOUNT CORPORATION BERHAD
Level 8 Uptown 1 1 Jalan SS21/58 Damansara Uptown, 47400, Petaling Jaya, Selangor Darul Ehsan, Malaysia
Tel.: (60) 377123333
Web Site: https://www.pcb.my
PARAMON—(KLS)
Rev.: $179,357,460

PARAMOUNT CORPORATION BERHAD

Paramount Corporation Berhad—(Continued)
Assets: $661,406,349
Liabilities: $309,030,899
Net Worth: $352,375,450
Earnings: $15,902,222
Emp.: 486
Fiscal Year-end: 12/31/22
Property Development Services
N.A.I.C.S.: 531311
Chiang Quan Teo *(Chm)*

Subsidiaries:

Berkeley Sdn. Bhd. (1)
Lot 75 Lot 1874 Jalan Delima/KU 1, Off Jalan Kapar, 41400, Kelang, Selangor Darul Ehsan, Malaysia
Tel.: (60) 327277512
Web Site: https://paramountproperty.my
Property Management Services
N.A.I.C.S.: 531311

Cambridge English For Life Sdn. Bhd. (1)
A-1-10 Merchant Square No 1 Jalan Tropicana Selatan 1 PJU3, 47410, Petaling Jaya, Selangor, Malaysia
Tel.: (60) 37 883 0912
Web Site: https://www.cambridgeforlife.org
Educational Support Services
N.A.I.C.S.: 611710
Elsie Chin *(CEO)*

KDU College (PG) Sdn Bhd (1)
SS22/41 Damansara Jaya, 47400, Petaling Jaya, Selangor Darul Ehsan, Malaysia
Tel.: (60) 3 7728 8123
Web Site: http://www.kdupg.edu.my
Sales Range: $25-49.9 Million
Emp.: 25
Education Services
N.A.I.C.S.: 611710

KDU College Sdn. Bhd. (1)
Jalan Ss 22/41 Damansara Jaya, 47400, Petaling Jaya, Selangor Darul Ehsan, Malaysia
Tel.: (60) 379536688
Web Site: http://www.kdu.edu.my
Education Services
N.A.I.C.S.: 611710

KDU Management Development Centre Sdn. Bhd. (1)
Level 3 Admin Block KDU University College Utropolis Glenmarie Campus, 40150, Shah Alam, Selangor Darul Ehsan, Malaysia
Tel.: (60) 355650799
Web Site: http://www.kmdc.com.my
Sales Range: $10-24.9 Million
Emp.: 40
Educational Support Services
N.A.I.C.S.: 611710

KDU Smart School Sdn. Bhd. (1)
No 3-5-7 Jalan Teknologi 2/1 Kota Damansara, Daerah, 47810, Petaling Jaya, Selangor Darul Ehsan, Malaysia
Tel.: (60) 361453888
Web Site: http://www.srikdu.edu.my
Emp.: 300
Education Services
N.A.I.C.S.: 611710
Teh Geok Lian *(CEO)*

KDU University College (PG) Sdn. Bhd. (1)
32 Jalan Anson, 10400, George Town, Penang, Malaysia
Tel.: (60) 42266368
Web Site: http://www.kdupg.edu.my
Education Services
N.A.I.C.S.: 611710

Paramount Engineering & Construction Sdn. Bhd. (1)
Wisma Paramount 1A Lorong BLM 1/1 Bandar Laguna Merbok, 08000, Sungai Petani, Kedah Darul Aman, Malaysia
Tel.: (60) 44419191
Web Site: http://www.pecsb.my
Emp.: 100
Civil Engineering Services
N.A.I.C.S.: 541330
Ooi Hun Peng *(CEO)*

Paramount Property (Cityview) Sdn. Bhd. (1)
No 204 Jalan Ampang, 50250, Kuala Lumpur, Malaysia
Tel.: (60) 327277519
Web Site: https://paramountproperty.my
Property Development Services
N.A.I.C.S.: 531390

Paramount Property (Sekitar 26 Enterprise) Sdn. Bhd. (1)
Persiaran Hulu Selangor Seksyen 26, 40400, Shah Alam, Selangor, Malaysia
Tel.: (60) 392120448
Web Site: https://paramountproperty.my
Property Development Services
N.A.I.C.S.: 236116

Paramount Property (Utara) Sdn. Bhd. (1)
No 1 Jalan Banyan 1 Bukit Banyan, Bukit Banyan, 08000, Sungai Petani, Kedah Darul Aman, Malaysia
Tel.: (60) 44413388
Web Site: https://paramountproperty.my
Sales Range: $50-74.9 Million
Property Development Services
N.A.I.C.S.: 531390
Ooi Hun Peng *(CEO)*

Subsidiary (Domestic):

Kelab Bandar Laguna Merbok Sdn. Bhd. (2)
Persiaran BLM 3 Bandar Laguna Merbok, 8000, Sungai Petani, Kedah Darul Aman, Malaysia
Tel.: (60) 44412288
Sales Range: $25-49.9 Million
Emp.: 7
Entertainment Services
N.A.I.C.S.: 561990
Ooi Hun Peng *(Gen Mgr)*

Paramount Property Holdings Sdn. Bhd. (1)
Level 8 Uptown 1 1 Jalan SS21/58 Damansara Uptown, 47400, Petaling Jaya, Selangor Darul Ehsan, Malaysia
Tel.: (60) 377123333
Web Site: http://www.ku.com.my
Sales Range: $50-74.9 Million
Emp.: 45
Investment Management & Property Development Services
N.A.I.C.S.: 523999
Jeffrey Chew *(CEO)*

R.E.A.L. Education Group Sdn. Bhd. (1)
Lot No 5 Jalan Merah Saga U9/5, 40250, Shah Alam, Selangor, Malaysia
Tel.: (60) 37 842 3228
Web Site: https://realschools.edu.my
Education Services
N.A.I.C.S.: 611310
Ee Ching Wah *(Pres)*

PARAMOUNT COSMETICS INDIA LIMITED
902-904 9th Floor Prestige Meridian-1 29 M G Road, Bengaluru, 560 001, Karnataka, India
Tel.: (91) 8025320870 In
Web Site:
https://www.parammount.com
Year Founded: 1985
507970—(BOM)
Rev.: $3,227,600
Assets: $5,155,219
Liabilities: $2,730,340
Net Worth: $2,424,879
Earnings: $25,382
Emp.: 52
Fiscal Year-end: 03/31/23
Cosmetics Products Mfr
N.A.I.C.S.: 325620
Hansraj Rathor *(Gen Mgr-Fin)*

PARAMOUNT INSURANCE COMPANY LIMITED
House No 22 Road No 113/A Gulshan 2, Dhaka, 1212, Bangladesh
Tel.: (880) 255049824
Web Site:
https://www.paramountinsure.com

Year Founded: 1999
PARAMOUNT—(CHT)
Rev.: $678,076
Assets: $15,515,310
Liabilities: $5,642,242
Net Worth: $9,873,068
Earnings: $644,479
Emp.: 204
Fiscal Year-end: 12/31/23
Insurance Services
N.A.I.C.S.: 524298
Nawaz Ahmad *(Chm)*

PARAMOUNT LIFE & GENERAL INSURANCE CORPORATION
14th & 15th Fl Sage House 110 V A Rufino St, Legaspi Village, Makati, Philippines
Tel.: (63) 2 772 9200 PH
Web Site:
http://www.paramount.com.ph
Year Founded: 1950
Life, Property & Casualty Insurance Products & Services
N.A.I.C.S.: 524298
Patrick L. Go *(Chm & CEO)*

PARAMOUNT PRINTPACKAGING LTD
A 309 TTC Industrial Estate Opp Electronic Bhavan, Mahape Road, Navi Mumbai, 400701, Maharashtra, India
Tel.: (91) 2227788437 In
Web Site: http://www.pppltd.in
Year Founded: 1985
Board Packaging Mfr
N.A.I.C.S.: 322212
Divyesh Sukhadia *(Mng Dir)*

PARAMOUNT RESOURCES LTD.
2800 TD Canada Trust Tower 421 Seventh Avenue S W, Calgary, T2P 4K9, AB, Canada
Tel.: (403) 290-3600 AB
Web Site:
https://www.paramountres.com
Year Founded: 1978
PRMRF—(OTCIQ)
Rev.: $1,081,893,240
Assets: $3,039,236,028
Liabilities: $1,000,301,436
Net Worth: $2,038,934,592
Earnings: $185,322,132
Emp.: 475
Fiscal Year-end: 12/31/21
Oil & Gas Production Services
N.A.I.C.S.: 213112
James H. T. Riddell *(Chm, Pres & CEO)*

Subsidiaries:

Fox Drilling Inc. (1)
2 3710 18 Ave N, Lethbridge, T1H 5S7, AB, Canada
Tel.: (403) 380-3330
Web Site: https://foxdrilling.ca
Sales Range: $50-74.9 Million
Emp.: 5
Oil & Gas Exploration Services
N.A.I.C.S.: 213111
Josh Berezay *(Pres)*

Fox Drilling Limited Partnership (1)
2 3710 18 Avenue N, Lethbridge, T1H5S7, AB, Canada
Tel.: (403) 380-3330
Web Site:
https://foxdrillinginc.squarespace.com
Oil & Gas Well Drilling Services
N.A.I.C.S.: 213111

Paramount Drilling U.S. LLC (1)
2273 3rd Ave W, Dickinson, ND 58601-2605
Tel.: (701) 225-9709

INTERNATIONAL PUBLIC

Sales Range: $75-99.9 Million
Emp.: 2
Well Drilling Services
N.A.I.C.S.: 213112

Paramount Resources (ACL) Ltd. (1)
421 7th Ave SW Ste 2800, Calgary, T2P 4K9, AB, Canada (100%)
Tel.: (403) 261-1200
Web Site: http://www.apachecorp.com
Sales Range: $600-649.9 Million
Emp.: 400
Oil & Gas Exploration & Production
N.A.I.C.S.: 211120
Grady L. Ables *(Pres & Reg VP)*

ProspEx Resources Ltd. (1)
255 5th Ave SW, Suite 2500 Bow Valley Square III, Calgary, T2P 3G6, AB, Canada
Tel.: (403) 268-3940
Web Site: http://www.psx.ca
Sales Range: $25-49.9 Million
Emp.: 23
Oil & Gas Exploration Services
N.A.I.C.S.: 211120

Summit Resources, Inc., (1)
5555 E Van Buren St 210, Phoenix, AZ 85008-3411
Tel.: (928) 607-3524
Natural Gas Generation Services
N.A.I.C.S.: 211130

PARAMOUNT TRADING (JAMAICA) LIMITED
39 Waltham Park Road, Kingston, 11, Jamaica
Tel.: (876) 9239040 JM
Web Site:
https://www.paramountjm.com
Year Founded: 1991
PTL—(JAM)
Rev.: $9,976,922
Assets: $11,460,767
Liabilities: $5,934,255
Net Worth: $5,526,512
Earnings: $441,643
Emp.: 70
Fiscal Year-end: 05/31/21
Chemical Raw Materials & Products Mfr & Distr
N.A.I.C.S.: 325998
Radcliff Olander Knibbs *(Chm)*

PARAMOUNT WINDOWS INC.
105 Panet Road, Winnipeg, R2J 0S1, MB, Canada
Tel.: (204) 233-4966
Web Site:
http://www.paramountwindows.com
Year Founded: 1948
Rev.: $10,259,504
Emp.: 75
Windows & Doors Mfr
N.A.I.C.S.: 321911
Bernie Dudeck *(Pres)*

PARANA BCO S.A.
Rua Comendador Araujo 614, 80420-063, Curitiba, PR, Brazil
Tel.: (55) 4133519765
Web Site:
http://www.paranabanco.com.br
PRBC4—(BRAZ)
Sales Range: Less than $1 Million
Financial Investment Services
N.A.I.C.S.: 523999

Subsidiaries:

JMalucelli Agenciamento e Servicos Ltda. (1)
Rua da Bahia 1182 LJ 07, Lourdes, Belo Horizonte, 30160-011, Minas Gerais, Brazil
Tel.: (55) 3222414126
Financial Investment Services
N.A.I.C.S.: 523940

JMalucelli Investimentos Ltda. (1)
Rua Visconde do Rio Branco 1488 4 andar Centro, Curitiba, 80420-210, Parana, Brazil
Tel.: (55) 4133519966

Web Site:
http://www.jmalucelliinvestimentos.com.br
Asset Management Services
N.A.I.C.S.: 531390

JMalucelli Resseguradora S.A. (1)
Rua Visconde de Nacar 1440 - 15 andar
Centro, Curitiba, 80410-201, Parana, Brazil
Tel.: (55) 4132819100
Reinsurance Services
N.A.I.C.S.: 524130

PARANAPANEMA S.A.
Rua Felipe Camarao 500, Bairro Utinga, 09220 580, Santo Andre, 09220 580, SP, Brazil
Tel.: (55) 1121997604
Web Site:
https://www.paranapanema.com.br
Year Founded: 1961
PMAM3—(BRAZ)
Rev.: $173,901,070
Assets: $318,953,353
Liabilities: $1,073,946,987
Net Worth: ($754,993,634)
Earnings: ($248,464,268)
Fiscal Year-end: 12/31/23
Copper Product Mfr
N.A.I.C.S.: 331420
Marcelo Jose Milliet (CEO)

PARANGUL SA
str 1 Decembrie 1918 nr 110, Petrosani, Hunedoara, Romania
Tel.: (40) 254 542 801
Web Site:
http://www.hotelpetrosani.ro
Year Founded: 1987
Sales Range: Less than $1 Million
Emp.: 26
Accommodation Services
N.A.I.C.S.: 721110

PARANOVUS ENTERTAINMENT TECHNOLOGY LTD.
No 11 Dongjiao East Road Shuangxi Shunchang, Nanping, 353200, Fujian, China
Tel.: (86) 5997828808
Web Site: https://pavs.ai
Year Founded: 2004
PAVS—(NASDAQ)
Rev.: $6,544,819
Assets: $7,728,826
Liabilities: $2,560,381
Net Worth: $5,168,445
Earnings: ($9,927,324)
Emp.: 7
Fiscal Year-end: 03/31/24
Holding Company
N.A.I.C.S.: 551112
Xuezhu Wang (Chm & CEO)

PARAS DEFENCE & SPACE TECHNOLOGIES LTD.
D-112 Ttc Industrial Area Nerul, Navi Mumbai, 400706, Maharashtra, India
Tel.: (91) 2269199999
Web Site:
https://www.parasdefence.com
Year Founded: 2009
543367—(BOM)
Rev.: $19,738,637
Assets: $49,516,194
Liabilities: $21,301,112
Net Worth: $28,215,082
Earnings: $2,154,803
Fiscal Year-end: 03/31/21
Defence & Space Optic Mfr
N.A.I.C.S.: 336414
Amit Mahajan (Dir-Technical & R&D)

Subsidiaries:

Ayatti Innovative Private Limited (1)
Gat No 343 Village-Nighoje MIDC Phase 3 Chakan Industrial Area, Pune, 410501, Maharashtra, India
Tel.: (91) 9324611972

Web Site: https://www.ayatti.co.in
Mechanical Engineering Services
N.A.I.C.S.: 541330

PARAS FLOWFORM ENGINEERING LIMITED
Plot No M-6 Addl MIDC, Ambarnath East, Thane, 421 506, Maharashtra, India
Tel.: (91) 251 2620333
Web Site:
http://www.parasflowform.com
Emp.: 230
Metal Products Mfr
N.A.I.C.S.: 332999
Sharad Shah (Chm)

PARASUCO JEANS INC.
128 Deslauriers, Montreal, H4N 1V8, QC, Canada
Tel.: (514) 334-0888
Web Site: http://www.parasuco.com
Sales Range: $50-74.9 Million
Emp.: 125
Jean Mfr
N.A.I.C.S.: 458110
Salvatore Parasuco (Founder)

PARATECH CO., LTD.
65-2 Chuneui-dong, Wonmi-gu, Bucheon, Gyeonggi, Korea (South)
Tel.: (82) 27952300
Web Site: http://www.paratech.co.kr
Year Founded: 1973
033540—(KRS)
Rev.: $164,176,848
Assets: $160,789,761
Liabilities: $86,571,545
Net Worth: $74,218,216
Earnings: ($4,236,881)
Emp.: 250
Fiscal Year-end: 12/31/22
Fire Fitting Equipment Mfr
N.A.I.C.S.: 333998

Subsidiaries:

Paratech Co., Ltd. - Seosan Plant (1)
1169 Suseok-dong Chung, Seosan, Cheongnam-do, Korea (South)
Tel.: (82) 416645400
Industrial Machinery Mfr
N.A.I.C.S.: 333310

PARC LOGISTIC TRANSILVANIA SRL
Str Orastie Nr 10, 400398, Cluj-Napoca, Romania
Tel.: (40) 264416 597
Web Site:
http://www.transilvaniaconstructii.ro
Storage, Production & Cold Storage Space Services
N.A.I.C.S.: 493110

Subsidiaries:

S.C. Transilvania Constructii S.A. (1)
Str Taietura Turcului nr 47 Et 3, Cluj-Napoca, Cluj, Romania (81.2%)
Tel.: (40) 264 416597
Web Site:
http://www.transilvaniaconstructii.ro
Rev.: $9,972,248
Assets: $69,579,298
Liabilities: $46,845,269
Net Worth: $22,734,029
Earnings: $2,294,268
Emp.: 19
Fiscal Year-end: 12/31/2019
Construction Services
N.A.I.C.S.: 236210
Mircea Timofte (Chm)

PARCELPAL LOGISTICS INC.
190 Alexander St Ste 305, Vancouver, V6A 2S5, BC, Canada
Tel.: (587) 883-9811
Web Site: http://www.parcelpal.com

PTNYF—(OTCQB)
Rev.: $5,884,273
Assets: $4,294,190
Liabilities: $4,131,785
Net Worth: $162,406
Earnings: ($3,209,389)
Emp.: 174
Fiscal Year-end: 12/31/21
Technology Investment Services
N.A.I.C.S.: 523999
Rod Santulan (Sr VP)

Subsidiaries:

TraderOS Technologies Inc. (1)
TraderOS Technologies Inc., New York, NY 10038
Tel.: (800) 668-6286
Web Site: http://www.traderos.com
Online Trading Services
N.A.I.C.S.: 561990

PARCOM CAPITAL MANAGEMENT B.V.
Stadionplein 16, 1076 CM, Amsterdam, Netherlands
Tel.: (31) 20 658 7500   NI
Web Site:
http://www.parcomcapital.com
Year Founded: 1982
Privater Equity Firm
N.A.I.C.S.: 523999
Erik Westerink (Partner)

Subsidiaries:

Ergon Capital Management SA (1)
Route dArlon 19-21, 8009, Strassen, Luxembourg
Tel.: (352) 2060042620
Web Site: http://www.ergoncapital.com
Rev.: $1,064,423,750
Emp.: 7
Privater Equity Firm
N.A.I.C.S.: 523999
Wolfgang de Limburg Stirum (Mng Partner)

Holding (Non-US):

Farmabios SpA (2)
Via Pavia 1, Gropello Cairoli, 27027, Milan, PV, Italy
Tel.: (39) 03828191
Web Site: https://www.farmabios.com
Active Pharmaceutical Ingredients Mfr & Distr
N.A.I.C.S.: 325412
Mario Di Giacomo (CEO)

Keesing Media Group B.V. (2)
Naritaweg 235, 1043 CB, Amsterdam, Netherlands
Tel.: (31) 20 564 1234
Web Site: https://www.keesing.com
Emp.: 400
Puzzle Magazines Publishing Services
N.A.I.C.S.: 511120

PharmaZell GmbH (2)
Rosenheimer Str 43, 83064, Raubling, Germany
Tel.: (49) 8035880
Web Site: https://pharmazell-group.com
Sales Range: $50-74.9 Million
Active Pharmaceutical Ingredients Mfr & Distr
N.A.I.C.S.: 325412
Oliver Bolzern (CEO & COO)

SVT GmbH (2)
Eisenwerkstrasse 21-27, 58332, Schwelm, Germany
Tel.: (49) 23364430
Web Site: https://www.svt-gmbh.com
Loading Arm Mfr
N.A.I.C.S.: 333131
Michael Schauerte (Mng Dir)

Subsidiary (US):

Connex SVT Inc. (3)
3402 Torchlite Terrace Ct Ste D, Katy, TX 77494
Tel.: (281) 391-1244
Web Site: http://www.connexsvt.com
Loading Arm Equipment Mfr
N.A.I.C.S.: 333131

Barry Craig (Pres)

Gamma Holding N.V. (1)
Panovenweg 12, PO Box 80, 5700 AB, Helmond, Netherlands
Tel.: (31) 492566600
Web Site: http://www.gammaholding.com
Sales Range: $800-899.9 Million
Emp.: 4,500
Holding Company; Textile Products Developer, Mfr & Whslr
N.A.I.C.S.: 551112

Subsidiary (US):

Clear Edge Filtration, Inc. (2)
2021 S Lewis Ave Ste 570, Tulsa, OK 74104
Tel.: (918) 728-8111
Web Site: http://www.clear-edge.com
Sales Range: $25-49.9 Million
Filtration Products Mfr
N.A.I.C.S.: 314999
Rick Von Drehle (CEO)

Subsidiary (Non-US):

Clear Edge Filtration (Australia) Pty. Ltd. (3)
6 Garden Boulevard, Dingley Village, Dingley, 3172, VIC, Australia
Tel.: (61) 385516400
Web Site: http://www.clear-edge.com
Sales Range: $10-24.9 Million
Emp.: 60
Filtration Products Mfr
N.A.I.C.S.: 314999
Kenneth Shue (Mng Dir-Asia Pacific)

Clear Edge Filtration (NZ) Ltd. (3)
126 Lansford Cres, Avondale, Auckland, New Zealand
Tel.: (64) 98282182
Web Site: http://www.clearedge.com
Sales Range: $10-24.9 Million
Emp.: 15
Filtration Products Mfr
N.A.I.C.S.: 314999
Tim Girdimeieer (Gen Mgr)

Clear Edge Filtration CFE GmbH (3)
Erzwsche 44, Salzgitter, 382229, Germany
Tel.: (49) 534181510
Web Site: http://www.clear-edge.com
Sales Range: $1-9.9 Million
Filtration Products Mfr
N.A.I.C.S.: 314999

Clear Edge Filtration GmbH (3)
Kevelaerer Strasse 78, 47608, Geldern, Walbeck, Germany
Tel.: (49) 28311220
Web Site: http://www.clear-edge.com
Sales Range: $25-49.9 Million
Emp.: 180
Filtration Products Mfr
N.A.I.C.S.: 314999
Peter Bonnes-Varkyser (Controller)

Clear Edge Filtration Polska Sp. z o.o. (3)
Ul Koscielna 15, Konstantynow Lodzki, 95050, Poland
Tel.: (48) 42 211 12 65
Filtration Products Mfr
N.A.I.C.S.: 314999
Collin Waudby (Gen Mgr)

Clear Edge Filtration South Africa Pty. Ltd. (3)
44 Jasper Rd Robertsham, PO Box 38262, Booysens, 2016, South Africa
Tel.: (27) 116805300
Web Site: http://www.clearedge.com
Sales Range: $1-9.9 Million
Filtration Products Mfr
N.A.I.C.S.: 314999
elsabath Kuman (Gen Mgr)

Clear Edge Filtration Sweden AB (3)
Brevensvgen, SE 640 10, Hogsjo, Sweden
Tel.: (46) 15147500
Web Site: http://www.clear-edge.com
Sales Range: $25-49.9 Million
Filtration Products Mfr
N.A.I.C.S.: 339999

Clear Edge Filtration UK Ltd. (3)
Knowsley Road Industrial Estate, Haslingden, BB4 4EJ, Lancs, United Kingdom

PARCOM CAPITAL MANAGEMENT B.V.

Parcom Capital Management B.V.—(Continued)
Tel.: (44) 1706 239 500
Filtration Products Mfr
N.A.I.C.S.: 314999

Subsidiary (Domestic):

Clear Edge Filtration, Inc.-Skaneateles Falls (3)
4563 Jordan Rd, Skaneateles Falls, NY 13153-0238
Tel.: (315) 685-3466
Sales Range: $10-24.9 Million
Filtration Product Mfr & Sales
N.A.I.C.S.: 314999

Industrial Fabrics Corp. (3)
7160 Northland Cir, Minneapolis, MN 55428
Tel.: (763) 535-3220
Web Site: http://www.ifcfabrics.com
Industrial Fabric Mfr
N.A.I.C.S.: 314999
Michael Burks (Supvr-Weaving)

Subsidiary (Non-US):

Deutsche Gamma GmbH (2)
Girmesgath 5, D47803, Krefeld, Germany
Tel.: (49) 2151890222
Sales Range: $250-299.9 Million
Emp.: 3,300
Holding Company
N.A.I.C.S.: 551112

Subsidiary (Domestic):

Verseidag AG (3)
Girmesgath 5, D 47803, Krefeld, Germany
Tel.: (49) 2151890
Web Site: http://www.verseidag.de
Sales Range: $300-349.9 Million
Screen & Filter Technology, Coating & Composites for Sailcloth Mfr
N.A.I.C.S.: 333998

Subsidiary (Domestic):

Verseidag-Indutex GmbH (4)
Industrie Strasse 56, 47803, Krefeld, Germany
Tel.: (49) 21518760
Web Site: http://www.verseidag.de
Sales Range: $50-74.9 Million
Coated Fabric Mfr
N.A.I.C.S.: 313320
Markus Simon (Mng Dir)

Subsidiary (Non-US):

Gamma Grundstucksverwaltungsgesellschaft mbH (2)
Girmesgath 5, 47803, Krefeld, Germany
Tel.: (49) 2151890222
Web Site: http://www.verseigag.de
Sales Range: $25-49.9 Million
Emp.: 16
Mfr of Textiles
N.A.I.C.S.: 313230

Subsidiary (Domestic):

Gamma Holding Nederland N.V. (2)
Panovenweg 12, PO Box 80, 5708 HR, Helmond, Netherlands
Tel.: (31) 492 56 66 00
Web Site: http://www.gammaholding.nl
Sales Range: $900-999.9 Million
Conveyor Belts, Flat Belts, Modular Belts, Endless Woven Belts, Engineered Belts & Timing Belts Mfr
N.A.I.C.S.: 326220

Koninklijke Ten Cate, B.V. (1)
Stationsstraat 11, 7607 GX, Almelo, Netherlands
Tel.: (31) 546544911
Web Site: http://www.tencate.com
Emp.: 3,796
Holding Company; Technical Textiles & Technical Components Mfr & Whslr
N.A.I.C.S.: 551112
Don M. Olsen (CEO-Protective Fabrics)

Subsidiary (Domestic):

GreenFields Holding BV (2)
G van der Muelenweg 2, 7443 RE, Nijverdal, Netherlands
Tel.: (31) 548633333
Web Site: http://www.greenfields.eu

Holding Company; Artificial Turf Installation Services
N.A.I.C.S.: 551112

Subsidiary (Domestic):

GreenFields BV (3)
G van der Muelenweg 2, 7443 RE, Nijverdal, Netherlands
Tel.: (31) 548633333
Web Site: http://www.greenfields.eu
Artificial Turf Installation Services
N.A.I.C.S.: 339999

Subsidiary (Non-US):

GreenFields Sports & Leisure Pty Ltd. (4)
20 Chesterfield Road, Pietermaritzburg, 3201, South Africa
Tel.: (27) 338977500
Web Site: http://www.greenfields.eu
Sport Goods Distr
N.A.I.C.S.: 532284

GreenFields Swiss AG (4)
Talstrasse 26, CH-8200, Schaffhausen, Switzerland
Tel.: (41) 526320101
Web Site: http://www.greenfields.eu
Artificial Turf Installation Services
N.A.I.C.S.: 339999

Subsidiary (US):

Polyloom Corporation of America (2)
1131 Broadway St, Dayton, TN 37321-1802
Tel.: (423) 775-0792
Web Site: http://www.tencategrass.com
Artificial Turf Fibers & Backing Mfr
N.A.I.C.S.: 325220

Subsidiary (Non-US):

SOLMAX (2)
Av Puente Cultural 10, San Sebastian de los Reyes, 28702, Madrid, Spain
Tel.: (34) 607499962
Web Site: http://www.tencategeo.eu
Geosynthetics & Industrial Fabrics Mfr
N.A.I.C.S.: 313220

Solmax (2)
Bd Mircea Voda 43 Bucuresti-Sector 3, Bucharest, Romania
Tel.: (40) 740955194
Web Site: http://www.tencategeo.eu
Geosynthetics & Industrial Fabrics Mfr
N.A.I.C.S.: 313220

Ten Cate Advanced Armour UK Limited (2)
Regus 2430/2440 The Quadrant Aztec West, Bristol, BS32 4AQ, United Kingdom
Tel.: (44) 1454877600
Web Site: http://www.tencateadvancedarmour.com
Customized Lightweight Ballistic Protection Solutions Mfr
N.A.I.C.S.: 336992

Subsidiary (Domestic):

Ten Cate Advanced Textiles BV (2)
G van der Muelenweg 2, PO Box 186, 7440 AD, Nijverdal, Netherlands
Tel.: (31) 548 633922
Web Site: http://eu.tencatefabrics.com
Holding Company
N.A.I.C.S.: 551112

Subsidiary (US):

Southern Mills, Inc. (3)
6501 Mall Blvd, Union City, GA 30291
Tel.: (770) 969-1000
Web Site: http://us.tencatefabrics.com
Industrial Textiles & Protective Fabrics Mfr
N.A.I.C.S.: 313210
Jean Harris (VP-HR)

Subsidiary (Non-US):

Ten Cate Danmark a/s (2)
Damsbovej 10, 5492, Vissenbjerg, Denmark
Tel.: (45) 65481600
Web Site: http://www.tencateadvancedarmour.com
Protective Fabrics Mfr
N.A.I.C.S.: 313220

Subsidiary (Domestic):

Ten Cate Advanced Armour Danmark a/s (3)
Damsbovej 10, 5492, Vissenbjerg, Denmark
Tel.: (45) 65481600
Web Site: http://www.tencateadvancedarmour.com
Customized Lightweight Ballistic Protection Solutions Mfr
N.A.I.C.S.: 336992
Helle Specht (Mng Dir)

Subsidiary (Non-US):

Ten Cate Geosynthetics (UK) Limited (2)
39 High Street, Wednesfield, Wolverhampton, WV11 1ST, W Midlands, United Kingdom
Tel.: (44) 1952588066
Web Site: http://www.tencategeo.eu
Geosynthetics & Industrial Fabrics Mfr
N.A.I.C.S.: 313220

Subsidiary (Domestic):

Ten Cate Thiobac bv (2)
Hoge Dijkje 2, 7442 AE, Nijverdal, Netherlands
Tel.: (31) 548633944
Web Site: http://www.tencate.com
Synthetic Turf Components Mfr
N.A.I.C.S.: 325220

Subsidiary (Non-US):

TenCate Advanced Armour SASU (2)
50 Route de Louvier, 38270, Primarette, France
Tel.: (33) 474795050
Web Site: http://www.tencateadvancedarmor.com
Customized Lightweight Ballistic Protection Solutions Mfr
N.A.I.C.S.: 336992

TenCate France SASU (2)
9 Rue Marcel Paul, BP 40080, F-95873, Bezons, Cedex, France
Tel.: (33) 134235363
Web Site: http://www.tencategeo.eu
Geosynthetics & Industrial Fabrics Mfr
N.A.I.C.S.: 325998

TenCate Geosynthetics (Thailand) Ltd (2)
555 Rasa Tower 26th Floor Phaholyothin Road Soi 19, Chatuchak, Bangkok, 10900, Thailand
Tel.: (66) 26926680
Web Site: http://www.tencategeo.asia
Geosynthetics & Industrial Fabrics Mfr
N.A.I.C.S.: 313220

TenCate Geosynthetics Asia Sdn. Bhd. (2)
14 Jalan Sementa 27/91 Seksyen 27, Shah Alam, 40400, Selangor Darul Ehsan, Malaysia
Tel.: (60) 351928568
Web Site: http://www.tencategeo.asia
Geosynthetics & Industrial Fabrics Mfr
N.A.I.C.S.: 314999

TenCate Geosynthetics Austria GES.M.B.H (2)
Schachermayerstrasse 18, A-4021, Linz, Austria
Tel.: (43) 73269830
Web Site: https://www.tencategeo.eu
Geosynthetics & Industrial Fabrics Mfr
N.A.I.C.S.: 314999

TenCate Geosynthetics France S.A.S. (2)
9 rue Marcel Paul, BP 40080, F-95873, Bezons, Cedex, France
Tel.: (33) 134235363
Web Site: https://www.tencategeo.eu
Geosynthetics Products Mfr
N.A.I.C.S.: 325998

TenCate Geosynthetics Malaysia Sdn Bhd (2)
14 Jalan Sementa 27/91 Seksyen 27, Shah Alam, 40400, Selangor, Malaysia
Tel.: (60) 351928568
Web Site: http://www.tencategeo.asia

Geosynthetics & Industrial Fabrics Mfr
N.A.I.C.S.: 313220

Subsidiary (Domestic):

TenCate Geosynthetics Netherlands B.V. (2)
Europalaan 206, 7559 SC, Hengelo, Netherlands
Tel.: (31) 546544811
Web Site: http://www.tencategeo.eu
Geosynthetics & Industrial Fabrics Mfr
N.A.I.C.S.: 313220

Subsidiary (Non-US):

TenCate Industrial Zhuhai Co. Ltd. (2)
South of Nangang West Road Gaolan Port Economic Zone, Zhuhai, 519050, Guangdong, China
Tel.: (86) 7568861616
Web Site: http://www.tencategeo.asia
Geosynthetics & Industrial Fabrics Mfr
N.A.I.C.S.: 313220
Nell Nong (Mgr-Production)

Subsidiary (Domestic):

TenCate Protective Fabrics Holding BV (2)
G van der Muelenweg 2, PO Box 186, 7440 AD, Nijverdal, Netherlands
Tel.: (31) 548 633922
Web Site: http://eu.tencatefabrics.com
Protective Workwear Mfr
N.A.I.C.S.: 339999

Subsidiary (US):

TenCate Protective Fabrics USA Inc. (2)
6501 Mall Blvd, Union City, GA 30291
Tel.: (770) 969-1000
Web Site: http://us.tencatefabrics.com
Protective Workwear Mfr
N.A.I.C.S.: 339999
Daniel Hauert (VP-Sls & Bus Dev-Americas)

Subsidiary (Non-US):

TigerTurf (UK) Limited (2)
229 Ikon Droitwich Road, Hartlebury, DY10 4EU, Worcs, United Kingdom
Tel.: (44) 1299 253 966
Web Site: http://www.tigerturf.com
Synthetic Turf Mfr
N.A.I.C.S.: 339999
Paul Langford (Mng Dir-EMEA)

TigerTurf Australia Pty Ltd (2)
2/12 Latitude Boulevard, Thomastown, Melbourne, 3074, VIC, Australia
Tel.: (61) 3 9464 5052
Web Site: http://www.tigerturf.com
Synthetic Turf Mfr
N.A.I.C.S.: 325130

TigerTurf NZ Limited (2)
384 Neilson Street, Onehunga, Auckland, 1061, New Zealand
Tel.: (64) 96344134
Web Site: http://www.tigerturf.co.nz
Synthetic Grass & Turf Mfr
N.A.I.C.S.: 339999
Peter Leeves (Gen Mgr)

Subsidiary (Domestic):

Xtra Grass (2)
G van der Muelenweg 2, 7443 RE, Nijverdal, Netherlands
Tel.: (31) 548633333
Web Site: http://www.xtragrass-hybrid-turf.com
Artificial Turf Installation Services
N.A.I.C.S.: 238990

MGG Group B.V. (1)
Industriestraat 14a, 5931 PJ, Tegelen, Netherlands
Tel.: (31) 77 373 9999
Web Site: http://www.mgg.com
Aluminium Sand-Castings & Sub-Assemblies Mfr
N.A.I.C.S.: 331523

Subsidiary (Domestic):

MGG Blerick (2)

Groot Egtenrayseweg 58, 5928 PA, Venlo, Netherlands
Tel.: (31) 77 3231515
Web Site: http://www.mgg.com
Aluminum Casting Mfr
N.A.I.C.S.: 331523

Subsidiary (Non-US):

MGG Schwabisch Gmund (2)
Lorcher Strasse 115, 73525, Schwabisch Gmund, Germany
Tel.: (49) 717191040
Web Site: http://www.mgg.com
Aluminum Casting Mfr
N.A.I.C.S.: 331523

MGG Trest (2)
Nadrazni 1444, 589 01, Trest, Czech Republic
Tel.: (420) 567224325
Web Site: http://www.mgg.com
Metal Product Distr
N.A.I.C.S.: 423510

Qizini Group B.V. (1)
De Pol 36, 7581 CZ, Losser, Netherlands
Tel.: (31) 53 478 9200
Web Site: http://www.qizini.nl
Emp.: 300
Prepared Food Mfr
N.A.I.C.S.: 311991
Jorca Crielaard (Mgr-HR)

Subsidiary (Domestic):

Qizini Alphen B.V. (2)
Van Foreestlaan 3, 2404 HC, Alphen aan den Rijn, Netherlands (100%)
Tel.: (31) 172430882
Web Site: http://www.qizini.com
Sales Range: $25-49.9 Million
Emp.: 200
Prepared Food Mfr
N.A.I.C.S.: 311991
Walther de Haan (Mgr-Ops)

PARDIS INVESTMENT COMPANY
Unit 4 4th Fl 29 Africa Building Jahan Kudak Junction, Tehran, Iran
Tel.: (98) 21 88786717
Web Site:
  http://www.pardisinvestment.com
Year Founded: 1956
AYEG1—(THE)
Sales Range: Less than $1 Million
Investment Management Service
N.A.I.C.S.: 523999

PARDIS PETROCHEMICAL COMPANY
Molasadara Street Sheikh Bahai St north of Arafi Shirazi Street, 7th floor, 19936 45853, Tehran, Iran
Tel.: (98) 21488603493
Web Site: https://www.paupc.ir
Year Founded: 2001
PRDZ1—(THE)
Sales Range: Less than $1 Million
Chemical Products Distr
N.A.I.C.S.: 424690
Amir Hossein Naraghi (Chm)

PAREKH ALUMINEX LIMITED
G-11 Everest Building 8th Floor Tardeo Road, Tardeo, Mumbai, 400 034, India
Tel.: (91) 22 2352 1777
Web Site:
  http://www.parekhaluminex.com
Year Founded: 1994
Sales Range: $250-299.9 Million
Aluminum Sheet, Plate & Foil Container Mfr
N.A.I.C.S.: 322220

PARENT CAPITAL CORP.
24 West 4th Avenue, Vancouver, V5Y 1G3, BC, Canada
Tel.: (604) 218-7400 AB

Web Site:
  http://www.centuryenergyltd.com
PAR.H—(TSXV)
Assets: $212,903
Liabilities: $102,107
Net Worth: $110,796
Earnings: ($223,529)
Emp.: 5
Fiscal Year-end: 08/31/22
Oil & Gas Exploration Services
N.A.I.C.S.: 211120

Subsidiaries:

Century Energy Ltd. - Houston Branch (1)
4605 Post Oak Place Dr Ste 250, Houston, TX 77027
Tel.: (713) 658-0161
Oil & Gas Exploration Services
N.A.I.C.S.: 213112

PARENTERAL DRUGS (INDIA) LIMITED
340 Laxmi Plaza Laxmi Industrial Estate New Link Road, Andheri West, Mumbai, 400 053, MH, India
Tel.: (91) 61725900
Web Site: http://www.pdindia.com
Year Founded: 1983
Rev.: $34,030,226
Assets: $138,549,723
Liabilities: $159,735,236
Net Worth: ($21,185,513)
Earnings: ($18,507,416)
Emp.: 900
Fiscal Year-end: 03/31/18
Pharmaceuticals Product Mfr
N.A.I.C.S.: 325412
Manoharlal Gupta (Chm)

Subsidiaries:

Parentech Healthcare Limited (1)
Shree Ganesh Chambers A B Road, Indore, 452 001, India
Tel.: (91) 1143181000
Web Site: http://www.parentech.net
Sales Range: $25-49.9 Million
Emp.: 3
Pharmaceuticals Product Mfr
N.A.I.C.S.: 325412
Manohar Lal Gupta (Mgr)

PARETO BANK ASA
Dronning Mauds gate 3, Postboks 1823, 0123, Oslo, Norway
Tel.: (47) 24028100
Web Site: http://www.paretobank.no
8PB—(BER)
Sales Range: Less than $1 Million
Commercial Banking Services
N.A.I.C.S.: 522110
Tiril Haug Villum (CEO & Officer-IR)

PARETO GROUP
Dronning Mauds gt 3, PO Box 1396, Vika, Oslo, Norway
Tel.: (47) 2287 87 00 NO
Web Site: http://www.pareto.no
Year Founded: 1985
Holding Company
N.A.I.C.S.: 551112
Svein Stole (Owner, Chm & CEO)

Subsidiaries:

Krogsveen AS (1)
Martin Linges vei 17, 1330, Fornebu, Norway
Tel.: (47) 67 52 95 50
Web Site: http://www.krogsveen.no
Property Management Services
N.A.I.C.S.: 531190
Stian Klofta (CEO)

Pareto Securities AS (1)
Dronning Mauds gt 3, PO Box 1396, Vika, Oslo, N-0114, Norway
Tel.: (47) 22878700
Web Site: http://www.paretosec.com
Emp.: 400
Financial Services

N.A.I.C.S.: 523999
Ole Henrik Bjorge (CEO)

PAREX RESOURCES INC.
2700 Eighth Avenue Place West Tower 585 8 Avenue SW, Calgary, T2P 1G1, AB, Canada
Tel.: (403) 265-4800 AB
Web Site:
  https://www.parexresources.com
Year Founded: 2009
PXT—(TSX)
Rev.: $1,057,184,000
Assets: $1,784,221,000
Liabilities: $390,530,000
Net Worth: $1,393,691,000
Earnings: $303,105,000
Emp.: 371
Fiscal Year-end: 12/31/21
Oil Exploration & Production Services
N.A.I.C.S.: 211120
Ryan W. Fowler (Sr VP-Exploration)

Subsidiaries:

Parex Resources (Colombia) Ltd. (1)
Calle 113 No 7-21 of 611 Edificio Teleport Torre A, Bogota, Colombia
Tel.: (57) 16291716
Oil Exploration Services
N.A.I.C.S.: 213112
Lee Distefano (Pres & Country Mgr)

Verano Energy (Switzerland) AG (1)

PARFAS LIMITED
119 Lees Road Sherwood House, Oldham, OL4 1JW, Lancs, United Kingdom
Tel.: (44) 1616208111 UK
Web Site: https://parfas.co.uk
Emp.: 100
Security Systems, Monitoring & Risk Management Services
N.A.I.C.S.: 561621

Subsidiaries:

SSS Management Services Limited (1)
Shannon House Coldharbour Lane, Aylesford, ME20 7NS, Kent, United Kingdom
Tel.: (44) 1622798200
Web Site: http://www.sss-support.co.uk
Sales Range: $25-49.9 Million
Emp.: 100
Administrative Management Consulting Services
N.A.I.C.S.: 541611
Stacey Anderson (Mng Dir)

PARFETTS
Didsbury Road, Stockport, SK4 2JP, United Kingdom
Tel.: (44) 161 429 0429
Web Site: http://www.parfetts.co.uk
Year Founded: 1980
Sales Range: $450-499.9 Million
Emp.: 593
Grocery Store Operator
N.A.I.C.S.: 445110
David Grimes (Co-Mng Dir)

PARI CAPITAL GMBH
Walter-Gropius-Str 15, 80807, Munich, Germany
Tel.: (49) 89 99 84 80 0
Web Site: http://www.parigroup.com
Private Investment Company
N.A.I.C.S.: 523999
Guido Krass (Owner)

Subsidiaries:

Renusol Europe GmbH (1)
Piccolominstr 2, 51063, Cologne, Germany
Tel.: (49) 2217887070
Web Site: http://www.renusol.com
PV Mounting Systems (for Roof-Integrated, Rooftop & Flat-Roof Installations)
N.A.I.C.S.: 335931

Stefan Drabant (Acct Mgr-Eastern Europe)

PARI MEDICAL HOLDING GMBH
Moosstrasse 3, 82319, Starnberg, Germany
Tel.: (49) 81 51 279 0
Web Site: http://www.pari.de
Emp.: 500
Respiratory Equipment Mfr
N.A.I.C.S.: 339112
Johann Zimmermann (CEO)

Subsidiaries:

PARI Japan KK (1)
Kikuko Okada Yasui Bldg No 1012-25-24, Mino-shi, Osaka, 562-0012, Hakunoshima, Japan
Tel.: (81) 72 737 7800
Web Site: http://www.pari-japan.jp
Medical Equipment Mfr
N.A.I.C.S.: 339112

PARI MEDICAL Ltd. (1)
The Old Sorting Office Rosemount Avenue, West Byfleet, KT14 6LB, Surrey, United Kingdom
Tel.: (44) 1932 341122
Web Site: http://www.parimedical.co.uk
Emp.: 11
Medical Equipment Mfr
N.A.I.C.S.: 339112
Mal Apter (Country Mgr)

PARI Pharma GmbH (1)
Lochhamer Schlag 21, 82166, Grafelfing, Germany
Tel.: (49) 89 742 846 0
Web Site: http://www.paripharma.com
Medical Equipment Mfr
N.A.I.C.S.: 339112
Oliver Denk (VP-BU Pharma)

PARI PulmoMed S.A.R.L. (1)
11 avenue de l ile Saint-Martin, Z A du Petit Nanterre, 92737, Nanterre, Cedex, France
Tel.: (33) 1 56 83 85 00
Web Site: http://www.pari-pulmomed.fr
Medical Equipment Mfr
N.A.I.C.S.: 339112

PARI Respiratory Equipment, Inc. (1)
2943 Oak Lake Blvd, Midlothian, VA 23112
Tel.: (804) 253-7274
Web Site: http://www.pari.com
Sales Range: $1-9.9 Million
Emp.: 12
Respiratory Equipment Mfr
N.A.I.C.S.: 339112
Jeff Hunzinker (Pres)

PARI synergy in medicine OOO (1)
Novocheremushkinskaya 49, 117418, Moscow, Russia
Tel.: (7) 4959818860
Web Site: http://www.pari.com.ru
Medical Equipment Mfr
N.A.I.C.S.: 339112

PARItec GmbH (1)
Holzhofstrasse 10b, 82362, Weilheim, Germany
Tel.: (49) 881 9410 0
Medical Equipment Mfr
N.A.I.C.S.: 339112

PARI MUTUEL URBAIN
2 rue du Pr Florian Delbarre, 75015, Paris, France
Tel.: (33) 156099100 FR
Web Site: http://www.pmu.fr
Year Founded: 1930
Sales Range: $5-14.9 Billion
Emp.: 1,040
Horse Race Betting
N.A.I.C.S.: 713290
Eric Brion (Mgr-TV & Multimedia)

PARIKSHA FIN-INVEST-LEASE LIMITED
Uttam Toyota A-11 Meerut Road Industrial Area, Ghaziabad, 201 003, Uttar Pradesh, India

PARIKSHA FIN-INVEST-LEASE LIMITED

Pariksha Fin-Invest-Lease Limited—(Continued)
Tel.: (91) 1204193799 In
Web Site: http://www.pfil.in
Year Founded: 1994
Rev.: $134,681
Assets: $607,606
Liabilities: $9,733
Net Worth: $597,873
Earnings: $53,269
Fiscal Year-end: 03/31/19
Finance Management Services
N.A.I.C.S.: 522291
Amita Adlakha *(Mng Dir)*

PARIN FURNITURE LTD.
Plot no 1-3 Survey No 33 National Highway 27, Village Billayala, Rajkot, 360311, India
Tel.: (91) 9898498984
Web Site:
  https://www.parinfurniture.com
PARIN—(NSE)
Rev.: $9,799,017
Assets: $17,251,520
Liabilities: $10,570,517
Net Worth: $6,681,002
Earnings: $368,755
Emp.: 254
Fiscal Year-end: 03/31/23
Furniture Product Distr
N.A.I.C.S.: 449110
Umesh Nandani *(Chm & Mng Dir)*

PARIS GROUP INTERNATIONAL LLC
3rd Floor Dubai Festive City Tower, Ras Al Khor, Dubai, United Arab Emirates
Tel.: (971) 4 232 8999
Web Site: http://www.parisgroup.ae
Holding Company
N.A.I.C.S.: 551112
Abdulkader Sankari *(Pres)*

Subsidiaries:

Gianfranco Ferre S.p.A. (1)
Via Pontaccio 21, 20121, Milan, Italy
Tel.: (39) 02721341
Web Site: http://www.gianfrancoferre.com
Designer Clothing Mfr
N.A.I.C.S.: 424250

Subsidiary (US):

Gianfranco Ferre USA Inc. (2)
85 5th Ave Fl 6, New York, NY 10003
Tel.: (212) 413-4400
Business Support Services
N.A.I.C.S.: 561499

PARIS MIKI HOLDINGS INC.
10F Shiodome Shiba-Rikyu Building 1-2-3 Kaigan, Minato-ku, Tokyo, 105-0022, Japan
Tel.: (81) 364320732
Web Site: https://www.paris-miki.com
Year Founded: 1950
7455—(TKS)
Rev.: $329,918,320
Assets: $264,538,810
Liabilities: $66,086,780
Net Worth: $198,452,030
Earnings: $11,170,900
Fiscal Year-end: 03/31/24
Optical Lens Mfr
N.A.I.C.S.: 333248
Mikio Tane *(Chm)*

Subsidiaries:

PARIS MIKI Inc. (1)
Cascade Mall Dr, Burlington, WA 98223
Tel.: (360) 757-7770
Web Site: http://www.parismikiusa.com
Sales Range: $25-49.9 Million
Emp.: 5
Optical Glass Retailers
N.A.I.C.S.: 456130

PARITY GROUP PLC
80 George Street, 5 Jewry Street, Edinburgh, EH2 3BU, United Kingdom
Tel.: (44) 1315539100
Web Site: https://www.parity.net
PTY—(AIM)
Rev.: $51,310,275
Assets: $16,114,618
Liabilities: $10,041,656
Net Worth: $6,072,961
Earnings: ($2,164,857)
Emp.: 35
Fiscal Year-end: 12/31/22
Information Technology Services
N.A.I.C.S.: 541512
Roger Antony *(Fin Dir)*

Subsidiaries:

Parity Holdings Limited (1)
The Ministry 2nd floor 79-81 Borough Road, London, SE1 1DN, United Kingdom (100%)
Tel.: (44) 2081711729
Web Site: https://www.parity.net
Sales Range: $25-49.9 Million
Custom Computer Programming Services
N.A.I.C.S.: 541511

Parity Solutions Limited (1)
2 Bath Place Rivington Steet, 1 Hartfield Road Wimbledon, London, EC2A 3DR, United Kingdom (100%)
Tel.: (44) 2085435353
Sales Range: $25-49.9 Million
Emp.: 150
Computer System Design Services
N.A.I.C.S.: 541512
Matthew Bayfield *(Mng Dir)*

PARK & BELLHEIMER AG
Zweibrucker Strabe 4, 66953, Pirmasens, Germany
Tel.: (49) 72727010
Web Site: https://www.park-bellheimer.de
Year Founded: 1995
PKB—(DEU)
Rev.: $26,879,347
Assets: $37,851,860
Liabilities: $23,269,677
Net Worth: $14,582,183
Earnings: $2,240,865
Emp.: 126
Fiscal Year-end: 12/30/23
Beverage Product Mfr & Distr
N.A.I.C.S.: 312120

PARK ELEKTRIK URETIM MADENCILIK SANAYI VE TICARET AS
Pasalimani Street No 41 Uskudar, Istanbul, Turkiye
Tel.: (90) 2165312400
Web Site:
  https://www.parkelektrik.com.tr
PRKME—(IST)
Rev.: $13,461,021
Assets: $104,362,393
Liabilities: $11,135,297
Net Worth: $93,227,097
Earnings: $11,445,834
Fiscal Year-end: 12/31/23
Eletric Power Generation Services
N.A.I.C.S.: 221118
Ali Coskun Duyak *(Vice Chm)*

PARK GEORGIA REALTY LTD
BC-435 North Road, Coquitlam, V3K 3V9, BC, Canada
Tel.: (604) 931-7227
Web Site:
  http://www.parkgeorgia.com
Year Founded: 1983
Sales Range: $10-24.9 Million
Real Estate & Rental Services
N.A.I.C.S.: 531210
Ernest Hui *(Pres)*

PARK LAWN COMPANY LIMITED
21 St Clair Avenue East Suite 1001, Toronto, M4T 1L9, ON, Canada
Tel.: (647) 933-9079 ON
Web Site: http://www.parklawnlp.ca
Year Founded: 1892
PRL—(CNSX)
Sales Range: Less than $1 Million
Cemeteries, Mausoleums & Crematoriums
N.A.I.C.S.: 812220

Subsidiaries:

Saber Management, LLC (1)
612 N Webster St, Kokomo, IN 46901
Tel.: (765) 454-7355
Web Site:
  http://www.sabermanagement.com
Office Administrative Services
N.A.I.C.S.: 561110
David Sullivan *(CEO)*

PARK REIT
53 Cherni Vrah Blvd, 1680, Sofia, Bulgaria
Tel.: (359) 24898715
Web Site: https://park.bg
Year Founded: 2005
PARK—(BUL)
Sales Range: Less than $1 Million
Financial & Insurance Services
N.A.I.C.S.: 524210
Zdravko Stoev *(Exec Dir)*

PARK STREET NORDICOM A/S
Svanevej 12, 2400, Copenhagen, Denmark
Tel.: (45) 33339303 DK
Web Site: https://www.nordicom.dk
Year Founded: 1989
PARKST.A—(CSE)
Rev.: $22,178,958
Assets: $406,225,492
Liabilities: $248,938,809
Net Worth: $157,286,684
Earnings: $7,955,318
Emp.: 35
Fiscal Year-end: 12/31/22
Real Estate Investment, Development & Property Management
N.A.I.C.S.: 531390
Andrew John Essex LaTrobe *(Chm)*

Subsidiaries:

Phoam Studio ApS (1)
Carl Jacobsens Vej 16 Stair 11 2 Floor, 2500, Valby, Denmark
Tel.: (45) 31909575
Web Site: http://www.phoam.dk
Architectural Design Services
N.A.I.C.S.: 541310

Pulse Living ApS (1)
Svanevej 12, 2400, Copenhagen, Denmark
Tel.: (45) 33339303
Web Site: https://www.pulseliving.dk
Information Technology Services
N.A.I.C.S.: 541519

PARK SYSTEMS CORP.
KANC 15F Gwanggyo-ro 109, Suwon, 16229, Korea (South)
Tel.: (82) 315466800
Web Site:
  https://www.parksystems.com
Year Founded: 1997
140860—(KRS)
Rev.: $95,508,383
Assets: $128,126,689
Liabilities: $36,498,509
Net Worth: $91,628,181
Earnings: $21,464,009
Emp.: 268
Fiscal Year-end: 12/31/22
Electronic Components Mfr
N.A.I.C.S.: 334419

INTERNATIONAL PUBLIC

Sang-il Park *(Founder & CEO)*

Subsidiaries:

Park Systems Europe GmbH (1)
Schildkrotstrasse 15, 68199, Mannheim, Germany
Tel.: (49) 62149089650
Analytical Laboratory Instrument Mfr
N.A.I.C.S.: 334516

Park Systems France SARL (1)
Tel.: (33) 607108736
Analytical Laboratory Instrument Mfr
N.A.I.C.S.: 334516

Park Systems Inc. (1)
3040 Olcott St, Santa Clara, CA 95054
Tel.: (408) 986-1110
Analytical Laboratory Instrument Mfr
N.A.I.C.S.: 334516

Park Systems Japan Inc. (1)
1-17-1 Kanda Nishiki-cho, Chiyoda-ku, Tokyo, 101-0054, Japan
Tel.: (81) 332191001
Analytical Laboratory Instrument Mfr
N.A.I.C.S.: 334516

Park Systems Microscopy S.A. de C.V. (1)
Rio de la Magdalena No 326 Despacho 104 Col La Otra Banda, Alvaro Obregon, 01090, Mexico, Mexico
Tel.: (52) 5571002354
Analytical Laboratory Instrument Mfr
N.A.I.C.S.: 334516

Park Systems Pte. Ltd. (1)
10 Science Park Rd 01-07 The Alpha Science Park 2, Singapore, 117684, Singapore
Tel.: (65) 66347470
Analytical Laboratory Instrument Mfr
N.A.I.C.S.: 334516

PARK'S MOTOR GROUP
14 Bothwell Road, Glasgow, Hamilton, ML3 0AY, Lanarkshire, United Kingdom
Tel.: (44) 1698303900
Web Site: http://www.parks.uk.com
Year Founded: 1971
Sales Range: $550-599.9 Million
Emp.: 1,084
New & Used Car Dealer
N.A.I.C.S.: 441110
Douglas Park *(Founder)*

PARK24 CO. LTD.
2-20-4 Nishigotanda, Shinagawa-ku, Tokyo, 141-8924, Japan
Tel.: (81) 367478109
Web Site: https://www.park24.co.jp
Year Founded: 1971
4666—(TKS)
Rev.: $2,340,572,070
Assets: $2,184,833,130
Liabilities: $1,770,663,690
Net Worth: $414,169,440
Earnings: $124,372,780
Emp.: 5,444
Fiscal Year-end: 10/31/23
Parking Equipment Sales
N.A.I.C.S.: 334514
Yasuji Iwabuchi *(Corp Officer-ICT)*

Subsidiaries:

GSPARK 24 Co., Ltd. (1)
13 Sungmun-gil Yomni-dong KT Mapo Building 7th Floor, Mapo-gu, Seoul, 121-872, Korea (South)
Tel.: (82) 232723500
Web Site: http://www.gspark24.co.kr
Parking Lot Management Services
N.A.I.C.S.: 812930

Park24 Business Support Co., Ltd. (1)
1-18-9 Nishigotanda, Shinagawa-ku, Tokyo, 141-0031, Japan
Tel.: (81) 35 436 7281
Web Site: https://www.park24bs.co.jp
Emp.: 231
Business Support Services
N.A.I.C.S.: 561499

AND PRIVATE COMPANIES

Secure Parking Corporation Sdn. Bhd.
Wisma Secure Parking L-G-05 Block L
Pusat Dagangan NZX, No 2 Jalan PJU
1A/41B Ara Jaya PJU 1A, 47301, Petaling
Jaya, Selangor, Malaysia
Tel.: (60) 37 885 0680
Web Site:
https://www.secureparking.com.my
Parking Lot Management Services
N.A.I.C.S.: 812930
Mak Jee Chew (Mgr-Risk Mgmt)

Secure Parking Pty. Ltd. (1)
Northpoint Level 13 100 Miller Street, North Sydney, 2060, NSW, Australia
Tel.: (61) 289124900
Web Site: http://www.secureparking.com.au
Emp.: 7,000
Parking Management Services
N.A.I.C.S.: 812930
Peter Anson (CEO)

Secure Parking Singapore Pte. Ltd. (1)
67 Ubi Avenue 1 02-05/06 North Wing Starhub Green, Singapore, 408942, Singapore
Tel.: (65) 65922700
Web Site: http://www.secureparking.com.sg
Emp.: 1,500
Parking Lot Management Services
N.A.I.C.S.: 812930
Steven Chew Wai Meng (Gen Mgr)

Taiwan Park24 Parking Co., Ltd. (1)
104 3rd Floor No 87 Songjiang Road, Zhongshan District, Taipei, 10491, Taiwan
Tel.: (886) 225046098
Web Site: https://www.park24.com.tw
Sales Range: $25-49.9 Million
Emp.: 24
Parking Services
N.A.I.C.S.: 812930
Kozakura Tatsuhiko (Mng Dir)

Times Communication Co., Ltd. (1)
2-20-4 Nishigotanda, Shinagawa-ku, Tokyo, 141-0031, Japan
Tel.: (81) 357598924
Web Site: http://www.timescom.co.jp
Road Services
N.A.I.C.S.: 237310

Times Innovation Capital LLC (1)
2-20-4 Nishigotanda, Shinagawa-ku, Tokyo, 141-0031, Japan
Tel.: (81) 367478111
Investment Business Services
N.A.I.C.S.: 523999

Times Mobility Co., Ltd. (1)
2-20-4 Nishigotanda, Shinagawa-ku, Tokyo, 141-0031, Japan
Tel.: (81) 367478161
Emp.: 1,105
Parking Lot Management Services
N.A.I.C.S.: 812930

Times Service Co., Ltd. (1)
2-20-4 Nishigotanda, Shinagawa-ku, Tokyo, 141-0031, Japan
Tel.: (81) 36 743 8924
Web Site: https://www.timesservice.co.jp
Emp.: 2,313
Parking Lot Management Services
N.A.I.C.S.: 812930

Times Support Co., Ltd. (1)
1-18-9 Gotanda Gotanda NT Building 3F, Shinagawa-nishi, Tokyo, 141-0031, Japan
Tel.: (81) 35 436 1189
Web Site: https://www.timessupport.co.jp
Emp.: 28
Insurance Agency Services
N.A.I.C.S.: 524210

Times24 Co., Ltd. (1)
2-20-4 Nishigotanda, Shinagawa-ku, Tokyo, 141-0031, Japan
Tel.: (81) 36 747 8124
Web Site: https://www.times24.co.jp
Emp.: 712
Parking Lot Management Services
N.A.I.C.S.: 812930

PARKANON LISTATEHDAS OY
Teollisuustie 11, 39700, Parkano, Finland
Tel.: (358) 333938150   FI
Web Site: http://www.parkanonlista.fi
Sales Range: $25-49.9 Million
Emp.: 85
Sawmill Operator
N.A.I.C.S.: 321113
Marjaleena Hussi (Asst Mgr)

PARKD LTD.
Tel.: (61) 894298863   AU
Web Site: http://www.parkdgroup.com
Year Founded: 2016
PKD—(ASX)
Rev.: $2,225,771
Assets: $636,543
Liabilities: $629,316
Net Worth: $7,227
Earnings: ($196,394)
Fiscal Year-end: 06/30/24
Parking Lot Construction Services
N.A.I.C.S.: 236220
Peter McUtchen (CEO)

PARKEN SPORT & ENTERTAINMENT A/S
Per Henrik Lings Alle 2, 2100, Copenhagen, Denmark
Tel.: (45) 35433131
Web Site: https://www.parken.dk
Year Founded: 1991
PARKEN—(CSE)
Rev.: $190,118,794
Assets: $459,751,704
Liabilities: $316,768,676
Net Worth: $142,983,027
Earnings: $27,814,675
Emp.: 734
Fiscal Year-end: 12/31/22
Professional Soccer Club Operator
N.A.I.C.S.: 711211

PARKER AGROCHEM EXPORTS LIMITED
Block H Plot 3 4 New Kandla, Kutch, 370 270, Gujarat, India
Tel.: (91) 2836270530
Web Site: https://www.parkeragrochem.com
524628—(BOM)
Rev.: $522,547
Assets: $582,855
Liabilities: $221,090
Net Worth: $361,765
Earnings: $78,257
Emp.: 18
Fiscal Year-end: 03/31/23
Commodities Trading Services
N.A.I.C.S.: 523160
Bharatkumar R. Thakkar (CFO)

PARKER CORPORATION
2-22-1 Nihonbashi-Ningyocho Chuo-ku, Tokyo, Japan
Tel.: (81) 356440600
Web Site: https://www.parkercorp.co.jp
9845—(TKS)
Rev.: $447,715,130
Assets: $458,700,950
Liabilities: $165,673,040
Net Worth: $293,027,910
Earnings: $23,802,610
Fiscal Year-end: 03/31/24
Industrial Machinery Mfr
N.A.I.C.S.: 333310
Yoshishige Satomi (Pres)

Subsidiaries:

Asahi Rubber Inc. (1)
2-7-2 Dotemachi, Omiya-ku, Saitama, 330-0801, Japan   (91%)
Tel.: (81) 486506051
Web Site: https://www.asahi-rubber.co.jp
Rev.: $67,992,320
Assets: $94,089,600
Liabilities: $48,825,920
Net Worth: $45,263,680
Earnings: $2,303,840
Emp.: 315
Fiscal Year-end: 03/31/2022
Industrial Rubber Product Mfr
N.A.I.C.S.: 326291
Shigeyoshi Yokoyama (Chm)

Subsidiary (US):

ARI INTERNATIONAL CORPORATION (2)
2015 S Arlington Heights Rd Ste 109, Arlington Heights, IL 60005
Tel.: (847) 364-1000
Web Site: https://www.ari-corp.com
Industrial Rubber Whslr
N.A.I.C.S.: 423840

Subsidiary (Domestic):

ASAHI FR R&D Co., Ltd. (2)
2-7-2 Dote-cho, Omiya-ku, Saitama, 330-0801, Japan
Tel.: (81) 486506051
Web Site: https://www.asahi-rubber.co.jp
Industrial Rubber Mfr
N.A.I.C.S.: 326299

Plant (Domestic):

Asahi Rubber Inc. - Fukushima Factory (2)
1 Bozukubo Oaza Izumizaki Izumizakimura, Nishi-Shirakawa-gun, Fukushima, 969-0101, Japan
Tel.: (81) 248533491
Industrial Rubber Mfr
N.A.I.C.S.: 326299

Asahi Rubber Inc. - Shirakawa Factory (2)
1-21 Tsukinoiri Kayane, Shirakawa-shi, Fukushima, 961-0004, Japan
Tel.: (81) 248211401
Industrial Rubber Mfr
N.A.I.C.S.: 326299

PARKER SOFTWARE LTD
Victoria Business Park Prospect Way, Knypersley, Stoke-on-Trent, ST8 7PL, United Kingdom
Tel.: (44) 1782822577
Web Site: http://www.parker-software.com
Year Founded: 2003
Sales Range: $1-9.9 Million
Emp.: 15
Software Publisher
N.A.I.C.S.: 513210
Stephen Parker (Founder & CEO)

Subsidiaries:

Parker Software Inc. (1)
4767 New Broad St Baldwin Park, Orlando, FL 32814
Tel.: (800) 680-7712
Software Publisher
N.A.I.C.S.: 513210

PARKERS CHRYSLER DODGE JEEP
1765 Main Street, Penticton, V2A 5H1, BC, Canada
Tel.: (250) 492-2839
Web Site: http://www.parkerschrysler.com
Year Founded: 1945
New & Used Car Dealers
N.A.I.C.S.: 441110
Janet Parker (Pres)

PARKIT ENTERPRISE INC.
100 Canadian Rd, Toronto, M1R 4Z5, ON, Canada
Tel.: (604) 424-8700   BC
Web Site: https://www.parkitenterprise.com
Year Founded: 2006
1TH—(DEU)
Rev.: $15,656,078
Assets: $245,060,025
Liabilities: $132,406,223
Net Worth: $112,653,802
Earnings: ($3,845,090)
Emp.: 1

PARKLAND CORPORATION

Fiscal Year-end: 12/31/23
Real Estate Investment Services
N.A.I.C.S.: 531390
Joanne Odette (CFO)

Subsidiaries:

FLY Away Airport Parking Services LLC (1)
1671 Murfreesboro Rd, Nashville, TN 37217-2917
Tel.: (615) 367-2200
Web Site: http://www.flyawayparking.com
Parking Lots & Garages
N.A.I.C.S.: 812930
J. R. Fraley (Pres)

Parkit Nashville LLC (1)

PARKLAND CORPORATION
1800 240-4 Ave SW, Calgary, T2P 4H4, AB, Canada
Tel.: (403) 567-2500   AB
Web Site: http://www.parkland.ca
Year Founded: 1969
PF6—(DEU)
Rev.: $23,972,815,247
Assets: $10,243,037,601
Liabilities: $7,893,181,650
Net Worth: $2,349,855,950
Earnings: $347,935,288
Fiscal Year-end: 12/31/23
Fuel Distr
N.A.I.C.S.: 424720
James Pantelidis (Chm)

Subsidiaries:

Elbow River Marketing Ltd. (1)
Suite 1500 335 8 Ave SW, Calgary, T2P 1C9, AB, Canada
Tel.: (403) 232-6868
Web Site: https://www.elbowriver.com
Liquid Petroleum Gas Distribution Services
N.A.I.C.S.: 221210
Craig Clark (Pres)

Neufeld Petroleum & Propane Ltd. (1)
101 14125 99 St, Grande Prairie, T8V 7G2, AB, Canada
Tel.: (780) 814-6111
Web Site: http://www.neufeldonline.com
Fiscal Year-end: 08/31/2006
Petroleum & Propane Products Distr
N.A.I.C.S.: 424690

Parkland (USA) LLC (1)
100 27th St NE, Minot, ND 58703
Tel.: (701) 852-1194
Fuel & Gas Distr
N.A.I.C.S.: 457120
Jay Erickson (Interim Pres & COO)

Subsidiary (Domestic):

Conrad & Bischoff Inc. (2)
2251 N Holmes Ave, Idaho Falls, ID 83401
Tel.: (208) 522-4217
Web Site: https://www.conradbischoff.com
Sales Range: $100-124.9 Million
Emp.: 250
Petroleum Bulk Stations
N.A.I.C.S.: 424710
Jeff Walbom (CFO)

Kellerstrass Enterprises LLC (2)
1500 W 2550 S, Ogden, UT 84401
Tel.: (801) 392-9516
Web Site: http://www.kellerstrassoil.com
Sales Range: $50-74.9 Million
Emp.: 30
Whslr of Petroleum Bulk Stations & Terminals
N.A.I.C.S.: 424710
Rick Reese (VP-Sls)

Ken Bettridge Distributing Inc. (2)
386 N 100 W, Cedar City, UT 84720-2520
Tel.: (435) 586-2411
Web Site: http://www.kboil.net
Emp.: 160
Petroleum Services
N.A.I.C.S.: 424710
Wayne Rowley (Controller)

Missouri Valley Petroleum, Inc. (2)
1722 Mandan Ave, Mandan, ND 58554

PARKLAND CORPORATION

Parkland Corporation—(Continued)
Tel.: (701) 663-5091
Web Site: http://www.mvpinc.net
Petroleum Product Distr
N.A.I.C.S.: 424720

Mort Distributing Inc. (2)
310 E Allard St, Glendive, MT 59330
Tel.: (406) 365-2177
Petroleum & Petroleum Products Merchant Whslr
N.A.I.C.S.: 424720

Rhinehart Oil Co. Inc. (1)
585 ES Rd, American Fork, UT 84003
Tel.: (801) 756-9681
Web Site: http://www.rhinehartoil.com
Sales Range: $25-49.9 Million
Emp.: 40
Engine Fuels & Oils
N.A.I.C.S.: 424720
Dave Jardine *(Controller)*

Branch (Domestic):

Rhinehart Oil Co. Inc. - American Fork (2)
585 E State Rd, American Fork, UT 84003
Tel.: (801) 756-9681
Web Site: https://www.rhinehartoil.com
Gasoline Service Stations & Convenience Stores
N.A.I.C.S.: 457120

Sparling's Propane Co. Ltd. (1)
82948 London Road Highway 4 South, Blyth, N0M 1H0, ON, Canada
Tel.: (519) 523-4256
Web Site: https://www.sparlings.com
Sales Range: $1-9.9 Million
Propane Gas Distribution Services
N.A.I.C.S.: 457210

PARKOMAT INTERNATIONAL LTD.
Golda meir 3, Ness Ziona, Israel
Tel.: (972) 86484849   IL
Web Site: https://www.parkomat.co.il
Year Founded: 2009
PRKM—(TAE)
Rev.: $25,726,205
Assets: $27,254,869
Liabilities: $17,711,838
Net Worth: $9,543,031
Earnings: $2,200,028
Emp.: 60
Fiscal Year-end: 12/31/23
Commercial & Service Industry Machinery Manufacturing
N.A.I.C.S.: 333310

Subsidiaries:

Jupiter EV (1)
Science Park, Ness Ziona, Israel
Tel.: (972) 86484849
Web Site: https://www.jupiter-ev.com
Automotive Parts Mfr & Distr
N.A.I.C.S.: 336390

PARKSIDE FORD LINCOLN LTD.
2000 Main Street, Winnipeg, R2V 2B8, MB, Canada
Tel.: (204) 339-2000
Web Site: http://www.parksideford.net
Year Founded: 1963
Rev.: $45,501,191
Emp.: 80
New & Used Car Dealers
N.A.I.C.S.: 441110

PARKSIDE RESOURCES CORPORATION
141 Adelaide Street West Suite 1220, Toronto, M5H 3L5, ON, Canada
Tel.: (416) 862-1500   BC
Web Site: http://www.parksideresources.com
Year Founded: 2005
Metal Mining
N.A.I.C.S.: 212290
Donald Goldman *(Chm)*

PARKSON HOLDINGS BERHAD
Level 14 Lion Office Tower No 1 Jalan Nagasari, 50200, Kuala Lumpur, Wilayah Persekutuan, Malaysia
Tel.: (60) 321420155
Web Site: http://www.lion.com.my
PARKSON—(KLS)
Rev.: $1,338,653,745
Assets: $2,362,214,498
Liabilities: $1,655,918,303
Net Worth: $706,296,195
Earnings: ($32,157,923)
Emp.: 10
Fiscal Year-end: 12/31/21
Department Stores
N.A.I.C.S.: 455110
Kwee Peng Lim *(Co-Sec)*

Subsidiaries:

Anshan Tianxing Parkson Shopping Centre Co Ltd (1)
No 88 Erdao Street, Tiedong District, Anshan, 114001, Liaoning, China (100%)
Tel.: (86) 4122288888
Web Site: http://www.parksongroup.com.cn
Department Stores Operation Services
N.A.I.C.S.: 455110

Chongqing Wanyou Parkson Plaza Co Ltd (1)
No 77 Daping Changjiang 2 Road, Yuzhong District, Chongqing, 400042, China
Tel.: (86) 2368770296
Department Stores Operation Services
N.A.I.C.S.: 455110

Mianyang Fulin Parkson Plaza Co. Ltd (1)
No 17 Cheong Road, Mianyang, 621000, Sichuan, China
Tel.: (86) 8162241772
Department Stores Operation Services
N.A.I.C.S.: 455110

Nanning Brilliant Parkson Commercial Co Ltd (1)
No 18 Chaoyang Road, Nanning, 530012, Guangxi, China
Tel.: (86) 7712624889
Department Stores Operation Services
N.A.I.C.S.: 455110

Parkson Corporation Sdn Bhd (1)
Level 5 Klang Parade 2112 Jalan Meru, 41050, Klang, Selangor, Malaysia
Tel.: (60) 1300880828
Web Site: https://www.parkson.com.my
Sales Range: $50-74.9 Million
Emp.: 200
Apparel Stores Operation Services
N.A.I.C.S.: 458110

Subsidiary (Non-US):

Parkson Hanoi Co Ltd (2)
198 Taay Son Street, Dong Da District, Hanoi, Vietnam
Tel.: (84) 435378666
Department Stores Operation Services
N.A.I.C.S.: 455110

Parkson Retail Development Co., Ltd. (1)
9th Floor Parkson Plaza No 101 Fuxingmennei Avenue, Beijing, 100031, China
Tel.: (86) 1066536868
Department Store Operations
N.A.I.C.S.: 455110

Xi'an Chang'an Parkson Store Co., Ltd. (1)
No 38 Mid Chang an Road, Xi'an, 710061, Shaanxi, China
Tel.: (86) 2985256609
Web Site: http://www.lion.com.my
Department Stores Operation Services
N.A.I.C.S.: 455110

PARKSON RETAIL ASIA LIMITED
80 Robinson Road 02-00, Singapore, 068898, Singapore
Tel.: (65) 62363333

Web Site: https://www.parkson.com.sg
Year Founded: 1987
O9E—(SES)
Rev.: $164,197,110
Assets: $218,679,511
Liabilities: $210,791,404
Net Worth: $7,888,107
Earnings: $21,911,078
Emp.: 2,241
Fiscal Year-end: 12/31/23
Consumer Goods Distr
N.A.I.C.S.: 455110
Heng Jem Cheng *(Chm)*

Subsidiaries:

PT. Tozy Sentosa (1)
Parkson Office Building 7th-8th floor CBD Bintaro Jaya Sektor VII, Jln Boulevard Bintaro Jaya Blok B7 /D05, Tangerang, 15524, Banten, Indonesia
Tel.: (62) 2180828100
Web Site: http://www.centro.co.id
Departmental Store Operator
N.A.I.C.S.: 455110

PARKSON RETAIL GROUP LIMITED
5th Floor Metro Plaza No 555 Loushanguan Road, Changning District, Shanghai, 200051, China
Tel.: (86) 2162298001
Web Site: http://www.parksongroup.com.cn
3368—(OTCIQ)
Department Stores
N.A.I.C.S.: 455110
Heng Jem Cheng *(Chm)*

Subsidiaries:

Guizhou Zunyi Parkson Retail Development Co., Ltd. (1)
Zone B Laocheng Xinjie Minzhu Road, Honghuagang, Zunyi, 563000, Guizhou, China
Tel.: (86) 85128253366
Shopping Mall & Supermarket Retailer
N.A.I.C.S.: 455110

Parkson Credit Sdn. Bhd. (1)
Level 5 Lion Office Tower No 1 Jalan Nagasari, 50200, Kuala Lumpur, Malaysia
Tel.: (60) 321422999
Web Site: https://www.parksoncredit.com.my
Credit Financial Services
N.A.I.C.S.: 522299
Utama William Cheng *(Chm)*

PARKSVILLE CHRYSLER LTD.
230 Shelly Road, Parksville, V9P 1V6, BC, Canada
Tel.: (250) 248-3281
Web Site: http://www.parksvillechrysler.com
Rev.: $21,415,914
Emp.: 40
New & Used Car Dealers
N.A.I.C.S.: 441110
Bruce Alexander *(Owner)*

PARKWAY CHRYSLER DODGE JEEP RAM
2260 Battleford Road, Mississauga, L5N 3K6, ON, Canada
Tel.: (905) 567-1700
Web Site: http://www.parkwaychrysler.com
Rev.: $23,408,000
Emp.: 50
New & Used Car Dealers
N.A.I.C.S.: 441110
Alex Cochrane *(Mgr-Used Car Sls)*

PARKWAY CORPORATE LIMITED
Warehouse 5 45 Bunnett Street, Sunshine, 3020, VIC, Australia
Tel.: (61) 390693200
Web Site: https://pwnps.com

INTERNATIONAL PUBLIC

Year Founded: 2010
4IP—(DEU)
Rev.: $28,464,365
Assets: $9,710,035
Liabilities: $2,283,727
Net Worth: $7,426,309
Earnings: ($1,786,905)
Fiscal Year-end: 06/30/22
Potash Mining Services
N.A.I.C.S.: 212390
Amanda Wilton-Heald *(Sec)*

PARKWAY LIFE REAL ESTATE INVESTMENT TRUST
9 Raffles Place 26-01 Republic Plaza, Singapore, 048619, Singapore
Tel.: (65) 62364333   SG
Web Site: https://plifereit.com
Year Founded: 2007
C2PU—(SES)
Rev.: $111,692,040
Assets: $1,767,881,541
Liabilities: $696,490,949
Net Worth: $1,071,390,592
Earnings: $76,092,555
Emp.: 23
Fiscal Year-end: 12/31/23
Trust Management Services
N.A.I.C.S.: 523940
Loo Hock Leong *(CFO)*

PARKWOOD HOLDINGS BERHAD
Unit 8-02 Level 8 Menara LGB No 1 Jalan Wan Kadir, Taman Tun Dr Ismail, 60000, Kuala Lumpur, Malaysia
Tel.: (60) 377106288   MY
Web Site: https://parkwood.my
Year Founded: 1969
PARKWD—(KLS)
Rev.: $3,897,375
Assets: $39,418,772
Liabilities: $7,012,124
Net Worth: $32,406,648
Earnings: $496,735
Fiscal Year-end: 12/31/22
Steel Product Mfr & Distr
N.A.I.C.S.: 332999
Ghazali Mat Ariff *(Chm)*

Subsidiaries:

Parkwood Developments Sdn. Bhd. (1)
No 28 Ground Floor Jalan Wan Kadir 1, Taman Tun Dr Ismail, 60000, Kuala Lumpur, Malaysia
Tel.: (60) 377106288
Web Site: http://www.parkwood.my
Steel Product Mfr & Whslr
N.A.I.C.S.: 331513
Noor Faridah Mohd Noor *(Mgr-HR & Admin)*

PARKWOOD HOLDINGS LIMITED
Parkwood House Berkeley Drive, Bamber Bridge, Preston, PR5 6BY, Lancs, United Kingdom
Tel.: (44) 1772627111   UK
Web Site: http://www.parkwood-holdings.co.uk
Year Founded: 1992
Sales Range: $200-249.9 Million
Emp.: 6,000
Holding Company
N.A.I.C.S.: 551112
Tony Hewitt *(Chm)*

Subsidiaries:

Civic Trees (Tree Movers) Limited (1)
Forestry House, PO Box 23, HP234AE, Tring, Hertfordshire, United Kingdom
Tel.: (44) 1442825401
Web Site: http://www.civictrees.co.uk
Sales Range: $10-24.9 Million
Emp.: 30
Nursery & Tree Production
N.A.I.C.S.: 111421

AND PRIVATE COMPANIES

Coblands Nurseries Limited (1)
Trench Road, Kent, Tonbridge, TN11 PNG, United Kingdom
Tel.: (44) 1732770999
Web Site: http://www.coblandsnurseries.co.uk
Sales Range: $10-24.9 Million
Emp.: 30
Soil Preparation Planting & Cultivating
N.A.I.C.S.: 115112
Gerald Bonner *(Gen Mgr)*

Glendale Countryside Limited (1)
Coach House Duxbury Hall Road Duxbury Park, Chorley, PR7 4AT, Lancashire, United Kingdom
Tel.: (44) 8458386619
Web Site: http://www.glendale-services.co.uk
Environmental Consulting Services
N.A.I.C.S.: 541620

Glendale Golf Limited (1)
Princes Close Gardens Off Stratford Road, Longbridge, Warwick, CV34 6RA, United Kingdom
Tel.: (44) 1159 235473
Web Site: http://www.glendale-golf.com
Golf Course Management Services
N.A.I.C.S.: 713910

Glendale Managed Services Limited (1)
Parkwood House Berkeley Drive Bamber Bridge, Preston, PR5 6BY, Lancashire, United Kingdom
Tel.: (44) 1772 627111
Web Site: http://www.parkwood-holdings.co.uk
Emp.: 30
Golf Course Management Services
N.A.I.C.S.: 713910

Glendale Recycling Limited (1)
Coach House Duxbury Hall Road Duxbury Park, Chorley, PR7 4AT, Lancashire, United Kingdom
Tel.: (44) 1257 460461
Web Site: http://www.glendale-services.co.uk
Emp.: 30
Waste Recycling Services
N.A.I.C.S.: 562998

Parkwood Community Leisure Limited (1)
Little Bowbrook Walton Road Hartlebury, Kidderminster, DY10 4JA, Worcs, United Kingdom
Tel.: (44) 1299 253400
Sales Range: $25-49.9 Million
Emp.: 50
Leisure Management Services
N.A.I.C.S.: 541618

Parkwood Consultancy Services (PCS) (1)
Avenue J Stoneleigh Park, Kenilworth, CV8 2LG, Warks, United Kingdom
Tel.: (44) 1789450085
Web Site: http://www.parkwoodconsultancy.co.uk
Sales Range: $25-49.9 Million
Emp.: 25
Management Consulting Services
N.A.I.C.S.: 541618
Simon Witney *(Mng Dir)*

Parkwood Group Trustees Limited (1)
Parkwood House Berkeley Drive Bamber Bridge, Preston, PR5 6BY, United Kingdom
Tel.: (44) 1772627111
Web Site: http://www.parkwood-holdings.co.uk
Sales Range: $10-24.9 Million
Emp.: 30
Business Support Services
N.A.I.C.S.: 561499

Parkwood Health & Fitness Limited (1)
Darkes Lane, Potters Bar, EN61AA, United Kingdom **(100%)**
Tel.: (44) 1707660777
Web Site: http://www.parkwoodhealthandfitness.uk
Sales Range: $10-24.9 Million
Emp.: 30
Ambulatory Health Care Services
N.A.I.C.S.: 621999

Parkwood Healthcare Limited (1)
No 15 Market Square Ste 4, Bishop's Stortford, CM233UT, United Kingdom
Tel.: (44) 1279505400
Web Site: http://www.parkwoodnurses.co.uk
Sales Range: $10-24.9 Million
Emp.: 3
Ambulatory Health Care Services
N.A.I.C.S.: 621999
Anthony Hewitt *(Mng Dir)*

Parkwood Leisure Limited (1)
Attwood House Perdiswell Park John Comyn Drive, Worcester, WR3 7NS, United Kingdom
Tel.: (44) 1299253400
Web Site: http://www.leisurecentre.com
Sales Range: $25-49.9 Million
Emp.: 30
Amusement & Recreation Industries
N.A.I.C.S.: 713990
Andrew Holt *(Mng Dir)*

Parkwood Project Management Limited (1)
Atherstone Barn Alscot Estate, Atherstone on Stour, Stratford-upon-Avon, CV37 8NE, Warks, United Kingdom
Tel.: (44) 1789450085
Web Site: http://www.parkwoodconsultancy.co.uk
Sales Range: $25-49.9 Million
Emp.: 20
Project Management Services
N.A.I.C.S.: 541618
Jacalyn Evans *(Mng Dir)*

PARLE INDUSTRIES LTD.
Unit No C/406 4th Floor Crystal Plaza Premises Co Op Soc Ltd, New Link Road Andheri West, Mumbai, 400 053, India
Tel.: (91) 2228769986
Web Site: https://www.parleindustries.com
Year Founded: 1983
532911—(BOM)
Rev.: $96,049
Assets: $2,538,229
Liabilities: $96,528
Net Worth: $2,441,701
Earnings: $4,688
Emp.: 8
Fiscal Year-end: 03/31/23
Software Development Services
N.A.I.C.S.: 541511
Rakeshkumar Dinesh Mishra *(Exec Dir)*

Subsidiaries:

Sun Beam Infotech Ltd. (1)
Sunbeam IT Park Second Floor Phase 2, Rajiv Gandhi Infotech Park, Pune, 411057, Maharashtra, India
Tel.: (91) 8282829806
Web Site: https://www.sunbeaminfo.in
Software Training Institute Services
N.A.I.C.S.: 611420

PARLEM TELECOM CO DE TELECOMUNICACIONS SA
Av/ Diagonal 452 Planta 4, 08018, Barcelona, Spain
Tel.: (34) 900730850
Web Site: https://www.parlem.com
Year Founded: 2014
PAR—(BAR)
Telecommunication Servicesb
N.A.I.C.S.: 517810
Ernest Perez-Mas *(Pres)*

PARLO BERHAD
Wisma Parlo No 72 Jalan Kampong Attap, 50460, Kuala Lumpur, Wilayah Persekutuan, Malaysia
Tel.: (60) 327266055 MY
Web Site: https://www.parlogroup.com
PARLO—(KLS)
Rev.: $26,153,866

Assets: $9,441,866
Liabilities: $3,140,565
Net Worth: $6,301,302
Earnings: ($1,936,153)
Emp.: 58
Fiscal Year-end: 06/30/22
Telecommunication Solution Services
N.A.I.C.S.: 517111

Subsidiaries:

V Care Industries (Malaysia) Sdn. Bhd. (1)
No 72 Jalan Kampong Attap, 50460, Kuala Lumpur, Malaysia
Tel.: (60) 380602262
Web Site: https://vcaremalaysia.com
Medical Equipment Mfr & Distr
N.A.I.C.S.: 339112

PARMAX PHARMA LIMITED
Plot No 20 Survey Rajkot-Gondal National Highway Hadamtala No 27, Tal Kotda Sangani, Rajkot, 360311, Gujarat, India
Tel.: (91) 2827270534
Web Site: https://www.parmaxpharma.com
Year Founded: 1994
540359—(BOM)
Rev.: $1,854,093
Assets: $2,111,700
Liabilities: $1,409,600
Net Worth: $702,100
Earnings: ($12,477)
Emp.: 94
Fiscal Year-end: 03/31/23
Pharmaceutical Preparation Mfr & Distr
N.A.I.C.S.: 325412
Alkesh M. Gopani *(Mng Dir)*

PARMESHWARI SILK MILLS LIMITED
Village Bajra Rahon Road, Ludhiana, 141 007, Punjab, India
Tel.: (91) 1612691873
Web Site: https://www.parmeshwarisilk.com
Year Founded: 1993
540467—(BOM)
Rev.: $13,819,714
Assets: $18,011,561
Liabilities: $13,998,051
Net Worth: $4,013,509
Earnings: $232,298
Emp.: 525
Fiscal Year-end: 03/31/21
Textile Product Mfr & Distr
N.A.I.C.S.: 313240

PARNASSOS ENTERPRISES S.A.
Politia Business Center 109-111 Mesogion Avenue Building G1, Ambelokipi, 115 26, Athens, Greece
Tel.: (30) 210 6971 200
Web Site: http://www.parnassos-sa.gr
Year Founded: 1934
Sales Range: $1-9.9 Million
Emp.: 12
Investment Management Service
N.A.I.C.S.: 523940

PARNAV SPORTS ACADEMY LIMITED
266 A 2F Elegance Jasola District Centre Old Mathura Road, New Delhi, 110 025, India
Tel.: (91) 1132319296 In
Web Site: http://www.parnavsports.com
Sports Management & Training Services
N.A.I.C.S.: 611620
Garima Baghla *(Officer-Compliance & Sec)*

PARQUEST CAPITAL SAS

PARNAX LAB LTD.
104-107 Bldg No 8 Jogani Industrial Estate, Chunabhatti Sion, Mumbai, 400 022, India
Tel.: (91) 2268252525
Web Site: https://www.naxparlab.com
Year Founded: 1985
506128—(BOM)
Rev.: $20,188,133
Assets: $17,393,790
Liabilities: $9,928,916
Net Worth: $7,464,875
Earnings: $1,035,075
Emp.: 8
Fiscal Year-end: 03/31/23
Pharmaceuticals Product Mfr
N.A.I.C.S.: 325412
Prakash M. Shah *(Chm & CEO)*

Subsidiaries:

Naxpar Pharma Private Limited (1)
104-107 Bldg No 8 Jogani Industrial Estate, Chunabhatti Sion, Mumbai, 400 022, India
Tel.: (91) 2268252525
Pharmaceuticals Product Mfr
N.A.I.C.S.: 325412

PARNELL PHARMACEUTICALS HOLDINGS LTD.
Unit 4 Century Estate 476 Gardeners Road, Alexandria, 2063, NSW, Australia
Tel.: (61) 296674411 AU
Web Site: https://www.parnell.com
PARNF—(OTCIQ)
Sales Range: $10-24.9 Million
Emp.: 84
Animal Health Pharmaceutical Mfr
N.A.I.C.S.: 325412
Brad McCarthy *(CEO)*

PARPRO CORPORATION
67-1 Dongyuan Road Chungli Industrial Zone, Taoyuan, 32063, Taiwan
Tel.: (886) 34525535
Web Site: https://www.parpro.com
4916—(TAI)
Rev.: $111,657,375
Assets: $118,875,727
Liabilities: $53,369,173
Net Worth: $65,506,554
Earnings: $2,626,639
Emp.: 455
Fiscal Year-end: 12/31/23
Electric Equipment Mfr
N.A.I.C.S.: 335999
Win-Jia Liao *(Chm)*

Subsidiaries:

Parpro (Nevada), Inc. (1)
194 Gallagher Crest Rd, Henderson, NV 89074
Tel.: (702) 331-2700
Sheet Metal Mfr
N.A.I.C.S.: 332322

PARQUE ARAUCO S.A.
Cerro Colorado 5240 Torre del Parque 1 Piso 15, Las Condes, Santiago, Chile
Tel.: (56) 222990510
Web Site: https://www.parauco.com
Year Founded: 1979
PARAUCO—(SGO)
Rev.: $300,013,311
Assets: $3,953,416,060
Liabilities: $2,102,161,801
Net Worth: $1,851,254,259
Earnings: $146,554,434
Emp.: 571
Fiscal Year-end: 12/31/23
Non Residential Building Operator
N.A.I.C.S.: 531120
Andres Torrealba Ruiz-Tagle *(CEO-Chile Div)*

PARQUEST CAPITAL SAS

PARQUEST CAPITAL SAS

Parquest Capital SAS—(Continued)
19 avenue de Opera, Paris, 75001, France
Tel.: (33) 1 70 08 60 90
Web Site: http://www.parquest.fr
Year Founded: 2002
Private Investment Firm
N.A.I.C.S.: 523999
Denis Le Chevallier *(Assoc Dir)*

Subsidiaries:

Acces Industrie SA (1)
Rue Albert Einstein, 47400, Tonneins, France
Tel.: (33) 5 53 88 27 98
Web Site: http://www.acces-industrie.com
Aerial Work Platforms & Telescopic Handlers Rental & Leasing Services
N.A.I.C.S.: 532412
Pascal Meynard *(Dir Gen)*

PARROT S.A.
174 quai de Jemmapes, 75010, Paris, France
Tel.: (33) 148036060
Web Site: https://www.parrot.com
Year Founded: 1994
PAOTF—(OTCEM)
Rev.: $69,508,599
Assets: $176,495,040
Liabilities: $55,537,698
Net Worth: $120,957,342
Earnings: ($46,657,055)
Emp.: 516
Fiscal Year-end: 12/31/20
Wireless Mobile Phone Accessories Mfr
N.A.I.C.S.: 334290
Henri Seydoux *(Chm & CEO)*

Subsidiaries:

Parrot Asia Pacific Ltd. (1)
Suite 708 9 7 F Wharf T and T Centre 7 Canton Road, Tsim Sha Tsui, Kowloon, China (Hong Kong)
Tel.: (852) 22479988
Wireless Electronic Product Mfr
N.A.I.C.S.: 334419
Anthony Yip *(Reg Sls Mgr)*

Parrot Drones S.A.S. (1)
174 quai de Jemmapes, 75010, Paris, France
Tel.: (33) 148036069
Wireless Drone Mfr
N.A.I.C.S.: 336411

Pix4D SA (1)
Route de Renens 24, 1008, Prilly, Switzerland
Tel.: (41) 215520590
Web Site: http://www.pix4d.com
Software Development Services
N.A.I.C.S.: 541511
Christoph Strecha *(Founder & CEO)*

Subsidiary (Non-US):

Pix4D Espagne SL (2)
Paseo de la Castellana 77, 28046, Madrid, Spain
Tel.: (34) 644824725
Software Development Services
N.A.I.C.S.: 541511

Pix4D GmbH (2)
Alte Jakobstrasse 85 86, 10179, Berlin, Germany
Tel.: (49) 30403666270
Software Development Services
N.A.I.C.S.: 541511

Subsidiary (US):

Pix4D Inc. (2)
201 Mission St Ste 560, San Francisco, CA 94105
Tel.: (415) 766-0503
Software Development Services
N.A.I.C.S.: 541511
Holden Greene *(Engr-Technical Support)*

PARS ANIMAL FEED COMPANY
No 29-Tohid St-Next To Tejarat Bank, PO Box 13145-633, Tehran, Iran
Tel.: (98) 21 66420017
Year Founded: 1966
Emp.: 110
Animal Feed Mfr
N.A.I.C.S.: 311119

PARS CARTON COMPANY
No 513 Next To The Shadmehr Azadi Avenue, Tehran, 14199, Iran
Tel.: (98) 21 66005590
Web Site: http://www.parscarton.com
Paper Products Mfr
N.A.I.C.S.: 322299
Namdari Masoud *(Mng Dir)*

PARS DAROU COMPANY
No 13 East 144 Ave 1st Sq Tehranpars, PO Box 11365-4688, 16547 13691, Tehran, Iran
Tel.: (98) 21 77704061
Web Site: http://www.parsdarou.ir
PDRO—(THE)
Sales Range: Less than $1 Million
Pharmaceuticals Product Mfr
N.A.I.C.S.: 325412

PARS ELECTRIC MANUFACTURING COMPANY PJSC
11th Km of Karaj Special Road, Tehran, 13145 1386, Iran
Tel.: (98) 21 4905113
Web Site: http://www.parselectric.ir
Year Founded: 1963
Electronic Products Mfr
N.A.I.C.S.: 334310

PARS KHAZAR INDUSTRIAL COMPANY
No 45 Gharani St, PO Box 15815-3383, Tehran, Iran
Tel.: (98) 21 88307426
Web Site: http://www.parskhazar.com
Year Founded: 1969
KHAZ—(THE)
Sales Range: Less than $1 Million
Electrical Appliance Mfr
N.A.I.C.S.: 335210

PARS OIL & GAS COMPANY
No 1 Parvin Etesami Ave Fatemi St, P.O.Box 1414713111, Tehran, Iran
Tel.: (98) 21 88966031
Web Site: http://www.pogc.ir
Year Founded: 1998
NPRS—(THE)
Sales Range: Less than $1 Million
Oil & Gas Operations
N.A.I.C.S.: 213112
Mohammad Meshkin Fam *(Chm & Mng Dir)*

PARS PAMCHAL CHEMICAL COMPANY
10 Pajoheshgah Dovvom Alley Bokharest Av Beheshti Av, PO Box 15875-7451, Tehran, Iran
Tel.: (98) 21 88731030
Web Site: http://www.parspamchal.com
Year Founded: 1970
Paints Mfr
N.A.I.C.S.: 325510
Hossein Maghzi *(Chm)*

PARS PUMP MANUFACTURING CO.
No 222 Next To The Navab And Eskandari Azadi Avenue, Tehran, 15815-1185, Iran
Tel.: (98) 21 66921082
Web Site: http://www.parspump.com
Turbine Pump Mfr
N.A.I.C.S.: 333611
A. Mozaffari Fard *(Mng Dir)*

PARS REFRACTORIES CO
3 4th Floor No31 2nd Saei Alley Vali-Asr Ave, Tehran, 19679-16961, Iran
Tel.: (98) 2188651320
Web Site: http://www.pars-ref.ir
Refractory Products Mfr
N.A.I.C.S.: 327120

PARS SHAHAB LAMP COMPANY
No 45 And 47-Sepahbod Gharani Ave, Po Box 15815-1445, Tehran, 15816 53134, Iran
Tel.: (98) 2188307425
Web Site: http://www.parsshahab.com
Year Founded: 1968
LAPS1—(THE)
Sales Range: Less than $1 Million
Emp.: 673
Electric Lighting Equipment Mfr
N.A.I.C.S.: 335132

PARS SWITCH COMPANY
7th Yavaran Street Eshragh Industrial Zone, Zanjan, Iran
Tel.: (98) 32221954
Web Site: http://www.parsswitch.com
Year Founded: 1976
SWIC—(THE)
Sales Range: Less than $1 Million
Emp.: 491
Circuit Breaker Mfr
N.A.I.C.S.: 335313

Subsidiaries:

Zangan Pars Co. (1)
7 Yavaran St, Ishraq Industrial Town, Zanjan, Iran
Tel.: (98) 2432221954
Web Site: http://www.zanganpars.com
Emp.: 50
Electrical Panel Mfr
N.A.I.C.S.: 335313

PARS TILE COMPANY
Seyed Khandan East Simorgh St Arsabaran St No19, Tehran, Iran
Tel.: (98) 302223429
Web Site: https://parstile.ir
Year Founded: 1973
KPRS1—(THE)
Sales Range: Less than $1 Million
Tiles Mfr
N.A.I.C.S.: 327120

PARS TOUSHEH INVESTMENT COMPANY
No 32 No 6 Mousavi Street, Tehran, Iran
Tel.: (98) 2188837997
Web Site: https://www.parstousheh.com
Year Founded: 1979
Emp.: 4,000
Electrical Appliance Mfr
N.A.I.C.S.: 335210
Hossein Mahrou *(Chm)*

Subsidiaries:

Khazar Plastic Production & Industrial Company (1)
4th Floor No 2 Sharif Alley Sepahbod Gharani St, Tehran, Iran
Tel.: (98) 2188839839
Web Site: http://www.khazarplastic.com
Plastics Product Mfr
N.A.I.C.S.: 326199
Mahmoud Koucheki *(Mng Dir)*

Khazar Sintech Electro-motor Manufacturing Company (1)
Nogreh deh Industrial Town, Astaneh, Tehran, Guilan, Iran
Tel.: (98) 134285482
Web Site: http://www.pknmotor.com
Electromotor Mfr
N.A.I.C.S.: 336320
Sam Mehran *(Sls Mgr)*

Nur Tousheh International Company (1)
11 Km of Karaj Special Road-Pars Shaid Complex-Pars Khazar Building, 1389835316, Tehran, Iran
Tel.: (98) 44904617009821
Web Site: http://www.nurtousheh.com
Home Appliance Mfr
N.A.I.C.S.: 335220

Pars Khazar Distribution Company (1)
Ground Floor Pars Sheed Building Kilometre-11 of Karaj Special Road, 1389913656, Tehran, Iran
Tel.: (98) 44905405
Home Appliance Distr
N.A.I.C.S.: 423620

Pars Khazar Noghreh Company (1)
Noghreh Deh Industrial Township, Kiashahr Astaneh-ye Ashrafiyeh, 4443178734, Tehran, Guilan, Iran
Tel.: (98) 42850482
Home Appliance Distr
N.A.I.C.S.: 423620

Pars Shahab Noghreh Company (1)
Opposite to Yas No 6 St Off Kaj Sq Kilometre-12, Noghredeh Industrial Township Bandar Kiashahr Astaneashrafieh, 4443178458, Tehran, Guilan, Iran
Tel.: (98) 42850540
Home Appliance Distr
N.A.I.C.S.: 423620

Pars Zarasa Home Appliances Design & Industrial Company (1)
Building 43 Sepahbod Gharani St, Tehran, Iran
Tel.: (98) 2188312866
Home Appliance Mfr
N.A.I.C.S.: 335220

Pras Khazar Company (1)
No 43 Sepahbod Gharani St, Mail Box 15815-3383, Tehran, Iran
Tel.: (98) 2188307426
Electrical Home Appliance Mfr
N.A.I.C.S.: 335210

Shahab Shisheh Industrial Company (1)
Mirza Kouchak Khan St Shahid Beheshti Ave, Rasht Industrial Township, 4337187774, Tehran, Iran
Tel.: (98) 33882307
Emp.: 73
Glass Products Mfr
N.A.I.C.S.: 327215

Shahab Tousheh Company (1)
Motahari St after Deputy Mayor No 318 Third Floor, Tehran, Iran
Tel.: (98) 2188835637
Web Site: http://www.shahabtousheh.com
Electronic Products Mfr
N.A.I.C.S.: 334111

PARSAN MAKINA PARCALARI SANAYII AS
Levent Mahallesi Tekirler Sokak No 10 Besiktas, Istanbul, Turkiye
Tel.: (90) 2123242041
Web Site: http://www.parsan.com
Year Founded: 1968
PARSN—(IST)
Rev.: $76,153,821
Assets: $225,539,244
Liabilities: $99,447,431
Net Worth: $126,091,812
Earnings: $22,499,924
Fiscal Year-end: 12/31/22
Automotive Components Mfr
N.A.I.C.S.: 336390
Tevfik Yamanturk *(Chm)*

Subsidiaries:

Belen Elektrik Uretim A.S. (1)
Ankara Street No 222, Karaoglan Golbasi, 06830, Ankara, Turkiye
Tel.: (90) 3124840570
Web Site: http://www.belenelektrik.com.tr
Electric Power Distribution Services
N.A.I.C.S.: 221122

AND PRIVATE COMPANIES

Bordo Elk. Enerjisi Toptan Satis A.S. (1)
Ankara Caddesi No 222 Gaziosmanpasa Mahallesi, Golbasi, 06830, Ankara, Turkiye
Tel.: (90) 3124856420
Web Site: https://www.bordoenerji.com
Financial Services
N.A.I.C.S.: 523999

Bordo Enerji A.S. (1)
No 222 Mahallesi, Karaoglan Golbasi, 06830, Ankara, Turkiye
Tel.: (90) 3124856420
Web Site: http://www.bordoenerji.com.tr
Electric Power Distribution Services
N.A.I.C.S.: 221122

Celik Holding A.S. (1)
Tugay Yolu Cad Cevizli Mah No 8, Maltepe, Istanbul, Turkiye
Tel.: (90) 2163050557
Web Site: https://www.celik-holding.com
Construction Services
N.A.I.C.S.: 541330

Subsidiary (Domestic):

Doktas Dokumculuk Ticaret ve Sanayi A.S (2)
Golyolu No 26 PK 18, Bursa, 16801, Orhangazi, Turkiye (90.01%)
Tel.: (90) 2245734263
Rev.: $326,334,220
Assets: $392,867,304
Liabilities: $241,608,632
Net Worth: $151,258,672
Earnings: $16,021,226
Emp.: 3,127
Fiscal Year-end: 12/31/2023
Iron Castings, Aluminium Castings & Light Alloy Wheel Mfr
N.A.I.C.S.: 331523
Tevfik Yamanturk *(Chm)*

Subsidiary (Non-US):

Componenta UK Ltd. (3)
3&4 The Mews Trent Park Eastern Avenue, Lichfield, WS13 6RN, Staffs, United Kingdom
Tel.: (44) 1543495555
Motor Vehicle Parts & Accessories Whslr
N.A.I.C.S.: 423120
Duncan John Ward *(Fin Dir)*

Subsidiary (Domestic):

Guris Holding A.S. (2)
Ankara Cad No 222 Gaziosmanpasa Mah, Golbasi, 06830, Ankara, Turkiye
Tel.: (90) 3124381150
Web Site: https://www.gurisholding.com.tr
Construction Services
N.A.I.C.S.: 236210

Guris Holding Co. Inc. (2)
Piyade Sokak No 19, Cankaya, 06550, Ankara, Turkiye
Tel.: (90) 3124381150
Web Site: http://www.gurisholding.com.tr
Construction Services
N.A.I.C.S.: 541330
Musfik Hamdi Yamanturk *(Chm & Gen Mgr)*

Derne Temiz Enerji Uretim A.S. (1)
Ankara Street No 222, Karaoglan Golbasi, 06830, Ankara, Turkiye
Tel.: (90) 3124840570
Web Site: http://www.derneenerji.com
Electric Power Distribution Services
N.A.I.C.S.: 221122

EOLOS Ruzgar Enerjisi Uretim A.S. (1)
Tel.: (90) 3124840570
Web Site: http://www.eolos.com.tr
Electric Power Distribution Services
N.A.I.C.S.: 221122

Gimak Enerji Uretim Ltd. (1)
Ankara Caddesi No 222 Gaziosmanpasa Mahallesi, Golbasi, 06830, Ankara, Turkiye
Tel.: (90) 3124840570
Power Generation Services
N.A.I.C.S.: 221114

Gurenerji Elektrik Uretim Ltd. Sti. (1)
Ankara Street No 222, Karaoglan Gazi District Golbasi, 06830, Ankara, Turkiye
Tel.: (90) 3124840570
Electric Power Generation Services

N.A.I.C.S.: 221118

Guris Is Makinalari Endustri A.S (1)
Cevizli Tugay Yolu No 8, Maltepe, Istanbul, Turkiye
Tel.: (90) 2163050557
Web Site: https://www.gurisendustri.com
Construction Machinery Distr
N.A.I.C.S.: 423810
Tevfik Yamanturk *(Deputy Chm)*

Kuzey Kibris Santral Madencilik Ltd. (1)
78 Girne Caddesi Ali Taner Fikri Ishani, Lefkosa, Turkiye
Tel.: (90) 3922272341
Automation Machinery Parts Mfr & Distr
N.A.I.C.S.: 333248

Mirage Park Otelcilik A.S. (1)
Goynuk Mahallesi Ahu-Unal Aysal Caddesi No 29, Kemer, 07994, Antalya, Turkiye
Tel.: (90) 2428152244
Web Site: https://www.mirageparkresort.com.tr
Resort Management Services
N.A.I.C.S.: 721110

Mogan Enerji Yatirim Holding A.S. (1)
Ankara Caddesi No 222, Gaziosmanpasa Mahallesi, Golbasi, 06830, Ankara, Turkiye
Tel.: (90) 3124840570
Web Site: https://www.mogan.com.tr
Electric Power Distribution Services
N.A.I.C.S.: 221122
Tarik Aygun *(Deputy Chm)*

Mogan Tarim A.S. (1)
Ankara Cad No 222 Gaziosmanpasa Mahallesi, Golbasi, 06830, Ankara, Turkiye
Tel.: (90) 3124841526
Web Site: https://www.mogantarim.com
Automation Machinery Parts Mfr & Distr
N.A.I.C.S.: 333248

OMTAS A.S. (1)
C Istasyon Mah 1496/1 Sok No 1, 41400, Gebze, Kocaeli, Turkiye
Tel.: (90) 2626555544
Web Site: http://www.omtas.com.tr
Industrial Machinery Mfr
N.A.I.C.S.: 333248

Omtas Otomotiv Sanayi Ve Ticaret A.S. (1)
Istasyon Mah 1496/1 Sok No 1, Gebze, 41400, Kocaeli, Turkiye
Tel.: (90) 2626555544
Web Site: https://www.omtas.com.tr
Industrial Equipment Whsr
N.A.I.C.S.: 423830

Ovid Wind LLC (1)
Levazim Mahallesi Koru Sokak Zorlu Center Apt No 2/445, Besiktas, Istanbul, Turkiye
Tel.: (90) 2124011900
Web Site: https://www.ovidistanbul.com
Stainless Steel Product Mfr & Distr
N.A.I.C.S.: 332996

Pokut Elektrik Uretim A.S. (1)
Ankara Street No 222, Golbasi, 06830, Ankara, Turkiye
Tel.: (90) 3124840570
Web Site: http://www.pokutelektrik.com
Electric Power Distribution Services
N.A.I.C.S.: 221122

PARSEQ PLC
Lowton Way, Hellaby, S66 8RY, United Kingdom
Tel.: (44) 1709 448000 UK
Web Site: http://www.parseq.com
Sales Range: $25-49.9 Million
Emp.: 50
Holding Company; Business Process Outsourcing Services
N.A.I.C.S.: 551112
Tony Strong *(CEO)*

Subsidiaries:

Intelligent Environments Europe Limited (1)
20 Old Bridge St, Kingston upon Thames, KT1 4BU, Surrey, United Kingdom
Tel.: (44) 2086149903
Web Site: http://www.ie.com

Sales Range: $25-49.9 Million
Emp.: 80
Financial Software Development Services
N.A.I.C.S.: 513210

Parseq Limited (1)
Lowton Way, Hellaby, Hellaby, Rotherham, S66 8RY, United Kingdom
Tel.: (44) 1709 448000
Web Site: http://www.parseq.com
Sales Range: $10-24.9 Million
Emp.: 2,500
Business Process Outsourcing Financial & Administrative Services
N.A.I.C.S.: 561499
Graham Stein *(Mng Dir)*

PARSHVA ENTERPRISES LIMITED
A-811/812 8th Floor Jaswanti Allied Business Centre, Ramchandra Extention Road Kanchpada Malad West, Mumbai, 400064, India
Tel.: (91) 2249729700
Web Site: https://www.parshvaenterprises.com
Year Founded: 2017
542694—(BOM)
Rev.: $2,193,550
Assets: $1,391,451
Liabilities: $132,966
Net Worth: $1,258,486
Earnings: $25,706
Emp.: 8
Fiscal Year-end: 03/31/23
Plastic Machine Mfr
N.A.I.C.S.: 333248
Dhaval Siriya *(CFO)*

PARSHWANATH CORPORATION LIMITED
50 Third Floor Harsiddha Chambers Income Tax Cross Roads Ashram Road, Ahmedabad, 380014, Gujarat, India
Tel.: (91) 7927540848
Web Site: https://www.parshwanath.co.in
Year Founded: 1967
511176—(BOM)
Rev.: $123,746
Assets: $1,384,857
Liabilities: $59,217
Net Worth: $1,325,640
Earnings: $34,650
Emp.: 4
Fiscal Year-end: 03/31/23
Residential Building Construction Services
N.A.I.C.S.: 236115
Rushabhbhai Navnitbhai Patel *(Chm & Co-Mng Dir)*

PARSIAN BANK
Shahrek Quds West Shahid Farhzadi Blvd Zarafshan St No 4, 1467793811, Tehran, Iran
Tel.: (98) 2181151000
Web Site: https://www.parsian-bank.ir
Year Founded: 2001
BPAR1—(THE)
Sales Range: Less than $1 Million
Banking Operations, Commercial Activities & Services
N.A.I.C.S.: 523150

Subsidiaries:

Lotus Parsian Construction Development Company (1)
Unit 1 No 79 Opposite Emdad Khodro Building Sheikh Bahai St, 19186 33814, Tehran, Iran
Tel.: (98) 2188641223
Web Site: http://www.parsian-lotus-hotels.com
Commercial Banking Services
N.A.I.C.S.: 522110

Parsian Brokerage Company (1)

PARSIAN OIL & GAS DEVELOPMENT CO.

No 24 8th Alley Opposite Tehran Clinic Ghaem Magham St, 15868 53714, Tehran, Iran
Tel.: (98) 2187148
Web Site: http://www.parsianbroker.com
Financial Services
N.A.I.C.S.: 523940

Parsian Construction Development Company (1)
No 79 Sheikh Bahai Square Sheikh Bahai Shomali St, Tehran, Iran
Tel.: (98) 2188604433
Web Site: http://www.pcdco.ir
Commercial Banking Services
N.A.I.C.S.: 522110

Parsian E-commerce Company (1)
street light 8 Nelson Mandela Blvd, Tehran, Iran
Tel.: (98) 8722661777
Web Site: http://www.pec.ir
Electronic Payment Services
N.A.I.C.S.: 522320

Parsian Exchange Company (1)
Parsian Bank Building Takhti Sq Shahid Beheshti St, Tehran, Iran
Tel.: (98) 2188535012
Web Site: http://www.parsian-exchange.ir
Commercial Banking Services
N.A.I.C.S.: 522110

PARSIAN INSURANCE COMPANY
No 15 Shahid Saneei St After Jahan Koodak Intersection Africa Blvd, Tehran, Iran
Tel.: (98) 21 88795002
Web Site: http://www.parsianinsurance.ir
Year Founded: 2003
IPAR—(THE)
Sales Range: $125-149.9 Million
Emp.: 445
General Insurance Services
N.A.I.C.S.: 524210
Mahdi Jalali *(Vice Chm)*

PARSIAN OIL & GAS DEVELOPMENT CO.
No 41 in front of Mobasher Alley Elahieh Entrance Roman Bridge, Shariati St, 19149 43346, Tehran, Iran
Tel.: (98) 2178329000
Web Site: https://www.pogdc.com
Year Founded: 2007
PASN1—(THE)
Sales Range: Less than $1 Million
Oil & Gas Development Services
N.A.I.C.S.: 213112

Subsidiaries:

Oil Industries Engineering & Construction Co. (1)
2 Pirooz St, South Kamranieh, Tehran, 1937956751, Iran
Tel.: (98) 2122218005
Web Site: http://www.oiecgroup.com
Oil & Gas Operation Services
N.A.I.C.S.: 213112

Shiraz Oil Refining Co. (1)
22 km of Shiraz-Isfahan Road, PO Box 1445-71365, 7341991475, Shiraz, Iran
Tel.: (98) 38217561071
Web Site: http://www.sorc.ir
Oil Refining Product Distr
N.A.I.C.S.: 424720

Tabriz Petrochemical Co. (1)
Tabriz Petrochemical Complex Special Rd Off Km 3 Bakeri Freeway, Kasaei Highway End Kasaei Highway End Production Complex, Tabriz, Iran
Tel.: (98) 4134280000
Web Site: http://www.tpco.ir
Polyethylene Product Mfr
N.A.I.C.S.: 325211

Zagros Petrohemical Co. (1)
No 88 Khoddami st, Vanak, 1994835555, Tehran, Iran
Tel.: (98) 2188612100

PARSIAN OIL & GAS DEVELOPMENT CO.

Parsian Oil & Gas Development Co.—(Continued)
Web Site: http://www.zpcir.com
Methanol Mfr
N.A.I.C.S.: 325199
Mehdi Ranjkesh (Chief Comml Officer)

PARSIAN OIL & GAS DEVELOPMENT GROUP COMPANY
No 41 in front of Mobasher Alley Elahieh Entrance Roman Bridge, 19149 43346, Tehran, Iran
Tel.: (98) 2178329000
Web Site: https://www.pogdc.com
Year Founded: 1974
PNTB1—(THE)
Sales Range: Less than $1 Million
Petrochemical & Oil Refining Product Mfr
N.A.I.C.S.: 324110

PARSIENA DESIGN, INC.
159 Rayette Rd 1, Concord, L4K 2E8, ON, Canada
Tel.: (905) 660-0747
Web Site: http://www.parsienadesign.com
Sales Range: $10-24.9 Million
Emp.: 10
Stone Casting Design Services
N.A.I.C.S.: 423320
Joe Bigio (Mng Partner)

Subsidiaries:

Da Vinci Stone Craft Ltd. (1)
159 Rayette Road, Concord, L4K 2E8, ON, Canada
Tel.: (416) 781-4417
Web Site: http://www.davincistonecraft.com
Other Concrete Product Mfr
N.A.I.C.S.: 327390

PARSVNATH DEVELOPERS LTD.
Parsvnath Tower Near Shahdara Metro Station, Shahdara, Delhi, 110 032, India
Tel.: (91) 1143050100
Web Site: https://www.parsvnath.com
Year Founded: 1984
PARSVNATH—(NSE)
Rev.: $58,643,499
Assets: $1,072,892,321
Liabilities: $1,047,881,207
Net Worth: $25,011,113
Earnings: ($58,403,272)
Emp.: 246
Fiscal Year-end: 03/31/21
Commercial & Residential Architectural & Construction Services
N.A.I.C.S.: 541310
Rajeev Jain (Dir-Mktg)

Subsidiaries:

Parsvnath Landmark Developers Private Limited (1)
Parsvnath Tower Near Shahdara Metro Station Shahdara, New Delhi, 110032, India
Tel.: (91) 1143050100
Real Estate Services
N.A.I.C.S.: 531390

Parsvnath Rail Land Project Private Limited (1)
Parsvnath Tower Near Shahdara Metro Station, Shahdara, New Delhi, 110032, India
Tel.: (91) 1143050100
Real Estate Services
N.A.I.C.S.: 531210

PARSVNATH ESTATE DEVELOPERS PVT. LTD.
6th Floor Arunachal Building 19 Barakhamba Road, New Delhi, 110 001, India
Tel.: (91) 1143686600
Web Site: http://www.parsvnath.com
Year Founded: 2007

Real Estate Services
N.A.I.C.S.: 531390
Pradeep Jain (Chm)

PARTANI APPLIANCES LTD.
702 East Alkarim Trade Centre, Secunderabad, 500003, India
Tel.: (91) 4066260041
Year Founded: 1985
Home Appliance Product Retailer
N.A.I.C.S.: 449210

PARTEC AG
Possartstr 20, 81679, Munich, Germany
Tel.: (49) 8999809100
Web Site: https://www.par-tec.com
Year Founded: 1999
JY0—(MUN)
Rev.: $105,618,282
Assets: $90,285,527
Liabilities: $55,778,551
Net Worth: $34,506,976
Earnings: ($19,262,532)
Emp.: 37
Fiscal Year-end: 12/31/23
Software Development Services
N.A.I.C.S.: 541511
Bernhard Frohwitter (Chm)

PARTENON M.A.M. SISTEM A.D.
Simina 9a, Belgrade, Serbia
Tel.: (381) 11 244 54 58
Web Site: http://www.partenon.rs
Year Founded: 2002
PTNN—(BEL)
Sales Range: Less than $1 Million
Emp.: 2
Books Publishing Services
N.A.I.C.S.: 513130
Momcilo Mitrovic (Exec Dir)

PARTER CAPITAL GROUP GMBH
Myliusstrasse 23, 60323, Frankfurt am Main, Germany
Tel.: (49) 69770619990
Web Site: http://www.parter-capital.com
Equity Investment Firm
N.A.I.C.S.: 523999
Rudiger G. Terhost (Mng Dir)

Subsidiaries:

Ampegon AG (1)
Spinnereistrasse 5, CH 5300, Turgi, Switzerland
Tel.: (41) 56 710 44 00
Web Site: http://www.ampegon.com
Sales Range: $100-124.9 Million
Emp.: 100
Radio Transmission Equipment Mfr
N.A.I.C.S.: 334220
Josef Troxler (Chm & CEO)

Subsidiary (Non-US):

Ampegon Antenna Systems GmbH (2)
Carl-Benz-Strasse 6-8, Schifferstadt, 67105, Germany
Tel.: (49) 62359250300
Web Site: http://www.ampegon.com
Sales Range: $25-49.9 Million,
Emp.: 20
Radio Transmission Equipment Mfr
N.A.I.C.S.: 334220
Weidlich Gunter (Gen Mgr)

Ampegon Science & Technology (Beijing) Co., Ltd. (2)
No 5 Longxiang Industrial Park, Erbozi New Village, Changping District, Beijing, 102208, China
Tel.: (86) 10 5256 8941
Radio Transmission Equipment Mfr
N.A.I.C.S.: 334220

Digital Film Technology GmbH (1)

Borsigstrasse 13, 64291, Darmstadt, Germany
Tel.: (49) 6151 8503 500
Web Site: https://www.dft-film.com
Film Post Production Services
N.A.I.C.S.: 512191
Sai Prasad (Mng Dir)

Subsidiary (Non-US):

Digital Film Technology (2)
St George's House 15 Hanover Square, London, W1S 1HS, United Kingdom
Tel.: (44) 203 012 1984
Film Post Production Services
N.A.I.C.S.: 512191
Simon Carter (Dir-Sls)

Subsidiary (US):

Digital Film Technology LLC (2)
3211 Cahuenga Blvd W Ste 103, Los Angeles, CA 90068
Tel.: (877) 363-8367
Film Post Production Services
N.A.I.C.S.: 512191
Craig Nichols (Sr Engr-Svc)

Guardian Autoglas GmbH (1)
Am Heegwald 19, D-76227, Karlsruhe, Germany
Tel.: (49) 7 21 9 40 07 0
Web Site: http://www.guardianautomotiveglass.com
Automotive Glass Mfr
N.A.I.C.S.: 327215
Herr Joachim Magin (CEO)

PARTICIPATIEMAATSCHAPPIJ VLAANDEREN
Oude Graanmarkt 63, 1000, Brussel, Belgium
Tel.: (32) 022295230
Web Site: https://www.pmv.eu
Emp.: 100
Financial Services
N.A.I.C.S.: 523999

PARTICIPATIONS INDUSTRIELLES ET MINIERES SA
106 rue de Rennes, 75006, Paris, France
Tel.: (33) 142226280
Holding Company
N.A.I.C.S.: 551112
Karl Akesson (Chm & CEO)

PARTNER COMMUNICATIONS COMPANY LTD.
8 Amal Street Afeq Industrial Park, PO Box 435, Rosh Ha'Ayin, 48103, Israel
Tel.: (972) 547814888
Web Site: https://www.partner.co.il
Year Founded: 1997
PTNR—(TAE)
Rev.: $1,044,278,760
Assets: $1,674,634,360
Liabilities: $1,097,377,680
Net Worth: $577,256,680
Earnings: $35,709,800
Emp.: 2,574
Fiscal Year-end: 12/31/21
Mobile Communications Operator
N.A.I.C.S.: 517112
Avi Gabbay (CEO)

PARTNER ONE CAPITAL, INC.
6900 Boulevard Arthur-Suave Suite 203, Laval, H7R 1K7, QC, Canada
Tel.: (514) 856-5643
Web Site: https://partnerone.com
Software Publisher
N.A.I.C.S.: 513210
Andrew Hall (Portfolio Mgr)

Subsidiaries:

Cincom Systems, Inc. (1)
55 Merchant St, Cincinnati, OH 45246-3732
Tel.: (513) 612-2300
Web Site: http://www.cincom.com

INTERNATIONAL PUBLIC

Sales Range: $350-399.9 Million
Emp.: 1,000
Mfr of Computer Software
N.A.I.C.S.: 541512
Brian Bish (CEO)

Subsidiary (Non-US):

Cincom Iberia, S.A. (2)
Calle Barbara de Braganza n 2 Torre 1 - Planta 3 B, Madrid, 28006, Spain
Tel.: (34) 915249820
Business Software Development Services
N.A.I.C.S.: 541511

Cincom Italia S.r.l. (2)
Via Buozzi 10, Turin, 10123, Italy
Tel.: (39) 0115154711
Business Software Development Services
N.A.I.C.S.: 541511

Cincom Monaco S.A.M. (2)
Gildo Pastor Center 7 rue du Gabian, Monaco, 98000, Monaco
Tel.: (377) 93100120
Web Site: https://www.cincom.com
Sales Range: $10-24.9 Million
Emp.: 4
Business Software Development Services
N.A.I.C.S.: 541511
Francis Barlet (Mgr-Fin)

Cincom Netherlands B.V. (2)
Postmastraat 46, 4105 DW, Culemborg, Netherlands
Tel.: (31) 345471050
Web Site: https://www.cincom.com
Emp.: 5
Business Software Development Services
N.A.I.C.S.: 541511

Cincom Systems (UK) Limited (2)
1 Grenfell Road, Maidenhead, SL61HN, Berkshire, United Kingdom
Tel.: (44) 1628542300
Web Site: https://www.cincom.com
Sales Range: $10-24.9 Million
Emp.: 120
Software Publisher
N.A.I.C.S.: 513210

Cincom Systems France S.A.R.L. (2)
50 Avenue Daumesnil, Paris, 75012, France
Tel.: (33) 153617000
Web Site: https://www.cincom.com
Sales Range: $10-24.9 Million
Emp.: 40
Business Software Development Services
N.A.I.C.S.: 541511
Oliver Le Gagic (Gen Mgr)

Cincom Systems GmbH & Co. oHG (2)
Am Kronberger Hang 4, 65824, Schwalbach, Germany
Tel.: (49) 619690030
Web Site: https://acquire.cincom.de
Sales Range: $10-24.9 Million
Emp.: 15
Business Software Development Services
N.A.I.C.S.: 541511
Monika Laurent (Mgr-Mktg)

Cincom Systems of Australia Pty Ltd. (2)
Level 4 Avaya Bldg 123 Epping Rd, North Ryde, 2113, NSW, Australia
Tel.: (61) 288751400
Web Site: https://www.cincom.com.au
Emp.: 40
Business Software Development Services
N.A.I.C.S.: 541511
Greg Mills (COO)

Cincom Systems of Canada, Ltd (2)
2085 Hurontario Street Suite 200, Mississauga, L5A 4G1, ON, Canada
Tel.: (905) 279-4220
Software Development Services
N.A.I.C.S.: 541511

Cincom Systems of Japan Ltd. (2)
11F CR Kamiyacho Bldg 1-11-9 Azabudai, Minato-Ku, Tokyo, 1060041, Japan
Tel.: (81) 335606061
Web Site: https://www.cincom.co.jp
Sales Range: $10-24.9 Million
Emp.: 10
Business Software Development Services

PARTNERA OYJ
Kauppurienkatu 12 B, 90100, Oulu, Finland
Tel.: (358) 83133410
Web Site: https://www.partnera.fi
Year Founded: 1882
PARTNE1—(HEL)
Rev.: $91,243,456
Assets: $163,245,306
Liabilities: $115,275,424
Net Worth: $47,969,882
Earnings: $25,810,451)
Emp.: 299
Fiscal Year-end: 12/31/22
Investment Management Service
N.A.I.C.S.: 523999
Jari Pirinen *(Chm)*

PARTNERBUD S.A.
Reja 4, Fugasowka, 42-440, Zawiercie, Poland
Tel.: (48) 3267152012
Web Site: http://www.awbud.pl
Construction Engineering Services
N.A.I.C.S.: 541330

PARTNERFONDS AG
Fraunhoferstrasse 15, D-82152, Planegg, Germany
Tel.: (49) 89614240200
Web Site: http://www.partnerfonds.ag
Year Founded: 2003
Sales Range: $50-74.9 Million
Investment Services
N.A.I.C.S.: 523999
Oliver Kolbe *(CEO)*

PARTNERPEDIA SOLUTIONS INC.
1690 West Broadway Suite 202, Vancouver, V6J 1X6, BC, Canada
Tel.: (604) 681-1660
Web Site: http://www.partnerpedia.com
Year Founded: 1996
Sales Range: $1-9.9 Million
Software Publisher
N.A.I.C.S.: 513210
Mark Sochan *(CEO)*

PARTNERS GROUP HOLDING AG
Zugerstrasse 57, 6341, Baar, Switzerland
Tel.: (41) 417846000   CH
Web Site: https://www.partnersgroup.com
Year Founded: 1996
PGPHF—(OTCIQ)
Rev.: $2,058,314,856
Assets: $5,326,496,674
Liabilities: $2,635,920,177
Net Worth: $2,690,576,497
Earnings: $1,112,416,851
Emp.: 1,931
Fiscal Year-end: 12/31/23
Holding Company
N.A.I.C.S.: 551112
Marcel Erni *(Co-Founder)*

Subsidiaries:

BluSky Restoration Contractors, LLC   (1)
9110 E Nicholas Ave Ste 180, Centennial, CO 80112
Tel.: (303) 789-4258
Web Site: http://www.goblusky.com
Commercial & Residential Restoration, Renovation, Environmental & Roofing Services
N.A.I.C.S.: 236220
Daniel F. Flanagan *(Chief Sls Officer)*

Subsidiary (Domestic):

J & R Contracting Co. Inc.   (2)
1300 Michigan Ave, Waterville, OH 43566
Tel.: (419) 843-3473
Sales Range: $1-9.9 Million
Emp.: 24
Residential Remodeling Services
N.A.I.C.S.: 236118
Michael J. Bostdorff *(Pres)*

Weston American, Inc.   (2)
13701 Green Ash Ct, Earth City, MO 63045
Tel.: (314) 298-2701
Web Site: http://www.usstl.com
Residential Remodeler
N.A.I.C.S.: 236118

Budderfly LLC   (1)
2 Trap Falls Rd, Shelton, CT 06484-4616
Tel.: (203) 513-8634
Web Site: http://www.budderfly.com
Plumbing, Heating & Air-Conditioning Contractors
N.A.I.C.S.: 238220
Ken Buda *(VP)*

Cote Restaurants Ltd.   (1)
Woolverstone House 61 Berners St, London, W1T 3NJ, United Kingdom
Tel.: (44) 203 2067940
Web Site: http://www.cote-restaurants.co.uk
Sales Range: $10-24.9 Million
Emp.: 1,124
Restaurant Operators
N.A.I.C.S.: 722511
Alex Scrimgeour *(Co-Mng Dir)*

DiversiTech Corporation   (1)
6650 Sugarloaf Pkwy #100, Duluth, GA 30097
Tel.: (678) 542-3600
Web Site: http://www.diversitech.com
Emp.: 1,250
Industrial Products Mfr & Distr
N.A.I.C.S.: 332510
Wayne M. Hewett *(CEO)*

Subsidiary (Domestic):

Packard, Inc.   (2)
2700 Barrett Lakes Blvd NW Ste 100, Kennesaw, GA 30144
Tel.: (770) 427-5765
Web Site: http://www.packardonline.com
Electrical Apparatus & Equipment, Wiring Supplies & Related Equipment Merchant Whslr
N.A.I.C.S.: 423610
Susan L. Kirkland *(Pres)*

Stride Tool Inc.   (2)
46 E Washington St, Ellicottville, NY 14731-9717
Tel.: (716) 699-2031
Web Site: http://www.stridetool.com
Sales Range: $10-24.9 Million
Emp.: 150
Mfr of Hand Tools
N.A.I.C.S.: 332216
Lori Northrup *(Chm)*

Fermaca S.A. de C.V.   (1)
Vito Alessio Robles 130, Col La Florida, 01030, Mexico, Mexico
Tel.: (52) 55 5148 670
Web Site: http://www.fermaca.mx
Energy & Infrastructure Services
N.A.I.C.S.: 236220
Fernando Calvillo Alvarez *(Pres & CEO)*

Form Technologies, Inc.   (1)
14045 Ballantyne Corporate Place Ste 400, Charlotte, NC 28277
Tel.: (704) 927-2790
Web Site: http://www.formtechnologies.com
Precision Component Mfr
N.A.I.C.S.: 335999
Simon Newman *(CEO)*

Subsidiary (Domestic):

Dynacast International Inc.   (2)
14045 Ballantyne Corporate Pl Ste 300, Charlotte, NC 28277
Tel.: (704) 927-2790
Web Site: http://www.dynacast.com
Emp.: 27
Zinc, Aluminium & Magnesium Castings Mfr
N.A.I.C.S.: 331523
Simon J. Newman *(Chm & CEO)*

Subsidiary (Non-US):

Dynacast (Shanghai) Ltd.   (3)
No 8 Dongbao Road Songjiang Industrial Zone, Shanghai, 201613, China
Tel.: (86) 2157741010
Web Site: http://www.dynacast.cn
Automotive Die Casting Equipment Mfr
N.A.I.C.S.: 331523

Dynacast (Singapore) Pte Ltd   (3)
6 Second Chin Bee Road, Jurong, 618773, Singapore
Tel.: (65) 6268 7644
Web Site: http://www.dynacast.com.sg
Metal Die Casting Products Mfr
N.A.I.C.S.: 331523

Dynacast - Peterborough   (3)
710 Neal Drive, Peterborough, K9J 6X7, ON, Canada
Tel.: (705) 748-9522
Web Site: http://www.dynacast.com
Small Precise Zinc Die Castings; Designers & Injected Metal Assembly & Injected Metal Machines Mfr
N.A.I.C.S.: 331529

Division (Domestic):

FisherTech   (4)
710 Neal Drive, PO Box 179, Peterborough, K9J 6Y9, ON, Canada
Tel.: (705) 748-9522
Web Site: http://www.fishertech.com
Custom Assembly Services & Fixturing Systems Mfr
N.A.I.C.S.: 333511
Doug Montgomery *(Gen Mgr)*

Subsidiary (Domestic):

Techmire   (4)
185 Voyageur, Montreal, H9R 6B2, QC, Canada
Tel.: (514) 694-4110
Web Site: http://www.techmire.com
Multiple-Slide Die Casting Machines Mfr
N.A.I.C.S.: 333517

Subsidiary (Non-US):

Dynacast Deutschland GmbH   (3)
Hufinger Strasse 24, Postfach 1263, Braunlingen, D-78199, Germany
Tel.: (49) 771 9208 0
Web Site: http://www.dynacast.de
Precision Die Casting Parts Mfr
N.A.I.C.S.: 331523

Dynacast Espana S.A.   (3)
Centro Industrial Santiga Calle Flassaders 22, Santa Perpetua de Mogoda, 08130, Barcelona, Spain
Tel.: (34) 937297112
Web Site: http://www.dynacast.es
Metal Products Die Casting Services
N.A.I.C.S.: 331523

Division (Domestic):

Dynacast International Inc. - Tooling Division   (3)
N117 W19048 Fulton Dr, Germantown, WI 53022
Tel.: (262) 250-0303
Web Site: http://www.dynacast.com
Emp.: 30
Special Die & Tool, Die Set, Jig & Fixture Mfr
N.A.I.C.S.: 333514

Subsidiary (Non-US):

Dynacast Osterreich GmbH   (3)
Neunkirchnerstrasse 83, Postfach 84, Wiener Neustadt, 2700, Austria
Tel.: (43) 2622 27831
Web Site: http://www.dynacast.at
Metal Die Casting Products Mfr
N.A.I.C.S.: 331523

Dynacast de Mexico, S.A. de C.V.   (3)
Av Tejocotes 77 A Interior 2-A San Martin Obispo, Cuautitlan Izcalli, 54763, Mexico
Tel.: (52) 5558999690
Web Site: http://www.dynacast.mx
Small Precision Zinc & Lead Diecastings Mfr
N.A.I.C.S.: 331523

Subsidiary (Domestic):

Signicast LLC   (3)
1800 Innovation Way, Hartford, WI 53027
Tel.: (262) 673-2700
Web Site: http://www.signicast.com
Steel Investment Casting
N.A.I.C.S.: 331512
Marc Riquelme *(Pres)*

Subsidiary (Non-US):

Cirex BV   (4)
Bornsestraat 365, 7601 PB, Almelo, Netherlands   (100%)
Tel.: (31) 546540400
Web Site: http://www.cirex.eu
Precision Foundry
N.A.I.C.S.: 331513
Jaroen Spoelder *(Mng Dir)*

Global Blue S.A.   (1)
route de Divonne 46, CH 1260, Nyon, Switzerland
Tel.: (41) 223637740
Web Site: http://www.global-blue.com
Sales Range: $550-599.9 Million
Tax Refund Transaction Processing Services
N.A.I.C.S.: 522320
David Baxby *(CEO)*

Subsidiary (Non-US):

Global Blue (UK) Limited   (2)
11th Floor GWII Great West House Great West Road, Brentford, TW8 9HU, United Kingdom
Tel.: (44) 8 707 666 789
Web Site: http://www.globalblue.com
Tax Refund Transaction Processing Services
N.A.I.C.S.: 522320
Jack Sten *(CEO)*

Hearthside Food Solutions, LLC   (1)
3333 Finley Rd Ste 800, Downers Grove, IL 60515
Tel.: (630) 967-3600
Web Site: https://www.hearthsidefoods.com
Sales Range: Less than $1 Million
Emp.: 13,000
All Other Miscellaneous Food Manufacturing
N.A.I.C.S.: 311999
Richard G. Scalise *(Founder & Chm)*

Subsidiary (Domestic):

Greencore USA - CPG Partners, LLC   (2)
1800 Averill Rd, Geneva, IL 60134
Tel.: (630) 845-9400
Web Site: http://www.hearthsidefoods.com
Integrated Food Packaging & Logistics Services
N.A.I.C.S.: 561910

Plant (Domestic):

Hearthside Food Solutions, LLC - Gibson City   (2)
310 W 10th St, Gibson City, IL 60936-1327
Tel.: (217) 784-4238
Web Site: http://www.hearthsidefoods.com
Food & Consumer Product Contract Packaging Services
N.A.I.C.S.: 561910
Vicky Smitley *(VP-Sls & Mktg)*

Hearthside Food Solutions, LLC - McComb   (2)
312 Rader Rd, McComb, OH 45858-9751
Tel.: (419) 293-2911
Web Site: http://www.hearthsidefoods.com
Cookies & Crackers Mfr
N.A.I.C.S.: 311821
Rich Scalise *(Chm & CEO)*

Subsidiary (Domestic):

Quality Bakery Products, LLC   (2)
888 E Las Olas Blvd Ste 700, Fort Lauderdale, FL 33301
Tel.: (856) 764-2006
Web Site: http://www.hearthsidefoods.com
Bakery Products Retailer
N.A.I.C.S.: 424420
Gerald J Mangano Jr. *(Head-Sls & Mktg)*

Ryt-way Industries, LLC   (2)
21850 Grenada Ave, Lakeville, MN 55044-9076
Tel.: (952) 469-1417

PARTNERS GROUP HOLDING AG

Partners Group Holding AG—(Continued)
Web Site: http://www.hearthsidefoods.com
Contract Food Packaging Services
N.A.I.C.S.: 424450

KinderCare Education LLC (1)
650 Holladay St Ste 1400, Portland, OR 97232
Tel.: (800) 633-1488
Web Site: http://www.kc-education.com
Holding Company; Child Day Care Centers Operator
N.A.I.C.S.: 551112
Tom Wyatt (CEO)

Subsidiary (Domestic):

KinderCare Learning Centers, Inc. (2)
650 NE Holladay St Ste 1400, Portland, OR 97232
Tel.: (503) 872-1300
Web Site: http://www.kindercare.com
Early Childhood Education & Care
N.A.I.C.S.: 624410

Subsidiary (Domestic):

Creme de la Creme, Inc. (3)
6400 S Fiddlers Green Cir Ste 1400, 80111, Greenwood Village, CO
Tel.: (303) 773-6607
Web Site: http://www.cremedelacreme.com
Sales Range: $1-9.9 Million
Emp.: 260
Child Day Care Services
N.A.I.C.S.: 624410
Bruce Karpas (Pres)

Pacific Bells, LLC (1)
111 W 39th St, Vancouver, WA 98660
Tel.: (360) 694-7855
Web Site: http://www.pacificbells.com
Franchise Limited-Service Restaurants Operator
N.A.I.C.S.: 722513
David Hawthorne (Chief People Officer)

Partners Group (Brazil) Investimentos Ltda. (1)
Rua Joaquim Floriano 1120-11 Andar, Sao Paulo, 04534-004, Brazil
Tel.: (55) 11 3528 6500
Web Site: http://www.partnersgroup.com
Holding Company
N.A.I.C.S.: 551112
Gonzalo Fernanders (Mng Dir)

Partners Group (Canada) Inc. (1)
Exchange Tower 130 King Street West Suite 1820, Toronto, M5X 1E3, ON, Canada
Tel.: (416) 865-2033
Private Equity Services
N.A.I.C.S.: 523940

Partners Group (France) SAS (1)
10 Rue Labie, 75017, Paris, France
Tel.: (33) 1 45 03 60 84
Holding Company
N.A.I.C.S.: 551112

Partners Group (Guernsey) Ltd. (1)
Tudor House Le Bordage, PO Box 477, Saint Peter Port, GY1 6BD, Guernsey
Tel.: (44) 148 171 1690
Private Equity Services
N.A.I.C.S.: 523940

Partners Group (India) Private Limited (1)
Suite 3103 Four Seasons Hotel Plot No 1/136 Dr E Moses Road, Worli, Mumbai, 400 018, India
Tel.: (91) 224 289 4200
Private Equity Services
N.A.I.C.S.: 523940

Partners Group (Luxembourg) S.a.r.l. (1)
2 Rue Jean Monnet, 2180, Luxembourg, Luxembourg
Tel.: (352) 2748281
Web Site: http://www.partnersgroup.com
Emp.: 14
Holding Company
N.A.I.C.S.: 551112
Venessa Tamilleri (Office Mgr)

Partners Group (Shanghai) Co., Ltd. (1)
Unit 1904-1906A Level 19 Tower I Jing An Kerry Center, No 1515 West Nanjing Road Jing An District, Shanghai, 200040, China
Tel.: (86) 212 221 8666
Private Equity Services
N.A.I.C.S.: 523940

Partners Group (Singapore) Pte. Limited (1)
71 Robinson Road Level 13, Singapore, 068895, Singapore
Tel.: (65) 6671 3500
Web Site: http://www.partnersgroup.com
Emp.: 250
Holding Company
N.A.I.C.S.: 551112
Adam Howarth (Mng Dir)

Partners Group (UK) Limited (1)
110 Bishopsgate 14th Floor, London, EC2N 4AY, United Kingdom
Tel.: (44) 20 7575 2500
Holding Company
N.A.I.C.S.: 551112
Philipp Mueller (VP)

Partners Group (USA) Inc. (1)
The Grace Bldg 1114 Avenue Of The Americas 37th Fl, New York, NY 10036
Tel.: (212) 908-2600
Web Site: http://www.partnersgroup.com
Holding Company
N.A.I.C.S.: 551112
Mina Lee (Office Mgr)

Partners Group Advisors (DIFC) Limited (1)
Office 601 Level 6 Index Tower DIFC, PO Box 507253, Dubai, United Arab Emirates
Tel.: (971) 4 316 9555
Private Equity Services
N.A.I.C.S.: 523940

Partners Group Global Opportunities Ltd. (1)
Tudor House Le Bordage, PO Box 477, Saint Peter Port, Guernsey
Tel.: (44) 1481711690
Web Site: http://www.pg-globalopportunities.net
Rev: $9,583
Assets: $70,696,499
Liabilities: $406,075
Net Worth: $70,290,425
Earnings: ($27,232,149)
Fiscal Year-end: 12/31/2017
Investment Fund Services
N.A.I.C.S.: 525910
John E. Hallam (Chm)

Partners Group Japan Kabushiki Kaisha (1)
Marunouchi Park Bldg 6F 2-6-1 Marunouchi, Chiyoda-ku, Tokyo, 100-6906, Japan
Tel.: (81) 35 219 3700
Private Equity Services
N.A.I.C.S.: 523940

Partners Group Prime Services Solutions (Philippines), Inc. (1)
18/F Seven/NEO Building 5th Avenue Corner 26th Street, Bonifacio Global City, Taguig, 1634, Metro Manila, Philippines
Tel.: (63) 28 804 7100
Private Equity Services
N.A.I.C.S.: 523940

Partners Group Private markets (Australia) Pty. Ltd. (1)
L32 Deutsche Bank Place 126 Phillip Street, Sydney, 2000, NSW, Australia
Tel.: (61) 28 216 1900
Web Site: https://www.partnersgroupaustralia.com
Emp.: 20
Private Equity Services
N.A.I.C.S.: 523940
Josh Peel (Mng Dir)

Partners Group Solis SARL (1)
Skygarden im Arnulfpark, Erika Mann Str 7, 80636, Munich, Germany
Tel.: (49) 89 38 38 92 0
Private Markets Investment Services
N.A.I.C.S.: 523999

Perennius Capital Partners SGR S.p.A. (1)
Via della Moscova 3, 20121, Milan, Italy
Tel.: (39) 02 888 369 1
Web Site: http://www.partnersgroup.com
Emp.: 12
Holding Company
N.A.I.C.S.: 551112

PremiStar, LLC (1)
10 Parkway North Suite #100, Deerfield, IL 60015
Tel.: (847) 729-9450
Web Site: https://premistar.com
Commercial Industrial Heat & Air Conditioning, Refrigeration & Food Equipment Sales & Services Provider
N.A.I.C.S.: 333415
Joe Kirmser (CEO)

Subsidiary (Domestic):

Arctic Engineering Co., Inc. (2)
8410 Minnesota St, Merrillville, IN 46410
Tel.: (219) 947-4999
Web Site: http://www.arcticengineering.com
Sales Range: $10-24.9 Million
Emp.: 65
Plumbing Services
N.A.I.C.S.: 238220
William K (Pres)

Capstone Mechanical, LP. (2)
7100 Imperial Dr, Waco, TX 76712
Tel.: (254) 399-8090
Web Site: http://www.capstonemechanical.com
Sales Range: $10-24.9 Million
Emp.: 125
Plumbing Services
N.A.I.C.S.: 238220
Rick Tullis (Pres)

Cs3, Inc (2)
1931 Thomas Rd, Memphis, TN 38134
Tel.: (901) 382-6202
Web Site: http://www.cs3.com
Rev: $5,000,000
Emp.: 46
Site Preparation Contractor
N.A.I.C.S.: 238910
John R. Jerkins (Pres)

Johansen & Anderson, Inc. (2)
925 Plainfield Rd, Joliet, IL 60435
Tel.: (815) 723-9383
Web Site: http://www.jnaonline.com
Refrigeration Equipment & Supplies Merchant Whslr
N.A.I.C.S.: 423740
Andy Weis (VP)

Page Mechanical Group, Inc. (2)
4611 Cummins Ct, Fort Myers, FL 33905
Tel.: (239) 275-4406
Web Site: http://www.pagemech.com
Sales Range: $10-24.9 Million
Emp.: 180
Plumbing & Mechanical Services
N.A.I.C.S.: 238220
William A. Jones (Owner & CFO)

Roger Schweitzer & Sons, Inc. (2)
2129 Freeman Ave, Cincinnati, OH 45214
Tel.: (513) 241-4423
Plumbing, Heating & Air-Conditioning Services
N.A.I.C.S.: 238220

Ruyle Mechanical Services, Inc (2)
1325 Ne Bond St, Peoria, IL 61603
Tel.: (309) 674-6644
Web Site: http://www.ruylecorp.com
Rev: $5,900,000
Emp.: 60
Site Preparation Contractor
N.A.I.C.S.: 238910
Chris Benson (Treas)

Tessendorf Mechanical Services, Inc. (2)
45 Center Dr, Gilberts, IL 60136-9739
Tel.: (847) 426-7524
Web Site: http://www.tessendorfmechanical.com
Rev: $1,200,000
Emp.: 17
Plumbing, Heating & Air-Conditioning Services
N.A.I.C.S.: 238220
Lisa Johnston (Office Mgr)

SPi Global Solutions Corporation (1)
SPi Global Building Pascor Drive,

INTERNATIONAL PUBLIC

Paranaque, 1700, Sto Nino, Philippines
Tel.: (63) 28558600
Web Site: http://www.straive.com
Emp.: 14,700
Telemarketing Services
N.A.I.C.S.: 561422
Maria Cecilia Ampeloquio (Chief People Officer)

Subsidiary (Non-US):

SPi Global (Xi'An) Information Technology Ltd. (2)
2nd Floor 01 Square 72 KeJi 2nd Road Xi'an Software Park, Xi'an, 710075, Shaanxi, China
Tel.: (86) 29 68913111
Web Site: http://www.spi-global.com
Telemarketing Services
N.A.I.C.S.: 561422
ZhiKui Chian (CEO)

SPi Technologies India Private Limited (2)
DLF SEZ IT Park Chennai Block 9B 6th Floor 1 124 Shivaji Gardens, Moonlight Stop Nandambakkam Mount Poonamallee Road, Chennai, 600 089, Manapakkam, India
Tel.: (91) 44 4395 0500
Web Site: http://www.spi-global.com
Telemarketing Services
N.A.I.C.S.: 561422

Scope e-Knowledge Center Pvt Ltd. (2)
No 41 Mount Poonamallee Road Jayant Tech Park 2nd Floor, Nandambakkam, Chennai, 600089, Tamilnadu, India
Tel.: (91) 44 4091 8900
Web Site: http://www.spi-global.com
Content & Data Solutions
N.A.I.C.S.: 519290
M. A. Eswaran (COO)

Surewerx Inc. (1)
49 Schooner St, Coquitlam, V3K 0B3, BC, Canada
Tel.: (604) 523-8665
Web Site: https://surewerx.com
Emp.: 350
Industrial Tools & Equipments Mfr
N.A.I.C.S.: 333515
Carlo Del Fante (Mgr-Bus Dev)

Subsidiary (US):

ADA Solutions Inc. (2)
323 Andover St Ste 3, Wilmington, MA 01887
Tel.: (800) 372-0519
Web Site: http://www.adatile.com
Detectable Warning & Way Finding Solutions Design & Mfr
N.A.I.C.S.: 334511

Footwear Specialties International LLC (2)
13136 NE Airport Way, Portland, OR 97230-1035
Web Site: http://www.footwearspecialties.com
Footwear Mfr
N.A.I.C.S.: 316210

Techem GmbH (1)
Hauptstrasse 89, 65760, Eschborn, Germany
Tel.: (49) 61965220
Web Site: http://www.techem.de
Energy Billing & Energy Management Services
N.A.I.C.S.: 561499
Robert Woggon (Head-Corp Comm)

Subsidiary (Non-US):

Danuvius EOOD (2)
bul Ovtscha kupel 72 Et 2, 1618, Sofia, Bulgaria
Tel.: (359) 2 955 04 11
Energy & Water Metering Equipment Mfr
N.A.I.C.S.: 334515
Asya Angelova (Country Mgr)

Subsidiary (US):

Metron Sustainable Services Inc. (2)
5661 Airport Blvd, Boulder, CO 80301
Tel.: (303) 217-5990

AND PRIVATE COMPANIES

Web Site:
http://www.metronsubmetering.com
Energy Billing & Energy Management Services
N.A.I.C.S.: 561499
Rick Minogue (Mng Dir)

Subsidiary (Non-US):

Techem (Schweiz) AG (2)
Steinackerstrasse 55, 8902, Urdorf, Switzerland
Tel.: (41) 43 455 65 00
Web Site: http://www.techem.ch
Energy Billing & Energy Management Services
N.A.I.C.S.: 561499
Marcel Sporrer (Mng Dir & Head-Fin)

Techem Danmark A/S (2)
Trindsovej 7A-B, 8000, Arhus, Denmark
Tel.: (45) 87 44 77 00
Web Site: http://www.techem.dk
Energy Billing & Energy Management Services
N.A.I.C.S.: 561499
Carsten Hejgaard (Mgr)

Techem Energy Services B.V. (2)
Takkebijsters 17 A1, 4817 BL, Breda, Netherlands
Tel.: (31) 76 57 25 800
Web Site: http://www.techem.nl
Energy Billing & Energy Management Services
N.A.I.C.S.: 561499
Maikel van Loo (Mng Dir)

Techem Energy Services Middle East FZCO (2)
Dubai Silicon Oasis Headquaters Building, PO Box 341002, Office 603 D-Wing, Dubai, United Arab Emirates
Tel.: (971) 4 5015516
Web Site: http://www.techem.me
Energy Billing & Energy Management Services
N.A.I.C.S.: 561499

Techem Energy Services S.R.L. (2)
Strada Ronda nr 8 Sector 2, 024102, Bucharest, Romania
Tel.: (40) 21 323 21 21
Web Site: http://www.techem.ro
Energy Billing & Energy Management Services
N.A.I.C.S.: 561499

Techem Enerji Hizmetleri Sanayi ve Ticaret Limited Sirketi (2)
Gulbahar Mah Avni Dilligil Sok Celik Is Merkezi, No 11/A Daire 5 Sisli, 34394, Istanbul, Turkiye
Tel.: (90) 212 447 07 47
Web Site: http://www.techem.com.tr
Energy Billing & Energy Management Services
N.A.I.C.S.: 561499

Techem Norge A/S (2)
Dicks vei 10b, 1366, Lysaker, Norway
Tel.: (47) 22 02 14 59
Web Site: http://www.techem.no
Energy Billing & Energy Management Services
N.A.I.C.S.: 561499

Techem S.r.l. (2)
Via dei Buonvisi 61/D, 00148, Rome, Italy
Tel.: (39) 06 65191810
Web Site: http://www.techem.it
Energy Billing & Energy Management Services
N.A.I.C.S.: 561499
Octavio Manuel Prieto (Mng Dir)

Techem SAS (2)
Gay Lussac building 20 avenue Edouard Herriot, CS 9002, 92356, Le Plessis-Robinson, Cedex, France
Tel.: (33) 1 46 01 59 70
Web Site: http://www.techem.fr
Energy Billing & Energy Management Services
N.A.I.C.S.: 561499
Bruno Macre (Dir)

Techem Services e.o.o.d. (2)
jk Geo Milev Prof Georgi Pavlov No 3, 1111, Sofia, Bulgaria

Tel.: (359) 700 1 28 28
Web Site: http://www.techem.net
Energy Billing & Energy Management Services
N.A.I.C.S.: 561499

Techem Sverige AB (2)
Foretagsgatan 9, Box 5, 233 51, Svedala, Sweden
Tel.: (46) 102022800
Web Site: http://www.techem.se
Energy Billing & Energy Management Services
N.A.I.C.S.: 561499
Carsten Hejgaard (CEO)

Techem Techniki Pomiarowe Sp. z o.o.
os Lecha 121, 61 298, Poznan, Poland
Tel.: (48) 61 623 35 00
Web Site: http://www.techem.pl
Energy Billing & Energy Management Services
N.A.I.C.S.: 561499
Wojciech Lubiniecki (Chm-Mgmt Bd)

Techem do Brasil Servicos de Medicao de Agua Ltda. (2)
Av Brig Luis Antonio 2 729, 13 andar Jardim Paulista, Sao Paulo, 01401 000, Brazil
Tel.: (55) 11 3059 3030
Web Site: http://www.techem.com.br
Energy Billing & Energy Management Services
N.A.I.C.S.: 561499
Eduardo Lacerda Soares (Mng Dir)

Techem spol. s r. o. (2)
Hattalova 12, 831 03, Bratislava, Slovakia
Tel.: (421) 2 49 10 64 11
Web Site: http://www.techem.sk
Energy Billing & Energy Management Services
N.A.I.C.S.: 561499
Eliana Kostolany (Mng Dir)

Techem spol. s r. o. (2)
Pocernicka 96, Malesice, 108 00, Prague, Czech Republic
Tel.: (420) 272 088 777
Web Site: http://www.techem.cz
Energy Billing & Energy Management Services
N.A.I.C.S.: 561499
Jiri Zerzan (Mng Dir)

Wedgewood Village Pharmacy LLC (1)
405 Heron Dr, Swedesboro, NJ 08085
Web Site:
http://www.wedgewoodpharmacy.com
Teleproduction & Other Postproduction Services
N.A.I.C.S.: 512191
George J. Malmberg (Co-Founder)

Subsidiary (Domestic):

Wildlife Pharmaceuticals, Inc. (2)
1230 W Ash St Ste D, Windsor, CO 80550-4677
Tel.: (970) 079-0920
Web Site: http://www.wildpharm.com
Veterinary Services
N.A.I.C.S.: 541940
William R. Lance (Owner)

PARTNERS VALUE INVESTMENTS INC.
Brookfield Place 181 Bay Street Office Suite 210, Toronto, M5J 2T3, ON, Canada
Tel.: (647) 503-6516   ON
Web Site: http://www.pvii.ca
Year Founded: 1988
Sales Range: $50-74.9 Million
Investment Services
N.A.I.C.S.: 523999

PARTNERS VALUE SPLIT CORPORATION
181 Bay St Ste 210, Toronto, M5J 2T3, ON, Canada
Tel.: (416) 363-9491

Web Site:
https://www.partnersvaluesplit.com
Year Founded: 2001
PVS.PR.F—(TSX)
Rev.: $105,479,000
Assets: $7,237,937,000
Liabilities: $831,825,000
Net Worth: $6,406,112,000
Earnings: $2,346,155,000
Fiscal Year-end: 12/31/21
Investment Services
N.A.I.C.S.: 523999
Loretta M. Corso (Co-Sec)

PARTRON CO., LTD.
22 Samsung 1-ro 2-gil, Hwaseong, 18449, Gyeonggi-do, Korea (South)
Tel.: (82) 312017700
Web Site: https://www.partron.co.kr
Year Founded: 2003
091700—(KRS)
Rev.: $937,205,574
Assets: $525,866,422
Liabilities: $141,547,088
Net Worth: $384,319,334
Earnings: $29,549,518
Emp.: 451
Fiscal Year-end: 12/31/22
Electronic Components Mfr
N.A.I.C.S.: 334419
Jong-Koo Kim (Chm & CEO)

Subsidiaries:

PARTRON PRECISION (1)
21-9 Seokwoo-dong, Hwaseong, Gyeonggi-do, Korea (South)
Tel.: (82) 31 371 1400
Web Site: http://www.partron.net
Electronic Equipment Mfr & Distr
N.A.I.C.S.: 334419

Solleds Co., Ltd. (1)
21-9 Seokwoo-dong, Hwaseong, Gyeonggi-do, Korea (South)
Tel.: (82) 31 371 1500
Web Site: http://www.solleds.com
Diode Mfr
N.A.I.C.S.: 334413

YANTAI PARTRON ELECTRONICS Co., Ltd. (1)
352 Muxim Road Muping Economy Development Zone, Yantai, 264100, Shandong, China
Tel.: (86) 5954268717
Web Site: http://www.partron.co.kr
Electronic Components Distr
N.A.I.C.S.: 423690

PARTS FOR TRUCKS, INC.
52 Wright Avenue, Dartmouth, B3B 1C6, NS, Canada
Tel.: (902) 468-6100
Web Site:
https://www.partsfortrucks.com
Year Founded: 1919
Rev.: $29,800,000
Emp.: 170
Truck & Trailer Parts Distr
N.A.I.C.S.: 423120
Angela Morris (Mgr-HR)

PARTY CRUISERS LIMITED
301 3rd Floor Raheja Point 1 near Pandit Jawaharlal Nehru Rd, P and T Colony Vakola Santacruz East, Mumbai, 400055, Maharashtra, India
Tel.: (91) 9967361117
Web Site:
https://www.partycruisersindia.com
Year Founded: 1994
PARTYCRUS—(NSE)
Rev.: $4,808,321
Assets: $3,529,477
Liabilities: $810,371
Net Worth: $2,719,106
Earnings: $457,670
Emp.: 67
Fiscal Year-end: 03/31/23
Wedding Event Services

N.A.I.C.S.: 812990
Rachana Zuzer Lucknowala (Mng Dir)

PARU CO., LTD.
12 Sandan4-gil, Seo-myeon, Suncheon, 57929, Jeollanam-do, Korea (South)
Tel.: (82) 617555114
Web Site: https://iparu.com
Year Founded: 1993
043200—(KRS)
Rev.: $31,097,735
Assets: $41,367,111
Liabilities: $23,300,679
Net Worth: $18,066,432
Earnings: ($3,554,365)
Emp.: 38
Fiscal Year-end: 12/31/22
Solar Tracking Control System Mfr
N.A.I.C.S.: 334519
Moon-Sik Kang (CEO)

Subsidiaries:

Sun Action Trackers LLC (1)
15143 Tradesman Dr, San Antonio, TX 78249
Tel.: (210) 585-8224
Web Site: https://sat-energy.com
Solar Power Generation Services
N.A.I.C.S.: 221114

PARVATI SWEETNERS & POWER LTD.
Hall No 2 Shopping Complex Gomantika Parisar, Jawahar Chowk, Bhopal, 462003, India
Tel.: (91) 7554009254
Web Site:
https://parvatisweetners.co.in
541347—(BOM)
Rev.: $10,694,086
Assets: $19,535,861
Liabilities: $7,550,079
Net Worth: $11,985,782
Earnings: $161,933
Emp.: 40
Fiscal Year-end: 03/31/23
Sugar Mfr & Distr
N.A.I.C.S.: 311313
Poonam Chouksey (Chm & Mng Dir)

PARX MATERIALS N.V.
Tel.: (31) 103400095
Web Site:
http://www.parxmaterials.com
Year Founded: 2012
MLPRX—(EUR)
Rev.: $138,366
Assets: $5,267,925
Liabilities: $995,793
Net Worth: $4,272,131
Earnings: ($177,006)
Fiscal Year-end: 12/31/22
Biotechnology Research & Development Services
N.A.I.C.S.: 541714
Michael Van Der Jagt (Member-Mgmt Bd)

PASAL DEVELOPMENT S.A.
116 Kifisias Ave & 1 Davaki Str, GR 115 26, Athens, Greece
Tel.: (30) 2106967600
Web Site: http://www.pasal.gr
Year Founded: 1991
PREMIA—(ATH)
Rev.: $20,965,352
Assets: $393,141,501
Liabilities: $230,597,546
Net Worth: $162,543,955
Earnings: $7,995,817
Emp.: 17
Fiscal Year-end: 12/31/23
Real Estate Services
N.A.I.C.S.: 531390
Sotiris Theodoridis (Chm & CEO)

PASAL DEVELOPMENT S.A.

Pasal Development S.A.—(Continued)

Subsidiaries:

Kaminos S.A. (1)
34 Ag Varvaras Halandri, 15231, Athens, Greece
Tel.: (30) 2109008400
Building Construction Services
N.A.I.C.S.: 236220

PASARI SPINNING MILLS LIMITED

No 18 III Floor Anjaneya Temple Road Yediyur Jayanagar 6th Block, Bengaluru, 560082, Karnataka, India
Tel.: (91) 8026760125
Web Site:
  https://www.pasariexports.com
Year Founded: 1991
521080—(BOM)
Rev.: $82,700
Assets: $316,628
Liabilities: $404,358
Net Worth: ($87,730)
Earnings: ($32,957)
Fiscal Year-end: 03/31/23
Handloom Fabric Mfr & Distr
N.A.I.C.S.: 313110
Tarun Kumar Gupta *(Mng Dir & CFO)*

PASCAL BIOSCIENCES, INC.

280 7th Avenue East, Vancouver, V5T 0B4, BC, Canada
Tel.: (206) 221-3443
Web Site:
  http://www.pascalbiosciences.com
Year Founded: 2013
PSCBF—(OTCIQ)
Rev.: $1,097
Assets: $14,725
Liabilities: $753,279
Net Worth: ($738,554)
Earnings: $375,713
Emp.: 7
Fiscal Year-end: 11/30/22
Pharmaceuticals Product Mfr
N.A.I.C.S.: 325412
Patrick W. Gray *(CEO)*

PASCHAL-WERK G. MAIER GMBH

Kreuzbuhlstrasse 5, 77790, Steinach, Germany
Tel.: (49) 7832710
Web Site: http://www.paschal.de
Year Founded: 1964
Rev.: $48,463,150
Emp.: 320
Concrete Formwork Mfr & Distr
N.A.I.C.S.: 327390

Subsidiaries:

PASCHAL AG (1)
Leuholz 21, Wangen, Switzerland
Tel.: (41) 554408087
Web Site: http://www.paschal.ch
Concrete Product Distr
N.A.I.C.S.: 423320

PASCHAL Concrete Forms Co. W.L.L (1)
Bahrain International Investment Park 115 Avenue 19 Bldg 96, Hidd, Bahrain
Tel.: (973) 17672580
Concrete Product Distr
N.A.I.C.S.: 423320

PASCHAL EMIRATES Co. L.L.C (1)
Marrakesh Street Umm Ramool, PO Box 638, Rashidiya, Dubai, United Arab Emirates
Tel.: (971) 42861139
Concrete Product Distr
N.A.I.C.S.: 423320

PASCHAL EMIRATES L.L.C (1)
Bldg 279 Mussaffah Commercial ME-10, Abu Dhabi, United Arab Emirates
Tel.: (971) 25591088

Web Site:
  http://www.paschalinternational.com
Concrete Product Distr
N.A.I.C.S.: 423320

PASCHAL Form Work (India) Pvt. Ltd (1)
Plot No 901 Road No 46 Jubilee Hills, 500033, Hyderabad, Andhra Pradesh, India
Tel.: (91) 4066580505
Web Site: http://www.paschalindia.com
Concrete Product Distr
N.A.I.C.S.: 423320

PASCHAL SARL (1)
70 avenue Albert Einstein Z I de Chasteau d'Eau, Moissy-Cramayel, Cedex, France
Tel.: (33) 164131111
Web Site: http://www.paschal.fr
Concrete Product Distr
N.A.I.C.S.: 423320

PASCHAL spol.s.r.o (1)
Vysehradska 23, Prague, Czech Republic
Tel.: (420) 221594594
Web Site: http://www.paschal.cz
Concrete Product Distr
N.A.I.C.S.: 423320

PASCHAL-Danmark A/S (1)
Systemforskallinger Bredskiftevej 24, Arhus, Denmark
Tel.: (45) 86244500
Web Site: http://www.paschal.dk
Concrete Product Distr
N.A.I.C.S.: 423320
Marie-louise Vestergaard *(Engr-Civil)*

PASDEC HOLDINGS BERHAD

Level 21 Menara Zenith Jalan Putra Square 6 Putra Square, 25200, Kuantan, Pahang Darul Makmur, Malaysia
Tel.: (60) 95133888
Web Site:
  https://www.pasdec.com.my
Year Founded: 1997
6912—(KLS)
Rev.: $30,446,836
Assets: $107,964,664
Liabilities: $15,846,848
Net Worth: $92,117,817
Earnings: $9,868,917
Fiscal Year-end: 12/31/20
Property Development Services
N.A.I.C.S.: 531312
Shakerah Enayetali *(Sec)*

Subsidiaries:

Kuantan Tembeling Resort Sdn. Bhd. (1)
Jalan Padang Golf, 25050, Kuantan, Pahang, Malaysia
Tel.: (60) 9 5676688
Web Site: http://www.pasdec.com.my
Property Development & Management Services
N.A.I.C.S.: 531210

Pasdec Bina Sdn. Bhd. (1)
13th Floor Menara Teruntum Jalan Mahkota, 25000, Kuantan, Pahang, Malaysia
Tel.: (60) 9 5136137
Sales Range: $50-74.9 Million
Emp.: 14
Construction Equipment Rental Services
N.A.I.C.S.: 532412

Pasdec Corporation Sdn.Bhd. (1)
Tingkat 14 Menara Teruntum Jalan Mahkota, 25000, Kuantan, Pahang, Malaysia
Tel.: (60) 95133888
Sales Range: $75-99.9 Million
Emp.: 100
Property Development & Management Services
N.A.I.C.S.: 531210
Mohd Khairuddin Abdul Manan *(CEO)*

Subsidiary (Domestic):

Pasdec Putra Sdn. Bhd. (2)
Community Bldg Tg Lumpur, 26060, Kuantan, Pahang, Malaysia

Tel.: (60) 95513288
Sales Range: $75-99.9 Million
Property Development Services
N.A.I.C.S.: 531390

Pasdec Land Sdn. Bhd. (1)
Tingkat 3 Menara Teruntum Jalan Mahkota, 25000, Kuantan, Pahang, Malaysia
Tel.: (60) 95179001
Web Site: http://www.pasdec.com.my
Sales Range: $50-74.9 Million
Emp.: 7
Property Development Services
N.A.I.C.S.: 531210

Pasdec Trading Sdn. Bhd. (1)
Lot 106 Tingkat 1 Block B Medan Warisan Lorong Sri Teruntum 1, 25100, Kuantan, Pahang, Malaysia
Tel.: (60) 9 5135773
Construction Materials Whslr
N.A.I.C.S.: 423320

PASECO CO., LTD.

248 Wonsi-ro, Danwon-gu, Ansan, 15429, Gyeonggi-do, Korea (South)
Tel.: (82) 315995651
Web Site: https://www.paseco.com
Year Founded: 1974
037070—(KRS)
Rev.: $153,764,519
Assets: $114,760,163
Liabilities: $32,983,524
Net Worth: $81,776,639
Earnings: $7,049,877
Emp.: 354
Fiscal Year-end: 12/31/22
Household Appliances Mfr
N.A.I.C.S.: 335220
Kim Ki Jun *(Chm)*

PASHA YATIRIM BANKASI A.S.

Sultan Selim Mahallesi Humeyra Sokak PASHA Plaza No 2/7, Kagithane, 34 415, Istanbul, Turkiye
Tel.: (90) 2127058900
Web Site:
  http://www.pashabank.com.tr
Year Founded: 1987
PBTR—(IST)
Sales Range: Less than $1 Million
Banking Services
N.A.I.C.S.: 522110
Jalal Gasimov *(Chm)*

PASHUPATI COTSPIN LTD.

Survey No 404 At-Balasar Kadi-Detroj Road, Ta-Kadi Dist, Mehsana, Gujarat, India
Tel.: (91) 9099977560
Web Site:
  https://www.pashupaticotspin.com
Year Founded: 2017
PASHUPATI—(NSE)
Rev.: $54,178,419
Assets: $37,022,804
Liabilities: $23,666,699
Net Worth: $13,356,106
Earnings: $465,032
Emp.: 398
Fiscal Year-end: 03/31/23
Cotton Product Mfr
N.A.I.C.S.: 311224
Hareshkumar Rameshchandra Shah *(CFO)*

PASINEX RESOURCES LIMITED

82 Richmond Street East, Toronto, M5C 1P1, ON, Canada
Tel.: (416) 861-9659   BC
Web Site: https://www.pasinex.com
Year Founded: 2006
PSXRF—(OTCIQ)
Assets: $2,283,969
Liabilities: $2,247,745
Net Worth: $36,224
Earnings: ($233,911)
Emp.: 3

INTERNATIONAL PUBLIC

Fiscal Year-end: 12/31/23
Gold Exploration & Mining Services
N.A.I.C.S.: 212220
Steven Williams *(Pres & CEO)*

Subsidiaries:

Pasinex Resources Limited - Nevada Branch (1)
PO Box 5924, Twin Falls, ID 83303
Tel.: (208) 358-3617
Zinc Ore Mining Services
N.A.I.C.S.: 212230

PASLIN DIGITAL TECHNOLOGY CO., LTD.

Economic Development Zone No 2888 Nansha Street, Changchun, 130000, Jilin, China
Tel.: (86) 43181912755
Web Site: https://www.paslin.cn
Year Founded: 1993
600215—(SHG)
Rev.: $157,054,037
Assets: $503,443,526
Liabilities: $275,495,520
Net Worth: $227,948,007
Earnings: $20,013,051
Fiscal Year-end: 12/31/22
Real Estate Management & Construction Engineering Services
N.A.I.C.S.: 531390
Chen Zhu *(Vice Chm)*

PASOFINO GOLD LIMITED

366 Bay Street Suite 200, Toronto, M5H 4B2, ON, Canada
Tel.: (416) 451-0049   BC
Web Site:
  https://www.pasofinogold.com
Year Founded: 2010
EFRGF—(OTCQB)
Assets: $1,720,805
Liabilities: $1,273,004
Net Worth: $447,802
Earnings: ($4,230,728)
Fiscal Year-end: 04/30/23
Mineral Mining Services
N.A.I.C.S.: 212220
Stephen Dunn *(CEO)*

PASON SYSTEMS INC.

6130 Third Street SE, Calgary, T2H 1K4, AB, Canada
Tel.: (403) 301-3400   AB
Web Site: https://www.pason.com
Year Founded: 1996
3PS—(DEU)
Rev.: $272,814,508
Assets: $360,402,600
Liabilities: $64,210,682
Net Worth: $296,191,918
Earnings: $70,788,949
Emp.: 715
Fiscal Year-end: 12/31/23
Instrumentation, Software & Monitoring Products to the Oil & Gas Drilling Industries
N.A.I.C.S.: 213112
Lars Olesen *(VP-Product & Tech)*

Subsidiaries:

Pason DGS Brasil Servicos - Petroliferos Ltda (1)
Avenida Luis Tarquinio 1404 Bagao 06, Lauro de Freitas, Salvador, 42700-000, Bahia, Brazil
Tel.: (55) 7133691385
Web Site: http://www.pason.com
Sales Range: $50-74.9 Million
Oilfield Equipment Leasing Services
N.A.I.C.S.: 532412

Pason DGS Colombia LTDA (1)
Transversal 93 53-32 Bodega 29 Parque Empresarial El Dorado, Bogota, Colombia
Tel.: (57) 1 7437900
Web Site: http://www.pason.com
Drilling Services
N.A.I.C.S.: 213111

AND PRIVATE COMPANIES — PASONA GROUP INC.

Pason DGS Peru S.A.C (1)
Avenida Victor Andres Belaunde 210 Piso 5, San Isidro, 2151, Lima, Peru
Tel.: (51) 14892250
Web Site: http://www.pason.com
Sales Range: $25-49.9 Million
Directional Drilling Software Development Services
N.A.I.C.S.: 541511

Pason DGS S.A. (1)
Teodoro Planas 4331, Q8304EOA, Neuquen, Argentina
Tel.: (54) 2994452827
Web Site: http://www.pason.com
Sales Range: $25-49.9 Million
Oilfield Equipment Rental Services
N.A.I.C.S.: 532490

Pason Offshore Corp. (1)
7701 W Little York Ste 800, Houston, TX 77040
Tel.: (713) 693-8700
Web Site: http://www.pason.com
Sales Range: $25-49.9 Million
Offshore Engineering Services
N.A.I.C.S.: 541330

Pason Systems Corp (1)
6130 Third Street SE, Calgary, T2H 1K4, AB, Canada
Tel.: (403) 301-3400
Web Site: http://www.pason.com
Sales Range: $125-149.9 Million
Drilling Rigs Mfr & Distr
N.A.I.C.S.: 333132

Pason Systems USA Corp. (1)
16035 Table Mtn Pkwy, Golden, CO 80403-1648 (100%)
Tel.: (720) 880-2000
Web Site: http://www.us.pason.com
Sales Range: $50-74.9 Million
Emp.: 50
Provider of Instrumentation, Software & Monitoring Products to the Oil & Gas Drilling Industries
N.A.I.C.S.: 213112
Lee Maassen *(Controller)*

Pason Systems USA Corp. (1)
7701 W Little York Ste 800, Houston, TX 77040 (100%)
Tel.: (281) 404-4000
Web Site: http://www.us.pason.com
Sales Range: $50-74.9 Million
Emp.: 50
Provider of Instrumentation, Software & Monitoring Products to the Oil & Gas Drilling Industries
N.A.I.C.S.: 213112

Pason de Mexico S.A. de C.V. (1)
Rivera Verde #502 Col Riveras de rancho Grande, CP 88560, Reynosa, Tamaulipas, Mexico
Tel.: (52) 899 9532245
Web Site: http://www.pason.com
Oilfield Instrumentation Equipment Services
N.A.I.C.S.: 213112
Russell Smith *(Gen Mgr-Pason Offshore & Intl)*

PASONA GROUP INC.
Job Hub Square Otemachi 2-6-2, Chiyoda-ku, Tokyo, 100-8228, Japan
Tel.: (81) 367340200
Web Site: https://www.pasona.co.jp
Year Founded: 1976
2168—(TKS)
Rev.: $2,358,005,130
Assets: $1,990,204,900
Liabilities: $967,789,930
Net Worth: $1,022,414,970
Earnings: $633,839,510
Emp.: 25,046
Fiscal Year-end: 05/31/24
Human Resources Management & Temporary Staffing Services
N.A.I.C.S.: 923130
Junko Fukasawa *(Exec Officer & VP)*

Subsidiaries:

Asahi Beer Communication Co., Ltd. (1)
Aquatelous U II -5F 2-20-3 Kaminarimon, Taito-ku, Tokyo, Japan
Tel.: (81) 358607565
Web Site: https://www.asahibeer-comm.jp
Brewery Distr
N.A.I.C.S.: 424810

Benefit One (Thailand) Co., Ltd. (1)
98 Sathorn Square Office Tower 26th Floor Unit No 2602-2604, North Sathorn Road Silom Bangrak, Bangkok, 10500, Thailand
Tel.: (66) 20070707
Web Site: https://www.benefit-one.co.th
HR Consulting Services
N.A.I.C.S.: 541612

Benefit One Inc. (1)
2-6-2 Otemachi JOB HUB SQUARE 9th floor, Chiyoda-ku, Tokyo, 100-0004, Japan (51.16%)
Tel.: (81) 368703800
Web Site: http://www.corp.benefit-one.co.jp
Emp.: 860
Outsourcing Services
N.A.I.C.S.: 541612

Benefit One Shanghai Inc. (1)
18th Floor Tower B 838 S Huangpi road, Huangpu District, Shanghai, China
Tel.: (86) 2168411000
Web Site: https://www.benefit-one.com.cn
Business Outsourcing Services
N.A.I.C.S.: 541618

Benefit One USA, Inc. (1)
440 N Wolfe Rd, Sunnyvale, CA 94085
Tel.: (408) 856-6477
Web Site: https://www.benefitoneusa.com
Professional Employer Organization Services
N.A.I.C.S.: 561330

Bewith, Inc. (1)
Shinjuku Park Tower N Building 32F 3-7-1 Nishi-Shinjuku, Shinjyuku-ku, Tokyo, 163-1032, Japan
Tel.: (81) 359083155
Web Site: https://www.bewith.net
Sales Range: $100-124.9 Million
Emp.: 9,358
Information Technology Consulting Services
N.A.I.C.S.: 541512

Chihou Sousei Inc. (1)
3-1-30 Minami-Aoyama, Minato-ku, Tokyo, 107-0062, Japan
Tel.: (81) 368327366
Web Site: https://www.chihousousei.jp
Supermarket Services
N.A.I.C.S.: 445110

GM7 Inc. (1)
22-2 Machinishi, Marumori-cho Igu-gun, Miyagi, 981-2165, Japan
Tel.: (81) 22 451 8804
Web Site: https://www.gm7.jp
Agricultural Services
N.A.I.C.S.: 115116

Gotop Co., Ltd. (1)
41-1 Koyocho, Matsusaka, 515-0053, Mie, Japan
Tel.: (81) 598202880
Web Site: https://www.gotop.co.jp
BPO Services
N.A.I.C.S.: 561422

Ihatov Touhoku Inc. (1)
2-13 Iwaicho, Ichinoseki, Iwate, Japan
Tel.: (81) 191260015
Web Site: https://www.ihatovtouhoku.com
Parking Lot Services
N.A.I.C.S.: 812930

MGR Consulting Co., Ltd. (1)
9F No 71 Sec 2 Dunhua S Rd, Taipei, Taiwan
Tel.: (886) 227082929
Web Site: https://www.mgr.com.tw
Recruitment Consulting Services
N.A.I.C.S.: 561311
Alex Hsu *(Gen Mgr)*

Nagasaki Diamond Staff KK (1)
2-25 Fuchi-machi, Nagasaki, 852-8012, Japan (66.7%)
Tel.: (81) 958618111
Web Site: https://www.diamondstaff.jp
Human Resource Consulting Services
N.A.I.C.S.: 541612

National Examination Center Inc. (1)
3rd Floor of MFPR Kojimachi Building 5-7-2, Kojimachi Chiyoda-ku, Tokyo, 102-0083, Japan
Tel.: (81) 352129901
Web Site: https://www.nexa.co.jp
Education & Training Services
N.A.I.C.S.: 611710

Nijigennomori Inc. (1)
924-1 Iwaya, Awaji, Hyogo, 656-2401, Japan
Tel.: (81) 799732280
Web Site: https://www.nijigennomori.com
Parking Lot Services
N.A.I.C.S.: 812930

PASONA Tech Vietnam Co.,Ltd. (1)
4th Floor E-town 1 Building 364 Cong Hoa Street, Ward 13 Tan Binh Dist, Ho Chi Minh City, Vietnam
Tel.: (84) 2838127150
Web Site: https://pasona.vn
Sales Range: $10-24.9 Million
Emp.: 45
Outsourcing Services
N.A.I.C.S.: 561311

PT Dutagriya Sarana (1)
Graha Mas Fatmawati Blok A 10-11 Jl RS Fatmawati No 71, Jakarta, 12150, Indonesia
Tel.: (62) 217252665
Web Site: https://www.dutagriyasarana.co.id
Recruitment Consulting Services
N.A.I.C.S.: 561311
Koichi Itabashi *(VP)*

PT Pasona HR Indonesia (1)
Pakuwon Tower 11th Floor Unit E and Y Jl Casablanca Kav 88, Jakarta Selatan, 12870, Indonesia
Tel.: (62) 2129568555
Web Site: https://www.pasona.co.id
Employment Placement Services
N.A.I.C.S.: 561311
Makiya Nambu *(Commissioner)*

PT. Benefit One Indonesia (1)
MidPlaza 2 16th Floor Jl Gen SudirmanKav 10-11, Jakarta Pusat, 10220, Indonesia
Tel.: (62) 21 574 9112
Web Site: https://www.benefit-one.co.id
Management Consulting Services
N.A.I.C.S.: 541611

Pasona Agri-Partners Inc. (1)
3-1-30 Minami-Aoyama, Minato-ku, Tokyo, 107-0062, Japan
Tel.: (81) 367341260
Web Site: https://www.pasona-nouentai.co.jp
Agricultural Product Mfr
N.A.I.C.S.: 325320

Pasona Art Now Inc. (1)
3-1-30 Minami-Aoyama, Minato-ku, Tokyo, 107-0062, Japan
Tel.: (81) 367341349
Web Site: https://www.pasona-artnow.co.jp
Art & Space Rental Services
N.A.I.C.S.: 531120

Pasona Asia Co., Limited (1)
Unit 1702 Level 17 Tower 2 Silvercord Center No 30 Canton Rd, Tsim Sha Tsui, Kowloon, China (Hong Kong)
Tel.: (852) 28823484
Web Site: https://www.pasona.com.hk
Emp.: 15
Recruitment Services
N.A.I.C.S.: 561311
Akemi Aota *(Mng Dir)*

Pasona Canada, Inc. (1)
25 Adelaide Street East Suite 818, Toronto, M5C 3A1, ON, Canada
Tel.: (416) 867-1162
Sales Range: $25-49.9 Million
Emp.: 3
Placement Services
N.A.I.C.S.: 561311
Joy Haywood *(Pres)*

Pasona Career Inc. (1)
1-5-1 Marunouchi Chiyoda-ku, Tokyo, 100-6514, Japan
Tel.: (81) 362255100
Web Site: http://www.pasonacareer.jp
Emp.: 1,500
Recruitment Services
N.A.I.C.S.: 561311

Takashi Watanabe *(VP)*

Pasona Education Co. Limited (1)
2/F Vulcan House 21-23 Leighton Road, Causeway Bay, China (Hong Kong)
Tel.: (852) 25778002
Web Site: https://www.pasona.edu.hk
Sales Range: $10-24.9 Million
Emp.: 45
Professional & Customer Training Services
N.A.I.C.S.: 611430
Akemi Aota *(Pres & Principal)*

Pasona Empower Inc. (1)
Ginza Toshiba Bldg Chuo Ku, Tokyo, 100-0004, Japan
Tel.: (81) 3 3574 1571
Web Site: http://www.pasona-emp.co.jp
Business Support Services
N.A.I.C.S.: 561499

Pasona Fortune Inc. (1)
Job Hub Square 5F 2-6-2 Otemachi, Chiyoda-Ku, Tokyo, 100-8228, Japan
Tel.: (81) 368324100
Web Site: http://www.pasona-fortune.co.jp
Employment Placement Services
N.A.I.C.S.: 561311

Pasona Foster Inc. (1)
3-1-30 Minami-Aoyama, Minato-ku, Tokyo, 107-0062, Japan
Tel.: (81) 367341280
Web Site: https://www.pasonafoster.co.jp
Child Care Services
N.A.I.C.S.: 624410

Pasona HR Consulting & Recruitment (Thailand) Co., Ltd. (1)
98 Sathorn Square Office Tower 26th Floor Unit No 2602-2604, North Sathorn Road Silom Bangrak, Bangkok, 10500, Thailand
Tel.: (66) 2 108 1250
Web Site: http://www.pasona.co.th
HR Consulting Services
N.A.I.C.S.: 541612

Pasona HR Consulting (Thailand) Co., Ltd. (1)
98 Sathorn Square Office Tower 26th Floor Unit No 2602-2604, North Sathorn Road Silom Bangrak, Bangkok, 10500, Thailand
Tel.: (66) 21081250
Career Consulting Services
N.A.I.C.S.: 541612

Pasona HR Consulting Inc. (1)
2-6-2 Otemachi, Chiyoda-Ku, Tokyo, 100-8228, Japan
Tel.: (81) 362255111
Web Site: http://www.pasona-hrc.co.jp
HR Consulting Services
N.A.I.C.S.: 541612

Pasona HR Malaysia Sdn. Bhd. (1)
1-41-02 Menera Bangkok Bank Laman Sentral Berjaya No 105, Jalan Ampang, 50450, Kuala Lumpur, Malaysia
Tel.: (60) 327709399
Web Site: https://www.pasonahr.my
Employment Placement Services
N.A.I.C.S.: 561311
Chua Chee Peng *(Mng Dir)*

Pasona HS Inc. (1)
12F Pasona Square 3-1-30 Minami Aoyama, Minato-ku, Tokyo, 107-0062, Japan
Tel.: (81) 362819620
Web Site: https://www.pasona-hs.co.jp
Temporary Staffing Services
N.A.I.C.S.: 561311

Pasona Heartful Inc. (1)
3-1-30 Minami Aoyama, Minato-ku, Tokyo, 107-0062, Japan
Tel.: (81) 367341093
Web Site: https://www.pasona-heartful.co.jp
Employment Placement Services
N.A.I.C.S.: 561311

Pasona Human Resources (Shanghai) Co., Ltd. (1)
Room 704 Ship Building No 1 Pudong Avenue, Pudong New District, Shanghai, 200120, China
Tel.: (86) 2153828210
Web Site: https://www.pasona.com.cn
Emp.: 50
Temporary Staffing & Placement Services

PASONA GROUP INC.

Pasona Group Inc.—(Continued)
N.A.I.C.S.: 561311
Hideaki Otaka (Chm)

Pasona Human Solutions Inc. (1)
2-6-2 Otemachi, Chiyoda-ku, Tokyo, 100-8228, Japan
Tel.: (81) 3 6281 9620
Web Site: http://www.pasona-hs.co.jp
Human Resource Consulting & Outsourcing Services
N.A.I.C.S.: 541612
Takako Yagi (Pres)

Pasona India Private Limited (1)
F-127 and 128 Rectangle-1 Behind Sheraton Hotel D-4, Saket, New Delhi, 110017, India
Tel.: (91) 1146525252
Web Site: https://www.pasona.in
Employment Placement Services
N.A.I.C.S.: 561311
Ranen Gupta (Mng Dir)

Pasona Job Hub Inc. (1)
Pasona Square 3-1-30 Minami Aoyama, Minato-ku, Tokyo, 107-0062, Japan
Tel.: (81) 368322901
Web Site: https://pasona-jobhub.co.jp
Business Outsourcing Services
N.A.I.C.S.: 541618

Pasona Knowledge Partner Inc. (1)
4F Midosuji Grand Tower 3-5-1 Bakuromachi, Chuo-ku, Osaka, 541-0059, Japan
Tel.: (81) 676366400
Web Site: https://www.pasona-kp.co.jp
Emp.: 107
Intellectual Property Management Services
N.A.I.C.S.: 533110

Pasona Korea Co., Ltd. (1)
1220 12F Chengdam Venture Plaza Seolleungno 704, Gangnam-gu, Seoul, 06069, Korea (South)
Tel.: (82) 220383786
Web Site: https://www.pasona.co.kr
Employment Placement Services
N.A.I.C.S.: 561311

Pasona Kyoto Inc. (1)
Shijo KM Bldg Tohokukado Sakaimachi Shijodori, Shimogyo-ku, Kyoto, 600 8006, Japan
Tel.: (81) 752414447
Web Site: https://www.pasona-kyoto.co.jp
Sales Range: $10-24.9 Million
Emp.: 50
Outsourcing & Recruitment Services
N.A.I.C.S.: 561311

Pasona Life Care Inc. (1)
3-1-30 Pasona Square Minami-Aoyama, Minato-ku, Tokyo, 107-0062, Japan
Tel.: (81) 368327380
Web Site: https://www.pasona-lc.co.jp
Temporary Staffing Services
N.A.I.C.S.: 561311

Pasona Logicom Inc. (1)
Kobe Kokusai Kaikan 18Fl, Kobe, 651 0087, Hyogo, Japan
Tel.: (81) 782651260
Web Site: http://www.pasona-logi.com
Sales Range: Less than $1 Million
Emp.: 10
Employment & Other Human Resource Services
N.A.I.C.S.: 541612
Yoshihiro Tamura (Pres)

Pasona Masters Inc. (1)
3-1-30 Pasona Square Minami-Aoyama, Minato-ku, Tokyo, 107-0062, Japan
Tel.: (81) 368327370
Web Site: https://www.pasona-masters.co.jp
Temporary Staffing Services
N.A.I.C.S.: 561311

Pasona NA, Inc. (1)
340 Madison Ave Ste 12-B, New York, NY 10173
Tel.: (212) 661-5110
Sales Range: $10-24.9 Million
Emp.: 295
Staffing & Recruiting Services
N.A.I.C.S.: 561311

Pasona Okayama Inc. (1)
1-6 Ekimotomachi Okayama Fukoku Seimei Building 11F, Kita-ku, Okayama, 700-0024, Japan
Tel.: (81) 862330333
Web Site: http://www.pasona-okayama.co.jp
Staffing Services
N.A.I.C.S.: 561311

Pasona Panasonic Business Service Co., Ltd. (1)
Kitahama Nexu Build 4-33 Kitahama Higashi, Chuo-ku, Osaka, 540-0031, Japan
Tel.: (81) 120551036
Web Site: https://www.pasona-pbs.co.jp
BPO Services
N.A.I.C.S.: 561422

Pasona Singapore Pte.Ltd. (1)
1 Finlayson Green 09-02, Singapore, 049246, Singapore
Tel.: (65) 67326933
Web Site: https://www.pasona.com.sg
Sales Range: $25-49.9 Million
Emp.: 10
Placement Services
N.A.I.C.S.: 561311
Misaki Morimura (Mng Dir)

Pasona Sourcing Inc. (1)
5 2 1 Ginza, Chuo ku, Tokyo, 104 0061, Japan
Tel.: (81) 335168311
Web Site: http://www.pasona-src.co.jp
Sales Range: $25-49.9 Million
Emp.: 100
Business & Placement Services
N.A.I.C.S.: 561499

Pasona Taiwan Co., Ltd. (1)
6th Floor No 65 Section 2 Dunhua South Rd Ye Caiji World Trade Center, Da'an District, Taipei, Taiwan
Tel.: (886) 227082929
Web Site: https://www.pasona.com.tw
Emp.: 100
Temporary Staffing & Placement Services
N.A.I.C.S.: 561311
Alex Hsu (Mng Dir)

Pasona Tech, Inc. (1)
2-6-2 Otemachi, Chiyoda-Ku, Tokyo, 100-8228, Japan
Tel.: (81) 36 734 1246
Web Site: https://www.pasonatech.co.jp
Information Technology Services
N.A.I.C.S.: 541511

Pasona Yaskawa Business Staff Inc. (1)
3-2-8 Kurosaki Fukuoka Kurosaki Fureai Building, Yahatanishi, Kitakyushu, 806-0021, Japan
Tel.: (81) 93 645 6848
Web Site: https://www.ybstaff.com
Temporary Staffing Services
N.A.I.C.S.: 561311

Tango Kingdom Brewery Inc. (1)
123 Tottori Yasaka-cho, Kyotango, 627-0133, Kyoto, Japan
Tel.: (81) 772654193
Web Site: https://www.tango-kingdom.com
Brewery Mfr
N.A.I.C.S.: 312120

Tangokura Inc. (1)
17 Izumi Mineyama-cho, Kyotango, Kyoto, Japan
Tel.: (81) 772620151
Web Site: https://www.tangokura.com
Beverage Whslr
N.A.I.C.S.: 424820

Yaskawa Business Staff Co., Ltd. (1)
3-2-8 Kurosaki, Yahatanishi-ku, Kitakyushu, 806-0021, Fukuoka, Japan
Tel.: (81) 93 645 6848
Web Site: http://www.ybstaff.com
Sales Range: $25-49.9 Million
Temporary Staffing & Employment Placement Services
N.A.I.C.S.: 561311
Yoshihisa Higuchi (Pres)

PASQUARELLI AUTO S.P.A.
Via Piana Sant'Angelo 202, San Salvo, 66050, Chieti, Italy
Tel.: (39) 087334561
Web Site: https://www.pasquarelliauto.it
Year Founded: 1986
PSQ—(ITA)
Car Retailer
N.A.I.C.S.: 441120

PASS MEXICO S.A. DE C.V.
Insurgentes Sur 933 1er Piso, Col Napoles, Mexico, 3810, Mexico
Tel.: (52) 5556828768 MX
Web Site: http://www.pass.mx
Sales Range: $1-9.9 Million
Emp.: 16
Predictive Analytics & Data Mining Software Distr & Technical Consulting Services
N.A.I.C.S.: 423430
Luis Ernesto Albarran (Gen Mgr)

PASSAT SA
2 rue Alfred de Vigny, CS-10117, Fourqueux, France
Tel.: (33) 130082440
Web Site: https://www.passat.fr
PSAT—(EUR)
Rev.: $41,187,331
Assets: $44,936,622
Liabilities: $9,462,817
Net Worth: $35,473,805
Earnings: $2,293,473
Emp.: 129
Fiscal Year-end: 12/31/19
Holding Company
N.A.I.C.S.: 551112
Borries Broszio (Chm & CEO)

PASSINI GROUP
Via Per Modena 152, Castelvetro Di Modena, 41014, Modena, Italy
Tel.: (39) 059704111
Web Site: http://www.passinigroup.com
Sales Range: $250-299.9 Million
Emp.: 2,000
Mfr, Designer & Distributor of Undercarriages & Components for Earthmoving & Agricultural Crawler Machines
N.A.I.C.S.: 333924

PASSION HOLDINGS LIMITED
Yirong Road Longyan Economic & Technological Development District, 364000, Fuzhou, Fujian, China
Tel.: (86) 5975279888 SG
Web Site: http://www.passion-holdings.com
Sales Range: $100-124.9 Million
Emp.: 1,000
Rattan Furniture, Wood Furniture, Bamboo Crafts, Wood Crafts, Photo Frames & Wire Crafts Mfr & Sales
N.A.I.C.S.: 337122
Huiling Chen (Chm)

PASSIVSYSTEMS GROUP PLC
Benyon House Newbury Business Park, Newbury, RG14 2PZ, Berkshire, United Kingdom
Tel.: (44) 1635525050
Web Site: http://www.passivsystems.com
Year Founded: 2008
Emp.: 60
Hot Water, Space Heating & Solar PV Monitoring Software
N.A.I.C.S.: 513210
Colin Calder (Founder & CEO)

PASSLOGY CO., LTD.
Tokyo Building 7F 161 Kanda Jinbocho, Chiyoda-Ku, Tokyo, 101-0052, Japan
Tel.: (81) 352832263
Web Site: https://www.passlogy.com 4426—(TKS)
Sales Range: Less than $1 Million
Software Development Services
N.A.I.C.S.: 541511
Hideharu Ogawa (Pres)

PASSUS SA
ul Goraszewska 19, 02-910, Warsaw, Poland
Tel.: (48) 695444803
Web Site: https://www.passus.com
Year Founded: 2014
PAS—(WAR)
Information Technology Consulting Services
N.A.I.C.S.: 541512
Tadeusz Dudek (CEO)

PASTURE HOLDINGS LTD.
2 Corporation Rd 03 0405 Corporation Place, Singapore, 609969, Singapore
Tel.: (65) 65156516 SG
Web Site: https://www.pasturegroup.com
Year Founded: 1996
UUK—(CAT)
Rev.: $9,704,000
Assets: $7,646,000
Liabilities: $3,818,000
Net Worth: $3,828,000
Earnings: ($1,298,000)
Fiscal Year-end: 06/30/23
Holding Company
N.A.I.C.S.: 551112

PASUKHAS GROUP BERHAD
DF2-11-01 Level 11 Persoft Tower, 6B Persiaran Tropicana Tropicana Golf & Country Resor, 47410, Petaling Jaya, Selangor Darul Ehsan, Malaysia
Tel.: (60) 376656088
Web Site: https://www.pasukhasgroup.com
PASUKGB—(KLS)
Rev.: $31,004,131
Assets: $42,591,827
Liabilities: $10,345,513
Net Worth: $32,246,314
Earnings: ($4,894,215)
Fiscal Year-end: 06/30/23
Engineering Services; Switchboard Mfr
N.A.I.C.S.: 541330
Ah Kiong Teng (Chm & Mng Dir)

PASUPATI ACRYLON LTD.
M-14 Connaught Circus Middle Circle, New Delhi, 110 001, India
Tel.: (91) 1147627400
Web Site: https://pasupatiacrylon.com
500456—(BOM)
Rev.: $70,192,040
Assets: $50,616,439
Liabilities: $18,748,657
Net Worth: $31,867,781
Earnings: $5,876,120
Emp.: 439
Fiscal Year-end: 03/31/21
Textile Fiber Products Mfr
N.A.I.C.S.: 314999
Satish Kumar Bansal (CFO)

PASUPATI FINCAP LIMITED
1501 Nirmal Tower 26 Barakhamba Road, New Delhi, 110001, India
Tel.: (91) 1147632200
Web Site: http://www.pasupatifincap.com
Year Founded: 1993
Assets: $143,040
Liabilities: $98,722
Net Worth: $44,318
Earnings: ($1,075)

Fiscal Year-end: 03/31/18
Financial Services
N.A.I.C.S.: 523999
Eladathuparambil Mohandas (CEO)

PASUPATI SPINNING & WEAVING MILLS LIMITED
Village Kaprivas, Dharuhera, Rewari, Haryana, India
Tel.: (91) 1147632200
Web Site:
https://www.pasupatitextiles.com
Year Founded: 1979
503092—(BOM)
Rev.: $16,628,607
Assets: $12,332,702
Liabilities: $8,767,184
Net Worth: $3,565,518
Earnings: $131,623
Emp.: 504
Fiscal Year-end: 03/31/23
Textile Products Mfr
N.A.I.C.S.: 313110
Vidit Jain (Co-Mng Dir)

PAT TECH FITWELL TUBE COMPONENTS LIMITED
Survey No 873/B/1 Road No 1 Anson Limbani Estate, Near GETCO 66 KV Substation GIDC POR NH 8 Vadodara, Gujarat, 391243, India
Tel.: (91) 2652830151
Web Site:
https://www.pftcpipefittings.com
Year Founded: 2012
PATTECH—(NSE)
Pipe & Tube Product Mfr
N.A.I.C.S.: 331210
Bharatbhai Jivrajbhai Limbani (Chm)

PATA SALDUS AS
Kuldigas Iela 86c, Saldus Novads, Riga, 3801, Latvia
Tel.: (371) 6380 7072
Web Site: http://www.patasaldus.lv
SMA1R—(TAL)
Rev.: $64,285,024
Assets: $44,346,425
Liabilities: $30,927,736
Net Worth: $13,418,689
Earnings: ($2,234,454)
Emp.: 239
Fiscal Year-end: 12/31/19
Wood Products Mfr
N.A.I.C.S.: 321999
Gatis Megnis (Mgr-Forest Resourse)

PATAGONIA GOLD CORP.
Av Del Liberator 498 Piso 26, C1001ABR, Buenos Aires, Argentina
Tel.: (54) 1152786950   BC
Web Site:
https://www.patagoniagold.com
Year Founded: 2006
HGLD—(OTCIQ)
Rev.: $8,220,000
Assets: $49,574,000
Liabilities: $42,314,000
Net Worth: $7,260,000
Earnings: ($6,407,000)
Fiscal Year-end: 12/31/23
Metal Exploration Services
N.A.I.C.S.: 212290
Christopher Van Tienhoven (CEO)

Subsidiaries:

Patagonia Gold Ltd   (1)
11-12 St James's Square, London, SW1Y 4LB, United Kingdom
Tel.: (44) 2074584100
Web Site: http://www.patagoniagold.com
Gold Ore Mining Services
N.A.I.C.S.: 212220
Carlos J. Miguens (Chm)

PATAGONIA LITHIUM LIMITED
Level 6 505 Little Collins Street, Melbourne, 3000, VIC, Australia
Tel.: (61) 433747380   AU
Web Site:
https://www.patagonialithium.com
Year Founded: 2021
PL3—(ASX)
Rev.: $95,474
Assets: $4,781,820
Liabilities: $139,913
Net Worth: $4,641,908
Earnings: ($723,709)
Fiscal Year-end: 12/31/23
Mineral Exploration Services
N.A.I.C.S.: 212390
Jarek Kopias (Sec)

PATANJALI AYURVED LIMITED
Patanjali Food Herbal park Vill - Padartha Laksar Road, Laksar Road, Haridwar, 249404, Uttrakhand, India
Tel.: (91) 18001804108
Web Site: https://patanjaliayurved.org
Year Founded: 2006
Agricultural Products Mfr & Marketer
N.A.I.C.S.: 325320
Acharya Balkrishna (Mng Dir)

Subsidiaries:

Patanjali Foods Limited   (1)
601,Part B-2, Metro Tower 6th Floor, Vijay Nagar AB Road, Indore, 452 010, India
Tel.: (91) 7314767109
Web Site: https://www.patanjalifoods.com
Rev.: $1,871,756,015
Assets: $1,191,677,429
Liabilities: $1,899,438,780
Net Worth: ($707,761,351)
Earnings: $867,202,352
Fiscal Year-end: 03/31/2018
Soya Food Mfr
N.A.I.C.S.: 424490
Sanjeev Asthana (CEO)

PATDIAM JEWELLERY LTD.
Unit No 102 Tower No 1 Seepz Special Economic Zone Andheri East, Mumbai, 400 096, India
Tel.: (91) 2228293455
Web Site: https://www.patdiam.com
Year Founded: 1999
539401—(BOM)
Rev.: $13,163,264
Assets: $8,396,211
Liabilities: $1,972,172
Net Worth: $6,424,039
Earnings: $986,751
Emp.: 38
Fiscal Year-end: 03/31/23
Jewelry Mfr
N.A.I.C.S.: 339910
Pravin Kakadia (Chm)

Subsidiaries:

Zest Corporation   (1)

PATEC PRECISION INDUSTRY CO., LTD.
2 Woodlands Walk, Singapore, 738221, Singapore
Tel.: (65) 62578122
Web Site: https://www.patec-intl.com
Year Founded: 1992
2236—(TAI)
Rev.: $59,426,042
Assets: $81,566,137
Liabilities: $29,954,968
Net Worth: $51,611,169
Earnings: $4,141,797
Emp.: 1,000
Fiscal Year-end: 12/31/23
Iron & Steel Forging
N.A.I.C.S.: 332111

Subsidiaries:

Patec Precision Kft   (1)
Mechatronikai Ipari Park 3/A, 3526, Miskolc, Hungary
Tel.: (36) 46526400
Machine Tool Component Mfr
N.A.I.C.S.: 333517
Tamas Gabor (Country Mgr)

Press Automation Technology Pte Ltd.   (1)
2 Woodlands Walk, Singapore, 738221, Singapore
Tel.: (65) 62578122
Machine Tool Component Mfr
N.A.I.C.S.: 333517
Hidaka Hiroyuki (Gen Mgr)

Subsidiary (Non-US):

PT. Patec Presisi Engineering   (2)
Jalan Angsana Raya L3-01, Delta Silicon Industrial Park Lippo Cikarang, Bekasi, 17550, Indonesia
Tel.: (62) 2189908366
Machine Tool Component Mfr
N.A.I.C.S.: 333517
Liju Joseph (Mgr-Mechanical)

Subsidiary (Domestic):

PT. PDF Presisi Engineering   (3)
Jl Akasia II Blok A8-07, Delta Silicon Industrial Park Lippo Cikarang, Bekasi, 17550, Indonesia
Tel.: (62) 2189905781
Web Site: http://www.pdf-presisi.com
Emp.: 40
Metal Forging Component Mfr
N.A.I.C.S.: 332111

Wuxi Jingxin Precision Machining Co. Ltd.   (1)
No 8 Suofang Industrial Park Xuedian South Road, New Dist, Wuxi, Jiangsu, China
Tel.: (86) 51085311462
Machine Tool Component Mfr
N.A.I.C.S.: 333517

PATEK PHILIPPE GENEVA
Chemin du Pont-du-Centenaire 141, 1228, Plan-les-Ouates, Switzerland
Tel.: (41) 228842020
Web Site: http://www.patek.com
Year Founded: 1845
Sales Range: $10-24.9 Million
Emp.: 1,600
Watch Mfr
N.A.I.C.S.: 334519
Thierry Stern (Pres)

Subsidiaries:

Patek Philippe   (1)
1 Rockefeller Plz Ste 930, New York, NY 10020
Tel.: (212) 218-1240
Web Site: http://www.patek.com
Watch Distr
N.A.I.C.S.: 423940
Theresa Henderson (Mgr-Inventory Sls)

PATEL ENGINEERING LTD.
Patel Estate, Jogeshwari W, Mumbai, 400 102, Maharashtra, India
Tel.: (91) 2226767500
Web Site: https://www.pateleng.com
Year Founded: 1949
531120—(BOM)
Rev.: $518,233,199
Assets: $1,049,095,378
Liabilities: $692,308,974
Net Worth: $356,786,404
Earnings: $21,437,803
Emp.: 4,426
Fiscal Year-end: 03/31/23
Civil Engineering Construction Services
N.A.I.C.S.: 237990
Rupen Patel (Chm & Mng Dir)

Subsidiaries:

ASI Constructors Inc.   (1)
1880 Office Club Pointe Ste 2000, Colorado Springs, CO 80920
Tel.: (719) 647-2821
Web Site: http://www.asiconstructors.com
Sales Range: $1-9.9 Million
Emp.: 110
Civil Engineering Construction Services
N.A.I.C.S.: 237990
John Bowen (Pres)

Subsidiary (Domestic):

Engineering & Construction Innovations Inc.   (2)
7002 6th St N, Oakdale, MN 55128
Tel.: (651) 298-9111
Web Site: https://eciconstructors.com
Sales Range: $1-9.9 Million
Emp.: 15
Civil Engineering Construction Services
N.A.I.C.S.: 237990
Shane McFadden (Pres)

PT Surya Geo Minerals   (1)
city lofts sudirman jakarta pusat, Jakarta, 10220, Indonesia
Tel.: (62) 2125558812
Dam & Tunnel Construction Services
N.A.I.C.S.: 237990

Patel Engineering Inc   (1)
12 Buell Mansion Pkwy, Englewood, CO 80113
Tel.: (303) 761-6700
Dams & Tunnel Construction Services
N.A.I.C.S.: 237990

Patel Hydro Power Pvt. Ltd.   (1)
E 29 Sector 8, Noida, 201 301, India
Tel.: (91) 1204509300
Web Site: www.patelenergy.com
Engineering Consulting Services
N.A.I.C.S.: 541330

Patel Realty (India) Ltd.   (1)
2nd Floor Patel Estate S V Road, Jogeshwari W, Mumbai, 400 102, India
Tel.: (91) 22 61366500
Web Site: http://www.patelrealty.in
Building Construction & Design Services
N.A.I.C.S.: 236220
Pravin Patel (Chm)

Subsidiary (Non-US):

Les Salines Development Ltd.   (2)
Near Bulk Sugar Terminal Les Salines, Port Louis, Mauritius
Tel.: (230) 2105788
Engineeering Services
N.A.I.C.S.: 541330

Subsidiary (Domestic):

PBSR Developers Pvt. Ltd.   (2)
1st Floor Patel Engineering Building 8-2-293/82/A/76 Road No 9A, Celebrations Hotel Lane Jubile, Hyderabad, 500 033, India
Tel.: (91) 4044604810
Engineeering Services
N.A.I.C.S.: 541330

PATEL INTEGRATED LOGISTICS LIMITED
Patel House 48 Gazdar Bandh North Avenue Road, Santacruz West, Mumbai, 400 054, India
Tel.: (91) 2226052915
Web Site: https://www.patel-india.com
Year Founded: 1959
526381—(BOM)
Rev.: $33,605,323
Assets: $20,627,960
Liabilities: $6,517,427
Net Worth: $14,110,533
Earnings: $587,111
Emp.: 272
Fiscal Year-end: 03/31/23
Logistic Services
N.A.I.C.S.: 541614
Sweta Parekh (Sec)

PATELS AIRTEMP (INDIA) LTD.
5th Floor Kalpana Complex Nr Memnagar Fire Station Navrangpura, Ahmedabad, 380009, Gujarat, India
Tel.: (91) 7927913694
Web Site:
https://www.patelsairtemp.com

PATELS AIRTEMP (INDIA) LTD.

Patels Airtemp (India) Ltd.—(Continued)
Year Founded: 1973
517417—(BOM)
Rev.: $33,907,332
Assets: $43,212,241
Liabilities: $27,678,221
Net Worth: $15,534,021
Earnings: $1,339,068
Emp.: 236
Fiscal Year-end: 03/31/23
Air Conditioner Equipment Mfr
N.A.I.C.S.: 333415
Narayanbhai Gangaram Patel *(Chm)*

Subsidiaries:

Patels Airtemp (USA) Inc. (1)
4548 Talisman St, Torrance, CA 90503
Tel.: (323) 207-7793
Air Conditioning & Refrigeration Equipment Mfr
N.A.I.C.S.: 333415

PATENTES TALGO S.L.
Paseo del Tren Talgo 2, Las Matas, 28290, Madrid, Spain
Tel.: (34) 916313800
Web Site: https://www.talgo.com
Year Founded: 1942
Sales Range: $125-149.9 Million
Emp.: 1,000
Train Mfr
N.A.I.C.S.: 336510
Carlos Palacio Oriol *(Pres)*

Subsidiaries:

Talgo (Deutschland) GmbH (1)
Revaler Strasse 99, 10245, Berlin, Germany
Tel.: (49) 30 23 88 00 0
Web Site: http://www.talgo.de
Emp.: 10
Train Mfr
N.A.I.C.S.: 336510

Talgo BH d.o.o (1)
Danijela Ozme 1, 71000, Sarajevo, Bosnia & Herzegovina
Tel.: (387) 33 26 11 55
Train Mfr
N.A.I.C.S.: 336510

Talgo, Inc. (1)
505 5th Ave S Ste 170, Seattle, WA 98104
Tel.: (206) 748-6140
Web Site: http://www.talgoamerica.com
Emp.: 70
Train Mfr
N.A.I.C.S.: 336510
Antonio Perez *(Pres & CEO)*

PATENTUS S.A.
Ul Gornoslaska 11, 43-200, Pszczyna, Poland
Tel.: (48) 322101100
Web Site: https://patentus.eu
Year Founded: 1992
PAT—(WAR)
Rev.: $62,190,549
Assets: $66,222,307
Liabilities: $23,187,246
Net Worth: $43,035,061
Earnings: $15,855,945
Fiscal Year-end: 12/31/23
All Other Miscellaneous Electrical Equipment & Component Manufacturing
N.A.I.C.S.: 335999
Stanislaw Duda *(Vice Chm-Mgmt Bd)*

PATERSON GLOBALFOODS INC.
22nd Fl 333 Main St, Winnipeg, R3C 4E2, MB, Canada
Tel.: (204) 956-2090
Web Site:
  http://www.patersonglobalfoods.com
Year Founded: 1908
Sales Range: $800-899.9 Million
Emp.: 70

International Agri-Food Services
N.A.I.C.S.: 111419
Andrew B. Paterson *(Pres & CEO)*

Subsidiaries:

Alliance Grain Terminal Ltd.
1155 Stewart St, Vancouver, V6A 4H4, BC, Canada
Tel.: (604) 254-4414
Grain Processing Services
N.A.I.C.S.: 493130
David Kushnier *(CEO)*

FeedMax Corp. (1)
Hwy 18, PO Box 1133, Killarney, Carberry, R0K 1G0, MB, Canada (100%)
Tel.: (204) 523-3333
Web Site: https://www.feedmax.com
Sales Range: $200-249.9 Million
Heavy & Civil Engineering Construction
N.A.I.C.S.: 237990
Keith Bruch *(Mng Dir)*

Global Grain Australia Pty Limited (1)
1 Bruce Street, 3031, Kensington, VIC, Australia (100%)
Tel.: (61) 393725722
Sales Range: $50-74.9 Million
Emp.: 8
Grain & Field Bean Whslr
N.A.I.C.S.: 424510

Growers International Organic Sales Inc. (1)
22nd Floor 333 Main Street, Winnipeg, R3C 4E2, MB, Canada (100%)
Tel.: (204) 956-2090
Web Site: http://www.giosi.com
Sales Range: $25-49.9 Million
Emp.: 30
Grain & Field Bean Whslr
N.A.I.C.S.: 424510
Ken Sabatier *(Gen Mgr)*

NutraSun Foods Ltd. (1)
6201 E Primrose Green Drive, PO Box 30059, Regina, S4V 3L7, SK, Canada
Tel.: (306) 751-2040
Web Site: http://www.nutrasunfoods.com
Emp.: 25
Bakery Product Distr
N.A.I.C.S.: 424490
Neil Tennent *(Mgr-Quality Control & R&D)*

PTC Construction Ltd. (1)
22nd Floor -333 Main Street, Winnipeg, R3C 4E2, MB, Canada (100%)
Tel.: (204) 956-2090
Web Site: http://www.ptcconstruction.com
Sales Range: $25-49.9 Million
Emp.: 40
Heavy & Civil Engineering Construction
N.A.I.C.S.: 237990
Ranon Cairo *(Mng Dir)*

Paterson Grain Ltd. (1)
22nd Floor 333 Main Street, Winnipeg, R3C 4E2, MB, Canada
Tel.: (204) 956-2090
Web Site: https://www.patersongrain.com
Sales Range: $75-99.9 Million
Grains & Agrifood Marketer, Trader & Handler
N.A.I.C.S.: 424510

Truck Freight International (1)
2200-333 Main Street, PO Box 27085, Winnipeg Square, Winnipeg, R3C 4E2, MB, Canada
Tel.: (204) 926-3450
Web Site: http://www.truck-freight.com
Local Freight Trucking
N.A.I.C.S.: 484110

PATH CORPORATION
JPR Harajuku Building 1711 Jingumae 6chome, Shibuya-ku, Tokyo, 150-0001, Japan
Tel.: (81) 368236664
Web Site: https://www.pathway.co.jp
Year Founded: 1990
3840—(TKS)
Rev.: $15,335,200
Assets: $11,084,970
Liabilities: $3,152,970
Net Worth: $7,932,000

Earnings: ($1,156,750)
Fiscal Year-end: 03/31/24
Payment Processing & Marketing Services
N.A.I.C.S.: 522320

Subsidiaries:

MadreX Co., Ltd. (1)
6-17-11 JPR Harajuku Building 6F Jingumae, Shibuya-ku, Tokyo, 150-0001, Japan
Tel.: (81) 354678431
Emp.: 46
Cosmetic Product Mfr & Distr
N.A.I.C.S.: 325620
Shinichiro Nakahara *(Pres)*

Zyva Studio Co., Ltd. (1)
6-17-11 JPR Harajuku Building 6F Jingumae, Shibuya-ku, Tokyo, 150-0001, Japan
Tel.: (81) 120998830
Emp.: 10
Cosmetic Product Mfr & Distr
N.A.I.C.S.: 325620

PATHE MOTORWAY S.A.
Moschochori, Larissa, 415 00, Greece
Tel.: (30) 2410 680300   GR
Web Site:
  http://www.aegeanmotorway.gr
Holding Company: Highway Construction
N.A.I.C.S.: 551112
Nikolaos Antzoulakos *(CFO)*

Subsidiaries:

Aegean Motorway S.A. (1)
Moschochori, 441500, Larissa, Greece (100%)
Tel.: (30) 2410680300
Web Site: http://www.aegeanmotorway.gr
Sales Range: $100-124.9 Million
Emp.: 410
Design, Construction, Financing, Operation & Maintenance of Highways
N.A.I.C.S.: 237310
Nikolaos Antzoulakos *(CFO)*

PATHE SA
2 Rue Lamennais, Paris, 75008, France
Tel.: (33) 1 71 72 30 00   FR
Web Site: http://www.pathe.com
Year Founded: 1896
Sales Range: $800-899.9 Million
Emp.: 1,920
Television & Motion Picture Entertainment Company
N.A.I.C.S.: 512110
Georges Bonopera *(Gen Mgr-Travels)*

Subsidiaries:

Europalaces Sarl (1)
2 Rue Lamennais, 75008, Paris, France
Tel.: (33) 171723000
Web Site: http://www.qruelamennais.com
Motion Picture & Video Production
N.A.I.C.S.: 512110

Pathe Entertainment Ltd (1)
6 Ramillies St, London, W1F 7TY, United Kingdom
Tel.: (44) 2073235151
Web Site: http://www.pathe.co.uk
Sales Range: $25-49.9 Million
Emp.: 20
Motion Picture & Video Distribution
N.A.I.C.S.: 512120
Camerin McCraken *(Mng Dir)*

Pathe Finance Sarl (1)
2 Rue Lamennais, 75008, Paris, France
Tel.: (33) 171723000
Web Site: http://www.pathe.com
Management Consulting Services
N.A.I.C.S.: 541618

Pathe Productions Ltd (1)
6 Ramillies Street, London, W1F 7TY, United Kingdom
Tel.: (44) 2073235151
Web Site: http://www.pathe.co.uk

INTERNATIONAL PUBLIC

Sales Range: $25-49.9 Million
Emp.: 25
Motion Picture & Video Production
N.A.I.C.S.: 512110

PATHFINDR LTD.
The Glasshouse Kings Lane, Norwich, NR1 3PS, United Kingdom
Tel.: (44) 1603327166
Web Site: https://pathfindr.io
Year Founded: 2016
Aircraft Repair Services
N.A.I.C.S.: 488190

PATIDAR BUILDCON LIMITED
Lati Bazar Joravarnagar, Surendranagar, 363020, Gujrat, India
Tel.: (91) 2752231526
Web Site:
  https://www.patidarbuildconltd.in
Year Founded: 1986
524031—(BOM)
Rev.: $137,054
Assets: $1,272,957
Liabilities: $437,744
Net Worth: $835,214
Earnings: $2,650
Emp.: 7
Fiscal Year-end: 03/31/23
Real Estate Development Services
N.A.I.C.S.: 531390
Rajnikant Ramjibhai Patel *(Mng Dir)*

PATIENTSKY GROUP AS
Postboks 748, Sentrum, NO-0106, Oslo, Norway
Tel.: (47) 45113331
Web Site: https://www.patientsky.com
Year Founded: 2014
CQDE—(OSL)
Rev.: $9,226,083
Assets: $13,576,103
Liabilities: $447,143
Net Worth: $13,128,960
Earnings: $2,953,285
Emp.: 29
Fiscal Year-end: 12/31/23
Software Development Services
N.A.I.C.S.: 541511
Christoffer Mathiesen *(CFO)*

Subsidiaries:

Hove Medical Systems AS (1)
Hove Medical Dyrmyrgata 35, 3611, Kongsberg, Norway
Tel.: (47) 21931918
Web Site: https://www.hovemedical.no
Medical Software Development Services
N.A.I.C.S.: 541511

PATIMAS COMPUTERS BERHAD
Patimas Technology Ctr Technology Pk Malaysia Bukit Jalil, 57000, Kuala Lumpur, Malaysia
Tel.: (60) 389941818
Web Site: http://www.patimas.com
Sales Range: $50-74.9 Million
Telecommunication Servicesb
N.A.I.C.S.: 541618
Jarnail Singh *(CEO)*

Subsidiaries:

Patimas Computer Security Sdn Bhd (1)
Patimas Technology Ctr Technology Pk Malaysia Bukit Jalil, 57000, Kuala Lumpur, Malaysia
Tel.: (60) 389941818
Computer Peripheral Distr
N.A.I.C.S.: 423430

Patimas Computer Systems Sdn Bhd (1)
Technology Park Malaysia Bukit Jalil, Kuala Lumpur, 57000, Malaysia
Tel.: (60) 389941818
Web Site: http://www.patimas.com
Emp.: 15

Computer Hardware & Software Distr
N.A.I.C.S.: 423430

Patimas Outsourcing Services Sdn Bhd (1)
Patimas Technology Centre Technology Park Malaysia Bukit Jalil, 57000, Kuala Lumpur, Wilayah Persekutuan, Malaysia
Tel.: (60) 389941628
Computer Software Development Services
N.A.I.C.S.: 541511

Patimas-HPD Systems Sdn Bhd (1)
Patimas Technology Centre Technology Park Malaysia Bukit Jalil, 57000, Kuala Lumpur, Malaysia
Tel.: (60) 389941818
Sales Range: $75-99.9 Million
Emp.: 120
Printer Distr
N.A.I.C.S.: 423430

PATISSERIE HOLDINGS PLC
146-158 Sarehole Road, Hall Green, Birmingham, B28 8DT, United Kingdom
Tel.: (44) 121 777 7000 UK
Web Site: http://investors.patisserie.co.uk
Year Founded: 2014
Rev.: $143,179,057
Assets: $124,026,161
Liabilities: $8,261,222
Net Worth: $115,764,938
Earnings: $20,517,020
Emp.: 2,949
Fiscal Year-end: 09/30/17
Holding Company; Retail Bakeries & Cafe Operator
N.A.I.C.S.: 551112
Luke Oliver Johnson *(Chm)*

Subsidiaries:

Patisserie Valerie Limited (1)
146-156 Sarehole Road, Hall Green, Birmingham, B28 8DT, United Kingdom
Tel.: (44) 121 777 7000
Web Site: http://www.patisserie-valerie.co.uk
Retail Bakeries & Cafe Operator
N.A.I.C.S.: 311811
Jose Peralta *(Dir-Food Production & Supply)*

PATKOL PUBLIC COMPANY LIMITED
348 Chaloem Phrakiat Rd Rama 9, Nong Bon Subdistrict Prawet District, Bangkok, 10250, Thailand
Tel.: (66) 23281035
Web Site: https://www.patkol.com
Year Founded: 1965
PK—(THA)
Rev.: $50,551,857
Assets: $102,016,099
Liabilities: $59,733,270
Net Worth: $42,282,829
Earnings: ($4,207,925)
Emp.: 945
Fiscal Year-end: 12/31/23
Refrigeration & Food Machinery Mfr
N.A.I.C.S.: 333415
Sangchai Chotechuangchutchaval *(Vice Chm & CEO)*

Subsidiaries:

PKB Enterprise Co., Ltd. (1)
838 Charoen Nakorn Re, Klongsan, Bangkok, 10600, Thailand
Tel.: (66) 24377622
Web Site: http://www.pkb.com
Sales Range: $25-49.9 Million
Emp.: 30
Sheet Insulation Finish Production & Installation Services
N.A.I.C.S.: 331315

PATLON AIRCRAFT & INDUSTRIES, LTD.
8130 5th Line, Halton Hills, L7G 0B8, ON, Canada
Tel.: (905) 864-8706
Web Site: http://www.patlon.com
Year Founded: 1953
Aircraft Spares & Custom Components & Systems Mfr
N.A.I.C.S.: 336412
Cheryl Patlon *(Dir-Ops)*

PATO CHEMICAL INDUSTRY PUBLIC CO., LTD.
Pato Building 3388 New Petchburi Road Bangkapi Huaykwang, Bangkok, 10310, Thailand
Tel.: (66) 23185612
Web Site: https://www.patochemical.com
Year Founded: 1972
PATO—(THA)
Rev.: $17,317,179
Assets: $16,589,846
Liabilities: $2,165,788
Net Worth: $14,424,058
Earnings: $2,067,906
Emp.: 72
Fiscal Year-end: 12/31/23
Agrochemical Products Formulator & Distr
N.A.I.C.S.: 325320
Metha Trillit *(Chm, Pres & Mgr-Factory-Acting)*

PATRIA BANK S.A.
42 Soseaua Pipera Globalworth Plaza Building Floors 7 8 & 10, PO Box 020112, Bucharest, Romania
Tel.: (40) 800410310
Web Site: http://www.en.patriabank.ro
Year Founded: 1993
Commercial Banking Services
N.A.I.C.S.: 522110
Dragos Horia Manda *(Chm)*

PATRIA INVESTIMENTOS SA
Avenida Cidade Jardim 803 10th Floor, Sao Paulo, 01453-000, Brazil
Tel.: (55) 11 3039 9000
Web Site: http://www.patria.com
Year Founded: 1988
Sales Range: $5-14.9 Billion
Private Equity Services
N.A.I.C.S.: 523999
Otavio Castello Branco *(Partner)*

Subsidiaries:

AlphaVille Urbanismo S.A. (1)
United Nations Avenue 8501, Pinheiros, Sao Paulo, 05425-070, Brazil
Tel.: (55) 1130305100
Web Site: http://www.alphavilleurbanismo.com.br
Urban Residential Development & Building
N.A.I.C.S.: 925120

PATRIA INVESTMENTS LIMITED
60 Nexus Way 4th floor, PO Box 757, Camana Bay, KY1-9006, Cayman Islands
Tel.: (345) 6404900 Ky
Web Site: https://www.patria.com
Year Founded: 2007
PAX—(NASDAQ)
Rev.: $258,877,000
Assets: $976,238,000
Liabilities: $462,780,000
Net Worth: $513,458,000
Earnings: $94,104,000
Emp.: 385
Fiscal Year-end: 12/31/22
Investment Services
N.A.I.C.S.: 523940
Marco Nicola D'Ippolito *(Chief Corp Dev Officer)*

PATRIA LATIN AMERICAN OP-
PORTUNITY ACQUISITION CORP.
18 Forum Lane 3rd floor, PO Box 757, Grand Cayman, Georgetown, KY1-9006, Cayman Islands
Tel.: (345) 6404900 Ky
Web Site: https://patrialatamgrowth.com
Year Founded: 2021
PLAO—(NASDAQ)
Assets: $241,327,491
Liabilities: $250,773,757
Net Worth: ($9,446,266)
Earnings: $9,256,245
Emp.: 2
Fiscal Year-end: 12/31/22
Investment Services
N.A.I.C.S.: 523999
Ana Cristina Russo *(CFO)*

PATRIA OYJ
Kaivokatu 10A, Helsinki, 100, Finland
Tel.: (358) 204691 FI
Web Site: http://www.patria.fi
Year Founded: 1997
Aerospace & Defense Group
N.A.I.C.S.: 541330
Pasi Niinikoski *(Chief Bus Dev Officer)*

Subsidiaries:

Millog Oy (1)
Sarvijaakonkatu 3 A, 33540, Tampere, Finland
Tel.: (358) 20 469 7000
Web Site: http://www.millog.fi
Optical Product Mfr
N.A.I.C.S.: 333310
Heikki Allonen *(Chm)*

Nammo AS (1)
Enggata 37, 2830, Raufoss, Norway (50%)
Tel.: (47) 61153600
Web Site: http://www.nammo.com
Rev.: $576,070,830
Assets: $707,271,383
Liabilities: $392,060,557
Net Worth: $315,210,826
Earnings: $21,826,922
Emp.: 2,377
Fiscal Year-end: 12/31/2019
Ordnance, Small Arms Ammunition & Missile Mfr; Joint Venture of Patria Oyj & The Norwegian Ministry of Trade & Industry
N.A.I.C.S.: 332994
Raimo Helasmaki *(Exec VP-Comml Ammunition)*

Subsidiary (US):

Capstone Precision Group, LLC (2)
4051 N Higley Rd, Mesa, AZ 85215
Tel.: (714) 441-7202
Web Site: http://www.bergerbullets.com
Rifle Bullets Mfr
N.A.I.C.S.: 332992

Subsidiary (Non-US):

Nammo Artillery Center Oy (2)
Hatanpaan valtatie 26, 33100, Tampere, Finland (100%)
Tel.: (358) 64310111
Sales Range: $25-49.9 Million
Emp.: 160
Small Arms Ammunition Mfr
N.A.I.C.S.: 332992

Nammo Australia Pty Ltd. (2)
14/38 Down Street, Collingwood, 3066, VIC, Australia (100%)
Tel.: (61) 408 762 370
Web Site: http://www.nammo.com
Sales & Industrial Specialty Munitions Mfr
N.A.I.C.S.: 332993
Robert Wellwood *(Mng Dir)*

Subsidiary (Domestic):

Nammo Bakelittfabrikken AS (2)
Bogstadfeltet, Aurskog, 1930, Oslo, Norway (100%)
Tel.: (47) 63865950
Web Site: http://www.nammo.com
Small Arms Ammunition Mfr
N.A.I.C.S.: 332992
John Vaagland *(Mgr)*

Subsidiary (Non-US):

Nammo Cheltenham Ltd. (2)
Unit 36 Cheltenham Trade Park, Cheltenham, GL51 8LZ, Glos, United Kingdom
Tel.: (44) 1242 548 780
Web Site: http://www.nammo.com
Emp.: 13
Aerospace Propulsion Equipment Mfr
N.A.I.C.S.: 336415

Nammo Germany GmbH (2)
PO Box 1462, Schonebeck, 39218, Bremen, Germany (100%)
Tel.: (49) 3928729102
Sales Range: $25-49.9 Million
Emp.: 4
Small Arms Ammunition Mfr
N.A.I.C.S.: 332992

Subsidiary (US):

Nammo Inc. (2)
2000 N 14th St Ste 250, Arlington, VA 22201 (100%)
Tel.: (703) 524-6100
Web Site: http://www.nammo.com
Sales Range: $25-49.9 Million
Emp.: 6
Law firm
N.A.I.C.S.: 541199
Peter Sioma *(CEO)*

Subsidiary (Non-US):

Nammo Ireland Limited (2)
Unit 15-17 Northwest Business Park, Ballycoolin, Dublin, 15, Ireland (100%)
Tel.: (353) 1 861 0010
Web Site: http://www.nammo.com
Aerospace Propulsion Equipment Mfr
N.A.I.C.S.: 336415

Nammo Lapua Oy (2)
Patruunatehtaantie 15, PO Box 5, Lapua, 62101, Finland
Tel.: (358) 64310111
Web Site: http://www.lapua.com
Sales Range: $25-49.9 Million
Emp.: 150
Ammunition Cartridges & Components Mfr
N.A.I.C.S.: 332992
Raimo Helarmaki *(Mgr)*

Subsidiary (Domestic):

Nordic Distribution Oy (3)
Patruunatehtaantie 15, Lapua, 62100, Finland (100%)
Tel.: (358) 643103011
Web Site: http://www.nordis.fi
Sporting & Recreational Goods & Supplies Whslr
N.A.I.C.S.: 423910

Affiliate (Domestic):

Nammo NAD AS (2)
Lokken Verk, 7332, Trondheim, Norway (50%)
Tel.: (47) 72497080
Web Site: http://www.nammo.com
Sales Range: $25-49.9 Million
Emp.: 10
Small Arms Ammunition Mfr
N.A.I.C.S.: 332992

Subsidiary (US):

Nammo Perry Inc. (2)
10625 Puckett Rd, Perry, FL 32348
Tel.: (850) 584-2634
Web Site: http://www.nammo.com
Sales Range: $50-74.9 Million
Emp.: 250
Ammunition & Pyrotechnic Products Mfr
N.A.I.C.S.: 332994
Michael Quesenberry *(Pres)*

Nammo Pocal Inc. (2)
100 Electric St, Scranton, PA 18509
Tel.: (570) 961-1999
Web Site: http://www.nammo.com
Sales Range: $1-9.9 Million
Emp.: 70
Mortar Training Ammunition Mfr
N.A.I.C.S.: 332993

PATRIA OYJ

Patria Oyj—(Continued)

Subsidiary (Domestic):

Nammo Raufoss AS (2)
Enggata 10, PO Box 162, 2831, Raufoss, Norway
Tel.: (47) 61153650
Sales Range: $100-124.9 Million
Emp.: 400
Ammunition & Missile System Mfr
N.A.I.C.S.: 332993

Subsidiary (Non-US):

Nammo Schonebeck GmbH (2)
Wilhelm-Dumling Str 12, PO Box 1462, 39218, Schonebeck, Germany
Tel.: (49) 3928 729 100
Web Site: http://www.nammo.com
Emp.: 70
Small Arms Ammunition Mfr
N.A.I.C.S.: 332992

Nammo Sweden AB (2)
Vingakersverken, 64392, Vingaker, Sweden (100%)
Tel.: (46) 15119500
Web Site: http://www.nammo.com
Sales Range: $350-399.9 Million
Emp.: 1,700
Small Arms Ammunition Mfr
N.A.I.C.S.: 332992

Subsidiary (Domestic):

Hansson PyroTech AB (3)
Kopingsvagen 35, 711 31, Lindesberg, Sweden
Tel.: (46) 58187250
Web Site: http://www.ikarossignals.com
Naval Pyrotechnic Distress Signal Equipment Mfr
N.A.I.C.S.: 325920

Nammo Demil Division AB (3)
Vingakersverken, Vingaker, 64392, Sweden
Tel.: (46) 15119500
Web Site: http://www.nammo.com
Sales Range: $25-49.9 Million
Emp.: 70
Ammunition Demilitarization & Disposal Services
N.A.I.C.S.: 541330
Urban Oholm (Sr VP)

Nammo LIAB AB (3)
Kengsvrigan, PO Box 154, S 711 23, Lindesberg, Sweden
Tel.: (46) 58187100
Web Site: http://www.nammo.com
Sales Range: $10-24.9 Million
Emp.: 135
Aerodynamics & Defence Systems
N.A.I.C.S.: 334511
Lars Pihl (Dir-Mktg)

Nammo Sweden AB (3)
Vingakersverken, SE-643 92, Vingaker, Sweden
Tel.: (46) 15119500
Web Site: http://www.nammo.com
Business Support Services (for Ammunition Mfg)
N.A.I.C.S.: 332992

Vanasverken AB (3)
PO Box 4, Karlsborg, 54623, Linkoping, Sweden (100%)
Tel.: (46) 50518100
Web Site: http://www.nammo.com
Ordnance & Accessories Mfr
N.A.I.C.S.: 332994
Peter Ambjornsson (Pres)

Subsidiary (US):

Nammo Talley, Inc. (2)
4051 N Higley Rd, Mesa, AZ 85215-4299
Tel.: (480) 898-2200
Web Site: http://www.nammo.com
Sales Range: $50-74.9 Million
Emp.: 225
Propellant-Based Propulsion Systems & Products Mfr
N.A.I.C.S.: 336415
Michael W. Trapp (Mgr-Bus Dev-Core Products & Advanced Tech)

Subsidiary (Non-US):

Nammo Vihtavuori Oy (2)

Vihtavuori Site Ruutitehtaantie 80, 41330, Vihtavuori, Finland
Tel.: (358) 14 3779 211
Web Site: http://www.nammo.com
Sales Range: $75-99.9 Million
Emp.: 100
Production & Sale of Propellants & Ignition Powders for Munitions & Associated Raw Materials
N.A.I.C.S.: 325998
Ilkka Heikkilae (Mng Dir)

Nammo Westcott Ltd. (2)
Building 47 Westcott Venture Park, Westcott, Aylesbury, HP18 0NZ, Bucks, United Kingdom
Tel.: (44) 1296 652 065
Web Site: http://www.nammo.com
Emp.: 22
Aerospace Propulsion Equipment Mfr
N.A.I.C.S.: 336415

Affiliate (Non-US):

Nammon Works Oy (2)
Caakolanpie, Usialoeonai, 26500, Uusikaupunki, Finland (50%)
Tel.: (358) 28481400
Ordnance & Accessories Mfr
N.A.I.C.S.: 332994
Raimo Helasmaaki (Exec VP)

Oricopa Oy (1)
Hatanpaan valtatie 30, 33100, Tampere, Finland
Tel.: (358) 20 734 3500
Web Site: http://www.oricopa.fi
Defense Equipment Mfr
N.A.I.C.S.: 336992
Mika Raty (Mng Dir)

Patria Aerostructures Oy (1)
Lentokonetehtaantie 3, Halli, 35600, Finland
Tel.: (358) 204691
Web Site: http://www.patria.com
Composite Structures Mfr
N.A.I.C.S.: 336413

Patria Aviation Oy (1)
Lentokonetehtaantie 3, 35600, Halli, Finland
Tel.: (358) 204691
Web Site: http://www.patria.fi
Sales Range: $125-149.9 Million
Emp.: 500
Aviation Maintenance & Support Services
N.A.I.C.S.: 488119
Birgitta Selonen (Chief Comm Officer)

Patria Czech s.r.o. (1)
Boruvkova 781, Horni Jircany, 252 42, Jesenice, Czech Republic
Tel.: (420) 606 768 437
Aircraft Engineering Services
N.A.I.C.S.: 541330

Patria Helicopters AB (1)
Helikoptervagen 1, PO Box 116, 190 46, Stockholm, Arlanda, Sweden
Tel.: (46) 859378700
Web Site: http://www.patriahelicopters.com
Sales Range: $25-49.9 Million
Emp.: 50
Helicopter Assembly, Maintenance & Support Services
N.A.I.C.S.: 541330
Youni Majuri (VP)

Patria Helicopters AS (1)
Bardufoss Lufthavn Troms, 9325, Bardufoss, Norway
Tel.: (47) 77 836 668
Web Site: http://www.patriahelicopters.com
Emp.: 8
Aircraft Engineering Services
N.A.I.C.S.: 541330
Dan Nordheim (Mng Dir & Country Mgr)

Patria Land Services Oy (1)
Autotehtaantie 6, PO Box 186, 13101, Hameenlinna, Finland
Tel.: (358) 204691
Web Site: http://www.patria.fi
Sales Range: $200-249.9 Million
Emp.: 1,000
Armored Wheeled Vehicle Mfr
N.A.I.C.S.: 336992

Patria Pilot Training Oy (1)
Helsinki-Malmi Airport, Helsinki, FI-00700, Finland
Tel.: (358) 204691

Pilot School & Training Services
N.A.I.C.S.: 611512
Mikko Paronen (CEO)

Patria Polska Sp. z o.o. (1)
ul Prusa 2, 00-493, Warsaw, Poland
Tel.: (48) 22 657 03 61
Aircraft Engineering Services
N.A.I.C.S.: 541330

PATRIMOINE ET COMMERCE
7 rue Nationale, 92100, Boulogne-Billancourt, France
Tel.: (33) 146994779 FR
Web Site: http://www.patrimoine-commerce.com
PAT—(EUR)
Rev.: $49,354,780
Assets: $996,243,740
Liabilities: $527,881,560
Net Worth: $468,362,180
Earnings: $35,237,280
Fiscal Year-end: 12/31/21
Commercial Real Estate Investment, Management & Leasing Services
N.A.I.C.S.: 531120
Eric Duval (Founder & Mng Dir)

PATRIOT BATTERY METALS INC.
Suite 500 666 Burrard Str, Vancouver, V6C 3P6, BC, Canada
Tel.: (778) 945-2950 BC
Web Site: http://www.gaiametalscorp.com
Year Founded: 2007
PMETF—(OTCQX)
Rev.: $21,796,558
Assets: $183,139,543
Liabilities: $33,021,349
Net Worth: $150,118,194
Earnings: $1,925,094
Emp.: 17
Fiscal Year-end: 03/31/24
Junior Exploration Company
N.A.I.C.S.: 212290
Dusan Berka (CFO)

PATRIOT FORGE CO.
280 Henry Street, PO Box 996, Brantford, N3S 7R5, ON, Canada
Tel.: (519) 758-8100
Web Site: http://www.patriotforge.com
Custom Forged Components
N.A.I.C.S.: 332111
Jim Anderson (Mgr-Sls-Western Canada & United States Pacific North West Reg)

Subsidiaries:

Patriot Forge (1)
1802 Cranberry St, Erie, PA 16502-1551
Tel.: (814) 456-2088
Web Site: http://www.patriotforge.com
Sales Range: $25-49.9 Million
Emp.: 4
Mfr of Precision Steel Forgings
N.A.I.C.S.: 331110

Patriot Special Metals, Inc. (1)
2201 Harrison Ave S W, Canton, OH 44076
Tel.: (330) 580-9600
Web Site: http://www.patriotspecialmetals.com
Stainless Steel Bar Mfr & Distr
N.A.I.C.S.: 331110
Paul Olah (VP-Bus Dev)

PATRIOT LITHIUM LIMITED
Suite 6 245 Churchill Avenue, Subiaco, 6008, WA, Australia
Tel.: (61) 413621652
Web Site: https://www.patriot-lithium.com
Year Founded: 2021
PAT—(ASX)
Exploration & Mining Services
N.A.I.C.S.: 213115
Cameron O'Brien (CFO)

INTERNATIONAL PUBLIC

PATRIS INVESTIMENTOS SGPS, S.A.
rua Duque de Palmela 37 3, 1250-097, Lisbon, Portugal
Tel.: (351) 210438893
Web Site: http://www.patris.pt
ALPTR—(EUR)
Sales Range: $25-49.9 Million
Securities Brokerage Services
N.A.I.C.S.: 523150
Goncalo Pereira Coutinho (Chm & CEO)

PATRIZIA SE
Fuggerstrasse 26, 86150, Augsburg, Germany
Tel.: (49) 82150910000
Web Site: https://www.patrizia.ag
Year Founded: 1984
PAT—(DEU)
Rev.: $370,551,410
Assets: $2,409,908,824
Liabilities: $850,652,003
Net Worth: $1,559,256,821
Earnings: $46,308,333
Emp.: 881
Fiscal Year-end: 12/31/20
Real Estate Services
N.A.I.C.S.: 531210
Theodor Seitz (Chm-Supervisory Bd)

Subsidiaries:

ADVANTAGE Investment Partners A/S (1)
Bredgade 40, 1260, Copenhagen, Denmark
Tel.: (45) 31501757
Web Site: https://www.advantage-ip.com
Investment Management Service
N.A.I.C.S.: 523940

PARRIZIA Activos Inmobiliarios Espana S.L.U. (1)
Genova 27, 28004, Madrid, Spain
Tel.: (34) 917698950
Real Estate Investment Services
N.A.I.C.S.: 523999
Alvaro Basterrechea (Assoc Dir)

PATRIZIA Acquisition & Consulting GmbH. (1)
Fuggerstrasse 26, 86150, Augsburg, Germany
Tel.: (49) 82150910200
Sales Range: $150-199.9 Million
Emp.: 280
Real Estate Services
N.A.I.C.S.: 531390

PATRIZIA Augsburg Kapitalverwaltungsgesellschaft mbH (1)
Fuggerstrasse 26, 86150, Augsburg, Germany
Tel.: (49) 82150910000
Real Estate Investment Services
N.A.I.C.S.: 523999

PATRIZIA Denmark A/S (1)
Adelgade 15 2, 1304, Copenhagen, Denmark
Tel.: (45) 33186868
Web Site: http://www.patrizia.dk
Emp.: 27
Real Estate Services
N.A.I.C.S.: 531390
Charlotte Svalgaard (Mgr-Asset-Residential)

PATRIZIA Deutschland GmbH (1)
Kurfurstendamm 21, 10719, Berlin, Germany
Tel.: (49) 30206086636
Real Estate Investment Services
N.A.I.C.S.: 523999

PATRIZIA Finland Oy (1)
Katariinankatu 1 3 OG, 00170, Helsinki, Finland
Tel.: (358) 306705350
Real Estate Investment Services
N.A.I.C.S.: 523999
Mikko Vaisanen (Mgr-Investment)

PATRIZIA France SAS (1)
2 rue de Clichy, 75009, Paris, France
Tel.: (33) 156640404
Real Estate Investment Services

AND PRIVATE COMPANIES

N.A.I.C.S.: 523999

PATRIZIA Hong Kong Limited (1)
4/F Lee Garden Three 1 Sunning Road, Causeway Bay, China (Hong Kong)
Tel.: (852) 37696229
Real Estate Investment Services
N.A.I.C.S.: 523999

PATRIZIA Immobilien Kapitalan- lagegesellschaft mbH. (1)
Fuggerstrasse 26, 86150, Augsburg, Bavaria, Germany
Tel.: (49) 82150910451
Real Estate Asset Management Services
N.A.I.C.S.: 531390

PATRIZIA Immobilien Kapitalverwaltungs-gesellschaft mbH (1)
Burchardstrasse 14, 20095, Hamburg, Germany
Tel.: (49) 40284067400
Real Estate Investment Services
N.A.I.C.S.: 523999

PATRIZIA Immobilienmanagement GmbH. (1)
Fuggerstrasse 26, 86150, Augsburg, Germany
Tel.: (49) 82150910100
Web Site: http://www.patrizia.ag
Sales Range: $150-199.9 Million
Emp.: 300
Real Estate Manangement Services
N.A.I.C.S.: 531390

PATRIZIA Investmentmanagement GmbH. (1)
Fuggerstrasse 26, Augsburg, 86150, Germany
Tel.: (49) 82150910500
Web Site: http://www.patrizia.ag
Sales Range: $50-74.9 Million
Emp.: 15
Real Estate Management Services
N.A.I.C.S.: 531390

PATRIZIA Ireland Ltd. (1)
Tel.: (353) 6698561
Real Estate Investment Services
N.A.I.C.S.: 523999
David Egan *(Assoc Dir & Mgr-Asset)*

PATRIZIA Japan KK (1)
6/F BIZCORE Akasaka Mitsuke 3-1-2 Akasak, Minato-ku, Tokyo, 107-0052, Japan
Tel.: (81) 345632900
Real Estate Investment Services
N.A.I.C.S.: 523999
Kazuko Ito *(Assoc Dir-Fund Svcs)*

PATRIZIA Multi Managers A/S (1)
Strandvejen 102 E 4th Floor, 2900, Hellerup, Denmark
Tel.: (45) 36347044
Real Estate Investment Services
N.A.I.C.S.: 523999

PATRIZIA Netherlands B.V. (1)
Fred Roeskestraat 111, 1076 EE, Amsterdam, Netherlands
Tel.: (31) 208203909
Real Estate Investment Services
N.A.I.C.S.: 523999
Rudo Mulder *(Assoc Dir-Transactions)*

PATRIZIA Projekt 110 GmbH. (1)
Fuggerstrasse 26, 86150, Augsburg, Germany
Tel.: (49) 82150910700
Web Site: http://www.patrizia.ag
Emp.: 600
Real Estate Property Development Services
N.A.I.C.S.: 531210

PATRIZIA Projekt 180 GmbH. (1)
Fuggerstr 26, 86150, Augsburg, Germany
Tel.: (49) 82150910600
Sales Range: $150-199.9 Million
Emp.: 300
Real Estate Project Management Services
N.A.I.C.S.: 531390

PATRIZIA Projekt 240 GmbH. (1)
Fugter St 26, 86150, Augsburg, Bavaria, Germany
Tel.: (49) 82150910600
Web Site: http://www.patrizia.ag
Emp.: 300

Real Estate Manangement Services
N.A.I.C.S.: 531311

PATRIZIA Projekt 280 Verwaltungs GmbH. (1)
Fukker Str 26, 86150, Augsburg, Bavaria, Germany
Tel.: (49) 82150910600
Web Site: http://www.patrizia.ag
Sales Range: $75-99.9 Million
Emp.: 180
Real Estate Property Development Services
N.A.I.C.S.: 531210

PATRIZIA Projektentwicklung GmbH. (1)
Fuggerstrasse 26, 86150, Augsburg, Germany
Tel.: (49) 82150910700
Sales Range: $150-199.9 Million
Emp.: 280
Real Estate Manangement Services
N.A.I.C.S.: 531312

PATRIZIA Real Estate Investment Management S.a.r.l. (1)
2-4 Rue Beck, 1222, Luxembourg, Luxembourg
Tel.: (352) 26638400
Real Estate Investment Services
N.A.I.C.S.: 523999

PATRIZIA Sweden AB (1)
Vasagatan 15-17, 111 20, Stockholm, Sweden
Tel.: (46) 703242070
Real Estate Investment Services
N.A.I.C.S.: 523999
Pauline Von Troil *(Assoc Dir & Mgr-Asset)*

PATRIZIA UK Limited (1)
166 Sloane Street, London, SW1X 9QF, United Kingdom
Tel.: (44) 2077613300
Real Estate Investment Services
N.A.I.C.S.: 523999
Tom Stenhouse *(Mng Dir)*

PATRIZIA Wohnen GmbH. (1)
Fuggerstrasse 26, 86150, Augsburg, Germany
Tel.: (49) 82150910500
Sales Range: $150-199.9 Million
Emp.: 280
Real Estate Asset Management Services
N.A.I.C.S.: 531390

Patrizia Infrastructure Ltd. (1)
5th Floor 17 St Swithins Lane, London, EC4N 8AL, United Kingdom
Tel.: (44) 2071836120
Real Estate Investment Services
N.A.I.C.S.: 531390

Patrizia Pty. Ltd. (1)
Level 1 39 Brisbane Avenue, Barton, 2600, ACT, Australia
Tel.: (61) 262731222
Real Estate Investment Services
N.A.I.C.S.: 531390

Projekt Wasserturm Bau GmbH & Co. KG. (1)
Fuggerstrasse 26, 86150, Augsburg, Germany
Tel.: (49) 821509100
Sales Range: $50-74.9 Million
Emp.: 350
Real Estate Manangement Services
N.A.I.C.S.: 531312

Projekt Wasserturm Verwaltungs GmbH. (1)
Fuggerstr 26, 86150, Augsburg, Germany
Tel.: (49) 82150910600
Sales Range: $150-199.9 Million
Real Estate Manangement Services
N.A.I.C.S.: 531312

Wohnungsgesellschaft Olympia mbH. (1)
Fugger Strasse 26, 86150, Augsburg, Germany
Tel.: (49) 821509100
Sales Range: $75-99.9 Million
Emp.: 130
Real Estate & Property Management Services
N.A.I.C.S.: 531312
Wolfgang Etter *(Mng Dir)*

PATRON CAPITAL ADVISERS LLP
One Vine Street, London, W1J 0AH, United Kingdom
Tel.: (44) 2076299417 UK
Web Site:
http://www.patroncapital.com
Year Founded: 1999
Privater Equity Firm
N.A.I.C.S.: 523999
Keith Breslauer *(Sr Partner & Mng Dir)*

Subsidiaries:

Patron Capital Europe S.a.r.l (1)
5 Rue Guillaume Kroll, 1882, Luxembourg, Luxembourg
Tel.: (352) 26 26 89 1
Financial Investment Advisory Services
N.A.I.C.S.: 523940
Geraldine Schmit *(Mng Dir)*

Patron Capital Iberia (1)
Passeig de Gracia 74, 8007, Barcelona, Spain
Tel.: (34) 93 467 91 00
Financial Investment Advisory Services
N.A.I.C.S.: 523940
Pedro Barcelo *(Mng Dir)*

Patron Capital Italia Srl (1)
Viale Tunisia 50, 20124, Milan, Italy
Tel.: (39) 02 798416
Web Site: http://www.patroncapital.it
Financial Investment Advisory Services
N.A.I.C.S.: 523940
Maria Matusiewicz *(Office Mgr)*

Powerleague Group Limited (1)
Anchor Grounds Blackhall Street, Paisley, PA1 1TD, United Kingdom
Tel.: (44) 1418877758
Web Site: http://www.powerleague.co.uk
Sales Range: $25-49.9 Million
Emp.: 685
Soccer Centers Operator
N.A.I.C.S.: 713990
Nigel Hargreaves *(Dir-Comml)*

Punch Taverns Limited (1)
Jubilee House Second Avenue, Burton-on-Trent, DE14 2WF, Staffs, United Kingdom
Tel.: (44) 1283501600
Web Site: http://www.punchpubs.com
Holding Company; Pub Operator
N.A.I.C.S.: 551112
Steve Dando *(CFO)*

Subsidiary (Domestic):

Punch Partnerships (PML) Limited (2)
Jubilee House Second Avenue, Burton-on-Trent, DE14 2WF, Staffs, United Kingdom
Tel.: (44) 1283501600
Web Site: http://www.punchtaverns.com
Pub Operator
N.A.I.C.S.: 722410

Punch Partnerships (PTL) Limited (2)
Elsley Court 20-22 Great Titchfield Street, London, W1W 8BE, United Kingdom
Tel.: (44) 1283501600
Web Site: http://www.punchtaverns.com
Pub Operator
N.A.I.C.S.: 722410

Punch Taverns (Services) Limited (2)
Jubilee House Second Avenue, Burton-on-Trent, DE14 2WF, Staffs, United Kingdom
Tel.: (44) 1283501600
Web Site: http://www.punchtaverns.com
Office Administrative & Technical Support Services
N.A.I.C.S.: 561110

Punch Taverns Finance PLC (2)
Elsley Court 20-22 Great Titchfield Street, London, W1W 8BE, United Kingdom
Tel.: (44) 1283501600
Web Site: http://www.punchtaverns.com
Financial Support Services
N.A.I.C.S.: 522299

PATRON EXIM LIMITED

411 Safal Prelude Corporate Road, Prahlad Nagar, Ahmedabad, 380015, Gujarat, India
Tel.: (91) 9979978393
Web Site:
https://www.patronexim.com
Year Founded: 1982
543798—(BOM)
Pharmaceutical Product Mfr & Distr
N.A.I.C.S.: 325412
Narendrakumar Patel *(Chm)*

PATRONALE LIFE NV
Bischoffsheimlaan 33, 1000, Brussels, Belgium
Tel.: (32) 2511 6006 BE
Web Site: http://www.patronale-life.be
Year Founded: 1926
Life Insurance Products & Services
N.A.I.C.S.: 524113
Filip Moeykens *(CEO)*

Subsidiaries:

Banimmo S.A. (1)
Bischoffsheimlaan 33, 1932, Zaventem, Belgium **(60.13%)**
Tel.: (32) 27105311
Web Site: https://www.banimmo.be
Sales Range: $1-9.9 Million
Real Estate Investment & Development Services
N.A.I.C.S.: 531390
Damien Darche *(Chief Dev Officer)*

Subsidiary (Domestic):

Immo Koningslo NV (2)
Lenneke Marelaan 8, 1932, Zaventem, Belgium
Tel.: (32) 27105311
Commercial Real Estate Management & Leasing Services
N.A.I.C.S.: 531312
Terlingen Christine *(Gen Mgr)*

PATRONUS RESOURCES LIMITED
Level 1 24 Outram Street, West Perth, 6005, WA, Australia
Tel.: (61) 892422227
Web Site:
https://www.patronusresources.com
Year Founded: 2011
PTN—(ASX)
Rev.: $628,703
Assets: $57,584,918
Liabilities: $1,497,585
Net Worth: $56,087,333
Earnings: $29,164,202
Fiscal Year-end: 06/30/24
Mineral Exploration Services
N.A.I.C.S.: 212290
Giuseppe Paolo Graziano *(Chm)*

Subsidiaries:

PNX Metals Limited (1)
Level 1 135 Fullarton Road, Rose Park, 5067, SA, Australia
Tel.: (61) 883643188
Web Site: https://www.pnxmetals.com.au
Rev.: $90,040
Assets: $18,984,739
Liabilities: $2,829,645
Net Worth: $16,155,094
Earnings: ($962,395)
Emp.: 130
Fiscal Year-end: 06/30/2021
Mineral Mining Services
N.A.I.C.S.: 212230
James Fox *(CEO & Mng Dir)*

PATRYS LIMITED
Level 4 100 Albert Road, Melbourne, 3205, VIC, Australia
Tel.: (61) 396703273
Web Site: https://www.patrys.com
Year Founded: 2006
PAB—(ASX)
Rev.: $930,931
Assets: $2,778,833

PATRYS LIMITED

Patrys Limited—(Continued)
Liabilities: $461,649
Net Worth: $2,317,184
Earnings: ($2,363,214)
Emp.: 10
Fiscal Year-end: 06/30/24
Pharmaceutical Mfr, Researcher & Developer
N.A.I.C.S.: 325412
Deanne Greenwood *(VP-Bus Dev & Intellectual Property)*

Subsidiaries:

Patrys GmbH (1)
Friedrich Bergius Ring 15, 97076, Wurzburg, Germany
Tel.: (49) 93123079514
Sales Range: $25-49.9 Million
Emp.: 8
Pharmaceuticals Product Mfr
N.A.I.C.S.: 325412

PATSPIN INDIA LTD.
3rd Floor Palal Towers M G Road, Ravipuram, Cochin, 682 016, India
Tel.: (91) 4842661900
Web Site: https://gtntextiles.com
PATSPINLTD—(NSE)
Rev.: $9,014,879
Assets: $11,714,010
Liabilities: $13,785,900
Net Worth: ($2,071,890)
Earnings: ($2,176,344)
Emp.: 512
Fiscal Year-end: 03/31/23
Yarn Spinning & Textile Products Mfr
N.A.I.C.S.: 313110
Umang Patodia *(Mng Dir)*

PATTERN SPA
Via Italia 4, 10093, Collegno, TO, Italy
Tel.: (39) 0114531597
Web Site: https://www.patterngroup.it
Year Founded: 2000
PTR—(ITA)
Rev.: $160,721,544
Assets: $119,275,572
Liabilities: $72,366,138
Net Worth: $46,909,435
Earnings: $25,813,919
Emp.: 793
Fiscal Year-end: 12/31/23
Fashion Designing Services
N.A.I.C.S.: 541490
Francesco Martorella *(Founder & Chm)*

Subsidiaries:

Dyloan Bond Factory S.R.L. (1)
Via di P Adalgiso 31-33-35, 66100, Chieti Scalo, CH, Italy
Tel.: (39) 0871574972
Luxury Product Mfr & Distr
N.A.I.C.S.: 315120

Idee Partners S.R.L. (1)
Via E Conti 21, 50018, Scandicci, FI, Italy
Tel.: (39) 0550946967
Emp.: 240
Luxury Product Mfr & Distr
N.A.I.C.S.: 315120

Nuova Nicol S.R.L. (1)
Via Ferrovia 2/A, 40012, Calderara di Reno, BO, Italy
Tel.: (39) 0516469032
Luxury Product Mfr & Distr
N.A.I.C.S.: 315120

S.M.T. - Societa' Manifattura Tessile S.R.L. (1)
Via della Costituzione 37, 42015, Correggio, RE, Italy
Tel.: (39) 0522345229
Luxury Product Mfr & Distr
N.A.I.C.S.: 315120

PATTON & COOKE CO
Unit 100 7795 128th Street, Surrey, V3W 4E6, BC, Canada
Tel.: (604) 591-5374
Web Site: http://www.pattonandcooke.com
Year Founded: 1961
Emp.: 150
Electric Equipment Mfr
N.A.I.C.S.: 335999

PATTYN BELGIUM NV
Hoge Hul 2 8000, Brugge, Belgium
Tel.: (32) 50450480
Web Site: https://www.pattyn.com
Year Founded: 1952
Packing & Machinery Mfg
N.A.I.C.S.: 339991

Subsidiaries:

Visio Nerf SA (1)
1 Rue des Compagnons, 49340, Neuilly, France (76%)
Tel.: (33) 241300010
Web Site: http://www.visionerf.eu
Electronic Products Mfr
N.A.I.C.S.: 334419

PAUL AYOTTE INSURANCE BROKER LTD.
101 Pine Street South, Timmins, P4N 2K1, ON, Canada
Tel.: (705) 360-5200
Web Site: http://www.paib.ca
Year Founded: 1974
Sales Range: $25-49.9 Million
Emp.: 30
Insurance Services
N.A.I.C.S.: 524210
Daniel Ayotte *(Owner)*

PAUL FIEREK SPEDITION GMBH
Fichtenstrasse 7, 69509, Morlenbach, Germany
Tel.: (49) 620118980
Web Site: http://www.fierek.de
Year Founded: 1974
Rev.: $10,345,500
Emp.: 8
Freight Transportation Services
N.A.I.C.S.: 488510
Paul Fierek *(Mng Dir)*

PAUL HARTMANN AG
Paul-Hartmann-Strasse 12, 89522, Heidenheim, Germany
Tel.: (49) 7321360
Web Site: https://www.hartmann.info
PHH2—(DEU)
Rev.: $2,597,693,116
Assets: $2,193,157,877
Liabilities: $1,019,302,519
Net Worth: $1,173,855,358
Earnings: $31,371,985
Emp.: 10,168
Fiscal Year-end: 12/31/23
Medical & Patient Care Products Developer
N.A.I.C.S.: 812199
Britta Fuenfstueck *(Chm-Mgmt Bd, CEO & Dir-Labor Rels)*

Subsidiaries:

Atemzentrum Bad Lippspringe GmbH (1)
Antoniusstrasse 21, Bad Lippspringe, 33175, Germany
Tel.: (49) 5252 93581 16
Health Care Srvices
N.A.I.C.S.: 621999

Bace Comercio Internacional Ltda. (1)
Av Presidente Kennedy No 2299 Part D, Osasco, 06298-190, SP, Brazil
Tel.: (55) 1131680226
Web Site: http://www.bace.com.br
Medical Care Product Mfr
N.A.I.C.S.: 339113

Bode Chemie GmbH & Co. (1)
Melanchthonstrasse 27, 22525, Hamburg, Germany
Tel.: (49) 40540060
Web Site: https://www.bode-chemie.de
Sales Range: $75-99.9 Million
Emp.: 280
Hygiene & Skin Care Products Mfr & Whslr
N.A.I.C.S.: 325180
Ruhneu Kaleus *(Dir-Mktg)*

CMC Consumer Medical Care GmbH (1)
Eichendorffstrasse 12-14, Brenz, Sontheim, Germany
Tel.: (49) 73 25 92 44 0
Web Site: http://www.care-innovation.de
Sales Range: $25-49.9 Million
Emp.: 15
Health Care Retail Store Operating Services
N.A.I.C.S.: 456199
Rainer Mangold *(Gen Mgr)*

D.A.S. Distributori Articoli Sanitari s.r.l. (1)
Via Invernizio Carolina 6, Turin, Italy
Tel.: (39) 011 6193945
Surgical Equipment Distr
N.A.I.C.S.: 423450

FORO.MED. Production s.r.l. (1)
Viale Dell Industria 9/15, Boffalora sopra Ticino, 20010, Italy
Tel.: (39) 0297255353
Surgical & Medical Equipment Mfr & Distr
N.A.I.C.S.: 339112

Genesi s.r.l. (1)
Via Fossano - Fr San Bernardo 128, 12041, Bene Vagienna, Cuneo, Italy
Tel.: (39) 0172 655241
Web Site: http://www.genesitalia.it
Elastic Bandages Mfr & Distr
N.A.I.C.S.: 339113

HARTMANN Beteiligungen GmbH (1)
Paul-Hartmann-Str 12, Heidenheim, 89522, Germany
Tel.: (49) 7321360
Investment Management Service
N.A.I.C.S.: 523999

HARTMANN Pardes GmbH (1)
Moselstrasse 24, 63477, Maintal, Germany
Tel.: (49) 61819460
Web Site: http://www.hartmann-pardes.de
Sales Range: $25-49.9 Million
Emp.: 60
Medical & Patient Care Products Developer
N.A.I.C.S.: 812199

HARTMANN USA, Inc. (1)
481 Lakeshore Pkwy, Rock Hill, SC 29730
Tel.: (803) 325-7600
Sales Range: $25-49.9 Million
Emp.: 70
Medical & Surgical Appliances Mfr & Distr
N.A.I.C.S.: 339112

HARTMANN-RICO A.S. (1)
Masarykovo Nam 77, 66471, Veverska Bityska, Czech Republic
Tel.: (420) 549456111
Web Site: http://www.hartmann.com
Sales Range: $350-399.9 Million
Emp.: 1,200
Medical & Patient Care Products Developer
N.A.I.C.S.: 812199
L'ubomir Palenik *(Mng Dir)*

HARTMANN-RICO Hungaria Kft. (1)
Budapark Paul Hartmann u 8, 2051, Biatorbagy, Hungary
Tel.: (36) 23530900
Web Site: http://www.hartmann.hu
Sales Range: $25-49.9 Million
Emp.: 70
Medical & Patient Care Products Developer
N.A.I.C.S.: 812199
Laszlo Hornyak *(Mng Dir)*

HARTMANN-RICO S.R.O. (1)
Vlckova 18, 81106, Bratislava, Slovakia
Tel.: (421) 257202081
Web Site: http://de.hartmann.info
Sales Range: $25-49.9 Million
Emp.: 32
Medical & Patient Care Products Developer

INTERNATIONAL PUBLIC

N.A.I.C.S.: 812199

HARTMANN-Scandicare AB (1)
Depagatan 2, PO Box 24, Anderstorp, 33421, Sweden
Tel.: (46) 371587400
Web Site: http://www.hartmann.se
Sales Range: $25-49.9 Million
Emp.: 30
Medical & Patient Care Products Developer
N.A.I.C.S.: 812199
Bengt Gustafson *(Mng Dir)*

HARTMANN-Vitamed (Pty) Ltd. (1)
Unit 15 Northlands Production Park Cnr Epsom Ave Newmarket St, PO Box 993, Randburg, 2169, Gauteng, South Africa
Tel.: (27) 117047420
Web Site: http://www.za.hartmann.info
Sales Range: $25-49.9 Million
Emp.: 52
Medical & Patient Care Products Developer
N.A.I.C.S.: 812199
Bill Kelly *(CEO)*

HYGIENE PARTNERS S.A.R.L. (1)
18 Rue des Goumiers, 67730, Chatenois, France
Tel.: (33) 3 88 82 43 10
Sales Range: $50-74.9 Million
Emp.: 10
Pharmaceutical Products Distr
N.A.I.C.S.: 424210
Alexandre Kleiber *(Gen Mgr)*

Hygiene Cotton Industries Pamuk Sanayi ve Ticaret Limited Sirketi (1)
Mumin Ozyurt Cd No 17, Serbest, Mersin, Turkiye
Tel.: (90) 324 239 38 70
Pharmaceutical Products Mfr & Distr
N.A.I.C.S.: 325412

IVF HARTMANN AG (1)
28 Victor von Bruns Street, Neuhausen, 8212, Switzerland
Tel.: (41) 526743111
Web Site: http://www.ivf.hartmann.info
Sales Range: $75-99.9 Million
Emp.: 318
Medical & Patient Care Products Developer
N.A.I.C.S.: 812199

IVF HARTMANN Holding AG (1)
Victor von Bruns-Strasse 28, PO Box 634, 8212, Neuhausen am Rheinfall, Switzerland
Tel.: (41) 526743111
Web Site: https://www.ivf.hartmann.info
Sales Range: Less than $1 Million
Holding Company
N.A.I.C.S.: 551112
Claus Martini *(CEO)*

KOB (Qingdao) Medical Devices Co., Ltd. (1)
No 71 Zhufeng Street, Jiaonan, 266400, Qingdao, China
Tel.: (86) 53286185812
Medical Device Distr
N.A.I.C.S.: 423450

KOB Medical Devices (Deutschland) GmbH (1)
Lauterstr 50, Wolfstein, 67752, Germany
Tel.: (49) 6304740
Emp.: 700
Medical Device Mfr & Distr
N.A.I.C.S.: 339112
Philip Strahattman *(Mgr)*

Karl Otto Braun KG (1)
Lauterstrasse 50, 67751, Wolfstein, Germany
Tel.: (49) 6304740
Web Site: http://www.kob.de
Sales Range: $150-199.9 Million
Emp.: 800
Medical & Patient Care Products Developer
N.A.I.C.S.: 812199
Gerhard F. Braun *(Mng Dir)*

Kistler AG (1)
Verbandwattefabrik, 8737, Gommiswald, Switzerland
Tel.: (41) 55 285 30 30
Pharmaceutical Products Distr
N.A.I.C.S.: 424210

Kneipp GmbH (1)
Winterhauser Str 85, 97084, Wurzburg, Germany

AND PRIVATE COMPANIES / PAUL HARTMANN AG

Tel.: (49) 93180020
Web Site: https://www.kneipp.com
Health & Fitness Services
N.A.I.C.S.: 812990
Carolin Mueller *(Head-Mktg-DACH)*

Kneipp Japan K.K. (1)
3014 Shinohara-cho, Kohoku-ku, Yokohama, 222-0026, Kanagawa, Japan
Tel.: (81) 45 309 87 01
Web Site: http://www.kneipp.jp
Cosmetic Product Distr
N.A.I.C.S.: 424210

Kneipp Nederland B.V. (1)
Aardvletterweg 10, Postbus 40, 3417 ZG, Montfoort, Netherlands
Tel.: (31) 348 479111
Web Site: http://www.kneipp.nl
Emp.: 20
Cosmetic Products Mfr & Distr
N.A.I.C.S.: 325620

Kneipp Verwaltungsgesellschaft mbH (1)
Steinbachtal 43, 97082, Wurzburg, Germany
Tel.: (49) 931 80020
Management Consulting Services
N.A.I.C.S.: 541611

Kneipp-Werke Kneipp-Mittel-Zentrale (1)
Steinbachtal 43, 97082, Wurzburg, Germany
Tel.: (49) 93180020
Web Site: http://www.kneipp.de
Medical & Patient Care Products Developer
N.A.I.C.S.: 812199

Laboratoires Paul Hartmann S.A.R.L. (1)
Villa No 10 Lotissements Communal No 3, Rouiba, Algeria
Tel.: (213) 21855330
Health Care Srvices
N.A.I.C.S.: 621999
Samir Aouis *(Dir-Sls & Comml)*

Laboratorios HARTMANN S.A. (1)
Carrasco i Formiguera 48, Mataro, 080302, Barcelona, Spain
Tel.: (34) 937 417 100
Pharmaceutical Products Distr
N.A.I.C.S.: 424210

MEDICUS GmbH (1)
Schillerstrasse 61, 75038, Oberderdingen, Germany
Tel.: (49) 70 45 20 08 0
Web Site: http://www.medicus-handel.de
Women Healthcare Services
N.A.I.C.S.: 621610

Max Lorne S.A. (1)
41 Grande Rue, 10190, Villemaur-sur-Vanne, France
Tel.: (33) 325405507
Medical Equipment Distr
N.A.I.C.S.: 423450
Marc Dubois *(Gen Mgr)*

N.V. PAUL HARTMANN S.A. (1)
1 Ave Paul Hartmann, 1480, Saintes, Belgium
Tel.: (32) 23914444
Web Site: http://www.en.hartmann.info
Sales Range: $25-49.9 Million
Emp.: 75
Medical & Patient Care Products Developer
N.A.I.C.S.: 812199
Marc Vander Gucht *(Mng Dir)*

NOGE Gesellschaft fur Medizinprodukte und -dienstleistungen mbH (1)
Paul-Hartmann-Str 12, 89522, Heidenheim, Germany
Tel.: (49) 7321360
Surgical & Medical Equipment Distr
N.A.I.C.S.: 423450
Michael Banz *(Gen Mgr)*

PAUL HARTMANN (Shanghai) Trade Co., Ltd. (1)
391 Guiping Road Block A Room 1001-1003, Shanghai, 200233, China
Tel.: (86) 800 820 2826
Web Site: http://www.hartmann.info
Sales Range: $25-49.9 Million
Emp.: 50
Medical & Patient Care Products Developer
N.A.I.C.S.: 812199

PAUL HARTMANN A/S (1)
Huginsvej 1 F, 3400, Hillerod, Denmark
Tel.: (45) 48220400
Web Site: http://www.dk.hartmann.info
Sales Range: $25-49.9 Million
Emp.: 7
Medical & Patient Care Products Developer
N.A.I.C.S.: 812199
Bengt Gustafson *(Mng Dir)*

PAUL HARTMANN AG & Co. Logistikzentrum Sud oHG (1)
Paul Hartmann Str 12, Heidenheim, 89522, Germany
Tel.: (49) 7321 360
Logistics Consulting Servies
N.A.I.C.S.: 541614

PAUL HARTMANN AS (1)
Hoffsveien 48, 0377, Oslo, Norway
Tel.: (47) 22133110
Web Site: http://en.hartmann.info
Medical & Patient Care Products Developer
N.A.I.C.S.: 812199

PAUL HARTMANN Adriatic d.o.o. (1)
Letaliska Cesta 3c, 1000, Ljubljana, Slovenia
Tel.: (386) 1 548 45 81
Web Site: http://www.si.hartmann.info
Medical & Surgical Equipment Mfr & Distr
N.A.I.C.S.: 339112

PAUL HARTMANN Asia-Pacific Ltd. (1)
Suite 3102 23 Wang Tai Road Manhattan Place, Kowloon Bay, Kowloon, China (Hong Kong)
Tel.: (852) 29537100
Web Site: http://www.hartmann.info
Medical & Patient Care Products Developer
N.A.I.C.S.: 812199
Andreas Joehle *(CEO)*

PAUL HARTMANN B.V. (1)
Karkanbos 1103, PO Box 26, 6546 BC, Nijmegen, Netherlands
Tel.: (31) 243723610
Sales Range: $25-49.9 Million
Emp.: 60
Medical & Patient Care Products Developer
N.A.I.C.S.: 812199
Rudolf Marinus Krouwel *(Mng Dir)*

PAUL HARTMANN Egypt S.A.E. (1)
6th of October City 6 Industrial Zone, pcs 17 & 18, Giza, 12515, Egypt
Tel.: (20) 2 5730913
Medical & Patient Care Products Developer
N.A.I.C.S.: 327910

PAUL HARTMANN Finance B.V. (1)
Kerkenbos 1103d, Nijmegen, 6546 BC, Netherlands
Tel.: (31) 243723610
Financial Management Services
N.A.I.C.S.: 523999

PAUL HARTMANN GmbH (1)
IZ No Sud Strasse 3 Ecoplus Wirtschaftspark Objekt 64, Postfach 110, 2355, Wiener Neudorf, Austria
Tel.: (43) 2236 646300
Web Site: http://www.at.hartmann.info
Medical & Patient Care Products Developer
N.A.I.C.S.: 812199

PAUL HARTMANN Hellas A.E. (1)
L Vouliagmenis 140, 16674, Glyfada, Athina, Greece
Tel.: (30) 2108986630
Web Site: http://www.gr.hartmann.info
Sales Range: $25-49.9 Million
Emp.: 23
Medical & Patient Care Products Developer
N.A.I.C.S.: 812199
Panos Koronakis *(Mng Dir)*

PAUL HARTMANN LDA (1)
Av Severiano Falcao 22-2, 2685-378, Loures, Portugal
Tel.: (351) 219409920
Web Site: http://www.es.hartmann.info
Sales Range: $25-49.9 Million
Emp.: 30
Medical & Patient Care Products Developer

N.A.I.C.S.: 812199
Jose Manuel Toscano De Mendonca *(Mng Dir)*

PAUL HARTMANN Ltd. (1)
Heywood Distribution Pk, Pilsworth Rd, Heywood, OL10 2TT, Lancashire, United Kingdom
Tel.: (44) 706363200
Web Site: http://www.hartmann.co.uk
Medical & Patient Care Products Developer
N.A.I.C.S.: 812199

PAUL HARTMANN Ltd. Sti. (1)
Barbaros Mah Dereboyu Cd Basil Sk Uphill Towers A1-A Blok D 9 West, 34746, Istanbul, Atasehir, Turkiye
Tel.: (90) 216 688 53 70
Web Site: http://tr.hartmann.info
Sales Range: $25-49.9 Million
Emp.: 11
Medical & Patient Care Products Developer & Distr
N.A.I.C.S.: 812199
Fritz Mader *(Mng Dir)*

PAUL HARTMANN Medical Private Ltd. (1)
Dynasty Business Park A-Wing Andheri East, Mumbai, 400053, India
Tel.: (91) 22 40309175
Medical & Surgical Equipment Mfr & Distr
N.A.I.C.S.: 339112

PAUL HARTMANN Middle East FZE (1)
Dubai Airport Free Zone, PO Box 54525, Dubai, United Arab Emirates
Tel.: (971) 42996996
Web Site: http://ae.hartmann.info
Sales Range: $25-49.9 Million
Emp.: 7
Medical & Patient Care Products Developer
N.A.I.C.S.: 812199

PAUL HARTMANN OOO (1)
Kozhevnicheskaya 7-1, 115114, Moscow, Russia
Tel.: (7) 4957969961
Web Site: http://www.paulhartmann.ru
Sales Range: $25-49.9 Million
Emp.: 60
Medical & Patient Care Products Developer
N.A.I.C.S.: 812199

PAUL HARTMANN Polska (1)
Ul Partyzancka 133/151, 95-200, Pabianice, Poland
Tel.: (48) 422252291
Web Site: http://www.paulhartmann.pl
Sales Range: $25-49.9 Million
Emp.: 200
Medical & Patient Care Products Developer
N.A.I.C.S.: 812199
Grazyna Zeromska-Tiszler *(Mng Dir)*

PAUL HARTMANN Pty. Ltd. (1)
Level 6 5 Rider Boulevard, Level 6 5 Rider Blvd Rds, Rhodes, 2142, NSW, Australia
Tel.: (61) 287627000
Web Site: http://www.hartmann.com.au
Sales Range: $25-49.9 Million
Emp.: 60
Medical & Patient Care Products Developer
N.A.I.C.S.: 812199
Mark Summerville *(Mng Dir)*

PAUL HARTMANN S.A. (1)
9 Loute De Selestat, 67730, Chatenois, France
Tel.: (33) 388824343
Web Site: http://www.hartmann.fr
Sales Range: $150-199.9 Million
Emp.: 900
Medical & Patient Care Products Developer
N.A.I.C.S.: 812199
Michel Kuehn *(Mng Dir)*

PAUL HARTMANN S.A.R.L. (1)
Villa N 10 Lotissement Commmunal N 3, Rouiba, Algeria
Tel.: (213) 21855330
Medical & Patient Care Products Developer
N.A.I.C.S.: 812199

PAUL HARTMANN S.A.R.L. (1)
7 Rue Lbn El Jaouzi, 20100, Casablanca, Morocco
Tel.: (212) 22483923
Sales Range: $25-49.9 Million
Emp.: 11
Medical & Patient Care Products Developer

N.A.I.C.S.: 812199

PAUL HARTMANN S.p.A. (1)
Via Della Metallurgia 12 ZAI 2, 37139, Verona, Italy
Tel.: (39) 0458182411
Web Site: http://it.hartmann.info
Medical & Patient Care Products Developer
N.A.I.C.S.: 812199
Rossiello Massimo *(Mgr-Intl)*

PAUL HARTMANN d.o.o. (1)
Karlovacka cesta 4f, 10020, Zagreb, Croatia
Tel.: (385) 14812844
Web Site: http://www.hr.hartmann.info
Sales Range: $25-49.9 Million
Emp.: 100
Medical & Patient Care Products Developer
N.A.I.C.S.: 812199
Alfred Racek *(Mng Dir)*

Paul Hartmann AG (Shanghai) Trade Co., Ltd. (1)
Room 1001-1003 Block A New Caohejing International Business Center, 391 Gui Ping Road, Shanghai, 200233, China
Tel.: (86) 2154263500
Health Care Srvices
N.A.I.C.S.: 621999
Glen Wang *(Mng Dir)*

Paul Hartmann Chile SpA (1)
Cerro El Plomo 5630 9th Floor Office 909, 7560742, Las Condes, Santiago, Chile
Tel.: (56) 226664276
Health Care Srvices
N.A.I.C.S.: 621999

Paul Hartmann Taiwan Limited (1)
7th Floor No 67 Shitan Road, Neihu District, Taipei, Taiwan
Tel.: (886) 227907992
Health Care Srvices
N.A.I.C.S.: 621999
Laura Hung *(Mgr-RA & QA)*

Pioneers Healthcare Pars Private Joint Stock Company (1)
3rd Floor No 4/1 Bahrami Alley, Lofti Street 7th Tir Square, Tehran, Iran
Tel.: (98) 218810150
Medical & Patient Care Products Developer
N.A.I.C.S.: 812199

Providom SAS (1)
9 Route De Selestat, 67730, Chatenois, France
Tel.: (33) 3 88 82 43 43
Web Site: http://www.providom.fr
Pharmaceutical Products Distr
N.A.I.C.S.: 424210

QMService GmbH (1)
Robin Bahr Paul-Hartmann-Strasse 12, 89522, Heidenheim, Germany
Tel.: (49) 7321 55789 11
Web Site: http://www.qmservice.info
Sales Range: $10-24.9 Million
Emp.: 5
Professional Health Care Training Services
N.A.I.C.S.: 611430

Reha-Service Loose GmbH (1)
Forsterweg 130, 22525, Hamburg, Germany
Tel.: (49) 40 830 50 51
Web Site: http://www.krankenbett-pflegebett.de
Health Care Srvices
N.A.I.C.S.: 621999

S.C. PAUL HARTMANN S.R.L. (1)
Str Kos Karoly nr 1A, RO 540 297, Tirgu Mures, Romania
Tel.: (40) 265210928
Web Site: http://ro.hartmann.info
Medical & Patient Care Products Developer
N.A.I.C.S.: 812199

Sanimed GmbH (1)
Gildestrasse 68, 49479, Ibbenburen, Germany
Tel.: (49) 5451923111
Web Site: http://www.sanimed.de
Sales Range: $75-99.9 Million
Emp.: 380
Medical & Patient Care Products Developer
N.A.I.C.S.: 812199
Karlheinz Westkamp *(Mng Dir)*

PAUL HARTMANN AG

PAUL HARTMANN AG—(Continued)

Unitex-Hartmann S.A. (1)
Poligono Industrial Pla d'en Boet II, c Carrasco i Formiguera 48, 08302, Mataro, 08302, Barcelona, Spain
Tel.: (34) 937417100
Web Site: http://www.es.hartmann.info
Sales Range: $25-49.9 Million
Emp.: 220
Medical & Patient Care Products Developer
N.A.I.C.S.: 812199
Mark Peres *(Gen Mgr)*

Vlesia GmbH (1)
Paul-Hartmann-Straaye 12-14, 89522, Heidenheim, Germany
Tel.: (49) 7321 36 14 32
Web Site: http://www.vlesia.info
Clothing Diapers Mfr
N.A.I.C.S.: 314999
Thilo Eckermann *(Co-Mng Dir)*

Whitestone Acquisition Corp. (1)
4265 W Vernal Pike, Bloomington, IN 47404-9660
Tel.: (812) 332-3703
Web Site: http://www.whitestonecorp.com
Rev.: $25,000,000
Emp.: 100
Sanitary Paper Products
N.A.I.C.S.: 322291

PAUL HENKE GMBH & CO. KG
Bruckenstrasse 94, Lohne, 32584, Germany
Tel.: (49) 573174070
Web Site: http://www.henke-beschlaege.de
Year Founded: 1929
Rev.: $29,312,250
Emp.: 152
Furniture Components Mfr
N.A.I.C.S.: 337126
Dieter Henke *(Mng Dir)*

PAUL KELLER GARTEN- LANDSCHAFTS- SPORTPLATZ- UND TIEFBAU GMBH
Am Anger 20, 39218, Schonebeck, Germany
Tel.: (49) 392848290
Web Site: http://www.paul-keller-gmbh.de
Year Founded: 1961
Rev.: $18,848,443
Emp.: 90
Gardening & Landscaping Services
N.A.I.C.S.: 236116
Hans-Jurgen Tersch *(Mng Dir)*

PAUL MERCHANTS LIMITED
Pml House Soo 829-830 Sector 22-A, Chandigarh, 160022, India
Tel.: (91) 1725041792
Web Site: https://www.paulmerchants.net
Year Founded: 1984
539113—(BOM)
Rev.: $840,813,548
Assets: $106,691,877
Liabilities: $45,452,647
Net Worth: $61,239,230
Earnings: $5,275,139
Emp.: 393
Fiscal Year-end: 03/31/23
Financial Services
N.A.I.C.S.: 541611
Rajneesh Bansal *(Mng Dir)*

Subsidiaries:

Paul Infotech Private Limited (1)
Shop No F3-01 Third Floor Taj Building Aambagan Road, Aambagan Sakchi, Jamshedpur, 831001, Jharkhand, India
Tel.: (91) 7903174066
Web Site: https://paulinfotechsolutions.com
Computer Education & Training Services
N.A.I.C.S.: 611420

PAULIC MEUNERIE SA
Moulin du Gouret, Saint-Gerand, 56920, Pontivy, France
Tel.: (33) 297514003
Web Site: https://www.paulicmeunerie.com
Year Founded: 1957
ALPAU—(EUR)
Sales Range: $10-24.9 Million
Flour Mill Product Mfr & Distr
N.A.I.C.S.: 311211
Jean Paulic *(Chm & CEO)*

PAULIG TEPPICHWEBEREI GMBH
Gewerbering Nord 1, 97359, Kitzingen, Germany
Tel.: (49) 932498200
Web Site: http://www.paulig-teppiche.de
Year Founded: 1750
Rev.: $15,431,849
Emp.: 30
Carpet Mfr
N.A.I.C.S.: 314110
Thomas Paulig *(Co-CEO)*

PAUSHAK LIMITED
1st Floor 1965 Alembic City Alembic Road, Vadodara, 390003, Gujarat, India
Tel.: (91) 2652280550
Web Site: https://www.paushak.com
Year Founded: 1969
532742—(BOM)
Rev.: $26,544,775
Assets: $49,726,371
Liabilities: $7,319,705
Net Worth: $42,406,666
Earnings: $6,475,091
Emp.: 335
Fiscal Year-end: 03/31/23
Phosgene Gas Producer
N.A.I.C.S.: 325998
Kirti Shah *(CFO)*

PAVE-TAR CONSTRUCTION LTD.
366 Watline Ave, Mississauga, L4Z 1X2, ON, Canada
Tel.: (905) 502-6673
Web Site: http://www.pavetarconstruction.com
Year Founded: 1974
Rev.: $15,000,000
Emp.: 50
Highway & Street Construction
N.A.I.C.S.: 237310
Vince Campana *(Founder)*

PAVEMENT MANAGEMENT SERVICES PTY LTD.
Rintoul Business Park Unit 7B 26 Powers Road, Seven Hills, Sydney, 2147, NSW, Australia
Tel.: (61) 2 9674 9488
Web Site: http://www.pavement.com.au
Year Founded: 1978
Sales Range: $25-49.9 Million
Civil Engineering Services
N.A.I.C.S.: 237990
John Yeaman *(Mng Dir)*

PAVILION PRIVATE EQUITY CO., LTD.
Seoul Mecenatpolice 45 Yanghwa-ro, Mapo-gu, Seoul, 04036, Korea (South)
Tel.: (82) 2 6970 3726
Web Site: http://www.pavilioninv.com
Financial Service Provider
N.A.I.C.S.: 525990
Young-Gak Yun *(Founder & Chm)*

PAVILION REIT MANAGEMENT SDN. BHD.
Level 10 Pavilion Kuala Lumpur 168, Jalan Bukit Bintang, 55100, Kuala Lumpur, Malaysia
Tel.: (60) 3 2118 8888   MY
Web Site: http://www.pavilion-reit.com
Real Estate Investment Trust Management Services
N.A.I.C.S.: 531390
Desmond Siew Choon Lim *(Chm)*

Subsidiaries:

Pavilion Real Estate Investment Trust (1)
6-2 Level 6 East Wing Menara Goldstone Holiday Inn Express, No 84 Jalan Raja Chulan, 50200, Kuala Lumpur, Malaysia (0.18%)
Tel.: (60) 321669818
Web Site: http://www.pavilion-reit.com
Rev.: $120,569,524
Assets: $1,372,100,741
Liabilities: $512,840,000
Net Worth: $859,260,741
Earnings: $84,190,265
Emp.: 22
Fiscal Year-end: 12/31/2022
Real Estate Investment Trust
N.A.I.C.S.: 525990
Desmond Siew Choon Lim *(Chm)*

PAVLODAR OIL CHEMISTRY REFINERY JSC
1 Khimkombinatovskaya Street, 140000, Pavlodar, Kazakhstan
Tel.: (7) 7182396544
Web Site: http://www.pnhz.kz
Sales Range: $750-799.9 Million
Emp.: 3,200
Oil Refining & Petrochemical Production Services
N.A.I.C.S.: 324110
Shukhrat Abdurashitovich Danbay *(Gen Dir)*

PAVLODARENERGO JSC
27 Krivenko St, Pavlodar, 150012, Kazakhstan
Tel.: (7) 7182399506
Web Site: http://www.pavlodarenergo.kz
Year Founded: 2000
PDEN—(KAZ)
Rev.: $183,596,520
Assets: $764,022,090
Liabilities: $553,543,858
Net Worth: $210,478,232
Earnings: ($110,507,897)
Fiscal Year-end: 12/31/21
Electric Power Generation & Distribution Services
N.A.I.C.S.: 221111
Oleg Perfilov *(Gen Dir)*

Subsidiaries:

Pavlodar Regional Electric Distribution Company JSC (1)
Krivenko street 27, Pavlodar, 140000, Kazakhstan
Tel.: (7) 7182322022
Electricity Distribution Services
N.A.I.C.S.: 221122

PAVLOVO BUS AO
Suvorov street house 1, Nizhny Novgorod Region, Pavlovo, 606108, Russia
Tel.: (7) 8317128114
Web Site: https://www.paz-bus.ru
PAZA—(MOEX)
Sales Range: Less than $1 Million
Steam & Hot Water Boiler Mfr
N.A.I.C.S.: 332410

PAVNA INDUSTRIES LIMITED
Vimlanchal Hari nagar Gopalpuri, Aligarh, Lucknow, 202001, Uttar Pradesh, India
Tel.: (91) 8006409330
Web Site: https://www.pavnagroup.com
Year Founded: 1971
543915—(BOM)
Rev.: $43,662,946
Assets: $33,419,279
Liabilities: $24,533,673
Net Worth: $8,885,606
Earnings: $1,035,382
Emp.: 695
Fiscal Year-end: 03/31/23
Electrical Products Mfr
N.A.I.C.S.: 336320

PAVONINE CO., LTD.
33 Hogupo-ro, Namdong-gu, Incheon, 21693, Korea (South)
Tel.: (82) 328146900
Web Site: https://www.pavonine.net
Year Founded: 1989
177830—(KRS)
Rev.: $90,535,099
Assets: $109,404,608
Liabilities: $50,362,210
Net Worth: $59,042,398
Earnings: $5,590,717
Emp.: 240
Fiscal Year-end: 12/31/22
Electrical Component Mfr
N.A.I.C.S.: 335999
Yongill Jeong *(Dir)*

Subsidiaries:

Pavonine Co., Ltd. - Gwangju Division (1)
Tel.: (82) 629466910
Electric Equipment Mfr
N.A.I.C.S.: 335999

Pavonine Co., Ltd. - Songdo Division (1)
7-42 Songdo-dong Yeonsu-gu, Incheon, Korea (South)
Tel.: (82) 328516060
Electric Equipment Mfr
N.A.I.C.S.: 335999

PAWANSUT HOLDINGS LIMITED
415 Usha Kiran Building Commercial Complex, Azadpur, Delhi, 110033, India
Tel.: (91) 1143619333
Web Site: https://www.pawansutholdings.com
Year Founded: 1984
Rev.: $216,852
Assets: $3,890,898
Liabilities: $92,992
Net Worth: $3,797,907
Earnings: $361
Emp.: 10
Fiscal Year-end: 03/31/18
Holding Company
N.A.I.C.S.: 551112
Ajay Kumar Jindal *(CFO)*

PAX CONSTRUCTION LTD.
4452 Juneau Street, Burnaby, V5C 4C8, BC, Canada
Tel.: (604) 291-8885   Ca
Web Site: http://www.paxconstruction.ca
Year Founded: 1988
General Contractors
N.A.I.C.S.: 236220
Peter Brauer *(Principal & Gen Mgr)*

PAX FORLAG AS
Dronningens gate 16, 0152, Oslo, Norway
Tel.: (47) 23136900   NO
Web Site: http://www.pax.no
Year Founded: 1964
Emp.: 10

AND PRIVATE COMPANIES

Book Publisher & Distr
N.A.I.C.S.: 513130
Bjorn Smith-Simonsen *(CEO & Publr)*

Subsidiaries:

De Norske Bokklubbene AS (1)
Gullhaug Torg 1, 0402, Oslo, Norway
Tel.: (47) 22028700
Web Site: http://www.bokklubben.no
Sales Range: $50-74.9 Million
Online & Mail Order Book Retailer
N.A.I.C.S.: 459210
Kari Moller *(CEO)*

PAX GLOBAL TECHNOLOGY LIMITED
Room 2504 25/F Sun Hung Kai Centre 30 Harbour Road, Wanchai, China (Hong Kong)
Tel.: (852) 25008500   BM
Web Site:
    http://www.paxglobal.com.hk
Year Founded: 2000
0327—(HKG)
Rev.: $1,027,994,505
Assets: $1,210,016,948
Liabilities: $329,521,073
Net Worth: $880,495,875
Earnings: $161,695,883
Emp.: 1,712
Fiscal Year-end: 12/31/22
Holding Company; Electronic Fund Transfer Point-of-Sale Products Mfr & Related Services
N.A.I.C.S.: 551112
Guoming Nie *(Chm)*

Subsidiaries:

Pax Italia S.r.l. (1)
Via Ronchi 43, 20134, Milan, Italy
Tel.: (39) 0284083818
Computer Equipment Distr
N.A.I.C.S.: 423430

Pax Japan Kabushiki Kaisha (1)
2-10-4 PMO Jimbocho 8F Kanda Jimbocho, Chiyoda-ku, Tokyo, 101-0051, Japan
Tel.: (81) 354887910
Web Site: https://www.paxjp.co.jp
Electronic Payment Terminal & Transactional Software Services
N.A.I.C.S.: 522320

Pax Pos Solutions India Private Ltd. (1)
Unit-402A 4th Floor Global Foyer Sector - 43 Golf Course Road, Gurgaon, 122002, India
Tel.: (91) 1244073854
Electronic Payment Terminal & Transactional Software Services
N.A.I.C.S.: 522320

Pax Technology Limited (1)
Room 2416 24/F Sun Hung Kai Centre 30 Harbour Road, Wanchai, China (Hong Kong)
Tel.: (852) 25008500
Web Site: http://www.paxglobal.com.hk
Emp.: 18
Electronic Fund Transfer Point-of-Sale Products Mfr & Related Services
N.A.I.C.S.: 334118

Subsidiary (Non-US):

Pax Computer Technology (Shenzhen) Co., Ltd (2)
4/F No 3 Building Software Park 2nd Central Science-Tech Road, High-Tech Industrial Park, Shenzhen, 518057, Guangdong, China
Tel.: (86) 75586169630
Web Site: http://www.pax.com.cn
Computer Terminal Mfr
N.A.I.C.S.: 334118

Subsidiary (US):

Pax Technology, Inc. (2)
8775 Baypine Rd, Jacksonville, FL 32356
Tel.: (904) 900-3751
Web Site: https://www.pax.us
Electronic Payment Terminal Product Distr
N.A.I.C.S.: 423420

Andy Chau *(Pres & CEO)*

PAXAN. CO
Km 8 of Fatah highway, 13186 933841, Tehran, 13186 933841, Iran
Tel.: (98) 2164562545
Web Site: https://www.paxanco.com
PAKS1—(THE)
Sales Range: Less than $1 Million
Detergents Mfr
N.A.I.C.S.: 325611

PAXMAN AB
Pirgatan 13, SE-374 35, Karlshamn, SE-374 35, Sweden
Tel.: (46) 709439671
Web Site: https://www.paxman.se
PAX—(OMX)
Rev.: $20,858,598
Assets: $16,590,625
Liabilities: $4,418,369
Net Worth: $12,172,256
Earnings: $826,930
Emp.: 91
Fiscal Year-end: 12/31/23
Health Care Srvices
N.A.I.C.S.: 621610
Richard Paxman *(CEO)*

Subsidiaries:

Paxman Coolers Limited (1)
International House Penistone Road Fenay Bridge, Huddersfield, HD8 0LE, West Yorkshire, United Kingdom
Tel.: (44) 1484349444
Web Site:
    https://www.paxmanscalpcooling.com
Medical Device Mfr
N.A.I.C.S.: 339112

PAXYS, INC.
15th Floor 6750 Ayala Office Tower Ayala Avenue, Makati, Philippines
Tel.: (63) 282503800
Web Site: https://www.paxys.com
PAX—(PHI)
Rev.: $929,344
Assets: $80,089,526
Liabilities: $1,829,464
Net Worth: $78,260,062
Earnings: ($278,990)
Emp.: 270
Fiscal Year-end: 12/31/21
Business Process Outsourcing Services
N.A.I.C.S.: 561422
Ana Maria A. Katigbak *(Asst Sec)*

Subsidiaries:

Scopeworks Asia, Inc. (1)
Building 1 LSL Compound Diode Street, Light Industry and Science Park LISP 1 Barangay Diezmo, Cabuyao, Laguna, Philippines
Tel.: (63) 82503830
Web Site: https://www.scopeworksasia.com
Medical Transcription Services
N.A.I.C.S.: 561410

PAY MY TIME LTD
30 Percy Street, London, W1T2DB, United Kingdom
Tel.: (44) 2074671700   UK
Web Site: http://www.paymytime.com
Year Founded: 2014
Software Development Services
N.A.I.C.S.: 541511
Thomas Brooks *(Chm & CEO)*

PAYCE CONSOLIDATED LIMITED
Level 37 Chifley Tower 2 Chifley Square, Sydney, 2000, NSW, Australia
Tel.: (61) 2 8080 2300   AU
Web Site: http://www.payce.com.au
Year Founded: 1978

Property Investment; Urban Land Developer
N.A.I.C.S.: 523999
Brian Michael Boyd *(Chm & Mng Dir)*

PAYCHEST, INC.
1B Glamour Court 1 Discovery Bay Road, Lantau Island, Tsuen Wan, China (Hong Kong)
Tel.: (852) 7142747206
PYCT—(OTCIQ)
Sales Range: Less than $1 Million
Financial Brokerage Services
N.A.I.C.S.: 523160
Peter Coorey *(Pres)*

PAYFACTO INC.
1 Place du Commerce Suite 402, Verdun, H3E 1A2, QC, Canada
Web Site: http://www.payfacto.com
Year Founded: 2018
Payment Solutions
N.A.I.C.S.: 522320
Martin Leroux *(Pres & CEO)*

PAYFARE INC.
40 University Avenue Suite 551, Toronto, M5J 1T1, ON, Canada   BC
Web Site: https://corp.payfare.com
Year Founded: 2012
PYFRF—(OTCQX)
Rev.: $96,925,984
Assets: $161,936,699
Liabilities: $124,916,071
Net Worth: $37,020,627
Earnings: ($2,190,514)
Emp.: 78
Fiscal Year-end: 12/31/22
Asset Management Services
N.A.I.C.S.: 523999

PAYNOVA AB
Tel.: (46) 851710000
Web Site: https://www.paynova.com
SILEON—(OMX)
Rev.: $3,900,371
Assets: $18,282,805
Liabilities: $15,685,866
Net Worth: ($2,596,939)
Earnings: ($5,362,638)
Emp.: 38
Fiscal Year-end: 12/31/23
Electronic Payment Process Services
N.A.I.C.S.: 522320
Daniel Ekberger *(Chm & CEO)*

PAYPOINT PLC
1 The Boulevard Shire Park, Welwyn Garden City, AL7 1EL, Hertfordshire, United Kingdom
Tel.: (44) 1707600300
Web Site: https://www.paypoint.com
Year Founded: 1996
PAY—(LSE)
Rev.: $197,064,912
Assets: $315,171,617
Liabilities: $202,130,565
Net Worth: $113,041,052
Earnings: $94,415,849
Emp.: 670
Fiscal Year-end: 03/31/22
Payment Processing Systems
N.A.I.C.S.: 522320
Nick Wiles *(CEO & Member-Exec Bd)*

Subsidiaries:

Appreciate Group plc (1)
Valley Road, Birkenhead, CH41 7ED, Merseyside, United Kingdom
Tel.: (44) 1516531700
Web Site: http://www.appreciategroup.co.uk
Rev.: $145,011,285
Assets: $267,932,465
Liabilities: $243,887,244
Net Worth: $24,045,221
Earnings: $1,155,420
Emp.: 355
Fiscal Year-end: 03/31/2021

PAYPOINT PLC

Cash Savings & Cash Lending
N.A.I.C.S.: 525990
Russell Fairbrother *(Sec)*

Subsidiary (Domestic):

Country Christmas Savings Club Limited (2)
Valley Rd, Birkenhead, CH417ED, United Kingdom   **(100%)**
Tel.; (44) 1516531700
Sales Range: $50-74.9 Million
Emp.: 150
Mail-Order Houses
N.A.I.C.S.: 522299

Family Christmas Savings Club Limited (2)
Valley Road, Birkenhead, CH41 7ED, United Kingdom
Tel.: (44) 845 888 1000
Web Site: http://www.familyhampers.co.uk
Online Shopping Services
N.A.I.C.S.: 455211

High Street Vouchers Limited (2)
Valley Rd, Birkenhead, CH41 7ED, United Kingdom   **(100%)**
Web Site:
    http://www.highstreetvouchers.com
Sales Range: $50-74.9 Million
Emp.: 150
Mail-Order Houses
N.A.I.C.S.: 561440
Peter Johnson *(Chm)*

Home Farm Hampers Limited (2)
Unit 22 Bridgemead Westleigh, Bridgemead, Swindon, SN5 7YZ, Wiltshire, United Kingdom
Tel.: (44) 1793513322
Savings Club Organization
N.A.I.C.S.: 525990

Park Christmas Savings Club Limited (2)
Valley Rd, Birkenhead, CH41 7ED, United Kingdom   **(100%)**
Tel.: (44) 1516531700
Web Site: http://www.getpark.co.uk
Sales Range: $50-74.9 Million
Emp.: 150
Mail-Order Houses
N.A.I.C.S.: 484230
Peter Johnson *(Chm)*

Park Direct Credit Limited (2)
730 Chesterfield Road, Woodseats, Sheffield, S8 0SE, United Kingdom
Tel.: (44) 11 4255 7774
Financial Management Services
N.A.I.C.S.: 523999

Park Financial Services Limited (2)
Valley Rd, Birkenhead, CH417ED, United Kingdom   **(100%)**
Tel.: (44) 1516531700
Web Site: http://www.parkgroup.co.uk
Sales Range: $100-124.9 Million
Emp.: 150
Financial Investment Activities
N.A.I.C.S.: 523999
Peter Johnson *(Chm)*

Park Retail Limited (2)
Valley Rd, Birkenhead, CH417ED, United Kingdom   **(100%)**
Tel.: (44) 1516531700
Web Site: http://www.parkgroup.co.uk
Sales Range: $50-74.9 Million
Emp.: 150
Mail-Order Houses
N.A.I.C.S.: 424490
Peter Johnson *(Chm)*

PayPoint Collections Limited (1)
1 The Boulevard Shire Park, Welwyn Garden City, AL71EL, Hertfordshire, United Kingdom
Tel.: (44) 1707600300
Web Site: http://www.paypoint.co.uk
Sales Range: $100-124.9 Million
Emp.: 250
Electronic Financial Payment Services
N.A.I.C.S.: 522320
Seimus Smith *(Mng Dir)*

PayPoint Network Limited (1)
1 The Boulevard Shire Park, Welwyn Gar-

PAYPOINT PLC

PayPoint plc—(Continued)
den City, AL7 1EL, Hertfordshire, United Kingdom
Tel.: (44) 3304000000
Web Site: http://www.my.paypoint.com
Sales Range: $200-249.9 Million
Emp.: 350
Electronic Financial Payment Services
N.A.I.C.S.: 522320

PayPoint Retail Solutions Limited (1)
1 The Boulevard Shire Park, Welwyn Garden City, AL7 1EL, Hertfordshire, United Kingdom
Tel.: (44) 1707600300
Web Site: http://www.paypoint.com
Sales Range: $100-124.9 Million
Emp.: 450
Transaction Processing Services
N.A.I.C.S.: 522320

PayPoint Services Romania SRL (1)
15 Charles De Gaulle Square Et 16, Bucharest, 011857, Romania
Tel.: (40) 214091410
Mobile Prepaid Cards Distr
N.A.I.C.S.: 517121
Iulian Stefan (Dir-IT)

PayPoint.net Limited (1)
1 Finsbury Square, London, EC2A 1AE, United Kingdom
Tel.: (44) 2030582116
Web Site: http://www.paypoint.net
Credit Card Processing Services
N.A.I.C.S.: 522210

Verrus UK Limited (1)
PO Box 271, Stroud, GL6 9WZ, United Kingdom
Tel.: (44) 87 0112 6412
Credit Card Processing Services
N.A.I.C.S.: 522210

PAYSAFE LIMITED
2 Gresham Street 1st floor, London, EC2V 7AD, United Kingdom
Tel.: (44) 2076088460   BM
Web Site: https://www.paysafe.com
PSFE—(NYSE)
Rev.: $1,601,138,000
Assets: $5,227,701,000
Liabilities: $4,344,388,000
Net Worth: $883,313,000
Earnings: ($20,251,000)
Emp.: 3,200
Fiscal Year-end: 12/31/23
Investment Holding Company
N.A.I.C.S.: 551112
Ismail Dawood (CFO)

Subsidiaries:

Foley Trasimene Acquisition Corp II (1)
1701 Village Ctr Cir, Las Vegas, NV 89134
Tel.: (877) 249-0020
Web Site: http://www.foleytrasimene2.com
Financial Investment Services
N.A.I.C.S.: 523999
William P. Foley II (Founder & Chm)

Paysafe Group PLC (1)
3rd Floor Queen Victoria House 41-43 Victoria Street, Douglas, IM1 2LF, Isle of Man
Tel.: (44) 1624698700
Web Site: http://www.paysafe.com
Online Payment Services
N.A.I.C.S.: 522320
Philip McHugh (CEO)

Subsidiary (US):

Leaders Merchant Services, LLC (2)
725 Via Alondra, Camarillo, CA 93012
Tel.: (800) 220-4143
Web Site:
    http://www.leadersmerchantservices.com
Financial Transactions Processing, Reserve & Clearinghouse Activities
N.A.I.C.S.: 522320

Subsidiary (Non-US):

Paysafe - Montreal (2)
3500 de Maisonneuve Blvd W Ste 700, Montreal, H3Z 3C1, QC, Canada
Tel.: (514) 380-2700
Web Site: https://www.paysafe.com
Provider of Business-to-Business Proprietary E-Commerce Solutions & Services
N.A.I.C.S.: 561499

Skrill Ltd. (2)
1st floor 2 Gresham Street, London, EC2V 7AD, United Kingdom
Tel.: (44) 8557192087
Web Site: https://www.skrill.com
Online Payment System Operator
N.A.I.C.S.: 522320
Jonathan Wilson (Sr VP)

PAYSAUCE LIMITED
85 The Esplanade Petone, Lower Hutt, 5012, New Zealand
Tel.: (64) 45550754   NZ
Web Site: https://www.paysauce.com
Year Founded: 2004
PYS—(NZX)
Rev.: $3,476,675
Assets: $21,532,297
Liabilities: $20,697,967
Net Worth: $834,330
Earnings: ($333,732)
Emp.: 37
Fiscal Year-end: 03/31/23
Electric Bulb Mfr
N.A.I.C.S.: 335139
Chris Mardon (Co-Founder)

PAYTON INDUSTRIES LTD.
PO Box 4068, Rishon le Zion, 75140, Israel
Tel.: (972) 39616601
Web Site:
    http://www.paytongroup.com
PAYT—(TAE)
Rev.: $54,856,000
Assets: $84,629,000
Liabilities: $9,407,000
Net Worth: $75,222,000
Earnings: $15,266,000
Emp.: 178
Fiscal Year-end: 12/31/23
Capacitor, Resistor, Coil, Transformer & Other Inductor Manufacturing
N.A.I.C.S.: 334416
David Yativ (Founder, Chm, Pres & Co-CEO)

PAYTON PLANAR MAGNETICS LTD.
3 Ha avoda Stree, Ness Ziona, Israel
Tel.: (972) 9544283326
Web Site:
    https://www.paytongroup.com
Year Founded: 1992
PAY—(EUR)
Rev.: $60,270,000
Assets: $75,046,000
Liabilities: $6,629,000
Net Worth: $68,417,000
Earnings: $13,917,000
Emp.: 178
Fiscal Year-end: 12/31/22
Planar Magnetic Component Mfr
N.A.I.C.S.: 334419
David Yativ (Founder, Chm, Pres & Co-CEO)

Subsidiaries:

Payton America Inc. (1)
1805 S Powerline Rd Ste 109, Deerfield Beach, FL 33442
Tel.: (954) 428-3326
Magnetic Component Mfr
N.A.I.C.S.: 334419
Jim Marinos (Exec VP-Engrg & Mktg)

PAZ CORP S.A.
Avenida Apoquindo 4501 Office 2104, Las Condes, Santiago, Chile
Tel.: (56) 8635000
Web Site: https://www.paz.cl
PAZ—(SGO)
Sales Range: Less than $1 Million

Real Estate Development Services
N.A.I.C.S.: 531390
Cesar Barros Soffia (CEO)

PAZ OIL COMPANY LTD.
Euro Park Holland Building, Yakum, 60972, Israel
Tel.: (972) 98631103
Web Site: http://www.paz.co.il
Year Founded: 1922
PZOL—(TAE)
Rev.: $3,669,843,844
Assets: $3,135,239,625
Liabilities: $2,259,428,062
Net Worth: $875,811,562
Earnings: ($1,381,406)
Emp.: 3,962
Fiscal Year-end: 12/31/23
All Other Petroleum & Coal Products Manufacturing
N.A.I.C.S.: 324199
Uri Kahalon (VP-Real Estate & Ops)

Subsidiaries:

Paz Aviation Assets Ltd. (1)
Street 23 Ben Gurion Airport, Tel Aviv, 70100, Israel
Tel.: (972) 39774001
Web Site: http://www.paz.co.il
Fuel Storage Services
N.A.I.C.S.: 493190
Shmuel Gotshel (Mgr)

Paz Aviation Services Ltd. (1)
Settlement Lod Airport, Tel Aviv, 70100, Israel
Tel.: (972) 39774000
Web Site:
    http://www.pazaviationservices.co.il
Sales Range: $25-49.9 Million
Emp.: 50
Airplane Refueling Services
N.A.I.C.S.: 424720
Shmuel Looly Gotshal (CEO)

Paz Lubricants & Chemicals Ltd. (1)
1 Elgazali Street, PO Box 55, Haifa, Israel
Tel.: (972) 48352004
Web Site: http://www.pazlub.co.il
Sales Range: $25-49.9 Million
Emp.: 145
Lubricant Oils, Chemicals & Solvents Mfr & Blending
N.A.I.C.S.: 324191

Pazgas Ltd. (1)
46 Hamaccabim Road, Rishon le Zion, 75359, Israel
Tel.: (972) 39688088
Web Site: http://www.pazgas.co.il
Natural Gas Storage Services
N.A.I.C.S.: 486210

Pazkar Ltd. (1)
PO Box 2030, Alon Tavor, Haifa, 18000, Israel
Tel.: (972) 46423154
Web Site: https://www.pazkar.co.il
Sales Range: $1-9.9 Million
Emp.: 72
Waterproofing Membranes & Bituminous Products For Road Construction
N.A.I.C.S.: 325220

PAZARDZHIK BTM AD
ul d-r Nikola Lambrev 24, Pazardzhik, 4400, Bulgaria
Tel.: (359) 34445607
Tobacco Product Mfr
N.A.I.C.S.: 312230
Sasha Atanasova Filipova (Dir-IR)

PB FINTECH LIMITED
Plot 119 Sector 44, Gurgaon, 122001, Haryana, India
Tel.: (91) 1244562907
Web Site: https://www.pbfintech.in
Year Founded: 2008
543390—(BOM)
Rev.: $130,686,902
Assets: $318,144,099
Liabilities: $46,272,463
Net Worth: $271,871,636

INTERNATIONAL PUBLIC

Earnings: ($20,507,992)
Fiscal Year-end: 03/31/21
Insurance Services
N.A.I.C.S.: 524210
Bhasker Joshi (Compliance Officer)

Subsidiaries:

MyLoanCare Ventures Private Limited (1)
Plot No-131 Sector-44, Gurgaon, 122001, India
Tel.: (91) 8448389600
Web Site: https://www.myloancare.in
Financial Services
N.A.I.C.S.: 522310

Paisabazaar Marketing and Consulting Private Limited (1)
135 P Sector 44, Gurgaon, 122001, Haryana, India
Tel.: (91) 1243509999
Web Site: https://www.paisabazaar.com
Insurance Services
N.A.I.C.S.: 524210

PB GLOBAL LTD.
A-201 Crystal Plaza Premises New Link Road Andheri West, Mumbai, 400053, India
Tel.: (91) 2249335800
Web Site: https://www.pbltd.in
Year Founded: 1960
Electronic Equipment Distr
N.A.I.C.S.: 423690
Himgauri Palkar (Chief Compliance Officer)

PB GROUP LTD.
Xiao Keshan Xingang Town, Fanchang County, Wuhu, Anhui, China
Tel.: (86) 23658331   Ky
Web Site: http://www.thepbg.com
Year Founded: 2002
8331—(HKG)
Rev.: $12,958,218
Assets: $22,507,243
Liabilities: $4,972,547
Net Worth: $17,534,696
Earnings: ($383,994)
Emp.: 130
Fiscal Year-end: 03/31/23
Clay Building Material Mfr & Distr
N.A.I.C.S.: 327120
Man Fung Chan (Co-Chm)

PB HOLDING NV
Pieter Braaijweg 6, 1114 AR, Amsterdam, Netherlands
Tel.: (31) 206136028
Web Site: http://www.stern.nl
Year Founded: 1993
STRN—(EUR)
Rev.: $922,478,250
Assets: $532,322,901
Liabilities: $378,317,572
Net Worth: $154,005,329
Earnings: ($33,615,701)
Emp.: 1,557
Fiscal Year-end: 12/31/20
Car Dealership Owner & Operator; Car Rental & Leasing Services; Car Repair Services
N.A.I.C.S.: 441110
H. Henk van der Kwast (Chm-Mgmt Bd & CEO)

PBA HOLDINGS BHD.
Level 32 KOMTAR Penang Road, Georgetown, 10000, Penang, Malaysia
Tel.: (60) 42006700
Web Site: https://www.pbahb.com.my
PBA—(KLS)
Rev.: $92,207,663
Assets: $360,165,653
Liabilities: $156,473,880
Net Worth: $203,691,773
Earnings: $7,476,709

Emp.: 1,497
Fiscal Year-end: 12/31/23
Water Supply Management Services
N.A.I.C.S.: 221310
Jaseni Maidinsa *(CEO)*

Subsidiaries:

Perbadanan Bekalan Air Pulau
Pinang Sdn. Bhd. (1)
Level 32 Komtar Jalan Penang, 10000,
George Town, Pulau Pinang, Malaysia
Tel.: (60) 4 200 6600
Web Site: https://www.pba.com.my
Water Distribution Services
N.A.I.C.S.: 221310

PBA INFRASTRUCTURE LIMITED

611/3 V N Purav Marg, Chembur
East, Mumbai, 400 071, India
Tel.: (91) 2261277200
Web Site: https://pbainfra.in
Year Founded: 1974
532676—(BOM)
Rev.: $1,585,600
Assets: $38,072,070
Liabilities: $52,392,267
Net Worth: ($14,320,197)
Earnings: ($16,123,374)
Emp.: 52
Fiscal Year-end: 03/31/23
Civil Engineering Services
N.A.I.C.S.: 541330
Narain Pirimal Belani *(Mng Dir)*

PBC HEALTH BENEFITS SOCIETY

4250 Canada Way, Burnaby, V5G
4W6, BC, Canada
Tel.: (604) 419-2000
Web Site:
https://www.pac.bluecross.ca
Sales Range: $750-799.9 Million
Emp.: 750
Health & Dental Benefits
N.A.I.C.S.: 524114
Lizanne Mailhot *(Chief Compliance Officer, Chief Risk Officer & CFO-Interim)*

Subsidiaries:

British Columbia Life and Casualty
Company (1)
4250 Canada Way, Burnaby, V5G 4W7,
BC, Canada
Tel.: (604) 419-8040
Web Site: http://www.pbchbs.com
Sales Range: $350-399.9 Million
Emp.: 600
Short & Long Term Disability Coverage &
Life Insurance
N.A.I.C.S.: 524113
Ken Martin *(Pres & CEO)*

PBG S.A.

ul Skorzewska 35 Wysogotowo k,
Przezmierowo, 62-081, Poznan, Poland
Tel.: (48) 616651700   PL
Web Site: https://www.pbg-sa.pl
Year Founded: 1994
PBG—(WAR)
Rev.: $3,557
Assets: $21,521,087
Liabilities: $1,532,990,088
Net Worth: ($1,511,469,000)
Earnings: ($76,925,813)
Emp.: 2,659
Fiscal Year-end: 12/31/23
Holding Company; Natural Gas,
Crude Oil & Fuel Facilities Contracting Services
N.A.I.C.S.: 551112
Maciej Stanczuk *(Vice Chm/VP-Mgmt Bd)*

Subsidiaries:

Aprivia SA (1)
Skorzewska 35 Wysogotowo, 62081,
Przezmierowo, Poland
Tel.: (48) 616646426
Web Site: http://www.aprivia-sa.pl
Road Construction Services
N.A.I.C.S.: 237310

Dromost Sp. z.o.o. (1)
Zabno 2A, Brodnica, 63-112, Poland
Tel.: (48) 612823597
Web Site: http://www.dromost.com
Sales Range: $50-74.9 Million
Emp.: 118
Road Construction Services
N.A.I.C.S.: 237310
Janusz Fajfer *(Gen Mgr)*

GasOil Engineering a.s. (1)
Karpatska 3256 15, Slovensko, 05801, Poprad, Slovakia
Tel.: (421) 527144111
Web Site: http://www.gasoil.sk
Sales Range: $100-124.9 Million
Emp.: 180
Natural Gas & Crude Oil Engineering Services
N.A.I.C.S.: 213112

Hydrobudowa 9 S.A. (1)
ul Skorzewska 35, Wysogotowo k Poznania, 62 081, Przezmierowo, Poland
Tel.: (48) 618469700
Web Site: http://www.hb9.pl
Sales Range: $150-199.9 Million
Emp.: 600
Environmental Protection Services
N.A.I.C.S.: 813312

Infra SA (1)
ul Skorzewska 35, 62081, Przezmierowo,
Poland
Tel.: (48) 616622570
Web Site: http://www.infra-sa.pl
Water Pipes & Sewage Systems Renovation Services
N.A.I.C.S.: 221320
Tomasz Danilos *(Pres)*

KWG S.A. (1)
ul Pomorska 35, 70 812, Szczecin, Poland
Tel.: (48) 91 4321130
Web Site: http://www.kwg.com.pl
Infrastructure Investment & Environmental
Protection Services
N.A.I.C.S.: 813312

Metorex Sp. z.o.o. (1)
ul Zwirki i Wigury 17A, 87 100, Torun, Poland
Tel.: (48) 566529002
Web Site: http://www.metorex.pl
Sales Range: $25-49.9 Million
Emp.: 100
Sewage Treatment Plants Construction
Services
N.A.I.C.S.: 237110
Rafal Damasiewicz *(Pres)*

P.R.G. Metro Sp. z.o.o. (1)
ul Wolczynska 163, Warsaw, 01 919, Poland
Tel.: (48) 228645750
Web Site: http://www.prgmetro.eu
Sales Range: $25-49.9 Million
Emp.: 40
Road & Subway Construction Services
N.A.I.C.S.: 237310
Henryk Zlocki *(Pres)*

PBG Dom Sp. z o.o. (1)
ul Skorzewska 35, Wysogotowo k Poznania, 62 081, Przezmierowo, Poland
Tel.: (48) 616651700
Web Site: http://www.pbgdom.com.pl
Real Estate Development Services
N.A.I.C.S.: 531210
Simon Schmidt *(VP)*

RAFAKO S.A. (1)
ul Lakowa 33, 47-400, Raciborz,
Poland (61.01%)
Tel.: (48) 324101000
Web Site: https://www.rafako.com.pl
Rev.: $325,625,791
Assets: $279,747,875
Liabilities: $337,152,967
Net Worth: ($57,405,092)
Earnings: ($88,483,306)
Emp.: 1,661
Fiscal Year-end: 12/31/2020

Boiler Mfr
N.A.I.C.S.: 332410

Wiertmar Sp. z.o.o. (1)
Kopanka 13 15, 92 701, Lodz, Poland
Tel.: (48) 426484062
Web Site: http://www.wiertmar.pl
Sales Range: $25-49.9 Million
Emp.: 30
Pipeline Renovation & Monitoring Services
N.A.I.C.S.: 541990

PBG S/A

Rodovia BR 101 Km 163, 88200-000,
Tijucas, 88200-000, SC, Brazil
Tel.: (55) 4832792222
Web Site:
https://www.portobello.com.br
PTBL3—(BRAZ)
Rev.: $391,632,960
Assets: $589,193,599
Liabilities: $520,194,298
Net Worth: $68,999,301
Earnings: ($6,275,004)
Emp.: 200
Fiscal Year-end: 12/31/23
Construction Related Services
N.A.I.C.S.: 237990
Claudio Avila da Silva *(Vice Chm)*

Subsidiaries:

Chubb Seguros Sa (1)
Matriz Av Paseo de la Reforma No 250
Torre Niza Piso 15, Colonia Juarez Delegacion Cuauhtemoc, 06600, Mexico, Mexico
Tel.: (52) 15552585800
Insurance Services
N.A.I.C.S.: 524210

Hdi Global Seguros Sa (1)
Blvd Manuel Avila Camacho 1 175 Col Polanco 1 Seccion, Del Miguel Hidalgo,
11510, Mexico, Mexico
Tel.: (52) 5552027534
Insurance Services
N.A.I.C.S.: 524210
German Cardenas *(Dir Gen)*

Tokio Marine Seguradora S.A (1)
Rua Sampaio Viana 44-loja, Sao Paulo,
4004-902, Brazil
Tel.: (55) 1130547000
Insurance Services
N.A.I.C.S.: 524210
Israel Matos *(Mgr-IT)*

PBM POLYTEX LIMITED

8th Floor Ram Krishna Chambers
Productivity Road, Alkapuri, Baroda,
300007, Gujarat, India
Tel.: (91) 2652333586
Web Site:
https://www.pbmpolytex.com
514087—(BOM)
Rev.: $24,614,064
Assets: $17,302,608
Liabilities: $2,409,280
Net Worth: $14,893,328
Earnings: $40,429
Emp.: 847
Fiscal Year-end: 03/31/23
Garments & Textile Products Mfr
N.A.I.C.S.: 314999
Gopal Patodia *(Mng Dir)*

PBO ANIOTA S.A.

ul Wrzesinska 70, 62-025, Kostrzyn,
Poland
Tel.: (48) 616576550
Web Site: http://www.pboaniola.pl
Sales Range: $25-49.9 Million
Construction & Engineering Services
N.A.I.C.S.: 236220
Waldemar Aniola *(Chm-Mgmt Bd)*

PBR PLANUNGSBURO ROHLING AG

Albert-Einstein-Strasse 2, 49076,
Osnabruck, Germany
Tel.: (49) 54194120
Web Site: http://www.pbr.de

Year Founded: 1960
Rev.: $32,418,068
Emp.: 500
Architecture & Constructional Engineering Services
N.A.I.C.S.: 237990
Heinrich Eustrup *(Chm)*

Subsidiaries:

pbr Holscher Brandschutz GmbH (1)
Zimmerstrasse 15 a, 40215, Dusseldorf,
Germany
Tel.: (49) 54194120
Web Site: http://www.pbr-hoelscher.de
Building Construction Services
N.A.I.C.S.: 236220
Martin Holscher *(Mng Partner & Mng Dir)*

PBS FINANSE S.A.

Ul Mickiewicza 29, 38-500, Sanok,
Poland
Tel.: (48) 881062626
Web Site: https://pbsfinanse.pl
Year Founded: 1991
PBF—(WAR)
Rev.: $244,411
Assets: $3,052,846
Liabilities: $792,429
Net Worth: $2,260,417
Earnings: $70,630
Fiscal Year-end: 12/31/23
Financial Services
N.A.I.C.S.: 523999
Dariusz Blicharz *(Chm-Mgmt Bd)*

PBS HOLDING AG

Vogelweiderstrasse 37, 4600, Wels,
Austria
Tel.: (43) 59614
Web Site: http://www.pbs-holding.com
Year Founded: 2000
Paper, Office & Stationery Supplies
Mfr
N.A.I.C.S.: 459410
Richard Scharmann *(CEO)*

Subsidiaries:

Office Depot s.r.o. (1)
Florianova 2461, 253 01, Hostivice, Czech
Republic
Tel.: (420) 311 614 111
Web Site: http://www.pbs-holding.com
Office Supplies Retailer
N.A.I.C.S.: 459410

PC CORP

9947 109 Street, Edmonton, T5K
1H6, AB, Canada
Tel.: (780) 428-3000
Web Site: http://www.pccorp.com
Year Founded: 1988
Rev.: $26,827,856
Emp.: 37
Computer & Computer Peripherals
Dealers
N.A.I.C.S.: 423430

PC DEPOT CORPORATION

2-5 Takashima 1-chome, Nishi-ku,
Yokohama, Kanagawa, Japan
Tel.: (81) 455237618
Web Site: https://www.pcdepot.co.jp
Year Founded: 1994
7618—(TKS)
Rev.: $292,858,720
Assets: $350,222,400
Liabilities: $92,821,520
Net Worth: $257,400,880
Earnings: $8,373,200
Emp.: 1,000
Fiscal Year-end: 03/31/23
Computer Peripheral Equipment Mfr
N.A.I.C.S.: 334118
Takahisa Nojima *(Pres & CEO)*

Subsidiaries:

ejworks Corporation (1)
Yokohama Gate Tower 18th Floor 1-2-5

PC DEPOT CORPORATION

PC DEPOT CORPORATION—(Continued)
Takashima, Nishi-ku, Yokohama, 220-0011, Kanagawa, Japan
Tel.: (81) 455222879
Emp.: 82
Telecommunication Servicesb
N.A.I.C.S.: 517111

PC DIRECT, INC.
8th floor 138 Wonhyo-ro, Yongsan-gu, Seoul, Korea (South)
Tel.: (82) 27853001
Web Site: https://www.pcdirect.co.kr
Year Founded: 1998
051380—(KRS)
Rev.: $239,505,405
Assets: $69,508,577
Liabilities: $35,122,979
Net Worth: $34,385,598
Earnings: ($3,178,828)
Emp.: 102
Fiscal Year-end: 12/31/22
Computer Peripheral Distr
N.A.I.C.S.: 423430
Yeon-Hak Kwon (Sr Mng Dir & CFO)

PC GUARD S.A.
Ul Rozana 63A, 02-569, Warsaw, Poland
Tel.: (48) 61 843 42 66
Web Site: http://www.pcguard.pl
Information Technology Services
N.A.I.C.S.: 519290
Aneta Frukacz (Chm-Mgmt Bd)

PC JEWELLER LIMITED
C - 54 Preet Vihar Vikas Marg, New Delhi, 110092, India
Tel.: (91) 1149714971
Web Site:
  https://corporate.pcjeweller.com
Year Founded: 2005
534809—(BOM)
Rev.: $316,039,806
Assets: $915,523,050
Liabilities: $473,037,588
Net Worth: $442,485,463
Earnings: ($24,363,048)
Emp.: 1,443
Fiscal Year-end: 03/31/23
Jewelry Mfr & Retailer
N.A.I.C.S.: 339910
Ramesh Kumar Sharma (COO)

Subsidiaries:
Transforming Retail Private Limited (1)
1st Floor 2716 Bank Street, karol bagh, New Delhi, 110005, India
Tel.: (91) 9910897647
Jewellery Distr
N.A.I.C.S.: 458310

PC PARTNER GROUP LIMITED
19/F Shatin Galleria 18-24 Shan Mei Street, Fo Tan, Sha Tin, New Territories, China (Hong Kong)
Tel.: (852) 27998011
Web Site: http://www.pcpartner.com
Year Founded: 1997
1263—(HKG)
Rev.: $1,373,851,770
Assets: $784,818,473
Liabilities: $421,297,485
Net Worth: $363,520,988
Earnings: $89,491,868
Emp.: 2,714
Fiscal Year-end: 12/31/22
Computer Product Mfr
N.A.I.C.S.: 334118
Tony Shik Ho Wong (Co-Founder, Chm & CEO)

Subsidiaries:
Active Smart Limited (1)
1518 15/F Yale Indsutrial Building 61 63 Au Pui Wan Street, Fo Tan, Sha Tin, New Territories, China (Hong Kong)
Tel.: (852) 26880100
Web Site: http://www.activesmartlimited.com
Computer Hardware Mfr & Distr
N.A.I.C.S.: 334118

Ask Technology Group Limited (1)
Unit A & B 21F Mai Wah Ind Bldg 1-7 Wah Sing Street, Kwai Chung, China (Hong Kong)
Tel.: (852) 23983223
Graphic Card Mfr
N.A.I.C.S.: 334118

Subsidiary (Domestic):
Innovision Multimedia Limited (2)
Unit A and B 21/F Mai Wah Industrial Building 1-7 Wah Sing Street, Kwai Chung, China (Hong Kong)
Tel.: (852) 2 398 9698
Web Site: https://www.inno3d.com
Emp.: 20
Graphic Card Mfr
N.A.I.C.S.: 334118

Innopartner Pte. Limited (1)
71 Nanyang Drive Innovation Centre 04-15, Singapore, 638075, Singapore
Tel.: (65) 31515672
Electronics Mfr
N.A.I.C.S.: 334419

Manli Technology Group Limited (1)
1601 16/F Seaview Centre 139 - 141 Hoi Bun Road, Kwun Tong, Kowloon, China (Hong Kong)
Tel.: (852) 2 344 2833
Web Site: https://www.manli.com
Sales Range: $25-49.9 Million
Emp.: 12
Computer Hardware Mfr & Distr
N.A.I.C.S.: 334118

Zotac USA Inc. (1)
5793 McCully St, Chino, CA 91710
Tel.: (909) 594-4300
Web Site: http://www.zotacusa.com
Graphic Card & Motherboard Mfr
N.A.I.C.S.: 334118

PC SPLASH WATER PUBLIC COMPANY LTD.
Kleomenous 2, Nicosia, Cyprus
Tel.: (357) 22443644
Soft Drink Distr
N.A.I.C.S.: 424490

PC SYSTEMS S.A.
74-76 Voriou Ipirou St, Amaroussio, 15125, Athens, Greece
Tel.: (30) 2108123000
Web Site: http://www.pcsystems.gr
Year Founded: 1987
Sales Range: $10-24.9 Million
Emp.: 170
Software Application Development & Consulting Services
N.A.I.C.S.: 541511
Grigorios Dedes (Chm & CEO)

PCA CORPORATION
PCA Bldg 1-2-21 Fujimi, Chiyoda-ku, Tokyo, 102-8171, Japan
Tel.: (81) 352112700
Web Site: https://www.pca.jp
Year Founded: 1980
9629—(TKS)
Rev.: $99,268,980
Assets: $221,811,770
Liabilities: $96,466,340
Net Worth: $125,345,430
Earnings: $10,648,710
Emp.: 672
Fiscal Year-end: 03/31/24
Computer Software Development Services
N.A.I.C.S.: 541511
Takuya Kitagawa (Auditor)

Subsidiaries:
Dream hop Co.,Ltd. (1)
Create Building 1-8-10 Iidabashi, Chiyoda-ku, Tokyo, 102-0072, Japan

Tel.: (81) 5017417172
Web Site: https://www.dreamhop.com
Healthcare Management Consulting Services
N.A.I.C.S.: 524114

Xronos, Inc. (1)
Sumitomo Fudosan Akihabara Ekimae Building 17F, 300 Kandaneribeicho Chiyoda-ku, Tokyo, 101-0022, Japan
Tel.: (81) 335258018
Web Site: https://www.xronos-inc.co.jp
Emp.: 110
Database Management Software Development Services
N.A.I.C.S.: 541511

PCA TECHNOLOGY LIMITED
3 Ang Mo Kio Street 62 05-01, Singapore, 569139, Singapore
Tel.: (65) 65454542
Web Site:
  http://www.pcatechnology.com
Year Founded: 1990
Sales Range: $25-49.9 Million
Computer Peripheral Mfr & Distr
N.A.I.C.S.: 334413
Kok Kong Phang (Exec Dir)

Subsidiaries:
PCA Technology (M) Sdn. Bhd - Tampoi Plant (1)
12& 12B Jalan Bayu Kawasan Perindustrian Hasil, 81200, Johor Bahru, Johor, Malaysia
Tel.: (60) 72323223
Web Site: http://www.pcatechnology.com
Printed Circuit Assemblies Mfr
N.A.I.C.S.: 334418

PCB SA
rond-point Schuman 6, 1040, Brussels, Belgium
Tel.: (32) 10887284
Web Site: http://www.pcb.be
PCBB—(EUR)
Pharmaceutical Products Distr
N.A.I.C.S.: 424210
Pascal Fournier Montigieux (Sec)

PCB TECHNOLOGIES LTD.
10 Hauman Street, Migdal, 2310502, Israel
Tel.: (972) 046544300
Web Site: http://www.pcb.co.il
Sales Range: Less than $1 Million
Contract Electronic Provider & Mfr
N.A.I.C.S.: 541990

Subsidiaries:
AMS Electronics Ltd. (1)
Amal 14, Rosh Ha'Ayin, Israel
Tel.: (972) 3 9011106
Web Site: http://www.amstech.co.il
Electronic Products Mfr
N.A.I.C.S.: 334419
Jacob Levi (CEO)

PCBL LIMITED
Duncan House 31 Netaji Subhas Road, Kolkata, 700001, West Bengal, India
Tel.: (91) 3366251443
Web Site: https://www.pcblltd.com
Year Founded: 1960
PCBL—(NSE)
Rev.: $697,160,842
Assets: $651,377,016
Liabilities: $310,953,780
Net Worth: $340,423,236
Earnings: $53,017,205
Emp.: 1,178
Fiscal Year-end: 03/31/23
Carbon Black Mfr
N.A.I.C.S.: 325180
Kaushik Mukherjee (Chief Legal Officer, Compliance Officer & Sec)

Subsidiaries:
PCBL (TN) Limited (1)

INTERNATIONAL PUBLIC

Duncan House 31 Netaji Subhas Road, Kolkata, 700 001, West Bengal, India
Tel.: (91) 3366251443
Web Site: https://www.pcblltn.com
Chemical Products Mfr
N.A.I.C.S.: 325998

PCC EXOL SA
ul Sienkiewicza 4, 56-120, Brzeg Dolny, Poland
Tel.: (48) 717942127
Web Site: https://pcc-exol.eu
Surfactants Mfr
N.A.I.C.S.: 325998
Miroslaw Siwirski (Pres)

PCC INTERMODAL S.A
ul Pulaskiego 6, 81-368, Gdynia, Poland
Tel.: (48) 587647660
Web Site:
  http://www.pccintermodal.pl
Sales Range: $10-24.9 Million
Emp.: 60
Intermodal Transportation Services
N.A.I.C.S.: 482111
Dariusz Andrzej Stefanski (Pres)

PCC SE
Moerser Str 149, 47198, Duisburg, Germany
Tel.: (49) 2066 2019 0
Web Site: http://www.pcc.eu
Sales Range: $800-899.9 Million
Emp.: 3,500
Holding Company; Chemicals, Energy & Logistics Services
N.A.I.C.S.: 551112
Alfred Pelzer (Mng Dir)

Subsidiaries:
3Services Factory S.A. (1)
Gospodarcza Str 12, 40-432, Katowice, Poland
Tel.: (48) 324288382
Web Site: http://www.eng.3s.pl
Telecommunication Servicesb
N.A.I.C.S.: 541618
Ryszard Kubis (Member-Mgmt Bd)

CATCH66 GmbH (1)
Moerser Strasse 149, 47198, Duisburg, Germany
Tel.: (49) 2066201966
Web Site: http://www.catch66.de
Fish Product Distr
N.A.I.C.S.: 424460

Chemi-Plan S.A. (1)
Henryka Sienkiewicza, Brzeg Dolny, Poland
Tel.: (48) 717942015
Logistics Consulting Servies
N.A.I.C.S.: 541614

Elpis Sp. z o.o. (1)
Zemborzycka 55, Lublin, 20-445, Poland
Tel.: (48) 814613630
Web Site: http://www.elpis.lublin.pl
Air Conditioning Installation Services
N.A.I.C.S.: 238220

GRID BH d.o.o. (1)
Juraja Najtharta 1, 71000, Sarajevo, Bosnia & Herzegovina
Tel.: (387) 33555285
Logistics Consulting Servies
N.A.I.C.S.: 541614

Locochem Sp. z o.o. (1)
ul Sienkiewicza 4, 56-120, Brzeg Dolny, Poland
Tel.: (48) 717942060
Plastic Raw Material Distr
N.A.I.C.S.: 424610

Novi Energii OOD (1)
Georgi Izmirliev Str 28 block 234 ap 67, Triaditsa, 1404, Sofia, Bulgaria
Tel.: (359) 29617585
Plastic Raw Material Distr
N.A.I.C.S.: 424610
Yordan Stanimirov (Mng Dir)

OOO PCC Consumer Products (1)

ul Spiridonovka 30/1, 123001, Moscow, Russia
Tel.: (7) 4957773747
Logistics Consulting Servies
N.A.I.C.S.: 541614

PCC Chemax, Inc. (1)
30 Old Augusta Rd, Piedmont, SC 29673
Tel.: (864) 277-7000
Web Site: http://www.pcc-chemax.com
Sales Range: $10-24.9 Million
Emp.: 29
Chemicals Mfr
N.A.I.C.S.: 325998

PCC Consumer Products Czechowice S.A. (1)
ul Lukasiewicza 5, 43-502, Czechowice-Dziedzice, Poland
Tel.: (48) 322152681
Logistics Consulting Servies
N.A.I.C.S.: 541614

PCC Consumer Products S.A. (1)
ul F Nullo 2, 00-486, Warsaw, Poland
Tel.: (48) 225298100
Logistics Consulting Servies
N.A.I.C.S.: 541614

PCC Energetyka Blachownia Sp. z o.o. (1)
ul Szkolna 15, 47- 225, Kedzierzyn-Kozle, Poland
Tel.: (48) 774886553
Logistics Consulting Servies
N.A.I.C.S.: 541614

PCC Energia EOOD (1)
Georgi Izmirliev Str 28 block 234 ap 67, Triaditsa, 1404, Sofia, Bulgaria
Tel.: (359) 29617585
Logistics Consulting Servies
N.A.I.C.S.: 541614

PCC Energy Trading GmbH (1)
Hilgerstrasse 20, 45141, Essen, Germany
Tel.: (49) 206620190
Logistics Consulting Servies
N.A.I.C.S.: 541614

PCC Exol Kimya San.ve Tic. Ltd. (1)
Agaoglu My Office 212 Kat 8 Daire 130, Bagcilar, 34127, Istanbul, Turkiye
Tel.: (90) 2126939598
Logistics Consulting Servies
N.A.I.C.S.: 541614

PCC HYDRO DOOEL Skopje (1)
Kosta Shahov Str No 12/2, 1000, Skopje, North Macedonia
Tel.: (389) 23085088
Web Site: http://www.pcc-hydro-mk.com
Power Plant Maintenance Services
N.A.I.C.S.: 237990
Kristian Gligorovski (Project Mgr)

PCC Insulations GmbH (1)
Moerser Strasse 149, 47198, Duisburg, Germany
Tel.: (49) 206620190
Polyol Product Mfr
N.A.I.C.S.: 325998

PCC Intermodal GmbH (1)
Georg-Richter-Strasse 15, 15234, Frankfurt, Germany
Tel.: (49) 3354016763
Logistics Consulting Servies
N.A.I.C.S.: 541614

PCC Intermodal S.A. (1)
ul Hutnicza 16, 81-061, Gdynia, Poland
Tel.: (48) 585858200
Web Site: http://www.pccintermodal.pl
Emp.: 400
Railway Freight Transportation Services
N.A.I.C.S.: 482111
Adam Adamek (VP)

PCC Morava - Chem s.r.o. (1)
Leose Janacka 798/20, 737 01, Cesky Tesin, Czech Republic
Tel.: (420) 558769111
Web Site: http://www.pccmorava-chem.cz
Industrial Chemical Products Mfr
N.A.I.C.S.: 325199

PCC Organic Oils Ghana Ltd. (1)
C188 A/C, PO Box 439, Akim Oda, Ghana
Tel.: (233) 206620190
Logistics Consulting Servies

N.A.I.C.S.: 541614

PCC Prodex Sp. z o.o. (1)
Artemidy 24, 01 497, Warsaw, Poland
Tel.: (48) 226380924
Web Site: http://www.pcc-prodex.eu
Polyurethane Products Mfr
N.A.I.C.S.: 325211

PCC Rokita SA (1)
Tel.: (48) 717942000
Web Site: http://www.pcc.rokita.pl
Rev.: $606,755,842
Assets: $641,488,311
Liabilities: $290,517,784
Net Worth: $350,970,528
Earnings: $68,058,689
Emp.: 3,300
Fiscal Year-end: 12/31/2023
Chemical Product Mfr & Distr
N.A.I.C.S.: 325998
Alfred Pelzer (Chm-Supervisory Bd)

PCC Seaview Residences ehf. (1)
Bakkavegur 2, Husavik, 640, Akureyri, Iceland
Tel.: (354) 8964701
Plastic Raw Material Distr
N.A.I.C.S.: 424610

PCC Silicium S.A. (1)
Zagorze 92, 26-140, Walbrzych, Poland
Tel.: (48) 412548211
Web Site: http://www.pccsilicium.pl
Road & Railway Construction Services
N.A.I.C.S.: 237990
Mariusz Antosiewicz (Chm-Supervisory Bd)

PCC Slovakia s.r.o. (1)
Letna 45, 040 01, Kosice, Slovakia
Tel.: (421) 911645460
Web Site: http://www.pccslovakia.sk
Fuel Distr
N.A.I.C.S.: 424720

PCC Specialties GmbH (1)
Otto-Roelen-Str 1, 46147, Oberhausen, Germany
Tel.: (49) 2083876490
Web Site: http://www.pcc-specialties.eu
Paint & Coating Mfr
N.A.I.C.S.: 325510
Uwe Zakrzewski (Mng Dir)

PCC Therm Sp. z o.o. (1)
Sienkiewicza 4, 56-120, Brzeg Dolny, Poland
Tel.: (48) 717942000
Polyol Product Mfr
N.A.I.C.S.: 325998

PolyU GmbH (1)
Hilgerstrasse 20, 45141, Essen, Germany
Tel.: (49) 20181503330
Web Site: http://www.polyu.eu
Polyurethane Chemical Mfr
N.A.I.C.S.: 326150
Klaus Langerbeins (Mng Dir)

S.C. Euro-Urethane S.R.L (1)
Str Uzinei Nr 1, 240401, Ramnicu Valcea, Romania
Tel.: (40) 250701851
Chemical Products Distr
N.A.I.C.S.: 424690

TEC artec valves GmbH & Co. KG i.L. (1)
Am Heidering 7a Gewerbepark Nord, Oranienburg, 16515, Germany
Tel.: (49) 3301203260
Industrial Machinery Mfr
N.A.I.C.S.: 333998
Matthias Richter (Mgr-Pur)

TzOW Petro Carbo Chem (1)
ul Strujska 98/408, 79026, Lvov, Ukraine
Tel.: (380) 322374000
Logistics Consulting Servies
N.A.I.C.S.: 541614

ZAO NOVOBALT Terminal (1)
ul Portvaja 36, 236039, Kaliningrad, Russia
Tel.: (7) 4012631828
Chemical Products Distr
N.A.I.C.S.: 424690

distripark GmbH (1)
Otto-Roelen-Strasse 1, 46147, Oberhausen, Germany
Tel.: (49) 2083876500

Web Site: http://www.distripark.de
Industrial Chemical Mfr & Whslr
N.A.I.C.S.: 325320
Tobias Jansen (Sls Mgr)

distripark.com Sp. z o.o. (1)
Sienkiewicza 4, 56-120, Brzeg Dolny, Poland
Tel.: (48) 667650174
Plastic Raw Material Distr
N.A.I.C.S.: 424610
Maciej Grech (Owner & Project Mgr)

PCCS GROUP BERHAD
Lot 1376 GM 127 Mukim Simpang Kanan Jalan Kluang, 83000, Batu Pahat, Johor, Malaysia
Tel.: (60) 74568871
Web Site: https://www.pccsgroup.net
Year Founded: 1973
PCCS—(KLS)
Rev.: $102,928,815
Assets: $97,660,283
Liabilities: $55,757,295
Net Worth: $41,902,988
Earnings: ($36,630)
Emp.: 2,296
Fiscal Year-end: 03/31/22
Textile Mfr
N.A.I.C.S.: 313210
Siew Chuan Chua (Co-Sec)

Subsidiaries:

Beauty Electronic Embroidering Centre Sdn. Bhd. (1)
PLO 10 Kawasan Perusahaan Parit Raja, Parit Raja, 86400, Batu Pahat, Johor, Malaysia
Tel.: (60) 74548800
Web Site: http://www.pccsgroup.net
Emp.: 100
Embroidering Services
N.A.I.C.S.: 313220

China Roots Packaging Pte. Ltd. (1)
No 13 Dongya Road East Area Of Economic Technology Development, 510730, Guangzhou, Guangdong, China
Tel.: (86) 2062952000
Web Site: http://www.cn.grahampackaging.com
Plastic Packaging Materials Mfr
N.A.I.C.S.: 326199

Keza Sdn. Bhd. (1)
PLO 10 Kawasan Perindustrian Parit Raja, Parit Raja, 86400, Batu Pahat, Johor, Malaysia
Tel.: (60) 74548822
Elastic Bands Mfr
N.A.I.C.S.: 339999

Mega Label (Malaysia) Sdn. Bhd. (1)
No 4 Jalan Palam 34/18A Seksyen 34, 40470, Shah Alam, Selangor, Malaysia
Tel.: (60) 3 5161 0880
Web Site: http://www.megalb.com
Sales Range: $25-49.9 Million
Label Printing Services
N.A.I.C.S.: 323111

Mega Labels & Stickers Sdn. Bhd. (1)
Lot 1376 GM 127 Mukim Simpang Kanan, Jalan Kluang, 83000, Batu Pahat, Johor, Malaysia
Tel.: (60) 74568888
Web Site: http://www.mgl.my
Sales Range: $25-49.9 Million
Emp.: 140
Label Printing Services
N.A.I.C.S.: 561910
Edmund Chan (Mng Dir)

PCCS (Hong Kong) Limited (1)
Unit 5 9/F Chevalier Commercial Centre 8 Wang Hoi Road, KowloonBay, Kowloon, China (Hong Kong)
Tel.: (852) 21211788
Web Site: http://www.pccsgroup.net
Sales Range: $50-74.9 Million
Emp.: 3
Apparel Distr
N.A.I.C.S.: 424310

PCCS Garments (Suzhou) Ltd. (1)
Tel.: (86) 51263786288
Sales Range: $350-399.9 Million
Emp.: 2,000
Apparels Mfr
N.A.I.C.S.: 315250

PCCS Garments Limited (1)
No 1 Confederation of Russia Sangkat Tuk Thla Khan Sen Sok, 12101, Phnom Penh, Cambodia
Tel.: (855) 23995750
Web Site: http://www.pccsgroup.net
Sales Range: $1-4.9 Billion
Emp.: 10,000
Garments Mfr
N.A.I.C.S.: 313220

Perfect Seamless Garments (Cambodia) Ltd. (1)
28A St Veng Sreng Phum Traparng Thleung Sangkat Chom Chao, Khan Porsenchey, Phnom Penh, Cambodia
Tel.: (855) 9 525 8153
Emp.: 150
Laser Perforation & Eyelet Mfr
N.A.I.C.S.: 339993

Perusahaan Chan Choo Sing Sdn Bhd (1)
Sales Range: $100-124.9 Million
Emp.: 300
Apparels Mfr
N.A.I.C.S.: 315250

Thirty Three (Shanghai) Ltd. (1)
Room 210 No 31 28 DanBa Road, PuTuo Area, Shanghai, 200062, China
Tel.: (86) 2161677833
Event Planning Services
N.A.I.C.S.: 561920

Wan He Da Manufacturing Company Ltd. (1)
National Road No 4 Phum Ang Sangkat Chom Chao, Khan Porsenchey, Phnom Penh, Cambodia
Tel.: (855) 24398888
Emp.: 2,638
Kid Knit & Woven Apparel Mfr
N.A.I.C.S.: 315990

PCD STORES (GROUP) LIMITED
76 132 Zhongshan Road, Siming District, Xiamen, 360001, China
Tel.: (86) 5922663323
Web Site: http://www.pcds.com.cn
Sales Range: $200-249.9 Million
Emp.: 3,500
Department Stores
N.A.I.C.S.: 455110
Alfred Chan (Chm & Exec Dir)

PCF GROUP PLC
Pinners Hall 105-108 Old Broad Street, London, EC2N 1ER, United Kingdom
Tel.: (44) 2072222426 UK
Web Site: http://pcf.bank
Year Founded: 1993
PCF—(AIM)
Rev.: $42,506,140
Assets: $532,748,962
Liabilities: $480,444,157
Net Worth: $52,304,805
Earnings: ($19,089,543)
Emp.: 152
Fiscal Year-end: 09/30/22
Financial Services
N.A.I.C.S.: 523999
Scott D. Maybury (CEO)

Subsidiaries:

PCF Asset Finance Limited (1)
39 Victoria Street Pinners Holl 105-108 Old Brodge St, London, SW1H 0EU, United Kingdom
Tel.: (44) 2072277502
Web Site: http://wwwpcfg.co.uk
Emp.: 43
Financial Management Services
N.A.I.C.S.: 523999
Robert John Murray (Mng Dir)

PCF GROUP PLC

PCF Group plc—(Continued)

PCF Equipment Leasing Limited (1)
180 Borough High Street, London, SE1
1LB, United Kingdom (100%)
Tel.: (44) 2072222426
Web Site: http://www.pcfg.co.uk
Sales Range: $25-49.9 Million
Emp.: 50
Equipment Leasing Services
N.A.I.C.S.: 532490

PCF Group Limited (1)
125 Old Broad Street, London, EC2N 1AR,
United Kingdom (100%)
Tel.: (44) 2072222426
Web Site: http://www.pcfg.co.uk
Sales Range: $50-74.9 Million
Emp.: 50
Financial Services
N.A.I.C.S.: 523999
Anthony Nelson *(Chm)*

PCF Leasing Limited (1)
Brandon 180 Borough St, London, SE11LB,
United Kingdom (100%)
Tel.: (44) 2072222426
Web Site: http://www.pcfg.co.uk
Sales Range: $50-74.9 Million
Emp.: 50
Leasing Services
N.A.I.C.S.: 525990

Private and Commercial Finance
Company Limited (1)
Brandon House 180 Borough High Street,
London, SE1 1LB, United
Kingdom (100%)
Tel.: (44) 2072222426
Web Site: http://www.pcfg.co.uk
Sales Range: $50-74.9 Million
Emp.: 50
Installment Credit Services
N.A.I.C.S.: 522390
Robert Murray *(Mng Dir)*

The Asset Management Corporation
Limited (1)
Brandon House 180 Borough High Street,
London, SE1 1LB, United
Kingdom (100%)
Tel.: (44) 2072222426
Web Site: http://www.pcfg.co.uk
Sales Range: $50-74.9 Million
Emp.: 50
Asset Management Services
N.A.I.C.S.: 523999
Scott Maybury *(CEO)*

PCF GROUP SA
al Solidarnosci 171, 00-877, Warsaw,
Poland
Tel.: (48) 228873430
Web Site:
https://www.peoplecanfly.com
Year Founded: 2002
PCF—(WAR)
Rev.: $38,141,260
Assets: $130,452,490
Liabilities: $21,743,140
Net Worth: $108,709,349
Earnings: ($19,200,965)
Emp.: 756
Fiscal Year-end: 12/31/23
Custom Computer Programming Services
N.A.I.C.S.: 541511
Adam Parsons *(Chief Dev Officer)*

PCH INTERNATIONAL LTD.
Heritage Business Park Bessboro
Road, Blackrock, Cork, Ireland
Tel.: (353) 21 733 7400
Web Site: http://www.pchintl.com
Sales Range: $450-499.9 Million
Emp.: 5,000
Business Management Services
N.A.I.C.S.: 541611
Liam Casey *(Founder & CEO)*

Subsidiaries:

Fab, Inc. (1)
235 Park Ave S 4th Fl, New York, NY
10003
Tel.: (855) 767-7322
Web Site: http://www.fab.com
ECommerce
N.A.I.C.S.: 445298
Bradford Shane Shellhammer *(Co-Founder)*

PCH Innovation Hub-Shenzhen (1)
Block D&E 4/F Du Shi Ming Yuan Jintang
St Cai Wu Wei, Luo Hu District, Shenzhen,
518010, Guangdong, China
Tel.: (86) 755 2598 8866
Web Site: http://www.pchintl.com
Emp.: 200
Designs Custom Manufacturing Solutions
for Startups & Fortune 500 Companies
N.A.I.C.S.: 561499
Ray Porter *(Mng Dir-Ops)*

PCH International Ltd. (1)
907 9/F Lippo Sun Plaza 28 Canton Road,
Tsim Sha Tsui, Hong Kong, China (Hong
Kong)
Tel.: (852) 2921 9200
Business Management Services
N.A.I.C.S.: 541611

PCH International Ltd. (1)
22F Shibuya Mark City West 1-12-1 Dogen-
zaka, Shibuya-ku, Tokyo, 150-0043, Japan
Tel.: (81) 3 4360 5411
Web Site: http://www.pchintl.com
Emp.: 2
Business Management Services
N.A.I.C.S.: 541611
Keisuke Suzuki *(Gen Mgr)*

PCH International Ltd. - Seoul (1)
Room 901 Woosung Characterville 467-18
Dogok-Dong, Gangnam-gu, Seoul, Korea
(South)
Tel.: (82) 2 571 9191
Web Site: http://www.pchintl.com
Business Management Services
N.A.I.C.S.: 541611

PCHOME ONLINE, INC.
12th Floor No 105 Section 2 Dunhua
South Road, Taipei, 106, Taiwan
Tel.: (886) 227000898
Web Site: https://corp.pchome.tw
Year Founded: 1996
8044—(TPE)
Rev.: $1,460,177,032
Assets: $831,443,267
Liabilities: $567,548,010
Net Worth: $263,895,257
Earnings: $1,362,974
Fiscal Year-end: 12/31/22
Online Marketing Services
N.A.I.C.S.: 541890
Yu-Shan Chang *(CEO)*

Subsidiaries:

PChome Bibian Inc. (1)
108-0014 PMO Tamachi IV 2F 5-29-19
Shiba, Minato-ku, Tokyo, Japan
Tel.: (81) 363817337
Web Site: https://www.bibian.co.jp
Ecommerce & Digital Marketing Services
N.A.I.C.S.: 522320

PCI BIOTECH HOLDING ASA
Ullernchausseen 64, 0379, Oslo, Norway
Tel.: (47) 67115400
Web Site: https://www.pcibiotech.no
Year Founded: 2000
PCIB—(OSL)
Rev.: $293,933
Assets: $4,330,345
Liabilities: $492,214
Net Worth: $3,838,131
Earnings: ($1,997,071)
Emp.: 7
Fiscal Year-end: 12/31/23
Medical Device Mfr.
N.A.I.C.S.: 334519
Anders Hogset *(Chief Scientific Officer)*

PCI GEOMATICS GROUP INC
90 All State Parkway Street 501,
Markham, L3R6H3, ON, Canada
Tel.: (905) 764-0614
Web Site:
http://www.pcigeomatics.com
Year Founded: 1982
Rev.: $10,433,394
Emp.: 88
Remote Sensing Services & Computer Software Services
N.A.I.C.S.: 423430
Robert Lang *(CFO)*

Subsidiaries:

Pci Geomatics USA Inc. (1)
1655 N Fort Myer Dr Ste 700, Arlington, VA
22209
Tel.: (866) 307-0313
Computer Software Development Services
N.A.I.C.S.: 541511

PCI TECHNOLOGY GROUP CO., LTD
PCI Intelligent Building No 2 Xincen
Fourth Road, Tianhe, Guangzhou,
510653, China
Tel.: (86) 2085521717
Web Site: https://www.pcitech.com
Year Founded: 1986
600728—(SHG)
Rev.: $749,228,229
Assets: $1,567,554,249
Liabilities: $805,394,519
Net Worth: $762,159,729
Earnings: ($36,800,539)
Emp.: 2,000
Fiscal Year-end: 12/31/22
Software & System Integration Services
N.A.I.C.S.: 541512
Liu Wei *(Chm & CEO)*

Subsidiaries:

Beijing Inforefiner Technology Co.,
Ltd. (1)
Room A023 3rd Floor Building 17 No 3
Yanjing Lizhong Street, Chaoyang District,
Beijing, China
Tel.: (86) 1059780065
Information Technology Services
N.A.I.C.S.: 541519

Chongqing PCI Technology&Service
Co., Ltd. (1)
Room 8 33rd Floor Huarun building Xieji-
awan, Jiulongpo District, Chongqing, China
Tel.: (86) 2368163991
Information Technology Services
N.A.I.C.S.: 541519

Guangdong Fundway Technology
Co., Ltd. (1)
411B Haizhu Zhongda Technology Building
No 135 Xingang West Road, Guangdong,
Guangdong, China
Tel.: (86) 2089250751
Information Technology Services
N.A.I.C.S.: 541519

Guangzhou Cloudwalk Information
Technology Co., Ltd. (1)
F5-6 Heung Kong Science & Technology
Innovation Center, Nansha, Guangzhou,
China
Tel.: (86) 4001515992
Web Site: https://www.cloudwalk.com
Information Technology Services
N.A.I.C.S.: 541511

Guangzhou PCI Data Service Co.,
Ltd. (1)
Room 2503 Tower C Wansheng Plaza No
1226 Xingang East Road, Pazhou Haizhu
District, Guangzhou, Guangdong, China
Tel.: (86) 2089557133
Information Technology Services
N.A.I.C.S.: 541519

Guangzhou Panyu Huicheng Small
Loan Co., Ltd. (1)
Unit 04-08 17th Floor Zhongyin Building No
338 Qinghe East Road, Panyu District,
Guangzhou, Guangdong, China
Tel.: (86) 2084629999
Information Technology Services

INTERNATIONAL PUBLIC

N.A.I.C.S.: 541519

Guangzhou XX-Motor Information
TechnologyCo., Ltd. (1)
Jiadu Intelligent Building No 2 Xincen 4th
Road, Tianhe District, Guangzhou, Guang-
dong, China
Tel.: (86) 4000990356
Web Site: https://www.xx-motor.com
Information Technology Services
N.A.I.C.S.: 541519

PCI Hong Kong Limited (1)
Rm G 10/F Effort Ind Bldg 2-8 Kung Yip St,
Kwai Hing NT, Hong Kong, China (Hong
Kong)
Tel.: (852) 35685225
Web Site: https://www.pci-hk.com
Information Technology Services
N.A.I.C.S.: 541511

PCI Service Support Technology Co.,
Ltd. (1)
PCI Intelligent Building No 2 Xincen Fourth
Road, Tianhe District, Guangzhou, China
Tel.: (86) 2085521717
Information Technology Services
N.A.I.C.S.: 541519

PCI Technology&Service Co.,
Ltd. (1)
PCI Intelligent Building No 2 Xincen Fourth
Road, Tianhe District, Guangzhou, China
Tel.: (86) 2085620012
Information Technology Services
N.A.I.C.S.: 541519

PCI-Jianxun Xinjiang Technology Co.,
Ltd. (1)
The 29th floor Xingle World Trade Plaza No
460 Qitai Road, Shayibake District Xinjiang,
Urumqi, China
Tel.: (86) 9915580333
Information Technology Services
N.A.I.C.S.: 541519

PCI-SUNTEK Payment Technology
Co., Ltd. (1)
Room 1306 No 26 Jinlong Road, Nansha
District, Guangzhou, Guangdong, China
Tel.: (86) 2085103909
Information Technology Services
N.A.I.C.S.: 541519

Shenzhen PCI Chuanghui Investment
Co., Ltd. (1)
Room 201 Building A No 1 Qianwan 1st
Road, Qianhai Hong Kong-Shenzhen Coop-
eration Zone Qianhai, Shenzhen, Guang-
dong, China
Tel.: (86) 2085521717
Information Technology Services
N.A.I.C.S.: 541519

Suzhou 1000video Visiual Technology
Co., Ltd. (1)
Room 1802 Building 2 Pioneer Park No 209,
Zhuyuan Road, High-tech Zone, Suzhou,
China
Tel.: (86) 4008702878
Web Site: https://www.1000video.com.cn
Information Technology Services
N.A.I.C.S.: 541511

PCI-PAL PLC
7 Gamma Terrace, Ransomes Eu-
ropark, Ipswich, IP3 9FF, Suffolk,
United Kingdom
Tel.: (44) 3301310330
Web Site: https://www.pcipal.com
PCIP—(AIM)
Rev.: $22,699,644
Assets: $19,615,728
Liabilities: $22,105,611
Net Worth: ($2,489,883)
Earnings: ($1,491,402)
Emp.: 114
Fiscal Year-end: 06/30/24
Holding Company; Secure Financial
Transaction Processing Services
N.A.I.C.S.: 551112
Geoffrey Forsyth *(Chief Information
Security Officer)*

Subsidiaries:

PCI-PAL Limited (1)

1 Cornhill, London, EC3V 3ND, United Kingdom
Tel.: (44) 207 030 3770
Web Site: http://www.pci-pal.com
Secure Payment Processing Services
N.A.I.C.S.: 522320
James Barham (CEO)

PCL EMPLOYEES HOLDINGS LTD.
5410 99th Street NW, Edmonton, T6E 3P4, AB, Canada
Tel.: (780) 733-5000   AB
Web Site: http://www.pcl.com
Year Founded: 1906
Sales Range: $5-14.9 Billion
Emp.: 3,408
Holding Company; Construction Services
N.A.I.C.S.: 551112
Ross A. Grieve (Chm)

Subsidiaries:

Mellow Industrial Services, Inc. (1)
2305 5th St NW, Nisku, T9E 7X1, AB, Canada
Tel.: (780) 955-8500
Web Site: http://www.melloy.com
Sales Range: $25-49.9 Million
Emp.: 45
Industrial Contractor
N.A.I.C.S.: 238990

PCL Construction Enterprises, Inc. (1)
2000 S Colorado Blvd Tower 2 Ste 2-500, Denver, CO 80222
Tel.: (303) 365-6500
Web Site: http://enterprises.pcl.com
Emp.: 1,434
Commercial Buildings, Civil & Heavy Industrial Construction
N.A.I.C.S.: 237990
Mike Kehoe (VP-Fin)

Subsidiary (Domestic):

Nordic PCL Construction, Inc. (2)
1099 Alakea St Ste 1560, Honolulu, HI 96813
Tel.: (808) 541-9101
Building Construction Services
N.A.I.C.S.: 236210
Glen Kaneshige (Pres)

Unit (Domestic):

PCL Civil Constructors, Inc.-SE (2)
3810 Northdale Blvd Ste 200, Tampa, FL 33624
Tel.: (813) 264-9500
Web Site: http://www.pcl.com
Sales Range: $25-49.9 Million
Emp.: 50
Infrastructure Construction
N.A.I.C.S.: 237310
Gayle Grady (District Mgr)

PCL Civil Constructors, Inc.-SW (2)
1711 W Greentree Dr Ste 201, Tempe, AZ 85284
Tel.: (480) 829-6333
Web Site: http://www.civil.pcl.com
Sales Range: $50-74.9 Million
Emp.: 180
Infrastructure Construction
N.A.I.C.S.: 237310
Tom O'Donnell (District Mgr)

Subsidiary (Non-US):

PCL Construction Resources Inc. (2)
10003 56th Ave NW, Edmonton, T6E 5L7, AB, Canada
Tel.: (780) 733-5910
Web Site: http://www.resources-pcl.com
Sales Range: $25-49.9 Million
Emp.: 50
Construction Equipment Distr & Supplier
N.A.I.C.S.: 423390

Subsidiary (Domestic):

PCL Construction Services, Inc. (2)
3650 131st Ave SE Ste 600, Bellevue, WA 98006
Tel.: (425) 454-8020
Building Construction Services
N.A.I.C.S.: 236210
Tom Doig (VP & District Mgr)

PCL Construction, Inc. (2)
4545 Fuller Dr Ste 406, Irving, TX 75038
Tel.: (972) 650-1065
Civil Engineering Services
N.A.I.C.S.: 541330
Doug Schmits (Area Mgr)

PCL Industrial Services, Inc. (2)
1500 S Union Ave, Bakersfield, CA 93307
Tel.: (661) 832-3995
Web Site: http://www.ndservices.pcl.com
Sales Range: $100-124.9 Million
Emp.: 300
Heavy Industrial General Contractor
N.A.I.C.S.: 237990
Joe Carrieri (Pres)

Teton Industrial Construction, Inc. (2)
6445 Shiloh Rd Ste E, Alpharetta, GA 30005
Tel.: (678) 965-3100
Web Site: http://www.tetonindustrial.com
Sales Range: $25-49.9 Million
Emp.: 70
Industrial Contractor
N.A.I.C.S.: 236220
Don Knicely (Sr Mgr-Fin & Admin)

The Nassal Company (2)
415 W Kaley St, Orlando, FL 32806
Tel.: (407) 648-0400
Web Site: http://www.nassal.com
Sales Range: $10-24.9 Million
Emp.: 53
Provider of Commercial & Office Building Construction Services
N.A.I.C.S.: 236220
Matt Brown (Partner)

PCL Construction Management Inc.-Calgary (1)
2882 11th St NE, Calgary, T2E 7S7, AB, Canada
Tel.: (403) 250-4800
Web Site: http://www.pcl.com
Sales Range: $25-49.9 Million
Emp.: 100
Construction Services
N.A.I.C.S.: 541618
Blaine Maciborsky (VP & District Mgr)

PCL Construction Management Inc.-Saskatoon (1)
3120 Faithfull Ave, Saskatoon, S7K 8H3, SK, Canada
Tel.: (306) 931-3322
Web Site: http://www.pcl.com
Sales Range: $25-49.9 Million
Emp.: 63
Construction Services
N.A.I.C.S.: 541618

PCL Constructors Canada Inc.-Atlantic Canada (1)
111 Ilsley Ave Suite 300, Dartmouth, B3B 1S8, NS, Canada
Tel.: (902) 481-8500
Web Site: http://canada.pcl.com
Sales Range: $25-49.9 Million
Emp.: 50
Design, Building, General Contracting & Construction Management Services
N.A.I.C.S.: 541618

PCL Constructors Canada Inc.-Ottawa (1)
49 Auriga Drive, Ottawa, K2E 8A1, ON, Canada
Tel.: (613) 225-6130
Web Site: http://www.canada.pcl.com
Sales Range: $25-49.9 Million
Emp.: 100
Design-build, General Contracting & Construction Management Services
N.A.I.C.S.: 541618
Paul Knowles (VP)

PCL Constructors Canada Inc.-Toronto (1)
2201 Bristol Circle Suite 500, Oakville, L6H 0J8, ON, Canada
Tel.: (905) 276-7600
Web Site: http://www.pcl.com

Design-Build, General Contracting & Construction Management Services
N.A.I.C.S.: 541618
Joe Watson (Dir-Bus Dev)

PCL Constructors Canada Inc.-Winnipeg (1)
1540 Gamble Place, Winnipeg, R3T 1N6, MB, Canada
Tel.: (204) 949-8900
Web Site: http://www.canada.pcl.com
Sales Range: $25-49.9 Million
Emp.: 40
Design-build, General Contracting & Construction Management Services
N.A.I.C.S.: 541618
Sharon Malenki (Mgr-Admin)

PCL Constructors Inc. (1)
9915 56th Ave NW, Edmonton, T6E 5L7, AB, Canada
Tel.: (780) 733-5000
Web Site: http://constructors.pcl.com
Sales Range: $150-199.9 Million
Emp.: 1,000
Independent Operating Company Consulting Services
N.A.I.C.S.: 541618
Todd Craigen (COO & Pres-Corp Svcs)

PCL Constructors Northern Inc. (1)
5400 99 Street NW, Edmonton, T6E 3P4, AB, Canada
Tel.: (780) 733-6000
Building Construction Services
N.A.I.C.S.: 236210
Alan Kuysters (VP & District Mgr)

PCL Constructors Pacific Rim Pty Ltd. (1)
55 Flemington Road Ste 116, North Melbourne, 3051, VIC, Australia
Tel.: (61) 7807335000
Building Construction Services
N.A.I.C.S.: 236210
Alex Pimentel (Sr Project Mgr-Controls)

PCL Constructors Westcoast Inc. (1)
13911 Wireless Way Suite 310, Richmond, V6V 3B9, BC, Canada
Tel.: (604) 241-5200
Emp.: 80
Building Construction Services
N.A.I.C.S.: 236210
Sean Hamelin (VP)

PCL Energy Inc. (1)
10003 56th Ave NW, Edmonton, T6E 5L7, AB, Canada
Tel.: (780) 733-5910
Web Site: http://www.pcl.com
General & Industrial Contracting Services
N.A.I.C.S.: 238990
Denis Dubord (VP & Gen Mgr)

PCL Industrial Constructors, Inc. (1)
5402 99th St NW, Edmonton, T6E 3P4, AB, Canada
Tel.: (780) 733-5500
Web Site: http://www.pcl.com
Sales Range: $50-74.9 Million
Emp.: 200
General Industrial Construction
N.A.I.C.S.: 236210

PCL Industrial Management Inc. (1)
5404 99th St NW, Edmonton, T6E 3P4, AB, Canada
Tel.: (780) 733-5700
Web Site: http://www.pcl.com
Emp.: 200
Construction Management
N.A.I.C.S.: 541618
Dave Kaminsky (Sr Mgr-Project Dev)

PCL Intracon Power Inc. (1)
5350 99th St NW, Edmonton, T6E 3P4, AB, Canada
Tel.: (780) 733-5300
Web Site: http://www.intracon.pcl.com
Sales Range: $25-49.9 Million
Emp.: 60
Electrical & Instrumentation Industrial Construction Company
N.A.I.C.S.: 238210
Brent Holdner (Mgr-Ops)

PCL INC
Star Valley Rm 701 99 Digital-ro 9-gil, Geumcheon-gu, Seoul, 08510, Korea (South)
Tel.: (82) 221443901
Web Site: https://www.pclchip.com
241820—(KRS)
Rev.: $28,545,613
Assets: $67,448,291
Liabilities: $41,643,635
Net Worth: $25,804,656
Earnings: ($3,076,618)
Emp.: 62
Fiscal Year-end: 12/31/22
Diagonistic Medical Device Mfr
N.A.I.C.S.: 334510
Soyoun Kim (CEO)

PCL TECHNOLOGIES TRADING, INC.
9th Floor No 97 Tun-HwaS Road Sec 2, Taipei, 106, Taiwan
Tel.: (886) 227006650
Web Site: https://www.pcltech.com
Year Founded: 2007
4977—(TAI)
Rev.: $92,838,821
Assets: $155,164,681
Liabilities: $38,835,944
Net Worth: $116,328,737
Earnings: $13,495,482
Emp.: 660
Fiscal Year-end: 12/31/22
Telecommunications Equipment
N.A.I.C.S.: 334290
Ming-Nan Chuang (CEO)

Subsidiaries:

PCL (Suzhou) Co., Ltd. (1)
368 Heshan Road New District, Suzhou, 215129, China
Tel.: (86) 51268093566
Engineeering Services
N.A.I.C.S.: 541330

PCL Technologies (Taiwan) Co., Ltd. (1)
26th Floor No 105 Tun-Hwa S Road Sec2, Taipei, 106, Taiwan
Tel.: (886) 227006650
Optical Component & Equipment Distr
N.A.I.C.S.: 423460

PCM POMEROY CONSTRUCTION & MAINTENANCE LTD.
109-3060 Norland Ave, Burnaby, V5B 3A6, BC, Canada
Tel.: (604) 294-6700
Web Site: https://www.pomeroyconstruction.com
Year Founded: 1991
Rev.: $12,223,500
Emp.: 40
General Contractors
N.A.I.C.S.: 236220
Randy L. Browne (Mgr-Sls & Mktg)

PCO AG
Donaupark 11, 93309, Kelheim, Germany
Tel.: (49) 944120050   De
Web Site: http://www.pco.de
Year Founded: 1987
Sales Range: $10-24.9 Million
Emp.: 50
Scientific Cameras Mfr
N.A.I.C.S.: 333310
Emil Ott (Founder)

Subsidiaries:

PCO-TECH Inc. (1)
6930 Metroplex Dr, Romulus, MI 48174
Tel.: (248) 276-8820
Web Site: http://www.pco-tech.com
Photonic Instrument Mfr & Distr
N.A.I.C.S.: 334413
Murad Karmali (VP-Sls)

PCS HOLDING AG

PCS HOLDING AG

PCS Holding AG—(Continued)
Schulstrasse 4, CH-8500, Frauenfeld, Switzerland
Tel.: (41) 52723360
Web Site: https://pcs-holding.ch
Emp.: 100
Holding Company
N.A.I.C.S.: 551112

PCS TECHNOLOGY LIMITED
S No 1A F1 Irani Market Compound, Yerwada, Pune, 411015, Maharashtra, India
Tel.: (91) 2241296111
Web Site: https://www.pcstech.com
517119—(BOM)
Rev.: $386,221
Assets: $6,291,442
Liabilities: $578,253
Net Worth: $5,713,189
Earnings: $61,318
Emp.: 10
Fiscal Year-end: 03/31/21
Software Development Services
N.A.I.C.S.: 541511
Mehul Monani (Compliance Officer & Sec)

PD EROZIJA A.D.
Pop Lukina br 8, 14000, Valjevo, Serbia
Tel.: (381) 14 227 311
Web Site: http://www.erozijava.co.rs
Year Founded: 1967
Sales Range: $1-9.9 Million
Emp.: 85
Hydraulic Structure Construction Services
N.A.I.C.S.: 237990

PD OMOLJICA AD
Kralja Petra I br 2, 26230, Omoljica, 26230, Serbia
Tel.: (381) 13617017
Web Site: https://www.pdomoljicaad.rs
Year Founded: 1954
OMOL—(BEL)
Rev.: $1,339,502
Assets: $13,555,367
Liabilities: $965,192
Net Worth: $12,590,175
Earnings: ($588,603)
Fiscal Year-end: 12/31/23
Farming Services
N.A.I.C.S.: 111998
Donko Rajkovic (Exec Dir)

PD ZAJECAR A.D.
Negotinski put bb, Zajecar, Serbia
Tel.: (381) 19 436 462
Year Founded: 1957
Sales Range: $1-9.9 Million
Emp.: 42
Cereal Crop Farming Services
N.A.I.C.S.: 111998

PDC BIOLOGICAL HEALTH GROUP CORPORATION
140 11120 Horseshoe Way, Richmond, V7A 5H7, BC, Canada
Tel.: (604) 304-6006
Web Site: http://www.eidam.com
Medical Devices
N.A.I.C.S.: 339112
Simon Cheng (CEO)

PDC CONSULTANTS PTY. LTD.
Level 2 21 Kintail Road, Applecross, 6153, WA, Australia
Tel.: (61) 8 9315 6600   AU
Web Site: http://www.pdcgroup.com
Year Founded: 1972
Sales Range: $75-99.9 Million
Emp.: 385

Engineering & Technical Consulting Services
N.A.I.C.S.: 541330
Martyn Weir (CEO)

PDD HOLDINGS INC.
28/F No 533 Loushanguan Road, Changning District, Shanghai, 200051, China
Tel.: (86) 2152661300   Ky
Web Site: http://www.pinduoduo.com
Year Founded: 2015
PDD—(NASDAQ)
Rev.: $14,394,070,155
Assets: $27,763,140,895
Liabilities: $16,254,841,149
Net Worth: $11,508,299,746
Earnings: $1,190,237,931
Emp.: 9,762
Fiscal Year-end: 12/31/21
Consumer Products Distr
N.A.I.C.S.: 551112
Colin Huang (Co-Founder & Chm)

PDG REALTY S.A. EMPREENDIMENTOS E PARTICIPACOES
Av Dr Cardoso de Melo 1855 6 andar, Vila Olimpia, Sao Paulo, 04548-005, SP, Brazil
Tel.: (55) 21104400
Web Site: http://www.pdg.com.br
Year Founded: 2003
PDGR3—(BRAZ)
Rev.: $74,328,963
Assets: $479,038,581
Liabilities: $1,697,970,734
Net Worth: ($1,218,932,153)
Earnings: ($225,260,911)
Fiscal Year-end: 12/31/19
Real Estate Manangement Services
N.A.I.C.S.: 531110
Augusto Alves dos Reis Neto (CEO, CFO, & Officer-IR & Dir-Investor Relations)

Subsidiaries:

Abyara Planejamento Imobiliario S.A.   (1)
Av Republica Do Libano 417, Ibirapuera, Sao Paulo, 04501-000, Brazil
Tel.: (55) 11 3888 3380
Web Site: http://www.abyara.com.br
Real Estate Manangement Services
N.A.I.C.S.: 531390

Agra Moab Incorporadora Ltda   (1)
Rua Delmira Ferreira 119 Vila Firmiano Pinto, Sao Paulo, 04125-120, Brazil
Tel.: (55) 11 5061 0294
Real Estate Manangement Services
N.A.I.C.S.: 531390

Bruxelas Empreendimentos Imobiliarios Spe Ltda   (1)
Av Paulista 1374, Sao Paulo, 01310-100, Brazil
Tel.: (55) 1932072035
Real Estate Manangement Services
N.A.I.C.S.: 531390

Condessa Empreendimentos Imobiliarios Ltda.   (1)
Zuquim Dr 1557, Sao Paulo, 02035-012, Brazil
Tel.: (55) 11 2971 4600
Real Estate Manangement Services
N.A.I.C.S.: 531390

Eltanin Incorporadora Ltda   (1)
R Braga 200, Sao Bernardo do Campo, 09725-160, Sao Paulo, Brazil
Tel.: (55) 11 4121 7915
Real Estate Manangement Services
N.A.I.C.S.: 531390

Gold Acre Empreendimentos Imobiliarios SPE Ltda.   (1)
Rua Marte 100, Barueri, Sao Paulo, 06414-000, Brazil
Tel.: (55) 11 4161 0657
Real Estate Manangement Services

N.A.I.C.S.: 531390

Gold Alaska Empreendimentos Imobiliarios Ltda   (1)
Avenida Governador Pedro de Toledo 370, Campinas, Sao Paulo, 13070-752, Brazil
Tel.: (55) 19 3236 0595
Real Estate Manangement Services
N.A.I.C.S.: 531390

Gold Amapa Empreendimentos Imobiliarios Ltda   (1)
Avenida Presidente Juscelino Kubitscheck de Oliveira 1600, Sao Jose do Rio Pardo, 15091-450, Sao Paulo, Brazil
Tel.: (55) 17 3216 1421
Real Estate Manangement Services
N.A.I.C.S.: 531390

Gold Ikralia Empreend. Imob. SPE Ltda.   (1)
Rua Dom Vital 248, Gloria, Porto Alegre, 90660-030, Brazil
Tel.: (55) 51 3519 3291
Real Estate Manangement Services
N.A.I.C.S.: 531390

Gold Polonia Empreendimentos imobiliarios SPE Ltda   (1)
Praca Santos Dumont 1101, Araraquara, Sao Paulo, Brazil
Tel.: (55) 16 3322 2229
Real Estate Manangement Services
N.A.I.C.S.: 531390

Gold Portugal Empreendimentos imobiliarios SPE Ltda   (1)
R Dr Gabriel Penteado 502 Vl, Campinas, Sao Paulo, 13035-451, Brazil
Tel.: (55) 19 32723606
Real Estate Manangement Services
N.A.I.C.S.: 531390

Gold Red Empreendimentos imobiliarios SPE Ltda   (1)
Rua Jose Cobra 401, Sao Jose dos Campos, Sao Paulo, Brazil
Tel.: (55) 12 3931 2231
Real Estate Manangement Services
N.A.I.C.S.: 531390

Gold Sao Paulo Empreendimentos Imobiliarios SPE Ltda.   (1)
Rua Alba 150 - Vila Santa Catarina, Sao Paulo, 04346-000, Brazil
Tel.: (55) 11 5031 1990
Real Estate Manangement Services
N.A.I.C.S.: 531390

Gold Withe Empreendimentos imobiliarios SPE Ltda   (1)
Rua Jasmim 610 - Chacara Primavera, Campinas, Sao Paulo, 13087-460, Brazil
Tel.: (55) 19 3256 5353
Real Estate Manangement Services
N.A.I.C.S.: 531390

Goldfarb 12 Empreendimento Imobiliario Ltda.   (1)
Avenida Joaquim Constantino 10100 Presidente Prudente, Sao Paulo, Brazil
Tel.: (55) 18 3909 4774
Real Estate Manangement Services
N.A.I.C.S.: 531390

Kochab Incorporadora Ltda.   (1)
R Braga 202, Sao Bernardo do Campo, 09725-160, Sao Paulo, Brazil
Tel.: (55) 11 4330 8526
Real Estate Manangement Services
N.A.I.C.S.: 531390

Matipu Empreendimentos Imobiliarios Ltda   (1)
Rua Monsenhor de Paula Rodrigues 129 - Vila Belmiro, Santos, Sao Paulo, 11075-350, Brazil
Tel.: (55) 13 3221 1051
Real Estate Manangement Services
N.A.I.C.S.: 531390

Orion Incorporadora Ltda   (1)
Rua Joao Balbi 167, Belem, 66055-280, Para, Brazil
Tel.: (55) 9132546811
Real Estate Manangement Services
N.A.I.C.S.: 531390

PDG Barao Geraldo
Rua Barao Geraldo de Rezende 97, Campi-

nas, Sao Paulo, 13020-440, Brazil
Tel.: (55) 19 3236 2591
Real Estate Management Services
N.A.I.C.S.: 531390

INTERNATIONAL PUBLIC

PDMS LTD.
Global House Isle of Man Business Park Cooil Road, Douglas, IM2 2QZ, Isle of Man
Tel.: (44) 1624 664000
Web Site: http://www.pdms.com
Year Founded: 1993
Emp.: 70
Software Development Services
N.A.I.C.S.: 513210
Simon Edwards (Mgr-Quality & Standards)

PDS LIMITED
Unit No 971 Solitaire Corporate Park Andheri Ghatkopar Link Road, Mumbai, 400093, Maharashtra, India
Tel.: (91) 8067653000
Web Site: https://pdsltd.com
PDSL—(NSE)
Rev.: $1,274,328,242
Assets: $372,763,911
Liabilities: $239,365,482
Net Worth: $133,398,429
Earnings: $39,178,514
Emp.: 180
Fiscal Year-end: 03/31/23
Apparel Mfr & Distr
N.A.I.C.S.: 315250
Deepak Seth (Co-Founder)

Subsidiaries:

Casa Forma Limited   (1)
2nd Floor 13 Golden Square Soho, London, W1F 9JG, United Kingdom
Tel.: (44) 2075849495
Web Site: https://www.casaforma.co.uk
Interior Design Services
N.A.I.C.S.: 541410
Faiza Seth (Founder)

DBS Lifestyle India Private Limited   (1)
B-107 Sector 2, Noida, 201301, Uttar Pradesh, India
Tel.: (91) 1202443932
Web Site: https://www.dbslifestyle.com
Clothing & Fashion Product Mfr
N.A.I.C.S.: 315990

Kleider Sourcing Limited   (1)
House 10 Road 12 Sector 06, Uttara, Dhaka, 1230, Bangladesh
Tel.: (880) 28412814
Web Site: https://www.kleidersourcing.com
Textile Clothing Product Whslr
N.A.I.C.S.: 458110

Nor Lanka Colombo Manufacturing Limited   (1)
Tel.: (94) 112003010
Web Site: https://norlankmfg.com
Textile Product Mfr & Whslr
N.A.I.C.S.: 314999

Norlanka Brands Private Limited   (1)
758 and 759 2Nd Floor 19th Main Sector-2 HSR Layout, Bengaluru, 560102, Karnataka, India   (75%)
Tel.: (91) 9868037938
Web Site: https://lillyandsid.co.in
Children Clothing Whslr
N.A.I.C.S.: 424350

PDS Trading (Shanghai) Co., Limited   (1)
Room 508 Can Hong Elite Plaza No 1059 Wu Zhongroad Near Lian Hua Road, Shanghai, 201103, China
Tel.: (86) 2154846606
Apparel Distr
N.A.I.C.S.: 424350

PG Home Group SPA   (1)
Avenida Del Valle 869 Of 204 Huechuraba, Santiago, Chile
Tel.: (56) 229492654
Apparel Distr
N.A.I.C.S.: 424350

AND PRIVATE COMPANIES

Progress Apparels Bangladesh Limited (1)
Ms-sfb-01 and 02 Adamjee Epz, Naryanganj, Dhaka, 1431, Bangladesh
Tel.: (880) 1704166674
Web Site: https://www.progress-mfg.com
Apparels Mfr
N.A.I.C.S.: 315250

Recovered Clothing Limited (1)
Quadrant House 4 Thomas More Square Floor 6, London, E1W 1YW, United Kingdom
Tel.: (44) 7904958053
Web Site: https://recoveredclothing.com
Clothing Product Whslr
N.A.I.C.S.: 458110

Simple Approach Limited (1)
7/F Park Fook Industrial Building 615-617 Tai Nan West Street, Cheung Sha Wan, China (Hong Kong)
Tel.: (852) 35881888
Web Site: https://www.simple-approach.com
Emp.: 40
Apparel Distr
N.A.I.C.S.: 424350

Subsidiary (Non-US):

Simple Approach (Canada) Limited (2)
418 North Service Rd E, Oakville, L6H 5R2, ON, Canada
Tel.: (905) 845-1885
Apparel Distr
N.A.I.C.S.: 424350

Spring Near East Manufacturing Company Limited (1)
7/F Park Fook Industrial Building 615-617 Tai Nan West Street, Cheung Sha Wan, Kowloon, China (Hong Kong)
Tel.: (852) 35881988
Web Site: https://www.springne.com
Textile Products Mfr
N.A.I.C.S.: 314999

Techno Design GMBH (1)
Tel.: (49) 2113687990
Web Site: https://www.techno-design.net
Apparel Distr
N.A.I.C.S.: 424350
Rajyve Ranjan *(Mng Dir)*

PDZ HOLDINGS BERHAD
No 1 Jalan Sungai Aur, 42000, Port Klang, Selangor Darul Ehsan, Malaysia
Tel.: (60) 331692233 MY
Web Site: https://www.pdzlines.com
PDZ—(KLS)
Rev.: $1,822,857
Assets: $23,274,074
Liabilities: $3,163,598
Net Worth: $20,110,476
Earnings: ($1,372,487)
Fiscal Year-end: 12/31/22
Holding Company; Freight Shipping Services
N.A.I.C.S.: 551112
Ho Jien Shiung *(Exec Dir)*

Subsidiaries:

PDZ Shipping Agency (Bintulu) Sdn. Bhd. (1)
No 61 2nd Floor Taman Sri Sihong Jalan Abahu Galau, Jalan Abang Galau, Bintulu, 97000, Sarawak, Malaysia
Tel.: (60) 86332722
Sales Range: $25-49.9 Million
Emp.: 4
Shipping Support Services
N.A.I.C.S.: 483111

PDZ Shipping Agency (Johor) Sdn.Bhd. (1)
No 8 Jalan Ros Merah 2/9, Taman Johor Jaya, 81100, Johor Bahru, Johor Darul Takzim, Malaysia
Tel.: (60) 73522866
Web Site: http://www.pdzlines.com.my
Emp.: 18
Shipping Support Services
N.A.I.C.S.: 488510
Kelvin Too *(Branch Mgr)*

PDZ Shipping Agency (Kuching) Sdn.Bhd. (1)
Lot 9842 Section 64 Jalan Pending, Kuching, 93450, Sarawak, Malaysia
Tel.: (60) 82336345
Sales Range: $25-49.9 Million
Emp.: 18
Shipping Support Services
N.A.I.C.S.: 488510
Chan Kheng Hwang *(Gen Mgr)*

PDZ Shipping Agency (Sabah) Sdn.Bhd. (1)
Unit No B920 9th Floor Wisma Merdeka Phase II, 88000, Kota Kinabalu, Sabah, Malaysia
Tel.: (60) 88264211
Sales Range: $25-49.9 Million
Emp.: 20
Shipping Support Services
N.A.I.C.S.: 488510
Alvin Wong *(Exec Dir)*

PDZ Shipping Agency (Sibu) Sdn.Bhd. (1)
No 6 1st Floor Lorong Kampung Datu 9, 96000, Sibu, Sarawak, Malaysia
Tel.: (60) 84320252
Sales Range: $25-49.9 Million
Emp.: 12
Shipping Support Services
N.A.I.C.S.: 488510
Ting Chiew Hook *(Exec Dir)*

PDZ Shipping Agency (Tawau) Sdn. Bhd. (1)
TB314 2nd Floor Fajar Complex, PO Box 62163, Tawau, 91031, Sabah, Malaysia
Tel.: (60) 89775850
Sales Range: $25-49.9 Million
Emp.: 9
Shipping Services
N.A.I.C.S.: 483111
Wong Kapison *(Mgr)*

Tong Joo Shipping Pte Ltd (1)
100 Beach Road Level 16, Singapore, 189702, Singapore
Tel.: (65) 62211333
Sales Range: $25-49.9 Million
Emp.: 21
Marine Cargo Handling & Support Services
N.A.I.C.S.: 488320

PEA ENCOM INTERNATIONAL CO., LTD
200 Ngamwongwan Road Ladyao, Chatuchak, Bangkok, 10900, Thailand
Tel.: (66) 25909938
Web Site: https://pea-encom.com
Power Generation & Distribution Services
N.A.I.C.S.: 221114

PEAB AB
Margretetorpsvagen 84, SE-269 73, Forslov, Sweden
Tel.: (46) 43189000
Web Site: https://www.peab.com
PEAB.B—(OMX)
Rev.: $7,306,732,160
Assets: $5,147,381,120
Liabilities: $3,628,339,680
Net Worth: $1,519,041,440
Earnings: $388,336,480
Emp.: 15,252
Fiscal Year-end: 12/31/20
Construction & Civil Engineering Services
N.A.I.C.S.: 541330
Mats Paulsson *(Vice Chm)*

Subsidiaries:

A-frakt AB (1)
Jarnvagsgatan 114, Arvidsjaur, 933 34, Sweden
Tel.: (46) 96 01 34 10
Freight Trucking Services
N.A.I.C.S.: 484110

AB Faresta Grus (1)
Gardsvagen 6, PO Box 808, 16970, Solna, Sweden
Tel.: (46) 86236800
Industrial Sand Mining
N.A.I.C.S.: 212322

AB Vendels Grustag (1)
Borjegatan 77, 752 19, Uppsala, Sweden
Tel.: (46) 18 22 70 30
Gravel Extraction Services
N.A.I.C.S.: 212321

ATS Kraftservice AB (1)
Kristinavagen 26, Box 1, 711 30, Lindesberg, Sweden
Tel.: (46) 581 133 20
Web Site: http://www.atskraftservice.se
Sales Range: $25-49.9 Million
Electric Power Line Construction Engineering Services
N.A.I.C.S.: 237130

ATS Service AB (1)
Gardsvagen 6, 169 70, Solna, Sweden
Tel.: (46) 86236700
Construction Engineering Services
N.A.I.C.S.: 541330
Thomas Eklund *(Gen Mgr)*

Aktiebolaget Smidmek Eslov (1)
Bruksgatan 7A, 241 39, Eslov, Sweden
Tel.: (46) 41313870
Web Site: https://smidmek.com
Prefabricated Concrete & Steel Frame Services
N.A.I.C.S.: 238120

Annehem Bygg Och Projekt AB (1)
Arenagatan 35, 215 32, Malmo, Sweden
Tel.: (46) 40167770
Web Site: http://www.annehem.se
Building Construction Services
N.A.I.C.S.: 236220

Arne Olav Lund A/S (1)
Ringdalskogen 103, 3270, Larvik, Norway
Tel.: (47) 33139660
Web Site: https://aol.no
Road & Sewage Construction Services
N.A.I.C.S.: 237110

Asfaltbelaggningar i Boden AB (1)
Flygfaltsvagen 34, Boden, 961 43, Sweden
Tel.: (46) 92114900
Civil Engineering Construction Services
N.A.I.C.S.: 237990

Asfaltti-System Oy (1)
Kisallintie 9, 45200, Kouvola, Finland
Tel.: (358) 57455500
Web Site: https://www.asfalttisystem.com
Asphalt Roofing Mfr
N.A.I.C.S.: 324122

BEFAB Entreprenad Mjolby AB (1)
Transformatorgatan 3, 595 35, Mjolby, Sweden
Tel.: (46) 13 473 3210
Web Site: http://peab.se
Civil Engineering Construction Services
N.A.I.C.S.: 237990
Fredrik Aslund *(Mng Dir)*

BEFAB Schakt AB (1)
Jagarvallsvagen 3a, Linkoping, 584 22, Sweden
Tel.: (46) 13141000
Digging Excavation Services
N.A.I.C.S.: 238910

Bjorn Bygg AS (1)
Hjalmar Johansens gt 25, PO Box 6342, 9293, Tromso, Norway
Tel.: (47) 77661030
Web Site: http://www.bjorn.no
Sales Range: $25-49.9 Million
Engineeering Services
N.A.I.C.S.: 541330

Bogstrand AS (1)
Molnholtet 42, 9414, Harstad, Norway
Tel.: (47) 48050200
Web Site: https://www.bogstrand.no
Painting & Building Wall Finishing Services
N.A.I.C.S.: 238320

Byggservice & Vedlikehold AS (1)
Sorkedalsveien 150A, 0754, Oslo, Norway
Tel.: (47) 416 51 414
Web Site: http://www.peab.no
Sales Range: $50-74.9 Million
Emp.: 120
New Housing Operative Builders

PEAB AB

N.A.I.C.S.: 236117

Carpenova AB (1)
Valhall Park By 10, 262 74, Angelholm, Sweden
Tel.: (46) 431 36 75 50
Human Resource Consulting Services
N.A.I.C.S.: 541612

CompWell AB (1)
Vikingavagen 31, 224 76, Lund, Sweden
Tel.: (46) 46 132760
Web Site: http://www.compwell.biz
Network Component Tools Distr
N.A.I.C.S.: 423830

Elvehavn Brygge Hus G AS (1)
Henrik Ibsens Gate 100, 0230, Oslo, Norway
Tel.: (47) 23303000
Web Site: http://www.peab.no
Sales Range: $50-74.9 Million
Emp.: 120
New Housing Operative Builders
N.A.I.C.S.: 236117

Fastighets AB Ekudden (1)
Sveagatan 6 A, 441 32, Alingsas, Sweden
Tel.: (46) 322611213
Real Estate Manangement Services
N.A.I.C.S.: 531390

Fastighetsforvaltnings- bolaget Gasellen 2 HB (1)
Gardsvagen 7, 169 70, Solna, Sweden
Tel.: (46) 8 6236800
Real Estate Manangement Services
N.A.I.C.S.: 531390

Ferdigbetong AS (1)
Stakkevollvegen 11, 9010, Tromso, Norway
Tel.: (47) 77681862
Web Site: http://www.ferdig-betong.no
Sales Range: $25-49.9 Million
Emp.: 2
Engineeering Services
N.A.I.C.S.: 541330

Flygstaden Intressenter i Soderhamn AB (1)
Margretetorpsvagen 84, Forslov, 260 92, Sweden
Tel.: (46) 43189148
Investment Management Service
N.A.I.C.S.: 523999

Froseth AS (1)
Venusvegen 21, Verdal, Norway
Tel.: (47) 97992400
Web Site: https://froeseth.no
Construction Materials Distr
N.A.I.C.S.: 423320

Glacell Sverige AB (1)
Drakenvagen 27, 262 74, Angelholm, Sweden
Tel.: (46) 101431000
Web Site: https://glacell.se
Solar Panels Installation Services
N.A.I.C.S.: 238210

HGT AS (1)
Postboks 56, Kokstad, Bergen, Norway
Tel.: (47) 55982750
Web Site: https://hgt.no
Construction Services
N.A.I.C.S.: 236220

Hagstrom i Nas AB (1)
Narsjovagen 23, Nas, 780 53, Vansbro, Sweden
Tel.: (46) 706208271
Web Site: http://www.hagstromab.se
Building Maintenance & Inspection Services
N.A.I.C.S.: 541350

Halsingebygg i Hudiksval AB (1)
Kopmanbergsvagen 4, 824 50, Hudiksvall, Sweden
Tel.: (46) 65035730
Web Site: https://www.halsingebygg.se
Private & Public Construction Services
N.A.I.C.S.: 236220

Huvudkontor Peab AB (1)
Margretetorpsvagen 84, 260 92, Forslov, Sweden (100%)
Tel.: (46) 43189000
Web Site: http://www.peab.se
Sales Range: $25-49.9 Million
Emp.: 100
Heavy & Civil Engineering Construction

PEAB AB

Peab AB—(Continued)
N.A.I.C.S.: 237990
Mats Paulsson *(CEO & Mng Dir)*

Incasec AB (1)
Valhall Park Bygg, Angelholm, 262 74, Sweden
Tel.: (46) 43189400
Construction Engineering Services
N.A.I.C.S.: 541330

Interoc AB (1)
Betonggatan 1, 721 36, Vasteras, Sweden
Tel.: (46) 733 37 56 45
Roofing Ceiling Device Mfr
N.A.I.C.S.: 335131

J.O.Z. Peab Group SIA (1)
Balasta dambis 80 A, Riga, Latvia
Tel.: (371) 7500371
Engineeering Services
N.A.I.C.S.: 541330

K.Nordang AS (1)
Morkevegen 41, Stranda, 6200, Lierstranda, Norway
Tel.: (47) 70268585
Web Site: http://www.nordang.no
Private & Public Construction Services
N.A.I.C.S.: 236220

Kompligens Fastigheter AB (1)
Margretetorpsvagen 84, Forslov, 260 91, Sweden
Tel.: (46) 43189000
Real Estate Manangement Services
N.A.I.C.S.: 531390

Kranor AS (1)
Eternitveien 10, 3470, Slemmestad, Norway
Tel.: (47) 31297800
Web Site: http://www.kranor.no
Sales Range: $25-49.9 Million
Heavy & Civil Engineering Construction
N.A.I.C.S.: 237990

Kungsfiskaren Bygg & Fastighet AB (1)
Gardsvagen 6, 169 28, Solna, Sweden
Tel.: (46) 8 799 25 00
Building Renovation & Decorating Services
N.A.I.C.S.: 236118

Lambertsson Oy (1)
Karhunkierros 1, Nurmijarvi, Finland
Tel.: (358) 92900330
Web Site: http://www.lambertsson.com
Sales Range: $25-49.9 Million
Emp.: 17
Engineeering Services
N.A.I.C.S.: 541330

Lambertsson Sverige AB (1)
Margretetorpsvagen 84, 269 73, Forslov, Sweden (100%)
Tel.: (46) 431 893 00
Web Site: http://www.lambertsson.com
Sales Range: $50-74.9 Million
Emp.: 105
Rental & Installation of Electrical & Heating Equipment for Construction Industry
N.A.I.C.S.: 532490

Subsidiary (Domestic):

Lambertssons Kran AB (2)
Ostra Lindomevagen 50, 437 34, Lindome, Sweden (100%)
Tel.: (46) 31996000
Sales Range: $50-74.9 Million
Cranes & Lifts Rentals
N.A.I.C.S.: 532490
Jan Heed *(CEO)*

Subsidiary (Domestic):

Bararelaget Krancenter AB (3)
Morsaregatan 15, 254 66, Helsingborg, Sweden
Tel.: (46) 42162030
Web Site: http://www.bararelaget.se
Sales Range: $10-24.9 Million
Cranes & Lifts Rentals
N.A.I.C.S.: 532490

Subsidiary (Domestic):

Ralling AB (4)
Hammarvagen 5, 23237, Malmo, Sweden (100%)
Tel.: (46) 40158050
Web Site: http://www.ralling.se
Rental of Mobil Cranes, Forklifts & Trucks; Contracting Work in the Heavy Lifting Field
N.A.I.C.S.: 532412

Lattklinkerbetong AB (1)
Presstorp 106, Ucklum, 444 94, Stenungsund, Sweden
Tel.: (46) 303 77 62 70
Web Site: http://www.lkb.se
Sales Range: $25-49.9 Million
Joists & Facade Walls Mfr
N.A.I.C.S.: 327390

Linje & Kabelplojning i Borlange AB (1)
Godsvagen 11, 784 72, Borlange, Sweden
Tel.: (46) 243 21 77 60
Web Site: http://www.peab.se
Sales Range: $25-49.9 Million
Emp.: 50
Construction Equipment Rental Services
N.A.I.C.S.: 532412

Ljungbyhed Park AB (1)
Thulinvagen 5, 264 51, Ljungbyhed, Sweden
Tel.: (46) 435440010
Web Site: http://www.ljungbyhedpark.se
Building Construction Services
N.A.I.C.S.: 236220

Ljungbyheds Golfcenter AB (1)
Monumentvagen 2, 260 70, Ljungbyhed, Sweden
Tel.: (46) 435440044
Golf Course Operation Services
N.A.I.C.S.: 713910

Molletofta i Klippan AB (1)
Lisakravagen 2 E, 264 94, Klippan, Sweden
Tel.: (46) 43522225
Real Estate Manangement Services
N.A.I.C.S.: 531390

Nordenfjeldske Spunt og Peleservice AS (1)
Leirfossveien 23, 7491, Trondheim, Norway
Tel.: (47) 91 63 44 00
Construction & Civil Engineering Services
N.A.I.C.S.: 237990

Olof Mobjer Entreprenad AB (1)
Akarevagen 11 A, 311 32, Falkenberg, Sweden
Tel.: (46) 346714480
Web Site: http://www.mobjerab.se
Sales Range: $25-49.9 Million
Emp.: 16
Wind Turbine Foundation Ring Construction Services
N.A.I.C.S.: 237990

Olsson & Zarins Baltinvest AB (1)
Gardsvagen 6, PO Box 808, 16970, Solna, Sweden
Tel.: (46) 86236800
Industrial Supplies Whslr
N.A.I.C.S.: 423840

Peab AS (1)
Strandveien 17, 1366, Lysaker, Norway
Tel.: (47) 23303000
Web Site: https://www.peab.no
Sales Range: $50-74.9 Million
New Housing Operative Builders
N.A.I.C.S.: 236117

Peab Asfalt A/S (1)
Norreskov Bakke 1, 8600, Silkeborg, Denmark
Tel.: (45) 87221500
Web Site: https://peabasfalt.dk
Emp.: 300
Paving Services
N.A.I.C.S.: 237310

Peab Asfalt AB (1)
Margretetorpsvagen 84, Box 1282, 262 24, Angelholm, Sweden (100%)
Tel.: (46) 43189000
Web Site: http://www.peabasfalt.se
Sales Range: $25-49.9 Million
Heavy & Civil Engineering Construction
N.A.I.C.S.: 237990

Peab Asfalt Norden AB (1)
Box 1282, 262 24, Angelholm, Sweden
Tel.: (46) 43189000
Construction Services
N.A.I.C.S.: 236220

Peab Asfalt Norge AS (1)
Strandveien 17, 1366, Lysaker, Norway
Tel.: (47) 23303000
Web Site: http://www.peabasfalt.no
Asphalt Mfr
N.A.I.C.S.: 324121

Peab Asfalt Syd AB (1)
Margretetorpsvagen 84, Forslov, 26973, Sweden (100%)
Tel.: (46) 43189000
Web Site: http://www.peab.se
Sales Range: $25-49.9 Million
Emp.: 100
Heavy & Civil Engineering Construction
N.A.I.C.S.: 237990
Mats Paulsson *(CEO & Mng Dir)*

Peab Bildrift AB (1)
Margretetorpsvagen 84, 269 73, Forslov, Sweden (100%)
Tel.: (46) 43189000
Web Site: http://www.peab.se
Sales Range: $25-49.9 Million
Emp.: 100
Heavy & Civil Engineering Construction
N.A.I.C.S.: 237990

Peab Bolig AS (1)
PO Box 2909, Solli, 0230, Oslo, Norway
Tel.: (47) 23303000
Web Site: http://www.peab.no
New Housing Operative Builders
N.A.I.C.S.: 236117

Peab Bolig Prosjekt AS (1)
Strandveien 15A, Lysaker, 1366, Norway
Tel.: (47) 23303000
Web Site: http://www.peab.no
Building Construction Services
N.A.I.C.S.: 236117
Stine Gabrielsen *(Mgr-PR)*

Peab Bostad AB (1)
Sales Range: $75-99.9 Million
Emp.: 400
Engineeering Services
N.A.I.C.S.: 541330
Mats Paulsson *(Gen Mgr)*

Peab Byggkonstruktion AB (1)
PO Box 101, Forslov, Sweden
Tel.: (46) 87998500
Construction & Civil Engineering Services
N.A.I.C.S.: 541330

Peab Construction i Goteborg AB (1)
Anders Personsgatan 2, Gothenburg, 40180, Jesper, Sweden
Tel.: (46) 317008400
Web Site: http://www.peab.se
Emp.: 100
Engineeering Services
N.A.I.C.S.: 541330
Jesper Goransson *(Gen Mgr)*

Peab Elevbyggen AB (1)
Savelundsgatan 6, Alingsas, 44138, Sweden (100%)
Tel.: (46) 32279500
Web Site: http://www.peab.se
Sales Range: $25-49.9 Million
Emp.: 20
Engineeering Services
N.A.I.C.S.: 541330
Henrik Johansson *(Mng Dir)*

Peab Energi AB (1)
Margretetorpsvagen 84, Forslov, 260 91, Sweden
Tel.: (46) 43189000
Civil Engineering Construction Services
N.A.I.C.S.: 237990

Peab Exploatering AB (1)
Gardsvagen 6, Solna, 169 70, Sweden
Tel.: (46) 86236800
Construction Engineering Services
N.A.I.C.S.: 541330

Peab Fastighetsutveckling Sverige AB (1)
PO Box 808, 169 28, Solna, Sweden
Tel.: (46) 8 623 68 00
Real Estate Manangement Services
N.A.I.C.S.: 531390

Peab Forvaltning Nykoping AB (1)
Gardsvagen 6, PO Box 808, 16970, Solna, Sweden

Tel.: (46) 86236800
Web Site: http://www.peab.se
Sales Range: $150-199.9 Million
Emp.: 350
Real Estate Agents & Brokers
N.A.I.C.S.: 531210

Peab Grundlaggning AB (1)
Flintyxegatan 2, 213 76, Malmo, Gunnilse, Sweden
Tel.: (46) 43189000
Web Site: https://www.peabgrundlaggning.se
Sales Range: $50-74.9 Million
Nonresidential Property Managers
N.A.I.C.S.: 531312
Kai Tamminen *(CEO)*

Peab Grundlaggning Norden AB (1)
Salsmastaregatan 32 A, 422 46, Hisings Backa, Vastra Gotaland, Sweden
Tel.: (46) 31 928330
Web Site: http://www.peab.se
Emp.: 25
Construction Engineering Services
N.A.I.C.S.: 541330
Kai Tamminen *(Gen Mgr)*

Peab I 5 AB (1)
Gardsvagen 6, PO Box 808, Solna, 169 70, Sweden
Tel.: (46) 86236800
Web Site: http://www.peab.se
Sales Range: $150-199.9 Million
Emp.: 300
Real Estate Property Lessors
N.A.I.C.S.: 531190

Peab Industri AB (1)
Drakenvagen 35, PO Box 1291, Angelholm, 262 24, Sweden
Tel.: (46) 431449600
Sales Range: $250-299.9 Million
Emp.: 1,000
Holding Company
N.A.I.C.S.: 551112
Mats Paulsson *(CEO & Mng Dir)*

Peab Industri B.V. (1)
Herengracht 469, 1017BS, Amsterdam, Netherlands
Tel.: (31) 104042396
Credit Intermediation Services
N.A.I.C.S.: 522390

Peab Industri Norge AS (1)
Sorkedalsveien 148, Oslo, 0754, Norway
Tel.: (47) 23303000
Web Site: http://www.peab.no
Sales Range: $50-74.9 Million
Emp.: 110
Industrial Building Construction Services
N.A.I.C.S.: 236210

Peab Industri Sverige AB (1)
Margretetorpsv 84, 269 73, Forslov, Sweden
Tel.: (46) 43189000
Web Site: http://www.peab.se
Asphalt & Concrete Mfr
N.A.I.C.S.: 324121

Peab Infra Oy (1)
Karvaamokuja 2a, 380, Helsinki, Finland
Tel.: (358) 207606200
Web Site: http://www.peab.fi
Emp.: 20
Civil Engineering Construction Services
N.A.I.C.S.: 237990

Peab Invest AS (1)
Sorkedalsveien 150A, 754, Oslo, Norway
Tel.: (47) 23 30 30 00
Property Leasing Services
N.A.I.C.S.: 531190

Peab Kiinteistokehitys Oy (1)
Karvaamokuja 2a, 00380, Helsinki, Finland
Tel.: (358) 207606200
Web Site: https://peab.fi
Construction Services
N.A.I.C.S.: 236220

Peab Norge AS (1)
93 Roa, 0754, Oslo, Norway
Tel.: (47) 8 623 68 00
Web Site: http://www.peab.no
Sales Range: $50-74.9 Million
Emp.: 120
New Housing Operative Builders
N.A.I.C.S.: 236117

AND PRIVATE COMPANIES

Peab Oy (1)
Karvaamokuja 2a, 00380, Helsinki, Finland
Tel.: (358) 207606200
Web Site: https://www.peabkoti.fi
Emp.: 160
Construction Engineering Services
N.A.I.C.S.: 541330
Mika Katajisto *(CEO & Mng Dir-Construction)*

Peab Park AB (1)
Margretetorpsvagen 84, Forslov, 26973, Sweden
Tel.: (46) 86236950
Web Site: http://www.peab.com
Emp.: 80
Real Estate Property Lessors
N.A.I.C.S.: 531190

Peab Projektfastigheter AB (1)
Gardsvagen 6, PO Box 808, 16970, Solna, Sweden
Tel.: (46) 86236800
Web Site: http://www.peab.com
Sales Range: $50-74.9 Million
Emp.: 100
Real Estate Property Lessors
N.A.I.C.S.: 531190

Peab Projektutveckling Nord AB (1)
Gardsvagen 6, PO Box 808, 16928, Solna, Sweden
Tel.: (46) 86236800
Web Site: http://www.peab.se
Sales Range: $150-199.9 Million
Emp.: 400
Real Estate Property Lessors
N.A.I.C.S.: 531190
Mats Paulsson *(Gen Mgr)*

Peab Seicon Oy (1)
Sentnerikuja No 5, Helsinki, 440, Finland
Tel.: (358) 207606200
Web Site: http://www.peab.fi
Sales Range: $75-99.9 Million
Emp.: 300
Engineering Services
N.A.I.C.S.: 541330
Mika Katajisto *(CEO)*

Peab Sp.z.o.o (1)
al Jana Pawla II 29, 00-867, Warsaw, Poland
Tel.: (48) 603308909
Web Site: https://peab.pl
New Housing Operative Builders
N.A.I.C.S.: 236117

Peab Sverige AB (1)
Gardsvagen 6, PO Box 808, 169 28, Solna, Sweden
Tel.: (46) 86236800
Web Site: http://www.peab.se
Floor Laying Contractor
N.A.I.C.S.: 238330
Jan Eskilsson *(Mgr)*

Peab Sverige AB (1)
Margretetorpsv 84, 269 73, Forslov, Sweden (100%)
Tel.: (46) 43189000
Web Site: http://www.peab.se
Sales Range: $25-49.9 Million
Heavy & Civil Engineering Construction
N.A.I.C.S.: 237990

Peab Sverige AB, finsk filial (1)
Centnergranden 5, 440, Helsinki, Finland
Tel.: (358) 207606200
Web Site: http://www.peab.fi
Emp.: 70
Construction Machinery Leasing Services
N.A.I.C.S.: 532412

Peab Transport & Maskin AB (1)
Margretetorpsv 12, 26092, Forslov, Sweden (100%)
Tel.: (46) 43189274
Web Site: http://www.peab.sa
Sales Range: $25-49.9 Million
Emp.: 13
General Automotive Repair
N.A.I.C.S.: 811111
Hakan Wenwiv *(Mng Dir)*

Peab Ugglarp AB (1)
Margretetorpsvagen 82, 269 73, Forslov, Sweden
Tel.: (46) 43189000
Web Site: http://www.peab.se

Property Leasing Services
N.A.I.C.S.: 531190

Peab Utvecklings AB (1)
Margretetorpsvagen 84, 26091, Forslov, Sweden (100%)
Tel.: (46) 43189000
Web Site: http://www.peab.se
Sales Range: $25-49.9 Million
Emp.: 100
Heavy & Civil Engineering Construction
N.A.I.C.S.: 237990
Mats Paulsson *(Pres & CEO)*

Peabskolan i Angelholm AB (1)
Sollentunavagen 15, Sollentuna, Sweden
Tel.: (46) 86236950
Real Estate Property Lessors
N.A.I.C.S.: 531190

Pionjaren Fastighets AB (1)
Pontonjarvagen 10, 961 43, Boden, Sweden
Tel.: (46) 921 572 81
Real Estate Manangement Services
N.A.I.C.S.: 531390

Raaen Entreprenor AS (1)
Verftsbassenget 5 PB 720, Horten, 3188, Norway
Tel.: (47) 33072000
Construction Engineering Services
N.A.I.C.S.: 541330

Riksten Friluftsstad AB (1)
Kanslivagen 29, 146 37, Tullinge, Sweden
Tel.: (46) 84499530
Web Site: https://www.riksten.se
Building Construction Services
N.A.I.C.S.: 236220

Rorman Installation & Service Sverige AB (1)
Signalistgatan 16, 72131, Vasteras, Sweden
Tel.: (46) 21800010
Carpentry Contractor
N.A.I.C.S.: 238350

Skandinaviska Byggelement AB (1)
Box 1292, 262 24, Angelholm, Sweden
Tel.: (46) 150482200
Web Site: https://www.byggelement.se
Emp.: 350
Concrete Panel Mfr
N.A.I.C.S.: 327390

Smefa Entreprenor AS (1)
Verpetveien 6, Vestby, 1540, Norway
Tel.: (47) 64 95 03 47
Construction Engineering Services
N.A.I.C.S.: 541330

Stockholm Entreprenad AB (1)
Kvastvagen 17, 128 62, Farsta, Sweden
Tel.: (46) 8 619 40 00
Outdoor Environment Maintenance Services
N.A.I.C.S.: 561790

Swerock AB (1)
Valhall Park Hus, Box 1281, 262 24, Angelholm, Sweden
Tel.: (46) 431449630
Web Site: https://swerock.se
Ready Mix Concrete Distr
N.A.I.C.S.: 423320
Karl-Gunnar Karlsson *(Gen Mgr)*

Subsidiary (Domestic):

Radasand AB (2)
Sandtagsvagen 1, 531 57, Lidkoping, Sweden
Tel.: (46) 104568900
Web Site: https://www.radasand.se
Sand Quarrying, Processing & Supplier
N.A.I.C.S.: 212321
Mark Dose *(Mgr-Quality)*

Swerock Oy (1)
Hairdressing alley 2a, 00380, Helsinki, Finland
Tel.: (358) 24845600
Web Site: https://www.swerock.fi
Construction Materials Distr
N.A.I.C.S.: 423320
Juha Helin *(Mng Dir)*

TGS Fastigheter Nr 2 AB (1)
Box 808, 169 28, Solna, Sweden
Tel.: (46) 8 623 68 00
Property Leasing Services

N.A.I.C.S.: 531190

Tranab Markbyggnad AB (1)
Osmundgatan 10, 703 83, Orebro, Sweden
Tel.: (46) 19167790
Web Site: http://www.tranab.se
Private & Public Construction Services
N.A.I.C.S.: 236220
Kjell Fransson *(Mng Dir)*

Ulriksdal Utveckling AB (1)
Gardsvagen 6, PO Box 808, Solna, Sweden
Tel.: (46) 86236800
Sales Range: $25-49.9 Million
Emp.: 20
Engineeering Services
N.A.I.C.S.: 541330

Varvstaden AB (1)
Margretetorpsvagen, 260 92, Forslov, Sweden
Tel.: (46) 431 89000
Property Management Services
N.A.I.C.S.: 531311

Vasa Betongstation OY (1)
Valimontie 7, Vaasa, 65100, Finland
Tel.: (358) 63208100
Sales Range: $25-49.9 Million
Emp.: 50
Concrete Products Mfr
N.A.I.C.S.: 327390

PEABODY

45 Westminster Bridge Road, London, SE1 7JB, United Kingdom
Tel.: (44) 020 7021 4444
Web Site: http://www.peabody.org.uk
Year Founded: 1862
Rev.: $716,996,300
Assets: $8,624,259,920
Liabilities: $5,049,430,580
Net Worth: $3,574,829,340
Earnings: $187,814,960
Emp.: 2,672
Fiscal Year-end: 03/31/19
Real Estate Development & Property Management
N.A.I.C.S.: 531210
David Lavarack *(Exec Dir-Corp Svcs)*

Subsidiaries:

Community Based Housing Association (1)
433-443 High Road, London, E11 4JU, United Kingdom (100%)
Tel.: (44) 2079228500
Web Site: http://www.cbha.org.uk
Sales Range: $50-74.9 Million
Emp.: 50
Community Housing Services
N.A.I.C.S.: 624229

Gallions Housing Association Limited (1)
15 Joyce Dawson Way, Thamesmead, SE28 8RA, United Kingdom
Tel.: (44) 300 123 1237
Web Site: http://www.gallionsha.co.uk
Building Construction Services
N.A.I.C.S.: 236117

Peabody Group Maintenance Ltd (1)
3 Saxon Close, Walthamstow, London, E17 8LE, United Kingdom
Tel.: (44) 8 8509 0044
Property Management Services
N.A.I.C.S.: 531312
Jason Munford *(Mng Dir)*

Peabody Pension Trust Limited (1)
45 Westminster Bridge Road, SE17JB, London, United Kingdom (100%)
Tel.: (44) 2079287811
Web Site: http://www.peabody.org.uk
Sales Range: $200-249.9 Million
Emp.: 400
Real Estate Investment Trust
N.A.I.C.S.: 525990
Steven Howlett *(CEO)*

PEACE ARCH ENTERTAINMENT GROUP INC.

1867 Yonge Street Ste 650, Toronto, M4S 1Y5, ON, Canada

Tel.: (647) 777-1177
Web Site: http://www.peacearch.com
Year Founded: 1983
Sales Range: $50-74.9 Million
Emp.: 90
Holding Company; Motion Picture Producer & Distr
N.A.I.C.S.: 551112
Richard K. Watson *(Sec)*

PEACE HILLS GENERAL INSURANCE COMPANY

300-10709 Jasper Ave NW, Edmonton, T5J 3N3, AB, Canada
Tel.: (780) 424-3986
Web Site:
http://www.peacehillsinsurance.com
Year Founded: 1982
Sales Range: $150-199.9 Million
Emp.: 200
Insurance Services
N.A.I.C.S.: 524210
Marvin Yellowbird *(Chm)*

PEACE LIVING CO., LTD.

3-4 Hinokami Furukawa Ojin-cho, Tokushima, 771-1151, Yubinbango, Japan
Tel.: (81) 88 665 5847
Web Site: http://www.peaceliving.net
Year Founded: 2007
1437—(TKS)
Sales Range: $10-24.9 Million
Real Estate Manangement Services
N.A.I.C.S.: 531210
Satoshi Kono *(Dir-Building Div)*

PEACH PROPERTY GROUP AG

Neptunstrasse 96, 8032, Zurich, Switzerland
Tel.: (41) 444855000
Web Site:
https://www.peachproperty.com
PEAN—(SWX)
Rev.: $450,539,600
Assets: $3,164,169,876
Liabilities: $1,895,319,912
Net Worth: $1,268,849,965
Earnings: $227,850,699
Emp.: 194
Fiscal Year-end: 12/31/21
Luxury Residential Property Developer
N.A.I.C.S.: 236117
Thomas Wolfensberger *(CEO)*

Subsidiaries:

Peach Property Group (Deutschland) GmbH (1)
Aachener Strasse 186, 50931, Cologne, Germany
Tel.: (49) 2212992330
Web Site: https://www.peachproperty.com
Sales Range: $25-49.9 Million
Luxury Residential Construction Services
N.A.I.C.S.: 236116

PEACH TELECOM LTD.

St Andrews House 4400 Parkway, Whiteley, Fareham, PO15 7FJ, Hampshire, United Kingdom
Tel.: (44) 800 988 2002
Web Site:
http://www.peachtelecom.co.uk
Sales Range: $10-24.9 Million
Emp.: 55
Telecommunications & Internet Services
N.A.I.C.S.: 517111
Darren Scott-Healey *(CEO)*

PEAK ENGINEERING & CONSTRUCTION LTD.

13580 County Road 2, Colborne, K0K 1S0, ON, Canada
Tel.: (905) 355-1500

PEAK ENGINEERING & CONSTRUCTION LTD.

PEAK Engineering & Construction Ltd.—(Continued)
Web Site: http://www.peakltd.ca
Year Founded: 1991
Rev.: $10,100,000
Emp.: 59
General Building Contractors
N.A.I.C.S.: 236220
Phil Smith *(Mgr-Ops-Building Projects)*

PEAK GLOBAL CONSULTANCY LTD.
Process House, 341 Great Western Road, Aberdeen, AB10 6NW, United Kingdom
Tel.: (44) 1224 379 792
Web Site: http://www.peak-ltd.com
Consulting Services
N.A.I.C.S.: 541611
John Hargreaves *(Mng Dir)*

PEAK MINERALS LIMITED
Level 1 Suite 23 513 Hay Street, Subiaco, 6008, WA, Australia
Tel.: (61) 861436748   AU
Web Site:
  https://www.peakminerals.com.au
PUA—(ASX)
Rev.: $50,455
Assets: $106,195
Liabilities: $545,745
Net Worth: ($439,550)
Earnings: ($602,474)
Fiscal Year-end: 06/30/24
High Purity Alumina Mfr
N.A.I.C.S.: 327999
Robert Boston *(Chm)*

PEAK RARE EARTHS LIMITED
Level 9 190 St Georges Terrace, Mezzanine Floor, Perth, 6000, WA, Australia
Tel.: (61) 892005360   AU
Web Site: https://peakrareearths.com
Year Founded: 2006
PKREF—(OTCIQ)
Rev.: $85,053
Assets: $47,186,977
Liabilities: $4,820,746
Net Worth: $42,366,230
Earnings: ($3,655,376)
Fiscal Year-end: 06/30/21
Gold Mining
N.A.I.C.S.: 212220
Rocky Smith *(CEO)*

PEAKO LIMITED
Level 1 10 Yarra Street, South Yarra, 3141, VIC, Australia
Tel.: (61) 386104723   AU
Web Site: https://www.peako.com.au
PKO—(ASX)
Rev.: $32,702
Assets: $118,379
Liabilities: $63,032
Net Worth: $55,347
Earnings: ($631,961)
Emp.: 6
Fiscal Year-end: 06/30/24
Crude Petroleum Extraction Services
N.A.I.C.S.: 211120
Robert Wright *(CFO & Sec)*

PEANUT COMPANY OF AUSTRALIA LIMITED
133 Haly Street, PO Box 26, Kingaroy, 4610, QLD, Australia
Tel.: (61) 741626311
Web Site: http://www.pca.com.au
Year Founded: 1924
Sales Range: $25-49.9 Million
Emp.: 262
Peanuts & Peanut Products Mfr, Developer & Marketer
N.A.I.C.S.: 311911

Donald C. Mackenzie *(Sec)*

PEARL & DEAN CINEMAS LIMITED
Corinthian House 279 Tottenham Court Road, London, W1T 7RJ, United Kingdom
Tel.: (44) 2071992400   UK
Web Site:
  http://www.pearlanddean.com
Year Founded: 1953
Sales Range: $25-49.9 Million
Emp.: 40
Cinema Advertising Services
N.A.I.C.S.: 541840
Allison McBride *(Acct Mgr-Innovations)*

PEARL ABYSS CORP.
48 Gwacheon-daero 2-gil, Gyeonggi-do, Gwacheon, 13824, Anyang, Korea (South)
Tel.: (82) 24768583   KR
Web Site:
  https://www.pearlabyss.com
Year Founded: 2010
263750—(KRS)
Rev.: $295,816,655
Assets: $937,699,567
Liabilities: $401,333,363
Net Worth: $536,366,205
Earnings: ($32,980,667)
Emp.: 895
Fiscal Year-end: 12/31/22
Online Game Developer
N.A.I.C.S.: 513210
Kyeong-in Jung *(CEO)*

Subsidiaries:

CCP hf   (1)
Grandagarour 8, 101, Reykjavik, Iceland
Tel.: (354) 5409100
Web Site: http://www.ccpgames.com
Rev.: $65,000,000
Emp.: 600
Computer Game Software Publisher
N.A.I.C.S.: 513210
Hilmar Veigar Petursson *(CEO)*

Subsidiary (Non-US):

CCP Games Shanghai   (2)
Room 401 Building 6800 Show No 800 Changde Road, Jing an district, Shanghai, 200040, China
Tel.: (86) 2161267605
Game Development Services
N.A.I.C.S.: 513210

CCP Games UK Ltd   (2)
New Eden House Fletcher Road, Gateshead, NE8 2ET, Tyne & Wear, United Kingdom
Tel.: (44) 191 500 8770
Game Development Services
N.A.I.C.S.: 513210
Maria Sayans *(Chief Customer Officer)*

Subsidiary (US):

CCP North America Inc.   (2)
250 E Ponce De Leon Ave Ste 700, Decatur, GA 30030-3440
Tel.: (770) 413-3022
Software Development Services
N.A.I.C.S.: 541511

PEARL AGENCY ALLGEMEINE VERMITTLUNGSGESELLSCHAFT MBH
PEARL-Strasse 1-3, 79426, Buggingen, Germany
Tel.: (49) 7631 360 0
Web Site: http://www.pearl.de
Sales Range: $150-199.9 Million
Emp.: 400
Computer Products Online Retailer
N.A.I.C.S.: 423430
Daniel C. Ludwig *(Mng Dir)*

PEARL GLOBAL INDUSTRIES LIMITED
Pearl Tower Plot no 51 Sector 32, Gurgaon, 122 001, Haryana, India
Tel.: (91) 1244651000
Web Site:
  https://www.pearlglobal.com
PGIL—(NSE)
Rev.: $206,719,886
Assets: $176,629,048
Liabilities: $104,263,191
Net Worth: $72,365,857
Earnings: $2,386,457
Emp.: 5,126
Fiscal Year-end: 03/31/21
Apparel Designer & Distr
N.A.I.C.S.: 315990
Sandeep Sabharwal *(Compliance Officer & Sec)*

Subsidiaries:

Alpha Clothing Limited   (1)
270 DOHS Baridhara, Dhaka, 1206, Bangladesh
Tel.: (880) 28411439
Web Site: https://www.alphaclothing.org
Cloth Mfr & Retailer
N.A.I.C.S.: 313310

Norwest Industries Ltd.   (1)
No 615-617 Fuk Industrial Bldg 7th Fl, Tai Nan W St Lai Chi Kok, Kowloon, China (Hong Kong)
Tel.: (852) 35881988
Apparels Mfr
N.A.I.C.S.: 315250

PT Pinnacle Apparels   (1)
Tel.: (62) 2129770089
Web Site:
  https://www.ptpinnacleapparels.com
Outerwear Mfr & Retailer
N.A.I.C.S.: 315250
Pulkit Seth *(Pres)*

Pearl Unlimited Inc.   (1)
525 7th Ave Ste 506, New York, NY 10018
Tel.: (212) 840-3183
Cloth Mfr & Retailer
N.A.I.C.S.: 313310

Poeticgem Ltd.   (1)
Unit 4 The Trident Ctr Imperial Way, Watford, WD24 4JH, Hertfordshire, United Kingdom
Tel.: (44) 1923249497
Apparels Mfr
N.A.I.C.S.: 315250

Zamira Fashion Ltd.   (1)
Flat A 10th Floor Park Fook Industrial Building 615-617, Tai Nan West Street Cheung Sha Wan, Kowloon, China (Hong Kong)
Tel.: (852) 35881818
Web Site: https://www.zamira.com.hk
Sales Range: $25-49.9 Million
Emp.: 60
Apparels Mfr
N.A.I.C.S.: 315250

PEARL GOLD AG
Kurfurstendamm 213, 10719, Berlin, Germany
Tel.: (49) 30590030436   De
Web Site:
  https://www.pearlgoldag.com
Year Founded: 2008
02P—(DEU)
Assets: $14,670,432
Liabilities: $375,316
Net Worth: $14,295,116
Earnings: ($596,090)
Fiscal Year-end: 12/31/23
Gold Mining & Extraction
N.A.I.C.S.: 212220
Jean Louis Dupuy *(CEO & Member-Mgmt Bd)*

PEARL GREEN CLUBS & RESORTS LIMITED
UP GF-01 Krushna Complex Near

INTERNATIONAL PUBLIC

Choice Navrangpura, Ahmedabad, 380009, Gujarat, India
Tel.: (91) 8488086694
Web Site:
  https://www.pearlgreenresort.com
Year Founded: 2018
543540—(BOM)
Rev.: $1,192,830
Assets: $2,397,866
Liabilities: $106,217
Net Worth: $2,291,649
Earnings: $21,186
Emp.: 9
Fiscal Year-end: 03/31/23
Resort Operator
N.A.I.C.S.: 721120

PEARL GULL IRON LIMITED
Suite 23 513 Hay Street, Subiaco, 6008, WA, Australia
Tel.: (61) 861436730   AU
Web Site:
  https://www.pearlgulliron.com.au
Year Founded: 2017
PLG—(ASX)
Rev.: $8,476
Assets: $7,292,821
Liabilities: $4,840,582
Net Worth: $2,452,240
Earnings: ($745,909)
Fiscal Year-end: 06/30/23
Iron Ore Mining Services
N.A.I.C.S.: 212210
Russell Clark *(Chm)*

PEARL HEALTHCARE LIMITED
Suite 7 13-25 Church Street, Hawthorn, 3122, VIC, Australia
Tel.: (61) 398531700
Web Site:
  http://www.pearlhealthcare.com.au
Sales Range: $10-24.9 Million
Dental Laboratories Owner & Operator
N.A.I.C.S.: 339116
Greg Plummer *(Chm)*

PEARL MUSICAL INSTRUMENT CO. LTD.
10-2-1 Yachiyodai Nishi, Yachiyo, 276 0034, Chiba, Japan
Tel.: (81) 474862811   JP
Web Site: http://www.pearldrum.com
Year Founded: 1946
Sales Range: $75-99.9 Million
Emp.: 350
Musical Instrument Mfr
N.A.I.C.S.: 339992

Subsidiaries:

Pearl Corporation   (1)
549 Metroplex Dr, Nashville, TN 37211-3140
Tel.: (615) 833-4477
Web Site: http://www.pearldrum.com
Sales Range: $50-74.9 Million
Emp.: 100
Distr of Drums & Percussion Gear
N.A.I.C.S.: 423990

Pearl Music Europe B.V   (1)
Craenakker 28, 5951 CC, Belfeld, Netherlands
Tel.: (31) 77 308 1200
Web Site: http://www.pearleurope.com
Musical Instrument Distr
N.A.I.C.S.: 459140
Hans van Dreumel *(Mgr-Fin)*

PEARL OF KUWAIT REAL ESTATE COMPANY K.S.C.C.
Sharq - Khaled Bin Al Waleed Street - Tower KBT - Floor 38, PO Box 23859, Safat, Kuwait, 13099, Kuwait
Tel.: (965) 22916112
Web Site: http://www.pearl.com.kw
Year Founded: 1975
Sales Range: $10-24.9 Million

AND PRIVATE COMPANIES

PEARSON PLC

Emp.: 17
Commercial & Industrial Real Estate
Construction & Other Real Estate Services
N.A.I.C.S.: 236220

PEARL POLYMERS LIMITED
A97/2 Okhla Industrial Area Phase 2,
New Delhi, 110020, India
Tel.: (91) 1147385300
Web Site: https://pearlpet.com
Year Founded: 1971
PEARLPOLY—(BOM)
Rev: $2,337,270
Assets: $5,425,082
Liabilities: $864,361
Net Worth: $4,560,722
Earnings: ($979,881)
Emp.: 75
Fiscal Year-end: 03/31/23
Resin Mfr
N.A.I.C.S.: 325211
Chand Seth *(Chm & Mng Dir)*

Subsidiaries:

Pearl Engineering Polymers Limited (1)
204 Rohit House 3 Tolstoy Marg, New Delhi, 110001, India
Tel.: (91) 1141417917
Web Site: http://www.pearlpet.net
Sales Range: $25-49.9 Million
Emp.: 138
Bottle Mfr
N.A.I.C.S.: 339999
Harish Seth *(Chm & Mng Dir)*

PEARL RIVER HOLDINGS LIMITED
502-383 Richmond Street, London,
N6A 3C4, ON, Canada
Tel.: (519) 679-1200
Year Founded: 1997
PRH—(TSXV)
Rev.: $34,228,486
Assets: $28,483,465
Liabilities: $11,585,685
Net Worth: $16,897,780
Earnings: ($526,093)
Fiscal Year-end: 12/31/23
Plastic Product Mfr & Distr
N.A.I.C.S.: 326199
George W. Lunick *(Pres & CEO)*

Subsidiaries:

Red Door China Pty Limited (1)
59 Hume St, Crows Nest, 2065, NSW, Australia
Tel.: (61) 1300 996 557
Plastic Product Distr
N.A.I.C.S.: 424990

Rodman Enterprises Limited (1)
Rm 802 Car Po Commercial Bldg 18-20 Lyndhurst Terrace, Central, Hong Kong, China (Hong Kong)
Tel.: (852) 28541491
Web Site: http://www.rodman.cn
Emp.: 3
Plastic Product Distr
N.A.I.C.S.: 424990
Josephine Lee *(Gen Mgr-Cooler Div)*

PEARL SANITARY PAPER CONVERTING CO. PLC
Abdoun - Mohamed Ali Bdair Street - Building No 84, PO Box 77, Na'ur, Amman, 11710, Jordan
Tel.: (962) 64652688
Year Founded: 1993
PERL—(AMM)
Sales Range: Less than $1 Million
Sanitary Paper Product Mfr
N.A.I.C.S.: 322291
Maen Sami Kradsheh *(Gen Mgr)*

PEARSON PLC
80 Strand, London, WC2R 0RL, United Kingdom
Tel.: (44) 2070102000
Web Site: https://www.pearson.com
Year Founded: 1897
PSO—(NYSE)
Rev.: $4,643,579,365
Assets: $8,502,275,010
Liabilities: $3,461,830,125
Net Worth: $5,040,444,885
Earnings: $480,283,113
Emp.: 18,360
Fiscal Year-end: 12/31/23
Holding Company; Multiple Platform Publishing, Educational & Professional Development Services
N.A.I.C.S.: 551112
Giovanni Giovannelli *(Pres-English Language Learning)*

Subsidiaries:

CTI Education Group Pty Ltd (1)
Bldg 1 Fourways Manor Office Park Cnr Roos And Macbeth Streets, Fourways, Sandton, 2191, South Africa
Tel.: (27) 114678422
Web Site: http://www.cti.co.za
Educational Support Services
N.A.I.C.S.: 611710

Cogmed Systems AB (1)
Gustavslundsvagen 137, Bromma, 167 51, Stockholm, Sweden
Tel.: (46) 850631550
Software Development Services
N.A.I.C.S.: 541511

Connections Academy of Florida, LLC (1)
13008 Telecom Dr Ste 340, Temple Terrace, FL 33637
Education Services
N.A.I.C.S.: 611710
Jamie Worrell *(Mgr-Special Education)*

Connections Academy of Iowa, LLC (1)
807 3rd St, Anita, IA 50020
Tel.: (712) 581-0200
Education Services
N.A.I.C.S.: 611710

Connections Academy of Maine, LLC (1)
600 Southborough Dr Ste 202, South Portland, ME 04106
Tel.: (207) 805-3254
Education Services
N.A.I.C.S.: 611710
Walter Wallace *(Principal)*

Connections Academy of Maryland, LLC (1)
10960 Grantchester Way, Columbia, MD 21044
Tel.: (443) 529-1000
Web Site: http://www.connectionsacademy.com
Education Services
N.A.I.C.S.: 611710

Connections Academy of Nevada, LLC (1)
555 Double Eagle Ct Ste 1000, Reno, NV 89521
Tel.: (775) 826-4200
Education Services
N.A.I.C.S.: 611710
Christine Dzarnoski *(Principal-High School)*

Connections Academy of New Mexico, LLC (1)
130 Siringo Rd, Santa Fe, NM 87505
Tel.: (505) 428-2130
Education Services
N.A.I.C.S.: 611710
Sandy Beery *(Exec Dir)*

Connections Academy of Oregon, LLC (1)
740 Overholt St, Prairie City, OR 97869
Tel.: (541) 262-4630
Education Services
N.A.I.C.S.: 611710
Miranda Pickner *(Principal)*

Connections Academy of Tennessee, LLC (1)
117 Edenway Dr, White House, TN 37188
Tel.: (615) 270-2431
Education Services
N.A.I.C.S.: 611710
Derek Sanborn *(Exec Dir)*

Connections Academy of Texas LLC (1)
10550 Richmond Ave Ste 140, Houston, TX 77042
Tel.: (281) 661-8293
Education Services
N.A.I.C.S.: 611710
Amanda Viola *(Principal)*

Connections Education LLC (1)
10960 Grantchester Way, Columbia, MD 21044
Web Site: http://www.connectionseducation.com
Educational Support Services
N.A.I.C.S.: 611710
Sarah Savage *(Coord)*

Dorling Kindersley Verlag GmbH (1)
Tel.: (49) 894423260
Web Site: http://www.dorlingkindersley.de
Sales Range: $25-49.9 Million
Emp.: 60
Illustrated Book Publisher
N.A.I.C.S.: 513130

Edexcel China Ltd (1)
Shui On Centre, Wanchai, China (Hong Kong)
Tel.: (852) 02511 2122
Books Publishing Services
N.A.I.C.S.: 513130

Editions Du Renouveau Pedagogique Inc (1)
1611 boul Cremazie East 10th floor, Montreal, H2M 2P2, QC, Canada
Tel.: (514) 334-2690
Web Site: https://www.pearsonerpi.com
Books Publishing Services
N.A.I.C.S.: 513130

Embanet ULC (1)
105 Gordon Baker Rd Suite 300, Toronto, M2H 3P8, ON, Canada
Web Site: http://www.ec.cratco.com
Online Learning Services
N.A.I.C.S.: 611710
Stephen Fireng *(Pres & CEO)*

FBH Inc Sarl (1)
17 rue Glesener, 1631, Luxembourg, Luxembourg
Tel.: (352) 27 48 92 45
Educational Book Publisher
N.A.I.C.S.: 513130

Franchise Support & Services SL (1)
Calle Tuset 20 Piso 5, Barcelona, 08006, Spain
Tel.: (34) 933063320
Books Publishing Services
N.A.I.C.S.: 513130

Frederick Warne & Co. Ltd. (1)
80 Strand, London, WC2R 0RL, United Kingdom
Tel.: (44) 2070103000
Web Site: http://www.us.penguingroup.com
Sales Range: $800-899.9 Million
Emp.: 3,000
Children Book Publisher
N.A.I.C.S.: 513130

Fronter AS (1)
Kirkens hus Radhusgata 1-3, 0151, Oslo, Norway
Tel.: (47) 24 14 99 99
Web Site: http://com.fronter.info
Learning Management Services
N.A.I.C.S.: 611710

Fronter GmbH (1)
Martin-Kollar-Strasse 10-12, 81829, Munich, Bavaria, Germany
Tel.: (49) 89 30 90 51980
Web Site: http://de.fronter.info
Sales Range: $10-24.9 Million
Emp.: 60
Educational Support Services
N.A.I.C.S.: 611710

Fronter Oy (1)
Urho Kekkosenkatu 4-6 E, Helsinki, 100, Finland
Tel.: (358) 456791000
Web Site: http://fi.fronter.info
Online Education & Career Training Services
N.A.I.C.S.: 611430

GED Testing Service LLC (1)
1919 M St NW Ste 600, Washington, DC 20036
Tel.: (952) 681-3444
Web Site: https://ged.com
Higher Educational Institution Services
N.A.I.C.S.: 611310
Vicki Greene *(Pres & CEO)*

Gas Logic Ltd (1)
Unit 2 1 Rowdell Road, Northolt, UB5 5QR, Middlesex, United Kingdom
Tel.: (44) 8458457222
Web Site: https://www.logic4training.co.uk
Sales Range: $10-24.9 Million
Emp.: 30
Vocational Training & Assessment Services
N.A.I.C.S.: 624310
Gayle Budd *(Co-Founder)*

Heinemann Publishers (Pty) Ltd (1)
Building No 5 Grayston Office Park 128 Peter Road, PO Box 781940, Sandton, 2146, South Africa
Tel.: (27) 11 322 8600
Web Site: http://www.heinemann.co.za
Book Publishers
N.A.I.C.S.: 513130

Lakeside Property Development Co., Ltd. (1)
Waterfront Lakeside, West Thurrock, RM20 1WL, Essex, United Kingdom (100%)
Tel.: (44) 1708666571
Land Management
N.A.I.C.S.: 531210

Longman Australasia Pty Ltd (1)
L 9 5 Queens Rd, Melbourne, 3004, VIC, Australia
Tel.: (61) 398112800
Educational Support Services
N.A.I.C.S.: 611710

Longman Group (Overseas) Holdings Ltd (1)
Edinburgh Gate, Harlow, CM20 2JE, United Kingdom
Tel.: (44) 1279623623
Investment Management Service
N.A.I.C.S.: 523940

Longman Kenya Ltd (1)
Kijabe Street Next to Simlaw Seeds, Nairobi, Kenya
Tel.: (254) 20 211 9177
Books Publishing Services
N.A.I.C.S.: 513130

Longman Malawi Ltd (1)
Alliance House Churchill Road, Limbe, Malawi
Tel.: (265) 1844000
Educational Support Services
N.A.I.C.S.: 611710

Longman Namibia (Pty) Ltd (1)
19 Joule Street Southern Industrial Area, Windhoek, Namibia
Tel.: (264) 61 231 214
Web Site: http://www.longmanafrica.co.za
Sales Range: $25-49.9 Million
Emp.: 9
Book Publishers
N.A.I.C.S.: 513130

Longman Zambia Ltd (1)
Plot 1281 Lungwebungu Road, Lusaka, 50496, Zambia
Tel.: (260) 211 25 1166
Sales Range: $25-49.9 Million
Emp.: 8
Educational Materials Publisher
N.A.I.C.S.: 513199
Chris Koveya *(Mng Dir)*

Maskew Miller Longman (Pty) Ltd (1)
Cnr Logan Way & Forest Drive, Pinelands, 7405, South Africa
Tel.: (27) 21 532 6000
Web Site: http://www.mml.co.za
Sales Range: $50-74.9 Million
Emp.: 250
Book Publishers

PEARSON PLC

Pearson plc—(Continued)
N.A.I.C.S.: 513130

Midrand Graduate Institute Pty Ltd (1)
44 Alsatian Road Glen Austin Extension 3, Midrand, 1685, South Africa
Tel.: (27) 11 690 1700
Web Site: http://www.mgi.ac.za
Educational Institute Operator
N.A.I.C.S.: 611710

NCS Pearson (India) Private Ltd (1)
4th Floor 18 Ramnath House Yousuf Sarai, New Delhi, 110 016, India
Tel.: (91) 80 4215 3440
Web Site: http://www.pearsonclinical.in
Sales Range: $10-24.9 Million
Emp.: 30
Educational Assessment Services
N.A.I.C.S.: 611710

NCS Pearson Pty Ltd (1)
459-471 Church Street, Richmond, Melbourne, 3121, VIC, Australia
Tel.: (61) 398727700
Sales Range: $10-24.9 Million
Emp.: 50
Educational Support Services
N.A.I.C.S.: 611710

National Computer Systems Japan Co Ltd (1)
Teikoku Hotel Tower 18F 1-1-1 Uchi Saiwai-Cho, Chiyoda-ku, Tokyo, 100-0011, Japan
Tel.: (81) 368910500
Software Testing Services
N.A.I.C.S.: 541511

Pearson (Singapore) Pte Ltd (1)
72 Circular Road 03-01, Singapore, 049426, Singapore
Tel.: (65) 6236 9500
Educational Support Services
N.A.I.C.S.: 611710

Pearson Amsterdam BV (1)
Coengebouw Kabelweg 37, 1014 BA, Amsterdam, Netherlands
Tel.: (31) 205755800
Sales Range: $25-49.9 Million
Emp.: 65
Book Publishers
N.A.I.C.S.: 513130
H. Dennery *(Gen Mgr)*

Pearson Assessment & Information BV (1)
Kabelweg 37, 1014 BA, Amsterdam, Netherlands
Tel.: (31) 205815500
Web Site: https://www.pearsonclinical.nl
Emp.: 80
Book Publishers
N.A.I.C.S.: 513130

Pearson Assessment & Information GmbH (1)
Baseler Str 35 -37, 60329, Frankfurt, Hessen, Germany
Tel.: (49) 69 756146 0
Web Site: http://www.pearsonassessment.de
Sales Range: $25-49.9 Million
Emp.: 15
Psychological Assessment Services
N.A.I.C.S.: 541720

Pearson Australia Group Pty. Ltd. (1)
250 Camberwell Road, Camberwell, 3124, Australia
Tel.: (61) 398112447
Web Site: http://www.pearson.com.au
Sales Range: $100-124.9 Million
Emp.: 300
Book Publishers
N.A.I.C.S.: 513130

Subsidiary (Domestic):

Dorling Kindersley Australia Pty Ltd (2)
707 Collins Street, Melbourne, 8012, VIC, Australia
Tel.: (61) 398112400
Books Publishing Services
N.A.I.C.S.: 513130

Division (Domestic):

Pearson Australia-Schools Division (2)
707 Collins St, PO Box 460, Port Melbourne, 3008, VIC, Australia
Tel.: (61) 392457111
Web Site: http://www.pearson.com.au
Sales Range: $50-74.9 Million
Emp.: 200
Publisher of Educational Book Titles
N.A.I.C.S.: 513130

Subsidiary (Domestic):

Pearson Education Australia Pty. Ltd. (2)
Unit 4 Level 3 14 Aquatic Dr, French's Forest, 2086, NSW, Australia
Sales Range: $25-49.9 Million
Emp.: 100
Book Publishers
N.A.I.C.S.: 513130

Subsidiary (Non-US):

Pearson New Zealand (2)
67 Apollo Drive Rosedale, North Shore City, Auckland, 632, New Zealand (100%)
Tel.: (64) 98869536
Web Site: https://www.pearson.com
Sales Range: $25-49.9 Million
Emp.: 30
Publisher of Primary, Secondary & Tertiary Textbooks
N.A.I.C.S.: 513130

Subsidiary (Domestic):

Penguin Group (NZ) Ltd (3)
Ground Floor Aon House Smales Farm 74 Taharoto Road, Takapuna, Auckland, 0622, New Zealand
Tel.: (64) 94427400
Web Site: https://www.penguin.co.nz
Book Distr
N.A.I.C.S.: 424920

Subsidiary (Domestic):

Penguin Books (NZ) Ltd (4)
Ground Floor Aon House Smales Farm 74 Taharoto Road, Takapuna, Auckland, 0622, New Zealand
Tel.: (64) 94427400
Book Whslr
N.A.I.C.S.: 424920

Subsidiary (Non-US):

Penguin Australia Pty. Ltd. (2)
Tel.: (61) 385374599
Web Site: http://www.penguin.com.au
Books Publishing Services
N.A.I.C.S.: 513130

Pearson Canada Assessment Inc. (1)
26 Prince Andrew Place, Toronto, M3C 2H4, ON, Canada
Web Site: http://www.pearsonclinical.ca
Education Management Services
N.A.I.C.S.: 611710

Pearson Canada Finance Unlimited (1)
80 Strand, London, WC2R 0RL, United Kingdom
Tel.: (44) 2070102000
Investment Management Service
N.A.I.C.S.: 561499

Pearson Canada Inc. (1)
357 Bay Street 3rd Floor, Toronto, M5H 4A6, ON, Canada (100%)
Tel.: (416) 447-5101
Web Site: https://www.pearsoncanadaschool.com
Sales Range: $25-49.9 Million
Emp.: 100
School Book Publisher
N.A.I.C.S.: 513130

Division (Domestic):

Pearson Canada Inc - Penguin Group (Canada) Division (2)
90 Eglinton Avenue East Suite 700, Toronto, M4P 2Y3, ON, Canada
Tel.: (416) 925-2249
Web Site: http://www.penguin.ca
Sales Range: $25-49.9 Million
Emp.: 65
Book Publishers
N.A.I.C.S.: 513130

Subsidiary (Domestic):

Pearson Education Canada (2)
26 Prince Andrew Place, PO Box 580, Don Mills, M3C 2H4, ON, Canada (100%)
Tel.: (416) 447-5101
Web Site: https://www.pearsoncanadaschool.com
Sales Range: $50-74.9 Million
Emp.: 250
Marketing of Books to Schools & Businesses
N.A.I.C.S.: 459210

Division (Domestic):

Pearson Penguin Canada Inc. (2)
320 Front St W, Toronto, M5V 3B6, ON, Canada
Tel.: (416) 925-2249
Web Site: http://www.penguin.ca
Book Publishers
N.A.I.C.S.: 513130

Pearson College Limited (1)
6 Mitre Passage North Greenwich, London, SE10 0ER, United Kingdom
Tel.: (44) 2034411303
Web Site: https://www.escapestudios.ac.uk
Higher Educational Institution Services
N.A.I.C.S.: 611310
Roxanne Stockwell *(Principal & VP)*

Pearson Deutschland GmbH (1)
St Martin-Strasse 82, 81541, Munich, Germany
Web Site: http://www.pearson.de
Digital Education Learning Services
N.A.I.C.S.: 611710

Pearson Driving Assessments Ltd (1)
The Lighthouse 14 The Quays, Salford, M50 3BF, United Kingdom
Tel.: (44) 1618557000
Web Site: http://www.pearsonvue.co.uk
Emp.: 300
Software Testing Services
N.A.I.C.S.: 541511

Subsidiary (Non-US):

Harcourt Education Ltd. (2)
Tel.: (44) 18456301111
Web Site: http://www.harcourteducation.co.uk
Sales Range: $150-199.9 Million
Publisher of School, Educational, Professional, Reference & College Textbooks
N.A.I.C.S.: 513130

Subsidiary (Non-US):

Heinemann Publishers, Ltd. (3)
Tel.: (44) 1865888000
Web Site: http://www.harcourt.co.uk
Sales Range: $100-124.9 Million
Emp.: 500
Publisher of Educational Titles
N.A.I.C.S.: 513130

Division (Domestic):

Pearson Education - Europe, Middle East & Africa (2)
Edinburgh Gate, Harlow, CM20 2JE, Essex, United Kingdom (100%)
Tel.: (44) 1279623623
Web Site: http://www.pearsoned.co.uk
Sales Range: $150-199.9 Million
Publishing Company
N.A.I.C.S.: 513130

Subsidiary (Non-US):

Alhambra Longman S.A. (3)
Nunez de Balboa 120, 28006, Madrid, Spain (100%)
Tel.: (34) 915903432
Web Site: http://www.longman.com
Book Publishing
N.A.I.C.S.: 513130

Longman Lesotho (Pty) Ltd. (3)
104 Christie House, PO Box 1174, Maseru, Lesotho, 100, South Africa (100%)
Tel.: (27) 266 314254
Web Site: http://www.longman-elt.com
Educational Materials Publisher
N.A.I.C.S.: 513130

Longman Nigeria Ltd. (3)
Pvt Mail Bag 21036, 52 Oba Akran Avenue, Ikeja, Nigeria (100%)
Tel.: (234) 14978925
Web Site: http://www.pearsoned.com
Publisher of Fiction & Non-Fiction, Textbooks
N.A.I.C.S.: 513130

Longman Zimbabwe (Pte) Ltd. (3)
Tourle Road, PO Box ST125, Ardbennie, Harare, Zimbabwe (100%)
Tel.: (263) 4621661
Web Site: http://www.longmanafrica.co.za
Sales Range: $25-49.9 Million
Emp.: 31
Publisher of Books on Africana, Books in Shona & Ndebele, Paperbacks
N.A.I.C.S.: 513130

Pearson Benelux (3)
Kabelweg 37, 1014 BA, Amsterdam, Netherlands (100%)
Tel.: (31) 205755800
Sales Range: $25-49.9 Million
Emp.: 60
Book Whslr
N.A.I.C.S.: 459210

Pearson Education Italia S.r.l. (3)
Via Costanza Arconati 1, 20135, Milan, Italy (100%)
Tel.: (39) 02748231
Sales Range: $25-49.9 Million
Emp.: 40
Publisher of Textbooks & Educational Materials
N.A.I.C.S.: 513130

Pearson Educacion Latinoamerica (1)
Antonio Dovali Jaime No 70 Piso 6 Torre B, Santa Fe, 01210, Mexico (100%)
Tel.: (52) 5553870700
Web Site: http://www.pearsoned.com
Sales Range: $75-99.9 Million
Emp.: 190
Publishing Company
N.A.I.C.S.: 513140

Pearson Educacion S.A (1)
Paseo de la castellana 85, 28046, Madrid, Spain
Tel.: (34) 913828300
Web Site: https://www.pearsoneducacion.net
Book Publishers
N.A.I.C.S.: 513130

Pearson Educacion de Chile (1)
Tel.: (56) 27199700 (100%)
Web Site: http://www.pearseducacion.cl
Sales Range: $25-49.9 Million
Emp.: 41
Publisher of College & School Texts
N.A.I.C.S.: 513130

Pearson Educacion de Colombia Ltda (1)
Carrera 7 N 156-68 Northpoint Torre 3 Piso 26, Bogota, Colombia
Tel.: (57) 12940800
Educational Support Services
N.A.I.C.S.: 611710

Pearson Educacion de Mexico SA de CV (1)
Atlacomulco No 500 5to piso Colonia Industrial Atoto, 53519, Naucalpan, Mexico
Tel.: (52) 5553870700
Educational Support Services
N.A.I.C.S.: 611710

Pearson Educacion de Peru SA (1)
Avenida Javier Prado Este 4491, Surco, Lima, Peru
Tel.: (51) 14372010
Educational Support Services
N.A.I.C.S.: 611710
Eduardo Guzman *(Gen Mgr)*

Pearson Educacion de Venezuela (1)

AND PRIVATE COMPANIES — PEARSON PLC

Torre A Piso 18, 1060-054, Caracas, Venezuela **(100%)**
Tel.: (58) 2122854505
Sales Range: $25-49.9 Million
Emp.: 4
Publisher of College & School Texts
N.A.I.C.S.: 513130

Pearson Education (Singapore) Pte Ltd
23/25 First Lok Yang Road Pioneer West, Singapore, 629734, Singapore
Tel.: (65) 63199388
Educational Book Publisher
N.A.I.C.S.: 513130

Pearson Education (South Africa) Pty Ltd
Auto Atlantic 4th Floor Corner Hertzog Boulevard and Heerengracht, Cape Town, 8001, South Africa
Tel.: (27) 215326000
Sales Range: $25-49.9 Million
Emp.: 63
Book Publishers
N.A.I.C.S.: 513130

Pearson Education Asia Ltd (1)
18/F 1063 King's Road, Quarry Bay, China (Hong Kong)
Tel.: (852) 31810123
Sales Range: $100-124.9 Million
Emp.: 500
Book Publishers
N.A.I.C.S.: 513130

Pearson Education Botswana (Proprietary) Ltd (1)
Plot 14386 New Lobatse Road West Industrial Site, Gaborone, Botswana
Tel.: (267) 3922969
Sales Range: $25-49.9 Million
Emp.: 11
Educational Book Publisher
N.A.I.C.S.: 513130
Christopher Koveya (Mng Dir)

Pearson Education Central Europe SpZoo (1)
ul Ostrobramska 101A, 04-041, Warsaw, Poland
Tel.: (48) 459596060
Web Site: https://www.pearson.pl
Book Publishers
N.A.I.C.S.: 513130

Pearson Education Hellas SA (1)
Tel.: (30) 2109373170
Web Site: http://www.pearsonelt.gr
Digital Learning & Publishing Services
N.A.I.C.S.: 611710

Pearson Education Holdings Ltd (1)
80 Strand, London, WC2R 0RL, United Kingdom
Tel.: (44) 1279623042
Investment Management Service
N.A.I.C.S.: 523999

Pearson Education Indochina Ltd (1)
Tel.: (66) 26815515
Web Site: http://www.pearson-indochina.com
Books Publishing Services
N.A.I.C.S.: 513130

Pearson Education Korea Ltd (1)
7F Shinhan DM Building Mapo Daero 25, Mapo-gu, Seoul, 120-111, Korea (South)
Tel.: (82) 23083210180
Book Publishers
N.A.I.C.S.: 513130

Pearson Education Ltd. (1)
Edinburgh Gate, Harlow, CM20 2JE, Essex, United Kingdom **(100%)**
Tel.: (44) 1279623623
Web Site: http://www.pearsoned.com
Sales Range: $200-249.9 Million
Emp.: 600
Textbooks & Technical Books Publisher
N.A.I.C.S.: 513130

Pearson Education South Asia Pte Ltd. (1)
63 Chulia Street 15-01, Singapore, 049514, Singapore **(100%)**
Tel.: (65) 64330933
Sales Range: $50-74.9 Million
Emp.: 190
Educational Book Publishing
N.A.I.C.S.: 323117

Pearson Education Taiwan Ltd (1)
Educational Book Publisher
N.A.I.C.S.: 513130

Pearson Education Yayincilik Sirketi (1)
Koza Is Merkezi B Block Kat 4 Murbasan Sok Balmumcu, Istanbul, 34349, Turkiye
Tel.: (90) 212 288 6941
Sales Range: $25-49.9 Million
Emp.: 40
Educational Books Distr
N.A.I.C.S.: 424920
Ozhan Toktas (Gen Mgr)

Pearson Education do Brasil (1) **(100%)**
Tel.: (55) 1136131200
Web Site: http://www.pearson.com.br
Sales Range: $50-74.9 Million
Emp.: 215
Publisher of College & School Texts
N.A.I.C.S.: 513130

Pearson Egitim Cozumleri Tikaret Limited Sirketi (1)
Nidakule Kozyatagi Kozyatagi Mahallesi Degirmen Sokak No 18 K 6, Kadikoy, Istanbul, Turkiye
Tel.: (90) 2162176600
Web Site: https://www.tr.pearson.com
Education Services
N.A.I.C.S.: 611710

Pearson France SAS (1)
15 Rue Henri Roleanguy, Montreuil, 93100, France
Tel.: (33) 1 43 62 31 00
Web Site: http://www.pearson.fr
Emp.: 30
Books Publishing Services
N.A.I.C.S.: 513130

Pearson Heinemann Ltd (1)
Halley Court Jordan Hill, Oxford, OX2 8EJ, United Kingdom
Tel.: (44) 1865 311366
Books Publishing Services
N.A.I.C.S.: 513130

Pearson Holdings Southern Africa (Pty) Ltd. (1)
Cnr Logan Way & Forest Drive, Pinelands, 7405, South Africa
Tel.: (27) 21 532 6184
Web Site: http://www.pearson.co.za
Book Publishers
N.A.I.C.S.: 513130

Pearson IOKI Spolka z ograniczona odpowiedzialnoscia (1)
ul Dabrowskiego 77A, 60-529, Poznan, Poland
Tel.: (48) 618433177
Emp.: 140
Information Technology Services
N.A.I.C.S.: 541511

Pearson India PvT Ltd (1)
7th Floor Knowledge Boulevard A-8 A Sector-62, Noida, 201 309, Uttar Pradesh, India
Tel.: (91) 1204190100
Educational Book Publisher
N.A.I.C.S.: 513130
Vikas Singh (Mng Dir)

Pearson International Finance Ltd (1)
80 Strand, London, WC2R 0RL, United Kingdom
Tel.: (44) 2070102000
Financial Management Services
N.A.I.C.S.: 523999

Pearson Italy Srl (1)
Corso Trapani 16, 10139, Turin, Italy
Tel.: (39) 011 75021 11
Web Site: http://www.pearson.it
Sales Range: $50-74.9 Million
Emp.: 200
Book Publishers
N.A.I.C.S.: 513130

Pearson Japan K.K. (1)
11F Kanda Square 2-2-1 Kanda-Nishiki-cho, Chiyoda-ku, Tokyo, 101-0054, Japan
Tel.: (81) 345400380
Web Site: http://www.pearson.co.jp
Education Services
N.A.I.C.S.: 611710
Toshinori Iwamoto (Country Mgr)

Pearson Lesotho (Proprietary) Ltd (1)
Lesotho 1st Floor Christie House Orpen Road Old Europa, Maseru, 100, Lesotho
Tel.: (266) 22314254
Sales Range: $25-49.9 Million
Emp.: 6
Book Publishers
N.A.I.C.S.: 513130

Pearson Loan Finance Unlimited (1)
80 Strand, London, WC2R 0RL, United Kingdom
Tel.: (44) 2070102000
Emp.: 1,000
Investment Management Service
N.A.I.C.S.: 523999

Pearson Luxembourg Holdings Ltd (1)
80 Strand Shell Mex House, London, WC2R 0RL, United Kingdom
Tel.: (44) 2070102000
Investment Management Service
N.A.I.C.S.: 523999

Pearson Luxembourg Holdings No.2 Ltd (1)
80 Strand, London, WC2R 0RL, United Kingdom
Tel.: (44) 2070102000
Investment Management Service
N.A.I.C.S.: 523999

Pearson Malaysia Sdn Bhd (1)
Web Site: http://www.pearson.com
Books Publishing Services
N.A.I.C.S.: 513130
Edward Teoh (Gen Mgr)

Pearson Management Services Ltd (1)
80 Strand, London, WC2R 0RL, United Kingdom
Tel.: (44) 2070102000
Business Management Services
N.A.I.C.S.: 561499

Pearson Overseas Holdings Ltd (1)
80 Strand, London, WC2R 0RL, United Kingdom
Tel.: (44) 2070102000
Investment Management Service
N.A.I.C.S.: 523999

Pearson Schweiz AG (1)
Gewerbestrasse 10, 6330, Cham, Switzerland
Tel.: (41) 417474747
Web Site: https://www.pearson.ch
Education Services
N.A.I.C.S.: 611710

Pearson Shared Services Ltd (1)
80 Strand, London, WC2R 0RL, United Kingdom
Tel.: (44) 1279623928
Book Publishers
N.A.I.C.S.: 513130
Adam Miles (Mgr-Contact Centre)

Pearson South Africa (Pty) Ltd. (1)
4th Floor Auto Atlantic Corner Hertzog Boulevard and Heerengracht, Cape Town, 8001, South Africa
Tel.: (27) 215326000
Education Management Services
N.A.I.C.S.: 611710
Jannie Theron (Sls Dir-Fin)

Pearson Sweden AB (1)
Gustavslundsvagen 137, 167 51, Bromma, Sweden
Tel.: (46) 86197600
Web Site: https://www.pearsonclinical.se
Emp.: 25
Books Publishing Services
N.A.I.C.S.: 513130
Catherine Mabon (Mng Dir)

Pearson, Inc. (1) **(100%)**
Tel.: (212) 641-2400
Web Site: http://www.pearson.com
Sales Range: $25-49.9 Million
Emp.: 40
Holding Company
N.A.I.C.S.: 551112

Subsidiary (Non-US):

Americas Choice Inc (2)
Tel.: (202) 783-3668
Educational Administrative Services
N.A.I.C.S.: 923110

Book Country LLC (2)
Web Site: http://www.bookcountry.com
Books Publishing Services
N.A.I.C.S.: 513130

Dominie Press Inc (2)
Tel.: (760) 431-8000
Education Material Publishing Services
N.A.I.C.S.: 513199

Dorling Kindersley Publishing Inc (2)
Tel.: (646) 674-4047
Web Site: https://www.dk.com
Books Publishing Services
N.A.I.C.S.: 513130

FT Publications Inc (2)
Tel.: (212) 641-6500
Web Site: http://www.ft.com
Publishing Services
N.A.I.C.S.: 513199

FT Search Inc (2)
Tel.: (203) 564-1501
Books Publishing Services
N.A.I.C.S.: 513130

Florida Sun Publications, Inc. (2)
Tel.: (941) 748-4140
Web Site: https://www.sunpubfla.com
Printing Company
N.A.I.C.S.: 513120

Money Media Inc (2)
Tel.: (212) 390-7302
Web Site: https://www.money-media.com
Sales Range: $1-9.9 Million
Emp.: 30
News Reporting Services
N.A.I.C.S.: 516210
Egon Smullyan (VP-Comml Ops)

Ncs Pearson, Inc. (2)
Web Site: http://www.ncspearson.com
Educational Support Services
N.A.I.C.S.: 611710

New York Institute of Finance (2) **(100%)**
Tel.: (212) 641-6616
Web Site: https://www.nyif.com
Sales Range: $10-24.9 Million
Emp.: 40
Financial Training Services
N.A.I.C.S.: 611410

PN Holdings Inc (2)
Tel.: (734) 765-5562
Investment Management Service
N.A.I.C.S.: 523999

Pearson Business Services Inc (2)
Tel.: (281) 391-5213
Secretarial Services
N.A.I.C.S.: 561492

Pearson Education Holdings Inc (2)
Tel.: (201) 236-7000
Investment Management Service
N.A.I.C.S.: 523999

Pearson Education, Inc. (2) **(100%)**
Tel.: (201) 236-7000
Web Site: http://www.pearsoned.com
Educational Publishing
N.A.I.C.S.: 513120

Pearson Holdings Inc (2)
Tel.: (212) 641-2400
Investment Management Service
N.A.I.C.S.: 523999

Pearson Real Estate Holdings Inc (2)
Tel.: (307) 684-9556
Sales Range: $50-74.9 Million
Emp.: 8
Investment Management Service
N.A.I.C.S.: 523999

Pearson Technology Centre Inc. (2) **(100%)**
Tel.: (201) 767-5000

PEARSON PLC

Pearson plc—(Continued)

Web Site: http://www.pearson.com
Sales Range: $100-124.9 Million
Emp.: 400
Business Research Services
N.A.I.C.S.: 513130

Pearson's Knowledge Technologies LLC (2)
Tel.: (303) 545-9092
Web Site: http://kt.pearsonassessments.com
Educational Research Services
N.A.I.C.S.: 611710

Rough Guides Inc (2)
Tel.: (212) 414-3635
Books Publishing Services
N.A.I.C.S.: 513130

SchoolNet, Inc. (2)
Tel.: (646) 496-9000
Web Site: http://www.schoolnet.com
Sales Range: $10-24.9 Million
Emp.: 110
Education Software Developer
N.A.I.C.S.: 513210

The SIOP Institute LLC (2)
Tel.: (877) 637-1604
Web Site: http://www.siop.pearson.com
Education Services
N.A.I.C.S.: 611710

Wall Street Institute International Inc (2)
Tel.: (443) 320-1110
Web Site: http://www.wallstreetinstitute.com
Language Training Services
N.A.I.C.S.: 611630

eCollege inc (2)
Tel.: (303) 658-1000
Web Site: http://www.pearson.com
Emp.: 500
Online Education Services
N.A.I.C.S.: 516210

Peter Honey Publications Limited (1)
Tel.: (44) 1628633946
Sales Range: $25-49.9 Million
Emp.: 10
Educational Book Publisher
N.A.I.C.S.: 513130

Smarthinking, Inc. (1)
8101 Biscayne Blvd Ste 708, Miami, FL 33138
Web Site: https://www.smarthinkinginc.com
Marketing & Advertising Services
N.A.I.C.S.: 541810
Abe Villareal (Dir-Comm)

Stark Verlagsgesellschaft mbH & Co KG (1)
Lilienthalstrasse 2, Hallbergmoos, 85399, Germany
Tel.: (49) 180 3 179000
Web Site: http://www.stark-verlag.de
Emp.: 500
Book Publishing & Educational Support Services
N.A.I.C.S.: 513130

Stark Verwaltungsgesellschaft mbH (1)
Buergermeister-Guenthner-Strasse 6, Oberhaid, Bamberg, 96173, Germany
Tel.: (49) 9503504510
Business Management Services
N.A.I.C.S.: 561499

TQ Catalis Limited (1)
80 Strand, London, WC2R 0RL, United Kingdom
Tel.: (44) 8458808108
Vocational Training Services
N.A.I.C.S.: 624100

TQ Clapham Ltd (1)
The Derby Conference Centre London Road, Derby, United Kingdom
Tel.: (44) 8458808108
Emp.: 20
Educational Support Services
N.A.I.C.S.: 611710
Bruce Cantrill (Mng Dir)

TQ Education & Training Ltd (1)
Bangrave Road South, Corby, NN17 1NN, Northants, United Kingdom
Tel.: (44) 1509 678 400
Web Site: http://www.tq.com
Sales Range: $10-24.9 Million
Emp.: 50
Education Training Services
N.A.I.C.S.: 611710
Christopher Samler (Chm)

TQ Group Ltd (1)
80 Strand, London, WC2R 0RL, United Kingdom
Tel.: (44) 1159540100
Books Publishing Services
N.A.I.C.S.: 513130

TQ Holdings Ltd. (1)
Bangrave Road South, Corby, NN17 1NN, Northants, United Kingdom
Tel.: (44) 1536 351 300
Web Site: http://www.tq.com
Emp.: 10
Education Training Services
N.A.I.C.S.: 611710

The Assessment Company Ltd (1)
T D S House Terrace Road South, Binfield, Bracknell, RG42 4BH, United Kingdom
Tel.: (44) 1344300070
Educational Support Services
N.A.I.C.S.: 611710

The Coaching Space Ltd (1)
33 St James's Square, London, SW1Y 4JS, United Kingdom
Tel.: (44) 2076984467
Web Site: https://www.ildynamics.com
Executive Coaching Consulting Services
N.A.I.C.S.: 611430

The Learning Edge International Pty Ltd (1)
Level 1 160 Collins Street, GPO Box 2217, Hobart, 7001, TAS, Australia
Tel.: (61) 362238544
Sales Range: $10-24.9 Million
Emp.: 25
Professional Training Services
N.A.I.C.S.: 611430

Ventura Publishing Ltd (1)
Edinburgh Gate, Harlow, CM20 2JE, Essex, United Kingdom
Tel.: (44) 1279623623
Book Publishers
N.A.I.C.S.: 513130
Rod Bristow (Pres)

WSI Education Brazil Licencia (1)
Av Brigadeiro Faria Lima 1571, Sao Paulo, Brazil
Tel.: (55) 1138160383
Sales Range: $10-24.9 Million
Emp.: 60
Language Training Services
N.A.I.C.S.: 611630

WSI Education GmbH (1)
Rosental 5, 80331, Munich, Germany
Tel.: (49) 895529890
Web Site: http://www.wallstreetinstitute.de
English Language School Operator
N.A.I.C.S.: 611630

dvn medienservice GmbH & Co. KG (1)
Brunecker Strasse 98, Nuremberg, 90461, Germany (100%)
Tel.: (49) 911439920
Web Site: http://www.dvn.de
Sales Range: $25-49.9 Million
Emp.: 200
Media Representatives
N.A.I.C.S.: 541840

m2p medienfabrik GmbH & Co. KG (1)
Mainstrasse 20, 90451, Nuremberg, Germany (100%)
Web Site: http://www.media2print.de
Sales Range: $10-24.9 Million
Emp.: 76
Printing Services
N.A.I.C.S.: 323111

PEATY MILLS PLC

Bridge House 1 Endeavour Park Addington, West Malling, ME19 5SH, Kent, United Kingdom
Tel.: (44) 1732879800
Web Site: http://www.peatymills.com
Year Founded: 1979
Sales Range: $10-24.9 Million
Emp.: 15
Label Supplier
N.A.I.C.S.: 561910
Colin Young (Dir-Fin)

PEAVEY INDUSTRIES LP

7740 40 Ave, Red Deer, T4P 2H9, AB, Canada
Tel.: (403) 346-8991
Web Site: http://www.peaveymart.com
Sales Range: $75-99.9 Million
Emp.: 1,000
Farm & Hardware Retailer
N.A.I.C.S.: 444140

Subsidiaries:

TSC Stores L.P. (1)
2209 Dundas Street E, London, N5V 1R4, ON, Canada
Tel.: (519) 000-0000
Web Site: https://www.peaveymart.com
Rev.: $72,425,143
Emp.: 500
Hardware Stores
N.A.I.C.S.: 444140

PEBBLE BEACH SYSTEMS GROUP PLC

Unit 1 First Quarter Blenheim Road, Epsom, KT19 9QN, Surrey, United Kingdom
Tel.: (44) 7555593602 UK
Web Site: https://www.pebbleplc.com
PEB—(AIM)
Rev.: $15,747,876
Assets: $16,511,718
Liabilities: $15,429,608
Net Worth: $1,082,110
Earnings: $1,947,797
Emp.: 90
Fiscal Year-end: 12/31/23
Software & Technology Products Mfr
N.A.I.C.S.: 513210
Peter Mayhead (CEO)

Subsidiaries:

Continental Microwave Limited (1)
27 Maylands Ave, Hemel Hempstead, HP2 7DE, Hartfordshire, United Kingdom (100%)
Tel.: (44) 494774400
Sales Range: $25-49.9 Million
Emp.: 65
Mfr of Broadcast & Telecommunications Equipment
N.A.I.C.S.: 334220

Subsidiary (US):

Microwave Radio Communications (2)
101 Billerica Ave Bldg 6, North Billerica, MA 01862 (100%)
Tel.: (978) 671-5700
Sales Range: $25-49.9 Million
Emp.: 70
Mfr & Designer of Broadcast & Telecommunication Equipment
N.A.I.C.S.: 334220
George Smith (CEO)

DC Machine Vision Limited (1)
Marlborough House, Charnham Ln, Hungerford, RG17 0EY, Berks, United Kingdom (100%)
Tel.: (44) 1488685500
Web Site: http://www.vislink.com
Sales Range: $25-49.9 Million
Emp.: 2
Reseller of Computer Imaging Systems
N.A.I.C.S.: 541512

Pebble Beach Systems Limited (1)
12 Horizon Business Village 1 Brooklands Rd, Weybridge, KT13 0TJ, Surrey, United Kingdom
Tel.: (44) 193 233 3790
Web Site: https://www.pebble.tv

INTERNATIONAL PUBLIC

Software Services
N.A.I.C.S.: 513210

PEC LTD.

15 Barakhamba Road, Hansalaya, New Delhi, 110001, India
Tel.: (91) 1123316397
Web Site: http://www.peclimited.com
Sales Range: $1-4.9 Billion
Emp.: 202
International Trade & Business Services
N.A.I.C.S.: 561499
Ravi Kumar (Exec Dir-Mktg)

PEC LTD.

14 International Business Park, Singapore, 609922, Singapore
Tel.: (65) 62689788 SG
Web Site: https://www.peceng.com
Year Founded: 1982
IX2—(SES)
Rev.: $319,332,535
Assets: $304,452,292
Liabilities: $124,786,943
Net Worth: $179,665,349
Earnings: $5,982,167
Emp.: 2,531
Fiscal Year-end: 06/30/23
Oil & Gas Engineering & Construction Services
N.A.I.C.S.: 237990
Edna Poh Thim Ko (Chm)

Subsidiaries:

Audex Fujairah LL FZE (1)
Room 6 Block C Next to Al Malik Corporation Limited, Fujairah Free Zone 1, Fujairah, United Arab Emirates
Tel.: (971) 92281075
Engineering Construction Services
N.A.I.C.S.: 541330

EBT Engineering Pte. Ltd. (1)
11 Neythal Rd, Singapore, 628577, Singapore
Tel.: (65) 68619022
Web Site: https://www.ebt.com.sg
Emp.: 120
Corrosion Protection Services
N.A.I.C.S.: 237120
Mat Zanes (Mgr)

Huizhou Tianxin Petrochemical Engineering Co., Ltd. (1)
No 360 Petrochemical Avenue, Daya Bay District, Huizhou, 516086, Guangdong, China (60%)
Tel.: (86) 7525556900
Web Site: https://www.txeng.com
Engineering Construction Services
N.A.I.C.S.: 541330

IT Re-Engineering Pte. Ltd. (1)
14 International Business Park, Singapore, 609922, Singapore
Tel.: (65) 65666788
Web Site: https://www.itr.com.sg
Engineering Equipment Distr
N.A.I.C.S.: 423490

Isotech Pte. Ltd. (1)
14 International Business Park, Singapore, 609922, Singapore
Tel.: (65) 62689788
Web Site: https://www.isotech.com.sg
Isolation Services
N.A.I.C.S.: 213112

PT Audex Indonesia (1)
Kebayoran Square Business Park No A-9 Jalan Boulevard Bintaro Jaya, Sektor 7, Tangerang, 15224, Indonesia
Tel.: (62) 212221339798
Engineering Construction Services
N.A.I.C.S.: 541330

Plant Engtech Private Limited (1)
60A Nethaji Street Ayyappa Nagar, Tiruchirappalli, 620021, India
Tel.: (91) 4314023703
Web Site: https://www.plantengtech.com
Engineering Construction Services
N.A.I.C.S.: 541330
Raja Ram (Engr-Mechanical)

Testing Inspection & Solution Pte. Ltd. (1)
14 International Business Park, Singapore, 609922, Singapore
Tel.: (65) 62689788
Web Site: https://www.tis.com.sg
Oil & Gas Field Exploration Services
N.A.I.C.S.: 213112

PECCA GROUP BERHAD
No 1 Jalan Perindustrian Desa Aman 1A Industri Desa Aman Kepong, 52200, Kuala Lumpur, Malaysia
Tel.: (60) 362751800 MY
Web Site: https://www.peccaleather.com
Year Founded: 2000
PECCA—(KLS)
Rev.: $46,827,090
Assets: $55,880,635
Liabilities: $10,754,709
Net Worth: $45,125,926
Earnings: $7,497,566
Emp.: 909
Fiscal Year-end: 06/30/23
Leather Product Mfr & Distr
N.A.I.C.S.: 316990
Hwa Cheng Teoh *(Founder & Mng Dir-Grp)*

PECOS HOTELS & PUBS LTD.
34 Resthouse Road, Bengaluru, 560 001, India
Tel.: (91) 8025580971
Web Site: https://www.pecospub.com
Year Founded: 1989
539273—(BOM)
Rev.: $1,068,606
Assets: $637,202
Liabilities: $64,585
Net Worth: $572,617
Earnings: $139,328
Emp.: 20
Fiscal Year-end: 03/31/23
Hotel & Pub Operator
N.A.I.C.S.: 721120
Liam Norman Timms *(Exec Dir)*

PEDIGREE WHOLESALE LTD.
Pedigree House Ambleside, Gamston, Nottingham, NG2 6NQ, United Kingdom
Tel.: (44) 115 982 3900
Web Site: http://www.petproducts.co.uk
Year Founded: 1972
Pet Product Wholesalers
N.A.I.C.S.: 459910
Chris Hindson *(Mgr-Sls Support)*

Subsidiaries:

Just for Pets Limited (1)
The Business Centre Edward Street, Redditch, B97 6HA, United Kingdom
Tel.: (44) 1299 252070
Web Site: http://www.justforpetstores.co.uk
Pet Supplies Retailer
N.A.I.C.S.: 459910

PEDRO RESOURCES LTD.
393 University Avenue Suite 1810, Toronto, M5G 1E6, ON, Canada
Tel.: (647) 946-2286
PED.H—(TSX)
Assets: $24,512
Liabilities: $144,777
Net Worth: ($120,265)
Earnings: ($190,884)
Fiscal Year-end: 12/31/20
Mineral Exploration Services
N.A.I.C.S.: 213115
Brian Stecyk *(CEO)*

PEE CEE COSMA SOPE LTD.
Hall H1-H2 First Floor Padam Plaza Plot No 5 Sector 16B, Awas Vikas Sikandra Yojna, Agra, 282 007, Uttar Pradesh, India
Tel.: (91) 5622527331
Web Site: https://doctorsoap.com
524136—(BOM)
Rev.: $14,993,178
Assets: $5,605,239
Liabilities: $1,963,935
Net Worth: $3,641,304
Earnings: $298,088
Emp.: 263
Fiscal Year-end: 03/31/23
Cosmetics Products Mfr
N.A.I.C.S.: 325620
Mayank Jain *(Chm)*

PEEK & CLOPPENBURG KG
Berliner Allee 2, 40212, Dusseldorf, Germany
Tel.: (49) 2113662601
Web Site: http://www.peek-cloppenburg.com
Year Founded: 1901
Sales Range: $1-4.9 Billion
Emp.: 10,200
Department Stores Owner & Operator
N.A.I.C.S.: 455110

PEEL CHRYSLER JEEP DODGE
212 Lakeshore Road West, Toronto, L5H 1G6, ON, Canada
Tel.: (905) 278-6181
Web Site: http://www.peelchryslerjeep.com
Rev.: $11,476,733
Emp.: 25
New & Used Car Dealers
N.A.I.C.S.: 441110
Kevin Murchie *(Mgr-Parts)*

PEEL HOLDINGS LTD.
Peel Dome The Trafford Center, Manchester, M17 8PL, United Kingdom
Tel.: (44) 1616298200 UK
Web Site: http://www.peelholdings.co.uk
Sales Range: $350-399.9 Million
Emp.: 1,068
Real Estate Holdings & Transport Services
N.A.I.C.S.: 551112
John Whittaker *(Chm)*

Subsidiaries:

City Airport Ltd (1)
Control Tower Liverpool Road, Eccles, Manchester, M30 7SA, United Kingdom
Tel.: (44) 161 789 1362
Web Site: http://www.cityairportandheliport.com
Oil Transportation Services
N.A.I.C.S.: 481111
Kay Nugent *(Bus Mgr & Mgr-Comml)*

Durham Tees Valley Airport Limited (1)
Tees Valley, Darlington, DL2 1LU, United Kingdom
Tel.: (44) 8712 242426
Web Site: http://www.durhamteesvalleyairport.com
Passenger Air Transportation Services
N.A.I.C.S.: 481111
Shaun Woods *(Mgr-Airport)*

Peel Airports Ltd. (1)
Peel Dome, The Trafford Ctr, Manchester, M17 8PL, United Kingdom (100%)
Tel.: (44) 1616298200
Web Site: http://www.peel.co.uk
Holding Company
N.A.I.C.S.: 551112

Peel Land and Property Holdings Ltd. (1)
Peel Dome, The Trafford Ctr, Manchester, M178PL, United Kingdom (100%)
Tel.: (44) 1616298200
Web Site: http://www.peel.co.uk
Real Estate Property Lessors
N.A.I.C.S.: 531190
John Whittaker *(Chm)*

Peel Media Limited (1)
Venus Building 1 Old Park Lane, Trafford, Manchester, M41 7HA, United Kingdom
Tel.: (44) 7570343729
Web Site: https://www.mediacityuk.co.uk
Real Estate Investment Services
N.A.I.C.S.: 531390
Jessica Hough *(Mgr-Sound Stage)*

Peel Ports Ltd (1)
Peel dome, The Trafford Centre, Manchester, M17 8PL, United Kingdom
Tel.: (44) 1519496000
Web Site: http://www.peel.co.uk
Marine Port Operation Services
N.A.I.C.S.: 488310
Gary Hodgson *(Gen Mgr)*

Subsidiary (Domestic):

The Mersey Docks & Harbour Company (2)
Maritime Center, Port of Liverpool, Liverpool, L21 1LA, United Kingdom
Tel.: (44) 1519496000
Web Site: http://www.merseydocks.co.uk
Sales Range: $550-599.9 Million
Emp.: 500
Port Facilities Management Services; Cargo Handling & Associated Services
N.A.I.C.S.: 488310
Stephen Carr *(Head-Bus Dev)*

Subsidiary (Domestic):

Heysham Port Ltd. (3)
Maritime Ctr, Liverpool, L21 1LA, United Kingdom (100%)
Tel.: (44) 1524852373
Web Site: http://www.merseydocks.co.uk
Sales Range: $25-49.9 Million
Emp.: 100
Dock Operator
N.A.I.C.S.: 488310

PEEL HOTELS PLC
19 Warwick Avenue, London, W9 2PS, United Kingdom
Tel.: (44) 2072661100
Web Site: http://www.peelhotels.co.uk
Rev.: $19,783,368
Assets: $44,652,643
Liabilities: $15,098,875
Net Worth: $29,553,768
Earnings: $270,087
Emp.: 442
Fiscal Year-end: 01/27/19
Hotel Operator
N.A.I.C.S.: 721110
Robert Edmund Guy Peel *(Chm)*

Subsidiaries:

Crown & Mitre (Carlisle) Limited (1)
English Street, Carlisle, CA3 8HZ, Cumbria, United Kingdom
Tel.: (44) 1228525491
Hotel Operator
N.A.I.C.S.: 721110
Maggie McLellan *(Gen Mgr)*

PEEL HUNT LLP
Moor House 120 London Wall, London, EC2Y 5ET, United Kingdom
Tel.: (44) 2074188900
Web Site: http://www.peelhunt.com
Sales Range: $75-99.9 Million
Emp.: 150
Investment Services
N.A.I.C.S.: 523150
Simon Hayes *(Chm)*

Subsidiaries:

Peel Hunt Inc. (1)
250 Park Ave, New York, NY 10017
Tel.: (646) 924-2597
Web Site: http://www.peelhunt.com
Brokerage Firm
N.A.I.C.S.: 531210
Harry Jaffe *(Head-Sls-North America)*

PEEL MINING LTD.
Unit 1 34 Kings Park Rd, West Perth, 6005, WA, Australia
Tel.: (61) 893823955
Web Site: https://www.peelmining.com.au
PEX—(ASX)
Rev.: $286,594
Assets: $73,974,108
Liabilities: $1,085,028
Net Worth: $72,889,080
Earnings: ($1,803,406)
Fiscal Year-end: 06/30/24
Tungsten & Mineral Ore Mining & Exploration Services
N.A.I.C.S.: 212390
Rob Tyson *(Mng Dir)*

PEEL MUTUAL INSURANCE COMPANY
103 Queen Street West, Brampton, L6Y 1M3, ON, Canada
Tel.: (905) 451-2386
Web Site: http://www.peelmutual.com
Year Founded: 1876
Rev.: $19,045,000
Emp.: 28
Insurance Services
N.A.I.C.S.: 524298

PEERAGE REALTY PARTNERS, INC.
1325 Lawrence Ave E Ste 200, Toronto, M3A 1C6, ON, Canada
Tel.: (647) 547-3430
Web Site: http://www.peeragerealty.com
Holding Company
N.A.I.C.S.: 523999
Miles S. Nadal *(Founder)*

Subsidiaries:

Four Seasons International Realty, LLC (1)
550 Hinesburg Rd, South Burlington, VT 05403
Tel.: (802) 864-0541
Web Site: http://www.fourseasonsir.com
Emp.: 220
Real Estate Agency
N.A.I.C.S.: 531210
Staige J. Davis *(CEO)*

PEERAPAT TECHNOLOGY PUBLIC COMPANY LIMITED
406 Ratchadaphisek Rd, Samsen Nok Huai Khwang, Bangkok, 10310, Thailand
Tel.: (66) 22901200
Web Site: https://www.peerapat.com
Year Founded: 1983
PRAPAT—(THA)
Rev.: $31,294,960
Assets: $36,494,341
Liabilities: $21,461,353
Net Worth: $15,032,989
Earnings: $1,491,710
Fiscal Year-end: 12/31/23
Chemical Product Mfr & Distr
N.A.I.C.S.: 325199
Veerapong Luesakul *(CEO)*

Subsidiaries:

Allies intertrade Co., Ltd. (1)
406 Ratchadaphisek Road, Samsen Nok Subdistrict Huai Khwang District, Bangkok, 10310, Thailand
Tel.: (66) 22901288
Web Site: https://alliesth.com
Washing Machine Distr
N.A.I.C.S.: 423620

Thai Steward Services Company Limited (1)
408 Ratchadapisek Road Samsen Nork, Huai Khwang, Bangkok, 10310, Thailand
Tel.: (66) 645851909
Web Site: https://thaisteward.com
Washing Machine Distr

PEERAPAT TECHNOLOGY PUBLIC COMPANY LIMITED

Peerapat Technology Public Company Limited—(Continued)
N.A.I.C.S.: 423620
Chanok Phothong *(Sls Mgr)*

PEERLESS ENGINEERING SALES LTD.
4015 East First Avenue, Burnaby, V5C 3W5, BC, Canada
Tel.: (604) 659-4100
Web Site:
   https://www.peerlessengineers.com
Year Founded: 1964
Industrial Machinery & Equipment Mfr
N.A.I.C.S.: 333248
Jeffrey Magnolo *(Pres)*

PEET LIMITED
Level 7 200 St Georges Terrace, Perth, 6000, WA, Australia
Tel.: (61) 894201111   AU
Web Site: https://www.peet.com.au
PPC—(ASX)
Rev.: $195,365,918
Assets: $730,558,224
Liabilities: $333,257,878
Net Worth: $397,300,346
Earnings: $23,969,017
Emp.: 193
Fiscal Year-end: 06/30/24
Real Estate Developer & Other Related Services
N.A.I.C.S.: 531390
Dom Scafetta *(Sec)*

Subsidiaries:

CIC Australia Limited (1)
Level 3 64 Allara Street, Canberra, 2601, ACT, Australia   (100%)
Tel.: (61) 262300800
Web Site: http://www.cicaustralia.com.au
Residential Real Estate Developer
N.A.I.C.S.: 237210

JTP Homes Pty Limited (1)
93 Pellatt St, Beaumaris, Melbourne, 3193, VIC, Australia
Tel.: (61) 40 095 1000
Web Site: https://www.jpthomes.com.au
Residential Building & Construction Services
N.A.I.C.S.: 236118
Gerry Flood *(Mng Dir)*

Peet Estates (QLD) Pty Limited (1)
Level 3 167 Eagle Street, Brisbane, 4000, QLD, Australia
Tel.: (61) 73 187 2040
Real Estate Development Services
N.A.I.C.S.: 531390

Peet Estates (VIC) Pty Limited (1)
Level 4 380 St Kilda Road, Melbourne, 3004, VIC, Australia
Tel.: (61) 39 868 5900
Real Estate Development Services
N.A.I.C.S.: 531390

Peet Estates (WA) Pty Limited (1)
Level 7 200 St Georges Terrace, Perth, 6000, WA, Australia
Tel.: (61) 89 420 1111
Real Estate Development Services
N.A.I.C.S.: 531390

Peet No 72 Avoca Pty. Limited (1)
Level 7 200 St Georges Terrace, Perth, 6000, WA, Australia
Tel.: (61) 894201111
Web Site: https://www.peet.com.au
Sales Range: $50-74.9 Million
Emp.: 80
Real Estate Agencies
N.A.I.C.S.: 531210
Brendan Gora *(CEO)*

Peet No 77 Pty. Limited (1)
Level 7 200 St Georges Terrace, Perth, 6000, WA, Australia
Tel.: (61) 894201111
Web Site: https://www.peet.com.au
Sales Range: $50-74.9 Million
Emp.: 70
Subdividers & Real Estate Developers

N.A.I.C.S.: 531390
Jo Aerthrell *(Mgr-Mktg)*

Peet Queens Park JV Pty. Limited (1)
Level 7 200 St Georges Terrace, Perth, 6000, WA, Australia
Tel.: (61) 894201111
Web Site: https://www.peet.com.au
Sales Range: $50-74.9 Million
Emp.: 70
Real Estate Developers
N.A.I.C.S.: 531190

Peet Southern JV Pty. Limited (1)
Level 7 200 St Georges Terrace, Perth, 6000, WA, Australia
Tel.: (61) 894201111
Web Site: https://www.peet.com.au
Sales Range: $50-74.9 Million
Emp.: 100
Real Estate Agencies
N.A.I.C.S.: 531210

Secure Living Pty. Limited (1)
No 52 Bellambi Ch, Lakelands, Mandurah, 6180, Western Australia, Australia
Tel.: (61) 895834011
Sales Range: $50-74.9 Million
Emp.: 2
Real Estate Agencies
N.A.I.C.S.: 531210

PEETI SECURITIES LIMITED
Survey No 71 Opp BSNL Office Beside M P Hardware Lane, Old Kurnool Road Kattedan, Hyderabad, 500077, India
Tel.: (91) 9963114257
Web Site:
   https://www.peetisecuritiesltd.com
Year Founded: 1994
531352—(BOM)
Rev.: $3,243,259
Assets: $1,479,695
Liabilities: $223,164
Net Worth: $1,256,531
Earnings: $70,679
Emp.: 29
Fiscal Year-end: 03/31/23
Fabric Curtain Mfr & Distr
N.A.I.C.S.: 314120
Sandeep Peeti *(Chm & Mng Dir)*

PEG PEREGO SPA
Via A De Gasperi 50, 20862, Arcore, MI, Italy
Tel.: (39) 03960881   IT
Web Site:
   http://www.it.pegperego.com
Year Founded: 1949
Sales Range: $300-349.9 Million
Emp.: 1,100
Baby Carriages, Strollers & Children's Vehicles Mfr
N.A.I.C.S.: 339930
Luchio Perego *(CEO)*

Subsidiaries:

Peg Perego USA Inc. (1)
3625 Independence Dr, Fort Wayne, IN 46808
Tel.: (260) 482-8191
Web Site: http://www.pegperego.com
Sales Range: $50-74.9 Million
Emp.: 56
Baby Carriages, Strollers & Children's Vehicles Mfr
N.A.I.C.S.: 423990

PEGASUS ASIA
1 Wallich Street Guoco Tower 15 03, Singapore, 078881, Singapore
Tel.: (65) 6 718 2111
Web Site: https://www.pegasus-asia.com
Year Founded: 2021
PGS—(SES)
Asset Management Services
N.A.I.C.S.: 531390
Neil Parekh *(CEO)*

PEGASUS DIGITAL MOBILITY ACQUISITION CORP.
71 Fort Street, Georgetown, KY1-1106, Cayman Islands
Tel.: (345) 7694900   Ky
Web Site:
   http://www.pegasusmobility.com
Year Founded: 2021
PGSS—(NYSE)
Rev.: $13,882,867
Assets: $231,085,639
Liabilities: $239,936,932
Net Worth: ($8,851,293)
Earnings: $11,838,568
Emp.: 3
Fiscal Year-end: 12/31/22
Investment Services
N.A.I.C.S.: 523999
Ralf Speth *(Chm & CEO)*

PEGASUS HEIGHTS BERHAD
1-40-1 Menara Bangkok Bank No 105 Jalan Ampang, Berjaya Central Park, 50450, Kuala Lumpur, Malaysia
Tel.: (60) 321813553   MY
Web Site:
   https://www.pegasusheights.com
Year Founded: 1974
4464—(KLS)
Rev.: $2,907,706
Assets: $29,031,781
Liabilities: $1,676,099
Net Worth: $27,355,682
Earnings: ($1,135,176)
Emp.: 47
Fiscal Year-end: 12/31/23
Property Development Services
N.A.I.C.S.: 531311
See Yang Lee *(Exec Dir)*

PEGASUS INTERNATIONAL HOLDINGS LIMITED
Unit 1110 11/F New Kowloon Plaza 38, Tai Kok Tsui, Kowloon, China (Hong Kong)
Tel.: (852) 23170167   BM
Web Site:
   http://www.pegasusholdings.com
Year Founded: 1956
0676—(HKG)
Rev.: $9,254,000
Assets: $99,614,000
Liabilities: $21,067,000
Net Worth: $78,547,000
Earnings: $1,683,000
Emp.: 212
Fiscal Year-end: 12/31/22
Footwear Mfr
N.A.I.C.S.: 316210
Yiu Lee *(Sec & Deputy Gen Mgr)*

PEGASUS RESOURCES INC.
700-838 West Hastings, Vancouver, V6C 0A6, BC, Canada
Tel.: (403) 597-3410   BC
Web Site:
   https://www.pegasusresources.com
Year Founded: 1995
PEGA—(TSXV)
Rev.: $623
Assets: $1,141,327
Liabilities: $359,254
Net Worth: $782,073
Earnings: ($802,804)
Fiscal Year-end: 05/31/24
Mineral Exploration Services
N.A.I.C.S.: 212290
Charles Desjardins *(Pres & CEO)*

PEGASUS SEWING MACHINE MANUFACTURING CO., LTD.
5-7-2 Sagisu, Fukushima-ku, Osaka, 553-0002, Japan
Tel.: (81) 664511351
Web Site: https://www.pegasus.co.jp
Year Founded: 1914

INTERNATIONAL PUBLIC

6262—(TKS)
Rev.: $115,952,620
Assets: $283,892,890
Liabilities: $81,607,060
Net Worth: $202,285,830
Earnings: ($475,920)
Emp.: 1,498
Fiscal Year-end: 03/31/24
Industrial Sewing Machine Mfr
N.A.I.C.S.: 333248
Shigemi Mima *(Pres)*

Subsidiaries:

PEGASUS-SHIMAMOTO AUTO PARTS (VIETNAM) CO., LTD. (1)
Lot B15 Long Duc Industrial Park, Long Duc Ward, Long Thanh, Dong Nai, Vietnam
Tel.: (84) 2513681171
Automobile Parts Distr
N.A.I.C.S.: 423120

Pegasus Corporation of America (1)
10675 NW 37th Terr, Doral, FL 33178
Tel.: (305) 468-9780
Web Site:
   http://www.pegasusofamerica.com
Sewing Machines Distr
N.A.I.C.S.: 423830
Melvyn Blore *(CEO)*

Pegasus Europa GmbH (1)
Weilerbacher Strasse 77, 67661, Kaiserslautern, Germany
Tel.: (49) 6313710990
Web Site: https://www.pegasus-europa.de
Sewing Machines Distr
N.A.I.C.S.: 423830

Pegasus Sewing Machine Manufacturing Co., Ltd. - Shiga Factory (1)
866-2 Motoayano Minakuchi-cho, Koka, 528-0037, Shiga, Japan
Tel.: (81) 748623341
Industrial Sewing Machine Mfr
N.A.I.C.S.: 333248

Pegasus Sewing Machine Pte Ltd. (1)
30 Tai Seng Street 09-04 Breadtalk iHQ, Singapore, 534013, Singapore
Tel.: (65) 6296 3638
Web Site: http://www.pegasus.com.sg
Sewing Machines Distr
N.A.I.C.S.: 423830

Pegasus Vietnam Sewing Machine Co., Ltd. (1)
Tan Truong Industrial Zone, Cam Giang District, Hai Duong, Vietnam
Tel.: (84) 2203570271
Sewing Machines Distr
N.A.I.C.S.: 423830

Tianjin Pegasus System Engineering Co., Ltd. (1)
No B1111-B1114 Building B Hi-Tech Information Plaza No 8 Huatian Road, Huayuan Industrial area, Tianjin, 300384, China
Tel.: (86) 22 2370 7121
Sewing Machines Distr
N.A.I.C.S.: 423830

Tianjin Pegasus-Shimamoto Auto Parts Co., Ltd. (1)
No 12 Xinye 1 West Zone of TEDA, Tianjin, 300452, China
Tel.: (86) 2266320977
Automobile Parts Distr
N.A.I.C.S.: 423120

PEGATRON CORPORATION
No 96 Ligong Street, Beitou, Taipei, 112, Taiwan
Tel.: (886) 281439001   TW
Web Site:
   https://www.pegatroncorp.com
Year Founded: 2007
PGRGS—(LUX)
Rev.: $41,341,925,898
Assets: $19,892,530,000
Liabilities: $13,183,707,720
Net Worth: $6,708,822,281
Earnings: $661,693,994
Emp.: 8,807
Fiscal Year-end: 12/31/22

AND PRIVATE COMPANIES

Electric Equipment Mfr
N.A.I.C.S.: 335999
T. H. Tung (Chm)

Subsidiaries:

Asuspower Investment Co., Ltd. (1)
7th Floor Office 2 No 167 Kuang-Ming Road, Beitou, Taipei, Taiwan
Tel.: (886) 2 2894 3447
Investment Management Service
N.A.I.C.S.: 523940

Subsidiary (Domestic):

Pega International Limited (2)
No 150 Li-Te Road, Beitou District, Taipei, 11259, Taiwan
Tel.: (886) 2 81439001
Investment Management Service
N.A.I.C.S.: 523940

Subsidiary (US):

Pegatron Technology Service Inc (2)
121 River Ridge Cir, Jeffersonville, IN 47130-8974
Tel.: (812) 282-2787
Consumer Electronics Whslr
N.A.I.C.S.: 423620

Lumens Integration Inc. (1)
4116 Clipper Ct, Fremont, CA 94538
Tel.: (510) 252-0200
Web Site: http://www.mylumens.com
Computer Peripheral Equipment Distr
N.A.I.C.S.: 423430

Pegatron Czech s.r.o. (1)
Na Rovince 862, Hrabova, 720 00, Ostrava, Czech Republic
Tel.: (420) 553031111
Web Site: https://www.pegaservice.eu
Emp.: 700
Electronic Components Mfr
N.A.I.C.S.: 334419

Unihan Corporation (1)
No 150 Lide Road, Beitou District, Taipei, Taiwan
Tel.: (886) 2 8143 9007
Computer Peripheral Equipment Mfr
N.A.I.C.S.: 334118

Subsidiary (Domestic):

AMA Precision Inc (2)
3F No 37 Sec 2 Jhongyang S Rd, Peitou District, Taipei, Taiwan
Tel.: (886) 2 2895 5056
Computer Peripheral Equipment Mfr
N.A.I.C.S.: 334118

PEGAVISION CORP.
No 5 Shing Yeh Street, GuiShan District, Taoyuan, 333, Taiwan
Tel.: (886) 33298808
Web Site:
https://www.pegavision.com
Year Founded: 2009
6491—(TAI)
Emp.: 1,708
Ophthalmic Product Mfr
N.A.I.C.S.: 339115
T. H. Tung (Chm)

PEGBOARD SOFTWARE PTY LTD
Suite 1 241 Blackburn Road, Mount Waverley, Melbourne, 3149, VIC, Australia
Tel.: (61) 1300 798 882
Web Site:
http://www.pegboard.com.au
Year Founded: 2000
Sales Range: $1-9.9 Million
Content Management Software
N.A.I.C.S.: 513210
Ashton Wynn-Yorke (Owner & Pres)

PEGMONT MINES LIMITED
13 Oden Street, Port Macquarie, 2444, NSW, Australia
Tel.: (61) 265837747 AU
Web Site:
https://www.pegmont.com.au
PMI—(NSXA)
Assets: $1,319,097
Liabilities: $17,528
Net Worth: $1,301,569
Earnings: ($386,343)
Fiscal Year-end: 12/31/21
Zinc, Copper & Gold Mining Services
N.A.I.C.S.: 212230
Malcolm A. Mayger (Mng Dir)

PEH WERTPAPIER AG
Bettinastrasse 5759, 60325, Frankfurt am Main, Germany
Tel.: (49) 6924747990
Web Site: https://www.peh.de
PEH—(BER)
Sales Range: Less than $1 Million
Financial Advisory Services
N.A.I.C.S.: 523940
Martin Stuerner (Chm-Mgmt Bd & CEO)

PEIJIA MEDICAL LIMITED
8 Zhongtian Street, Suzhou Industrial Park, Suzhou, Jiangsu, China
Tel.: (86) 51281877166 Ky
Web Site:
http://www.peijiamedical.com
Year Founded: 2012
9996—(HKG)
Medical Instrument Mfr
N.A.I.C.S.: 339112
Yi Zhang (Chm & CEO)

Subsidiaries:

Achieva Medical (Shanghai) Co., Ltd. (1)
Suite 301 328 Edison Road, Pilot Free Trade Zone, Shanghai, 201203, China
Tel.: (86) 2158958455
Web Site: http://www.achievamedical.com
Medical Device Mfr & Distr
N.A.I.C.S.: 339112

Achieva Medical (Suzhou) Co., Ltd. (1)
No 8 Zhongtian Street, Suzhou Industrial Park, Suzhou, 215028, Jiangsu, China
Tel.: (86) 51281880766
Medical Device Mfr & Distr
N.A.I.C.S.: 339112

PEINTURES DE PARIS
41 bis rue du Chateau, 92500, Paris, France
Tel.: (33) 147492020
Web Site:
http://www.peinturesdeparis.com
Year Founded: 1950
Paints Mfr
N.A.I.C.S.: 325510

PEIPORT HOLDINGS LTD.
Unit 316 3/F Lakeside 1 Phase Two Science Park Pak Shek Kok, New Territories, Hong Kong, China (Hong Kong)
Tel.: (852) 28859525
Web Site: http://www.peiport.com
2885—(HKG)
Rev.: $31,315,530
Assets: $53,521,823
Liabilities: $8,585,468
Net Worth: $44,936,355
Earnings: ($460,020)
Emp.: 149
Fiscal Year-end: 12/31/22
Optoelectronic Product Mfr
N.A.I.C.S.: 334413
Chin Ching Leung (Sec)

PEIXIN INTERNATIONAL GROUP N.V.
Shuangyang Overseas Chinese Economic-Develop Zone, Luojiang District, Quanzhou, 362012, Fujian, China
Tel.: (86) 595 22458888 NL
Web Site: http://www.peixin.com
Year Founded: 1985
Hygiene Products Mfr
N.A.I.C.S.: 325611
Qiulin Xie (Chm-Mgmt Bd & CEO)

PEKABESKO AD
St 10 Br 44 s Kadino, Ilinden, 1041, Skopje, North Macedonia
Tel.: (389) 22656565
Web Site:
https://www.pekabesko.com.mk
Year Founded: 1972
PKB—(MAC)
Rev.: $98,256,555
Assets: $42,788,083
Liabilities: $15,064,853
Net Worth: $27,723,230
Earnings: $2,633,917
Emp.: 45
Fiscal Year-end: 12/31/23
Veal Product Mfr
N.A.I.C.S.: 424470
Marko Kutrevski (Chm & Mgr-Cigarette Div)

PEKARA 1 MAJ A.D.
2 Oktobar br 92, 26300, Vrsac, Serbia
Tel.: (381) 13831303 RS
Web Site:
https://www.pekara1maj.co.rs
Year Founded: 1946
PKMJ—(BEL)
Sales Range: $1-9.9 Million
Emp.: 90
Bakery Products Mfr
N.A.I.C.S.: 311824
Dragan Rabljac (Exec Dir & Dir)

PEKARA A.D.
Ekstravilan bb, Bela Crkva, Serbia
Tel.: (381) 13 851 526
Year Founded: 2001
Sales Range: Less than $1 Million
Bakery Products Mfr
N.A.I.C.S.: 311813

PEKARSKA INDUSTRIJA A.D.
Milosa Obrenovica 39, Pancevo, Serbia
Tel.: (381) 13 318 400
Year Founded: 1999
PKRP—(BEL)
Sales Range: $1-9.9 Million
Emp.: 182
Bakery Products Mfr
N.A.I.C.S.: 311813
Zorica Mislopoljac (CFO)

PEKER GAYRIMENKUL YATIRIM ORTAKLIGI AS
Cumhuriyet Mah Silahsor Cad Yeniyol Sok No 8, Bomonti Business Center sisli, Istanbul, Turkiye
Tel.: (90) 2124443264
Web Site: https://www.pekergyo.com
Year Founded: 2017
PEKGY—(IST)
Rev.: $30,356,485
Assets: $200,002,203
Liabilities: $87,238,772
Net Worth: $112,763,431
Earnings: $34,023,323
Emp.: 31
Fiscal Year-end: 12/31/23
Construction Services
N.A.I.C.S.: 236220
Hasan Peker (Chm)

PEKING UNIVERSITY RESOURCES HOLDINGS COMPANY LIMITED
Unit 1408 14th Floor Cable TV Tower 9 Hoi Shing Road, Tsuen Wan, New Territories, China (Hong Kong)
Tel.: (852) 2989 1200 BM
Web Site: http://www.pku-resources.com
Rev.: $3,453,230,529
Assets: $5,515,276,200
Liabilities: $5,357,345,316
Net Worth: $157,930,884
Earnings: ($242,314,951)
Emp.: 1,205
Fiscal Year-end: 12/31/19
Computer Products Whslr
N.A.I.C.S.: 423430
Fu Shuang Zheng (Exec Dir)

PELAGIA SHETLAND LIMITED
Point of Scattland, Gremista, Lerwick, ZE1 0PX, Shetland, United Kingdom
Tel.: (44) 4757844400
Web Site: http://pelagia.com
Year Founded: 1985
Fish & Seafood Production
N.A.I.C.S.: 311710
Darren Leask (Sec)

Subsidiaries:

SFP (Shetland Fish Products) Limited (1)
The Factory Heogan, Shetland, Woodford, ZE29EW, United Kingdom
Tel.: (44) 1595820223
Fish Meal Producer
N.A.I.C.S.: 311119

PELANGI INDAH CANINDO TBK
Jl Daan Mogot Km 14 No 700, Jakarta, 11840, Indonesia
Tel.: (62) 216192222
Web Site: https://www.pic.co.id
Year Founded: 1983
PICO—(INDO)
Rev.: $35,575,316
Assets: $47,798,717
Liabilities: $34,489,164
Net Worth: $13,309,553
Earnings: $367,537
Emp.: 171
Fiscal Year-end: 12/31/23
Gas Mfr
N.A.I.C.S.: 325120

PELANGI PUBLISHING GROUP BHD
66 Jalan Pingai Taman Pelangi, 80400, Johor Bahru, Johor Darul Takzim, Malaysia
Tel.: (60) 7331 6288
Web Site:
http://www.pelangipublishing.com
Rev.: $16,747,826
Assets: $34,432,673
Liabilities: $10,566,435
Net Worth: $23,866,238
Earnings: $446,769
Emp.: 400
Fiscal Year-end: 09/30/19
Books Publishing Services
N.A.I.C.S.: 513130
Chuan Sen Huan (Co-Sec)

Subsidiaries:

Dickens Publishing Ltd. (1)
Suite G7-G8 Davina House 137-149 Goswell Road, London, EC1V 7ET, United Kingdom
Tel.: (44) 2072536888
Web Site:
http://www.dickenspublishing.co.uk
Books Publishing Services
N.A.I.C.S.: 513130

P.T. Penerbitan Pelangi Indonesia (1)
Pusat Niaga Terpadu Block 11 No 8D Jl Daan Mogot Raya KM 19 6, 15122,

PELANGI PUBLISHING GROUP BHD

Pelangi Publishing Group Bhd—(Continued)
Tangerang, Banten, Indonesia
Tel.: (62) 21 54365043
Sales Range: $25-49.9 Million
Emp.: 25
Books Publishing Services
N.A.I.C.S.: 513130

Pelangi Education Sdn. Bhd. (1)
4B Jalan Maju Jaya, 80400, Johor Bahru,
Johor Darul Takzim, Malaysia
Tel.: (60) 73313975
Books Publishing Services
N.A.I.C.S.: 513130

Pelangi Multimedia Technologies
Sdn. Bhd. (1)
Lot 8 Jalan P10/10 Kws Perusahaan Bangi,
43650, Bandar Baru Bangi, Selangor Darul
Ehsan, Malaysia
Tel.: (60) 389269553
Web Site: http://pmt.pelangibooks.com
Sales Range: $25-49.9 Million
Emp.: 40
Multimedia Design Services
N.A.I.C.S.: 541430

Pelangi Publishing (Thailand) Co.
Ltd. (1)
1213/364 Soi Latphrao 94 Latphrao Rd
Plubpla, Wangthonglang, Bangkok, 10310,
Thailand
Tel.: (66) 29356368
Web Site: http://www.e-pelangithai.com
Sales Range: $25-49.9 Million
Emp.: 15
Educational Books & Discs Retailer
N.A.I.C.S.: 334610

Penerbitan Pelangi Sdn. Bhd. (1)
66 Jalan Pingai Taman Pelangi, Johor
Bahru, 804000, Johor, Malaysia
Tel.: (60) 73316288
Web Site: http://www.pelangibooks.com
Sales Range: $50-74.9 Million
Emp.: 200
Books Publishing Services
N.A.I.C.S.: 513130

Subsidiary (Domestic):

Comtech Marketing Sdn. Bhd. (2)
No 8 10 Jalan Rosmerah 1/4 Taman Johor
Jaya, 81100, Johor Bahru, Johor, Malaysia
Tel.: (60) 73541219
Printing & Typesetting Services
N.A.I.C.S.: 323111

Pelangi Formpress Sdn. Bhd. (2)
16 Jalan Bukit 2 Kawasan Miel Seri Alam,
81750, Masai, Johor Darul Takzim, Malaysia
Tel.: (60) 73864001
Web Site: http://www.pelangipublishing.com
Sales Range: $25-49.9 Million
Emp.: 16
Printing Services
N.A.I.C.S.: 323111

The Commercial Press Sdn.
Bhd. (1)
Lot 8 Jalan P10/10 Kawasan Perusahaan,
43650, Bangi, Selangor Darul Ehsan,
Malaysia (100%)
Tel.: (60) 389251276
Web Site: http://www.thecompress.com
Sales Range: $25-49.9 Million
Emp.: 40
Printing Services
N.A.I.C.S.: 323111

Tunas Pelangi Sdn. Bhd. (1)
66 Jalan Pingai Taman Pelangi, 80400, Johor Bahru, Johor Darul Takzim, Malaysia
Tel.: (60) 389223993
Web Site: http://www.pelangibooks.com
Sales Range: $50-74.9 Million
Emp.: 200
Books Publishing Services
N.A.I.C.S.: 513130
Wong Mei-Mei (Gen Mgr)

PELANGIO EXPLORATION INC.
82 Richmond Street East, Toronto,
M5C 1P1, ON, Canada
Tel.: (905) 336-3828 AB
Web Site: https://www.pelangio.com

Year Founded: 1997
PGXPF—(OTCIQ)
Rev.: $5,200
Assets: $495,353
Liabilities: $438,548
Net Worth: $56,805
Earnings: ($1,065,773)
Emp.: 4
Fiscal Year-end: 12/31/19
Gold Exploration & Development Services
N.A.I.C.S.: 212220
Ingrid J. Hibbard (Pres & CEO)

PELATRO PLC
49 Queen Victoria Street, London,
EC4N 4SA, United Kingdom
Tel.: (44) 2076531554 UK
Web Site: http://www.pelatro.com
Year Founded: 2017
PTRO—(AIM)
Sales Range: $1-9.9 Million
Emp.: 105
Software Development Services
N.A.I.C.S.: 541511
Subash Menon (Co-Founder, CEO & Mng Dir)

PELHAMS LIMITED
Pelhams House 3rd Floor 94/96
Rober Mugabe Road, Harare, Zimbabwe
Tel.: (263) 4 705271
Year Founded: 1949
Household Appliance & Furniture Mfr
N.A.I.C.S.: 337121

PELICAN INTERNATIONAL INC.
1000 Place paul-Kane, Laval, H7C
2T2, QC, Canada
Tel.: (450) 664-1222
Web Site: http://pelicansport.com
Water Sport Equipment Mfr
N.A.I.C.S.: 713940
Christian Elie (Co-Owner)

Subsidiaries:

Advanced Elements, Inc. (1)
5370 Gateway Plz Dr, Benicia, CA 94510
Tel.: (707) 745-9800
Web Site:
http://www.advancedelements.com
Sporting & Recreational Goods & Supplies
Merchant Whslr
N.A.I.C.S.: 423910
Clay Haller (Pres)

PELICAN RESOURCES LIMITED
Level 11 BGC Centre 28 The Esplanade, Perth, 6000, WA, Australia
Tel.: (61) 64249299
Web Site:
http://www.pelicanresources.com.au
Sales Range: Less than $1 Million
Gold, Nickel & Iron Mining Services
N.A.I.C.S.: 212220
Antonio Torresan (Exec Dir)

Subsidiaries:

Sibuyan Nickel Properties Dev.
Corp. (1)
Manila Memorial Bldg 2283 Pasong Tamo
Ext, Makati, Philippines
Tel.: (63) 28171342
Mineral Mining & Exploration Services
N.A.I.C.S.: 212390

Sunrise Exploration Pty Ltd (1)
Level 1 284 Oxford St, Leederville, 6007,
WA, Australia
Tel.: (61) 892421166
Sales Range: $50-74.9 Million
Mineral Mining & Exploration Services
N.A.I.C.S.: 212390
John Palermo (Mng Dir)

PELIKAN INTERNATIONAL CORPORATION BERHAD
No 9 Jalan Pemaju U1/15 Seksyen
U1 Hicom Glenmarie Industrial Park,
40150, Shah Alam, Selangor Darul
Ehsan, Malaysia
Tel.: (60) 355695511 MY
Web Site: https://www.pelikan.com
Year Founded: 1838
PELIKAN—(KLS)
Rev.: $289,297,800
Assets: $311,754,218
Liabilities: $205,818,030
Net Worth: $105,936,188
Earnings: $23,030,618
Emp.: 1,558
Fiscal Year-end: 12/31/21
Writing Instrument, Stationery & Art
Product Mfr
N.A.I.C.S.: 339940
Siew Chuan Chua (Co-Sec)

Subsidiaries:

Molkari Vermietungsgesellschaft mbH
& Co. Objekt Falkensee KG (1)
Am Borsigturm 100, 13507, Berlin, Germany
Tel.: (49) 3043930
Building Rental Services
N.A.I.C.S.: 531110

Pelikan (Thailand) Co. Ltd. (1)
1427 Kanchanaphisek Road, Bang Khae
Nuea Subdistrict Bang Khae District, Bangkok, 10160, Thailand
Tel.: (66) 280414159
Web Site: https://www.pelikan.co.th
Colour Brush & Cryon Mfr
N.A.I.C.S.: 339940

Pelikan Argentina S.A. (1)
Stationery Product Mfr
N.A.I.C.S.: 322230

Pelikan Hardcopy Holding AG (1)
Haldenstrasse 28, 8620, Wetzikon, Switzerland
Tel.: (41) 417903883
Web Site: http://www.pelikan-hardcopy.com
Printing Machinery Mfr
N.A.I.C.S.: 333248

Subsidiary (Domestic):

Pelikan Hardcopy Production AG (2)
Haldenstrasse 28, 8620, Wetzikon, Switzerland
Tel.: (41) 44 986 12 62
Web Site: http://www.pelikan-hardcopy.com
Printing Supplies Development Services
N.A.I.C.S.: 541715
Flaeio Monti (Gen Mgr)

Pelikan Holding AG (1)
Chaltenbodenstrasse 8, 8834, Schindellegi,
Switzerland (96.49%)
Tel.: (41) 44 786 7020
Web Site: http://www.pelikan.ch
Rev.: $328,949,605
Assets: $206,817,517
Liabilities: $184,276,553
Net Worth: $22,540,964
Earnings: $15,316,576
Emp.: 1,264
Fiscal Year-end: 12/31/2014
Holding Company; Office, Arts & Crafts
Supplies Mfr & Whslr
N.A.I.C.S.: 551112
Hooi Keat Loo (Pres)

Subsidiary (Domestic):

Pelikan (Schweiz) AG (2)
Alpenblickstrasse 7, 8853, Lachen,
Switzerland (100%)
Tel.: (41) 447867020
Web Site: https://www.pelikan.com
Office, Arts & Crafts Supplies Mfr & Whslr
N.A.I.C.S.: 339940
Thomas Pister (Mng Dir)

Subsidiary (Non-US):

Pelikan AG (2)
Am Borsigturm 100, 13507, Berlin,
Germany (51.4%)
Tel.: (49) 30 4393 0

INTERNATIONAL PUBLIC

Web Site: http://www.pelikan-ag.com
Sales Range: $125-149.9 Million
Emp.: 1,171
Holding Company; Pulp & Paper Mills Operator & Paper Products Whslr
N.A.I.C.S.: 551112
Hooi Keat Loo (Member-Mgmt Bd)

Subsidiary (Domestic):

Convex Schreibwaren-Handels
GmbH (3)
Am Borsigturm 100, 13507, Berlin, Germany
Tel.: (49) 30 43933511
Stationery Product Distr
N.A.I.C.S.: 424120
Karsten Tews (Gen Mgr)

Subsidiary (Non-US):

DELMET PROD srl (3)
Industriei nr 3, Buftea, 070000, Ilfov, Romania
Tel.: (40) 31 824 1081
Web Site: https://www.delmet.ro
Sales Range: $25-49.9 Million
Emp.: 29
Stationery Article Mfr
N.A.I.C.S.: 327110

Subsidiary (Domestic):

Falken Office Products GmbH (3)
Am Bahnhof 5, 03185, Peitz, Germany
Tel.: (49) 35601840
Web Site: http://www.falken-office-products.com
Sales Range: $125-149.9 Million
Emp.: 260
Stationery & Office Suppliers Mfr & Supplier
N.A.I.C.S.: 322230
Marcus Peters (Dir-Sls)

Subsidiary (Non-US):

Herlitz Benelux BV (3)
Hoge Bergen 15, 4704 RH, Roosendaal,
Netherlands
Tel.: (31) 165574242
Web Site: http://www.herlitz.sk
Sales Range: $25-49.9 Million
Emp.: 15
Stationery & Office Supplies Sales
N.A.I.C.S.: 424120

Subsidiary (Non-US):

Herlitz Bulgaria EooD (4)
10 Poruchik Nedelcho Bonchev str, Iskar
Railway Station, 1528, Sofia, Bulgaria
Tel.: (359) 29732020
Web Site: http://www.herlitzbg.com
Stationery Products Mfr & Distr
N.A.I.C.S.: 322230

Subsidiary (Non-US):

Herlitz Hungaria Kft. (3)
Campona utca 1, Campona utca 1 - 6-os
epulet, 1225, Budapest, Hungary
Tel.: (36) 613052000
Web Site: https://www.shop.herlitz.hu
Sales Range: $1-9.9 Million
Emp.: 100
Stationery & Office Supplies Sales
N.A.I.C.S.: 424120

Subsidiary (Domestic):

Herlitz PBS AG (3)
Strasse der Einheit 142-148, 14612, Falkensee, Germany
Tel.: (49) 332 2260
Web Site: https://www.herlitz.de
Stationery & Office Supplies Mfr
N.A.I.C.S.: 322230

Subsidiary (Non-US):

Herlitz Romania srl (3)
Strada Depozitelor no 22, Judetul Mures,
540240, Targu Mures, Mures, Romania
Tel.: (40) 735003004
Web Site: https://www.herlitz.ro
Sales Range: $1-9.9 Million
Emp.: 88
Stationery & Office Supplies Sales
N.A.I.C.S.: 424120

Herlitz Slovakia s.r.o. (3)

Odborarska 52, 83102, Bratislava, Slovakia
Tel.: (421) 244461766
Web Site: http://www.herlitz.sk
Sales Range: $1-9.9 Million
Emp.: 17
Stationery & Office Supplies Sales
N.A.I.C.S.: 424120

Herlitz Spol. s.r.o. (3)
Bucharova 1281/2, PO Box 101, Stodulky, 158 00, Prague, Cestlice, Czech Republic
Tel.: (420) 29 654 4230
Web Site: https://www.herlitz.de
Sales Range: $1-9.9 Million
Emp.: 34
Stationery & Office Supplies Sales
N.A.I.C.S.: 424120

Subsidiary (Non-US):

Herlitz Spolka z.o.o. (4)
Baranowo ul Szamotulska 2, 62-081, Przezmierowo, Poland
Tel.: (48) 616501100
Web Site: http://www.herlitz.de
Consumer Goods Distr
N.A.I.C.S.: 424990

Subsidiary (Non-US):

Herlitz UK Ltd. (5)
Saint Marys Industrial Park, Hyde, SK14 4HN, United Kingdom
Tel.: (44) 161 367 7305
Web Site: http://www.herlitz.de
Sales Range: $1-9.9 Million
Emp.: 35
Stationery Product Distr
N.A.I.C.S.: 424120

Subsidiary (Non-US):

Pelikan Benelux N.V./S.A. (3)
Stationsstraat 43, 1702, Groot-Bijgaarden, Belgium
Tel.: (32) 24818700
Web Site: https://www.pelikan.com
Sales Range: $25-49.9 Million
Emp.: 20
Pens Producer
N.A.I.C.S.: 339940
Sven Vergauwen (Mng Dir)

Pelikan Colombia S.A.S. (3)
Carrera 65B N 18A-17, Bogota, DC, Colombia
Tel.: (57) 3105762817
Web Site: https://pelikancolombia.com
Stationery Product Distr
N.A.I.C.S.: 424120

Affiliate (Non-US):

Pelikan Japan K.K. (3)
1-1-12 Ueno, Taito-ku, Tokyo, 110-0005, Japan (25%)
Tel.: (81) 338366541
Web Site: http://www.pelikan.com
Stationery Product Distr
N.A.I.C.S.: 424120

Pelikan Mexico S.A. de C.V. (3)
Street Carretera A Tehuacan 1033, 72220, Puebla, Mexico (49.9%)
Tel.: (52) 222 309 8000
Web Site: http://www.pelikan.com
Stationery Products Mfr & Distr
N.A.I.C.S.: 322230

Subsidiary (Domestic):

Pelikan Vertriebsgesellschaft mbH & Co. KG (3)
Werftstrasse 9, 30163, Hannover, Germany
Tel.: (49) 51169690
Web Site: http://www.pelikan.com
School & Office Suplies Whslr
N.A.I.C.S.: 424120
Torsten Jahn (Mng Dir)

Susy Card GmbH (3)
Strasse der Einheit 142-148, 14612, Falkensee, Germany
Tel.: (49) 3322260
Web Site: http://www.susy-card.com
Stationery Mfr & Supplier
N.A.I.C.S.: 322230

Subsidiary (Non-US):

Pelikan Asia Sdn. Bhd. (2)

No 9 Jalan Pemaju U1/15 Seksyen U1 Hicom Glenmarie Industrial Park, 40150, Shah Alam, Selangor Darul Ehsan, Malaysia
Tel.: (60) 355695511
Sales Range: $25-49.9 Million
Emp.: 100
Stationery Product Whslr
N.A.I.C.S.: 424120
Hooi Keat Loo (Pres)

Pelikan Austria GesmbH (2)
Dr Kraitschekgasse 7-9, 2486, Pottendorf, Austria (100%)
Tel.: (43) 2236440000
Web Site: http://www.pelikan.at
Office Supplies Distr
N.A.I.C.S.: 424120

Pelikan PBS-Produktion Verwaltungs-GmbH (2)
Pelikanstrasse 11, 31228, Peine, Germany (100%)
Tel.: (49) 51712990
Web Site: http://www.pelikan.com
Sales Range: $150-199.9 Million
Office Supplies Distr
N.A.I.C.S.: 424120

Pelikan Italia S.p.A. (1)
Street Street Antonio Cechov 48, 20151, Milan, Italy
Stationery Product Mfr
N.A.I.C.S.: 322230
Emanuele Crespi (Mgr-IT & Gen Svcs)

Pelikan Middle East FZE (1)
Street Block Q4-Office 202 Saif Zone, 120318, Sharjah, United Arab Emirates
Tel.: (971) 65574571
Stationery Product Mfr
N.A.I.C.S.: 322230
Shinas Muhammed (Mgr-Acct)

Pelikan N.V./S.A (1)
Street Stationsstraat 43, 1702, Groot-Bijgaarden, Belgium
Tel.: (32) 24818700
Stationery Product Mfr
N.A.I.C.S.: 322230

Pelikan PBS-Produktionsgesellschaft mbH & Co. KG (1)
Street Pelikanstrasse 11 Vohrum, 31228, Peine, Germany
Tel.: (49) 51712990
Stationery Product Mfr
N.A.I.C.S.: 322230

Pelikan Singapore Pte. Ltd. (1)
Street 18 Tannery Lane 01-03 Lian Tong Building, Singapore, 347780, Singapore
Tel.: (65) 62585231
Stationery Product Mfr
N.A.I.C.S.: 322230

Pelikan Taiwan Co., Ltd. (1)
Street 1 F 32 Lane 21 Hwang Chi Street, Taipei, Taiwan
Tel.: (886) 288665818
Stationery Product Mfr
N.A.I.C.S.: 322230

Pelikan-Artline Pty., Ltd. (1)
2 Coronation Ave, Kings Park, 2148, NSW, Australia
Tel.: (61) 296740900
Web Site: http://www.pelikanartline.com.au
Office Supplies Distr; Owned 50% by Pelikan International Corp Berhad & 50% by ACCO Brands Corporation
N.A.I.C.S.: 459410

eCom Logistik GmbH (1)
Strasse der Einheit 142-148, 14612, Falkensee, Germany
Tel.: (49) 3322260
Emp.: 170
Logistic Services
N.A.I.C.S.: 541614
Sebastian Fechner (Mgr-Sls)

PELION GREEN FUTURE GMBH
Leopoldstraße 20, 80802, Munich, Germany
Tel.: (49) 17684848418
Web Site:
https://www.peliongreenfuture.com

Year Founded: 2016
Renewable Energy Power Generation
N.A.I.C.S.: 221114

PELION S.A.
Ul Zbaszynska 3, 91-342, Lodz, Poland
Tel.: (48) 422007474
Web Site: http://www.pelion.eu
Year Founded: 1990
Sales Range: $1-4.9 Billion
Pharmaceuticals, Herbs & Cosmetics Retailer & Distr
N.A.I.C.S.: 456110
Jacek Szwajcowski (Pres & Member-Mgmt Bd)

Subsidiaries:

PGF - Bydgaszcz S.A. (1)
Ul Magazynowa 13, 85-790, Bydgoszcz, Poland
Tel.: (48) 50 323 6231
Pharmaceutical Product Whslr
N.A.I.C.S.: 424210

PGF - Lodz Sp. z o.o. (1)
Ul Zbaszynska 3, 91-342, Lodz, Poland
Tel.: (48) 426133301
Emp.: 50
Pharmaceutical Product Whslr
N.A.I.C.S.: 424210

PGF Aptekarz Sp. z o.o. (1)
Ul Boya Zelenskiego 2, 35-105, Rzeszow, Poland
Tel.: (48) 17 875 2200
Pharmaceutical Product Whslr
N.A.I.C.S.: 424210

PGF Cefarm Krakow Sp. z o.o. (1)
Ul Albatrosow 1, 30-716, Krakow, Poland
Tel.: (48) 12 646 9405
Pharmaceutical Product Whslr
N.A.I.C.S.: 424210

PGF Cefarm Lublin Sp. z o.o. (1)
Al Spokiziekzosci Pracy 78, 20-147, Lublin, Poland
Tel.: (48) 81 535 3200
Pharmaceutical Product Whslr
N.A.I.C.S.: 424210

PGF Cefarm Poznan Sp. z o.o. (1)
Ul Wladyslawa Wegorka 15, 60-318, Poznan, Poland
Tel.: (48) 61 861 2600
Pharmaceutical Product Whslr
N.A.I.C.S.: 424210

PGF Cefarm Sp. z o.o. (1)
Ul Spokiziekza 25, 11-001, Dywity, Poland
Tel.: (48) 89 511 9202
Pharmaceutical Product Whslr
N.A.I.C.S.: 424210

PGF Sp. z o.o. (1)
Ul Nawagrodzka 151 A, 18-400, Lomza, Poland
Tel.: (48) 86 215 5656
Pharmaceutical Product Whslr
N.A.I.C.S.: 424210

PGF Urtica Sp. z o.o. (1)
Ul Krzemieniecka 120, 54-613, Wroclaw, Poland
Tel.: (48) 71 782 6601
Web Site: http://www.urtica.com.pl
Hospital Supplies Sales
N.A.I.C.S.: 423450

Pharmapoint Sp. z o.o. (1)
ul Zbaszynska 3, Lodz, 91342, Poland
Tel.: (48) 42 200 8016
Web Site: http://www.pharmapoint.pl
Emp.: 63
Pharmaceutical & Cosmetic Products Whslr
N.A.I.C.S.: 424210
Jednej Kosinski (CEO)

Polska Grupa Farmaceutyczna - HURT Sp. z o.o. (1)
ul Zbaszynska 3, 91-342, Lodz, Poland
Tel.: (48) 42 200 7444
Web Site: http://www.pgf.com.pl
Pharmaceutical & Cosmetic Products Whslr
N.A.I.C.S.: 424210

PELISTERKA AD
Boulevard Koco Racin 97, 1000, Skopje, North Macedonia
Tel.: (389) 23221109
Web Site: https://www.pelisterka.mk
LOZP—(MAC)
Rev.: $8,934,664
Assets: $19,843,367
Liabilities: $10,056,364
Net Worth: $9,787,003
Earnings: $58,537
Fiscal Year-end: 12/31/23
Electrical & Electronic Product Mfr
N.A.I.C.S.: 336320

PELLICANO PTY LTD
Level 2 395 Ferntree Gully Rd, Mount Waverley, 3149, VIC, Australia
Tel.: (61) 385624300
Web Site:
http://www.pellicano.com.au
Year Founded: 1967
Sales Range: $50-74.9 Million
Emp.: 100
Asset & Property Management Services; Commercial & Industrial Building Construction
N.A.I.C.S.: 525990
Antonio Pellicano (Mng Dir)

Subsidiaries:

Pellicano Builders Pty Ltd (1)
395 Ferntree Gully Road Level 2, Mt Waverley, Melbourne, 3149, VIC, Australia
Tel.: (61) 385413400
Web Site: http://www.pellicano.com.au
Sales Range: $50-74.9 Million
Emp.: 54
Commercial & Institutional Building Construction
N.A.I.C.S.: 236220

PELORUS PRIVATE EQUITY LIMITED
Level 1 50 Yeo Street, PO Box 612, Neutral Bay, 2089, NSW, Australia
Tel.: (61) 290338688
Web Site: http://www.pelorus.com.au
Rev.: $2,033,712
Assets: $31,102,717
Liabilities: $15,297,848
Net Worth: $15,804,869
Earnings: ($414,197)
Emp.: 20
Fiscal Year-end: 06/30/19
Real Estate Investment Services
N.A.I.C.S.: 531390
Joseph Glew (Chm)

Subsidiaries:

Planloc Pty Ltd (1)
Level 6 80 Alfred St S, Milsons Point, 2061, NSW, Australia
Tel.: (61) 299691095
Financial Services
N.A.I.C.S.: 523910

PELOTON CAPITAL MANAGEMENT, INC.
8 King Street East Suite 1100, Toronto, M5C 1B5, ON, Canada
Tel.: (647) 957-8320
Web Site:
http://www.pelotonmanagement.com
Privater Equity Firm
N.A.I.C.S.: 523999
Nora Nestor (CFO)

Subsidiaries:

123Dentist, Inc. (1)
4321 Still Creek Drive Suite 200, Burnaby, V5C 6S7, BC, Canada
Web Site: https://www.123dentist.com
Dental Services
N.A.I.C.S.: 339116

Subsidiary (Domestic):

Altima Dental Canada Inc. (2)

PELOTON CAPITAL MANAGEMENT, INC.

Peloton Capital Management, Inc.—(Continued)

1 Yorkdale Road Suite 320, Toronto, M6A 3A1, ON, Canada
Tel.: (416) 785-1828
Web Site: http://www.altimadental.com
Sales Range: $25-49.9 Million
Emp.: 300
Dental Clinics Operator
N.A.I.C.S.: 621210
George Christodoulou *(Founder & Co-CEO)*

Glass, Lewis & Co., LLC (1)
255 California St Ste 1100, San Francisco, CA 94111
Tel.: (415) 678-4110
Web Site: http://www.glasslewis.com
Sales Range: $75-99.9 Million
Emp.: 300
Shareholder Services Research & Analysis
N.A.I.C.S.: 541910
Katherine Rabin *(CEO)*

Subsidiary (Non-US):

CGI Glass Lewis Pty Limited (2)
Suite 503 Level 5 255 George Street, Sydney, 2000, NSW, Australia
Tel.: (61) 2 9299 9266
Web Site: http://www.glasslewis.com
Emp.: 10
Shareholder Services Research & Analysis
N.A.I.C.S.: 541910
Aaron Bertinetti *(Gen Mgr)*

Glass Lewis Europe, Ltd. (2)
15 Henry Street, Limerick, Ireland
Tel.: (353) 61 292800
Shareholder Services Research & Analysis
N.A.I.C.S.: 541910

PELOTON MINERALS CORPORATION

380 Wellington Street Tower B 6th Floor, London, N6A 5B5, ON, Canada
Tel.: (519) 964-2836
Web Site:
  https://pelotonminerals.com
Year Founded: 2000
PMCCF—(OTCQB)
Assets: $114,391
Liabilities: $2,847,902
Net Worth: ($2,733,511)
Earnings: ($2,137,063)
Emp.: 3
Fiscal Year-end: 12/31/22
Mineral Exploration & Mining Services
N.A.I.C.S.: 212220
John F. O'Donnell *(Chm)*

PELSIS HOLDING (UK) LIMITED

Sterling House Grimbald Crag Close, Knaresborough, HG5 8PJ, North Yorkshire, United Kingdom
Tel.: (44) 8009885359
Web Site: http://www.pelsis.com
Year Founded: 2009
Holding Company
N.A.I.C.S.: 551112

Subsidiaries:

Pelsis Limited (1)
Sterling House Grimbald Crag Close, Knaresborough, HG5 8PJ, United Kingdom
Tel.: (44) 8009885359
Web Site: https://www.pelsis.com
Sales Range: $25-49.9 Million
Emp.: 100
Washroom Hygiene Product Mfr & Supplier
N.A.I.C.S.: 325612
Peter Mangion *(Mng Dir)*

Subsidiary (US):

Bird B Gone, Inc. (2)
1921 E Edinger Ave, Santa Ana, CA 92705
Tel.: (949) 472-3122
Web Site: http://www.birdbgone.com
Soap & Detergent Mfr
N.A.I.C.S.: 325611
Bruce Donoho *(Founder & CEO)*

Holding (Domestic):

SX Environmental Supplies Limited (2)
Unit 2 Scimitar Park Courtauld Road, Basildon, SS13 1ND, Essex, United Kingdom
Tel.: (44) 1702 524040
Web Site: http://www.pestcontrolonline.com
Sales Range: $50-74.9 Million
Emp.: 17
Pest Control Product Distr
N.A.I.C.S.: 424690
Mark Sutton *(Gen Mgr)*

PELWATTE DAIRY INDUSTRIES LIMITED

27 Melbourne Avenue, Colombo, 04, Sri Lanka
Tel.: (94) 112501196
Web Site:
  http://www.pelwattesugar.com
Dairy Products Mfr
N.A.I.C.S.: 311514
M.J.C. Amarasuriya *(Chm)*

PEMA 2B

19 Blvd du Parc, 92200, Neuilly-sur-Seine, France
Tel.: (33) 1 41 43 83 00
Web Site: http://www.pema-group.com
Year Founded: 1942
Rev.: $27,000,000
Emp.: 40
N.A.I.C.S.: 541810
Jean-Louis Courtois *(Pres)*

PEMA HOLDING AG

Gotthardstrasse 31, 6460, Altdorf, Switzerland
Tel.: (41) 41 875 11 00
Holding Company
N.A.I.C.S.: 551112
Ulrich Graf *(Chm)*

Subsidiaries:

Daetwyler Cabling Solutions AG (1)
Gotthardstrasse 31, 6460, Altdorf, Switzerland (100%)
Tel.: (41) 418751122
Web Site: http://www.cabling.datwyler.com
Sales Range: $100-124.9 Million
Emp.: 500
Fabricated Wire Product Mfr
N.A.I.C.S.: 332618
Johannes Mueller *(CEO)*

Subsidiary (Non-US):

Daetwyler (Suzhou) Cabling Systems Co. Ltd (2)
Block 31 #15 Dong Fu Road Suzhou Singapore Industrial Park, 215123, Suzhou, China (100%)
Tel.: (86) 51262653600
Web Site: http://www.datwyler-china.com
Sales Range: $25-49.9 Million
Emp.: 100
Fiber Optic Cable Mfr
N.A.I.C.S.: 335921

Daetwyler (Thelma) Cables & Systems Pte Ltd (2)
30 Toh Guan Road 01-01A, Singapore, 608840, Singapore (100%)
Tel.: (65) 68631166
Web Site: http://www.tabling.datwyler.com
Sales Range: $25-49.9 Million
Emp.: 21
Fabricated Wire Product Mfr
N.A.I.C.S.: 332618
Eyphan Lim *(CEO)*

Daetwyler Cables+Systems (Shanghai) Co. Ltd (2)
Bldg 16 No 1-111 Kang Qiao Dong Rd, Kang Qiao Industrial Zone Pudo, 201319, Shanghai, China (100%)
Tel.: (86) 2168130066
Web Site: http://www.datwyler-china.com
Sales Range: $25-49.9 Million
Emp.: 100
Cable Networks
N.A.I.C.S.: 516210

Daetwyler Kabel+Systeme GmbH (2)
Lilienthalstrasse 7, Hallbergmoos, 85399, Neufahrn, Germany (100%)
Tel.: (49) 816595010
Sales Range: $25-49.9 Million
Emp.: 40
Nonferrous Metal Rolling Drawing & Extruding
N.A.I.C.S.: 331491

Daetwyler Holding AG (1)
Gotthardstrasse 31, CH-6460, Altdorf, Switzerland
Tel.: (41) 418751100
Web Site: https://www.datwyler.com
Rev.: $1,368,552,419
Assets: $1,427,145,240
Liabilities: $968,148,328
Net Worth: $458,996,912
Earnings: $79,391,491
Emp.: 8,056
Fiscal Year-end: 12/31/2023
Holding Company
N.A.I.C.S.: 551112
Paul J. Halg *(Chm)*

Subsidiary (US):

Columbia Engineered Rubber, Inc. (2)
875 Center Dr, Vandalia, OH 45377
Tel.: (937) 890-7464
Web Site: http://www.columbiaerd.com
Sales Range: $75-99.9 Million
Emp.: 70
Custom Rubber Component Mfr & Distr
N.A.I.C.S.: 326299
Mark Bueltel *(Co-Pres & Mgr-Engrg)*

Subsidiary (Non-US):

Daetwyler (UK) Ltd (2)
Unit B Omega Enterprise Park, Electron Way, Chandlers Ford, SO53 4SE, Hamps, United Kingdom (100%)
Tel.: (44) 2380279999
Web Site: http://www.datwyler.com
Sales Range: $25-49.9 Million
Emp.: 7
Fabricated Wire Product Mfr
N.A.I.C.S.: 332618

Daetwyler Inter GmbH (2)
Allerfeldstrasse 5, 31832, Springe, Germany (100%)
Tel.: (49) 504591090
Web Site: http://www.daetwyler-rubber.com
Sales Range: $25-49.9 Million
Emp.: 30
Industrial Building Construction
N.A.I.C.S.: 236210

Daetwyler Pharma Packaging Deutschland GmbH (2)
Tornadostrasse 4, 76307, Karlsbad, Ittersbach, Germany
Tel.: (49) 72489230
Web Site: http://www.datwyler.com
Medicinal Rubber & Aluminum Closures Mfr
N.A.I.C.S.: 326299

Daetwyler Pharma Packaging Italy Srl (2)
Via Bernarde 11, Montegaldella, 36040, Vicenza, Italy (100%)
Tel.: (39) 0444737200
Fabricated Wire Product Mfr
N.A.I.C.S.: 332618

Subsidiary (US):

Daetwyler Pharma Packaging USA (2)
9012 Pennsuaken Hwy, Pennsauken, NJ 08110 (100%)
Tel.: (856) 663-2202
Web Site: http://www.datwyler.com
Sales Range: $50-74.9 Million
Emp.: 220
Rubber Products Mfr
N.A.I.C.S.: 326299

Subsidiary (Domestic):

Daetwyler Teco Holding AG (2)
Gotthardstrasse 31, 6460, Altdorf, Switzerland (100%)
Tel.: (41) 418751122
Web Site: http://www.daetwyler-cables.com

INTERNATIONAL PUBLIC

Sales Range: $150-199.9 Million
Emp.: 300
Industrial Machinery & Equipment Whslr
N.A.I.C.S.: 423830

Subsidiary (Non-US):

Distrelec Gesellschaft mbH (2)
Trestner Strasse 47, 1200, Vienna, Austria (100%)
Tel.: (43) 13341010
Web Site: http://www.distrelec.ch
Sales Range: $25-49.9 Million
Emp.: 15
Electronic Parts & Equipment Whslr
N.A.I.C.S.: 423690

Distrelec Italia Srl (2)
Via Canova 40-42, 20020, Lainate, Italy (100%)
Tel.: (39) 02937551
Web Site: http://www.distrelec.it
Electronic Parts & Equipment Whslr
N.A.I.C.S.: 423690

Helvoet Pharma N.V. (2)
Industriepark 1519, B 3570, Alken, Belgium (100%)
Tel.: (32) 0011590811
Web Site: http://www.helvoetpharma.be
Sales Range: $200-249.9 Million
Emp.: 500
Mfr of Rubber Closures & Aluminum & Plastic Caps for Pharmaceutical Packaging
N.A.I.C.S.: 326199

Subsidiary (Non-US):

Helvoet (Tilburg) B.V (3)
Centaurusweg 146, 5015 TA, Tilburg, Netherlands
Tel.: (31) 135478600
Sales Range: $25-49.9 Million
Emp.: 100
Plastics Product Mfr
N.A.I.C.S.: 326199

Subsidiary (Domestic):

Kaved AG (2)
Gotthardstrasse 31, Altdorf, 6460, Switzerland (100%)
Tel.: (41) 418753800
Web Site: http://www.daetwyler.com
Emp.: 400
Miscellaneous Electrical Equipment & Component Mfr
N.A.I.C.S.: 335999
Johannes Mueller *(Mgr)*

Mader Technic AG (2)
Gotthardstrasse 31, 6460, Altdorf, Switzerland (100%)
Tel.: (41) 418751122
Web Site: http://www.daetwyler-cables.com
Sales Range: $250-299.9 Million
Emp.: 700
Refrigeration Equipment & Supplies Whslr
N.A.I.C.S.: 423740

Subsidiary (Non-US):

Matrijzenmakerij Maro B.V. (2)
Scherpdeel 30, 4703RJ, Roosendaal, Netherlands (100%)
Tel.: (31) 165553160
Web Site: http://www.daetwyler.ch
Sales Range: $25-49.9 Million
Emp.: 15
Unclassified Establishments
N.A.I.C.S.: 811210
Erik Thielens *(Mng Dir)*

Subsidiary (US):

Parco Inc. (2)
1801 S Archibald Ave, Ontario, CA 91761
Tel.: (909) 947-2200
Web Site: http://www.parcoinc.com
Sales Range: $125-149.9 Million
Emp.: 200
Gaskets & Sealing Devices
N.A.I.C.S.: 339991
Debra Kiefert *(Controller)*

Subsidiary (Domestic):

Proditec AG (2)
Grabenstrasse No 6, Naenikon, 8606, Zurich, Switzerland (100%)
Tel.: (41) 448071111

Web Site: http://www.proditec.ch
Sales Range: $25-49.9 Million
Emp.: 50
Electronic Parts & Equipment Whslr
N.A.I.C.S.: 423690
Jurg Detzel *(Mng Dir)*

Subsidiary (Non-US):

Schuricht Distrelec GmbH (2)
Lise-Meitner-Str 4, 28359, Bremen,
Germany (100%)
Tel.: (49) 1805223435
Web Site: http://www.distrelec.de
Sales Range: $25-49.9 Million
Emp.: 60
Electronic Parts & Equipment Whslr
N.A.I.C.S.: 423690
Jorg-Lothar Loch *(Mng Dir)*

Wachendorf GmbH (2)
Engeler Strasse 29, Hannover,
Germany (100%)
Tel.: (49) 424793090
Web Site: http://www.wachendorf.de
Sales Range: $25-49.9 Million
Emp.: 10
Custom Computer Programming Services
N.A.I.C.S.: 541511
Heinrich Wachendorf *(Mng Dir)*

PEMBINA PIPELINE CORPORATION
Ste 4000 585-8th Ave SW, Calgary,
T2P 1G1, AB, Canada
Tel.: (403) 231-7500 AB
Web Site: https://www.pembina.com
Year Founded: 1954
PBA—(NYSE)
Rev.: $6,740,784,517
Assets: $24,095,442,122
Liabilities: $12,414,124,252
Net Worth: $11,681,317,870
Earnings: $1,223,313,880
Emp.: 2,837
Fiscal Year-end: 12/31/23
Railways Transportation Services
N.A.I.C.S.: 488210
J. Scott Burrows *(Pres & CEO)*

Subsidiaries:

Alliance Pipeline L.P. (1)
6385 Old Shady Oak Rd Ste 150, Eden
Prairie, MN 55344
Tel.: (952) 944-3183
Web Site: http://www.alliancepipeline.com
Pipeline Transportation Services
N.A.I.C.S.: 486990
Brian Troicuk *(Mgr-Regulatory Affairs)*

Aux Sable Canada L.P (1)
8th Ave Place, Calgary, T2P 3H5, AB,
Canada
Tel.: (403) 231-7500
Web Site: http://www.auxsable.com
Pipeline Transportation Services
N.A.I.C.S.: 486990

Kinder Morgan Canada Limited (1)
300 5th Avenue SW Suite 3000, Calgary,
T2P 5J2, AB, Canada
Tel.: (403) 514-6400
Web Site:
   http://www.kindermorgancanadaltd.com
Rev.: $281,313,886
Assets: $3,935,755,712
Liabilities: $3,281,579,987
Net Worth: $654,175,725
Earnings: ($713,326,404)
Emp.: 153
Fiscal Year-end: 12/31/2018
Pipeline System Development Services
N.A.I.C.S.: 213112

Subsidiary (Domestic):

KM Canada Rail Holdings GP
Limited (2)
2700-300 5 Ave SW, Calgary, T2P 5J2, AB,
Canada
Tel.: (403) 514-6400
Holding Company
N.A.I.C.S.: 551112

Pembina Midstream Limited
Partnership (1)
700 9 Ave SW, Calgary, T2P 3V4, AB,
Canada
Tel.: (403) 231-7500
Web Site: http://www.pembina.com
Pipeline Oil Transmission Services
N.A.I.C.S.: 486990

Pembina NGL Corporation (1)
4000 585 - 8th Avenue SW, Calgary, T2P
1G1, AB, Canada (100%)
Tel.: (403) 231-7500
Web Site: https://www.pembina.com
Sales Range: $125-149.9 Million
Emp.: 286
Natural Gas Liquids Infrastructure & Logistics Services
N.A.I.C.S.: 237120

PEMBRIDGE RESOURCES PLC
154 Southgate Street Discovery
House, Gloucester, GL1 2EX, United
Kingdom
Tel.: (44) 1452541285
Web Site:
   https://www.pembridgeresource.com
Year Founded: 2010
PERE—(AIM)
Rev.: $58,278,000
Assets: $74,345,000
Liabilities: $85,167,000
Net Worth: ($10,822,000)
Earnings: ($27,275,000)
Emp.: 107
Fiscal Year-end: 12/31/20
Metal Mining
N.A.I.C.S.: 212290
Gati Al-Jebouri *(Chm & CEO)*

PEMBROKE VCT PLC
3 Cadogan Gate, London, SW1X
0AS, United Kingdom
Tel.: (44) 2077666900 UK
Web Site:
   https://www.pembrokevct.com
Year Founded: 2012
PEMB—(LSE)
Assets: $270,249,525
Liabilities: $2,072,637
Net Worth: $268,176,888
Earnings: ($11,492,586)
Fiscal Year-end: 03/31/23
Portfolio Management & Investment
Advice
N.A.I.C.S.: 523940
Andrew Wolfson *(Mng Dir & CIO)*

PEMTRON CORPORATION
1406 Byucksan Digital Valley VI
Gasan-Dong 219 Gasan digital 1-ro,
Geumcheon-gu, Seoul, 08501, Korea
(South)
Tel.: (82) 218335220
Web Site: https://pemtron.com
Year Founded: 2002
168360—(KRS)
Software Development Services
N.A.I.C.S.: 541511

Subsidiaries:

Pemtron Europe GmbH (1)
Kapellenstrasse 11, Feldkirchen bei, 85622,
Munich, Germany
Tel.: (49) 8987768842
Inspection Equipment Mfr & Distr
N.A.I.C.S.: 334519

Pemtron Technologies Asia Pte.
Limited (1)
Flat/RM 1704 17/F Singga Commercial
Centre 144 151 Connaught Road, West Sai
Ying Pun, Hong Kong, China (Hong Kong)
Tel.: (852) 35905175
Semiconductor Mounting Inspection Equipment Mfr & Distr
N.A.I.C.S.: 334413

Pemtron Technologies Co., Ltd. (1)
F Zone 4th Floor Building 1 Baisha Industry
Park, Nanshan District, Shenzhen, China
Tel.: (86) 75521659772
Semiconductor Mounting Inspection Equipment Mfr & Distr
N.A.I.C.S.: 334413

Pemtron Technology Mexico, S de
R.L. de C.V. (1)
Nicolas Bravo 3647 Miguel de la Madrid,
Jalisco, 45239, Zapopan, Mexico
Tel.: (52) 3327339111
Web Site: https://pemtron.mx
Inspection Equipment Mfr & Distr
N.A.I.C.S.: 334519

Pemtron Technology, Corp. (1)
15111 S Figueroa St, Gardena, CA 90248
Semiconductor Mounting Inspection Equipment Mfr & Distr
N.A.I.C.S.: 334413

Pemtron Vina Co., Ltd. (1)
Lot A31-A32 V2 Building Home City Apartment Trung Kinh Street, Cau Giay district,
Hanoi, Vietnam
Tel.: (84) 865840329
Inspection Equipment Mfr & Distr
N.A.I.C.S.: 334519

PENAFLOR S.A.
Arenales 480 Vicente Lopez, 1638,
Buenos Aires, Argentina
Tel.: (54) 11 5198 8000
Web Site:
   http://www.grupopenaflor.com.ar
Year Founded: 1883
Sales Range: $200-249.9 Million
Emp.: 1,500
Wine Producer
N.A.I.C.S.: 312130
Martin A. Ramos *(CEO)*

PENDER FINANCIAL GROUP CORPORATION
Suite 1640-1066 West Hastings
Street, Vancouver, V6E 3X1, BC,
Canada
Tel.: (604) 688-1511 BC
Web Site:
   http://www.penderfund.com
Venture Capital Investment & Fund
Management Services
N.A.I.C.S.: 523999
David Barr *(Pres, CEO & Portfolio
Mgr-PenderFund Capital)*

Subsidiaries:

ActiveState Software Inc. (1)
1000 1177 West Hastings Street, Vancouver, V6E 2K3, BC, Canada
Tel.: (778) 786-1100
Web Site: http://www.activestate.com
Software Publisher
N.A.I.C.S.: 513210
Bart Copeland *(Pres & CEO)*

PENDER GROWTH FUND INC.
Suite 1803 - 1066 West Hastings
Street, Vancouver, V6E 3X2, BC,
Canada
Tel.: (604) 688-1511
Web Site:
   https://www.pendergrowthfund.com
PNDDF—(OTCIQ)
Rev.: $6,818,860
Assets: $56,395,256
Liabilities: $3,622,805
Net Worth: $52,772,451
Earnings: $777,417
Fiscal Year-end: 12/31/23
Investment Services
N.A.I.C.S.: 523999
Kelly Edmison *(Chm)*

PENDERFUND CAPITAL MANAGEMENT LTD.
885 W Georgia St Ste 2200, Vancouver, V6C 3E8, BC, Canada
Tel.: (604) 688-1511
Web Site:
   http://www.penderfund.com
Sales Range: $1-9.9 Million
Emp.: 10
Investment Services
N.A.I.C.S.: 523999
Kelly Edmison *(Chm & Partner)*

PENEQUITY REALTY CORPORATION
33 Young St Ste 901, Toronto, M5E
1G4, ON, Canada
Tel.: (416) 408-3080
Web Site: http://www.penequity.com
Rev.: $27,387,659
Emp.: 36
Real Estate Services
N.A.I.C.S.: 531210
David V. Johnston *(Pres & CEO)*

PENFUND MANAGEMENT LTD.
Bay Adelaide Centre 333 Bay Street
Suite 610, Toronto, M5H 2R2, ON,
Canada
Tel.: (416) 865-0707
Web Site: http://www.penfund.com
Year Founded: 1979
Investment Management Service
N.A.I.C.S.: 523940
Richard Bradlow *(Partner)*

PENGANA CAPITAL GROUP LIMITED
Level 27 Governor Phillip Tower 1
Farrer Place, Sydney, 2000, NSW,
Australia
Tel.: (61) 285249900
Web Site: https://www.pengana.com
Year Founded: 2003
PCG—(ASX)
Rev.: $26,508,413
Assets: $62,022,569
Liabilities: $13,125,668
Net Worth: $48,896,902
Earnings: ($2,902,644)
Fiscal Year-end: 06/30/24
Investment Services; Holding Company
N.A.I.C.S.: 551112
Katrina Glendinning *(CFO)*

Subsidiaries:

Hunter Hall Investment Management
Ltd (1)
Level 2 56 Pitt street, Sydney, 2000, NSW,
Australia
Tel.: (61) 282240300
Web Site: http://www.hunterhall.com.au
Sales Range: $50-74.9 Million
Emp.: 30
Investment Management Service
N.A.I.C.S.: 523999
Peter James MacDonald Hall *(Chm)*

Pengana International Equities
Ltd (1)
Suite 1 Level 27 Gosvernor Phillip Tower 1
Farrer Place, Sydney, 2000, NSW, Australia
Tel.: (61) 285249900
Web Site: http://www.pengana.com
Rev.: $35,632,345
Assets: $234,946,580
Liabilities: $12,634,215
Net Worth: $222,312,366
Earnings: $22,452,591
Fiscal Year-end: 06/30/2024
Investment Services
N.A.I.C.S.: 523999
Russel Pillemer *(Mng Dir)*

PENGDU AGRICULTURE & ANIMAL HUSBANDRY CO., LTD.
No 25 Hongqiao Commercial Villa
2188 Hongqiao Road, Changning
District, Shanghai, 200336, China
Tel.: (86) 2155082178
Web Site:
   http://www.dakangmuye.com
002505—(SSE)
Rev.: $2,726,615,736

PENGDU AGRICULTURE & ANIMAL HUSBANDRY CO., LTD.

Pengdu Agriculture & Animal Husbandry Co., Ltd.—(Continued)

Assets: $2,308,779,720
Liabilities: $1,464,137,532
Net Worth: $844,642,188
Earnings: $2,383,992
Fiscal Year-end: 12/31/22
Pig Breeder & Distr
N.A.I.C.S.: 112210
Junjie Ge *(Chm)*

PENGQI TECHNOLOGY DEVELOPMENT CO., LTD.
18F Golden Tower Fortune Plaza, No 39 Guoquan Road Yangpu District, Shanghai, 200433, China
Tel.: (86) 21 35071889
Web Site: http://www.600614.com
Rev.: $235,098,689
Assets: $617,676,282
Liabilities: $595,962,918
Net Worth: $21,713,364
Earnings: ($132,364,867)
Fiscal Year-end: 12/31/19
Pharmaceutical Product Mfr & Distr
N.A.I.C.S.: 325412
Xueyun Song *(Pres)*

PENGUEN GIDA SANAYI A.S.
Balkan Mah Mumin Gencoglu Cad No 1, Nilufer, 16240, Bursa, Turkiye
Tel.: (90) 2243242424
Web Site: https://www.penguen.com.tr
Year Founded: 1989
PENGD—(IST)
Rev.: $26,444,681
Assets: $63,227,526
Liabilities: $18,418,282
Net Worth: $44,809,244
Earnings: $2,480,426
Emp.: 868
Fiscal Year-end: 12/31/22
Fruit & Vegetable Mfr
N.A.I.C.S.: 311421
Orhan Umit Gencoglu *(Chm-Mgmt Bd)*

PENGUIN VENTURES B.V.
Spoetnik 58, Amersfoort, 3824MG, Netherlands
Tel.: (31) 334506120
Web Site: http://www.penguin-ventures.com
Year Founded: 2000
Sales Range: $25-49.9 Million
Emp.: 12
Privater Equity Firm
N.A.I.C.S.: 523999
Serge Kremer *(Co-Founder)*

PENINSULA CAPITAL ADVISORS LLP
10 Brook Street, London, W1S 1BG, United Kingdom
Tel.: (44) 203 642 3420   UK
Web Site: http://www.peninsulacapital.co.uk
Investment Advisory & Asset Management Services
N.A.I.C.S.: 523940
Ramon Arocena Soria *(Partner)*

PENINSULA CONSUMER SERVICES CO-OP ASSOCIATION LTD
Ste 1 2132 Keating X Rd, Saanichton, V8M 2A6, BC, Canada
Tel.: (250) 652-1188
Web Site: http://www.peninsulaco-op.com
Sales Range: $50-74.9 Million
Emp.: 300
Grocery Product Distr
N.A.I.C.S.: 445110
Erik Gault *(Mgr-Ops)*

PENINSULA ENERGY LIMITED
Web Site: http://www.pel.net.au
N.A.I.C.S.: 325413
PENMF—(OTCQB)
Rev.: $18,300,000
Assets: $88,185,000
Liabilities: $14,746,000
Net Worth: $73,439,000
Earnings: ($4,619,000)
Emp.: 38
Fiscal Year-end: 06/30/22
Uranium Exploration & Mining Services
N.A.I.C.S.: 212290
Wayne Heili *(CEO & Mng Dir)*

PENINSULA FORD LINCOLN
Sunset Strip, Owen Sound, N4K 6H6, ON, Canada
Tel.: (519) 376-3252
Web Site: http://www.peninsulaford.com
Year Founded: 1980
Rev.: $39,359,670
Emp.: 81
New & Used Car Dealers
N.A.I.C.S.: 441110
Ryan Carson *(Gen Mgr)*

PENINSULAR GOLD LIMITED
First Island House Peter Street, Saint Helier, JE2 4SP, Jersey   JE
Tel.: (44) 326988381
Year Founded: 2005
Sales Range: $10-24.9 Million
Emp.: 251
Gold Mining Services
N.A.I.C.S.: 212220
Andrew Yeow Kam Tai *(Chm & CEO)*

PENN-CO CONSTRUCTION CANADA (2003) LTD
25 Penner Drive, PO Box 60, Blumenort, R0A 0C0, MB, Canada
Tel.: (204) 326-1341
Web Site: http://www.penn-co.com
Year Founded: 1959
Rev.: $14,519,807
Emp.: 50
Construction Services
N.A.I.C.S.: 236220
Dan Reimer *(Pres)*

PENNANT INTERNATIONAL GROUP PLC
Unit D1 Staverton Connection, Cheltenham, GL51 0TF, Gloucestershire, United Kingdom
Tel.: (44) 1452714914
Web Site: https://www.pennantplc.com
PEN—(AIM)
Rev.: $19,783,508
Assets: $23,819,140
Liabilities: $11,317,592
Net Worth: $12,501,547
Earnings: ($1,183,955)
Emp.: 140
Fiscal Year-end: 12/31/23
Computer Training Services
N.A.I.C.S.: 611420
Philip H. Walker *(CEO)*

Subsidiaries:

Pennant Australasia Pty Ltd.   (1)
Ste 6 334 Highbury Rd, PO Box 2050, Mount Waverley, 3149, VIC, Australia
Tel.: (61) 398867977
Web Site: https://www.pennantaust.com.au
Sales Range: $25-49.9 Million
Emp.: 4
Software Development Services
N.A.I.C.S.: 541511

Pennant Canada Limited   (1)
1400 Blair Pl Ste 100, Ottawa, K1J 9B8, ON, Canada
Tel.: (613) 745-3811
Web Site: https://www.pennantcanada.ca

Emp.: 8
Computer Software Packages Distr
N.A.I.C.S.: 423430

Pennant Information Services Limited   (1)
Renold House Heald Green Styal Road, Manchester, M22 5WZ, United Kingdom
Tel.: (44) 161 493 1600
Computer Software Training Services
N.A.I.C.S.: 611420

Pennant Software Services Limited   (1)
Unit 6 Dartmouth Bldg Ft Fareham Indus Estate Newgate Ln, Fareham, PO14 1AH, Hampshire, United Kingdom
Tel.: (44) 1329226300
Web Site: http://www.pennantplc.co.uk
Sales Range: $25-49.9 Million
Emp.: 7
Software Support Services
N.A.I.C.S.: 541511

Pennant Training Systems Limited   (1)
Pennant Ct Staverton Tech Park, Cheltenham, GL51 6TL, Gloucestershire, United Kingdom
Tel.: (44) 1452714914
Web Site: http://www.pennantplc.co.uk
Sales Range: $10-24.9 Million
Emp.: 100
Computer Software Training Services
N.A.I.C.S.: 611420

PENNAR INDUSTRIES LIMITED
D No 2-91/14/8/PIL/10&11 Whitefield Kondapur, Hyderabad, 500081, Telangana, India
Tel.: (91) 4043904952
Web Site: https://www.pennarindia.com
Year Founded: 1988
PENIND—(NSE)
Rev.: $210,757,365
Assets: $258,331,710
Liabilities: $163,232,160
Net Worth: $95,099,550
Earnings: $387,660
Emp.: 2,718
Fiscal Year-end: 03/31/21
Engineeering Services
N.A.I.C.S.: 541330
Nrupender Rao *(Founder & Chm)*

Subsidiaries:

Ascent Building LLC   (1)
214 Fountainhead Rd, Portland, TN 37148
Web Site: https://ascentbuildings.net
Emp.: 150
Steel Building Construction Services
N.A.I.C.S.: 238120

Cadmum S.A.R.L.   (1)
ZA Champ Noyer, 03310, Villebret, France
Tel.: (33) 470090796
Web Site: https://cadnum.com
Pipe Mold Mfr & Distr
N.A.I.C.S.: 333511

Oneworks BIM Technologies Private Limited   (1)
Prime Plaza No 54/1 1st Street Sripuram Colony St Thomas Mount, Chennai, 600 016, India
Tel.: (91) 444 017 8300
Web Site: http://www.pebspennar.in
Architectural Design & Planning Services
N.A.I.C.S.: 541310

Pennar Engineered Building Systems Limited   (1)
9th Floor West Wing DHFLVC Silicon Towers, Kondapur, Hyderabad, 500 084, Andhra Pradesh, India
Tel.: (91) 40 40210525
Web Site: http://www.pebspennar.in
Sales Range: $50-74.9 Million
Emp.: 250
Engineered Building Structure Mfr
N.A.I.C.S.: 339999
P. V. Rao *(Mng Dir)*

Pennar Global Inc.   (1)

INTERNATIONAL PUBLIC

21 Waterway Ave Ste 300, The Woodlands, TX 77380
Tel.: (281) 362-2707
Web Site: https://www.pennarglobal.com
Emp.: 300
Steel Tube Mfr
N.A.I.C.S.: 331210

PENNEO A/S
Enghavevej 40 4 sal, 1674, Copenhagen, Denmark
Tel.: (45) 71999893
Web Site: https://www.penneo.com
Year Founded: 2014
PENNEO—(CSE)
Rev.: $10,426,363
Assets: $21,992,260
Liabilities: $6,726,796
Net Worth: $15,265,464
Earnings: ($2,931,387)
Emp.: 107
Fiscal Year-end: 12/31/22
Software Development Services
N.A.I.C.S.: 541511
Christian Stendevad *(CEO)*

PENNER INTERNATIONAL INC.
20 PTH 12 N, Steinbach, R5G 1B7, MB, Canada
Tel.: (204) 326-3487
Web Site: https://www.penner.ca
Year Founded: 1923
Sales Range: $50-74.9 Million
Emp.: 564
Truck Transportation Services
N.A.I.C.S.: 484122
Milton Penner *(Pres)*

PENNEY GROUP
1309 Topsail Road, PO Box 8274, Saint John's, A1B 3N4, NL, Canada
Tel.: (709) 782-3404
Web Site: http://www.penneygroup.ca
Sales Range: $1-4.9 Billion
Emp.: 3,000
Holding Company; Civil Construction, Automotive Sales, Real Estate Development, Energy Services & Marine Transportation
N.A.I.C.S.: 551112
Edward J. Murphy *(Sr VP-Fin)*

Subsidiaries:

Ocean Choice International L.P.   (1)
1315 Topsail Road, PO Box 8190, Saint John's, A1B 3N4, NL, Canada
Tel.: (709) 782-6244
Web Site: http://www.oceanchoice.com
Sales Range: $25-49.9 Million
Emp.: 50
Seafood Processing & Marketing
N.A.I.C.S.: 311710
Greg Viscount *(Gen Mgr-Newfoundland)*

Subsidiary (Non-US):

Ocean Choice International Limited   (2)
42A High St, Theale, Reading, RG7 5AN, Berkshire, United Kingdom
Tel.: (44) 1189325180
Web Site: http://www.oceanchoice.com
Sales Range: $25-49.9 Million
Emp.: 7
Seafood Whslr
N.A.I.C.S.: 424460

Ocean Choice International, K.K.   (2)
2-1-18 Axis Bldg Tachibana-dori, Chuo-ku, Kobe, 650 0016, Japan
Tel.: (81) 783515300
Web Site: http://www.oceanchoice.com
Sales Range: $25-49.9 Million
Emp.: 7
Seafood Processing & Marketing
N.A.I.C.S.: 311710
Shigeho Ueda *(Pres)*

Pennecon Limited   (1)
1309 Topsail Rd, PO Box 8274 Station A, Saint John's, A1B 3N4, NL, Canada

Tel.: (709) 782-3404
Web Site: http://www.penneygroup.ca
Sales Range: $600-649.9 Million
Emp.: 1,200
Civil Engineering, Ready Mix Concrete Mfr, Energy Services & Real Estate Services
N.A.I.C.S.: 237990
Jerry David White (CFO)

Subsidiary (Domestic):

ABc Precast & Ready Mix Ltd. (2)
1941 Trans Canada Hwy, Nanaimo, V9X 1R4, BC, Canada
Tel.: (250) 753-1223
Emp.: 15
Precast & Ready Mix Concrete
N.A.I.C.S.: 327320

Allstar Rebar Limited (2)
206 McNamara Drive, PO Box 1024, Station C, Saint John's, A1L 0A6, NL, Canada
Tel.: (709) 754-5591
Web Site: http://www.penneygroup.ca
Emp.: 25
Rebar Mfr & Whslr
N.A.I.C.S.: 327390
Greg Gulliver (Gen Mgr)

Capital Precast Limited (2)
Trans-Canada Highway Station A, PO Box 8274, Saint John's, A1B 3N4, NL, Canada
Tel.: (709) 364-5008
Web Site: http://www.pennecon.com
Sales Range: $50-74.9 Million
Emp.: 150
Precast Concrete Mfr
N.A.I.C.S.: 327390
Gary Guinchard (Gen Mgr)

Capital Ready Mix Limited (2)
2800 Trans-Canada Highway, PO Box 8056 Station A, Saint John's, A1B 3M7, NL, Canada
Tel.: (709) 364-5008
Web Site: http://www.penneygroup.ca
Sales Range: $25-49.9 Million
Emp.: 15
Readymix Concrete Mfr
N.A.I.C.S.: 327320
Jason Coish (Gen Mgr)

Concrete Products Limited (2)
260 East White Hills Road, PO Box 8056, Saint John's, A1B 3M7, NL, Canada
Tel.: (709) 368-3171
Web Site: http://www.concreteproducts.ca
Emp.: 70
Concrete Products Mfr
N.A.I.C.S.: 327390
Jason Coish (Gen Mgr)

Octagon Development Corporation (2)
1288 Topsail Road Unit C, PO Box 8274 Station A, Paradise, A1L 1N7, NL, Canada
Tel.: (709) 782-5920
Web Site: http://www.penneygroup.ca
Sales Range: $300-349.9 Million
Emp.: 1,000
Real Estate Development
N.A.I.C.S.: 531390

Pennecon Energy Ltd. (2)
650 Water Street, Saint John's, A1C 5M5, NL, Canada
Tel.: (709) 726-5888
Web Site: http://www.pennecon.com
Sales Range: $25-49.9 Million
Emp.: 20
Holding Company; Energy Services for the Oil & Gas Industry
N.A.I.C.S.: 551112
Paul Stanley (Sr VP)

Subsidiary (Domestic):

Bay Bulls Marine Terminal Inc. (3)
650 Water Street, Saint John's, A1C 5M5, NL, Canada
Tel.: (709) 334-2820
Web Site: http://csomerton54.wix.com
Emp.: 25
Marine Terminal Management & Operation
N.A.I.C.S.: 488310
David Elliott (Gen Mgr)

Subsidiary (Domestic):

Pennecon Heavy Civil Limited (2)
1309 Topsail Rd, PO Box 8274 Station A, Saint John's, A1B 3N4, NL, Canada
Tel.: (709) 782-3404
Web Site: http://www.pennecon.com
Sales Range: $25-49.9 Million
Emp.: 50
Civil Construction & Site Development Services
N.A.I.C.S.: 237990
Brad Cole (VP)

Branch (Domestic):

Pennecon Heavy Civil Limited (3)
110-2433 Dollarton Hwy, North Vancouver, V7H 0A1, BC, Canada
Tel.: (604) 987-9588
Web Site: http://www.penneygroup.ca
Sales Range: $25-49.9 Million
Emp.: 1
Civil Construction & Site Development
N.A.I.C.S.: 237990

Shamrock Waters of Canada Inc. (1)
1288 Topsail Road, Paradise, A1L 1N7, NL, Canada
Tel.: (709) 368-9020
Web Site: http://www.shamrockwaters.ca
Water Bottler & Distr
N.A.I.C.S.: 312112

PENNINE TELECOM LTD.
Pennine House Salford Street, Bury, BL9 6YA, Lancs, United Kingdom
Tel.: (44) 1617633333 UK
Web Site:
  http://www.wearepennine.com
Year Founded: 1976
Emp.: 200
Business Communication Systems Provider
N.A.I.C.S.: 517810
Andrew Roberts (Mng Dir)

PENNON GROUP PLC
Peninsula House Rydon Lane, Exeter, EX2 7HR, Devon, United Kingdom
Tel.: (44) 1392446677 UK
Web Site: https://www.pennon-group.co.uk
PNN—(OTCIQ)
Emp.: 5,382
Holding Company, Operator & Investor in Water & Sewer Services, Waste Management, Environmental Instrumentation & Construction Services
N.A.I.C.S.: 551112
Susan Jane Davy (CEO)

Subsidiaries:

Bristol Water plc (1)
Bridgwater Road, Bristol, BS13 7AT, United Kingdom
Tel.: (44) 3456003600
Web Site: http://www.bristolwater.co.uk
Water Supply Services
N.A.I.C.S.: 221310
Mel Karam (CEO)

Pennon Water Services Limited (1)
Peninsula House Rydon Lane, Exeter, EX2 7HR, United Kingdom
Tel.: (44) 1392 446 677
Water Supply Services
N.A.I.C.S.: 221310

SSWB Limited (1)
Green Lane, Walsall, WS2 7PD, West Midlands, United Kingdom
Tel.: (44) 192 263 8282
Web Site: https://www.south-staffordshire.com
Water Distribution Services
N.A.I.C.S.: 221310
Phil Newland (CEO)

South West Water Ltd. (1)
Penninsula House, Rydon Ln, Exeter, EX2 7HR, Devon, United Kingdom (100%)
Tel.: (44) 3443462020
Web Site: http://www.southwestwater.co.uk
Sales Range: $500-549.9 Million
Emp.: 1,300
Water & Sewerage Services, Waste Management Services, Construction Services; Mfr of Environmental Instrumentation
N.A.I.C.S.: 221310
Louise Rowe (Dir-Fin)

PENNPETRO ENERGY PLC
88 Whitfield Street 1st Floor, London, W1T 4EZ, United Kingdom
Tel.: (44) 2032390033 UK
Web Site:
  http://www.pennpetroenergy.co.uk
Year Founded: 2016
PPP—(LSE)
Assets: $6,163,136
Liabilities: $4,985,355
Net Worth: $1,177,781
Earnings: ($318,902)
Emp.: 3
Fiscal Year-end: 03/31/23
Oil & Gas Exploration Services
N.A.I.C.S.: 213112

PENNY HYDRAULICS LTD
Station Road, Clowne, Chesterfield, S43 4AB, Derbyshire, United Kingdom
Tel.: (44) 1246811475
Web Site:
  http://www.pennyhydraulics.com
Sales Range: $10-24.9 Million
Emp.: 60
Hydraulic Lifting Equipment Mfr
N.A.I.C.S.: 423830
Martin Oke (Area Mgr-Sls)

PENPOWER TECHNOLOGY LTD.
7F No 47 Lane 2 Sec 2 Guangfu Rd, Hsinchu, 300, Taiwan
Tel.: (886) 35722691
Web Site:
  https://www.penpowerinc.com
Year Founded: 1991
5211—(TPE)
Rev.: $4,613,857
Assets: $20,839,696
Liabilities: $2,538,661
Net Worth: $18,301,035
Earnings: $801,738
Fiscal Year-end: 12/31/22
Software Development Services
N.A.I.C.S.: 541511
Cheng-An Hung (CEO)

PENSAFE INC.
1175 Barton St Unit 4, Stoney Creek, L8E 5H1, ON, Canada
Tel.: (905) 643-7188
Web Site: http://www.pensafe.ca
Year Founded: 1937
Sales Range: $1-9.9 Million
Emp.: 50
Designer & Mfr of High Strength Forged Components
N.A.I.C.S.: 332312
Al Payne (VP-Global Ops & Gen Mgr)

PENSANA METALS LTD.
Level 1 10 Outram Street, West Perth, 6005, WA, Australia
Tel.: (61) 892210090
Web Site:
  http://www.pensanametals.com
Year Founded: 2006
PRE—(LSE)
Assets: $74,571,607
Liabilities: $23,615,793
Net Worth: $50,955,814
Earnings: ($5,818,045)
Emp.: 51
Fiscal Year-end: 06/30/24
Gold Mining Services
N.A.I.C.S.: 212220
Graeme Clatworthy (Mng Dir-Ozango Minerais)

PENSANA PLC
Rex House 4-12 Regent Street 4th Floor, London, SW1Y 4PE, United Kingdom UK
Web Site: https://www.pensana.co.uk
Year Founded: 2019
PRE—(LSE)
Assets: $71,625,693
Liabilities: $14,865,091
Net Worth: $56,760,602
Earnings: ($4,302,823)
Emp.: 56
Fiscal Year-end: 06/30/23
Mineral Exploration Services
N.A.I.C.S.: 213115
Rocky Smith (COO)

PENSION INSURANCE CORPORATION
14 Cornhill, London, EC3V 3ND, United Kingdom
Tel.: (44) 2071052000
Web Site:
  http://www.pensioncorporation.com
Year Founded: 2006
Rev.: $13,377,008,400
Assets: $76,905,666,000
Liabilities: $4,194,496,800
Net Worth: $72,711,169,200
Earnings: $418,400,400
Emp.: 130
Fiscal Year-end: 12/31/19
Pension Insurance Services
N.A.I.C.S.: 524292
Tracy Blackwell (CEO)

PENSIONBEE GROUP PLC
209 Blackfriars Road, London, SE1 8NL, United Kingdom
Tel.: (44) 2034578444 UK
Web Site:
  https://www.pensionbee.com
Year Founded: 2014
PBEE—(LSE)
Rev.: $22,294,875
Assets: $32,370,613
Liabilities: $2,665,993
Net Worth: $29,704,620
Earnings: ($27,955,062)
Emp.: 185
Fiscal Year-end: 12/31/22
Software Development Services
N.A.I.C.S.: 541511
Christoph J. Martin (CFO)

Subsidiaries:

PensionBee Limited (1)
209 Blackfriars Road, London, SE1 8NL, United Kingdom
Tel.: (44) 2034578444
Web Site: https://www.pensionbee.com
Software Solution Provider Services
N.A.I.C.S.: 541714

PENSONIC HOLDINGS BERHAD
1165 Lorong Perindustrian Bukit Minyak 16, Taman Perindustrian Bukit Minyak, 14100, Seberang Perai, Penang, Malaysia
Tel.: (60) 45070393
Web Site: https://www.pensonic.com
PENSONI—(KLS)
Rev.: $57,820,967
Assets: $57,993,321
Liabilities: $28,642,524
Net Worth: $29,350,797
Earnings: ($845,874)
Fiscal Year-end: 05/31/23
Holding Company; Consumer Electronic Appliances Mfr & Distr
N.A.I.C.S.: 551112
Dixon Chuon Jin Chew (CEO-Grp)

Subsidiaries:

Amtek Marketing Services Pte. Ltd. (1)

PENSONIC HOLDINGS BERHAD

Pensonic Holdings Berhad—(Continued)

2 Leng Kee Road 06-03 Thye Hong Centre, Singapore, 159086, Singapore **(100%)**
Tel.: (65) 64726508
Web Site: http://sg.cornellappliances.com
Sales Range: $50-74.9 Million
Emp.: 8
Household Appliance Distr
N.A.I.C.S.: 423620

Cornell Sales & Service Sdn. Bhd. (1)
11B Jalan 223 Seksyen 51A, 46100, Petaling Jaya, Selangor, Malaysia **(100%)**
Tel.: (60) 379545200
Web Site: https://my.cornellappliances.com
Household Electrical & Electronic Appliances Distr
N.A.I.C.S.: 423620

Keat Radio Co. Sdn. Bhd. (1)
98 Lrg Perusahaan Maju 8 Kaw Perusahaan Perai 4, Perai, 13600, Penang, Malaysia **(100%)**
Tel.: (60) 45070321
Emp.: 500
Electrical & Electronic Appliances Mfr & Whslr
N.A.I.C.S.: 335210
Chew Weng Khak *(Chm)*

Subsidiary (Non-US):

Pensonic (H.K.) Corporation Limited (2)
Unit 1303 Wanchi Commercial Centre 194-204 Johnston Road, Hong Kong, China (Hong Kong) **(100%)**
Tel.: (852) 27270997
Sales Range: $50-74.9 Million
Emp.: 8
Electrical & Electronic Appliances Wholesale Trade Distr
N.A.I.C.S.: 425120

Subsidiary (Domestic):

Pensonic Industries Sdn. Bhd. (2)
1165 Lorong Perindustrian Bukit Manyak 16 Taman Perindustrian, Perai, 14100, Simpang, Malaysia **(100%)**
Tel.: (60) 45070393
Web Site: http://www.pensonic.com
Emp.: 500
Electrical & Electronic Appliances Distr
N.A.I.C.S.: 423620
Dixon Chew *(CEO)*

Pensia Electronic Sdn. Bhd. (1)
Plot 98 Lorong Perusahaan Maju 8 Bukit Tengah Industrial Park, 13600, Perai, Penang, Malaysia **(100%)**
Tel.: (60) 45070393
Sales Range: $125-149.9 Million
Emp.: 400
Electrical & Electronic Appliances Mfr & Distr
N.A.I.C.S.: 335220
Dixon Choun Jin Chew *(CEO)*

Pensonic (Cambodia) Co., Ltd. (1)
Lot 1529 National Road 2, Sangkat Chak Angre Krom Khan Mean Chey, Phnom Penh, Cambodia
Tel.: (855) 89308474
Household Appliance Whslr
N.A.I.C.S.: 423620

Pensonic Sales & Service Sdn. Bhd.
Lot 11A Jalan 51a/223 Sec 51A, 46100, Petaling Jaya, Selangor Darul Ehsan, Malaysia **(100%)**
Tel.: (60) 79545200
Sales Range: $50-74.9 Million
Emp.: 80
Household Electrical & Electronic Appliances Distr
N.A.I.C.S.: 423620

PENTA CAPITAL LLP

150 St Vincent Street, Glasgow, G2 5NE, United Kingdom
Tel.: (44) 141 572 7300 UK
Web Site:
    http://www.pentacapital.com
Year Founded: 1999
Privater Equity Firm

N.A.I.C.S.: 523999
David Calder *(Partner)*

PENTA GOLD LTD.

2224 Manek Chowk Opp Old Sharer Bazar, Ahmedabad, 380001, Gujarat, India
Tel.: (91) 2222402255
Web Site: http://www.pentagold.in
PENTAGOLD—(NSE)
Rev.: $21,228,400
Assets: $58,564,382
Liabilities: $53,409,183
Net Worth: $5,155,198
Earnings: $10,128
Emp.: 3
Fiscal Year-end: 03/31/21
Jewellery Product Mfr & Distr
N.A.I.C.S.: 339910
Ketan Madhusudan Shroff *(Chm & Mng Dir)*

PENTA INVESTMENTS LIMITED

3rd floor Osprey House 5-7 Old Street, Channel Islands, JE2 3RG, Saint Helier, Jersey
Tel.: (44) 1534 828 711 JE
Web Site:
    http://www.pentainvestments.com
Year Founded: 1994
Privater Equity Firm
N.A.I.C.S.: 523999

Subsidiaries:

Amersport Sp. z o.o. Sp. k. (1)
Poleczki 21 budynek C, 02-822, Warsaw, Poland
Tel.: (48) 22 461 0304
Web Site: http://www.amersport.pl
Shoe Distr
N.A.I.C.S.: 458210

Ceska Lekarna Holding, a.s. (1)
Nove Sady 996/25, 602 00, Brno, Czech Republic
Tel.: (420) 516770100
Web Site: http://www.drmax.cz
Holding Company; Pharmacies Operator
N.A.I.C.S.: 551112
Daniel Horak *(Dir Gen)*

Subsidiary (Domestic):

Dr. Max BDC, s.r.o. (2)
Florentinum budova D Na Florenci 2116/15, 110 00, Prague, 1, Czech Republic
Tel.: (420) 222 811 999
Web Site: http://www.drmax.cz
Pharmacies Operator
N.A.I.C.S.: 456110
Daniel Horak *(Dir Gen)*

Subsidiary (Non-US):

Dr. Max Sp. z o.o. (2)
ul Krzemieniecka 60a, 54 613, Wroclaw, Poland
Tel.: (48) 71 799 4600
Web Site: http://www.drmax.pl
Pharmacies Operator
N.A.I.C.S.: 456110
Marcin Fakadej *(CFO)*

EMC Instytut Medyczny S.A. (1)
 (73.53%)
Tel.: (48) 717472700
Web Site: https://www.emc-sa.pl
Rev.: $173,325,203
Assets: $116,886,687
Liabilities: $63,098,577
Net Worth: $53,788,110
Earnings: $4,404,726
Emp.: 2,500
Fiscal Year-end: 12/31/2023
Hospitals & Clinics Operator
N.A.I.C.S.: 622110
Agnieszka Szpara *(Chm-Mgmt Bd)*

Empik Sp. z o.o. (1)
ul Marszalkowska 104/122, PL-00-017, Warsaw, Poland
Tel.: (48) 22 551 3333
Web Site: http://www.empik.com

Books, Music CDs, DVDs, Games, Software & Stationery Products Distr
N.A.I.C.S.: 459210
Ewa Szmidt-Belcarz *(Chm)*

Fortuna Entertainment Group N.V. (1)
Strawinskylaan 809, WTC T A/L 8, 1077XX, Amsterdam, Netherlands **(68.25%)**
Tel.: (31) 20 238 0320
Web Site: http://www.fortunagroup.eu
Rev.: $252,143,541
Assets: $403,113,430
Liabilities: $310,932,114
Net Worth: $92,181,316
Earnings: $18,491,365
Emp.: 6,064
Fiscal Year-end: 12/31/2017
Online Betting
N.A.I.C.S.: 713290
Per Widerstrom *(Chm-Mgmt Bd)*

GRY-OnLine S.A. (1)
ul Gabrieli Zapolskiej 16A, 30-126, Krakow, Poland
Tel.: (48) 12 6261250
Web Site: http://www.firma.gry-online.pl
Online Gambling Services
N.A.I.C.S.: 541511

Gandalf Sp. z o.o. (1)
ul Beskidzka 37, 92-612, Lodz, Poland
Tel.: (48) 42 252 39 23
Web Site: http://www.gandalf.com.pl
Online Book Distr
N.A.I.C.S.: 459210
Aleksander Gandalf *(Mgr-Brand & Product)*

Penta Investments Ltd. (1)
Agias Fylaxeos & Polygnostou 212, C&I Center 2nd Floor, 3082, Limassol, Cyprus
Tel.: (357) 2573 3104
Web Site: http://www.pentainvestments.com
Emp.: 10
Private Equity & Real Estate Investment Firm
N.A.I.C.S.: 523999
Jozef Oravkin *(Mng Partner-Real Estate Div)*

Pol Perfect Sp. z o.o. (1)
ul Stagiewna 2c, 03-117, Warsaw, Poland
Tel.: (48) 22 51 939 51
Web Site: http://www.polperfect.com.pl
Magazine Distr
N.A.I.C.S.: 424920

Spiele Max GmbH (1)
Haynauer Strasse 72 a, 12249, Berlin, Germany
Tel.: (49) 30 376 79 04 19
Web Site: http://www.spielemax.de
Online Shopping Services
N.A.I.C.S.: 455211
Falk Siegmundt *(Co-Chm, CEO & Mng Dir)*

ZSNP, a.s. (1)
Priemyselna 12, 965 63, Ziar nad Hronom, Slovakia **(96%)**
Tel.: (421)-45 601 11 11
Web Site: http://www.zsnp.sk
Sales Range: $10-24.9 Million
Emp.: 250
Aluminum Mfr
N.A.I.C.S.: 331313
Jan Klimko *(Chm & CEO)*

Joint Venture (Domestic):

Slovalco AS (2)
Priemyselna 14, 965 48, Ziar nad Hronom, Slovakia **(44.7%)**
Tel.: (421) 456089999
Web Site: https://www.slovalco.sk
Sales Range: $400-449.9 Million
Emp.: 500
Aluminium Products Mfr
N.A.I.C.S.: 331313
Milan Vesely *(CEO)*

e-Muzyka S.A. (1)
ul Zwyciezcow 18, 03-941, Warsaw, Poland
Tel.: (48) 22 427 31 90
Web Site: http://www.e-muzyka.pl
Multimedia Content Development Services
N.A.I.C.S.: 541840
Jan Ejsmont *(CFO)*

PENTA-OCEAN CONSTRUCTION CO., LTD.

2-8 Koraku 2-chome, Bunkyo-ku, Tokyo, 112-8576, Japan
Tel.: (81) 338177181 JP
Web Site: https://www.penta-ocean.co.jp
Year Founded: 1896
1893—(TKS)
Rev.: $4,083,049,880
Assets: $3,741,445,080
Liabilities: $2,597,492,040
Net Worth: $1,143,953,040
Earnings: $118,153,750
Emp.: 3,976
Fiscal Year-end: 03/31/24
Large-Scale Civil & Engineering Services
N.A.I.C.S.: 541330
Makoto Shimoishi *(Sr Mng Exec Officer)*

Subsidiaries:

Domi Environmental Solutions Co., Ltd. (1)
Minamisode Address 29, Sodegaura, 299-0268, Chiba, Japan
Tel.: (81) 43 838 4739
Web Site: https://www.domi-es.jp
Environmental Consulting Services
N.A.I.C.S.: 541620

Jaiwat Co., Ltd. (1)
14 Chidoricho, Ichikawa, 272-0126, Chiba, Japan
Tel.: (81) 47 318 2871
Web Site: https://www.jaiwat.co.jp
Recycling Services
N.A.I.C.S.: 562111

Kegoya Dock Co., Ltd. (1)
6-1-11 Kegoya, Kure, 737-0012, Japan
Tel.: (81) 823281111
Web Site: https://www.kegoya-dock.com
Sales Range: $50-74.9 Million
Emp.: 250
Ship Building & Repairing
N.A.I.C.S.: 336611

PT. Penta Ocean Construction (1)
Mid Plaza 2 Lt 24 Jl Jend Sudirman No 10-11, Jakarta, 10220, Indonesia
Tel.: (62) 21 570 5484
Web Site: https://www.poc.co.id
Construction Services
N.A.I.C.S.: 236220

Penta Techno Service K.K. (1)
Gijutsu Kenkyujo, Nasushiobara, Japan
Tel.: (81) 287392129
Physical Engineering & Life Sciences Research & Development
N.A.I.C.S.: 541715

Penta-Ocean Construction (Hong Kong) Ltd. (1)
Unit 601 K Wah Centre, 191 Java Road, North Point, China (Hong Kong)
Tel.: (852) 28331098
Residential Care Facilities
N.A.I.C.S.: 623990

Penta-Ocean Construction (India) Pvt. Ltd. (1)
Unit No 1120 11th Floor JMD Megapolis Sector-48 Sohana Road, Gurgaon, 122018, Haryana, India
Tel.: (91) 124 436 8355
Environmental Consulting Services
N.A.I.C.S.: 541620

Penta-Ocean Dredging Co., Ltd. (1)
Teban Garden Post Office, Singapore, Singapore
Tel.: (65) 68735897
Heavy & Civil Engineering Construction
N.A.I.C.S.: 237990

Yoshin Construction Co., Ltd. (1)
Hakatako Ctr Bldg 5th Floor, Fukuoka, Japan
Tel.: (81) 922828118
Heavy & Civil Engineering Construction
N.A.I.C.S.: 237990

PENTAGON CHEMICAL SPECIALTIES LTD.

Northside, Workington, CA14 1JJ,
Cumbria, United Kingdom
Tel.: (44) 900604371
Rev.: $114,496,200
Emp.: 75
Chemicals Contract Mfr & Processor
N.A.I.C.S.: 325998
Allan Laing *(CEO)*

Subsidiaries:

Pentagon Fine Chemicals Ltd. (1)
Lowr Rd, Halebank, Widnes, WA8 8NS,
United Kingdom (100%)
Tel.: (44) 514243671
Sales Range: $25-49.9 Million
Fine Chemicals Mfr
N.A.I.C.S.: 325998
Allan Laing *(CEO)*

PENTAIR PLC
70 London Road Regal House,
Twickenham, London, TW13QS,
United Kingdom
Tel.: (44) 7494216154   IE
Web Site: https://www.pentair.com
Year Founded: 1966
PNR—(NYSE)
Rev.: $4,104,500,000
Assets: $6,563,300,000
Liabilities: $3,346,200,000
Net Worth: $3,217,100,000
Earnings: $622,700,000
Emp.: 10,500
Fiscal Year-end: 12/31/23
Holding Company; Water Processing
& Flow Control Products Mfr
N.A.I.C.S.: 551112
John L. Stauch *(Pres & CEO)*

Subsidiaries:

Combinatie Nijuis-Ippel V.o.f. (1)
Parallelweg 4, 7102 DE, Winterswijk, Netherlands
Tel.: (31) 543547474
Web Site: http://www.pentair.com
Emp.: 150
Industrial & Commercial Machinery Equipment Mfr
N.A.I.C.S.: 333310

D.A.S. International, Ltd. (1)
Edward House Unit 80 Lancaster Way Business Park, Ely, CB6 3NW, Cambridgeshire,
United Kingdom
Tel.: (44) 1353772020
Emp.: 8
Fruit & Vegetable Whslr
N.A.I.C.S.: 424480
Ian Dennis *(Mng Dir)*

Dritte Korschenbroicher Armaturen
GmbH (1)
Werner-Von-Siemens-Str, 41352, Korschenbroich, Nordrhein-Westfalen, Germany
Tel.: (49) 2161615493
Fire Alarm Security Equipment Mfr
N.A.I.C.S.: 333998

ERICO B.V. (1)
Jules Verneweg 75, 5015 BG, Tilburg, Netherlands
Tel.: (31) 5835100
Water Processing Services
N.A.I.C.S.: 562910

ERICO France Sarl (1)
Rue Charles Dalliere BP 31, 42161,
Andrezieux-Boutheon, France
Tel.: (33) 477365656
Water Processing Services
N.A.I.C.S.: 562910

ERICO Products Australia Pty
Limited (1)
323 Parramatta Rd, Auburn, 2144, NSW,
Australia
Tel.: (61) 294798500
Emp.: 5
Water Processing Services
N.A.I.C.S.: 562910

Emerson Automation Solutions Finall
Control UK Ltd. (1)
Sharp Street, Worsley, Manchester, M28
3NA, United Kingdom

Tel.: (44) 161 790 7741
Fire Protection Equipment Mfr
N.A.I.C.S.: 339999

Emirates Techno Casting FZE (1)
Hamriyah Free Zone, PO Box 41608,
Sharjah, United Arab Emirates
Tel.: (971) 65133100
Web Site:
http://www.emiratestechnocasting.com
Steel Products Mfr
N.A.I.C.S.: 333511

Emirates Techno Casting LLC (1)
PO Box 2895, Ajman, United Arab Emirates
Tel.: (971) 67433363
Web Site:
http://www.emiratestechnocasting.com
Valve Mfr
N.A.I.C.S.: 332911

Erichs Armatur AB (1)
Travbanegatan 8, PO Box 9144, Malmo,
21377, Sweden
Tel.: (46) 40 31 15 50
Web Site: http://www.auma.se
Emp.: 60
Valve & Actuator Mfr
N.A.I.C.S.: 332911
Ulf Elowsson *(Mng Dir)*

Erwin Burbach Maschinenfabrik
GmbH (1)
Nobelstr 14, 41189, Monchengladbach,
Germany
Tel.: (49) 2166 95 50
Web Site: http://www.pentair.com
Emp.: 120
Steel Pole Mfr
N.A.I.C.S.: 331210

Faradyne Motors LLC (1)
2077 Division St, Palmyra, NY 14522
Tel.: (315) 502-0125
Web Site: https://www.faradynemotors.com
Emp.: 20
Submersible Pump Motor & Control Box Mfr
N.A.I.C.S.: 335312
Dante Volpe *(Pres)*

Filtrix B.V. (1)
Marssteden 50, Enschede, 7547 TC, Netherlands
Tel.: (31) 534287450
Web Site: http://www.filtrix.com
Water Purifier & Related Equipment Whslr
N.A.I.C.S.: 423840

Flow Control Holding GmbH & Co.
KG (1)
Werner-von-Siemens-Str, 41352, Korschenbroich, Germany
Tel.: (49) 2161 6150
Web Site: http://www.pentair.com
Emp.: 15
Investment Management Service
N.A.I.C.S.: 523999

Haffmans B.V. (1)
Marinus Dammeweg 30, 5928 PW, Venlo,
Netherlands
Tel.: (31) 773232300
Web Site: http://www.haffmans.nl
Sales Range: $50-74.9 Million
Emp.: 160
Quality Control Equipment & Carbon Dioxide Systems Mfr & Distr
N.A.I.C.S.: 333310
Olaf Muller *(Mng Dir)*

Subsidiary (US):

Haffmans North America, Inc. (2)
293 Wright St, Delavan, WI 53115
Tel.: (763) 545-1730
Sales Range: $25-49.9 Million
Emp.: 4
Quality Control Equipment & Carbon Dioxide Systems Mfr & Distr
N.A.I.C.S.: 333310

Hypro EU Limited (1)
Station Rd Longstanton, Cambridge, CB24
3DS, United Kingdom
Tel.: (44) 1954260097
Web Site: https://www.hypro-eu.com
Emp.: 10,000
Pump & Pumping Equipment Mfr
N.A.I.C.S.: 333914

Investim Chile S.A. (1)

Avda Manuel Montt 1953, Santiago, Chile
Tel.: (56) 2 3411933
Financial Management Services
N.A.I.C.S.: 523999

JCF Fluid Flow India Private
Limited (1)
1st Floor Chona Centre 45 College Rd,
Chennai, 600 006, India
Tel.: (91) 44 4225 4600
Fluid Power Valve Mfr
N.A.I.C.S.: 332912

Jung Pumpen Hungary Kft. (1)
Magyarorszagi Kozvetlen Kereskedelmi Andrassy ut 121, 1062, Budapest, Hungary
Tel.: (36) 13880255
Sales Range: $50-74.9 Million
Emp.: 4
Water Treatment Service Equipment Whslr
N.A.I.C.S.: 423830
Kormoozy Richard *(Gen Mgr)*

Ken's Beverage Inc. (1)
10015 S Mandel St, Plainfield, IL 60585
Web Site: http://www.kensbeverage.com
Water Filtration & Treatment Services
N.A.I.C.S.: 488390
Ken Reimer *(Founder)*

Leushuis Projects International
B.V. (1)
Marssteden 50, 7547 TC, Enschede, Netherlands
Tel.: (31) 534287000
Fluid Control & Thermal Management Products & Services
N.A.I.C.S.: 334519

MECAIR S.r.l. (1)
Via Per Cinisello 97, Nova Milanese, 20384,
Italy
Tel.: (39) 03623751
Web Site: http://www.cleanairsystems.com
Industrial Valve Mfr
N.A.I.C.S.: 332911

Mecafrance (Deutschland)
GmbH (1)
Koernerstr 22, Bad Godesberg, 53175,
Bonn, Germany
Tel.: (49) 228935500
Web Site: https://www.mecafrance-bonn.de
Emp.: 7
Industrial Valve Mfr
N.A.I.C.S.: 332911

Milperra Developments Pty
Limited (1)
Lvl 23 91 King William St, Adelaide, 5000,
SA, Australia
Tel.: (61) 88113 5325
Real Estate Development Services
N.A.I.C.S.: 531390

PT Pentair Eurapipe Indonesia (1)
Jl Letjen S Parman Kav 77 Wisma 77 Lt 5,
Karawang, 11410, Indonesia
Tel.: (62) 267 432044
Piping Equipment Mfr
N.A.I.C.S.: 326122

Pentair Canada, Inc. (1)
269 Trillium Dr, Kitchener, N2G 4W5, ON,
Canada
Tel.: (519) 748-5470
Emp.: 35
Water Treatment Service Equipment Whslr
N.A.I.C.S.: 423830

Pentair Clean Process Technologies
India Private Limited (1)
161 Greams Rd, Chennai, 600006, Tamil
Nadu, India
Tel.: (91) 4442122046
Sales Range: $25-49.9 Million
Emp.: 25
Fluid Control & Thermal Management Products & Services
N.A.I.C.S.: 334519

Pentair Control Beijing Co., Ltd. (1)
Building a-3 Dixing Industrial Park No 15
Shuangyang Rd, Beijing, 100023, China
Tel.: (86) 1067821000
Emp.: 136
Industrial Valve Distr
N.A.I.C.S.: 423840

Pentair European Investments
(Deutschland) GmbH (1)

Im Petersfeld 6, 65624, Altendiez, Germany
Tel.: (49) 64321001
Web Site: http://www.cleanairsystems.com
Emp.: 6
Investment Management Service
N.A.I.C.S.: 523999

Pentair European Security Holdings
SA (1)
Zone d'Activite du Vert Galant rue des
Oziers, 95310, Saint-Ouen-l'Aumone,
France
Tel.: (33) 1 3440 7332
Emp.: 30
Holding Company
N.A.I.C.S.: 551112
Bollen Frederic *(Mgr)*

Pentair Flow Control International Pty.
Limited (1)
114 Albatross Rd, Nowra, 2541, NSW, Australia
Tel.: (61) 24448 0300
Web Site: http://www.pentair.com
Emp.: 50
Industrial Valve Mfr
N.A.I.C.S.: 332911

Pentair Flow Control Pacific Pty.
Limited (1)
114 Albatross Road, Nowra, 2541, NSW,
Australia (100%)
Tel.: (61) 244480300
Web Site: http://valves.pentair.com
Sales Range: $25-49.9 Million
Emp.: 150
Flow Control Products
N.A.I.C.S.: 332919

Pentair France SARL (1)
140 Avenue Roland Garros, Buc, 95300,
France
Tel.: (33) 139241500
Water Treatment Service Equipment Whslr
N.A.I.C.S.: 423830

Pentair International Armaturen Holding GmbH (1)
Werner-von-Siemens-Strasse, Korschenbroich, 41352, Germany
Tel.: (49) 2161615493
Holding Company
N.A.I.C.S.: 551112

Pentair International PLT Deutschland
GmbH (1)
Nobelstrasse 14, 41189, Monchengladbach,
Germany
Tel.: (49) 213131060
Web Site: http://www.nordic-water.de
Surveillance System Installation Services
N.A.I.C.S.: 238210

Subsidiary (Domestic):

Pentair International PLT Klartechnik
GmbH (2)
Hansemannstr 41, Neuss, 41468, Germany
Tel.: (49) 2131310634
Security System Installation Services
N.A.I.C.S.: 238210

Pentair International PLT Umwelttechnik GmbH (2)
Hansemannstr 41, Neuss, 41468,
Nordrhein-Westfalen, Germany
Tel.: (49) 2131310634
Industrial Valve Mfr
N.A.I.C.S.: 332911

Pentair Manufacturing Belgium
BVBA (1)
Toekomstlaan 30 Industriepark Wolfstee,
2200, Herentals, Belgium
Tel.: (32) 14283500
Web Site: http://www.pentair.com
Emp.: 200
Water Treatment Equipment Mfr
N.A.I.C.S.: 333310

Pentair Technical Products India Private Limited (1)
No 10C II Phase, Bengaluru, 560058, Karnataka, India
Tel.: (91) 8067152072
Web Site: http://www.pentair.com
Emp.: 50
Water Treatment Equipment Whslr
N.A.I.C.S.: 423830

PENTAIR PLC

Pentair plc—(Continued)

Pentair Thailand Ltd. (1)
1023 TPS Building Patanakaran Rd, Suanluang, Bangkok, 10250, Thailand
Tel.: (66) 27178153
Water Treatment Equipment Mfr
N.A.I.C.S.: 333310

Pentair Thermal Management Norway AS (1)
PO Box 146, Drobak, 1443, Norway
Tel.: (47) 66817990
Water Processing Services
N.A.I.C.S.: 562910

Pentair Umwelttechnik GmbH (1)
Im Petersfeld 6, 65624, Altendiez, Germany
Tel.: (49) 64329529900
Web Site: http://www.cleanairsystems.com
Sales Range: $25-49.9 Million
Emp.: 6
Environmental Consulting Services
N.A.I.C.S.: 541620

Pentair Water Germany GmbH (1)
Wiesenstr 4a, 64347, Griesheim, Germany
Tel.: (49) 615584170
Water Treatment Equipment Whslr
N.A.I.C.S.: 423830

Pentair Water Latinamerica S.A. (1)
San Jose 165 Capital Federal 1076, Buenos Aires, Argentina
Tel.: (54) 1148131996
Web Site: http://www.pentair.com
Emp.: 40
Water Treatment Service Equipment Whslr
N.A.I.C.S.: 423830

Pentair Water Polska Sp.z.o.o. (1)
Ul Plonow 21, 41-200, Sosnowiec, Poland
Tel.: (48) 322951200
Sales Range: $25-49.9 Million
Emp.: 10
Fluid Control & Thermal Management Products & Services
N.A.I.C.S.: 334519
Marezna Spyra *(VP)*

Pentair, Inc. (1)
5500 Wayzata Blvd Ste 900, Golden Valley, MN 55416-1261
Tel.: (763) 545-1730
Web Site: http://www.pentair.com
Fluid Filtration, Fluid Control, Enclosure & Thermal Management Products & Services
N.A.I.C.S.: 334519

Subsidiary (Non-US):

Alberta Electronic Company Limited (2)
7th ningjin Center 28th Floor Room B Shing Yip st, Kowloon, Kwun Tong, China (Hong Kong)
Tel.: (852) 23342788
Web Site: http://www.alberta.com.hk
Electric Power Transmission Services
N.A.I.C.S.: 237130

Subsidiary (Domestic):

Alliance Integrated Systems, Inc. (2)
7433 Harwin Dr, Houston, TX 77036
Tel.: (713) 868-4800
Web Site: http://www.pentair.com
Electrical Engineering Services
N.A.I.C.S.: 541330

Applied Wastewater Systems (2)
1101 Myers Pkwy, Ashland, OH 44805-1969
Tel.: (419) 289-1144
Web Site: http://www.femyers.com
Sales Range: $200-249.9 Million
Emp.: 600
Water System, Industrial Pump, Waste Handling Product & Grey Iron Casting Mfr
N.A.I.C.S.: 333914

Everpure Inc. (2)
1040 Muirfield Dr, Hanover Park, IL 60133-5468
Tel.: (630) 307-3000
Web Site: http://www.everpure.com
Sales Range: $100-124.9 Million
Emp.: 350
Mfr of Water Conditioning & Filtration Products
N.A.I.C.S.: 333310

Subsidiary (Non-US):

Everpure Japan Inc. (2)
Hashimoto MN Bldg 7F 3-25-1 Hashimoto, Midori-ku, Sagamihara, 252-0143, Kanagawa, Japan
Tel.: (81) 427753011
Web Site: https://www.everpure.co.jp
Water Treatment Services Including Sales & Distribution
N.A.I.C.S.: 562219

Subsidiary (Domestic):

Hoffman Enclosures Inc. (2)
2100 Hoffman Way, Anoka, MN 55303-1745
Tel.: (763) 421-2240
Web Site: http://www.hoffman.nvent.com
Sales Range: $500-549.9 Million
Emp.: 2,000
Designer & Mfr of Metal Enclosures to Protect Electronic Controls & Electrical Systems
N.A.I.C.S.: 332322
John Humbert *(CFO)*

Subsidiary (Non-US):

Hoffman Schroff PTE Ltd (2)
390 Havelock Road 04-01 Kings Centre, Singapore, 169662, Singapore
Tel.: (65) 67685800
Sales Range: $25-49.9 Million
Emp.: 10
Electronic Equipment Supply Whslr
N.A.I.C.S.: 449210

Subsidiary (Domestic):

Hydromatic Pentair (2)
1101 Myers Pkwy, Ashland, OH 44805-3524 (100%)
Tel.: (419) 289-3042
Web Site: http://www.hydromatic.com
Sales Range: $200-249.9 Million
Emp.: 350
Mfr of Pumps
N.A.I.C.S.: 333914

Subsidiary (Non-US):

Jung Pumpen GmbH (2)
Industriestr 4-6, 33803, Steinhagen, Germany
Tel.: (49) 5204170
Web Site: https://www.jung-pumpen.de
Sales Range: $100-124.9 Million
Emp.: 365
Waste Water Technology
N.A.I.C.S.: 333914

Pentair Private, Limited (2)
L/52 - 55 Vena Industrial Estate, Vena, Goa, 403722, India (100%)
Tel.: (91) 8322783014
Web Site: http://www.pentair.com
Sales Range: $25-49.9 Million
Emp.: 3
Mfr of Pressure Vessels
N.A.I.C.S.: 332420

Subsidiary (Domestic):

Pentair Pump Group, Inc. (2)
1101 Myers Pkwy, Ashland, OH 44805
Tel.: (419) 289-1144
Web Site: http://www.pentair.com
Sales Range: $150-199.9 Million
Emp.: 250
Pumps Mfr
N.A.I.C.S.: 333914

Subsidiary (Non-US):

F.E. Myers Company (3)
269 Trillium Dr, PO Box 9138, Kitchener, N2G 4W5, ON, Canada (100%)
Tel.: (519) 748-5470
Web Site: http://www.pentairpump.com
Sales Range: $10-24.9 Million
Emp.: 20
Water Pumps & Systems for Home & Farm
N.A.I.C.S.: 333914

Subsidiary (Domestic):

Hypro (3)
375 5th Ave NW, New Brighton, MN 55112
Tel.: (651) 766-6300
Web Site: http://www.shurflo.com
Pumps & Accessories Mfr
N.A.I.C.S.: 333914
Bob Olson *(Owner)*

Shurflo Pump Manufacturing Co. (3)
5900 Katella Ave, Cypress, CA 90630
Tel.: (562) 795-5200
Web Site: http://www.shurflo.com
Sales Range: $100-124.9 Million
Emp.: 100
Mfr of Pumps
N.A.I.C.S.: 333914

Subsidiary (Non-US):

Pentair Technical Products China (2)
21f of Cloud Nine Plaza No 1118 West Yan an Road, Changning District, Shanghai, 200052, China
Tel.: (86) 4008201133
Fluid Control & Thermal Management Products & Services
N.A.I.C.S.: 237130

Subsidiary (Domestic):

Pentair Technical Products, Inc. (2)
170 Commerce Dr, Warwick, RI 02886-2430 (100%)
Tel.: (401) 732-3770
Web Site: http://www.pentair.com
Sales Range: $75-99.9 Million
Emp.: 200
Electronic Components Mfr & Distr
N.A.I.C.S.: 334111

Pentair Thermal Management LLC (2)
307 Constitution Dr, Menlo Park, CA 94025-3032
Tel.: (713) 865-9899
Web Site: http://us.thermal.pentair.com
Sales Range: $125-149.9 Million
Emp.: 350
Heat Tracing, Floor Heating, Snow Melting & De-Icing, Temperature Measurement, Wiring & Leak Detection Systems
N.A.I.C.S.: 333415

Subsidiary (Non-US):

Nvent Solutions (UK) Limited (3)
3 Rutherford Road, Stephenson Industrial Estate, Washington, NE37 3HX, Tyne & Wear, United Kingdom
Tel.: (44) 1914198200
Web Site: http://www.pentairthermal.com
Security System Installation Services
N.A.I.C.S.: 238210

Pentair Thermal Controls Norway AS (3)
Sagaveien 13, PO Box 146, 1441, Drobak, Norway
Tel.: (47) 66 81 79 90
Electrical Heat Tracing System Distr
N.A.I.C.S.: 423610

Pentair Thermal Management Canada Ltd. (3)
250 W St, Trenton, K8V 5S2, ON, Canada (100%)
Tel.: (613) 392-6571
Web Site: http://www.pentair.com
Sales Range: $50-74.9 Million
Emp.: 185
Mineral Insulated Power, Heating & Thermoelectric Cables Mfr
N.A.I.C.S.: 335999

Subsidiary (Domestic):

Pentair Thermal Management Holdings B LLC (3)
307 Constitution Dr, Menlo Park, CA 94025-1164
Tel.: (650) 216-1526
Holding Company
N.A.I.C.S.: 551112

Pentair Thermal Management Holdings LLC (3)
307 Constitution Dr, Menlo Park, CA 94025-1164
Tel.: (650) 216-1526
Holding Company
N.A.I.C.S.: 551112

Subsidiary (Non-US):

Pentair Thermal Management India Private Limited (3)

INTERNATIONAL PUBLIC

A-26 Sector-63, Noida, 201 307, Uttar Pradesh, India
Tel.: (91) 8826754400
Heat Tracing Equipment Mfr
N.A.I.C.S.: 333414

Pentair Thermal Management Japan Co., Ltd. (3)
4F KC Bldg 3-16-1 Shin-Yokohama, Kohoku-ku, Yokohama, 222-0033, Kanagawa, Japan
Tel.: (81) 45 471 7630
Web Site: http://www.tycothermalcontrols.com
Electronic Connector Mfr & Distr
N.A.I.C.S.: 334417

Pentair Thermal Management KZ LLP (3)
4 A Smagulova St, Atyrau, 060005, Kazakhstan
Tel.: (7) 7122 325554
Sales Range: $25-49.9 Million
Emp.: 15
Heating Equipment Mfr
N.A.I.C.S.: 333414
Ilya Krotikov *(Mgr-Sls)*

Pentair Thermal Management Korea Ltd. (3)
4th Floor Bibong Bldg 840-10 Yeoksam-Dong, Gangnam-Gu, 135-936, Seoul, Korea (South)
Tel.: (82) 2 2129 7700
Electronic Connectors Distr
N.A.I.C.S.: 423690

Pentair Thermal Management Nordic AB (3)
Flojelbergsgatan 20B, 431 37, Molndal, Sweden
Tel.: (46) 31 335 58 00
Heat Tracing Equipment Mfr
N.A.I.C.S.: 333414

Pentair Thermal Management Polska Sp. z o.o. (3)
ul Cybernetyki 19, 02-677, Warsaw, Poland
Tel.: (48) 22 33 12 950
Security System Installation Services
N.A.I.C.S.: 238210
Krzysztof Czyzewski *(Gen Mgr)*

Subsidiary (Domestic):

Tracer Industries, Inc. (3)
7433 Harwin Dr, Houston, TX 77036-2007
Tel.: (713) 868-5500
Heat Tracing Products Mfr
N.A.I.C.S.: 335999

Subsidiary (Domestic):

Tracer Construction LLC (4)
7433 Harwin Dr, Houston, TX 77036
Tel.: (713) 868-5500
Construction Engineering Services
N.A.I.C.S.: 541330

Subsidiary (Non-US):

Tracer Industries Canada Limited (4)
11004 174 St NW, Edmonton, T5S 2P3, AB, Canada
Tel.: (780) 455-8111
Security System Services
N.A.I.C.S.: 561621

Subsidiary (Non-US):

Tyco Thermal Controls (Shanghai) Engineering Co., Ltd. (3)
20/F Innovation Building 1009 Yishan Road, Shanghai, 200233, China
Tel.: (86) 2124121688
Heat Tracing Equipment Mfr
N.A.I.C.S.: 333414

Tyco Thermal Controls (Shanghai) Trading Co. Ltd (3)
20/F Innovation Building 1009 Yishan Road, Shanghai, 200233, China
Tel.: (86) 2124121688
Heat Tracing Equipment Mfr
N.A.I.C.S.: 333414

Tyco Thermal Controls Finland Oy (3)
Pappilankatu 25, 05800, Hyvinkaa, Finland

Tel.: (358) 800116799
Emp.: 1
Electronic Connector Mfr & Distr
N.A.I.C.S.: 334417
Lars Alsterberg (Mgr-Bus Dev)

Subsidiary (Non-US):

Pentair Water (Suzhou) Co. Ltd. (2)
No 371 Heshan Road, High-Tech District, Suzhou, 215011, Jiangsu, China
Tel.: (86) 51266617690
Water Treatment Service Equipment Whslr
N.A.I.C.S.: 423830

Pentair Water Belgium N.V. (2)
Toekomstlaan 30 Industriepark Wolfstee, Herentals, 2200, Belgium (100%)
Tel.: (32) 14259911
Web Site: http://www.pentairpooleurope.com
Sales Range: $75-99.9 Million
Emp.: 200
Water Treatment Equipment Mfr
N.A.I.C.S.: 333414

Subsidiary (Domestic):

Pentair Water Group, Inc. (2)
293 Wright St, Delavan, WI 53115
Tel.: (262) 728-5551
Web Site: http://www.pentair.com
Sales Range: $450-499.9 Million
Emp.: 1,700
Mfr of Pumps, Valves, Filters, Related Fluid Handling Equipment & Pool & Spa Accessories
N.A.I.C.S.: 333914

Unit (Domestic):

Aurora Pump (3)
800 Airport Rd, North Aurora, IL 60542
Tel.: (630) 859-7000
Web Site: http://www.aurorapump.com
Sales Range: $75-99.9 Million
Emp.: 205
Pumps for Sewage & Waste Handling & Chemical, Commercial HVAC, Petrochemical, Water & Wastewater Treatment Markets
N.A.I.C.S.: 423830

Subsidiary (Domestic):

Pentair Water Group, Inc. - Dover (3)
47 Crosby Rd, Dover, NH 03820-4340
Tel.: (603) 749-1610
Sales Range: $50-74.9 Million
Emp.: 130
Household Type Water Filters & Softeners
N.A.I.C.S.: 333310
Jason Racine (Mgr-Ops)

Division (Domestic):

Pentair Water Pool & Spa, Inc. (3)
400 Regency Forest Dr, Cary, NC 27518 (100%)
Tel.: (919) 566-8000
Web Site: http://www.pentairpool.com
Sales Range: $125-149.9 Million
Emp.: 350
Mfr Of Swimming Pool Filters Pumps Heaters & Accessory Products
N.A.I.C.S.: 333310

Unit (Domestic):

Paragon Aquatics (4)
1351 Route 55, Lagrangeville, NY 12540
Tel.: (845) 463-7200
Web Site: http://www.paragonaquatics.com
Sales Range: $50-74.9 Million
Emp.: 45
Commercial Swimming Pool Equipment Mfr
N.A.I.C.S.: 332322

Pentair Water Pool & Spa, Inc. - California (4)
10951 W Los Angeles Ave, Moorpark, CA 93021-9744
Tel.: (805) 553-5000
Sales Range: $75-99.9 Million
Swimming Pool Equipment Mfr
N.A.I.C.S.: 334512

Division (Domestic):

Pentair Water Treatment (3)
20580 Enterprise Ave, Brookfield, WI 53045
Tel.: (262) 784-4190

Water-Conditioning Control Valves Mfr
N.A.I.C.S.: 333914

Subsidiary (Non-US):

Pentair Water Italy S.r.l. (2)
Corso Europa 2 angolo Via Trieste, Lainate, 20020, Milan, Italy (100%)
Tel.: (39) 029327111
Web Site: http://www.pentairwater.com
Sales Range: $25-49.9 Million
Emp.: 45
Distribution of Pressure Vessels & Other Products for Water Treatment
N.A.I.C.S.: 332420

Schroff GmbH (2)
Langenalber Str 96 100, 75334, Straubenhardt, Germany (100%)
Tel.: (49) 7082794214
Web Site: https://schroff.nvent.com
Sales Range: $150-199.9 Million
Emp.: 800
Mfr of Electronic Enclosures, Cabinets, Cases, Subracks, Microcomputer Packaging Systems, Backplanes, Power Supplies & Technical Workstations
N.A.I.C.S.: 333414

Schroff K.K. (2)
Nisso No 13 Bldg 4F 2-5-1 Shinyokohama, Kohoku-ku, Yokohama, 222-0033, Kanagawa, Japan
Tel.: (81) 454760281
Web Site: http://www.schroff.co.jp
Sales Range: $25-49.9 Million
Emp.: 60
Water Treatment Service Equipment Whslr
N.A.I.C.S.: 423830

Subsidiary (Domestic):

Sudmo North America, Inc. (2)
1330 Anvil Rd, Machesney Park, IL 61115
Tel.: (815) 639-0322
Water Treatment Service Equipment Whslr
N.A.I.C.S.: 423830

Webster Electric Company, LLC (2)
280 E Howard St, Des Plaines, IL 60018
Tel.: (847) 827-4444
Electrical Equipment Supply Whslr
N.A.I.C.S.: 423830

Safety Systems UK Pte. Ltd. (2)
3 International Business Park 05-14 Nordic European Centre, Singapore, 609927, Singapore
Tel.: (65) 6899 2280
Fire Protection Equipments Distr
N.A.I.C.S.: 423850

Schroff GmbH (1)
Langenalber Strasse 96-100, 75334, Straubenhardt, Germany
Tel.: (49) 70827940
Water Processing Services
N.A.I.C.S.: 562910

Schroff Scandinavia AB (1)
Flygfaltsgatan 11, PO Box 2003, Skarpnack, 128 21, Sweden
Tel.: (46) 86836100
Web Site: http://www.schroff.se
Sales Range: $25-49.9 Million
Emp.: 12
Computer System Integration Services
N.A.I.C.S.: 541512

Spensall Engineering Limited (1)
Kitson Road, Leeds, LS10 1NR, United Kingdom
Tel.: (44) 1132450726
Sales Range: $25-49.9 Million
Emp.: 45
Fire Alarm Mfr
N.A.I.C.S.: 334290
Catherine Judge (Mgr-HR)

Sudmo (UK) Ltd. (1)
8 De Salis Court, Hampton Lovett, Droitwich, WR9 ONX, Worcestershire, United Kingdom
Tel.: (44) 1905797280
Sales Range: $50-74.9 Million
Emp.: 7
Water Treatment Equipment Whslr
N.A.I.C.S.: 423830

Sudmo Holding GmbH (1)

Industriestrasse 7, 73469, Riesburg, Germany
Tel.: (49) 9081 8030
Web Site: http://www.suedmo.com
Valve Mfr
N.A.I.C.S.: 332912

TopAq Pty Limited (1)
L 8 499 St Kilda Rd, Melbourne, 3000, VIC, Australia
Tel.: (61) 39863 3500
Waste Treatment Services
N.A.I.C.S.: 221310

Union Engineering A/S (1)
Snaremosevej 17, Fredericia, 7000, Denmark
Tel.: (45) 76207700
Water Processing Services
N.A.I.C.S.: 562910

Union Engineering North America LLC (1)
1 Industry Dr, Palm Coast, FL 32137
Tel.: (386) 445-4200
Water Processing Services
N.A.I.C.S.: 562910

Valvulas Crosby Industria e Comercio Ltda. (1)
Av das Nacoes Unidas 8501 17 andar, Sao Paulo, 05425-070, Brazil
Tel.: (55) 1134346530
Web Site: http://www.crosby.com.br
Industrial Valve Mfr
N.A.I.C.S.: 332911

Vierte Korschenbroicher Armaturen Verwaltungs GmbH (1)
Werner-von-Siemens-Strasse, 41352, Korschenbroich, Germany
Tel.: (49) 2161615493
Pipe Fitting Mfr
N.A.I.C.S.: 332919

Water Reticulation Systems (Virginia) Pty Limited (1)
Shop 4 Brady St, Virginia, 5120, SA, Australia
Tel.: (61) 88380 9994
Emp.: 4
Water Irrigation & Reticulation Services
N.A.I.C.S.: 221310
Tony White (Gen Mgr)

X-Flow B.V. (1)
Marssteden 50, PO Box 739, 7547 TC, Enschede, Netherlands
Tel.: (31) 534287000
Web Site: https://xflow.pentair.com
Water Treatment Equipment Whslr
N.A.I.C.S.: 423830

PENTAL LIMITED

Level 6 390 St Kilda Rd, Melbourne, 3004, VIC, Australia
Tel.: (61) 392512311
Web Site: https://www.pental.com.au
PTL—(ASX)
Rev.: $89,975,224
Assets: $80,664,483
Liabilities: $25,642,847
Net Worth: $55,021,636
Earnings: $4,878,332
Emp.: 156
Fiscal Year-end: 06/26/22
Personal Care & Home Products Mfr
N.A.I.C.S.: 325620
Oliver Carton (Sec)

Subsidiaries:

DCS International Pty. Ltd. (1)
Unit 21 296 Bay Road, Cheltenham, Melbourne, 3192, VIC, Australia
Tel.: (61) 38 585 3300
Web Site: https://www.dcsinternational.com.au
Sales Range: $25-49.9 Million
Emp.: 6
Organic Chemical Mfr
N.A.I.C.S.: 325199

Hampers with Bite Pty. Ltd. (1)
55 Victoria St, Fitzroy, VIC, Australia
Tel.: (61) 1300943518
Web Site: https://www.hamperswithbite.com.au

Gift Hamper Distr
N.A.I.C.S.: 424990

PENTAMASTER CORPORATION BERHAD

Plot 18 and 19 Technoplex Medan Bayan Lepas, Taman Perindustrian Bayan Lepas Phase IV, 11900, Penang, Malaysia
Tel.: (60) 46469212
Web Site: https://www.pentamaster.com.my
Year Founded: 1991
PENTA—(KLS)
Rev.: $127,108,357
Assets: $245,115,209
Liabilities: $56,175,349
Net Worth: $188,939,860
Earnings: $27,627,586
Emp.: 802
Fiscal Year-end: 12/31/22
Automation Solutions & Services
N.A.I.C.S.: 332216
Pei Joo Gan (CFO)

Subsidiaries:

Pentamaster Automation (Germany) GmbH (1)
Lilienthalstr 2a, 82205, Gilching, Germany
Tel.: (49) 81057759988
Information Technology Services
N.A.I.C.S.: 541512

Pentamaster Automation (Japan) Co., Ltd. (1)
YS Yokohama Nishiguchi Building 7F 2-25-1 Tsuruya-cho, Kanagawa-ku, Yokohama, 220-1835, Kanagawa, Japan
Tel.: (81) 455948456
Technical Consulting Services
N.A.I.C.S.: 541690

Pentamaster Equipment Manufacturing Sdn. Bhd. (1)
Plot 18 & 19 Technoplex Medan Bayan Lepas Taman Perindustrian Phase IV, 11900, Bayan Lepas, Penang, Malaysia
Tel.: (60) 46469212
Precision Machining Parts Mfr
N.A.I.C.S.: 332216

Pentamaster International Ltd. (1)
Plot 18 & 19 Technoplex Medan Bayan Lepas, Taman Perindustrian Bayan Lepas Phase IV, 11900, Penang, Malaysia
Tel.: (60) 46469212
Web Site: http://www.pentamaster.com.my
Rev.: $150,598,608
Assets: $252,294,516
Liabilities: $67,712,016
Net Worth: $184,582,500
Earnings: $30,960,601
Emp.: 920
Fiscal Year-end: 12/31/2023
Automation Equipment Mfr
N.A.I.C.S.: 334413
Choon Chuah (Chm)

TP Concept Sdn. Bhd. (1)
Plot 197 Jalan Permatang Damar Laut, 11900, Bayan Lepas, Penang, Malaysia
Tel.: (60) 46262079
Web Site: https://www.tp-concept.com
High Precision Metal Components Mfr & Distr
N.A.I.C.S.: 332510

PENTAMEDIA GRAPHICS LIMITED

No 25 First Main Road United India Colony Kodambakkam, Chennai, 600 024, India
Tel.: (91) 44 2483 3067
Web Site: http://www.pentamedia.in
Rev.: $504,362
Assets: $17,716,803
Liabilities: $177,695
Net Worth: $17,539,108
Earnings: $16,836
Emp.: 18
Fiscal Year-end: 03/31/18
Information Technology Software
N.A.I.C.S.: 513210

PENTANET LIMITED

Pentamedia Graphics Limited—(Continued)

PENTANET LIMITED
150C ST Georges Terrace, Perth, 6000, WA, Australia
Tel.: (61) 894662670   AU
Web Site:
  https://www.pentanet.com.au
Year Founded: 2017
5GG—(ASX)
Rev.: $13,663,689
Assets: $31,360,110
Liabilities: $11,046,489
Net Worth: $20,313,621
Earnings: ($4,935,124)
Emp.: 69
Fiscal Year-end: 06/30/23
Telecommunication Servicesb
N.A.I.C.S.: 517810
Mart-Marie Derman (CFO)

PENTEL CO., LTD.
7 2 Nihonbashi Koami cho, Chuo ku, Tokyo, 103-8538, Japan
Tel.: (81) 336673333   JP
Web Site: http://www.pentel.co.jp
Year Founded: 1946
Sales Range: $125-149.9 Million
Emp.: 900
Stationery Product Mfr
N.A.I.C.S.: 339940

Subsidiaries:

Pentel of America, Ltd.   (1)
2715 Columbia St, Torrance, CA 90503
Tel.: (310) 320-3831
Web Site: http://www.pentel.com
Sales Range: $75-99.9 Million
Emp.: 108
Mfr of Pens, Liquid Ink Ball Pens, Porous Point Pens, Plastic Point Pens, Mechanical Pencils, Markers, Art Materials, Sliding Sleeve Automatic Pencils & Leads
N.A.I.C.S.: 424120
I. Nakayama (Pres)

Division (Domestic):

Pentel of America   (2)
1250 Arthur Ave, Elk Grove Village, IL 60007-5221
Tel.: (847) 640-7570
Web Site: http://www.pentel.com
Sales Range: $25-49.9 Million
Emp.: 20
Sales & Distribution Center
N.A.I.C.S.: 424120

PENTLAND GROUP LIMITED
8 Manchester Square, London, W1U 3PH, United Kingdom
Tel.: (44) 2075353800   UK
Web Site: http://www.pentland.com
Year Founded: 1932
Sales Range: $400-449.9 Million
Emp.: 2,000
Holding Company; Branded Apparel Licensing & Marketer
N.A.I.C.S.: 551112
Robert Stephen Rubin (Chm)

Subsidiaries:

Acme Refrigeration Ltd.   (1)
Cunliffe Rd, Whitebirk Industrial Est, Blackburn, BB1 5ST, Lancashire, United Kingdom   (100%)
Tel.: (44) 254277999
Sales Range: $50-74.9 Million
Emp.: 105
Mfr of Refrigeration Equipment
N.A.I.C.S.: 333415

JD Sports Fashion plc   (1)
Hollinsbrook Way Pilsworth, Bury, BL9 8RR, Lancashire, United Kingdom (51.9%)
Tel.: (44) 1617671000
Web Site: https://www.jdplc.com
Rev.: $13,324,064,688
Assets: $10,169,615,755
Liabilities: $6,544,236,591
Net Worth: $3,625,379,164
Earnings: $764,661,273
Emp.: 81,866
Fiscal Year-end: 02/03/2024
Sports Apparel Product Distr
N.A.I.C.S.: 551112
Dominic Platt (CFO)

Subsidiary (Domestic):

Blacks Outdoor Retail Limited   (2)
Hollinsbrook Way, Pilsworth, Bury, BL9 8RR, Lancs, United Kingdom   (100%)
Tel.: (44) 161 767 1000
Web Site: http://www.blacks.co.uk
Retailer of Outdoor Footwear, Apparel & Equipment
N.A.I.C.S.: 424340

Go Outdoors Limited   (2)
Cuthbert House Arley Street, Sheffield, S2 4QP, United Kingdom
Tel.: (44) 3300081555
Web Site: http://www.gooutdoors.co.uk
Electronic Shopping Services
N.A.I.C.S.: 459110
Louise Ayling (Head-Fin)

Subsidiary (US):

Hibbett, Inc.   (2)
2700 Milan Ct, Birmingham, AL 35211
Tel.: (205) 942-4292
Web Site: https://www.hibbett.com
Rev.: $1,708,316,000
Assets: $939,160,000
Liabilities: $562,929,000
Net Worth: $376,231,000
Earnings: $128,057,000
Emp.: 3,800
Fiscal Year-end: 01/28/2023
Sporting Good Stores Operator
N.A.I.C.S.: 459110
Michael E. Longo (Pres & CEO)

Subsidiary (Domestic):

Hibbett Sporting Goods Inc.   (3)
413 Eagle Ridge Dr, Lake Wales, FL 33859
Tel.: (863) 679-8013
Web Site: http://www.hibbett.com
Rev.: $8,000,000
Emp.: 13
Sporting & Recreational Goods & Supplies Merchant Whslr
N.A.I.C.S.: 423910

Subsidiary (Domestic):

City Gear, LLC   (4)
4841 Summer Ave, Memphis, TN 38122   (100%)
Tel.: (901) 762-7850
Web Site: http://www.citygear.com
Men's Clothing Retailer
N.A.I.C.S.: 424350
Benjamin Knighten (COO & Sr VP-Ops)

Subsidiary (US):

Shoe Palace Corporation   (2)
755 Jarvis Dr, Morgan Hill, CA 95037
Tel.: (909) 885-8111
Web Site: http://www.shoepalace.com
Shoe Stores
N.A.I.C.S.: 458210
Mike Lopez (Mgr-Site)

The Finish Line, Inc.   (2)
3308 N Mitthoeffer Rd, Indianapolis, IN 46235
Tel.: (317) 899-1022
Web Site: http://www.finishline.com
Athletic Apparel & Accessories Retailer
N.A.I.C.S.: 339920
Glenn S. Lyon (Chm)

Subsidiary (Domestic):

Garry Gribble's Running Sports, LLC   (3)
8600 Ward Pkwy, Kansas City, MO 64114
Tel.: (816) 363-4800
Web Site: http://www.garrygribbles.com
Shoe Stores
N.A.I.C.S.: 458210
David Williford (Mgr)

Spike's Holding, LLC   (3)
3308 N Mitthoeffer Rd, Indianapolis, IN 46235   (100%)
Tel.: (317) 899-1022
Holding Company

N.A.I.C.S.: 551112
The Finish Line Puerto Rico, Inc.   (3)
725 W Main Ave, Bayamon, PR 00961-4470
Tel.: (787) 779-6603
Shoe Store Operator
N.A.I.C.S.: 458210

Pentland Asia   (1)
13th Fl Harbour Crystal Ctr 100 Granville Rd, Tsim Sha Tsui E, Kowloon, China (Hong Kong)   (100%)
Tel.: (852) 27343288
Web Site: http://www.pentland.com
Sales Range: $25-49.9 Million
Emp.: 70
Business Development & Sourcing of Various Fashion Brands
N.A.I.C.S.: 459999

Pentland Asia Bangkok (Thailand)   (1)
The Offices At CentralWorld 19th Floor Unit 1910 999/9 Rama 1 Road, Pathumwan, Bangkok, Thailand
Tel.: (66) 2 696 2499
Sports Goods Whslr
N.A.I.C.S.: 423910

Pentland Asia Ho Chi Minh City (Vietnam) Ltd   (1)
Floor 2 Room 203-204 Saigon Riverside Building 2A-4A Ton Duc Thang Str, Ben Nghe Ward District 1, Ho Chi Minh City, Vietnam
Tel.: (84) 8 6256 3500
Sports Goods Whslr
N.A.I.C.S.: 423910

Pentland Asia Pacific Ltd   (1)
Green Office Park 6 Wing B 3rd Floor Zone 9B, Jl BSD City, Tangerang, 15345, Indonesia
Tel.: (62) 2129580200
Web Site: http://www.pentland.com
Sports Goods Whslr
N.A.I.C.S.: 423910

Pentland Asia Shenzhen (China) Co Ltd   (1)
Room 18B Benyuan Building No 6015 Shennan Road, Futian District, Shenzhen, 518040, China
Tel.: (86) 755 3396 0777
Sports Goods Whslr
N.A.I.C.S.: 423910

Pentland Brands PLC   (1)
Lakeside Squires Lane, London, N3 2QT, United Kingdom   (100%)
Tel.: (44) 2083462600
Web Site: http://www.pentlandbrands.com
Sales Range: $100-124.9 Million
Emp.: 550
Athletic Footwear Mfr
N.A.I.C.S.: 316210
Andy Long (CEO)

Pentland Group plc - Pentland Distribution Great Harwood Unit   (1)
Premier Mill West Street, Great Harwood, BB6 7LT, United Kingdom
Tel.: (44) 1254 885 556
Sports Goods Whslr
N.A.I.C.S.: 423910

Pentland Group plc - Pentland Distribution Washington Unit   (1)
Glover Distribution Centre Spire Road Glover Industrial Estate, District 11 Tyne & Wear, Washington, NE37 3ES, United Kingdom
Tel.: (44) 191 415 4037
Sports Goods Whslr
N.A.I.C.S.: 423910
Tim Marriner (Mgr)

Pentland Group plc - Pentland Shipping Unit   (1)
Unit 2 Walker Industrial Park Walker Road Guide, Lancashire, Blackburn, BB1 2QE, United Kingdom
Tel.: (44) 1254 505 900
Sports Goods Whslr
N.A.I.C.S.: 423910

Pentland Shipping Services, Ltd.   (1)
Pentland Ctr Lakeside House, Squires Ln, London, N3 2QL, United Kingdom   (100%)

INTERNATIONAL PUBLIC

Tel.: (44) 2083462600
Web Site: http://www.pentland.com
Sales Range: $200-249.9 Million
Emp.: 500
Freight Forwarder
N.A.I.C.S.: 488510

Pentland Trading Private Ltd   (1)
145 Santhome High Road, MRC Nagar, Chennai, 600 028, India
Tel.: (91) 44 4314 446
Sports Goods Whslr
N.A.I.C.S.: 423910
M. A. Lakshmi Priya (Mgr-HR)

Pentland USA Inc.   (1)
3333 New Hyde Pk Rd Ste 200 & 212, New Hyde Park, NY 11042
Tel.: (516) 365-1333
Sports Goods Whslr
N.A.I.C.S.: 423910

Speedo International Ltd.   (1)
Speedo House Enterprise Way, NG2 Business Park, Nottingham, NG21EN, United Kingdom   (100%)
Tel.: (44) 1158555000
Web Site: http://www.speedo.com
Sales Range: $25-49.9 Million
Emp.: 200
Mfr of Swimwear
N.A.I.C.S.: 315210
David Robinson (Pres)

PENTOKEY ORGANY (INDIA) LIMITED
509 Western Edge I Off Western Express Highway Borivali East, Fort, Mumbai, 400066, India
Tel.: (91) 2228545118
Web Site: https://www.pentokey.com
Year Founded: 1986
524210—(BOM)
Rev.: $253,025
Assets: $852,221
Liabilities: $69,441
Net Worth: $782,780
Earnings: ($61,671)
Emp.: 3
Fiscal Year-end: 03/31/20
Organic Chemical Mfr
N.A.I.C.S.: 325199

Subsidiaries:

PENTOKEY ORGANY (INDIA) LIMITED - RATNAGIRI FACTORY   (1)
D-1/1 MIDC Lote Parshuram M G Road, Tal Khed, Ratnagiri, 415 722, India
Tel.: (91) 2356 273078
Chemical Products Mfr
N.A.I.C.S.: 325199

PENYAO ENVIRONMENTAL PROTECTION CO., LTD.
Pengyao Technology Innovation Park, Industrial Concentration Zone Gaocheng Town, Yixing, 214214, China
Tel.: (86) 51088568063
Web Site:
  https://www.penyao.com.cn
Year Founded: 1984
300664—(CHIN)
Rev.: $292,505,125
Assets: $1,115,620,088
Liabilities: $497,255,206
Net Worth: $618,364,881
Earnings: $36,321,173
Fiscal Year-end: 12/31/23
Water Treatment Equipment Mfr & Distr
N.A.I.C.S.: 333310
Wang Pengyao (Chm & Gen Mgr)

PEOPLE & TECHNOLOGY INC.
33 Cheomdangieop-ro, Gumi, 39422, Gyeongsangbuk-do, Korea (South)
Tel.: (82) 544696900
Web Site: https://www.epnt.co.kr
Year Founded: 2003

137400—(KRS)
Rev.: $320,463,713
Assets: $834,413,520
Liabilities: $655,552,925
Net Worth: $178,860,595
Earnings: $45,768,274
Emp.: 459
Fiscal Year-end: 12/31/22
Industrial Machinery Mfr
N.A.I.C.S.: 333248
Joonsup Kim (CEO)

Subsidiaries:

People & Technology Inc. - 2th Factory (1)
970 Inpyeung-ri Buksam-eup, Chilgok, 718-844, Gyung-buk, Korea (South)
Tel.: (82) 549759269
Semiconductor Devices Mfr
N.A.I.C.S.: 334413

PEOPLE CO., LTD.
VORT Higashi-Nihonbashi Mori Bldg 2-15-5 Higashi-Nihonbashi, Chuo-Ku, Tokyo, 103-0004, Japan
Tel.: (81) 338622768
Web Site: https://www.people-kk.co.jp
Year Founded: 1977
7865—(TKS)
Rev.: $43,463,200
Assets: $25,884,320
Liabilities: $4,162,400
Net Worth: $21,721,920
Earnings: $3,213,760
Emp.: 50
Fiscal Year-end: 01/31/21
Toy & Bicycle Mfr
N.A.I.C.S.: 339930
Masato Kiribuchi (Exec Officer)

PEOPLE CORPORATION
1403 Kenaston Boulevard, Winnipeg, R3P 2T5, MB, Canada
Tel.: (866) 940-3950
Web Site: http://www.peoplecorporation.com
Year Founded: 2006
PEO—(TSXV)
Rev.: $124,346,990
Assets: $250,598,594
Liabilities: $151,223,245
Net Worth: $99,375,350
Earnings: ($1,996,852)
Emp.: 925
Fiscal Year-end: 08/31/19
Human Resouce Services
N.A.I.C.S.: 541612
Laurie Goldberg (Co-Founder & Chm)

Subsidiaries:

BPA Financial Group Ltd. (1)
90 Burnhamthorpe Road West Suite 300, Mississauga, L5B 3C3, ON, Canada
Tel.: (905) 275-6466
Web Site: https://www.bpagroup.com
Financial Services
N.A.I.C.S.: 522110
Jeffrey C. Baldwin (Pres)

Bencom Financial Services Group Inc. (1)
1060 Guelph Street Main Floor, Kitchener, N2B 2E3, ON, Canada
Tel.: (519) 579-4730
Web Site: http://www.bencomfsgi.com
Financial Services
N.A.I.C.S.: 522110
Dino Costabile (Mng Partner)

Benefit Partners Inc. (1)
1-2140 Regent St, Sudbury, P3E 3Z8, ON, Canada
Tel.: (705) 524-1559
Web Site: http://www.benefitpartners.com
Insurance Services
N.A.I.C.S.: 524210
Jennifer Tagliabracci (Acct Mgr)

Coughlin & Associates Ltd. (1)
466 Tremblay Road, Ottawa, K1G 3R1, ON, Canada
Tel.: (613) 231-2266
Web Site: https://www.coughlin.ca
Insurance Services
N.A.I.C.S.: 524210
Sarah Welsh (Fin Mgr)

Lane Quinn Benefit Consultants Ltd. (1)
250 1011-9th Avenue S E, Calgary, T2G 0H7, AB, Canada
Tel.: (403) 261-6084
Web Site: http://www.lanequinn.com
Insurance Services
N.A.I.C.S.: 524210
Jay B. Quinn (Founder & Pres)

Life Benefit Solutions Inc. (1)
Unit 100 - 6 Roslyn Road, Winnipeg, R3L 0G5, MB, Canada
Tel.: (204) 237-5433
Web Site: https://www.lifeinc.ca
Insurance Services
N.A.I.C.S.: 524210
Romelyn Avila (Office Mgr)

People First HR Services Ltd. (1)
1403 Kenaston Boulevard, Winnipeg, R3P 2T5, MB, Canada
Tel.: (204) 940-3900
Web Site: https://www.peoplefirsthr.com
Career Development Services
N.A.I.C.S.: 611430
Gord Clunie (VP-Professional & Mgmt Recruitment)

Silverberg & Associates Inc. (1)
9913 - 112 Street, Edmonton, T5K 1L6, AB, Canada
Tel.: (780) 448-0676
Web Site: http://www.silverberggroup.com
Insurance Services
N.A.I.C.S.: 524210
Doug K. Silverberg (Partner)

Sirius Benefit Plans Inc. (1)
1403 Kenaston Blvd, Winnipeg, R3P 2T5, MB, Canada
Tel.: (204) 488-7600
Web Site: http://www.siriusbenefits.ca
Insurance Services
N.A.I.C.S.: 524210
Ed Melna (Pres)

Skipwith & Associates Insurance Agencies Inc. (1)
6 Cumberland Street, Barrie, L4N 2P4, ON, Canada
Tel.: (705) 734-6279
Web Site: http://www.skipwith.ca
Insurance Services
N.A.I.C.S.: 524210

PEOPLE&TECHNOLOGY MS, INC.
16 25-gil Seongseogongdan-ro, Dalseo-Gu, Daegu, 35886, Korea (South)
Tel.: (82) 535823577
Web Site: https://www.ms-mc.co.kr
Year Founded: 2001
257370—(KRS)
Rev.: $10,630,021
Assets: $44,526,902
Liabilities: $28,048,434
Net Worth: $16,478,469
Earnings: ($4,451,149)
Emp.: 50
Fiscal Year-end: 12/31/21
General Purpose Machinery Mfr
N.A.I.C.S.: 333998
Kum Sanghwan (CEO)

PEOPLE'S BANK OF CHINA
32 Chengfang Street, Xi Cheng District, Beijing, 100800, China
Tel.: (86) 1066194114
Web Site: http://www.pbc.gov.cn
Year Founded: 1948
Banking Services
N.A.I.C.S.: 521110
Zhou Xiaochuan (Governor)

PEOPLE'S GARMENT PUBLIC COMPANY LIMITED
666 Rama III Road Bangpongpang, Yannawa, Bangkok, 10120, Thailand
Tel.: (66) 26856500
Web Site: https://www.pg.co.th
Year Founded: 1980
PG—(THA)
Rev.: $22,424,127
Assets: $50,029,327
Liabilities: $6,394,545
Net Worth: $43,634,781
Earnings: $758,571
Emp.: 727
Fiscal Year-end: 12/31/23
Garment & Textile Mfr & Distr
N.A.I.C.S.: 424350
Chailert Manoonpol (Vice Chm)

PEOPLE'S INSURANCE COMPANY (GROUP) OF CHINA LIMITED
PICC Building No 88 West Chang'an Street, Xicheng District, Beijing, 100031, China
Tel.: (86) 1069009192 CN
Web Site: https://www.picc.com
Year Founded: 1949
1339—(OTCIQ)
Rev.: $85,253,101,462
Assets: $208,953,118,077
Liabilities: $167,283,728,401
Net Worth: $41,669,389,677
Earnings: $4,766,836,509
Emp.: 177,852
Fiscal Year-end: 12/31/22
Health, Personal & Life Insurance
N.A.I.C.S.: 524210
Houjie Zhou (CFO & Officer-Fin)

Subsidiaries:

PICC (Hong Kong) Limited (1)
15/F Guangdong Investment Tower 148 Connaught Road Central, Hong Kong, China (Hong Kong)
Tel.: (852) 25172332
Web Site: https://www.picchk.com
Finance Services
N.A.I.C.S.: 541611

PICC Asset Management Company Limited (1)
Floor 20 21 and 22 Tower 1 Century Plaza No 1198 Century Avenue, Pudong New District, Shanghai, 200122, China
Tel.: (86) 2138571800
Web Site: https://www.piccamc.com
Asset Management Services
N.A.I.C.S.: 523940

PICC Capital Insurance Asset Management Co., Ltd. (1)
8th Floor No 88 West Changan Street, Xicheng, Beijing, 100031, China
Tel.: (86) 1083561999
Web Site: https://www.picccim.com.cn
Insurance Services
N.A.I.C.S.: 524210

PICC Capital Investment Management Company Limited (1)
8th Floor 88 West Chang an Street, Xicheng District, Beijing, 100031, China
Tel.: (86) 1083561999
Web Site: http://www.picc.com
Financial Consulting Services
N.A.I.C.S.: 541611
Casey Chai (Asst Mgr)

PICC Health Insurance Company Limited (1)
6th Floor No 88 West Chang'an Street, Xicheng District, Beijing, 100032, China
Tel.: (86) 1058332833
Web Site: https://www.picchealth.com
Health Insurance Services
N.A.I.C.S.: 524114

PICC Investment Holding Company Limited (1)
7th Floor PICC Building No 88 West Chang'an Street, Xicheng District, Beijing, 100031, China
Tel.: (86) 1069009888
Web Site: https://www.picc-inv.com
Finance Services
N.A.I.C.S.: 541611

PICC Property & Casualty Company Limited (1)
Tower 2 No 2 Jianguomenwai Avenue, Chaoyang District, Beijing, 100022, China
Tel.: (86) 1085176084
Web Site: http://www.piccnet.com.cn
Rev.: $66,368,580,270
Assets: $99,096,381,210
Liabilities: $69,981,731,700
Net Worth: $29,114,649,510
Earnings: $3,197,186,280
Emp.: 180,616
Fiscal Year-end: 12/31/2020
Insurance Services
N.A.I.C.S.: 524126
Jianmin Miao (Chm)

PEOPLE'S LEASING AND FINANCIAL SERVICES LIMITED
Paramount Heights 12 Floor 65/2/1 Box Culvert Road Purana Paltan, Dhaka, 1000, Bangladesh
Tel.: (880) 247118938 BD
Web Site: https://www.plfsbd.com
Year Founded: 1996
PLFSL—(CHT)
Rev.: $4,151,321
Assets: $142,216,869
Liabilities: $474,651,939
Net Worth: ($332,435,071)
Earnings: ($29,576,937)
Emp.: 24
Fiscal Year-end: 12/31/22
Leasing & Financial Services
N.A.I.C.S.: 522220
Nizamul Ahsan (Vice Chm)

PEOPLE, DREAMS & TECHNOLOGIES GROUP CO., LTD.
1-20-4 Nihonbashi Kakigara-cho, Chuo-ku, Tokyo, 1030014, Japan
Tel.: (81) 336393317
Web Site: https://www.pdt-g.co.jp
9248—(TKS)
Rev.: $263,045,920
Assets: $239,451,602
Liabilities: $102,695,738
Net Worth: $136,755,864
Earnings: $7,948,464
Emp.: 2,036
Fiscal Year-end: 09/30/23
Management Consulting Services
N.A.I.C.S.: 541618

Subsidiaries:

Effect Co., Ltd. (1)
Hakata Sun City Building 5th Floor 2 1-5 Hakataeki minami, Hakata-ku, Fukuoka, 812-001, Japan
Tel.: (81) 924091723
Web Site: https://effect-effect.com
Emp.: 37
Software Development Services
N.A.I.C.S.: 541511

PEOPLE.CN CO., LTD.
No 2 Jintai Xilu, Chaoyang District, Beijing, 100733, China
Tel.: (86) 1065369999
Web Site: https://en.people.cn
Year Founded: 1997
603000—(SHG)
Rev.: $277,678,992
Assets: $772,143,419
Liabilities: $220,592,998
Net Worth: $551,550,421
Earnings: $43,552,234
Fiscal Year-end: 12/31/22
Internet Advertising Services
N.A.I.C.S.: 513120
Ye Zhenzhen (Chm & Pres)

PEOPLEBIO CO.
242 Pangyo-Ro 6Fl Pdc C-Dong,

PEOPLEBIO CO.

PeopleBio Co.—(Continued)
Bundang-Gu, Seongnam, 13487, Gyeonggi-do, Korea (South)
Tel.: (82) 315267825
Web Site: https://www.peoplebio.net
Year Founded: 2002
304840—(KRS)
Rev.: $3,409,187
Assets: $32,456,134
Liabilities: $27,912,495
Net Worth: $4,543,639
Earnings: ($10,970,431)
Emp.: 54
Fiscal Year-end: 12/31/22
Pharmaceutical Preparation Mfr & Distr
N.A.I.C.S.: 325412
Sungkee Lee *(Acct Mgr)*

PEOPLEIN LIMITED
Level 6 540 Wickham Street, Fortitude Valley, 4006, QLD, Australia
Tel.: (61) 732380800 AU
Web Site:
https://www.peoplein.com.au
Year Founded: 1996
PPE—(ASX)
Rev.: $788,763,351
Assets: $261,272,034
Liabilities: $154,413,728
Net Worth: $106,858,306
Earnings: $3,598,424
Emp.: 15,000
Fiscal Year-end: 06/30/24
Workforce Management Services
N.A.I.C.S.: 541612
Thomas Reardon *(CEO-Industrial & Specialist Svcs & Exec Dir)*

Subsidiaries:

AWX Pty Ltd (1)
69-75 Sandgate Road, Albion, 4010, QLD, Australia
Tel.: (61) 732380800
Web Site: https://www.awx.com.au
Staffing Services
N.A.I.C.S.: 561311

Australian Healthcare Academy Pty Ltd (1)
8/30 Atchison Street, Saint Leonards, 2065, NSW, Australia
Tel.: (61) 1300953276
Web Site:
http://www.healthcareacademy.com.au
Nursing Services
N.A.I.C.S.: 611519

Carestaff Nursing Services Pty Ltd (1)
Level 2 Suite 201 Varsity One 1 Lake Orr Drive, Varsity Lakes, 4227, QLD, Australia
Tel.: (61) 1300227378
Web Site:
https://www.carestaffnursing.com.au
Hospital & Health Care Services
N.A.I.C.S.: 622110

Edmen Community Staffing Solutions Pty Ltd (1)
Family Services House O136 Level 1 Ste 103 Stockland Civic Plaza, 211 Lake Entrance Rd, Shellharbour, 2529, NSW, Australia
Tel.: (61) 1300665880
Web Site: https://www.edmencss.com.au
Staffing Services
N.A.I.C.S.: 561311

Expect A Star Services Pty Ltd (1)
Level 3 1 Marshall Avenue, Saint Leonards, 2065, NSW, Australia
Tel.: (61) 1300669653
Web Site: https://www.expectastar.com.au
Staffing Services
N.A.I.C.S.: 561311

First Choice Care Pty Ltd (1)
PO Box 975, Capalaba, 4157, QLD, Australia
Tel.: (61) 1300307241
Web Site: http://www.firstchoicecare.com.au
Staffing Services
N.A.I.C.S.: 561311

Halcyon Knights New Zealand Ltd. (1)
Level 3 Stanbeth House 28 Customs Street East, Auckland, 1010, New Zealand
Tel.: (64) 225007035
Staffing Services
N.A.I.C.S.: 561311

Halcyon Knights Pte Ltd (1)
101B Telok Ayer St 03-00, Singapore, 068574, Singapore
Tel.: (65) 94278839
Staffing Services
N.A.I.C.S.: 561311

Halcyon Knights Pty Ltd (1)
Level 18 31 Queen Street, Melbourne, 3000, VIC, Australia
Tel.: (61) 392351111
Web Site:
https://www.halcyonknights.com.au
Staffing Services
N.A.I.C.S.: 561311

Illuminate Search & Consulting Pty. Ltd. (1)
Level 10 50 Margaret Street, Sydney, NSW, Australia
Tel.: (61) 292486866
Web Site:
https://www.illuminatesearch.com.au
Information Technology Consulting Services
N.A.I.C.S.: 541512

Mobilise Group Pty Ltd (1)
Westminster Business Center Printing House Lane, Hayes, London, UB3 1AP, Middlesex, United Kingdom
Tel.: (44) 2085737777
Web Site: http://www.mobilisecase.com
Mobile Accessory Distr
N.A.I.C.S.: 449210

Network Nursing Agency Pty Ltd (1)
8/30 Atchison St, Saint Leonards, 2065, NSW, Australia
Tel.: (61) 1300568773
Web Site: https://www.nursing-agency.com.au
Hospital & Health Care Services
N.A.I.C.S.: 622110

Perigon Group Pty. Ltd. (1)
Level 15 20 Hunter Street, Sydney, NSW, Australia
Tel.: (61) 297755900
Web Site: https://www.perigongroup.com.au
Finance & Accounting Consultant Services
N.A.I.C.S.: 541219

Project Partners Corporation Pty Ltd (1)
A Lvl 6 540 Wickham Street, Brisbane CBD, Fortitude Valley, 4006, QLD, Australia
Tel.: (61) 1300001372
Web Site: https://www.project-partners.com.au
Business Consultancy Services
N.A.I.C.S.: 541611

Supreme Nursing Global Pty Ltd (1)
12 Glasgow Street, Ashgrove, Brisbane, 4060, QLD, Australia
Tel.: (61) 1300911884
Web Site:
http://www.supremenursing.com.au
Nursing Care Services
N.A.I.C.S.: 623110

Techforce Personnel Pty. Ltd. (1)
Level 4 45 St Georges Terrace, Perth, WA, Australia
Tel.: (61) 863637040
Web Site: https://www.techforce.com.au
Emp.: 8,500
Building & Civil Engineering Services
N.A.I.C.S.: 541330

Timberwolf Planting Pty Ltd (1)
Level 6/540 Wickham Street, Fortitude Valley, 4006, QLD, Australia
Tel.: (61) 1300840845
Web Site:
https://www.timberwolfplanting.com.au
Landscaping Services
N.A.I.C.S.: 561730

Victorian Nurse Specialists Pty Ltd (1)
Suite 3 107 Union Road, Surry Hills, 3127, VIC, Australia
Tel.: (61) 398987000
Web Site:
http://www.nursespecialists.com.au
Hospital & Health Care Services
N.A.I.C.S.: 622110

Vision Surveys (QLD) Pty. Ltd. (1)
4/2 Myer Lasky Dr, Cannonvale, QLD, Australia
Tel.: (61) 749483781
Web Site:
https://www.visionsurveysqld.com.au
Building Design & Planning Services
N.A.I.C.S.: 541310

PEOPLES ADVERTISING
Laivasillankatu 14, C 00100, Helsinki, Finland
Tel.: (358) 50 5606022
Web Site: http://www.peoples.fi
Advetising Agency
N.A.I.C.S.: 541810
Klaus Suhonen *(Dir-Art)*

PEOPLES INSURANCE COMPANY LIMITED
15th Floor 36 Dilkusha C/A, Dhaka, 1000, Bangladesh
Tel.: (880) 2223384166
Web Site:
https://www.peoplesinsurance.com
Year Founded: 1985
PEOPLESINS—(CHT)
Rev.: $753,720
Assets: $26,098,438
Liabilities: $12,173,033
Net Worth: $13,925,405
Earnings: $1,087,485
Emp.: 336
Fiscal Year-end: 12/31/23
Insurance Agency Services
N.A.I.C.S.: 524210
Mohamed Ali Hossain *(Chm)*

PEOPLES INVESTMENTS LIMITED
New Hind House 3 Narottam Morarji Marg Ballard Estate, Mumbai, 400 001, India
Tel.: (91) 2266046000
Web Site:
https://www.pplsinvestments.com
501144—(BOM)
Rev.: $6,825
Assets: $6,392
Liabilities: $381
Net Worth: $6,012
Earnings: ($1,313)
Emp.: 1
Fiscal Year-end: 03/31/21
Investment Management Service
N.A.I.C.S.: 523150
Suryakant Laxman Khare *(CFO & Sec)*

PEOPLES LEASING & FINANCE PLC
No 1161 Maradana Road, Borella, Colombo, Sri Lanka
Tel.: (94) 112631631
Web Site: https://www.plc.lk
Year Founded: 1995
PLC—(COL)
Rev.: $134,367,035
Assets: $666,907,038
Liabilities: $505,635,703
Net Worth: $161,271,335
Earnings: $11,808,476
Emp.: 2,114
Fiscal Year-end: 03/31/23
Commercial Banking Services
N.A.I.C.S.: 522110
A. S. Ibrahim *(CEO & Gen Mgr)*

Subsidiaries:

Lankan Alliance Finance Limited (1)
Laila Tower 8 South Gulshan Avenue, Dhaka, 1212, Bangladesh
Tel.: (880) 2 984 0411
Web Site: https://www.lankanalliance.com
Financial Services
N.A.I.C.S.: 522320
Shubho Sadi *(Asst Mgr)*

People's Insurance PLC (1)
No 07 Havelock Road, Colombo, 05, Sri Lanka
Tel.: (94) 112126126
Web Site: http://www.peoplesinsurance.lk
General Insurance Services
N.A.I.C.S.: 524210

People's Leasing Fleet Management Limited (1)
No 1161 Maradana Road, Borella, Colombo, Sri Lanka
Tel.: (94) 112338111
Insurance Brokerage Services
N.A.I.C.S.: 524210

People's Leasing Property Development Limited (1)
No 1161 Maradana Road, Borella, Colombo, Sri Lanka
Tel.: (94) 112631631
Finance Leasing Services
N.A.I.C.S.: 522220

PEOPLES TRUST COMPANY
Suite 1400 - 888 Dunsmuir Street, Vancouver, V6C 3K4, BC, Canada
Tel.: (604) 683-2881
Web Site:
https://www.peoplestrust.com
Year Founded: 1985
Sales Range: $10-24.9 Million
Emp.: 80
Residential Mortgages; Commercial & Industrial Real Estate Financing; Mortgage Banking; Mortgage Financing; Deposit Services; Mortgage Backed Securities; Retirement Savings Plan
N.A.I.C.S.: 522299
Eskandar Ghermezian *(Chm)*

PEPCAP RESOURCES INC.
Suite 717 1030 W Georgia Street, Vancouver, V6E 2Y3, BC, Canada
Tel.: (604) 341-4691 AB
Web Site:
http://www.pepcapresources.com
Year Founded: 2012
WAV—(TSXV)
Sales Range: Less than $1 Million
Investment Services
N.A.I.C.S.: 523999
Saliba Sassine *(Chm)*

PEPINIERES JEAN REY
559 Quartier La Pascalette, La Londe-les-Maures, 83250, Aix-en-Provence, Var, France
Tel.: (33) 494051787
Web Site: http://www.jeanrey.fr
Rev.: $26,200,000
Emp.: 300
Ornamental Nursery Products
N.A.I.C.S.: 111421
Jean-Marie Rey *(Pres)*

PEPPER FOOD SERVICE CO., LTD.
17th floor Olinas Tower 4-1-3 Taihei, Sumida-ku, Tokyo, 130-0012, Japan
Tel.: (81) 338293210
Web Site: https://www.pepper-fs.co.jp
Year Founded: 1985
3053—(TKS)
Sales Range: $650-699.9 Million
Restaurant Operators
N.A.I.C.S.: 722511

PEPPERMINT INNOVATION LIMITED
Level 2 East The Wentworth Building

AND PRIVATE COMPANIES — PER AARSLEFF HOLDING A/S

300 Murray Street, Perth, 6000, WA, Australia
Tel.: (61) 893169100 AU
Web Site: https://pepltd.com.au
Year Founded: 2007
PIL—(ASX)
Rev.: $582,381
Assets: $1,065,325
Liabilities: $762,855
Net Worth: $302,470
Earnings: ($2,587,312)
Emp.: 13
Fiscal Year-end: 06/30/24
Mobile Banking, Payments & Remittance Services
N.A.I.C.S.: 541519
Christopher Kain (CEO & Mng Dir)

Subsidiaries:

Peppermint Bizmoto Inc. (1)
Unit 25 PH 2nd floor 125 Col, Bonny Serrano Ave Cubao Metro Manila, Quezon City, 1109, Philippines
Tel.: (63) 9283987007
Web Site: https://www.bizmoto.com.ph
Business Software Development Services
N.A.I.C.S.: 561499

PEPPERMINT PR
26 Park Rd, Hale, WA15 9NN, Cheshire, United Kingdom
Tel.: (44) 1619414252
Web Site: http://www.peppermintpr.com
Sales Range: $10-24.9 Million
Emp.: 20
Public Relations
N.A.I.C.S.: 541820
Emma Jones (Acct Mgr)

PEPTIDREAM INC.
3-25-23 Tonomachi, Kawasaki-ku, Kawasaki, 210-0821, Kanagawa, Japan
Tel.: (81) 442701300
Web Site: https://www.peptidream.com
Year Founded: 2006
4587—(TKS)
Rev.: $203,568,080
Assets: $492,499,760
Liabilities: $206,425,350
Net Worth: $286,074,410
Earnings: $21,518,150
Emp.: 713
Fiscal Year-end: 12/31/23
Biopharmaceutical Mfr
N.A.I.C.S.: 325412
Kiichi Kubota (Chm & CEO)

PEPTONIC MEDICAL AB
Farogatan 33, 164 53, Kista, Sweden
Tel.: (46) 853020110
Web Site: https://www.peptonicmedical.se
Year Founded: 2009
28L—(DEU)
Rev.: $4,259,887
Assets: $7,872,034
Liabilities: $3,548,988
Net Worth: $4,323,046
Earnings: ($3,383,473)
Emp.: 34
Fiscal Year-end: 12/31/22
Pharmaceutical Product Mfr & Distr
N.A.I.C.S.: 325412
Anders Blom (Chm)

Subsidiaries:

Pharmiva AB (1)
Scheelevagen 4, 223 81, Lund, Sweden
Tel.: (46) 766119661
Web Site: https://www.pharmiva.com
Pharmaceutical Product Mfr & Distr
N.A.I.C.S.: 325412
Anna Linton (CEO)

PEPTRON, INC.
37-24 Yuseong-daero 1628 beon-gil, Yuseong-gu, Daejeon, 34054, Korea (South)
Tel.: (82) 423608880
Web Site: https://www.peptron.com
Year Founded: 1997
087010—(KRS)
Rev.: $4,459,335
Assets: $52,366,595
Liabilities: $11,631,707
Net Worth: $40,734,888
Earnings: ($11,553,160)
Emp.: 40
Fiscal Year-end: 12/31/22
Pharmaceuticals Mfr
N.A.I.C.S.: 325412
Ho-Il Choi (Founder & CEO)

PER AARSLEFF HOLDING A/S
Hasselager Alle 5, 8260, Viby, Denmark
Tel.: (45) 87442222 DK
Web Site: https://www.aarsleff.com
Year Founded: 1947
PAAL.B—(OMX)
Rev.: $2,425,505,731
Assets: $1,472,043,253
Liabilities: $867,317,232
Net Worth: $604,726,022
Earnings: $78,017,859
Emp.: 7,658
Fiscal Year-end: 09/30/21
Construction Services
N.A.I.C.S.: 237990
Hans Christensen (Mgr-Pipe Technologies Div)

Subsidiaries:

Aarsleff Baltic SIA LLC (1)
Uriekstes Str 3 2, Riga, LV-1005, Latvia
Tel.: (371) 67382392
Construction Contracting Services
N.A.I.C.S.: 236220

Aarsleff Biz Sp. z o.o. (1)
Ul Jana Soltana 1, 72-602, Swinoujscie, Poland
Tel.: (48) 913221200
Web Site: https://www.aarsleff.biz
Prefabricated Concrete Element Mfr
N.A.I.C.S.: 327390
Jens Kristian Worm (Dir-)

Aarsleff Ground Engineering Limited (1)
Hawton Lane, Balderton, Newark, NG24 3BU, Nottinghamshire, United Kingdom
Tel.: (44) 1636611140
Web Site: https://www.aarsleff.co.uk
Engineering Contractor Services
N.A.I.C.S.: 541330
Kevin Hague (Mng Dir)

Aarsleff Grundbau GmbH (1)
Friedrich-Ebert-Damm 111, D-22047, Hamburg, Germany
Tel.: (49) 40696720
Web Site: https://www.aarsleff-grundbau.de
Construction Services
N.A.I.C.S.: 238110

Aarsleff Grundlaggnings AB (1)
Langavallsgatan 8, 424 57, Gunnilse, Sweden
Tel.: (46) 313303230
Web Site: http://www.aarsleff.nu
Foundation Engineering Services
N.A.I.C.S.: 238110

Aarsleff Hulin s.r.o. (1)
Mierova 23, 920 01, Hlohovec, Slovakia
Tel.: (421) 337369111
Web Site: https://www.aarsleff.sk
Sewer Rehabilitation Services
N.A.I.C.S.: 237110

Aarsleff Leidingrenovatie B.V. (1)
Molenwerf 40, 1911 DB, Uitgeest, Netherlands
Tel.: (31) 251743200
Web Site: https://www.aarsleff-bv.nl
Sewer Rehabilitation Services
N.A.I.C.S.: 237110

Aarsleff Rail A/S (1)
Hasselager Alle 5, 8260, Viby, Denmark
Tel.: (45) 87343000
Web Site: http://aarsleffrail.com
Emp.: 50
Railway Track Construction Services
N.A.I.C.S.: 237990
Bo Clausen (Chief Engr)

Aarsleff Rorteknik AB (1)
Symmetrivagen 29, Box 2013, 19202, Sollentuna, Sweden
Tel.: (46) 859476400
Web Site: http://www.aarsleff.com
Sales Range: $25-49.9 Million
Emp.: 40
Plumbing Heating & Air-Conditioning Contractors
N.A.I.C.S.: 238220

Aarsleff Spezialtiefbau GmbH (1)
Rubbertstr 27, D-21109, Hamburg, Germany
Tel.: (49) 4075242460
Web Site: https://www.aarsleff.de
Emp.: 180
Civil Engineering Services
N.A.I.C.S.: 541330

Aarsleff Srl (1)
Via Guido d'Arezzo 4, 20145, Milan, Italy
Tel.: (39) 0248559423
Testing Laboratories
N.A.I.C.S.: 541380

Anker AB (1)
Christian IV Vag 4, 302 67, Halmstad, Sweden
Tel.: (46) 35 250 0350
Web Site: https://www.ankerab.se
Railway Track Construction Services
N.A.I.C.S.: 237990

BL Grundvandsaenkning A/S (1)
Norgesvej 49A, 6100, Haderslev, Denmark
Tel.: (45) 74204060
Web Site: https://bl-grundvand.dk
Groundwater Lowering Services
N.A.I.C.S.: 562998

Banedrift AS (1)
Tomteveien 33C, 1618, Fredrikstad, Norway
Tel.: (47) 6 987 7010
Web Site: https://www.banedrift.no
Railway Maintenance & Renewal Services
N.A.I.C.S.: 488210

Bluelight GmbH (1)
Motorstrasse 25, 70499, Stuttgart, Germany
Tel.: (49) 711887724200
Web Site: https://www.bluelight-gmbh.de
Water & Sewer Line Services
N.A.I.C.S.: 237110
Niklas Ernst (Mng Dir)

Brodrene Hedegaard A/S (1)
Teknikervej 9-11, 2770, Kastrup, Denmark
Tel.: (45) 4535 0920
Web Site: http://www.aarsleff.com
Construction Engineering Services
N.A.I.C.S.: 541330

CP Test A/S (1)
Skomagervej 13 c, 7100, Vejle, Denmark
Tel.: (45) 75723999
Web Site: https://www.cptest.dk
Engineering Services
N.A.I.C.S.: 541330

Cannon Piling Ltd. (1)
Building 11 Grange Farm Business Centre Woodham Road, Battlesbridge, Wickford, Essex, United Kingdom
Tel.: (44) 1245401333
Web Site: https://www.cannonpiling.com
Foundation Piling Services
N.A.I.C.S.: 238910

Centrum Paele A/S (1)
Gronlandsvej 96, 7100, Vejle, Denmark
Tel.: (45) 75830111
Web Site: https://www.centrumpaele.dk
Emp.: 65
Concrete Pile Mfr
N.A.I.C.S.: 327390
Lars G. Christensen (Mgr)

Centrum Pali Sp. z o.o. (1)
Ul Lakoszynska 127, 99-300, Kutno, Poland
Tel.: (48) 242547064
Web Site: https://www.centrumpali.pl
Prefabricated Concrete Element Mfr
N.A.I.C.S.: 327390

Centrum Pfahle GmbH (1)
Friedrich-Ebert-Damm 111, 22047, Hamburg, Germany
Tel.: (49) 40696720
Web Site: https://www.aarsleff-grundbau.de
Sales Range: $25-49.9 Million
Emp.: 47
Construction Engineering Services
N.A.I.C.S.: 541330
Peter Wardinghus (Mng Dir)

Centrum Pile Limited (1)
Hawton Lane, Balderton Newark-on-Trent, Newark, NG24 3BU, Nottinghamshire, United Kingdom
Tel.: (44) 1636615700
Web Site: https://www.centrumpile.co.uk
Emp.: 70
Reinforced Precast Concrete Pile Equipment Mfr & Distr
N.A.I.C.S.: 333120
Eamonn Walsh (Mgr)

DMT Ingenieure GmbH (1)
Zum Audorfer See 9, 24782, Budelsdorf, Germany
Tel.: (49) 4331437550
Web Site: https://www.dmt-ingenieure.eu
Engineeering Services
N.A.I.C.S.: 541330

Dan Jord A/S (1)
Viengevej 8, 8240, Risskov, Denmark
Tel.: (45) 86212655
Web Site: https://danjord.dk
Sales Range: $25-49.9 Million
Emp.: 200
Construction Engineering Services
N.A.I.C.S.: 541330

Danpipe A/S (1)
Birkemosevej 32, 8381, Hasselager, Denmark
Tel.: (45) 32884600
Engineeering Services
N.A.I.C.S.: 541330
Bent Rasmussen (Mgr)

E. Klink A/S (1)
Roskildevej 338, 2630, Taastrup, Denmark
Tel.: (45) 44912891
Web Site: https://www.eklink.dk
Ventilation Contractor Services
N.A.I.C.S.: 238220

Entreprenorfirmaet Ostergaard A/S (1)
Sverigesvej 4, 7100, Vejle, Denmark
Tel.: (45) 75823455
Web Site: https://www.oestergaardas.dk
Emp.: 100
Construction Services
N.A.I.C.S.: 236220

FRP Prolining GmbH (1)
Eichhorster Strasse 5, D-17034, Neubrandenburg, Germany
Tel.: (49) 3953513560
Web Site: https://www.frp-prolining.de
Pipe Distr
N.A.I.C.S.: 423510

Handvaerkergarden A/S (1)
Lind Hansens Vej 5, 5000, Odense, Denmark
Tel.: (45) 6 591 4884
Web Site: https://www.hvg-as.dk
Construction Services
N.A.I.C.S.: 236220

Hansson & Knudsen A/S (1)
Cikorievej 5, 5220, Odense, Denmark
Tel.: (45) 66120810
Web Site: https://www.hansson-knudsen.dk
Civil Engineering Services
N.A.I.C.S.: 541330

Holmskov Rustfri Stainless Steel Company A/S (1)
Industrivej 21, 3550, Slangerup, Denmark
Tel.: (45) 4 819 2434
Web Site: https://www.holmskov.dk
Engineering Contractor Services
N.A.I.C.S.: 541330
Lasse Holmskov (Controller)

Insituform Linings PLC. (1)
12-20 Brunel Close, Park Farm Industrial

PER AARSLEFF HOLDING A/S

Per Aarsleff Holding A/S—(Continued)
Estate, Wellingborough, NN8 6QX, United Kingdom
Tel.: (44) 1933678266
Web Site: http://www.northants-chamber.co.uk
Sales Range: $25-49.9 Million
Emp.: 35
Water Sewer & Pipeline Construction
N.A.I.C.S.: 237120
Mark Bates *(Mng Dir)*

Insituform Rohrsanierungstechniken GmbH (1)
Sulzbacher Strasse 47, 90552, Rothenbach, Germany
Tel.: (49) 911957730
Industrial Machinery Equipment Mfr
N.A.I.C.S.: 333248

Metris Sp. z o.o. (1)
Ul Lakoszynska 127 A, 99-300, Kutno, Poland
Tel.: (48) 242535055
Web Site: https://www.metris.com.pl
Engineering Contractor Services
N.A.I.C.S.: 541330

Neidhardt Grundbau GmbH (1)
Rubbertstrasse 27, D-21109, Hamburg, Germany
Tel.: (49) 407524240
Web Site: https://www.neidhardt-grundbau.de
Emp.: 80
Foundation Engineering Services
N.A.I.C.S.: 541330

Olimb Rorfornying Holding AS (1)
Sarpsborgveien 115, 1640, Rade, Norway
Tel.: (47) 69281700
Web Site: https://olimb.no
Emp.: 130
Construction Contracting Services
N.A.I.C.S.: 236220

Ostergaard A/S (1)
Sverigesvej 4, 7100, Vejle, Denmark
Tel.: (45) 75823455
Web Site: http://www.oestergaardas.dk
Sales Range: $25-49.9 Million
Emp.: 100
Civil Engineering Services
N.A.I.C.S.: 237310
Morten Hansen *(Gen Mgr)*

PAA International Engineering Corp. (1)
20th Floor 3241, Wen Hsin Rd Sec 3, Taichung, Taiwan
Tel.: (886) 422535055
Water Sewer & Pipeline Construction
N.A.I.C.S.: 237120
Jack Loai *(Gen Mgr)*

PAA Project Finance A/S (1)
Industriholmen 2, DK-2650, Hvidovre, Denmark
Tel.: (45) 36344550
Web Site: https://www.paaprojectfinance.dk
Project Management Services
N.A.I.C.S.: 541611
Anne Ulderup *(Co-COO)*

PH Byg Faaborg A/S (1)
L Frandsensvej 7, 5600, Faborg, Denmark
Tel.: (45) 6 261 8292
Web Site: https://www.phbygfaaborg.dk
Masonry Contracting Services
N.A.I.C.S.: 238140

Per Aarsleff Gronland ApS (1)
Tel.: (299) 87442222
Construction Contracting Services
N.A.I.C.S.: 236220

Per Aarsleff OY (1)
Alhonnituntie 6, 01900, Nurmijarvi, Finland
Tel.: (358) 92902280
Web Site: http://www.aarsleff.fi
Sales Range: $25-49.9 Million
Emp.: 32
Water Sewer & Pipeline Construction
N.A.I.C.S.: 237120
Juha-tekka Maumukfela *(Gen Mgr)*

Per Aarsleff Polska Sp. z o.o. (1)
ul Krolowej Marysienki 20 lokal 2, 02954, Warsaw, Poland
Tel.: (48) 226516972

Web Site: http://www.aarsleffpipe.pl
Sales Range: $25-49.9 Million
Emp.: 100
Water Sewer & Pipeline Construction
N.A.I.C.S.: 237120
Arkadiusz Bachan *(Mng Dir)*

Per Aarsleff ZAO (1)
7 building 1 BC Central Yard st Baumanskaya, 105005, Moscow, Russia
Tel.: (7) 8123630777
Web Site: http://www.aarsleff.ru
Sales Range: $25-49.9 Million
Emp.: 30
Plastics Product Mfr
N.A.I.C.S.: 326199

Petri & Haugsted as (1)
Roskildevej 338, 2630, Taastrup, Denmark
Tel.: (45) 44887700
Web Site: https://www.petri-haugsted.dk
Sales Range: $50-74.9 Million
Emp.: 300
Road Construction Services
N.A.I.C.S.: 237310
Jacob Thor Hanson *(CEO)*

Ponel Bau GmbH (1)
Lesumstrasse 6, 26135, Oldenburg, Germany
Tel.: (49) 441972810
Web Site: https://www.ponel-bau.de
Engineering Services
N.A.I.C.S.: 541330

Rock Armour Trading AB (1)
Sandengatan 2, 45330, Lysekil, Sweden
Tel.: (46) 705915152
Construction Contracting Services
N.A.I.C.S.: 236220

S T B - Woltjen GmbH (1)
Am Koppelberg 38, Steimbke, 31634, Nienburg, Germany
Tel.: (49) 5026474400
Web Site: https://www.stb-woeltjen.de
Civil Engineering Services
N.A.I.C.S.: 541330

S&H Klimateknik A/S (1)
Erhvervsvej 19, DK-2600, Glostrup, Denmark
Tel.: (45) 70260039
Web Site: https://www.klimateknik.eu
Refrigeration Installation Services
N.A.I.C.S.: 238220

Steg Entreprenor AS (1)
Apalveien 1, 3360, Geithus, Norway
Tel.: (47) 32783606
Web Site: https://www.steg.no
Emp.: 45
Engineering Construction Services
N.A.I.C.S.: 541330

Trym Anlegg AS (1)
Dybdahls veg 1, 7051, Trondheim, Norway
Tel.: (47) 73575000
Civil Engineering Services
N.A.I.C.S.: 541330

UAB Aarsleff (1)
Tel.: (370) 37370717
Web Site: http://www.aarsleff.com
Sales Range: $25-49.9 Million
Emp.: 25
Commercial & Institutional Building Construction
N.A.I.C.S.: 236220

VG Entreprenor A/S (1)
Rugmarken 8, 7620, Lemvig, Denmark
Tel.: (49) 96640910
Web Site: http://www.vg-e.dk
Sales Range: $25-49.9 Million
Emp.: 20
Construction Engineering Services
N.A.I.C.S.: 541330
Uffe Larsen *(CEO)*

Wicotec Kirkebjerg A/S (1)
Roskildevej 338, 2630, Taastrup, Denmark (80%)
Tel.: (45) 44220000
Web Site: https://wicoteckirkebjerg.dk
Emp.: 1,350
Construction Engineering Services
N.A.I.C.S.: 541330

PERA GAYRIMENKUL YATIRIM ORTAKLIGI A.S.
Kizilirmak Mah Dumlupinar Boulevard, 3-B Interior Door no 77 Next Level Plaza Cankaya, 34425, Ankara, Turkiye
Tel.: (90) 3129850533
Web Site: https://www.peraholding.com.tr
PEGYO—(IST)
Real Estate Investment Services
N.A.I.C.S.: 523999
Aysegul Bensel *(Chm & Gen Mgr)*

PERAK CORPORATION BERHAD
No 1-A Blok B Menara PKNP Jalan Meru Casuarina Bandar Meru Raya, 30020, Ipoh, Perak Darul Ridzuan, Malaysia
Tel.: (60) 55019998
Web Site: https://www.perakcorp.com.my
Year Founded: 1991
PRKCORP—(KLS)
Rev.: $31,534,603
Assets: $111,462,222
Liabilities: $60,078,095
Net Worth: $51,384,127
Earnings: $6,277,249
Fiscal Year-end: 12/31/22
Property Development Services
N.A.I.C.S.: 531312
Salmah Mohamed Isimail *(Head-HR & Admin)*

Subsidiaries:

Casuarina Meru Sdn. Bhd. (1)
No 1-C Jalan Meru Casuarina, Bandar Meru Raya, 30020, Ipoh, Perak, Malaysia
Tel.: (60) 5 529 9999
Web Site: https://www.casuarinahotels.com.my
Hotel Services
N.A.I.C.S.: 721110

Labu Sayong Cafe Sdn. Bhd. (1)
No 1-A Blok A Menara PKNP Jalan Casuarina Meru Bandar Meru Raya, 30020, Ipoh, Perak, Malaysia
Tel.: (60) 52375238
Web Site: http://www.labusayong.com.my
Cafe Services
N.A.I.C.S.: 722513

Lumut Maritime Terminal Sdn. Bhd. (1)
Lot 1 Lumut Port Industrial Park Jalan Kg Acheh, 32000, Sitiawan, Perak Darul Ridzuan, Malaysia
Tel.: (60) 5 698 3333
Web Site: https://www.lumutport.com
Emp.: 250
Marine Cargo Handling Services
N.A.I.C.S.: 488320
Izudin Ismail *(COO)*

PCB Transportation Travel & Tours Sdn. Bhd. (1)
Tingkat 2 Wisma Wan Mohamed Jalan Panglima Bukit Gantang, 30000, Ipoh, Perak, Malaysia
Tel.: (60) 52427277
Sales Range: $25-49.9 Million
Emp.: 20
Travel & Tour Operating Agencies
N.A.I.C.S.: 561510

Premium Meridian Sdn. Bhd. (1)
3rd Floor Wisma Wan Mohamed Jalan Panglima Bukit Gantang Wahab, 30000, Ipoh, Perak, Malaysia
Tel.: (60) 5 242 2661
Sales Range: $25-49.9 Million
Emp.: 8
Property Development & Project Management Services
N.A.I.C.S.: 236116

PERAK TRANSIT BERHAD
E-6-2A SOHO Ipoh 2 Jalan Sultan Idris Shah, 30000, Ipoh, Perak, Malaysia

INTERNATIONAL PUBLIC

Tel.: (60) 52551128
Web Site: https://www.peraktransit.com.my
Year Founded: 2008
PTRANS—(KLS)
Rev.: $37,693,797
Assets: $275,522,253
Liabilities: $134,236,499
Net Worth: $141,285,754
Earnings: $14,172,824
Emp.: 228
Fiscal Year-end: 12/31/23
Investment Holding Services
N.A.I.C.S.: 551112
Kong Fitt Cheong *(Mng Dir)*

PERCEPT HOLDINGS PVT. LTD.
P2 Raghuvanshi Estate 11/12 Senapati Bapat Marg, Mumbai, 400013, India
Tel.: (91) 2230448400
Web Site: http://www.perceptholdings.com
Year Founded: 1984
Rev.: $419,796,597
Emp.: 1,000
Advertising And Media Agencies
N.A.I.C.S.: 551112
Harindra Singh *(Vice Chm & Mng Dir)*

Subsidiaries:

Allied Media (1)
P2 Level 3 Raghuvanshi Estate 11/12 Senapati Bapat Marg, Lowerpanel, Mumbai, 400 013, India
Tel.: (91) 22 4004 6800
N.A.I.C.S.: 541830
Priya Iyer *(Dir-Bus-South Ops)*

Clea PR (1)
Arch 25/28 Below Mahalaxmi Bridge Off Dr E Moses Road, Mahalaxmi, Mumbai, 400034, India
Tel.: (91) 22 2498 8669
Emp.: 175
N.A.I.C.S.: 541820
Vinod G. Nair *(Mng Dir)*

Media Agency Middle East (MAME) (1)
Suite 108 Rose Building, PO Box 74248, Satwa, Dubai, United Arab Emirates
Tel.: (971) 4 344 1429
Web Site: http://www.mediaagencyme.com
N.A.I.C.S.: 541840
Bipin Pathak *(CEO)*

Percept / H (1)
P22 Raghuvanshi Estate 11/12 Senapati Bapat Marg, Lower Parel, Mumbai, 400 013, India
Tel.: (91) 22 3044 8200
Emp.: 150
N.A.I.C.S.: 541833
Ajay Chandwani *(Exec Dir)*

Subsidiary (Domestic):

AMO Communications (2)
P2 Level 3 B Raghuvanshi Estate, 11/12 Senapati Bapat Marg, Lower Parel, Mumbai, 400 013, India
Tel.: (91) 22 3049 7000
Web Site: http://www.amogroup.com
Emp.: 50
N.A.I.C.S.: 541810
Elvis Dias *(Mng Dir)*

IBD India (2)
IBD House Ajay Bus Ctr T H Kataria Rd Mahim, Mumbai, 400016, India
Tel.: (91) 22 2432 3203
Web Site: http://www.ibdbrands.com
Emp.: 50
N.A.I.C.S.: 541810
Rahul Gupta *(Mng Dir)*

Subsidiary (Non-US):

Percept Gulf (2)
PO Box 74155, Dubai, United Arab Emirates
Tel.: (971) 3434674
N.A.I.C.S.: 541810

Dolly Nader *(Acct Mgr)*

Subsidiary (Domestic):

Percept Swift Advertising Private
Limited (2)
201 Navneet Plaza Old Palasia, Indore,
452001, India
Tel.: (91) 731 256 0301
N.A.I.C.S.: 541810
Rahul Jain *(Mng Dir)*

Percept OOH (1)
P2 Level 3 B Raghuvanshi Estate 11/12
Senapati Bapat Marg, Lower Parel, Mumbai, 400013, India
Tel.: (91) 22 3042 8855
N.A.I.C.S.: 541810
Sanjay Pareek *(Pres)*

Percept Profile (1)
P2 Level 3 B Raghuvanshi Estate 11/12
Senapati Bapat Marg, Mumbai, 400013,
India
Tel.: (91) 22 3040 8800
Emp.: 35
N.A.I.C.S.: 541820
Rahat Beri *(COO)*

PERCEVA SAS
32 Avenue de lOpera, 75002, Paris,
France
Tel.: (33) 1 4297 1990   FR
Web Site: http://www.perceva.fr
Private Equity Services
N.A.I.C.S.: 523999
Jean-Louis Grevet *(Dir-Publ)*

Subsidiaries:

KEYOR (1)
22 Rue d'Artagnan, 33100, Bordeaux,
France
Tel.: (33) 557778686
Web Site: http://www.keyor.fr
Door Mfr & Distr
N.A.I.C.S.: 332510
Lucie Garreaud *(Sls Mgr)*

Oniris S.A. (1)
61 rte de la Reine, Boulogne, 92100,
France
Tel.: (33) 1 46 047587
Web Site: http://www.oniris-sa.fr
Bathroom Design Services
N.A.I.C.S.: 449129

PERCHERON THERAPEUTICS LIMITED
L30 Collins Place 35 Collins Street,
Melbourne, 3000, VIC, Australia
Tel.: (61) 398278999
Web Site: https://percherontx.com
ATHJF—(OTCIQ)
Rev.: $1,388,399
Assets: $17,190,743
Liabilities: $992,384
Net Worth: $16,198,359
Earnings: ($4,452,951)
Emp.: 9
Fiscal Year-end: 06/30/22
Pharmaceuticals Mfr
N.A.I.C.S.: 325412
Mark Diamond *(CEO & Mng Dir)*

PERCON CONSTRUCTION INC.
20 Airview Road, Toronto, M9W 4P2,
ON, Canada
Tel.: (416) 744-9967
Web Site:
   http://www.perconstruction.com
Sales Range: $10-24.9 Million
General Building Contractors
N.A.I.C.S.: 236220
Frank Perricone *(Pres)*

PERCY DALTON'S FAMOUS PEANUT COMPANY LIMITED
Spitalfield House Helion's Bumstead
Rd, Haverhill, CB9 7AA, Suffolk,
United Kingdom
Tel.: (44) 1440764500

Web Site:
   http://www.percydaltons.com
Year Founded: 1930
Sales Range: $25-49.9 Million
Emp.: 150
Nuts & Dried Fruits Mfr & Processor
N.A.I.C.S.: 311423
Calum Ryder *(Mng Dir)*

PEREGRINE CORPORATION
270 The Parade, Kensington, 5068,
SA, Australia
Tel.: (61) 883339777
Web Site:
   http://www.peregrine.com.au
Year Founded: 1984
Emp.: 3,500
Convenience Food Distr
N.A.I.C.S.: 445131
Fred Shahin *(Founder)*

PEREGRINE GOLD LIMITED
Tel.: (61) 292999690   AU
Web Site:
   https://www.peregrinegold.com.au
Year Founded: 2020
PGD—(ASX)
Rev.: $22,665
Assets: $5,155,006
Liabilities: $394,445
Net Worth: $4,760,561
Earnings: ($2,703,359)
Fiscal Year-end: 06/30/23
Gold Exploration Services
N.A.I.C.S.: 212220

PEREGRINE HOLDINGS LIMITED
1 Park Lane, Wierda Valley, Sandton,
2196, South Africa
Tel.: (27) 117227400
Web Site: http://www.peregrine.co.za
PGR—(JSE)
Rev.: $113,941,780
Assets: $653,894,381
Liabilities: $521,385,876
Net Worth: $132,508,505
Earnings: $36,209,090
Emp.: 704
Fiscal Year-end: 03/31/19
Holding Company; Financial Planning
& Asset Management Services
N.A.I.C.S.: 551112
Sean Alan Melnick *(Chm)*

Subsidiaries:

Peregrine Financial Products (Pty)
Ltd (1)
Simeka House Vineyard Office Park 99 Jip
De Jager, Bellville, Cape Town, 7530, South
Africa
Tel.: (27) 11 722 7572
Web Site: http://www.peregrine.co.za
Sales Range: $50-74.9 Million
Emp.: 34
Financial Planning & Consulting Services
N.A.I.C.S.: 523940

Peregrine Management Services
(Pty) Ltd (1)
6A Sandown Vly Crescent, Sandown, Johannesburg, 195, Gauteng, South Africa
Tel.: (27) 117227400
Sales Range: $150-199.9 Million
Emp.: 300
Property Management Services
N.A.I.C.S.: 531311
Sean Melnick *(Chm)*

Stenham Ltd (1)
180 Great Portland St, London, W1W 5QZ,
United Kingdom
Tel.: (44) 2070796616
Web Site:
   http://www.stenhamassetmanagement.com
Sales Range: $50-74.9 Million
Emp.: 90
Investment Management Service
N.A.I.C.S.: 523999

PEREKOP BROMINE
Severnaya Str 1, AR of Crimea Krasnoperekopsk, Kiev, Ukraine
Tel.: (380) 56 787 37 49
Web Site:
   http://www.perekopbromine.com
Year Founded: 1932
Chemical Products Mfr
N.A.I.C.S.: 325998

PERENCO GAS LTD.
15-19 Britten St, London, SW3 3TY,
United Kingdom
Tel.: (44) 442073559100
Web Site: http://www.perenco.com
Sales Range: $1-4.9 Billion
Emp.: 4,000
Oil & Gas Exploration & Production
N.A.I.C.S.: 211120
Jean-Michel Jacoulot *(CEO)*

Subsidiaries:

Perenco SA (1)
7 rue de Logelbach, 75116, Paris, France
Tel.: (33) 1 53 57 66 00
Web Site: http://www.perenco.com
Oil & Gas Exploration
N.A.I.C.S.: 211120
Jean-Michel Jacoulot *(CEO)*

Subsidiary (Non-US):

Perence Colombia Limited (2)
Carretera 7 No 71 21Torre B Piso 17, Bogota, D.C., Colombia (100%)
Tel.: (57) 1 313 5000
Web Site: http://www.perenco-colombia.com
Sales Range: $75-99.9 Million
Emp.: 300
Petroleum Exploration, Production & Distribution
N.A.I.C.S.: 211120
Mauro Da Silva Pereira *(Pres)*

PERENNIAL ENERGY HOLDINGS LIMITED
Unit 1003 10/F Tower 2 Lippo Centre
89 Queensway, Hong Kong, China
(Hong Kong)
Tel.: (852) 25688086   Ky
Web Site:
   http://www.perennialenergy.hk
Year Founded: 1990
2798—(HKG)
Rev.: $250,478,233
Assets: $572,832,562
Liabilities: $227,077,484
Net Worth: $345,755,077
Earnings: $104,451,282
Emp.: 3,619
Fiscal Year-end: 12/31/22
Holding Company
N.A.I.C.S.: 551112
Bangping Yu *(Founder, Chm & CEO)*

PERENNIAL INTERNATIONAL LIMITED
1 Science Museum Road Concordia
Plaza Unit 2006, Kowloon, Tsimshatsui, China (Hong Kong)
Tel.: (852) 35244800
Web Site:
   http://www.perennialcable.com
Year Founded: 1989
0725—(HKG)
Rev.: $41,376,810
Assets: $84,383,453
Liabilities: $12,205,065
Net Worth: $72,178,388
Earnings: $2,020,620
Emp.: 790
Fiscal Year-end: 12/31/22
Holding Company; Power Cords,
Power Cord Sets, Cables, Wires,
Wire Harnesses & Plastic Resins Mfr
N.A.I.C.S.: 551112
Chung Hung Mon *(Deputy Chm & CEO)*

PERENNIAL REAL ESTATE HOLDINGS LIMITED
8 Shenton Way 36-01 AXA Tower,
Singapore, 068811, Singapore
Tel.: (65) 6602 6800   SG
Web Site:
   http://www.perennialrealestate.com
Rev.: $92,065,152
Assets: $5,599,371,250
Liabilities: $2,744,795,685
Net Worth: $2,854,575,565
Earnings: $4,044,401
Emp.: 446
Fiscal Year-end: 12/31/19
Real Estate Owner, Developer &
Property Manager
N.A.I.C.S.: 531210
Seck Guan Pua *(CEO)*

Subsidiaries:

Shanghai Dolly Pte Ltd (1)
3B River Valley Road, Singapore, 179021,
Singapore
Tel.: (65) 63367676
Nightclub Operator
N.A.I.C.S.: 722410

The St. James Pte Ltd (1)
3 Sentosa Gateway, Singapore, 098544,
Singapore
Tel.: (65) 6270 7676
Nightclub Operator
N.A.I.C.S.: 722410
Gordon Foo *(Gen Mgr)*

PERENTI GLOBAL LIMITED
Level 2 202 Pier Street, Perth, 6000,
WA, Australia
Tel.: (61) 894216500
Web Site:
   https://www.perentigroup.com
Year Founded: 1987
AUSDF—(OTCIQ)
Rev.: $1,867,707,651
Assets: $2,137,113,846
Liabilities: $1,123,934,838
Net Worth: $1,013,179,008
Earnings: $32,552,348
Emp.: 9,000
Fiscal Year-end: 06/30/22
Mining Industry Supply Services
N.A.I.C.S.: 333131
Mark Norwell *(CEO & Mng Dir)*

Subsidiaries:

African Mining Services (Ghana) Pty
Ltd (1)
13 Patrice Lumumba Road, Airport Residential Area PMB KIA, Accra, Ghana
Tel.: (233) 302611333
Web Site: http://www.amsgh.com
Sales Range: $10-24.9 Million
Emp.: 40
Mining Industry Supply Services
N.A.I.C.S.: 333131

Ausdrill (Ghana) Pty. Ltd. (1)
6-12 Uppsala Place, Canning Vale, 6155,
WA, Australia
Tel.: (61) 893533055
Mining Support Services
N.A.I.C.S.: 541330

Ausdrill Mining Services Pty. Ltd. (1)
6-12 Uppsala Place, PO Box 1540, Canning
Vale, 6155, WA, Australia
Tel.: (61) 861594407
Web Site: http://www.amsaus.com.au
Sales Range: $50-74.9 Million
Emp.: 70
Mining Support Services
N.A.I.C.S.: 213114

Ausdrill Northwest Pty. Ltd. (1)
6-12 Uppsala Place, Canning Vale, 6155,
WA, Australia
Tel.: (61) 861594407
Sales Range: $100-124.9 Million
Emp.: 150
Exploration Drilling Services
N.A.I.C.S.: 213111
Wayne Bucknall *(Gen Mgr)*

PERENTI GLOBAL LIMITED

Perenti Global Limited—(Continued)

Barminco Limited (1)
390 Stirling Crescent, Midland, 6055, WA, Australia
Tel.: (61) 894161000
Web Site: http://www.barminco.com.au
Underground Mining Services
N.A.I.C.S.: 213114
Michael Ellis *(VP-Fin)*

Brandrill Limited (1)
Tel.: (61) 894946500
Web Site: http://www.brandrill.com
Sales Range: $100-124.9 Million
Emp.: 516
Drilling & Blasting Services
N.A.I.C.S.: 213111

Subsidiary (Non-US):

DT Hi Load Australia Pty. Ltd. (2)
Tel.: (61) 861485555
Web Site: http://www.dthiload.com
Sales Range: $25-49.9 Million
Emp.: 64
Light Weight Heavy Duty Trays Mfr
N.A.I.C.S.: 336211

RockTek Limited (2)
Tel.: (61) 894946570
Web Site: http://www.rocktek.com
Drilling Equipment Mfr
N.A.I.C.S.: 237990

DDH1 Limited (1)
21 Baile Rd, Canning Vale, 6155, WA, Australia
Tel.: (61) 894351700
Web Site: http://ddh1.com.au
Drilling Services
N.A.I.C.S.: 213115
Sy Van Dyk *(CEO & Mng Dir)*

Subsidiary (Domestic):

Swick Mining Services Ltd. (2)
64 Great Eastern Highway, Guildford, 6055, WA, Australia
Tel.: (61) 892778800
Web Site: http://www.swickmining.com
Rev.: $115,735,298
Assets: $112,648,319
Liabilities: $43,875,104
Net Worth: $68,773,214
Earnings: $3,768,122
Fiscal Year-end: 06/30/2021
Mineral Drilling Services
N.A.I.C.S.: 213114
Kent Swick *(Mng Dir)*

Subsidiary (Non-US):

SMS Mining Services (Canada) Inc. (3)
1648 Pioneer Rd, Sudbury, P3G 1E2, ON, Canada
Tel.: (705) 522-1800
Web Site: http://www.swickmining.ca
Sales Range: $50-74.9 Million
Emp.: 30
Mineral Drilling Services
N.A.I.C.S.: 213115

Drill Rigs Australia Pty. Ltd. (1)
6-12 Uppsala Place, Canning Vale, 6155, WA, Australia
Tel.: (61) 893115666
Web Site: http://www.drillrigsaus.com.au
Drilling Support Equipments Mfr & Maintenance Services
N.A.I.C.S.: 333131
Eddie Banner *(Gen Mgr)*

Supply Direct Pty. Ltd. (1)
6-12 Uppsala Place, Canning Vale, 6155, WA, Australia
Tel.: (61) 893115777
Web Site: http://www.supplydirect.net
Mining Equipments & Parts Distr
N.A.I.C.S.: 423830

Subsidiary (Non-US):

Logistics Direct Ltd. (2)
Tel.: (233) 302770418
Web Site: http://www.logisticsdirect.com
Sales Range: $25-49.9 Million
Emp.: 45
Logistics & Freight Forwarding Services
N.A.I.C.S.: 488510

Peter Gralla *(Gen Mgr)*

Supply Direct South Africa Pty. Ltd. (2)
249 Flemming Road, Meadowdale, 1614, Gauteng, South Africa
Tel.: (27) 114530380
Web Site: https://supplydirect.net
Sales Range: $25-49.9 Million
Emp.: 14
Mining Equipments & Parts Distr
N.A.I.C.S.: 423830

Synegex Holdings Pty. Ltd. (1)
Forrest St 149, PO Box 2131, Boulder, Kalgoorlie, 6432, WA, Australia
Tel.: (61) 890809170
Web Site: http://www.ausdrill.com.au
Emp.: 10
Blasting Services & Bulk Explosives Mfr
N.A.I.C.S.: 213114
Garry Billing *(Gen Mgr)*

PERESEC SOUTH AFRICA PROPRIETARY LIMITED

4th Fl 6A Sandown Vly Crescent, Sandown, Johannesburg, 2196, Gauteng, South Africa
Tel.: (27) 117227330
Web Site: https://www.peresec.com
Emp.: 45
Securities Brokerage Services
N.A.I.C.S.: 523150
Gavin Betty *(Mng Dir)*

Subsidiaries:

African Phoenix Investments Ltd (1)
59 16th Road, Private Bag x170, Midrand, 1685, South Africa
Tel.: (27) 117227330
Web Site: http://www.phoenixinvestments.co.za
Sales Range: $1-4.9 Billion
Emp.: 13,074
Bank Holding Company
N.A.I.C.S.: 551111

Subsidiary (Domestic):

African Bank Limited (2)
59 16th Rd, Halfway House, Johannesburg, South Africa
Tel.: (27) 112569128
Web Site: http://www.africanbank.co.za
Commericial Banking
N.A.I.C.S.: 522110
Antonio Fourie *(Exec Dir)*

Credit Indemnity Property (Pty) Limited (2)
59 16th Avenue, Halfway House, Johannesburg, South Africa
Tel.: (27) 112569000
Sales Range: $350-399.9 Million
Emp.: 1,000
Credit Union
N.A.I.C.S.: 522130

The SPAR Group Limited (2)
22 Chancery Lane, PO Box 1589, Pinetown, 3600, South Africa
Tel.: (27) 860313141
Web Site: http://www.spar.co.za
Rev.: $8,132,201,378
Assets: $3,354,507,268
Liabilities: $2,797,838,932
Net Worth: $556,668,336
Earnings: $24,098,550
Emp.: 10,512
Fiscal Year-end: 09/30/2023
Financial Investment Activities
N.A.I.C.S.: 523999
Graham Owen O'Connor *(CEO)*

Peresec Prime Brokers (Pty) Ltd (1)
6A Sandown Vly Crescent, Sandown, Johannesburg, 2196, Gauteng, South Africa
Tel.: (27) 117227516
Web Site: http://www.peregrine.co.za
Sales Range: $50-74.9 Million
Emp.: 50
Fund Management Services
N.A.I.C.S.: 523940
Gavin Betty *(Mng Dir)*

PERFECT CORP.

14F No 98 Minquan Road Xindian District, New Taipei City, 231, Taiwan
Tel.: (886) 286671265
Web Site: https://www.perfectcorp.com
PERF—(NYSE)
Rev.: $53,505,000
Assets: $170,363,000
Liabilities: $30,957,000
Net Worth: $139,406,000
Earnings: $5,416,000
Emp.: 321
Fiscal Year-end: 12/31/23
Beauty Technology Solutions
N.A.I.C.S.: 456120
Alice H. Chang *(CEO)*

PERFECT GROUP CORP., LTD.

Hangji Industrial Park, Yangzhou, 225111, Jiangsu, China
Tel.: (86) 51487492116
Web Site: https://www.toothbrush.com.cn
603059—(SHG)
Rev.: $147,409,653
Assets: $222,685,365
Liabilities: $59,119,281
Net Worth: $163,566,084
Earnings: $13,662,113
Fiscal Year-end: 12/31/22
Toilet Product Mfr
N.A.I.C.S.: 325611
Zhang Wensheng *(Chm & Gen Mgr)*

PERFECT GROUP INTERNATIONAL HOLDINGS LTD.

26/F YHC Tower 1 Sheung Yuet Road, Kowloon, China (Hong Kong)
Tel.: (852) 23346841
Web Site: http://www.hkperjew.com.hk
Year Founded: 1985
3326—(HKG)
Rev.: $47,691,248
Assets: $106,657,193
Liabilities: $24,176,933
Net Worth: $82,480,260
Earnings: $3,495,413
Emp.: 150
Fiscal Year-end: 12/31/22
Holding Company
N.A.I.C.S.: 551112
Kin Kwong Kan *(Chm & CEO)*

Subsidiaries:

Hong Kong Perfect Jewellery DMCC (1)
Unit No B3-19-11 Gold Tower Jumeirah Lakes Towers, Dubai, United Arab Emirates
Tel.: (971) 44523649
Logistics Consulting Servies
N.A.I.C.S.: 541614

Perfect Group International Holdings Ltd. - China Factory (1)
No 22 Xinhou Road Lin Village Tangxia town, Dongguan, Guangdong, China
Tel.: (86) 76982621838
Jewelry Mfr
N.A.I.C.S.: 339910

PERFECT HOLDING SA

Avenue de Florimont 3, CH-1006, Lausanne, Switzerland
Tel.: (41) 21 552 6016
Web Site: http://www.perfect.aero
PRFN—(SWX)
Assets: $154,016
Liabilities: $607,004
Net Worth: ($452,988)
Earnings: ($161,943)
Emp.: 10
Fiscal Year-end: 12/31/21
Aviation Services
N.A.I.C.S.: 488190
Jean-Claude Roch *(Chm, CEO & CFO)*

INTERNATIONAL PUBLIC

Subsidiaries:

4M Systems Inc. (1)
46555 Old Ironsides Dr Ste 485, Santa Clara, CA 95054
Tel.: (408) 970-8505
Optical Discs Equipment Mfr
N.A.I.C.S.: 333310

4M Systems Ltd (1)
Unit A 25th Floor CDW Building, Tsuen Wan, China (Hong Kong)
Tel.: (852) 23114018
Web Site: http://www.asia4m.com.hk
Optical Discs Equipment Mfr
N.A.I.C.S.: 333310

4M Systems SA (1)
Avenue Des Sports 42, CH-1400, Yverdon-les-Bains, Switzerland
Tel.: (41) 244237111
Optical Discs Equipment Mfr
N.A.I.C.S.: 333310

PERFECT INFRAENGINEERS LIMITED

R-637 TTC Industrial Area TB Road, Masjid Bandar East, Mumbai, 400701, India
Tel.: (91) 9821433953
Web Site: https://www.perfectinfra.com
Year Founded: 1996
PERFECT—(NSE)
Rev.: $867,154
Assets: $4,160,530
Liabilities: $1,600,899
Net Worth: $2,559,631
Earnings: $71,782
Emp.: 50
Fiscal Year-end: 03/31/23
Plumbing & Heating Contracting & Engineering
N.A.I.C.S.: 238220
Nimesh Natvarlal Mehta *(Chm & Mng Dir)*

Subsidiaries:

Perfect Control Panels Private Limited (1)
R 637 TTC Industrial Area MIDC Rabale, Navi Mumbai, India
Tel.: (91) 8454981097
Plumbing Contracting Services
N.A.I.C.S.: 238220

PERFECT MEDICAL HEALTH MANAGEMENT LIMITED

51st Floor Langham Place Office Tower 8 Argyle Street, Mong Kok, Kowloon, China (Hong Kong)
Tel.: (852) 29702778
1830—(HKG)
Rev.: $177,130,778
Assets: $165,277,485
Liabilities: $87,212,678
Net Worth: $78,064,808
Earnings: $40,243,845
Emp.: 1,317
Fiscal Year-end: 03/31/23
Holding Company; Weight Loss Management, Spa Treatment & Other Beauty Services & Products
N.A.I.C.S.: 551112
Kong Au-Yeung *(Chm & CEO)*

Subsidiaries:

I-Medi Asia Limited (1)
Mong Kok, Kowloon, China (Hong Kong)
Tel.: (852) 81019288
Web Site: http://www.imedi-asia.com
Medical Aesthetic Device Distr
N.A.I.C.S.: 423450

Perfect Shape & Skin (YL) Limited (1)
Rm 805 8/F Kwong Wah Plz, Yuen Long, New Territories, China (Hong Kong)
Tel.: (852) 24698879
Slimming & Beauty Treatment Services
N.A.I.C.S.: 812112

AND PRIVATE COMPANIES

Perfect Shape & Skin Limited (1)
Hollywood Plaza, Mong Kok, Kowloon, China (Hong Kong)
Tel.: (852) 27703718
Slimming & Beauty Treatment Services
N.A.I.C.S.: 812112

Perfect Shape & Skin Management Co. Limited (1)
Rm 1205-06 Tower I Silvercord Centre 30 Canton Road, Hong Kong, China (Hong Kong)
Tel.: (852) 27702099
Slimming & Beauty Treatment Services
N.A.I.C.S.: 812112

Perfect Shape & Spa (CWB) Limited (1)
19-4 Hand Loom Center Paterson Street 2 Causeway Bay, Wanchai, China (Hong Kong)
Tel.: (852) 29702778
Slimming & Beauty Treatment Services
N.A.I.C.S.: 812112

PERFECT MOMENT LTD.
307 Canalot Studios 222 Kensal Road, London, W10 5BN, United Kingdom
Tel.: (44) 2045588849   DE
Web Site:
https://www.perfectmoment.com
Year Founded: 1984
PMNT—(NYSEAMEX)
Rev.: $24,443,000
Assets: $12,609,000
Liabilities: $4,846,000
Net Worth: $7,763,000
Earnings: ($8,722,000)
Emp.: 39
Fiscal Year-end: 03/31/24
Clothing Accessory Retailer
N.A.I.C.S.: 424350

PERFECT OPTRONICS LTD
Flat 903 9/F New Lee Wah Centre No 88 Tokwawan Road, Tokwawan, Kowloon, China (Hong Kong)
Tel.: (852) 31615555
Web Site: http://www.perfect-optronics.com
Year Founded: 2000
8311—(HKG)
Rev.: $38,418,045
Assets: $19,603,125
Liabilities: $5,662,530
Net Worth: $13,940,595
Earnings: $444,083
Emp.: 65
Fiscal Year-end: 12/31/22
Display Components Distr
N.A.I.C.S.: 423690
Wai Tak Cheng (Founder)

Subsidiaries:

Fayeking Technology Limited (1)
88 To Kwa Wan Road Room 903 9/F New Lever Centre, Kowloon, China (Hong Kong)
Tel.: (852) 3 161 5555
Web Site: https://www.fayeking.com.hk
Electronic Product Mfr & Whslr
N.A.I.C.S.: 334419

Yuan Mei Xin Technology (Shenzhen) Company Limited (1)
Room 705 7/F Block A New Technology Plaza Futian District, Shenzhen, 518040, China
Tel.: (86) 75583435566
Electronic Components Distr
N.A.I.C.S.: 423690

PERFECT PRESENTATION FOR COMMERCIAL SERVICES COMPANY
4077 Alsheikg Abdullah Bin Gabreen Street 7537, PO Box 105523, Riyadh, 13531, Saudi Arabia
Tel.: (966) 115109988
Web Site: https://www.2p.com.sa
Year Founded: 2004
7204—(SAU)
Rev.: $301,238,142
Assets: $314,225,465
Liabilities: $212,355,161
Net Worth: $101,870,303
Earnings: $34,477,256
Emp.: 4,500
Fiscal Year-end: 12/31/23
Information Technology Services
N.A.I.C.S.: 541512
Nasser Abdullah Albassam (Chm)

PERFECT WORLD CO., LTD.
Perfect World Plaza Tower 306 86 Beiyuan Road, Chaoyang District, Beijing, 100101, China
Tel.: (86) 10 5780 5700   Ky
Web Site: http://www.pwrd.com
Year Founded: 2004
Sales Range: $600-649.9 Million
Holding Company; Online Game Developer & Operator
N.A.I.C.S.: 551112
Michael Yufeng Chi (Chm)

Subsidiaries:

Beijing Perfect World Game Software Co., Ltd. (1)
8/F Huakong Mansion No 1 Yard Shangdi East Road, Haidian Dist, Beijing, 100085, China
Tel.: (86) 1057801326
Sales Range: $700-749.9 Million
Emp.: 400
Gaming Software Development Services
N.A.I.C.S.: 541511
Michael Yufeng Chi (Chm)

Cryptic Studios, Inc. (1)
980 University Ave, Los Gatos, CA 95032
Tel.: (408) 399-1969
Web Site: http://www.crypticstudios.com
Sales Range: $25-49.9 Million
Emp.: 100
Video Game Developer
N.A.I.C.S.: 513210
Stephen D'Angelo (CTO)

Perfect World Entertainment Inc. (1)
101 Redwood Shores Pkwy Ste 400, Redwood City, CA 94065
Tel.: (650) 590-7700
Web Site: http://www.perfectworld.com
Emp.: 100
Online Gambling Services
N.A.I.C.S.: 541511
Bryan Huang (Pres)

Perfect World Europe B.V. (1)
Joan Muyskenweg 22 4th Fl, Amsterdam, 1906 CJ, Noord Holland, Netherlands
Tel.: (31) 202201000
Sales Range: $25-49.9 Million
Emp.: 40
Online Games Publishing Services
N.A.I.C.S.: 516210

Runic Games, Inc. (1)
1417 4th Ave, Seattle, WA 98111
Tel.: (206) 623-0576
Web Site: http://www.runicgames.com
Online Game Software Development Services
N.A.I.C.S.: 541511

PERFECT-OCTAVE MEDIA PROJECTS LTD.
702 7th Floor Crystal Paradise Jeevan Nagar Veera Desai Road, Andheri West, Mumbai, 400093, India
Tel.: (91) 9819790246   In
Web Site:
https://www.perfectoctave.com
Year Founded: 1991
521062—(BOM)
Rev.: $189,485
Assets: $1,447,131
Liabilities: $447,371
Net Worth: $999,760
Earnings: $50,429
Emp.: 8
Fiscal Year-end: 03/31/23

PERFETTI VAN MELLE HOLDING B.V.

Entertainment & Media Services
N.A.I.C.S.: 541830
Ganeshkumar Kuppan (Mng Dir)

PERFECTECH INTERNATIONAL HOLDINGS LIMITED
15/F Sun Hing Industrial Building, 46 Wong Chuk Hang Road, Aberdeen, China (Hong Kong)
Tel.: (852) 39650088
Web Site:
https://www.perfectech.com.hk
0765—(HKG)
Rev.: $22,625,895
Assets: $20,098,845
Liabilities: $6,515,123
Net Worth: $13,583,723
Earnings: ($761,303)
Emp.: 700
Fiscal Year-end: 12/31/22
Novelties & Decoration Products Mfr
N.A.I.C.S.: 459420
Albert Wai Yip Poon (Exec Dir)

Subsidiaries:

Benefit Packing Materials Limited (1)
7 Fl Etat Factory Bldg 4 Heung Yip Rd, Wong Chuk Hang, Aberdeen, China (Hong Kong)
Tel.: (852) 26931116
Sales Range: $25-49.9 Million
Emp.: 30
Packaging Material Distr
N.A.I.C.S.: 423840

Dream Creation Ltd (1)
7 F E Tat Factory Bldg 4 Heung Yip Rd, Wong Chuk Hang, Aberdeen, China (Hong Kong)
Tel.: (852) 39650088
Sales Range: $25-49.9 Million
Emp.: 30
Toys Mfr & Sales
N.A.I.C.S.: 339930

Perfectech Colour Centre Limited (1)
15th Floor Sun Hing Industrial Building, 46 Wong Chuk Hang Road, Aberdeen, China (Hong Kong)
Tel.: (852) 25546366
Sales Range: $25-49.9 Million
Emp.: 25
Industrial Dyes Mfr
N.A.I.C.S.: 325130
Benjamin Yan Lee Tsui (Dir-Sls)

Perfectech International Trading Ltd (1)
15/F Sun Hing Industrial Building 46 Wong Chuk Hang Road, Wong Chuk Hang, Aberdeen, China (Hong Kong)
Tel.: (852) 3 965 0088
Web Site: http://www.perfectech.com
Sales Range: $25-49.9 Million
Emp.: 30
Novelties & Decorative Products Sales
N.A.I.C.S.: 424950
Steve Lui (Mgr-Mktg)

Shouji Mold Engineering Co Ltd (1)
Tai Long Shan Rd Man Fung Ind Est, Shajing Po On, Shenzhen, Guangdong, China
Tel.: (86) 75533850289
Web Site: http://www.sj-mold.com
Plastic Injection Mold Mfr
N.A.I.C.S.: 333511

Shouji Tooling Factory Ltd (1)
15/F Sun Hing Industrial Building 46 Wong Chuk Hang Road, Aberdeen, China (Hong Kong)
Tel.: (852) 3 965 0088
Web Site: https://www.shoujitooling.com
Emp.: 400
Plastic Injection Mold Mfr
N.A.I.C.S.: 333511

Plant (Non-US):

Shouji Tooling Factory Ltd - China Factory (2)
No 1 WeiFa Industrial Park, Ya Kou Village Nan Lang Town, Zhongshan, 518104, Guangdong, China
Tel.: (86) 7608 996 9889
Web Site: https://www.shoujitooling.com
Plastic Injection Mold Mfr
N.A.I.C.S.: 333511

PERFECTENERGY INTERNATIONAL LIMITED
479 You Dong Road, Minhang District, Shanghai, 201100, China
Tel.: (86) 2154880958   NV
Web Site:
http://www.perfectenergy.com.cn
Sales Range: $50-74.9 Million
Emp.: 150
Solar Cells, Solar Modules & Photovoltaic Systems Mfr
N.A.I.C.S.: 334413
Jack Li (Founder & CEO)

Subsidiaries:

Perfectenergy GmbH (1)
Tannenweg 8-10, 53757, Saint Augustin, Germany
Tel.: (49) 2241 23425 0
Web Site: http://www.perfectenergy-gmbh.de
Sales Range: $25-49.9 Million
Emp.: 7
Electric Power Equipment Mfr
N.A.I.C.S.: 335999
Xiaochun Haas (CEO)

PERFECTPAC LIMITED
910 Chiranjiv Tower 43-Nehru Place, New Delhi, 110 019, India
Tel.: (91) 1126441022
Web Site:
https://www.perfectpac.com
Year Founded: 1973
526435—(BOM)
Rev.: $11,994,653
Assets: $5,428,092
Liabilities: $1,628,200
Net Worth: $3,799,892
Earnings: $339,548
Emp.: 141
Fiscal Year-end: 03/31/23
Polystyrene Product Mfr
N.A.I.C.S.: 326140
Sanjay Rajgarhia (Mng Dir)

PERFEKTA HOLDING JOSSEFORS AB
Kokerigatan 4, 671 60, Arvika, Sweden
Tel.: (46) 570 388 40
Year Founded: 1954
Holding Company
N.A.I.C.S.: 551112
Ake Lindeberg (Mng Dir)

PERFETTI VAN MELLE HOLDING B.V.
Zoete Inval 20, 4815 HK, Breda, Netherlands
Tel.: (31) 765275000
Web Site:
http://www.perfettivanmelle.com
Year Founded: 1900
Sales Range: $1-4.9 Billion
Emp.: 19,000
Confectionery Products
N.A.I.C.S.: 311352
Sameer Suneja (Global CEO)

Subsidiaries:

Perfetti Van Melle Benelux B.V. (1)
Zoete Inval 20, 4815 HK, Breda, Netherlands
Tel.: (31) 765275000
Web Site: http://www.perfettivanmelle.com
Sales Range: $25-49.9 Million
Emp.: 400
Whslr & Retailer of Candy & Confections
N.A.I.C.S.: 445292
Walter Dorhaut Mees (Mgr-Mktg & Adv)

PERFETTI VAN MELLE HOLDING B.V.

INTERNATIONAL PUBLIC

Perfetti Van Melle Holding B.V.—(Continued)

Subsidiary (Non-US):

Frisk Int. N.V. (2)
Technologielaan 2, Leuven, 3001, Brabant, Belgium (100%)
Tel.: (32) 16395001
Web Site: http://www.frisk.com
Sales Range: $25-49.9 Million
Emp.: 64
Mfr of Candy & Confectionery Products
N.A.I.C.S.: 311352

Subsidiary (Domestic):

Look-o-Look International BV (2)
Geurdeland 5, 6673 DR, Andelst, Netherlands
Tel.: (31) 488470200
Web Site: http://www.lookolook.com
Sales Range: $25-49.9 Million
Emp.: 40
Confectionery Mfr
N.A.I.C.S.: 551112
Adrie W. Gerritsen *(Gen Mgr)*

PVM Tab Tech B.V. (2)
Nusterweg 1216136, Sittard, Netherlands
Tel.: (31) 4645727
Candy Product Mfr & Distr
N.A.I.C.S.: 311351

Perfetti Van Melle B.V. (2)
Zoete Inval 20, 4815 HK, Breda, Netherlands (100%)
Tel.: (31) 765275000
Web Site: http://www.perfettivanmelle.com
Mfr of Confections
N.A.I.C.S.: 311352

Van Melle Nederland B.V. (2)
Zoete Inval 20, PO Box 3000, Breda, 4815 HK, Netherlands (100%)
Tel.: (31) 765275000
Web Site: http://www.perfettivanmelle.nl
Confectionery Mfr
N.A.I.C.S.: 311352
Kees De Waard *(Gen Mgr)*

Perfetti Van Melle International Holding B.V. (1)
Zoete Inval 20, 4815 HK, Breda, Netherlands (100%)
Tel.: (31) 765275000
Web Site: http://www.perfettivanmelle.com
Sales Range: $150-199.9 Million
Emp.: 350
Holding Company: Confectionery Mfr
N.A.I.C.S.: 551112

Subsidiary (Non-US):

CFP Brands Susswarenhandels GmbH & Co. KG (2)
Kortrijker Strasse 1, 53177, Bonn, Germany (66%)
Tel.: (49) 228 92362 0
Web Site: http://www.cfp-brands.de
Sales Range: $50-74.9 Million
Emp.: 100
Holding Company
N.A.I.C.S.: 551112
Jorg Beiss *(Gen Mgr)*

Subsidiary (Non-US):

Chupa Chups Industrial Mexicana S. A de C. V. (3)
Avda Central Manzanas 4 Parque Ind, Toluca, 2000, Mexico
Tel.: (52) 722 2790110
Candy Product Mfr & Distr
N.A.I.C.S.: 311351

Chupa Chups Perfetti Van Melle Uk Ltd (3)
The Boatyard105 Straight Road Old, Windsor, SL4 2 SE, WindsorBerkshire, United Kingdom
Tel.: (44) 1753 442100
Candy Product Mfr & Distr
N.A.I.C.S.: 311351

Chupa Chups Portugal Ltd (3)
A Urb Casal da Serra Av Casal da Serra LT 1-3 Sala, Lisbon, Portugal
Tel.: (351) 121 95 33880
Candy Product Mfr & Distr
N.A.I.C.S.: 311351

Jessica Marquez *(Brand Mgr)*

Chupa Chups S.A. (3)
Delesmasies 16 Santesteve Sesrovirs Pl de la Pau, Cornella de Llobreget, Barcelona, 08940, Spain
Tel.: (34) 934952727
Web Site: http://www.chupachups.es
Confectionery Mfr
N.A.I.C.S.: 311351
Ubalbo Traldi *(Pres)*

Chupa-Chups Rus (3)
Repischeva str 18 Kolomiagi Ch Ch Factory, 197349, Saint Petersburg, Russia
Tel.: (7) 8124482323
Web Site: http://www.perfettivanmelle.it
Candy Product Mfr & Distr
N.A.I.C.S.: 311351

Subsidiary (Non-US):

GELCO S.r.l. (2)
Via E Mattei, Zona Industriale, 64020, Teramo, Castelnuovo Vomano, Italy (100%)
Tel.: (39) 086157223
Web Site: http://www.gelco.it
Sales Range: $25-49.9 Million
Emp.: 185
Mfr of Candy & Confectionery Products
N.A.I.C.S.: 311352

Gum Base Company S.p.A. (2)
Via Nerviano 25, Lainate, 20020, Milan, Italy (100%)
Tel.: (39) 02931721
Web Site: http://www.gumbase.com
Mfr of Candy & Confectionery Products
N.A.I.C.S.: 311352

Subsidiary (Non-US):

Gum Base Shanghai Food Co. Ltd. (3)
7171 Beijing Hwy, Chonggu Town, Shanghai, 201706, Quingpu, China (90%)
Tel.: (86) 2159781803
Web Site: http://www.gumbase.com
Mfr of Candy & Confectionery Products
N.A.I.C.S.: 311352

Subsidiary (Non-US):

La Giulia Ind. S.p.A. (2)
Via E Fermi 17, 34170, Gorizia, Italy (100%)
Tel.: (39) 0481528211
Web Site: http://www.lagiulia.it
Sales Range: $25-49.9 Million
Emp.: 130
Mfr of Candy & Confectionery Products
N.A.I.C.S.: 311352
Ubaldo Traldi *(Pres)*

PT. Perfetti Indonesia (2)
Gedung Ambhara Jl Dr, Saharjo No 181, Jakarta, 12860, Indonesia
Tel.: (62) 218307681
Mfr of Candy & Confectionery Products
N.A.I.C.S.: 311352

Perfetti CR s.r.o. (2)
Tomickova 9, 14000, Prague, Czech Republic
Tel.: (420) 244466500
Sales Range: $10-24.9 Million
Emp.: 30
Mfr of Candy & Confectionery Products
N.A.I.C.S.: 311352

Perfetti Confectionery Vietnam Ltd. (2)
70/1 Hwy n 1, Thu Duc District, Linh Xuan Village, Ho Chi Minh City, Vietnam
Tel.: (84) 88967095
Mfr of Candy & Confectionery Products
N.A.I.C.S.: 311352

Perfetti S.A. (2)
Riera de Targa No 53, Vilassar de Dalt, 08339, Barcelona, Spain (100%)
Tel.: (34) 937530501
Mfr of Candy & Confectionery Products
N.A.I.C.S.: 311352

Perfetti Van Melle Asia Pacific Pte Ltd (2)
331 North Bridge Road, Singapore, 188720, Singapore
Tel.: (65) 6336 3545

Web Site: http://www.perfettivanmelle.com
Candy Product Mfr
N.A.I.C.S.: 311351

Perfetti Van Melle Brasil Ltda. (2)
Rua Parsch 100 Distrito Industrial, Caixa Portal 277 1, Vinhedo, CEP 13280000, SP, Brazil (100%)
Tel.: (55) 1938767812
Sales Range: $150-199.9 Million
Mfr of Candies & Confections
N.A.I.C.S.: 311352

Perfetti Van Melle Canada Ltd. (2)
3800 Steeles Av West Suite 014, Woodbridge, L4L 4G9, ON, Canada
Tel.: (905) 581-2455
Candy Product Mfr & Distr
N.A.I.C.S.: 311351

Perfetti Van Melle Confectionery (Shenzhen) Co., Ltd. (2)
Tuyang Kuichong, Longgang District, Shenzhen, 518119, Guangdong, China
Tel.: (86) 755 8423 1333
Candy Product Mfr & Distr
N.A.I.C.S.: 311351
Nazmul Haider *(Mgr-Fin)*

Perfetti Van Melle Confectionery China Co Ltd (2)
318 Lu Chun Rd, Minhang, Shanghai, 200245, China (100%)
Tel.: (86) 2134054668
Web Site: http://www.perfettivanmelle.com.cn
Sales Range: $150-199.9 Million
Mfr of Candy & Confectionery Products
N.A.I.C.S.: 311352

Perfetti Van Melle Export Far East Ltd (2)
Ste 713 A Ocean Ctr Harbour City, Canton Rd, Kowloon, China (Hong Kong) (100%)
Tel.: (852) 27367009
Web Site: http://www.perfettivanmelle.com
Sales Range: $25-49.9 Million
Emp.: 7
N.A.I.C.S.: 311352

Perfetti Van Melle Gida Sanayi ve Ticaret A.S. (2)
Kirac Merkez Mah Ataturk Cad No 1734900 Buyukcekmece, Istanbul, Turkiye
Tel.: (90) 212 6891151
Candy Product Mfr & Distr
N.A.I.C.S.: 311351
Cemal Demirsu *(Mgr-IT)*

Perfetti Van Melle Hellas S.A. (2)
Pentelis 36175 64, Faliro, Athens, Greece
Tel.: (30) 210 9480366
Web Site: http://www.perfettivanmelle.com
Emp.: 90
Candy Product Mfr & Distr
N.A.I.C.S.: 311351
Stanatis Karavisiliavis *(Mgr-Comml)*

Perfetti Van Melle India Pvt. Ltd. (2)
Global Business Park 1st Floor Tower A, Mehrauli Gurgaon Road, Gurgaon, 122 002, Manesar, India (100%)
Tel.: (91) 124 6726371
Web Site: http://www.perfettiit.com
Mfr of Candy & Confectionery Products
N.A.I.C.S.: 311352
Rajesh Ramakrishnan *(Mng Dir)*

Plant (Domestic):

Perfetti Van Melle India Pvt. Ltd. - Chennai Factory (3)
No 7 Karanaipuducherry Village - Post Near Urapakkam Via Guduvanchery, Chennai, 603 202, India
Tel.: (91) 44 66094800
Candy Product Mfr
N.A.I.C.S.: 311351
Karthik Panneerselvam *(Area Mgr-Sls)*

Perfetti Van Melle India Pvt. Ltd. - Manesar Factory (3)
47th Milestone Delhi - Jaipur Highway Village, Manesar, Gurgaon, 122 050, Haryana, India
Tel.: (91) 124 6730452
Web Site: http://www.pvmindia.com
Emp.: 700
Candy Product Mfr
N.A.I.C.S.: 311351

Ajay Mittal *(Mgr-Plant)*

Perfetti Van Melle India Pvt. Ltd. - Rudrapur Factory (3)
14-B Sector-9 IIE SIDCUL Pant Nagar, Rudrapur, 263 153, Uttarakhand, India
Tel.: (91) 5944 664911
Candy Product Mfr
N.A.I.C.S.: 311351

Subsidiary (Domestic):

Perfetti Van Melle International Trust B.V. (2)
Zoete Inval 20, PO Box 3000, Breda, 3000, Netherlands (100%)
Tel.: (31) 765275000
Web Site: http://www.perfettivanmelle.nl
Sales Range: $200-249.9 Million
Holding Co
N.A.I.C.S.: 551112
Kees Waarg *(Gen Mgr)*

Subsidiary (Non-US):

Perfetti Van Melle Indonesia (3)
Bogor St 47 4 Kibino, PO Box 4091, Jakarta, 16912, Indonesia (70%)
Tel.: (62) 218754266
Sales Range: $150-199.9 Million
Emp.: 1,000
N.A.I.C.S.: 311352

Plant (Domestic):

Perfetti Van Melle Indonesia - Cikampek factory (4)
Kawasan Industri Kota Bukit Indah Blok A II 20-21 Cikampek, Purwakarta, 41181, Indonesia
Tel.: (62) 264 351271
Candy Product Mfr
N.A.I.C.S.: 311351

Subsidiary (Non-US):

Perfetti Van Melle Polska SP. z.o.o. (3)
The Park Krakowiakow 50, 02-255, Warsaw, Mazowieckie, Poland (100%)
Tel.: (48) 22 7118500
Web Site: http://www.mentos.pr
Sales Range: $25-49.9 Million
Emp.: 50
Mfr of Confectionery Products
N.A.I.C.S.: 311352

Subsidiary (US):

Perfetti Van Melle USA, Inc. (2)
3645 Turfway Rd, Erlanger, KY 41018 (100%)
Tel.: (859) 283-1234
Web Site: http://www.Perfetti.com
Sales Range: $75-99.9 Million
Emp.: 200
Mfr of Confectionery Products
N.A.I.C.S.: 424450
Rick Tyrrell *(VP-Sls)*

Subsidiary (Non-US):

Van Melle Far East Limited (2)
Ste 713A Ocean Ctr 5, Canton Rd, Kowloon, NIL, China (Hong Kong) (100%)
Tel.: (852) 27367009
Emp.: 7
N.A.I.C.S.: 311352

Subsidiary (Non-US):

Perfetti Van Melle OOO (2)
Village Leshkovo Istra district, PO Box 123103, 143591, Moscow, Russia
Tel.: (7) 495 9602800
Candy Product Mfr & Distr
N.A.I.C.S.: 311351

Perfetti Van Melle Phils., Inc. (2)
16 Fl Octagon Ctr San Miguel Ave, Orpigas Ctr, Pasig, 1605, Philippines (100%)
Tel.: (63) 26347653
Web Site: http://www.perfettivanmelle.it
Sales Range: $10-24.9 Million
Emp.: 22
Mfr of Candies & Confections
N.A.I.C.S.: 311352

Perfetti Van Melle Romania Srl (2)
Aurel Vlaicu 186 3400, Cluj-Napoca, 500481, Romania

Tel.: (40) 264 444 575
Candy Product Mfr & Distr
N.A.I.C.S.: 311351

Perfetti Van Melle Slovakia s.r.o. (2)
Odborarska 3, 831 02, Bratislava, Slovakia
Tel.: (421) 244 455 006
Web Site: http://www.perfettivanmelle.cz
Candy Product Mfr & Distr
N.A.I.C.S.: 311351

Perfettie Van Melle Brasil Ltda (2)
Rua Iracema Lucas n 100, Distrito Industrial, Vinhedo, 13280 000, Sao Paulo, Brazil
Tel.: (55) 19 3876 7800
Web Site: http://www.perfettivanmelle.com
Candy & Confectionery Products Mfr & Distr
N.A.I.C.S.: 311352

Van Melle A.G. (2)
Steistegstrasse 13, Postfach 647, 6430, Schwyz, Switzerland
Tel.: (41) 41 817 7777
Candy Product Mfr & Distr
N.A.I.C.S.: 311351

PERFORMA PARTNERS
Surubim Street 577 cj 94 Brooklin Novo, Sao Paulo, 04571-050, Brazil
Tel.: (55) 11 3814 4111
Web Site: http://www.performapartners.com
Year Founded: 2006
Emp.: 4
Private Equity Firm Services
N.A.I.C.S.: 523999
Andre Pimentel *(Sr Partner)*

PERFORMANCE AUTO GROUP
105 Van Kirk Drive, Brampton, L7A 1A4, ON, Canada
Tel.: (905) 863-7359
Web Site: http://www.performance.ca
Year Founded: 1964
New Car Retailer
N.A.I.C.S.: 441110
Neil Van Lochem *(CFO)*

Subsidiaries:

Grimsby Hyundai (1)
569 Main Street West, Grimsby, L3M 1V1, ON, Canada
Tel.: (905) 643-1221
Web Site: https://www.grimsbyhyundai.com
Emp.: 50
New & Used Car Dealers
N.A.I.C.S.: 441110

PERFORMANCE CARS (ST. CATHARINES) LTD.
371 Ontario St, Saint Catharines, L2R 7A7, ON, Canada
Tel.: (905) 934-2277
Web Site: http://www.performancecars.-benz.ca
Rev.: $11,302,844
Emp.: 25
New & Used Car Dealers
N.A.I.C.S.: 441110
Steve Champion *(Gen Mgr)*

PERFORMANCE EQUIPMENT LTD.
6950 Tomken Rd, Mississauga, L5T 2S3, ON, Canada
Tel.: (905) 564-8333
Web Site: http://www.volvotrucks.com
Rev.: $74,500,000
Emp.: 140
Truck Retailer
N.A.I.C.S.: 441227
Boyd Brenton *(Controller)*

PERFORMANCE ONE AG
S6 35, 68161, Mannheim, Germany
Tel.: (49) 62158679490
Web Site: https://www.performance.one

Year Founded: 2009
PO1—(MUN)
Rev.: $13,842,530
Assets: $4,978,454
Liabilities: $4,238,861
Net Worth: $739,593
Earnings: ($518,819)
Emp.: 81
Fiscal Year-end: 12/31/23
Digital Marketing Services
N.A.I.C.S.: 541810

PERFORMANCE PR LTD.
The Warehouse 47-49 Cowleaze Road, Kingston upon Thames, KT2 6DZ, United Kingdom
Tel.: (44) 2085413434
Web Site: http://www.performancepr.com
Year Founded: 2002
Advertising Agencies
N.A.I.C.S.: 541810

Subsidiaries:

Performance Communications Ltd (1)
9 Mulberry Avenue, Portishead, Bristol, BS20 7LG, United Kingdom
Tel.: (44) 7954 203 745
Medical Consulting Services
N.A.I.C.S.: 541840

Performance PR Middle East (1)
Office 1905 Building 1, PO Box 502058, Dubai Media City, Dubai, United Arab Emirates
Tel.: (971) 4 4347365
Web Site: http://www.performancepr.com
Emp.: 10
Advertising Agencies
N.A.I.C.S.: 541810

PERFORMANCE SHIPPING INC.
373 Syngrou Avenue, Palaio Faliro, 175 64, Athens, Greece
Tel.: (30) 2166002400
Web Site: https://www.pshipping.com
Year Founded: 2010
PSHG—(NASDAQ)
Rev.: $108,938,000
Assets: $296,266,000
Liabilities: $63,082,000
Net Worth: $233,184,000
Earnings: $56,924,000
Emp.: 209
Fiscal Year-end: 12/31/23
Freight Transportation Services
N.A.I.C.S.: 483111
Symeon Palios *(Chm)*

PERFUMERIA JULIA, S.A.
Av Carlemany 115, Escaldes-Engordany, AD700, Andorra
Tel.: (376) 801926
Web Site: http://www.julia.ad
Sales Range: $75-99.9 Million
Emp.: 300
Perfume Sales & Mfr
N.A.I.C.S.: 456120
Bonet Fite Julia *(Chm)*

PERGAMON STATUS DIS TI-CARET AS
Alsancak Mah 1456 Sokak Baro Han No 16 Ic Kapi No 11 Konak, 35220, Izmir, Turkiye
Tel.: (90) 2324641616
Web Site: https://www.psdisticaret.com.tr
Year Founded: 2001
PSDTC—(IST)
Sales Range: Less than $1 Million
Manmade Fibre Product Distr
N.A.I.C.S.: 424690
Ibrahim Anar *(Member-Exec Bd)*

PERIHELION CAPITAL LTD.

1066 West Hastings Street Suite 2600, Vancouver, V6E 3X2, BC, Canada
Tel.: (778) 867-0482 Ca
Year Founded: 2018
PCL.P—(TSXV)
Assets: $89,531
Liabilities: $42,957
Net Worth: $46,575
Earnings: ($69,345)
Fiscal Year-end: 12/31/20
Business Consulting Services
N.A.I.C.S.: 522299

PERIMETER MEDICAL IMAGING AI, INC.
555 Richmond Street W, Toronto, M5V 3B1, ON, Canada
Tel.: (647) 360-0302
Web Site: https://perimetermed.com
PINK—(TSXV)
Rev.: $403,533
Assets: $20,541,371
Liabilities: $5,476,566
Net Worth: $15,064,805
Earnings: ($14,035,994)
Fiscal Year-end: 12/31/23
Medical Technology Services
N.A.I.C.S.: 621511
Jeremy Sobotta *(CEO)*

PERION NETWORK LTD.
4 HaNechoshet Street, Holon, 5885849, Israel
Tel.: (972) 733981000 Il
Web Site: https://www.perion.com
Year Founded: 1999
PERI—(NASDAQ)
Rev.: $640,256,000
Assets: $870,218,000
Liabilities: $287,084,000
Net Worth: $583,134,000
Earnings: $99,225,000
Emp.: 440
Fiscal Year-end: 12/31/22
E-Mail Customization Software Developer
N.A.I.C.S.: 513210
Maoz Sigron *(CFO)*

Subsidiaries:

IncrediMail USA (1)
1230 Ave of the Americas 7th Fl, New York, NY 10020
Tel.: (212) 682-1995
E-Mail Customization Solutions
N.A.I.C.S.: 513210
Yaron Adler *(Co-Founder)*

Subsidiary (Domestic):

Smilebox, Inc. (2)
15809 Bear Creek Pkwy, Redmond, WA 98052
Tel.: (425) 881-9475
Web Site: http://www.smilebox.com
Sales Range: $25-49.9 Million
Emp.: 50
Online Electronic Invitation Design Software
N.A.I.C.S.: 513210

Intercept Interactive, Inc. (1)
1 World Trade Ctr 71st Fl Ste J, New York, NY 10007
Tel.: (212) 685-8000
Web Site: https://www.undertone.com
Advertising, Market Research, Media Buying Services, Media Planning
N.A.I.C.S.: 541810
Louise Peddell *(VP-HR)*

PERISAI PETROLEUM TEKNOLOGI BHD.
Suite 3A-17 Level 17 Block 3A Plaza Sentral Jalan Stesen Sentral 5, 50470, Kuala Lumpur, Malaysia
Tel.: (60) 322781133 MY
Web Site: http://www.perisai.biz
PERISAI—(KLS)
Rev.: $28,132,315

Assets: $223,766,420
Liabilities: $345,263,402
Net Worth: ($121,496,982)
Earnings: ($57,044,347)
Fiscal Year-end: 06/30/19
Offshore Drilling, Production, Support & Construction
N.A.I.C.S.: 237120
Zainol Izzet Mohamed Ishak *(Mng Dir)*

Subsidiaries:

Corro-Pro (L) Inc. (1)
Level 1 Lot 7 Block F Saguking Commercial Building, 87000, Labuan, Wilayah Persekutuan, Malaysia
Tel.: (60) 87410745
Marine Vessel Operating Services
N.A.I.C.S.: 488330
Eugene Sin *(Sr Mgr-Vessel Ops)*

PERISSON PETROLEUM CORPORATION
Suite 2000 530 - 8th Avenue SW, Calgary, T2P 3S8, AB, Canada
Tel.: (403) 800-0042
Web Site: http://www.perisson.com
POG—(TSXV)
Rev.: $1,677,170
Assets: $3,916,983
Liabilities: $13,507,814
Net Worth: ($9,590,831)
Earnings: ($3,690,265)
Fiscal Year-end: 12/31/19
Oil & Gas Exploration
N.A.I.C.S.: 211120
Chien-Yeh Chen *(CEO)*

PERIYA CORP.
625 Richmond Street W Apt 0, Toronto, M6J 1C2, ON, Canada
Tel.: (647) 444-3845 NV
Year Founded: 2013
Mobile Application Software
N.A.I.C.S.: 513210
Christopher Park *(Pres, CEO, CFO & Treas)*

PERK LABS, INC.
997 Seymour St Suite 250, Vancouver, PMB 955, BC, Canada
Tel.: (778) 819-1352
Web Site: https://www.perklabs.io
PKLBF—(OTCQB)
Rev.: $24,710
Assets: $373,806
Liabilities: $195,310
Net Worth: $178,496
Earnings: ($2,642,909)
Emp.: 20
Fiscal Year-end: 11/30/22
Mobile Application Development Services
N.A.I.C.S.: 541511
Gary Zhang *(CTO)*

Subsidiaries:

Perk Hero Software Inc. (1)
Two Bentall Centre 555 Burrard Street Suite 1755, Box 240, Vancouver, V7X 1M9, BC, Canada
Web Site: http://www.perkhero.com
Software Development Services
N.A.I.C.S.: 541511
Jonathan Hoyles *(CEO)*

PERK.COM, INC.
150 Caroline St S Ste 406, Waterloo, N2L 0A5, ON, Canada
Tel.: (519) 504-0482
Web Site: http://www.perk.com
Consumer Reward Software
N.A.I.C.S.: 513210
Edward William Hastings *(CEO)*

Subsidiaries:

AppRedeem, Inc. (1)

PERK.COM, INC.

Perk.com, Inc.—(Continued)

1804 N Shoreline Blvd Ste 220, Mountain View, CA 94043
Tel.: (650) 625-0604
Web Site: http://www.appredeem.com
Software Publisher
N.A.I.C.S.: 513210
James Ransom *(VP-Engrg)*

PERKAPALAN DAI ZHUN SDN. BHD.

No 1 Jln Sungai Aur, 42000, Port Klang, Selangor, Malaysia
Tel.: (60) 331692233 MY
Web Site: http://www.pdzlines.com
Year Founded: 1989
Container Trucking Services
N.A.I.C.S.: 484121
Tan Chor How Christopher *(CEO & Exec Dir)*

PERLITE CANADA, INC.

1775 52nd Avenue, Lachine, H8T 2Y1, QC, Canada
Tel.: (514) 631-4251
Web Site:
   htttp://www.perlitecanada.com
Year Founded: 1993
Rev.: $6,013,169
Assets: $3,284,774
Liabilities: $1,167,181
Net Worth: $2,117,592
Earnings: $732,741
Emp.: 27
Fiscal Year-end: 10/31/18
Perlite Production Services
N.A.I.C.S.: 325180
Richard Barabe *(Pres & CEO)*

PERM ENERGY RETAIL COMPANY OJSC

Timiryazeva 37, Perm, 614007, Russia
Tel.: (7) 3422628892
PMSB—(MOEX)
Sales Range: Less than $1 Million
Electric Power Distribution Services
N.A.I.C.S.: 221122

PERMA FUNDS MANAGEMENT

Level 2 175 Macquarie Street, Sydney, NSW, Australia
Tel.: (61) 92792290
Web Site:
   http://www.permafunds.com.au
Privater Equity Firm
N.A.I.C.S.: 523999
Hussein Rifai *(Mng Dir)*

Subsidiaries:

Shepparton Partners Collective Pty Ltd. (1)
175 Macquarie St Ste 2 Level 2, Sydney, 2000, NSW, Australia
Tel.: (61) 292792290
Web Site: http://www.spc.com.au
Food Products Mfr & Distr
N.A.I.C.S.: 311999
Hussein Rifai *(Chm)*

Subsidiary (Domestic):

SPC Ardmona Limited (2)
50 Camberwell Rd, Hawthorn, 3123, VIC, Australia
Tel.: (61) 398618900
Web Site: http://www.spcardmona.com.au
Packaged Fruit Distr
N.A.I.C.S.: 311411
Reg Weine *(Mng Dir)*

Subsidiary (Domestic):

Ardmona Foods Limited (3)
Andrew Failey Ave, Shepparton, 3630, VIC, Australia
Tel.: (61) 358333777
Web Site: http://www.spcardmona.com.au
Emp.: 700

Canned Fruit Jam & Vegetable Mfr
N.A.I.C.S.: 311411

Henry Jones Foods Pty Ltd (3)
PO Box 207, Shepparton, 3632, VIC, Australia
Tel.: (61) 358521111
Specialty Food Mfr & Distr
N.A.I.C.S.: 311412

Subsidiary (Non-US):

SPC Ardmona (Germany) GmbH (3)
Agnesstrasse 30, 22301, Hamburg, Germany
Tel.: (49) 4023841120
Web Site: http://www.spcardmona.de
Sales Range: $25-49.9 Million
Emp.: 1
Packaged Fruits & Vegetables Distr
N.A.I.C.S.: 424480

SPC Ardmona (Spain), S.L.U. (3)
Carretera De Caravaca Moratalla km 1, Moratalla, Murcia, 30440, Spain
Tel.: (34) 968607500
Convenience Food Retailer
N.A.I.C.S.: 445131

Subsidiary (Domestic):

SPC Ardmona Operations Limited
50 Camberwell Road, Hawthorn East, 3123, VIC, Australia
Tel.: (61) 398618900
Processed Fruit & Vegetable Mfr
N.A.I.C.S.: 311411

Shepparton Partners Collective Pty Ltd. (1)
175 Macquarie St Ste 2 Level 2, Sydney, 2000, NSW, Australia
Tel.: (61) 292792290
Web Site: http://www.spc.com.au
Food Products Mfr & Distr
N.A.I.C.S.: 311999
Hussein Rifai *(Chm)*

Subsidiary (Domestic):

SPC Ardmona Limited (2)
50 Camberwell Rd, Hawthorn, 3123, VIC, Australia
Tel.: (61) 398618900
Web Site: http://www.spcardmona.com.au
Packaged Fruit Distr
N.A.I.C.S.: 311411
Reg Weine *(Mng Dir)*

Subsidiary (Domestic):

Ardmona Foods Limited (3)
Andrew Failey Ave, Shepparton, 3630, VIC, Australia
Tel.: (61) 358333777
Web Site: http://www.spcardmona.com.au
Emp.: 700
Canned Fruit Jam & Vegetable Mfr
N.A.I.C.S.: 311411

Henry Jones Foods Pty Ltd (3)
PO Box 207, Shepparton, 3632, VIC, Australia
Tel.: (61) 358521111
Specialty Food Mfr & Distr
N.A.I.C.S.: 311412

Subsidiary (Non-US):

SPC Ardmona (Germany) GmbH (3)
Agnesstrasse 30, 22301, Hamburg, Germany
Tel.: (49) 4023841120
Web Site: http://www.spcardmona.de
Sales Range: $25-49.9 Million
Emp.: 1
Packaged Fruits & Vegetables Distr
N.A.I.C.S.: 424480

SPC Ardmona (Spain), S.L.U. (3)
Carretera De Caravaca Moratalla km 1, Moratalla, Murcia, 30440, Spain
Tel.: (34) 968607500
Convenience Food Retailer
N.A.I.C.S.: 445131

Subsidiary (Domestic):

SPC Ardmona Operations Limited (3)

50 Camberwell Road, Hawthorn East, 3123, VIC, Australia
Tel.: (61) 398618900
Processed Fruit & Vegetable Mfr
N.A.I.C.S.: 311411

PERMAJU INDUSTRIES BERHAD

1st Floor Wisma Cergaz Lot 45182 Sungai Penchala Off Jalan Damansara, Alamesra Sulaman Coastal Highway, 60000, Kuala Lumpur, Sabah, Malaysia
Tel.: (60) 377258855
Web Site:
   https://www.permaju.com.my
Year Founded: 1996
PERMAJU—(KLS)
Rev.: $10,343,259
Assets: $62,278,570
Liabilities: $5,707,483
Net Worth: $56,571,088
Earnings: ($3,900,874)
Emp.: 60
Fiscal Year-end: 06/30/23
Plywood Mfr
N.A.I.C.S.: 321211
Woon Yun Chai *(Exec Dir)*

Subsidiaries:

Autohaus Car Rental Sdn. Bhd. (1)
1st Floor Wisma Cergaz Lot 45182 Sungai Penchala Off Jalan Damansara, 60000, Kuala Lumpur, Malaysia
Tel.: (60) 377258855
Web Site:
   https://www.autohauscarrental.com
Electric Car Rental Services
N.A.I.C.S.: 532111

PERMANENT MAGNETS LIMITED

B-3 MIDC Industrial Area Mira-gaon Miraroad-East, Thane, 401 107, Maharashtra, India
Tel.: (91) 2268285400
Web Site: https://www.pmlindia.com
504132—(BOM)
Rev.: $22,563,563
Assets: $18,135,975
Liabilities: $4,833,391
Net Worth: $13,302,584
Earnings: $3,567,184
Emp.: 103
Fiscal Year-end: 03/31/23
Magnetic Products Mfr
N.A.I.C.S.: 332999
Sharadkumar Jaiprakash Taparia *(Mng Dir)*

PERMANENT TSB GROUP HOLDINGS PLC

56-59 St Stephen's Green, Dublin, 2, Ireland
Tel.: (353) 17042000 IE
Web Site:
   https://www.permanenttsbgroup.ie
Year Founded: 1884
IL0A—(ISE)
Rev.: $838,933,449
Assets: $28,108,606,113
Liabilities: $25,511,597,659
Net Worth: $2,597,008,454
Earnings: $240,624,323
Emp.: 2,614
Fiscal Year-end: 12/31/22
Bank Holding Company
N.A.I.C.S.: 551111
Conor Ryan *(Sec)*

Subsidiaries:

permanent tsb plc (1)
56-59 Saint Stephen's Green, Dublin, D02 H489, Ireland
Tel.: (353) 12124290
Web Site: https://www.ptsb.ie
Commericial Banking
N.A.I.C.S.: 522110

INTERNATIONAL PUBLIC

Conor Ryan *(Sec)*

PERMARK INTERNATIONAL (PTY.) LTD.

50 Angus Crescent Longmeadow Business Park East, Edenvale, Modderfontein, South Africa
Tel.: (27) 115790000
Web Site: http://www.permark.co.za
Year Founded: 1957
Sales Range: $75-99.9 Million
Emp.: 300
Manufacture & Marketing of Licensed & Owned Brands
N.A.I.C.S.: 339999

PERMEX PETROLEUM CORP.

Standard Life Building 625 Howe Street Suite 1290, Vancouver, V6C 2T6, BC, Canada
Tel.: (604) 259-2525
Web Site:
   https://www.permexpetroleum.com
75P—(DEU)
Rev.: $878,951
Assets: $12,567,558
Liabilities: $2,104,453
Net Worth: $10,463,105
Earnings: ($2,714,616)
Emp.: 2
Fiscal Year-end: 09/30/22
Oil & Gas Exploration Services
N.A.I.C.S.: 213112

PERMIRA ADVISERS LLP

80 Pall Mall, London, SW1Y 5ES, United Kingdom
Tel.: (44) 2076321000 UK
Web Site: http://www.permira.com
Year Founded: 1985
Privater Equity Firm
N.A.I.C.S.: 523999
Benoit Vauchy *(Partner)*

Subsidiaries:

Acromas Holdings Ltd. (1)
Enbrook Park, Folkestone, CT20 3SE, Kent, United Kingdom
Tel.: (44) 1303776023
Web Site: http://www.acromas.com
Sales Range: $1-4.9 Million
Emp.: 31,302
Holding Company; Financial, Insurance, Travel, Healthcare & Lifestyle Products & Services
N.A.I.C.S.: 551112
John Andrew Goodsell *(Chm & CEO)*

Subsidiary (Domestic):

Saga Group Limited (2)
Enbrook Park, Middleburg Square, Folkestone, CT20 3SE, Kent, United Kingdom
Tel.: (44) 1303771111
Web Site: http://www.saga.co.uk
Sales Range: $125-149.9 Million
Emp.: 6,000
Holding Company; Insurance, Travel, Financial & Lifestyle Products & Services
N.A.I.C.S.: 551112
Robin Shaw *(CEO-Saga Shipping)*

Subsidiary (Domestic):

Acromas Holidays Limited (3)
Enbrook Park, Middleburg Square, Folkestone, CT20 3SE, Kent, United Kingdom
Tel.: (44) 1303 771 111
Web Site: http://www.travel.saga.co.uk
Vacation & Tour Travel Agency
N.A.I.C.S.: 561510
Susan Hooper *(CEO)*

Acromas Shipping Limited (3)
Enbrook Park, Middleburg Square, Folkestone, CT20 3SE, Kent, United Kingdom
Tel.: (44) 1303 771 111
Web Site: http://www.saga.co.uk
Cruise Vacation Travel Agency
N.A.I.C.S.: 561510

Allied Healthcare (3)
Beaconsfield Court Beaconsfield Road, Hat-

AND PRIVATE COMPANIES — PERMIRA ADVISERS LLP

field, AL10 8HU, Herts, United Kingdom
Tel.: (44) 8458501435
Web Site: http://www.alliedhealthcare.com
Holding Company; Health & Social Care Staffing
N.A.I.C.S.: 551112
John Rennocks *(Chm)*

Subsidiary (Domestic):

Nestor Primecare Services Ltd. (4)
Beaconfields Court Beaconsfield Road, Hatfield, AL10 8HU, Herts, United Kingdom
Tel.: (44) 1707 286800
Web Site: http://www.nestor-healthcare.co.uk
Sales Range: $10-24.9 Million
Health Care Srvices
N.A.I.C.S.: 621999

Subsidiary (US):

Allied Healthcare International Inc. (3)
245 Park Ave 39th Fl, New York, NY 10167
Tel.: (212) 750-0064
Web Site: http://www.alliedhealthcare.com
Sales Range: $250-299.9 Million
Emp.: 1,160
Holding Company; Healthcare Staffing
N.A.I.C.S.: 551112

Subsidiary (Non-US):

Allied Healthcare Group Holdings Limited (4)
Stone Business Park, Brooms Road, Stone, ST15 0TL, Staffs, United Kingdom
Tel.: (44) 1785810600
Web Site: http://www.alliedhealthcare.co.uk
Holding Company
N.A.I.C.S.: 551112

Subsidiary (Domestic):

Allied Healthcare Holdings Limited (5)
Stone Business Park, Brooms Road, Stone, ST15 0TL, Staffs, United Kingdom
Tel.: (44) 1785810600
Web Site: http://www.alliedhealthcare.co.uk
Sales Range: $150-199.9 Million
Emp.: 200
Holding Company; Healthcare Staffing Services
N.A.I.C.S.: 551112

Subsidiary (Domestic):

Allied Healthcare Group Limited (6)
Stone Business Park, Brooms Road, Stone, ST15 0TL, Staffordshire, United Kingdom
Tel.: (44) 1785810600
Web Site: http://www.alliedhealthcare.co.uk
Sales Range: $25-49.9 Million
Nursing & Healthcare Services
N.A.I.C.S.: 621610

Subsidiary (Domestic):

Saga Services Limited (2)
Enbrook Park, Middleburg Square, Folkestone, CT20 1AZ, Kent, United Kingdom
Tel.: (44) 1303771111
Web Site: http://www.saga.co.uk
Financial Information & Advisory Services
N.A.I.C.S.: 525990
Andrew Goodsell *(CEO)*

Subsidiary (Domestic):

The Automobile Association Limited (2)
Fanum House Basingview, Basingstoke, RG21 4EA, Hants, United Kingdom
Tel.: (44) 8705448866
Web Site: http://www.theaa.com
Sales Range: $300-349.9 Million
Automobile Services Club
N.A.I.C.S.: 561599
Michael Cutbill *(Dir-Mktg & Sls)*

Akindo Sushiro Co., Ltd. (1)
1-22-2 Esaka-cho, Suita, 564-0063, Osaka, Japan
Tel.: (81) 66 368 1001
Web Site: http://www.akindo-sushiro.co.jp
Sales Range: $1-4.9 Billion
Emp.: 1,387
Sushi Restaurant Operator
N.A.I.C.S.: 722513
Koichi Mizutome *(Pres & CEO)*

Alter Domus Luxembourg Sarl (1)
15 Boulevard FW Raiffeisen, L-2411, Luxembourg, Luxembourg
Tel.: (352) 4818281
Web Site: https://alterdomus.com
Emp.: 100
Investment Services
N.A.I.C.S.: 523999

BorsodChem Nyrt. (1)
Bolyai Ter 1, 3700, Kazincbarcika, Hungary (95.23%)
Tel.: (36) 48511211
Web Site: http://www.borsodchem-group.com
Sales Range: $1-4.9 Billion
Emp.: 300
Polymers for Plastics
N.A.I.C.S.: 325998
Jason Ding *(CEO)*

Subsidiary (Domestic):

BC-Ablakprofil Kft. (2)
3702 Kazincbarcika Pf 434, Bolyai ter 1, 3704, Kazincbarcika, Hungary
Tel.: (36) 48320322
Web Site: http://www.bcablakprofil.hu
Sales Range: $50-74.9 Million
Producer & Sales of PVC Window Profiles & Pipes
N.A.I.C.S.: 326122

BC-KC Formalin Kft. (2)
Bolyai Ter 1, Kazincbarcika, 3700, Hungary
Tel.: (36) 48512934
Web Site: http://www.borsodchem.hu
Sales Range: Less than $1 Million
Emp.: 18
Producer & Sales of Formaldehyde; Joint Venture of BorsodChem Rt (66.67%) & Dynea Austria Gmbh (33.33%)
N.A.I.C.S.: 325998
Luudadanyi Atila *(Pres)*

BC-Ongrobau Kft. (2)
Bolyai Ter 1, Kazincbarcika, 3700, Hungary
Tel.: (36) 48511380
Sales Range: $25-49.9 Million
Emp.: 88
Maintenance, Renovation & Building; Corrosion Protection; Transportation of Liquid Communal & Hazardous Waste Waters
N.A.I.C.S.: 237120

BC-Ongroelektro Kft. (2)
Bolyai Ter 1, 3700, Kazincbarcika, Hungary
Tel.: (36) 48512771
Web Site: http://www.ongroelektro.mtt.hu
Sales Range: $50-74.9 Million
Mfr & Maintenance of Electric & Process Control Equipment
N.A.I.C.S.: 335314
Tibor Turey *(Gen Mgr)*

BC-Ongropack Kft. (2)
Bolyai ter 1, Pf 441, H-3704, Kazincbarcika, Hungary
Tel.: (36) 48320822
Web Site: http://old.ongropack.hu
Sales Range: $50-74.9 Million
Producer & Sales of PVC Films & Corrugated Sheets
N.A.I.C.S.: 325992

Subsidiary (Non-US):

BorsodChem MCHZ, s.r.o. (2)
Chemicka 2039/1, Ostrava Marianske, 709 00, Hory, Czech Republic
Tel.: (420) 596641111
Web Site: http://www.borsodchem-cz.com
Chemical Products Distr
N.A.I.C.S.: 325998
Miroslava Jerabkova *(Dir-HR)*

CABB GmbH (1)
Otto-Volger-Strasse 3c, Taunus, 65843, Sulzbach, Germany
Tel.: (49) 6196 9674 0
Web Site: http://www.cabb-chemicals.com
Sales Range: $400-449.9 Million
Chemicals Mfr
N.A.I.C.S.: 325998
Robert Dahinden *(Gen Mgr-Custom Mfg Bus Unit)*

Subsidiary (Non-US):

CABB AG (2)
Dungerstrasse 81, Post box 1964, 4133, Pratteln, Switzerland
Tel.: (41) 618253111
Web Site: http://www.cabb-chemicals.com
Sales Range: $150-199.9 Million
Chemicals Mfr & Distr
N.A.I.C.S.: 325998
Joerg Schrickel *(Mgr-Mktg)*

CABB Oy (2)
Kemirantie 1, 67900, Kokkola, Finland
Tel.: (358) 467100600
Web Site: http://www.cabb-chemicals.com
Sales Range: $100-124.9 Million
Chemicals Mfr
N.A.I.C.S.: 325998
Ulf Bjorkqvist *(CEO)*

Cambrex Corporation (1)
1 Meadowlands Plz, East Rutherford, NJ 07073
Tel.: (201) 804-3000
Web Site: http://www.cambrex.com
Rev.: $514,997,000
Assets: $1,223,428,000
Liabilities: $569,701,000
Net Worth: $653,727,000
Earnings: $92,418,000
Emp.: 1,732
Fiscal Year-end: 12/31/2018
Pharmaceutical Ingredients & Intermediates Mfr
N.A.I.C.S.: 325412
Thomas W. Loewald *(Pres & CEO)*

Subsidiary (Non-US):

AS Cambrex Tallinn (2)
Teaduspargi 3/1, EE-12618, Tallinn, Estonia
Tel.: (372) 6204398
Web Site: http://www.cambrex.com
Emp.: 25
Pharmaceutical Preparation Mfr
N.A.I.C.S.: 325412
Kaarel Siirde *(Mgr)*

Subsidiary (Domestic):

Cambrex Charles City, Inc. (2)
1205 11th St, Charles City, IA 50616-3466 (100%)
Tel.: (641) 257-1000
Web Site: http://www.cambrex.com
Sales Range: $75-99.9 Million
Emp.: 200
Mfr of Fine Chemical Intermediaries
N.A.I.C.S.: 325411

Cambrex High Point, Inc. (2)
4180 Mendenhall Oaks Pkwy, High Point, NC 27265
Tel.: (336) 841-5250
Emp.: 75
Pharmaceutical Ingredient Mfr
N.A.I.C.S.: 325412
Brian Swierenga *(VP)*

Subsidiary (Non-US):

Cambrex IEP GmbH (2)
Rheingau strasse 190-196, 65203, Wiesbaden, Germany
Tel.: (49) 6119624639
Web Site: http://www.cambrex.com
Pharmaceutical Preparation Mfr
N.A.I.C.S.: 325412
Antje Gupta *(Gen Mgr)*

Cambrex Karlskoga AB (2)
Bjorkborns Industriomrade, 691 85, Karlskoga, Sweden (100%)
Tel.: (46) 586783000
Web Site: http://www.cambrex.com
Sales Range: $100-124.9 Million
Emp.: 300
Mfr of Pharmaceutical Active Ingredients, Advanced Intermediates & Specialty Chemicals
N.A.I.C.S.: 325998
Bjarne Sandberg *(Mng Dir & Mgr-Site)*

Cambrex Mirabel (2)
17800 rue Lapointe, Mirabel, J7J 0W8, QC, Canada
Tel.: (450) 433-7673
Pharmaceutical Ingredient & Intermediate Mfr
N.A.I.C.S.: 325412

Cambrex Profarmaco Milano S.r.l. (2)
Via Cucchiari 17, 20155, Milan, Italy (100%)
Tel.: (39) 0023459881
Web Site: http://www.profarmaco.it
Sales Range: $75-99.9 Million
Emp.: 230
Developer & Sales of Active Pharmaceutical Ingredients
N.A.I.C.S.: 325412

Subsidiary (Domestic):

Cambrex Whippany (2)
30 N Jefferson Rd, Whippany, NJ 07981
Tel.: (973) 428-4000
Pharmaceutical Ingredient & Intermediate Mfr
N.A.I.C.S.: 325412

Halo Pharmaceutical, Inc. (2)
30 N Jefferson Rd, Whippany, NJ 07981
Tel.: (973) 428-4000
Web Site: http://www.halopharma.com
Pharmaceutical Development & Mfr
N.A.I.C.S.: 325412
Lee Karras *(CEO)*

PharmaCore, Inc. (2)
4180 Mendenhall Oaks Pky, High Point, NC 27265 (100%)
Tel.: (336) 841-5250
Web Site: http://www.pharmacore.com
Sales Range: $10-24.9 Million
Emp.: 60
Develops & Discovers Drugs in Pharmaceutical, Discovery Platform & Biotechnology Companies
N.A.I.C.S.: 325412
Brian Swierenga *(COO)*

Subsidiary (Non-US):

Zenara Pharma Private Limited (2)
P No 87-95 Phase-3 Ida, Cherlapally, Hyderabad, 500051, India
Tel.: (91) 4027260848
Pharmaceuticals Product Mfr
N.A.I.C.S.: 325412

Corin Group PLC (1)
The Corinium Centre, Cirencester, GL7 1YJ, Glos, United Kingdom
Tel.: (44) 1285659866
Web Site: http://www.coringroup.com
Orthopedic Device Mfr
N.A.I.C.S.: 339113
Stefano Alfonsi *(Chm & CEO)*

Subsidiary (Non-US):

Corin Australia Pty Ltd (2)
17 Bridge Street, Pymble, 2073, NSW, Australia
Tel.: (61) 2 9497 7400
Web Site: http://www.coringroup.com
Medical Equipment & Supplies Distr
N.A.I.C.S.: 423450

Corin Germany GmbH (2)
Am Felsbrunnen 8, 66119, Saarbrucken, Germany
Tel.: (49) 681 883 997 0
Web Site: http://www.coringroup.com
Medical Equipment & Supplies Distr
N.A.I.C.S.: 423450

Corin Japan KK (2)
5-1-18-10F Miyahara, Yodogawa-Ku, Osaka, 532-0003, Japan
Tel.: (81) 6 6391 8651
Medical Equipment & Supplies Distr
N.A.I.C.S.: 423450

Corin South Africa (proprietary) Ltd (2)
35 Golf Course Road, Sybrand Park, Rondebosch, 7700, South Africa
Tel.: (27) 21 510 0169
Medical Equipment & Supplies Distr
N.A.I.C.S.: 423450

Subsidiary (US):

Corin USA (2)
12750 Citrus Park Ln, Tampa, FL 33625
Tel.: (813) 977-4469
Web Site: http://www.coringroup.com
Medical Equipment & Supplies Distr
N.A.I.C.S.: 423450

Ergomed Plc (1)

PERMIRA ADVISERS LLP

Permira Advisers LLP—(Continued)
1 Occam Court The Surrey Research Park, Guildford, GU2 7HJ, Surrey, United Kingdom
Tel.: (44) 1483503205
Web Site: http://www.ergomedplc.com
Rev.: $160,999,795
Assets: $143,904,743
Liabilities: $52,613,008
Net Worth: $91,291,735
Earnings: $17,207,743
Emp.: 1,371
Fiscal Year-end: 12/31/2021
Pharmaceuticals Mfr
N.A.I.C.S.: 325412
Miroslav Reljanovic *(Founder & Chm)*

Subsidiary (Non-US):

Ergomed Clinical Research FZ LLC (2)
Dubai International Academic City Block N 03 Office N EO 05, PO Box 501708, Dubai, United Arab Emirates
Tel.: (971) 43749785
Pharmaceutical Preparation Mfr
N.A.I.C.S.: 325412

Ergomed Clinical Research LLC (2)
Skakovaya Street 17 Building 2 Office 2714, Moscow, 125040, Russia
Tel.: (7) 4957218533
Pharmaceutical Preparation Mfr
N.A.I.C.S.: 325412

Ergomed Clinical Research Limited (2)
Room 205 Fl 2 No 467 Section 6 Zhongxiao E Rd, Nangang District, Taipei, 115, Taiwan
Tel.: (886) 227836668
Pharmaceutical Preparation Mfr
N.A.I.C.S.: 325412

Ergomed GmbH (2)
Herriotstrasse 1, 60528, Frankfurt am Main, Germany
Tel.: (49) 6934872880
Pharmaceutical Preparation Mfr
N.A.I.C.S.: 325412

Ergomed Istrazivanja Zagreb d.o.o. (2)
Oreskoviceva 20A, 10020, Zagreb, Croatia
Tel.: (385) 14628500
Pharmaceutical Preparation Mfr
N.A.I.C.S.: 325412

Ergomed Spolka z o.o. (2)
Ul Armii Krajowej 18, 30-150, Krakow, Poland
Tel.: (48) 126224470
Pharmaceutical Preparation Mfr
N.A.I.C.S.: 325412

Ergomed Virtuoso Sarl (2)
18 Avenue Louis-Casai, 1209, Geneva, Switzerland
Tel.: (41) 227477801
Pharmaceutical Preparation Mfr
N.A.I.C.S.: 325412

Ergomed d.o.o. Novi Sad (2)
Belgrade Office Park Djordja Stanojevica 12, 11070, Belgrade, Serbia
Tel.: (381) 114048651
Pharmaceutical Preparation Mfr
N.A.I.C.S.: 325412

Ergomed d.o.o. Sarajevo (2)
Zmaja Od Bosne 7-7a, 71000, Sarajevo, Bosnia & Herzegovina
Tel.: (387) 33215715
Pharmaceutical Preparation Mfr
N.A.I.C.S.: 325412

Subsidiary (Domestic):

Haemostatix Limited (2)
BioCity Nottingham Pennyfoot Street, Nottingham, NG1 1GF, United Kingdom
Tel.: (44) 1159124512
Web Site: http://www.haemostatix.com
Pharmaceutical Preparation Mfr
N.A.I.C.S.: 325412

MedSource UK Ltd. (2)
1 Occam Court, Guildford, GU2 7HJ, Surrey, United Kingdom
Tel.: (44) 1483503205
Biotechnology Research & Development Services
N.A.I.C.S.: 541714

PrimeVigilance Limited (2)
1 Occam Court Surrey Research Park, Guildford, GU2 7HJ, Surrey, United Kingdom
Tel.: (44) 1483307920
Web Site: https://www.primevigilance.com
Pharmaceutical Preparation Mfr
N.A.I.C.S.: 325412
Jonathan West *(Pres)*

Subsidiary (Non-US):

PrimeVigilance s.r.o. (2)
Stetkova 18, 140 00, Prague, Czech Republic
Tel.: (420) 774497834
Pharmaceutical Preparation Mfr
N.A.I.C.S.: 325412

Exclusive Networks SA (1)
20 Quai du Point du Jour Arcs de Seine, 92100, Boulogne-Billancourt, France (57.28%)
Web Site: https://www.exclusive-networks.com
Rev.: $1,682,495,144
Assets: $3,704,942,802
Liabilities: $2,667,817,829
Net Worth: $1,037,124,973
Earnings: $48,564,645
Emp.: 2,658
Fiscal Year-end: 12/31/2023
Information Technology Services
N.A.I.C.S.: 541512
Nathalie Buhnemann *(CFO)*

Subsidiary (Non-US):

Compendium CE Sp. z o.o (2)
ul Tatarska 5, 30-103, Krakow, Poland
Tel.: (48) 122984777
Web Site: https://www.compendium.pl
Information Technology & Education Services
N.A.I.C.S.: 611710

Exclusive Networks Asia Pte. Ltd. (2)
3 Kallang Junction 04-02 Vanguard Campus, Singapore, 339265, Singapore
Tel.: (65) 67470118
Global Operation Services
N.A.I.C.S.: 561990

Exclusive Networks Austria GmbH (2)
Heinrich Bablik-Strasse 17 K21 Top N06, 2345, Brunn am Gebirge, Austria
Tel.: (43) 133603370
Digital Infrastructure Services
N.A.I.C.S.: 541810

Exclusive Networks BH d.o.o. (2)
Fra Andela Zvizdovica 1, 71000, Sarajevo, Bosnia & Herzegovina
Tel.: (387) 33266675
Digital Infrastructure Services
N.A.I.C.S.: 541810

Exclusive Networks Bilisim A.S. (2)
Icerenkoy Kayisdagi Cad Ciftligi Yolu Kar Plaza No 47 Kat 1, Atasehiristanbul, Karaman, Turkiye
Tel.: (90) 2164640490
Global Operation Services
N.A.I.C.S.: 561990

Exclusive Networks Denmark A/S (2)
Strandvejen 58 4th floor, 2900, Hellerup, Denmark
Tel.: (45) 70234235
Digital Infrastructure Services
N.A.I.C.S.: 541810

Exclusive Networks Deutschland GmbH (2)
Hardenbergstrasse 9a, 10623, Berlin, Germany
Tel.: (49) 303251310
Digital Infrastructure Services
N.A.I.C.S.: 541810

Exclusive Networks Finland OY (2)
Saterinkatu 6, 02600, Espoo, Finland
Tel.: (358) 207551640
Digital Infrastructure Services
N.A.I.C.S.: 541810

Exclusive Networks Ireland Ltd. (2)
Unit 8 Orchard Business Centre 2009 Orchard Avenue Citywest 24, Dublin, D24 YC8C, Ireland
Tel.: (353) 16876500
Digital Infrastructure Services
N.A.I.C.S.: 541810

Exclusive Networks Malaysia Sdn. Bhd. (2)
A-28-05 05th Floor Block A 3 Two Square Jalan 19/1, 46300, Petaling Jaya, Selangor Darul Ehsan, Malaysia
Tel.: (60) 379568688
Digital Infrastructure Services
N.A.I.C.S.: 541810

Exclusive Networks PH Inc. (2)
Unit 1505 The Orient Square Bldg F Ortigas Jr Road Ortigas Ctr, Pasig, 1605, Philippines
Tel.: (63) 24709013
Digital Infrastructure Services
N.A.I.C.S.: 541810

Exclusive Networks Poland S.A. (2)
ul Zawila 61, 30-390, Krakow, Poland
Tel.: (48) 122525555
Digital Infrastructure Services
N.A.I.C.S.: 541810

Exclusive Networks Singapore Pte. Ltd. (2)
3 Kallang Junction 04-02 Vanguard Campus, Singapore, 339265, Singapore
Tel.: (65) 67470118
Digital Infrastructure Services
N.A.I.C.S.: 541810

Exclusive Networks Switzerland AG (2)
Thurgauerstrasse 40, 8050, Zurich, Switzerland
Tel.: (41) 445216333
Digital Infrastructure Services
N.A.I.C.S.: 541810

Exclusive Networks Technology Romania S.R.L. (2)
Str Grigore Romniceanu no 20 sector 5, 050576, Bucharest, Romania
Tel.: (40) 376201200
Digital Infrastructure Services
N.A.I.C.S.: 541810

Exclusive Networks Vietnam Co., Ltd. (2)
12th Floor ICON4 Tower 243A De La Thanh Street, Lang Thuong Ward Dong Da District, Hanoi, Vietnam
Tel.: (84) 2422203299
Global Operation Services
N.A.I.C.S.: 561990

Ignition Technology Group Limited (2)
Cody Technolgy Park Ively Road, Farnborough, GU14 0LX, Hampshire, United Kingdom
Tel.: (44) 2038736580
Technology Consultancy Services
N.A.I.C.S.: 541690

Ignition Technology Ltd. (2)
Cody Technology Park Ively Road, Farnborough, GU14 0LX, Hampshire, United Kingdom
Tel.: (44) 2038736580
Technology Consultancy Services
N.A.I.C.S.: 541715

Itec Intelligent Services Ltd. (2)
Rosa Mulberry Business Park Fishponds Road, Wokingham, RG41 2GY, United Kingdom
Tel.: (44) 1189777100
Web Site: https://www.itec-is.com
Wired & Wireless Telecommunication Services
N.A.I.C.S.: 517111

P.T. Exclusive Networks Indonesia (2)
Gedung Menara Anugrah 18th Floor Kantor Taman E3 3 Jl, Mega Kuningan Lot 8 6 - 8 7 Kawasan Mega Kuningan Setiabudi, Jakarta Selatan, 12950, Indonesia

INTERNATIONAL PUBLIC

Tel.: (62) 2157941901
Digital Infrastructure Services
N.A.I.C.S.: 541810

Genesys Telecommunications Laboratories, Inc. (1)
2001 Junipero Serra Blvd, Daly City, CA 94014
Tel.: (650) 466-1100
Web Site: http://www.genesys.com
Sales Range: $350-399.9 Million
Emp.: 2,000
Call Center Software & Contact Center Solutions
N.A.I.C.S.: 541511
Slava Zhakov *(CTO)*

Subsidiary (Domestic):

Angel.com Incorporated (2)
8219 Leesburg Pike 5th Fl, Vienna, VA 22182
Tel.: (703) 269-1070
Web Site: http://www.angel.com
Sales Range: $10-24.9 Million
Emp.: 75
Cloud-Based Customer Experience Management Solutions
N.A.I.C.S.: 513210

Subsidiary (Non-US):

Genesys Japan Co., Ltd. (2)
6th Floor Uchisaiwaicho Tokyu Bldg 1-3-2 Uchisaiwaicho, Chiyoda-ku, Tokyo, 100-0011, Japan (100%)
Tel.: (81) 3 6361 8000
Web Site: http://www.genesyslab.co.jp
Sales Range: $25-49.9 Million
Emp.: 45
Call Center Software & Contact Center Solutions
N.A.I.C.S.: 541511

Genesys Laboratories Australasia Pty. Ltd. (2)
Level 17 124 Walker Street, North Sydney, 2060, NSW, Australia (100%)
Tel.: (61) 2 9463 8500
Web Site: http://www.genesyslab.com
Sales Range: $25-49.9 Million
Emp.: 20
Call Center Software & Contact Center Solutions
N.A.I.C.S.: 541511
Gordon Clubb *(Mng Dir)*

Genesys Telecommunications Laboratories - Europe Limited (2)
Unit 100 Frimley Business Park Frimley Bldg 3, Camberley, GU16 7SG, Surrey, United Kingdom (100%)
Tel.: (44) 1276 457 000
Web Site: http://www.genesyslab.co.uk
Call Center Software & Contact Center Solutions
N.A.I.C.S.: 541511

Subsidiary (Non-US):

GCTI Telecommunications Laboratories AB (3)
Kungsgatan 10 3rd Floor, Stockholm, 11143, Sweden
Tel.: (46) 73 502 8090
Web Site: http://www.genesyslab.com
Call Center Software & Contact Center Solutions
N.A.I.C.S.: 541511

Genesys Telecommunication Laboratories S.L. (3)
Paseo de la Castellana 216, 28046, Madrid, Spain (100%)
Tel.: (34) 911 981 700
Web Site: http://www.genesyslab.com
Sales Range: $25-49.9 Million
Emp.: 23
Call Center Software & Contact Center Solutions
N.A.I.C.S.: 541511
Xavier Velasco *(Mng Dir)*

Genesys Telecommunications Laboratories B.V. (3)
Gooimeer 6-02, 1411 DD, Naarden, Netherlands (100%)
Tel.: (31) 206500000
Web Site: http://www.genesyslab.com

AND PRIVATE COMPANIES / PERMIRA ADVISERS LLP

Sales Range: $25-49.9 Million
Emp.: 25
Call Center Software & Contact Center Solutions
N.A.I.C.S.: 541511
Roger Stanton (VP-Fin)

Genesys Telecommunications Laboratories GmbH (3)
Joseph-Wild-Strasse 20, 81829, Munich, Germany (100%)
Tel.: (49) 89 451 2590
Web Site: http://www.genesyslab.com
Sales Range: $10-24.9 Million
Emp.: 30
Call Center Software & Contact Center Solutions
N.A.I.C.S.: 541511
Mark Alloy (Mng Dir)

Genesys Telecommunications Laboratories S.r.l. (3)
Via Torri Bianche 7 Edificio Faggio 6 piano, 20871, Vimercate, MB, Italy (100%)
Tel.: (39) 02 9475 1800
Web Site: http://www.genesys.com
Sales Range: $10-24.9 Million
Emp.: 35
Call Center Software & Contact Center Solutions
N.A.I.C.S.: 541511
Paolo Mariottini (VP-Italy)

Genesys Telecommunications SAS (3)
65 Rue Camille Desmoulins, Issy-les-Moulineaux, 92130, France (100%)
Tel.: (33) 1 4110 1717
Web Site: http://www.genesys.com
Emp.: 25
Call Center Software & Contact Center Solutions
N.A.I.C.S.: 541511

Subsidiary (Non-US):

Genesys Telecommunications Laboratories Asia Pte. Ltd. (2)
9 Raffles Place 18-02 Republic Plaza 1, Singapore, 048619, Singapore (100%)
Tel.: (65) 6521 9521
Web Site: http://www.genesyslab.com
Emp.: 30
Call Center Software & Contact Center Solutions
N.A.I.C.S.: 541511

Subsidiary (Domestic):

Interactive Intelligence Group, Inc. (2)
7601 Interactive Way, Indianapolis, IN 46278
Tel.: (317) 872-3000
Web Site: http://www.inin.com
Holding Company; Interaction Management Software Developer & Distr
N.A.I.C.S.: 551112

Subsidiary (Non-US):

Interactive Intelligence (South Africa) (Pty) Ltd (3)
6 Coombe Place Tuscany Office Park Bldg 7, Rivonia, 2128, Gauteng, South Africa
Tel.: (27) 877400900
Web Site: http://www.inin.com
Software Development Services
N.A.I.C.S.: 513210

Subsidiary (Domestic):

Interactive Intelligence, Inc. (3)
7601 Interactive Way, Indianapolis, IN 46278
Tel.: (317) 872-3000
Web Site: http://www.inin.com
Interaction Management Software Developer & Distr
N.A.I.C.S.: 513210

Subsidiary (Non-US):

ININ UK Limited (4)
Genesys House Frimley Business Park, Frimley, Camberley, GU16 7SG, United Kingdom
Tel.: (44) 1753418800
Interaction Management Software Developer & Marketer

N.A.I.C.S.: 423430

Subsidiary (Domestic):

SoundBite Communications, Inc. (2)
22 Crosby Dr, Bedford, MA 01730
Tel.: (781) 897-2500
Web Site: http://www.soundbite.com
Rev.: $48,071,000
Assets: $38,332,000
Liabilities: $6,961,000
Net Worth: $31,371,000
Earnings: ($1,823,000)
Emp.: 140
Fiscal Year-end: 12/31/2012
On-Demand Automated Voice Messaging Services
N.A.I.C.S.: 541519
Timothy R. Segall (CTO)

Subsidiary (Domestic):

SmartReply Technologies, Inc. (3)
2 Venture Ste 340, Irvine, CA 92618
Tel.: (949) 340-0700
Sales Range: $10-24.9 Million
Emp.: 45
Voice & Message-Based Services for Businesses
N.A.I.C.S.: 541613

Branch (Domestic):

SoundBite Communications - Washington, DC (3)
2020 14th St N Ste 500, Arlington, VA 22201
Tel.: (703) 879-3400
Web Site: http://www.soundbite.com
Wireless Communication Services
N.A.I.C.S.: 517112

Subsidiary (Non-US):

SoundBite Communications UK, Ltd. (3)
Standard House Weyside Park, Catteshall Lane, Godalming, Surrey, United Kingdom
Tel.: (44) 8000518975
Wired Telecommunication Services
N.A.I.C.S.: 517111

Subsidiary (Domestic):

Utopy, Inc. (2)
2001 Junipero Serra Blvd, Daly City, CA 94014
Tel.: (888) 436-3797
Web Site: http://www.utopy.com
Sales Range: $10-24.9 Million
Emp.: 15
Performance Optimization & Customer Intelligence Solutions
N.A.I.C.S.: 517810

Hugo Boss AG (1)
Dieselstrasse 12, 72555, Metzingen, Germany (55.62%)
Tel.: (49) 7123940
Web Site: https://www.group.hugoboss.com
Rev.: $4,633,468,375
Assets: $3,832,285,021
Liabilities: $2,385,351,584
Net Worth: $1,446,933,437
Earnings: $297,814,328
Emp.: 18,738
Fiscal Year-end: 12/31/2023
Clothing Designer & Mfr
N.A.I.C.S.: 315250
Sinan Piskin (Deputy Chm-Supervisory Bd)

Subsidiary (Non-US):

Hugo Boss (Schweiz) AG (2)
Baarerstrasse 135, 6300, Zug, Switzerland
Tel.: (41) 417680404
Web Site: http://www.hugoboss.com
Sales Range: $125-149.9 Million
Men's & Women's Fashion Apparel Whslr
N.A.I.C.S.: 424350

Hugo Boss Australia Pty. Ltd. (2)
Albert Street 6, Preston, 3072, VIC, Australia
Tel.: (61) 394746300
Web Site: http://www.hugoboss.com.au
Sales Range: $25-49.9 Million
Emp.: 30
Men's & Women's Fashion Apparel Whslr
N.A.I.C.S.: 424350
Keighran Mattews (Mng Dir)

Hugo Boss Benelux B.V. (2)
PO Box 75564, 1118 ZP, Schiphol, Netherlands
Tel.: (31) 206556000
Web Site: http://www.hugoboss.com
Sales Range: $25-49.9 Million
Emp.: 35
Men's & Women's Fashion Apparel Whslr
N.A.I.C.S.: 424350

Hugo Boss Canada Inc. (2)
2600 Steeles Avenue West, Concord, L4K 3C8, ON, Canada
Tel.: (905) 739-2677
Web Site: http://www.hugoboss.com
Sales Range: $25-49.9 Million
Emp.: 45
Men's & Women's Fashion Apparel Whslr
N.A.I.C.S.: 424350

Hugo Boss Espana S.A. (2)
Ribera del Loira 8-10 Edificio Paris- 1 planta, 28042, Madrid, Spain
Tel.: (34) 913601000
Web Site: http://www.group.hugoboss.com
Sales Range: $25-49.9 Million
Emp.: 48
Mens & Womens Fashion Apparel Distr
N.A.I.C.S.: 424350

Hugo Boss France S.A.S. (2)
15 Ave de la Grande Armee, 75116, Paris, France
Tel.: (33) 144171670
Web Site: http://www.group.hugoboss.com
Sales Range: $25-49.9 Million
Emp.: 30
Men's & Women's Fashion Apparel Whslr
N.A.I.C.S.: 424350

Hugo Boss Hong Kong Ltd. (2)
Millenium City 6 Level 33 & 35, No 392 Kwun Tong Road, Kowloon, China (Hong Kong)
Tel.: (852) 23774404
Web Site: http://group.hugoboss.com
Sales Range: $25-49.9 Million
Emp.: 40
Men's & Women's Fashion Apparel Whslr
N.A.I.C.S.: 424350

Hugo Boss Italia S.p.A. (2)
Via Morimondo 26, 20143, Milan, Italy
Tel.: (39) 0689970194
Web Site: http://www.hugoboss.com
Sales Range: $50-74.9 Million
Emp.: 55
Men & Women Fashion Apparel Distr
N.A.I.C.S.: 424350
Pozzi Nazzario (Gen Mgr)

Hugo Boss Japan K.K. (2)
3F 5 2 1 Minami Aoyama, Minatu-ku, Tokyo, 107-0062, Japan
Tel.: (81) 357747670
Web Site: http://www.hugoboss.com
Sales Range: $50-74.9 Million
Mens & Womens Fashion Apparel Distr
N.A.I.C.S.: 424350

Hugo Boss Mexico S.A. de C.V. (2)
Lamartine N 415, Col Bosque de Chapultepec, Mexico, 11580, DF, Mexico
Tel.: (52) 5552621000
Web Site: http://www.hugoboss.com
Sales Range: $25-49.9 Million
Emp.: 10
Men's & Women's Fashion Apparel Whslr
N.A.I.C.S.: 424350
Gerrit Rutzel (Mng Dir)

Plant (Non-US):

Hugo Boss Textile Industry Ltd. (2)
Aegen Free Zone, Izmir, 35410, Turkiye
Tel.: (90) 2322983000
Web Site: http://www.hugoboss.com
Sales Range: $750-799.9 Million
Clothing Mfr
N.A.I.C.S.: 315250

Subsidiary (Non-US):

Hugo Boss UK Ltd. (2)
39 Plender Street, London, NW1 0DT, United Kingdom
Tel.: (44) 2075545700
Web Site: http://www.hugoboss.co.uk
Sales Range: $25-49.9 Million
Men's & Women's Fashion Apparel Whslr
N.A.I.C.S.: 424350

Subsidiary (US):

Hugo Boss USA Inc. (2)
55 Water st 4408, New York, NY 10041
Tel.: (212) 940-0600
Web Site: http://www.hugoboss.com
Sales Range: $200-249.9 Million
Emp.: 510
Holding Company
N.A.I.C.S.: 551112
Anthony Lucia (Pres & CEO)

Subsidiary (Domestic):

Hugo Boss Fashions Inc. (3)
601 W 26th St 8th Fl, New York, NY 10001
Tel.: (212) 940-0600
Web Site: http://www.hugoboss.com
Sales Range: $25-49.9 Million
Emp.: 65
Men's & Women's Fashion Apparel Whslr
N.A.I.C.S.: 424350

Subsidiary (Non-US):

Hugo Boss do Brasil Ltda. (2)
Av Marg Rio Pinheiros 5200, Edificio Quebec, 05693 000, Sao Paulo, SP, Brazil
Tel.: (55) 1137598700
Web Site: http://www.group.hugoboss.com
Sales Range: $25-49.9 Million
Emp.: 30
Men's & Women's Fashion Apparel Whslr
N.A.I.C.S.: 424350

I-MED Radiology Network Ltd. (1)
Level 5 24 York Street, Sydney, 2000, NSW, Australia
Tel.: (61) 2 8274 1000
Web Site: http://www.i-med.com.au
Medical Imaging Clinic Operator
N.A.I.C.S.: 621512
Steven Rubic (CEO)

Ideal Snacks Corporation (1)
89 Mill St, Liberty, NY 12754
Tel.: (845) 292-7000
Web Site: http://www.idealsnacks.com
Snack Food Mfr
N.A.I.C.S.: 311919
Gunther Brinkman (VP-Contract Mfg)

Informatica Corporation (1)
2100 Seaport Blvd, Redwood City, CA 94063
Tel.: (650) 385-5000
Web Site: http://www.informatica.com
Sales Range: $1-4.9 Billion
Emp.: 3,664
Enterprise Data Integration Software & Services
N.A.I.C.S.: 513210
Charles Race (Exec VP-Worldwide Field Ops)

Subsidiary (Non-US):

AddressDoctor GmbH (2)
Rontgenstr 9, 67133, Maxdorf, Germany
Tel.: (49) 623797740
Web Site: http://www.addressdoctor.com
Enterprise Data Integration Software Provider
N.A.I.C.S.: 541511
Earl E. Fry (Mng Dir)

Subsidiary (Domestic):

Compact Solutions LLC (2)
1 Lincoln Ctr 18 W 140th W Butterfield Rdd 15th Fl, Oakbrook Terrace, IL 60181
Tel.: (708) 524-9500
Web Site: http://www.compactbi.com
Business Data Services
N.A.I.C.S.: 541512
Grzegorz Swietlik (Dir-Polish Ops)

Subsidiary (Non-US):

I.D.I. Informatica Data Integration Ltd. (2)
Kiryat Atidim Bldg 8 29th Fl, Tel Aviv, 6158101, Israel
Tel.: (972) 35633600
Web Site: http://www.informatica.com
Sales Range: $25-49.9 Million
Emp.: 66
Data Integration Software Services
N.A.I.C.S.: 541511

IS Informatica Software Ltda. (2)

PERMIRA ADVISERS LLP

Permira Advisers LLP—(Continued)
Av Das Nacoes Unidas 12901-3 Andar,
Torre Norte Brooklin Novo, Sao Paulo,
04578-000, Brazil
Tel.: (55) 1130135446
Web Site: http://www.informatica.com
Sales Range: $25-49.9 Million
Data Integration Software Provider
N.A.I.C.S.: 541511

Group (Non-US):

Informatica Australia Pty. Ltd. - Asia/Pacific Headquarters (2)
Level 5 255 George St, Sydney, 2000, NSW, Australia
Tel.: (61) 289074400
Web Site: http://www.informatica.com
Sales Range: $75-99.9 Million
Emp.: 20
Enterprise Data Integration Software & Services
N.A.I.C.S.: 513210

Subsidiary (Non-US):

Informatica (Beijing) Information Technology Co., Ltd. (3)
19F-06 E Tower Twin Towers B-12 Jian Guo Men Wai Da Jie, Chao Yang District, Beijing, 100022, China
Tel.: (86) 1058793366
Web Site: http://www.informatica.com
Sales Range: $100-124.9 Million
Enterprise Data Integration Software & Services
N.A.I.C.S.: 513210
Wang Qun *(Pres-Greater China)*

Informatica Business Solutions Pvt. Ltd. (3)
206 Navkar Chamber, MVRoad Marol Naka, Andheri E, Mumbai, 59, India
Tel.: (91) 2240262643
Web Site: http://www.informatica.com
Sales Range: $100-124.9 Million
Enterprise Data Integration Software & Services
N.A.I.C.S.: 513210

Informatica Hong Kong (3)
2/F Shui On Centre, 6-8 Harbour Road, Wanchai, China (Hong Kong)
Tel.: (852) 28248860
Web Site: http://www.informatica.com
Sales Range: $100-124.9 Million
Enterprise Data Integration Software & Services
N.A.I.C.S.: 513210

Informatica Japan K.K (3)
Sumitomo Ichigaya Bldg 1-1 Ichigaya-Honmuracho, Shinjuku-ku, Tokyo, 162-0845, Japan
Tel.: (81) 352297211
Web Site: http://www.informatica.com
Sales Range: $100-124.9 Million
Enterprise Data Integration Software & Services
N.A.I.C.S.: 513210

Informatica Korea Corporation (3)
Samsung Life Insurance Yoido B/D 20F Yoido-Dong, Youngdeungpo-Ku, Seoul, Korea (South)
Tel.: (82) 262935000
Web Site: http://www.informatica.com
Sales Range: $10-24.9 Million
Emp.: 15
Enterprise Data Integration Software & Services
N.A.I.C.S.: 513210
S. C. Choi *(Country Mgr)*

Informatica S.E.A. Pte., Ltd. (3)
600 North Bridge Road, Parkview Square, Singapore, 188778, Singapore
Tel.: (65) 63966679
Web Site: http://www.informatica.com
Sales Range: $25-49.9 Million
Emp.: 25
Enterprise Data Integration Software & Services
N.A.I.C.S.: 513210

Informatica Taiwan Co. Ltd. (3)
Dunhua S Rd, Taipei, 105, Taiwan
Tel.: (886) 225770257
Web Site: http://www.informatica.com
Sales Range: $100-124.9 Million
Emp.: 25
Enterprise Data Integration Software & Services
N.A.I.C.S.: 513210

Subsidiary (Non-US):

Informatica International do Brazil Ltd. - Latin America Region Headquarters (2)
Av Das Nacoes Unidas 12901 - 3 Andar Torre Norte, Brooklin Novo, Sao Paulo, 04578-000, Brazil
Tel.: (55) 1130135446
Web Site: http://www.informatica.com
Sales Range: $100-124.9 Million
Emp.: 30
Enterprise Data Integration Software & Services
N.A.I.C.S.: 513210

Branch (Domestic):

Informatica - Rio de Janeiro (3)
Praia de Botafogo 501 1 andar, Torre Pao de Azucar, 22250-040, Rio de Janeiro, Brazil
Tel.: (55) 2125866091
Web Site: http://www.informatica.com
Sales Range: $100-124.9 Million
Emp.: 10
Enterprise Data Integration Software & Services
N.A.I.C.S.: 513210

Subsidiary (Non-US):

Informatica Software Services de Mexico S.A. de C.V. (3)
Blvd Manuel Avila Camacho No 36, Piso 10 Lomas de Chapultepec, 11000, Mexico, Mexico
Tel.: (52) 5591721463
Web Site: http://www.informatica.com
Sales Range: $25-49.9 Million
Emp.: 50
Enterprise Data Integration Software & Services
N.A.I.C.S.: 513210

Group (Non-US):

Informatica Nederland B.V. - EMEA Headquarters (2)
Edisonbaan 14A, 3439 MN, Nieuwegein, Netherlands
Tel.: (31) 306086700
Web Site: http://www.informatica.com
Sales Range: $100-124.9 Million
Emp.: 55
Enterprise Data Integration Software & Services
N.A.I.C.S.: 513210

Subsidiary (Non-US):

Informatica CZ, s.r.o. (3)
Krenova 439/13, 162 00, Prague, 6, Czech Republic
Tel.: (420) 235010244
Web Site: http://www.informatica.cz
Sales Range: $100-124.9 Million
Emp.: 10
Enterprise Data Integration Software & Services
N.A.I.C.S.: 513210
Radek Stastny *(Mng Dir)*

Informatica France S.A.S. (3)
Tour CB 21 16 Place de l'Iris, rue Du General Leclerc, Paris, 92800, France
Tel.: (33) 141389200
Web Site: http://www.informatica.com
Rev.: $13,100,000
Emp.: 50
Enterprise Data Integration Software & Services
N.A.I.C.S.: 513210

Informatica GmbH (3)
Lyoner Strasse 15, 60528, Frankfurt, Germany
Tel.: (49) 699288090
Web Site: http://www.informatica.com
Sales Range: $100-124.9 Million
Enterprise Data Integration Software & Services
N.A.I.C.S.: 513210

Informatica Ireland Limited (3)
George's Quay House Townsend St, Dublin, 2, Ireland
Tel.: (353) 14004900
Web Site: http://www.informatica.com
Sales Range: $75-99.9 Million
Emp.: 50
Data Quality Software & Support Services
N.A.I.C.S.: 518210

Informatica Middle East FZ-LLC (3)
Al-Shatha Tower 2407, Dubai Internet City, Dubai, United Arab Emirates
Tel.: (971) 4 3642960
Web Site: http://www.informatica.com
Sales Range: $100-124.9 Million
Enterprise Data Integration Software & Services
N.A.I.C.S.: 513210

Informatica Software (Schweiz) AG (3)
Dreikonigstrasse 31A, 8002, Zurich, Switzerland
Tel.: (41) 432155600
Web Site: http://www.informatica.com
Sales Range: $100-124.9 Million
Enterprise Data Integration Software & Services
N.A.I.C.S.: 513210

Informatica Software Italia S.r.l. (3)
Via Conca del Naviglio 18, Milan, 20123, Italy
Tel.: (39) 0289827360
Web Site: http://www.informatica.com
Sales Range: $100-124.9 Million
Enterprise Data Integration Software & Services
N.A.I.C.S.: 513210

Informatica Software Ltd. (3)
6 Waltham Park Waltham Road, White Waltham, Maidenhead, SL6 3TN, Berkshire, United Kingdom
Tel.: (44) 1628511311
Web Site: http://www.informatica.com
Sales Range: $75-99.9 Million
Emp.: 130
Enterprise Data Integration Software & Services
N.A.I.C.S.: 513210

Informatica South Africa (3)
Kid House 812 Hammets Crossing 2 Selborne Rd Fourways, Maroelandal Fourways, Johannesburg, 2040, South Africa
Tel.: (27) 114629676
Web Site: http://www.informatica.co.za
Sales Range: $1-9.9 Million
Emp.: 5
Enterprise Data Integration Software & Services
N.A.I.C.S.: 513210

Informatica Turkey (3)
Idealtepe Mah Dik Sok No15/2, 34841 Kucukyali, Istanbul, Turkiye
Tel.: (90) 216 518 4447
Web Site: http://www.informatica.com.tr
Sales Range: $100-124.9 Million
Enterprise Data Integration Software & Services
N.A.I.C.S.: 513210

Itemfield Limited (3)
Street 8 Kiryat Atidim Building 29th Floor, Tel Aviv, 6158101, Israel
Tel.: (972) 35633600
Web Site: http://www.informatica.com
Sales Range: $10-24.9 Million
Emp.: 65
Enterprise Data Integration Software & Services
N.A.I.C.S.: 561210

Subsidiary (Non-US):

Informatica Research and Development Center LLC (2)
Office 702 Building 88A Sredniy Prospect VO, 199106, Saint Petersburg, Russia
Tel.: (7) 8123209143
Web Site: http://www.informatica.com
Sales Range: $25-49.9 Million
Emp.: 55
Data Integration Software Services
N.A.I.C.S.: 541511

Informatica Software Limited (2)

INTERNATIONAL PUBLIC

Unit36 Level23 One Island East 8 Westlands Road, Hong Kong, China (Hong Kong)
Tel.: (852) 37507620
Web Site: http://www.informatica.com
Emp.: 100
Enterprise Data Integration Software Provider
N.A.I.C.S.: 541511

Informatica Software Ltd. (2)
Bankers Hall West Tower 888-3rd Street SW 10th Floor, Calgary, T2P 5C5, AB, Canada
Tel.: (403) 668-6000
Web Site: http://www.informatica.com
Data Migration & Consolidation & Synchronization & Warehousing Service Provider
N.A.I.C.S.: 518210

Informatica Software de Mexico S. de R.L. de C.V. (2)
Blvd Del Centro No 26 Ofic 14, Naucalpan, 53140, Mexico, Mexico
Tel.: (52) 5591721434
Web Site: http://www.informatica.com
Enterprise Data Integration Software Services
N.A.I.C.S.: 541511

Subsidiary (Domestic):

StrikeIron, LLC (2)
15501 Weston Pkwy Ste 150, Cary, NC 27513
Tel.: (919) 467-4545
Web Site: http://www.strikeiron.com
Sales Range: $1-9.9 Million
Emp.: 25
Information Technology Services
N.A.I.C.S.: 541512

WisdomForce Technologies, Inc. (2)
8501 SE 76th Pl, Mercer Island, WA 98040
Tel.: (206) 407-9238
Web Site: http://www.wisdomforce.com
Software Publishing Services
N.A.I.C.S.: 513210
Sohaib Abbasi *(Chm, CEO & Pres)*

Just Group plc (1)
Enterprise House Bancroft Road, Reigate, RH2 7RP, Surrey, United Kingdom
Tel.: (44) 1737233297
Web Site: https://www.justgroupplc.co.uk
Rev.: $1,962,888,160
Assets: $40,189,346,125
Liabilities: $38,670,790,204
Net Worth: $1,518,555,920
Earnings: $162,837,667
Emp.: 1,181
Fiscal Year-end: 12/31/2023
Financial Investment Services
N.A.I.C.S.: 551112
David Richardson *(CEO & Mng Dir-Corp Bus)*

Subsidiary (Domestic):

Just Retirement (Holdings) Limited (2)
Vale House Roebuck Close Bancroft Road, Reigate, RH2 7RU, Surrey, United Kingdom
Tel.: (44) 1737233297
Web Site: http://www.justretirement.com
Holding Company; Retirement Planning Products & Services
N.A.I.C.S.: 551112

Subsidiary (Domestic):

Just Retirement Limited (3)
Vale House Roebuck Close Bancroft Road, Reigate, RH2 7RU, Surrey, United Kingdom
Tel.: (44) 17 3723 3296
Web Site: http://www.justretirement.com
Sales Range: $75-99.9 Million
Pension Retirement Services
N.A.I.C.S.: 623311

Just Retirement Solutions Limited (3)
Vale House Roebuck Close Bancroft Road, Reigate, RH2 7RU, Surrey, United Kingdom
Tel.: (44) 17 3723 3415
Web Site: http://www.justretirementsolutions.com
Pension & Property Assets Retirement Services
N.A.I.C.S.: 525110

AND PRIVATE COMPANIES — PERMIRA ADVISERS LLP

Subsidiary (Domestic):

Partnership Assurance Group Limited (2)
5th Floor 110 Bishopsgate, London, EC2N 4AY, United Kingdom
Tel.: (44) 20 7398 5933
Holding Company; Retirment Income & Defined Benefit Products & Services
N.A.I.C.S.: 551112
Jane Kennedy (COO)

Kroll, LLC (1)
Tel.: (212) 593-1000
Web Site: https://www.kroll.com
Emp.: 4,000
Financial Advisory & Investment Banking Services
N.A.I.C.S.: 523999
Noah Gottdiener (Chm)

Subsidiary (Non-US):

Duff & Phelps (Switzerland) SA (2)
Bleicherweg 10, Zurich, 8002, Switzerland
Tel.: (41) 44 562 04 23
Web Site: http://www.duffandphelps.com
Financial Advisory & Investment Banking Services
N.A.I.C.S.: 523150
Nadine Stuttle (Mng Dir-Legal Mgmt Consulting Practice)

Duff & Phelps B.V. (2)
Amstelplein 1 Rembrandt Tower, Amsterdam, 1096, Netherlands
Tel.: (31) 208515151
Web Site: http://www.duffphelps.com
Sales Range: $100-124.9 Million
Emp.: 25
Financial Advisory & Investment Banking Services
N.A.I.C.S.: 523150
Henk Oosterhout (Mng Dir)

Duff & Phelps Canada Limited (2)
333 Bay Street 14th Fl, Toronto, M5H 2R2, ON, Canada
Tel.: (416) 364-9700
Financial Advisory & Investment Banking Services
N.A.I.C.S.: 525990
Robert Kofman (Mng Dir)

Duff & Phelps GmbH (2)
Leopoldstrasse 8, 80802, Munich, Germany
Tel.: (49) 89388884100
Web Site: http://www.duffandphelps.com
Sales Range: $1-4.9 Billion
Emp.: 20
Financial Advisory & Investment Banking Services
N.A.I.C.S.: 523150

Duff & Phelps K.K. (2)
Fukoku Seimei Building 22F 2 2 2 Uchisaiwaicho Chiyoda ku, Tokyo, 100 0011, Japan
Tel.: (81) 335930101
Web Site: http://www.duffandphelps.com
Financial Advisory & Investment Banking Services
N.A.I.C.S.: 523150
Katsumi Asai (Mng Dir-Valuation Svcs)

Duff & Phelps SAS (2)
4 Square Edouard VII, 75009, Paris, France
Tel.: (33) 1 56 43 15 27
Web Site: http://www.duffandphelps.com
Financial Advisory & Investment Banking Services
N.A.I.C.S.: 523150
Yann Magnan (Mng Dir)

Duff & Phelps, Ltd. (2)
The Shard 32 London Bridge Street, London, SE1 9SG, United Kingdom
Tel.: (44) 207 089 4700
Web Site: http://www.duffandphelps.com
Financial Advisory & Investment Banking Services
N.A.I.C.S.: 523150
Mathias Schumacher (Mng Dir-Valuation Advisory)

Subsidiary (Domestic):

Kroll Holdco, LLC (2)
55 E 52nd St, New York, NY 10055
Tel.: (212) 593-1000
Emp.: 4,000
Holding Company; Business Consulting, Corporate Advisory, Intelligence Investigation, Background Screening & Security Services
N.A.I.C.S.: 551112

Subsidiary (Non-US):

Kroll Associates (Asia) Ltd. (3)
Level 3 Three Pacific place 1 Queens Road East, Hong Kong, China (Hong Kong)
Tel.: (852) 28847788
Web Site: http://www.kroll.com
Business Consulting Services
N.A.I.C.S.: 541611
David Liu (Mng Dir & Head-Asia Pacific)

Kroll Associates Brasil Ltda. (3)
Tower Bridge Avenida Jornalista Roberto Marinho 85 5th Floor, Sao Paulo, 04576-010, Brazil
Tel.: (55) 1138970900
Web Site: http://www.kroll.com
Risk Managemeng Srvices
N.A.I.C.S.: 541611
Fernanda Barroso (Mng Dir & Gen Dir)

Kroll Associates SA (3)
Avenida del Libertador 6250 Piso 5, Buenos Aires, C1428BOJ, Argentina
Tel.: (54) 1147066000
Web Site: http://www.kroll.com
Risk Managemeng Srvices
N.A.I.C.S.: 541611
Juan Cruz Amirante (Assoc Mng Dir & Head-Argentina Office)

Kroll Canada (3)
70 University Avenue Suite 200, Mailbox 9, Toronto, M5J 2M4, ON, Canada
Tel.: (416) 956-5000
Risk Managemeng Srvices
N.A.I.C.S.: 541611

Subsidiary (Domestic):

Kroll Factual Data, LLC (3)
55 E 52nd St 31st Fl, New York, NY 10055
Tel.: (212) 871-2000
Web Site: http://www.kroll.com
Verification Services to Mortgage Lenders, Banks, Credit Unions, Property Management Firms & Other Businesses
N.A.I.C.S.: 519290
Timothy Gallagher (Mng Dir & Head-New York Office)

Subsidiary (Non-US):

Kroll Holdings Limited (3)
The Shard 32 London Bridge Street, London, SE1 9SG, United Kingdom
Tel.: (44) 2070295000
Web Site: http://www.kroll.com
Risk Managemeng Srvices
N.A.I.C.S.: 541611
Andrew Beckett (Mng Dir-Cyber Risk)

Subsidiary (Non-US):

Kroll Associates Iberia, S.L. (4)
Paseo de la Castellana 81, 28046, Madrid, Spain
Tel.: (34) 910389000
Web Site: http://www.kroll.com
Risk Managemeng Srvices
N.A.I.C.S.: 541611
Marcelo Correia (Assoc Mng Dir & Head-Madrid Office)

Kroll Associates Srl (4)
Piazza della Repubblica 24, 20124, Milan, Italy
Tel.: (39) 0286998088
Web Site: http://www.kroll.com
Risk Managemeng Srvices
N.A.I.C.S.: 541611

Kroll France SAS (4)
4 Square Edouard VII, 75009, Paris, Cedex, France
Tel.: (33) 1 56 43 15 27
Web Site: http://www.kroll.com
Risk Managemeng Srvices
N.A.I.C.S.: 541611

Subsidiary (Non-US):

Kroll Mexico (3)
Paseo de la Reforma 505 Piso 42 Suite E - Torre Mayor Col Cuauhtemoc, Mexico, 06500, Mexico
Tel.: (52) 5552797250
Web Site: http://www.kroll.com
Risk Managemeng Srvices
N.A.I.C.S.: 541611
Bryan Weihs (Mng Dir & Head-Mexico Office)

Resolver Inc. (3)
111 Peter Street Suite 804, Toronto, M5V 2H1, ON, Canada
Tel.: (888) 316-6747
Web Site: http://www.resolver.com
Emp.: 225
Risk Management Software
N.A.I.C.S.: 513210

Subsidiary (US):

Agiliance, Inc. (4)
845 Stewart Dr Ste D, Sunnyvale, CA 94085
Tel.: (408) 200-0400
Web Site: http://www.riskvisioninc.com
Sales Range: $1-9.9 Million
Emp.: 60
Security Software & Cloud Computing Services
N.A.I.C.S.: 513210
Joseph Fantuzzi (Pres & CEO)

Subsidiary (Domestic):

Kroll Securities, LLC (2)
311 S Wacker Dr Ste 4200, Chicago, IL 60606
Tel.: (312) 697-4600
Financial Advisory & Investment Banking Services
N.A.I.C.S.: 523940
Stephen M. Burt (Pres)

Lowell Financial Services GmbH (1)
Am EUROPA-CENTER 1b, 45145, Essen, Germany
Tel.: (49) 2011020
Web Site: http://www.gfkl.com
Emp.: 1,465
Financial Services
N.A.I.C.S.: 523999
Anke Blietz (Mng Dir-Competence Center Insurance, Banking & eCommerce Key Acct)

Subsidiary (Non-US):

IS Inkasso Service GmbH (2)
Sudtirolerstrasse 9, 4020, Linz, Austria
Tel.: (43) 732 60 06 31
Web Site: http://www.inkasso.at
Debt Collection Services
N.A.I.C.S.: 561440
Christian Kren (Mng Dir)

Lowell Financial Ltd. (2)
Ellington House 9 Savannah Way Leeds Valley Park West, Leeds, LS10 1AB, W Yorkshire, United Kingdom
Tel.: (44) 345 300 9410
Web Site: http://www.lowellgroup.co.uk
Financial Management Services
N.A.I.C.S.: 523999
Jonathan Trott (Mgr-Comml Fin)

Subsidiary (Domestic):

Hoist Finance UK Limited (3)
Carolina Way Quays Reach, Hoist, Salford, M50 2ZY, United Kingdom
Tel.: (44) 8001216902
Web Site: http://www.hoistfinance.co.uk
Emp.: 1,380
Financial Services
N.A.I.C.S.: 525990
Sean Gallacher (Head-Ops)

Subsidiary (Domestic):

Lowell GFKL Collections GmbH (2)
Werdener Strasse 4, 40227, Dusseldorf, Germany
Tel.: (49) 211 586765 00
Web Site: http://www.gfkl.com
Debt Collection Services
N.A.I.C.S.: 561440

Lowell GFKL PayProtect GmbH (2)
Am EUROPA-CENTER 1b, 45145, Essen, Germany
Tel.: (49) 201 7696 166
Web Site: http://www.gfkl.com
Debt Collection Services
N.A.I.C.S.: 561440

Lowell Inkasso Becker Wuppertal GmbH & Co. KG (2)
Friedrich-Engels-Allee 32, 42103, Wuppertal, Germany
Tel.: (49) 202 49371 0
Web Site: http://www.gfkl.com
Emp.: 160
Debt Collection Services
N.A.I.C.S.: 561440

Lowell Proceed Collection Services GmbH (2)
Am Europa-Center 1b, 45145, Essen, Germany
Tel.: (49) 201 769 5161
Web Site: http://www.gfkl.com
Emp.: 180
Collection Services
N.A.I.C.S.: 561440

Lowell Sirius Inkasso GmbH (2)
Werdener Strasse 4, 40227, Dusseldorf, Germany
Tel.: (49) 211 882910
Web Site: http://www.gfkl.com
Emp.: 200
Debt Collection Services
N.A.I.C.S.: 561440
Anita Gluszak-Haefs (Mng Dir)

Lowell Zyklop Inkasso Deutschland GmbH (2)
Kreuzweg 64, 47809, Krefeld, Germany
Tel.: (49) 21 51 52 99 0
Web Site: http://www.gfkl.com
Emp.: 120
Debt Collection Services
N.A.I.C.S.: 561440
Gerhard Liebchen (Mng Dir)

Lytx, Inc. (1)
9785 Towne Ctr Dr, San Diego, CA 92121
Tel.: (858) 430-4000
Web Site: http://www.lytx.com
Emp.: 400
Driving Improvement & Safety Technologies Developer & Mfr
N.A.I.C.S.: 334310
Gretchen Griswold (Sr Dir-Corp Comm)

McAfee, LLC (1)
2821 Mission College Blvd, Santa Clara, CA 95054
Tel.: (408) 970-5151
Web Site: http://www.mcafee.com
Emp.: 7,330
Computer Security Software, Products & Services
N.A.I.C.S.: 513210
Steve Grobman (CTO & Sr VP)

Subsidiary (Non-US):

McAfee Co., Ltd. (2)
Shibuya Mark City West 16/20th Fl 1-12-1 Dougenzaka, Shibuya-ku, Tokyo, 150 0043, Japan
Tel.: (81) 3 5428 1100
Web Site: http://www.mcafee.com
Computer Security Software, Products & Services
N.A.I.C.S.: 513210
Sanjay Manohar (Mng Dir-India)

McAfee International BV (2)
Boeingavenue 30, 1119 PE, Schiphol-Rijk, Netherlands
Tel.: (31) 205863800
Web Site: http://www.mcafee.com
Data Security, Protection & Encryption Software Services
N.A.I.C.S.: 513210

Opodo Limited (1)
26-28 Hammersmith Grove, Hammersmith Emban, London, W6 7BA, United Kingdom
Tel.: (44) 8703525000
Web Site: http://www.opodo.com
Internet Travel Agency Services
N.A.I.C.S.: 561599
Caroline Noble (Mng Dir)

Permira (Guernsey) Limited (1)
Trafalgar Court, PO Box 503, Les Banques, Saint Peter Port, GY1 6DJ, Guernsey
Tel.: (44) 1481743200
Web Site: http://www.permira.com

PERMIRA ADVISERS LLP

Permira Advisers LLP—(Continued)

Privater Equity Firm
N.A.I.C.S.: 523999
Alistair Boyle (Head-Guernsey & Sr Dir-Fin)

Permira Advisers LLC (1)
320 Park Ave 33rd Fl, New York, NY 10022
Tel.: (212) 386-7480
Web Site: http://www.permira.com
Sales Range: $50-74.9 Million
Emp.: 15
Privater Equity Firm
N.A.I.C.S.: 523999
Tom Lister (Mng Partner-Global)

Permira Beteiligungsberatung GmbH (1)
Bockenheimer Landstrasse 33, Frankfurt am Main, 60325, Germany
Tel.: (49) 699714660
Web Site: http://www.permira.com
Sales Range: $50-74.9 Million
Emp.: 32
Privater Equity Firm
N.A.I.C.S.: 523999
Jorg Rockenhauser (Partner)

Permira Luxembourg S.ar.l. (1)
488 route de Longwy, 1940, Luxembourg, Luxembourg
Tel.: (352) 2686811
Emp.: 9
Privater Equity Firm
N.A.I.C.S.: 523999
Severina Michelle (Mng Dir)

R. Griggs Group Limited (1)
Cobbs Lane, Wollaston, NN29 7SW, Northants, United Kingdom
Tel.: (44) 1933663281
Holding Company; Footwear Designer, Licensor & Marketer
N.A.I.C.S.: 551112
Max Griggs (Pres)

Subsidiary (Domestic):

AirWair International Limited (2)
Cobbs Lane, Wollaston, NN29 7SW, Northants, United Kingdom
Tel.: (44) 1933663281
Web Site: http://www.drmartens.com
Leather Footwear & Accessories Designer & Marketer
N.A.I.C.S.: 424340
Max Griggs (Pres)

Subsidiary (US):

Dr. Martens Airwair USA LLC (3)
10 NW 10th Ave, Portland, OR 97209-3106
Tel.: (503) 222-6300
Web Site: http://www.dmusastore.com
Sales Range: $75-99.9 Million
Emp.: 220
Leather Footwear & Accessories Whslr
N.A.I.C.S.: 424340
Robert Bradford (VP-Sls)

Squarespace Inc. (1)
225 Varick St 12th Fl, New York, NY 10014
Tel.: (646) 580-3456
Web Site: https://www.squarespace.com
Rev.: $866,972,000
Assets: $730,517,000
Liabilities: $1,033,508,000
Net Worth: ($302,991,000)
Earnings: ($252,221,000)
Emp.: 1,800
Fiscal Year-end: 12/31/2022
Software Publisher
N.A.I.C.S.: 513210
Marcela Martin (CFO)

Synamedia Ltd. (1)
One London Road, Staines-upon-Thames, TW1 84EX, Mddx, United Kingdom
Tel.: (44) 1784774333
Web Site: http://www.synamedia.com
Broadcast Media Services
N.A.I.C.S.: 541840
Paul Segre (CEO)

Subsidiary (Non-US):

Unitymedia GmbH (2)
Aachenerstrasse 746-750, 50933, Cologne, Germany
Tel.: (49) 8007001177
Web Site: http://www.unitymedia.de
Internet, Television & Telecommunications Services
N.A.I.C.S.: 517810

Subsidiary (Domestic):

Kabel BW GmbH (3)
Im Breitspiel 2, 69126, Heidelberg, Germany
Tel.: (49) 62213342512
Web Site: http://www.unitymedia.de
Sales Range: $750-799.9 Million
Cable Television, Internet & Telecommunications Services
N.A.I.C.S.: 516210

Unitymedia Management GmbH (3)
Aachener Strasse 746-750, 50933, Cologne, Nordrhein-Westfalen, Germany
Tel.: (49) 221377920
Cable Channel Operating Services
N.A.I.C.S.: 516210

Unitymedia NRW GmbH (3)
PO Box 10 13 30, 44713, Bochum, Germany
Tel.: (49) 221377920
Web Site: http://www.unitymedia.de
Broadband Service Distr
N.A.I.C.S.: 334220

TBS Group SpA (1)
AREA Science Park Padriciano 99, 34149, Trieste, Italy
Tel.: (39) 04092291
Web Site: http://www.tbsgroup.com
Sales Range: $250-299.9 Million
Clinical & Medical Engineering & Consulting Services
N.A.I.C.S.: 541330
Alessandro Dogliani (Chm & CEO)

Subsidiary (Domestic):

Crimo Italia s.r.l. (2)
Z Industriale Nord, 06023, Gualdo Tadino, Perugia, Italy
Tel.: (39) 0759142064
Web Site: http://www.crimoitalia.it
Medical & Surgical Instrument Repair & Maintenance Services
N.A.I.C.S.: 811210

Elettronica Bio Medicale S.p.a. (2)
Via F Bettini 13, 06034, Foligno, Perugia, Italy
Tel.: (39) 0742326601
Web Site: http://www.ebm.it
Clinical Engineering Services
N.A.I.C.S.: 541715
Fabio Faltoni (VP)

Subsidiary (Non-US):

MSI Medserv International Deutschland GmbH (2)
Im Goldacker 14, 88630, Pfullendorf, Germany
Tel.: (49) 7552 928010
Web Site: http://www.medservinternational.com
Endoscopy Equipments Maintenance Services
N.A.I.C.S.: 811210
Luigi Cuorvo (Mng Dir)

Subsidiary (Domestic):

S.L.T. s.r.l. (2)
Via Torino 30, 20063, Cernusco sul Naviglio, Milan, Italy
Tel.: (39) 0248464064
Web Site: http://www.slt.eu.com
Medical Instrument Distr
N.A.I.C.S.: 423450
Vincent Ventimiglia (CEO)

Subsidiary (Non-US):

STB Servicos Telematicos e Biomedicos Unipessoal LDA (2)
Rua dos Bombeiros Voluntarios do Dafundo N 1, Dafundo, 1495-714, Oeiras, Portugal
Tel.: (351) 214195436
Web Site: http://www.tbspt.com
Medical & Surgical Instrument Repair & Maintenance Services
N.A.I.C.S.: 327910

Surgical Technologies BV (2)
Lichtenhorststraat 35a, 6942 GS, Didam, Gelderland, Netherlands
Tel.: (31) 316296543
Web Site: http://www.surgical.nl
Surgical Equipments Maintenance Services
N.A.I.C.S.: 811310

TBS BE Telematic & Biomedical Services BVBA (2)
Rue Marie Curie 10, B-3341, Loncin, Liege, Belgium
Tel.: (32) 42392313
Web Site: http://www.tbsbe.com
Medical & Surgical Instrument Repair & Maintenance Services
N.A.I.C.S.: 811210

TBS FR Telematic & Biomedical Services Sarl (2)
Les Bureaux Verts 16 chemin du Professeur Depere, 69160, Tassin-la-Demi-Lune, Rhone, France
Tel.: (33) 437225900
Web Site: http://www.tbsfr.com
Medical & Surgical Instrument Repair & Maintenance Services
N.A.I.C.S.: 811210

TBS GB Telematic & Biomedical Services Ltd (2)
Wrest Park House Park Avenue Silsoe, London, MK45 4HR, United Kingdom
Tel.: (44) 844 809 4778
Web Site: http://www.tbsgb.com
Biomedical Engineering Services
N.A.I.C.S.: 811210
Victoria Sawford (Mgr-Procurement)

Subsidiary (Non-US):

TBS INDIA Telematic & Biomedical Services Pvt Ltd. (3)
5th Floor Arden Fair Opp Benniganahalli Ring Road Flyover Pai Layout, Old Madras Road, Bengaluru, Karnataka, India
Tel.: (91) 8040545050
Web Site: http://www.tbs-india.com
Biomedical Equipment Repair & Maintenance Services
N.A.I.C.S.: 811210
Chelvadorai Nithyanandam (CEO)

Subsidiary (Domestic):

Tesan S.p.A (2)
Via Ludovico Lazzaro Zamenhof 200, 36100, Vicenza, Italy
Tel.: (39) 0444914700
Web Site: http://www.tesan.it
Telemedical Consulting Services
N.A.I.C.S.: 524114

Subsidiary (Domestic):

Tesan Televita S.r.l (3)
Via Manin 16, 33100, Udine, Italy
Tel.: (39) 0432 272727
Web Site: http://www.tesantelevita.it
Telemedical Consulting Services
N.A.I.C.S.: 621491

The Knot Worldwide Inc. (1)
2 Wisconsin Cir 3rd Fl, Chevy Chase, MD 20815
Tel.: (877) 331-7752
Web Site: http://www.weddingwire.com
Online Wedding Planning Services
N.A.I.C.S.: 513199
Timothy R. Chi (CEO)

Subsidiary (Domestic):

XO Group Inc. (2)
195 Broadway 25th Fl, New York, NY 10007
Tel.: (212) 219-8555
Web Site: http://www.xogroupinc.com
Rev.: $160,556,000
Assets: $204,120,000
Liabilities: $31,031,000
Net Worth: $173,089,000
Earnings: $5,534,000
Emp.: 741
Fiscal Year-end: 12/31/2017
Online Wedding Resource
N.A.I.C.S.: 519290
Dhanusha Sivajee (Chief Mktg Officer)

Subsidiary (Domestic):

WEDDINGPAGES, LLC (3)
11106 Mockingbird Dr, Omaha, NE 68137

INTERNATIONAL PUBLIC

Tel.: (212) 219-8555
Publishing Services
N.A.I.C.S.: 513199

The Ultimate Software Group of Canada, Inc. (1)
144 Bloor St. West Suite 400, Toronto, M5H 1M4, ON, Canada
Tel.: (416) 861-8530
Software Development Services
N.A.I.C.S.: 541511

Tilney Smith & Williamson Ltd. (1)
6 Chesterfield Gardens, London, W1J 5BQ, United Kingdom
Tel.: (44) 2031 316 167
Web Site: http://group.tilney.co.uk
Holding Company; Investment & Wealth Management Services
N.A.I.C.S.: 551112
Chris Woodhouse (CEO)

Subsidiary (Domestic):

Smith & Williamson Holdings Limited (2)
25 Moorgate, London, EC2R 6AY, United Kingdom
Tel.: (44) 2071314000
Web Site: http://www.smithandwilliamson.com
Sales Range: $700-749.9 Million
Emp.: 1,700
Holding Company; Accounting, Investment, Asset Management & Other Financial Services
N.A.I.C.S.: 551112
Andrew Sykes (Chm)

Subsidiary (Non-US):

Shaws IPM Limited (3)
Elia House 77 Limassol Avenue, 2121, Nicosia, Cyprus
Tel.: (357) 22418888
Web Site: http://www.ipm.com.cy
Property Management Services
N.A.I.C.S.: 531311
Andreas Athinodorou (Mng Dir)

Smith & Williamson (Channel Islands) Limited (3)
3rd Floor 37 Esplanade, Saint Helier, Jersey
Tel.: (44) 1534 714557
Chartered Accountancy Services
N.A.I.C.S.: 541211

Subsidiary (Domestic):

Smith & Williamson Fund Administration Limited (3)
206 St Vincent Street, Glasgow, G2 5SG, United Kingdom
Tel.: (44) 141 222 1150
Fund Administration Services
N.A.I.C.S.: 524292

Smith & Williamson Investment Management Limited (3)
25 Moorgate, London, EC2R 6AY, United Kingdom
Tel.: (44) 2071314000
Web Site: http://www.smith.williamson.co.uk
Sales Range: $75-99.9 Million
Emp.: 750
Investment Management Service
N.A.I.C.S.: 523940
Peter Fernandes (Head-Private Client Investment Mgmt)

Smith & Williamson Limited (3)
25 Moorgate, London, EC2R 6AY, United Kingdom
Tel.: (44) 2071314000
Web Site: http://www.smith.williamson.co.uk
Accounting, Auditing & Tax Consultation Services
N.A.I.C.S.: 541211
Joss Dalrymple (Head-Private Client Tax & Bus Svcs)

Subsidiary (Domestic):

Tilney Investment Management (2)
Royal Liver Building Pier Head, Liverpool, L3 1NY, United Kingdom
Tel.: (44) 151 236 6000
Web Site: http://www.tilney.co.uk
Fund Management Services

AND PRIVATE COMPANIES

N.A.I.C.S.: 523940
John Mulhern *(Mng Dir)*

Tilney Investment Management Services Limited (2)
6 Chesterfield Gardens, London, W1J 5BQ, United Kingdom
Tel.: (44) 2031 316 167
Web Site: http://www.bestinvest.co.uk
Investment & Wealth Management Services
N.A.I.C.S.: 523940
Donald Reid *(COO)*

Zendesk, Inc. (1)
989 Market St, San Francisco, CA 94103
Tel.: (415) 418-7506
Web Site: http://www.zendesk.com
Rev.: $1,338,603,000
Assets: $2,451,279,000
Liabilities: $1,962,061,000
Net Worth: $489,218,000
Earnings: ($223,644,000)
Emp.: 5,860
Fiscal Year-end: 12/31/2021
Computer Software Publisher & Retailer
N.A.I.C.S.: 513210
Tom Eggemeier *(CEO)*

Subsidiary (Non-US):

Base spolka z ograniczona odpowiedzialnoscia (2)
ul Parowcowa 4C, 02-445, Warsaw, Poland
Tel.: (48) 226145204
Web Site: http://www.base.waw.pl
Machine Tools Mfr
N.A.I.C.S.: 333517

We Are Cloud SAS (2)
1 Place Francis Ponge, Montpellier, 34000, France
Tel.: (33) 467416064
Web Site: http://www.bimeanalytics.com
Software Development Services
N.A.I.C.S.: 541511

Zendesk APAC (2)
Level 1 482 Bourke Street, Melbourne, 3000, VIC, Australia
Tel.: (61) 3 9008 6775
Computer Software Publisher & Retailer
N.A.I.C.S.: 513210
Adam Clark *(VP-Sls-Australia & New Zealand)*

Zendesk EMEA (2)
30 Eastbourne Terrace Bishops Bridge, London, W2 6LA, United Kingdom
Tel.: (44) 20 3355 7960
Computer Software Publisher & Retailer
N.A.I.C.S.: 513210

Zendesk Korea LLC (2)
373 Gangnam-daero Seocho-dong, Seocho-gu, Seoul, Korea (South)
Tel.: (82) 50409200518
Software Development Services
N.A.I.C.S.: 541511

Zendesk Singapore PTE. LTD (2)
401 Commonwealth Drive Haw Par Technocentre 07-01, Singapore, 149598, Singapore
Tel.: (65) 63379102
Web Site: http://www.zopim.com
Software Development Services
N.A.I.C.S.: 541511

PERMODALAN NASIONAL BERHAD
Level 3 Menara PNB, Kuala Lumpur, 50400, Malaysia
Tel.: (60) 320505500
Web Site: http://www.pnb.com.my
Year Founded: 1978
Sales Range: $550-599.9 Million
Emp.: 2,000
Holding Company; Investment Services
N.A.I.C.S.: 551112
Idris Bin Kechot *(Deputy Pres-Unit Trust)*

Subsidiaries:

Amanah Saham Nasional Berhad (1)
Level UG Balai PNB, 201-A Jalan Tun Razak, 50400, Kuala Lumpur, Malaysia (100%)
Tel.: (60) 321612399
Web Site: http://www.asnb.com.my
Trusts Estates & Agency Accounts
N.A.I.C.S.: 525920

Duopharma Biotech Berhad (1)
Suite 18 06 Level 18 CIMB HUB No 26, Jalan Sultan Ismail, 50250, Kuala Lumpur, Wilayah Persekutuan, Malaysia
Tel.: (60) 321620218
Web Site: https://www.duopharmabiotech.com
Rev.: $147,453,333
Assets: $258,607,196
Liabilities: $119,935,873
Net Worth: $138,671,323
Earnings: $14,838,519
Emp.: 1,500
Fiscal Year-end: 12/31/2022
Holding Company; Pharmaceutical Products Mfr
N.A.I.C.S.: 551112
Noor Azwah Samsudin *(Sec)*

FEC Cables (Malaysia) Sdn. Bhd. (1)
Persiaran Raja Muda, Shah Alam, 40700, Selangor Darul Ehsan, Malaysia (71.13%)
Tel.: (60) 355191110
Web Site: http://www.fec.com.my
Sales Range: $25-49.9 Million
Emp.: 200
Energy & Telecommunication Cable Mfr & Whslr
N.A.I.C.S.: 335929
Ithnin Nohaned *(Gen Mgr)*

Federal Power Sdn. Bhd. (1)
Lot No 8 Jalan Ragum 15 17, PO Box 016, 40702, Shah Alam, Malaysia (51%)
Tel.: (60) 355183600
Web Site: http://www.federalpower.com.my
Sales Range: $100-124.9 Million
Emp.: 400
Steel Wire & Cables Mfr & Sales
N.A.I.C.S.: 332618

Heveafil Sdn. Berhad (1)
1 Jalan Heveafil, Batang Kali, Kuala Lumpur, 44300, Selangor, Malaysia (91.3%)
Tel.: (60) 360573001
Web Site: http://www.heveafil.com.my
Sales Range: $125-149.9 Million
Emp.: 450
Mechanical Use Rubber Product Mfr
N.A.I.C.S.: 326291

PNB (UK) Limited (1)
PNB House 7th Floor, EC43 4AY, London, United Kingdom
Tel.: (44) 20 7382 1500
Investment Management Service
N.A.I.C.S.: 523940
Khairul Hadi M. Rahim *(Mgr-Fund)*

PNB Asset Management (Japan) Co Ltd (1)
The New Otani Garden Court 19F 4-1 Kioi-Cho, Chiyoda-ku, Tokyo, 102-0094, Japan
Tel.: (81) 3 6261 0017
Emp.: 4
Investment Management Service
N.A.I.C.S.: 523940
Tadashi Mizushima *(Dir-Representative)*

PNB Equity Resource Corporation Sdn. Bhd. (1)
23rd Floor Menara PNB 201-A Jalan Tun Razak, 50400, Kuala Lumpur, Malaysia
Tel.: (60) 3 2050 5100
Investment Management Service
N.A.I.C.S.: 523940
Edree Ahmad *(Mgr)*

PNB Investment Institute Sdn. Berhad (1)
21 Floor Menara PNB 201 A Jalan Tun Razak, Kuala Lumpur, 50400, Malaysia (51%)
Tel.: (60) 320505500
Web Site: http://www.pnb.com.my
Trusts, Estates & Agency Accounts
N.A.I.C.S.: 525920

PNB Management Services Sdn. Berhad (1)
10 Jalan Binjai, Kuala Lumpur, 50450, Malaysia (100%)
Tel.: (60) 374903333
Web Site: http://www.pnbdarbypark.com
Sales Range: $100-124.9 Million
Emp.: 250
Trusts Estates & Agency Accounts
N.A.I.C.S.: 525920
Taha Zainar *(Mng Dir)*

PNB Merdeka Ventures Sdn Bhd (1)
19th Floor Menara PNB, 201-A Jalan Tun Razak, Kuala Lumpur, 50400, Malaysia (100%)
Tel.: (60) 320505608
Web Site: http://www.pnb.com
Sales Range: $50-74.9 Million
Emp.: 8
Trusts Estates & Agency Accounts
N.A.I.C.S.: 525920
Abdul Aziz *(CEO)*

PNB NJI Holdings Sdn. Berhad (1)
23rd Fl Menara Pnb, Kuala Lumpur, 50400, Malaysia (100%)
Tel.: (60) 321610588
Web Site: http://www.pnb.com.my
Credit Union
N.A.I.C.S.: 522130

PNB Nomura Jafco Management Sdn. Berhad (1)
23rd Fl Tower Blk, Pnb Bldg 201-A, Kuala Lumpur, Malaysia (100%)
Tel.: (60) 321610588
Portfolio Management
N.A.I.C.S.: 523940

PNB Property Management Sdn. Berhad (1)
24th Fl Menara Pnb, Kuala Lumpur, Malaysia (100%)
Tel.: (60) 321610588
Sales Range: $50-74.9 Million
Emp.: 100
Trusts Estates & Agency Accounts
N.A.I.C.S.: 525920

Pelaburan Hartanah Nasional Berhad (1)
Level 31 Menara PNB, 201-A Jalan Tun Razak, Kuala Lumpur, 50400, Malaysia (100%)
Tel.: (60) 320505318
Web Site: http://www.bmb.com.my
Sales Range: $50-74.9 Million
Emp.: 15
Trusts Estates & Agency Accounts
N.A.I.C.S.: 525920
Hafis Mohd *(CEO)*

Pengurusan Pelaburan ASW 2020 Berhad (1)
Amanah Saham Nasional, 50400, Kuala Lumpur, Malaysia (100%)
Tel.: (60) 321610588
Sales Range: $350-399.9 Million
Emp.: 1,000
Trusts Estates & Agency Accounts
N.A.I.C.S.: 525920

Projek Lintasan Kota Holdings Sdn Bhd (1)
Peti 2 Tingkat 12 Menara PNB 201- A Jalan Tun Razak, 50400, Kuala Lumpur, Malaysia
Tel.: (60) 3 2164 2450
Web Site: http://www.prolintas.com.my
Holding Company
N.A.I.C.S.: 551112
Malik Parvez Ahmad *(COO-Comml & Fin)*

PERMSIN STEEL WORKS PLC
4 95-96 Rama 2 Road, Khok Kham Subdistrict Muang District, Bangkok, 74000, Samut Sakhon, Thailand
Tel.: (66) 34825090
Web Site: https://www.permsinsteel.com
Year Founded: 1989
PERM—(THA)
Rev.: $105,745,868
Assets: $124,119,002
Liabilities: $102,388,207
Net Worth: $21,730,794
Earnings: ($10,827,594)
Fiscal Year-end: 12/31/23
Steel Products Mfr
N.A.I.C.S.: 331110
Chukiat Yongvongpaibul *(Pres)*

PERNOD RICARD S.A.

PERN S.A.
ul Wyszogrodzka 133, 09-410, Plock, Poland
Tel.: (48) 24 266 2300   PL
Web Site: http://www.pern.pl
Year Founded: 1959
Crude Oil Pipeline Network Operator
N.A.I.C.S.: 486110
Igor Wasilewski *(Chm-Mgmt Bd)*

Subsidiaries:

GAZ-SYSTEM S.A. (1)
ul Mszczonowska 4, 02-337, Warsaw, Poland
Tel.: (48) 222201800
Web Site: https://www.gaz-system.pl
Natural Gas Distribution
N.A.I.C.S.: 221210

PERNOD RICARD S.A.
5 Cours Paul Ricard, 75380, Paris, Cedex 08, France
Tel.: (33) 170931600   FR
Web Site: https://www.pernod-ricard.com
Year Founded: 1975
RI—(EUR)
Rev.: $13,098,424,347
Assets: $40,660,479,171
Liabilities: $22,621,411,612
Net Worth: $18,039,067,559
Earnings: $2,463,846,320
Emp.: 20,617
Fiscal Year-end: 06/30/23
Alcoholic Beverage Distr
N.A.I.C.S.: 424820
Gilles Bogaert *(CEO-Europe, Middle East, Asia & Latin America)*

Subsidiaries:

Castle Brands Inc. (1)
122 E 42nd St Ste 5000, New York, NY 10168
Tel.: (646) 356-0200
Web Site: https://castlebrandsinc.com
Rev.: $95,841,703
Assets: $84,980,566
Liabilities: $65,631,038
Net Worth: $19,349,528
Earnings: $5,663,616
Emp.: 59
Fiscal Year-end: 03/31/2019
Vodka, Rum, Irish Whiskey & Liqueurs Importer & Marketer
N.A.I.C.S.: 424820
T. Kelley Spillane *(Sr VP-Sls-Global)*

Subsidiary (Non-US):

Castle Brands Spirits Company Limited (2)
Suite 16 the Mall Beacon Court Business Park, Sandyford, Dublin, Ireland
Tel.: (353) 12932962
Web Site: http://www.castlebrandsinc.com
Sales Range: $25-49.9 Million
Emp.: 6
Alcoholic Beverages Mfr
N.A.I.C.S.: 312140

Champagne Perrier-Jouet (1)
28 avenue de Champagne, 51200, Epernay, France
Tel.: (33) 326533800
Web Site: https://www.perrier-jouet.com
Alcoholic Beverages Mfr
N.A.I.C.S.: 312120

Chivas Brothers Pernod Ricard Ltd (1)
111-113 Renfrew Rd, Paisley, PA3 4DY, Renfrewshire, United Kingdom
Tel.: (44) 1415311801
Beverage Product Mfr
N.A.I.C.S.: 312120

Subsidiary (Domestic):

Chivas Brothers (Holdings) Ltd (2)
Chivas House 72 Chancellors Road, London, W6 9RS, United Kingdom
Tel.: (44) 2082501000
Investment Management Service
N.A.I.C.S.: 523999

PERNOD RICARD S.A.

Pernod Ricard S.A.—(Continued)
Jean-Christophe Coutures *(Chm & CEO)*

Domaines Jean Martell (1)
Domaine Jean Martell No 4, 16170, Rouillac, France
Tel.: (33) 545218111
Alcoholic Beverage Distr
N.A.I.C.S.: 424820

G.H. Mumm & Cie - Ste Vinicole de Champagne Successeur (1)
29 rue du Champ de Mars, 51100, Reims, France
Tel.: (33) 326495969
Web Site: https://www.mumm.com
Alcoholic Beverage Mfr & Distr
N.A.I.C.S.: 312120

Irish Distillers Ltd. (1)
Simmonscourt House Simmonscourt Road, Ballsbridge, Dublin, 4, Ireland **(100%)**
Tel.: (353) 1 212 9000
Web Site: https://www.irishdistillers.ie
Sales Range: $25-49.9 Million
Emp.: 140
Whiskey Distiller
N.A.I.C.S.: 312130
Conor McQuaid *(Chm & CEO)*

Martell & Co. SA (1)
Place Edouard Martell, BP 21, 16100, Cognac, France
Tel.: (33) 545363333
Web Site: https://www.martell.com
Emp.: 500
Spirits & Cognacs Mfr
N.A.I.C.S.: 312140

Martell Mumm Perrier-Jouet (1)
112 Avenue Kleber, 75116, Paris, France
Tel.: (33) 1 53 23 26 50
Sales Range: $150-199.9 Million
Emp.: 40
Alcoholic Beverage Distr
N.A.I.C.S.: 424820

Pernod (1)
120 Ave Du Marechal Foch, 94015, Creteil, Cedex, France **(100%)**
Tel.: (33) 149815151
Web Site: http://www.pernod.com
Rev.: $354,143,520
Emp.: 500
Producer of Aperitifs
N.A.I.C.S.: 312130

Pernod Ricard (China) Trading Co Ltd (1)
15F Infinitus Tower 168 Hu Bin Road, Luwan Dist, Shanghai, 200021, China
Tel.: (86) 2123011000
Web Site: https://www.pernod-ricard-china.com
Sales Range: $75-99.9 Million
Emp.: 185
Alcoholic Beverage Distr
N.A.I.C.S.: 424820
Constantine Constandis *(Gen Mgr)*

Pernod Ricard (Holding) (1)
12 place des Etats-Unis, 75783, Paris, France
Tel.: (33) 1 41 00 41 00
Web Site: http://www.pernod-ricard.com
Investment Management Service
N.A.I.C.S.: 523999

Pernod Ricard Africa & Midle East (1)
2 Bis Rue de Solferino, 75340, Paris, France
Tel.: (33) 1 44 11 77 00
Alcoholic Beverage Distr
N.A.I.C.S.: 424820

Subsidiary (Non-US):

Pernod Ricard Gulf (2)
7th Floor 705-707 Jafza View 19 Jebel Ali Free Zone, PO Box 17497, Dubai, 17497, United Arab Emirates
Tel.: (971) 4 886 4434
Emp.: 2
Alcoholic Beverage Distr
N.A.I.C.S.: 424820

Pernod Ricard Istanbul (2)
Ahi Evran Cad N 1 Polaris Plaza Kat 9 N 42 PK, Maslak, 34398, Istanbul, Turkiye
Tel.: (90) 212 346 0203
Sales Range: $50-74.9 Million
Emp.: 60
Alcoholic Beverage Distr
N.A.I.C.S.: 424820
Selcuk Tuemay *(Mng Dir)*

Pernod Ricard South Africa Pty Ltd (2)
21 Woodlands Drive Country Club Estate Woodmead Building 6, De Waterkant, Johannesburg, 2191, South Africa
Tel.: (27) 11 802 0600
Web Site: https://www.pernod-ricard.com
Alcoholic Beverage Mfr & Distr
N.A.I.C.S.: 312120
Brigitte Staley *(Dir-Fin)*

Pernod Ricard Argentina Corp. (1)
Jujuy 1197, Bella Vista, B1661KTA, San Miguel, Buenos Aires, Argentina
Tel.: (54) 1151698000
Web Site: https://www.pernod-ricard.com.ar
Beverage Product Distr
N.A.I.C.S.: 424820

Pernod Ricard Asia Duty Free Ltd (1)
Unit 2318 23rd Floor Miramar Tower 132 Nathan Road, Tsimshatsui, Kowloon, China (Hong Kong)
Tel.: (852) 2378 6900
Alcoholic Beverage Product Distr
N.A.I.C.S.: 424820

Pernod Ricard Australia Pty Ltd (1)
Level 43 Tower One 100 Barangaroo Avenue, Barangaroo, 2000, NSW, Australia
Tel.: (61) 28 874 8222
Web Site: https://www.pernod-ricard.com
Sales Range: $75-99.9 Million
Emp.: 25
Spirit & Wine Distr
N.A.I.C.S.: 424820
Julien Hamard *(Mng Dir)*

Subsidiary (Domestic):

Pernod Ricard Winemakers Pty Ltd (2)
Level 3 167 Fullarton Road, Dulwich, 5067, SA, Australia
Tel.: (61) 288748222
Web Site: https://www.pernod-ricard-winemakers.com
Emp.: 20
Alcoholic Beverage Mfr & Distr
N.A.I.C.S.: 312120

Subsidiary (Domestic):

Orlando Wyndham (3)
167 Fullerton Rd, Dulwich, 5065, SA, Australia **(100%)**
Tel.: (61) 882082466
Web Site: http://www.orlandowyndhamgroup.com.au
Sales Range: $25-49.9 Million
Importer of Spirits & Exporter of Wines
N.A.I.C.S.: 312130

Pernod Ricard Chile SA (1)
Avenida Vitacura 5250 Of 1001, Santiago, Chile
Tel.: (56) 2 345 37 00
Web Site: http://www.pernod-ricard.com
Sales Range: $25-49.9 Million
Emp.: 50
Alcoholic Beverage Distr
N.A.I.C.S.: 424820
Juan Miguel Casellas *(Mng Dir)*

Pernod Ricard Colombia SA (1)
Calle 103 N 19-60 Piso 1 y 2, Bogota, Colombia
Tel.: (57) 16369066
Beverage Product Distr
N.A.I.C.S.: 424820
Juan Fernando Rodriguez Castro *(CFO)*

Pernod Ricard Europe SA (1)
23 Rue De L Amiral D Estaing, Paris, 75016, France **(100%)**
Tel.: (33) 144117700
Web Site: http://www.pernod-ricard-europe.com
Sales Range: $1-9.9 Million
Emp.: 80
Export & Distribution of Pernod Ricard Aperitifs & Brandies

N.A.I.C.S.: 445320

Subsidiary (Non-US):

Jan Becher Karlovarska Becherovka, A/S (2)
TG Masaryka 282/57, 360 01, Karlovy Vary, Czech Republic
Tel.: (420) 359578111
Web Site: https://www.pernod-ricard.cz
Sales Range: $50-74.9 Million
Emp.: 130
Spirits & Wines Mfr & Distr
N.A.I.C.S.: 312140

Pernod Ricard Armenia (2)
2/4 Janibekyan St, 0031, Yerevan, Armenia
Tel.: (374) 10354879
Web Site: https://pernod-ricard.am
Emp.: 28
Alcoholic Beverage Mfr & Distr
N.A.I.C.S.: 312120
Manuk Abrahamyan *(Office Mgr)*

Pernod Ricard Belgium SA (2)
Boulevard de Waterloo 16, 1000, Brussels, Belgium
Tel.: (32) 26636262
Web Site: https://www.pernod-ricard.com
Emp.: 60
Alcoholic Beverage Distr
N.A.I.C.S.: 424820

Pernod Ricard Bulgaria EOOD (2)
Business Park Sofia Building 12 - Entrance A - Floor 3, Mladost region-Mladost 4 living district-1 Business Park Sofia Street, 1715, Sofia, 1766, Bulgaria
Tel.: (359) 29761101
Emp.: 8
Alcoholic Beverage Distr
N.A.I.C.S.: 424820
Miroslava Simova *(Pres)*

Pernod Ricard Deutschland GmbH (2)
Habsburgerring 2, 50674, Cologne, Germany
Tel.: (49) 221 430 9090
Web Site: https://www.pernod-ricard.de
Emp.: 225
Spirits Producer & Distr
N.A.I.C.S.: 424820
Thomas Drosse *(Mng-Dir-Sales)*

Subsidiary (Domestic):

Black Forest Distillers GmbH (3)
Ausserer Vogelsberg 7, 72290, Lossburg, Germany **(100%)**
Tel.: (49) 744 691 7660
Web Site: https://www.monkey47.com
Gin Distillery & Whslr
N.A.I.C.S.: 312140
Julien Nicolay *(Gen Mgr-APAC)*

Subsidiary (Non-US):

Pernod Ricard Austria GmbH (3)
Schottenfeldgasse 20, 1070, Vienna, Austria
Tel.: (43) 1290 281 8100
Web Site: https://www.pernod-ricard.at
Sales Range: $25-49.9 Million
Emp.: 30
Spirit Producer & Distr
N.A.I.C.S.: 424820
Gregory Chevillat *(Dir-Fin)*

Pernod Ricard Denmark A/S (3)
Vesterbrogade 149, 1620, Copenhagen, Denmark
Tel.: (45) 3 323 9000
Web Site: https://www.pernod-ricard-denmark.com
Sales Range: $50-74.9 Million
Emp.: 150
Alcoholic Beverage Producer & Distr
N.A.I.C.S.: 424810

Pernod Ricard Swiss S.A. (3)
Richtiarkade 16, 8304, Wallisellen, Switzerland
Tel.: (41) 445758000
Web Site: https://www.pernod-ricard-swiss.com
Sales Range: $25-49.9 Million
Emp.: 51
Spirits Producer & Distr
N.A.I.C.S.: 424810

INTERNATIONAL PUBLIC

Subsidiary (Non-US):

Pernod Ricard Espana S.A (2)
C/ Manuel Maranon 8, 28043, Madrid, Spain
Tel.: (34) 91 368 3067
Sales Range: $150-199.9 Million
Emp.: 50
Beverage Product Distr
N.A.I.C.S.: 424820

Subsidiary (Domestic):

Domecq Bodegas (3)
Edificio Igara II Camino de Portuetxe 35A, 20018, San Sebastian, Guipuzcoa, Spain
Tel.: (34) 943445700
Web Site: http://www.domecqbodegas.com
Wine Production & Sales
N.A.I.C.S.: 312130

Subsidiary (Non-US):

Pernod Ricard Estonia OU (2)
Veskiposti 2, Tallinn, EE-10138, Estonia
Tel.: (372) 6512420
Web Site: http://www.pernod-ricard.com
Sales Range: $25-49.9 Million
Emp.: 24
Beverage Product Distr
N.A.I.C.S.: 424820
Rein Aksalu *(Mgr-Public Affairs)*

Pernod Ricard Italia S.p.A. (2)
Via Gaetano De Castillia 23, 20124, Milan, Italy
Tel.: (39) 02205671
Distilled Beverage Mfr
N.A.I.C.S.: 312120

Pernod Ricard Nederland BV (2)
Stadionstraat 38, Breda, 4815 NG, Netherlands
Tel.: (31) 76 5025111
Web Site: https://www.pernod-ricard.com
Sales Range: $25-49.9 Million
Emp.: 50
Alcoholic Beverage Distr
N.A.I.C.S.: 424820
Erik Zaal *(Mng Dir)*

Pernod Ricard Nordic
Besoksadress Marieviksgatan 19b, 117 43, Stockholm, Sweden
Tel.: (46) 8 744 7000
Web Site: https://www.pernod-ricard-sweden.com
Sales Range: $100-124.9 Million
Emp.: 375
Alcoholic Beverage Mfr & Distr
N.A.I.C.S.: 312120
Mia Avelin-Mangefors *(Dir-HR)*

Subsidiary (Non-US):

Pernod Ricard Finland Oy (3)
Fabianinkatu 8, 00130, Helsinki, Finland
Tel.: (358) 207212200
Emp.: 100
Alcoholic Beverages Mfr
N.A.I.C.S.: 312120
Jori Manninen *(Pres)*

Subsidiary (Domestic):

Pernod Ricard Sweden AB (3)
Marieviksgatan 19b, 117 43, Stockholm, Sweden
Tel.: (46) 87447000
Web Site: https://www.pernod-ricard-sweden.com
Sales Range: $150-199.9 Million
Emp.: 30
Beverage Product Distr
N.A.I.C.S.: 424820
Helene Reuterwall Thideman *(Mgr-PR)*

Subsidiary (Non-US):

Pernod-Ricard Norway A/S (3)
Fridtjof Nansens vei 17-19, Oslo, 0369, Norway
Tel.: (47) 22933000
Alcoholic Beverage Distr
N.A.I.C.S.: 424820

Subsidiary (Domestic):

AS Premium Brands Norway (4)
Fridtjof Nansens Vei 17, 369, Oslo, Norway
Tel.: (47) 22933000

AND PRIVATE COMPANIES — PERNOD RICARD S.A.

Alcoholic Beverage Distr
N.A.I.C.S.: 424820

Subsidiary (Non-US):

Pernod Ricard Southern Central Europe (2)
Vurnikova Ulica 2, 1000, Ljubljana, Slovenia
Tel.: (386) 1 4740 200
Alcoholic Beverage Distr
N.A.I.C.S.: 424820

Subsidiary (Non-US):

Pernod Ricard Croatia d.o.o. (3)
Avenija Veceslava Holjevca 40, 10020, Zagreb, Croatia
Tel.: (385) 13440888
Web Site: https://pernod-ricard-croatia.com
Alcoholic Beverage Distr
N.A.I.C.S.: 424820

Pernod Ricard Serbia d.o.o (3)
Bulevar Oslobodjenja 211, 11000, Belgrade, Serbia
Tel.: (381) 113091500
Web Site: https://www.pernod-ricard.com
Sales Range: $25-49.9 Million
Emp.: 24
Alcoholic Beverage Distr
N.A.I.C.S.: 424820
Predrag Amidzic *(Mng Dir)*

Subsidiary (Domestic):

Pernod Ricard Slovenja d.o.o. (3)
Vurnikova Ulica 2, 1000, Ljubljana, Slovenia
Tel.: (386) 14740200
Alcoholic Beverage Distr
N.A.I.C.S.: 424820

Subsidiary (Non-US):

Pernod Ricard UK Limited (2)
Building 7 Chiswick Park 566 Chiswick High Road, London, W4 5YG, United Kingdom
Tel.: (44) 208 538 4484
Web Site: http://www.pernod-ricard-uk.com
Emp.: 300
Wine & Distilled Beverages Mfr & Whslr
N.A.I.C.S.: 424820
Chris Shead *(Dir-Channel-Off-Trade Spirits)*

Pernod Ricard Ukraine (2)
11 Solomyanska Str Eleven Business Center, Kiev, 03110, Ukraine
Tel.: (380) 80 050 5453
Web Site: http://www.pernod-ricard.com
Sales Range: $75-99.9 Million
Emp.: 200
Beverage Product Distr
N.A.I.C.S.: 424820

UAB Pernod Ricard Lietuva (2)
Menulio G 7, 04326, Vilnius, Lithuania
Tel.: (370) 524 622 77
Web Site: http://www.pernod-ricard.lt
Sales Range: $25-49.9 Million
Emp.: 20
Alcoholic Beverage Distr
N.A.I.C.S.: 424820
Darius Augaitis *(Gen Mgr)*

Watercourse Distillery Ltd (2)
Bow Street, Dublin, 7, Ireland
Tel.: (353) 18072355
Web Site: http://www.ojd.ie
Alcoholic Beverage Distr
N.A.I.C.S.: 424820

Wyborowa SA (2)
53 E Plater Str, 00-113, Warsaw, Poland
Tel.: (48) 22 597 10 50
Web Site: http://www.pernod-ricard.com
Spirit & Vodka Mfr
N.A.I.C.S.: 312140

Yerevan Brandy Company (2)
2 Admiral Isakov ave, Yerevan, 0082, Armenia
Tel.: (374) 1 054 0000
Web Site: https://en.araratbrandy.com
Alcoholic Beverage Products Mfr
N.A.I.C.S.: 312130

Pernod Ricard Finance SA (1)
12 Place Des Etats Unis, 75116, Paris, France
Tel.: (33) 141004100

Sales Range: $100-124.9 Million
Emp.: 20
Financial Management Services
N.A.I.C.S.: 523999
Gilles Bogaert *(Gen Mgr)*

Pernod Ricard Hong Kong Ltd (1)
Unit 2318 23rd Floor Miramar Tower 132 Nathan Road, Tsimshatsui, Kowloon, China (Hong Kong)
Tel.: (852) 2398 3636
Alcoholic Beverage Distr
N.A.I.C.S.: 424820
Xavier Beysecker *(VP-Digital-Asia)*

Pernod Ricard India PTE Ltd (1)
Building No 8C 15th Floor DLF Cyber City DLF Phase II, Gurgaon, 122002, Haryana, India
Tel.: (91) 124 235 8001
Web Site: https://www.pernod-ricard.com
Emp.: 1,363
Alcoholic Beverage Distr
N.A.I.C.S.: 424820
Paul-Robert Bouhier *(Mng Dir)*

Subsidiary (Domestic):

Seagram Distilleries Pte Ltd (2)
Bldg No 8a 4TH Flr DLF Cyber City DLF City Phase II 4th Fl, Gurgaon, 122 002, India
Tel.: (91) 12 4235 8001
Web Site: http://www.pernod-ricard.com
Emp.: 150
Alcoholic Beverages Mfr
N.A.I.C.S.: 312120
Guillaump Reydet *(Mng Dir)*

Pernod Ricard Japan K.K. (1)
34F Sumitomo Fudosan Iidabashi First Tower 2-6-1 Koraku, Bunkyo-ku, Tokyo, 112-0004, Japan
Tel.: (81) 358022670
Web Site: https://www.pernod-ricard-japan.com
Alcoholic Beverage Distr
N.A.I.C.S.: 424820
Jean-Etienne Gourgues *(Pres & CEO)*

Pernod Ricard Kazakhstan LLP (1)
Al-Farabi Ave 19/1 BC Nurly Tau Block 3 B 10th floor, 050059, Almaty, Kazakhstan
Tel.: (7) 7273110520
Web Site: https://www.pernod-ricard.com
Beverage Product Distr
N.A.I.C.S.: 424820

Pernod Ricard Korea Ltd (1)
21F Nara Building 1328-3 Seocho-Dong, Seocho-Gu, Seoul, 137-070, Korea (South)
Tel.: (82) 2 3466 5700
Web Site: http://www.pernod-ricard.com
Alcoholic Beverage Distr
N.A.I.C.S.: 424820
Jean-Manuel Spriet *(CEO)*

Pernod Ricard Minsk LLC (1)
Liberty Residense Internatsionalnaya 20a Office 65, 220088, Minsk, Belarus
Tel.: (375) 172241122
Sales Range: $25-49.9 Million
Emp.: 4
Beverage Product Distr
N.A.I.C.S.: 424820

Pernod Ricard New Zealand Limited (1)
Level 3 4 Graham St Auckland Central, Auckland, 1010, New Zealand
Tel.: (64) 93368300
Web Site: https://www.pernod-ricard.com
Emp.: 800
Alcoholic Beverage Mfr & Distr
N.A.I.C.S.: 312120
Kieran Stevens *(Deputy Mng Dir-Domestic Sls & Mktg)*

Pernod Ricard North America SAS (1)
2 Rue De Solferino N 2 Et 2 B, 75007, Paris, France
Tel.: (33) 1 41 00 41 00
Sales Range: $75-99.9 Million
Emp.: 200
Alcoholic Beverage Distr
N.A.I.C.S.: 424820

Subsidiary (Non-US):

Corby Spirit and Wine Limited (2)
225 King Street West Suite 1100, Toronto, M5V 3M2, ON, Canada
Tel.: (416) 479-2400
Web Site: https://www.corby.ca
Rev.: $124,689,956
Assets: $198,318,150
Liabilities: $55,000,542
Net Worth: $143,317,607
Earnings: $18,306,917
Emp.: 205
Fiscal Year-end: 06/30/2022
Spirits & Wine Producer & Marketer
N.A.I.C.S.: 312140
George F. McCarthy *(Chm)*

Hiram Walker & Sons Ltd. (2)
2072 Riverside Dr E, Windsor, N8Y 4S5, ON, Canada
Tel.: (519) 254-5171
Web Site: http://www.hiramwalker.com
Sales Range: $75-99.9 Million
Distilled & Blended Liquor Producer
N.A.I.C.S.: 312140

Subsidiary (US):

Pernod Ricard USA, Inc. (2)
100 Manhattanville Rd, Purchase, NY 10577 (100%)
Tel.: (914) 848-4800
Web Site: http://www.pernod-ricard-usa.com
Sales Range: $100-124.9 Million
Emp.: 300
Mfr of Spirits
N.A.I.C.S.: 312140
Mark Orr *(VP-North American Affairs)*

Division (Domestic):

Pernod Ricard USA Llc - Continental Division (3)
909 Lk Carolyn Pkwy Ste 1080, Irving, TX 75039
Tel.: (972) 764-7151
Web Site: http://www.pernod-ricard.com
Alcoholic Beverages Mfr
N.A.I.C.S.: 312120

Pernod Ricard USA Llc - East Division (3)
100 Manhattanville Rd, Purchase, NY 10577
Tel.: (914) 848-4800
Web Site: http://www.pernodricardusa.com
Sales Range: $25-49.9 Million
Emp.: 200
Alcoholic Beverages Mfr
N.A.I.C.S.: 312120
Brian Fry *(CEO)*

Pernod Ricard USA Llc - West Division (3)
3161 Michelson Dr Ste 950, Irvine, CA 92612
Tel.: (949) 242-6800
Web Site: http://www.pernod-ricard-usa.com
Alcoholic Beverages Mfr
N.A.I.C.S.: 312130

Pernod Ricard Pacific Holding Pty Ltd (1)
167 Fullarton Rd, Dulwich, 5065, SA, Australia
Tel.: (61) 288748222
Web Site: http://www.premium-wine-brands.com
Emp.: 14
Investment Management Service
N.A.I.C.S.: 523999
Bryan Fry *(Mng Dir)*

Pernod Ricard Pacific Travel Retail (1)
Level 3 16 Byfield Street, North Ryde, 2113, NSW, Australia
Tel.: (61) 2 8874 8222
Web Site: http://www.pernod-ricard-pacific-travel-retail.com
Sales Range: $75-99.9 Million
Emp.: 200
Alcoholic Beverage Distr
N.A.I.C.S.: 424820
Tim Peach *(Mng Dir)*

Pernod Ricard Philippines Inc. (1)
4-C Palm Coast Avenue OneE-com Center Building Mall of Asia Complex, Pasay, 1300, Philippines
Tel.: (63) 2 556 6598
Web Site: http://www.pernod-ricard.com

Emp.: 12
Alcoholic Beverage Distr
N.A.I.C.S.: 424820
Kevin Lee *(Mng Dir)*

Pernod Ricard Rouss CJSC (1)
Yakimansky lane bld 6, Business Center Imperial House, 119049, Moscow, Russia
Tel.: (7) 4959374377
Alcoholic Beverage Distr
N.A.I.C.S.: 424820

Pernod Ricard Singapore PTE Ltd (1)
1 Kim Seng Promenade 11-09/12 Great World City West Tower, Singapore, 237994, Singapore
Tel.: (65) 62355055
Alcoholic Beverage Distr
N.A.I.C.S.: 424820
Paul-Robert Bouhier *(Mng Dir)*

Pernod Ricard Taiwan Ltd (1)
Suite B 3rd Floor No 209 Civic Boulevard Section 3, Taipei, 10492, Taiwan
Tel.: (886) 2 87720272
Alcoholic Beverage Distr
N.A.I.C.S.: 424820

Pernod Ricard Thailand Ltd (1)
14th Floor President Tower 973 Ploenchit Road, Lumpini Pathumwan, Bangkok, 10330, Thailand
Tel.: (66) 2648 8222
Web Site: http://www.pernod-ricard.com
Emp.: 92
Alcoholic Beverage Distr
N.A.I.C.S.: 424820
Quentin Job *(Mng Dir)*

Pernod Ricard Uruguay SA (1)
World Trade Center Luis Alberto de Herrera 1248, Torre A - Piso 20 - Of 2001, 11300, Montevideo, Uruguay
Tel.: (598) 2 623 1430
Sales Range: $25-49.9 Million
Emp.: 4
Beverage Product Distr
N.A.I.C.S.: 424820

Pramsur SA (1)
Avenida Doctor Luis Alberto De Herrera 1248, Torre A Piso 20 Oficina 2001, Montevideo, 11300, Uruguay
Tel.: (598) 26231430
Beverage Product Distr
N.A.I.C.S.: 424810

Ricard SA (1)
4 Et 6 Rue Berthelot, 13014, Marseilles, Cedex, France
Tel.: (33) 491111111
Web Site: http://www.ricard-sa.com
Sales Range: $350-399.9 Million
Emp.: 1,200
Producer of Aperitifs & Fruit Juices
N.A.I.C.S.: 312130
Savinel Philippe *(Chm & CEO)*

Spirits Partners SAS (1)
Chemin Des Meches, Creteil, 94015, France
Tel.: (33) 149815815
Sales Range: $25-49.9 Million
Emp.: 11
Alcoholic Beverage Mfr & Distr
N.A.I.C.S.: 312120
Bruno Gazaniol *(CEO)*

Suntory Allied Ltd. (1)
16th Fl Tradepia Odaiba 2-3-1 Daiba Minato ku, Minato-ku, Tokyo, 135 0091, Japan
Tel.: (81) 355302245
Emp.: 12
Wine & Liquor Distr
N.A.I.C.S.: 445320

The Absolut Company SA (1)
Marieviksgatan 19B, 117 97, Stockholm, Sweden
Tel.: (46) 87447000
Web Site: https://www.theabsolutcompany.com
Sales Range: $150-199.9 Million
Emp.: 500
Spirits Producer & Distr
N.A.I.C.S.: 312140
Krister Asplund *(VP-Manufacturing)*

Subsidiary (US):

The Absolut Spirits Company Inc. (2)

PERNOD RICARD S.A.

Pernod Ricard S.A.—(Continued)

401 Park Ave S, New York, NY 10019
Tel.: (212) 641-8700
Web Site: http://www.absolut.com
Sales Range: $25-49.9 Million
Emp.: 30
Spirits Distr
N.A.I.C.S.: 424820

The Glenlivet Distillers Ltd (1)
Glenlivet Distillery, Ballindalloch, AB37 9DB, Banffshire, United Kingdom
Tel.: (44) 1340 821 720
Web Site: http://www.theglenlivet.com
Emp.: 4
Beverages Mfr
N.A.I.C.S.: 312120
Fadi Bikawi (Gen Mgr)

PERPETUAL EQUITY INVESTMENT COMPANY LIMITED

Level 18 123 Pitt Street, Sydney, 2000, NSW, Australia
Tel.: (61) 292293138
Web Site:
   https://www.perpetualequity.com.au
PIC—(ASX)
Rev.: $29,115,251
Assets: $335,912,792
Liabilities: $13,029,514
Net Worth: $322,883,279
Earnings: $19,067,842
Fiscal Year-end: 06/30/24
Investment Management Service
N.A.I.C.S.: 523940
Sylvie Dimarco (Sec)

Subsidiaries:

United Malt Group Limited (1)
Level 28 175 Liverpool Street, Sydney, 2000, NSW, Australia
Tel.: (61) 280733160
Web Site: http://www.unitedmalt.com
Brewery Product Distr
N.A.I.C.S.: 424810
Mark L. Palmquist (CEO & Mng Dir)

PERPETUAL GLOBAL LIMITED

Level 2 Kalpataru Synergy, Opposite Grand Hyatt Santacruz, Mumbai, 400055, India
Tel.: (91) 22 6193 3333
Web Site: http://www.perpetual-global.com
Sales Range: $10-24.9 Million
Plastic Mfr
N.A.I.C.S.: 326199
Vivek Tandon (Chm)

PERPETUAL INCOME & GROWTH INVESTMENT TRUST PLC

Park Drive, Oxfordshire, Henley-on-Thames, RG9 1HH, United Kingdom
Tel.: (44) 1491417000
Web Site:
   http://www.invescoperpetual.co.uk
Rev.: $54,238,595
Assets: $845,174,054
Liabilities: $130,388,779
Net Worth: $714,785,275
Earnings: ($296,087,142)
Fiscal Year-end: 03/31/19
Investment Management Service
N.A.I.C.S.: 525990
Mark Barnett (Mgr-Fund)

PERPETUAL LIMITED

Angel Place Level 18 123 Pitt Street, Sydney, 2000, NSW, Australia
Tel.: (61) 292299000   AU
Web Site:
   https://www.perpetual.com.au
Year Founded: 1886
PPT—(ASX)
Rev.: $906,450,317
Assets: $2,269,764,948
Liabilities: $1,107,171,470
Net Worth: $1,162,593,478
Earnings: $315,304,486
Emp.: 1,877
Fiscal Year-end: 06/30/24
Holding Company; Financial & Investment Management Services
N.A.I.C.S.: 551112
Anthony Cay (Portfolio Mgr)

Subsidiaries:

Barrow, Hanley, Mewhinney & Strauss, LLC (1)
2200 Ross Ave 31 St Fl, Dallas, TX 75201   (75%)
Tel.: (214) 665-1900
Web Site: https://www.barrowhanley.com
Asset Management
N.A.I.C.S.: 523940
Robert D. Barkley (Mng Dir-Client Dev)

Fordham Business Advisors Pty. Ltd. (1)
Level 29 Rialto South Tower 525 Collins Street, Melbourne, VIC, Australia
Tel.: (61) 396116611
Web Site:
   https://www.fordhamgroup.com.au
Wealth Management Services
N.A.I.C.S.: 523940

Laminar Capital Pty. Ltd. (1)
Level 5 Rialto North 525 Collins Street, Melbourne, VIC, Australia
Tel.: (61) 390016990
Web Site: https://laminarcapital.com.au
Investment Management Service
N.A.I.C.S.: 523940

Pendal Group Limited (1)
Level 14 The Chifley Tower 2 Chifley Square, Sydney, 2000, NSW, Australia
Tel.: (61) 292202000
Web Site: http://www.pendalgroup.com
Rev.: $480,719,865
Assets: $1,319,070,405
Liabilities: $258,485,689
Net Worth: $1,060,584,716
Earnings: $126,193,025
Emp.: 346
Fiscal Year-end: 09/30/2021
Investment Management Service
N.A.I.C.S.: 523940
Emilio Gonzalez (CEO-Grp & Mng Dir)

Subsidiary (Non-US):

JOHCM (Singapore) Pte Limited (2)
138 Market Street 15-04 CapitaGreen, Singapore, 048946, Singapore
Tel.: (65) 65116300
Web Site: https://www.johcm.com
Investment Management Service
N.A.I.C.S.: 523940

Subsidiary (US):

JOHCM (USA) Inc. (2)
53 State St 13th Fl, Boston, MA 02109
Tel.: (857) 444-0633
Web Site: https://www.johcm.com
Investment Management Service
N.A.I.C.S.: 523940

Thompson, Siegel & Walmsley, LLC (2)
6641 W Broad St Ste 600, Richmond, VA 23230   (100%)
Tel.: (804) 353-4500
Web Site: https://www.tswinvest.com
Asset Management
N.A.I.C.S.: 523940
Lori N. Anderson (Dir-Ops)

Perpetual Investment Management Limited (1)
Level 18 123 Pitt St, PO Box 4171, Sydney, 2001, NSW, Australia
Tel.: (61) 292299000
Web Site: http://www.perpetual.com.au
Sales Range: $350-399.9 Million
Emp.: 1,000
Investment Management Service
N.A.I.C.S.: 523940
Rob Lane (CEO)

Perpetual Legal Services Pty Limited (1)
Level 12 123 Pitt Street, Sydney, 2000, NSW, Australia
Tel.: (61) 292299000
Web Site: http://www.perpetual.com.au
Emp.: 2,000
Real Estate Property Lessors
N.A.I.C.S.: 531110
Karen Robinson (Office Mgr)

Perpetual Mortgage Services Pty Limited (1)
Level 12 123 Pitt St, Sydney, 2000, NSW, Australia
Tel.: (61) 398533355
Web Site: http://www.perpetual.com.au
Mortgage Loan Services
N.A.I.C.S.: 522310

Perpetual Nominees Limited (1)
Level 12 Angel Pl, 123 Pitt Rd, Sydney, 2000, New South Wales, Australia
Tel.: (61) 292293345
Web Site: http://www.perpetual.com.au
Trust Management Services
N.A.I.C.S.: 541618

Perpetual Superannuation Ltd (1)
Level 12 123 Pitt Street, Sydney, 2000, NSW, Australia
Tel.: (61) 292299000
Web Site: http://www.perpetual.com.au
Financial Planning Services
N.A.I.C.S.: 523940

Perpetual Trust Services Limited (1)
Level 12 1243 Pitt St, PO Box 4172, Sydney, 2000, NSW, Australia
Tel.: (61) 292299000
Web Site: http://www.perpetual.com.au
Trust Management Services
N.A.I.C.S.: 523940

Perpetual Trustee Company (Canberra) Limited (1)
Ngunnawal Ngambri people Level 9-Nishi Building 2 Phillip Law Street, Canberra, 2601, ACT, Australia
Tel.: (61) 262436500
Web Site: http://www.perpetual.com.au
Emp.: 4
Investment Management Service
N.A.I.C.S.: 523940

Perpetual Trustee Company Limited (1)
Angel Place Level 18 123 Pitt Street, Sydney, 2000, NSW, Australia
Tel.: (61) 292292900
Web Site: http://www.perpetual.com.au
Investment Management Service
N.A.I.C.S.: 523940

Perpetual Trustees Queensland Limited (1)
Central Plaza 1 Level 15 345 Queen Street, Brisbane, 4000, QLD, Australia
Tel.: (61) 73 834 5656
Web Site: https://www.perpetual.com.au
Sales Range: $50-74.9 Million
Emp.: 20
Investment Management Service
N.A.I.C.S.: 523940

Perpetual Trustees Victoria Limited (1)
Rialto South Tower Level 28 and 29 525 Collins Street, Melbourne, 3000, VIC, Australia
Tel.: (61) 38 628 0400
Web Site: https://www.perpetual.com.au
Sales Range: $100-124.9 Million
Emp.: 160
Investment Management Service
N.A.I.C.S.: 523940

Perpetual Trustees WA Limited (1)
Exchange Tower Level 29 2 The Esplanade, Perth, 6000, WA, Australia
Tel.: (61) 89 224 4400
Web Site: https://www.perpetual.com.au
Sales Range: $50-74.9 Million
Emp.: 50
Investment Management Service
N.A.I.C.S.: 523940

Trillium Asset Management UK Limited (1)
93 George Street, Edinburgh, United Kingdom
Tel.: (44) 1313767426

INTERNATIONAL PUBLIC

Web Site:
   https://www.trilliumassetmanagement.co.uk
Investment Financing Services
N.A.I.C.S.: 523940

Trillium Asset Management, LLC (1)
60 S St Ste 1100, Boston, MA 02111
Tel.: (617) 423-6655
Web Site: https://www.trilliuminvest.com
Rev.: $9,130,000
Emp.: 22
Portfolio Management
N.A.I.C.S.: 523940
Matthew W. Patsky (CEO)

PERPETUAL RESOURCES LIMITED

2/68 Hay St, Subiaco, 2008, WA, Australia
Tel.: (61) 862565390   AU
Web Site:
   https://www.perpetualresources.co
PEC—(ASX)
Rev.: $41,127
Assets: $1,815,354
Liabilities: $328,789
Net Worth: $1,486,565
Earnings: ($3,631,249)
Fiscal Year-end: 06/30/24
Coal Mining
N.A.I.C.S.: 212115
George Karafotias (Sec)

PERRIGO COMPANY PLC

The Sharp Building Hogan Place, Dublin, 2, Ireland
Tel.: (353) 17094000   IE
Web Site: http://www.perrigo.com
PRGO—(NYSE)
Rev.: $4,655,600,000
Assets: $10,809,100,000
Liabilities: $6,041,200,000
Net Worth: $4,767,900,000
Earnings: ($12,700,000)
Emp.: 9,140
Fiscal Year-end: 12/31/23
Holding Company; Drug Mfr & Distr
N.A.I.C.S.: 551112
Sharon Kochan (Pres-RX Pharmaceuticals)

Subsidiaries:

Adriatic BST Trgovina in Storitve D.o.o. (1)
Verovskova Ulica 55, 1000, Ljubljana, Slovenia
Tel.: (386) 59077100
Pharmaceutical Preparation Drug Distr
N.A.I.C.S.: 424210

Biover NV (1)
Venecoweg 26, 9810, Nazareth, Belgium
Tel.: (32) 93810200
Web Site: http://www.biover.pt
Pharmaceuticals Product Mfr
N.A.I.C.S.: 325412

Cinetic Laboratories Argentina SA (1)
Av Triunvirato 2734/36, C1427AAN, Buenos Aires, Argentina
Tel.: (54) 1145526260
Web Site: http://www.cineticlab.com
Pharmaceuticals Product Mfr
N.A.I.C.S.: 325412

Cosmediet - Biotechnie SAS (1)
470 avenue de Lossburg, 69480, Anse, France
Tel.: (33) 474099700
Web Site: https://www.cosmediet.fr
Pharmaceuticals Product Mfr
N.A.I.C.S.: 325412

Dr. Fresh, LLC (1)
6 Centerpointe Dr Ste 640, La Palma, CA 90623
Tel.: (714) 690-1573
Web Site: http://www.drfresh.com
Oral Care Product Mfr
N.A.I.C.S.: 339114

Elan Pharma International Limited (1)

AND PRIVATE COMPANIES — PERRIGO COMPANY PLC

Treasury Building Grand Canal Street Lower, Dublin, 2, Ireland **(100%)**
Tel.: (353) 17094000
Therapeutic Products Mfr & Distr
N.A.I.C.S.: 325412

Geiss, Destin & Dunn, Inc. (1)
725 Hwy 74 S, Peachtree City, GA 30269
Tel.: (770) 486-0381
Web Site: https://www.perrigodirect.com
Health & Personal Care Products Distr
N.A.I.C.S.: 456199
Chris Calloway *(Gen Mgr & Dir)*

Gelcaps Exportadora de Mexico, S.A. de C.V. (1)
Torre Polanco Mariano Escobedo 476 piso 14 Oficina 1401, Col Nueva Anzures, Mexico, 11590, Mexico
Tel.: (52) 5553402230
Web Site: http://www.gelcaps.com.mx
Pharmaceuticals Product Mfr
N.A.I.C.S.: 325412

Interdelta S.A. (1)
Route Andre-Piller 21, PO Box 71, 1762, Givisiez, Switzerland
Tel.: (41) 264697500
Web Site: http://www.interdelta.ch
Pharmaceutical Products Distr
N.A.I.C.S.: 424210
Christian Egger *(Mgr-Sls & HR)*

Laboratoire de la Mer SAS (1)
ZAC de la Madeleine Avenue du General Patton, 35400, Saint-Malo, France
Tel.: (33) 299215370
Web Site: https://www.laboratoiredelamer.com
Pharmaceuticals Product Mfr
N.A.I.C.S.: 325412

Laboratoires Omega Pharma France SAS (1)
20 Rue Andre Gide BP 80, 92321, Chatillon, Cedex, France
Tel.: (33) 155481800
Pharmaceutical Preparation Drug Distr
N.A.I.C.S.: 424210

Medgenix Benelux NV (1)
Vliegveld 21, 8560, Wevelgem, Belgium
Tel.: (32) 56426711
Web Site: https://www.medgenix.be
Pharmaceutical Products Distr
N.A.I.C.S.: 424210

Oce Bio BVBA (1)
Nijverheidsstraat 96, Wommelgem, 2160, Belgium
Tel.: (32) 33662121
Pharmaceutical Preparation Drug Distr
N.A.I.C.S.: 424210

Omega Pharma Austria Healthcare GmbH (1)
Rennweg 17, 1030, Vienna, Austria
Tel.: (43) 171201360
Pharmaceuticals Product Mfr
N.A.I.C.S.: 325412

Omega Pharma Hungary Kft. (1)
Madarasz u 47-49, 1138, Budapest, Hungary
Tel.: (36) 19201570
Pharmaceuticals Product Mfr
N.A.I.C.S.: 325412

Omega Pharma Kisisel Bakim Urunleri Sanayi VE Ticaret Limited Sirketi (1)
Merdivenkoy Mah Bora Sok No 1A Office Block 5th Floor Nida Kule, Goztepe, 34732, Istanbul, Turkiye
Tel.: (90) 2162507500
Pharmaceutical Preparation Drug Distr
N.A.I.C.S.: 424210

Omega Pharma Limited (1)
32 Vauxhall Bridge Road, London, SW1V 2SA, United Kingdom
Tel.: (44) 2035989601
Pharmaceutical Products Distr
N.A.I.C.S.: 424210

Omega Pharma Luxembourg SarL (1)
16 Zone D Activite Zare Ilot Ouest Esch-sur-alzette, 4384, Mondercange, Luxembourg
Tel.: (352) 26551741
Pharmaceutical Preparation Drug Distr
N.A.I.C.S.: 424210

Omega Pharma Manufacturing GmbH & Co. KG (1)
Benzstr 25, 71083, Herrenberg, Germany
Tel.: (49) 70329220
Pharmaceutical Preparation Drug Distr
N.A.I.C.S.: 424210

Omega Pharma Poland Sp.z.o.o. (1)
Al Niepodleglosci 18 BTD Office Center 2 Pietro, 02-653, Warsaw, Poland
Tel.: (48) 224895451
Web Site: http://www.omega-pharma.pl
Pharmaceuticals Product Mfr
N.A.I.C.S.: 325412

Perrigo Company (1)
515 Eastern Ave, Allegan, MI 49010
Tel.: (269) 673-8451
Web Site: http://www.perrigo.com
Rev.: $3,539,800,000
Assets: $5,350,800,000
Liabilities: $3,018,200,000
Net Worth: $2,332,600,000
Earnings: $441,900,000
Emp.: 9,900
Fiscal Year-end: 06/29/2013
Pharmaceutical & Nutritional Product Mfr
N.A.I.C.S.: 325412

Subsidiary (Domestic):

L. Perrigo Company (2)
515 Eastern Ave, Allegan, MI 49010
Tel.: (269) 673-8451
Web Site: http://www.perrigo.com
Over-The-Counter Pharmaceuticals Mfr
N.A.I.C.S.: 325412

Subsidiary (Non-US):

Omega Pharma NV (2)
Industrial Zoning De Prijkels, Venecoweg 26, 9810, Nazareth, Belgium
Tel.: (32) 93810481
Web Site: http://www.omega-pharma.com
Emp.: 2,500
Pharmaceuticals, Cosmetics & Dietetic Products Mfr & Whslr
N.A.I.C.S.: 325412

Subsidiary (Non-US):

Bional Nederland BV (3)
Postbus 25258, 3001 HG, Rotterdam, Netherlands
Tel.: (31) 8000202020
Web Site: https://www.bional.nl
Emp.: 50
Health & Personal Care Product Mfr
N.A.I.C.S.: 325412

Omega Pharma Deutschland GmbH (3)
Benzstr 25, 71083, Herrenberg, Germany
Tel.: (49) 7032 9154 200
Web Site: http://www.omega-pharma.de
Non-Prescription Drugs & Home Diagnostics Distr
N.A.I.C.S.: 424210
Stephan Tomat *(Mng Dir)*

Omega Pharma Espana SA (3)
Pz Xavier Cugat 2 Ed D Pl 1, Sant Cugat del Valles, 08174, Barcelona, Spain
Tel.: (34) 902 88 90 10
Web Site: http://www.omegapharma.es
Non-Prescription Drugs & Home Diagnostics Marketer
N.A.I.C.S.: 424210

Omega Pharma Holding (Nederland) B.V. (3)
Kralingseweg 201, 3062 CE, Rotterdam, Netherlands
Tel.: (31) 102211000
Web Site: http://www.omega-pharma.nl
Emp.: 50
Holding Company; Pharmaceutical Products Mfr
N.A.I.C.S.: 551112

Omega Pharma Nederland B.V. (3)
Kralingseweg 201 Gebouw Taxus, 3062 CE, Rotterdam, Netherlands
Tel.: (31) 10 22 11 000
Web Site: http://www.omega-pharma.nl
Emp.: 55
Pharmaceuticals Mfr
N.A.I.C.S.: 325412
Joost Hunfeld *(Gen Mgr)*

Samenwerkende Apothekers Nederland BV (3)
Postbus 6612, 3002 AP, Rotterdam, Netherlands
Tel.: (31) 10 2211080
Web Site: http://www.samenwerkendeapothekers.nl
Over-The-Counter Pharmaceuticals Mfr
N.A.I.C.S.: 325412

Subsidiary (Non-US):

Orion Laboratories (NZ) Ltd. (2)
Whangaparaoa, PO Box 781, Auckland, 0943, New Zealand
Tel.: (64) 94243102
Pharmaceutical Products Distr
N.A.I.C.S.: 424210
Shane Byrne *(Mng Dir)*

Orion Laboratories PTY Limited (2)
25-29 Delawney St, Balcatta, 6021, WA, Australia
Tel.: (61) 1800805546
Web Site: http://www.perrigo.com.au
Emp.: 100
Pharmaceuticals & Nutritional Products Mfr
N.A.I.C.S.: 325412

Subsidiary (Domestic):

P2C, Inc. (2)
515 Eastern Ave, Allegan, MI 49010
Tel.: (269) 673-8451
Pharmaceutical Sales
N.A.I.C.S.: 424210

PBM Nutritionals, LLC (2)
147 Industrial Park Rd, Georgia, VT 05468
Tel.: (802) 527-0521
Web Site: http://www.perrigonutritionals.com
Emp.: 300
Infant Formula & Pediatric Nutritional Products Mfr & Distr
N.A.I.C.S.: 311999

PBM Products, LLC (2)
652 Peter Jefferson Pkwy Ste 300, Charlottesville, VA 22911
Tel.: (434) 297-1070
Nutritional Healthcare Product Mfr
N.A.I.C.S.: 325412

Paddock Laboratories, LLC (2)
3940 Quebec Ave N, Minneapolis, MN 55427-9841
Tel.: (763) 546-4676
Sales Range: $50-74.9 Million
Emp.: 200
Researches, Develops & Manufactures Generic Prescription & Over-The-Counter Specialty Products
N.A.I.C.S.: 325412
Joseph C. Papa *(Chm & CEO)*

Perrigo Company of South Carolina, Inc. (2)
4615 Dairy Dr, Greenville, SC 29607-3792 **(100%)**
Tel.: (864) 288-5521
Sales Range: $200-249.9 Million
Emp.: 400
Vitamins & Nutritional Products Mfr
N.A.I.C.S.: 325412
Rod Hochmuth *(VP)*

Perrigo International, Inc. (2)
515 Eastern Ave, Allegan, MI 49010
Tel.: (269) 673-8451
Pharmaceutical Products Distr
N.A.I.C.S.: 424210

Subsidiary (Non-US):

Perrigo Israel Agencies Ltd. (2)
29 Lechi, 51200, Bnei Brak, Israel
Tel.: (972) 35773700
Sales Range: $300-349.9 Million
Emp.: 1,000
Pharmaceutical & Nutritional Healthcare Product Mfr & Distr
N.A.I.C.S.: 325412

Perrigo Israel Pharmaceuticals Ltd. (2)
29 Lehi Street, 51200, Bnei Brak, Israel
Tel.: (972) 35773700

Emp.: 450
Pharmaceuticals Developer & Mfr
N.A.I.C.S.: 325412
Shlomi Leibovitch *(VP & Head-Pharmaceutical Div)*

Subsidiary (Domestic):

Perrigo New York, Inc. (2)
Bathgate Industrial Park 1700 Bathgate Ave, Bronx, NY 10457
Tel.: (718) 901-2800
Emp.: 500
Generic Pharmaceuticals & Cosmetic Products Mfr
N.A.I.C.S.: 325412
Nesseem Awad *(Dir-Quality)*

Perrigo Pharmaceuticals Company (2)
515 Eastern Ave, Allegan, MI 49010-9070
Tel.: (269) 673-8451
Pharmaceuticals & Nutritional Products Mfr
N.A.I.C.S.: 325412

Perrigo Research & Development Company (2)
515 Eastern Ave, Allegan, MI 49010
Tel.: (269) 673-8451
Sales Range: $200-249.9 Million
Research & Development of Pharmaceuticals & Nutritionals
N.A.I.C.S.: 325412
Bruce D. Johnson *(VP-R&D-Consumer Health Care)*

Perrigo Sales Corporation (2)
515 Eastern Ave, Allegan, MI 49010
Tel.: (269) 673-8451
Sales Range: $1-4.9 Billion
Emp.: 3,000
Sales of Private Label OTC Pharmaceuticals & Nutritionals
N.A.I.C.S.: 424210
Amy Buzzell *(Mgr-Sls Ops)*

Subsidiary (Non-US):

Perrigo UK Acquisition Limited (2)
Wrafton, Braunton, EX33 2DL, Devon, United Kingdom
Tel.: (44) 1271815815
Investment Management Service
N.A.I.C.S.: 523940

Perrigo de Mexico S.A. de C.V. (2)
Calle Industria Automotriz, 25900, Ramos Arizpe, Coahuila, Mexico
Tel.: (52) 844 488 3646
Web Site: http://www.perrigo.com.mx
Private label OTC Pharmaceuticals & Nutritionals Mfr
N.A.I.C.S.: 325412

Quimica y Farmacia S.A. de C.V. (2)
Autopista Saltillo Monterrey Km 11 5 Colonia, Capellania subdivision, Ramos Arizpe, Coahuila, Mexico **(100%)**
Tel.: (52) 8444383900
Web Site: https://www.quifa.com.mx
Sales Range: $50-74.9 Million
Emp.: 150
Mfr & Distr of Generic & Over-the-Counter Pharmaceuticals
N.A.I.C.S.: 325412

Wrafton Laboratories Limited (2)
Wrafton, Braunton, EX33 2DL, Devon, United Kingdom **(100%)**
Tel.: (44) 1271 815 815
Web Site: http://www.perrigouk.co.uk
Emp.: 600
Contract Manufacturing Services for Over-the-Counter & Prescription Medicines
N.A.I.C.S.: 325412

Perrigo Norge AS (1)
Nydalsveien 36 B, 0484, Oslo, Norway
Tel.: (47) 23007040
Web Site: https://www.perrigo.no
Pharmaceutical Products Distr
N.A.I.C.S.: 424210

Ranir, LLC (1)
4701 E Paris Ave SE, Grand Rapids, MI 49512
Tel.: (616) 698-8880
Web Site: http://www.ranir.com
Oral Care Products Mfr & Marketer
N.A.I.C.S.: 339114
Rich Sorota *(Pres & CEO)*

PERRIGO COMPANY PLC

Perrigo Company plc—(Continued)

Subsidiary (Non-US):

Ranir GmbH (2)
Auf dem Seidenberg 1, 53721, Siegburg, Germany
Tel.: (49) 2241252200
Web Site: https://www.ranir.com
Sales Range: $10-24.9 Million
Emp.: 10
Oral Product Mfr
N.A.I.C.S.: 339114
Andreas Lanvers (Gen Mgr)

Plant (Domestic):

Ranir GmbH - Schonau im Schwarzwald (3)
Oberfeldstrasse 1-5, Schonau im Schwarzwald, 79677, Germany
Tel.: (49) 7673 829 0
Web Site: http://www.ranir.com
Sales Range: $10-24.9 Million
Emp.: 100
Dental Product Mfr
N.A.I.C.S.: 339114

Richard Bittner AG (1)
Reisnerstrasse 55-57, 1030, Vienna, Austria
Tel.: (43) 427637888
Pharmaceutical Preparation Drug Distr
N.A.I.C.S.: 424210

PERROT DUVAL HOLDING S.A.

Rue de Candolle 16, 1205, Geneva, Switzerland
Tel.: (41) 227766144
Web Site:
 https://www.perrotduval.com
Year Founded: 1896
PEDU—(SWX)
Rev.: $18,455,654
Assets: $23,990,022
Liabilities: $8,889,135
Net Worth: $15,100,887
Earnings: ($1,980,044)
Emp.: 233
Fiscal Year-end: 04/30/23
Holding Company; Financial Services
N.A.I.C.S.: 551112
Nicolas Eichenberger (Chm)

Subsidiaries:

Fuell Engineering B.V. (1)
Frankweg 65, 2153 PD, Nieuw-Vennep, Netherlands
Tel.: (31) 252222012
Web Site: http://fuell-dispensing.com
Sales Range: $50-74.9 Million
Emp.: 5
Printing Inks Mfr & Sales
N.A.I.C.S.: 325910

Fuell Systembau GmbH (1)
Richard-Klinger-Strasse 31, 65510, Idstein, Germany
Tel.: (49) 61265980
Web Site: http://www.fuell-dispensing.com
Sales Range: $25-49.9 Million
Emp.: 30
Automated Storage & Dispensing Systems Mfr
N.A.I.C.S.: 333248
Uwe Fuell (Mng Dir)

Full Lab Automation GmbH (1)
Riedstrasse 25, 73760, Ostfildern, Germany
Tel.: (49) 71144706680 0
Web Site: https://fuell-labautomation.com
Automation Machinery Mfr
N.A.I.C.S.: 333998

Full Systembau GmbH (1)
Richard-Klinger-Strasse 31, D-65510, Idstein, Germany
Tel.: (49) 61265980
Web Site: https://fuell-dispensing.com
Dispensing Plant Mfr
N.A.I.C.S.: 333914

Infranor Inter AG (1)
Glatttalstrasse 37, CH-8052, Zurich, Switzerland (78%)
Tel.: (41) 44 308 500

Web Site: http://www.infranor.com
Sales Range: Less than $1 Million
Emp.: 208
Industrial Machinery & Plant & Automation Equipment Mfr, Sales & Service
N.A.I.C.S.: 333248

Subsidiary (Domestic):

Cybelec SA (2)
Rue des Uttins 27, 1401, Yverdon-les-Bains, Switzerland
Tel.: (41) 244470200
Web Site: http://www.cybelec.ch
Emp.: 70
Metal Forming Machine Controls Developer, Mfr & Sales
N.A.I.C.S.: 333517

Subsidiary (Non-US):

CYBELEC Numerical Control Technology (Shanghai) (3)
Room B 4-1 Forward Hi-tech Zone, 33 Forward Rd, Shanghai, 201818, Jiading, China
Tel.: (86) 2159900200
Sales Range: $25-49.9 Million
Emp.: 3
Metal Forming Machine Controls Sales & Services
N.A.I.C.S.: 334513

Cybelec Srl (3)
Via Cesare Cantu 29, I-20092, Milan, Cinisello Banlsamo, Italy
Tel.: (39) 0220480897
Web Site: http://www.cybelec.it
Sales Range: $25-49.9 Million
Emp.: 4
Metal Forming Machine Controls Sales & Services
N.A.I.C.S.: 334513

Cynum Industrie SA (3)
3 Avenue Louis Delage, F-91301, Linas, France
Tel.: (33) 1 69 63 94 24
Sales Range: $50-74.9 Million
Emp.: 1
Metal Forming Machine Controls Sales & Services
N.A.I.C.S.: 423830

Subsidiary (Non-US):

Infranor B.V. (2)
Albert Einsteinstraat 6, NL-3261 LP, Oud-Beijerland, Netherlands
Tel.: (31) 186610155
Web Site: http://www.infranor.nl
Industrial Machinery, Plant & Equipment Automation Mfr, Engineering, Sales & Services
N.A.I.C.S.: 333248

Infranor Electronics SAS (2)
Avenue Jean Moulin, F-65104, Lourdes, Cedex, France
Tel.: (33) 562941067
Web Site: http://www.infranor.com
Intelligent Drives Developer, Mfr & Sales
N.A.I.C.S.: 333612

Infranor GmbH (2)
Donaustrasse 19a, 63452, Hanau, Germany
Tel.: (49) 6181180120
Web Site: http://www.de.infranor.com
Emp.: 5
Industrial Machinery, Plant & Equipment Automation Mfr, Engineering, Sales & Services
N.A.I.C.S.: 333248
Judith Frank (Mgr-Comml)

Infranor GmbH (2)
Wolfener Str 32-34, 12681, Berlin, Germany
Tel.: (49) 306139080
Web Site: http://www.infranor.com
Intelligent Drives Developer, Mfr & Sales
N.A.I.C.S.: 333612

Infranor Ltd. (2)
Building 720 Bentwaters Business Park, Rendlesham, IP12 2TW, Suffolk, United Kingdom
Tel.: (44) 2081442152
Web Site: http://uk.infranor.com
Industrial Machinery, Plant & Equipment Automation Mfr, Engineering, Sales & Services

N.A.I.C.S.: 333248
Adrian Hazelwood (Mng Dir)

Subsidiary (Domestic):

Infranor SA (2)
Althardstrasse 158, 8105, Regensdorf, Switzerland
Tel.: (41) 443085000
Web Site: http://www.ch.infranor.com
Industrial Machinery, Plant & Equipment Automation Mfr, Engineering, Sales & Services
N.A.I.C.S.: 333248
Raymond Kaser (Gen Mgr)

Subsidiary (Non-US):

Infranor SA (2)
Occitania 24, 08911, Badalona, Spain
Tel.: (34) 934601631
Web Site: http://es.infranor.com
Emp.: 20
Industrial Machinery, Plant & Equipment Automation Mfr, Engineering, Sales & Services
N.A.I.C.S.: 333248

Infranor SAS (2)
Immeuble Newton Silic 8 1 rue Georges Besse, 92160, Antony, France
Tel.: (33) 156451600
Web Site: http://fr.infranor.com
Industrial Machinery, Plant & Equipment Automation Mfr, Engineering, Sales & Services
N.A.I.C.S.: 333248

Subsidiary (US):

Infranor, Inc. (2)
299 Ballardvale St Ste 4, Wilmington, MA 01887
Tel.: (978) 988-9002
Web Site: https://www.infranorusa.com
Industrial Machinery, Plant & Equipment Automation & Metal Forming Machine Controls Mfr, Engineering, Sales & Services
N.A.I.C.S.: 333248
Daniel D'Aquila (Mng Dir)

Subsidiary (Non-US):

Mavilor Motors SA (2)
Pol Ind Can Bernades - Subira C/ Emporda 11-13, Santa Perpetua de Mogoda, 08130, Barcelona, Spain
Tel.: (34) 935743690
Web Site: http://www.mavilor.es
Emp.: 60
AC, DC & Generators Developer, Mfr & Sales
N.A.I.C.S.: 335311

Perrot Duval Management S.A (1)
Place de la Gare 5, 1296, Coppet, Vaud, Switzerland
Tel.: (41) 227766144
Sales Range: $25-49.9 Million
Emp.: 2
Business Management Services
N.A.I.C.S.: 561110
Nicolas Eichenberger (Mgr)

PERROTT ENGINEERING GROUP LTD.

Woodroyde, Sutcliffe Wood Lane, Halifax, HX3 8PS, West Yorkshire, United Kingdom
Tel.: (44) 1422 202575 UK
Year Founded: 1963
Holding Company
N.A.I.C.S.: 551112
Graham Perrott (Chm)

Subsidiaries:

Clean Air Limited (1)
Mill Street Farnworth, Dunscar, Bolton, BL4 7BH, Lancashire, United Kingdom
Tel.: (44) 1204572900
Web Site: www.cleanairltd.co.uk
Sales Range: $1-9.9 Million
Emp.: 25
Design & Installation of Fume Extraction System Mfr
N.A.I.C.S.: 333413
Will Perrott (Mng Dir)

INTERNATIONAL PUBLIC

PERSEUS FINTECH SA

17 Carbunarilor Str 1st District, 013988, Bucharest, Romania
Tel.: (40) 213110087
Web Site:
 https://www.perseusfintech.com
PVBS—(BUC)
Rev.: $473,638
Assets: $1,226,033
Liabilities: $463,266
Net Worth: $762,767
Earnings: $232,306
Emp.: 41
Fiscal Year-end: 12/31/23
Business & Management Consulting Services
N.A.I.C.S.: 541611
Federico Salmoiraghi (Pres & Gen Mgr)

PERSEUS MINING LIMITED

Level 2 437 Roberts Road, Subiaco, 6008, WA, Australia
Tel.: (61) 861441700 AU
Web Site:
 https://www.perseusmining.com
Year Founded: 2003
P4Q—(DEU)
Rev.: $862,382,856
Assets: $1,523,712,859
Liabilities: $265,508,587
Net Worth: $1,258,204,272
Earnings: $214,472,671
Fiscal Year-end: 06/30/22
Gold Ore & Silver Ore Mining
N.A.I.C.S.: 212220
Terence Sean Harvey (Chm)

Subsidiaries:

Occidental Gold Sarl (1)
Deux Plateaux Vallon A l'intersection des rues J75 et J44, BP 571, Lot 1438 ilot 145 28, 28, Abidjan, Cote d'Ivoire
Tel.: (225) 22419126
Web Site: http://www.perseusmining.com
Sales Range: $50-74.9 Million
Emp.: 50
Gold Exploration Services
N.A.I.C.S.: 212220

Orca Gold, Inc. (1)
885 West Georgia Street Suite 2000, Vancouver, V6C 3E8, BC, Canada
Tel.: (604) 689-7842
Mineral Exploration Services
N.A.I.C.S.: 212390

Perseus Mining Cote d'Ivoire SA (1)
Deux Plateaux Vallon A l'intersection Des Rues J75 et J44 Lot 1438, BP 571, Ilot 145 28, Abidjan, Cote d'Ivoire
Tel.: (225) 2 241 9126
Gold Mining & Exploration Services
N.A.I.C.S.: 212220

PERSEUS PROTEOMICS INC.

3F A I Nihombashi EAST 30-1 Nihombashi Hakozakicho, Chuo-ku, Tokyo, 103-0015, Japan
Tel.: (81) 362648268
Web Site: https://www.ppmx.com
Year Founded: 2001
4882—(TKS)
Emp.: 21
Biotechnology Research & Development Services
N.A.I.C.S.: 541714

PERSEUS SPECIALTY FOOD PRODUCTS S.A.

Vocha Corinthia, 200 01, Zevgolatio, Greece
Tel.: (30) 27410 58300 GR
Web Site:
 http://www.perseusgroup.gr
Year Founded: 1968
Food Products Mfr
N.A.I.C.S.: 311999

AND PRIVATE COMPANIES

PERSHING SQUARE HOLDINGS, LTD.
Northern Trust International, PO Box 255, Trafalgar Court Les Banques, Saint Peter Port, GY1 3QL, Guernsey
Tel.: (44) 1481745001 GY
Web Site:
http://www.pershingsquare.com
PSH—(EUR)
Rev.: $202,833,597
Assets: $15,128,600,308
Liabilities: $3,065,993,281
Net Worth: $12,062,607,027
Earnings: $2,486,054,201
Fiscal Year-end: 12/31/23
Law firm
N.A.I.C.S.: 541110
William Albert Ackman *(CEO & Portfolio Mgr)*

PERSIAN GULF FAJR ENERGY COMPANY
Imam Khomeini Port-Site 2-Petzone, PO Box 117, 63571 76349, Tehran, Iran
Tel.: (98) 6152121544
Web Site: https://www.fepg.ir
Year Founded: 1998
Eletric Power Generation Services
N.A.I.C.S.: 221112

PERSIAN GULF PETROCHEMICAL INDUSTRY COMMERCIAL COMPANY
No 38 Karimkhan Zand Blvd Haft Tir Sq, Tehran, Iran
Tel.: (98) 2143349000
Web Site: http://www.pgpicc.com
PKLJ1—(THE)
Sales Range: Less than $1 Million
Petrochemical Mfr
N.A.I.C.S.: 325110
Jafar Rabiee *(Vice Chm & CEO)*

Subsidiaries:

Arvand Petrochemical Company (1)
9 th floor No 46 Karim khan-e-Zand Blvd Hafte-e-Tir Sq, 1584893117, Tehran, Iran
Tel.: (98) 2188310653
Web Site: http://www.arvandpvc.ir
Petrochemical Products Mfr
N.A.I.C.S.: 325110

Karoon Petrochemical Co. (1)
No 17 Shahid Khalilzadeh Ally Vanak Sq Valiasr St, 1965754351, Tehran, Iran
Tel.: (98) 2188786992
Web Site: http://www.krnpc.ir
Polyurethane Product Mfr & Distr
N.A.I.C.S.: 326150

Khouzestan Petrochemical Co. (1)
Site 4 Petrochemical Special Economic Zone, 6356178776, Ahvaz, Khouzestan, Iran
Tel.: (98) 6152170201
Web Site: http://www.kzpc.ir
Petrochemical Products Mfr
N.A.I.C.S.: 325110
Manouchehr Tavakol *(Gen Mgr)*

Mehr Petrochemical Co. (1)
1st floor No 22 5th St Khaled Eslamboli Vozara Ave, 1513643911, Tehran, Iran
Tel.: (98) 21885547845
Web Site: http://www.mehrpc.com
Petrochemical Products Mfr
N.A.I.C.S.: 325110

Nouri Petrochemical Co. (1)
Pars Special Economic Energy Zone, Post Box 75391-115, 7511811366, Asaluyeh, Bushehr, Iran
Tel.: (98) 77373232504
Web Site: http://www.bpciran.com
Emp.: 1,300
Petrochemical Products Mfr
N.A.I.C.S.: 325110

Pars Petrochemical Co. (1)
No 52 Pardis St North Shiraz St Molla Sadra St, PO Box 163-75391, 1137075118, Tehran, Iran
Tel.: (98) 88034126021
Web Site: http://www.parspc.net
Oil & Gas Operation Services
N.A.I.C.S.: 213112

PERSIMMON PLC
Persimmon House Fulford, York, YO19 4FE, United Kingdom
Tel.: (44) 1904642199
Web Site:
http://www.persimmonhomes.com
Year Founded: 1972
PSN—(OTCIQ)
Rev.: $3,008,376,720
Assets: $3,968,884,440
Liabilities: $1,257,340,320
Net Worth: $2,711,544,120
Earnings: $442,292,400
Emp.: 5,862
Fiscal Year-end: 12/31/22
Home Design & Construction Services
N.A.I.C.S.: 236115
Michael Hugh Killoran *(Dir-Grp Fin)*

Subsidiaries:

Abbot Walk (Chatteris) Residents Management Company Limited (1)
Abbot Walk Doddington Road, Chatteris, PE16 6UA, Cambridgeshire, United Kingdom
Tel.: (44) 1354700633
House Construction & Design Services
N.A.I.C.S.: 532412

Agusta Park Yeovil Management Company Limited (1)
Tel.: (44) 1935319565
Residential Building Construction Services
N.A.I.C.S.: 236117

Avalon (Mansfield) Management Company Limited (1)
Fountain House Southwell Road West, Mansfield, NG18 4LE, Nottinghamshire, United Kingdom
Tel.: (44) 1623703364
Residential Building Construction Services
N.A.I.C.S.: 236117

Aykley Woods (Durham) Management Company Limited (1)
Aykley Heads, Durham, DH1 5TT, United Kingdom
Tel.: (44) 1913385420
Residential Building Construction Services
N.A.I.C.S.: 236117

Backbridge (Malmesbury) Management Company Limited (1)
Backbridge Farm Sillars Green Tetbury Road, Malmesbury, SN16 0FA, Wiltshire, United Kingdom
Tel.: (44) 1666337953
House Construction & Design Services
N.A.I.C.S.: 532412

Bishops Mead (Lydney) Management Company Limited (1)
Par Four Lane, Lydney, GL15 5GB, Gloucestershire, United Kingdom
Tel.: (44) 1594800592
Residential Building Construction Services
N.A.I.C.S.: 236117

Bootham Crescent (York) Residents Management Company Limited (1)
Bootham Crescent, York, YO30 7AQ, North Yorkshire, United Kingdom
Tel.: (44) 1904233953
House Construction & Design Services
N.A.I.C.S.: 532412

Bradley Barton View Management Company Limited (1)
Bradley Barton Avenue Emblett Drive, Newton Abbot, TQ12 1YJ, Devon, United Kingdom
Tel.: (44) 1626242632
House Construction & Design Services
N.A.I.C.S.: 532412

Bramble Rise (Hetton) Management Company Limited (1)
North Road, Hetton-le-Hole, Houghton le Spring, DH5 9JY, Durham, United Kingdom
Tel.: (44) 1919170529
Residential Building Construction Services
N.A.I.C.S.: 236117

Branshaw Park (Keighley) Management Company Limited (1)
Camborne Way, Oakworth, Keighley, BD22 7LB, West Yorkshire, United Kingdom
Tel.: (44) 1535280430
Residential Building Construction Services
N.A.I.C.S.: 236117

Brindle Park (Bamber Bridge) Management Company Limited (1)
Brindle Park Brindle Road, Bamber Bridge, Preston, PR5 6YL, Lancashire, United Kingdom
Tel.: (44) 1772348171
House Construction & Design Services
N.A.I.C.S.: 532412

Buttercup Leys (Boulton Moor) Residential Management Company Limited (1)
Snelsmoor Lane, Boulton Moor, Derby, DE24 5AR, Derbyshire, United Kingdom
Tel.: (44) 3309124590
Residential Building Construction Services
N.A.I.C.S.: 236117

Calder Grange (Dewsbury) Management Company Limited (1)
Rumble Road, Dewsbury, WF12 7LR, West Yorkshire, United Kingdom
Tel.: (44) 1924664299
Residential Building Construction Services
N.A.I.C.S.: 236117

Castle Park (West Durrington) Management Company Limited (1)
Castle Park West Durrington Sunflower Street, West Durrington, Worthing, BN13 3FP, West Sussex, United Kingdom
Tel.: (44) 1903254834
House Construction & Design Services
N.A.I.C.S.: 532412

Castle View (Netherton) Management Company Limited (1)
Castle View Netherton Moor Road, Netherton, HD4 7LE, West Yorkshire, United Kingdom
Tel.: (44) 1484796243
House Construction & Design Services
N.A.I.C.S.: 532412

Cayton Meadows (Scarborough) Management Company Limited (1)
Church Lane, Cayton, Scarborough, YO11 3SA, North Yorkshire, United Kingdom
Tel.: (44) 1723336934
Residential Building Construction Services
N.A.I.C.S.: 236117

Chancery Park (Exning) Residents Management Company Limited (1)
Chancery Park Burwell Road, Exning, CB8 7EY, Suffolk, United Kingdom
Tel.: (44) 1638596803
House Construction & Design Services
N.A.I.C.S.: 532412

Charles Church Essex Limited (1)
Persimmon House Gershwin Boulevard Drury Road, Witham, CM8 1FQ, Essex, United Kingdom
Tel.: (44) 1376518811
Residential Building Construction Services
N.A.I.C.S.: 236117
Richard Hush *(Mng Dir)*

Charles Church London Limited (1)
Vanwall Business Park 2 Vanwall Road, Maidenhead, SL6 4UB, Berkshire, United Kingdom
Tel.: (44) 1628502800
Residential Building Construction Services
N.A.I.C.S.: 236117
Karl Endersby *(Mng Dir)*

Charles Church Thames Valley Limited (1)
Persimmon House Knoll Road, Camberley, GU15 3TQ, Surrey, United Kingdom
Tel.: (44) 1276808080
Residential Building Construction Services
N.A.I.C.S.: 236117
Dan Castle *(Mng Dir)*

Chaucers Meadow (North Petherton) Management Company Limited (1)

PERSIMMON PLC

Chaucers Meadow Taunton Road, North Petherton, Bridgwater, TA6 6NW, Somerset, United Kingdom
Tel.: (44) 1278554351
House Construction & Design Services
N.A.I.C.S.: 532412

Coastal Dunes (Lytham St Annes) Management Company Limited (1)
Ashworth Road, Lytham Saint Anne's, FY8 2FW, Lancashire, United Kingdom
Tel.: (44) 1253208829
Residential Building Construction Services
N.A.I.C.S.: 236117

Coatham Vale And Berrymead Gardens Residents Management Company Limited (1)
Coatham Vale, Beaumont Hill, Darlington, DL1 3NG, County Durham, United Kingdom
Tel.: (44) 1325525115
House Construction & Design Services
N.A.I.C.S.: 532412

Coquet Grange (Amble) Management Company Limited (1)
Tel.: (44) 1670335219
Residential Building Construction Services
N.A.I.C.S.: 236117

Edinburgh Park (Liverpool) Management Company Limited (1)
Edinburgh Park Townsend Lane Anfield, Liverpool, L6 0BB, Merseyside, United Kingdom
Tel.: (44) 1514593872
House Construction & Design Services
N.A.I.C.S.: 532412

Eve Parc (Falmouth) Management Company Limited (1)
Eve Parc Bickland Water Road Kergilliack, Falmouth, TR11 4PB, Cornwall, United Kingdom
Tel.: (44) 1326331509
House Construction & Design Services
N.A.I.C.S.: 532412

Eve Park (Falmouth) Management Company Limited (1)
Bickland Water Road Kergilliack, Falmouth, TR11 4PB, Cornwall, United Kingdom
Tel.: (44) 132 633 1509
Residential Building Construction Services
N.A.I.C.S.: 236117

Fallow (Benton) Residents Management Company Limited (1)
Fallow Park Station Road, Wallsend, NE28 9FE, Tyne and Wear, United Kingdom
Tel.: (44) 1919332436
House Construction & Design Services
N.A.I.C.S.: 532412

Fatherford View (Okehampton) Management Company Limited (1)
Fatherford View Exeter Road, Okehampton, EX20 1QF, Devon, United Kingdom
Tel.: (44) 1837510342
House Construction & Design Services
N.A.I.C.S.: 532412

Festival Park (Easton) Residents Management Company Limited (1)
Festival Park Dereham Road Easton, Norwich, NR9 5EG, Norfolk, United Kingdom
Tel.: (44) 1603989118
House Construction & Design Services
N.A.I.C.S.: 532412

FibreNest Limited (1)
PO Box 745, York, YO1 0JF, United Kingdom
Tel.: (44) 3332342220
Web Site: https://www.fibrenest.com
Internet Broadband Services
N.A.I.C.S.: 517111

Forest View (Calverton) Management Company Limited (1)
Forest View 1 Butterfly Lane Collyer Road, Calverton, Nottingham, NG14 6TF, United Kingdom
Tel.: (44) 1156662072
House Construction & Design Services
N.A.I.C.S.: 532412

Foundry Meadows (Bexhill) Residents Management Company Limited (1)

5815

PERSIMMON PLC

Persimmon plc—(Continued)
Tel.: (44) 1424237312
Residential Building Construction Services
N.A.I.C.S.: 236117

Foxfields (Stoke-On-Trent) Management Company Limited (1)
Foxfields The Wood, Stoke-on-Trent, ST3 6HR, Staffordshire, United Kingdom
Tel.: (44) 1782498698
House Construction & Design Services
N.A.I.C.S.: 532412

Galliford Homes Limited (1)
Sterling House Langston Rd, Loughton, IG10 3TS, United Kingdom
Tel.: (44) 2084181000
Web Site: https://www.galliardhomes.com
Emp.: 700
Residential Property Development Services
N.A.I.C.S.: 531390
Stephen Conway *(Founder & Chm)*

Garendon Park Residents Management Company Ltd. (1)
Garendon Park William Railton Road Derby Road, Loughborough, LE12 5BT, Leicestershire, United Kingdom
Tel.: (44) 1509972753
House Construction & Design Services
N.A.I.C.S.: 532412

Harebell Meadows And Hartburn Grange Residents Management Company Limited (1)
Harebell Meadows Yarm Back Lane, Stockton-on-Tees, TS21 1AU, County Durham, United Kingdom
Tel.: (44) 1642130763
House Construction & Design Services
N.A.I.C.S.: 532412

Harlow Hill Grange (Harrogate) Management Company Limited (1)
Tel.: (44) 1423226557
Residential Building Construction Services
N.A.I.C.S.: 236117

Hartley Grange (Whittlesey) Residents Management Company Limited (1)
Hartley Grange Wetland Way, Whittlesey, PE7 1FQ, Cambridgeshire, United Kingdom
Tel.: (44) 1733307815
House Construction & Design Services
N.A.I.C.S.: 532412

Heugh Hall (Coxhoe) Residents Management Company Limited (1)
Heugh Hall Grange Station Road, Coxhoe, Durham, DH6 4AZ, County Durham, United Kingdom
Tel.: (44) 1913496283
House Construction & Design Services
N.A.I.C.S.: 532412

Hill Barton Vale Exeter Management Company Limited (1)
Tel.: (44) 1392966897
Residential Building Construction Services
N.A.I.C.S.: 236117

Hillfield Meadows (Sunderland) Management Company Limited (1)
Hillfield Meadows Silksworth Road, Sunderland, SR3 2PG, Tyne and Wear, United Kingdom
Tel.: (44) 1918142322
Residential Building Construction Services
N.A.I.C.S.: 236117

Hillies View (Wombwell) Management Company Limited (1)
Tel.: (44) 1226449672
Residential Building Construction Services
N.A.I.C.S.: 236117

Horsebridge Network Systems Limited (1)
4 Herrick Way, Staverton Staverton Bridge, Cheltenham, GL51 6TQ, United Kingdom
Tel.: (44) 1242382810
Web Site: https://www.horsebridge.net
Network Infrastructure Services
N.A.I.C.S.: 541512

Kingsbury Meadows (Wakefield) Management Company Limited (1)
Tel.: (44) 1924614667

Residential Building Construction Services
N.A.I.C.S.: 236117

Knightswood Place (Rainham) Residents Management Company Limited (1)
Tel.: (44) 1708201315
Residential Building Construction Services
N.A.I.C.S.: 236117

Lakedale Whiteley Meadows (North Whiteley) Management Company Limited (1)
Lakedale at Whiteley Meadows Bluebell Way, Whiteley, PO15 7PF, Hampshire, United Kingdom
Tel.: (44) 1329759010
House Construction & Design Services
N.A.I.C.S.: 532412

Lavender Fields (South Wootton) Residents Management Company Ltd. (1)
Lavender Fields Nursery Lane, South Wootton, King's Lynn, PE30 3NA, Norfolk, United Kingdom
Tel.: (44) 1553602873
House Construction & Design Services
N.A.I.C.S.: 532412

Lindley Moor Meadows (Huddersfield) Management Company Limited (1)
Tel.: (44) 1484508929
Residential Building Construction Services
N.A.I.C.S.: 236117

Llys Ystrad (Bridgend) Management Company Limited (1)
Llys Ystrad Llangewydd Road Cefn Glas, Bridgend, CF31 4JP, Mid Glamorgan, United Kingdom
Tel.: (44) 1656337370
House Construction & Design Services
N.A.I.C.S.: 532412

Lodmoor Sands (Weymouth) Management Company Limited (1)
Tel.: (44) 1305236741
Residential Building Construction Services
N.A.I.C.S.: 236117

Low Moor Meadows (Morley) Management Company Limited (1)
Tel.: (44) 1134872417
Residential Building Construction Services
N.A.I.C.S.: 236117

Manor Gardens (Selsey) Management Company Limited (1)
Manor Gardens Manor Road, Selsey, PO20 0FR, West Sussex, United Kingdom
Tel.: (44) 1243214373
House Construction & Design Services
N.A.I.C.S.: 532412

Meon Way Gardens Management Company Limited (1)
Meon Way Gardens Langate Fields, Long Marston, Stratford-upon-Avon, CV37 8GP, Warwickshire, United Kingdom
Tel.: (44) 1789330893
House Construction & Design Services
N.A.I.C.S.: 532412

Meridian Place (Hertford) Residents Management Company Limited (1)
Tel.: (44) 1992949992
Residential Building Construction Services
N.A.I.C.S.: 236117

Mill Gardens (Cullompton) Management Company Limited (1)
Mill Gardens Willand Road, Cullompton, EX15 1FE, Devon, United Kingdom
Tel.: (44) 1884212142
House Construction & Design Services
N.A.I.C.S.: 532412

Millbeck Grange (Bowburn) Management Company Limited (1)
Tursdale Road, Bowburn, DH6 5FL, Durham, United Kingdom
Tel.: (44) 1919170633
Residential Building Construction Services
N.A.I.C.S.: 236117

Moorfield Park Management Company Limited (1)
Tel.: (44) 1253547095

Residential Building Construction Services
N.A.I.C.S.: 236117

Mulberry Grange (Castleford) Management Company Limited (1)
Tel.: (44) 1977800712
Residential Building Construction Services
N.A.I.C.S.: 236117

Norton Hall Meadow Management Limited (1)
Norton Hall Lane, Norton Canes, Cannock, WS11 9PG, Staffordshire, United Kingdom
Tel.: (44) 1543223434
Residential Building Construction Services
N.A.I.C.S.: 236117

Oak Tree Gardens (Audley) Management Company Limited (1)
Tel.: (44) 1952953565
Residential Building Construction Services
N.A.I.C.S.: 236117

Oakhurst Village (Shirley) Management Company Limited (1)
Tel.: (44) 1218097322
Residential Building Construction Services
N.A.I.C.S.: 236117

Oakland Gardens (Wilthorpe) Management Company Limited (1)
Tel.: (44) 1226449707
Residential Building Construction Services
N.A.I.C.S.: 236117

Oakwood Meadows (Colchester) Residents Management Company Limited (1)
Tel.: (44) 1206586416
Residential Building Construction Services
N.A.I.C.S.: 236117

Orchard Manor (Cheddington) Residents Management Company Limited (1)
Tel.: (44) 1296796426
Residential Building Construction Services
N.A.I.C.S.: 236117

Orchard Meadows (Iwade) Residents Management Company Limited (1)
Orchard Meadows Grovehurst Road, Iwade, Sittingbourne, ME9 8RD, Kent, United Kingdom
Tel.: (44) 1795503073
House Construction & Design Services
N.A.I.C.S.: 532412

Orchard Mews Pershore Management Company Limited (1)
Orchard Mews Station Road, Pershore, WR10 2DG, Worcestershire, United Kingdom
Tel.: (44) 1386579753
House Construction & Design Services
N.A.I.C.S.: 532412

Paragon Park (Coventry) Management Company Limited (1)
Tel.: (44) 2477717729
Residential Building Construction Services
N.A.I.C.S.: 236117

Parklands (Hessle) Residents Management Company Limited (1)
Parklands Ferriby Road, Hessle, HU13 0HX, East Yorkshire, United Kingdom
Tel.: (44) 1482422554
House Construction & Design Services
N.A.I.C.S.: 532412

Perry Park View (Perry Barr) Management Company Limited (1)
Tel.: (44) 1217968411
Residential Building Construction Services
N.A.I.C.S.: 236117

Persimmon Finance Ltd. (1)
Persimmon House Fulford, York, YO19 4FE, United Kingdom (100%)
Tel.: (44) 1904642199
Sales Range: $1-4.9 Billion
Emp.: 100
Home Financing Services
N.A.I.C.S.: 921130

Persimmon Holdings Limited (1)
Persimmon House Fulford, York, YO19 4FE, United Kingdom (100%)
Tel.: (44) 1904642199

Sales Range: $50-74.9 Million
Holding Company
N.A.I.C.S.: 551112

Subsidiary (Domestic):

Charles Church (North East) Ltd (2)
Persimmon House Roseden Way, Aycliffe Industrial Est, Newcastle upon Tyne, NE13 9EA, United Kingdom (100%)
Tel.: (44) 191 238 9950
Web Site: http://www.charleschurch.com
Sales Range: $25-49.9 Million
Designs & Constructs Homes
N.A.I.C.S.: 236118

Charles Church (North London) Ltd (2)
Persimmon House 2 Vanwall Road, Vanwall Business Park, Maidenhead, SL6 4UB, Berkshire, United Kingdom (100%)
Tel.: (44) 162 850 2800
Web Site: http://www.charleschurch.com
Sales Range: $25-49.9 Million
Designs & Constructs Homes
N.A.I.C.S.: 236118

Charles Church (North West) Ltd. (2)
56-62 Middlewich Rd, Sandbach, CW111HU, Cheshire, United Kingdom
Tel.: (44) 01270757470
Web Site: http://www.persimmonhomes.com
Sales Range: $25-49.9 Million
Emp.: 28
New Single-Family Housing Construction
N.A.I.C.S.: 236115

Charles Church (South East) Ltd (2)
Scholars House 60 College Road, Maidstone, ME15 6SJ, United Kingdom (100%)
Tel.: (44) 1622626816
Web Site: http://www.charleschurch.com
Designs & Constructs Homes
N.A.I.C.S.: 236118

Subsidiary (Non-US):

Charles Church (Southern) Ltd (2)
(100%)
Tel.: (44) 1276808080
Sales Range: $25-49.9 Million
Emp.: 45
Designs & Constructs Homes
N.A.I.C.S.: 236118

Subsidiary (Domestic):

Charles Church (Special Projects) (2)
Persimmon House Knoll Road, Camberley, GU15 3TQ, Surrey, United Kingdom
Tel.: (44) 1276808080
Web Site: http://www.charleschurch.com
Sales Range: $25-49.9 Million
Emp.: 30
New Single-Family Housing Construction
N.A.I.C.S.: 236115

Charles Church (Western) Ltd (2)
Churchward House Churchward Rd Yate, Bristol, BS37 5NN, United Kingdom (100%)
Tel.: (44) 1454333800
Web Site: http://www.charleschurch.com
Sales Range: $25-49.9 Million
Emp.: 35
Designs & Constructs Homes
N.A.I.C.S.: 236118

Charles Church (Yorkshire) Ltd (2)
Persimmon House, Fulford, York, YO19 4FE, United Kingdom (100%)
Tel.: (44) 190 464 2199
Web Site: http://www.charleschurch.com
Sales Range: $25-49.9 Million
Designs & Constructs Homes
N.A.I.C.S.: 236118

Subsidiary (Non-US):

Charles Church Developments Ltd. (2)
Tel.: (44) 1276808080
Sales Range: $25-49.9 Million
Emp.: 45
New Single-Family Housing Construction
N.A.I.C.S.: 236115

Persimmon North Division (1)
Persimmon House Fulford, York, YO19

INTERNATIONAL PUBLIC

AND PRIVATE COMPANIES

PERSIMMON PLC

4FE, United Kingdom (100%)
Tel.: (44) 1904642199
Web Site: http://www.persimmonhomes.com
Sales Range: $75-99.9 Million
Emp.: 200
Holding Company
N.A.I.C.S.: 551112

Subsidiary (Domestic):

Persimmon Homes (East Yorkshire) Ltd. (2)
Persimmon House, Morton Ln, Beverley, HU17 9DD, East Yorkshire, United Kingdom (100%)
Tel.: (44) 1482871885
Web Site: https://www.persimmonplc.com
Sales Range: $10-24.9 Million
Emp.: 40
Designs & Constructs Homes
N.A.I.C.S.: 624229

Persimmon Homes (Lancashire) Ltd (2)
Persimmon House Gershwin Boulevard Drury Road, Lancaster Business Park, Lancaster, LA1 3RQ, United Kingdom (100%)
Tel.: (44) 152 454 2000
Sales Range: $25-49.9 Million
Emp.: 50
Designs & Constructs Homes
N.A.I.C.S.: 236118

Persimmon Homes (Mercia) Ltd. (2)
Charles Church NW 56 62 Middlewich Rd, Sandbach, CW11 1HU, Cheshire, United Kingdom (100%)
Tel.: (44) 1270750085
Web Site: https://www.persimmonhomes.com
Sales Range: $10-24.9 Million
Emp.: 28
Designs & Constructs Homes
N.A.I.C.S.: 624229

Persimmon Homes (North East) Ltd. (2)
Persimmon House Roseden Way, Newcastle upon Tyne, NE13 9EA, United Kingdom (100%)
Tel.: (44) 1912389950
Sales Range: $10-24.9 Million
Designs & Constructs Homes
N.A.I.C.S.: 624229
Stuart Grimes (Mng Dir)

Subsidiary (Non-US):

Persimmon Homes (North West) Ltd. (2)
(100%)
Tel.: (44) 1617463737
Sales Range: $10-24.9 Million
Designs & Constructs Homes
N.A.I.C.S.: 624229

Persimmon Homes (South Yorkshire) Ltd. (2)
(100%)
Tel.: (44) 1302436110
Sales Range: $25-49.9 Million
House Builder
N.A.I.C.S.: 236118

Subsidiary (Domestic):

Persimmon Homes (Teesside) Ltd (2)
Radcliffe Crescent, Thornaby, Stockton-on-Tees, TS17 6BS, United Kingdom (100%)
Tel.: (44) 164 266 0200
Sales Range: $25-49.9 Million
Emp.: 40
Designs & Constructs Homes
N.A.I.C.S.: 236118
Neil Foster (Mng Dir)

Persimmon Homes (West Yorkshire) Ltd. (2)
3 Hepton Court York Road, Leeds, LS9 6PW, United Kingdom (100%)
Tel.: (44) 1132409726
Sales Range: $25-49.9 Million
Emp.: 40
Designs & Constructs Homes
N.A.I.C.S.: 531210
Chris Hull (Mng Dir)

Persimmon Homes (Yorkshire) Ltd. (2)

Persimmon House Fulford, York, YO19 4FE, United Kingdom (100%)
Tel.: (44) 1904642199
Sales Range: $10-24.9 Million
Designs & Constructs Homes
N.A.I.C.S.: 624229
Scott Waters (Mng Dir)

Persimmon Partnerships (Scotland) Limited (1)
Tel.: (44) 1417662600
Residential Building Construction Services
N.A.I.C.S.: 236117

Persimmon South Division (1)
Persimmon House Fulford, Fulford, York, YO19 4FE, United Kingdom (100%)
Tel.: (44) 1904642199
Web Site: http://www.persimmonhomes.com
Sales Range: $50-74.9 Million
Emp.: 200
Holding Company
N.A.I.C.S.: 551112

Subsidiary (Domestic):

Elvetham Heath Developments (2)
The Community Ctr, The Key Elvetham Heath, Fleet, GU51 1HA, Hampshire, United Kingdom (100%)
Tel.: (44) 1252619810
Web Site: http://www.elvethamheath.co.uk
Sales Range: $25-49.9 Million
Emp.: 6
Designs & Constructs Homes
N.A.I.C.S.: 236118

Persimmon Homes (Anglia) Ltd. (2)
Persimmon House Bankside 100 Peachman Way, Broadland Business Park, Norwich, NR7 0WF, Norfolk, United Kingdom (100%)
Tel.: (44) 1603977200
Sales Range: $10-24.9 Million
Designs & Constructs Homes
N.A.I.C.S.: 624229
Michelle Baker (Mng Dir)

Persimmon Homes (East Midlands) Ltd. (2)
Persimmon House 19 Commerce Road Lynch Wood, Peterborough Business Park, Peterborough, PE2 6LR, Cambridgeshire, United Kingdom (100%)
Tel.: (44) 1733397200
Sales Range: $10-24.9 Million
Emp.: 45
Designs & Constructs Homes
N.A.I.C.S.: 624229
Ben Shaw (Mng Dir)

Persimmon Homes (Essex) Ltd. (2)
Persimmon House Gershwin Boulevard Drury Road, Witham, CM8 1FQ, Essex, United Kingdom (100%)
Tel.: (44) 137 651 8811
Sales Range: $25-49.9 Million
Emp.: 50
Designs & Constructs Homes
N.A.I.C.S.: 236118
David Thornton (Reg Chm)

Persimmon Homes (Midlands) Ltd. (2)
3 Waterside Way Bedford Road, Northampton, NN4 7XD, United Kingdom (100%)
Tel.: (44) 1604884600
Sales Range: $10-24.9 Million
Designs & Constructs Homes
N.A.I.C.S.: 624229
Zac Hurst (Mng Dir)

Subsidiary (Non-US):

Persimmon Homes (North Midlands) Ltd. (2)
(100%)
Tel.: (44) 1162815600
Sales Range: $10-24.9 Million
Emp.: 50
Designs & Constructs Homes
N.A.I.C.S.: 624229
Dan Endersby (Mng Dir)

Persimmon Homes (South Coast) Ltd. (2)
(100%)
Tel.: (44) 1329514300
Sales Range: $25-49.9 Million
Designs & Constructs Homes
N.A.I.C.S.: 531210

Andrew Barron (Mng Dir)

Persimmon Homes (South East) Ltd. (2)
(100%)
Tel.: (44) 1622626816
Sales Range: $10-24.9 Million
Emp.: 30
Designs & Constructs Homes
N.A.I.C.S.: 541330
Martin Crick (Mng Dir)

Persimmon Homes (South Midlands) Ltd. (2)
(100%)
Tel.: (44) 1527851200
Sales Range: $25-49.9 Million
Emp.: 40
House Builder
N.A.I.C.S.: 236118
Russell Griffin (Mng Dir)

Subsidiary (Domestic):

Persimmon Homes (South West) Ltd. (2)
Mallard Road Sowton Trading Estate, Exeter, EX2 7LD, Devon, United Kingdom (100%)
Tel.: (44) 1392252541
Sales Range: $25-49.9 Million
Designs & Constructs Homes
N.A.I.C.S.: 531210
Daniel Heathcote (Mng Dir)

Subsidiary (Non-US):

Persimmon Homes (Thames Valley) Ltd. (2)
(100%)
Tel.: (44) 1276808080
Web Site: http://www.persimmon.com
Sales Range: $10-24.9 Million
Emp.: 30
Designs & Constructs Homes
N.A.I.C.S.: 624229
Dan Castle (Mng Dir)

Subsidiary (Domestic):

Persimmon Homes (Wales) Ltd. (2)
Llantrisant Business Park, Rhondda Cynon Taff, Llantrisant, CF72 8YP, United Kingdom (100%)
Tel.: (44) 1443223653
Sales Range: $25-49.9 Million
Designs & Constructs Homes
N.A.I.C.S.: 531210
Lee Woodfine (Mng Dir)

Persimmon Homes (Wessex) Ltd. (2)
Verona House Tetbury Hill, Malmesbury, SN16 9JR, Wiltshire, United Kingdom (100%)
Tel.: (44) 1666824721
Sales Range: $10-24.9 Million
Designs & Constructs Homes
N.A.I.C.S.: 624229
Julian Roper (Mng Dir)

Subsidiary (Non-US):

Persimmon Homes (West Midlands) Ltd (2)
(100%)
Tel.: (44) 1902787989
Sales Range: $25-49.9 Million
Emp.: 50
Designs & Constructs Homes
N.A.I.C.S.: 236118
Daniel Hassell (Mng Dir)

Pottery Gardens (Cheadle) Residents Management Company Limited (1)
Pottery Gardens Froghall Road, Cheadle, ST10 1TF, Staffordshire, United Kingdom
Tel.: (44) 1538710450
House Construction & Design Services
N.A.I.C.S.: 532412

Rainton Gardens (Chilton Moor) Management Company Limited (1)
Rainton Gardens Black Boy Road, Chilton Moor, Houghton le Spring, DH4 6LX, Tyne and Wear, United Kingdom
Tel.: (44) 1915947893
House Construction & Design Services
N.A.I.C.S.: 532412

Saltram Meadow Plymouth Management Company Limited (1)
Tel.: (44) 1752967050
Residential Building Construction Services
N.A.I.C.S.: 236117

Saxons Chase (Headcorn) Residents Management Company Limited (1)
Tel.: (44) 1622391869
Residential Building Construction Services
N.A.I.C.S.: 236117

Space4 Limited (1)
Tameside Drive, Castle Bromwich, Birmingham, B35 7AG, United Kingdom
Tel.: (44) 1217488383
Residential Building Construction Services
N.A.I.C.S.: 236117
Gareth Wicks (Mng Dir)

St Michaels Place (Colchester) Residents Management Company Limited (1)
St Michaels Place Berechurch Hall Road, Colchester, CO2 9PN, Essex, United Kingdom
Tel.: (44) 1206586390
House Construction & Design Services
N.A.I.C.S.: 532412

St Michaels Way (South Ryhope) Residents Management Company Limited (1)
St Michaels Way A1018, South Ryhope, Sunderland, SR2 0GW, Tyne and Wear, United Kingdom
Tel.: (44) 1913387183
House Construction & Design Services
N.A.I.C.S.: 532412

Stanford Meadows (Stanford-Le-Hope) Residents Management Company Limited (1)
Tel.: (44) 1375808234
Residential Building Construction Services
N.A.I.C.S.: 236117

Stephenson Park (Wallsend) Residents Management Company Limited (1)
Stephenson Park Norman Terrace Howdon Green, Wallsend, NE28 6SP, Tyne and Wear, United Kingdom
Tel.: (44) 1919332356
House Construction & Design Services
N.A.I.C.S.: 532412

Swan Park (Dawlish) Management Company Limited (1)
Swan Park Exeter Road, Dawlish, EX7 0SB, Devon, United Kingdom
Tel.: (44) 1626244781
House Construction & Design Services
N.A.I.C.S.: 532412

The Hamptons (Newcastle) Resident Management Company Limited (1)
The Hamptons Keele Road, Newcastle-under-Lyme, ST5 2GQ, Staffordshire, United Kingdom
Tel.: (44) 1782498720
House Construction & Design Services
N.A.I.C.S.: 532412

The Maples (NGP) Management Company Limited (1)
The Maples Primrose Lane, Newcastle upon Tyne, NE13 9ET, Tyne and Wear, United Kingdom
Tel.: (44) 1919332475
House Construction & Design Services
N.A.I.C.S.: 532412

The Maples (Weston) Residents Management Company Limited (1)
The Maples High Road, Spalding, Weston, PE12 6RA, Lincolnshire, United Kingdom
Tel.: (44) 1733797022
House Construction & Design Services
N.A.I.C.S.: 532412

The View (Redditch) Management Company Limited (1)
The View Brockhill, Redditch, B97 6BP, Worcestershire, United Kingdom
Tel.: (44) 1527396673
House Construction & Design Services
N.A.I.C.S.: 532412

PERSIMMON PLC

Persimmon plc—(Continued)

Trelawny Place (Felixstowe) Residents Management Company Limited (1)
Trelawny Place Candlet Road, Felixstowe, IP11 9QZ, Suffolk, United Kingdom
Tel.: (44) 1394330582
House Construction & Design Services
N.A.I.C.S.: 532412

Trinity Pastures (Calvert Lane Hull) Residents Management Company Limited (1)
Trinity Pastures Calvert Lane, Hull, HU4 6BN, East Yorkshire, United Kingdom
Tel.: (44) 1482422511
House Construction & Design Services
N.A.I.C.S.: 532412

Walmsley Park (Leigh) Management Company Limited (1)
Tel.: (44) 1942363605
Residential Building Construction Services
N.A.I.C.S.: 236117

Weavers Place (Skelmanthorpe) Management Company Limited (1)
Weavers Place Cumberworth Road, Skelmanthorpe, Huddersfield, HD8 9AW, West Yorkshire, United Kingdom
Tel.: (44) 1484508970
House Construction & Design Services
N.A.I.C.S.: 532412

White Rose Park (Norwich) Residents Management Company Limited (1)
White Rose Park Drayton High Road, Norwich, NR6 5AH, Norfolk, United Kingdom
Tel.: (44) 1603514073
Residential Building Construction Services
N.A.I.C.S.: 236117

Whitworth Dale Management Company Limited (1)
Whitworth Dale Dale Road South, Darley Dale, Matlock, DE4 2EU, Derbyshire, United Kingdom
Tel.: (44) 1629704297
House Construction & Design Services
N.A.I.C.S.: 532412

Woodhorn Meadows (Ashington) Residents Management Company Limited (1)
Woodhorn Meadows Summerhouse Lane, Ashington, NE63 9DF, Northumberland, United Kingdom
Tel.: (44) 1670335339
House Construction & Design Services
N.A.I.C.S.: 532412

PERSIS HOLDINGS LIMITED

Suite 2600 1055 W Georgia Street, Vancouver, V6E 3P3, BC, Canada
Tel.: (604) 694-8800
Web Site: https://www.persisholdings.com
Year Founded: 1981
Emp.: 6
Holding Company
N.A.I.C.S.: 551112
Hassan Khosrowshahi (Chm)

Subsidiaries:

DRI Capital Inc. (1)
100 King St West Suite 7250, Toronto, M5X 1B1, ON, Canada (100%)
Tel.: (416) 324-5738
Web Site: https://drihealthcare.com
Rev.: $3,000,000,000
Emp.: 30
Pharmaceutical & Biotechnology Investment Services
N.A.I.C.S.: 523999
Jeff McGrath (Sr Legal Counsel & VP)

PERSIST OIL AND GAS INC.

1800 700 4th Ave SW, Calgary, T2P 3J4, AB, Canada
Tel.: (587) 686-6907
Web Site:
https://www.persistoilandgas.com
Year Founded: 2018
Oil & Gas Company
N.A.I.C.S.: 213112
Mass Geremia (Pres & Dir)

Subsidiaries:

Hawkley Oil & Gas Limited (1)
Suite 106 Ground Floor 101 Moray Street, South Melbourne, 3205, VIC, Australia
Tel.: (61) 386792219
Web Site: https://www.hawkleyoilandgas.com
Rev.: $47,004
Assets: $48,481
Liabilities: $773,898
Net Worth: ($725,417)
Earnings: ($911,487)
Fiscal Year-end: 06/30/2021
Oil & Gas Exploration Services
N.A.I.C.S.: 211120
Murray Wylie (Sec)

PERSISTENCE CAPITAL PARTNERS LP

600 De Maisonneuve Boulevard West Suite 2000, Montreal, H3A 3J2, QC, Canada
Tel.: (866) 379-5842
Web Site:
http://www.persistencecapital.com
Year Founded: 2008
Privater Equity Firm
N.A.I.C.S.: 523999
Stuart M. Elman (Mng Partner)

Subsidiaries:

Neighbourly Pharmacy Inc. (1)
400-190 Attwell Drive, Toronto, M9W 6H8, ON, Canada (50.2%)
Tel.: (416) 309-9102
Web Site:
https://www.neighbourlypharmacy.ca
Rev.: $558,865,154
Assets: $822,092,746
Liabilities: $362,938,698
Net Worth: $459,154,048
Earnings: ($11,040,054)
Emp.: 3,648
Fiscal Year-end: 03/25/2023
Pharmaceutical Product Mfr & Distr
N.A.I.C.S.: 325412
Roy Wieschkowski (Sr VP)

PERSISTENT SYSTEMS LTD.

Bhageerath 402 Senapati Bapat Road, Pune, 411 016, India
Tel.: (91) 2067030000
Web Site: https://www.persistent.com
Year Founded: 1990
PERSISTENT—(NSE)
Rev.: $799,166,687
Assets: $739,024,241
Liabilities: $279,262,211
Net Worth: $459,762,030
Earnings: $94,237,689
Emp.: 18,599
Fiscal Year-end: 03/31/22
Infrastructure Software Developer
N.A.I.C.S.: 513210
Anand Deshpande (Founder, Chm & Mng Dir)

Subsidiaries:

PARX Consulting GmbH (1)
An der Alster 62, 20099, Hamburg, Germany
Tel.: (49) 40232054000
Information Technology Services
N.A.I.C.S.: 541511

PARX Werk AG (1)
Birmensdorferstrasse 108, 8003, Zurich, Switzerland
Tel.: (41) 435009700
Software Development Services
N.A.I.C.S.: 541511

Persistent Systems Australia Pty. Ltd. (1)
Level 12 680 George Street, Sydney, 2000, NSW, Australia
Tel.: (61) 282807355
Software Development Services
N.A.I.C.S.: 541511

Persistent Systems France S.A.S. (1)
1 Rue Hector Berlioz, 38600, Fontaine, France
Tel.: (33) 476533580
Sales Range: $25-49.9 Million
Emp.: 30
Scientific Instruments Control Software Developer
N.A.I.C.S.: 513210

Persistent Systems Germany GmbH (1)
Lyoner Strasse 14, 60528, Frankfurt am Main, Germany
Tel.: (49) 8920000320
Software Development Services
N.A.I.C.S.: 541511

Persistent Systems Inc. USA (1)
Tel.: (650) 481-9180
Software Developer
N.A.I.C.S.: 513210
Tom Klein (Gen Counsel & Sr VP-Corp Dev)

Subsidiary (Domestic):

Akshat Corporation (2)
4062 148th Ave NE, Redmond, WA 98052-5164
Tel.: (425) 867-1350
Web Site: http://www.rgensolutions.com
Custom Computer Programming Services
N.A.I.C.S.: 541511
Vandana Mishra (Exec VP)

CloudSquads, Inc. (2)
260 Sheridan Ave Ste B10, Palo Alto, CA 94306
Tel.: (408) 720-8275
Web Site: http://www.cloudsquads.com
Software Developer
N.A.I.C.S.: 513210
Ashish Seth (Co-Founder)

Persistent Systems Lanka (Private) Limited (1)
4th Floor 123 Bauddhaloka Mawatha, 400003, Colombo, Sri Lanka
Tel.: (94) 112510300
Information Technology Services
N.A.I.C.S.: 541511

Persistent Systems Malaysia Sdn. Bhd. (1)
601-602 Level 6 Uptown 1 Jalan SS21/58 Damansara Utama, 47400, Petaling Jaya, Selangor Darul Ehsan, Malaysia
Tel.: (60) 376638301
Software Publisher
N.A.I.C.S.: 513210

Persistent Systems Pte. Ltd. (1)
Tel.: (65) 62234355
Software Developer
N.A.I.C.S.: 513210

Persistent Systems Switzerland AG (1)
Birmensdorferstrasse 108, 8003, Zurich, Switzerland
Tel.: (41) 435009700
Software Development Services
N.A.I.C.S.: 541511

Persistent Systems and Solutions Limited (1)
Bhageerath 402 Senapati Bapat Road, Pune, 411016, Maharashtra, India
Tel.: (91) 20 2570 2000
Software Development Services
N.A.I.C.S.: 541511

Persistent Systems, Inc. (1)
2055 Laurelwood Rd Ste 210, Santa Clara, CA 95054
Tel.: (408) 216-7010
Information Technology Services
N.A.I.C.S.: 541511
Dhanashree Bhat (COO)

Youperience Limited (1)
Tel.: (44) 1932895000
Information Technology Services
N.A.I.C.S.: 541511

PERSOL HOLDINGS CO., LTD.

1-15-5 Minami-Aoyama, Minato-ku, Tokyo, 107-0062, Japan
Tel.: (81) 333752220 JP
Web Site: https://www.persol-group.co.jp
Year Founded: 2008
2181—(TKS)
Rev.: $8,772,283,030
Assets: $3,428,805,300
Liabilities: $2,051,829,930
Net Worth: $1,376,975,370
Earnings: $198,108,310
Emp.: 65,730
Fiscal Year-end: 03/31/24
Holding Company; Personnel Recruitment, Placement & Outsourcing Services
N.A.I.C.S.: 551112
Takao Wada (Pres & CEO)

Subsidiaries:

Avanti Staff Corporation (1)
7th Peace Building 6-7 Nihonbashi Kabutocho, Chuo-ku Kabutocho, Tokyo, 103-0026, Japan
Tel.: (81) 36 703 8333
Web Site: https://www.avantistaff.com
Temporary Staffing Services
N.A.I.C.S.: 561320

Bizer Inc. (1)
KS Floor 5th Floor Resona Kudan Building 1-5-6 Kudanminami, Chiyoda-ku, Tokyo, 102-0074, Japan
Tel.: (81) 36 869 4084
Web Site: https://www.bizer.jp
Software Development Services
N.A.I.C.S.: 541511

Persol AVC Technology Co., Ltd. (1)
1-1 Saiwaicho 6th Floor Techno Center, Takatsuki, 569-1194, Osaka, Japan
Tel.: (81) 72 690 7535
Web Site: https://www.persol-avct.co.jp
Digital Audiovisual Product Mfr & Distr
N.A.I.C.S.: 334310

Persol Business Expert Co., Ltd. (1)
TS Ikebukuro Building 2-63-4 Higashiikebukuro, Toshima-ku, Tokyo, 170-0013, Japan
Tel.: (81) 36 362 5720
Web Site: https://www.persol-businessexpert.co.jp
Call Center Services
N.A.I.C.S.: 561422

Persol Career Consulting Co., Ltd. (1)
20th Floor of Morinaga Plaza Building Main Building 5-33-1, Shiba Minato-ku, Tokyo, 108-0014, Japan
Tel.: (81) 35 427 7880
Web Site: https://www.persol-cc.co.jp
Paid Employment Agency Services
N.A.I.C.S.: 561311
Noriyuki Osawa (Pres)

Persol Excel Associates Co., Ltd. (1)
2-1-61 Shiromi TWIN21 Gallery fourth Floor MID Tower 4th Floor, Chuo-ku, Osaka, 540-0001, Japan
Tel.: (81) 66 945 6214
Web Site: https://www.pea.persol-group.co.jp
Baked Goods Mfr & Distr
N.A.I.C.S.: 311812

Persol Excel HR Partners Co., Ltd. (1)
2-1-61 Shiromi TWIN21MID Tower 2nd Floor, Chuo-ku, Osaka, 540-6102, Japan
Tel.: (81) 66 945 0390
Web Site: https://www.persol-hrpartners.co.jp
Paid Employment Agency Services
N.A.I.C.S.: 561311

Persol Facility Management Co., Ltd. (1)
5th Floor of Stadium Place Aoyama 2-9-5 Kita-Aoyama, Minato-ku, Tokyo, 107-0061, Japan
Tel.: (81) 36 385 6844
Web Site: https://www.fm.persol-group.co.jp
Consulting Services
N.A.I.C.S.: 541611

AND PRIVATE COMPANIES — PERSOL HOLDINGS CO., LTD.

Persol Factory Partners Co., Ltd. (1)
2-2-16 Sonezakishinchi Nishi-Umeda MID Building 3F, Kita-ku, Osaka, 530-0002, Japan
Tel.: (81) 66 341 6262
Web Site: https://www.persol-factorypartners.co.jp
Paid Employment Agency Services
N.A.I.C.S.: 561311

Persol Field Staff Co., Ltd. (1)
Shinjuku Maynds Tower 2-1-1 Yoyogi, Shibuya-ku, Tokyo, 151-0053, Japan
Tel.: (81) 12 078 8264
Web Site: https://www.pfs.persol-group.co.jp
Paid Employment Agency Services
N.A.I.C.S.: 561311

Persol Nextage Co., Ltd. (1)
Morinaga Plaza Building 17F 5-33-1 Shiba, Minato-ku, Tokyo, 108-0014, Japan
Tel.: (81) 36 385 0800
Web Site: https://nextage.persol-group.co.jp
Paid Employment Agency Services
N.A.I.C.S.: 561311

Persol Process & Technology Co., Ltd. (1)
7F Toyosufront 3-2-20, Toyosu Koto-ku, Tokyo, 135-0061, Japan
Tel.: (81) 36 385 0900
Web Site: https://www.persol-pt.co.jp
Emp.: 3,152
Software Development Services
N.A.I.C.S.: 541511

Persol Process & Technology Vietnam Co., Ltd. (1)
6th Floor An Phu Plaza 117-119 Ly Chinh Thang, Ward 7 District 3, Ho Chi Minh City, 70000, Vietnam
Tel.: (84) 283 848 1200
Web Site: https://www.persol-pt.vn
Software Development Services
N.A.I.C.S.: 541511

Persol Technology Staff Co., Ltd. (1)
51F Shinjuku Mitsui Building 2-1-1 Nishi-Shinjuku, Shinjuku-ku, Tokyo, 163-0451, Japan
Tel.: (81) 36 370 6840
Web Site: https://www.persol-tech-s.co.jp
Paid Employment Agency Services
N.A.I.C.S.: 561311

Persol Tempstaff Co., Ltd. (1)
Shinjuku Maynds Tower 2-1-1 Yoyogi, Shibuya-ku, Tokyo, 151-0053, Japan
Tel.: (81) 3 5350 1212
Web Site: http://www.tempstaff.co.jp
Emp.: 54,760
Staffing & Human Resource Support Services
N.A.I.C.S.: 561311
Takao Wada (Officer-Sls & Strategy)

Subsidiary (Domestic):

Careerrise Corporation (2)
1-3-22 Yaesu Yaesuryumeikan Building 7 Fl, 103-0028, Tokyo, Japan
Tel.: (81) 0342846111
Web Site: http://www.career-rise.co.jp
Temporary Staffing
N.A.I.C.S.: 561320
Takumi Endo (Pres)

DRD Co., Ltd. (2)
1-1 Ageo-shi, Ageo, 362-0046, Saitama, Japan (100%)
Tel.: (81) 48 726 4580
Web Site: http://www.ndrd.co.jp
Sales Range: $25-49.9 Million
Emp.: 520
Automobile Design & Testing Services
N.A.I.C.S.: 541420
Mikio Miyamura (Pres & CEO)

HOWCOM Co., Ltd. (2)
Sumitomo Seimei Kawasaki Ohdori Building 2F 2-11 Higashida-cho, Kawasaki-ku, Kawasaki, 210-0005, Kanagawa, Japan
Tel.: (81) 4 4220 3481
Web Site: http://www.howcom.co.jp
Sales Range: $25-49.9 Million
Emp.: 200
Information Technology Support Services
N.A.I.C.S.: 541512
Yoshinori Hirabayashi (Pres)

Intelligence Holdings, Ltd. (2)
27-28F Marunouchi Bldg 2-4-1 Marunouchi, Chiyoda-ku, Tokyo, 100-6328, Japan (100%)
Tel.: (81) 3 6213 9000
Web Site: http://www.inte.co.jp
Emp.: 5,166
Holding Company; Temporary Staffing, Recruitment Consulting & Online Career Services
N.A.I.C.S.: 551112
Taro Mineo (Pres & CEO)

Subsidiary (Non-US):

Intelligence Asia Pte. Ltd. (3)
8 Marina View #11-01 Asia Square Tower 1, 018960, Singapore, Singapore (60%)
Tel.: (65) 6225 0900
Web Site: http://inteasia.com
Sales Range: $25-49.9 Million
Emp.: 10
Recruitment Services
N.A.I.C.S.: 561311
Takayuki Yamazaki (CEO)

Subsidiary (Domestic):

Persol Career Co., Ltd. (3)
Marunouchi Building 27F 2-4-1 Marunouchi, Chiyoda-ku, Tokyo, 100-6328, Japan (100%)
Tel.: (81) 36 213 9000
Web Site: https://www.persol-career.co.jp
Sales Range: $1-9.9 Million
Emp.: 4,540
Temporary Staffing, Recruitment Consulting & Online Career Services
N.A.I.C.S.: 561311
Taro Mineo (Pres & CEO)

Subsidiary (Domestic):

Japan IDEX Co., Ltd. (2)
65-18 2-chome Ikebukuro, Toshima-ku, Tokyo, 170-0014, Japan
Tel.: (81) 369074481
Web Site: http://www.jix.co.jp
Sales Range: $150-199.9 Million
Emp.: 650
Business Process Outsourcing Services
N.A.I.C.S.: 561439
Yoshiyuki Ito (CEO)

Persol Research & Development Co., Ltd. (2)
Nadya Park Business Centre Bldg 20F 3-18-1 Sakae, Naka-Ku, Nagoya, 460-0008, Aichi, Japan (100%)
Tel.: (81) 522429001
Web Site: http://www.persol-rd.co.jp
Emp.: 2,567
Staffing & Employment Consulting Services
N.A.I.C.S.: 561311
Eiji Isoda (Pres)

Personal Inc. (2)
Kojimachi Building 2F 3-3-6 Kudanminami, Chiyoda-ku, Tokyo, 102-0074, Japan
Tel.: (81) 353571870
Web Site: http://www.personal.co.jp
Emp.: 130
Staffing & Employment Consulting Services
N.A.I.C.S.: 561311

Support-A Ltd. (2)
1-13-9 Shibuya Shibuyatakugin Bldg 6 Fl, 1248, Shibuya-ku, Tokyo, 150-0002, Japan
Tel.: (81) 364184580
Web Site: http://www.support-a.com
Sales Range: $25-49.9 Million
Emp.: 25
Employment Placement Services
N.A.I.C.S.: 561311

Subsidiary (Non-US):

Suzhou Tempstaff Data Co., Ltd. (2)
No 135 Suzhou Industrial Park, Suzhou, Jiangsu, China
Tel.: (86) 51262621020
Data Entry & Data Processing Services
N.A.I.C.S.: 518210

Subsidiary (Domestic):

Temp Research Institute Co., Ltd. (2)
Mitomi Building 7F 1-20-22 Ebisu, Shibuya-ku, Tokyo, 150-0013, Japan
Tel.: (81) 354213880
Web Site: http://www.iccworld.co.jp
Sales Range: $10-24.9 Million
Emp.: 18
Overseas Study & Educational Consulting Services
N.A.I.C.S.: 611710

Tempbros Co., Ltd. (2)
2-1-1 Yoyogi Shinjuku Maynds Tower 16F, Shibuya-ku, Tokyo, 151-0053, Japan
Tel.: (81) 363326416
Web Site: https://pfs.persol-group.co.jp
Staffing & Employment Consulting Services
N.A.I.C.S.: 561311

Tempstaff Creative Co., Ltd. (2)
3-5-14 Kitaaoyama, Minato-ku, Tokyo, 107-0061, Japan
Tel.: (81) 357757330
Web Site: http://www.tempcreative.co.jp
Employment Placement Services
N.A.I.C.S.: 561311

Tempstaff Cross Co., Ltd. (2)
3-3-3 Akasaka Sumitomo Seimei Building 9th Floor, Tokyo, 107-0052, Japan
Tel.: (81) 335822234
Web Site: http://www.tempcross.co.jp
Emp.: 204
Temporary & Permanent Office Personnel Placement Services
N.A.I.C.S.: 561320
Kentaro Kasamatsu (Pres)

Tempstaff Familie Co., Ltd. (2)
1-10-6 Minamichitose, Nagano, 380-0823, Japan
Tel.: (81) 262271360
Web Site: http://www.tempstaff-familie.co.jp
Temporary Staffing Services
N.A.I.C.S.: 561320

Affiliate (Domestic):

Tempstaff Forum Co., Ltd. (2)
1-7-10 Higashiodori 6th floor Niigata Central Building, Chuo-Ku, Niigata, 950-0087, Japan
Tel.: (81) 252403200
Staffing & Employment Consulting Services
N.A.I.C.S.: 561311

Subsidiary (Domestic):

Tempstaff Frontier Co., Ltd. (2)
2-6-1 Ginza Chuoginza Building 4F, Chuo-Ku, Tokyo, 104-0061, Japan
Tel.: (81) 355245591
Web Site: http://www.tempfrontier.co.jp
Staffing & Employment Consulting Services
N.A.I.C.S.: 561311

Tempstaff Fukuoka Co., Ltd. (2)
5-23-8 Watanabedori, Chuo-Ku, Fukuoka, 810-0004, Japan
Tel.: (81) 927220641
Web Site: http://www.tempfuk.co.jp
Staffing & Employment Consulting Services
N.A.I.C.S.: 561311

Tempstaff Grow Co., Ltd. (2)
206 Takasaki Center Building 7F, Takasaki, 371-0831, Gunma, Japan (100%)
Tel.: (81) 272216006
Web Site: http://www.tempstaff-grow.co.jp
Employment Placement Services
N.A.I.C.S.: 561311
Takuro Ito (Pres)

Subsidiary (Non-US):

Tempstaff Guangzhou Ltd. (2)
Unit 10 11F Grand Tower 228 Tian He Road, Guangzhou, Guangdong, China
Tel.: (86) 20 3835 0377
Web Site: http://www.tempstaff.com.cn
Recruitment & Employment Consulting Services
N.A.I.C.S.: 561311

Tempstaff Indonesia Co., Ltd. (2)
Wisma Kyoei Prince 14th Floor Jl Jend Sudirman Kav 3-4, Jakarta, 10220, Indonesia
Tel.: (62) 21 579 05805
Recruitment & Employment Consulting Services
N.A.I.C.S.: 561311

Subsidiary (Domestic):

Tempstaff Integration Co., Ltd. (2)
TS Ikebukuro Building 2-63-4 Higashi-Ikebukuro, Toshima-ku, Tokyo, 170-0013, Japan
Tel.: (81) 363625720
Web Site: https://persol-businessexpert.co.jp
Emp.: 600
Comprehensive Contract Business Services
N.A.I.C.S.: 518210
Masamichi Mizuta (Pres & Dir)

Affiliate (Domestic):

Tempstaff Kamei Corporation (2)
Kakyoin Square 8F 1-1-20 Kakyoin, Aoba-ku, Sendai, 980-0013, Miyagi, Japan
Tel.: (81) 222663171
Web Site: https://www.persol-tempstaffkamei.co.jp
Emp.: 30,000
Temporary Staffing & Placement Services
N.A.I.C.S.: 561311
Hijiri Iwasaki (Pres)

Subsidiary (Non-US):

Tempstaff Korea Co., Ltd. (2)
Daeil-Building No 18 Namdaemunro 1-Ga, Jung-ku, Seoul, 100-91, Korea (South)
Tel.: (82) 25576604
Web Site: http://www.tempstaff.co.kr
Staffing & Employment Consulting Services
N.A.I.C.S.: 561320

Subsidiary (Domestic):

Tempstaff Learning Co., Ltd. (2)
2-1-1 Yoyogi Shinjuku Mines Tower 16F, Shibuya-ku, Tokyo, 151-0053, Japan
Tel.: (81) 353522165
Web Site: http://www.templearn.co.jp
Sales Range: $25-49.9 Million
Emp.: 50
Employee Training & Human Resource Consulting Services
N.A.I.C.S.: 541612
Shinya Iwasaki (Pres)

Tempstaff Plus Co., Ltd. (2)
2-7-5 Yoyogi Shinjukutaguchi Building 2F, Shibuya-ku, Tokyo, 151-0053, Japan
Tel.: (81) 353334781
Web Site: http://www.tempstaffplus.co.jp
Temporary Staffing Services
N.A.I.C.S.: 561320

Subsidiary (Non-US):

Tempstaff Shanghai Co., Ltd. (2)
918 Huaihai Zhong Road, Shanghai, China
Tel.: (86) 2164155368
Web Site: http://www.tempstaff-sh.com
Employment Placement Services
N.A.I.C.S.: 561311

Tempstaff Taiwan Co., Ltd. (2)
201-3 Tung Hwa North Road 8F Formosa Plastic Group Building, 10508, Taipei, Taiwan
Tel.: (886) 227132468
Web Site: http://www.tempstaff.com.tw
Staffing & Employment Consulting Services
N.A.I.C.S.: 561311

Subsidiary (Domestic):

Tempstaff Technologies Co., Ltd. (2)
2-1-1 Yoyogi Shinjuku Maynds Tower, Shibuya-Ku, Tokyo, 151-0053, Japan
Tel.: (81) 353345528
Web Site: http://www.temptech.co.jp
Staffing & Employment Consulting Services
N.A.I.C.S.: 561311

Tempstaff Welfare Co., Ltd. (2)
5-8-5 Osaki Green Plaza Gotanda No 2, Shinagawa-ku, Tokyo, 141-0032, Japan
Tel.: (81) 354367641
Nursing Services
N.A.I.C.S.: 623110

Thanks Temp Co., Ltd. (2)
2-3-13 Yayoicho Kawamoto Building, Nakano-ku, Tokyo, 164-0013, Japan
Tel.: (81) 333738281
Web Site: http://www.thankstemp.co.jp
Physically Challenged People Employment Support Services
N.A.I.C.S.: 561311

Persol Thanks Co., Ltd. (1)

PERSOL HOLDINGS CO., LTD.

Persol Holdings Co., Ltd.—(Continued)
3-1-1 Higashiikebukuro Sunshine 60 2F,
Toshima-ku, Tokyo, 170-6002, Japan
Tel.: (81) 36 362 5781
Web Site: https://www.thanks.persol-group.co.jp
Paid Employment Agency Services
N.A.I.C.S.: 561311

Persol Works Design Co., Ltd. (1)
Ikebukuro West Building 2-65-18 Ikebukuro,
Toshima-ku, Tokyo, 171-0014, Japan
Tel.: (81) 36.907 4481
Web Site: https://www.persol-wd.co.jp
Paid Employment Agency Services
N.A.I.C.S.: 561311
Yoshinori Hirabayashi *(Pres)*

Postas Co., Ltd. (1)
5-4-18 Tsukiji Shiodome East Side Building
2nd and 3rd Floor, Chuo-ku, Tokyo, 104-0045, Japan
Tel.: (81) 36 264 0910
Web Site: https://www.postas.co.jp
Software Development Services
N.A.I.C.S.: 541511

Programmed Maintenance Services Limited (1)
47 Burswood Road, Burswood, 6100, WA,
Australia **(100%)**
Tel.: (61) 892162100
Web Site: https://www.programmed.com.au
Rev.: $2,691,375,000
Assets: $1,293,579,000
Liabilities: $685,749,000
Net Worth: $607,830,000
Earnings: $12,285,000
Fiscal Year-end: 03/31/2017
Staffing, Maintenance & Project Services
N.A.I.C.S.: 561311
Stephen Leach *(CFO)*

Subsidiary (Domestic):

PeopleCo. Pty Ltd (2)
Unit 1 37-39 Little Boundary Road, Laverton, VIC, Australia
Tel.: (61) 3 8348 4600
Web Site: http://www.peopleco.com.au
Temporary Staffing Services
N.A.I.C.S.: 561320
Bev Myers *(Bus Mgr)*

Programmed Electrical Technologies Ltd
Unit 4 40-44 Cook Street, Port Melbourne,
3207, VIC, Australia **(100%)**
Tel.: (61) 93203444
Web Site: http://www.programmed.com.au
Electrical, Data, Audio Visual & Communications Cabling Design & Installation
N.A.I.C.S.: 238210

Programmed Facility Management Pty. Ltd. (2)
Level 32 Tower 2 727 Collins Street, Melbourne, 3008, VIC, Australia **(100%)**
Tel.: (61) 386466444
Web Site: http://www.programmed.com.au
Facility Management Services
N.A.I.C.S.: 541618

Programmed Industrial Maintenance Pty. Ltd. (2)
168 Abernethy Road, Belmont, 6104, WA,
Australia
Tel.: (61) 892298383
Web Site: http://www.programmed.com.au
Construction Engineering Services
N.A.I.C.S.: 541330
Malcolm Roberts *(Gen Mgr)*

Subsidiary (Domestic):

Programmed Industrial Maintenance Services Pty. Ltd. (3)
Suite 2 38 Colin Street, West Perth, 6005,
WA, Australia
Tel.: (61) 892298383
Web Site: http://www.extraman.com.au
Industrial Maintenance Human Resource Management Services
N.A.I.C.S.: 561330

Subsidiary (Domestic):

Programmed Integrated Workforce Limited (2)
47 Burswood Road, Burswood, 6100, WA,
Australia
Tel.: (61) 892162100
Web Site: http://www.intgroup.com.au
General Labor Employment Organization
N.A.I.C.S.: 561330

Subsidiary (Non-US):

Programmed Integrated Workforce (3)
635 Great South Road, Penrose, Auckland,
1061, New Zealand
Tel.: (64) 9 571 1825
Web Site: http://www.programmed.co.nz
Emp.: 3
Recruitment & Office Management Services
N.A.I.C.S.: 561311
Nic Fairbank *(CEO)*

Subsidiary (Non-US):

Programmed Maintenance Services (N.Z.) Ltd. (2)
4 Arthur Brown Place, Auckland, 1060, New
Zealand
Tel.: (64) 95710439
Web Site: http://www.programmed.co.nz
Property Maintenance Services
N.A.I.C.S.: 561730
Craig Lahood *(Gen Mgr)*

Reline Co., Ltd. (1)
Minamiyama Bldg 1F 2-10-6 Hirakawa-cho,
Chiyoda-ku, Tokyo, 102-0093, Japan
Tel.: (81) 352140410
Accounting & Financial Services
N.A.I.C.S.: 541219

TS Consulting International, Inc. (1)
300 N Sepulveda Blvd Ste 1018, El Segundo, CA 90245
Tel.: (310) 965-9810
Web Site: https://ts2tech.space
Sales Range: $25-49.9 Million
Emp.: 13
Recruitment & Employment Consulting Services
N.A.I.C.S.: 561311
Yoshimi Iyadomi *(Pres)*

Tempstaff (Hong Kong) Limited (1)
Unit 2001 20F Hing Wai Building 36
Queen's Road, Central, China (Hong Kong) **(51%)**
Tel.: (852) 25258121
Web Site: http://www.tempstaff.com.hk
Recruitment & Employment Consulting Services
N.A.I.C.S.: 561311

Tempstaff Career Co., Ltd. (1)
2-1-1 Yoyogi Shinjuku Mines Tower,
Shibuya-ku, Tokyo, 151-0053, Japan
Tel.: (81) 353044801
Web Site: http://www.tscareer.co.jp
Personnel Consulting Services
N.A.I.C.S.: 541612

Tempstaff Career Transition Co., Ltd. (1)
1-8-4 Kandasudacho Yoyu Building,
Chiyoda-ku, Tokyo, 101-0041, Japan
Tel.: (81) 352983271
Staffing & Employment Consulting Services
N.A.I.C.S.: 561311

Tempstaff Data Co., Ltd. (1)
1-51-7 Minamiotsuka Misakiotsuka Building
2F, Toshima-ku, Tokyo, 170-0005, Japan
Tel.: (81) 353192231
Web Site: http://www.tsdata.co.jp
Sales Range: $25-49.9 Million
Emp.: 10
Data Entry & Data Processing Services
N.A.I.C.S.: 518210

Tempstaff Medical Co., Ltd. (1)
2-11-17 Yoyogi Raundo Cross Shinjuku
Building 9F, Shibuya-ku, Tokyo, 151-0053,
Japan
Tel.: (81) 3 3378 1380
Web Site: http://www.tempmedical.co.jp
Physical Examination & Healthcare Support Services
N.A.I.C.S.: 621491

Tempstaff SP Co., Ltd. (1)
124 Kokuba, Tokyo, Japan
Tel.: (81) 357784260

Web Site: http://www.temp-sp.co.jp
Staffing & Employment Consulting Services
N.A.I.C.S.: 561311

PERSONAL ASSETS TRUST PLC

Juniper Partners 28 Walker Street,
Edinburgh, EH3 7HR, United Kingdom
Tel.: (44) 1313780500 UK
Web Site: https://www.patplc.co.uk
PNL—(LSE)
Assets: $2,343,085,101
Liabilities: $273,823,893
Net Worth: $2,069,261,208
Earnings: ($17,735,319)
Fiscal Year-end: 04/30/23
Portfolio Management & Investment Advice
N.A.I.C.S.: 523940
Hamish N. Buchan *(Chm)*

PERSONAL GROUP HOLDINGS PLC

John Ormond House 899 Silbury
Boulevard, Milton Keynes, MK9 3XL,
United Kingdom
Tel.: (44) 1908605000
Web Site:
   https://www.personalgroup.com
Year Founded: 1984
PGH—(AIM)
Rev.: $109,385,256
Assets: $58,834,890
Liabilities: $19,731,129
Net Worth: $39,103,762
Earnings: ($9,155,516)
Emp.: 262
Fiscal Year-end: 12/31/22
Employee Benefit Administration & Management Services
N.A.I.C.S.: 524128
Ashley Doody *(CIO)*

Subsidiaries:

B M Agency Services Limited (1)
John Ormand House 899 Silbury Boulevard,
Milton Keynes, MK9 3XL, Buckinghamshire,
United Kingdom
Tel.: (44) 8440964
Web Site:
   http://www.bmagencyservices.co.uk
Emp.: 8
General Insurance Services
N.A.I.C.S.: 524113
Simon Ingman *(Dir-Fin)*

Berkeley Morgan Group Limited (1)
John Ormond House 899 Silbury Boulevard,
Milton Keynes, MK9 3XL, Buckinghamshire,
United Kingdom
Tel.: (44) 1908605000
General Insurance Services
N.A.I.C.S.: 524113

Berkeley Morgan Limited (1)
John Ormond House 899 Silbury Boulevard
Central, Milton Keynes, MK9 3XL, Buckinghamshire, United Kingdom
Tel.: (44) 1908605000
Web Site: http://www.berkeleymorgan.co.uk
Financial Management Consulting Services
N.A.I.C.S.: 541611

Innecto People Consulting Limited (1)
20 Eastbourne Terrace, London, W2 6LG,
United Kingdom
Tel.: (44) 2034570894
Web Site: https://www.innecto.com
Human Resource Consultancy Services
N.A.I.C.S.: 541612
Deborah Frost *(Founder)*

Let's Connect IT Solutions Limited (1)
John Ormond House 899 Silbury Boulevard
Central, Milton Keynes, MK9 3XL, United
Kingdom
Tel.: (44) 3302000231
Web Site: https://www.lets-connect.co.uk
Information Technology Services

INTERNATIONAL PUBLIC

N.A.I.C.S.: 541511

Personal Assurance Plc (1)
John Ormond House 899 Silbury Boulevard,
Milton Keynes, MK9 3XL, Buckinghamshire,
United Kingdom
Tel.: (44) 1908605000
Web Site: https://www.personal-group.com
Sales Range: $100-124.9 Million
Emp.: 120
Personal insurance services
N.A.I.C.S.: 524126

Personal Assurance Services Limited (1)
John Ormond House 899 Silbury Boulevard,
Milton Keynes, MK9 3XL, Buckinghamshire,
United Kingdom
Tel.: (44) 1908605000
Emp.: 250
General Insurance Services
N.A.I.C.S.: 524114
Deborah Frost *(CEO)*

Personal Group Benefits Limited (1)
899 Silbury Boulevard, Milton Keynes, MK9
3XL, United Kingdom
Tel.: (44) 1908605000
Sales Range: $25-49.9 Million
Emp.: 150
Employee Benefits Management
N.A.I.C.S.: 541611
Jason Graves *(Mgr-Sls & Admin)*

Personal Group Trustees Limited (1)
John Ormond House 899 Silbury Boulevard,
Milton Keynes, MK9 3XL, Buckinghamshire,
United Kingdom
Tel.: (44) 1908605000
Financial Management Consulting Services
N.A.I.C.S.: 541611

Personal Management Solutions Limited (1)
Tel.: (44) 1908605000
Sales Range: $25-49.9 Million
Emp.: 150
Flexible Benefits & Salary Management Services
N.A.I.C.S.: 541611

Universal Provident Limited (1)
John Ormond House 899 Silbury Boulevard,
Milton Keynes, MK9 3XL, Buckinghamshire,
United Kingdom
Tel.: (44) 1908605000
Web Site:
   http://www.universalprovident.co.uk
Sales Range: $50-74.9 Million
Emp.: 10
General Insurance Services
N.A.I.C.S.: 524114

PERSONAS SOCIAL INCORPORATED

302-155 University Ave, Toronto,
M5H 3M7, ON, Canada
Tel.: (416) 716-9281 AB
Web Site: http://peeks.social
Year Founded: 2008
PRSN—(DEU)
Rev.: $2,252,925
Assets: $6,347,727
Liabilities: $5,282,952
Net Worth: $1,064,775
Earnings: ($3,451,650)
Fiscal Year-end: 02/29/20
Online Social Networking Services
N.A.I.C.S.: 541519
William Lavin *(CFO)*

PERSPECTUM GROUP PLC

Gemini One 5520 John Smith Drive,
Oxford Business Park South, Oxford,
OX4 2LL, Oxfordshire, United Kingdom
Tel.: (44) 1865 655 343
Web Site:
   http://www.perspectum.com
Year Founded: 2021
SCAN—(NASDAQ)
Rev.: $8,610,000
Assets: $36,429,000
Liabilities: $5,891,000
Net Worth: $30,538,000

Earnings: ($13,067,000)
Emp.: 192
Fiscal Year-end: 12/31/20
Biotechnology Research & Development Services
N.A.I.C.S.: 541714
Rajarshi Banerjee (CEO)

PERTAMA DIGITAL BERHAD
No 1001 Block A Pusat Dagangan Phileo Damansara 1, No 9 Jalan 16/11 Off Jalan Damansara, 46350, Petaling Jaya, Selangor, Malaysia
Tel.: (60) 378031126   MY
Web Site: https://www.pertamadigital.com
Year Founded: 1999
8532—(KLS)
Rev.: $1,857,989
Assets: $33,657,143
Liabilities: $30,283,386
Net Worth: $3,373,757
Earnings: ($2,099,048)
Fiscal Year-end: 12/31/22
Textile Product Mfr & Distr
N.A.I.C.S.: 313210
Ding Pan (Mng Dir)

Subsidiaries:

Television Airtime Services Sdn. Bhd. (1)
Unit 548 - 550 Block A Kelana Center Point No 3 Jalan SS7/19, Kelana Jaya, 47301, Petaling Jaya, Selangor, Malaysia
Tel.: (60) 378062755
Web Site: http://www.tas.com.my
Broadcasting Services
N.A.I.C.S.: 516120
Sabri Ab Rahman (Pres)

PERUSA GMBH
Theatinerstrasse 40, 80333, Munich, Germany
Tel.: (49) 89 2388789 0   De
Web Site: http://www.perusa.de
Year Founded: 2007
Privater Equity Firm
N.A.I.C.S.: 523999
Christian Hollenberg (Co-Founder & Partner)

Subsidiaries:

Maredo Restaurants Holding GmbH (1)
Elisabethstrasse 22, 40217, Dusseldorf, Germany
Tel.: (49) 211386280
Web Site: http://www.maredo.com
Holding Company; Full-Service Steak Restaurants Owner & Operator
N.A.I.C.S.: 551112
Klaus Farrenkopf (CEO)

Subsidiary (Domestic):

Maredo Gaststatten-GmbH & Co. Betriebs-KG (2)
Elisabethstrasse 22, Dusseldorf, 40217, Germany
Tel.: (49) 211386280
Web Site: http://www.maredo.com
Full-Service Steak Restaurants Operator
N.A.I.C.S.: 722511

Perusa Partners Management Limited (1)
3 Cornet Street, Saint Peter Port, GY1 1BZ, Channel Islands, Guernsey
Tel.: (44) 148 174 9700
Web Site: http://www.perusafund.gg
Private Equity Fund Management Services
N.A.I.C.S.: 523940
Michael Geary (Dir-Investment)

Holding (Non-US):

BACTEC International Limited (2)
37 Riverside Sir Thomas Longley Road, Rochester, ME2 4DP, Kent, United Kingdom
Tel.: (44) 1634 296757
Web Site: http://www.bactec.com

Sales Range: $10-24.9 Million
Emp.: 27
Explosive Ordnance Disposal & Landmine Clearance Services
N.A.I.C.S.: 928110
Kevin Kannbona (CEO)

Subsidiary (Non-US):

BACTEC Cambodia (3)
56 St 242 Sangkat Chaktomuk, Khuan Duan Penh, Phnom Penh, Cambodia
Tel.: (855) 23 727 501
Explosive Ordnance Disposal & Landmine Clearance Services
N.A.I.C.S.: 928110

BACTEC Lao Ltd (3)
Unit 8 Phonsavanh Neua Village Sisattanak District, PO Box 6089, Sisattanak District, Vientiane, Lao People's Democratic Republic
Tel.: (856) 21 264 923
Web Site: http://www.bactec.com
Explosive Ordnance Disposal & Landmine Clearance Services
N.A.I.C.S.: 928110

BACTEC Mozambique Limited (3)
Av Das Industrias 4152, Matola, Mozambique
Tel.: (258) 21 734004
Explosive Ordnance Disposal & Landmine Clearance Services
N.A.I.C.S.: 928110

BACTEC SE Asia Pty. Ltd (3)
1A/75 Old Pittwater Road, Brookvale, 2210, NSW, Australia
Tel.: (61) 2 9905 7831
Explosive Ordnance Disposal & Landmine Clearance Services
N.A.I.C.S.: 928110

Holding (Non-US):

Schuberth Holding GmbH (2)
Brahmsstrasse 32, 81677, Munich, Germany
Tel.: (49) 391 8106 0
Holding Company; Motorcycle Helmet Mfr & Distr
N.A.I.C.S.: 551112

Subsidiary (Domestic):

Schuberth GmbH (3)
Stegelitzer Strasse 12, 39126, Magdeburg, Germany
Tel.: (49) 391 8106 0
Web Site: http://www.schuberth.com
Motorcycle Helmet Mfr & Distr
N.A.I.C.S.: 339113
Jan-Christian Becker (CEO)

Schuberth North America, LLC (3)
Romereschstr 33, Osnabruck, 49090, Germany
Tel.: (49) 9492150893
Web Site: http://www.schuberthnorthamerica.com
Motorcycle Helmet Distr
N.A.I.C.S.: 423990
Randy Northrup (Pres)

Holding (Non-US):

trovicor GmbH (2)
Machtlfinger Strasse 7, 81379, Munich, Germany
Tel.: (49) 89 20 80 35 500
Information Technology Monitoring & Intelligence Services
N.A.I.C.S.: 541519

PERUSAHAAN PERSEROAN INDONESIA TBK
Jl Japati No 1, Bandung, 40133, West Java, Indonesia
Tel.: (62) 224521404   Id
Web Site: https://www.telkom.co.id
TLK—(NYSE)
Rev.: $9,690,087,040
Assets: $18,640,507,480
Liabilities: $8,473,371,200
Net Worth: $10,167,136,280
Earnings: $2,091,587,520
Emp.: 6,960

Fiscal Year-end: 12/31/23
Holding Company; Telecommunication & Information Network Services
N.A.I.C.S.: 551112
Honesti Basyir (Dir-Grp Bus Dev)

Subsidiaries:

P.T. Citra Sari Makmur (1)
Chase Plaza 16th Floor, Jl Jendral Sudirman Kav 21, Jakarta, 12910, Indonesia
Tel.: (62) 215700194
Web Site: http://www.csmcom.com
Sales Range: $25-49.9 Million
Emp.: 300
Telecommunication Network Service; Owned 38.29% by PT Tigatra Media, 36.71% by Media Trio Ltd & 25.00% by Perusahaan Perseroan Persero PT Telekomunikasi Indonesia, Tbk
N.A.I.C.S.: 517111

P.T. Collega Inti Pratama (1)
Jl TB Simatupang RT 3/RW 3 Talavera Office Park, Cilandak Bar Kec Cilandak Kota, Jakarta Selatan, Indonesia
Tel.: (62) 2175924428
Web Site: https://www.collega.co.id
Information Technology Services
N.A.I.C.S.: 541519

P.T. Graha Telkomsigma (1)
Jl CBD lot VIII Nomor 8 Kelurahan lengkong gudang, Tangerang, Indonesia
Tel.: (62) 2180864830
Web Site: https://www.telkomsigma.co.id
Information Technology Services
N.A.I.C.S.: 541512

P.T. Metra TV (1)
Kawasan The Telkom Hub Gedung Telkom Landmark Tower II lantai 22, Jl Jenderal Gatot Subroto Kav 52 Kuningan Barat Mampang Prapatan, Jakarta, Indonesia
Tel.: (62) 1500039
Web Site: https://www.metra.tv
Subscription Television Broadcasting Services
N.A.I.C.S.: 516120

P.T. Nuon Digital Indonesia (1)
Telkom Landmark Tower 45 FL, Jl Jend Gatot Subroto Kav 52, Jakarta Selatan, Indonesia
Tel.: (62) 217244493
Web Site: https://nuon.id
Digital Content Services
N.A.I.C.S.: 518210

P.T. Pojok Celebes Mandiri (1)
Gedung STO Telkom Pasar Minggu Lt 2 Jalan Taman Margasatwa No 20, Pasar Minggu, Jakarta Selatan, Indonesia
Tel.: (62) 2127844132
Web Site: https://pointer.co.id
Travel Agency Services
N.A.I.C.S.: 561599

P.T.Bosnet Distribution Indonesia (1)
Mayapada Tower 11th Floor Jl Jenderal Sudirman Kav 28, Jakarta Selatan, 12920, Indonesia
Tel.: (62) 2183702981
Web Site: https://www.bosnetdis.com
Logistic Services
N.A.I.C.S.: 621491

PT Administrasi Medika (1)
Telkom Gambir Gedung C Jl Medan Merdeka Selatan No 12, Jakarta Pusat, 10110, Jakarta, Indonesia
Tel.: (62) 2134831100
Web Site: https://www.admedika.co.id
Emp.: 1,838
Information Technology Services
N.A.I.C.S.: 541519

PT Balebat Dedikasi Prima (1)
Jl Veteran II No 17 Teluk Pinang Ciawi, Bogor, 16720, Indonesia
Tel.: (62) 251 8247760
Web Site: http://www.balebat.co.id
Commercial Printing & Publishing Services
N.A.I.C.S.: 323111

PT Digital Aplikasi Solusi (1)
88 at Kasablanka 35th Floor, Jakarta, 12870, Indonesia
Tel.: (62) 2180640600

Web Site: https://www.digiserve.co.id
Information Technology Services
N.A.I.C.S.: 541511

PT Graha Yasa Selaras (1)
Jl WR Supratman No 66-68 Bandung Hotel Mercure Nexa Supratman, Bandung, Indonesia
Tel.: (62) 2287245817
Web Site: http://www.gys.co.id
Hotel Services
N.A.I.C.S.: 721110

PT Infomedia Nusantara (1)
Jl RS Fatmawati No 77-81, Jakarta Selatan, 12150, Indonesia
Tel.: (62) 217201221
Web Site: http://www.infomedia.co.id
Information Technology Services
N.A.I.C.S.: 541519

PT Infrastruktur Telekomunikasi Indonesia (1)
Telkom Landmark Tower Lt 19 Jl Gatot Subroto Kav 52, Jakarta Selatan, 12710, Indonesia
Tel.: (62) 2183708471
Web Site: http://www.telkominfra.co.id
Telecommunication Servicesb
N.A.I.C.S.: 517810

PT Melon Indonesia (1)
Telkom Landmark Tower 45 FL Jl Jend Gatot Subroto Kav 52, Jakarta Selatan, 12710, Indonesia
Tel.: (62) 217244493
Web Site: http://melon.id
Digital Advertising Services
N.A.I.C.S.: 541810

PT Metra Digital Media (1)
Telkom Landmark Tower Lt 18 Jl Jend Gatot Subroto Kav 52, Jakarta, 12710, Indonesia
Tel.: (62) 217518777
Web Site: https://www.mdmedia.co.id
Digital Marketing Services
N.A.I.C.S.: 541613

PT Multimedia Nusantara (1)
Telkom Landmark Tower 2 41st Floor, Jl Jendral Gatot Subroto Kav 52, Jakarta, 12710, Indonesia
Tel.: (62) 215210123
Web Site: https://www.telkommetra.co.id
Investment Management Service
N.A.I.C.S.: 523999

Subsidiary (Domestic):

PT Finnet Indonesia (2)
Telkom Landmark Tower lt 28 Jl Jendral Gatot Subroto kav 52, Jakarta, 12710, Indonesia
Tel.: (62) 8111337001
Web Site: https://www.finpay.id
Electronic Payment Services
N.A.I.C.S.: 522320
Syaiful Rahim (Dir-Bus & Mktg)

Subsidiary (Non-US):

PT Metra-Net (2)
Tel.: (62) 2179187250
Web Site: http://www.metranet.co.id
Internet Service Provider
N.A.I.C.S.: 517810

Subsidiary (Domestic):

PT Sigma Cipta Caraka (2)
Jl CBD lot VIII Nomor 8 Kelurahan lengkong gudang, Bumi Serpong Damai, Tangerang, 15321, Indonesia
Tel.: (62) 2180864830
Web Site: https://www.telkomsigma.co.id
Sales Range: $150-199.9 Million
Emp.: 100
Information Technology Consulting Services
N.A.I.C.S.: 541512
Sihmirmo Adi (CEO)

Subsidiary (Domestic):

P.T. Sigma Solusi Integrasi (3)
Menara Dea 8th Floor Jl Mega Kuningan Barat IX Kav E 4 3 No 1, Jakarta, 12950, Indonesia
Tel.: (62) 21 5761208
Information Technology Consulting Services
N.A.I.C.S.: 541512

PERUSAHAAN PERSEROAN INDONESIA TBK

Perusahaan Perseroan Indonesia Tbk—(Continued)

PT Sigma Metrasys (3)
The East Tower 36th Floor Unit 01 Jl Lingkar Mega Kuningan, Kav E3 2 No 1, Jakarta, 12950, Indonesia
Tel.: (62) 21 579 58175
Web Site: http://www.telkomsigma.co.id
Information Technology Consulting Services
N.A.I.C.S.: 541512

PT Signet Pratama (3)
Menara Dea 7th Floor Jl Mega Kuningan Barat IX Kav E 4 3 No 1, Jakarta, 12950, Indonesia
Tel.: (62) 215764040
Sales Range: $25-49.9 Million
Emp.: 10
System Integration & Networking Services
N.A.I.C.S.: 541512
Syarif Idrus *(Mng Dir)*

PT Nutech Integrasi (1)
Gedung Philips baru lt 1 Jl Warung Buncit kav 99, Pejaten Barat Pasar Minggu, Jakarta Selatan, 12510, Indonesia
Tel.: (62) 2127808111
Web Site: http://www.nutech-integrasi.com
Information Technology Services
N.A.I.C.S.: 541519

PT PINS Indonesia (1)
The Telkom Hub Tower II lt 42 Jl Jendral Gatot Subroto Kav 52, Jakarta Selatan, 12710, Indonesia
Tel.: (62) 2150820790
Web Site: http://www.pins.co.id
Telecommunication Servicesb
N.A.I.C.S.: 517810

PT Pramindo Ikat Nusantara (1)
Plaza Kuningan Annex Building 7th Floor Jl HR Rasuna Said Kav C11-C14, Jakarta, 12940, Indonesia
Tel.: (62) 21 5202560
Web Site: http://www.pramindo.com
Telecommunication Servicesb
N.A.I.C.S.: 517810

PT Telekomunikasi Indonesia International (1)
Tel.: (62) 2129952300
Web Site: http://www.telin.co.id
Sales Range: $50-74.9 Million
Emp.: 150
Telecommunication Servicesb
N.A.I.C.S.: 517810

Subsidiary (Non-US):

PT Telekomunikasi Indonesia International (Hong Kong) Ltd (2)
05 9/FL Ocean Center No 5 Canton Road, Tsim Sha Tsui, Kowloon, China (Hong Kong)
Tel.: (852) 3102 3309
Web Site: http://www.telin.hk
Emp.: 100
Telecommunication Servicesb
N.A.I.C.S.: 517810

PT Telekomunikasi Indonesia International Pte. Ltd. (2)
1 Maritime Square 09-63 HarbourFront Centre, Singapore, 99253, Singapore
Tel.: (65) 6278 8189
Web Site: http://www.telin.sg
Emp.: 14
Telecommunication Servicesb
N.A.I.C.S.: 517810

PT Telkom Akses (1)
Tel.: (62) 2129337000
Web Site: http://www.telkomakses.co.id
Broadband Network Services
N.A.I.C.S.: 517111

PT Telkom Landmark Tower (1)
The Telkom Hub Telkom Landmark Tower 3rd Floor Jl Jend Gatot Subroto, Kav 52, Jakarta, 12710, Indonesia
Tel.: (62) 2122533000
Web Site: https://www.tlt.co.id
Real Estate Services
N.A.I.C.S.: 531390
Didit Sulistyo *(Pres)*

PT Telkom Satelit Indonesia (1)
Telkom Landmark Tower Lt 21 Jl Jenderal Gatot Subroto Kav 52, Kuningan Barat Mampang Prapatan, Jakarta Selatan, 12710, Indonesia
Tel.: (62) 2127933230
Web Site: http://www.telkomsat.co.id
Telecommunication Servicesb
N.A.I.C.S.: 517810
Edi Witjara *(Co-Pres)*

PT. Telekomunikasi Selular (1)
Wisnamulia Gatot Sucbroto 42 M Floor 19th, 12710, Jakarta, Indonesia
Tel.: (62) 215240811
Web Site: http://www.telkomsel.com
Rev.: $827,368,000
Emp.: 2,500
GSM Operator
N.A.I.C.S.: 517112

Pt Graha Sarana Duta (1)
Jl Kebon Sirih No 10, Jakarta, 10110, Indonesia
Tel.: (62) 213800900
Web Site: http://www.telkomproperty.co.id
Property Management Services
N.A.I.C.S.: 531312
Rakhmad Tunggal Afifuddin *(Chm)*

TS Global Network Sdn. Bhd. (1)
Jalan teknokrat 1/2 cyber 3, 63000, Cyberjaya, Selangor, Malaysia
Web Site: http://www.tsgn.com.my
Satellite Equipment Services
N.A.I.C.S.: 811210

Telekomunikasi Indonesia International (Malaysia) Sdn. Bhd. (1)
Suite 7 03 Level 7 Wisma UOA II No 21 Jalan Pinang, 50450, Kuala Lumpur, Malaysia
Tel.: (60) 323320680
Telecommunication Servicesb
N.A.I.C.S.: 517810

Telekomunikasi Indonesia International Australia Pty. Ltd. (1)
Level 4-5 241 Commonwealth Street Surry Hills, Sydney, 2010, NSW, Australia
Tel.: (61) 292884600
Telecommunication Servicesb
N.A.I.C.S.: 517810

Telekomunikasi Indonesia International Inc. (1)
800 Wilshire Blvd 6th Fl Ste 620, Los Angeles, CA 90017
Tel.: (213) 289-3009
Telecommunication Servicesb
N.A.I.C.S.: 517810

Telekomunikasi Indonesia International Ltd. (1)
Suite 905 9/F Ocean Centre 5 Canton Road, Tsim Sha Tsui, Kowloon, China (Hong Kong)
Tel.: (852) 3 102 3309
Telecommunication Servicesb
N.A.I.C.S.: 517810

Telekomunikasi Indonesia International S.A. (1)
Timor Plaza 4th Floor Rua Presidente Nicolao Lobato, Comoro, Dili, Timor-Leste
Tel.: (670) 7 373 7373
Telecommunication Servicesb
N.A.I.C.S.: 517810

Telekomunikasi Indonesia Intl (Malaysia) Sdn. Bhd. (1)
Suite 7 03 Level 7 Wisma UOA 2 No 21 Jalan Pinang, 50450, Kuala Lumpur, Malaysia
Tel.: (60) 323320680
Telecommunication Servicesb
N.A.I.C.S.: 517810

PERUSAHAAN SADUR TIMAH MALAYSIA (PERSTIMA) BERHAD

PLO 255 Jalan Timah 3 Kawasan Perindustrian Pasir Gudang, 81700, Pasir Gudang, Johor, Malaysia
Tel.: (60) 72541200
Web Site: https://www.perstima.com.my
Year Founded: 1979
PERSTIM—(KLS)
Rev.: $309,549,206
Assets: $201,455,238
Liabilities: $86,800,212
Net Worth: $114,655,026
Earnings: $8,146,455
Emp.: 491
Fiscal Year-end: 03/31/23
Tin Plate Mfr
N.A.I.C.S.: 331110
Hoe Soon Wee *(Chm)*

Subsidiaries:

Perstima (Vietnam) Co., Ltd. (1)
No 15 VSIP Street 6, Vietnam Singapore Industrial Park, Thuan An, Binh Duong, Vietnam
Tel.: (84) 2743784090
Web Site: http://www.perstima.com.vn
Tinplate Product Mfr
N.A.I.C.S.: 331110

PERUVIAN METALS CORP.

10545 - 45 Avenue NW 250 Southridge NW Suite 300, Edmonton, T6H 4M9, AB, Canada
Tel.: (647) 370-5268
Web Site: https://www.peruvianmetals.com
Year Founded: 1997
DUVNF—(OTCQB)
Rev.: $839,084
Assets: $2,282,264
Liabilities: $1,147,078
Net Worth: $1,135,185
Earnings: $381,903
Fiscal Year-end: 12/31/20
Mineral Exploration Services
N.A.I.C.S.: 213114
Jeffrey J. Reeder *(Chm & CEO)*

Subsidiaries:

Minera Aguila de Oro SAC (1)
Calle Juan De Arona No 670 Dpto 401 Miraflores, San Isidro, Lima, Peru
Tel.: (51) 1 4221467
Mineral Mining Services
N.A.I.C.S.: 212390

PERVASIVE COMMODITIES LTD.

C-806 Titanium City Canter Near Sachin Tower 100 Ft Road, Satellite Jodhpur Char Rasta Ahmedabad, Ahmedabad, 380015, Gujarat, India
Tel.: (91) 8347056404
Web Site: https://pervasiveindia.com
Year Founded: 1956
517172—(BOM)
Rev.: $471,345
Assets: $26,386
Liabilities: $23,272
Net Worth: $3,114
Earnings: $1,104
Fiscal Year-end: 03/31/21
Electric Power Equipment Distr
N.A.I.C.S.: 423610
Bhavinkumar Patel *(CFO & Sec)*

PERVEZ AHMED CONSULTANCY SERVICES LTD.

20-K Gulberg II, Lahore, Pakistan
Tel.: (92) 4235714809
Web Site: http://pervezahmed.net
Year Founded: 2005
PASL—(PSX)
Rev.: $2,159
Assets: $300,949
Liabilities: $2,327,912
Net Worth: ($2,026,964)
Earnings: ($9,338)
Fiscal Year-end: 06/30/23
Financial Brokerage Services
N.A.I.C.S.: 523160

PERWYN LLP

Anchor House 15-19 Britton Street, London, SW3 3TY, United Kingdom
Tel.: (44) 20 7368 9209

INTERNATIONAL PUBLIC

Web Site: http://www.perwyn.co.uk
Holding Company
N.A.I.C.S.: 551112
Andrew Wynn *(Founder & Mng Partner)*

Subsidiaries:

Lowe Rental Ltd (1)
Knockmore Industrial Estate Moira Road Unit J Lisburn, London, United Kingdom
Tel.: (44) 2892604619
Refrigerator Mfr
N.A.I.C.S.: 333415
Rodney Lowry *(CEO)*

Subsidiary (Domestic):

PKL Group (UK) Ltd (2)
Stella Way Bishops Cleeve, Cheltenham, GL52 7DQ, Gloucestershire, United Kingdom
Tel.: (44) 1242663000
Web Site: http://www.pkl.co.uk
Sales Range: $50-74.9 Million
Catering Equipment Rental Services
N.A.I.C.S.: 532490
Lee Vines *(COO)*

Sumo Digital Ltd. (1)
Unit 32 Jessops Riverside, 800 Brightside Lane, Sheffield, S9 2RX, South Yorkshire, United Kingdom
Tel.: (44) 1142426766
Web Site: http://www.sumo-digital.com
Interactive Entertainment Software Publisher
N.A.I.C.S.: 513210
Paul Porter *(Co-Founder & Mng Dir)*

PESACARA A.D.

Edvina Zdovca 4, 24000, Subotica, Serbia
Tel.: (381) 24 558 616
Web Site: http://www.pescara.rs
Year Founded: 1997
Sales Range: Less than $1 Million
Emp.: 3
Agricultural Raw Material Whslr
N.A.I.C.S.: 424590

PESONA METRO HOLDINGS BHD

39 Jalan SB Indah 1/19 Taman Sungai Besi Indah, 43300, Seri Kembangan, Selangor, Malaysia
Tel.: (60) 389410818
Web Site: https://www.pesona.com.my
PESONA—(KLS)
Rev.: $74,176,068
Assets: $120,551,798
Liabilities: $84,821,975
Net Worth: $35,729,824
Earnings: ($630,688)
Emp.: 254
Fiscal Year-end: 12/31/22
Construction Services
N.A.I.C.S.: 236220
Subhi Dziyauddin *(Deputy Chm)*

Subsidiaries:

PM2 Building System Sdn. Bhd. (1)
39 Ground Floor Jalan SB Indah 1/19 Taman Sungai Besi Indah, 43300, Seri Kembangan, Selangor, Malaysia
Tel.: (60) 389410818
Web Site: http://www.pm2.com.my
Construction Services
N.A.I.C.S.: 236220

Pesona Saferay Sdn. Bhd. (1)
Lot 5930 Kawasan Perusahaan Kamunting, 34600, Perak, Malaysia
Tel.: (60) 5 891 1128
Web Site: http://www.gaudidecor.com
Polyurethane Products Mfr
N.A.I.C.S.: 325211

PESQUERA EXALMAR SAA

Av Victor Andres Belaunde 214, San Isidro, Lima, Peru
Tel.: (51) 14414420

AND PRIVATE COMPANIES — PETER WARREN AUTOMOTIVE HOLDINGS LTD.

Web Site:
https://www.exalmar.com.pe
Year Founded: 1976
EXALMC1—(LIM)
Rev.: $254,351,000
Assets: $679,102,000
Liabilities: $410,859,000
Net Worth: $268,243,000
Earnings: ($11,609,000)
Emp.: 1,320
Fiscal Year-end: 12/31/23
Food Mfr
N.A.I.C.S.: 311999
Cesar Mendoza Suarez *(Mgr-Innovation & Continuous Improvement)*

PESQUERA JARAMILLO LTDA
Carrera 92 64 C 54, Bogota, 917, Colombia
Tel.: (57) 12916400
Web Site:
http://www.pesquerajaramillo.com
Sales Range: $50-74.9 Million
Emp.: 170
Seafood Importer & Exporter
N.A.I.C.S.: 424460
Henry Arturo Garcia Gonzalez *(CEO)*

PESQUERA VERAZ S.A.
2820 Virrey Vertiz Av CP 7600, Mar del Plata, Argentina
Tel.: (54) 223 480 8414
Web Site:
http://www.pesqueraveraz.com.ar
Year Founded: 1987
Fishing Operations
N.A.I.C.S.: 114119
Evelina Contessi *(Pres)*

Subsidiaries:

Explotacion Pesquera De La Patagonia S.A. (1)
Carlos Pellegrini 855-9 Piso, C1009ABQ, Buenos Aires, Argentina
Tel.: (54) 1143259553
Web Site: http://www.pespasa.com.ar
Sales Range: $25-49.9 Million
Emp.: 22
Seafood Distr
N.A.I.C.S.: 424460

PESTECH INTERNATIONAL BERHAD
No 26 Jalan Utarid U5/14 Seksyen U5, 40150, Shah Alam, Selangor Darul Ehsan, Malaysia
Tel.: (60) 378452186
Web Site: https://www.pestech-international.com
Year Founded: 1991
5219—(KLS)
Rev.: $176,984,775
Assets: $750,109,140
Liabilities: $520,557,098
Net Worth: $229,552,043
Earnings: $9,239,175
Emp.: 780
Fiscal Year-end: 06/30/22
Power System Engineering
N.A.I.C.S.: 237130
Ah Hock Lim *(Chm)*

Subsidiaries:

ENERSOL Co. Ltd. (1)
1st Floor Lot 2 Bukit Garden Kg Bukit Kalam Jalan Mohd Salleh, Daerah Timur Laut, 87000, Labuan, Malaysia
Tel.: (60) 42811371
Laboratory Testing Services
N.A.I.C.S.: 541380

PESTECH (Cambodia) PLC (1)
AAA Tower 10th Floor Mao Tse Tong Blvd, SangKat Bueong Keng Kong I Khan ChamkarMorn, Phnom Penh, Cambodia
Tel.: (855) 23882105
Web Site: https://www.pestech.com.kh

Power Transmission Line Construction Services
N.A.I.C.S.: 237130

PESTECH Energy Sdn. Bhd. (1)
No 5 Jalan Jasmine 5 Seksyen BB10, Bukit Beruntung, 48300, Petaling Jaya, Malaysia
Tel.: (60) 78252186
Web Site: http://www.pestechenergy.com
Power Transmission Services
N.A.I.C.S.: 221121

Subsidiary (Non-US):

SystemCorp Energy Pty Ltd (2)
15/50 William St, Beckenham, Perth, 6107, WA, Australia
Tel.: (61) 862452100
Web Site: http://www.systemcorp.com.au
Electricity Utility Services
N.A.I.C.S.: 926130

PESTECH Technology Sdn. Bhd. (1)
B2-8-01 Block B2 Meritus Oasis Corporate Park No 2 Jalan PJU 1A/2, Ara Damansara, 47301, Petaling Jaya, Selangor Darul Ehsan, Malaysia
Tel.: (60) 378312186
Web Site: https://www.pestech-technology.com
Eletric Power Generation Services
N.A.I.C.S.: 221118

PESTELL NUTRITION INC.
141 Hamilton Road, New Hamburg, N3A 2H1, ON, Canada
Tel.: (519) 662-2877
Web Site: http://www.pestell.com
Year Founded: 1972
Pet Product Mfr

Subsidiaries:

Pestell Pet Products (1)
141 Hamilton Road, New Hamburg, N3A 2H1, ON, Canada
Tel.: (519) 662-2877
Web Site: https://www.pestellpet.com
Pet Product Mfr
N.A.I.C.S.: 459910

Subsidiary (US):

BPV Environmental (2)
511 76th St SW, Byron Center, MI 49315
Tel.: (616) 281-4502
Web Site:
https://www.bpvenvironmental.com
Administrative Management & General Management Consulting Service
N.A.I.C.S.: 541611

PET PLASTICS LIMITED
323 3rd Floor Panchratna Bldg Opera House Charni Road, Mumbai, 400 004, Maharashtra, India
Tel.: (91) 2223615564
Web Site:
https://www.petplasticslimited.com
Year Founded: 1985
Rev.: $36,785,240
Assets: $39,467,006
Liabilities: $17,215,895
Net Worth: $22,251,111
Earnings: $547,245
Fiscal Year-end: 03/31/18
Plastic Tank Mfr
N.A.I.C.S.: 326122
Afrin Shaikh *(Sec)*

PET PROTECT LIMITED
Furness House 53 Brighton Rd, RH1 6RD, Redhill, United Kingdom - England
Tel.: (44) 8456031294
Web Site: http://www.petprotect.co.uk
Year Founded: 1983
Sales Range: $25-49.9 Million
Emp.: 28
Pet Health Care Plans
N.A.I.C.S.: 812910

PETAL S.A.
99 A I Cuza Street, 735100, Husi, Vaslui, Romania
Tel.: (40) 235481781
Web Site: https://www.petal.ro
Year Founded: 1949
PETY—(BUC)
Rev.: $14,573,834
Assets: $19,288,895
Liabilities: $14,764,306
Net Worth: $4,524,588
Earnings: $1,241,564
Emp.: 119
Fiscal Year-end: 12/31/23
Oil Field Equipment & Metallurgical Equipment Mfr
N.A.I.C.S.: 333131

PETALING TIN BERHAD
No 118 Jalan Semangat, 46300, Petaling Jaya, Selangor, Malaysia
Tel.: (60) 379681222
Web Site: http://www.petalingtin.com
Sales Range: $1-9.9 Million
Property Development Services
N.A.I.C.S.: 531311

Subsidiaries:

Lembah Langat Development Sdn. Bhd. (1)
1st Floor No 118 Jln Semangat, 46300, Petaling Jaya, Selangor, Malaysia
Tel.: (60) 3 7968 1222
Residential Property Development Services
N.A.I.C.S.: 531390

PETAQUILLA MINERALS LTD.
777 Hornby Street Suite 1230, Vancouver, V6Z 1S4, BC, Canada
Tel.: (604) 694-0021
Web Site: http://www.petaquilla.com
Year Founded: 1985
Sales Range: $100-124.9 Million
Gold Exploration & Mining Services
N.A.I.C.S.: 212220
Richard Fifer *(Chm)*

PETARDS GROUP PLC
Parallel House 32 London Road, Guildford, GU1 2AB, United Kingdom
Tel.: (44) 1483230345
Web Site: https://www.petards.com
PEG—(AIM)
Rev.: $18,429,691
Assets: $15,490,227
Liabilities: $5,005,914
Net Worth: $10,484,314
Earnings: $1,174,428
Emp.: 87
Fiscal Year-end: 12/31/21
Security & Surveillance Systems
N.A.I.C.S.: 561621
Osman Abdullah *(CEO)*

Subsidiaries:

Petards (1)
390 Princesway North, Team Valley, Gateshead, NE11 0TU, Tyne and Wear, United Kingdom (100%)
Tel.: (44) 1914203000
Web Site: http://www.petards.com
Security System Services
N.A.I.C.S.: 561621

Petards EIMC Ltd. (1)
390 Princes Way, Team Vly Trading Est, Gateshead, NE110TU, Tyne and Wear, United Kingdom (100%)
Tel.: (44) 1914203030
Web Site: http://www.petards.com
Electrical Equipment & Component Mfr
N.A.I.C.S.: 335999

Petards Inc. (1)
The Natty Boh Tower 3600 O'Donnell St Ste 250, Baltimore, MD 21224 (100%)
Tel.: (410) 327-3001
Web Site: http://www.petards.com
Sales Range: $25-49.9 Million
Emp.: 10
Security System Services

N.A.I.C.S.: 561621

Petards International Ltd. (1)
390 Princes Way, Team Vly Trading Est, Gateshead, NE11 0TU, Tyne and Wear, United Kingdom (100%)
Tel.: (44) 8700704141
Web Site: http://www.petards.com
Sales Range: $25-49.9 Million
Computer Peripheral Equipment Mfr
N.A.I.C.S.: 334118

Petards Joyce-Loebl Ltd. (1)
390 Princesway Team Valley, Gateshead, NE11 0TU, Tyne & Wear, United Kingdom
Tel.: (44) 1914203000
Web Site: http://www.petards.com
Sales Range: $25-49.9 Million
Emp.: 100
Security Systems
N.A.I.C.S.: 561621

Petards Ltd. (1)
390 Princesway N, Team Valley, Gateshead, NE11 0TU, Tyne and Wear, United Kingdom (100%)
Tel.: (44) 1914203000
Web Site: http://www.petards.com
Sales Range: $25-49.9 Million
Security System Services
N.A.I.C.S.: 561621

Water Hall Group plc (1)
Parallel House 32 London Road, Guildford, GU1 2AB, Surrey, United Kingdom
Tel.: (44) 1483452333
Web Site: http://www.waterhallgroupplc.com
Emp.: 4
Holding Company
N.A.I.C.S.: 551112
Roger Dixon Musson *(Sec)*

Subsidiary (Domestic):

Water Hall (England) Limited (2)
Water Hall Quarry Lower Hadfield Road, Hertford, SG13 8LF, United Kingdom
Tel.: (44) 1992 582253
Sales Range: $25-49.9 Million
Emp.: 9
Waste Management Services
N.A.I.C.S.: 562219

PETER LANE CONCRETE LTD
14802 91 Street, Grande Prairie, T8V 8L7, AB, Canada
Tel.: (780) 532-8415
Web Site: http://www.peterlane.ca
Year Founded: 1978
Rev.: $15,584,196
Emp.: 20
Concrete Contract Services
N.A.I.C.S.: 327390
Wapady Gravel *(Owner)*

PETER RUPPEL GMBH & CO. KG
Bahnhofstrasse 70-100, 97922, Lauda, Germany
Tel.: (49) 93435050
Web Site: http://www.ruppel.de
Rev.: $33,212,500
Emp.: 202
Warehousing Services
N.A.I.C.S.: 493110
Thomas Rainer *(Mng Dir)*

PETER SMITH GM
42 Towncentre Drive, Belleville, K8N 4Z5, ON, Canada
Tel.: (866) 809-0224
Web Site:
http://www.petersmithgm.com
Year Founded: 2004
New & Used Car Dealers
N.A.I.C.S.: 441110
Cheryl Donaldson *(Mgr-Fin Svc)*

PETER WARREN AUTOMOTIVE HOLDINGS LTD.
13 Hume Highway, Warwick Farm, Sydney, 2170, NSW, Australia
Tel.: (61) 287775858
Web Site: https://www.pwah.com.au

PETER WARREN AUTOMOTIVE HOLDINGS LTD.

Peter Warren Automotive Holdings Ltd.—(Continued)
Year Founded: 1958
PWR—(ASX)
Rev.: $1,343,402,882
Assets: $785,586,490
Liabilities: $450,292,104
Net Worth: $335,294,386
Earnings: $36,749,038
Emp.: 1,800
Fiscal Year-end: 06/30/23
Holding Company
N.A.I.C.S.: 551112
Victor Cuthell *(Sec)*

Subsidiaries:

Burwood Mazda Pty. Limited (1)
59-63 Burwood Highway, Burwood, 3125, VIC, Australia
Tel.: (61) 391169081
Web Site: https://www.burwoodmazda.com.au
Automobile Parts Mfr & Distr
N.A.I.C.S.: 332999

Lismore Mazda Pty. Limited (1)
Corner Bruxner Hwy and Snow St, Lismore, 2480, NSW, Australia
Tel.: (61) 266260440
Web Site: https://www.lismoremazda.com.au
Automobile Parts Distr
N.A.I.C.S.: 441120

Robina Mazda Pty. Limited (1)
44 Brabham Circuit, Robina, 4226, QLD, Australia
Tel.: (61) 755885500
Web Site: https://www.robinamazda.com.au
Automobile Parts Distr
N.A.I.C.S.: 441120

Southport Mazda Pty. Limited (1)
Cnr Bay and High Street, Southport, 4215, QLD, Australia
Tel.: (61) 755838800
Web Site: https://www.southportmazda.com.au
Automobile Parts Distr
N.A.I.C.S.: 441120

Sunshine Group Pty. Limited (1)
125 Bunting Rd, Brooklyn, 3012, VIC, Australia
Tel.: (61) 393148300
Web Site: https://www.sunshinegroupe.com.au
Waste Management Recycling Services
N.A.I.C.S.: 562998

Sydney North Shore Automotive Pty. Limited (1)
555 Pacific Highway, Artarmon, 2064, NSW, Australia
Tel.: (61) 291052888
Web Site: https://www.sydneynorthshore.com.au
Automobile Parts Distr
N.A.I.C.S.: 441120

Tweed Heads Mazda Pty. Limited (1)
117-123 Minjungbal Drive, Tweed Heads, 2486, NSW, Australia
Tel.: (61) 755096710
Web Site: https://www.tweedmazda.com.au
Automobile Parts Distr
N.A.I.C.S.: 441120

PETERHOUSE CORPORATE FINANCE LIMITED
3rd Floor New Liverpool House, 15 Eldon Street, London, EC2M 7LD, United Kingdom
Tel.: (44) 20 7469 0930 UK
Web Site: http://www.pcorpfin.com
Emp.: 13
Financial Advisory & Brokerage Services
N.A.I.C.S.: 523940
Peter Greensmith *(CEO)*

PETERLABS HOLDINGS BHD
Lot 16014 PT No 24341 Jalan Nilam 3, Bandar Nilai Utama, 71800, Nilai, Negeri Sembilan, Malaysia
Tel.: (60) 67999090
Web Site: https://www.peterlabs.com.my
PLABS—(KLS)
Rev.: $34,208,004
Assets: $22,481,451
Liabilities: $6,311,394
Net Worth: $16,170,057
Earnings: $852,564
Fiscal Year-end: 12/31/22
Animal Health & Nutrition Products Mfr
N.A.I.C.S.: 311119
Tong Seng Lim *(Mng Dir)*

Subsidiaries:

PeterLabs Sdn Bhd (1)
Lot 16014 PT No 24341 Jalan Nilam 3, Bandar Nilai Utama, 71800, Nilai, Negeri Sembilan, Malaysia
Tel.: (60) 67999090
Web Site: http://plabs.peterlabs.com.my
Sales Range: $25-49.9 Million
Emp.: 80
Animal Nutrition Products Mfr & Distr
N.A.I.C.S.: 311119
Evon Yap *(Gen Mgr)*

PETERS MACGREGOR INVESTMENTS LIMITED
Suite 507 19a Boundary Street Rushcutters Bay, Sydney, 2011, NSW, Australia
Tel.: (61) 293322133
Web Site: http://www.petersmacgregor.com
Sales Range: $1-9.9 Million
Investment Services
N.A.I.C.S.: 523940
Leslie Wayne Peters *(Founder & Chief Investment Officer)*

PETERSBURG SOCIAL COMMERCIAL BANK, JSC
42 liter A Shpalernaya st, 191123, Saint Petersburg, Russia
Tel.: (7) 8123322626
Web Site: http://www.pscb.ru
Year Founded: 1993
Rev.: $18,094,262
Assets: $403,034,645
Liabilities: $354,068,398
Net Worth: $48,966,246
Earnings: $6,655,215
Emp.: 302
Fiscal Year-end: 12/31/18
Commercial Banking Services
N.A.I.C.S.: 522110
Nikolay A. Alekseev *(Deputy Chm-Mgmt Bd)*

PETERSEN PONTIAC BUICK GMC
10 Automall Rd, Sherwood Park, T8H 2N1, AB, Canada
Tel.: (780) 464-5123
Web Site: http://www.petersenpontiac.com
Sales Range: $50-74.9 Million
Emp.: 150
Automobile Dealers
N.A.I.C.S.: 441110
Pat Ehli *(Mgr-Parts)*

PETERSHILL PARTNERS PLC
Peterborough Court 133 Fleet Street, London, EC4A 2BB, United Kingdom
Tel.: (44) 2896930221 UK
Web Site: https://www.petershillpartners.com
Year Founded: 2007
PHLL—(LSE)
Rev.: $393,600,000
Assets: $5,722,100,000
Liabilities: $1,002,800,000
Net Worth: $4,719,300,000
Earnings: ($452,900,000)
Emp.: 1,800
Fiscal Year-end: 12/31/22
Investment Management Service
N.A.I.C.S.: 523999
Ali Raissi *(Mng Dir)*

PETGO CORPORATION
12F Harmony Tower 1-32-2 Honmachi, Nakano-ku, Tokyo, 164-0012, Japan
Tel.: (81) 353332830
Web Site: https://corp.petgo.jp
Year Founded: 2004
7140—(TKS)
Rev.: $65,472,050
Assets: $21,806,390
Liabilities: $14,383,360
Net Worth: $7,423,030
Earnings: $1,136,920
Emp.: 52
Fiscal Year-end: 03/31/24
Pet Care Product Mfr
N.A.I.C.S.: 311111
Fumihiko Koide *(CEO, CTO & Exec VP)*

PETKIM PETROKIMYA HOLDING A.S.
Siteler Mahallesi Necmettin Giritlioglu Cad SOCAR Turkiye, Aliaga Yonetim Binas No 6/1, 35800, Izmir, Turkiye
Tel.: (90) 2123050000
Web Site: https://www.petkim.com.tr
Year Founded: 1965
PETKM—(IST)
Rev.: $2,046,913,517
Assets: $3,244,059,244
Liabilities: $1,503,740,713
Net Worth: $1,740,318,531
Earnings: $251,071,586
Emp.: 2,383
Fiscal Year-end: 12/31/23
Petrochemical Products Mfr
N.A.I.C.S.: 325211
Riza Bozoklar *(VP-Supply Chain & Procurement)*

Subsidiaries:

Petlim Limancilik Ticaret A.S. (1)
Siteler Mahallesi Necmettin Giritlioglu Caddesi No 6/12, Aliaga, 35800, Izmir, Turkiye
Tel.: (90) 2324556555
Web Site: https://www.petlim.com.tr
Port Operation Services
N.A.I.C.S.: 488310

PETMIN LIMITED
37 Peter Place Lyme Park, Bryanston, 2021, South Africa
Tel.: (27) 11 706 1644
Web Site: http://www.petmin.co.za
Sales Range: $75-99.9 Million
Anthracite & Silica Mining Services
N.A.I.C.S.: 212322
Bradley Doig *(COO)*

Subsidiaries:

Tendele Coal Mining (Pty) Ltd (1)
Postnet Ste 208, Nkolokotho, Natal, 3935, South Africa
Tel.: (27) 828951378
Sales Range: $100-124.9 Million
Emp.: 250
Mining Support Services
N.A.I.C.S.: 213114

PETO MACCALLUM LTD.
165 Cartwright Avenue, Toronto, M6A 1V5, ON, Canada
Tel.: (416) 785-5110
Web Site: http://www.petomaccallum.com
Year Founded: 1973
Rev.: $12,927,280
Emp.: 150
Engineeering Services

INTERNATIONAL PUBLIC

N.A.I.C.S.: 541330
Judy Singh *(Sec)*

PETPAL PET NUTRITION TECHNOLOGY CO., LTD.
No 2 Chongle Road Shuitou Town Industrial Park, Pingyang County, Wenzhou, 325405, Zhejiang, China
Tel.: (86) 57758189955
Web Site: http://www.peidibrand.com
Year Founded: 2002
300673—(CHIN)
Rev.: $243,144,720
Assets: $405,559,440
Liabilities: $135,793,476
Net Worth: $269,765,964
Earnings: $17,847,648
Fiscal Year-end: 12/31/22
Pet Food Mfr & Distr
N.A.I.C.S.: 311111
Chen Zhenbiao *(Chm & Gen Mgr)*

PETRA DIAMONDS LIMITED
One Heddon Street, London, W1B 4BD, United Kingdom
Tel.: (44) 2074948203
Web Site: https://www.petradiamonds.com
PDL—(LSE)
Rev.: $367,000,000
Assets: $772,000,000
Liabilities: $555,000,000
Net Worth: $217,000,000
Earnings: ($104,000,000)
Emp.: 3,004
Fiscal Year-end: 06/30/24
Diamond Mining Services
N.A.I.C.S.: 212311
Adonis Pouroulis *(Chm)*

Subsidiaries:

Cullinan Diamond Mine (Pty) Ltd (1)
Oak Av 1015 Pb X, Cullinan, Pretoria, South Africa
Tel.: (27) 12 3052911
Diamond Mining Services
N.A.I.C.S.: 212290

Dancarl Diamonds (Pty) Ltd (1)
District Barkly West, Barkly West, 8375, Northern Cape, South Africa
Tel.: (27) 53 5216
Diamond Mining Services
N.A.I.C.S.: 212319

Messina Diamond Mine (Pty) Ltd (1)
Bellsbank Farm, Warrenton, 8530, Northern Cape, South Africa
Tel.: (27) 535519200
Emp.: 108
Diamond Mining Services
N.A.I.C.S.: 212311
Christo du Preez *(Gen Mgr)*

Subsidiary (Domestic):

Sedibeng Diamond Mine JV (2)
86 Bellsbank, Windsorton, South Africa
Tel.: (27) 53 5519200
Diamond Mining Services
N.A.I.C.S.: 212390

PETRA EDUCATION COMPANY
7th Circle Royal Jordanian Building Third Floor Office No 308, PO Box 143203, Amman, 11814, Jordan
Tel.: (962) 65857469
Web Site: https://petraeduco.com
Year Founded: 1990
PEDC—(AMM)
Rev.: $33,937,828
Assets: $72,300,972
Liabilities: $12,311,262
Net Worth: $59,989,710
Earnings: $6,514,009
Emp.: 505
Fiscal Year-end: 12/31/20
Educational Support Services
N.A.I.C.S.: 611710

AND PRIVATE COMPANIES

Mohammed Hisham Al-ansari *(Chm)*

PETRA ENERGY BERHAD
Suite 13 02 Level 13 Menara OBYU 4 Jalan PJU 8/8A, Bandar Damansara Perdana, 47820, Petaling Jaya, Selangor, Malaysia
Tel.: (60) 377265576
Web Site:
https://www.petraenergy.com.my
PENERGY—(KLS)
Rev.: $78,460,106
Assets: $133,334,815
Liabilities: $51,360,635
Net Worth: $81,974,180
Earnings: $2,767,407
Emp.: 70
Fiscal Year-end: 12/31/22
Marine Services
N.A.I.C.S.: 211120
Ahmadi Yusoff *(Exec Dir)*

Subsidiaries:

Jurutera Perunding Akal Sdn Bhd (1)
Lot 908 Jalan Desa Senadin 1A Off Jalan Marigold, Senadin Industrial Estate, 98100, Miri, Sarawak, Malaysia
Tel.: (60) 85668178
Web Site: http://www.akal.com.my
Sales Range: $25-49.9 Million
Engineering Consulting Services
N.A.I.C.S.: 541330

Petra Fabricators Sdn Bhd (1)
Lot 58 Jalan Utas 15/7 Kawasan Perusahaan Seksyen 15, 40000, Shah Alam, Selangor, Malaysia
Tel.: (60) 355112000
Web Site: http://sa.petra.com.my
Sales Range: $50-74.9 Million
Emp.: 120
Pressure Vessels Mfr
N.A.I.C.S.: 333249
Ng Teik Heng *(Gen Mgr)*

Petra Marine Sdn. Bhd. (1)
Lot 651 H S Chin Building Lorong 2 Krokop 2, 98000, Miri, Sarawak, Malaysia
Tel.: (60) 85463888
Marine Services
N.A.I.C.S.: 211120

Petra Resources Sdn Bhd (1)
Lot 2000 Piasau Industrial Estate, PO Box 1618, 98000, Miri, Sarawak, Malaysia
Tel.: (60) 85652699
Sales Range: $100-124.9 Million
Emp.: 268
Oil Field Equipment Mfr
N.A.I.C.S.: 333914

PETRATHERM LIMITED
169 Fullarton Road, Dulwich, 5065, SA, Australia
Tel.: (61) 881335000
Web Site:
http://www.petratherm.com.au
PTR—(ASX)
Rev.: $38,684
Assets: $3,852,137
Liabilities: $199,310
Net Worth: $3,652,827
Earnings: ($701,614)
Fiscal Year-end: 06/30/24
Eletric Power Generation Services
N.A.I.C.S.: 221118
Donald Clinton Stephens *(Sec)*

PETREL RESOURCES PLC
162 Clontarf Road, Dublin, D03 F6Y0, Ireland
Tel.: (353) 18332833 IE
Web Site:
https://www.petrelresources.com
Year Founded: 1997
PET—(AIM)
Assets: $850,746
Liabilities: $1,094,380
Net Worth: ($243,634)
Earnings: ($527,143)

Emp.: 3
Fiscal Year-end: 12/31/23
Oil & Gas Exploration Services
N.A.I.C.S.: 211120
David Horgan *(Mng Dir)*

PETRICHOR ENERGY INC.
Suite 303 - 595 Howe Street, Box 4, Vancouver, V6C 2T5, BC, Canada
Tel.: (604) 336-8615
Web Site:
https://www.petrichorenergy.com
ODEFF—(OTCEM)
Assets: $180
Liabilities: $8,744,305
Net Worth: ($8,744,126)
Earnings: ($535,045)
Fiscal Year-end: 12/31/22
Oil & Gas Exploration Services
N.A.I.C.S.: 213112
Richard Barnett *(CFO & Sec)*

PETRO IVOIRE S.A.
Abidjan Vridi, BP 12, CI-737, Abidjan, Cote d'Ivoire
Tel.: (225) 21 75 88 40
Web Site: http://www.petroivoire.ci
Sales Range: $75-99.9 Million
Gas Stations
N.A.I.C.S.: 457110

PETRO MATAD LIMITED
Victory House, Douglas, Isle of Man
Tel.: (44) 1624627099 IM
Web Site:
https://www.petromatadgroup.com
Year Founded: 2007
MATD—(AIM)
Rev.: $351,000
Assets: $21,403,000
Liabilities: $348,000
Net Worth: $21,055,000
Earnings: ($5,926,000)
Fiscal Year-end: 12/31/23
Oil & Gas Exploration Services
N.A.I.C.S.: 213112
John Rene Henriksen *(CFO)*

PETRO RIO S.A.
Praia de Botafogo 370, Rio de Janeiro, Brazil
Tel.: (55) 2137213800
Web Site: https://prio3.com.br
PETR4—(BRAZ)
Rev.: $91,523,924,561
Assets: $187,856,486,667
Liabilities: $119,509,480,028
Net Worth: $68,347,006,638
Earnings: $22,374,644,120
Emp.: 211
Fiscal Year-end: 12/31/23
Oil & Natural Gas Exploration & Other Related Services
N.A.I.C.S.: 211120
Roberto Bernardes Monteiro *(CEO & Officer-IR)*

Subsidiaries:

Dommo Energia S.A. (1)
Rua Lauro Muller 116 38 andar, Botafogo, Rio de Janeiro, 22290-160, Brazil
Tel.: (55) 21 2196 4606
Web Site: http://www.dommoenergia.com.br
Sales Range: $125-149.9 Million
Oil & Gas Field Related Services
N.A.I.C.S.: 213112
Marko Jovovic *(Chm)*

Subsidiary (Domestic):

Oleo e Gas Participacoes S.A. (2)
Rua Lauro Muller 116 - 38 andar, Botafogo, Rio de Janeiro, 22290-160, Brazil
Tel.: (55) 21 21964699
Web Site: http://www.ogpar.com.br
Oil & Natural Gas Exploration & Production Services
N.A.I.C.S.: 211120

HRT America Inc. (1)
1254 Enclave Pkwy Ste 640 6th Fl, Houston, TX 77077
Tel.: (281) 501-5600
Oil & Gas Exploration Services
N.A.I.C.S.: 213112

HRT O&G Exploracao e Producao de Petroleo Ltda. (1)
Atlantica Ave 1130, E 10 andares Copacabana, Rio de Janeiro, Brazil
Tel.: (55) 21 2105 9700
Oil & Gas Exploration Services
N.A.I.C.S.: 213112

PETRO VIETNAM OIL CORPORATION
Floor 14-18 PetroVietnam Tower 1 - 5 Le Duan, Ben Nghe Ward Distrist 1, Ho Chi Minh City, 70000, Vietnam
Tel.: (84) 2839106990 VN
Web Site: http://www.pvoil.com.vn
Year Founded: 2008
Oil Import & Export Services
N.A.I.C.S.: 213112
Cao Hoai Duong *(Pres, CEO & Member-Mgmt Bd)*

Subsidiaries:

Petro Vietnam Oil Corporation Ba Ria Vung Tau Unit (1)
9 Nguyen Thai Hoc Ward 7, Vung Tau, Vietnam
Tel.: (84) 643859623
Oil Import & Export Services
N.A.I.C.S.: 213112

Petro Vietnam Oil Corporation Dinh Vu Unit (1)
Lo F6 KCN Dinh Vu Dong Hai 2, Hai An, Haiphong, Vietnam
Tel.: (84) 313741788
Oil Import & Export Services
N.A.I.C.S.: 213112

Petro Vietnam Oil Corporation Ha Tinh Unit (1)
417 Tran Phu P Thach Linh Thanh pho, Ha Tinh, Vietnam
Tel.: (84) 393692555
Oil Import & Export Services
N.A.I.C.S.: 213112

Petro Vietnam Oil Corporation Mien Dong Unit (1)
54B Duong 30/4 P Thang Nhat TP, Vung Tau, Vietnam
Tel.: (84) 643594568
Oil Import & Export Services
N.A.I.C.S.: 213112

Petro Vietnam Oil Corporation Nha Be Unit (1)
Ap 4 Xa Phu Xuan Huyen, Nha Be, Ho Chi Minh City, Vietnam
Tel.: (84) 837827612
Oil Import & Export Services
N.A.I.C.S.: 213112

Petro Vietnam Oil Corporation PV TECH PRO Unit (1)
17th Floor DMC Tower 353 - Kim Ma, Ba Dinh, Hanoi, Vietnam
Tel.: (84) 444564888
Oil Import & Export Services
N.A.I.C.S.: 213112

Societe Shell du Laos (1)
143 Sithane Road, Vientiane, Lao People's Democratic Republic
Tel.: (856) 21212842
Petroleum Marketing
N.A.I.C.S.: 211120

PETRO VIKING ENERGY INC.
Macleod Place II Suite 500 5940 Macleod Trail SW, Calgary, T2H 2G4, AB, Canada
Tel.: (587) 315-0326 AB
Web Site: http://www.petroviking.com
Year Founded: 2010
Sales Range: Less than $1 Million
Oil & Gas Extraction
N.A.I.C.S.: 211130
Lars Glimhagen *(CFO)*

PETRO WELT TECHNOLOGIES AG
Kaerntner Ring 11-13, A-1010, Vienna, Austria
Tel.: (43) 153523200
Web Site: http://pewete.com
O2C—(DEU)
Rev.: $15,888,193
Assets: $175,683,143
Liabilities: $148,429,743
Net Worth: $27,253,400
Earnings: ($444,432,333)
Emp.: 114
Fiscal Year-end: 12/31/22
Oil & Gas Exploration Services
N.A.I.C.S.: 213112
Maurice Gregoire Dijols *(Chm-Supervisory Bd)*

Subsidiaries:

OOO Kat-Oil Drilling (1)
314 Kirova Ave, Samara, 443125, Samara region, Russia
Tel.: (7) 8463130092
Oil Field Services
N.A.I.C.S.: 213112

OOO Katkonef (1)
8 Yantarnaya St, Kogalym, 628481, Tyumen region, Russia
Tel.: (7) 3466750110
Oil Field Services
N.A.I.C.S.: 213112

OOO Katobneft (1)
66 A Industrialnaya St, Nizhnevartovsk, 628600, Tyumen region, Russia
Tel.: (7) 3466311166
Oil Field Services
N.A.I.C.S.: 213112

OOO Petro Welt Technologies (1)
4 Building 1 2nd Kazachiy Lane, Moscow, 119180, Russia
Tel.: (7) 4957807327
Hydraulic Fracturing Proppant Mfr
N.A.I.C.S.: 327999
Christian Jennevin *(VP-Global BD & Ops)*

OOO Wellprop (1)
Etkulskiy Tract 11, Kopeysk, 456658, Chelyabinsk, Russia
Tel.: (7) 3512472030
Proppant Mfr
N.A.I.C.S.: 327999

Too Petro Welt Kazakhstan (1)
74/1 Micro District 14 St 2nd Floor BC K7 Group, Aktau, Kazakhstan
Tel.: (7) 7242272929
Oil Field Services
N.A.I.C.S.: 213112

PETRO-KING OILFIELD SERVICES LIMITED
Room 705-710 F7 Building A Tiley Central Plaza No 3 Haide Road, Nanshan District, Shenzhen, 518054, Guangdong, China
Tel.: (86) 75586331788
Web Site: http://www.petro-king.cn
2178—(HKG)
Rev.: $40,005,803
Assets: $104,985,030
Liabilities: $71,613,818
Net Worth: $33,371,213
Earnings: ($3,511,350)
Emp.: 248
Fiscal Year-end: 12/31/22
Oilfield Engineering & Consulting
N.A.I.C.S.: 541330
Jinlong Wang *(Chm)*

Subsidiaries:

Petro-king Group Middle East Corporation FZCO (1)
Room 342-341 Building 5WB DAFZA, PO Box 371823, Dubai, United Arab Emirates
Tel.: (971) 42323310
Well Drilling & Completion Services
N.A.I.C.S.: 213111
Andrew Rumford *(Dir-Global Ops)*

PETRO-KING OILFIELD SERVICES LIMITED

Petro-King Oilfield Services Limited—(Continued)

Petro-king International Company Limited **(1)**
Level 17 Tower 2 Silvercord No 30 Canton Road, Tsim Sha Tsui, Kowloon, China (Hong Kong)
Tel.: (852) 23978392
Well Drilling & Completion Services
N.A.I.C.S.: 213111

Petro-king Oilfield Technology Limited **(1)**
Room 705-710 7/F Building A Tiley Central Plaza No 3 Haide Road, Nanshan, Shenzhen, Guangdong, China
Tel.: (86) 75586331788
Web Site: https://www.petro-king.cn
Well Drilling & Completion Services
N.A.I.C.S.: 213111
Wang Jinlong *(Chm & Exec Dir)*

Star Petrotech Pte. Ltd. **(1)**
No 33 Gul Avenue, Singapore, 629673, Singapore
Tel.: (65) 68631720
Web Site: https://www.starpetrotech.com
Downhole Completion Equipment Mfr
N.A.I.C.S.: 333132

PETROBRESS
13 Pl Comte Andre D Estampes, 71270, Chalon-sur-Saone, France
Tel.: (33) 385762205
Web Site: http://www.livraison-fioul-saone-loire.fr
Sales Range: $25-49.9 Million
Emp.: 10
Oil & Fuel Mfr & Distr
N.A.I.C.S.: 213112
Rene Thibert *(Pres)*

PETROCAPITA INCOME TRUST
8561 - 8A Avenue SW Suite 2210, Calgary, T3H 0V5, AB, Canada
Tel.: (587) 887-1541   AB
Web Site: http://www.petrocapita.com
Year Founded: 2010
Oil & Gas Related Services
N.A.I.C.S.: 213112
Richard Mellis *(Pres & CEO)*

PETROCART SA
Strada Decebal Nr 171, Piatra Neamt, 610052, Romania
Tel.: (40) 233218330
Web Site: http://www.petrocart.ro
Sales Range: $10-24.9 Million
Emp.: 254
Paper & Cardboard Mfr
N.A.I.C.S.: 322130

PETROCHEMICAL INDUSTRIES INVESTMENT CO.
3 Jaleh Alley South Shiraz Ave, Tehran, 14369 54111, Iran
Tel.: (98) 2188052043
Web Site: http://www.piicgroup.com
Year Founded: 1992
Petrochemical Mfr
N.A.I.C.S.: 325110
A. H. Pahlevan *(Vice Chm & Supvr)*

PETROCHEMICAL TRANSPORTATION ENGINEERING CO.
No 32 Darya Blv Saadat Abad, Tehran, Iran
Tel.: (98) 2188576451
Web Site: https://www.ptec-ir.com
Year Founded: 1991
HJPT1—(THE)
Sales Range: Less than $1 Million
Logistic Services
N.A.I.C.S.: 541614
Mohsen Kafaeekhoo *(Vice Chm)*

Subsidiaries:

Jahan Deniz Kala W.S.C **(1)**
No 32 Darya Street, Saadatabad, Tehran, Iran
Tel.: (98) 2188377176
Web Site: http://www.wsc-ir.com
Cargo Services
N.A.I.C.S.: 481112
Forough Naderi *(Head-Mktg Dept)*

Terminals and Tanks Petrochemical Co. **(1)**
North Sheikh Bahai St Above Sheikh Bahai Square 12 Meters 2-No 6, PO Box 1995863793, Second Floor, Tehran, Iran
Tel.: (98) 2188062248
Web Site: http://www.ttpc.ir
Offshore & Terminal Services
N.A.I.C.S.: 488310

PETROENERGY RESOURCES CORPORATION
7th Floor JMT Building ADB Ave Ortigas Business Center, Pasig, 1600, Philippines
Tel.: (63) 26372917
Web Site: https://www.petroenergy.com.ph
PERC—(PHI)
Rev.: $60,487,290
Assets: $395,094,148
Liabilities: $166,350,476
Net Worth: $228,743,672
Earnings: $17,047,584
Fiscal Year-end: 12/31/23
Technical Services for Oil Exploration
N.A.I.C.S.: 213112
Arlan P. Profeta *(Officer-Alternate Information, Compliance Officer & Asst Sec)*

PETROFAC LIMITED
26 New Street, St Helier, Jersey, JE2 3RA, United Kingdom
Tel.: (44) 2078114900
Web Site: https://www.petrofac.com
Year Founded: 1981
PFC—(LSE)
Rev.: $2,591,000,000
Assets: $3,267,000,000
Liabilities: $3,155,000,000
Net Worth: $112,000,000
Earnings: ($523,000,000)
Fiscal Year-end: 12/31/22
Petroleum Factories Operator & Builder
N.A.I.C.S.: 333132
Rob Jewkes *(COO-IES)*

Subsidiaries:

Oilennium Limited **(1)**
36 North Quay, Great Yarmouth, Norfolk, NR30 1JE, United Kingdom
Tel.: (44) 1493278300
Learning Management System Services
N.A.I.C.S.: 611430

Petrofac Energy Limited **(1)**
Petrofac House Al-Khan Road, PO Box 23467, Sharjah, United Arab Emirates
Tel.: (971) 65740999
Web Site: http://www.petrofac.com.ae
Sales Range: $25-49.9 Million
Emp.: 10
Petroleum Refining Services
N.A.I.C.S.: 324110

Petrofac Engineering India Private Limited **(1)**
7th Floor Ventura Central Avenue Hiranandani Business Park, Powai, Mumbai, 400076, India
Tel.: (91) 2230513100
Emp.: 17
Oil & Natural Gas Services
N.A.I.C.S.: 211130

Petrofac Engineering Services India Private Limited **(1)**
12th Floor Building 14 Tower B DLF Cyber City Sector 24 & 25A, Delhi, 122 002, India
Tel.: (91) 1243878000

Engineering Services
N.A.I.C.S.: 541330

Petrofac Inc. **(1)**
16340 Park Ten Pl Ste 130, Houston, TX 77084
Tel.: (832) 460-4985
Web Site: https://www.petrofac.com
Sales Range: $25-49.9 Million
Emp.: 50
Oil & Gas Field Machinery
N.A.I.C.S.: 333132

Petrofac International Ltd **(1)**
5th Floor 23 Novoslobodskaya Street, 127055, Moscow, Russia **(100%)**
Tel.: (7) 959670258
Sales Range: $25-49.9 Million
Emp.: 10
N.A.I.C.S.: 333132

Petrofac International Ltd. **(1)**
40 Jabbar Jabarli St Castem BussCtr 6th Fl, 370065, Baku, Azerbaijan **(100%)**
Tel.: (994) 12978063
Web Site: http://www.petrofac.com
Sales Range: $25-49.9 Million
Emp.: 25
Oil & Gas Field Machinery
N.A.I.C.S.: 333132

Petrofac International Ltd. **(1)**
Petrofac House Al-Khan Road, PO Box 23467, Sharjah, 23467, United Arab Emirates **(100%)**
Tel.: (971) 65740999
Web Site: http://www.petrofac.com
Sales Range: $800-899.9 Million
Emp.: 4,000
N.A.I.C.S.: 333132

Petrofac International, Damascus **(1)**
Mezzah Eastern Villas Jadet El Shafei Farabi Street, PO Box 30180, Building 167/A First Floor, Damascus, Syria
Tel.: (963) 116132399
Web Site: http://www.petrofac.com
N.A.I.C.S.: 333132

Petrofac Mexico SA de CV **(1)**
Prol 27 de Febrero No 4506 Tabasco 2000, Villahermosa, 86035, Mexico
Tel.: (52) 9933108560
Oil & Natural Gas Services
N.A.I.C.S.: 211130

Petrofac South East Asia Pte Ltd **(1)**
10th Floor Shinawatra Tower 3 1010 Viphavadi Rangsit Road, Chatuchak, Bangkok, 10900, Thailand
Tel.: (66) 62490025
Oil & Natural Gas Services
N.A.I.C.S.: 211130

Sakhalin Technical Training Centre **(1)**
6G Mira Avenue, 693012, Yuzhno-Sakhalinsk, Russia
Tel.: (7) 4242495900
Web Site: http://en.sttc.net.ru
Emp.: 12,500
Oil & Natural Gas Services
N.A.I.C.S.: 211130

Scotvalve Services Limited **(1)**
Tofthills Avenue Midmill Business Park, Kintore, Edinburgh, AB51 0QP, Aberdeenshire, United Kingdom
Tel.: (44) 1467631400
Oil & Gas Equipment Mfr
N.A.I.C.S.: 333132

W&W Energy Services Inc. **(1)**
110 W 5th St, Odessa, TX 79761
Tel.: (432) 561-8669
Web Site: https://wandwenergy.com
Emp.: 300
Oil & Renewable Energy Distr
N.A.I.C.S.: 486210

PETROFRONTIER CORP.
Suite 900 903 - 8 Avenue SW, Calgary, T2P 0P7, AB, Canada
Tel.: (403) 718-0366   AB
Web Site: https://www.petrofrontier.com
Year Founded: 2009
PFC—(TSXV)
Rev.: $2,845,947

INTERNATIONAL PUBLIC

Assets: $14,174,265
Liabilities: $14,815,221
Net Worth: ($640,956)
Earnings: ($10,220,948)
Fiscal Year-end: 12/31/23
Oil & Gas Exploration
N.A.I.C.S.: 211120
Michael John Hibberd *(Dir-Ops)*

PETROGRESS, INC.
10 Sp Trikoupi Str, 18538, Piraeus, Greece
Tel.: (30) 2104599741   DE
Web Site: https://www.petrogressinc.com
Year Founded: 2010
PGAS—(OTCEM)
Rev.: $15,961,220
Assets: $12,407,099
Liabilities: $3,893,258
Net Worth: $8,513,841
Earnings: ($2,984,681)
Emp.: 12
Fiscal Year-end: 12/31/19
Holding Company; Oil & Gas Whslr & Shipping Services
N.A.I.C.S.: 551112
Evangelos Makris *(CFO)*

PETROKEMIJA D.D.
Aleja Vukovar 4, 44320, Kutina, Croatia
Tel.: (385) 44647122
Web Site: http://en.petrokemija.hr
PTKM-R-A—(ZAG)
Rev.: $295,222,778
Assets: $200,189,064
Liabilities: $96,546,660
Net Worth: $103,642,404
Earnings: $43,374,259
Emp.: 1,381
Fiscal Year-end: 12/31/20
Fertilizer Mfr
N.A.I.C.S.: 325311
Gordana Jugovic *(Mgr-Corp Comm)*

Subsidiaries:

Petrokemija d.o.o. Novi Sad **(1)**
Ilije Ognjanovica 28, Novi Sad, 21000, Vojvodina, Serbia
Tel.: (381) 21424472
Web Site: http://www.petrokemija.rs
Sales Range: $50-74.9 Million
Emp.: 4
Fertilizer Whslr
N.A.I.C.S.: 424910

Restoran Petrokemija d.o.o. **(1)**
Aleja Vukovar 4, Kutina, 44320, Sisak-Moslavina, Croatia
Tel.: (385) 44647145
Web Site: http://www.restoran-petrokemija.hr
Sales Range: $10-24.9 Million
Emp.: 6
Restaurant Management Services
N.A.I.C.S.: 722511

PETROKENT TURIZM A.S.
Billur Street No 1, Barbaros District Kavaklidere, Ankara, Türkiye
Tel.: (90) 3124671515
Web Site: https://www.petrokent.com.tr
Year Founded: 1989
PKENT—(IST)
Home Management Services
N.A.I.C.S.: 721110
Ali Ercan *(Chm)*

PETROL AD-SOFIA
Cherni vrah No 43, 1407, Sofia, Bulgaria
Tel.: (359) 29690453   BG
Web Site: https://www.petrol.bg
Year Founded: 1932
PET—(BUL)
Rev.: $273,795,465
Assets: $69,581,508

AND PRIVATE COMPANIES

Liabilities: $67,744,851
Net Worth: $1,836,656
Earnings: ($13,905,565)
Emp.: 1,189
Fiscal Year-end: 12/31/21
Petroleum Product Mfr
N.A.I.C.S.: 324199
Georgi Tatarski *(Deputy Chm-Mgmt Bd & Exec Dir)*

PETROL, SLOVENSKA ENERGETSKA DRUZBA, D.D.
Dunajska cesta 50, 1000, Ljubljana, Slovenia
Tel.: (386) 14714232
Web Site: https://www.petrol.eu
PETG—(LJU)
Rev.: $3,782,282,305
Assets: $2,201,102,437
Liabilities: $1,185,753,967
Net Worth: $1,015,348,469
Earnings: $88,838,651
Emp.: 5,157
Fiscal Year-end: 12/31/20
Oil & Petroleum Products Distr
N.A.I.C.S.: 424720
Zoran Gracner *(Member-Mgmt Bd & Dir-Labor)*

Subsidiaries:

Atet d.o.o. (1)
Zgornji Brnik 130a, 4210, Ljubljana, Slovenia
Tel.: (386) 13208230
Web Site: https://www.atet.si
Car Rental Services
N.A.I.C.S.: 532111

Beogas d.o.o. (1)
Omladinskih brigada 88-90, 11090, Belgrade, Serbia
Tel.: (381) 117850800
Web Site: https://www.beogas.rs
Natural Gas Distribution Services
N.A.I.C.S.: 221210

Crodux Derivati Dva d.o.o. (1)
Savska Opatovina 36, Zagreb, 10000, Croatia
Tel.: (385) 1 665 14 00
Web Site: http://www.crodux-derivati.hr
Natural Gas Distr Services
N.A.I.C.S.: 221210
Ivan Cermak *(Founder)*

Cypet Oils Ltd. (1)
333 28th October St, PO Box 3311, Ariadne House Ofc No 52, 57019, Limassol, Cyprus
Tel.: (357) 25586039
Web Site: http://www.petrol.si
Oil Trading Services
N.A.I.C.S.: 213112

Geoplin d.o.o. (1)
Cesta Ljubljanske Brigade 11, P P 3706, 1001, Ljubljana, Slovenia
Tel.: (386) 15820800
Web Site: https://www.geoplin.si
Natural Gas Distribution Services
N.A.I.C.S.: 221210
Joze Bajuk *(Mgr)*

IGES d.o.o. (1)
Dunajska cesta 50, 1000, Ljubljana, Slovenia
Tel.: (386) 5 331 1974
Oil & Gas Distr
N.A.I.C.S.: 424720

MBills d.o.o. (1)
Trzaska 118, 1000, Ljubljana, Slovenia
Tel.: (386) 12003336
Web Site: https://www.mbills.si
Paperless & Cashless Payment Services
N.A.I.C.S.: 522320
Primoz Zupan *(Gen Mgr)*

Petrol - Invest d.o.o. (1)
Donje polje b.b., 81250, Cetinje, Montenegro
Tel.: (382) 41230660
Web Site: http://www.petrol.si
Sales Range: $50-74.9 Million
Emp.: 3
Investment Services
N.A.I.C.S.: 525910

Petrol BH Oil Company d.o.o. (1)
Dzemala Bijedica 202, Ilidza, 71210, Sarajevo, Bosnia & Herzegovina
Tel.: (387) 33560070
Web Site: https://www.petrol.ba
Petroleum Product Distr
N.A.I.C.S.: 457210

Petrol Crna Gora MNE d.o.o. (1)
Ulica Slobode br 2, 81000, Podgorica, Montenegro
Tel.: (382) 20246586
Web Site: https://www.petrol.me
Petroleum Product Distr
N.A.I.C.S.: 424720

Petrol GEO d.o.o. (1)
Mlinska ulica 5D, 9220, Lendava, Slovenia
Tel.: (386) 25772240
Drilling Oil & Gas Field Services
N.A.I.C.S.: 213111
Matej Prkic *(Mng Dir)*

Petrol Gas Group d.o.o. (1)
Kninska 139B, Veternik, 21203, Novi Sad, Serbia
Tel.: (381) 1 47 14 911
Web Site: http://www.petrol.si
Gas Distribution Services
N.A.I.C.S.: 221210

Petrol Hidroenergija d.o.o. (1)
Branka Radicevica br 1, 74270, Teslic, Bosnia & Herzegovina
Tel.: (387) 33560070
Eletric Power Generation Services
N.A.I.C.S.: 221118
Gregor Znidarsic *(Gen Mgr)*

Petrol Power d.o.o. (1)
Tesanjska 24a, 71000, Sarajevo, Bosnia & Herzegovina
Tel.: (387) 33560070
Eletric Power Generation Services
N.A.I.C.S.: 221118
Ales Weiss *(Gen Mgr)*

Petrol Trade Handelsgesellschaft m.b.H. (1)
Elisabethstrasse 10/4, 1010, Vienna, Austria
Tel.: (43) 1 585 5473
Petroleum Product Distr
N.A.I.C.S.: 457210
Marko Malgaj *(Gen Mgr)*

Petrol Trgovina d.o.o. (1)
Oreskoviceva 6 H, Otok, Zagreb, 10010, Croatia
Tel.: (385) 16680000
Web Site: http://www.petrol.si
Sales Range: $25-49.9 Million
Emp.: 14
Petroleum Products Trading Services
N.A.I.C.S.: 324199

Petrol d.o.o. (1)
Oreskoviceva 6h, 10010, Zagreb, Croatia
Tel.: (385) 1 668 0091
Petroleum Product Distr
N.A.I.C.S.: 457210

Petrol d.o.o. (1)
Rakovica Patrijarha Dimitrija 12v, Belgrade, 11100, Serbia
Tel.: (381) 11 715 2230
Petroleum Product Distr
N.A.I.C.S.: 457210

Petrol d.o.o. Beograd (1)
Omladinskih brigada 88-90 building 2300 floor 7, Novi Beograd, 11070, Belgrade, Serbia
Tel.: (381) 117152230
Web Site: http://www.petroldoobeograd.com
Sales Range: Less than $1 Million
Emp.: 50
Fuel Trading Services
N.A.I.C.S.: 457210

Petrol-Trade Handelsges.m.b.H. (1)
Elisabethstrasse 10, 1010, Vienna, Austria
Tel.: (43) 15855473
Sales Range: $50-74.9 Million
Emp.: 5
Oil & Petroleum Products Distr
N.A.I.C.S.: 211130

Subsidiary (Non-US):

Cypet-Trade Ltd. (2)
333 28th October St, PO Box 3311, Ariadne House Ofc no 52, 57019, Limassol, Cyprus
Tel.: (357) 25586039
Web Site: http://www.petrol.si
Rev.: $1,162,433,750
Oil & Petroleum Products Trading Services
N.A.I.C.S.: 213112

Rodgas AD Backa Topola (1)
Marsala Tita br 61, Backa Topola, Serbia
Tel.: (381) 24715828
Rev.: $30,866
Gas Distribution Services
N.A.I.C.S.: 221210

Vjetroelektrane Glunca d.o.o. (1)
Krapanjska cesta 8, 22000, Sibenik, Croatia
Tel.: (385) 333 7500
Electricity Production Services
N.A.I.C.S.: 221118
Boris Antolovic *(Gen Mgr)*

Zagorski Metalac d.o.o. (1)
2F Josipa Broza Tita Street, 49210, Zabok, Croatia
Tel.: (385) 49587151
Web Site: https://www.zagorski-metalac.hr
Gas Distribution Services
N.A.I.C.S.: 221210

PETROLEO BRASILEIRO S.A. - PETROBRAS
Av Republica do Chile n 65 - Centro, Rio de Janeiro, 20031-912, RJ, Brazil
Tel.: (55) 8007289001 BR
Web Site: https://www.petrobras.com.br
Year Founded: 1953
PBR—(NYSE)
Rev.: $102,409,000,000
Assets: $217,067,000,000
Liabilities: $138,092,000,000
Net Worth: $78,975,000,000
Earnings: $24,995,000,000
Emp.: 46,730
Fiscal Year-end: 12/31/23
Oil Explorer, Producer, Refiner & Transporter
N.A.I.C.S.: 324110
Eduardo Bacellar Leal Ferreira *(Chm)*

Subsidiaries:

Companhia Locadora de Equipamentos Petroliferos S.A. (1)
Avenida Republica Do Chile 65 Sala 401 C Parte Centro, 20031-170, Rio de Janeiro, Brazil
Tel.: (55) 2132294230
Eletric Power Generation Services
N.A.I.C.S.: 221118

Engenharia/IEEPT/IETR (1)
Rua General Canabarro 500, 9 Andar Maracana, 20271 900, Rio de Janeiro, RJ, Brazil
Tel.: (55) 2138763700
Construction & Conversion of Tankers
N.A.I.C.S.: 541330

Innova S.A. (1)
BR 386 Rodovia Tabai/Canoas Km 419 Complexo Basico Via do Contorno 212, III Polo Petroquimico, Triunfo, 95853-000, Brazil
Tel.: (55) 5134575800
Sales Range: $100-124.9 Million
Emp.: 200
Oil & Gas Exploration Services
N.A.I.C.S.: 213112

Petrobas Transporte S.A. (1)
Av Pres Vargas 328, 20035 900, Rio de Janeiro, RJ, Brazil
Tel.: (55) 21 3224 4477
Web Site: http://www.transpetro.com.br
Distribution of Oil & Oil Products, Ethanol, Biofuels & Natural Gas Transportation & Storage Activities
N.A.I.C.S.: 486110

Petrobras Comercializadora de Energia Ltda. (1)
Av Almirante Barroso 81-Centro, Rio de Janeiro, 20031-004, Brazil
Tel.: (55) 21 3229 4288
Sales Range: $50-74.9 Million
Emp.: 30
Electric Power Distribution Services
N.A.I.C.S.: 221122

Petrobras Internacional S.A. (1)
Rua General Canabarro 500-10 O Andar Maracana, 20721-900, Rio de Janeiro, RJ, Brazil
Tel.: (55) 2125341000
Worldwide Exploration & Production, Marketing & Services
N.A.I.C.S.: 211120

Subsidiary (Non-US):

Braspetro Oil Services Co. - Brasoil (2)
2nd Floor - Anderson Square Building, Georgetown, Cayman Islands
Oil Production
N.A.I.C.S.: 211120

Subsidiary (US):

Petrobras America Inc. (2)
757 N Eldridge Pkwy ste 1100, Houston, TX 77079 (100%)
Tel.: (713) 808-2000
Sales Range: $50-74.9 Million
Emp.: 120
Exploration, Production & Commercialization of Oil & Petroleum Products
N.A.I.C.S.: 424720

Subsidiary (Non-US):

Petrobras Bolivia S.A. (2)
Avenida Leique Castedo No 1700, Santa Cruz, Bolivia
Web Site: http://www.petrobras.com
Sales Range: $150-199.9 Million
Emp.: 400
Natural Gas & Petroleum Products
N.A.I.C.S.: 211120

Subsidiary (Domestic):

Petrobras Bolivia Internacional S.A (3)
Av Leigue Castedo 1700 Centro Empresarial 2do Piso, Santa Cruz, Bolivia
Tel.: (591) 33664009
Web Site: http://www.petrobras.com
Emp.: 55
Oil & Gas Exploration Services
N.A.I.C.S.: 213112

Subsidiary (Non-US):

Petrobras Energia de Mexico S.A. de C.V. (2)
Avda Paseo De La Reforma 115-Oficina 1101, Mexico, 11000, Mexico
Tel.: (52) 5530679109
Web Site: http://www.petrobras.com
Sales Range: $50-74.9 Million
Emp.: 4
Oil & Gas Exploration Services
N.A.I.C.S.: 213112

Petroleo Brasileiro Nigeria Limited (2)
35 Maloney Street, PO Box 2293, Marina, Lagos, Nigeria
Web Site: http://www2.petrobras.com.br
Provider of Natural Gas Services
N.A.I.C.S.: 211120

Petrobras Quimica S.A. (1)
Tel.: (55) 2132244477
Web Site: http://www.petrobras.com.br
Gas Exploration
N.A.I.C.S.: 211120

Vibra Energia S.A. (1)
Rua Correia Vasques, 250, 20211-140, Rio de Janeiro, Brazil
Tel.: (55) 2132242401
Web Site: https://www.vibraenergia.com.br
Rev.: $33,580,010,215
Assets: $8,960,535,783
Liabilities: $5,718,701,685
Net Worth: $3,241,834,098
Earnings: $982,174,134
Fiscal Year-end: 12/31/2023
Natural Gas Distr
N.A.I.C.S.: 211120
Ernesto Peres Pousada Jr. *(Pres, CEO & Member-Exec Bd)*

Subsidiary (Domestic):

Liquigas Distribuidora S.A. (2)

PETROLEO BRASILEIRO S.A. - PETROBRAS

Petroleo Brasileiro S.A. -
PETROBRAS—(Continued)

Av Paulista 1842 6th floor, Ed Cetenco
Plaza - Torre Norte, Sao Paulo, 01310-923,
Brazil **(100%)**
Tel.: (55) 30043002
Web Site: https://www.liquigas.com.br
Liquefied Petroleum Gas Distr
N.A.I.C.S.: 457210

PETROLEOS DE VENEZUELA S.A.

Edificio Petroleos de Venezuela
Avenida Libertador, La Campina
Apartado 169, Caracas, 1050 A, Venezuela
Tel.: (58) 2127084111 **VE**
Web Site: http://www.pdvsa.com
Sales Range: $25-49.9 Billion
Emp.: 98,422
Petroleum Products, Bitumen, Natural Gas, Coal & Petrochemicals Mfr
N.A.I.C.S.: 211120
Rafael Ramirez Carreno *(CEO)*

Subsidiaries:

Bitor America Corp. (1)
370 W Camino Blvd Ste 213, Boca Raton, FL 33432
Tel.: (561) 392-0026
Sales Range: $50-74.9 Million
Emp.: 7
Fuel Development, Production & Marketing
N.A.I.C.S.: 211120

Bitumenes Orinoco, S.A. (1)
Av Ernesto Blohm La Estancia piso 9 Chuao, Apartado Postal 3470, Caracas, 1010 A, Venezuela
Tel.: (58) 2 908 2811
Web Site: http://www.pdvsa.com
Development, Production & Marketing of Fossil Fuel
N.A.I.C.S.: 211120

Carbozulia, S.A. (1)
Ave 5 De Julio Esquina Ave 11 Edif Exploracion Producion Y Mejoramient, 1Er Piso, 4001, Maracaibo, Zulia, Venezuela **(100%)**
Tel.: (58) 2617981267
Web Site: http://www.pdvsa.com
Sales Range: $50-74.9 Million
Emp.: 20
N.A.I.C.S.: 211120

Citgo Petroleum Corporation (1)
6100 S Yale, Tulsa, OK 74136 **(100%)**
Tel.: (918) 495-4000
Web Site: http://www.citgo.com
Sales Range: $1-4.9 Billion
Emp.: 4,000
Refining, Marketing & Transportation of Petroleum
N.A.I.C.S.: 324110
Frank Gygax *(VP)*

Plant (Domestic):

Citgo Petroleum - Lake Charles Refinery (2)
PO Box 1562, Lake Charles, LA 70602-1562
Tel.: (337) 708-6011
Web Site: http://www.citgo.com
Sales Range: $650-699.9 Million
Emp.: 1,200
Oil Refinery
N.A.I.C.S.: 211120
Eduardo Assef *(VP-Petroleum Refining)*

Subsidiary (Domestic):

Citgo Petroleum Corporation (2)
PO Box 26868, Oklahoma City, OK 73126-0868 **(100%)**
Tel.: (405) 270-6200
Web Site: http://www.citgo.com
Sales Range: $50-74.9 Million
Emp.: 108
Mfr of Oil & Grease
N.A.I.C.S.: 324191

Citgo Pipeline Company (2)
6100 S Yale Ave, Tulsa, OK 74136-1905 **(100%)**
Tel.: (918) 495-5211

Sales Range: $25-49.9 Million
Emp.: 50
Operation of Crude Petroleum Pipelines
N.A.I.C.S.: 486110

Intevep, S.A. (1)
Sector El Tambor, Los Teques, Miranda, Venezuela
Tel.: (58) 212 3306111
Oil & Gas Exploration Services
N.A.I.C.S.: 213112

MC BITOR Limited (1)
New Pier Takeshiba Noth Tower 23rd Floor 11-1 Kaigan 1-Chome, Minato-Ku, Tokyo, Japan
Tel.: (81) 354044822
Web Site: http://www.sovereign-publications.com
N.A.I.C.S.: 211120

PDV Brasil Combustibles y Lubrificantes LTDA (1)
Av Gov Jose Malcher 815 Paladium Center 7 andar, Belem, Para, Brazil
Tel.: (55) 591 3241 6335
Oil & Gas Exploration Services
N.A.I.C.S.: 213112

PDV Ecuador S.A. (1)
Av Juan Tanca Marengo Km 6 5 Via a Daule, Guayaquil, Ecuador
Tel.: (593) 4 2252705
Oil & Gas Exploration Services
N.A.I.C.S.: 213112

PDV Marina, S.A. (1)
Avda Francisco de Miranda Centro Empresarial Miranda Los Ruices Piso 3, Caracas, Venezuela
Tel.: (58) 212 708 8432
Web Site: http://www.pdvsa.com
Oil Transportation & Deep Sea Transportation Services
N.A.I.C.S.: 211120

PDVSA Argentina S.A. (1)
Avenida Del Libertador 602 Ciudad De Floor 20, Buenos Aires, 1001, Argentina
Tel.: (54) 1148 189652
Oil & Gas Exploration Services
N.A.I.C.S.: 213112
Miguel Tarazona *(Gen Mgr)*

PDVSA Cuba SA (1)
C/Lamparilla No 2 Edif Lonja del Comercio, Piso 4 Ofc F La Habana Vieja, Havana, Cuba
Tel.: (53) 7 8644497
Oil & Gas Exploration Services
N.A.I.C.S.: 213112

PDVSA Ecuador SA (1)
Av Orellana y 6 de Diciembre Edificio Alisal de Orellana piso 11, Quito, EC170, Ecuador
Tel.: (593) 2 4000300
Oil & Gas Exploration Services
N.A.I.C.S.: 213112

PDVSA Services B.V. (1)
President Kennedy Laan 19, 2517 JK, Hague, Netherlands **(100%)**
Tel.: (31) 703488588
Web Site: http://www.pdvsa.com
Sales Range: $50-74.9 Million
Emp.: 7
Petroleum
N.A.I.C.S.: 211120
Francisca Thijssen *(Sec)*

PDVSA Services, Inc. (1)
1293 Eldridge Pkwy, Houston, TX 77077-6800
Tel.: (281) 531-0004
Web Site: http://www.pdvsa.com
Sales Range: $10-24.9 Million
Emp.: 27
Petroleum Oil & Gas Trading Services
N.A.I.C.S.: 561409
Frank Rodriguez *(Coord-Quality Assurance & Inspection Svcs)*

PDVSA USA, Inc. (1)
750 Lexington Ave 59th St 21st Fl, New York, NY 10022
Tel.: (646) 723-2080
Oil & Gas Exploration Services
N.A.I.C.S.: 213112

PDVSA do Brasil LTDA. (1)
Praia do Flamengo 78-5 andar Flamengo,

Rio de Janeiro, 22210-030, Brazil
Tel.: (55) 521 2556 0353
Oil & Gas Exploration Services
N.A.I.C.S.: 213112

Pdvsa Uruguay S A (1)
Peatonal Sarandi 675 Ofc 401, Montevideo, Uruguay
Tel.: (598) 2 915 6994
Oil & Gas Exploration Services
N.A.I.C.S.: 213112

Petroleos de Venezuela (1)
Edif Lagoven Av Leonardo Da Vinci 313549, Los Chaguaramos, Caracas, 1010 A, Venezuela **(100%)**
Tel.: (58) 2127084111
Web Site: http://www.pdvsa.com
Sales Range: $50-74.9 Million
Emp.: 50
Natural Gas & Petroleum Production
N.A.I.C.S.: 211120

Refineria Isla (Curazao), S.A. (1)
PO Box 3843, Emmastad, Curacao **(100%)**
Tel.: (599) 94662700
Web Site: http://www.refineriaisla.com
Sales Range: $750-799.9 Million
Emp.: 1,050
N.A.I.C.S.: 211120
Manuel Madina *(Gen Mgr)*

PETROLEOS DEL PERU S.A.

Av Enrique Canaval Moreyra 150, Lima, 27, Peru
Tel.: (51) 1 2117800
Web Site:
http://www.petroperu.com.pe
Sales Range: $1-4.9 Billion
Emp.: 4,000
Fuel & Petroleum Products Transportation, Refinery, Distribution & Trading Services
N.A.I.C.S.: 324110
James Atkins Lerggios *(Chm)*

Subsidiaries:

Petroleos del Peru S.A. - Conchan Refinery (1)
Panamericana Sur km 26 5, Lurin, Peru
Tel.: (51) 1 625 4000
Petroleum Refinery Services
N.A.I.C.S.: 324110

Petroleos del Peru S.A. - El Milagro Refinery (1)
Av Enrique Canaval Moreyra 150, Lima, Utcubamba, Peru
Tel.: (51) 6145000
Web Site: http://www.petroperu.com.pe
Petroleum Refinery Services
N.A.I.C.S.: 324110

Petroleos del Peru S.A. - Iquitos Refinery (1)
Loreto, Iquitos, Maynas, Peru
Tel.: (51) 65 23 3331
Petroleum Refinery Services
N.A.I.C.S.: 324110

Petroleos del Peru S.A. - Talara Refinery (1)
Parinas, Talara, Piura, Peru
Tel.: (51) 73 28 4200
Petroleum Refinery Services
N.A.I.C.S.: 324110

PETROLEOS DELTA, S.A.

Calle Miguel A Brostella Edificio Camino de Cruces Stage 7, Apartado, Panama, Panama
Tel.: (507) 279 3000
Web Site: http://www.petrodelta.com
Year Founded: 1983
PDEL—(PAN)
Sales Range: Less than $1 Million
Petroleum Product Whslr
N.A.I.C.S.: 424720

PETROLEOS MEXICANOS

Avenida Marina Nacional No 329 Col Veronica Anzures, CP 11300, Mexico, Mexico

Tel.: (52) 5591268700
Web Site: http://www.pemex.com
Year Founded: 1938
PEMEX—(LUX)
Rev.: $119,812,930,293
Assets: $112,884,202,872
Liabilities: $201,802,896,123
Net Worth: ($88,918,693,251)
Earnings: $5,026,923,087
Emp.: 120,054
Fiscal Year-end: 12/31/22
Petroleum & Basic Petrochemicals Exploration, Drilling, Transportation, Refining, Distribution & Sales
N.A.I.C.S.: 325110
Norma Rocio Nahle Garcia *(Co-Owner & Chm)*

Subsidiaries:

III Servicios, S.A. de C.V. (1)
Avenida Jaime Balmes Miguel Hidalgo, 11510, Mexico, Mexico
Tel.: (52) 5553953334
Petrochemical Product Distr
N.A.I.C.S.: 424720

Kot Insurance Company, AG. (1)
Schaffhauserstrasse 418 3rd floor, 8050, Zurich, Switzerland
Tel.: (41) 433360660
Web Site: https://www.koticag.ch
Insurance Services
N.A.I.C.S.: 524210

P.M.I. Comercio Internacional, S.A. de C.V. (1)
Marina Nacional 329, Anahuac Miguel Hidalgo, 11311, Mexico, Mexico
Tel.: (52) 5519440000
Crude Oil & Refined Products Importing & Exporting Services
N.A.I.C.S.: 486110

Subsidiary (Non-US):

Hijos de J. Barreras, S.A. (2)
Avda Beiramar 2, PO Box 35, 36208, Vigo, Spain **(51%)**
Tel.: (34) 966213297
Web Site: https://www.hjbarreras.es
Ship Builders
N.A.I.C.S.: 332111
Jose Garcia Costas *(Chm)*

P.M.I. Holdings Petroleos Espana, S.L. (2)
Calle Alfonso Rodriguez Santamaria 18, 28002, Madrid, Spain
Tel.: (34) 911310440
Holding Company
N.A.I.C.S.: 551112
Elliott Guedero *(Gen Mgr)*

Subsidiary (US):

P.M.I. Services North America, Inc. (2)
909 Fannin St, Houston, TX 77010
Tel.: (713) 567-0039
Oil Transportation Services
N.A.I.C.S.: 486990

Subsidiary (Non-US):

P.M.I. Trading Limited (2)
25/28 North Wall Quay, Dublin, Ireland
Tel.: (353) 19440000
Petrochemical Product Distr
N.A.I.C.S.: 424720

PEMEX Exploracion Y Produccion (1)
Ave Marina Nacional 329 Colonia Huasteca, Miguel Hidalgo, 11311, Mexico, DF, Mexico **(100%)**
Tel.: (52) 5519442500
Web Site: http://www.pemex.com
Petroleum Exploration & Production
N.A.I.C.S.: 211120

PEMEX Finance, Ltd. (1)
Apo 3rd Floor, PO Box 10632, Georgetown, KY1-1006, Cayman Islands
Tel.: (345) 345 945 9208
Financial Services
N.A.I.C.S.: 522220

AND PRIVATE COMPANIES

PETROLIAM NASIONAL BERHAD

PEMEX Gas Y Petroquimica Basica (1)
Ave Marina Nacional 329 Colonia Huasteca, Miguel Hidalgo, 11330, Mexico, DF, Mexico
Tel.: (52) 5519442500 (100%)
Web Site: http://www.pemexgas.com.mx
Sales Range: $25-49.9 Million
Emp.: 50
Gas & Petrochemicals
N.A.I.C.S.: 325110

PEMEX Procurement International, Inc. (1)
777 N Eldridge Pkwy Ste 700, Houston, TX 77079
Tel.: (713) 430-3100
Web Site: https://www.pemexprocurement.com
Petrochemical Product Mfr & Distr
N.A.I.C.S.: 325110

PEMEX Refinacion (1)
Avenida Marina Nacional 329 Colonia Veronica Anzures, Miguel Hidalgo, 11311, Mexico, DF, Mexico
Tel.: (52) 5519442500 (100%)
Web Site: https://www.pemex.com
Sales Range: $1-4.9 Billion
Emp.: 15,000
Petroleum Refining
N.A.I.C.S.: 324110

PETROLEUM ADVISORY FORUM
Bolshoy Znamensky Pereulok 2/3, Moscow, Russia
Tel.: (7) 4951398011
Web Site: http://www.paf.ru
Year Founded: 1991
Investment Services
N.A.I.C.S.: 523940
Glenn Waller *(Pres)*

PETROLEUM CORPORATION OF JAMAICA LIMITED
36 Trafalgar Road, Box 579, Kingston, 10, Jamaica
Tel.: (876) 0009295380
Sales Range: $25-49.9 Million
Emp.: 112
Petroleum Products
N.A.I.C.S.: 324199
Russell Hadeed *(Chm)*

Subsidiaries:

Jamaica Aircraft Refuelling Services Ltd. (1)
96 Marcus Garvey Drive, Kingston, Jamaica
Tel.: (876) 923 8611
Petroleum Product Distr
N.A.I.C.S.: 424720

Petcom Limited (1)
695 Spanish Town Road, Kingston, Jamaica
Tel.: (876) 765 0012
Web Site: http://www.petcomja.com
Petroleum Product Distr
N.A.I.C.S.: 424720
Craig Plunkett *(Brand Mgr)*

PETROLEUM INTERIOR DECORATION JOINT STOCK COMPANY
62 Tran Thai Tong, Cau Giay, Hanoi, Vietnam
Tel.: (84) 4 62811820
Web Site: http://www.pvcid.com
Construction, Architectural Design, Interior & Exterior Decoration
N.A.I.C.S.: 541310
Trong Nghia Tran *(Chm & Gen Mgr)*

PETROLEUM PHUONGDONG TOURISM JOINST-STOCK COMPANY
No 218 Le Duan Street, Vinh, Nghe An, Vietnam
Tel.: (84) 383845527
Web Site: https://www.phuongdongpv.com.vn

PDC—(HNX)
Rev.: $846,041
Assets: $11,148,536
Liabilities: $6,076,359
Net Worth: $5,072,177
Earnings: ($592,628)
Fiscal Year-end: 12/31/21
Business Travel, Hotel & Restaurant Services
N.A.I.C.S.: 561510
Nguyen Thi Mai Huong *(Chm)*

PETROLEUM REAL ESTATE JSC
2A Do Quang Street Trung Hoa Ward, Cau Giay District, Hanoi, Vietnam
PVL—(HNX)
Rev.: $277,000
Assets: $40,968,400
Liabilities: $15,615,200
Net Worth: $25,353,200
Earnings: $5,800
Fiscal Year-end: 12/31/22
Real Estate Development Services
N.A.I.C.S.: 531390
Bui Quang Minh *(Chm)*

PETROLEXPORTIMPORT S.A.
B-dul Unirii nr 72 bl J3C Sector 3, Bucharest, Romania
Tel.: (40) 21 318 84 59
Web Site: http://www.petex.ro
Year Founded: 1948
PEI—(BUC)
Petroleum Product Whslr
N.A.I.C.S.: 424720
Iancu Valeriu *(Gen Mgr)*

PETROLIA SE
205 Christodoulou Chatzipavlou Street Loulloupis Court 4th Floor, Office 401, 3036, Limassol, Cyprus
Tel.: (357) 25725777 CY
Web Site: https://www.petrolia.eu
Year Founded: 1997
0PE—(DEU)
Rev.: $55,504,000
Assets: $63,859,000
Liabilities: $24,845,000
Net Worth: $39,014,000
Earnings: ($711,000)
Emp.: 259
Fiscal Year-end: 12/31/22
Holding Company; Oilfield Drilling & Support Services
N.A.I.C.S.: 551112
Berge Gerdt Larsen *(Chm)*

Subsidiaries:

Catch Fishing Services BV (1)
Jacob Le Mairestraat 235, 7825 XE, Emmen, Netherlands
Tel.: (31) 591635123
Web Site: http://www.catch-fishing.com
Oil Field Equipment Distr
N.A.I.C.S.: 423830

Catch Oil Tools Pty Ltd. (1)
640 Karel Avenue, Jandakot, 6164, WA, Australia
Tel.: (61) 894945100
Oil & Gas Services
N.A.I.C.S.: 325412

IOT Group Limited (1)
50 Paraite Road, Bell Block, New Plymouth, New Zealand
Tel.: (64) 67551970
Web Site: http://www.iotgroup.com
Oil & Gas Services
N.A.I.C.S.: 325412

Independent Oil Tools AS (1)
Midtgardveien 30, 4031, Stavanger, Norway
Tel.: (47) 51819400
Oil & Gas Services
N.A.I.C.S.: 325412
Sven Olav Borgen *(Mng Dir)*

Independent Oil Tools Srl (1)

Blv Ecaterina Teodoroiu no 46, Gorj County, Targu Jiu, Romania
Tel.: (40) 253216781
Oil & Gas Services
N.A.I.C.S.: 325412
Mihai Filipas *(Gen Mgr)*

PETROLIAM NASIONAL BERHAD
Tower 1 Petronas Twin Towers, Kuala Lumpur City Centre, 50088, Kuala Lumpur, Malaysia
Tel.: (60) 320515000 MY
Web Site: http://www.petronas.com
Year Founded: 1974
Rev.: $58,427,156,340
Assets: $151,360,338,780
Liabilities: $44,624,989,080
Net Worth: $106,735,349,700
Earnings: $9,841,980,960
Emp.: 47,669
Fiscal Year-end: 12/31/19
Natural Gas & Crude Oil Exploration
N.A.I.C.S.: 211120
Md Arif Mahmood *(CEO-Downstream & Exec VP)*

Subsidiaries:

BASF PETRONAS Chemicals Sdn. Bhd. (1)
Lot 19 01 Level 19 1powerhouse No 1 Persiaran Bandar Utama, Bandar Utama, 47800, Petaling Jaya, Selangor, Malaysia
Tel.: (60) 376121088
Web Site: https://www.basf-petronas.com.my
Sales Range: $25-49.9 Million
Emp.: 48
Chemical Product Mfr; Owned 60% by BASF Aktiengesellschaft & 40% by Petroliam Nasional Berhad
N.A.I.C.S.: 325180

BP Petronas Acetyls Sdn Bhd (1)
Kertih Integrated Petrochemical Complex, 24300, Terengganu, Kertih, Malaysia
Tel.: (60) 95200222
Web Site: https://www.ineos-pcg.com
Sales Range: $100-124.9 Million
Emp.: 90
Acetid Acid Mfg; Owned 70% by BP plc & 30% by Petroliam Nasional Berhad
N.A.I.C.S.: 325180

Bekalan Air KIPC Sdn Bhd (1)
Tower 1 PETRONAS Twin Towers, 50088, Kuala Lumpur, Malaysia
Tel.: (60) 3 21774444
Petrochemical Product Whslr
N.A.I.C.S.: 424720

E&P O&M Services Sdn Bhd (1)
A-25-1 Hampshire Place Office 157 Hampshire 1 Jalan Mayang Sari, 50450, Kuala Lumpur, Malaysia
Tel.: (60) 32 203 0600
Web Site: https://www.epoms.com.my
Facility Support Services
N.A.I.C.S.: 561210
Rizalman Abdul Razak *(Head)*

Engen Limited (1)
Cnr Riebeeck and Long Street, PO Box 35, Cape Town, 8000, South Africa
Tel.: (27) 214034911
Web Site: http://www.engen.co.za
Petroleum Product Distr
N.A.I.C.S.: 424720

Japan Malaysia LNG Co., Ltd. (1)
17F Nisseki Yokohama Bldg 1-1-8 Sakuragi-cho, Sakuragi-cho Naka-ku, Yokohama, 231-0062, Japan
Tel.: (81) 45 683 1330
Web Site: https://www.jamalco.co.jp
Emp.: 8
Crude Petroleum Extraction Services
N.A.I.C.S.: 211120

KBB Joint Operating Co. Sdn. Bhd (1)
Level 29 Tower 1 PETRONAS Twin Towers, 50088, Kuala Lumpur, Malaysia
Tel.: (60) 3 2168 2288
Oil & Gas Exploration Services
N.A.I.C.S.: 213112

Idris Bin Dusa *(Gen Mgr)*

KLCC (Holdings) Sdn. Bhd. (1)
Level 54 Tower 2 Petronas Twin Towers Kuala Lumpur City Centre, 50088, Kuala Lumpur, Malaysia
Tel.: (60) 3 2382 8000
Holding Company
N.A.I.C.S.: 551112
Hashim Wahir *(CEO & Mng Dir)*

KLCC Property Holdings Berhad (1)
Level 33 and 34 Menara Dayabumi Jalan Sultan Hishamuddin, 50050, Kuala Lumpur, Malaysia
Tel.: (60) 327836000
Web Site: http://www.klcc.com.my
Rev.: $308,836,190
Assets: $3,832,689,524
Liabilities: $622,683,598
Net Worth: $3,210,005,926
Earnings: $192,921,481
Emp.: 946
Fiscal Year-end: 12/31/2022
Commercial Property Development Services
N.A.I.C.S.: 236220
Kok Leong Yeap *(Co-Sec)*

MISC Berhad (1)
Level 17 Menara Dayabumi Jalan Sultan Hishamuddin, 50050, Kuala Lumpur, Malaysia (62%)
Tel.: (60) 322640888
Web Site: https://www.misc.com.my
Rev.: $2,934,808,889
Assets: $13,262,273,228
Liabilities: $5,155,588,571
Net Worth: $8,106,684,656
Earnings: $388,358,095
Emp.: 9,355
Fiscal Year-end: 12/31/2022
Gas & Petroleum Shipping Services
N.A.I.C.S.: 488510
Yang Chien Yee *(Pres & CEO)*

Subsidiary (US):

American Eagle Tankers Agencies Inc. (2)
1900 W Loop S Ste 920, Houston, TX 77027
Tel.: (832) 615-2000
Web Site: http://www.aet-tankers.com
Sales Range: $25-49.9 Million
Emp.: 27
Provider of Petroleum Tanking Services
N.A.I.C.S.: 488510

Subsidiary (Non-US):

Eagle Shipmanagement Pte Ltd (3)
1 HarbourFront Ave 11-02 Keppel Bay Tower, Singapore, 098632, Singapore (100%)
Tel.: (65) 61002288
Web Site: http://www.eagleshipmgt.com
Sales Range: $25-49.9 Million
Ship Management Services
N.A.I.C.S.: 488330
Abdul Rahim *(VP)*

Subsidiary (Non-US):

MISC Agencies (Australia) Pty Ltd (2)
Suite 40 Albert Square 37-39 Albert Road, Melbourne, 3004, VIC, Australia (100%)
Tel.: (61) 3 9862 6016
Web Site: http://www.miscaust.com.au
Shipping Services
N.A.I.C.S.: 488330

Subsidiary (Domestic):

Petronas Maritime Services Sdn. Bhd. (2)
Tingkat 16 Menara Dayabumi, Jalan Sultan Hishamuddin, 50050, Kuala Lumpur, Malaysia (100%)
Tel.: (60) 327836000
Sales Range: $50-74.9 Million
Emp.: 130
Management & Operation of Ports & Marine Vessels; Marine Support Services
N.A.I.C.S.: 488330

MTBE Malaysia Sdn. Bhd. (1)
Lot 111 Kawasan Perindustrian Gebeng, PO Box 1, 26080, Kuantan, Pahang, Malaysia (100%)

PETROLIAM NASIONAL BERHAD

Petroliam Nasional Berhad—(Continued)

Tel.: (60) 95856700
Web Site: http://www.petronas.com.my
Management & Operation of the MTBE/Propylene Plant in Kuantan; Markets Methyl-Tertiary-Butyl-Ether (MTBE) & Propylene to Domestic & Export Markets
N.A.I.C.S.: 325199

Malaysia LNG Sdn. Bhd. (1)
Level 81 Tower 2 PETRONAS Twin Towers, Kuala Lumpur City Centre, 50088, Kuala Lumpur, Malaysia (90%)
Tel.: (60) 3 2051 7800
Holding Company; Liquefied Natural Gas Mfr & Marketer
N.A.I.C.S.: 551112
Dzafri Sham Ahmad (CEO & Grp VP)

Subsidiary (Domestic):

Malaysia LNG Dua Sdn. Bhd. (2)
Tanjung Kidurong, PO Box 89, 97007, Bintulu, Sarawak, Malaysia (60%)
Tel.: (60) 86 856 000
Liquified Natural Gas Refinery
N.A.I.C.S.: 324110
Dzafri Sham Ahmad (CEO)

Malaysia LNG Tiga Sdn. Bhd. (2)
Tanjung Kidurong, PO Box 89, 97007, Bintulu, Sarawak, Malaysia (60%)
Tel.: (60) 86 856 000
Liquified Natural Gas Refinery
N.A.I.C.S.: 324110
Dzafri Sham Ahmad (CEO)

Malaysian International Trading Corporation Sdn. Bhd. (1)
Level 13 15 Tower 1 Petronas Twin Tower, Kuala Lumpur City Ctr, 50088, Kuala Lumpur, Malaysia (100%)
Tel.: (60) 320514224
Web Site: http://www.mitco.com.my
Sales Range: $150-199.9 Million
Emp.: 350
Trading of Non-Oil Petroleum Products including Petrochemicals, Fertilizers, Nitrogenous Chemicals & Olefins & Polymers; Trading House for General Merchandise & Other Non-Oil Commodities
N.A.I.C.S.: 424690

Malaysian Refining Company Sdn Bhd (1)
Bangunan Pentadbiran Persiaran Penapisan, 76300, Sungai Udang, Melaka, Malaysia
Tel.: (60) 6 3522 020
Oil Refinery Services
N.A.I.C.S.: 324110
Datuk Nur Iskandar Abd Samad (CEO & Mng Dir)

Nada Properties Co., Ltd. (1)
PETRONAS Sudan Complex No 13 Block 7 Nile Avenue, PO Box 11150, Khartoum, Sudan
Tel.: (249) 15 655 6000
Web Site: https://www.nadaproperties.com
Real Estate Services
N.A.I.C.S.: 531210

OGP Technical Services Sdn Bhd (1)
Level 8 Menara Dayabumi Jalan Sultan Hishamuddin, 50050, Kuala Lumpur, Malaysia
Tel.: (60) 3 2783 6366
Engineering Consulting Services
N.A.I.C.S.: 541330
Hj Mohd Radzi Salleh (CEO & Mng Dir)

PETRONAS Aviation Sdn Bhd (1)
Level 73 Tower 2 PETRONAS Twin Towers, 50088, Kuala Lumpur, Malaysia
Tel.: (60) 3 2331 4639
Aviation Fuel Distr
N.A.I.C.S.: 424720

PETRONAS Base Oil (M) Sdn Bhd (1)
Level 26 Integra Tower The Intermark 348 Jalan Tun Razak, 50400, Kuala Lumpur, Malaysia
Tel.: (60) 3 2301 4000
Petrochemical Product Whslr
N.A.I.C.S.: 424720
Phillip James (CEO & Mng Dir)

PETRONAS Capital Limited (1)
Unit Level 13 E Main Office Tower Financial Park Labuan, Jalan Merdeka, 87000, Labuan, Labuan, Malaysia
Tel.: (60) 3 2331 4908
Holding Company
N.A.I.C.S.: 551112

PETRONAS Chemicals Ammonia Sdn Bhd (1)
Kompleks Pentadbiran Petrokimia Petronas KM 105, Jalan Kuantan-Kuala Terengganu Kemaman, 24300, Kerteh, Terengganu, Malaysia
Tel.: (60) 9 830 5000
Oil & Gas Operation Services
N.A.I.C.S.: 213112

PETRONAS Chemicals Derivatives Sdn Bhd (1)
Administration Building Petronas Petroleum Industry Complex, KM 106 Jalan Kuantan-Kuala Terengganu, 24300, Kerteh, Terengganu, Malaysia
Tel.: (60) 9 830 7700
Oil & Gas Operation Services
N.A.I.C.S.: 213112

PETRONAS Chemicals Fertiliser Kedah Sdn Bhd (1)
KM 3 Jalan Jeniang, PO Box 22, 08300, Gurun, Kedah, Malaysia
Tel.: (60) 4 466 6666
Oil & Gas Operation Services
N.A.I.C.S.: 213112

PETRONAS Chemicals Glycols Sdn Bhd (1)
Administration Building Petronas Petroleum Industry Complex, KM 106 Jalan Kuantan-Kuala Terengganu, 24300, Kerteh, Terengganu, Malaysia
Tel.: (60) 9 830 7700
Oil & Gas Operation Services
N.A.I.C.S.: 213112

PETRONAS Chemicals MTBE Sdn Bhd (1)
Lot 111/112 Kawasan Perindustrian Gebeng, 26080, Kuantan, Pahang, Malaysia
Tel.: (60) 9 585 6700
Oil & Gas Operation Services
N.A.I.C.S.: 213112

PETRONAS Chemicals Marketing Sdn Bhd (1)
Level 34 Tower 1 Petronas Twin Towers Kuala Lumpur City Centre, 50088, Kuala Lumpur, Malaysia
Tel.: (60) 32 331 5000
Oil & Gas Operation Services
N.A.I.C.S.: 213112

PETRONAS Chemicals Methanol Sdn Bhd (1)
Kawasan Perindustrian Rancha-Rancha, PO Box 80079, 87010, Labuan, Malaysia
Tel.: (60) 8 759 4000
Oil & Gas Operation Services
N.A.I.C.S.: 213112

PETRONAS Chemicals Polyethylene Sdn Bhd (1)
Lot 3834 Kawasan Bukit Tengah KM 105 Jalan Kuantan-Kuala, Kemaman, 24300, Kerteh, Terengganu, Malaysia
Tel.: (60) 9 830 2000
Oil & Gas Operation Services
N.A.I.C.S.: 213112

PETRONAS Dagangan Berhad (1)
Level 27-32 Tower 1 Petronas Twin Towers Kuala Lumpur City Centre, 50088, Kuala Lumpur, Malaysia (69.86%)
Tel.: (60) 320515000
Web Site: https://www.mymesra.com.my
Rev.: $7,777,544,127
Assets: $2,382,547,513
Liabilities: $1,157,708,148
Net Worth: $1,224,839,365
Earnings: $166,738,201
Emp.: 2,010
Fiscal Year-end: 12/31/2022
Petroleum Products Marketer
N.A.I.C.S.: 424720
Kok Leong Yeap (Co-Sec)

PETRONAS Gas Berhad (1)
Level 49-50 Tower 1 PETRONAS Twin Towers, Kuala Lumpur City Centre, 50088, Kuala Lumpur, Malaysia (60.66%)
Tel.: (60) 323315000
Web Site: http://www.petronas.com
Rev.: $1,303,740,952
Assets: $4,166,857,566
Liabilities: $1,328,795,979
Net Worth: $2,838,061,587
Earnings: $372,162,540
Emp.: 1,763
Fiscal Year-end: 12/31/2022
Natural Gas Processor & Distr
N.A.I.C.S.: 221210
Burhan Abdullah (Head-Gas Transmission & Regasification)

PETRONAS India (Holdings) Company Pte Ltd (1)
12th Floor Mohan Dev Building 13 Tolstoy Marg, 110 001, New Delhi, India
Tel.: (91) 11 2331 7050
Holding Company
N.A.I.C.S.: 551112

PETRONAS South Africa (Pty) Ltd (1)
2nd Floor Triangle House 22 Riebeek Street, 8001, Cape Town, South Africa
Tel.: (27) 2721 4188 740
Holding Company
N.A.I.C.S.: 551112
Rizan Ismail (CEO & Mng Dir)

PETRONAS Technology Ventures Sdn Bhd (1)
Tower 1 Petronas Twin Towers Kuala Lumpur City Centre, 50088, Kuala Lumpur, Malaysia
Tel.: (60) 32 051 5000
Oil & Gas Operation Services
N.A.I.C.S.: 213112

Petronas Argentina S.A. (1)
San Martin 323 Piso 19, 1004, Buenos Aires, Argentina (100%)
Tel.: (54) 1143944100
Holding Company
N.A.I.C.S.: 551112

Petronas Carigali Sdn. Bdh. (1)
Tower 1 Petronas Twin Towers, Kuala Lumpur City Ctr, 50088, Kuala Lumpur, Malaysia (100%)
Tel.: (60) 320515000
Web Site: http://www.petronas.com
Sales Range: $50-74.9 Million
Emp.: 100
Exploration, Development & Production of Oil & Gas
N.A.I.C.S.: 211120

Subsidiary (Domestic):

Petronas Carigali Overseas Sdn. Bhd. (2)
Tower 1 Petronas Twin Towers, 50088, Kuala Lumpur, Malaysia (100%)
Tel.: (60) 320515000
Web Site: http://www.petronas.com
Sales Range: $50-74.9 Million
Emp.: 100
Exploration, Development & Production of Oil & Gas Overseas
N.A.I.C.S.: 211120

Petronas Chemicals Group Berhad (1)
Tower 1 Petronas Twin Towers Kuala Lumpur City Centre, 50088, Kuala Lumpur, Malaysia
Tel.: (60) 320515000
Web Site: https://www.petronas.com
Rev.: $6,127,619,048
Assets: $11,731,216,931
Liabilities: $3,322,116,402
Net Worth: $8,409,100,529
Earnings: $1,339,047,619
Emp.: 6,288
Fiscal Year-end: 12/31/2022
Petrochemical Mfr
N.A.I.C.S.: 325110
Mazuin Ismail (CEO, Mng Dir & Sr VP)

Petronas Fertilizer (Kedah) Sdn. Bhd. (1)
Km 3 Jalan Jeniang, PO Box 22, 08300, Gurun, Kedah, Malaysia (100%)
Tel.: (60) 44685202
Web Site: http://www.petronas.com
Sales Range: $125-149.9 Million
Emp.: 420
Ammonia, Granular Area, Methanol & Formaldehyde Production
N.A.I.C.S.: 325110

Petronas Methanol (Labuan) Sdn. Bhd. (1)
Kawasan Perindustrian Rancha Rancha, PO Box 80079, Labuan, 87000, Sabah, Malaysia (100%)
Tel.: (60) 87594000
Web Site: http://www.petronas.com
Sales Range: $125-149.9 Million
Emp.: 280
Production of Methanol
N.A.I.C.S.: 325110

Petronas NGV Sdn. Bhd. (1)
Level 47 Tower 1 Petronas Twin Towers, Kuala Lumpur City Centre, 50088, Kuala Lumpur, Malaysia (100%)
Tel.: (60) 320515000
Web Site: http://www.petronas.com.my
Promoter of the Use of Natural Gas for Vehicles
N.A.I.C.S.: 221210

Petronas Penapisan (Melaka) Sdn. Bhd. (1)
Bangunan Pentadbiran Persiaran Penapisan, Kampong Sungai Udang, 76300, Melaka, Malaysia (100%)
Tel.: (60) 63522020
Web Site: http://www.petronas.com
Sales Range: $450-499.9 Million
Emp.: 1,200
Management & Operation of Refinery
N.A.I.C.S.: 324110

Petronas Penapisan (Terengganu) Sdn Bhd (1)
Lot 1119 Ladang Bukit Tengah, 24300, Kerteh, Terengganu, Malaysia
Tel.: (60) 9 830 3000
Crude Oil Refining Services
N.A.I.C.S.: 324110

Petronas Philippines, Inc. (1)
15 Fl Citibank Tower Valero St Salcedo Vlg, Makati, 1200, Metro Manila, Philippines (100%)
Tel.: (63) 28481665
Web Site: http://www.petronas.com
Sales Range: $50-74.9 Million
Emp.: 100
Holding Company
N.A.I.C.S.: 551112

Petronas Technical Services Sdn. Bhd. (1)
Level 69 Tower 1 Petronas Twin Tower, Kuala Lumpur City Centre, 50088, Kuala Lumpur, Malaysia (100%)
Tel.: (60) 320513475
Holding Company for Petronas Investment in the Business of Project Management, Engineering, Procurement & Construction Management Services for the Oil, Gas & Petrochemical Industry
N.A.I.C.S.: 551112

Petronas Trading Corporation Sdn. Bhd. (PETCO) (1)
Level 35 Tower 1 Petronas Twin Towers, 50088, Kuala Lumpur, Malaysia (100%)
Tel.: (60) 323314875
Web Site: http://www.petronas.com.my
Sales Range: $50-74.9 Million
Emp.: 100
Marketing & Trading of Crude Oil & Petroleum Products Internationally
N.A.I.C.S.: 424720

Petrosains Sdn Bhd (1)
Level 4 Suria KLCC Petronas Twin Towers Kuala Lumpur City Centre, 50088, Kuala Lumpur, Malaysia
Tel.: (60) 32 331 8787
Web Site: https://petrosains.com.my
Oil & Gas Operation Services
N.A.I.C.S.: 213112
Ezarisma Azni Mohamad (CEO)

Polyproplylene Malaysia Sdn. Bhd. (1)
Lot 112 Kawasan Perindustrian Gebeng Balok, PO Box 2, 26080, Kuantan, Pahang, Malaysia (100%)

Tel.: (60) 95856700
Web Site: http://www.petronas.com
Sales Range: $200-249.9 Million
Emp.: 620
Management & Operation of Propylene Plant
N.A.I.C.S.: 325199

PrimeSourcing International Sdn Bhd (1)
Level 12 Tower 1 PETRONAS Twin Towers, 50088, Kuala Lumpur, Malaysia
Tel.: (60) 3 2051 3633
Oil & Gas Exploration Services
N.A.I.C.S.: 213112
Yaacob Salim *(CEO & Mng Dir)*

Progress Energy Canada Ltd (1)
Tel.: (403) 216-2510
Web Site: http://www.progressenergy.com
Sales Range: $450-499.9 Million
Emp.: 142
Natural Gas & Crude Oil Exploration Services
N.A.I.C.S.: 211120
Art MacNichol *(Sr VP-Strategy & Corp Dev)*

Vestigo Petroleum Sdn Bhd (1)
Level 13 Menara Binjai No 2 Jalan Binjai Off Jalan Ampang, 50450, Kuala Lumpur, Malaysia
Tel.: (60) 32 776 9999
Web Site: https://vestigopetroleum.com
Oil & Gas Operation Services
N.A.I.C.S.: 213112
Hazanie B. Jamian *(CEO)*

PETROLIMEX INSTALLATION NO. III JOINT STOCK COMPANY
2286 Huynh Tan Phat Hamlet 3 Phu Xuan, Nha Be District, Ho Chi Minh City, Vietnam
Tel.: (84) 839404602
Web Site: https://www.penjico.petrolimex.com
PEN—(HNX)
Rev.: $15,729,300
Assets: $23,488,300
Liabilities: $16,272,300
Net Worth: $7,216,000
Earnings: $41,400
Fiscal Year-end: 12/31/23
Construction Services
N.A.I.C.S.: 236210

PETROLIMEX INTERNATIONAL TRADING JSC
54-56 Bui Huu Nghia Street, Ward 5 Dist 5, Ho Chi Minh City, Vietnam
Tel.: (84) 2838383400
Web Site: https://www.pitco.com.vn
PIT—(HNX)
Bed Dryer Equipment Mfr
N.A.I.C.S.: 335210
Huy Thang Ha *(Gen Dir)*

PETROLIMEX SAIGON TRANSPORTATION & SERVICE JSC
No 118 Huynh Tan Phat Tan Thuan Tay ward, District 07, Ho Chi Minh City, Vietnam
Tel.: (84) 838721014
Web Site: http://www.ptssaigon.petrolimex.com
PSC—(HNX)
Rev.: $78,090,400
Assets: $24,583,500
Liabilities: $12,754,000
Net Worth: $11,829,500
Earnings: $561,700
Fiscal Year-end: 12/31/22
Petroleum Product Whslr
N.A.I.C.S.: 424720
Dinh Trung Bui *(Chm-Mgmt Bd)*

PETROLINA (HOLDINGS) PUBLIC LTD
Tel.: (357) 24848000   CY

Web Site: http://www.petrolina.com.cy
Year Founded: 1959
PHL—(CYP)
Sales Range: Less than $1 Million
Petroleum Products Mfr & Whslr
N.A.I.C.S.: 324199
Kostakis Lefkaritis *(Chm)*

PETROLINVEST D.D.
Tvornicka 3 Stup, 71 000, Sarajevo, Bosnia & Herzegovina
Tel.: (387) 3 377 9800
Web Site: http://www.petrolinvest.com
Year Founded: 1969
PINSR—(SARE)
Rev.: $2,352,913
Assets: $4,775,874
Liabilities: $1,054,091
Net Worth: $3,721,783
Earnings: ($561,623)
Emp.: 60
Fiscal Year-end: 12/31/20
Oil & Gas Pipeline Construction Services
N.A.I.C.S.: 237120
Mustafa Cerimagic *(Mng Dir)*

PETROLINVEST S.A.
ul Slaska 35-37, woj pomorskie, 81-310, Gdynia, Poland
Tel.: (48) 586662200
Web Site: http://www.petrolinvest.pl
Year Founded: 1991
Sales Range: Less than $1 Million
Emp.: 82
Petroleum & Liquid Gas Exploration Services
N.A.I.C.S.: 424720
Bertrand Le Guern *(Chm-Mgmt Bd)*

PETROLYMPIC LTD.
82 Richmond Street East 1st Floor, Toronto, M5C 1P1, ON, Canada
Tel.: (845) 656-0184
Web Site: https://www.petrolympic.com
PCQRF—(OTCIQ)
Assets: $328,220
Liabilities: $1,577,114
Net Worth: ($1,248,894)
Earnings: ($859,851)
Fiscal Year-end: 12/31/23
Oil & Gas Exploration Services
N.A.I.C.S.: 213112
Mendel Ekstein *(Pres & CEO)*

Subsidiaries:

Oil-lympia Oil and Gas Inc. (1)
5 Seven Springs Rd, Monroe, NY 10950-2400
Tel.: (845) 782-3371
Web Site: http://www.petrolympic.com
Oil & Gas Exploration Services
N.A.I.C.S.: 213112

PETROMAROC CORPORATION
Queensway House Hilgrove Street, Saint Helier, JE1 1ES, Jersey
Tel.: (44) 772 249 1084
Web Site: http://petromaroc.co
Year Founded: 2006
Rev.: $14,169,093
Assets: $11,493,588
Liabilities: $8,389,226
Net Worth: $3,104,362
Earnings: $10,897,693
Emp.: 7
Fiscal Year-end: 12/31/17
Oil & Gas Exploration Services
N.A.I.C.S.: 211120
Martin Arch *(CFO & Sec)*

PETROMIN RESOURCES LTD.

24 West 4th Avenue, Vancouver, V6C 2V6, BC, Canada
Tel.: (604) 682-8831
Web Site: http://www.petromin.ca
Sales Range: Less than $1 Million
Gas & Petroleum Exploration Services
N.A.I.C.S.: 211120
Arthur Ross Gorrell *(Chm, Pres & CEO)*

PETRON CORPORATION
Tel.: (63) 288849200
Web Site: https://www.petron.com
PCOR—(PHI)
Rev.: $14,462,886,927
Assets: $8,014,877,599
Liabilities: $6,215,924,831
Net Worth: $1,798,952,768
Earnings: $182,973,728
Emp.: 2,251
Fiscal Year-end: 12/31/23
Oil Refining & Distribution Services
N.A.I.C.S.: 324110
Ramon S. Ang *(Pres & CEO)*

Subsidiaries:

Petron Freeport Corporation (1)
40 San Miguel Ave St SMC SMT Ofc Park, Mandaluyong Metro Manila, Manila, CP 1550, Philippines
Tel.: (63) 28863888
Web Site: http://www.petron.com
Petroleum Retail Services
N.A.I.C.S.: 424720

Petron Marketing Corporation (1)
40 San Miguel Ave, Mandaluyong, Philippines
Tel.: (63) 28849200
Sales Range: $50-74.9 Million
Emp.: 72
Oil & Petroleum Whslr
N.A.I.C.S.: 424720

PETRONE GROUP S.R.L.
Via Artemisia Gentileschi 26, 80126, Naples, Italy
Tel.: (39) 0812415111   IT
Web Site: http://www.petrone.it
Holding Company; Pharmaceutical & Health Care Products & Services
N.A.I.C.S.: 551112
Claudia Rinaldi *(Mgr-Bus Dev)*

Subsidiaries:

Fin Posillipo S.p.A. (1)
Via Artemisia Gentileschi 26, 80126, Naples, Italy
Tel.: (39) 081 241 5111
Web Site: http://www.finposillipo.it
Pharmaceutical & Health Care Industry Investment Management, Financial Advisory & Business Consulting Services
N.A.I.C.S.: 523940
Gianluca Petrone *(Dir-Admin)*

Subsidiary (Domestic):

Pierrel S.p.A. (2)
Appia 7 bis 46/48, 81043, Capua, CE, Italy   (75.63%)
Tel.: (39) 0823626111
Web Site: http://www.pierrelgroup.com
Sales Range: $10-24.9 Million
Contract Pharmaceutical Mfr; Biopharmaceutical Research & Development Services
N.A.I.C.S.: 325412
Raffaele Petrone *(Chm)*

PETRONEFT RESOURCES PLC
20 Holles Street, Dublin, 2, Ireland
Tel.: (353) 16470280   IE
Web Site: http://www.petroneft.com
Year Founded: 2005
P8ET—(ISE)
Rev.: $5,815,255
Assets: $41,895,429
Liabilities: $14,846,201
Net Worth: $27,049,228

Earnings: ($4,871,064)
Emp.: 37
Fiscal Year-end: 12/31/21
Oil & Gas Exploration & Production Services
N.A.I.C.S.: 211120
Karl Johnson *(VP-Bus Dev & Ops)*

Subsidiaries:

Stimul-T OOO (1)
13 Sovpartshkolnyi Lane Office 9, 634009, Tomsk, Russia
Tel.: (7) 3822515124
Web Site: http://www.petroneft.com
Sales Range: $50-74.9 Million
Oil & Gas Exploration Services
N.A.I.C.S.: 211120
Aleksei Nikolaevich *(Gen Dir)*

PETRONET LNG LIMITED
1st Floor World Trade Center Babar Road Barakhamba Lane, New Delhi, 110001, India
Tel.: (91) 1123411411
Web Site: https://petronetlng.in
532522—(NSE)
Rev.: $7,244,460,164
Assets: $2,727,952,761
Liabilities: $897,779,510
Net Worth: $1,830,173,251
Earnings: $398,755,470
Emp.: 523
Fiscal Year-end: 03/31/23
Oil & Natural Gas Mfr
N.A.I.C.S.: 213112
Rajan Kapur *(Sec)*

Subsidiaries:

Petronet LNG Limited - Kochi LNG Terminal Facility (1)
Survey No 347 Puthuvypu, PO 682508, Kochi, 682 508, Kerela, India
Tel.: (91) 4842502268
Web Site: http://petronetlng.in
Natural Gas Mfr
N.A.I.C.S.: 333618

PETRONOR E&P LIMITED
48 Dover Street, London, W1S 4FF, United Kingdom
Tel.: (44) 2036557810
Web Site: https://petronorep.com
FQ00—(DEU)
Rev.: $146,066,000
Assets: $184,467,000
Liabilities: $74,542,000
Net Worth: $109,925,000
Earnings: $34,275,000
Emp.: 35
Fiscal Year-end: 12/31/22
Oil & Gas Exploration
N.A.I.C.S.: 211120
Jens Pace *(Interim CEO)*

Subsidiaries:

PetroNor E&P AS (1)
Froyas gate 13, 0273, Oslo, Norway
Tel.: (47) 22554607
Oil & Gas Services
N.A.I.C.S.: 213112

PETROPAVLOVSK PLC
11 Grosvenor Place, London, SW1X 7HH, United Kingdom
Tel.: (44) 2072018900
Web Site: http://www.petropavlovsk.net
Year Founded: 1994
POG—(LSE)
Rev.: $988,534,000
Assets: $1,731,012,000
Liabilities: $1,059,371,000
Net Worth: $671,641,000
Earnings: $48,882,000
Emp.: 8,889
Fiscal Year-end: 12/31/20
Gold Mining, Exploration & Development Services

PETROPAVLOVSK PLC

Petropavlovsk PLC—(Continued)
N.A.I.C.S.: 212220
Alya Samokhvalova (*Deputy CEO-Strategic Dev*)

Subsidiaries:

IRC Limited (1)
6H 9 Queen's Road, Central, China (Hong Kong)
Tel.: (852) 27720007
Web Site: https://www.ircgroup.com.hk
Rev.: $278,757,000
Assets: $593,952,000
Liabilities: $145,681,000
Net Worth: $448,271,000
Earnings: ($87,840,000)
Emp.: 1,804
Fiscal Year-end: 12/31/2022
Iron Ore Mining & Production Services
N.A.I.C.S.: 212210
Yury Makarov (*CEO*)

LLC Transit (1)
Odesskaya st 9, 690014, Vladivostok, Russia
Tel.: (7) 423 279 5739
Web Site: https://www.transitllc.ru
Cargo Transportation Services
N.A.I.C.S.: 488510

PETROPLAN LIMITED
99 Walnut Tree Close, Guildford, GU1 4UQ, Surrey, United Kingdom
Tel.: (44) 1483 881500
Web Site: http://www.petroplan.com
Year Founded: 1976
Sales Range: $200-249.9 Million
Emp.: 60
Human Resource Consulting Services
N.A.I.C.S.: 541612
John Reeder (*Founder & Chm*)

PETRORECONCAVO S.A.
Estrada do Vinte Mil, Km 3,5 Estacao de Sao Roque Mata de Sao Joao, Bahia, 48280-000, Brazil
Tel.: (55) 7136350200
Web Site: https://petroreconcavo.com.br
Year Founded: 1999
Oil & Gas Exploration
N.A.I.C.S.: 211120

Subsidiaries:

Maha Energy Brasil Ltda. (1)
Av das Americas 3500 Ed Londres salas 515 e 516 Cep 22 640 102, Barra da Tijuca, Rio de Janeiro, Brazil
Tel.: (55) 2135544300
Oil & Gas Exploration & Production
N.A.I.C.S.: 211120

PETROS PETROPOULOS S.A.
96-104Iera Odos street, 10447, Athens, Greece
Tel.: (30) 2103499200
Web Site: https://www.petropoulos.com
Year Founded: 1922
PETRO—(ATH)
Rev.: $16,850,166,094
Assets: $9,382,656,310
Liabilities: $4,310,141,578
Net Worth: $5,072,514,732
Earnings: $706,083,008
Emp.: 178
Fiscal Year-end: 12/31/22
Automotive Products Mfr & Distr
N.A.I.C.S.: 441330

Subsidiaries:

PMS S.A. (1)
145 Liossion, 10445, Athens, Greece
Tel.: (30) 210 8831457
Car Alarms Whslr
N.A.I.C.S.: 441330

PETROSAUDI INTERNATIONAL LTD.
Dhahran Road, PO Box 1648, Al Khobar, 31952, Saudi Arabia
Tel.: (966) 38995555
Web Site: http://www.petrosaudi.com
Year Founded: 2005
Oil Exploration & Production
N.A.I.C.S.: 213112
Tarek Essam Ahmad Obaid (*Founder & CEO*)

Subsidiaries:

PetroSaudi Energy & Trading (UK) Ltd (1)
1 Curzon Street, London, W1J 5HD, United Kingdom
Tel.: (44) 2075140100
Oil & Gas Exploration services
N.A.I.C.S.: 213111
Tim Myers (*Pres*)

Petrosaudi International Sa (1)
Rue Du Rhone 86, 1204, Geneva, Switzerland
Tel.: (41) 228186119
Oil & Gas Exploration services
N.A.I.C.S.: 213111

PETROSIBIR AB
Nybrogatan 34 1st Floor, Stockholm, Sweden
Tel.: (46) 84071850
Web Site: http://www.petrosibir.com
Year Founded: 2007
Sales Range: $10-24.9 Million
Emp.: 36
Oil Exploration & Production Services
N.A.I.C.S.: 211120
Gunnar Danielsson (*Deputy CEO & CFO*)

Subsidiaries:

Shelton Canada Corp. (1)
145 Evans Ave Ste 212, Toronto, M8Z 5X8, ON, Canada
Tel.: (416) 252-4101
Web Site: http://www.sheltonpetroleum.com
Sales Range: $1-9.9 Million
Emp.: 5
Oil & Gas Exploration Services
N.A.I.C.S.: 211120
Zenon Potoczny (*Pres*)

Joint Venture (Non-US):

Kashtan Petroleum Ltd. (2)
Geroiv Stalingrada Ave 24 Apt 141, Kiev, 04210, Ukraine
Tel.: (380) 444673115
Petroleum Services
N.A.I.C.S.: 211120

PETROTX LP
Midtown Tower Menachem Begin 144/A, Tel Aviv, 6492124, Israel
Tel.: (972) 35665005
Web Site: http://www.petrotxlp.com
PTX—(TAE)
Rev.: $19,457,000
Assets: $38,397,000
Liabilities: $26,036,000
Net Worth: $12,361,000
Earnings: ($1,115,000)
Fiscal Year-end: 12/31/22
Natural Gas Extraction Services
N.A.I.C.S.: 211130
Yossi Levy (*CEO*)

PETROVIETNAM COATING JOINT STOCK COMPANY
Road 2B Phu My 1 Industrial Zone, Phu My Ward, Vung Tau, Vietnam
Tel.: (84) 2543924456
Web Site: https://www.pvcoating.vn
PVB—(HNX)
Rev.: $24,447,200
Assets: $49,799,700
Liabilities: $12,859,000
Net Worth: $36,940,700
Earnings: $336,400
Emp.: 251
Fiscal Year-end: 12/31/23
Coating Mfr
N.A.I.C.S.: 325510
Nguyen Tuan Thanh (*Member-Mgmt Bd & Deputy Dir*)

PETROVIETNAM ENGINEERING CONSULTANCY JSC
10th floor PV Gas Tower 673 Nguyen Huu Tho, Nha Be District, Ho Chi Minh City, Vietnam
Tel.: (84) 2837816111
Web Site: https://www.pve.vn
Year Founded: 1988
Rev.: $63,578,432
Assets: $62,145,853
Liabilities: $49,255,156
Net Worth: $12,890,697
Earnings: $815,906
Fiscal Year-end: 12/31/17
Engineering Consultancy Services
N.A.I.C.S.: 541330
Ngo Ngoc Thuong (*Pres, CEO, Member-Mgmt Bd & Deputy Gen Dir*)

PETROVIETNAM OIL PHU YEN JOINT STOCK COMPANY
157-159 Hung Vuong street ward 5, Tuy Hoa, Phu Yen, Vietnam
Tel.: (84) 2573828643
Web Site: http://www.pvoilphuyen.com.vn
Year Founded: 1981
PPY—(HNX)
Rev.: $181,914,892
Assets: $16,351,456
Liabilities: $9,937,028
Net Worth: $6,414,428
Earnings: $437,874
Emp.: 308
Fiscal Year-end: 12/31/23
Petroleum Product Distr
N.A.I.C.S.: 424720
Nguyen Anh Toan (*Chm-Mgmt Bd*)

PETROVIETNAM PACKAGING JOINT STOCK COMPANY
Lot A1-3 Tra Kha Industrial Zone Ward No 8, Bac Lieu, Vietnam
Tel.: (84) 2913957555
Web Site: https://www.pbp.vn
PBP—(HNX)
Rev.: $35,973,300
Assets: $12,507,200
Liabilities: $5,802,700
Net Worth: $6,704,500
Earnings: $802,000
Emp.: 210
Fiscal Year-end: 12/31/23
Packaging Mfr
N.A.I.C.S.: 326112
Thuan Duc Nguyen (*Chm*)

PETROVIETNAM POWER ENGINEERING CONSULTING JSC
12th Floor Diamond Flower Tower Building No 48 Le Van Luong, Nhan Chinh Ward Thanh Xuan District, Hanoi, Vietnam
Tel.: (84) 2435572222
Web Site: https://www.pvpe.vn
Year Founded: 2007
PPE—(HNX)
Rev.: $179,508
Assets: $663,650
Liabilities: $203,899
Net Worth: $459,751
Earnings: $30,653
Emp.: 2
Fiscal Year-end: 12/31/23
Oil & Gas Distribution Services
N.A.I.C.S.: 213112
Hoa My Quach (*Chm-Mgmt Bd*)

INTERNATIONAL PUBLIC

PETROVIETNAM POWER NHON TRACH 2 JOINT STOCK COMPANY
Oil and Gas Power Center, Phuoc Khanh Commune, Nhon Trach, Dong Nai, Vietnam
Tel.: (84) 2512225899
Web Site: https://pvpnt2.vn
Year Founded: 2007
Power Generation Services
N.A.I.C.S.: 221118
Hai Ngoc Uong (*Chm & Chm-Mgmt Bd*)

PETROVIETNAM SECURITIES INCORPORATED
Hanoitourist Tower No 18 Ly Thuong Kiet Street, Hoan Kiem district, Hanoi, Vietnam
Tel.: (84) 2439343888
Web Site: https://www.psi.vn
Year Founded: 2006
PSI—(HNX)
Rev.: $12,344,303
Assets: $92,870,774
Liabilities: $64,741,350
Net Worth: $28,129,424
Earnings: $1,007,587
Emp.: 151
Fiscal Year-end: 12/31/23
Investment Banking & Securities Brokerage Services
N.A.I.C.S.: 523150
Tran Hung Dung (*Member-Mgmt Bd & Deputy Gen Dir*)

PETROVSKY MLYN A.D.
Industrijska zona bb, Backi Petrovac, Serbia
Tel.: (381) 21 780 334
Year Founded: 1992
Sales Range: Less than $1 Million
Grain Mill Product Mfr
N.A.I.C.S.: 311230
Rastislav Struhar (*Exec Dir*)

PETROWEST CORP.
Suite 800 407 2nd Street SW, Calgary, T2P 2Y3, AB, Canada
Tel.: (403) 237-0881
Year Founded: 2011
PRW—(TSX)
Sales Range: $100-124.9 Million
Oil Field Services
N.A.I.C.S.: 213111

Subsidiaries:

Petrowest Civil Services LP (1)
8223 93 St, Fort Saint John, V1J 6X1, BC, Canada
Tel.: (250) 787-0969
Oil Filed Construction Services
N.A.I.C.S.: 237120

Petrowest Construction LP (1)
10014B Franklin Ave, Fort McMurray, T9H 2K6, AB, Canada
Tel.: (780) 743-0486
Oilfield Construction
N.A.I.C.S.: 237990

Subsidiary (Domestic):

Enviro-Mulch Land Clearing Solutions (2)
8823 72nd Street, Fort Saint John, V1J 0B4, BC, Canada
Tel.: (250) 261-5655
Web Site: http://www.enviro-mulch.com
Land Clearing & Construction Site Preparation Services
N.A.I.C.S.: 237990
Jeff Doyle (*Mgr-Ops*)

Jim Moffatt Construction Ltd. (2)
PO Box 318, Worsley, T0H 3W0, AB, Canada
Tel.: (780) 685-3600

AND PRIVATE COMPANIES

Sales Range: $25-49.9 Million
Emp.: 50
Oil Filed Construction Services
N.A.I.C.S.: 213111

Quigley Contracting (2)
PO Box 280, Charlie Lake, V0C1H0, BC, Canada
Tel.: (250) 787-0254
Road Building Construction
N.A.I.C.S.: 237310
Darren Seminoff *(Mgr-Ops)*

Roy Larson Construction
10226 - 84 Ave, Clairmont, T0H 0W0, AB, Canada
Tel.: (780) 830-3051
Construction Services Supplies
N.A.I.C.S.: 423320

Petrowest Corp. - Civil Division (1)
407 2nd Street SW Suite 800, Calgary, T2P 2Y3, AB, Canada
Tel.: (403) 237-0881
Custom Aggregate Crushing & Separation, Sand Screening & Oil Safety Supervision Services
N.A.I.C.S.: 212321

Subsidiary (Domestic):

R. Bee Crushing Ltd (2)
PO Box 1110, Gibbons, T0A 1N0, AB, Canada
Tel.: (780) 942-2434
Emp.: 20
Specialized Trucking & Hauling Capabilities
N.A.I.C.S.: 484230
David Howells *(Gen Mgr)*

S.O.S Oilfield Safety (2)
11309 86 Avenue, Grande Prairie, T8V 6Z6, AB, Canada
Tel.: (780) 539-5393
Emp.: 4
Oilfield Safety Supervision Services
N.A.I.C.S.: 238910
Brad Spurrell *(Mgr-Ops)*

Petrowest Corp. - Transportation & Hauling Division (1)
407 2nd Street SW, Calgary, T2P 2Y3, AB, Canada
Tel.: (403) 237-0881
General Heavy Duty Hauling & Equipment Transportation
N.A.I.C.S.: 488510

Subsidiary (Domestic):

CJM Trucking Ltd. (2)
55229 Boysdale Road, Fort Saskatchewan, T8L 5C5, AB, Canada
Tel.: (780) 998-1242
Web Site: http://www.cjmtrucking.com
Emp.: 18
Heavy Haul, Oversized Load & Equipment Hauling Rentals
N.A.I.C.S.: 532412
Dan Howard *(Mgr-Ops)*

Cutbank Trucking Ltd. (2)
PO Box 549, Grande Prairie, T8V 3A7, AB, Canada
Tel.: (780) 532-2424
Road Construction
N.A.I.C.S.: 237310
Ray Wardill *(Mgr)*

Murtron Hauling Ltd. (2)
9824 104 Ave, PO Box 3005, Clairmont, T0H 0W0, AB, Canada
Tel.: (780) 567-3612
Gravel, Heavy Equipment & Logs Transportation
N.A.I.C.S.: 488510
Keith Paton *(Controller)*

Trans Carrier Limited (2)
11579 Chevron Front, PO Box 6924, Fort Saint John, V1J 4J3, BC, Canada
Tel.: (250) 785-5553
Oilfield Site Maintenance
N.A.I.C.S.: 811310

PETROX RESOURCES CORP.
Suite 3001 505 6th Street SW, Calgary, T2P 1X5, AB, Canada
Tel.: (403) 270-2290 **AB**

Web Site:
https://petroxresourcescorp.com
Year Founded: 2011
PTC—(TSXV)
Rev.: $430,467
Assets: $404,199
Liabilities: $289,112
Net Worth: $115,087
Earnings: ($56,087)
Fiscal Year-end: 12/31/23
Oil & Gas Exploration Services
N.A.I.C.S.: 211120
Tam Edwin *(CEO)*

PETRUS RESOURCES LTD.
2400 240 4th Ave SW, Calgary, T2P 4H4, AB, Canada
Tel.: (403) 984-4014
Web Site:
https://www.petrusresources.com
6P4—(DEU)
Rev.: $94,846,334
Assets: $330,621,460
Liabilities: $92,638,375
Net Worth: $237,983,085
Earnings: $38,307,785
Emp.: 17
Fiscal Year-end: 12/31/23
Oil & Gas Exploration Services
N.A.I.C.S.: 213112
Don T. Gray *(Chm)*

PETS AT HOME GROUP PLC
Chester House Epsom Avenue, Handforth, Wilmslow, SK9 3RN, Cheshire, United Kingdom **UK**
Web Site:
https://www.petsathomeplc.com
Year Founded: 1991
PETS—(LSE)
Rev.: $1,879,821,777
Assets: $2,143,602,809
Liabilities: $885,168,686
Net Worth: $1,258,434,123
Earnings: $100,827,499
Emp.: 8,369
Fiscal Year-end: 03/28/24
Other Miscellaneous Nondurable Goods Merchant Wholesalers
N.A.I.C.S.: 424990
Mike Iddon *(CFO)*

Subsidiaries:

Aberdeen Vets4Pets Limited (1)
Inside Pets at Home Beach Boulevard Retail Park Links Road, Aberdeen, AB11 5EJ, Aberdeenshire, United Kingdom
Tel.: (44) 1224577930
Pet Healthcare Services
N.A.I.C.S.: 541940

Accrington Vets4Pets Limited (1)
Inside Pets at Home Eastgate Retail Park Stanley Street, Accrington, BB5 6PW, Lancashire, United Kingdom
Tel.: (44) 1254300290
Veterinary Care Services
N.A.I.C.S.: 541940

Bearsden Vets4Pets Limited (1)
1 Hillfoot Drive, Bearsden, Glasgow, G61 3QL, United Kingdom
Tel.: (44) 1419420283
Pet Healthcare Services
N.A.I.C.S.: 541940

Bicester Vets4Pets Limited (1)
Inside Pets at Home Launton Road, Bicester, OX26 4JG, Oxfordshire, United Kingdom
Tel.: (44) 1869328450
Pet Healthcare Services
N.A.I.C.S.: 541940

Bishop Auckland Vets4Pets Limited (1)
89 Cockton Hill Road, Bishop Auckland, DL14 6JN, Durham, United Kingdom
Tel.: (44) 1388660280
Pet Healthcare Services
N.A.I.C.S.: 541940

Blackpool Warbreck Vets4Pets Limited (1)
Inside Pets at Home Holyoake Avenue, Blackpool, FY2 0QX, Lancashire, United Kingdom
Tel.: (44) 1253356770
Pet Healthcare Services
N.A.I.C.S.: 541940

Bodmin Vets4Pets Limited (1)
Inside Pets at Home Bodmin Retail Park Launceston Road, Bodmin, PL31 2GA, Cornwall, United Kingdom
Tel.: (44) 1208261690
Pet Healthcare Services
N.A.I.C.S.: 541940

Bolton Central Vets4Pets Limited (1)
Inside Pets at Home Central Retail Park, Manchester Road Trinity Street Junction, Bolton, BL2 1HQ, Greater Manchester, United Kingdom
Tel.: (44) 1204368030
Pet Healthcare Services
N.A.I.C.S.: 541940

Borehamwood Vets4Pets Limited (1)
Inside Pets at Home Borehamwood Shopping Centre 25 Theobald Street, Borehamwood, WD6 4PR, Hertfordshire, United Kingdom
Tel.: (44) 2082363930
Pet Healthcare Services
N.A.I.C.S.: 541940

Bracknell Vets4Pets Limited (1)
Inside Pets at Home The Peel Centre Skimped Hill Ln, Bracknell, RG12 1EN, Berkshire, United Kingdom
Tel.: (44) 1344356970
Pet Healthcare Services
N.A.I.C.S.: 541940

Bradford Vets4Pets Limited (1)
Crossley Hall Retail Park Thornton Road, Bradford, BD8 0HH, West Yorkshire, United Kingdom
Tel.: (44) 1274488457
Pet Healthcare Services
N.A.I.C.S.: 541940

Bramley Vets4Pets Limited (1)
Old School House Lower Town Street, Bramley, Leeds, LS13 4BN, West Yorkshire, United Kingdom
Tel.: (44) 1132554466
Pet Healthcare Services
N.A.I.C.S.: 541940

Bridlington Vets4Pets Limited (1)
Inside Pets at Home Bessingby Road, Bridlington, YO16 4SH, East Yorkshire, United Kingdom
Tel.: (44) 1262426410
Pet Healthcare Services
N.A.I.C.S.: 541940

Brighton Vets4Pets Limited (1)
Inside Pets at Home Hollingbury Retail Park Carden Avenue, Brighton, BN1 8LW, East Sussex, United Kingdom
Tel.: (44) 1273762988
Pet Healthcare Services
N.A.I.C.S.: 541940

Bromborough Vets4Pets Limited (1)
Inside Pets at Home Croft Retail Park Welton Road, Wirral, Birkenhead, CH62 3PN, United Kingdom
Tel.: (44) 1514823530
Pet Healthcare Services
N.A.I.C.S.: 541940

Cambridge Perne Road Vets4Pets Limited (1)
255 Barnwell Road, Cambridge, CB5 8SL, Cambridgeshire, United Kingdom
Tel.: (44) 1223243535
Veterinary Clinics Operator
N.A.I.C.S.: 541940

Companion Care (Chippenham) Limited (1)
Inside Pets at Home Bumpers Way, Chippenham, SN14 6RZ, Wiltshire, United Kingdom
Tel.: (44) 1249736941
Veterinary Care Services
N.A.I.C.S.: 541940

Companion Care (Ely) Limited (1)

PETS AT HOME GROUP PLC

Cathedral Veterinary Surgery 64 Newnham Street, Ely, CB7 4PE, Cambridgeshire, United Kingdom
Tel.: (44) 1353662079
Pet Healthcare Services
N.A.I.C.S.: 541940

Companion Care (Llantrisant) Limited (1)
Inside Pets at Home Glamorgan Retail Park Newpark, Llantrisant, CF72 8RP, Mid Glamorgan, United Kingdom
Tel.: (44) 1443228315
Veterinary Care Services
N.A.I.C.S.: 541940

Companion Care (Maidstone) Limited (1)
Inside Pets at Home South Aylesford Retail Park, Aylesford, Maidstone, ME20 7TP, Kent, United Kingdom
Tel.: (44) 1622711363
Pet Healthcare Services
N.A.I.C.S.: 541940

Corby Vets4Pets Limited (1)
Inside Pets at Home The Peel Centre Phoenix Way, Corby, NN17 5DT, Northamptonshire, United Kingdom
Tel.: (44) 1536206531
Pet Healthcare Services
N.A.I.C.S.: 541940

Crewe Vets4Pets Limited (1)
Inside Pets at Home Grand Junction Retail Park Grand Junction Way, Crewe, CW1 2RP, Cheshire, United Kingdom
Tel.: (44) 1270849494
Pet Healthcare Services
N.A.I.C.S.: 541940

Doncaster Vets4Pets Limited (1)
Unit 2a Wentworth Road, Wheatley, Doncaster, DN2 4DB, South Yorkshire, United Kingdom
Tel.: (44) 1302556868
Pet Healthcare Services
N.A.I.C.S.: 541940

Dorchester Vets4Pets Limited (1)
Inside Pets at Home Weymouth Avenue Retail Park Weymouth Avenue, Dorchester, DT1 2RY, Dorset, United Kingdom
Tel.: (44) 1305268794
Pet Healthcare Services
N.A.I.C.S.: 541940

Dundee Vets4Pets Limited (1)
Inside Pets at Home Kingsway East Retail Park, Dundee, DD4 8JT, United Kingdom
Tel.: (44) 1382519200
Pet Healthcare Services
N.A.I.C.S.: 541940

East Kilbride South Vets4Pets Limited (1)
Inside Pets at Home East Kilbride Retail Park Howard Avenue, East Kilbride, G74 4ZA, United Kingdom
Tel.: (44) 1355271540
Pet Healthcare Services
N.A.I.C.S.: 541940

Evesham Vets4Pets Limited (1)
Inside Pets at Home Four Pools Retail Park Four Pools lane, Evesham, WR11 1DJ, Worcestershire, United Kingdom
Tel.: (44) 1386769300
Pet Healthcare Services
N.A.I.C.S.: 541940

Gillingham Vets4Pets Limited (1)
Inside Pets at Home Gillingham Retail Park Ambley Road, Gillingham, ME8 0PU, Medway, United Kingdom
Tel.: (44) 1634224620
Pet Healthcare Services
N.A.I.C.S.: 541940

Grantham Vets4Pets Limited (1)
95-97 London Rd, Grantham, NG31 6HS, Lincolnshire, United Kingdom
Tel.: (44) 1476571773
Pet Healthcare Services
N.A.I.C.S.: 541940

Guildford Vets4Pets Limited (1)
Inside Pets at Home Woodbridge Rd, Guildford, GU1 1EE, Surrey, United Kingdom
Tel.: (44) 3452668521
Pet Healthcare Services

PETS AT HOME GROUP PLC

Pets at Home Group Plc—(Continued)
N.A.I.C.S.: 541940

Handforth Vets4Pets Limited (1)
Inside Pets at Home Handforth Shopping Park Long Marl Drive, Handforth, SK9 3TJ, Cheshire, United Kingdom
Tel.: (44) 3452668522
Pet Healthcare Services
N.A.I.C.S.: 541940

Hemsworth Vets4Pets Limited (1)
Wakefield Road Hemsworth, Wakefield, WF9 4AB, West Yorkshire, United Kingdom
Tel.: (44) 1977624430
Veterinary Care Services
N.A.I.C.S.: 541940

Huddersfield Vets4Pets Limited (1)
144 New Hey Rd, Huddersfield, HD3 4BZ, West Yorkshire, United Kingdom
Tel.: (44) 1484646800
Pet Healthcare Services
N.A.I.C.S.: 541940

Kendal Vets4Pets Limited (1)
Inside Pets at Home South Lakeland Retail Park Queen Katherines Avenue, Kendal, LA9 6DU, Cumbria, United Kingdom
Tel.: (44) 1539742910
Pet Healthcare Services
N.A.I.C.S.: 541940

Kilmarnock Vets4Pets Limited (1)
Inside Pets at Home Queens Drive Queens Drive Retail Park, Kilmarnock, KA1 3XB, East Ayrshire, United Kingdom
Tel.: (44) 1563522225
Pet Healthcare Services
N.A.I.C.S.: 541940

Lancaster Vets4Pets Limited (1)
Inside Pets At Home Lancaster City Retail Park Mellishaw Lane, Morecambe, LA3 3FE, Lancashire, United Kingdom
Tel.: (44) 1524581346
Pet Healthcare Services
N.A.I.C.S.: 541940

Leamington Spa Myton Road Vets4Pets Limited (1)
Myton Road, Leamington Spa, Warwick, CV31 3NY, United Kingdom
Tel.: (44) 1926310430
Pet Healthcare Services
N.A.I.C.S.: 541940

Leamington Spa Vets4Pets Limited (1)
Inside Pets at Home Myton Road, Leamington Spa, CV31 3NY, Warwickshire, United Kingdom
Tel.: (44) 1926310430
Pet Healthcare Services
N.A.I.C.S.: 541940

Leeds Kirkstall Vets4Pets Limited (1)
Inside Pets at Home Kirkstall Bridge Shopping Park Bridge Road, Kirkstall, Leeds, LS5 3BL, West Yorkshire, United Kingdom
Tel.: (44) 1132399930
Pet Healthcare Services
N.A.I.C.S.: 541940

Liverpool OS Vets4Pets Limited (1)
8 Broad Green Rd, Old Swan, Liverpool, L13 5SG, United Kingdom
Tel.: (44) 1512520000
Veterinary Care Services
N.A.I.C.S.: 541940

Maidstone Vets4Pets Limited (1)
128 Sutton Road, Maidstone, ME15 9BY, Kent, United Kingdom
Tel.: (44) 1622686817
Pet Healthcare Services
N.A.I.C.S.: 541940

Market Harborough Vets4Pets Limited (1)
Inside Pets at Home Springfield Retail Park, Market Harborough, LE16 8BD, Leicestershire, United Kingdom
Tel.: (44) 1858438900
Pet Healthcare Services
N.A.I.C.S.: 541940

Newark Vets4Pets Limited (1)
Inside Pets at Home Northgate Retail Park, Newark, NG24 1GA, Nottinghamshire, United Kingdom
Tel.: (44) 1636593900
Pet Healthcare Services
N.A.I.C.S.: 541940

Newtownards Vets4Pets Limited (1)
2a Portaferry Road, Newtownards, BT23 8NN, Down, United Kingdom
Tel.: (44) 2891824200
Veterinary Care Services
N.A.I.C.S.: 541940

Northwich Vets4Pets Limited (1)
Inside Pets at Home Chester Way Retail Park Chester Way, Northwich, CW9 5JF, Cheshire, United Kingdom
Tel.: (44) 1606333450
Pet Healthcare Services
N.A.I.C.S.: 541940

Pentland Vets4Pets Limited (1)
Inside Pets at Home Straiton Mains Straiton Retail Park, Loanhead, EH20 9PW, Midlothian, United Kingdom
Tel.: (44) 1314403904
Pet Healthcare Services
N.A.I.C.S.: 541940

Perth Vets4Pets Limited (1)
Inside Pets at Home St Catherines Retail Park St Catherines Road, Perth & Kinross, Perth, PH1 5XD, United Kingdom
Tel.: (44) 1738783826
Veterinary Care Services
N.A.I.C.S.: 541940

Pet City Limited (1)
Avenue Retail Park Weaverthorpe Road Tong Street, Bradford, BD4 9RQ, United Kingdom
Tel.: (44) 1274680398
Web Site: https://www.petcitybradford.co.uk
Home Pet Distr
N.A.I.C.S.: 424990

Prescot Vets4Pets Limited (1)
Inside Pets at Home Unit A Cables Retail Park Steley Way, Prescot, Liverpool, L34 5NQ, United Kingdom
Tel.: (44) 1514306474
Pet Healthcare Services
N.A.I.C.S.: 541940

Rawtenstall Vets4Pets Limited (1)
Inside Pets at Home New Hall Hey Retail Park, Rawtenstall, BB4 6HR, Lancashire, United Kingdom
Tel.: (44) 1706833050
Pet Healthcare Services
N.A.I.C.S.: 541940

Runcorn Vets4Pets Limited (1)
3 Jack Search Way Murdishaw Avenue, Runcorn, WA7 6SA, Cheshire, United Kingdom
Tel.: (44) 1928750260
Pet Healthcare Services
N.A.I.C.S.: 541940

Scunthorpe Vets4Pets Limited (1)
Inside Pets At Home Lakeside Retail Park, Scunthorpe, DN16 3UA, Lincolnshire, United Kingdom
Tel.: (44) 1724407950
Pet Healthcare Services
N.A.I.C.S.: 541940

Selby Vets4Pets Limited (1)
Inside Pets at Home Three Lakes Retail Park Bawtry Road, Selby, YO8 8LY, North Yorkshire, United Kingdom
Tel.: (44) 1757211610
Pet Healthcare Services
N.A.I.C.S.: 541940

Sheffield Drakehouse Vets4Pets Limited (1)
Inside Pets at Home Drakehouse Retail Park Drakehouse Way, Sheffield, S20 7JJ, South Yorkshire, United Kingdom
Tel.: (44) 1142474558
Pet Healthcare Services
N.A.I.C.S.: 541940

Sidcup Vets4Pets Limited (1)
278 Sherwood Park Avenue, Sidcup, DA15 9JN, United Kingdom
Tel.: (44) 2083043641
Pet Healthcare Services
N.A.I.C.S.: 541940

South Shields Quays Vets4Pets Limited (1)
Inside Pets at Home, South Shields, NE33 1RD, Tyne and Wear, United Kingdom
Tel.: (44) 1914969700
Pet Healthcare Services
N.A.I.C.S.: 541940

St Austell Vets4Pets Limited (1)
Inside Pets at Home Pentewan Retail Park Pentewan Road, St Austell, Saint Austell, PL25 5BU, Cornwall, United Kingdom
Tel.: (44) 1726626820
Pet Healthcare Services
N.A.I.C.S.: 541940

Staines Vets4Pets Limited (1)
Inside Pets at Home Two Rivers Retail Park Mustard Mill Road, Staines, TW18 4WB, Surrey, United Kingdom
Tel.: (44) 1784278917
Veterinary Care Services
N.A.I.C.S.: 541940

Vets4Pets UK Limited (1)
Isambard House Fire Fly Avenue, Swindon, SN2 2EH, United Kingdom
Tel.: (44) 1367820820
Pet Healthcare Services
N.A.I.C.S.: 541940

PETSEC ENERGY LTD.
Macquarie Business Centre Level 7 165 Macquarie Street, Sydney, 2000, NSW, Australia
Tel.: (61) 29 247 4605 AU
Web Site: http://www.petsec.com.au
Year Founded: 1967
PSJEY—(OTCIQ)
Assets: $1,597,000
Liabilities: $23,595,000
Net Worth: ($21,998,000)
Earnings: ($3,021,000)
Emp.: 35,000
Fiscal Year-end: 12/31/21
Oil & Gas Exploration & Production
N.A.I.C.S.: 211120
Terrence N. Fern *(Chm)*

Subsidiaries:

Ginida Pty. Limited (1)
Level 13 1 Alfred St, Sydney, 2000, NSW, Australia
Tel.: (61) 292474605
Oil & Gas Exploration Services
N.A.I.C.S.: 211120

Najedo Pty. Ltd. (1)
L13-1 Alfred St, Sydney, 2000, NSW, Australia **(100%)**
Tel.: (61) 292474605
Sales Range: $50-74.9 Million
Emp.: 4
Financial Investment Activities
N.A.I.C.S.: 523999
Terry N. Fern *(Chm & Mng Dir)*

Osglen Pty. Limited (1)
Level 13-1 Alfred St, 2000, Sydney, NSW, Australia
Tel.: (61) 292474605
Financial Investment Activities
N.A.I.C.S.: 523999
Terry N. Fern *(Chm & Mng Dir)*

Petsec (U.S.A.) Inc. (1)
301 E Kaliste Saloom Rd, Lafayette, LA 70508
Tel.: (337) 989-1942
Web Site: http://www.petsecenergy.com
Sales Range: $50-74.9 Million
Emp.: 4
Oil & Gas Exploration Services
N.A.I.C.S.: 211120
Ross Keogh *(Pres)*

Petsec America Pty. Limited (1)
Level 13 1 Alfred Street, Sydney, 2000, NSW, Australia
Tel.: (61) 292474605
Web Site: http://www.petsec.com.au
Oil & Gas Exploration Services
N.A.I.C.S.: 211120
Terrance N. Fern *(CEO)*

Petsec Energy, Inc. (1)
3861 Ambassador Caffery Pkwy Ste 500, Lafayette, LA 70503
Tel.: (337) 989-1942
Web Site: http://www.petsec.com
Sales Range: $100-124.9 Million
Oil & Gas Exploration & Production
N.A.I.C.S.: 211120
Ross A. Keogh *(Pres)*

Petsec Investments Pty Limited (1)
Level 13-1 Alfred St, Sydney, 2000, NSW, Australia **(100%)**
Tel.: (61) 292474605
Web Site: http://www.petsec.com
Securities Brokerage
N.A.I.C.S.: 523150
Terry N. Fern *(Chm & Mng Dir)*

Western Medical Products Pty Limited (1)
Level 13-1 Alfred St, Sydney, 2000, NSW, Australia **(100%)**
Tel.: (61) 292474605
Web Site: http://www.petsec.com
Sales Range: $25-49.9 Million
Surgical & Medical Instrument Mfr
N.A.I.C.S.: 339112
Terry N. Fern *(Chm & Mng Dir)*

PETSERVICE HOLDING N.V.
Industrieweg 16, 1521 NC, Wormerveer, Netherlands
Tel.: (31) 356255187
Web Site:
https://www.petserviceholding.com
Year Founded: 2021
MLPET—(EUR)
Rev.: $1,334,009
Assets: $2,635,355
Liabilities: $1,602,816
Net Worth: $1,032,539
Earnings: ($1,126,178)
Emp.: 7
Fiscal Year-end: 12/31/23
Holding Company
N.A.I.C.S.: 551112
Ron Van Veldhoven *(CEO)*

PETTENATI S.A. INDUSTRIA TEXTI
Rodovia RSC 453 - Km 2 4 - s/n Distrito Industrial, Caxias do Sul, 95010-550, RS, Brazil
Tel.: (55) 5432277200
Web Site:
https://www.pettenati.com.br
Year Founded: 1964
PTNT4—(BRAZ)
Rev.: $171,175,491
Assets: $161,269,320
Liabilities: $73,741,457
Net Worth: $87,527,863
Earnings: $13,961,587
Emp.: 2,505
Fiscal Year-end: 06/30/23
Textile Product Mfr & Whslr
N.A.I.C.S.: 314999
Carla Francisca Pettenati *(Pres)*

PETTY WOOD & CO. LTD.
Livingstone Road, Walworth Business Park, Andover, SP10 5NS, Hants, United Kingdom
Tel.: (44) 1264 345500
Web Site:
http://www.pettywood.co.uk
Sales Range: $25-49.9 Million
Emp.: 55
Retail Food Distribution, Sales & Marketing Services
N.A.I.C.S.: 424410
John Potter *(CEO)*

Subsidiaries:

Tree of Life UK Ltd. (1)
Coaldale Road Lymedale Business Park, Newcastle-under-Lyme, ST5 9QH, Staffordshire, United Kingdom
Tel.: (44) 1782567100
Web Site: http://www.treeoflifeuk.com

Sales Range: $50-74.9 Million
Organic & Natural Products Distr
N.A.I.C.S.: 424490

PEWO ENERGIETECHNIK GMBH
Geierswalder Strasse 13, 02979, Bautzen, Germany
Tel.: (49) 357148980
Web Site: http://www.pewo.com
Sales Range: $10-24.9 Million
Heat Distribution Equipments Mfr
N.A.I.C.S.: 333414
Egbert Petrick (Mng Dir)

Subsidiaries:

PEWO Austria GmbH (1)
St Peter 12, 8843, Sankt Peter am Kammersberg, Austria
Tel.: (43) 353673908
Emp.: 280
Heat Distribution Services
N.A.I.C.S.: 221330
Christian Auer (Product Mgr)

PEWO Energietechnik Schweiz GmbH (1)
Pra Pury 7, 3280, Murten, Switzerland
Tel.: (41) 317556518
Heat Distribution Services
N.A.I.C.S.: 221330

PEWO Energiteknik AB (1)
Domherrevagen 11, 19255, Stockholm, Sweden
Tel.: (46) 703813813
Heat Distribution Services
N.A.I.C.S.: 221330
Diana Westling (Mgr-Sls)

PEWO d.o.o. (1)
Visokog Stefana 54, 11380, Belgrade, Serbia
Tel.: (381) 112928086
Heat Distribution Services
N.A.I.C.S.: 221330
David Piegazki (Country Mgr)

PEXA AB
Arvid Wallgrens Backe 20, 413 46, Gothenburg, Sweden
Tel.: (46) 705864380
Web Site: https://www.pexa.se
Year Founded: 2004
FA0—(DEU)
Medical Instrument Mfr
N.A.I.C.S.: 339112
Claes Holmberg (Chm)

PEXA GROUP LIMITED
Tower 4 Level 16 Collins Square 727 Collins Street, Melbourne, 3008, VIC, Australia
Tel.: (61) 370024500   AU
Web Site: https://www.pexa.com.au
Year Founded: 2010
PXA—(ASX)
Rev.: $183,665,645
Assets: $1,097,484,515
Liabilities: $287,712,069
Net Worth: $809,772,446
Earnings: ($14,240,073)
Emp.: 968
Fiscal Year-end: 06/30/23
Financial Investment Services
N.A.I.C.S.: 523999
Glenn King (Grp CEO & Mng Dir)

Subsidiaries:

I.D. (informed decisions) Pty. Ltd. (1)
10 Easey St, PO Box 1689, Collingwood, 3066, VIC, Australia
Tel.: (61) 394172205
Web Site: https://home.id.com.au
Digital Platform Services
N.A.I.C.S.: 541810

Optima Legal Services Ltd. (1)
Hepworth House Claypit Lane, Leeds, LS2 8AE, United Kingdom
Tel.: (44) 3031231113

Web Site: https://www.optimalegal.co.uk
Mortgage Finance Services
N.A.I.C.S.: 522310

Property Exchange Australia Ltd. (1)
Tower 4 Level 16 Collins Square 727 Collins Street, Melbourne, 3008, VIC, Australia
Tel.: (61) 370024500
Information & Communication Technology Services
N.A.I.C.S.: 541430

PEXIP HOLDING ASA
Lilleakerveien 2A 8 floor, 0283, Oslo, Norway
Tel.: (47) 99234596
Web Site: https://www.pexip.com
Year Founded: 2011
PEXIP—(OSL)
Rev.: $91,777,388
Assets: $186,685,664
Liabilities: $43,066,322
Net Worth: $143,619,342
Earnings: ($7,369,850)
Emp.: 298
Fiscal Year-end: 12/31/23
Holding Company
N.A.I.C.S.: 551112
Ian Mortimer (CTO)

PEYTO EXPLORATION & DEVELOPMENT CORP.
Suite 300 600 3rd Ave SW, Calgary, T2P 0G5, AB, Canada
Tel.: (403) 261-6081
Web Site: https://www.peyto.com
Year Founded: 1998
PEY—(OTCIQ)
Rev.: $506,692,143
Assets: $2,960,300,065
Liabilities: $1,578,788,891
Net Worth: $1,381,511,174
Earnings: $119,100,565
Emp.: 55
Fiscal Year-end: 12/31/21
Natural Gas Exploration & Services
N.A.I.C.S.: 221210
Jean-Paul H. Lachance (COO & VP-Engrg)

PEZM GOLD, INC.
837 West Hastings Streett Suite 507, Vancouver, V6C 3N6, BC, Canada
Tel.: (604) 685-1017
Mineral Exploration Services
N.A.I.C.S.: 213114
Arness Cordick (CEO)

PF COLLINS CUSTOMS BROKER LTD.
100 251 East White Hills Road, PO Box 5514, Saint John's, A1C 5W4, NL, Canada
Tel.: (709) 726-7596
Web Site: https://www.pfcollins.com
Year Founded: 1921
Sales Range: $10-24.9 Million
Emp.: 100
Brokerage & Freight Forwarding Services
N.A.I.C.S.: 425120
Raymonds Collins (Pres)

PF GROUP HOLDINGS LIMITED
Suite 4409 44/F COSCO Tower 183 Queen s Road, Central, China (Hong Kong)
Tel.: (852) 2 877 3188   Ky
Web Site: http://www.pfs.com.hk
8221—(HKG)
Rev.: $960,127
Assets: $25,727,125
Liabilities: $5,950,105
Net Worth: $19,777,019
Earnings: ($3,197,543)
Emp.: 19
Fiscal Year-end: 03/31/22

Financial Security Brokerage Services
N.A.I.C.S.: 523150
Yuk Tong Fok (Exec Dir)

PFA HOLDING A/S
Sundkrogsgade 4, 2100, Copenhagen, Denmark
Tel.: (45) 3917 5000   DK
Web Site: http://www.pfa.dk
Rev.: $5,437,590,750
Assets: $88,186,833,000
Liabilities: $86,976,029,100
Net Worth: $1,210,803,900
Earnings: $17,459,100
Emp.: 1,337
Fiscal Year-end: 12/31/18
Holding Company; Pension Fund Administration, Real Estate & Investment Management Services
N.A.I.C.S.: 551112
Allan Polack (CEO)

Subsidiaries:

PFA Pension Forsikringsaktieselskab (1)
Sundkrogsgade 4, 2100, Copenhagen, Denmark
Tel.: (45) 39175000
Web Site: http://www.pfa.dk
Emp.: 2,623
Pension Fund Management Services
N.A.I.C.S.: 551112
Anders Damgaard (CFO)

Joint Venture (Domestic):

TDC Holding A/S (2)
Teglholmsgade 1, 0900, Copenhagen, C, Denmark   (16.66%)
Tel.: (45) 70110330
Web Site: http://www.tdcgroup.com
Rev.: $2,302,027,000
Assets: $9,226,189,000
Liabilities: $6,451,042,500
Net Worth: $2,775,146,500
Earnings: $246,246,000
Emp.: 6,433
Fiscal Year-end: 12/31/2022
Holding Company; Telecommunications Services
N.A.I.C.S.: 551112
Mike Parton (Chm)

Subsidiary (Domestic):

Nuuday A/S (3)
Teglholmsgade 1, 2450, Copenhagen, Denmark
Tel.: (45) 70110330
Web Site: https://nuuday.com
Emp.: 3,075
Digital Media Streaming & Telecommunications Services
N.A.I.C.S.: 517121

Punktum dk A/S (3)
Ørestads Boulevard 108 11, 2300, Copenhagen, Denmark
Tel.: (45) 33646000
Web Site: https://www.punktum.dk
Sales Range: $10-24.9 Million
Emp.: 43
Internet Domain Name Registration & Hosting Services
N.A.I.C.S.: 518210
Jakob Bring Truelsen (CEO)

TDC Solutions A/S (3)
Teglholmsgade 1 G 455, 0900, Copenhagen, C, Denmark
Tel.: (45) 70110330
Telecommunications, Internet & Business Management Services
N.A.I.C.S.: 517111

YouSee A/S (3)
Teglholmsgade 1, DK-0900, Copenhagen, Denmark
Tel.: (45) 70704040
Web Site: http://yousee.dk
Cable Television & Internet Services
N.A.I.C.S.: 516210

Subsidiary (Domestic):

DKTV A/S (4)

Teglholmsgade 1,, 2450, Copenhagen, Denmark
Tel.: (45) 43324700
Web Site: https://www.dktv.dk
Emp.: 422
Cable Television & Internet Services
N.A.I.C.S.: 516210

Branch (Domestic):

Dansk Kabel TV A/S - Esbjerg (5)
Skjoltsgate 49, 6700, Esbjerg, Denmark
Tel.: (45) 43324700
Web Site: https://www.dktv.dk
Cable Television & Internet Services
N.A.I.C.S.: 516210

PFC DEVICE INC.
1/F Shell Industrial Building 12 Lee Chung Street, Chai Wan, China (Hong Kong)
Tel.: (852) 2 558 0181   Ky
Web Site: http://www.pfc-device.com
8231—(HKG)
Rev.: $21,098,000
Assets: $26,988,000
Liabilities: $3,797,000
Net Worth: $23,191,000
Earnings: $646,000
Emp.: 138
Fiscal Year-end: 12/31/20
Semiconductor Product Mfr & Distr
N.A.I.C.S.: 334413
James Man-fai Hong (CEO)

Subsidiaries:

PFC Device Inc. - Shunde Factory (1)
No 18 San Le Dong Lu Beijiao Industrial park, Beijiao Town Shunde District, Foshan, Guangdong, China
Tel.: (86) 75726655813
Rectifier Mfr
N.A.I.C.S.: 334413

PFERDEWETTEN.DE AG
Kaistr 4, 40221, Dusseldorf, Germany
Tel.: (49) 21178178210
Web Site: https://www.pferdewetten.ag
Year Founded: 1997
EMH—(MUN)
Rev.: $16,344,846
Assets: $38,105,988
Liabilities: $17,880,174
Net Worth: $20,225,814
Earnings: ($2,654,838)
Emp.: 90
Fiscal Year-end: 12/31/22
Horse Racecourse Operator
N.A.I.C.S.: 711219

PFG GLASS INDUSTRIES
27413 55 Ave, Langley, V4W 3Y1, BC, Canada
Tel.: (604) 607-4500
Web Site: https://www.pfgglass.com
Year Founded: 1990
Emp.: 100
Glass Products Distr & Mfr
N.A.I.C.S.: 327215
Ole Nielsen (Pres & CEO)

PFIFFNER INTERNATIONAL AG
Lindenplatz 17, Hirschthal, 5042, Aarau, Switzerland
Tel.: (41) 62 739 2828
Web Site: http://www.pfiffner-group.com
Year Founded: 1927
Emp.: 250
Transformer & Other Electronic Parts Mfr
N.A.I.C.S.: 335311

Subsidiaries:

Haefely Test AG (1)

PFIFFNER INTERNATIONAL AG

PFIFFNER International AG—(Continued)
Birsstrasse 300, 4052, Basel, Switzerland **(100%)**
Tel.: (41) 613734111
Web Site: http://www.haefely-hipotronics.com
Sales Range: $25-49.9 Million
Emp.: 120
Supplier of High Voltage Test Systems
N.A.I.C.S.: 334519
Markus Schneider (Dir-Fin)

PFK ELECTRONICS (PTY) LTD.
28 Wiganthorpe Road, Willowton, Pietermaritzburg, 3200, KwaZulu-Natal, South Africa
Tel.: (27) 338159800
Web Site: http://www.pfk.co.za
Year Founded: 1969
Automotive Electronic System Mfr
N.A.I.C.S.: 334419
Alan Sullivan (CTO)

PFL INFOTECH LTD.
102 Block B2 Radha Krishna Towers Mayur Marg Begumpet, Hyderabad, 500016, Telangana, India
Tel.: (91) 9666699809
Web Site: https://www.pflinfotech.in
Rev.: $102,186
Assets: $1,472,159
Liabilities: $60,052
Net Worth: $1,412,107
Earnings: $60,447
Fiscal Year-end: 03/31/18
Software Publishing Services
N.A.I.C.S.: 513210
P. Amresh Kumar (Chm & Mng Dir)

PFLEIDERER GMBH
Ingolstadter Strasse 51, 92318, Neumarkt, Germany
Tel.: (49) 918128 480
Web Site: http://www.pfleiderer.com
Year Founded: 1890
Sales Range: $1-4.9 Billion
Emp.: 5,592
Wood-Based Products & Infrastructure Technology Services
N.A.I.C.S.: 488210

Subsidiaries:

Duropal GmbH **(1)**
Westring 19-21, 59759, Arnsberg, Germany
Tel.: (49) 29323020
Web Site: http://www.duropal.com
Sales Range: $150-199.9 Million
Emp.: 300
Decorative Lamination Sheets Mfr & Distr
N.A.I.C.S.: 322220
Meinolf Hering (Gen Mgr)

Heller Holz GmbH **(1)**
Ingolstadter Strasse 51, 92318, Neumarkt, Germany
Tel.: (49) 91 81 28 0
Web Site: http://www.hellerholz.com
Wood & Timber Products Mfr
N.A.I.C.S.: 321999

JURA Spedition GmbH **(1)**
Ingolstadter Str 51, Neumarkt, 92318, Germany
Tel.: (49) 9181280
Sales Range: $25-49.9 Million
Emp.: 10
Freight Forwarding Services
N.A.I.C.S.: 488510
Andreas Ott (Mgr-Logistics & Transport)

Subsidiary (Non-US):

Jura Polska Sp. z o.o. **(2)**
Wiorowa 1, Grajewo, 19230, Poland
Tel.: (48) 86 27 29 437
Web Site: http://www.jura-polska.pl
Sales Range: $25-49.9 Million
Logistics Consulting Servies
N.A.I.C.S.: 541614
Krzysztof Brzostek (Chm)

Kunz Faserplattenwerk Baruth GmbH **(1)**
An der Birkenpfuhlheide 3, Baruth, 15837, Brandenburg, Germany
Tel.: (49) 33 70 47 01 00
Wood Products Mfr & Distr
N.A.I.C.S.: 321999

Pfleiderer Accessories and Services, GmbH **(1)**
Unterer Auenweg 9, Leutkirch, 88299, Germany
Tel.: (49) 75619770
Emp.: 11
Flooring Equipment Maintenance Services
N.A.I.C.S.: 811411

Pfleiderer Benelux B.V. **(1)**
De Ketting 16a, Vught, 5261 LJ, Netherlands
Tel.: (31) 736840744
Web Site: http://www.pfleiderer.nl
Flooring Materials Mfr & Distr
N.A.I.C.S.: 327120

Pfleiderer Europols GmbH & Co. KG-Werk Regensburg **(1)**
Donaustaufer St 139, 93059, Regensburg, Germany **(100%)**
Tel.: (49) 941466580
Web Site: http://www.pfleiderer.com
Sales Range: $250-299.9 Million
Emp.: 560
Provider of Construction Materials.
N.A.I.C.S.: 423320

Pfleiderer France S. A. S. **(1)**
Par Techno Henri Farman 12 Rue Clement Ader, Reims, 51100, France
Tel.: (33) 326352080
Flooring Materials Distr
N.A.I.C.S.: 423320

Pfleiderer Grajewo S.A. **(1)**
Ul Wiorowa 1, P 19203, Grajewo, Poland **(85.65%)**
Tel.: (48) 862723261
Web Site: http://www.pfleiderer.pl
Sales Range: $125-149.9 Million
Emp.: 500
Wood Products
N.A.I.C.S.: 321999

Pfleiderer Holzwerkstoffe GmbH & Co. KG **(1)**
Holzstrasse 10, 33332, Gutersloh, Germany **(100%)**
Tel.: (49) 52418720
Web Site: http://www.yestyy-wood.com
Sales Range: $800-899.9 Million
Emp.: 4,000
Provider of Construction Equipment
N.A.I.C.S.: 333120

Pfleiderer Holzwerkstoffe GmbH & Co. KG-Werk Arnsberg **(1)**
Westring 19 21, Arnsberg, 59759, Germany **(100%)**
Tel.: (49) 29323020
Web Site: http://www.pfleiderer.com
Sales Range: $150-199.9 Million
Emp.: 400
Provider of Construction Materials.
N.A.I.C.S.: 423320
Michael Wolff (Gen Mgr)

Pfleiderer Holzwerkstoffe Nidda Verwaltungs-GmbH **(1)**
Ingolstadter Str 51, Neumarkt, 92318, Germany
Tel.: (49) 9181280
Wood Products Mfr & Distr
N.A.I.C.S.: 321999

Pfleiderer Holzwerkstoffe Verwaltungs GmbH **(1)**
Ingolstadter Str 51, 92318, Neumarkt, Germany
Tel.: (49) 9181 280
Wood Products Mfr
N.A.I.C.S.: 321999
Michael Wolff (CEO)

Pfleiderer Industrie Ltd. **(1)**
Oakfield House Springwood Way Tytherington Business Park, Macclesfield, SK10 2XA, Cheshire, United Kingdom
Tel.: (44) 1 625 660 410
Web Site: http://www.duropal.co.uk

Emp.: 7
Decorative Laminates Mfr
N.A.I.C.S.: 322220
Jason Taylor (Gen Mgr-Sls)

Pfleiderer Infrastrukturtechnik GmbH & Co. KG **(1)**
Muehlenweg 1, Betonschwellenwerk Coswig, D 01640, Coswig, Germany **(100%)**
Tel.: (49) 352391801
Web Site: http://www.pfleiderer.de
Sales Range: $50-74.9 Million
Emp.: 100
Provider of Construction Materials.
N.A.I.C.S.: 423320

Pfleiderer Infrastrukturtechnik GmbH & Co. KG **(1)**
Bautzner Str 65, 4347, Leipzig, Germany **(100%)**
Tel.: (49) 918128197
Web Site: http://www.pfleiderer.com
Wood Products
N.A.I.C.S.: 321219

Pfleiderer Infrastrukturtechnology GmbH & Co. KG **(1)**
Ingolstadterstrasse 151, PO Box 80, 92318, Neumarkt, Germany **(100%)**
Tel.: (49) 918128609
Web Site: http://www.railone.com
Sales Range: $250-299.9 Million
Emp.: 800
Provider of Construction Materials.
N.A.I.C.S.: 423320

Pfleiderer Leutkirch GmbH **(1)**
Wurzacher Strasse 32, Leutkirch, 88299, Germany
Tel.: (49) 7561 89 0
Web Site: http://www.pfleiderer.com
Interior Wood Products Mfr & Distr
N.A.I.C.S.: 321999

Subsidiary (Non-US):

Thermopal-Fiderisspan AG **(2)**
Seestrasse 295, 8804, Wadenswil, Switzerland
Tel.: (41) 44 307 55 55
Web Site: http://www.fiderisspan.ch
Wood Materials & Panel Distr
N.A.I.C.S.: 423310

Pfleiderer MDF Sp. z o.o. **(1)**
ul Wiorowa 1, Grajewo, 19-203, Poland
Tel.: (48) 86 27 29 600
Web Site: http://www.pfleiderer.pl
Timber & Wood Products Mfr
N.A.I.C.S.: 321999

Pfleiderer Prospan S. A. **(1)**
ul Boles Awiecka 10, Wieruszow, 98-400, Poland
Tel.: (48) 62 783 3100
Veneer Chipboard Furniture Mfr
N.A.I.C.S.: 321211

Pfleiderer Service Sp. z o.o. **(1)**
Wiorowa 1, 19-203, Grajewo, Poland
Tel.: (48) 86 272 94 60
Wood Products Mfr
N.A.I.C.S.: 321999

Pfleiderer dritte Erwerbergesellschaft mbH & Co **(1)**
Ingolstadter Str 51, 92318, Neumarkt, Germany
Tel.: (49) 9181280
Flooring Materials Mfr & Distr
N.A.I.C.S.: 327120
Michael Wolff (CEO)

Silekol Sp. z o.o. **(1)**
ul Mostowa 30K, 47-220, Kedzierzyn-Kozle, Poland
Tel.: (48) 77 405 42 00
Web Site: http://www.silekol.pl
Adhesive Resins & Hardeners Mfr
N.A.I.C.S.: 325520
Janusz Zowade (Pres & Gen Mgr)

Unitherm Baruth GmbH **(1)**
An der Birkenphulheide 3, Baruth, 15837, Germany
Tel.: (49) 33704700
Eletric Power Generation Services
N.A.I.C.S.: 221118

Zaklady Plyt Wiorowych Prospan S.A. **(1)**

INTERNATIONAL PUBLIC

Ul Boleslawiecka 10, P 98400, Wieruszow, Poland **(48.61%)**
Tel.: (48) 627833320
Web Site: http://www.pfleiderer.pl
Sales Range: $125-149.9 Million
Emp.: 500
Wood Products
N.A.I.C.S.: 321999
Rafal Karcz (Dir-Fin)

PFNONWOVENS A.S.
Hradcanske Namesti 67/8 Hradcany, 118 00, Prague, Czech Republic
Tel.: (420) 515262411
Web Site: http://www.pfnonwovens.cz
PEGAS—(PRA)
Rev.: $287,888,950
Assets: $509,868,217
Liabilities: $268,424,912
Net Worth: $241,443,305
Earnings: $20,825,444
Fiscal Year-end: 12/31/19
Nonwoven Fabric Product Mfr
N.A.I.C.S.: 313230
Carl Allen Bodford (Chm)

Subsidiaries:

PFNonwovens Czech s.r.o. **(1)**
Primeticka 86, 669 02, Znojmo, Czech Republic
Tel.: (420) 515262411
Textile Products Mfr
N.A.I.C.S.: 314999

PFNonwovens Egypt LLC **(1)**
Plot No O6 O8 in Zone No 3 at the Northern Expansions Area and, its Extension 6th of October City, Giza, Egypt
Tel.: (20) 238642230
Textile Products Mfr
N.A.I.C.S.: 314999

PFNONWOVENS HOLDING S.R.O.
Hradcanske namesti 67/8, Hradcany, 118 00, Prague, Czech Republic
Tel.: (420) 515262411
Web Site: http://www.pfnonwovens.cz
PGS—(PRA)
Producer of Non-Woven Textiles
N.A.I.C.S.: 313230
Cedric Ballay (CEO)

PG ELECTROPLAST LIMITED
P42 to 46 SiteB UPSIDC Industrial Area Surajpur, District Gautam Budh Nagar, Noida, 201306, Uttar Pradesh, India
Tel.: (91) 1202569323
Web Site: https://www.pgel.in
Year Founded: 2003
533581—(BOM)
Rev.: $259,496,817
Assets: $180,824,327
Liabilities: $133,353,816
Net Worth: $47,470,511
Earnings: $9,288,244
Emp.: 890
Fiscal Year-end: 03/31/23
Consumer Electronic Components Mfr & Assembler
N.A.I.C.S.: 334419
Promod Gupta (Co-Chm & Mng Dir)

PG INDUSTRIES (ZIMBABWE) LIMITED
146 Seke Road Graniteside, PO Box 1285, Harare, Zimbabwe
Tel.: (263) 4749540
Web Site: http://www.pgzim.co.zw
Year Founded: 1949
Sales Range: $25-49.9 Million
Emp.: 1,790
Building Materials Mfr & Distr, Including Glass, Timber Boards, Hardware, Cement & Cement Products
N.A.I.C.S.: 444180
H. M. Munyati (CEO)

AND PRIVATE COMPANIES

PG PLC
PAMA Shopping Village Valletta Road, Mosta, MST 9017, Malta
Tel.: (356) 23496100
Web Site: https://www.pggroup.com.mt
Year Founded: 2016
PG—(MAL)
Rev.: $187,710,986
Assets: $137,737,967
Liabilities: $70,312,972
Net Worth: $67,424,995
Earnings: $13,671,487
Emp.: 393
Fiscal Year-end: 04/30/23
Investment Management Service
N.A.I.C.S.: 523940
John Zarb *(Chm)*

Subsidiaries:

PG Developments Limited (1)
Unit E Broughton Business Park Oliver's Place, Fulwood, Preston, PR2 9ZA, United Kingdom
Tel.: (44) 8006440055
Web Site: https://www.pgdevelopments.co.uk
Window & Door Installation Services
N.A.I.C.S.: 238350

Pama Shopping Village Limited (1)
Valletta Road, Mosta, MST 9017, Malta
Tel.: (356) 23496000
Investment Services
N.A.I.C.S.: 523999

Pavi Shopping Complex PLC (1)
Triq Manuel Dimech, Qormi, QRM 9061, Malta
Tel.: (356) 22700000
Investment Services
N.A.I.C.S.: 523999

PG TECHNOLOGY, LTD.
5 Falcon Business Centre 2-4 Willow Lane, Mitcham, CR4 4NA, Surrey, United Kingdom
Tel.: (44) 2086489461   UK
Web Site: http://www.pgtechnology.co.uk
Year Founded: 1934
Sales Range: $10-24.9 Million
Emp.: 40
Machine Tools Marketer & Mfr
N.A.I.C.S.: 333517
Vincent Bootes *(Owner)*

Subsidiaries:

PGT Ceewrite Ltd (1)
5 Falcon Business Centre 2 - 4 Willow Lane, Mitcham, CR4 4NA, Surrey, United Kingdom
Tel.: (44) 20 8648 9461
Web Site: http://www.pgt-uk.co.uk
Precision Equipment Mfr
N.A.I.C.S.: 332721
Ian Baker *(Mgr-Quality)*

PGE POLSKA GRUPA ENERGETYCZNA S.A.
Aleja Krasnicka 27, 20-718, Lublin, Poland
Tel.: (48) 223401177
Web Site: https://www.gkpge.pl
Year Founded: 1990
PGE—(WAR)
Rev.: $18,448,223,886
Assets: $26,573,380,897
Liabilities: $12,911,370,145
Net Worth: $13,662,010,752
Earnings: $851,630,407
Emp.: 38,013
Fiscal Year-end: 12/31/22
Electricity Generation Services
N.A.I.C.S.: 221122
Anna Kowalik *(Chm-Supervisory Bd)*

Subsidiaries:

Agencja Rynku Energii S.A. (1)
ul Bobrowiecka 3, 00-728, Warsaw, Poland
Tel.: (48) 224442000
Web Site: http://www.are.waw.pl
Energy Market Agency
N.A.I.C.S.: 541613
Stanislaw Okrasa *(CEO)*

BESTGUM Sp. z o.o. (1)
Ul Sw Barbary 3, 97-427, Rogowiec, Poland
Tel.: (48) 44 737 1850
Web Site: https://www.bestgum.pl
Belt Vulcanizing & Rubber Product Mfr
N.A.I.C.S.: 326220
Mariusz Skowronek *(Chm)*

BETRANS Sp. z o.o. (1)
Kalisko 13 Skr Poczt 98, 97-400, Belchatow, Poland
Tel.: (48) 44 737 7200
Web Site: https://www.betrans.pl
Vehicle Repair & Maintenance Services
N.A.I.C.S.: 811111

ELBEST Security Sp. z o.o. (1)
Ul 1 Maja 63, 97-400, Warsaw, Poland
Tel.: (48) 447378131
Web Site: https://www.elbestsecurity.pl
Electronic Security Services
N.A.I.C.S.: 561621

ELBEST Sp. z o.o. (1)
Ul Wojska Polskiego 73, 97-400, Belchatow, Poland
Tel.: (48) 60 389 8668
Web Site: https://www.elbest.pl
Catering Services
N.A.I.C.S.: 722320

ELECTRA Deutschland GmbH (1)
Erste Brunnenstrasse 12, Hamburg, 20459, Germany
Tel.: (49) 40 80 90 35 0
Web Site: http://www.electra-deutschland.de
Sales Range: $75-99.9 Million
Emp.: 6
Electric Power Distribution Services
N.A.I.C.S.: 221122

ELMEN Sp. z o.o. (1)
Sw Barbary 8, 97-427, Rogowiec, Poland
Tel.: (48) 44 735 4920
Web Site: https://www.elmen.pl
Construction Renovation Services
N.A.I.C.S.: 236118

EPC S.A. (1)
Ul Wojciech Gorskiego 9, 00-033, Warsaw, Poland (100%)
Tel.: (48) 223213101
Web Site: http://www.epc.pl
Sales Range: $25-49.9 Million
Emp.: 100
Energy Related Consulting Services
N.A.I.C.S.: 541690
Krzysztof Lipko *(Pres)*

Eltur Serwis Sp. z o.o. (1)
Ul Mlodych Energetykow 12, Bogatynia, 59-916, Zgorzelec, Poland
Tel.: (48) 75 772 3001
Web Site: https://www.eltur-serwis.com.pl
Power Equipment Maintenance Services
N.A.I.C.S.: 811310

Energo-Utech S.A. (1)
ul Krzywoustego 7, 61-144, Poznan, Poland
Tel.: (48) 612275710
Web Site: https://www.enut.pl
Sales Range: $50-74.9 Million
Emp.: 20
Leasing & Financial Services to Electric Power Companies
N.A.I.C.S.: 525990
Krzysztof Kwiatkowski *(Chm-Mgmt Bd)*

Energopomiar Sp. z o.o. (1)
ul gen J Sowinskiego 3, PO Box 402, 44 101, Gliwice, Poland
Tel.: (48) 322376800
Web Site: http://www.energopomiar.com.pl
Sales Range: $100-124.9 Million
Emp.: 300
Construction Services
N.A.I.C.S.: 236210
Adam Smolik *(Pres & Mng Dir)*

MEGAZEC Sp. z o.o. (1)
street Energetyczna 6, 85-950, Bydgoszcz, Poland
Tel.: (48) 525233700
Web Site: https://www.megazec.pl
Construction Remodeling Services
N.A.I.C.S.: 236118

MegaSerwis Sp. z o.o. (1)
Ul Zgorzelecka 4, Bogatynia, 59-920, Zgorzelec, Poland
Tel.: (48) 75 648 0421
Web Site: https://www.mega-serwis.com.pl
Catering Services
N.A.I.C.S.: 722320

PGE Baltica Sp. z o.o. (1)
ul Mokotowska 49, 00-542, Warsaw, Poland
Tel.: (48) 223405060
Web Site: https://pgebaltica.pl
Offshore Wind Farm Services
N.A.I.C.S.: 237130
Monika Morawiecka *(Co-Pres)*

PGE Dom Maklerski S.A. (1)
ul Mysia 2, 00-496, Warsaw, Poland
Tel.: (48) 223401360
Web Site: https://www.dmpge.pl
Financial Brokerage Services
N.A.I.C.S.: 523150

PGE Ekoserwis Sp. z o.o. (1)
Pl Staszica 30, 50-222, Wroclaw, Poland
Tel.: (48) 713238817
Web Site: https://www.pgeekoserwis.pl
Heat Product Mfr & Distr
N.A.I.C.S.: 333414
Lech Sekyra *(Pres)*

PGE Elektrownia Opole S.A. (1)
Brzezie k, Opole, 46-021, Poland
Tel.: (48) 774 23 50 50
Sales Range: $500-549.9 Million
Emp.: 700
Fossil Fuel Electric Power Generation Services
N.A.I.C.S.: 221112
Adam Zurek *(Branch Mgr)*

PGE Energetyka Kolejowa SA (1)
Ul Hoza 63 67, Warsaw, 00-681, Poland
Tel.: (48) 223919000
Web Site: https://pgeenergetykakolejowa.pl
Electric Power Supply Services
N.A.I.C.S.: 221122
Wojciech Orzech *(Chm-Mgmt Bd)*

PGE Energia Ciepla S.A. (1)
ul Zlota 59 Skylight Building 12th floor, 00-120, Warsaw, Poland
Tel.: (48) 225565300
Web Site: https://www.pgeenergiaciepla.pl
Electricity Distribution Services
N.A.I.C.S.: 221122

PGE Energia Jadrowa S.A. (1)
ul Mokotowska 49, 00-542, Warsaw, Poland
Tel.: (48) 223402980
Web Site: http://pgeej1.pl
Nuclear Power Plant Construction Engineering Services
N.A.I.C.S.: 237130

PGE Energia Odnawialna S.A. (1)
ul Ogrodowa 59a, 00-876, Warsaw, Poland
Tel.: (48) 224331300
Web Site: https://pgeeo.pl
Emp.: 100
Electrical Energy Distr
N.A.I.C.S.: 221122
Arkadiusz Sekscinski *(Pres-Acting-Mgmt Bd & VP-Mgmt Bd)*

PGE Gornictwo i Energetyka Konwencjonalna S.A. (1)
ul Weglowa 5, 97-400, Belchatow, Poland
Tel.: (48) 447377300
Web Site: https://www.pgegiek.pl
Coal Mining Services
N.A.I.C.S.: 213113

PGE Obrot S.A. (1)
ul 8-go Marca 6, 35-959, Rzeszow, Poland
Tel.: (48) 422222222
Web Site: https://www.pge-obrot.pl
Electricity Distribution Services
N.A.I.C.S.: 221122

PGE Systemy S.A. (1)
ul Sienna 39, 00-121, Warsaw, Poland
Tel.: (48) 223401609
Web Site: https://pgesystemy.pl
Information Technology Consulting Services
N.A.I.C.S.: 541512

PGE Ventures Sp. z o.o. (1)
2 Mysia Str, 00-496, Warsaw, Poland
Tel.: (48) 223401555
Web Site: https://pgeventures.pl
Portfolio Investment Services
N.A.I.C.S.: 523940
Tomasz Jakubiak *(Pres)*

PSE-Centrum Sp. z o.o. (1)
Pruszka 17, 02-119, Warsaw, Poland (100%)
Tel.: (48) 226909601
Web Site: http://www.pse-centrum.com.pl
Sales Range: $25-49.9 Million
Emp.: 150
Electricity Grid Maintenance, Repairer & Support Services
N.A.I.C.S.: 811310

PSE-ELECTRA S.A. (1)
2 Mysia Street, 00-496, Warsaw, Poland (100%)
Tel.: (48) 223401277
Web Site: http://www.pseelectra.pl
Electricity Distr & Consulting Services
N.A.I.C.S.: 221122

PSE-Info Sp. z o.o. (1)
Ul Mysia 2, 00-496, Warsaw, Poland (100%)
Tel.: (48) 226932406
Web Site: http://www.pseinfo.pl
Sales Range: $50-74.9 Million
Emp.: 130
IT Consulting Services
N.A.I.C.S.: 541690

PSE-Operator SA (1)
2 Mysia, 00-496, Warsaw, Poland (100%)
Tel.: (48) 223402600
Web Site: http://www.pse-operator.pl
Electricity & Data Transmission; Telecommunications & IT Activities
N.A.I.C.S.: 221122
Stefania Kasprzyk *(Pres)*

PSE-Polnoc Sp. z o.o. (1)
Ul Marzalka Focha 16, 85-950, Bydgoszcz, Poland (100%)
Tel.: (48) 523751000
Web Site: http://www.pse-polnoc.pl
Sales Range: $25-49.9 Million
Emp.: 140
Electricity Grid Maintenance, Repairer & Support Services
N.A.I.C.S.: 811310

PSE-Poludnie Sp. z o.o. (1)
25th St Jordana, 40952, Katowice, Poland (100%)
Tel.: (48) 322578777
Web Site: http://www.pse-poludnie.pl
Electricity Grid Maintenance, Repairer & Supporting Services
N.A.I.C.S.: 811310

PSE-Serwis Sp. z.o.o. (1)
ul Mysia 2, 00-496, Warsaw, Poland
Tel.: (48) 226931212
Web Site: http://www.pseserwis.pl
Electrical Power Investments
N.A.I.C.S.: 221122

PSE-WSCHOD Sp. z.o.o. (1)
Ul Zeromskiego 75, 26-600, Radom, Poland
Tel.: (48) 483660606
Web Site: http://www.pse.com.pl
Operation & Repair of Electricity Networks
N.A.I.C.S.: 221122

PSE-Zachod Sp. z.o.o. (1)
ul Marcelinska 71, 60-354, Poznan, Poland
Tel.: (48) 618611000
Sales Range: $75-99.9 Million
Emp.: 100
Electric Power Distr
N.A.I.C.S.: 221122
Adam Hoffr *(Mng Dir)*

Ramb Sp. z o.o. (1)
Piaski 2, 97-400, Belchatow, Poland
Tel.: (48) 44 737 7801
Web Site: https://www.ramb.pl
Construction & Engineering Equipment Mfr
N.A.I.C.S.: 333120

PGF CAPITAL BHD
2449 Lorong Perusahaan Sepuluh Kawasan Perusahaan Perai, 13600, Perai, Penang, Malaysia
Tel.: (60) 43908460

PGF CAPITAL BHD

PGF Capital Bhd—(Continued)

Web Site: https://pgfcapital.com.my
PGF—(KLS)
Rev.: $28,002,300
Assets: $68,875,210
Liabilities: $22,768,049
Net Worth: $46,107,161
Earnings: $2,276,051
Emp.: 271
Fiscal Year-end: 02/29/24
Fiberglass Wool Products Mfr
N.A.I.C.S.: 327993
Ming Chong Tan (COO)

Subsidiaries:

Golden Approach Sdn. Bhd. (1)
Diamond Creeks Darul Ridzuan, 35900, Tanjung Malim, Perak, Malaysia
Tel.: (60) 44549119
Sales Range: $25-49.9 Million
Emp.: 7
Beauty Care Services
N.A.I.C.S.: 812112
Fong Wern Sheng (Mng Dir)

Poly Insulation Solutions Sdn Bhd (1)
2449 Lorong Perusahaan Sepuluh Kawasan Perusahaan Perai, 13600, Perai, Penang, Malaysia
Tel.: (60) 43908460
Web Site: http://www.ecowool.com.my
Insulated Fiber Materials Distr
N.A.I.C.S.: 423390

PGF CONSULTANTS INC.

291 Dalhousie St Ste 202, Ottawa, K1N 7E5, ON, Canada
Tel.: (613) 241-2251
Web Site: http://www.pgf.ca
Year Founded: 1988
Rev.: $26,800,000
Emp.: 8
Consulting Services
N.A.I.C.S.: 541618
Benoit Hubert (Owner & Pres)

PGF POLSKA GRUPA FOTOWOLTAICZNA S.A.

Chlodna 51, 00-867, Warsaw, Poland
Tel.: (48) 601783164
Web Site: https://pgfgroup.pl
PGV—(WAR)
Rev.: $29,788,110
Assets: $49,680,386
Liabilities: $16,923,526
Net Worth: $32,756,860
Earnings: ($51,762,195)
Fiscal Year-end: 12/31/23
Real Estate Services
N.A.I.C.S.: 531390
Wiktor Niedziela (Pres & VP)

Subsidiaries:

CSY S.A. (1)
ul Grunwaldzka 13, 14-200, Ilawa, Poland
Tel.: (48) 6482131
Web Site: http://www.csy.ilawa.pl
Industrial Machinery & Equipment Mfr
N.A.I.C.S.: 333998
Grzegorz Wrona (Pres)

PGGM VERMOGENSBEHEER B.V.

Noordweg Noord 150, 3704 JG, Zeist, Netherlands
Tel.: (31) 302779911 NI
Web Site: http://www.pggm.nl
Rev.: $216,202,224,000
Emp.: 1,300
Pension Fund & Investment Management Services
N.A.I.C.S.: 524292

PGM BUDUCNOST AD

Dimitrija Tucovica 38, 17523, Presevo, Serbia
Tel.: (381) 17664157

Web Site: https://www.pgmbuducnost.rs
Year Founded: 1960
BDPR—(BEL)
Rev.: $1,748,931
Assets: $3,560,238
Liabilities: $1,400,853
Net Worth: $2,159,385
Earnings: ($235,124)
Emp.: 41
Fiscal Year-end: 12/31/23
Lime & Stone Mining Services
N.A.I.C.S.: 212311
Destan Jasari (Gen Mgr)

PGO AUTOMOBILES

ZA La Pyramide, Saint-Christol-les, 30380, Ales, France
Tel.: (33) 4 66 60 56 05
Web Site: http://www.pgo.fr
Rev.: $292,810
Earnings: ($6,771,237)
Fiscal Year-end: 12/31/18
Automobile Mfr
N.A.I.C.S.: 336110

PGP GLASS CEYLON PLC

148 Maligawa Road Borupana, Ratmalana, Sri Lanka
Tel.: (94) 117800200
Web Site: https://pgpglassceylon.com
Year Founded: 1955
GLAS—(COL)
Rev.: $66,799,735
Assets: $43,191,870
Liabilities: $10,872,304
Net Worth: $32,319,566
Earnings: $10,586,532
Emp.: 800
Fiscal Year-end: 03/31/23
Glass Container Mfr
N.A.I.C.S.: 327213
Niloni Boteju (Controller-Fin)

PGS ASA

Lilleakerveien 4C, 0283, Oslo, Norway NO
Web Site: http://www.pgs.com
Year Founded: 1991
PGEJF—(OTCIQ)
Rev.: $825,100,000
Assets: $1,953,300,000
Liabilities: $1,443,000,000
Net Worth: $510,300,000
Earnings: ($32,800,000)
Emp.: 900
Fiscal Year-end: 12/31/22
Oil & Gas Exploration Services
N.A.I.C.S.: 213112
Gottfred Langseth (CFO & Exec VP)

Subsidiaries:

Atlantis (UK) Ltd. (1)
Seymour House South Street, Bromley, BR1 1RH, Kent, United Kingdom
Tel.: (44) 2083155800
Software Development Services
N.A.I.C.S.: 541511

MTEM Limited (1)
Birch House 10 Bankhead Crossway South, Edinburgh, EH11 4EP, United Kingdom
Tel.: (44) 1314663511
Oil & Gas Exploration Services
N.A.I.C.S.: 213112

Multiklient Invest A.S. (1)
Lilleakerveien 4C, N-0216, Oslo, Norway (100%)
Tel.: (47) 67526400
Web Site: http://www.pgs.com
Sales Range: $75-99.9 Million
Emp.: 300
Seismic Data Services
N.A.I.C.S.: 334519

Natuna Ventures Pte. Ltd. (1)
111 Somerset Road Unit 15-05/06 Tripleone Somerset, Singapore, 238164, Singapore
Tel.: (65) 67356411
Web Site: http://www.pgs.com

Oil & Gas Exploration Services
N.A.I.C.S.: 213112

PGS Americas, Inc. (1)
15150 Memorial Dr 1009, Houston, TX 77079-4320
Tel.: (281) 509-8000
Oil & Gas Exploration Services
N.A.I.C.S.: 213112

PGS Angola Ltd. (1)
House 29 Rua Maria Antunes, Luanda, Angola
Tel.: (244) 22 239 7288
Oil & Gas Services
N.A.I.C.S.: 213112

PGS Australia Pty. Ltd. (1)
Level 28 QV1 250 St Georges Terrace, West Perth, 6000, WA, Australia (100%)
Tel.: (61) 893209000
Sales Range: $50-74.9 Million
Emp.: 50
Oil & Gas Operations
N.A.I.C.S.: 213112

PGS Bergen Warehouse (1)
Hegrenesveien 15, Sandviken, 5042, Bergen, Norway
Tel.: (47) 55 25 90 60
Web Site: http://www.pgs.com
Geophysical Exploration Services
N.A.I.C.S.: 541360

PGS Data Processing & Technology (1)
PGS House Strandveien 4, Lysaker, 1366, Norway
Tel.: (47) 67526400
Web Site: http://www.pgs.com
Sales Range: $100-124.9 Million
Emp.: 400
Data Processing Services
N.A.I.C.S.: 518210

PGS Data Processing & Technology Sdn. Bhd. (1)
Ground Level Right Wing Quill Building 3 3501 Jalan Teknokrat 5, 63000, Cyberjaya, Selangor, Malaysia
Tel.: (60) 3 8317 3904
Data Processing Services
N.A.I.C.S.: 518210
Stuart Surridge (Mgr-Svc)

PGS Data Processing Middle East SAE (1)
Block B-1 Road 14 Public Free Zone, Nasr City, Cairo, 7069, Egypt
Tel.: (20) 222746181
Emp.: 90
Data Processing Services
N.A.I.C.S.: 518210

PGS Data Processing, Inc. (1)
15375 Memorial Dr, Houston, TX 77079
Tel.: (281) 509-8000
Data Processing Services
N.A.I.C.S.: 518210

PGS Exploration (Norway) AS (1)
Lilleakerveien 4C, PO Box 251, Lilleaker, Oslo, 0216, Norway
Tel.: (47) 67526400
Web Site: http://www.pgs.com
Emp.: 500
Oil & Gas Exploration Services
N.A.I.C.S.: 213112
Jon Erik Reinhardsen (Gen Mgr)

PGS Exploration (UK) Ltd. (1)
3 The Heights Brooklands, Weybridge, KT13 0NY, Surrey, United Kingdom (100%)
Tel.: (44) 1932376000
Web Site: https://www.pgs.com
Sales Range: $100-124.9 Million
Emp.: 300
Oil & Gas Operations
N.A.I.C.S.: 213112

PGS Exploration (US), Inc. (1)
15730 Park Row Ste 200, Houston, TX 77084
Tel.: (281) 599-1967
Web Site: http://www.pgs.com
Oil & Gas Exploration Services
N.A.I.C.S.: 213112

PGS Falcon AS (1)
Lilleakerveien 4C, Lysaker, 216, Norway

INTERNATIONAL PUBLIC

Tel.: (47) 67526400
Web Site: http://www.pgs.com
Emp.: 50
Geophysical Engineering Services
N.A.I.C.S.: 541330
Jon Erik Reinhardsen (Pres & CEO)

PGS Geophysical (Netherlands) B.V. (1)
Haagse Schouwweg 8H, Leiden, 2332 KG, Netherlands
Tel.: (31) 71 5730840
Geophysical Engineering Services
N.A.I.C.S.: 541330

PGS Geophysical AS (1)
Lilleakerveien 4C, PO Box 251, 0283, Oslo, Norway (100%)
Tel.: (47) 67526400
Sales Range: $200-249.9 Million
Emp.: 315
Oil & Gas Operations
N.A.I.C.S.: 213112
Jon Erik Reinhardsen (Pres & CEO)

PGS Geophysical Nigeria Ltd. (1)
No 10A Fabac Close Victoria Island, Lagos, Nigeria
Tel.: (234) 9030069602
Geophysical Mapping Services
N.A.I.C.S.: 541360

PGS Ghana Limited (1)
Imperial Square Building 6th Senchi Street Airport Residential Area, Accra, Ghana
Tel.: (233) 302737223
Geophysical Mapping Services
N.A.I.C.S.: 541360

PGS Investigacao Petrolifera Limitada (1)
Rua Victor Civita 77 Bloco 1 Edificio 6 2 Sala 101, Rio de Janeiro, 22775-044, Brazil
Tel.: (55) 21 3970 7300
Sales Range: $25-49.9 Million
Emp.: 2
Geophysical Surveying Services
N.A.I.C.S.: 541360

PGS Japan K.K. (1)
BUREX Kyobashi Building 814 2-7-14 Kyobashi, Chuo-ku, Tokyo, 104-0031, Japan
Tel.: (81) 62710752
Sales Range: $25-49.9 Million
Emp.: 4
Seismic & Electromagnetic Services
N.A.I.C.S.: 541360

PGS Marine Geophysical Group (1)
Lilleakerveien 4C, 1366, Oslo, Norway
Tel.: (47) 67526400
Web Site: http://www.pgs.com
Marine Geophysical Data Acquisition Services
N.A.I.C.S.: 561499

PGS Multi Transient EM (1)
10 Bankhead Crossway South, Edinburgh, EH11 4EP, United Kingdom
Tel.: (44) 1314663511
Sales Range: $25-49.9 Million
Emp.: 100
Geophysical Data Acquisition Services
N.A.I.C.S.: 541330
Dan Whealiang (CEO)

PGS MultiClient (1)
15150 Memorial Dr, Houston, TX 77079
Tel.: (281) 509-8124
Web Site: http://www.pgs.com
Geophysical Data Acquisition Services
N.A.I.C.S.: 541330

PGS Overseas AS (1)
Strandveien 4, PO Box 89, 1326, Lysaker, Norway (100%)
Tel.: (47) 67526400
Sales Range: $200-249.9 Million
Emp.: 400
Oil & Gas Operations
N.A.I.C.S.: 213112
Jon Erik Reinhardsen (Pres & CEO)

PGS Pension Trustee Ltd. (1)
4 Heights Brooklands, Weybridge, KT13 0NY, Surrey, United Kingdom
Tel.: (44) 1932260001
Pension Fund Management Services
N.A.I.C.S.: 525110

PGS Production AS (1)

Lilleakerveien 4C, PO Box 89, Lysaker, Oslo, 0216, Norway (100%)
Tel.: (47) 67526400
Web Site: http://www.pgs.com
Sales Range: $350-399.9 Million
Emp.: 1,500
Scientific & Technical Consulting Services
N.A.I.C.S.: 541690

PGS Shipping AS (1)
Strandveien 4, 1366, Lysaker, Norway
Tel.: (47) 67 52 64 00
Web Site: http://www.pgs.com
Sales Range: $125-149.9 Million
Emp.: 60
Marine Vessel Service
N.A.I.C.S.: 488330
Jon Erik Reinhardsen (Pres & CEO)

PGS Suporte Logistico e Servicos Ltda. (1)
Rua do Passeio 38/40 Tower 2 Office 1602, Ed Passeio Corporate 20 021-290 Centro, Rio de Janeiro, 22775-044, Brazil
Tel.: (55) 2124218400
Sales Range: $25-49.9 Million
Emp.: 10
Petroleum Geological Data Processing Services
N.A.I.C.S.: 518210

PGS Tanker AS (1)
Lilleakerveien 4 C, PO Box 251, Oslo, 0283, Norway (100%)
Tel.: (47) 6 752 6400
Web Site: https://www.pgs.com
Emp.: 400
Water Transportation Services
N.A.I.C.S.: 488390
Jon Erik Reinhardsen (Gen Mgr)

PGS Venture AS (1)
Strandveien 4, Lysaker, 1366, Norway
Tel.: (47) 67526400
Financial Management Services
N.A.I.C.S.: 523999

PGS-Kazakhstan LLP (1)
32 Kunayev Street BC Etalon 3 Floor, Almaty, 050004, Kazakhstan
Tel.: (7) 727 271 02 01
Web Site: http://www.pgs.com
Geophysical Engineering Services
N.A.I.C.S.: 541330

PT PGS Nusantara (1)
Pondok Indah Tower 3 17th Floor Unit M59, Jalan Sultan Iskandar Muda Kav V-TA, 12310, Jakarta, Selatan, Indonesia (100%)
Tel.: (62) 2129659040
Web Site: http://www.pgs.com
Sales Range: $50-74.9 Million
Oil & Gas Operations
N.A.I.C.S.: 213112

PT Petroprima Geo-Servis Nusantara (1)
Pondok Indah Tower 3 17th Floor Unit M59, Jalan Sultan Iskandar Muda Kav V-TA, Jakarta, 12310, Indonesia
Tel.: (62) 2129659040
Geophysical Mapping Services
N.A.I.C.S.: 541360

Panoceanic Energy Limited (1)
4 Heights Brooklands, Weybridge, KT13 0NY, United Kingdom
Tel.: (44) 1932376000
Web Site: http://www.pgs.com
Sales Range: $200-249.9 Million
Oil & Gas Exploration Services
N.A.I.C.S.: 213112

Petroleum Geo-Services (1)
4 The Heights Brooklands, KT13 0NY, Surrey, United Kingdom (100%)
Tel.: (44) 1932376000
Web Site: http://www.pgs.com
Sales Range: $10-24.9 Million
Emp.: 300
Oil & Gas Operations
N.A.I.C.S.: 213112

Petroleum Geo-Services (UK) Ltd. (1)
4 The Heights Brooklands, KT13 0NY, Surrey, United Kingdom (100%)
Tel.: (44) 1932376000

Web Site: http://www.pgs.com
Sales Range: $200-249.9 Million
Oil & Gas Operations
N.A.I.C.S.: 213112

Petroleum Geo-Services Asia Pacific Pte Ltd.
Unit No 202/A 2nd Floor Everest Nivara Infotech Park-I TTC, Industrial Area MIDC Turbhe, Navi Mumbai, 400 705, India
Tel.: (91) 22 6628 8500
Sales Range: $50-74.9 Million
Emp.: 2
Oil Exploration Services
N.A.I.C.S.: 213112
Ashok Pandey (Mgr-Center)

Petroleum Geo-Services Asia Pacific Pte. Ltd. (1)
Triple One Summerset Road Unit no 15-05, Public/06, Singapore, 238164, Singapore (100%)
Tel.: (65) 67356411
Web Site: http://www.pgs.com
Sales Range: $50-74.9 Million
Emp.: 80
Oil & Gas Operations
N.A.I.C.S.: 213112
Jon Erik Reinhardsen (Pres & CEO)

Petroleum Geo-Services Exploration (M) Sdn. Bhd. (1)
Menara Dion Level 11 27 Jalan Sultan Ismail, 50250, Kuala Lumpur, Malaysia
Tel.: (60) 321753800
Geophysical Mapping Services
N.A.I.C.S.: 541360

Petroleum Geo-Services, Inc. (1)
15730 Park Row Ste 200, Houston, TX 77084
Tel.: (281) 509-8000
Web Site: http://www.pgs.com
Oil & Gas Exploration Services
N.A.I.C.S.: 213112

Pgs Onshore, Inc. (1)
3201 C St Ste 403, Anchorage, AK 99503
Tel.: (907) 569-4049
Sales Range: $1-9.9 Million
Emp.: 50
Oil & Gas Field Services
N.A.I.C.S.: 333132

PGT HOLDINGS JSC
12th Floor Pax Sky Building 144-146-148 Le Lai Ben Thanh Ward, District 1, Ho Chi Minh City, Vietnam
Tel.: (84) 2866840446
Web Site: https://www.pgt-holdings.com
Year Founded: 2004
PGT—(HNX)
Rev.: $156,955
Assets: $2,129,960
Liabilities: $845,624
Net Worth: $1,284,336
Earnings: $34,615
Emp.: 26
Fiscal Year-end: 12/31/21
Petroleum Product Whslr
N.A.I.C.S.: 424720

Subsidiaries:

PGT Solutions JSC (1)
A2/D21 Alley 82 Dich Vong Hau, Cau Giay District, Hanoi, Vietnam
Tel.: (84) 705133339
Web Site: https://pgt-solutions.com
Emp.: 50
Web Application & Cloud Infrastructure Services
N.A.I.C.S.: 518210

PH TRADING LIMITED
113 Park Street B Block 10th Floor, Poddar Point, Kolkata, 700016, India
Tel.: (91) 3340675050
Web Site: https://www.phtradinglimited.com
Year Founded: 1982
512026—(BOM)
Rev.: $3,837
Assets: $266,411

Liabilities: $839
Net Worth: $265,572
Earnings: ($45,801)
Fiscal Year-end: 03/31/23
Phenol Product Whslr
N.A.I.C.S.: 424690
Tushar Suresh Dave (CEO)

PH VITRES D'AUTOS
2635 St Joseph, Sainte-Perpetue, J0C 1R0, QC, Canada
Tel.: (819) 336-6660
Web Site: http://www.ph.ca
Year Founded: 1967
Rev.: $39,522,650
Emp.: 275
Automobile Windshields & Windows Installation Services
N.A.I.C.S.: 326199
Mario Jutras (Pres)

PHAARMASIA LIMITED
Plot No 16 Phase 3 IDA Jeedimetla, Hyderabad, 500 055, India
Tel.: (91) 4023095690
Web Site: https://phaarmasia.in
Year Founded: 1981
523620—(BOM)
Rev.: $3,357,796
Assets: $3,407,793
Liabilities: $2,111,732
Net Worth: $1,296,061
Earnings: ($150,974)
Emp.: 13
Fiscal Year-end: 03/31/23
Pharmaceutical Product Mfr & Distr
N.A.I.C.S.: 325412
Maneesh Ramakant Sapte (Mng Dir)

PHAGELUX, INC.
12th Floor Huasheng Building 398 Hankou Rd, Huangpu District, Shanghai, 200001, China
Tel.: (86) 2161500300
Web Site: http://www.phagelux.com
Anti-Bacterial Product Mfr
N.A.I.C.S.: 325998
Bryan Li (Exec VP)

Subsidiaries:

Omnilytics, Inc. (1)
9100 S 500 W, Sandy, UT 84070
Tel.: (801) 746-3600
Web Site: http://www.omnilytics.com
Rev.: $4,000,000
Emp.: 14
Research & Development in Biotechnology
N.A.I.C.S.: 541714
Justin Reber (Pres)

PHANTOM DIGITAL EFFECTS LIMITED
7th Floor, Techniplex - I, Techniplex Complex, Veer Savarkar Flyover, Goregaon (West), Mumbai, 400 104, IN, India
Tel.: (91) 2240122204
Web Site: https://phantomfx.com
Year Founded: 2010
PHANTOMFX—(NYSE)
Animation & Post-production
N.A.I.C.S.: 513210

PHANTOM INDUSTRIES INC
207 Weston Road, Toronto, M6N 4Z3, ON, Canada
Tel.: (416) 762-7177
Web Site: http://www.phantom.ca
Year Founded: 1956
Rev.: $46,142,351
Emp.: 530
Fashion Products Mfr
N.A.I.C.S.: 315990

PHANTOM MFG. (INTL.) LTD.
30451 Simpson Rd, Abbotsford, V2T 6C7, BC, Canada

Tel.: (604) 855-3654
Web Site: http://www.phantomscreens.com
Year Founded: 1992
Sales Range: $10-24.9 Million
Emp.: 100
Retractable Screen Solutions for Doors & Windows
N.A.I.C.S.: 332321
C. Esther De Wolde (CEO)

Subsidiaries:

PHANTOM SCREENS (UK) LTD. (1)
23 King Street Industrial Estate, Langtoft, Peterborough, PE6 9NF, United Kingdom
Tel.: (44) 1778 560070
Web Site: http://www.phantom-fly-screens.co.uk
Window Screen Mfr
N.A.I.C.S.: 332321

Phantom Screens (Mfg) Australia Pty Ltd (1)
5 Piringa Ave, Somerton, 4044, SA, Australia
Tel.: (61) 8 8275 6300
Web Site: http://www.phantomscreens.com.au
Emp.: 6
Window Screen Mfr
N.A.I.C.S.: 332321

PHARMA AIDS LIMITED
345 Segun Bagicha 1st Floor Ramna, Dhaka, 1000, Bangladesh
Tel.: (880) 29337741
Web Site: https://www.pharmaaids.com
Year Founded: 1981
PHARMAID—(DHA)
Rev.: $3,747,367
Assets: $4,405,902
Liabilities: $829,017
Net Worth: $3,576,885
Earnings: $403,272
Fiscal Year-end: 06/30/22
Amopule Mfr
N.A.I.C.S.: 325412

PHARMA DEKO PLC.
Plot C1/1 Okene Close Agbara Industrial Estate, Agbara, Ogun, Nigeria
Tel.: (234) 8169622189
Web Site: https://www.pharmadekoplc.com
Year Founded: 1962
PHARMDEKO—(NIGE)
Rev.: $372,725
Assets: $1,728,600
Liabilities: $760,536
Net Worth: $968,064
Earnings: ($51,656)
Emp.: 110
Fiscal Year-end: 12/31/21
Pharmaceutical Product Mfr & Distr
N.A.I.C.S.: 325412
Folarin R. A. Williams (Chm)

PHARMA FOODS INTERNATIONAL CO., LTD.
1-49 Ohara Goryo, Nishikyo-ku, Kyoto, 615-8245, Japan
Tel.: (81) 753948600
Web Site: https://www.pharmafoods.co.jp
Year Founded: 1997
2929—(TKS)
Rev.: $386,554,340
Assets: $227,484,060
Liabilities: $155,425,360
Net Worth: $72,058,700
Earnings: $19,935,100
Emp.: 670
Fiscal Year-end: 07/31/24
Functional Food Ingredient Mfr & Whslr
N.A.I.C.S.: 311999
Mujo Kim (CEO)

PHARMA FOODS INTERNATIONAL CO., LTD.

Pharma Foods International Co., Ltd.—(Continued)

Subsidiaries:

FUTURE LABO Co., Ltd. (1)
4F Tanakakoma Building 8-5-32 Akasaka, Minato-ku, Tokyo, 107-0052, Japan
Tel.: (81) 120766153
Cosmetics Mfr & Sales
N.A.I.C.S.: 325620
Inoue Yasunori (Mng Dir)

PHARMA RESEARCH BIO CO., LTD.
641-3 Saimdang-ro, Gangneung, Gangwon-do, Korea (South)
Tel.: (82) 336557560
Web Site: https://www.pr-bio.co.kr
Year Founded: 2009
217950—(KRS)
Biotechnology Research & Development Services
N.A.I.C.S.: 541714

PHARMABCINE INC.
2F Research Building 2 70 Yuseong-daero 1689 beon-gil, Yuseong-gu, Daejeon, 34047, Korea (South)
Tel.: (82) 428632017
Web Site: https://www.pharmabcine.com
Year Founded: 2008
208340—(KRS)
Rev.: $158,461
Assets: $30,953,577
Liabilities: $11,939,344
Net Worth: $19,014,233
Earnings: ($23,430,669)
Emp.: 57
Fiscal Year-end: 12/31/22
Health Care Srvices
N.A.I.C.S.: 621610
WeonSup Lee (Head-R&D Center)

Subsidiaries:

Wincal Biopharm, Inc. (1)
400 Oyster Point Blvd Ste 321, South San Francisco, CA 94080
Tel.: (650) 410-5022
Web Site: https://www.wincalbio.com
Vascular Therapeutics Services
N.A.I.C.S.: 622310

PHARMABLOCK SCIENCES (NANJING), INC.
No 81 Huasheng Road, Jiangbei New District, Nanjing, 210032, Jiangsu, China
Tel.: (86) 4000255188
Web Site: https://www.pharmablock.com
Year Founded: 2006
300725—(CHIN)
Rev.: $242,994,983
Assets: $718,902,935
Liabilities: $319,976,692
Net Worth: $398,926,244
Earnings: $27,798,283
Fiscal Year-end: 12/31/23
Pharmaceutical Product Mfr & Distr
N.A.I.C.S.: 325412
Shijie Zhang (CTO)

Subsidiaries:

PharmaBlock (USA), Inc. (1)
777 Schwab Rd Unit D, Hatfield, PA 19440
Tel.: (267) 649-7271
Pharmaceutical Research & Development Services
N.A.I.C.S.: 541714

PHARMACARE LABORATORIES PTY. LTD.
18 Jubilee Avenue, Warriewood, 2102, NSW, Australia
Tel.: (61) 299971466
Web Site: http://www.pharmacare.com.au

Year Founded: 1985
Pharmaceutical Products Distr
N.A.I.C.S.: 424210
Vincent Tan (Gen Mgr)

PHARMACIELO LTD.
1 Toronto St Ste 805, Toronto, M5C 2V6, ON, Canada
Tel.: (416) 315-8741
Web Site: http://www.pharmacielo.com
Cannabis Product Mfr
N.A.I.C.S.: 325412
Simon Langelier (Chm)

PHARMACO NZ LTD.
4 Fisher Crescent Mt Wellington, PO Box 4079, Auckland, 1140, New Zealand
Tel.: (64) 93773336
Web Site: http://www.pharmaco.co.nz
Year Founded: 1967
Sales Range: $10-24.9 Million
Emp.: 50
Pharmaceutical Sales & Marketing, Warehousing, Distribution, Regulatory & Administration Services
N.A.I.C.S.: 541613

PHARMACOSMOS A/S
Roervangsvej 30,, 4300, Holbaek, Denmark
Tel.: (45) 59485959
Web Site: https://pharmacosmos.com
Pharmaceuticals Mfr
N.A.I.C.S.: 325412

Subsidiaries:

Pharmacosmos Therapeutics Inc. (1)
E Tower, 120 Headquarters Plaza 6th fl., Morristown, NJ 07960
Tel.: (908) 769-7100
Web Site: https://www.pharmacosmos.us
Pharmaceutical Services
N.A.I.C.S.: 325412
Joshua B. Franklin (Pres)

PHARMACY WON INC.
7171 Yonge Street, Thornhill, L3T 2A9, ON, Canada
Tel.: (905) 886-7171
Year Founded: 1963
Sales Range: $25-49.9 Million
Emp.: 200
Drug Stores Owner & Operator
N.A.I.C.S.: 456110
Marv Turk (Pres)

PHARMADRUG INC.
2905 - 77 King St West, Toronto, M5K 1H1, ON, Canada
Tel.: (647) 202-1824
Web Site: https://pharmadrug.ca
LMLLF—(OTCIQ)
Rev.: $534,822
Assets: $10,708,318
Liabilities: $2,171,336
Net Worth: $8,536,982
Earnings: ($4,245,915)
Fiscal Year-end: 12/31/20
Medical Cannabis Distr
N.A.I.C.S.: 424210
Daniel Cohen (Chm & CEO)

PHARMAENGINE, INC.
11F No 10 Sec 3 Mingshen E Road, Taipei, 104, Taiwan
Tel.: (886) 225158228
Web Site: https://www.pharmaengine.com
Pharmaceuticals Product Mfr
N.A.I.C.S.: 325412
Yufang Hu (Pres)

PHARMAESSENTIA CORP.
2F-5 No 3 Park Street, Nangang District, Taipei, 115, Taiwan
Tel.: (886) 226557688
Web Site: https://hq.pharmaessentia.com
Year Founded: 2003
6446—(TPE)
Rev.: $90,111,684
Assets: $479,399,306
Liabilities: $99,784,667
Net Worth: $379,614,639
Earnings: ($42,985,649)
Emp.: 489
Fiscal Year-end: 12/31/22
Therapeutic Product Distr
N.A.I.C.S.: 423450
Ching-Leou Teng (Chm)

Subsidiaries:

Panco Healthcare Co., Ltd. (1)
2F-5 No 3 Park Street, Nangang District, Taipei, Taiwan
Tel.: (886) 227126811
Web Site: https://www.pancohc.com.tw
Healthcare Product Mfr & Distr
N.A.I.C.S.: 325412

PharmaEssentia Asia (Hong Kong) Limited (1)
19/F Cheung Kong Center 2 Queens Road, Central, China (Hong Kong)
Tel.: (852) 34695130
Development Research Services
N.A.I.C.S.: 541714

PharmaEssentia Biotechnology (Beijing) Limited (1)
Room 1423 14F Jiatai International Building, 41 Middle Road of East Fourth Ring Chaoyang, Beijing, 10025, China
Tel.: (86) 1085711234
Development Research Services
N.A.I.C.S.: 541714

PharmaEssentia Japan KK (1)
12th Floor Akasaka Center Building 1-3-13 Motoakasaka, Minato-ku, Tokyo, 107-0051, Japan
Tel.: (81) 369105103
Web Site: https://jp.pharmaessentia.com
Pharmaceutical Mfr & Distr
N.A.I.C.S.: 325411

PharmaEssentia Korea Corporation (1)
Unit 2022 20F Gwanghwamun Building 149 Sejong-daero, Jongno-gu, Seoul, Korea (South)
Tel.: (82) 221094928
Development Research Services
N.A.I.C.S.: 541714

PharmaEssentia USA Corporation (1)
35 Corporate Dr Ste 325, Burlington, MA 01803
Tel.: (617) 245-2200
Health Care Srvices
N.A.I.C.S.: 524114

PHARMAIDS PHARMACEUTICALS LIMITED
Unit 201 2nd Floor Brigade Rubix 20/14 HMT Factory Main Road, Peenya Plantation, Hyderabad, 560013, Telangana, India
Tel.: (91) 9611551732
Web Site: https://www.pharmaids.com
524572—(BOM)
Assets: $2,947,944
Liabilities: $255,050
Net Worth: $2,692,895
Earnings: ($905,900)
Emp.: 9
Fiscal Year-end: 03/31/23
Pharmaceutical Product Mfr & Distr
N.A.I.C.S.: 325412
Ghisulal Jain (Chm & Mng Dir)

PHARMALA BIOTECH HOLDINGS INC.
82 Richmond St E, Toronto, M5C 1P1, ON, Canada
Web Site: https://www.pharmala.ca
Year Founded: 2021
MDMA—(CNSX)
Holding Company
N.A.I.C.S.: 551112
Nicholas Kadysh (Pres & CEO)

PHARMALLY INTERNATIONAL HOLDING CO., LTD.
Room 1807 No 333 Sec 1 Keelung Road, Xinyi District, Taipei, 11012, Taiwan
Tel.: (886) 2 27576000
Web Site: http://www.pharmally.com
Rev.: $169,086,176
Assets: $335,483,749
Liabilities: $89,955,895
Net Worth: $245,527,853
Earnings: $35,925,151
Emp.: 1,200
Fiscal Year-end: 12/31/18
Pharmaceuticals Mfr
N.A.I.C.S.: 325412
Wen-Lai Huang (Chm)

PHARMALUNDENSIS AB
Scheelevagen 22, Medicon Village, 223 63, Lund, Sweden
Tel.: (46) 46132780
Web Site: https://www.pharmalundensis.se
Year Founded: 2006
Biotechnology Research & Development Services
N.A.I.C.S.: 541714
Staffan Skogvall (CEO)

PHARMANUTRA S.P.A.
Via Delle Lenze 216/B, 56122, Pisa, Italy
Tel.: (39) 0507846500
Web Site: https://www.pharmanutra.it
Year Founded: 2003
PHNM—(AIM)
Rev.: $90,390,202
Assets: $108,557,338
Liabilities: $53,335,140
Net Worth: $55,222,198
Earnings: $16,310,427
Emp.: 90
Fiscal Year-end: 12/31/22
Biotechnology Research & Development Services
N.A.I.C.S.: 541714
Roberto Lacorte (Vice Chm)

Subsidiaries:

Akern S.R.L. (1)
Via Lisbona 32 34, Pontassieve, 50065, Florence, Italy
Tel.: (39) 0558315658
Web Site: https://www.akern.com
Medical Devices & Equipment Mfr
N.A.I.C.S.: 339112

Alesco S.r.l. (1)
Via delle Lenze 216/B, 56122, Pisa, Italy
Tel.: (39) 0507846511
Web Site: https://www.alescosrl.com
Functional Ingredient Mfr
N.A.I.C.S.: 311999

PHARMARESEARCH CO., LTD.
77-19 Gwahakdanji-ro, Gangneung, 25452, Gangwon-do, Korea (South)
Tel.: (82) 336457640
Web Site: https://pharmaresearch.co.kr
Year Founded: 1993
214450—(KRS)
Rev.: $149,379,880
Assets: $366,668,331
Liabilities: $81,608,144
Net Worth: $285,060,187
Earnings: $31,122,328
Emp.: 315

Fiscal Year-end: 12/31/22
Biopharmaceutical Mfr
N.A.I.C.S.: 325412
SangSoo Jung *(Chm)*

PHARMARESOURCES (SHANGHAI) CO., LTD.
Bldg 12 No 59 Kai Qing Rd West
Campus, Pudong, Shanghai, China
Tel.: (86) 2150720228202
Web Site:
 https://www.pharmaresources.cn
Year Founded: 2007
301230—(CHIN)
Rev.: $68,974,239
Assets: $209,459,704
Liabilities: $52,059,042
Net Worth: $157,400,661
Earnings: $5,298,479
Emp.: 700
Fiscal Year-end: 12/31/23
Pharmaceutical Product Mfr & Distr
N.A.I.C.S.: 325412
Chen Ping *(Chm)*

Subsidiaries:

PharmaResources (Chengdu) Co., Ltd. (1)
Bldg 5 3rd Floor No 670 Haifa Road Chengdu Strait, Science and Technology Industrial Development Park Wenjiang, Chengdu, China
Tel.: (86) 2150720228
Drug Research & Development Services
N.A.I.C.S.: 621999

PharmaResources (Kaiyuan) Co., Ltd. (1)
No 3 Beihuan Road, Economic Development District Kaiyuan City, Tieling, 112300, Liaoning, China
Tel.: (86) 2150720228
Drug Research & Development Services
N.A.I.C.S.: 621999

PharmaResources CMC Co., Ltd. (1)
Bldg 1 1st Floor Zone C No 178 Renqing Road, Pudong, Shanghai, China
Tel.: (86) 2150720228202
Pharmaceutical Preparation Mfr
N.A.I.C.S.: 325412

PHARMARISE HOLDINGS CORPORATION
Sumitomo Nakano Sakue Building 8F/11F, 1-38-1 Chuo Nakano-ku, Tokyo, 164-0011, Japan
Tel.: (81) 333627130
Web Site: http://www.pharmarise.com
Year Founded: 1984
2796—(TKS)
Rev.: $360,020,260
Assets: $194,902,460
Liabilities: $145,710,840
Net Worth: $49,191,620
Earnings: ($2,320,110)
Emp.: 1,869
Fiscal Year-end: 05/31/24
Pharmaceuticals Whslr
N.A.I.C.S.: 424210
Yoshio Odaka *(Auditor)*

Subsidiaries:

Hokkaido Pharmarise Co., Ltd. (1)
2-5 Kita Gojo-nishi, Chuo-ku, Sapporo, 060-0005, Hokkaido, Japan
Tel.: (81) 11 769 2628
Web Site: http://www.h-pharmarise.co.jp
Pharmacy Retailer
N.A.I.C.S.: 456110

PHARMARON BEIJING CO., LTD.
6 Taihe Road BDA, Beijing, 100176, China
Tel.: (86) 10 5733 0000
Web Site: http://www.pharmaron.com
Year Founded: 2003
Emp.: 4,000
Life Sciences Research & Development Services
N.A.I.C.S.: 541715
Boliang Lou *(Chm & CEO)*

Subsidiaries:

Absorption Systems LLC (1)
436 Creamery Way Ste 600G, Exton, PA 19341-2556
Tel.: (610) 280-7300
Web Site: http://www.absorption.com
Research & Pharmaceuticals Services
N.A.I.C.S.: 541714
Patrick Dentinger *(CEO)*

Subsidiary (Domestic):

TGA Sciences, Inc. (2)
47 Hall St, Medford, MA 02155
Tel.: (781) 393-6910
Pharmaceutical, Biotechnology & Research Laboratories
N.A.I.C.S.: 541714

Aesica Pharmaceuticals Limited (1)
Q5 Quorum Business Park Benton Lane, Newcastle, NE12 8BS, Tyne & Wear, United Kingdom
Tel.: (44) 191 218 1960
Web Site: http://www.aesica-pharma.com
Sales Range: $250-299.9 Million
Emp.: 1,200
Pharmaceuticals Product Mfr
N.A.I.C.S.: 325412
David Lloyd *(VP-HR)*

Pharmaron - Radiolabelled Sciences (1)
Newmarket Road, Fordham, CB7 5WW, United Kingdom
Tel.: (44) 2920 474 900
Web Site: http://www.pharmaron.co.uk
Biotechnology Research & Development Services
N.A.I.C.S.: 541714
Anthony Rees *(Mgr-Quality Control)*

Pharmaron, Inc. (1)
6 Venture Ste 250, Irvine, CA 92618
Tel.: (949) 788-0586
Web Site: http://www.pharmaron.com
Pharmaceutical Research Services
N.A.I.C.S.: 541715
Hua Yang *(Chief Scientific Officer)*

Xceleron, Inc. (1)
20340 Seneca Meadows Pkwy, Germantown, MD 20876
Tel.: (240) 361-1900
Web Site: http://www.xceleron.com
Sales Range: $1-9.9 Million
Emp.: 14
Biomedical Research & Drug Development
N.A.I.C.S.: 541715
Michael J. Butler *(CEO)*

PHARMASAVE DRUGS (NATIONAL) LTD.
8411 - 200th Street Suite 201, Langley, V2Y 0E7, BC, Canada
Tel.: (604) 455-2400
Web Site:
 https://www.pharmasave.com
Year Founded: 1981
Sales Range: $10-24.9 Million
Emp.: 55
Independent Pharmacy & Drugstore Retailer
N.A.I.C.S.: 456110

Subsidiaries:

Pharmasave Alberta Division (1)
Ste 203 7003 5th St S E, Calgary, T2H 2G2, AB, Canada
Tel.: (403) 255-5022
Web Site: http://www.pharmasave.com
Pharmacy Operator
N.A.I.C.S.: 456110
Vinod Thakrar *(Mgr)*

Pharmasave Atlantic Canada Division (1)
Suite 100 239 Brownlow Avenue, Dartmouth, B3B 2B2, NS, Canada
Tel.: (902) 468-7257
Web Site: http://www.pharmasave.com
Pharmacy Operator
N.A.I.C.S.: 456110
Greg van den Hoogen *(Gen Mgr)*

Pharmasave British Columbia Division (1)
6350 203rd Street, Langley, V2Y 1L9, BC, Canada
Tel.: (604) 532-2250
Pharmacy Operator
N.A.I.C.S.: 456110

Pharmasave Central Division (1)
Suite 206 584 Pembina Highway, Winnipeg, R3M 3X7, MB, Canada
Tel.: (204) 985-0220
Web Site: http://www.pharmasave.com
Pharmacy Operator Services
N.A.I.C.S.: 456110
Paul Melnyk *(CEO)*

Pharmasave Drugs (Pacific) Ltd. (1)
5685 176A Street, Cloverdale, Surrey, V3S 4C5, BC, Canada
Tel.: (604) 574-2621
Pharmacy Store Operator
N.A.I.C.S.: 456110
Dave Reston *(CEO)*

Pharmasave Ontario Division (1)
3100 Steeles Avenue E, Markham, L3R 8T3, ON, Canada
Tel.: (905) 477-7820
Web Site: http://www.pharmasave.com
Pharmacy Operator
N.A.I.C.S.: 456110
Doug Sherman *(CEO)*

PHARMASCIENCE INC.
6111 Royalmount Avenue, Montreal, H4P 2T4, QC, Canada
Tel.: (514) 340-9800
Web Site:
 http://www.pharmascience.com
Year Founded: 1983
Sales Range: $700-749.9 Million
Emp.: 1,500
Pharmaceutical Product Mfr & Distr
N.A.I.C.S.: 325412
Ted Wise *(Co-Founder)*

Subsidiaries:

Pendopharm (1)
6111 Royalmount Avenue, Montreal, H4P 2T4, QC, Canada
Tel.: (514) 340-5045
Web Site: http://pendopharm.com
Pharmaceutical Developer, Licensor & Marketer
N.A.I.C.S.: 325412

PHARMASGP HOLDING SE
Lochhamer Schlag 1, 82166, Grafelfing, Germany
Tel.: (49) 898589639
Web Site: https://pharmasgp.com
Year Founded: 2012
PSG—(DEU)
Rev.: $111,601,257
Assets: $144,938,131
Liabilities: $101,059,298
Net Worth: $43,878,832
Earnings: $18,103,468
Emp.: 96
Fiscal Year-end: 12/31/23
Pharmaceutical Product Mfr & Distr
N.A.I.C.S.: 325412
Natalie Weigand *(CEO)*

Subsidiaries:

Restaxil GmbH (1)
Am Haag 14, 82166, Grafelfing, Germany
Tel.: (49) 8589639150
Web Site: https://restaxil.de
Healthcare Product Mfr & Distr
N.A.I.C.S.: 325412

PHARMASIMPLE SA
Boulevard Millenium 11, 7100, La Louviere, Hainaut, Belgium
Tel.: (32) 26 50 06 90
Web Site:
 http://www.pharmsimple.com
ALPHS—(EUR)
Sales Range: $50-74.9 Million
Cosmetic Product Distr
N.A.I.C.S.: 456120
Michael Willems *(Founder, Chm & CEO)*

PHARMAUST LTD.
Level 4 96-100 Albert Road, Western Australia, South Melbourne, 3205, VIC, Australia
Tel.: (61) 396927222
Web Site:
 https://www.pharmaust.com
Year Founded: 2000
PAA—(ASX)
Rev.: $578,379
Assets: $7,428,452
Liabilities: $598,696
Net Worth: $6,829,756
Earnings: ($5,942,792)
Emp.: 4
Fiscal Year-end: 06/30/24
Pharmaceutical Preparations
N.A.I.C.S.: 325412
Sam Wright *(Sec)*

Subsidiaries:

Epichem Pty Ltd (1)
5/3 Brodie Hall Drive, Bentley, 6102, WA, Australia
Tel.: (61) 86 167 5200
Web Site: http://www.epichem.com.au
Sales Range: $25-49.9 Million
Synthetic & Medicinal Chemistry Services
N.A.I.C.S.: 541715
Wayne Best *(Chm)*

PHARMAX LIMITED
1-1060 Meyerside Drive, Mississauga, L5T 1J4, ON, Canada
Tel.: (289) 562-0025
Web Site: https://www.pharmax.ca
Year Founded: 1972
Pharmaceuticals Mfr
N.A.I.C.S.: 325412
Gary Hodgins *(Pres & CEO)*

PHARMAXIS LTD.
20 Rodborough Road, Locked Bag 5015, French's Forest, 2086, NSW, Australia
Tel.: (61) 294547200   AU
Web Site:
 http://www.pharmaxis.com.au
Year Founded: 1998
SNT—(ASX)
Rev.: $3,908,253
Assets: $6,931,757
Liabilities: $3,806,757
Net Worth: $3,125,000
Earnings: ($9,125,267)
Emp.: 107
Fiscal Year-end: 06/30/24
Pharmaceutical Product Research & Development Services
N.A.I.C.S.: 325412
David M. McGarvey *(CFO & Sec)*

Subsidiaries:

Pharmaxis Pharmaceuticals Limited (1)
25 Moorgate, London, EC2R 6AY, Buckinghamshire, United Kingdom
Tel.: (44) 1628902121
Web Site: http://www.pharmaxis.com
Sales Range: $25-49.9 Million
Emp.: 14
Pharmaceuticals Mfr
N.A.I.C.S.: 325412

PHARMEDIC PHARMACEUTICAL MEDICINAL JSC
No 367 Nguyen Trai, Nguyen Cu Trinh district 1, Ho Chi Minh City, Vietnam

PHARMEDIC PHARMACEUTICAL MEDICINAL JSC

Pharmedic Pharmaceutical Medicinal JSC—(Continued)
Tel.: (84) 839200300
Web Site: https://pharmedic.com.vn
PMC—(HNX)
Rev.: $47,227,400
Assets: $49,412,400
Liabilities: $6,634,200
Net Worth: $42,778,200
Earnings: $8,341,600
Fiscal Year-end: 12/31/22
Pharmaceuticals Product Mfr
N.A.I.C.S.: 325412
Trung Viet Tran *(Gen Dir & Member-Mgmt Bd)*

PHARMESIS INTERNATIONAL LTD.
5 Kallang Sector 03-02, Singapore, 349279, Singapore
Tel.: (65) 68460766
Web Site: https://www.pharmesis.com
Year Founded: 1996
BFK—(SES)
Rev.: $6,427,606
Assets: $12,097,887
Liabilities: $4,465,493
Net Worth: $7,632,394
Earnings: ($6,427,606)
Emp.: 750
Fiscal Year-end: 12/31/23
Pharmaceuticals Product Mfr
N.A.I.C.S.: 325412
Xuedan Wu *(CEO)*

PHARMGEN SCIENCE INC.
216 Dongjak-daero, Seocho-gu, Seoul, 06554, Korea (South)
Tel.: (82) 221943500
Web Site: https://www.wooridulpharm.com
Year Founded: 1966
004720—(KRS)
Rev.: $115,763,859
Assets: $243,439,263
Liabilities: $84,581,602
Net Worth: $158,857,660
Earnings: $53,735,761
Emp.: 265
Fiscal Year-end: 12/31/22
Pharmaceuticals Product Mfr
N.A.I.C.S.: 325412
Hye-Youn Kim *(Co-CEO)*

Subsidiaries:

Wooridul Pharmaceutical Ltd. - Hyangnam Plant (1)
50 Pharmaceutical Industrial Complex 2-gil, Hwaseong, Gyeonggi-do, Korea (South)
Tel.: (82) 313706000
Pharmaceutical Preparation Mfr
N.A.I.C.S.: 325412

PHARMHOLD AD
Yapadzha 6 Office No 3, Kremikovtsi, 1839, Sofia, 1839, Bulgaria
Tel.: (359) 52555541
Web Site: https://www.pharmhold.bg
PHRM—(BUL)
Sales Range: Less than $1 Million
Pharmaceutical Products Distr
N.A.I.C.S.: 424210
Veselin Mareshki *(Dir-IR)*

PHARMICELL CO., LTD.
7th floor Ssangbong Building 874 Unju-ro, Gangnam-gu, Seoul, Korea (South)
Tel.: (82) 234960114
Web Site: https://www.pharmicell.com
Year Founded: 1968
005690—(KRS)
Rev.: $46,159,446
Assets: $86,436,443
Liabilities: $25,297,404
Net Worth: $61,139,039
Earnings: $8,348,612
Emp.: 115
Fiscal Year-end: 12/31/22
Pharmaceuticals Product Mfr
N.A.I.C.S.: 325412
Jung Gilsu *(Dir)*

Subsidiaries:

PHARMICELL CO., LTD. - Ulsan Plant (1)
8 Seokdang-gil Onsan-eup, Ulju-gun, Ulsan, 689-896, Korea (South)
Tel.: (82) 52 231 5643
Pharmaceuticals Product Mfr
N.A.I.C.S.: 325412

PHARMING GROUP N.V.
Darwinweg 24, 2333 CR, Leiden, Netherlands
Tel.: (31) 715247400
Web Site: https://www.pharming.com
PHAR—(NASDAQ)
Rev.: $205,622,000
Assets: $425,797,000
Liabilities: $221,159,000
Net Worth: $204,638,000
Earnings: $13,674,000
Emp.: 332
Fiscal Year-end: 12/31/22
Pharmaceutical Preparations
N.A.I.C.S.: 325412
Sijmen de Vries *(CEO)*

PHARMOCANN GLOBAL LTD.
Horesh Haalonim 1, Ramat Yishai, 3009500, Israel
Tel.: (972) 49533757
Web Site: https://www.pharmocann.co.il
Year Founded: 2008
PMCN.M—(TAE)
Rev.: $3,982,042
Assets: $1,962,149
Liabilities: $1,751,899
Net Worth: $210,250
Earnings: ($2,689,322)
Fiscal Year-end: 12/31/23
Pharmaceutical Preparation Manufacturing
N.A.I.C.S.: 325412

PHARMSVILLE CO., LTD.
37 Magok Jungang 8-Ro 3-Gil, Gangseo-Gu, Seoul, Korea (South)
Tel.: (82) 25531323
Web Site: https://www.pharmsville.net
Year Founded: 2000
318010—(KRS)
Rev.: $20,028,841
Assets: $57,398,334
Liabilities: $9,332,935
Net Worth: $48,065,398
Earnings: $3,116,143
Emp.: 35
Fiscal Year-end: 12/31/22
Health Food Mfr & Distr
N.A.I.C.S.: 311999
Byung-Wook Lee *(Pres & CEO)*

PHARMSYNTHEZ PJSC
25 Krasnovo Kursanta Str, 197 110, Saint Petersburg, Russia
Tel.: (7) 8123298080
Web Site: http://www.en.pharmsynthez.com
Year Founded: 1996
LIFE—(MOEX)
Sales Range: Less than $1 Million
Pharmaceuticals Product Mfr
N.A.I.C.S.: 325412
Dmitry D. Genkin *(Chm)*

PHARNEXT SAS
11 rue des Peupliers, 92130, Issy-les-Moulineaux, France
Tel.: (33) 141092230
Web Site: http://www.pharnext.com
Year Founded: 2007
ALPHA—(EUR)
Rev.: $595
Assets: $8,374,492
Liabilities: $43,236,381
Net Worth: ($34,861,889)
Earnings: ($40,991,023)
Fiscal Year-end: 12/31/22
Biopharmaceutical Product Mfr
N.A.I.C.S.: 325412
Daniel Cohen *(Co-Founder & CEO)*

PHAROL SGPS, S.A.
Gorgel do Amaral Street No 4, Edificio Amoreiras Square, 1250-133, Lisbon, Portugal
Tel.: (351) 212697690
Web Site: https://pharol.pt
Year Founded: 1994
PHR—(EUR)
Rev.: $1,550,706
Assets: $105,336,083
Liabilities: $30,121,582
Net Worth: $75,214,502
Earnings: $1,067,659
Emp.: 7
Fiscal Year-end: 12/31/23
Telecommunication Servicesb
N.A.I.C.S.: 517111
Luis Sousa de Macedo *(Dir-IR)*

PHAROS ENERGY PLC
Eastcastle House 27/28 Eastcastle Street, London, W1W 8DH, United Kingdom
Tel.: (44) 2077472000
Web Site: https://www.pharos.energy
Year Founded: 1997
SOCLF—(OTCIQ)
Rev.: $199,100,000
Assets: $572,900,000
Liabilities: $242,300,000
Net Worth: $330,600,000
Earnings: $24,400,000
Fiscal Year-end: 12/31/22
Oil & Natural Gas Exploration & Production
N.A.I.C.S.: 211120
Ed Story *(Pres & CEO)*

Subsidiaries:

SOCO Exploration (Thailand) Co., Ltd. (1)
4 Fl 1769 Ritratana Bldg Ramkhamhaeng Rd Hua Mark, Bangkapi, Bangkok, 10240, Thailand
Tel.: (66) 23199865
Oil & Gas Exploration Services
N.A.I.C.S.: 213112

SOCO Management Services, Inc. (1)
5970 Keswick Ave, Riverside, CA 92506
Tel.: (951) 249-7766
Web Site: http://www.homesforrentinriverside.com
Management Services
N.A.I.C.S.: 561110

PHAROS IBIO CO., LTD.
38 427beongil Heungan-daero 1408ho, Dongan-gu, Anyang, 1408, Gyeonggi-do, Korea (South)
Tel.: (82) 7076628585
Web Site: https://www.pharosibio.com
Year Founded: 2016
388870—(KRS)
Emp.: 32
Biotechnology Research & Development Services
N.A.I.C.S.: 541714
Jeonghyeok Yoon *(CEO)*

PHARVARIS N.V.

INTERNATIONAL PUBLIC

Emmy Noetherweg 2, 2333 BK, Leiden, Netherlands
Tel.: (31) 712036410
Web Site: https://www.pharvaris.com
Year Founded: 2015
PHVS—(NASDAQ)
Assets: $430,276,781
Liabilities: $15,806,240
Net Worth: $414,470,541
Earnings: ($108,865,819)
Emp.: 82
Fiscal Year-end: 12/31/23
Biotechnology Research & Development Services
N.A.I.C.S.: 541714
Stefan Abele *(Chief Technical Ops Officer)*

PHASE HOLOGRAPHIC IMAGING PHI AB
Skiffervagen 48, 224 78, Lund, Sweden
Tel.: (46) 46386080
Web Site: https://phiab.com
Year Founded: 2004
L5W—(DEU)
Biotechnical Imaging Equipment Mfr
N.A.I.C.S.: 334510
Peter Egelberg *(CEO)*

PHAT DAT REAL ESTATE DEVELOPMENT CORPORATION
Viettel Complex Building 8th-9th Floors Tower B, 285 Cach Mang Thang Tam Street Ward 12 District 10, Ho Chi Minh City, Vietnam
Tel.: (84) 906098118
Web Site: https://www.phatdat.com.vn
Year Founded: 2004
PDR—(HOSE)
Rev.: $61,751,500
Assets: $2,106,782,300
Liabilities: $1,148,843,100
Net Worth: $957,939,200
Earnings: $68,405,900
Emp.: 267
Fiscal Year-end: 12/31/23
Real Estate Development Services
N.A.I.C.S.: 531390

Subsidiaries:

Phat Dat Industrial Park Investment & Development JSC (1)
10th Floor Tower B Viettel Building 285 Cach Mang Thang Tam, Ward 12 District 10, Ho Chi Minh City, Vietnam
Tel.: (84) 2822266868
Real Estate Investment Services
N.A.I.C.S.: 531210

Phu Hung Real Estate Investment Co., Ltd. (1)
6 Hoa Mai St, Ward 2 Phu Nhuan Dist, Ho Chi Minh City, Vietnam
Tel.: (84) 2835174499
Web Site: https://www.hungphu.com
Construction Development Services
N.A.I.C.S.: 236220
Nguyen Anh Khiem *(Chm)*

PHATISA GROUP LIMITED
Suite A Block 7 Uniciti Office Park Black River Road, Bambous, Mauritius
Tel.: (230) 460 0525
Web Site: http://www.phatisa.com
Privater Equity Firm
N.A.I.C.S.: 523999
Valentine Chitalu *(Chm)*

Subsidiaries:

Rolfes Holdings Limited (1)
First Floor The Oval West Wanderers Office Park, 52 Corlett Drive, Illovo, 2196, South Africa
Tel.: (27) 11 268 6100
Web Site: http://www.rolfesza.net
Rev.: $114,812,292

Assets: $82,669,812
Liabilities: $44,805,406
Net Worth: $37,864,407
Earnings: ($70,907)
Emp.: 493
Fiscal Year-end: 06/30/2018
Investment Management Service
N.A.I.C.S.: 523940
Richard Buttle *(CEO)*

PHATRA LEASING PUBLIC COMPANY LIMITED
252/6 29TH Floor Muang Thai Phatra Complex 1 Rachadaphisek Rd, Huay Kwang, Bangkok, 10320, Thailand
Tel.: (66) 22907575
Web Site: https://www.pl.co.th
Year Founded: 1987
PL—(THA)
Rev.: $78,800,597
Assets: $359,216,669
Liabilities: $266,565,854
Net Worth: $92,650,815
Earnings: $3,135,479
Emp.: 155
Fiscal Year-end: 12/31/23
Car Lending Services
N.A.I.C.S.: 532112
Poomchai Lamsan *(Vice Chm)*

PHAXIAM THERAPEUTICS S.A.
60 Avenue Rockefeller, 69008, Lyon, France
Tel.: (33) 478744438
Web Site: https://phaxiam.com
Year Founded: 2004
PHXM—(NASDAQ)
Rev.: $38,072,984
Assets: $56,266,903
Liabilities: $27,419,230
Net Worth: $28,847,673
Earnings: ($280,039)
Emp.: 49
Fiscal Year-end: 12/31/22
Pharmaceuticals Product Mfr
N.A.I.C.S.: 325412
Thibaut du Fayet *(CEO)*

Subsidiaries:

Erytech Pharma, Inc. (1)
1 Main St Ste 300, Cambridge, MA 02142
Tel.: (857) 706-1585
Web Site: https://erytech.com
Biopharmaceutical Product Development Services
N.A.I.C.S.: 541714

Pherecydes Pharma SA (1)
22 Boulevard Benoni Goullin, 44200, Nantes, France
Tel.: (33) 141506204
Web Site: https://www.pherecydes-pharma.com
Biotechnology Research & Development Services
N.A.I.C.S.: 541714
Thibaut du Fayet *(CEO)*

PHC CO., LTD
207 Geunmgok-Dong, Bundang-gu, 463-869, Seongnam, Gyeonggi, Korea (South)
Tel.: (82) 317780800
Web Site: http://www.topfield.co.kr
Year Founded: 1998
057880—(KRS)
Rev.: $8,916,379
Assets: $20,043,832
Liabilities: $5,517,409
Net Worth: $14,526,423
Earnings: ($51,914,523)
Emp.: 76
Fiscal Year-end: 12/31/22
Broadcasting Receiver Mfr
N.A.I.C.S.: 334220

PHC HOLDINGS CORPORATION
15F Dai-Ichi Life Hibiya First 1-13-2 Yurakucho, Minato-ku, Tokyo, 100-8403, Japan
Tel.: (81) 354087280
Web Site: https://www.phchd.com
Year Founded: 1969
6523—(TKS)
Rev.: $2,339,279,000
Assets: $3,730,201,470
Liabilities: $2,810,334,040
Net Worth: $919,867,430
Earnings: ($85,222,730)
Emp.: 9,245
Fiscal Year-end: 03/31/24
Laboratory Equipment Design & Mfr
N.A.I.C.S.: 339112
Kyoko Deguchi *(Chm & Pres)*

Subsidiaries:

PHC Corporation (1)
2-38-5 Nishishimbashi, Minato-ku, Tokyo, 105-8433, Japan (100%)
Tel.: (81) 3 5408 7290
Web Site: http://www.phchd.com
Sales Range: $1-4.9 Billion
Emp.: 2,300
Electronic Healthcare Device Designer, Mfr & Distr
N.A.I.C.S.: 334510
Kenji Yamane *(Pres & CEO)*

Subsidiary (Non-US):

Ascensia Diabetes Care Holdings AG (2)
Peter Merian Strasse 90, 4052, Basel, Switzerland
Tel.: (41) 41 799 7000
Web Site: http://www.ascensia.com
Holding Company; Blood Monitoring & Diabetes Care Management Equipment Designer, Mfr & Whslr
N.A.I.C.S.: 551112
Brian B. Hansen *(Pres-Continuous Glucose Monitoring)*

Subsidiary (Non-US):

Ascensia Diabetes Care Canada Inc. (3)
2920 Matheson Blvd East - Suite 201, Mississauga, L4W 5R6, ON, Canada
Web Site: https://www.ascensiadiabetes.ca
Blood Monitoring & Diabetes Care Management Equipment Whslr
N.A.I.C.S.: 423450

Ascensia Diabetes Care UK Limited (3)
Ascensia House Albert Road, Newbury, RG14 1LD, Berks, United Kingdom
Tel.: (44) 1635 566 381
Web Site: http://www.diabetes.ascensia.co.uk
Blood Monitoring & Diabetes Care Management Equipment Whslr
N.A.I.C.S.: 423450
Ros Barker *(Mng Dir & Country Head-UK)*

Subsidiary (US):

Ascensia Diabetes Care US Inc. (3)
5 Wood Hollow Rd, Parsippany, NJ 07054
Web Site: http://www.contournext.com
Blood Monitoring & Diabetes Care Management Equipment Designer, Mfr & Whslr
N.A.I.C.S.: 334510

Subsidiary (Domestic):

LSI Medience Corporation (2)
13-4 Uchikanda 1-chome, Chiyoda-ku, Tokyo, 101-8517, Japan
Tel.: (81) 3 5577 0450
Web Site: http://www.medience.co.jp
Emp.: 3,501
Vitro Diagnostic Reagent Mfr & Distr
N.A.I.C.S.: 325413
Akio Ito *(Pres & CEO)*

Subsidiary (Non-US):

PT. Panasonic Healthcare Indonesia (2)
Kawasan Industri MM2100 Blok O-1, Cikarang Barat, Bekasi, 17520, Indonesia
Tel.: (62) 21 898 0005

Web Site: http://www.panasonic.net
Emp.: 600
Healthcare Device Mfr
N.A.I.C.S.: 334510
Hiairano Dauguru *(Pres & Mng Dir)*

Panasonic Healthcare Singapore Pte. Ltd. (2)
2 Corporation Road 03-08 Lobby C Corporation Place, Singapore, 618494, Singapore
Tel.: (65) 6262 1111
Web Site: http://www.panasonic.net
Health Care Srvices
N.A.I.C.S.: 621999

PHENIX OPTICAL COMPANY LIMITED
No 197 Fenghuang West Avenue, Shangrao, 334100, Jiangxi, China
Tel.: (86) 57185009981
Web Site: https://www.phenixoptics.com.cn
600071—(SHG)
Rev.: $261,808,836
Assets: $292,889,802
Liabilities: $206,654,563
Net Worth: $86,235,238
Earnings: $672,277
Emp.: 7,470
Fiscal Year-end: 12/31/22
Optical Instruments & Lenses Mfr
N.A.I.C.S.: 333310
Liu Rui *(Exec VP)*

Subsidiaries:

Phenix Optics Japan Co., Ltd. (1)
4F 2-12-1 Shinyokohama, Kohoku-ku, Yokohama, 2220033, Japan
Tel.: (81) 456249989
Optical Instrument & Lens Mfr
N.A.I.C.S.: 333310

PHENIXCOM SA
23 Burospace, 91570, Bievres, France
Tel.: (33) 160106443
Web Site: http://www.phenixcom.com
Sales Range: Less than $1 Million
Internet Services
N.A.I.C.S.: 517121
Marchal Christian *(Chm & CEO)*

PHENOM RESOURCES CORP.
1100 736 Granville St, Vancouver, V6Z 1G3, BC, Canada
Tel.: (604) 340-7711
Web Site: http://phenomresources.com
Year Founded: 2006
PHNMF—(OTCQX)
Rev.: $3,778
Assets: $14,647,477
Liabilities: $406,927
Net Worth: $14,240,550
Earnings: ($1,586,167)
Emp.: 2
Fiscal Year-end: 11/30/22
Mineral Exploration Services
N.A.I.C.S.: 213114
Paul Cowley *(Pres & CEO)*

PHI ASSET MANAGEMENT PARTNERS SGEIC S.A.
Calle General Castanos 4 2nd Izquierda, 28004, Madrid, Spain
Tel.: (34) 91 561 3371
Web Site: http://www.phi-industrial.com
Investment Management Service
N.A.I.C.S.: 523940
Alexander Wit *(Mng Partner)*

Subsidiaries:

PHI Asset Management Partners SGEIC S.A. - Barcelona (1)
Paseo de Gracia 37 Planta 3rd Puerta 2, 08007, Barcelona, Spain
Tel.: (34) 93 487 9735
Web Site: http://www.phi-industrial.com

Investment Management Service
N.A.I.C.S.: 523940
Jordi Bricio *(Mng Partner)*

Holding (Non-US):

Boglioli S.p.A. (2)
Via Brescia 47, Gambara, 25020, Brescia, Italy
Tel.: (39) 02 5456387
Web Site: http://www.bogliolimilano.com
Men's Apparel Mfr & Distr
N.A.I.C.S.: 315250

Subsidiary (US):

Boglioli USA Corporation (3)
79 Mercer St 5th Fl, New York, NY 10012
Tel.: (646) 781-9754
Web Site: http://www.boglioli.it
Men's Apparel Distr
N.A.I.C.S.: 458110

Holding (Non-US):

intimus International GmbH (2)
Bergheimer Strasse 6-12, 88677, Markdorf, Germany
Tel.: (49) 7544600
Web Site: http://www.intimus.com
Sales Range: $50-74.9 Million
Emp.: 280
Information Security, Business Information & Cash Management Machinery Whslr
N.A.I.C.S.: 333310
Javier Ortiz de Zarate Martinez *(Mng Dir)*

Subsidiary (Non-US):

intimus International Austria Ges.m.b.H. (3)
Ernst Melchior Gasse 20, 4 OG Top 6, 1020, Vienna, Austria (100%)
Tel.: (43) 125836210
Web Site: http://www.intimus.com
Information Security, Business Information & Cash Management Machinery Whslr
N.A.I.C.S.: 423420

intimus International Iberica, S.A.U. (3)
Anton Fortuny 14-16 N1 Escalera C Planta 1, 08950, Esplugues de Llobregat, Spain
Tel.: (34) 934803310
Web Site: http://www.intimus.com
Information Security, Business Information & Cash Management Machinery Mfr & Whslr
N.A.I.C.S.: 333310
Jose Oliveira *(Gen Mgr)*

intimus International Limited (3)
Unit 39 Basepoint Business Centre Metcalf Way, Crawley, RH11 7XX, W Sussex, United Kingdom
Tel.: (44) 1293 44 1900
Web Site: http://www.intimus.com
Information Security, Business Information & Cash Management Machinery Whslr
N.A.I.C.S.: 423420
Fritz Nueschel *(Pres)*

intimus International Netherlands B.V. (3)
Rivium Quadrant 2 6e verdieping, 2909 LC, Capelle aan den IJssel, Netherlands
Tel.: (31) 102421100
Web Site: http://www.intimus.com
Information Security, Business Information & Cash Management Machinery Whslr
N.A.I.C.S.: 423420
Victor Dake *(Gen Mgr)*

Subsidiary (Non-US):

intimus International Belgium (4)
Wayenborgstraat 26, 2800, Mechelen, Belgium
Tel.: (32) 1529 4630
Web Site: http://www.intimus.com
Information Security, Business Information & Cash Management Machinery Whslr
N.A.I.C.S.: 423420

intimus International Luxembourg S.a.r.l. (4)
1 Route des Trois Cantons 9 rez-de-chaussee, 8399, Luxembourg, Luxembourg
Tel.: (352) 2610 8866
Web Site: http://www.intimus.com

PHI ASSET MANAGEMENT PARTNERS SGEIC S.A.

PHI Asset Management Partners SGEIC S.A.—(Continued)
Information Security, Business Information & Cash Management Machinery Whslr
N.A.I.C.S.: 423420

Subsidiary (US):

intimus International North America, Inc. (3)
251 Wedcor Ave, Wabash, IN 46992
Web Site: http://www.intimus.com
Information Security, Business Information & Cash Management Machinery Whslr
N.A.I.C.S.: 423420
Larry Koenig (Head-Natl Sls)

PHICHEM CORPORATION
2999 Panjing Road Baoshan District, Shanghai, 201908, China
Tel.: (86) 2150551001
Web Site:
   https://www.phichem.com.cn
Year Founded: 2002
300398—(CHIN)
Rev.: $408,116,124
Assets: $886,487,004
Liabilities: $350,320,464
Net Worth: $536,166,540
Earnings: $61,013,628
Emp.: 1,900
Fiscal Year-end: 12/31/22
Specialty Chemicals & Materials Mfr
N.A.I.C.S.: 325998
Jinshan Zhang (Founder, Chm & Pres)

Subsidiaries:

PhiChem America, Inc. (1)
7085 Las Positas Rd Ste A, Livermore, CA 94551
Tel.: (925) 373-3128
Web Site: https://www.phichem.com
Optical Fiber Cable Distr
N.A.I.C.S.: 423610

PHIHONG TECHNOLOGY CO., LTD.
No 568 Fuxing 3rd Road, Guishan District, Taoyuan, 333611, Taiwan
Tel.: (886) 33277288   CN
Web Site:
   https://www.phihong.com.tw
Year Founded: 1972
2457—(TAI)
Rev.: $403,296,267
Assets: $509,452,415
Liabilities: $202,044,206
Net Worth: $307,408,210
Earnings: $8,584,780
Emp.: 2,690
Fiscal Year-end: 12/31/23
Electronic Components Mfr
N.A.I.C.S.: 334419
Jim Chen (VP-New Tech Dev)

Subsidiaries:

Phihong Technology Japan Co., Ltd. (1)
3-23-24 Toyo Vort Toyocho Building 5th Floor, Koto-ku, Tokyo, 135-0016, Japan
Tel.: (81) 356771678
Web Site: http://www.phihong.co.jp
Power Supply Product Mfr
N.A.I.C.S.: 334515

Phihong USA Corp. (1)
47800 Fremont Blvd, Fremont, CA 94538
Tel.: (510) 445-0100
Power Supply Product Mfr
N.A.I.C.S.: 334515

Phihong Vietnam Co., Ltd. (1)
Lot CN5, An Duong Industrial Zone Hong Phong Commune, Haiphong, An Duong, Vietnam
Tel.: (84) 22588315579
Power Supply Product Mfr & Distr
N.A.I.C.S.: 335999

Zerova Technologies (Dongguan) Co., Ltd. (1)
Room 201 Building 5 No 133 Tiesong Road, Qingxi Town, Dongguan, Guangdong, China
Tel.: (86) 76986818881
Electric Vehicle Charging Equipment Distr
N.A.I.C.S.: 423620

Zerova Technologies Europe B.V. (1)
Spaces Zuidas IIBarbara Strozzilaan 101, Amsterdam, Netherlands
Tel.: (31) 202149195
Electric Vehicle Charging Equipment Distr
N.A.I.C.S.: 423620

Zerova Technologies Japan Co., Ltd. (1)
5F VORT Toyocho Building 3-23-24 Toyo, Koto-ku, Tokyo, 135-0016, Japan
Tel.: (81) 356771678
Charging Equipment Mfr & Distr
N.A.I.C.S.: 336320

Zerova Technologies Taiwan Limited (1)
No 99 Zhengnan 1st St, Yongkang Dist, Tainan City, 71046, Taiwan
Tel.: (886) 62547588
Web Site: https://www.zerovatech.com
Electric Vehicle Charging Equipment Distr
N.A.I.C.S.: 423620

Zerova Technologies USA LLC (1)
47775 Fremont Blvd, Fremont, CA 94538
Tel.: (510) 936-9000
Electric Vehicle Charging Equipment Distr
N.A.I.C.S.: 423620

PHIL COMPANY, INC.
Phil Park TOKYO GINZA Shintomi Lab 1-12 Tsukiji 3-chome, Chuo-ku, Tokyo, 104-0045, Japan
Tel.: (81) 362641100
Web Site: https://www.philcompany.jp
3267—(TKS)
Rev.: $42,277,670
Assets: $38,640,500
Liabilities: $19,284,800
Net Worth: $19,355,700
Earnings: $269,420
Fiscal Year-end: 11/30/23
Parking Lot Operator
N.A.I.C.S.: 812930
Yuichi Nomi (Pres)

PHILADELPHIA INSURANCE COMPANY LTD.
Jabal Al-Hussein, PO Box 8663, Amman, 11121, Jordan
Tel.: (962) 65668131
Year Founded: 1980
PHIN—(AMM)
Sales Range: $1-9.9 Million
Emp.: 53
General Insurance Services
N.A.I.C.S.: 524298
Hatem Hussein (Gen Mgr)

PHILADELPHIA INTERNATIONAL EDUCATIONAL INVESTMENT COMPANY PLC
University of Jordan st-abu Al-Haj complex, PO Box 1101, Amman, 11910, Jordan
Tel.: (962) 65163498
Year Founded: 1991
PIEC—(AMM)
Rev.: $18,154,731
Assets: $42,568,744
Liabilities: $13,173,456
Net Worth: $29,395,288
Earnings: $1,848,328
Emp.: 631
Fiscal Year-end: 12/31/20
Education Services
N.A.I.C.S.: 611710
Rebhi Suboh (Gen Mgr)

PHILADELPHIA PHARMACEUTICALS
10th St King Abdullah II Industrial City, PO Box 276, Sahab, 11512, Jordan
Tel.: (962) 64029181
Web Site:
   https://www.philapharma.com
Year Founded: 1993
PHIL—(AMM)
Rev.: $10,797,293
Assets: $21,167,246
Liabilities: $5,015,922
Net Worth: $16,151,324
Earnings: $199,876
Emp.: 168
Fiscal Year-end: 12/31/20
Pharmaceutical Products Marketing & Mfr
N.A.I.C.S.: 424210
Kayed G. Al-Shaabani (Vice Chm & CEO)

PHILCOMSAT HOLDINGS CORPORATION
12/F Telecom Plaza Building 316 Sen Gil Puyat Avenue Metro Manila, Makati, 1200, Philippines
Tel.: (63) 28158406   PH
Web Site: https://www.phc.com.ph
PHC—(PHI)
Rev.: $1,010,175
Assets: $27,439,543
Liabilities: $1,106,512
Net Worth: $26,333,031
Earnings: $323,030
Fiscal Year-end: 12/31/23
Investment Holding Company
N.A.I.C.S.: 551112
Katrina C. Ponce-Enrile (Chm & Exec VP)

PHILENERGY CO., LTD.
1-19 Jigotjungang-ro, Osan, 18102, Gyeonggi-do, Korea (South)
Tel.: (82) 317899000
Web Site:
   https://www.philenergy.co.kr
Year Founded: 2020
378340—(KRS)
Emp.: 216
Battery Mfr
N.A.I.C.S.: 335910
Kim Woo Young (Principal & Mgr)

PHILEO AUSTRALIA LIMITED
Level 14 303 Collins Street, Melbourne, 3000, VIC, Australia
Tel.: (61) 396638018   AU
Web Site: http://www.palltd.com.au
Rev.: $117,714,153
Assets: $265,814,298
Liabilities: $103,602,956
Net Worth: $162,211,342
Earnings: $66,418,553
Fiscal Year-end: 06/30/18
Real Estate Manangement Services
N.A.I.C.S.: 531390
Tejas Gandhi (Sec & Controller)

Subsidiaries:

Phileo 303 Collins Pty Ltd (1)
L 14 303 Collins St, Melbourne, 3000, VIC, Australia
Tel.: (61) 396638018
Web Site: http://www.palltd.com.au
Sales Range: $50-74.9 Million
Emp.: 8
Financial Management Services
N.A.I.C.S.: 523999

PHILEX MINING CORPORATION
2nd Floor LaunchPad Reliance Street corner Sheridan Street, Metro Manila, Mandaluyong, 1550, Philippines
Tel.: (63) 26311381
Web Site:
   https://www.philexmining.com.ph
Year Founded: 1955

INTERNATIONAL PUBLIC

PX—(PHI)
Rev.: $139,497,299
Assets: $819,921,307
Liabilities: $247,777,266
Net Worth: $572,144,041
Earnings: $18,380,464
Emp.: 2,199
Fiscal Year-end: 12/31/23
Gold Mining
N.A.I.C.S.: 212220
Manuel V. Pangilinan (Chm)

Subsidiaries:

PXP Energy Corporation (1)
2/F LaunchPad Reliance cor Sheridan St, Mandaluyong, 1550, Philippines
Tel.: (63) 286311381
Web Site: https://www.pxpenergy.com.ph
Rev.: $1,335,318
Assets: $64,359,714
Liabilities: $9,934,704
Net Worth: $54,425,010
Earnings: ($65,380,120)
Emp.: 9
Fiscal Year-end: 12/31/2021
Petroleum Exploration Services
N.A.I.C.S.: 211120
Manuel V. Pangilinan (Chm)

Subsidiary (Non-US):

FEC Resources Inc. (2)
Bentall 5 550 Burrard Street Suite 2300, Vancouver, V6C 2B5, BC, Canada (54.99%)
Tel.: (403) 290-1676
Web Site: https://www.fecresources.com
Rev.: $38
Assets: $2,279,788
Liabilities: $304,624
Net Worth: $1,975,164
Earnings: ($193,182)
Fiscal Year-end: 12/31/2022
Investment Services
N.A.I.C.S.: 523999
Daniel Carlos (Pres & CEO)

Forum Energy Limited (2)
16 High Holborn, London, WC1V 6BX, United Kingdom (69.5%)
Tel.: (44) 208 616 7297
Sales Range: $1-9.9 Million
Emp.: 17
Oil, Gas & Coal Explorer
N.A.I.C.S.: 213112
Paul Forrest (Sec)

PHILI-ORIENT LINES (PENANG) SDN. BHD.
No 316-F Wisma Phili-Orient Jalan Dato Ismail Hashim, Sungai Ara, 11900, Bayan Lepas, Penang, Malaysia
Tel.: (60) 4 646 4336   MY
Web Site: http://www.pol-group.com
Year Founded: 1989
Sales Range: $10-24.9 Million
Emp.: 80
Holding Company; Freight Forwarding Services
N.A.I.C.S.: 551112
Jay Shanker (Mng Dir)

Subsidiaries:

Phili-Orient Airfreight (Malaysia) Sdn Bhd (1)
No 25 Jalan PJS 8/18 Dataran Mentari Bandar Sunway, 46150, Petaling Jaya, Selangor Darul Ehsan, Malaysia
Tel.: (60) 356300027
Emp.: 20
Logistic Services
N.A.I.C.S.: 541614
Jay Shanker (Dir-Ops)

Phili-Orient Airfreight (Penang) Sdn Bhd (1)
No 316-F Wisma Phili-Orient Jalan Dato Ismail Hashim, Sungai Ara, 11900, Bayan Lepas, Penang, Malaysia (100%)
Tel.: (60) 46464336
Web Site: http://www.pol-group.com
Logistic Services
N.A.I.C.S.: 541614
Shanmugam Paramasivan (Gen Mgr)

PHILION SE
Wallstr 15 a, 10179, Berlin, Germany
Tel.: (49) 3028493640
Web Site: https://www.philion.de
PH6—(DEU)
Rev.: $560,500
Assets: $8,003,940
Liabilities: $14,449,690
Net Worth: ($6,445,750)
Earnings: ($22,296,690)
Emp.: 3
Fiscal Year-end: 12/31/19
Telecommunication Servicesb
N.A.I.C.S.: 517112
Rene Schuster (Chm)

Subsidiaries:

Fexcom GmbH (1)
Stohrerstrasse 17, 04347, Leipzig, Germany
Tel.: (49) 341944330
Web Site: http://www.fexcom.de
Communication Service
N.A.I.C.S.: 517810

System Repair Center GmbH (1)
Stohrerstrasse 17, 04347, Leipzig, Germany
Tel.: (49) 34194433102
Web Site: http://www.src-leipzig.de
Cell Phone Repair Services
N.A.I.C.S.: 811210

PHILIP MORRIS CR AS
Vitezna 1, Kutna Hora, 28403, Prague, Czech Republic
Tel.: (420) 266702111
TABAK—(PRA)
Rev.: $919,810,588
Assets: $711,075,740
Liabilities: $330,228,546
Net Worth: $380,847,194
Earnings: $149,530,705
Emp.: 1,301
Fiscal Year-end: 12/31/23
Consumer Products Distr
N.A.I.C.S.: 423620

PHILIPP HOLZMANN AG
Taunusanlage 1, Frankfurt, 60299, Germany
Tel.: (49) 6102453862
Sales Range: Less than $1 Million
Engineeering Services
N.A.I.C.S.: 541330
Johannes A. Ohlinger (CFO & Member-Mgmt Bd)

PHILIPPE LEVESQUE SA
Route De La Cense, 02400, Essomes-sur-Marne, Aisne, France
Tel.: (33) 323702829
Web Site: http://www.coceral.com
Rev.: $24,000,000
Emp.: 12
Chemical Products Sales
N.A.I.C.S.: 424690
Philippe Levesque (Gen Mgr)

PHILIPPI, PRIETOCARRIZOSA & URIA
El Golf 40 Piso 20, Las Condes, 7550107, Santiago, Chile
Tel.: (56) 2 2364 37 00
Web Site: http://www.ppulegal.com
Year Founded: 2015
Law Services
N.A.I.C.S.: 541110

Subsidiaries:

Estudio Ferrero Abogados (1)
Victor Andres Belaunde 395 San Isidro, Lima, Peru
Tel.: (51) 1 513 7200
Web Site: http://www.ferrero.com.pe
Emp.: 50
Law firm
N.A.I.C.S.: 541110
Guillermo Ferrero (Partner)

PHILIPPINE BANK OF COMMUNICATIONS
PBCOM Tower 6795 Ayala Avenue, corner V A Rufino St, PO Box 3281, Makati, 1226, Philippines
Tel.: (63) 288307000 PH
Web Site: https://www.pbcom.com.ph
Year Founded: 1939
PBC—(PHI)
Rev.: $142,257,071
Assets: $2,647,224,536
Liabilities: $2,330,303,805
Net Worth: $316,920,730
Earnings: $34,061,399
Fiscal Year-end: 12/31/22
Commericial Banking
N.A.I.C.S.: 522110
Eric O. Recto (Chm)

PHILIPPINE BUSINESS BANK INC.
350 Rizal Avenue Extension cor 8th Avenue, Grace Park Caloocan City, Manila, Philippines
Tel.: (63) 23633333
Web Site: http://www.pbb.com.ph
Sales Range: $500-549.9 Million
Banking Services
N.A.I.C.S.: 522110
Francis T. Lee (Chm)

Subsidiaries:

Bright Kindle Resources and Investments Inc. (1)
16th Floor Citibank Tower 8741 Paseo de Roxas, Makati, 1605, Philippines
Tel.: (63) 28330769
Web Site: https://bkr.com.ph
Rev.: $46,065
Assets: $52,314,134
Liabilities: $30,190,160
Net Worth: $22,123,974
Earnings: $597,183
Fiscal Year-end: 12/31/2023
Property Investment Services
N.A.I.C.S.: 523999
Diane Madelyn C. Ching (Officer-Compliance & Sec)

PHILIPPINE ESTATES CORPORATION
35th Floor One Corporate Center Julia Vargas Avenue cor, Meralco Avenue Ortigas Center, Pasig, 1605, Philippines
Tel.: (63) 86373112 PH
Web Site: https://www.phes.com.ph
Year Founded: 1983
PHES—(PHI)
Rev.: $5,003,609
Assets: $55,993,683
Liabilities: $8,780,125
Net Worth: $47,213,558
Earnings: $1,055,732
Emp.: 67
Fiscal Year-end: 12/31/23
Real Estate Developers
N.A.I.C.S.: 531311
Kenneth T. Gatchalian (Vice Chm)

PHILIPPINE INFRADEV HOLDINGS INC.
35/F Rufino Pacific Tower, 6784 Ayala Avenue, Makati, 1223, Philippines
Tel.: (63) 27502000
Web Site: http://www.interportresources.com
INFRA—(PHI)
Rev.: $9,795,958
Assets: $2,232,455,892
Liabilities: $405,586,845
Net Worth: $1,826,869,047
Earnings: ($796,603,411)
Emp.: 23
Fiscal Year-end: 12/31/23
Real Estate Development Services
N.A.I.C.S.: 531312

Delfin P. Angcao (Officer-Corp Info & Sec)

PHILIPPINE NATIONAL BANK
PNB Financial Center, President Diosdado Macapagal Blvd, Pasay, 1300, Philippines
Tel.: (63) 285263131
Web Site: https://www.pnb.com.ph
Year Founded: 1916
PNB—(PHI)
Rev.: $881,969,442
Assets: $24,768,320,970
Liabilities: $21,414,883,485
Net Worth: $3,353,437,485
Earnings: $659,152,790
Emp.: 8,656
Fiscal Year-end: 12/31/21
Banking Services
N.A.I.C.S.: 522110
Florencia G. Tarriela (Chm)

Subsidiaries:

Allied Banking Corporation (Hong Kong) Limited (1)
1402 World Wide House 19 Des Voeux Road, Central, China (Hong Kong)
Tel.: (852) 28462288
Web Site: http://www.abchkl.com.hk
Banking Services
N.A.I.C.S.: 522110

PNB Capital & Investment Corporation (1)
9th Floor PNB Financial Center Pres Diosdado Macapagal Blvd, Pasay, 1300, Philippines (100%)
Tel.: (63) 25263698
Investment Banking Services
N.A.I.C.S.: 523150
Florencia G. Tarriela (Chm)

PNB Corporation (1)
Ste 114/114C Micronesia Mall 1088 W Marine Corps Dr, Dededo, GU 96929
Tel.: (671) 646-9143
Remittance Services
N.A.I.C.S.: 522320
Mario R. Palisoc (Gen Mgr)

PNB Europe PLC (1)
238 Vauxhall Bridge Road, London, SW1V 1AU, United Kingdom (100%)
Tel.: (44) 2073132300
Web Site: https://www.pnb.com.ph
Secondary Market Financing
N.A.I.C.S.: 522299

PNB Forex, Incorporated (1)
Pres Diosdado P Macapagal Boulevard, PNB Financial Center, Pasay, 1300, Philippines (100%)
Tel.: (63) 28916040
Currency Exchange Services
N.A.I.C.S.: 523150

PNB Global Remittance & Financial Company (HK) Limited (1)
Unit 01 9/F Tung Wai Commercial Bldg 109-111 Gloucester Road, Wanchai, China (Hong Kong)
Tel.: (852) 25372345
Banking Services
N.A.I.C.S.: 522110

PNB Holdings Corporation (1)
2nd Floor PNB Financial Center, Pres Diosdado Macapagal Blvd, Manila, 1300, Pasay City, Philippines (100%)
Tel.: (63) 526 3131
Commericial Banking
N.A.I.C.S.: 522110

PNB International Investments Corporation (1)
316 W 2nd St 7th Fl, Los Angeles, CA 90012
Tel.: (213) 401-1008
Investment Management Service
N.A.I.C.S.: 523940
Nelson V. Javier (Pres & CEO)

Subsidiary (Domestic):

PNB Remittance Centers, Inc. (2)
225 W Broadway Ste 301, Glendale, CA 91204
Tel.: (213) 401-1008
Web Site: https://www.pnbwebremit.com
Remittance Services
N.A.I.C.S.: 522320

Subsidiary (Domestic):

PNB RCI Holding Co. Ltd. (3)
316 W 2nd St 7th Fl, Los Angeles, CA 90012
Tel.: (213) 401-1008
Holding Company
N.A.I.C.S.: 551112
Felix Enrico R. Alfiler (Chm)

PNB Remittance Co. (1)
Unit 104 3050 Confederation Parkway, Mississauga, L5B 3Z6, ON, Canada
Tel.: (905) 896-9743
Web Site: https://www.pnb.com.ph
Remittance Services
N.A.I.C.S.: 522320

PNB Securities Inc. (1)
3rd Floor PNB Finance Center Macapagal Blvd, 3rd Fl PNB Finance Center, Pasay, 1300, Philippines (100%)
Tel.: (63) 85263510
Web Site: https://www.pnb.com.ph
Sales Range: $50-74.9 Million
Emp.: 10
Securities Brokerage
N.A.I.C.S.: 523150

PNB-IBJL Equipment Rentals Corporation (1)
5th Floor PNB Makati Center 6754 Ayala Avenue cor Legaspi Street, Makati, 1226, Philippines
Tel.: (63) 28925555
Investment Services
N.A.I.C.S.: 523999
Modette Ines V. Carino (Pres & CEO)

PNB-Mizuho Equipment Rentals Corporation (1)
6754 Ayala Ave Cor Legaspi St, Makati, 1226, Metro Manila, Philippines
Tel.: (63) 28925555
Web Site: https://pnb-mizuholeasing.com.ph
Financial Lending Services
N.A.I.C.S.: 522220

PHILIPPINE NATIONAL OIL COMPANY
PNOC Building 6 Energy Center Merritt Road Fort Bonifacio, Taguig, Philippines
Tel.: (63) 3 789 7662 PH
Web Site: http://www.pnoc.com.ph
Year Founded: 1973
Sales Range: $150-199.9 Million
Oil, Gas & Coal Exploration & Production Services
N.A.I.C.S.: 211120
Antonio M. Cailao (Pres & CEO)

Subsidiaries:

PNOC Alternative Fuels Corporation (1)
2nd Floor PNOC Building 5 Energy Center Rizal Drive, Bonifacio Global City, Taguig, 1634, Philippines
Tel.: (63) 2 817 9694
Web Site: http://www.pnoc-afc.gov.ph
Sales Range: $1-9.9 Million
Alternative Fuels Exploration & Development
N.A.I.C.S.: 213112
Sabino R. Dapat (Chm)

PNOC Development & Management Corporation (1)
2/F PNOC Bldg 5 Energy Center Rizal Drive, Bonifacio Global City, Taguig, 1634, Philippines
Tel.: (63) 2 840 2652
Web Site: http://www.pnoc-dmc.com.ph
Real Estate Development & Management Services
N.A.I.C.S.: 531390
Joseph John M. Literal (VP)

PNOC Exploration Corporation (1)
Building 1 Energy Center Rizal Drive, Boni-

Philippine National Oil Company—(Continued)

facio Global City, Taguig, 1634, Metro Manila, Philippines **(99.78%)**
Tel.: (63) 284799400
Web Site: http://www.pnoc-ec.com.ph
Rev.: $101,981,894
Assets: $348,316,999
Liabilities: $61,245,771
Net Worth: $287,071,228
Earnings: $23,153,759
Emp.: 150
Fiscal Year-end: 12/31/2019
Oil & Gas Exploration Services
N.A.I.C.S.: 211120
Candido M. Magsombol (VP-Mgmt Svcs Div)

PNOC Renewables Corporation (1)
PNOC Building 5 Energy Center Rizal Dirve, Bonifacio Global City, Taguig, 1634, Metro Manila, Philippines
Tel.: (63) 2 840 3079
Web Site: http://www.pnoc-rc.com.ph
Rev.: $589
Assets: $22,193,552
Liabilities: $1,175,627
Net Worth: $21,017,925
Earnings: ($456,157)
Fiscal Year-end: 12/31/2015
Renewable Energy Sources Implementation & Development
N.A.I.C.S.: 237990
Carlos Jose P. Gatmaitan (Pres & CEO)

PHILIPPINE RACING CLUB, INC.
Saddle & Clubs Leisure Park Brgy Sabang Naic, Cavite, 4110, Philippines
Tel.: (63) 8805209195 **PH**
Web Site: http://prci.powersites.ph
Year Founded: 1937
PRC—(PHI)
Rev.: $6,184,406
Assets: $143,781,993
Liabilities: $36,554,768
Net Worth: $107,227,225
Earnings: $5,155,401
Emp.: 160
Fiscal Year-end: 12/31/21
Horse Racing Club
N.A.I.C.S.: 711310
Allan V. Abesamis (CFO & Exec VP)

PHILIPPINE REALTY & HOLDINGS CORPORATION
1 Balete Drive corner N Domingo St Brgy Kaunlaran, Quezon City, 1111, Philippines
Tel.: (63) 286313179 **PH**
Web Site: https://www.philrealty.com.ph
Year Founded: 1981
RLT—(PHI)
Rev.: $15,766,047
Assets: $154,242,789
Liabilities: $37,106,515
Net Worth: $117,136,274
Earnings: $3,237,973
Fiscal Year-end: 12/31/22
Real Estate Services
N.A.I.C.S.: 531390
Gerardo Domenico Antonio V. Lanuza (Chm)

PHILIPPINE SEVEN CORPORATION
7th Floors The Columbia Tower Ortigas Avenue, Mandaluyong, 1550, Philippines
Tel.: (63) 87110711
Web Site: https://www.7-eleven.com.ph
SEVN—(PHI)
Rev.: $944,876,878
Assets: $591,104,065
Liabilities: $446,098,614
Net Worth: $145,005,451
Earnings: ($9,588,904)
Emp.: 3,146
Fiscal Year-end: 12/31/21
Grocery Items Retailing & Merchandising Services
N.A.I.C.S.: 445110
Violeta B. Apolinario (Head-HR & Admin Div)

PHILIPPINE STOCK EXCHANGE, INC.
PSE Tower 5th Avenue cor 28th Street, Bonifacio Global City, Taguig, 1634, Philippines
Tel.: (63) 288764888
Web Site: https://www.pse.com.ph
Year Founded: 1927
PSE—(PHI)
Rev.: $24,933,094
Assets: $127,102,406
Liabilities: $28,674,282
Net Worth: $98,428,125
Earnings: $13,635,082
Emp.: 132
Fiscal Year-end: 12/31/23
Market for Exchange, Purchase & Sale of Securities
N.A.I.C.S.: 523210
Roel A. Refran (COO & Sr VP)

PHILIPPINE TELEGRAPH & TELEPHONE CORPORATION
Spirit of Communications Center 106 Carlos Palanca St, Legaspi Village Manila, Makati, 1229, Philippines
Tel.: (63) 88159961
Web Site: https://www.ptt.com.ph
Year Founded: 1962
PTT—(PHI)
Rev.: $9,546,124
Assets: $20,107,551
Liabilities: $19,433,181
Net Worth: $674,370
Earnings: $142,762
Emp.: 248
Fiscal Year-end: 12/31/23
Telecommunication Servicesb
N.A.I.C.S.: 517112
James C. Velasquez (Pres & CEO)

PHILIPPINE TRUST COMPANY
Philtrust Bank Bldg 1000 United Nations Avenue corner San Marcelino St, Manila, Philippines
Tel.: (63) 285249061 **PH**
Web Site: http://www.philtrustbank.com
Year Founded: 1916
PTC—(PHI)
Rev.: $169,274,712
Assets: $3,185,639,367
Liabilities: $2,767,236,861
Net Worth: $418,402,506
Earnings: $18,581,006
Fiscal Year-end: 12/31/23
Commercial Banking Services
N.A.I.C.S.: 522110
Martin B. Isidro (Sec)

PHILIPPOS NAKAS S.A.
19th Km Lavriou Avenue, 19002, Peania, Greece
Tel.: (30) 2106686000
Web Site: https://www.nakas.gr
Year Founded: 1937
NAKAS—(ATH)
Rev.: $28,133,401
Assets: $32,574,836
Liabilities: $12,193,914
Net Worth: $20,380,922
Earnings: $1,822,810
Emp.: 391
Fiscal Year-end: 06/30/23
Musical Instruments & Audiovisual Systems Distr
N.A.I.C.S.: 449210
Stelios D. Vasilakis (VP)

Subsidiaries:

NAKAS MUSIC CYPRUS LTD (1)
2K Nikis Avenue, Nicosia, 1086, Cyprus
Tel.: (357) 22512088
Web Site: http://www.nakas.gr
Musical Instrument Retailer
N.A.I.C.S.: 459140
George Avlonitis (Gen Mgr)

PHILLIP CAPITAL PTE. LTD.
250 North Bridge Road 06-00 Raffles City Tower, Singapore, 179 101, Singapore
Tel.: (65) 65336001
Web Site: http://www.phillip.com.sg
Year Founded: 1975
Sales Range: $150-199.9 Million
Emp.: 3,500
Financial Services
N.A.I.C.S.: 561499
Hoon Sun Loh (Mng Dir)

Subsidiaries:

Agility Partners Pte. Ltd. (1)
250 North Bridge Road 06-00 Raffles City Tower, Singapore, 179101, Singapore
Tel.: (65) 65330220
Real Estate Services
N.A.I.C.S.: 531390

Asha Phillip Securities Ltd (1)
Level 4, Millennium House, 46/58 Navam Mawatha, 2, Colombo, Sri Lanka
Tel.: (94) 112429100
Web Site: http://www.ashaphillip.net
Securities Exchange
N.A.I.C.S.: 523210

CKS Property Consultants Pte Ltd (1)
250 North Bridge Road, Raffles City Tower 09-02, Singapore, 179101, Singapore
Tel.: (65) 330220
Web Site: http://www.cks.com.sg
Sales Range: $25-49.9 Million
Emp.: 50
Licensed Estate Agents
N.A.I.C.S.: 531390

CyberQuote (Thailand) Co., Ltd. (1)
119 BIS Building 3rd Floor 3E12 Mahaesak Road, Suriyawong Bangrak, Bangkok, 10500, Thailand
Tel.: (66) 263570977099
Financial & Information Training Services
N.A.I.C.S.: 611430

CyberQuote Japan, Ltd. (1)
4th floor Nihonbashi Kabutocho Building Gamocho, Chuo-ku, Tokyo, 103-0026, Japan
Tel.: (81) 345893310
Financial & Information Training Services
N.A.I.C.S.: 611430

CyberQuote Pte Ltd (1)
36 Purvis Street, 02-13 Talib Centre, Singapore, 188613, Singapore
Tel.: (65) 311558
Web Site: http://www.cyberquote.com.sg
Sales Range: $25-49.9 Million
Emp.: 20
Information Technology Solutions
N.A.I.C.S.: 541990

Subsidiary (Non-US):

CyberQuote (HK) Ltd (2)
11 F United Ctr 95 Queensway, Hong Kong, China (Hong Kong)
Tel.: (852) 22776600
Web Site: http://www.cyberquote.com.hk
Information Technology Solutions
N.A.I.C.S.: 541990

First Finance PLC (1)
Yothapol Khemarak Phoumin Blvd 271, Phnom Penh, Cambodia
Tel.: (855) 93666635
Web Site: http://www.firstfinance.biz
Home Loan Services
N.A.I.C.S.: 522310
Chun Sothany (CEO)

King & Shaxson Asset Management (1)
6th Fl Candlewick House, 120 Cannon St, London, United Kingdom
Tel.: (44) 2074265950
Web Site: http://www.kingandshaxson.com
Sales Range: $50-74.9 Million
Emp.: 70
Asset Management
N.A.I.C.S.: 525990
David Wilamin (CEO)

King & Shaxson Capital Limited (1)
6th Floor Candlewick House, 120 Cannon Street, London, EC4N 6AS, United Kingdom
Tel.: (44) 2074265950
Web Site: http://www.kasl.co.uk
Sales Range: $50-74.9 Million
Emp.: 65
Securities & Commodity Exchanges
N.A.I.C.S.: 523210
David Wileman (CEO)

King & Shaxson Capital Limited (1)
3rd Floor 35 Rue de la Bienfaisance, 75008, Paris, 75008, France
Tel.: (33) 145633100
Web Site: http://www.kingandshaxson.com
Financial Management
N.A.I.C.S.: 525990

King & Shaxson Ltd (1)
7th Floor Candlewick House, 120 Cannon Street, London, EC4N 6AS, United Kingdom
Tel.: (44) 2079295300
Web Site: http://www.kingandshaxson.com
Sales Range: $50-74.9 Million
Emp.: 100
Financial Advisors
N.A.I.C.S.: 525990
Elizabeth Mahoney (Head-Ops)

PC Quote (M) Sdn Bhd (1)
B-2-6 Megan Avenue II, No12 Jalan Yap Kwan Seng, 50450, Kuala Lumpur, Malaysia
Tel.: (60) 327153068
Sales Range: $25-49.9 Million
Emp.: 80
Computer Programming
N.A.I.C.S.: 541511
Andy Lim (Mng Dir)

PT CyberQuote Indonesia (1)
Anz Tower Level 23B J1 Jendral Sudirman Kav 33A, Jakarta, 10220, Indonesia
Tel.: (62) 2157900800
Financial & Information Training Services
N.A.I.C.S.: 611430

PT Phillip Commodities Indonesia (1)
Level 23B Jl Jend Sudirman Kav 33A, Jakarta, 10220, Indonesia
Tel.: (62) 2157906529
Financial Investment Services
N.A.I.C.S.: 523999

PT Phillip Futures (1)
Level 23B Jl Jend Sudirman Kav 33A, Jakarta, 10220, Indonesia
Tel.: (62) 2157906525
Web Site: http://www.phillipfutures.co.id
Financial Investment Services
N.A.I.C.S.: 523999

PT Phillip Securities Indonesia (1)
Wisma Standard Chartered Bank Level 23B, Jl Jend Sudirman Kav 33A, 10220, Jakarta, Indonesia
Tel.: (62) 2157900800
Web Site: http://www.phillip.co.id
Securities Exchange
N.A.I.C.S.: 523210

Phillip Asset Management (HK) Ltd (1)
11/F United Centre 95 Queensway, Hong Kong, China (Hong Kong)
Tel.: (852) 22776698
Web Site: http://www.phillip.com.hk
Sales Range: $100-124.9 Million
Emp.: 200
Asset Management
N.A.I.C.S.: 523999

Phillip Bank Plc (1)
Ground Floor of B-Office Centre 61-64 Norodom Blvd Corner Street 306, Sangkat Boeung Keng Kang 1, Phnom Penh, Cambodia

AND PRIVATE COMPANIES — PHILOPTICS

Tel.: (855) 7796 6151
Commercial Banking Services
N.A.I.C.S.: 522110

Phillip Capital Limited (1)
Level 10 330 Collins Street, Melbourne, 3000, VIC, Australia
Tel.: (61) 386339803
Web Site: http://www.phillipcapital.com.au
Sales Range: $50-74.9 Million
Emp.: 30
Financial Management
N.A.I.C.S.: 525990

Phillip Capital Management Sdn Bhd (1)
B-2-6 Megan Avenue II, No. 12, Jalan Yap Kwan Seng, Kuala Lumpur, Malaysia
Tel.: (60) 21668099
Web Site: http://www.poems.com.my
Fund Management
N.A.I.C.S.: 525910

Phillip Capital Menkul Degerler A.S. (1)
Hurriyet Mah Dr Cemil Bengu Cad Hak is Merkezi No 2 K 6/A, Caglayan Kagithane, 34403, Istanbul, Türkiye
Tel.: (90) 2129822500
Web Site: http://www.phillipcapital.com.tr
Financial Services
N.A.I.C.S.: 523210

Phillip Commodities (HK) Ltd (1)
11/F United Centre 95 Queensway, Hong Kong, China (Hong Kong)
Tel.: (852) 22776600
Web Site: http://www.phillip.com.hk
Sales Range: $350-399.9 Million
Commodity Exchange
N.A.I.C.S.: 523210

Phillip Commodities Pte. Ltd. (1)
250 North Bridge Road 06-00 Raffles City Tower, Singapore, 179101, Singapore
Tel.: (65) 65380500
Financial Investment Services
N.A.I.C.S.: 523999

Phillip Commodities Vietnam Company Limited (1)
Room 3 01B Floor 3th Satra Dong Khoi Tower No 58 Dong Khoi, Ben Nghe Ward District 1, Ho Chi Minh City, Vietnam
Tel.: (84) 2822534358
Financial Investment Services
N.A.I.C.S.: 523999

Phillip Finance & Investment Services India Pvt. Ltd. (1)
No 1 18th Floor Urmi Estate 95 Ganpatrao Kadam Marg Lower Parel West, Mumbai, 400-013, Maharashtra, India
Tel.: (91) 2224831919
Financial Services
N.A.I.C.S.: 523999

Phillip Finance (HK) Ltd (1)
11-12/F United Centre 95 Queensway bay, Hong Kong, China (Hong Kong)
Tel.: (852) 22776600
Web Site: http://www.poems.com.hk
Sales Range: $200-249.9 Million
Emp.: 300
Licensed Moneylender
N.A.I.C.S.: 522310

Phillip Financial Advisors (HK) Ltd (1)
11-12/F United Centre 95 Queensway, Hong Kong, China (Hong Kong)
Tel.: (852) 22776600
Web Site: http://www.poems.com.hk
Financial Advisory Services
N.A.I.C.S.: 523940

Phillip Financial Advisory (Guangzhou) Co. Ltd (1)
No 3-15 Lin He Xi Road China Shine Plaza Building B Unit 1911, Guangzhou, China
Tel.: (86) 20 22371800
Financial Advisory Services
N.A.I.C.S.: 523940

Phillip Financial Advisory (Shanghai) Co. Ltd (1)
No 550 Yan An East Rd Ocean Tower, Ocean Tower Unit 2318, 200001, Shanghai, China
Tel.: (86) 2151699200

Sales Range: $50-74.9 Million
Emp.: 30
Financial Advisors
N.A.I.C.S.: 525990

Phillip Financials K.K. (1)
SK Building 344 Yamabuki-Cho, Shinjuku-ku, Tokyo, Japan
Tel.: (81) 352284832
Financial Management
N.A.I.C.S.: 525990

Phillip Futures DMCC (1)
Unit No 601 Plot No 58 White Crown Bldg Sheikh Zayed Road, Dubai, United Arab Emirates
Tel.: (971) 4 3325052
Financial Services
N.A.I.C.S.: 523210

Phillip Futures Inc (1)
141 W Jackson Blvd Ste 3050, Chicago, IL 60604
Tel.: (312) 356-9003
Web Site: http://www.phillipusa.com
Financial Services
N.A.I.C.S.: 523210
Lynette Lim (CEO)

Phillip Futures Sdn. Bhd. (1)
Block B-2-6 Megan Avenue II Jalan Yap Kwan Seng, 50450, Kuala Lumpur, Malaysia
Tel.: (60) 321621628
Web Site: http://www.phillipfutures.com.my
Online Trading Platform Services
N.A.I.C.S.: 523160

Phillip Life Assurance (Thailand) Public Co. Ltd (1)
Vorawat Building 2nd Floor 849 Silom Road, Bangrak, Bangkok, 10500, Thailand
Tel.: (66) 2 632 5000
Web Site: http://www.philliplife.com
Insurance Services
N.A.I.C.S.: 524113

Phillip Mutual Berhad (1)
B-2-7 Megan Avenue II, No 12 Jalan Yap Kwan Seng, 50450, Kuala Lumpur, Malaysia
Tel.: (60) 327830300
Web Site: http://www.poems.com.my
Sales Range: $50-74.9 Million
Emp.: 56
Trust Management
N.A.I.C.S.: 523991
Andy Lim (Mng Dir)

Phillip Private Equity Pte. Ltd. (1)
250 North Bridge Road 06-00 Raffles City Tower, Singapore, 179101, Singapore
Tel.: (65) 65336001
Financial Investment Services
N.A.I.C.S.: 523999
Jie Xiang Yong (Mgr-Investment)

Phillip Securities (HK) Ltd (1)
11/F United Center 95 Queensway, Hong Kong, China (Hong Kong)
Tel.: (852) 22776600
Web Site: http://www.phillip.com.hk
Securities Exchange
N.A.I.C.S.: 523210
Limwah Sai (Mng Dir)

Phillip Securities (Thailand) Public Co. Ltd (1)
15th Floor Vorawat Building, 849 Silom Road Bangrak, 10500, Bangkok, Thailand
Tel.: (66) 26351700
Web Site: http://www.phillip.co.th
Sales Range: $100-124.9 Million
Emp.: 200
Securities Exchange
N.A.I.C.S.: 523210
Chiam Toon Tong (Mng Dir)

Phillip Securities Japan Ltd. (1)
4-2 Nihonbashi Kabuto-cho, Chuo-ku, Tokyo, 103-0026, Japan (100%)
Tel.: (81) 336662101
Web Site: http://www.phillip.co.jp
Securities Brokerage Services
N.A.I.C.S.: 523150
Hitoshi Shimoyama (Pres & CEO)

Phillip Securities Pte. Ltd. (1)
250 North Bridge Road 06-00 Raffles City Tower, Singapore, 179101, Singapore
Tel.: (65) 33 6001

Web Site: http://www.phillip.com.sg
Securities, Fund Management, Corporate Finance, Securities Financing & Custodial Services
N.A.I.C.S.: 523150
Luke Lim (Mng Dir)

Subsidiary (Domestic):

Phillip Capital Management (S) Ltd (2)
250 North Bridge Road Unit 06-00, 06-00 Raffles City Tower, Singapore, 179101, Singapore
Tel.: (65) 383638
Web Site: http://www.phillipfunds.com
Sales Range: $50-74.9 Million
Emp.: 18
Fund Management Services
N.A.I.C.S.: 525910
Jeffrey Lee (Mng Dir & Co-Chief Investment Officer)

Phillip Financial Pte Ltd (2)
250 N Bridge Rd, #06-00 Raffles City Tower, Singapore, 179 101, Singapore
Tel.: (65) 65341458
Web Site: http://www.phillip.com.sg
Securities Financing
N.A.I.C.S.: 523150

Phillip Futures Pte Ltd (2)
250 North Bridge Road, 07-01 Raffles City Tower, Singapore, 179101, Singapore
Tel.: (65) 351155
Web Site: http://www.phillipfutures.com.sg
Sales Range: $50-74.9 Million
Holder of a Capital Markets Services License to Trade in Futures Contracts & Leveraged Foreign Exchange Granted by the Monetary Authority of Singapore
N.A.I.C.S.: 522299

Phillip Securities Research Pte Ltd (2)
250 North Bridge Road, #09-00 Raffles City Tower, 179 101, Singapore, Singapore
Tel.: (65) 65311410
Financial Advisors
N.A.I.C.S.: 523999

Phillip Trading Pte Ltd (2)
250 North Bridge Road, 07-01 Raffles City Tower, 179101, Singapore, Singapore
Tel.: (65) 65351155
Web Site: http://www.phillip.com.sg
Commodity Exchange
N.A.I.C.S.: 523210

Phillip Ventures IFSC Pvt. Ltd. (1)
Unit No 521 522 Signature Building 5th floor Block 13B Zone I Gift Sez, Gandhinagar, 382355, Gujarat, India
Tel.: (91) 7966518002
Financial Services
N.A.I.C.S.: 523999

Phillip Wealth Planner Sdn. Bhd. (1)
B-2-6 Megan Avenue II No 12 Jalan Yap Kwan Seng, 50450, Kuala Lumpur, Malaysia
Tel.: (60) 327830300
Web Site: http://www.phillipwealth.com.my
Financial Planning & Wealth Management Services
N.A.I.C.S.: 541611
Jun Jiang Pow (Dir-Wealth Plng)

PhillipCapital (India) Pvt. Ltd (1)
No 1 18th Floor Urmi Estate 95 Ganpatrao Kadam Marg Lower Parel West, Mumbai, 400013, Maharashtra, India
Tel.: (91) 22 24831919
Web Site: http://www.phillipcapital.in
Financial Services
N.A.I.C.S.: 523210

PhillipCapital Asset Management K.K. (1)
Kabuto-cho Bldg 4F 4-3 Nihonbashi Kabuto-cho, Chuo-ku, Tokyo, 103-0026, Japan
Tel.: (81) 356239077
Financial Investment Services
N.A.I.C.S.: 523999

PhillipCapital CKS Japan K.K. (1)
Kabuto-cho Bldg 4F 4-3, Nihonbashi Kabuto-cho, Tokyo, 103-0026, Japan
Tel.: (81) 3 5623 9066

Financial Services
N.A.I.C.S.: 523210

PhillipCapital UK (1)
5th Floor Candlewick House 120 Cannon Street, London, EC4N 6AS, United Kingdom
Tel.: (44) 20 7426 5968
Web Site: http://www.kingandshaxson.com
Financial Services
N.A.I.C.S.: 523210
Elizabeth Mahoney (Head-Ops)

Walker, Crips, Weddle, Beck PLC (1)
Walker Crips Group Plc. Finsbury Tower, 103-105 Bunhill Row, London, EC1 Y8LZ, United Kingdom
Tel.: (44) 2031008000
Sales Range: $100-124.9 Million
Emp.: 200
Financial Management
N.A.I.C.S.: 525990

PHILLIPS RIVER MINING LTD.
Suite 4 Level 3 South Shore Centre, 85 South Perth Esplanade, South Perth, 6151, WA, Australia
Tel.: (61) 8 6313 3800 AU
Sales Range: Less than $1 Million
Gold, Silver & Base Metals Exploration
N.A.I.C.S.: 213114
Christopher John West (Chm & Sec)

PHILOKTIMATIKI PUBLIC LTD
20 25th March Str Office 101, PO Box 27785, Engomi, 2433, Nicosia, Cyprus
Tel.: (357) 22591919
Web Site: https://www.philoktimatiki.com
Year Founded: 1989
PES—(CYP)
Sales Range: Less than $1 Million
Real Estate Development Services
N.A.I.C.S.: 531390
Yannis Kyriakopoulos (Chm)

PHILOMAXCAP AG
Marienplatz 2, 80331, Munich, Germany
Tel.: (49) 8913928890
Web Site: https://www.philomaxcap.com
Year Founded: 1997
HBD1—(DEU)
Assets: $1,181,146
Liabilities: $77,271
Net Worth: $1,103,875
Earnings: ($275,969)
Fiscal Year-end: 12/31/23
Investment Management Service
N.A.I.C.S.: 523999

PHILOPTICS
1-19 Jigotjungang-ro, Gwonseon-gu, Osan, 18102, Gyeonggi-do, Korea (South)
Tel.: (82) 312928321
Web Site: https://www.philoptics.com
Year Founded: 2008
161580—(KRS)
Rev.: $233,158,587
Assets: $248,008,343
Liabilities: $170,237,568
Net Worth: $77,770,774
Earnings: $1,919,132
Emp.: 319
Fiscal Year-end: 12/31/22
Laser Glass Cutting Equipment Mfr
N.A.I.C.S.: 333517
Kwang-Il Kim (Pres)

Subsidiaries:

Philoptics USA Inc. (1)
6595 N Oracle Rd Ste 153B, Tucson, AZ 85704
Tel.: (520) 229-6250
Web Site: https://philopticsusa.com

PHILOPTICS

Philoptics—(Continued)
Automotive 3D Inspection Services
N.A.I.C.S.: 541380

PHILTER COMMUNICATIONS INC.
167 King St E 2nd Fl, Toronto, M5A 1J4, ON, Canada
Tel.: (416) 365-0460
Sales Range: $10-24.9 Million
Emp.: 10
N.A.I.C.S.: 541810
Scott Reid (Dir-Creative)

PHILWEB CORPORATION
41F One San Miguel Avenue Bldg 1 San Miguel Avenue cor Shaw Blvd, Ortigas Center, Pasig, 1605, Philippines
Tel.: (63) 23385577
Web Site: http://www.philweb.com.ph
Year Founded: 1969
WEB—(PHI)
Rev.: $11,185,885
Assets: $26,369,383
Liabilities: $13,906,336
Net Worth: $12,463,047
Earnings: ($1,085,870)
Fiscal Year-end: 12/31/21
Internet Services
N.A.I.C.S.: 541511
Dennis O. Valdes (Pres)

PHINERGY LTD.
Derekh Hayaim 2, Kfar Saba, Israel
Tel.: (972) 89137900
Web Site: https://www.phinergy.com
PNRG—(TAE)
Rev.: $861,125
Assets: $31,401,768
Liabilities: $14,697,142
Net Worth: $16,704,626
Earnings: ($9,018,763)
Fiscal Year-end: 06/30/23
Metal Air Battery Mfr
N.A.I.C.S.: 335910
Dekal Tzidon (Co-Founder & Chief Innovation Officer)

PHINMA CORPORATION
12th Floor Phinma Plaza 39 Plaza Drive Rockwell Center, Makati, Philippines
Tel.: (63) 288700100   PH
Web Site: https://www.phinma.com.ph
Year Founded: 1957
PHN—(PHI)
Rev.: $384,107,932
Assets: $785,031,247
Liabilities: $591,831,465
Net Worth: $193,199,782
Earnings: $29,369,017
Fiscal Year-end: 12/31/23
Investment Management & Real Estate Services
N.A.I.C.S.: 531311
Rizalina P. Andrada (VP-Fin)

Subsidiaries:

Cagayan de Oro College, Inc. (1)
Max Suniel Street, Carmen, Cagayan de Oro, 9000, Misamis Oriental, Philippines
Tel.: (63) 9173765105
Web Site: https://coc.phinma.edu.ph
Educational Institution Services
N.A.I.C.S.: 611710
Ramon R. Del Rosario Jr. (Chm)

P & S Holdings Corporation (1)
9th Floor Fort legend Tower 31st Street 3rd Avenue, Fort Bonifacio, Taguig, 1634, Philippines
Tel.: (63) 29081724
Web Site: http://www.phinmacorp.com.ph
Paper Bag Mfr
N.A.I.C.S.: 322299

PHINMA Education Holdings, Inc. (1)
2F PHINMA Plaza 39 Plaza Drive Rockwell Center, Makati, 1210, Philippines
Tel.: (63) 28969537
Web Site: https://www.phinma.edu.ph
Educational Institution Services
N.A.I.C.S.: 611710
Chito B. Salazar (Pres & CEO)

PHINMA Solar Energy Corporation (1)
3rd Floor PHINMA Plaza 39 Plaza Drive Rockwell Center, Makati, Philippines
Tel.: (63) 288700482
Educational Institution Services
N.A.I.C.S.: 611710

PHINMA University of Iloilo (1)
Rizal Street, Iloilo, 5000, Philippines
Tel.: (63) 33 338 1071
Web Site: http://www.ui.phinma.edu.ph
Emp.: 300
Academic Institution
N.A.I.C.S.: 611310
Ramon R. del Rosario (Chm)

Pamantasan ng Araullo (Araullo University), Inc. (1)
Maharlika Highway Barangay Bitas, Cabanatuan, 3100, Nueva Ecija, Philippines
Tel.: (63) 444643399
Web Site: https://www.au.phinma.edu.ph
Educational Support Services
N.A.I.C.S.: 611710

PhilCement Corporation (1)
Garcia Road Mariveles Diversion Road, Mariveles, 2106, Bataan, Philippines
Tel.: (63) 288700548
Educational Institution Services
N.A.I.C.S.: 611710

Phinma Property Holdings Corporation (1)
29 Epifanio de los Santos Ave, Kalakhang Maynila, Mandaluyong, 1550, Philippines
Tel.: (63) 9175356800
Web Site: https://www.phinmaproperties.com
Property Development Services
N.A.I.C.S.: 236116

Republican College, Inc. (1)
42 18th Avenue, Cubao, Quezon City, Metro Manila, Philippines
Tel.: (63) 289121286
Educational Institution Services
N.A.I.C.S.: 611710

Rizal College of Laguna (1)
Manila S Rd, Calamba, Laguna, Philippines
Tel.: (63) 495571879
Educational Institution Services
N.A.I.C.S.: 611710

Southwestern University (1)
Urgello Street Sambag 2, Cebu, 6000, Philippines
Tel.: (63) 9178352881
Web Site: https://swu.phinma.edu.ph
Educational Institution Services
N.A.I.C.S.: 611710

St. Jude College, Inc. (1)
1338 Don Quijote Street corner Dimasalang, Sampaloc, Manila, 1008, Philippines
Tel.: (63) 253385833
Web Site: https://www.sjc.phinma.edu.ph
Educational Institution Services
N.A.I.C.S.: 611710
Raymundo P. Reyes (Pres)

Union Galvasteel Corporation (1)
Bacnotan Drive Brgy Real, Calamba, Laguna, Philippines
Tel.: (63) 39190032303
Web Site: https://www.ugc.ph
Galvanized Sheets Mfr
N.A.I.C.S.: 326299

University of Pangasinan, Inc. (1)
Arellano Street, Dagupan, 2400, Pangasinan, Philippines
Tel.: (63) 755225635
Web Site: https://up.phinma.edu.ph
Educational Programming Services
N.A.I.C.S.: 611710

PHIPPS DICKSON INTEGRIA INC.
18103 Trans-Canada Highway, Kirkland, H9J 3Z4, QC, Canada
Tel.: (514) 695-1333
Web Site: http://www.groupepdi.com
Year Founded: 2007
Sales Range: $25-49.9 Million
Emp.: 200
Printing Services
N.A.I.C.S.: 323111

Subsidiaries:

PDI Graphica (1)
4148 Portland Blvd, Sherbrooke, J1L 2Y4, QC, Canada
Tel.: (819) 562-3861
Sales Range: $25-49.9 Million
Emp.: 50
Lithographic Commercial Printing
N.A.I.C.S.: 323111

PHISON ELECTRONICS CORPORATION
No 1 Qunyi Road, Miaoli, Zhunan, 350, Taiwan
Tel.: (886) 37586896
Web Site: https://www.phison.com
Year Founded: 2000
8299—(TPE)
Rev.: $1,884,005,315
Assets: $1,875,678,829
Liabilities: $699,059,313
Net Worth: $1,176,619,517
Earnings: $168,875,528
Emp.: 4,251
Fiscal Year-end: 12/31/22
Electronic Components Mfr & Distr
N.A.I.C.S.: 334419
Khein Seng Pua (Chm)

Subsidiaries:

Super Storage Technology Corporation (1)
No 38 Keyi Street Township, Miaoli County, Zhunan, Taiwan
Tel.: (886) 37580885
Web Site: https://www.sstek.com.tw
Information Technology Services
N.A.I.C.S.: 541511

PHL SA
Chemin Departemental 138 1 Route De Darnetal, 76240, Le Mesnil-Esnard, Seine Maritime, France
Tel.: (33) 235798450
Sales Range: $25-49.9 Million
Emp.: 48
Car Dealership
N.A.I.C.S.: 441110
Alain Delaunay (Mgr & Fin)

PHM GROUP HOLDING OYJ
Takomotie 1–3, 00380, Helsinki, Finland
Tel.: (358) 102708001
Web Site: https://www.phmgroup.com
Emp.: 10,200
Real Estate Property Managers
N.A.I.C.S.: 531311
Ville Rantala (Grp CEO)

Subsidiaries:

Investis SA (1)
Route de la Chocolatiere 21, 1026, Echandens, Switzerland
Tel.: (41) 58 787 00 40
Web Site: http://www.investis-sa.ch
Real Estate Investment
N.A.I.C.S.: 531390
Stephane Bonvin (CEO)

Subsidiary (Domestic):

Aatest AG (2)
Niederlenzer Kirchweg 1, 5600, Lenzburg, Switzerland
Tel.: (41) 628913349
Web Site: https://www.aatest.ch
Material Testing Laboratory Services
N.A.I.C.S.: 541380

INTERNATIONAL PUBLIC

Analysis Lab S.A. (2)
Eckweg 8a, 2504, Biel, Switzerland
Tel.: (41) 325455167
Web Site: https://analysis-lab.ch
Material Testing Laboratory Services
N.A.I.C.S.: 541380

Hauswartprofis AG (2)
Alte Bahnhofstrasse 7, 5506, Magenwil, Switzerland
Tel.: (41) 848999777
Web Site: https://www.hauswartprofis.ch
House Maintenance Services
N.A.I.C.S.: 561720

Privera AG (2)
Worbstrasse 142, Postfach 60, 3073, Gumligen, Switzerland
Tel.: (41) 587156000
Web Site: https://www.privera.ch
Emp.: 460
Third-Party Property Management Services
N.A.I.C.S.: 531312
Andreas Stockler (Head-Co-ownership)

PHOCOMEX
16 Avenue de Rome ZI des Estroublans, 13127, Vitrolles, Bouches Du Rhone, France
Tel.: (33) 4 42 893333
Web Site: http://www.phocomex.fr
Rev.: $25,600,000
Emp.: 200
Heavy Equipment Rental & Leasing
N.A.I.C.S.: 532490
Philippe Thirion (Pres)

PHOEBUS HOLDINGS LTD.
Radcliffe House Blenheim Court, Solihull, B91 2AA, W Midlands, United Kingdom
Tel.: (44) 8456187070
Web Site: http://www.phoebus.co.uk
Year Founded: 2007
Sales Range: $50-74.9 Million
Emp.: 200
Holding Company
N.A.I.C.S.: 551112
Robert Lintonbon (CEO)

PHOENICIA FINANCE COMPANY PLC
The Phoenicia Malta The Mall, FRN 1478, Floriana, Malta
Tel.: (356) 2 122 5241
Web Site: http://www.phoeniciafinance.com
Year Founded: 1947
PH28A—(MAL)
Rev.: $1,580,731
Assets: $30,992,617
Liabilities: $30,652,104
Net Worth: $340,514
Earnings: $37,266
Fiscal Year-end: 12/31/21
Restaurant & Hotel Operator
N.A.I.C.S.: 722511
Mark D. Shaw (Chm)

PHOENITRON HOLDINGS LIMITED
Suite 710 North Tower World Finance Centre Harbour City T S T, Kowloon, China (Hong Kong)
Tel.: (852) 23771888   Ky
Web Site: http://www.phoenitron.com
8066—(HKG)
Rev.: $7,456,482
Assets: $10,808,558
Liabilities: $6,130,772
Net Worth: $4,677,786
Earnings: ($986,280)
Emp.: 139
Fiscal Year-end: 12/31/22
Holding Company
N.A.I.C.S.: 551112
Lily Wu (Chm, CEO & Compliance Officer)

PHOENIX A.M.D. INTERNATIONAL INC.
41 Butler Court, Bowmanville, L1C 4P8, ON, Canada
Tel.: (905) 427-7440
Web Site:
  https://www.phoenixamd.com
Year Founded: 1991
Rev.: $12,886,000
Emp.: 30
Home Furnishings Services
N.A.I.C.S.: 423220
Albert Marrache *(Pres)*

PHOENIX ACQUISITION LIMITED
3 Temasek Avenue Level 34 Centennial Tower, Singapore, 039190, Singapore
Tel.: (65) 31051635   VG
Year Founded: 2021
Investment Services
N.A.I.C.S.: 523999
Wayne Christopher Farmer *(Chm & CEO)*

PHOENIX APPS INC.
1258-720 King Street West Suite 200, Toronto, M5V 3S5, ON, Canada
Tel.: (239) 451-3016   NV
Year Founded: 2015
Liabilities: $145,616
Net Worth: ($145,616)
Earnings: ($94,744)
Fiscal Year-end: 12/31/18
Mobile Software Application Development Services
N.A.I.C.S.: 541511
Yi Xing Wang *(Pres, CEO, CFO & Sec)*

PHOENIX ASSET MANAGEMENT PARTNERS LTD.
64-66 Glentham Road, London, SW13 9JJ, United Kingdom
Tel.: (44) 20 8600 0100
Web Site:
  http://www.phoenixasset.com
Year Founded: 1998
Investment Management
N.A.I.C.S.: 523940
Roger Canham *(Chm)*

Subsidiaries:

Hornby PLC   (1)
Enterprise Road Westwood Industrial Estate, Margate, CT9 4JX, Kent, United Kingdom   **(71.5%)**
Tel.: (44) 1843233525
Web Site: https://www.hornby.plc.uk
Rev.: $70,997,223
Assets: $69,579,652
Liabilities: $38,885,383
Net Worth: $30,694,269
Earnings: ($15,257,511)
Emp.: 193
Fiscal Year-end: 03/31/2024
Model Trains & Entertainment Products Mfr
N.A.I.C.S.: 339930
Lyndon Charles Davies *(CEO)*

Subsidiary (Domestic):

Airfix   (2)
Westwood, Margate, CT9 4JX, Kent, United Kingdom   **(100%)**
Tel.: (44) 1843233525
Web Site: http://www.airfix.com
Sales Range: $25-49.9 Million
Emp.: 50
Mfr of Scale Plastic Model Kits
N.A.I.C.S.: 459120
Richard Ames *(CEO)*

Subsidiary (US):

Hornby America Inc.   (2)
3900-C2 Industry Dr E, Fife, WA 98424
Tel.: (877) 358-6405
Web Site: http://www.hornbyamerica.com
Sales Range: $25-49.9 Million
Emp.: 11
Toy Trains Mfr & Distr
N.A.I.C.S.: 339930

Subsidiary (Non-US):

Hornby Deutschland GmbH   (2)
Ostpreubenstrasse 13, Rodental, 96472, Bavaria, Germany
Tel.: (49) 9563 5036 0
Web Site: http://www.hornby.de
Model Railway Equipment Distr
N.A.I.C.S.: 423860

Hornby Espana S.A   (2)
C Federico Chueca S/n, 28806, Alcala de Henares, Madrid, Spain
Tel.: (34) 918796333
Web Site: http://www.electrotren.es
Electronic Toy Trains Mfr
N.A.I.C.S.: 339930

Hornby France S.A.S.   (2)
Parc D Activite De Gomberville Rue Amedee Gordini, Magny-les-Hameaux, 78114, Yvelines, France
Tel.: (33) 130527300
Web Site: http://www.hornby.fr
Emp.: 11
Home Entertainment Products Distr
N.A.I.C.S.: 423920
Olivier Lanter *(Gen Mgr)*

Subsidiary (Domestic):

Hornby Hobbies Limited   (2)
3F Gateway Innovation Way Discovery Park, Sandwich, CT13 9FF, Kent, United Kingdom
Tel.: (44) 1843 233500
Web Site: http://www.hornby.com
Sales Range: $50-74.9 Million
Emp.: 160
Toy Trains Mfr
N.A.I.C.S.: 339930
Richard Anes *(CEO)*

Subsidiary (Non-US):

Hornby Italia s.r.l.   (2)
Via Ferri 14, Borgosatollo, 25010, Brescia, Italy
Tel.: (39) 0302501493
Web Site: http://www.hornby.it
Toy & Doll Sets Distr
N.A.I.C.S.: 423920

PHOENIX BEVERAGES LIMITED
Pont Fer, Phoenix, Mauritius
Tel.: (230) 6012000
Web Site: https://phoenixbev.mu
Year Founded: 1961
MBL—(MAU)
Rev.: $228,652,217
Assets: $195,012,005
Liabilities: $64,180,062
Net Worth: $130,831,943
Earnings: $15,774,740
Emp.: 1,787
Fiscal Year-end: 06/30/23
Beverages Mfr
N.A.I.C.S.: 312120
Bernard Theys *(CEO)*

Subsidiaries:

Edena S.A.   (1)
10 rue Eugene Delouise - Riviere des Galets, 97419, La Possession, Reunion
Tel.: (262) 262421530
Web Site: https://www.edena.re
Consumer Services
N.A.I.C.S.: 624190

PHOENIX CANADA OIL COMPANY LIMITED
3219 Yonge Street, Box 307, Toronto, M4N 3S1, ON, Canada
Tel.: (416) 368-4440   Ca
Web Site: http://www.phoenix-pco.com
Year Founded: 1944
Sales Range: Less than $1 Million
Gas Exploration Services
N.A.I.C.S.: 213112
Michael D. Kindy *(CFO)*

PHOENIX CAPITAL CO., LTD.
6th Fl Marunouchi 2-chome Building 251 Marunouchi, Chiyoda-ku, Tokyo, 100-0005, Japan
Tel.: (81) 3 3215 3260
Web Site:
  http://www.phoenixcapital.co.jp
Year Founded: 2002
Investment Company
N.A.I.C.S.: 523999
Tomohiko Mimura *(Pres)*

Subsidiaries:

Endeavour United Co., Ltd.   (1)
6F Marunouchi 2-chome Building 2-5-1 Marunouchi, Chiyoda-ku, Tokyo, 100-0005, Japan
Tel.: (81) 3 6880 3379
Web Site: http://www.endeavourunited.co.jp
Alternative Investment Management Services
N.A.I.C.S.: 523940
Tomohiko Mimura *(CEO)*

Holding (Domestic):

Java Holdings Co., Ltd.   (2)
8-2 Minatojima-Nakamachi 6-chome, Chuo-ku, Kobe, 650-0046, Hyogo, Japan
Tel.: (81) 78 302 8282
Web Site: http://www.java.gr.jp
Womens Apparel Retail Operating Services
N.A.I.C.S.: 315210
Masayoshi Kitada *(Pres)*

Palemo Holdings Co., Ltd.   (2)
5-27-13 Meieki Nishikibashi Building 6th Floor, Nakamura-ku, Nagoya, 450-0002, Aichi, Japan   **(50.16%)**
Tel.: (81) 525816800
Web Site: https://www.palemo.co.jp
Rev.: $113,021,690
Assets: $59,740,340
Liabilities: $48,098,560
Net Worth: $11,641,780
Earnings: $2,913,990
Emp.: 1,585
Fiscal Year-end: 02/29/2024
Holding Company; Women's Clothing Retailer
N.A.I.C.S.: 551112

Subsidiary (Domestic):

Palemo Co., Ltd   (3)
1 Tenpo Gotanda-cho, Inazawa, 492-8680, Aichi, Japan   **(100%)**
Tel.: (81) 587 24 9771
Web Site: http://www.palemo.co.jp
Women's Clothing Retailer
N.A.I.C.S.: 458110
Kaori Yoshida *(Pres)*

Holding (Domestic):

Sunrise Inc.   (2)
2-44-10 Kami-igusa, Suginami-ku, Tokyo, 167-0023, Japan
Tel.: (81) 333970211
Web Site: http://www.sunrise-inc.co.jp
Animated Film Production Services
N.A.I.C.S.: 512110
Makoto Asanuma *(Pres & CEO)*

PHOENIX CAPITAL HOLDING AD
Todor Aleksandrov 109-115, 1303, Sofia, 1303, Bulgaria
Tel.: (359) 28051921
Web Site:
  https://www.phoenixcapital.bg
0PHA—(BUL)
Sales Range: Less than $1 Million
Holding Company
N.A.I.C.S.: 551112
Georgi Rimpev *(CEO)*

PHOENIX CONTACT GMBH & CO. KG
Flachsmarktstr 8, 32825, Munich, Germany
Tel.: (49) 5235 300
Web Site:
  http://www.phoenixcontact.com
Electrical Connection, Electronical Interface & Industrial Automation Technology Mfr
N.A.I.C.S.: 334417
Frank Stuhrenberg *(CEO & Chm)*

Subsidiaries:

Etherwan Systems Inc.   (1)
4th Floor-6 Far East Ctr, 79 Hsin Taiwu Rd Sec 1, Taipei, Taiwan   **(100%)**
Tel.: (886) 226629 8986
Web Site: http://www.etherwan.com
Computer System Design Services
N.A.I.C.S.: 541512

Innominate Security Technologies AG   (1)
Rudower Chaussee 13, 12489, Berlin, Germany
Tel.: (49) 30 921028 0
Web Site: http://www.innominate.com
Computer Peripheral Equipment Mfr
N.A.I.C.S.: 334118
Dirk Seewald *(CEO)*

PHOENIX CONTACT (Israel) Ltd.   (1)
Industrial Park Hasharon, P O B 1799, Tzoran-Kadima, 60920, Israel
Tel.: (972) 9 8915700
Electronic Equipment Distr
N.A.I.C.S.: 423690

PHOENIX CONTACT (Pty) Ltd.   (1)
36 Lyn Road Ferndale Ext 4, PO Box 916, Ferndale, 2160, Johannesburg, South Africa
Tel.: (27) 11 801 8200
Electronic Equipment Distr
N.A.I.C.S.: 423690
Peter Miuff *(Gen Mgr)*

PHOENIX CONTACT A/S   (1)
Hammerholmen 48, PO Box 1181, 2650, Hvidovre, Denmark
Tel.: (45) 36 77 44 11
Electronic Equipment Distr
N.A.I.C.S.: 423690
Brian Lumby *(Product Mgr-Interface)*

PHOENIX CONTACT AB   (1)
Linvagen 2, 14144, Huddinge, Sweden
Tel.: (46) 8 608 64 00
Electronic Equipment Distr
N.A.I.C.S.: 423690

PHOENIX CONTACT AS   (1)
Stromsveien 344, 1081, Oslo, Norway
Tel.: (47) 22 07 68 00
Electronic Equipment Distr
N.A.I.C.S.: 423690

PHOENIX CONTACT B.V.   (1)
Hengelder 56, 6902 PA, Zevenaar, Netherlands
Tel.: (31) 316 59 17 20
Electronic Equipment Distr
N.A.I.C.S.: 423690

PHOENIX CONTACT GmbH   (1)
Ada-Christen-Gasse 4, 1100, Vienna, Austria
Tel.: (43) 1 680 76
Web Site: http://www.phoenixcontact.com
Emp.: 65
Electronic Equipment Distr
N.A.I.C.S.: 423690
Lutzky Thomas *(Gen Mgr)*

PHOENIX CONTACT Ind. Com. Ltda.   (1)
Rua Francisco Corazza 20 a 100 Pq Residencial da Lapa, Sao Paulo, Brazil
Tel.: (55) 11 3871 6400
Electronic Equipment Distr
N.A.I.C.S.: 423690

PHOENIX CONTACT Ltd   (1)
21 Bell Road South Lower Hutt, Wellington, New Zealand
Tel.: (64) 4 912 2892
Electronic Equipment Distr
N.A.I.C.S.: 423690

PHOENIX CONTACT Middle East FZ LLC   (1)
Office 301 Third Floor Block 10 Dubai Inter-

PHOENIX CONTACT GMBH & CO. KG

PHOENIX CONTACT GmbH & Co. KG—(Continued)
national Academic City, PO Box 345002,
Dubai, United Arab Emirates
Tel.: (971) 4 437 0324
Electronic Equipment Distr
N.A.I.C.S.: 423690
Hesham Hammad *(Mgr-Mktg)*

PHOENIX CONTACT PTY. LTD. (1)
130-140 Parraweena Road, Miranda, 2228,
NSW, Australia
Tel.: (61) 1300 786 411
Electronic Equipment Distr
N.A.I.C.S.: 423690

PHOENIX CONTACT S.p.A. (1)
Via Bellini 39/41, Cusano Milanino, 20095,
Milan, Italy
Tel.: (39) 02 660591
Web Site: http://www.phoenixcontact.com
Electronic Equipment Distr
N.A.I.C.S.: 423690
Fabio Grandi *(Mgr-ICT)*

PHOENIX CONTACT SAS (1)
52 Boulevard de Beaubourg, Emerainville,
77436, Marne-la-Vallee, Cedex, France
Tel.: (33) 1 60 17 98 98
Electronic Equipment Distr
N.A.I.C.S.: 423690

PHOENIX CONTACT SEA Pte. Ltd. (1)
105 Eunos Avenue 3 04-00, Singapore,
409836, Singapore
Tel.: (65) 6435 9800
Electronic Equipment Distr
N.A.I.C.S.: 423690
Siang Leng Tan *(Dir-Segment)*

PHOENIX CONTACT SRL (1)
Floreasca Business Park Calea Floreasca
169 A Corp A Floor 2, Bucharest, 014459,
Romania
Tel.: (40) 21 350 88 12
Electronic Equipment Distr
N.A.I.C.S.: 423690
Natalia Toma *(Mgr-Fin)*

PHOENIX CONTACT Sp. z o.o (1)
ul Bierutowska 57-59 Budynek nr 3/A, 51-317, Wroclaw, Poland
Tel.: (48) 71 39 80 410
Emp.: 50
Electronic Equipment Distr
N.A.I.C.S.: 423690
Maciej Merek *(CEO)*

PHOENIX CONTACT Wielkopolska sp. z o.o. (1)
ul Celna 5, 64-300, Nowy Tomysl, Poland
Tel.: (48) 61 44 35 500
Electronic Equipment Distr
N.A.I.C.S.: 423690
Lidia Pietruszynska *(Project Mgr)*

PHOENIX CONTACT nv/sa (1)
Minervastraat 10-12, 1930, Zaventem, Belgium
Tel.: (32) 2 723 98 11
Web Site: http://www.phoenixcontact.be
Emp.: 40
Electronic Equipment Distr
N.A.I.C.S.: 423690
Steven Criel *(Gen Mgr)*

PHOENIX CONTACT s.a r.l. (1)
10a op Bourmicht Rue des Merovingiens,
8070, Bertrange, Luxembourg
Tel.: (352) 45 02 35 1
Electronic Equipment Distr
N.A.I.C.S.: 423690

PHOENIX CONTACT, S.A.U. (1)
Parque Tecnologico de Asturias p 16-17,
Llanera, 33428, Asturias, Spain
Tel.: (34) 985 791 636
Electronic Equipment Distr
N.A.I.C.S.: 423690

PHOENIX CONTACT, s.r.o. (1)
Mokran zahon 4, 821 04, Bratislava, Slovakia
Tel.: (421) 2 3210 1470
Electronic Equipment Distr
N.A.I.C.S.: 423690
Jozef Tomasko *(Acct Mgr)*

PHOENIX CONTACT, s.r.o. (1)
Dornych 47, 617 00, Brno, Czech Republic

Tel.: (420) 542 213 401
Electronic Equipment Distr
N.A.I.C.S.: 423690

Perle Systems Limited (1)
60 Renfrew Drive Suite 100, Markham, L3R 0E1, ON, Canada
Tel.: (905) 475-6070
Web Site: http://www.perle.com
Communications Hardware Systems Mfr
N.A.I.C.S.: 334118
Joseph Perle *(CEO)*

Subsidiary (Non-US):

Perle Systems Asia Pacific (Pte) Ltd. (2)
Level 8-09 The Metropolis Tower 2, 11
North Buona Vista Drive, Singapore,
138589, Singapore
Tel.: (65) 31 63 09 31
Communications Hardware Systems Sales
N.A.I.C.S.: 423430
Alan Carney *(Dir-Sls-Asia)*

Perle Systems Europe Limited (2)
314 Midsummer Court, Midsummer Boulevard, Milton Keynes, MK9 2UB, Bucks,
United Kingdom
Tel.: (44) 1908 847140
Communication Equipment Mfr & Distr
N.A.I.C.S.: 334118
Miriam Webster *(Mgr-Mktg)*

Perle Systems GmbH (2)
Teerhof 59, 28199, Bremen, Germany
Tel.: (49) 421 3677 198
Web Site: http://www.perlesystems.de
Sales Range: $25-49.9 Million
Emp.: 2
Communications Hardware Systems Sales
N.A.I.C.S.: 423430
Roman Wenskowski *(Mgr-Sls)*

Subsidiary (US):

Perle Systems Inc. (2)
830 Fesslers Pkwy Ste 108, Nashville, TN 37210
Tel.: (800) 467-3753
Web Site: http://www.perle.com
Communication Equipment Mfr & Distr
N.A.I.C.S.: 334118

Subsidiary (Non-US):

Perle Systems K.K. (2)
4-3-9 Nihonbashi Muromachi, Chuo-ku, Tokyo, 103-0022, Japan
Tel.: (81) 3 5413 7956
Communications Hardware Systems Sales
N.A.I.C.S.: 423430
Alan Carney *(Dir-Sls-Asia)*

Perle Systems S.A.R.L. (2)
8 rue des freres Caudron, 78147, Velizy-Villacoublay, Cedex, France
Tel.: (33) 1 86 26 55 90
Communications Hardware Systems Sales
N.A.I.C.S.: 423430

Phoenix Contact (1)
500 Avis Dr, Ann Arbor, MI 48108
Tel.: (734) 205-5000
Sales Range: $25-49.9 Million
Emp.: 25
Electrical Connection, Electronical Interface
& Industrial Automation Technology Mfr
N.A.I.C.S.: 334417
Bryan Bridges *(Engr-Software)*

Phoenix Contact (Ireland) Ltd. (1)
A4 Nutgrove Office Park Nutgrove Avenue,
Rathfarnham, Dublin, Ireland
Tel.: (353) 1 2051 300
Electronic Equipment Distr
N.A.I.C.S.: 423690

Phoenix Contact E-Mobility GmbH (1)
Hainbergstrasse 2, 32816, Schieder-Schwalenberg, Germany
Tel.: (49) 5235 343890
Web Site: http://www.phoenixcontact-emobility.com
Electronic Equipment Distr
N.A.I.C.S.: 423690
Vitalij Manin *(Project Mgr)*

Phoenix Contact Electrical Equipment Trading LLC (1)
Shop No 2 Building No 1 Plot No C14 Block
No M44, Mussafah Industrial Area, Abu Dhabi, United Arab Emirates
Tel.: (971) 2 551 1412
Electronic Equipment Distr
N.A.I.C.S.: 423690

Phoenix Contact Elektronik Tic. Ltd. Sti. (1)
Kisikli Mah Hanim Seti Sok No 38/A, B
Camlica - Uskudar, 34692, Istanbul, Turkiye
Tel.: (90) 216 481 0300
Electronic Equipment Distr
N.A.I.C.S.: 423690
Kerem Kokel *(Product Mgr)*

Phoenix Contact Kft. (1)
Csorsz utca 49-51, Budapest, 1124, Hungary
Tel.: (86) 15551000
Web Site: http://www.phoenixcontact.com
Emp.: 30
Electronic Equipment Distr
N.A.I.C.S.: 423690
Gabor Palos *(Gen Mgr)*

Phoenix Contact Oy (1)
Niittytie 11, 01300, Vantaa, Finland
Tel.: (358) 9 350 9020
Electronic Equipment Distr
N.A.I.C.S.: 423690
Mika Luokkala *(Acct Mgr)*

Phoenix Contact Power Supplies GmbH (1)
Oberes Feld 1, 33106, Paderborn, Germany
Tel.: (49) 5251 2886 0
Electronic Equipment Distr
N.A.I.C.S.: 423690
Bernd Seiffert *(Engr-Electrical)*

Phoenix Contact S.A. (1)
Ruta Panamericana Ramal Campana Km
37 500 Centro Industrial Gari, Garin, 1619,
Buenos Aires, Argentina
Tel.: (54) 3327 41 7000
Electronic Equipment Distr
N.A.I.C.S.: 423690

Phoenix Contact S.A. (1)
Sintra Business Park Edificio no 1 Industrial
da Abrunheira, 2710-089, Sintra, Portugal
Tel.: (351) 21 911 2760
Web Site: http://www.phoenixcontact.com
Emp.: 30
Electronic Equipment Distr
N.A.I.C.S.: 423690
Mitchell Bethesda *(Gen Mgr)*

Phoenix Contact S.A. de C.V. (1)
Newton No 293 - Piso 1 Colonia Polanco V
Seccion, Distrito Federal, Mexico, 11560,
Mexico
Tel.: (52) 55 1101 1380
Electronic Equipment Distr
N.A.I.C.S.: 423690

Phoenix Contact Software (1)
Room 1902 QiLai Building 889 YiShan
Road, 200233, Shanghai, China
Tel.: (86) 21 5228 9958
Software Development Services
N.A.I.C.S.: 541511

Phoenix Contact Software (1)
Yusen Shinyokohama 1-chome Bldg 6F 7-9
Shinyokohama 1-chome, Yokohama, 222-0033, Kanagawa, Japan
Tel.: (81) 45 473 7531
Software Development Services
N.A.I.C.S.: 541511

Phoenix Contact Software (1)
500 Avis Dr, Ann Arbor, MI 48108
Tel.: (734) 205-5137
Software Development Services
N.A.I.C.S.: 541511

Phoenix Contact Software GmbH (1)
Langenbruch 6, 32657, Lemgo, Germany
Tel.: (49) 5261 9373 0
Web Site: http://www.phoenixcontact.com
Software Development Services
N.A.I.C.S.: 541511
Thomas Guse *(Mgr-Sls)*

Phoenix Contact UAB (1)
Svitrigailos str 11b, 03228, Vilnius, Lithuania
Tel.: (370) 52106321
Electronic Equipment Distr

INTERNATIONAL PUBLIC

N.A.I.C.S.: 423690
Marius Manasovas *(Mgr-Bus Dev & Engr)*

Phoenix Contact d.o.o. (1)
Capraska ulica 6, 10000, Zagreb, Croatia
Tel.: (385) 1 645 8990
Web Site: http://www.phoenixcontact.hr
Emp.: 3
Electronic Equipment Distr 423690
N.A.I.C.S.: 423690
Daniel Prebeg *(Engr-Sls)*

Phoenix Contact, Inc (1)
586 Fulling Mill Rd, Middletown, PA 17057
Tel.: (717) 944-1300
Emp.: 675
Electric Equipment Mfr
N.A.I.C.S.: 334419
Jack Nehlig *(Pres)*

Phoenix Feinbau GmbH & Co KG (1)
Gustavstrasse 3, 58511, Ludenscheid, Germany
Tel.: (49) 23 51 4306 3 01 53
Electronic Equipment Distr
N.A.I.C.S.: 423690

Sutron electronic GmbH (1)
Kurze Str 29, Filderstadt, 70794, Germany
Tel.: (49) 711770980
Web Site: http://www.suetron.de
Electronic Equipment Distr
N.A.I.C.S.: 423690
Uwe Harasko *(Product Mgr)*

PHOENIX EQUITY PARTNERS LTD.
123 Victoria Street, London, SW1E 6DE, United Kingdom
Tel.: (44) 2074346999
Web Site: http://www.phoenix-equity.com
Year Founded: 2001
Investment Management Service
N.A.I.C.S.: 523940
David Burns *(Mng Partner)*

Subsidiaries:

Vivid Imaginations Ltd (1)
Ashbourne House The Guilway, Old Portsmouth Rd, Guildford, GU3 1LS, Surrey,
United Kingdom
Tel.: (44) 1483449944
Web Site:
http://www.vividimaginations.co.uk
Sales Range: $100-124.9 Million
Emp.: 100
Toy Developer & Distr
N.A.I.C.S.: 339930

PHOENIX FINANCE & INVESTMENTS LIMITED
Eunoos Ctr Level 11 52-53 Dilkusha
C/A, Dhaka, 1000, Bangladesh
Tel.: (880) 29569007
Web Site:
http://www.phoenixfinance.com.bd
Year Founded: 1995
Sales Range: $10-24.9 Million
Financial & Investment Services
N.A.I.C.S.: 523999
M. Shah Alam *(Deputy Mng Dir)*

PHOENIX FOREST PRODUCTS
110 West Beaver Creek, Richmond
Hill, L4B 1C2, ON, Canada
Tel.: (905) 764-8930
Year Founded: 1982
Rev.: $18,800,625
Emp.: 10
Lumber Whslr
N.A.I.C.S.: 423310
Michael Cohen *(Pres)*

PHOENIX GLOBAL RESOURCES PLC
6th Floor Kings House 10 Haymarket,
London, SW1Y 4BP, United Kingdom
Tel.: (44) 2039122800   UK
Web Site:
http://www.phoenixglobalresources.com

PGR—(AIM)
Rev.: $78,370,000
Assets: $516,762,000
Liabilities: $515,715,000
Net Worth: $1,047,000
Earnings: ($25,021,000)
Emp.: 80
Fiscal Year-end: 12/31/21
Oil & Gas Exploration Services
N.A.I.C.S.: 211130
Nigel Duxbury (Sec)

Subsidiaries:

PGR Operating LLC   (1)
20 Greenway Plz Ste 1075, Houston, TX 77046
Tel.: (346) 444-9230
Oil & Gas Production Services
N.A.I.C.S.: 213112

PHOENIX GROUP HOLDINGS PLC
20 Old Bailey, London, EC4M 7AN, United Kingdom
Tel.: (44) 2035679100   Ky
Web Site:
    https://www.thephoenixgroup.com
Year Founded: 2008
PHNX—(LSE)
Assets: $343,486,060,500
Liabilities: $337,238,319,000
Net Worth: $6,247,741,500
Earnings: ($1,159,933,500)
Fiscal Year-end: 12/31/22
Holding Company
N.A.I.C.S.: 551112
Andy Moss (CEO-Phoenix Life & Dir-Heritage Bus)

Subsidiaries:

Pearl Life Holdings Limited   (1)
1 Wythall Green Way, Wythall, Birmingham, B47 6WG, United Kingdom
Tel.: (44) 1733472200
Financial Management Services
N.A.I.C.S.: 523999

Phoenix Life Limited   (1)
1 Wythall Green Way, Wythall, Birmingham, B47 6WG, United Kingdom
Tel.: (44) 1512555177
Web Site: http://www.phoenixlifegroup.co.uk
Life Insurance Products & Services
N.A.I.C.S.: 524113

Subsidiary (Domestic):

Phoenix Life Assurance Limited   (2)
1 Wythall Green Way, Wythall, Birmingham, B47 6WG, United Kingdom
Tel.: (44) 1733470470
Web Site: http://www.phoenixlife.co.uk
Auto, Home, Travel & Commercial Insurance Carrier
N.A.I.C.S.: 524298

Phoenix Life Holdings Limited   (2)
1 Wythall Green Way, Wythall, Birmingham, B47 6WG, United Kingdom
Tel.: (44) 8450020366
Web Site: http://www.thephoenixgroup.com
Holding Company
N.A.I.C.S.: 551112

Subsidiary (Domestic):

Abbey Life Assurance Company Limited   (3)
100 Holdenhurst Rd, Bournemouth, BH8 8AL, Dorset, United Kingdom
Tel.: (44) 3456005405
Web Site: http://www.abbeylife.co.uk
Fire Insurance Services
N.A.I.C.S.: 524113

Subsidiary (Non-US):

Scottish Mutual International Ltd.   (3)
16 Joyce Way Park West Business Park, Dublin, 12, Ireland
Tel.: (353) 18044000
Web Site: http://www.smi.ie
Sales Range: $50-74.9 Million
Emp.: 30

Investment & Life Insurance Products & Services
N.A.I.C.S.: 524113

Phoenix Wealth Services Limited   (1)
1 Wythall Green Way, Wythall, Birmingham, B47 6WG, United Kingdom
Tel.: (44) 345 129 9993
Web Site: https://www.phoenixwealth.co.uk
Pension Claim Insurance Services
N.A.I.C.S.: 524292

ReAssure Group Plc   (1)
Windsor House Telford Centre, Telford, TF3 4NB, United Kingdom
Tel.: (44) 2074045959
Web Site:
    http://www.reassuregroupplc.co.uk
Holding Company
N.A.I.C.S.: 551112
Ian Patrick (CFO)

Subsidiary (Domestic):

Old Mutual Wealth Life Assurance Ltd.   (2)
Old Mutual House Portland Terrace, Southampton, SO14 7EJ, United Kingdom
Tel.: (44) 2380334411
Web Site: http://www.oldmutualwealth.co.uk
Long-Term Investments for Wealth Building & Wealth Management
N.A.I.C.S.: 523940
Paul Feeney (CEO)

ReAssure Limited   (2)
Windsor House, Telford Centre, Telford, TF3 4NB, Shropshire, United Kingdom
Tel.: (44) 1952292929
Web Site: http://www.reassure.co.uk
Life Assurance & Pensions
N.A.I.C.S.: 524113
Matthew Cuhls (CEO)

Subsidiary (Non-US):

Ark Life Assurance Company dac   (3)
3rd Floor College Park House Nassau Street, Dublin, D02 VY46, Ireland
Tel.: (353) 1890252364
Web Site: http://www.arklife.ie
Life Insurance Asset Management Services
N.A.I.C.S.: 524292
Ann Kelleher (CEO)

ReAssure Life Limited   (1)
Windsor House Ironmasters Way, Telford, TF3 4NB, Shropshire, United Kingdom
Tel.: (44) 195 229 2929
Web Site: https://www.reassure.co.uk
Pension Fund Claim Services
N.A.I.C.S.: 524292

SLF of Canada UK Limited   (1)
Matrix House Basing View, Basingstoke, RG21 4DZ, Hampshire, United Kingdom
Tel.: (44) 8450720223
Web Site: http://www.sloc.co.uk
Financial Management Services
N.A.I.C.S.: 523999

Standard Life Assurance Limited   (1)
30 Lothian Rd Standard Life House, Edinburgh, EH1 2DH, United Kingdom
Tel.: (44) 1312252552
Web Site: http://www.standardlife.co.uk
Sales Range: $350-399.9 Million
Emp.: 1,000
Life Insurance
N.A.I.C.S.: 524113
Susan McInnes (CEO)

Subsidiary (Non-US):

Standard Life International Limited   (2)
90 Saint Stephen's Green, Dublin, Ireland
Tel.: (353) 6397171
Web Site: http://www.standardlife.ie
Sales Range: $75-99.9 Million
Mutual Fund Management Services
N.A.I.C.S.: 523940

Subsidiary (Domestic):

Standard Life Investment Funds Limited   (2)
1 George St, Edinburgh, EH2 2LL, United Kingdom
Tel.: (44) 1312252552

Web Site: http://www.standardlife.co.uk
Mutual Fund Management Services
N.A.I.C.S.: 523940

Standard Life Investments Limited   (2)
1 George Street, Edinburgh, EH2 2LL, United Kingdom
Tel.: (44) 1312252345
Web Site:
    http://www.standardlifeinvestments.com
Sales Range: $300-349.9 Million
Emp.: 1,600
Financial Investment Services
N.A.I.C.S.: 523940
Keith Skeoch (CEO)

Subsidiary (Domestic):

Ignis Asset Management Limited   (3)
50 Bothwell Street, Glasgow, G2 6HR, United Kingdom
Tel.: (44) 1412228000
Web Site: http://www.ignisasset.com
Emp.: 250
Holding Company; Asset Management Services
N.A.I.C.S.: 551112

Subsidiary (Domestic):

Standard Life Trustee Company Limited   (2)
30 Lothian Road, Edinburgh, EH1 2DH, United Kingdom
Tel.: (44) 1312252552
Mutual Fund Management Services
N.A.I.C.S.: 523940

The Standard Life Assurance Company   (2)
30 Lothian Road, PO Box 23966, Edinburgh, EH3 1BF, United Kingdom
Tel.: (44) 1312451377
Web Site: http://www.standardlife.co.uk
General Insurance Services
N.A.I.C.S.: 524113
Barry O'Dwyer (CEO-UK & Europe)

Standard Life International Designated Activity Company   (1)
90 St Stephen's Green, Dublin, D02 F653, Ireland
Tel.: (353) 1 639 7000
Web Site: https://www.standardlife.ie
Emp.: 350
Financial Investment Services
N.A.I.C.S.: 523940

Vebnet (Holdings) Limited   (1)
5 Devonshire Square, London, EC2M 4YD, United Kingdom
Tel.: (44) 1312705500
Sales Range: $25-49.9 Million
Emp.: 3
Computer Software Development Services
N.A.I.C.S.: 541511

Subsidiary (Domestic):

Vebnet Limited   (2)
Prospect House 5-9 Thistle Street, Edinburgh, EH2 1DF, Scotland, United Kingdom
Tel.: (44) 1312705500
Web Site: http://www.vebnet.com
Sales Range: $250-299.9 Million
Emp.: 1,000
Employee Benefits Technology & Services
N.A.I.C.S.: 513210
Richard Morgan (Dir-Consultancy Svcs)

PHOENIX INSURANCE CO. LTD.
Dilkusha Commercial Area Purbani Annex Building 1st Floor, GPO Box No 3647, Dhaka, 1000, Bangladesh
Tel.: (880) 29563609
Web Site:
    https://www.phoenixinsurance.com
Year Founded: 1986
PHENIXINS—(CHT)
Rev.: $385,529
Assets: $21,237,909
Liabilities: $7,243,282
Net Worth: $13,994,627
Earnings: $761,970
Emp.: 249

Fiscal Year-end: 12/31/22
Insurance Services
N.A.I.C.S.: 524298
Mohammad Shoeb (Chm)

PHOENIX INTERNATIONAL LTD.
3rd Floor Gopala Tower 25 Rajendra Place, New Delhi, 110008, India
Tel.: (91) 1125747696
Web Site:
    https://www.phoenixindia.com
526481—(BOM)
Rev.: $3,965,506
Assets: $56,224,303
Liabilities: $15,002,937
Net Worth: $41,221,366
Earnings: $258,414
Emp.: 13
Fiscal Year-end: 03/31/23
Footwear Mfr
N.A.I.C.S.: 316210
Narender Makkar (Compliance Officer & Sec)

Subsidiaries:

Phoenix Industries Limited   (1)
Plot No 16 Survey No 328/1/1/2 Masat Industrial Area, Village Masat, Silvassa, 396230, Dadra & Nagar Haveli, India
Tel.: (91) 2240441111
Web Site: https://www.phoenixalloys.com
Metal Alloy Mfr
N.A.I.C.S.: 331110

PHOENIX LIVING SPACES PVT. LTD.
Phoenix House Plot No 1335 Road No 45 Jubilee Hills, Hyderabad, 500 033, Telangana, India
Tel.: (91) 4023553351
Web Site:
    http://www.phoenixindia.net
Real Estate Support Services
N.A.I.C.S.: 531390
Suresh Chukkapalli (Founder & Chm)

PHOENIX MECANO AG
Hofwisenstrasse 6, CH-8260, Stein am Rhein, Switzerland
Tel.: (41) 527427500
Web Site: https://www.phoenix-mecano.com
PMN—(SWX)
Rev.: $856,044,817
Assets: $663,883,431
Liabilities: $349,594,878
Net Worth: $314,288,553
Earnings: $50,172,204
Emp.: 6,722
Fiscal Year-end: 12/31/23
Motor & Generator Manufacturing
N.A.I.C.S.: 335312
Benedikt A. Goldkamp (Chm)

Subsidiaries:

AVS-Phoenix Mecano GmbH   (1)
Birostrasse 17, 1230, Vienna, Austria
Tel.: (43) 16150801
Web Site: https://www.avs-phoenix.at
Sales Range: $25-49.9 Million
Emp.: 20
Industrial Supplies Whslr
N.A.I.C.S.: 423840

BEWATEC Kommunikationstechnik GmbH   (1)
Orkotten 65, 48291, Telgte, Germany
Tel.: (49) 25 047 3370
Web Site: https://en.bewatec.de
Emp.: 100
Software Development Services
N.A.I.C.S.: 541511
Eva-Catharina Vossfanger (Head-Sales)

Bewatec Connected.Care GmbH   (1)
Alt-Moabit 98, 10559, Berlin, Germany
Tel.: (49) 25 047 3370
Emp.: 40
Software Development Services

PHOENIX MECANO AG

Phoenix Mecano AG—(Continued)
N.A.I.C.S.: 541511
Anja Ogunkoya *(Ops Mgr)*

Bond Tact Industrial Limited (1)
Rm 09 9/F New City Centre 2 Lei Yue Mun Road, Kwun Tong, Kowloon, China (Hong Kong)
Tel.: (852) 23475809
Web Site: https://www.bondtact.com
Industrial Component Mfr
N.A.I.C.S.: 334419

Bopla Gehause Systeme GmbH (1)
Borsigstrasse 17-25, 32257, Bunde, Germany
Tel.: (49) 52239690
Web Site: https://www.bopla.de
Sales Range: $75-99.9 Million
Emp.: 240
Plastics Materials & Whslr
N.A.I.C.S.: 424610

Datatel Elektronik GmbH (1)
Am Pferdemarkt 61 A, 30853, Langenhagen, Germany
Tel.: (49) 511 90 89 08
Web Site: http://www.phoenix-mecano.com
Toroidal Transformer Mfr
N.A.I.C.S.: 334416

DewertOkin AB (1)
Box 172, 351 04, Vaxjo, Sweden
Tel.: (46) 470724990
Web Site: https://www.phoenix-mecano.se
Mechanical Component Mfr & Distr
N.A.I.C.S.: 333613

DewertOkin AG (1)
Hofwisenstrasse 6, 8260, Stein am Rhein, Switzerland
Tel.: (41) 527427500
Mechanical Component Mfr & Distr
N.A.I.C.S.: 333613
M. Kleinle *(Mng Dir)*

DewertOkin GmbH (1)
Weststrasse 1, 32278, Kirchlengern, Germany
Tel.: (49) 52239790
Web Site: https://www.dewertokin.com
Sales Range: $25-49.9 Million
Emp.: 15
Medical Actuator Mfr
N.A.I.C.S.: 333995

Subsidiary (Domestic):

Dewert Antriebs- und Systemtechnik GmbH (2)
Weststrasse 1, 32278, Kirchlengern, Germany
Tel.: (49) 52239790
Web Site: http://www.dewert.de
Sales Range: $50-74.9 Million
Speed Changer Industrial High-Speed Drive & Gear Mfr
N.A.I.C.S.: 333612

Subsidiary (Non-US):

Dewert Australia Pty Ltd. (2)
64 Butler Way, Tullamarine, 3043, VIC, Australia
Tel.: (61) 39 338 5699
Web Site: https://www.phoenix-mecano.com.au
Sales Range: $50-74.9 Million
Emp.: 10
Electronic Parts & Equipment Whslr
N.A.I.C.S.: 423690

Subsidiary (US):

Dewert Motorized Systems Inc (2)
7330 Executive Way, Frederick, MD 21704-8318
Tel.: (301) 696-9366
Web Site: http://www.dewert.com
Sales Range: $25-49.9 Million
Emp.: 3
Electronic Components Mfr
N.A.I.C.S.: 334419
Shana Bell *(Gen Mgr)*

Okin America Inc. (2)
291 CDF Blvd, Shannon, MS 38868
Tel.: (662) 566-1000
Web Site: https://www.okinamerica.com
Electronic Components Distr
N.A.I.C.S.: 423690

Subsidiary (Non-US):

Okin Scandinavia AB (2)
Palvaen 8, Box 73, Ingelstad, Vaxjo, 360 44, Sweden
Tel.: (46) 470 724990
Web Site: http://www.phoenix-mecano.se
Sales Range: $25-49.9 Million
Emp.: 12
Electric Actuator Mfr
N.A.I.C.S.: 333995

DewertOkin Kft. (1)
Szent Istvan korut 24, 6000, Kecskemet, Hungary
Tel.: (36) 76515600
Web Site: https://www.dewertokin.hu
Mechanical Component Mfr & Distr
N.A.I.C.S.: 333613

DewertOkin Services GmbH (1)
Weststrasse 1, 32278, Kirchlengern, Germany
Tel.: (49) 5 223 9790
Mechanical Component Mfr & Distr
N.A.I.C.S.: 333613
M. Kersting *(Mng Dir)*

DewertOkin Technology Group Co., Ltd. (1)
No 1507 Taoyuan Road Gaozhao Street, Xiuzhou Development Zone, Jiaxing, 314031, Zhejiang, China
Tel.: (86) 4008878573
Web Site: https://en.okindewert.cn
Emp.: 846
Electro Technical Component Mfr & Distr
N.A.I.C.S.: 335999

DewertOkin do Brasil Ltda. (1)
Av Prof Alceu Maynard Araujo 185 - Ground Floor St Amaro, Sao Paulo, 04726-160, SP, Brazil
Tel.: (55) 1156434190
Web Site: https://phoenixmecano.com.br
Electromechanical Product Mfr & Distr
N.A.I.C.S.: 334419

Gotz-Udo Hartmann GmbH + Co. KG (1)
Auf der Struth 1, Gravenwiesbach, Hessen, 61279, Germany
Tel.: (49) 608696140
Web Site: http://www.hartu.de
Sales Range: $25-49.9 Million
Emp.: 40
Motor Vehicle Steering & Suspension Components Mfr
N.A.I.C.S.: 336330

HPC Sekure GmbH (1)
Im Hollbichl 7, Neuhochstadt, 82234, Wessling, Germany
Tel.: (49) 81539530450
Web Site: https://www.der-plomben-shop.de
Security Seal Distr
N.A.I.C.S.: 423840
Manfred Bergler *(Mng Dir)*

Haining My Home Mechanism Co., Ltd. (1)
Building 1 No 1 Qi'er Road, Chang'an town Nongfa District Jiaxing, Haining, Zhejiang, China
Tel.: (86) 57387500562
Mechanical Component Mfr & Distr
N.A.I.C.S.: 333613

Hartmann Codier GmbH (1)
Industriestrasse 3, 91083, Baiersdorf, Germany
Tel.: (49) 23 897 9880
Web Site: https://www.ptr-hartmann.com
Sales Range: $25-49.9 Million
Emp.: 260
Switchgear & Switchboard Apparatus Mfr
N.A.I.C.S.: 335313
Peter Scherer *(Mng Dir)*

Hartmann Electronic GmbH (1)
Motorstr 43, 70499, Stuttgart, Germany
Tel.: (49) 71 113 9890
Web Site: https://www.hartmann-electronic.com
Backplane Mfr
N.A.I.C.S.: 334412

Hartmann Elektronik GmbH (1)
Motorstr 43, 70499, Stuttgart, Germany
Tel.: (49) 71 113 9890
Web Site: https://www.hartmann-elektronik.com
Sales Range: $25-49.9 Million
Emp.: 7,000
Fabricated Wire Product Mfr
N.A.I.C.S.: 332618

Hartu Electronique S.a.r.l. (1)
Rue Annabe Lot 119-Zl, 2013, Ben Arous, Tunisia
Tel.: (216) 71387802
Sales Range: $100-124.9 Million
Emp.: 400
Electronic Components Mfr
N.A.I.C.S.: 334419

Hartu S.a.r.l. (1)
Rue Annaba Lot 119-Z l, 2013, Ben Arous, Tunisia
Tel.: (216) 71 387 802
Sales Range: $100-124.9 Million
Emp.: 40
Electronic Components Mfr
N.A.I.C.S.: 334419

IFINA Beteiligungsgesellschaft mbH (1)
Erbeweg 13-15, 32457, Porta Westfalica, Germany
Tel.: (49) 5715041114
Web Site: https://ifina.de
Sales Range: $50-74.9 Million
Emp.: 13
Financial Investment Services
N.A.I.C.S.: 523999
Martina Sochor *(Gen Mgr)*

Kundisch Beteiligungs-GmbH (1)
Steinkirchring 56, 78056, Villingen-Schwenningen, Germany
Tel.: (49) 772097610
Sales Range: $25-49.9 Million
Emp.: 35
Printed Circuit Board Mfr
N.A.I.C.S.: 334412

Kundisch GmbH + Co. KG (1)
Steinkirchring 56, 78056, Villingen-Schwenningen, Germany
Tel.: (49) 772097610
Web Site: https://www.kundisch.de
Electronic Components Mfr
N.A.I.C.S.: 334419

Lohse GmbH (1)
Heinkelstrasse 12, 76461, Muggensturm, Germany
Tel.: (49) 722282295
Electrical Wiring Supplies Mfr
N.A.I.C.S.: 335931
Ewald Sorg *(Mgr)*

Mazaka Endustriyel Urunler San Tic ve Teknoloji A.S. (1)
Ivedik OSB 1434 Cad No 5, Yenimahalle, 06374, Ankara, Turkiye
Tel.: (90) 312 394 2106
Web Site: https://www.mazaka.com.tr
Automation Equipment Mfr
N.A.I.C.S.: 335314

Mecano Components (Shanghai) Co. Ltd. (1)
No 1001 Jiaqian Road, Nanxiang Town Jiading District, Shanghai, 201802, China
Tel.: (86) 2169176590
Web Site: https://www.mecano.com.cn
Sales Range: $25-49.9 Million
Emp.: 100
Electronic Components Mfr
N.A.I.C.S.: 334419

Okin Vietnam Company Ltd. (1)
Lot H5-2 B1 Zone D9 Street, Rach Bap Industrial Park An Dien Ward, Ben Cat, Binh Duong, Vietnam
Tel.: (84) 2743591539
Mechanical Component Mfr & Distr
N.A.I.C.S.: 333613
S. Li *(Mng Dir)*

PM International B.V. (1)
Havenstraat 100, 7005AG, Doetinchem, Netherlands
Tel.: (31) 314368368
Sales Range: $25-49.9 Million
Emp.: 30
Holding Company
N.A.I.C.S.: 551112

Ger Hartman *(Gen Mgr)*

PM Komponenten B.V. (1)
Havenstraat 100, 7005 AG, Doetinchem, Netherlands
Tel.: (31) 314368368
Web Site: http://www.pmkomponenten.nl
Electrical Apparatus & Equipment Wiring Supplies & Construction Material Whslr
N.A.I.C.S.: 423610

PM Komponenten N.V. (1)
Karrewegstraat 124, 9800, Deinze, Belgium
Tel.: (32) 92207050
Web Site: http://www.pmk.be
Sales Range: $25-49.9 Million
Emp.: 19
Electrical Apparatus & Equipment Wiring Supplies & Construction Material Whslr
N.A.I.C.S.: 423610
Mark Lutin *(Mng Dir)*

PM Special Measuring Systems B.V. (1)
Euregioweg 330B, 7532 SN, Enschede, Netherlands
Tel.: (31) 537400740
Web Site: https://www.pm-sms.com
Measuring Component Mfr
N.A.I.C.S.: 334519

PTR HARTMANN GmbH (1)
Gewerbehof 38, 59368, Werne, Germany
Tel.: (49) 238979880
Web Site: https://www.ptr-hartmann.com
Sales Range: $25-49.9 Million
Emp.: 260
Electronic Components Mfr
N.A.I.C.S.: 334419

PTR Hartmann (Shaoguan) Co. Ltd. (1)
No 19 Le Yuan Road, Lechang Industrial Zone, Shaoguan, GuangDong, China
Tel.: (86) 7515566636
Web Site: https://www.ptr-hartmann.cn
Emp.: 150
Mechanical Component Mfr & Distr
N.A.I.C.S.: 333613

PTR Messtechnik Verwaltungs-GmbH (1)
Gewerbehof 38, 59368, Werne, Germany
Tel.: (49) 2389 798 80
Web Site: http://www.ptr.eu
Electronic Terminal Box Mfr
N.A.I.C.S.: 334419

Phoenix Mecano (India) Ltd. (1)
388 Bhare Taluka Mulshi Pirangut industrial area, Pune, 412 115, India
Tel.: (91) 2066745000
Web Site: https://www.phoenixmecano.co.in
Electronic Parts & Equipment Whslr
N.A.I.C.S.: 423690

Phoenix Mecano ApS (1)
Coriolisvej 1, Sonderborg, 6400, Odense, Denmark
Tel.: (45) 70702029
Web Site: http://www.phoenix-mecano.dk
Electronic Components Mfr
N.A.I.C.S.: 334419

Phoenix Mecano B.V. (1)
Havenstraat 100, 7005 AG, Doetinchem, Netherlands
Tel.: (31) 314368368
Web Site: https://www.phoenixmecano.nl
Automation Equipment Mfr
N.A.I.C.S.: 335314

Phoenix Mecano Beteiligungen AG (1)
Hofwisenstrasse 6, 8260, Stein am Rhein, Schaffhausen, Switzerland
Tel.: (41) 527427500
Web Site: http://www.phoenix-mecano.com
Financial Management Services
N.A.I.C.S.: 523999

Phoenix Mecano Comercial e Tecnica Ltda. (1)
Alameda Caiapos 657 - Tambore, 06460-110, Barueri, Sao Paulo, Brazil
Tel.: (55) 1156434190
Web Site: http://www.phoenix-mecano.com.br
Electronic Parts & Equipment Whslr
N.A.I.C.S.: 423690

AND PRIVATE COMPANIES   PHOENIX MEDIA INVESTMENT (HOLDINGS) LIMITED

Phoenix Mecano Components (Shanghai) Co. Ltd. (1)
No 1001 Jiaqian Road, Nanxiang Town Jiading District, Shanghai, 201802, China
Tel.: (86) 216 917 6590
Web Site: https://www.mecano.com.cn
Sales Range: $25-49.9 Million
Emp.: 20
Electronic Components Mfr
N.A.I.C.S.: 334419

Phoenix Mecano Digital Elektronik GmbH (1)
Am Schunkenhofe 7, Wutha-Farnroda, 99848, Erfurt, Germany
Tel.: (49) 36 921 2010
Web Site: https://www.pmde.de
Sales Range: $25-49.9 Million
Emp.: 150
Electronic Components Mfr
N.A.I.C.S.: 334419
Rolf Bormet (Mng Dir)

Phoenix Mecano ELCOM S.a.r.l. (1)
4 Rue Electronique Z I 2, Djebel El Quest, TN-1111, Zaghouan, Tunisia
Tel.: (216) 72640089
Sales Range: $200-249.9 Million
Emp.: 60
Electronic Components Mfr
N.A.I.C.S.: 334419
Carl Vieth (Gen Mgr)

Phoenix Mecano Hartu S.a.r.l. (1)
Rue Annabe Lot 119-Z I, 2013, Ben Arous, Tunisia
Tel.: (216) 71 387 802
Web Site: http://www.phoenix-mecano.com
Electronic Components Mfr
N.A.I.C.S.: 334419

Phoenix Mecano Holding Ltda. (1)
Av Prof Alceu Maynard Araujo 185, Sao Paulo, 04726-160, SP, Brazil
Tel.: (55) 1156434190
Mechanical Component Mfr & Distr
N.A.I.C.S.: 333613
D. Weber (Mng Dir)

Phoenix Mecano Hong Kong Ltd. (1)
Rm 09 9/F New City Centre 2 Lei Yue Mun Road, Kwun Tong, Kowloon, China (Hong Kong)
Tel.: (852) 27277790
Mechanical Component Mfr & Distr
N.A.I.C.S.: 333613

Phoenix Mecano Inc. (1)
7330 Executive Way, Frederick, MD 21704-8353
Tel.: (301) 696-9411
Web Site: https://www.phoenixmecano.com
Sales Range: $25-49.9 Million
Emp.: 80
Metal Coating Engraving & Allied Services to Mfr
N.A.I.C.S.: 332812
Philip Brown (Pres & CEO)

Phoenix Mecano Kecskemet KFT (1)
Szent Istvan krt 24, 6000, Kecskemet, Hungary
Tel.: (36) 76515500
Web Site: https://www.phoenix-mecano.hu
Sales Range: $450-499.9 Million
Emp.: 44
Plastics Product Mfr
N.A.I.C.S.: 326199

Phoenix Mecano Komponenten AG (1)
Hofwisenstrasse 6, Stein am Rhein, 8260, Zurich, Switzerland
Tel.: (41) 52 742 7500
Web Site: https://www.phoenix-mecano.com
Sales Range: $25-49.9 Million
Emp.: 30
Logistics Consulting Servies
N.A.I.C.S.: 541614

Phoenix Mecano Korea Co. Ltd. (1)
2020 ho Daelim Acrotel C-dong Dogok-2 dong 467-6, Kangnam-gu, 135-971, Seoul, Korea (South)
Tel.: (82) 226376922
Web Site: http://www.pmecano.co.kr
Sales Range: $25-49.9 Million
Emp.: 10
Electronic Components Mfr
N.A.I.C.S.: 334419

Phoenix Mecano Ltd. (1)
26 Faraday Road, Aylesbury, Buckingham, HP19 8RY, United Kingdom
Tel.: (44) 1296611660
Web Site: https://www.phoenix-mecano.co.uk
Sales Range: $25-49.9 Million
Emp.: 25
Electronic Parts & Equipment Whslr
N.A.I.C.S.: 423690

Phoenix Mecano Management AG (1)
Lindenstrasse 23, 8302, Kloten, Switzerland
Tel.: (41) 432554255
Sales Range: $25-49.9 Million
Emp.: 6
Management Consulting Services
N.A.I.C.S.: 541618

Phoenix Mecano N.V. (1)
Karrewegstraat 124, 9800, Deinze, Belgium
Tel.: (32) 92207050
Web Site: https://www.phoenix-mecano.be
Mechanical Component Mfr & Distr
N.A.I.C.S.: 333613

Phoenix Mecano OOO (1)
Sosnovaya Alley building 6A building 1 room 31, Zelenograd, Moscow, 124489, Russia
Tel.: (7) 4959842511
Web Site: https://www.rose-rf.ru
Mechanical Component Mfr & Distr
N.A.I.C.S.: 333613

Phoenix Mecano Plastic S.r.l. (1)
Str Europa Unita 10, 550018, Sibiu, Romania
Tel.: (40) 269253084
Web Site: https://phoenix-mecano.ro
Sales Range: $75-99.9 Million
Emp.: 311
Plastics & Fiber Glass Products Mfr
N.A.I.C.S.: 326199

Phoenix Mecano S.E. Asia Pte Ltd. (1)
53 Ubi Ave 3 03-01 Travelite Building, Singapore, 408863, Singapore
Tel.: (65) 67491611
Web Site: https://www.phoenixmecano.com.sg
Sales Range: $25-49.9 Million
Emp.: 40
Electronic Components Mfr
N.A.I.C.S.: 334419

Phoenix Mecano S.a.r.l. (1)
76 rue du Bois Galon, 94124, Fontenay-sous-Bois, France
Tel.: (33) 153995050
Web Site: https://www.phoenix-mecano.fr
Sales Range: $25-49.9 Million
Emp.: 30
Electronic Parts & Equipment Whslr
N.A.I.C.S.: 423690
Jen-Pierre Schreiber (Mng Dir)

Phoenix Mecano S.r.l. (1)
Viale Virgilio 42 B, 41123, Modena, MO, Italy
Tel.: (39) 0598779400
Web Site: https://www.phoenix-mecano.it
Emp.: 2
Electronic Components Distr
N.A.I.C.S.: 423690

Phoenix Mecano Saudi Arabia LLC (1)
Building No 3267 King Abdul Aziz Road Unit No 1, Dharan, Dammam, 3451, Saudi Arabia
Tel.: (966) 533378211
Mechanical Component Mfr & Distr
N.A.I.C.S.: 333613
S. Shukla (Mng Dir)

Phoenix Mecano Trading AG (1)
Hofwisenstrasse 6, Stein am Rhein, 8260, Switzerland
Tel.: (41) 527427522
Web Site: http://www.phoenix-mecano.com
Sales Range: $50-74.9 Million
Emp.: 10
Chemical & Products Merchant Whslr
N.A.I.C.S.: 424690

Phoenix Mecano Tunisie S.a.r.l. (1)
23 rue Jamel Abdelnacer, Borj Cedria, 2084, Tunis, Tunisia
Tel.: (216) 71430666
Sales Range: $25-49.9 Million
Emp.: 30
Motor & Generator Mfr
N.A.I.C.S.: 335312

RK Antriebs- und Handhabungs-Technik GmbH (1)
Am Klaepenberg 5, Bienenbuttel, 29553, Uelzen, Germany
Tel.: (49) 582398010
Web Site: https://www.rk-aht.de
Automation Equipment Mfr
N.A.I.C.S.: 335314
Franz Hadrian (Comml Dir)

RK Rose + Krieger GmbH (1)
Potsdamer Str 9, 32423, Minden, Germany
Tel.: (49) 57193350
Web Site: https://www.rk-rose-krieger.com
Sales Range: $50-74.9 Million
Emp.: 200
Bolt, Nut, Screw, Rivet & Washer Mfr
N.A.I.C.S.: 332722

RK Schmidt Systemtechnik GmbH (1)
Essener Strasse 8, Marpingen-Alsweiler, 66606, Sankt Wendel, Germany
Tel.: (49) 6851802550
Web Site: https://www.rk-schmidt.de
Industrial Machinery Mfr
N.A.I.C.S.: 333248
Jorg-Udo Schmidt (Mng Dir)

ROSE Systemtechnik GmbH & Co. KG. (1)
Erbeweg 13 - 15, 32457, Porta Westfalica, Germany
Tel.: (49) 333430980
Web Site: https://www.rose-systemtechnik.com
Sales Range: $25-49.9 Million
Emp.: 38
Switchgear & Switchboard Apparatus Mfr
N.A.I.C.S.: 335313

Redur GmbH + Co. KG (1)
Neue Strasse 20A, Niederzier, 52382, Duren, Germany
Tel.: (49) 24289053710
Web Site: https://www.redur.de
Instrument Transformer Mfr
N.A.I.C.S.: 335311
Lothar Schunk (Gen Mgr)

Rose Systemtechnik GmbH (1)
Erbeweg 13-15, 32457, Porta Westfalica, Germany
Tel.: (49) 57150410
Web Site: https://www.rose-systemtechnik.com
Sales Range: $150-199.9 Million
Emp.: 360
Electronic Parts & Equipment Whslr
N.A.I.C.S.: 423690

Rose Systemtechnik Middle East (FZE) (1)
Warehouse No Q4-102 SAIF Zone, PO Box 8993, Sharjah, 8993, United Arab Emirates
Tel.: (971) 65578500
Web Site: http://www.rose-pw.de
Emp.: 6
Industrial Electrical Equipment Mfr
N.A.I.C.S.: 335999

Shenzhen Elcom Trading Co. Ltd. (1)
1903 19F Dongfeng Buidung 2010 Shennan Road, Shenzhen, 518031, China
Tel.: (86) 755 837 856 74
Sales Range: $50-74.9 Million
Emp.: 7
Electronic Components Distr
N.A.I.C.S.: 423690
Eddy Lam (Gen Mgr)

Sistemas Phoenix Mecano Espana S.A. (1)
C/ Tarento N 15 Plataforma Logistica Plaza, Carretera de Logrono Km 247, 50197, Zaragoza, Spain
Tel.: (34) 976786080
Web Site: https://www.phoenix-mecano.es
Sales Range: $25-49.9 Million
Emp.: 18
Electronic Parts & Equipment Whslr
N.A.I.C.S.: 423690

W-IE-NE-R Plein & Baus GmbH (1)
Linde 18, 51399, Burscheid, Germany
Tel.: (49) 2174 67 80
Web Site: http://www.wiener-d.com
Sales Range: $25-49.9 Million
Emp.: 25
Electronic Components Mfr
N.A.I.C.S.: 334419

Wiener Power Electronics GmbH (1)
Linde 18, 51399, Burscheid, Germany
Tel.: (49) 2 174 6780
Web Site: https://www.wiener-d.com
Electro Technical Component Mfr & Distr
N.A.I.C.S.: 335999

ismet GmbH (1)
Lupfenstrasse 65, 78056, Villingen-Schwenningen, Germany
Tel.: (49) 77 209 7320
Web Site: https://www.ismet.de
Instrument Transformer Mfr
N.A.I.C.S.: 335311
Lothar Schunk (Mng Dir)

ismet Transformatory s.r.o. (1)
Beharovice 100, Beharovice, 67139, Znojmo, Czech Republic
Tel.: (420) 515252576
Web Site: https://www.ismet.de
Mechanical Component Mfr & Distr
N.A.I.C.S.: 333613

PHOENIX MEDIA INVESTMENT (HOLDINGS) LIMITED
No 2-6 Dai King Street Tai Po Industrial Estate, Tai Po, New Territories, China (Hong Kong)
Tel.: (852) 22008888
Web Site: http://www.ifeng.com
2008—(HKG)
Rev.: $382,975,958
Assets: $920,474,520
Liabilities: $355,663,035
Net Worth: $564,811,485
Earnings: ($57,073,208)
Emp.: 2,803
Fiscal Year-end: 12/31/22
Satellite Television Broadcasting Services
N.A.I.C.S.: 516120
Wei Xu (Chm)

Subsidiaries:

Phoenix Chinese News & Entertainment Limited (1)
7th Floor The Chiswick Center, 414 Chiswick High Road, London, W4 5TF, United Kingdom
Tel.: (44) 2089874320
Web Site: http://www.phoenixcne.com
Television Broadcasting Services
N.A.I.C.S.: 516120

Phoenix Metropolis Media (Beijing) Company Limited (1)
Rm 1501 No 42 Liang Ma Qiao Rd Beijing Guangming Hotel, Chaoyang District, Beijing, 100025, China
Tel.: (86) 10 84418800
LED Displays Mfr
N.A.I.C.S.: 334513

Phoenix Metropolis Media (Shanghai) Company Limited (1)
Rm 303 Garden State Ln 10, 396 S Rd Urumqi, Shanghai, China
Tel.: (86) 21 64378093
Outdoor Media Services
N.A.I.C.S.: 541910

Phoenix New Media Limited (1)
Sinolight Plaza Floor 16 No 4 Qiyang Road Wangjing, Chaoyang District, Beijing, 100102, China
Tel.: (86) 1060676000
Web Site: https://ir.ifeng.com
Rev.: $95,815,795
Assets: $243,512,406
Liabilities: $82,399,341
Net Worth: $161,113,065
Earnings: ($15,107,859)
Emp.: 743
Fiscal Year-end: 12/31/2023

PHOENIX MEDIA INVESTMENT (HOLDINGS) LIMITED — INTERNATIONAL PUBLIC

Phoenix Media Investment (Holdings) Limited—(Continued)
Internet, Mobile & TV
N.A.I.C.S.: 516120
Xiaoyan Chi (Sr VP)

Phoenix Satellite Television (U.S.) Inc. (1)
12803 Schabarum Ave, Irwindale, CA 91706
Tel.: (626) 388-1188
Web Site: http://www.ifengus.com
Sales Range: $25-49.9 Million
Emp.: 50
Television Broadcasting Services
N.A.I.C.S.: 516120
Glenn Lin (Dir-Acctg)

Phoenix Satellite Television Company Limited (1)
No 2-6 Dai King Street Tai Po Industrial Estate, Tai Po, New Territories, China (Hong Kong)
Tel.: (852) 22008888
Web Site: http://www.ifeng.com
Television Broadcasting Services
N.A.I.C.S.: 516120
Wang Ji Yan (Exec VP)

Shenzhen Phoenix Metropolis Media Company Limited (1)
No 2 21E China Phoenix Bldg Shennan Rd, Futian District, Shenzhen, China
Tel.: (86) 75582525128
Sales Range: $25-49.9 Million
Emp.: 20
Outdoor Media Services
N.A.I.C.S.: 541910

PHOENIX PETROLEUM PHILIPPINES, INC.
Phoenix Bulk Depot Lanang, Davao, 8000, Philippines
Tel.: (63) 822358888   PH
Web Site: https://www.phoenixfuels.ph
Year Founded: 2002
PNX—(PHI)
Rev.: $2,269,559,780
Assets: $1,526,520,664
Liabilities: $1,275,992,526
Net Worth: $250,528,138
Earnings: ($58,391,555)
Fiscal Year-end: 12/31/22
Refined Petroleum Products, Lubricants & Chemical Distr
N.A.I.C.S.: 424720
Dennis A. Uy (Co-Founder, Chm & Chief Strategy Officer)

Subsidiaries:

PNX Energy International Holdings, Pte. Ltd. (1)
350 Orchard Road 17-05/06 Shaw House, Singapore, 238868, Singapore
Tel.: (65) 63600780
Chemical Product Whslr
N.A.I.C.S.: 424690

Philippine FamilyMart CVS, Inc. (1)
15th-17th Floor Udenna Tower Rizal Drive Cor 4th Avenue, Bonifacio Global City, Taguig, 1634, Metro Manila, Philippines
Tel.: (63) 84034013
Web Site: http://www.familymart.com.ph
Convenience Food Distr
N.A.I.C.S.: 445131

Phoenix LPG Philippines, Inc. (1)
Matab-ang Dalipuga, Iligan, 9200, Philippines
Tel.: (63) 632251214
Liquified Petroleum Gas Bottling & Marketing
N.A.I.C.S.: 424720
Julgin Anthony G. Villanueva (Gen Mgr-Luzon)

PHOENIX PHARMAHANDEL GMBH & CO. KG
Pfingstweidstrasse 10-12, D-68199, Mannheim, Germany
Tel.: (49) 62185050   De
Web Site: http://www.phoenixgroup.eu
Rev.: $33,558,959,557
Assets: $11,651,988,625
Liabilities: $8,173,092,171
Net Worth: $3,478,896,454
Earnings: $48,533,904
Emp.: 32,009
Fiscal Year-end: 01/31/20
Holding Company; Pharmaceutical Products Whslr, Retailer & Logistics Services
N.A.I.C.S.: 551112
Helmut Fischer (Member-Exec Bd-Fin-Phoenix Grp)

Subsidiaries:

ADG Apotheken Dienstleistungsgesellschaft mb (1)
Salzachstrasse 15, 68199, Mannheim, Germany
Tel.: (49) 621 8505 520
Web Site: http://www.adg.de
Software Development Services
N.A.I.C.S.: 541511

Aesculap 98 Bt. (1)
Dozsa Eng Road 103rd, Sarmellek, Zala, Hungary
Tel.: (36) 83 355 012
Pharmaceutical Products Distr
N.A.I.C.S.: 424210

Aveszt Bt. (1)
Kossuth Lutca 4, 5440, Kunszentmarton, Hungary
Tel.: (36) 56 461 009
Pharmaceutical Products Distr
N.A.I.C.S.: 424210

Belvarosi Kigyo Patika Bt. (1)
Gabor Aron utca 3, 2100, Godollo, Hungary
Tel.: (36) 28430069
Pharmaceutical Products Distr
N.A.I.C.S.: 424210

Brocacef Groep N.V. (1)
Straatweg 2, 3604 BB, Maarssen, Netherlands
Tel.: (31) 30 245 2911
Web Site: http://www.brocacef.nl
Emp.: 5,000
Holding Company; Pharmaceutical Product Distr & Pharmacies Operator
N.A.I.C.S.: 551112
Peter de Jong (Chm)

Subsidiary (Domestic):

BENU Nederland B.V. (2)
Straatweg 2, 3604 BB, Maarssen, Netherlands   (100%)
Tel.: (31) 30 245 2581
Web Site: http://www.benuapotheek.nl
Pharmacies Operator
N.A.I.C.S.: 456110
Bart Tolhuisen (Mng Dir)

Brocacef B.V. (2)
Straatweg 2, 3604 BB, Maarssen, Netherlands
Tel.: (31) 302452911
Web Site: http://www.brocacef.nl
Pharmaceutical & Medical Supplies Distr
N.A.I.C.S.: 424210

Comifar S.p.A. (1)
Via Fratelli Di Dio 2, 20026, Novate Milanese, Milan, Italy
Tel.: (39) 02333301
Web Site: http://www.comifar.it
Pharmaceutical Products Distr
N.A.I.C.S.: 424210
Mauro Giombini (Chm-Grp)

Dosis Alfa Bt. (1)
Hunyadi ter 27, 7200, Dombovar, Hungary
Tel.: (36) 74 565 488
Pharmaceutical Products Distr
N.A.I.C.S.: 424210

Gyogyito Patikus Bt. (1)
Ola utca 1, 8900, Zalaegerszeg, Hungary
Tel.: (36) 92 511 519
Pharmaceutical Products Distr
N.A.I.C.S.: 424210

Hajnal Bt. (1)
Gesztenyes ut 56, 2091, Etyek, Hungary
Tel.: (36) 27 305 095
Pharmaceutical Products Distr
N.A.I.C.S.: 424210

Health Logistics GmbH (1)
Vichystrasse 14, 76646, Bruchsal, Germany
Tel.: (49) 7251 93 25 7 0
Web Site: http://www.health-logistics.de
Logistics Consulting Servies
N.A.I.C.S.: 541614
Clemens Homburg (Mng Dir)

Kiralyfi es Tarsa Bt. (1)
Fo utca 27, 5350, Tiszafured, Hungary   (69%)
Tel.: (36) 59 510 180
Pharmaceutical Products Distr
N.A.I.C.S.: 424210

Libra AG (1)
Akad St Mladenov No 3, Sofia, 1700, Bulgaria
Tel.: (359) 2 9658 104
Web Site: http://www.libra-ag.com
Logistics & Warehousing Services
N.A.I.C.S.: 493110

Masodik PHN 2007. Kft (1)
Koszegi ut 6, 9700, Szombathely, Hungary   (74.67%)
Tel.: (36) 94 801 230
Pharmaceutical Products Distr
N.A.I.C.S.: 424210

Mixtura 36 Bt. (1)
Koztarsasag utja 55, 8900, Zalaegerszeg, Hungary   (51%)
Tel.: (36) 92 510 113
Pharmaceutical Products Distr
N.A.I.C.S.: 424210

Mixtura Bt. (1)
Wagner utca 105, 5600, Bekescsaba, Hungary   (74.9%)
Tel.: (36) 66 450 968
Pharmaceutical Products Distr
N.A.I.C.S.: 424210

Nozsobe Bt. (1)
Jerevani ut 28, Gyor, 9028, Hungary
Tel.: (36) 96 429 677
Pharmaceutical Products Distr
N.A.I.C.S.: 424210

PHOENIX Arzneiwaren- grosshandlung Ges.m.b.H. (1)
Albert-Schweitzer-Gasse 3, 1140, Vienna, Austria
Tel.: (43) 1 491 49 0
Web Site: http://www.phoenix-gh.at
Logistics & Warehousing Services
N.A.I.C.S.: 493110
Gerhard Waberer (Mng Dir)

PHOENIX Farmacija d.d. (1)
Ozaljska ulica 95, 10000, Zagreb, Croatia
Tel.: (385) 1 3650 111
Web Site: http://www.phoenix-farmacija.hr
Emp.: 179
Pharmaceuticals Product Mfr
N.A.I.C.S.: 325412
Tomislav Kulic (Dir-Logistics & Fin)

PHOENIX Lekarensky velkoobchod a.s (1)
K perovne 945/7, Hostivar, 102 00, Prague, Czech Republic
Tel.: (420) 296808111
Web Site: http://www.phoenix.cz
Pharmaceutical Products Distr
N.A.I.C.S.: 424210

PHOENIX Medical Supplies Ltd. (1)
Rivington Road Whitehouse Industrial Estate, Runcorn, WA7 3DJ, Cheshire, United Kingdom
Tel.: (44) 1928 750500
Web Site: http://www.phoenixmedical.co.uk
Emp.: 6,440
Pharmaceutical Products Distr
N.A.I.C.S.: 424210
Paul Smith (CEO)

PHOENIX Pharma DOOEL (1)
Jadranska magistrala 31, 1000, Skopje, North Macedonia
Tel.: (389) 22786060
Web Site: http://www.phoenixpharma.com.mk
Pharmaceutical Products Distr
N.A.I.C.S.: 424210

PHOENIX Pharma Polska Sp. z o.o. (1)
ul Oplotek 26, 01-940, Warsaw, Poland
Tel.: (48) 225960900
Web Site: http://www.pharma.com.pl
Pharmaceutical Products Distr
N.A.I.C.S.: 424210
Izabela Kubisiak (Chm & Mng Dir)

PHOENIX Pharma S.A.S. (1)
ZA des bouvets 1 rue des Bouvets, 94015, Creteil, cedex, France
Tel.: (33) 145176300
Web Site: http://www.phoenixpharma.fr
Pharmaceutical Products Distr
N.A.I.C.S.: 424210

PHOENIX Pharma Zrt. (1)
Keleti M u 19, 2151, Fot, Hungary
Tel.: (36) 27889100
Web Site: http://www.phoenix.hu
Pharmaceutical Products Distr
N.A.I.C.S.: 424210

PHOENIX Pharma d.o.o. (1)
Bore Stankovica 2, 11000, Belgrade, Serbia
Tel.: (381) 113538100
Web Site: http://www.phoenixpharma.rs
Pharmaceutical Products Distr
N.A.I.C.S.: 424210
Aleksandar Zecevic (Mgr-IT)

PLUS PHARMACIE SA (1)
26 boulevard paul Vaillant Couturier, Ivry-sur-Seine, 94200, France
Tel.: (33) 1 45 21 00 47
Web Site: http://www.phoenixpharma.fr
Pharmaceutical Products Distr
N.A.I.C.S.: 424210

Pharmacies BENU S.A. (1)
Rue du Center 6, PO Box 108, 1752, Villars-sur-Glane, Switzerland
Tel.: (41) 264097700
Web Site: http://www.benu.ch
Pharmaceutical Products Distr
N.A.I.C.S.: 424210

Tamro Oyj (1)
Tamrotalo Rajatorpantie 41 B, 01640, Vantaa, Finland   (100%)
Tel.: (358) 2044511
Web Site: http://www.tamro.fi
Sales Range: $1-4.9 Billion
Emp.: 470
Pharmaceuticals Whslr
N.A.I.C.S.: 423450
Hanne Bergholm (Head-Mktg & Comm)

Subsidiary (Non-US):

Apokjeden A/S (2)
Skarersletta 55, 1473, Lorenskog, Norway
Tel.: (47) 21611000
Web Site: http://www.apotek1.no
Sales Range: $50-74.9 Million
Emp.: 300
Whslr of Pharmaceuticals
N.A.I.C.S.: 424210
Oyvind Winther (Mng-Dir)

Nomeco A/S (2)
Borgmester Christiansens Gade 40, Copenhagen, 1790, Denmark   (100%)
Tel.: (45) 36454536
Web Site: http://www.nomeco.dk
Sales Range: $200-249.9 Million
Emp.: 750
Pharmaceuticals Whslr
N.A.I.C.S.: 423450
Per Hansen (Dir-Logistics)

Tamro AB (2)
Importgatan 18, Gothenburg, 42246, Sweden   (100%)
Tel.: (46) 317677500
Web Site: http://www.tamro.com
Sales Range: $125-149.9 Million
Emp.: 300
Whslr of Pharmaceuticals
N.A.I.C.S.: 424210
Lars Schenatz (Mng Dir)

Branch (Domestic):

Tamro AB (3)
Formvagen 7, PO Box 3000, S 906 02, Umea, Sweden   (100%)
Tel.: (46) 902072200
Web Site: http://www.tamro.com

AND PRIVATE COMPANIES

Sales Range: $25-49.9 Million
Emp.: 45
Whslr of Pharmaceuticals
N.A.I.C.S.: 424210
Lars Schenatz *(Mng Dir)*

Group (Non-US):

Tamro Baltics (2)
Parnu mnt 501 Laagri, 76401, Harjumaa, Estonia
Tel.: (372) 650 3600
Web Site: http://www.tamrobaltics.com
Regional Managing Office; Pharmaceutical Distr & Logistics Svcs
N.A.I.C.S.: 551114
Leon Jankelevitsh *(Mng Dir & Member-Mgmt Bd)*

Subsidiary (Domestic):

Tamro Eesti OU (3)
Parnu mnt 501 Laagri, 76401, Harjumaa, Estonia
Tel.: (372) 650 3600
Web Site: http://www.tamrobaltics.com
Sales Range: $25-49.9 Million
Emp.: 70
Pharmaceutical Distr & Logistics Services
N.A.I.C.S.: 424210

Subsidiary (Non-US):

Tamro SIA (3)
Noliktavu Street 5 Dreilini, Stopinu, Riga, LV-2130, Latvia (100%)
Tel.: (371) 67067800
Web Site: http://www.tamrobaltics.com
Sales Range: $25-49.9 Million
Emp.: 100
Retailer & Wholesaler of Pharmaceuticals
N.A.I.C.S.: 424210

UAB Tamro (3)
9 ojo Forto g 70, 48179, Kaunas, Lithuania
Tel.: (370) 837401099
Web Site: http://www.tamrobaltics.com
Sales Range: $25-49.9 Million
Emp.: 80
Whslr of Pharmaceuticals
N.A.I.C.S.: 424210

Veszter Kft. (1)
Vandor Sandor utca 1, 1181, Budapest, Hungary (74%)
Tel.: (36) 1 290 8631
Pharmaceutical Products Distr
N.A.I.C.S.: 424210

Zalar Patika Kft. (1)
Zalar Jozsef utca 9, 3300, Eger, Hungary (74.67%)
Tel.: (36) 36 310 191
Pharmaceutical Products Distr
N.A.I.C.S.: 424210

transmed Transport GmbH (1)
Dr-Gessler-Str 37, 93051, Regensburg, Germany
Tel.: (49) 941 92041 0
Web Site: http://www.transmed.de
Emp.: 350
Logistics Consulting Servies
N.A.I.C.S.: 541614
Marco Grasmeder *(Mng Dir)*

PHOENIX PLUS CORP.
Tel.: (60) 81200914 NV
Web Site: http://www.phoenixpluscorp.com
Year Founded: 2018
PXPC—(OTCIQ)
Rev.: $1,232,326
Assets: $921,631
Liabilities: $244,571
Net Worth: $677,060
Earnings: ($437,781)
Fiscal Year-end: 07/31/24
Technical Consultancy Services
N.A.I.C.S.: 541690
Chong Chow Lee *(Pres, CEO, Treas & Sec)*

PHOENIX POWER CO SAOG
MGM 3RD Floor Building 4 Office number 305 B, PO Box 96, Qurum, 102, Muscat, Oman
Tel.: (968) 22009960
Web Site: https://www.phoenixpoweroman.com
Year Founded: 2011
PHPC—(MUS)
Rev.: $985,082,848
Assets: $4,021,213,514
Liabilities: $2,653,884,577
Net Worth: $1,367,328,936
Earnings: $113,628,824
Fiscal Year-end: 12/31/21
Electric Power Distribution Services
N.A.I.C.S.: 221118
Paul Atkinson *(CEO)*

PHOENIX RISING COMPANIES, INC.
Level 11 Tower 4 Puchong Financial Corporate Centre Jalan Puteri 1/2, Bandar Puteri, 47100, Puchong, Malaysia
Tel.: (60) 386000313 NV
Web Site: http://www.phoenix-cos.com
Year Founded: 2012
PRCX—(OTCIQ)
Rev.: $13,430,991
Assets: $19,284,954
Liabilities: $14,178,664
Net Worth: $5,106,290
Earnings: $10,350,864
Emp.: 20
Fiscal Year-end: 12/31/21
Online Discounted Travel-Related Services
N.A.I.C.S.: 513199
Ding-Shin Chang *(Chm, Pres & CEO)*

PHOENIX SHIPPING (WUHAN) CO., LTD.
12th Floor Huijiang Building No 39 Minquan Road, Jianghan District, Wuhan, 430021, China
Tel.: (86) 2266312981
Year Founded: 2006
000520—(SSE)
Rev.: $146,306,628
Assets: $108,509,544
Liabilities: $30,770,064
Net Worth: $77,739,480
Earnings: $5,086,692
Fiscal Year-end: 12/31/22
Cargo Transportation Services
N.A.I.C.S.: 483111

PHOENIX SILICON INTERNATIONAL CORP.
No 6 Lixing Rd, East Dist, Hsinchu, 300094, Taiwan
Tel.: (886) 35641888
Web Site: https://www.psi.com.tw
Year Founded: 1997
8028—(TAI)
Rev.: $108,823,044
Assets: $300,336,887
Liabilities: $171,639,615
Net Worth: $128,697,271
Earnings: $10,202,884
Emp.: 442
Fiscal Year-end: 12/31/23
Wafer Equipment Mfr
N.A.I.C.S.: 333242
Mike Liang *(Chm & Pres)*

Subsidiaries:

Phoenix Battery Co., Ltd. (1)
Building H No 1 Sec 6 Zhonghua Rd, Hsinchu, 300104, Taiwan
Tel.: (886) 35183690
Web Site: https://www.phoenixbattery.com.tw
Battery Mfr
N.A.I.C.S.: 335910
Mike Yang *(Chm)*

PHOENIX SOLAR AG
Hirschbergstrasse 4, Sulzemoos, 85254, Dachau, Germany
Tel.: (49) 8135938000 De
Web Site: http://www.phoenixsolar.com
PS4—(DEU)
Sales Range: $125-149.9 Million
Emp.: 111
Mfr of Solar Power Systems
N.A.I.C.S.: 334419
Thomas Zinser *(Vice Chm-Supervisory Bd)*

Subsidiaries:

Phoenix Solar E.P.E. (1)
104 Pentelis Ave & 1 Metamorphoseos St, Halandri, 15234, Greece
Tel.: (30) 2106838386
Web Site: http://www.phoneixsolar.gr
Sales Range: $25-49.9 Million
Emp.: 11
Solar Energy Equipment Services
N.A.I.C.S.: 333414
Christos Protogeropoulos *(Gen Mgr)*

Phoenix Solar Pty Ltd. (1)
Level 5 23 Peel St, Adelaide, 5000, South Australia, Australia
Tel.: (61) 874209936
Sales Range: $25-49.9 Million
Emp.: 3
Solar Energy Equipment Mfr & Services
N.A.I.C.S.: 335999

Phoenix Solar S.L. (1)
Teide 4, Madrid, 28703, Spain
Tel.: (34) 916587857
Web Site: http://www.phoenixsolar.es
Sales Range: $25-49.9 Million
Emp.: 6
Photovoltaic Systems Mfr
N.A.I.C.S.: 334413
Irene Dieguez *(Gen Mgr)*

Phoenix Solar S.R.L. (1)
Viale Santi Pietro e Palo 50, Rome, 00144, Italy
Tel.: (39) 065924358
Web Site: http://www.phoenixsolar.it
Sales Range: $25-49.9 Million
Emp.: 4
Solar Energy Equipment Services
N.A.I.C.S.: 333414

PHOENIX SPREE DEUTSCHLAND LIMITED
12 Castle Street, Saint Helier, Jersey
Tel.: (44) 1534847000 JE
Web Site: https://www.phoenixspree.com
Year Founded: 2007
PSDL—(LSE)
Rev.: $34,950,987
Assets: $902,653,091
Liabilities: $498,281,351
Net Worth: $404,371,739
Earnings: ($125,722,470)
Fiscal Year-end: 12/31/23
Real Estate Investment Services
N.A.I.C.S.: 531390
Robert Hingley *(Chm)*

PHOENIX TOURS INTERNATIONAL, INC.
4F & 5F No 25 Sec 1 Chang-an East Road, Zhongshan District, Taipei, 104, Taiwan
Tel.: (886) 225370000
Web Site: https://www.travel.com.tw
5706—(TAI)
Rev.: $72,031,457
Assets: $103,050,783
Liabilities: $55,123,743
Net Worth: $47,927,040
Earnings: $5,829,262
Fiscal Year-end: 12/31/23
Travel Agency Services
N.A.I.C.S.: 561510
Wei-Yao Chang *(Chm)*

PHOENIX TOWNSHIP LTD.
Durga Bhavan Hede Centre Tonca, Panaji, 403 001, Goa, India
Tel.: (91) 8326642724
Web Site: https://www.hbgindia.com
537839—(BOM)
Rev.: $3,145,315
Assets: $5,876,398
Liabilities: $2,948,756
Net Worth: $2,927,642
Earnings: $81,446
Emp.: 156
Fiscal Year-end: 03/31/23
Hotel Operator
N.A.I.C.S.: 721110
Prafulla Rajaram Hede *(Chm)*

PHOENIX TREE HOLDINGS LIMITED
Room 212 Chao Yang Shou Fu 8 Chao Yang Men Nei Street, Dongcheng District, Beijing, 100010, China
Tel.: (86) 105 717 6925 Ky
Year Founded: 2015
DNK—(NYSE)
Rev.: $1,020,172,493
Assets: $1,288,689,197
Liabilities: $1,234,447,714
Net Worth: $54,241,483
Earnings: ($491,524,459)
Emp.: 4,506
Fiscal Year-end: 12/31/19
Holding Company
N.A.I.C.S.: 551112
Derek Boyang Shen *(Chm)*

PHOENIXBIO CO., LTD.
3-4-1 Kagamiyama, Higashi-hiroshima, 739-0046, Japan
Tel.: (81) 824310016
Web Site: https://www.phoenixbio.co.jp
Year Founded: 2002
6190—(TKS)
Rev.: $11,336,150
Assets: $17,946,150
Liabilities: $6,067,980
Net Worth: $11,878,170
Earnings: $171,860
Emp.: 70
Fiscal Year-end: 03/31/24
Life Science Research Services
N.A.I.C.S.: 541715
Kenji Kuramoto *(Chm)*

Subsidiaries:

KMT Hepatech Inc. (1)
2011-94 Street NW, Edmonton, T6N 1H1, AB, Canada
Tel.: (780) 695-7400
Web Site: https://www.kmthepatech.com
Research & Development Services
N.A.I.C.S.: 541715
Norman Kneteman *(Co-Founder & Pres)*

KMT Hepatech, Inc. (1)
11421 Saskatchewan Drive, Edmonton, T6G 2M9, AB, Canada
Tel.: (780) 641-1919
Web Site: http://kmthepatech.com
Vivo Research Services
N.A.I.C.S.: 541714
Norman Kneteman *(Pres)*

PhoenixBio USA Corporation (1)
65 Broadway Ste 605, New York, NY 10006
Tel.: (212) 379-6411
Research & Development Services
N.A.I.C.S.: 541715

PHOL DHANYA PUBLIC COMPANY LIMITED
1/11 Village No 3 Lam Luk Ka Road Lat Sawai Subdistrict, Lamlukka, Pathumthani, 12150, Thailand
Tel.: (66) 27910111
Web Site: https://www.pdgth.com
Year Founded: 1961

PHOL DHANYA PUBLIC COMPANY LIMITED

Phol Dhanya Public Company Limited—(Continued)
PHOL—(THA)
Rev.: $28,357,829
Assets: $18,781,753
Liabilities: $7,852,410
Net Worth: $10,929,344
Earnings: $1,743,352
Fiscal Year-end: 12/31/23
Protective Equipment & Safety Products Distr
N.A.I.C.S.: 423450
Drekachidd Chungcharoen *(Chm)*

Subsidiaries:

Phol Water Company Limited (1)
1/11 Village No 3 Lam Luk Ka Road, Lat Sawai Subdistrict Lam Luk Ka District, Pathumthani, 12150, Thailand
Tel.: (66) 27910111
Web Site: www.pholwater.com
Waste Water Treatment Services
N.A.I.C.S.: 562211

PHONE WEB SA
88 rue de Courcelles, 75008, Paris, France
Tel.: (33) 156793210
Web Site: https://phoneweb.fr
MLPHW—(EUR)
Sales Range: $1-9.9 Million
Tele Marketing & Customer Care Services
N.A.I.C.S.: 561422
Mohamed Boukerdenna *(Chm & CEO)*

PHONG PHU PHARMACEUTICAL JSC
Lot 12 No 8 Street Tan Tao Industrial Zone Tan Tao A Ward, Binh Tan district, Ho Chi Minh City, Vietnam
Tel.: (84) 837547997
Web Site: https://duocphongphu.com.vn
Year Founded: 2000
PPP—(HNX)
Rev.: $5,331,571
Assets: $6,241,201
Liabilities: $1,577,871
Net Worth: $4,663,330
Earnings: $674,111
Fiscal Year-end: 12/31/21
Pharmaceuticals Mfr
N.A.I.C.S.: 325412
Thai Nha Ngon *(Vice Chm-Mgmt Bd & Gen Dir)*

PHOSCO LTD
Level 4 100 Albert Road, South Melbourne, 3205, VIC, Australia
Tel.: (61) 396927222
Web Site: https://www.phosco.com.au
Year Founded: 2009
PHO—(ASX)
Rev.: $6,727
Assets: $523,950
Liabilities: $6,313,186
Net Worth: ($5,789,235)
Earnings: ($1,320,270)
Fiscal Year-end: 06/30/24
Gold Mining Services
N.A.I.C.S.: 212220
Robin Widdup *(Founder & Chm)*

PHOSLOCK ENVIRONMENTAL TECHNOLOGIES LIMITED
Suite 3 Level 12 75 Elizabeth Street, Sydney, 2000, NSW, Australia
Tel.: (61) 391100002 AU
Web Site: https://petwatersolutions.com
Rev.: $12,259,234
Assets: $15,941,768
Liabilities: $4,970,503
Net Worth: $10,971,265
Earnings: $84,313
Emp.: 15
Fiscal Year-end: 06/30/18
Water Technologies & Solutions For Metals
N.A.I.C.S.: 327992
Cherry Wang *(CFO)*

Subsidiaries:

Phoslock (Beijing) Ecological Engineering Technology Co., Ltd. (1)
Room 902 Tower T6 Han's Plaza, Yizhuang Economic and Technological Development Zone, Beijing, China
Tel.: (86) 1067862208
Web Site: http://www.phoslock.cn
Waste Treatment Services
N.A.I.C.S.: 221310

PHOSPHORE SARL
10 Grand Rue, Logelheim Alsace, 68280, Strasbourg, France
Tel.: (33) 0389410052
Web Site: http://www.groupe-phosphore.com
Artisan & Craftsman Management Consulting Services
N.A.I.C.S.: 541618
Christophe Le Bihan *(Grp Comms Mgr)*

Subsidiaries:

Groupe Rivalis SA (1)
10 Grand Rue, Logelheim, 68280, Colmar, France (100%)
Tel.: (33) 389410052
Web Site: http://www.rivalis.fr
Artisan & Craftsman Management Consulting Services
N.A.I.C.S.: 541618
Damien Valdan *(Deputy CEO)*

PHOTOCAT A/S
Langebjerg 4, 4000, Roskilde, Denmark
Tel.: (45) 70225055
Web Site: https://www.photocat.net
Year Founded: 2009
PCAT—(OMX)
Rev.: $2,147,206
Assets: $3,271,916
Liabilities: $1,222,259
Net Worth: $2,049,658
Earnings: ($432,077)
Emp.: 9
Fiscal Year-end: 12/31/22
Finishing Material Distr
N.A.I.C.S.: 444180
Mette Therkildsen *(Chm)*

PHOTOCURE ASA
Hoffsveien 4, 0275, Oslo, Norway
Tel.: (47) 22062210 NO
Web Site: https://www.photocure.com
0IMT—(LSE)
Rev.: $36,313,689
Assets: $66,417,329
Liabilities: $23,674,580
Net Worth: $42,742,749
Earnings: ($6,637,447)
Emp.: 105
Fiscal Year-end: 12/31/22
Pharmaceutical & Medical Device Mfr
N.A.I.C.S.: 325412
Grete Hogstad *(VP-Strategic Mktg & Bus Dev-Global)*

PHOTOGLOB AG
Industriestrasse Ost 10, 4614, Hagendorf, Switzerland
Tel.: (41) 622092300
Web Site: http://www.photoglob.ch
Year Founded: 1889
Sales Range: $25-49.9 Million
Emp.: 80
Postcards Publisher; Travel Literature Distr
N.A.I.C.S.: 513199

PHOTOLINK CREATIVE GROUP
Old School House Thirsk St, Manchester, M12 6PN, United Kingdom
Tel.: (44) 1612737551
Web Site: http://www.photolink.co.uk
Sales Range: $10-24.9 Million
Emp.: 110
N.A.I.C.S.: 541810
David Walter *(CEO)*

PHOTOMYNE LTD.
8 Hakishon St, Bene Beraq, Israel
Tel.: (972) 35518114
Web Site: https://www.photomyne.com
Year Founded: 2014
PHTM—(TAE)
Rev.: $13,326,000
Assets: $17,833,000
Liabilities: $4,954,000
Net Worth: $12,879,000
Earnings: $2,503,000
Fiscal Year-end: 12/31/23
Custom Computer Programming Services
N.A.I.C.S.: 541511

PHOTON CAPITAL ADVISORS LIMITED
90A Road No 9 Jubliee Hills, Hyderabad, 500 033, India
Tel.: (91) 4040062950
Web Site: https://www.pcalindia.com
509084—(BOM)
Rev.: $24,723
Assets: $1,230,969
Liabilities: $3,885
Net Worth: $1,227,085
Earnings: ($44,662)
Emp.: 4
Fiscal Year-end: 03/31/23
Financial Services
N.A.I.C.S.: 523999
Tejaswy Nandury *(Exec Dir)*

PHOTON ENERGY N.V.
Barbara Strozzilaan 201, 1083 HN, Amsterdam, Netherlands
Tel.: (31) 202402570 NI
Web Site: https://www.photonenergy.com
Year Founded: 2010
PEN—(PRA)
Rev.: $45,170,982
Assets: $241,494,092
Liabilities: $178,193,059
Net Worth: $63,301,033
Earnings: ($7,901,268)
Emp.: 141
Fiscal Year-end: 12/31/21
Electricity Power Generation Services
N.A.I.C.S.: 237130
Georg Hotar *(Co-Founder & CEO)*

Subsidiaries:

Photon Energy Australia Pty. Ltd. (1)
Level 5 219-241 Cleveland Street, Redfern, 2016, NSW, Australia
Tel.: (61) 280213383
Web Site: https://www.photonenergy.com.au
Solar Battery Storage Services
N.A.I.C.S.: 221118

Photon Energy Operations CZ s.r.o. (1)
Karolinska 661/4, 186 00, Prague, Czech Republic
Tel.: (420) 277002910
Solar Battery Storage Services
N.A.I.C.S.: 221118

Photon Energy Operations SK s.r.o. (1)
Vajnorska 134/B, 831 04, Bratislava, Slovakia
Tel.: (421) 901702159
Solar Battery Storage Services
N.A.I.C.S.: 221118

INTERNATIONAL PUBLIC

Photon Water Technology s.r.o. (1)
Generala Svobody 25/108 Liberec XII, Stare Pavlovice, 460 01, Liberec, Czech Republic
Tel.: (420) 704296693
Web Site: https://www.photonwater.com
Renewable Energy Services
N.A.I.C.S.: 221111
Petr Kvapil *(Mng Dir)*

PHOTON INFOTECH PRIVATE LIMITED
1/124 Mt Ponamalee Rd BLS IT Pk Shivaji Grdn, 6th Blk Fidelity Bldg, Chennai, 600089, India
Tel.: (91) 4430618000
Web Site: http://www.photoninfotech.com
Sales Range: $200-249.9 Million
Emp.: 1,108
IT Consulting Services
N.A.I.C.S.: 541690
Srinivasanian Balasubramanian *(Chm & CEO)*

PHOTOQUIP INDIA LTD.
10116 Salt pan Division Vidyalankar College Road, Antop Hill Wadala East, Mumbai, 400037, India
Tel.: (91) 2224110110
Web Site: https://www.photoquip.com
526588—(BOM)
Rev.: $1,430,070
Assets: $2,268,701
Liabilities: $1,370,613
Net Worth: $898,088
Earnings: ($491,973)
Emp.: 13
Fiscal Year-end: 03/31/23
Photographic Equipment Mfr & Distr
N.A.I.C.S.: 333310
Jayant Purshottam Soni *(Chm & Mng Dir)*

PHOTOVOLTECH N.V.
Industrial Area West Grijpen, Grijpenlaan 18, 3300, Tienen, Belgium
Tel.: (32) 16805850
Web Site: http://www.photovoltech.be
Sales Range: $50-74.9 Million
Emp.: 200
Mfr of Silicon Solar Cells
N.A.I.C.S.: 334419

PHOTOZOU HOLDINGS, INC.
4-30-4F Yotsuya Shinjuku-ku, Tokyo, 160-0004, Japan
Year Founded: 2014
PTZH—(OTCIQ)
Rev.: $73,901
Assets: $156,413
Liabilities: $824,223
Net Worth: ($667,810)
Earnings: ($263,837)
Emp.: 1
Fiscal Year-end: 11/30/23
Investment Services
N.A.I.C.S.: 523999

PHP VENTURES ACQUISITION CORP.
CT 10-06 Level 10 Corporate Tower Subang Square Jalan SS15/4G, 47500, Subang Jaya, Selangor, Malaysia
Tel.: (60) 358888485 DE
Year Founded: 2021
PPHP—(NASDAQ)
Rev.: $802,841
Assets: $59,854,796
Liabilities: $65,033,008
Net Worth: $5,178,212
Earnings: ($1,848,123)
Fiscal Year-end: 12/31/22
Investment Services
N.A.I.C.S.: 523999

Marcus Choo Yeow Ngoh *(Chm & CEO)*

PHRIKOLAT CHEMISCHE ER-ZEUGNISSE GMBH
Dammstrasse 70-80, D 53721, Siegburg, Germany
Tel.: (49) 224161041 De
Web Site: http://www.phrikolat.com
Year Founded: 1956
Sales Range: $700-749.9 Million
Emp.: 20
Industrial Chemicals; Specialty Chemicals; Oil Field Chemicals, Specialties for Horizontal Drilling
N.A.I.C.S.: 325998
Irmhild Lauter *(Mng Dir)*

Subsidiaries:

Phrikolat Drilling Specialties GmbH (1)
Reisertstrasse 24, 53773, Hennef, Germany (100%)
Tel.: (49) 2242933920
Web Site: http://www.phrikolat.de
Sales Range: $1-9.9 Million
Emp.: 14
Horizontal Drilling Specialty Chemical Distr
N.A.I.C.S.: 424690

Phrikolat Drilling Specialties GmbH (1)
Reisertstr 24, 53773, Hennef, Germany (100%)
Tel.: (49) 2242 933 92 0
Web Site: http://www.phrikolat.com
Sales Range: $25-49.9 Million
Drilling Chemicals Mfr
N.A.I.C.S.: 424690

PHSC PLC
The Old Church 31 Rochester Rd, Aylesbury, ME20 7PR, Kent, United Kingdom
Tel.: (44) 1622717700
Web Site: https://www.phsc.plc.uk
PHSC—(AIM)
Rev.: $4,268,841
Assets: $5,388,489
Liabilities: $870,645
Net Worth: $4,517,845
Earnings: $302,079
Emp.: 34
Fiscal Year-end: 03/31/23
Health Safety Products Consultancy
N.A.I.C.S.: 525120
Nicola C. Coote *(Co-Founder, Deputy Chm & Deputy CEO)*

Subsidiaries:

Inspection Services UK Limited (1)
The Old Church 31 Rochester Rd, Aylesford, ME20 7PR, Kent, United Kingdom
Tel.: (44) 1622715353
Web Site: http://www.safeinspect.co.uk
Sales Range: $25-49.9 Million
Emp.: 2
Equipment Inspection Services
N.A.I.C.S.: 334519
Stephen King *(Mng Dir)*

Personnel Health & Safety Consultants Ltd. (1)
The Old Church 31 Rochester Rd, Aylesford, ME20 7PR, Kent, United Kingdom
Tel.: (44) 1622717700
Web Site: http://www.phsc.co.uk
Sales Range: $10-24.9 Million
Emp.: 12
Health & Safety Consulting Services
N.A.I.C.S.: 621999
Stephen King *(CEO)*

Quality Leisure Management Limited (1)
6 Blotts Barn Brooks Road, Raunds, Northampton, NN9 6NS, Northamptonshire, United Kingdom
Tel.: (44) 1933626444
Web Site: http://www.qlmconsulting.co.uk

Sales Range: $25-49.9 Million
Emp.: 9
Leisure Management Services
N.A.I.C.S.: 541611
Peter Mills *(Founder)*

RSA Environmental Health Ltd. (1)
Unit 6 Blotts Barn Brooks Road, Wellingborough, NN9 6NS, Northamptonshire, United Kingdom
Tel.: (44) 1933626444
Web Site: http://www.rsaenvironmentalhealth.co.uk
Sales Range: $25-49.9 Million
Emp.: 5
Health & Safety Consulting Services
N.A.I.C.S.: 813920
Justin Smith *(Mng Dir)*

Division (Domestic):

In House (2)
Unit 6 Blotts Barn Brooks Road, Raunds, Wellingborough, NN9 6NS, Northants, United Kingdom
Tel.: (44) 1933626444
Web Site: http://www.inhousesafety.co.uk
Sales Range: $25-49.9 Million
Emp.: 4
Food & Health Safety Consulting Services
N.A.I.C.S.: 541690
Hazel Bourne *(Bus Mgr)*

PHU HOA TAN WATER SUPPLY JSC
86 Tan Hung Ward 12, District 5, Ho Chi Minh City, Vietnam
Tel.: (84) 8 9552650
Web Site: http://www.phuwaco.com.vn
Water Supply
N.A.I.C.S.: 221310
Dang Van Nguyen *(CTO)*

PHU NHUAN JEWELRY JOINT STOCK COMPANY
170E Phan Dang Luu, Ward 3 Phu Nhuan District, Ho Chi Minh City, Vietnam
Tel.: (84) 2839951703
Web Site: https://www.pnj.com.vn
Year Founded: 1988
PNJ—(HOSE)
Sales Range: Less than $1 Million
Jewelry Mfr & Distr
N.A.I.C.S.: 339910
Cao Thi Ngoc Dung *(Chm)*

Subsidiaries:

CAO Fashion Company Limited (1)
1170E Phan Dang Luu Ward 3, Ho Chi Minh City, Phu Nhuan District, Vietnam
Tel.: (84) 8 3990 0776
Web Site: http://www.caofinejewellery.com
Jewelry Mfr & Sales
N.A.I.C.S.: 339910

Dai Viet Energy Joint Stock Company (1)
Block A 87/1 Street 5 Vinh Lock Industrial Centre, Ho Chi Minh City, Vietnam
Tel.: (84) 8 3765 6565
Web Site: http://www.nangluongdaiviet.com
Energy Services
N.A.I.C.S.: 221122

Dong A Land Joint Stock Company (1)
43R/12 Ho Van Hue Ward 9, Phu Nhuan District, Ho Chi Minh City, 7000, Vietnam
Tel.: (84) 8 3845 6858
Web Site: http://www.diaocdonga.com
Real Estate Development Services
N.A.I.C.S.: 531390

PNJ Jewelry Production & Trading Company Limited (1)
No 23 Street 14, Ward 5 Go Vap District, Ho Chi Minh City, Vietnam
Tel.: (84) 2835886678
Web Site: http://export.pnj.com.vn
Jewelry Mfr & Distr
N.A.I.C.S.: 339910

PNJ Laboratory Limited Company (1)
205 Phan Dang Luu Ward 1, Phu Nhuan District, Ho Chi Minh City, Vietnam
Tel.: (84) 3 3844 6199
Web Site: http://www.pnj.com.vn
Laboratory Testing Services
N.A.I.C.S.: 541380

Saigon Fuel Corporation (1)
146E Nguyen DinhChinh Street, District 1, Ho Chi Minh City, Vietnam
Tel.: (84) 839979292
Web Site: http://www.sfc.com.vn
Petroleum Distr
N.A.I.C.S.: 324199

PHU PHONG PRODUCTION - TRADE - SERVICE - STOCK COMPANY
04th Block B Road Tan Tao Industrial Zone, Binh Tan Dist, Ho Chi Minh City, Vietnam
Tel.: (84) 8 7505932
Web Site: http://www.phuphong.com
Glass Products Mfr
N.A.I.C.S.: 327212
Trong Tuan Luong *(Deputy Chm)*

PHU TAI JOINT STOCK COMPANY
278 Nguyen Thi Dinh St, Nguyen Van Cu Ward, Quy Nhon, Binh Dinh, Vietnam
Tel.: (84) 563847668
Web Site: https://www.phutai.com.vn
Year Founded: 1994
PTB—(HOSE)
Rev.: $688,652,200
Assets: $523,829,800
Liabilities: $247,703,700
Net Worth: $276,126,100
Earnings: $48,729,200
Emp.: 7,408
Fiscal Year-end: 12/31/22
Furniture Mfr
N.A.I.C.S.: 337211

Subsidiaries:

Binh Dinh Toyota Co., Ltd. (1)
No 278A Nguyen Thi Dinh Street, Nguyen Van Cu Ward, Quy Nhon, Binh Dinh, Vietnam
Tel.: (84) 2563946717
Car Repair Services
N.A.I.C.S.: 811198

Granite Manufacturing Co., Ltd. - Granida (1)
No 10 Tan Lap 1, Hiep Phu Ward District 9, Ho Chi Minh City, Vietnam
Tel.: (84) 838960451
Construction Machinery Mfr
N.A.I.C.S.: 333120

Phu Tai Dong Nai Company Limited (1)
Lot 14, Tam Phuoc Industrial Park Tam Phuoc Commune, Bien Hoa, Dong Nai, Vietnam
Tel.: (84) 6133512837
Wooden Furniture Mfr
N.A.I.C.S.: 337211

Phu Tai Ninh Thuan Stone JSC (1)
No 08 Trieu Quang Phuc street, My Hai Ward, Phan Rang-Thap Cham, Ninh Thuan, Vietnam
Tel.: (84) 2563847668
Construction Machinery Mfr
N.A.I.C.S.: 333120

Phu Tai Real Estates Company Limited (1)
2nd Floor Phu Tai Building 278 Nguyen Dinh Street, Nguyen Van Cu Ward, Quy Nhon, Binh Dinh, Vietnam
Tel.: (84) 2563847668
Real Estate Development Services
N.A.I.C.S.: 531390

Phu Yen Construction Materials JSC (1)
Lot A7 A8 A17 A18, An Phu Industrial Zone An Phu Commune, Tuy Hoa, Phu Yen, Vietnam
Tel.: (84) 2573846462
Construction Machinery Mfr
N.A.I.C.S.: 333120

Phutai Quartz Stone Company Limited (1)
B112-114, Nhon Trach Textile Industrial Zone Hiep Phuoc Townlet, Nhon Trach, Dong Nai, Vietnam
Tel.: (84) 2513685881
Web Site: http://www.phutaiquartz.com
Compound Stone Mfr
N.A.I.C.S.: 327991

Thanh Chau Phu Yen Granite Company Limited (1)
Lanh Truong Hamlet, Dong Xuan, Xuan Lanh, Phu Yen, Vietnam
Tel.: (84) 2573679282
Construction Machinery Mfr
N.A.I.C.S.: 333120

Tuan Dat Minerals Co., Ltd. (1)
Tel.: (84) 2563847668
Construction Machinery Mfr
N.A.I.C.S.: 333120

Universal Stone JSC (1)
194/6 Nguyen Trong Tuyen, Phu Nhuan District, Ho Chi Minh City, Vietnam
Tel.: (84) 839998989
Construction Machinery Mfr
N.A.I.C.S.: 333120

Vina G7 Joint Stock Company (1)
Tam Phuoc 1 Long Khanh 3 Hamlet, Industrial Cluster Tam Phuoc Commune, Bien Hoa, Dong Nai, Vietnam
Tel.: (84) 613513634
Emp.: 500
Wooden Furniture Mfr
N.A.I.C.S.: 337211

PHU THINH - NHA BE GARMENT JSC
No 13A Tong Van Tran street ward 5, district 11, Ho Chi Minh City, Vietnam
Tel.: (84) 8 8650561
Web Site: http://www.phuthinhnb.com
Rev.: $48,400
Assets: $2,480,221
Liabilities: $1,215,161
Net Worth: $1,265,061
Earnings: $26,230
Fiscal Year-end: 12/31/18
Garment Mfr & Whslr
N.A.I.C.S.: 315250

PHUC HUNG HOLDINGS CONSTRUCTION JOINT STOCK COMPANY
1st Floor Tower A The Light Building To Huu, Nam Tu Liem, Hanoi, Vietnam
Tel.: (84) 2466645618
Web Site: https://www.phuchung.com.vn
Year Founded: 2001
Sales Range: $75-99.9 Million
Civil Construction Services
N.A.I.C.S.: 237990
Tran Huy Tuong *(Gen Dir)*

PHUC THINH DESIGN CONSTRUCTION TRADING CORPORATION
361 Le Trong Tan Street Son Ky Ward, Tan Phu District, Ho Chi Minh City, Vietnam
Tel.: (84) 2838116823
Web Site: https://www.phucthinh.com.vn
PTD—(HNX)
Rev.: $19,074,117
Assets: $9,892,450
Liabilities: $7,622,000
Net Worth: $2,270,450
Earnings: $125,990
Fiscal Year-end: 12/31/23
Construction Services

Phuc Thinh Design Construction Trading Corporation—(Continued)
N.A.I.C.S.: 236220

PHUMELELA GAMING AND LEISURE LIMITED
Turffontein Racecourse 14 Turf Club Street Turffontein, Johannesburg, 2190, South Africa
Tel.: (27) 116811500
Web Site: http://www.phumelela.com
PHM—(JSE)
Sales Range: $100-124.9 Million
Horse Racing
N.A.I.C.S.: 711219
Freda Moloi (Sec & Head-CSI)

Subsidiaries:

East Cape Racing (Pty) Limited (1)
Dryfontein Rd, Port Elizabeth, 6390, Eastern Cape, South Africa
Tel.: (27) 413721859
Web Site: http://www.phumelela.com
Sales Range: $25-49.9 Million
Emp.: 50
Horse Racecourse Operation Services
N.A.I.C.S.: 711212

PHUOC HOA RUBBER JOINT STOCK COMPANY
Phuoc Hoa Commune, Phu Giao District, Ho Chi Minh City, Binh Duong, Vietnam
Tel.: (84) 6503657106
Web Site: https://phr.vn
PHR—(HOSE)
Rev.: $55,662,189
Assets: $253,813,918
Liabilities: $96,667,313
Net Worth: $157,146,606
Earnings: $27,245,066
Emp.: 2,187
Fiscal Year-end: 12/31/23
Rubber Products Mfr
N.A.I.C.S.: 326299
Phi Hung Le (Chm)

PHUONG NAM CULTURAL JOINT STOCK CORPORATION
940 3 Thang 2 Street, Ward 15 11 District, Ho Chi Minh City, Vietnam
Tel.: (84) 88663447
Web Site: https://www.pnc.com.vn
Year Founded: 1982
PNC—(HOSE)
Rev.: $26,917,155
Assets: $21,742,146
Liabilities: $14,233,694
Net Worth: $7,508,453
Earnings: $691,336
Emp.: 913
Fiscal Year-end: 12/31/23
Movie Production Services
N.A.I.C.S.: 512110

PHUONG NAM EDUCATION INVESTMENT & DEVELOPMENT JSC
No 231 Nguyen Van Cu Street Ward 4, District 5, Ho Chi Minh City, Vietnam
Tel.: (84) 838306501
Web Site: http://www.sachhoctro.com.vn
SED—(HNX)
Rev.: $90,736,900
Assets: $49,138,400
Liabilities: $21,451,200
Net Worth: $27,687,200
Earnings: $3,791,200
Fiscal Year-end: 12/31/22
Magazine Publishing Services
N.A.I.C.S.: 513120
Anh Lan Pham (Chief Acctg Officer)

PHX ENERGY SERVICES CORP.
Tel.: (403) 543-4466 AB
Web Site: https://www.phxtech.com
Year Founded: 1985
PHX—(TSX)
Rev.: $182,845,808
Assets: $169,395,485
Liabilities: $66,108,993
Net Worth: $103,286,492
Earnings: ($6,079,221)
Emp.: 438
Fiscal Year-end: 12/31/20
Oil & Gas Exploration Services
N.A.I.C.S.: 211120
John M. Hooks (Chm & CEO)

Subsidiaries:

Phoenix Technology Services Inc. (1)
Suite 1400 250-2nd Street SW, Calgary, T2P 0C1, AB, Canada
Tel.: (403) 543-4466
Web Site: https://www.phxtech.com
Sales Range: $50-74.9 Million
Oil & Gas Field Drilling Services
N.A.I.C.S.: 213111

Phoenix Technology Services LP (1)
1600 215 9th Avenue SW, Calgary, T2P 1K3, AB, Canada
Tel.: (403) 543-4466
Web Site: https://www.phxtech.com
Sales Range: $50-74.9 Million
Emp.: 60
Oil & Gas Field Drilling Services
N.A.I.C.S.: 213111
Cameron Ritchie (Sr VP)

RMS Systems Inc. (1)
Suite 1400 250-2nd, Calgary, T2P 0C1, AB, Canada
Tel.: (403) 717-9695
Web Site: http://www.streamservices.com
Sales Range: $1-9.9 Million
Software Development Services
N.A.I.C.S.: 541511

Subsidiary (US):

RigManager Inc. (2)
10700 Hammerly Blvd, Houston, TX 77043
Tel.: (713) 467-0009
Software Development Services
N.A.I.C.S.: 541511
Bob Hooks (Gen Mgr)

PHYNOVA GROUP LTD.
16 Blenheim Office Park, Long Hanborough, 0X29 8LN, Oxon, United Kingdom
Tel.: (44) 1993880700 UK
Web Site: http://www.phynova.com
Year Founded: 2002
Sales Range: Less than $1 Million
Emp.: 8
Anti-Infective & Anti-Cancer Pharmaceutical & Drug Mfr
N.A.I.C.S.: 325412
Robert Miller (CEO)

PHYSICAL PROPERTY HOLDINGS INC.
23/F AIA Tower No 183 Electric Road, North Point, China (Hong Kong)
Tel.: (852) 2917 0000 DE
Year Founded: 1988
Sales Range: Less than $1 Million
Emp.: 3
Fitness & Spa Facilities Owner & Operator
N.A.I.C.S.: 713940
Ngai Keung Luk (Chm & CEO)

PHYSIK INSTRUMENTE (PI) GMBH & CO. KG
Auf der Romerstr 1, D-76228, Karlsruhe, Germany
Tel.: (49) 721 4846 0
Web Site: http://www.physikinstrumente.com
Sales Range: $100-124.9 Million
Emp.: 750
NanoPositioning, MicroPositioning & Piezo Technology Services
N.A.I.C.S.: 334513
Brian Lula (Chm, Pres & CEO)

Subsidiaries:

ACS Motion Control Ltd. (1)
5 HaTnufa Street Yokneam Illit, Migdal Ha'Emeq, 2066717, Israel
Tel.: (972) 46546440
Web Site: http://www.acsmotioncontrol.com
Motion Control Devices & Equipment Mfr
N.A.I.C.S.: 334513
Alexander Ivanovski (System Engr)

PI (Physik Instrumente) L.P. (1)
5420 Trabuco Rd Ste 100, Irvine, CA 92620
Tel.: (949) 679-9191
Web Site: http://www.pi-usa.us
Emp.: 5
NanoPositioning, MicroPositioning & Piezo Technology Services
N.A.I.C.S.: 334513
William Culpi (Chief Engineer)

PI (Physik Instrumente) Ltd. (1)
Trent House University Way, Cranfield Technology Park, Cranfield, MK43 0AN, Bedford, United Kingdom
Tel.: (44) 1234 756 360
Web Site: http://www.physikinstrumente.co.uk
Emp.: 12
NanoPositioning, MicroPositioning & Piezo Technology Services
N.A.I.C.S.: 334513

PI (Physik Instrumente) Singapore LLP (1)
20 Sin Ming Lane, #05-60 Midview City, Singapore, 573968, Singapore
Tel.: (65) 665 98400
NanoPositioning, MicroPositioning & Piezo Technology Services
N.A.I.C.S.: 334513

PI Benelux B.V. (1)
Hertog Hendrikstraat 7a, 5492 BA, Sint-Oedenrode, Netherlands
Tel.: (31) 499375375
Measuring & Controlling Equipment Distr
N.A.I.C.S.: 423830
Dick Moerman (Mng Dir)

PI Ceramic GmbH (1)
Lindenstrasse, D-07589, Munchenbernsdorf, Germany
Tel.: (49) 36604 882 0
NanoPositioning, MicroPositioning & Piezo Technology Services
N.A.I.C.S.: 334513

PI France S.A.S. (1)
244 Bis Avenue Marx Dormoy, 92120, Montrouge, France
Tel.: (33) 1 55 22 60 00
NanoPositioning, MicroPositioning & Piezo Technology Services
N.A.I.C.S.: 334513

PI Korea Ltd (1)
Cheonho-Daero 1111, Gangdong-gu, Seoul, 134-814, Korea (South)
Tel.: (82) 2475 0060
NanoPositioning, MicroPositioning & Piezo Technology Services
N.A.I.C.S.: 334513

PI miCos GmbH (1)
Freiburger Strasse 30, D-79427, Eschbach, Germany
Tel.: (49) 7634 5057 0
NanoPositioning, MicroPositioning & Piezo Technology Services
N.A.I.C.S.: 334513

PI-Japan Co., Ltd. (1)
2-38-5 Akebono-cho, Tachikawa, 190-0012, Tokyo, Japan
Tel.: (81) 42 526 7300
Web Site: http://www.pi-japan.jp
Emp.: 13
Nano-Positioning Micro-Positioning & Piezo Technology Services
N.A.I.C.S.: 334513

Karl Spanner (Pres & CEO)

Physik Instrumente (PI Shanghai) Co., Ltd. (1)
Building No 7-106, Longdong Avenue 3000, 201203, Shanghai, China
Tel.: (86) 21 518 792 98
NanoPositioning, MicroPositioning & Piezo Technology Services
N.A.I.C.S.: 334513

Physik Instrumente (PI) S. r. l. (1)
Via G Marconi 28, I-20091, Bresso, Italy
Tel.: (39) 02 665 011 01
NanoPositioning, MicroPositioning & Piezo Technology Services
N.A.I.C.S.: 334513

Physik Instrumente (PI) Taiwan Ltd. (1)
M01 2F No 97-100 Sec 2 Dunhua S Road, Taipei, 10601, Taiwan
Tel.: (886) 921089036
Web Site: http://www.pi-taiwan.com.tw
Measuring & Controlling Equipment Distr
N.A.I.C.S.: 423830

PHYSIOMICS PLC
Bee House 140 Eastern Avenue, Milton Park, Abingdon, OX14 4SB, Oxfordshire, United Kingdom
Tel.: (44) 1235841575
Web Site: https://www.physiomics.co.uk
PYC—(AIM)
Rev.: $1,036,006
Assets: $1,397,984
Liabilities: $187,230
Net Worth: $1,210,754
Earnings: ($312,050)
Fiscal Year-end: 06/30/22
Pharmaceutical Mathematical Modeling Services
N.A.I.C.S.: 541715
Paul B. Harper (Chm)

PHYSIOTHERM GMBH
Physiothermstrasse 1, Thaur, 6065, Austria
Tel.: (43) 5223 54777 AT
Web Site: http://www.physiotherm.com
Year Founded: 1996
Sales Range: $10-24.9 Million
Low-Temperature Infrared Sauna Mfr & Distr
N.A.I.C.S.: 321992
Josef Gunsch (CEO)

Subsidiaries:

Manufactur fur Glas und Spiegel GmbH (1)
Emailwerkstrasse 25, 9523, Villach, Austria
Tel.: (43) 4242 41671 0
Web Site: http://www.neher.at
Sales Range: $1-9.9 Million
Emp.: 35
Shower Frame, Enclosure & Other Related Products Mfr
N.A.I.C.S.: 332999

PHYSTECH II JSC
4 Microdistrict 73, Oblast Region, 130000, Aktau, Mangistau, Kazakhstan
Tel.: (7) 292336374
PHYS—(KAZ)
Sales Range: Less than $1 Million
Geological Exploration Services
N.A.I.C.S.: 213114
Bayzhaliyev Ernar (CEO & Gen Dir)

PHYTO CHEM INDIA LTD
8-3-229/23 First Floor Thaherville Yousufguda Checkpost, Hyderabad, 500 045, Telangana, India
Tel.: (91) 4023557712
Web Site: https://www.phytochemindia.com
524808—(BOM)
Rev.: $3,227,444

Assets: $4,798,633
Liabilities: $3,526,251
Net Worth: $1,272,382
Earnings: $26,665
Emp.: 77
Fiscal Year-end: 03/31/23
Chemicals Agrochemicals Pesticides
N.A.I.C.S.: 424910
Nayudamma Yarlagadda *(CEO & Mng Dir)*

PHZ BALTONA S.A.
ul. Marcina Flisa 4, 02-234, Warsaw, Poland
Tel.: (48) 22 519 20 00
Web Site: http://www.baltona.pl
Rev.: $129,072,540
Assets: $77,458,022
Liabilities: $51,746,221
Net Worth: $25,711,801
Earnings: $1,152,931
Fiscal Year-end: 12/31/18
Duty Free Stores
N.A.I.C.S.: 455219
Magdalena Przybysz *(Chm-Supervisory Bd)*

Subsidiaries:

BH Travel Retail Poland Sp. z o.o (1)
Ul Marcina Flisa 4, 02-247, Warsaw, Poland
Tel.: (48) 225192000
Web Site: http://www.bisnode.pl
Food & Beverage Whslr
N.A.I.C.S.: 424490
Karina Brazhko *(Mgr-Store)*

Baltona Shipchandlers Sp. z o.o. (1)
ul Finska 1, 72-602, Swinoujscie, Poland
Tel.: (48) 913216265
Web Site: http://www.baltona-ship.pl
Seagoing Crew Distr
N.A.I.C.S.: 483111

PI INDUSTRIES LTD.
5th Floor Vipul Square B Block, Sushant Lok Phase-1, Gurgaon, 122009, Haryana, India
Tel.: (91) 1246790000
Web Site: https://www.piindustries.com
Year Founded: 1946
523642—(BOM)
Rev.: $797,434,207
Assets: $1,016,689,647
Liabilities: $153,611,894
Net Worth: $863,077,753
Earnings: $147,413,225
Emp.: 3,384
Fiscal Year-end: 03/31/23
Fine Chemicals, Agricultural Chemicals & Pharmaceutical Intermediates Mfr
N.A.I.C.S.: 325998
Mayank Singhal *(Vice Chm, CEO & Mng Dir)*

Subsidiaries:

Archimica S.p.A. (1)
Viale Milano 86, 26900, Lodi, LO, Italy
Tel.: (39) 037149021
Web Site: http://www.archimica.com
Pharmaceutical Ingredient & Fine Chemical Product Mfr
N.A.I.C.S.: 325199

Isagro (ASIA) Agrochemicals Pvt, Ltd. (1)
Unit 1 Ground 2 & 3 Floor Brady Gladys Plaza, 1/447 Senapati Bapat Marg Lowe, Mumbai, 400013, India (100%)
Tel.: (91) 2266955656
Web Site: http://www.isagroasia.com
Sales Range: $25-49.9 Million
Emp.: 270
Pesticide & Agricultural Chemical Mfr
N.A.I.C.S.: 325320
Chinmoy Bhattacharya *(Mgr-Sls)*

Jivagro Ltd. (1)
Tel.: (91) 2262665600
Web Site: https://www.jivagro.com
Insecticides Mfr
N.A.I.C.S.: 325320
Rajnish Sarna *(Chm)*

PI Health Sciences Ltd. (1)
Udaisagar Road, Udaipur, 313001, Rajasthan, India
Tel.: (91) 2946651100
Web Site: https://pihealthsciences.com
Pharmaceuticals Mfr
N.A.I.C.S.: 325412

PI Japan Co.Ltd. (1)
Tohan Bldg 4F 2-11-4 Uchi-Kanda, Chiyoda-ku, Tokyo, 101-0047, Japan
Tel.: (81) 352564431
Sales Range: $25-49.9 Million
Emp.: 5
Agrochemical Mfr
N.A.I.C.S.: 325320

Plant Health Care plc (1)
1 Scott Place 2 Hardman Street, Manchester, M3 3AA, United Kingdom
Tel.: (44) 1494775111
Web Site: https://www.planthealthcare.com
Rev.: $8,432,000
Assets: $18,210,000
Liabilities: $3,852,000
Net Worth: $14,358,000
Earnings: ($6,304,000)
Emp.: 46
Fiscal Year-end: 12/31/2021
Organic Fertilizer Mfr
N.A.I.C.S.: 325314
Christopher G. J. Richards *(CEO)*

PI MLINPRODUKT AD ADA
Veliki put bb, 24430, Ada, Serbia
Tel.: (381) 24853444
MPRO—(BEL)
Sales Range: Less than $1 Million
Wheat Producer
N.A.I.C.S.: 111140

PIA CORPORATION
Higashi 1-2-20 Shibuya First Tower, Shibuya-ku, Tokyo, 150-0011, Japan
Tel.: (81) 357745200   JP
Web Site: https://www.pia.jp
Year Founded: 1972
4337—(TKS)
Rev.: $261,670,070
Assets: $596,691,310
Liabilities: $560,045,470
Net Worth: $36,645,840
Earnings: $7,389,980
Emp.: 448
Fiscal Year-end: 03/31/24
Digital Content, Event Ticketing & Publishing
N.A.I.C.S.: 561599
Hiroshi Yanai *(Pres & CEO)*

PIALA, INC.
13/F Yebisu Garden Place Tower 4-20-3 Ebisu, Shibuya-ku, Tokyo, 150-6013, Japan
Tel.: (81) 368200730
Web Site: https://www.piala.co.jp
Year Founded: 2004
7044—(TKS)
Rev.: $64,263,760
Assets: $25,119,870
Liabilities: $20,993,490
Net Worth: $4,126,380
Earnings: ($6,962,380)
Fiscal Year-end: 12/31/23
Digital Marketing Services
N.A.I.C.S.: 541870
Shinkichi Negoro *(Mng Dir)*

Subsidiaries:

Channel J (Thailand) Co., Ltd. (1)
24 Prime Building 10 Fl Unit A Sukhumvit 21 Asoke Rd, Klongtoey-Nua Wattana, Bangkok, 10110, Thailand
Tel.: (66) 22581720
Web Site: https://www.channelj.co.th
Food Media Entertainment Services
N.A.I.C.S.: 722310

PG-Trading (Hangzhou) Co., Ltd. (1)
Room 216 Block A Hualian Creative Plaza 125 Jiangsu North Road, Changning District, Shanghai, 200050, China
Tel.: (86) 2162166309
Web Site: http://www.pg-mtrade.com.cn
Web Operation Services
N.A.I.C.S.: 541511

PIALA VENTURES Inc. (1)
13F Ebisu Garden Place Tower 4-20-3 Ebisu, Shibuya-ku, Tokyo, 150-6013, Japan
Tel.: (81) 363626835
Web Site: https://piala.vc
Venture Capital Services
N.A.I.C.S.: 523910

PIALab. Inc. (1)
Amico East Building 6F 1-5 Terashima Honmachi Nishi, Tokushima, 770-0831, Japan
Tel.: (81) 886563011
Web Site: https://www.pialab.co.jp
Call Center Services
N.A.I.C.S.: 561422
Takao Asuka *(CEO)*

PIATEC (Thailand) Co., Ltd. (1)
24 Prime Building 10 Fl Room A Sukhumvit 21 Asoke Rd, Klongtoey-Nua Wattana, Bangkok, 10110, Thailand
Tel.: (66) 22581720
Web Site: https://www.piatec.co.th
Emp.: 21
Web Application Development Services
N.A.I.C.S.: 541511

PIANEGONDA SRL
Via De Gasperi 82-84, 36040, Vicenza, Italy
Tel.: (39) 0444415209
Web Site: http://www.pianegonda.com
Sales Range: $10-24.9 Million
Jewelry
N.A.I.C.S.: 339910
Franco Pianegonda *(Dir-Creative)*

Subsidiaries:

Pianegonda Corp. (1)
1562 Alton Rd, Miami Beach, FL 33139
Tel.: (305) 672-8476
Web Site: http://store.pianegonda.com
Jewelry
N.A.I.C.S.: 339910

Pianegonda France S.A. (1)
Rue Saint Honore 350, Paris, France
Tel.: (33) 142964459
Jewelry Stores
N.A.I.C.S.: 458310

PIANO SOFTWARE B.V.
Herengracht 433, 1017 BR, Amsterdam, Netherlands
Web Site: https://piano.io
Software Publisher
N.A.I.C.S.: 513210
Sven Adler *(CFO)*

PIAZAR AGRO INDUSTRIAL COMPANY
24 K M From Tabriz Alley Khosro Shahr-Next To Piazar Bridge, PO Box 51385-1187, Tabriz, Azerbaijan, Iran
Tel.: (98) 412 2682777
Year Founded: 1969
PIAZ—(THE)
Sales Range: Less than $1 Million
Emp.: 122
Food Products Mfr
N.A.I.C.S.: 311423

PIC INVESTMENT GROUP INC.
70 24th Street E, Saskatoon, S7K 4B8, SK, Canada
Tel.: (306) 664-3955
Web Site: http://www.picgroup.ca
Year Founded: 1976
Sales Range: $150-199.9 Million
Holding Company; Investment Services

N.A.I.C.S.: 551112
Greg Yuel *(Pres & CEO)*

Subsidiaries:

Adventure Destinations International (1)
11 Hangar Road, Saskatoon, S7L 5X4, SK, Canada
Tel.: (306) 933-9453
Web Site: http://www.adventuredestinations.ca
Emp.: 5
Recreational Camp Services
N.A.I.C.S.: 721214
James Yuel *(Pres)*

ClearTech Industries Inc. (1)
1500 Quebec Ave, Saskatoon, S7K 1V7, SK, Canada
Tel.: (306) 664-2522
Web Site: http://www.cleartech.ca
Emp.: 40
Chemical & Laboratory Product Distr
N.A.I.C.S.: 424690
Randy M. Bracewell *(Pres)*

G Mechanical Ltd. (1)
229 Avenue I South, Saskatoon, S7M 1X8, SK, Canada
Tel.: (306) 343-1999
Web Site: http://www.gmechanical.ca
Mechanical Engineering Services
N.A.I.C.S.: 541330

Hydor-Tech Limited (1)
11750-180th Street, Edmonton, T5S 1N7, AB, Canada
Tel.: (780) 452-9888
Web Site: http://www.chemtradelogistics.cm
Emp.: 12
Chemical Products Mfr
N.A.I.C.S.: 325199

Kipp & Zonen B.V. (1)
Delftechpark 36, 2628 XH, Delft, Netherlands
Tel.: (31) 15 2755 210
Web Site: http://www.kippzonen.com
Solar Radiation Measuring Instrument Mfr
N.A.I.C.S.: 334519

Subsidiary (Non-US):

Kipp & Zonen France S.A.R.L (2)
88 Avenue de l'Europe, 77184, Emerainville-Malnoue, France
Tel.: (33) 1 64 02 50 28
Web Site: http://www.kippzonen.com
Solar Radiation Measuring Instrument Mfr
N.A.I.C.S.: 334519
Kamal Sabra *(Gen Mgr)*

Panther Industries Inc. (1)
108 Internal Road, PO Box 698, Davidson, S0G 1A0, SK, Canada
Tel.: (306) 567-2814
Web Site: http://www.pantherindustriesinc.com
Emp.: 35
Wooden Pallet Distr
N.A.I.C.S.: 423830
Kevin Williams *(VP-Fin)*

PICARD AUTOS 33
142 Avenue Du General De Gaulle, 33500, Libourne, Gironde, France
Tel.: (33) 557554545
Web Site: http://concessions.peugeot.fr
Rev.: $23,000,000
Emp.: 48
N.A.I.C.S.: 441110
Albert Picard *(Pres)*

PICARD AUTOS RAMONVILLE
A 9 7 Boulevard Des Cretes, Ramonville-Saint-Agne, 31522, Haute Garonne, France
Tel.: (33) 562191919
Web Site: http://www.ramonville.peugeot.fr
Rev.: $24,000,000
Emp.: 48
N.A.I.C.S.: 441110
Fabrice Picard *(Pres)*

PICCADILLY AD

Picard Autos Ramonville—(Continued)

PICCADILLY AD
21 Istoria Slavyanobalgarska Str,
1220, Sofia, Bulgaria
Tel.: (359) 2 803 8220   BG
Web Site: http://www.piccadilly.bg
Year Founded: 1994
Supermarkets & Convenience Stores
Operator
N.A.I.C.S.: 445110
Erikjan Lantink *(COO)*

PICCADILY AGRO INDUSTRIES LTD.
Village Bhadson Umri Indri Road,
Tehsil Indri Distt, Karnal, 160017,
Haryana, India
Tel.: (91) 1744271653
Web Site: https://www.picagro.com
530305—(BOM)
Rev.: $76,296,085
Assets: $71,046,124
Liabilities: $43,289,287
Net Worth: $27,756,837
Earnings: $2,793,082
Emp.: 324
Fiscal Year-end: 03/31/23
Food Products & Sugar Mfr
N.A.I.C.S.: 311313
Harvinder Singh Chopra *(Mng Dir)*

PICCADILY SUGAR & ALLIED INDUSTRIES LIMITED
Jakhal Road Patran, Patiala, 147001,
Punjab, India
Tel.: (91) 4242500
Web Site:
https://www.psailpatran.com
Year Founded: 1994
507456—(BOM)
Rev.: $2,613,404
Assets: $6,379,198
Liabilities: $4,689,047
Net Worth: $1,690,150
Earnings: ($248,690)
Emp.: 37
Fiscal Year-end: 03/31/23
Sugar Mfr & Whslr
N.A.I.C.S.: 111930
Devinder Sharma *(Chm)*

PICHARD PERE ET FILS S.A.S.
4 rue des Livraindieres, ZI Nord,
28100, Dreux, Eure Et Loir, France
Tel.: (33) 237468062
Web Site: http://www.pichard-sas.com
Year Founded: 1935
Emp.: 70
Meat Packing Plants
N.A.I.C.S.: 311611
Declo Mesnl *(Dir-Publ)*

PICK N PAY STORES LTD.
Pick N Pay Office Park 101 Rosmead
Ave, Kenilworth, Cape Town, 7708,
South Africa
Tel.: (27) 216581000
Web Site:
https://www.picknpayinvestor.co.za
Year Founded: 1967
PIK—(JSE)
Rev.: $6,283,093,768
Assets: $2,533,092,534
Liabilities: $2,543,036,930
Net Worth: ($9,944,396)
Earnings: ($173,732,846)
Emp.: 90,000
Fiscal Year-end: 02/25/24
Grocery & Cloth Whslr
N.A.I.C.S.: 458110
Richard Brasher *(CEO)*

PICKALBATROS HOTELS & NILE CRUISES
7 Abdel Moneim Riyadh, Mohandesin, Giza, Egypt
Tel.: (20) 2 333 86 800
Web Site:
http://www.pickalbatros.com
Year Founded: 1992
Hotels, Resorts, Cruises
N.A.I.C.S.: 721110
Kamel Hassan Abou Ali *(Chm)*

PICKERINGS AUTO GROUP PTY. LTD.
783-797 Flinders St, PO Box 5453,
Townsville, 4810, QLD, Australia
Tel.: (61) 747265555
Web Site:
http://www.pickerings.com.au
Automotive Retailer
N.A.I.C.S.: 441110
Nicole Dowling *(Bus Mgr)*

PICKLES CORPORATION
3F Daini Rings Bldg 3-18-3 Kusunokidai, Tokorozawa, 359-0037, Saitama, Japan
Tel.: (81) 429987771
Web Site: http://www.pickles.co.jp
Year Founded: 1977
2925—(TKS)
Rev.: $435,658,080
Assets: $252,560,880
Liabilities: $90,353,120
Net Worth: $162,207,760
Earnings: $20,599,040
Emp.: 237
Fiscal Year-end: 02/28/22
Food Product Mfr & Distr
N.A.I.C.S.: 311999

PICKSTOCK ASHBY LTD.
The Abattoir Coal Lane Hartshorn,
Telford, DE11 7BF, Derbys, United Kingdom
Tel.: (44) 1283 551692
Web Site:
http://www.pickstocksashbyltd.com
Year Founded: 2003
Sales Range: $75-99.9 Million
Emp.: 60
Meat Product Whslr
N.A.I.C.S.: 311612
Gareth Roberts *(Mgr-Sls)*

PICNIC CORPORATION PUBLIC CO. LTD.
805 Srinakarin Road, Suan Luang,
Bangkok, 10250, Thailand
Tel.: (66) 27213600
Sales Range: $350-399.9 Million
Emp.: 200
Liquefied Petroleum Gas Whslr & Construction Services
N.A.I.C.S.: 424720
Watcharakiti Watcharothai *(Pres)*

PICO (THAILAND) PUBLIC COMPANY LIMITED
10 Soi Lasalle 56 Bangna Tai,
Bangna, Bangkok, 10260, Thailand
Tel.: (66) 27487000
Web Site: https://www.picothai.com
Year Founded: 1981
PICO—(THA)
Rev.: $30,229,052
Assets: $21,312,556
Liabilities: $9,859,694
Net Worth: $11,452,862
Earnings: $668,752
Emp.: 149
Fiscal Year-end: 10/31/23
Trade & Merchandise Exhibition Services
N.A.I.C.S.: 561499
Song Heng Chia *(Chm)*

Subsidiaries:

Andrew Bethell Associates
Limited   (1)
1st Floor Bristol and West House 100 Cross
Brook Street, Cheshunt, EN8 8JJ, Hurts,
United Kingdom
Tel.: (44) 2088001047
Educational Support Services
N.A.I.C.S.: 611710

G&S Joint Venture Company
Limited   (1)
18 Soi Lasalle 56, Bangna Tai Bangna,
Bangkok, 10260, Thailand
Tel.: (66) 27487007
Building Design & Decoration Services
N.A.I.C.S.: 541410

Multi Designs Company Limited   (1)
Spring Bank House 33 Stamford St, Altrincham, WA14 1ES, Cheshire, United Kingdom
Tel.: (44) 1614770766
Sales Range: $25-49.9 Million
Emp.: 50
Interior Decorators & Designers
N.A.I.C.S.: 541410

NXH Joint Venture Company
Limited   (1)
10 Soi Lasalle 56, Bangna Tai Bangna,
Bangkok, 10260, Thailand
Tel.: (66) 27487007
Building Design & Decoration Services
N.A.I.C.S.: 541410

Nox Bangkok Company Limited   (1)
10 Soi Lasalle 56, Bangna, Bangkok,
10260, Thailand
Tel.: (66) 27458058
Web Site: http://www.picothai.com
Sales Range: $25-49.9 Million
Emp.: 5
Business Consulting Services
N.A.I.C.S.: 541618

PX System Company Limited   (1)
79/90 Moo 12 Bangna-Trad Road, Bang
Kaeo Bang Phli, Bangkok, 10540, Samut
Prakarn, Thailand
Tel.: (66) 218001716
Web Site: https://www.pxsystem.com
Exhibition Supplies & Services
N.A.I.C.S.: 561920

TCBN Company Limited   (1)
10 Soi Lasalle 56 Sukhumvit Road, Bangna
Tai Bangna, Bangkok, 10260, Thailand
Tel.: (66) 274581123
Web Site: https://www.tcbn.co.th
Media Communication Services
N.A.I.C.S.: 541840

PICO FAR EAST HOLDINGS LIMITED
Pico House 4 Dai Fu Street Tai Po
Industrial Estate, Tai Po, NT, China
(Hong Kong)
Tel.: (852) 26650990
Web Site: http://www.pico.com
0752—(HKG)
Rev.: $585,700,502
Assets: $646,399,264
Liabilities: $364,425,767
Net Worth: $281,973,496
Earnings: $19,811,457
Emp.: 2,200
Fiscal Year-end: 10/31/22
Holding Company; Exhibition Services
N.A.I.C.S.: 551112
Lawrence Song Huat Chia *(Chm)*

Subsidiaries:

Albert Smith (China) Company
Limited   (1)
Albert Smith Building 36 Cao Lian Road
Lian Xi Cun, Anting Town Jiading District,
Shanghai, China
Tel.: (86) 2169596990
Web Site: http://www.albertsmithchina.com
Sales Range: $125-149.9 Million
Emp.: 350
Signage Mfr & Sales
N.A.I.C.S.: 339950

INTERNATIONAL PUBLIC

Asia Game Show Holdings Ltd.   (1)
Pico House 4 Dai Fu Street Tai Po Industrial Estate, Tai Po, New Territories, China
(Hong Kong)
Tel.: (852) 25093430
Web Site: http://www.asiagameshow.com
Emp.: 10
Game Hosting Services
N.A.I.C.S.: 711310

Beijing Pico Exhibition Services Co.,
Ltd.   (1)
Pico Centre 8 Li Shui Qiao Bei, Chaoyang
District, Beijing, 102218, China
Tel.: (86) 1084823991
Web Site: http://www.pico.com
Sales Range: $25-49.9 Million
Emp.: 200
Trade Show Organizing Services
N.A.I.C.S.: 561920

Camron Public Relations Limited   (1)
7th Floor 17 Slingsby Place, London, WC2E
9AB, United Kingdom
Tel.: (44) 2074201700
Web Site: http://camronpr.com
Business Innovation Services
N.A.I.C.S.: 541820
Bethan Beckett *(Sr Acct Mgr)*

Chengdu Pico Exhibition Services
Co., Ltd.   (1)
Room 1703 Tower A Times Plaza 2 Zongfu
Road, Jinjiang District, Chengdu, 610016,
China
Tel.: (86) 2886727990
Exhibition Shows Organizing Services
N.A.I.C.S.: 561920
Allen Li *(Mgr)*

Chenzhou International Convention &
Exhibition Center Limited   (1)
Chenzhou Road, Chenzhou, 423000, Hunan, China
Tel.: (86) 7358899600
Web Site: http://www.chenzhoucec.com
Exhibition & Event Management Services
N.A.I.C.S.: 561920

Dongguan Pico Exhibition Services
Co Limited   (1)
1st Road Reservoir Industrial District Guan
Jing Tou Feng Gang, Dongguan, 523705,
Guangdong, China
Tel.: (86) 769 8777 4471
Sales Range: $25-49.9 Million
Emp.: 140
Exhibition Organizing Services
N.A.I.C.S.: 561920

Epicentro Digital Limited   (1)
4 Dai Fu Street Industrial Estate, Tai Po,
New Territories, China (Hong Kong)
Tel.: (852) 26604433
Web Site: https://www.epicentro.com.hk
Application Development Services
N.A.I.C.S.: 513210
Alison Lam *(Sr Mgr)*

Fairtrans International Ltd.   (1)
Iwasei Nihonbashi Building 6F 6-5 Nihonbashi Odenmacho, Chuo-Ku, Tokyo, 103-0011, Japan
Tel.: (81) 338080915
Web Site: https://fairtrans.info
Sales Range: $25-49.9 Million
Emp.: 12
Transportation Services
N.A.I.C.S.: 481111
Takashi Oide *(Exec Dir)*

Global-Link MP Events International
Inc.   (1)
3973 Yague Street Brgy Sta Cruz, Makati,
1205, Philippines
Tel.: (63) 9955298672
Web Site: http://www.globallinkmp.com
Event Management Services
N.A.I.C.S.: 541921
Jing Lagandaon *(COO)*

Guangzhou Pico Exhibition Services
Co., Ltd.   (1)
Room 1901 Block H Winter Tower GT Land
Plaza No 12 Zhujiang Road East,
Guangzhou, 510623, Guangdong, China
Tel.: (86) 2087322990
Exhibition Contract Organizing Services
N.A.I.C.S.: 561920

AND PRIVATE COMPANIES — PICO FAR EAST HOLDINGS LIMITED

Guangzhou Pico IES Exhibition Services Co., Ltd. (1)
Room 702 Dongshan Plaza 69 Xien Lie road Central, Guangzhou, 510095, Guangdong, China
Tel.: (86) 20 8908 9045
Web Site: http://www.pico.com
Exhibition Contract Organizing Services
N.A.I.C.S.: 238990

Local Projects, LLC (1)
123 William St Ste 801, New York, NY 10038
Tel.: (212) 480-0479
Web Site: https://localprojects.com
Design Services
N.A.I.C.S.: 541420

MP International (Asia Pacific) Ltd. (1)
Pico House 4 Dai Fu Street Tai Po Industrial Estate, Tai Po, New Territories, China (Hong Kong)
Tel.: (852) 25093430
Web Site: http://www.mphk.com
Emp.: 10
Exhibition Contract Organizing Services
N.A.I.C.S.: 561920

MP International Pte. Ltd. (1)
20 Kallang Avenue 2nd Floor Pico Creative Centre, Singapore, 339411, Singapore
Tel.: (65) 63896610
Web Site: https://www.mpinetwork.com
Exhibition Organizing Services
N.A.I.C.S.: 561920

Subsidiary (Non-US):

MP International (Shanghai) Pte. Ltd. (2)
Flat 11E Jin Ming Building 8 Zun Yi Road South, Changning District, Shanghai, 200336, China
Tel.: (86) 2162959990
Web Site: http://www.picoworld.com
Emp.: 10
Exhibition Contract Organizing Services
N.A.I.C.S.: 561920

MP Zhongmao International (Shanghai) Pte. Ltd. (2)
A10 Huading Tower 2368 Zhongshan Road West, Shanghai, 200235, China
Tel.: (86) 2154592323
Web Site: http://www.mpzhongmao.com
Sales Range: $10-24.9 Million
Emp.: 50
Exhibition Contract Organizing Services
N.A.I.C.S.: 561920

Marina Bay Carnival Pte Ltd. (1)
12A Bayfront Ave, Singapore, 018970, Singapore
Tel.: (65) 94458408
Web Site: https://marinabaycarnival.sg
Carnival Ride & Entertainment Operator
N.A.I.C.S.: 713990
Tracey Khoo *(Dir-Project)*

Not Ordinary Media, LLC (1)
2202 S Figueroa St Ste 346, Los Angeles, CA 90007
Tel.: (323) 848-4270
Web Site: https://nomology.com
Video Technology Development Services
N.A.I.C.S.: 512110
Loren Rochelle *(Co-Founder & CEO)*

PT Pico TBA (1)
Grand Slipi Tower 38th Floor Unit 38H Jalan S Parman Kav 22-24, Jakarta, 11410, Indonesia
Tel.: (62) 2129022312
Brand Marketing Services
N.A.I.C.S.: 541613
Ariawan Tjondronugroho *(Mgr-Ops)*

Parico Electrical Engineering Sdn. Bhd. (1)
19-20 Jalan Tembaga Sd 5/2 Bandar, Sri Damansara, 52200, Kuala Lumpur, Malaysia
Tel.: (60) 362754133
Web Site: http://www.pico.com.my
Sales Range: $25-49.9 Million
Emp.: 50
Electrical Contractor Services
N.A.I.C.S.: 238210

Pico Art Exhibit, Inc. (1)
20910 Normandie Ave Unit D, Torrance, CA 90502
Tel.: (310) 328-6990
Exhibition Contract Organizing Services
N.A.I.C.S.: 561920

Pico Art International Pte. Ltd. (1)
Pico Creative Centre 20 Kallang Avenue, Singapore, 339411, Singapore
Tel.: (65) 62940100
Sales Range: $75-99.9 Million
Emp.: 300
Exhibition Organizing Services
N.A.I.C.S.: 561920
Ng Meng Chuen *(Gen Mgr)*

Pico Chicago, Inc. (1)
311 S Wacker Dr Ste 420, Chicago, IL 60606
Tel.: (312) 922-7779
Web Site: https://www.pico.net
Exhibition Organizing Services
N.A.I.C.S.: 561920

Pico Concepts India Private Ltd. (1)
14/5 Mathura Road Opp Spring Field Colony Sector 31, Faridabad, 121003, Delhi, Haryana, India
Tel.: (91) 1294077920
Web Site: http://www.in.pico.com
Exhibition Contract Organizing Services
N.A.I.C.S.: 561920

Pico Contracts Limited (1)
Pico House 4 Dai Fu Street, Tai Po Industrial Estate, Tai Po, New Territories, China (Hong Kong)
Tel.: (852) 26650990
Exhibition Installation & Organizing Services
N.A.I.C.S.: 561920

Pico Global Services Ltd. (1)
Pico House 4 Dai Fu Street Tai Po Industrial Estate, Tai Po, New Territories, China (Hong Kong)
Tel.: (852) 26650990
Event Marketing Services
N.A.I.C.S.: 561920

Pico Global Services Ltd. (1)
1st Floor 46-48 London Road, Twickenham, TW1 3RJ, Middlesex, United Kingdom
Tel.: (44) 2089486211
Web Site: http://uk.pico.com
Sales Range: $25-49.9 Million
Emp.: 10
Exhibition Contract Organizing Services
N.A.I.C.S.: 561920

Pico Hanoi Limited (1)
14th Floor Icon 4 Tower 243A De La Thanh, Dong Da District, Hanoi, Vietnam
Tel.: (84) 437711389
Web Site: http://www.picoworld.com
Emp.: 20
Exhibition Contract Organizing Services
N.A.I.C.S.: 561920

Pico Hochiminh City Ltd. (1)
10th Floor ACB Tower 444A-446 Cach Mang Thang Tam Street, Ward 11 District 3, Ho Chi Minh City, Vietnam
Tel.: (84) 2838464990
Web Site: http://www.picoworld.com
Sales Range: $10-24.9 Million
Emp.: 50
Design & Project Management Services
N.A.I.C.S.: 561110
Low Wan Thiam *(Mgr)*

Pico IES Group (China) Co., Ltd. (1)
No 188 Xin Chen Road BeiCai Town, Pudong Area, Shanghai, 201204, China
Tel.: (86) 2151960990
Emp.: 300
Exhibition Shows Organizing Services
N.A.I.C.S.: 561920

Pico IES Group Ltd. (1)
Pico House 4 Dai Fu Street, Tai Po Industrial Estate, Tai Po, New Territories, China (Hong Kong)
Tel.: (852) 37130400
Emp.: 200
Exhibition Organizing Services
N.A.I.C.S.: 561920

Pico International (Dubai) LLC (1)
12th Floor Mazaya Business Centre Building AA1 Jumeirah Lake Towers, PO Box 37679, Dubai, United Arab Emirates
Tel.: (971) 44204028
Web Site: http://uae.pico.com
Sales Range: $25-49.9 Million
Emp.: 250
Exhibition Contract Organizing Services
N.A.I.C.S.: 561920

Pico International (HK) Limited (1)
Pico House 4 Dai Fu St Tai Po Industrial Estate, Tai Po, New Territories, China (Hong Kong)
Tel.: (852) 26650990
Exhibition Contract Organizing Services
N.A.I.C.S.: 561920

Pico International (Henan) Exhibition Services Company Limited (1)
512 5/F Block B Graham Building 18 CBD Outer Ring Road, Zhengzhou, 450000, Henan, China
Tel.: (86) 37156678977
Exhibition & Event Management Services
N.A.I.C.S.: 561920

Pico International (LA) Inc. (1)
8530 Ste A Washington Blvd, Culver City, CA 90232
Tel.: (310) 450-1028
Exhibition & Event Management Services
N.A.I.C.S.: 561920

Pico International (M) Sdn. Bhd. (1)
Level 4 Wisma Pico 19-20 Jalan Tembaga Sd 502, Bandar Sri Damansara, Kuala Lumpur, 52200, Malaysia
Tel.: (60) 362755990
Web Site: http://www.pico.com.my
Sales Range: $75-99.9 Million
Emp.: 300
Exhibition Organizing Services
N.A.I.C.S.: 561920

Pico International (Macao) Ltd. (1)
Block D 7th Floor World Trade Center, 918 Friendship Avenue, Macau, China (Macau)
Tel.: (853) 28727990
Web Site: http://mo.pico.com
Sales Range: $25-49.9 Million
Emp.: 6
Exhibition Contract Organizing Services
N.A.I.C.S.: 238990

Pico International (Qatar) WLL (1)
No 2 1st Floor Faisaliya Building Al Sadd Area, PO Box 24403, Al Asad Area, Doha, Qatar
Tel.: (974) 4677988
Web Site: http://qa.pico.com
Sales Range: $25-49.9 Million
Emp.: 20
Exhibition Contract Organizing Services
N.A.I.C.S.: 561920

Pico International Limited (1)
Iwasei Nihombashi Building 6F 6-5 Nihonbashi Odenmacho, Chuo-ku, Tokyo, 103 0011, Japan (100%)
Tel.: (81) 338080891
Sales Range: $10-24.9 Million
Emp.: 27
Exhibition Services
N.A.I.C.S.: 561920

Pico International Taiwan Ltd. (1)
3F No 343 Nanking East Road Section 5, Taipei, 10504, Taiwan
Tel.: (886) 227535990
Sales Range: $10-24.9 Million
Emp.: 38
Exhibition Contract Organizing Services
N.A.I.C.S.: 561920

Pico International, Inc. (1)
20910 Normandie Ave B, Torrance, CA 90502-1602
Tel.: (310) 328-6990
Management Services
N.A.I.C.S.: 561110

Pico Myanmar Company Limited (1)
No 37 Kabar Aye Pagoda Road, Mayangone Township, Yangon, Myanmar
Tel.: (95) 1657998
Web Site: http://mm.pico.com
Exhibition & Event Management Services
N.A.I.C.S.: 561920

Pico North Asia Ltd. (1)
4F Jinsung B/D Yeongdong-daero 85-gil 38, Gangnam-gu, Seoul, 06180, Korea (South)
Tel.: (82) 25583240
Web Site: http://kr.pico.com
Sales Range: $10-24.9 Million
Emp.: 40
Exhibition Organizing Services
N.A.I.C.S.: 561920

Pico Projects (International) Limited (1)
Pico House 4 Dai Fu Street, Tai Po Industrial Estate, Tai Po, New Territories, China (Hong Kong)
Tel.: (852) 26604506
Sales Range: $25-49.9 Million
Emp.: 15
Interior Design Services
N.A.I.C.S.: 541410

Shanghai Pico Exhibition Services Co., Ltd. (1)
Pico Building 188 Xin Chen Road Beicai Town, Pu Dong Area, Shanghai, 201204, China
Tel.: (86) 2159100990
Sales Range: $75-99.9 Million
Emp.: 300
Exhibition Shows Organizing Services
N.A.I.C.S.: 561920

Shanghai Pixels Information Technology Co., Ltd. (1)
No 99 Lane 4499 Cao An Highway, Jiading District, Shanghai, China
Tel.: (86) 2160108777
Web Site: http://www.pixelslab.net
Interactive Technology Development Services
N.A.I.C.S.: 541511

TBA Creative Network Group (1)
Pico Creative Centre No 3 Shunxing Road, Shunyi District, Beijing, 101300, China
Tel.: (86) 1089414020
Web Site: https://www.tbacreative.net
Brand Marketing Services
N.A.I.C.S.: 541613
Iris Zhang *(Asst Gen Mgr-Acct Svc)*

World Image International Ltd. (1)
Pico House 4 Dai Fu St Tai Po Industrial Estate, Tai Po, New Territories, China (Hong Kong)
Tel.: (852) 26650990
Brand Design & Development Services
N.A.I.C.S.: 541490

Subsidiary (Non-US):

World Image (China) Company Ltd. (2)
Room F&G 5th Floor Jun Li Wealth Tower No 5199 Gong He Xin Road, Baoshan District, Shanghai, 200435, China
Tel.: (86) 2161359299
Web Site: http://www.worldimagegroup.com
Sales Range: $25-49.9 Million
Emp.: 100
Advertising & Branding Services
N.A.I.C.S.: 541890
Bill Chai *(Mgr)*

World Image (Middle East) L.L.C. (2)
PO Box 54175, Dubai, United Arab Emirates
Tel.: (971) 43389080
Web Site: http://www.worldimage-me.com
Sales Range: $25-49.9 Million
Emp.: 100
Exhibition Contract Organizing Services
N.A.I.C.S.: 561920

World Image (Shanghai) Design & Engineering Co., Ltd. (2)
Rm F&G 5th Floor Jun Li Wealth Tower No 5199 Gong He Xin Road, Baoshan District, Shanghai, 200435, China
Tel.: (86) 2161359299
Web Site: http://www.worldimage-group.com
Sales Range: $25-49.9 Million
Emp.: 70
Signage Mfr & Sales
N.A.I.C.S.: 339950

World Image Signs (Beijing) Company Ltd. (2)
1501 International Exhibition Center 25 Nanli Ganlu Yard, Beijing, 100000, Chaoyang, China

PICO FAR EAST HOLDINGS LIMITED

Pico Far East Holdings Limited—(Continued)
Tel.: (86) 10 6510 4162
Web Site: http://www.worldimage-group.com
Sales Range: $25-49.9 Million
Emp.: 80
Electrical Signs Mfr & Sales
N.A.I.C.S.: 339950

World Image Plus Pte Ltd. (1)
20 Kallang Avenue, Singapore, 339411, Singapore
Tel.: (65) 91637507
Web Site: https://world-image-plus-pte-ltd.business.site
Design Services
N.A.I.C.S.: 541420

Yangon Convention Centre Ltd. (1)
37 Kabar Aye Pagoda Road, Mayangone Township, Yangon, Myanmar
Tel.: (95) 9799288980
Web Site: https://www.yangoncc.com
Convention Center Operator
N.A.I.C.S.: 711310

PICOGRAM CO., LTD.
118 Bupyeongbuk-Ro, Bupyeong-Gu, Incheon, 21310, Korea (South)
Tel.: (82) 326785114
Web Site: https://www.picogram.com
Year Founded: 2002
376180—(KRS)
Water Purification Equipment Mfr
N.A.I.C.S.: 333413
Suk Rim Choi (CEO)

Subsidiaries:

PicoLead (Beijing) Water Treatment Technology Co., Ltd. (1)
Room No 1011 Ronghua International Building No 3, Beijing Economic and Technological Development Zone, Beijing, 100176, China
Tel.: (86) 106 781 7987
Water Purification Equipment Mfr
N.A.I.C.S.: 333310

Picogram Malaysia Sdn. Bhd. (1)
Unit F1 2-02 Bukit Jalil City Signture, Pusat Perdagangan Bandar Bukit Jalil Persiaran Jalil 2, 57000, Kuala Lumpur, Malaysia
Tel.: (60) 39 765 1248
Web Site: https://www.picogram.my
Water Purifier Equipment Mfr & Distr
N.A.I.C.S.: 333310

PICOP RESOURCES INC
2f Moredel Building 2280 Passion Tamo Extension, Makati, Philippines
Tel.: (63) 813 2081
Year Founded: 1952
Paper Products Mfr
N.A.I.C.S.: 322299
Eleanore B. Gutierrez (CFO & Treas)

PICS LTD.
Avenida Manuel Bandeira 291 Block A 2nd floor, Sao Paulo, 05317-020, Brazil
Tel.: (55) 11977231925   Ky
Year Founded: 2021
Emp.: 1,846
Holding Company
N.A.I.C.S.: 551112
Jose Antonio Batista Costa (CEO)

PICTET & CIE
Route des Acacias 601211, 1211, Geneva, Switzerland
Tel.: (41) 583232323
Web Site: http://www.pictet.com
Assets: $365,000,000,000
Emp.: 3,000
Private Banking Services
N.A.I.C.S.: 525910
Nicolas Pictet (Sr Partner)

PICTON MAHONEY TACTICAL INCOME FUND
33 Yonge Street Suite 830, Toronto, M5E 1G4, ON, Canada

Tel.: (416) 955-4108   ON
Web Site: http://www.pictonmahoney.com
Year Founded: 2012
PMB.UN—(TSX)
Rev.: $1,396,091
Assets: $28,937,470
Liabilities: $8,121,493
Net Worth: $20,815,977
Earnings: $825,287
Fiscal Year-end: 12/31/21
Investment Services
N.A.I.C.S.: 523999
David K. Picton (Pres)

PICTON PROPERTY INCOME LIMITED
Trafalgar Court Les Banques, PO Box 255, Saint Peter Port, GY1 3QL, Guernsey
Tel.: (44) 2070119978   GY
Web Site: https://www.picton.co.uk
Year Founded: 2005
PCTN—(LSE)
Rev.: $69,035,597
Assets: $976,919,971
Liabilities: $314,871,245
Net Worth: $662,048,726
Earnings: ($6,045,191)
Emp.: 12
Fiscal Year-end: 03/31/24
Real Estate Investment Services
N.A.I.C.S.: 531190
Michael Morris (CEO)

Subsidiaries:

Picton Capital Limited (1)
1st Floor 28 Austin Friars, London, EC2N 2QQ, United Kingdom
Tel.: (44) 20 7628 4800
Real Estate Investment Services
N.A.I.C.S.: 531190
Jay Cable (Head-Asset Mgmt)

PICTUREHOUSE MEDIA LIMITED
4th Floor Punnaiah Plaza Plot No 8384 Road No 2 Banjara Hills, Hyderabad, 500 034, India
Tel.: (91) 4067309999
Web Site: https://www.pvpcinema.com
532355—(BOM)
Rev.: $1,893,280
Assets: $4,226,621
Liabilities: $12,776,320
Net Worth: ($8,549,499)
Earnings: $24,583,718
Emp.: 3
Fiscal Year-end: 03/31/23
Motion Picture Production Services
N.A.I.C.S.: 512110
Prasad V. Potluri (Mng Dir)

PIDILITE INDUSTRIES LIMITED
Regent Chambers 7th Floor Jamnalal Bajaj Marg 208, Nariman Point, Mumbai, 400021, Maharashtra, India
Tel.: (91) 2268837000
Web Site: https://www.pidilite.com
Year Founded: 1959
PIDILITIND—(NSE)
Rev.: $1,006,293,015
Assets: $1,205,352,330
Liabilities: $409,147,830
Net Worth: $796,204,500
Earnings: $153,716,745
Emp.: 6,376
Fiscal Year-end: 03/31/21
Adhesives & Industrial Chemicals Mfr
N.A.I.C.S.: 325520
Bharat Puri (Mng Dir)

Subsidiaries:

Chemson Asia Pte Ltd (1)
31 A Venoi Rd Poineer Lot, Singapore, 627779, Singapore   (75%)

Tel.: (65) 67638681
Sales Range: $50-74.9 Million
Emp.: 10
Chemical & Allied Products Whslr
N.A.I.C.S.: 424690

Cipy Polyurethanes Pvt. Ltd. (1)
T-127, MIDC Bhosari, Pune, 411026, Maharashtra, India
Tel.: (91) 2066316400
Web Site: https://www.cipypolyurethane.com
Floor Coating Product Mfr
N.A.I.C.S.: 325510

Nina Percept Private Limited (1)
Tel.: (91) 2266166000
Web Site: https://www.ninapercept.com
Engineeering Services
N.A.I.C.S.: 541330

Pidilite Bamco Ltd. (1)
Tel.: (66) 27228535
Web Site: https://www.dr-fixit.co.th
Construction Chemicals Mfr
N.A.I.C.S.: 325520

Pidilite Industries Egypt SAE (1)
Plot No 178-Fifth Industrial Zone, Sadat City, Egypt
Tel.: (20) 482657107
Chemical Products Mfr
N.A.I.C.S.: 325998

Pidilite Innovation Centre Pte (1)
61 Science Park Road The Galen 03-11/12 Singapore Science Park II, Singapore, 117525, Singapore
Tel.: (65) 63168695
Web Site: https://www.pidilite.com.sg
Sales Range: $25-49.9 Million
Product Testing & Consulting Services
N.A.I.C.S.: 541380

Pidilite Lanka (Pvt) Ltd. (1)
Tel.: (94) 112300872
Floor Coating Product Mfr
N.A.I.C.S.: 325510

Pidilite Middle East Ltd. (1)
Jebel Ali Free Zone, PO Box 61013, Dubai, United Arab Emirates
Tel.: (971) 48849880
Chemical Products Mfr
N.A.I.C.S.: 325998

Pidilite Speciality Chemicals Bangladesh Pvt. Ltd. (1)
House No B101 North Road No 7 New DOHS Mohakhali, Dhaka, 1206, Bangladesh
Tel.: (880) 28714577
Chemical Products Mfr
N.A.I.C.S.: 325998

Pidilite USA Inc. (1)
Tel.: (570) 454-3596
Sales Range: $25-49.9 Million
Emp.: 20
Construction Chemicals Mfr
N.A.I.C.S.: 325520

PIE FACE HOLDINGS PTY LTD
27 Cadogan Street, Marrickville, 2204, NSW, Australia
Tel.: (61) 1300048411
Web Site: http://www.pieface.com.au
Year Founded: 2003
Sales Range: $10-24.9 Million
Emp.: 80
Bakeries
N.A.I.C.S.: 311811
Bob Ozdemir (Mgr-Franchising Dev)

PIENO ZVAIGZDES AB
Perkunkiemio St 3, 12127, Vilnius, Lithuania
Tel.: (370) 52461414
Web Site: https://www.pienozvaigzdes.lt
Year Founded: 1998
PZV1L—(RSE)
Rev.: $191,043,637
Assets: $82,880,839
Liabilities: $50,531,443
Net Worth: $32,349,396
Earnings: $4,602,625

INTERNATIONAL PUBLIC

Emp.: 1,672
Fiscal Year-end: 12/31/19
Dairy Products Distr
N.A.I.C.S.: 424490
Julius Kvaraciejus (Chm-Mgmt Bd)

PIERER KONZERNGESELL-SCHAFT MBH
Edisonstrasse 1, 4600, Wels, Austria
Tel.: (43) 7242 643600   AT
Private Investment Firm
N.A.I.C.S.: 523999
Stefan Pierer (Owner)

Subsidiaries:

PIERER Mobility AG (1)
Edisonstrasse 1, 4600, Wels, Austria   (62.98%)
Tel.: (43) 724269402
Web Site: https://www.pierermobility.com
Rev.: $2,937,629,883
Assets: $3,259,639,800
Liabilities: $2,261,454,314
Net Worth: $998,185,486
Earnings: $88,508,297
Emp.: 6,184
Fiscal Year-end: 12/31/2023
Investment Holding Company; Motorcycle & Automotive Parts Mfr
N.A.I.C.S.: 551112
Friedrich Roithner (CFO & Member-Exec Bd)

Subsidiary (Domestic):

CROSS Finanzierungs GmbH (2)
EdisonStr 1, 4600, Wels, Austria
Tel.: (43) 7242643600
Transaction Financing Services
N.A.I.C.S.: 522299
Stefan Pierer (CEO)

Subsidiary (Non-US):

Die Wethje GmbH (2)
Donaustr 29 - 41, 94491, Hengersberg, Germany
Tel.: (49) 9901 93 33 0
Web Site: http://www.wethje-gmbh.com
Automobile Parts Mfr
N.A.I.C.S.: 336390
Alfred F. Hortenhuber (Co-Mng Dir)

Subsidiary (Domestic):

Durmont Teppichbodenfabrik GmbH (2)
Wiesengasse 55, 8230, Hartberg, Austria
Tel.: (43) 3332 6010 0
Web Site: http://www.durmont.at
Flooring Mfr
N.A.I.C.S.: 321918

Subsidiary (US):

Felt Racing, LLC (2)
30161 Avenida de las Banderas Unit A, Rancho Santa Margarita, CA 92688
Tel.: (949) 268-4458
Web Site: http://www.feltbicycles.com
Bicycle Mfr & Whslr
N.A.I.C.S.: 336991

Subsidiary (Domestic):

KTM AG (2)
Stallhofnerstrasse 3, A-5230, Mattighofen, Austria   (50.1%)
Tel.: (43) 7742 6000 0
Web Site: http://www.ktm.com
Rev.: $1,221,449,457
Assets: $1,130,205,984
Liabilities: $672,379,728
Net Worth: $457,826,255
Earnings: $77,034,117
Emp.: 2,931
Fiscal Year-end: 12/31/2016
Holding Company; Motorcycle & Other Recreational Vehicle Mfr & Distr
N.A.I.C.S.: 551112
Hubert Trunkenpolz (Member-Exec Bd)

Subsidiary (Non-US):

KTM Canada Inc. (3)
8701 Rue Samuel-Hatt, Chambly, J3L 6V4, QC, Canada
Tel.: (450) 441-4451

AND PRIVATE COMPANIES

Automotive Part Whslr
N.A.I.C.S.: 423120
Andy White *(Mgr-Team)*

KTM Central East Europe s.r.o. (3)
H-Business Center Roznavska 24, 82104,
Bratislava, Slovakia
Tel.: (421) 232 132 506
Web Site: http://www.ktm.com
Emp.: 15
Automotive Part Whslr
N.A.I.C.S.: 423120
Hans Steiner *(Gen Mgr)*

KTM Nordic Oy (3)
Tuupakantie 3 C, 01740, Vantaa, Finland
Tel.: (358) 10 841 1200
Automotive Part Whslr
N.A.I.C.S.: 423120

Subsidiary (Domestic):

KTM Technologies GmbH (3)
St Leonharder-Strasse 4, 5081, Salzburg,
Austria
Tel.: (43) 6246 73488 9000
Web Site: http://www.ktm-technologies.com
Motor Vehicle Parts Mfr
N.A.I.C.S.: 336390

Subsidiary (Non-US):

KTM-Racing AG (3)
Zurcherstrasse 305, 8500, Frauenfeld, Switzerland
Tel.: (41) 52 723 05 50
Web Site: http://www.rallye-adventure.de
Automotive Part Whslr
N.A.I.C.S.: 423120

Subsidiary (Domestic):

KTM-Sportmotorcycle AG (3)
Stallhofnerstrasse 3, 5230, Mattighofen,
Austria
Tel.: (43) 7742 6000 0
Web Site: http://www.ktm.com
Motorcycle & Other Recreational Vehicle
Mfr & Distr
N.A.I.C.S.: 336991
Philipp Habsburg *(Member-Exec Bd-R&D)*

Subsidiary (US):

KTM North America, Inc. (4)
1119 Milan Ave, Amherst, OH
44001-1319 (100%)
Tel.: (440) 985-3553
Web Site: http://www.ktm.com
Sales Range: $25-49.9 Million
Emp.: 60
Motorcycles & Dirt Bikes Distr
N.A.I.C.S.: 423110
John Hinz *(Pres)*

Subsidiary (Non-US):

KTM-Sportmotorcycle Belgium S.A. (3)
Rue Edouard Belin 1, 1435, Mont-Saint-Guibert, Belgium
Tel.: (32) 10 47 11 40
Automotive Part Whslr
N.A.I.C.S.: 423120

KTM-Sportmotorcycle Espana S.L. (3)
C/ Cinca 8-10 Pol Ind Sta Margarida, 8223,
Barcelona, Spain
Tel.: (34) 937363535
Motor Vehicle Parts Mfr
N.A.I.C.S.: 336390

KTM-Sportmotorcycle Italia s.r.l. (3)
Via Spallanzani 16/a, Albano
Sant'Alessandro, 24061, Bergamo, Italy
Tel.: (39) 035 303100
Web Site: http://www.ktminfoservice.it
Motor Vehicle Parts Mfr
N.A.I.C.S.: 336390
Paolo Carrubba *(Mgr-Mktg & Comm)*

KTM-Sportmotorcycle Scandinavia AB (3)
Hjalmarberget Mosasvagen, 702 31, Orebro, Sweden
Tel.: (46) 19 58 57 50
Automotive Part Whslr
N.A.I.C.S.: 423120

KTM-Sportmotorcycle UK Ltd. (3)
KTM House Ward Road, Brackley, NN13
7LE, Northamptonshire, United Kingdom
Tel.: (44) 1280 709500
Motor Vehicle Parts Mfr
N.A.I.C.S.: 336390
Shaun Sisterson *(Mng Dir)*

Subsidiary (Non-US):

SMP Automotive Technology Iberica, S.L. (2)
Ctra B-142 Sentmenat 18-20, 08213,
Polinya, Spain
Tel.: (34) 937452300
Emp.: 310
Automotive Part Whslr
N.A.I.C.S.: 423120

SMP Deutschland GmbH (2)
Schlossmattenstr 18, 79268, Botzingen,
Germany
Tel.: (49) 7663 61 0
Web Site: http://www.smp-automotive.com
Automotive Part Whslr
N.A.I.C.S.: 423120
Dirk Laforet *(VP-Production & Quality Sys)*

Subsidiary (Domestic):

W Verwaltungs AG (2)
Gewerbegebiet Nord 8, A-5222, Munderfing, Austria
Tel.: (43) 7744 20240 0
Web Site: http://www.wp-group.com
Motorcycle Parts Mfr
N.A.I.C.S.: 336991
Johann Grubbauer *(Member-Mgmt Bd)*

Subsidiary (Domestic):

WP Performance Systems GmbH (3)
Gewerbegebiet Nord 8, 5222, Munderfing,
Austria
Tel.: (43) 7744 20240 0
Web Site: http://www.wp-group.com
Motorcycle Parts Mfr
N.A.I.C.S.: 336991
Hannes Haunschmid *(Chm)*

Subsidiary (Non-US):

WP Cooling Systems (Dalian) Co., Ltd. (4)
Development Zone, Dalian, 116600, Liaoning, China
Tel.: (86) 411 39211 188
Heat Exchanger Mfr
N.A.I.C.S.: 332410

WP Germany GmbH (4)
Hohenburger Strasse 55, 92289, Ursensollen, Germany
Tel.: (49) 9628 9299292
Web Site: http://www.wp-germany.com
Suspension Product Mfr
N.A.I.C.S.: 336330
Rainer Mengel *(Mng Dir)*

WP Radiator Italia S.r.l. (4)
Via Cottolengo 8, Vinovo, 10048, Turin, Italy
Tel.: (39) 011 9658191
Radiator Whslr
N.A.I.C.S.: 423120

Subsidiary (US):

WP Suspension North America, Inc. (4)
38340 Innovation Ct Ste 701, Murrieta, CA
92563
Tel.: (951) 234-2254
Web Site: http://www.wpfactoryservices.com
Suspension Product Mfr
N.A.I.C.S.: 336330

Pierer Industrie AG (1)
Edisonstrasse 1, 4600, Wels, Austria
Tel.: (43) 7242 69402
Web Site: http://www.piererindustrie.at
Holding Company
N.A.I.C.S.: 551112
Stefan Pierer *(Chm-Mgmt Bd & CEO)*

Subsidiary (US):

CP-Carrillo, LLC (2)
1902 McGaw Ave, Irvine, CA 92614
Tel.: (949) 567-9000
Web Site: http://www.cp-carrillo.com
Industrial Machinery & Equipment Distr

N.A.I.C.S.: 423830
Barry Calvert *(CEO)*

Subsidiary (Non-US):

Moto Italia SRL (2)
Via Biondi 1, 20154, Milan, Italy
Tel.: (39) 0287068247
Web Site: http://www.officinamotoitalia.it
Motor Cycle Distr
N.A.I.C.S.: 423910

Subsidiary (Domestic):

Pankl Racing Systems AG (2)
Industriestrasse West 4, 8605, Kapfenberg,
Austria (94.5%)
Tel.: (43) 3862339990
Web Site: http://www.pankl.com
Rev.: $452,007,948
Assets: $408,899,437
Liabilities: $246,050,337
Net Worth: $162,849,100
Earnings: $15,014,902
Emp.: 2,434
Fiscal Year-end: 12/31/2023
Engine Systems Mfr & Distr
N.A.I.C.S.: 333618
Stefan Pierer *(Chm-Supervisory Bd)*

Subsidiary (US):

CP Pistons LLC (3)
1902 McGaw Ave, Irvine, CA 62614
Tel.: (949) 567-9000
Web Site: http://www.cppistons.com
Sales Range: $25-49.9 Million
Emp.: 100
Carburetor Piston Piston Ring & Valve Mfr
N.A.I.C.S.: 336310

Subsidiary (Non-US):

Pankl - APC Turbosystems GmbH (3)
Rudolf-Diesel-Str 24, 68169, Mannheim,
Germany
Tel.: (49) 621 860 854 430
Web Site: http://www.pankl-apc.com
Emp.: 52
Automobile Mfr
N.A.I.C.S.: 336110
Thomas Schofer *(Co-Partner)*

Subsidiary (US):

Pankl Aerospace Innovations, LLC (3)
Stamford iCenter 175 Atlantic St, Stamford,
CT 06901
Tel.: (562) 704-2493
Aircraft Part Mfr
N.A.I.C.S.: 336413

Subsidiary (Domestic):

Pankl Aerospace Systems Europe GmbH (3)
Industriestrasse W 4, 8605, Kapfenberg,
Austria
Tel.: (43) 3862339990
Web Site: http://www.pankl.com
Sales Range: $125-149.9 Million
Emp.: 400
Transportation Equipment & Supplies except Motor Vehicle Whslr
N.A.I.C.S.: 423860
Wolfgang Plasser *(CEO)*

Subsidiary (US):

Pankl Aerospace Systems Inc. (3)
16615 Edwards Rd, Cerritos, CA 90703
Tel.: (562) 207-6300
Web Site: http://www.pankl.com
Sales Range: $25-49.9 Million
Emp.: 70
Search Detection Navigation Guidance
Aeronautical & Nautical System & Instrument Mfr
N.A.I.C.S.: 334511

Subsidiary (Non-US):

Pankl Automotive Slovakia s.r.o. (3)
Odbojarov 294-10, 95588, Tovarniky, Slovakia
Tel.: (421) 385369811
Web Site: http://www.pankl.com

PIERER KONZERNGESELLSCHAFT MBH

Sales Range: $25-49.9 Million
Emp.: 150
Other Engine Equipment Mfr
N.A.I.C.S.: 333618

Subsidiary (Domestic):

Pankl Drivetrain Systems GmbH And Co KG (3)
Industriestrasse West 4, Steiermark, 8605,
Kapfenberg, Austria
Tel.: (43) 3862339999
Web Site: http://www.pankl.com
Sales Range: $75-99.9 Million
Emp.: 800
Other Metalworking Machinery Mfr
N.A.I.C.S.: 333519
Wolfgang Plasser *(Pres & CEO)*

Pankl Engine Systems AG (3)
Kaltschmidstrasse 2-6, 8600, Bruck an der
Mur, Austria
Tel.: (43) 3862512500
Web Site: http://www.pankl.com
Sales Range: $75-99.9 Million
Emp.: 400
Motor & Generator Manufacturing of High
Performance Vehicles
N.A.I.C.S.: 335312

Pankl High Performance Pistons GmbH (3)
Industriestrasse West 4, 8605, Kapfenberg,
Austria
Tel.: (43) 3862339990
Web Site: http://www.pankl.com
Motor & Generator Mfr
N.A.I.C.S.: 335312
Wolfgang Plasser *(CEO)*

Subsidiary (US):

Pankl Inc (3)
16615 Edwards Rd, Cerritos, CA 90703
Tel.: (562) 677-7251
Web Site: http://www.pankl.com
Sales Range: $25-49.9 Million
Emp.: 50
Automotive Parts & Accessories Stores
N.A.I.C.S.: 441330

Subsidiary (Non-US):

Pankl Japan Inc. (3)
301 Storia Shinagawa 2-16-8 Konan,
Minato-ku, Tokyo, Japan
Tel.: (81) 357153877
Sales Range: $25-49.9 Million
Emp.: 3
Other Engine Equipment Mfr
N.A.I.C.S.: 333618

Pankl Racing Systems UK Ltd (3)
Telford Road Oxon, Bicester, OX264LD,
United Kingdom
Tel.: (44) 1869243344
Web Site: http://www.pankl.com
Emp.: 30
All Other Automotive Repair & Maintenance
N.A.I.C.S.: 811198
Eric Newell *(Head-Ops)*

Subsidiary (Domestic):

Pankl Schmiedetechnik GmbH & Co KG (3)
Industriestrasse West 2, 8605, Kapfenberg,
Austria
Tel.: (43) 3862339990
Web Site: http://www.pankl.com
Sales Range: $75-99.9 Million
Emp.: 500
Aluminum Sheet Plate & Foil Mfr
N.A.I.C.S.: 331315
Wolfgang Plasser *(CEO)*

Subsidiary (Non-US):

SHW AG (2)
Stiewingstr 111, 73433, Aalen,
Germany (74.86%)
Tel.: (49) 73615021
Web Site: http://www.shw.de
Rev.: $509,933,089
Assets: $394,955,752
Liabilities: $257,393,697
Net Worth: $137,562,055
Earnings: ($7,280,380)
Emp.: 1,700
Fiscal Year-end: 12/31/2022
Pumps & Engine Components Mfr

PIERER KONZERNGESELLSCHAFT MBH

Pierer Konzerngesellschaft mbH—(Continued)
N.A.I.C.S.: 336310
Klaus Rinnerberger (Chm-Supervisory Bd)

Subsidiary (Domestic):

SHW Automotive GmbH (3)
Enzisholzweg 11, 88427, Bad Schussen-ried, Germany
Tel.: (49) 7583 9460
Sales Range: $150-199.9 Million
Emp.: 350
Automotive Distr
N.A.I.C.S.: 423110
Thomas Weber (Mgr-Sls)

PIERIDAE ENERGY (CANADA) LIMITED

3100 308-4th Avenue SW, Calgary, T2P 0H7, AB, Canada
Tel.: (403) 261-5900 Ca
Web Site:
 http://www.pieridaeenergy.com
Year Founded: 2003
PTOAF—(OTCIQ)
Rev.: $277,992,142
Assets: $482,175,080
Liabilities: $350,477,621
Net Worth: $131,697,459
Earnings: $6,781,733
Emp.: 261
Fiscal Year-end: 12/31/23
Oil & Gas Exploration Services
N.A.I.C.S.: 213112
Thomas Dawson (Sr VP-Mktg & Bus Dev)

Subsidiaries:

Ikkuma Resources Corp. (1)
Suite 2700 605 - 5th Avenue SW, Calgary, T2P 3H5, AB, Canada
Tel.: (403) 261-5900
Web Site: http://www.ikkumarescorp.com
Rev.: $38,738,968
Assets: $259,909,792
Liabilities: $176,487,701
Net Worth: $83,422,091
Earnings: ($28,636,614)
Emp.: 43
Fiscal Year-end: 12/31/2017
Oil & Gas Exploration Services
N.A.I.C.S.: 213112
Robert Dales (Chm)

PIERRE & VACANCES SA

LArtois Espace Pont de Flandre, 11 rue de Cambral, 75947, Paris, Cedex 19, France
Tel.: (33) 33158215821
Web Site:
 https://www.pierreetvacances.com
VAC—(EUR)
Rev.: $1,972,033,337
Assets: $4,811,256,210
Liabilities: $5,281,255,106
Net Worth: ($469,998,896)
Earnings: ($69,781,433)
Emp.: 8,318
Fiscal Year-end: 09/30/23
Traveler Accommodation Services
N.A.I.C.S.: 561599
Gerard Bremond (Chm)

Subsidiaries:

Bonavista de Bonmont SL (1)
Gulf of Bonmont Urb Terres Noves, Mont Roig Del Camp, 43300, Tarragona, Spain
Tel.: (34) 977832050
Real Estate Services
N.A.I.C.S.: 531190

Center Parcs Europe NV (1)
Rivium Boulevard 231, 2909 LK, Capelle aan den IJssel, Netherlands
Tel.: (31) 104989754
Web Site: https://www.centerparcs.eu
Nature Parks Services
N.A.I.C.S.: 712190

Clubhotel Multivacances SA (1)
11 rue de Cambrai, 75947, Paris, Cedex, France
Tel.: (33) 155264964
Web Site: http://multivacances.groupepvcp.com
Real Estate Services
N.A.I.C.S.: 531390

Cobim SARL (1)
29 Bld Thiers, 64500, Saint-Jean-de-Luz, France
Tel.: (33) 559269192
Web Site: http://www.tagimmobilier.com
Vacation Camp Services
N.A.I.C.S.: 721214

Les Senioriales Ville de Dijon SNC (1)
112 Avenue Jean Jaures, 21000, Dijon, France
Tel.: (33) 562478610
Senior Residence Services
N.A.I.C.S.: 623311

Les Senioriales Ville de Nimes SCI (1)
7 Boulevard Natoire, 30000, Nimes, France
Tel.: (33) 562478610
Senior Residence Services
N.A.I.C.S.: 623311

Les Senioriales Ville de Rillieux la Pape SCI (1)
21 rue de la Republique, 69140, Rillieux-la-Pape, France
Tel.: (33) 562478610
Senior Residence Services
N.A.I.C.S.: 623311

Les Senioriales Ville de St Etienne SCI (1)
52 rue Desire Claude, 42100, Saint-Etienne, France
Tel.: (33) 562478610
Senior Residence Services
N.A.I.C.S.: 623311

Les Senioriales de Juvignac SCI (1)
107 rue Jupiter, Juvignac, 34990, Montpellier, France
Tel.: (33) 562478610
Senior Residence Services
N.A.I.C.S.: 623311

Les Senioriales de Mordelles SCCV (1)
4 bis rue Jeanne d'Arc, Mordelles, 35310, Maure-de-Bretagne, France
Tel.: (33) 562478610
Senior Residence Services
N.A.I.C.S.: 623311

Les Senioriales en Ville Manosque SCI (1)
Rue Leon Mure, 04100, Manosque, France
Tel.: (33) 562478610
Senior Residence Services
N.A.I.C.S.: 623311

Les Senioriales en Ville d'Emerainville SCI (1)
2 Rue Willy Brandt, 77184, Emerainville-Malnoue, France
Tel.: (33) 562478610
Senior Residence Services
N.A.I.C.S.: 623311

Les Senioriales en Ville de Marseille - St Loup SCI (1)
159 Boulevard du pont de vivaux, 13010, Marseille, France
Tel.: (33) 562478610
Senior Residence Services
N.A.I.C.S.: 623311

Les Senioriales en Ville de Saint Avertin SCI (1)
23-27 Boulevard Paul Doumer, 37550, Saint-Avertin, France
Tel.: (33) 562478610
Senior Residence Services
N.A.I.C.S.: 623311

PVCP China Real Estate Brokerage Company Limited (1)
1788 International Center Nanjing West Road, Jing'an District, Shanghai, China
Tel.: (86) 4008215808
Web Site: http://www.puweiproperty.com
Real Estate Services
N.A.I.C.S.: 531390

Pierre & Vacances Developpement SA (1)
11 rue de Cambrai, 75947, Paris, Cedex, France
Tel.: (33) 158215357
Web Site:
 http://developpement.groupepvcp.com
Real Estate Services
N.A.I.C.S.: 531190

SAS PV Senioriales Promotion et Commercialisation (1)
2 Place Auguste Albert, 31500, Toulouse, France
Tel.: (33) 562479494
Web Site: https://www.senioriales.com
Emp.: 183
Real Estate Services
N.A.I.C.S.: 531190

PIERRE FABRE S.A.

17 Avenue Jean Moulin, Castres, France
Tel.: (33) 563714200
Web Site: http://www.pierre-fabre.com
Year Founded: 1961
Sales Range: $1-4.9 Billion
Emp.: 10,000
Perfumes, Cosmetics & Pharmaceuticals Mfr, Marketer & Distr
N.A.I.C.S.: 325620
Roch Doliveux (Chm-Supervisory Bd)

Subsidiaries:

Les Entretiens du Carla (1)
Les Fontaines 29 Avenue Du Sidobre, 81106, Castres, Cedex, France
Tel.: (33) 5 63 62 38 50
Web Site: http://www.entretiens-du-carla.com
Pharmaceuticals Product Mfr
N.A.I.C.S.: 325412

ORFAGEN (1)
Parc Technologique du Canal 4 rue Marie Curie, 31521, Ramonville-Saint-Agne, France
Tel.: (33) 5 62 24 76 83
Web Site: http://www.orfagen.com
Pharmaceuticals Product Mfr
N.A.I.C.S.: 325412

PIERRE FABRE USA KLORANE (1)
8 Campus Dr, Parsippany, NJ 07054
Tel.: (800) 522-8285
Cosmetics Mfr
N.A.I.C.S.: 325620

Pierre Fabre (Switzerland) S.A. (1)
Hegenheimermattweg 183, Allschwil, 4123, Switzerland
Tel.: (41) 61 487 89 00
Web Site: http://www.pierre-fabre.com
Pharmaceutical Testing Laboratory
N.A.I.C.S.: 541380

Pierre Fabre Dermo-Cosmetique Argentina S.A. (1)
Mt De Alvear 684 7 Piso, C1058AAH, Buenos Aires, Argentina
Tel.: (54) 114 318 96 00
Pharmaceuticals Product Mfr
N.A.I.C.S.: 325412

Pierre Fabre Dermo-Cosmetique, S.A. (1)
Les Cauquillous, 81506, Lavaur, Cedex, France
Tel.: (33) 5 63 58 88 00
Web Site: http://www.piere-fabre.com
Pharmaceuticals Product Mfr
N.A.I.C.S.: 325412

Pierre Fabre Iberica, S.A (1)
C/Ramon Trias Fargas 7-11, Barcelona, Spain
Tel.: (34) 93 483 30 00
Web Site: http://www.pierre-fabre.es
Pharmaceuticals Product Mfr
N.A.I.C.S.: 325412

Pierre Fabre Italia SpA (1)
1 Via Winckelmann, 20146, Milan, Italy
Tel.: (39) 02 47 79 41
Pharmaceuticals Product Mfr
N.A.I.C.S.: 325412

INTERNATIONAL PUBLIC

Pierre Fabre Medicament S.A. (1)
45 place Abel Gance, 92654, Boulogne-sur-Mer, France
Tel.: (33) 1 49 10 80 00
Pharmaceuticals Product Mfr
N.A.I.C.S.: 325412

Subsidiary (US):

Pierre Fabre Pharmaceuticals Inc (2)
8 Campus Dr, Parsippany, NJ 07054
Tel.: (973) 647-1600
Web Site: http://www.pierre-fabre.com
Emp.: 50
Pharmaceutical Product Whslr
N.A.I.C.S.: 424210
Kim DeWitt (Mgr-Fin & Ops)

ROBAPHARM A.G. (1)
Hegenheimermattweg 183, Allschwil, 4123, Switzerland
Tel.: (41) 61 487 88 88
Pharmaceutical Products Mfr & Lab Testing
N.A.I.C.S.: 325412

PIERSON DIFFUSION

Route de Bar le Duc Chauvoncourt, 55300, Saint-Mihiel, France
Tel.: (33) 329890162
Web Site: http://www.pierson.fr
Rev.: $25,500,000
Emp.: 89
Furniture & Fixtures
N.A.I.C.S.: 337127
Franck Souquet (Pres)

PIESAT INFORMATION TECHNOLOGY CO., LTD.

5F Building No 1 Area A Yiyuan Cultural and Creative Industry Base, Xingshikou Road Haidian District, Beijing, 100195, China
Tel.: (86) 1082556572
Web Site: http://www.piesat.com.cn
Year Founded: 2008
688066—(SHG)
Rev.: $344,969,876
Assets: $837,991,454
Liabilities: $457,596,089
Net Worth: $380,395,365
Earnings: $37,072,873
Emp.: 3,500
Fiscal Year-end: 12/31/22
Information Technology Services
N.A.I.C.S.: 541512
Yuxiang Wang (Chm & Gen Mgr)

PIETRO CO., LTD.

3-4-5 Tenjin, Chuo-ku, Fukuoka, 810-0001, Japan
Tel.: (81) 927160300 JP
Web Site: https://www.pietro.co.jp
Year Founded: 1979
2818—(TKS)
Rev.: $66,734,560
Assets: $69,953,630
Liabilities: $27,457,940
Net Worth: $42,495,690
Earnings: $720,490
Emp.: 291
Fiscal Year-end: 03/31/24
Food Products Mfr
N.A.I.C.S.: 325412
Keiko Nishikawa (Chm)

PIGEON CORPORATION

4-4 Nihonbashi-Hisamatsucho, Chuo-ku, Tokyo, 103-8480, Japan
Tel.: (81) 336614200 JP
Web Site: https://www.pigeon.com
Year Founded: 1949
PGENY—(OTCIQ)
Rev.: $669,746,438
Assets: $712,138,684
Liabilities: $137,216,447
Net Worth: $574,922,237
Earnings: $52,630,480
Emp.: 4,148
Fiscal Year-end: 12/31/23

AND PRIVATE COMPANIES

Childcare & Nursing Care Products Mfr
N.A.I.C.S.: 325620
Shigeru Yamashita *(Chm)*

Subsidiaries:

PHP Hyogo Co., Ltd. (1)
1009-28 Nakamura Kamikawacho, Kanzaki-gun, Hyogo, 679-2413, Japan **(100%)**
Tel.: (81) 790312940
Web Site: http://www.php-hyogo.co.jp
Emp.: 79
Mfr of Personal Wipes for Babies, Mothers & Elder Care Patients
N.A.I.C.S.: 325620

PHP Ibaraki Co., Ltd.
2068 1 Okadacho, Hitachiota, 313-0031, Ibaraki, Japan
Tel.: (81) 294741700
Sales Range: $25-49.9 Million
Emp.: 70
Tissues Mfr & Supplier
N.A.I.C.S.: 322291
Isao Omura *(Pres)*

Pigeon Hearts Corporation (1)
4-4 Nihonbashi Hisamatsu-cho, Chuo-ku, Tokyo, 103-0005, Japan
Tel.: (81) 336614290
Web Site: https://www.pigeonhearts.co.jp
Child Care Services
N.A.I.C.S.: 624410
Nobuo Takubo *(Auditor)*

Pigeon Home Products Corporation (1)
3885-10 Obuchi, Fuji City Ukishima Industrial Park, Fuji, 417-0801, Shizuoka, Japan
Tel.: (81) 545673344
Web Site: https://www.pigeonhomeproducts.com
Baby Care Product Mfr & Distr
N.A.I.C.S.: 325620

Pigeon India Pvt. Ltd. (1)
Unit No 216 Suncity Business Tower Sector 54 Golf Course Road, Gurgaon, 122002, Haryana, India
Tel.: (91) 1244320000
Web Site: https://www.pigeon-in.com
Infant Product Mfr
N.A.I.C.S.: 311514

Pigeon Industries (Thailand) Co., Ltd. (1)
700/103 Moo 1 Amata City Chonburi Industrial Estate, Tambol Ban Kao Phan Thong District, Phan Thong, 20160, Chon Buri, Thailand
Tel.: (66) 3821434344
Web Site: https://www.pigeon.co.th
Sales Range: $50-74.9 Million
Emp.: 484
Baby Products Mfr
N.A.I.C.S.: 458110

Pigeon Manufacturing Hyogo Corporation (1)
28-1009 Nakamura Kamikawa-cho, Kanzaki, 679-2413, Hyogo, Japan
Tel.: (81) 790312940
Web Site: https://www.pigeonmanufacturing.com
Emp.: 79
Plastic Sanitary Product Mfr
N.A.I.C.S.: 326199

Pigeon Singapore Pte. Ltd. (1)
80 Bendemeer Road 06-01B, Singapore, 339949, Singapore
Tel.: (65) 67423001
Web Site: https://www.pigeon.com.sg
Sales Range: $25-49.9 Million
Baby Products Mfr & Whslr
N.A.I.C.S.: 424350
Yusuke Nakata *(Pres)*

Thai Pigeon Co., Ltd. (1)
944 Moo 15 Theparaks Road, T Bang Sao Thong, Bang Sao Thong, 10570, Samutprakarn, Thailand
Tel.: (66) 2 313 1360
Infant Product Mfr
N.A.I.C.S.: 311514

PIHLAJALINNA OY

Kehrasaari B, 33200, Tampere, Finland
Tel.: (358) 207706896 FI
Web Site: https://www.pihlajalinna.fi
Year Founded: 2014
PIHLIS—(HEL)
Rev.: $745,176,991
Assets: $714,050,291
Liabilities: $581,427,801
Net Worth: $132,622,491
Earnings: $8,265,703
Emp.: 7,016
Fiscal Year-end: 12/31/22
Holding Company; Health Care & Social Care Services
N.A.I.C.S.: 551112
Mikko Wiren *(Chm)*

Subsidiaries:

Etela-Karjalan Liikuntakeskus Oy (1)
Pelitie 36, 53810, Lappeenranta, Finland
Tel.: (358) 55419600
Web Site: http://www.huhtari.fi
Health Care Srvices
N.A.I.C.S.: 621498

Forever Hameenlinna Oy (1)
Vanajantie 10b, 13110, Hameenlinna, Finland
Tel.: (358) 36883355
Health Care Srvices
N.A.I.C.S.: 621498

Forever Herttoniemi Oy (1)
Hitsaajankatu 10, 00810, Helsinki, Finland
Tel.: (358) 504388884
Health Care Srvices
N.A.I.C.S.: 621498

Forever Hiekkaharju Oy (1)
Tennistie 3, 01370, Vantaa, Finland
Tel.: (358) 98735400
Health Care Srvices
N.A.I.C.S.: 621498

Forever Jarvenpaa Oy (1)
Wartsilankatu 8B, Jarvenpaa, Finland
Tel.: (358) 438267155
Health Care Srvices
N.A.I.C.S.: 621498

Forever Lahti Oy (1)
Svinhufvudinkatu 23, 15110, Lahti, Finland
Tel.: (358) 3877550
Health Care Srvices
N.A.I.C.S.: 621498

Forever Matinkyla Oy (1)
Matinkar Anontie 1, 02230, Espoo, Finland
Tel.: (358) 982560011
Health Care Srvices
N.A.I.C.S.: 621498

Forever Varisto Oy (1)
Martinkylantie 39, 01720, Vantaa, Finland
Tel.: (358) 438250754
Health Care Srvices
N.A.I.C.S.: 621498

Hammaslaakarikeskus Mandipula Oy (1)
Tasalanaukio 3, 21200, Raisio, Finland
Tel.: (358) 24398330
Web Site: http://www.mandibula.fi
Health Care Srvices
N.A.I.C.S.: 621498

Jamsan Terveys Oy (1)
Sairaalantie 11, 42100, Jamsa, Finland
Tel.: (358) 206306020
Web Site: https://www.jamsanterveys.fi
Health Care Srvices
N.A.I.C.S.: 621498

Keravan Forever Oy (1)
Kultasepankatu 5, 04250, Kerava, Finland
Tel.: (358) 958400110
Health Care Srvices
N.A.I.C.S.: 621498

Kuusiolinna Terveys Oy (1)
Salmentie 10, 63300, Alavus, Finland
Tel.: (358) 625257612
Web Site: https://www.kuusiolinna.fi
Health Care Srvices
N.A.I.C.S.: 621498

Leaf Areena Oy (1)
Karsamaentie 35, 20360, Turku, Finland
Tel.: (358) 102814400
Web Site: http://www.leafareena.fi
Health Care Srvices
N.A.I.C.S.: 621498

Pihlajalinna Ikioma Oy (1)
Porrassalmenkatu 21, 50100, Mikkeli, Finland
Tel.: (358) 15321320
Health Care Srvices
N.A.I.C.S.: 621610

Pihlajalinna Terveys Oy (1)
Kehrasaari B 4th floor, 33200, Tampere, Finland
Tel.: (358) 10312144
Health Care & Social Care Services
N.A.I.C.S.: 622110
Kimmo Saarinen *(Dir-Medical)*

PIHSIANG MACHINERY MFG. CO., LTD.

No 108 Xinhe Road Xinfeng Township, Hsin-chu, 304, Taiwan
Tel.: (886) 35688585
Web Site: http://www.pihsiang.com.tw
Year Founded: 1983
Sales Range: $50-74.9 Million
Medical Mobility Device Mfr
N.A.I.C.S.: 336991
Ching-Ming Chiang *(Gen Mgr)*

Subsidiaries:

Pihsiang Energy Technology Co., Ltd. (1)
No 7 Gongyeh 5 Road Hsinchu Industry Park, Hukou, 30352, Hsinchu, Taiwan
Tel.: (886) 35977360
Web Site: http://www.phet.com.tw
Emp.: 120
Battery Mfr
N.A.I.C.S.: 335910

Shoprider Japan Ltd. (1)
3-41-8 Hagasha Nappori, Arakawa-ku, Tokyo, 116-0014, Japan
Tel.: (81) 356153351
Web Site: http://www.shopriderjapan.co.jp
Electric Wheelchairs & Carts Mfr
N.A.I.C.S.: 336999

Shoprider Mobility Products, Inc. (1)
1338 Storm Pkwy Ste D, Torrance, CA 90501
Tel.: (310) 328-8866
Web Site: http://www.shoprider.com
Emp.: 16
Shopping Scooters Retailer Distr
N.A.I.C.S.: 441227
Alain Muril *(Gen Mgr)*

Yangming Industry (Zhejiang) Ltd. (1)
No 501 Xingping 3rd Road Economic Development Zone, Pinghu, 314200, Zhejiang, China
Tel.: (86) 57385072960
Web Site: http://www.pihsiang.com.cn
Shopping Scooter & Electric Wheelchairs Mfr
N.A.I.C.S.: 339113

PIIPPO OYJ

Sysmajarventie 3, 83500, Outokumpu, Finland
Tel.: (358) 13562556
Web Site: https://www.piippo.fi
PIIPPO—(HEL)
Rev.: $24,109,648
Assets: $22,836,175
Liabilities: $14,569,393
Net Worth: $8,266,782
Earnings: $485,646
Emp.: 89
Fiscal Year-end: 12/31/22
Ropes, Twines & Net Wraps Mfr
N.A.I.C.S.: 314994
Arja Karvonen *(Mgr-Fin)*

PIK D.D.

Kresimirova 26, 51000, Rijeka, Croatia
Tel.: (385) 51650318

PIL ITALICA LIFESTYLE LTD.

Web Site: http://www.pikrijeka.hr
Pasta & Bakery Product Mfr
N.A.I.C.S.: 311824

PIK GROUP OF COMPANIES PJSC

19 Bld 1 Barrikadnaya Street, 123242, Moscow, Russia
Tel.: (7) 4955059733
Web Site: http://www.pik.ru
Year Founded: 1994
Construction Services
N.A.I.C.S.: 236220
Yuri Ilyin *(VP-Capital Markets & Corp Fin)*

PIK PESTER A.D.

Karadordeva 11, 11000, Belgrade, Serbia
Tel.: (381) 112633149
Web Site: https://www.pikpester.com
Year Founded: 2001
PKPT—(BEL)
Sales Range: Less than $1 Million
Dairy Cattle Farming Services
N.A.I.C.S.: 112120
Ersin Malicevic *(Gen Mgr & Exec Dir)*

PIK VRBAS A.D.

Aleksandra Dubceka 14, Belgrade, Serbia
Tel.: (381) 11 3778 357
Year Founded: 1991
Sales Range: Less than $1 Million
Retail Store Operator
N.A.I.C.S.: 455219

PIKE WHEATON

3110 50 Ave, Red Deer, T4R 1M6, AB, Canada
Tel.: (403) 347-3301
Web Site: http://www.pikewheaton.com
Rev.: $13,824,247
Emp.: 50
New & Used Car Dealers
N.A.I.C.S.: 441110
Gordon Pike *(Owner)*

PIKO A.D.

Boze Tatarevica 16, 78430, Prnjavor, Bosnia & Herzegovina
Tel.: (387) 51645183
PIKO—(BANJ)
Sales Range: Less than $1 Million
Emp.: 7
Real Estate Prorperty Leasing Services
N.A.I.C.S.: 531190
Miladin Stanic *(Chm-Mgmt Bd & Pres)*

PIKOLIN S.A.

Ronda Ferrocarril 24 Poligono Industrial Plaza, 50197, Zaragoza, Spain
Tel.: (34) 976300864 ES
Web Site: http://www.pikolin.com
Year Founded: 1948
Sales Range: $125-149.9 Million
Emp.: 1,000
Mattress Mfr
N.A.I.C.S.: 337910
Alfonso Solans *(Chm)*

Subsidiaries:

COFEL (1)
57 Rue Yves Kermen, 92100, Boulogne-Billancourt, Cedex, France
Tel.: (33) 14 190 2828
Web Site: https://www.cofel.fr
Mfr of Mattresses & Bed Bases; Joint Venture of Recticel S.A. (50%) & Pikolin S.A. (50%)
N.A.I.C.S.: 337910

PIL Italica Lifestyle Ltd.—(Continued)

Kodiyat Road Sisarma, Udaipur, 313031, Rajasthan, India
Tel.: (91) 9314411101
Web Site: https://www.italica.com
500327—(BOM)
Rev.: $10,233,583
Assets: $10,453,450
Liabilities: $2,113,123
Net Worth: $8,340,327
Earnings: $364,918
Emp.: 203
Fiscal Year-end: 03/31/23
Plastic Molded Furniture Mfr
N.A.I.C.S.: 337126
Narendra Bhanawat (CFO)

PILA PHARMA AB

Norra Vallgatan 72, 211 22, Malmo, Sweden
Tel.: (46) 739036969
Web Site: https://www.pilapharma.com
Year Founded: 2014
PILA—(NASDAQ)
Pharmaceutical Product Mfr & Distr
N.A.I.C.S.: 325412
Dorte X. Gram (CEO)

Subsidiaries:

Xenia Pharma Pvt. Ltd. (1)
Copenhagen Bio Science Park COBIS Ole Maaloes Vej 3, 2200, Copenhagen, Denmark
Tel.: (45) 739036969
Web Site: https://www.xeniapharma.com
Medical Device Distr
N.A.I.C.S.: 423450

PILANI INVESTMENT & INDUSTRIES CORPORATION LIMITED

Birla Building 14th Floor 9/1 R N Mukherjee Road, Kolkata, 700 001, India
Tel.: (91) 3340823700
Web Site: https://www.pilaniinvestment.com
Year Founded: 1948
Sales Range: $1-9.9 Million
Emp.: 5
Non Banking Financial Services
N.A.I.C.S.: 523999
Rajkumar Singh Kashyap (Chief Risk Officer & Sec)

PILATUS AIRCRAFT LTD.

PO Box 992, 6371, Stans, Switzerland
Tel.: (41) 416193333
Web Site: http://www.pilatus-aircraft.com
Year Founded: 1939
Sales Range: $600-649.9 Million
Emp.: 2,000
Aircrafts & Training Systems Developer, Mfr & Marketer
N.A.I.C.S.: 336411
Oscar J. Schwenk (Chm)

Subsidiaries:

Altenrhein Aviation Ltd (1)
Flughafenstrasse 11, 9423, Altenrhein, Switzerland
Tel.: (41) 71 858 51 85
Web Site: http://www.altenrhein-aviation.com
Sales Range: $10-24.9 Million
Maintenance, Modernization & Overhauling of Aircraft
N.A.I.C.S.: 488190
Timo Nielsen (Mgr-Quality & Safety)

DTC Dynamic Test Center AG (1)
Route Principale 127, CH 2537, Vauffelin, Switzerland
Tel.: (41) 32 321 66 00
Web Site: http://www.dtc-ag.ch
Rev.: $7,555,240
Emp.: 23
Automotive Testing Center
N.A.I.C.S.: 541380
Bernhard Gerster (CEO)

Pilatus Australia Pty Ltd (1)
17 James Schofield Drive, Adelaide Airport, Adelaide, 5950, SA, Australia
Tel.: (61) 8 8238 1600
Web Site: http://www.pilatus-aircraft.com
Emp.: 8
Aircraft Sales & Marketing
N.A.I.C.S.: 488190
Sebastian Lip (CEO)

Pilatus Business Aircraft Ltd (1)
Rocky Mountain Metropolitan Airport 11755 Airport Way, Broomfield, CO 80021
Tel.: (303) 465-9099
Web Site: http://www.pilatus-aircraft.com
Emp.: 100
Completion of Aircraft Interiors & Exteriors; Aircraft Marketing, Sales & Servicing
N.A.I.C.S.: 336413
Thomas Bosshard (Pres & CEO)

Skytech Inc. (1)
200 Airport Dr, Westminster, MD 21157
Tel.: (410) 876-0353
Web Site: http://www.skytechinc.com
Emp.: 100
Aircraft Parts Whslr
N.A.I.C.S.: 423860
Michael J. Fitzgerald (Exec VP-Sls & Mktg)

PILBARA MINERALS LIMITED

Level 2 146 Colin Street, West Perth, 6005, WA, Australia
Tel.: (61) 862666266
Web Site: http://www.pilbaraminerals.com.au
PLS—(ASX)
Rev.: $2,649,813,523
Assets: $3,389,733,977
Liabilities: $1,179,378,627
Net Worth: $2,210,355,350
Earnings: $1,559,063,050
Emp.: 292
Fiscal Year-end: 06/30/23
Metal Mining & Exploration Services
N.A.I.C.S.: 212290
John Holmes (Mgr-Exploration & Geology)

PILERSUISOQ

JM Jensenip Aqq 2, PO Box 50, Sisimiut, 3911, Greenland
Tel.: (299) 862444
Web Site: http://www.kni.gl
Sales Range: $125-149.9 Million
Emp.: 800
Grocery Stores
N.A.I.C.S.: 445110
Claus Jensen (Pres)

PILI INTERNATIONAL MULTIMEDIA CO., LTD.

32F No 95 Sec 1 Xintai 5th Rd, Xizhi Dist, Taipei, Taiwan
Tel.: (886) 289780555
Web Site: https://pili.com.tw
Year Founded: 1996
8450—(TPE)
Rev.: $12,508,739
Assets: $54,439,890
Liabilities: $22,595,754
Net Worth: $31,844,136
Earnings: $(3,852,015)
Fiscal Year-end: 12/31/22
Broadcasting Services
N.A.I.C.S.: 711190
Liang-Hsun Huang (Vice Chm & Pres)

PILIPINAS SHELL PETROLEUM CORPORATION

41st Floor The Finance Center 26th Street Corner 9th Avenue, Bonifacio Global City Brgy Fort Bonifacio, 1635, Taguig, 1635, Metro Manila, Philippines
Tel.: (63) 234994001
Web Site: https://pilipinas.shell.com.ph
SHLPH—(PHI)
Rev.: $4,645,258,709
Assets: $2,080,803,759
Liabilities: $1,537,247,442
Net Worth: $543,556,318
Earnings: $21,233,091
Fiscal Year-end: 12/31/22
Petroleum Product Mfr & Distr
N.A.I.C.S.: 324110
Cesar G. Romero (Pres & CEO)

PILKINGTON'S TILES GROUP PLC

PO Box 4, Rake Ln Clifton Jct, Swinton, M27 8LP, Manchester, United Kingdom
Tel.: (44) 617271000
Year Founded: 1891
Sales Range: $25-49.9 Million
Emp.: 391
Ceramic Wall & Floor Tiles Mfr
N.A.I.C.S.: 327120

Subsidiaries:

Pilkington's Tiles Ltd. (1)
PO Box 4, Clifton Jct, Swinton, M27 8LP, Manchester, United Kingdom (100%)
Tel.: (44) 617271000
Sales Range: $125-149.9 Million
Emp.: 310
Wall & Floor Tiles Mfr
N.A.I.C.S.: 327120

Quiligotti Contracts Ltd. (1)
PO Box 4, Rake Ln, Clifton Junction, Swinton, M27 8LP, Manchester, United Kingdom (100%)
Tel.: (44) 617271130
Installation of Terrazzo Tiles
N.A.I.C.S.: 238340

Quiligotti Terrazzo Ltd. (1)
PO Box 4, Clifton Junction, Swinton, M27 8LP, Lancashire, United Kingdom (100%)
Tel.: (44) 1617271189
Web Site: http://www.pilkingtons.com
Terrazzo Tiles Mfr
N.A.I.C.S.: 238340

PILLAR RESOURCE SERVICES, INC.

502 550-11th Avenue SW, Calgary, T2R 1M7, AB, Canada
Tel.: (403) 266-7070
Web Site: https://www.pillar.ca
Year Founded: 1983
Sales Range: $100-124.9 Million
Emp.: 500
Mechanical & Fabrication Services
N.A.I.C.S.: 541330
Joe Samaska (Pres)

Subsidiaries:

Pillar Resource Services, Inc. - Edmonton Facility (1)
4155-84th Avenue, Edmonton, T6B 2Z3, AB, Canada
Tel.: (780) 440-2212
Fabricated Pipe Mfr
N.A.I.C.S.: 332996

PILLER INDUSTRIEVENTILATOREN GMBH

Nienhagener Strasse 6, Moringen, 37186, Northeim, Germany
Tel.: (49) 55542010
Web Site: http://www.piller.de
Year Founded: 1909
Sales Range: $50-74.9 Million
Centrifugal Fan Mfr
N.A.I.C.S.: 333413
Nils Englund (Mng Dir)

Subsidiaries:

Piller BC Shanghai Ltd. (1)
Unit 30988 88 Keyuan Road, Zhangjiang Hi-Tech Park Pudong, 201203, Shanghai, China
Tel.: (86) 2150203878
Compressor Distr
N.A.I.C.S.: 423830

Piller SEA Pte. Ltd. (1)
25 International Business Park 03-56 German Centre, Singapore, 609916, Singapore
Tel.: (65) 65629551
Web Site: http://www.piller.com.sg
Compressor Distr
N.A.I.C.S.: 423830
Elizabeth Belisario (Mgr-After Sls & Mktg)

Piller TSC Blower Corporation (1)
445 Duane Ave, Schenectady, NY 12304
Tel.: (518) 372-2496
Web Site: http://www.piller-tsc.com
Compressor Mfr
N.A.I.C.S.: 333912
James Flynn (VP)

PILOT CORPORATION

2-6-21 Kyobashi, Chuo-ku, Tokyo, 104-8304, Japan
Tel.: (81) 335383700
Web Site: https://www.pilot.co.jp
Year Founded: 1918
7846—(TKS)
Rev.: $840,803,100
Assets: $1,180,258,120
Liabilities: $241,932,070
Net Worth: $938,326,050
Earnings: $96,856,490
Emp.: 1,105
Fiscal Year-end: 12/31/23
Fountain & Ball-Point Pens, Building Materials, Computer Supplies, Jewelry, Gift Products & Magnetic Boards Mfr
N.A.I.C.S.: 339940
Hiromoto Watanabe (Chm)

Subsidiaries:

Pilot Corporation of Europe S.A. (1)
PAE de La Caille - Saint-Martin Bellevue, Allonzier-La-Caille, 74350, Annecy, France
Tel.: (33) 450083000
Web Site: http://www.pilotpen.eu
Emp.: 240
Stationery Product Mfr
N.A.I.C.S.: 322230

Subsidiary (Non-US):

Comercial Arge, S.A. (2)
Plaza Lopez de la Plata 4, 28043, Madrid, Spain
Tel.: (34) 915016705
Web Site: http://www.pilot-es.es
Home & Office Equipment Whslr
N.A.I.C.S.: 423430

Nykor Pilot Pen Italia Srl (2)
Via del Lavoro 89, Casalecchio di Reno, BO, Italy
Tel.: (39) 051750566
Web Site: http://www.pilotpen.it
Stationery Product Distr
N.A.I.C.S.: 424120

Division (Non-US):

Pilot Corporation of Europe S.A. - Benelux Division (2)
Leuvensesteenweg 542 C2, 1930, Zaventem, Belgium
Tel.: (32) 22458086
Web Site: http://www.pilotpen.be
Stationery Product Mfr
N.A.I.C.S.: 322230
Frank Schelkens (Mng Dir)

Subsidiary (Non-US):

Pilot Nordic AB (2)
Maskingatan 6, 195 60, Arlandastad, Sweden
Tel.: (46) 854480550
Web Site: https://www.pilotnordic.com
Stationery Product Distr

N.A.I.C.S.: 424120
Jan-Olof Vegholm *(Mng Dir)*

Pilot Pen (Deutschland) GmbH (2)
Senefelder-Ring 81, 21465, Reinbek, Germany
Tel.: (49) 402519320
Web Site: http://www.pilotpen.de
Stationery Product Mfr
N.A.I.C.S.: 322230

Subsidiary (Domestic):

Pilot Pen France, SA (2)
PAE de La Caille - Saint-Martin Bellevue, Allonzier-La-Caille, 74350, Annecy, France
Tel.: (33) 450083000
Web Site: https://www.pilotpen.fr
Stationery Product Distr
N.A.I.C.S.: 424120
Monsieur Julien Barabant *(Dir-Publication)*

Subsidiary (Non-US):

Pilot Pen Norsk AS (2)
Grini Naeringspark 12, 1361, Osteras, Norway
Tel.: (47) 67162200
Web Site: http://www.pilotpen.no
Stationery Product Distr
N.A.I.C.S.: 424120
Alexis Bjornskau *(Sls Mgr)*

Pilot Pen Petersburg Ltd. (2)
31A st Vozrozhdenija, 198188, Saint Petersburg, Russia
Tel.: (7) 8123321681
Web Site: http://www.pilotpen.ru
Stationery Product Distr
N.A.I.C.S.: 424120

Pilot Pen UK Ltd. (2)
4 Dukes Meadow Millboard Road, Bourne End, Buckingham, SL8 5XF, United Kingdom
Tel.: (44) 175771666
Web Site: http://www.pilotpen.co.uk
Stationery Product Distr
N.A.I.C.S.: 424120
Mark Knibbs *(Mng Dir)*

Pilotpen Iberica, Unipessoal, Lda (2)
Parque Empresarial Vialonga Nave 11 Granja de Alpriate Casal Bagulho, 2625-607, Vialonga, Portugal
Tel.: (351) 210995603
Stationery Product Distr
N.A.I.C.S.: 424120

Plumor-Novimex AG (2)
Achslenstrasse 15, 9016, Saint Gallen, Switzerland
Tel.: (41) 713139680
Web Site: http://www.pilotpen.ch
Stationery Product Distr
N.A.I.C.S.: 424120

Pulse Design doo (2)
Veljka Mladenovica bb, 78000, Banja Luka, Bosnia & Herzegovina
Tel.: (387) 51389890
Web Site: http://www.pilotpen.ba
Stationery Product Mfr
N.A.I.C.S.: 322230

Pulse Office doo (2)
Prva industrijska br 5, 22330, Nova Pazova, Serbia
Tel.: (381) 607000462
Web Site: http://www.pulseserbia.com
Bag Mfr
N.A.I.C.S.: 322220

S. C. Dacris Impex Srl (2)
Strada Paroseni Nr 2-4 Sector 2, Bucharest, Romania
Tel.: (40) 730597748
Web Site: http://www.dacris.ro
Machinery Equipment Mfr
N.A.I.C.S.: 333922

Socrates P. Kyprianides Ltd. (2)
6 Prince Charles Str, Ayios Dhometios, 2373, Nicosia, Cyprus
Tel.: (357) 22771204
Stationery Product Mfr
N.A.I.C.S.: 322230

Vaclav Cizek s.r.o. (2)
Do Certous 2620/11, Horni Pocernice, 193 00, Prague, Czech Republic
Tel.: (420) 255734111
Web Site: https://www.vaclav-cizek.cz
Stationery Product Distr
N.A.I.C.S.: 424120
Jan Fiala *(Mgr-Acct)*

WPC Sp. z o.o. (2)
ul Sosnkowskiego 1, 02-495, Warsaw, Poland
Tel.: (48) 225320800
Stationery Product Distr
N.A.I.C.S.: 424120

Pilot Pen (Malaysia) Sdn. Bhd. (1)
No 6 Jalan BP 4/6 Bandar Bukit Puchong, Puchong, 47100, Kuala Selangor, Malaysia
Tel.: (60) 380681818
Web Site: http://www.pilotpen.com.my
Writing Instrument Stationery Whslr
N.A.I.C.S.: 424120
Lai Yoke Ng *(Supvr-Acct)*

Pilot Pen (S) Pte. Ltd. (1)
21/23 Tampines Industrial Avenue 5 T5 Tampines, Singapore, 528620, Singapore
Tel.: (65) 67892121
Web Site: https://www.pilotpen.com.sg
Writing Equipment Mfr
N.A.I.C.S.: 339940
Tracy Chee *(Mgr-Marketing)*

Pilot Pen Australia Pty. Ltd. (1)
39 Enterprise Circuit, Preston, 2170, NSW, Australia
Tel.: (61) 1300325866
Web Site: http://www.pilotpen.com.au
Home & Office Equipment Whslr
N.A.I.C.S.: 423430
Scott Thornton *(Mng Dir)*

Pilot Pen South Africa (Pty) Ltd. (1)
62 Milky Way Off Lepus Road, Amalgam, Johannesburg, South Africa
Tel.: (27) 118378494
Web Site: http://www.pilotpensa.co.za
Stationery Product Distr
N.A.I.C.S.: 424120

The Pilot Corporation of America (1)
3855 Regent Blvd, Jacksonville, FL 32224-6505
Tel.: (904) 565-7600
Web Site: http://www.pilotpen.com
Sales Range: $150-199.9 Million
Emp.: 306
Writing Instrument Mfr & Distr
N.A.I.C.S.: 424120

Division (Domestic):

The Pilot Corporation of America (2)
4200 Business Dr, Fremont, CA 94538 (100%)
Tel.: (510) 226-6466
Sales Range: $25-49.9 Million
Emp.: 8
Mfr of Pens
N.A.I.C.S.: 424120

The Pilot Corporation of America (2)
3901 Regent Blvd E Pk, Jacksonville, FL 32224
Tel.: (904) 645-9999
Web Site: http://www.pilotpen.com
Sales Range: $25-49.9 Million
Emp.: 150
Mfr of Pilot Pens
N.A.I.C.S.: 339940

PILOT ENERGY LTD.
Suite 301 35 Spring Street, Bondi Junction, 2022, NSW, Australia
Tel.: (61) 497832046 AU
Web Site: https://www.pilotenergy.com.au
PGY—(ASX)
Rev.: $286,821
Assets: $10,893,241
Liabilities: $2,692,121
Net Worth: $8,201,120
Earnings: ($2,854,812)
Fiscal Year-end: 09/30/23
Oil & Gas Exploration Services
N.A.I.C.S.: 211120
Lisa Dadswell *(Sec)*

PILSEN STEEL S.R.O.
Tylova 1/57, 301 00, Plzen, Czech Republic
Tel.: (420) 378132509 CZ
Web Site: http://www.pilsensteel.cz
Year Founded: 1859
Steel Products Mfr
N.A.I.C.S.: 332111
Michal Berka *(Dir-Sls)*

PIM KOREA CO., LTD.
26 Secheon-ro 8-gil Dasa-eup, Dalseong-gun, Daegu, 42921, Korea (South)
Tel.: (82) 535869600
Web Site: https://www.pimkorea.com
Year Founded: 2001
448900—(KRS)
Emp.: 75
Automobile & Light Duty Motor Vehicle Mfr & Distr
N.A.I.C.S.: 336120

PIM LIMITED
Quay Road, PO Box 1173, Port Louis, Mauritius
Tel.: (230) 2163000
Web Site: https://pimltd.mu
Year Founded: 1970
PIM—(MAU)
Rev.: $6,731,035
Assets: $6,377,515
Liabilities: $4,607,830
Net Worth: $1,769,684
Earnings: $262,175
Emp.: 165
Fiscal Year-end: 06/30/23
Plastics Product Mfr
N.A.I.C.S.: 326199
M. Paul Eric Piat Corson *(Mng Dir)*

PIMA ZINC CORP.
65 International Blvd Suite 202, Toronto, M9W 6L9, ON, Canada
Tel.: (775) 315-0728
Web Site: https://www.cybeats.com
RAEWF—(OTCIQ)
Sales Range: Less than $1 Million
Mineral Exploration Services
N.A.I.C.S.: 213114
Albert Contardi *(CEO)*

PINAR ENTEGRE ET VE UN SANAYI AS
Kemalpasa OSB Mahallesi 503 Sokak Dis Kapi No 224, Kemalpasa, 35170, Izmir, Turkiye
Tel.: (90) 2328770900
PETUN—(IST)
Sales Range: Less than $1 Million
Meat Product Distr
N.A.I.C.S.: 424470

PINAR SU SANAYI VE TICARET AS
Kemalpasa St No 262, Pinarbasi, 35060, Izmir, Turkiye
Tel.: (90) 2324365250
Web Site: https://www.pinarsu.com.tr
Year Founded: 1984
PINSU—(IST)
Rev.: $29,800,540
Assets: $57,655,207
Liabilities: $46,289,620
Net Worth: $11,365,587
Earnings: ($5,403,455)
Emp.: 375
Fiscal Year-end: 12/31/20
Bottled Product Mfr
N.A.I.C.S.: 312112
Emine Feyhan Yasar *(Chm)*

PINAR SUT MAMULLERI SANAYII AS
Kemalpasa Caddesi No 317, Pinarbasi, 35060, Izmir, Turkiye
Tel.: (90) 2324361515

PNSUT—(IST)
Rev.: $279,750,234
Assets: $260,320,756
Liabilities: $109,361,343
Net Worth: $150,959,413
Earnings: $5,828,293
Emp.: 1,033
Fiscal Year-end: 12/31/19
Dairy Products Distr
N.A.I.C.S.: 424430
Gurkan Hekimoglu *(Gen Mgr)*

PINCHIN LTD
2360 Meadowpine Boulevard Unit 2, Mississauga, L5N 6S2, ON, Canada
Tel.: (905) 363-0678
Web Site: https://www.pinchin.com
Year Founded: 1981
Emp.: 1,000
Environmental Services
N.A.I.C.S.: 541620
Jeff Grossi *(CEO)*

Subsidiaries:

Ransom Consulting, LLC (1)
12 Kent Way Ste 100, Byfield, MA 01922-1221
Tel.: (978) 465-1822
Web Site: http://www.ransomenv.com
Environmental Consulting Services
N.A.I.C.S.: 541620
Stephen B. Ransom *(Pres)*

PINCON LIFESTYLE LTD.
No 103 K H Road Shanthinagar Samskruthi Chambers 3rd Floor, Bengaluru, 560027, India
Tel.: (91) 8022229135
Fashion Apparels Mfr
N.A.I.C.S.: 315990
Partho Basu *(CFO)*

PINDAO HOLDINGS LIMITED
Block F Building 3 Crown Science & Technology Park Tairan 9th Road, Futian, Shenzhen, Guangdong, China Ky
Web Site: https://www.naixuecha.com
Year Founded: 2014
2150—(HKG)
Rev.: $715,005,538
Assets: $1,044,024,701
Liabilities: $376,411,165
Net Worth: $667,613,536
Earnings: $1,546,023
Emp.: 7,199
Fiscal Year-end: 12/31/23
Holding Company
N.A.I.C.S.: 551112
Bin Deng *(COO)*

PINE CAPITAL GROUP LIMITED
80 Robinson Road #02-00, Singapore, 068898, Singapore
Tel.: (65) 6 532 2533 SG
Year Founded: 1988
Sales Range: $1-9.9 Million
Investment Holding Company
N.A.I.C.S.: 551112
Pan Mi Keay *(Sec)*

Subsidiaries:

BIOMASS Energy Corporation (1)
735-3 Meshiro-machi, Isahaya, 854-0007, Nagasaki, Japan
Tel.: (81) 957468511
Web Site: http://www.transcu.com.sg
Biomass Energy Research & Development Services
N.A.I.C.S.: 541715

PINE CLIFF ENERGY LTD.
Suite 850 1015-4th Street SW, Calgary, T2R 1J4, AB, Canada
Tel.: (403) 269-2289 Ca

PINE CLIFF ENERGY LTD.

Pine Cliff Energy Ltd.—(Continued)
Web Site:
https://www.pinecliffenergy.com
Year Founded: 2004
PIFYF—(OTCQX)
Rev.: $142,605,922
Assets: $360,246,609
Liabilities: $284,788,977
Net Worth: $75,457,631
Earnings: $6,887,450
Emp.: 103
Fiscal Year-end: 12/31/23
Petroleum & Natural Gas Services
N.A.I.C.S.: 213112
George F. Fink (Chm)

Subsidiaries:

Certus Oil & Gas Inc. (1)

PINE TECHNOLOGY HOLDINGS LIMITED
Unit 1201 12/F 148 Electric Road, North Point, China (Hong Kong)
Tel.: (852) 2 773 9911
Web Site: http://www.pinegroup.com
Year Founded: 1989
1079—(HKG)
Rev.: $12,219,000
Assets: $39,616,000
Liabilities: $6,223,000
Net Worth: $33,393,000
Earnings: ($2,091,000)
Emp.: 106
Fiscal Year-end: 06/30/21
Video Graphics Technology & Computer Peripherals Mfr & Distr
N.A.I.C.S.: 334118
Hang Tai Chiu (Founder)

Subsidiaries:

Elite View Development Ltd. (1)
Unit C Young Ya Industrial Building 381-389 Sha Tsui Road, Tsuen Wan, New Territories, China (Hong Kong)
Tel.: (852) 29549729
Consumer Electronics Product Mfr
N.A.I.C.S.: 334419

Pine Group Hong Kong Limited (1)
1201 148 Electric Rd, North Point, China (Hong Kong)
Tel.: (852) 27739911
Web Site: http://www.pinegroup.com
Electronic Products Mfr
N.A.I.C.S.: 334118

Pine Lab TW Co. Ltd. (1)
Floor 6 Room 3 No 79 Section 1 Hsin Tai Wu Road His Chilh, Taipei, Taiwan
Tel.: (886) 226988033
Computer Peripherals Mfr
N.A.I.C.S.: 334112

Pine Technology (Macao Commercial Offshore) Ltd. (1)
Avenida Da Praia Grande No 619 Floor 14 Room 12, Edf Si Toi Comercial Centre, Macau, 999078, China (Macau)
Tel.: (853) 2 871 7466
Web Site: http://www.pinegroup.com
Emp.: 10
Electronic Products Mfr
N.A.I.C.S.: 334118

Pine Technology Limited (1)
Room A 32/f Manulife Tower 169 Electric Road, North Point, China (Hong Kong)
Tel.: (852) 27739911
Computer Peripheral Equipment Distr
N.A.I.C.S.: 423430

Pineview Industries Limited (1)
China Merchants Tower Room 1001, Central, China (Hong Kong)
Tel.: (852) 27739911
Computer Component Mfr
N.A.I.C.S.: 335999

Samtack Inc. (1)
10 Sims Crescent Unit 4 and 5, Richmond Hill, L4B 1K9, ON, Canada
Tel.: (905) 707-2388
Web Site: http://www.samtack.com

Computer Peripheral Distr
N.A.I.C.S.: 423430

PINE TRAIL REAL ESTATE INVESTMENT TRUST
161 Bay Street 27th Floor, Toronto, M5J 2S1, ON, Canada
Tel.: (403) 268-6854
Web Site: https://pinereit.com
Year Founded: 2018
PINE.UN—(TSXV)
Rev.: $320,912
Assets: $2,989,753
Liabilities: $286,970
Net Worth: $2,702,783
Earnings: $600,470
Fiscal Year-end: 12/31/21
Real Estate Investment Services
N.A.I.C.S.: 531390
Andrew Shapack (CEO)

PINE TREE FORD LINCOLN
100 Auto Park Circle, Vaughan, L4L 9T5, ON, Canada
Tel.: (416) 798-4777
Web Site:
http://www.pinetreefordlincoln.net
Rev.: $38,789,240
Emp.: 80
New & Used Car Dealers
N.A.I.C.S.: 441110
Brian Coy (Mgr-Fin)

PINEAPPLE EXPRESS CANNABIS COMPANY
Kleonos 8A, Lakatamia, Nicosia, 2333, Cyprus
Tel.: (357) 22000344 NV
Web Site: http://www.minaro-corp.com
Year Founded: 2017
Rev.: $30,250
Assets: $32,322
Liabilities: $48,235
Net Worth: ($15,913)
Earnings: ($19,507)
Fiscal Year-end: 01/31/21
Graphic Design Services
N.A.I.C.S.: 541430
Yulia Lazaridou (Pres, CEO, CFO, Chief Acctg Officer & Treas)

PINEAPPLE FINANCIAL INC.
Unit 200 111 Gordon Baker Road, North York, M2H 3R1, ON, Canada
Tel.: (416) 669-2046 Ca
Web Site:
https://www.gopineapple.com
Year Founded: 2015
PAPL—(NYSEAMEX)
Rev.: $2,688,987
Assets: $4,096,592
Liabilities: $2,747,276
Net Worth: $1,349,316
Earnings: ($4,102,659)
Emp.: 55
Fiscal Year-end: 08/31/24
Financial Investment Services
N.A.I.C.S.: 523999

PINEAPPLE POWER CORPORATION PLC
Studio 16 Cloisters House 8 Battersea Park Road, London, SW8 4BG, United Kingdom UK
Web Site: https://www.pineapple-powercorp.com
Year Founded: 2014
PNPL—(LSE)
Assets: $409,028
Liabilities: $63,748
Net Worth: $345,280
Earnings: ($464,474)
Fiscal Year-end: 12/31/22
Investment Management Service
N.A.I.C.S.: 523999

Claudio Morandi (Chm)

PINEAPPLE RESOURCES BERHAD
Wisma Pineapple Lot 135 Jalan 1/89B 3 1/2 Miles off Jalan Sungei Besi, 57100, Kuala Lumpur, Malaysia
Tel.: (60) 379816266 MY
Web Site:
https://www.pineappleresources.com
Year Founded: 2000
PINEAPP—(KLS)
Rev.: $10,049,836
Assets: $5,079,763
Liabilities: $1,291,690
Net Worth: $3,788,072
Earnings: ($608,868)
Emp.: 168
Fiscal Year-end: 06/30/23
Computer Accessory Distr
N.A.I.C.S.: 423430
Mark Loong Heng Lim (Mng Dir)

PINEHILL PACIFIC BERHAD
No 2-3 Third Floor Jalan Suria Puchong 6 Pusat Perniagaan, Suria Puchong, 47110, Puchong, Selangor Darul Ehsan, Malaysia
Tel.: (60) 89470222
Web Site:
https://www.pinepac.com.my
Year Founded: 1917
PINEPAC—(KLS)
Rev.: $198,281
Assets: $38,785,469
Liabilities: $1,750,990
Net Worth: $37,034,479
Earnings: ($2,955,952)
Emp.: 30
Fiscal Year-end: 06/30/23
Palm Oil Cultivation Services
N.A.I.C.S.: 311225
Abdul Latip Mohd Zain (Dir-Plantation)

Subsidiaries:

Benta Plantations (Perak) Sdn Bhd (1)
Batu 7 Jalan Changkat Jong, Teluk Intan, 36000, Perak, Malaysia
Tel.: (60) 56211931
Emp.: 500
Oil Palm Cultivation & Processing Services
N.A.I.C.S.: 115112
N. Amarution (Mgr)

PINENEX CO., LTD.
934 Gumuncheon-ri, Hyangnam-eup, Hwaseong, 445-922, Gyunggi-do, Korea (South)
Tel.: (82) 31 2973551
Web Site:
http://www.sapphiretek.com
Year Founded: 2000
Rev.: $10,536,111
Assets: $41,969,507
Liabilities: $40,432,167
Net Worth: $1,537,340
Earnings: ($26,010,651)
Emp.: 60
Fiscal Year-end: 12/31/18
Sapphire Ingot Mfr
N.A.I.C.S.: 334413
Kim Yong-Seok (Pres & CEO)

PINESOLUTIONS.CO.UK
Rouen House, Rouen Road, Norwich, NR1 1RB, Norfolk, United Kingdom
Tel.: (44) 1603 697 610
Web Site:
http://www.pinesolutions.co.uk
Year Founded: 2003
Sales Range: $10-24.9 Million
Online Furniture Retailer
N.A.I.C.S.: 423210
Kevin Johnson (CEO)

INTERNATIONAL PUBLIC

PINESTONE CAPITAL LIMITED
Unit 1807 18th Floor China Resources Building 26 Harbour Road, Wanchai, China (Hong Kong)
Tel.: (852) 37280828 Ky
Web Site:
http://www.pinestone.com.hk
Year Founded: 2015
0804—(HKG)
Rev.: $2,482,553
Assets: $21,667,605
Liabilities: $696,915
Net Worth: $20,970,690
Earnings: ($5,287,425)
Emp.: 17
Fiscal Year-end: 12/31/22
Financial Security Brokerage Services
N.A.I.C.S.: 523150
Henry Cheung (Chm)

PINETREE CAPITAL LTD.
1965 Queen Street East Suite 200, Toronto, M4L 1H9, ON, Canada
Tel.: (416) 941-9600
Web Site:
https://www.pinetreecapital.com
Year Founded: 1992
PNP—(TSX)
Rev.: $1,904,682
Assets: $13,948,029
Liabilities: $251,764
Net Worth: $13,696,266
Earnings: $1,467,730
Emp.: 2
Fiscal Year-end: 12/31/19
Merchant Banking & Venture Capital Services
N.A.I.C.S.: 523910
Peter Tolnai (Chm)

Subsidiaries:

Emerald Capital Corp (1)
325 Howe St Ste 603, Vancouver, V6C 1Z7, BC, Canada
Tel.: (604) 687-8446
Web Site:
http://www.emeraldcapitalcorp.com
Mortgage Brokerage Services
N.A.I.C.S.: 522310

Pinetree Resource Partnership (1)
1965 Queen Street East Suite 200, Toronto, M4L 1H9, ON, Canada
Tel.: (416) 941-9600
Web Site: http://www.pinetree.com
Sales Range: $50-74.9 Million
Brokerage Services
N.A.I.C.S.: 523160

PINEWOOD TECHNOLOGIES GROUP PLC
Sentinel House 193 Old Marylebone Rd, Little Oak Drive Annesley, London, W1H 4AD, United Kingdom
Tel.: (44) 1216976600
Web Site:
https://www.pinewoodtech.com
PDG—(LSE)
Rev.: $4,569,553,143
Assets: $2,043,675,839
Liabilities: $1,688,967,432
Net Worth: $354,708,407
Earnings: $57,434,991
Emp.: 5,334
Fiscal Year-end: 12/31/22
Automobile Sales
N.A.I.C.S.: 441110
Martin S. Casha (COO)

Subsidiaries:

CFC Solutions Ltd. (1)
1310 Solihull Parkway, Birmingham Business Park, Birmingham, B37 7YB, United Kingdom
Tel.: (44) 1217177444
Web Site: http://www.cfcsolutions.co.uk
Sales Range: $25-49.9 Million
Emp.: 160

AND PRIVATE COMPANIES / PING AN INSURANCE (GROUP) COMPANY OF CHINA, LTD.

Fleet Management Software Development Services
N.A.I.C.S.: 541511

Evans Halshaw (Cardiff) Limited (1)
505 Newport Road, South Glamorgan, Cardiff, CF23 9UE, United Kingdom
Tel.: (44) 2920490511
Car Retailer
N.A.I.C.S.: 441120
Colin Craythorne *(Mgr-Kia Brand)*

Evans Halshaw Motors Limited (1)
Loxley House 2 Oakwood Ct, Little Oak Dr Annesley, Nottingham, NG15 0DR, United Kingdom
Tel.: (44) 1623725000
Web Site: http://www.evanshalshaw.com
Sales Range: $200-249.9 Million
Emp.: 694
Truck & Auto Franchise Operator
N.A.I.C.S.: 441227

Executive Motor Group Limited (1)
13123 Kuykendahl Rd, Houston, TX 77090
Tel.: (713) 517-4744
Web Site: http://www.executivemotorgroup.com
Car Retailer
N.A.I.C.S.: 441120

National Fleet Solutions Limited (1)
Pendragon House Sir Frank Whittle Road, Derby, DE21 4AZ, United Kingdom
Tel.: (44) 1332287126
Sales Range: $25-49.9 Million
Emp.: 15
Motor Vehicle Distr
N.A.I.C.S.: 423110
Neal Francis *(Gen Mgr)*

Pendragon Contracts Limited (1)
Pendragon House Sir Frank Whittle Rd, Derby, DE21 4AZ, United Kingdom
Tel.: (44) 1332267367
Web Site: http://www.pendragon-contracts.co.uk
Sales Range: $50-74.9 Million
Emp.: 70
Fleet Leasing Services
N.A.I.C.S.: 532411
Marisa Fravolini *(Dir-Customer Svcs)*

Pendragon Finance & Insurance Limited (1)
Loxley House 2 Oak Wood Court, Annesley, Nottingham, NG15 0DR, United Kingdom
Tel.: (44) 1623725000
Web Site: http://www.pendragonplc.com
Sales Range: $200-249.9 Million
Emp.: 400
Insurance Brokerage Services
N.A.I.C.S.: 524210

Pendragon Javelin Limited (1)
2 Oakwood Court Little Oak Drive, Nottingham, NG15 0DR, United Kingdom
Tel.: (44) 1623725000
Automobile Sales & Support Services
N.A.I.C.S.: 441110

Pendragon Motor Group Limited (1)
2 Oakwood Court Little Oak Drive, Annesley, Nottingham, NG15 0DR, United Kingdom
Tel.: (44) 1623725200
Web Site: http://www.pendragonplc.uk.com
Sales Range: $100-124.9 Million
Emp.: 400
New & Used Car Sales
N.A.I.C.S.: 441110

Pendragon Motorcycles Limited (1)
2 Loxham Road, London, E4 8SE, United Kingdom
Tel.: (44) 2085319026
Motor Vehicle Distr
N.A.I.C.S.: 423110

Pendragon Vehicle Management Limited (1)
Pendragon House Sir Frank Whittle Road, Derby, DE21 4AZ, United Kingdom
Tel.: (44) 1332267367
Web Site: http://www.pendragonvehicle.co.uk
Vehicle Leasing Services
N.A.I.C.S.: 532112

Penegon Properties, Inc. (1)
PO Box 20256, Atlanta, GA 30325

Tel.: (404) 355-5978
Web Site: http://www.pentagonhomes.biz
Real Estate Services
N.A.I.C.S.: 531390

Pinewood Technologies PLC (1)
2960 Trident Court Solihull Parkway, Birmingham Business Park, Birmingham, B37 7YN, United Kingdom
Tel.: (44) 1216976600
Web Site: http://www.pinewood.co.uk
Sales Range: $25-49.9 Million
Software Development Services
N.A.I.C.S.: 541511
Neville Briggs *(Mng Dir)*

Stratstone Limited (1)
Loxley House 2 Oakwood Court Little Oak Drive, Annesley, NG15 0DR, Nottinghamshire, United Kingdom
Tel.: (44) 3333237098
Web Site: http://www.stratstone.com
Luxury Automotive Retailer
N.A.I.C.S.: 441227
Trevor Fussey *(Mng Dir)*

Stripestar Limited (1)
Loxley House Oakwood Court, Little Oak Drive Annesley, Nottingham, NG15 0DR, United Kingdom
Tel.: (44) 1623 725200
Motor Vehicle Distr
N.A.I.C.S.: 441110

The Mcgill Group Limited (1)
20-2400 Wyecroft Rd, Oakville, L6L 6M8, ON, Canada
Web Site: https://www.mcgillgroupltd.com
Property Management Services
N.A.I.C.S.: 531311

Trust Motors Limited (1)
10 Norman Spencer Drive, Manukau, Manukau, New Zealand
Tel.: (64) 9 887 8668
Web Site: https://www.trustmotors.co.nz
Fire Insurance Services
N.A.I.C.S.: 524210

PING AN HEALTHCARE & TECHNOLOGY COMPANY LIMITED
17-19/F Block B Shanghai Ping An Building No 166 Kaibin Road, Shanghai, China — Ky
Web Site: https://www.pagd.net
Year Founded: 2014
1833---(HKG)
Rev.: $647,092,656
Assets: $2,287,333,989
Liabilities: $450,411,913
Net Worth: $1,836,922,076
Earnings: $(46,363,813)
Emp.: 1,753
Fiscal Year-end: 12/31/23
Health Care Services
N.A.I.C.S.: 621610
Cheng Liu *(Sec)*

PING AN INSURANCE (GROUP) COMPANY OF CHINA, LTD.
47th 48th 109th 110th 111th 112th Floors Ping An Finance Center, No 5033 Yitian Road Futian District, Shenzhen, Guangdong, China
Tel.: (86) 4008866338 — CN
Web Site: https://www.group.pingan.com
Year Founded: 1988
2318---(HKG)
Rev.: $180,855,825,240
Assets: $1,553,859,803,460
Liabilities: $1,388,741,862,630
Net Worth: $165,117,940,830
Earnings: $15,568,893,780
Fiscal Year-end: 12/31/21
Investment Management Service
N.A.I.C.S.: 551112
Mingzhe Ma *(Founder & Chm)*

Subsidiaries:

Autohome Inc. (1)
18th Floor Tower B CEC Plaza 3 Dan Ling Street, Haidian District, Beijing, 100080, China **(53.3%)**
Tel.: (86) 1059857001
Web Site: https://ir.autohome.com.cn
Rev.: $961,014,067
Assets: $4,114,396,738
Liabilities: $640,672,491
Net Worth: $3,473,724,247
Earnings: $252,634,304
Emp.: 5,355
Fiscal Year-end: 12/31/2022
Automotive Distr
N.A.I.C.S.: 513199

China PA Asset Management (Hong Kong) Company Limited (1)
Suite 2301 23rd Floor Two International Finance Centre, 8 Finance Street Central, Hong Kong, China (Hong Kong)
Tel.: (852) 37629228
Fire Insurance Services
N.A.I.C.S.: 524113

China PA Securities (Hong Kong) Company Limited (1)
Units 3601 36th Floor, The Center 99 Queen Road Central, Hong Kong, China (Hong Kong)
Tel.: (852) 37629778
Fire Insurance Services
N.A.I.C.S.: 524113

China Ping An Insurance Overseas (Holdings) Limited (1)
23rd Floor Two International Finance Centre 8 Finance Street, 8 Connaught Road, Central, China (Hong Kong)
Tel.: (852) 37629228
Web Site: https://overseas.pingan.com.hk
General Insurance Services
N.A.I.C.S.: 524210

Ningbo Beilun Port Expressway Co., Ltd. (1)
Panhuo Town Beilun, Ningbo, 315000, Zhejiang, China
Tel.: (86) 57488239198
General Insurance Services
N.A.I.C.S.: 524210

Ping An Annuity Insurance Company of China, Ltd (1)
18 F Yinhe Intl Mansion No 51 Beijing St, Shenhe Dist, Shenyang, 110002, Liaoning, China
Tel.: (86) 2431581935
Web Site: http://www.pingan.com
Emp.: 200
General Insurance Services
N.A.I.C.S.: 524210

Ping An Asset Management Co., Ltd. (1)
29-31F No 1333 Lujiazui Ring Road, Pudong New District, Shanghai, 200120, Guangdong, China **(100%)**
Tel.: (86) 4008866338
Web Site: http://www.pingan.com
Asset Management Services
N.A.I.C.S.: 523940
Jack Wan *(Chm)*

Ping An Bank Co., Ltd. (1)
No 5047 Shennan East Road, Luohu District, Shenzhen, 518001, Guangdong, China **(59%)**
Tel.: (86) 75582088888
Web Site: https://bank.pingan.com
Rev.: $25,951,169,430
Assets: $754,004,629,800
Liabilities: $693,418,041,720
Net Worth: $60,586,588,080
Earnings: $5,567,038,560
Emp.: 34,626
Fiscal Year-end: 12/31/2021
Banking Services
N.A.I.C.S.: 522110
Wei Qiu *(Chm-Supervisory Bd)*

Ping An Life Insurance Company of China, Ltd. (1)
Ping An Building Ba Gua No 3 Road, Shenzhen, 518029, Guangdong, China **(99.33%)**
Tel.: (86) 755 8226 2888
Web Site: http://www.pingan.com
Life Insurance Products & Services
N.A.I.C.S.: 524113

Ping An Property & Casualty Insurance Company of China, Ltd. (1)
Ping An Building Ba Gua No 3 Road, Shenzhen, 518029, Guangdong, China **(99.08%)**
Tel.: (86) 75582262888
Web Site: http://www.pingan.com
Property & Casualty Insurance Products & Services
N.A.I.C.S.: 524126
Peng Wu *(Pres)*

Subsidiary (Non-US):

China Ping An Insurance (Hong Kong) Company Limited (2)
17th Floor Union Kashima Building 138 Gloucester Road, Wanchai, China (Hong Kong) **(75%)**
Tel.: (852) 28271883
Web Site: http://www.pingan.com.hk
Sales Range: $50-74.9 Million
Emp.: 40
Property & Casualty Insurance Services
N.A.I.C.S.: 524126

Ping An Securities Co., Ltd. (1)
Ping An Building Ba Gua No 3 Road, Shenzhen, 518000, Guangdong, China **(86.66%)**
Tel.: (86) 75522627052
Web Site: http://www.pingan.com
Securities Trading, Brokerage & Investment Banking Services
N.A.I.C.S.: 523150

Ping An Tradition International Money Broking Co. Ltd. (1)
Unit 02-03 11/F Tower One Kerry Plaza Zhongxinsi Road, Futian District, Shenzhen, China
Tel.: (86) 75533351888
Web Site: http://www.pingantradition.com.cn
Inter Dealer Broking Services
N.A.I.C.S.: 523150

Ping An of China Asset Management (Hong Kong) Company Limited (1)
Suite 2301 23rd Floor Two International Finance Centre, 8 Finance Street, Central, China (Hong Kong)
Tel.: (852) 37629228
Web Site: https://www.asset.pingan.com.hk
Integrated Financial Services
N.A.I.C.S.: 561499
Tony Fung *(Mgr-Portfolio)*

Shanghai Jahwa United Company Ltd. (1)
11F Block A Shuangshihui No 399 East Changzhi Road, Hongkou District, Shanghai, 200080, China
Tel.: (86) 2135907000
Web Site: http://www.jahwa.com.cn
Rev.: $997,726,331
Assets: $1,722,635,806
Liabilities: $704,808,168
Net Worth: $1,017,827,638
Earnings: $66,274,318
Fiscal Year-end: 12/31/2022
Cosmetics Mfr
N.A.I.C.S.: 456120
Alex Pan *(Chm, CEO & Gen Mgr)*

Subsidiary (Non-US):

Mayborn Group Limited (2)
Mayborn House Balliol Business Park Benton Lane, Newcastle upon Tyne, NE12 8EW, Northd, United Kingdom
Tel.: (44) 1912501864
Web Site: https://www.mayborngroup.com
Baby Accessory Mfr & Distr
N.A.I.C.S.: 326199
Steve Parkin *(CEO)*

Subsidiary (Domestic):

Gro-group International Limited (3)
Malvern House Matford Court Yeoford Way, Exeter, EX2 8LB, Devon, United Kingdom
Tel.: (44) 808 597 9899
Web Site: http://www.gro.co.uk
Baby Apparel & Accessory Distr
N.A.I.C.S.: 424350

Subsidiary (Non-US):

Jackel China Ltd. (3)
Su Jiu Ind Area, Changping, Dongguan, Guangdong, China
Tel.: (86) 769 8339 3963
Web Site: http://www.mayborngroup.com

PING AN INSURANCE (GROUP) COMPANY OF CHINA, LTD.

Ping An Insurance (Group) Company of China, Ltd.—(Continued)
Baby Feeding Products Mfr
N.A.I.C.S.: 326199

Mayborn Morocco sarl (3)
Zone Franche d'Exportation Gzanaya iLot A 1 - Tangier Free Zone, Tangiers, 90100, Morocco
Tel.: (212) 5 39 39 41 32
Web Site: http://www.mayborngroup.com
Baby Feeding Bottles Mfr & Distr
N.A.I.C.S.: 326199

Subsidiary (US):

Mayborn USA Inc. (3)
11th Fl 1010 Washington Blvd, Stamford, CT 06901
Tel.: (203) 290-3212
Web Site: http://www.tommeetippee.us
Baby Feeding Products Sales & Marketer
N.A.I.C.S.: 423990

Subsidiary (Non-US):

Product Marketing Mayborn Ltd (3)
14/ F China Aerospace Centre 143 Hoi Bun Road, Hong Kong, China (Hong Kong)
Tel.: (852) 2793 0703
Web Site: http://www.mayborngroup.com
Baby Feeding Products Sales & Marketer
N.A.I.C.S.: 423990

PINGDINGSHAN TIANAN COAL MINING CO. LTD.
No 21 Kuangong Road, Pingdingshan, 467099, Henan, China
Tel.: (86) 3752726764
Web Site: http://www.pmta.com.cn
Year Founded: 1998
601666—(SHG)
Rev.: $5,060,620,225
Assets: $10,411,681,677
Liabilities: $6,933,268,756
Net Worth: $3,478,412,920
Earnings: $803,767,536
Emp.: 78,300
Fiscal Year-end: 12/31/22
Coal Mining, Processing & Distribution
N.A.I.C.S.: 213113
Jiao Zhenying (Chm)

PINGPROPERTIES BV
Hoogoorddreef 7, 1101 BA, Amsterdam, Netherlands
Tel.: (31) 205640420 NI
Web Site: http://www.pingproperties.com
Sales Range: $1-4.9 Billion
Emp.: 30
Real Estate Industry Equity Investment & Management Firm
N.A.I.C.S.: 523999
Michael Van Der Kooij (Treas)

PINGTAN MARINE ENTERPRISE LTD.
18-19/F Zhongshan Building A No 154 Hudong Road, Fuzhou, 350001, China
Tel.: (86) 5918 727 1266 Ky
Web Site: http://www.ptmarine.com
Year Founded: 2010
PME—(NASDAQ)
Rev.: $164,083,044
Assets: $576,235,498
Liabilities: $484,145,619
Net Worth: $92,089,879
Earnings: ($2,480,719)
Emp.: 2,356
Fiscal Year-end: 12/31/21
Ocean Fishing Services
N.A.I.C.S.: 114119
Xinrong Zhuo (Founder, Chm & CEO)

Subsidiaries:

China Dredging Group Co., Ltd. (1)
Floor 18 Tower A Zhongshan Building 154, Hudong Road Gulou District, Fuzhou, 350001, Fujian, China (100%)
Tel.: (86) 59187271266
Web Site: http://www.ptmarine.com
Sales Range: $200-249.9 Million
Emp.: 106
Holding Company; Contract Dredging Services
N.A.I.C.S.: 551112

Subsidiary (Domestic):

Fujian Xing Gang Port Service Co., Ltd. (2)
Floor 18 Tower A Zhongshan Building No 154 Hudong Road, Gulou District, Fuzhou, 350001, Fujian, China
Tel.: (86) 591 8727 1266
Contract Dredging Services
N.A.I.C.S.: 237990

PINK N PAY HOLDINGS LIMITED RF
101 Rosmead Avenue, Kenilworth, Cape Town, 7708, South Africa
Tel.: (27) 216581000 ZA
Web Site: http://www.picknpay.co.za
Year Founded: 1967
Investment Holding Company
N.A.I.C.S.: 551112

Subsidiaries:

Pick n Pay Holdings Limited (1)
101 Rosmead Avenue, Kenilworth, Cape Town, 7708, South Africa
Tel.: (27) 216581000
Web Site: http://www.picknpayinvestor.co.za
Rev.: $5,844,431,886
Assets: $1,337,224,288
Liabilities: $1,035,886,397
Net Worth: $301,337,891
Earnings: $91,857,345
Emp.: 52,900
Fiscal Year-end: 02/26/2017
Food, Clothing & General Investment Services
N.A.I.C.S.: 455211

Subsidiary (Domestic):

Boxer Superstores (Pty) Limited (2)
41 The Blvd Westend Ofc Park, Westville, Durban, 3610, Kwazulu-Natal, South Africa
Tel.: (27) 312757000
Web Site: http://www.boxer.co.za
Sales Range: $100-124.9 Million
Emp.: 302
Supermarket Management Services
N.A.I.C.S.: 445110
Eugene Stoop (Mng Dir)

Pick n Pay Franchise Financing (Pty) Limited (2)
101 Rosmead Ave, Cape Town, 7708, Western Cape, South Africa
Tel.: (27) 216581000
Financial Services
N.A.I.C.S.: 522299
Jaques Lombard (Mgr)

Pick n Pay Garages (Pty) Limited (2)
Corner Shannon Rd & Bell Dr, Krugersdorp, 1739, Gauteng, South Africa
Tel.: (27) 119541411
Sales Range: $25-49.9 Million
Emp.: 32
Parking Garages Operation Services
N.A.I.C.S.: 812930

Pick n Pay Wholesalers (Pty) Limited (2)
101 Romead Ave Kenilworth, Cape Town, 8000, Western Cape, South Africa
Tel.: (27) 216581000
Web Site: http://www.pnp.co.za
Grocery Product Whslr
N.A.I.C.S.: 445110
Glen Edson (Reg Mgr)

PINKI A.D.
Gradski Park 2, 11080, Zemun, Serbia
Tel.: (381) 11 3163 966
Web Site: http://www.pinki-zemun.co.rs
Year Founded: 1973

PNKZ—(BEL)
Sales Range: Less than $1 Million
Emp.: 26
Sports Club Operator
N.A.I.C.S.: 711211
Petar Dukic (Mng Dir)

PINLIVE FOODS CO., LTD.
Room 308 Building No 10 No 652 Changshou Road, Putuo District, Shanghai, 200060, China
Tel.: (86) 2151863006
Web Site: http://www.pinlive.com
Year Founded: 1997
300892—(SSE)
Rev.: $216,040,500
Assets: $202,753,044
Liabilities: $41,891,148
Net Worth: $160,861,896
Earnings: $1,572,480
Fiscal Year-end: 12/31/22
Dairy Products Mfr
N.A.I.C.S.: 333241
Mu Wang (Chm & Gen Mgr)

PINNACLE INVESTMENT MANAGEMENT GROUP LIMITED
Level 25 Australia Square Tower 264 George Street, Sydney, 2000, NSW, Australia
Tel.: (61) 1300010311 AU
Web Site: https://www.pinnacleinvestment.com
PNI—(ASX)
Sales Range: $1-9.9 Million
Offices of Other Holding Companies
N.A.I.C.S.: 551112
Ian Macoun (Mng Dir)

Subsidiaries:

Next Financial Limited (1)
Level 14 167 Macquarie St, Sydney, 2000, NSW, Australia
Tel.: (61) 2 8198 0120
Investment Management Service
N.A.I.C.S.: 523940
Peter Hastings Warne (Chm)

Wilson HTM Ltd (1)
Level 30 Waterfront Place 1 Eagle Street, Brisbane, 4000, QLD, Australia
Tel.: (61) 0732121333
Web Site: http://www.wilsonhtm.com.au
Sales Range: $200-249.9 Million
Investment Advisory Services
N.A.I.C.S.: 523940

Subsidiary (Domestic):

Wilson HTM Corporate Finance Limited (2)
Riparian Plz 71 Eagle St, Brisbane, 4000, QLD, Australia
Tel.: (61) 732121333
Web Site: http://www.wilsonhtm.com.au
Sales Range: $100-124.9 Million
Emp.: 110
Financial Investment Advisory Services
N.A.I.C.S.: 523940
Steven Wilson (Chm)

Wilson HTM Services Pty Ltd. (2)
L 38 Riparian Plz 71 Eagle St, Brisbane, 4000, QLD, Australia
Tel.: (61) 732121333
Sales Range: $100-124.9 Million
Investment Management Service
N.A.I.C.S.: 523940

PINNACLE MINERALS LIMITED
L1/389 Oxford Street, Mount Hawthorn, Perth, 6016, WA, Australia
Tel.: (61) 894260666
Web Site: https://www.pinnacleminerals.com
Year Founded: 2021
PIM—(ASX)
Rev.: $55,091
Assets: $2,888,831
Liabilities: $201,065

INTERNATIONAL PUBLIC

Net Worth: $2,687,766
Earnings: ($2,203,818)
Fiscal Year-end: 06/30/24
Mineral Exploration Services
N.A.I.C.S.: 212390
Jay Stephenson (Sec)

PINOVA CAPITAL GMBH
Rindermarkt 7, 80331, Munich, Germany
Tel.: (49) 89 1894 254 40 De
Web Site: http://www.pinovacapital.com
Privater Equity Firm
N.A.I.C.S.: 523999
Marko Maschek (Partner & Member-Mgmt Bd)

Subsidiaries:

INVENT Umwelt- und Verfahrenstechnik AG (1)
Am Pestalozziring 21, Erlangen, 91058, Germany
Tel.: (49) 9131 69098 0
Web Site: http://www.invent-uv.de
Sales Range: $10-24.9 Million
Emp.: 60
Water & Wastewater Treatment Technologies Developer, Mfr & Whslr
N.A.I.C.S.: 333248
Marcus Hofken (Pres & CEO)

WENDT-SIT GmbH (1)
Beindersheimer Strasse 79, Frankenthal, 67227, Germany
Tel.: (49) 6233 7704 0
Web Site: http://www.wendt-sit.de
Emp.: 100
Sound & Thermal Insulation Products Mfr & Distr
N.A.I.C.S.: 326140
Stefan Trubner (Mng Dir)

PINTARAS JAYA BERHAD
No 8 Jalan Majistret U1/26 Hicom Glenmarie Industrial Park, 40150, Shah Alam, Selangor Darul Ehsan, Malaysia
Tel.: (60) 355691516
Web Site: https://www.pintaras.com.my
PTARAS—(KLS)
Rev.: $109,676,583
Assets: $146,335,656
Liabilities: $47,285,296
Net Worth: $99,050,360
Earnings: $10,197,740
Emp.: 293
Fiscal Year-end: 06/30/22
Construction Services
N.A.I.C.S.: 236220
Yok Kee Khoo (Exec Dir)

Subsidiaries:

Pintaras Geotechnics Sdn. Bhd. (1)
8 Jalan Majistret U1/26 Hicom Glenmarie Industrial Park, 40150, Shah Alam, Selangor Darul Ehsan, Malaysia
Tel.: (60) 355691516
Web Site: http://www.pintaras.com.my
Emp.: 200
Geotechnical & Foundation Engineering Services
N.A.I.C.S.: 541330

Prima Packaging Sdn. Bhd. (1)
Lot 18 Taman Perindustrian Subang Utama Seksyen 22, 40000, Shah Alam, Selangor, Malaysia
Tel.: (60) 351916228
Web Site: https://www.primapac.com.my
Industrial Metal Container Mfr
N.A.I.C.S.: 332439

Primapac Sdn. Bhd. (1)
Lot 18 Seksyen 22, Taman Perindustrian Subang Utama, 40000, Shah Alam, Selangor, Malaysia
Tel.: (60) 351916228
Web Site: https://www.primapac.com.my
Industrial Metal Container Mfr
N.A.I.C.S.: 332439

PINTEC TECHNOLOGY HOLDINGS LIMITED
3rd Floor No 11 Building No 109 Yard Tianjizhigu Jinghai 3rd St BDA, Chaoyang District, Beijing, China
Tel.: (86) 1065060227 Ky
Web Site: https://www.pintec.com
Year Founded: 2012
PT—(NASDAQ)
Rev.: $26,542,101
Assets: $116,628,508
Liabilities: $126,591,602
Net Worth: ($9,963,094)
Earnings: ($15,585,901)
Emp.: 124
Fiscal Year-end: 12/31/21
Information Technology Services
N.A.I.C.S.: 541512
Wei Wei *(Co-Founder & CEO)*

PINTEL CO., LTD.
5F Geonyeong Building 56 Baumoero 37gil, Seocho-gu, Seoul, 06729, Korea (South)
Tel.: (82) 264936024
Web Site: https://www.pintel.co.kr
Year Founded: 2015
291810—(KRS)
Software Development Services
N.A.I.C.S.: 541511

PIOLAX INC.
51 Iwai-cho, Hodogaya-ku, Yokohama, 240-0023, Kanagawa, Japan
Tel.: (81) 457311211
Web Site: https://www.piolax.co.jp
Year Founded: 1939
5988—(TKS)
Rev.: $426,682,110
Assets: $802,559,760
Liabilities: $89,049,920
Net Worth: $713,509,840
Earnings: $26,525,930
Emp.: 2,883
Fiscal Year-end: 03/31/24
Automobile Parts Mfr & Distr
N.A.I.C.S.: 332613
Yukihiko Shimazu *(Pres)*

Subsidiaries:

Dongguan Piolax Co., Ltd. (1)
No 8 Xifu West Lake Industrial Zone Lincun Tangxia Town, Dongguan, Guangdong, China
Tel.: (86) 76987987779
Mold Product Mfr & Distr
N.A.I.C.S.: 333511

KHK Sales Co., Ltd. (1)
51 Iwai-cho, Hodogaya-ku, Yokohama, 240-0023, Kanagawa, Japan
Tel.: (81) 45 742 9990
Metal & Plastic Fastener Distr
N.A.I.C.S.: 423710

P.M.T. Inc. (1)
252-5 Katsuuri, Moka, 321-4366, Tochigi, Japan
Tel.: (81) 285827655
Mold Product Mfr & Distr
N.A.I.C.S.: 333511

P.N.S. INC. (1)
187-28 Kamigoya, Nasushiobara, 329-3127, Tochigi, Japan
Tel.: (81) 287681221
Spring Mfr & Distr
N.A.I.C.S.: 332613

PIOLAX CORPORATION (1)
139 Etowah Industrial Ct, Canton, GA 30114-8088
Tel.: (770) 479-2227
Web Site: https://www.piolaxusa.com
Industrial Fastener Product Mfr & Distr
N.A.I.C.S.: 332722

PIOLAX Co., Ltd. (1)
47 Harmony-ro 187Beon-gil, Yeonsu-gu, Incheon, 22013, Korea (South)
Tel.: (82) 325718251
Web Site: https://www.piolax.co.kr

Industrial Fastener Product Mfr & Distr
N.A.I.C.S.: 332722

PIOLAX Harness Fastening Systems, Inc. (1)
2996-3 Gouhara, Annaka, 379-0135, Gunma, Japan
Tel.: (81) 273857521
Industrial Fastener Product Mfr
N.A.I.C.S.: 332722

PIOLAX INDIA PRIVATE LIMITED (1)
200 North Belerica Road Sri City DTZ, Post Box No 1, Tirupati District, Tirupati, 517646, Andhra Pradesh, India
Tel.: (91) 8576696100
Industrial Fastener Product Mfr & Distr
N.A.I.C.S.: 332722

PIOLAX KYUSYU CO., LTD. (1)
115-49 Hiratsune, Iizuka, 820-0073, Fukuoka, Japan
Tel.: (81) 948244661
Industrial Fastener Product Mfr & Distr
N.A.I.C.S.: 332722

PIOLAX MEXICANA S. A. de C. V. (1)
Avenida Industrial 211 Parque Industrial La Silla, 66600, Apodaca, Mexico
Tel.: (52) 8183866000
Plastic Product Mfr & Distr
N.A.I.C.S.: 326199

PT. PIOLAX INDONESIA (1)
Jl Harapan VII Lot LL-4b KIIC Industrial Estate Sirnabaya Village, Telukjambe Timur, Karawang, 41361, Indonesia
Tel.: (62) 2678457062
Motorcycle Mfr & Distr
N.A.I.C.S.: 336991
Hendri Yono *(Mgr-Production Engrg)*

Piolax (China) Co., Ltd. (1)
Room 1505 15 Floors T1 Building No 421 Zi Yun Road, Changning District, Shanghai, 200051, China
Tel.: (86) 216 268 8022
Automobile Parts Distr
N.A.I.C.S.: 441330

Piolax (Thailand) Ltd. (1)
107/14 Moo 4, Eastern Seaboard Industrial Estate Rayong T Pluakdaeng A Pluakdaeng, Rayong, 21140, Thailand
Tel.: (66) 38955412
Web Site: http://www.piolax.co.th
Industrial Fastener Product Mfr & Distr
N.A.I.C.S.: 332722

Piolax Business Service Co., Ltd. (1)
51 Iwai-cho, Hodogaya-ku, Yokohama, 240-0023, Kanagawa, Japan
Tel.: (81) 45 741 1211
Human Affair Services
N.A.I.C.S.: 541612

Piolax Inc. - Fuji Plant (1)
2264-1 Minami-matsuno, Fuji, 421-3303, Shizuoka, Japan
Tel.: (81) 545850015
Industrial Fastener Product Mfr & Distr
N.A.I.C.S.: 332722

Piolax Inc. - Moka Plant (1)
14-2 Matsuyama-cho, Moka, 321-4346, Tochigi, Japan
Tel.: (81) 285824651
Industrial Fastener Product Mfr & Distr
N.A.I.C.S.: 332722

Piolax Ltd. (1)
Shorten Brook Drive, Altham Business Park Altham, Accrington, BB5 5YH, Lancashire, United Kingdom
Tel.: (44) 1282684000
Web Site: http://www.piolax.co.uk
Industrial Fastener Product Mfr & Distr
N.A.I.C.S.: 332722

Piolax Medical Devices, Inc. (1)
2265-3 Kamiyabe-cho, Totsuka-ku, Yokohama, 245-0053, Kanagawa, Japan
Tel.: (81) 455179730
Web Site: http://www.piolax-md.co.jp
Emp.: 218
Medical Device Mfr & Distr
N.A.I.C.S.: 339112
Kazutaka Nanaumi *(Exec VP)*

Saga Tekkosho Co., Ltd. (1)
1-5-30 Kamizono, Saga, 840-0806, Japan
Tel.: (81) 95 231 2111
Web Site: https://www.dextech.co.jp
Emp.: 1,940
Industrial Fastener Mfr & Distr
N.A.I.C.S.: 332722

Wuhan PIOLAX Co., Ltd. (1)
No 1148 Hannan Avenue Shamao Street, Hannan District, Wuhan, Hubei, China
Tel.: (86) 2784737830
Plastic Product Mfr & Distr
N.A.I.C.S.: 326199
Liu Chang *(Engr-Quality)*

PIOLINK INC.
IT Castle 1-401 98 Gasan Digital 2-ro, Geumcheon-Gu, Seoul, 08506, Korea (South)
Tel.: (82) 220256900
Web Site: https://www.piolink.com
Year Founded: 2000
170790—(KRS)
Rev.: $47,275,757
Assets: $72,662,260
Liabilities: $17,008,506
Net Worth: $55,653,753
Earnings: $9,315,344
Emp.: 373
Fiscal Year-end: 12/31/22
Application Networking & Web Security Technology
N.A.I.C.S.: 334290
Young-Cheol Cho *(CEO)*

Subsidiaries:

PIOLINK China (1)
Rm 2204 Suncome Liauw, Shanghai, China
Tel.: (86) 21 60457915
Web Site: http://www.piolink.com
Communication Equipment Distr
N.A.I.C.S.: 423690

PIOLINK Japan (1)
Shinjuku Building 9F 1-8-1 Nishi-Shinjuku, Shinjuku-ku, Tokyo, 160-0023, Japan
Tel.: (81) 359905411
Web Site: https://www.piolink.co.jp
Emp.: 381
Communication Equipment Distr
N.A.I.C.S.: 423690

PION GROUP AB
Torsgatan 11, Box 207, SE-101 24, Stockholm, Sweden
Tel.: (46) 770111222
Web Site: https://www.piongroup.se
PION.B—(OMX)
Rev.: $178,552,987
Assets: $60,900,829
Liabilities: $41,331,405
Net Worth: $19,569,424
Earnings: $864,326
Emp.: 4,312
Fiscal Year-end: 12/31/20
Staffing & Outsourcing Services
N.A.I.C.S.: 541612

PIONEER AGRO EXTRACTS LIMITED
Chhoti Nehar Malakpur, 145025, Pathankot, 145025, Punjab, India
Tel.: (91) 1862245352
Web Site: https://www.pioneeragro.co.in
Year Founded: 1993
519439—(BOM)
Rev.: $247,527
Assets: $649,050
Liabilities: $16,354
Net Worth: $632,696
Earnings: $8,609
Fiscal Year-end: 03/31/23
Edible Oil Mfr
N.A.I.C.S.: 311224
Jagat Mohan Aggarwal *(Chm & Mng Dir)*

PIONEER CEMENT LTD.
135 Ferozpur Road, Lahore, Pakistan
Tel.: (92) 4237503570
Web Site: https://www.pioneercement.com
PIOC—(KAR)
Rev.: $69,887,629
Assets: $303,551,811
Liabilities: $207,904,568
Net Worth: $95,647,243
Earnings: $5,674,907
Emp.: 1,059
Fiscal Year-end: 06/30/19
Cement Mfr & Sales
N.A.I.C.S.: 325520
Sajid Feroze *(CEO & Mng Dir)*

PIONEER CREDIT LIMITED
Level 6 108 St Georges Terrace, Perth, 6000, WA, Australia
Tel.: (61) 1300720823
Web Site: http://www.pioneercredit.com.au
PNC—(ASX)
Rev.: $55,806,624
Assets: $245,683,760
Liabilities: $216,173,877
Net Worth: $29,509,882
Earnings: ($6,703,392)
Emp.: 400
Fiscal Year-end: 06/30/24
Retail Debt Portfolio Acquirer & Servicer
N.A.I.C.S.: 525990
Keith R. John *(Mng Dir)*

Subsidiaries:

Sphere Legal Pty Limited (1)
Level 6 108 St Georges Terrace, Perth, 6000, WA, Australia
Tel.: (61) 893235060
Web Site: http://www.spherelegal.com.au
Law firm
N.A.I.C.S.: 541110

PIONEER EMBROIDERIES LIMITED
Unit No 101B 1st Floor Abhishek Premises Plot No C5-6, Dalia Industrial Estate Off New Link Road Andheri West, Mumbai, 400 058, Maharashtra, India
Tel.: (91) 2242232323
Web Site: https://www.pelhakoba.com
Year Founded: 1991
514300—(BOM)
Rev.: $31,100,419
Assets: $25,718,634
Liabilities: $10,642,386
Net Worth: $15,076,248
Earnings: $2,561,696
Emp.: 1,045
Fiscal Year-end: 03/31/21
Garment Accessories Mfr
N.A.I.C.S.: 339999
Raj Kumar Sekhani *(Chm)*

Subsidiaries:

Crystal Lace (I) Limited (1)
68 Vrindavan Society Near Raghukul Market, Out side Kamela Subway Anjana, Surat, 395002, India
Tel.: (91) 2612342063
Web Site: https://www.crystallace.in
Embroidery Lace Mfr
N.A.I.C.S.: 313220

PIONEER GARAGE LTD
33320 First Ave, Mission, V2V 1G8, BC, Canada
Tel.: (604) 826-6201
Web Site: http://www.pioneerchryslerjeep.com
Year Founded: 1939
Rev.: $13,347,016
Emp.: 30
New & Used Car Dealers
N.A.I.C.S.: 441110

Pioneer Garage Ltd—(Continued)
Arlene Sater (Controller)

PIONEER GLOBAL GROUP LIMITED
18th Floor 68 Yee Wo Street, Causeway Bay, China (Hong Kong)
Tel.: (852) 25266068
Web Site:
https://www.pioneerglobalgroup.com
0224—(HKG)
Sales Range: $75-99.9 Million
Emp.: 17
Real Estate & Financial Investment Services
N.A.I.C.S.: 523999
Kenneth Gaw (Mng Dir)

Subsidiaries:

InterContinental Hong Kong (1)
18 Salisbury Road, Kowloon, China (Hong Kong)
Tel.: (852) 27211211
Web Site: http://www.hongkong-ic.intercontinental.com
Emp.: 750
Home Management Services
N.A.I.C.S.: 721110

Pioneer Industries (Holdings) Limited (1)
20 F Lyndhurst Tower 1 Lyndhurst Ter, Central, China (Hong Kong)
Tel.: (852) 25266068
Web Site:
http://www.pioneerglobalgroup.com
Investment Management Service
N.A.I.C.S.: 523999

PIONEER INSURANCE COMPANY LIMITED
Rangs Babylonia 5th Floor 246 Bir Uttam Mir Shawkat Sarak, Tejgaon, Dhaka, 1212, Bangladesh
Tel.: (880) 8878901
Web Site:
https://www.pioneerinsurance.com
Year Founded: 1996
PIONEERINS—(CHT)
Rev.: $1,088,152
Assets: $54,584,549
Liabilities: $15,580,918
Net Worth: $39,003,631
Earnings: $6,228,093
Emp.: 445
Fiscal Year-end: 12/31/23
Insurance Agency Services
N.A.I.C.S.: 524210
Tapan Chowdhury (Chm)

PIONEER INVESTCORP LTD
1218 12th Floor Maker Chamber V, Nariman Point, Mumbai, 400 021, India
Tel.: (91) 2266186400
Web Site: https://www.pinc.co.in
Year Founded: 1984
507864—(BOM)
Rev.: $4,918,070
Assets: $48,640,648
Liabilities: $30,906,215
Net Worth: $17,734,433
Earnings: $487,933
Emp.: 250
Fiscal Year-end: 03/31/24
Finance
N.A.I.C.S.: 522291
Amit J. Chandra (Compliance Officer & Sec)

Subsidiaries:

Infinity.Com Financial Securities Ltd (1)
No 1216 Maker Chambers, 5 Nariman Point, Mumbai, 400 021, India
Tel.: (91) 2266186633
Web Site: https://www.infinityfinsec.com
Emp.: 150

Investment Services
N.A.I.C.S.: 523999
Gaurang Gandhi (Mng Dir)

PINC Finserve Private Limited (1)
1218 12th Floor Maker Chamber V Nariman Point, Mumbai, 400021, India
Tel.: (91) 8657858689
Web Site: https://pincfinserve.com
Financial Services
N.A.I.C.S.: 523999

Pioneer Commodity Intermediaries Pvt. Ltd. (1)
1219 Maker Chambers, 5 Nariman Point, Mumbai, 400021, Maharastra, India
Tel.: (91) 2222021171
Web Site: http://www.pinc.co.in
Sales Range: $25-49.9 Million
Investment Management Service
N.A.I.C.S.: 541618
Gurang Gandhi (Mng Dir)

PIONEER JELLICE INDIA PVT. LTD
23-A Vallabhai Road, Chokkikulam, Madurai, 625002, India
Tel.: (91) 4522534099
Web Site:
http://www.pioneerjellice.com
Emp.: 100
Pharmaceuticals Product Mfr
N.A.I.C.S.: 325412

PIONEER MEDIA HOLDINGS INC.
3104-1055 Dunsmuir Street, Vancouver, V7X 1G4, BC, Canada   BC
Web Site: https://www.p10neer.com
Year Founded: 2017
6NU—(DEU)
Rev.: $359,277
Assets: $11,610,166
Liabilities: $1,809,334
Net Worth: $9,800,832
Earnings: ($20,505,868)
Fiscal Year-end: 05/31/22
Holding Company
N.A.I.C.S.: 551112
Darcy Taylor (CEO)

PIONEER MOTOR PCL
78 78/4 78/5 Moo 3 Dontoom-Nakornchaisri Rd, Donfaek Subdistrict Nakorn chai sri District, Nakhon Pathom, 73120, Thailand
Tel.: (66) 342651118
Web Site:
https://www.pioneermotor.th.com
Year Founded: 2001
PIMO—(THA)
Rev.: $27,991,549
Assets: $37,207,625
Liabilities: $7,271,600
Net Worth: $29,936,025
Earnings: $2,147,995
Emp.: 525
Fiscal Year-end: 12/31/23
Air Conditioner Electric Motor Mfr & Distr
N.A.I.C.S.: 333415
Wasun Itthirojanakul (Mng Dir)

PIONEER PROPERTY GROUP ASA
Radhusgaten 23, 0158, Oslo, Norway
Tel.: (47) 46296719
Web Site:
https://www.pioneerproperty.no
PPG—(OSL)
Rev.: $12,404,349
Assets: $253,019,057
Liabilities: $126,836,147
Net Worth: $126,182,909
Earnings: $2,461,268
Emp.: 4
Fiscal Year-end: 12/31/23
Pre-School & Kindergarten Real Estate Services

N.A.I.C.S.: 531390
Martin P. Hoff (CFO)

PIONEER TRUCK LINES LTD.
PO Box 72032, Edmonton, T6B 3A7, AB, Canada
Tel.: (780) 467-8880
Web Site:
http://www.pioneertrucklines.com
Year Founded: 1987
Rev.: $23,649,026
Emp.: 120
Oilfield Transportation Services
N.A.I.C.S.: 213112
Dale Dubinsky (Co-Owner & Pres)

PIONEERING TECHNOLOGY CORP.
2785 Skymark Ave Unit 13, Mississauga, L4W 4Y3, ON, Canada
Tel.: (905) 712-2061
Web Site:
https://www.pioneeringtech.com
2PX—(DEU)
Rev.: $2,142,522
Assets: $3,501,329
Liabilities: $1,316,778
Net Worth: $2,184,551
Earnings: ($501,172)
Fiscal Year-end: 06/30/23
Technology Solutions
N.A.I.C.S.: 541690
John Bergsma (Chm)

PIONEERS HOLDING COMPANY
Sheraton Al Matar El Nozha Cairo Governorate, Heliopolis, 11361, Cairo, Egypt
Tel.: (20) 222668452
Web Site:
https://www.pioneersholding.com
PIOH.CA—(EGX)
Rev.: $582,586,258
Assets: $1,008,460,017
Liabilities: $468,633,546
Net Worth: $539,826,471
Earnings: $84,214,798
Fiscal Year-end: 12/31/19
Financial Services
N.A.I.C.S.: 523999
Waleed Mohamed Zaki (Founder, Founder, Chm, Chm & CEO)

Subsidiaries:

Al Giza General For Contracting & Real Estate Co. (1)
46 El-Falaki St, Bab El-Louk, Cairo, Egypt
Tel.: (20) 22 399 0561
Web Site: https://www.al-giza.com
Real Estate Investment Services
N.A.I.C.S.: 531390
Mohamed Ezzat El Maayergy (Mng Dir & Chm)

El Kahera Housing (1)
Al Nabouy Al Mohands St Administrative Business Center, Embassies District, Nasr, Egypt (80.5%)
Tel.: (20) 2 26777181
Real Estate Manangement Services
N.A.I.C.S.: 531390

Electro Cable Egypt (1)
Mostorod Industrial Zone Km 4 6 6 th October Road, PO Box 208, Qualubia Governorate, Cairo, Egypt (68.14%)
Tel.: (20) 242205848
Web Site: https://www.ececables.com
Sales Range: Less than $1 Million
Power & Communication Cable Mfr
N.A.I.C.S.: 335929

Electro Cables Egypt Co. (1)
6 th October Road Ismaellia Canal Road, PO Box 208, Mostorod Industrial Zone 4 6, Cairo, Qualubia, Egypt
Tel.: (20) 24 220 5848
Web Site: https://www.ececables.com
Power Cable Mfr & Distr
N.A.I.C.S.: 335929

Pioneers Securities Co. (1)
4 Abbas El Akkad St 4th Floor, Nasr City, Cairo, Egypt
Tel.: (20) 22 671 0057
Web Site: https://www.pioneers-securities.com
Emp.: 556
Financial Investment Services
N.A.I.C.S.: 523999

PIONIR AD
Salas preko bare 27, 21480, Srbobran, Serbia
Tel.: (381) 21 730 446
Web Site: http://www.pionirad.co.rs
Year Founded: 1989
Sales Range: $1-9.9 Million
Emp.: 62
Cereal Crop Farming Services
N.A.I.C.S.: 111998

PIOVAN SPA
Via Delle Industrie 16, Santa Maria di Sala, 30036, Venice, Italy
Tel.: (39) 0415799111
Web Site: https://www.piovan.com
Year Founded: 1934
PVN—(ITA)
Rev.: $617,175,185
Assets: $557,175,185
Liabilities: $368,040,623
Net Worth: $189,134,562
Earnings: $53,990,507
Emp.: 1,805
Fiscal Year-end: 12/31/23
Automation Equipment Mfr & Distr
N.A.I.C.S.: 333111
Nicola Piovan (Chm & Pres)

Subsidiaries:

Doteco S.p.A. (1)
Via E Mattei 30, San Martino Spino, 41037, Modena, MO, Italy
Tel.: (39) 053531653
Web Site: https://www.doteco.com
Emp.: 71
Plastics Product Mfr
N.A.I.C.S.: 326199
Marco Reggiani (CEO)

Energys S.r.l. (1)
Piazza Manifattura 1, 38068, Rovereto, Trento, Italy
Tel.: (39) 0492143390
Web Site: https://www.energysynt.com
Hydroelectric Power Generation Services
N.A.I.C.S.: 221111

FDM GmbH (1)
Junkersring 24, 53844, Troisdorf, Germany
Tel.: (49) 22412660600
Web Site: https://www.piovan.com
Machinery Mfr
N.A.I.C.S.: 333248
Guido Faust (Gen Mgr)

FEA Process & Technological Plants S.r.l. (1)
Via Saluzzo 49, Scarnafigi, 12030, Cuneo, Italy
Tel.: (39) 017574134
Web Site: https://www.piovan.com
Machinery Mfr
N.A.I.C.S.: 333248

Piovan Asia Pacific Ltd. (1)
555 Rasa Tower Building A Unit 1402-4 Floor 14 Phahonyothin Road, Sub-district Chatuchak District Chatuchak, Bangkok, 10900, Thailand
Tel.: (66) 20266645
Plastic Mfr
N.A.I.C.S.: 325211

Piovan Canada Ltd. (1)
6535 Millcreek Drive Unit 2 3, Mississauga, L5N 2M2, ON, Canada
Tel.: (905) 629-8822
Machinery Mfr
N.A.I.C.S.: 333248

Piovan Central Europe GmbH (1)
Campus 21 Europaring F10 302, Brunn am Gebirge, 2345, Vienna, Austria
Tel.: (43) 22363121100

AND PRIVATE COMPANIES

Machinery Mfr
N.A.I.C.S.: 333248

Piovan Czech Republic s.r.o. (1)
Sevce Matouse 298/12, 140 00, Prague,
Czech Republic
Tel.: (420) 602177915
Machinery Mfr
N.A.I.C.S.: 333248

Piovan Do Brasil Ltda. (1)
Rua Costante Piovan 40, Parque Industrial
Agua Vermelha, Osasco, 06276-038, Sao
Paulo, Brazil
Tel.: (55) 1136939500
Machinery Mfr
N.A.I.C.S.: 333248

Piovan France SAS (1)
1 Parc d'activite La Croix Chalon, Volognat,
01460, Nurieux, France
Tel.: (33) 474767700
Machinery Mfr
N.A.I.C.S.: 333248

Piovan GmbH (1)
Zeppelinstrasse 30 Postfach 1344, Garching, 85748, Munich, Germany
Tel.: (49) 893294570
Machinery Mfr
N.A.I.C.S.: 333248

Piovan Gulf Fze (1)
Jafza One A902 Jebel Ali Free Zone, PO
Box 263851, 263851, Dubai, United Arab
Emirates
Tel.: (971) 543298327
Machinery Mfr
N.A.I.C.S.: 333248

Piovan Hungary Kft. (1)
Montevideo u 3/a, 1037, Budapest, Hungary
Tel.: (36) 705645439
Machinery Mfr
N.A.I.C.S.: 333248

Piovan India Private Limited (1)
501 Wellington Business Park-1 Marol
Naka, Andheri Kurla Road Andheri E, Mumbai, 400 059, Maharashtra, India
Tel.: (91) 2228510024
Machinery Mfr
N.A.I.C.S.: 333248

Piovan Japan Inc. (1)
22F Kobe Kokusai Kaikan 8-1-6 Goko-Dori,
Chuo-ku, Kobe, Hyogo, Japan
Tel.: (81) 785705711
Machinery Mfr
N.A.I.C.S.: 333248

Piovan Maroc Sarl. AU (1)
Bir Rami Angel Avenue Mohamed V et Rue
N 2 Immeuble C Bureau N 4, Kenitra, Morocco
Tel.: (212) 537316776
Machinery Mfr
N.A.I.C.S.: 333248

Piovan Mexico S.A. de C.V. (1)
Parque Tecnologico Innovacion Queretaro
Carretera Estatal, N 431 Km2200 N19 Local 2 Col Hacienda La Machorra, El
Marques, Queretaro, Mexico
Tel.: (52) 4422215056
Machinery Mfr
N.A.I.C.S.: 333248

**Piovan Muhendslik Limited
Sirketi** (1)
Kavacik Mhallesi-Hulagu Cad No15,
Beykoz, 34810, Istanbul, Turkiye
Tel.: (90) 2163314401
Machinery Mfr
N.A.I.C.S.: 333248

Piovan UK Limited (1)
Unit 7B Silver Birches Business Park, Aston
Fields, Bromsgrove, B60 3EU, United Kingdom
Tel.: (44) 1527879419
Machinery Mfr
N.A.I.C.S.: 333248

**Piovan Vietnam Company
Limited** (1)
Office No 23 9th Floor TNR Tower 180 -
192 Nguyen Cong Tru Street, Nguyen Thai
Binh Ward District 1, Ho Chi Minh City,
Vietnam
Tel.: (84) 902348049
Machinery Mfr
N.A.I.C.S.: 333248

Progema S.r.l. (1)
Via Sagra San Michele 117, 10141, Turin,
Italy
Tel.: (39) 0110160217
Web Site: http://www.progemasrl.com
Engineeering Services
N.A.I.C.S.: 541330

Republic Machine Inc. (1)
4237 Produce Rd, Louisville, KY 40218
Tel.: (502) 637-6778
Web Site: https://www.republicmachine.com
Engineeering Services
N.A.I.C.S.: 541330

Studio Ponte S.r.l. (1)
Via Uccellino 71, Poggio Renatico, 44028,
Ferrara, Italy
Tel.: (39) 0532826351
Web Site: http://www.studio-ponte.it
Engineeering Services
N.A.I.C.S.: 541330

TOBA PNC Co. Ltd. (1)
Ace Techno Tower10th 470-5 11F Gasan-
Dong, Kumcheon-Gu, Seoul, Korea (South)
Tel.: (82) 1090796036
Machinery Mfr
N.A.I.C.S.: 333248

PIPED BITS CO., LTD.
2F+3F Orix Akasaka 2 chome Bldg
2-9-11, Akasaka Minato-ku, Tokyo,
107-0052, Japan
Tel.: (81) 3 55756601
Web Site: http://www.pi-pe.co.jp
Year Founded: 2000
Sales Range: $25-49.9 Million
Emp.: 242
Application Software Development
Services
N.A.I.C.S.: 541512
Nobuaki Satani *(Founder & CEO)*

PIPEHAWK PLC
2a & 3 Crabtree Road, Forest Vale
Industrial Estate, Cinderford, GL14
2YQ, Hampshire, United Kingdom
Tel.: (44) 1252338959
Web Site: https://www.pipehawk.com
PIP—(AIM)
Rev.: $8,034,446
Assets: $9,610,290
Liabilities: $16,380,584
Net Worth: ($6,770,294)
Earnings: ($3,084,631)
Emp.: 93
Fiscal Year-end: 06/30/23
Land Mines & Utilities Detection Electronic Systems Developer
N.A.I.C.S.: 334419
Gordon G. Watt *(Chm)*

Subsidiaries:

Adien Limited (1)
Unit 5 Third Ave Delta Court, Sky Business
Park, Doncaster, DN9 3GN, United
Kingdom (100%)
Tel.: (44) 130 249 5803
Web Site: https://www.adien-utility-
detection.com
Sales Range: $25-49.9 Million
Emp.: 30
Utilities Detection & Mapping Services
N.A.I.C.S.: 541330
Bob Tallentire *(Mng Dir)*

QM Systems Limited (1)
4 Manor Park Estate Wyndham Street, Aldershot, GU12 4NZ, Hampshire, United
Kingdom
Tel.: (44) 125 233 6612
Web Site: https://www.qm-systems.com
Sales Range: $25-49.9 Million
Emp.: 10
Software Development Services
N.A.I.C.S.: 541511

Sumo Services Ltd (1)
Unit 8 Hayward Business Center, New
Lane, Havant, PO9 2NL, Hampshire, United
Kingdom
Tel.: (44) 845 456 1104
Web Site: https://www.sumoservices.com
Emp.: 20
Utility Mark Out Services
N.A.I.C.S.: 541330

PIPETECH DESIGN & CONSTRUCTION LTD
Pipetech House 8 Bentalls Business
Park, Bentalls, Basildon, SS14 3BN,
Essex, United Kingdom
Tel.: (44) 1268 532432
Web Site:
http://www.pipetechservices.co.uk
Year Founded: 2001
Sales Range: $10-24.9 Million
Emp.: 50
Mechanical & Electrical Contractor
N.A.I.C.S.: 238210
Juan Garcia *(Mng Dir)*

PIPIS BROS FARM PUBLIC COMPANY LIMITED
100 Papaflessa Kokkinotrimithia,
2660, Nicosia, Cyprus
Tel.: (357) 22872727
Sales Range: $10-24.9 Million
Poultry Processing Services
N.A.I.C.S.: 311615
Christos Pipis *(Gen Dir)*

PIQUADRO SPA
Localita Sassuriano 246, 40041, Gaggio Montano, Bologna, Italy
Tel.: (39) 0534409001
Web Site: https://www.piquadro.com
Year Founded: 1987
PQ—(ITA)
Rev.: $191,667,386
Assets: $207,278,221
Liabilities: $141,382,474
Net Worth: $65,895,748
Earnings: $7,017,052
Emp.: 1,039
Fiscal Year-end: 03/31/23
Leather Product Mfr & Whslr
N.A.I.C.S.: 316990
Marco Palmieri *(Chm & CEO)*

Subsidiaries:

Lancel Sogedi S.A. (1)
48-50 Rue Ampere, 75017, Paris, France
Tel.: (33) 185533830
Web Site: https://lancel.com
Luxury Product Mfr & Distr
N.A.I.C.S.: 315990

Piquadro Retail San Marino srl (1)
Str Degli Angariari 41, Falciano, San Marino
Tel.: (378) 3459965654
Travel Accessories Mfr & Distr
N.A.I.C.S.: 316990

Piquadro UK Limited (1)
67 Regent Street, Saint James South, London, W1B 5RA, United Kingdom
Tel.: (44) 7492227774
Travel Accessories Mfr & Distr
N.A.I.C.S.: 316990

The Bridge S.p.A. (1)
Via E Codignola 14/16, Scandicci, 50018,
Florence, Italy
Tel.: (39) 0534409022
Web Site: https://www.thebridge.it
Travel Accessories Mfr & Distr
N.A.I.C.S.: 316990

PIRAEUS FINANCIAL HOLDINGS S.A.
4 Amerikis Street, 105 64, Athens,
Greece
Tel.: (30) 2103335000   GR
Web Site:
http://www.piraeusholdings.gr
Year Founded: 1916
BPIRY—(OTCIQ)
Rev.: $1,824,951,435
Assets: $81,654,435,571
Liabilities: $74,552,126,052
Net Worth: $7,102,309,519
Earnings: $1,023,095,187
Emp.: 8,658
Fiscal Year-end: 12/31/22
Financial Holding Company
N.A.I.C.S.: 551111
Christos I. Megalou *(CEO & Mng Dir)*

Subsidiaries:

Agricultural Bank of Greece, S.A. (1)
23 Panepistimiou Str, 10564, Athens,
Greece
Tel.: (30) 2103298911
Web Site: http://www.atebank.gr
Sales Range: $1-4.9 Billion
Emp.: 8,915
Banking Services
N.A.I.C.S.: 522110

Subsidiary (Domestic):

ATE Leasing S.A. (2)
111 Messogion Street, Athens, 11526,
Greece
Tel.: (30) 210 3712400
Web Site: http://www.ateleasing.gr
Leasing Programs
N.A.I.C.S.: 525990
Nikolaos Marantos *(Gen Mgr)*

Hellenic Sugar Industry S.A. (2)
Mitropoleos 34 str, PO Box 10108, 541 10,
Thessaloniki, Greece (82.56%)
Tel.: (30) 231 029 6400
Web Site: https://www.ebz.gr
Sales Range: $25-49.9 Million
Emp.: 6
Cane Sugar Refining
N.A.I.C.S.: 311314

ETVA Industrial Parks S.A. (1)
75 Vas Sofias Avenue, 115 21, Athens,
Greece
Tel.: (30) 210 954 0000
Industrial Management Services
N.A.I.C.S.: 541611

EXUS S.A. (1)
1 Estius Str and 73-75 Mesogion Av, 11526,
Athens, Greece
Tel.: (30) 2107450300
Web Site: http://www.exus.co.uk
Financial Software
N.A.I.C.S.: 513210

Euroterra S.A. (1)
Kifisias 164 Psychiko, 11525, Athens,
Greece
Tel.: (30) 210 324 1091
Real Estate Services
N.A.I.C.S.: 531390

Geniki Information S.A. (1)
Lmesogeion, 109-111, Athens, Greece
Tel.: (30) 210 697 5138
Web Site: https://www.geniki-information.gr
Assessment & Collection Debt Services
N.A.I.C.S.: 561440

Philoktimatiki Ergoliptiki Ltd. (1)
20 25th March Str Office 101, PO Box
27785, Engomi, 2433, Nicosia, Cyprus
Tel.: (357) 2 259 1919
Web Site: https://www.philoktimatiki.com
Construction Services
N.A.I.C.S.: 236220
Yannis Kyriakopoulos *(Chm)*

Picar S.A (1)
5 Korai Str, 10564, Athens, Greece
Tel.: (30) 2107728400
Web Site: http://www.pbre.gr
Sales Range: $50-74.9 Million
Real Estate Development Services
N.A.I.C.S.: 531390

**Piraeus Asset Management Mutual
Funds S.A** (1)
87 Syngrou Ave, 117 45, Athens, Greece
Tel.: (30) 2103288222
Web Site: https://www.piraeusaedak.gr
Asset Management Services
N.A.I.C.S.: 541618

**Piraeus Asset Management Single
Member S.A.** (1)
94 Vas Sofias Av and 1 Kerasountos, 115

PIRAEUS FINANCIAL HOLDINGS S.A.

Piraeus Financial Holdings S.A.—(Continued)
28, Athens, Greece
Tel.: (30) 210 328 8222
Web Site: https://www.piraeusaedak.gr
Mutual Fund Investment Services
N.A.I.C.S.: 523940
Hercules Bablekos (CEO & Chm)

Piraeus Bank S.A. (1)
4 Amerikis Str, 105 64, Athens, Greece
Banking Services
N.A.I.C.S.: 522110
Christos Megalou (CEO)

Subsidiary (Domestic):

Trastor Real Estate Investment Company S.A. (2)
Chimarras 5, 105 64, Athens, Greece (98.36%)
Tel.: (30) 2106910016
Web Site: https://www.trastor.gr
Rev.: $29,103,016
Assets: $541,350,283
Liabilities: $247,022,844
Net Worth: $294,327,439
Earnings: $24,311,873
Emp.: 17
Fiscal Year-end: 12/31/2023
Real Estate Investment Services
N.A.I.C.S.: 531390
Konstantinos Markazos (Vice Chm & CEO)

Piraeus Best Leasing S.A. (1)
87 Syngrou Ave, 117 45, Athens, Greece
Tel.: (30) 2109009860
Web Site: http://www.piraeusleasing.gr
Automobile Leasing Services
N.A.I.C.S.: 532112

Piraeus Capital Management S.A (1)
94 Vas Sofias Av 1 Kerasountos Str, 115 28, Athens, Greece
Tel.: (30) 2103288551
Commercial Banking Services
N.A.I.C.S.: 522110

Piraeus Card Services S.A (1)
87 Sigrou Av, 117 45, Athens, Greece
Tel.: (30) 210 9294981
Web Site: http://www.piraeusbank.gr
Credit Card Processing Services
N.A.I.C.S.: 522320
Michael G. Sallas (Pres)

Piraeus Direct Services S.A. (1)
Salaminos Str-72,kallithea, 17675, Greece
Tel.: (30) 2103898922
Web Site: http://www.pds.gr
Sales Range: $25-49.9 Million
Emp.: 218
Call Center Services
N.A.I.C.S.: 561439

Piraeus Direct Solutions Single Member S.A. (1)
72-74 Salaminos Street, Kallithea, Athens, Greece
Tel.: (30) 210 389 8990
Web Site: https://www.pds.gr
Telecommunication Servicesb
N.A.I.C.S.: 517112

Piraeus Factoring S.A. (1)
170 Alexandras Av, 115 21, Athens, Greece
Tel.: (30) 2109008000
Web Site: https://www.piraeus-factoring.gr
Sales Range: $75-99.9 Million
Emp.: 60
Business Financial Services
N.A.I.C.S.: 522299
Eleni Vrettou (Chm)

Piraeus Insurance and Reinsurance Brokerage SA (1)
2 4 Mesogion av 163, 106 78, Athens, Greece
Tel.: (80) 2103288015
Web Site: http://www.piraeusbank.com
Sales Range: $50-74.9 Million
Emp.: 60
Insurance Services
N.A.I.C.S.: 524210

Piraeus Leasing S.A. (1)
27 Sinopis, 115 27, Athens, Greece
Tel.: (30) 2107760600
Web Site: http://www.piraeusleasing.gr

Sales Range: $25-49.9 Million
Emp.: 50
Leasing Services
N.A.I.C.S.: 532112
Ioannis Mavrelos (Mng Dir)

Piraeus Multifin S.A. (1)
13 Posidonos Ave, Alimos District, 174 55, Athens, Greece
Tel.: (30) 2109890300
Web Site: http://www.multifin.gr
Car Finance Services
N.A.I.C.S.: 522220

Piraeus Real Estate S.A (1)
Korai 5, 10564, Athens, Greece
Tel.: (30) 210 7728400
Web Site: http://www.pbre.gr
Real Estate Manangement Services
N.A.I.C.S.: 531390

Piraeus Securities S.A. (1)
Stadiou 10, 10564, Athens, Greece
Tel.: (30) 2103354100
Web Site: https://www.piraeus-sec.gr
Sales Range: $100-124.9 Million
Emp.: 150
Securities Brokerage Services
N.A.I.C.S.: 523150
Damianos Papakomstantiou (Vice Chm & Mng Dir)

Thriacio Logistics Center S.A. (1)
Vasilissis Sofias 75, 115 21, Athens, Greece
Tel.: (30) 210 954 0016
Web Site: https://www.thriasiologistics.gr
Logistic Services
N.A.I.C.S.: 484110

Tirana Bank S.A. (1)
Rr Ibrahim Rugova, PO Box 2400/1, Tirana, Albania
Tel.: (355) 4 2277 700
Web Site: http://www.tiranabank.al
Sales Range: $25-49.9 Million
Emp.: 464
Banking Services
N.A.I.C.S.: 522110
Manjola Capo (Head-Credit)

PIRAMAL ENTERPRISES LTD.
Piramal Ananta Agastya Corporate Park Opposite Fire Brigade, Kamani Junction LBS Marg Kurla West, Mumbai, 400070, Maharashtra, India
Tel.: (91) 2238023000   In
Web Site: https://www.piramal.com 500302—(BOM)
Rev.: $1,089,471,854
Assets: $10,041,623,404
Liabilities: $6,317,736,347
Net Worth: $3,723,887,057
Earnings: $1,195,201,727
Emp.: 180
Fiscal Year-end: 03/31/23
Holding Company
N.A.I.C.S.: 551112
Ajay G. Piramal (Chm)

Subsidiaries:

Ash Stevens Inc. (1)
18655 Krause St, Riverview, MI 48193
Tel.: (734) 282-3370
Web Site: http://www.ashstevens.com
Pharmaceutical Preparation Mfr
N.A.I.C.S.: 325412
Vince Ammoscato (VP-Ops)

Plant (Domestic):

Ash Stevens, Inc. (2)
18655 Krause St, Riverview, MI 48193
Tel.: (734) 282-3370
Web Site: http://www.ashstevens.com
Emp.: 80
Pharmaceutical Preparation Mfr
N.A.I.C.S.: 325412
Dumitru Ionescu (Sr Dir-Process Chemistry)

Coldstream Laboratories Inc. (1)
1500 Bull Lea Rd Ste 250, Lexington, KY 40511
Tel.: (859) 977-8600
Web Site: http://www.coldstreamlabs.com
Emp.: 140
Chemicals Mfr
N.A.I.C.S.: 325412

Sara Jull (Dir-Project Mgmt)

Dewan Housing Finance Corporation Limited (1)
10th Floor TCG Financial Centre BKC Road Bandra Kurla Complex, Bandra East, Mumbai, 400 098, India
Tel.: (91) 2266006999
Web Site: http://www.dhfl.com
Rev.: $1,851,532,044
Assets: $15,286,726,800
Liabilities: $14,148,507,942
Net Worth: $1,138,218,858
Earnings: ($138,511,494)
Emp.: 3,320
Fiscal Year-end: 03/31/2019
Housing Finance Services
N.A.I.C.S.: 522310
Kapil Wadhawan (Chm & Mng Dir)

Subsidiary (Domestic):

DHFL Vysya Housing Finance Ltd. (2)
No 3 8 A Main Rd JVT Tower, Sampangi Ramnagar, Bengaluru, 560027, Karnataka, India
Tel.: (91) 8022217637
Web Site: http://www.dvhousing.com
Sales Range: $25-49.9 Million
Emp.: 25
Housing Loan Services
N.A.I.C.S.: 921130
R. Nambirajan (Mng Dir)

Minrad International, Inc. (1)
50 Cobham Dr Orchard Park, New York, NY 14127
Tel.: (716) 855-1068
Web Site: http://www.minrad.com
Sales Range: $10-24.9 Million
Emp.: 139
Acute Medical Care Devices & Pharmaceuticals Mfr
N.A.I.C.S.: 325412

Piramal Capital & Housing Finance Limited (1)
Tel.: (91) 8002666444
Web Site: https://www.piramalfinance.com
Housing Financial Services
N.A.I.C.S.: 522292
Vaibhav Rekhi (Partner)

Piramal Consumer Products Private Limited (1)
Piramal Ananta Agastya Corporate Park 109 A 109A/1 to 109/21A, 111 and 110 110/1 to 110/13 Opposite Fire Brigade Kamani Junction, Mumbai, 400 070, Maharashtra, India
Tel.: (91) 2238023000
Pharmaceuticals Product Mfr
N.A.I.C.S.: 325412

Piramal Critical Care B.V. (1)
Rouboslaan 32 Ground Floor, 2252 TR, Voorschoten, Netherlands
Tel.: (31) 71 203 4050
Pharmaceuticals Product Mfr
N.A.I.C.S.: 325412

Piramal Critical Care Deutschland GmbH (1)
Am Soldnermoos 17, 85399, Hallbergmoos, Germany
Tel.: (49) 811998 866 8540
Pharmaceuticals Product Mfr
N.A.I.C.S.: 325412

Piramal Critical Care Italia, S.p.A. (1)
Via XXIV Maggio 62/A, San Giovanni Lupatoto, 37057, Verona, Italy
Tel.: (39) 045 875 3281
Pharmaceuticals Product Mfr
N.A.I.C.S.: 325412
Renata Ferrari (Country Mgr)

Piramal Critical Care Limited (1)
Suite 4 Ground Floor Heathrow Boulevard-East Wing 280 Bath Road, West Drayton, UB7 0DQ, United Kingdom
Tel.: (44) 208 759 3411
Pharmaceuticals Product Mfr
N.A.I.C.S.: 325412
John Vaughan (Country Mgr)

Piramal Critical Care South Africa (Pty) Ltd. (1)

INTERNATIONAL PUBLIC

2 Ground Floor Kipersol House Stonemill Office Park 300 Acacia Road, Darrenwood, Johannesburg, 2194, Gauteng, South Africa
Tel.: (27) 82 454 1781
Pharmaceuticals Product Mfr
N.A.I.C.S.: 325412
Bertus Bouwer (Country Mgr)

Piramal Critical Care, Inc. (1)
3950 Schelden Cir, Bethlehem, PA 18017
Web Site: https://www.piramalcriticalcare.com
Pharmaceutical Product Mfr & Distr
N.A.I.C.S.: 325412
Mahesh Sane (VP-Finance)

Piramal Fund Management Private Limited (1)
Piramal Towers A Wing Ground Floor Peninsula Corporate Park G K Marg, Lower Parel West, Mumbai, 400 013, India
Tel.: (91) 2261513456
Web Site: https://www.piramalfundmanagement.com
Fund Management Services
N.A.I.C.S.: 523940
Vaibhav Rekhi (Partner)

Piramal Healthcare (Canada) Limited (1)
110 Industrial Parkway North, Aurora, L4G 3H4, ON, Canada
Tel.: (905) 727-9417
Pharmaceuticals Product Mfr
N.A.I.C.S.: 325412

Piramal Healthcare Limited (1)
247 Business Park A-Wing 6th Floor, LBS Marg Vikhroli, Mumbai, 400083, India
Tel.: (91) 22 3095 6666
Web Site: http://www.piramal.com
Pharmaceuticals Product Mfr
N.A.I.C.S.: 325412

Piramal Healthcare UK Limited (1)
Whalton Road, Morpeth, NE61 3YA, Northumberland, United Kingdom
Tel.: (44) 167 056 2400
Pharmaceuticals Product Mfr
N.A.I.C.S.: 325412

Piramal Pharma Limited (1)
Piramal Ananta Ground Floor Piramal Ananta Agastya Corporate Park, LBS Marg Kamani Junction Kurla West, Mumbai, 400 070, Maharashtra, India
Tel.: (91) 223 802 3000
Pharmaceuticals Product Mfr
N.A.I.C.S.: 325412
Peter DeYoung (CEO-Global Pharma)

PIRAMAL GLASS LIMITED
Piramal Tower Annexe 6th Floor Peninsula Corporate Park, Off Worli Naka Lower Parel West, Mumbai, 400 013, Maharashtra, India
Tel.: (91) 22 30466969   In
Web Site: http://www.piramalglass.com
Glass Mfr
N.A.I.C.S.: 327215
Vijay Shah (Vice Chm)

Subsidiaries:

Piramal Glass - USA, Inc. (1)
1000 Taylor Ave, Park Hills, MO 63601-1769
Tel.: (573) 431-5743
Glass Container Mfr
N.A.I.C.S.: 327213

Subsidiary (Domestic):

Piramal Glass Williamstown LLC (2)
918 E Malaga Rd, Williamstown, NJ 08094
Tel.: (856) 728-9300
Web Site: http://www.piramal.com
Sales Range: $50-74.9 Million
Emp.: 120
Glass Products Mfr
N.A.I.C.S.: 327215
James Moore (Gen Mgr)

Piramal Glass Flat River LLC (1)
1000 Taylor Ave, Flat River, MO 63601
Tel.: (314) 846-5136
Glass Container Mfr
N.A.I.C.S.: 327213

PIRAMAL PHYTOCARE LIMITED
Piramal Tower Ganpatrao Kadam Marg, Lower Parel, Mumbai, 400 013, India
Tel.: (91) 2238023083 In
Web Site: http://www.piramalphytocare.com
532979—(BOM)
Rev.: $3,609,751
Assets: $1,138,696
Liabilities: $4,800,645
Net Worth: ($3,661,948)
Earnings: ($1,181,200)
Emp.: 141
Fiscal Year-end: 03/31/19
Pharmaceuticals Product Mfr
N.A.I.C.S.: 325412
Maneesh Sharma (Officer-Compliance & Sec)

PIRANSHAHR SUGAR COMPANY
Plate 24 Vanak Square Dedar North Eastern Kish, First Floor, Tehran, Iran
Tel.: (98) 2188199340
Web Site: https://pirasugar.ir
Year Founded: 1968
Beet Sugar Mfr
N.A.I.C.S.: 311313

PIRELLI DE VENEZUELA, C.A.
Carretera Nacional Guacara-Los Guayos, Zona Postal 2015, Municipio Guacara Fabrica de Cauchos, Valencia, Carabobo, Venezuela
Tel.: (58) 2454001391
Web Site: http://www.pirelli.com
Tire Dealers
N.A.I.C.S.: 441340

PIRIOU SAS
ZI du Moros, BP 521, 29185, Concarneau, Cedex, France
Tel.: (33) 2 9897 0948 FR
Web Site: http://www.piriou.com
Year Founded: 1965
Ship Building, Ship Repair & Naval Engineering Services
N.A.I.C.S.: 336611
Vincent Faujour (Gen Mgr)

Subsidiaries:
Kership SAS (1)
ZI du Moros, BP 521, 29185, Concarneau, Cedex, France (55%)
Tel.: (33) 2 9860 6313
Web Site: http://www.kership.com
Military & Law Enforcement Ship Building & Repair Services
N.A.I.C.S.: 336611

Subsidiary (Domestic):
Kership Lorient SAS (2)
ZI de Rohu, 56000, Lorient, France
Tel.: (33) 297768910
Military & Law Enforcement Ship Building & Repair Services
N.A.I.C.S.: 336611

PIRSON MONTAGE SA
Rue Fanny 74, Seraing, 4100, Belgium
Tel.: (32) 4 385 90 90
Web Site: http://www.pirsonmontagesa.be
Emp.: 30
Industrial Services
N.A.I.C.S.: 238120
Laurent Pirson (Mng Dir)

Subsidiaries:
DSD Steel Construction AG (1)
Zugerstrasse 40, 6314, Unterageri, Switzerland
Tel.: (41) 41 754 53 10
Holding Company; Steel Construction
N.A.I.C.S.: 551112

Subsidiary (Non-US):
DSD Steel Group GmbH (2)
Henry Ford Strasse 110, Saarlouis, 66740, Germany
Tel.: (49) 6831180
Web Site: http://www.dsd-steel.com
Sales Range: $300-349.9 Million
Emp.: 2,000
Steel Structure Bridge Process Equipment & Special Construction Gas Treating Plant & Environmental Technology Air Conditioning & Erection of Industrial Plant Services
N.A.I.C.S.: 236210

Subsidiary (Domestic):
DSD Bruckenbau GmbH (3)
Landsberger Allee 117A, 10407, Berlin, Germany
Tel.: (49) 3020928220
Web Site: http://www.dsd-brueckenbau.com
Sales Range: $25-49.9 Million
Steel & Composite Bridge Construction Service
N.A.I.C.S.: 237310
Harald Stutzer (Mng Dir)

Subsidiary (Non-US):
DSD Ferrometalco SAE (3)
Ismailia Desert Road, PO Box 9024 Nasr City, Heliopolis, Cairo, Egypt (100%)
Tel.: (20) 2 624 0060
Web Site: http://www.ferrometalco.com
Steel Engineering, Fabrication & Erection
N.A.I.C.S.: 238120

Subsidiary (Domestic):
DSD HILGERS Stahlbau GmbH (3)
Hilgersstrasse, 56598, Rheinbrohl, Germany
Tel.: (49) 2635 963 0
Web Site: http://www.dsd-hilgers.de
Steel Structure Erection & Maintenance Services
N.A.I.C.S.: 238120

DSD Industrie Rohrtechnik GmbH (3)
Carl Friedrich Benz Strasse 2, Delitzsch, 4509, Germany
Tel.: (49) 34202 9879 10
Web Site: http://www.dsd-irt.com
Emp.: 100
Industrial Pipeline Construction
N.A.I.C.S.: 237120
Thomas Roeder (Mng Dir)

Subsidiary (Non-US):
DSD International Contractors S.a.r.l. (3)
Parc d' activites economiques, ZA Gadderscheider, L-4984, Sanem, Luxembourg
Tel.: (352) 57 48 48
Web Site: http://www.dsd-steel.com
Structural Steel Components Fabrication & Installation Services
N.A.I.C.S.: 238120
Laurent Bouzonville (Mng Dir)

Subsidiary (Domestic):
DSD Montagetechnik GmbH (3)
Henry Ford Strasse 110, 66740, Saarlouis, Germany
Tel.: (49) 6831 18 2638
Emp.: 40
Planning & Erection of Industrial Plants
N.A.I.C.S.: 238120
Dittmar Wachter (Mng Dir)

DSD NOELL GmbH (3)
Alfred Nobel Str 20, 97080, Wurzburg, Germany
Tel.: (49) 931 903 1215
Web Site: http://www.dsd-noell.com
Sales Range: $25-49.9 Million
Emp.: 50
Hydromechanical Equipment Services
N.A.I.C.S.: 238290
Ioan Gische (Mng Dir)

Subsidiary (Non-US):
DSD Steel Bulgaria Ltd. (3)
20 Chataldzha Blvd entr A fl 1 office 3, 9000, Varna, Bulgaria
Tel.: (359) 52 305525
Web Site: http://www.dsd-steel.bg
Maintenance, Service & Repair of Industrial Plants
N.A.I.C.S.: 236210

Subsidiary (Domestic):
Ferrostaal Maintenance Eisenhuttenstadt GmbH (3)
Strasse 22 (Industriepark ArcelorMittal), 15890, Eisenhuttenstadt, Germany
Tel.: (49) 3364 428 100
Web Site: http://www.dsd-ehs.com
Mechanical Engineering Services
N.A.I.C.S.: 541330
Dieter Zellin (Mng Dir)

IMB Industrie Montage GmbH (3)
Werkstrasse 16, D-15890, Eisenhuttenstadt, Germany
Tel.: (49) 3364 37 64 20
Web Site: http://www.imb-ehst.de
Steel Construction, Maintenance & Repair of Industrial Plants
N.A.I.C.S.: 238120
Thierry Putters (Mng Dir)

Pirson Refractories B.V. (1)
Rooswijkweg 215, Velsen-Noord, Velsen, 1951 MD, North Holland, Netherlands
Tel.: (31) 251 27 24 12
Web Site: http://www.pirsonholland.com
Installation of Blast Furnace Linings & Refractories for Hot Blast Systems
N.A.I.C.S.: 236210

PIRTEK FLUID SYSTEMS PTY. LTD.
3-7 Garling Road, Kings Park, 2148, NSW, Australia
Tel.: (61) 2 8822 9000 AU
Web Site: http://www.pirtek.com.au
Year Founded: 1980
Hydraulic Components Sale & Services Shop Franchisor Services
N.A.I.C.S.: 533110

Subsidiaries:
PIRTEK (MONGOLIA) LLC (1)
Dundgol Street 3rd Khoroo, Bayangol, 016020, Ulaanbaatar, Mongolia
Tel.: (976) 77117733
Web Site: http://www.pirtek.mn
Hydraulic Equipment Distr
N.A.I.C.S.: 423830

PIRTEK (NEW ZEALAND) LTD (1)
10 Ross Reid Place, East Tamaki, Manukau, 2013, New Zealand
Tel.: (64) 92746925
Web Site: http://www.pirtek.co.nz
Hydraulic Equipment Distr
N.A.I.C.S.: 423830
Chris Bourke (Gen Mgr)

PIRTEK ASIA PTE LTD (1)
101A Pioneer Road, Singapore, 639606, Singapore
Tel.: (65) 68731878
Web Site: http://www.pirtekasia.com
Hydraulic Equipment Distr
N.A.I.C.S.: 423830

PIRTEK DEUTSCHLAND (GERMANY) GMBH (1)
Maarweg 165, 50825, Cologne, Germany
Tel.: (49) 221945440
Hydraulic Equipment Distr
N.A.I.C.S.: 423830

Pirtek B.V (1)
Hongkongstraat 29, Rotterdam, 3047 BR, Netherlands
Tel.: (31) 881118888
Web Site: http://www.pirtek.nl
Hydraulic Equipment Distr
N.A.I.C.S.: 423830
Michel Schutte (Mgr-Ops & Technical)

Pirtek Europe Ltd. (1)
199 The Vale, Acton, London, W3 7QS, United Kingdom
Tel.: (44) 2087498444
Web Site: http://www.pirtek-europe.com
Hydraulic Equipment Maintenance Services
N.A.I.C.S.: 811310

Pirtek Fluid Systems (Delta) ltd (1)
1090 Cliveden Avenue, Annacis Island, Delta, V3M 6E6, BC, Canada
Tel.: (604) 516-0611
Web Site: http://www.pirtek.ca
Hydraulic Equipment Distr
N.A.I.C.S.: 423830

Pirtek Southern Africa (Pty) Ltd (1)
7 Guernsey Drive Longmeadow Business Estate East, Johannesburg, 1609, Gauteng, South Africa
Tel.: (27) 116082299
Web Site: http://www.pirtek.co.za
Hydraulic Equipment Distr
N.A.I.C.S.: 423830

Pirtek USA LLC (1)
501 Haverty Ct Ste A, Rockledge, FL 32955
Tel.: (321) 504-4422
Web Site: http://www.pirtekusa.com
Emp.: 40
Hydraulic Components Sales & Service Shops Franchisor
N.A.I.C.S.: 533110
Gwyn O'Kane (VP-Franchise Dev)

PISANI & RICKERTSEN GMBH
Messberg 1, 20095, Hamburg, Germany
Tel.: (49) 403029060
Web Site: http://www.pisani.de
Year Founded: 1905
Rev.: $82,267,496
Emp.: 10
Hazelnut Producer
N.A.I.C.S.: 311911
Thomas Haas-Rickertsen (Mng Dir)

PISCINES DESJOYAUX SA
42 avenue Benoit Fourneyron, CS 50280, 42484, La Fouillouse, France
Tel.: (33) 477361212
Web Site: https://www.desjoyaux.eu
ALPDX—(EUR)
Sales Range: $125-149.9 Million
Swimming Pool Mfr & Marketer
N.A.I.C.S.: 339920
Jean-Louis Desjoyaux (Chm & CEO)

Subsidiaries:
DESJOYAUX PISCINES France SARL (1)
23 Rue de la Planche aux Joncs, 57155, Marly, Moselle, France
Tel.: (33) 387569584
Sales Range: $25-49.9 Million
Emp.: 7
Swimming Pool Construction Services
N.A.I.C.S.: 238990

Subsidiary (Domestic):
DESJOYAUX PISCINES 06 SARL (2)
Avenue Leon Berenger, 06700, Saint-Laurent-du-Var, Alpes-Maritimes, France
Tel.: (33) 493268818
Swimming Pool Construction Services
N.A.I.C.S.: 238990

DESJOYAUX PISCINES 24 SARL (2)
2 Impasse du Moulin Rond Point la Cavaille, 24100, Saint-Laurent-des-Vignes, Dordogne, France
Tel.: (33) 553248598
Swimming Pool Construction Services
N.A.I.C.S.: 237110

DESJOYAUX PISCINES 77 SARL (2)
Route Nationale 7 Route d'Antibes, 77780, Bourron-Marlotte, Seine-et-Marne, France
Tel.: (33) 1 64 78 36 90
Swimming Pool Construction Services
N.A.I.C.S.: 237110

DESJOYAUX PISCINES 78 SARL (2)
Boulevard de la renaissance, 78240, Chambourcy, France
Tel.: (33) 139080730
Web Site: http://chambourcy.piscinedesjoyaux.fr
Swimming Pool Construction Services

PISCINES DESJOYAUX SA

Piscines Desjoyaux SA—(Continued)
N.A.I.C.S.: 238990

DESJOYAUX PISCINES CAEN SARL (2)
5 rue de Vienne, Paris, 75008, France
Tel.: (33) 2 31 79 80 80
Web Site: http://www.piscine-bonheur.fr
Emp.: 2
Swimming Pool Construction Services
N.A.I.C.S.: 238990

DESJOYAUX PISCINES ST ETIENNE SARL
ZI du bas Rollet, 42480, La Fouilouse, Loire, France
Tel.: (33) 4 77 55 69 06
Swimming Pool Construction Services
N.A.I.C.S.: 238990

Desjoyaux Piscinas Lisboa, LDA (1)
Av 23 de Julho de 1833 E N 378 Lote 43, Fernao Ferro, 2865-067, Seixal, Portugal
Tel.: (351) 212122005
Web Site: http://www.desjoyaux.pt
Sales Range: $25-49.9 Million
Emp.: 2
Swimming Pool Construction Services
N.A.I.C.S.: 238990
Frederick Maleuzaux (Gen Mgr)

FOREZ PISCINES SA (1)
Ld La Gouyonniere, 42480, La Fouilouse, Loire, France
Tel.: (33) 477361212
Web Site: http://www.desjoyaux.com
Swimming Pool Equipment Mfr & Distr
N.A.I.C.S.: 326199

Subsidiary (Non-US):

DESJOYAUX DEUTSCHLAND GmbH. (2)
Wilpertingerstr 1, 85375, Neufahrn bei Freising, Germany
Tel.: (49) 81656099425
Web Site: http://www.desjoyaux.de
Emp.: 10
Swimming Pool Construction Services
N.A.I.C.S.: 238990

Subsidiary (Non-US):

DESJOYAUX IBERICA DISA (3)
Calle de la Trepadella 8-89, 08755, Castellbisbal, Barcelona, Spain
Tel.: (34) 937711944
Swimming Pool Construction Services
N.A.I.C.S.: 237110

VIP SARL (1)
17 Rue du Nouveau Siecle, 59800, Lille, Nord, France
Tel.: (33) 320149214
Swimming Pool Construction Services
N.A.I.C.S.: 238990

PISCINES GROUPE GA SA
Parc dActivites RN 8 Quartier du Douard, 13420, Gemenos, France
Tel.: (33) 442320332
Web Site: http://www.piscinesgroupega.com
Sales Range: $10-24.9 Million
Holding Company
N.A.I.C.S.: 551112
Gerard Andrei (Chm & CEO)

PISCINES MAGILINE SAS
3 rue du Labourat, ZAC des Ecrevolles, 10000, Troyes, France
Tel.: (33) 3 2545 1240   FR
Web Site: http://www.piscines-magiline.fr
Year Founded: 1994
Sales Range: $10-24.9 Million
Emp.: 97
Custom Swimming Pool Liner & Related Products Designer, Mfr & Distr
N.A.I.C.S.: 326199
Herve Ricard (Chm & CEO)

PISEC GROUP GMBH
Gusshausstrasse 12, 1040, Vienna, Austria
Tel.: (43) 5053215
Web Site: http://www.pisec.com
Steel & Other Industrial Products Mfr
N.A.I.C.S.: 331513
Jurgen Hackl (CFO)

Subsidiaries:

Zimmer Staal Bvba (1)
Grote Markt 41, 2500, Lier, Belgium
Tel.: (32) 3 491 82 82
Web Site: http://www.zimmer.be
Steel Product Distr
N.A.I.C.S.: 423390
Pieter Adams (Dir-Comml)

PITANGO VENTURE CAPITAL
11 HaMenofim St Building B, 46725, Herzliyya, Israel
Tel.: (972) 99718100
Web Site: http://www.pitango.com
Rev.: $1,600,000,000
Emp.: 30
Investment Services
N.A.I.C.S.: 523999
Rami Kalish (Mng Gen Partner)

PITER TRUST INVESTMENT COMPANY JSC
Moika Embankment 11n, 191186, Saint Petersburg, Russia
Tel.: (7) 8123366586
Web Site: http://www.piter-trust.ru
Emp.: 100
Real Estate Manangement Services
N.A.I.C.S.: 531190
Ruslan Lienkha (Head-Customer Svc Dept)

PITTARDS PLC
Sherborne Road, Yeovil, BA21 5BA, Somerset, United Kingdom
Tel.: (44) 193 547 4321
Web Site: http://www.corporate.pittards.com
PTD—(LSE)
Rev.: $26,685,987
Assets: $38,741,182
Liabilities: $21,001,213
Net Worth: $17,739,970
Earnings: $373,373
Emp.: 1,108
Fiscal Year-end: 12/31/21
Leather Processing Services
N.A.I.C.S.: 316110
Reginald H. Hankey (CEO)

Subsidiaries:

Ethiopia Tannery Share Company (1)
PO Box 5628, 5628, Addis Ababa, Ethiopia
Tel.: (251) 11 551 3691
Web Site: http://www.ethiopiatannery.com.et
Leather Product Mfr
N.A.I.C.S.: 316990
Dagnachew Demelash (Gen Mgr)

Pittards Group Limited (1)
Sherborne Rd, Yeovil, BA21 5BA, United Kingdom (100%)
Tel.: (44) 1935474321
Web Site: http://www.pittards.com
Sales Range: $25-49.9 Million
Leather & Hide Tanning & Finishing
N.A.I.C.S.: 316110

PITTI ENGINEERING LIMITED
6-3-648/401 4th Floor Padmaja Landmark Somajiguda, Hyderabad, 500082, Telangana, India
Tel.: (91) 4023312770
Web Site: https://www.pitti.in
Year Founded: 1987
513519—(BOM)
Rev.: $134,044,518
Assets: $117,253,882
Liabilities: $77,204,112
Net Worth: $40,049,769
Earnings: $7,053,786
Emp.: 1,331
Fiscal Year-end: 03/31/23
Electrical Laminations Mfr
N.A.I.C.S.: 339999
Sharad B. Pitti (Chm & Mng Dir)

Subsidiaries:

Pitti Castings Pvt Ltd. (1)
6-3-648/401 4th Floor Padmaja Landmark Somajiguda, Hyderabad, 500 082, Telangana, India
Tel.: (91) 4023312770
Web Site: http://www.pitticastings.com
Emp.: 2,500
Iron & Steel Product Mfr
N.A.I.C.S.: 331110

PITTLER MASCHINENFABRIK AG
Gutleutstrasse 175, D-60327, Frankfurt am Main, Germany
Tel.: (49) 6924000858
Web Site: https://www.pittler-maschinenfabrik.de
Year Founded: 1889
PIT—(MUN)
Rev.: $7,969,941
Assets: $26,117,564
Liabilities: $13,378,904
Net Worth: $12,738,660
Earnings: $474,664
Emp.: 122
Fiscal Year-end: 12/31/23
Precision Equipment Mfr & Distr
N.A.I.C.S.: 333310
Markus Hoehne (Member-Mgmt Bd)

PIVARA TUZLA D.D.
Marsala Tita 163, 75000, Tuzla, Bosnia & Herzegovina
Tel.: (387) 3 530 0100
Web Site: http://www.pivaratuzla.ba
PITZRK1—(SARE)
Rev.: $16,798,133
Assets: $23,585,394
Liabilities: $7,868,158
Net Worth: $15,717,236
Earnings: $1,929,970
Emp.: 206
Fiscal Year-end: 12/31/20
Alcoholic Beverages Mfr
N.A.I.C.S.: 312120

PIVOTAL THERAPEUTICS INC.
81 Zenway Blvd Unit 10, Woodbridge, L4H 0S5, ON, Canada
Tel.: (905) 856-9797   Ca
Web Site: http://www.pivotaltherapeutics.us
Year Founded: 2011
PVTTF—(OTCIQ)
Sales Range: Less than $1 Million
Pharmaceuticals Mfr
N.A.I.C.S.: 325412
Eugene G. Bortoluzzi (Founder)

PIVOTREE INC.
6300 Northam Drive, Toronto, L4V 1H7, ON, Canada
Web Site: https://www.pivotree.com
Year Founded: 1998
8AV0—(DEU)
Rev.: $67,814,161
Assets: $48,398,593
Liabilities: $4,986,193
Net Worth: $43,412,400
Earnings: ($5,459,561)
Emp.: 600
Fiscal Year-end: 12/31/23
Ecommerce Hosting Services
N.A.I.C.S.: 518210
Bill Di Nardo (CEO)

Subsidiaries:

Bridge Solutions Group Corp. (1)
1 Bridge Plz N Ste 275, Fort Lee, NJ 07024
Web Site: http://www.bridgesgi.com
Computer System Design Services
N.A.I.C.S.: 541512

INTERNATIONAL PUBLIC

Doug Brochu (CEO)

PIX TRANSMISSIONS LIMITED
J-7 MIDC Hingna Road, Nagpur, 440 016, Maharashtra, India
Tel.: (91) 7104669000
Web Site: https://www.pixtrans.com
PIXTRANS—(NSE)
Rev.: $62,439,714
Assets: $75,701,071
Liabilities: $25,904,929
Net Worth: $49,796,142
Earnings: $9,397,124
Emp.: 749
Fiscal Year-end: 03/31/22
Transmission Belt Mfr
N.A.I.C.S.: 326220
Amarpal Singh Sethi (Chm & Co-Mng Dir)

Subsidiaries:

PIX EUROPE LIMITED (1)
Unit 24 Farthing Road Industrial Estate, Sproughton, Ipswich, IP1 5AP, Suffolk, United Kingdom
Tel.: (44) 1473 744612
Web Site: http://www.pixeuro.com
Sales Range: $25-49.9 Million
Emp.: 40
Belt & Hose Mfr
N.A.I.C.S.: 326220
Stewart Booth (Dir-Ops)

PIX GERMANY GmbH (1)
Karl-Schurz-Str 35, 33100, Paderborn, Germany
Tel.: (49) 5251 284 4070
Web Site: https://www.pixgermany.com
Sales Range: $25-49.9 Million
Emp.: 12
Transmission Belt Mfr
N.A.I.C.S.: 326220

PIX Hydraulics Europe Limited (1)
Unit 24 Farthing Road Industrial Estate, Sproughton, Ipswich, IP1 5AP, Suffolk, United Kingdom
Tel.: (44) 1473 463680
Web Site: http://www.pixhydraulics.com
Sales Range: $25-49.9 Million
Emp.: 30
Belt & Hydraulic Hose Mfr
N.A.I.C.S.: 326220
Joseth Deacon (Dir-Ops)

PIX MIDDLE EAST FZC (1)
Warehouse No 16/1, PO Box 54526, Ras al Khaimah, United Arab Emirates
Tel.: (971) 72444366
Web Site: http://www.pixmiddle-east.com
Belt & Hydraulic Hose Mfr
N.A.I.C.S.: 326220

PIXART IMAGING, INC.
No 5 Innovation Road 1 Hsinchu Science Park, Hsinchu, Taiwan
Tel.: (886) 35795317
Web Site: https://www.pixart.com
Year Founded: 1998
3227—(TPE)
Rev.: $163,396,398
Assets: $352,801,551
Liabilities: $67,250,008
Net Worth: $285,551,543
Earnings: $32,453,741
Emp.: 645
Fiscal Year-end: 12/31/22
Optical Instrument Mfr
N.A.I.C.S.: 333310
Sen-Huang Huang (Chm & Pres)

Subsidiaries:

Audiowise Technology Inc. (1)
2F No 1-1 Innovation Road I Hsinchu Science Park, Baoshan Township, Hsinchu, 30076, Taiwan
Tel.: (886) 35795317
Web Site: http://www.audiowise-t.com
Wireless Audio Services
N.A.I.C.S.: 512290

PixArt Imaging (Penang) Sdn. Bhd. (1)

Ground and First Floor Kompleks Eureka
Universiti Sains, 11800, Penang, Malaysia
Tel.: (60) 46136300
IC Design Services
N.A.I.C.S.: 541420

PixArt Imaging (USA), Inc. (1)
1263 Oakmead Pkwy Ste 200, Sunnyvale,
CA 94085
Tel.: (408) 501-6008
IC Design Services
N.A.I.C.S.: 541420

PixArt Technology (Shenzhen) Co.,
Ltd. (1)
Room 808 Block A Hailrun Complex
No6021 ShenNan Blvd, Fu Tian District,
Shenzhen, 518040, China
Tel.: (86) 75589812394
IC Design Services
N.A.I.C.S.: 541420

PIXEL COMPANYZ INC.
5F Edomisaka Mori Building 1-40
Toranomon 4-chome, Minato-ku, To-
kyo, 105-0001, Japan
Tel.: (81) 367313410   JP
Web Site: https://www.pixel-cz.co.jp
Year Founded: 1986
2743—(TKS)
Rev.: $4,317,810
Assets: $8,054,240
Liabilities: $808,260
Net Worth: $7,245,980
Earnings: ($3,615,900)
Emp.: 91
Fiscal Year-end: 12/31/23
Investment Services
N.A.I.C.S.: 523999
Hiroaki Yoshida (CEO)

Subsidiaries:

HYBRID (HONGKONG) CO.,
LTD. (1)
Suite C 6/F Cameron Plaza 23-25A Cam-
eron Road, Tsim Sha Tsui, Kowloon, China
(Hong Kong)
Tel.: (852) 3118 7136
Printing Equipment Distr
N.A.I.C.S.: 423610

HYBRID INTERNATIONAL TRADING
(SHANGHAI) CO., LTD. (1)
641Lane No 1 703 TianShan Rd, Shanghai,
China
Tel.: (86) 21 5206 7070
Printing Equipment Distr
N.A.I.C.S.: 423610

Tokyo Chuo Sato Product Sales Co.,
Ltd. (1)
5F No 1 Fuji Bldg 2-15 Kanda-Jimbocho,
Chiyoda-ku, Tokyo, 101-0051, Japan
Tel.: (81) 3 3556 5361
Web Site: http://www.chuosato.com
Printing Equipment Distr
N.A.I.C.S.: 423610

PIXELA CORPORATION
25F Namba Parks Tower 2-10-70
Namba-naka, Naniwa-ku, Osaka,
556-0011, Japan
Tel.: (81) 666333500
Web Site: https://www.pixela.co.jp
Year Founded: 1982
6731—(TKS)
Rev.: $10,287,590
Assets: $6,948,200
Liabilities: $3,204,680
Net Worth: $3,743,520
Earnings: ($10,018,170)
Emp.: 55
Fiscal Year-end: 09/30/23
Hardware Product Mfr & Whslr
N.A.I.C.S.: 334310
Hiroshi Fujioka (Pres)

PIXELPLUS CO., LTD.
30 Geumto-ro 40beon-gil, Sujeong-
gu, Seongnam, 13453, Gyeonggi-do,
Korea (South)
Tel.: (82) 3180168800   KR
Web Site: https://www.pixelplus.com
Year Founded: 2000
087600—(KRS)
Rev.: $48,215,418
Assets: $72,798,791
Liabilities: $7,843,094
Net Worth: $64,955,697
Earnings: $190,072
Emp.: 112
Fiscal Year-end: 12/31/22
Fabless Semiconductor Mfr
N.A.I.C.S.: 334413
Seo-Kyu Lee (CEO)

Subsidiaries:

Pixelplus Shanghai Co., Ltd. (1)
Flat F 17/E First Trade Tower, 985
Dongfang Road, Shanghai, 200122, Pu-
dong, China
Tel.: (86) 2158209982
Web Site: http://www.pixelplus.co.kr
Semiconductor Mfr
N.A.I.C.S.: 334413

Pixelplus Technology Inc. (1)
6F-2 No 29 Puding Rd, Hsin-chu, 300, Tai-
wan
Tel.: (886) 36667933
Web Site: http://www.solun.com.tw
Sales Range: $25-49.9 Million
Emp.: 15
Semiconductor Mfr
N.A.I.C.S.: 334413
Taniear Lin (Mng Dir)

PIXIE DUST TECHNOLOGIES, INC.
2-20-5 Kanda Misaki-cho, Chiyoda-
ku, Tokyo, 101-0061, Japan
Tel.: (81) 352444880   JP
Web Site: https://www.pixiedusttech.com
Year Founded: 2017
PXDT—(NASDAQ)
Rev.: $6,561,088
Assets: $22,349,521
Liabilities: $12,930,978
Net Worth: $9,418,544
Earnings: ($13,046,154)
Emp.: 80
Fiscal Year-end: 04/30/24
Information Technology Services
N.A.I.C.S.: 541512
Takayuki Hoshi (Chief Res Officer)

PIXIUM VISION
74 rue du Faubourg Saint Antoine,
75012, Paris, France
Tel.: (33) 176214730
Web Site: http://www.pixium-vision.com
Year Founded: 2011
PIX—(EUR)
Sales Range: $1-9.9 Million
Medical Device Mfr
N.A.I.C.S.: 339112
Bernard Gilly (Chm)

PIXTA INC.
JustCo Shibuya Hikarie Shibuya
Hikarie 33F 2-21-1 Shibuya, Shibuya-
ku, Tokyo, 150-8510, Japan
Tel.: (81) 357742692
Web Site: https://pixta.co.jp
Year Founded: 2005
3416—(TKS)
Rev.: $18,582,890
Assets: $16,342,450
Liabilities: $9,337,530
Net Worth: $7,004,920
Earnings: $1,850,490
Emp.: 116
Fiscal Year-end: 12/31/23
Stock Photos, Illustrations, Vectors &
Footage Website
N.A.I.C.S.: 513199
Daisuke Komata (Founder, Founder
& CEO)

Subsidiaries:

Snapmart Inc. (1)
3-11-11 Shibuya Shibuya-Ku, Tokyo, Japan
Tel.: (81) 8043378267
Web Site: http://www.snapmart.jp
Stock Photo Services
N.A.I.C.S.: 519290

PIZU GROUP HOLDING LIMITED
Unit A 11F Two Chinachem Plaza No
68 Connaught Road, Hong Kong,
China (Hong Kong)
Tel.: (852) 3 118 2308   Ky
Web Site: http://www.pizugroup.com
Year Founded: 2003
8053—(HKG)
Rev.: $250,872,642
Assets: $504,733,645
Liabilities: $284,632,312
Net Worth: $220,101,333
Earnings: $31,947,349
Emp.: 1,343
Fiscal Year-end: 03/31/22
Explosive Equipment Mfr & Distr
N.A.I.C.S.: 325920
Zeke Xiong (Chm)

PIZZA PIZZA ROYALTY CORP.
500 Kipling Avenue, Toronto, M8Z
5E5, ON, Canada
Tel.: (416) 967-1010   Ca
Web Site: http://www.pizzapizza.ca
Year Founded: 2012
PZRIF—(OTCIQ)
Rev.: $24,969,595
Assets: $284,012,230
Liabilities: $56,974,235
Net Worth: $227,037,995
Earnings: $18,714,484
Emp.: 5,200
Fiscal Year-end: 12/31/21
Restaurant Management Services
N.A.I.C.S.: 722511

PJ ELECTRONICS CO LTD
6th Fl 101-Dong Bucheon Techno
Park, Ojeong-gu, Bucheon, 14501,
Gyeonggi-do, Korea (South)
Tel.: (82) 323267000
Web Site: https://www.pjems.co.kr
Year Founded: 1969
006140—(KRS)
Rev.: $120,978,407
Assets: $142,387,055
Liabilities: $49,852,528
Net Worth: $92,534,527
Earnings: $5,335,975
Emp.: 233
Fiscal Year-end: 12/31/22
Electronic Products
N.A.I.C.S.: 334419
Myung-Wook Kim (CEO)

Subsidiaries:

PJ Electronics Co., Ltd. - Factory
II (1)
501 303 Dong Bucheon Techno-park 365,
Samjeong-dong Ojeong-gu, Bucheon,
Gyeonggi, Korea (South)
Tel.: (82) 323268423
Printed Circuit Board Mfr
N.A.I.C.S.: 334412

PJ METAL CO., LTD.
13FL Saman BL 945 Daechi-dong,
Gangnam-gu, Seoul, 135-846, Korea
(South)
Tel.: (82) 25554451
Web Site: http://www.pjmetal.co.kr
Year Founded: 1984
128660—(KRS)
Rev.: $206,360,275
Assets: $86,744,102
Liabilities: $39,913,412
Net Worth: $46,830,690
Earnings: $4,435,041
Emp.: 91
Fiscal Year-end: 12/31/22
Aluminum Deoxidizer Product Mfr
N.A.I.C.S.: 331314
Byeng Hyuk Choi (Dir)

Subsidiaries:

DAWONALLOY Co., Ltd. (1)
123-90 Injusandan-ro Inju-myeo, Asan,
31435, Chungcheongnam-do, Korea
(South)
Tel.: (82) 415319611
Web Site: https://www.dawonalloy.com
Aluminum Alloy Mfr & Distr
N.A.I.C.S.: 331313

PJ ALTEK Co., Ltd. (1)
117 Poseunggongdansunhwan-ro,
Poseung-eup, Pyeongtaek, 17960,
Gyeonggi-do, Korea (South)
Tel.: (82) 316866777
Web Site: https://www.pjaltek.co.kr
Aluminum Alloy Mfr
N.A.I.C.S.: 331313

PJ Chemtek Co., Ltd. (1)
67-2 Yusangongdan 8-gil, Yangsan,
Gyeongsangnam-do, Korea (South)
Tel.: (82) 553882341
Web Site: https://www.pjzinc.co.kr
Chemical Product Mfr & Distr
N.A.I.C.S.: 325130

Poong Jeon Nonferrous Metal. Co.
Ltd. (1)
48 Saryeom-ro 680-3Gyeongseo-dong,
Seo-gu, Incheon, 22744, Korea (South)
Tel.: (82) 325619111
Web Site: https://www.poongjeon.net
Nonferrous Metal Mfr & Distr
N.A.I.C.S.: 331523

PJBUMI BERHAD
No 11 Jalan Ruang U8/109 Seksyen
U8 Bukit Jelutong, 40150, Shah
Alam, Selangor Darul Ehsan, Malay-
sia
Tel.: (60) 378310075
Web Site: http://www.pjbumi.com.my
PJBUMI—(KLS)
Rev.: $3,041,775
Assets: $8,019,495
Liabilities: $1,998,810
Net Worth: $6,020,685
Earnings: $309,870
Emp.: 16
Fiscal Year-end: 12/31/22
Fiber Reinforced Plastic Mfr
N.A.I.C.S.: 326199
Seck Wah Lim (Co-Sec)

PJP MAKRUM S.A.
Plac Koscieleckich 3, 85-033, Bydgo-
szcz, Poland
Tel.: (48) 602314270
Web Site: https://www.projprzem.com
Year Founded: 1990
PJP—(WAR)
Rev.: $108,537,855
Assets: $103,287,601
Liabilities: $62,245,427
Net Worth: $41,042,175
Earnings: $4,488,567
Fiscal Year-end: 12/31/23
Building Construction Services
N.A.I.C.S.: 236220
Dariusz Skrocki (Chm-Supervisory
Bd)

PJSC AEROFLOT RUSSIAN AIRLINES
St Arbat house 1, 119019, Moscow,
Russia
Tel.: (7) 4952235555   RU
Web Site: http://www.aeroflot.ru
Year Founded: 1932
AFLT—(MOEX)
Rev.: $6,842,320,924
Assets: $12,451,022,554
Liabilities: $13,554,768,361
Net Worth: ($1,103,745,807)

PJSC AEROFLOT RUSSIAN AIRLINES

PJSC Aeroflot Russian Airlines—(Continued)
Earnings: ($156,708,791)
Emp.: 31,500
Fiscal Year-end: 12/31/23
Airline Services
N.A.I.C.S.: 481111
Vitaly Saveliev (Chm)

Subsidiaries:

JSC Aurora Airlines (1)
50A Gorkogo St, Sakhalin Region, 693023, Yuzhno-Sakhalinsk, Russia
Tel.: (7) 4242300206
Web Site: http://www.flyaurora.ru
Airline Services
N.A.I.C.S.: 481111

ZAO Aeromar (1)
Sheremetyevskoe highway ow 31, 141425, Moscow, Khimki, Russia
Tel.: (7) 4952349475
Web Site: http://www.aeromar.ru
Sales Range: $200-249.9 Million
Emp.: 2,500
Airline Catering Services; Owned 51% by Aeroflot Russian Airlines & 49% by Deutsche Lufthansa AG
N.A.I.C.S.: 722320

PJSC ALCHEVSKKOKS
1 Krasnyh Partizan Str, Lugansk reg, 94200, Alchevsk, Ukraine
Tel.: (380) 6442 7 62 86
Web Site: http://www.akz.lg.ua
Chemical Products Mfr
N.A.I.C.S.: 325998

PJSC ALROSA
Ozerkovskaya emb 24, Moscow, 115184, Russia
Tel.: (7) 4956209250
Web Site: https://www.alrosa.ru
ALRS—(MOEX)
Rev.: $4,404,326,310
Assets: $5,707,750,860
Liabilities: $2,697,219,330
Net Worth: $3,010,531,530
Earnings: $1,230,066,930
Emp.: 30,000
Fiscal Year-end: 12/31/21
Diamond Mining Services
N.A.I.C.S.: 212390
Sergey Barsukov (Deputy CEO)

Subsidiaries:

ALROSA Belgium NV (1)
Lange Herentalsestraat 62/70, 2018, Antwerp, Belgium
Tel.: (32) 32270658
Diamond Mining Services
N.A.I.C.S.: 212390

ALROSA Hong Kong Ltd. (1)
Suite 6405 64 F Central Plaza 18 Harbour Road, Wanchai, China (Hong Kong)
Tel.: (852) 25219292
Diamond Mining Services
N.A.I.C.S.: 212390

ALROSA Israel Ltd. (1)
Diamond Exchange Maccabi Bldg 2031 1 Jabotinsky Str, 52520, Ramat Gan, Israel
Tel.: (972) 36128680
Diamond Mining Services
N.A.I.C.S.: 212390

ALROSA USA Inc. (1)
580 5th Ave, New York, NY 10036
Tel.: (212) 921-4300
Diamond Mining Services
N.A.I.C.S.: 212390
Rebecca Foerster (Pres)

Almazdortrans LLC (1)
2 ul Pervomayskaya, Lensk, 678144, Russia
Tel.: (7) 4113749999
Diamond Mining Services
N.A.I.C.S.: 212390

Hidrochicapa S.A. (1)
Salvador Allende No 100, Luanda, Angola
Tel.: (244) 929505050
Web Site: http://www.hidrochicapa.com

Hydro Power Station Construction Services
N.A.I.C.S.: 237130
Sergey Ermolaev (Fin Dir)

JSC ALROSA Air Company (1)
Airport Administrative Building Office 24, 678170, Mirny, Russia
Tel.: (7) 4113648121
Web Site: http://www.alrosa.aero
Airline Transportation Services
N.A.I.C.S.: 488190

JSC ALROSA-Gaz (1)
Chernyshevskoe Highway 21, PO Box 20, Mirny, Russia
Tel.: (7) 4113635051
Web Site: http://www.alrosa-gaz.ru
Gas Production & Transportation Services
N.A.I.C.S.: 486210

JSC ALROSA-Lena Shipping Company (1)
Naberezhnaya d 59, 678144, Lensk, Russia
Tel.: (7) 4113746538
Web Site: http://www.alrosalena.ru
Water Transportation Services
N.A.I.C.S.: 488390

JSC ALROSA-Torg (1)
23/1 Leningradsky Prospect, 678174, Mirny, Russia
Tel.: (7) 4113633602
Diamond Mining Services
N.A.I.C.S.: 212390

JSC Almazy Anabara (1)
Kirov Street 18 Block B, 677000, Yakutsk, Russia
Tel.: (7) 4112496000
Web Site: http://www.alanab.ykt.ru
Diamond Mining Services
N.A.I.C.S.: 212390

JSC Golubaya Volna Resort (1)
st Tourist 27, Gelendzhik, 353465, Krasnodar, Russia
Tel.: (7) 8614170484
Web Site: http://www.golubaya-volna.ru
Hospitality Services
N.A.I.C.S.: 721110

JSC IC Bourevestnik (1)
3 bld 1 Lyotchik Parshin st, 197350, Saint Petersburg, Russia
Tel.: (7) 8126151239
Web Site: http://www.bourevestnik.com
X-Ray Sorter & Analytical Instrument Mfr
N.A.I.C.S.: 334517
Yury A. Vedin (Fin Dir)

JSC Non-State Pension Fund Almaznaya Osen (1)
Ozerkovskaya nab 24, 115184, Moscow, Russia
Tel.: (7) 4956209250
Diamond Mining Services
N.A.I.C.S.: 212390

OJSC Vilyuiskaya HPP-3 (1)
pos Light st Voropaya 22 A, Mirninskiy Ulus, Mirny, 678196, Russia
Tel.: (7) 4113671685
Web Site: http://www.shpp.ru
Hydroelectric Power Generation Services
N.A.I.C.S.: 221111

PJSC Severalmaz (1)
ul Karla Marksa 15, Arkhangelsk, Russia
Tel.: (7) 8182657507
Web Site: http://www.severalmaz.ru
Diamond Mining Services
N.A.I.C.S.: 212390
Pismenniy Andry (Chm & CEO)

PJSC AUTOKRAZ
Kievskaya str 62, Kremenchuk, 39631, Ukraine
Tel.: (380) 536 766 200
Web Site:
http://www.autokraz.com.ua
KRAZ—(UKR)
Motor Vechicle & Spare Part Mfr
N.A.I.C.S.: 336211
Roman Chernyak (CEO)

Subsidiaries:

KrAZ , PJSC (1)

2 Yaroslavskyi proizd, 39631, Kremenchuk, Ukraine
Tel.: (380) 536766210
Trucks Mfr
N.A.I.C.S.: 336212
Vladimir Belov (Acct Mgr)

PJSC CENTRENERGO
Narodnogo Opolchenya Street 1, 04053, Kiev, Ukraine
Tel.: (380) 443640265
Web Site:
https://www.centrenergo.com
Year Founded: 1995
CEEN—(UKR)
Sales Range: Less than $1 Million
Eletric Power Generation Services
N.A.I.C.S.: 221118
Denys I. Kudin (Chm-Supervisory Bd)

PJSC CHERKIZOVO GROUP
Lesnaya Str 5B 12th Floor White Square Office Center, 125047, Moscow, 125047, Russia
Tel.: (7) 4956602440
Web Site: https://cherkizovo-group.com
Year Founded: 1974
GCHE—(MOEX)
Rev.: $1,937,358,170
Assets: $2,329,946,240
Liabilities: $1,341,435,320
Net Worth: $988,510,920
Earnings: $107,280,630
Emp.: 30,355
Fiscal Year-end: 12/31/19
Meat Processing & Distribution Services
N.A.I.C.S.: 424470
Yury N. Dyachuk (Member-Mgmt Bd & Head-Legal Support & Real Estate Ops)

Subsidiaries:

CJSC Petelinskaya (1)
Chastsy, Odintsovsky District, Moscow, 143060, Russia
Tel.: (7) 495 514 1560
Web Site: http://www.cherkizovo.com
Chilled Poultry Meat Mfr
N.A.I.C.S.: 311615

LLC MPP Salsky (1)
8 Promyshlennaya str, Sal'sk, 347632, Rostov, Russia
Tel.: (7) 8637250102
Veal Product Mfr
N.A.I.C.S.: 311613

LLC Tambovmyasoprom (1)
106A Sovetskaya Str, Tambov, 392000, Russia
Tel.: (7) 4752729986
Pig Breeding Services
N.A.I.C.S.: 112210

OOO Pit-Product (1)
Pr Obukhovskoy Oborony 70, 192029, Saint Petersburg, Russia
Tel.: (7) 812 3366 888
Web Site: http://www.pitproduct.ru
Food Processing Services
N.A.I.C.S.: 311612

PJSC CONCERN GALNAFTOGAZ
72 Heroyiv UPA Str, L'viv, Ukraine
Tel.: (380) 322989601
Web Site:
http://www.galnaftogas.com
Sales Range: $700-749.9 Million
Emp.: 10,000
Petroleum Products & Filling Stations
N.A.I.C.S.: 424720
Nazar Kupybida (Member-Mgmt Bd)

Subsidiaries:

Terrin Ltd. (1)
Bud 72 Vul Geroiv Upa, L'vlv, 79015, Ukraine
Tel.: (380) 322988913
Restaurant Management Services

INTERNATIONAL PUBLIC

N.A.I.C.S.: 722511

Tobi-GNG PP (1)
Bud 72 Vul Geroiv Upa, L'viv, 79015, Ukraine
Tel.: (380) 322989601
Web Site: http://www.okko.com.ua
Gasoline Distr
N.A.I.C.S.: 457110

PJSC CONCERN KHLIBPROM
2 Khlibna st, 79035, L'viv, Ukraine
Tel.: (380) 32 297 72 70
Web Site:
http://www.hlibprom.com.ua
Year Founded: 2003
Bakery Products Mfr
N.A.I.C.S.: 311919

PJSC DNIPROSPETSSTAL
Yuzhnoe Shosse 81, 69008, Zaporizhzhya, Ukraine
Tel.: (380) 61 283 4040
Web Site: http://www.dss.com.ua
Year Founded: 1932
Rev.: $344,497,901
Assets: $285,032,315
Liabilities: $234,855,804
Net Worth: $50,176,511
Earnings: ($15,325,621)
Fiscal Year-end: 12/31/18
Metal Products Mfr
N.A.I.C.S.: 332999
Sergiy G. Kiyko (Chm-Mgmt Bd & Dir-Engrg Sciences)

PJSC EL5-ENERGO
10 Khokhryakova Street Sverdlovsk Oblast, Yekaterinburg, 620014, Russia
Tel.: (7) 4955393131
Web Site: https://www.el5-energo.ru
Year Founded: 2004
ENRU—(MOEX)
Rev.: $649,912,912
Assets: $1,232,778,670
Liabilities: $654,937,451
Net Worth: $577,841,219
Earnings: $34,749,394
Emp.: 1,411
Fiscal Year-end: 12/31/21
Electric & Thermal Power Distribution Services
N.A.I.C.S.: 221122
Carlo Tamburi (Deputy Chm)

PJSC ENERGOMASHINOSTROITELNY ALLIANCE
Lenina Street Bldg 220, Rostov Region, Taganrog, 347928, Russia
Tel.: (7) 8634313601
Web Site: http://www.em-alliance.com
Sales Range: $400-449.9 Million
Emp.: 5,000
Power Machines & Equipment Mfr
N.A.I.C.S.: 332410
Roman Serikov (Member-Mgmt Bd)

Subsidiaries:

EMAlliance Ivanovo (1)
Of 6 Bagaeva str 59, Ivanovo, 153000, Russia
Tel.: (7) 4932 595 220
Power Generating Equipment Mfr
N.A.I.C.S.: 335312

RO ZKTI (1)
60 Aref eva str, Rostov-na-Donu, Russia
Tel.: (7) 863 252 07 29
Power Generating Equipment Mfr
N.A.I.C.S.: 335312

TETRA Energie Technologie Transfer GmbH (1)
Allee der Kosmonauten 28, 12681, Berlin, Germany
Tel.: (49) 30 54982734
Power Generating Equipment Mfr
N.A.I.C.S.: 335312

PJSC FIDOBANK
10 Chervonoarmiyska str, 01601,
Kiev, Ukraine
Tel.: (380) 44 2386767   UA
Web Site: http://www.fidobank.ua
Banking Services
N.A.I.C.S.: 522110
Alexander Adarich (Chm)

PJSC GAZPROM
2/3 Lakhtinsky Avenue Bldg 1, Saint
Petersburg, 197229, Russia
Tel.: (7) 4957193001   RU
Year Founded: 1989
GAZP—(MOEX)
Rev.: $123,549,718,990
Assets: $352,962,273,240
Liabilities: $117,211,241,930
Net Worth: $235,751,031,310
Earnings: $20,477,309,210
Emp.: 462,000
Fiscal Year-end: 12/31/19
Holding Company; Gas Exploration,
Production, Transmission, Storage,
Processing & Marketing
N.A.I.C.S.: 551112

Subsidiaries:

Belgazprombank OJSC (1)
60/2 Pritytskogo Str, 220121, Minsk,
Belarus   **(49.66%)**
Tel.: (375) 17 229 1629
Web Site: http://www.belgazprombank.by
Commercial Banking Services
N.A.I.C.S.: 522110
Viktor D. Babariko (Chm-Mgmt Bd)

Electrogaz (1)
39 ul Krasnoarmeiskaya, Krasnodar,
350760, Russia
Tel.: (7) 8612624089
Web Site: http://www.elektrogaz.ru
N.A.I.C.S.: 211120

GAZPROM Schweiz AG (1)
Pelikanplatz 15, 8001, Zurich, Switzerland
Tel.: (41) 044 266 28
Web Site: http://www.gazprom-schweiz.ch
Natural Gas Distribution Services
N.A.I.C.S.: 221210
Slawa Margulis (CEO)

Gas Oil LLC (1)
14 Nakhimov St, Kaliningrad, 236010, Russia
Tel.: (7) 4012 92 94 59
Web Site: http://www.gasoil.ru
Natural Gas Distr
N.A.I.C.S.: 221210
Dmitry S. Komarchuk (Exec Dir)

Gazavtomatika (1)
St Bolshaya Cheremushkinskaya d 13,
Moscow, 117447, Russia
Tel.: (7) 4992462692
Web Site: http://www.gazauto.gazprom.ru
Equipment Repair; Instrumentation & Equipment for Gas Industry
N.A.I.C.S.: 811310

Gazexport (1)
Golutvinsky Pereulok Building 10, Moscow,
119180, Russia
Tel.: (7) 952309507
Web Site: http://www.gazexport.ru
N.A.I.C.S.: 541330

Gazmash (1)
13 ul Verhnyaya Radishchevskaya, Moscow, 109004, Russia
Tel.: (7) 0959151111
Gas Powered Equipment; Gas Infrared
Burner; Gas Pressure Regulators; Water
Loop Heating Device; Gas Ovens; Three
Burner Gas Ovens; Two Burner Gas Burners; Low Melting Point Fluotine-Free Enamels
N.A.I.C.S.: 333414

Gazprom EP International B.V. (1)
Museumplein 9, 1071 DJ, Amsterdam,
Netherlands
Tel.: (31) 2030 50 980
Web Site: http://www.gazprom-international.com
Hydrocarbon Mfr

N.A.I.C.S.: 325110
Andrey Fick (Mng Dir)

Gazprom Gerosgaz Holding B.V. (1)
Concertgebouwplein 13, Amsterdam, 1071
LL, Netherlands
Tel.: (31) 207547831
Investment Management Service
N.A.I.C.S.: 523999

Gazprom Global LNG Ltd. (1)
20 Triton Street, London, NW1 3BF, United
Kingdom
Tel.: (44) 207 756 0000
Natural Gas Exploration Service
N.A.I.C.S.: 211130

Gazprom Transgaz Kazan LLC (1)
Adelya Kutuya 41, 420073, Kazan, Tatarstan, Russia   **(100%)**
Tel.: (7) 8432882230
Web Site: http://www.kazan-tr.gazprom.ru
Main Truck Gas Pipeline Operation & Repair; Gas Distribution System Operation &
Repair; Compressor Station Operation &
Repair; Natural Gas; LPG; LPG Car Filling;
Consumer Gas Supply
N.A.I.C.S.: 221210

Gazprom Transgaz Stavropol (1)
October Revolution 6, 355000, Stavropol,
Russia
Tel.: (7) 8652229002
Web Site: http://stavropol-tr.gazprom.ru
Natural Gas Supplier
N.A.I.C.S.: 211130
Alexey Zavgorodnev (Dir Gen)

Gazpromavia (1)
Ostafyevo Airport, Ryazanovskoye borough,
108824, Moscow, Russia
Tel.: (7) 4958173311
Web Site: http://avia.gazprom.com
Sales Range: $1-4.9 Billion
Passenger & Cargo Transportation
N.A.I.C.S.: 481112

Gazstroidetal (1)
108 Skuratovskaya Str, Tula, 300026, Russia
Tel.: (7) 231393
Mfr of Non-Standard Process Equipment
N.A.I.C.S.: 211120

JSC Gazprom Neft (1)
3-5 Pochtamtskaya St, Saint Petersburg,
190000, Russia   **(75%)**
Tel.: (7) 8123633152
Web Site: http://www.gazprom-neft.com
Rev.: $40,088,018,040
Assets: $61,705,040,790
Liabilities: $26,006,173,180
Net Worth: $35,698,867,610
Earnings: $6,808,279,440
Emp.: 73,251
Fiscal Year-end: 12/31/2019
Oil & Gas Operations
N.A.I.C.S.: 213111
Alexei Miller (Chm)

Subsidiary (Non-US):

Gazprom Neft Trading GmbH (2)
Schwarzenbergplatz 5/4th Floor, 1030, Vienna, Austria
Tel.: (43) 1 90393 1012
Emp.: 50
Oil & Petroleum Products Distr
N.A.I.C.S.: 424720

Naftna Industrija Srbije a.d. Novi Sad (2)
Narodnog fronta 12, 21102, Novi Sad, Serbia
Tel.: (381) 214811111
Web Site: https://www.nis.rs
Sales Range: Less than $1 Million
Emp.: 5,973
Holding Company; Petroleum & Natural
Gas Exploration, Extraction, Refining, Distribution & Gasoline Stations Operator
N.A.I.C.S.: 551112
Vadim Vladislavovich Yakovlev (Chm)

Shell Salym Development B.V. (2)
Carel van Bylandtlaan 30, Hague, 2596 HR,
Netherlands
Tel.: (31) 703779111
Crude Oil & Natural Gas Extracting Services
N.A.I.C.S.: 211120

Sibir Energy Limited (2)
78 Pall Mall, London, SW1Y 5ES, United
Kingdom
Tel.: (44) 2031783650
Web Site: http://www.sibirenergy.com
Sales Range: $1-4.9 Billion
Emp.: 1,003
Oil & Gas Exploration Services
N.A.I.C.S.: 211120
Andrew Harrison (Sec)

Subsidiary (Non-US):

Eurosov Petroleum Holdings (Cyprus) Limited (3)
Gr17 Totalserve House Xenopoulou, 3106,
Limassol, Cyprus
Tel.: (357) 25866000
Holding Company
N.A.I.C.S.: 551112

Fabula Limited (3)
Technikerstrasse 36, Innsbruck, Austria
Tel.: (43) 6765852838
Civic & Social Organizations
N.A.I.C.S.: 813410

Nord Stream AG (1)
Industriestrasse 18, 6302, Zug, Switzerland
Tel.: (41) 41 766 91 91
Web Site: http://www.nord-stream.com
Oil & Gas Pipeline Construction Services
N.A.I.C.S.: 237120
Olivier Escola (Deputy Dir-Maintenance)

OAO Gazpromneft Omsk (1)
54 Ul Frunze, Omsk, 644043, Russia
Tel.: (7) 3812270270
Natural Gas Distribution Services
N.A.I.C.S.: 221210

OAO Krasnoyarskgazprom (1)
Chapeva Street 50B, Khimki District, Moscow, Russia
Tel.: (7) 495 9724578
Web Site:
http://www.krasnoyarskgazprom.com
Crude Oil Refinery Services
N.A.I.C.S.: 324110

OAO Lazurnaya (1)
103 Kurortniy Prospekt, 354024, Sochi,
Russia
Tel.: (7) 8622663005
Web Site: http://www.eng.lazurnaya.ru
Home Management Services
N.A.I.C.S.: 721110

OAO Tsentrgaz (1)
11 Mendeleevskaya St, 300000, Tula, Russia
Tel.: (7) 4872307150
Web Site: http://en.cgaz.ru
Oil & Gas Pipeline Construction Services
N.A.I.C.S.: 237120

OJSC Mosenergo (1)
Vernadskogo prospect 101 bld 3, 119526,
Moscow, 119526, Russia
Tel.: (7) 4959571957
Web Site: https://mosenergo.gazprom.com
Rev.: $3,032,878,260
Assets: $5,105,911,260
Liabilities: $849,876,180
Net Worth: $4,256,035,080
Earnings: $38,982,180
Emp.: 8,654
Fiscal Year-end: 12/31/2021
Fossil Fuel Power Generation Services
N.A.I.C.S.: 221112
Elena Lushpaeva (Dir-PR & Govt Rels)

OOO Gazprom Burenie (1)
Nametkina st 12A, 117420, Moscow, Russia
Tel.: (7) 4995803580
Web Site: http://www.burgaz.ru
Gas Well Drilling Services
N.A.I.C.S.: 213111

OOO Gazprom Inform (1)
st Bolshaya Cheremushkinskaya 13 building
3, 117447, Moscow, Russia
Tel.: (7) 4995801000
Web Site: http://inform.gazprom.ru
Information Technology Consulting Services
N.A.I.C.S.: 541512

OOO Gazprom PKhG (1)
N 101 P Gazoprovoda, Moscow, 142770,
Russia
Tel.: (7) 4954284498

Gas Exploration Services
N.A.I.C.S.: 213112

OOO Gazprom dobycha Astrakhan (1)
St Lenin st Babushkina 30/33 Building A,
Astrakhan Region, 414000, Astrakhan, Russia
Tel.: (7) 8512316039
Web Site:
http://www.astrakhandobycha.gazprom.ru
Gas Processing & Preparation Services
N.A.I.C.S.: 213112

OOO Gazprom dobycha Krasnodar (1)
Kubanskaya Naberezhnaya st 62 Krasnodar Region, 350063, Krasnodar, Russia
Tel.: (7) 8612131082
Web Site: http://www.krasnodar-dobycha.gazprom.ru
Gas Processing & Preparation Services
N.A.I.C.S.: 213112

OOO Gazprom dobycha Nadym (1)
Yamalo-Nenets Autonomous Okrug St Pionerskaya 14, 629736, Nadym, Russia
Tel.: (7) 3499567700
Web Site:
http://www.nadymdobycha.gazprom.ru
Gas Processing & Preparation Services
N.A.I.C.S.: 213112

OOO Gazprom dobycha Noyabrsk (1)
st 40 years of Victory 2, Yamal-Nenets Autonomous Okrug, 629806, Noyabr'sk, Russia
Tel.: (7) 3496368607
Web Site: http://noyabrsk-dobycha.gazprom.ru
Gas Exploration Services
N.A.I.C.S.: 213112

OOO Gazprom dobycha Orenburg (1)
11 60 Ljet Oktyabrya St, 460021, Orenburg,
Russia
Tel.: (7) 3532 73 11 10
Web Site: http://www.ogp.gazprom.ru
Oil & Gas Exploration Services
N.A.I.C.S.: 213112
Sergey Ivanov (Gen Dir)

OOO Gazprom dobycha Urengoy (1)
st Railway 8, Yamalo-Nenets, 629307,
Novvy Urengoy, Russia
Tel.: (7) 3494 94 81 11
Web Site: http://urengoy-dobycha.gazprom.ru
Gas Exploration Services
N.A.I.C.S.: 213112

OOO Gazprom dobycha Yamburg (1)
9 Geologorazvedchikov St, 629300, Novvy
Urengoy, Yanao, Russia
Tel.: (7) 3494966020
Web Site: http://yamburg-dobycha.gazprom.com
Oil & Gas Exploration Services
N.A.I.C.S.: 213112
Oleg Andreev (Dir Gen)

OOO Gazprom invest Zapad (1)
6 Tobolskaya St, 194044, Saint Petersburg,
Russia
Tel.: (7) 812 332 73 40
Web Site: http://www.zapad-invest.gazprom.ru
Oil & Gas Pipeline Construction Services
N.A.I.C.S.: 237130

OOO Gazprom pererabotka (1)
St Smolyachkova House 6 Office 901,
194044, Saint Petersburg, Russia
Tel.: (7) 8126098888
Web Site:
http://www.pererabotka.gazprom.ru
Gas Processing & Preparation Services
N.A.I.C.S.: 213112

OOO Gazprom podzemremont Urengoy (1)
3A Yubileynaya St, POB 955, Tyumen
Oblast, 629300, Novvy Urengoy, Yamal-Nenets, Russia
Tel.: (7) 3494 22 07 28
Web Site: http://www.gazprom.com

PJSC GAZPROM

PJSC Gazprom—(Continued)

Oil & Gas Well Drilling Services
N.A.I.C.S.: 213111

OOO Gazprom transgas Moskva (1)
101/1 Gazoprovod Settlement Kommunarka, Leninskiy District, Moscow, 142770, Russia
Tel.: (7) 498 617 9330
Natural Gas Distribution Services
N.A.I.C.S.: 221210

OOO Gazprom transgas Tchaikovsky (1)
30 Primorsky Blvd, Perm Territory, 617760, Chaykovskiy, Perm Krai, Russia
Tel.: (7) 3424176000
Web Site: http://tchaikovsky-tr.gazprom.ru
Oil & Gas Transportation Services
N.A.I.C.S.: 486210

OOO Gazprom transgas Ufa (1)
59 Zorge Str, 450054, Ufa, Bashkortostan, Russia
Tel.: (7) 3472373584
Web Site: http://ufa-tr.gazprom.ru
347 237 56 40
N.A.I.C.S.: 221210

OOO Gazprom transgas Volgograd (1)
st Workers and Peasants 58, 400074, Volgograd, Russia **(100%)**
Tel.: (7) 8442931274
Web Site: http://volgograd-tr.gazprom.ru
Natural Gas Distribution Services
N.A.I.C.S.: 221210
Yury Maramygin *(Dir Gen)*

OOO Gazprom transgas Yugorsk (1)
st Mira 15, Tyumen, 628260, Yugorsk, Khanty-Mansi Autonomous Okrug, Russia
Tel.: (7) 3467520007
Web Site: http://yugorsk-tr.gazprom.ru
Pipeline Gas Transmission Services
N.A.I.C.S.: 486210

OOO Gazprom transgaz Krasnodar (1)
St Dzerzhinsky 36, 350051, Krasnodar, Russia
Tel.: (7) 8612240868
Web Site: http://www.krasnodar-tr.gazprom.ru
Natural Gas Distr
N.A.I.C.S.: 221210

OOO Gazprom transgaz Makhachkala (1)
St Hadji Bulacha 3rd 13, 367030, Makhachkala, Russia
Tel.: (7) 8722519343
Web Site: http://www.makhachkala-tr.gazprom.ru
Gas Transmission Services
N.A.I.C.S.: 221210

OOO Gazprom transgaz Moskva (1)
St Nametkina 16, 117420, Moscow, Russia
Tel.: (7) 4958179330
Web Site: http://www.moskva-tr.gazprom.ru
Gas Processing & Preparation Services
N.A.I.C.S.: 213112

OOO Gazprom transgaz Nizhny Novgorod (1)
St Zvezdinka 11, 603000, Nizhniy Novgorod, Russia
Tel.: (7) 8314311333
Web Site: http://www.n-novgorod-tr.gazprom.ru
Gas Transmission Services
N.A.I.C.S.: 221210

OOO Gazprom transgaz Samara (1)
St Novo-Sadovaya 106 A Building 1, 443068, Samara, Russia
Tel.: (7) 8462123871
Web Site: http://www.samara-tr.gazprom.ru
Gas Transmission Services
N.A.I.C.S.: 221210

OOO Gazprom transgaz Sankt-Peterburg (1)
Varshavskaya st 3 Bldg 2, Moscow Zastava, 196128, Saint Petersburg, Russia
Tel.: (7) 8124551200
Web Site: http://www.spb-tr.gazprom.ru
Gas Processing & Preparation Services
N.A.I.C.S.: 213112

OOO Gazprom transgaz Saratov (1)
House 118A Building 1, 410052, Saratov, Russia
Tel.: (7) 8452306691
Web Site: http://www.saratov-tr.gazprom.ru
Gas Transmission Services
N.A.I.C.S.: 221210

OOO Gazprom transgaz Surgut (1)
Universitetskaya st 1 Khanty-Mansiysk Autonomous Okrug Khmao-Yugra, 628412, Surgut, Russia
Tel.: (7) 8614163691
Web Site: http://www.surgut-tr.gazprom.ru
Gas Processing & Preparation Services
N.A.I.C.S.: 213112

OOO Gazprom transgaz Tomsk (1)
Frunze Ave 9, 634029, Tomsk, Russia
Tel.: (7) 3822603209
Web Site: http://tomsk-tr.gazprom.ru
Gas Processing & Preparation Services
N.A.I.C.S.: 213112

OOO Gazprom transgaz Uhta (1)
Gazovikov Embankment 10/1 Komi Republic, 169300, Ukhta, Komi Republic, Russia
Tel.: (7) 8216760056
Web Site: http://www.ukhta-tr.gazprom.ru
Gas Processing & Preparation Services
N.A.I.C.S.: 213112

OOO Gazprom transgaz Yekaterinburg (1)
St Clara Zetkin 14, 620075, Yekaterinburg, Russia
Tel.: (7) 3433597530
Web Site: http://www.ekaterinburg-tr.gazprom.ru
Gas Transmission Services
N.A.I.C.S.: 221210

OOO GazpromPurInvest (1)
13 Str 1 Ul Donskaya, Moscow, 119049, Russia
Tel.: (7) 4959333317
Web Site: http://www.gazprompurinvest.ru
Investment Management Service
N.A.I.C.S.: 523999

OOO Gazpromneftfinans (1)
125a Ul Profsoyuznaya, Moscow, 100000, Russia
Tel.: (7) 4957773117
Oil & Gas Exploration Services
N.A.I.C.S.: 213112

OOO Kovyktaneftegaz (1)
14 Ul Nizhnyaya Naberezhnaya, Irkutsk, 664011, Russia
Tel.: (7) 3952243671
Oil & Gas Exploration Services
N.A.I.C.S.: 213112

Orenburggazprom (1)
11 60 Ljet Oktyabrya St, Orenburg, 460021, Russia
Tel.: (7) 3532731324
N.A.I.C.S.: 213111

Private company Kaunas Heat and Power Plant UAB (1)
Taikos pr 147, 51142, Kaunas, Lithuania
Tel.: (370) 37 308 059
Web Site: http://www.kte.lt
Sales Range: $75-99.9 Million
Emp.: 15
Electric Power Distribution Services
N.A.I.C.S.: 221122

Promgaz (1)
Nametkina Str 6, Moscow, 117420, Russia
Tel.: (7) 4955044270
Web Site: http://www.oao-promgaz.ru
Emp.: 800
N.A.I.C.S.: 541360
Yury Spektor *(Gen Dir)*

SCHWARZMEER UND OSTSEE Versicherungs-AG (1)
Grosse Elbstrasse 14, 22767, Hamburg, Germany **(50.9%)**
Tel.: (49) 402271280
Web Site: http://www.sovag.de
Sales Range: $125-149.9 Million
Emp.: 116
Insurance Services
N.A.I.C.S.: 524210
Gerd H. Meyer *(Chm)*

SEFE Securing Energy for Europe GmbH (1)
Markgrafenstrasse 23, 10117, Berlin, Germany
Tel.: (49) 30201950
Web Site: https://www.sefe.eu
Sales Range: $500-549.9 Million
Natural Gas Distribution Services
N.A.I.C.S.: 221210
Egbert Laege *(CEO)*

Samaratransgaz (1)
190 Samarskaya ul, Samara, 443100, Russia
Tel.: (7) 8462334371
Gas Transportation & Consumer Supply; Natural Gas; LPG; LPG Car Filling; Gas Car Fuel Sytem Hook-Up
N.A.I.C.S.: 211120

Severnipigaz (1)
1a ul Sevastopolakaya, Ukhta, 169400, Komi, Russia
Tel.: (7) 214767014
Geological Survey & Prospective Evaluation, Drilling, Development, Exploration, Designing of Gas & Gas Condensate Fields Infrastructure Arrangement
N.A.I.C.S.: 541360

Spetsgaszavtotrans (1)
182 Votkinskoye shosse, Izhevsk, 426039, Udmurtiya, Russia
Tel.: (7) 3412218288
Gas Car Fuel System Hook-Up; Domestic Gas Ovens; Spare Parts for Gas Equipment
N.A.I.C.S.: 221210

Surgutgazprom (1)
1 Universitetskaya St, 628412, Surgut, Tyumen Region, Russia **(100%)**
Tel.: (7) 3462750009
Web Site: http://surgut-tr.gazprom.ru
Gas Production & Transportation; Stable Condensate; Diesel Oil; C5-C6 Fraction; Wide Fraction Light Hydrocarbons; Straight Run Gasoline Fraction; Light Boiler Fuel
N.A.I.C.S.: 221210

Tomsktransgaz (1)
68 ul Starodepovskaya, Tomsk, 634059, Russia
Tel.: (7) 3822271732
Main Trunk Gas Pipeline Operation & Repair; Gas Distribution System Operation & Repair; Compressor Station Operation & Repair; Natural Gas; LPG; Consumer Gas Supply
N.A.I.C.S.: 221210

TyumenNIIgiprogaz (1)
2 Vorovskogo Str, Tyumen, 625019, Russia
Tel.: (7) 3452286481
Web Site: http://www.tyumenniigiprogaz.gazprom.ru
Gas & Oil Field Design & Development; Gas, Oil & Condensate Research; Study of Gas Industry Economics
N.A.I.C.S.: 213112

Uraltransgaz (1)
14 K Zetkin Street, Yekaterinburg, 620000, Sverdlovsk Region, Russia
Tel.: (7) 3432597265
Web Site: http://www.energogas.ru
N.A.I.C.S.: 221210

Volta S.p.A. (1)
Via del Vigneto 23, 39100, Bolzano, Italy
Tel.: (39) 0471 561 000
Web Site: http://www.volta.it
Eletric Power Generation Services
N.A.I.C.S.: 221118
Fischnaller Peter *(Mgr-Sls)*

WINGAS Holding GmbH (1)
Friedrich-Ebert-Strasse 160, 34119, Kassel, Hessen, Germany **(49.96%)**
Tel.: (49) 5613010
Web Site: http://www.wintershall.com
Investment Management Service
N.A.I.C.S.: 523999

Subsidiary (Domestic):

WINGAS GmbH (2)
Konigstor 20, 34117, Kassel, Germany
Tel.: (49) 561998580
Web Site: https://www.wingas.com
Rev: $2,194,307,584
Emp.: 400

INTERNATIONAL PUBLIC

Commercial & Industrial Natural Gas Supply Services
N.A.I.C.S.: 221210

Subsidiary (Non-US):

WINGAS Belgium s.p.r.l./b.v.b.a. (3)
Avenue des Arts Kunstlaan 21, 1000, Brussels, Belgium
Tel.: (32) 22806724
Web Site: http://www.wintershall.com
Commercial & Industrial Natural Gas Supply Services
N.A.I.C.S.: 221210

Subsidiary (Domestic):

WINGAS Transport GmbH & Co. KG (3)
Baumbachstrasse 1, 34119, Kassel, Germany
Tel.: (49) 5619340
Web Site: http://www.wingas-transport.de
Sales Range: $50-74.9 Million
Emp.: 250
Commercial & Industrial Natural Gas Supply Services
N.A.I.C.S.: 486210
Bjorn Kaiser *(Mng Dir)*

Subsidiary (Non-US):

WINGAS UK Ltd. (3)
Bridge House Berleith House 73-75 Sheen Rd, 3 Heron Square, Richmond, TW9 1Yj, Surrey, United Kingdom
Tel.: (44) 2084399680
Web Site: http://www.wingas-uk.com
Sales Range: $75-99.9 Million
Emp.: 23
Commercial & Industrial Natural Gas Supply Services
N.A.I.C.S.: 221210

Subsidiary (Domestic):

WINGAS Verwaltungs-GmbH (3)
Friedrich-Ebert-Str 160, 34119, Kassel, Germany
Tel.: (49) 5613010
Web Site: http://www.wingas.de
Investment Management Service
N.A.I.C.S.: 523999

ZAO Gazprom invest Yug (1)
8 Str 1 Nauchny Proezd, 117246, Moscow, Russia
Tel.: (7) 495 411 57 03
Web Site: http://www.gazprominvestyug.ru
Oil & Gas Pipeline Construction Services
N.A.I.C.S.: 237120
Nikolay Panyukov *(Sec-Press & Deputy Head-Admin Directorate)*

ZAO Gazpromneft Severo Zapad (1)
5 Liter A Galernaya Ul, Saint Petersburg, 197706, Russia
Tel.: (7) 8124493084
Oil Products Whslr
N.A.I.C.S.: 424720

ZAO Nortgaz (1)
1 Ofis 4 35 Yakimanka B Ul, Moscow, 119180, Russia
Tel.: (7) 4957774971
Web Site: http://www.northgas.ru
Gas Exploration Services
N.A.I.C.S.: 213112

PJSC IC RUSS-INVEST

5 Bld 4 Naschchiokinsky Pereulok, 119019, Moscow, Russia
Tel.: (7) 4953639380 RU
Web Site: http://www.russ-invest.com
Year Founded: 1992
Sales Range: $150-199.9 Million
Brokerage Services
N.A.I.C.S.: 523150
Olga Nikolaevna Ilina *(Sec)*

Subsidiaries:

ABR Financial B.V. (1)
Strawinskylaan 611, Amsterdam, 1077 XX, Noord-Holland, Netherlands
Tel.: (31) 208200082
Web Site: http://www.abrfinancial.nl
Securities Brokerage Services
N.A.I.C.S.: 523150

AND PRIVATE COMPANIES

PJSC KHIMPROM
st Industrial 101, Chuvash Republic, Novocheboksarsk, 429965, Russia
Tel.: (7) 8352735555
Web Site: https://www.himprom.com
Year Founded: 1960
HIMC—(MOEX)
Sales Range: Less than $1 Million
Chemical Products Mfr
N.A.I.C.S.: 325998

PJSC KUIBYSHEVAZOT
6 Novozavodskaya street, Tolyatti, 445007, Samara, Russia
Tel.: (7) 8482561009
Web Site: https://www.kuazot.ru
Year Founded: 1961
KAZT—(MOEX)
Rev.: $926,523,330
Assets: $1,056,579,520
Liabilities: $542,693,850
Net Worth: $513,885,670
Earnings: $40,808,900
Emp.: 5,500
Fiscal Year-end: 12/31/19
Chemical Products Mfr
N.A.I.C.S.: 325998
Victor I. Gerasimenko *(Chm)*

Subsidiaries:

JV Granifert (1)
Novozavodskaya st 6, Togliatti, 445007, Samara Oblast, Russia
Tel.: (7) 8482566038
Ammonium Sulphate & Nitrogen Fertilizer Mfr
N.A.I.C.S.: 325311

OOO Kurskkhimvolokno (1)
Silicatnyy st 1, Kursk, 305026, Russia
Tel.: (7) 4712328311
Chemical Yarn Mfr
N.A.I.C.S.: 325220

PJSC LSR GROUP
Kazanskaya st 36, Saint Petersburg, 190031, Russia
Tel.: (7) 8007707577 RU
Web Site: https://www.lsrgroup.ru
Year Founded: 1993
LSRG—(MOEX)
Rev.: $2,639,907,734
Assets: $5,315,659,209
Liabilities: $3,989,273,139
Net Worth: $1,326,386,069
Earnings: $316,781,775
Emp.: 10,000
Fiscal Year-end: 12/31/23
Real Estate Development Services
N.A.I.C.S.: 531390
Andrey Molchanov *(Co-CEO)*

Subsidiaries:

LSR Construction-Urals Ltd. (1)
ul 40th Anniversary of Komsomol 34, Yekaterinburg, 620092, Russia
Tel.: (7) 3432159933
Web Site: https://www.lsrconstruction-ural.ru
Concrete Products Mfr
N.A.I.C.S.: 327390

LSR Wall Materials Ltd. (1)
Tel.: (7) 8123348700
Web Site: https://www.sm.lsr.ru
Bricks Mfr
N.A.I.C.S.: 327331

LSR-Stroy OOO (1)
Office C301-305 47/49 Marata, 191002, Saint Petersburg, Russia
Tel.: (7) 8124588398
Real Estate Development Services
N.A.I.C.S.: 531390

OOO H+H (1)
Ul Fucika D K office 602, 192102, Saint Petersburg, Russia
Tel.: (7) 812 609 0900
Emp.: 20
Aircrete Mfr
N.A.I.C.S.: 327331

S&G Development Partners Objekt Leipzig GmbH & Co KG (1)
Sachsenseite 5, 04103, Leipzig, Germany
Tel.: (49) 34122170610
Web Site: http://www.sg-development.de
Emp.: 20
Terminal Development Services
N.A.I.C.S.: 236220

PJSC LUKOIL
Tel.: (7) 4956274444 RU
Web Site: https://www.lukoil.com
Year Founded: 1991
LKOH—(MOEX)
Rev.: $127,091,376,210
Assets: $92,468,169,030
Liabilities: $31,540,880,550
Net Worth: $60,927,288,480
Earnings: $10,446,160,110
Emp.: 100,000
Fiscal Year-end: 12/31/21
Oil Production & Sales
N.A.I.C.S.: 324110
Vagit Alekperov *(Pres & CEO)*

Subsidiaries:

LICARD OOO (1)
st Bolshaya Ordynka 3, 115035, Moscow, Russia
Tel.: (7) 4955870777
Web Site: http://www.licard.ru
Oil & Gas Services
N.A.I.C.S.: 213112
Alexey Filippov *(Gen Dir)*

LITASCO Central Asia LLP (1)
17 Av Kabanbay Batyr Z05H0B4, Yessil District, Astana, Kazakhstan
Tel.: (7) 7172591727
Oil & Gas Distribution Services
N.A.I.C.S.: 221210
Farid Kerimov *(Gen Dir)*

LITASCO Middle East DMCC (1)
Almas Tower Office 18C Jumeirah Lakes Towers, PO Box 102648, Dubai, United Arab Emirates
Tel.: (971) 42795900
Oil & Gas Services
N.A.I.C.S.: 213112
Valery Kildiyarov *(Fin Dir)*

LITASCO SA (1)
9 rue du Conseil General, 1205, Geneva, Switzerland
Tel.: (41) 22 705 20 00
Web Site: http://www.litasco.com
Petroleum Product Distr
N.A.I.C.S.: 424720

Subsidiary (Non-US):

LUKOIL Asia Pacific PTE Ltd. (2)
8 Marina Boulevard 04-02 Marina Bay Financial Center Tower 1, Singapore, 018981, Singapore
Tel.: (65) 6796 2311
Petroleum Product Distr
N.A.I.C.S.: 424720

LUKOIL Benelux B.V. (2)
Wilhelminakade 85 Maastoren building 36th floor, 3072 AP, Rotterdam, Netherlands
Tel.: (31) 10 264 2700
Petroleum Product Distr
N.A.I.C.S.: 424720

LUKOIL Hamburg GmbH (2)
Grimm 8 Weco Haus, 20457, Hamburg, Germany
Tel.: (49) 4027 1690
Petroleum Product Distr
N.A.I.C.S.: 424720

LLC Lukoil EPU Service (1)
Oktyabrskaya St 10, 626483, Kogalym, Tyumen, Russia
Tel.: (7) 3466748910
Web Site: http://www.lukoil-epu.ru
Oil & Gas Services
N.A.I.C.S.: 213112

LLC Lukoil-ENERGOSETI (1)
Pokrovsky Boulevard 3 Bldg 1, 109028, Moscow, Russia
Tel.: (7) 4956278015
Web Site: http://www.es.lukoil.ru

Electric Power Transportation Services
N.A.I.C.S.: 221118

LLC Lukoil-Ekoenergo (1)
Socialist 59 St, 344002, Rostov-na-Donu, Russia
Tel.: (7) 8632109600
Web Site: http://ekoenergo.lukoil.ru
Oil & Gas Services
N.A.I.C.S.: 213112

LLC Lukoil-Georgia (1)
Right bank of the River Mtkvari Adjacent to Gotua Street, Tbilisi, 0160, Georgia
Tel.: (995) 322380013
Web Site: http://www.lukoil.ge
Emp.: 500
Oil & Gas Distribution Services
N.A.I.C.S.: 221210

LLC Lukoil-KGPZ (1)
PO Box No 5, 403805, Kstovo, Volgograd, Russia
Tel.: (7) 8445547182
Web Site: http://www.kgpz.lukoil.ru
Oil & Gas Services
N.A.I.C.S.: 213112

LLC Lukoil-KMN (1)
St Kievskaya 23, 236039, Kaliningrad, Russia
Tel.: (7) 4012680022
Web Site: http://www.kmn.lukoil.ru
Oil & Gas Services
N.A.I.C.S.: 213112

LLC Lukoil-Komi (1)
St Neftyanikov 31, 169712, Usinsk, Republic of Komi, Russia
Tel.: (7) 8214455111
Web Site: http://komi.lukoil.ru
Oil & Gas Services
N.A.I.C.S.: 213112
Ovcharov Alexander *(Project Mgr)*

LLC Lukoil-Kubanenergo (1)
Tram 13 St, 350911, Krasnodar, Russia
Tel.: (7) 8612191314
Web Site: http://www.kubanenergo.lukoil.ru
Heat & Electricity Services
N.A.I.C.S.: 333414

LLC Lukoil-Nizhegorodnefteorgsintez (1)
Building 9 Central Highway Industrial Area, Kstovsky District, 607650, Kstovo, Nizhny Novgorod, Russia
Tel.: (7) 8314553771
Web Site: http://www.nnos.lukoil.ru
Oil & Gas Services
N.A.I.C.S.: 213112

LLC Lukoil-Nizhegorodniinefteproekt (1)
St Maxim Gorky 147A, 603006, Nizhniy Novgorod, Russia
Tel.: (7) 8314223333
Web Site: http://www.nneft.lukoil.ru
Oil & Gas Services
N.A.I.C.S.: 213112

LLC Lukoil-Rostovenergo (1)
Peskova 17 St, 344055, Rostov-na-Donu, Russia
Tel.: (7) 8632037118
Web Site: http://www.rostovenergo.lukoil.ru
Oil & Gas Services
N.A.I.C.S.: 213112

LLC Lukoil-Severo-Zapadnefteprodukt (1)
Aptekarskaya Embankment 8 Letter A, 197022, Saint Petersburg, Russia
Tel.: (7) 8123468080
Web Site: http://www.sznp.lukoil.ru
Petroleum Product Services
N.A.I.C.S.: 424720

LLC Lukoil-West Siberia (1)
Khanty-Mansiysk Autonomous Okrug-Yugra St Pribaltiyskaya 20, 628484, Kogalym, Tyumen, Russia
Tel.: (7) 3466761494
Web Site: http://zs.lukoil.ru
Oil & Gas Services
N.A.I.C.S.: 213112

LLC Lukoil-Yugnefteprodukt (1)
St Stavropolskaya 2/1, 350033, Krasnodar, Russia
Tel.: (7) 8612134040

Web Site: http://www.ugnp.lukoil.ru
Oil & Gas Services
N.A.I.C.S.: 213112

LLC TZK-Arkhangelsk (1)
Talazhskoe Highway 60, 163053, Arkhangelsk, Russia
Tel.: (7) 8182636730
Web Site: http://www.tzkarhangelsk.lukoil.ru
Petroleum Products Marketing Services
N.A.I.C.S.: 424720

LUKOIL - Nizhnevolzhskneft OOO (1)
1 Admiralteiskaya Str, Astrakhan, 414000, Russia
Tel.: (7) 851 240 2800
Web Site: http://www.nvn.lukoil.com
Oil & Gas Exploration Services
N.A.I.C.S.: 211130

LUKOIL - Perm OOO (1)
Lenina St 62, 614068, Perm, Perm Territory, Russia
Tel.: (7) 3422356807
Web Site: http://perm.lukoil.ru
Oil Drilling Services
N.A.I.C.S.: 213111

LUKOIL - Permnefteorgsintez OOO (1)
84 Promyshlennaya St, 614055, Perm, Russia
Tel.: (7) 3422202467
Web Site: http://pnos.lukoil.ru
Oil Refinery Services
N.A.I.C.S.: 324110
Vasily I. Anisimov *(Gen Dir)*

LUKOIL Italia S.r.l. (1)
Societa Unipersonale Via Bissolati 20, 00187, Rome, Italy
Tel.: (39) 06 4203 3511
Web Site: http://www.lukoil.it
Petroleum Product Distr
N.A.I.C.S.: 424720
Svyatoslav Smoliyaninov *(Gen Dir)*

LUKOIL Lubricants Mexico S.de R.L.de C.V. (1)
Emerson 304 Interior 4001 Colonia Polanco Reforma, Delegacion Miguel Hidalgo, 11550, Mexico, Mexico
Tel.: (52) 5543350810
Web Site: http://lukoil-lubricants.mx
Oil & Gas Services
N.A.I.C.S.: 213112

LUKOIL Mid-East Limited (1)
West Qurna-2 project, Dubai, United Arab Emirates
Tel.: (971) 4448 75 75
Web Site: http://www.lukoil-overseas.com
Oil & Gas Exploration Services
N.A.I.C.S.: 211130

LUKOIL Overseas Cyprus Limited (1)
6 Georgiou Davaris Office 301, Strovolos, 2024, Nicosia, Cyprus
Tel.: (357) 22 517600
Web Site: http://www.lukoiloverseascy.com
Gasoline Distr
N.A.I.C.S.: 424710
Andreas Poyiatzis *(Gen Dir)*

LUKOIL Technology Services GmbH (1)
Zaunergasse 1-3, 1030, Vienna, Austria
Tel.: (43) 1 7151333
Web Site: http://www.lukoil-technology.com
Information Technology Services
N.A.I.C.S.: 541512

LUKOIL-Bulgaria EOOD (1)
42 Todor Alexandrov Blvd, 1303, Sofia, Bulgaria
Tel.: (359) 29174100
Web Site: http://www.lukoil.bg
Oil & Gas Distribution Services
N.A.I.C.S.: 221210
Valentin Zlatev *(Gen Mgr)*

Lukoil Accounting & Finance Europe s.r.o. (1)
Kutvirtova 339/5, 150 00, Prague, Czech Republic
Tel.: (420) 257414555
Web Site: http://www.lafe.lukoil.com
Oil & Gas Services

PJSC LUKOIL

PJSC Lukoil—(Continued)

N.A.I.C.S.: 213112
Ivan Vrublevskiy *(Mng Dir)*

Lukoil Americas LLC (1)
1500 Hempstead Tpke, East Meadow, NY 11554-1551
Tel.: (212) 421-4141
Web Site: http://www.lukoilamericas.com
Sales Range: $100-124.9 Million
Emp.: 140
Oil Production
N.A.I.C.S.: 211120

Subsidiary (Domestic):

Lukoil Americas Holding Limited (2)
1500 Hempstead Tpke, East Meadow, NY 11554
Tel.: (212) 421-4141
Web Site: http://www.lukoilamericas.com
Sales Range: $25-49.9 Million
Gasoline Stations with Convenience Stores
N.A.I.C.S.: 457110

Subsidiary (Domestic):

Getty Petroleum Marketing Inc. (3)
1500 Hempstead Tpke, East Meadow, NY 11554-1558 **(100%)**
Tel.: (516) 542-4900
Web Site: http://www.getty.com
Independent Marketer & Wholesale Distr of Gasoline, Heating Oil & Petroleum Products
N.A.I.C.S.: 424720

Subsidiary (Domestic):

Getty Terminals (4)
1500 Hempstead Tpke, East Meadow, NY 11554-1558
Tel.: (516) 542-4900
Web Site: http://www.getty.com
Sales Range: $50-74.9 Million
Emp.: 125
Wholesale Distributor of Gasoline & Petroleum Products
N.A.I.C.S.: 424720

Kingston Oil Supply Corp. (4)
15 N Broadway PO Box 760, Port Ewen, NY 12466-0788
Tel.: (845) 331-0770
Web Site: http://www.koscocomfort.com
Sales Range: $25-49.9 Million
Emp.: 28
Fuel Oil Distributor
N.A.I.C.S.: 457210
Barry Motzkin *(Pres)*

Lukoil Aviation Bulgaria EOOD (1)
Todor Alexandrov Blvd N 42, 1303, Sofia, Bulgaria
Tel.: (359) 29174171
Web Site: http://www.aero-bulgaria.lukoil.com
Oil & Gas Distribution Services
N.A.I.C.S.: 221210
Mikhail Sizov *(Gen Mgr)*

Lukoil Belorussia FLLC (1)
St Nemiga 36, Minsk, 220004, Belarus
Tel.: (375) 172089800
Web Site: http://www.lukoil.by
Oil & Gas Distribution Services
N.A.I.C.S.: 221210

Lukoil International Upstream West Inc. (1)
Phoenix Tower 3200 Sw Fway Ste 3120, Houston, TX 77027
Tel.: (713) 386-2716
Web Site: http://www.upstreamwest.lukoil.com
Oil & Gas Services
N.A.I.C.S.: 213112
H. Daniel Hogan *(Gen Mgr)*

Lukoil Lubricants Central Asia LLP (1)
Dostyk ave D 38 203c Office, Almaty, 050010, Kazakhstan
Tel.: (7) 7273212040
Oil & Gas Distribution Services
N.A.I.C.S.: 221210

Lukoil Lubricants East Europe S.R.L. (1)
No 235 Mihai Bravu Street, Prahova, Ploiesti, 100410, Romania
Tel.: (40) 244504802
Web Site: http://www.lukoil-lubricants.ro
Oil & Gas Services
N.A.I.C.S.: 213112
Adrian Epure *(Controller-Fin)*

Lukoil Lubricants Middle East Madeni Yag Sanayi ve Ticaret Limited Sirketi (1)
Akatlar Mah Ebulula Mardin Cd Maya Park Tower 1 No 22, Besiktas, Istanbul, 34335, Turkiye
Tel.: (90) 212 274 3776
Web Site: https://www.lukoil.com.tr
Oil & Gas Services
N.A.I.C.S.: 213112
Ozlem Tekin *(Mgr-Treasury)*

Lukoil Macedonia Ltd. (1)
Partisan Squads No 18, 1000, Skopje, North Macedonia
Tel.: (389) 23293033
Web Site: http://www.lukoil.com.mk
Oil & Gas Distribution Services
N.A.I.C.S.: 221210
Ryupin Denis *(Gen Dir)*

Lukoil Marine Lubricants DMCC (1)
Jbc 4 Tower Unit No 1506 15th Floor Jumeirah Lakes Towers, PO Box 487718, Dubai, United Arab Emirates
Tel.: (971) 44300769
Oil & Gas Services
N.A.I.C.S.: 213112

Lukoil Marine Lubricants Germany GmbH (1)
Alsterufer 20, 20354, Hamburg, Germany
Tel.: (49) 4018 042 2060
Web Site: https://www.lukoilmarine.com
Oil & Gas Services
N.A.I.C.S.: 213112

Lukoil Marine Lubricants USA Inc. (1)
250 S President St Ste 3200, Baltimore, MD 21202
Tel.: (443) 835-1766
Oil & Gas Services
N.A.I.C.S.: 213112

Lukoil Montenegro DOO (1)
Bulevar Svetog Petra Cetinjskog br 130, 81000, Podgorica, Montenegro
Tel.: (382) 2 021 9415
Web Site: https://www.lukoil.co.me
Emp.: 140
Oil & Gas Services
N.A.I.C.S.: 213112

Lukoil Neftochim Burgas AD (1)
Industrial Zone Burgas, PO Box 8104, 8104, Burgas, Bulgaria
Tel.: (359) 55112600
Web Site: http://www.neftochim.bg
Sales Range: $1-4.9 Billion
Oil & Gas Exploration
N.A.I.C.S.: 211120
Natalia Vasilievna Ivanova *(Head-PR, Protocol & Adv)*

Lukoil Romania S.R.L. (1)
Str Siriului no 20 Corp A Sector 1, 014354, Bucharest, Romania
Tel.: (40) 212272106
Web Site: http://www.lukoil.ro
Oil & Gas Distribution Services
N.A.I.C.S.: 221210
Cristian Zecheru *(Mgr-Environment)*

Lukoil-Moldova S.R.L. (1)
Str Columna 92, MD-2012, Chisinau, Moldova
Tel.: (373) 22211238
Web Site: https://www.lukoil.md
Oil & Gas Services
N.A.I.C.S.: 213112

OOO Eni-Nefto (1)
Eningradskoje Shosse 63, 125455, Moscow, Russia
Tel.: (7) 4952341921
Natural Gas Producer
N.A.I.C.S.: 221210

OOO LUKOIL-Volgogradnefteperera botka (1)
40 let VLKSM St 55, 400029, Volgograd, Russia
Tel.: (7) 8442963490

Web Site: http://vnpz.lukoil.ru
Crude Oil Mfr
N.A.I.C.S.: 211120

OOO Wolgodeminoil (1)
Ul Rabotche-Krestyanskaya Street 30 A, 400074, Volgograd, Russia
Tel.: (7) 8442333420
Web Site: http://www.basf.ru
Chemical Product Mfr; Owned 50% by Wintershall AG & 50% by OAO Lukoil
N.A.I.C.S.: 325998

Oy Teboil AB (1)
Plaza Loiste Ayritie 20, 01510, Vantaa, Finland
Tel.: (358) 204 7001
Web Site: https://www.teboil.fi
Oil & Gas Distribution Services
N.A.I.C.S.: 221210
Alexey Moskalenko *(Gen Dir)*

PJSC EL5-Energo (1)
7 bld 1 Pavlovskaya street, 115093, Moscow, Russia **(56.4%)**
Tel.: (7) 4955393131
Web Site: http://www.enelrussia.ru
Hydroelectric Power Generation Services
N.A.I.C.S.: 221111

Petrotel-Lukoil S.A. (1)
235 Mihai Bravu Street, Romania Prahova County, Ploiesti, 100410, Romania
Tel.: (40) 244504000
Web Site: http://www.petrotel.lukoil.com
Oil & Gas Services
N.A.I.C.S.: 213112
Danulescu Dan *(Chief Engr)*

PJSC M2M PRIVATE BANK

Leontievsky per 21/1 build 1, 125009, Moscow, Russia
Tel.: (7) 495 223 223 5
Web Site: http://www.m2mbank.ru
Sales Range: $25-49.9 Million
Banking Services
N.A.I.C.S.: 522110

PJSC MAGNITOGORSK IRON & STEEL WORKS

93 Kirov Street, Chelyabinsk region, 455000, Magnitogorsk, Russia
Tel.: (7) 3519244009
Web Site: http://www.mmk.ru
Year Founded: 1992
Iron & Steel Mfr
N.A.I.C.S.: 332312
Pavel V. Shilyaev *(CEO)*

PJSC MEGAFON

41 Oruzheyniy lane, Moscow, 127006, Russia
Tel.: (7) 4997552155
Web Site: http://www.megafon.com
Year Founded: 1993
MFON—(MOEX)
Rev.: $5,628,740,930
Assets: $11,180,606,280
Liabilities: $9,492,617,910
Net Worth: $1,687,988,370
Earnings: $130,443,310
Emp.: 40,334
Fiscal Year-end: 12/31/19
Wireless Telecommunication Services
N.A.I.C.S.: 517112
Gevork Vermishyan *(CEO, Gen Dir & Member-Mgmt Bd)*

Subsidiaries:

LLC Scartel (1)
Rusakovskaya street 13, Moscow, 107140, Russia
Tel.: (7) 4959267585
Wireless Telecommunication Services
N.A.I.C.S.: 517112

MegaLabs (1)
11 2-y Kazachiy pereulok Bldg 1, Moscow, 119180, Russia
Tel.: (7) 499 755 00 80
Wireless Telecommunication Services
N.A.I.C.S.: 517112

Nakhodka Telecom (1)

Ul Nakhimovskaya 30, Nakhodka, 692900, Russia
Tel.: (7) 4236692777
Wireless Telecommunication Services
N.A.I.C.S.: 517112

PJSC MMC NORILSK NICKEL

Tel.: (7) 4957877667 RU
Web Site: https://www.nornickel.com
Year Founded: 1935
GMKN—(MOEX)
Rev.: $16,876,000,000
Assets: $25,795,000,000
Liabilities: $17,228,000,000
Net Worth: $8,567,000,000
Earnings: $5,854,000,000
Emp.: 78,000
Fiscal Year-end: 12/31/22
Mineral Mining Services
N.A.I.C.S.: 212290
Andrey Evgenyevich Bougrov *(Member-Mgmt Bd & Sr VP-Sustainable Dev)*

Subsidiaries:

Gipronickel Institute, Ltd. (1)
11 Grazhdansky Prospect, 195220, Saint Petersburg, Russia
Tel.: (7) 8123353124
Web Site: http://www.nickel.spb.ru
Non-Ferrous Metallurgy Research & Development Services
N.A.I.C.S.: 541715
Kolesnikov Gennady Kuzmich *(CEO)*

JSC Third Generation Company of the Wholesale Electricity Market (1)
28 50 let Oktyabrya Avenue, Ulan-Ude, 123001, Buryatia, Russia **(60.15%)**
Tel.: (7) 4952314344
Web Site: http://www.ogk3.ru
Sales Range: $1-4.9 Billion
Emp.: 6,495
Electric Power Wholesale Distr
N.A.I.C.S.: 221122
Aleksander Nikulov *(Chm-Mgmt Bd & Gen Dir)*

Subsidiary (Non-US):

JSC TransService (2)
St Academician Williams 4, PO Box 04073, 03191, Kiev, Ukraine
Tel.: (380) 443643407
Web Site: http://www.trans-service.com.ua
Sales Range: $25-49.9 Million
Emp.: 26
Transport Shipping Agency Services
N.A.I.C.S.: 488999

Kola Mining and Metallurgical Company (1)
22 Voznesensky Pereulok, Moscow, 125009, Russia
Tel.: (7) 495 787 7667
Web Site: http://www.nornik.ru
Copper & Nickel Mining Services
N.A.I.C.S.: 212230

LLC Norilskgeologiya (1)
1 Promzona, Noril'sk, 663300, Russia
Tel.: (7) 3919452373
Nickel Mining Services
N.A.I.C.S.: 212230

MPI Nickel Pty. Ltd. (1)
Suite 1 45 Ord Street, West Perth, 6005, VIC, Australia
Tel.: (61) 894260100
Emp.: 4
Nickel & Other Metal Ore Mining Services
N.A.I.C.S.: 212230

NORMETIMPEX (1)
15 1st Krasnogvardeysky Drive, 123112, Moscow, Russia **(100%)**
Tel.: (7) 4957877649
Web Site: http://www.normet.ru
Sales Range: $50-74.9 Million
Emp.: 100
Non-Ferrous & Precious Metals Distr & Whslr
N.A.I.C.S.: 423510
Ravil Nasybullov *(Gen Dir)*

Norilsk Nickel (Cyprus) Limited (1)
3403 Maximus Plaza Tower 3 4 floor Con-

stantinos Paparigopoulos 6, Limassol, 3106, Cyprus
Tel.: (357) 25875575
Web Site: http://www.nornickel.com
Investment Management Service
N.A.I.C.S.: 523999

Norilsk Nickel Asia Ltd. (1)
Unit 6310 63/F The Center 99 Queen's Road Central, Hong Kong, China (Hong Kong)
Tel.: (852) 25206199
Web Site: http://www.nornik.ru
Sales Range: $50-74.9 Million
Emp.: 10
Non-Ferrous & Precious Metals Distr & Whslr
N.A.I.C.S.: 423510

Norilsk Nickel Marketing (Shanghai) Co., Ltd. (1)
1805 GC Tower 1088 Yuan Shen Road, Shanghai, 200122, China
Tel.: (86) 21 3857 1333
Web Site: http://www.nornik.ru
Nickel Mining Services
N.A.I.C.S.: 212230

Norilsk Nickel South Africa (1)
Knightsbridge Manor Office Park Block C Unit 1, 33 Sloane Street, Bryanston, 2021, South Africa
Tel.: (27) 11 463 4223
Web Site: http://www.nornik.ru
Nickel & Other Metal Ore Mining
N.A.I.C.S.: 212220
Gerhard Potgieter (Mng Dir)

Norilsk Nickel USA (1)
2 Penn Ctr W Ste 330, Pittsburgh, PA 15276
Tel.: (412) 722-1120
Web Site: http://www.nornickel.com
Sales Range: $50-74.9 Million
Emp.: 10
Non-Ferrous & Precious Metals Distr & Whslr
N.A.I.C.S.: 423510

OJSC Norilsko Taimyrskaya Energeticheskaya Kompaniya (1)
19 Ul Veteranov, Noril'sk, 663305, Russia
Tel.: (7) 3919431110
Web Site: http://www.oao-mtek.ru
Electric Power Generation & Distribution Services
N.A.I.C.S.: 221118

OJSC Norilsky Kombinat (1)
Pl Gvardeyskaya d 2, Noril'sk, 663310, Russia
Tel.: (7) 3919 42 80 33
Nickel Mining Services
N.A.I.C.S.: 212230

OJSC RAO Norilsk Nickel (1)
Korp 2 1 ul Korotkaya, Dudinka, Taymyr, Russia
Tel.: (7) 495 797 8244
Non Ferrous & Precious Metal Mfr
N.A.I.C.S.: 332999

OJSC Taimyrenergo (1)
19 Ul Veteranov Krasnoyark Krai, Noril'sk, 663310, Russia
Tel.: (7) 3919357705
Electric Power Distribution Services
N.A.I.C.S.: 221122

PJSC MOESK
2nd Paveletsky PR d 3 p 2, 115114, Moscow, Russia
Tel.: (7) 4956624070
Web Site: https://rossetimr.ru
Year Founded: 2004
MSRS—(MOEX)
Rev.: $2,487,983,112
Assets: $5,150,724,441
Liabilities: $2,650,825,485
Net Worth: $2,499,898,957
Earnings: $140,865,623
Emp.: 15,448
Fiscal Year-end: 12/31/21
Electric Power Distribution Services
N.A.I.C.S.: 221122
Aleksey Sergeyevich Starostin (Deputy Dir Gen-Corp Mgmt & Property Rels)

Subsidiaries:

Jsc Energotsentr (1)
Radchenko 13 Noginsk St building Office Room 50, 142400, Moscow, Russia
Tel.: (7) 4951980905
Web Site: http://www.energo-centr.ru
Construction Equipment Services
N.A.I.C.S.: 811310

Jsc Moesk-Engineering (1)
Yuzhnoportovaya 17 St Building 3, 115088, Moscow, Russia
Tel.: (7) 4952520801
Web Site: http://www.enesk.ru
Construction Equipment Services
N.A.I.C.S.: 811310

PJSC NOVOROSSIYSK COMMERCIAL SEA PORT
Portovaya St 14 Krasnodar Region, 353901, Novorossiysk, Russia
Tel.: (7) 8137878736
Web Site: http://www.nmtp.info
NMTP—(MOEX)
Rev.: $867,192,000
Assets: $3,011,810,000
Liabilities: $1,359,982,000
Net Worth: $1,651,828,000
Earnings: ($943,280,000)
Emp.: 7,557
Fiscal Year-end: 12/31/19
Cargo & Stevedoring Services
N.A.I.C.S.: 488320
Maksim S. Grishanin (First VP-Transneft)

Subsidiaries:

JSC Novoroslesexport (1)
2 Mira Str, Krasnodar Region, 353900, Novorossiysk, Russia
Tel.: (7) 8617600401
Web Site: http://www.nle.ru
Container Terminal Equipment Distr
N.A.I.C.S.: 488310

LLC Primorsk Trade Port (1)
PO Box 25, Primorsk Vyborg District, 188910, Saint Petersburg, Leningrad, Russia
Tel.: (7) 8137862999
Web Site: http://www.ptport.ru
Oil & Petroleum Product Distr
N.A.I.C.S.: 424720
Sergey Volynets (CEO)

OJSC Novorossiysk Shipyard (1)
Suhumskoe Shosse, 353920, Novorossiysk, Krasnodar Krai, Russia
Tel.: (7) 8617265084
Web Site: http://www.nsrz.ru
Sales Range: $400-449.9 Million
Emp.: 1,052
Ship Repair & Maintenance Services
N.A.I.C.S.: 336611

PJSC Fleet of NCSP (1)
14 Portovaya St, Krasnodar, 353901, Novorossiysk, Krasnodar Krai, Russia
Tel.: (7) 8617602300
Web Site: http://www.fleetncsp.ru
Sales Range: $200-249.9 Million
Emp.: 800
Ship Repair & Maintenance Services
N.A.I.C.S.: 336611

PJSC PHOSAGRO
Bld 1 55/1 Leninsky Prospekt, 119333, Moscow, 119333, Russia
Tel.: (7) 4952329689
Web Site: https://www.phosagro.com
Year Founded: 2001
PHOR—(MOEX)
Rev.: $5,663,973,360
Assets: $5,461,371,090
Liabilities: $3,243,629,880
Net Worth: $2,217,741,210
Earnings: $1,746,708,780
Emp.: 18,370
Fiscal Year-end: 12/31/21
Agricultural Fertilizer Mfr
N.A.I.C.S.: 325311
Boris Levin (Deputy Gen Dir)

Subsidiaries:

Agro-Cherepovets, CJSC (1)
40 Severnoe Shosse, Cherepovets, 162610, Russia
Tel.: (7) 8202 51 92 81
Nitrogen Fertilizer Mfr
N.A.I.C.S.: 325311

Apatit, OJSC (1)
1 Leningradskaya Street, Kirovsk, Murmansk, 184250, Russia
Tel.: (7) 8153135460
Phosphatic Fertilizer Mfr
N.A.I.C.S.: 325312
Vladimir Davydenko (CEO)

Balakovo Mineral Fertilizers (1)
18 Promzona, Balakovo, 413858, Saratov Region, Russia
Tel.: (7) 8453 49 40 34
Phosphatic Fertilizer Mfr
N.A.I.C.S.: 325312
Alexander Abaev (Dir-Information Policy)

Metachem, LLC (1)
20 Kirovsky Prospekt, Volkhov, 187400, Russia
Tel.: (7) 81363 64 902
Phosphatic Fertilizer Mfr
N.A.I.C.S.: 325312
Yuri Chernenko (CEO)

NIUIF, OJSC (1)
Severnoe shosse 75, 162622, Cherepovets, Vologda, Russia
Tel.: (7) 8202593796
Web Site: https://www.niuif.ru
Fertilizer Research & Development Services
N.A.I.C.S.: 541715
Boris Levin (CEO)

PhosAgro Balkans DOO (1)
Bulevar Mihaila Pupina 6, 11000, Belgrade, Serbia
Tel.: (381) 114300060
Phosphate-Based Fertilizer Mfr
N.A.I.C.S.: 325312

PhosAgro Trading SA (1)
Baarerstrasse 63, 6300, Zug, Switzerland
Tel.: (41) 417470370
Phosphate-Based Fertilizer Mfr
N.A.I.C.S.: 325312

PhosAgro-Cherepovets, OJSC (1)
75 Severnoe Shosse, Cherepovets, 162622, Vologda Region, Russia
Tel.: (7) 8202 59 33 09
Phosphatic Fertilizer Mfr
N.A.I.C.S.: 325312
Alexey Salnikov (Head-Info Policy Dept)

PhosAgro-Kursk, LLC (1)
Magistralnyi proezd 36, Kursk, 305025, Russia
Tel.: (7) 4712999014
Web Site: http://www.phosagro.com
Fertilizer Distr
N.A.I.C.S.: 424910

PhosAgro-Trans, LLC (1)
Dobrolyubova Prospekt 8 lit A, Saint Petersburg, 197198, Russia
Tel.: (7) 812 740 3460
Freight Forwarding Services
N.A.I.C.S.: 488510

Phosagro Deutschland GmbH (1)
Ballindamm 39, 20095, Hamburg, Germany
Tel.: (49) 40999993013
Phosphate-Based Fertilizer Mfr
N.A.I.C.S.: 325312

Phosagro France SAS (1)
Centre international d affaires - Parme activites 24, Boulevard Marcel Assault, 64200, Biarritz, France
Tel.: (33) 783878078
Phosphate-Based Fertilizer Mfr
N.A.I.C.S.: 325312

Phosint Trading Limited (1)
21 Vasili Michailidi Street, 3026, Limassol, Cyprus
Tel.: (357) 25 50 82 00
Web Site: http://www.phosinttrading.innovatico.com
Chemical Products Distr
N.A.I.C.S.: 424690

PJSC POLYUS
Tel.: (7) 4956413377   JE
Web Site: https://polyus.com
Year Founded: 2006
PLZL—(MOEX)
Rev.: $5,436,000,000
Assets: $9,284,000,000
Liabilities: $9,911,000,000
Net Worth: ($627,000,000)
Earnings: $1,729,000,000
Emp.: 20,385
Fiscal Year-end: 12/31/23
Gold Exploration & Mining Services
N.A.I.C.S.: 551112
Victor Drozdov (Dir-IR & Comm Dept)

Subsidiaries:

JSC Polyus Krasnoyarsk (1)
3 bldg 1 Krasina St, Moscow, 123056, Russia
Tel.: (7) 4956413377
Web Site: https://www.polyus.com
Gold Mining & Exploration Services
N.A.I.C.S.: 213114

OJSC Polyus Gold (1)
15-1 Building Tverskoy Boulevard, Moscow, 123104, Russia   (92.95%)
Tel.: (7) 4956413377
Web Site: http://www.polyusgold.com
Sales Range: $1-4.9 Billion
Gold Mining & Production
N.A.I.C.S.: 212220
German R. Pikhoya (Gen Dir)

Subsidiary (Domestic):

CJSC Tonoda (2)
2 ul Mira, Bodaybo, 666910, Russia
Tel.: (7) 3956176016
Gold Mining Services
N.A.I.C.S.: 212220

Lenzoloto OAO (2)
2 ul Mira, Bodaybo, 666904, Russia   (64.08%)
Tel.: (7) 3956152900
Sales Range: Less than $1 Million
Emp.: 3
Real Estate Prorperty Leasing Services
N.A.I.C.S.: 531190

PJSC RAO ENERGY SYSTEM OF EAST
str Malaya Dmitrovka 7, 127006, Moscow, Russia
Tel.: (7) 8003338000
Web Site: http://www.rao-esv.ru
Year Founded: 2008
Eletric Power Generation Services
N.A.I.C.S.: 221118
Andrey Kazachenkov (Member-Mgmt Bd)

PJSC ROSTELECOM
30 building 1 Goncharnaya st, 115172, Moscow, 115172, Russia
Tel.: (7) 4999998283   RU
Web Site: https://www.company.rt.ru
Year Founded: 1993
RTKM—(MOEX)
Rev.: $7,813,839,240
Assets: $14,855,901,360
Liabilities: $11,792,796,420
Net Worth: $3,063,104,940
Earnings: $428,777,040
Emp.: 126,812
Fiscal Year-end: 12/31/21
Telecommunications Network & ISDN Services
N.A.I.C.S.: 517111
Alexey Sapunov (Sr VP-Technical Infrastructure)

Subsidiaries:

CJSC GNC Alfa (1)
1 Khaghaghutyan Str, Abovyan, Kotayk, Armenia
Tel.: (374) 60464646
Web Site: http://www.rtarmenia.am
Telecommunication Servicesb

PJSC ROSTELECOM

PJSC Rostelecom—(Continued)

CJSC Globaltel (1)
Bytlerova str Bldg 7, 117485, Moscow, Russia
Tel.: (7) 4959842666
Web Site: http://old.globaltel.ru
Communication Service
N.A.I.C.S.: 517810

CJSC Makomnet (1)
Kapelskiy per 8 bl 1, 129110, Moscow, Russia
Tel.: (7) 4957969400
Web Site: http://www.macomnet.com
Telecommunication Servicesb
N.A.I.C.S.: 517810

JSC AIST (1)
Yubileynaya street house number 31 building Zh, Box Number 0007, Samara, 445027, Togliatti, Russia
Tel.: (7) 8482202020
Web Site: http://www.smr.aist.net.ru
Telecommunication Servicesb
N.A.I.C.S.: 517810
Dobrynin Vyacheslav Aleksandrovich *(Gen Dir)*

JSC Bashinformsvyaz (1)
ul Lenina 32/1, Ufa, 450077, Russia
Tel.: (7) 3472506340
Web Site: http://www.bashtel.ru
Sales Range: Less than $1 Million
Emp.: 6,042
Telecommunication Servicesb
N.A.I.C.S.: 517112

JSC Netris (1)
2nd Yuzhnoportovy passage 16 bldg 6 floor 2 3, 115088, Moscow, Russia
Tel.: (7) 4958705525
Web Site: http://www.netris.ru
Software Development Services
N.A.I.C.S.: 541511

LLC LekStar Communication (1)
Jubilee prospect 66, Reutov, Moscow, Russia
Tel.: (7) 4959559027
Web Site: http://svsreut.ru
Broadband Internet Services
N.A.I.C.S.: 517111

LLC Prometey (1)
st Komissar Smirnov 3B, 195009, Saint Petersburg, Russia
Tel.: (7) 8123138813
Web Site: http://www.prometeyhome.ru
Telecommunication Servicesb
N.A.I.C.S.: 517810

LLC Solar Security (1)
Nikitsky Lane 7 bld 1, 125009, Moscow, Russia
Tel.: (7) 4997550770
Web Site: http://en.rt-solar.ru
Commercial Security & Surveillance Solution Services
N.A.I.C.S.: 561621

Lukoil Inform Company (1)
11 Sretensky Building, 101000, Moscow, Russia **(100%)**
Tel.: (7) 4959274850
Telecommunication Servicesb
N.A.I.C.S.: 517810

OAO Lipetselektrosvyaz (1)
Ul Zegelya 2, 398000, Lipetsk, Russia
Tel.: (7) 42726835
Web Site: http://www.lipetsk.ru
Sales Range: $750-799.9 Million
Emp.: 3,600
Provider of Telecommunication & Data Transmission Services
N.A.I.C.S.: 517111

OJSC North-West Telecom (1)
14/26 ul Gorokhovaya, 16 ul Bolshaya Morskaya, 191186, Saint Petersburg, Russia
Tel.: (7) 8125954556
Web Site: http://www.nwtelecom.ru
Sales Range: $700-749.9 Million
Emp.: 6,546
Telecommunication Servicesb
N.A.I.C.S.: 517111
Vladimir A. Akulich *(CEO)*

Subsidiary (Domestic):

CJSC Novgorod Deitacom (2)
Nikolskaya 16-5, Velikiy Novgorod, Russia
Tel.: (7) 8162663073
Web Site: http://www.deitacom.ru
Emp.: 100
Internet Services
N.A.I.C.S.: 517810

CJSC St.Petersburg Tranzit Telecom (2)
22 Bolshaya Morskaya ul, 191186, Saint Petersburg, Russia
Tel.: (7) 8123804861
Web Site: http://www.ptt.spb.ru
Wireline Telecommunication Services
N.A.I.C.S.: 517112

OAO Lensvyaz (2)
61 Bolshaya Morskaya ul, 190000, Saint Petersburg, Russia **(50.66%)**
Tel.: (7) 8125718478
Web Site: http://www.lenobl.nwtelecom.ru
Telecommunications & Data Transmission Services
N.A.I.C.S.: 517111

OAO Novgorodtelecom (2)
2 Ludogotsha ul, Velikiy Novgorod, 173001, Russia **(50.66%)**
Tel.: (7) 8162782510
Web Site: http://www.novgorod.nwtelecom.ru
Sales Range: $450-499.9 Million
Emp.: 2,300
Telecommunications & Data Transmission Services
N.A.I.C.S.: 517111

OAO Petersburg Telephone Network (2)
24 Bolshaya Morskaya ul, 191186, Saint Petersburg, Russia **(50.94%)**
Tel.: (7) 8123141550
Web Site: http://www.ptn.ru
Telecommunications & Data Transmission Services
N.A.I.C.S.: 517111

OJSC SibirTelecom (1)
53 Gorky Street, 630099, Novosibirsk, Russia
Tel.: (7) 3832191106
Web Site: http://www.sibirtelecom.ru
Sales Range: $1-4.9 Billion
Emp.: 25,355
Telecommunication Servicesb
N.A.I.C.S.: 517810

OJSC Southern Telecommunications Company (1)
66 Karasunskaya Street, Krasnodar, Russia **(50.69%)**
Tel.: (7) 861 253 20 56
Web Site: http://www.stcompany.ru
Sales Range: $5-14.9 Billion
Telecommunication Servicesb
N.A.I.C.S.: 517111
Alexander Petrovich Shipulin *(Gen Dir)*

OJSC VolgaTelecom (1)
Dom Svyazi Maxim Gorky Square, 603000, Nizhniy Novgorod, Russia
Tel.: (7) 8314375000
Web Site: http://www.vt.ru
Sales Range: $1-4.9 Billion
Telecommunication Servicesb
N.A.I.C.S.: 517112

Subsidiary (Domestic):

CJSC Ulyanovsk-GSM (2)
Goncharov Str 52, Ulyanovsk, Russia
Tel.: (7) 08422424242
Cellular & Wireless Telecommunications
N.A.I.C.S.: 517112

Branch (Domestic):

VolgaTelecom - Chuvashian Republic Branch (2)
Pr Lenina 2, Cheboksary, 428000, Chuvashian Republic, Russia
Tel.: (7) 8352 62 43 04
Web Site: http://www.vt.ru
Sales Range: $1-4.9 Billion
Emp.: 3,400
Telecommunication Servicesb
N.A.I.C.S.: 517111

VolgaTelecom - Kirov Branch (2)
Ul Drelevskogo 43/1, 610000, Kirov, Russia
Tel.: (7) 8332649831
Web Site: http://www.vt.ru
Sales Range: $1-4.9 Billion
Emp.: 5,200
Telecommunication & Data Transmission Services
N.A.I.C.S.: 517111

VolgaTelecom - Marii-El Republic Branch (2)
Ul Sovetskaya 138, Yoshkar-Ola, 424000, Mariy El Republic, Russia
Tel.: (7) 8362664571
Web Site: http://www.vt.ru
Sales Range: $500-549.9 Million
Emp.: 2,300
Telecommunication Servicesb
N.A.I.C.S.: 517111

VolgaTelecom - Orenburg Branch (2)
11 Volodarskogo St, Orenburg, 460000, Russia
Tel.: (7) 3532773410
Web Site: http://www.vt.ru
Sales Range: $1-4.9 Billion
Emp.: 6,500
Telecommunication & Data Transmission Services
N.A.I.C.S.: 517111

VolgaTelecom - Saratov Branch (2)
Ul Kiseleva 40, Saratov, 410012, Russia
Tel.: (7) 8452 27 14 18
Web Site: http://www.vt.ru
Sales Range: $1-4.9 Billion
Emp.: 6,500
Telecommunication, Internet & Data Transmission Services
N.A.I.C.S.: 517111

VolgaTelecom - Udmurtia Republic Branch (2)
Ul Pushkinskaya 278, 426008, Izhevsk, Udmurtia Republic, Russia
Tel.: (7) 3412 22 69 91
Web Site: http://www.vt.ru
Sales Range: $1-4.9 Billion
Emp.: 3,800
Telecommunication Servicesb
N.A.I.C.S.: 517111

VolgaTelecom - Ulyanovsk Branch (2)
60 L Tolstogo St, Ulyanovsk, 432980, Russia
Tel.: (7) 8422 41 20 10
Web Site: http://www.vt.ru
Sales Range: $1-4.9 Billion
Emp.: 3,500
Telecommunication & Data Transmission Services
N.A.I.C.S.: 517111

PJSC Giprosvyaz (1)
st3rd Horoshevskaya 11, 123298, Moscow, Russia
Tel.: (7) 4991970000
Web Site: http://www.giprosvyaz.ru
Telecommunication Servicesb
N.A.I.C.S.: 517810

SC RPK Svyazist (1)
Shaumyan Ave 4 Building 1 Letter A Metro Novocherkasskaya BC, Bazin Office 203, 195027, Saint Petersburg, Russia
Tel.: (7) 8123150807
Web Site: http://www.rpk-svyazist.ru
Telecommunication Servicesb
N.A.I.C.S.: 517810

SC RT Labs (1)
22 km Kievskoe highway 6 building 1, 108811, Moscow, Russia
Tel.: (7) 4951222333
Web Site: http://www.rtlabs.ru
Telecommunication Servicesb
N.A.I.C.S.: 517810
Farit Khusnoyarov *(CEO)*

SC RTComm.RU (1)
Moskovsky settlement Kievskoe highway 22nd km house building 6 bldg 1, 108811, Moscow, Russia
Tel.: (7) 4959887778
Web Site: http://www.rtcomm.ru
Telecommunication Servicesb
N.A.I.C.S.: 517810

Ratiev Sergey Yurievich *(CEO)*

SC Severen-Telecom (1)
st Republican 28A pom 12H, 195112, Saint Petersburg, Russia
Tel.: (7) 8127407070
Web Site: http://www.severen.ru
Telecommunication Servicesb
N.A.I.C.S.: 517810

SC TKT-stroy (1)
Trefoleva street 29 letter A, 198095, Saint Petersburg, Russia
Tel.: (7) 88126440682
Web Site: http://www.tkt-stroy.ru
Telecommunication Servicesb
N.A.I.C.S.: 517810
Grigorieva Lyubov Pavlovna *(CEO)*

PJSC RUSHYDRO

51 Arkhitektora Vlasova Street, 117393, Moscow, Russia
Tel.: (7) 8002006112   RU
Web Site: https://www.rushydro.ru
Year Founded: 2004
HYDR—(MOEX)
Rev.: $5,469,264,510
Assets: $12,533,659,890
Liabilities: $4,056,274,980
Net Worth: $8,477,384,910
Earnings: $566,790,660
Fiscal Year-end: 12/31/21
Electric Energy Distribution Services
N.A.I.C.S.: 221122
Sergey Anatolevich Kirov *(Member-Mgmt Bd & Deputy Gen Dir)*

Subsidiaries:

JSC ChirkeiGESstroy (1)
7 A Car Lane Kazbekova St, 367000, Makhachkala, Russia **(74.99%)**
Tel.: (7) 8722 64 68 69
Web Site: http://www.chges.ru
Construction Engineering Services
N.A.I.C.S.: 237990

JSC Lenhydroproject (1)
22 Prospect Ispitateley, 197227, Saint Petersburg, Russia
Tel.: (7) 8123952901
Electric Energy Distribution Services
N.A.I.C.S.: 221122

JSC VNIIG (1)
21 Gzhatskaya St, 195220, Saint Petersburg, Russia
Tel.: (7) 8125345445
Electric Energy Distribution Services
N.A.I.C.S.: 221122

PhosAgro Polska Sp.z o.o (1)
Rondo Onz 1, 124, Wykroty, Poland
Tel.: (48) 222034500
Medical Laboratory Services
N.A.I.C.S.: 621511

RusHydro International AG (1)
Via Nassa 42, 6900, Lugano, Switzerland
Tel.: (41) 919932565
Emp.: 1
Hydroelectric Power Generation Services
N.A.I.C.S.: 221111
Thomas Kern *(Gen Mgr)*

Sakhalinenergo PJSC (1)
43 Communist, Yuzhno-Sakhalinsk, 693000, Russia **(76.59%)**
Tel.: (7) 4242782359
Web Site: http://www.sahen.elektra.ru
Sales Range: Less than $1 Million
Electric Power Transmission Services
N.A.I.C.S.: 221121
Igor Butovsky *(Chm-Mgmt Bd & Gen Dir)*

PJSC RUSPOLYMET

Vosstaniya str 1/15, Kulebaki, Nizhniy Novgorod, 607018, Russia
Tel.: (7) 8317679000
Web Site: https://www.ruspolymet.ru
RUSP—(MOEX)
Sales Range: Less than $1 Million
Alloy Product Mfr
N.A.I.C.S.: 331110

Artyom V. Biserov *(Head-Gen Machine Building-Nuclear & Power En-grg Sls Office)*

PJSC S.P. KOROLEV ROCKET & SPACE CORPORATION ENERGIA
4A Lenin Street Korolev, 141070, Moscow, Russia
Tel.: (7) 4955138655 RU
Web Site: http://www.energia.ru
Year Founded: 1946
RKKE—(MOEX)
Sales Range: Less than $1 Million
Space Vehicle Mfr
N.A.I.C.S.: 336419

PJSC STROYTRANSGAZ
10 Testovskaya Street, 123112, Moscow, Russia
Tel.: (7) 4952589494
Web Site: http://www.stroytransgaz.ru
Year Founded: 1990
Oil & Gas Pipeline, Storage & Processing Facility, Industrial Plant & Infrastructure Engineering & Construction Services
N.A.I.C.S.: 237990
Mikhail Vladimirovich Khryapov *(Member-Mgmt Bd & First VP)*

Subsidiaries:

STG Engineering LLC (1)
58 Novocheremushikinskaya Street, Moscow, 117418, Russia
Tel.: (7) 4952871869
Emp.: 200
Oil & Gas Field Engineering Services
N.A.I.C.S.: 333132

PJSC TATNEFT
75 Lenin Street, 423450, Almetyevsk, Tatarstan, Russia
Tel.: (7) 8553371111 RU
Web Site: http://www.tatneft.ru
Year Founded: 1950
TATN—(MOEX)
Rev.: $17,044,668,600
Assets: $20,235,832,830
Liabilities: $7,528,571,580
Net Worth: $12,707,261,250
Earnings: $2,678,994,420
Emp.: 64,329
Fiscal Year-end: 12/31/21
Oil & Gas Producer & Tire Mfr
N.A.I.C.S.: 211120
Nail Ulfatovich Maganov *(Chm-Mgmt Bd & Gen Dir)*

Subsidiaries:

Aytemiz Akaryakit Dagitim A.S. (1)
Sogutlucesme Cad No 83 Kadikoy, 34714, Istanbul, Turkiye
Tel.: (90) 2164182020
Web Site: http://www.aytemiz.com.tr
Rev.: $1,536,122,943
Assets: $391,308,948
Liabilities: $265,686,117
Net Worth: $125,622,832
Earnings: $30,927,249
Fiscal Year-end: 12/31/2021
Petroleum Product Distr
N.A.I.C.S.: 424720
Ismail Aytemiz *(Pres)*

JSC Almetyevsk Heating Networks (1)
St Rizy Fakhretdin 4, 423462, Almetyevsk, Russia
Tel.: (7) 8553312741
Web Site: http://www.apts.tatneft.ru
Oil & Energy Services
N.A.I.C.S.: 213112

JSC TANECO (1)
Republic of Tatarstan, 423570, Nizhnekamsk, Russia
Tel.: (7) 8555490232
Web Site: http://www.taneco.ru
Oil & Energy Services
N.A.I.C.S.: 213112

Aidar Minraufovich Khismatullin *(Gen Dir-Acting)*

JSC Yarpolimermash-Tatneft (1)
9 Polushkina Roshcha, 150003, Yaroslavl, Russia
Tel.: (7) 4852251593
Oil & Energy Services
N.A.I.C.S.: 213112

TatITneft LLC (1)
Room No 56 7 Universitetskiy Str, 420500, Innopolis, Russia
Tel.: (7) 9172551952
Web Site: http://www.tatneft.ru
Oil & Energy Services
N.A.I.C.S.: 213112

Tatneft- AZS - Tashkent LLC (1)
St Tashkent yuli 56, Nurafshon, Tashkent, Uzbekistan
Tel.: (998) 702020290
Oil & Energy Services
N.A.I.C.S.: 213112

Tatneft-AZS -Zapad LLC (1)
32-a Pulkovskoe highway, 196158, Saint Petersburg, Russia
Tel.: (7) 8127030616
Oil & Energy Services
N.A.I.C.S.: 213112

Tatneft-AZS Center LLC (1)
St R Fakhretdin 37, 423450, Almetyevsk, Russia
Tel.: (7) 8553315513
Oil & Energy Services
N.A.I.C.S.: 213112

Tatneft-AZS-Ukraine LLC (1)
St Polovka 62, Poltava, 36010, Ukraine
Tel.: (380) 532610106
Oil & Energy Services
N.A.I.C.S.: 213112

Tatneft-Energosbyt LLC (1)
5 Ob ezdnaya Str, 423450, Almetyevsk, Tatarstan, Russia
Tel.: (7) 8555318745
Web Site: http://www.energosbyt.tatneft.ru
Oil & Energy Services
N.A.I.C.S.: 213112

Tatneft-NAO LLC (1)
Lenin str 31 Nenets Autonomous Okrug, 166000, Naryan-Mar, Russia
Tel.: (7) 8556940805
Oil & Energy Services
N.A.I.C.S.: 213112
Gabidullin Rinat Nailovich *(Gen Dir)*

Tatneft-Neftekhimservis LLC (1)
5 Ob'ezdnaya Str, 423450, Almetyevsk, Tatarstan, Russia
Tel.: (7) 8553316286
Oil & Energy Services
N.A.I.C.S.: 213112

Tatneft-Samara LLC (1)
St Sovetskaya 165 A, 423462, Almetyevsk, Tatarstan, Russia
Tel.: (7) 8553302820
Oil & Energy Services
N.A.I.C.S.: 213112

Tatneft-Trans LLC (1)
Promsona, 423570, Nizhnekamsk, Tatarstan, Russia
Tel.: (7) 8553306063
Web Site: http://www.tn-trans.tatneft.ru
Oil & Energy Services
N.A.I.C.S.: 213112

Trading House KAMA LLC (1)
33 Chaikovsky Str, PO Box 107, Leninogorsk, 423259, Kazan, Tatarstan, Russia
Tel.: (7) 8559526291
Oil & Energy Services
N.A.I.C.S.: 213112

PJSC TERRITORIAL GENERATING COMPANY NO 1
16 Dobroljubova Pr Corp 2 Litera A Arena Hall Business Centre, Saint Petersburg, 197198, Russia
Tel.: (7) 8126883606
Web Site: https://www.tgc1.ru
TGKA—(MOEX)
Rev.: $1,568,733,602

Assets: $2,943,792,891
Liabilities: $819,903,030
Net Worth: $2,123,889,861
Earnings: $128,882,345
Emp.: 7,098
Fiscal Year-end: 12/31/19
Thermal & Electrical Power Energy Mfr
N.A.I.C.S.: 221111
Vadim Vederchik *(Mng Dir)*

Subsidiaries:

JSC St. Petersburg Heating Grid (1)
St Chernyakhovsky 36, Saint Petersburg, 191119, Russia
Tel.: (7) 8126884945
Web Site: http://www.teplosetspb.ru
Heating Energy Power Distribution Services
N.A.I.C.S.: 221122

PJSC TRANSCONTAINER
Oruzheyniy Pereulok 19, 125047, Moscow, Russia
Tel.: (7) 4957881717
Web Site: http://www.trcont.com
Year Founded: 2006
Rev.: $1,390,067,270
Assets: $1,360,710,670
Liabilities: $579,470,250
Net Worth: $781,240,420
Earnings: $189,527,500
Emp.: 53
Fiscal Year-end: 12/31/19
Logistic Services
N.A.I.C.S.: 488510
Victor Markov *(CEO)*

Subsidiaries:

JSC Logistika-Terminal (1)
54 Lit A Moskovskoe shosse, Shushary, 196626, Saint Petersburg, Russia
Tel.: (7) 8126000326
Web Site: http://www.logistika-terminal.ru
Containers Handling Services
N.A.I.C.S.: 488320

PJSC UNITED AIRCRAFT CORPORATION
22 Ulansky Pereulok bldg1, Moscow, 101000, Russia
Tel.: (7) 4959261420
Web Site: http://www.uacrussia.ru
Year Founded: 2006
UNAC—(MOEX)
Sales Range: $5-14.9 Billion
Emp.: 96,787
Aircraft Mfr
N.A.I.C.S.: 336411
Vladimir A. Dmitriev *(Chm)*

Subsidiaries:

JSC Aerokompozit (1)
Ulitsa Polikarpova 23B Building 2, 125284, Moscow, Russia
Tel.: 495940874010
Aviation Equipment Mfr
N.A.I.C.S.: 336413

JSC Aviastar-Sp (1)
Antonova Ave 1, 432072, Ulyanovsk, Russia
Tel.: (7) 8422281281
Web Site: http://www.aviastar-sp.ru
Aviation Equipment Mfr
N.A.I.C.S.: 336413

JSC Aviation Holding Company (1)
Polikarpov str 23B, 125284, Moscow, Russia
Tel.: (7) 4995500106
Aviation Equipment Mfr
N.A.I.C.S.: 336413
Ilya S. Tarasenko *(Gen Dir)*

JSC Flight Research Institute N.A. M.M. Gromov (1)
Ulitsa Garnaeva 2A, 140180, Zhukovskiy, Moscow, Russia
Tel.: (7) 4955565938
Web Site: http://www.lii.ru
Aviation Equipment Mfr

N.A.I.C.S.: 336413
Pavel Nikolaevich Vlasov *(Gen Dir)*

JSC Russian Aircraft Corporation (1)
Leningradskoe highway 6, 125284, Moscow, Russia
Tel.: (7) 4957218100
Web Site: http://www.migavia.ru
Aviation Equipment Mfr
N.A.I.C.S.: 336413
Andrey Leonidovich Gerasimchuk *(Mng Dir)*

Joint-Stock Company Aerocomposit-Ulyanovsk (1)
Antonova Prospekt 1, Zavolzhsky District, 432072, Ulyanovsk, Russia
Tel.: (7) 8422590600
Air-Borne Vehicle Mfr
N.A.I.C.S.: 333912
Yury V. Solodkov *(Gen Dir)*

Joint-Stock Company Kapo-Composit (1)
Dementyeva Str 1, Kazan, Tatarstan, Russia
Tel.: (7) 8432020744
Air-Borne Vehicle Mfr
N.A.I.C.S.: 333912
Alexei B. Slobodinskiy *(Gen Dir)*

OJSC Experimental Design Bureau N.A. A.S. Yakovlev (1)
Leningradsky Prospect 68, 125315, Moscow, Russia
Tel.: (7) 4951583432
Web Site: http://www.yak.ru
Aviation Equipment Mfr
N.A.I.C.S.: 336413
Demchenko Oleg Fedorovich *(Gen Dir)*

OJSC Experimental Machine-Building Plant N.A. V.M. Myasishchev (1)
Ulitsa Narkomvod 7, 140180, Zhukovskiy, Moscow, Russia
Tel.: (7) 4956647676
Web Site: http://www.emz-m.ru
Aviation Equipment Mfr
N.A.I.C.S.: 336413

OJSC Ilyushin Aviation Complex (1)
Leningradsky Prospect 45 G, 125190, Moscow, Russia
Tel.: (7) 4950000010
Web Site: http://www.ilyushin.org
Air-Borne Vehicle Mfr
N.A.I.C.S.: 333912
Yury Grudinin *(Gen Dir)*

PJSC Scientific & Production Corporation (1)
Bld 1 68 Leningradsky Av, 125315, Moscow, Russia
Tel.: (7) 4957772101
Aviation Equipment Mfr
N.A.I.C.S.: 336413
Ravil Rashidovich Hakimov *(Gen Dir)*

PJSC Taganrog Aviation Scientific-Technical Complex N.A. G.M. Beriev (1)
Ploschad Aviatorov 1, 347923, Taganrog, Russia
Tel.: (7) 8634390901
Aviation Equipment Mfr
N.A.I.C.S.: 336413
Tikhonov Mikhailovich *(Mng Dir)*

Pjsc Tupolev (1)
17 Academician Tupolev Embankment, 105005, Moscow, Russia
Tel.: (7) 4992637777
Web Site: http://www.tupolev.ru
Emp.: 12,000
Aviation Equipment Mfr
N.A.I.C.S.: 336413
Ronis N. Sharipov *(Gen Dir)*

Sukhoi Company (JSC) (1)
23B Polikarpov str, PB 604, Moscow, 125284, Russia
Tel.: (7) 495 940 26 63
Web Site: http://www.sukhoi.org
Aircraft Mfr
N.A.I.C.S.: 336411

PJSC VSEUKRAINSKYI AKSIONERNYI BANK
5 Zoolohichna Street, 04119, Kiev, Ukraine

PJSC VSEUKRAINSKYI AKSIONERNYI BANK

PJSC Vseukrainskyi Aksionernyi Bank—(Continued)
Tel.: (380) 444963396 UA
Web Site: http://www.vab.ua
Year Founded: 1992
Sales Range: $75-99.9 Million
Emp.: 2,035
Retail & Commercial Banking
N.A.I.C.S.: 522110
Zhanna Makeyenko *(Deputy Chm-Mgmt Bd)*

PJSC VTB BANK
43 bld 1 Vorontsovskaya str, 109147, Moscow, 109147, Russia
Tel.: (7) 4957397799 RU
Web Site: https://www.vtb.com
Year Founded: 1990
VTBR—(MOEX)
Rev.: $14,221,626,000
Assets: $244,375,434,000
Liabilities: $221,172,012,000
Net Worth: $23,203,422,000
Earnings: $1,014,291,000
Emp.: 79,217
Fiscal Year-end: 12/31/20
Retail, Corporate & Investment Banking & Other Financial Services
N.A.I.C.S.: 522110
Yuri A. Soloviev *(Co-Chm-Mgmt Bd)*

Subsidiaries:

Banco VTB Africa S.A (1)
Rua da Missao No 22 r c, Luanda, Angola
Tel.: (244) 222390307
Web Site: http://www.vtb.ao
Banking Services
N.A.I.C.S.: 522110

Bank VTB (Kazakhstan) JSC
26/29 Timiryazev Street, Almaty, 050040, Kazakhstan
Tel.: (7) 727 330 50 50
Web Site: http://www.vtb-bank.kz
Sales Range: $100-124.9 Million
Emp.: 200
Commercial Banking Services
N.A.I.C.S.: 522110

Bank VTB North-West OJSC (1)
38 Nevskiy Prospekt, 191011, Saint Petersburg, Russia
Tel.: (7) 8123298329
Web Site: http://www.vtb-sz.ru
Commercial Banking Services
N.A.I.C.S.: 522110

Coop Pank AS (1)
Maakri 30, 15014, Tallinn, Estonia (59%)
Tel.: (372) 6690900
Web Site: https://www.cooppank.ee
Rev.: $121,014,461
Assets: $2,192,528,977
Liabilities: $1,987,401,479
Net Worth: $205,127,498
Earnings: $43,276,300
Emp.: 396
Fiscal Year-end: 12/31/2023
Commericial Banking
N.A.I.C.S.: 522110
Margus Rink *(Chm-Mgmt Bd)*

Subsidiary (Non-US):

AS Eesti Krediidipank Latvijas (2)
21-8 Kr Valdemara str, Riga, LV-1010, Latvia
Tel.: (371) 67775888
Web Site: http://www.ekp.lv
Banking Services
N.A.I.C.S.: 522110

JSC Commercial Bank - Bank of Moscow (1)
8/15 bld 3 Rozhdestvenka St, Moscow, 107996, Russia (100%)
Tel.: (7) 4957458000
Web Site: http://www.bm.ru
Sales Range: $1-4.9 Billion
Banking Services
N.A.I.C.S.: 522110

Subsidiary (Non-US):

BM Bank, JSC (2)

T Shevchenko Avenue 37/122, Kiev, 1032, Ukraine
Tel.: (380) 444990101
Web Site: http://www.bmbank.com.ua
Banking Services
N.A.I.C.S.: 522110
Oksana Kuzminova *(Deputy Chm)*

Subsidiary (Domestic):

Bezhitsa-Bank (2)
16 Arsenalskaya Ul Bryanskaya Oblast, Bryansk, 241050, Russia
Tel.: (7) 483 2 66 05 05
Web Site: http://www.bm.ru
Banking Services
N.A.I.C.S.: 522110

OJSC Mosvodokanalbank (2)
3 Pleteshkovsky Per, Moscow, 107005, Russia
Tel.: (7) 495 632 16 91
Web Site: http://www.mvkb.ru
Banking Services
N.A.I.C.S.: 522110

JSC TransCreditBank (1)
37A Novaya Basmannaya St, 105066, Moscow, Russia (99.6%)
Tel.: (7) 4957880880
Web Site: http://www.tcb.ru
Sales Range: $1-4.9 Billion
Banking Services
N.A.I.C.S.: 522110
Mikhail M. Zadornov *(Chm)*

Joint Venture (Domestic):

TKB BNP Paribas Investment Partners JSC (2)
69/71 lit A Marata Street, 191119, Saint Petersburg, Russia (50%)
Tel.: (7) 8123327332
Web Site: http://www.tkbip.com
Emp.: 90
Investment Fund Asset Management Services
N.A.I.C.S.: 523940
Tanya Landwehr *(CFO & Head-Comml Dev & Intl Sls)*

Multicarta Ltd (1)
43 Ul Vorontsovskaya, 109147, Moscow, Russia
Tel.: (7) 4957846055
Web Site: http://multicarta.ru
Sales Range: $200-249.9 Million
Emp.: 300
Financial Management Services
N.A.I.C.S.: 523999

NPF VTB Pension Fund JSC (1)
St Vorontsovskaya 43 building 1, Moscow, Russia
Tel.: (7) 84956686111
Web Site: http://www.vtbnpf.ru
Pension Services
N.A.I.C.S.: 525110
Irina Reshetova *(Mgr-HR)*

OJSC VTB Bank (Azerbaijan) (1)
38 Khatai ave Messenat Plasa 1st floor, Baku, Azerbaijan
Tel.: (994) 124920080
Web Site: http://en.vtb.az
Banking Services
N.A.I.C.S.: 522110
Tural Valiyev *(Dir-Retail Banking Dept)*

Pjsc Sarovbusinessbank (1)
Silkina street 13, Sarov, Nizhniy Novgorod, Russia
Tel.: (7) 88312808558
Web Site: http://www.sbbank.ru
Banking Services
N.A.I.C.S.: 522110

Tele2 Russia (1)
Kievskoe highway 22nd kilometer household 6 building 1, Moskovsky settlement, 108811, Moscow, Russia
Tel.: (7) 4952298400
Web Site: https://msk.tele2.ru
Sales Range: $800-899.9 Million
Emp.: 9,000
Cellular Telecommunications Services
N.A.I.C.S.: 517112
Ritvars Krievs *(CTO)*

VTB Bank (Austria) AG (1)

Parkring 6, PO Box 560, Vienna, 1010, Austria
Tel.: (43) 1515350
Web Site: http://www.vtb.at
Sales Range: $100-124.9 Million
Emp.: 180
Commercial Banking Services
N.A.I.C.S.: 522110
Andrey Girichev *(CEO)*

VTB Bank (Belarus) CJSC (1)
Moskovskaya str 14, Minsk, 220007, Belarus (97.3%)
Tel.: (375) 173091515
Web Site: http://www.vtb.by
Commercial Banking Services
N.A.I.C.S.: 522110

VTB Bank (Deutschland) AG (1)
13 Walter Kolb Strasse, 60594, Frankfurt am Main, Germany
Tel.: (49) 69 21 680
Web Site: http://www.vtb.de
Commercial Banking Services
N.A.I.C.S.: 522110

VTB Bank (Europe) SE (1)
Wipplingerstrasse 35/11, 1010, Vienna, Austria
Tel.: (43) 1515350
Banking Services
N.A.I.C.S.: 522110
Ulrike Bader *(Dir-Trade & Export Fin)*

VTB Bank (France) SA (1)
79-81 boulevard Haussmann, 75382, Paris, France
Tel.: (33) 140064321
Web Site: http://www.en.vtb.fr
Sales Range: $50-74.9 Million
Emp.: 60
Commercial Banking Services
N.A.I.C.S.: 522110

VTB Factoring Ltd (1)
10 Presnenskaya emb, 123112, Moscow, Russia
Tel.: (7) 4957833534
Web Site: http://eng.vtbf.ru
Factoring Services
N.A.I.C.S.: 522299

VTB Leasing (Europe) Ltd (1)
30 Ekaterinis Kornarou Street Flat 301, Nicosia, 2024, Strovolos, Cyprus
Tel.: (357) 22767630
Emp.: 2
Financial Lending Services
N.A.I.C.S.: 523999
Anastasia Dementyeva *(Gen Mgr)*

VTB Leasing JSC (1)
Presnenskaya embankment 10 Block C, 123112, Moscow, Russia
Tel.: (7) 8007700621
Web Site: http://www.vtb-leasing.ru
Leasing Services
N.A.I.C.S.: 532490
Ivanter Dmitry *(Gen Dir)*

VTB Specialized Depository CJSC (1)
st Shchepkina d 4 floor 8 room / room II/1, vn ter g municipal district Meshchansky, 129090, Moscow, Russia
Tel.: (7) 4959563070
Web Site: http://www.vtbsd.ru
Non Banking Depositary Services
N.A.I.C.S.: 522180

VTB-Capital CJSC (1)
Federation Tower West 12 Presnenskaya Emb, 123112, Moscow, Russia
Tel.: (7) 4959609999
Web Site: https://www.vtbcapital.ru
Financial Management Services
N.A.I.C.S.: 523999
Damian Chunilal *(CEO-Asia)*

Subsidiary (Non-US):

VTB Bank (Armenia) CJSC (2)
Moskovyan Str 35 68-73 Non-Residential Premises, Yerevan, Armenia
Tel.: (374) 80 00 87 87
Web Site: http://www.vtb.am
Securities Brokerage Services
N.A.I.C.S.: 523150
Armen Sargsyan *(Deputy Chm-Mgmt Bd)*

VTB Capital Plc (2)

INTERNATIONAL PUBLIC

14 Cornhill, London, EC3V 3ND, United Kingdom
Tel.: (44) 2033348000
Web Site: http://www.vtbcapital.com
Sales Range: $150-199.9 Million
Emp.: 300
Commercial Banking Services
N.A.I.C.S.: 522110

VTB-Development CJSC (1)
29 Ul B Morskaya, Saint Petersburg, 190000, Russia
Tel.: (7) 8123292219
Web Site: http://www.vtb.com
Financial Management Services
N.A.I.C.S.: 523999

Vozrozhdenie Bank JSC (1)
7/4 Luchnikov Pereulok Building 1 GSP, Moscow, 101990, Russia (96.3%)
Tel.: (7) 4957770888
Web Site: http://www.vbank.ru
Rev.: $325,694,820
Assets: $3,550,753,690
Liabilities: $3,310,567,810
Net Worth: $240,185,880
Earnings: ($95,005,130)
Emp.: 5,546
Fiscal Year-end: 12/31/2018
Banking Services
N.A.I.C.S.: 522110
Anatoly Pechatnikov *(Deputy Chm)*

Subsidiary (Domestic):

NPF Garmonia (2)
Ul Ostryakova, Moscow, Russia
Tel.: (7) 4957907935
Non Government Pension Fund Services
N.A.I.C.S.: 525110

PJSC YUZHNIIGIPROGAZ
169-G Artyoma str, Donetsk, 83004, Ukraine
Tel.: (380) 62 206 53 75
Web Site: http://www.ungg.org
Year Founded: 1930
Oil & Gas Pipeline Mfr
N.A.I.C.S.: 237120
Iurii M. Kostenko *(Head-Project Enrg & Deputy Dir)*

PJSC ZAPOROZHYE FERRO ALLOYS PLANT
11 Diahonalne shose, Zaporizhzhya, 69035, Ukraine
Tel.: (380) 612 700 41 71
Web Site: http://www.zfz.com.ua
Year Founded: 1931
Iron & Ferroalloy Mfr
N.A.I.C.S.: 331110
P. A. Kravchenko *(Chm)*

PJX RESOURCES INC.
5600 - 100 King Street West, Toronto, M5X 1C9, ON, Canada
Tel.: (416) 799-9205 AB
Web Site:
https://www.pjxresources.com
Year Founded: 2010
PJXRF—(OTCQB)
Rev.: $454
Assets: $1,034,374
Liabilities: $204,754
Net Worth: $829,620
Earnings: ($1,248,784)
Fiscal Year-end: 12/31/20
Metal Mining
N.A.I.C.S.: 212290
John Keating *(Pres & CEO)*

PKA A/S
Tuborg Boulevard 3, 2900, Hellerup, Denmark
Tel.: (45) 39454540 DK
Web Site: http://www.pka.dk
Year Founded: 1954
Emp.: 100
Pension Administration Services
N.A.I.C.S.: 524292
Peter Damgaard *(CEO)*

AND PRIVATE COMPANIES

Subsidiaries:

TDC Holding A/S (1)
Teglholmsgade 1, 0900, Copenhagen, C, Denmark (16.66%)
Tel.: (45) 70110330
Web Site: http://www.tdcgroup.com
Rev.: $2,302,027,000
Assets: $9,226,189,000
Liabilities: $6,451,042,500
Net Worth: $2,775,146,500
Earnings: $246,246,000
Emp.: 6,433
Fiscal Year-end: 12/31/2022
Holding Company; Telecommunications Services
N.A.I.C.S.: 551112
Mike Parton (Chm)

Subsidiary (Domestic):

Nuuday A/S (2)
Teglholmsgade 1, 2450, Copenhagen, Denmark
Tel.: (45) 70110330
Web Site: https://nuuday.com
Emp.: 3,075
Digital Media Streaming & Telecommunications Services
N.A.I.C.S.: 517121

Punktum dk A/S (2)
Ørestads Boulevard 108 11, 2300, Copenhagen, Denmark
Tel.: (45) 33646000
Web Site: https://www.punktum.dk
Sales Range: $10-24.9 Million
Emp.: 43
Internet Domain Name Registration & Hosting Services
N.A.I.C.S.: 518210
Jakob Bring Truelsen (CEO)

TDC Solutions A/S (2)
Teglholmsgade 1 G 455, 0900, Copenhagen, C, Denmark
Tel.: (45) 70110330
Telecommunications, Internet & Business Management Services
N.A.I.C.S.: 517111

YouSee A/S (2)
Teglholmsgade 1, DK-0900, Copenhagen, Denmark
Tel.: (45) 70704040
Web Site: http://yousee.dk
Cable Television & Internet Services
N.A.I.C.S.: 516210

Subsidiary (Domestic):

DKTV A/S (3)
Teglholmsgade 1,, 2450, Copenhagen, Denmark
Tel.: (45) 43324700
Web Site: https://www.dktv.dk
Emp.: 422
Cable Television & Internet Services
N.A.I.C.S.: 516210

Branch (Domestic):

Dansk Kabel TV A/S - Esbjerg (4)
Skjoltsgate 49, 6700, Esbjerg, Denmark
Tel.: (45) 43324700
Web Site: https://www.dktv.dk
Cable Television & Internet Services
N.A.I.C.S.: 516210

PKB VELEPRODAJA PRODUKT AD

Zrenjaninski put 194, Belgrade, Serbia
Tel.: (381) 11 20 74 400
Web Site:
http://www.pkbveleprodukt.rs
Year Founded: 1976
Sales Range: Less than $1 Million
Emp.: 44
Supermarket Operator
N.A.I.C.S.: 445110

PKO BANK POLSKI SA

ul Pulawska 15, 02-515, Warsaw, Poland
Tel.: (48) 225219182 PL
Web Site: http://www.pkobp.pl
Year Founded: 1919
PKO—(WAR)
Rev.: $4,601,818,821
Assets: $125,990,051,751
Liabilities: $114,628,196,754
Net Worth: $11,361,854,997
Earnings: $1,382,203,688
Fiscal Year-end: 12/31/23
Financial Investment Services
N.A.I.C.S.: 523999
Piotr Mazur (Vice Chm-Mgmt Bd)

Subsidiaries:

Bankowe Towarzystwo Kapitalowe SA (1)
ul Chlodna 52, 00-872, Warsaw, Poland
Tel.: (48) 227788880
Web Site: http://www.btksa.pl
Investment Banking Services
N.A.I.C.S.: 523150

Subsidiary (Domestic):

PKO BP Faktoring SA (2)
al Solidarnosci 171, 00-877, Poland
Tel.: (48) 224223550
Web Site: http://www.pkofaktoring.pl
Banking & Financial Security Services
N.A.I.C.S.: 523150
Piotr Mierzejewski (Chm-Mgmt Bd)

Centrum Finansowe Pulawska Sp. z o.o. (1)
ul Pulawska 15, 02-515, Warsaw, Poland (100%)
Tel.: (48) 225216804
Web Site: http://www.cfp.com.pl
Property & Facility Management Services
N.A.I.C.S.: 531390

Centrum Haffnera Sp. z o.o. (1)
ul Reja 13/15, 81-874, Sopot, Poland (49.43%)
Tel.: (48) 585557412
Web Site: http://www.centrum-haffnera.eu
Financial Investment Services
N.A.I.C.S.: 523999
Jacek Girdziusz (Gen Mgr)

Finanse Agent Transferowy Sp. z o.o. (1)
Ul Kolejowa 5/7, 01 217, Warsaw, Poland (100%)
Tel.: (48) 225348484
Web Site: http://www.finat.pl
Financial Investment Services
N.A.I.C.S.: 523999

Fort Mokotow Sp. z o.o. (1)
ul Pulawska 15, 05-515, Warsaw, Poland
Tel.: (48) 22 521 4300
Web Site: http://www.fortmokotow.com.pl
Investment Banking & Securities Dealing
N.A.I.C.S.: 523150

Inteligo Financial Services S.A. (1)
Bank Polski Spolka Akcyjna Kancelaria ul Partyzantow 15, Powszechna Kasa Oszczednosci, 22-411, Zamosc, Poland (100%)
Tel.: (48) 815356789
Web Site: http://www.inteligo.pl
Sales Range: $100-124.9 Million
Emp.: 168
Financial Services
N.A.I.C.S.: 522320

KREDOBANK SA (1)
ul Sacharowa 78A, 79026, L'viv, Ukraine
Tel.: (380) 32 297 23 20
Web Site: http://www.kredobank.com.ua
Commercial Banking Services
N.A.I.C.S.: 522110

Molina sp. z o.o. (1)
Ul Chlodna 52, 00-872, Warsaw, Poland
Tel.: (48) 223585605
Web Site: http://www.molina.com.pl
Real Estate Management Services
N.A.I.C.S.: 531390

PKO Bank Hipoteczny SA (1)
ul Pulawska 15, 02-515, Warsaw, Poland
Tel.: (48) 225215750
Web Site: http://www.pkobh.pl
Financial Management Services
N.A.I.C.S.: 541611

PKO Inwestycje Sp. z o.o. (1)
Mooktowska, 00650, Warsaw, Poland (100%)
Tel.: (48) 225216804
Web Site: http://www.pkoinwestycje.pl
Sales Range: $25-49.9 Million
Emp.: 40
Real Estate Services
N.A.I.C.S.: 531390

PKO Leasing SA (1)
Al Marshal Edward Smigly-Rydza 20, 93-281, Lodz, Poland
Tel.: (48) 222603666
Web Site: http://www.pkoleasing.pl
Financial Services
N.A.I.C.S.: 541611

PKO Towarzystwo Funduszy Inwestycyjnych SA (1)
Ul Chlodna 52, 00-872, Warsaw, Poland
Tel.: (48) 223585656
Web Site: http://www.pkotfi.pl
Financial Management Services
N.A.I.C.S.: 541611
Piotr Zochowski (Pres)

PKO Zycie Towarzystwo Ubezpieczen SA (1)
Ul Chlodna 52, 00-872, Warsaw, Poland
Tel.: (48) 225410892
Web Site: http://www.pkoubezpieczenia.pl
Financial Management Services
N.A.I.C.S.: 541611

PKO/Credit Suisse Towarzystwo Funduszy Inwestycyj-nych S.A. (1)
ul Grojecka 5, 02 019, Warsaw, Poland (100%)
Tel.: (48) 22 358 56 56
Web Site: http://www.pko-cs.pl
Financial Investment Services
N.A.I.C.S.: 523999

Pomeranka Sp. z o.o. (1)
Ul Pulawska 15, 05-515, Warsaw, Poland (100%)
Tel.: (48) 225216804
Web Site: http://www.neptunpark.pl
Investment Services
N.A.I.C.S.: 523150

Powszechne Towarzystwo Emerytalne Bankowy S.A. (1)
ul Chlodna 52, 00-872, Warsaw, Poland (100%)
Tel.: (48) 225803700
Web Site: http://www.pkopte.pl
Financial Investment Services
N.A.I.C.S.: 523999

Qualia Development (1)
ul Chlodna 52, 00-872, Warsaw, Poland
Tel.: (48) 22 378 98 00
Web Site: http://www.qualia.pl
Real Estate Development Services
N.A.I.C.S.: 531390

ZenCard sp. z o.o. (1)
Al Jana Pawla II 80 Budynek Babka Tower, 00-175, Warsaw, Poland
Tel.: (48) 225994490
Web Site: http://www.zencard.pl
Financial Management Services
N.A.I.C.S.: 541611

PKSHA TECHNOLOGY, INC.

2-35-10 Hongo Bunkyo-Ku, Tokyo, 113-0033, Japan
Web Site: http://www.pkshatech.com
3993—(TKS)
Rev.: $98,607,720
Assets: $261,521,740
Liabilities: $57,230,480
Net Worth: $204,291,260
Earnings: $5,388,400
Fiscal Year-end: 09/30/23
Software Development Services
N.A.I.C.S.: 541511
Katsuya Uenoyama (Founder & Pres)

PKU HEALTHCARE CORP., LTD.

10th Floor Unit 1 Liangjiang Tiandi No 56 Jinkai Avenue, Yubei District, Chongqing, 401121, China

PLACEMENTS CMI INC.

Tel.: (86) 2367525366
Web Site: https://www.pku-hc.com
Year Founded: 1965
000788—(SSE)
Rev.: $302,960,518
Assets: $353,332,902
Liabilities: $155,466,783
Net Worth: $197,866,119
Earnings: $6,002,768
Emp.: 2,910
Fiscal Year-end: 12/31/20
Pharmaceutical Research & Development, Manufacturing & Export
N.A.I.C.S.: 325412
Pingdong Yuan (Pres)

PLACEMENTS CMI INC.

11535 1st Avenue Bureau 500, Saint-Georges, G5Y7H5, QC, Canada
Tel.: (418) 228-8031
Year Founded: 1973
Investment Holding Company
N.A.I.C.S.: 551112
Marcel Dutil (Pres & CEO)

Subsidiaries:

Canam Group Inc. (1)
11505 1re Avenue Bureau 500, Saint-Georges, G5Y 7X3, QC, Canada
Tel.: (418) 228-8031
Web Site: http://www.groupecanam.com
Fabricated Steel Mfr
N.A.I.C.S.: 332312
Marcel C. M. Dutil (Chm)

Subsidiary (US):

Canam Steel Corporation (2)
4010 Clay St, Point of Rocks, MD 21777
Tel.: (301) 874-5141
Web Site: http://www.groupecanam.com
Steel Products Mfr
N.A.I.C.S.: 331110
Randy Leonard (Ops Mgr)

Plant (US):

Canam-Bridge (2)
386 River Rd, Claremont, NH 03743
Tel.: (603) 542-5202
Web Site: http://www.canambridges.com
Bridge Construction Services
N.A.I.C.S.: 237310

Subsidiary (Non-US):

Steel Plus Limited (2)
Gn 37 B Sector 5 Salt Lake, Kolkata, 700091, West Bengal, India
Tel.: (91) 3323575865
Web Site: http://www.groupecanam.com
Steel Joists Mfr
N.A.I.C.S.: 332312
Partha Pratim Ghosh (Gen Mgr)

Subsidiary (US):

Stonebridge Inc. (2)
165 Ryan St, South Plainfield, NJ 07080
Tel.: (908) 753-1100
Web Site:
http://www.stonebridgesteelerection.com
Structural Steel & Precast Concrete Contractors
N.A.I.C.S.: 238120
Jack Falcone (VP-Bus Dev)

Subsidiary (Non-US):

Technyx Euro Services S.R.L. (2)
9 Ionescu Crum Street, 500446, Brasov, Romania
Tel.: (40) 268318057
Web Site: http://www.groupecanam.com
Construction Product Mfr
N.A.I.C.S.: 332312
Mihu Anghelescu (Deputy Mgr)

Manac Inc. (1)
2275 107th Street, Saint-Georges, G5Y 8G6, QC, Canada
Tel.: (418) 228-2018
Web Site: https://www.manac.com
Sales Range: $200-249.9 Million
Trailer Mfr
N.A.I.C.S.: 336212
Marcel Dutil (Founder)

PLACEMENTS CMI INC.

Placements CMI Inc.—(Continued)

Subsidiary (Domestic):

Peerless Limited (2)
575 Page Ave, Penticton, V2A 6P3, BC, Canada
Tel.: (250) 492-0408
Web Site: https://www.peerless.ca
Truck Trailer Mfr
N.A.I.C.S.: 336212
Tim Libby *(Mgr-Custom Products-Drilling & Well Servicing)*

PLACES FOR PEOPLE GROUP LIMITED

80 Cheapside, London, EC2V 6EE, United Kingdom
Tel.: (44) 2074290400   UK
Web Site: http://www.placesforpeople.co.uk
Rev.: $1,058,654,464
Assets: $6,443,397,120
Liabilities: $5,785,566,208
Net Worth: $657,830,912
Earnings: $156,497,920
Emp.: 12,513
Fiscal Year-end: 03/31/18
Holding Company; Residential Housing Development, Property Management & Resident Support Services
N.A.I.C.S.: 551112
David Cowans *(CEO)*

Subsidiaries:

Brio Retirement Living (Chapelton) Limited (1)
19 Landale Court, Chapelton, Stonehaven, AB39 8BF, United Kingdom
Tel.: (44) 156 973 0008
Residential Management Services
N.A.I.C.S.: 531311

Brio Retirement Living (Holdings) Limited (1)
305 Gray's Inn Road, London, WC1X 8QR, United Kingdom
Tel.: (44) 145 188 5494
Web Site: https://www.brioretirement.co.uk
Residential Management Services
N.A.I.C.S.: 531311
Helen Kings *(CEO)*

Castle Rock Edinvar Housing Association Limited (1)
1 Hay Avenue, Edinburgh, EH16 4RW, United Kingdom
Tel.: (44) 131 657 0600
Web Site:
   http://www.castlerockedinvar.co.uk
Residential Property Management Services
N.A.I.C.S.: 531311
Graham Waddell *(Chm)*

Subsidiary (Domestic):

with You (2)
Hays Business Centre Unit 3/2 4 Hay Avenue, Edinburgh, EH16 4AQ, United Kingdom
Tel.: (44) 1312012931
Web Site: http://www.withyou.support
Healthcare Services
N.A.I.C.S.: 623210
Jane Scott *(Chm)*

Cotman Housing Association Limited (1)
Cotman House Bowthorpe Hall, Bowthorpe Hall Road, Norwich, NR5 9AD, United Kingdom
Tel.: (44) 1603 731699
Web Site: http://www.cotman-housing.org.uk
Emp.: 50
Housing Association & Rented Services
N.A.I.C.S.: 624229
Jane Warnes *(Mng Dir)*

Derwent Facilities Management Limited (1)
1175 Thorpe Park Century Way, Leeds, LS15 8ZB, West Yorkshire, United Kingdom
Tel.: (44) 113 531 1000
Web Site: https://www.derwentfm.com
Commercial Property Development Services
N.A.I.C.S.: 531390

Janice Boucher *(Mng Dir)*

Girlings Retirement Rentals Limited (1)
2 Crescent Office Park Clarks Way, Bath, BA2 2AF, United Kingdom
Tel.: (44) 182 334 6823
Web Site: https://www.girlings.co.uk
Commercial Property Development Services
N.A.I.C.S.: 531390

Millwood Designer Homes Limited (1)
6 Alexander Grove Kings Hill, West Malling, ME19 4XR, Kent, United Kingdom
Tel.: (44) 173 277 0991
Web Site:
   https://www.millwooddesignerhomes.co.uk
Residential Management Services
N.A.I.C.S.: 531311
Chris Pitchford *(Dir)*

Osterna Limited (1)
Chelford House Gadbrook Park, Northwich, CW9 7LN, Cheshire, United Kingdom
Tel.: (44) 345 002 4420
Web Site: https://www.osterna.co.uk
Residential Management Services
N.A.I.C.S.: 531311

PFP Capital Limited (1)
107 Cheapside, London, EC2V 6DN, United Kingdom
Tel.: (44) 207 429 0436
Web Site: https://www.pfpcapital.co.uk
Commercial Property Development Services
N.A.I.C.S.: 531390
Chris Jones *(Mng Dir)*

Places for People Capital Markets Plc (1)
305 Grays Inn Road, London, WC1X 8QR, United Kingdom
Tel.: (44) 20 7843 3800
Residential Property Management Services
N.A.I.C.S.: 531311

Places for People Developments Limited (1)
Saltire Studio 3 Saltire Street, Edinburgh, EH5 1QS, United Kingdom
Tel.: (44) 1315592200
Residential Property Management Services
N.A.I.C.S.: 531311

Places for People Homes Limited (1)
305 Gray's Inn Road, London, WC1X 8QR, United Kingdom
Tel.: (44) 207 843 3800
Web Site: http://www.placesforpeople.co.uk
Sales Range: $350-399.9 Million
Emp.: 1,385
Residential Property Management Services
N.A.I.C.S.: 531311

Subsidiary (Domestic):

Places for People Individual Support Limited (2)
4 The Pavilions Ashton On Ribble, Preston, PR2 2YB, Lancashire, United Kingdom
Tel.: (44) 1254776699
Residential Property Management Services
N.A.I.C.S.: 531311

Places for People Landscapes Limited (2)
Westwood Nurseries Pippin Street, Brindle, Chorley, PR6 8ND, United Kingdom
Tel.: (44) 1772 336647
Residential Property Management Services
N.A.I.C.S.: 531311

Places for People Leisure Management Limited (1)
Waters Edge Riverside Way Watchmoor Park, Camberley, GU15 3YL, Surrey, United Kingdom
Tel.: (44) 1276 418200
Web Site:
   http://www.placesforpeopleleisure.co.uk
Sales Range: $50-74.9 Million
Emp.: 6,500
Leisure Centers Management Services
N.A.I.C.S.: 531312
Sandra Dodd *(CEO)*

Residential Management Group Limited (1)

Essex Road, Hoddesdon, EN11 0DR, Hertfordshire, United Kingdom
Tel.: (44) 345 002 4487
Web Site: http://www.rmgltd.co.uk
Residential Property Management Services
N.A.I.C.S.: 531311
Alan Inglis *(Dir-Fin)*

Residential Management Group Scotland Limited (1)
RMG House Essex Road, Hoddesdon, EN11 0DR, Hertfordshire, United Kingdom
Tel.: (44) 345 002 4499
Web Site: https://www.rmgscotland.com
Residential Management Services
N.A.I.C.S.: 531311
Hugh McGeever *(Mng Dir)*

Tila Commercial Limited (1)
1 Poultry, London, EC2R 8EJ, United Kingdom
Tel.: (44) 203 950 9672
Web Site: https://www.tilacommercial.com
Commercial Property Development Services
N.A.I.C.S.: 531390
Beata Nzekwe *(Head-Accounting)*

Touchstone Corporate Property Services Limited (1)
2 Crescent Office Park Clarks Way, Bath, BA2 2AF, United Kingdom
Tel.: (44) 1225 838 490
Web Site: http://www.touchstonecps.com
Emp.: 530
Residential Property Management Services
N.A.I.C.S.: 531311
Helen Kings *(Mng Dir)*

PLACO CO., LTD

550 Sasakubo Shinden, Iwatsuki-ku, Saitama, 339-8558, Japan
Tel.: (81) 487980222
Web Site: https://www.placo.co.jp
Year Founded: 1960
6347—(TKS)
Sales Range: Less than $1 Million
Emp.: 80
Blow Molding Machinery Mfr
N.A.I.C.S.: 333248
Hideo Kurosawa *(Pres)*

PLAINTREE SYSTEMS INC.

10 Didak Drive, Arnprior, K7S 0C3, ON, Canada
Tel.: (613) 623-3434   Ca
Web Site: https://www.plaintree.com
Year Founded: 1988
PTEEF—(OTCIQ)
Rev.: $17,880,479
Assets: $11,069,385
Liabilities: $10,408,913
Net Worth: $660,472
Earnings: $791,834
Fiscal Year-end: 03/31/24
Infrared Transceivers Mfr for Wireless Networks
N.A.I.C.S.: 334210
William David Watson *(Pres & CEO)*

Subsidiaries:

Hypernetics Ltd. (1)
10 Didak Drive, Arnprior, K7S 0C3, ON, Canada
Tel.: (613) 623-3434
Sales Range: $25-49.9 Million
Emp.: 25
Electromagnetic Indicators Mfr & Distr
N.A.I.C.S.: 334511

Summit Aerospace USA Inc. (1)
137 Market Way, Mount Pocono, PA 18344
Tel.: (570) 839-8615
Sales Range: $1-9.9 Million
Emp.: 43
Aerospace Machinery Mfr
N.A.I.C.S.: 334511

Triodetic Inc (1)
4465 E Genesee St, Syracuse, NY 13214-2253
Web Site: https://triodetic.com
Building Roofs Mfr
N.A.I.C.S.: 332322

INTERNATIONAL PUBLIC

PLAISIO COMPUTERS S.A.

Thesi Sklri, Magoula, 19600, Greece
Tel.: (30) 2105587323
Web Site: http://www.plaisio.gr
Year Founded: 1989
PLAIS—(ATH)
Rev.: $355,162,479
Assets: $223,275,447
Liabilities: $118,681,643
Net Worth: $104,593,804
Earnings: $2,180,367
Emp.: 1,403
Fiscal Year-end: 12/31/19
Computer Peripheral Equipment Whslr
N.A.I.C.S.: 423430
Gerardos Konstantinos Georgios *(Vice Chm & CEO)*

PLAMA-PUR D.D.

Podgrad 17, 6244, Podgrad, Slovenia
Tel.: (386) 5 7149 200
Web Site: http://www.plama-pur.si
Year Founded: 1955
Flexible Polyurethane Foam Mfr
N.A.I.C.S.: 326150
Uros Barba *(Dir)*

PLAN B MEDIA PUBLIC COMPANY LIMITED

No 1213/420 Lat Phrao 94 Sriwara Road Town in Town Village, Plubpla Wangthonglang, Bangkok, 10310, Thailand
Tel.: (66) 253080536
Web Site:
   https://www.planbmedia.co.th
PLANB—(THA)
Rev.: $246,552,199
Assets: $474,215,866
Liabilities: $212,951,726
Net Worth: $261,264,140
Earnings: $27,653,738
Emp.: 944
Fiscal Year-end: 12/31/23
Outdoor Advertising
N.A.I.C.S.: 541850
Palin Lojanagosin *(CEO)*

Subsidiaries:

Golink Online Co., Ltd. (1)
1213/420 Soi Lat Phrao 94 Panchamitra Plubpla, Wang Thonglang, Bangkok, 10310, Thailand
Tel.: (66) 899999199
Web Site: www.golink.co.th
Software Programming Services
N.A.I.C.S.: 541511

Tuna Advertising Co., Ltd. (1)
Village Klang Muang Ladprao 87 580/78 Soi Ladprao 87 Chantrasuk, Khlong Chao Khun Sing Subdistrict Wang Thonglang District, Bangkok, 10310, Thailand
Tel.: (66) 21582978
Web Site: https://tuna.co.th
Advertising Management Services
N.A.I.C.S.: 541810

PLAN OPTIK AG

Ueber Der Bitz 3, 56479, Elsoff, Germany
Tel.: (49) 266450680
Web Site: https://www.planoptik.com
Year Founded: 2005
P4O—(DEU)
Rev.: $14,299,590
Assets: $17,494,064
Liabilities: $4,446,363
Net Worth: $13,047,701
Earnings: $1,802,288
Emp.: 107
Fiscal Year-end: 12/31/23
Glass Wafer Mfr
N.A.I.C.S.: 325180

PLAN SAS

81 rue du Petit Mas Parc d Activite,

Avignon Courtine, BP 70930, Avignon, France
Tel.: (33) 490276900
Web Site: http://www.plan-sas.com
Year Founded: 1920
Sales Range: $50-74.9 Million
Emp.: 200
Horticulture & Gardening Products Mfr
N.A.I.C.S.: 111998
Jean-Claude Plan *(Pres)*

PLANA-INNOVA GMBH
Schnieringshof 12, 45329, Essen, Germany
Tel.: (49) 2018381819
Web Site: http://www.plana-innova.de
Halls & Tents Mfr
N.A.I.C.S.: 314910
Heinz Kremeyer *(Mng Dir)*

Subsidiaries:

plana-innova ag (1)
Werkstrasse 71, CH-3250, Lyss, Switzerland
Tel.: (41) 323873900
Web Site: http://www.plana-innova.de
Halls & Tents Mfr
N.A.I.C.S.: 314910

PLANDAI BIOTECHNOLOGY, INC.
17 Hanover Square, London, W1S 1BN, United Kingdom
Tel.: (44) 2037909494
Web Site: http://www.plandaibiotech.com
PLPL—(OTCIQ)
Sales Range: Less than $1 Million
Proprietary Botanical Extracts Mfr
N.A.I.C.S.: 325412
Roger Baylis-Duffield *(Pres & CEO)*

PLANET BASED FOODS GLOBAL INC.
2250-1055 West Hastings Street, Vancouver, V6E 2E9, BC, Canada
Tel.: (619) 363-7456   BC
Web Site: https://www.planetbasedfoods.com
Year Founded: 2017
PBF—(CNSX)
Rev.: $11,747
Assets: $6,607,745
Liabilities: $755,826
Net Worth: $5,851,919
Earnings: ($4,336,563)
Fiscal Year-end: 12/31/21
Food Products Distr
N.A.I.C.S.: 424490
Braelyn Davis *(Pres & CEO)*

PLANET COMMUNICATIONS ASIA PUBLIC COMPANY LIMITED
157 Soi Ramindra 34 Ramindra Road, Tarang Bangkhen, Bangkok, 10230, Thailand
Tel.: (66) 27922400
Web Site: https://www.planetcomm.com
PLANET—(THA)
Rev.: $16,150,159
Assets: $37,462,649
Liabilities: $22,313,062
Net Worth: $15,149,587
Earnings: ($6,043,038)
Emp.: 167
Fiscal Year-end: 12/31/23
Satellite Communication Consulting, Development & Implementation
N.A.I.C.S.: 517410
Prapat Rathlertkarn *(Vice Chm, Co-Pres & CEO)*

Subsidiaries:

Planet Cloud Company Limited (1)
157 Ramintra Road Soi Ram Inthra 34, Tha Raeng Subdistrict Bang Khen District, Bangkok, 10230, Thailand
Tel.: (66) 27922388
Web Site: https://www.planetcloud.cloud
Information Technology Services
N.A.I.C.S.: 541511

PLANET IMAGE INTERNATIONAL LIMITED
No 756 Guangfu Road Hi-tech Development Zone, Xinyu, Jiangxi, China
Tel.: (86) 7907138216   Ky
Year Founded: 2019
Rev.: $132,791,000
Assets: $112,375,000
Liabilities: $100,073,000
Net Worth: $12,302,000
Earnings: $4,234,000
Emp.: 1,317
Fiscal Year-end: 12/31/20
Holding Company
N.A.I.C.S.: 551112
Weidong Gu *(Co-Founder & Chm)*

PLANET PAYMENT GROUP HOLDINGS LTD.
Martin House IDA Business Park Dangan, Galway, H91 A06C, Ireland
Tel.: (353) 91 558 233
Web Site: http://www.planetpayment.com
Tax Services
N.A.I.C.S.: 541213
Patrick Waldron *(CEO)*

Subsidiaries:

Planet Payment Inc. (1)
670 Long Beach Blvd, Long Beach, NY 11561
Tel.: (516) 670-3200
Web Site: http://www.planetpayment.com
Sales Range: $50-74.9 Million
Multi-Currency Payment Processing Services
N.A.I.C.S.: 522320
E. Drew Soinski *(Mng Dir-Wholesale)*

PLANET VENTURES INC.
750 West Pender Street Suite 303, Vancouver, V6C 2T7, BC, Canada
Tel.: (604) 681-0084   BC
Web Site: https://www.planetventuresinc.com
Year Founded: 1996
PNXPF—(OTCIQ)
Rev.: $229,017
Assets: $4,830,300
Liabilities: $488,624
Net Worth: $4,341,676
Earnings: ($1,354,245)
Fiscal Year-end: 03/31/23
Gold Exploration Services
N.A.I.C.S.: 212220
Zula Kropivnitski *(CFO & Sec)*

PLANETA CORPORACION SRL
Av Diagonal 662-664, 08034, Barcelona, Spain
Tel.: (34) 934928000   ES
Web Site: http://www.planeta.es
Year Founded: 1949
Publishing & Communication Services
N.A.I.C.S.: 513130
Jose Manuel Lara *(Founder)*

PLANETEL S.P.A.
Via Boffalora 4, Treviolo, 24048, Bergamo, Italy
Tel.: (39) 035204070
Web Site: https://www.planetel.it
Year Founded: 2001
PLN—(EUR)

Emp.: 150
Telecommunication Servicesb
N.A.I.C.S.: 517810
Bruno Mario Pianetti *(CEO)*

Subsidiaries:

Sitis S.R.L. (1)
Via Boffalora, 4 24048, Treviolo, Italy
Tel.: (39) 035204033
Web Site: https://www.sitis.it
Emp.: 27
Telecommunication Servicesb
N.A.I.C.S.: 517810

PLANETMEDIA SA
47 rue de la Chaussee d Antin, 75009, Paris, France
Tel.: (33) 1 53 06 62 66
Web Site: http://www.planet.fr
ALPLA—(EUR)
Sales Range: $1-9.9 Million
Website Owner & Operator
N.A.I.C.S.: 518210
Thierry Casseville *(Chm-Exec Bd)*

PLANETREE INTERNATIONAL DEVELOPMENT LIMITED
8th Floor China United Centre 28 Marble Road North Point, Hong Kong, China (Hong Kong)
Tel.: (852) 31980238   BM
Web Site: http://www.planetreeintl.com
0613—(HKG)
Rev.: $19,804,193
Assets: $307,624,605
Liabilities: $37,294,388
Net Worth: $270,330,218
Earnings: ($195,330)
Emp.: 44
Fiscal Year-end: 12/31/22
Property Investment & Management Services
N.A.I.C.S.: 523940
Hiu Lo Lam *(Exec Dir)*

PLANIGRUPO LATAM SAB DE CV
Av Conscripto 360 Paseo Hipodromo PB local SA002 Col Lomas Hipodromo, Naucalpan de Juarez, 53900, Mexico, Mexico
Tel.: (52) 5591770870
Web Site: https://www.planigrupo.com.mx
Year Founded: 1975
PLAN—(MEX)
Real Estate Manangement Services
N.A.I.C.S.: 531390
Karime Garza Serna *(Dir-Ops)*

PLANINKA A.D.
Kosovska 38, Kursumlija, Serbia
Tel.: (381) 27 381 344
Web Site: http://www.planinka.rs
Year Founded: 1964
Sales Range: $10-24.9 Million
Beverage Product & Bottled Water Mfr
N.A.I.C.S.: 312112

PLANINSKO DOBRO GACKO A.D.
Tel.: (387) 59472365
Year Founded: 2001
PLDG-R-A—(BANJ)
Sales Range: Less than $1 Million
Emp.: 15
Dairy Cattle Farming Services
N.A.I.C.S.: 112120
Desimir Kovacevic *(Chm-Mgmt Bd)*

PLANSEE HOLDING AG
6600 Reutte, Reutte, 6600, Tirol, Austria
Tel.: (43) 56726000

Web Site: http://www.plansee.com
Sales Range: $1-4.9 Billion
Emp.: 6,000
Powder Metallurgical Products & Components
N.A.I.C.S.: 332117

Subsidiaries:

Ceratazit S.A. (1)
Rte de Holzem BP 51, 8201, Mamer, Luxembourg
Tel.: (352) 3120851
Web Site: http://www.ceratizit.com
Emp.: 1,100
Cutting Tool & Wear Protection Metal Component Mfr
N.A.I.C.S.: 332999

Subsidiary (Non-US):

CERATIZIT America Latina Ltda. (2)
Praca das Orquideas 52 Terreo-Centro Comercial de Alphaville, Barueri, 06453-002, Sao Paulo, Brazil
Tel.: (55) 11 4133 2300
Web Site: http://www.ceratizit.com
Emp.: 20
Building Materials Distr
N.A.I.C.S.: 423320
Alain Breton *(Mgr-Wood & Stone)*

CERATIZIT Deutschland GmbH (2)
Robert-Bosch-Strasse 23, 72186, Empfingen, Germany
Tel.: (49) 7485 9980 20
Machine Tools Mfr
N.A.I.C.S.: 333517
Frank Taome *(Gen Mgr)*

CERATIZIT Hitzacker GmbH (2)
Am Rasenberg 3, 29456, Hitzacker, Germany
Tel.: (49) 5862 969 10 0
Machine Tools Mfr
N.A.I.C.S.: 333517

CERATIZIT Iberica S.L. (2)
Via de las Dos Castillas 9c Portal 2 Piso 1 C, Pozuelo de Alarcon, 28224, Madrid, Spain
Tel.: (34) 91 351 0609
Metal Product Distr
N.A.I.C.S.: 423510

CERATIZIT India Pvt. Ltd. (2)
58 Motilal Gupta Road, Barisha, Kolkata, 700 008, India
Tel.: (91) 33 2494 0335
Industrial Machinery & Equipment Distr
N.A.I.C.S.: 423830

CERATIZIT Italia S.p.A. (2)
Via Milanese 6, Alserio, 22040, Como, Italy
Tel.: (39) 031 6349 211
Web Site: http://www.ceratizit.com
Emp.: 25
Metal Product Distr
N.A.I.C.S.: 423510
Josef Laemmle *(Mng Dir)*

CERATIZIT Japan Ltd. (2)
3-13-9 Mizuho, Shizuoka, 421-0115, Japan
Tel.: (81) 54 268 1060
Metal Product Distr
N.A.I.C.S.: 423510

CERATIZIT Logistik GmbH (2)
Daimlerstrasse 70, 87437, Kempten, Germany
Tel.: (49) 831 570 11 0
Logistics Consulting Servies
N.A.I.C.S.: 541614

CERATIZIT Mexico, S.A. de C.V. (2)
Calle Rufino Tamayo N 19 Fraccionamiento Pueblo Nuevo, Corregidora, 76040, Queretaro, Mexico
Tel.: (52) 442 225 9173
Metal Product Distr
N.A.I.C.S.: 423510

CERATIZIT Nederland B.V. (2)
Bergrand 224, 4707 AT, Roosendaal, Netherlands
Tel.: (31) 1655 508 00
Metal Product Distr
N.A.I.C.S.: 423510

CERATIZIT Schweiz AG (2)

PLANSEE HOLDING AG — INTERNATIONAL PUBLIC

PLANSEE Holding AG—(Continued)
Hauptstrasse 211, 2552, Orpund, Switzerland
Tel.: (41) 32 344 93 93
Metal Product Distr
N.A.I.C.S.: 423510

CERATIZIT UK Ltd. (2)
Sheffield Business Park Europa Link, Sheffield, S9 1XU, United Kingdom
Tel.: (44) 1142428820
Web Site: http://www.ceratizit.com
Emp.: 3
Metal Product Distr
N.A.I.C.S.: 423510
Nathan Paxton (Gen Mgr)

Subsidiary (US):

CERATIZIT USA, Inc. (2)
11350 Stephens Rd, Warren, MI 48089
Tel.: (586) 759-2280
Machine Tool Distr
N.A.I.C.S.: 423830

Subsidiary (Domestic):

Best Carbide Cutting Tools, Inc. (3)
1454 W 135th St, Gardena, CA 90249
Tel.: (310) 324-6631
Web Site: http://www.bestcarbide.com
Sales Range: $1-9.9 Million
Emp.: 60
Machine Tool (Metal Cutting Types) Mfr
N.A.I.C.S.: 333517
Mark A. Nunez (Pres)

Subsidiary (Domestic):

CERATOOL S.a r.l. (2)
Rue Geespelt 7, 3378, Livange, Luxembourg
Tel.: (352) 51 73 48
Machine Tools Mfr
N.A.I.C.S.: 333517

CERATUNGSTEN S.a r.l. (2)
Zone Industrielle Haneboesch Route de Bascharage, 4562, Niedercorn, Luxembourg
Tel.: (352) 58 53 15
Machine Tools Mfr
N.A.I.C.S.: 333517

Subsidiary (US):

PCT-GW Carbide Tools USA, Inc (2)
13701 Excelsior Dr, Santa Fe Springs, CA 90670
Tel.: (562) 921-7898
Metal Product Distr
N.A.I.C.S.: 423510
Chirayu Shah (Engr-Mfr)

PROMAX Tools L.P. (2)
11312 Sunrise Gold Cir, Rancho Cordova, CA 95742
Tel.: (916) 638-0501
Web Site: http://www.promaxtools.com
Machine Tools Mfr
N.A.I.C.S.: 333517
Nancy Owens (Pres)

Subsidiary (Non-US):

VIMIKE SA (2)
Filikon 5, Peristeri, 12131, Athens, Greece
Tel.: (30) 2105 751 920
Metal Product Distr
N.A.I.C.S.: 423510
Siggeniotis Kostas (Gen Mgr)

Subsidiary (US):

Xceliron Corp. (2)
9540 Vassar Ave, Chatsworth, CA 91311-4141
Tel.: (818) 700-8404
Web Site: http://www.xceliron.com
Machine Tools Mfr
N.A.I.C.S.: 333517
Randy Jones (Mng Dir)

Global Tungsten & Powders Corp. (1)
1 Hawes St, Towanda, PA 18848
Tel.: (570) 268-5000
Web Site: http://www.globaltungsten.com
Refractory Material Mfr
N.A.I.C.S.: 332117
Andreas Lackner (Pres & CEO)

Subsidiary (Non-US):

Global Tungsten & Powders spol. s r.o. (2)
Zahradni 1442/46, Bruntal, 792 01, Czech Republic
Tel.: (420) 555 559 301
Refractory Material Distr
N.A.I.C.S.: 423840
Stepan Pelc (Mgr-Sls & Mktg)

PLANSEE Bondingshop K.K. (1)
1622-1 Mutsuzaki Sakura, Chiba, 285-0812, Japan
Tel.: (81) 4 3483 5691
Web Site: http://www.plansee.com
Emp.: 20
Metal Plating Services
N.A.I.C.S.: 332812
Shiro Furusawa (Gen Mgr)

PLANSEE China Ltd. (1)
Rm 1201-1203 Hollywood Centre 233 Hollywood Rd, Sheung Wan, Hong Kong, China (Hong Kong)
Tel.: (852) 2542 1838
Refractory Material Mfr
N.A.I.C.S.: 327120

PLANSEE Composite Materials GmbH (1)
Siebenburgerstrasse 23, 86983, Lechbruck, Germany
Tel.: (49) 8862 773 0
Web Site: http://www.plansee-cm.com
Powder Metallurgical Component Mfr
N.A.I.C.S.: 332117
Mathias Hochstrasser (Mng Dir)

PLANSEE India HPM Pvt. Ltd. (1)
Plot No 311 Hebbal Industrial Area, Metagalli Post, Mysore, 570016, India
Tel.: (91) 8212513746
Web Site: http://www.plansee.com
Emp.: 270
Metallic Wire Mfr
N.A.I.C.S.: 331492
Mahadeva Kothegala (Gen Mgr-Fin & Comml)

PLANSEE Japan Ltd. (1)
Ark Hills Sengokuyama Mori Tower 1-9-10 Roppongi, Minato-ku, Tokyo, 106-0032, Japan
Tel.: (81) 3 3568 2451
Powder Metallurgical Component Mfr
N.A.I.C.S.: 332117

PLANSEE Korea HPM Inc. (1)
PLANSEE Korea Bonding 2Ba-904 Shiwalndustrial Park 2203-4, Jeongwang-Dong, Siheung, 429-926, Kyunggi-Do, Korea (South)
Tel.: (82) 31 433 1281
Web Site: http://www.plansee.co.kr
Powder Metallurgical Component Mfr
N.A.I.C.S.: 332117

PLANSEE MW GmbH (1)
Boulevard Stoletov 157, 5301, Gabrovo, Bulgaria
Tel.: (359) 66812 313
Refractory Material Mfr
N.A.I.C.S.: 327120

PLANSEE Mexico S.A. de C.V. (1)
Rufino Tamayo 19 Pueblo Nuevo, 76040, Queretaro, Mexico
Tel.: (52) 442 295 8991
Refractory Material Distr
N.A.I.C.S.: 423840
Adriana Archila (Mgr-Admin)

PLANSEE Nederland (1)
Markerkant 1201 38, 1314 AJ, Almere, Netherlands
Tel.: (31) 36 534 5691
Metal Product Distr
N.A.I.C.S.: 423510
Astrid Van Zoomeren (Brand Mgr)

PLANSEE Powertech AG (1)
Retterswil 13, 5703, Seon, Switzerland
Tel.: (41) 62 769 60 80
Web Site: http://www.plansee-powertech.com
Metal Plating Services
N.A.I.C.S.: 332812

PLANSEE SE (1)
Mitallwerk Plansee 71, Reutte, 6600, Tirol, Austria
Tel.: (43) 56726000
Web Site: http://www.plansee.com
Sales Range: $400-449.9 Million
Emp.: 2,000
Refractory Metal & Composite Material Products Mfr
N.A.I.C.S.: 332117
Michael Schwarzkopf (Chm-Exec Bd)

Subsidiary (US):

PLANSEE USA LLC (2)
115 Constitution Blvd, Franklin, MA 02038
Tel.: (508) 553-3800
Web Site: http://www.plansee.com
Sales Range: $25-49.9 Million
Emp.: 100
Refractory Metal & Composite Material Products Mfr
N.A.I.C.S.: 332117
Egon Okorn (Pres & CEO)

Subsidiary (Domestic):

PLANSEE Thermal Management Solutions Inc. (1)
10113 Carroll Canyon Rd, San Diego, CA 92131-1109
Tel.: (858) 271-1993
Web Site: http://www.plansee-tms.com
Sales Range: $50-74.9 Million
Thermal Management Material Mfr
N.A.I.C.S.: 332117
Vim Dutt (Pres & CEO)

PLANSEE Shanghai High Performance Materials Ltd. (1)
No 555 Yitian Road Lingang Industrial Zone, Shanghai, 201306, China
Tel.: (86) 21 6023 0666
Refractory Material Mfr
N.A.I.C.S.: 327120

PLANSEE South America Ltda. (1)
Rua Alvaro Anes 46 - cj 23, Pinheiros, 05421-010, Sao Paulo, Brazil
Tel.: (55) 11 3819 4051
Web Site: http://www.plansee.com
Emp.: 2
Metal Product Distr
N.A.I.C.S.: 423510
Elisio Ferreira Neto (Mng Dir)

PLANSEE Taiwan Co., Ltd. (1)
Taipei World Trade Center Hsin-Yi Rd Sec 5, No 5 Room 7C25, Taipei, 00110, Taiwan
Tel.: (886) 2 8780 8979
Metal Product Distr
N.A.I.C.S.: 423510
Jerry Tsai (Mgr)

PLANSEE Tungsten Alloys SAS (1)
la marque de CIME BOCUZE 446 avenue des Digues, BP 301, 74807, Saint-Pierre-en-Faucigny, France
Tel.: (33) 4 5025 3700
Web Site: http://www.plansee-ta.com
Composite Material Mfr
N.A.I.C.S.: 332117

Plansee Mitsubishi Materials Global Sinter Holding, S.A. (1)
101 Route de Holzem, 8232, Mamer, Luxembourg
Tel.: (352) 26394012
Web Site: http://www.pmgsinter.com
Sales Range: $200-249.9 Million
Emp.: 1,000
Powder Metallurgical Component Mfr
N.A.I.C.S.: 332117

WNT Ceska republika s.r.o. (1)
Sokolovska 250, 594 01, Velke Mezirici, Czech Republic
Tel.: (420) 566 522 411
Web Site: http://www.wnt.com
Industrial Supplies Whslr
N.A.I.C.S.: 423840

WNT France S.A.S. (1)
20 Rue Lavoisier, 95300, Pontoise, France
Tel.: (33) 1 34 20 14 40
Web Site: http://www.wnt.com
Industrial Supplies Whslr
N.A.I.C.S.: 423840

WNT Iberica S.L. (1)
Via de las Dos Castillas 9c Portal 2 Piso 1D, Pozuelo de Alarcon, 28224, Madrid, Spain
Tel.: (34) 91 352 54 73
Web Site: http://www.wnt.com
Industrial Supplies Whslr
N.A.I.C.S.: 423840
Elena Gonzalo Symth (Mgr-Cutomer Svc)

WNT Italia S.p.A. (1)
Via C Cantu 29, 20092, Cinisello Balsamo, Italy
Tel.: (39) 02 641673 1
Web Site: http://www.wnt.com
Industrial Supplies Whslr
N.A.I.C.S.: 423840

WNT Onasya Kesici Takimlar San.ve Tic. Ltd. Sti. (1)
Serifali Mah Hattat Sok No 16/2, Umraniye, 34775, Istanbul, Turkiye
Tel.: (90) 216 526 63 05
Web Site: http://www.wnt.com
Industrial Supplies Whslr
N.A.I.C.S.: 423840

WNT Polska Sp. z o.o. (1)
ul Jozefa Marcika 2, 30-443, Krakow, Poland
Tel.: (48) 12 2528570
Web Site: http://www.wnt.com
Industrial Supplies Whslr
N.A.I.C.S.: 423840

WNT Scandinavia AB (1)
Munkerodsvagen 27, 444 32, Stenungsund, Sweden
Tel.: (46) 303 726 360
Web Site: http://www.wnt.com
Industrial Supplies Whslr
N.A.I.C.S.: 423840

Wincut Machining Solutions India Pvt. Ltd. (1)
P-107 Lake Terrace, Kolkata, 700029, India
Tel.: (91) 33 4061 4553
Web Site: http://www.wnt.com
Industrial Supplies Whslr
N.A.I.C.S.: 423840

PLANT ADVANCED TECHNOLOGIES SA

19 avenue de la Foret de Haye, 54500, Nancy, France
Tel.: (33) 383940342
Web Site:
    https://www.plantadvanced.com
Year Founded: 2005
ALPAT—(EUR)
Sales Range: $1-9.9 Million
Emp.: 10
Plant Extract Pharmaceutical & Cosmetics Products Mfr
N.A.I.C.S.: 541715
Jean-Paul Fevre (Founder & Pres)

Subsidiaries:

Couleurs de Plantes SAS (1)
18 rue de l Arsenal, ZI de l'Arsenal, 17300, Rochefort, France
Tel.: (33) 546993249
Web Site: http://www.couleurs-de-plantes.com
Chemical Products Mfr
N.A.I.C.S.: 325199

Straticell SA/NV (1)
Science Park Crealys Rue Jean Sonet 10 Les Isnes, 5032, Gembloux, Belgium
Tel.: (32) 81728582
Web Site: http://www.straticell.com
Pharmaceuticals Product Mfr
N.A.I.C.S.: 325412
Michel Salmon (Founder & CEO)

Temisis Therapeutics SA (1)
19 avenue de la Foret de Haye, Vandoeuvre-les, 54500, Nancy, France
Tel.: (33) 383940342
Web Site: http://www.temisis.com
Biotechnology Research & Development Services
N.A.I.C.S.: 541713
Paul Hannewald (CEO)

PLANT CO., LTD.

15-8-1 Shimoshinjo Sakai-cho, Sakai, 919-0521, Fukui, Japan
Tel.: (81) 776720300
Web Site: https://www.plant-co.jp
Year Founded: 1982
7646—(TKS)
Sales Range: $700-749.9 Million
Emp.: 620
Departmental Store Operator
N.A.I.C.S.: 455110
Masami Mitsuta *(Pres)*

PLANT VEDA FOODS LTD.
1668 Fosters Way, Delta, V3M 6S6, BC, Canada
Tel.: (604) 200-3335   BC
Web Site: https://www.plantveda.com
Year Founded: 2019
PLVFF—(OTCIQ)
Rev.: $230,236
Assets: $2,520,350
Liabilities: $2,670,119
Net Worth: ($149,769)
Earnings: ($2,961,819)
Fiscal Year-end: 12/31/22
Food Product Mfr & Distr
N.A.I.C.S.: 311412

PLANT-BASED INVESTMENT CORP.
240 Richmond Street West Suite 4164, Toronto, M5V 1V6, ON, Canada
Tel.: (647) 660-0566
Web Site: http://cgocorp.com
CGOC—(CNSX)
Rev.: $330,599
Assets: $19,233,546
Liabilities: $1,605,408
Net Worth: $17,628,138
Earnings: ($6,094,289)
Fiscal Year-end: 10/31/19
Financial Investment Services
N.A.I.C.S.: 523999

PLANTARC BIO LTD.
Birkat Am St 61-63, Givat Hen, Ra'anana, Israel
Tel.: (972) 98320911
Web Site: https://www.plantarcbio.com
Year Founded: 2014
PLNT—(TAE)
Rev.: $1,320,072
Assets: $3,643,321
Liabilities: $339,550
Net Worth: $3,303,771
Earnings: ($582,401)
Fiscal Year-end: 12/31/23
Bio Technology Services
N.A.I.C.S.: 541714
Oded Shoseyov *(Chm)*

PLANTFUEL LIFE INC.
2500 Meadowpine Blvd Unit 202, Mississauga, L5N 6C4, ON, Canada
Tel.: (416) 262-0871   BC
Web Site: http://sirebioscience.com
Year Founded: 2014
SIRE—(CNSX)
Rev.: $2,849
Assets: $5,845,797
Liabilities: $3,843,800
Net Worth: $2,001,997
Earnings: ($4,894,557)
Fiscal Year-end: 09/30/19
Digital Product Researcher & Developer; Software Solutions
N.A.I.C.S.: 513210

PLANTHEON CO., LTD.
195 Empire Tower 43rd Floor, Yannawa Sathorn, Bangkok, 10120, Thailand
Tel.: (66) 22877000
Web Site: http://www.plantheon.co.th
Emp.: 100

Agricultural Plantation & All Other Agricultural Product Trading
N.A.I.C.S.: 111998
Subsidiaries:

Siam Food Products Public Company Limited   (1)
1 Empire Tower 43rd Floor South Sathorn Road Yannawa, Sathorn, Bangkok, 10120, Thailand   **(100%)**
Tel.: (66) 22877000
Web Site: http://www.siamfood.co.th
Rev.: $77,624,197
Assets: $57,962,574
Liabilities: $11,296,386
Net Worth: $46,666,187
Earnings: ($1,974,305)
Emp.: 501
Fiscal Year-end: 09/30/2023
Food Products Mfr
N.A.I.C.S.: 311999
Thien Mekanontchai *(Chm & Chm-Exec Bd)*

PLANTX LIFE INC.
100 Park Royal S Suite 504, West Vancouver, V7T 1A2, BC, Canada
Tel.: (604) 355-6100   BC
Web Site: https://www.plantx.com
Year Founded: 2011
WNT—(DEU)
Rev.: $5,394,597
Assets: $1,660,341
Liabilities: $10,576,710
Net Worth: ($8,916,369)
Earnings: ($3,704,447)
Emp.: 80
Fiscal Year-end: 03/31/24
Holding Company; Plant-Based Products Online Retailer
N.A.I.C.S.: 551112
Lorne Rapkin *(CFO)*
Subsidiaries:

EH Coffee Inc.   (1)
163 Sterling Road Unit 161, Toronto, M6R 2B2, ON, Canada
Tel.: (416) 399-1936
Web Site: https://ehroasters.com
Coffee Product Mfr & Distr
N.A.I.C.S.: 311920

PlantX Living Inc.   (1)
100 Park Royal S Suite 504, West Vancouver, V7T 1A2, BC, Canada   **(100%)**
Web Site: https://www.plantx.com
Sales Range: Less than $1 Million
Plant-Based Products Online Retailer
N.A.I.C.S.: 445110
Sean Dollinger *(Founder)*

Portfolio Coffee Inc.   (1)
163 Sterling Rd Unit 161, Toronto, M6R 2B2, ON, Canada
Tel.: (416) 616-2920
Web Site: https://portfoliocoffee.ca
Coffee Product Mfr & Distr
N.A.I.C.S.: 311920

PLANTYNET CO. LTD.
6FL U-Space 2A 670 Daewangpangyo-ro, Bundang-gu, Seongnam, 13494, Gyeonggi-do, Korea (South)
Tel.: (82) 7044897000   KR
Web Site: https://www.plantynet.com
Year Founded: 2000
075130—(KRS)
Rev.: $24,487,579
Assets: $70,103,921
Liabilities: $10,772,687
Net Worth: $59,331,234
Earnings: ($1,195,175)
Emp.: 80
Fiscal Year-end: 12/31/22
Internet Services
N.A.I.C.S.: 513199
Tae Joo Kim *(CEO)*
Subsidiaries:

Beijing Plantynet Co., Ltd   (1)
Room701 Building4 China Central Plaza 89 Jianguo Road, Chaoyang, Beijing, China
Tel.: (86) 10 62698388
Web Site: http://www.plantynet.com.cn
Information Technology Consulting Services
N.A.I.C.S.: 541512
Terry Chul Rhee *(CEO)*

PLASAN SASA LTD.
Kibbutz, Sasa, 13870, Israel
Tel.: (972) 4 6809000
Web Site: http://www.plasan.com
Year Founded: 1985
Vehicle Armor Mfr
N.A.I.C.S.: 336992
Dan Ziv *(CEO)*
Subsidiaries:

Plasan North America, Inc.   (1)
222 Bowen Rd, Bennington, VT 05201
Tel.: (802) 445-3095
Web Site: http://www.plasansasa.com
Sales Range: $50-74.9 Million
Emp.: 115
Vehicle Armor Mfr
N.A.I.C.S.: 336992

Plasan USA, Inc.   (1)
139 Shields Dr, Bennington, VT 05201
Tel.: (802) 445-1700
Web Site: http://www.plasancarbon.com
Sales Range: $25-49.9 Million
Emp.: 70
Carbon Fiber Automotive Part Mfr
N.A.I.C.S.: 336211
Robert Willig *(Pres & CEO)*

PLASCAR PARTICIPACOES INDUSTRIAIS S.A.
Av Wilhelm Winter 300 Distrito Industrial, Jundiai, 13213-000, Brazil
Tel.: (55) 21525300   BR
Web Site: https://www.plascar.com.br
PLAS3—(BRAZ)
Rev.: $169,147,472
Assets: $144,678,632
Liabilities: $226,155,748
Net Worth: ($81,477,116)
Earnings: ($19,368,033)
Emp.: 2,186
Fiscal Year-end: 12/31/22
Automotive Parts Mfr & Sales
N.A.I.C.S.: 336310
Paulo Silvestri *(Chm)*

PLASCOBEL BVBA
Fabrieksstraat 145, Overpelt, 3990, Belgium
Tel.: (32) 11660711   BE
Web Site: http://www.plascobel.be
Year Founded: 1958
Sales Range: $10-24.9 Million
Emp.: 100
Injection Moulding Products
N.A.I.C.S.: 326199
Tony Beeuwsaert *(Gen Mgr)*

PLASMAPP CO., LTD.
13F 476 Gangnam-daero, Gangnam-gu, Seoul, 06120, Korea (South)
Tel.: (82) 7050574404
Web Site: https://www.plasmapp.com
Year Founded: 2014
405000—(KRS)
Software Development Services
N.A.I.C.S.: 541511
Seongho Han *(Head)*

PLASMEQ PJSC
ul Stanislavskogo d 3/9, Moscow, 109004, Russia
Tel.: (7) 4955405519
Web Site: http://www.plasmeq.ru
Industrial Equipment Mfr & Distr
N.A.I.C.S.: 333992

PLASSON INDUSTRIES LTD.
Maagan Michael D N Menashe, Tel Aviv, 3780500, Israel
Tel.: (972) 46394711

Web Site: https://www.plasson.com
Year Founded: 1963
PLSN—(TAE)
Rev.: $445,979,340
Assets: $589,421,127
Liabilities: $269,200,423
Net Worth: $320,220,704
Earnings: $34,588,146
Emp.: 2,000
Fiscal Year-end: 09/30/23
Plastic Product Mfr & Distr
N.A.I.C.S.: 326130
Gal Wexsler *(CEO)*
Subsidiaries:

Plasson (Qingdao) Livestock Technology Co., Ltd.   (1)
Songshan Rd West Liuting Airport Industrial Park, Qingdao, Shandong, China
Tel.: (86) 53267762109
Web Site: https://www.plasson.cn
Poultry Farm Equipment Mfr & Distr
N.A.I.C.S.: 333111

Plasson Italia S.r.l.   (1)
Via Fabbriche 22, 15069, Serravalle Scrivia, Italy
Tel.: (39) 0143609920
Web Site: https://www.plasson.it
Fitting Tubing Mfr
N.A.I.C.S.: 332919

Plasson Polska Sp. z o.o.   (1)
ul Julianowska 37a, 05-500, Piaseczno, Poland
Tel.: (48) 227279064
Web Site: https://www.plasson.pl
Fitting Tubing Mfr & Distr
N.A.I.C.S.: 332919

Plasson Romania SRL   (1)
Strada Margeanului 32A, 430013, Baia Mare, Romania
Tel.: (40) 262220329
Web Site: https://www.plasson.ro
Fitting Tubing Mfr
N.A.I.C.S.: 332919

PLASTEC TECHNOLOGIES, LTD.
Unit 01 21/F Aitken Vanson Centre 61 Hoi Yuen Road, Kwun Tong, Kowloon, China (Hong Kong)
Tel.: (852) 21917155   Ky
Web Site: https://www.plastec.com.hk
Year Founded: 1993
PLTYF—(OTCIQ)
Rev.: $14,446
Assets: $13,194,783
Liabilities: $1,566,592
Net Worth: $11,628,192
Earnings: ($387,069)
Fiscal Year-end: 12/31/21
Plastics Product Mfr
N.A.I.C.S.: 326199
Kin Sun Sze-To *(Chm, CEO & COO)*

PLASTECH HOLDING GMBH
Am Hof 4, 1010, Vienna, Austria
Tel.: (43) 405 97 71 0   AU
Web Site: http://www.plastech.at
Holding Company
N.A.I.C.S.: 551112
Paul Neumann *(Co-Owner)*
Subsidiaries:

PLASTECH Beteiligungs GmbH   (1)
Am Hof 4, 1010, Vienna, Austria
Tel.: (43) 1 405 9771 0
Web Site: http://www.plastech.at
Investment Services
N.A.I.C.S.: 523999
Rudolf Knunz *(CEO)*

Subsidiary (Non-US):

Kautex Maschinenbau GmbH   (2)
Kautexstrasse 54, D-53229, Bonn, Germany   **(74.9%)**
Tel.: (49) 2284890
Web Site: http://www.kautex-group.com
Blow Molding Machines Mfr
N.A.I.C.S.: 333511

PLASTECH HOLDING GMBH

PLASTECH Holding GmbH—(Continued)
Andreas Lichtenauer *(Mng Partner)*

Subsidiary (Non-US):

Kautex Italy (3)
Via Carlo Ferrari 12, 21057, Olgiate Olona, Italy
Tel.: (39) 0331 642046
Web Site: http://www.kautex-group.com
Plastic Product Distr
N.A.I.C.S.: 424610

OOO Kautex Maschinenbau (3)
Medovy Pereulok 5 Building 1 5th Floor Business Center ULEJ, 107023, Moscow, Russia
Tel.: (7) 8124680050
Web Site: http://www.kautex-group.com
Plastic Product Distr
N.A.I.C.S.: 424610

Shunde Kautex Plastics Technology Co., Ltd. (3)
Fu'An Industrial District, Shunde, Foshan, Guangdong, China
Tel.: (86) 75727330910
Web Site: http://www.kautex-group.com
Emp.: 130
Plastic Product Distr
N.A.I.C.S.: 424610

PLASTENE INDIA LIMITED
HB Jirawla House 13 Navbharat Society Opp Panchshil Bus Stop, Usmanpura, Ahmedabad, 380 013, Gujarat, India
Tel.: (91) 79 27550764
Web Site: http://www.champalalgroup.com
Sales Range: $150-199.9 Million
Emp.: 1,135
Plastic Packaging
N.A.I.C.S.: 322220
Champalal G. Parekh *(Chm)*

PLASTIBLENDS INDIA LIMITED
Fortune Terraces A-Wing 10th Floor Opp Citi Mall, Link Road Andheri West, Mumbai, 400 053, India
Tel.: (91) 2226736468
Web Site: https://www.plastiblends.com
523648—(BOM)
Rev.: $92,767,292
Assets: $58,083,772
Liabilities: $10,733,086
Net Worth: $47,350,686
Earnings: $3,219,351
Emp.: 468
Fiscal Year-end: 03/31/23
Masterbatches Mfr
N.A.I.C.S.: 339999
Shreevallabh G. Kabra *(Chm)*

Subsidiaries:

Plastiblends India Limited - Works I (1)
74/1 74/2 & 75/3 Daman Industrial Estate, Kadaiya Village, Daman, 396210, India
Tel.: (91) 260 222 1772
Web Site: http://www.plastiblends.com
Emp.: 450
Plastic Colorants Mfr
N.A.I.C.S.: 325998
S. V. Kabra *(Chm)*

Plastiblends India Limited - Works II (1)
Khasara No 216 Raipur Bhagwanpur, Roorkee, Haridwar, 247667, Uttarakhand, India
Tel.: (91) 1332 235046
Web Site: http://www.plastiblends.com
Plastic Colorants Mfr
N.A.I.C.S.: 325998

PLASTICOS COMPUESTOS, S.A.
Carrer de l'Orfebreria 3, Palau Solita i Plegamans, 08184, Barcelona, Spain
Tel.: (34) 938639670
Web Site: https://www.kompuestos.com
Year Founded: 2007
ALKOM—(EUR)
Rev.: $72,360,578
Assets: $51,004,883
Liabilities: $32,820,087
Net Worth: $18,184,796
Earnings: ($451,755)
Emp.: 80
Fiscal Year-end: 12/31/21
Plastics Product Mfr
N.A.I.C.S.: 326199
Ignacio Duch Tuesta *(Chm)*

PLASTIGRAY
Zac De Gray Sud, 70100, Gray, Haute Saone, France
Tel.: (33) 384647700
Web Site: http://www.plastigray.com
Rev.: $24,500,000
Emp.: 134
Design, Industrialization & Manufacture of Structural Parts & Technical Parts in Plastic Injection
N.A.I.C.S.: 326199
Emmanuel Gauss *(Mgr-Mktg)*

PLASTIKA A.S.
Novozamocka 222C, PO Box 52, 949 05, Nitra, Slovakia
Tel.: (421) 376513818
Web Site: http://www.plastika.sk
Plastic Pipes Distr
N.A.I.C.S.: 423320
Roman Sustek *(Chm-Mgmt Bd)*

PLASTIKA KRITIS S.A.
P Street Industrial Zone, 714 08, Iraklion, Crete, Greece
Tel.: (30) 2810308500
Web Site: https://www.plastikakritis.com
Year Founded: 1970
PLAKR—(ATH)
Rev.: $410,270,449
Assets: $518,037,311
Liabilities: $59,958,053
Net Worth: $458,079,258
Earnings: $46,897,009
Emp.: 1,201
Fiscal Year-end: 12/31/23
Plastics Product Mfr
N.A.I.C.S.: 326199

Subsidiaries:

Agripolyane SA (1)
Z I Le Clos Marquet, PO Box 188, 42408, Saint-Chamond, Cedex, France
Tel.: (33) 477311000
Web Site: https://www.agripolyane.com
Plastics Product Mfr
N.A.I.C.S.: 326199

Global Colors Polska SA (1)
ul Szkolna 15, 47-225, Kedzierzyn-Kozle, Poland
Tel.: (48) 774886616
Web Site: https://globalcolors.pl
Emp.: 500
Masterbatch Product Mfr
N.A.I.C.S.: 325211
Tomasz Barciak *(Mgr-Sls)*

Senkroma SA (1)
Beykujduzu Organize Sanayi Bolgesi Mermerciler Sanayi Sitesi, 1 Bulvar No 9 Beylikduzu, 34520, Istanbul, Türkiye
Tel.: (90) 2128765636
Web Site: https://www.senkroma.com.tr
Emp.: 500
Masterbatch Product Mfr
N.A.I.C.S.: 325211

PLASTIQUES DU VAL DE LOIRE S.A.
Les Vallees Zone Industrielle Nord, 37130, Paris, France
Tel.: (33) 247961515
Web Site: http://www.groupe-plastivaloire.com
Sales Range: $450-499.9 Million
Emp.: 4,500
N.A.I.C.S.: 326199
Alain Audiger *(Mgr-DP)*

Subsidiaries:

Amiens Injection S.A. (1)
2 Rue de la Croix de Pierre - Z I Nord, 80015, Amiens, France
Tel.: (33) 3 22 67 52 00
Plastics Product Mfr
N.A.I.C.S.: 326199

BOURBON Automotive Plastics GmbH (1)
Westhafenplatz 1, 60237, Frankfurt am Main, Germany
Tel.: (49) 69 710 456 315
Plastic Product Distr
N.A.I.C.S.: 424610

Bourbon Automotive Plastic SA (1)
19 Rue Du Jura, BP 1, 39171, Saint-Lupicin, Cedex, France
Tel.: (33) 3 84 41 40 50
Plastics Product Mfr
N.A.I.C.S.: 326199

Bourbon Automotive Plastics Marinha Grande, S.A. (1)
Zi Do Casal da Lebre - Appartado 360, Marinha Grande, Portugal
Tel.: (351) 244 555 987
Web Site: http://www.inteplastico.pt
Plastic Product Distr
N.A.I.C.S.: 424610

Cardonaplast, S.A. (1)
Calle Dels Forns 4-5, Cardona, 08261, Barcelona, Spain
Tel.: (34) 93 868 49 60
Plastic Product Distr
N.A.I.C.S.: 424610
Jordi Blanch *(Mgr-Quality)*

Elbromplast S.A. (1)
Calea Vidrighin Stan n 13A, 300571, Timisoara, Romania
Tel.: (40) 256 290 696
Plastic Product Distr
N.A.I.C.S.: 424610

FABRYKA PLASTIKOW GLIWICE - SP Z.O.O. (1)
Ul Wyczolkowskiego 20a, 44109, Gliwice, Poland
Tel.: (48) 32 234 57 50
Plastic Product Distr
N.A.I.C.S.: 326199
John Oriard *(Plant Dir)*

Fabrika Plastikow Pomerania - Sp z o.o. (1)
Ul Zielna 13, 82-500, Kwidzyn, Poland
Tel.: (48) 55 279 68 31
Web Site: http://www.fpk.pl
Plastic Product Distr
N.A.I.C.S.: 424610

Injection Plastiques Systemes (1)
ZI Sidi Abdelhamid, BP 04, 4061, Sousse, Tunisia
Tel.: (216) 73 321 803
Plastics Product Mfr
N.A.I.C.S.: 326199

SAS Ere Plastique (1)
Zac des Tribouilleres, 38460, Cremieu, France
Tel.: (33) 4 74 90 87 87
Plastics Product Mfr
N.A.I.C.S.: 326199

PLASTMO LTD.
255 Summerlea Road, Brampton, L6T 4T8, ON, Canada
Tel.: (905) 793-9462
Web Site: http://www.plastmo.com
Rev.: $374,850,314
Emp.: 34
Rain Ware Window Mfr
N.A.I.C.S.: 321911
Geoff Card *(VP)*

PLASTO CARGAL GROUP LTD.

INTERNATIONAL PUBLIC

PO Box 175, Yavne, 81101, Israel
Tel.: (972) 89326211
Web Site: http://www.cargal.co.il
PLCR—(TAE)
Rev.: $191,146,359
Assets: $228,376,444
Liabilities: $176,493,140
Net Worth: $51,883,304
Earnings: ($23,305,135)
Fiscal Year-end: 12/31/22
Plastic Packaging Materials Mfr
N.A.I.C.S.: 326112
Gabriel Nagar *(Vice Chm & CEO)*

PLASTOFORM HOLDINGS LIMITED
Rm 902-4 Seapower Centre, 73 Lei Muk Road, Kwai Chung, New Territories, China (Hong Kong)
Tel.: (852) 24227106
Web Site: http://www.plastoform.com
Rev.: $5,574,052
Assets: $1,888,407
Liabilities: $2,002,179
Net Worth: ($113,772)
Earnings: ($6,950,805)
Emp.: 621
Fiscal Year-end: 12/31/18
Speaker Mfr
N.A.I.C.S.: 334310
Enzo Sheung Chun Lai *(Deputy CEO)*

PLASTOPIL HAZOREA COMPANY LTD.
Hazorea, Tel Aviv, Israel
Tel.: (972) 49598800
Web Site: https://www.plastopil.com
Year Founded: 1960
PPIL—(TAE)
Rev.: $106,479,041
Assets: $112,313,052
Liabilities: $74,997,018
Net Worth: $37,316,035
Earnings: $544,710
Fiscal Year-end: 09/30/23
Plastic Packaging Materials Mfr
N.A.I.C.S.: 326112
Ronen Elad *(Chm)*

Subsidiaries:

Plastopil BV (1)
De Steiger 46, 1351 AC, Almere, Netherlands
Tel.: (31) 367671000
Flexible Packaging Container Mfr
N.A.I.C.S.: 326112

Plastopil Inc. (1)
400 Frenchtown Rd Unit B, East Greenwich, RI 02818
Tel.: (401) 642-8444
Flexible Packaging Container Mfr
N.A.I.C.S.: 326112

PLASTRO MAYER GMBH
Muhltalstrasse 11, 72818, Trochtelfingen, Germany
Tel.: (49) 7124490
Web Site: http://www.plastromayer.de
Year Founded: 1957
Rev.: $36,716,391
Emp.: 212
Injection Moulds Mfr
N.A.I.C.S.: 336310
Johannes Grupp *(Owner & Mng Partner)*

PLASTRON PRESICION CO., LTD.
3F No 1 Ln 11 Ziqiang St, Tucheng Dist, New Taipei City, 23678, Taiwan
Tel.: (886) 222672346
Web Site: https://www.plastronconn.com
Year Founded: 1988
6185—(TPE)
Rev.: $18,434,043

AND PRIVATE COMPANIES

Assets: $80,512,866
Liabilities: $12,818,435
Net Worth: $67,694,431
Earnings: $1,371,510
Emp.: 152
Fiscal Year-end: 12/31/22
Electronic Connector Mfr & Distr
N.A.I.C.S.: 334417
Wen-Keng Chen *(Chm)*

Subsidiaries:

Plastron Electronic Technology (Anhui) Co., Ltd. (1)
No 18 West Wuyuanshan Road Economic Development Zone, Langxi County, Xuancheng, 242199, Anhui, China
Tel.: (86) 5637378618
Connector Whslr
N.A.I.C.S.: 423610

Plastron Electronic Technology (Suzhou) Co., Ltd. (1)
No169 Chang Bang Road Wujiang Economic and Technology Development Zone, Suzhou, 215200, Jiangsu, China
Tel.: (86) 51263408897
Connector Whslr
N.A.I.C.S.: 423610

Plastron Technology (Shenzhen) Co., Ltd. (1)
No 2071 Jincheng Road, Shajing Town Baoan District, Shenzhen, 518104, Guangdong, China
Tel.: (86) 75527568616
Connector Whslr
N.A.I.C.S.: 423610

PLAT'HOME CO., LTD.
Nihon Building Kudan Bekkan 3rd floor Kudan-kita 4-1-3, Chiyoda-ku, Tokyo, 102-0073, Japan
Tel.: (81) 352134794
Web Site: https://www.plathome.com
Year Founded: 1993
6836—(TKS)
Sales Range: $10-24.9 Million
Emp.: 43
Computer Peripheral Distr
N.A.I.C.S.: 423430
Tomoyasu Suzuki *(Founder & Pres)*

PLATA LATINA MINERALS CORPORATION
1100-1111 Melville Street, Vancouver, V6E 3V6, BC, Canada
Tel.: (604) 685-5254 BC
Web Site: https://www.plminerals.com
PLA—(TSXV)
Rev.: $745
Assets: $577,306
Liabilities: $67,992
Net Worth: $509,315
Earnings: $(426,715)
Fiscal Year-end: 12/31/19
Silver & Gold Mining
N.A.I.C.S.: 212220
William Durand Eppler *(Chm & Interim CEO)*

PLATA MANAGEMENT PUBLIC LTD.
Anexartisias 1 & Athinon 79 Nora Court Office 203, Limassol, Cyprus
Tel.: (357) 25817577
Financial Management Services
N.A.I.C.S.: 541611

PLATEER CO., LTD.
Business Park D Unit 6F 26 Beobwon-Ro 9Gil, Songpa-Gu, Seoul, Korea (South)
Tel.: (82) 25544668
Web Site: https://www.plateer.com
Year Founded: 2005
367000—(KRS)
Emp.: 184
Software Development Services

N.A.I.C.S.: 541511
Sang-Hun Lee *(CEO)*

PLATIGE IMAGE S.A.
Wladyslawa Szpilmana 4 St, 02-634, Warsaw, Poland
Tel.: (48) 228446474
Web Site: https://www.platige.com
Animation Services
N.A.I.C.S.: 512199
Karol Zbikowski *(CEO)*

PLATINA PARTNERS LLP
Berkeley Square House Berkeley Square, London, W1J 6BD, United Kingdom
Tel.: (44) 20 7042 9600 UK
Web Site: http://www.platinapartners.com
Year Founded: 2002
Emp.: 32
Investment Management Service
N.A.I.C.S.: 523940
Thomas Rottner *(Founder & Mng Partner)*

Subsidiaries:

Compobaie Solutions SAS (1)
Chemin de la Vialette, 81150, Marssac-sur-Tarn, France
Tel.: (33) 5 63 53 23 76
Investment Management Service
N.A.I.C.S.: 523940

Entap Limited (1)
20 Manchester Square, London, W1U 3PZ, United Kingdom
Tel.: (44) 207 036 62 00
Web Site: http://www.entap.co.uk
Emp.: 35
Financial Management Services
N.A.I.C.S.: 541611
Thomas Rottner *(Gen Mgr)*

PLATINA RESOURCES LIMITED
Level 2 Suite 9 389 Oxford Street, Mount Hawthorn, 6016, WA, Australia
Tel.: (61) 755809094
Web Site: https://www.platinaresources.com
PTNUF—(OTCIQ)
Rev.: $7,731,748
Assets: $18,590,341
Liabilities: $219,211
Net Worth: $18,371,130
Earnings: $15,371,732
Fiscal Year-end: 06/30/21
Other Metal Ore Mining
N.A.I.C.S.: 212290
Brian Moller *(Chm)*

PLATINUM ASIA INVESTMENTS LIMITED
Level 8 7 Macquarie Place, Sydney, 2000, NSW, Australia
Tel.: (61) 292557500
Web Site: https://www.platinum.com.au
Year Founded: 2015
PAI—(ASX)
Rev.: $16,113,782
Assets: $255,807,958
Liabilities: $607,639
Net Worth: $255,200,319
Earnings: $9,163,328
Emp.: 100
Fiscal Year-end: 06/30/24
Investment Management Service
N.A.I.C.S.: 523940
Joanne Jefferies *(Gen Counsel & Sec-Grp)*

PLATINUM ASSET MANAGEMENT LTD.
Level 8 7 Macquarie Place, Sydney, 2000, NSW, Australia
Tel.: (61) 292557500 AU

Web Site: https://www.platinum.com.au
PTM—(ASX)
Rev.: $123,517,628
Assets: $231,174,545
Liabilities: $19,636,752
Net Worth: $211,537,793
Earnings: $30,138,221
Emp.: 100
Fiscal Year-end: 06/30/24
Investment Fund Management Services
N.A.I.C.S.: 523940
Kerr Neilson *(Co-Founder)*

Subsidiaries:

Platinum Asset Pty Limited (1)
Level 8 7 Macquarie Pl, Sydney, 2000, NSW, Australia
Tel.: (61) 2 2557500
Web Site: http://www.platinum.com.au
Sales Range: $25-49.9 Million
Emp.: 70
Asset Management Services
N.A.I.C.S.: 541618

Platinum Investment Management Limited (1)
Tel.: (61) 29 255 7500
Web Site: https://www.platinum.com.au
Emp.: 110
Investment Management Service
N.A.I.C.S.: 541618

PLATINUM CAPITAL LIMITED
Level 8 7 Macquarie Place, Sydney, 2000, NSW, Australia
Tel.: (61) 292557500 AU
Web Site: https://www.platinumcapital.com.au
Year Founded: 1994
PMC—(ASX)
Rev.: $16,764,156
Assets: $305,494,123
Liabilities: $7,464,610
Net Worth: $298,029,513
Earnings: $8,545,005
Emp.: 100
Fiscal Year-end: 06/30/24
Asset Management Services
N.A.I.C.S.: 531390
Matthew Githens *(Chief Compliance Officer)*

PLATINUM GROUP METALS LTD.
1100 Melville Street Suite 838, Vancouver, V6E 4A6, BC, Canada
Tel.: (604) 899-5450 BC
Web Site: https://www.platinumgroupmetal.net
Year Founded: 2000
PLG—(NYSEAMEX)
Assets: $52,093,000
Liabilities: $2,343,000
Net Worth: $49,750,000
Earnings: $(4,607,000)
Emp.: 73
Fiscal Year-end: 08/31/24
Metal Mining Services
N.A.I.C.S.: 212290
R. Michael Jones *(Co-Founder)*

Subsidiaries:

Platinum Group Metals RSA Pty Ltd (1)
1st Fl Tech House Greenacres Office Park Cor Victory & Rustenburg Rd, Victory Park, Johannesburg, 2193, Gauteng, South Africa
Tel.: (27) 117822186
Web Site: http://www.platinumgroupmetals.net
Metal Mining Services
N.A.I.C.S.: 212290
Mlibo Mgudlwa *(VP)*

PLATINUM INSURANCE COMPANY LIMITED
Suit No 1014 10th Floor Uni-Plaza I I

Chundrigar Road, Karachi, Pakistan
Tel.: (92) 2423231
Insurance Services
N.A.I.C.S.: 524298

PLATINUM ONE BUSINESS SERVICES LIMITED
Ashar IT Park B Wing 1st Floor 16 Z Road Wagle Estate, Wagle Industrial Estate Thane West, Thane, 400604, Maharashtra, India
Tel.: (91) 9819216509
Web Site: https://www.platinumone.in
Year Founded: 2008
543352—(BOM)
Emp.: 500
Business Process Management Services
N.A.I.C.S.: 561990
Amey Saxena *(Mng Dir)*

PLATO CAPITAL LIMITED
50 Raffles Place 32-01 Singapore Land Tower, Singapore, 048623, Singapore
Tel.: (65) 65365355 SG
YYN—(CAT)
Rev.: $380,683
Assets: $40,429,970
Liabilities: $3,822,880
Net Worth: $36,607,091
Earnings: $1,896,855
Emp.: 7
Fiscal Year-end: 12/31/22
Investment Management Service
N.A.I.C.S.: 523999
Kian Onn Lim *(Chm)*

PLATO GOLD CORP.
1240 Bay Street Suite 800, Toronto, M5R 2A7, ON, Canada
Tel.: (416) 968-0608
Web Site: https://www.platogold.com
Year Founded: 2005
PGC—(TSXV)
Sales Range: Less than $1 Million
Gold Exploration Services
N.A.I.C.S.: 212220
Anthony J. Cohen *(Pres & CEO)*

PLATO INCOME MAXIMISER LIMITED
Level 25 264 George Street, Sydney, 2000, NSW, Australia
Tel.: (61) 1300010311
Web Site: http://www.plato.com.au
Year Founded: 2017
PL8—(ASX)
Rev.: $56,661,992
Assets: $549,565,302
Liabilities: $465,411
Net Worth: $549,099,891
Earnings: $44,031,116
Fiscal Year-end: 06/30/24
Investment Management Service
N.A.I.C.S.: 523940
Jonathan Trollip *(Chm)*

PLATO INVESTMENT MANAGEMENT LIMITED
Grosvenor Place Level 12 225 George Street, Sydney, 2000, NSW, Australia
Tel.: (61) 1300737760
Web Site: http://www.plato.com.au
Year Founded: 2006
Sales Range: $25-49.9 Million
Emp.: 5
Investment Management Service
N.A.I.C.S.: 523940
Don Hamson *(Mng Dir)*

PLATT NERA INTERNATIONAL LIMITED
170/9-10 4th Floor Ocean Tower 1 Sukhumvit Soi 16 Ratchadapisek Rd,

PLATT NERA INTERNATIONAL LIMITED

Platt Nera International Limited—(Continued)
Klongtoey, Bangkok, Thailand
Tel.: (66) 26619922
Web Site: http://www.plattnera.com
Year Founded: 2004
1949—(HKG)
Rev.: $14,151,158
Assets: $47,707,065
Liabilities: $33,768,220
Net Worth: $13,938,845
Earnings: $230,441
Emp.: 60
Fiscal Year-end: 12/31/23
Information Technology Services
N.A.I.C.S.: 541512
Prapan Asvaplungprohm *(Chm)*

Ky

PLATYNOWE INWESTYCJE S.A.
Ul Grojecka 43 Lokal 1A, 02-031, Warsaw, Poland
Tel.: (48) 22 290 57 97
Web Site: http://www.platyn.pl
PIW—(WAR)
Sales Range: Less than $1 Million
Real Estate Development Services
N.A.I.C.S.: 531390

PL

PLATZ CO., LTD.
2-3-17 Nakahata, Onojo City, Fukuoka, 816-0921, Japan
Tel.: (81) 120773433
Web Site: https://www.platz-ltd.co.jp
Year Founded: 1992
7813—(TKS)
Rev.: $39,727,140
Assets: $39,024,280
Liabilities: $19,157,600
Net Worth: $19,866,680
Earnings: $404,300
Emp.: 140
Fiscal Year-end: 06/30/24
Nursing Care Beds, Mattresses & Other Bed Related Items Mfr
N.A.I.C.S.: 337910
Akitoshi Fukuyama *(Chm & Co-CEO)*

PLATZER FASTIGHETER HOLDING AB
Lilla Bommen 8, Box 211, 401 23, Gothenburg, Sweden
Tel.: (46) 31631200
Web Site: https://www.platzer.se
Year Founded: 1969
PLAZ.B—(OMX)
Rev.: $1,687,613
Assets: $2,955,605,904
Liabilities: $1,716,699,456
Net Worth: $1,238,906,448
Earnings: $33,652,988
Emp.: 85
Fiscal Year-end: 12/31/23
Real Estate Services
N.A.I.C.S.: 531390
Per-Gunnar Persson *(CEO)*

PLAVA LAGUNA DD
Rade Koncara 12, Pula, 52440, Croatia
Tel.: (385) 52 410 101
Hotels & Travel Services
N.A.I.C.S.: 721110
Djenio Radic *(CEO)*

Subsidiaries:
Istraturist Umag d.d. (1)
Jadranska 66, 52470, Umag, Croatia **(93.04%)**
Tel.: (385) 52 519 000
Web Site: http://www.istraturist.com
Accommodation & Catering Services
N.A.I.C.S.: 721199
Ronald Korotaj *(CEO)*

PLAY ADVERTISING
1455 Lakeshore Rd Ste 208 S, Burlington, L7S 2J1, ON, Canada
Tel.: (905) 631-8299
Web Site: http://www.playadvertising.com
Year Founded: 1997
Sales Range: $10-24.9 Million
Emp.: 7
Advertising Agencies
N.A.I.C.S.: 541810
Brian Torsney *(Pres-Brand Builder)*

PLAYA HOTELS & RESORTS N.V.
Nieuwezijds Voorburgwal 104, 1012 SG, Amsterdam, Netherlands
Tel.: (31) 205711202
Web Site: https://www.playaresorts.com
Year Founded: 2016
PLYA—(NASDAQ)
Rev.: $977,504,000
Assets: $1,933,725,000
Liabilities: $1,378,928,000
Net Worth: $554,797,000
Earnings: $53,852,000
Emp.: 14,100
Fiscal Year-end: 12/31/23
Holding Company; Hotel & Resort Developer, Owner & Operator
N.A.I.C.S.: 551112
Brandon B. Buhler *(Sr VP)*

NI

Subsidiaries:
Cameron del Pacifico, S. de R.L. de C.V. (1)
Calle Barra De Navidad Puerto Vallarta, 48343, Jalisco, Mexico
Tel.: (52) 3222265000
Hotel & Resort Operator
N.A.I.C.S.: 721110

Hotel Capri Caribe, S. de R.L. de C.V. (1)
Carretera Federal Chetumal Cancun 387 Km 299 Lobby-bar Rendezvous, 77710, Playa del Carmen, Quintana Roo, Mexico
Tel.: (52) 9848734880
Hotel & Resort Operator
N.A.I.C.S.: 721110

PLAYD CO., LTD.
11 Hwangsaeul-ro 5th Floor 359beon-gil, Bundang-Gu, Seongnam, 13590, Gyeonggi-do, Korea (South)
Tel.: (82) 15663265
Web Site: https://www.playd.com
Year Founded: 2010
237820—(KRS)
Rev.: $31,906,058
Assets: $130,455,245
Liabilities: $62,326,365
Net Worth: $68,128,880
Earnings: $2,727,012
Emp.: 338
Fiscal Year-end: 12/31/21
Advertising Agency Services
N.A.I.C.S.: 541810
Jun-Yong Lee *(CEO)*

PLAYFAIR MINING LTD.
1489 Marine Dr No 738, Vancouver, V7T 1B8, BC, Canada
Tel.: (604) 687-7178
Web Site: https://www.playfairmining.com
Year Founded: 1988
P1J1—(DEU)
Assets: $124,555
Liabilities: $227,305
Net Worth: ($102,750)
Earnings: ($2,632,317)
Fiscal Year-end: 02/29/24
Tungsten Exploration & Development Services
N.A.I.C.S.: 212290
Donald G. Moore *(CEO)*

BC

PLAYGON GAMES, INC.
1100 - 1199 West Hastings Street, Vancouver, V6E 3T5, BC, Canada
Tel.: (604) 563-2640
Web Site: https://www.playgon.com
PLGNF—(OTCIQ)
Rev.: $9,499
Assets: $10,703,002
Liabilities: $3,615,194
Net Worth: $7,087,808
Earnings: ($4,999,799)
Fiscal Year-end: 12/31/20
Computer Game Development Services
N.A.I.C.S.: 541511
James Penturn *(Chm)*

PLAYGRAM CO., LTD.
648 Samseong-ro, Gangnam-gu, Gangnam-gu, Seoul, Korea (South)
Tel.: (82) 0221565380
Web Site: https://www.playgram.co.kr
Year Founded: 1974
009810—(KRS)
Emp.: 100
Flexible Industrial Packaging Mfr & Sales
N.A.I.C.S.: 561499
Jaewook Kim *(CEO)*

PLAYGROUND VENTURES INC.
1100-736 Granville Street, Vancouver, V6Z 1G3, BC, Canada
Tel.: (416) 361-1913
Web Site: https://playgroundventures.com
PLAY—(CNSX)
Assets: $1,209,714
Liabilities: $164,653
Net Worth: $1,045,061
Earnings: ($116,765)
Fiscal Year-end: 12/31/20
Software Development Services
N.A.I.C.S.: 541511
Jon Gill *(Chm)*

PLAYJAM LTD.
Morelands Block D 5-23 Old Street, London, EC1V 9HL, United Kingdom
Tel.: (44) 2082 376 600
Web Site: http://www.playjam.com
Emp.: 40
Branded Interactive Television & Mobile Device Videogame Platform Developer
N.A.I.C.S.: 541511
Anthony Johnson *(Chief Comml Officer)*

UK

PLAYMATES HOLDINGS, LTD.
23/F The Toy House 100 Canton Road, Tsimshatsui, Kowloon, China (Hong Kong)
Tel.: (852) 23779109
Web Site: http://www.playmates.net
635—(OTCIQ)
Rev.: $91,968,893
Assets: $850,225,312
Liabilities: $75,767,633
Net Worth: $774,457,679
Earnings: ($26,582,489)
Emp.: 77
Fiscal Year-end: 12/31/22
Investment Holding & Development; Toy Mfr & Marketer
N.A.I.C.S.: 551112
Alain Bing Kin Cheng *(Exec Dir)*

Subsidiaries:
Playmates Toys Inc. (1)
909 N Pacific Coast Hwy Ste 800, El Segundo, CA 90245-2732 **(100%)**
Tel.: (310) 252-8000
Web Site: https://www.playmatestoys.com

INTERNATIONAL PUBLIC

Sales Range: $150-199.9 Million
Emp.: 53
Toys Developer, Marketer & Distr
N.A.I.C.S.: 423920

Playmates Toys Limited (1)
23/F The Toy House 100 Canton Road, Tsimshatsui, Kowloon, China (Hong Kong) **(100%)**
Tel.: (852) 23779109
Web Site: http://www.playmatestoys.com
Rev.: $37,306,175
Assets: $140,665,330
Liabilities: $17,909,647
Net Worth: $122,755,683
Earnings: ($3,877,526)
Emp.: 65
Fiscal Year-end: 12/31/2020
Toy & Hobby Goods & Supplies Whslr
N.A.I.C.S.: 423920
Sidney Shu Sing To *(Chm)*

PLAYSIDE STUDIOS LIMITED
Level 1 75 Crockford Street, Port Melbourne, 3207, VIC, Australia
Tel.: (61) 407880693
Web Site: https://www.playsidestudios.com
Year Founded: 2011
PLY—(ASX)
Rev.: $25,450,218
Assets: $31,439,656
Liabilities: $6,135,489
Net Worth: $25,304,166
Earnings: ($4,544,565)
Fiscal Year-end: 06/30/23
Software Development Services
N.A.I.C.S.: 541511
Darren Briggs *(CFO)*

AU

PLAYTECH PLC
Ground Floor St George's Court, Upper Church Street, Douglas, IM1 1EE, Isle of Man
Tel.: (44) 1624645954
Web Site: https://www.playtech.com
Year Founded: 1999
PTEC—(LSE)
Rev.: $2,157,103,131
Assets: $4,203,488,365
Liabilities: $1,920,626,892
Net Worth: $2,282,861,472
Earnings: $132,836,198
Emp.: 7,700
Fiscal Year-end: 12/31/23
Gaming Software Services
N.A.I.C.S.: 513210
Mor Weizer *(CEO)*

Subsidiaries:
OU Playtech (Estonia) (1)
Vanemuise 7, 51001, Tartu, Estonia
Tel.: (372) 6977900
Web Site: http://www.playtech.ee
Sales Range: $75-99.9 Million
Emp.: 400
Programming & Software Services
N.A.I.C.S.: 541511

Playtech Bulgaria (1)
115 Tsarigradsko Shose European Trade Center Building C, Sofia, Bulgaria
Tel.: (359) 29874953
Web Site: http://www.playtech.bg
Software Development Services
N.A.I.C.S.: 541511

Techplay Marketing Ltd (1)
132 Menachem Begin St, Azrieli Ctr 1, 67011, Tel Aviv, Israel
Tel.: (972) 36112424
Computer Softwares Mfr
N.A.I.C.S.: 423430

PLAYTIKA HOLDING CORP.
c/o Playtika Ltd. HaChoshlim St 8, Herzliya Pituach, Israel
Tel.: (972) 733163251
Web Site: https://www.playtika.com
Year Founded: 2016
PLTK—(NASDAQ)
Rev.: $2,567,000,000

DE

Assets: $3,175,000,000
Liabilities: $3,396,500,000
Net Worth: ($221,500,000)
Earnings: $235,000,000
Emp.: 3,600
Fiscal Year-end: 12/31/23
Holding Company; Mobile Games Developer & Promoter
N.A.I.C.S.: 551112
Michael D. Cohen (Chief Legal Officer & Sec)

Subsidiaries:

Playtika Ltd. (1)
8 HaChoshlim St, PO Box 12625, Herzliya Pituach, 4672408, Pituach, Israel
Tel.: (972) 733993800
Web Site: https://www.playtika.com
Emp.: 2,000
Mobile Game Developer
N.A.I.C.S.: 541511
Michael D. Cohen (Chief Legal Officer & Sec)

Subsidiary (Non-US):

Wooga GmbH (2)
Saarbrucker Strasse 38, 10405, Berlin, 10405, Germany
Tel.: (49) 30521070550
Web Site: http://www.wooga.com
Sales Range: $25-49.9 Million
Emp.: 30
Online & Mobile Social Games Developer
N.A.I.C.S.: 513210
Jens Begemann (Co-Founder)

PLAYWAY SA
ul Bluszczanska 76 paw 6, 00-712, Warsaw, 00-712, Poland
Tel.: (48) 535535311
Web Site: https://www.playway.com
PLW—(WAR)
Rev.: $69,602,642
Assets: $135,911,331
Liabilities: $33,780,996
Net Worth: $102,130,335
Earnings: $32,087,144
Fiscal Year-end: 12/31/23
Software Development Services
N.A.I.C.S.: 541511
Krzysztof Kostowski (Chm)

PLAYWITH INC.
5F 6F 23F 60 Mabang-ro, Seocho-gu, Seoul, 13487, Korea (South)
Tel.: (82) 25385950
Web Site: http://www.playwith.co.kr
Year Founded: 1984
023770—(KRS)
Rev.: $11,125,709
Assets: $26,026,522
Liabilities: $5,210,320
Net Worth: $20,816,203
Earnings: ($2,311,735)
Emp.: 56
Fiscal Year-end: 12/31/22
Online Game Services
N.A.I.C.S.: 334610
Weonyoung Lee (Gen Mgr)

PLAYWIZE PLC
2nd Floor Britannia Business Centre, 11-13 Cricklewood Lane Cricklewood, London, NW2 1ET, United Kingdom
Tel.: (44) 20 8282 7200
Web Site:
  http://www.playwizeplc.com
Sales Range: Less than $1 Million
Emp.: 15
Video Games Software; Online Gambling Services
N.A.I.C.S.: 513210
John H. Corre (Chm)

PLAZA CENTERS N.V.
Tolstraat 112, 1074 VK, Amsterdam, Netherlands
Tel.: (31) 203449560   Nl

Web Site:
  https://www.plazacenters.com
Year Founded: 1993
PLAZ.L—(TAE)
Rev.: $192,982
Assets: $8,851,592
Liabilities: $137,635,758
Net Worth: ($128,784,166)
Earnings: ($9,059,501)
Fiscal Year-end: 12/31/22
Shopping Center Operator
N.A.I.C.S.: 531120

PLAZA CENTRES P.L.C.
The Plaza Management Office Level 3 The Plaza Commercial Centre, Bisazza Street, Sliema, SLM 1640, Malta
Tel.: (356) 21343832   Mt
Web Site: https://www.plaza-shopping.com
Year Founded: 1957
PZC—(MAL)
Rev.: $195,338
Assets: $8,959,637
Liabilities: $139,315,778
Net Worth: ($130,356,141)
Earnings: ($9,170,084)
Emp.: 17
Fiscal Year-end: 12/31/22
Real Estate Lending Services
N.A.I.C.S.: 531120
Charles J. Farrugia (Chm)

PLAZA CREATE HONSHA CO., LTD.
1-8-10 Harumi Harumi Island Triton Square Office Tower X 27th floor, Chuo-ku, Tokyo, 104-6027, Japan
Tel.: (81) 335328800   JP
Web Site:
  https://www.plazacreate.co.jp
Year Founded: 1988
7502—(TKS)
Rev.: $116,587,180
Assets: $72,888,470
Liabilities: $58,042,410
Net Worth: $14,846,060
Earnings: $383,380
Emp.: 566
Fiscal Year-end: 03/31/24
Photo Finishing Store Franchise Services
N.A.I.C.S.: 333310
Yasuhiro Oshima (Board of Directors & Pres)

Subsidiaries:

Plaza Create Mobiling Co., Ltd. (1)
1 Gobancho Osato Building 2F, Chiyoda-ku, Tokyo, 102-0076, Japan
Tel.: (81) 332220990
Web Site: http://www.plazacreate-mobiling.co.jp
Photo Developing & Printing Services
N.A.I.C.S.: 541921

Plaza Heart Co., Ltd. (1)
1 Gobancho Ichiga Yaosato Building 2 F, Chiyoda-ku, Tokyo, 102-0076, Japan
Tel.: (81) 332223366
Web Site: http://www.plazaheart.com
Sales Range: $25-49.9 Million
Emp.: 70
Wedding Chapel Photography Services
N.A.I.C.S.: 541921

PLAZA FORD SALES LIMITED
33 Terminal Road, PO Box 1000, Sydney, B1P 6J4, NS, Canada
Tel.: (902) 567-1616
Web Site: https://www.plazaford.ca
Rev.: $13,650,357
Emp.: 38
New & Used Car Dealers
N.A.I.C.S.: 441110
Sheldon Saccary (Mgr-Sls)

PLAZA KIA
7079 Yonge Street, Thornhill, L3T 2A7, ON, Canada
Tel.: (905) 763-3688
Web Site: http://www.plazakia.com
Sales Range: $25-49.9 Million
Emp.: 95
Car Dealer
N.A.I.C.S.: 441110

PLAZA RETAIL REIT
98 Main Street, Fredericton, E3A 9N6, NB, Canada
Tel.: (506) 460-8289   NB
Web Site: https://plaza.ca
Year Founded: 1999
PLZ.UN—(TSX)
Rev.: $86,545,201
Assets: $950,340,342
Liabilities: $560,848,605
Net Worth: $389,491,736
Earnings: $78,610,535
Emp.: 84
Fiscal Year-end: 12/31/21
Real Estate Investment Trust
N.A.I.C.S.: 525990
Michael A. Zakuta (Pres & CEO)

PLAZA WIRES LIMITED
A-74 Okhla Industrial Area Phase-II, New Delhi, 110020, India
Tel.: (91) 1166369666
Web Site:
  https://www.plazacables.com
Year Founded: 2006
PLAZACABLE—(NSE)
Electrical Equipment Mfr & Distr
N.A.I.C.S.: 333414
Ajay Kumar Batla (CFO)

PLB ENGINEERING BERHAD
1320 Jalan Baru Taman Chai Leng, 13700, Perai, Pulau Pinang, Malaysia
Tel.: (60) 43905737
Web Site: https://plb.com.my
PLB—(KLS)
Rev.: $9,483,184
Assets: $88,973,029
Liabilities: $72,486,848
Net Worth: $16,486,180
Earnings: ($3,421,226)
Emp.: 89
Fiscal Year-end: 08/31/23
Industrial & Residential Construction Services
N.A.I.C.S.: 236115
Guat Beng Ong (Exec Dir)

Subsidiaries:

Gaintrend Sdn. Bhd. (1)
No 2 Jalan Industrial Beringin Taman Perindustrian Beringin Juru, 14100, Seberang Perai Tengah, Pulau Pinang, Malaysia
Tel.: (60) 45076789
Property Development Services
N.A.I.C.S.: 236116

PLC FINANCIAL SOLUTIONS LIMITED
1 Alfred Place, South Melbourne, 3205, VIC, Australia
Tel.: (61) 8 9364 2387
Web Site:
  http://www.plcfinancial.com.au
Rev.: $18,676
Assets: $1,052,191
Liabilities: $380,258
Net Worth: $671,933
Earnings: $1,278,907
Fiscal Year-end: 06/30/18
Gold Trading Business
N.A.I.C.S.: 212220
Eryn Kestel (Sec)

Subsidiaries:

G-Vest Corporation Sdn. Bhd. (1)
43 Jalan Chew Boon Juan, Ipoh, 30250, Perak, Malaysia
Tel.: (60) 52555077
Sales Range: $50-74.9 Million
Emp.: 5
Money Lending Services
N.A.I.C.S.: 522291
Dhamo Munusamy (Mgr)

PLC HOLDING CO.
La Pouge, Saint-Auvent, 87310, France
Tel.: (33) 5 55 48 47 47
Sales Range: $50-74.9 Million
Emp.: 8
Material Handling Systems, Automation Systems, Heat Treating Industrial Ovens & Furnaces Mfr
N.A.I.C.S.: 333414
Philippe Blandinieres (Pres)

Subsidiaries:

Wisconsin Oven Corporation (1)
2675 Main St, East Troy, WI 53120
Tel.: (262) 642-3938
Web Site: http://www.wisoven.com
Sales Range: $10-24.9 Million
Industrial Furnace & Oven Mfr
N.A.I.C.S.: 333994
Dave Strand (Pres & CEO)

PLC S.P.A
Via Lanzone 31, 20123, Milan, Italy
Tel.: (39) 0818039717
Web Site: http://www.plc-spa.com
Renewable Energy Systems
N.A.I.C.S.: 335929
Giuseppe Garofano (Pres)

PLC S.P.A.
Via Lanzone 31, 20123, Milan, Italy
Tel.: (39) 0249535741
Web Site: https://plc-spa.it
PLC—(ITA)
Rev.: $72,103,985
Assets: $89,583,839
Liabilities: $75,654,046
Net Worth: $13,929,794
Earnings: $3,153,770
Emp.: 233
Fiscal Year-end: 12/31/23
Investment Management Service
N.A.I.C.S.: 523940
Francesco Esposito (Founder)

PLDT INC.
Ramon Cojuangco Bldg Makati Ave cor Ayala Ave, Legazpi Village, Makati, 1200, Philippines
Tel.: (63) 288168056   PH
Web Site: https://www.pldt.com
Year Founded: 1928
PHI—(NYSE)
Rev.: $4,269,096,000
Assets: $12,982,569,600
Liabilities: $10,612,180,800
Net Worth: $2,370,388,800
Earnings: $223,288,000
Emp.: 17,155
Fiscal Year-end: 12/31/22
Telecommunication Servicesb
N.A.I.C.S.: 517112
Manuel V. Pangilinan (Chm)

Subsidiaries:

ABM Global Solutions, Inc. (1)
224 Nicanor Garcia, Makati, 1209, Metro Manila, Philippines
Tel.: (63) 28 359 4909
Web Site: https://www.ags.com.ph
Information Technology Services
N.A.I.C.S.: 541511

Airborne Access Corporation (1)
3rd Floor Topys Pl, Calle Industria cor Economia S, 1110, Manila, Philippines
Tel.: (63) 26334112
Wired Telecommunications Carriers
N.A.I.C.S.: 517111

Bonifacio Communications Corporation (1)

PLDT INC.

PLDT Inc.—(Continued)
Bonifacio Centre Fort Bonifacio, Taguig, 1630, Philippines
Tel.: (63) 28179496
Telecommunication Servicesb
N.A.I.C.S.: 517810

BusinessWorld Publishing Corporation (1)
Raul L Locsin Building I 95 Balete Drive Extension, New Manila, Quezon City, 1112, Philippines
Tel.: (63) 285277777
Web Site: https://www.bworldonline.com
Sales Range: $50-74.9 Million
Emp.: 200
Newspaper Publishers
N.A.I.C.S.: 513110
Wilfredo G. Reyes (Editor-in-Chief)

Curo Teknika, Inc. (1)
25th and 26th Floors Robinsons Cyberscape Alpha, Garnet and Sapphire Streets Ortigas Center, Pasig, 1605, Philippines
Tel.: (63) 28 575 9000
Web Site: https://www.curoteknika.com
Business Process Management Services
N.A.I.C.S.: 541611
Jemuel C. Luciano (Asst VP)

Digital Telecommunications Phils., Inc. (1)
110 Eulogio Rodriguez Jr Ave, Bagumbayan, Quezon City, 1110, Philippines
Tel.: (63) 283978888
Telecommunication Servicesb
N.A.I.C.S.: 517111

Subsidiary (Domestic):

Digitel Mobile Phils., Inc. (2)
URC Compound 110 E Rodriguez Jr Avenue, Bagumbayan, 1110, Quezon City, Philippines (100%)
Tel.: (63) 23978888
Web Site: http://www.suncellular.com.ph
Mobile Telecommunications Services
N.A.I.C.S.: 517112

I-Contacts Corporation (1)
1487 Universal Tower Building Quezon Ave, Quezon City, Philippines
Tel.: (63) 2 848 8888
Communication Service
N.A.I.C.S.: 517810

Liberty Telecoms Holdings, Inc. (1)
Technology Centre Building, 2298 Chino Roces Avenue Extension, Makati, 1231, Philippines
Tel.: (63) 28130377
Web Site: http://www.libertytelecomsholdingsinc.net
Sales Range: $1-9.9 Million
Emp.: 47
Holding Company; Telecommunications Tower Construction & Maintenance Services
N.A.I.C.S.: 551112

Mabuhay Philippines Satellite Corp. (1)
FL 2 Bldg Tower 1 6799 Ayala Ave, Makati, 1200, Philippines
Tel.: (63) 28875788
Web Site: http://www.mabuhaysat.com
Sales Range: $25-49.9 Million
Emp.: 50
Marketing Satellite Transponder
N.A.I.C.S.: 517410

Multisys Technologies Corporation (1)
14 Mt Olives St, Multinational Village Moonwalk, Paranaque, Philippines
Tel.: (63) 288359697
Web Site: https://www.multisyscorp.com
Emp.: 400
Software Development Services
N.A.I.C.S.: 541511

PLDT Clark Telecom, Inc. (1)
Bldg 5665 Manuel Roxas Hi-Way cor Ninoy Aquino Ave, Clark Freeport Zone, Pampanga, 2023, Philippines
Tel.: (63) 45 599 2000
Web Site: https://www.pldtclarktel.com
Telecommunication Servicesb
N.A.I.C.S.: 517112
Chito F. Franco (Pres & CEO)

PLDT Singapore Pte Ltd. (1)
545 Orchard Rd 08-01 Far E Shipping Ctr, Singapore, 238882, Singapore (100%)
Tel.: (65) 63329873
Web Site: http://www.pldtglobal.com
Sales Range: $10-24.9 Million
Emp.: 30
Telephone Answering Services
N.A.I.C.S.: 561421

PLDT US (1)
624 S Grand Ave Ste 901-F, Los Angeles, CA 90017
Tel.: (213) 623-1150
Web Site: http://www.pldtglobal.com
Telecommunication Servicesb
N.A.I.C.S.: 517810

PLDT-Philcom, Inc. (1)
Ramon Cojuangco Building Makati Avenue, Makati, 1200, Philippines
Tel.: (63) 28168408
Web Site: http://www.philcom.ph
Telecommunication Servicesb
N.A.I.C.S.: 517810

Pacific Global One Aviation Company, Inc. (1)
PLDT Hangar General Aviation Area Domestic Airport Road, Pasay, 1300, Metro Manila, Philippines
Tel.: (63) 28 854 4801
Web Site: https://www.pacificglobalone.com
Aircraft Rental Services
N.A.I.C.S.: 532411

Parlance Systems, Inc. (1)
Ground Floor PLDT - Jupiter Warehouse, Makati, Philippines
Tel.: (63) 28168085
Teleproduction & Postproduction Services
N.A.I.C.S.: 512191

Smart Communications, Inc. (1)
6799 Ayala Ave, 6799 Ayala Avenue, Makati, 1226, Philippines (100%)
Tel.: (63) 28110211
Web Site: https://www.smart.com.ph
Telecommunication Servicesb
N.A.I.C.S.: 517112

Subsidiary (Domestic):

PLDT Communications and Energy Ventures, Inc. (2)
6799 Ayala Ave, Makati, 1226, Philippines
Tel.: (63) 25116122
Web Site: http://www.pcev.com.ph
Wireless Telecommunication Services
N.A.I.C.S.: 517112
Deborah Anne N. Tan (Officer-Corp Information & IR)

Smart Communications, Inc. (1)
SMART Tower, 6799 Ayala Ave, 1226, Makati, Philippines (100%)
Tel.: (63) 26727277
Web Site: http://smart.com.ph
Wireless Communication Equipment Mfr
N.A.I.C.S.: 517112
Manuel V. Pangilinan (Chm)

Subsidiary (Domestic):

Connectivity Unlimited Resource Enterprise, Inc. (2)
28th Floor Smart Tower 6799 Ayala Avenue, Makati, 1226, Philippines
Tel.: (63) 25113914
Cellular Mobile Telephone Services
N.A.I.C.S.: 517112

Subic Telecommunications Company, Inc. (1)
Bldg 60 Sampson Ave, Subic Bay Freeport Zone, 2222, Subic, Philippines
Tel.: (63) 472522000
Web Site: http://www.pldtsubictel.com
Sales Range: $25-49.9 Million
Emp.: 30
Telecommunications Resellers
N.A.I.C.S.: 517121
Rossano Danoog (COO)

Tighe Publishing Services, Inc. (1)
1700 W Irving Pk Rd Ste 210, Chicago, IL 60613
Tel.: (773) 281-9100
Web Site: http://www.tighepub.com

Sales Range: $1-9.9 Million
Emp.: 19
Periodical Publishers
N.A.I.C.S.: 513120
Suzanne H. Tighe (Pres)

ePLDT, Inc. (1)
5th Fl Locsin Building Ayala Corner Makati Avenue, Makati, 1200, Philippines (100%)
Web Site: http://www.epldt.com
Sales Range: $1-4.9 Billion
Emp.: 11,000
Information Technology Consulting, Management & Investment Services
N.A.I.C.S.: 541690

Subsidiary (Domestic):

BayanTrade, Inc. (2)
4/F SM Cyber One Bldg 69 Jupiter Street, Bel Air Village, Makati, 1225, Philippines
Tel.: (63) 2 8582900
Sales Range: $25-49.9 Million
Emp.: 200
Knowledge Process Outsourcing Services
N.A.I.C.S.: 561499

Subsidiary (Non-US):

Infocom Technologies, Inc. (2) (99.6%)
Tel.: (63) 28400772
Sales Range: $1-9.9 Million
Emp.: 145
Internet Service Provider
N.A.I.C.S.: 517810

Subsidiary (Domestic):

SPi CRM Inc. (2)
5th Floor Locsin Building 6752 Ayala Avenue Corner Makati Avenue, Makati, 1226, Philippines
Tel.: (63) 28179496
Business Process Outsourcing Services
N.A.I.C.S.: 561499

ePLDT VENTUS, INC. (2)
6th Floor MGO Building Legaspi Corner Dela Rosa Streets, Barangay San Lorenzo, Makati, 1229, Philippines
Tel.: (63) 2 884 6111
Business Process Outsourcing Services
N.A.I.C.S.: 561499

PLEASANT HOTELS INTERNATIONAL

7th Floor No 30 Section 3 Bade Road, Taoyuan, 33050, Taiwan
Tel.: (886) 33255688
Web Site: https://www.pleasanthotels.com.tw
2718—(TPE)
Rev.: $2,895,695
Assets: $131,526,936
Liabilities: $83,350,467
Net Worth: $48,176,469
Earnings: ($1,498,734)
Emp.: 14
Fiscal Year-end: 12/31/22
Hotel & Restaurant Operator
N.A.I.C.S.: 721110
Hsien-Ling Yang (Chm)

PLEASS GLOBAL LTD.

Pleass Drive, PO Box 502, Pacific Harbour, Suva, Namosi, Fiji
Tel.: (679) 330 8803
Web Site: http://www.pleass.com
Year Founded: 1996
PBP—(SPSE)
Rev.: $5,341,079
Assets: $14,227,809
Liabilities: $5,732,775
Net Worth: $8,495,034
Earnings: $542,917
Emp.: 120
Fiscal Year-end: 12/31/21
Bottled Water Mfr
N.A.I.C.S.: 312112
Warwick Pleass (Chm & Mng Dir)

PLEJD AB

Krokslatts Fabriker 27A, 431 37, Molndal, Sweden
Tel.: (46) 102078901
Web Site: https://www.plejd.com
Year Founded: 2009
Electric Equipment Mfr
N.A.I.C.S.: 335999
Rikard Skoldin (Mgr-Sls)

PLENITUDE BERHAD

2nd Floor No 2 Jalan Sri Hartamas 8 Sri Hartamas, 50480, Kuala Lumpur, Wilayah Persekutuan, Malaysia
Tel.: (60) 362010051 MY
Web Site: https://www.plenitude.com.my
PLENITU—(KLS)
Rev.: $67,500,180
Assets: $545,356,103
Liabilities: $127,879,290
Net Worth: $417,476,813
Earnings: $4,706,708
Emp.: 333
Fiscal Year-end: 06/30/22
Holding Company; Property Investment & Development Services
N.A.I.C.S.: 551112
Yuet Chyn Wong (Co-Sec)

Subsidiaries:

Plenitude Bangsar Residences Sdn Bhd (1)
136 Jalan Ara, Bangsar, 59100, Kuala Lumpur, Malaysia
Tel.: (60) 320923232
Residence Operator Services
N.A.I.C.S.: 531110

Plenitude Bayu Sdn Bhd (1)
G3-18 18A Gurney Walk Drive, George Town, 10250, Penang, Malaysia
Tel.: (60) 42910888
Property Development Services
N.A.I.C.S.: 531390

Plenitude Heights Sdn. Bhd. (1)
Bukit Bintang Sales Gallery Persiaran Bukit Bintang, 08000, Sungai Petani, Kedah, Malaysia (100%)
Tel.: (60) 44300333
Sales Range: $25-49.9 Million
Emp.: 28
Residential Property Development Services
N.A.I.C.S.: 236116
Tankok Siang (Gen Mgr)

Subsidiary (Domestic):

Plenitude Builders Sdn. Bhd. (2)
No 8 Ground Floor Jalan Sri Hartamas 8, Sri Hartamas, 50480, Kuala Lumpur, Malaysia (100%)
Tel.: (60) 362010888
Emp.: 22
Residential Property Development Services
N.A.I.C.S.: 236116
Elsie Chua (Chm)

Plenitude Permai Sdn. Bhd. (1)
No 31 Jalan PP 2/2 Taman Putra Prima, 47130, Puchong, Selangor Darul Ehsan, Malaysia (100%)
Tel.: (60) 380682006
Emp.: 20
Residential Property Development Services
N.A.I.C.S.: 531390

Plenitude Tebrau Sdn. Bhd. (1)
No 61 Jalan Harmonium 35/1 Taman Desa Tebrau, 81100, Johor Bahru, Johor, Malaysia (100%)
Tel.: (60) 73508282
Web Site: http://www.plenitude.com.my
Sales Range: $50-74.9 Million
Emp.: 20
Residential Township Development Services
N.A.I.C.S.: 531210

The Nomad Residences Bangsar Sdn. Bhd. (1)
136 Jalan Ara, Bangsar, 59100, Kuala Lumpur, Malaysia
Tel.: (60) 32 092 3232
Web Site: https://www.thenomadresidences.com

Sales Range: $50-74.9 Million
Emp.: 20
Residential Property Management Services
N.A.I.C.S.: 531311

PLENTEX LIMITED
246 Esplanade, Brighton, 3186, VIC, Australia
Tel.: (61) 395538896
Web Site: http://www.plentex.com.au
Sales Range: Less than $1 Million
Emp.: 1
Mining Services
N.A.I.C.S.: 212230
David J. Streader *(Sec)*

PLENTI GROUP LTD.
Level 5 14 Martin Place, Sydney, 2000, NSW, Australia
Tel.: (61) 1300768710   AU
Web Site: https://www.plenti.com.au
Year Founded: 2014
PLT—(ASX)
Rev.: $93,536,546
Assets: $1,245,405,229
Liabilities: $1,216,039,643
Net Worth: $29,365,586
Earnings: ($8,855,056)
Fiscal Year-end: 03/31/23
Financial Investment Services
N.A.I.C.S.: 523999
Georgina Koch *(Gen Counsel)*

PLENTY CO., LTD.
2-25-5 Kume Building Kamiosaki, Shinagawa-ku, Tokyo, 141-0021, Japan
Tel.: (81) 354364877   JP
Web Site: http://www.plenty.co.jp
Year Founded: 1995
Sales Range: $25-49.9 Million
Emp.: 96
LED Rental Systems
N.A.I.C.S.: 335139
Omochi Shigemi *(Pres & CEO)*

PLENUM AG
k26 Neue Mainzer Str 28, 60549, Frankfurt am Main, Germany
Tel.: (49) 6964357225
Web Site: https://www.plenum.de
PLEK—(MUN)
Rev.: $26,084,610
Assets: $19,307,144
Liabilities: $14,072,955
Net Worth: $5,234,190
Earnings: $733,866
Emp.: 137
Fiscal Year-end: 12/31/22
Management Consulting Services
N.A.I.C.S.: 541611
Volker Elders *(Member-Mgmt Bd)*

Subsidiaries:

IN:SIGHT Customer Information Management GmbH (1)
Herrenkellergraben 22, 89073, Ulm, Germany
Tel.: (49) 73140342240
Customer Information Management Services
N.A.I.C.S.: 561110

plenum International Management Consulting GmbH (1)
Hagenauer Strasse 53, 65203, Wiesbaden, Germany
Tel.: (49) 61198820
Business Management & Consulting Services
N.A.I.C.S.: 541618

plenum Management Consulting GmbH (1)
Hagenauer Strasse 53, 65203, Wiesbaden, Germany
Tel.: (49) 61198820
Web Site: http://www.plenum.com
Personnel Development & Skills Management Services

N.A.I.C.S.: 541612

PLENUS COMPANY LIMITED
19-21 Kamimuta 1-chome, Hakata-ku Fukuoka-shi, Fukuoka, 812-8580, Japan
Tel.: (81) 92 452 3600
Web Site: http://www.plenus.co.jp
Year Founded: 1960
9945—(TKS)
Rev.: $1,384,588,480
Assets: $782,095,600
Liabilities: $278,222,560
Net Worth: $503,873,040
Earnings: $21,557,360
Emp.: 1,178
Fiscal Year-end: 02/28/22
Restaurant Operators
N.A.I.C.S.: 722511
Tatsuo Shioi *(Pres)*

Subsidiaries:

PLENUS AusT PTY. LTD. (1)
Shop 2 38-42 Bridge Street, Sydney, 2000, NSW, Australia
Tel.: (61) 2 9247 8166
Web Site: http://www.yayoi.com.au
Restaurant Operators
N.A.I.C.S.: 722511

Plenus, Inc. (1)
389 Hillsdale Mall, San Mateo, CA 94403
Tel.: (650) 315-2287
Web Site: https://www.yayoi-us.com
Restaurant Services
N.A.I.C.S.: 722511

PLETHICO PHARMACEUTICALS LTD.
AB Road, Manglia, Indore, 453 774, Madhya Pradesh, India
Tel.: (91) 7312422881
Web Site: http://www.plethico.com
Sales Range: $300-349.9 Million
Emp.: 1,000
Herbal & Pharmaceutical Product Mfr; Hospital Supplies & Veterinary Products Mfr
N.A.I.C.S.: 325412
Shashikant Patel *(Chm & Mng Dir)*

Subsidiaries:

Natrol Global FZ-LLC (1)
Dubai Academic City Du Biotic Fl 1 Flat 1, 345012, Dubai, United Arab Emirates
Tel.: (971) 4 4345801
Sales Range: $25-49.9 Million
Emp.: 4
Herbal Products Mfr
N.A.I.C.S.: 311920

Plethico Global Holdings BV (1)
Orlyplein 10-24e Etage, 1043 DP, Amsterdam, North Holland, Netherlands
Tel.: (31) 205773530
Pharmaceutical Products Mfr & Sales
N.A.I.C.S.: 325412

Plethico Pharmaceuticals Ltd. - Manglia Plant (1)
A B Road, Manglia, 453 771, Indore, Madhya Pradesh, India
Tel.: (91) 7312806271
Health Care Products Mfr
N.A.I.C.S.: 325412

PLEXBIO CO., LTD.
6F-1 No 351 Yangguang St, Neihu District, Taipei, 11491, Taiwan
Tel.: (886) 226275878
Web Site: https://www.plexbio.com
Year Founded: 2009
6572—(TAI)
Biotechnology Products Mfr
N.A.I.C.S.: 325414
Dean Tsao *(Chm & CEO)*

PLEXIAN AB
Gustav Adolfs Torg 8B, 211 39, Malmo, Sweden
Tel.: (46) 406025415

Web Site: https://www.plexian.se
Year Founded: 2017
53C—(DEU)
Information Technology Services
N.A.I.C.S.: 541512
Johan Mollerstrom *(CEO)*

PLEXUS COTTON LIMITED
20 Chapel Street, Liverpool, L3 9AG, United Kingdom
Tel.: (44) 151 650 8888
Web Site: http://www.plexus-cotton.com
Year Founded: 1990
Sales Range: $500-549.9 Million
Emp.: 1,413
Cotton Whslr
N.A.I.C.S.: 424590
Nick Earlam *(Founder & Chm)*

PLEXUS HOLDINGS PLC
Highdown House Yeoman Way, Worthing, BN99 3HH, West Sussex, United Kingdom
Tel.: (44) 1224774222
Web Site: https://www.plexusplc.com
POS—(LSE)
Rev.: $1,846,557
Assets: $23,134,734
Liabilities: $8,829,198
Net Worth: $14,305,536
Earnings: ($4,985,827)
Emp.: 36
Fiscal Year-end: 06/30/23
Crude Petroleum Extraction Services
N.A.I.C.S.: 211120
Graham Paul Stevens *(Dir-Fin)*

Subsidiaries:

Plexus Ocean Systems (Malaysia) Sdn Bhd (1)
Lot 2-2 Level 2 Tower B The Troika 19 Persiaran KLCC, 50450, Kuala Lumpur, Malaysia
Tel.: (60) 321786165
Petroleum Product Distr
N.A.I.C.S.: 424720

Plexus Ocean Systems Limited (1)
Plexus House Burnside Drive, Dyce, Aberdeen, AB21 0HW, United Kingdom
Tel.: (44) 1224774222
Petroleum Product Distr
N.A.I.C.S.: 424720

PLIM COOPERATION AG
Mettlenwaldweg 17, PO Box 46, Herrenschwanden, 3037, Bern, Switzerland
Tel.: (41) 319791717
Web Site: http://www.plimswiss.com
Sales Range: $50-74.9 Million
Emp.: 35
Consumer Products Developer, Mfr & Distr
N.A.I.C.S.: 339999
Claude Kiener *(CEO)*

PLOEGER MACHINES B.V.
Electronweg 5, Roosendaal, 4706 PP, Netherlands
Tel.: (31) 165319333   NI
Web Site: http://www.ploeger.com
Year Founded: 1959
Sales Range: $250-299.9 Million
Emp.: 700
Holding Company; Farm Harvester & Other Agricultural Machinery Mfr & Distr
N.A.I.C.S.: 551112
Ad Ploeger *(Pres & Gen Mgr)*

Subsidiaries:

Oxbo International Corporation (1)
7275 Batavia Byron Rd, Byron, NY 14422
Tel.: (585) 548-2665
Web Site: http://www.oxbocorp.com

Sales Range: $100-124.9 Million
Emp.: 400
Farm Machinery & Equipment Mfr
N.A.I.C.S.: 333111
Gary Stich *(Pres)*

Ploeger Agro B.V. (1)
Electronweg, 4706 PP, Roosendaal, Netherlands
Tel.: (31) 165 319 333
Web Site: http://www.ploeger.com
Sales Range: $50-74.9 Million
Emp.: 140
Farm Harvester & Other Agricultural Machinery Mfr & Distr
N.A.I.C.S.: 333111

Subsidiary (Non-US):

Standen Engineering Limited (2)
Hereward Works Station Road, Ely, CB7 4BP, Cambridgeshire, United Kingdom (100%)
Tel.: (44) 1353661111
Web Site: http://www.standen.co.uk
Sales Range: $10-24.9 Million
Emp.: 30
Potato Harvesters
N.A.I.C.S.: 115113
Owen Blake *(Mng Dir)*

PLOMBCO INC.
66 Edmond Street, Valleyfield, J6S3E8, QC, Canada
Tel.: (450) 371-8800
Web Site: http://www.plombco.com
Year Founded: 1985
Rev.: $799,000,000
Emp.: 150
Wheel Balancing Weights Mfr & Distr
N.A.I.C.S.: 327910
Martin Lussier *(Owner)*

PLOTECH CO., LTD.
No 33 Ta Yeou St Lu Chu Area, Taoyuan, Taiwan
Tel.: (886) 33543961
Web Site: https://www.plotech.com
Year Founded: 1990
6141—(TAI)
Rev.: $84,049,214
Assets: $236,527,346
Liabilities: $176,846,980
Net Worth: $59,680,367
Earnings: ($15,119,788)
Emp.: 400
Fiscal Year-end: 12/31/23
Printed Circuit Board Mfr
N.A.I.C.S.: 334412
Lee Chi Liang *(Chm)*

Subsidiaries:

Plotech Technology (Kunshan) Co., Ltd. (1)
East Industrial District, Kunshan, 215331, Jiangsu, China
Tel.: (86) 51257876868
Web Site: http://www.plotech.com.tw
Telecommunications Equipment & Computer Parts Mfr
N.A.I.C.S.: 334118

PLOTINUS NYRT
Szirmai u 2/a, 3508, Miskolc, Hungary
Tel.: (36) 30 9006092
Web Site: http://www.plotinus.hu
Sales Range: Less than $1 Million
Investment Services
N.A.I.C.S.: 523999

PLOVDIV TECH PARK AD
14 Valko Shopov St, 4023, Plovdiv, Bulgaria
Tel.: (359) 32620189
Web Site: https://www.optela.com
Year Founded: 1980
PTP—(BUL)
Sales Range: Less than $1 Million
Laser Source Mfr
N.A.I.C.S.: 339999

PLOVDIV TECH PARK AD

Plovdiv Tech Park AD—(Continued)
Venelin Yordanov *(Co-CEO)*

PLOVER BAY TECHNOLOGIES LIMITED
Unit A8 5/F HK Spinners Ind Bldg Phase 6 481 Castle Peak Road, Cheung Sha Wan, Kowloon, China (Hong Kong)
Tel.: (852) 29907667 Ky
Web Site: http://www.ploverbay.com
Year Founded: 2006
1523—(HKG)
Rev.: $86,757,000
Assets: $83,290,000
Liabilities: $39,999,000
Net Worth: $43,291,000
Earnings: $22,659,000
Emp.: 202
Fiscal Year-end: 12/31/22
Network Router Mfr & Distr
N.A.I.C.S.: 334210
Alex Wing Hong Chan *(Founder & Chm)*

PLS PLANTATIONS BERHAD
Unit No 9-01 Level 9 Menara TSR No 12 Jalan PJU 7/3, Mutiara Damansara, 47810, Petaling Jaya, Selangor, Malaysia
Tel.: (60) 377175888
Web Site: https://www.plsplantations.my
Year Founded: 1987
PLS—(KLS)
Rev.: $24,353,577
Assets: $105,676,098
Liabilities: $40,003,179
Net Worth: $65,672,919
Earnings: ($4,543,508)
Emp.: 359
Fiscal Year-end: 06/30/24
Construction Services
N.A.I.C.S.: 237310
Thiam Wah Lim *(Co-Sec)*

Subsidiaries:

Aramijaya Sdn. Bhd. (1)
G-12 Blok 6 Jalan Skudai, Danga Bay, 80200, Johor Bahru, Johor, Malaysia
Tel.: (60) 72328382
Web Site: https://www.aramijaya.com
Forestry Plantation Services
N.A.I.C.S.: 115310
Shahir Nasir *(Chm)*

Dulai Fruits Enterprise Sdn. Bhd. (1)
Level 2 122 Jalan Desa Gombak 1 Jalan Gombak, 53000, Kuala Lumpur, Malaysia
Tel.: (60) 340228036
Web Site: https://www.dulaifruits.com
Dulai Fruit Whslr
N.A.I.C.S.: 424480
Qi Seong Liew *(Mgr-Bus Dev)*

PLUKON FOOD GROUP BV
Industrieweg 36, Wezep, 8091, Netherlands
Tel.: (31) 38 376 66 37
Web Site: http://www.plukon.com
Poultry Processing
N.A.I.C.S.: 311615
Brett J Bos *(Dir-Legal Affairs)*

Subsidiaries:

Duc S.A. (1)
Grande Rue, 89771, Chailley, Cedex, France
Tel.: (33) 03 86 43 55 88
Web Site: http://www.duc.fr
Chicken & Poultry Products Production, Packaging, Slaughtering & Sales
N.A.I.C.S.: 311615
Brett J Bos *(Dir-Legal Affairs)*

PLUMBASE LTD.
Hoo Farm Industrial Estate Edwin Ave, Hampton-in-Arden, Kidderminster, DY11 7RA, United Kingdom
Tel.: (44) 1562828505
Web Site: http://www.plumbase.com
Sales Range: $25-49.9 Million
Emp.: 10
Plumbing & Heating Merchant Services
N.A.I.C.S.: 238220
Danny Taylor *(Dir-Sls Dev)*

PLUMBFAST CO., LTD.
30 Myeonghak 2-gil Yeondongmyeon, Sejong, Korea (South)
Tel.: (82) 448659681
Web Site: https://www.plumbfast.co.kr
Year Founded: 1992
035200—(KRS)
Rev.: $23,184,753
Assets: $31,280,914
Liabilities: $3,032,235
Net Worth: $28,248,680
Earnings: $1,015,777
Emp.: 66
Fiscal Year-end: 12/31/22
Plastics Product Mfr
N.A.I.C.S.: 326122
Hee Won Jae *(CEO)*

PLUMBLINE LIFE SCIENCES, INC.
4F 18 Seocho-daero 34-gil, Seocho-gu, Seoul, 06661, Korea (South)
Tel.: (82) 269083540
Web Site: https://www.plumblinels.com
Year Founded: 2014
Biopharmaceutical Mfr
N.A.I.C.S.: 325412
Jin Ho Hwang *(Auditor)*

PLURI INC.
MATAM Advanced Technology Park Building No 5, Haifa, 3508409, Israel
Tel.: (972) 747108600 NV
Web Site: https://www.pluri-biotech.com
Year Founded: 2001
PLUR—(NASDAQ)
Rev.: $326,000
Assets: $39,527,000
Liabilities: $34,112,000
Net Worth: $5,415,000
Earnings: ($21,344,000)
Emp.: 106
Fiscal Year-end: 06/30/24
Stem Cell Researcher & Developer
N.A.I.C.S.: 325413
Yaky Yanay *(Pres & CEO)*

PLURIBUS TECHNOLOGIES INC.
111 Peter St. Ste 503, Toronto, M5V 2H1, ON, Canada
Tel.: (800) 851-9383
Web Site: http://www.pluribustechnology.com
Year Founded: 2017
Holding Company
N.A.I.C.S.: 551112
Diane Pedreira *(COO)*

Subsidiaries:

The Learning Network Inc. (1)
19772 MacArthur Blvd Ste 225, Irvine, CA 92612
Tel.: (949) 221-8600
Web Site: http://www.learning.net
Education & Training Services
N.A.I.C.S.: 611710
Christine Quach *(Project Mgr)*

PLURILOCK SECURITY, INC.
330-702 Fort Street, Victoria, V8W 1H2, BC, Canada
Tel.: (250) 590-2383
Web Site: https://www.plurilock.com
PLCKF—(OTCQB)
Rev.: $374,969
Assets: $1,743,330
Liabilities: $431,172
Net Worth: $1,312,158
Earnings: ($3,597,106)
Fiscal Year-end: 12/31/20
Information Technology Services
N.A.I.C.S.: 541512
Roland Sartorius *(CFO & Sec)*

Subsidiaries:

Aurora Systems Consulting, Inc. (1)
2510 W 237th St Ste 202, Torrance, CA 90505
Tel.: (310) 530-8260
Web Site: http://www.aurorait.com
Sales Range: $1-9.9 Million
Emp.: 10
Management Consulting Services
N.A.I.C.S.: 541611
Philip de Souza *(Pres)*

Integra Network Corporation (1)
2733 Lancaster Rd Suite 220, Ottawa, K1B 0A9, ON, Canada
Tel.: (613) 526-4945
Web Site: https://www.integranetworks.com
Information Technology Services
N.A.I.C.S.: 541512

PLURITEC LTD.
1100 place du Technoparc bureau 200, Trois Rivieres, G9A 0A9, QC, Canada
Tel.: (819) 379-8010
Web Site: http://www.pluritec.qc.ca
Year Founded: 1972
Engineering Consultancy Firm
N.A.I.C.S.: 541330
Jonathan Dugay *(Gen Mgr)*

PLUS ALPHA CONSULTING CO., LTD.
25F Shiodome Sumitomo Bldg 1-9-2 Higashi Shimbashi, Minato, Tokyo, 105-0021, Japan
Tel.: (81) 364324016
Web Site: https://www.pa-consul.co.jp
Year Founded: 2006
4071—(TKS)
Rev.: $79,202,390
Assets: $85,193,440
Liabilities: $18,228,390
Net Worth: $66,965,050
Earnings: $18,575,800
Emp.: 429
Fiscal Year-end: 09/30/23
Management Consulting Services
N.A.I.C.S.: 541618

PLUS BANK PJSC
Building 1 The Limestone Lane 7, Moscow, 109004, Russia
Tel.: (7) 84959894299
Web Site: http://www.plus-bank.ru
Sales Range: Less than $1 Million
Mortgage Banking Services
N.A.I.C.S.: 522292
Kantar Orynbaev *(Chm-Mgmt Bd)*

PLUS CORPORATION
4-1-28 Toranomon Towers Office 12F, Toranomon Minato-ku, Tokyo, 105-0001, Japan
Tel.: (81) 358607030 JP
Web Site: http://www.plus.co.jp
Year Founded: 1948
Sales Range: $1-4.9 Billion
Emp.: 5,055
Office Furniture, Stationery, Office Automation Supplies, Electronic & Optical Devices, Office Equipment & Education Equipment Mfr & Sales
N.A.I.C.S.: 337214
Yoshihisa Imaizumi *(Chm & CEO)*

INTERNATIONAL PUBLIC

Subsidiaries:

Biznet Corporation (1)
6-14 Sanbancho Chiyoda-Ku, Tokyo, 102-0075, Japan
Tel.: (81) 3 5860 1000
Web Site: http://www.biznet.co.jp
Sales Range: $150-199.9 Million
Office Supplies, Industrial Supplies & Consumable Goods Distr
N.A.I.C.S.: 423420

Hankyu Cargo Service Co., Ltd. (1)
5-3-1 Sagisu Fukushima-Ku, Osaka, Japan
Tel.: (81) 666145408
Freight Transportation Services
N.A.I.C.S.: 488510

Jointex Company (1)
No 41 No 24 Higashi Center Building, Toshima-ku, Tokyo, 170-0013, Japan
Tel.: (81) 3 6907 7325
Web Site: http://www.jointex.co.jp
Office Equipment Distr
N.A.I.C.S.: 423420

PLUS Vision Corp. of Japan (1)
1 20 11 Otowa, Bunkyo Ku, Tokyo, 112 8654, Japan
Tel.: (81) 339423192
Web Site: http://www.plus-vision.com
Sales Range: $450-499.9 Million
Emp.: 1,400
Office Furniture, Stationary, Office Machines & Educational Equipment Mfr & Distr
N.A.I.C.S.: 459410

Subsidiary (US):

PLUS Vison Corp. of America (2)
9610 SW Sunshine Ct Ste 100, Beaverton, OR 97005
Tel.: (503) 748-8700
Web Site: http://www.plus-america.com
Sales Range: $25-49.9 Million
Emp.: 15
Portable Digital Projectors, Electronic Copyboards & Real-Time Interactive White Boards
N.A.I.C.S.: 333310
Tsutomu Oishi *(Pres & CEO)*

Plus Europe GmbH (1)
Werftstrasse 23, 40549, Dusseldorf, Nordrhein-Westfalen, Germany
Tel.: (49) 211 5228570
Web Site: http://www.plus-europe.com
Emp.: 10
Stationery Product Distr
N.A.I.C.S.: 424120
Yoshi Ikeda *(Gen Mgr)*

Plus Logistics Corp. (1)
3-3-20 Komagome Komagome Toriobiru third floor Yubinbango, Toshima-ku, Tokyo, 170-0003, Japan
Tel.: (81) 3 5394 1267
Web Site: http://www.plc.co.jp
Logistics Consulting Servies
N.A.I.C.S.: 541614
Koike Ryu *(Mgr-HR)*

Subsidiary (Domestic):

PLUS Cargo Service Co., Ltd. (2)
154-4 Azakomimae, Furugome Narita, Chiba, 286-0104, Japan
Tel.: (81) 476327274
Logistics Consulting Servies
N.A.I.C.S.: 541614

Plus Stationery Shanghai Co., Ltd. (1)
Room 249 28th Floor Number 140 Tianlin Rd, Xuhui District, Shanghai, China
Tel.: (86) 21 6485 1010
Web Site: http://www.plus-china.cn
Stationery Product Distr
N.A.I.C.S.: 424120

Plus Vietnam Industrial Co., Ltd. (1)
Bien Hoa Industrial Zone 2 3 St 1A, Bien Hoa, Dong Nai, Vietnam
Tel.: (84) 61 3836592
Web Site: http://www.plusvietnam.com.vn
Stationery Product Mfr
N.A.I.C.S.: 322230

Plant (Domestic):

Plus Vietnam Industrial Co., Ltd. - Nhon Trach Factory (2)

Lot T1&T3 No 10 Road Nhoh Trach Industrial Zone 3, Hiep Phuoc, Nhon Trach, Dong Nai, Vietnam
Tel.: (84) 61 3569855
Stationery Product Mfr
N.A.I.C.S.: 322230

Shantou Plus Instruments Co., Ltd. (1)
1/F-5/F A1 Factory Building Xuntai industry zone South area of Zhujin, industry park Shaoshan road Longhu, Shantou, Guangdong, China
Tel.: (86) 754 8832 1887
Digital Projector Mfr & Distr
N.A.I.C.S.: 333310

Taiwan Plus Corporation (1)
6F No 36 Nanjing W Rd, Taipei, Taiwan
Tel.: (886) 2 25560909
Web Site: http://www.taiwan-plus.com.tw
Stationery Product Mfr
N.A.I.C.S.: 322230

PLUS GROUP HOLDINGS INC.
Suite 4503 45/F Far East Financial Centre 16 Harcourt Road, Admiralty, Hong Kong, China (Hong Kong) Ky
Year Founded: 2004
2486—(HKG)
Holding Company
N.A.I.C.S.: 551112

PLUS500UK LTD.
Building 10 2 Matam, Haifa, 3115001, Israel
Tel.: (972) 48189503 Il
Web Site: https://www.plus500.com
Year Founded: 2008
PLUS—(LSE)
Rev.: $718,700,000
Assets: $822,800,000
Liabilities: $161,500,000
Net Worth: $661,300,000
Earnings: $310,600,000
Fiscal Year-end: 12/31/21
Financial Commodity Brokerage Services
N.A.I.C.S.: 523160
Gal Haber (Mng Dir)

PLUSPETROL RESOURCES CORPORATION BV
Muiderstraat 7A, 1011 PZ, Amsterdam, Netherlands
Tel.: (31) 206622199 NI
Web Site: http://www.pluspetrol.net
Sales Range: $400-449.9 Million
Emp.: 2,242
Holding Company Oil & Gas Exploration & Production
N.A.I.C.S.: 551112
Christian Garzon Maceda (CFO & Sr VP-Corp Svcs)

Subsidiaries:

LSC Lithium Corporation (1)
40 University Avenue Suite 605, Toronto, M5J 1T1, ON, Canada
Tel.: (416) 304-9384
Web Site: http://www.lsclithium.com
Assets: $105,090,000
Liabilities: $8,581,000
Net Worth: $96,509,000
Earnings: ($3,966,000)
Fiscal Year-end: 08/31/2017
Lithium Mining
N.A.I.C.S.: 212390
Ian Stalker (Pres & CEO)

Subsidiary (Domestic):

Dajin Lithium Corp. (2)
Suite 202 8661 - 201 Street, Langley, V2Y 0G9, BC, Canada
Tel.: (604) 681-6151
Web Site: https://www.heliosx.ca
Assets: $2,875,588
Liabilities: $219,825
Net Worth: $2,655,762
Earnings: ($724,652)
Fiscal Year-end: 11/30/2020

Mineral Exploration Services
N.A.I.C.S.: 213114
Brian Findlay (Pres & CEO)

Pluspetrol S.A. (1)
Lima 339, Buenos Aires, C1073AAG, Argentina
Tel.: (54) 11 4340 2222
Web Site: http://www.pluspetrol.net
Sales Range: $250-299.9 Million
Emp.: 430
Oil & Gas Exploration & Production; Electric Power Generation & Natural Gas Distribution
N.A.I.C.S.: 211120
Christian Garzon-Maceda (CFO, Member-Exec Bd & Sr VP-Corp Svcs)

Subsidiary (Non-US):

Pluspetrol Venezuela S.A. (2)
Torre Forum Pb Oficina B Guicapuro con Av Principal de las Mercedes, Urb El Rozal, Caracas, 1060, Venezuela
Tel.: (58) 212 952 8475
Web Site: http://www.pluspetrol.net
Oil & Gas Exploration & Production
N.A.I.C.S.: 211120

PLUTON RESOURCES LIMITED
Suite 8 Level 1 12 - 20 Railway Road, Subiaco, 6008, WA, Australia
Tel.: (61) 8 6145 1800 AU
Web Site: http://www.plutonresources.com
Year Founded: 2006
Sales Range: $25-49.9 Million
Iron Ore Mining Services
N.A.I.C.S.: 212210
Iain Nish (Mgr-Contracts)

PLUTUS POWERGEN PLC
27/28 Eastcastle Street, London, W1W 8DH, United Kingdom
Tel.: (44) 20 3705 8352
Web Site: http://www.plutuspowergen.com
Rev.: $1,618,001
Assets: $660,610
Liabilities: $539,591
Net Worth: $121,019
Earnings: ($2,094,773)
Emp.: 5
Fiscal Year-end: 04/30/19
Electric Power Generation
N.A.I.C.S.: 221118
James Longley (CEO-Interim, CFO & Sec)

Subsidiaries:

IPSO Management Limited (1)
Elizabeth House 39 York Rd, London, SE1 7NQ, United Kingdom
Tel.: (44) 2079212990
Business Management Services
N.A.I.C.S.: 561110

IPSol Energy Limited (1)
Elizabeth House 39 York Rd, London, SE1 7NQ, United Kingdom
Tel.: (44) 2079212990
Sales Range: $50-74.9 Million
Solar Photovoltaic Business & Technical Solutions
N.A.I.C.S.: 926130
Peter Khoury (CEO)

Medermica Limited (1)
Elizabeth House 39 York Rd, London, SE1 7NQ, United Kingdom
Tel.: (44) 2079212990
Sales Range: $25-49.9 Million
Emp.: 2
Laboratory & Healthcare Diagnostic Devices Mfr
N.A.I.C.S.: 334510
Eleni Bitziou (Officer-Tech)

PLYCRETE, INC.
1777 rue Cedar, Mascouche, J7L 1W6, QC, Canada
Tel.: (450) 477-8161 NV

Year Founded: 2007
Sales Range: Less than $1 Million
Emp.: 2
Modular Residential & Commercial Units & Homes Wholesale Distr
N.A.I.C.S.: 459930
Clement Guevremont (Pres)

PLYMOUTH REALTY CAPITAL CORP.
880-580 Hornby Street, Vancouver, V6C3B6, BC, Canada
Tel.: (604) 617-5421 ON
Year Founded: 2013
Assets: $22,751
Liabilities: $15,871
Net Worth: $6,880
Earnings: ($26,363)
Fiscal Year-end: 12/31/18
Investment Services
N.A.I.C.S.: 523999
Gunther Roehlig (CEO & CFO)

PLYZER TECHNOLOGIES INC.
68 Admiral Road, Toronto, M5R 2L5, ON, Canada
Tel.: (416) 860-0211 NV
Year Founded: 2005
PLYZ—(OTCEM)
Assets: $206,941
Liabilities: $2,729,795
Net Worth: ($2,522,854)
Earnings: ($25,565,021)
Fiscal Year-end: 03/31/19
Investment Services
N.A.I.C.S.: 523999
Terence Robinson (Chm, Pres, CEO, CFO, Treas & Sec)

PM CAPITAL ASIAN OPPORTUNITIES FUND LIMITED
Level 27 420 George Street, Sydney, 2000, NSW, Australia
Tel.: (61) 282430888
Web Site: http://www.pmcapital.com.au
PAF—(ASX)
Rev.: $12,429,906
Assets: $52,015,310
Liabilities: $1,964,859
Net Worth: $50,050,451
Earnings: $8,172,209
Fiscal Year-end: 06/30/21
Investment Fund
N.A.I.C.S.: 525990
Richard Matthews (COO, Sec & Head-Risk & Compliance)

PM CAPITAL GLOBAL OPPORTUNITIES FUND LIMITED
Level 11 68 York Street, Sydney, 2000, NSW, Australia
Tel.: (61) 282430888 AU
Web Site: http://www.pmcapital.com.au
PGF—(ASX)
Rev.: $128,323,199
Assets: $526,440,762
Liabilities: $88,421,054
Net Worth: $438,019,708
Earnings: $82,657,932
Fiscal Year-end: 06/30/23
Closed-End Investment Fund
N.A.I.C.S.: 525990
Ben Skilbeck (Exec Dir)

PM ENGINEERING SRL
Via Vincenzo Monti 3, 20030, Senago, MI, Italy
Tel.: (39) 029989701 IT
Web Site: http://www.plastecomilano.com
Year Founded: 1956
Sales Range: $25-49.9 Million
Emp.: 65
Plastics Product Mfr

N.A.I.C.S.: 326199
Vittorio Cigognetti (Founder)

PM&E, INC.
Suite 205 4610 Dufferin Street, Toronto, M3H 5S4, ON, Canada
Tel.: (647) 761-3413
Web Site: https://www.pme-holding.com
PMEA—(OTCIQ)
Sales Range: Less than $1 Million
Holding Company; Photovoltaic Modular Energy Generation & Alternatives
N.A.I.C.S.: 551112
Jack Merck (Pres & CEO)

PMB TECHNOLOGY BERHAD
Lot 1797 Jalan KPB 1 Bukit Belimbing, 43300, Seri Kembangan, Selangor Darul Ehsan, Malaysia
Tel.: (60) 389618355
Web Site: https://www.pmbtechnology.com
PMBTECH—(KLS)
Rev.: $250,393,862
Assets: $363,209,312
Liabilities: $171,164,233
Net Worth: $192,045,079
Earnings: $23,355,556
Emp.: 1,234
Fiscal Year-end: 12/31/22
Aluminum & Related Products Mfr
N.A.I.C.S.: 331314
Yit Chan Tai (Co-Sec)

Subsidiaries:

Everlast Aluminium (M) Sdn. Bhd. (1)
Lot 1797 Jalan Balakong Bukit Belimbing, 43300, Seri Kembangan, Selangor, Malaysia
Tel.: (60) 38 961 5223
Web Site: http://www.everlas.com
Sales Range: $50-74.9 Million
Emp.: 200
Ladders Mfr
N.A.I.C.S.: 332323

Subsidiary (Domestic):

Everlast Access Technologies Sdn. Bhd. (2)
Lot 1797 Jalan Balakong Bukit Belimbing, 43300, Seri Kembangan, Selangor, Malaysia
Sales Range: $25-49.9 Million
Emp.: 100
Ladders Distr
N.A.I.C.S.: 423830

PMB Central Sdn. Bhd. (2)
Lot 1797 Jalan Balakong Bukit Belimbing, 43300, Seri Kembangan, Selangor, Malaysia
Tel.: (60) 389611088
Web Site: http://www.pmbtechnology.com
Curtain Wall Mfr
N.A.I.C.S.: 332323

PMB Eastern Sdn. Bhd. (2)
Block B Lot 86 Jalan Industri Semambu 7 Semambu Industrial Estate, 25350, Kuantan, Pahang, Malaysia
Tel.: (60) 95663923
Sales Range: $25-49.9 Million
Emp.: 14
Extruded Aluminum Products Distr
N.A.I.C.S.: 423510
Kenny Choy (Mgr)

PMB Northern Sdn. Bhd. (2)
Lot 10-08 Jalan PKNK2 Kaw Perindustrian Sungai Petani, Sungai Petani, 08000, Kedah, Malaysia
Tel.: (60) 44424149
Sales Range: $25-49.9 Million
Emp.: 50
Curtain Wall Mfr
N.A.I.C.S.: 332323
Eng Chen Ching (Branch Mgr)

PMB Quick Access Sdn. Bhd. (2)
Lot 1797 Jalan Balakong Bukit Belimbing,

PMB TECHNOLOGY BERHAD

PMB Technology Berhad—(Continued)
43300, Seri Kembangan, Selangor, Malaysia
Tel.: (60) 38 961 8686
Web Site: http://www.qaccess-scaffolds.com
Sales Range: $25-49.9 Million
Emp.: 200
Aluminum Scaffold Mfr
N.A.I.C.S.: 331318

PMB Facade Technology Sdn. Bhd. (1)
Lot 1797 Jalan KPB 1 Bukit Belimbing, 43300, Seri Kembangan, Selangor Darul Ehsan, Malaysia
Tel.: (60) 389618355
Aluminum & Related Product Mfr
N.A.I.C.S.: 331314

PMB-Cyberwall Limited (1)
Unit 1508-18 15/F 41 Heung Yip Road, Wong Chuk Hang, Hong Kong, China (Hong Kong)
Tel.: (852) 2 397-6008
Web Site: https://www.pmbc.com.hk
Sales Range: $25-49.9 Million
Emp.: 30
Curtain Wall Mfr
N.A.I.C.S.: 332999

PMC COMMUNICATIONS CO., LTD.
Rm 1803 Tower South Yuexiu City Plaza, No 437 Dongfeng Rd (M), Guangzhou, 510200, China
Tel.: (86) 20 8356 9288
Web Site: http://www.pmc.com.cn
Advetising Agency
N.A.I.C.S.: 541810
Judy Huang *(Mng Dir)*

Subsidiaries:

PMC Beijing (1)
Room 1805-010 18/Floor Fuli Gemini B San Huan Middle Road No55, Chaoyang District, Beijing, China
Tel.: (86) 10 5617 4619
Web Site: http://www.pmc.com.cn
Advetising Agency
N.A.I.C.S.: 541810

PMC Hong Kong (1)
Street 1111 Tower II Silvercord Canton Road, Tsim Sha Tsui, Hong Kong, China (Hong Kong)
Tel.: (852) 3128 9625
Advetising Agency
N.A.I.C.S.: 541810

PMC Shanghai (1)
Room 525 No 109 Yan Dang Road, Lu Wan District, Shanghai, 200020, China
Tel.: (86) 21 5383 3321
Advetising Agency
N.A.I.C.S.: 541810

PMC FINCORP LIMITED
B-10 VIP Colony Civil Lines, Rampur, 244901, Uttar Pradesh, India
Tel.: (91) 1147631025
Web Site: https://pmcfincorp.com
Year Founded: 1985
534060—(BOM)
Rev.: $1,085,115
Assets: $16,059,517
Liabilities: $3,665,823
Net Worth: $12,393,693
Earnings: ($762,916)
Emp.: 13
Fiscal Year-end: 03/31/23
Financial Management Services
N.A.I.C.S.: 523999
Raj Kumar Modi *(Mng Dir)*

PMD ACADEMY CORP
78 Yanghwa-ro Mapo-gu, Seoul, Korea (South)
Tel.: (82) 7076025096
Web Site: http://www.m.pmd.co.kr
Educational Support Services
N.A.I.C.S.: 611710
Yoo Joon-Chul *(CEO)*

PME AFRICAN INFRASTRUCTURE OPPORTUNITIES PLC
Millennium House 46 Athol Street, Douglas, IM1 1JB, Isle of Man
Tel.: (44) 1624 692 600
Web Site: http://www.pmeinfrastructure.com
Rev.: $270,000
Assets: $3,749,000
Liabilities: $92,000
Net Worth: $3,657,000
Earnings: ($1,513,000)
Fiscal Year-end: 12/31/18
Investment Management
N.A.I.C.S.: 523940
Lawrence Albert Kearns *(Exec Dir)*

PME S.A.
Ul Reymonta 24, 40-029, Katowice, Poland
Tel.: (48) 32 202 80 61
Web Site: http://www.pemug.com.pl
Steel Construction & Equipment Mfr
N.A.I.C.S.: 331110

PMGC TECHNOLOGY GROUP LIMITED
3rd Floor Sutherland House 5-6 Argyll Street, London, W1F 7TE, United Kingdom
Tel.: (44) 20 7287 9928
Web Site: http://www.pmgroupuk.com
Year Founded: 1998
Sales Range: $25-49.9 Million
Emp.: 83
Telecommunication Servicesb
N.A.I.C.S.: 517112
Shez Cheema *(CEO)*

PMPG POLSKIE MEDIA S.A.
Al Jerozolimskie 212, Batory Office Building II, 02-486, Warsaw, Poland
Tel.: (48) 223475000
Web Site: https://www.pmpg.pl
Year Founded: 1998
PGM—(WAR)
Rev.: $11,992,378
Assets: $10,704,014
Liabilities: $2,186,992
Net Worth: $8,517,022
Earnings: $617,632
Fiscal Year-end: 12/31/23
Media & Marketing Sector Services
N.A.I.C.S.: 541613
Tomasz Bielanowicz *(Chm-Supervisory Bd)*

PN POONGNYUN CO. LTD.
620 Byeolmang-ro, Danwon-gu, An-san, 425 866, Gyeonggi, Korea (South)
Tel.: (82) 314912965
Web Site: https://www.pnshop.co.kr
Year Founded: 1954
024940—(KRS)
Rev.: $44,209,341
Assets: $41,768,057
Liabilities: $6,294,728
Net Worth: $35,473,329
Earnings: $1,360,371
Emp.: 162
Fiscal Year-end: 12/31/22
Kitchen Utensil Mfr
N.A.I.C.S.: 332215
Jae Won Yoo *(CEO)*

PNC INFRATECH LIMITED
3/22-D Civil Lines Bypass Road NH-2, Agra, 282002, India
Tel.: (91) 8047636259
Web Site: https://www.pncinfratech.com
PNCINFRA—(NSE)
Rev.: $805,198,881
Assets: $1,307,021,379
Liabilities: $890,329,863
Net Worth: $416,691,516
Earnings: $67,827,191
Emp.: 8,564
Fiscal Year-end: 03/31/21
Infrastructure Construction Services
N.A.I.C.S.: 237310
Pradeep Kumar Jain *(Chm & Mng Dir)*

Subsidiaries:

PNC Delhi Industrialinfra Private Limited (1)
NBCC Plaza Tower II 4th Floor Pushp Vihar Near Saket, New Delhi, 110 017, India
Tel.: (91) 1129574800
Web Site: https://www.pncnarela.com
Infrastructure Developing Services
N.A.I.C.S.: 237310

PNC PROCESS SYSTEMS CO LTD
No 170 Zihai Road, Minhang District, Shanghai, 200241, China
Tel.: (86) 2180238200
Web Site: http://www.pnc-systems.com
Year Founded: 2000
603690—(SHG)
Rev.: $428,153,352
Assets: $1,381,247,478
Liabilities: $720,067,893
Net Worth: $661,179,585
Earnings: $39,654,857
Fiscal Year-end: 12/31/22
Integrated Solution Mfr & Distr
N.A.I.C.S.: 325998
Jiang Yuan *(Chm, Pres & Gen Mgr)*

Subsidiaries:

Nanolink Aps (1)
Lundagervej 25D, 8722, Hedensted, Denmark
Tel.: (45) 88709000
Web Site: https://www.nanolink.com
Fleet Management Services
N.A.I.C.S.: 532112

PHARMAC Ltd. (1)
10F Bldg 3A Tianhua Information Park No 299 Longcao Road, Xuhui District, Shanghai, China
Tel.: (86) 2133560600
Web Site: https://en.pharmachamp.com
Emp.: 300
Cleaning Liquid Mfr
N.A.I.C.S.: 325611

PNC TECH CO LTD
62 Jeonpa-ro 104 beon-gil, Donganh-gu, Anyang, 14042, Gyeonggi-do, Korea (South)
Tel.: (82) 314525791   KR
Web Site: https://www.pnctech.com
Year Founded: 1999
237750—(KRS)
Rev.: $16,872,411
Assets: $59,619,649
Liabilities: $6,913,794
Net Worth: $52,705,854
Earnings: $2,259,429
Emp.: 69
Fiscal Year-end: 12/31/22
Digital Power Equipment Mfr
N.A.I.C.S.: 334515
Kwang-Sik Cho *(Pres & CEO)*

PNE AG
Peter Henlein Str 2-4, 27472, Cuxhaven, Germany
Tel.: (49) 472171806
Web Site: https://www.pne-ag.com
PNE3—(MUN)
Rev.: $134,153,321
Assets: $1,216,122,540
Liabilities: $982,576,764
Net Worth: $233,545,776
Earnings: ($10,541,958)
Emp.: 608
Fiscal Year-end: 12/31/23

INTERNATIONAL PUBLIC

Wind Farm Services
N.A.I.C.S.: 333111
Jorg Klowat *(CFO)*

Subsidiaries:

BGZ Fondsverwaltung GmbH (1)
Otto-Hahn-Strasse 12-16, 25813, Husum, Germany
Tel.: (49) 48418944825
Web Site: https://www.bgz-gmbh.de
Renewable Energy Services
N.A.I.C.S.: 221118
Marco Lange *(Mng Dir)*

Coliaenergia ESPANA, S.L. (1)
C/ Teodoro Camino 2 Entreplanta A, 02001, Albacete, Spain
Tel.: (34) 967993046
Wind & Solar Energy Generation Services
N.A.I.C.S.: 221115

Energy Consult Polska Sp.z o.o. (1)
Wojska Polskiego 24-26, 75-712, Koszalin, Poland
Tel.: (48) 664706701
Web Site: https://www.energy-consult-polska.net
Wind Solar Energy Services
N.A.I.C.S.: 221115

Energy Consult Sverige AB (1)
Strandvagen 169, 59146, Motala, Sweden
Tel.: (46) 733771052
Web Site: https://www.energy-consult-sverige.net
Wind & Solar Energy Generation Services
N.A.I.C.S.: 221115

MEB Safety Services GmbH (1)
Tilsiter Str 2-4, 28217, Bremen, Germany
Tel.: (49) 42169107081
Web Site: https://www.meb-services.eu
Safety Services
N.A.I.C.S.: 922190

PNE Sverige AB (1)
Lilla Bommen 1, 411 04, Gothenburg, Sweden
Tel.: (46) 702378828
Web Site: https://www.pne-sverige.se
Wind & Solar Energy Generation Services
N.A.I.C.S.: 221115

PNE WIND Yenilenebilir Enerjiler Ltd. (1)
2146 Sok Demirler Atlas Plaza 14/5, Cankaya, 06530, Ankara, Turkiye
Tel.: (90) 3122194010
Wind Energy Services
N.A.I.C.S.: 221115

Pavana GmbH (1)
Otto-Hahn-Str 12-16, 25813, Husum, Germany
Tel.: (49) 48418944227
Web Site: https://www.pavana-wind.com
Wind Energy Services
N.A.I.C.S.: 221115

Pavana Polska Sp. z o.o. (1)
ul Wojska Polskiego 24-26, 75-712, Koszalin, Poland
Tel.: (48) 600906634
Wind Solar Energy Services
N.A.I.C.S.: 221115

Plambeck Neue Energien Betriebs- und Beteiligungsgesellschaft mbH (1)
Peter-Henlein-Strasse 2-4, 27472, Cuxhaven, Niedersachsen, Germany
Tel.: (49) 4721718441
Sales Range: $50-74.9 Million
Emp.: 153
Wind Farms Mfr
N.A.I.C.S.: 333611

Plambeck Neue Energien Biomasse AG (1)
Peter-Henlein-Strasse 2-4, Cuxhaven, 27472, Niedersachsen, Germany
Tel.: (49) 4721718440
Web Site: http://www.pnewind.com
Wind Power Plants Mfr
N.A.I.C.S.: 333613

Plambeck Neue Energien Biomasse Betriebsgesellschaft mbH (1)
Peter-Henlein-Strasse 2, 27472, Cuxhaven,

Lower Saxony, Germany
Tel.: (49) 472171806
Sales Range: $50-74.9 Million
Emp.: 183
Wind Turbines Mfr & Installation Services
N.A.I.C.S.: 333611

Plambeck Neue Energien Grundstucks GmbH (1)
Peter-Henlein-Strasse 2-4, 27472, Cuxhaven, Lower Saxony, Germany
Tel.: (49) 4721718440
Energy Consulting Services
N.A.I.C.S.: 541690
Rainer Heinsohn (Mgr-PR)

S.C. PNE WIND Romania Energy Holding S.R.L (1)
Tel.: (40) 214104255
Wind Energy Services
N.A.I.C.S.: 221115

Sachsenkraft Plus GmbH (1)
Burgerstrasse 28, 01127, Dresden, Germany
Tel.: (49) 3518584281
Web Site: https://www.sachsenkraft.de
Solar Energy Construction Services
N.A.I.C.S.: 221114

Sevivon Sp. z o.o. (1)
ul Wojska Polskiego 24-26, 75-712, Koszalin, Poland
Tel.: (48) 943425451
Web Site: https://www.sevivon.pl
Renewable Energy Services
N.A.I.C.S.: 221114

VKS Vindkraft Sverige AB (1)
Strandvagen 169, 59146, Motala, Sweden
Tel.: (46) 141441100
Web Site: https://www.vksvind.se
Renewable Energy Services
N.A.I.C.S.: 221114

WKN France S.A.S.U. (1)
Immeuble Le Sanitat 10 rue Charles Brunelliere, 44100, Nantes, France
Tel.: (33) 240587310
Web Site: https://www.wkn-france.fr
Renewable Energy Services
N.A.I.C.S.: 221114

WKN GmbH (1)
Otto-Hahn-Str 12-16, 25813, Husum, Germany
Tel.: (49) 48418944100
Web Site: https://www.wkn-group.com
Renewable Energy Services
N.A.I.C.S.: 221114

WKN Italia s.r.l. (1)
Tel.: (39) 0683361086
Web Site: https://www.wkn-italia.com
Renewable Energy Services
N.A.I.C.S.: 221114

WKN Wertewind GmbH (1)
Otto-Hahn-Strasse 12-16, 25813, Husum, Germany
Tel.: (49) 48418944200
Web Site: http://www.wknwertewind.de
Wind Energy Services
N.A.I.C.S.: 221115

WKN Windcurrent SA (Pty) Ltd. (1)
PO Box 762, Cape Town, 6560, South Africa
Tel.: (27) 448770564
Renewable Energy Services
N.A.I.C.S.: 221114
Mike Mangnall (Mng Dir)

energy consult GmbH (1)
Peter-Henlein-Strasse 2-4, 27472, Cuxhaven, Germany
Tel.: (49) 472171808
Web Site: https://www.energy-consult.net
Renewable Energy Services
N.A.I.C.S.: 221114
Tanja Grefe-Totz (Mng Dir)

energy consult Prufgesellschaft GmbH (1)
Otto-Hahn-Strasse 12-16, 25813, Husum, Germany
Tel.: (49) 48418944216
Web Site: https://www.energy-consult-pruefgesellschaft.net
Renewable Energy Services
N.A.I.C.S.: 221114

PNE PCB BERHAD
No 6 Jalan Firma 2/1 Kawasan Perindustrian Tebrau, 81100, Johor Bahru, Malaysia
Tel.: (60) 73546448   MY
Web Site: https://www.pnepcb.com
Year Founded: 1976
6637—(KLS)
Rev.: $12,493,370
Assets: $19,429,836
Liabilities: $8,941,430
Net Worth: $10,488,406
Earnings: ($3,360,902)
Fiscal Year-end: 03/31/24
Printed Circuit Board Mfr
N.A.I.C.S.: 334412
Sor Hua Tea (Sec)

Subsidiaries:

PNE Electronics (Dong Guan) Corporation Limited (1)
Bai Shi Gang Chang Ping Zhen, Guangzhou, Dongguan, China
Tel.: (86) 76983820333
Web Site: http://www.pne.com.sg
Printed Circuit Board Mfr
N.A.I.C.S.: 334412

PNE PCB Pte. Ltd. (1)
996 Bendemeer Road 07-06, Singapore, 339944, Singapore
Tel.: (65) 62910698
Web Site: http://www.pne.com.sg
Printed Circuit Board Distr
N.A.I.C.S.: 423690

Qisda (Suzhou) Co., Ltd. (1)
No 169 Zhujiang Rd New Area, 215015, Suzhou, Jiangsu, China
Tel.: (86) 51266658800
Web Site: http://www.qisda.com
Sales Range: $25-49.9 Million
Emp.: 10
Computer Peripherals Mfr
N.A.I.C.S.: 334118

PNG AIR LTD.
Jackson's Airport Boroko NCD, PO Box 170, Port Moresby, Papua New Guinea
Tel.: (675) 7373 7100   PG
Web Site: http://www.apng.com
CGA—(PNGX)
Sales Range: $25-49.9 Million
Emp.: 700
Oil Transportation Services
N.A.I.C.S.: 488190
Murray Woo (Chm)

PNGS GARGI FASHION JEWELLERY LTD.
S No 37 /1 & 37 /2 Near Lokmat New Pape, Wadgaon Khurd, Pune, 411041, Maharashtra, India
Tel.: (91) 7219621832
Web Site: https://www.gargibypng.com
Year Founded: 2009
543709—(BOM)
Rev.: $3,456,316
Assets: $2,903,675
Liabilities: $435,849
Net Worth: $2,467,826
Earnings: $562,256
Emp.: 24
Fiscal Year-end: 03/31/23
Jewelry Product Distr
N.A.I.C.S.: 458310

PO VALLEY ENERGY LIMITED
Level 5 / 191 St Georges Terrace, Perth, 6000, WA, Australia
Tel.: (61) 893169100   AU
Web Site: https://www.povalley.com
Year Founded: 1999
PVE—(ASX)
Rev.: $2,580,103
Assets: $16,493,277
Liabilities: $1,546,237
Net Worth: $14,947,041
Earnings: $647,596
Emp.: 14
Fiscal Year-end: 12/31/23
Oil & Natural Gas Exploration Services
N.A.I.C.S.: 211120
Michael George Masterman (Founder, Chm & CEO)

PO YUEN CULTURAL HOLDINGS (HONG KONG) CO., LTD.
Room A 16/F Winbase Centre 208 Queeen's Road Central, Sheung Wan, China (Hong Kong)
Tel.: (852) 23501928   NV
Year Founded: 2014
POYN—(OTCBB)
Assets: $1,000
Liabilities: $68,122
Net Worth: ($67,122)
Earnings: ($40,460)
Fiscal Year-end: 03/31/19
Investment Holding Company; Business Development Services
N.A.I.C.S.: 551112
Peter H. Tong (CFO, Treas & Sec)

POBEDA A.D.
Kraljice Marije bb, Ljig, Serbia
Tel.: (381) 143445390
Year Founded: 1946
PBLJ—(BEL)
Rev.: $35,009
Assets: $195,521
Liabilities: $976,853
Net Worth: ($781,332)
Earnings: ($113,842)
Emp.: 7
Fiscal Year-end: 12/31/22
Leather Cloth Mfr
N.A.I.C.S.: 315250

POBEDA A.D.
Timocka 10, Belgrade, Serbia
Tel.: (381) 69 8233 462
Web Site: http://www.pobeda-ad.rs
Year Founded: 1953
Sales Range: Less than $1 Million
Heating & Air Conditioning System Maintenance Services
N.A.I.C.S.: 238220
Zoran Stojanovic (Exec Dir)

POBEDA METALAC A.D.
Rade Koncara 1, Petrovaradin, Serbia
Tel.: (381) 21431301
Year Founded: 1991
PBMT—(BEL)
Sales Range: $1-9.9 Million
Emp.: 51
Industrial Machinery Mfr
N.A.I.C.S.: 333998
Jadranko Protic (Exec Dir)

POBEDA ZARA A.D.
Rade Koncara 1, 21131, Petrovaradin, Serbia
Tel.: (381) 21431301
Web Site: http://www.pobeda.co.rs
Year Founded: 1991
PBZR—(BEL)
Sales Range: Less than $1 Million
Emp.: 9
Holding Company
N.A.I.C.S.: 551112
Aleksandar Vujic (Dir)

POBJEDA D.D.
Bukva bb, 74260, Tesanj, Bosnia & Herzegovina
Tel.: (387) 32665300
Web Site: http://www.pobjeda-tesanj.ba
Year Founded: 1954
PBJTRK1—(SARE)
Rev.: $14,542,382
Assets: $17,480,319
Liabilities: $5,155,674
Net Worth: $12,324,646
Earnings: $1,129,968
Emp.: 280
Fiscal Year-end: 12/31/21
Automobile Parts Mfr
N.A.I.C.S.: 336390
Bejdzakic Kasim (CEO)

POBJEDA TECHNOLOGY D.O.O. GORAZDE
Visegradska bb, 73000, Gorazde, Bosnia & Herzegovina
Tel.: (387) 3 824 1050
Web Site: http://www.pobjeda-technology.ba
PSPGRK4—(SARE)
Rev.: $14,923,630
Assets: $15,682,704
Liabilities: $9,481,586
Net Worth: $6,201,118
Earnings: $245,322
Emp.: 174
Fiscal Year-end: 12/31/20
Ammunition Product Mfr
N.A.I.C.S.: 332992

POBJEDA-RUDET D.D.
Visegradska bb, 73000, Gorazde, Bosnia & Herzegovina
Tel.: (387) 3 822 1336
Web Site: http://www.pobjeda.com
PRDGRK3—(SARE)
Rev.: $12,899,522
Assets: $24,522,795
Liabilities: $4,007,070
Net Worth: $20,515,724
Earnings: $2,514,866
Emp.: 312
Fiscal Year-end: 12/31/20
Explosives Mfr
N.A.I.C.S.: 325920
Esad Hodzic (Exec Dir-HR, Economic & Legal Affairs)

POCHET S.A.
121-127 quai de Valmy, 75010, Paris, France
Tel.: (33) 144721100
Web Site: http://www.pochet.com
Sales Range: $500-549.9 Million
Emp.: 50
Luxury Glass Perfume Bottles & Cosmetic Containers Mfr
N.A.I.C.S.: 327213
Gabriel Colonna De Giovellina (Pres)

Subsidiaries:

Qualipac S.A. (1)
30 Rue D Orleans, 92200, Neuilly-sur-Seine, France (100%)
Tel.: (33) 155615000
Web Site: http://www.qualipac.fr
Sales Range: $450-499.9 Million
Mfr Plastic Packaging for Cosmetics & Perfumes
N.A.I.C.S.: 322220
Thierry Sarfati (Gen Mgr)

Subsidiary (Domestic):

Lisi Cosmetics S.A.S. (2)
193 rue de Bercy, Tour Gamma A, Paris, Cedex 12, France (100%)
Tel.: (33) 153029640
Web Site: http://www.lisi-cosmetics.com
Sales Range: $25-49.9 Million
Emp.: 35
Bolt Nut Screw Rivet & Washer Mfr
N.A.I.C.S.: 327910

Priminter (2)
30 Rue D Orleans, 92200, Neuilly-sur-Seine, France
Tel.: (33) 155615050
Web Site: http://www.qualipac.fr

POCHET S.A.

Pochet S.A.—(Continued)
Sales Range: $25-49.9 Million
Plastics Products
N.A.I.C.S.: 326199

Subsidiary (Non-US):

Priminter (HKG) Ltd. (2)
Room 170123 Sasson Tower 7 Cheung Shun Street, Kowloon, China (Hong Kong)
Tel.: (852) 28771250
Sales Range: $25-49.9 Million
Emp.: 20
N.A.I.C.S.: 326199
Galy Yung *(Gen Mgr)*

Subsidiary (US):

Qualipac America (2)
1 Garrett Mtn Plz 5th Fl, Woodland Park, NJ 07424
Tel.: (973) 389-7730
Web Site: http://www.qualipac.fr
Packaging for Skin Care & Perfume Products
N.A.I.C.S.: 561910
Virginie Lecaro *(Coord-HR)*

POCHIN'S LTD.
Brooks Lane, Middlewich, CW10 0JQ, Cheshire, United Kingdom
Tel.: (44) 1606833333
Web Site: http://www.pochins.com
Year Founded: 1934
Sales Range: $100-124.9 Million
Emp.: 158
Construction & Contracting Services
N.A.I.C.S.: 236220

Subsidiaries:

Liberty Pochin Limited (1)
C-o Pochins Plc, Brooks Lane Cheshire, CW100JQ, Middlewich, United Kingdom **(50%)**
Tel.: (44) 1606832276
Real Estate Agency
N.A.I.C.S.: 531210

Manchester Technopark Limited (1)
Kilburn House Lloyd Street North, Manchester Science Park, Manchester, M15 5RN, United Kingdom **(50%)**
Tel.: (44) 1612261000
Web Site: http://www.manchestertechnopark.co.uk
Amusement & Theme Parks
N.A.I.C.S.: 713110

P.B. Developments Limited (1)
15 Summer Street, Aberdeen, AB10 1SB, United Kingdom **(100%)**
Tel.: (44) 1224626888
Web Site: http://www.pbdeco.com
Emp.: 4
Land Subdivision
N.A.I.C.S.: 237210

Pochin (Contractors) Limited (1)
Brooks Lane Cheshire, Middlewich, CW10 0JQ, United Kingdom **(100%)**
Tel.: (44) 8448054220
Web Site: http://www.pochins.com
Sales Range: $25-49.9 Million
Emp.: 50
Industrial Building Construction
N.A.I.C.S.: 236210
James Nicholson *(CEO)*

Pochin Construction Limited (1)
Brooks Ln, Middlewich, CW10 0JQ, United Kingdom
Tel.: (44) 1606 833 333
Web Site: http://www.pochinconstruction.co.uk
Sales Range: $25-49.9 Million
Emp.: 70
Construction Engineering Services
N.A.I.C.S.: 541330
Mark Hatton *(Dir-Comml)*

Pochin Developments Limited (1)
Brooks Lane Cheshire, Middlewich, CW10 0JQ, United Kingdom **(100%)**
Tel.: (44) 1606833333
Web Site: http://www.pochins.com

Sales Range: $75-99.9 Million
Emp.: 150
Real Estate Property Lessors
N.A.I.C.S.: 531190
James Nicholson *(CEO)*

Pochin Homes Limited (1)
Brooks Lane Cheshire, Middlewich, CW10 0JQ, United Kingdom **(100%)**
Tel.: (44) 1606831664
Web Site: http://www.pochinhomes.co.uk
Sales Range: $25-49.9 Million
New Single-Family Housing Construction
N.A.I.C.S.: 236115
John Russell *(Dir-Comml)*

Pochin Plant Limited (1)
Brooks Lane Cheshire, CW100JQ, Middlewich, United Kingdom **(100%)**
Tel.: (44) 1606833333
Web Site: http://www.pochins.plc.uk
Sales Range: $50-74.9 Million
Emp.: 150
Commercial & Institutional Building Construction
N.A.I.C.S.: 236220
Richard Fildes *(Chm)*

POCHIRAJU INDUSTRIES LIMITED
1/102 Sathyamangalam Village Thumanapalli Post, Krishnagiri District, Hosur, 635105, Tamil Nadu, India
Tel.: (91) 4344254988
Web Site: http://www.pochiraju.co.in
Year Founded: 1995
Assets: $16,559,746
Liabilities: $11,182,210
Net Worth: $5,377,536
Earnings: ($1,718,812)
Emp.: 200
Fiscal Year-end: 03/31/18
Biotechnology Products Mfr
N.A.I.C.S.: 325414
Sudhakar Pochiraju *(Chm & Mng Dir)*

POCL ENTERPRISES LIMITED
Willingdon Crescent 1st Floor No 6/2 Pycrofts Garden Road, Nungambakkam, Chennai, 600 006, India
Tel.: (91) 4449145454
Web Site: https://poel.in
Year Founded: 1988
539195—(BOM)
Rev.: $104,896,961
Assets: $19,509,310
Liabilities: $13,329,920
Net Worth: $6,179,390
Earnings: $1,545,507
Emp.: 405
Fiscal Year-end: 03/31/23
Chemical Products Mfr
N.A.I.C.S.: 325998
Devakar Bansal *(Co-Mng Dir)*

POCO HOLDING CO., LTD.
13F Block B Zhigu Industrial Park 3157 Shahe West Road, Nanshan District, Shenzhen, 518052, China
Tel.: (86) 75526654881
Web Site: https://www.pocomagnetic.com
Year Founded: 2009
300811—(SSE)
Rev.: $149,621,472
Assets: $315,702,036
Liabilities: $86,977,800
Net Worth: $228,724,236
Earnings: $27,105,624
Fiscal Year-end: 12/31/22
Holding Company
N.A.I.C.S.: 551112
Jianghua Du *(Chm & Gen Mgr)*

POD POINT GROUP HOLDINGS PLC
222 Grays Inn Road, London, WC1X 8HB, United Kingdom
Tel.: (44) 2073534200

Web Site: https://www.investors.pod-point.com
Year Founded: 2009
PODP—(LSE)
Rev.: $90,140,116
Assets: $294,476,142
Liabilities: $62,013,380
Net Worth: $232,462,762
Earnings: ($25,512,497)
Emp.: 540
Fiscal Year-end: 12/31/22
Holding Company
N.A.I.C.S.: 551112
David Wolffe *(CFO)*

Subsidiaries:

Pod Point Limited (1)
28-42 Banner Street, London, EC1Y 8QE, United Kingdom
Tel.: (44) 2072474114
Web Site: https://pod-point.com
Electric Charging Vehicle Distr
N.A.I.C.S.: 423620

Pod Point Norge AS (1)
Engebrets vei 3, 0275, Oslo, Norway
Tel.: (47) 21939730
Web Site: https://pod-point.no
Electric Vehicle Charging Installation Services
N.A.I.C.S.: 238210

PODAK CO., LTD.
10F No 129 Section 2 Zhongshan North Road, Zhongshan District, Taipei, 104, Taiwan
Tel.: (886) 225219090
Web Site: https://podak.com.tw
Year Founded: 1976
3537—(TPE)
Rev.: $87,933,996
Assets: $63,588,187
Liabilities: $27,956,414
Net Worth: $35,631,773
Earnings: $7,397,430
Fiscal Year-end: 12/31/22
Electric & Electronic Component Mfr
N.A.I.C.S.: 335999

PODDAR HOUSING AND DEVELOPMENT LIMITED
Poddar Group Building Mathuradas Mill Compound 126 NM Joshi Marg, Lower Parel West, Mumbai, 400 013, India
Tel.: (91) 2266164444
Web Site: https://www.poddarhousing.com
Year Founded: 1982
523628—(BOM)
Rev.: $8,077,060
Assets: $82,502,156
Liabilities: $56,516,924
Net Worth: $25,985,232
Earnings: ($267,458)
Emp.: 114
Fiscal Year-end: 03/31/21
Construction Engineering Services
N.A.I.C.S.: 541330
Dipak Kumar Poddar *(Founder & Chm)*

Subsidiaries:

Shiv Shakti Developers (1)
North near Holy Child school Panchavati Ambika Nagar, Borishana, Kalol, 382721, Gujarat, India
Tel.: (91) 9376655155
Web Site: https://www.shivshaktidevelopers.co.in
Real Estate Services
N.A.I.C.S.: 531390

PODDAR PIGMENTS LTD.
E-10-11 and F-14 to 16 RIICO Industrial Area, Sitapura, Jaipur, 302 022, Rajasthan, India
Tel.: (91) 1412770202

INTERNATIONAL PUBLIC

Web Site: https://www.poddarpigmentsltd.com
Year Founded: 1991
PODDARMENT—(NSE)
Rev.: $41,515,557
Assets: $39,758,755
Liabilities: $4,544,260
Net Worth: $35,214,496
Earnings: $3,278,041
Emp.: 337
Fiscal Year-end: 03/31/23
Plastic Raw Material Mfr
N.A.I.C.S.: 326199
S. S. Poddar *(Mng Dir)*

PODIUM MINERALS LIMITED
Level 1 234 Churchill Ave, Subiaco, 6008, WA, Australia
Tel.: (61) 892188878
Web Site: https://www.podiumminerals.com
POD—(ASX)
Rev.: $88,506
Assets: $14,965,300
Liabilities: $344,156
Net Worth: $14,621,144
Earnings: ($1,619,626)
Fiscal Year-end: 06/30/24
Mineral Exploration Services
N.A.I.C.S.: 213114
Russell Thomson *(CFO & Sec)*

PODRAVKA D.D.
Ante Starcevica 32, 48000, Koprivnica, Croatia
Tel.: (385) 48651144
Web Site: https://www.podravka.com
Year Founded: 1936
PODR—(ZAG)
Rev.: $713,307,177
Assets: $787,128,665
Liabilities: $221,972,042
Net Worth: $565,156,624
Earnings: $53,545,823
Emp.: 6,299
Fiscal Year-end: 12/31/22
Food & Pharmaceuticals
N.A.I.C.S.: 311423
Hrvoje Kolaric *(Member-Mgmt Bd)*

Subsidiaries:

Belupo d.d (1)
Josipa Vargovica 4/3, 48000, Koprivnica, Croatia
Tel.: (385) 48659011
Web Site: https://www.belupo.hr
Emp.: 1,300
Pharmaceutical Product Whslr
N.A.I.C.S.: 424210
Miroslav Vitkovic *(Chm-Supervisory Bd)*

Belupo d.o.o. (1)
Dvorzakova 6, 10000, Ljubljana, Slovenia **(100%)**
Tel.: (386) 13009510
Web Site: http://www.belupo.hr
Sales Range: $25-49.9 Million
Emp.: 7
Pharmaceutical Preparation Mfr
N.A.I.C.S.: 325412

Danica d.o.o. (1)
Delekovecka cesta 21, 48000, Koprivnica, Croatia **(100%)**
Tel.: (385) 48652300
Sales Range: $100-124.9 Million
Emp.: 400
Mayonnaise Dressing & Prepared Sauce Mfr
N.A.I.C.S.: 311941

Farmavita d.o.o. (1)
Igmanska 5a, 71320, Vogosca, Bosnia & Herzegovina
Tel.: (387) 33476320
Web Site: https://farmavita.ba
Emp.: 200
Pharmaceutical Product Whslr
N.A.I.C.S.: 424210

Ital-Ice d.o.o (1)

M Vlasica 47, Porec, 52000, Rijeka, Croatia **(100%)**
Tel.: (385) 52434908
Sales Range: $25-49.9 Million
Emp.: 35
Ice Cream & Frozen Dessert Mfr
N.A.I.C.S.: 311520

KONAR Lebensmittelhandels GmbH (1)
Hoglworther Str 1, Munich, 81369, Germany
Tel.: (49) 8972441750
Web Site: http://www.podravka-vegeta.de
Sales Range: $25-49.9 Million
Emp.: 5
Dried & Dehydrated Food Mfr
N.A.I.C.S.: 311423
Alen Ipsa *(Mng Dir)*

Mirna d.d. (1)
Giordano Paliaga 8, 52 210, Rovinj, Croatia
Tel.: (385) 52702100
Web Site: https://www.mirna-rovinj.hr
Fish Production Services
N.A.I.C.S.: 112511

Podravka - International s.r.o. (1)
Jesenskeho 1486, 960 01, Zvolen, Slovakia
Tel.: (421) 455240911
Web Site: http://www.podravka.sk
Sales Range: $25-49.9 Million
Emp.: 40
Chemical & Allied Products Merchant Whslr
N.A.I.C.S.: 424690

Podravka DOOEL (1)
Multifunctional Zone Cojlija Street 9 No 4, Petrovec, 1043, Skopje, North Macedonia
Tel.: (389) 22650134
Food Products Distr
N.A.I.C.S.: 445110
Mislav Matijevic *(Mktg Dir)*

Podravka EOOD (1)
247 Botevgradsko Chaussee blvd, Poduiane region, 1113, Sofia, Bulgaria
Tel.: (359) 29714452
Food Products Distr
N.A.I.C.S.: 445110
Denis Krsnik *(Gen Mgr)*

Podravka Gulf FZE (1)
Jafza One office BB 1209, Jebel Ali, Dubai, United Arab Emirates
Tel.: (971) 48818449
Web Site: https://en.podravka.ae
Food Products Distr
N.A.I.C.S.: 445110
Martina Dalic *(Co-Pres)*

Podravka International Kft. (1)
Llka u 34, 1143, Budapest, Hungary
Tel.: (36) 12732060
Web Site: http://www.vegeta.hu
Sales Range: $25-49.9 Million
Emp.: 28
Dried & Dehydrated Food Mfr
N.A.I.C.S.: 311423

Podravka International Pty Ltd (1)
Unit 4-59-63 Cawarra Road, Caringbah, 2229, NSW, Australia
Tel.: (61) 295310044
Web Site: http://www.podravka.com.au
Sales Range: $50-74.9 Million
Emp.: 8
Grocery & Related Products Whslr
N.A.I.C.S.: 424490
Ivan Hudaly *(Mng Dir)*

Podravka International USA Inc (1)
420 Lexington Ave Ste 2034, New York, NY 10017
Tel.: (212) 661-0125
Web Site: http://www.podravka.com
Sales Range: $25-49.9 Million
Emp.: 2
Food Products Mfr
N.A.I.C.S.: 311412
Domagoj Kero *(Pres)*

Podravka Inzenjering d.o.o (1)
13 Trg Kralja Tomislava, Koprivnica, 48000, Croatia
Tel.: (385) 48651524
Food Products Mfr
N.A.I.C.S.: 311412

Podravka Polska Sp. z.o.o. (1)
ul Lentza 10 A, 02-956, Warsaw, Poland
Tel.: (48) 224273010
Web Site: http://www.podravka.pl
Sales Range: $25-49.9 Million
Emp.: 10
Dried & Dehydrated Food Mfr
N.A.I.C.S.: 311423

Podravka d.o.o (1)
Tosin bunar 272, 11000, Belgrade, Serbia
Tel.: (381) 112184703
Web Site: http://www.podravka.com
Sales Range: $25-49.9 Million
Emp.: 60
Food Products Mfr
N.A.I.C.S.: 311991

Podravka d.o.o (1)
Cesta v Gorice 40, Ljubljana, 1000, Slovenia
Tel.: (386) 14797100
Web Site: http://www.podravka.com
Sales Range: $25-49.9 Million
Emp.: 36
Food Products Mfr
N.A.I.C.S.: 311991
Alga Ucakar *(Mgr-Mktg)*

Podravka d.o.o (1)
Safeta Zajke 269, 71000, Sarajevo, Bosnia & Herzegovina
Tel.: (387) 33475760
Web Site: http://www.podravka.com
Sales Range: $25-49.9 Million
Emp.: 100
Food Products Mfr
N.A.I.C.S.: 311999
Branislav Lovric *(Mgr-Sls)*

Podravka trgovacko poduzece d.o.o. (1)
Cesta V Gorice 40, Ljubljana, 1000, Slovenia
Tel.: (386) 14797100
Web Site: http://www.podravka.hr
Sales Range: $25-49.9 Million
Emp.: 40
Perishable Prepared Food Mfr
N.A.I.C.S.: 311991
Miroslav Vitkovic *(Mng Dir)*

Podravka- Int Deutschland - Konar Gmbh (1)
Hoglworther Str 1, Munich, 81369, Germany
Tel.: (49) 8972441750
Web Site: http://www.podravka-vegeta.de
Sales Range: $25-49.9 Million
Emp.: 9
Food Products Mfr
N.A.I.C.S.: 311919
Alan Ipsa *(Mng Dir)*

Podravka-International s.r.l. (1)
Splaiul Unirii no 4 Bl B3, District 4, Bucharest, Romania
Tel.: (40) 213114507
Web Site: https://www.podravka.ro
Food Products Distr
N.A.I.C.S.: 445110

Podravka-Lagris a.s. (1)
Dolni Lhota 39, Dolni Lhota u Luhacovic, 763 23, Zlin, Czech Republic
Tel.: (420) 577658200
Web Site: https://www.podravka.cz
Sales Range: $100-124.9 Million
Emp.: 300
Dried & Dehydrated Food Mfr
N.A.I.C.S.: 311423
Dalibor Kezele *(Gen Mgr)*

Zito Maloprodaja d.o.o. (1)
Moskovska Ulica 1, 1000, Ljubljana, Slovenia
Tel.: (386) 15876100
Web Site: https://www.zito.si
Food Products Distr
N.A.I.C.S.: 445110
Karmen Pangos *(CEO)*

Zito d.o.o. (1)
Moskovska ulica 1, 1000, Ljubljana, Slovenia
Tel.: (386) 15876100
Web Site: https://www.zito.si
Sales Range: $125-149.9 Million
Baking & Milling Services
N.A.I.C.S.: 311811
Erik Zunic *(Member-Mgmt Bd-Fin, Acctg & IT)*

Subsidiary (Domestic):

Intes Storitve, d.o.o. (2)
St Jozica flander 2, 2000, Maribor, Slovenia **(100%)**
Tel.: (386) 5876102
Web Site: http://www.zito.si
Breads & Cakes Mfr
N.A.I.C.S.: 311812

PODRAVSKA BANKA D.D.
Opaticka 3, 48000, Koprivnica, Croatia
Tel.: (385) 72655000
Web Site: https://www.poba.hr
Year Founded: 1872
Rev.: $21,701,435
Assets: $493,521,585
Liabilities: $432,538,508
Net Worth: $60,983,077
Earnings: $3,718,932
Emp.: 223
Fiscal Year-end: 12/31/16
Banking & Financial Services
N.A.I.C.S.: 523150
Sigilfredo Montinari *(Deputy Chm-Supervisory Bd)*

PODUNAVLJE A.D.
Proleterska bb, Celarevo, Serbia
Tel.: (381) 21 761 814
Year Founded: 1998
Sales Range: $1-9.9 Million
Emp.: 83
Fruit Farming Services
N.A.I.C.S.: 111339
Nikola Milicevic *(Gen Mgr)*

PODUNAVLJE A.D.
Jugoslovenske armije 42, 21400, Backa Palanka, 21400, Serbia
Tel.: (381) 217550900
Web Site: https://www.podunavlje.rs
Year Founded: 1953
PDBP—(BEL)
Sales Range: $25-49.9 Million
Emp.: 578
Retail Store Operator
N.A.I.C.S.: 455219
Jovo Zivkov *(Exec Dir & Dir)*

PODUNAVLJE A.D.
Jugoslovenske armije 42, 21400, Backa Palanka, Serbia
Tel.: (381) 217550900
Web Site: https://podunavlje.rs
Year Founded: 2003
PDBC—(BEL)
Sales Range: $10-24.9 Million
Emp.: 474
Grocery Store Operator
N.A.I.C.S.: 445110
Branko Jelic *(CEO & Exec Dir)*

PODVIS TERM A.D.
Dobrivoja Radosavljevica 146, 19350, Knjazevac, Serbia
Tel.: (381) 19731002
Web Site: http://www.podvisterm.rs
Year Founded: 1996
PDVS—(BEL)
Sales Range: Less than $1 Million
Emp.: 31
Boiler & Water Heater Mfr
N.A.I.C.S.: 332410
Dusko Kostic *(Exec Dir & Dir)*

POENINA HOLDING AG
Vega-Strasse 3 Glattpark, 8152, Opfikon, Switzerland
Tel.: (41) 587339090
Web Site: http://www.poenina.ch
PNHO—(SWX)
Sales Range: Less than $1 Million
Plumbing Contract Services
N.A.I.C.S.: 238220
Jean-Claude Bregy *(Chm-Mgmt Bd, CEO & CFO-Interim)*

Subsidiaries:

Albis Technik AG (1)
Fischmarkt 1, 6302, Zug, Switzerland
Tel.: (41) 7290906
Web Site: http://www.albis-technik.ch
Heating & Plumbing Services
N.A.I.C.S.: 238220

Banz AG (1)
Neuhaltenstrasse 3, Ebikon, 6030, Lucerne, Switzerland
Tel.: (41) 4401515
Web Site: http://www.banz.ch
Heating & Plumbing Services
N.A.I.C.S.: 238220

Demuth AG (1)
Tafernstrasse 31, 5405, Baden-Dattwil, Switzerland
Tel.: (41) 564833000
Web Site: http://www.demuth-ag.ch
Construction Services
N.A.I.C.S.: 236220

Elsener-Klima AG (1)
Soodring 13a, 8134, Adliswil, Switzerland
Tel.: (41) 447118040
Web Site: http://www.elsener-klima.ch
Heating & Plumbing Services
N.A.I.C.S.: 238220

Hans Ziegler AG (1)
Sagenriet 9, 8853, Lachen, Switzerland
Tel.: (41) 554515020
Web Site: http://www.hansziegler.ch
Heating & Plumbing Services
N.A.I.C.S.: 238220

Lauber IWISA AG (1)
Kehrstrasse 14, Naters, 3904, Brig, Switzerland
Tel.: (41) 279227777
Web Site: http://www.lauber-iwisa.ch
Sanitary & Heating Services
N.A.I.C.S.: 238220

Ospelt Haustechnik AG (1)
Arinstrasse 15, 9475, Sevelen, Switzerland
Tel.: (41) 817400806
Heating & Ventilation Contract Services
N.A.I.C.S.: 238220

Sada AG (1)
Vega-Strasse 3 Glattpark, 8152, Opfikon, Switzerland
Tel.: (41) 442979797
Web Site: http://www.sada.ch
Sanitary & Ventilation Services
N.A.I.C.S.: 238220

Scherrer Haustechnik AG (1)
Rheinweg 1, 8200, Schaffhausen, Switzerland
Tel.: (41) 526350111
Web Site: http://www.scherrerht.ch
Sanitary & Ventilation Services
N.A.I.C.S.: 236220

Shz Gebaudetechnik AG (1)
Sagenriet 9, 8853, Lachen, Switzerland
Tel.: (41) 554516040
Web Site: http://www.shz.ch
Heating & Ventilation Services
N.A.I.C.S.: 238220

Spescha Haustechnik AG (1)
Plam dil Blasi 5, 7078, Lenzerheide, Switzerland
Tel.: (41) 813851111
Web Site: http://www.spescha-haustechnik.ch
Heating & Plumbing Services
N.A.I.C.S.: 238220

Willi Haustechnik AG (1)
Industriestrasse 19, 7001, Chur, Switzerland
Tel.: (41) 812869944
Web Site: http://www.willihaustechnik.ch
Construction Services
N.A.I.C.S.: 236220

POET TECHNOLOGIES INC.
1107-120 Eglinton Avenue East, Toronto, M4P 1E2, ON, Canada
Tel.: (416) 368-9411 ON
Web Site: https://www.poet-technologies.com

POET TECHNOLOGIES INC.

POET Technologies Inc.—(Continued)

POET—(NASDAQ)
Rev.: $552,748
Assets: $15,390,453
Liabilities: $3,945,405
Net Worth: $11,445,048
Earnings: ($21,036,690)
Emp.: 53
Fiscal Year-end: 12/31/22
Semiconductor Product Mfr & Sales
N.A.I.C.S.: 334413
Thomas R. Mika *(CFO & Exec VP)*

POGAGNA
Rue De Cornen, 44510, Le Pouliguen, Loire-Atlantique, France
Tel.: (33) 240421046
Rev.: $30,800,000
Emp.: 72
Grocery Stores
N.A.I.C.S.: 445110
Pierrette Lehuede *(Mgr-Fin)*

POH HUAT RESOURCES HOLDINGS BERHAD
Plo 1 Jorak Industrial Area Mukim Sungai Raya, Bukit Pasir, 84300, Muar, Johor, Malaysia
Tel.: (60) 69859688
Web Site: https://www.pohhuat.com
POHUAT—(KLS)
Rev.: $93,189,226
Assets: $134,339,639
Liabilities: $17,880,229
Net Worth: $116,459,410
Earnings: $5,814,285
Emp.: 2,802
Fiscal Year-end: 10/31/23
Wooden Furniture Mfr & Distr
N.A.I.C.S.: 337121
Kah Man Pang *(Sec)*

Subsidiaries:

Poh Huat Furniture Industries (M) Sdn. Bhd. (1)
Plo 1 Jalan Raja Bukit Pasir Industrial Area Mukim Sg Raya, Bukit Pasir, 84300, Muar, Johor Darul Takzim, Malaysia
Tel.: (60) 69859688
Sales Range: $75-99.9 Million
Emp.: 120
Home Furnishing Mfr
N.A.I.C.S.: 423220
Patrick Chen *(Mgr-Mktg)*

Poh Huat Furniture Industries Vietnam Joint Stock Company (1)
No 17 Road 26 Song Than II Industrial Zone, Di An, 53000, Binh Duong, Vietnam
Tel.: (84) 6503729101
Wooden Furniture Mfr
N.A.I.C.S.: 321999

Poh Huat Furniture Industries Vietnam Joint Stock Company - Dong Nai Factory (1)
No 25 Tam Phuoc Industrial Zone, Long Thanh Ward, Bien Hoa, Dong Nai, Vietnam
Tel.: (84) 2513512888
Furniture Mfr
N.A.I.C.S.: 337214

Poh Huat International Furniture S.A. (Proprietary) Limited (1)
Unit 3 Hambleton Park 98 Richards Drive, Halfway House, Midrand, 1685, South Africa
Tel.: (27) 110216451
Web Site: http://www.pohhuat.co.za
Home & Office Furnitures Distr
N.A.I.C.S.: 423210

POH KONG HOLDINGS BERHAD
1620 Jalan 524, 46200, Petaling Jaya, Selangor Darul Ehsan, Malaysia
Tel.: (60) 379403333
Web Site:
https://www.pohkong.com.my
POHKONG—(KLS)
Rev.: $223,517,208
Assets: $200,060,540
Liabilities: $51,022,364
Net Worth: $149,038,176
Earnings: $9,098,425
Emp.: 1,046
Fiscal Year-end: 07/31/21
Jewelry Mfr
N.A.I.C.S.: 339910
Yim Kong Ng *(Sec)*

Subsidiaries:

Poh Kong Jewellery Manufacturer Sdn. Bhd. (1)
Lot 1 Jalan Astaka U8/81 Section U8, Shah Alam, 40150, Malaysia
Tel.: (60) 378468899
Jewellery Mfr & Distr
N.A.I.C.S.: 339910

POHJOLAN VOIMA OY
Toolonkatu 4, PO Box 40, FIN-00101, Helsinki, Finland
Tel.: (358) 9693061
Web Site: http://www.pvo.fi
Year Founded: 1943
Sales Range: $125-149.9 Million
Emp.: 860
Energy & Power Generation Services
N.A.I.C.S.: 335311
Seppo Parvi *(Deputy Chm)*

Subsidiaries:

Kaukaan Voima Oy (1)
Kaukaantie 16, 53200, Lappeenranta, Finland
Tel.: (358) 204 15 161
Electricity Power Generation Services
N.A.I.C.S.: 221118
Jukka Kiuru *(Mng Dir)*

Kokkolan Voima Oy (1)
Voimalantie 10, 67900, Kokkola, Finland
Tel.: (358) 10 478 5000
Electricity Power Generation Services
N.A.I.C.S.: 221118
Veli-Matti Tuliniemi *(Mng Dir)*

Mussalon Voima Oy (1)
Janskantie 1, PO Box 108, 48101, Kotka, Finland
Tel.: (358) 5 2299 5800
Electricity Power Generation Services
N.A.I.C.S.: 221118
Mikko Kurki *(Mng Dir)*

PVO-Pool Oy (1)
Voimalaitoksentie 51, 29200, Harjavalta, Finland
Tel.: (358) 253 55 50 00
Electricity Power Generation Services
N.A.I.C.S.: 221118

PVO-Vesivoima Oy (1)
Voimatie 23, 91100, Helsinki, Finland
Tel.: (358) 10 478 5000
Web Site: http://www.pohjolanvoima.fi
Electricity Power Generation Services
N.A.I.C.S.: 221111
Pertti Pietinen *(Mng Dir)*

Porin Prosessivoima Oy (1)
Titaanitie, 28840, Pori, Finland
Tel.: (358) 9 693 061
Electricity Power Generation Services
N.A.I.C.S.: 221118
Timo Maki *(Mng Dir)*

Powest Oy (1)
Toolonkatu 4, PO Box 40, 00101, Helsinki, Finland
Tel.: (358) 9693061
Web Site: http://www.powest.com
Sales Range: $25-49.9 Million
Emp.: 15
Power Distribution Services
N.A.I.C.S.: 335311

Rauman Biovoima Oy (1)
Tikkalantie 1, PO Box 95, 26101, Rauma, Finland
Tel.: (358) 204 14 101
Electricity Power Generation Services
N.A.I.C.S.: 221118
Timo Pitkanen *(Mng Dir)*

Wisapower Oy (1)
Alholmintie 42, PO Box 118, 68601, Pietarsaari, Finland
Tel.: (358) 204 15 111
Electricity Power Generation Services
N.A.I.C.S.: 221118

POIANA BRASOV SA
Str Muresenil No 28, 500030, Brasov, Romania
Tel.: (40) 268417866
Web Site:
https://www.poianabrasovsa.ro
Year Founded: 1895
POBR—(BUC)
Assets: $94
Liabilities: $23,624
Net Worth: ($23,531)
Earnings: ($1,802)
Fiscal Year-end: 12/31/22
Travel Agency Services
N.A.I.C.S.: 561510

POINCARE GESTION SAS
23 rue Lepois, 54000, Nancy, France
Tel.: (33) 3 83 32 48 37
Web Site: http://www.fonds-gei.com
Investment Services
N.A.I.C.S.: 523999
Serge Peiffer *(Pres)*

Subsidiaries:

Rollpack SASU (1)
496 Zone Industrielle de Neuilly, 88170, Chatenois, France
Tel.: (33) 3 29 94 78 38
Web Site: http://www.rollpack.com
Sales Range: $25-49.9 Million
Emp.: 38
Packaging Paper Products Mfr
N.A.I.C.S.: 322220
Jean Goulet *(CEO)*

POINT ENGINEERING CO., LTD.
89 Asanvalley-Ro, Dunpo-Myeon, Asan, Chungcheongnam-do, Korea (South)
Tel.: (82) 415465131
Web Site: https://www.pointeng.co.kr
Year Founded: 1998
256630—(KRS)
Rev.: $30,212,057
Assets: $78,449,876
Liabilities: $18,637,778
Net Worth: $59,812,098
Earnings: $598,225
Emp.: 193
Fiscal Year-end: 12/31/22
Semiconductor Components Mfr
N.A.I.C.S.: 334413
Bum-Mo Ahn *(CEO)*

POINT LISAS INDUSTRIAL PORT DEVELOPMENT CORPORATION LIMITED
PLIPDECO House Orinoco Drive Point Lisas Industrial Estate, Couva, Trinidad & Tobago
Tel.: (868) 6362201
Web Site: https://www.plipdeco.com
Year Founded: 1966
PLD—(TRI)
Rev.: $54,168,627
Assets: $486,877,760
Liabilities: $53,222,623
Net Worth: $433,655,137
Earnings: $7,782,360
Fiscal Year-end: 12/31/23
Other Activities Related to Real Estate
N.A.I.C.S.: 531390
Ian R. H. Atherly *(Chm)*

POINT LOMA RESOURCES LTD.
2000 350 7 Avenue SW, Calgary, T2P 3N9, AB, Canada
Tel.: (403) 705-5051
Web Site: http://www.pointloma.ca
Year Founded: 2010
Rev.: $4,083,376
Assets: $25,572,590
Liabilities: $26,090,800
Net Worth: ($518,210)
Earnings: ($10,194,147)
Emp.: 14
Fiscal Year-end: 12/31/18
Oil & Gas Exploration
N.A.I.C.S.: 211120
Brad Johnston *(VP-Land)*

POINTCLICKCARE CORP.
5570 Explorer Drive, Mississauga, L4W 0C4, ON, Canada
Tel.: (905) 858-8885
Web Site:
https://www.pointclickcare.com
Year Founded: 1995
Customized Software for Nursing Homes & Long-Term Care Facilities
N.A.I.C.S.: 513210
Mike Wessinger *(Co-Founder & CEO)*

Subsidiaries:

American HealthTech, Inc. (1)
805 S Wheatley St Ste 600, Ridgeland, MS 39157-6080
Web Site: https://www.healthtech.net
Healthcare Software Publisher
N.A.I.C.S.: 513210
Mechelle Green *(VP-AHT Client Rels)*

POINTER LIMITED
65 North Wallace Street, Glasgow, G4 0DT, United Kingdom
Tel.: (44) 1415642500
Web Site: http://www.pointer.co.uk
Year Founded: 1972
Rev.: $22,082,385
Emp.: 177
Security & Fire Systems Services
N.A.I.C.S.: 561621
Jim Gemmell *(Mgr-EMEA Solutions)*

Subsidiaries:

Pointer Asia Limited (1)
2034/72 15th Floor ItalThai Tower New Phetchburi Road, Bangkapi Huay-kwang, Bangkok, 10320, Thailand
Tel.: (66) 27161800
Web Site: www.pointer.co.th
Security System Installation Services
N.A.I.C.S.: 561621
Zaruth Phanrithi-udom *(Country Mgr)*

Pointer LLC (1)
Jawarth Al Jebel Shatti Complex 1322, PO Box 3390, Way 217 Shatti Al Qurum, Ruwi, 112, Oman
Tel.: (968) 96795797
Web Site: http://www.pointeroman.com
Security System Installation Services
N.A.I.C.S.: 561621
Chris Webster *(Gen Mgr)*

POINTERRA LIMITED
Level 2 27 Railway Road, Subiaco, 6008, WA, Australia
Tel.: (61) 863236100
Web Site: https://www.pointerra 3DP—(ASX)
Rev.: $5,074,111
Assets: $3,402,188
Liabilities: $3,848,448
Net Worth: ($446,259)
Earnings: ($3,490,781)
Fiscal Year-end: 06/30/24
Investment Services
N.A.I.C.S.: 523999
Ian Olson *(Mng Dir)*

Subsidiaries:

Pointerra US, Inc. (1)
919 N Market St Ste 950, Wilmington, DE 19801

AND PRIVATE COMPANIES

Tel.: (571) 528-8799
Software Development Services
N.A.I.C.S.: 541511

POINTON YORK GROUP LIMITED
Pointon York House Welland Business Park Valley Way, Market Harborough, LE16 7PS, United Kingdom
Tel.: (44) 1858419300
Web Site: http://www.pointonyork.co.uk
Sales Range: $1-9.9 Million
Holding Company; Financial & Insurance Services
N.A.I.C.S.: 551112
Geoffrey Pointon *(Founder & Chm)*

POINTPACK SA
60a Jozefa Bema St, 01-225, Warsaw, Poland
Tel.: (48) 223790270
Web Site: https://www.pointpack.com
Online Shopping Retailer
N.A.I.C.S.: 334513
Marek Piosik *(Founder & CEO)*

POINTS NORTH CONTRACTING, LTD.
8011 93 Street, Fort Saint John, V1J 6X1, BC, Canada
Tel.: (250) 787-5525
Rev.: $20,900,000
Emp.: 20
Oil Field Services
N.A.I.C.S.: 213112

POINTSBET HOLDINGS LIMITED
Level 2 165 Cremorne Street, Cremorne, 3121, VIC, Australia
Tel.: (61) 484036681   AU
Web Site: https://www.pointsbet.com.au
Year Founded: 2015
PBTHF—(OTCQX)
Rev.: $137,118,080
Assets: $395,624,307
Liabilities: $68,666,623
Net Worth: $326,957,684
Earnings: ($180,161,048)
Emp.: 698
Fiscal Year-end: 06/30/23
Holding Company
N.A.I.C.S.: 551112
A. J. Hensher *(Sec)*

POITOU CARBURANTS SAE DES ETS TABAUD
Parc D" Activites D Alpespace Voie Galilee, Francin, 73800, Chambery, France
Tel.: (33) 549484028
Sales Range: $25-49.9 Million
Emp.: 30
Coal & Other Minerals & Ores
N.A.I.C.S.: 423520
Frederic Tabaud *(Co-Pres)*

POJAZDY SZYNOWE PESA BYDGOSZCZ S.A. HOLDING
Zygmunta Augusta 11 Str, 85-082, Bydgoszcz, Poland
Tel.: (48) 525868100
Web Site: http://www.pesa.pl
Year Founded: 1851
Sales Range: $400-449.9 Million
Emp.: 1,500
Transportation Services
N.A.I.C.S.: 488210
Robert Swiechowicz *(Pres & CEO)*

Subsidiaries:

Zaklad Produkcyjno - Remontowy "REM-SUW" Sp. z o.o.   (1)
ul Zygmunta Augusta 11, 85-082, Bydgoszcz, Poland
Tel.: (48) 52 349 32 07
Web Site: http://www.remsuw.pl
Emp.: 80
Railway Rolling Stock Repairing Services
N.A.I.C.S.: 488210

POKARNA LIMITED
Surya Towers 105 Sardar Patel Road, Secunderabad, 500 003, Telangana, India
Tel.: (91) 4066310111
Web Site: https://www.pokarna.com
Year Founded: 1991
POKARNA—(NSE)
Rev.: $88,642,204
Assets: $132,388,142
Liabilities: $71,582,423
Net Worth: $60,805,719
Earnings: $7,890,522
Emp.: 304
Fiscal Year-end: 03/31/23
Crushed & Broken Granite Mining & Quarrying Services
N.A.I.C.S.: 212313
Gautam Chand Jain *(Chm & Mng Dir)*

POKFULAM DEVELOPMENT COMPANY LIMITED
23/F Beverly House 93-107 Lockhart Road, Wanchai, China (Hong Kong)
Tel.: (852) 2 520 1010   HK
Web Site:
   http://www.pokfulam.com.hk
Year Founded: 1970
0225—(HKG)
Rev.: $22,280,650
Assets: $735,760,993
Liabilities: $23,412,192
Net Worth: $712,348,801
Earnings: $17,679,547
Emp.: 74
Fiscal Year-end: 09/30/21
Investment Management Service
N.A.I.C.S.: 523999
Abraham Tat Chang Wong *(Chm & Mng Dir)*

Subsidiaries:

Elephant Holdings Limited   (1)
3/F Beverly House 93-107 Lockhart Road, Wanchai, China (Hong Kong)   (99.76%)
Tel.: (852) 2520 2330
Web Site: http://www.elephant.com.hk
Electronic Control System Installation Services
N.A.I.C.S.: 238210

POKHARA FINANCE LIMITED
Newroad, Kaski, Pokhara, 9, Nepal
Tel.: (977) 61581145
Web Site:
   https://www.pokharafinance.com.np
PFL—(NEP)
Sales Range: Less than $1 Million
Banking Services
N.A.I.C.S.: 522110
Bhuwansing Gurung *(Chm)*

POLA ORBIS HOLDINGS INC.
Pola Ginza Building 1-7-7 Ginza, Chuo-ku, Tokyo, 104-0061, Japan
Tel.: (81) 335635517
Web Site: https://www.po-holdings.co.jp
PORBF—(OTCIQ)
Rev.: $1,706,690,480
Assets: $1,972,222,560
Liabilities: $328,026,160
Net Worth: $1,644,196,400
Earnings: $44,837,760
Emp.: 146
Fiscal Year-end: 12/31/20
Holding Company
N.A.I.C.S.: 551112
Satoshi Suzuki *(Pres)*

POLAR CAPITAL GLOBAL FINANCIALS TRUST PLC

Subsidiaries:

Jurlique International Pty Ltd   (1)
44-50 Oborn Road, Mount Barker, 5251, SA, Australia
Tel.: (61) 883917479
Web Site: http://www.jurlique.com
Sales Range: $100-124.9 Million
Skin Care & Cosmetic Products Mfr & Retailer
N.A.I.C.S.: 325620

Kayaku Co., Ltd.   (1)
1-2-5 Kitano, Tokorozawa, 359-1152, Saitama, Japan
Tel.: (81) 4 2948 1351
Web Site: http://www.kayaku.co.jp
Emp.: 174
Pharmaceutical Products Mfr & Distr
N.A.I.C.S.: 325412

ORBIS Inc.   (1)
2-1-14 Hiratsuka, Shinagawa-ku, Tokyo, 142-0051, Japan
Tel.: (81) 120080270
Web Site: https://corp.orbis.co.jp
Sales Range: $400-449.9 Million
Emp.: 1,055
Cosmetics Mfr & Sales
N.A.I.C.S.: 325620
Takuma Kobayashi *(Pres)*

ORLANE JAPON INC   (1)
7F 1-9-2 Shinjuku, Shinjuku-ku, Tokyo, 60-0022, Japan
Tel.: (81) 3 5368 0881
Web Site: http://www.orlane.co.jp
Cosmetics Mfr & Sales
N.A.I.C.S.: 325620

P.O. REAL ESTATE INC.   (1)
2-2-10 Nishigotanda, Shinagawa-ku, Tokyo, 141-0031, Japan
Tel.: (81) 334947139
Web Site: https://www.po-realestate.co.jp
Sales Range: $50-74.9 Million
Emp.: 13
Office Building Rental Services
N.A.I.C.S.: 531120

Subsidiary (Domestic):

P.O. MEDIA SERVICE INC   (2)
Pola Gotanada Building 3 3F 8-9-5 Nishi Gotanda, Shinagawa-ku, Tokyo, 141-0031, Japan
Tel.: (81) 3 3495 1051
Web Site: http://www.po-mediaservice.co.jp
Commercial Printing Services
N.A.I.C.S.: 323111

Subsidiary (Non-US):

P.O. TECHNO SERVICE INC.   (2)
Tel.: (81) 337792788
Web Site: https://www.po-technoservice.co.jp
Facility Management Services
N.A.I.C.S.: 561210

POLA COSMETICS (HONGKONG) CO., LTD   (1)
Level 16 Millennium City 2 C78 Kwun Tong Road, Kowloon, China (Hong Kong)
Tel.: (852) 25110881
Web Site: http://www.pola.com.hk
Emp.: 40
Cosmetics Whslr
N.A.I.C.S.: 424210

POLA COSMETICS (THAILAND) CO., LTD   (1)
518/5 6th Floor Maneeya Building Ploenchit Road, Pathum Wan, Bangkok, Bangkok, Thailand
Tel.: (66) 22548140
Cosmetics Mfr & Sales
N.A.I.C.S.: 325620

POLA Chemical Industries, Inc.   (1)
Tel.: (81) 458267111
Web Site: https://www.pola-rm.co.jp
Holding Company; Cosmetics Research & Development & Mfr
N.A.I.C.S.: 551112

Holding (Domestic):

POLA Inc.   (2)
2-2-3 Nishigotanda, Shinagawa-ku, Tokyo, 141-8523, Japan

Tel.: (81) 334947111
Web Site: https://www.pola.co.jp
Sales Range: $800-899.9 Million
Cosmetics Mfr
N.A.I.C.S.: 325620

POLA ORBIS Travel Retail Limited   (1)
Room 2401 24/F World Trade Centre, Causeway Bay, China (Hong Kong)
Tel.: (852) 37483124
Personalized Beauty Care Product Distr
N.A.I.C.S.: 456120

POLA TRADING (SHANGHAI) CO., LTD.   (1)
Tel.: (86) 2164671785
Cosmetic Products Sales
N.A.I.C.S.: 424210

POLA U.S.A. INC   (1)
251 E Victoria St, Carson, CA 90746
Tel.: (800) 765-2872
Web Site: http://www.pola.com
Cosmetics Mfr & Sales
N.A.I.C.S.: 325620

Pola Chemical Industries, Inc. - Fukuroi Plant   (1)
1234 Aino, Fukuroi, 437-8765, Shizuoka, Japan
Tel.: (81) 53 842 7111
Web Site: http://www.pola-rm.co.jp
Cosmetics Products Mfr
N.A.I.C.S.: 325620

Taiwan ORBIS Inc.   (1)
No 45 Nanjing West Road, Datong District, Taipei, 10666, Taiwan
Tel.: (886) 22 558 8123
Web Site: http://www.orbis.com.tw
Sales Range: $50-74.9 Million
Cosmetics Products Mfr & Sales
N.A.I.C.S.: 424210
Akiko Egami *(Mng Dir)*

Tricot, Inc.   (1)
2-3-15 5F, Shinjyuku-ku, Tokyo, 160-0022, Japan
Tel.: (81) 364164866
Web Site: https://tricot-inc.com
Personalized Beauty Care Product Distr
N.A.I.C.S.: 456120

decencia INC.   (1)
Pola Daini Gotanda Building 1F 2-2-10 Nishigotanda, Shinagawa-ku, Tokyo, 141-0031, Japan
Tel.: (81) 334941570
Web Site: https://www.decencia.co.jp
Sales Range: $25-49.9 Million
Cosmetics Mfr & Sales
N.A.I.C.S.: 325620

pdc INC.   (1)
Tengenji Square 4F Minami Azabu, Minato-ku, Tokyo, 106-0047, Japan
Tel.: (81) 357390822
Web Site: http://www.p-dc.com
Cosmetics Retailer
N.A.I.C.S.: 456120

POLAMCO LTD
Weston Lock Lower Bristol Road, Bath, BA2 1EP, United Kingdom
Tel.: (44) 1225322500
Web Site: http://www.polamco.com
Rev.: $13,828,409
Emp.: 91
Electrical Component Mfr
N.A.I.C.S.: 335999
David Polson *(Chm)*

POLAR CAPITAL GLOBAL FINANCIALS TRUST PLC
16 Palace Street, London, SW1E 5JD, United Kingdom
Tel.: (44) 2072272700   UK
Web Site:
   https://www.polarcapitaltrust.com
Year Founded: 2013
PCFT—(LSE)
Rev.: $24,370,465
Assets: $718,409,933
Liabilities: $96,897,518
Net Worth: $621,512,415

POLAR CAPITAL GLOBAL FINANCIALS TRUST PLC

Polar Capital Global Financials Trust plc—(Continued)
Earnings: ($19,764,481)
Fiscal Year-end: 11/30/23
Investment Management Trust Services
N.A.I.C.S.: 523940
Nick Brind *(Mgr-Fund)*

POLAR CAPITAL GLOBAL HEALTHCARE TRUST PLC
16 Palace Street, London, SW1E 5JD, United Kingdom
Tel.: (44) 2072272700   UK
Web Site:
https://www.polarcapitaltrust.co.uk
Year Founded: 2010
PCGH—(LSE)
Rev.: $91,713,195
Assets: $575,865,675
Liabilities: $53,394,390
Net Worth: $522,471,285
Earnings: $85,360,590
Fiscal Year-end: 09/30/21
Investment Management Trust Services
N.A.I.C.S.: 523940
Lisa Arnold *(Chm)*

POLAR CAPITAL HOLDINGS PLC
16 Palace Street, London, SW1E 5JD, United Kingdom
Tel.: (44) 2072272700   UK
Web Site:
https://www.polarcapital.co.uk
Year Founded: 2001
POLR—(AIM)
Rev.: $227,096,659
Assets: $300,118,224
Liabilities: $122,720,885
Net Worth: $177,397,339
Earnings: $44,222,982
Emp.: 167
Fiscal Year-end: 03/31/23
Investment Management Service
N.A.I.C.S.: 523999
Brian Ashford-Russell *(Founder)*

Subsidiaries:

Polar Capital (America) Corporation   (1)
10 Corbin Dr, Darien, CT 06820
Tel.: (203) 604-1550
Investment Management Service
N.A.I.C.S.: 523999
John Mansell *(COO)*

Polar Capital Partners (Jersey) Limited   (1)
12 Castle Street, Saint Helier, JE23RT, Jersey
Tel.: (44) 153 484 7000
Investment Management Service
N.A.I.C.S.: 523999
Bob Jones *(Mng Dir)*

POLAR CAPITAL TECHNOLOGY TRUST PLC
16 Palace Street, London, SW1E 5JD, United Kingdom
Tel.: (44) 2072272700
Web Site:
https://www.polarcapitaltrust.co.uk
Year Founded: 1996
PCT—(LSE)
Assets: $3,602,702,313
Liabilities: $92,697,759
Net Worth: $3,510,004,554
Earnings: $130,538,898
Fiscal Year-end: 04/30/23
Investment Services
N.A.I.C.S.: 523999
Ben Rogoff *(Partner)*

POLAR ELECTRO OY
Professorintie 5, 90440, Kempele, Finland
Tel.: (358) 85202100   FI
Web Site: http://www.polar.com
Year Founded: 1977
Sales Range: $150-199.9 Million
Emp.: 1,200
Wireless Heart Rate Measurement Monitor Manufacturing
N.A.I.C.S.: 334519
Marco Suvilaakso *(Grp Dir-Product)*

Subsidiaries:

Polar Electro (UK) Ltd   (1)
Polar House Unit L Heathcote Way Heathcote Industrial Estate, Warwick, CV34 6TE, United Kingdom
Tel.: (44) 1926 310 330
Electronic Equipment Distr
N.A.I.C.S.: 423690

Polar Electro Austria GmbH   (1)
Handelskai 388/ Top 432 Eingang Wehlistrasse 299, 1020, Vienna, Austria
Tel.: (43) 259 68 63 60
Electronic Equipment Distr
N.A.I.C.S.: 423690

Polar Electro Belgium NV   (1)
Vriesenrot 3 IZ Hoogveld - Zone B, 9200, Dendermonde, Belgium
Tel.: (32) 52 25 94 20
Electronic Equipment Distr
N.A.I.C.S.: 423690

Polar Electro Canada Inc   (1)
2350 46th Avenue, Lachine, H8T 2P3, QC, Canada
Tel.: (514) 636-3302
Electronic Equipment Distr
N.A.I.C.S.: 423690

Polar Electro Danmark ApS   (1)
Skovlytoften 26 A, 2840, Holte, Denmark
Tel.: (45) 4541 0530
Electronic Equipment Distr
N.A.I.C.S.: 423690

Polar Electro Europe AG   (1)
Antennestraat 46, 1322 AS, Almere, Netherlands
Tel.: (31) 36 546 03 13
Electronic Equipment Distr
N.A.I.C.S.: 423690

Polar Electro France S.A.S.   (1)
1 Chemin De L'aviation CS 70233, 64200, Bassussarry, Cedex, France
Tel.: (33) 559 435 290
Electronic Equipment Distr
N.A.I.C.S.: 423690

Polar Electro GmbH   (1)
Darmstadter Str 59, 64572, Buttelborn, Germany
Tel.: (49) 6152 92 36 600
Electronic Equipment Distr
N.A.I.C.S.: 423690

Polar Electro Iberica S.A   (1)
Av Ports d Europa 100, 08040, Barcelona, Spain
Tel.: (34) 902 159 951
Electronic Equipment Distr
N.A.I.C.S.: 423690

Polar Electro Inc.   (1)
1111 Marcus Ave, Lake Success, NY 11042-1034   (100%)
Tel.: (516) 364-0400
Web Site: http://www.polarusa.com
Wireless Heart Rate Monitoring Devices Distribution & Sales
N.A.I.C.S.: 334519
Steve Stardy *(Mgr-Natl Accts)*

Polar Electro Italia SrL   (1)
via Cimarosa 53, Casalecchio di Reno, 40033, Bologna, Italy
Tel.: (39) 051 29 87 611
Electronic Equipment Distr
N.A.I.C.S.: 423690

Polar Electro Norge AS   (1)
PO Box 6307 Etterstad, 0604, Oslo, Norway
Tel.: (47) 23172500
Electronic Equipment Distr
N.A.I.C.S.: 423690

Polar Electro Singapore Pte Ltd   (1)
1 Commonwealth Lane 07-04 One Commonwealth, Singapore, 149544, Singapore
Tel.: (65) 6692 7722
Electronic Equipment Distr
N.A.I.C.S.: 423690

Polar Electro Sverige AB   (1)
Salkhallen Gustavslundvagen 159, 167 51, Bromma, Sweden
Tel.: (46) 8 704 00 29
Electronic Equipment Distr
N.A.I.C.S.: 423690

POLAR WINDOWS OF CANADA LTD.
672 Kimberly Avenue, Winnipeg, R2K 0Y2, MB, Canada
Tel.: (204) 956-6500
Web Site:
http://www.polarwindows.com
Year Founded: 1976
Metal Window & Door Mfr & Distr
N.A.I.C.S.: 332321
Stephen Segal *(Pres)*

POLARAY OPTOELECTRONICS CO., LTD.
15 Kon 4 Road, Linkou-Hsiang, Taipei, Hsien, Taiwan
Tel.: (886) 2 2602 0978
Year Founded: 1998
Sales Range: $10-24.9 Million
Emp.: 50
Optoelectronic Product Mfr
N.A.I.C.S.: 334413
Mei Li Gung *(Pres)*

Subsidiaries:

Beijing SWT Optical Communications Technologies, Co., Ltd.   (1)
10th Floor Tower C2 Oriental Plaza No1 East Chang An Avenue, Dong Cheng District, Beijing, 100738, China
Tel.: (86) 1085180588
Web Site: http://www.swt-oc.com
Sales Range: $1-9.9 Million
Optoelectronic Products Mfr; Owned 50% by Beijing SWT Communications Co., Ltd. & 50% by Polaray Optoelectronics Co., Ltd.
N.A.I.C.S.: 334413

POLARCOOL AB
Medicon Village, 223 81, Lund, Sweden
Tel.: (46) 733992317
Web Site: https://www.polarcool.se
98H—(DEU)
Medical Device Mfr
N.A.I.C.S.: 339112
Matz Johansson *(CEO)*

POLARCUS LIMITED
Reef Tower Level 20 Jumeirah Lakes Towers, PO Box 283373, Dubai, United Arab Emirates
Tel.: (971) 44360800
Web Site: http://www.polarcus.com
Sales Range: $250-299.9 Million
Seismic & Navigation Systems Mfr
N.A.I.C.S.: 334511
Imane Mabrouk *(Head-Tax)*

Subsidiaries:

Polarcus DMCC   (1)
Reef Tower Level 20 Cluster O, PO Box 283373, Jumeirah Lakes Towers, Dubai, United Arab Emirates
Tel.: (971) 44360800
Web Site: http://www.polarcus.com
Geophysical Surveying Services
N.A.I.C.S.: 541360

Polarcus Seismic Limited   (1)
Almas Tower Level 32, PO Box 283373, Jumeirah Lakes Towers, Dubai, 283373, United Arab Emirates
Tel.: (971) 44360800
Web Site: http://www.polarcus.com
Emp.: 130
Seismic Geophysical Services

INTERNATIONAL PUBLIC

N.A.I.C.S.: 541360

POLARIS AI CO., LTD.
4FL 19 Seoun-ro, Seocho-gu, Seoul, 06732, Korea (South)
Tel.: (82) 234896800
Web Site: https://www.polarisai.co.kr
Year Founded: 1991
039980—(KRS)
Rev.: $62,014,932
Assets: $75,426,609
Liabilities: $21,919,347
Net Worth: $53,507,261
Earnings: ($2,173,007)
Emp.: 137
Fiscal Year-end: 12/31/22
Wireless Communication Services
N.A.I.C.S.: 517112
Kim Woong *(Co-CEO)*

POLARIS AI CO., LTD.
Web Site:
http://www.estechpharma.com
Year Founded: 1996
041910—(KRS)
Rev.: $47,581,867
Assets: $95,352,679
Liabilities: $6,312,326
Net Worth: $89,040,353
Earnings: ($4,881,075)
Emp.: 168
Fiscal Year-end: 12/31/22
Pharmaceutical Product Mfr & Distr
N.A.I.C.S.: 325412
Jeong Hee Yoon *(Sr Mng Dir & CFO)*

POLARIS BANK LIMITED
3 Akin Adesola Street, Victoria Island, Lagos, Nigeria
Tel.: (234) 1 270-1600   NG
Web Site:
http://www.polarisbanklimited.com
Year Founded: 2018
Commericial Banking
N.A.I.C.S.: 522110
Adetokunbo Mukhail Abiru *(CEO & Mng Dir)*

POLARIS CAPITAL GROUP CO., LTD.
GranTokyo North Tower 38F 1-9-1 Marunouchi, Chiyoda-ku, Tokyo, 100-6738, Japan
Tel.: (81) 352236780   JP
Web Site: http://www.polaris-cg.com
Year Founded: 2004
Investment Management Service
N.A.I.C.S.: 523940
Yuji Kimura *(Founder, Pres & CEO)*

Subsidiaries:

CARTA HOLDINGS, INC.   (1)
Shibuya Solasta 15F 1-2-1 Dogenzaka, Shibuya, Tokyo, 150-0043, Japan   (62%)
Tel.: (81) 354594226
Web Site: http://cartaholdings.co.jp
Rev.: $170,946,990
Assets: $353,528,670
Liabilities: $184,552,700
Net Worth: $168,975,970
Earnings: ($16,732,400)
Fiscal Year-end: 12/31/2023
Online Media Research Services
N.A.I.C.S.: 541910
Shinsuke Usami *(CEO)*

Subsidiary (Domestic):

Research Panel, Inc.   (2)
8-16 Shinsencho Shibuya First Place 8f, Shibuya-Ku, Tokyo, 150-0045, Japan
Tel.: (81) 3 5459 5562
Web Site: http://www.research-panel.jp
Information Services
N.A.I.C.S.: 519290

VOYAGE Ventures Inc   (2)
Shibuya First Place Bldg 8F Shinsen-Cho 8-16, Shibuya, Tokyo, 150-0045, Japan
Tel.: (81) 3 5459 1166

AND PRIVATE COMPANIES POLARIS LTD.

Web Site: http://www.voyage-ventures.com
Sales Range: $25-49.9 Million
Emp.: 250
Online Marketing Services
N.A.I.C.S.: 541613
Hidenori Nagaoka (Pres & CEO)

Subsidiary (Domestic):

cyber communications inc. (3)
Tsukiji Shochiku Bldg 1-13-1 Tsukiji, Chuo-ku, Tokyo, 104-0045, Japan
Tel.: (81) 368376011
Web Site: http://www.cci.co.jp
N.A.I.C.S.: 541810
Akio Niizawa (Pres)

Subsidiary (Domestic):

adingo, Inc. (2)
Shibuya First Place Bldg 8F Shinsen-cho 8-16, Shibuya, Tokyo, 150-0045, Japan
Tel.: (81) 3 5459 1182
Web Site: http://www.adingo.jp
Sales Range: $10-24.9 Million
Emp.: 5
Online Advertising Services
N.A.I.C.S.: 541890
Kazuyuki Furuya (Gen Dir)

LB Co., Ltd. (1)
3469 1 Kurohama, Hasuda, Saitama, 349-0101, Japan
Tel.: (81) 487691133
Web Site: http://www.elbee.jp
Emp.: 366
Chilled Tea & Fruit Juice Mfr & Distr
N.A.I.C.S.: 311411
Hiroshi Shiraishi (Pres)

Novarese Inc. (2)
Ginza YOMIKO Bldg 4F Ginza 1-8-14, Chuo-ku, Tokyo, 104-0061, Japan
Tel.: (81) 3 5524 1122
Web Site: http://www.novarese.co.jp
Emp.: 2,002
Bridal Services
N.A.I.C.S.: 812990
Hiroki Ogino (Pres & CEO)

Subsidiary (Domestic):

MARRY MARBLE Co., Ltd. (2)
2-1-7 4F Shinkawa, Chou-ku, Tokyo, 104-0033, Japan
Tel.: (81) 3 5542 3135
Web Site: http://www.marry-marble.com
Emp.: 92
Event Management Services
N.A.I.C.S.: 812990
Yoshitomo Nishida (Dir)

Subsidiary (Non-US):

Novarese KOREA INC. (2)
201 Mecenatpolis 490 Seogyo-dong, Mapo-ku, Seoul, Korea (South)
Tel.: (82) 2 3443 1123
Restaurant Operators
N.A.I.C.S.: 722511

Shanghai Novarese Co., Ltd. (2)
630 Yongjia Rd, Xuhui, Shanghai, China
Tel.: (86) 21 5466 0320
Restaurant Operators
N.A.I.C.S.: 722511
Koji Nakagawa (Gen Mgr)

Subsidiary (Domestic):

TIMELESS Inc. (2)
4-1 Nihonbashi Kodenma-cho Iimon Kodenma Town Building 2F, Chuo-ku, Tokyo, 103-0001, Japan
Tel.: (81) 3 6661 7090
Web Site: http://www.timeless-gift.com
Event Management Services
N.A.I.C.S.: 812990
Akihiko Sanbuku (Pres & Dir)

VRESS ET ROSE Co., Ltd. (2)
1-11-14 Shirakane, Showa-ku, Nagoya, 466-0058, Aichi, Japan
Tel.: (81) 52 882 4617
Web Site: http://www.vresset.com
Flower Distr
N.A.I.C.S.: 459310

O-net, Inc. (1)
Rakuten Crimson House 1-14-1 Tamagawa, Setagaya-ku, Tokyo, 1581194, Japan

Tel.: (81) 5058175600
Web Site: http://onet.rakuten.co.jp
Event Organizing Services
N.A.I.C.S.: 711310

Sogo Medical Co. Ltd. (1)
Fukuoka Tenjin Center Bldg 16F 2-14-8 Tenjin, Chuo Ku, Fukuoka, Japan
Tel.: (81) 927137611
Web Site: http://www.sogo-medical.co.jp
Rev.: $1,202,627,280
Assets: $796,962,240
Liabilities: $472,602,480
Net Worth: $324,359,760
Earnings: $37,766,640
Emp.: 6,059
Fiscal Year-end: 03/31/2018
Medical Supplies & Equipment Whslr
N.A.I.C.S.: 423450
Kenji Sakamoto (Pres & CEO)

Subsidiary (Domestic):

Aoba Pharmacy Co., Ltd. (2)
2-15-15 Fujigaoka, Hyogo, Akashi, 674-0091, Japan
Tel.: (81) 789250306
Pharmaceutical Products Distr
N.A.I.C.S.: 456110

Beauty Drug Saito Co., Ltd. (2)
9-32-20 Tokiwa, Urawa-ku, Saitama, 330-0061, Japan
Tel.: (81) 488228178
Pharmaceutical Products Distr
N.A.I.C.S.: 456110

Hokendohjinsha Inc. (2)
1-4-4 Chiyoda-ku, Tokyo, 102-8155, Japan
Tel.: (81) 332346111
Web Site: http://www.hokendohjin.co.jp
Healthcare Management Consulting Services
N.A.I.C.S.: 524114

MEDI-QOL Inc. (2)
Gate City Osaki W Tower 1 Fl, Osaki 1-11-1, 141-0032, Tokyo, Japan
Tel.: (81) 337798839
Management Consulting Services
N.A.I.C.S.: 541618

SME Co., Ltd. (2)
Daihyaku Seimei Togoshi Building 4th Floor, Shinagawa-Ku, Tokyo, 1420041, Japan
Tel.: (81) 337846335
Custom Computer Programming Services
N.A.I.C.S.: 541511

Shokando Co., Ltd. (2)
9F Shinosaka Brick Building 1-6-1 Miyahara, Yodogawaku, Osaka, 532-0003, Japan
Tel.: (81) 663972100
Web Site: http://www.shokando.co.jp
Pharmaceutical Products Distr
N.A.I.C.S.: 456110

Sogo Media Supply Co., Ltd. (2)
Kejitenjin Bldg 3rd Fl, Fukuoka, Japan
Tel.: (81) 927131291
Commercial & Industrial Machinery & Equipment Rental & Leasing
N.A.I.C.S.: 532490

Sogo Medical Pharmacy Chubu Co., Ltd. (2)
1-47-1 Nagono Nakamura-Ku, Nagoya, Japan
Tel.: (81) 525637231
Web Site: http://www.sogo-medical.co.jp
Pharmacies & Drug Stores
N.A.I.C.S.: 456110
Moritaka Nakashima (CEO)

Sogo Medipro Co., Ltd. (2)
Gate City Osaki W Tower 22nd Fl, Shinagawa-Ku, Tokyo, Japan
Tel.: (81) 120788231
Pharmacies & Drug Stores
N.A.I.C.S.: 456110

Sogo Pharmaceutical Co., Ltd. (2)
Nippon Bldg 2 6 2 Ohtemachi, Chiyoda Ku, Tokyo, 100 0004, Japan (100%)
Tel.: (81) 332796891
Web Site: http://www.sogo-pharma.co.jp
Sales Range: $25-49.9 Million
Emp.: 133
Provider of Pharmaceuticals
N.A.I.C.S.: 325412

Jun Sawada (Mgr-Mktg)

Space Value Holdings Co., Ltd. (1)
SVHD Building 3-4-12 Shiba, Minato-ku, Tokyo, 105-0014, Japan (81.7%)
Tel.: (81) 354396070
Web Site: http://www.svh.co.jp
Rev.: $750,296,800
Assets: $766,414,000
Liabilities: $515,750,400
Net Worth: $250,663,600
Earnings: $3,184,720
Emp.: 1,380
Fiscal Year-end: 03/31/2021
Holding Company
N.A.I.C.S.: 551112
Naoki Morioka (CEO)

Subsidiary (Non-US):

P-Parking International Pte. Ltd. (2)
No 33 Ubi Avenue 3 06-24 Vertex, Singapore, 408868, Singapore
Tel.: (65) 67494119
Web Site: http://www.pparking.com.sg
Emp.: 100
Automated Parking Management Services
N.A.I.C.S.: 812930

Subsidiary (Domestic):

Urban-staff Co., Ltd. (2)
2569-18 Nakaokamotocho, Utsunomiya, 329-1105, Tochigi Prefecture, Japan
Tel.: (81) 286712555
Web Site: http://www.urban-staff.net
Civil Engineering Services
N.A.I.C.S.: 541330

POLARIS CAPITAL PUBLIC COMPANY LIMITED
503/34 KSL Tower Building 18th Floor Sri-Ayutthaya Road, Thanon Phayathai Ratchathewi, Bangkok, 10400, Thailand
Tel.: (66) 953685396
POLAR—(THA)
Rev.: $1,121,847
Assets: $100,475,842
Liabilities: $16,011,212
Net Worth: $84,464,630
Earnings: ($1,290,577)
Fiscal Year-end: 12/31/23
Real Estate Manangement Services
N.A.I.C.S.: 531390
Tischuan Nanavaratorn (Chm)

POLARIS HOLDING COMPANY LIMITED
Stevedore House 38 Front Street, Hamilton, HM12, Bermuda
Tel.: (441) 2923366
Web Site: http://www.polaris.bm
Year Founded: 2011
POLAR—(BERM)
Rev.: $11,109,093
Assets: $16,708,876
Liabilities: $5,830,720
Net Worth: $10,878,156
Earnings: $740,819
Fiscal Year-end: 03/31/24
Holding Company
N.A.I.C.S.: 551112
Cheryl Hayward-Chew (Chm)

Subsidiaries:

East End Asphalt Company Limited (1)
8 Ducks Puddle Drive, Hamilton, Bermuda
Tel.: (441) 2361776
Line Painting Services
N.A.I.C.S.: 237310

Equipment Sales and Rentals LTD (1)
628 Bizzell Dr, Lexington, KY 40510
Tel.: (859) 231-5343
Web Site: http://www.equipmentsalesandrentals.com
Construction Equipment Rental Services
N.A.I.C.S.: 532412
Mark Hall (Mgr-Store)

POLARIS HOLDINGS CO., LTD.
Yamazaki Kyodo Building 1123 Iwamotocho, Chiyoda-ku, Tokyo, 101-0032, Japan
Tel.: (81) 358223010
Web Site: https://www.polaris-holdings.com
Year Founded: 1912
3010—(TKS)
Rev.: $149,022,450
Assets: $153,404,880
Liabilities: $107,895,030
Net Worth: $45,509,850
Earnings: $21,793,170
Emp.: 687
Fiscal Year-end: 03/31/24
Holding Company; Real Estate & Hotel Services
N.A.I.C.S.: 551112
Takakura Shigeru (Chm)

Subsidiaries:

Fino Hotels Co., Ltd. (1)
Iwamoto-chou 1-12-3, Chiyoda-ku, Tokyo, Japan
Tel.: (81) 358223090
Web Site: https://www.finohotels.com
Hotel Services
N.A.I.C.S.: 721110
Shigeru Takakura (CEO)

KOKO Hotels Co., Ltd. (1)
1-12-3 Iwamotocho, Chiyoda-ku, Tokyo, 101-0032, Japan
Tel.: (81) 366732939
Web Site: https://www.koko-hotels.com
Home Management Services
N.A.I.C.S.: 721110

POLARIS LTD.
81 Ubi Avenue 4 03-11 UB One, Singapore, 408830, Singapore
Tel.: (65) 63099088
Web Site: https://wearepolaris.sg
Year Founded: 1984
5BI—(SES)
Rev.: $52,034,828
Assets: $24,246,758
Liabilities: $16,888,477
Net Worth: $7,358,281
Earnings: ($4,606,150)
Emp.: 28
Fiscal Year-end: 12/31/22
Mobile Phones, Electronics & Related Accessories Retailer
N.A.I.C.S.: 449210
Carl Johan Pontus Soennerstedt (CEO)

Subsidiaries:

CarrierNet Corporation (Singapore) Pte. Ltd. (1)
81 Ubi Avenue 4 #03-11, Singapore, 408830, Singapore
Tel.: (65) 6309 9088
Calling Cards Distr
N.A.I.C.S.: 517121

Mastro Luxe Pte. Ltd. (1)
81 Ubi Avenue 4 03 11 UB One, Singapore, 408830, Singapore
Tel.: (65) 63099088
Web Site: https://www.mastroluxe.com
Textile Bags Merchant Distr
N.A.I.C.S.: 314910

Uni 3 Pte Ltd (1)
29 Roberts Lane, Singapore, 218308, Singapore
Tel.: (65) 62966065
Calling Cards Distr
N.A.I.C.S.: 517121

Vikay America Incorporated (1)
9311 Eton Ave, Chatsworth, CA 91311 (100%)
Tel.: (818) 772-6050
Web Site: http://www.vikay.com
Sales Range: $25-49.9 Million
Emp.: 20
Liquid Crystal Modules

POLARIS LTD.

Polaris Ltd.—(Continued)
N.A.I.C.S.: 334118

POLARIS MANAGEMENT A/S
Malmogade 3, DK-2100, Copenhagen, Denmark
Tel.: (45) 35263574   DK
Web Site: http://www.polarisequity.dk
Year Founded: 1998
Sales Range: $10-24.9 Million
Privater Equity Firm
N.A.I.C.S.: 523999
Jan Johan Kuhl *(Mng Partner)*

Subsidiaries:

BabySam AmbA   (1)
Egelund A27-29, DK-6200, Abenra, Denmark
Tel.: (45) 74632510
Web Site: http://www.babysam.dk
Sales Range: $75-99.9 Million
Baby Equipment Retailer
N.A.I.C.S.: 459999

Falck Safety Services Holding A/S   (1)
Falck-Huset Polititorvet, Copenhagen, 1780, Denmark
Tel.: (45) 7033 311
Web Site: http://www.falcksafety.com
Emp.: 500
Safety Health & Survival Training & Consultancy Services For Oil & Gas, Shipping, Renewable Energy Military & Aviation Industries
N.A.I.C.S.: 611430
Claus Nexo Hansen *(Mng Dir)*

Subsidiary (Domestic):

Falck Safety Services A/S   (2)
Uglviggardsvej 3, 6705, Esbjerg, Denmark
Tel.: (45) 76121314
Healtcare Services
N.A.I.C.S.: 621610
Duncan Bonner *(Mng Dir-UK)*

Subsidiary (Non-US):

Falck Safety Services de Mexico, S.A.P.I. de C.V   (2)
Av Poniente Central S/N Laguna Azul Industrial Port, CP 24114, Ciudad del Carmen, Mexico
Tel.: (52) 9381120206
Web Site: http://www.falck.mx
Survival Training Services
N.A.I.C.S.: 611699

Molslinjen A/S   (1)
Hveensgade 4, 8000, Arhus, Denmark   (77%)
Tel.: (45) 70 10 14 18
Web Site: http://www.molslinjen.dk
Emp.: 230
Ferry Passenger Transportation Services
N.A.I.C.S.: 483212
Frantz Palludan *(Chm)*

POLARIS MEDIA ASA
Ferjemannsveien 10, 7014, Trondheim, Norway
Tel.: (47) 46407200
Web Site: http://www.polarismedia.no
POL—(OSL)
Sales Range: Less than $1 Million
Holding Company; Media Production, Publishing & Digital Services
N.A.I.C.S.: 551112
Per Axel Koch *(CEO)*

POLARIS NORTHSTAR CAPITAL CORP
Suite 810 - 789 West Pender Street, Vancouver, V6C 1H2, BC, Canada
Tel.: (416) 319-5744   BC
Web Site: http://www.globalcarecapital.com
Year Founded: 2004
HLTH—(CNSX)
Rev.: $7,078
Assets: $556,942
Liabilities: $1,620,380
Net Worth: ($1,063,438)
Earnings: ($41,758,313)
Fiscal Year-end: 12/31/20
Investment Services
N.A.I.C.S.: 523999
Alexander Somjen *(Pres & CEO)*

POLARIS OFFICE CORP.
15F Pan-Pacific building 12 Digital-ro 31-gil, Guro-gu, Seoul, 08380, Korea (South)
Tel.: (82) 25370538
Web Site: http://www.infraware-global.com
Year Founded: 1997
041020—(KRS)
Rev.: $18,548,495
Assets: $58,047,573
Liabilities: $8,653,052
Net Worth: $49,394,521
Earnings: $9,784,109
Emp.: 138
Fiscal Year-end: 12/31/22
Software Development Services
N.A.I.C.S.: 541511
Lee Sung Youp *(Mng Dir)*

Subsidiaries:

Infraware Technology, Inc.   (1)
18th 20th floor of Daeryung Techno Town 19 Gasan Digital 1-ro, Geumcheon-gu, Seoul, Korea (South)
Tel.: (82) 2 6003 8800
Web Site: http://www.infrawaretech.com
Information Technology Consulting Services
N.A.I.C.S.: 541511

POLARIS UNO, Inc.   (1)
158-15 Wanjusandan 3-ro chonbuk, Bongdong-eup, Wonju, 55321, Jeollabuk-do, Korea (South)   (65%)
Tel.: (82) 632617555
Web Site: http://www.unon.co.kr
Rev.: $74,434,542
Assets: $85,784,994
Liabilities: $19,249,905
Net Worth: $66,535,089
Earnings: $2,843,250
Emp.: 113
Fiscal Year-end: 12/31/2022
Timber Product Mfr
N.A.I.C.S.: 339999
Kim Dong Hyun *(Deputy Gen Mgr)*

POLARIS RENEWABLE ENERGY INC.
7 St Thomas Street Suite 606, Toronto, M5S 2B7, ON, Canada
Tel.: (647) 245-7199
Web Site: http://www.polarisinfrastructure.com
PIF—(TSX)
Rev.: $59,517,000
Assets: $502,700,000
Liabilities: $241,876,000
Net Worth: $260,824,000
Earnings: $542,000
Emp.: 151
Fiscal Year-end: 12/31/21
Investment Services
N.A.I.C.S.: 523999
Marc Murnaghan *(CEO)*

Subsidiaries:

Empresa de Generacion Electrica S.A.   (1)
Ave Ricardo J Alfaro Plaza Edison 8th Floor Zona 08, PO Box 05290, El Dorado, Panama, Panama
Tel.: (507) 512 0201
Web Site: https://www.egesa.net
Energy Power Distr
N.A.I.C.S.: 221122

Polaris Renewable Energy S.A.   (1)
Prime Time Tower Costa del Este Office 7-C, Panama, Panama
Tel.: (507) 932707292
Renewable Energy Consulting Services
N.A.I.C.S.: 541690

POLARIS WORKS, INC.
114 Gwahaksaneop 1-ro Oksanmyeon, Heungdeok-gu, Cheongju, Chungcheongbuk-do, Korea (South)
Tel.: (82) 432187866
Web Site: http://www.optopac.com
Year Founded: 2003
123010—(KRS)
Rev.: $12,524,473
Assets: $61,321,127
Liabilities: $18,997,306
Net Worth: $42,323,821
Earnings: ($4,029,302)
Emp.: 82
Fiscal Year-end: 12/31/22
Semiconductor Devices Mfr
N.A.I.C.S.: 334413

POLARX LIMITED
Unit 25 22 Railway Road, Subiaco, 6008, WA, Australia
Tel.: (61) 892261356
Web Site: https://www.polarx.com.au
Year Founded: 1984
PXX—(ASX)
Rev.: $67
Assets: $24,261,136
Liabilities: $803,612
Net Worth: $23,457,523
Earnings: ($7,883,124)
Emp.: 1
Fiscal Year-end: 06/30/24
Mineral Exploration Services
N.A.I.C.S.: 213114
Ian Cunningham *(CFO & Sec)*

Subsidiaries:

PolarX Limited   (1)
Unit 25 22 Railway Rd, Subiaco, 6008, WA, Australia
Tel.: (61) 892261356
Web Site: https://www.polarx.com.au
Emp.: 2
Gold Exploration & Mining Services
N.A.I.C.S.: 212220
Ian Cunningham *(CFO & Sec)*

POLCOLORIT S.A.
ul Jeleniogorska 7, Piechowice, 58-573, Warsaw, Poland
Tel.: (48) 75 75 473 10
Web Site: http://www.polcolorit.pl
Year Founded: 1984
Ceramic Tile Mfr
N.A.I.C.S.: 327120

POLDIS
Kervent BP 99, 29250, Saint-Pol-de-Leon, Finistere, France
Tel.: (33) 298690911
Sales Range: $25-49.9 Million
Emp.: 102
Grocery Stores
N.A.I.C.S.: 445110
Antoine Polard *(Mng Partner)*

POLE TO WIN HOLDINGS, INC.
11th Floor Shinjuku NS Building, 2-4-1 Nishi-Shinjuku Shinjuku-ku, Tokyo, 163-0811, Japan
Tel.: (81) 359097911
Web Site: http://www.poletowin-pitcrew-holdings.co.jp
Year Founded: 2009
3657—(TKS)
Rev.: $333,088,200
Assets: $173,251,240
Liabilities: $77,954,550
Net Worth: $95,296,690
Earnings: $13,946,030
Emp.: 3,292
Fiscal Year-end: 01/31/24
Internet-Related Services
N.A.I.C.S.: 551112
Tamiyoshi Tachibana *(Chm)*

Subsidiaries:

Daiichi Shorin Co., Ltd.   (1)
Shinjuku NS Building 11F 2-4-1 Nishi-Shinjuku, Shinjuku-ku, Tokyo, 163-0811, Japan
Tel.: (81) 35 977 8033
Web Site: https://www.daiichi-shorin.jp
Digital Book Publisher
N.A.I.C.S.: 513130

ENTALIZE Co., Ltd.   (1)
MSB-21 Minami-Otsuka Building 2-37-5 Minami-Otsuka, Toshima-ku, Tokyo, 170-0005, Japan
Tel.: (81) 35 977 8033
Web Site: https://www.entalize.co.jp
Information Technology Services
N.A.I.C.S.: 541511
Hiroshi Takao *(Pres & CEO)*

MIRAIt Service Design Co. Ltd.   (1)
2-4-4 Sotokanda 1st Radio Building New Building 3F, Chiyoda-ku, Tokyo, 101-0021, Japan
Tel.: (81) 36 869 4510
Web Site: https://www.msdcorp.co.jp
Information Technology Services
N.A.I.C.S.: 541511

MSD Secure Service Inc.   (1)
2-4-4 Sotokanda Daiichi Denpa Building 3F, Chiyoda-ku, Tokyo, 101-0021, Japan
Tel.: (81) 36 869 4510
Web Site: https://www.msdss.co.jp
Information Technology Services
N.A.I.C.S.: 541511

PITCREW Co., Ltd.   (1)
7F Kanda Iwamotocho Plaza Building 2-4-1 Iwamotocho, Chiyoda-ku, Tokyo, 101-0032, Japan
Tel.: (81) 35 820 7711
Web Site: https://www.pit-crew.co.jp
Network Research & Development Services
N.A.I.C.S.: 518210

PTW International UK Limited   (1)
6th Floor One Lampton Road, Hounslow, TW3 1JB, United Kingdom
Tel.: (44) 2086077900
Web Site: http://www.poletowineurope.com
Game Software Development Services
N.A.I.C.S.: 541511

Pole To Win Co., Ltd.   (1)
3F 3-801 Kamiyashiro, Kamiyashiro Meito-ku, Nagoya, 465-0025, Aichi, Japan
Tel.: (81) 52 709 4555
Web Site: http://www.ptw.co.jp
Game Publishers & Developers Outsourcing Services
N.A.I.C.S.: 541519

Subsidiary (Non-US):

PTW (Singapore) Pte. Ltd   (2)
57 Ubi Avenue 1 Ubi Centre 05-09, Singapore, 408936, Singapore
Tel.: (65) 65348851
Web Site: http://www.poletowinasia.com
Emp.: 20
Interactive Entertainment Testing Services
N.A.I.C.S.: 541519
Winston Wong *(Mng Dir)*

Subsidiary (US):

Pole To Win America, Inc.   (2)
1196 Borregas Ave Ste 101, Sunnyvale, CA 94089
Tel.: (408) 541-0400
Web Site: http://www.poletowinamerica.com
Outsourcing Services
N.A.I.C.S.: 561499
Deborah Kirkham *(CEO)*

Subsidiary (Domestic):

Pole To Win America Hunt Valley Inc.   (3)
10720 Gilroy Rd, Hunt Valley, MD 21031
Tel.: (410) 568-3075
Web Site: http://www.poletowinamerica.com
Interactive Entertainment Testing Services
N.A.I.C.S.: 541519

Subsidiary (Non-US):

Pole To Win India Ltd.   (2)
PTWI Pvt Ltd 6th Floor B Wing Smartworks - Purva Summit, Kukatpally Hyderabad,

Hyderabad, 500081, Telangana, India **(100%)**
Tel.: (91) 8049103999
Web Site: http://www.ptw.com
Interactive Entertainment Testing Services
N.A.I.C.S.: 513210

Pole To Win Viet Nam Joint Stock Company **(1)**
31th Floor Keangnam Ha Noi Landmark72 Lot E6 Pham Hung Street, Me Tri Ward Nam Tu Liem District, Hanoi, Vietnam
Tel.: (84) 247 305 4886
Web Site: https://www.ptw-v.com
Software Development Services
N.A.I.C.S.: 541511

QaaS Co., Ltd. **(1)**
2-4-1 Nishi-Shinjuku Shinjuku NS Building 14F, Shinjuku-ku, Tokyo, Japan
Tel.: (81) 36 890 1010
Web Site: https://www.qaas.co.jp
Information Technology Services
N.A.I.C.S.: 541511

SIDE UK Limited **(1)**
Unit A12 Tileyard London 105 Blundell Street, King's Cross, London, N7 9BN, United Kingdom
Tel.: (44) 207 631 4800
Web Site: https://www.side.com
Video & Audio Studio Services
N.A.I.C.S.: 512240

POLENERGIA S.A.
ul Krucza 24/26, 00 526, Warsaw, Poland
Tel.: (48) 225223900 **PL**
Web Site: https://www.polenergia.pl
Year Founded: 1997
PEP—(WAR)
Rev.: $1,775,921,972
Assets: $1,569,445,310
Liabilities: $794,930,161
Net Worth: $774,515,148
Earnings: $40,174,346
Emp.: 404
Fiscal Year-end: 12/31/22
Renewable Energy Plant Outsourcing, Biomass Fuel Distribution & Wind Farm Development & Operation Services
N.A.I.C.S.: 561499
Michal Michalski *(Chm-Mgmt Bd)*

POLESTAR AUTOMOTIVE HOLDING UK PLC
Assar Gabrielssons Vag 9, SE-405 31, Gothenburg, Sweden
Tel.: (46) 9497351834 **UK**
Web Site: https://www.polestar.com
Year Founded: 2017
PSNY—(NASDAQ)
Rev.: $2,378,562,000
Assets: $4,121,304,000
Liabilities: $5,383,603,000
Net Worth: ($1,262,299,000)
Earnings: ($1,194,831,000)
Emp.: 2,515
Fiscal Year-end: 12/31/23
Holding Company
N.A.I.C.S.: 551112
Dennis Nobelius *(COO)*

POLET A.D.
Sabacki put bb, Hrtkovci, Serbia
Tel.: (381) 22 455 290
Year Founded: 1991
Sales Range: Less than $1 Million
Grain Farming Services
N.A.I.C.S.: 111191

POLET IGK A.D
Zeleznicka 13, 23272, Novi Becej, Serbia
Tel.: (381) 23771200
Web Site: http://www.polet.rs
Year Founded: 1907
PLTNN—(BEL)
Sales Range: Less than $1 Million
Raw Material Product Distr

N.A.I.C.S.: 424590
Majda Petkovic *(Mng Dir)*

POLIAN FINANCIAL SERVICES SP. Z O.O.
Atrium Plaza Floor 6 Jana Pawla II Avenue 29, 00-867, Warsaw, Poland
Tel.: (48) 226536950 **PL**
Web Site: http://www.poloniafs.pl
Year Founded: 1994
Sales Range: $10-24.9 Million
Emp.: 20
Private Equity Firm Services
N.A.I.C.S.: 523999
Witold Radwanski *(CEO & Partner)*

Subsidiaries:
Krokus Private Equity Sp. z o.o. **(1)**
Al Jana Pawla II 25, 00-854, Warsaw, Poland
Tel.: (48) 226534700
Web Site: http://www.krokuspe.pl
Sales Range: $125-149.9 Million
Emp.: 10
Privater Equity Firm
N.A.I.C.S.: 523999
Witold Radwanski *(CEO & Mng Partner)*

POLIGHT ASA
Kongeveien 77, 3188, Horten, Norway
Tel.: (47) 33071260
Web Site: https://www.polight.com
Year Founded: 2005
PLT—(OSL)
Rev.: $2,212,949
Assets: $21,964,532
Liabilities: $2,348,610
Net Worth: $19,615,922
Earnings: ($8,404,015)
Emp.: 22
Fiscal Year-end: 12/31/23
Camera Lenses Mfr
N.A.I.C.S.: 333310
Oyvind Isaksen *(CEO)*

POLIGRAFICA S. FAUSTINO S.P.A.
Via Valenca 15, 25030, Castrezzato, BS, Italy
Tel.: (39) 03070491 **IT**
Web Site: http://www.psf.it
Year Founded: 1957
Sales Range: $25-49.9 Million
Emp.: 230
Provider of Graphics & Communications Services
N.A.I.C.S.: 541430
Anna Lambiase *(Mgr-IR)*

Subsidiaries:
BB S.r.l. **(1)**
Via Valenca 15, 25030, Milan, BS, Italy **(100%)**
Tel.: (39) 03070491
Web Site: http://www.cantoalto.it
Sales Range: $25-49.9 Million
Emp.: 100
E-commerce
N.A.I.C.S.: 541512

Litografia Spada S.r.l. **(1)**
286 Via Druento, Venaria Reale, 10078, Turin, Italy
Tel.: (39) 0114509243
Label Printing Services
N.A.I.C.S.: 561910
Giuseppe Frigoli *(Mng Dir)*

PSFInteractive S.R.L. **(1)**
via Valenca 17, 25030, Castrezzato, BS, Italy **(97%)**
Tel.: (39) 030 7049 1
Web Site: http://www.psfinteractive.it
Emp.: 100
Web Agency & Internet Services
N.A.I.C.S.: 541890
David Borselli *(Dir-Comml)*

POLIMEX-MOSTOSTAL S.A.

al Jana Pawla II 12, 00-124, Warsaw, Poland
Tel.: (48) 228297100 **PL**
Web Site: https://www.polimex-mostostal.pl
Year Founded: 1945
PXM—(WAR)
Rev.: $765,658,281
Assets: $627,283,535
Liabilities: $390,106,452
Net Worth: $237,177,083
Earnings: ($31,304,116)
Emp.: 4,605
Fiscal Year-end: 12/31/23
Engineering & Construction Services
N.A.I.C.S.: 237990
Joanna Makowiecka *(Vice Chm-Mgmt Bd)*

Subsidiaries:
Instal-Lubin S.A. **(1)**
Ul Anny Walentynowicz 9, 20-328, Lublin, Poland
Tel.: (48) 81 744 0031
Web Site: https://www.instal.com.pl
Heat & Ventilation Installation Services
N.A.I.C.S.: 238220
Aneta Binkiewicz *(Pres)*

Mostostal Siedlce Sp. z o.o. Sp.k. **(1)**
Ul Teresposka 12, 08-110, Siedlce, Poland
Tel.: (48) 256439507
Web Site: https://www.mostostal.siedlce.pl
Engineering Construction Services
N.A.I.C.S.: 541330

Naftoremont-Naftobudowa Sp. z o.o. **(1)**
Al Jana Pawla II 12, 00-124, Warsaw, Poland
Tel.: (48) 228297202
Engineering Construction Services
N.A.I.C.S.: 541330
Miroslaw Miskiewicz *(Pres)*

Polimex Budownictwo Sp. z o.o. Sp.k. **(1)**
Ul Teresposka 12, 08-110, Siedlce, Poland
Tel.: (48) 256439643
Engineering Construction Services
N.A.I.C.S.: 541330
Andrzej Rudolf *(Mng Dir)*

Polimex Energetyka Sp. z o.o. **(1)**
Al Jana Pawla II 12, 00-124, Warsaw, Poland
Tel.: (48) 228297248
Power Plant Maintenance Services
N.A.I.C.S.: 811310
Mariusz Kowolik *(Pres)*

Polimex Infrastruktura Sp. z o.o. **(1)**
Al Jana Pawla II 12, 00-124, Warsaw, Poland
Tel.: (48) 228297100
Engineering Construction Services
N.A.I.C.S.: 541330
Przemyslaw Janiszewski *(Pres)*

Polimex Operator Sp. z o.o. Sp.k. **(1)**
Al Jana Pawla II 12, 00-124, Warsaw, Poland
Tel.: (48) 22 529 7100
Construction Equipment Distr
N.A.I.C.S.: 423390
Wojciech Demediuk *(Pres)*

Polimex Power Engineering Sp z.o.o. **(1)**
12 John Paul II, Warsaw, 00-124, Poland
Tel.: (48) 22 829 72 48
Web Site: http://www.polimex-energetyka.pl
Sales Range: $125-149.9 Million
Drilling Platforms Mfr
N.A.I.C.S.: 213112
Andrzej Orlinski *(Deputy Chm-Mgmt Bd & COO)*

Stalfa Sp. z o.o. **(1)**
Ul Oleksiaka Wichury 2, 08-300, Sokolow, Podlaski, Poland
Tel.: (48) 25787380002
Web Site: https://www.stalfa.pl
Steel & Aluminum Product Mfr
N.A.I.C.S.: 332999

POLISAN HOLDING A.S.
Hilltown Ofis Aydinevler Mah Siteler Yolu Cad 28 No 1/A, Kucukyali-Maltepe, Istanbul, Turkiye
Tel.: (90) 2165785600
Web Site: https://www.polisanholding.com
Year Founded: 2009
POLHO—(IST)
Rev.: $129,620,364
Assets: $180,146,438
Liabilities: $58,895,751
Net Worth: $121,250,688
Earnings: $50,400,466
Emp.: 1,154
Fiscal Year-end: 12/31/22
Holding Company
N.A.I.C.S.: 551112
Mehmet Emin Bitlis *(Chm)*

Subsidiaries:
Polisan Hellas S.A. **(1)**
B'Industrial Area of Volos, P P Box 1061, 375 00, Volos, Greece
Tel.: (30) 2425022250
Web Site: https://www.polisanhellas.com
Plastics Product Mfr
N.A.I.C.S.: 326199

Polisan Kimya Sanayii A.S. **(1)**
Hilltown Office Aydinevler Mah Siteler Yolu Cad 28 No 1/A, Kucukyali-Maltepe, Istanbul, Turkiye
Tel.: (90) 2165785600
Web Site: https://www.polisankimya.com.tr
Paints Mfr
N.A.I.C.S.: 325510

POLITIKA A.D.
Cetinjska 1, 11103, Belgrade, Serbia
Tel.: (381) 113373031
Web Site: https://www.politika-ad.com
Year Founded: 1904
PLTK—(BEL)
Rev.: $7,682,509
Assets: $29,953,005
Liabilities: $56,128,503
Net Worth: ($26,175,499)
Earnings: ($4,286,306)
Emp.: 197
Fiscal Year-end: 12/31/22
Printing & Publishing Services
N.A.I.C.S.: 513110
Zefirino Grasi *(Chm & CEO)*

POLITO FORD LINCOLN SALES
2 Harvest St, PO Box 656, Lindsay, K9V4S5, ON, Canada
Tel.: (705) 328-3673
Web Site: http://www.politofordsales.com
Rev.: $13,292,400
Emp.: 30
New & Used Car Dealers
N.A.I.C.S.: 441110

POLJOOPREMA D.D.
Rajlovacka cesta bb, Sarajevo-Novi Grad, Sarajevo, Bosnia & Herzegovina
Tel.: (387) 3 356 8250
Web Site: http://www.poljooprema.ba
POPMRK2—(SARE)
Rev.: $7,536
Assets: $3,589,788
Liabilities: $660,259
Net Worth: $2,929,529
Earnings: ($117,817)
Emp.: 2
Fiscal Year-end: 12/31/20
Gardening & Farming Material Distr
N.A.I.C.S.: 444240

POLJOPRIVREDA NOVO SELO A.D.
Jokai Mor 2, Orom, Serbia

POLJOPRIVREDA NOVO SELO A.D.

Poljoprivreda Novo Selo a.d.—(Continued)

Tel.: (381) 24 799 028
Web Site:
   http://www.poljoprivrednanovo.com
Year Founded: 1990
Sales Range: Less than $1 Million
Grain Farming Services
N.A.I.C.S.: 111191

POLJOPRIVREDNA STRUCNA SLUZBA SUBOTICA A.D.
Trg Cara Jovana Nenada 15/III, 24000, Subotica, Serbia
Tel.: (381) 24555932
Web Site: https://www.pss-subotica.rs
Year Founded: 1998
PSSS—(BEL)
Rev.: $290,984
Assets: $247,316
Liabilities: $75,116
Net Worth: $172,199
Earnings: ($28,200)
Emp.: 16
Fiscal Year-end: 12/31/22
Agricultural Consulting Services
N.A.I.C.S.: 541690
Damir Varga (Exec Dir)

POLJOPROMET A.D.
15 Maj 143, Ruma, Serbia
Tel.: (381) 22 490 130
Year Founded: 1956
Sales Range: Less than $1 Million
Emp.: 3
Grain Product Whslr
N.A.I.C.S.: 424510

POLLARD BANKNOTE LIMITED
140 Otter Street, Winnipeg, R3T 0M8, MB, Canada
Tel.: (204) 474-2323   Ca
Web Site:
   https://www.pollardbanknote.com
Year Founded: 1907
PBKOF—(OTCIQ)
Rev.: $359,077,472
Assets: $360,947,903
Liabilities: $199,049,581
Net Worth: $161,898,322
Earnings: $15,411,698
Emp.: 2,064
Fiscal Year-end: 12/31/21
Gaming Products Mfr & Sales
N.A.I.C.S.: 339999
Jennifer Westbury (Exec VP-Sls & Customer Dev)

Subsidiaries:

Diamond Game Enterprises   (1)
560 Arvin Avenue Unit 3, Stoney Creek, L8E 5P1, ON, Canada   (100%)
Tel.: (905) 643-6040
Web Site: https://www.diamondgame.com
Gaming & Gambling Services
N.A.I.C.S.: 713290

Fastrak Retail (UK) Limited   (1)
Heapy Street, Macclesfield, SK11 7JB, Cheshire, United Kingdom
Tel.: (44) 1625439966
Web Site: https://www.fastrakretail.co.uk
Gold Retailer
N.A.I.C.S.: 458310

Next Generation Lotteries GmbH   (1)
Mariahilfer Strasse 36, 1030, Vienna, Austria
Tel.: (43) 12057740000
Web Site: https://www.nextgl.com
Lottery Services
N.A.I.C.S.: 713290

Schafer Systems, Inc.   (1)
1000 Flag Rd, Adair, IA 50002
Tel.: (641) 742-3266
Web Site: http://www.ssi-ia.com
Gambling Products Mfr
N.A.I.C.S.: 339999

POLLARD WINDOWS INC.
1217 King Road, PO Box 507, Burlington, L7R 3Y3, ON, Canada
Tel.: (905) 634-2365
Web Site:
   https://www.pollardwindows.com
Year Founded: 1947
Rev.: $43,434,170
Emp.: 350
Window Mfr
N.A.I.C.S.: 321911
Gary L. Pollard (Dir-Bus Dev)

POLLEN STREET LIMITED
11-12 Hanover Square, London, W1S 1JJ, United Kingdom
Tel.: (44) 2037286750   UK
Web Site:
   http://www.honeycombplc.com
Year Founded: 2015
POLN—(LSE)
Rev.: $74,633,868
Assets: $866,147,970
Liabilities: $381,126,939
Net Worth: $485,021,031
Earnings: $28,106,162
Fiscal Year-end: 12/31/20
Investment Management Service
N.A.I.C.S.: 523940
Julian Dale (CFO)

Subsidiaries:

Pollen Street Capital Limited   (1)
11 - 12 Hanover Square, London, W1S 1JJ, United Kingdom
Tel.: (44) 2037286750
Web Site: http://www.pollencap.com
Holding Company
N.A.I.C.S.: 551112
Julian Dale (CFO)

Subsidiary (Domestic):

Mattioli Woods plc   (2)
1 New Walk Place, Leicester, LE1 6RU, United Kingdom
Tel.: (44) 1162408700
Web Site: https://www.mattioliwoods.com
Rev.: $85,013,638
Assets: $168,581,304
Liabilities: $51,699,262
Net Worth: $116,882,042
Earnings: $1,888,589
Emp.: 636
Fiscal Year-end: 05/31/2021
Pension Funds
N.A.I.C.S.: 525110
Murray Smith (Dir)

Subsidiary (Domestic):

Custodian Capital Limited   (3)
1 New Walk Place, Leicester, LE1 6RU, United Kingdom
Tel.: (44) 116 240 8740
Web Site: https://www.custodiancapital.com
Investment Management Service
N.A.I.C.S.: 541611
Richard Shepherd-Cross (Mng Dir)

Custodian Property Income REIT plc   (3)
1 New Walk Place, Leicester, LE1 6RU, United Kingdom
Tel.: (44) 1162408740
Web Site: https://www.custodianreit.com
Rev.: $52,303,768
Assets: $793,433,344
Liabilities: $253,454,960
Net Worth: $539,978,384
Earnings: $160,399,096
Fiscal Year-end: 03/31/2022
Lessors of Other Real Estate Property
N.A.I.C.S.: 531190
Richard Shepherd-Cross (Mng Dir & Mgr-Custodian Capital & Fund)

Subsidiary (Domestic):

Drum Income Plus REIT PLC   (4)
115 George Street, Edinburgh, EH2 4JN, United Kingdom
Tel.: (44) 1312850050
Web Site: http://www.dripreit.co.uk
Rev.: $5,627,749

Assets: $72,898,702
Liabilities: $35,031,891
Net Worth: $37,866,811
Earnings: ($4,648,833)
Fiscal Year-end: 09/30/2020
Real Estate Investment Trust Services
N.A.I.C.S.: 531190
Hugh Little (Chm)

Subsidiary (Domestic):

Maven Capital Partners UK LLP   (3)
Kintyre House 205 West George Street, Glasgow, G2 2LW, United Kingdom
Tel.: (44) 141 306 7400
Web Site: http://www.mavencp.com
Privater Equity Firm
N.A.I.C.S.: 523999
Bill Nixon (Mng Partner)

Holding (Domestic):

Fundamental Tracker Investment Management Limited   (4)
Kintyre House, 205 West George Street, Glasgow, G2 2LW, Scotland, United Kingdom
Tel.: (44) 141 306 7400
Web Site:
   http://www.fundamentaltracker.com
Sales Range: $50-74.9 Million
Emp.: 2
Investment Management Service
N.A.I.C.S.: 523999

Joint Venture (Domestic):

Indigo Telecom Group Limited   (4)
102 Wales One Business Park, Magor, NP26 3DG, Monmouthshire, United Kingdom
Tel.: (44) 1291435500
Web Site: http://www.indigotg.com
Management & Maintenance of Telecommunication Network
N.A.I.C.S.: 517810
Mark Orchart (Dir-Grp Product & Bid)

Holding (Domestic):

Westfield Medical Limited   (4)
Second Avenue Westfield Trading Estate, Midsomer Norton, Radstock, BA3 4DP, United Kingdom
Tel.: (44) 1761408800
Web Site: http://www.westmed.co.uk
Emp.: 100
Sterilized Barrier Packaging Products Mfr & Distr
N.A.I.C.S.: 326112
Stephen Kilbane (Mgr-Sls)

Subsidiary (Domestic):

Pole Arnold Financial Management Limited   (3)
Long Barn 16 Narborough Wood Park Desford Road, Enderby, Leicester, LE19 4XT, United Kingdom
Tel.: (44) 116 204 3428
Web Site: https://www.polearnold.co.uk
Wealth Management Services
N.A.I.C.S.: 523999
Mike Pole (Mng Dir)

SSAS Solutions (UK) Ltd.   (3)
Rivers Edge 11 Ravenhill Road, Belfast, BT6 8DN, United Kingdom
Tel.: (44) 289 693 1260
Web Site: https://www.ssassolutions.com
Insurance & Pension Fund Services
N.A.I.C.S.: 524292
Judith Sloss (Mgr-Administration)

Joint Venture (Domestic):

Proactis Holdings PLC   (2)
Riverview Court Castle Gate, Wetherby, LS22 6LE, United Kingdom
Tel.: (44) 1937545070
Web Site: http://www.proactis.com
Sales Range: $50-74.9 Million
B2B E-commerce Sales Software Applications
N.A.I.C.S.: 513210
Tim Sykes (CEO)

Subsidiary (US):

Intesource, Inc.   (3)

INTERNATIONAL PUBLIC

2111 E Highland Ave Ste B-375, Phoenix, AZ 85016
Tel.: (757) 283-9797
Web Site: http://www.intesource.com
Emp.: 25
Purchasing Service
N.A.I.C.S.: 561499
Gabriel Gabaldon (CTO & VP)

Subsidiary (Domestic):

PROACTIS Group Limited   (3)
Riverview Court Castle Gate, Wetherby, LS22 6LE, West Yorkshire, United Kingdom
Tel.: (44) 1937545070
Web Site: http://www.proactis.com
Sales Range: $25-49.9 Million
Emp.: 60
Application Software Development Services & Sales
N.A.I.C.S.: 541511
Craig Slater (CEO)

Subsidiary (US):

Perfect Commerce, LLC   (3)
1 BayPort Way Ste 120, Newport News, VA 23606
Tel.: (757) 766-8211
Web Site: http://www.proactis.com
Sourcing & Procurement Software & Online Applications Services
N.A.I.C.S.: 423430

POLLUX BV
Ettenseweg 6, 4706 PB, Roosendaal, Netherlands
Tel.: (31) 165527286   Nl
Web Site: http://www.pollux.nl
Year Founded: 2005
Sales Range: $10-24.9 Million
Emp.: 10
Computer Aided Design & Manufacturing Software & Technology Distr
N.A.I.C.S.: 423430
Grzegorz Pawnuk (Co-Owner & Gen Dir)

POLLUX PROPERTIES LTD.
554 Havelock Road, Singapore, 169639, Singapore
Tel.: (65) 69220333   SG
Web Site: https://pollux.com.sg
Year Founded: 2000
5AE—(CAT)
Rev.: $10,441,269
Assets: $283,037,076
Liabilities: $125,554,145
Net Worth: $157,482,931
Earnings: $1,491,044
Fiscal Year-end: 12/31/23
Real Estate Development Services
N.A.I.C.S.: 531390
Bee Leng Chew (Sec)

POLMED S.A.
Os Kopernika 21, Starogard, 83-200, Gdansk, Poland
Tel.: (48) 801 033 200
Web Site: http://www.polmed.pl
Year Founded: 1999
POM—(WAR)
Sales Range: $10-24.9 Million
Medical Center Operator
N.A.I.C.S.: 621111
Radoslaw Szubert (Chm)

Subsidiaries:

POLMED Zdrowie Sp. z o.o.   (1)
Startowa 1, 80-461, Gdansk, Poland
Tel.: (48) 587693760
Health Care Srvices
N.A.I.C.S.: 621999

POLNOC NIERUCHOMOSCI S.A.
ul Balicka 35, 30-149, Krakow, Poland
Tel.: (48) 126384888
Web Site: http://www.polnoc.pl
Year Founded: 1999

Sales Range: $1-9.9 Million
Real Estate Services
N.A.I.C.S.: 531390
Piotr Sumara *(Pres)*

POLNONAKUP SARIS AS
Bardejovska 44, Presov, 080 01, Slovakia
Tel.: (421) 517764227
Web Site: http://www.pnsaris.sk
1PSA01AE—(BRA)
Sales Range: Less than $1 Million
Agricultural Services
N.A.I.C.S.: 115116
Stanislav Biros *(Chm-Mgmt Bd)*

POLNORD S.A.
ul A Branickiego 15, 02-972, Warsaw, Poland
Tel.: (48) 223519600
Web Site: http://www.polnord.pl
PND—(WAR)
Rev.: $73,264,361
Assets: $238,622,914
Liabilities: $119,679,609
Net Worth: $118,943,304
Earnings: ($17,991,075)
Emp.: 108
Fiscal Year-end: 12/31/20
Engineering & Construction Services
N.A.I.C.S.: 541330
Marcin Gomola *(Member-Mgmt Bd)*

Subsidiaries:

OSIEDLE TECZOWY LAS PD Development Sp. z o.o. S.K.A. (1)
ul Kartuska 246, 80 125, Gdansk, Pomeranian, Poland
Tel.: (48) 583053188
Industrial Construction Services
N.A.I.C.S.: 236210

PD Development Sp. z o. o. (1)
ul Kartuska 246, 80 125, Gdansk, Pomeranian, Poland
Tel.: (48) 583209740
Industrial Construction Management Services
N.A.I.C.S.: 236210

POLNORD - APARTAMENTY Sp. z o.o. (1)
Mysliwska 33, 80 125, Gdansk, Pomeranian, Poland
Tel.: (48) 583209743
Web Site: http://www.polnord.pl
Industrial Construction Services
N.A.I.C.S.: 236210

POLNORD - LODZ I Sp. z o.o. (1)
Ul Piotrkowska 79, 90 423, Lodz, Poland
Tel.: (48) 426303045
Industrial Construction & Engineering Services
N.A.I.C.S.: 236210

POLNORD - LODZ II Sp. z o.o. (1)
Zeligowskiego 43, 90 644, Lodz, Poland
Tel.: (48) 426303350
Industrial Construction & Engineering Services
N.A.I.C.S.: 236210

POLNORD - Wydawnictwo Oskar Sp. z o.o. (1)
Na Piaskach 10, 80 846, Gdansk, Pomeranian, Poland
Tel.: (48) 583058028
Books Publishing Services
N.A.I.C.S.: 513130

POLNORD Inzynieria Sp. z o.o. (1)
ul Okrezna 38, 02-925, Warsaw, Poland
Tel.: (48) 22 885 23 51
Residential Building Construction Services
N.A.I.C.S.: 236115

POLNORD Sopot II Sp. z o.o. (1)
Ul Slaska 35/37, 81-310, Gdynia, Masovian, Poland
Tel.: (48) 224039086
Industrial Construction Management Services
N.A.I.C.S.: 236210

POLNORD Szczecin I Sp. z o.o. (1)
ul Kazimierska 1A/1, 71-043, Szczecin, Masovian, Poland
Tel.: (48) 914830685
Web Site: http://www.polnord.pl
Industrial Construction Services
N.A.I.C.S.: 236210

POLNORD WARSZAWA - WILANOW I Sp. z o.o. (1)
ul Herbu Janina 11c lok 10 pietro 2, 02-972, Warsaw, Masovian, Poland
Tel.: (48) 222218192
Web Site: http://www.polnard.pr
Sales Range: $25-49.9 Million
Emp.: 10
Industrial Construction Services
N.A.I.C.S.: 236210

POLNORD WARSZAWA - WILANOW II Sp. z o.o. (1)
Al Rzeczypospolitej 3, 02 972, Masovian, Poland
Tel.: (48) 224039082
Industrial Construction Management Services
N.A.I.C.S.: 236210

POLNORD WARSZAWA - WILANOW III Sp. z o.o. (1)
Al Rzeczypospolitej 3, 02 972, Warsaw, Masovian, Poland
Tel.: (48) 224039083
Sales Range: $25-49.9 Million
Emp.: 3
Industrial Construction Management Services
N.A.I.C.S.: 236210

Pomorskie Biuro Projektow GEL Sp. z o.o. (1)
ul M Reja 13/15, 81-874, Sopot, Poland
Tel.: (48) 585513393
Web Site: http://www.gel.pl
Emp.: 20
Industrial Construction Services
N.A.I.C.S.: 236210

POLO HOTELS LIMITED
Hotel North Park Sector 32, Near Ghaggar Bridge, Panchkula, 134108, Haryana, India
Tel.: (91) 9041953535
Web Site: http://www.polohotelsltd.com
Year Founded: 1984
526687—(BOM)
Sales Range: Less than $1 Million
Hotel Operator
N.A.I.C.S.: 721110
Amardeep Singh Dahiya *(Mng Dir & CEO, Officer-Compliance)*

POLO QUEEN INDUSTRIAL & FINTECH LIMITED
304 A-Z Industrial Estate Ganpatrao Kadam Marg, Lower Parel, Mumbai, 400 013, India
Tel.: (91) 2245370000
Web Site: https://www.poloqueen.com
Year Founded: 1984
540717—(BOM)
Rev.: $9,366,645
Assets: $26,237,142
Liabilities: $3,926,429
Net Worth: $22,310,712
Earnings: $282,572
Emp.: 19
Fiscal Year-end: 03/31/23
Chemical Product Mfr & Distr
N.A.I.C.S.: 325611
Umesh Kumar Agarwal *(Exec Dir)*

POLO RESOURCES LIMITED
Sunninghill, PO Box 38, Sandton, 2157, South Africa
Tel.: (27) 787312919
Web Site: http://www.poloresources.com
Rev.: $134,000
Assets: $60,462,000
Liabilities: $300,000
Net Worth: $60,162,000
Earnings: ($4,190,000)
Fiscal Year-end: 06/30/19
Uranium & Coal Mining Services
N.A.I.C.S.: 212290
Michael Tang *(Chm)*

POLPAR S.A.
Av Brigadeiro Faria Lima 1355 - 10 Andar/par, 1452919, Sao Paulo, Brazil
Tel.: (55) 1135039320
Year Founded: 1988
PPAR3—(BRAZ)
Sales Range: Less than $1 Million
Financial Investment Services
N.A.I.C.S.: 523999
Orlando de Souza Dias *(Dir-IR)*

POLSIB SA
Sos Alba Iulia 40, Sibiu, Romania
Tel.: (40) 269 210085
Web Site: http://www.polsib.com
Sales Range: Less than $1 Million
Emp.: 24
Printing Services
N.A.I.C.S.: 323120
Teodor Raducanu *(Pres)*

POLSKA ZEGLUGA MORSKA
Pl Rodla 8, 70-419, Szczecin, Poland
Tel.: (48) 913594333
Web Site: http://www.polsteam.com
Year Founded: 1951
Sales Range: $100-124.9 Million
Emp.: 2,970
Sea Freight Transportation Services
N.A.I.C.S.: 483111
Robert Dabrowski *(Pres)*

Subsidiaries:

Cyfadaco Ship Management Ltd. (1)
Chrysalia Court 5th Floor B, 206 arch Makarios III Avenue, Limassol, 3030, Cyprus
Tel.: (357) 99203212
Sales Range: $25-49.9 Million
Emp.: 1
Sea Freight Transportation
N.A.I.C.S.: 483111
Krystian Piwko *(Gen Mgr)*

Kpt. Grzegorz Gorski Polsteam (Morocco) S.A.R.L. (1)
21 Rue Ain Kharzouza Hay Essalam, 20 200, Casablanca, Morocco
Tel.: (212) 22363591
Sea Freight Transportation
N.A.I.C.S.: 483111

Marine Medical Services (1)
Pl. Rodla 8, 70-419, Szczecin, Poland
Tel.: (48) 913594200
Medical Devices
N.A.I.C.S.: 622110

Pazim (1)
Pl Rodla 8, 70 419, Szczecin, Poland
Tel.: (48) 913594614
Web Site: http://www.pazim.pl
Sales Range: $50-74.9 Million
Emp.: 130
Sea Freight Transportation
N.A.I.C.S.: 483111
Przemyslaw Janasik *(Chm)*

Polbaltica A/B (1)
Papparvagen 27, PO Box 151, 12320, Farsta, Sweden
Tel.: (46) 86040495
Web Site: http://polsteam.com.pl
Sea Freight Transportation
N.A.I.C.S.: 483111

Polhansa Shipping GmbH (1)
Jungfernstieg 38, Hamburg, 20354, Germany
Tel.: (49) 403551310
Sales Range: $25-49.9 Million
Emp.: 4
Sea Freight Transportation
N.A.I.C.S.: 483111

Polsteam (Iberia) S.A. (1)
C/ Santa Hortensia 62-1 piso B, 28002, Madrid, Spain
Tel.: (34) 915103420
Sea Freight Transportation
N.A.I.C.S.: 483111

Polsteam (Luxembourg) S.A. (1)
5 Boulevard Royal Royal Rome II, 2449, Luxembourg, Luxembourg
Tel.: (352) 2232725
Sales Range: $25-49.9 Million
Emp.: 2
Sea Freight Transportation
N.A.I.C.S.: 483111

Polsteam (UK) Ltd. (1)
35 City Business Centre, Lower Road, London, SE 16 2X8, Rotherhithe, United Kingdom
Tel.: (44) 2072314940
Web Site: http://www.polsteam.co.uk
Sales Range: $25-49.9 Million
Emp.: 4
Sea Freight Transportation
N.A.I.C.S.: 483111

Polsteam Benelux B.V. (1)
Albert Plesmanweg 43-E, 3088 GB, Rotterdam, Netherlands
Tel.: (31) 104360588
Ocean Freight Transportation
N.A.I.C.S.: 483111

Polsteam Brokers (1)
Pl Rodla 8, Biuro 1604, 70-419, Szczecin, Poland
Tel.: (48) 913594762
Web Site: http://www.polsteambrokers.com.pl
Sales Range: $50-74.9 Million
Emp.: 10
Sea Freight Transportation
N.A.I.C.S.: 483111
Zbigniew Janeczko *(Gen Mgr)*

Polsteam Brokers Gdynia Ltd. (1)
Zygmunta Augusta 13/21, 81-366, Gdynia, Poland
Tel.: (48) 586618985
Sales Range: $50-74.9 Million
Emp.: 3
Sea Freight Transportation
N.A.I.C.S.: 483111
Jaroslaw Berndt *(Pres)*

Polsteam Shipping Agency Ltd. (1)
Pl Rodla 8, 70-419, Szczecin, Poland
Tel.: (48) 913594242
Web Site: http://www.polsteamagency.pl
Sales Range: $25-49.9 Million
Emp.: 30
Sea Freight Transportation
N.A.I.C.S.: 483111
Elzbieta Peta *(Chm)*

Polsteam USA Inc. (1)
17 Battery Pl Ste 907, New York, NY 10004
Tel.: (212) 422-0182
Web Site: http://www.polsteam.com.pl
Sales Range: $25-49.9 Million
Emp.: 5
Sea Freight Transportation
N.A.I.C.S.: 483111
Piotr Cichocki *(Pres)*

Polsteam Zegluga Szczecinska Sp. z o.o. (1)
ul Jana z Kolna 21 B, 71-602, Szczecin, Poland
Tel.: (48) 601795777
Web Site: http://www.polsteam.szczecin.pl
Marine Transportation Services
N.A.I.C.S.: 483111
Aleksandra Turbaczewska *(Pres)*

Polsteam Zeluga Szczecinska Ltd. (1)
ul. Jana z Kolna (Ladoga), 71-603, Szczecin, Poland
Tel.: (48) 601795777
Web Site: http://polsteam.com.pl
Sea Freight Transportation
N.A.I.C.S.: 483111

Unity Line (1)
Pl Rodla 8, 70-419, Szczecin, Poland
Tel.: (48) 913595695
Web Site: http://www.unityline.pl
Sales Range: $25-49.9 Million
Emp.: 70
Sea Freight Transportation

POLSKA ZEGLUGA MORSKA

Polska Zegluga Morska—(Continued)
N.A.I.C.S.: 483111

Zegluga Polska S.A. (1)
Plac Rodla 8, Szczecin, 70-419, Poland
Tel.: (48) 913594075
Sea Freight Transportation
N.A.I.C.S.: 483111
Andrea Cieslinski *(Pres)*

POLSKI BANK KOMOREK MACIERZYSTYCH SA
Al Jana Pawla II 29, 00-867, Warsaw, Poland
Tel.: (48) 224364050
Web Site: http://www.pbkm.pl
BKM—(WAR)
Sales Range: Less than $1 Million
Health Care Srvices
N.A.I.C.S.: 621999
Jakub Julian Baran *(Chm-Mgmt Bd)*

POLSKI HOLDING NIERUCHOMOSCI S.A.
al Jana Pawla II 12, 00-124, Warsaw, Poland
Tel.: (48) 228509100
Web Site: https://www.phnsa.pl
Year Founded: 2011
PHN—(WAR)
Rev.: $145,045,731
Assets: $1,175,279,469
Liabilities: $599,872,966
Net Worth: $575,406,503
Earnings: ($42,428,862)
Fiscal Year-end: 12/31/23
Holding Company; Real Estate Management & Development Services
N.A.I.C.S.: 551112
Marcin Mazurek *(CEO)*

Subsidiaries:

BUDEXPO Sp. z o.o. (1)
ul Bartycka 26, Warsaw, Poland
Tel.: (48) 22 522 89 00
Real Estate Management & Development Services
N.A.I.C.S.: 531390

DALMOR S.A. (1)
ul Hryniewickiego 10, 81-340, Gdynia, Poland
Tel.: (48) 58 620 09 21
Warehousing & Storage Services
N.A.I.C.S.: 493110
Krzysztof Rychlicki *(Pres)*

Warszawski Holding Nieruchomosci S.A. (1)
36 Swietokrzyska Str, 00-116, Warsaw, Poland
Tel.: (48) 22 850 90 80
Web Site: http://www.whnsa.pl
Holding Company
N.A.I.C.S.: 551112
Artur Lebiedzinski *(Pres & Member-Mgmt Bd)*

Subsidiary (Domestic):

AGROMAN Sp. z o.o. (2)
ul Swietokrzyska 36 lok 18/19, 00-116, Warsaw, Poland
Tel.: (48) 22 434 55 55
Real Estate Development Services
N.A.I.C.S.: 531390
Pawel Wiesik *(Pres)*

Wroclawskie Centrum Prasowe Sp. z o.o. (1)
ul Podwale 62, 50-010, Wroclaw, Poland
Tel.: (48) 71 342 48 42
Web Site: http://www.wcp.phnsa.pl
Real Estate Management & Development Services
N.A.I.C.S.: 531390
Dariusz Gutarowski *(Pres)*

POLSKIE GORNICTWO NAFTOWE I GAZOWNICTWO S.A.
25 M Kasprzaka Street, 01-224, Warsaw, Poland
Tel.: (48) 225894555 PL
Web Site: http://www.pgnig.pl
Year Founded: 1982
PGN—(WAR)
Sales Range: $5-14.9 Billion
Oil & Natural Gas Exploration & Production Services
N.A.I.C.S.: 211120
Magdalena Zegarska *(Vice Chm-Mgmt Bd)*

Subsidiaries:

BUD-GAZ Sp. z o.o. (1)
ul Kasprzaka 25, 01-224, Warsaw, Poland
Tel.: (48) 22 632 83 15
Web Site: http://www.bud-gaz.pl
Sales Range: $25-49.9 Million
Emp.: 4
Network Construction Services
N.A.I.C.S.: 237990
Mieczyslaw Wiecaszek *(Gen Mgr)*

Biuro Studiow i Projektow Gazownictwa GAZOPROJEKT SA (1)
ul Strzegomska 55a, 53-611, Wroclaw, Poland
Tel.: (48) 717851100
Web Site: http://www.gazoprojekt.pl
Sales Range: $50-74.9 Million
Emp.: 170
Engineeering Services
N.A.I.C.S.: 237990
Adam Kalak *(Pres & Mng Dir)*

Dolnoslaska Spolka Gazownictwa Sp. z o.o. (1)
ul Ziebicka 44, 50-507, Wroclaw, Poland
Tel.: (48) 71 364 95 05
Web Site: http://www.dolnoslaskiosd.pl
Natural Gas Distr
N.A.I.C.S.: 221210

GAZ MEDIA Sp. z o.o. (1)
ul Pilsudskiego 4, 05-200, Wolomin, Poland
Tel.: (48) 22 763 88 50
Web Site: http://www.gazmedia.pl
Gas Installation Services
N.A.I.C.S.: 237120

GAZ Sp. z o.o. (1)
ul Emilii Plater 12c, 05-870, Blonie, Mazowieckie, Poland
Tel.: (48) 22 725 49 92
Web Site: http://www.gaz-blonie.pl
Pipeline Construction & Gas Installation Services
N.A.I.C.S.: 237120

Geofizyka Krakow Sp. Z.o.o. (1)
ul Lukasiewicza 3, 31-429, Krakow, Poland
Tel.: (48) 122991200
Web Site: http://www.gk.com.pl
Sales Range: $200-249.9 Million
Emp.: 900
Seismic Data Analysis & Processing
N.A.I.C.S.: 541360
Wojciech Dawidziuk *(Chm-Supervisory Bd)*

Geofizyka Torun Sp. Z.o.o. (1)
Chrobrego 50, 87-100, Torun, Poland
Tel.: (48) 566593101
Web Site: http://www.gtservices.pl
Sales Range: $25-49.9 Million
Emp.: 100
3D Seismic Technological Services
N.A.I.C.S.: 541360
Piotr Antonik *(Pres & CEO)*

Geovita Sp. z o.o. (1)
ul Krucza 6/14, 00-537, Warsaw, Poland
Tel.: (48) 22 583 52 11
Web Site: http://www.geovita.pl
Hotel & Resort Services
N.A.I.C.S.: 721110

Gornoslaska Spolka Gazownictwa Sp. z o.o. (1)
ul Szczesc Boze 11, 41-800, Zabrze, Poland
Tel.: (48) 32 398 50 00
Web Site: http://www.gsgaz.pl
Natural Gas Distr
N.A.I.C.S.: 221210

Karpacka Spolka Gazownictwa Sp. z o.o. (1)
ul Wita Stwosza 7, 33-100, Tarnow, Poland
Tel.: (48) 14 632 31 00

Web Site: http://www.ksgaz.pl
Natural Gas Distr
N.A.I.C.S.: 221210

Mazowiecka Spolka Gazownictwa Sp. z o.o. (1)
ul Krucza 6/14, 00-537, Warsaw, Poland
Tel.: (48) 22 667 39 00
Web Site: http://www.msgaz.pl
Natural Gas Distribution Services
N.A.I.C.S.: 221210

NYSAGAZ Sp. z o.o. (1)
Plac Solidarnosci 1/3/5, 53-661, Wroclaw, Poland
Tel.: (48) 71 78 88 501
Web Site: http://www.nysagaz.pl
Electric Power Generation & Transmission Services
N.A.I.C.S.: 221118

Operator Systemu Magazynowania Sp. z o.o. (1)
ul Marcina Kasprzaka 25D, 01-224, Warsaw, Poland
Tel.: (48) 22 691 79 14
Web Site: http://www.osm.pgnig.pl
Oil & Gas Exploration Services
N.A.I.C.S.: 213112

PGNiG Technologie Sp. z o.o. (1)
ul Naftowa 8, 38-400, Krosno, Poland
Tel.: (48) 134362511
Web Site: http://www.technologiepgnig.pl
Oil & Gas Field Construction Services
N.A.I.C.S.: 237120
Marcin Dziadowiec *(Chm-Supervisory Bd)*

PGNiG Energia SA (1)
ul M Kasprzaka 25 budynek C14, 01-224, Warsaw, Poland
Tel.: (48) 22 589 44 28
Web Site: http://www.energia.pgnig.pl
Eletric Power Generation Services
N.A.I.C.S.: 221118

PGNiG Gazoprojekt S.A. (1)
Strzegomska 55a, 53-611, Wroclaw, Poland
Tel.: (48) 71 785 1100
Web Site: https://www.gazoprojekt.pl
Design & Consulting Services
N.A.I.C.S.: 541618

PGNiG Norway AS (1)
Vestre Svanholmen 44, 4313, Sandnes, Norway
Tel.: (47) 51 95 07 50
Crude Oil & Natural Gas Extraction Services
N.A.I.C.S.: 211120
Geir Kvael *(Gen Mgr)*

PGNiG Obrot Detaliczny Sp. z o.o. (1)
Ul Jana Kazimierza 3, 01-248, Warsaw, Poland
Tel.: (48) 22 515 1515
Oil & Gas Exploration Services
N.A.I.C.S.: 213112

PGNiG Supply & Trading GmbH (1)
Arnulfstrasse 19, 80335, Munich, Germany
Tel.: (49) 89 159 2590
Web Site: https://www.pst-energie.com
Natural Gas Distribution Services
N.A.I.C.S.: 221210
Bartlomiej Korzeniewski *(Mng Dir)*

PGNiG Upstream North Africa B.V. (1)
Strawinskylaan 615 Tower A Floor 6 Office A-615, 1077 XX, Amsterdam, Netherlands
Tel.: (31) 20 665 8935
Oil & Gas Exploration Services
N.A.I.C.S.: 213112

PGNiG Upstream Norway AS (1)
Vestre Svanholmen 4, 4313, Sandnes, Norway
Tel.: (47) 5 195 0750
Web Site: https://norway.pgnig.pl
Gas & Oil Distr
N.A.I.C.S.: 424720
Przemyslaw Waclawski *(Chm)*

Polska Spolka Gazownictwa Sp. z o.o. (1)
Ul Wojciecha Bandrowskiego 16, 33-100, Tarnow, Poland
Tel.: (48) 14 632 3999

INTERNATIONAL PUBLIC

Web Site: https://www.psgaz.pl
Gas Distribution Services
N.A.I.C.S.: 221210
Kazimierz Kujda *(Co-Chm)*

Pomorska Spolka Gazownictwa Sp. z o.o. (1)
Walowa 41/43, 80-858, Gdansk, Poland
Tel.: (48) 224443333
Web Site: http://www.psgaz.pl
Natural Gas Distribution Services
N.A.I.C.S.: 221210

Poszukiwania Naftowe DIAMENT Sp. z o.o. (1)
Ul Naftowa 3, 65-705, Gora Zielona, Poland
Tel.: (48) 683295555
Web Site: http://www.pn-diament.com.pl
Sales Range: $200-249.9 Million
Emp.: 500
Oil & Gas Services
N.A.I.C.S.: 213112

Poszukiwania Nafty i Gazu Jaslo Sp. z o.o. (1)
Ul Asnyka 6, 38-200, Jaslo, Poland
Tel.: (48) 134462061
Web Site: http://www.pnig.jaslo.pl
Sales Range: $75-99.9 Million
Emp.: 100
Gas & Oil Exploration Services
N.A.I.C.S.: 211120
Jan Kruczak *(Pres)*

Poszukiwania Nafty i Gazu NAFTA Sp. z o.o. (1)
Plac Staszica 9, 64-920, Pila, Poland (100%)
Tel.: (48) 672151300
Web Site: http://www.nafta.com.pl
Sales Range: $400-449.9 Million
Emp.: 750
Oil & Gas Exploration Services
N.A.I.C.S.: 211120
Stanislaw Wais *(Pres)*

Przedsiebiorstwo Energetyki Cieplnej Sp. z o.o. (1)
ul Nasienna 6, 73-110, Stargard Szczecinski, Poland
Tel.: (48) 915788400
Web Site: https://www.pec.stargard.pl
Steam Heat Distr
N.A.I.C.S.: 221330
Andrzej Haftman *(Chm & CEO)*

The Central Measurement and Research Laboratory (1)
MKasbrzaka 25B, 01-224, Warsaw, Poland
Tel.: (48) 226322368
Sales Range: $25-49.9 Million
Emp.: 40
Natural Gas Measuring Services
N.A.I.C.S.: 541715

Wielkopolska Spolka Gazownictwa Sp. z o.o. (1)
ul Grobla 15, 61-859, Poznan, Poland
Tel.: (48) 61 854 51 00
Web Site: http://www.wsgaz.pl
Natural Gas Distr
N.A.I.C.S.: 221210

ZRG Krosno Sp. z o.o. (1)
ul Lukasiewicza 93, 38-400, Krosno, podkarpackie, Poland
Tel.: (48) 13 43 72 100
Web Site: http://www.zrg.krosno.pl
Oil & Gas Exploration Services
N.A.I.C.S.: 213112

ZRUG Sp. z o.o. (1)
ul Tadeusza Kosciuszki 76/3, 61-892, Poznan, Poland
Tel.: (48) 61 650 08 57
Web Site: http://www.zrug.pl
Sales Range: $50-74.9 Million
Emp.: 150
Infrastructure Engineering Services
N.A.I.C.S.: 237990
Pawel Wilczynski *(Pres)*

Zaklad Gospodarki Mieszkaniowej Sp. z o.o. (1)
Plac Tadeusza Kosciuszki 1, 26-300, Opoczno, Poland
Tel.: (48) 44 755 26 19
Web Site: http://www.zgmopoczno.pl
Real Estate Manangement Services

AND PRIVATE COMPANIES

N.A.I.C.S.: 531390

Zaklad Remontowy Urzadzen Gazowniczych Sp. z o.o. (1)
Pogorska Wola 450, 33-152, Pogorska Wola, Poland
Tel.: (48) 146225503
Web Site: http://www.zrug.tarnow.pl
Oil & Gas Services
N.A.I.C.S.: 213112
Miron J. Jamroz *(Chm)*

Zaklad Urzadzen Naftowych Naftomet Sp. Z.o.o. (1)
Ul Naftowa 8, Krosno, 38-400, Poland
Tel.: (48) 134362511
Web Site: http://www.naftomet.pl
Sales Range: $100-124.9 Million
Emp.: 500
Oilfield Equipment
N.A.I.C.S.: 333132
Zbigniew Skiba *(Mng Dir)*

POLSKIE KOLEJE PANSTWOWE S.A.
Al Jerozolimskie 142A, 02-305, Warsaw, Poland
Tel.: (48) 723996246
Web Site: http://www.pkp.pl
Year Founded: 2001
Sales Range: $1-4.9 Billion
Emp.: 145,000
Railway Services
N.A.I.C.S.: 485112
Jakub Karnowski *(Pres)*

Subsidiaries:

PKP Cargo, S.A. (1)
ul Grojecka 17, 02-021, Warsaw, Poland
Tel.: (48) 327221414
Web Site: https://www.pkpcargo.com
Rev.: $1,354,092,348
Assets: $1,924,383,259
Liabilities: $1,112,219,263
Net Worth: $812,163,995
Earnings: $37,180,325
Emp.: 19,971
Fiscal Year-end: 12/31/2022
Rail Freight Transportation Services
N.A.I.C.S.: 482111
Czeslaw Warsewicz *(CEO & Member-Mgmt Bd)*

PKP Linia Hutnicza Szerokotorowa Sp. z o.o. (1)
ul Szczebrzeska 11, 22-420, Zamosc, Poland
Tel.: (48) 84 6386223
Web Site: http://www.pkp-lhs.pl
Metal Products Long Haul Railway Service
N.A.I.C.S.: 482111

PKP Polskie Linie Kolejowe S.A. (1)
ul Targowa 74, 03-734, Warsaw, Poland
Tel.: (48) 224732000
Web Site: http://www.plk-sa.pl
Railway Infrastructure Management Services
N.A.I.C.S.: 488210

POLSON LIMITED
615/616 Churchgate Chambers 5 New Marine Lines Road, Taluka Shahuwadi, Kolhapur, 415101, Maharashtra, India
Tel.: (91) 2222626439
Web Site: https://www.polsonltd.com
Year Founded: 1900
507645—(BOM)
Rev.: $10,316,288
Assets: $21,694,575
Liabilities: $7,765,410
Net Worth: $13,929,165
Earnings: $579,042
Emp.: 50
Fiscal Year-end: 03/31/23
Specialty Chemicals Mfr
N.A.I.C.S.: 325998
Amol Jagdish Kapadia *(Mng Dir)*

POLTAVA AUTOMOBILE UNIT PLANT, PJSC
57 Zenkovskaya Street, 36009, Poltava, Ukraine
Tel.: (380) 532 51 92 00
Web Site: http://www.paaz.com.ua
Year Founded: 1945
PAAZ—(UKR)
Automobile Parts Mfr
N.A.I.C.S.: 336390
Andrian Lytovchenko *(Gen Dir)*

POLTRONESOFA HOLDING SRL
Rotonda Gilles Villeneuve 2, Centro Commerciale Le Rotonde di Zola, Bologna, Italy
Tel.: (39) 0510195294   IT
Web Site: https://www.poltronesofa.com
Holding Company
N.A.I.C.S.: 551112

Subsidiaries:

Poltronesofa SpA (1)
Via Lunga 16 Crespellano Valsamoggia, 40053, Bologna, Italy
Tel.: (39) 0510195294
Web Site: https://www.poltronesofa.com
Furniture Mfr & Distr
N.A.I.C.S.: 423210

Subsidiary (Non-US):

SCS Group PLC (2)
45 - 49 Villiers Street, Sunderland, SR1 1HA, United Kingdom
Tel.: (44) 1917313000
Web Site: http://www.scsplc.co.uk
Rev.: $440,605,937
Assets: $319,339,817
Liabilities: $258,907,700
Net Worth: $60,432,117
Earnings: $25,883,574
Emp.: 1,855
Fiscal Year-end: 07/31/2021
Furniture Retailer
N.A.I.C.S.: 423210
Chris Muir *(CFO)*

POLTTIMO OY
PO Box 20, 15141, Lahti, Finland
Tel.: (358) 3 86411
Web Site: http://www.polttimo.com
Year Founded: 1883
Sales Range: $150-199.9 Million
Emp.: 197
Holding Company
N.A.I.C.S.: 551112
Par-Gustaf Relander *(Chm)*

Subsidiaries:

Viking Malt Oy (1)
Niemenkatu 18, PO Box 22, 15141, Lahti, Finland
Tel.: (358) 3 864 15
Web Site: http://www.vikingmalt.com
Malt Mfr & Distr
N.A.I.C.S.: 311213
Timo Huttunen *(Dir-Special Malts)*

Subsidiary (Non-US):

Viking Malt A/S (2)
Spirevej 5, DK 4760, Vordingborg, Denmark   (100%)
Tel.: (45) 55975000
Web Site: http://www.vikingmalt.com
Malt Beverages Mfr & Distr
N.A.I.C.S.: 312120
Kim G. Jorgensen *(Mng Dir)*

POLUDNIOWY KONCERN ENERGETYCZNY S.A.
ul Lwowska 23, 40-389, Katowice, Poland
Tel.: (48) 327742000
Web Site: http://www.pke.pl
Year Founded: 2000
Sales Range: $1-4.9 Billion
Emp.: 6,000
Electronic Services
N.A.I.C.S.: 221122
Jan Kurp *(Chm-Mgmt Bd & CEO)*

Subsidiaries:

Kopalnia Wapienia Czatowice Sp. z o.o. (1)
Czatkowice 248, Krzeszowice, 32063, Poland
Tel.: (48) 122821020
Web Site: http://www.czatowice.com.pl
Limestone Mining & Distr
N.A.I.C.S.: 212312
Andrzej Piotrowski *(Mgr-Sls)*

Polska Energia - Pierwsza Kompania Handlow Sp. z o.o. (1)
Ul Jordana 25, 40-043, Katowice, Poland
Tel.: (48) 322578619
Web Site: http://www.polskaenergia.pl
Electrical Energy Distr
N.A.I.C.S.: 221122

Przedsiebiorstwo Produkcyjno-Uslugowe Elektro Sp. z o.o. (1)
ul Wyzwolenia 30, Laziska Gorne, 43-170, Bytom, Poland
Tel.: (48) 323243533
Web Site: http://www.elektro.net.pl
Appliance Repair & Maintenance
N.A.I.C.S.: 811412

Przedsiebiorstwo Swiadczen Zdrowotnych i Promocji Zdrowia Elvita-Jaworzno III Sp. z o.o. (1)
ul Promienna 51, Jaworzno, 43 603, Bytom, Poland
Tel.: (48) 327151199
Electronic Components Mfr
N.A.I.C.S.: 334419

Przedsiebiorstwo Uslug Remontowych Energetyki - Jaworzno III Sp. z o.o. (1)
Ul Energetykow 15, Jaworzno, 43-603, Bytom, Poland
Tel.: (48) 327152756
Sales Range: $25-49.9 Million
Emp.: 25
Bridge & Tunnel Construction
N.A.I.C.S.: 237310

POLUS BIOPHARM INC.
Capital Tower 10F 142 Teheran-Ro, Gangnam-Gu, Seoul, Korea (South)
Tel.: (82) 25543377
Web Site: http://www.pbp00.cafe24.com
Year Founded: 2016
007630—(KRS)
Rev.: $25,092
Assets: $112,377,430
Liabilities: $64,042,244
Net Worth: $48,335,185
Earnings: ($457,103)
Emp.: 2
Fiscal Year-end: 12/31/21
Pharmaceutical Preparation Mfr
N.A.I.C.S.: 325412
S. H. Nam *(CEO)*

POLWAX S.A.
3 Maja 101, 38-200, Jaslo, Poland
Tel.: (48) 134262200
Web Site: https://www.polwax.pl
Year Founded: 2012
PWX—(WAR)
Rev.: $64,133,384
Assets: $28,407,774
Liabilities: $14,631,098
Net Worth: $13,776,677
Earnings: ($9,915,396)
Fiscal Year-end: 12/31/23
Oil & Gas Refinig Services
N.A.I.C.S.: 213112
Andrzej Nowak *(Mgr-Foreign Sls-Paraffin Sls Office)*

POLY CULTURE GROUP CORPORATION LIMITED
District A 20/F 1 North Street of Chaoyangmen, Dongcheng District, Beijing, 100010, China
Tel.: (86) 1064082666   CN

POLY CULTURE GROUP CORPORATION LIMITED

Web Site:
http://en.polyculture.com.cn
3636—(HKG)
Rev.: $367,432,978
Assets: $1,676,504,747
Liabilities: $1,210,961,232
Net Worth: $465,543,515
Earnings: ($39,551,944)
Emp.: 8,175
Fiscal Year-end: 12/31/22
Investment Management Service
N.A.I.C.S.: 523940
Niansha Xu *(Chm)*

Subsidiaries:

Beijing Poly Art Center Corporation Limited (1)
15/F New Poly Plaza No 1 Chaoyangmen North Street Dongcheng District, Beijing, 100010, China
Tel.: (86) 10 84192359
Artwork Distr
N.A.I.C.S.: 424990

Beijing Poly Art Investment Management Corporation Limited (1)
7/F New Poly Plaza No 1 Chaoyangmen North Street Dongcheng District, Beijing, 100010, China
Tel.: (86) 1064082311
Web Site: http://www.polyartinvest.com
Port Management Consulting Services
N.A.I.C.S.: 541611

Beijing Poly International Auction Corporation Limited (1)
Floor 3 New Poly Plaza 1 North Chaoyangmen Street, Dongcheng District, Beijing, 100010, China
Tel.: (86) 106 408 3188
Web Site: https://en.polypm.com.cn
Art Auction Services
N.A.I.C.S.: 459920
Li Xiaowen *(Sr Mgr-Modern & Contemporary Arts)*

Beijing Poly Performing Arts Corporation Limited (1)
Dongzhimen South Street No 14 Poly Plaza 7 room 788, Dongcheng District, Beijing, 100027, China
Tel.: (86) 1065512811
Web Site: https://en.polyperformingarts.com
Theater Management Services
N.A.I.C.S.: 711310

Beijing Poly Theatre Management Corporation Limited (1)
Gate 7 Poly Plaza No 14 Dongzhimen South Street, Dongcheng District, Beijing, 100027, China
Tel.: (86) 1065001188
Web Site: http://www.polytheatre.com
Theater Operator
N.A.I.C.S.: 711310

Changzhou Poly Grand Theatre Management Corporation Limited (1)
No 2 Jinling North Road, Xinbei District, Changzhou, 213000, Jiangsu, China
Tel.: (86) 51989607000
Web Site: https://czpoly.polyt.cn
Theater Management Services
N.A.I.C.S.: 711310

Chongqing Poly Theatre Management Corporation Limited (1)
Chongqing Theatre Wenhuajie East Road Jiangbeizui, Jiangbei District, Chongqing, 400020, China
Tel.: (86) 2361863112
Web Site: http://www.cqdjy.com.cn
Theater Management Services
N.A.I.C.S.: 711310

Dongguan Poly Yulan Grand Theatre Management Corporation Limited (1)
No 96 Hongfu Road, Nancheng District, Dongguan, 523071, Guangdong, China
Tel.: (86) 76922837303
Web Site: https://dgyldjy.polyt.cn
Theater Management Services
N.A.I.C.S.: 711310

Hefei Poly Grand Theatre Management Corporation Limited (1)

POLY CULTURE GROUP CORPORATION LIMITED

Poly Culture Group Corporation Limited—(Continued)
No 516 Tian'ehu Road, New Municipal & Cultural Development District, Hefei, 230071, Anhui, China
Tel.: (86) 5513501218
Web Site: http://www.hfgrandtheatre.com
Theater Management Services
N.A.I.C.S.: 711310

Henan Poly Art Center Management Corporation Limited (1)
Henan Art Center No 1 CBD, Zhengdong New District, Zhengzhou, 450046, Henan, China
Tel.: (86) 37169092292
Web Site: https://hnbljy.polyt.cn
Art Center Operation Management Services
N.A.I.C.S.: 711310

Huizhou Poly Culture & Arts Center Management Corporation Limited (1)
Yunshan West Road Jiangbei, Huizhou, 516000, Guangdong, China
Tel.: (86) 7522898066
Web Site: http://www.hzpolytheatre.com
Art Center Operation Management Services
N.A.I.C.S.: 711310

Lishui Poly Grand Theatre Management Corporation Limited (1)
No 6 Huayuan Road, Lishui, 323000, Zhejiang, China
Tel.: (86) 5782291122
Web Site: https://lsgrandtheatre.polyt.cn
Theater Management Services
N.A.I.C.S.: 711310

Ma'anshan Poly Grand Theatre Management Corporation Limited (1)
Ma'anshan Grand Theatre Tower 3 No 2006 Taibai Avenue, Ma'anshan, 243000, Anhui, China
Tel.: (86) 5558356204
Web Site: http://www.masdjy.com
Theater Management Services
N.A.I.C.S.: 711310

Ningbo Culture Square Poly Grand Theatre Management Co., Ltd. (1)
No 1900 Ningchuan East Street, Jiangdong District, Ningbo, 315040, Zhejiang, China
Tel.: (86) 57487033589
Web Site: http://www.nbpolytheatre.com
Theater Management Services
N.A.I.C.S.: 711310

Poly (Beijing) Theatre Construction Engineering Consulting Corporation Limited (1)
Room 764 Poly Plaza No 14 Dongzhimen South Road, Beijing, 100027, China
Tel.: (86) 1065519510
Engineering Consulting Services
N.A.I.C.S.: 541330

Poly Film Investment Corporation Limited (1)
5A Care City Shopping Mall No 16 South Third Ring West Road, Fengtai District, Beijing, 100068, China
Tel.: (86) 10 87578500
Web Site: http://www.polycinemas.com
Television Program Production Services
N.A.I.C.S.: 512110
Jiang Yingchun (Chm)

Qingdao Poly Grand Theatre Management Corporation Limited (1)
Qingdao Grand Theatre No 5 Yunling Road, Laoshan District, Qingdao, 266061, Shandong, China
Tel.: (86) 53288038058
Web Site: http://www.qingdaograndtheatre.com
Theater Management Services
N.A.I.C.S.: 711310

Shanghai Oriental Art Center Management Corporation Limited (1)
No 425 Dingxiang Rd, Shanghai, 200135, China
Tel.: (86) 2138424800
Web Site: http://www.shoac.com.cn
Art Center Operation Management Services
N.A.I.C.S.: 711310

Shanxi Poly Grand Theatre Management Co., Ltd (1)
Shanxi Grand Theatre, Changfeng West Street Changfeng Culture and Business District, Taiyuan, Shanxi, China
Tel.: (86) 3517781180
Web Site: http://www.sxdjypoly.com
Theater Management Services
N.A.I.C.S.: 711310

Taizhou Poly Grand Theatre Management Corporation Limited (1)
No 300 Hailing South Road Hailing District, Taizhou, 225300, Jiangsu, China
Tel.: (86) 52386899105
Web Site: http://www.tzdjy.cn
Theater Management Services
N.A.I.C.S.: 711310

Wenzhou Poly Grand Theatre Management Corporation Limited (1)
Room 1914 19/F Municipal Administrative Center No 500 Shifu Road, Wenzhou, 325088, Zhejiang, China
Tel.: (86) 57788956733
Web Site: http://www.wzdjy.com
Theater Management Services
N.A.I.C.S.: 711310

Wuhan Qintai Grand Theatre Management Corporation Limited (1)
Wuhan Qintai Theatre North Side of Yuehu Lake, Hanyang District, Wuhan, 430050, Hubei, China
Tel.: (86) 2784550088
Web Site: http://www.whqtdjy.com
Theater Management Services
N.A.I.C.S.: 711310

Yantai Poly Grand Theatre Management Corporation Limited (1)
Yantai Grand Theatre Cultural Center South Street Zhifu District, Yantai, 264000, Shandong, China
Tel.: (86) 5356860878
Theater Management Services
N.A.I.C.S.: 711310

POLY MEDICURE LTD.
Plot No 104-105 and 115-116 Sector - 59 HSIDC Industrial Area, Ballabgarh, Faridabad, 121 004, Haryana, India
Tel.: (91) 1292307000
Web Site: https://www.polymedicure.com
Year Founded: 1995
POLYMED—(NSE)
Rev.: $138,051,172
Assets: $189,102,476
Liabilities: $40,235,238
Net Worth: $148,867,238
Earnings: $21,495,414
Emp.: 2,339
Fiscal Year-end: 03/31/23
Pharmaceuticals Product Mfr
N.A.I.C.S.: 325412
Himanshu Baid (Co-Mng Dir)

Subsidiaries:

Plan1 Health s.r.l. (1)
Via Solari 5 Amaro, 33020, Udine, Italy
Tel.: (39) 0433468376
Web Site: http://www.p1h.it
Medical Equipment Mfr
N.A.I.C.S.: 339112

POLY PLASTIC MASTERBATCH (SUZHOU) CO., LTD.
Shiyuan Road Beiqiao Street, Xiangcheng, Suzhou, 215144, Jiangsu, China
Tel.: (86) 51265999276
Web Site: https://www.ppm-sz.com
Year Founded: 2002
300905—(SSE)
Rev.: $111,167,316
Assets: $200,741,112
Liabilities: $18,823,428
Net Worth: $181,917,684
Earnings: $6,583,356
Fiscal Year-end: 12/31/22
Chemical Product Mfr & Distr
N.A.I.C.S.: 325520

Yiming Xu (Chm)

POLY PROPERTY GROUP CO., LIMITED
Room 2503 Admiralty Centre Tower 1, 18 Harcourt Road, Hong Kong, China (Hong Kong)
Tel.: (852) 28106216
Web Site: http://www.polyhongkong.com.hk
0119—(HKG)
Rev.: $4,709,387,796
Assets: $30,399,468,517
Liabilities: $24,399,471,888
Net Worth: $5,999,996,630
Earnings: $336,212,553
Emp.: 9,700
Fiscal Year-end: 12/31/21
Property Investment & Management Services
N.A.I.C.S.: 531390
LiWen Wen Ye (Exec Dir)

POLY UNION CHEMICAL HOLDING GROUP CO.,LTD.
Poly Jiuhe Building No 9 Aoxing Road, Guanshanhu District, Guiyang, 550002, Guizhou, China
Tel.: (86) 85186749901
Web Site: https://www.gzjiulian.com
Year Founded: 2002
002037—(SSE)
Rev.: $893,495,772
Assets: $2,285,212,176
Liabilities: $1,755,593,892
Net Worth: $529,618,284
Earnings: ($110,382,480)
Fiscal Year-end: 12/31/22
Explosives Mfr
N.A.I.C.S.: 325920
Liu Wensheng (Chm)

POLY-CLIP SYSTEM GMBH & CO. KG
Niedeckerstrasse 1, 65795, Hattersheim, Germany
Tel.: (49) 6190 8886 0
Web Site: http://www.polyclip.com
Clip Closure System Mfr
N.A.I.C.S.: 332510
Joachim Meyrahn (Pres & CEO)

POLYARD PETROLEUM INTERNATIONAL GROUP LIMITED
Room 801-802 8/F Shanghai Industrial Investment Building, 48-62 Hennessy Road, Wanchai, China (Hong Kong)
Tel.: (852) 25878800
Web Site: http://www.ppig.com.hk
008011—(HKG)
Rev.: $33,660
Assets: $70,246,890
Liabilities: $29,154,405
Net Worth: $41,092,485
Earnings: $16,951,763
Emp.: 39
Fiscal Year-end: 12/31/21
Oil & Gas Exploration Services
N.A.I.C.S.: 213112
Chun Liang Lai (CEO)

Subsidiaries:

Polyard Petroleum International Company Limited (1)
Ave do Dr Rodrigo Rodrigues No 600E Edf First Int l Commerical Center, 5 Andar, Macau, China (Macau)
Tel.: (853) 28702686
Investment Holding Services
N.A.I.C.S.: 551112

Sinotech Polyard (Beijing) Resource Science & Technology Limited (1)
Room 1901 Building B No 60 Anli Road Chaoyang District, Beijing, 100029, China

INTERNATIONAL PUBLIC

Tel.: (86) 1064827253
Oil & Gas Exploration Consulting Services
N.A.I.C.S.: 541611

POLYBOIS INC.
739 Monfette street E, Thetford Mines, G6G 7K7, QC, Canada
Tel.: (418) 338-4638
Web Site: http://www.polybois.ca
Year Founded: 1971
Sales Range: $10-24.9 Million
Emp.: 70
Wooden Furniture Mfr
N.A.I.C.S.: 337211

POLYCAB INDIA LIMITED
29 The Ruby 21st Floor Senapati Bapat Marg Tulsi Pipe Road Dadar West, Mahim West, Mumbai, 400016, India
Tel.: (91) 2224327074
Web Site: https://www.polycab.com
Year Founded: 1996
542652—(BOM)
Rev.: $1,707,464,061
Assets: $1,130,085,247
Liabilities: $330,551,166
Net Worth: $799,534,081
Earnings: $153,738,145
Emp.: 4,485
Fiscal Year-end: 03/31/23
Electrical Wire Mfr
N.A.I.C.S.: 335929
Inder T. Jaisinghani (Chm & Mng Dir)

Subsidiaries:

Silvan Innovation Labs Private Limited (1)
No 13 Zain Burj 8th Cross 2nd Main Indiranagar 1st Stage, Bengaluru, 560038, India
Tel.: (91) 9108001821
Web Site: https://www.silvan.co.in
Automation Technology Services
N.A.I.C.S.: 541330

POLYCHEM LIMITED
7 Jamshedji Tata Road 5th Floor Oriental House Churchgate Reclamation, Mumbai, 400 020, India
Tel.: (91) 2222820048
Web Site: https://www.polychemltd.com
Year Founded: 1956
506605—(BOM)
Rev.: $6,815,946
Assets: $5,225,370
Liabilities: $673,329
Net Worth: $4,552,041
Earnings: $1,156,897
Emp.: 25
Fiscal Year-end: 03/31/23
Chemical Products Mfr
N.A.I.C.S.: 325998
Tanil R. Kilachand (Chm)

Subsidiaries:

Gujarat Poly Electronics Limited (1) B-18 Gandhinagar Electronic Estate, Gandhinagar, 382 024, Gujarat, India (53.99%)
Tel.: (91) 7935333658
Web Site: http://www.gpelindia.com
Rev.: $2,446,952
Assets: $2,281,302
Liabilities: $1,424,687
Net Worth: $856,615
Earnings: $635,298
Emp.: 34
Fiscal Year-end: 03/31/2023
Electronic Capacitor Mfr
N.A.I.C.S.: 334416
Tanil Ramdas Kilachand (Chm)

POLYCON INTERNATIONAL LIMITED
48-49 Gopalbadi Lane No 2 Ajmer Road, Jaipur, 302001, Rajasthan, India
Tel.: (91) 1412363048

Web Site: https://www.polyconltd.com
Year Founded: 1991
531397—(BOM)
Rev.: $3,146,934
Assets: $4,488,184
Liabilities: $4,035,418
Net Worth: $452,767
Earnings: $7,709
Emp.: 105
Fiscal Year-end: 03/31/23
Plastics Product Mfr
N.A.I.C.S.: 326199
C. S. Gajanand Gupta *(CFO & Sec)*

POLYFAIR HOLDINGS LTD.
Unit 1206-07 Fortress Tower 250 Kings Road, North Point, China (Hong Kong)
Tel.: (852) 35952227
Web Site: https://www.polyfaircurtainwall.com
Year Founded: 2006
8532—(HKG)
Rev.: $46,702,884
Assets: $32,730,739
Liabilities: $23,827,894
Net Worth: $8,902,845
Earnings: $342,700
Emp.: 117
Fiscal Year-end: 03/31/22
Construction Engineering Services
N.A.I.C.S.: 541330
Mo Lam Chow *(Chm)*

Subsidiaries:

Shenzhen Polyfair Curtainwall Technology Company Limited (1)
Room 1213-1214 Blk East Baihuo Square No 123 Shennan East Road, Luohu District, Shenzhen, China
Tel.: (86) 75582322657
Engineering Design Services
N.A.I.C.S.: 541330

POLYGENTA TECHNOLOGIES LIMITED
Kaledonia HDIL Building Unit No 1B 5th floor, Sahar Road Off Western Express Highway Andheri East, Mumbai, 400 069, India
Tel.: (91) 22 6215 4087   In
Web Site: http://www.polygenta.com
Year Founded: 1981
Rev.: $13,714,776
Assets: $30,380,724
Liabilities: $1,608,948
Net Worth: $28,771,776
Earnings: ($3,448,770)
Emp.: 241
Fiscal Year-end: 03/31/19
Polyester Filament Yarn Mfr
N.A.I.C.S.: 313110
Paresh Damania *(Officer-Compliance & Sec)*

Subsidiaries:

POLYGENTA TECHNOLOGIES LIMITED - Nashik Factory (1)
Gat 265/1-266, Avankhed Dindori, Nashik, 422 201, Maharashtra, India
Tel.: (91) 2557 228100
Polyester Yarn Mfr
N.A.I.C.S.: 313110

POLYGIENE GROUP AB
Styrmansgatan 2, 211 18, Malmo, Sweden
Tel.: (46) 40262222
Web Site: https://polygiene.com
Year Founded: 2006
POLYG—(OMX)
Rev.: $16,256,334
Assets: $58,248,148
Liabilities: $2,747,946
Net Worth: $55,500,201
Earnings: $2,045,670
Emp.: 37

Fiscal Year-end: 12/31/22
Clothing Apparel Distr
N.A.I.C.S.: 458110
Ulrika Bjork *(CEO)*

POLYGON GLOBAL PARTNERS LLP
4 Sloane Terrace, London, SW1X 9DQ, United Kingdom
Tel.: (44) 2079018300
Web Site: http://www.polygoninv.com
Year Founded: 2009
Investment Firm
N.A.I.C.S.: 523940
Reade Grifith *(CIO & Principal)*

POLYGON REAL ESTATE LTD.
8 Granit Kiryat Arie 10033, Petah Tiqwa, 4900, Israel
Tel.: (972) 732333900
Year Founded: 1962
POLY—(TAE)
Rev.: $7,914,353
Assets: $47,158,170
Liabilities: $2,270,479
Net Worth: $44,887,691
Earnings: $4,652,576
Fiscal Year-end: 12/31/23
Other Activities Related to Real Estate
N.A.I.C.S.: 531390
Yehuda Bachar *(Chm)*

POLYGONE INTERNATIONAL SA
173 Chaussee de wavre, 1050, Brussels, Belgium
Tel.: (32) 22137400
Web Site: http://www.polygonegroup.be
Year Founded: 2006
Sales Range: $10-24.9 Million
Emp.: 104
Advertising Services
N.A.I.C.S.: 541890
Thierry Goor *(Mng Dir & Mng Partner)*

POLYGREEN RESOURCES CO., LTD.
Lot 3 Lingkaran Sultan Hishamuddin Kaw 20, PKNS Industrial Estate Selat Klang Utara, 42000, Port Klang, Selangor Darul Ehsan, Malaysia
Tel.: (60) 331762602
8423—(TPE)
Rev.: $10,045,337
Assets: $16,867,461
Liabilities: $5,321,515
Net Worth: $11,545,946
Earnings: $917,331
Emp.: 149
Fiscal Year-end: 12/31/22
Rubber & Plastic Product Mfr
N.A.I.C.S.: 326220

Subsidiaries:

Jeng Yuan Reclaimed Rubber Sdn. Bhd. (1)
Lot 3 Lingkaran Sultan Hishamuddin Kaw 20 PKNS Industrial Estate, Selat Klang Utara, 42000, Port Klang, Selangor Darul Ehsan, Malaysia
Tel.: (60) 331762602
Web Site: https://www.jeng-yuan.com
Reclaimed Rubber Mfr
N.A.I.C.S.: 326299

POLYLINK POLYMERS (INDIA) LTD.
506 Saffron Building Near Center Point Ambavadi, Ahmedabad, 380 006, Gujarat, India
Tel.: (91) 7926427800
Web Site: https://www.polylinkpolymers.com

531454—(BOM)
Rev.: $6,072,430
Assets: $3,607,685
Liabilities: $479,755
Net Worth: $3,127,930
Earnings: $77,226
Emp.: 36
Fiscal Year-end: 03/31/23
Polythene Compounds Mfr
N.A.I.C.S.: 326140
Uma Shankar Bhartia *(Chm & Mng Dir)*

POLYLITE TAIWAN CO., LTD.
No 406 Changfa Rd, Dayuan Dist, Taoyuan, 33759, Taiwan
Tel.: (886) 33853934
Web Site: https://www.gialens.com.tw
Year Founded: 1994
1813—(TPE)
Rev.: $11,320,139
Assets: $35,566,645
Liabilities: $9,873,777
Net Worth: $25,692,868
Earnings: ($306,038)
Fiscal Year-end: 12/31/22
Polycarbonate Lens Mfr & Distr
N.A.I.C.S.: 339115
I-Hsin Sung *(Chm & CEO)*

POLYMAC THERMOFORMERS LTD.
29A Weston Street 3rd Floor Room No C-5, Kolkata, 700012, West Bengal, India
Tel.: (91) 3340041400
Web Site: https://www.polythermoformers.com
Year Founded: 1999
537573—(BOM)
Rev.: $1,271,709
Assets: $2,189,968
Liabilities: $959,118
Net Worth: $1,230,850
Earnings: $53,769
Emp.: 3
Fiscal Year-end: 03/31/23
Disposable Plastic Glasses, Cups & Bowls Mfr
N.A.I.C.S.: 326199
Pramod Kumar Agrawal *(Chm)*

POLYMECHPLAST MACHINES LTD.
Gold Coin House 775 GIDC Makarpura Industrial Estate, Vadodara, 390010, India
Tel.: (91) 2652632210   In
Web Site: https://www.polymechplast.com
Year Founded: 1978
526043—(BOM)
Rev.: $8,374,906
Assets: $5,182,891
Liabilities: $2,163,935
Net Worth: $3,018,956
Earnings: $185,744
Emp.: 116
Fiscal Year-end: 03/31/23
Plastic Processing Machinery Mfr
N.A.I.C.S.: 333248
K. R. Bhuva *(Chm & Mng Dir)*

POLYMER LINK HOLDINGS BHD
PTT 522 Jalan Sultan Mohamed 1 Kawasan Perindustrian, Bandar Sultan Suleiman, 42000, Port Klang, Selangor, Malaysia
Tel.: (60) 331790609
Web Site: http://www.polymerlink.net
Year Founded: 2014
Rev.: $17,438,581
Assets: $12,773,236
Liabilities: $5,576,258
Net Worth: $7,196,978

Earnings: $2,327,133
Fiscal Year-end: 09/30/19
Plastic Materials Mfr
N.A.I.C.S.: 325211
Eddie Koh *(Gen Mgr)*

Subsidiaries:

Polymer Link India Pvt. Ltd. (1)
A/442 Neo Corporate Plaza Ramachandra Lane Malad West, Mumbai Suburban, Mumbai, 400064, Maharashtra, India
Tel.: (91) 9137628080
Compounded Plastic Powder Mfr & Distr
N.A.I.C.S.: 325211

Polymer Link Philippines Inc. (1)
Building N12347 Clark Civil Aviation Complex IE-5 SCTEX Clark, South Interchange Road Clark Freeport Zone, Pampanga, Philippines
Tel.: (63) 452802057
Compounded Plastic Powder Mfr & Distr
N.A.I.C.S.: 325211

Polymer Link Sdn. Bhd. (1)
PTT 522 Jalan Sultan Mohamed 1 Sultan Suleiman, Kawasan Perindustrian Bandar, 42000, Port Klang, Selangor, Malaysia
Tel.: (60) 331790609
Web Site: http://www.polymerlink.net
Compounded Plastic Powder Mfr & Distr
N.A.I.C.S.: 325211

POLYMER LOGISTICS N.V.
Esdoornlaan 45B, 4902 TN, Oosterhout, Netherlands
Tel.: (31) 162372290
Web Site: http://www.polymerlogistics.com
Year Founded: 1994
Sales Range: $50-74.9 Million
Emp.: 102
Fiscal Year-end: 12/31/14
Retail Ready Packaging Services
N.A.I.C.S.: 561910
Gideon Feiner *(CEO)*

Subsidiaries:

Polymer Logistics, Inc. (1)
1725 Sierra Rdg Dr, Riverside, CA 92507-7133
Tel.: (951) 567-2900
Web Site: http://www.polymerlogistics.com
Sales Range: $1-9.9 Million
Emp.: 30
Packaging Solution & Logistic Services Retailer
N.A.I.C.S.: 424610
Tony Mosco *(VP-Sls-North America)*

POLYMETALS RESOURCES LTD.
Tel.: (61) 68302557   AU
Web Site: https://www.polymetals.com
Year Founded: 2020
POL—(ASX)
Rev.: $739
Assets: $14,045,386
Liabilities: $2,034,177
Net Worth: $12,011,209
Earnings: ($5,085,347)
Fiscal Year-end: 06/30/23
Metal Exploration Services
N.A.I.C.S.: 213114
David Sproule *(Chm)*

Subsidiaries:

Endeavor Operations Pty Ltd (1)
Via Louth Rd, PO Box 109, Cobar, 2835, NSW, Australia
Tel.: (61) 268302555
Web Site: www.cbhresources.com.au
Sales Range: $50-74.9 Million
Zinc, Lead & Silver Mining & Exploration
N.A.I.C.S.: 212230

POLYMIX
6 Rue De l'Industrie, 68126, Bennwihr Gare, France
Tel.: (33) 389201380

POLYMIX

Polymix—(Continued)
Web Site: http://www.polymix.fr
Industrial Polymers Mfr
N.A.I.C.S.: 423830
Julie Fath (Dir-Publication)

POLYNESIAN LIMITED
Beach Road, PO Box 599, Apia, Samoa (Western)
Tel.: (685) 21261
Year Founded: 1959
Sales Range: $75-99.9 Million
Emp.: 280
Airline Operator
N.A.I.C.S.: 481111
Alyson Pavitt-Sefo (Mgr-Airport Svcs)

POLYNET PUBLIC COMPANY LIMITED
888 Moo 11, Bang Sao Thong, 10570, Samutprakarn, Thailand
Tel.: (66) 23979094
Web Site: https://www.polynet.co.th
Year Founded: 1999
POLY—(THA)
Rev.: $28,063,229
Assets: $45,711,563
Liabilities: $7,707,217
Net Worth: $38,004,346
Earnings: $5,109,943
Emp.: 568
Fiscal Year-end: 12/31/23
Plastic Fabrication Product Mfr
N.A.I.C.S.: 315990
Chaiyaporn Nitaswarakul (Chm)

POLYNOVO LIMITED
2/320 Lorimer Street, Port Melbourne, 3207, VIC, Australia
Tel.: (61) 386814050   AU
Web Site: https://polynovo.com
PNV—(ASX)
Rev.: $32,096,161
Assets: $26,794,837
Liabilities: $13,221,715
Net Worth: $13,573,122
Earnings: ($913,706)
Emp.: 152
Fiscal Year-end: 06/30/22
Medical Device Mfr
N.A.I.C.S.: 334510
Paul Brennan (CEO & Mng Dir)

Subsidiaries:

PolyNovo Biomaterials Pty Ltd.   (1)
2/230 Lorimer Street, Port Melbourne, 3207, VIC, Australia
Tel.: (61) 386814050
Web Site: http://www.polynovo.com
Medical Materials Mfr
N.A.I.C.S.: 325412

Polynovo Limited   (1)
2/320 Lorimer Street, Port Melbourne, 3207, VIC, Australia
Tel.: (61) 386814050
Web Site: https://polynovo.com
Pharmaceuticals Mfr
N.A.I.C.S.: 325412

POLYPEPTIDE LABORATORIES AB
Limhamnsvagen 108, 200 61, Limhamn, Sweden
Tel.: (46) 40 366 200
Web Site: http://www.polypeptide.com
Polypeptide Mfr
N.A.I.C.S.: 325412

POLYPID LTD.
18 Hasivim Street, Petah Tiqwa, 495376, Israel
Tel.: (972) 747195700   II
Web Site: https://www.polypid.com
Year Founded: 2008
PYPD—(NASDAQ)
Assets: $25,971,000
Liabilities: $20,142,000
Net Worth: $5,829,000
Earnings: ($39,557,000)
Emp.: 65
Fiscal Year-end: 12/31/22
Pharmaceuticals Mfr
N.A.I.C.S.: 325412
Noam Emanuel (Chief Scientific Officer)

Subsidiaries:

PolyPid Inc.   (1)
47 Maple St Ste 302A, Summit, NJ 07901
Biopharmaceutical Mfr
N.A.I.C.S.: 325412

POLYPLEX CORPORATION LIMITED
B-37 Sector - 1 Gautam Budh Nagar, Noida, 201301, Uttar Pradesh, India
Tel.: (91) 1202443716
Web Site: https://www.polyplex.com
Year Founded: 1984
POLYPLEX—(NSE)
Rev.: $679,404,153
Assets: $843,124,846
Liabilities: $186,778,847
Net Worth: $656,345,999
Earnings: $117,658,031
Emp.: 933
Fiscal Year-end: 03/31/21
Biaxially Oriented Polyester (BOPET) Film Mfr & Exporter
N.A.I.C.S.: 322220
Sanjiv Saraf (Chm)

Subsidiaries:

Polyplex (Asia) Pte. Ltd.   (1)
B-37 Sector 1 Gautan Budh Nagar, Noida, 201301, Uttar Pradesh, India   (100%)
Tel.: (91) 1202443716
Holding Company; Plastic Films Mfr & Distr
N.A.I.C.S.: 551112

Subsidiary (Non-US):

Polyplex (Thailand) Public Company Limited   (2)
75/26 Ocean Tower-II 18C Floor Sukhumvit Road Kwaeng North Klongtoey, Khet Wattana, Bangkok, 10110, Thailand
Tel.: (66) 26652706
Web Site: https://www.polyplexthailand.com
Rev.: $575,070,670
Assets: $738,134,016
Liabilities: $178,121,409
Net Worth: $560,012,606
Earnings: $9,901,181
Emp.: 782
Fiscal Year-end: 03/31/2024
Biaxially Oriented Polyester (BOPET) Film Mfr & Exporter; Owned 53.5% by Polyplex (Asia) Pte. Ltd. & 16.5% by Polyplex Corporation Limited
N.A.I.C.S.: 322220
Sanjiv Saraf (Vice Chm)

Subsidiary (US):

Polyplex (Americas) Inc.   (3)
12200 Ford Rd Ste A-210, Farmers Branch, TX 75234
Tel.: (972) 247-3836
Sales Range: $50-74.9 Million
Emp.: 10
Plastic Films Distr; Owned 80.24% by Polyplex Thailand Public Company Limited & 9.88% by Polyplex Corporation Limited
N.A.I.C.S.: 424610

Subsidiary (Non-US):

Polyplex (Singapore) Pte. Limited   (3)
Levels 21 & 34 Centennial Tower 3 Temasek Avenue, Singapore, 039190, Singapore
Tel.: (65) 65497878
Web Site: https://www.polyplex.com
Plastic Product Mfr & Distr
N.A.I.C.S.: 326111

Subsidiary (Non-US):

Polyplex Trading (Shenzhen) Company Limited   (4)
Room 1309 A Block Galaxy Century Building Caitian South Rd, Futian District, Shenzhen, 518000, China   (100%)
Tel.: (86) 7558 256 1002
Web Site: https://www.polyplexthailand.com
Plastic Product Distr
N.A.I.C.S.: 424610
Amit Prakash (Dir)

Subsidiary (Non-US):

Polyplex Europa Polyester Film San ve tic A.S.   (3)
Karamehmet Mh Avrupa Serbest Bolgesi 3 Sokak No 4, Velimise Mevkil Corlu, Tekirdag, 59850, Turkiye   (100%)
Tel.: (90) 282 691 1241
Web Site: https://www.polyplex.com
Sales Range: $125-149.9 Million
Emp.: 300
Polyester Film Mfr
N.A.I.C.S.: 322220
Neeraj Gupta (Chm)

POLYRAM PLASTIC INDUSTRIES LTD.
Moshav Ram-On M P Gilboa, Tel Aviv, Israel
Tel.: (972) 465999999
Web Site: https://www.polyram-group.com
Year Founded: 1986
POLP—(TAE)
Rev.: $271,364,351
Assets: $283,726,479
Liabilities: $114,686,568
Net Worth: $169,039,911
Earnings: $23,074,399
Emp.: 280
Fiscal Year-end: 09/30/23
Thermoplastic Compound Distr
N.A.I.C.S.: 424610
Ishay Davidi (Chm)

POLYROCKS CHEMICAL CO., LTD.
XiongXing Industrial Park, Qingyuan, 511540, Guangdong, China
Tel.: (86) 7633125898
Web Site: https://www.polyrocks.net
Year Founded: 2007
688669—(SHG)
Rev.: $555,621,136
Assets: $573,527,780
Liabilities: $331,321,522
Net Worth: $242,206,258
Earnings: $6,324,795
Emp.: 1,000
Fiscal Year-end: 12/31/22
Chemical Product Mfr & Distr
N.A.I.C.S.: 325520
Gang Chen (Chm & Gen Mgr)

POLYSPIN EXPORTS LIMITED
1 Railway Feeder Road Cholapuram South, Rajapalayam, 626139, Tamilnadu, India
Tel.: (91) 4563284503
Web Site: https://www.polyspin.in
Year Founded: 1972
539354—(BOM)
Rev.: $29,473,521
Assets: $19,380,888
Liabilities: $12,207,050
Net Worth: $7,173,838
Earnings: $644,398
Emp.: 1,878
Fiscal Year-end: 03/31/23
Plastic Bag Mfr & Whslr
N.A.I.C.S.: 326111
R. Ramji (CEO & Mng Dir)

POLYTAINERS INC.
197 Norseman St, Toronto, M8Z 2R5, ON, Canada
Tel.: (416) 239-7311
Web Site:
    http://www.polytainersinc.com
Sales Range: $125-149.9 Million

INTERNATIONAL PUBLIC

Emp.: 900
Plastic Container Mfr
N.A.I.C.S.: 326199

POLYTEC ASSET HOLDINGS LIMITED
23rd Floor Pioneer Centre 750 Nathan Road, Kowloon, China (Hong Kong)
Tel.: (852) 2380 9682   Ky
Web Site:
    http://www.polytecasset.com
Sales Range: $200-249.9 Million
Emp.: 260
Investment Holding Company
N.A.I.C.S.: 551112
Koc Leng Chio (Exec Dir)

Subsidiaries:

JSC Caspi Neft TME   (1)
Business Center White Tower 135 Abylaykhan Avenue 2nd Floor, Almaty, 050091, Kazakhstan   (100%)
Tel.: (7) 3272506030
Sales Range: $100-124.9 Million
Oil & Gas Exploration, Drilling & Extraction Services
N.A.I.C.S.: 211120

POLYTEC HOLDING AG
Polytec Strasse 1, A-4063, Horsching, Austria
Tel.: (43) 72217010   AT
Web Site: https://www.polytec-group.com
Year Founded: 1986
P4N—(MUN)
Rev.: $702,050,281
Assets: $588,384,787
Liabilities: $348,933,307
Net Worth: $239,451,480
Earnings: ($15,531,451)
Emp.: 3,291
Fiscal Year-end: 12/31/23
Automobile Parts Mfr
N.A.I.C.S.: 551112
Fred Duswald (Chm-Supervisory Bd)

Subsidiaries:

POLYTEC AUTOMOTIVE GmbH & Co KG   (1)
Meyerfelder Weg 45, 49393, Lohne, Germany
Tel.: (49) 44429500
Web Site: http://www.polytec-automotive.com
Sales Range: $150-199.9 Million
Emp.: 550
Automobiles Design Services
N.A.I.C.S.: 541420

POLYTEC AVO NV   (1)
Metropoolstraat 8, 2900, Schoten, Belgium
Tel.: (32) 36801820
Web Site: http://www.polytec-group.com
Sales Range: $25-49.9 Million
Emp.: 40
Car Styling Services
N.A.I.C.S.: 541490

POLYTEC CAR STYLING Bromyard Ltd.   (1)
Porthouse Industrial Estate, Bromyard, Hereford, HR7 4NS, United Kingdom
Tel.: (44) 1885483000
Web Site: http://www.polytec-group.com
Sales Range: $75-99.9 Million
Emp.: 280
Automotive Products Mfr
N.A.I.C.S.: 336390

POLYTEC COMPOSITES SWEDEN AB   (1)
Box 302, S-34126, Ljungby, Sweden
Tel.: (46) 37267500
Web Site: http://www.polytec-composites-se.com
Sales Range: $50-74.9 Million
Emp.: 108
Automotive Composite Mfr
N.A.I.C.S.: 336330

POLYTEC Composites Bohemia s.r.o. (1)
Marianskolazenska 200, Chodova Plana, 34813, Czech Republic
Tel.: (420) 374331401
Sales Range: $50-74.9 Million
Emp.: 150
Injection Molded Plastic Products Mfr
N.A.I.C.S.: 326199

POLYTEC Composites Germany GmbH & Co KG (1)
Tel.: (49) 725892790
Sales Range: $100-124.9 Million
Plastic Spare Parts Mfr
N.A.I.C.S.: 326199

POLYTEC Composites Verwaltungs GmbH (1)
Alte Munzesheimer Str 4, Kraichtal, Karlsruhe, 76703, Germany
Tel.: (49) 725892790
Web Site: http://www.polytec-group.com
Emp.: 50
Plastic Spare Parts Mfr
N.A.I.C.S.: 326199

POLYTEC Composites Weiden GmbH (1)
Friedrich Ochs Str 2, Weiden, 92637, Germany
Tel.: (49) 961391737800
Web Site: http://www.polytecgroup.com
Sales Range: $100-124.9 Million
Emp.: 150
Injection Molded Plastic Products Mfr
N.A.I.C.S.: 326199

POLYTEC Compounds GmbH & Co. KG (1)
Alte Munzesheimer Strasse 8, Gochsheim, 76703, Kraichtal, Germany
Tel.: (49) 725892790
Plastic Spare Parts Mfr
N.A.I.C.S.: 326199

POLYTEC ELASTOFORM GmbH & Co KG (1)
Kiesstrasse 12, 4614, Marchtrenk, Austria
Tel.: (43) 724 353 4510
Web Site: https://www.polytec-industrial.com
Sales Range: $25-49.9 Million
Plastic Mfr
N.A.I.C.S.: 326199

POLYTEC EMC Engineering GmbH (1)
Kiesstrasse 12, 4614, Marchtrenk, Austria
Tel.: (43) 7243539520
Web Site: https://www.polytec-industrial.com
Sales Range: $25-49.9 Million
Emp.: 40
Motor Vehicle Spare Parts Mfr
N.A.I.C.S.: 336390

POLYTEC FOHA Corp (1)
205 Riviera Drive Unit 5, Markham, L3R, ON, Canada
Tel.: (905) 940-5006
Web Site: http://www.polytec-group.com
Car Design Services
N.A.I.C.S.: 541490

POLYTEC FOHA Inc. (1)
7020 Murtham Ave, Warren, MI 48092
Tel.: (586) 978-9386
Emp.: 30
Car Design Services
N.A.I.C.S.: 541420

POLYTEC FOR Car Styling GmbH & Co KG (1)
Linzer Strasse 50, Horsching, 4063, Austria
Tel.: (43) 72217010
Web Site: http://www.polytec-group.com
Emp.: 250
Plastics Product Mfr
N.A.I.C.S.: 326199

POLYTEC INTERIOR GmbH (1)
Dieselweg 10, D-82538, Geretsried, Germany
Tel.: (49) 81713810
Sales Range: $100-124.9 Million
Emp.: 270
Automotive Interior Design Services
N.A.I.C.S.: 336360

POLYTEC Industrial Plastics GmbH (1)
Am Vorort 27, Bochum, 44894, Germany
Tel.: (49) 234893680
Web Site: http://www.polytech-Industrial.com
Sales Range: $25-49.9 Million
Emp.: 60
Plastic Spare Parts Mfr
N.A.I.C.S.: 326199

Subsidiary (Non-US):

POLYTEC EMC Engineering GmbH & Co KG (2)
Kiesstrasse 12, 4614, Marchtrenk, Austria
Tel.: (43) 724353952
Web Site: https://www.polytec-industrial.com
Sales Range: $25-49.9 Million
Emp.: 30
Industrial Equipment Mfr
N.A.I.C.S.: 333248

Subsidiary (Domestic):

POLYTEC THELEN GmbH (2)
Am Vorort 27, 44894, Bochum, Germany
Tel.: (49) 234893680
Web Site: https://www.polytec-industrial.com
Sales Range: $25-49.9 Million
Emp.: 50
Plastic Spare Parts Mfr
N.A.I.C.S.: 326199
Peter Stinshoff (Coord-Data Production)

POLYTEC Industrielackierung GmbH & Co. KG (1)
Lochfeldstr 20-24, Rastatt, 76437, Germany
Tel.: (49) 72225990
Web Site: http://www.polytec-group.de
Sales Range: $100-124.9 Million
Plastic Spare Parts Mfr
N.A.I.C.S.: 326199

POLYTEC Industrielackierung Weiden GmbH (1)
Meerbodenreuth 33, 92665, Altenstadt, Germany
Tel.: (49) 960263800
Web Site: https://www.win-coatings.de
Automotive Painting Services
N.A.I.C.S.: 811121

POLYTEC Interior Polska Sp. z o.o. (1)
Piaskowa 120, Tomaszow Mazowiecki, 97-200, Poland
Tel.: (48) 447256100
Web Site: http://www.polska.com
Emp.: 900
Automobile Spare Parts Mfr
N.A.I.C.S.: 336390
Marzena Kepa (Dir)

POLYTEC Interior South Africa (Pty) Ltd. (1)
Trio Industrial Park, Pretoria, 200, South Africa
Tel.: (27) 125411878
Sales Range: $25-49.9 Million
Emp.: 71
Automobile Spare Parts Mfr
N.A.I.C.S.: 336390

POLYTEC Interior Zaragoza S.L. (1)
Carretera Logrono S n Km 27 5 Pg Ind Logistico, Figueruelas, 50639, Aragon, Spain
Tel.: (34) 976656285
Automobile Spare Parts Mfr
N.A.I.C.S.: 327910
Zaberr Gallego (Gen Mgr)

POLYTEC PLASTICS Germany GmbH & Co KG (1)
Tel.: (49) 44429500
Web Site: http://www.polytec-group.com
Sales Range: $200-249.9 Million
Emp.: 600
Plastics Product Mfr
N.A.I.C.S.: 326199

Subsidiary (Domestic):

POLYTEC Deutschland Verwaltungs GmbH (2)
Meyerfelder Weg 45, Lohne, 49393, Germany
Tel.: (49) 39201282500
Plastics Product Mfr
N.A.I.C.S.: 326199

POLYTEC Plastics Idstein GmbH & Co. KG (1)
Black And Decker Strasse 25, 65510, Idstein, Germany
Tel.: (49) 61265820
Web Site: http://www.polytec-croubh.com
Sales Range: $50-74.9 Million
Emp.: 250
Mfr of Thermoplastic Injection Moulded Articles
N.A.I.C.S.: 326199

POLYTEX INDIA LIMITED
401 4th Floor Nisarg Apartment Besant Road Vile Parle West, Mumbai, 400056, India
Tel.: (91) 2267147827
Web Site: https://www.polytexindia.com
Year Founded: 1987
512481—(BOM)
Assets: $353,936
Liabilities: $24,591
Net Worth: $329,345
Earnings: ($8,980)
Emp.: 1
Fiscal Year-end: 03/31/23
Investment Management Service
N.A.I.C.S.: 523999
Arvind Mulji Kariya (CFO)

POLYTRONICS TECHNOLOGY CORP.
No 24-1 Industry E Rd IV, Hsinchu Science Park, Hsin-chu, 300, Taiwan
Tel.: (886) 35643931
Web Site: https://www.pttc.com.tw
Year Founded: 1988
6224—(TAI)
Rev.: $91,361,781
Assets: $141,570,092
Liabilities: $49,528,335
Net Worth: $92,041,757
Earnings: ($947,349)
Emp.: 590
Fiscal Year-end: 12/31/23
Polymeric Positive Temperature Coefficient Thermistors Mfr
N.A.I.C.S.: 334512
Zhu Fuhua (Chm)

Subsidiaries:

Kunshan Polystar Electronics Co., Ltd. (1)
998 Han-Pu Rd Hi-Tech Industrial Park, Kunshan, 215316, Jiangsu, China
Tel.: (86) 51286162818
Thermal Conductive Board Mfr
N.A.I.C.S.: 334513

TCLAD Inc. (1)
1600 Orrin Rd, Prescott, WI 54021
Tel.: (715) 262-5898
Web Site: https://www.tclad.com
Emp.: 312
Automotive LED Light Mfr
N.A.I.C.S.: 336320

TCLAD Technology Co., Ltd. (1)
No 24-1 Industry E Rd IV Hsinchu Science Park, Hsinchu, 300, Taiwan
Tel.: (886) 35643931
Industrial Automation Services
N.A.I.C.S.: 532490

Tclad Europe GmbH (1)
Bischheimerstrasse 14, 67292, Kirchheimbolanden, Germany
Tel.: (49) 63526788210
Automotive LED Light Mfr
N.A.I.C.S.: 336320

POLYURETHANE FOAM SYSTEMS INC.
440 Conestogo Rd, Waterloo, N2L 4E2, ON, Canada
Tel.: (519) 884-0688
Web Site: http://www.polyurethanefoam.com
Year Founded: 2000
Rev.: $15,010,000
Emp.: 8
Polyurethane Foam Product Mfr
N.A.I.C.S.: 326150
Dan Clayton (Founder & Pres)

POLYWERT GMBH
Strasberger Strasse 5, Bobingen, 86399, Germany
Tel.: (49) 823496020
Web Site: http://www.polywert.de
Year Founded: 1992
Rev.: $11,035,200
Emp.: 45
Polyester Fibre Products Mfr
N.A.I.C.S.: 424690
Christoph Adelmann (Mng Dir)

POMERLEAU INC.
521 6th Avenue, Saint-Georges, G5Y 0H1, QC, Canada
Tel.: (418) 228-6688
Web Site: http://www.pomerleau.ca
Year Founded: 1964
Sales Range: $800-899.9 Million
Emp.: 4,000
General Contracting Services
N.A.I.C.S.: 236220
Pierre Pomerleau (Pres & CEO)

Subsidiaries:

Beaubois Ltee (1)
521 6th Avenue, Saint-Georges, G5Y 0H1, QC, Canada
Tel.: (418) 228-5104
Web Site: http://www.beaubois.ca
Sales Range: $100-124.9 Million
Emp.: 400
Custom-Made Furniture & Architectural Woodwork Mfr
N.A.I.C.S.: 337122

Borea Construction Ulc (1)
562 Olivier Rd, Levis, G7A 2N6, QC, Canada
Tel.: (418) 626-2314
Web Site: http://www.boreaconstruction.com
Wind Energy Construction Services
N.A.I.C.S.: 237130
Marc Richard (Sr VP)

Hotel Le Georgesville (1)
300 118e Rue, Saint-Georges, G5Y 3E3, QC, Canada (100%)
Tel.: (418) 227-3000
Web Site: http://www.georgesville.com
Emp.: 60
Hotels & Motels
N.A.I.C.S.: 721110
Mireille Vezina (Gen Mgr)

La Chateau Bonne Entente (1)
3400 Chemin, Sainte-Foy, G1X 1S6, QC, Canada (100%)
Tel.: (418) 653-5221
Web Site: https://www.lebonneentente.com
Sales Range: $50-74.9 Million
Emp.: 200
Hotels & Motels
N.A.I.C.S.: 721110

POMIFRUTAS S/A
Rodovia da Maca Km 28, Caixa Postal 02, Fraiburgo, Brazil
Tel.: (55) 4932562201
Web Site: http://www.renar.agr.br
FRTA3—(BRAZ)
Sales Range: Less than $1 Million
Crop Farming Services
N.A.I.C.S.: 111998
Marcos Kassardjian (CEO)

POMINA STEEL CORPORATION
Road 27 Than II Industrial Zone, Di An, Binh Duong, Vietnam
Tel.: (84) 6503710051
Web Site: https://www.pomina-steel.com
POM—(HNX)
Rev.: $135,297,422
Assets: $428,656,048

POMINA STEEL CORPORATION

Pomina Steel Corporation—(Continued)
Liabilities: $362,952,883
Net Worth: $65,703,164
Earnings: ($39,429,306)
Emp.: 300
Fiscal Year-end: 12/31/23
Steel Mfrs
N.A.I.C.S.: 331110
Chieu Xuan Do *(Chm)*

Subsidiaries:

Pomina Steel Joint Stock Company 2 (1)
Phu My Industrial Park, Tan Thanh, Vung Tau, Ba Ria-Vung Tau, Vietnam
Tel.: (84) 2543922517
Web Site: https://pomina-steel.com
Steel Products Mfr
N.A.I.C.S.: 331110

POMONA ACQUISITION LTD.
Suite 56 theDesk 5/F United Centre 95 Queensway, Central, China (Hong Kong)
Tel.: (852) 98380771   Ky
Year Founded: 2021
PMACU—(NASDAQ)
Investment Services
N.A.I.C.S.: 523999
Gary Ka Leung Chan *(CEO)*

POMONA-GRUPPEN AB
Arsenalsgatan 2, 111 47, Stockholm, Sweden
Tel.: (46) 8 679 1350   SE
Web Site: http://www.pomona.se
Year Founded: 1986
Sales Range: Less than $1 Million
Investment Services
N.A.I.C.S.: 523999

Subsidiaries:

Argynnis Group AB (1)
Hedekullevagen 24, Trollhattan, 46111, Sweden
Tel.: (46) 520473200
Web Site: http://www.binarelektronik.se
Sales Range: $25-49.9 Million
Emp.: 250
Industrial Electronics & Industrial Production Equipment Mfr
N.A.I.C.S.: 333248
Ingemar Pettersson *(CEO)*

Subsidiary (Domestic):

Binar Elektronik AB (2)
Hedekullevagen 24, 461 38, Trollhattan, Sweden
Tel.: (46) 520473200
Web Site: http://www.binarelektronik.se
Sales Range: $25-49.9 Million
Emp.: 30
Electronic Components Mfr
N.A.I.C.S.: 334419
Anders Wilhelmsson *(Mgr-Sls)*

Subsidiary (Non-US):

Binar Handling GmbH (2)
In den Wieden 3, 34355, Staufenberg, Germany
Tel.: (49) 5543 30379 0
Industrial Machinery Mfr
N.A.I.C.S.: 333998

Binar Handling Sud Gmbh (2)
Autenbachstrasse 11, 71711, Berlin, Germany
Tel.: (49) 7144 80767 0
Industrial Machinery Mfr
N.A.I.C.S.: 333998

Subsidiary (Domestic):

Binar Olofstrom AB (2)
Vastra Storgatan 20, 293 38, Olofstrom, Sweden
Tel.: (46) 454323055
Web Site: http://www.binarolofstrom.se
Sales Range: $50-74.9 Million
Emp.: 6
Press Line Automation Mfr

N.A.I.C.S.: 423830
Ingemar Pettersson *(Gen Mgr)*

Binar Quick-Lift Systems AB (2)
Hedekullevagen 24, 461 38, Trollhattan, Sweden
Tel.: (46) 520474000
Web Site: http://www.kahlman.se
Sales Range: $25-49.9 Million
Emp.: 18
Portable Lifts & Cranes Mfr
N.A.I.C.S.: 333923
Johan Ahlstrom *(Mgr)*

Ircon Drying Systems AB (2)
Svetsargatan 8, 462 56, Vanersborg, Sweden
Tel.: (46) 521 276970
Web Site: http://www.ircon.se
Industry Machinery Mfr
N.A.I.C.S.: 333998
Fredrik Liljesater *(Engr-Electrical & Automation)*

Mabema AB (2)
Teknikringen 4C, 583 30, Linkoping, Sweden
Tel.: (46) 13 15 3700
Web Site: http://www.dynamis.se
Material Handling & Measurement Systems
N.A.I.C.S.: 334513

Subsidiary (Non-US):

Mercura S.A.S (2)
4 Rue Louis Pasteur, 41260, Paris, France
Tel.: (33) 2 54 57 52 52
Web Site: http://www.mercura.fr
Automobile Parts Mfr
N.A.I.C.S.: 334290
Denis Lahoreau *(CEO)*

Subsidiary (Domestic):

Nohab Industri AB (2)
Nohabgatan 18, 461 53, Trollhattan, Sweden
Tel.: (46) 520 383 45
Web Site: http://www.nohab.se
Steel Products Mfr
N.A.I.C.S.: 331110

Subsidiary (Non-US):

Solaronics SA (2)
Zone Industrielle 3 Rue Du Kemmel, Armentieres, 59280, France
Tel.: (33) 320105949
Web Site: http://www.ircon-solaronics.com
Burner Mfr
N.A.I.C.S.: 333414

Subsidiary (Domestic):

Standby AB (2)
Nohabgatan 12C, 461 53, Trollhattan, Sweden
Tel.: (46) 520 49 44 40
Web Site: http://www.standby.eu
Automobile Parts Mfr
N.A.I.C.S.: 334290
Daniel Tibell *(Mgr-Sls & Mktg)*

POMORAVLJE A.D.
Bulevar 12 Februar 129, 18000, Nis, Serbia
Tel.: (381) 18 585 132
Web Site: http://www.pomoravlje-nis.co.rs
Year Founded: 1998
PMNI—(BEL)
Sales Range: Less than $1 Million
Emp.: 11
Paint, Varnish & Coating Product Mfr
N.A.I.C.S.: 325510
Dejan Andrijasevic *(Mng Dir)*

POMORAVLJE A.D.
Hajduk Veljkov venac 4-6, Belgrade, Serbia
Tel.: (381) 11 2646 977
Year Founded: 1993
Sales Range: Less than $1 Million
Mobile Food Services
N.A.I.C.S.: 722330
Saric Zivojin *(Dir)*

POMORAVLJE TERM A.D.
Majakovskog 34, Nis, Serbia
Tel.: (381) 18 277 040
Year Founded: 1993
Sales Range: Less than $1 Million
Emp.: 5
Plumbing Equipment Whslr
N.A.I.C.S.: 423720

POMPES RUTSCHI SAS
61 avenue de Fribourg, 68110, Illzach, France
Tel.: (33) 389616800
Web Site: https://www.grupperutschi.com
Nuclear Grade Pumps & Related Customisation Services
N.A.I.C.S.: 221118

POMVOM LTD.
Hamenofim 10, Herzliya, Israel
Tel.: (972) 35772022
Web Site: https://www.pomvom.com
Year Founded: 2016
PMVM—(TAE)
Rev.: $60,350,047
Assets: $16,161,624
Liabilities: $7,801,077
Net Worth: $8,360,547
Earnings: ($7,175,300)
Fiscal Year-end: 12/31/23
Computer Software Publisher
N.A.I.C.S.: 513210
Matan Mandelbaum *(COO& Partner)*

Subsidiaries:

Pomvom UK Limited (1)
1 Park Row, Leeds, LS1 5AB, United Kingdom
Web Site: http://www.pomvom.com
Computer Software Publisher
N.A.I.C.S.: 513210

Subsidiary (Domestic):

Picsolve International Ltd. (2)
9 Victoria Way Pride Park, Derby, DE24 8AN, United Kingdom
Tel.: (44) 1332370740
Web Site: http://www.picsolve.biz
Attraction Photography Services
N.A.I.C.S.: 541921
David Hockley *(CEO)*

Subsidiary (US):

Freeze Frame, Inc. (3)
4205 Vineland Rd Ste L9, Orlando, FL 32811
Tel.: (407) 648-2111
Web Site: http://www.freezeframe.com
Sales Range: $1-9.9 Million
Emp.: 20
Photography Studio
N.A.I.C.S.: 541921
Cliff David *(Pres)*

PON HOLDINGS B.V.
Rondebeltweg 31, 1329 BN, Almere, Netherlands
Tel.: (31) 886060100   Nl
Web Site: http://www.pon.com
Year Founded: 1898
Sales Range: $1-4.9 Billion
Emp.: 13,000
Automobile Component Industrial Component & Bicycle Mfr
N.A.I.C.S.: 551112

Subsidiaries:

Dutchlease B.V. (1)
Aploniastraat 16, Rotterdam, 3084 CC, Netherlands (100%)
Tel.: (31) 104105700
Web Site: http://www.dutchlease.nl
Sales Range: $50-74.9 Million
Emp.: 25
Motor Vehicle Leasing
N.A.I.C.S.: 532112
Hans Groenhuijsen *(Mng Dir)*

Nimpon Trade and Services b.v. (1)

INTERNATIONAL PUBLIC

Driebergseweg 17, 3708 JA, Zeist, Netherlands (40%)
Tel.: (31) 30 697 1410
Web Site: http://www.nimpon.com
Sales Range: $50-74.9 Million
Emp.: 100
Holding Company
N.A.I.C.S.: 551112
Marc Renne *(CEO)*

Subsidiary (Non-US):

Scanpocon Metric A/S (2)
Aggerhaten 5, Markaervej, 5220, Odense, Denmark
Tel.: (45) 66176260
Web Site: http://www.coromatic.dk
Sales Range: $25-49.9 Million
Emp.: 40
Power Supply Solutions
N.A.I.C.S.: 332410
Micheal Peterson *(Mng Dir)*

Pon Bicycle Group (1)
Rondebeltweg 31, 1329 BN, Almere, Netherlands
Tel.: (31) 886060100
Web Site: http://www.pon.com
Emp.: 6
Bicycle Mfr
N.A.I.C.S.: 336991
Markus Schmautz *(Sr VP)*

Subsidiary (Non-US):

Cervelo Cycles Inc. (2)
15 Leswyn road Unit 1, Toronto, M6A1J8, ON, Canada
Tel.: (416) 425-9517
Web Site: http://www.cervelo.com
Sales Range: $25-49.9 Million
Emp.: 50
Bicycle Mfr
N.A.I.C.S.: 336991
Phil White *(Co-Founder & CEO)*

Derby Cycle AG (2)
Siemensstrasse 1 3, 49661, Cloppenburg, Germany
Tel.: (49) 44719660
Web Site: http://www.derby-cycle.com
Sales Range: $350-399.9 Million
Emp.: 714
Bicycle Mfr
N.A.I.C.S.: 336991

Subsidiary (Domestic):

Koninklijke Gazelle N.V. (2)
Wilhelminaweg 8, 6950 AA, Dieren, Netherlands
Tel.: (31) 9007070707
Web Site: http://www.gazelle.nl
Sales Range: $200-249.9 Million
Bicycle Mfr
N.A.I.C.S.: 336991
Adriaan Heuzinkveld *(Mgr-HR)*

Pon North America, Inc. (1)
230 Park Ave Ste 1000, New York, NY 10169-1099
Tel.: (212) 808-6560
Holding Company
N.A.I.C.S.: 551111

Subsidiary (Domestic):

Equipment Depot, Inc. (2)
840 Gessner Rd Ste 950, Houston, TX 77024
Tel.: (713) 365-2547
Web Site: http://www.eqdepot.com
Emp.: 27
Material-Handling Equipment Sales, Rental & Service
N.A.I.C.S.: 532490
Rick Green *(Dir-Sls-Matl Handling-Central Reg)*

Subsidiary (Domestic):

Equipment Depot Kentucky, Inc. (3)
922 E Division St, Evansville, IN 47711-5667
Tel.: (812) 425-8164
Web Site: http://www.eqdepot.com
Sales Range: $50-74.9 Million
Material Handling Equipment Dealer
N.A.I.C.S.: 423830

Equipment Depot Ltd. (3)

AND PRIVATE COMPANIES — PONSSE OYJ

4100 S Interstate 35, Waco, TX 76706
Tel.: (254) 662-4322
Web Site: http://www.eqdepot.com
Industrial, Construction & Agricultural Equipment Supplier
N.A.I.C.S.: 423830
E. G. White-Swift *(Dir-Mktg & Adv)*

Branch (Domestic):

Equipment Depot (4)
700 W Cavalcade St, Houston, TX 77009-3007 **(100%)**
Tel.: (713) 869-6801
Web Site: http://www.eqdepot.com
Sales Range: $50-74.9 Million
Emp.: 90
Material-Handling Equipment Sales, Rental & Service
N.A.I.C.S.: 532490

Subsidiary (Domestic):

Equipment Depot Ohio, Inc. (3)
4331 Rossplain Dr, Cincinnati, OH 45236-1207
Tel.: (513) 891-0700
Web Site: http://www.portmanpeople.com
Sales Range: $75-99.9 Million
Retailer of Industrial & Material Handling Equipment
N.A.I.C.S.: 532490

Equipment Depot Pennsylvania, Inc. (3)
741 Independence Ave, Mechanicsburg, PA 17055-5498
Tel.: (717) 918-8700
Web Site: http://www.eqdepot.com
Sales Range: $75-99.9 Million
Material Handling Equipment Dealer
N.A.I.C.S.: 423830
Jake Briscoe *(Gen Mgr)*

Equipment Depot of Illinois, Inc. (3)
751 Expressway Dr, Itasca, IL 60143
Tel.: (630) 562-4900
Web Site: http://www.eqdepot.com
Sales Range: $50-74.9 Million
Material Handling Equipment Sales & Leasing
N.A.I.C.S.: 423830

RH Marine Group B.V. (1)
Droogdokweg 71, 3089 JN, Rotterdam, Netherlands **(100%)**
Tel.: (31) 104283222
Web Site: http://www.rhmarinegroup.com
Holding Company; Marine Vessel Electrical Monitoring Device, Electronic Propulsion System Navigation System, Climate Control System & Training Simulation System Mfr
N.A.I.C.S.: 551112
Erik van der Noordaa *(CEO)*

Subsidiary (Domestic):

Free Technics B.V. (2)
Jan Evertsenweg 2, 3115 JS, Schiedam, Netherlands
Tel.: (31) 104871911
Web Site: http://www.freetechnics.eu
Maritime Software Development Services
N.A.I.C.S.: 541511

RH Marine Netherlands B.V. (2)
Jan Evertsenweg 2, 3115 JA, Schiedam, Netherlands
Tel.: (31) 104871911
Web Site: http://www.rhmarine.com
Marine Satellite & Radio Communications Technologies, Automation Systems, Observation Products & Navigation Systems; Supplier of Satellite Airtime & Onboard Information Technology Services
N.A.I.C.S.: 517410

Subsidiary (Non-US):

Radio Holland Egypt (3)
24 Syria St Roushdy, Alexandria, Egypt
Tel.: (20) 35233454
Web Site: http://www.radioholland.com
Electronic Communications Equipment Whslr
N.A.I.C.S.: 423690

Radio Holland Hong Kong (3)
Unit 2003 One Midtown 11 Hoi Shing Road, Tseun Wan, Hong Kong, China (Hong Kong)
Tel.: (852) 24239007
Web Site: http://www.radioholland.com
Marine Electronics Retailer & Installer
N.A.I.C.S.: 517410

Radio Holland Middle East (3)
W-116 Maritime, PO Box 333764, Dubai, United Arab Emirates
Tel.: (971) 44377550
Web Site: http://www.radioholland.com
Marine Electronics Retailer & Installer
N.A.I.C.S.: 517410

Subsidiary (Domestic):

Radio Holland Netherlands B.V. (3)
Droogdokweg 71, 3089 JN, Rotterdam, Netherlands
Tel.: (31) 10 4283344
Web Site: http://www.radioholland.com
Developer of Marine Satellite & Radio Communications Technology Automation System Observation Product & Navigation System Supplier of Satellite Airtime & Onboard Information Technology Services
N.A.I.C.S.: 517410
Erik van der Noordaa *(CEO)*

Subsidiary (Domestic):

Radio Holland Netherlands (4)
Zijlvest 12, 9936 GZ, Delfzijl, Netherlands
Tel.: (31) 596633985
Web Site: http://www.radioholland.com
Marine Electronics Retailer & Installer
N.A.I.C.S.: 517410
Paul Smulders *(CEO)*

Subsidiary (Non-US):

Radio Holland Norway AS (3)
Ostre Akervei 19, 0581, Oslo, Norway
Tel.: (47) 23338000
Web Site: http://www.radioholland.com
Marine Electronics Retailer & Installer
N.A.I.C.S.: 517410
Jan Erik Skjonsberg *(Mgr-Technical)*

Radio Holland South Africa (3)
16 Paarden Eiland Road, 7404, Cape Town, South Africa
Tel.: (27) 215084700
Web Site: http://www.radioholland.com
Full-Service Systems Integrator of Innovative & Sustainable Marine Technology Products
N.A.I.C.S.: 488330

Branch (Domestic):

Radio Holland South Africa (4)
16 Paarden Eiland Road, Paarden Eiland, 7404, Cape Town, South Africa
Tel.: (27) 215084700
Web Site: http://www.radioholland.co.za
Marine Electronics Retailer
N.A.I.C.S.: 517410
Julian Hurrie *(Gen Mgr)*

Subsidiary (Non-US):

Radio-Holland Curacao (3)
De Rouvilleweg z/n, PO Box 4201, Willemstad, Curacao
Tel.: (599) 94626866
Web Site: http://www.radioholland.com
Marine Electronics Retailer
N.A.I.C.S.: 517410

Radio-Holland Singapore Pte. Ltd. (3)
2 Bukit Batok Street 23 Suite 06-01, Singapore, 659554, Singapore
Tel.: (65) 68622218
Web Site: http://www.radioholland.com.sg
Sales Range: $25-49.9 Million
Emp.: 55
Marine Electronics Retailer & Installers
N.A.I.C.S.: 517410
Denny Tan *(Mng Dir)*

POND SECURITY SERVICE GMBH
Ruckinger Strasse 12, 63526, Erlensee, Germany
Tel.: (49) 61838060
Web Site: http://www.pond-security.de
Year Founded: 1983
Rev.: $185,171,159
Emp.: 3,600
Security Services
N.A.I.C.S.: 561612
Daniel M. Pond *(Founder)*

POND TECHNOLOGIES HOLDINGS INC.
250 Shields Court Unit 8, Markham, L3R 9W2, ON, Canada
Tel.: (416) 287-3835 AB
Web Site: https://www.pondtech.com
Year Founded: 1972
PNDHF—(OTCQB)
Rev.: $3,432,776
Assets: $30,280,312
Liabilities: $33,886,010
Net Worth: ($3,605,698)
Earnings: ($2,623,287)
Emp.: 18
Fiscal Year-end: 12/31/23
Microalgal Biomass Production
N.A.I.C.S.: 541715
Steven Martin *(Co-CEO)*

Subsidiaries:

Pond Naturals Inc. (1)
1135 Hamilton Road, Agassiz, Chilliwack, V0M 1A3, BC, Canada
Tel.: (416) 287-3835
Web Site: https://www.pondnaturals.com
Algae Product Services
N.A.I.C.S.: 112519

Pond Technologies Inc. (1)
250 Shields Court Unit 8, Markham, L3R 9W7, ON, Canada
Tel.: (416) 287-3835
Web Site: https://www.pondtech.com
Algae Product Services
N.A.I.C.S.: 112519
Grant Smith *(CEO)*

PONDY OXIDES & CHEMICALS LIMITED
4 th Floor KRM Centre No 2 Harrington Road, Chetpet, Chennai, 600 031, Tamil Nadu, India
Tel.: (91) 4442965454
Web Site: https://pocl.com
Year Founded: 1995
POCL—(NSE)
Rev.: $177,501,792
Assets: $56,718,554
Liabilities: $24,974,834
Net Worth: $31,743,720
Earnings: $9,066,411
Emp.: 503
Fiscal Year-end: 03/31/23
Zinc Oxide Mfr
N.A.I.C.S.: 339999
Anil Kumar Bansal *(Chm)*

Subsidiaries:

Lohia Metals Private Limited (1)
No 2 Harrington Road KRM Centre 4th Floor, Chetpet, Chennai, 600 031, Tamilnadu, India
Tel.: (91) 44 42965454
Web Site: http://www.lmpl.co.in
Sales Range: $50-74.9 Million
Emp.: 200
Metal Refining Services
N.A.I.C.S.: 331410
Ashish Bansal *(Mgr)*

PONG MARKETING & PROMOTIONS INC.
201 Creditview Road, Vaughan, L4L 9T1, ON, Canada
Tel.: (905) 264-3555
Web Site: http://www.pongmarketing.com
Emp.: 50
Phone Cards & Promotional Calling Cards; Mobile Gaming Software Developer
N.A.I.C.S.: 517121

Karla Pena *(Mgr-Bus Dev & Mktg)*

PONISAVLJE A.D.
Ul Decanska 53, 18300, Pirot, Serbia
Tel.: (381) 10322623
Web Site: https://www.ponisavlje.co.rs
Year Founded: 1902
POPI—(BEL)
Sales Range: Less than $1 Million
Emp.: 15
Carpet & Rug Product Mfr
N.A.I.C.S.: 314110
Lela Panic *(Exec Dir & Dir)*

PONMART
Z I Le Pont Rouge Rue Christophe Colomb, 11000, Carcassonne, Aude, France
Tel.: (33) 468710711
Rev.: $26,100,000
Emp.: 42
Miscellaneous General Merchandise Stores
N.A.I.C.S.: 444180
Michael Nazieres *(Dir)*

PONOKA FORD SALES
6305 42 Avenue, Ponoka, T4J 1J8, AB, Canada
Tel.: (403) 783-5501
Web Site: http://www.legacyfordponoka.ca
Rev.: $16,258,706
Emp.: 35
New & Used Car Dealers
N.A.I.C.S.: 441110
Al Raugust *(Mgr-Fixed Ops)*

PONSSE OYJ
Tel.: (358) 20768800
Web Site: https://www.ponsse.com
Year Founded: 1970
PON1V—(HEL)
Rev.: $781,930,746
Assets: $582,141,543
Liabilities: $268,893,670
Net Worth: $313,247,873
Earnings: $39,652,500
Emp.: 1,782
Fiscal Year-end: 12/31/20
Forst Machinery Mfr & Distr
N.A.I.C.S.: 333120
Mammu Kaario *(Vice Chm)*

Subsidiaries:

Epec Oy (1)
Tel.: (358) 207608111
Web Site: http://epec.fi
Auto Parts Mfr
N.A.I.C.S.: 336390

Ponsse AB (1)
Lisjovagen 40, 735 91, Surahammar, Sweden
Tel.: (46) 22039900
Emp.: 74
Construction Equipment Mfr
N.A.I.C.S.: 333120

Ponsse AS (1)
Klettvegen 7, 2211, Kongsvinger, Norway
Tel.: (47) 62888870
Construction Equipment Mfr
N.A.I.C.S.: 333120

Ponsse Chile SpA (1)
Ruta 5 Sur km, 410, Chillan, Chile
Tel.: (56) 224147211
Forest Machinery Distr
N.A.I.C.S.: 423810

Ponsse China Ltd. (1)
1 Gangwan Road, Guangxi Industry Park Hepu, Beihai, 536100, China
Tel.: (86) 7797201872
Construction Equipment Mfr
N.A.I.C.S.: 333120

Ponsse Czech s.r.o. (1)
K Capka 385, CZ-543 71, Hostin u Vojkovic, Czech Republic

PONSSE OYJ

Ponsse Oyj—(Continued)
Tel.: (420) 735127056
Spare Parts Distr
N.A.I.C.S.: 423140

Ponsse North America, Inc. (1)
4400 International Ln, Rhinelander, WI 54501
Tel.: (715) 369-4833
Construction Equipment Mfr
N.A.I.C.S.: 333120

Ponsse S.A.S. (1)
ZAC Croix Saint Nicolas, Gondreville, 54840, Saint-Nicolas, France
Tel.: (33) 383651200
Construction Equipment Mfr
N.A.I.C.S.: 333120

Ponsse UK Ltd. (1)
4 Other Business Park, Dumfries, DG12 6TZ, United Kingdom
Tel.: (44) 1461207510
Construction Equipment Mfr
N.A.I.C.S.: 333120

Ponsse Uruguay S.A. (1)
Route 90 no 3102, 60000, Paysandu, Uruguay
Tel.: (598) 47243800
Construction Equipment Mfr
N.A.I.C.S.: 333120

PONTEX POLYBLEND CO., LTD.
No 23-6 Longxing Ln Sec 2 Fengxing Rd, Tanzi Dist, Taichung, 42742, Taiwan
Tel.: (886) 425384121
Web Site: https://pontex.com
Year Founded: 1982
8935—(TPE)
Rev.: $29,593,315
Assets: $53,811,056
Liabilities: $27,613,732
Net Worth: $26,197,324
Earnings: $855,329
Fiscal Year-end: 12/31/22
Electronic Components Mfr
N.A.I.C.S.: 334419
Morgan Shen (Chm)

Subsidiaries:

Pontex (Q.Y) Polyblend Co., Ltd. (1)
Longwan Industrial Park Longwan Avenue 33, Qingxin District Taiping Town, Qingyuan, Guangdong, China
Tel.: (86) 7636829996
Injection Mould Mfr
N.A.I.C.S.: 333511

VietNam Pontex Polyblend Co., Ltd. (1)
Lot J 2 CN My Phuoc 2 Industrial Park, Chanh Phu Hoa ward, Ben Cat, Binh Duong, Vietnam
Tel.: (84) 2742221898
Plastic Compound Material Mfr
N.A.I.C.S.: 325211

PONTIGGIA SARL
7 Rue De Selestat, 68180, Horbourg-Wihr, Haut Rhin, France
Tel.: (33) 389292660
Web Site: http://www.funramp.fr
Sales Range: $25-49.9 Million
Emp.: 67
Skating Modules Mfr & Installer
N.A.I.C.S.: 237310
Jean-Pierre Schittly (Mgr)

PONTIVY AUTOMOBILES
6 Rue Victor Et Helene Basch, 56300, Pontivy, Morbihan, France
Tel.: (33) 297257378
Web Site: http://www.pontivyauto.fr
Sales Range: $10-24.9 Million
Emp.: 21
New Car Dealers
N.A.I.C.S.: 441110
Denis Le Thuaut (Mng Partner)

PONTOS GROUP
Aleksanterinkatu 46 A, 00100, Helsinki, Finland
Tel.: (358) 10 239 6350
Web Site: http://www.pontos.fi
Sales Range: $50-74.9 Million
Emp.: 10
Private Equity & Real Estate Investment
N.A.I.C.S.: 523999
Ilpo Kokkila (Chm)

PONTUS PROTEIN LTD.
17686 - 66A Avenue, Surrey, V3S 2A7, BC, Canada
Tel.: (778) 999-3353
Web Site: http://www.pontuswaterlentils.com
HUL—(TSXV)
Assets: $4,503,741
Liabilities: $3,207,574
Net Worth: $1,296,167
Earnings: ($6,842,414)
Fiscal Year-end: 11/30/21
Business Consulting Services
N.A.I.C.S.: 522299
Avtar Dhaliwal (CEO)

PONY GROUP INC.
Engineer Experiment Building A202 7 Gaoxin South Avenue, Nanshan District, Shenzhen, 518000, Guangdong, China
Tel.: (86) 75586665622
Year Founded: 2016
Rev.: $112,844
Assets: $69,809
Liabilities: $425,353
Net Worth: ($355,544)
Earnings: ($269,078)
Emp.: 3
Fiscal Year-end: 12/31/22
Holding Company
N.A.I.C.S.: 551112
Wenxian Fan (Founder, Chm, Pres, CEO & CFO)

PONY TESTING CO., LTD.
101 5th Floor Building No 1 No 66 Jindai Road, Haidian District, Beijing, 100095, China
Tel.: (86) 1083055180
Web Site: http://www.ponytest.com
Year Founded: 2002
300887—(SSE)
Rev.: $307,444,975
Assets: $426,027,983
Liabilities: $116,543,783
Net Worth: $309,484,200
Earnings: $33,750,631
Emp.: 8,000
Fiscal Year-end: 12/31/21
Testing Services
N.A.I.C.S.: 541380
Wei Song (Chm)

PONYLINK CO., LTD
Feelingk Tower 272 Youngdeungpo-ro, Yeongdeungpo-gu, Seoul, 07303, Korea (South)
Tel.: (82) 221027300
Web Site: https://www.ponylink.co.kr
Year Founded: 2000
064800—(KRS)
Rev.: $73,276,590
Assets: $157,826,029
Liabilities: $27,863,411
Net Worth: $129,962,618
Earnings: ($14,839,606)
Emp.: 85
Fiscal Year-end: 12/31/22
Mobile Application Development Services
N.A.I.C.S.: 513210
Jung-Il Hwang (Mng Dir)

POOJAWESTERN METALIKS LIMITED
Plot No 1 Phase II GIDC Dared Khambhaliya Bypass After Lords Hotel, Jamnagar, 361 004, Gujarat, India
Tel.: (91) 2882730088
Web Site: https://www.poojametal.com
Year Founded: 1991
540727—(BOM)
Rev.: $3,808,585
Assets: $3,495,666
Liabilities: $2,023,991
Net Worth: $1,471,674
Earnings: $127,570
Emp.: 60
Fiscal Year-end: 03/31/23
Metal Product Mfr & Distr
N.A.I.C.S.: 331410
Sunil Devram Panchmatiya (Chm & Mng Dir)

POOLBEG PHARMA PLC
40 Bank Street Floor 24, London, E14 5NR, United Kingdom
Tel.: (44) 2071831499
Web Site: https://www.poolbegpharma.com
Year Founded: 2021
POLB—(AIM)
Rev.: $263,822
Assets: $24,348,649
Liabilities: $1,219,389
Net Worth: $23,129,260
Earnings: ($5,915,173)
Emp.: 12
Fiscal Year-end: 12/31/22
Pharmaceutical Product Mfr & Distr
N.A.I.C.S.: 325412

Subsidiaries:

Poolbeg Pharma (Ireland) Limited (1)
4th Floor Fitzwilliam Hall Fitzwilliam Place 2, Dublin, D02 T292, Ireland
Tel.: (353) 15634396
Pharmaceutical Infection Disease Research & Development Services
N.A.I.C.S.: 813212

POONA DAL & OIL INDUSTRIES LTD.
71/A Industrial Estate, Hadapsar, Pune, 411 013, Maharashtra, India
Tel.: (91) 2026816020
Web Site: https://www.pdbmgroup.com
Year Founded: 1993
519359—(BOM)
Rev.: $22,218,093
Assets: $7,282,442
Liabilities: $123,968
Net Worth: $7,158,474
Earnings: $148,519
Emp.: 15
Fiscal Year-end: 03/31/21
Edible Oil Mfr & Distr
N.A.I.C.S.: 311225
Swati P. Runwal (Compliance Officer & Sec)

POONAWALLA FINCORP LIMITED
Development House 24 Park Street, Kolkata, 700016, India
Tel.: (91) 3344027736
Web Site: https://poonawallafincorp.com
POONAWALLA—(NSE)
Rev.: $240,786,524
Assets: $2,784,078,892
Liabilities: $1,960,007,194
Net Worth: $824,071,698
Earnings: $82,132,966
Emp.: 2,452
Fiscal Year-end: 03/31/23

INTERNATIONAL PUBLIC

Financial Services
N.A.I.C.S.: 522291
Sanjay Chamria (Vice Chm & Mng Dir)

POONGSAN HOLDINGS CORPORATION
Poongsan Bldg 23 Chungjeong-ro, Seodaemun-gu, Seoul, 120-837, Korea (South)
Tel.: (82) 222786700
Web Site: https://www.poongsanhc.co.kr
Year Founded: 2008
005810—(KRS)
Rev.: $297,343,991
Assets: $876,513,328
Liabilities: $136,696,137
Net Worth: $739,817,190
Earnings: $56,080,820
Emp.: 311
Fiscal Year-end: 12/31/22
Holding Company; Non-ferrous Metal Products Mfr
N.A.I.C.S.: 551112
Jin Ryu (Chm & CEO)

Subsidiaries:

Poongsan Corporation (1)
Poongsan Bldg 23 Chungjeong-ro, Seodaemun-gu, Seoul, 120-837, Korea (South)
Tel.: (82) 234065114
Web Site: https://www.poongsan.co.kr
Rev.: $3,354,077,578
Assets: $2,604,192,946
Liabilities: $1,191,194,678
Net Worth: $1,412,998,268
Earnings: $134,425,910
Fiscal Year-end: 12/31/2022
Fabricated Non-Ferrous Metal Products & Ammunition Mfr
N.A.I.C.S.: 325920
Jin Roy Ryu (Chm & CEO)

Subsidiary (US):

PMX Industries, Inc. (2)
5300 Willow Creek Dr SW, Cedar Rapids, IA 52404-4303 (100%)
Tel.: (319) 368-7700
Web Site: https://www.ipmx.com
Sales Range: $100-124.9 Million
Emp.: 450
Mfr & Developer of Propellants & Explosives; Tubing; Coin & Metal Products
N.A.I.C.S.: 331529

Subsidiary (Non-US):

Poongsan (H.K.) Ltd. (2)
Unit1907B 19/F Exchange Tower 33 Wang Chiu Road, Kowloon Bay, Kowloon, China (Hong Kong) (100%)
Tel.: (852) 27356330
Sales Range: $25-49.9 Million
Emp.: 7
Mfr & Developer of Propellants & Explosives; Tubing; Coin & Metal Products
N.A.I.C.S.: 325920

Plant (Domestic):

Poongsan Corp. - Busan Plant (2)
230 Seonsuchon-ro, Haeundae-gu, Busan, 612-723, Korea (South)
Tel.: (82) 515208114
Web Site: https://www.poongsan.co.kr
Small Arms Ammunition Mfr
N.A.I.C.S.: 332992
Choi Han Myung (Vice Chm)

Poongsan Corp. - Ulsan Plant (2)
94 Sanam-ro, Ulju-gun, Ulsan, 689-892, Korea (South)
Tel.: (82) 522319114
Web Site: http://www.poongsan.co.kr
Emp.: 3,900
Copper & Copper Alloy Products Mfr
N.A.I.C.S.: 331529

Subsidiary (Non-US):

Siam Poongsan Metal Co., Ltd. (2)
38/14 Laemchabang Industrial Estate Moo 5 T Tungsukla, A Sriracha, Chon Buri,

20230, Thailand (100%)
Tel.: (66) 38400056
Web Site: https://www.siam-poongsan.com
Sales Range: $50-74.9 Million
Emp.: 240
Mfr & Developer of Propellants & Explosives; Tubing; Coin & Metal Products
N.A.I.C.S.: 325920

Poongsan Holdings Corp. - Busan Plant (1)
230 Seonsuchon-ro, Haeundae-gu, Busan, 612-723, Korea (South)
Tel.: (82) 51 520 8114
Web Site: http://www.poongsan.co.kr
Metal Processing Facilities Mfr
N.A.I.C.S.: 333515

Poongsan Holdings Corp. - Changwon Plant (1)
670 Gongdan-ro, Seongsan-gu, Changwon, Gyeongsangnam-do, Korea (South)
Tel.: (82) 55 239 0700
Web Site: http://www.poongsanhc.co.kr
Sales Range: $125-149.9 Million
Emp.: 415
Metal Fittings, Ammunition Parts & Multi-Gauge Strips Mfr
N.A.I.C.S.: 332999

Poongsan Metal Service Corporation (1)
680-1 Naegi-ri, Poseung-Eup, Pyeongtaek, Gyeonggi-do, Korea (South)
Tel.: (82) 316507500
Web Site: http://www.poongsan.co.kr
Sales Range: $25-49.9 Million
Emp.: 50
Copper Product Mfr
N.A.I.C.S.: 331410

Poongsan Special Metal Corporation (1)
Web Site: http://www.poongsansm.co.kr
Sales Range: $50-74.9 Million
Emp.: 150
Copper Product Mfr
N.A.I.C.S.: 331410

Poongsan Valinox Corporation (1)
324-6 Hyosung-Dong, Keyang-Gu, Incheon, 407717, Korea (South)
Tel.: (82) 32 556 4424
Titanium & Steel Tube Mfr
N.A.I.C.S.: 331210
Jong Inn Ryu (Pres)

POONGWON PRECISION CO., LTD.
24 Sandan-ro 35beon-gil, Danwon-gu, Ansan, Gyeonggi-do, Korea (South)
Tel.: (82) 314932107
Web Site:
https://www.poongwon.com
Year Founded: 1996
371950—(KRS)
Rev.: $34,449,025
Assets: $83,018,592
Liabilities: $21,851,929
Net Worth: $61,166,663
Earnings: $5,013,205
Emp.: 240
Fiscal Year-end: 12/31/22
Electronic Component Mfr & Distr
N.A.I.C.S.: 334419
Kim Seong Hoe (Gen Mgr)

POP CULTURE GROUP CO., LTD.
Room 1207-08 No 2488 Huandao East Road, Huli District, Xiamen, 361008, Fujian, China
Tel.: (86) 5925968189   Ky
Web Site: https://www.cpop.cn
Year Founded: 2020
CPOP—(NASDAQ)
Rev.: $47,381,918
Assets: $42,234,757
Liabilities: $26,909,583
Net Worth: $15,325,174
Earnings: ($12,632,115)
Emp.: 26
Fiscal Year-end: 06/30/24
Holding Company
N.A.I.C.S.: 551112
Zhuoqin Huang (Chm & CEO)

POP MART INTERNATIONAL GROUP LIMITED
Floor 36 & 37 Block A Puxiang Center Hongtai East Street, Dawangjing Technology Business Park Chaoyang, Beijing, 100102, China
Tel.: (86) 13810354609   Ky
Web Site: https://www.popmart.com
Year Founded: 2010
9992—(HKG)
Rev.: $872,424,956
Assets: $1,380,270,132
Liabilities: $303,012,987
Net Worth: $1,077,257,144
Earnings: $150,749,197
Emp.: 4,704
Fiscal Year-end: 12/31/23
Collectible Toys Mfr & Distr
N.A.I.C.S.: 339930
De Si (COO)

Subsidiaries:

Pop Mart Japan, Inc. (1)
2nd Floor Akiba CO Building 3-16-12 Sotokanda, Chiyoda-ku, Tokyo, 101-0021, Japan
Tel.: (81) 368228583
Web Site: https://www.popmart.co.jp
Emp.: 8
Toy Shop Operator
N.A.I.C.S.: 561720

Pop Mart Korea Co., Ltd. (1)
6th floor Cheongha Building 161-7 Donggyo-dong 174 Donggyo-ro, Mapo-gu, Seoul, 03995, Korea (South)
Tel.: (82) 5053046600
Web Site: https://popmart.co.kr
Art Toy Distr
N.A.I.C.S.: 423920

POPLAR CO., LTD.
665-1 Hisachi, Asakita-ku, Hiroshima, 731-3395, Japan
Tel.: (81) 828373500
Web Site: https://www.poplar-cvs.co.jp
Year Founded: 1976
7601—(TKS)
Rev.: $87,703,300
Assets: $27,005,810
Liabilities: $23,623,880
Net Worth: $3,381,930
Earnings: $3,275,580
Fiscal Year-end: 02/29/24
Convenience Store Operator
N.A.I.C.S.: 445131
Shunji Meguro (Founder, Chm & Pres)

POPLAR CREEK RESOURCES INC.
36 Lott Creek View, Calgary, T3Z 3V5, AB, Canada
Tel.: (403) 616-5387   AB
Year Founded: 2006
Oil & Gas Exploration
N.A.I.C.S.: 211120
Richard Edgar (Pres & CEO)

POPOVA KULA WINERY
Wine Boulevard no 1 Demir Kapija 1442, Demir Kapija, Skopje, North Macedonia
Tel.: (389) 76432630
Web Site:
https://www.popovakula.com.mk
POPK—(MAC)
Rev.: $1,051,240
Assets: $3,221,535
Liabilities: $1,063,684
Net Worth: $2,157,851
Earnings: $30,788
Fiscal Year-end: 12/31/23
Tobacco Product Mfr
N.A.I.C.S.: 312230
Lence Nedeva (Mgr-Wine Tourism)

POPOVO POLJE A.D.
Republike Srpske 37, 89101, Trebinje, Bosnia & Herzegovina
Tel.: (387) 59273590
Web Site: https://popovopolje.com
Year Founded: 1977
POPO—(BANJ)
Sales Range: $350-399.9 Million
Emp.: 21
Crop Farming Services
N.A.I.C.S.: 111998
Dusan Vasiljevic (Chm-Mgmt Bd & Pres)

POPPINS CORP.
Hiroo 5 chome No 6 Hiroo No 6 Plaza 5F, Yubinbango, 1500012, Tokyo, Shibuya-ku, Japan
Tel.: (81) 334472100
Web Site: http://www.poppins.co.jp
Education & Care Services
N.A.I.C.S.: 611710
Noriko Nakamura (Chm)

Subsidiaries:

Tempstaff Wish Co., Ltd. (1)
2-1-1 Yoyogi Shinjuku Mines Tower 18F, Shibuya-Ku, Tokyo, 151-0053, Japan
Tel.: (81) 353086170
Web Site: http://www.temp-wish.co.jp
Staffing & Employment Services for Nursery Schools, Kindergartens & Manages & Operates Child-Care Facilities
N.A.I.C.S.: 561311
Takaaki Nishiuchi (Pres)

POPPINS HOLDINGS, INC.
Hiroo Plaza 5F 5-6-6, Hiroo Shibuya-ku, Tokyo, 150-0012, Japan
Tel.: (81) 334472100
Web Site: https://www.poppins.co.jp
Year Founded: 2016
7358—(TKS)
Rev.: $204,851,370
Assets: $103,669,980
Liabilities: $46,127,540
Net Worth: $57,542,440
Earnings: $4,799,930
Emp.: 5,685
Fiscal Year-end: 12/31/23
Holding Company
N.A.I.C.S.: 551112
Noriko Nakamura (Founder & Chm)

Subsidiaries:

Poppins Sitter Co., Ltd. (1)
5-6-6 Hiroo, Shibuya-ku, Tokyo, Japan
Tel.: (81) 120795501
Web Site: http://www.smartsitter.jp
Childcare & Senior Care Services
N.A.I.C.S.: 624410

POPREACH CORPORATION
1 University Avenue 3rd Floor, Toronto, M5J 2P1, ON, Canada
Tel.: (416) 583-5918
Web Site: https://popreach.com
Year Founded: 2018
INIKF—(OTCQB)
Rev.: $140,637,000
Assets: $139,456,000
Liabilities: $138,547,000
Net Worth: $909,000
Earnings: ($56,195,000)
Fiscal Year-end: 12/31/23
Game Development Services
N.A.I.C.S.: 513210
Jeff Collins (COO)

Subsidiaries:

Crucial Interactive Inc. (1)
1 University Ave 3rd Floor, Toronto, M5J 2P1, ON, Canada
Tel.: (416) 645-0135

Web Site:
https://www.advertisers.contobox.com
Advertising Technologies Services
N.A.I.C.S.: 541840

Jet Marketing Agency LLC (1)
211 N 1st St Ste 207, Brighton, MI 48116
Web Site:
https://www.jetmarketingagency.com
Marketing & Advertising Services
N.A.I.C.S.: 541613

Mosten Media B.V. (1)
Paulus Potterstraat 32-1, 1071DB, Amsterdam, Netherlands
Tel.: (31) 208081143
Web Site: https://www.mostenmedia.com
Marketing & Advertising Services
N.A.I.C.S.: 541613

OpenMoves LLC (1)
315 Main St 2nd Fl, Huntington, NY 11743
Tel.: (631) 546-7779
Web Site: http://www.openmoves.com
Sales Range: $1-9.9 Million
Marketing Services
N.A.I.C.S.: 541613
Ronen Yaari (Founder)

SHIFT44, Inc. (1)
4250 Veterans Memorial Hwy Ste 300E, Holbrook, NY 11741
Tel.: (631) 910-9988
Web Site: https://shift44.com
Marketing & Advertising Services
N.A.I.C.S.: 541613

Schiefer Chopshop (1)
660 Baker St Bldg D, Costa Mesa, CA 92626
Tel.: (949) 838-0355
Web Site: https://wearescs.com
Media Buying Agencies
N.A.I.C.S.: 541830
James Schiefer (CEO)

Sedulen LLC (1)
PBM 113 2500 Regency Pkwy, Cary, NC 27518
Tel.: (919) 378-1780
Web Site: https://www.sedulen.com
Software Development Services
N.A.I.C.S.: 541511

POPULAR ESTATE MANAGEMENT LIMITED
81 8TH Floor A wing New York Tower Opp Muktidham Derasar S G Highway, Ahmedabad, 380054, Gujarat, India
Tel.: (91) 7926858881   In
Web Site:
https://www.popularmanagement.in
Year Founded: 1994
531870—(BOM)
Sales Range: Less than $1 Million
Emp.: 10
Real Estate Manangement Services
N.A.I.C.S.: 531390
Ramanbhai Bholidas Patel (Chm)

POPULAR LIFE INSURANCE COMPANY LIMITED
Peoples Insurance Bhaban 36 Dilkusha C/A 17 Floor, Dhaka, 1000, Bangladesh
Tel.: (880) 2957753438
Web Site:
https://www.popularlifeins.com
Year Founded: 2000
POPULARLIF—(CHT)
Rev.: $230,977,795
Assets: $210,783,261
Liabilities: $20,244,680
Net Worth: $190,538,580
Earnings: $156,153,667
Fiscal Year-end: 12/31/22
Insurance Services
N.A.I.C.S.: 524298
Mohammad Motaher Hussain (Chm)

PORN PROM METAL PUBLIC COMPANY LIMITED

PORN PROM METAL PUBLIC COMPANY LIMITED

Porn Prom Metal Public Company Limited—(Continued)
229 Nakhonratchasima Road, Dusit, Bangkok, 10300, Thailand
Tel.: (66) 26286100 TH
Web Site: http://www.ppm.co.th
Year Founded: 1992
PPM—(THA)
Rev.: $71,339,336
Assets: $61,515,363
Liabilities: $29,573,801
Net Worth: $31,941,562
Earnings: $4,841,196
Fiscal Year-end: 12/31/23
Metal Product Distr
N.A.I.C.S.: 423510

Subsidiaries:

Premium Flexible Packaging Co., Ltd. (1)
88/8 Moo 5 Salaya-Bang Phat Rd, Salaya Sub-district Phutthamonthon District, Nakhon Pathom, 73170, Thailand
Tel.: (66) 24298414
Web Site: http://www.pfppack.com
Flexible Packaging Products Mfr
N.A.I.C.S.: 326112

Solar PPM Company Limited (1)
205/1 Nakhonratchasima Road, Dusit, Bangkok, 10300, Thailand
Tel.: (66) 26286100
Web Site: http://www.solarppm.com
Solar Power Generation Services
N.A.I.C.S.: 221114

PORR AG
Absberggasse 47, 1100, Vienna, Austria
Tel.: (43) 506260 AT
Web Site: https://www.porr-group.com
Year Founded: 1869
POS—(VIE)
Rev.: $6,244,345,996
Assets: $4,475,280,596
Liabilities: $3,613,069,286
Net Worth: $862,211,310
Earnings: $69,515,433
Emp.: 18,515
Fiscal Year-end: 12/31/22
Building Construction & Civil Engineering
N.A.I.C.S.: 236220
Klaus Ortner (Deputy Chm-Supervisory Bd)

Subsidiaries:

A. Niedermuhlbichler Baugesellschaft m.b.H. (1)
An der Sandleiten 5, 9871, Seeboden, Austria
Tel.: (43) 506269500
Web Site: https://nmbbau.at
Emp.: 40
Construction Services
N.A.I.C.S.: 236220

ABAP Beteiligungs Holding GmbH (1)
Absberggasse 47, 1100, Vienna, Austria
Tel.: (43) 5 06 26 0
Investment Management Service
N.A.I.C.S.: 523940

ABW Abbruch Boden- und Wasserreinigungs-Gesellschaft m.b.H. (1)
Allecgasse 38, 1110, Vienna, Austria
Tel.: (43) 176930030
Web Site: https://www.abwwien.at
Hazardous & Non-Hazardous Waste Disposal Services
N.A.I.C.S.: 562211

ALPINE Bau CZ s. r.o. (1)
Jiraskova 613/13 Krasno nad Becvou, 757 01, Valasske Mezirici, Czech Republic
Tel.: (420) 571 750 111
Web Site: http://www.alpine.cz
Construction Engineering Services
N.A.I.C.S.: 541330

ARIWA Abwasserreinigung im Waldviertel GmbH (1)
Absberggasse 47, 1103, Vienna, Austria
Tel.: (43) 506261556
Web Site: https://www.ariwa.at
Wastewater Discharge & Treatment Services
N.A.I.C.S.: 221320

Allgemeine Strassenbau GmbH (1)
Wildpretstrasse 7, 1110, Vienna, Austria (52.5%)
Tel.: (43) 506262053
Commercial & Institutional Building Construction
N.A.I.C.S.: 236220
Uber Allbau (Mng Dir)

Alois Felser Gesellschaft m.b.H. (1)
Porr-Strasse 1, Kematen, 6175, Linz, Austria (52.5%)
Tel.: (43) 506263110
Painting & Wall Covering Contractors
N.A.I.C.S.: 238320

Altlastensanierung und Abraumdeponie Langes Feld Gesellschaft m.b.H. (1)
Wagramer Strasse 315-317, 1210, Vienna, Austria
Tel.: (43) 12594521
Web Site: http://www.langesfeld.at
Waste Management Services
N.A.I.C.S.: 562998

Aschauer Zimmerei GmbH (1)
Wienerstr 112, Gars Am Kamp, 3571, Vienna, Austria (52.55%)
Tel.: (43) 298522350
Carpentry Contractor
N.A.I.C.S.: 238350

Asdag Baugesellschaft m.b.H. (1)
Absberggasse 47, 1100, Vienna, Austria (52.5%)
Tel.: (43) 506262012
Heavy & Civil Engineering Construction
N.A.I.C.S.: 237990

Asphalt-Unternehmung Carl Gunther Gesellschaft m.b.H. (1)
Wildpretstrasse 7, 1110, Vienna, Austria (52.5%)
Tel.: (43) 506262159
Highway & Street Construction
N.A.I.C.S.: 237310

Asphaltmischwerk Greinsfurth GmbH & Co OG (1)
Bauwesenstrasse 2, A-3300, Amstetten, Austria
Tel.: (43) 747263005
Web Site: https://www.amg-greinsfurth.at
Asphalt Mix Product Mfr
N.A.I.C.S.: 324121

Asphaltmischwerk LEOPOLDAU - TEERAG- ASDAG + Mayreder-Bau GmbH & Co. KG (1)
Verlangerte Thayagasse, 1210, Vienna, Austria
Tel.: (43) 1 292 25 91
Construction Engineering Services
N.A.I.C.S.: 541330

Asphaltunternehmung Raimund Guckler Bauunternehmung Gesellschaft m.b.H. (1)
Wildpretstrasse 7, 1110, Vienna, Austria (52.5%)
Tel.: (43) 176816320
Highway & Street Construction
N.A.I.C.S.: 237310

Asw-Asphalt- und Schotterwerk Neustift GmbH And Co. KG (1)
Puchstrasse 176, 8055, Graz, Austria (100%)
Tel.: (43) 3162941260
Dimension Stone Mining & Quarrying
N.A.I.C.S.: 212311

BBGS Spolka z ograniczona odpowiedzialnoscia (1)
Ul Holubcowa 123, 02-854, Warsaw, Poland
Tel.: (48) 222669900
Construction Services
N.A.I.C.S.: 236220

BZW Liegenschaftsverwaltungs GmbH (1)
Absberggasse 47, 1103, Vienna, Austria
Tel.: (43) 4262 274 09 0
Construction Engineering Services
N.A.I.C.S.: 541330

Baugesellschaft m.b.H. Erhard Mortl (1)
Auenfischerstrasse 1, Wolfsberg, A-9400, Vienna, Austria (52.5%)
Tel.: (43) 43524242
Web Site: http://www.moertl-bau.at
Highway & Street Construction
N.A.I.C.S.: 237310

Baumgasse 131 Bautrager- und Verwertungsgesellschaft m.b.H. (1)
Absberggasse 47, Vienna, 1100, Austria
Tel.: (43) 50 626 1451
Construction Engineering Services
N.A.I.C.S.: 541330

Bautech Labor GmbH (1)
7 Haidequerstrasse 5b, 1110, Vienna, Austria
Tel.: (43) 506262341
Web Site: https://www.bautechlabor.at
Emp.: 80
Asphalt Mix Product Mfr
N.A.I.C.S.: 324121

Bitu - Bau Gesellschaft m.b.H. (1)
Grazer Strasse 36 A, Stegersbach, 7551, Graz, Austria (52.5%)
Tel.: (43) 3326523670
Web Site: http://www.teerag-asdag.at
Nonresidential Buildings Lessors
N.A.I.C.S.: 531120

Bosch Baugesellschaft m.b.H. (1)
7 Haidequerstrasse 3, 1110, Vienna, Austria (52.5%)
Tel.: (43) 506262997
Asphalt Shingle & Coating Materials Mfr
N.A.I.C.S.: 324122

Dike Liegenschaftsverwertung Gesellschaft m.b.H. (1)
Absberggasse 47, 1103, Vienna, Austria (100%)
Tel.: (43) 506262012
Web Site: http://www.put.at
Real Estate Agents & Brokers
N.A.I.C.S.: 531210

EPS MARIA LANZENDORFER-STRASSE 17 Errichtungs- und Beteiligungs GmbH (1)
Absberggasse 47, 1100, Vienna, Austria
Tel.: (43) 50 626 1451
Construction Engineering Services
N.A.I.C.S.: 541330

EPS TRIESTER STRASSE Errichtungs- und Beteiligungsverwaltungs GmbH (1)
Absberggasse 47, 1100, Vienna, Austria
Tel.: (43) 5 06 26 1451
Construction Engineering Services
N.A.I.C.S.: 541330

EPS Tamussinostrasse Errichtungs- und Beteiligungs GmbH (1)
Absberggasse 47, Vienna, Austria
Tel.: (43) 5 06 26 1451
Construction Engineering Services
N.A.I.C.S.: 541330

Eisenschutzgesellschaft m.b.H. (1)
7 Haidequerstrasse 3, 1110, Vienna, Austria (52.5%)
Tel.: (43) 506267123
Web Site: http://eisenschutz.at
Sales Range: $25-49.9 Million
Emp.: 120
Painting & Wall Covering Contractors
N.A.I.C.S.: 238320

Emil Mayr Hoch- und Tiefbau GmbH (1)
Kapellenstrasse 7, Ettringen, 86833, Koblenz, Germany (93.94%)
Tel.: (49) 82498040
Web Site: http://www.emilmayr.de
Sales Range: $25-49.9 Million
Emp.: 50
Single-Family Housing Construction
N.A.I.C.S.: 236115

INTERNATIONAL PUBLIC

Josef Lampert (Mng Dir)
Esikas Beteiligungsverwaltungs GmbH (1)
Absberggasse 47, 1100, Vienna, Austria
Tel.: (43) 5 06 26 0
Construction Engineering Services
N.A.I.C.S.: 541330

Esoro Beteiligungsverwaltungs GmbH & Co. KG (1)
Absberggasse 47, 1100, Vienna, Austria
Tel.: (43) 50 626 1702
Web Site: http://www.porr-solutions.com
Construction Engineering Services
N.A.I.C.S.: 541330

Euphalt-Handelsgesellschaft m.b.H. (1)
Gewerbeallee 5, Steyregg, 4221, Linz, Austria (52.5%)
Tel.: (43) 732640500
Web Site: http://euphalt.at
Sales Range: $25-49.9 Million
Petroleum & Coal Products Mfr
N.A.I.C.S.: 324199

FMA Gebaudemanagement GmbH (1)
Absberggasse 47, 1103, Vienna, Austria (50%)
Tel.: (43) 506262012
Waste Management Services
N.A.I.C.S.: 562998

FPS Infrastruktur Holding GmbH (1)
Absberggasse 47, 1100, Vienna, Austria
Tel.: (43) 5 06 26 1451
Investment Management Service
N.A.I.C.S.: 523999

Fehberger Stahlbau GmbH (1)
Hans-Wiegele-Strasse 2/OG1/3, 9100, Volkermarkt, Austria
Tel.: (43) 4232201100
Web Site: http://www.fehberger.at
Construction Services
N.A.I.C.S.: 236220

Forum am Bahnhof Quickborn GmbH & Co. KG (1)
Winsbergring 42, 22525, Hamburg, Germany
Tel.: (49) 40 54777172
Construction Engineering Services
N.A.I.C.S.: 541330

Franki Polska Spolka z ograniczona odpowiedzialnoscia (1)
ul Jasnogorska 44, 31-358, Krakow, Poland
Tel.: (48) 126227560
Web Site: http://frankipolska.pl
Construction Services
N.A.I.C.S.: 236220

Franz Bocks Nachf. Ing. Eva And Karl Schindler Gesellschaft m.b.H. And Co.Nfg.KG (1)
Absberggasse 47, 1100, Vienna, Austria (52.5%)
Tel.: (43) 506262012
Real Estate Agents & Brokers
N.A.I.C.S.: 531210

Franz Greiner Gesellschaft m.b.H. (1)
Wildpretstrasse 7, 1111, Vienna, Austria (52.5%)
Tel.: (43) 506262053
Highway & Street Construction
N.A.I.C.S.: 237310

G. Hinteregger & Sohne Baugesellschaft m.b.H. (1)
Bergerbrauhofstrasse 27, Postfach 178, 5021, Salzburg, Austria
Tel.: (43) 662889800
Web Site: http://www.hinteregger.co.at
Construction Services
N.A.I.C.S.: 236220

GREENPOWER Anlagenerrichtungs- und Betriebs-GmbH (1)
Absberggasse 47, Vienna, 1103, Austria
Tel.: (43) 50 626 2015
Construction Engineering Services
N.A.I.C.S.: 541330

Gesellschaft fur Bauwesen GmbH (1)

AND PRIVATE COMPANIES — PORR AG

Wildpretstrasse 7, 1110, Vienna, Austria **(52.5%)**
Tel.: (43) 16171460
Water Sewer & Pipeline Construction
N.A.I.C.S.: 237120

Gesellschaft zur Schaffung von Wohnungseigentum Gesellschaft m.b.H. (1)
Absberggasse 47, 1100, Vienna, Austria
Tel.: (43) 5 06 26 1451
Construction Engineering Services
N.A.I.C.S.: 541330

Giral Beteiligungsverwaltungs GmbH (1)
Absberggasse 47, 1100, Vienna, Austria
Tel.: (43) 5 06261451
Construction Engineering Services
N.A.I.C.S.: 541330

Giral Beteiligungsverwaltungs GmbH & Co. KG (1)
Absberggasse 47, 1103, Vienna, Austria
Tel.: (43) 56 626 0
Construction Engineering Services
N.A.I.C.S.: 541330

Goidinger Bau GmbH (1)
Hinterfeldweg 10, 6511, Zams, Austria
Tel.: (43) 506264693
Web Site: http://goidingerbau.at
Construction Services
N.A.I.C.S.: 236220

Gostena Beteiligungsverwaltungs GmbH (1)
Absberggasse 47, 1100, Vienna, Austria
Tel.: (43) 50 626 0
Construction Engineering Services
N.A.I.C.S.: 541330

Gradevinsko preduzece Porr d.o.o. (1)
Milutina Milankovica 11a, 11000, Belgrade, Serbia
Tel.: (381) 11 3642 200
Web Site: http://www.porr.rs
Construction Engineering Services
N.A.I.C.S.: 541330

Grazer Transportbeton Gesellschaft m.b.H.
Thalerhofstrasse 88, Unterpremstatten, A-8141, Graz, Austria **(100%)**
Tel.: (43) 50 626 3392
Web Site: http://www.beton-schotter-kratochwill.at
Sales Range: $25-49.9 Million
Emp.: 60
Sand, Chippings, Broken Gravel & Hard Rock Products Mfr
N.A.I.C.S.: 212321
Thomas Hittler (Mng Dir)

Grund- Pfahl- und Sonderbau GmbH (1)
Industriestrasse 27a, 2325, Himberg, Austria
Tel.: (43) 2235877770
Web Site: http://www.gps-bau.com
Excavation, Stake-Drilling & Foundation Contracting Services
N.A.I.C.S.: 238110

Gunimperm-Bauveg SA (1)
Via San Bernardino, Castione, 6532, Bellinzona, Switzerland
Tel.: (41) 91 829 16 18
Construction Engineering Services
N.A.I.C.S.: 541330

Haidacker Projektentwicklung GmbH (1)
Absberggasse 47, 1100, Vienna, Austria
Tel.: (43) 5 06 26 1451
Construction Engineering Services
N.A.I.C.S.: 541330

Hernalser Hof Beteiligungsverwaltungs GmbH (1)
Absberggasse 47, 1100, Vienna, Austria
Tel.: (43) 5 06 26 1451
Construction Engineering Services
N.A.I.C.S.: 541330

Hernalser Hof Beteiligungsverwaltungs GmbH & Co. KG (1)
Absberggasse 47, 1103, Vienna, Austria
Tel.: (43) 5 06 26 1451
Construction Engineering Services
N.A.I.C.S.: 541330

Hospitals Projektentwicklungsges.m.b.H. (1)
Absberggasse 47, 1100, Vienna, Austria **(52.5%)**
Tel.: (43) 506261782
Web Site: http://www.hospitals.at
Residential Buildings & Dwellings Lessors
N.A.I.C.S.: 531110

Hotel am Kanzleramt Verwaltungs GmbH (1)
Storkower Str 113, 10407, Berlin, Germany
Tel.: (49) 30 421842328
Construction Engineering Services
N.A.I.C.S.: 541330

IAT GmbH (1)
Badenerstr 54, 2514, Traiskirchen, Austria
Tel.: (43) 2252 20 69 85 0
Web Site: http://www.i-a-t.at
Concrete Coating & Sealing Services
N.A.I.C.S.: 238390

Subsidiary (Non-US):

IAT Deutschland GmbH (2)
LogoWalter-Gropius-Strasse 23, 80807, Munich, Germany
Tel.: (49) 89710010
Web Site: https://www.i-a-t.at
Civil Engineering in Waterproofing Against Wetness & Confined Water
N.A.I.C.S.: 541330
Robert Giefing (Mng Dir)

IAT Impermeabilizzazioni Srl (1)
Via Mulini 19, Val Di Vizze, Bolzano, 39049, Italy
Tel.: (39) 0472764498
Construction Engineering Services
N.A.I.C.S.: 541330

IAT UK Waterproofing Systems Limited (1)
239 High Street Kensington, London, W8 6SA, United Kingdom
Tel.: (44) 506262084
Construction Services
N.A.I.C.S.: 236220

ISG Ingenieurservice Grundbau GmbH (1)
Hittfelder Kirchweg 24, 21220, Seevetal, Germany
Tel.: (49) 4105580570
Web Site: http://www.ingenieurservice-grundbau.de
Construction Engineering Services
N.A.I.C.S.: 236220
Arne Kindler (Head-Metrology)

Ing. Otto Richter And Co Strassenmarkierungen GmbH (1)
Hirschackergasse 1, 2514, Traiskirchen, Austria **(52.5%)**
Tel.: (43) 225280345
Web Site: http://www.rimak.at
Sales Range: $50-74.9 Million
Emp.: 60
Credit Intermediation
N.A.I.C.S.: 522299
Friedrich Reidinger (Gen Mgr)

Ing. RADL-BAU GmbH (1)
Absberggasse 47, 1100, Vienna, Austria **(100%)**
Tel.: (43) 506262746
Web Site: http://www.porr-group.com
Industrial Building Construction
N.A.I.C.S.: 236210

Ishap Personaldokumentations GmbH (1)
Giefinggasse 6/2/2 4, 1210, Vienna, Austria
Tel.: (43) 123641320
Web Site: https://www.ishap.at
Software Services
N.A.I.C.S.: 541511

Jandl Baugesellschaft m.b.H. (1)
Thalerhofstrasse 88, Unterpremstatten, 8141, Graz, Austria **(100%)**
Tel.: (43) 506263462
Single-Family Housing Construction
N.A.I.C.S.: 236115

Joiser Hoch- und Tiefbau GmbH (1)
Absberggasse 47, 1103, Vienna, Austria
Tel.: (43) 50 6262470
Construction Engineering Services
N.A.I.C.S.: 541330

Koller Transporte - Kies - Erdbau GmbH (1)
Industriepark Nord Percostrasse 17, 1222, Vienna, Austria
Tel.: (43) 12593600
Web Site: https://www.koller-gmbh.at
Construction Services
N.A.I.C.S.: 236220

Kraft And Warme Rohr- und Anlagentechnik GmbH (1)
Absberggasse 47, 1100, Vienna, Austria **(52.5%)**
Tel.: (43) 506264953
Web Site: https://www.kw.co.at
Residential Buildings & Dwellings Lessors
N.A.I.C.S.: 531110
Reinald Krammer (Mng Dir)

LD Recycling GmbH (1)
Barbaraweg 51, 8700, Leoben, Austria **(100%)**
Tel.: (43) 6646266442
Web Site: http://www.schwarzl-gruppe.at
Security System Services
N.A.I.C.S.: 561621

M.E.G. Mikrobiologische Erddekontamination GmbH (1)
Pummererstrasse 17, A-4020, Linz, Austria
Tel.: (43) 506265929
Web Site: https://www.meg.co.at
Construction Engineering Services
N.A.I.C.S.: 541330

MSO Mischanlagen GmbH (1)
Neudorf 117, 8262, Linz, Austria
Tel.: (43) 33858422
Construction Engineering Services
N.A.I.C.S.: 541330

Mast Bau GmbH (1)
Lorenzweg 40, 39140, Magdeburg, Germany **(93.94%)**
Tel.: (49) 391536010
Single-Family Housing Construction
N.A.I.C.S.: 236115

Nagele Hoch- und Tiefbau GmbH (1)
Bundesstrasse 20, Rothis, 6832, Feldkirch, Austria
Tel.: (43) 506268840
Web Site: https://naegele-hochtiefbau.at
Construction Services
N.A.I.C.S.: 236220
Gunter Summer (Mgr-Building Construction)

Nagele Tiefbau GmbH (1)
Absberggasse 47, 1100, Vienna, Austria
Tel.: (43) 5 06 26 0
Construction Engineering Services
N.A.I.C.S.: 541330

OBA - Osterreichische Betondecken Ausbau GmbH (1)
Lagergasse 346, 8055, Graz, Austria
Tel.: (43) 506263179
Web Site: https://oebatech.at
Construction Services
N.A.I.C.S.: 236220

OBA Betondecken Ausbau Deutschland GmbH (1)
Walter-Gropius-Strasse 23, 80807, Munich, Germany
Tel.: (49) 8971001700
Construction Services
N.A.I.C.S.: 236220

OBALOVNA PRIBRAM, s.r.o. (1)
Dubecska 3238, Prague, 1000, Czech Republic
Tel.: (420) 267226111
Web Site: http://www.porr.cz
Sales Range: $200-249.9 Million
Emp.: 1,500
Construction Engineering Services
N.A.I.C.S.: 237990

PKM - Muldenzentrale GmbH (1)
Alberner Hafenzufahrtsstrasse 9, A-1110, Vienna, Austria
Tel.: (43) 50626626
Web Site: https://www.pkm-muldenzentrale.at
Emp.: 60
Hazardous & Non-Hazardous Waste Disposal Services
N.A.I.C.S.: 562211

PNC Norge AS (1)
Hoffsveien 1C, 0275, Oslo, Norway
Tel.: (47) 90622724
Web Site: https://www.pnc-norge.no
Construction Services
N.A.I.C.S.: 236220

PORR (Slovensko) A.S. (1)
Plynarenska 1, 82109, Bratislava, Slovakia **(100%)**
Tel.: (421) 2581070
Web Site: http://www.porr.sk
Housing Operative Builders
N.A.I.C.S.: 236117

PORR Financial Services AG (1)
Seedorferstrasse 56, 6460, Altdorf, Uri, Switzerland
Tel.: (41) 41 8750101
Sales Range: $100-124.9 Million
Emp.: 150
Financial Management Services
N.A.I.C.S.: 523999
Robert Fortunati (Gen Mgr)

PPP Campus Bednar Park Errichtungs- und Betriebs GmbH (1)
Absberggasse 47, 1100, Vienna, Austria
Tel.: (43) 50 626 1451
Construction Engineering Services
N.A.I.C.S.: 541330

PWW Deponija Dva d.o.o. (1)
Bulevar Oslobodenja 147, 16000, Leskovac, Serbia
Tel.: (381) 16234540
Construction Services
N.A.I.C.S.: 236220

PWW Deponija d.o.o. (1)
7 n 66, 35000, Jagodina, Serbia
Tel.: (381) 358150070
Construction Services
N.A.I.C.S.: 236220

PWW d.o.o. (1)
25 Maj 65b, 18000, Nis, Serbia
Tel.: (381) 18538444
Construction Services
N.A.I.C.S.: 236220

Panitzky Gesellschaft m.b.H. (1)
Wildpretstrasse 7, 1110, Vienna, Austria **(52.5%)**
Tel.: (43) 17697783
Web Site: http://www.panitzky.at
Sales Range: $25-49.9 Million
Emp.: 50
Printing & Writing Paper Whslr
N.A.I.C.S.: 424110

Pichlingerhof Liegenschaftsverwertungs GmbH (1)
Absberggasse 47, 1100, Vienna, Austria
Tel.: (43) 5 06 26 0
Construction Engineering Services
N.A.I.C.S.: 541330

Pichlingerhof Liegenschaftsverwertungs GmbH & Co KG (1)
Absberggasse 47, 1100, Vienna, Austria
Tel.: (43) 5 06 26 0
Construction Engineering Services
N.A.I.C.S.: 541330

Porr (Polska) S.A. (1)
ul Holubcowa 123, 02-854, Warsaw, Poland **(100%)**
Tel.: (48) 222669900
Web Site: http://www.porr.pl
Sales Range: $25-49.9 Million
Emp.: 200
Housing Operative Builders
N.A.I.C.S.: 236117
Dariusz Wietrzynski (Member-Exec Bd)

Porr - living Solutions GmbH (1)
Absberggasse 47, 1100, Vienna, Austria
Tel.: (43) 50 626 1451
Construction Engineering Services
N.A.I.C.S.: 541330

Porr A.S. (1)

PORR AG

PORR AG—(Continued)

Dubecska 3238/36, 100 00, Prague, 10,
Czech Republic
Tel.: (420) 267226111
Web Site: https://porr.cz
Construction Services
N.A.I.C.S.: 236220

Porr Alpha Baugesellschaft mbH (1)
Absberggasse 47, 1103, Vienna,
Austria **(100%)**
Tel.: (43) 506262012
Web Site: http://www.porr.at
Bridge & Tunnel Construction
N.A.I.C.S.: 237310

Porr Austriarail GmbH (1)
Absberggasse 47, 1100, Vienna, Austria
Tel.: (43) 506266677
Web Site: https://austriarail.at
Construction Services
N.A.I.C.S.: 236220

Porr Bau GmbH (1)
Absberggasse 47, 1100, Vienna, Austria
Tel.: (43) 506260
Web Site: https://porr.at
Construction Engineering Services
N.A.I.C.S.: 541330
Sandra Muellner (Sec)

Porr Beteiligungen und Management GmbH (1)
Absberggasse 47, 1100, Vienna, Austria
Tel.: (43) 506260
Construction Services
N.A.I.C.S.: 236220

Porr Beteiligungsverwaltungs GmbH (1)
Absberggasse 47, 1103, Vienna,
Austria **(100%)**
Tel.: (43) 506262012
Sales Range: $1-4.9 Billion
Emp.: 10,000
Holding Company
N.A.I.C.S.: 551112
Wolfgang Hesoun (CEO)

Porr Construct S.R.L. (1)
Blvd Dimitrie Pompeiu no 5-7 floor 3,
020335, Bucharest, Romania
Tel.: (40) 213126500
Web Site: https://www.porr.ro
Construction Engineering Services
N.A.I.C.S.: 541330

Porr Design & Engineering Deutschland GmbH (1)
Valeska-Gert-Strasse 1, 10243, Berlin, Germany
Tel.: (49) 304218420
Construction Services
N.A.I.C.S.: 236220

Porr Design & Engineering GmbH (1)
Absberggasse 47, 1100, Vienna, Austria
Tel.: (43) 506260
Web Site: http://www.pde-porr.com
Design & Engineering Services
N.A.I.C.S.: 541330

Porr Deutschland GmbH (1)
Walter Gropius Str 23, Munich, 80807,
Germany **(93.94%)**
Tel.: (49) 89710010
Web Site: http://www.porr-ag.de
Sales Range: $25-49.9 Million
Emp.: 100
Single-Family Housing Construction
N.A.I.C.S.: 236115

Subsidiary (Domestic):

FRANKI Grundbau GmbH & Co. KG (2)
Hittfelder Kirchweg 24-28, 21220, Seevetal,
Germany **(100%)**
Tel.: (49) 41058690
Web Site: http://www.franki.de
Bored Pile Foundations & Curtain Foundation Contractor
N.A.I.C.S.: 238910

Porr Equipment Services Cesko s.r.o. (1)
Dubecska 3238/36, 100 00, Prague, Czech Republic
Tel.: (420) 720038947
Web Site: https://porr.cz
Construction Services
N.A.I.C.S.: 236220

Porr Equipment Services GmbH (1)
Absberggasse 47, 1100, Vienna, Austria
Tel.: (43) 506261367
Construction Engineering Services
N.A.I.C.S.: 541330

Porr GmbH (1)
Absberggasse 47, 1103, Vienna,
Austria **(100%)**
Tel.: (43) 506262012
Web Site: http://www.porr-gmbh.at
Sales Range: $650-699.9 Million
Emp.: 2,000
Residential Buildings & Dwellings Lessors
N.A.I.C.S.: 531110

Porr Hrvatska D.o.o. Za graditeljstvo (1)
Kresimira Purica 23, 10000, Zagreb, Croatia
Tel.: (385) 15390700
Sales Range: $50-74.9 Million
Emp.: 5
Construction Services
N.A.I.C.S.: 236210

Porr Industriebau GmbH (1)
Dr-Emil-Brichta-Strasse 5, 94036, Passau, Germany
Tel.: (49) 8513793290
Construction Services
N.A.I.C.S.: 236220

Porr Infrastruktur Investment AG (1)
Absberggasse 47, 1100, Vienna, Austria
Tel.: (43) 5 06 26 1451
Construction Engineering Services
N.A.I.C.S.: 541330

Porr International GmbH (1)
Absberggasse 47, 1103, Vienna,
Austria **(100%)**
Tel.: (43) 506262012
Web Site: http://www.porr.at
Sales Range: $300-349.9 Million
Emp.: 1,000
Residential Buildings & Dwellings Lessors
N.A.I.C.S.: 531110

Porr Oevermann GmbH (1)
Robert-Bosch-Strasse 7-9, 48153, Munster, Germany
Tel.: (49) 25176010
Web Site: https://www.oevermann.com
Construction Services
N.A.I.C.S.: 236220
Kirchhoff Strassenbau (Mng Dir)

Porr Projekt und Hochbau Aktiengesellschaft (1)
Absberggasse 47, 1103, Vienna,
Austria **(100%)**
Tel.: (43) 506262012
Web Site: http://www.porr.at
Residential Buildings & Dwellings Lessors
N.A.I.C.S.: 531110

Porr Solutions Deutschland GmbH (1)
Storkower Str 113, Berlin, 10407, Germany
Tel.: (49) 30421842328
Real Estate Development Services
N.A.I.C.S.: 531390

Porr Solutions Immobilien- und Infrastrukturprojekte GmbH (1)
Absberggasse 47, Vienna, 1100,
Austria **(100%)**
Tel.: (43) 506262012
Web Site: http://www.porr-solutions.com
Holding Company
N.A.I.C.S.: 551112

Porr Solutions S.R.L. (1)
Str Sfanta Vineri Nr 29 Corp B Etaj 3,
030203, Bucharest, Romania
Tel.: (40) 213 126 500
Construction Engineering Services
N.A.I.C.S.: 541330

Porr Suisse AG (1)
Seedorferstrasse 56, 6460, Altdorf,
Switzerland **(100%)**
Tel.: (41) 418750101
Web Site: https://porr.ch
Sales Range: $50-74.9 Million
Emp.: 140
Highway & Street Construction
N.A.I.C.S.: 237310
Werner Pattermann (Mng Dir & Member-Mgmt Bd)

Porr Technics And Services GmbH And Co KG (1)
Absberggasse 47, 1103, Vienna,
Austria **(100%)**
Tel.: (43) 506262012
Engineeering Services
N.A.I.C.S.: 541330
Wolfgang Hesoun (CEO)

Porr Technobau und Umwelt GmbH (1)
Fuerstenrieder Strasse 281, Munich, 81377,
Germany **(93.94%)**
Tel.: (49) 89710010
Web Site: http://www.ptu.at
Sales Range: $75-99.9 Million
Emp.: 118
Road & Building Construction; Engineering Services
N.A.I.C.S.: 237310

Porr Tunnelbau GmbH (1)
Absberggasse 47, Vienna, 1103, Austria
Tel.: (43) 50 626 1234
Web Site: http://www.porr-tunnelbau.at
Bridge & Tunnel Construction
N.A.I.C.S.: 237310

Porr UK Ltd. (1)
Stockley Park 4 Longwalk, Uxbridge, London, UB11 1FW, United Kingdom
Tel.: (44) 2031785402
Construction Services
N.A.I.C.S.: 236220

Porr Umwelttechnik Deutschland GmbH (1)
Carl-Zeiss-Str 6, 85748, Garching, Germany
Tel.: (49) 893294400
Construction Services
N.A.I.C.S.: 236220

Porr Umwelttechnik GmbH (1)
Absberggasse 47, 1100, Vienna,
Austria **(100%)**
Tel.: (43) 506260
Web Site: https://put.at
Sales Range: $350-399.9 Million
Emp.: 700
Environmental Consulting Services
N.A.I.C.S.: 541620

Subsidiary (Non-US):

Thorn Abwassertechnik GmbH (2)
Carl-Zeiss-Strasse 6, 85748, Garching, Germany
Tel.: (49) 893294400
Web Site: http://www.thorn-abwassertechnik.de
Waste Management Services
N.A.I.C.S.: 562998

Porreal Cesko, s.r.o. (1)
Vaclavske namesti 837/11, 110 00, Prague,
Czech Republic
Tel.: (420) 12350297
Construction Services
N.A.I.C.S.: 236220

Prajo & Co GmbH (1)
Absberggasse 47, 1100, Vienna, Austria
Tel.: (43) 140602950
Web Site: https://prajo.at
Construction Services
N.A.I.C.S.: 236220

Projekt Ost - IBC Business Center Entwicklungs- und Errichtungs-GmbH And Co KG (1)
Thalerhofstrasse 86, Unterpremstatten,
8141, Graz, Austria **(100%)**
Tel.: (43) 506263464
Engineeering Services
N.A.I.C.S.: 541330

Projekt West - IBC Business Center Entwicklungs- und Errichtungs-GmbH And Co KG (1)
Thalerhofstrasse 86, 8141, Unterpremstatten, Austria **(100%)**
Tel.: (43) 506263464
Web Site: http://www.ibc-graz.at
Sales Range: $25-49.9 Million
Emp.: 60
Heavy & Civil Engineering Construction

INTERNATIONAL PUBLIC

N.A.I.C.S.: 237990

Projektentwicklungsges.m.b.H. (1)
Absberggasse 47, 1100, Vienna, Austria
Tel.: (43) 506263691
Construction Services
N.A.I.C.S.: 236220

Projektierungsteam Munchen GmbH (1)
Furstenrieder Strasse 285, 81377, Munich,
Germany **(100%)**
Tel.: (49) 8971001222
Single-Family Housing Construction
N.A.I.C.S.: 236115

Pronat Steinbruch Preg GmbH (1)
Preg 14, St Lorenzen, 8715, Graz,
Austria **(68.77%)**
Tel.: (43) 38322215
Web Site: http://www.porr-stmk.ag
Emp.: 27
Dimension Stone Mining & Quarrying
N.A.I.C.S.: 212311
Karl-Heinz Strauss (CEO)

Pulmetall Bodenmarkierungen Gesellschaft mbH (1)
Anton Freunschlag Gasse 61, 1230, Vienna, Austria **(52.5%)**
Tel.: (43) 16091492
Web Site: http://www.pulmetall.at
Sales Range: $50-74.9 Million
Coating & Pavement Marketing Services
N.A.I.C.S.: 332812

RCH Recycling Center Himberg GmbH (1)
Industriestrasse 36, A-2325, Himberg, Austria
Tel.: (43) 506262183
Web Site: https://rch-himberg.at
Hazardous & Non-Hazardous Waste Disposal Services
N.A.I.C.S.: 562211

Radmer Kies GmbH & Co. KG (1)
Am Kiesgrund 100, 85609, Aschheim, Germany
Tel.: (49) 8994384210
Web Site: http://www.radmerkies.de
Sand & Gravel Processing Services
N.A.I.C.S.: 212321

Radmer Kiesvertrieb Verwaltungs GmbH (1)
Aschheim, 85609, Aschheim, Bavaria, Germany
Tel.: (49) 8994384210
Construction Engineering Services
N.A.I.C.S.: 541330

SC Schwarzl Beton SRL (1)
Dimitrie Pompeiu Blvd, Bucharest, 020337,
Romania
Tel.: (40) 213126500
Web Site: http://www.porr.ro
Emp.: 5
Construction Engineering Services
N.A.I.C.S.: 541330

SFZ Freizeitbetriebs-GmbH And Co KG (1)
Thalerhofstrasse 85, 8141, Unterpremstatten, Austria
Tel.: (43) 3135 535770
Web Site: http://www.schwarzlsee.at
Amusement & Theme Parks Operator
N.A.I.C.S.: 713110

SFZ Immobilien GmbH And Co KG (1)
Thalerhofstrasse 86, Unterpremstatten,
8141, Graz, Austria **(100%)**
Tel.: (43) 506263464
Sales Range: $75-99.9 Million
Emp.: 200
Real Estate Agents & Brokers
N.A.I.C.S.: 531210

STANOGRAD ULAGANJA d.o.o. za promet nekretninama, usluge i graditeljstvo (1)
Kresimira Purica 23/2, Samobor, Croatia
Tel.: (385) 1 4854323
Construction Engineering Services
N.A.I.C.S.: 541330

Sabelo Beteiligungsverwaltungs GmbH (1)

Absberggasse 47, 1100, Vienna, Austria
Tel.: (43) 506260
Construction Engineering Services
N.A.I.C.S.: 541330

Sakela Beteiligungsverwaltungs GmbH (1)
Absberggasse 47, 1100, Vienna, Austria
Tel.: (43) 50 626 0
Construction Engineering Services
N.A.I.C.S.: 541330

Salzburger Reststoffverwertung GmbH (1)
Scherenbrandtnerhofstr 5, 5021, Salzburg, Austria (50%)
Tel.: (43) 506262834
Emp.: 2
Commercial & Institutional Building Construction
N.A.I.C.S.: 236220

Schatzl & Jungmayr Garten- und Landschaftsbau GmbH (1)
Dieselstrasse 3, Mauer, 3362, Amstetten, Austria (52.52%)
Tel.: (43) 506261035
Web Site: http://www.schatzl-jungmayr.at
Landscape Architectural Services
N.A.I.C.S.: 541320

Schotter- und Betonwerk Karl Schwarzl Betriebsgesellschaft m.b.H. (1)
Thalerhofstrasse 86, Premstatten, 8141, Graz, Austria (100%)
Tel.: (43) 506263392
Web Site: https://schwarzl-gruppe.at
Sales Range: $100-124.9 Million
Emp.: 250
Construction Sand & Gravel Mining
N.A.I.C.S.: 212321
Guill Emette *(Office Mgr)*

Schotterwerk Gradenberg Gesellschaft m.b.H. (1)
Judenburgerstr 230, 8580, Koflach, Austria (100%)
Tel.: (43) 506263121
Building Construction Services
N.A.I.C.S.: 236220

Schwarzl Beton D.o.o. (1)
Steinbruch Bojna Jukinacka 41, Gllina, 44400, Sisak, Croatia (75%)
Tel.: (385) 44880330
Residential Buildings & Dwellings Lessors
N.A.I.C.S.: 531110

Schwarzl Transport GmbH (1)
Thalerhofstrasse 88, Premstatten, 8141, Unterpremstatten, Austria
Tel.: (43) 506263392
Construction Engineering Services
N.A.I.C.S.: 541330

Senuin Beteiligungsverwaltungs GmbH (1)
Absberggasse 47, 1100, Vienna, Austria
Tel.: (43) 5 6260 1451
Construction Engineering Services
N.A.I.C.S.: 541330

Somax Beteiligungsverwaltungs GmbH (1)
Absberggasse 47, 1100, Vienna, Austria
Tel.: (43) 5 06 26 0
Construction Engineering Services
N.A.I.C.S.: 541330

Sovelis Beteiligungsverwaltungs GmbH (1)
Absberggasse 47, 1100, Vienna, Austria
Tel.: (43) 50 626 0
Construction Engineering Services
N.A.I.C.S.: 541330

Stal-Service Spolka z ograniczona odpowiedzialnoscia (1)
ul Struzanska 30, Stanislawow Pierwszy, 05-126, Nieporet, Poland
Tel.: (48) 227725025
Web Site: https://www.stalservice.com.pl
Steel Product Distr
N.A.I.C.S.: 423510
Jacek Mroczkowski *(Mgr-Sls)*

Strauss Property Management GmbH (1)
Euro Plaza Lehrbachgasse 2, 1120, Vienna, Austria
Tel.: (43) 506268989
Web Site: https://strauss-pm.at
Property Management Services
N.A.I.C.S.: 531311
Birgit Wagner *(Mng Dir)*

Stump-Hydrobudowa Spolka z ograniczona odpowiedzialnoscia (1)
ul Poleczki 35, 02-822, Warsaw, Poland
Tel.: (48) 222669100
Web Site: http://www.stump-hydrobudowa.pl
Construction Services
N.A.I.C.S.: 236220

TEERAG-ASDAG Slovakia s.r.o. (1)
Plynarenska 1, 821 09, Bratislava, Slovakia
Tel.: (421) 253630147
Construction Engineering Services
N.A.I.C.S.: 541330

TKDZ GmbH (1)
Josef-Schnuch-Strasse 26, Wellen, 54441, Trier, Germany
Tel.: (49) 6584790
Web Site: https://tkdz-wellen.de
Hazardous & Non-Hazardous Waste Disposal Services
N.A.I.C.S.: 562211
Wolfgang Hirzi *(Mgr-Technical)*

Tancsos und Binder Gesellschaft m.b.H. (1)
Hirschackergasse 1, 2514, Traiskirchen, Austria (52.5%)
Tel.: (43) 2252259200
Web Site: http://www.tancsos-binder.at
Sales Range: $25-49.9 Million
Emp.: 20
Converted Paper Product Mfr
N.A.I.C.S.: 322299

Technisches Buro Sepp Stehrer Baustoff-Grobhandlung Gesellschaft m.b.H (1)
7 Haidequerstrasse 3, A 1111, Vienna, Austria (100%)
Tel.: (43) 1769 1930
Printing & Writing Paper Whslr
N.A.I.C.S.: 424110

Teerag-Asdag AG (1)
7 Haidequerstrasse 1, Vienna, 1110, Austria (52.5%)
Tel.: (43) 1 767 15 760
Web Site: http://www.teerag-asdag.at
Sales Range: $25-49.9 Million
Emp.: 100
Pavement, Road Marking & Concrete Ceiling Works & Landscape Architecture
N.A.I.C.S.: 324121

Teerag-Asdag Aktiengesellschaft (1)
7 Haidequerstrasse 3, 1111, Vienna, Austria (52.5%)
Tel.: (43) 506262997
Web Site: http://www.teerag-asdag.at
Highway & Street Construction
N.A.I.C.S.: 237310

Teerag-Asdag Polska Spolka Z Ograniczona Odpowiedzialnoscia (1)
Ul Wybrzeze Gdynskie 6A, 01-531, Warsaw, Poland (100%)
Tel.: (48) 225288960
Web Site: http://www.teerag-asdag.at
Sales Range: $25-49.9 Million
Emp.: 80
Excavation Contractor
N.A.I.C.S.: 238910

Teerag-asdag Hochbau Burgenland GmbH (1)
Grazerstrasse 36A, 7551, Stegersbach, Austria
Tel.: (43) 506267440
Construction Services
N.A.I.C.S.: 236220

Track Experts d.o.o. (1)
Milutina Milankovica 11a, 11070, Novi Beograd, Serbia
Tel.: (381) 113642200
Construction Services
N.A.I.C.S.: 236220

UBM Development AG (1)
Laaer-Berg-Strasse 43, 1100, Vienna, Austria (41.8%)
Tel.: (43) 506262600
Web Site: https://www.ubm-development.com
Rev.: $144,554,284
Assets: $1,566,836,823
Liabilities: $1,025,665,875
Net Worth: $541,170,948
Earnings: $18,314,267
Emp.: 292
Fiscal Year-end: 12/31/2022
Property Development, Leasing & Sales
N.A.I.C.S.: 531390
Iris Ortner *(Deputy Chm-Supervisory Bd)*

Subsidiary (Non-US):

FMP Planning and Facility Management Poland Sp. z o.o (2)
Ul Poleczki 35, Warsaw, 02-822, Poland
Tel.: (48) 223568000
Web Site: http://www.fmp.net.pl
Emp.: 30
Facility Management Services
N.A.I.C.S.: 541611

Subsidiary (Domestic):

Rainbergstrasse - Immobilienprojektentwicklungs GmbH (2)
Floridsdorfer Hauptstrasse 1, 1210, Vienna, Austria
Tel.: (43) 664 626 10 77
Real Estate Development Services
N.A.I.C.S.: 531390

Strauss & Partner Development GmbH (2)
Floridsdorfer Hauptstrabe 1, 1210, Vienna, Austria
Tel.: (43) 50 626 2600
Web Site: http://www.strauss-partner.com
Sales Range: $300-349.9 Million
Emp.: 100
Real Estate Development Services
N.A.I.C.S.: 531390

Subsidiary (Non-US):

ALBA BauProjektManagement GmbH (3)
Keltenring 7, 82041, Oberhaching, Germany
Tel.: (49) 89 641608 0
Web Site: http://www.alba-bpm.de
Sales Range: $25-49.9 Million
Construction & Real Estate Project Management
N.A.I.C.S.: 236220
Marc Kirschbaum *(Mng Dir & Exec Dir)*

Subsidiary (Domestic):

PORREAL Immobilien Management GmbH (3)
Am Euro Platz 2, Vienna, 1120, Austria
Tel.: (43) 50 626 8989
Web Site: http://www.porreal.com
Sales Range: $25-49.9 Million
Emp.: 35
Real Estate Development Services
N.A.I.C.S.: 531390

Subsidiary (Domestic):

UBM Seevillen Errichtungs-GmbH (2)
Floridsdorfer Hauptstrasse 1, 1210, Vienna, Austria
Tel.: (43) 50 626 1471
Web Site: http://www.ubm.at
Emp.: 80
Real Estate Development Services
N.A.I.C.S.: 531390

Subsidiary (Non-US):

UBM d.o.o. za poslovanje nekretninama (2)
Radnicka Cesta 80, Zagreb, Croatia
Tel.: (385) 1 53 90 706
Real Estate Development Services
N.A.I.C.S.: 531390

Subsidiary (Domestic):

Zenit Bauplanungs- und Errichtungsgesellschaft m.b.H. (2)
Floridsdorfer Hauptstrasse 1, 1210, Vienna, Austria
Tel.: (43) 50626 0
Real Estate Development Services
N.A.I.C.S.: 531390

Vorspann-Technik GmbH (1)
Furstenrieder Strasse 285, 81377, Munich, Germany (100%)
Tel.: (49) 8971001200
Web Site: http://www.vorspanntechnik.com
Holding Company
N.A.I.C.S.: 551112

Vorspann-Technik GmbH And Co.KG (1)
Innsbrucker Bundesstrasse 126, 5020, Salzburg, Austria (100%)
Tel.: (43) 662 45 40 00 0
Web Site: http://www.vorspanntechnik.com
Bridge & Tunnel Construction
N.A.I.C.S.: 237310

W 3 Errichtungs und Betriebs-Aktiengesellschaft (1)
Laaer-Berg-Strasse 43, 1100, Vienna, Austria (53.33%)
Tel.: (43) 506260
Web Site: http://www.w3.co.at
Commercial & Institutional Building Construction
N.A.I.C.S.: 236220

Wibeba Hochbau GmbH And Co. Nfg. KG (1)
Absberggasse 47, 1103, Vienna, Austria (100%)
Tel.: (43) 506262012
Sales Range: $1-4.9 Billion
Emp.: 4,000
Real Estate Agents & Brokers
N.A.I.C.S.: 531210

Wiener Betriebs- und Baugesellschaft m.b.H. (1)
7 Haidequerstrasse 1, 1110, Vienna, Austria
Tel.: (43) 506264956
Web Site: https://wibeba.at
Natural Gas Pipeline Construction Services
N.A.I.C.S.: 237120
Mario Posch *(Head-Urban Civil Engrg)*

Wiener Stadtwerke Holding AG (1)
Thomas-Klestil-Platz 13, 1030, Vienna, Austria
Tel.: (43) 1 53 1230
Web Site: http://www.wienerstadtwerke.at
Emp.: 15,000
Investment Management Service
N.A.I.C.S.: 523940

Wohnpark Laaer Berg Verwertungs- und Beteiligungs-GmbH & Co. Bauplatz 3 turkis Projekt-OG (1)
Absberggasse 47, 1103, Vienna, Austria
Tel.: (43) 5 06 26 0
Construction Engineering Services
N.A.I.C.S.: 541330

Wohnpark Laaer Berg Verwertungs- und Beteiligungs-GmbH & Co. Bauplatz 4 blau Projekt-OG (1)
Absberggasse 47, 1103, Vienna, Austria
Tel.: (43) 5 06 26 0
Construction Engineering Services
N.A.I.C.S.: 541330

bpp Bautechnik GmbH (1)
Kaplanstrasse 7, Pichl Bei, 4632, Wels, Austria
Tel.: (43) 724720280
Web Site: http://www.bpp-bautechnik.at
Construction Services
N.A.I.C.S.: 236220

PORSCHE AUTOMOBIL HOLDING SE

Porscheplatz 1, 70435, Stuttgart, Germany
Tel.: (49) 71191124420   De
Web Site: https://www.porsche-se.com
Year Founded: 1931
PAH3—(DUS)
Assets: $68,835,125,460
Liabilities: $7,762,413,840
Net Worth: $61,072,711,620
Earnings: $5,625,321,520
Emp.: 41
Fiscal Year-end: 12/31/23

PORSCHE AUTOMOBIL HOLDING SE

Porsche Automobil Holding SE—(Continued)

Holding Company; Motor Vehicles, Engines & Components Mfr & Sales
N.A.I.C.S.: 551112
Wolfgang Porsche *(Chm-Supervisory Bd)*

Subsidiaries:

DDS Digital Data Services GmbH (1)
Stumpfstraaye 1, 76131, Karlsruhe, Germany
Tel.: (49) 7219651400
Web Site: http://www.ddsgeo.com
Software Services
N.A.I.C.S.: 541519
Ernest McCutcheon *(Mng Dir)*

Locatienet B.V. (1)
Energieweg 1, 3542 DZ, Utrecht, Netherlands
Tel.: (31) 346581671
Web Site: http://www.locatienet.com
Internet Marketing Services
N.A.I.C.S.: 541613
Vincent Beaufort *(Mgr-Bus Unit & Consultancy)*

PTV Austria Planung Transport Verkehr GmbH (1)
Siegelgasse 1/2/1, 1030, Vienna, Austria
Tel.: (43) 171021470
Web Site: http://www.discover.ptvgroup.com
Transportation Services
N.A.I.C.S.: 484110
Thomas Epp *(Mng Dir)*

PTV Distribution Planning Software Ltd. (1)
4-5 Centre Court Vine Lane, Halesowen, B63 3EB, West Midlands, United Kingdom
Tel.: (44) 1215856633
Software Services
N.A.I.C.S.: 541519

PTV Transport Consult GmbH (1)
Stumpfstr 1, 76131, Karlsruhe, Germany
Tel.: (49) 72196510
Software Services
N.A.I.C.S.: 541519

Transport Technologie-Consult Karlsruhe GmbH (1)
Gerwigstrasse 53, 76131, Karlsruhe, Germany
Tel.: (49) 721625030
Web Site: http://www.ttk.de
Emp.: 30
Transportation Services
N.A.I.C.S.: 484110
Marc Perez *(Dir-Dept Transport Plng)*

Volkswagen AG (1)
Berliner Ring 2, 38440, Wolfsburg, Germany (52.2%)
Tel.: (49) 536190
Web Site: http://www.volkswagenag.com
Rev.: $290,081,880,000
Assets: $612,869,274,600
Liabilities: $443,418,327,000
Net Worth: $169,450,947,600
Earnings: $17,887,223,200
Emp.: 672,789
Fiscal Year-end: 12/31/2021
Passenger & Commercial Vehicle Mfr
N.A.I.C.S.: 336110
Hans Dieter Potsch *(Chm-Supervisory Bd)*

Subsidiary (Domestic):

AZU Autoteile und Zubehor Vertriebs GmbH (2)
An Der Trift 67, 63303, Dreieich, Germany
Tel.: (49) 61038060
Sales Range: $25-49.9 Million
Emp.: 160
Motor Vehicle Parts & Accessories Distr
N.A.I.C.S.: 441330

Audi AG (2)
Auto-Union-Strasse 1, 85045, Ingolstadt, Germany (99.55%)
Tel.: (49) 841890
Web Site: http://www.audi.com
Rev.: $60,666,147,200
Assets: $69,565,708,800
Liabilities: $38,539,552,000
Net Worth: $31,026,156,800
Earnings: $6,990,758,400
Emp.: 83,172
Fiscal Year-end: 12/31/2022
Automobile Mfr
N.A.I.C.S.: 336110
Peter Mosch *(Vice Chm-Supervisory Bd)*

Subsidiary (Domestic):

Audi Akademie Gesellschaft fur Personal und Organisations Entwicklung mbH (3)
Egerlandstr 7, Ingolstadt, 80503, Germany
Tel.: (49) 841966020
Web Site: http://www.audi-akademie.de
Sales Range: $10-24.9 Million
Emp.: 240
Business School
N.A.I.C.S.: 611410
Ralph Linda *(Gen Mgr)*

Audi Synko GmbH (3)
Auto Union Str, Ingolstadt, 85057, Germany
Tel.: (49) 841890
Web Site: http://www.audi.de
Emp.: 50,000
Motor Vehicle Distr
N.A.I.C.S.: 336320

Subsidiary (Non-US):

Audi Brazil Distribuidora De Veiculos Ltd. (4)
659 Rua Columbia, Ava Washington Louis 2480 Mara, Sao Paulo, 01438 001, Brazil
Tel.: (55) 1138966000
Web Site: http://www.audi.com.br
Sales Range: $25-49.9 Million
Emp.: 70
Motor Vehicle Distr
N.A.I.C.S.: 336320
Jan Ebercold *(Dir-Fin)*

Audi Hungaria Motor Kft. (4)
Kordan 1, Gyor, 9027, Hungary
Tel.: (36) 96661000
Web Site: http://www.audi.hu
Sales Range: $800-899.9 Million
Emp.: 5,000
Motor Vehicle Mfr & Distr
N.A.I.C.S.: 336110
Thomas Faustmann *(Mng Dir)*

Audi Japan K.K. (4)
Akumori Building 31F 1-12-32 Asksaka, Minato-ku, Tokyo, 107-0052, Japan
Web Site: http://www.audi.co.jp
Motor Vehicle Mfr & Distr
N.A.I.C.S.: 336110

Subsidiary (Domestic):

Audi Zentrum Hannover GmbH (4)
Vahrenwalder Strasse 303, 30179, Hannover, Germany
Tel.: (49) 511860569
Web Site: http://www.audizentrum-hannover.de
Sales Range: $25-49.9 Million
Emp.: 160
Motor Vehicle Distr
N.A.I.C.S.: 336320

Subsidiary (US):

Audi of America, Inc. (4)
2200 Ferdinand Porsche Dr, Herndon, VA 20171
Tel.: (248) 754-5000
Web Site: http://www.audiusa.com
Sales Range: $75-99.9 Million
Emp.: 1,200
Motor Vehicle Distr
N.A.I.C.S.: 423100
Bradley Stertz *(Mgr-PR & Corp Comm)*

Subsidiary (Non-US):

Automobili Lamborghini Holding S.p.A. (4)
Via Modena 12, Sant' Agata Bolognese, Bologna, 40019, Italy
Tel.: (39) 0516817611
Web Site: http://www.lamborghini.com
Sales Range: $75-99.9 Million
Emp.: 567
Motor Vehicle Mfr & Distr
N.A.I.C.S.: 336110
Fintan Knight *(Member-Mgmt Bd)*

Holding (Domestic):

Autogerma S.p.A. (5)
Via Gerhard R Gumpert 1, Casella Postale 47, I-37137, Verona, Italy
Tel.: (39) 0458091111
Web Site: http://www.volkswagengroup.it
Distr of Automobiles
N.A.I.C.S.: 423100
Monica Girelli *(Dir-Network Plng)*

Automobili Lamborghini S.p.A. (5)
Via Modena 12, Sant Agata Bolognese, 40019, Bologna, Italy
Tel.: (39) 0516817611
Web Site: http://www.lamborghini.com
Sales Range: $125-149.9 Million
Motor Vehicle Mfr & Distr
N.A.I.C.S.: 336110
Matteo Ortenzi *(CEO-Asia Pacific)*

Subsidiary (Domestic):

Italdesign-Giugiaro S.p.A. (6)
Via Achelle Grandi 25, Moncalieri, 10024, TO, Italy
Tel.: (39) 0116891611
Web Site: http://www.italdesign.it
Transportation Vehicle Concept & Design Engineering
N.A.I.C.S.: 541490

Unit (Domestic):

Giugiaro Design (7)
Via Achille Grandi 25, Moncalieri, 10024, Turin, Italy (100%)
Tel.: (39) 0116893311
Web Site: http://www.italdesign.it
Sales Range: $25-49.9 Million
Emp.: 650
Innovative Design Technologies for Industrial & Transport Industries
N.A.I.C.S.: 561499
Fabrizio Giugiaro *(Mng Dir & Dir-Styling Center)*

Holding (Domestic):

Lamborghini ArtiMarca S.p.A. (5)
Via Modena 12, Sant Agata Bolognese, 40019, Bologna, 40019, Italy
Tel.: (39) 0516817611
Web Site: http://www.lamborghini.com
Sales Range: $125-149.9 Million
Motor Vehicle Distr
N.A.I.C.S.: 336211

Motori Marini Lamborghini S.p.A. (5)
Via Modena 12, Sant Agata Bolognese, 40019, Bologna, Italy
Tel.: (39) 0516817611
Car Engine Mfr
N.A.I.C.S.: 333618

Subsidiary (Non-US):

Design Center Europe, S.L. (4)
Av Navarra S/N, Sitges, 08870, Barcelona, Spain
Engineering Design Services
N.A.I.C.S.: 541330

Ducati Motor Holding S.p.A. (4)
Via Cavalieri Ducati 3, 40100, Bologna, Italy
Tel.: (39) 0516413111
Web Site: http://www.ducati.com
Sales Range: $600-649.9 Million
Motorcycle Mfr
N.A.I.C.S.: 336991
Sergi Canovas Garriga *(Mng Dir-Natl Sls-India)*

Subsidiary (US):

Ducati North America Inc. (5)
10443 Bandley Dr, Cupertino, CA 95014-1912
Tel.: (408) 253-0499
Sales Range: $10-24.9 Million
Emp.: 45
Motor Cycle Distr
N.A.I.C.S.: 336991

Subsidiary (Domestic):

GIF Gewerbe- und Industriepark Bad Friedrichshall GmbH (4)
Schultheiss Seeber Str 1 B 6, Bad Friedrichshall, 74177, Germany
Tel.: (49) 7136910002

INTERNATIONAL PUBLIC

Web Site: http://www.gif-bfh.de
Sales Range: $50-74.9 Million
Emp.: 3
Property Management
N.A.I.C.S.: 531390

Subsidiary (Non-US):

Racing Technology Norfolk Ltd. (4)
Hingham Industrial Estate, Ironside Way Hingham, Norwich, NR94LF, United Kingdom
Tel.: (44) 953851411
Sales Range: $25-49.9 Million
Emp.: 32
Motor Vehicles Mfr
N.A.I.C.S.: 336110

Subsidiary (US):

Silvercar, Inc. (3)
2415 Highway 71 E, Del Valle, TX 78617
Tel.: (512) 666-9680
Web Site: http://www.silvercar.com
Car Rental Services
N.A.I.C.S.: 532111

Subsidiary (Non-US):

AutoEuropa Automoveis Lda. (2)
Quinta da Marqueza, Quinta Do Anjo, 2954-024, Palmela, Portugal
Tel.: (351) 212112552
Web Site: http://www.volkswagenautoeuropa.pt
Sales Range: $900-999.9 Million
Emp.: 3,600
Automotive Assembly Plant
N.A.I.C.S.: 336110

Subsidiary (Domestic):

Automobilmanufaktur Dresden GmbH (2)
Lennestr 3, 1069, Dresden, Germany
Tel.: (49) 35145690
Web Site: http://www.glaesernemanufaktur.de
Mfr of Automobiles
N.A.I.C.S.: 336110

Autostadt GmbH (2)
Stadtbruecke, D-38440, Wolfsburg, Germany
Tel.: (49) 5361400
Web Site: http://www.autostadt.de
Emp.: 1,500
Public Relations Company
N.A.I.C.S.: 541820

CARIAD SE (2)
Berliner Ring 2, 38440, Wolfsburg, Germany
Tel.: (49) 15222998466
Web Site: https://cariad.technology
Software Develoopment
N.A.I.C.S.: 513210
Peter Bosch *(CEO)*

Subsidiary (Domestic):

Paragon Semvox GmbH (3)
Konrad-Zuse-Strasse 19, Limbach, 66459, Zwickau, Germany
Tel.: (49) 6841809010
Web Site: http://www.semvox.de
Software Development Services
N.A.I.C.S.: 541511
Norbert Pfleger *(Co-CEO)*

Subsidiary (Domestic):

Dr. Ing. h.c. F. Porsche AG (2)
Porsche Platz 1, 70435, Stuttgart, Germany (100%)
Tel.: (49) 0711 911 0
Web Site: http://www.porsche.com
Rev.: $23,874,457,320
Assets: $34,483,068,900
Liabilities: $21,667,583,700
Net Worth: $12,815,485,200
Earnings: $2,824,113,600
Emp.: 27,612
Fiscal Year-end: 12/31/2016
Automobile & Motor Vehicle Components Mfr
N.A.I.C.S.: 336110
Wolfgang Porsche *(Chm-Supervisory Bd)*

Subsidiary (Domestic):

Karosseriewerk Porsche GmbH & Co. KG (3)

AND PRIVATE COMPANIES
PORSCHE AUTOMOBIL HOLDING SE

Schwieberdinger Str 130, Stuttgart, 70435, Germany
Tel.: (49) 7119110
Motor Vehicle Body Mfr
N.A.I.C.S.: 336211

Mieschke Hofmann und Partner Gesellschaft fur Management- und IT-Beratung mbH (3)
Konigsallee 49, Ludwigsburg, 71638, Germany
Tel.: (49) 7141 7856 0
Web Site: http://www.mhp.com
Rev.: $128,174,830
Emp.: 750
Information Technology Consulting Services
N.A.I.C.S.: 541512
Ralf Hofmann *(Co-Founder)*

PIKS Porsche Information Kommunikation Services GmbH (3)
Porscheplatz 1, Stuttgart, 70435, Germany **(100%)**
Tel.: (49) 71191122911
Web Site: http://www.porsche.de
Information & Communication Services for Vehicle Mfr
N.A.I.C.S.: 336110

Subsidiary (Non-US):

Porsche Austria GmbH & Co. OG (3)
Jurgen Lenzeder Vogelweiderstrasse 75, Salzburg, A5020, Austria
Tel.: (43) 66246812252
Car Dealer
N.A.I.C.S.: 441110

Porsche Cars Australia Pty. Ltd. (3)
109 111 Victoria Parade, Collingwood, 3066, VIC, Australia **(100%)**
Tel.: (61) 394730911
Web Site: http://www.porsche.com.au
Sales Range: $25-49.9 Million
Emp.: 100
Vehicle Mfr
N.A.I.C.S.: 336110

Subsidiary (Domestic):

Porsche Centre Melbourne Pty. Ltd. (4)
109-111 Victoria Parade, Collingwood, 3066, VIC, Australia **(100%)**
Tel.: (61) 3 9473 0901
Web Site: http://www.porschemelbourne.com.au
Sales Range: $25-49.9 Million
Emp.: 60
Automobile Sales, Parts & Service
N.A.I.C.S.: 441110
Fay Williams *(Bus Mgr)*

Subsidiary (Domestic):

Porsche Classic GmbH (3)
Porschestrasse 15 19, 71634, Ludwigsburg, Germany **(100%)**
Tel.: (49) 7119110
Web Site: http://www.porsche.de
Sales Range: $1-4.9 Billion
Emp.: 10,000
After Sale Services for Motor Vehicles
N.A.I.C.S.: 423120
Wendelin Wiedeking *(Mng Dir)*

Porsche Consulting GmbH (3)
Porsche Platz 1, Stuttgart, 70435, Badin Wirttemberg, Germany **(100%)**
Tel.: (49) 7119110
Web Site: http://www.porscheconsulting.de
Sales Range: $25-49.9 Million
Emp.: 12
Management Consultants
N.A.I.C.S.: 541611

Subsidiary (Non-US):

Porsche Engineering Japan Co. Ltd. (3)
Custom Parkside 3-13-10, Nishiazaby, Tokyo, 106-0031, Japan **(100%)**
Web Site: http://www.porsche.jp
Vehicle Mfr
N.A.I.C.S.: 336110

Subsidiary (Domestic):

Porsche Engineering Services GmbH (3)
Etzelstr 1, 74 321, Bietigheim-Bissingen, Germany **(100%)**
Tel.: (49) 7142986308
Web Site: http://www.porscheengineering.com
Sales Range: $75-99.9 Million
Emp.: 350
Engineeering Services
N.A.I.C.S.: 541330
Peter Schafer *(Mng Dir)*

Subsidiary (US):

Porsche Enterprises, Inc. (3)
980 Hammond Dr Ste 1000, Atlanta, GA 30328 **(96%)**
Tel.: (770) 290-3500
Web Site: http://www.porsche.com
Sales Range: $50-74.9 Million
Emp.: 200
Holding Company for Northern American Activities of Porsche
N.A.I.C.S.: 441330
Detlev Vonpanpane *(CEO)*

Subsidiary (Domestic):

Porsche Cars North America, Inc. (4)
980 Hammond Dr NE Ste 1000, Atlanta, GA 30328-8187
Tel.: (770) 290-3500
Web Site: http://www.porsche.com
Cars & Parts Mfr
N.A.I.C.S.: 423110
Detlev von Platen *(Chm)*

Subsidiary (Domestic):

Porsche Aviation Products Inc. (5)
980 Hammond Dr, Atlanta, GA 30328
Tel.: (770) 290-3500
Web Site: http://www.us.porsche.com
Sales Range: $150-199.9 Million
Aircraft Engine Services
N.A.I.C.S.: 423110

Subsidiary (Non-US):

Porsche Cars Canada (5)
5925 Airport Rd Suit 420, Mississauga, L4V 1W1, ON, Canada **(100%)**
Tel.: (905) 629-9900
Web Site: http://www.porsche.com
Sales Range: $50-74.9 Million
Emp.: 20
Vehicle Mfr
N.A.I.C.S.: 336110
Margareta Mahlstedt-Karayiannis *(Dir-Mktg)*

Subsidiary (Domestic):

Porsche Motorsports (5)
3203 S Shannon St, Santa Ana, CA 92704 **(100%)**
Tel.: (714) 546-6939
Web Site: http://www.us.porsche.com
Sales Range: $50-74.9 Million
Emp.: 12
Racing Cars Mfr
N.A.I.C.S.: 441110

Subsidiary (Domestic):

Porsche Financial Services (4)
4343 Commerce Ct Ste 300, Lisle, IL 60532
Tel.: (630) 505-1515
Web Site: http://www.porsche.com
Sales Range: $25-49.9 Million
Emp.: 80
Financial Services
N.A.I.C.S.: 532112

Porsche Latin America (4)
200 S Biscayne Blvd Ste 4540, Miami, FL 33131 **(100%)**
Tel.: (786) 425-2430
Web Site: http://www.porsche.com
Sales Range: $10-24.9 Million
Emp.: 20
Vehicle Mfr
N.A.I.C.S.: 441110

Subsidiary (Domestic):

Porsche Erste Vermogensverwaltung GmbH (3)
Porscheplatz 1, 70435, Stuttgart, Baden-Wurttemberg, Germany
Tel.: (49) 711 9110

Investment Management Service
N.A.I.C.S.: 523999

Subsidiary (Non-US):

Porsche Financial Management Services Ltd. (3)
1 Exchange Pl IFSC, Dublin, Ireland **(100%)**
Tel.: (353) 16701533
Web Site: http://www.porsche.com
Sales Range: $25-49.9 Million
Emp.: 4
Financial Management Services
N.A.I.C.S.: 541611
Dan Ludford *(Mng Dir)*

Subsidiary (Domestic):

Porsche Financial Services GmbH (3)
Porschestrasse 1, 70435, Bietigheim-Bissingen, Germany
Tel.: (49) 71191112003
Web Site: http://www.porsche.com
Financial Services
N.A.I.C.S.: 522220
Albert Moser *(Mng Dir)*

Subsidiary (Non-US):

Porsche Cars Great Britain Ltd (4)
Bath Rd, Reading, RG31 7SE, United Kingdom **(100%)**
Tel.: (44) 1189303666
Web Site: http://www.porsche.co.uk
Sales Range: $25-49.9 Million
Car Mfr
N.A.I.C.S.: 336110
Ragnar Schulte *(Gen Mgr-Mktg)*

Porsche Financial Services France S.A. (4)
122 Ave Du General LeClerc, 92514, Boulogne-Billancourt, Boulogne Billancourt, France **(100%)**
Tel.: (33) 155199112
Web Site: http://www.porsche.fr
Sales Range: $25-49.9 Million
Emp.: 30
Financial Services
N.A.I.C.S.: 523940

Porsche Financial Services Italia S.p.A. (4)
179 181 Via Del Santo, 35010, Limena, Padua, Italy **(100%)**
Tel.: (39) 0498704864
Web Site: http://www.porsche.com
Sales Range: $50-74.9 Million
Emp.: 8
Financial Services
N.A.I.C.S.: 523940

Porsche Financial Services Japan K.K. (4)
Arukotawa 16 Fl 1 8 1, Meguro Ku Shimomeguro, Tokyo, 153 0064, Japan **(100%)**
Tel.: (81) 354365944
Web Site: http://www.porsche.co.jp
Vehicle Financing
N.A.I.C.S.: 532112
Shuichi Ohnishi *(Gen Mgr)*

Porsche Services Espana (4)
Ave De Burgos 87, 28050, Madrid, Spain **(90%)**
Tel.: (34) 912035400
Web Site: http://www.porsche.es
Sales Range: Less than $1 Million
Emp.: 40
N.A.I.C.S.: 336110

Subsidiary (Non-US):

Porsche France S.A. (3)
122 Ave Du General LeClerc, Cydec, 92100, Boulogne, France **(100%)**
Tel.: (33) 155199112
Web Site: http://www.porsche.fr
Sales Range: $25-49.9 Million
Emp.: 30
Vehicle Mfr
N.A.I.C.S.: 336110

Porsche Iberica S.A. (3)
Avda De Burgos 87, Madrid, 28050, Spain **(40%)**
Tel.: (34) 912035620

Web Site: http://www.porsche.es
Sales Range: $25-49.9 Million
Emp.: 35
Sale of Cars & Spare Parts
N.A.I.C.S.: 441120
Rafel Sanroman *(Dir-Sls)*

Subsidiary (Domestic):

Porsacentre Barcelona S.L. (4)
Carrera de la Botanica 89, ES 08908, L'Hospitalet de Llobregat, Barcelona, Spain **(95%)**
Tel.: (34) 902200911
Web Site: http://www.porsche-barcelona.com
Automobile Sales
N.A.I.C.S.: 441110
Jose Velasco *(Mgr)*

Porsamadrid S.L. (4)
Pol Ind El Carralero II C/ de la Ciruela 5, Majadahonda, 28220, Madrid, Spain **(100%)**
Tel.: (34) 916 347 810
Web Site: http://www.porsche-madridoeste.com
Sales Range: $10-24.9 Million
Emp.: 27
Automobile Sales
N.A.I.C.S.: 441110
Thomas Billrn *(Gen Mgr)*

Subsidiary (Non-US):

Porsche International Financing Ltd. (3)
No 1 Exch Pl IFSC, Dublin, 1, Ireland **(100%)**
Tel.: (353) 16701533
Web Site: http://www.porsche.com
Sales Range: $50-74.9 Million
Emp.: 4
Financial Services for Vehicle Mfr
N.A.I.C.S.: 532112
Din Laford *(Mng Dir)*

Subsidiary (Domestic):

Porsche International Insurance Ltd. (4)
No 1 Exchange Place International Financial Service Center, Dublin, 1, Ireland **(100%)**
Tel.: (353) 16701533
Web Site: http://www.porsche.com
Emp.: 4
Vehicle Insurance Services
N.A.I.C.S.: 524298
Dan Ludford *(Mng Dir)*

Subsidiary (Non-US):

Porsche Italia S.p.A (3)
Corso Stati Uniti 35, 35127, Padua, Italy **(100%)**
Tel.: (39) 0498704864
Web Site: http://www.porsche.it
Sales Range: $25-49.9 Million
Emp.: 55
Sale of Cars & Spare Parts
N.A.I.C.S.: 441120

Subsidiary (Domestic):

Centro Porsche Padova S.r.L. (4)
35 Corso Stati Uniti, 35127, Padua, Italy **(100%)**
Tel.: (39) 0498292930
Web Site: http://www.porsche.com
Sales Range: $25-49.9 Million
Emp.: 18
Vehicle Mfr
N.A.I.C.S.: 336110

Centro Porsche S.R.L. (4)
Via Lancetti 46, 20158, Milan, Italy **(100%)**
Tel.: (39) 026939621
Web Site: http://www.porsche.com
Sales Range: $50-74.9 Million
Emp.: 27
Vehicle Mfr
N.A.I.C.S.: 336110

Subsidiary (Non-US):

Porsche Japan KK (3)
Arukotawa 16 Fl 1 8 1, Meguro Ku Shimomeguro, Tokyo, 153 0064, Japan **(100%)**
Tel.: (81) 354365925

PORSCHE AUTOMOBIL HOLDING SE
INTERNATIONAL PUBLIC

Porsche Automobil Holding SE—(Continued)
Web Site: http://www.porsche.co.jp
Sales Range: $25-49.9 Million
Emp.: 55
Vehicle Mfr
N.A.I.C.S.: 336110
Ito Tomohiko (COO)

Subsidiary (Domestic):

Porsche Leasing GmbH (3)
Porschestrasse 15 19, 78634, Ludwigsburg,
Badin Wirttamberg, Germany (100%)
Tel.: (49) 7119110
Web Site: http://www.porsche.de
Leasing Services
N.A.I.C.S.: 532112
Bernard Maier (Mng Dir)

Porsche Leipzig GmbH (3)
Porschestr 1, 04158, Leipzig,
Germany (100%)
Tel.: (49) 3419990
Web Site: http://www.porsche-leipzig.com
Sales Range: $100-124.9 Million
Emp.: 300
Vehicle Mfr
N.A.I.C.S.: 336110
Karen Comlad (Sec)

Subsidiary (Non-US):

Porsche Middle East (3)
Office No 2 E 401 4th Fl Dubai Airport Free
Zone New E Wing Bldg, PO Box 54299,
Dubai, United Arab Emirates (100%)
Tel.: (971) 42995911
Web Site: http://www.porsche.com
Sales Range: $25-49.9 Million
Emp.: 34
Vehicle Mfr
N.A.I.C.S.: 336110
George Wills (Mng Dir-Middle East & Africa)

Subsidiary (Domestic):

Porsche Niederlassung Stuttgart GmbH (3)
Porsche Platz 1, 70 435, Stuttgart,
Germany (100%)
Tel.: (49) 7119110
Web Site: http://www.porsche.de
Sales Range: $800-899.9 Million
Emp.: 5,000
Vehicle Mfr
N.A.I.C.S.: 336110

Subsidiary (Non-US):

Porsche Slovakia (3)
Vajnorska 160, 831 01, Bratislava, Slovakia
Tel.: (421) 249262607
Web Site: http://www.vw.sk
Sales Range: $150-199.9 Million
Emp.: 808
Motor Vehicle Mfr & Distr
N.A.I.C.S.: 336110

Subsidiary (Domestic):

Porsche Zwischenholding GmbH (3)
Porscheplatz 1, Stuttgart, 70435, Germany
Tel.: (49) 7119110
Web Site: http://www.porsche.de
Emp.: 1,500
Investment Management Service
N.A.I.C.S.: 523940
Thomas Egeland (Gen Mgr)

Subsidiary (Non-US):

Farsund Aluminium Casting AS (4)
Lundevaagen S, PO Box 158, 4552, Farsund, Norway
Tel.: (47) 3838 9000
Web Site: http://www.fac.no
Sales Range: $25-49.9 Million
Emp.: 200
Die Casting Aluminum Products Mfr & Distr
N.A.I.C.S.: 331523

Mieschke Hofmann und Partner (Schweiz) AG (4)
Althardstrasse 80, 8105, Regensdorf, Switzerland
Tel.: (41) 44 842 72 82
Sales Range: $125-149.9 Million
Emp.: 700
Information Technology Consulting Services
N.A.I.C.S.: 541512

Porsche Asia Pacific Pte. Ltd. (4)
20 McCallum Street 12-01 Tokio Marine
Centre, Singapore, 69046, Singapore
Tel.: (65) 6645 4911
Web Site: http://www.porsche.com
Emp.: 32
New Car Dealers
N.A.I.C.S.: 441110
Nico Kuhlmann (Dir-Sls)

Porsche Consulting Brasil Ltda. (4)
Rua Florida 1703 Cj 121, Sao Paulo,
4565001, Brazil
Tel.: (55) 11 2538 9111
Management Consulting Services
N.A.I.C.S.: 541618
Ruediger Leutz (Pres & CEO)

Porsche Design Italia S.r.L. (4)
Corso Stati Uniti 35, Padua, 35127, Italy
Tel.: (39) 049761009
Automobile Mfr
N.A.I.C.S.: 336110
Slavia Stivanello (Mgr)

Subsidiary (Domestic):

Porsche Deutschland GmbH (4)
Porschestrasse 1, Bietigheim-Bissingen,
74321, Germany
Tel.: (49) 711 911 12002
Web Site: http://www.porsche.com
Motor Vehicle Distr
N.A.I.C.S.: 441227

Porsche Dienstleistungs GmbH (4)
Porscheplatz 1, Stuttgart, 70435, Germany
Tel.: (49) 7119110
Web Site: http://www.porsche.de
Catering Services
N.A.I.C.S.: 722320

Porsche Engineering Group GmbH (4)
Porschestrabe, 71287, Weissach, Germany
Tel.: (49) 711 911 88888
Web Site:
 http://www.porscheengineering.com
Automotive Engineering & Design Services
N.A.I.C.S.: 541330

Subsidiary (Non-US):

Porsche Financial Services Australia, Pty. Ltd. (4)
109 111 Victoria Pde, Collingwood, Melbourne, 3066, VIC, Australia
Tel.: (61) 394730917
Web Site:
 http://www.porschemelbourne.com.au
Financial Management Services
N.A.I.C.S.: 523999
Piero Pellegrini (Gen Mgr)

Subsidiary (Domestic):

Porsche Financial Services GmbH & Co. KG (4)
Porschestrasse 1, 74304, Bietigheim-Bissingen, Germany
Tel.: (49) 711 911 12003
Financial Management Services
N.A.I.C.S.: 523999

Subsidiary (Non-US):

Porsche Financial Services Great Britain Ltd. (4)
Bath Road, Reading, RG31 7SE, Berkshire,
United Kingdom
Tel.: (44) 1189 303666
Financial Management Services
N.A.I.C.S.: 523999

Subsidiary (Domestic):

Porsche Financial Services Verwaltungs- gesellschaft mbH (4)
Porschestrasse 1, 74304, Bietigheim-Bissingen,
Germany
Tel.: (49) 711 911 12003
Financial Services
N.A.I.C.S.: 523999

Subsidiary (US):

Porsche Funding LLC (4)
4343 Commerce Ct Ste 300, Lisle, IL 60532
Tel.: (630) 225-3200
Financial Investment Services
N.A.I.C.S.: 523999

Porsche Funding Ltd. Partnership (4)
4343 Commerce Ct, Lisle, IL 60532
Tel.: (630) 225-3200
Sales Range: $25-49.9 Million
Emp.: 100
Car Mfr & Distr
N.A.I.C.S.: 336110
Ross Dupper (Gen Mgr)

Porsche Leasing Ltd. (4)
980 Hammond Dr Ste 1000, Atlanta, GA
30328
Tel.: (630) 505-1515
Business Support Services
N.A.I.C.S.: 561499

Subsidiary (Domestic):

Porsche Lizenz- und Handelsgesellschaft mbH & Co. KG (4)
Porschestrasse 1, Bietigheim-Bissingen,
74321, Germany
Tel.: (49) 711 911 12911
Web Site: http://www.porsche-design.com
Sales Range: $25-49.9 Million
Emp.: 100
Apparel & Accessories Designer & Marketer
N.A.I.C.S.: 533110
Frank Angelkotter (Member-Mgmt Bd)

Porsche Logistik GmbH (4)
Porscheplatz 1, Stuttgart, 70435, Germany
Tel.: (49) 7119110
Logistics Consulting Servies
N.A.I.C.S.: 541614

Porsche Niederlassung Berlin GmbH (4)
Franklinstr 23, 10587, Berlin, Germany
Tel.: (49) 30 978 911 100
Web Site: http://www.porschezentrum-berlin.de
Sales Range: $25-49.9 Million
Emp.: 80
Car Distr
N.A.I.C.S.: 441110
Stephan Blassing (Mng Dir)

Porsche Niederlassung Berlin-Potsdam GmbH (4)
Albert-Einstein-Ring 49, 14532, Kleinmachnow, Germany
Tel.: (49) 30 978 911 300
Web Site: http://www.porsche-berlin-potsdam.de
Emp.: 15
Car Mfr & Distr
N.A.I.C.S.: 441110
Patrick Henkel (Mng Dir)

Porsche Niederlassung Hamburg GmbH (4)
Eiffestrasse 498, 20537, Hamburg, Germany
Tel.: (49) 40211050
Web Site: http://www.porsche-hamburg.de
Emp.: 100
Car Mfr & Distr
N.A.I.C.S.: 441110
Andreas Tetzloff (Mng Dir)

Porsche Niederlassung Leipzig GmbH (4)
Poststrasse 7, 4158, Leipzig, Germany
Tel.: (49) 341 919 36 0
Web Site: http://www.porsche-leipzig.de
Sales Range: $10-24.9 Million
Emp.: 2
Used Car Distr
N.A.I.C.S.: 441120
Markus Neu (Mng Dir)

Subsidiary (Non-US):

Porsche Retail Group Australia Pty. Ltd. (4)
109-111 Victoria Pde, Collingwood, Collingwood, 3066, VIC, Australia
Tel.: (61) 394730901
Web Site: http://www.porsche.com.au
Emp.: 10
Car Distr
N.A.I.C.S.: 441110
Sakai Ken (CFO)

Porsche Schweiz AG (4)
Blegisstrasse 7, 6300, Rotkreuz, Switzerland
Tel.: (41) 414879132
Web Site: http://www.porsche.ch
Sales Range: $10-24.9 Million
Emp.: 3
Automobile Driving School Operating Services
N.A.I.C.S.: 611692
Stephan Altrichter (Gen Mgr)

Subsidiary (Non-US):

Europcar Mobility Group SA (2)
13 ter Boulevard Berthier, FR-75017, Paris,
France
Tel.: (33) 180209000
Web Site:
 http://www.europcar-mobility-group.com
Rev.: $3,328,046,622
Assets: $7,732,816,749
Liabilities: $5,818,641,269
Net Worth: $1,914,175,480
Earnings: $59,718,325
Emp.: 8,198
Fiscal Year-end: 12/31/2022
Holding Company; Car Rental Services
N.A.I.C.S.: 551112
Caroline Parot (CEO & Member-Mgmt Bd)

Holding (Domestic):

Europcar International S.A. (3)
13 Ter Boulevard Berthier, 75017, Paris,
France (100%)
Tel.: (33) 180209000
Web Site: http://www.europcar.com
Sales Range: $1-4.9 Billion
Emp.: 60
Car Rental Services
N.A.I.C.S.: 532111

Subsidiary (Domestic):

Europcar France S.A. (4)
3 Ave Du Centre, Les Quadrants, 78881,
Saint-Quentin-en-Yvelines, France (99.9%)
Tel.: (33) 130449000
Web Site: http://www.europcar.fr
Sales Range: $150-199.9 Million
Car Rental Services
N.A.I.C.S.: 532111

Subsidiary (Non-US):

Europcar IB, S.A. (5)
Mostrador Terminal A / Counter, 7611, Madrid, Spain (100%)
Tel.: (34) 911505000
Web Site: http://www.europcar.es
Emp.: 100
Car Rental Services
N.A.I.C.S.: 532111

Europcar International S.A. & Co. OHG (5)
Tangstedter Landstrasse 81, Hamburg,
22415, Germany (99%)
Tel.: (49) 40520180
Web Site: http://www.europcar.de
Sales Range: $125-149.9 Million
Emp.: 430
Car Rental Services
N.A.I.C.S.: 532111

Subsidiary (Domestic):

Europcar Autovermietung GmbH (6)
Anckelmannsplatz 1, 20537, Hamburg, Germany
Tel.: (49) 40520180
Web Site: http://www.europcar.de
Car Rental Services
N.A.I.C.S.: 532111

Subsidiary (Domestic):

Europcar Holding S.A.S. (4)
Parc d'affaires Le val Saint Quentin 2 rue
Rene Caudron, Les Quadrants, 78881,
Voisins-le-Bretonneux, France (100%)
Tel.: (33) 130449000
Web Site: https://www.europcar.com
Sales Range: $50-74.9 Million
Holding Company
N.A.I.C.S.: 551112
Philippe Jerome (Gen Mgr)

Subsidiary (Non-US):

Europcar Italia S.p.A. (5)
Via Cesare Giulio Viola 48, Parco De
Medici, 00148, Rome, Italy (100%)

PORSCHE AUTOMOBIL HOLDING SE — AND PRIVATE COMPANIES

Tel.: (39) 06967091
Car Rental Services
N.A.I.C.S.: 532111

Europcar S.A. (5)
Brixtonlaan 43, PO Box 88, 1930,
Zaventem, Brussels, Belgium **(99.9%)**
Tel.: (32) 72100592
Web Site: http://www.europcar.com
Sales Range: $25-49.9 Million
Emp.: 70
Car Rental Services
N.A.I.C.S.: 532111

Europcar UK Limited (5)
Europcar House Aldenham Road, Watford,
WD23 2QQ, United Kingdom **(100%)**
Tel.: (44) 1923811000
Web Site: http://www.europcar.co.uk
Sales Range: $25-49.9 Million
Emp.: 100
Car Rental Services
N.A.I.C.S.: 532111
Robert Shaw *(Dir-Ops)*

Holding (US):

Fox Rent A Car, Inc. (3)
5500 W Century Blvd, Los Angeles, CA
90045
Tel.: (323) 673-9084
Web Site: http://www.foxrentacar.com
Passenger Car Rental
N.A.I.C.S.: 532111
Mike Jaberi *(Co-Mng Dir)*

Joint Venture (Non-US):

**FAW-Volkswagen Automotive Co.,
Ltd.** (2)
Dongfeng Street, Changchun, 130011, Jilin,
China **(40%)**
Tel.: (86) 431 85990151
Web Site: http://www.faw-volkswagen.com
Sales Range: $1-4.9 Billion
Emp.: 9,800
Motor Vehicle Mfr & Distr
N.A.I.C.S.: 336110

Subsidiary (Domestic):

Fahrzeugteile Service-Zentrum Mellendorf GmbH (2)
Industrie Strasse 44, 30900, Wedemark,
Mellendorf, Germany
Tel.: (49) 5.13097651e+011
Web Site: http://www.fs-zm.de
Sales Range: $25-49.9 Million
Emp.: 250
Vehicle Wheel Assembly
N.A.I.C.S.: 336390

Subsidiary (Non-US):

Groupe Volkswagen France S.A. (2)
11 Ave De Boursonne, Villers-Cotterets,
26001, France
Tel.: (33) 323738080
Web Site: http://www.volkswagengroup.fr
Sales Range: $150-199.9 Million
Emp.: 675
Motor Vehicle Mfr & Sales
N.A.I.C.S.: 336110
Ravoal Jack *(Pres)*

**HOLAD Holding & Administration
AG** (2)
St Jakobs-Strasse 7, PO Box 2879, 4002,
Basel, Switzerland
Tel.: (41) 61 234582
Sales Range: $25-49.9 Million
Emp.: 1
Motor Vehicle Distr
N.A.I.C.S.: 423110

**INIS International Insurance Services
s.r.o.** (2)
, Prague, Czech Republic
Provider of Insurance Services
N.A.I.C.S.: 524298

Subsidiary (Non-US):

**INIS International Insurance Service
s.r.o.** (3)
, Bratislava, Slovakia
Provider of Insurance Services
N.A.I.C.S.: 524298

Subsidiary (Non-US):

Import Volkswagen Group s.r.o. (2)
Radlicka 740/5, Prague, 15800, Czech Republic
Tel.: (420) 251033111
Web Site: http://www.volkswagen.cz
Sales Range: $25-49.9 Million
Emp.: 150
Motor Vehicle Distr
N.A.I.C.S.: 336320
Vratislav Strasil *(Mng Dir)*

Subsidiary (Domestic):

**Ingenieurgesellschaft Auto und
Verkehr** (2)
Carnotstrasse 1, D-10587, Berlin,
Germany **(50%)**
Tel.: (49) 30399780
Web Site: http://www.iav.de
Sales Range: $500-549.9 Million
Emp.: 5,200
Developer of Automotive Technology
N.A.I.C.S.: 541715
Michael Schubert *(Member-Mgmt Bd & Dir-Comml)*

Subsidiary (Non-US):

IAV Automotive Engineering (Shanghai) Co. Ltd. (2)
8F No 185 Mo Yu Road, Anting Town Jiading District, Shanghai, 201805, China
Tel.: (86) 21 39570917 0
Web Site: http://www.iav.com
Sales Range: $25-49.9 Million
Emp.: 50
Automotive Engineering
N.A.I.C.S.: 541330

Subsidiary (US):

IAV Automotive Engineering Inc. (3)
15620 Technology Dr, Northville, MI 48168
Tel.: (734) 971-1070
Web Site: http://www.iav-usa.com
Sales Range: $25-49.9 Million
Emp.: 140
Developer of Automotive Technology
N.A.I.C.S.: 541330

Subsidiary (Non-US):

IAV Co. Ltd. Japan (3)
1-28 Kanda Sudacho, Aqua Kanda Building 6F, Chiyoda-ku, Tokyo, 101 0041, Japan
Tel.: (81) 3 4550 1302
Web Site: http://www.iav.com
Automotive Engineering
N.A.I.C.S.: 541330

IAV France S.A.S.U. (3)
4 rue Guynemer, 78280, Guyancourt,
France
Tel.: (33) 130120000
Web Site: http://www.iav.com
Automotive Engineering
N.A.I.C.S.: 541330
Thomas Roelle *(Mng Dir)*

IAV Korea Co., Ltd. (3)
9F Anyangventuretel 1107-1 Bisandong
Dongangu Anyangsi, Kyoungkido, Seoul,
431 050, Korea (South)
Tel.: (82) 314408540
Web Site: http://www.iav.com.kr
Sales Range: $25-49.9 Million
Emp.: 5
Automotive Engineering
N.A.I.C.S.: 541330

IAV U.K, Ltd. (3)
Alexander House Christy Ct, Southfields
Business Park, Basildon, SS15 6TL, Essex,
United Kingdom
Tel.: (44) 1268564672
Web Site: http://www.iav.com
Automotive Engineering
N.A.I.C.S.: 541330

Joint Venture (Non-US):

**Krupp Modulos Automotivos do Brasil
Ltda.** (2)
Av Leste Km 4 Sn Campo Largo Da Roseira, 03090 900, Sao Jose dos Pinhais,
Brazil **(49%)**
Tel.: (55) 4121064796

Web Site: http://www.tka-as.thyssenkrupp.com
Sales Range: $10-24.9 Million
Emp.: 296
Motor Vehicles Mfr
N.A.I.C.S.: 336110

Subsidiary (Domestic):

**Kunden Club GmbH des
Volkswagen-Konzerns** (2)
John F Kennedy Allee 64, 38444, Wolfsburg, Germany
Tel.: (49) 536130850
Web Site: http://www.vw-club.de
Sales Range: $25-49.9 Million
Emp.: 25
Advertising Services
N.A.I.C.S.: 541870

LGI Logistikzentrum im Guterverkehrszentrum Ingolstadt Betreibergesellschaft mbH (2)
Rathausplatz 4, 85049, Ingolstadt, Germany
Tel.: (49) 8413050
Group Business Services
N.A.I.C.S.: 561499

**MMI Marketing Management Institut
GmbH** (2)
Klostergang 53, 38104, Braunschweig,
38104, Germany
Tel.: (49) 53137020
Web Site: http://www.mmi-akademei.de
Sales Range: $25-49.9 Million
Emp.: 22
Consulting Services
N.A.I.C.S.: 541611
Rainer Jung *(Mng Dir)*

**Neuland Wohnungsgesellschaft
mbH** (2)
Erfurter Ring 15, 38444, Wolfsburg, Germany
Tel.: (49) 53617910
Web Site: http://www.nld.de
Property Manager
N.A.I.C.S.: 531390

Subsidiary (Non-US):

SEAT, S.A. (2)
Autovia A2 Km 585, 08760, Martorell, Spain
Tel.: (34) 937 08 5000
Web Site: http://www.seat.es
Rev: $11,441,719,148
Assets: $6,041,406,910
Liabilities: $4,225,810,508
Net Worth: $1,815,596,402
Earnings: $336,838,232
Emp.: 14,106
Fiscal Year-end: 12/31/2017
Motor Vehicle Mfr & Distr
N.A.I.C.S.: 336110
Holger Kintscher *(VP-Fin, IT & Org)*

Subsidiary (Domestic):

Gearbox del Prat, S.A. (3)
Pl Pratense 113 S/N, 08820, Llobregat,
Spain
Tel.: (34) 9340282600
Web Site: http://www.seat.com
Sales Range: $350-399.9 Million
Emp.: 1,500
Vehicle Parts Mfr
N.A.I.C.S.: 336340

Subsidiary (Non-US):

SEAT Deutschland GmbH (3)
Starkenburgstrasse 10, 64546, Morfelden,
Germany
Tel.: (49) 61052080
Web Site: http://www.seat.de
Sales Range: $50-74.9 Million
Emp.: 150
N.A.I.C.S.: 336110

Subsidiary (Domestic):

Servilease S.A. (3)
Av De Bruselas 34, Alcobendas, 28100,
Spain
Tel.: (34) 914535151
Sales Range: $50-74.9 Million
Emp.: 25
Vehicle Rental
N.A.I.C.S.: 532120

Volkswagen Navarra, S.A. (3)
Poligino Industrial Landaben S N, 31012,
Pamplona, Spain
Tel.: (34) 948424104
Sales Range: $800-899.9 Million
Emp.: 4,500
Motor Vehicles Mfr
N.A.I.C.S.: 336110

Joint Venture (Non-US):

**Shanghai-Volkswagen Automotive
Company Ltd.** (2)
63 Anting Luo Pu Road, Shanghai, 201805,
China
Tel.: (86) 2159561888
Web Site: http://www.csvw.com
Automobile Mfr
N.A.I.C.S.: 336110

Subsidiary (Non-US):

Svenska Volkswagen AB (2)
Hantverksvagen 9, Sodertalje, 151 88,
Sweden
Tel.: (46) 855386500
Web Site: http://www.volkswagengroup.se
Sales Range: $75-99.9 Million
Emp.: 450
Motor Vehicle Distr
N.A.I.C.S.: 336320
Claes Gerveland *(Mng Dir)*

Subsidiary (Domestic):

Traton SE (2)
Hanauer Str 26, 80995, Munich, Germany
Tel.: (49) 893609870
Web Site: https://www.traton.com
Rev: $46,017,699
Assets: $27,703,379,020
Liabilities: $11,988,851,716
Net Worth: $15,714,527,304
Earnings: ($281,316,641)
Emp.: 100,356
Fiscal Year-end: 12/31/2022
Heavy Duty Truck Mfr
N.A.I.C.S.: 336120
Karina Schnur *(Chm-Supervisory Bd-Group Works Council)*

Subsidiary (Domestic):

MAN SE (3)
Dachauer Str 641, 80995, Munich,
Germany **(100%)**
Tel.: (49) 89360980
Web Site: http://www.man.eu
Rev: $13,844,434,160
Assets: $22,590,996,290
Liabilities: $16,088,550,140
Net Worth: $6,502,446,150
Earnings: $772,058,250
Emp.: 230
Fiscal Year-end: 12/31/2018
Holding Company; Commercial Vehicle, Engine & Mechanical Engineering Equipment Mfr
N.A.I.C.S.: 551112
Jurgen Kerner *(Deputy Chm-Supervisory Bd)*

Subsidiary (US):

MAN Capital Corporation (4)
2 Amboy Ave, Woodbridge, NJ
07095 **(100%)**
Tel.: (732) 582-8220
Web Site: http://www.man.de
Sales Range: $350-399.9 Million
Emp.: 1,800
Financing
N.A.I.C.S.: 333248

Subsidiary (Domestic):

MAN Diesel & Turbo SE (4)
Stadtbachstrasse 1, Augsburg, 86153,
Germany **(100%)**
Tel.: (49) 8213220
Web Site: http://www.mandieselturbo.com
Sales Range: $1-4.9 Billion
Emp.: 6,700
Mfr of Four & Two-Stroke Diesel Engines;
Gas & Dual Engines & Exhaust Gas Turbochargers
N.A.I.C.S.: 333618
Georg Pachta-Reyhofen *(Chm-Supervisory Bd)*

PORSCHE AUTOMOBIL HOLDING SE

Porsche Automobil Holding SE—(Continued)

Subsidiary (Non-US):

MAN Diesel & Turbo (5)
Teglholmsgade 41, Copenhagen, 2450,
Denmark **(100%)**
Tel.: (45) 33851100
Web Site: http://www.mandieselturbo.com
Sales Range: $125-149.9 Million
Emp.: 900
Mfr of Diesel Engines
N.A.I.C.S.: 333618
Thomas Knudsen *(Mgr)*

MAN Diesel & Turbo France SAS (5)
Avenue de Chatonay Porte No 7, 44608,
Saint Nazaire, France **(100%)**
Tel.: (33) 240 906 500
Web Site: http://www.mandieselturbo.com
Sales Range: $25-49.9 Million
Emp.: 700
Mfr of High & Medium Speed Diesel Engines, Reconditioning, Retrofit & Upgrade & Training Services
N.A.I.C.S.: 333618
Stephan Timmermann *(Mgr-Engines & Marine Sys-After Sales)*

MAN Diesel & Turbo Japan Ltd. (5)
Kobe Kokusai Kaikan 15 Fl 8 1 6 Goko Dori
Chuo Ku, 8 1 6 Goko Dori, Kobe, 6510087,
Hyogo, Japan **(100%)**
Tel.: (81) 782619645
Web Site: http://www.mandieselturbo.com
Sales Range: $25-49.9 Million
Emp.: 15
Diesel Engine Mfr
N.A.I.C.S.: 333618
Kimihiko Sugiura *(Pres)*

MAN Diesel & Turbo Ltd. (5)
710 Dorval Dr Ste 600, Oakville, L6K 3V7,
ON, Canada **(100%)**
Tel.: (905) 842-2020
Web Site: http://www.mandieselturbo.com
Sales Range: $10-24.9 Million
Emp.: 35
Sales, Service & Spare Parts Support on a Range of Engines
N.A.I.C.S.: 336412

MAN Diesel & Turbo Norge AS (5)
Haakon VII St Gate 1, N-0110, Oslo, Vika,
Norway **(100%)**
Tel.: (47) 22832101
Web Site: http://www.manbw.com
Sales Range: $25-49.9 Million
Emp.: 6
Mfr of Diesel Engines
N.A.I.C.S.: 333618

Subsidiary (US):

MAN Diesel & Turbo North America Inc. (5)
1600 Brittmoore Rd, Houston, TX 77043
Tel.: (713) 780-4200
Web Site:
 http://www.mandieselturbo.us.com
Emp.: 100
Compressor & Turbine Mfr
N.A.I.C.S.: 333912
Nicole Sandoval *(Mgr-Mktg)*

Division (Domestic):

MAN Diesel & Turbo North America Inc. - Baton Rouge (6)
12612 Ronaldson Rd, Baton Rouge, LA 70807-1504
Tel.: (225) 775-2542
Web Site: http://www.brmw.net
Sales Range: $1-9.9 Million
Emp.: 75
Industrial Machinery Repair Services
N.A.I.C.S.: 811310
David Antoniazzi *(Dir-Sls-Cruise, Ferry & Merchant-Fort Lauderdale)*

MAN Diesel & Turbo North America Inc. - Woodbridge (6)
2 Amboy Ave, Woodbridge, NJ 07095
Tel.: (732) 582-8200
Web Site:
 http://www.mandieselturbo.us.com
Diesel Engines & Parts for Power Plants
N.A.I.C.S.: 333618

Unit (Domestic):

MAN Diesel & Turbo SE - Oberhausen (5)
Steinbrinkstrasse 1, 46145, Oberhausen,
Germany **(100%)**
Tel.: (49) 20869201
Web Site: http://www.mandieselturbo.com
Sales Range: $600-649.9 Million
Emp.: 3,000
Turbocompressors, Gas & Steam Turbines, Process Gas Expanders & Process Screw Compressors Mfr
N.A.I.C.S.: 333611

Subsidiary (Non-US):

MAN Diesel & Turbo Schweiz AG (5)
Hardstrasse 319, CH 8005, Zurich,
Switzerland **(100%)**
Tel.: (41) 12782211
Web Site: http://www.manturbo.com
Rev.: $1,223,600,000
Emp.: 306
Turbomachinery Mfr
N.A.I.C.S.: 333611

Subsidiary (US):

MAN Engines & Components Inc. (5)
591 SW 13th Ter, Pompano Beach, FL 33069-3520
Tel.: (954) 946-9092
Web Site: http://www.man-mec.com
Sales Range: $25-49.9 Million
Emp.: 36
Marine Propulsion Machinery & Equipment Distr
N.A.I.C.S.: 423860

Unit (Domestic):

Man DWE GmbH (5)
Werftstrasse 17, Deggendorf, 94669,
Germany **(100%)**
Tel.: (49) 9913810
Web Site: http://www.dwe.de
Sales Range: $75-99.9 Million
Emp.: 500
Shipbuilding, Dredger Building, Chemical Apparatus Construction & Plant Construction
N.A.I.C.S.: 336611
Reinharc Nessel *(Mgr-Sls)*

Subsidiary (Domestic):

MAN Truck & Bus AG (4)
Dachauer Strasse 667, 80995, Munich,
Germany **(100%)**
Tel.: (49) 8915800
Web Site: http://www.mantruckandbus.com
Rev.: $8,944,959,488
Emp.: 6,500
Commercial Vehicle Mfr
N.A.I.C.S.: 336110
Karina Schnur *(Chm-Supervisory Bd-Gen & Grp Works Council)*

Subsidiary (Non-US):

MAN Truck & Bus (S.A.) (Pty) Ltd. (5)
105 Andr Greyvensteyn Avenue, Isando,
1600, Gauteng, South Africa **(100%)**
Tel.: (27) 119286800
Web Site: http://www.mantruckandbus.co.za
Sales Range: $125-149.9 Million
Emp.: 300
Mfr of Commercial Vehicles
N.A.I.C.S.: 336120
Patience Dumisani *(Dir-Sls & Mktg)*

Subsidiary (Domestic):

MAN Truck & Bus Deutschland GmbH - Flensburg (5)
Werftstrasse 24, D 24939, Flensburg, Germany
Tel.: (49) 46148110
Web Site: http://www.maneurope.de
Sales Range: $10-24.9 Million
Emp.: 20
Commercial Vehicle Distr
N.A.I.C.S.: 423110

Subsidiary (Non-US):

MAN Truck & Bus Osterreich AG (5)
Schoenauer Strasse 5, PO Box 222, Steyr,
4400, Austria **(100%)**
Tel.: (43) 72525850
Web Site: http://www.man.at
Sales Range: $900-999.9 Million
Emp.: 3,500
Mfr of Commercial Vehicles
N.A.I.C.S.: 333310
Loose Byoern *(Mgr-Mktg)*

Subsidiary (Domestic):

MAN Truck & Bus Osterreich AG - Vienna (6)
Brunnerstrasse 44 0, A 1230, Vienna,
Austria **(100%)**
Tel.: (43) 1866310
Web Site: http://www.man-mn.at
Sales Range: $400-449.9 Million
Emp.: 1,000
Commercial Vehicle Mfr
N.A.I.C.S.: 333310
Wolfgang Schirmer *(Gen Mgr)*

MAN Truck & Bus Vertrieb Osterreich AG (6)
Brunner Strasse 44, Vienna, 1230,
Austria **(100%)**
Tel.: (43) 1863250
Web Site: http://www.mantruckandbus.au
Sales Range: $400-449.9 Million
Emp.: 1,000
Sale of Commercial Vehicles
N.A.I.C.S.: 333310

Subsidiary (Non-US):

MAN Truck & Bus Polska Sp. z o.o. (5)
Wolica 16C, 05-830, Nadarzyn, Poland **(100%)**
Tel.: (48) 227386900
Web Site: http://www.man-mn.pl
Sales Range: $25-49.9 Million
Emp.: 250
Trucks & Buses Mfr & Importer
N.A.I.C.S.: 333924

MAN Turkiye A.S. (5)
Esenboga Haralimani Yolu 22 Km Akyurt,
6750, Ankara, Turkiye **(100%)**
Tel.: (90) 3123980220
Web Site: http://www.man.com.tr
Sales Range: $300-349.9 Million
Emp.: 2,000
Mfr of Commercial Vehicles
N.A.I.C.S.: 333310

Subsidiary (Domestic):

NEOPLAN Bus GmbH (5)
Vaihinger Str 118 122, D70567, Stuttgart,
Germany **(100%)**
Tel.: (49) 71178350
Web Site: http://www.neoplan.de
Sales Range: $300-349.9 Million
Emp.: 1,474
Bus Mfr
N.A.I.C.S.: 333310

Plant (Domestic):

MAN Truck & Bus Deutschland GmbH - Salzgitter (6)
Heinrich Bussing Strasse 33, 38239,
Salzgitter, Germany
Tel.: (49) 5341280
Web Site: http://www.neoman.de
Sales Range: $300-349.9 Million
Bus Mfr
N.A.I.C.S.: 333310

Subsidiary (US):

Navistar International Corporation (3)
2701 Navistar Dr, Lisle, IL 60532 **(16.7%)**
Tel.: (331) 332-5000
Web Site: http://www.navistar.com
Rev.: $7,503,000,000
Assets: $6,637,000,000
Liabilities: $10,459,000,000
Net Worth: ($3,822,000,000)
Earnings: ($347,000,000)
Emp.: 12,100
Fiscal Year-end: 10/31/2020
Holding Company; Trucks & Engines Mfr
N.A.I.C.S.: 336120
Stefan Palmgren *(Exec VP-Production & Logistics)*

INTERNATIONAL PUBLIC

Joint Venture (Non-US):

Mahindra Navistar Automotives Limited (4)
Marketing Department 3rd Floor Mahindra
Towers, Worli, Mumbai, 400018, Maharashtra, India
Tel.: (91) 2027473600
Web Site: http://www.mahindranavistar.com
Sales Range: $150-199.9 Million
Emp.: 800
Trucks Mfr
N.A.I.C.S.: 333924

Subsidiary (Domestic):

Monaco RV, LLC (4)
91320 Coburg Industrial Way, Coburg, OR 97408-9492 **(100%)**
Tel.: (541) 686-8011
Web Site: http://www.monaco-online.com
Sales Range: $1-4.9 Billion
Recreational Vehicle Mfr
N.A.I.C.S.: 336213

Subsidiary (Non-US):

Navistar Mexico, S. de R.L. de C.V. (4)
Ejercito Nacional 904-8 Piso, Mexico, 11510, DF, Mexico
Tel.: (52) 5552626666
Motor Vehicle Parts Mfr
N.A.I.C.S.: 336390
Rene Reyes *(Dir-HR)*

Subsidiary (Non-US):

Scania AB (3)
Vagnmakarvagen 1, SE 151 87, Sodertalje, Sweden **(70.94%)**
Tel.: (46) 8 55 38 10 00
Web Site: http://www.scania.com
Sales Range: $5-14.9 Billion
Emp.: 42,129
Truck, Bus & Diesel Engine Mfr
N.A.I.C.S.: 336120
Christian Levin *(Pres & CEO)*

Subsidiary (Domestic):

Ferruform AB (4)
Tiknikv. 1, PO Box 815, Lulea, 97125, Sweden
Tel.: (46) 92076600
Web Site: http://www.ferruform.com
Sales Range: $200-249.9 Million
Emp.: 713
Bus & Truck Mfr
N.A.I.C.S.: 336120
Lennart Wiksten *(Mng Dir)*

Subsidiary (Non-US):

Scania (Great Britain) Ltd. (4)
Delaware Drive, Tongwell, Milton Keynes,
MK15 8HB, United Kingdom
Tel.: (44) 1908210210
Web Site: http://www.scania.co.uk
Sales Range: $25-49.9 Million
Emp.: 100
Motor Vehicle Distr
N.A.I.C.S.: 423110
Martin Hay *(Dir-Sls)*

Scania Argentina S.A. (4)
Ruta Panamericana-Km34, 1615 Malvinas
Argentinas, Buenos Aires, 1615, Argentina
Tel.: (54) 3327451000
Web Site: http://www.scania.com.ar
Sales Range: $25-49.9 Million
Emp.: 2,000
Motor Vehicle Distr
N.A.I.C.S.: 423110
Jose Mannucci *(Dir Gen)*

Scania Australia Pty Ltd (4)
212-216 Northbourne Road, Private Bag 11,
Campbellfield, Melbourne, 3061, VIC, Australia
Tel.: (61) 392173300
Web Site: http://www.scania.com.au
Sales Range: $100-124.9 Million
Emp.: 400
Motor Vehicle & Engine Distr
N.A.I.C.S.: 423110
Trevor O'Brien *(Natl Mgr-Bus & Coach)*

Subsidiary (Domestic):

Scania CV AB (4)

AND PRIVATE COMPANIES — PORSCHE AUTOMOBIL HOLDING SE

Verkstadsvagen 11, Sodertalje, 15187, Sweden
Tel.: (46) 855381000
Web Site: http://www.scania.com
Sales Range: $1-4.9 Billion
Emp.: 8,000
Truck, Bus & Engine Distr
N.A.I.C.S.: 336120
Peter Harnwall *(Mgr-Svcs)*

Subsidiary (Non-US):

Scania Deutschland GmbH (4)
August-Horch-Strasse 10, 56070, Koblenz, Germany
Tel.: (49) 2618970
Web Site: http://www.scania.de
Motor Vehicle Distr
N.A.I.C.S.: 441227

Scania Suomi Oy (4)
Muonamiehentie 1, Helsinki, 00390, Finland
Tel.: (358) 10555010
Web Site: http://www.scania.fi
Sales Range: $50-74.9 Million
Emp.: 545
Commercial Truck Dealer, Maintenance & Repair Services
N.A.I.C.S.: 423830
Jukka Tiusanen *(CFO)*

Subsidiary (US):

Scania USA Inc. (4)
121 Interpark Blvd Ste 1002, San Antonio, TX 78216-1850
Tel.: (210) 403-0007
Web Site: http://www.scania.com
Sales Range: $1-9.9 Million
Emp.: 3
Truck & Automobile Mfr
N.A.I.C.S.: 336120

Subsidiary (Non-US):

V.A.G. Holding Financiere S.A. (2)
, Villers-Cotterets, France
N.A.I.C.S.: 336110

Subsidiary (Domestic):

VW AUDI Vertrieb GmbH (2)
Goerzallee 251, 14167, Berlin, Germany
Tel.: (49) 3084789730
Web Site: http://www.volkswagen.de
Sales Range: $50-74.9 Million
Emp.: 200
Motor Vehicle Distr
N.A.I.C.S.: 423110

VW AUDI Vertriebszentrum Westfalen GmbH & Co. KG (2)
Max Planck Strasse 14, Unna, 59423, Germany
Tel.: (49) 23031050
Sales Range: $125-149.9 Million
Emp.: 450
Motor Vehicle Distr
N.A.I.C.S.: 423110

VW Kraftwerk GmbH (2)
Brieffach 1012, 38436, Wolfsburg, Germany
Tel.: (49) 5361925165
Web Site: http://www.vw-kraftwerk.de
Sales Range: $150-199.9 Million
Emp.: 505
Power Sector Engineering Services
N.A.I.C.S.: 541330

VW Original Teile Logistik GmbH & Co. KG Vertriebszentrum Sudwest Franken (2)
Unterer Kirchbergweg 65, Wurzburg, 97084, Germany
Tel.: (49) 931610400
Web Site: http://www.volkswagen-otlg.de
Sales Range: $125-149.9 Million
Emp.: 300
Motor Vehicle Distr
N.A.I.C.S.: 423110

VW-Versicherungsvermittlungs-GmbH (2)
PO Box 0310, 38436, Wolfsburg, Germany
Tel.: (49) 361925477
Web Site: http://www.volkswagen.com
Sales Range: $50-74.9 Million
Emp.: 100
Insurance Services
N.A.I.C.S.: 524298

Subsidiary (Non-US):

Volkswagen (China) Investment Company Limited (2)
Volkswagen Group Ctr Unit 2 A A3 Sanlitun Rd, Chaoyang District, Beijing, 100270, China
Tel.: (86) 1065313131
Web Site: http://www.volkswagen.com.cn
Sales Range: $150-199.9 Million
Emp.: 400
Financial Services
N.A.I.C.S.: 523940

Volkswagen Argentina S.A. (2)
Delcasse y Avenida Henry Ford, Gral Pacheco, B1610BKK, Buenos Aires, Argentina
Tel.: (54) 1143179066
Web Site: http://www.volkswagen.com.ar
Motor Vehicle Distr
N.A.I.C.S.: 423120
Emilio Saenz *(Pres)*

Volkswagen Bruxelles S.A. (2)
Blvd De La Deuxieme Armee Britannique 201, Britse Tweedelegeriaan, 1190, Brussels, Belgium
Tel.: (32) 23482111
Web Site: http://www.audi.de
Sales Range: $700-749.9 Million
Emp.: 2,600
Motor Vehicle Mfr & Distr
N.A.I.C.S.: 336110
Patrick Danau *(Mng Dir & Dir-Fin)*

Volkswagen Canada, Inc. (2)
777 Bayly Street West, Ajax, L1S 7G7, ON, Canada
Tel.: (905) 428-6700
Web Site: http://www.vw.com
Sales Range: $25-49.9 Million
Emp.: 100
Motor Vehicle Mfr & Distr
N.A.I.C.S.: 336110

Volkswagen Comercio e Participacoes Ltda. (2)
Rua Volkswagen 291 9 Andar - Lado Menor, Sao Paulo, 04344-901/94, SP, Brazil
Tel.: (55) 1155825122
Web Site: http://www.vw.com.br
Sales Range: $1-4.9 Billion
Emp.: 3,000
Holding Company
N.A.I.C.S.: 551112

Subsidiary (Domestic):

Banco Volkswagen S.A. (3)
Rua Volkswagen 291, Sao Paulo, 04344-900, SP, Brazil
Tel.: (55) 155825173
Web Site: http://www.volkswagen.com.br
Provider of Financial Services
N.A.I.C.S.: 523940

VVD Volkswagen Corretagem de Seguros Ltda (3)
Str Volkswagen 291, 04393-000 5582, Sao Paulo, Brazil
Tel.: (55) 1155825074
Web Site: http://www.volkswagen.com.br
Insurance Services
N.A.I.C.S.: 524128

Volkswagen Servicos S.A. (3)
Via Anchieta KM 23.5 Sao Bernardo do Campo CPI 1048, Sao Paulo, CEP 09823-990, SP, Brazil
Tel.: (55) 1 800 019 5775
Web Site: http://www.vw.com.br
Consulting & Financial Services
N.A.I.C.S.: 541611
Decio C. deAlmeida *(CEO-Volkswagen Bank)*

Volkswagen do Brasil (3)
Estr Marginal Da Via Anchieta S N Km 23 5 Ala 4, Sao Bernardo do Campo, 9823910, SP, Brazil
Tel.: (55) 1143472355
Web Site: http://www.volkswagen.com.br
Sales Range: $75-99.9 Million
Emp.: 110
Motor Vehicle Leasing Services
N.A.I.C.S.: 532120
Thomas Schmell *(Pres)*

Volkswagen do Brasil Ltda. (3)
Via Anchieta Km 23 5, Sao Bernardo do Campo, SP, Brazil
Tel.: (55) 1143472355
Web Site: http://www.volkswagen.com.br
Sales Range: $1-4.9 Billion
Emp.: 10,000
Motor Vehicle Mfr & Distr
N.A.I.C.S.: 336110
Ralf Berckhan *(VP-Sls & Mktg)*

Subsidiary (Domestic):

Consorcio Nacional Volkswagen Ltda. (4)
Via Anchieta Km 23 5, 09700, Sao Bernardo do Campo, Brazil
Tel.: (55) 1143472355
Motor Vehicle Retailers
N.A.I.C.S.: 441110

Subsidiary (US):

Volkswagen Credit Auto Receivables Corp. (2)
3800 Hamlin Rd, Auburn Hills, MI 48326
Tel.: (248) 340-5000
Web Site: http://www.vw.com
Rev.: $111,500,000
Emp.: 70
Vehicle Credit Provider
N.A.I.C.S.: 522220

Subsidiary (Non-US):

Volkswagen Finance Luxemburg S.A. (2)
291 Route d'Arlon, 1150, Luxembourg, Luxembourg
Tel.: (352) 27 44 06 30
Financial Services
N.A.I.C.S.: 523999

Subsidiary (Non-US):

Skoda Auto a.s. (3)
Tr Vaclava Klementa 869, 293 01, Mlada Boleslav, Czech Republic
Tel.: (420) 326811111
Web Site: http://www.skoda-auto.com
Rev.: $20,205,959,220
Assets: $10,634,356,350
Liabilities: $5,809,716,090
Net Worth: $4,824,640,260
Earnings: $1,394,632,890
Emp.: 33,881
Fiscal Year-end: 12/31/2019
Motor Vehicle Mfr & Distr
N.A.I.C.S.: 336110
Michael Oeljeklaus *(Member-Mgmt Bd-Production & Logistics)*

Subsidiary (Non-US):

Skoda Auto Deutschland GmbH (4)
Geuhtenwegstrasse 15, 64331, Weiterstadt, Germany
Tel.: (49) 61501330
Web Site: http://www.skoda-auto.de
Sales Range: $50-74.9 Million
Emp.: 200
Motor Vehicle Mfr & Distr
N.A.I.C.S.: 336110

Skoda Auto India Pvt. Ltd. (4)
A-1/1 MIDC Five Star Industrial Area, Shendra, Aurangabad, 431 201, India
Tel.: (91) 2406631111
Web Site: http://www.skoda-auto.com
Sales Range: $150-199.9 Million
Emp.: 1,000
Automobile Mfr
N.A.I.C.S.: 336110
Pawel Szuflak *(Dir-Sls & Mktg)*

Skoda Auto Polska, S.A. (4)
Warszawska 349, 61 060, Poznan, Poland
Tel.: (48) 618732300
Web Site: http://www.skoda-auto.pl
Sales Range: $50-74.9 Million
Emp.: 110
Motor Vehicle Mfr & Distr
N.A.I.C.S.: 336110

SkodaAuto Slovensko s.r.o. (4)
Sabinovska 6, Bratislava, 82102, Slovakia
Tel.: (421) 248247100
Web Site: http://www.skoda-auto.sk
Motor Vehicle Mfr & Distr
N.A.I.C.S.: 336110

Subsidiary (Domestic):

Volkswagen Financial Services AG (2)
Gifhorner Strasse 57, 38112, Braunschweig, Nidersachsen, Germany
Tel.: (49) 5312123071
Web Site: http://www.vwfsag.de
Sales Range: $1-4.9 Billion
Emp.: 11,305
Financial Services Products
N.A.I.C.S.: 523999
Daniela Cavallo *(Deputy Chm-Supervisory Bd)*

Joint Venture (Domestic):

FleetCompany GmbH (3)
Keltenring 13, 82041, Oberhaching, Germany (60%)
Tel.: (49) 89 63 89 82 0
Web Site: http://www.fleetlogistics.de
Fleet Management Services
N.A.I.C.S.: 485310
Arnd K. Martin *(Mng Dir)*

Subsidiary (Domestic):

LogPay Financial Services GmbH (3)
Schwalbacher Strasse 72, 65760, Eschborn, Germany
Tel.: (49) 6196 8012 701
Web Site: http://www.logpay.de
Financial Transaction Management & Networking Services
N.A.I.C.S.: 522320

Subsidiary (Non-US):

SkoFIN S.R.O. (3)
Pekarska 6, 155 00, Prague, Czech Republic
Tel.: (420) 224992410
Web Site: http://www.skofin.cz
Sales Range: $75-99.9 Million
Emp.: 250
Vehicle Credit Provider
N.A.I.C.S.: 522220

Subsidiary (Domestic):

Volim Volkswagen Immobilien Vernietgesellschaft fur VW Audi Handlerbetriebe GmbH (3)
Gifhorner Strasse 57, 38112, Braunschweig, Germany
Tel.: (49) 2123148
Property Management
N.A.I.C.S.: 531390

Subsidiary (Domestic):

Mobil Laser Tec GmbH (4)
Heinenkamp 24, 38444, Wolfsburg, Germany
Tel.: (49) 53084049330
Web Site: http://www.mobil-lasertechnik.de
Electric Equipment Mfr
N.A.I.C.S.: 335999

Subsidiary (Domestic):

Volkswagen Bank GmbH (3)
Gifhorner Strasse 57, 38112, Braunschweig, Germany
Tel.: (49) 53121202
Web Site: http://www.volkswagenbank.de
Sales Range: $1-4.9 Billion
Emp.: 3,500
Financial Services
N.A.I.C.S.: 522320

Subsidiary (Non-US):

Volkswagen Bank (4)
Via C.I. Petitti 15, 20149, Milan, Italy
Tel.: (39) 02 330271
Web Site: http://www.vwfs.it
Sales Range: $50-74.9 Million
Emp.: 99
Automotive Leasing & Banking Services
N.A.I.C.S.: 525990

Volkswagen Bank Polska S.A. (4)
Jana Pawla II 15, 00-828, Warsaw, Poland
Tel.: (48) 225387000
Web Site: http://www.volkswagenbank.pl

PORSCHE AUTOMOBIL HOLDING SE — INTERNATIONAL PUBLIC

Porsche Automobil Holding SE—(Continued)
Sales Range: $50-74.9 Million
Emp.: 150
Financial Services
N.A.I.C.S.: 522299

Subsidiary (Domestic):

Volkswagen Leasing Polska Sp. z o.o. (5)
Lomdonz 100124, Warsaw, Poland
Tel.: (48) 225387500
Web Site: http://www.volkswagenbank.pl
Car Lending Services
N.A.I.C.S.: 522220
Nigel Kerr (Head-Sls)

Subsidiary (Non-US):

Volkswagen Dogus Tuketici Finansmani Anonim Sirketi
Polaris Plaza Kat 13 1 Ahi Evran Caddesi, Maslak, 34398, Istanbul, Turkiye
Tel.: (90) 212 335 7000
Web Site: http://www.vdf.com.tr
Vehicle Credit Services
N.A.I.C.S.: 522299
Guy Edmunds (Dir-Sls-Middle East)

Volkswagen Finance, S.A. (3)
Ava De Bruselas 34, E-28108, Madrid, Spain
Tel.: (34) 902 120 210
Web Site: http://www.vw-finance.es
Sales Range: $125-149.9 Million
Emp.: 200
Automobile Financing
N.A.I.C.S.: 525990

Volkswagen Financial Consultant Service K.K. (3)
, Tokyo, Japan
Financial Consulting Services
N.A.I.C.S.: 525990

Subsidiary (Domestic):

Volkswagen Finance Japan K.K. (4)
Gotenyama Trust Tower 17F 4-7-35 Kitashinagawa, Shinagawa-ku, Tokyo, 140-0001, Japan
Tel.: (81) 355758450
Web Site: http://www.vsj.co.jp
Sales Range: $25-49.9 Million
Emp.: 54
Vehicle Credit Provider
N.A.I.C.S.: 522210

Subsidiary (Non-US):

Volkswagen Financial Services (U.K.) Ltd.
Yeomans Drive MK14 5LR, Milton Keynes, MK14 5AN, United Kingdom
Tel.: (44) 8709006040
Web Site: http://www.vwfs.co.uk
Sales Range: $150-199.9 Million
Emp.: 420
Vehicle Credit Provider
N.A.I.C.S.: 522220
Ian Tilbrook (Dir-Fleet)

Volkswagen Financne Sluzby Slovensko s.r.o. (3)
Vajnorska 98, 831 04, Bratislava, Slovakia
Tel.: (421) 249292010
Web Site: http://www.vwfs.sk
Sales Range: $50-74.9 Million
Emp.: 90
Credit Services
N.A.I.C.S.: 522299
Busum Benobac (Mng Dir)

Volkswagen Holding Financiere S.A. (3)
11 Avenue De Boursonne, 02600, Villers-Cotterets, France
Tel.: (33) 825022525
Sales Range: $250-299.9 Million
Emp.: 900
Holding Company
N.A.I.C.S.: 551112

Subsidiary (Domestic):

Volkswagen Finance S.A. (4)
11 Ave De Boursonne, 02601, Villers-Cotterets, France
Tel.: (33) 323737400
Emp.: 350
Vehicle Credit Services
N.A.I.C.S.: 522390
Chierry Lestiaucq (Pres)

Subsidiary (Domestic):

Volkswagen Leasing GmbH (3)
Gifhorner Strasse 57, Braunschweig, 38094, Germany
Tel.: (49) 53121202
Web Site: http://www.volkswagon.de
Sales Range: $1-4.9 Billion
Emp.: 3,500
Vehicle Credit Provider
N.A.I.C.S.: 522220

Subsidiary (Non-US):

Volkswagen Leasing Thailand Co., Ltd. (3)
48/13 7th Fl Tisco Tower Bldg, Sathorn Nua Road, Bangrak, 10500, Thailand
Tel.: (66) 26380808
Credit Services
N.A.I.C.S.: 522299

Subsidiary (Domestic):

Volkswagen-Versicherungsdienst GmbH (3)
Braunschweiger Str 101, 38444, Wolfsburg, Germany
Tel.: (49) 1803224295
Web Site: http://www.vvb.de
Sales Range: $150-199.9 Million
Emp.: 400
Insurance Service Provider
N.A.I.C.S.: 524298
Herrn Joerg Waelder (Mng Dir)

Subsidiary (Non-US):

COISSA Correduria Internacional de Seguros, S.L. (4)
C Villarroel 216 218, Barcelona, 08036, Spain
Tel.: (34) 934443301
Web Site: http://www.coissa.es
Volkswagen Insurance Services
N.A.I.C.S.: 524128

Volkswagen Versicherungsdienst GmbH Osterreich (4)
Trattnerhof 1, Postfach 1000, 1011, Vienna, Austria (100%)
Tel.: (43) 1 534 00 0
Web Site: http://www.vvd.at
Emp.: 140
Auto Insurance Products & Services
N.A.I.C.S.: 524126
Temtler Maximilian (Gen Mgr)

Volkswagen-Versicherungsdienst AG (4)
Geerenstrasse 1, 8304, Wallisellen, Switzerland
Tel.: (41) 432336000
Sales Range: $25-49.9 Million
Emp.: 20
Automobile Sales Financing
N.A.I.C.S.: 522220
Urs Schmid (Mng Dir)

Subsidiary (Non-US):

Volkswagen Group Australia Pty. Ltd. (2)
24 Muir Road, Chullora, 2190, NSW, Australia
Tel.: (61) 296956000
Web Site: http://www.volkswagen.com.au
Sales Range: $25-49.9 Million
Emp.: 134
Motor Vehicle Distr
N.A.I.C.S.: 441227

Volkswagen Group Japan K.K. (2)
5-10 Akemi-cho, 4418550, Toyohashi, Aichi, Japan
Tel.: (81) 532442222
Web Site: http://www.volkswagen.jp
Sales Range: $125-149.9 Million
Emp.: 300
Motor Vehicle Distr
N.A.I.C.S.: 423110
Shigeru Shoji (Pres)

Volkswagen Group Services (2)
Ave Louise 143-1, PO Box 7, 1050, Brussels, Belgium
Tel.: (32) 26454811
Web Site: http://www.volkswagenag.de
Sales Range: $10-24.9 Million
Emp.: 50
Business Consulting Services
N.A.I.C.S.: 541611
Danny Paredis (Mng Dir)

Volkswagen Group Singapore Pte. Ltd. (2)
247 Alexandra Rd, Singapore, 159934, Singapore
Tel.: (65) 63057100
Web Site: http://www.volkswagen.com.sg
Motor Vehicle Distr
N.A.I.C.S.: 336320

Volkswagen Group United Kingdom Ltd. (2)
Yeomans Dr, Milton Keynes, MK14 5AN, United Kingdom
Tel.: (44) 1908548000
Web Site: http://www.volkswagen.co.uk
Sales Range: $25-49.9 Million
Emp.: 100
Motor Vehicle Mfr & Distr
N.A.I.C.S.: 336110
Alison Jones (Brand Dir)

Subsidiary (Domestic):

Bentley Motors Limited (3)
Pyms Ln, Crewe, CW1 3PL, Cheshire, United Kingdom
Tel.: (44) 1270255155
Web Site: http://www.bentleymotors.com
Emp.: 5,000
Motor Vehicles Mfr
N.A.I.C.S.: 336110
Andrea Baker (Head-Media Rels)

Subsidiary (Non-US):

Bentley Motor Cars International S.A. (4)
Chemin des Charmettes 7, 1003, Lausanne, Switzerland
Tel.: (41) 218230111
Distribution of Automobiles
N.A.I.C.S.: 425120

Subsidiary (Domestic):

Bentley Motors Services Limited (4)
Pyms Ln, Crewe, CW1 3PL, Cheshire, United Kingdom
Tel.: (44) 1270255155
Web Site: http://www.bentleymotors.co.uk
Group Insurance Services
N.A.I.C.S.: 524298

Subsidiary (Domestic):

Volkswagen Group Insurance & Risk Management Services (UK) Ltd. (3)
Yeomans Dr Blakelands, Milton Keynes, MK14 5AN, United Kingdom
Tel.: (44) 1908548000
Web Site: http://www.volkswagen.co.uk
Sales Range: $75-99.9 Million
Group Insurance Services
N.A.I.C.S.: 524298

Volkswagen Insurance Service (Great Britain) Limited (3)
Yeomans Dr, Milton Keynes, MK14 5AN, United Kingdom
Tel.: (44) 1908548000
Web Site: http://www.volkswagen.co.uk
Sales Range: $75-99.9 Million
Group Insurance Services
N.A.I.C.S.: 524298

Subsidiary (US):

Volkswagen Group of America, Inc. (2)
2200 Ferdinand Porsche Dr, Herndon, VA 20171
Tel.: (248) 754-5000
Web Site: http://www.volkswagengroupamerica.com
Sales Range: $300-349.9 Million
Emp.: 800
Motor Vehicle Mfr & Distr
N.A.I.C.S.: 423110
Eric Johnson (Exec Dir-Svc & Parts)

Subsidiary (Domestic):

VW Credit, Inc. (3)
1401 Franklin Blvd, Libertyville, IL 60048
Web Site: http://www.vw.com
Credit Provider for Vehicle Purchase
N.A.I.C.S.: 522291
Anthony Bandmann (Pres & CEO)

Subsidiary (Domestic):

Volkswagen Immobilien Service GmbH (2)
Poststrasse 28, Wolfsburg, 38440, Germany
Tel.: (49) 53612640
Web Site: http://www.vwimmobilien.de
Sales Range: $75-99.9 Million
Emp.: 320
Property Management Services
N.A.I.C.S.: 531210
Roland Stoeckigt (Mng Dir)

Subsidiary (Non-US):

Volkswagen Insurance Company Ltd. (2)
Volkswagen House 14 Fitzwilliam Square, Dublin, 2, Ireland
Web Site: http://www.vwfsag.de
Insurance Service Provider
N.A.I.C.S.: 524128

Volkswagen Investments Ltd. (2)
Volkswagon House 14 Fitzwilliam Sq, Dublin, 2, Ireland
Tel.: (353) 14497250
N.A.I.C.S.: 336110

Subsidiary (Domestic):

Volkswagen Logistics GmbH & Co. OHG (2)
Hesslinger Strasse 12, 38436, Wolfsburg, Germany
Tel.: (49) 53612630
Web Site: http://www.vw-transport.de
Rev: $2,030,695,420
Emp.: 1,519
Transportation Management & Logistics Services
N.A.I.C.S.: 488999

Subsidiary (Non-US):

VWT Participacoes Ltda. (3)
Estr Marg Via Anchieta Km23, Sao Bernardo do Campo, 09823-990, Brazil
Motor Vehicle Distr
N.A.I.C.S.: 336320

Subsidiary (Domestic):

Volkswagen Transport of South America Ltda. (4)
Estr Marg Via Anchieta Km23, Sao Bernardo do Campo, 09823-990, SP, Brazil
Motor Vehicle Distr
N.A.I.C.S.: 336320

Subsidiary (Domestic):

Volkswagen OTLG Ltd. (2)
Dr Rudolf-Leidig Platz 1, 34225, Kassel, Baunatal, Germany
Tel.: (49) 5614901500
Web Site: http://www.volkswagen-otlg.de
Sales Range: $125-149.9 Million
Emp.: 500
Motor Vehicle Distr
N.A.I.C.S.: 423110

Subsidiary (Non-US):

Volkswagen Poznan Sp. z o.o. (2)
Warszawska 349, 61-060, Poznan, Poland
Tel.: (48) 618714126
Web Site: http://www.volkswagen-poznan.pl
Car Bodies Mfr
N.A.I.C.S.: 336211

Subsidiary (Domestic):

Volkswagen Retail GmbH (2)
Brieffach 0918, PO Box 1966, Wolfsburg, 38436, Germany
Tel.: (49) 5361971381
Web Site: http://www.volkswagen.com
Sales Range: $25-49.9 Million
Emp.: 22
Holding Company

N.A.I.C.S.: 551112

Subsidiary (Domestic):

Auto-Lackier-Center GmbH (3)
Roehrsdorfer Allee 27, Chemnitz OT, 9247, Rohrdorf, Germany
Tel.: (49) 372252270
Sales Range: Less than $1 Million
Emp.: 30
Vehicle Painting
N.A.I.C.S.: 325510

Lackier Center Glauchau GmbH (3)
Weidensdorfer Str 12, 08371, Glauchau, Germany
Tel.: (49) 376379340
Web Site: http://www.lackiercenter-glauchau.de
Automotive Paint Spraying
N.A.I.C.S.: 811121
Ingolf Hirsch (Mng Dir)

Lackier Centrum Oberland GmbH (3)
Gewerbegebiet Leithen, Dittersdorf, 07907, Zwickau, Germany
Automotive Paint Spraying
N.A.I.C.S.: 811121

Subsidiary (Domestic):

Volkswagen Sachsen Immobilienverwaltungs GmbH (2)
Glauchauer Strasse 40, U 8058, Zwickau, Sachsen, Germany
Tel.: (49) 375550
Web Site: http://www.volkswagen-sachsen.de
Sales Range: $1-4.9 Billion
Emp.: 6,200
N.A.I.C.S.: 336110

Subsidiary (Non-US):

Volkswagen Sarajevo, d.o.o. (2)
36 Igmanska, Vogosca, Sarajevo, 71320, Bosnia & Herzegovina
Tel.: (387) 33433858
Sales Range: $75-99.9 Million
Emp.: 350
Motor Vehicle Kit Assembler & Distr
N.A.I.C.S.: 336110

Volkswagen Slovakia a.s. (2)
, Bratislava, Slovakia
Web Site: http://www.volkswagen.sk
Motor Vehicle Mfr & Distr
N.A.I.C.S.: 336110

Volkswagen de Mexico S.A. de C.V. (2)
Brieffach 2363 Km 116 Autopista, 72000, Puebla, Mexico
Tel.: (52) 2222309616
Web Site: http://www.volkswagen.com
Rev.: $1,450,700,600
Emp.: 14,057
Motor Vehicle Mfr & Distr
N.A.I.C.S.: 336110

Subsidiary (Domestic):

Volkswagen Comercial S.A. de C.V. (3)
Av Hermanos Serdan No 652, 72100, Puebla, Mexico
Tel.: (52) 12222684833
Sales Range: $50-74.9 Million
Emp.: 200
Motor Vehicle Distr
N.A.I.C.S.: 423120

Volkswagen Financial Services, S.A. de C.V. (3)
Autovisat Mexico, KM 116, 72 700, Puebla, Mexico
Tel.: (52) 18007378489
Web Site: http://www.vwfs.co.uk
Vehicle Credit Services
N.A.I.C.S.: 522390

Subsidiary (US):

Volkswagen of America Administration Center West (2)
5388 Sterling Center Dr, Westlake Village, CA 91361-4688
Tel.: (818) 575-5500
Web Site: http://www.vw.com
Automotive Distr

N.A.I.C.S.: 423110

Subsidiary (Non-US):

Volkswagen of South Africa (Pty.) Ltd. (2)
Algoa Rd, PO Box 80, Uitenhage, 6230, South Africa
Tel.: (27) 419944111
Web Site: http://www.vw.co.za
Sales Range: $700-749.9 Million
Emp.: 5,000
Motor Vehicle Mfr & Distr
N.A.I.C.S.: 336110
Petra Hoffman (Dir-Mktg)

Subsidiary (Domestic):

Volkswagen-Bildungsinstitut GmbH (2)
Reichenbacher Str 76, 8056, Zwickau, Sachsen, Germany
Tel.: (49) 3752702611
Web Site: http://www.vw-bi.de
Sales Range: $10-24.9 Million
Emp.: 70
Business School
N.A.I.C.S.: 611410

Subsidiary (Non-US):

Volkswagen-Verzekerings Service N.V. (2)
Databankweg 18, 3821 AL, Amersfoort, Netherlands
Tel.: (31) 206607272
Sales Range: $25-49.9 Million
Emp.: 50
Insurance Services
N.A.I.C.S.: 524210

Subsidiary (Domestic):

V.V.S. Verzekeringen B.V. (3)
Diemerhof 36, PO Box 53, 1110 AB, Diemen, Netherlands
Tel.: (31) 206607272
Sales Range: $50-74.9 Million
Vehicle Insurance Service Provider
N.A.I.C.S.: 524298
J. Gonker (Mng Dir)

Subsidiary (Non-US):

Volkswagen Ubezpieczenia Sp. z o.o. (3)
, Warsaw, Poland
Motor Vehicle Mfr & Distr
N.A.I.C.S.: 336110

Subsidiary (Domestic):

Wolfsburg AG (2)
Major Hirst Str 11, Niadersachen, 38442, Wolfsburg, Germany
Tel.: (49) 53618971150
Web Site: http://www.wolfsburg-ag.com
Sales Range: $600-649.9 Million
Emp.: 3,000
Consulting Services
N.A.I.C.S.: 541611
Thomas Krause (Mng Dir)

PORT CO., LTD.
Sumitomo Realty & Development Shinjuku Grand Tower 12F 8-17-1, Nishi-Shinjuku, Tokyo, 160-0023, Japan JP
Web Site: http://www.theport.jp
Year Founded: 2011
7074—(TKS)
Recruitment Marketing & Support Services
N.A.I.C.S.: 561311
Hirofumi Kasuga (CEO)

PORT MORESBY STOCK EXCHANGE LIMITED
Level 1 Harbourside West Building Stanley Esplanade, Port Moresby, Papua New Guinea
Tel.: (675) 3201980
Web Site: http://www.pomsox.com.pg
Year Founded: 1999
Stock Exchange Services
N.A.I.C.S.: 523210

PORT OF CORK COMPANY LTD.
Custom House Street, Cork, Ireland
Tel.: (353) 21 427 3125
Web Site: http://www.portofcork.ie
Year Founded: 1959
Sales Range: $25-49.9 Million
Emp.: 113
Port & Harbour Operator
N.A.I.C.S.: 488510
Brendan Keating (CEO)

Subsidiaries:

Bantry Bay Port Company Limited (1)
Wolfe Tone Square, Bantry, Cork, Ireland
Tel.: (353) 2753277
Web Site: http://www.bantrybayport.com
Cost Management Services
N.A.I.C.S.: 488310
Olan O'Keeffe (Mgr-Terminal)

PORT OF HAI PHONG JOINT STOCK COMPANY
No 8A Tran Phu street, May To Ward Ngo Quyen District, Haiphong, Vietnam
Tel.: (84) 2253859945
Web Site: https://haiphongport.com
Year Founded: 1874
PHP—(HNX)
Rev.: $88,845,575
Assets: $291,654,058
Liabilities: $55,347,792
Net Worth: $236,306,267
Earnings: $30,709,656
Emp.: 1,435
Fiscal Year-end: 12/31/23
Port & Harbor Operation Services
N.A.I.C.S.: 488310
Pham Hong Minh (Chm & Chm)

Subsidiaries:

Hai Phong Port Operations And Engineering Training One Member Limited Company (1)
No 5 CuChinhLan road, Hong Bang, Haiphong, Vietnam
Tel.: (84) 2253747913
Engineeering Services
N.A.I.C.S.: 541330

PORT OF ROTTERDAM AUTHORITY NV
World Port Center Wilhelminakade 909, 3072 AP, Rotterdam, Netherlands
Tel.: (31) 102521010
Web Site: http://www.portofrotterdam.com
Sales Range: $800-899.9 Million
Emp.: 1,100
Marine Cargo Handling Services
N.A.I.C.S.: 488310
Rutger P. M. van Slobbe (Chm-Supervisory Bd)

PORT OF TAURANGA LIMITED
Salisbury Avenue, Mount Maunganui, New Zealand
Tel.: (64) 75728899
Web Site: https://www.port-tauranga.co.nz
Year Founded: 1988
PTAUY—(OTCIQ)
Rev.: $251,751,794
Assets: $1,689,156,100
Liabilities: $413,010,167
Net Worth: $1,276,145,933
Earnings: $70,057,416
Emp.: 172
Fiscal Year-end: 06/30/23
Cargo Shipping Services
N.A.I.C.S.: 488510
David Allan Pilkington (Chm)

Subsidiaries:

C3 Limited (1)
58 Cross Road Sulphur Point, Tauranga, 3110, New Zealand
Tel.: (64) 75728972
Web Site: https://www.c3.co.nz
Emp.: 800
Marine Cargo Handling Services
N.A.I.C.S.: 488320
Chris Sutherland (Gen Mgr-Logistics-New Zealand)

Tapper Transport Limited (1)
373a Neilson Street, PO Box 13835, Onehunga, Auckland, 1061, New Zealand
Tel.: (64) 96344780
Web Site: http://www.tapper.co.nz
Sales Range: $75-99.9 Million
Emp.: 110
Sea Freight Handling & Transportation Services
N.A.I.C.S.: 488320
Martyn Freer (Mgr-Logistics)

PORT OF TYNE DISTRIBUTION LTD
Maritime House Tyne Dock, South Shields, NE34 9PT, Tyne & Wear, United Kingdom
Tel.: (44) 1914552671
Web Site: http://www.portoftyne.co.uk
Year Founded: 1999
Sales Range: $50-74.9 Million
Emp.: 489
Cargo Business Services
N.A.I.C.S.: 488320
Andrew N. Moffat (CEO)

PORT SERVICES CORPORATION SAOG
Port Sultan Qaboos, PO Box 133, 100, Muscat, Oman
Tel.: (968) 24711205
Web Site: http://www.pscoman.com
Year Founded: 1976
PSCS—(MUS)
Sales Range: $10-24.9 Million
Port Facility Services
N.A.I.C.S.: 488310
Saud Ahmed Al Nahari (CEO)

PORTAGE BIOTECH INC.
6 Adelaide Street East Suite 300, Toronto, M5C 1H6, ON, Canada
Tel.: (416) 929-1806 VG
Web Site: https://www.portagebiotech.com
Year Founded: 2013
PRTG—(NASDAQ)
Rev.: $217,000
Assets: $99,129,000
Liabilities: $23,734,000
Net Worth: $75,395,000
Earnings: ($104,666,000)
Emp.: 7
Fiscal Year-end: 03/31/23
Pharmaceuticals Mfr
N.A.I.C.S.: 325412
Ian B. Walters (Chm)

PORTAGE RESOURCES INC.
Av Benavides 441 Apto 101B, Miraflores, Lima, 18, Peru
Tel.: (51) 11 511 733 5100
Year Founded: 2006
POTG—(OTCIQ)
Mineral Exploration Services
N.A.I.C.S.: 212290
Paul Belfiore (Pres, CFO, Treas & Sec)

PORTALE SARDEGNA S.P.A.
Via Senatore Mannironi 55, 08100, Nuoro, Italy
Tel.: (39) 078430638
Web Site: http://www.portalesardegna.com
PSA—(ITA)

PORTALE SARDEGNA S.P.A.

Portale Sardegna S.p.A.—(Continued)
Sales Range: Less than $1 Million
Online Travel Agency Services
N.A.I.C.S.: 561599
Massimiliano Cossu *(CEO & CFO)*

PORTER AVIATION HOLDINGS INC.
Billy Bishop Toronto City Centre Airport, Toronto, M5V 1A1, ON, Canada
Tel.: (416) 203-8100 ON
Web Site: http://www.flyporter.com
Sales Range: $125-149.9 Million
Emp.: 850
Holding Company; Airline Operator
N.A.I.C.S.: 551112
Donald J. Carty *(Chm)*

Subsidiaries:

Porter Airlines Inc. (1)
Billy Bishop Toronto City Airport, Toronto, M5V 1A1, ON, Canada
Tel.: (416) 203-8100
Web Site: http://www.flyporter.com
Airline
N.A.I.C.S.: 481111
Robert J. Deluce *(Chm)*

PORTER DAVIS HOMES
Level 10/720 Bourke St, Docklands, 3008, VIC, Australia
Tel.: (61) 387512700
Web Site:
    http://www.porterdavis.com.au
Year Founded: 1999
Residential Building Construction Services
N.A.I.C.S.: 236116
Anthony Roberts *(Founder & Mng Dir)*

PORTER HOLDING INTERNATIONAL, INC.
36th Floor Shenzhen Development Center 2010, Luohu District, Shenzhen, 518001, Guangdong, China
Tel.: (86) 75522230666 NV
Web Site: http://www.cnporter.com
Year Founded: 2013
ULNV—(OTCEM)
Rev.: $550,249
Assets: $1,033,878
Liabilities: $3,886,944
Net Worth: ($2,853,066)
Earnings: ($2,288,484)
Emp.: 28
Fiscal Year-end: 12/31/20
Digital Financial Operator
N.A.I.C.S.: 522320
Zonghua Chen *(Chm, Pres, CEO, CFO & Treas)*

PORTERET ET GOBILLOT SA
Z I De La Republique Rue Joseph Cugnot, 86000, Poitiers, Vienne, France
Tel.: (33) 472114383
Web Site: http://www.gobillot.com
Rev.: $85,500,000
Emp.: 71
N.A.I.C.S.: 423120
Bernard Chevallier *(Personnel Dir)*

PORTERS CORPORATION
Toda Building Aoyama 3rd floor 8-5-34 Akasaka, Minato-ku, Tokyo, 107-0052, Japan
Tel.: (81) 364320017
Web Site:
    https://www.portershrbc.com
Year Founded: 2001
5126—(TKS)
Rev.: $11,251,830
Assets: $10,422,300
Liabilities: $2,708,380
Net Worth: $7,713,920
Earnings: $1,893,030
Emp.: 66
Fiscal Year-end: 12/31/23
Software Development Services
N.A.I.C.S.: 541511

PORTES NOUVELLES DIMENSIONS INC
4065 rue Alfred Laliberte, Boisbriand, J7H 1P7, QC, Canada
Tel.: (450) 430-4486
Web Site:
    http://www.portesdimensions.com
Year Founded: 1988
Rev.: $24,829,200
Emp.: 70
Door Mfr
N.A.I.C.S.: 332321
Francois Audette *(Founder)*

PORTFOLIO STRATEGIES CORP
1850 14th St SW, Calgary, T2T 3S9, AB, Canada
Tel.: (403) 252-5222
Web Site:
    http://www.portfoliostrategies.ca
Sales Range: $100-124.9 Million
Emp.: 250
Mutual Fund Services
N.A.I.C.S.: 525190
Mark S. Kent *(Founder, Pres & CEO)*

PORTICO INTERNATIONAL HOLDINGS LTD.
Unit 1301 Jing An Kerry Centre, No 1515 Nanjing West Road, Shanghai, 200040, China
Tel.: (86) 27904822 BM
Web Site: http://www.portico-intl.com
Sales Range: $300-349.9 Million
Holding Company
N.A.I.C.S.: 551112
Alfred Kai Tai Chan *(Chm)*

Subsidiaries:

Ports 1961 USA Inc. (1)
3 9th Ave 2nd Fl, New York, NY 10014
Tel.: (212) 414-1050
Web Site: http://www.ports1961.com
Garment Distr
N.A.I.C.S.: 424350

PORTIGON AG
Herzogstrasse 15, 40217, Dusseldorf, Germany
Tel.: (49) 21182601 De
Web Site: http://www.portigon.com
Year Founded: 1969
Sales Range: $5-14.9 Billion
Emp.: 4,972
Investment & Portfolio Management Services
N.A.I.C.S.: 523940
Doris Ludwig *(Vice Chm-Supervisory Bd)*

Subsidiaries:

Portigon AG - Milan Branch (1)
Via Canova 36 38 40 Markato 5, 20145, Milan, Italy
Tel.: (39) 02349741
Web Site: http://www.portigon.com
Investment & Portfolio Management Services
N.A.I.C.S.: 523940

Portigon AG - Sydney Branch (1)
Level 8 16 Spring St, Sydney, 2000, Australia
Tel.: (61) 297779900
Sales Range: $50-74.9 Million
Emp.: 10
Investment & Portfolio Management Services
N.A.I.C.S.: 523940

Portigon AG - Tokyo Branch (1)
Roppongi Hills Mori Tower 37th Fl, 6-10-1 Roppongi, Tokyo, 106 6137, Japan
Tel.: (81) 364398000
Web Site: http://www.westlb.co.jp
Sales Range: $75-99.9 Million
Emp.: 100
Investment & Portfolio Management Services
N.A.I.C.S.: 523940

Portigon Securities Inc. (1)
7 World Trade Ctr 250 Greenwich St, New York, NY 10007
Tel.: (212) 852-6000
Web Site: http://www.portigon.com
Sales Range: $200-249.9 Million
Emp.: 300
International Banking Services
N.A.I.C.S.: 523150

Portigon UK Limited (1)
Woolgate Exchange 25 Basinghall Street, London, EC2V 5HA, United Kingdom
Tel.: (44) 20 7020 2000
Web Site: http://www.portigon.com
Sales Range: $700-749.9 Million
Emp.: 1,400
Banking Services
N.A.I.C.S.: 522110

RN Beteiligungs-GmbH i.L. (1)
Am Hauptbahnhof 2, Stuttgart, 70173, Baden-Wurttemberg, Germany
Tel.: (49) 711 1270
Business Management & Financial Services
N.A.I.C.S.: 523999

Schloss Krickenbeck GmbH (1)
Schloss Krickenbeck Poelvenn, 41334, Nettetal, Germany
Tel.: (49) 2642405250
Web Site: http://www.chateauform.com
Emp.: 50
Castle & Guest House Services
N.A.I.C.S.: 721199

PORTLAND INVESTMENT COUNSEL INC.
1375 Kerns Road Ste 100, PO Box 5104, Burlington, L7P 4V7, ON, Canada
Tel.: (905) 331-4242
Web Site: http://www.portlandic.com
Emp.: 100
Investment & Fund Management Services
N.A.I.C.S.: 523940
Michael A. Lee-Chin *(Founder, Chm & CEO)*

Subsidiaries:

Portland Holdings Limited (1)
1375 Kerns Road Suite 100, Burlington, L7P 4V7, ON, Canada
Tel.: (905) 331-4292
Web Site: http://www.portlandholdings.com
Sales Range: $25-49.9 Million
Investment Holding Company
N.A.I.C.S.: 551112
Michael A. Lee-Chin *(Chm)*

Holding (Non-US):

National Commercial Bank Jamaica Limited (2)
32 Trafalgar Road, Kingston, 10, Jamaica
Tel.: (876) 9299050
Web Site: http://www.jncb.com
Sales Range: Less than $1 Million
Banking Services
N.A.I.C.S.: 522110
Patrick A. A. Hylton *(Chm)*

Subsidiary (Non-US):

NCB (Cayman) Limited (3)
Phase II Cricket Square 171 Elgin Avenue, PO Box 3110, Georgetown, KY1-1205, Grand Cayman, Cayman Islands
Tel.: (345) 949 8002
Web Site: http://www.ncbcayman.com
Emp.: 5
Banking Services
N.A.I.C.S.: 522110

Subsidiary (Domestic):

NCB Capital Markets Ltd. (3)
32 Trafalgar Road, Kingston, 10, Jamaica
Tel.: (876) 960 7108
Web Site: http://www.ncbcapitalmarkets.com
Investment Services
N.A.I.C.S.: 523940
Alessandro Sax *(Portfolio Mgr-Cayman Islands)*

NCB Insurance Company Limited (3)
32 Trafalgar Road, Kingston, 10, Jamaica
Tel.: (876) 960 7108
Web Site: http://www.ncbinsurance.com
Insurance Services
N.A.I.C.S.: 524113
Vernon James *(Gen Mgr)*

NCB Jamaica (Nominees) Ltd. (3)
32 Trafalgar Road, Kingston, 10, Jamaica
Tel.: (876) 929 9050
Financial Services to Corporations
N.A.I.C.S.: 561499

West Indies Trust Co. Limited. (3)
32 Trafalgar Road, Kingston, 10, Jamaica
Tel.: (876) 929 9050
Trust & Will Management Services
N.A.I.C.S.: 523991

Portland Private Equity, L.P. (1)
1375 Kerns Road Suite 100, Burlington, L7P 4V7, ON, Canada
Tel.: (905) 331-4242
Web Site: http://www.portlandpe.com
Private Equity Fund Management Services
N.A.I.C.S.: 523940
Kip Thompson *(Mng Partner)*

PORTLAND STREET HONDA
36 Baker Drive, Dartmouth, B2W 6K1, NS, Canada
Tel.: (902) 435-3330
Web Site:
    http://www.portlandstreethonda.com
Year Founded: 1993
Rev.: $34,256,310
Emp.: 75
New & Used Car Dealers
N.A.I.C.S.: 441110
Dave McPherson *(Mgr-Fin)*

PORTLOGIC SYSTEMS INC.
2 Toronto Street Suite 209, Toronto, M5C 2B5, ON, Canada
Tel.: (437) 886-2432
Web Site:
    http://www.portlogicsystems.com
Year Founded: 2006
Sales Range: Less than $1 Million
Emp.: 1
Mobile & Internet Software Development Services
N.A.I.C.S.: 541511

PORTMEIRION GROUP PLC
London Road, Stoke-on-Trent, ST4 7QQ, Staffordshire, United Kingdom
Tel.: (44) 1782744721 UK
Web Site:
    https://www.portmeiriongroup.com
PMP—(LSE)
Rev.: $143,942,759
Assets: $128,394,150
Liabilities: $44,287,469
Net Worth: $84,106,681
Earnings: $4,400,371
Emp.: 866
Fiscal Year-end: 12/31/21
Ceramic Housewares Mfr
N.A.I.C.S.: 327110
Philip E. Atherton *(Dir-Sls & Mktg)*

Subsidiaries:

Nambe LLC (1)
810 Calle Mejia Ste 103, Santa Fe, NM 87501
Web Site: https://www.nambe.com
Interior Design Services
N.A.I.C.S.: 541410

Portmeirion Canada Inc. (1)
20 Voyager Court South, Toronto, M9W 5M7, ON, Canada (100%)

AND PRIVATE COMPANIES

Tel.: (416) 675-3755
Web Site: http://www.portmeirion.ca
Sales Range: $50-74.9 Million
Pottery & Accessories Marketer & Distr
N.A.I.C.S.: 423220
Robert Burke (Pres)

Portmeirion Group Designs, LLC (1)
105 Progress Ln, Waterbury, CT 06705
Web Site: https://www.portmeirion.com
Interior Design Services
N.A.I.C.S.: 541410

Portmeirion Group UK Limited (1)
London Road, Stoke-on-Trent, ST4 7QQ,
Staffordshire, United Kingdom
Tel.: (44) 1782 744721
Tableware & Kitchenware Mfr
N.A.I.C.S.: 327110

Portmeirion Group USA, Inc. (1)
105 Progress Ln, Waterbury, CT 06705-3830
Tel.: (203) 729-8255
Web Site: http://www.portmeirion.com
Dinnerware Retailer
N.A.I.C.S.: 424490

Portmeirion Potteries Limited (1)
London Road, Stoke-on-Trent, ST4 7QQ,
United Kingdom (100%)
Tel.: (44) 1782744721
Sales Range: $25-49.9 Million
Emp.: 500
Pottery Mfr
N.A.I.C.S.: 327110

Subsidiary (Domestic):

Portmeirion Enterprises Limited (2)
London Road, Stoke-on-Trent, ST4 7QQ,
United Kingdom (100%)
Tel.: (44) 1782744721
Web Site: http://www.portmeirion.com
Holding Company
N.A.I.C.S.: 551112

PORTO AVIATION GROUP S.P.A.
Via Confalonieri 22, Cremella, 23894,
Lecco, LC, Italy
Tel.: (39) 0399212128
Web Site:
https://www.portoaviationgroup.com
Year Founded: 1994
PAG—(EUR)
Aircraft Mfr
N.A.I.C.S.: 336411
Alberto Rodolfo Porto (Pres)

PORTO EDITORA LDA.
Rua da Restauracao 365, 4099-023,
Porto, Portugal
Tel.: (351) 22 608 83 00   PT
Web Site: http://www.portoeditora.pt
Sales Range: $100-124.9 Million
Emp.: 185
Educational & Reference Book &
Multimedia Product Publisher
N.A.I.C.S.: 513130
Antonio Cardoso (Dir-Fin)

Subsidiaries:

Circulo de Leitores (1)
Rua Prof Jorge da Silva Horta 1, 1500-499,
Lisbon, Portugal (100%)
Tel.: (351) 21 762 60 00
Web Site: http://www.circuloleitores.pt
Book Club Services
N.A.I.C.S.: 459210
Paulo Oliveira (Chm)

PORTO SEGURO SA
Rua Barao De Piracicaba 618 11th
Floor Campos Eliseos, Sao Paulo,
01216-012, Brazil
Tel.: (55) 1123937109
Web Site:
http://www.portoseguro.com.br
PSSA3—(BRAZ)
Rev.: $5,790,936,190
Assets: $7,908,260,100
Liabilities: $5,674,156,729
Net Worth: $2,234,103,371
Earnings: $413,803,282
Emp.: 14,000
Fiscal Year-end: 12/31/23
Insurance Services
N.A.I.C.S.: 524126
Roberto De Souza Santos (CEO)

PORTOBELLO CAPITAL ADVISORS SL
c/Almagro 36 planta 2, 28010, Madrid, Spain
Tel.: (34) 91 431 80 71   ES
Web Site:
http://www.portobellocapital.es
Emp.: 19
Privater Equity Firm
N.A.I.C.S.: 523999
Carolina Alvarez (Office Mgr)

Subsidiaries:

Industrias Alimentarias de Navarra S.A.U. (1)
Poligono Penalfons s/n, 31330, Villafranca,
Navarra, Spain
Tel.: (34) 948843360
Web Site: http://www.grupoian.com
Preserved Vegetables Mfr & Distr
N.A.I.C.S.: 311411

Ramon Sabater, S.A.U. (1)
Av Alto de las Atalayas 231 Apartado de
Correos 1, 30110, Cabezo de Torres, Murcia, Spain
Tel.: (34) 96 887 99 00
Web Site: http://www.rsabater.com
Spice, Herbs & Other Food Products Mfr & Distr
N.A.I.C.S.: 311942
Jose Sabater (CEO)

PORTOBELLO S.P.A.
Piazzale della stazione snc, Pomezia
Santa Palomba Industrial Area, 71,
Rome, Italy
Tel.: (39) 062294725
Web Site:
https://www.portobellospa.com
Year Founded: 2016
POR—(ITA)
Rev.: $114,271,732
Assets: $128,461,441
Liabilities: $115,095,980
Net Worth: $13,365,461
Earnings: $(49,542,149)
Emp.: 343
Fiscal Year-end: 12/31/23
Media Advertising Services
N.A.I.C.S.: 541840
Pietro Peligra (Chm)

PORTOFINO RESOURCES INC.
Suite 520 470 Granville St, Vancouver, V6C 1V5, BC, Canada
Tel.: (604) 683-1991   BC
Web Site:
https://portofinoresources.com
Year Founded: 2011
PFFOF—(OTCQB)
Assets: $261,435
Liabilities: $559,048
Net Worth: $(297,612)
Earnings: $(1,828,178)
Fiscal Year-end: 05/31/23
Metal Mining
N.A.I.C.S.: 212290
David G. Tafel (CEO)

PORTOLAN COMMERCE SOLUTIONS GMBH
Renntalstrasse 20, Ilsfeld, 74360,
Germany
Tel.: (49) 70629190   De
Web Site: http://www.portolancs.com
Year Founded: 1990
Sales Range: $10-24.9 Million
Emp.: 50
Business Management Software & Services
N.A.I.C.S.: 513210
Joachim Nurk (Mng Dir)

PORTON PHARMA SOLUTIONS LTD.
No 7 Yuntu Road, Beibei District,
Chongqing, 400714, China
Tel.: (86) 2365936900
Web Site:
http://www.portonpharma.com
Year Founded: 2005
300363—(CHIN)
Rev.: $987,685,920
Assets: $1,424,258,316
Liabilities: $515,548,800
Net Worth: $908,709,516
Earnings: $281,563,776
Emp.: 5,000
Fiscal Year-end: 12/31/22
Chemicals Mfr
N.A.I.C.S.: 325998
Nianfeng Ju (Chm, CEO & Gen Mgr)

Subsidiaries:

J-Star Research, Inc. (1)
3001 Hadley Rd Ste 1-5A, South Plainfield,
NJ 07080
Tel.: (908) 791-9100
Web Site: https://www.jstar-research.com
Rev.: $4,000,000
Emp.: 30
Fiscal Year-end: 12/31/2006
Commercial Nonphysical Research
N.A.I.C.S.: 541720

Porton Biologics Ltd. (1)
Building 3 Ascendas Park No 388 Xinping
Street, Suzhou Industrial Park, Jiangsu,
215021, China
Tel.: (86) 5128885038
Pharmaceuticals Product Mfr
N.A.I.C.S.: 325412

PORTS OF AUCKLAND LTD.
Ports of Auckland Building 1 Sunderland Street Mechanics Bay, Auckland,
1010, New Zealand
Tel.: (64) 9 348 5000
Web Site: http://www.poal.co.nz
Year Founded: 1988
Rev.: $166,187,127
Assets: $958,936,282
Liabilities: $423,106,923
Net Worth: $535,829,360
Earnings: $36,125,044
Emp.: 500
Fiscal Year-end: 06/30/19
Port Operations
N.A.I.C.S.: 488310
Wayne Thompson (Deputy CEO & CFO)

PORTSERCO LOGISTICS JOINT STOCK COMPANY
59 Ba Dinh p Thach Thang, Hai
Chau district, Da Nang, Vietnam
Tel.: (84) 2363894717
Web Site: https://www.portserco.com
Year Founded: 1993
PRC—(HNX)
Rev.: $4,157,039
Assets: $2,344,074
Liabilities: $905,617
Net Worth: $1,438,457
Earnings: $4,738
Fiscal Year-end: 12/31/23
Freight Transportation & Marine
Cargo Handling Services
N.A.I.C.S.: 483111
Nguyen Le Minh (Deputy Chm & Mgr)

PORVAIR PLC

PORVAIR PLC
7 Regis Place Bergen Way, King's
Lynn, PE30 2JN, Norfolk, United
Kingdom
Tel.: (44) 1553765500   UK
Web Site: https://www.porvair.com
Year Founded: 1982
PRV—(LSE)
Rev.: $224,077,658
Assets: $249,611,713
Liabilities: $70,823,679
Net Worth: $178,788,034
Earnings: $20,330,999
Emp.: 976
Fiscal Year-end: 11/30/23
Filtration & Separation Equipment Mfr
N.A.I.C.S.: 334513
Ben Stocks (CEO)

Subsidiaries:

J.G. Finneran Associates, Inc. (1)
3600 Reilly Ct, Vineland, NJ 08360
Tel.: (856) 696-3605
Laboratory & Medical Equipment Mfr
N.A.I.C.S.: 339112

Porvair Filtration Group Ltd (1)
1 Concorde Close, Segensworth, Fareham,
PO15 5RT, Hampshire, United Kingdom
Tel.: (44) 1489864330
Sales Range: $100-124.9 Million
Emp.: 200
Metals Filtration Services
N.A.I.C.S.: 213114
Tom Liddell (Mng Dir)

Subsidiary (US):

Porvair Filtration Group Inc. (2)
301 Business Ln, Ashland, VA 23005
Tel.: (804) 550-1600
Filter Equipment Mfr & Whslr
N.A.I.C.S.: 333413

Porvair Filtration India Private Limited (1)
401 Centrum IT Park Plot No C-3 Wagle
Estate, Thane, 400604, India
Tel.: (91) 2220811148
Aerospace Material Mfr
N.A.I.C.S.: 336413
Harish Shah (Mgr-Sls-Natl)

Porvair Sciences Limited (1)
7 Regis Place Bergen Way, Kings Lynn,
Norfolk, PE30 2JN, Surrey, United Kingdom
Tel.: (44) 1372824290
Web Site: https://www.porvairsciences.com
Sales Range: $25-49.9 Million
Emp.: 5
Biotechnological Products Research & Mfr
N.A.I.C.S.: 541714

Porvair Sciences Limited (1)
Clywedog Road South, Wrexham Industrial
Estate, Wrexham, LL13 9XS, United Kingdom
Tel.: (44) 1978661144
Web Site: https://www.microplates.com
Sales Range: $25-49.9 Million
Emp.: 60
Vacuum Manifolds, Sealers, Evaporators & Microtiter Plates
N.A.I.C.S.: 333998

Porvair Selee Filtration Technology (Hubei) Company Limited (1)
Chengdong Area Square Industrial Park,
Xiaonan Economic Development Zone
North District, Xiaogan, 432000, China
Tel.: (86) 7122886575
Aerospace Material Mfr
N.A.I.C.S.: 336413

Rohasys B.V. (1)
Provincienbaan 4, 5121 DL, Rijen, Netherlands
Tel.: (31) 161240152
Web Site: https://www.rohasys.com
Laboratory Product Mfr
N.A.I.C.S.: 334516

SEAL Analytical GmbH (1)
Werkstrasse 5, 22844, Norderstedt, Germany
Tel.: (49) 40609292920
Analytical Equipments Mfr & Whslr
N.A.I.C.S.: 423490

SEAL Analytical Inc (1)
6501 W Donges Bay Rd, Mequon, WI
53092

PORVAIR PLC

Porvair plc—(Continued)
Tel.: (262) 241-7900
Sales Range: $25-49.9 Million
Emp.: 12
Analytical Equipment Mfr
N.A.I.C.S.: 423490

Seal Analytical Limited (1)
Porvair Sciences Clywedog Road South, South Wrexham Industrial Estate, Wrexham, LL13 9XS, United Kingdom
Tel.: (44) 1978807273
Web Site: https://www.seal-analytical.com
Aerospace Material Mfr
N.A.I.C.S.: 336413
Lalicia Potter (Gen Mgr)

Selee Corporation
700 Shepherd St, Hendersonville, NC 28792
Tel.: (828) 697-2411
Web Site: https://selee.com
Sales Range: $100-124.9 Million
Emp.: 140
Metals Filtration Services
N.A.I.C.S.: 213114

Subsidiary (Non-US):

Porvair Selee Advanced Materials Wuhan Co Ltd (2)
A115 116 Hanzheng St 21 Jiefang Ave, Wuhan, 430034, China
Tel.: (86) 2783311025
Web Site: http://www.selee.com
Sales Range: $25-49.9 Million
Emp.: 50
Metals Filtration Services
N.A.I.C.S.: 213114

PORWAL AUTO COMPONENTS LTD.
209 and 215 Industrial Area Sector-1, Distt Dhar, Pithampur, 454 775, MP, India
Tel.: (91) 7292405101
Web Site: http://www.porwalauto.com
532933—(BOM)
Rev.: $16,863,066
Assets: $9,101,421
Liabilities: $2,038,163
Net Worth: $7,063,258
Earnings: ($123,686)
Emp.: 399
Fiscal Year-end: 03/31/23
Automotive Components Mfr
N.A.I.C.S.: 336390
Surendra Utsavlal Jain (Chm & CEO)

POS MALAYSIA BERHAD
Tingkat 8 Ibu Pejabat Pos Kompleks Dayabumi, 50670, Kuala Lumpur, Malaysia
Tel.: (60) 322672267
Web Site: https://www.pos.com.my
POS—(KLS)
Rev.: $577,234,845
Assets: $784,457,438
Liabilities: $501,464,453
Net Worth: $282,992,985
Earnings: ($76,234,455)
Emp.: 22,000
Fiscal Year-end: 12/31/20
Mail Services & Logistics
N.A.I.C.S.: 541614
Charles Brewer (CEO-Grp)

Subsidiaries:

Datapos (M) Sdn. Bhd. (1)
No 2 Jalan P/9A Kawasan Perusahaan Seksyen 13, 43650, Bandar Baru Bangi, Selangor, Malaysia
Tel.: (60) 389259286
Web Site: http://www.pos.com.my
Business Support Services
N.A.I.C.S.: 561439

PSH Express Sdn. Bhd. (1)
Level 4 Kompleks Dayabumi Pos Malaysia Jalan Sultan Hishamuddin, 50050, Kuala Lumpur, Malaysia
Tel.: (60) 322672260
Web Site: http://www.asiaxpress.net.my

Sales Range: $10-24.9 Million
Emp.: 30
Courier Service
N.A.I.C.S.: 492110

Pos Digicert Sdn. Bhd. (1)
8-3A-02 Star Central Lingkaran Cyberpoint Timur, 63000, Cyberjaya, Selangor Darul Ehsan, Malaysia
Tel.: (60) 388008008
Web Site: https://www.posdigicert.com.my
Sales Range: $25-49.9 Million
Emp.: 76
Digital Certification Services
N.A.I.C.S.: 518210

POSAVINA A.D.
Danka Mitrova 2, 78240, Srbac, Bosnia & Herzegovina
Tel.: (387) 51740018
PSVN—(BANJ)
Sales Range: Less than $1 Million
Emp.: 2
Grocery Store Operator
N.A.I.C.S.: 445110
Slobodan Dukic (Pres & Member-Mgmt Bd)

POSCO HOLDINGS INC.
440 Teheran-ro, Gangnam-gu, Seoul, 06194, Korea (South)
Tel.: (82) 234570114 KR
Web Site: https://www.posco-inc.com:4453
Year Founded: 1968
PKX—(NYSE)
Rev.: $59,738,870,436
Assets: $78,187,254,923
Liabilities: $31,974,583,501
Net Worth: $46,212,671,421
Earnings: $1,429,703,118
Emp.: 65,350
Fiscal Year-end: 12/31/23
Iron, Steel & Rolled Products Mfr & Distr
N.A.I.C.S.: 331110
Hag-Dong Kim (Sr Exec VP & Head-Steel Production & Tech Div)

Subsidiaries:

KOBRASCO (1)
Av Dante Michelini No 5500 Jardim Camburi, Ponta do Tubarao, Vitoria, 29090-900, ES, Brazil
Tel.: (55) 2733335164   (50%)
Web Site: http://www.posco.com
Metal Pellet Mfr & Distr
N.A.I.C.S.: 332991

Myanmar POSCO Steel Co., Ltd. (1)
Plot 22 No 3 Trunk Rd Pynmabin Industrial Complex Mi, Yangon, Myanmar   (100%)
Tel.: (95) 1703528
Web Site: http://www.posco.com
Sales Range: $50-74.9 Million
Emp.: 100
N.A.I.C.S.: 324199

POS-HiMetal Co., Ltd. (1)
868-11 Geumho-dong, Gwangyang, 545-826, Jeollanam-do, Korea (South)
Tel.: (82) 61 790 0224
Web Site: http://www.poshimetal.com
Ferromanganese Mfr
N.A.I.C.S.: 331110

POS-MPC S.A. de C.V. (1)
Carretera 190 Acceso al Aeropuerto Hermanos Serdan Km O 55, Ana Xalmimilulco, Huejotzingo, 74169, Mexico
Tel.: (52) 22 7102 6104 5
Web Site: http://www.posco.com
Emp.: 130
Seal Products Distr
N.A.I.C.S.: 423510

POS-NP Pty. Ltd. (1)
Ste C Level 49 1 Farrer Pl, Sydney, 2000, NSW, Australia
Tel.: (61) 292412345
Sales Range: $25-49.9 Million
Emp.: 14
Steel Product Distr
N.A.I.C.S.: 423510

Soo-Cheol Shin (Mng Dir)

POS-Ore Pty. Ltd. (1)
Suite C Level 49 Governor Phillip Tower 1 Farrer Place, Sydney, 2000, NSW, Australia
Tel.: (61) 292412345
Sales Range: $50-74.9 Million
Emp.: 15
Iron Ore Mining Services
N.A.I.C.S.: 212210
Sc Shin (Mng Dir)

POS-Qingdao Coil Center Co., Ltd. (1)
HuaXian-Lu DanShan Industrial Park, ChengYang-Qu, Qingdao, Shandong, China
Tel.: (86) 532 8965 6001
Web Site: http://www.posco.com
Steel Products Mfr
N.A.I.C.S.: 331110

POS-Thai Steel Service Center Co., Ltd. (1)
700 453 Moo 7 Bangpakong Industrial Park 2, T Donghuaroh A Muang, Chon Buri, 20000, Thailand
Tel.: (66) 38454200   (18.5%)
Web Site: http://www.posco.com
Sales Range: Less than $1 Million
Emp.: 80
Steel Processing Mill
N.A.I.C.S.: 331110

POSCO (Liaoning) Automotive Processing Center Ltd. (1)
No 111 Jianshe Rd, Shenbei New Dist, Shenyang, 110042, China
Tel.: (86) 2429875980
Automotive Steel Parts Mfr
N.A.I.C.S.: 336390

POSCO (Suzhou) Automotive Processing Center Co., Ltd. (1)
Pengqiao Road Cao'an Development Zone, Huaqiao, Kunshan, 215334, Jiangsu, China
Tel.: (86) 512 5760 5951
Web Site: http://www.posco.com
Sales Range: $50-74.9 Million
Emp.: 25
Automobile Parts Mfr
N.A.I.C.S.: 336390

POSCO (Thailand) Co., Ltd. - Wellgrow Factory 3 (1)
128/1 Moo 5 Wellgrow Industrial Estate, T Bangsamak, Bang Pakong, 24180, Chachoengsao, Thailand
Tel.: (66) 3854 5300 99
Sales Range: $50-74.9 Million
Emp.: 23
Automobile Parts Mfr
N.A.I.C.S.: 336390
Jong Geun Kim (Gen Mgr)

POSCO A&C Co., Ltd. (1)
682-20 Yeoksam-dong, Gangnam-gu, Seoul, 135-080, Korea (South)
Tel.: (82) 2 2018 7700
Web Site: http://www.poscoanc.com
Sales Range: $150-199.9 Million
Emp.: 800
Construction Engineering Services
N.A.I.C.S.: 541330

POSCO AST Co., Ltd. (1)
No 603 Seonggok-Dong, Danwon-Gu, Ansan, 425833, Kyungki-Do, Korea (South)
Tel.: (82) 3 1490 5114
Web Site: http://www.poscoast.com
Sales Range: $125-149.9 Million
Emp.: 325
Stainless Steel Sheet Mfr & Distr
N.A.I.C.S.: 331221
Tai-Han Yun (CEO)

POSCO America Corporation (1)
2 Executive Dr No 805, Fort Lee, NJ 07024-3308   (100%)
Tel.: (201) 585-3060
Sales Range: $50-74.9 Million
Emp.: 25
Steel Trade
N.A.I.C.S.: 423510
Sean You (Mgr-Sls)

Joint Venture (Domestic):

USS-POSCO Industries (2)
900 Loveridge Rd, Pittsburg, CA 94565-2808

INTERNATIONAL PUBLIC

Tel.: (925) 439-6000
Web Site: http://www.usspusco.com
Steel Mills
N.A.I.C.S.: 331110
Michael Piekut (Pres)

POSCO Asia Co., Ltd. (1)
18 Harbour Road Central Plaza Room 5508, Wanchai, China (Hong Kong)   (100%)
Tel.: (852) 28278787
Web Site: http://www.posco.com
Sales Range: $25-49.9 Million
Emp.: 20
Steel Trade
N.A.I.C.S.: 331513

POSCO Australia Pty. Ltd. (1)
Ste C Level 49 Governor Philip Tower, Sydney, 2000, NSW, Australia   (100%)
Tel.: (61) 292412345
Sales Range: $50-74.9 Million
Emp.: 12
Coal Mining
N.A.I.C.S.: 213113
Sungoom Yoon (Mng Dir)

POSCO Canada Ltd. (1)
2350 650 W Georgia St, PO Box 11617, Vancouver, V6B 4N9, BC, Canada   (100%)
Tel.: (604) 669-6689
Web Site: http://www.posco.com
Sales Range: $50-74.9 Million
Emp.: 5
Coal Mining
N.A.I.C.S.: 213113

POSCO China Dalian Plate Processing Center Ltd. (1)
Xingang Village Economic & Technological Development Zone, Changxing Island, Dalian, China
Tel.: (86) 411 3911 0910
Web Site: http://www.posco-china.com
Sales Range: $25-49.9 Million
Emp.: 80
Rolled Steel Plate Mfr
N.A.I.C.S.: 331210

POSCO Coated & Color Steel Co., Ltd. (1)
173 Cheolgang-ro Dong Nam-Gu, Pohang, Gyeongsangbuk-do, Korea (South)
Tel.: (82) 542806114
Web Site: http://www.poscocnc.com
Rev.: $892,270,786
Assets: $411,607,369
Liabilities: $156,882,169
Net Worth: $254,725,199
Earnings: $17,019,480
Emp.: 422
Fiscal Year-end: 12/31/2022
Steel Mfrs
N.A.I.C.S.: 331110
Yun Yang Su (CEO)

POSCO E&C Co., Ltd. (1)
568-1 Goedong-Dong, Nam-Gu, Pohang, 790-300, Kyungbuk, Korea (South)
Tel.: (82) 54 223 6114
Web Site: http://www.poscoenc.com
Construction Engineering Services
N.A.I.C.S.: 541330

POSCO E&E Co., Ltd. (1)
892 Posco Center Daechi 4-Dong, Gangnam-gu, Seoul, Korea (South)
Tel.: (82) 2 3469 6252
Web Site: http://www.poscoene.co.kr
Electric Power Generation Services
N.A.I.C.S.: 221118

POSCO Engineering Co., Ltd. (1)
9-3 Sunae-Dong, Bundang-Gu, Seongnam, 463-825, Korea (South)
Tel.: (82) 3 1738 0114
Web Site: http://www.poscoengineering.com
Construction Engineering Services
N.A.I.C.S.: 541330

POSCO Future M Co., Ltd (1)
110 Shinhang-ro Nam-gu, Pohang, Gyeongbuk, Korea (South)
Tel.: (82) 542900114
Rev.: $2,532,569,422
Assets: $3,556,944,200
Liabilities: $1,523,899,762
Net Worth: $2,033,044,438
Earnings: $90,710,527
Emp.: 1,951

AND PRIVATE COMPANIES

POSCO HOLDINGS INC.

Fiscal Year-end: 12/31/2022
Construction Materials Mfr
N.A.I.C.S.: 327120
Kyungzoon Min (CEO)

POSCO International Osaka (1)
POSCO Osaka Bldg 2nd And 3rd Fl 3-7
Nanba 2-Chome, Chou-Ku, Osaka, 542
0076, Japan (100%)
Tel.: (81) 725314577
Steel Trade
N.A.I.C.S.: 331513

POSCO Investment Co., Ltd. (1)
Rm 5401 Central Plz 18 Harbour Rd, Wanchai, China (Hong Kong) (100%)
Tel.: (852) 28027188
Web Site: http://www.posco-investments.co.hk
Sales Range: Less than $1 Million
Emp.: 7
Financing
N.A.I.C.S.: 522299

POSCO Ltd. - Pohang Works (1)
5 Dongchon Dong, Pohang, 40044, Kyongsangbuk Do, Korea (South)
Tel.: (82) 5622200114
Sales Range: $1-4.9 Billion
Emp.: 9,000
Steel Works
N.A.I.C.S.: 331513

POSCO M-TECH Co., Ltd. (1)
131 Hyeongsangangbuk-ro, Nam-gu, Pohang, 37835, Gyeongsangbuk-do, Korea (South)
Tel.: (82) 542808114
Web Site: https://www.poscomtech.com
Rev.: $262,448,924
Assets: $122,508,183
Liabilities: $34,602,698
Net Worth: $87,905,485
Earnings: $3,701,088
Emp.: 1,029
Fiscal Year-end: 12/31/2022
Engineeering Services
N.A.I.C.S.: 541330
Chi-Young Song (CEO)

Subsidiary (Domestic):

9Digit Co., Ltd. (2)
20BL-10 L Nonhyn-dong 428-9, Namdonggu, Incheon, Korea (South)
Tel.: (82) 32 817 2310
Web Site: http://www.9digit.co.kr
Metal Products Mfr
N.A.I.C.S.: 332999

POSCO MC Materials Co., Ltd. (1)
2408 Jecheol-ro, Gwangyang, 57812, Jeonnam, Korea (South)
Tel.: (82) 617608964
Web Site: https://www.poscomcm.com
Emp.: 181
Needle Coke Mfr & Distr
N.A.I.C.S.: 339993

POSCO P&S Co., Ltd. (1)
Posteel Tower 735 - 3 Yeoksam-Dong, Kangnam-Gu, Seoul, 135923, Korea (South)
Tel.: (82) 234695000
Web Site: http://www.poscopns.com
Steel Product Mfr & Distr
N.A.I.C.S.: 331110
Young-Tae Kwon (Pres)

POSCO TMC Co., Ltd. (1)
115 Gunsu1-gil Jiksan-eup Cheonan-si, Cheonan, Chungnam, Korea (South)
Tel.: (82) 41 580 1331
Web Site: http://www.poscotmc.com
Industrial Motor Core Mfr
N.A.I.C.S.: 332999

Plant (Non-US):

POSCO TMC Co., Ltd - Chinese Factory (2)
Fangda Street Longpu Road Suzhou Industrial Park, Suzhou, China
Tel.: (86) 512 8818 8906
Compressor Motor Core Mfr
N.A.I.C.S.: 332999

Plant (Domestic):

POSCO TMC Co., Ltd. - Pohang Factory (2)
1166 Haean-ro Heunghae-eup, Buk-gu, Pohang, 711941, Gyeongsangbuk, Korea (South)
Tel.: (82) 54 288 2504
Web Site: http://www.poscotmc.com
Emp.: 15
Industrial Motor Core Mfr
N.A.I.C.S.: 332999

POSCO WA Pty. Ltd. (1)
Bgc Building L 9 28 The Esplanade, Perth, 6000, WA, Australia
Tel.: (61) 894867052
Web Site: http://www.poscoenc.com
Emp.: 4
Textile Products Mfr
N.A.I.C.S.: 314999

POSCO-CTPC Co., Ltd. (1)
No 168 Huanghai Road, Teda, Tianjin, China
Tel.: (86) 22 2561 7002
Metal Rolled Products Mfr & Distr
N.A.I.C.S.: 331210

POSCO-China Holding Corp. (1)
8th Floor Office Tower A Gate Way Bd No 18 Dong San Huan, Chao Yang District, Beijing, 100027, China
Tel.: (86) 10 5166 6677
Web Site: http://www.posco.com
Investment Management Service
N.A.I.C.S.: 523999

POSCO-Foshan Steel Processing Center Co., Ltd. (1)
Guanglong Industry Area Chencun Town, Shunde District, Foshan, Guangdong, China
Tel.: (86) 757 2381 3988
Steel Processing Services & Distr
N.A.I.C.S.: 423510

POSCO-India Private Ltd. (1)
Fortune Towers 5th Floor, Chandraseskarpur, Bhubaneswar, 751 023, Orrisa, India
Tel.: (91) 6742303690
Web Site: http://www.posco-india.com
Hot & Cold-Rolled Steel Products Mfr
N.A.I.C.S.: 331221

POSCO-JKPC Co., Ltd. (1)
85 7 Hibikimachi 1-Chome, Kitakyushu, 808 011, Japan
Tel.: (81) 9 3751 6641
Automotive Steel Plate Mfr
N.A.I.C.S.: 331221

POSCO-JOPC Co., Ltd. (1)
3-2 Ozushimacho, Izumiotsu, 595-0054, Osaka, Japan
Tel.: (81) 725 31 4577
Steel Products Mfr
N.A.I.C.S.: 331110

POSCO-Japan Co., Ltd. (1)
4Fl Posco Tokyo Building 11-14 Ginza 5-Chome, Chuo-ku, Tokyo, 104-0061, Japan
Tel.: (81) 3 3546 1212
Steel Products Mfr & Distr
N.A.I.C.S.: 331110

POSCO-Mexico Co., Ltd. (1)
Boulevard De Los Rios Colonei, Altamira, 89603, Zacatecas, Mexico
Tel.: (52) 833 260 7700
Web Site: http://www.poscomexico.com.mx
Emp.: 40
Copper Rolling & Extruding Services
N.A.I.C.S.: 331420

POSCO-Thainox Public Company Limited (1)
Emporium Tower Floor 15/6-8 622 Sukhumvit Road Klongtan, Klongtoey, Bangkok, 10110, Thailand
Tel.: (66) 2494313047
Web Site: https://www.poscothainox.com
Rev.: $412,275,024
Assets: $339,160,657
Liabilities: $77,989,565
Net Worth: $261,171,091
Earnings: ($2,133,323)
Emp.: 550
Fiscal Year-end: 12/31/2023
Stainless Steel Mfr
N.A.I.C.S.: 331221
Do Soon Kim (Chm)

POSCO-Vietnam Co., Ltd (1)
Lot 1 Phu My2 Industrial Zone, Phu My, Ba Ria-Vung Tau, Vietnam
Tel.: (84) 64 3923 090
Web Site: http://www.poscovietnam.com
Steel Products Mfr
N.A.I.C.S.: 331110
Hoon Yun (Chm)

Subsidiary (Domestic):

POSCO-Vietnam Processing Center Co., Ltd. (2)
Nhon Trach 5 Industrial Zone, Nhon Trach, Dong Nai, Vietnam
Tel.: (84) 61 3569 350
Stainless Steel Processing Services & Distr
N.A.I.C.S.: 423510

POSVINA Co., Ltd. (2)
Phuoc Long Village, Thu Duc District, Ho Chi Minh City, Vietnam
Tel.: (84) 88960827
Mfr & Sales of Galvanized Products
N.A.I.C.S.: 331110

VSC-POSCO Steel Corp. (2)
Anhung Vlg Hongbang District, Haiphong, Vietnam
Tel.: (84) 31850124
Web Site: http://www.steelvps.com.vn
Sales Range: $50-74.9 Million
Emp.: 220
Bar & Wire Rod Producing
N.A.I.C.S.: 331491

Vietnam Steel Pipe Corp. (2)
10 Vat Cach Anhai District, Haiphong, Vietnam (100%)
Tel.: (84) 31850116
Sales Range: $50-74.9 Million
Emp.: 150
Pipe Producing
N.A.I.C.S.: 331210

POSMETAL (1)
85 7 Hibikimachi 1 Chome, Wakamatuku Kitakyushu Shi, Fukuoka, 808 011, Japan (50%)
Tel.: (81) 937516641
Web Site: http://www.posmetal.co.jp
Steel Trade
N.A.I.C.S.: 425120

Posco DX Co Ltd (1)
68 Hodong-ro, Nam-gu, Pohang, Gyeongsangbuk-do, Korea (South)
Tel.: (82) 542801114
Web Site: https://www.poscodx.com
Rev.: $884,105,713
Assets: $653,172,434
Liabilities: $335,640,179
Net Worth: $317,532,255
Earnings: $34,961,276
Emp.: 2,064
Fiscal Year-end: 12/31/2022
Information Technology Consulting Services
N.A.I.C.S.: 541512
Dukkyoon Jung (CEO)

Posco International Corporation (1)
165 Convensia-daero Yeonsu-gu, Incheon, 21998, Korea (South) (68.15%)
Tel.: (82) 27592114
Web Site: http://www.poscointl.com
Steel, Metal, Non-Ferrous Metal, Chemical, Machinery, Industrial, Automotive, Media, Electronic & Textile Industries Mfr, Distr & Trading Services
N.A.I.C.S.: 238990
Jeong Tak (Pres)

Subsidiary (Non-US):

Al-Bab Care of Daewoo (2)
King Faisal Foundation Bldg S Twr 8th Fl, PO Box 59644, Riyadh, 11692, Saudi Arabia
Tel.: (966) 014646211
N.A.I.C.S.: 333120

Daewoo Corp. Amsterdam B.V. (2)
Overschiestrat St No 180, Koningin, Wihelminacein 2 4, 1062 HK, Amsterdam, Netherlands
Tel.: (31) 206178105
Metal, Machinery & Automotive Components Mfr
N.A.I.C.S.: 333120

Daewoo Global Nigeria Ltd. (2)
12th Floor Forshure Towers 2A Osborne Road Ikyoe, Lagos, Nigeria
Tel.: (234) 12701102
Web Site: http://www.daewoo.com
Sales Range: $25-49.9 Million
Emp.: 10
Metal, Machinery & Automotive Components Mfr
N.A.I.C.S.: 333120

Daewoo International (Japan) Corp. (2)
24F Marunouchi Trust Tower Main 8-3 Marunouchi 1 chome Chiyoda-Ku, Tokyo, 100-0005, Japan
Tel.: (81) 3 5220 6123
Web Site: http://www.daewoo.com
Sales Range: $25-49.9 Million
Emp.: 50
Metal, Machinery & Automotive Components Mfr
N.A.I.C.S.: 333120

Daewoo International (Japan) Corp. (2)
Nihon Seimei Yodoyabashi Bldg 8th Fl, 5 29 3 Chome Kitahama Chuo-ku, Osaka, 541-0041, Japan
Tel.: (81) 662220848
Web Site: http://www.daewoo.com
Sales Range: $25-49.9 Million
Emp.: 50
N.A.I.C.S.: 333120

Daewoo International (Shanghai) Co., Ltd. (2)
Roomm 2003 Building 3 Dawning Centre, 500 Hongbaoshi Road, Shanghai, 201103, China
Tel.: (86) 2122113500
Web Site: http://www.daewoo.com
Sales Range: $25-49.9 Million
Emp.: 25
Industrial Machinery & Equipment Distr
N.A.I.C.S.: 423830

Subsidiary (US):

Daewoo International America Corp. (2)
85 Challenger Rd, Ridgefield Park, NJ 07660-2104
Tel.: (201) 229-4500
Web Site: http://www.daewoo.com
Sales Range: $25-49.9 Million
Emp.: 15
Import/Export; International Trading
N.A.I.C.S.: 423430

Daewoo International America Corp. (2)
Ste 1020 222 S Harbor Blvd, Anaheim, CA 92805-3762
Tel.: (714) 808-1000
Importer/Exporter of Seafood
N.A.I.C.S.: 423510

Subsidiary (Non-US):

Daewoo International Singapore Pte. Ltd. (2)
7 Temasek Boulevard 27-03 Suntec Tower One, Singapore, 38987, Singapore
Tel.: (65) 6333 5507
Web Site: http://www.daewoo.com
Seal Products Distr
N.A.I.C.S.: 423510

Daewoo Intl. Mexico S.A. de C.V. (2)
C V Paseo De Los Tamarindos 400 A 40 Piso Arcos Torre 1 Seccionponien, Colonia Bosqies De Las Lomas, Mexico, Mexico
Tel.: (52) 55 5596 5137
Web Site: http://www.daewoo.com
Emp.: 3
Galvanized Steel Sheet Distr
N.A.I.C.S.: 332322

Daewoo Italia S.R.L. (2)
Centro Direzionale Colleoni Palazzo Licorno, Via Parcelso 6, 20041, Milan, Agrate Brianza, Italy
Tel.: (39) 03964116200
Sales Range: $100-124.9 Million
Emp.: 9
Metal, Machinery & Automotive Components Mfr
N.A.I.C.S.: 333120
Jeong Won (Gen Mgr)

POSCO HOLDINGS INC.

POSCO Holdings Inc.—(Continued)

Daewoo Nigeria Limited (2)
Flat No 6 Plot 1608 Adeola Hopewell St,
PO Box 8686, Victoria Island, Lagos, Nigeria
Tel.: (234) 12613422
Sales Range: $25-49.9 Million
Emp.: 30
Metal, Machinery & Automotive Components Mfr
N.A.I.C.S.: 333120

Daewoo Paper Manufacturing Co. Ltd. (2)
No 8 Gunghua St, Yangming District, Mudanjiang, Heilongjiang, China
Tel.: (86) 453 632 5700
Web Site: http://www.daewoo.com
Paper Products Mfr
N.A.I.C.S.: 322299

Daewoo Singapore Pte. Ltd. (2)
7 Temasek Blvd 27-03 Suntec Tower One, Singapore, 038987, Singapore
Tel.: (65) 63335507
Sales Range: $25-49.9 Million
Emp.: 40
Trading Services
N.A.I.C.S.: 238990

Daewoo Textile Bukhara LLC (2)
Alpomish Str, Bukhara, Uzbekistan
Tel.: (998) 65 222 2161
Emp.: 740
Textile Products Mfr
N.A.I.C.S.: 314999

Gezira Tannery Co., Ltd. (2)
Plot No 21 Block 2 Mogran, PQ Box 607, Khartoum, Sudan
Tel.: (249) 183780915
Semi-Finished Leather Good Mfr
N.A.I.C.S.: 316110

Myanmar Daewoo Ltd. (2)
22 Yaw Mingyi Road, Dagon Township, Yangon, Myanmar
Tel.: (95) 1379120
Sales Range: $25-49.9 Million
Emp.: 100
Construction & Engineering Services
N.A.I.C.S.: 333120

PT. RISMAR Daewoo Apparel (2)
Kawasan Berikat Nusantara Jl Kalimantan Blok D27 Cakung-Cilicing, Jakarta, 14140, Indonesia
Tel.: (62) 21 440 4290
Textile Products Distr
N.A.I.C.S.: 424350

Senex Energy Limited (2)
Level 30 180 Ann Street, Brisbane, 4000, QLD, Australia
Tel.: (61) 733359000
Web Site: http://www.senexenergy.com.au
Rev.: $88,915,583
Assets: $513,132,767
Liabilities: $244,370,937
Net Worth: $268,761,830
Earnings: $50,314,165
Emp.: 191
Fiscal Year-end: 06/30/2021
Oil & Gas Exploration Services
N.A.I.C.S.: 213112
Ian R. Davies (CEO & Mng Dir)

The Blue Sea Company W.L.L. (2)
PO Box 4743, Safat, Kuwait, 13048, Kuwait
Tel.: (965) 2421476
N.A.I.C.S.: 333120

Posco Silicon Solution Co Ltd. (1)
17 Nojanggongdan-gil, Jeondong-myeon, Sejong, Korea (South)
Tel.: (82) 448679012
Web Site: https://www.poscosilicon.com
Silicon Anode Material Mfr & Distr
N.A.I.C.S.: 334413

The Siam United Steel Co., Ltd. (2)
9 Soi G5 Pakorn Songkrohraj Rd, Huay Pong Muang, Rayong, 21150, Thailand
Tel.: (66) 38685144
Cold-Rolled Steel Products Mfr
N.A.I.C.S.: 331221

Xenesys Inc. (1)
8F 11-14 Ginza 5-Chome, Chuo-Ku, Tokyo, 104-0061, Japan

Tel.: (81) 3 5148 2030
Web Site: http://www.xenesys.com
Sales Range: $25-49.9 Million
Emp.: 24
Electric Power Generation System Mfr
N.A.I.C.S.: 333611
Masaru Nagaya (Pres)

Plant (Domestic):

Xenesys Inc. - Imari Plant (2)
5-91 Nanatsujima Shioya Kurogawacho, Imari, 848-0121, Saga, Japan
Tel.: (81) 955 20 7570
Power Generation System Mfr
N.A.I.C.S.: 333611

Zhangjiagang POSCO Steel Co., Ltd. (1)
North of Yan Jiang Road Lian Xing Cun, Jinfeng Town, Zhangjiagang, Jiangsu, China (90%)
Tel.: (86) 520 855 497 1
Galvanized Steel Sheet Mfr & Distr
N.A.I.C.S.: 332322

Zhangjiagang Pohang Stainless Steel Co., Ltd. (1)
North of Riverside Road Lian Xing Cun, Jinfeng Town, Zhangjiagang, 215636, Jiangsu, China (60%)
Tel.: (86) 51258569211
Web Site: http://www.zpss.com
Emp.: 2,000
Stainless CR Coils Mfr & Distr
N.A.I.C.S.: 331110

POSEIDON CONCEPTS CORP.
Suite 1200 645 7th Avenue SW, Calgary, T2P 4G8, AB, Canada
Tel.: (403) 206-4999 AB
Web Site: http://www.poseidonconcepts.com
Sales Range: $75-99.9 Million
Oil & Gas Tanks
N.A.I.C.S.: 333132
Brad Wanchulak (Sr VP-Global Dev)

Subsidiaries:

Poseidon Concepts Inc. (1)
370-17th St Ste 5600, Denver, CO 80202
Tel.: (303) 629-2400
Fluid Handling Tank Rental Services
N.A.I.C.S.: 531130

Poseidon Concepts Ltd. (1)
645 7 Ave SW Unit 1200, Calgary, T2P4G8, AB, Canada
Tel.: (403) 262-2936
Sales Range: $50-74.9 Million
Emp.: 25
Fluid Handling Tank Rental Services
N.A.I.C.S.: 531130

POSEIDON NICKEL LIMITED
Level 1 3 Ord Street, West Perth, 6005, WA, Australia
Tel.: (61) 861676600
Web Site: https://www.poseidon-nickel.com.au
POS—(ASX)
Rev.: $1,833,600
Assets: $57,992,788
Liabilities: $43,412,794
Net Worth: $14,579,995
Earnings: ($40,090,812)
Fiscal Year-end: 06/30/24
Mining Industry
N.A.I.C.S.: 212220
Brendan Shalders (CFO & Co-Sec)

POSIFLEX TECHNOLOGY INC.
23 Datong St, Tucheng Dist, New Taipei City, 23679, Taiwan
Tel.: (886) 222685577
Web Site: https://www.posiflex.com.tw
Year Founded: 1984
8114—(TAI)
Rev.: $322,630,944
Assets: $486,076,472
Liabilities: $279,076,186
Net Worth: $207,000,286

Earnings: $23,877,595
Emp.: 1,400
Fiscal Year-end: 12/31/23
Touch Screen Terminals & Peripherals Mfr
N.A.I.C.S.: 334118
Mao Chiang Chen (Chm & Gen Mgr)

Subsidiaries:

European Portwell Technology B.V. (1)
Schillingweg 3, 2153 PL, Nieuw Vennep, Netherlands
Tel.: (31) 252278800
Web Site: https://www.portwell.eu
Computer Hardware Parts Mfr & Distr
N.A.I.C.S.: 334111

GANLOT, Inc. (1)
No 242 9F Bo-Ai St, Shu-Lin Dist, New Taipei City, 238, Taiwan
Tel.: (886) 277318989
Web Site: https://www.ganlot.com
Software Development Services
N.A.I.C.S.: 541511

KIOSK Embedded Systems GmbH (1)
Am Technologiepark 10 D, 82229, Seefeld, Germany
Tel.: (49) 81523962500
Computer Hardware Parts Mfr & Distr
N.A.I.C.S.: 334111

Kiosk Information Systems, Inc. (1)
346 S Arthur Ave, Louisville, CO 80027
Tel.: (303) 466-5471
Web Site: http://kiosk.com
Computer Peripheral Equipment Mfr
N.A.I.C.S.: 334118
Dan Houck (COO)

MEDWEL, Inc. (1)
No 242 Bo-Ai Street, Shu-Lin Dist, New Taipei City, 238, Taiwan
Tel.: (886) 277050080
Web Site: https://www.medwel.net
Software Development Services
N.A.I.C.S.: 541511

Portwell (UK) Ltd. (1)
Trident House Trident Park Basil Hill Road, Didcot, OX11 7HJ, United Kingdom
Tel.: (44) 1235750760
Computer Hardware Parts Mfr & Distr
N.A.I.C.S.: 334111

Portwell Inc. (1)
No 242 Bo-Ai Street, Shu-Lin Dist, New Taipei City, 238, Taiwan
Tel.: (886) 277318888
Web Site: https://www.portwell.com.tw
Emp.: 720
Telecommunication Servicesb
N.A.I.C.S.: 517810

Portwell India Technology Private Limited (1)
3rd Floor Jeet Dynasty Old Madras Rd next to Gopalan Signature Mall, Nagavarapalya Bennigana Halli, Bengaluru, 560093, Karnataka, India
Tel.: (91) 8040782700
Web Site: https://www.portwell.in
Computer Hardware Parts Mfr & Distr
N.A.I.C.S.: 334111

Portwell Japan, Inc. (1)
4-27-10 Sengoku, Bunkyo-ku, Tokyo, 112-0011, Japan
Tel.: (81) 369029225
Web Site: https://www.portwell.co.jp
Emp.: 39
Computer Hardware Parts Mfr & Distr
N.A.I.C.S.: 334111

Portwell Korea, Inc. (1)
Room 1901 Orbiz Tower 126 Beolmal-ro, Dongan-gu, Anyang, 14057, Gyeonggi, Korea (South)
Tel.: (82) 314503043
Web Site: https://www.portwell.co.kr
Computer Hardware Parts Mfr & Distr
N.A.I.C.S.: 334111

Posiflex Business Machines (Beijing) Co., Ltd. (1)
Room A816 Shouke Mansion 14 Courtyard of West 3rd Ring South Rd, Fengtai Dist,

INTERNATIONAL PUBLIC

Beijing, China
Tel.: (86) 1063634602
Computer Peripheral Equipment Mfr & Distr
N.A.I.C.S.: 334210

Posiflex Business Machines Sdn. Bhd. (1)
B-G-31 Block B Merchant Square 1 Jalan Tropicana Selatan 1 PJU 3, 47410, Petaling Jaya, Malaysia
Tel.: (60) 378859199
POS Machine Mfr & Distr
N.A.I.C.S.: 334118

Posiflex Business Machines, Inc. (1)
30689 Huntwood Ave, Hayward, CA 94544
Tel.: (510) 429-7097
Web Site: http://www.posiflexusa.com
Emp.: 35
Touch Screen Peripheral Distr
N.A.I.C.S.: 423690

Posiflex GmbH (1)
Kaiserswerther Str 85, 40878, Ratingen, Germany
Tel.: (49) 2102714650
Web Site: http://www.posiflex.de
Touch Screen Peripheral Distr
N.A.I.C.S.: 423690
Yicheng Yehmorosch (Gen Mgr)

Posiflex Technologies South Cone (1)
Darregueyra 2478 1er Piso, C1425FLR, Buenos Aires, Argentina
Tel.: (54) 1147728948
Touch Screen Peripheral Distr
N.A.I.C.S.: 423690

Posiflex Technology (India) Pvt Ltd. (1)
985 1st A Main Road 4th Cross Near Mahalakshmi Saw Mill / BDA Park, New Thippasandra, Bengaluru, 560075, India
Tel.: (91) 8040782700
Web Site: https://www.posiflexindia.com
Emp.: 30
Touch Screen Peripheral Distr
N.A.I.C.S.: 423690
Dinesh Kadi Ullal (Mng Dir)

Posiflex Technology Pte. Ltd. (1)
BLK 63 UBI Rd 1 01-51 Oxley Bizhub, Singapore, 408728, Singapore
Tel.: (65) 63855669
POS Machine Mfr & Distr
N.A.I.C.S.: 334118

Quinta Systems Pvt. Ltd. (1)
7/3 3rd Floor Jeet Dynasty Swamy Vivekananda Road Nagavarapalya, Bengaluru, 560093, Karnataka, India
Tel.: (91) 8040782700
Web Site: https://www.quinta.co.in
Warehouse & Storage Management Services
N.A.I.C.S.: 531130

POSITIVE THINKING
Willoughby House, 493 Richmond Rd, Richmond, TW1 2AG, United Kingdom
Tel.: (44) 208 744 4350
Web Site: http://www.positive-thinking.co.uk
Year Founded: 1994
Rev.: $34,762,200
Emp.: 42
N.A.I.C.S.: 541810
Tim Miller (CEO)

POSITIVE-A JSC
Tel.: (7) 273468667
PZVA—(KAZ)
Assets: $7,898,993
Liabilities: $8,786,741
Net Worth: ($887,748)
Earnings: ($424,487)
Fiscal Year-end: 12/31/22
Business Consulting Services
N.A.I.C.S.: 541611
Vostretsova Natalia (CEO)

POSITIVO TECNOLOGIA S.A.

Rua Joao Bettega 5200 - CIC, Curitiba, 81350-000, Parana, Brazil
Tel.: (55) 4132397300 BR
Web Site:
 https://www.positivotecnologia.com
Year Founded: 1989
POSI3—(BRAZ)
Sales Range: $500-549.9 Million
Emp.: 2,092
Computer Mfr & Sales
N.A.I.C.S.: 334111
Marielva Andrade Dias *(VP-Govt Market & Strategic Acct)*

Subsidiaries:

Positivo Informatica da Amazonia Ltda   (1)
Av Djalma Batista 3000, Manaus, 69055-038, Amazonas, Brazil
Tel.: (55) 4133167700
Computer Peripheral Equipments & Software Distr
N.A.I.C.S.: 423430

POSLOVNI OBJEKTI A.D.

Resavska 32, 11000, Belgrade, Serbia
Tel.: (381) 113612025
Web Site: https://poslovniobjekti.rs
Year Founded: 1984
PSOB—(BEL)
Rev.: $2,544,395
Assets: $906,669
Liabilities: $310,845
Net Worth: $595,824
Earnings: $21,719
Fiscal Year-end: 12/31/23
Management Consulting Services
N.A.I.C.S.: 541611
Zoran Nesic *(Head-Engrg)*

POSLOVNI SISTEM RMK D.D.

Bulevar kralja Tvrtka I br 17, 72 000, Zenica, Bosnia & Herzegovina
Tel.: (387) 32247774
Web Site: http://www.zeps.com
RMKZR—(SARE)
Rev.: $19,782
Assets: $842,568
Liabilities: $218,535
Net Worth: $624,032
Earnings: ($227,573)
Emp.: 3
Fiscal Year-end: 12/31/21
Marketing & Advertising Services
N.A.I.C.S.: 541810

POST & TELECOMMUNICATION EQUIPMENT JOINT STOCK COMPANY

61 Tran Phu Str Dien Bien Ward, Ba Dinh Dist, Hanoi, Vietnam
Tel.: (84) 38455946
Web Site: https://www.postef.com.vn
Year Founded: 1954
POT—(HNX)
Rev.: $115,771,800
Assets: $228,156,500
Liabilities: $197,067,900
Net Worth: $31,088,600
Earnings: $261,300
Emp.: 650
Fiscal Year-end: 12/31/23
Telecommunications Devices & Cable Mfr
N.A.I.C.S.: 334220

Subsidiaries:

POSTEF Development Energy System Company Limited   (1)
63 Tran Phu Str, Ba Dinh Dist Dien Bien Ward, Hanoi, Vietnam
Tel.: (84) 437342518
Web Site: http://www.pde.vn
Telecommunications Equipment Mfr
N.A.I.C.S.: 334220

Post & Telecommunication Equipment Joint Stock Company - Bac Ninh Factory   (1)
No 12 Str 15 VSIP Industrial Park, Bac Ninh, Vietnam
Tel.: (84) 2413765120
Telecommunications Equipment Mfr
N.A.I.C.S.: 334220

Post & Telecommunication Equipment Joint Stock Company - Da Nang Factory   (1)
Lot K Str 7 Lien Chieu Industrial Park, Da Nang, Vietnam
Tel.: (84) 5113774897
Telecommunications Equipment Mfr
N.A.I.C.S.: 334220

Post & Telecommunication Equipment Joint Stock Company - Ho Chi Minh Factory   (1)
Lot J9-J10 Str 3 Le Minh Xuan Industrial Park, Binh Chanh Dist, Ho Chi Minh City, Vietnam
Tel.: (84) 837662054
Telecommunications Equipment Mfr
N.A.I.C.S.: 334220

POST & TELECOMMUNICATIONS INVESTMENT & CONSTRUCTION JOINT STOCK COMPANY

France Van Hoang Liet, Hoang Mai, Hanoi, Vietnam
Tel.: (84) 438611513
Web Site: http://www.pticjsc.com
PTC—(HOSE)
Rev.: $4,437,982
Assets: $47,635,770
Liabilities: $26,133,572
Net Worth: $21,502,198
Earnings: $577,665
Fiscal Year-end: 12/31/23
Building Construction Services
N.A.I.C.S.: 236220

POST & TELECOMMUNICATONS INSURANCE JSC

8th Floor HAREC Building No 4A Lang Ha Street, Ba Dinh District, Hanoi, Vietnam
Tel.: (84) 437724466
Web Site: https://www.pti.com.vn
PTI—(HNX)
Rev.: $243,180,423
Assets: $311,890,210
Liabilities: $231,044,096
Net Worth: $80,846,113
Earnings: $9,565,859
Fiscal Year-end: 12/31/20
Insurance Services
N.A.I.C.S.: 524210
Bui Xuan Thu *(CEO)*

POST OFFICE LTD.

108 Dawes Rd, London, SW6 1PT, United Kingdom
Tel.: (44) 8457 22 3344 UK
Web Site: http://www.postoffice.co.uk
Counter & Financial Services
N.A.I.C.S.: 522110
Jane MacLeod *(Sec)*

POSTAL SAVINGS BANK OF CHINA CO., LTD.

No 3 Jinrong Street, Xicheng District, Beijing, 100808, China
Tel.: (86) 95580 CN
Web Site: https://www.psbc.com
Year Founded: 2007
1658—(HKG)
Rev.: $66,583,296,000
Assets: $1,975,046,392,800
Liabilities: $1,859,102,107,200
Net Worth: $115,944,285,600
Earnings: $11,983,842,000
Emp.: 195,102
Fiscal Year-end: 12/31/22
Commercial Banking Services
N.A.I.C.S.: 522110
Xuewen Zhang *(VP)*

Subsidiaries:

YOU BANK Co., Ltd.   (1)
25-26/F No 1080 Dongdaming Road, Hongkou District, Shanghai, 200082, China
Tel.: (86) 2135905606
Banking Services
N.A.I.C.S.: 522110

POSTE ITALIANE S.P.A.

Viale Europa 190, 00144, Rome, Italy
Tel.: (39) 0659581 IT
Web Site: https://www.posteitaliane.it
Year Founded: 1862
PST—(ITA)
Rev.: $21,413,228,864
Assets: $150,104,131,141
Liabilities: $145,584,661,132
Net Worth: $4,519,470,009
Earnings: $1,147,779,540
Emp.: 553
Fiscal Year-end: 12/31/18
Mail Delivery, Banking, Insurance, Telecommunication & Internet Services
N.A.I.C.S.: 491110
Matteo Del Fante *(CEO)*

Subsidiaries:

Banca del Mezzogiorno-MedioCredito Centrale SpA   (1)
Viale America 351, 00144, Rome, Italy
Tel.: (39) 09 06 47911
Web Site: http://www.mcc.it
Financial Services
N.A.I.C.S.: 541611
Claudia La Chioma *(Mgr-Risk)*

BancoPosta Fondi SpA   (1)
Via Marmorata 4, 153, Rome, Italy
Tel.: (39) 06 57018390
Web Site: http://www.bancopostafondi.it
Asset Management Services
N.A.I.C.S.: 531390
Mark Fardelli *(Mgr-Mktg)*

Mistral Air Srl   (1)
Viale Lincoln 3, 00144, Rome, Italy
Tel.: (39) 06 96663333
Web Site: http://www.mistralair.it
Aircraft Charter Services
N.A.I.C.S.: 481212
Luca Sanfilippo *(Mgr-MCC)*

Poste Insurance Broker Srl   (1)
Viale Europa 190, Rome, 00144, Italy
Tel.: (39) 011 652 3250
Web Site:
 https://posteinsurancebroker.poste.it
Insurance Broker Services
N.A.I.C.S.: 524210

Poste Vita SpA   (1)
Konrad Adenauer 3, 00144, Rome, Italy
Tel.: (39) 05927271006
Web Site: http://www.postevita.it
General Insurance Services
N.A.I.C.S.: 524210

Poste Welfare Servizi Srl   (1)
Viale Europa 175, 00144, Rome, Italy
Tel.: (39) 064 575 6001
Web Site: https://www.postewelfareservizi.it
Health Insurance Services
N.A.I.C.S.: 524114

Postel SpA   (1)
Viale Cassala 46, 20143, Milan, Italy
Tel.: (39) 02 581661
Web Site: http://www.postel.it
Mail Delivery Services
N.A.I.C.S.: 491110

Subsidiary (Domestic):

Address Software Srl   (2)
Via dell Elettronica 6, 37139, Verona, Italy
Tel.: (39) 045 8513590
Web Site: http://www.address.it
Application Software Development Services
N.A.I.C.S.: 541511
Alessio Fornasiero *(Project Mgr)*

SDA Express Courier   (1)
Via Eugenio Gra 19, Rome, 00163, Italy
Tel.: (39) 06665921
Web Site: http://www.sda.it
Sales Range: $650-699.9 Million
Emp.: 3,100
Courier Service
N.A.I.C.S.: 492110

Subsidiary (Domestic):

Italia Logistica Srl   (2)
Via del Pescaccio 30, 00166, Rome, Italy
Tel.: (39) 06 665481
Web Site: http://www.italialogistica.it
Logistics Consulting Servies
N.A.I.C.S.: 541614

Kipoint SpA   (2)
Via Giovan Battista Valente 190 Centro Commerciale Auchan, Rome, Italy
Tel.: (39) 06 2155786
Web Site: http://www.kipoint.it
Logistics Consulting Servies
N.A.I.C.S.: 541614
Giorgio Vaccaro *(CEO)*

Sennder Italia Srl   (1)
Via Ferrante Aporti 10, 20125, Milan, Italy
Tel.: (39) 028 295 4676
Web Site: https://www.sennder.com
Truck Transportation Services
N.A.I.C.S.: 484110

POSTE SRPSKE

Kralja Petra I Karadordevica 93, 78000, Banja Luka, Republika Srpska, Bosnia & Herzegovina
Tel.: (387) 51246020
Web Site:
 https://www.postesrpske.com
Year Founded: 1996
POST-R-A—(BANJ)
Sales Range: Less than $1 Million
Courier Service
N.A.I.C.S.: 491110
Snjezana Martic *(Exec Dir-Legal, Gen Affairs, HR & Investments)*

POSTEN NORGE AS

PO Box 1500, Sentrum, 0001, Oslo, Norway
Tel.: (47) 23149000 NO
Web Site: http://www.posten.no
Year Founded: 1996
Sales Range: $1-4.9 Billion
Emp.: 20,541
Postal, Communications & Logistics Services
N.A.I.C.S.: 491110
Gro Bakstad *(Exec VP-Mail Div)*

Subsidiaries:

Bring Frigoscandia AB   (1)
Landskronavagen 9, PO Box 912, Helsingborg, 25109, Sweden   (100%)
Tel.: (46) 42178000
Web Site: http://www.bring.com
Sales Range: $25-49.9 Million
Emp.: 300
Logistics Services for Temperature-Controlled Distribution; Freezing & Storage of Foodstuffs
N.A.I.C.S.: 541614
Hakan Nilsson *(Mng Dir)*

Subsidiary (Non-US):

Bring Cargo/Bring Frigo   (2)
Griendwerkersstraat 10, 3334 KB, Zwijndrecht, Netherlands
Tel.: (31) 78 610 00 30
Web Site: http://www.bring.nl
Sales Range: $25-49.9 Million
Emp.: 40
International & Local Freight & Cargo Services
N.A.I.C.S.: 488510
Rob Van Rooijen *(Mng Dir)*

Bring Frigoscandia   (2)
Olav Ingstadsvei 12, PO Box 125, NO 1305, Rud, Norway   (100%)
Tel.: (47) 67151100
Web Site: http://www.bringfrigoscandia.no

POSTEN NORGE AS

Posten Norge AS—(Continued)
Sales Range: $10-24.9 Million
Emp.: 40
Refrigerated Warehousing & Storage Services
N.A.I.C.S.: 493120

Bring Frigoscandia A/S (2)
Birkedam 11, 6000, Kolding, Denmark
Tel.: (45) 75509988
Web Site: http://www.bringfrigoscandia.dk
Sales Range: $10-24.9 Million
Emp.: 100
Refrigerated Warehousing & Storage Services
N.A.I.C.S.: 493120

Bring Logistics Netherlands B.V. (1)
Griendwerkersstraat 10, Zwijndrecht, 3334 KB, Netherlands (100%)
Tel.: (31) 786100030
Web Site: http://www.bring.com
Sales Range: $10-24.9 Million
Emp.: 45
Trucking, Freight & Warehousing Facilities
N.A.I.C.S.: 484121

POSTI GROUP OYJ
Postintaival 7 A, FI-00230, Helsinki, Finland
Tel.: (358) 204511
Web Site: http://www.posti.com
Postal & Logistics Services
N.A.I.C.S.: 541614
Markku Pohjola *(Chm)*

Subsidiaries:

Suomen Transval Oy (1)
Postintaival 7 A, 00230, Helsinki, Finland
Tel.: (358) 9 565 8520
Web Site: http://www.transval.fi
Outsourced Logistics Services
N.A.I.C.S.: 488999
Sakari Kiiskinen *(Dir)*

Subsidiary (Domestic):

Transval Teollisuuspalvelut Vindea Oy (2)
Vaihdemiehentie 1, 01450, Vantaa, Uusimaa, Finland
Tel.: (358) 19 460 4400
Logistics Consulting Servies
N.A.I.C.S.: 541614

POSTNL N.V.
Waldorpstraat 3, 2521 CA, Hague, Netherlands
Tel.: (31) 888686161 NI
Web Site: https://www.postnl.nl
Year Founded: 1946
PNL—(EUR)
Rev.: $3,393,049,860
Assets: $2,396,935,031
Liabilities: $2,203,755,666
Net Worth: $193,179,365
Earnings: ($1,071,659,832)
Emp.: 8,716
Fiscal Year-end: 12/31/22
Mail Delivery Services
N.A.I.C.S.: 491110
Pim Berendsen *(CFO & Member-Mgmt Bd)*

Subsidiaries:

Cendris Customer Contact B.V. (1)
Beursplein 1, 8911 BE, Leeuwarden, Netherlands
Tel.: (31) 88 225 5120
Web Site: https://www.cendris.nl
Customer Contact Services
N.A.I.C.S.: 561422

Cendris Document Presentment B.V. (1)
Hardwareweg 7, 3821 BL, Amersfoort, Netherlands
Tel.: (31) 703344960
Sales Range: $25-49.9 Million
Emp.: 50
Data & Document Services
N.A.I.C.S.: 518210

DM Productions B.V. (1)
Hoofdweg 679, 2131 BC, Hoofddorp, Netherlands
Tel.: (31) 235553090
Web Site: https://www.dmsolutions.nl
Advertising Agency Services
N.A.I.C.S.: 541810

Koninklijke PostNL BV (1)
Waldorpstraat 3, 2521 CA, Hague, Netherlands
Tel.: (31) 888686161
Web Site: https://www.postnl.nl
Mail Services
N.A.I.C.S.: 491110

POSTNORD AB
Terminalvagen 24, Solna, Sweden
Tel.: (46) 87811000
Web Site: http://www.postnord.com
Sales Range: $1-4.9 Billion
Emp.: 30,000
Postal Service
N.A.I.C.S.: 491110
Gunilla Berg *(CFO)*

Subsidiaries:

Addresspoint AB (1)
11136 Stockholm, 87813245, Stockholm, Sweden
Tel.: (46) 87813245
Web Site: http://www.addresspoint.se
Sales Range: $25-49.9 Million
Emp.: 6
Management Consulting Services
N.A.I.C.S.: 541618

DPD Dynamic Parcel Distribution GmbH & Co. KG (1)
Wailandstrasse 1, D-63741, Aschaffenburg, Germany (100%)
Tel.: (49) 6021 843 0
Web Site: http://www.dpd.com
Sales Range: $50-74.9 Million
Emp.: 200
Local Freight Trucking & Logistic Services
N.A.I.C.S.: 484121
John Acton *(Dir-Mgmt Exec Bd)*

DPD Parcel Holding A/S (1)
Venusvej 30, 6000, Kolding, Denmark (100%)
Tel.: (45) 70100510
Sales Range: $25-49.9 Million
Emp.: 200
Couriers
N.A.I.C.S.: 492110

Data Scanning Finland Ab (1)
Atomitie 5, 00370, Helsinki, Finland
Tel.: (358) 50 554 5651
Web Site: http://www.datascanning.fi
Direct Mailing Service
N.A.I.C.S.: 561431

Direct Link Worldwide Distribution Pte. Ltd (1)
Block 4 Kaki Bukit Avenue 1 05-01, Singapore, 417939, Singapore
Tel.: (65) 6 745 0773
Direct Mailing Service
N.A.I.C.S.: 561431
Bjorn Moberg *(Reg Mgr-Bus Dev)*

Subsidiary (Non-US):

Direct Link Worldwide Company Ltd. (2)
Units 1-6 21st floor Block B 11-13 Tai Yuen Street, Tung Chun Industrial Building, Kwai Chung, New Territories, China (Hong Kong)
Tel.: (852) 2850 4183
Web Site: http://www.directlink.com
Emp.: 30
Logistics Consulting Servies
N.A.I.C.S.: 541614
Ulrica Phillips *(Gen Mgr)*

Direct Link Worldwide Pty. Ltd (2)
Unit 5 1-7 Jabez Street, Marrickville, 2204, NSW, Australia
Tel.: (61) 2 9550 0500
Logistics Consulting Servies
N.A.I.C.S.: 541614

Direct Link Worldwide GmbH (1)
Kurhessenstrasse 1, 64546, Morfelden, Germany
Tel.: (49) 6105408160

Web Site: http://www.directlink.com
Sales Range: $25-49.9 Million
Emp.: 5
Direct Selling Establishments
N.A.I.C.S.: 541211
Stefan Ekonomakos *(Mng Dir)*

Subsidiary (Domestic):

PostNord Logistics GmbH (2)
Spenglerstrasse 23 A, 23556, Lubeck, Germany
Tel.: (49) 451 2035260
Web Site: http://www.postnordlogistics.com
Logistics Consulting Servies
N.A.I.C.S.: 541614

Direct Link Worldwide Inc. (1)
700 Dowd Ave, Elizabeth, NJ 07201
Tel.: (908) 289-0703
Direct Mailing Service
N.A.I.C.S.: 561431
John Cucciniello *(Pres)*

Direct Link Worldwide Ltd. (1)
Fairview Business Center, 25 Clayton Rd Middlesex, Hayes, UB3 1AN, United Kingdom
Tel.: (44) 2087074400
Web Site: http://www.directlink.com
Sales Range: $25-49.9 Million
Emp.: 50
Direct Selling Establishments
N.A.I.C.S.: 541211
Andy Packham *(Mgr-Sls)*

PostNord AS (1)
Alfaset 3 industrivei 25, 0668, Oslo, Norway
Tel.: (47) 22329000
Web Site: http://www.postnord.no
Logistics Consulting Servies
N.A.I.C.S.: 541614
Ole A. Hagen *(Dir-Comm & Mktg)*

PostNord Logistics (1)
Tietgensgade 37, 1566, Copenhagen, Denmark
Tel.: (45) 33 61 60 01
Web Site: http://www.postnord.com
Sales Range: $25-49.9 Million
Emp.: 12
Transportation, Logistics, Mail & Communication Services
N.A.I.C.S.: 561431
Serbaz Shali *(Mgr-Global Ops)*

PostNord Oy (1)
Osumakuja 3, PL 179, 01530, Vantaa, Finland
Tel.: (358) 10 572 8080
Web Site: http://www.postnordlogistics.fi
Logistics Consulting Servies
N.A.I.C.S.: 541614
Toni Karinen *(Mgr-Sls)*

Posten Forsakrings AB (1)
Terminalvagen 24, 10500, Stockholm, Sweden
Tel.: (46) 87811000
Postal Service
N.A.I.C.S.: 491110

Posten Leasing AB (1)
Karlsbodavagen 39, Bromma, Sweden
Tel.: (46) 87811606
Postal Service
N.A.I.C.S.: 491110

Posten Logistik AB (1)
Terminalvagen 24, Fack 610329, 10654 Stolkholm, 17173, Solna, Sweden
Tel.: (46) 87811000
Web Site: http://www.posten.se
Local Freight Trucking
N.A.I.C.S.: 484110

Posten Meddelande AB (1)
Terminalvagen 24, Solna, Sweden
Tel.: (46) 87811000
Web Site: http://www.posten.se
Postal Service
N.A.I.C.S.: 491110
Andreas Falkenmark *(Pres)*

Stralfors AB (1)
Helsingborgsvagen 20, 341 33, Ljungby, Sweden (100%)
Tel.: (46) 37285000
Web Site: http://www.stralfors.se
Sales Range: $600-649.9 Million
Emp.: 2,500
Information Logistics Services

INTERNATIONAL PUBLIC

N.A.I.C.S.: 541614
Stefan Lager *(VP-Ops-Info Logistics)*

Subsidiary (Domestic):

Hultberg Inrikes Transporter AB (2)
Stensatrav 2, 12739, Stockholm, Sweden
Tel.: (46) 86033670
Local Freight Trucking
N.A.I.C.S.: 484110

Subsidiary (Non-US):

Post Danmark A/S (2)
Tietgensgade 37 Copenhagen V, 1566, Copenhagen, Denmark
Tel.: (45) 33 61 00 00
Web Site: http://www.postdanmark.dk
Emp.: 1,500
Logistics Consulting Servies
N.A.I.C.S.: 541614
Isa Merethe Rogild *(Chm)*

Subsidiary (Domestic):

Data Scanning A/S (3)
Bernstorffsgade 38 Kobenhavn V, Copenhagen, 1577, Denmark
Tel.: (45) 46 55 00 70
Web Site: http://www.datascanning.dk
Direct Mailing Service
N.A.I.C.S.: 561431

Distribution Services A/S (3)
Borgmester Christiansens Gade 47-49, 2450, Copenhagen, Denmark
Tel.: (45) 33 266 266
Web Site: http://www.distributionservices.dk
Logistics Consulting Servies
N.A.I.C.S.: 541614

Logsite ApS (3)
Baldersbaekvej 8 C, 2635, Ishoj, Denmark
Tel.: (45) 43 46 20 04
Web Site: http://www.logsite.dk
Logistics Consulting Servies
N.A.I.C.S.: 541614

Subsidiary (Domestic):

Postakeriet Sverige AB (2)
Galgbacken 3, 17677, Jarfalla, Sweden
Tel.: (46) 858352072
Sales Range: $25-49.9 Million
Emp.: 91
Postal Service
N.A.I.C.S.: 491110

Subsidiary (Non-US):

Posten Logistik SCM Oy (2)
Osumakuja 1-3, PO Box 179, 01530, Vantaa, Finland
Tel.: (358) 10 804 848
Web Site: http://www.postenlogistik.fi
Sales Range: $100-124.9 Million
Emp.: 300
Local Freight Trucking
N.A.I.C.S.: 484110
Jari Rinnekoski *(Mng Dir & Country Mgr)*

Stralfors A/S (2)
Hedegaardsvej 88, 2300, Copenhagen, Denmark
Tel.: (45) 33868686
Web Site: http://www.stralfors.dk
Emp.: 130
Product Labeling, Branding & Packaging Solutions
N.A.I.C.S.: 561910
Brian Kluge *(Mng Dir)*

Stralfors AG (2)
Pfeffingerring 201 Aesch, Basel, Switzerland
Tel.: (41) 617562020
Web Site: http://www.esonpat.com
Sales Range: $50-74.9 Million
Emp.: 120
Paperboard Mills
N.A.I.C.S.: 322130

Stralfors AS (2)
Haraldrudveien 11, 0581, Oslo, Norway
Tel.: (47) 23258500
Web Site: http://www.stralfors.no
Sales Range: $50-74.9 Million
Emp.: 160
Book Periodical & Newspaper Whslr
N.A.I.C.S.: 424920
Thomas Barreth *(Gen Mgr)*

AND PRIVATE COMPANIES / POU SHENG INTERNATIONAL (HOLDINGS) LIMITED

Stralfors Deutschland GmbH & Co. KG
Im Emerten 11, 31737, Rinteln, Germany
Tel.: (49) 575170400
Process Physical Distribution & Logistics Consulting Services
N.A.I.C.S.: 541614

Stralfors Finance SAS (2)
22 Terrasse Bellini, 5 rue Bellini, Puteaux, 92806, France
Tel.: (33) 147479600
Web Site: http://www.stralfors.com
Sales Range: $25-49.9 Million
Emp.: 4
Graphic Design Services
N.A.I.C.S.: 541430

Stralfors France S.A. (2)
Tour Arago Defense, 5 rue Bellini, Puteaux, France
Tel.: (33) 147479600
Sales Range: $10-24.9 Million
Emp.: 50
Graphic Design Services
N.A.I.C.S.: 541430

Subsidiary (Domestic):

Stralfors Goteborg AB (2)
Amalia Jonssons Gata 5 Vastra Frolunda, PO Box 126, SE 42122, Gothenburg, Sweden
Tel.: (46) 313367800
Web Site: http://www.stralfors.com
Sales Range: $200-249.9 Million
Emp.: 800
Paperboard Mills
N.A.I.C.S.: 322130
Per Samuelson (Pres)

Subsidiary (Non-US):

Stralfors Information Logistics A/S (2)
Midtager 33, Brondby, 2605, Denmark
Tel.: (45) 33868686
Web Site: http://www.stralfors.dk
Sales Range: $50-74.9 Million
Emp.: 80
Books Printing
N.A.I.C.S.: 323117
Thomas Knudsen (Country Mgr)

Stralfors Information Logistics OY (2)
Toinen Savu 4, PO Box 260, 01511, Vantaa, Finland
Tel.: (358) 207404100
Web Site: http://www.Stralfors.fi
Sales Range: $25-49.9 Million
Emp.: 70
Data Processing Services
N.A.I.C.S.: 518210

Subsidiary (Domestic):

Stralfors Maila Nordic AB (2)
Terminal vagen 24 7th floor, Stockholm, 10500, Sweden
Tel.: (46) 37285000
Web Site: http://www.stralfors.se
Sales Range: $25-49.9 Million
Emp.: 200
Management Consulting Services
N.A.I.C.S.: 541618
Per Samuelson (Mng Dir)

Subsidiary (Non-US):

Stralfors Medigrafik A/S (2)
Walgerholm 20-22, 3500, Vaerlose, Denmark
Tel.: (45) 44655600
Books Printing
N.A.I.C.S.: 323117

Stralfors NV (2)
Industriepark Noord 19, 9100, Saint-Niklaas, Belgium
Tel.: (32) 37807070
Metalworking Machines Mfr
N.A.I.C.S.: 333519

Stralfors Oy (2)
Toinen Savu 4, Vantaa, Finland
Tel.: (358) 96152615
Office Equipment Whslr
N.A.I.C.S.: 423420

Stralfors PLC

Stralfors PLC (3)
Cardrew Way Cornwall, Redruth, TR151SH, United Kingdom
Tel.: (44) 1209312800
Web Site: http://www.stralfors.com
Emp.: 100
Process Physical Distribution & Logistics Consulting Services
N.A.I.C.S.: 541614

Subsidiary (Domestic):

Stralfors PLC (3)
2nd Floor North Wing Riverbridge House Anchor Boulevard, Crossways Business Park, Dartford, DA2 6SL, United Kingdom
Tel.: (44) 1322425110
Web Site: http://www.stralfors.co.uk
Sales Range: $25-49.9 Million
Emp.: 50
Data Processing Hosting & Related Services
N.A.I.C.S.: 518210
Tony Plummer (Mng Dir)

Subsidiary (Non-US):

Stralfors SAS (2)
22 Terrasse Bellini, 92806, Puteaux, France
Tel.: (33) 147479600
Web Site: http://www.stralfors.fr
Sales Range: $25-49.9 Million
Emp.: 20
Graphic Design Services
N.A.I.C.S.: 541430
Bernard Sanguinetti (Mng Dir)

Stralfors Sp.zO.o (2)
ul Parkowa 56, Laskowice, 86130, Poland
Tel.: (48) 523318166
Web Site: http://www.stralfors.pl
Printing Services
N.A.I.C.S.: 323111

Subsidiary (Domestic):

Stralfors Svenska AB (2)
Helsingborgsvagen 20, 34184, Ljungby, Sweden
Tel.: (46) 37285000
Web Site: http://www.stralfors.com
Sales Range: $200-249.9 Million
Emp.: 550
Commercial Printing
N.A.I.C.S.: 323111
Anne Marie Dreshol (CEO)

Stralfors Tandsbyn AB (2)
Forfattarvagen 2, Tandsbyn, Ostersund, 83021, Sweden
Tel.: (46) 6327500
Web Site: http://www.stralfors.se
Sales Range: $25-49.9 Million
Emp.: 40
Commercial Printing Mfr
N.A.I.C.S.: 323111
John Nilsen (Mng Dir)

Subsidiary (Non-US):

TH Stralfors (Data Products) Ltd. (2)
Tregoniggie Industrial Estate, Falmouth, TR114RR, United Kingdom
Tel.: (44) 1326372778
Business Services
N.A.I.C.S.: 561499

Svensk Adressandring AB (1)
Drottninggatan 82, 11136, Stockholm, Sweden
Tel.: (46) 87813245
Management Consulting Services
N.A.I.C.S.: 541618

Tidningstjanst AB (1)
Kallargrand, Hudiksvall, 824 30, Sweden
Tel.: (46) 65 017 085
Direct Mailing Service
N.A.I.C.S.: 561431

Transbothnia AB (1)
Kontaktvagen 1, Box 3113, 903 03, Umea, Sweden
Tel.: (46) 10 437 29 00
Web Site: http://www.transbothnia.se
Logistics Consulting Servies
N.A.I.C.S.: 541614
Henrik Holm (CEO)

POTASH RIDGE CORPORATION
36 Toronto Street Suite 1000, Toronto, M5C 2C5, ON, Canada
Tel.: (416) 362-8640 ON
Web Site: http://www.potashridge.com
Year Founded: 2011
Sales Range: Less than $1 Million
Emp.: 3
Potash Mining
N.A.I.C.S.: 212390

POTASIOS DE CHILE SA
Calle El Trovador 4285 Piso 11, Las Condes, Santiago, Chile
Tel.: (56) 24294900
Year Founded: 2011
Mineral Exploration Services
N.A.I.C.S.: 213114
Ricardo Moreno (CEO)

POTEN ENVIRONMENT GROUP CO LTD
Floor 12A Shougang International Trade Tower, No 60 Xizhimen North Street Haidian District, Beijing, 100082, China
Tel.: (86) 1082293399
Web Site: http://www.poten.cn
Year Founded: 1995
603603—(SHG)
Rev.: $93,865,290
Assets: $1,123,934,109
Liabilities: $858,931,679
Net Worth: $265,002,431
Earnings: $224,234,735
Emp.: 2,400
Fiscal Year-end: 12/31/22
Water Environmental Solution Services
N.A.I.C.S.: 562910
Lijun Zhao (Chm)

POTHIER MOTORS LIMITED
18 Falmouth Back Road, Falmouth, B0P 1L0, NS, Canada
Tel.: (902) 798-9584
Web Site: https://www.pothiermotors.com
Year Founded: 1957
Sales Range: $10-24.9 Million
New & Used Car Dealers
N.A.I.C.S.: 441110
John Pothier (Pres & Principal-Dealer)

POTIS CAPITAL SA
Str Observatorului Nr 4 Hala C2, Sat Baciu Comuna Baciu, Cluj-Napoca, Romania
Tel.: (40) 740212457
POTI—(BUC)
Rev.: $121
Assets: $970,271
Liabilities: $55,694
Net Worth: $914,577
Earnings: ($17,439)
Emp.: 3
Fiscal Year-end: 12/31/23
Management Consulting Services
N.A.I.C.S.: 541611
Anamaria Octavia Buhos (Pres)

POTISJE PRECIZNI LIV A.D.
Molski put 4, 24430, Ada, Serbia
Tel.: (381) 24853122
Web Site: https://ppl.rs
Year Founded: 1998
PPLA—(BEL)
Rev.: $1,940,699
Assets: $2,229,706
Liabilities: $494,723
Net Worth: $1,734,982
Earnings: $21,408
Emp.: 73
Fiscal Year-end: 12/31/23
Steel Casting Services
N.A.I.C.S.: 331513

Milutin Vico (CEO)

POTKOZARJE A.D.
Vidovdanska bb, 78400, Banja Luka, Bosnia & Herzegovina
Tel.: (387) 51813588
Year Founded: 2001
PTKZ—(BANJ)
Sales Range: Less than $1 Million
Emp.: 4
Real Estate Prorperty Leasing Services
N.A.I.C.S.: 531190
Damir Janusic (Chm-Mgmt Bd & Pres)

POU CHEN CORPORATION
No 600 Sec 4 Taiwan Blvd, Xitun Dist, Taichung, 40764, Taiwan
Tel.: (886) 424615678 TW
Web Site: https://www.pouchen.com
Year Founded: 1969
9904—(TAI)
Rev.: $8,065,460,109
Assets: $10,712,623,782
Liabilities: $4,085,092,753
Net Worth: $6,627,531,029
Earnings: $522,367,651
Emp.: 204,781
Fiscal Year-end: 12/31/23
Holding Company; Design, Production, Processing & Sale of Shoes & Shoe Materials; Electronic Components Mfr & Sales
N.A.I.C.S.: 551112
Chi-Jui Tsai (Founder)

Subsidiaries:

Barits Development Corporation (1)
25 Hsin Gung 2nd-Road Ta Hsin Industrial Park, Tienchung Chen, Chang-Hua, 52046, Taiwan
Tel.: (886) 48752380
Web Site: http://www.primeasia.com.tw
Sales Range: $25-49.9 Million
Emp.: 200
Leather Mfr
N.A.I.C.S.: 316990

LNC Technology Co., Ltd (1)
6F No 633 Sec 2 Taiwan Blvd, Xitun Dist, Taichung, 40764, Taiwan
Tel.: (886) 423106859
Web Site: https://www.lnc.com.tw
Sales Range: $50-74.9 Million
Emp.: 100
Precision Tools Mfr & Distr
N.A.I.C.S.: 423830

Pou Yu Biotechnology Co., Ltd. (1)
6 Fu Gung Road, Fushing Hsiang, Chang-Hua, 50662, Taiwan
Tel.: (886) 47695147
Medical Appliances Whslr
N.A.I.C.S.: 423450

Windsor Entertainment Co., Ltd. (1)
78 3 Chung Kang Road Section 3, Taichung, 40764, Taiwan
Tel.: (886) 424655660
Web Site: http://www.windsortaiwan.com
Sales Range: $25-49.9 Million
Emp.: 100
Entertainment & Resort Services
N.A.I.C.S.: 721110

POU SHENG INTERNATIONAL (HOLDINGS) LIMITED
22nd Floor C Bons International Center 108 Wai Yip Street Kwun Tong, Kowloon, China (Hong Kong)
Tel.: (852) 31825800
Web Site: http://www.pousheng.com
3813—(HKG)
Rev.: $2,616,778,148
Assets: $1,909,280,084
Liabilities: $758,853,716
Net Worth: $1,150,426,368
Earnings: $14,073,415
Emp.: 25,800
Fiscal Year-end: 12/31/22

POU SHENG INTERNATIONAL (HOLDINGS) LIMITED

Pou Sheng International (Holdings) Limited—(Continued)

Sportswear Retailer
N.A.I.C.S.: 458110
Pan-Tsu Wu (Chm)

Subsidiaries:

Yue-Shen (Taicang) Footwear Co. Ltd. (1)
No 33 Changsheng Rd N Rd Economic Dev Zone, Taicang, 215400, Jiangsu, China
Tel.: (86) 51253442388
Sportswear Mfr
N.A.I.C.S.: 424350

POUJOULAT SA
BP 01, 79270, Saint-Symphorien, France
Tel.: (33) 549044040
Web Site: https://www.poujoulat.fr
ALPJT—(EUR)
Sales Range: $250-299.9 Million
Emp.: 1,400
Chimneys & Metal Roof Tops Mfr & Distr
N.A.I.C.S.: 332999
Frederic Coirier (Chm-Mgmt Bd)

Subsidiaries:

BEIRENS S.A.S. (1)
ZI Val de l'Indre, 36500, Buzancais, Indre, France
Tel.: (33) 254384807
Web Site: http://www.beirens.com
Rev.: $22,890,330
Emp.: 170
Industrial Chimney Mfr
N.A.I.C.S.: 327390

POUJOULAT BV
Schoorsteensystemen-Ettensestraat 60, 7061 AC, Terborg, Gelderland, Netherlands
Tel.: (31) 315340050
Web Site: http://www.poujoulat.nl
Emp.: 8
Chimney Mfr
N.A.I.C.S.: 327390

POUJOULAT BeLux S.A. (1)
Rue de l'industrie 39, 1400, Nivelles, Walloon Brabant, Belgium
Tel.: (32) 67840202
Web Site: http://fr.poujoulat.be
Chimneys & Metal Roof Tops Mfr & Distr
N.A.I.C.S.: 423330
Bruno Haemers (Dir-Sls)

POUJOULAT Sp. z o.o. (1)
ul Olszankowa 45, 05 120, Legionowo, Masovian, Poland
Tel.: (48) 227740625
Sales Range: $25-49.9 Million
Emp.: 22
Chimney Mfr
N.A.I.C.S.: 423620

TOLERIE FOREZIENNE S.A.S. (1)
10 rue de l'industrie, 42160, Bonson, Loire, France
Tel.: (33) 4 77 55 17 10
Web Site: http://www.tolerie-forezienne.com
Thin Metal Sheets Mfr
N.A.I.C.S.: 331491
Frederic Coirier (Gen Mgr)

WESTAFLEX BATIMENT S.A.S. (1)
330 Rue Des Trois Pierres, BP 60234, 59334, Tourcoing, Nord, France
Tel.: (33) 3 20 68 44 00
Web Site: http://www.westafrance.com
Chimney Mfr
N.A.I.C.S.: 327390

POULAILLON SA
Pretzels Moricettes MFP POULAILLON SA ZA HEIDEN EST, 8 rue du Luxembourg, 68310, Wittelsheim, France
Tel.: (33) 389338989 FR
Web Site: https://www.poulaillon.fr
Year Founded: 1973
ALPOU—(EUR)
Sales Range: $75-99.9 Million
Emp.: 754

Catering Services
N.A.I.C.S.: 722320
Fabien Poulaillon (CEO)

POULINA GROUP HOLDING S.A.
GP1 Km 12 Ezzahra Ben Arous, 2034, Tunis, Tunisia
Tel.: (216) 70 020 520
Web Site: htttp://www.poulinagroupholding.com
Year Founded: 1967
Sales Range: $750-799.9 Million
Emp.: 6,000
Holding Company
N.A.I.C.S.: 551112
M. Abdelwaheb Ben Ayed (CEO)

Subsidiaries:

Almes (1)
ZI route du Bac, Rades, Tunis, Tunisia
Tel.: (216) 71449403
Web Site: http://www.almes.com.tn
Sales Range: $100-124.9 Million
Emp.: 300
Edible Oils Processor
N.A.I.C.S.: 311225

Aster Informatique (1)
10th Ave Abdelaziz Thaalbi, El Menzah 9, 2092, Tunis, Tunisia
Tel.: (216) 71881002
Web Site: http://www.astershop.com
Sales Range: $25-49.9 Million
Emp.: 16
Computer Equipment & Software Whslr
N.A.I.C.S.: 423430

Carthago Ceramic (1)
GP1 Km 12 Ezzahra, Tunis, Tunisia
Tel.: (216) 71455444
Web Site: http://www.carthagoceramic.com
Sales Range: $125-149.9 Million
Emp.: 260
Ceramic Tile Mfr
N.A.I.C.S.: 327120

El Mazraa (1)
GP1 Km 25 Fondouk Djedid, Tunis, Tunisia
Tel.: (216) 72250222
Web Site: http://www.elmazraa.com
Sales Range: $25-49.9 Million
Emp.: 182
Poultry Processing Services
N.A.I.C.S.: 311615

Societe Tunisienne de l'Industrie du Bois (1)
BP 293 ZI Bir El Kassaa 2013, Ben Arous, Tunisia
Tel.: (216) 71381760
Sales Range: $50-74.9 Million
Emp.: 200
Wood Products Mfr
N.A.I.C.S.: 321999

Technique de l'Embellage en Carton (1)
Route Agareb km 14, 3075, Sfax, Tunisia
Tel.: (216) 74 84 23 33
Web Site: http://www.groupeunipack.com
Sales Range: $125-149.9 Million
Emp.: 275
Paperboard & Flexible Packaging Mfr
N.A.I.C.S.: 322219

POUNDSTRETCHER LTD.
Trident Business Park Leeds Road, Deighton, Huddersfield, HD2 1UA, United Kingdom
Tel.: (44) 1484431444
Web Site: http://www.poundstretcher.co.uk
Year Founded: 1981
Sales Range: $400-449.9 Million
Emp.: 6,000
Consumer Product Retailer
N.A.I.C.S.: 459999
Aziz Tayub (Chm)

Subsidiaries:

Poundstretcher Limited (1)
Unit 2 London Rd, Redhill, RH1 1LY, Surrey, United Kingdom
Tel.: (44) 1737778473
Commercial Appliances Retailer
N.A.I.C.S.: 449210

POVAL KOGYO CO., LTD.
30 Nakafuka Noda-cho, Nakamura-ku, Nagoya, 453-0858, Japan
Tel.: (81) 524111050
Web Site: https://www.poval.co.jp
4247—(TKS)
Rev.: $23,723,290
Assets: $45,456,970
Liabilities: $7,608,110
Net Worth: $37,848,860
Earnings: $1,222,850
Emp.: 200
Fiscal Year-end: 03/31/24
Rubber & Plastic Hoses & Belting Mfr
N.A.I.C.S.: 326220
Takao Kanda (Chm)

Subsidiaries:

POBAL DEVICE KOREA CO., LTD. (1)
C 432 Sandong-Myeon Bongsan-Ri, Gumi, 730-853, Gyeongsangbuk-Do, Korea (South)
Tel.: (82) 544711282
Industrial Belt Distr
N.A.I.C.S.: 423840

POVAL KOBASHI (THAILAND) CO., LTD. (1)
Sindhorn Bldg Tower III 15th Floor 130-132 Wireless Rd Patumwan, Bangkok, 10330, Thailand
Tel.: (66) 26514842
Industrial Belt Distr
N.A.I.C.S.: 423840

POVAL KUSHAN CO., LTD. (1)
1333 Jinmao Road, Zhoushi Town, Kunshan, 215314, Jiangsu, China
Tel.: (86) 51250131711
Industrial Belt Distr
N.A.I.C.S.: 423840

Poval Kogyo Co., Ltd. - Daian Factory (1)
2246 Shinki Katahi Daian-cho, Inabe, 511-0271, Mie, Japan
Tel.: (81) 594783032
Industrial Belt Mfr
N.A.I.C.S.: 332618

POWDERTECH CO., LTD.
217 Toyofuta, Kashiwa, 277, Chiba, Japan
Tel.: (81) 471455751
Year Founded: 1966
5695—(TKS)
Rev.: $85,544,125
Assets: $149,377,375
Liabilities: $30,034,630
Net Worth: $119,342,745
Earnings: $7,916,672
Emp.: 200
Fiscal Year-end: 03/31/22
Printer Machinery Mfr & Distr
N.A.I.C.S.: 333248
Akira Nakako (Sr Mng Dir)

Subsidiaries:

PTS Co., Ltd. (1)
217 Toyofuta, Kashiwa, 277-8557, Chiba, Japan
Tel.: (81) 471452129
Oxygen Absorber Packaging Services
N.A.I.C.S.: 561910

Powdertech International Corporation (1)
2501 Chicago St Ste B, Valparaiso, IN 46383-6087
Tel.: (219) 548-3693
Ferrite Powder Mfr
N.A.I.C.S.: 327110

Wonderkeep Takahagi Co., Ltd. (1)
1201-12 Takada, Kashiwa, 277-0861, Chiba, Japan
Tel.: (81) 471465822

Oxygen Absorber Mfr
N.A.I.C.S.: 332420

POWEL AS
Klaebuveien 194, 7037, Trondheim, Norway
Tel.: (47) 73804500 NO
Web Site: http://www.powel.com
Year Founded: 1996
Sales Range: $75-99.9 Million
Emp.: 280
Energy & Public Sector Software Developer & Distr
N.A.I.C.S.: 513210
Bard Benum (CEO)

Subsidiaries:

Powel AB (1)
Ostra Storg 67, 553 21, Jonkoping, Sweden
Tel.: (46) 36 34 49 00
Web Site: http://www.powel.com
Emp.: 65
Software Development Services
N.A.I.C.S.: 541511

Powel Danmark A/S (1)
Niels Bohrs Alle 185, 5220, Odense, Denmark
Tel.: (45) 738 04500
Web Site: http://www.powel.dk
Software Development Services
N.A.I.C.S.: 541511

Powel Enerji Cozumleri Limited Sirketi (1)
Buyukdere Caddesi No 127 Astoria is Merkezi B Kule, 1305, Istanbul, Turkiye
Tel.: (90) 212 215 21 66
Web Site: http://www.powel.com
Emp.: 2
Software Development Services
N.A.I.C.S.: 541511
Serhat Simsek (Gen Mgr)

Powel sp. z.o.o. (1)
Gdansk Science and Technology Park Trzy Lipy 3, 80-172, Gdansk, Poland
Tel.: (48) 73 80 45 00
Software Development Services
N.A.I.C.S.: 541511

POWELL MOTORS LTD
804 Main St Hwy 10A, Swan River, R0L 1Z0, MB, Canada
Tel.: (204) 734-3464
Web Site: http://www.powellmotors.ca
Rev.: $13,737,302
Emp.: 30
New & Used Car Dealers
N.A.I.C.S.: 441110
Wayne Grier (Bus Mgr)

POWER & INSTRUMENTATION (GUJARAT) LTD.
B-1104 Sankalp Iconic Opp Vikram Nagar, Iscon Temple Cross Road S G Highway, Ahmedabad, 380054, Gujarat, India
Tel.: (91) 7940031612
Web Site: https://www.grouppower.org
Year Founded: 1975
543912—(BOM)
Rev.: $11,423,776
Assets: $12,797,794
Liabilities: $7,361,669
Net Worth: $5,436,125
Earnings: $432,828
Emp.: 47
Fiscal Year-end: 03/31/23
Engineeering Services
N.A.I.C.S.: 541330
Padmaraj Padmnabhan Pillai (Mng Dir)

POWER ASSETS HOLDINGS LIMITED
Unit 2005 20/F Cheung Kong Center

2 Queen's Road, GPO Box 338, Central, China (Hong Kong)
Tel.: (852) 21229122 HK
Web Site:
https://www.powerassets.com
6—(HKG)
Rev.: $165,118,151
Assets: $12,230,756,451
Liabilities: $888,212,967
Net Worth: $11,342,543,484
Earnings: $767,185,962
Emp.: 13
Fiscal Year-end: 12/31/23
Holding Company
N.A.I.C.S.: 551112
Ivan Kee Ham Chan *(CFO)*

Subsidiaries:

Associated Technical Services
Ltd. (1)
Hong Kong Electric Ctr 44 Kennedy Rd,
Wanchai, China (Hong Kong) **(100%)**
Tel.: (852) 28433111
Web Site: http://www.hec.com.hk
Sales Range: $350-399.9 Million
Provider of Consultancy, Project Management & Engineering Services
N.A.I.C.S.: 541330
Chi Tin Wan *(Mng Dir)*

CitiPower (1)
PO Box 14090, Melbourne, 8001, VIC,
Australia **(50%)**
Tel.: (61) 1300301101
Web Site: http://www.citipower.com.au
Sales Range: $650-699.9 Million
Emp.: 1,500
Electric Power Distr
N.A.I.C.S.: 221122
Peter Tulloch *(Chm)*

Hongkong Electric International
Ltd. (1)
44 Kennedy Rd, Wanchai, China (Hong Kong) **(100%)**
Tel.: (852) 28433111
Web Site: http://www.hec.com.hk
Sales Range: $50-74.9 Million
Emp.: 100
Provider of Investment Services
N.A.I.C.S.: 523940
Chi Tin Wan *(Mng Dir)*

Powercor Australia Limited (1)
40 Market St, Melbourne, 3000, VIC,
Australia **(50%)**
Tel.: (61) 396834444
Web Site: http://www.powercor.com.au
Sales Range: $75-99.9 Million
Emp.: 80
Electric Power Distr
N.A.I.C.S.: 221122

SA Power Networks (1)
1 ANZAC Highway, Keswick, 5035, SA,
Australia **(50%)**
Tel.: (61) 131261
Web Site:
https://www.sapowernetworks.com.au
Sales Range: $1-4.9 Billion
Emp.: 2,000
Electricity Distr
N.A.I.C.S.: 221122
David Syme *(Gen Mgr-People & Culture)*

The Hongkong Electric Co., Ltd. (1)
44 Kennedy Rd, PO Box 915, Wanchai,
China (Hong Kong) **(100%)**
Tel.: (852) 28433111
Web Site: http://www.hec.hk
Sales Range: $500-549.9 Million
Emp.: 1,000
Providers of Electrical Services
N.A.I.C.S.: 221122

POWER CAPITAL GLOBAL LIMITED
Nemours Chambers Qwomar Complex 4th Floor, PO Box 3170, Tortola,
SW1A 1LE, Virgin Islands (British)
Web Site:
http://www.powercapitalglobal.com
Venture Capital Investment Services
N.A.I.C.S.: 523999
Simon Dewhurst *(CEO)*

POWER CEMENT LIMITED
Arif Habib Center 23 M T Khan Road,
Karachi, 74000, Pakistan
Tel.: (92) 2132468231
Web Site:
https://www.powercement.com.pk
Year Founded: 1981
POWER—(LAH)
Rev.: $27,703,707
Assets: $287,260,334
Liabilities: $199,509,676
Net Worth: $87,750,657
Earnings: $4,179,521
Emp.: 360
Fiscal Year-end: 06/30/19
Cement Mfr
N.A.I.C.S.: 327120
Muhammad Kashif A. Habib *(CEO)*

POWER CONSTRUCTION CORPORATION OF CHINA
No 22 Chegongzhuang West Road,
Haidian District, Beijing, 100048,
China
Tel.: (86) 1058368779
Web Site: https://en.powerchina.cn
Year Founded: 2011
601669—(SHG)
Rev.: $80,394,857,787
Assets: $146,026,966,518
Liabilities: $112,282,669,999
Net Worth: $33,744,296,519
Earnings: $1,605,536,310
Emp.: 210,000
Fiscal Year-end: 12/31/22
Power Plant Design & Construction Services
N.A.I.C.S.: 237990
Yan Zhiyong *(Chm)*

Subsidiaries:

Hydrochina Corporation (1)
No 2 Beixiaojie Liupukang Dewai, Beijing,
100120, China
Tel.: (86) 10 5197 3399
Web Site: http://www.hydrochina.com.cn
Power Station Design & Construction Services
N.A.I.C.S.: 237990
Bin Wang *(Pres)*

SINOHYDRO Corporation (1)
22 Chegongzhuang West Road, Haidian
District, Beijing, 100048, China
Tel.: (86) 1058960134
Web Site: https://www.sinohydro.com
Sales Range: $5-14.9 Billion
Emp.: 130,000
Hydropower Construction Services
N.A.I.C.S.: 237130

TLT-Turbo GmbH (1)
Gleiwitzstrasse 7, 66482, Zweibrucken,
Germany **(100%)**
Tel.: (49) 63328080
Web Site: https://www.tlt-turbo.com
Sales Range: $25-49.9 Million
Emp.: 345
Industrial Fans & Ventilation Systems Mfr
N.A.I.C.S.: 333413
Rainer Redinger *(Mng Dir)*

POWER CORPORATION OF CANADA
751 Victoria Square, Montreal, H2Y
2J3, QC, Canada
Tel.: (514) 286-7400 Ca
Web Site:
https://www.powercorporation.com
Year Founded: 1925
POW—(TSX)
Rev.: $50,547,804,480
Assets: $492,135,477,120
Liabilities: $461,835,425,880
Net Worth: $30,300,051,240
Earnings: $2,764,577,520
Emp.: 30,000
Fiscal Year-end: 12/31/20
Financial Investment Services
N.A.I.C.S.: 551112

Andre Desmarais *(Deputy Chm & Deputy Chm)*

Subsidiaries:

Gesca, ltee. (1)
7 rue Saint Jacques W, Montreal, H2Y 1K9,
QC, Canada **(100%)**
Tel.: (514) 285-7272
Web Site: http://www.lapresse.ca
Sales Range: $200-249.9 Million
Emp.: 800
Newspaper Publishers
N.A.I.C.S.: 513110
Guy Crevrer *(Pres & CEO)*

Lumenpuies Group Inc. (1)
1220 Marie-Victorin Blvd, Longueuil, J4G
2H9, QC, Canada
Tel.: (514) 937-3003
Web Site: https://www.lmpg.com
Emp.: 800
Lighting Product Mfr
N.A.I.C.S.: 335132
Francois Xavier Souvay *(Founder & CEO)*

Lumenpulse Inc. (1)
1220 Marie-Victorin Blvd, Longueuil, J4G
2H9, QC, Canada **(55.7%)**
Tel.: (514) 937-3003
Web Site: https://www.lumenpulse.com
Emp.: 392
LED Lighting Mfr
N.A.I.C.S.: 334419
Francois-Xavier Souvay *(Founder & CEO)*

Potentia Renewables Inc. (1)
200 Wellington Street West-Suite 1102, Toronto, M5V 3C7, ON, Canada
Tel.: (416) 703-1911
Web Site:
https://www.potentiarenewables.com
Renewable Energy Services
N.A.I.C.S.: 221112
Jeff Jenner *(CEO)*

Power Energy Corporation (1)
751 Square Victoria, Montreal, H2Y 2J3,
QC, Canada
Tel.: (514) 286-7400
Privater Equity Firm
N.A.I.C.S.: 523940
Pierre Lorochelle *(Pres & CEO)*

Holding (US):

Nautilus Solar Energy, LLC (2)
396 Springfield Ave 2nd Fl, Summit, NJ
07901
Tel.: (484) 492-8663
Web Site: http://www.nautilussolar.com
Power & Communication Line Construction
N.A.I.C.S.: 237130
David Munsky *(VP-Bus Dev)*

Power Financial Corporation (1)
751 Victoria Square, Montreal, H2Y 2J3,
QC, Canada **(66.1%)**
Tel.: (514) 286-7430
Web Site: https://www.powerfinancial.com
Rev.: $36,580,002,480
Assets: $360,712,709,280
Liabilities: $334,914,938,400
Net Worth: $25,797,770,880
Earnings: $2,425,045,560
Emp.: 28,400
Fiscal Year-end: 12/31/2019
Holding Company that Provides Life, Health
& Disability Insurance & Investments
N.A.I.C.S.: 551112
Andre Desmarais *(Deputy Chm)*

Subsidiary (Domestic):

Great-West Lifeco, Inc. (2)
100 Osborne Street North, Winnipeg, R3C
1V3, MB, Canada **(68.2%)**
Tel.: (204) 946-1190
Web Site: https://www.greatwestlifeco.com
Rev.: $50,392,130,760
Assets: $493,218,152,640
Liabilities: $469,371,911,400
Net Worth: $23,846,241,240
Earnings: $2,551,797,360
Emp.: 28,000
Fiscal Year-end: 12/31/2021
Financial Holding Company
N.A.I.C.S.: 551112
R. Jeffrey Orr *(Chm)*

Subsidiary (US):

Great-West Life & Annuity Insurance
Company (3)
8515 E Orchard Rd, Greenwood Village,
CO 80111 **(100%)**
Tel.: (303) 737-3000
Web Site: http://www.greatwest.com
Rev.: $2,775,920,000
Assets: $62,461,262,000
Liabilities: $60,011,673,000
Net Worth: $2,449,589,000
Earnings: $369,116,000
Emp.: 5,800
Fiscal Year-end: 12/31/2017
Life, Medical & Accident Insurance & Annuity Services
N.A.I.C.S.: 524113
Richard G. Schultz *(Chief Legal Officer & Gen Counsel)*

Subsidiary (Domestic):

Great-West Financial Retirement Plan
Services, LLC (4)
11500 Outlook St, Overland Park, KS
66211-1804
Tel.: (847) 857-3000
Web Site: http://www.retireonline.com
Retirement Planning & Financial Investment
Advisory Services
N.A.I.C.S.: 523940

Subsidiary (US):

PanAgora Asset Management,
Inc. (3)
1 International Pl 24th Fl, Boston, MA
02110-3112
Tel.: (617) 439-6300
Web Site: http://www.panagora.com
Sales Range: $50-74.9 Million
Emp.: 70
Asset Management Services
N.A.I.C.S.: 523940
Eric Sorensen *(Pres & CEO)*

Subsidiary (Domestic):

The Canada Life Assurance
Company (3)
330 University Ave, Toronto, M5G 1R8, ON,
Canada
Tel.: (416) 597-1456
Web Site: http://www.canadalife.com
Emp.: 11,275
Insurance Services
N.A.I.C.S.: 524113

Subsidiary (Domestic):

GWL Realty Advisors, Inc. (4)
33 Yonge Street Suite 1000, Toronto, M5E
1G4, ON, Canada
Tel.: (416) 507-2929
Web Site:
https://www.gwlrealtyadvisors.com
Sales Range: $50-74.9 Million
Emp.: 40
Real Estate Investment Services
N.A.I.C.S.: 523940
Ralf Dost *(Pres)*

Investment Planning Counsel
Inc. (4)
5015 Spectrum Way Suite 200, Mississauga, L4W 0E4, ON, Canada
Tel.: (905) 212-9799
Web Site: https://www.ipcc.ca
Emp.: 20
Wealth Management Services
N.A.I.C.S.: 523940

Subsidiary (Non-US):

Irish Life Group Limited (4)
Irish Life Centre Lower Abbey Street, Dublin, 1, Ireland
Tel.: (353) 17041010
Web Site: http://www.irishlifegroup.ie
Holding Company; Insurance Products & Services
N.A.I.C.S.: 551112

Subsidiary (Domestic):

Irish Life Assurance plc (5)
Irish Life Centre Lower Abbey Street, PO
Box 129, Dublin, Ireland **(100%)**
Tel.: (353) 17041010

POWER CORPORATION OF CANADA

Power Corporation of Canada—(Continued)

Web Site: http://www.irishlife.ie
Life Insurance Products & Services
N.A.I.C.S.: 524113

Subsidiary (Domestic):

Laketon Investments (4)
130 Adelaide St W Ste 800, Toronto, M5H 1P9, ON, Canada (100%)
Tel.: (416) 864-0947
Sales Range: $10-24.9 Million
Emp.: 47
Investment Services
N.A.I.C.S.: 523160

London Insurance Group, Inc. (4)
255 Dufferin Ave, London, N6A 4K1, ON, Canada
Tel.: (519) 432-5281
Web Site: http://www.londonlife.com
Sales Range: $5-14.9 Billion
Financial Services
N.A.I.C.S.: 523940

Subsidiary (Domestic):

London Life Insurance Company (5)
255 Dufferin Avenue, London, N6A 4K1, ON, Canada (100%)
Tel.: (519) 432-5281
Web Site: http://www.londonlife.com
Rev.: $13,381,100,320
Assets: $70,870,136,330
Liabilities: $67,749,883,040
Net Worth: $3,120,253,290
Earnings: $450,776,550
Emp.: 2,500
Fiscal Year-end: 12/31/2018
Life, Health, Savings & Retirement Products
N.A.I.C.S.: 524114
Paul A. Mahon *(Co-Pres & CEO)*

Subsidiary (Non-US):

The Canada Life Group (U.K.) Limited (4)
Canada Life Place, Potters Bar, EN6 5BA, Herts, United Kingdom
Tel.: (44) 8453454333
Sales Range: $50-74.9 Million
Emp.: 300
Insurance Services & Products
N.A.I.C.S.: 524113
Ian McMullen *(Mng Dir-Grp Insurance)*

Subsidiary (Domestic):

Canada Life Limited (5)
Canada Life Place, Potters Bar, EN6 5BA, Hertfordshire, United Kingdom
Tel.: (44) 3456060708
Web Site: https://www.canadalife.co.uk
Insurance Services
N.A.I.C.S.: 524298
Jon Ford *(Dir-Individual Protection)*

Subsidiary (Domestic):

Canada Life (U.K.) Limited (6)
Canada Life Place, High Street, Potters Bar, EN6 5BA, Herts, United Kingdom (100%)
Tel.: (44) 1707651122
Web Site: http://www.canadalife.co.uk
Sales Range: $150-199.9 Million
Emp.: 1,200
Coordinates MetLife's Diversification & Expansion in the United Kingdom
N.A.I.C.S.: 524298

Subsidiary (Domestic):

Canada Life Management (U.K.) Limited (7)
Canada Life Pl High St, Potters Bar, EN6 5BA, Herts, United Kingdom
Tel.: (44) 8457226232
Web Site: http://www.canadalife.co.uk
Sales Range: $50-74.9 Million
Emp.: 500
Insurance Services
N.A.I.C.S.: 524113

Subsidiary (Domestic):

Canada Life Trustee Limited (5)
Canada Life Pl High St, Potters Bar, EN6 5BA, Herts, United Kingdom
Tel.: (44) 8457226232

Web Site: http://www.canadalife.co.uk
Sales Range: $50-74.9 Million
Insurance Services
N.A.I.C.S.: 524113

The Canada Life Assurance Company (U.K.) Limited (5)
Canada Life Place, High Street, Potters Bar, EN6 5BA, Herts, United Kingdom
Tel.: (44) 1707651122
Web Site: http://www.canadalife.co.uk
Sales Range: $50-74.9 Million
Emp.: 500
Life Insurance
N.A.I.C.S.: 524113

Subsidiary (Domestic):

IGM Financial Inc. (2)
447 Portage Avenue, Winnipeg, R3B 3H5, MB, Canada (57.6%)
Tel.: (204) 943-0361
Web Site: https://www.igmfinancial.com
Rev.: $2,360,906,959
Assets: $12,565,258,287
Liabilities: $8,620,384,526
Net Worth: $3,944,873,761
Earnings: $598,135,982
Emp.: 3,525
Fiscal Year-end: 12/31/2020
Premier Mutual Fund, Managed Asset & Personal Financial Services
N.A.I.C.S.: 523150
R. Jeffrey Orr *(Chm)*

Subsidiary (Domestic):

Investors Group, Inc. (3)
447 Portage Ave, Winnipeg, R3B 3H5, MB, Canada (100%)
Tel.: (204) 943-0361
Web Site: https://www.ig.ca
Sales Range: $700-749.9 Million
Emp.: 1,300
Financial Planning Services
N.A.I.C.S.: 523940

MacKenzie Financial Corporation (3)
180 Queen Street West, Toronto, M5V 3K1, ON, Canada (100%)
Tel.: (416) 922-3217
Web Site:
https://www.mackenzieinvestments.com
Rev.: $1,077,393
Assets: $1,018,689
Liabilities: $300,658
Net Worth: $718,030
Earnings: $718,030
Fiscal Year-end: 12/31/2016
Common Stock & Bond Portfolio Management Services
N.A.I.C.S.: 523940
Barry McInerney *(Pres & CEO)*

Subsidiary (Domestic):

Mackenzie Cundill Investment Management Ltd. (4)
200 Burrard St Ste 400, Vancouver, V6C 3L6, BC, Canada
Tel.: (604) 601-8300
Web Site: http://www.mackenziecundill.com
Sales Range: $50-74.9 Million
Emp.: 22
Investment Research & Management Services
N.A.I.C.S.: 523940

Affiliate (Domestic):

Wealthsimple Financial Corp. (3)
80 Spadina Avenue 4th Floor, Toronto, M5V 2J4, ON, Canada (36.3%)
Web Site: https://www.wealthsimple.com
Online Investment Management Services
N.A.I.C.S.: 523999
Paul Desmarais III *(Chm)*

Subsidiary (Non-US):

Power Financial Europe B.V. (2)
Veerkade 5, 3016 DE, Rotterdam, Netherlands (100%)
Tel.: (31) 4139154
Holding Company
N.A.I.C.S.: 551112
Jocelyn Lefebvre *(Mng Dir)*

Joint Venture (Domestic):

Parjointco N.V. (3)

Veerkade 5, Rotterdam, 3016DE, Netherlands (100%)
Tel.: (31) 4139154
Holding Company; Joint Venture Between Power Financial Europe BV & Agesca Netherland NV
N.A.I.C.S.: 551112

Holding (Non-US):

Pargesa Holding S.A. (4)
11 Grand-Rue, CH-1204, Geneva, Switzerland
Tel.: (41) 228177777
Web Site: http://www.pargesa.ch
Rev.: $5,770,980,992
Assets: $35,020,798,912
Liabilities: $11,115,023,488
Net Worth: $23,905,775,424
Earnings: $866,543,040
Emp.: 94,000
Fiscal Year-end: 12/31/2019
Holding Company
N.A.I.C.S.: 551112
Andre Desmarais *(Vice Chm)*

Sagard Capital Partners Management Corp. (1)
280 Park Ave, New York, NY 01007 (100%)
Tel.: (203) 629-6700
Web Site: http://www.sagardcapital.com
Private Equity & Investment Management Firm
N.A.I.C.S.: 523999
Greg Martinsen *(CFO)*

Subsidiary (Domestic):

Sagard Capital Partners, L.P. (2)
325 Greenwich Ave, Greenwich, CT 06830
Tel.: (203) 629-6700
Web Site: http://www.sagardcapital.com
Emp.: 48
Privater Equity Firm
N.A.I.C.S.: 523999

Sagard Holdings ULC (1)
280 Park Ave 3F W, New York, NY 10017
Tel.: (212) 380-5605
Web Site: http://www.sagardholdings.com
Asset Management Services
N.A.I.C.S.: 523940
Paul Desmarais III *(Chm & CEO)*

Holding (Domestic):

IntegraMed America, Inc. (2)
2 Manhattanville Rd, Purchase, NY 10577-2113
Tel.: (914) 253-8000
Web Site: http://www.integramed.com
Sales Range: $250-299.9 Million
Emp.: 1,259
Management Support to Reproductive Healthcare Specialists
N.A.I.C.S.: 561499

Joint Venture (Domestic):

9938982 Canada Inc. (3)
100 Domain Dr, Exeter, NH 03833-4801
Tel.: (603) 610-5802
Holding Company
N.A.I.C.S.: 551112
Paul Desmarais III *(Chm)*

Subsidiary (Domestic):

Bauer Hockey, Inc. (4)
100 Domain Dr, Exeter, NH 03833-4801
Tel.: (603) 430-2111
Web Site: http://www.bauer.com
Hockey Equipment Designer, Mfr & Marketer
N.A.I.C.S.: 423910

Combat Sports (4)
6651 S 216th St, Kent, WA 98032
Tel.: (253) 891-8377
Web Site:
http://www.combatsportsgroup.com
Sporting & Athletic Goods Distr
N.A.I.C.S.: 423910

Easton Baseball/Softball Inc. (4)
3500 Willow Ln, Thousand Oaks, CA 91361
Web Site: https://easton.rawlings.com
Sports Equipment, Sport Bags & Accessories Mfr & Whslr
N.A.I.C.S.: 339920

INTERNATIONAL PUBLIC

Subsidiary (Non-US):

Inaria International Inc. (4)
600 Steeprock Dr, Toronto, M6M 4L5, ON, Canada
Tel.: (416) 766-8825
Web Site: http://www.inariasoccer.com
Sporting & Athletic Goods Whslr
N.A.I.C.S.: 423910

Subsidiary (Domestic):

Maverik Lacrosse (4)
535 W 24th St 5th Fl, New York, NY 10011-1140
Tel.: (800) 537-1702
Web Site: http://www.maveriklacrosse.com
Sporting & Athletic Goods Whslr
N.A.I.C.S.: 423910

Division (Domestic):

IntegraMed America Consumer Services Division (3)
2 Manhattanville Rd 3rd Fl, Purchase, NY 10577-2113
Tel.: (914) 253-8000
Sales Range: $10-24.9 Million
Emp.: 50
Business Support Services
N.A.I.C.S.: 561499

IntegraMed America Fertility Centers (3)
2 Manhattanville Rd, Purchase, NY 10577-2113
Tel.: (914) 253-8000
Sales Range: $100-124.9 Million
Business Support Services for Fertility Centers
N.A.I.C.S.: 561499
Joe Travia *(Pres)*

IntegraMed America Vein Clinics (3)
2 Manhattanville Rd, Purchase, NY 10577-2113
Tel.: (914) 253-8000
Sales Range: $100-124.9 Million
Emp.: 50
Business Support Services for Vein Disease Treatment Centers
N.A.I.C.S.: 561499

Subsidiary (Domestic):

Reproductive Partners, Inc. (3)
6330 San Vicente Blvd Ste 408, Los Angeles, CA 90048
Tel.: (310) 855-2229
Web Site:
https://www.reproductivepartners.com
Sales Range: $10-24.9 Million
Emp.: 20
Infertility Treatment Services
N.A.I.C.S.: 621410

Sagard SAS (1)
49/51 Avenue George V, 75008, Paris, France
Tel.: (33) 15 383 3000
Web Site: https://www.sagard.com
Sales Range: $50-74.9 Million
Emp.: 10
Privater Equity Firm
N.A.I.C.S.: 523999
Rik Battey *(Partner)*

Holding (Domestic):

ALVEST SAS (2)
100-104 boulevard du Montparnasse, 75014, Paris, France
Tel.: (33) 14 064 1610
Web Site: https://alvest.fr
Sales Range: $450-499.9 Million
Holding Company; Airport Ground Support Equipment Mfr & Distr
N.A.I.C.S.: 551112

Subsidiary (Domestic):

Adhetec SAS (4)
Zone Bastillac Sud, BP 123, 65001, Tarbes, France
Tel.: (33) 56 251 7880
Web Site: https://www.adhetec.com
Adhesive Film Technologies Mfr & Distr
N.A.I.C.S.: 325520

Subsidiary (US):

Sage Parts Plus, Inc. (3)

30 Hub Dr, Melville, NY 11747
Tel.: (631) 501-1300
Web Site: https://www.sagegse.com
Emp.: 50
Airport Ground Support Equipment Parts Distr
N.A.I.C.S.: 423120
Mark Pollack *(Pres & CEO)*

Subsidiary (Domestic):

TLD Group SAS (3)
3 Rue Eiffel, 37270, Montlouis-sur-Loire, France
Tel.: (33) 247457777
Web Site: http://www.tld-gse.com
Emp.: 1,200
Holding Company; Airport Ground Support Equipment Designer, Mfr & Distr
N.A.I.C.S.: 551112
Jean-Marie Fulconis *(Chm)*

Subsidiary (US):

TLD America Corporation (4)
812 Bloomfield Ave, Windsor, CT 06095
Web Site: http://www.tld-group.com
Airport Ground Support Equipment Designer, Mfr & Distr
N.A.I.C.S.: 333924
Michael Rawls *(Mgr-Svc)*

Subsidiary (Non-US):

TLD Asia Limited (4)
Unit 1412 Fo Tan Industrial Center 26-28 Au Pui Wan Street, Hong Kong, China (Hong Kong)
Tel.: (852) 2692 2181
Web Site: http://www.tld-group.com
Airport Ground Support Equipment Designer, Mfr & Distr
N.A.I.C.S.: 333924
Allen Fu *(Chm-CSEA)*

TLD China (4)
No 3109 South Shenjiang Road, Pudong New District, 201321, Shanghai, China
Tel.: (86) 21 58153322
Aircraft Equipment Distr
N.A.I.C.S.: 423860
Chris Tam *(Exec Dir-Sls & Svc)*

Subsidiary (Domestic):

TLD Europe SAS (4)
3 Rue Gustave Eiffel, CS 30002, 37270, Mont Louis, Sur Loire, France
Tel.: (33) 247457777
Web Site: http://www.tld-gse.com
Airport Ground Support Equipment Designer, Mfr & Distr
N.A.I.C.S.: 333924

Subsidiary (Non-US):

TLD MIDDLE EAST (4)
Dubai Airport Free Zone Airbus Building West Ring Road, PO Box 549, Plot 20/22 Office 1 104, Dubai, United Arab Emirates
Tel.: (971) 47 030 410
Aircraft Equipment Distr
N.A.I.C.S.: 423860
Christophe Lesbaudy *(Dir-Sls & Svc)*

Holding (Domestic):

EuroDough S.A.S. (2)
rue Francois Jacob, 62800, Lievin, France
Tel.: (33) 3 2172 7575
Web Site: http://www.eurodough.com
Mfr of Refrigerated Dough Products
N.A.I.C.S.: 311812

Victoria Square Ventures Inc. (1)
751 Square-Victoria, Montreal, H2Y 2J3, QC, Canada
Tel.: (514) 286-7400
Web Site: http://www.powercorp.ca
Sales Range: $50-74.9 Million
Emp.: 100
Investment Management Service
N.A.I.C.S.: 523999
Andre Desmarais *(Pres)*

POWER DEVELOPMENT SERVICES (PTY) LIMITED
275 Granville Avenue North Robertville Ext 10, PO Box 6337, Weltevreden Park, Roodepoort, 1715, South Africa
Tel.: (27) 114720669 ZA
Web Site: http://www.pdspower.co.za
Year Founded: 1994
Power Generating Equipments Mfr & Distr
N.A.I.C.S.: 423610
Stephen Mackie *(Mgr-Projects)*

Subsidiaries:

Durapower Manufacturing (Pty) Limited (1)
275 Granville Avenue North Robertville Ext 10, Roodepoort, 1709, South Africa
Tel.: (27) 116724720
Web Site: http://www.durapower.co.za
Power Equipment & Supply Mfr
N.A.I.C.S.: 335999
Rainer Krisch *(Mgr)*

Subsidiary (Domestic):

Gillespie Diesel Services (Pty) Limited (2)
6 Tungsten Road, Isando, 1600, South Africa
Tel.: (27) 11 392 3065
Web Site: http://www.gillespiedieselservices.co.za
Emp.: 30
Diesel Generators Assembling & Distr
N.A.I.C.S.: 423610

POWER ENGINEERING CONSULTING JOINT STOCK COMPANY 2
32 Ngo Thoi Nhiem, Ward Vo Thi Sau District 3, Ho Chi Minh City, Vietnam
Tel.: (84) 2822216468
Web Site: https://www.pecc2.com
Year Founded: 1981
Rev.: $73,616,602
Assets: $87,707,760
Liabilities: $59,746,427
Net Worth: $27,961,333
Earnings: $9,004,195
Emp.: 743
Fiscal Year-end: 12/31/18
Engineering Consulting Services
N.A.I.C.S.: 541330
Nguyen Chon Hung *(Chm)*

POWER ENGINEERING CONSULTING JOINT STOCK COMPANY 3
32 Ngo Thoi Nhiem St Ward 7, District 3, Ho Chi Minh City, Vietnam
Tel.: (84) 2822211169
Web Site: https://www.pecc3.com.vn
TV3—(HNX)
Rev.: $20,092,600
Assets: $28,394,900
Liabilities: $13,452,000
Net Worth: $14,942,900
Earnings: $1,482,800
Emp.: 400
Fiscal Year-end: 12/31/23
Hydroelectric Power Generation Services
N.A.I.C.S.: 221111
Thai Tuan Tai *(Chm)*

POWER ENGINEERING CONSULTING JOINT STOCK COMPANY 4
11 Hoang Hoa Tham St, Nha Trang, Khanh Hoa, Vietnam
Tel.: (84) 2583563999
Web Site: https://pecc4.vn
Year Founded: 1976
TV4—(HNX)
Rev.: $29,970,500
Assets: $40,596,000
Liabilities: $15,062,100
Net Worth: $25,533,900
Earnings: $4,151,500
Emp.: 445
Fiscal Year-end: 12/31/22
Engineering Consulting Services
N.A.I.C.S.: 541330

POWER FINANCE CORPORATION LIMITED
Urjanidhi 1 Barakhamba Lane Connaught Place, New Delhi, 110 001, India
Tel.: (91) 1123456000 In
Web Site: https://pfcindia.com
Year Founded: 1988
532810—(BOM)
Rev.: $9,307,018,764
Assets: $107,441,023,919
Liabilities: $94,014,816,858
Net Worth: $13,426,207,062
Earnings: $2,539,247,048
Emp.: 519
Fiscal Year-end: 03/31/23
Financial Investment Services
N.A.I.C.S.: 523999
Rajeev Sharma *(Chm & Mng Dir)*

Subsidiaries:

PFC CONSULTING LTD. (1)
1st Fl Urja Nidhi 1 Barakhamba Ln, Connaught Pl, New Delhi, India
Tel.: (91) 1123456387
Power Sector Consulting Services
N.A.I.C.S.: 541690

REC Limited (1)
Core-4 SCOPE Complex 7 Lodhi Road, New Delhi, 110003, India (52.63%)
Tel.: (91) 11 4309 1500
Web Site: http://www.recindia.com
Electric Power Distr
N.A.I.C.S.: 221122

Subsidiary (Domestic):

REC Power Distribution Company Limited (2)
Core-4 Scope Complex, 7 Lodi Rd, Delhi, 110003, India
Tel.: (91) 11 24365165
Web Site: http://www.recindia.nic.in
Financial Support Services
N.A.I.C.S.: 561499
Rajiv Sharma *(Mng Dir)*

REC Transmission Projects Company Limited (2)
Core 4 Scope Complex, 7 Lodi Rd, Delhi, 110003, India
Tel.: (91) 1124365161
Web Site: http://www.recindia.com
Sales Range: $75-99.9 Million
Emp.: 450
Financial Support Services
N.A.I.C.S.: 561499
Rajiv Sharma *(Mng Dir)*

REC Power Development & Consultancy Ltd. (1)
Core-4 Scope Complex 7 Lodhi Road, New Delhi, 110003, India
Tel.: (91) 1124369690
Web Site: https://www.recpdcl.in
Electric Power Transmission Services
N.A.I.C.S.: 221121

POWER GENERATION ENGINEERING & SERVICES COMPANY
41 Al Salam Avenue New Cairo, PO Box 11835, Central District, Cairo, Egypt
Tel.: (20) 2 2618 5545 EG
Web Site: http://www.pgesco.com
Year Founded: 1993
Engineering & Construction Management Services
N.A.I.C.S.: 541330
Sherin Mosbeh *(Gen Mgr)*

POWER GRID COMPANY OF BANGLADESH LTD.
Grid Bhaban Avenue-3 Jahurul Islam City Aftabnagar Badda, Dhaka, 1212, Bangladesh
Tel.: (880) 2226600936
Web Site: https://www.pgcb.org.bd
Year Founded: 1996
POWERGRID—(CHT)
Rev.: $222,580,359
Assets: $4,988,693,479
Liabilities: $3,951,941,361
Net Worth: $1,036,752,118
Earnings: ($57,153,508)
Emp.: 3,387
Fiscal Year-end: 06/30/23
Power Transmission Services
N.A.I.C.S.: 221121
Md. Nizam Uddin *(Exec Dir)*

POWER GRID CORPORATION OF INDIA LIMITED
B-9 Qutab Institutional Area, Katwaria Sarai, New Delhi, 110016, India
Tel.: (91) 1126560112
532898—(BOM)
Rev.: $5,587,871,231
Assets: $30,009,657,694
Liabilities: $20,056,476,230
Net Worth: $9,953,181,464
Earnings: $1,848,464,720
Emp.: 8,342
Fiscal Year-end: 03/31/23
Electricity Distribution Services
N.A.I.C.S.: 221122
Ravi P. Singh *(Dir-Personnel)*

Subsidiaries:

Central Transmission Utility of India Limited (1)
Floors No 5-10 Tower 1 Plot No 16 Ircon International Tower, Institutional Area Sector 32, Gurgaon, 122001, Haryana, India
Tel.: (91) 1242822000
Web Site: https://ctuil.in
Electric Power Transmission Services
N.A.I.C.S.: 237130

POWER GROUP PROJECTS CORP.
520-999 West Hastings Street, Vancouver, V6C 2W2, BC, Canada
Tel.: (604) 290-7073 BC
Web Site: https://www.powergroupproject.com
Year Founded: 2009
PGPGF—(OTCIQ)
Rev.: $11,679
Assets: $565,164
Liabilities: $62,773
Net Worth: $502,391
Earnings: ($1,858,244)
Fiscal Year-end: 01/31/22
Metal Exploration Services
N.A.I.C.S.: 212230
Aleem Nathwani *(Chm & CEO)*

POWER HF CO., LTD.
No 78 Wenshui Road, Anqiu Economic Development Zone, Weifang, 262100, Shandong, China
Tel.: (86) 5368192707
Web Site: https://www.powerhf.com
Year Founded: 2004
605100—(SHG)
Rev.: $104,567,337
Assets: $311,899,316
Liabilities: $62,793,507
Net Worth: $249,105,809
Earnings: $3,312,527
Fiscal Year-end: 12/31/22
Engine Parts Mfr
N.A.I.C.S.: 333618
Huadong Xu *(Chm & Gen Mgr)*

POWER LINE ENGINEERING PUBLIC COMPANY LIMITED
2 Soi Sukhumvit 81 Siripot Sukhumvit Rd Bangjak, Phrakhanong, Bangkok, 10260, Thailand

POWER LINE ENGINEERING PUBLIC COMPANY LIMITED

Power Line Engineering Public Company Limited—(Continued)
Tel.: (66) 23320345
Web Site: https://www.ple.co.th
Year Founded: 1988
PLE—(THA)
Rev.: $273,340,471
Assets: $466,414,993
Liabilities: $392,939,680
Net Worth: $73,475,313
Earnings: $6,705,104
Fiscal Year-end: 12/31/23
Civil Construction Services
N.A.I.C.S.: 237990
Jurin Rungrukrutanakorn (VP)

POWER MECH PROJECTS LTD.
Plot No 77 Jublee Enclave Opp Hitex Madhapur, Hyderabad, 500 081, Telangana, India
Tel.: (91) 4030444444
Web Site: https://www.powermechprojects.in
Year Founded: 1999
539302—(BOM)
Rev.: $433,809,724
Assets: $366,185,480
Liabilities: $213,271,387
Net Worth: $152,914,094
Earnings: $24,855,824
Emp.: 11,648
Fiscal Year-end: 03/31/23
Commercial Building Construction Services
N.A.I.C.S.: 236220
Murugesan Rajendran (COO)

Subsidiaries:

Hydro Magus Private Limited (1)
H-113 Sector-63, Gautam Budh Nagar, Noida, 201301, Uttar Pradesh, India
Tel.: (91) 1204021744
Web Site: http://www.hydromagus.com
Emp.: 6,000
Electrical & Mechanical Equipment Mfr
N.A.I.C.S.: 333248

Power Mech BSCPL Consortium Private Limited (1)
Plot No 77 Jubile Enclave Opp Hitex Arcade, Madhapur, Hyderabad, 500081, Telangana, India
Tel.: (91) 4030444444
Medical Device Mfr
N.A.I.C.S.: 333248

Power Mech Industri Private Limited (1)
Tel.: (91) 9560095987
Electrical & Mechanical Equipment Mfr
N.A.I.C.S.: 333248

Power Mech Projects Limited LLC (1)
Block No 308 Building No 5790 Way No 857 Near Street Treat Al Mouj St, Al Mawalih North, 112, Seeb, Muscat, Oman
Tel.: (968) 90994099
Electrical & Mechanical Equipment Mfr
N.A.I.C.S.: 333248

POWER METAL RESOURCES PLC
74-76 Temple Chambers 3-7 Temple Avenue, London, EC4Y 0DT, United Kingdom
Tel.: (44) 2037781396   UK
Web Site: https://www.powerresources.com
Year Founded: 2011
POW—(AIM)
Rev.: $45,288
Assets: $16,541,442
Liabilities: $962,370
Net Worth: $15,579,072
Earnings: ($3,339,990)
Fiscal Year-end: 09/30/22
Iron & Gold Mining
N.A.I.C.S.: 212210

Andrew Bell (Chm)

POWER METALS CORP.
Suite 300 - 1055 West Hastings Street, Vancouver, V6E 2E9, BC, Canada
Tel.: (515) 401-7479   BC
Web Site: https://www.powermetalscorp.com
Year Founded: 2005
PWRMF—(OTCQB)
Assets: $6,523,406
Liabilities: $628,961
Net Worth: $5,894,445
Earnings: ($2,609,892)
Emp.: 1
Fiscal Year-end: 11/30/22
Mining Exploration & Development Services
N.A.I.C.S.: 212390
Cyrus H. Driver (CFO)

POWER MINERALS LIMITED
Level 1 6/68 North Terrace, Kent Town, 5067, SA, Australia
Tel.: (61) 882185000
Web Site: https://www.powerminerals.com.au
Year Founded: 2002
PNN—(ASX)
Rev.: $1,009,007
Assets: $24,594,887
Liabilities: $1,332,792
Net Worth: $23,262,095
Earnings: ($2,483,112)
Fiscal Year-end: 06/30/24
Mineral Mining Services
N.A.I.C.S.: 212220
Stephen Ross (Chm)

Subsidiaries:

PepinNini Resources Curnamona Pty Ltd. (1)
96 Babbage Road Roseville Chase, Sydney, 2069, NSW, Australia
Tel.: (61) 294176212
Web Site: http://www.pepinnini.com.au
Sales Range: $50-74.9 Million
Emp.: 20
Mineral Mining Services
N.A.I.C.S.: 212390
Rebecca Holland-Kennedy (Mng Dir)

POWER NICKEL INC.
The Canadian Venture Building 82 Richmond St East Suite 202, Toronto, M5C 1P1, ON, Canada
Tel.: (437) 238-1962
Web Site: https://powernickel.com
PNPN—(OTCIQ)
Assets: $393,246
Liabilities: $1,423,776
Net Worth: ($1,030,530)
Earnings: ($1,595,155)
Fiscal Year-end: 12/31/20
Metal Mining
N.A.I.C.S.: 212290
Terry Lynch (CEO)

Subsidiaries:

Chilean Metals Exploration Ltd. (1)
209 - 475 Howe St, Vancouver, 6046817748, BC, Canada
Tel.: (604) 681-7748
Web Site: http://www.chileanmetals.com
Metal Exploration Services
N.A.I.C.S.: 213114

POWER OF THE DREAM VENTURES, INC.
Soroksari ut 94-96, 1095, Budapest, Hungary
Tel.: (36) 14566061
Web Site: http://www.powerofthedream.com
Year Founded: 2006
Emp.: 2

Software Development Services
N.A.I.C.S.: 541511
Viktor Rozsnyay (Chm & CEO)

Subsidiaries:

Genetic Immunity, Inc. (1)
8300 Greensboro Dr 800, McLean, VA 22102
Tel.: (703) 879-6803
Pharmaceutical & Vaccine Mfr
N.A.I.C.S.: 325414

POWER QUOTIENT INTERNATIONAL CO., LTD.
8F No 49 Sec 4 Jhongyang Road, Tu Cheng District, New Taipei City, 23675, Taiwan
Tel.: (886) 2 2269 9889
Web Site: http://www.pqigroup.com
Rev.: $91,348,242
Assets: $203,361,588
Liabilities: $118,892,853
Net Worth: $84,468,735
Earnings: ($69,135,843)
Emp.: 120
Fiscal Year-end: 12/31/17
Storage & Memory Device Mfr
N.A.I.C.S.: 334112

Subsidiaries:

PQI Corporation (1)
46539 Fremont Blvd, Fremont, CA 94538
Tel.: (510) 651-7281
Web Site: http://www.pqigroup.com
Computer Peripheral Equipment Mfr
N.A.I.C.S.: 334112

PQI Japan Co Ltd (1)
B 10F Makuhari Techno Garden 1-3 Nakase, Mihama, Chiba, 261-0023, Japan
Tel.: (81) 432127575
Web Site: http://www.pqigroup.com
Sales Range: $25-49.9 Million
Emp.: 16
Computer Peripheral Equipment Mfr
N.A.I.C.S.: 334112

Power Quotient International (H.K.) Co., Ltd. (1)
Flat F 4/F Yeung Yiu Chung No 8 Industrial Building, 20 Wang Hoi Road Kowloon Bay, Kowloon, China (Hong Kong)
Tel.: (852) 27074118
Web Site: http://www.pqigroup.com
Sales Range: $25-49.9 Million
Emp.: 7
Computer Storage Device Mfr
N.A.I.C.S.: 334112

Power Quotient International (Shenzhen) Co., Ltd. (1)
Room 2412 West Building ShengTang Business Building, TaiRan 9th Road, FuTian District, Shenzhen, China
Tel.: (86) 755 2216 7256
Web Site: http://www.pqigroup.com
Computer Peripheral Equipment Mfr
N.A.I.C.S.: 334118

POWER RESOURCE EXPLORATION, INC.
104 1240 Kensington Road N W, Calgary, T2N 3P7, AB, Canada
Tel.: (403) 243-6333
Year Founded: 2005
Oil & Gas Exploration Services
N.A.I.C.S.: 213112
Keith Diakiw (Chm, Pres, CEO & Sec)

POWER ROOT BERHAD
No 30 Jalan Tago 9 Taman Perindustrian Tago, 52200, Kuala Lumpur, Malaysia
Tel.: (60) 362720303
Web Site: https://powerroot.com.my
PWROOT—(KLS)
Rev.: $77,030,463
Assets: $86,309,601
Liabilities: $20,474,387
Net Worth: $65,835,213

INTERNATIONAL PUBLIC

Earnings: $7,014,009
Fiscal Year-end: 03/31/21
Investment Services; Beverage Mfr & Sales
N.A.I.C.S.: 312111
Thuan Po See (Exec Dir)

POWER SOLUTION TECHNOLOGIES PUBLIC COMPANY LIMITED
PSTC Building 389 Vibhavadi Rangsit Road, Samsen nai District Phayathai, Bangkok, 10400, Thailand
Tel.: (66) 24086230
Web Site: https://www.pst.co.th
Year Founded: 2001
PSTC—(THA)
Rev.: $48,112,767
Assets: $216,202,170
Liabilities: $56,838,551
Net Worth: $159,363,618
Earnings: ($2,482,084)
Emp.: 49
Fiscal Year-end: 12/31/23
Power Supply Solutions
N.A.I.C.S.: 335311
Sakul Pochanart (Chm)

Subsidiaries:

Thai Pipeline Network Company Limited (1)
389 PSTC building 7th floor Vibhavadi - Rangsit Road, Samsennai Phayathai, Bangkok, 10400, Thailand
Tel.: (66) 25269999
Web Site: https://www.tpnthai.com
Pipeline Product Distr
N.A.I.C.S.: 237120
Chakkrit Charuchinda (Chm)

POWER SOLUTIONS, LTD.
1-13-5 Kudankita, Chiyoda-Ku, Tokyo, 102-0073, Japan
Tel.: (81) 362728531
Web Site: https://www.powersolutions.co.jp
Year Founded: 2002
4450—(TKS)
Rev.: $42,050,790
Assets: $35,003,330
Liabilities: $15,193,870
Net Worth: $19,809,460
Earnings: $3,162,140
Emp.: 333
Fiscal Year-end: 12/31/23
Information Technology Services
N.A.I.C.S.: 541512
Katsuhiko Fujita (Chm)

POWER SURVEY & EQUIPMENT LTD.
7850 Trans-Canada Route, Saint Laurent, H4T 1A5, QC, Canada
Tel.: (514) 333-8392   Ca
Web Site: http://www.powersurvey.com
Year Founded: 1948
Measuring & Analyzing the Intensity of Harmonic Currents & Voltages Solutions Provider
N.A.I.C.S.: 334513
Jacques Poulin (COO)

Subsidiaries:

Power Standards Lab. Inc. (1)
980 Atlantic Ave, Alameda, CA 94501-1096
Tel.: (510) 522-4400
Web Site: http://www.powerstandards.com
Instrument Mfr
N.A.I.C.S.: 334515
Alex McEachern (Founder)

POWER WIND HEALTH INDUSTRY, INC.
No 238 Boai 4th Road, Zuoying District, Kaohsiung, 81367, Taiwan
Tel.: (886) 73488000

Web Site:
https://powerwindhealth.com.tw
Year Founded: 2005
8462—(TAI)
Rev.: $140,495,335
Assets: $329,980,268
Liabilities: $271,810,808
Net Worth: $58,169,461
Earnings: $3,715,687
Fiscal Year-end: 12/31/23
Health & Fitness Training Services
N.A.I.C.S.: 713940

POWERBAND SOLUTIONS INC.
1100 Burloak Drive Suite 300, Burlington, L7L 6B2, ON, Canada BC
Web Site:
https://www.powerbandsolution.com
Year Founded: 2009
PBX—(OTCIQ)
Rev.: $1,529,529
Assets: $6,935,059
Liabilities: $8,013,097
Net Worth: ($1,078,038)
Earnings: ($6,160,268)
Fiscal Year-end: 12/31/19
Web-based Auction & Financing Solutions for Automotive Industry
N.A.I.C.S.: 513210
Kelly Jennings *(Pres & CEO)*

POWERCELL SWEDEN AB
Ruskvadersgatan 12, SE-418 34, Gothenburg, Sweden
Tel.: (46) 317203620
Web Site: https://powercellgroup.com
Year Founded: 2008
PCELL—(OMX)
Rev.: $30,802,609
Assets: $42,201,641
Liabilities: $14,858,936
Net Worth: $27,342,705
Earnings: ($6,250,124)
Emp.: 151
Fiscal Year-end: 12/31/23
Fuel Cell Systems Mfr
N.A.I.C.S.: 336310
Per Ekdunge *(CEO-Powercell Germany GmbH)*

Subsidiaries:

Powercell Deutschland GmbH (1)
Grosse Gallusstrasse 16-18, 60312, Frankfurt, Germany
Tel.: (49) 6930855470
Eletric Power Generation Services
N.A.I.C.S.: 221118

POWERCHIP TECHNOLOGY CORPORATION
No 12 Li-Hsin 1st Road, Hsinchu Science Park, Hsin-chu, Taiwan
Tel.: (886) 35795000
Web Site: http://www.powerchip.com
Year Founded: 1994
Sales Range: $1-4.9 Billion
Emp.: 3,728
Memory Products Mfr
N.A.I.C.S.: 334413
Frank Chongren Huang *(CEO)*

POWERCOM CO., LTD.
9th Floor No 246 LianCheng Rd, ZhongHe Dist, New Taipei City, Taiwan
Tel.: (886) 22258552
Web Site:
https://www.upspowercom.com
Year Founded: 1987
3043—(TAI)
Rev.: $43,393,863
Assets: $41,937,210
Liabilities: $29,038,130
Net Worth: $12,899,081
Earnings: ($23,415)
Emp.: 2,600
Fiscal Year-end: 12/31/23
Power Protection Products Mfr
N.A.I.C.S.: 335999
Yang Shu-Yen *(Chm & Gen Mgr)*

Subsidiaries:

Powercom America INC (1)
7550 Jurupa Ave, Riverside, CA 92504-1021
Tel.: (714) 525-8889
Web Site: https://www.powercom-usa.com
Power Protection Products, Mfr & Distr
N.A.I.C.S.: 335999

POWERFUL TECHNOLOGIES LTD.
A 181 Sector 63, Noida, 201307, India
Tel.: (91) 9205852962
Web Site: http://www.powerfultech.in
Rev.: $8,188,344
Assets: $7,072,836
Liabilities: $3,521,586
Net Worth: $3,551,249
Earnings: $137,882
Fiscal Year-end: 03/31/19
Electric Appliances Mfr
N.A.I.C.S.: 335210
Pallavi Sharma *(CFO)*

POWERGRID INFRASTRUCTURE INVESTMENT TRUST
Plot No 2 Sector 29, Gurgaon, 122001, India
Tel.: (91) 1242823177
Web Site: https://www.pginvit.in
Year Founded: 2020
543290—(BOM)
Investment Management Service
N.A.I.C.S.: 523940
Anjana Luthra *(Compliance Officer)*

POWERHOUSE ENERGY GROUP PLC
Unit 3/3A Garth Drive, Brackla Industrial Estate, Bridgend, CF31 2AQ, United Kingdom
Tel.: (44) 2033686399
Web Site:
https://www.powerhouseenergy.com
PHE—(AIM)
Rev.: $480,027
Assets: $11,547,550
Liabilities: $352,570
Net Worth: $11,194,980
Earnings: ($58,316,939)
Emp.: 4
Fiscal Year-end: 12/31/22
Waste Recycling Services
N.A.I.C.S.: 423930
Bruce Nicholson *(Project Mgr-Comml)*

POWERHOUSE VENTURES LIMITED
Level 1 Awly Building Suite 146 287-293 Durham Street North, Christchurch, 8013, New Zealand
Tel.: (64) 33723321 NZ
Web Site: http://www.powerhouse-ventures.co.nz
Year Founded: 2006
PVL—(ASX)
Rev.: $847,885
Assets: $6,427,290
Liabilities: $57,683
Net Worth: $6,369,607
Earnings: $429,035
Emp.: 7
Fiscal Year-end: 06/30/23
Investment Management Service
N.A.I.C.S.: 523940
Russell Yardley *(Chm)*

POWERLEADER SCIENCE & TECHNOLOGY GROUP LTD.
16/F Block B Building 7 Baoneng Science and Technology Park No1, Qingxiang Road Longhua New District, Shenzhen, 518110, China
Tel.: (86) 755 29528988
Web Site:
http://www.powerleader.com.cn
Year Founded: 1997
Rev.: $560,239,946
Assets: $655,362,673
Liabilities: $356,316,376
Net Worth: $299,046,296
Earnings: $16,204,219
Emp.: 766
Fiscal Year-end: 12/31/19
Computer Related Products Mfr & Sales
N.A.I.C.S.: 334118
Yunxia Zhang *(Founder & Chm)*

POWERLINES PLUS PTY LTD.
11-15 Cooper Avenue, Kenwick, WA, Australia
Tel.: (61) 8 9390 6999
Web Site:
http://www.powerlinesplus.com.au
Year Founded: 2009
Electronic Services
N.A.I.C.S.: 238210
Mike Green *(CFO)*

POWERLOGICS
163 Gwahaksaneop 4 Sa-ro Oksanmyeon, CheongWonGun, Cheongju, 363-911, Chungcheongbuk-do, Korea (South)
Tel.: (82) 432195600
Web Site:
http://www.powerlogics.co.kr
Year Founded: 1997
047310—(KRS)
Rev.: $570,550,813
Assets: $241,944,164
Liabilities: $111,866,201
Net Worth: $130,077,963
Earnings: ($38,111,201)
Emp.: 338
Fiscal Year-end: 12/31/22
Circuit Module Mfr
N.A.I.C.S.: 334412
Dong Hoon Jang *(CEO)*

POWERLONG COMMERCIAL MANAGEMENT HOLDINGS LIMITED
Powerlong Tower 1399 Xinzhen Road, Minhang District, Shanghai, China
Tel.: (86) 2151759999 Ky
Web Site:
https://www.powerlongcm.com
Year Founded: 1993
9909—(HKG)
Rev.: $364,940,463
Assets: $777,184,592
Liabilities: $353,843,459
Net Worth: $423,341,133
Earnings: $62,637,212
Emp.: 5,798
Fiscal Year-end: 12/31/23
Holding Company
N.A.I.C.S.: 551112
Deli Chen *(CEO)*

POWERLONG REAL ESTATE HOLDINGS LIMITED
Tel.: (86) 2151759999
Web Site: http://www.powerlong.com
1238—(HKG)
Rev.: $3,171,223,831
Assets: $29,741,612,068
Liabilities: $22,082,268,913
Net Worth: $7,659,343,155
Earnings: ($356,845,370)
Emp.: 9,234
Fiscal Year-end: 12/31/23
Holding Company
N.A.I.C.S.: 551112

Subsidiaries:

Changzhou Powerlong Real Estate Development Co., Ltd. (1)
400 Qinye Rd, Zhonglou, Changzhou, Jiangsu, China
Tel.: (86) 51983283888
Holding Company
N.A.I.C.S.: 551112

Jinjiang Jinlong Industrial Development Co., Ltd. (1)
Opposite Gymnasium Shiji Blvd, Qingyang, Jinjiang, 362200, Fujian, China
Tel.: (86) 59585933333
Holding Company
N.A.I.C.S.: 551112

Powerlong Real Estate (Hong Kong) Holdings Limited (1)
Rm 5813 58/F The Center, Central District, Hong Kong, China (Hong Kong)
Tel.: (852) 21691988
Holding Company
N.A.I.C.S.: 551112

Xiamen Powerlong Industry Co., Ltd. (1)
Northern Industrial Zone, Powerlong Industrial District Jimei, Xiamen, 361021, Fujian, China
Tel.: (86) 5926103999
Holding Company
N.A.I.C.S.: 551112

POWERMATIC DATA SYSTEMS LIMITED
9 Harrison Road 05-01, Singapore, 369651, Singapore
Tel.: (65) 62888220 SG
Web Site: https://powermatic.com.sg
Year Founded: 1989
BCY—(SES)
Rev.: $22,909,226
Assets: $63,209,337
Liabilities: $8,557,984
Net Worth: $54,651,352
Earnings: $7,030,752
Emp.: 84
Fiscal Year-end: 03/31/23
Computer Product Mfr & Distr
N.A.I.C.S.: 334118
Mun Chen *(Founder, Chm & CEO)*

Subsidiaries:

Compex (Suzhou) Co., Ltd (1)
12 ChuangTou Industrial Square Lou Feng North, Suzhou Industrial Park, Suzhou, 215122, China
Tel.: (86) 51262950050
Wireless Connectivity Product Mfr
N.A.I.C.S.: 334220

Compex Inc. (1)
20653 Lycoming St Unit A7, Walnut, CA 91789
Tel.: (909) 217-3998
Computer Peripheral Equipment Distr
N.A.I.C.S.: 423430

Compex Technologies Sdn. Bhd. (1)
No 67 Jalan i-Park 1/7 Kawasan Perindustrian i-Park, Bandar Indahpura Kulai, 81000, Johor, Malaysia
Tel.: (60) 6562888220
Wireless Connectivity Product Mfr
N.A.I.C.S.: 334290

PM DATA Sdn Bhd. (1)
Unit No 3A22 Block A Kelana Centre Point No 3 Jalan SS7/19, Petaling Jaya, Selangor, Malaysia
Tel.: (60) 378044204
Computer Peripheral Equipment Distr
N.A.I.C.S.: 423430

Powermatic Data Systems (Hong Kong) Limited (1)
22/F On Hong Commercial Building 145 Hennessy Road, Wanchai, China (Hong Kong)
Tel.: (852) 85225271632
Computer Peripheral Equipment Distr

POWERMATIC DATA SYSTEMS LIMITED

Powermatic Data Systems Limited—(Continued)
N.A.I.C.S.: 423430

POWERNET CO., LTD.
17th floor Building B Hyundai Knowledge Industry Center 70 Doosan-ro, Geumcheon-Gu, Seoul, 08584, Korea (South)
Tel.: (82) 232820700
Web Site:
https://www.gopowernet.com
Year Founded: 1988
037030—(KRS)
Rev.: $161,904,062
Assets: $109,089,638
Liabilities: $39,253,763
Net Worth: $69,835,875
Earnings: $1,272,251
Emp.: 121
Fiscal Year-end: 12/31/22
Computer Hardware Mfr
N.A.I.C.S.: 335999
Sang-Woo Kim *(Co-CEO)*

POWERSOFT S.P.A.
Via Enrico Conti 5, Scandicci, 50018, Florence, Italy
Tel.: (39) 0557350230
Web Site: https://www.powersoft.it
Year Founded: 1995
PWS—(ITA)
Rev.: $77,642,761,905
Assets: $66,012,820,409
Liabilities: $28,058,793,469
Net Worth: $37,954,026,940
Earnings: $13,314,955,295
Emp.: 146
Fiscal Year-end: 12/31/23
Audio Equipment Mfr
N.A.I.C.S.: 334310
Claudio Lastrucci *(Co-Founder & Dir-R&D)*

POWERSPEED ELECTRICAL LIMITED
Graniteside Kelvin Road North Cripps Road, Graniteside, Harare, Zimbabwe
Tel.: (263) 4771097
Web Site: http://www.powerspeed-ir.com
Year Founded: 1970
PWS—(ZIM)
Rev.: $74,250,007
Assets: $85,381,585
Liabilities: $62,830,098
Net Worth: $22,551,486
Earnings: $1,605,506
Emp.: 440
Fiscal Year-end: 09/30/22
Electric Equipment Mfr
N.A.I.C.S.: 335999
Simba Makoni *(Chm)*

POWERSTONE METALS CORP.
1040 West Georgia Street 19th Floor, Vancouver, V6E 4H3, BC, Canada
Tel.: (647) 987-5083
Web Site:
https://www.powerstonemetals.com
Year Founded: 2021
PS—(CNSX)
Mineral Exploration Services
N.A.I.C.S.: 213115
Carlo Rigillo *(CFO)*

POWERSTREAM INC.
161 Cityview Boulevard, Vaughan, L4H 0A9, ON, Canada
Tel.: (905) 417-6900
Web Site: http://www.powerstream.ca
Electric Power Distr
N.A.I.C.S.: 221122
Brian Bentz *(Pres & CEO)*

POWERTAP HYDROGEN CAPITAL CORP.
810 - 789 West Pender Street, Vancouver, V6C 1H2, BC, Canada
Tel.: (604) 687-2038
Year Founded: 1980
MOTNF—(OTCIQ)
Rev.: $347,226
Assets: $96,898,503
Liabilities: $909,720
Net Worth: $95,988,783
Earnings: ($45,262,609)
Emp.: 800
Fiscal Year-end: 06/30/21
Investment Management Service
N.A.I.C.S.: 525990

POWERTECH CO., LTD.
No 16 Guangming Ave New Light Source Industrial Base, Nanhai National High-tech Zone, Foshan, 528226, Guangdong, China
Tel.: (86) 75783207313
Web Site:
https://www.powertechsemi.com
Year Founded: 1998
301369—(CHIN)
Rev.: $32,747,162
Assets: $220,291,122
Liabilities: $17,869,074
Net Worth: $202,422,048
Earnings: $3,403,758
Fiscal Year-end: 12/31/23
Semiconductor Product Mfr & Distr
N.A.I.C.S.: 334413
Chimei Zhang *(Chm)*

Subsidiaries:

Powertech Semi Sdn. Bhd. (1)
F-5-13 The Latitude Jalan C180/1 Dataran C180 Batu 11, Darul Ehsan, 43200, Cheras, Selangor, Malaysia
Tel.: (60) 75783207605
Automated Equipment Mfr & Distr
N.A.I.C.S.: 334112

POWERTECH INDUSTRIAL CO., LTD.
10F No 407 Sec 2 Zhong Shan Rd, Zhonghe Dist, New Taipei City, 23558, Taiwan
Tel.: (886) 282215588
Web Site: https://www.power-tech.com.tw
Year Founded: 2000
3296—(TAI)
Rev.: $48,731,938
Assets: $69,167,923
Liabilities: $31,753,686
Net Worth: $37,414,237
Earnings: ($2,867,916)
Emp.: 126
Fiscal Year-end: 12/31/23
Outlets Mfr
N.A.I.C.S.: 335931
Yu-Ren Chen *(Dir-Dongguan Factory)*

Subsidiaries:

Dongguan Quan Sheng Electric Co., Ltd. (1)
No 168 Yong-Tai Rd, Hou-Chieh Village Hou-Chieh Town, Dongguan, 523963, Guangdong, China
Tel.: (86) 76985818977
Power Product Mfr
N.A.I.C.S.: 335999

POWERTECH TECHNOLOGY INC.
No 10 Datong Rd Hsinchu Industrial Park, Hukou, 303035, Hsinchu, Taiwan
Tel.: (886) 35980300
Web Site: https://www.pti.com.tw
Year Founded: 1997
PWRCT—(LUX)
Rev.: $2,303,572,463
Assets: $3,634,996,592
Liabilities: $1,375,063,946
Net Worth: $2,259,932,646
Earnings: $310,969,543
Emp.: 11,559
Fiscal Year-end: 12/31/23
Integrated Circuits Backend Services
N.A.I.C.S.: 541380
Duh-Kung Tsai *(Chm)*

Subsidiaries:

Powertech Semiconductor (Xian) Co., Ltd. (1)
Sub-zone B Shaanxi Xian Export Processing Zone No 28 Xinxi Boulevard, Xi'an, 710119, China
Tel.: (86) 2981022888
Web Site: http://www.ptixa.com
IC Backend Chip Probing & Packaging Mfr
N.A.I.C.S.: 334413

Powertech Technology (Singapore) Pte. Ltd. (1)
12 Ang Mo Kio St 65, Singapore, 569-6060, Singapore
Tel.: (65) 64128181
Sales Range: $50-74.9 Million
Emp.: 175
Flip Chip Bumping Services
N.A.I.C.S.: 334413

Powertech Technology (Xian) Ltd. (1)
Part B Shaanxi Xian Export Processing Zone No 28 Xinxi Avenue, Xi'an, 710119, Shaanxi, China
Tel.: (86) 2981022888
IC Backend Chip Probing & Packaging Mfr
N.A.I.C.S.: 334413

Powertech Technology Inc. - Plant 1 (1)
No 879 Litoushan Sec Wunshan Road, Hsinpu, 30550, Hsinchu, Taiwan
Tel.: (886) 3 5889698
Web Site: http://www.pti.com.tw
Integrated Circuits Mfr
N.A.I.C.S.: 334413

Powertech Technology Inc. - Plant 2 (1)
No 7 Sanmin Road Hsinchu Industrial Park, Hukou, 30352, Hsinchu, Taiwan
Tel.: (886) 3 5980300
Integrated Circuits Mfr
N.A.I.C.S.: 334413

Powertech Technology Japan Ltd. (1)
3F Shiodome Building 1-2-20 Kaigan, Minato-ku, Tokyo, 105-0022, Japan
Tel.: (81) 367218888
Web Site: http://www.pti-jp.com
Investment Management Service
N.A.I.C.S.: 523940
D. K. Tsai *(Exec Dir)*

Powertech Technology USA Inc. (1)
1735 N 1st St Ste 308, San Jose, CA 95112
Tel.: (408) 453-4560
Integrated Circuit Distr
N.A.I.C.S.: 423690

Tera Probe, Inc. (1)
Kakiya Building 2-7-17 Shin-Yokohama, Kouhoku-ku, Yokohama, 222 0033, Kanagawa, Japan (59.4%)
Tel.: (81) 454761011
Web Site: https://www.teraprobe.com
Rev.: $251,007,270
Assets: $492,315,420
Liabilities: $144,862,880
Net Worth: $347,452,540
Earnings: $29,026,460
Emp.: 261
Fiscal Year-end: 12/31/2023
Semiconductor Technology Test Services
N.A.I.C.S.: 334413
Tsuyoshi Yokoyama *(Pres)*

Subsidiary (Non-US):

TeraPower Technology, Inc. (2)
No 20 Wenhua Road, Hsinchu Industrial Zone Hukou Township, Hsin-chu, 303, Taiwan
Tel.: (886) 35982828

INTERNATIONAL PUBLIC

Web Site: https://www.terapower.com.tw
Business Management Consulting Services
N.A.I.C.S.: 561499

POWERTEK ENERGY SDN BHD
Level 43 Menara Maxis, Kuala Lumpur City Ctr, 50088, Kuala Lumpur, Malaysia
Tel.: (60) 323816666
Web Site:
http://www.powertek.com.my
Year Founded: 1990
Sales Range: $75-99.9 Million
Emp.: 100
Power Generation Services
N.A.I.C.S.: 221122
Ajeet Singh Ahluwalia *(Deputy CEO)*

Subsidiaries:

Pahlawan Power Sdn Bhd (1)
Stesen Janakuasa Elektrik Tanjong Kl, Kuala Lumpur, Malaysia
Tel.: (60) 6 63515942
Power Generation Services
N.A.I.C.S.: 221122

Panglima Power Sdn Bhd (1)
Level 43 Menara Maxis, Kuala Lumpur, 50088, Malaysia
Tel.: (60) 323816666
Web Site: http://www.powertek.com.my
Power Generation Services
N.A.I.C.S.: 221122

POWERTIP IMAGE CORP.
No 8 6 th Road Taichung Industrial Park, ShituenDistrict, Taichung, Taiwan
Tel.: (886) 423550816
Web Site: https://ptic.com.tw
Year Founded: 2003
6498—(TAI)
Optical Lens Product Mfr
N.A.I.C.S.: 333310
Hsi-Hsun Cheng *(VP)*

POWERTIP TECH CORP.
No 8 6th Road, Taichung Industrial Park, 407, Taichung, 407, Taiwan
Tel.: (886) 423558168
Web Site:
https://www.powertip.com.tw
Year Founded: 1991
6167—(TPE)
Rev.: $67,340,556
Assets: $73,401,620
Liabilities: $17,413,407
Net Worth: $55,988,212
Earnings: $7,786,449
Emp.: 900
Fiscal Year-end: 12/31/22
Electronic Components Mfr
N.A.I.C.S.: 334419
Shih-Yueh Wang *(Chm & Pres)*

POWERWELL HOLDINGS BERHAD
No 1B Jalan Anggerik Mokara 31/48 Seksyen 31 Kota Kemuning, 40460, Shah Alam, Selangor, Malaysia
Tel.: (60) 355213333
Web Site:
https://www.powerwell.com.my
Year Founded: 2001
PWRWELL—(KLS)
Rev.: $33,668,861
Assets: $32,689,951
Liabilities: $16,527,189
Net Worth: $16,162,762
Earnings: $1,442,009
Emp.: 254
Fiscal Year-end: 03/31/23
Holding Company
N.A.I.C.S.: 551112
Hoh Moon Heng *(Project Dir)*

AND PRIVATE COMPANIES

Subsidiaries:

Kejuruteraan Powerwell Sdn. Bhd. (1)
No 1B Jalan Anggerik Mokara 31/48 Seksyen 31, Kota Kemuning, 40460, Shah Alam, Selangor, Malaysia
Tel.: (60) 355213333
Electricity Distribution Product Mfr & Distr
N.A.I.C.S.: 335313

PT. Powerwell Listrik Indonesia (1)
Ruko Rich Palace Jl Meruya Ilir raya No 36-40 Blok A2 RT 008 / RW 07, Keluruhan Srengseng Kecamatan Kembangan, Jakarta Barat, 11630, Jakarta, Indonesia
Tel.: (62) 2122548258
Electricity Distribution Product Mfr
N.A.I.C.S.: 335999

Powerwell International Sdn. Bhd. (1)
No 4 Jalan Anggerik Mokara 31/44 Seksyen 31, Kota Kemuning, 40460, Shah Alam, Selangor, Malaysia
Tel.: (60) 355258788
Electricity Distribution Product Mfr & Distr
N.A.I.C.S.: 335313

Powerwell Sdn. Bhd. (1)
No 7D Jalan Anggerik Mokara 31/56 Seksyen 31, Kota Kemuning, 40460, Shah Alam, Selangor, Malaysia
Tel.: (60) 355258788
Electricity Distribution Product Mfr & Distr
N.A.I.C.S.: 335313

Powerwell Vietnam Co. Ltd. (1)
Warehouse A1 Lot D NO 7 Doc Lap Boulevard, Industrial Area Song Than 1 Di An Ward, Di An, Binh Duong, Vietnam
Tel.: (84) 2743737131
Electricity Distribution Product Mfr & Distr
N.A.I.C.S.: 335313

POWERWIN TECH GROUP LIMITED
Block B Building 1 Zhubang 2000 Business Center, Chaoyang, Beijing, China
Tel.: (86) 4001760388 Ky
Web Site: https://www.empowerwin.com
Year Founded: 2013
2405—(HKG)
Rev.: $16,429,000
Assets: $140,038,000
Liabilities: $133,725,000
Net Worth: $6,313,000
Earnings: $5,494,000
Emp.: 83
Fiscal Year-end: 12/31/22
Digital Marketing Services
N.A.I.C.S.: 541810
Lu Yu (Deputy COO)

POWR LITHIUM CORP.
1021 West Hastings Street 9th floor, Vancouver, V6E 0C3, BC, Canada
Tel.: (778) 383-7240 BC
Web Site: https://www.powrlithium.com
Year Founded: 2018
PWRLF—(OTCQB)
Assets: $1,863,903
Liabilities: $152,211
Net Worth: $1,711,693
Earnings: ($1,932,210)
Fiscal Year-end: 08/31/22
Mineral Exploration Services
N.A.I.C.S.: 212390
Matt Chatterton (CEO)

POWSZECHNE TOWARZYSTWO INWESTYCYJNE S.A.
ul Dabrowskiego 49/13, 60-842, Poznan, Poland
Tel.: (48) 61 8534274
Web Site: http://www.ptisa.pl
Investment Services
N.A.I.C.S.: 523999

POWSZECHNY ZAKLAD UBEZPIECZEN S.A.
al Jana Pawla II 24, 00-133, Warsaw, Poland
Tel.: (48) 225822623 PL
Web Site: http://www.pzu.pl
PZU—(WAR)
Rev.: $6,710,043,712
Assets: $109,561,121,439
Liabilities: $99,574,687,233
Net Worth: $9,986,434,206
Earnings: $1,321,157,614
Emp.: 38,130
Fiscal Year-end: 12/31/22
Insurance & Financial Services
N.A.I.C.S.: 525190
Tomasz Kulik (Member-Mgmt Bd)

Subsidiaries:

PZU Centrum Operacji SA (1)
ul Postepu 18A, 02-676, Warsaw, Poland
Tel.: (48) 801 102 102
Insurance Management Services
N.A.I.C.S.: 524298
Andrzej Szymanski (Deputy CEO & Head-Ops)

PZU Ukraina (1)
62 Dehtiarivska str, Kiev, 04112, Ukraine
Tel.: (380) 44 238 62 38
Web Site: http://www.pzu.com.ua
Investment Fund Management Services
N.A.I.C.S.: 523940

Tower Inwestycje Sp. z o.o. (1)
ul Ogrodowa 58, 00-876, Warsaw, Poland
Tel.: (48) 22 520 27 49
Web Site: http://www.towerinwestycje.pl
Investment Fund Management Services
N.A.I.C.S.: 523940
Agnieszka Pogorzelska (Sec)

POXEL SA
Immeuble Le Sunway 259-261 Avenue Jean Jaures, 69007, Lyon, France
Tel.: (33) 437372010
Web Site: https://www.poxel.com
POXEL—(EUR)
Rev.: $727,390
Assets: $37,463,846
Liabilities: $57,149,795
Net Worth: ($19,685,949)
Earnings: ($33,885,172)
Emp.: 37
Fiscal Year-end: 12/31/22
Pharmaceuticals Mfr
N.A.I.C.S.: 325412
Pascale Fouqueray-Grellier (Co-Founder & Exec VP-Clinical Dev & Regulatory Affairs)

POYA INTERNATIONAL CO., LTD.
No 74 Sec 3 Minzu Rd, West Central Dist, Tainan City, Taiwan
Tel.: (886) 62411000
Web Site: https://www.poya.com.tw
5904—(TPE)
Rev.: $608,953,788
Assets: $762,456,211
Liabilities: $572,653,972
Net Worth: $189,802,239
Earnings: $64,661,695
Emp.: 3,381
Fiscal Year-end: 12/31/22
Personal Care Product Distr
N.A.I.C.S.: 456120
Chen Jen-Zhao (Chm)

POZAVAROVALNICA SAVA, D.D.
Dunajska cesta 56, 1000, Ljubljana, Slovenia
Tel.: (386) 14750200
Web Site: https://www.sava-re.si
Year Founded: 1990
POSR—(LJU)
Rev.: $670,265,502
Assets: $2,112,003,330
Liabilities: $1,681,107,130
Net Worth: $430,896,200
Earnings: $56,210,911
Emp.: 2,723
Fiscal Year-end: 12/31/19
Reinsurance Services
N.A.I.C.S.: 524130
Mateja Lovsin Heric (Chm-Supervisory Bd)

Subsidiaries:

3 Zivljenjska Zavarovalnica Vita d.d. (1)
Trg Republike 3, 1000, Ljubljana, Slovenia
Tel.: (386) 1 476 5800
Web Site: https://www.zav-vita.si
Health Insurance Services
N.A.I.C.S.: 524114
Irena Prelog (Pres)

Bro-Dil, a.d. (1)
Ulica 27 Mart Broj 5/4, Skopje, North Macedonia (100%)
Tel.: (389) 2 3298851
Web Site: http://www.sava-re.si
Sales Range: $25-49.9 Million
Emp.: 5
Security Dealing & Financial Consultancy Services
N.A.I.C.S.: 523150
Iskra Kostova (CEO)

Diagnosticni Center Bled d.o.o. (1)
Pod Skalo 4, 4260, Bled, Slovenia
Tel.: (386) 4 579 8000
Web Site: https://www.dc-bled.si
Diagnostic Center Services
N.A.I.C.S.: 621512
Zvone Novina (CEO)

Drustvo Za Upravuvanje So Zadolzitelni I Dobovolin Penzisko Fondovi Sava Penzisko Drustvo A.D (1)
Ulica Vita Kraigherja 5 p p 1552, 2113, Maribor, Slovenia
Tel.: (386) 2 229 7440
Web Site: https://www.infond.si
Fund Management Services
N.A.I.C.S.: 523940
Jozica Palcic (Pres)

Sava Osiguruvanje A.D. (1)
Zagreb no 28A, 1000, Skopje, North Macedonia
Tel.: (389) 2 510 1500
Web Site: https://mk.sava.insure
Property & Casualty Reinsurance Services
N.A.I.C.S.: 524130

Sava Pokojninska Druzba, d.d. (1)
Ulica Vita Kraigherja 5, 2000, Maribor, Slovenia
Tel.: (386) 802929
Web Site: https://www.sava-pokojninska.si
Pension Fund Services
N.A.I.C.S.: 525110

Sava zivotno osiguranje a. d. o. (1)
Sremska 6, Belgrade, 11000, Serbia
Tel.: (381) 11 3643 610
Web Site: http://www.sava-re.si
Sales Range: $50-74.9 Million
Emp.: 13
Fire Insurance Services
N.A.I.C.S.: 524210
Gorica Drobnjak (Exec Dir)

So Poslovno Savjetovanje d.o.o. (1)
R Frangesa Mihanovica 9, 10110, Zagreb, Croatia
Tel.: (385) 1 666 6290
Web Site: https://www.sava-osiguranje.hr
Fire Insurance Services
N.A.I.C.S.: 524113

Tbs Team 24 Podjetje Za Storitvene Dejavnosti In Trgovino d.o.o. (1)
Ljubljanska ulica 42, 2000, Maribor, Slovenia
Tel.: (386) 2 618 2301
Web Site: https://www.tbs-team24.com
Customer Care Services
N.A.I.C.S.: 561422
Edvard Hojnik (Gen Mgr)

Zavarovalnica Sava Zavarovalna Druzba, d.d. (1)
Cankarjeva ulica 3, 2000, Maribor, Slovenia
Tel.: (386) 2 233 2100
Web Site: https://www.zav-sava.si
Fire Insurance Services
N.A.I.C.S.: 524113
David Kastelic (Chm)

Zavarovalnica Tilia, d. d. (1)
Seidlova Cesta 5, Novo Mesto, 8000, Slovenia
Tel.: (386) 73917200
Web Site: http://www.zav-tilia.si
Sales Range: $200-249.9 Million
Emp.: 400
Insurance Services
N.A.I.C.S.: 524210
Andrej Kavsek (Pres)

Zs Svetovanje, Storitve Zavarovalnega Zastopanja, d.o.o. (1)
Betnavska cesta 2, 2000, Maribor, Slovenia
Tel.: (386) 2 460 4060
Web Site: https://www.zs-svetovanje.si
Fire Insurance Services
N.A.I.C.S.: 524113

POZNANSKA KORPORACJA BUDOWLANA PEKABEX SA
ul Szarych Szeregów 23, Poznan, 60 462, Poland
Tel.: (48) 618210580
Construction Services
N.A.I.C.S.: 236220
Robert Waldemar Jedrzejowski (Chm)

POZZI MILANO SPA
Via Fornaci 4/AB, 25040, Monticelli Brusati, Brescia, Italy
Tel.: (39) 0306850825
Web Site: https://www.pozzimilano.it
Year Founded: 1876
7TL—(DEU)
Tableware Product Distr
N.A.I.C.S.: 424130
Fabio Sanzogni (VP)

POZZONI S.P.A.
Via Luigi e Pietro Pozzoni 11, 24034, Cisano Bergamasco, BG, Italy
Tel.: (39) 0354366111 IT
Web Site: http://www.pozzoni.it
Year Founded: 1913
Printing Services
N.A.I.C.S.: 323111
Fausto Tomasello (Product Mgr)

Subsidiaries:

Capriolo Venturini S.r.l. (1)
Via Pozzoni 11, Cisano bergamasco, 24034, Bergamo, Italy
Tel.: (39) 035 4366111
Emp.: 100
Printing Services
N.A.I.C.S.: 323111
Mario Pozzoni (Pres)

Elcograf S.p.A. (1)
Via Mondadori 15, 37131, Verona, Italy (80%)
Tel.: (39) 045934111
Web Site: http://www.elcograf.com
Book & Magazine Printing Services
N.A.I.C.S.: 323117

Subsidiary (Non-US):

Clays Limited (2)
Popson Street, Bungay, NR35 1ED, Suffolk, United Kingdom
Tel.: (44) 19868893211
Web Site: http://www.clays.co.uk
Book Printing Services
N.A.I.C.S.: 323117
Paul Hulley (Mng Dir)

PP BUDUCNOST A.D.
Gospodinacka 1b, 21238, Curug, Serbia
Tel.: (381) 21 4804 340
Web Site: http://www.globalseed.info
Emp.: 36
Vegetable Crop Production

PP Buducnost a.d.—(Continued)
N.A.I.C.S.: 111419
Zoran Jaksic *(Gen Mgr)*

PP PACK MAKING JOINT STOCK COMPANY
263 Tran Nguyen Han Street, Le Chan District, Haiphong, Vietnam
Tel.: (84) 313783922
Web Site: http://www.haipacpp.com
Year Founded: 1993
Sales Range: $125-149.9 Million
Emp.: 300
Plastic & Carton Packagings & Containers Mfr
N.A.I.C.S.: 322220
Binh Van Mai *(Chm & Gen Dir)*

PP PRIME PUBLIC COMPANY LIMITED
62 Moo 2, Nong Chumphon Subdistrict Khao Yoi District, Phetchaburi, 76140, Thailand
Tel.: (66) 328998814
Web Site: https://www.thailuxe.com
Year Founded: 1987
PPPM—(THA)
Rev.: $38,077,381
Assets: $33,115,893
Liabilities: $17,400,064
Net Worth: $15,715,829
Earnings: ($7,341,574)
Emp.: 420
Fiscal Year-end: 12/31/23
Shrimp & Fish Feed Mfr
N.A.I.C.S.: 115210

Subsidiaries:

Betagro-Thai Luxe Holding Company Limited (1)
69 5 Moo 5 Rama II Rd, Muang District Samutsongkram, Bangkok, 75000, Thailand
Tel.: (66) 3477 1401
Web Site: http://www.thailuxe.com
Agricultural Industries Operation Services
N.A.I.C.S.: 311119

PPAP AUTOMOTIVE LIMITED
54 Okhla Industrial Estate Phase III, New Delhi, 110020, India
Tel.: (91) 1204093901
Web Site: https://www.ppapco.in
Year Founded: 1978
532934—(BOM)
Rev.: $61,449,901
Assets: $65,702,740
Liabilities: $30,363,383
Net Worth: $35,339,356
Earnings: ($712,703)
Emp.: 1,213
Fiscal Year-end: 03/31/23
Automotive Sealing Systems & Exterior Products Mfr
N.A.I.C.S.: 339991
Ajay Kumar Jain *(Chm & Mng Dir)*

Subsidiaries:

PPAP Technology Limited (1)
B-45 Phase-II, Noida, 201305, Uttar Pradesh, India
Tel.: (91) 1204350634
Web Site: https://www.ppaptech.in
Lithium Battery Mfr & Distr
N.A.I.C.S.: 335910

PPC LTD.
Tel.: (27) 113869000 ZA
Web Site: https://www.ppc.co.za
Year Founded: 1913
PPC—(JSE)
Rev.: $531,163,181
Assets: $504,599,741
Liabilities: $193,179,053
Net Worth: $311,420,688
Earnings: $26,933,110
Emp.: 2,361
Fiscal Year-end: 03/31/24

Cement Mfr
N.A.I.C.S.: 327310
Mmakeaya Magoro Tryphosa Ramano *(CFO)*

Subsidiaries:

3Q Mahuma Concrete (Pty) Ltd. (1)
Plot 307 JQ Waterfall Hexriver, PO Box 20641, Rustenburg, 0305, South Africa
Tel.: (27) 145922202
Web Site: http://www.3qconcrete.co.za
Cement Distr
N.A.I.C.S.: 423320
Andre Beukes *(Supvr-Plant Production)*

CIMERWA Limitada (1)
Cimerwa House Kmihurura Sector, PO Box 644, Kigali, Rwanda (51%)
Tel.: (250) 788451135
Web Site: http://www.cimerwa.rw
Cement Mfr
N.A.I.C.S.: 327310
Regis A. Rugemanshuro *(Chm)*

PPC Aggregate Quarries (Pty) Ltd. (1)
Pierre Van Ryneveld Rd, Laudium, Pretoria, 0023, South Africa
Tel.: (27) 123183000
Aggregate Whslr
N.A.I.C.S.: 423320

PPC Botswana (Pty) Ltd. (1)
Plot 22034 Takatokwane Way, PO Box 2424, Gaborone West Industrial, Gaborone, Botswana
Tel.: (267) 3901553
Cement Mfr
N.A.I.C.S.: 327310
Tuelo Botlhole *(Gen Mgr)*

PPC Cement SA (Pty) Ltd. (1)
181 Beyers Naude Drive, Rustenburg, South Africa
Tel.: (27) 145970100
Cement Mfr
N.A.I.C.S.: 327310

Subsidiary (Domestic):

Safika Cement Holding (Pty) Ltd. (2)
Safika House, Johannesburg, South Africa
Tel.: (27) 114830840
Web Site: http://www.safika.co.za
Investment Services
N.A.I.C.S.: 523999
Sakumzi Saki Macozoma *(Chm)*

PPC Zimbabwe Ltd. (1)
Cnr J M N Nkomo Street and 13th Avenue, Bulawayo, Zimbabwe
Tel.: (263) 8677004215
Cement Mfr
N.A.I.C.S.: 327310

Ulula Ash (Pty) Ltd. (1)
Cnr of Tenesse and Malibongwe Drive, Kya-Sand, Johannesburg, South Africa
Tel.: (27) 117080010
Web Site: http://www.ululaflyash.com
Cement Mfr & Distr
N.A.I.C.S.: 327310
Counselor Dlodlo *(Gen Mgr)*

PPF GROUP N.V.
Strawinskylaan 933, 1077 XX, Amsterdam, Netherlands
Tel.: (31) 208813120 NI
Web Site: https://www.ppf.eu
Year Founded: 1991
Rev.: $5,389,517,120
Assets: $48,709,541,920
Liabilities: $38,248,621,840
Net Worth: $10,460,920,080
Earnings: ($357,417,840)
Emp.: 111,000
Fiscal Year-end: 12/31/20
Holding Company
N.A.I.C.S.: 551112
Jiri Smejc *(CEO)*

Subsidiaries:

Air Bank a.s. (1)
Hraskeho 2231/25 Praha 11, Chodov, Prague, 148 00, Czech Republic
Tel.: (420) 5 4713 4134

Web Site: http://www.airbank.cz
Commercial Banking Services
N.A.I.C.S.: 522110

Subsidiary (Domestic):

PPF banka, a.s. (2)
Evropska 2690/17, PO Box 177, 160 41, Prague, Czech Republic
Tel.: (420) 224 175 888
Web Site: http://www.ppfbanka.cz
Emp.: 1,500
Financial Investment Services
N.A.I.C.S.: 523940
Petr Jirasko *(Chm & CEO)*

Anthemona Ltd. (1)
15 Nafpliou Street 4th Floor, Limassol, 3025, Cyprus
Tel.: (357) 25960000
Financial Investment Services
N.A.I.C.S.: 523940

Central European Media Enterprises Ltd. (1)
O'Hara House 3 Bermudiana Road, Hamilton, HM 08, Bermuda
Tel.: (441) 296 1431
Web Site: http://www.cme.net
Rev.: $694,804,000
Assets: $1,447,862,000
Liabilities: $836,274,000
Net Worth: $611,588,000
Earnings: $119,134,000
Emp.: 2,550
Fiscal Year-end: 12/31/2019
TV Stations & Networks Operator
N.A.I.C.S.: 516120
Mark Kobal *(Head-IR)*

Subsidiary (Non-US):

CME Holdco L.P. (2)
Walker House, PO Box 265 GT, Mary Street, Georgetown, E9 00000, Grand Cayman, Cayman Islands
Holding Company
N.A.I.C.S.: 551112
Ronald S. Lauder *(Owner)*

RTL Hrvatska d.o.o. (2)
Krapinska 45, 10000, Zagreb, Croatia
Tel.: (385) 13660000
Web Site: http://www.rtl.hr
Television Broadcasting Services
N.A.I.C.S.: 516120
Tonko Weissmann *(Exec VP)*

Ceska Pojistovna a.s. (1)
Na Pankraci 123 Praha 4, Prague, 140 21, Czech Republic
Tel.: (420) 224 550 444
Fire Insurance Services
N.A.I.C.S.: 524113
Jaroslav Mlynar *(CEO)*

Ceska telekomunikacni infrastruktura a.s. (1)
Olsanska 2681/6, 130 00, Prague, Czech Republic
Tel.: (420) 238 461 111
Web Site: http://www.cetin.cz
Telecommunication Servicesb
N.A.I.C.S.: 517111

GP Reinsurance EAD (1)
Blvd Knyaz Al Donduvok 68, 1504, Sofia, Bulgaria
Tel.: (359) 29267111
Fire Insurance Services
N.A.I.C.S.: 524113

Generali Biztosito (1)
Terez Krt 42-44, 1066, Budapest, Hungary
Tel.: (36) 1 3017100
Fire Insurance Services
N.A.I.C.S.: 524113
Tibor Radnoti *(COO)*

Generali Romania Asigurare Reasigurare S.A. (1)
Charles de Gaulle Plaza Etaj 6 - 7 Piata Charles de Gaulle nr 15, Sector 1, 011857, Bucharest, Romania
Tel.: (40) 21 312 3635
Web Site: http://www.generali.ro
Fire Insurance Services
N.A.I.C.S.: 524113

Generali Towarzystwo Ubezpiec. (1)
ul Senatorska 18, 00-082, Warsaw, Poland

Tel.: (48) 913913913
Web Site: http://www.generali.pl
Fire Insurance Services
N.A.I.C.S.: 524113

Hofplein Offices Rotterdam B.V. (1)
Hofplein 20, 3012 CN, Rotterdam, Netherlands
Tel.: (31) 103070980
Web Site: https://hofpleinoffices.nl
Commercial Building Leasing Services
N.A.I.C.S.: 531120

Home Credit & Finance Bank LLC (1)
Building 1 8/1 Pravda Street, Moscow, 125040, Russia
Tel.: (7) 4957858222
Web Site: http://www.homecredit.ru
Sales Range: Less than $1 Million
Commercial Banking Services
N.A.I.C.S.: 522110

Home Credit Consumer Finance Co., Ltd. (1)
Floor 26-27 No 79 First Avenue TEDA, TEDA MSD-C District, Tianjin, China
Tel.: (86) 2259851768
Web Site: https://www.homecreditcfc.cn
Financial Payment Services
N.A.I.C.S.: 522320

Home Credit India Finance Private Ltd. (1)
DLF Infinity Towers Tower C 3rd Floor, DLF Cyber City Phase II, Gurgaon, 122 002, India
Tel.: (91) 1246628888
Web Site: https://www.homecredit.co.in
Financial Payment Services
N.A.I.C.S.: 522320

Home Credit International a.s. (1)
Evropska 2690/17, PO Box 177, 160 41, Prague, Czech Republic
Tel.: (420) 224174777
Web Site: https://www.homecredit.net
Financial Payment Services
N.A.I.C.S.: 522320

Home Credit Slovakia, a.s. (1)
Teplicka 7434/147, Piestany, Slovakia
Tel.: (421) 850111118
Web Site: https://www.homecredit.sk
Financial Payment Services
N.A.I.C.S.: 522320

Home Credit Vietnam Finance Company Ltd. (1)
Floor G 8 and 10 Phu Nu Building 20 Nguyen Dang Giai Str, Ward Thao Dien Thu Duc City, Ho Chi Minh City, Vietnam
Tel.: (84) 1900633999
Web Site: https://www.homecredit.vn
Financial Payment Services
N.A.I.C.S.: 522320

In Vino Natukhaevskoe LLC (1)
Natuchaevskaja Raevskaya 2 Krasnodarskiy kraj, Novorossiysk, 353982, Russia
Tel.: (7) 8617 27 05 53
Financial Investment Services
N.A.I.C.S.: 523940

Katerinska Office Building s.r.o. (1)
Katerinska 466/40, New Town, 120 00, Prague, Czech Republic
Tel.: (420) 724128244
Web Site: https://www.katerinska40.cz
Commercial Building Rental Services
N.A.I.C.S.: 531120

Mobi Banka a.d. (1)
Youth Brigade 88 Airport City, Belgrade, Serbia
Tel.: (381) 639005
Web Site: https://www.mobibanka.rs
Mobile Application Services
N.A.I.C.S.: 541511

O2 Czech Republic a.s. (1)
Za Brumlovkou 266/2 Michle, 140 22, Prague, 4, Czech Republic (83.2%)
Tel.: (420) 800020202
Web Site: http://www.o2.cz
Rev.: $1,712,869,200
Assets: $1,878,346,800
Liabilities: $1,254,417,030
Net Worth: $623,929,770
Earnings: $240,294,600

Emp.: 5,116
Fiscal Year-end: 12/31/2019
Fixed & Mobile Telecommunications & Internet Services
N.A.I.C.S.: 517111
Jindrich Fremuth (Chm & CEO)

Oribase Pharma SAS (1)
1682 Rue de la Valsiere, 34000, Montpellier, France
Tel.: (33) 4 67 72 76 70
Web Site: http://www.oribase-pharma.com
Biopharmaceutical Product Research & Development Services
N.A.I.C.S.: 325412
A. Yasri (Co-Founder & CEO)

PPF a.s. (1)
Evropska 2690/17, 160 00, Prague, Czech Republic
Tel.: (420) 224 174 748
Web Site: http://www.ppf.eu
Financial Investment Services
N.A.I.C.S.: 523940

RAV Agro LLC (1)
Bulvar TSVETNOY d 11 str 3, 127051, Moscow, Russia
Tel.: (7) 4991512230
Financial Investment Services
N.A.I.C.S.: 523940

SCTbio a.s. (1)
Jankovcova 1518/2, 170 00, Prague, Czech Republic
Tel.: (420) 224175111
Web Site: https://www.sctbio.com
Pharmaceuticals Mfr
N.A.I.C.S.: 325412

Skoda Electric a.s. (1)
Prumyslova 610/2a, 301 00, Plzen, Czech Republic
Tel.: (420) 378181410
Automotive Electrical Parts Mfr
N.A.I.C.S.: 336320

Skoda Pars a.s. (1)
Zerotinova 1833/56/1, 787 01, Sumperk, Czech Republic
Tel.: (420) 583365111
Automotive Electrical Parts Mfr
N.A.I.C.S.: 336320

Skoda Transtech Oy (1)
Tutkijantie 8, 90590, Oulu, Finland
Tel.: (358) 88706900
Web Site: https://www.skodatranstech.info
Automotive Electrical Parts Mfr
N.A.I.C.S.: 336320

Skoda Vagonka a.s. (1)
1 Maje 3176/102, 703 00, Ostrava, Czech Republic
Tel.: (420) 597477111
Automotive Electrical Parts Mfr
N.A.I.C.S.: 336320

Sotio Medical Research (Beijing) Co., Ltd. (1)
99 Kechuang 14 Street Building 30-B, Beijing, 100176, China
Tel.: (86) 10 5661 0700
Biotechnology Research & Development Services
N.A.I.C.S.: 541714

Sotio a.s. (1)
Jankovcova 1518/2, 170 00, Prague, Czech Republic
Tel.: (420) 224 175 111
Web Site: http://www.sotio.com
Biotechnology Research & Development Services
N.A.I.C.S.: 541714

Timeworth Ltd. (1)
18 Spyrou Kyprianou Avenue, Nicosia, Cyprus
Tel.: (357) 22451222
Financial Investment Services
N.A.I.C.S.: 523940

Yettel Bulgaria EAD (1)
Mladost 4 Business Park Sofia Bldg 6, 1766, Sofia, Bulgaria (100%)
Tel.: (359) 89123
Web Site: https://www.yettel.bg
Mobile Telecommunications Services
N.A.I.C.S.: 517112
Jason King (CEO)

Yettel Magyarorszag Zrt (1)
Pannon Ut 1, 2045, Torokbalint, Hungary
Tel.: (36) 209304000
Web Site: https://www.yettel.hu
Telecommunication Servicesb
N.A.I.C.S.: 517810
Peter Gazik (CEO)

Yettel d.o.o. (1)
Omladinskih Brigada 90, 11070, Belgrade, Serbia
Tel.: (381) 639000
Web Site: https://www.yettel.rs
Mobile Telecommunications Services
N.A.I.C.S.: 517112

PPHE HOTEL GROUP LIMITED
Motion Building 9th Floor Radarweg 60, 1043 NT, Amsterdam, Netherlands
Tel.: (31) 207178600 GY
Web Site: https://www.pphe.com
PPH—(LSE)
Rev.: $527,814,133
Assets: $2,449,096,127
Liabilities: $1,772,873,336
Net Worth: $676,222,791
Earnings: $34,557,607
Emp.: 5,120
Fiscal Year-end: 12/31/23
Holding Company; Hotel Owner & Operator
N.A.I.C.S.: 551112
Eli Papouchado (Chm)

Subsidiaries:

Park Plaza Germany Holdings GmbH (1)
Maerkisches Ufer 10, 10179, Berlin, Germany
Tel.: (49) 304005570
Hotel & Resort Operator
N.A.I.C.S.: 721110

Park Plaza Hotels Europe B.V (1)
Vinoly Tower 5th Floor Claude Debussylaan 14, 1082 MD, Amsterdam, Netherlands
Tel.: (31) 207178608
Web Site: http://www.pphe.com
Home Management Services
N.A.I.C.S.: 541618

Park Plaza Nurnberg GmbH (1)
Bahnhofstrasse 5, Nuremberg, Germany
Tel.: (49) 911215550
Hotel & Resort Operator
N.A.I.C.S.: 721110

The Mandarin Hotel B.V. (1)
Geldropseweg 17, Eindhoven, 5611 SC, Netherlands
Tel.: (31) 402125055
Web Site: http://www.parkplaza.com
Sales Range: $25-49.9 Million
Emp.: 40
Home Management Services
N.A.I.C.S.: 541618

art otel Berlin City Center West GmbH (1)
Markisches Ufer 12, Berlin, 10179, Germany
Tel.: (49) 304005570
Web Site: http://www.artotels.com
Sales Range: $25-49.9 Million
Emp.: 25
Home Management Services
N.A.I.C.S.: 541618

art otel Budapest Szallodauzemelteto Kft (1)
Bem Quay 16-19, 1011, Budapest, Hungary
Tel.: (36) 14879487
Web Site: http://www.artotel.com
Sales Range: $25-49.9 Million
Emp.: 40
Home Management Services
N.A.I.C.S.: 541618

PPI TRADING PRETZER & PILSL GMBH
Gotting 6 a, 94113, Biberach, Germany
Tel.: (49) 850991290
Web Site: http://www.ppi-trading.de
Year Founded: 1992
Sales Range: $50-74.9 Million
Emp.: 6
Photographic & Related Products Distr
N.A.I.C.S.: 423410
Josef Pretzer (Co-Founder)

PPK GROUP LIMITED
Level 13 120 Edward Street, Brisbane, 4000, QLD, Australia
Tel.: (61) 730544500
Web Site: https://www.ppkgroup.com.au
PPK—(ASX)
Rev.: $18,820,780
Assets: $82,028,579
Liabilities: $19,315,572
Net Worth: $62,713,007
Earnings: ($10,610,978)
Fiscal Year-end: 06/30/24
Holding Company
N.A.I.C.S.: 551112
Glenn Robert Molloy (Exec Dir)

Subsidiaries:

BNNT Technology Limited (1)
Level 27 10 Eagle Street, Brisbane, QLD, Australia
Tel.: (61) 412057422
Web Site: www.bnnt.com.au
Boron Nitride Nanotube Research & Development Services
N.A.I.C.S.: 541713

Li-S Energy Limited (1)
Level 27 10 Eagle Street, Brisbane, 4000, QLD, Australia
Tel.: (61) 730544500
Battery Equipment Distr
N.A.I.C.S.: 423610

PPK Mining Equipment Pty Limited (1)
13B Old Punt Road, Tomago, 2310, NSW, Australia
Tel.: (61) 249645400
Industrial Equipment Distr
N.A.I.C.S.: 423830

PPK Mining Repairs Alternators Pty Ltd (1)
Lot 1 / 201 Old Port Road, Port Kembla, 2505, NSW, Australia
Tel.: (61) 242073000
Mining Equipment Mfr & Distr
N.A.I.C.S.: 333131

Rambor Pty Ltd (1)
25 Thrift Close, Mount Thorley, 2330, NSW, Australia
Tel.: (61) 265746500
Web Site: http://www.rambor.com.au
Mining Equipment Mfr
N.A.I.C.S.: 333131

PPM D.D.
Mitra Trifunovica Uce 125, Tuzla, 75000, Bosnia & Herzegovina
Tel.: (387) 35302435
PPMTRK3—(SARE)
Rev.: $1,031,087
Assets: $3,896,064
Liabilities: $3,276,003
Net Worth: $620,062
Earnings: $376,834
Emp.: 3
Fiscal Year-end: 12/31/20
Dairy Product & Milk Production Services
N.A.I.C.S.: 112120

PPS INTERNATIONAL (HOLDINGS) LIMITED
24/F SUP Tower 75 83 Kings Road, North Point, China (Hong Kong)
Tel.: (852) 28319918
Web Site: http://www.hkpps.com.hk
8201—(HKG)
Rev.: $44,201,704
Assets: $37,966,424
Liabilities: $11,817,019
Net Worth: $26,149,405
Earnings: $2,667,306
Emp.: 939
Fiscal Year-end: 06/30/21
Holding Company; Pest Control, Hotel Housekeeping, Upholstery Cleaning & Waste Management Services
N.A.I.C.S.: 551112
Shaoheng Yu (Chm, CEO & Officer-Compliance)

Subsidiaries:

Pollution & Protection Services Limited (1)
Unit A 12/F Tower A Capital Tower No 38 Wai Yip Street Kowloon Bay, Kowloon, China (Hong Kong)
Tel.: (852) 28319918
Web Site: https://www.hkpps.com.hk
Environmental Services
N.A.I.C.S.: 541620
Candy Lee (Mgr-Acctg)

Shanghai PPS Sheng Mao Environmental Services Limited (1)
Room 1010 1011 1018 101 Nanmatou Rd, Pudong Xinqu, Shanghai, China
Tel.: (86) 2164478399
Web Site: http://www.ppssm.com.cn
Housekeeping Services
N.A.I.C.S.: 561720

PPT INZENJERING A.D. BEOGRAD
Boulevard 37-39, 11 000, Belgrade, Serbia
Tel.: (381) 11 3690 168
Web Site: http://www.ppt-inzenjering.rs
Year Founded: 1958
Emp.: 50
Engineeering Services
N.A.I.C.S.: 541330
Ivica Burgic (Gen Mgr)

PPX MINING CORP.
82 Richmond St E, Toronto, M5C 1P1, ON, Canada
Tel.: (416) 361-0737 BC
Web Site: https://ppxmining.com
Year Founded: 1987
PPX—(LIM)
Rev.: $4,578,212
Assets: $9,200,657
Liabilities: $11,231,447
Net Worth: ($2,030,789)
Earnings: $234,280
Fiscal Year-end: 09/30/22
Gold & Silver Exploration Services
N.A.I.C.S.: 212220
Brian Imrie (Chm)

Subsidiaries:

Sienna Minerals SAC (1)
Av Paz Soldan 170 Office 401, San Isidro, Lima, Peru
Tel.: (51) 1 422 8380
Web Site: http://www.siennaminerals.com
Gold Mining Services
N.A.I.C.S.: 212220

PR ENGINEERING LTD.
249 Toronto Avenue, Oshawa, L1H 3C2, ON, Canada
Tel.: (905) 579-9721
Web Site: http://www.prengineering.com
Year Founded: 1965
Rev.: $10,000,000
Emp.: 40
Mining Equipment Mfr
N.A.I.C.S.: 333131
Gary Robinson (Gen Mgr)

PR GAZ, INC.
Retelco Drive cor E Rodriguez Jr Avenue, Brgy Bagong Ilog, Pasig, Philippines

PR GAZ, INC.

PR Gaz, Inc.—(Continued)
Tel.: (63) 2 571 7771 PH
Web Site: http://www.prgaz.com.ph
Liquified Petroleum Gas Distr & Retail Franchisor
N.A.I.C.S.: 221210
Nelson C. Par (Founder)
Subsidiaries:
PR Gaz Haus Holdings, Inc. (1)
Retelco Drive cor E Rodriguez Jr Avenue, Brgy Bagong Ilog, Pasig, Philippines
Tel.: (63) 2 571 7711
Web Site: http://www.prgazhaus.com
Holding Company; Liquified Petroleum Gas Distr & Retail Franchisor
N.A.I.C.S.: 551112
Nelson C. Par (Founder, Chm & CEO)

PR Gaz Industrial Solutions, Inc. (1)
Retelco Drive cor E Rodriguez Jr Avenue, Brgy Bagong Ilog, Pasig, Philippines
Tel.: (63) 2 570 6597
Web Site: http://www.prgisi.com
Liquified Petroleum Gas Wholesale Trade Distr & Engineering Support Services
N.A.I.C.S.: 425120
Nelson C. Par (Founder, Chm & CEO)

PR POMEROY RESTORATION & CONSTRUCTION LTD.
18 - 2075 Brigantine Drive, Coquitlam, V3K 7B8, BC, Canada
Tel.: (604) 529-9200
Web Site:
   https://www.prconstruction.ca
Year Founded: 2001
Rev.: $13,911,192
Emp.: 32
Residential Remodeler
N.A.I.C.S.: 236118
Susan Turner (Office Mgr)

PRABHAT DAIRY LIMITED
Gat No 122 At Ranjankhol Post Tilaknagar Taluka Rahata, Ahmednagar, 413720, Maharashtra, India
Tel.: (91) 22 41287716
Web Site: http://www.prabhatdairy.in
Year Founded: 1998
Rev.: $34,233,179
Assets: $208,710,225
Liabilities: $96,855,400
Net Worth: $111,854,825
Earnings: $7,005,793
Emp.: 803
Fiscal Year-end: 03/31/19
Dairy Products Mfr
N.A.I.C.S.: 311514
Sarangdhar R. Nirmal (Chm & Co-Mng Dir)
Subsidiaries:
Sunfresh Agro Industries Private Limited (1)
D-37/4 Turbhe MIDC Thane Belapur Road, TTC Industrial Area, Navi Mumbai, 400 705, India
Tel.: (91) 2241287700
Agrochemical Distr
N.A.I.C.S.: 424910

PRABHAT TECHNOLOGIES (INDIA) LTD.
402 Western Edge I Western Express Highway, Mumbai, 400 066, Maharashtra, India
Tel.: (91) 2240676000 In
Web Site:
   https://www.prabhatgroup.net
Year Founded: 1997
540027—(BOM)
Rev.: $322,127
Assets: $10,221,653
Liabilities: $6,584,797
Net Worth: $3,636,856
Earnings: ($162,748)
Emp.: 7
Fiscal Year-end: 03/31/23

Electronic Equipment Distr
N.A.I.C.S.: 423690
Vishwamani Matamani Tiwari (Chm & Mng Dir)

PRABHAV INDUSTRIES LIMITED
9th Floor Galav Chamber Opp Sardar Patel Statue, Sayajigunj, Vadodara, 390 020, India
Tel.: (91) 2652362200 In
Web Site: http://www.prabhavind.com
Year Founded: 1995
Rev.: $3,665,469
Assets: $27,611,842
Liabilities: $6,267,381
Net Worth: $21,344,461
Earnings: $7,702
Fiscal Year-end: 03/31/17
Iron & Steel Mfr
N.A.I.C.S.: 331110
Jayesh Raichandbhai Thakkar (Mng Dir)

PRABHHANS INDUSTRIES LIMITED
Tel.: (91) 9417694151 In
Web Site: https://prabhhansindltd.in
Year Founded: 1993
530361—(BOM)
Assets: $615,036
Liabilities: $79,548
Net Worth: $535,489
Earnings: ($18,428)
Emp.: 10
Fiscal Year-end: 03/31/21
Real Estate Manangement Services
N.A.I.C.S.: 531390
Venkata Panati Krishna Reddy (Mng Dir)

PRABHU BANK LTD.
Prabhu Building Babarmahal, PO Box 19441, Kathmandu, Nepal
Tel.: (977) 5719000 NP
Web Site:
   https://www.prabhubank.com
Year Founded: 2014
PRVU—(NEP)
Rev.: $108,717,805
Assets: $1,823,647,913
Liabilities: $1,672,049,540
Net Worth: $151,598,373
Earnings: $18,628,282
Emp.: 2,424
Fiscal Year-end: 07/15/21
Commericial Banking
N.A.I.C.S.: 522110
Ashok Sherchan (CEO)

PRABHU INSURANCE LIMITED
PO Box 10811, Kathmandu, 977, Nepal
Tel.: (977) 1 4499220
Web Site:
   http://www.prabhuinsurance.com
Year Founded: 1996
Insurance Services
N.A.I.C.S.: 524298
Rajendra Malla (Vice Chm)

PRABHU STEEL INDUSTRIES LIMITED
Old Motor Stand Itwari, Nagpur, 440 008, India
Tel.: (91) 7122768745 In
Web Site: https://www.prabhusteel.in
Year Founded: 1972
Rev.: $4,370,197
Assets: $280,705,281,712
Liabilities: $179,577,832,408
Net Worth: $101,127,449,304
Earnings: $343,363
Fiscal Year-end: 03/31/18
Steel Product Mfr & Distr

N.A.I.C.S.: 331110
Harish Gangaram Agarwal (Exec Dir)

PRACTICUS LTD.
Riverside Barns Remenham Church Lane, Henley-on-Thames, RG9 3DB, Oxfordshire, United Kingdom
Tel.: (44) 1491 577122
Web Site: http://www.practicus.com
Year Founded: 2004
Sales Range: $50-74.9 Million
Emp.: 69
Management Consultancy Services
N.A.I.C.S.: 541618
Darren Tolhurst (CEO & Member-Exec Bd)
Subsidiaries:
Practicus Ltd. (1)
1801 Winway Building 50 Wellington Street, Central, China (Hong Kong)
Tel.: (852) 22905777
Business Management Consulting Services
N.A.I.C.S.: 541611
Philip Munro (Dir-Asia & Middle East)

Practicus Pty. Ltd. (1)
Level 6 23 Hunter Street, Sydney, 2000, NSW, Australia
Tel.: (61) 282815000
Business Management Consulting Services
N.A.I.C.S.: 541611
Jon Webster (Head-Mktg)

PRADA S.P.A.
Via Antonio Fogazzaro 28, 20135, Milan, Italy
Tel.: (39) 02550281 IT
Web Site:
   http://www.pradagroup.com
Year Founded: 1913
PRDSF—(OTCIQ)
Rev.: $5,100,810,490
Assets: $8,218,272,178
Liabilities: $4,034,364,343
Net Worth: $4,183,907,835
Earnings: $726,734,297
Emp.: 14,191
Fiscal Year-end: 12/31/23
Men's & Women's Apparel, Shoes & Accessories Mfr & Marketer
N.A.I.C.S.: 315250
Carlo Mazzi (Chm)
Subsidiaries:
Prada U.S.A. Corp. (1)
610 W 52nd St, New York, NY 10019
Tel.: (212) 307-9300
Web Site: http://www.prada.com
Sales Range: $50-74.9 Million
Emp.: 180
Apparel Mfr & Retailer
N.A.I.C.S.: 315250
Abilio Hagihara (Dir-Prada East Coast Visual Mdsg)
Subsidiary (Domestic):
Prada Hawaii Corp. (2)
2155 Kalakaua Ave Ste 414, Honolulu, HI 96815-2341
Tel.: (808) 923-2448
Web Site: http://www.prada.com
Sales Range: $25-49.9 Million
Emp.: 10
Men's Clothing, Women's Clothing, Accessories, Handbags & Shoes
N.A.I.C.S.: 458110
Davide Sesia (CEO)

PRADEEP METALS LIMITED
R-205 MIDC Rabale, Navi Mumbai, 400701, India
Tel.: (91) 2227691026
Web Site:
   https://www.pradeepmetals.com
Year Founded: 1982
513532—(BOM)
Rev.: $32,417,793
Assets: $25,030,466
Liabilities: $13,707,931

INTERNATIONAL PUBLIC

Net Worth: $11,322,535
Earnings: $3,144,680
Emp.: 513
Fiscal Year-end: 03/31/23
Metal Forging Mfr
N.A.I.C.S.: 332112
Pradeep Goyal (Founder, Chm & Mng Dir)
Subsidiaries:
Dimensional Machine Works LLC (1)
Tel.: (713) 849-5414
Web Site: https://www.dimensional.us
Emp.: 30
Precision Machined Components Mfr
N.A.I.C.S.: 332721

PRADELLA DEVELOPMENTS PTY LTD
PO Box 3301, Brisbane, 4101, QLD, Australia
Tel.: (61) 731150300 AU
Web Site: http://www.pradella.com.au
Year Founded: 1959
Holding Company; Residential & Commercial Property Development & Construction
N.A.I.C.S.: 551112
Phil Goodman (CEO)
Subsidiaries:
Pradella Constructions Pty Ltd (1)
154 Melbourne Street, PO Box 3301, Brisbane, 4101, QLD, Australia
Tel.: (61) 731150300
Web Site: http://www.pradella.com.au
Sales Range: $25-49.9 Million
Emp.: 100
Residential & Commercial Construction
N.A.I.C.S.: 236116
Kim Pradella (Mng Dir)

Pradella Developments Pty Ltd (1)
Suite 6 Terrace Suites 19 Lang Parade, Brisbane, 4064, QLD, Australia
Tel.: (61) 731150300
Web Site: http://www.pradella.com.au
Sales Range: $25-49.9 Million
Emp.: 50
Property Development
N.A.I.C.S.: 925120
Kim Pradella (Mng Dir)

PRADHIN LTD.
No 54 Old No 61 Sembudoss Street 1st Floor, Chennai, 600001, India
Tel.: (91) 4425233049
Web Site: http://www.pradhin.com
530095—(BOM)
Rev.: $2,060,884
Assets: $834,267
Liabilities: $104,994
Net Worth: $729,273
Earnings: ($12,277)
Fiscal Year-end: 03/31/23
Steel Distr
N.A.I.C.S.: 423510
Ajaybhai N. Chaudhari (Mng Dir)

PRADIP OVERSEAS LIMITED
104/105 Chacharwadi Opp Zydus Cadilla, Sarkhej Bawla Highway, Ahmedabad, 382 213, India
Tel.: (91) 2717 294 110
Web Site:
   http://www.pradipoverseas.com
PRADIP—(BOM)
Rev.: $36,813,777
Assets: $571,738,713
Liabilities: $2,050,835,105
Net Worth: ($1,479,096,391)
Earnings: ($225,497,727)
Emp.: 61
Fiscal Year-end: 03/31/21
Linens Mfr & Exporter
N.A.I.C.S.: 812331
Pradipkumar J. Karia (Chm & Mng Dir)

PRAEMIUM LIMITED
Level 19 367 Collins Street, Melbourne, 3000, VIC, Australia
Tel.: (61) 386221222
Web Site: https://www.praemium.com
PPS—(ASX)
Rev.: $55,239,646
Assets: $89,866,680
Liabilities: $16,983,957
Net Worth: $72,882,723
Earnings: $5,843,062
Emp.: 60
Fiscal Year-end: 06/30/24
Financial Services
N.A.I.C.S.: 523940
Christine Silcox (Dir)

Subsidiaries:

Plum Software Limited (1)
Waterside Centre Birmingham Business Park 4200 Solihull Parkway, Birmingham, B37 7YN, United Kingdom
Tel.: (44) 2038735567
Web Site: http://www.plumsoftware.co.uk
Emp.: 14
Software Development Services
N.A.I.C.S.: 541511
David Felix-Davies (Founder & Sr Mgr-Sls)

Praemium International Limited (1)
3rd Floor East Salisbury House 1-9 Union Street, Saint Helier, JE2 3RF, Jersey
Tel.: (44) 1534765450
Wealth Management Services
N.A.I.C.S.: 523940
Nadine Irons (Assoc Dir-Client Svcs & Ops)

PRAESEPE PLC
Seebeck House 1A Seebeck Place Knowlhill, Wolverton Road Great Linford, Milton Keynes, MK5 8FR, United Kingdom
Tel.: (44) 1908351200
Web Site: http://www.praesepeplc.com
Year Founded: 2007
Sales Range: $50-74.9 Million
Emp.: 279
Low-Stake Casino Operator
N.A.I.C.S.: 713290
Nick Harding (CEO)

PRAG BOSIMI SYNTHETICS LIMITED
No 19 Ambikagiri Nagar Milan Path, R G Barua Road, Guwahati, 781024, Assam, India
Tel.: (91) 2222660300
Web Site: https://www.pragbosimi.com
500192—(BOM)
Rev.: $381,317
Assets: $34,765,156
Liabilities: $27,058,131
Net Worth: $7,707,025
Earnings: ($1,663,925)
Emp.: 163
Fiscal Year-end: 03/31/21
Textile Products Mfr
N.A.I.C.S.: 314999
Hemant Bhanushankar Vyas (Mng Dir)

PRAGATI INSURANCE LIMITED
Pragati Insurance Bhaban 20-21 Kawran Bazar, Dhaka, 1215, Bangladesh
Tel.: (880) 255012680
Web Site: https://www.pragatiinsurance.com
Year Founded: 1986
PRAGATIINS—(DHA)
Rev.: $5,380,220
Assets: $57,971,309
Liabilities: $20,842,169
Net Worth: $37,129,140
Earnings: $3,377,796
Emp.: 575
Fiscal Year-end: 12/31/23
Insurance Services
N.A.I.C.S.: 524298
Khan Mohammed Ameer (Vice Chm)

PRAGATI LIFE INSURANCE LIMITED
Pragati Insurance Bhaban 6th Floor 20-21 Kawran Bazar, Dhaka, 1215, Bangladesh
Tel.: (880) 255014395
Web Site: https://www.pragatilife.com
Year Founded: 2000
PRAGATILIF—(CHT)
Rev.: $52,528,164
Assets: $65,852,412
Liabilities: $62,175,226
Net Worth: $3,677,187
Earnings: $57,903,917
Emp.: 972
Fiscal Year-end: 12/31/23
Insurance Services
N.A.I.C.S.: 524298
Khalilur Rahman (Chm)

PRAGMA FAKTORING S.A.
ul Brynowska 72, 40-584, Katowice, Poland
Tel.: (48) 32 44 20 200
Web Site: http://www.pragmafaktoring.pl
Year Founded: 1996
PRF—(WAR)
Sales Range: $1-9.9 Million
Financial Intermediary Services
N.A.I.C.S.: 522320
Tomasz Boduszek (Pres)

PRAGMA INKASO S.A.
ul Czarnohucka 3, 42-600, Tarnowskie Gory, Poland
Tel.: (48) 324500100
Web Site: http://www.pragmainkaso.pl
Year Founded: 2002
PRI—(WAR)
Sales Range: $25-49.9 Million
Emp.: 70
Debt Collection & Other Financial Services
N.A.I.C.S.: 561440
Tomasz Boduszek (Chm)

Subsidiaries:

LeaseLink Sp. z o.o. (1)
O ul Grochowska 306/308, 03-840, Warsaw, Poland
Tel.: (48) 226900666
Web Site: https://www.leaselink.pl
Loan Services
N.A.I.C.S.: 522390

Mint Software Sp. z o.o. (1)
Jasnogorska 23 Street, 31-358, Krakow, Poland
Tel.: (48) 608007200
Web Site: http://www.mintsoftware.pl
Software Programming Services
N.A.I.C.S.: 541511
Wojciech Bublik (CEO)

PRAGMATIC PLAY LTD.
144 Tower Road, Sliema, Malta
Tel.: (356) 277 813 45
Web Site: http://www.pragmaticplay.com
Mobile & Online Gaming Software Developer & Publisher
N.A.I.C.S.: 541511
Melissa Summerfield (Chief Comml Officer)

Subsidiaries:

Extreme Live Gaming Limited (1)
995 Great West Road, Brentford, London, TW8 9FY, United Kingdom
Tel.: (44) 2032878992
Web Site: http://www.extremelivegaming.com
Mobile & Online Gaming Software Developer & Publisher
N.A.I.C.S.: 541511
Darwyn David Palenzuela (CEO)

PRAIRIE NORTH CONST. LTD.
52520 Highway 60, Acheson, T7X 5A6, AB, Canada
Tel.: (780) 463-3363
Web Site: http://www.dirtmoving.com
Construction Services
N.A.I.C.S.: 236210
F. Craig Robertson (Pres)

PRAIRIE PROVIDENT RESOURCES INC.
1100 640 5th Avenue SW, Calgary, T2P 3G4, AB, Canada
Tel.: (403) 292-8000 AB
Web Site: https://www.ppr.ca
Year Founded: 2016
PPR—(TSX)
Rev.: $52,444,833
Assets: $172,348,800
Liabilities: $232,513,955
Net Worth: ($60,165,155)
Earnings: ($71,009,902)
Emp.: 32
Fiscal Year-end: 12/31/20
Petroleum & Natural Gas Exploration & Extraction
N.A.I.C.S.: 211120
Brad Likuski (VP-Ops)

Subsidiaries:

Prairie Provident Resources Canada Ltd. (1)
1100 640 5th Avenue SW, Calgary, T2P 3G4, AB, Canada
Tel.: (403) 292-8000
Web Site: https://www.ppr.ca
Oil & Gas Exploration Services
N.A.I.C.S.: 213112
Ryan Rawlyk (VP)

PRAIRIESKY ROYALTY LTD.
Suite 1700 350 7th Ave SW, Calgary, T2P 3N9, AB, Canada
Tel.: (587) 293-4000 AB
Web Site: http://www.prairiesky.com
Year Founded: 2013
PSK—(TSX)
Rev.: $134,082,792
Assets: $2,039,951,556
Liabilities: $208,242,936
Net Worth: $1,831,708,620
Earnings: $24,798,276
Emp.: 58
Fiscal Year-end: 12/31/20
Oil & Gas Exploration
N.A.I.C.S.: 211120
Andrew M. Phillips (Pres & CEO)

PRAJ INDUSTRIES LTD.
Praj Tower S 274 275/2 Bhumkar Chowk Hinjewadi Road, Hinjewadi, Pune, 411057, India
Tel.: (91) 2071802000
Web Site: https://www.praj.net
Year Founded: 1985
PRAJIND—(NSE)
Rev.: $427,269,181
Assets: $313,970,002
Liabilities: $184,713,099
Net Worth: $129,256,903
Earnings: $28,750,567
Emp.: 1,192
Fiscal Year-end: 03/31/23
Ethanol, Bio-Diesel & Brewery Facility Engineering & Manufacturing Services
N.A.I.C.S.: 541330
Pramod Chaudhari (Chm)

Subsidiaries:

PRAJ-Matrix (1)
402/403/1098 Urawade At Pirangut, Tal Mulshi, Pune, 412 108, Maharastra, India
Tel.: (91) 2066754000
Web Site: http://praj.net
Sales Range: $50-74.9 Million
Biochemical Services
N.A.I.C.S.: 325180

Praj Far East Co., Limited (1)
15 Sukhumvit Soi 31 Sukhumvit Road Klongtoey Nua, Wattana, Bangkok, 10110, Thailand
Tel.: (66) 26623177
Web Site: http://praj.net
Sales Range: $25-49.9 Million
Distilleries Services
N.A.I.C.S.: 312140

Praj Jaragua Bioenergia S.A. (1)
300 Jaragua Ave, Industrial Dist, 18087-380, Sorocaba, Brazil
Tel.: (55) 1521029000
Web Site: http://www.pjbioenergia.com
Methanol Mfr
N.A.I.C.S.: 325193

Praj Schneider Inc (1)
5634 S 85th Circle, Omaha, NE 68127
Tel.: (402) 331-7230
Sales Range: $25-49.9 Million
Emp.: 25
Engineeering Services
N.A.I.C.S.: 541330
Charles U. J. Schneider (Pres)

PRAJAY ENGINEERS SYNDICATE LIMITED
1-10-63 and 64 5thFloor Prajay Corporate House Chikoti Gardens, Begumpet, Hyderabad, 500 016, Telangana, India
Tel.: (91) 4066255566
Web Site: https://www.prajayengineers.com
Year Founded: 1986
PRAENG—(NSE)
Rev.: $5,382,086
Assets: $166,259,675
Liabilities: $88,413,630
Net Worth: $77,846,046
Earnings: ($691,495)
Emp.: 75
Fiscal Year-end: 03/31/21
Real Estate Manangement Services
N.A.I.C.S.: 531390
P. Bhaskara Rao (CFO)

PRAKASH CERAMICS LTD.
No 647 Opposite Tansi Honda Showroom Varthur Main Road, Ramagondanahalli Whitefield, Bengaluru, 560066, Karnataka, India
Tel.: (91) 9916120060
Web Site: http://www.prakashceramic.com
Sanitary Ware & Bathroom Accessory Mfr
N.A.I.C.S.: 327110

PRAKASH INDUSTRIES LIMITED
Srivan Bijwasan, New Delhi, 110 061, India
Tel.: (91) 1125305800
Web Site: https://www.prakash.com
Year Founded: 1980
506022—(BOM)
Rev.: $414,260,536
Assets: $509,646,904
Liabilities: $155,496,673
Net Worth: $354,150,231
Earnings: $22,837,959
Emp.: 2,355
Fiscal Year-end: 03/31/23
Iron & Steel Products Mfr
N.A.I.C.S.: 331110
Ved Prakash Agarwal (Chm)

Subsidiaries:

Prakash Industries Limited - Coal Mining Division (1)

PRAKASH INDUSTRIES LIMITED

Prakash Industries Limited—(Continued)
A-9 Shatabdi Nagar Songanga Colony
Seepat Road, Bilaspur, 495006, Chhattisgarh, India
Tel.: (91) 9893051093
Web Site: http://www.prakash.com
Sales Range: $50-74.9 Million
Emp.: 25
Coal Mining Services
N.A.I.C.S.: 212115
B. K. Verma *(Sr Gen Mgr)*

Prakash Industries Limited - PVC Pipe Division (1)
5 km Stone Moradabad Road US Nagar,
Kashipur, Uttaranchal, India
Tel.: (91) 5947 275095
Web Site: http://www.prakash.com
Plastic Tank Mfr
N.A.I.C.S.: 326122

Prakash Industries Limited - Wind Mill Division (1)
8/125 A Kumarapuram Road Aralvoimozhy,
Kanyakumari, 629301, Tamilnadu, India
Tel.: (91) 4652 263832
Emp.: 26
Eletric Power Generation Services
N.A.I.C.S.: 221118
R. Rajendran *(Deputy Gen Mgr)*

PRAKASH PIPES LIMITED
Darjiyan Wali Gali Rayya Teh-Baba Bakala, Amritsar, 143112, Punjab, India
Tel.: (91) 1853500453
Web Site:
https://www.prakashplastics.in
Year Founded: 1981
PPL—(NSE)
Pipe Product Mfr
N.A.I.C.S.: 332996
Ved Prakash Agarwal *(Chm)*

PRAKASH STEELAGE LTD.
101 1st Floor Shatrunjay Apartment 28 Sindhi Lane, Nanubhai Desai Road, Mumbai, 400 004, India
Tel.: (91) 2266134500
Web Site:
https://www.prakashsteelage.com
Year Founded: 1991
533239—(BOM)
Rev.: $9,364,133
Assets: $7,564,688
Liabilities: $46,009,519
Net Worth: ($38,444,832)
Earnings: $1,970,722
Emp.: 58
Fiscal Year-end: 03/31/19
Steel Pipes & Tubes Mfr
N.A.I.C.S.: 331210
Prakash C. Kanugo *(Founder, Chm & Mng Dir)*

PRAKASH WOOLLEN & SYNTHETIC MILLS LTD.
18th KM Stone Delhi Moradabad Road NH-24 Village Amhera, Moradabad, 244102, UP, India
Tel.: (91) 9760091983
Web Site:
https://www.prakashwoollen.com
Year Founded: 1973
531437—(BOM)
Rev.: $12,435,657
Assets: $14,236,892
Liabilities: $8,583,131
Net Worth: $5,653,762
Earnings: ($604,160)
Emp.: 419
Fiscal Year-end: 03/31/23
Mink Blanket Mfr & Distr
N.A.I.C.S.: 313210
Jai Kishan Gupta *(Mng Dir)*

PRAKIT HOLDINGS PUBLIC COMPANY LIMITED
88 Soi Sukhumvit 62 Section 3, Sukhumvit Road Bangchak Prakanong, Bangkok, 10260, Thailand
Tel.: (66) 27153000
Web Site: https://www.prakit.com
Year Founded: 1986
PRAKIT—(THA)
Rev.: $21,514,099
Assets: $36,926,012
Liabilities: $8,499,597
Net Worth: $28,426,416
Earnings: $6,780,382
Emp.: 197
Fiscal Year-end: 12/31/23
Advertising & Media Services
N.A.I.C.S.: 541890

Subsidiaries:

Prakit Advertising Limited (1)
88 Soi Sukhumvit 62 intersection 3 Sukhumvit Road Bangchak, Prakhanong, Bangkok, 10260, Thailand
Tel.: (66) 27153000
Web Site: http://www.prakitadvertising.com
Advertisement Creative Services
N.A.I.C.S.: 541810

PRAKTIKER AG
Am Tannenwald 2, 66459, Kirkel, Germany
Tel.: (49) 68499500   De
Web Site: http://www.praktiker.com
Year Founded: 1978
PRA—(DEU)
Sales Range: $1-4.9 Billion
Emp.: 19,523
Holding Company; Home-Improvement Store Operator
N.A.I.C.S.: 551112
Rudiger Wolff *(Vice Chm-Supervisory Bd)*

Subsidiaries:

Batiself S.A. (1)
2 Route D, L 8008, Strassen, Luxembourg
Tel.: (352) 4508311
Web Site: http://www.batiself.com.lu
Home Furnishing Mfr
N.A.I.C.S.: 236118

Praktiker Deutschland GmbH (1)
Am Tannenwald 2, 66459, Kirkel, Germany
Tel.: (49) 68499500
Web Site: http://www.praktiker.de
Sales Range: $200-249.9 Million
Emp.: 600
Home Improvement Store Operator
N.A.I.C.S.: 444110

Praktiker Hellas A.E. (1)
Pireos St 176, 177 78, Tavros, Greece
Tel.: (30) 2103493207
Web Site: http://www.praktiker.gr
Sales Range: $25-49.9 Million
Emp.: 40
Home Furnishing Mfr
N.A.I.C.S.: 236118
Costas Stamatakis *(Dir-Mktg)*

Praktiker Hungary Kft. (1)
Mester Ut 87, Budapest, 1095, Hungary
Tel.: (36) 14766100
Web Site: http://www.praktiker.hu
Sales Range: $25-49.9 Million
Emp.: 80
Home Furnishing Mfr
N.A.I.C.S.: 236118
Karl-Heinz Keth *(Mng Dir)*

Praktiker Yapi Merketleri A.S. (1)
Kucuksu Caddesi, Inkilap Mahallesi No 115, 81230, Istanbul, Turkiye
Tel.: (90) 2165228888
Web Site: http://www.praktiker.com.tr
Sales Range: $25-49.9 Million
Emp.: 90
Home Furnishing Mfr
N.A.I.C.S.: 236118

PRAKTIKER EOOD
Obikolna Nr 21 Druzba 2, 1582, Sofia, Bulgaria
Tel.: (359) 28072390
Web Site: http://www.praktiker.bg
Sales Range: $50-74.9 Million
Emp.: 200
Home Furnishings Services
N.A.I.C.S.: 236118
Michel Krahm *(Mgr)*

PRAMARA PROMOTIONS LIMITED
A-208 Boomerang Chandivali Farm Road, Chandivali Sakinaka Andheri East, Mumbai, 400 072, India
Tel.: (91) 2261983000
Web Site: https://www.pramara.com
Year Founded: 2006
PRAMARA—(NSE)
Rev.: $6,137,654
Assets: $7,360,734
Liabilities: $5,436,041
Net Worth: $1,924,693
Earnings: $266,878
Emp.: 83
Fiscal Year-end: 03/31/23
Toy Mfr
N.A.I.C.S.: 339930

PRANDA JEWELRY PUBLIC COMPANY LIMITED
28 Soi Bangna-Trad 28, Bangna, Bangkok, 10260, Thailand
Tel.: (66) 27699999   TH
Web Site: https://www.pranda.com
PDJ—(THA)
Rev.: $100,585,675
Assets: $109,285,471
Liabilities: $40,399,327
Net Worth: $68,886,144
Earnings: $2,399,443
Emp.: 2,105
Fiscal Year-end: 12/31/23
Holding Company; Jewelry Designer, Mfr, Whslr & Retailer
N.A.I.C.S.: 551112
Pranee Khunprasert *(Mng Dir-Mktg)*

Subsidiaries:

H.Gringoire S.A.R.L. (1)
53 rue Boissiere, 75116, Paris, France (100%)
Tel.: (33) 153019541
Web Site: http://www.h-gringoire.fr
Jewelry Mfr
N.A.I.C.S.: 339910

Pranda And Kroll GmbH And Co.KG (1)
Ebereschenweg 3, 75180, Pforzheim, Germany (51%)
Tel.: (49) 7231154470
Web Site: http://www.cai-jewels.com
Emp.: 30
Jewelry Mfr
N.A.I.C.S.: 339910

Pranda North America Inc. (1)
1 Wholesale Way, Cranston, RI 02920 (100%)
Tel.: (401) 946-2104
Web Site: http://www.pranda.com
Jewelry Mfr
N.A.I.C.S.: 339910

Pranda U.K. Limited (1)
Signal House West 1 Armfield Close, PO Box 59, West Molesey, KT8 2RT, Surrey, United Kingdom (100%)
Tel.: (44) 2089793896
Web Site: http://www.prandaonline.co.uk
Sales Range: $25-49.9 Million
Emp.: 35
Jewelry Mfr
N.A.I.C.S.: 339910

Primagold International Co. Ltd. (1)
589/64 Central City Bangna Building 12th Floor Bangna-Trad Road, Bangna Nuea Subdistrict Bangna District, Bangkok, 10260, Thailand (100%)
Tel.: (66) 27456111
Web Site: https://www.primagold.co.th
Sales Range: $50-74.9 Million
Emp.: 117
Jewelry Mfr

INTERNATIONAL PUBLIC

N.A.I.C.S.: 339910

PRANTALAY MARKETING PUBLIC COMPANY LIMITED
11259 1094/10 Wichienchodok Road, Mahachai Sub-District, Muang District, Samut Sakhon, 74000, Thailand
Tel.: (66) 3441 1388
Web Site: http://www.prantalay.com
Sales Range: $1-4.9 Billion
Emp.: 8,500
Frozen Seafood Products Processor & Distr
N.A.I.C.S.: 311710
Thongchai Tavannapong *(Mng Dir)*

PRAP JAPAN, INC.
Totate International Building 10F 2-12-19 Shibuya, Shibuya-ku, Tokyo, 150-8343, Japan
Tel.: (81) 3 3486 6831   JP
Web Site: http://www.prap.co.jp
Year Founded: 1970
Rev.: $4,630,000
Emp.: 232
Public Relations
N.A.I.C.S.: 541820
Hisashi Yajima *(Chm)*

Subsidiaries:

PRAP China Public Relations Consultants, Inc. (1)
Tower W Benzaiten Ste 902 The Tower Oriental Plz No 1, Dongcheng Dt E Chang An Ave, Beijing, 100738, China
Tel.: (86) 10 8518 5208
Emp.: 100
N.A.I.C.S.: 541820
Yuki X. Wei *(Mng Dir)*

PRARAM 9 HOSPITAL PCL
99 Rama IX Road Bangkapi Huai Khwang, Bangkok, 10310, Thailand
Tel.: (66) 22029999
Web Site: https://praram9.com
PR9—(THA)
Rev.: $124,147,914
Assets: $172,525,768
Liabilities: $24,239,644
Net Worth: $148,286,125
Earnings: $16,285,028
Emp.: 951
Fiscal Year-end: 12/31/23
Health Care Srvices
N.A.I.C.S.: 621999
Bhanapot Damapong *(Chm)*

PRASHKOVSKY INVESTMENTS & CONSTRUCTION LTD.
10 Moti Kind St, Rehovot, 75322, Israel
Tel.: (972) 549668165
Web Site:
https://www.prashkovsky.co.il
Year Founded: 2006
PRSK—(TAE)
Rev.: $103,576,183
Assets: $1,384,802,575
Liabilities: $887,738,900
Net Worth: $497,063,675
Earnings: $42,791,545
Fiscal Year-end: 12/31/23
Other Activities Related to Real Estate
N.A.I.C.S.: 531390
Arnon Prashkovsky *(Pres)*

PRASIDHA ANEKA NIAGA TBK
Plaza Sentral P608 Jl Jend Sudirman No 47, Jakarta, 12930, Indonesia
Tel.: (62) 2157904488
Web Site: https://www.prasidha.co.id
Year Founded: 1984
PSDN—(INDO)
Rev.: $17,282,597

Assets: $9,869,156
Liabilities: $5,577,777
Net Worth: $4,291,379
Earnings: $9,312,229
Emp.: 90
Fiscal Year-end: 12/31/23
Coffee Product Mfr
N.A.I.C.S.: 311920
Mansjur Tandiono *(Founder)*

Subsidiaries:

PT Aneka Bumi Kencana (1)
Jl Raya Mulyosari No 326, Surabaya, 60113, Jawa Timur, Indonesia
Tel.: (62) 31596584849
Coffee Bean Mfr
N.A.I.C.S.: 311920

PT. Aneka Coffee Industry (1)
39th floor Wisma 46 Kota BNI Jl Jend Sudirman Kav 1, Jakarta, 10220, Indonesia
Tel.: (62) 2139737378
Web Site: https://www.anekacoffee.com
Coffee Mfr
N.A.I.C.S.: 311920

Tirtha Harapan Bali.PT (1)
Jl Erlangga No 26, Singaraja, Bali, Indonesia
Tel.: (62) 36221088
Coffee Bean Mfr
N.A.I.C.S.: 311920

PRATAAP SNACKS LIMITED
Khasra No 378/2 Nemawar Road, Gram Palda, Indore, 452020, Madhya Pradesh, India
Tel.: (91) 7312437642 In
Web Site:
   https://www.yellowdiamond.in
Year Founded: 2009
540724—(BOM)
Rev.: $199,111,888
Assets: $109,300,042
Liabilities: $28,221,797
Net Worth: $81,078,245
Earnings: $2,435,322
Emp.: 1,503
Fiscal Year-end: 03/31/23
Food Product Mfr & Distr
N.A.I.C.S.: 311919
Arvind Mehta *(Chm)*

Subsidiaries:

Avadh Snacks Private Limited (1)
Survey No 128 Pot No 1 Opp Super Tech Industry, 15 Km from Metoda Gidc Rajkot Kalavad road Nikava Kalavad, Jamnagar, India
Tel.: (91) 9909777977
Web Site: https://www.avadhgroup.com
Snack Food Mfr & Distr
N.A.I.C.S.: 311919

PICL (India) Private Limited (1)
Plot - 619 Sector-69 IMT, Faridabad, 121006, Haryana, India
Tel.: (91) 1294009655
Web Site: https://www.piclindia.com
Automobile Parts Mfr
N.A.I.C.S.: 336390

Sidwal Refrigeration Industries Private Limited (1)
108 A Madangir, New Delhi, 110062, India
Tel.: (91) 1140775500
Web Site: http://www.sidwal.com
Air Conditioner Product Mfr
N.A.I.C.S.: 333415

PRATIBHA INDUSTRIES LIMITED
Unit No 1/B-56 & 1/B-57 1st Floor Phoenix Paragon, Plaza Phoenix Market City LBS Road Kurla W, Mumbai, 400070, Maharashtra, India
Tel.: (91) 2239559999
Web Site:
   https://www.pratibhagroup.com
Year Founded: 1982
PRATIBHA—(NSE)
Industrial Design Services
N.A.I.C.S.: 541420
Ajit B. Kulkarni *(Chm & Mng Dir)*

PRATICA KLIMAQUIP INDUSTRIA E COMERCIO SA
Highway BR 459 Km 101, Pouso Alegre, Minas Gerais, Brazil
Tel.: (55) 3534491200
Web Site: https://www.praticabr.com
PTCA3—(BRAZ)
Rev.: $56,575,676
Assets: $44,347,973
Liabilities: $30,470,852
Net Worth: $13,877,120
Earnings: $5,194,580
Fiscal Year-end: 12/31/23
Food Product Machinery Mfr
N.A.I.C.S.: 333241
Andre Luiz Rosa Rezende *(Chm, CEO, CFO & Dir-IR)*

PRATICA PARTICIPACOES S.A.
Av Doutor Joao Beraldo 408, 37550000, Pouso Alegre, MG, Brazil
Tel.: (55) 3534491200
Industrial Equipment Mfr
N.A.I.C.S.: 333248
Andre Luiz Rosa Rezende *(Chm, CEO, CFO & Dir-IR)*

PRATIK PANELS LTD.
44 and 56 Rawabhatta Industrial Estate Bilaspur Road, Raipur, 493 221, India
Tel.: (91) 771 256 2244
Web Site:
   http://www.pratikpanels.com
Rev.: $286
Assets: $54,959
Liabilities: $29,086
Net Worth: $25,873
Earnings: ($15,600)
Emp.: 1
Fiscal Year-end: 03/31/19
Plywood & Panel Mfr
N.A.I.C.S.: 321211
Gunwant Raj M. Singhvi *(Mng Dir)*

PRATIKSHA CHEMICALS LTD.
3rd Floor H K Complex Nr Dharnidhar Derasar Paldi, Ahmedabad, 380007, Gujarat, India
Tel.: (91) 7926609530
Web Site:
   https://www.dharapratiksha.com
Year Founded: 1991
531257—(BOM)
Rev.: $1,195,012
Assets: $1,287,573
Liabilities: $857,838
Net Worth: $429,734
Earnings: $10,539
Emp.: 21
Fiscal Year-end: 03/31/23
Chemical Products Mfr
N.A.I.C.S.: 325998
Harishbhai Krishnkant Bhatt *(Chm)*

PRAVEG LIMITED
214 Athena Avenue Behind Jaguar Showroom, SG Highway Gota, Ahmedabad, 382481, Gujarat, India
Tel.: (91) 7927496737
Web Site:
   https://www.dizcoverpraveg.com
Year Founded: 1986
531637—(BOM)
Rev.: $10,174,210
Assets: $15,060,536
Liabilities: $1,576,812
Net Worth: $13,483,724
Earnings: $3,409,028
Emp.: 171
Fiscal Year-end: 03/31/23
Pharmaceutical Preparation Mfr & Distr
N.A.I.C.S.: 325412
Pravinbhai M. Patel *(Chm & Mng Dir)*

PRAXIS FUND SERVICES (JERSEY) LIMITED
Charter Place 23/27 Seaton Place, Saint Helier, JE1 1JY, Jersey
Tel.: (44) 1534835835
Forestry Investment Services
N.A.I.C.S.: 523999

PRAXIS HOME RETAIL LIMITED
iThink Techno Campus Jolly Board Tower D Ground Floor Kanjurmarg East, Mumbai, 400 042, India
Tel.: (91) 2268824900 In
Web Site: https://www.praxisretail.in
Year Founded: 2007
PRAXIS—(NSE)
Rev.: $47,409,220
Assets: $37,451,352
Liabilities: $39,603,465
Net Worth: ($2,152,113)
Earnings: ($2,519,501)
Emp.: 831
Fiscal Year-end: 03/31/23
Home Furnishing Product Distr
N.A.I.C.S.: 449129
Viraj Didwania *(Chm & Mng Dir)*

PRAZSKE SLUZBY A.S.
Pod Sancemi 444/1, Prague 9, Prague, 180 77, Czech Republic
Tel.: (420) 284 098 448
Web Site: http://www.psas.cz
Waste Disposal & Recycling Services
N.A.I.C.S.: 562219

PRC REIT
bul Tsarigradsko shose 139, Sofia, 1784, Bulgaria
Tel.: (359) 29427409
Web Site: http://www.prcbg.com
PRC—(BUL)
Sales Range: Less than $1 Million
Real Estate Investment Services
N.A.I.C.S.: 531210

PRE-BUILT PUBLIC COMPANY LIMITED
503 Floor 1 Bondstreet Road, Bangpood Pakkred, Nonthaburi, 11120, Thailand
Tel.: (66) 29601380
Web Site: https://www.prebuilt.co.th
Year Founded: 1995
PREB—(THA)
Rev.: $142,338,483
Assets: $202,860,202
Liabilities: $128,881,727
Net Worth: $73,978,475
Earnings: $4,944,336
Fiscal Year-end: 12/31/23
Building Construction Services
N.A.I.C.S.: 236115
Wirot Charoentra *(Vice Chm, CEO & Mng Dir)*

PRE-TECH CO., LTD.
Keio-Fuchu 2-chome Bldg 2-1-14 Fuchu-cho, Fuchu, 183-0055, Tokyo, Japan
Tel.: (81) 42 360 6701
Web Site: http://www.pre-tech.co.jp
Year Founded: 1982
Emp.: 67
Industrial Electronic Cleaning Systems & Equipment Mfr & Whslr
N.A.I.C.S.: 333248
Hiroshi Amano *(Pres & CEO)*

PREATO CAPITAL AB
Riddargatan 19, SE-114 57, Stockholm, Sweden
Tel.: (46) 868442090
Web Site: http://www.preato.com
Privater Equity Firm
N.A.I.C.S.: 551112
Simon Hallqvist *(Chm)*

Subsidiaries:

Boreo Oyj (1)
Luomannotko 6, PO Box 73, 02201, Espoo, Finland (51.79%)
Tel.: (358) 102891200
Web Site: https://www.boreo.com
Rev.: $178,054,973
Assets: $132,023,402
Liabilities: $84,998,344
Net Worth: $47,025,058
Earnings: $3,090,849
Emp.: 341
Fiscal Year-end: 12/31/2023
Electronic Components Distr
N.A.I.C.S.: 423690
Janne Silvennoinen *(CEO)*

Subsidiary (Non-US):

ZAO YEInternational Russia (2)
Obukhovskoy Oborony 70 Building 3A, 192029, Saint Petersburg, Russia
Tel.: (7) 8123133440
Web Site: http://www.yeint.ru
Emp.: 70
Electronic Components Mfr
N.A.I.C.S.: 334419

PREATO OY
Mannerheimintie 16A 4, 00100, Helsinki, Finland
Tel.: (358) 9624084
Web Site: http://www.preato.fi
Sales Range: $25-49.9 Million
Emp.: 100
Privater Equity Firm
N.A.I.C.S.: 523999
Simon Hallqvist *(Chm & CEO)*

Subsidiaries:

Sefina Svensk Pantbelaning AB (1)
Vejatan 14, 113 29, Stockholm, Sweden
Tel.: (46) 854498190
Web Site: http://www.sefina.se
Sales Range: $75-99.9 Million
Emp.: 70
Owns & Operates Pawnshops
N.A.I.C.S.: 522291

PREAXIA HEALTH CARE PAYMENT SYSTEMS, INC.
1610-37th Street SW, PO Box 34075, Westbrook PO, Calgary, T3C 3W2, AB, Canada
Tel.: (403) 850-4120 NV
Web Site: http://www.preaxia.com
PAXH—(OTCIQ)
Assets: $14
Liabilities: $2,396,193
Net Worth: ($2,396,179)
Earnings: ($99,449)
Fiscal Year-end: 05/31/24
Healthcare Payment Systems
N.A.I.C.S.: 522320

PREBET AIUD S.A.
Str Arenei nr 10, 515200, Aiud, 515200, Romania
Tel.: (40) 258861661
Web Site: https://www.prebet.ro
Sales Range: $1-9.9 Million
Emp.: 307
Concrete Products Producer
N.A.I.C.S.: 327390
Ioan Campean *(Dir-Economic)*

PREBONA AB
Lastgatan 2, Simrishamn, 27 236, Skanes Fagerhult, Sweden
Tel.: (46) 705233047
Web Site: https://www.prebona.com
Nanotechnology Research Services

PREBONA AB

Prebona AB—(Continued)
N.A.I.C.S.: 541713
Orvar Otterstedt *(COO)*

PRECEDENT COMMUNICATIONS
11 Curtain Rd, London, EC2A 3LT, United Kingdom
Tel.: (44) 2074268900
Web Site: http://www.precedent.co.uk
Year Founded: 1990
Sales Range: $10-24.9 Million
Emp.: 75
N.A.I.C.S.: 541810
Mark Sherwin *(Dir-Bus Dev)*

PRECIA SA
PO Box 106, 07001, Privas, France
Tel.: (33) 475664600
Web Site:
   https://www.preciamolen.com
Year Founded: 1887
ALPM—(EUR)
Rev.: $168,923,397
Assets: $176,843,131
Liabilities: $79,217,594
Net Worth: $97,625,537
Earnings: $7,099,826
Emp.: 1,350
Fiscal Year-end: 12/31/22
Weighing Equipment Mfr
N.A.I.C.S.: 333993
Anne-Marie Escharavil *(Chm-Supervisory Bd)*

Subsidiaries:

Precia Molen Australia Pty Ltd (1)
Unit 6 6-8 McLachlan Avenue, Artarmon, 2064, NSW, Australia
Tel.: (61) 280068037
Weighing Machinery Mfr
N.A.I.C.S.: 333998

Precia Molen CZ S.R.O (1)
Jinonicka 804/80, 158 00, Prague, Czech Republic
Tel.: (420) 603885673
Web Site: https://cs.preciamolen.com
Weighing Machinery Mfr
N.A.I.C.S.: 333993

Precia Molen Ireland Limited (1)
Unit D1 Clane Business Park College Road, Clane, Kildare, W91 E778, Ireland
Tel.: (353) 18353084
Web Site: https://ie.preciamolen.com
Weighing Machinery Mfr
N.A.I.C.S.: 333993

Precia Molen NZ Ltd. (1)
1/21 McKee St, Pukete, Hamilton, 3200, New Zealand
Tel.: (64) 800662274
Web Site: https://nz.preciamolen.com
Weighing Machinery Mfr
N.A.I.C.S.: 333993

Precia Molen Nederland BV (1)
Franse Akker 1, 4824 AL, Breda, Netherlands
Tel.: (31) 765242526
Web Site: https://nl.preciamolen.com
Weighing Machinery Mfr
N.A.I.C.S.: 333993

Precia Molen Scandinavia AS (1)
Ringeriksvelen 48, 3414, Lierstranda, Norway
Tel.: (47) 47471547
Web Site: http://no.preciamolen.com
Weighing Machinery Mfr
N.A.I.C.S.: 333993

Precia Polska Sp. z o.o. (1)
Ul Czerwonego Pradnika 6, 31-431, Krakow, Poland
Tel.: (48) 124115050
Web Site: https://pl.preciamolen.com
Weighing Machinery Mfr
N.A.I.C.S.: 333993

Precia-Molen India Pvt. Limited (1)
DP 55-57, SIDCO Industrial Estate Thirumazhisai, Chennai, 600124, India

Tel.: (91) 4426810525
Web Site: https://in.preciamolen.com
Weighing Machinery Mfr
N.A.I.C.S.: 333993

Precia-Molen UK Limited (1)
Pitreavie Business Park, Dunfermline, KY11 8UL, Fife, United Kingdom
Tel.: (44) 3333001851
Web Site: https://uk.preciamolen.com
Weighing Machinery Mfr
N.A.I.C.S.: 333993

PRECINCT PROPERTIES NEW ZEALAND LIMITED
Level 12 188 Quay Street, Auckland, 1010, New Zealand
Tel.: (64) 92220070   NZ
Web Site: https://www.precinct.co.nz
Year Founded: 1997
PCT—(NZX)
Rev.: $132,850,410
Assets: $2,210,815,320
Liabilities: $885,891,930
Net Worth: $1,324,923,390
Earnings: ($92,916,390)
Emp.: 82
Fiscal Year-end: 06/30/23
Portfolio Management & Investment Advice
N.A.I.C.S.: 523940
Craig Hamilton Stobo *(Chm)*

PRECIO FISHBONE AB
Stortorget 8, 702 11, Orebro, Sweden
Tel.: (46) 771440080
PRCO.B—(OMX)
Rev.: $30,524,883
Assets: $25,183,883
Liabilities: $10,598,986
Net Worth: $14,584,898
Earnings: $2,464,795
Emp.: 246
Fiscal Year-end: 12/31/20
Financial Consulting Services
N.A.I.C.S.: 541611
Christer Johansson *(CEO)*

PRECIOUS METALS & MINING TRUST
2 Queen Street East 20th Floor, Toronto, M5C 3G7, ON, Canada
Tel.: (416) 681-7071
Web Site: http://www.ci.com
Year Founded: 2006
Rev.: $4,921,258
Assets: $22,223,335
Liabilities: $221,154
Net Worth: $22,002,180
Earnings: $4,351,920
Fiscal Year-end: 12/31/19
Financial Investment Services
N.A.I.C.S.: 523999

PRECIOUS METALS EXPLORATION CORP.
6 Rietfontein Road Edenburg, Sandton, 2128, South Africa
Tel.: (27) 11 2347976   NV
Web Site:
   http://www.preciousmetals.com
Year Founded: 2015
Emp.: 2
Precious Metal Exploration Services
N.A.I.C.S.: 213114
Robert Russel *(Chm, Pres, CEO & CFO)*

PRECIOUS SHIPPING PUBLIC COMPANY LIMITED
No 8 North Sathorn Road G 7th 8th and 9th floors Silom Bangrak, Bangkok, 10500, Thailand
Tel.: (66) 26968800
Web Site:
   https://www.preciousshipping.com
Year Founded: 1989

PSGFF—(OTCIQ)
Rev.: $151,593,205
Assets: $710,702,420
Liabilities: $236,456,975
Net Worth: $474,245,445
Earnings: $20,714,689
Emp.: 138
Fiscal Year-end: 12/31/23
Freight Shipping Services
N.A.I.C.S.: 483111
Shrilal Gopinathan *(VP-Comml)*

Subsidiaries:

Geepee Shipping Agencies Pvt., Ltd. (1)
1003 Dalamal House, 206 Nariman Point, Mumbai, 400 021, India
Tel.: (91) 22 56306439
Recruiting Services
N.A.I.C.S.: 541612

Geepee Shipping Agencies Pvt., Ltd. (1)
2/33 Venugopal Avenue, Chetput, Chennai, 600 031, India
Tel.: (91) 4428361069
Web Site: http://www.gcship.net
Sales Range: $25-49.9 Million
Emp.: 3
Recruitment Services
N.A.I.C.S.: 541612

Geepee Shipping Agencies Pvt., Ltd. (1)
4 Jagannath Sarkar Lane, Kidderpore, Kolkata, 700 023, India
Tel.: (91) 332 459 5670
Web Site: http://www.geepeeshipping.com
Sales Range: $25-49.9 Million
Emp.: 1
Recruitment Services
N.A.I.C.S.: 541612
Bholenath Baneerji *(Mng Dir)*

Great Circle Shipping Agency Limited (1)
8/35 North Sathorn Road, GPO Box 1228, Bangkok, 10500, Thailand
Tel.: (66) 26968900
Web Site: https://www.gcship.net
Emp.: 200
Technical Management Services
N.A.I.C.S.: 541611

PRECIOUS TRADING & INVESTMENTS LTD.
Ground and 3rd Floor Prius Infinity Paranjape B Scheme, Subash Road Vile Parle, Mumbai, 400 057, India
Tel.: (91) 224 260 2400
Web Site: http://www.ptil.co.in
Year Founded: 1986
506107—(BOM)
Rev.: $84,002,783
Assets: $217,938,767
Liabilities: $27,466,394
Net Worth: $190,472,373
Earnings: $175,726,688
Emp.: 3
Fiscal Year-end: 03/31/20
Real Estate Related Services
N.A.I.C.S.: 531390
Ashwin Sheth *(Chm & Mng Dir)*

PRECIOUS WOODS HOLDING AG
Untermuli 6, 6300, Zug, Switzerland
Tel.: (41) 41 726 1313   CH
Web Site:
   http://www.preciouswoods.com
Year Founded: 1990
Sales Range: $25-49.9 Million
Emp.: 1,300
Holding Company; Forest Management Services & Timber Producer
N.A.I.C.S.: 551112
Katharina Lehmann *(Chm)*

Subsidiaries:

Compagnie Equatoriale des Bois S.A. (1)

INTERNATIONAL PUBLIC

Rue Kringer Rendjombe Quartier Batterie IV, PO Box 2262, Libreville, Gabon
Tel.: (241) 73 45 79
Sales Range: $75-99.9 Million
Emp.: 400
Timber Logging Services
N.A.I.C.S.: 113110

Madeiras Preciosas de Amazonia Manejo Ltda. (1)
Estrada Torquato Tapajos Km 227, 69100-000, Itacoatiara, AM, Brazil
Tel.: (55) 923 521 9200
Web Site: http://www.preciouswoods.com
Sawmill; Sustainable Forestry & Small Parts Mfr
N.A.I.C.S.: 321113

Subsidiary (Domestic):

BK Energia Itacoatiara Ltda. (2)
Rodovia AM 363 KM 1 5 Zona Rural, Caixa Postal 101, Amazonas, BR-69100-000, Itacoatiara, Brazil
Tel.: (55) 9235213331
Web Site: http://www.preciouswoods.com
Electricity Production
N.A.I.C.S.: 221118

MIL Madeiras Preciosas Ltda (2)
Precious Woods Amazon Estr Torquato Tapajos Km 227, Caixa Postal 39, 69100-000, Itacoatiara, AM, Brazil
Tel.: (55) 923 521 92 00
Timber Logging Services
N.A.I.C.S.: 113110

Maderas Preciosas de Costa Rica S.A. (1)
Km 239 Carretera Interamericana Norte, PO Box 63-5000, Liberia, Guanacaste, Costa Rica
Tel.: (506) 2 666 0636
Web Site: http://www.preciouswoods.com
Sales Range: $25-49.9 Million
Emp.: 205
Reforestation of Abandoned Pastureland
N.A.I.C.S.: 115310

Precious Woods Europe B.V. (1)
Weypoort 75, Postbus 129, Nieuwerbrug, 2410 AC, Rijn, Netherlands
Tel.: (31) 34 868 4100
Web Site: http://www.preciouswoods.eu
Sales Range: $25-49.9 Million
Emp.: 27
Forestry Trading
N.A.I.C.S.: 236220

PRECIPITATE GOLD CORP.
625 Howe Street Suite 1020, Vancouver, V6C 2T6, BC, Canada
Tel.: (604) 558-0335   BC
Web Site:
   https://www.precipitategold.com
Year Founded: 2011
PRG—(TSXV)
Rev.: $55,111
Assets: $4,845,800
Liabilities: $287,645
Net Worth: $4,558,155
Earnings: $270,790
Fiscal Year-end: 11/30/23
Gold Mining
N.A.I.C.S.: 212220
Adrian W. Fleming *(Chm)*

PRECIS MARKETING
Charter House Sindford St, Lichfield, WS13 6QA, United Kingdom
Tel.: (44) 8456444567
Web Site:
   http://www.precismarketing.co.uk
Year Founded: 2005
Sales Range: $10-24.9 Million
Emp.: 11
Brand Development & Integration, Business-To-Business, Collateral, Internet/Web Design, Logo & Package Design, Search Engine Optimization
N.A.I.C.S.: 541810
Andy Frost *(Dir)*

Subsidiaries:

Adstorm (1)
Charter House Sandford St, Lichfield, WS13 6QG, United Kingdom
Tel.: (44) 1543 308636
Web Site: http://www.adstorm.co.uk
N.A.I.C.S.: 541810
Andreas Dannenberg *(Pres & CEO)*

PRECISE BIOMETRICS AB
Scheelevagen 27 8th floor, 223 62, Lund, Sweden
Tel.: (46) 46311100
Web Site: https://www.precisebiometrics.com
PREC—(OMX)
Rev.: $7,452,201
Assets: $21,111,542
Liabilities: $5,295,729
Net Worth: $15,815,812
Earnings: ($2,621,061)
Emp.: 31
Fiscal Year-end: 12/31/23
Biometric Security Solutions
N.A.I.C.S.: 561621
Torgny Hellstrom *(Chm)*

Subsidiaries:

EastCoast Solutions AB (1)
Osterlanggatan 43, 11131, Stockholm, Sweden
Tel.: (46) 86608210
Web Site: https://www.eastcoast.se
Management Consulting Services
N.A.I.C.S.: 541611

Precise Biometrics Inc. (1)
8300 Boone Blvd Ste 500, Vienna, VA 22182
Tel.: (703) 848-9266
Biometric Systems Mfr
N.A.I.C.S.: 334419

Precise Biometrics Solutions AB (1)
Scheelevagen 30, 22363, Lund, Sweden
Tel.: (46) 54101371
Web Site: http://www.precisebiometrics.com
Sales Range: $25-49.9 Million
Biometric Systems Mfr
N.A.I.C.S.: 334419
Hakan Persnon *(Gen Mgr)*

PRECISE CORPORATION PUBLIC COMPANY LIMITED
1842 Krungthep-Nonthaburi Road, Wongsawang Bangsue, Bangkok, 10800, Thailand
Tel.: (66) 2910970012
Web Site: https://www.precise.co.th
Year Founded: 1983
PCC—(THA)
Rev.: $135,028,400
Assets: $191,994,761
Liabilities: $96,667,067
Net Worth: $95,327,694
Earnings: $10,185,861
Emp.: 961
Fiscal Year-end: 12/31/23
Electric Equipment Mfr
N.A.I.C.S.: 335999
Kitti Sumrit *(CEO)*

PRECISION ASSESSMENT TECHNOLOGY CORPORATION
Ste 1030 885 West Georgia Street, PO Box 1022, Vancouver, V6C 3E8, BC, Canada
Tel.: (604) 669-3373 AB
Year Founded: 1987
Sales Range: $10-24.9 Million
Emp.: 60
Drilling Services
N.A.I.C.S.: 213111
Robert E. Nowack *(Chm)*

Subsidiaries:

Groundwater Protection (1)
2300 Silver Star Rd, Orlando, FL 32804
Tel.: (407) 426-7885
Web Site: http://www.groundwaterprotection.com
Drilling Service Provider
N.A.I.C.S.: 213111
Roy Rushing *(Mgr-Ops)*

PRECISION BIOSENSOR, INC.
306 Techno 2-Ro, Yuseong-Gu, Daejeon, Korea (South)
Tel.: (82) 428676300
Web Site: https://www.precision-bio.com
Year Founded: 2009
335810—(KRS)
Rev.: $15,691,300
Assets: $45,260,316
Liabilities: $19,661,614
Net Worth: $25,598,703
Earnings: ($5,220,154)
Emp.: 90
Fiscal Year-end: 12/31/22
Pharmaceutical Preparation Mfr & Distr
N.A.I.C.S.: 325412
Hanshin Kim *(CEO)*

PRECISION CAMSHAFTS LIMITED
E102 MIDC Akkalkot Road, Solapur, 413006, India
Tel.: (91) 2173295433
Web Site: https://www.pclindia.in
PRECAM—(NSE)
Rev.: $133,060,848
Assets: $133,150,567
Liabilities: $47,241,544
Net Worth: $85,909,022
Earnings: $5,549,535
Emp.: 1,070
Fiscal Year-end: 03/31/23
Camshaft Manufacturing
N.A.I.C.S.: 333517
Yatin Shah *(Chm & Mng Dir)*

Subsidiaries:

Emoss Mobile Systems B.V. (1)
Visserijweg 2, 4906 CJ, Oosterhout, Netherlands
Tel.: (31) 162420005
Web Site: https://www.emoss.nl
Electronic Services
N.A.I.C.S.: 238210

Memco Engineering Private Limited (1)
Plot No - F 5 / C-16 M I D C Satpur, Nashik, 422007, Maharashtra, India
Tel.: (91) 8888823710
Web Site: https://www.memcoindia.com
Tool Mfr
N.A.I.C.S.: 333517

Mft Motoren Und Fahrzeugtechnik GmbH (1)
Koblitzer Strasse 7, Cunewalde, 02733, Bautzen, Germany
Tel.: (49) 35877260
Web Site: https://mft.gmbh
Emp.: 150
Shaft Machining Mfr
N.A.I.C.S.: 333517
Jana Ain *(Mgr-Supply Chain)*

PRECISION CONTAINEURS LIMITED
Madhav Niwas CHSL Flat No B-11st floor Natakwala Lane, Opp S V Road Borivali West, Mumbai, 400092, Maharashtra, India
Tel.: (91) 2228990841 In
Web Site: http://www.precisioncontainers.com
Year Founded: 1981
523874—(BOM)
Rev.: $9,316
Assets: $62,586
Liabilities: $2,434,434
Net Worth: ($2,371,848)
Earnings: ($25,178)
Fiscal Year-end: 03/31/23
Barrel Mfr
N.A.I.C.S.: 332439
Jayesh Vinodrai Valia *(Mng Dir & Compliance Officer)*

PRECISION DRILLING CORPORATION
525-8th Ave S W Suite 800, Calgary, T2P 1G1, AB, Canada
Tel.: (403) 716-4500 AB
Web Site: https://www.precisiondrilling.com
Year Founded: 1952
PDS—(NYSE)
Rev.: $1,265,098,522
Assets: $2,249,933,500
Liabilities: $1,287,315,274
Net Worth: $962,618,226
Earnings: ($26,826,728)
Emp.: 4,802
Fiscal Year-end: 12/31/22
Contract Drilling, Technology Service & Oilfield Rental Equipment
N.A.I.C.S.: 213111
Kevin A. Neveu *(Pres & CEO)*

Subsidiaries:

Axis Energy Services Holdings Inc. (1)
525 8 Ave Sw Suite 800, Calgary, T2P 1g1, AB, Canada
Tel.: (403) 264-4301
Web Site: http://www.precisiondrilling.com
Investment Management Service
N.A.I.C.S.: 523940

Columbia Oilfield Supply Ltd. (1)
Ste 800 525 8th Ave SW, Calgary, T2P1G1, AB, Canada **(100%)**
Tel.: (780) 437-5110
Web Site: http://www.precisiondrilling.com
Sales Range: $10-24.9 Million
Emp.: 43
N.A.I.C.S.: 213111

LRG Catering Ltd. (1)
3050 Parsons Rd, Edmonton, T6N 1B1, AB, Canada **(100%)**
Tel.: (780) 431-3484
Web Site: http://www.toughnecks.com
Sales Range: $50-74.9 Million
Emp.: 15
N.A.I.C.S.: 213111

Precision Diversified Oilfield Services Corp. (1)
150 6 Ave Sw Suite 4200, Calgary, T2P 3Y7, AB, Canada
Tel.: (403) 716-4500
Web Site: http://www.precision.com
Emp.: 2,000
Oil & Gas Exploration Services
N.A.I.C.S.: 213112

Precision Drilling Company LP (1)
10350 Richmond Ave 600, Houston, TX 77042
Tel.: (713) 435-6100
Emp.: 75
Oil & Gas Drilling Services
N.A.I.C.S.: 213111
Kevin Neveu *(Pres)*

Precision Drilling Corporation (1)
504 204 Ave, Nisku, T9E 7X6, AB, Canada **(100%)**
Tel.: (780) 955-2029
Sales Range: $50-74.9 Million
Emp.: 100
Provider of Oilfield Drilling & Energy Service
N.A.I.C.S.: 213111

Precision Drilling Corporation - Middle East (1)
Bageen Buttin Das Tower 8th Floor, PO Box 2146, Abu Dhabi, 2146, United Arab Emirates **(100%)**
Tel.: (971) 26747333
Web Site: http://www.precisiondrilling.com
Emp.: 40
Provider of Oilfield Drilling & Energy Service
N.A.I.C.S.: 213111

Precision Limited Partnership (1)
150 6 Ave SW Suite 4200, Calgary, T2P 3Y7, AB, Canada
Tel.: (403) 781-5555
Web Site: http://www.precisiondrilling.com
Emp.: 1,000
Oil & Gas Exploration Services
N.A.I.C.S.: 213112

Precision Rentals Ltd. (1)
800 525 8th Ave SW, Calgary, T2P 1G1, AB, Canada **(100%)**
Tel.: (403) 716-4500
Web Site: http://www.precisiondrilling.com
Sales Range: $200-249.9 Million
Emp.: 220
Provider of Oilfield Drilling & Energy Service
N.A.I.C.S.: 213111

Precision Well Servicing (1)
Ste 800 525 8 Avenue SW, Calgary, T2P 1G1, AB, Canada
Tel.: (403) 781-5555
Web Site: http://www.precision.com
Sales Range: $50-74.9 Million
Emp.: 25
Provider of Drilling Services
N.A.I.C.S.: 213111

Precisionenergy Services (1)
4500 Petro Canada Ctr, 150 6th Ave SW, Calgary, T2P 3Y7, AB, Canada
Tel.: (403) 265-6060
Web Site: http://www.precision-es.com
Sales Range: $200-249.9 Million
Emp.: 500
Wire Line Services
N.A.I.C.S.: 213112

Rostel Industries Ltd. (1)
9699 Sheppard Rd SE, Calgary, T2C 4K5, AB, Canada **(100%)**
Tel.: (403) 720-3999
Web Site: https://rostelindustries.com
Sales Range: $10-24.9 Million
Emp.: 150
N.A.I.C.S.: 213111

PRECISION ELECTRONICS LIMITED
D-10 Sector-3, Noida, 201301, Uttar Pradesh, India
Tel.: (91) 1202551556
Web Site: https://pel-india.in
Year Founded: 1979
517258—(BOM)
Rev.: $4,336,850
Assets: $4,637,084
Liabilities: $3,028,919
Net Worth: $1,608,165
Earnings: $971
Emp.: 136
Fiscal Year-end: 03/31/23
Telecommunication Equipment Mfr & Distr
N.A.I.C.S.: 334290
Ashok Kumar Kanodia *(Founder & Mng Dir)*

PRECISION METAL FABRICATING LTD.
240 103rd Street East, Saskatoon, S7N 1Y7, SK, Canada
Tel.: (306) 955-3700
Year Founded: 1985
Rev.: $17,326,669
Emp.: 100
Farm Equipment Mfr
N.A.I.C.S.: 333111
Loren Katzenberger *(Pres & CEO)*

PRECISION METALIKS LIMITED
9-19-43 Suryadev Apartments Flat No 202 CBM Compound, Visakhapatnam, 530003, India
Tel.: (91) 8914884132
Web Site: https://www.precision-metaliks.com
Year Founded: 2012
PRECISION—(NSE)
Rev.: $22,667,526
Assets: $13,276,398
Liabilities: $7,538,601

Precision Metaliks Limited—(Continued)

Net Worth: $5,737,797
Earnings: $851,783
Emp.: 16
Fiscal Year-end: 03/31/23
Engineeering Services
N.A.I.C.S.: 541330

PRECISION SYSTEM SCIENCE CO., LTD.
88 Kamihongou, Matsudo, 271-0064, Chiba, Japan
Tel.: (81) 473034800 JP
Web Site: https://www.pss.co.jp
Year Founded: 1985
7707—(TKS)
Rev.: $24,749,380
Assets: $39,783,120
Liabilities: $14,019,880
Net Worth: $25,763,240
Earnings: ($6,972,620)
Emp.: 158
Fiscal Year-end: 06/30/24
Analytical Laboratory Instrument Mfr
N.A.I.C.S.: 334516
Hideji Tajima (Pres & Pres)

Subsidiaries:

Precision System Science Europe GmbH (1)
Spiesheimer Weg 32, 55286, Worrstadt, Germany
Tel.: (49) 673293880
Laboratory Equipment Distr
N.A.I.C.S.: 423450

Precision System Science USA, Inc. (1)
5673 W Las Positas Blvd Ste 202, Pleasanton, CA 94588
Tel.: (925) 960-9180
Web Site: https://www.pssbio.com
Emp.: 5
Laboratory Equipment Distr
N.A.I.C.S.: 423450
Paul Race (CEO)

PRECISION WIRES INDIA LTD
Saiman House J A Raul Street Off Sayani Road Prabhadevi, Mumbai, 400025, India
Tel.: (91) 2224376281
Web Site: https://precisionwires.in
Year Founded: 1989
523539—(BOM)
Rev.: $366,341,286
Assets: $111,293,615
Liabilities: $57,302,967
Net Worth: $53,990,648
Earnings: $7,133,038
Emp.: 648
Fiscal Year-end: 03/31/23
Copper Winding Wires Mfr
N.A.I.C.S.: 335139
Mahendra Ratilal Mehta (Chm & Mng Dir)

PRECOMP SOLUTIONS AB
Bronasgatan 6, 523 37, Ulricehamn, Sweden
Tel.: (46) 321530800
Web Site: https://www.precomp.se
Year Founded: 1956
PCOM.B—(OMX)
Rev.: $17,518,480
Assets: $10,183,914
Liabilities: $7,644,650
Net Worth: $2,539,264
Earnings: ($428,501)
Emp.: 131
Fiscal Year-end: 12/31/20
Motor Vehicle Part & Accessory Mfr
N.A.I.C.S.: 336390
Stig-Arne Blom (Chm)

Subsidiaries:

Precomp Solutions EAD (1)
8 Iliyensko Shosse str, 1220, Sofia, Bulgaria
Tel.: (359) 8362052
Automotive Products Mfr
N.A.I.C.S.: 336110

PRECOT LTD.
SF No 559/4 D Block 4th Floor Hanudev Info Park, Nava India Road, Coimbatore, 641 028, Tamil Nadu, India
Tel.: (91) 4224321100
Web Site: https://www.precot.com
PRECOT—(NSE)
Rev.: $115,228,200
Assets: $108,696,133
Liabilities: $60,052,335
Net Worth: $48,643,798
Earnings: ($3,120,029)
Emp.: 1,462
Fiscal Year-end: 03/31/23
Yarn & Textile Manufacturer
N.A.I.C.S.: 313110
Ashwin Chandran (Chm & Mng Dir)

Subsidiaries:

Suprem Associates Partnership Firm (1)

PREDATOR OIL & GAS HOLDINGS PLC
3rd Floor IFC5 Castle Street, Saint Helier, JE2 4SZ, Jersey
Tel.: (44) 1534834600 JE
Web Site: https://www.predatoroilandgas.com
Year Founded: 2017
PRD—(LSE)
Rev.: $46,461
Assets: $33,005,584
Liabilities: $6,387,225
Net Worth: $26,618,460
Earnings: ($6,131,106)
Fiscal Year-end: 12/31/23
Oil & Gas Exploration Services
N.A.I.C.S.: 213112
Paul Griffiths (CEO)

PREDICTA - ADNETWORK IAS LTDA.
Rua Gomes de Carvalho 1510 - 13 andar, Sao Paulo, SP, Brazil
Tel.: (55) 11 4095 1800
Web Site: http://www.predicta.net
Year Founded: 1999
Sales Range: $10-24.9 Million
Emp.: 150
Digital Marketing Software Developer
N.A.I.C.S.: 513210
Marcelo Marzola (CEO)

PREDICTA A.E.
18 Chatzikonstanti Str, 11524, Athens, Greece
Tel.: (30) 2106931040 GR
Web Site: http://www.predicta.gr
Year Founded: 2001
Sales Range: $1-9.9 Million
Emp.: 18
Predictive Analytics & Data Mining Software Distr
N.A.I.C.S.: 423430
Ionna Koutrouvis (Mng Dir)

PREDICTIV AI, INC.
151 Bloor Street West Suite 703, Toronto, M5S 1S4, ON, Canada
Tel.: (416) 792-9088
Web Site: http://www.predictiv.ai
PAI—(TSXV)
Rev.: $85,264
Assets: $56,306
Liabilities: $660,721
Net Worth: ($604,415)
Earnings: ($375,002)
Fiscal Year-end: 01/31/23
Information Technology Services

N.A.I.C.S.: 541512
Khurram Qureshi (CFO)

Subsidiaries:

AI Labs Inc. (1)
301 W Warner Rd 134, Tempe, AZ 85284
Tel.: (480) 626-8085
Web Site: http://www.ailabsinc.com
Software Development Services
N.A.I.C.S.: 541511

Weather Telematics Inc. (1)
151 Bloor Street West Suite 703, Toronto, M5S 1S4, ON, Canada
Tel.: (416) 580-6559
Web Site: http://www.weathertelematics.com
Weather Forecasting Services
N.A.I.C.S.: 541990

PREDICTIVE DISCOVERY LIMITED
Suite 2 Level 2 20 Kings Park Road, West Perth, 6005, WA, Australia
Tel.: (61) 892161000 AU
Web Site: https://www.predictivediscovery.com
PDI—(ASX)
Rev.: $1,045,384
Assets: $117,915,348
Liabilities: $4,436,489
Net Worth: $113,478,859
Earnings: ($5,787,881)
Emp.: 41
Fiscal Year-end: 06/30/24
Mineral Mining Services
N.A.I.C.S.: 212390
Paul Roberts (Dir-Technical)

PREDICTIVE SOLUTIONS SP. Z O.O.
Ul Raclawicka 58, 30-017, Krakow, Poland
Tel.: (48) 126369680 PL
Web Site: http://www.predictivesolutions.pl
Year Founded: 1991
Sales Range: $1-9.9 Million
Emp.: 30
Predictive Analytics & Data Mining Software Distr
N.A.I.C.S.: 423430
Piotr Komornicki (Mng Dir)

PREDICTMEDIX, INC.
77 King St West 3000, Toronto, M5K 1A2, ON, Canada
Tel.: (647) 889-6916
Web Site: https://www.predictmedix.com
PMEDF—(OTCQB)
Rev.: $27,395
Assets: $561,470
Liabilities: $681,463
Net Worth: ($119,993)
Earnings: ($1,617,565)
Emp.: 1
Fiscal Year-end: 01/31/23
Health Care Srvices
N.A.I.C.S.: 621610
Rahul Kushwah (CEO-Interim)

PREDILIFE SA
39 Rue Camille Desmoulins, 94805, Villejuif, Cedex, France
Tel.: (33) 972226708
Web Site: https://www.predilife.com
Year Founded: 2014
ALPRE—(EUR)
Sales Range: Less than $1 Million
Pharmaceuticals Product Mfr
N.A.I.C.S.: 325412
Stephane Ragusa (Chm & CEO)

PREDUZECE ZA PUTEVE VALJEVO A.D.
Milovana Glisica 94, 14000, Valjevo, Serbia

Tel.: (381) 14221486
Web Site: https://www.pzp-va.rs
Year Founded: 1962
PPVA—(BEL)
Rev.: $42,257,834
Assets: $40,053,024
Liabilities: $9,690,471
Net Worth: $30,362,553
Earnings: $5,150,168
Emp.: 531
Fiscal Year-end: 12/31/23
Road Construction Services
N.A.I.C.S.: 237310
Mihajlo Markovic (Mng Dir)

PREECHA GROUP PUBLIC COMPANY LIMITED
1919 Preecha Group Building Pattanakarn Road, Suan Luang, Bangkok, 10250, Thailand
Tel.: (66) 27228855 TH
Web Site: https://www.preecha.com
Year Founded: 1989
PRECHA—(THA)
Rev.: $5,022,770
Assets: $14,447,690
Liabilities: $3,902,966
Net Worth: $10,544,723
Earnings: $26,857
Fiscal Year-end: 12/31/23
Real Estate Development Services
N.A.I.C.S.: 531390
Phachara Yutithamdamrong (Chm)

PREEM AB
Warfvinges vag 45, 112 80, Stockholm, Sweden
Tel.: (46) 104501000 SE
Web Site: http://www.preem.se
Year Founded: 1996
Rev.: $10,262,384,860
Assets: $4,031,413,890
Liabilities: $2,888,017,160
Net Worth: $1,143,396,730
Earnings: $62,372,940
Emp.: 1,536
Fiscal Year-end: 12/31/19
Crude Oil Refining & Petroleum Products Marketer & Distr
N.A.I.C.S.: 324110
Mohammed H. Ali Al-Amoudi (Founder)

Subsidiaries:

Svensk Petroleum Forvaltning AB (1)
Sandhamnsgatan 51, 115 28, Stockholm, Sweden
Tel.: (46) 84501634
Petroleum Product Distr
N.A.I.C.S.: 424720

PREFERRED DENTAL TECHNOLOGIES, INC.
B01-185 Provencher Boulevard, Winnipeg, R2H-0G4, MB, Canada
Tel.: (204) 691-3722
Web Site: http://www.prefdent.com
Dental Device Mfr
N.A.I.C.S.: 339114
Erik Siegmund (Pres & CEO)

PREHRANA-PROMET D.D.
Ul Ahmeta Kobica bb, Gornja, Tuzla, 75208, Bosnia & Herzegovina
Tel.: (387) 35 394 160
PREHRK5—(SARE)
Rev.: $36,132
Assets: $3,819,324
Liabilities: $788,909
Net Worth: $3,030,415
Earnings: $397,583
Emp.: 1
Fiscal Year-end: 12/31/20
Tobacco & Food Product Distr
N.A.I.C.S.: 459991

PRELIOS S.P.A.
Viale Piero e Alberto Pirelli 27, 20126, Milan, Italy
Tel.: (39) 02 62811   IT
Web Site: http://www.prelios.com
Rev.: $82,156,032
Assets: $141,312,654
Liabilities: $3,851,064
Net Worth: $137,461,590
Earnings: ($31,878,252)
Emp.: 400
Fiscal Year-end: 12/31/16
Real Estate Services
N.A.I.C.S.: 531390
Riccardo Serrini (CEO & Gen Mgr)

Subsidiaries:

Ingest Facility S.p.A. (1)
C so Ferrucci 112A, 10138, Turin, Italy
Tel.: (39) 0110059711
Web Site: http://www.ingestfacility.com
Sales Range: $250-299.9 Million
Emp.: 380
Integrated Facility Management Services
N.A.I.C.S.: 541611

PREMA SEMICONDUCTOR GMBH
Robert Bosch Str 6, 55129, Mainz, Germany
Tel.: (49) 613150620
Web Site: http://www.prema.com
Year Founded: 1970
Rev.: $14,111,262
Emp.: 60
Digital Multimeters Mfr
N.A.I.C.S.: 334515
Christian V. der Luhe (Chm-Supervisory Bd)

PREMCO GLOBAL LTD.
Tower A 11th Floor 95 Ganpatrao Kadam Marg Lower Parel West, Andheri East, Mumbai, 400093, Maharastra, India
Tel.: (91) 2261055000
Web Site:
  https://www.premcoglobal.com
530331—(BOM)
Rev.: $11,566,489
Assets: $15,541,718
Liabilities: $2,512,487
Net Worth: $13,029,231
Earnings: $1,130,891
Emp.: 213
Fiscal Year-end: 03/31/23
Textile Apparel Mfr
N.A.I.C.S.: 315250
Ashok B. Harjani (Chm & Mng Dir)

PREMEDIA GLOBAL PVT. LTD.
12th Floor Phase II Ascendas International Tech Park, Chennai, 600113, India
Tel.: (91) 44 4291 3999   In
Web Site:
  http://www.premediaglobal.com
Year Founded: 2005
Sales Range: $150-199.9 Million
Emp.: 1,000
Publishing, Packaging & Corporate Logo Content Development, Editorial & Layout Design Services
N.A.I.C.S.: 541430
Jane Petlinski (Sr VP-PreK-12)

Subsidiaries:

PreMedia Global, Inc. (1)
4 Collins Ave, Plymouth, MA 02360
Tel.: (508) 746-0300
Web Site: http://www.premediaglobal.com
Sales Range: $25-49.9 Million
Emp.: 80
Publishing, Packaging & Corporate Logo Content Development, Editorial & Layout Design Services
N.A.I.C.S.: 541430

Branch (Domestic):
PreMedia Global, Inc. - New York (2)
345 7th Ave 22nd Fl, New York, NY 10001
Tel.: (646) 453-1000
Web Site: http://www.premediaglobal.com
Publishing, Packaging & Corporate Logo Content Development, Editorial & Layout Design Services
N.A.I.C.S.: 541430

PreMedia Global, Inc. - Ohio (2)
1797 Seddon Ct, Ashland, OH 44805
Tel.: (419) 289-0558
Web Site: http://www.premediaglobal.com
Sales Range: $25-49.9 Million
Emp.: 75
Publishing, Packaging & Corporate Logo Content Development, Editorial & Layout Design Services
N.A.I.C.S.: 541430

PREMIA FINANCE S.P.A.
Viale U Tupini 103, 00144, Rome, Italy
Tel.: (39) 0800970855
Web Site:
  https://www.premiafinancespa.it
Year Founded: 2011
PFI—(EUR)
Investment Management Service
N.A.I.C.S.: 523999

PREMIA REAL ESTATE INVESTMENT COMPANY SA
8B Chimarras str Maroussi, 115 21, Athens, Greece
Tel.: (30) 2102886000   GR
Web Site:
  https://www.premia.properties
Year Founded: 1991
PREMIA—(ATH)
Rev.: $20,496,991
Assets: $384,358,824
Liabilities: $225,446,058
Net Worth: $158,912,766
Earnings: $7,817,193
Emp.: 17
Fiscal Year-end: 12/31/23
Real Estate Investment Services
N.A.I.C.S.: 531190
Elias Georgiadis (Chm)

Subsidiaries:

Thesmia S.A. (1)
Loutsas Rd Industrial Area, Rest of Area, 19600, Mandra, Attica, Greece
Tel.: (30) 21055507516
Web Site: https://www.wiw.gr
Real Estate Investment & Management Services
N.A.I.C.S.: 531390

Zonas S.A. (1)
8 Chaidariou & 29 Polydevkous, 185 45, Piraeus, Greece
Tel.: (30) 2104133919
Web Site: https://www.zonas.gr
Real Estate Services
N.A.I.C.S.: 531311

PREMIER AFRICAN MINERALS LIMITED
The Croft 87 Main Road, Blue Hills R55, Midrand, ZA 1685, Gauteng, South Africa
Tel.: (27) 100201281   VG
Web Site:
  http://www.premierminerals.com
PREM—(AIM)
Rev.: $34,000
Assets: $51,055,000
Liabilities: $34,265,000
Net Worth: $16,790,000
Earnings: ($5,803,000)
Emp.: 19
Fiscal Year-end: 12/31/22
Mineral Mining
N.A.I.C.S.: 212390
George Roach (CEO)

PREMIER ANTI-AGING CO., LTD.
1-23-1 Toranomon, Minato-Ku, Tokyo, 105-6308, Japan
Tel.: (81) 335022020
Web Site: https://www.p-antiaging.co.jp
Year Founded: 2009
4934—(TKS)
Rev.: $126,632,980
Assets: $68,432,440
Liabilities: $30,341,160
Net Worth: $38,091,280
Earnings: ($9,224,260)
Fiscal Year-end: 07/31/24
Beauty Product Mfr & Distr
N.A.I.C.S.: 325620
Kiyoshi Matsuura (Founder, Pres & CEO)

PREMIER BUSINESS & PROJECTS CO. LTD.
200 Princess Basma Street, PO Box 5310, Abdoun, Amman, 11183, Jordan
Tel.: (962) 65933815
Web Site: https://premier.com.jo
Year Founded: 1973
ACDT—(AMM)
Rev.: $227,382
Assets: $4,121,571
Liabilities: $389,776
Net Worth: $3,731,795
Earnings: ($111,033)
Emp.: 2
Fiscal Year-end: 12/31/23
Investment Management Service
N.A.I.C.S.: 523999
Basim Muasher (Gen Mgr)

PREMIER CEMENT MILLS LIMITED
TK Bhaban 12th Floor 13 Kawran Bazar, Dhaka, 1215, Bangladesh
Tel.: (880) 255012191
Web Site:
  https://www.premiercement.com
Year Founded: 2001
PREMIERCEM—(CHT)
Rev.: $199,151,355
Assets: $307,027,898
Liabilities: $249,790,792
Net Worth: $57,237,106
Earnings: ($7,683,753)
Emp.: 1,845
Fiscal Year-end: 06/30/23
Cement Mfr
N.A.I.C.S.: 327310
Mohammed Shafiqul Islam Talukder (CFO)

PREMIER CHENNAI PROPERTIES LIMITED
498 Karumuttu Centre 3rd Floor South Wing Nandanam Anna Salai, Chennai, 600 035, Tamil Nadu, India
Tel.: (91) 4424313535
Web Site:
  http://www.premierchennai.co.in
Year Founded: 2007
Rev.: $2,077,672
Assets: $19,594,951
Liabilities: $2,307,000
Net Worth: $17,287,951
Earnings: $1,056,630
Emp.: 2
Fiscal Year-end: 03/31/19
Real Estate Support Services
N.A.I.C.S.: 531390
Suresh Ananthanarayanan Kootala (Mng Dir & CFO)

PREMIER DIVERSIFIED HOLDINGS INC.
1199 West Pender Street Suite 680, Vancouver, V6E 2R1, BC, Canada

Tel.: (604) 678-9115   BC
Web Site: https://www.pdh-inc.com
Year Founded: 2010
PRDGF—(OTCIQ)
Rev.: $68,835
Assets: $2,923,883
Liabilities: $2,936,890
Net Worth: ($13,007)
Earnings: ($1,637,986)
Fiscal Year-end: 09/30/22
Holding Company; Miscellaneous Financial Investments
N.A.I.C.S.: 551112
Simon Sutcliffe (Chm)

Subsidiaries:

Premier Diagnostic Health Services (Vancouver) Inc (1)
Unit 300 3185 Willingdon Green, Burnaby, V5G 4P3, BC, Canada
Tel.: (604) 689-7776
Web Site: http://www.pet-ct.ca
Sales Range: $10-24.9 Million
Emp.: 8
General Health Care Services
N.A.I.C.S.: 621512

PREMIER ENTERPRISE PUBLIC COMPANY LIMITED
No 1 Premier Corporate Park Premier Ally 2 Srinakarin Rd, Nong Bon Pravet, Bangkok, 10250, Thailand
Tel.: (66) 23011550
Web Site: http://www.pe.premier.co.th
Year Founded: 1974
PE—(THA)
Rev.: $15,902,198
Assets: $40,727,237
Liabilities: $36,383,832
Net Worth: $4,343,406
Earnings: ($69,774)
Emp.: 314
Fiscal Year-end: 12/31/20
Financial Services
N.A.I.C.S.: 523999
Akapun Nuanmuang (Dir-Internal Audit Office)

PREMIER EXPLOSIVES LTD
Premier House 11 Ishaq Colony Near AOC Centre, Secunderabad, 500015, Telangana, India
Tel.: (91) 4066146801
Web Site: https://www.pelgel.com
PREMEXPLN—(NSE)
Rev.: $24,482,453
Assets: $42,682,957
Liabilities: $19,185,528
Net Worth: $23,497,428
Earnings: $835,106
Emp.: 822
Fiscal Year-end: 03/31/23
manufacture of explosives
N.A.I.C.S.: 325920
T. V. Chowdary (Deputy Mng Dir)

Subsidiaries:

Premier Wire Products Limited (1)
204 IInd Fl, Minerva Complex S D Rd, Secunderabad, 500 003, Andhra Pradesh, India
Tel.: (91) 4027814748
Web Site: http://www.pelgel.com
Sales Range: $25-49.9 Million
Emp.: 50
Metalic Wire Products Mfr
N.A.I.C.S.: 335929

PREMIER FOODS PLC
Premier House Centrium Business Park Griffiths Way, Saint Albans, AL1 2RE, Hertfordshire, United Kingdom
Tel.: (44) 1727815850   UK
Web Site:
  https://www.premierfoods.co.uk
PFODF—(OTCIQ)
Rev.: $1,249,043,040
Assets: $2,985,962,490

PREMIER FOODS PLC

Premier Foods plc—(Continued)
Liabilities: $1,339,146,900
Net Worth: $1,646,815,590
Earnings: $113,684,760
Fiscal Year-end: 04/01/23
Mfr & Distr of Fresh Produce & Grocery Products
N.A.I.C.S.: 424410
Mark Hughes *(Dir-Procurement & Central Ops)*

Subsidiaries:

High Wycombe - Food Technology Centre (1)
The Lord Rank Ctr, Lincoln Rd, High Wycombe, HP12 3QS, Buckinghamshire, United Kingdom (100%)
Tel.: (44) 494428000
Sales Range: $300-349.9 Million
Emp.: 2,059
Flour Milling
N.A.I.C.S.: 561110

Knighton Foods Limited (1)
Newport Road, Adbaston Knighton, Powys, ST20 0QJ, Staffordshire, United Kingdom
Tel.: (44) 791 721 5525
Specialty Food Powder Mfr
N.A.I.C.S.: 311514
Richard Ilsley *(Mgr)*

PREMIER FUND
5 Tsar Asen St 2nd Floor, 9000, Varna, Bulgaria
Tel.: (359) 885831898
Web Site: https://4pr.eu
Year Founded: 2006
PREM—(BUL)
Sales Range: Less than $1 Million
Real Estate Investment Trust Services
N.A.I.C.S.: 531190
Antonia Stoyanova Vidinlieva *(Exec Dir)*

PREMIER HEALTH OF AMERICA, INC.
1114 Cure-Labelle Blvd suite 01, Blainville, J7C 2M9, QC, Canada
Web Site: https://www.premierhealthgroup.ca
Year Founded: 2017
PHA—(TSXV)
Rev.: $52,122,423
Assets: $30,609,235
Liabilities: $17,062,552
Net Worth: $13,546,683
Earnings: $1,170,907
Emp.: 589
Fiscal Year-end: 09/30/21
Health Care Srvices
N.A.I.C.S.: 621610
Jean-Robert Pronovost *(VP-Corp Dev)*

PREMIER INSURANCE COMPANY (NEPAL) LIMITED
Premier Bhawan Naxal, PO Box 9183, Kathmandu, Nepal
Tel.: (977) 14413543
Web Site: https://www.premier-insurance.com.np
Year Founded: 1994
PIC—(NEP)
Rev.: $10,396,231
Assets: $76,810,600
Liabilities: $49,226,929
Net Worth: $27,583,671
Earnings: $2,816,443
Fiscal Year-end: 07/15/21
General Insurance Services
N.A.I.C.S.: 524210
Suresh Lal Shrestha *(Chm)*

PREMIER INSURANCE LIMITED
State Life Building No 2A 5th Floor Wallace Road, Karachi, 74000, Pakistan
Tel.: (92) 2132416331
Web Site: https://pil.com.pk
PINL—(LAH)
Rev.: $1,438,239
Assets: $19,045,012
Liabilities: $11,593,784
Net Worth: $7,451,228
Earnings: ($1,544,061)
Emp.: 143
Fiscal Year-end: 12/31/19
Insurance Services
N.A.I.C.S.: 524210

PREMIER INVESTMENTS LIMITED
Level 7 417 St Kilda Road, Melbourne, 3004, VIC, Australia
Tel.: (61) 396506500
Web Site: https://www.premierinvestment.com
PMV—(ASX) AU
Rev.: $1,162,215,222
Assets: $1,765,864,143
Liabilities: $480,565,861
Net Worth: $1,285,298,283
Earnings: $218,497,467
Emp.: 9,000
Fiscal Year-end: 07/30/22
Financial Services
N.A.I.C.S.: 523940
Solomon Lew *(Chm)*

Subsidiaries:

Dotti Pty. Ltd. (1)
457 St Kilda Road, Melbourne, 3004, VIC, Australia
Tel.: (61) 39 420 0442
Web Site: https://www.dotti.com.au
Women Clothing Distr
N.A.I.C.S.: 458110

Just Group Limited (1)
457 St Kilda Road, Melbourne, 3004, VIC, Australia
Tel.: (61) 394200200
Emp.: 2,600
Clothing Retailer
N.A.I.C.S.: 458110
Mark McInnes *(CEO)*

Subsidiary (Domestic):

Jacqueline-Eve Fashions Pty. Limited (2)
658 Church Street, Richmond, 3121, VIC, Australia
Tel.: (61) 394200200
Sales Range: $200-249.9 Million
Emp.: 600
Fashion Apparel Stores
N.A.I.C.S.: 458110

Subsidiary (Domestic):

Jacqueline-Eve (Leases) Pty. Limited (3)
658 Church Street, Richmond, 3121, VIC, Australia
Tel.: (61) 394200200
Store Space Leasing Services
N.A.I.C.S.: 531190

Jacqueline-Eve (Retail) Pty. Limited (3)
658 Church Street, PO Box 2196, Richmond, 3121, VIC, Australia
Tel.: (61) 394200200
Emp.: 400
Womens Retail Clothing Stores
N.A.I.C.S.: 458110
Mark McInnes *(Gen Mgr)*

Subsidiary (Domestic):

Jay Jays Trademark Pty. Limited (2)
658 Church Street, Richmond, 3121, VIC, Australia
Tel.: (61) 394200200
Web Site: http://www.jayjays.com.au
Sales Range: $1-4.9 Billion
Emp.: 300
Clothing Apparels Mfr
N.A.I.C.S.: 315210

Just Jeans Pty. Ltd. (2)
457 St Kilda Rd, Melbourne, 3004, VIC, Australia
Tel.: (61) 394200200
Web Site: http://www.justjeans.com.au
Sales Range: $100-124.9 Million
Emp.: 300
Clothing Apparel Stores
N.A.I.C.S.: 458110

Just-Shop Pty. Limited (2)
457 St Kilda Road, Melbourne, 3004, VIC, Australia
Tel.: (61) 394200200
Web Site: http://www.justshop.com.au
Emp.: 600
Men & Women Clothing Stores
N.A.I.C.S.: 458110

Portmans Pty. Limited (2)
457 St Kilda Road, Melbourne, 3004, VIC, Australia
Tel.: (61) 394200200
Web Site: http://www.portmans.com.au
Sales Range: $25-49.9 Million
Emp.: 324
Women's Clothing Store
N.A.I.C.S.: 458110

Peter Alexander Sleepwear Pty. Limited (1)
658 Church St, PO Box 805, Richmond, 3121, VIC, Australia
Tel.: (61) 394200449
Web Site: http://www.peteralexander.com.au
Sales Range: $25-49.9 Million
Emp.: 25
Family Clothing Stores
N.A.I.C.S.: 458110

Premfin Pty. Ltd. (1)
Level 53 101 Collins St, Melbourne, 3000, VIC, Australia
Tel.: (61) 396000999
Web Site: http://www.premierinvestments.com.au
Sales Range: $50-74.9 Million
Emp.: 10
Financial Planning Services
N.A.I.C.S.: 523999

Smiggle Pty. Limited (1)
457 St Kilda Road, Melbourne, 3004, VIC, Australia
Tel.: (61) 39 420 0200
Web Site: https://www.smiggle.com.au
Stationery Product Distr
N.A.I.C.S.: 459410

Smiggle Singapore Pte. Ltd. (1)
01-85/86 United Sq S/C 101 Thomson Road United Square, Singapore, 307591, Singapore
Tel.: (65) 6 258 2595
Web Site: https://www.smiggle.sg
Stationery Product Distr
N.A.I.C.S.: 459410

Smiggle UK Limited (1)
Level 2 17-18 Margaret Street, London, W1W 8RP, United Kingdom
Tel.: (44) 161 386 6334
Web Site: https://www.smiggle.co.uk
Stationery Product Distr
N.A.I.C.S.: 459410

PREMIER LEASING & FINANCE LIMITED
Happy Rahman Plaza 25-27 Kazi Nazrul Islam Avenue, Bangla Motor Crossing, Dhaka, 1000, Bangladesh
Tel.: (880) 241060022
Web Site: https://www.plfbd.com
Year Founded: 2001
PREMIERLEA—(CSE)
Rev.: $9,203,432
Assets: $168,829,765
Liabilities: $191,498,064
Net Worth: ($22,668,299)
Earnings: ($19,700,395)
Fiscal Year-end: 12/31/22
Financial Services
N.A.I.C.S.: 523999
A. Z. M. Akamul Haq *(Chm)*

Subsidiaries:

Premier Leasing Securities Limited (1)

INTERNATIONAL PUBLIC

Happy Rahman Plaza 5th Floor 25-27 Kazi Nazrul Islam Avenue, Dhaka, 1000, Bangladesh
Tel.: (880) 9666777880
Web Site: http://www.plsl.com.bd
Financial Services
N.A.I.C.S.: 523999
Raihan Uddin Ahmed *(CEO)*

PREMIER LTD.
58 Nariman Bhavan, Nariman Point, Mumbai, 400021, India
Tel.: (91) 2261179000
Web Site: http://www.premier.co.in
Year Founded: 1944
PREMIER—(NSE) In
Rev.: $1,007,438
Assets: $29,660,535
Liabilities: $68,322,659
Net Worth: ($38,662,124)
Earnings: ($11,315,850)
Emp.: 324
Fiscal Year-end: 03/31/21
Machine Tools Mfr
N.A.I.C.S.: 333517
K. G. Rathi *(COO)*

Subsidiaries:

Premier Ltd. - Chinchwad Plant (1)
Mumbai Pune Road, Chinchwad, Pune, 411019, Maharashtra, India
Tel.: (91) 206 631 0000
Web Site: https://www.premier.co.in
Sales Range: $300-349.9 Million
Industrial Machinery Mfr
N.A.I.C.S.: 811310
M. D. Adhikari *(Pres)*

PREMIER MARKETING PUBLIC COMPANY LIMITED
Premier Corporate Park Soi Premier 2 Srinakarin Road, Nongbon Prawet District, Bangkok, 10250, Thailand
Tel.: (66) 23011600
Web Site: https://www.premier-marketing.co.th
Year Founded: 1977
PM—(THA)
Rev.: $124,815,487
Assets: $75,601,108
Liabilities: $31,935,849
Net Worth: $43,665,259
Earnings: $11,447,756
Emp.: 1,905
Fiscal Year-end: 12/31/23
Snack Food Distr
N.A.I.C.S.: 311919
Somchai Choonharas *(Chm)*

Subsidiaries:

Infinite Green Co., Ltd. (1)
2 Premier Place Soi Premier 2 Srinakarin Road Nong Bon, Pravet, Bangkok, 10250, Thailand
Tel.: (66) 2 301 1586
Web Site: https://www.infinitegreen.co.th
Renewable Energy Services
N.A.I.C.S.: 221114

Khon Thai Shop Ltd. (1)
Luzernerstrasse 107, 5054, Moosleerau, Switzerland
Tel.: (41) 763432468
Grocery Distr
N.A.I.C.S.: 445110

P.M. Food Co., Ltd. (1)
One Premier Corporate Park Soi Premier 2 Srinakarin Rd Nongbon, Pravet, Bangkok, 10250, Thailand
Tel.: (66) 23011700
Web Site: http://www.pmfood.n4.biz
Emp.: 400
Fish & Seafood Distr
N.A.I.C.S.: 424460

PMSE Co., Ltd. (1)
No 1 Premier Corporate Park Soi Premier 2 Srinakarin Road Nongbon, Prawet, 10250, Bangkok, Thailand
Tel.: (66) 23011655
Coffee Distr

AND PRIVATE COMPANIES

N.A.I.C.S.: 445298

Premier Assets Co., Ltd. (1)
Grosvenor House 160 Gillett Road, Thornton Heath, London, CR7 8SN, Surrey, United Kingdom
Tel.: (44) 208 689 0208
Web Site: https://www.premierassets.co.uk
Property Management Services
N.A.I.C.S.: 531312

Premier Canning Industry Co., Ltd. (1)
326 Ratanaraj Road, Bang-Boo District, Samut Prakan, 10560, Thailand
Tel.: (66) 2338132731
Web Site: http://www.premiercanning.com
Emp.: 573
Canned Food Product Mfr
N.A.I.C.S.: 311422

Tamarind Village Co., Ltd. (1)
50/1 Rajdamnoen Road, Tambon Sri Pum, Amphur Muang, 50200, Chiang Mai, Thailand
Tel.: (66) 53 418 8969
Web Site: https://www.tamarindvillage.com
Boutique Hotel Operator
N.A.I.C.S.: 721110

PREMIER MITON GLOBAL RENEWABLES TRUST PLC
Premier Miton Investors Eastgate Court High Street, Guildford, GU1 3DE, Surrey, United Kingdom
Tel.: (44) 2079822725
Web Site:
  http://www.premierfunds.co.uk
PMGR—(LSE)
Assets: $58,875,960
Liabilities: $19,669,485
Net Worth: $39,206,475
Earnings: ($5,528,655)
Fiscal Year-end: 12/31/22
Portfolio Management & Investment Advice
N.A.I.C.S.: 523940
Gillian Nott (Chm)

PREMIER MITON GROUP PLC
Eastgate Court High Street, Guildford, GU1 3DE, Surrey, United Kingdom
Tel.: (44) 1483306090   UK
Web Site:
  https://www.premiermiton.com
Year Founded: 2007
PMI—(AIM)
Rev.: $102,158,406
Assets: $319,948,398
Liabilities: $176,430,726
Net Worth: $143,517,672
Earnings: $10,835,154
Fiscal Year-end: 09/30/22
Financial Holding Company
N.A.I.C.S.: 551112
Michael O'Shea (CEO)

Subsidiaries:

Miton Group Limited (1)
Paternoster House 65 St Paul's Churchyard, London, EC4M 8AB, United Kingdom
Tel.: (44) 3334561122
Investment Management Service
N.A.I.C.S.: 523940

Premier Asset Management Limited (1)
Eastgate Ct High St, Guildford, GU1 3DE, Surrey, United Kingdom   (50.2%)
Tel.: (44) 1483306090
Web Site: http://www.premiermiton.com
Investment Management Service
N.A.I.C.S.: 523940
David BArron (CEO)

Subsidiary (Domestic):

Premier Fund Managers Limited (2)
Eastgate Ct High St, Guildford, GU1 3DE, United Kingdom
Tel.: (44) 1483306090
Web Site: http://www.premierfunds.co.uk

Investment Advisory Services
N.A.I.C.S.: 523940
Mike O'Shea (CEO)

Premier Portfolio Managers Limited (2)
Eastgate Court High Street, Guildford, GU1 3DE, Surrey, United Kingdom
Tel.: (44) 3334561122
Portfolio Management Services
N.A.I.C.S.: 523940
Mike O'Shea (CEO)

PREMIER MITON INVESTORS
6th Floor Paternoster House 65 St Paul s Churchyard, London, EC4M 8AB, United Kingdom
Tel.: (44) 2037141500
Investment Services
N.A.I.C.S.: 525910
Mike Hammond (Dir-Bus Dev)

PREMIER PAINTS PLC
Kilometre 2 Ifo-Ibogun Road, Ifo, Ogun, Nigeria
Tel.: (234) 8051199620
Web Site:
  http://www.premierpaintsplc.com
PREMPAINTS—(NIGE)
Rev.: $360,891
Assets: $653,485
Liabilities: $1,056,991
Net Worth: ($403,506)
Earnings: ($45,333)
Emp.: 30
Fiscal Year-end: 12/31/19
Paints Mfr
N.A.I.C.S.: 325510
Ogo-Oluwa G. O. Bankole (Chm)

PREMIER PAPER GROUP LIMITED
Midpoint Park Kingsbury Road, Minworth, Birmingham, B76 1AF, United Kingdom
Tel.: (44) 121 313 1115
Web Site: http://www.paper.co.uk
Sales Range: $250-299.9 Million
Emp.: 340
Tape Distr
N.A.I.C.S.: 424110
David Jones (Dir-Mktg)

Subsidiaries:

Premier Hedsorboard (1)
Unit 7 Langley Park Waterside Drive, Langley, SL3 6 EZ, Berkshire, United Kingdom   (100%)
Tel.: (44) 1753597050
Sales Range: $25-49.9 Million
Emp.: 20
Carton & Graphic Boards from Stock, Ex-Mill & Managed Inventories
N.A.I.C.S.: 322130
David Tovey (Mgr-Technical Svcs)

PREMIER PIPES LIMITED
Som Biz-ness Xquare 4th Floor 1The Mall, Kanpur, 208001, UP, India
Tel.: (91) 7522002351
Web Site:
  http://www.premierpipesltd.com
Year Founded: 1975
Rev.: $21,915,031
Assets: $7,066,325
Liabilities: $5,172,300
Net Worth: $1,894,025
Earnings: $158,634
Fiscal Year-end: 03/31/18
Steel Pipe & Tube Mfr
N.A.I.C.S.: 331210

PREMIER POLYFILM LTD.
305 Elite House 3rd Floor 36 Community Center Kailash Colony Extn, Zamroodpur, New Delhi, 110048, India
Tel.: (91) 8920831225

Web Site:
  https://www.premierpoly.com
Year Founded: 1992
514354—(BOM)
Rev.: $23,658,817
Assets: $12,471,107
Liabilities: $5,046,220
Net Worth: $7,424,887
Earnings: $1,149,078
Emp.: 276
Fiscal Year-end: 03/31/21
Polyvinyl Chloride Sheet Mfr
N.A.I.C.S.: 325220
Sumat Parsad Jain (Exec Dir)

PREMIER PRODUCTS PUBLIC COMPANY LIMITED
No 2 Premier Place Soi Premier 2 Srinakarin Road, Nong Bon, Nong Bon, Bangkok, 10250, Thailand
Tel.: (66) 23012100
Web Site: https://www.premier-products.co.th
Year Founded: 1975
PPP—(THA)
Rev.: $32,351,350
Assets: $38,284,788
Liabilities: $11,994,676
Net Worth: $26,290,112
Earnings: ($2,679,143)
Emp.: 466
Fiscal Year-end: 12/31/23
Water Treatment & Water Storage Systems Mfr
N.A.I.C.S.: 221310
Suradej Boonyawatana (Chm & Chm)

PREMIER PUMP & TANK CO., LTD.
Bourne End Mills Upper Bourne End Lane, Hemel Hempstead, HP1 2UJ, Hertfordshire, United Kingdom
Tel.: (44) 1442 872296
Web Site:
  http://www.premiergroup.org.uk
Sales Range: $10-24.9 Million
Emp.: 100
Fuel Storage & Dispensing Equipment Mfr
N.A.I.C.S.: 333132
Ken Owen (Mng Dir)

Subsidiaries:

Pumptronics Europe Ltd (1)
Lyngate Industrial Estate Folgate Road, North Walsham, NR28 0AJ, Norfolk, United Kingdom
Tel.: (44) 1692 500640
Web Site: http://www.pumptronics.co.uk
Emp.: 9
Pumping Equipment
N.A.I.C.S.: 333914
Andrew Olive (Gen Mgr)

PREMIER QUALITY STARCH PUBLIC COMPANY LIMITED
185 Moo 14, Kham Pa Lai Subdistrict Mueang Mukdahan District, Manorom, 49000, Thailand
Tel.: (66) 42643818
Web Site: https://www.pqstarch.com
Year Founded: 2005
PQS—(THA)
Rev.: $69,907,041
Assets: $73,327,541
Liabilities: $13,929,113
Net Worth: $59,398,428
Earnings: $3,965,019
Emp.: 506
Fiscal Year-end: 12/31/23
Starch Product Mfr
N.A.I.C.S.: 325520

PREMIER RECRUITMENT (INTERNATIONAL) UNLIMITED COMPANY

PREMIER TECH LTD.

6 Lapp's Quay, Cork, T12 XE1V, Ireland
Tel.: (353) 212300300   IE
Web Site:
  http://www.morganmckinley.com
Year Founded: 1988
Emp.: 800
Corporate Recruitment Consulting Services
N.A.I.C.S.: 541612
Patrick Fitzgerald (Founder & CEO)

Subsidiaries:

Accreate Limited (1)
77 Sir John Rogersons Quay, Dublin, 2, Ireland
Tel.: (353) 1 522 5400
Web Site: http://www.accreate.com
Recruitment Services
N.A.I.C.S.: 541612
David Burke (Mng Partner)

Morgan McKinley Group Limited (1)
61 Aldwych, London, WC2B 4AE, United Kingdom
Tel.: (44) 2070920000
Web Site: http://www.morganmckinley.co.uk
Corporate Recruitment Consulting Services
N.A.I.C.S.: 541612
Chris Leeson (Mng Dir-Fin Svcs-UK)

PREMIER SYNTHETICS LIMITED
Surana House Behind Klassic Chambers Swastik X Road, Opp Narnarayan Complex Navrangpura, Ahmedabad, 380009, Gujarat, India
Tel.: (91) 7926431558   In
Web Site:
  https://www.premiersyntheticsltd.com
Year Founded: 1970
509835—(BOM)
Rev.: $6,342,183
Assets: $5,052,633
Liabilities: $1,664,826
Net Worth: $3,387,808
Earnings: $2,949
Emp.: 30
Fiscal Year-end: 03/31/23
Woven Fabric Mfr & Whslr
N.A.I.C.S.: 313210
Sanjaykumar Vinodbhai Majethia (Exec Dir)

PREMIER TANK CORPORATION PUBLIC COMPANY LIMITED
No 2034/69 Italthai Tower 15th Floor New Petchburi Road, Bangkapi Huaykwang, Bangkok, 10310, Thailand
Tel.: (66) 23184013
Web Site:
  https://www.premiertankcorp.com
Year Founded: 2013
PTC—(THA)
Rev.: $5,197,997
Assets: $26,429,963
Liabilities: $603,394
Net Worth: $25,826,569
Earnings: $2,192,433
Emp.: 78
Fiscal Year-end: 12/31/23
Fuel & Petroleum Distr
N.A.I.C.S.: 424720
Patthaya Chunhachinda (Chm)

PREMIER TECH LTD.
1 Ave Premier, Riviere-du-Loup, G5R 6C1, QC, Canada
Tel.: (418) 867-8883   QC
Web Site:
  http://www.premiertech.com
Year Founded: 1987
Sales Range: $200-249.9 Million
Emp.: 1,500
Gardening Products & Sphagnum Peat Moss Producer & Distr

PREMIER TECH LTD.

Premier Tech Ltd.—(Continued)
N.A.I.C.S.: 111998
Bernard Belanger *(Chm & CEO)*

Subsidiaries:

CHRONOS RICHARDSON INDIA PVT. LTD. (1)
A 21 Third Floor Green Park Main, New Delhi, 110016, India
Tel.: (91) 129 2241014
Industrial Packaging Equipment Mfr
N.A.I.C.S.: 333993
Saurabh Sachan *(Engr-Svc)*

Changshu Premier Tech Chronos Equipment & Engineering Co., Ltd. (1)
Bld 16 HuanHu HongShun Ind Park Xin An Jiang Road, Changshu, 215500, JiangSu, China
Tel.: (86) 512 5230 6066
Industrial Packaging Equipment Mfr
N.A.I.C.S.: 333993

Chronos Richardson Limited (1)
Arnside Rd, Bestwood, Nottingham, NG5 5HD, United Kingdom
Tel.: (44) 59351351
Web Site:
  http://www.chronosrichardson.com
Sales Range: $25-49.9 Million
Emp.: 70
Mfr of Industrial Weighing & Process Control Equipment; Batch Blending
N.A.I.C.S.: 334513

Chronos Richardson Ltd. (1)
333 3 Sukhumvit 71 Road Prakanong Nua Watlana, Bangkok, 101 10, Thailand
Tel.: (66) 27405001
Web Site: http://www.ptchronos.com
Emp.: 50
Weighing, Batching, Bagging & Palletizing Services for Food, Feed, Chemical, Plastic, Fertilizer & Milling Industries
N.A.I.C.S.: 561910

Conder Aqua Solutions (1)
2 Whitehouse Way South West Industrial Estate, Durham, SR8 2RA, Peterlee, United Kingdom
Tel.: (44) 870 264 0004
Web Site: http://www.premiertech.co.uk
Industrial Equipment Mfr
N.A.I.C.S.: 334513
Stuart Wray *(Mng Dir)*

Premier Horticulture Ltd. (1)
1 Premier Ave, Riviere-du-Loup, G5R 6C1, QC, Canada (100%)
Tel.: (204) 422-8805
Web Site: http://www.premierhort.com
Sales Range: $50-74.9 Million
Emp.: 15
Peat Moss, Sphagnum, Soilless Potting Media, Retail Soils & Soil Mixes, Composts & Potting Mixes Mfr
N.A.I.C.S.: 424910
Pernard Belanger *(Pres)*

Premier Tech (1)
Reiser Strasse 21, 53773, Hennef, Germany (100%)
Tel.: (49) 22429335
Web Site:
  http://www.premiertechsystems.com
Sales Range: $25-49.9 Million
Emp.: 15
Bagging
N.A.I.C.S.: 313240

Premier Tech Biotechnologies (1)
1 Avenue Premier, Riviere-du-Loup, G5R 6C1, QC, Canada
Tel.: (418) 867-8883
Web Site: http://www.premiertech.com
Sales Range: $450-499.9 Million
Growth Supplements Mfr
N.A.I.C.S.: 325314
Martin Pelletier *(Gen Mgr)*

Premier Tech Chronos B.V. (1)
Meerheide 40, 5521 DZ, Eersel, Netherlands
Tel.: (31) 497 514 988
Industrial Packaging Equipment Mfr
N.A.I.C.S.: 333993
Ingo Jonas *(Mng Dir)*

Premier Tech Chronos Limited (1)
Unit 1 Centurion Business Centre Blenheim Industrial Estate Dabell Ave, Nottingham, NG6 8WN, United Kingdom
Tel.: (44) 115 9351351
Industrial Packaging Equipment Mfr
N.A.I.C.S.: 333993

Premier Tech Chronos S.A. (1)
15 rue Lavoisier, 91160, Longjumeau, France
Tel.: (33) 1 60 11 31 32
Industrial Packaging Equipment Mfr
N.A.I.C.S.: 333993

Premier Tech Chronos S.r.l. (1)
Via G Di Vittorio 78, 43044, Collecchio, Italy
Tel.: (39) 0521 296011
Industrial Packaging Equipment Mfr
N.A.I.C.S.: 333993
Fabrizio Ferrari *(Gen Mgr)*

Premier Tech Environment (1)
1 Ave Premier Premier Tech Campus, Riviere-du-Loup, G5R 6C1, QC, Canada
Tel.: (418) 867-8883
Web Site: http://www.premiertech.com
Sales Range: $250-299.9 Million
Emp.: 800
Water Treatment Product & Services
N.A.I.C.S.: 237110
Bernard Belanger *(Pres)*

Premier Tech Home & Garden, Inc. (1)
150 Savanah Oaks Dr, Brantford, N3V 1E7, ON, Canada
Tel.: (519) 754-2900
Web Site:
  http://www.pthomeandgarden.com
Lawn & Garden Product Mfr & Distr
N.A.I.C.S.: 333112
David Suske *(VP-Mktg)*

Premier Tech Iberoto, Unipessoal Lda. (1)
Rua de Ceramica-Broega, 2870-502, Montijo, Portugal
Tel.: (351) 21 192 67 20
Web Site: http://www.premiertech.pt
Industrial Equipment Mfr
N.A.I.C.S.: 334513

Premier Tech Prairie, Inc. (1)
5008 Nw 57th Ave, Johnston, IA 50131
Tel.: (515) 270-1019
Web Site: http://www.ptchronos.com
Engineeering Services
N.A.I.C.S.: 541330

Premier Tech Systems (1)
101-1 Av Premier, Riviere-du-Loup, G5R 6C1, QC, Canada
Tel.: (418) 868-8324
Web Site:
  https://www.pthomeandgarden.com
Packaging Machinery Mfr
N.A.I.C.S.: 333993

Premier Tech Water France (1)
Zone Industrielle de la Gare, Rue de la Gironniere, BP 98410, Sainte-Luce-sur-Loire, Cedex, France
Tel.: (33) 251850036
Water Treatment Products & Services
N.A.I.C.S.: 237110

PREMIER TECHNOLOGY PUBLIC COMPANY LIMITED

ONE Premier Corporate Park Soi Premier 2 Srinakarin Road Kwang Nongbon, Khet Prawet, Bangkok, 10250, Thailand
Tel.: (66) 23011550
Web Site: https://www.premier-technology.co.th
Year Founded: 1973
PT—(THA)
Rev.: $103,864,496
Assets: $59,127,550
Liabilities: $38,176,903
Net Worth: $20,950,647
Earnings: $7,417,429
Emp.: 404
Fiscal Year-end: 12/31/23
Electronics & IT Product Whslr
N.A.I.C.S.: 423690

Kulthida Verathaworn *(Sec)*

Subsidiaries:

Advanced Cyber Technology Co., Ltd. (1)
Room 702 The Dusit Thani Building 946 Rama 4 Rd, Silom Bangrak, Bangkok, 10500, Thailand
Tel.: (66) 2236 8586
Web Site: http://www.act-thai.net
Information Technology Services
N.A.I.C.S.: 541511

Datapro Computer Systems Co., Ltd. (1)
2 Premier Place Soi Premier 2 Srinakarin Road, Nongbon Prawet, Bangkok, 10250, Thailand
Tel.: (66) 27145995
Web Site: https://www.datapro.co.th
Computer Solutions & Services
N.A.I.C.S.: 541511

PREMIER TRADING AG

Theresienhohe 28 1 Floor, 80339, Munich, Germany
Tel.: (49) 89 4805 8060
Web Site:
  http://www.premiertradingag.com
Year Founded: 2011
Sales Range: $1-9.9 Million
Software Developer
N.A.I.C.S.: 513210
Pily Wong *(CEO)*

PREMIER1 LITHIUM LTD.

PO Box 7054, Cloisters Square, Perth, 6850, WA, Australia
Tel.: (61) 861888181   AU
Web Site:
  https://premier1lithium.com.au
Year Founded: 2019
PLC—(ASX)
Rev.: $2,902,405
Assets: $10,239,318
Liabilities: $1,931,539
Net Worth: $8,307,779
Earnings: ($5,463,943)
Fiscal Year-end: 06/30/23
Metal Mining Services
N.A.I.C.S.: 213114

Subsidiaries:

Intrepid Geophysics Pty. Ltd. (1)
Suite 110 / 3 Male Street, Brighton, 3186, VIC, Australia
Tel.: (61) 395931077
Web Site: https://www.intrepid-geophysics.com
Software Development Services
N.A.I.C.S.: 541511

SensOre Technologies Corporation (1)
24165 W Interstate 10 Ste 217-617, San Antonio, TX 78257-9997
Tel.: (630) 391-1628
Web Site:
  https://www.sensortechnologies.com
Geoscience Software Services
N.A.I.C.S.: 541511

PREMIERE EASTERN ENERGY LIMITED

Level 6 105 St Georges Terrace, Perth, 6000, WA, Australia
Tel.: (61) 8 6558 0886
Web Site: http://www.group-premiere.com
Sales Range: $300-349.9 Million
Petrochemical Products Wholesale Distr
N.A.I.C.S.: 424690
Zhan Aiping *(CEO)*

PREMIERE HORIZON ALLIANCE CORPORATION

1705 East Tower Philippine Stock Exchange Center Exchange Road,

INTERNATIONAL PUBLIC

Ortigas Center Metro Manila, Pasig, 1605, Philippines
Tel.: (63) 26327715
Web Site:
  https://www.premierehorizon.com
Year Founded: 1988
PHA—(PHI)
Rev.: $9,647,865
Assets: $84,658,382
Liabilities: $37,168,145
Net Worth: $47,490,238
Earnings: $125,097
Fiscal Year-end: 12/31/23
Investment Management Service
N.A.I.C.S.: 523999
Raul Ma. F. Anonas *(COO & Exec VP)*

PREMIERE ISLAND POWER REIT CORPORATION

9th Floor Vista Campus Tower 1 Cayetano Blvd Bgy Ususan, Taguig, Philippines
Tel.: (63) 287345732
Web Site: https://www.preit.com.ph
Year Founded: 2022
PREIT—(PHI)
Rev.: $11,624,339
Assets: $178,119,416
Liabilities: $13,852,134
Net Worth: $164,267,282
Earnings: $12,711,195
Emp.: 21
Fiscal Year-end: 12/31/23
Real Estate Investment Services
N.A.I.C.S.: 531190

PREMIUM BRANDS HOLDINGS CORPORATION

100 - 10991 Shellbridge Way, Richmond, V6X 3C6, BC, Canada
Tel.: (604) 656-3100   Ca
Web Site:
  https://www.premiumbrands.com
Year Founded: 1917
PBH—(TSX)
Rev.: $3,183,019,092
Assets: $2,770,757,532
Liabilities: $1,520,674,092
Net Worth: $1,250,083,440
Earnings: $65,476,836
Emp.: 8,724
Fiscal Year-end: 12/26/20
Food Mfr & Distr
N.A.I.C.S.: 424470
Will Kalutycz *(CFO)*

Subsidiaries:

Belmont Meat Products Ltd. (1)
230 Signet Drive, Toronto, M9L 1V2, ON, Canada
Web Site: https://www.belmontmeats.com
Meat Products Supplier
N.A.I.C.S.: 424470

Buddy's Kitchen, Inc. (1)
12105 Nicollet Ave S, Burnsville, MN 55337
Tel.: (952) 894-2540
Web Site: http://www.buddyskitchen.com
Frozen Specialty Food Mfr
N.A.I.C.S.: 311412

Centennial Foodservice Inc. (1)
Bay 132 2880-45 Ave SE, Calgary, T2B 3M1, AB, Canada
Tel.: (403) 299-0525
Web Site:
  http://www.centennialfoodservice.com
Frozen Food Distr
N.A.I.C.S.: 424420

Clearwater Seafoods Incorporated (1)
757 Bedford Highway, Bedford, B4A 3Z7, NS, Canada (50%)
Tel.: (902) 443-0550
Web Site: http://www.clearwater.ca
Rev.: $471,574,559
Assets: $549,058,935
Liabilities: $405,614,697
Net Worth: $143,444,238

Earnings: $40,437,577
Emp.: 1,845
Fiscal Year-end: 12/31/2019
Holding Company; Shellfish Fishing, Packaging & Whslr
N.A.I.C.S.: 551112
Ian D. Smith (CEO)

Subsidiary (Domestic):

Clearwater Seafoods Limited Partnership (2)
757 Bedford Highway, Bedford, B4A 3Z7, NS, Canada
Tel.: (902) 443-0550
Web Site: http://www.clearwater.ca
Sales Range: $25-49.9 Million
Emp.: 150
Shellfish Fishing, Packaging & Whslr
N.A.I.C.S.: 311710

Subsidiary (Non-US):

Clearwater Fine Foods Europe Limited (3)
New Covent Garden Market Unit A1-A136, London, SW8 5LL, United Kingdom (100%)
Tel.: (44) 2076274422
Web Site: http://www.clearwater.ca
Packaged Fish & Seafood Whslr
N.A.I.C.S.: 424460

Glaciar Pesquera S.A. (3)
Santiago Del Estero 1718 Piso 1 Oficina 7, Mar del Plata, 7600, Buenos Aires, Argentina
Tel.: (54) 2234922215
Sales Range: $50-74.9 Million
Emp.: 150
Seafood Whslr
N.A.I.C.S.: 424460
Eduardo Lemmi (Pres)

Concord Premium Meats Ltd. (1)
125 Edilcan Drive, Concord, L4K 3S6, ON, Canada
Tel.: (905) 738-7979
Web Site: https://www.concordpremiummeats.com
Meat Product Distr
N.A.I.C.S.: 424470

Frandon Seafoods Inc. (1)
6790 Boulevard des Grandes-Prairies, Saint Leonard, H1P 3P3, QC, Canada
Tel.: (514) 856-0752
Web Site: http://www.frandonseafoods.ca
Seafood Distr
N.A.I.C.S.: 424460

Hempler Foods Group LLC (1)
5470 Nielsen Ave, Ferndale, WA 98248
Tel.: (360) 312-1413
Web Site: http://www.hemplers.com
Frozen Meat Mfr & Distr
N.A.I.C.S.: 311612

Leadbetter Foods Inc. (1)
255 Hughes Road, Orillia, L3V 2M2, ON, Canada
Tel.: (705) 325-9922
Web Site: http://www.leadbetterfoods.ca
Meat Product Distr
N.A.I.C.S.: 424470

McLean Meats Inc. (1)
443 Wismer Street, Waterloo, N2K 2K6, ON, Canada
Tel.: (778) 285-1333
Web Site: http://www.mcleanmeats.com
Meat Product Distr
N.A.I.C.S.: 424470
Garth J. McLean (Pres & CEO)

Oberto Sausage Company Inc. (1)
7060 S 238th St, Kent, WA 98032
Tel.: (877) 453-7591
Web Site: http://www.oberto.com
Sausages & Other Prepared Meats Processor
N.A.I.C.S.: 311612
Tom Hernquist (Pres & CEO)

Piller Sausages & Delicatessens Ltd. (1)
443 Wismer Street, PO Box 338, Waterloo, N2K 2K6, ON, Canada
Tel.: (519) 743-1412
Web Site: http://www.pillers.com

Sales Range: $150-199.9 Million
Emp.: 600
Sausages & Delicatessen Meats Mfr
N.A.I.C.S.: 445240

Raybern Foods, LLC (1)
3170 Crow Canyon Pl Ste 200, San Ramon, CA 94583
Tel.: (925) 302-7800
Web Site: https://www.rayberns.com
Restaurant Operators
N.A.I.C.S.: 722511

Ready Seafood Co. (1)
40 Commercial St, Portland, ME 04101
Tel.: (207) 541-3672
Web Site: http://www.readyseafood.com
Fish & Seafood Markets
N.A.I.C.S.: 445250
John Ready (Pres)

SK Food Group Inc. (1)
4600 37th Ave SW, Seattle, WA 98126
Tel.: (206) 935-8100
Web Site: http://www.skfoodgroup.com
Confectionery Product Distr
N.A.I.C.S.: 424420
Stephen Sposari (CEO)

The Meat Factory Limited (1)
46 Community Ave, Stoney Creek, L8E 2Y3, ON, Canada
Tel.: (905) 662-2284
Web Site: http://www.tmffoods.com
Food Mfr
N.A.I.C.S.: 311999
Lou Albanese (Chm & CEO)

PREMIUM CAPITAL MARKET & INVESTMENTS LIMITED
401 Starlit Tower YN Road, Indore, 452001, Madhya Pradesh, India
Tel.: (91) 7314755137
Web Site: http://www.premiumcapital.in
511660—(BOM)
Sales Range: Less than $1 Million
Financial Investment Services
N.A.I.C.S.: 523999
Sudarshan Kumar Bandi (Chm)

PREMIUM CATERING (HOLDINGS) LIMITED
6 Woodlands Walk, Singapore, 738398, Singapore
Tel.: (65) 69701488 Ky
Web Site: https://www.premiumcaterings.com
Year Founded: 2012
PC—(NASDAQ)
Rev.: $3,809,054
Assets: $4,900,182
Liabilities: $5,972,774
Net Worth: ($1,072,592)
Earnings: ($1,081,875)
Emp.: 40
Fiscal Year-end: 06/30/24
Holding Company
N.A.I.C.S.: 551112

PREMIUM EXPLORATION INC.
1600 East Railway Street, Vancouver, V7J 1B5, BC, Canada
Tel.: (843) 290-8930 BC
Web Site: http://www.premiumexploration.com
Year Founded: 2004
PMMEF—(OTCIQ)
Gold Exploration Services
N.A.I.C.S.: 212220
Lisa Maxwell (Sec)

PREMIUM GROUP CO., LTD.
19th Floor The Okura Prestige Tower 2-10-4 Toranomon, Minato-ku, Tokyo, 105-0001, Japan
Tel.: (81) 351145701
Web Site: https://www.premium-group.co.jp
7199—(TKS)
Rev.: $208,519,060

Assets: $828,061,140
Liabilities: $726,591,030
Net Worth: $101,470,110
Earnings: $30,458,880
Emp.: 703
Fiscal Year-end: 03/31/24
Subsidiary Management Services
N.A.I.C.S.: 551114
Yohichi Shibata (Pres)

Subsidiaries:

CIFUT Co., Ltd. (1)
313 Tsuji, Itako, 311-2421, Ibaraki, Japan
Tel.: (81) 299777500
Web Site: https://www.cifut.com
Communication Equipment Mfr & Distr
N.A.I.C.S.: 334290

Premium Financial Services Co., Ltd. (1)
19th Floor The Okura Prestige Tower 2-10-4 Toranomon, Minato-ku, Tokyo, 105-0001, Japan
Tel.: (81) 351145700
Web Site: http://p-fs.co.jp
Financial Planning Services
N.A.I.C.S.: 523940

PREMIUM INCOME CORPORATION
121 King Street West Suite 2600, Toronto, M5H 3T9, ON, Canada
Tel.: (416) 681-3992
Year Founded: 1996
PIC.A—(TSX)
Rev.: $9,863,298
Assets: $200,922,758
Liabilities: $156,561,339
Net Worth: $44,361,419
Earnings: ($25,641,127)
Fiscal Year-end: 10/31/22
Investment Services
N.A.I.C.S.: 523999

PREMIUM NICKEL RESOURCES LTD.
3400One First Canadian Place, Vancouver, M5X 1A4, BC, Canada
Tel.: (604) 770-4334
Web Site: https://premiumnickelresources.ca
PNRLF—(OTCQX)
Assets: $27,760,951
Liabilities: $20,636,391
Net Worth: $7,124,560
Earnings: ($23,668,447)
Emp.: 193
Fiscal Year-end: 12/31/23
Nickel Mining Services
N.A.I.C.S.: 212230
Mark M. Fedikow (Pres)

PREMIUM TEXTILE MILLS LIMITED
1st Floor Haji Adam Chamber Altaf Hussain Road New Challi, Karachi, 74000, Pakistan
Tel.: (92) 2132410931
Web Site: https://www.premiumtextile.com
PRET—(KAR)
Rev.: $60,973,989
Assets: $56,475,691
Liabilities: $41,190,175
Net Worth: $15,285,515
Earnings: $3,314,686
Emp.: 794
Fiscal Year-end: 06/30/19
Yarn Mill
N.A.I.C.S.: 313110
Abdul Kadir Adam (CEO)

Subsidiaries:

Pinnacle Fibre Pvt Ltd (1)
Office No 405 4th Floor Business Arcade Near Lal Kothi PECHS Block VI, Shahra-e Faisal, Karachi, 75400, Sindh, Pakistan
Tel.: (92) 234370214

Web Site: https://www.pinnaclefiber.com.pk
Polyester Staple Fiber Mfr
N.A.I.C.S.: 325220

PREMOULE INC
2375 Dalton Avenue Office 200, Quebec, G1P 3S3, QC, Canada
Tel.: (418) 652-7777
Web Site: http://www.premoule.com
Sales Range: $50-74.9 Million
Emp.: 400
Thermoplastic Countertops & Kitchen Doors Mfr
N.A.I.C.S.: 332321
Anne Deslauriers (Dir-Sls & Strategic Dev-America)

Subsidiaries:

Premoule Inc - Portes Evolution Plant (1)
1500 boulevard Saint-Jude Sud, Alma, G8B 3L4, QC, Canada
Tel.: (418) 652-7777
Web Site: http://www.premoule.com
Emp.: 40
Plastic Door Mfr
N.A.I.C.S.: 326199

Premoule Inc - Portes et Moulures Ouellet Plant (1)
1906 Boyer Street, Baie Comeau, G5C 2Y5, QC, Canada
Tel.: (418) 652-7777
Thermoplastic Countertop & Door Mfr
N.A.I.C.S.: 326199

Premoule Inc - Premoule Comptoirs Plant (1)
270 Grands-Lacs Street, Saint-Augustin-de-Desmaures, G3A 2K1, QC, Canada
Tel.: (418) 652-7777
Plastic Door Mfr
N.A.I.C.S.: 326199

Premoule Inc - Premoule Portes Thermo Plant (1)
1245 Tessier Street, Hawkesbury, K6A 3R1, ON, Canada
Tel.: (418) 652-7777
Plastic Door Mfr
N.A.I.C.S.: 326199

PRENCO PROGRESS AND ENGINEERING CORPORATION LIMITED.
1135 Squires Beach Rd, Pickering, L1W 3T9, ON, Canada
Tel.: (416) 703-4580
Web Site: http://www.prencocorp.com
Year Founded: 1939
Rev.: $11,183,386
Emp.: 45
Aircraft Part Mfr
N.A.I.C.S.: 336413
Josef Chmel (Founder)

PRENETICS GLOBAL LIMITED
Unit 703-706 K11 ATELIER Kings Road 728 Kings Road, Quarry Bay, China (Hong Kong)
Tel.: (852) 22109588 Ky
Web Site: https://www.prenetics.com
Year Founded: 2007
PRE—(NASDAQ)
Rev.: $275,761,298
Assets: $312,131,231
Liabilities: $68,668,371
Net Worth: $243,462,860
Earnings: ($190,453,387)
Emp.: 400
Fiscal Year-end: 12/31/22
Investment Management Service
N.A.I.C.S.: 523999
Peter Yung Ho Wong (CTO)

PREOBRAZHENSKAYA BASE OF TRAWLING FLEET OAO
1 Portovaya Street, Lazovsky Region, 692998, Preobrazhenie, Russia
Tel.: (7) 4237724215 RU

Preobrazhenskaya Base of Trawling Fleet OAO—(Continued)

Web Site: http://pbtf.ru
Year Founded: 1930
Fishing, Seafood Processing & Whslr
N.A.I.C.S.: 311710
Sergey Mstislavovich *(Gen Dir)*

PRERNA INFRABUILD LTD.
Survey No 820/1 In lane of Panchwati Auto Opp to Honest Restaurant, Circle P Building Prahladnagar SG Road makarba, Ahmedabad, 380058, Gujarat, India
Tel.: (91) 9925005244
Web Site:
   https://www.prernagroup.com
Year Founded: 1988
531802—(BOM)
Rev.: $2,236,137
Assets: $10,402,218
Liabilities: $4,652,707
Net Worth: $5,749,511
Earnings: $1,178,287
Fiscal Year-end: 03/31/23
Real Estate Development Services
N.A.I.C.S.: 531390
Vijay Chandulal Shah *(Chm & Mng Dir)*

PRESBIA PLC
Suite 7 Sandyford Office Centre 17 Corrig Road Sandyford, Dublin, 18, Ireland
Tel.: (353) 551 1487   IE
Web Site: http://www.presbia.com
Rev.: $21,000
Assets: $4,530,000
Liabilities: $2,986,000
Net Worth: $1,544,000
Earnings: ($8,460,000)
Emp.: 20
Fiscal Year-end: 12/31/18
Optical Lens Mfr
N.A.I.C.S.: 339310
Zohar Loshitzer *(Chm & CEO)*

Subsidiaries:

Presbia Deutchland GmbH   (1)
Malmedyweg 45A, 45481, Mulheim an der Ruhr, Germany
Tel.: (49) 20888369675
Web Site: http://presbia.de
Medical Device Mfr & Distr
N.A.I.C.S.: 339113

PRESCIENT THERAPEUTICS LIMITED
Level 7 440 Collins Street, Melbourne, 3000, VIC, Australia
Tel.: (61) 1300805795
Web Site:
   https://www.ptxtherapeutics.com
PTX—(ASX)
Rev.: $2,478,876
Assets: $13,617,021
Liabilities: $1,552,860
Net Worth: $12,064,161
Earnings: ($5,500,835)
Emp.: 1
Fiscal Year-end: 06/30/24
Biopharmaceutical Developer
N.A.I.C.S.: 325412
Steven Yatomi-Clarke *(CEO & Mng Dir)*

PRESERVATION CAPITAL PARTNERS LTD.
1 Wilder Walk, Soho, Soho, London, W1B 5AP, United Kingdom
Tel.: (44) 203 728 7000
Web Site:
   http://www.preservationcapital.com
Privater Equity Firm
N.A.I.C.S.: 523999
Jatender Aujla *(Founder & Mng Partner)*

Subsidiaries:

Parmenion Capital Partners LLP   (1)
Aurora Counterslip, Bristol, BS1 6BX, United Kingdom
Tel.: (44) 3300945900
Web Site: http://www.parmenion.co.uk
Investment Management Service
N.A.I.C.S.: 523940
Martin Jennings *(CEO)*

PRESIDENT AUTOMOBILE INDUSTRIES PUBLIC COMPANY LIMITED
88/8 Moo 9 Soi WorPorAor 11 Piset Satetakit 1 Road, Suanluang Krathum Baen, Samut Sakhon, 74110, Thailand
Tel.: (66) 28109900
Web Site: https://paco.co.th
Year Founded: 1991
PACO—(THA)
Rev.: $30,790,765
Assets: $39,746,323
Liabilities: $10,349,840
Net Worth: $29,396,483
Earnings: $2,136,820
Fiscal Year-end: 12/31/23
Automotive Components Mfr
N.A.I.C.S.: 336330
Somchai Lertkajornkitti *(CEO)*

PRESIDENT HOTEL
43 Kifissias Ave, 115 23, Athens, Greece
Tel.: (30) 210 6989000
Web Site: http://www.president.gr
Year Founded: 1972
Emp.: 129
Hotel Services
N.A.I.C.S.: 721110
Manousakis M. Emmanouel *(Pres)*

PRESONA AB
Nygatan 39, 273 36, Tomelilla, Sweden
Tel.: (46) 41719900
Web Site: http://www.presona.se
Sales Range: $10-24.9 Million
Emp.: 45
Compacting Equipment Mfr
N.A.I.C.S.: 333998
Stefan Ekstrom *(CEO)*

Subsidiaries:

Presona Deutschland GmbH   (1)
Burglen 16, 88090, Immenstadt, Germany
Tel.: (49) 7545 5018265
Web Site: http://www.presona-deutschland.com
Compacting Equipment Mfr
N.A.I.C.S.: 333998

Presona Service GmbH   (1)
Venloer Strasse 280, 50823, Cologne, Germany
Tel.: (49) 221 50 80 831
Web Site: http://www.presona-service.de
Emp.: 6
Compacting Equipment Mfr
N.A.I.C.S.: 333998
Thomas Zout *(Gen Mgr)*

Presona UK Ltd   (1)
Unit 11 and 12 Blake Mill Business Park, Bridgwater, TA6 5LT, Somerset, United Kingdom
Tel.: (44) 1278 444527
Web Site: http://www.presona.co.uk
Emp.: 14
Compacting Equipment Mfr
N.A.I.C.S.: 333998
Dean Clarke *(Mng Dir)*

PRESS CORPORATION LIMITED
NBM Top Mandala House Kaohsiung Road, PO Box 1227, Blantyre, Malawi
Tel.: (265) 1833569   MW
Web Site: https://www.presscorp.com
Year Founded: 1961
PCL—(MALA)
Rev.: $102,907,545
Assets: $790,957,136
Liabilities: $598,630,159
Net Worth: $192,326,978
Earnings: $21,051,930
Fiscal Year-end: 12/31/22
Financial Services
N.A.I.C.S.: 523999
Elizabeth Mafeni *(Controller-Fin Grp)*

Subsidiaries:

Presscane Limited   (1)
PO Box 236, Chikhwawa, Malawi
Tel.: (265) 888816825
Web Site: https://www.presscane.com
Emp.: 83
Ethanol Distillery Product Mfr
N.A.I.C.S.: 325193
Francis Mndolo *(Chief HR & Admin Officer)*

PRESS CORPORATION PLC
NBM Top Mandala House Kaohsiung Road, PO Box 1227, Blantyre, Malawi
Tel.: (265) 1833569   MW
Web Site: http://www.presscorp.com
Year Founded: 1961
PCL—(MALA)
Rev.: $141,410,606
Assets: $955,299,630
Liabilities: $721,901,334
Net Worth: $233,398,296
Earnings: $44,665,128
Fiscal Year-end: 12/31/23
Real Estate Investment Services
N.A.I.C.S.: 531390
Radson Mwadiwa *(Chm)*

Subsidiaries:

Ethanol Company Limited   (1)
Tel.: (265) 1295200
Web Site: https://www.ethanolmw.com
Sales Range: $50-74.9 Million
Emp.: 14
Methanol Mfr
N.A.I.C.S.: 325193

Press Properties Limited   (1)
2nd Floor PCL House Top MANDALA Kaohsiung Road, PO Box 925, Blantyre, Malawi
Tel.: (265) 111824444
Web Site: https://www.pressproperties.com
Sales Range: $50-74.9 Million
Emp.: 1
Property Management Services
N.A.I.C.S.: 531311

PRESS KOGYO CO., LTD.
1-1-1 Shiohama, Kawasaki-ku, Kawasaki, 210-8512, Kanagawa, Japan
Tel.: (81) 442662581
Web Site:
   https://www.presskogyo.co.jp
Year Founded: 1925
7246—(TKS)
Rev.: $1,307,570,370
Assets: $1,267,414,620
Liabilities: $471,279,780
Net Worth: $796,134,840
Earnings: $53,395,580
Emp.: 5,602
Fiscal Year-end: 03/31/24
Automotive Parts & Construction Machinery Mfr
N.A.I.C.S.: 336390
Masahiko Sato *(Exec Mng Officer)*

Subsidiaries:

BANKIN KOGYO CO., LTD.   (1)
17 Kirihara Town, Fujisawa, 252-0811, Kanagawa, Japan
Tel.: (81) 466 44 7711
Web Site: http://www.bankinkogyo.co.jp
Automobile Parts Mfr
N.A.I.C.S.: 336390

KYOWA Manufacturing Co., Ltd   (1)
18-2 Matsuyama-cho, Moka, 321-4346, Tochigi, Japan
Tel.: (81) 285831121
Web Site: https://www.kyowass.co.jp
Emp.: 345
Automotive Parts & Construction Machinery Mfr
N.A.I.C.S.: 333120

ONOMICHI PRESS KOGYO CO., LTD.   (1)
2-165-34 Chojyahara, Onomichi, 722-0221, Hirosima, Japan
Tel.: (81) 848483121
Construction Machinery Parts Mfr
N.A.I.C.S.: 333120

PK MANUFACTURING (SUZHOU) CO., LTD.   (1)
No 101 Wang Mi Road, Suzhou New District, Suzhou, 215129, Jiangsu, China
Tel.: (86) 51268789330
Construction Machinery Parts Distr
N.A.I.C.S.: 423810

PK SERVICE CO., LTD.   (1)
5-27-1 Ishikawa, Fujisawa, 252-0815, Kanagawa, Japan
Tel.: (81) 466477100
Web Site: https://pk-service.co.jp
Emp.: 70
Facility Support Services
N.A.I.C.S.: 561210

PK U.S.A., Inc.   (1)
600 W Northridge Dr, Shelbyville, IN 46176
Tel.: (317) 395-5500
Web Site: https://www.pkusa.com
Automobile Parts Distr
N.A.I.C.S.: 423120
Peter Sandstrom *(Pres)*

PKC CO., LTD.   (1)
5-27-1 Ishikawa, Ota-ku, Fujisawa, 252-0815, Kanagawa, Japan
Tel.: (81) 466479913
Web Site: https://www.pkc.co.jp
Emp.: 20
Automobile Parts Distr
N.A.I.C.S.: 423120

PM Cabin Manufacturing Co., Ltd.   (1)
333 Lian Gang Rd, New District, Suzhou, 215129, Jiangsu, China
Tel.: (86) 51266656333
Construction Machinery Mfr & Distr
N.A.I.C.S.: 333998

PRESS KOGYO MINI CABIN (SUZHOU) CO., LTD.   (1)
No 133 Qinglian Road Xushuguan Town, Suzhou New District, Suzhou, 215151, Jiangsu, China
Tel.: (86) 51281880088
Construction Machinery Parts Distr
N.A.I.C.S.: 423810

PT. PK Manufacturing Indonesia (1)
Jl Harapan Raya Lot JJ-2B Kawasan Industri KIIC, Karawang, 41361, Jawa Barat, Indonesia
Tel.: (62) 2189114015
Automotive & Construction Machinery Parts Distr
N.A.I.C.S.: 423120
Elsye Fatmawati *(Mgr-Acctg & Fin)*

Press Kogyo Co., Ltd. - Onomichi Plant   (1)
21050-1 Oyamada, Takasu-cho, Onomichi, 722-0221, Hirosima, Japan
Tel.: (81) 848371211
Automobile Parts Mfr
N.A.I.C.S.: 336390

Press Kogyo Co., Ltd. - Saitama Plant   (1)
1100 Oaza-Ishidahongo, Kawagoe, 350-0835, Saitama, Japan
Tel.: (81) 492230822
Automobile Parts Mfr
N.A.I.C.S.: 336390

Press Kogyo Co., Ltd. - Utsunomiya Plant   (1)
1704 Shimotsuboyama, Shimotsuke, 323-0115, Tochigi, Japan
Tel.: (81) 285481511
Automobile Parts Mfr.

AND PRIVATE COMPANIES

N.A.I.C.S.: 336390

Press Kogyo Sweden AB (1)
Grondalsgatan 19, 572 35, Oskarshamn, Sweden
Tel.: (46) 491 76 75 00
Web Site: http://www.presskogyo.se
Emp.: 160
Automobile Parts Distr
N.A.I.C.S.: 423120
Rasmus Olheden *(CFO)*

TECMO CO., LTD. (1)
Tel.: (81) 466877821
Web Site: http://www.tecm.co.jp
Emp.: 180
Automobile Parts Mfr
N.A.I.C.S.: 336390

THAI SUMMIT PKK BANGPAKONG CO., LTD. (1)
Amata Nakorn Industrial Estate 700/409 Moo 7 Tumbol Donhuaroh, Amphur Muang, Chon Buri, 20000, Thailand
Tel.: (66) 38454390
Automobile Parts Distr
N.A.I.C.S.: 423120

THAI SUMMIT PKK CO., LTD. (1)
206 Moo 3 Laemchabang Industrial Estate, Tungsukala, Si Racha, 20230, Chonburi, Thailand
Tel.: (66) 38490580
Automobile Parts Distr
N.A.I.C.S.: 423120

Thai Summit PK Corporation Ltd. (1)
500/9 Moo3 Tambol Tasit, Amphur, Pluak Daeng, 21140, Rayong, Thailand
Tel.: (66) 38953400
Automobile Parts Distr
N.A.I.C.S.: 423120

PRESS METAL ALUMINIUM HOLDINGS BHD
Suite 61 & 62 Setia Avenue No 2 Jalan Setia Prima S U13/S, Setia Alam Seksyen U13, 40170, Shah Alam, Selangor, Malaysia
Tel.: (60) 333622188
Web Site:
 https://www.pressmetal.com
Holding Company
N.A.I.C.S.: 551112

Subsidiaries:

PMB Aluminium Sabah Sdn. Bhd. (1)
No 2 Lrg Neutron 1 Neutron Park, 88450, Kota Kinabalu, Sabah, Malaysia
Tel.: (60) 88435248
Curtain Wall Mfr
N.A.I.C.S.: 332323
Jason Lim *(Mgr)*

Press Metal Berhad (1)
Suite 61 & 62 Setia Avenue No 2 Jalan Setia Prima S U13/S, Setia Alam Seksyen U13, 40170, Shah Alam, Selangor Darul Ehsan, Malaysia
Tel.: (60) 3 3362 2188
Web Site: http://www.pressmetal.com
Sales Range: $1-4.9 Billion
Aluminium Products Mfr
N.A.I.C.S.: 331314
Poh Keong Koon *(CEO)*

Subsidiary (Domestic):

ACE Extrusion Sdn. Bhd. (2)
Lot 6463 Batu 5 3/4 Jalan Kapar Sementa, 42100, Kelang, Selangor Darul Ehsan, Malaysia
Tel.: (60) 332906308
Web Site: http://www.aceextrusion.com.my
Sales Range: $50-74.9 Million
Emp.: 100
Aluminium Extrusion Products Mfr & Distr
N.A.I.C.S.: 325180

Angkasa Jasa Sdn. Bhd. (2)
Lot 27 Jalan 3a Kawasan Miel Balakong, Taman Cheras Jaya, Cheras, 43200, Selangor, Malaysia
Tel.: (60) 390752136
Web Site: http://www.angkasajasa.com
Emp.: 60
Steel & Aluminium Fabrication Services

N.A.I.C.S.: 332312
Koon Poh Weng *(Mng Dir)*

BI-PMB Waste Management Sdn. Bhd. (2)
No 14 Jln 5 Off Jalan Bukit Rimau, 42450, Shah Alam, Selangor, Malaysia
Tel.: (60) 351226382
Waste Water Treatment Services
N.A.I.C.S.: 221320

PMS Marketing Sdn. Bhd. (2)
Lot 211 212 Block 293 Mukah Land District KM38 Jalan Mukah Balingian, Mukah, 96400, Sarawak, Malaysia
Tel.: (60) 86855199
Web Site: http://www.pressmetal.com
Sales Range: $250-299.9 Million
Emp.: 800
Aluminum Extrusion Products Distr
N.A.I.C.S.: 423510

Subsidiary (Non-US):

Press Metal International (Hubei) Ltd. (2)
No 1 Qili Road, Zhangjin Town, 433140, Qianjiang, Hubei, China
Tel.: (86) 728 664 1446
Web Site: http://www.pressmetal.com
Aluminium Die Casting Products Mfr
N.A.I.C.S.: 331524

Subsidiary (Domestic):

Press Metal Sarawak Sdn. Bhd. (2)
Lot 211 212 Block 293 Mukah Land District KM 38 Jalan Mukah Balingian, 96407, Mukah, Sarawak, Malaysia
Tel.: (60) 86855042
Aluminum Extrusion Product Mfr
N.A.I.C.S.: 331318

Subsidiary (Non-US):

Press Metal UK Limited (2)
Beldray Road, Bilston, WV14 7NH, West Midlands, United Kingdom
Tel.: (44) 1902498867
Sales Range: $25-49.9 Million
Emp.: 20
Extruded Aluminum Products Mfr
N.A.I.C.S.: 331318
Poh Keong Koon *(Mng Dir)*

Press Metal Bintulu Sdn Bhd (1)
Lot 36 Block 1 Samalaju Industrial Park, Kemena Land District, 97000, Kuching, Samalaju, Malaysia
Tel.: (60) 86297016
Web Site: http://www.pressmetal.com
Aluminum Smelting Services
N.A.I.C.S.: 331314

Joint Venture (Non-US):

Japan Alumina Associates (Australia) Pty. Ltd. (2)
Level 16 37 St George Tr, PO Box 3085, Perth, 6000, WA, Australia (50%)
Tel.: (61) 892213877
Sales Range: $150-199.9 Million
Emp.: 4
Miner of Bauxite & Alumina
N.A.I.C.S.: 331313

PRESSE-DRUCK- UND VERLAGS-GMBH
Curt-Frenzel-Str 2, 86167, Augsburg, Germany
Tel.: (49) 8217770 De
Web Site: http://www.presse-druck.de
Newspaper Publishers
N.A.I.C.S.: 513110
Andreas Ullman *(Dir-Technical)*

Subsidiaries:

Sudkurier GmbH (1)
Max-Stromeyer-Strasse 178, 78467, Konstanz, Germany (51%)
Tel.: (49) 7531 999 0
Web Site: http://www.suedkurier.de
Sales Range: $100-124.9 Million
Emp.: 300
Newspaper Publishing
N.A.I.C.S.: 513110
Rainer Wiesner *(Mng Dir)*

PRESSE-VERTRIEB HERMANN TRUNK GMBH & CO. KG
Muthmannstrasse 1, 80939, Munich, Germany
Tel.: (49) 89324714901
Web Site: http://www.presse.trunk.de
Sales Range: $10-24.9 Million
Freight Transportation Services
N.A.I.C.S.: 488510
Holger Bingmann *(Mng Dir)*

Subsidiaries:

PGV Austria Trunk GmbH (1)
St Leonharder Strasse 10, 5081, Anif, Salzburg, Austria
Tel.: (43) 62468820
Web Site: http://www.pgvaustria.at
Emp.: 300
Magazine Retailer Services
N.A.I.C.S.: 424920

PRESSMART MEDIA LTD.
8 2 268 R 5 Banjara Hills, Road No 2, Hyderabad, 500034, India
Tel.: (91) 4066124000
Web Site: http://www.pressmart.com
Sales Range: $50-74.9 Million
Emp.: 300
Digital Publishing Technical Support Services
N.A.I.C.S.: 541511
Sanjiv Gupta *(Founder, Chm & CEO)*

PRESSOR
Z I Petite Montagne Sud 2 Rue De L Oisans, 91090, Lisses, France
Tel.: (33) 169111800 FR
Web Site: http://www.pressor.fr
Rev.: $22,500,000
Emp.: 31
Waste Disposal Equipment Supplier
N.A.I.C.S.: 333519
Jean-Francois Bedos *(Pres)*

PRESSTONIC ENGINEERING LIMITED
Survey No 02 Khata No 145 Srigandhadakavalu Hoysala Main Road, Pillappa Industrial Layout Sunkadakatte, Bengaluru, 560091, Karnataka, India
Tel.: (91) 7899787639
Web Site:
 https://www.presstonic.com
Year Founded: 1996
PRESSTONIC—(NSE)
Rev.: $2,561,295
Assets: $3,445,001
Liabilities: $2,850,697
Net Worth: $594,304
Earnings: $295,098
Fiscal Year-end: 03/31/23
Automobile Product Mfr & Distr
N.A.I.C.S.: 336110

PRESSURE TECHNOLOGIES PLC
Tel.: (44) 3330150710 UK
Web Site:
 https://www.pressuretechnology.com
PRES—(AIM)
Rev.: $40,661,856
Assets: $34,296,506
Liabilities: $16,995,484
Net Worth: $17,301,021
Earnings: $(865,688)
Emp.: 247
Fiscal Year-end: 09/30/23
Gas Cylinder Mfr
N.A.I.C.S.: 332420
Joanna Allen *(CFO & Sec)*

Subsidiaries:

Al-Met Limited (1)
Unit A1-A3 Coedcae Lane Industrial Estate Coedcae Lane, Pontyclun, CF72 9HG, South Wales, United Kingdom

Tel.: (44) 1443220800
Web Site: https://almet.co.uk
Sales Range: $25-49.9 Million
Emp.: 45
Precision Engineering Tools & Tungsten Carbide Mfr
N.A.I.C.S.: 332216

Chesterfield Special Cylinders Limited (1)
Meadowhall Road, Sheffield, S9 1BT, South Yorkshire, United Kingdom
Tel.: (44) 1142427500
Sales Range: $25-49.9 Million
Emp.: 75
Seamless Steel Gas Cylinders Mfr
N.A.I.C.S.: 333995
Stephen Butler *(Dir-Integrity Mgmt)*

Division (Domestic):

Greenlane Biogas Europe Ltd (2)
Meadowhall Rd, Sheffield, S9 1BT, South Yorkshire, United Kingdom
Tel.: (44) 1142612344
Web Site: http://www.greenlanebiogas.com
Biogas Upgrading Systems Mfr & Services
N.A.I.C.S.: 333248

PRESTAR RESOURCES BERHAD
Lot 1298 Rawang Industrial Estate 16 1/2 Miles Jalan Ipoh, 48000, Rawang, Selangor Darul Ehsan, Malaysia
Tel.: (60) 360908218 MY
Web Site:
 https://www.prestar.com.my
Year Founded: 1984
PRESTAR—(KLS)
Rev.: $128,456,508
Assets: $138,122,751
Liabilities: $49,976,296
Net Worth: $88,146,455
Earnings: $3,215,026
Emp.: 614
Fiscal Year-end: 12/31/22
Steel Processing & Products Mfr
N.A.I.C.S.: 331110
Yew Seng Toh *(Exec Dir)*

Subsidiaries:

Dai Dong Steel Sdn. Bhd. (1)
Lot 1298 Rawang Industrial Estate 16 1/2 Miles Jalan Ipoh, 48000, Rawang, Selangor Darul Ehsan, Malaysia
Tel.: (60) 360908018
Sales Range: $25-49.9 Million
Emp.: 30
Steel Materials Stockist & Distr
N.A.I.C.S.: 423510
Phung Y. M. *(Mgr)*

Prestar Engineering Sdn. Bhd. (1)
Lot 1298 16 1/2 Miles Jalan Ipoh, Rawang Industrial Estate, 48000, Rawang, Selangor Darul Ehsan, Malaysia (75%)
Tel.: (60) 360908218
Web Site: https://www.prestar.com.my
Highway Guardrails & Accessories Mfr & Distr
N.A.I.C.S.: 332322

Prestar Galvanising Sdn. Bhd. (1)
Lot 1298 16 1/2 Miles Jalan Ipoh, Rawang Industrial Estate, 48000, Rawang, Selangor Darul Ehsan, Malaysia
Tel.: (60) 360908618
Sales Range: $100-124.9 Million
Emp.: 500
Galvanizing & Powder Coating Services
N.A.I.C.S.: 332812
S. B. Yeo *(Head-Ops)*

Prestar Manufacturing Sdn. Bhd. (1)
Lot 39 16 1/2 Miles Jalan Ipoh, Rawang Industrial Estate, 48000, Rawang, Selangor, Malaysia
Tel.: (60) 360913288
Web Site: http://www.prestar.com.my
Material Handling Equipment Mfr
N.A.I.C.S.: 333924

Prestar Marketing Sdn. Bhd. (1)
Lot 17494 8 1/2 Miles Jalan Ipoh Selayang Indus Estate, 68100, Batu Caves, Selangor, Malaysia

PRESTAR RESOURCES BERHAD

Prestar Resources Berhad—(Continued)
Tel.: (60) 361380033
General Hardware & Materials Handling Equipment Distr
N.A.I.C.S.: 423710

Prestar Precision Tube Sdn. Bhd. (1)
Lot 1298 16 1/2 Miles Jalan Ipoh, Rawang Industrial Estate, 48000, Rawang, Selangor Darul Ehsan, Malaysia
Tel.: (60) 360908818
Emp.: 200
Steel Pipes & Tubes Mfr
N.A.I.C.S.: 331210

Prestar Steel Pipes Sdn. Bhd. (1)
Lot 1298 Rawang Industrial Estate 16 1/2 Miles Jalan Ipoh, 48000, Rawang, Selangor, Malaysia
Tel.: (60) 360929800
Sales Range: $25-49.9 Million
Emp.: 100
Steel Pole Mfr
N.A.I.C.S.: 331210

Prestar Storage System Sdn. Bhd. (1)
Lot 3 Jalan RP Rawang Perdana, 48000, Rawang, Selangor Darul Ehsan, Malaysia
Tel.: (60) 360941354
Web Site:
    https://www.prestarstoragesystem.com
Storage Racks & Material Handling Systems Mfr
N.A.I.C.S.: 332313
Toh Yew Keat *(Mng Dir)*

Tashin Steel Sdn. Bhd.
Plot 40 Lorong Perusahaan Maju 7 Kawasan Perusahaan 4, 13600, Prai, Penang, Malaysia **(51%)**
Tel.: (60) 45090888
Web Site: https://www.tashin.com.my
Sales Range: $75-99.9 Million
Emp.: 150
Steel Products Stockist & Distr
N.A.I.C.S.: 423510

PRESTEIGNE LIMITED

Unit 9 The Brunei Center, Newton Road, Crawley, RH10 9TU, Surrey, United Kingdom
Tel.: (44) 1293 651 300
Web Site: http://www.presteigne.tv
Year Founded: 1991
Rental of Broadcast Equipment
N.A.I.C.S.: 334220
Tony Ridler *(Mgr-Prep & Maintenance)*

Subsidiaries:

Presteigne Charter Limited (1)
Unit 2/3 Manor Gate Manor Royal, Crawley, RH10 9SX, United Kingdom
Tel.: (44) 1293 651 300
Web Site: http://www.presteignecharter.com
Sales Range: $50-74.9 Million
Broadcasting Equipment Rental Services
N.A.I.C.S.: 532490
Mike Ransome *(Mng Dir)*

PRESTEVE FOODS LIMITED.

20954 Erie Street South, PO Box 902, Wheatley, N0P 2P0, ON, Canada
Tel.: (519) 825-4677
Web Site:
    http://www.prestevefoods.com
Rev.: $54,937,495
Emp.: 125
Fish & Seafood Distr
N.A.I.C.S.: 424460
Dan Walda *(CFO)*

PRESTIGE BIOLOGICS CO. LTD.

197 Osongsaengmyeong 1-Ro Osong-Eup, Heungdeok-Gu, Cheongju, 28161, Chungcheongbuk-do, Korea (South)
Tel.: (82) 432321552
Web Site:
    https://www.prestigebiopharma.com
Year Founded: 2015
950210—(KRS)
Rev.: $764,137
Assets: $534,660,548
Liabilities: $25,845,810
Net Worth: $508,814,738
Earnings: ($6,506,613)
Emp.: 69
Fiscal Year-end: 06/30/21
Pharmaceutical Preparation Mfr
N.A.I.C.S.: 325412
Jinwoo Michael Kim *(COO)*

PRESTIGE ESTATES PROJECTS LTD.

Prestige Falcon Tower No 19 Brunton Road, Bengaluru, 560025, India
Tel.: (91) 8025591080
Web Site:
    https://www.prestigeconstruct.com
Year Founded: 1997
533274—(BOM)
Rev.: $1,051,735,507
Assets: $4,386,175,889
Liabilities: $3,156,213,656
Net Worth: $1,229,962,232
Earnings: $127,906,001
Emp.: 1,292
Fiscal Year-end: 03/31/23
Residential & Commercial Property Developer
N.A.I.C.S.: 236117
Irfan Razack *(Chm & Co-Mng Dir)*

Subsidiaries:

Apex Realty Ventures LLP (1)
245 2nd Floor Satra Plaza Sector 19D, Vashi, Navi Mumbai, 400 703, India
Tel.: (91) 2264610777
Web Site: https://apexrealty.co.in
Real Estate Services
N.A.I.C.S.: 531390

PRESTIGE INTERNATIONAL INC.

14th floor Kojimachi Odori Building 2-4-1 Kojimachi, Chiyoda-ku, Tokyo, 102-0083, Japan
Tel.: (81) 352130220
Web Site: https://www.prestigein.com
Year Founded: 1986
4290—(TKS)
Rev.: $388,258,180
Assets: $448,395,960
Liabilities: $136,245,320
Net Worth: $312,150,640
Earnings: $38,278,510
Emp.: 4,982
Fiscal Year-end: 03/31/24
Data Processing Outsourcing Services
N.A.I.C.S.: 518210
Shinichi Tamagami *(CEO)*

Subsidiaries:

Entrust Inc. (1)
3-7-9 Nishiki Taiyo Seimei Nagoya No 2 Building 7F, Naka-ku, Nagoya, 460-0003, Aichi, Japan **(56.8%)**
Tel.: (81) 526848661
Web Site: https://www.entrust-inc.jp
Business Management Services
N.A.I.C.S.: 541618

Japanese Help Desk Inc. (1)
Unit LP-11 Medical Plaza Makati Amorsolo St, Legaspi Village, Makati, Philippines
Tel.: (63) 28 833 6852
Web Site: https://www.j-helpdesk.jp
Medical Assistance Services
N.A.I.C.S.: 621610

P. I. Philippines, Inc. (1)
5th Floor King's Court II Building 2129 Chino Roces Ave, Makati, Philippines
Tel.: (63) 28 887 5169
Business Process Outsourcing Services
N.A.I.C.S.: 541611

P.I Myanmar Pte. Limited (1)
Lanmadaw Street No 170/174 7th Floor, Latha Township, Yangon, Myanmar
Tel.: (95) 996 992 8611
Business Process Outsourcing Services
N.A.I.C.S.: 541611

P.I. Assistance (Thailand) Co., Ltd. (1)
Unit 5-6 Floor 22nd 399 Interchange 21 Building Sukhumvit Road, Klongtoey-Nua Wattana, Bangkok, 10110, Thailand
Tel.: (66) 2 615 6000
Business Process Outsourcing Services
N.A.I.C.S.: 541611

P.I. Prestige International (Cambodia) Co., Ltd. (1)
No 888 Russian Confederation Blvd, Sangkat Toeuk Thla Khan Sen Sok, Phnom Penh, Cambodia
Tel.: (855) 2 399 0681
Business Process Outsourcing Services
N.A.I.C.S.: 541611

P.I. Prestige International India Private Limited (1)
C-982 Ground Floor Sushant Lok Phase-1, Gurgaon, 122002, Haryana, India
Tel.: (91) 997 144 4696
Business Process Outsourcing Services
N.A.I.C.S.: 541611

PI EIS Insurance Technology Inc. (1)
2-4-1 Kojimachi, Chiyoda-ku, Tokyo, 102-0083, Japan
Tel.: (81) 35 213 0220
Web Site: https://www.pi-eis.co.jp
Insurance Agency Services
N.A.I.C.S.: 524210
Shinichi Tamagami *(CEO)*

Premier Aid Inc. (1)
14th Floor Kojimachi Odori Building 2-4-1 Kojimachi, Chiyoda-ku, Tokyo, 102-0083, Japan
Tel.: (81) 35 213 0850
Web Site: https://www.premier-aid.co.jp
Safe Driving Support Services
N.A.I.C.S.: 488490

Premier Assist Inc. (1)
14th floor Kojimachi Odori Building 2-4-1 Kojimachi, Chiyoda-ku, Tokyo, 102-0083, Japan
Tel.: (81) 352130280
Emp.: 696
Motor Vehicle Towing Services
N.A.I.C.S.: 488410
Hashimoto Mikio *(CEO)*

Premier Assist Network Inc. (1)
14th Floor Kojimachi Odori Building 2-4-1 Kojimachi, Chiyoda-ku, Tokyo, 102-0083, Japan
Tel.: (81) 35 213 0280
Web Site: https://www.premier-assist.co.jp
Road Operation Services
N.A.I.C.S.: 488490

Premier IT & Process Management Inc. (1)
5-1 Hamanota Kisakatamachi, Nikaho, 018-0113, Akita, Japan
Tel.: (81) 35 213 0223
Web Site: https://www.premier-itsolution.co.jp
Information Technology Services
N.A.I.C.S.: 541511

Premier Insurance Partners Inc. (1)
14th Floor Kojimachi Odori Building 2-4-1 Kojimachi, Chiyoda-ku, Tokyo, 102-0083, Japan
Tel.: (81) 35 213 0915
Web Site: https://www.pip-pi.co.jp
Insurance Brokerage Services
N.A.I.C.S.: 524210

Premier Insurance Solutions Inc. (1)
5th Floor of World Building 2-7-22 Kanda Nishikicho, Chiyoda-ku, Tokyo, 101-0054, Japan
Tel.: (81) 35 213 0910
Web Site: https://www.premier-insurancesolutions.co.jp
Insurance Agency Services
N.A.I.C.S.: 524210

INTERNATIONAL PUBLIC

Premier Life Inc. (1)
14F Kojimachi Odori Building 2-4-1 Kojimachi, Chiyoda-ku, Tokyo, 112-0083, Japan
Tel.: (81) 35 213 0316
Web Site: https://www.premier-life.co.jp
Rental Guarantee Services
N.A.I.C.S.: 531110

Premier Lotas Network Inc. (1)
14th Floor Kojimachi Odori Building 2-4-1 Kojimachi, Chiyoda-ku, Tokyo, 102-0083, Japan
Tel.: (81) 35 213 0329
Web Site: https://www.premier-ln.com
Road Service Network Management Services
N.A.I.C.S.: 488490

Premier Park Assist Inc. (1)
Razu Building 2F 3-19 Haramachi, Shinjuku-ku, Tokyo, 162-0053, Japan
Tel.: (81) 3 5155 1882
Web Site: http://www.premier-parkassist.com
Facility Maintenance Services
N.A.I.C.S.: 561210

Premier X-Value Inc. (1)
2-4-1 Kojimachi, Chiyoda-ku, Tokyo, 102-0083, Japan
Tel.: (81) 35 213 0206
Internet Communication Services
N.A.I.C.S.: 517810

Prestige Humansolution Inc. (1)
1-172 Arayatorikimachi Prestige International Akita BPO Main Campus, Akita, 010-1633, Japan
Tel.: (81) 18 888 9343
Web Site: https://www.prestige-hs.com
Employment Recruiting Services
N.A.I.C.S.: 561320

Prestige Internacional Mexico Ltda. (1)
Rio Lerma 232 piso 23 Of 2387 Torre Diana, 06500, Cuauhtemoc, Mexico
Tel.: (52) 553 300 6096
Business Process Outsourcing Services
N.A.I.C.S.: 541611

Prestige Internacional do Brasil Ltda. (1)
Rua Coronel Oscar Porto 736- Sala 45 Paraiso, Sao Paulo, 04003-003, Brazil
Tel.: (55) 1139390890
Web Site: https://www.prestigein-br.com
Business Process Outsourcing Services
N.A.I.C.S.: 561499

Prestige International (HK) Co., Ltd. (1)
Suite 701 7th Floor South Tower World Finance Centre Canton Road, Harbor City Tsim Sha Tsui, Kowloon, China (Hong Kong)
Tel.: (852) 36515700
Business Process Outsourcing Services
N.A.I.C.S.: 561499

Prestige International (M) Sdn. Bhd. (1)
A-12-10 Menara UOA Bangsar No 5 Jalan Bangsar Utama 1, 59000, Kuala Lumpur, Malaysia
Tel.: (60) 32 330 9966
Business Process Outsourcing Services
N.A.I.C.S.: 541611

Prestige International (S) Pte. Ltd. (1)
583 Orchard Road 09-03 Forum, Singapore, 238884, Singapore
Tel.: (65) 68320733
Business Process Outsourcing Services
N.A.I.C.S.: 561499

Prestige International (Taiwan) Co., Limited (1)
10 Floor 1 No 97, Song Ren Rd, Xinyi Dist, Taipei, 110, Taiwan
Tel.: (886) 27 718 1277
Business Process Outsourcing Services
N.A.I.C.S.: 541611

Prestige International (Thailand) Co., Ltd. (1)
399 Interchange 21 Bldg Unit No 2202 22nd Floor Sukhumvit Road, Klongtoey-Nua Wattana, Bangkok, 10110, Thailand

AND PRIVATE COMPANIES

Tel.: (66) 26156000
Web Site: https://www.prestigein.com
Business Process Outsourcing Services
N.A.I.C.S.: 561499

Prestige International Australia Pty. Ltd.
Suite 1201 Level 12 307 Pitt Street, Sydney, 2000, NSW, Australia
Tel.: (61) 282185000
Business Process Outsourcing Services
N.A.I.C.S.: 561499

Prestige International China Co., Ltd. (1)
Room 021 32nd Floor Hang Seng Bank Tower Lu Jia Zui Ring Road, Pudong NewArea, Shanghai, 200120, China
Tel.: (86) 2168412027
Web Site: https://www.prestigein.com
Business Process Outsourcing Services
N.A.I.C.S.: 561499

Prestige International U.K. Ltd. (1)
Suite A 4th Floor Corinthian House 17 Lansdowne Road, Croydon, London, CR0 2BX, Surrey, United Kingdom
Tel.: (44) 2086035854
Business Process Outsourcing Services
N.A.I.C.S.: 561499

Prestige International USA, Inc. (1)
19800 MacArthur Blvd Ste 400, Irvine, CA 92612
Tel.: (949) 437-9600
Business Process Outsourcing Services
N.A.I.C.S.: 561499
Shinichi Tamagami *(Chm & CEO)*

Prestige International Vietnam Co., Ltd. (1)
No 107 Nguyen Phong Sac Street 13Flr, Dich Vong Hau Cau Giay, Hanoi, Vietnam
Tel.: (84) 243 201 6065
Business Process Outsourcing Services
N.A.I.C.S.: 541611

Time Commerce Co., Ltd. (1)
Minamiaoyama HK Building 4F 7-3-6, Minamiaoyama Minato-ku, Tokyo, 107-0062, Japan
Tel.: (81) 35 464 8061
Web Site: http://www.time-commerce.com
Supply Chain Management Services
N.A.I.C.S.: 541614

PRESTIGE WEALTH INC.
Suite 3201 Champion Tower 3 Garden Road, Central, China (Hong Kong)
Tel.: (852) 21228560   Ky
Web Site: https://ir.prestigewm.hk
Year Founded: 2018
PWM—(NASDAQ)
Emp.: 6
Asset Management Services
N.A.I.C.S.: 523999
Hongtao Shi *(Chm)*

PRESTON CHEVROLET BUICK GMC CADILLAC LTD.
19990 Langley Bypass, Langley, V3A 4Y1, BC, Canada
Tel.: (604) 534-4154
Web Site: https://www.prestongm.com
Rev.: $37,164,356
Emp.: 90
New & Used Car Dealers
N.A.I.C.S.: 441110
Peter Heppner *(Pres-General & Acctg)*

PRESTON NORTH END PLC
Sir Tom Finney Way, Deepdale, Preston, PR1 6RU, United Kingdom
Tel.: (44) 8448561964
Web Site: http://www.pne.com
Sales Range: $10-24.9 Million
Emp.: 106
Football League Operator
N.A.I.C.S.: 711211
Kevin Abbott *(Dir-Fin)*

Subsidiaries:

Preston North End Football Club Limited (1)
Sir Tom Finney Way, Preston, PR1 6RU, Lancashire, United Kingdom
Tel.: (44) 8448561964
Web Site: http://www.pne.com
Emp.: 400
Professional Football League Club
N.A.I.C.S.: 711211
Kevin Aubert *(Dir-Fin)*

PREVAS AB
Glodgargrand 14, PO Box 4, SE-721 03, Vasteras, Sweden
Tel.: (46) 213601900
Web Site: https://www.prevas.com
PREV.B—(OMX)
Rev.: $94,203,154
Assets: $55,484,628
Liabilities: $27,307,709
Net Worth: $28,176,919
Earnings: $5,607,501
Emp.: 519
Fiscal Year-end: 12/31/20
Information Technology Services
N.A.I.C.S.: 541512
Goran Lundin *(Founder)*

Subsidiaries:

Zetiq Development AB (1)
Bofors Industriomrade, Karlskoga, 691 80, Sweden
Tel.: (46) 5 86 22 23 30
Electric Equipment Mfr
N.A.I.C.S.: 334419

PREVECEUTICAL MEDICAL, INC.
2500 885 Cambie St, Vancouver, V6B 0R6, BC, Canada
Tel.: (604) 416-7777   Ca
Web Site: https://www.preveceutical.com
Year Founded: 2015
PREV—(OTCQB)
Assets: $139,718
Liabilities: $3,563,768
Net Worth: ($3,424,050)
Earnings: ($1,095,135)
Fiscal Year-end: 12/31/22
Biotechnology Research & Development Services
N.A.I.C.S.: 541714
Stephen Van Deventer *(Co-Founder, Chm & CEO)*

PREVENT DEV GMBH
Hannoversche Strasse 2c, Wolfsburg, Germany
Tel.: (49) 536130340   De
Web Site: http://www.preventgroup.com
Sales Range: $5-14.9 Billion
Emp.: 12,000
Textiles & Motor Vehicle Interiors Designer, Developer, Mfr & Sales
N.A.I.C.S.: 314999
Nijaz Hastor *(Chm)*

Subsidiaries:

AD Boats Ltd. (1)
Matoseva 8, 21000, Solin, Croatia
Tel.: (385) 21275022
Sanitary Products Mfr
N.A.I.C.S.: 322291

CarTrim Zepce d.o.o. (1)
Polje Business Zone, Zepce, 72230, Zenica, Bosnia & Herzegovina
Tel.: (387) 32888216
Modern Furniture Mfr
N.A.I.C.S.: 337127

Eisenwerk Erzgebirge 1566 GmbH (1)
Giessereistrasse, 08304, Schonheide, Germany
Tel.: (49) 37755570

Web Site: http://www.esguss.de
Rocker Lever Mfr
N.A.I.C.S.: 336310

NEUE HALBERG-GUSS GmbH (1)
Kirchstr 16, 66130, Saarbrucken, Germany
Tel.: (49) 681 8705 0
Web Site: http://www.halberg-guss.de
Automotive Parts, Including Engine Blocks, Cast-Iron Cylinder Heads & Crankshafts Mfr
N.A.I.C.S.: 333618
Barbaros Arslan *(Mng Dir)*

Neofacture Furniture GmbH (1)
Hannoversche Strasse 2c, 38448, Wolfsburg, Germany
Tel.: (49) 536130340
Protective Face Shield & Mask Mfr
N.A.I.C.S.: 339113

PREVENT TURKEY Otomotive LIMITED SIRKETI (1)
Nurettin Baransel cad No 3, Istanbul, Turkiye
Tel.: (90) 5361 3034 362
Automobile Component Distr
N.A.I.C.S.: 423120

Prevent Apparel GmbH (1)
Goldbachstrasse 17, 37269, Eschwege, Germany
Tel.: (49) 5361 3034 602
Apparels Mfr
N.A.I.C.S.: 313310

Prevent Austria GmbH (1)
Dr Franz-Wilhelm-Strasse 2, AT-3500, Krems, Austria
Tel.: (43) 27328810
Web Site: http://www.eybl-international.com
Holding Company; Motor Vehicle Seating & Interior Products Mfr
N.A.I.C.S.: 551112

Subsidiary (Domestic):

Eybl Austria GmbH (2)
Dr Franz-Wilhelm-Strasse 2, 3500, Krems an der Donau, Austria   (100%)
Tel.: (43) 27328810
Web Site: http://www.eybl-international.com
Sales Range: $100-124.9 Million
Emp.: 380
Motor Vehicle Textile Products Mfr
N.A.I.C.S.: 314999
Josef Wagenleitner *(Dir-Tech)*

Subsidiary (Domestic):

Eybl Development GmbH (3)
Dr Franz Wilhelm-Strasse 2, Krems, 3500, Austria   (100%)
Tel.: (43) 27328810
Web Site: http://www.eybl-inrenational.com
Sales Range: $10-24.9 Million
Emp.: 40
Motor Vehicle Seating & Interior Textile Products Developer
N.A.I.C.S.: 541715

Subsidiary (Non-US):

Eybl Hungaria Textilipari Kft. (2)
Jokai u 4, H-9545, Janoshaza, Hungary   (100%)
Tel.: (36) 95 551 0
Sales Range: $150-199.9 Million
Motor Vehicle Seat Cover & Interior Special Components Mfr
N.A.I.C.S.: 336360

Eybl Slovakia s.r.o. (2)
Ul 1 maja 882, SK-02001, Puchov, Slovakia   (100%)
Tel.: (421) 424711218
Sales Range: $25-49.9 Million
Emp.: 35
Motor Vehicle Seat Cover Mfr
N.A.I.C.S.: 336360

Eybl Trier GmbH & Co. KG (2)
Im Speyer 11, 54294, Trier, Germany
Tel.: (49) 6518160
Sales Range: $50-74.9 Million
Emp.: 125
Motor Vehicle Textile Products Mfr
N.A.I.C.S.: 314999

Subsidiary (Domestic):

Eybl Verwaltungs GmbH (3)

Im Speyer 11, D-54294, Trier, Germany
Tel.: (49) 651 8160
Textile Mill Management Services
N.A.I.C.S.: 541611

Subsidiary (Non-US):

Prevent Halog, d.o.o. (2)
Kidriceva 14, Lenart, Slovenia
Tel.: (386) 27291950
Web Site: http://www.prevent-halog.com
Sales Range: $25-49.9 Million
Emp.: 40
Car Seat Covers Mfr
N.A.I.C.S.: 336390

Prevent Lamitex, d.o.o. (2)
Kidriceva 6, Slovenj Gradec, Slovenia
Tel.: (386) 28824703
Web Site: http://www.prevent.se
Sales Range: $10-24.9 Million
Emp.: 30
Lamination of Textiles
N.A.I.C.S.: 313310

Prevent Mezica, d.o.o. (2)
Glancnik 6, Mezica, Slovenia
Tel.: (386) 28279103
Web Site: http://www.preventmezica.com
Car Seat Covers Mfr
N.A.I.C.S.: 336390

Prevent Mislinja, d.o.o. (2)
Gozdarska 38, Mislinja, Slovenia
Tel.: (386) 28857800
Web Site: http://www.prevent.com
Sales Range: $25-49.9 Million
Emp.: 100
Protective Gloves & Work Clothing Mfr
N.A.I.C.S.: 315250
Andreas Oder *(Gen Mgr)*

Prevent SG, d.o.o. (2)
Kidriceva 6, 2380, Slovenj Gradec, Slovenia
Tel.: (386) 28823000
Web Site: http://www.prevent.com
Car Seat Covers Mfr
N.A.I.C.S.: 336390

Prevent TRO, d.o.o. (2)
Perzonali 2, Prevalje, Slovenia
Tel.: (386) 28246000
Web Site: http://www.prevent-tro.si
Sales Range: $50-74.9 Million
Emp.: 140
Tools, Industrial Knives & Saws Mfr
N.A.I.C.S.: 332216

Sepic, d.o.o. (2)
Gradisce 51, Obrov, Slovenia
Tel.: (386) 56890100
Moulding of Soft Polyurethane Foam
N.A.I.C.S.: 326150

Prevent Automotive Romania s.r.l. (1)
Aleea Austriei Nr 6, 305200, Deta, Romania
Tel.: (40) 256 407500
Automobile Component Distr
N.A.I.C.S.: 423120
Alexandru Ognean *(Mgr-Quality)*

Prevent Avto Rus OOO (1)
Per Sovetsky 3 Lit 32 B, 140560, Ozyory, Russia
Tel.: (7) 499 755 20 10
Automobile Component Distr
N.A.I.C.S.: 423120
Sergey Makeenko *(Gen Mgr)*

Prevent BH d.o.o. (1)
Topuzovo polje bb, 71300, Visoko, Bosnia & Herzegovina
Tel.: (387) 32 730 850
Web Site: http://www.prevent.ba
Automobile Component Distr
N.A.I.C.S.: 423120

Prevent Components d.o.o (1)
Industrijska zona bb, Potocari, 75430, Srebrenica, Bosnia & Herzegovina
Tel.: (387) 62945716
Seat Cover Mfr & Whslr
N.A.I.C.S.: 336360

Prevent Direkt d.o.o. (1)
Rajlovacka bb, 71000, Sarajevo, Bosnia & Herzegovina
Tel.: (387) 33782755
Seat Cover Mfr & Whslr
N.A.I.C.S.: 336360

PREVENT DEV GMBH

Prevent DEV GmbH—(Continued)

Prevent FAD dd (1)
Titova bb, 74264, Jelah, Bosnia & Herzegovina
Tel.: (387) 32 667 000
Automobile Component Distr
N.A.I.C.S.: 423120

Prevent Fabrics d.o.o. (1)
Topuzovo polje bb, 71300, Visoko, Bosnia & Herzegovina
Tel.: (387) 32942133
Fabric Textile Mfr
N.A.I.C.S.: 313310

Prevent Gorazde d.o.o. (1)
Prve Drinske Brigade 23, 73000, Gorazde, Bosnia & Herzegovina
Tel.: (387) 38241768
Fabric Textile Mfr
N.A.I.C.S.: 313310

Prevent Home d.o.o. (1)
Zgon bb, Kljuc, 79280, Sarajevo, Bosnia & Herzegovina
Tel.: (387) 37831002
Seat Cover Mfr & Whslr
N.A.I.C.S.: 336360

Prevent Interior d.o.o. (1)
Gorusa bb, 71300, Visoko, Bosnia & Herzegovina
Tel.: (387) 32942270
Seat Cover Mfr & Whslr
N.A.I.C.S.: 336360

Prevent Leather d.o.o. (1)
Topuzovo polje bb, 71300, Visoko, Bosnia & Herzegovina
Tel.: (387) 32942199
Footwear Mfr
N.A.I.C.S.: 316210

Prevent Moldova, d.o.o. (1)
Alba, Iulia 75, Chisinau, Moldova
Tel.: (373) 2581151
Web Site: http://www.prevent.si
Sales Range: $50-74.9 Million
Emp.: 200
Car Seat Covers Mfr
N.A.I.C.S.: 336390

Prevent Premium & Interior Kft. (1)
Ipari utca 1, 9900, Kormend, Hungary
Tel.: (36) 94 591 130
Automobile Component Distr
N.A.I.C.S.: 423120

Prevent ROM s.a.r.l. (1)
Aleea Austriei 6, 305200, Deta, Romania
Tel.: (40) 256407500
Protective Face Shield & Mask Mfr
N.A.I.C.S.: 339113

Prevent Safety d.o.o. (1)
Ul Prve Drinske brigade br 23, 73000, Gorazde, Bosnia & Herzegovina
Tel.: (387) 38 230 510
Automobile Component Distr
N.A.I.C.S.: 423120

Prevent Sarajevo, d.o.o. (1)
Gorusa bb, Visoko, 71300, Sarajevo, Bosnia & Herzegovina
Tel.: (387) 32745982
Web Site: http://www.prevent.ba
Car Seat Covers Mfr
N.A.I.C.S.: 336390
Kenan Nalbantic (Mng Dir)

Prevent Spare Parts d.o.o. (1)
Kidriceva 6, 2380, Slovenj Gradec, Slovenia
Tel.: (386) 2 878 77 84
Automobile Component Distr
N.A.I.C.S.: 423120

Prevent Srebrenica d.o.o. (1)
Industrijska zona bb, Potocari, 75430, Srebrenica, Bosnia & Herzegovina
Tel.: (387) 33774830
Seat Cover Mfr & Whslr
N.A.I.C.S.: 336360

Prevent Step d.o.o. (1)
Armije BiH bb, 72300, Bugojno, Bosnia & Herzegovina
Tel.: (387) 30257517
Seat Cover Mfr & Whslr
N.A.I.C.S.: 336360

Prevent TWB GmbH & Co. KG (1)
Sedanstrasse 3, 58089, Hagen, Germany
Tel.: (49) 2331 9166 0
Web Site: http://www.prevent-twb.com
Emp.: 500
Automotive Components Mfr
N.A.I.C.S.: 336330
Jan Rene Zander (Key Acct Mgr)

Prevent TWB do Brasil Industria E Comercio Ltda. (1)
Rodovia Dom Pedro I Km 87 5, 12954-260, Atibaia, Brazil
Tel.: (55) 11 4414 5851
Motor Vehicle Seating Mfr
N.A.I.C.S.: 336360

Prevent Thierry Brasil Ltda (1)
Rua Jose Alves Cardoso n 1 510 Bairro Cachoeirinha, 37 600-000, Cambui, Brazil
Tel.: (55) 35 3431 9511
Automobile Component Distr
N.A.I.C.S.: 423120

Prevent Travnik d.o.o. (1)
Tvornicka bb, 72270, Travnik, Bosnia & Herzegovina
Tel.: (387) 30961476
Seat Cover Mfr & Whslr
N.A.I.C.S.: 336360

Prevent Vigo SA (1)
Avenida Peinador 59, Mos, 36416, Pontevedra, Spain
Tel.: (34) 986288390
Sales Range: $50-74.9 Million
Emp.: 180
Car Seat Covers Mfr
N.A.I.C.S.: 336360

Prevent Visoko d.o.o. (1)
Gorusa bb, 71300, Visoko, Bosnia & Herzegovina
Tel.: (387) 32941310
Seat Cover Mfr & Whslr
N.A.I.C.S.: 336360

Prevent Zenica d.o.o. (1)
Gorazdanska 84a, 72000, Zenica, Bosnia & Herzegovina
Tel.: (387) 32941353
Modern Furniture Mfr
N.A.I.C.S.: 337127

Prevent Zlatar, d.o.o. (1)
Silvija Strahimira Kranjcevica b b, 4290, Zlatar, Croatia
Tel.: (385) 49587051
Sales Range: $100-124.9 Million
Emp.: 382
Car Seat Covers Mfr
N.A.I.C.S.: 336390

Thierry Prevent Development Pariz S.A. (1)
81 rue de Miromesnil, Paris, France
Tel.: (33) 144699840
Web Site: http://www.prevent.si
Motor Vehicle Parts Developer
N.A.I.C.S.: 336390

PREVENTION INSURANCE COM INC

552 Lonsdale Street Level 7, Melbourne, 3000, Australia
Tel.: (61) 38 393 1459 NV
Year Founded: 1975
PVNC—(OTCIQ)
Assets: $5,261
Liabilities: $153,216
Net Worth: ($147,955)
Earnings: ($55,995)
Emp.: 1
Fiscal Year-end: 04/30/22
Investment Services
N.A.I.C.S.: 523999
Marino Sussich (Pres, CEO, Treas, CFO & Sec)

PREVEST DENPRO LIMITED

Export Promotion Industrial Park, Bari Brahmana, Jammu, 180012, India
Tel.: (91) 8899074151
Web Site:
https://www.prevestdenpro.com
Year Founded: 1999
543363—(BOM)
Dental Equipment Mfr
N.A.I.C.S.: 339114
Atul Modi (Chm & Mng Dir)

Subsidiaries:

Denvisio Biomed Limited (1)
Unit No-312A 3rd Floor Centrum Plaza Golf Course, Gurgaon, 122011, Haryana, India
Tel.: (91) 8899074151
Web Site: https://www.prevestdirect.com
Dental Product Mfr & Distr
N.A.I.C.S.: 339114

PREVOZ RADNIKA KREKA D.D.

18 Hrvatske brigade bb, Tuzla, 75000, Bosnia & Herzegovina
Tel.: (387) 3 528 2469
PRAKRK3—(SARE)
Assets: $934,799
Liabilities: $178,721
Net Worth: $756,078
Earnings: ($64,323)
Emp.: 3
Fiscal Year-end: 12/31/20
Passenger Transportation Services
N.A.I.C.S.: 485999

PRFOODS AS

Karsa Port Saaremaa, 94129, Suure-Rootsi, Estonia
Tel.: (372) 4521470
Web Site: https://www.prfoods.ee
Sales Range: $75-99.9 Million
Emp.: 450
Ice Cream & Other Frozen Foods Mfr & Distr
N.A.I.C.S.: 311520
Katre Kovask (Chm & CEO)

Subsidiaries:

AB Premia KPC (1)
Taikos pr 96, Kaunas, 51178, Lithuania
Tel.: (370) 37 322816
Web Site: https://www.premia.lt
Frozen Food Product Distr
N.A.I.C.S.: 424420
Aiste Daugele (Mgr-Sls)

AS Premia FFL (1)
Meza street 4, Riga, 1048, Latvia
Tel.: (371) 6780 5165
Web Site: https://www.premia.lv
Frozen Food Product Distr
N.A.I.C.S.: 424420
Agnese Skalbe (Brand Mgr)

Subsidiary (Non-US):

Overumans Fisk Ab (2)
Box 210, 923 24, Storuman, Sweden
Tel.: (46) 951 261 33
Web Site: http://www.overumans.se
Fish Farming & Distr
N.A.I.C.S.: 112511

Vettel OU (1)
Suure-Rootsi Kula, Suure-Rootsi, Estonia
Tel.: (372) 452 1470
Emp.: 150
Fish Product Distr
N.A.I.C.S.: 424460
Aivar Jogi (Mgr)

PRG CORPORATION PUBLIC COMPANY LIMITED

88 Moo 2 Tiwanon Road Tumbol Bangkadee, Amphur Mueng, Bangkok, 12000, Pathumtani, Thailand
Tel.: (66) 25012175
Web Site: https://www.prg.co.th
Year Founded: 1979
PRG—(THA)
Rev.: $68,303,371
Assets: $308,497,236
Liabilities: $75,859,129
Net Worth: $232,638,107
Earnings: $10,112,390
Fiscal Year-end: 12/31/23
Milled Rice Mfr & Distr
N.A.I.C.S.: 311212

INTERNATIONAL PUBLIC

Suvait Theeravachirakul (Vice Chm)

Subsidiaries:

PRG Granary Co., Ltd. (1)
88 Moo 2 Tiwanon Road Tumbol Bangkadee, Amphur Mueng, Pathumthani, 12000, Thailand
Tel.: (66) 25012175
Rice Product Mfr
N.A.I.C.S.: 311212

Ratchasima Rice Co., Ltd. (1)
109/2 Moo 14 Mitraparp Road 199 KM Tumbol Lardbuakhow Amphur, Sikhiu, Nakhon Ratchasima, 30340, Thailand
Tel.: (66) 44323334
Rice Product Mfr
N.A.I.C.S.: 311212

Simapac Co., Ltd. (1)
109/2 Moo 14 Mitraparp Road 199 KM Tumbol Lardbuakhow Amphur, Sikhiu, Nakhon Ratchasima, 30340, Thailand
Tel.: (66) 44323456
Rice Product Mfr
N.A.I.C.S.: 311212

PRG HOLDINGS BERHAD

Lot C601 Capital 3 Oasis Square No 2 Jalan PJU 1A/7A Ara Damansara, 47301, Petaling Jaya, Selangor, Malaysia
Tel.: (60) 378590877 MY
Web Site: https://www.prg.com.my
Year Founded: 1983
PRG—(KLS)
Rev.: $65,086,138
Assets: $102,874,709
Liabilities: $49,521,270
Net Worth: $53,353,439
Earnings: $9,126,349
Emp.: 954
Fiscal Year-end: 12/31/22
Investment Holdings & Management Services
N.A.I.C.S.: 523940
Chong Keat Yeoh (Co-Sec)

Subsidiaries:

Furnitech Components (Vietnam) Co., Ltd. (1)
Street No 2 Nhon Trach Industrial Zone I, Nhon Trach, Dong Nai, Vietnam (71.57%)
Tel.: (84) 2513560385
Web Site: http://www.furniweb.com.my
Recliner Mechanism Mfr
N.A.I.C.S.: 337126

Furniweb Manufacturing (Vietnam) Co., Ltd. (1)
no 18 Road 3A Bien Hoa Industrial Zone II, Bien Hoa, Dong Nai, Vietnam
Tel.: (84) 61 832742
Textile Products Mfr
N.A.I.C.S.: 314999

Furniweb Manufacturing Sdn. Bhd. (1)
Lot 1883 Jalan KPB 9 Kg Bharu Balakong, 43300, Seri Kembangan, Selangor Darul Ehsan, Malaysia
Tel.: (60) 389612278
Emp.: 44
Webbing & Yarn Mfr
N.A.I.C.S.: 313110

Furniweb Safety Webbing Sdn. Bhd. (1)
Lot 1883 Jalan KPB 9 Kg Bharu Balakong, 43300, Seri Kembangan, Selangor Darul Ehsan, Malaysia
Tel.: (60) 389612278
Web Site: http://www.furniweb.com
Sales Range: $25-49.9 Million
Emp.: 100
Mfr of Motor Vehicle Safety Accessories
N.A.I.C.S.: 336340

Premier Elastic Webbing & Accessories (Vietnam) Co., Ltd. (1)
Street No 8 Nhon Trach Industrial Zone I, Nhon Trach, Dong Nai, Vietnam
Tel.: (84) 61 549385
Elastic Products Mfr
N.A.I.C.S.: 314999

AND PRIVATE COMPANIES

Texstrip Manufacturing Sdn. Bhd. (1)
Lot 1908 Batu 7 Jalan Bukit Kemuning
Seksyen 34, 40470, Shah Alam, Selangor
Darul Ehsan, Malaysia
Tel.: (60) 351212662
Emp.: 40
Elastic Tape Mfr
N.A.I.C.S.: 314999

Webtex Trading Sdn. Bhd. (1)
No 47 Jalan Jalak Taman Bukit Mewah,
Cheras, 56100, Kuala Lumpur, Malaysia
Tel.: (60) 391318923
Furniture Webbing Sales
N.A.I.C.S.: 314999

PRICE STEEL LTD.
13500 156 Street, Edmonton, T5V
1L3, AB, Canada
Tel.: (780) 447-9999
Web Site: https://www.pricesteel.com
Year Founded: 1978
Rev.: $19,127,889
Emp.: 50
Steel Service Center
N.A.I.C.S.: 423510
Brenda Bauman *(VP)*

PRICECHECK TOILETRIES LIMITED
201 Upwell Street, Sheffield, S4 8AL,
South Yorkshire, United Kingdom
Tel.: (44) 114 244 0887 UK
Web Site:
  http://www.pricecheck.uk.com
Year Founded: 1978
Sales Range: $50-74.9 Million
Emp.: 70
Toiletries Whslr
N.A.I.C.S.: 424210

PRICER AB
Vastra Jarnvagsgatan 7, S-111 64,
Stockholm, Sweden
Tel.: (46) 850558200 SE
Web Site: http://www.pricer.com
PCRBF—(OTCIQ)
Rev.: $266,162
Assets: $199,346
Liabilities: $104,326
Net Worth: $95,020
Earnings: ($4,791)
Emp.: 221
Fiscal Year-end: 12/31/23
Electronic Shelf Labeling Solutions
N.A.I.C.S.: 561910
Charles Jackson *(Head-Americas Reg)*

Subsidiaries:

Pricer E.S.L. Israel Ltd. (1)
2 Levontin, 65111, Tel Aviv, Israel
Tel.: (972) 36887879
Sales Range: $25-49.9 Million
Emp.: 3
Electronic Labelling Software Development Services
N.A.I.C.S.: 541511

Pricer Inc. (1)
303 Perimeter Ctr N Ste 525, Atlanta, GA 30346
Tel.: (212) 835-1515
Web Site: http://www.pricer.com
Sales Range: $25-49.9 Million
Emp.: 2
Business Software Solutions
N.A.I.C.S.: 513210

Pricer SAS (1)
Parc Ariane - Bat Saturne 2 rue Helene
Boucher, 78280, Guyancourt, France
Tel.: (33) 16 108 4020
Web Site: https://www.pricer.com
Sales Range: $25-49.9 Million
Business Software Services
N.A.I.C.S.: 513210

PRICEWATERHOUSECOOPERS & ASSOCIADOS - SOCIEDADE DE REVISORES OFI-

CIAIS DE CONTAS, LDA.
Palacio Sottomayor Avenida Fontes
Pereira de Melo n 16, 1050-121, Lisbon, Portugal
Tel.: (351) 213 599 000 PT
Web Site: http://www.pwc.pt
Accounting & Business Consulting Services
N.A.I.C.S.: 541211

Subsidiaries:

PricewaterhouseCoopers & Associados - Sociedade de Revisores Oficiais de Contas, Lda. - Praia Branch (1)
BAI Center Building 2nd Floor Right Avenue
City of Lisbon, CP 303, Praia, Cape Verde
Tel.: (238) 261 5934
Web Site: http://www.pwc.com
Accounting, Tax & Business Consulting Services
N.A.I.C.S.: 541211

PRICEWATERHOUSECOOPERS (CAMBODIA) LTD.
58C Sihanouk Boulevard Sangkat
Tonle Bassac Khan, Chamkarmon,
Phnom Penh, 12210, Cambodia
Tel.: (855) 23860606 KH
Web Site: http://www.pwc.com
Year Founded: 1998
Sales Range: $50-74.9 Million
Emp.: 200
Accounting, Tax Preparation, Risk
Management, Business Assurance,
Human Resource, Regulatory, Operational Management & Advisory Services
N.A.I.C.S.: 541211
Boonlert Kamolchanokkul *(Partner)*

PRICEWATERHOUSECOOPERS (GHANA) LIMITED
No 12 Airport City Una Home 3rd
Floor Airport City, Accra, Ghana
Tel.: (233) 302 761 500 GH
Web Site: http://www.pwc.com
Emp.: 300
Accounting & Business Consulting Services
N.A.I.C.S.: 541211
Ayesha Bedwei *(Partner-Ghana)*

Subsidiaries:

PricewaterhouseCoopers (Ghana) Limited - Freetown Branch (1)
No 2 MIK Drive Off Barracks Road Murray Town, Freetown, Sierra Leone
Tel.: (232) 7836 1701
Accounting, Tax & Business Consulting Services
N.A.I.C.S.: 541211

PRICEWATERHOUSECOOPERS (VIETNAM) LTD.
29 Le Duan Street, District 1 Ben
Nghe Ward, Ho Chi Minh City, Vietnam
Tel.: (84) 2838230796 VN
Web Site: http://www.pwc.com
Accounting, Tax Preparation, Risk
Management, Business Assurance,
Human Resource, Regulatory, Operational Management & Advisory Services
N.A.I.C.S.: 541211
Dinh Thi Quynh Van *(Partner & Gen Dir-Tax & Legal Svcs)*

Subsidiaries:

PricewaterhouseCoopers Legal Vietnam Co., Ltd. (1)
Saigon Tower 3rd Floor 29 Le Duan Street, District 1, Ho Chi Minh City, 70000, Vietnam
Tel.: (84) 8 3823 0796
Business Consulting Services
N.A.I.C.S.: 541611

PRICEWATERHOUSECOOPERS AG
Birchstrasse 160, 8050, Zurich, Switzerland
Tel.: (41) 58 792 4400 CH
Web Site: http://www.pwc.ch
Accounting, Tax & Business Consulting Services
N.A.I.C.S.: 541211
Urs Honeggar *(CEO)*

PRICEWATERHOUSECOOPERS AG WIRTSCHAFTSPRUFUNGSGESELLSCHAFT
Friedrich-Ebert-Anlage 35-37, 60327,
Frankfurt am Main, Germany
Tel.: (49) 69 9585 0 De
Web Site: http://www.pwc.de
Accounting, Tax & Consulting Services
N.A.I.C.S.: 541211
Peter Bartels *(Member-Exec Bd-Markets)*

Subsidiaries:

PwC Strategy& (Germany) GmbH (1)
Hofgarten Palais Goltsteinstrasse 14, Dusseldorf, 40211, Germany
Tel.: (49) 211 3890 0
Web Site: http://www.strategyand.pwc.com
Management Consulting Services
N.A.I.C.S.: 541611
Klaus-Peter Gushurst *(CEO)*

PRICEWATERHOUSECOOPERS AUDIT AZERBAIJAN LLC
The Landmark Office Plaza III 12th
Floor 90A Nizami Street, Baku,
AZ1010, Azerbaijan
Tel.: (994) 12 497 2515 Az
Web Site: http://www.pwc.com
Sales Range: $25-49.9 Million
Emp.: 100
Accounting, Tax Preparation, Risk
Management, Business Assurance,
Human Resource, Regulatory, Operational Management & Advisory Services
N.A.I.C.S.: 541211
Movlan Pashayev *(Mng Partner-Azerbaijan)*

PRICEWATERHOUSECOOPERS AUDIT CALEDONIE SELARL
6 rue Jean Jaures, Noumea, New Caledonia
Tel.: (687) 28 61 00 Nc
Web Site: http://www.pwc.com
Year Founded: 2003
Accounting, Tax Preparation, Risk
Management & Business Assurance Services
N.A.I.C.S.: 541211

PRICEWATERHOUSECOOPERS AUDIT LLC
Central Tower 6th Floor Suite 601
Sukhbaatar Square 2 SBD-8, Ulaanbaatar, 14200, Mongolia
Tel.: (976) 70009089 Mn
Web Site: http://www.pwc.com
Sales Range: $25-49.9 Million
Emp.: 80
Accounting, Tax Preparation, Risk
Management, Business Assurance,
Human Resource, Regulatory, Operational Management & Advisory Services
N.A.I.C.S.: 541211
Tsendmaa Choijamts *(Exec Dir-Tax)*

Subsidiaries:

PricewaterhouseCoopers Advisory LLC (1)
Central Tower Floor 6 Suite 601 Sukhbaatar Square SDB-8, Ulaanbaatar, 14200, Mongolia
Tel.: (976) 11 329088
Business Consulting Services
N.A.I.C.S.: 541611

PRICEWATERHOUSECOOPERS AUDIT S.R.L.
Lakeview Building 301-311 Barbu Vacarescu Street, Bucharest, Romania
Tel.: (40) 212253500 RO
Web Site: http://www.pwc.ro
Accounting, Tax & Business Consulting Services
N.A.I.C.S.: 541211

PRICEWATERHOUSECOOPERS AUDIT SH.P.K.
Str Ibrahim Rugova Sky Tower 9/1
Floor, Tirana, Albania
Tel.: (355) 42 242 254 Al
Web Site: http://www.pwc.com
Year Founded: 2004
Accounting, Tax Preparation, Risk
Management, Business Assurance,
Human Resource, Regulatory, Operational Management & Advisory Services
N.A.I.C.S.: 541211
Rolanda Duro *(Office Mgr)*

PRICEWATERHOUSECOOPERS AUSTRALIA (INTERNATIONAL) PTY. LTD.
One International Towers Sydney Watermans Quay, Barangaroo, Sydney, 2000, NSW, Australia
Tel.: (61) 2 8266 0000 AU
Web Site: http://www.pwc.com.au
Emp.: 185,000
Accounting, Tax & Consulting Services
N.A.I.C.S.: 541211
Luke Sayers *(CEO)*

Subsidiaries:

PwC Strategy& (Australia) Pty. Ltd. (1)
Level 7 7 Macquarie Place, Sydney, 2000, NSW, Australia
Tel.: (61) 2 9321 1900
Sales Range: $25-49.9 Million
Emp.: 120
Management Consulting Services
N.A.I.C.S.: 541611
Vanessa Miscamble Wallace *(Sr Partner)*

PRICEWATERHOUSECOOPERS BULGARIA EOOD
9-11 Maria Louisa Blvd, 1000, Sofia, Bulgaria
Tel.: (359) 2 9355 200 BG
Web Site: http://www.pwc.bg
Year Founded: 1992
Accounting, Tax Preparation, Risk
Management, Business Assurance,
Human Resource, Regulatory, Operational Management & Advisory Services
N.A.I.C.S.: 541211
Philipp A. Hofstetter *(Mng Dir)*

Subsidiaries:

PricewaterhouseCoopers Audit OOD (1)
9-11 Maria Louisa Blvd 8th Floor, Sofia, 1000, Bulgaria
Tel.: (359) 2 9355 200
Business Consulting Services
N.A.I.C.S.: 541611
Milka Damianova *(Dir-Assurance)*

PRICEWATERHOUSECOO-

PRICEWATERHOUSECOO — INTERNATIONAL PUBLIC

PRICEWATERHOUSECOO—(CONTINUED)

PERS CESKA REPUBLIKA, S.R.O.
City Green Court Hvezdova 1734/2c,
Prague, 4, Czech Republic
Tel.: (420) 251 151 111 CZ
Web Site: http://www.pwc.com
Year Founded: 1990
Sales Range: $200-249.9 Million
Emp.: 600
Accounting, Tax Preparation, Risk Management, Business Assurance, Human Resource, Regulatory, Operational Management & Advisory Services
N.A.I.C.S.: 541211
Jiri Moser *(Mng Partner)*

Subsidiaries:

PricewaterhouseCoopers Audit, s.r.o. (1)
Namesti Svobody 20, 602 00, Brno, Czech Republic
Tel.: (420) 542 520 111
Business Consulting Services
N.A.I.C.S.: 541611
Filip Herberger *(Asst Mgr)*

PricewaterhouseCoopers Legal s.r.o. (1)
Hvezdova 1734/2c, 140 00, Prague, Czech Republic
Tel.: (420) 251 151 111
Business Consulting Services
N.A.I.C.S.: 541611

PRICEWATERHOUSECOOPERS CO., LTD.
Otemachi Park Building 1-1-1
Otemachi, Chiyoda-ku, Tokyo, 100-0004, Japan
Tel.: (81) 362126800 JP
Web Site: http://www.pwc.co.jp
Year Founded: 1999
Emp.: 1,700
Accounting, Tax Preparation, Risk Management, Business Assurance, Human Resource, Regulatory, Operational Management & Advisory Services
N.A.I.C.S.: 541211
Koichiro Kimura *(CEO)*

Subsidiaries:

PricewaterhouseCoopers Aarata LLC (1)
Sumitomo Fudosan Shiodome Hamarikyu Bldg 8-21-1 Ginza, Chuo-ku, Tokyo, 104-0061, Japan
Tel.: (81) 335468450
Web Site: http://www.pwcaarata.or.jp
Sales Range: $400-449.9 Million
Emp.: 1,969
Accounting & Auditing Services
N.A.I.C.S.: 541211

PricewaterhouseCoopers Consultants Co., Ltd. (1)
Sumitomo Fudosan Shiodome Hamarikyu Bldg 8-21-1 Ginza, Chuo-ku, Tokyo, 104-0061, Japan (100%)
Tel.: (81) 335468480
Sales Range: $400-449.9 Million
Emp.: 1,200
Business Consulting Services
N.A.I.C.S.: 541611

Subsidiary (Domestic):

PricewaterhouseCoopers PRTM Management Consultants Japan LLC (2)
Shinjuku Mitsui Building 30F 2-1-1 Nishishinjuku Shinjuku-ku, Tokyo, 163-0430, Japan
Tel.: (81) 3 5326 9090
Business Consulting Services
N.A.I.C.S.: 541611
Shimpei Yamamoto *(Dir-HR & Bus Mgr)*

PwC Strategy& Japan, Inc. (2)
Roppongi Hills Mori Tower 27th FL 6-10-1 Roppongi Minato-ku, Tokyo, 106-6127, Japan
Tel.: (81) 367578600
Web Site: http://www.strategyand.pwc.com
Management Consulting Services
N.A.I.C.S.: 541611
Vanessa Miscamble Wallace *(Chm & Sr Partner)*

PricewaterhouseCoopers IAC (1)
Kasumigaseki Building 15th Floor 2-5 Kasumigaseki 3-chome Chiyoda-ku, Tokyo, 100-0013, Japan
Tel.: (81) 3 3539 6300
Business Consulting Services
N.A.I.C.S.: 541611

PricewaterhouseCoopers Kyoto (1)
Kyoto Mitsui Building 7th Floor Shijo Karasuma, Kyoto, 600-8008, Japan
Tel.: (81) 75 241 1901
Business Consulting Services
N.A.I.C.S.: 541611

PwC Advisory Co., Ltd. (1)
Sumitomo Fudosan Shiodome Hamarikyu Bldg 8-21-1 Ginza, Chuo-ku, Tokyo, 104-0061, Japan
Tel.: (81) 335468460
Web Site: http://www.pwcadvisory.co.jp
Sales Range: $125-149.9 Million
Emp.: 470
Corporate Transaction, Valuation & Advisory Services
N.A.I.C.S.: 561499

Zeirishi-Hojin PricewaterhouseCoopers (1)
Kasumigaseki Bldg 15th Floor 3-2-5 Kasumigaseki, Chiyoda-ku, Tokyo, 100-6015, Japan
Tel.: (81) 352512400
Sales Range: $200-249.9 Million
Emp.: 560
Tax Preparation Services
N.A.I.C.S.: 541211
Kazuya Miyakawa *(CEO)*

PRICEWATERHOUSECOOPERS CONSULTANTS (SHENZHEN) LIMITED
36/F The Exchange Tower Two 189 Nanjing Road, Heping District, Tianjin, 300051, Shenzhen, China
Tel.: (86) 22 2318 3333 CN
Web Site: http://www.pwccn.com
Accounting, Tax Preparation, Risk Management, Business Assurance, Human Resource, Regulatory, Operational Management & Advisory Services
N.A.I.C.S.: 541211

Subsidiaries:

PricewaterhouseCoopers Business Consulting (Shanghai) Co., Limited (1)
26/F Office Tower A Beijing Fortune Plaza 7 Dongsanhuan Zhong Road, Chaoyang, Beijing, 100020, China
Tel.: (86) 10 6533 8888
Web Site: http://www.pwccn.com
Business Consulting Services
N.A.I.C.S.: 541611

PricewaterhouseCoopers Information Technologies (Shanghai) Co., Ltd. (1)
Building 16 No 498 Guo Shou Jing Rd Z J Hi-Tech Park Pudong New Area, Shanghai, 201203, China
Tel.: (86) 21 5080 6700
Web Site: http://www.pwccn.com
Business Consulting Services
N.A.I.C.S.: 541611
Sarah Yuan *(Dir-Fin)*

PricewaterhouseCoopers International Assignment Services (Shanghai) Limited (1)
11/F PricewaterhouseCoopers Center 2 Corporate Avenue 202 Hu Bin Road, Huangpu District, Shanghai, 200021, China
Tel.: (86) 21 2323 8888
Web Site: http://www.pwcias.com
Expatriate Compensation & Benefits, Tax Planning & Compliance, Assignment Management & Visa Services
N.A.I.C.S.: 541219

PricewaterhouseCoopers Management Consulting (Shanghai) Limited (1)
8/F DBS Bank Tower 1318 Lu Jia Zui Road, Pudong New Area, Shanghai, 200120, China
Tel.: (86) 21 2323 8888
Management Consulting Services
N.A.I.C.S.: 541611

PricewaterhouseCoopers WMS (Shanghai) Co., Ltd (1)
5/F Infinitus Tower 168 Hu Bin Road, Huangpu District, Shanghai, 200021, China
Tel.: (86) 21 2323 8888
Accounting Services
N.A.I.C.S.: 541219

PwC Strategy& (China) Co., Ltd. (1)
6/F Infinitus Tower 168 Hu Bin Road, Huangpu District, Shanghai, 200021, China
Tel.: (86) 2123232020
Web Site: http://www.strategyand.pwc.com
Management Consulting Services
N.A.I.C.S.: 541611
Huchu Xu *(Partner & Mng Dir)*

PRICEWATERHOUSECOOPERS D.O.O.
Ljudevita Posavskog 31, 10000, Zagreb, Croatia
Tel.: (385) 1 6328 888 HR
Web Site: http://www.pwc.hr
Year Founded: 1997
Sales Range: $25-49.9 Million
Emp.: 100
Accounting Tax Preparation Risk Management Business Assurance Human Resource Regulatory Operational Management & Advisory Services
N.A.I.C.S.: 541211
John Mathias Gasparac *(Mng Partner)*

PRICEWATERHOUSECOOPERS D.O.O.
Cesta v Klece 15, 1000, Ljubljana, Slovenia
Tel.: (386) 1 5836 000 SI
Web Site: http://www.pwc.com
Year Founded: 1993
Accounting, Tax & Business Consulting Services
N.A.I.C.S.: 541211

PRICEWATERHOUSECOOPERS D.O.O.
Omladinskih brigada 88a Airport City Belgrade, Belgrade, 11000, Serbia
Tel.: (381) 11 3302 100 RS
Web Site: http://www.pwc.rs
Year Founded: 2001
Sales Range: $50-74.9 Million
Emp.: 230
Accounting, Tax Preparation, Risk Management, Business Assurance, Human Resource, Regulatory, Operational Management & Advisory Services
N.A.I.C.S.: 541211
Emmanuel Koenig *(Mng Partner-Serbia)*

PRICEWATERHOUSECOOPERS D.O.O.E.L
16 8th September Blvd Hyperium Business Center 2nd Floor, 1000, Skopje, North Macedonia
Tel.: (389) 2 3140 900 MK
Web Site: http://www.pwc.com
Year Founded: 1992
Accounting, Tax & Business Consulting Services
N.A.I.C.S.: 541211

PRICEWATERHOUSECOOPERS DOO
Fra Andjela Zvizdovica 1 Tower B 12th Floor, 71000, Sarajevo, Bosnia & Herzegovina
Tel.: (387) 33821600
Web Site: http://www.pwc.ba
Year Founded: 1998
Accounting, Tax & Business Consulting Services
N.A.I.C.S.: 541211

PRICEWATERHOUSECOOPERS EHF
Skogarhlid 12, 105, Reykjavik, Iceland
Tel.: (354) 550 5300 IS
Web Site: http://www.pwc.com
Sales Range: $50-74.9 Million
Emp.: 120
Accounting, Tax Preparation, Risk Management, Business Assurance, Human Resource, Regulatory, Operational Management & Advisory Services
N.A.I.C.S.: 541211
Fridgeir Sigurdsson *(CEO)*

PRICEWATERHOUSECOOPERS FAS LTD.
15th Floor Bangkok City Tower 179/74-80 South Sathorn Road, Bangkok, 10120, Thailand
Tel.: (66) 2 344 1000 TH
Web Site: http://www.pwc.com
Sales Range: $400-449.9 Million
Emp.: 1,350
Accounting, Tax Preparation, Risk Management, Business Assurance, Human Resource, Regulatory, Operational Management & Advisory Services
N.A.I.C.S.: 541211
Sira Intarakumthornchai *(CEO)*

Subsidiaries:

PricewaterhouseCoopers Legal & Tax Consultants Ltd. (1)
15th Floor Bangkok City Tower 179/74-80 South Sathorn Road, Bangkok, 10120, Thailand
Tel.: (66) 2 344 1000
Web Site: http://www.pwc.co.th
Emp.: 1,800
Legal & Tax Consulting Services
N.A.I.C.S.: 541611
Sira Intarakumthornchai *(CEO)*

PRICEWATERHOUSECOOPERS FRANCE SARL
63 Rue de Villiers, 92200, Neuilly-sur-Seine, France
Tel.: (33) 1 5657 5859 FR
Web Site: http://www.pwc.fr
Sales Range: $800-899.9 Million
Emp.: 4,000
Accounting, Tax Preparation, Risk Management, Business Assurance, Human Resource, Regulatory, Operational Management & Advisory Services
N.A.I.C.S.: 541211
Matthieu Moussy *(Partner-Auditing)*

Subsidiaries:

PricewaterhouseCoopers Audit SAS (1)
63 rue de Villiers, 92200, Neuilly-sur-Seine, France
Tel.: (33) 156575859
Web Site: http://www.pwc.fr
Business Consulting Services
N.A.I.C.S.: 541611
Nicolas Le Moual *(Sr Mgr)*

PricewaterhouseCoopers Corporate Finance SAS (1)

AND PRIVATE COMPANIES

63 rue de Villiers, 92200, Neuilly-sur-Seine, France
Tel.: (33) 156575859
Web Site: http://www.pwc.fr
Business Consulting Services
N.A.I.C.S.: 541611
Tarique Shakir-Khalil *(Head-Corp Fin)*

PricewaterhouseCoopers Entreprises Sarl (1)
63 rue de Villiers, 92200, Neuilly-sur-Seine, France
Tel.: (33) 156575859
Web Site: http://www.pwc.fr
Business Consulting Services
N.A.I.C.S.: 541611
Areski Djaouani *(Mgr)*

PwC Strategy& France SAS (1)
140 boulevard Malesherbes, 75017, Paris, France
Tel.: (33) 1 4434 3131
Web Site: http://www.strategyand.pwc.com
Management Consulting Services
N.A.I.C.S.: 541611
Viren Doshi *(Sr Partner & Head-Energy Practice-Global)*

PRICEWATERHOUSECOOPERS HUNGARY LIMITED LIABILITY COMPANY
Bajcsy-Zsilinszky ut 78, 1055, Budapest, Hungary
Tel.: (36) 1 461 9100
Web Site: http://www.pwc.com
Year Founded: 1854
Sales Range: $200-249.9 Million
Emp.: 900
Accounting, Tax Preparation, Risk Management, Business Assurance, Human Resource, Regulatory, Operational Management & Advisory Services
N.A.I.C.S.: 541211
Arpad Balazs *(Partner-Svcs Line Reader)*

Subsidiaries:

PricewaterhouseCoopers Auditing Limited Liability Company (1)
Bajcsy-Zsilinszky ut 78, 1055, Budapest, Hungary
Tel.: (36) 1 461 9100
Business Consulting Services
N.A.I.C.S.: 541611

PRICEWATERHOUSECOOPERS INTERAMERICA, S. DE R.L.
Colonia Loma Linda Norte diagonal Gema No 1 Bloque F Calle 3, Tegucigalpa, Honduras
Tel.: (504) 2231 1911 HN
Web Site: http://www.pwc.com
Ventilation Equipment Mfr
N.A.I.C.S.: 541211

PRICEWATERHOUSECOOPERS INTERAMERICAS
Plaza PwC 7th Floor 58E Street and Ricardo Arango Avenue, Panama, Panama
Tel.: (507) 206 9200
Web Site: http://www.pwc.com
Accounting & Business Consulting Services
N.A.I.C.S.: 541211

Subsidiaries:

Price Waterhouse y Compania de El Salvador (1)
Centro Profesional Presidente Avenida La Revolucion y, Calle Circunvalacion Colonia San Benito, San Salvador, El Salvador
Tel.: (503) 2 243 5844
Accounting, Tax & Business Consulting Services
N.A.I.C.S.: 541211

PricewaterhouseCoopers Consultores, S.A. (1)
Los Yoses San Pedro de Montes de Oca De La Camara de Industrias, Costa Rica 125 al oeste, San Jose, Costa Rica
Tel.: (506) 2224 1555
Web Site: http://www.pwc.com
Accounting, Tax & Business Consulting Services
N.A.I.C.S.: 541211

PRICEWATERHOUSECOOPERS INTERNATIONAL LIMITED
1 Embankment Place, London, WC2N 6RH, United Kingdom
Tel.: (44) 2075835000 UK
Web Site: http://www.pwc.com
Year Founded: 1998
Sales Range: $25-49.9 Billion
Emp.: 284,000
Accounting, Tax Preparation, Risk Management, Business Assurance, Human Resource, Regulatory, Operational Management & Advisory Services Organization
N.A.I.C.S.: 813920

Subsidiaries:

PwC Strategy& Inc. (1)
18th Fl 101 Park Ave, New York, NY 10178
Tel.: (212) 697-1900
Web Site: http://www.strategyand.pwc.com
Sales Range: $250-299.9 Million
Emp.: 400
Management Consulting Services Organization
N.A.I.C.S.: 813920
Tony Poulter *(Chm)*

PRICEWATERHOUSECOOPERS LIMITED
14G Finance and IT Center of Macau Avenida Doutor Mario Soares No 320, Macau, China (Macau)
Tel.: (853) 8799 5111 Mo
Web Site: http://www.pwchk.com
Emp.: 61
Accounting & Business Consulting Services
N.A.I.C.S.: 541211

PRICEWATERHOUSECOOPERS LIMITED
Communications House 10th Floor 1 Colville Street, PO Box 8053, Kampala, 8053, Uganda
Tel.: (256) 41 4 236 018 UG
Web Site: http://www.pwc.com
Emp.: 200
Accounting, Tax Preparation, Risk Management, Business Assurance, Human Resource, Regulatory, Operational Management & Advisory Services
N.A.I.C.S.: 541211
Francis Kamulegeya *(Sr Partner-Uganda)*

PRICEWATERHOUSECOOPERS LIMITED
21/F Edinburgh Tower The Landmark 15 Queens Road Central, Hong Kong, China (Hong Kong)
Tel.: (852) 2289 8888 HK
Web Site: http://www.pwc.com
Emp.: 17,000
Accounting, Tax Preparation, Risk Management, Business Assurance, Human Resource, Regulatory, Operational Management & Advisory Services
N.A.I.C.S.: 541211
Silas S.S. Yang *(Partner)*

Subsidiaries:

PricewaterhouseCoopers Consulting Hong Kong Ltd. (1)
21/F Edinburgh Tower The Landmark 15 Queen's Road Central, Hong Kong, China (Hong Kong)
Tel.: (852) 2289 8888
Web Site: http://www.pwchk.com
Business Consulting Services
N.A.I.C.S.: 541611

PwC International Assignment Services (Hong Kong) Ltd. (1)
19/F Tower A Manulife Financial Centre, Hong Kong, China (Hong Kong)
Tel.: (852) 2289 8888
Web Site: http://www.pwcias.com
Expatriate Compensation & Benefits, Tax Planning & Compliance, Assignment Management & Visa Services
N.A.I.C.S.: 541219

PRICEWATERHOUSECOOPERS LIMITED
327 Main Street, Gibraltar, GX11 1AA, Gibraltar
Tel.: (350) 200 73520
Web Site: http://www.pwc.gi
Sales Range: $25-49.9 Million
Emp.: 55
Accounting, Tax Preparation, Risk Management, Business Assurance, Human Resource, Regulatory, Operational Management & Advisory Services
N.A.I.C.S.: 541211
Colin Vaughan *(Partner)*

PRICEWATERHOUSECOOPERS LLP
34 Al-Farabi Avenue Building A 4th Floor, Almaty, 050059, Kazakhstan
Tel.: (7) 727 330 3200
Accounting & Business Consulting Services
N.A.I.C.S.: 541211
Carine Schneider *(Founder)*

Subsidiaries:

PricewaterhouseCoopers Tax & Advisory LLP (1)
Kabanbay Batyr Avenue Q2 Business Center 4th Floor, Nur-Sultan, 010000, Kazakhstan
Tel.: (7) 7172 55 07 07
Accounting & Business Consulting Services
N.A.I.C.S.: 541211

PRICEWATERHOUSECOOPERS LLP (CANADA)
PwC Tower 18 York Street Ste 2600, 77 King Street West Suite 2500, Toronto, M5J 0B2, ON, Canada
Tel.: (416) 863-1133
Web Site: http://www.pwc.com
Year Founded: 1910
Sales Range: $1-4.9 Billion
Emp.: 5,200
Accounting, Tax Preparation, Risk Management, Business Assurance, Human Resource, Regulatory, Operational Management & Advisory Services
N.A.I.C.S.: 541211
Tahir Ayub *(Mng Partner-Natl-Markets & Industries)*

PRICEWATERHOUSECOOPERS LLP (UK)
1 Embankment Place, London, WC2N 6RH, United Kingdom
Tel.: (44) 2075835000 UK
Web Site: http://www.pwc.co.uk
Rev.: $5,371,761,660
Assets: $2,805,803,220
Liabilities: $1,955,559,820
Net Worth: $850,243,400
Earnings: $1,289,324,320
Emp.: 24,207
Fiscal Year-end: 06/30/19

PRICEWATERHOUSECOOPERS ME LIMITED

Accounting, Tax Preparation, Risk Management, Business Assurance, Human Resource, Regulatory, Operational Management & Advisory Services
N.A.I.C.S.: 541211
Kevin Ellis *(Chm-Mgmt Bd & Sr Partner)*

Subsidiaries:

PRPi Consulting Limited (1)
7 More London Riverside, London, SE1 2RT, United Kingdom
Tel.: (44) 20 7212 6334
Web Site: http://www.prpiconsulting.com
Business Consulting Services
N.A.I.C.S.: 541611
Charles Humble *(CTO)*

PricewaterhouseCoopers Legal LLP (1)
1 Embankment Place, London, WC2N 6DX, United Kingdom
Tel.: (44) 2072121616
Web Site: http://www.pwclegal.co.uk
Emp.: 500
Law firm
N.A.I.C.S.: 541110
Laura Cox *(Partner & Head-Fin Svcs)*

PwC Strategy& (UK) Ltd. (1)
7 Savoy Court, Strand, London, WC2R 0JP, United Kingdom
Tel.: (44) 20 7393 3333
Web Site: http://www.strategyand.pwc.com
Emp.: 150
Management Consulting Services
N.A.I.C.S.: 541611
Viren Doshi *(Sr Partner & Head-Energy Practice-Global)*

PRICEWATERHOUSECOOPERS LTD.
City House 6 Karaiskakis Street, 3032, Limassol, Cyprus
Tel.: (357) 25555000 CY
Web Site: http://www.pwc.com.cy
Accounting, Tax & Business Consulting Services
N.A.I.C.S.: 541211

Subsidiaries:

SA Evangelou & Co. LLC (1)
Julia House Annex 1st Floor 3 Themistocles Dervis Street, 1066, Nicosia, Cyprus
Tel.: (357) 22 559 999
Web Site: http://www.pwclegal.com
Emp.: 37
Business Consulting Services
N.A.I.C.S.: 541611
George Polemidiotis *(Sr Mgr)*

PRICEWATERHOUSECOOPERS LTD.
Abacus House Tropicana Plaza Leeward Highway, Providenciales, Turks & Caicos Islands
Tel.: (649) 946 4890 TC
Accounting Tax Preparation Risk Management Business Assurance Regulatory & Advisory Services
N.A.I.C.S.: 541211
Joseph Connolly *(Partner)*

PRICEWATERHOUSECOOPERS ME LIMITED
13th Floor TJ Tower Building no 683 Road no 2811 Block no 428, Seef District, Manama, Bahrain
Tel.: (973) 1 711 8800 BH
Web Site: http://www.pwc.com
Emp.: 60
Accounting, Tax Preparation, Risk Management, Business Assurance, Human Resource, Regulatory, Operational Management & Advisory Services
N.A.I.C.S.: 541211
Mudassir Zubaire *(Sr Partner)*

PRICEWATERHOUSECOOPERS MYANMAR CO., LTD

PricewaterhouseCoopers ME Limited—(Continued)

PRICEWATERHOUSECOOPERS MYANMAR CO., LTD
Unit 02 04 06 08 10 Level 11 Myanmar Centre Tower 1 No 192, Kabar Aye Pagoda Road Bahan Township, Yangon, Myanmar
Tel.: (95) 193453349   MM
Web Site: http://www.pwc.com
Year Founded: 2012
Accounting & Business Consulting Services
N.A.I.C.S.: 541211

PRICEWATERHOUSECOOPERS PVT. LTD.
1701 17th Floor Shapath V Opp Karnavati Club S G Highway, Ahmedabad, 380 051, Gujarat, India
Tel.: (91) 79 3091 7000   In
Web Site: http://www.pwc.in
Accounting, Tax Preparation, Risk Management, Business Assurance, Human Resource, Regulatory, Operational Management & Advisory Services
N.A.I.C.S.: 541211
Neil Wilson (Co-COO)

Subsidiaries:

Diamond Management & Technology Consultants Private Limited (1)
B G House - 1st Floor Number 101 Hiranandani Business Park Village, Powai Mumbai Surburban Taluka-Kurla, Mumbai, 400 076, Maharashtra, India
Tel.: (91) 22 3304 0700
Web Site: http://www.pwc.in
Business Consulting Services
N.A.I.C.S.: 541611

PRTM Management Consultants (India) Private Limited (1)
Hulkul Brigade Center 2nd & 3rd Floor South Wing No 82 Lavelle Road, Bengaluru, 560001, Karnataka, India
Tel.: (91) 80 4010 0900
Web Site: http://www.pwc.in
Emp.: 130
Business Consulting Services
N.A.I.C.S.: 541611
Bala Chandran (Gen Mgr)

PricewaterhouseCoopers Service Delivery Center (Bangalore) Pvt. Ltd. (1)
Pine Valley 4th Floor Embassy Golf Links Business Park, Challaghatta Village, Bengaluru, 560071, India
Tel.: (91) 80 4017 0300
Emp.: 1,000
Business Consulting Services
N.A.I.C.S.: 541611
Sadashiv Hegde (Gen Mgr)

PricewaterhouseCoopers Service Delivery Center (Kolkata) Pvt. Ltd. (1)
Plot No X-1/1 Block EP 13th Floor Sector V Salt Lake City, Kolkata, 700 091, West Bengal, India
Tel.: (91) 3323579260
Web Site: http://www.pwc.in
Business Consulting Services
N.A.I.C.S.: 541611
Partha Bhattacharya (Sr Mgr-Fin)

PwC Strategy& (India) Pvt. Ltd. (1)
One Indiabulls Centre Tower 1 8th Floor, 841 S B Marg Elphinstone Road, Mumbai, 400 013, India
Tel.: (91) 22 6128 1111
Web Site: http://www.strategyand.pwc.com
Emp.: 60
Management Consulting Services
N.A.I.C.S.: 541611
Jaivardhan Sinha (Partner & Mng Dir)

PRICEWATERHOUSECOOPERS RUSSIA B.V.
White Square Business Center Butyrsky Val 10, Moscow, Russia
Tel.: (7) 495 967 6000   NL
Web Site: http://www.pwc.ru
Year Founded: 1989
Sales Range: $400-449.9 Million
Emp.: 2,000
Accounting, Tax Preparation, Risk Management, Business Assurance, Human Resource, Regulatory, Operational Management & Advisory Services
N.A.I.C.S.: 541211
Igor Lotakov (Mng Partner-Russia)

Subsidiaries:

PricewaterhouseCoopers Legal CIS B.V. (1)
White Square Office Centre 10 Butyrsky Val, Moscow, 125047, Russia
Tel.: (7) 495 967 6000
Web Site: http://www.pwc.ru
Business Consulting Services
N.A.I.C.S.: 541611

PwC Strategy& LLC (1)
Butyrsky Val 10, Moscow, 125047, Russia
Tel.: (7) 495 604 4100
Web Site: http://www.strategyand.pwc.com
Emp.: 30
Management Consulting Services
N.A.I.C.S.: 541611
Alexey Khokhlov (Partner)

ZAO PricewaterhouseCoopers Audit (1)
White Square Office Center 10 Butyrsky Val, Moscow, 125047, Russia
Tel.: (7) 495 967 6000
Web Site: http://www.pwc.ru
Accounting & Auditing Services
N.A.I.C.S.: 541211

PRICEWATERHOUSECOOPERS S.A.
268 Kifissias Avenue, 15232, Halandri, Athens, Greece
Tel.: (30) 210 6874 400   GR
Web Site: http://www.pwc.com
Sales Range: $200-249.9 Million
Emp.: 800
Accounting Tax Preparation Risk Management Business Assurance Human Resource Regulatory Operational Management & Advisory Services
N.A.I.C.S.: 541211
Marios Psaltis (Mng Partner)

Subsidiaries:

PricewaterhouseCoopers Auditing Company S.A. (1)
260 Kifissias Avenue, 152 32, Halandri, Athens, Greece
Tel.: (30) 210 68 74 400
Web Site: http://www.pwc.gr
Business Consulting Services
N.A.I.C.S.: 541611

PRICEWATERHOUSECOOPERS S.P.A.
Via Monte Rosa 91, Milan, 20149, Italy
Tel.: (39) 02 77851   IT
Web Site: http://www.pwc.com
Sales Range: $800-899.9 Million
Emp.: 3,100
Accounting, Tax Preparation, Risk Management, Business Assurance, Human Resource, Regulatory, Operational Management & Advisory Services
N.A.I.C.S.: 541211

Subsidiaries:

PricewaterhouseCoopers Advisory SpA (1)
Via Don Luigi Guanella 17, 70124, Bari, Italy
Tel.: (39) 080 5640311
Business Consulting Services
N.A.I.C.S.: 541611

Elia Alessandro Manconi (Sr Mgr-Corp Fin Div)

PwC Strategy& (Italia) S.r.l. (1)
Via Monte Rosa 91, 20149, Milan, Italy
Tel.: (39) 02 72 5091
Web Site: http://www.strategyand.pwc.com
Emp.: 40
Management Consulting Services
N.A.I.C.S.: 541611
Luigi Pugliese (Mng Partner)

TLS Associazione Professionale di Avvocati e Commercialisti (1)
Via Angelo Finelli 8, 40126, Bologna, Italy
Tel.: (39) 051 616 7711
Business Consulting Services
N.A.I.C.S.: 541611
Domenico Vito (Sr Mgr-Tax)

PRICEWATERHOUSECOOPERS S.R.L.
Pasaje Villegas No 383 Ana Maria Building 1st 2nd and 3rd Floors, San Jorge, La Paz, Bolivia
Tel.: (591) 2 240 8181   BO
Web Site: http://www.pwc.com
Accounting, Tax Preparation, Risk Management, Business Assurance, Human Resource, Regulatory, Operational Management & Advisory Services
N.A.I.C.S.: 541211
Harold Aguilar Soliz (Mgr)

PRICEWATERHOUSECOOPERS SA
Immeuble Alpha 2000 2nd & 20th Floor, Rue Gourgas - Plateau, Abidjan, Cote d'Ivoire
Tel.: (225) 2031 5400   CI
Accounting Tax Preparation Risk Management Business Assurance Regulatory & Advisory Services
N.A.I.C.S.: 541211
Edouard Messou (Partner)

PRICEWATERHOUSECOOPERS SA
Avenue Amilcar Cabral Enceinte BCI siege, Brazzaville, Congo, Republic of
Tel.: (242) 6 693 01 0   CG
Web Site: http://www.pwc.com
Accounting & Business Consulting Services
N.A.I.C.S.: 541211

Subsidiaries:

PricewaterhouseCoopers Tax & Legal SA (1)
88 avenue du General de Gaulle, Pointe Noire, Congo, Republic of
Tel.: (242) 5 534 09 0
Web Site: http://www.pwc.com
Accounting & Business Consulting Services
N.A.I.C.S.: 541211
Patrice Bazolo (Sr Mgr)

PRICEWATERHOUSECOOPERS SARL
Rue Christian Tobie Kouoh Immeuble PWC Bonanjo, PO Box 5689, Douala, Cameroon
Tel.: (237) 33 43 24 44   CM
Web Site: http://www.pwc.com
Accounting, Tax Preparation, Risk Management, Business Assurance, Human Resource, Regulatory, Operational Management & Advisory Services
N.A.I.C.S.: 541211

PRICEWATERHOUSECOOPERS SARL
Rue Augustin Rajakoba Ankadivato, Antananarivo, 101, Madagascar
Tel.: (261) 20 22 217 63   MG
Web Site: http://www.pwc.com

INTERNATIONAL PUBLIC

Accounting, Tax Preparation, Risk Management, Business Assurance, Human Resource, Regulatory, Operational Management & Advisory Services
N.A.I.C.S.: 541211
Vivian Lyng (Partner)

Subsidiaries:

PricewaterhouseCoopers Conseil SA (1)
Rue Augustin Rajakoba Ankadivato, Antananarivo, 101, Madagascar
Tel.: (261) 20 22 217 63
Web Site: http://www.pwc.com
Operational Management & Advisory Services
N.A.I.C.S.: 541611

PRICEWATERHOUSECOOPERS SLOVENSKO, S.R.O.
Twin City Business Center A Karadzicova 2 Karadzicova 2, 815 32, Bratislava, Slovakia
Tel.: (421) 259 350 111   Sk
Web Site: http://www.pwc.com
Sales Range: $100-124.9 Million
Emp.: 350
Accounting, Tax Preparation, Risk Management, Business Assurance, Human Resource, Regulatory, Operational Management & Advisory Services
N.A.I.C.S.: 541211
Philipp A. Hofstetter (Mng Dir)

Subsidiaries:

PricewaterhouseCoopers Legal, s.r.o. (1)
Namestie 1 maja 18, 815 32, Bratislava, Slovakia
Tel.: (421) 259 350 111
Business Consulting Services
N.A.I.C.S.: 541611

PRICEWATERHOUSECOOPERS TAX & LEGAL SA
3 Place de l Independance Immeuble SDIH, PO Box 6454, Dakar, Senegal
Tel.: (221) 33 849 05 00   SN
Web Site: http://www.pwc.com
Accounting, Tax Preparation, Risk Management, Business Assurance, Operational Management & Advisory Services
N.A.I.C.S.: 541211

PRICEWATERHOUSECOOPERS Y CIA, S.A.
Los Yoses San Pedro de Montes de Oca de la Camara de Industrias, 125 metros al oeste, San Jose, Costa Rica
Tel.: (506) 2224 1555   CR
Web Site: http://www.pwc.com
Emp.: 200
Accounting, Tax Preparation, Risk Management, Business Assurance, Human Resource, Regulatory, Operational Management & Advisory Services
N.A.I.C.S.: 541211
Oscar Piedra (Partner)

PRICEWATERHOUSECOOPERS, S.A.
Edificio Tivoli Plaza 6a Calle 6-38 Zona 9 4to Nivel, Guatemala, Guatemala
Tel.: (502) 2420 7800   GT
Web Site: http://www.pwc.com
Accounting, Tax Preparation, Risk Management, Business Assurance, Human Resource, Regulatory, Operational Management & Advisory Services
N.A.I.C.S.: 541211

PRICEWATERHOUSECOOPERS, S.L.
Torre PwC Paseo de la Castellana 259 B, 28046, Madrid, Spain
Tel.: (34) 915 684 400 ES
Web Site: http://www.pwc.es
Accounting, Tax Preparation, Risk Management, Business Assurance, Human Resource, Regulatory, Operational Management & Advisory Services
N.A.I.C.S.: 541211
Gonzalo Sanchez *(Chm)*

Subsidiaries:

PricewaterhouseCoopers Tax & Legal Services S.L. (1)
Calle Enrique Marinas 36 Planta 5, 15009, A Coruna, Spain
Tel.: (34) 981 136 753
Web Site: http://www.pwc.es
Accounting, Tax & Business Consulting Services
N.A.I.C.S.: 541211

PricewaterhouseCoopers Asesores de Negocios S.L. (1)
Edificio Alta Diagonal Avinguda Diagonal 640 Plantas 3 4 7, 08017, Barcelona, Spain
Tel.: (34) 932 532 700
Web Site: http://www.pwc.es
Accounting, Tax & Business Consulting Services
N.A.I.C.S.: 541211

PricewaterhouseCoopers Corporate Finance, S.L. (1)
Torre PwC Paseo de la Castellana 259B, 28046, Madrid, Spain
Tel.: (34) 915 684 400
Web Site: http://www.pwc.es
Accounting, Tax & Business Consulting Services
N.A.I.C.S.: 541211

PRICEWATERHOUSE COOPERSDONGO-SORIA, GAVEGLIO Y ASOCIADOS SOCIEDAD CIVIL
Av Santo Toribio No 143 Piso 8 27, Lima, Peru
Tel.: (51) 1 211 6500
Web Site: http://www.pwc.pe
Accounting & Business Consulting Services
N.A.I.C.S.: 541211

PRICEWATERHOUSECOOPERSISLA LIPANA & CO.
29th Floor Philamlife Tower 8767 Paseo de Roxas, Makati, 1226, Philippines
Tel.: (63) 2 845 2728 PH
Web Site: http://www.pwc.com
Sales Range: $200-249.9 Million
Emp.: 650
Accounting, Tax Preparation, Risk Management, Business Assurance, Human Resource, Regulatory, Operational Management & Advisory Services
N.A.I.C.S.: 541211
Alexander B. Cabrera *(Chm & Sr Partner)*

PRICEWORTH INTERNATIONAL BERHAD
1st Floor Lot 5 Block 4 Bandar Indah Mile 4, Jalan Utara, 90000, Sandakan, Malaysia
Web Site: http://www.pwibhmalaysia.com.my
PWORTH—(KLS)
Rev.: $27,303,093
Assets: $76,132,229
Liabilities: $25,573,427
Net Worth: $50,558,802
Earnings: $3,629,560
Emp.: 351
Fiscal Year-end: 12/31/22
Wood Products Processing & Mfr
N.A.I.C.S.: 321999
Nyuk Foh Lim *(Mng Dir)*

Subsidiaries:

Sinora Sdn Bhd (1)
11KM Jalan Sinora Batu Sapi, Sandakan, Sabah, Malaysia
Tel.: (60) 89614829
Web Site: https://www.snr.com.my
Plywood & Veneer Product Mfr & Whslr
N.A.I.C.S.: 321211
Lim Nyuk Foh *(Mng Dir)*

PRICOL LIMITED
CPM Towers 109 Race Course Road, Coimbatore, 641 018, Tamil Nadu, India
Tel.: (91) 4224336000
Web Site: https://www.pricol.com
PRICOLLTD—(BOM)
Rev.: $235,375,097
Assets: $156,616,893
Liabilities: $72,175,589
Net Worth: $84,441,304
Earnings: $14,949,380
Emp.: 1,872
Fiscal Year-end: 03/31/23
Automotive Components Mfr
N.A.I.C.S.: 336110
T. G. Thamizhanban *(Officer-Compliance & Sec)*

Subsidiaries:

Pricol Corporate Services Ltd (1)
No 702/12 Avinashi Road, Papanaickenpalayam, Coimbatore, 641 037, India
Tel.: (91) 422 4332012
Web Site: http://www.pricolcorporate.com
Strategic Planning & Advisory Services
N.A.I.C.S.: 561499

Pricol Limited - PLANT I (1)
132 Ooty Main Road, Perianaickenpalayam, Coimbatore, 641 020, Tamil Nadu, India
Tel.: (91) 422 4331100
Web Site: http://www.pricol.com
Motor Vehicle Parts Mfr
N.A.I.C.S.: 336390

Pricol Limited - PLANT II (1)
Plot No 34 & 35 Sector 4 IMT Manesar, Gurgaon, 122050, India
Tel.: (91) 124 4312200
Sales Range: $100-124.9 Million
Emp.: 40
Motor Vehicle Parts Mfr
N.A.I.C.S.: 336390
K. K. Anand *(VP)*

Pricol Packing Limited (1)
SF 45 Opp Madras Oxygen Ltd Thekkupalayam Post Mettupalayam Road, Coimbatore, 641020, India
Tel.: (91) 4222696913
Web Site: http://www.pricolpack.com
Packaging Products Mfr
N.A.I.C.S.: 322220

Pricol Properties Limited (1)
109 Race Course, Coimbatore, 641018, India
Tel.: (91) 4224336000
Web Site: http://www.pricolproperty.com
Sales Range: $50-74.9 Million
Emp.: 65
Residential Property Development Services
N.A.I.C.S.: 531390

Pricol Travel Limited (1)
No 122 Appusamy Layout Road Red Fields Puliakulam, Coimbatore, 641 045, Tamil Nadu, India
Tel.: (91) 4224332922
Web Site: http://www.pricoltravel.com
Sales Range: $25-49.9 Million
Emp.: 35
Travel Management Services
N.A.I.C.S.: 561599

PRIDE-CHEM INDUSTRIES PTE LTD
2 Tuas View Lane, Singapore, 637657, Singapore
Tel.: (65) 68617641
Web Site: http://www.pridechem.com.sg
Ammonia, Copper & Water Treatment Products Mfr
N.A.I.C.S.: 325998
Raymond Lim *(Owner)*

Subsidiaries:

Pride Chem Industries Sdn Bhd (1)
Plo 232 Jalan Keluli 1, Pasir Gudang Industrial Estate, Pasir Gudang, 81700, Johor Bahru, Malaysia
Tel.: (60) 72526755
Sales Range: $50-74.9 Million
Emp.: 7
Chemical & Fertilizer Mineral Mining
N.A.I.C.S.: 212390
Lim Kaming *(Gen Mgr)*

PRIEMA METALWARENFABRIEK BV
Zuiderinslag 22, 3871 MR, Hoevelaken, Netherlands
Tel.: (31) 33 2536804
Web Site: http://www.priemabv.nl
Year Founded: 1958
Sales Range: $25-49.9 Million
Emp.: 170
Metal Drawing & Assembling Product Mfr
N.A.I.C.S.: 332999

Subsidiaries:

Breclav Production s.r.o. (1)
Bratislavska 2939, CZ 69002, Breclav, Czech Republic
Tel.: (420) 519325000
Metal Drawing, Pressing, Punching & Assembling of Products
N.A.I.C.S.: 332999

Priema Cetra BV (1)
De Nieuwe Haven 10, Hardenberg, 7772 BC, Netherlands (100%)
Tel.: (31) 523 281100
Web Site: http://www.cetra.nl
Sales Range: $10-24.9 Million
Emp.: 90
Metal Component Mfr
N.A.I.C.S.: 332119
B. J. Roesink *(Gen Mgr)*

PRIJEDORCANKA A.D.
Brezicani Bb, 79101, Prijedor, Bosnia & Herzegovina
Tel.: (387) 52339959
Web Site: https://www.prijedorcanka.com
Year Founded: 1972
PDNK—(BANJ)
Sales Range: $1-9.9 Million
Alcoholic Beverages Mfr
N.A.I.C.S.: 312130
Ljiljana Vukelic *(CEO & Exec Dir)*

PRILAM S.A.S.
Et de la rue Charcot Angle de la rue Montebello, 62200, Boulogne-sur-Mer, France
Tel.: (33) 321833356 FR
Sales Range: $10-24.9 Million
Emp.: 31
Fish & Seafood Distr
N.A.I.C.S.: 424460
Eric Lavalette *(Pres)*

PRILEPSKA PIVARNICA AD
Cane Kuzmanoski 1, 7500, Prilep, North Macedonia
Tel.: (389) 48421450
Web Site: https://prilepskapivarnica.com.mk
Year Founded: 1924
PPIV—(MAC)
Rev.: $36,486,419
Assets: $47,538,504
Liabilities: $4,248,160
Net Worth: $43,290,344
Earnings: $2,142,429
Fiscal Year-end: 12/31/23
Beverage Distr
N.A.I.C.S.: 445320

PRIM S.A.
Calle F Numero 15 Polig Industrial Numero 1, 28938, Mostoles, Madrid, Spain
Tel.: (34) 913342400
Web Site: http://www.prim.es
Sales Range: $125-149.9 Million
Emp.: 351
Hospital Supplies Distr; Real Estate Services
N.A.I.C.S.: 237210
Jose Luis Meijide Garcia *(Vice Sec)*

Subsidiaries:

Enraf Nonius Iberica, S.A. (1)
Poligono Indus N 1 Calle F N 15, 28938, Mostoles, Madrid, Spain
Tel.: (34) 902161024
Web Site: http://www.enraf.es
Sales Range: $25-49.9 Million
Emp.: 42
Physiotherapy Equipments Mfr
N.A.I.C.S.: 339112

Subsidiary (Non-US):

Enraf Nonius Iberica Portugal, LDA. (2)
Rua Aquiles Machado 5-J, 1900-077, Lisbon, Portugal
Tel.: (351) 218429330
Web Site: http://www.enraf.nonius.com
Sales Range: $25-49.9 Million
Emp.: 4
Medical Equipment Distr
N.A.I.C.S.: 423450

Establecimientos Ortopedicos Prim, S.A. (1)
Calle Conde Penalver 24, 28006, Madrid, Spain
Tel.: (34) 914011100
Web Site: http://www.eoprim.es
Sales Range: $25-49.9 Million
Emp.: 30
Orthopaedic Product Mfr
N.A.I.C.S.: 339113

Luga Suministros Medicos, S.L. (1)
Avenida de la Constitucion Parcela 221 Poligono Indus Monte Boyal, 45950, Casarrubios del Monte, Toledo, Spain
Tel.: (34) 91 818 31 40
Sales Range: $25-49.9 Million
Emp.: 58
Silicone Foot Care Products Mfr & Retailer
N.A.I.C.S.: 339113

PRIMA AFP
Calle ChinchOn 980, San Isidro, Lima, Peru
Tel.: (51) 6157272
Year Founded: 2005
Financial Investment Services
N.A.I.C.S.: 523999
Alvaro Malachowski *(Chm)*

PRIMA AGRO LIMITED
Tel.: (91) 4842551533
Web Site: https://www.primaagro.in
Year Founded: 1987
519262—(BOM)
Rev.: $1,811,902
Assets: $3,076,366
Liabilities: $1,218,413
Net Worth: $1,857,953
Earnings: $225,348
Emp.: 58
Fiscal Year-end: 03/31/23
Animal Feed Mfr
N.A.I.C.S.: 311119
Sajjan Kumar Gupta *(Chm & Mng Dir)*

PRIMA BANKA SLOVENSKO AS

PRIMA AGRO LIMITED—(Continued)

PRIMA BANKA SLOVENSKO AS
Hodzova 11, Zilina, 010 11, Slovakia
Tel.: (421) 415111111
Commercial Banking Services
N.A.I.C.S.: 522110
Jan Rollo *(Chm & CEO)*

PRIMA CONSTRUCT S.A.
30 Tabacului Street, 700445, Iasi, Romania
Tel.: (40) 742078787
Web Site:
https://www.primaconstruct.ro
Year Founded: 2002
PCTM—(BUC)
Rev.: $105,471
Assets: $778,815
Liabilities: $98,808
Net Worth: $680,007
Earnings: ($9,322)
Emp.: 3
Fiscal Year-end: 12/31/22
Building Construction Services
N.A.I.C.S.: 237990
Florea Mocanu *(Pres)*

PRIMA INDUSTRIE SPA
Via Torino Pianezza 36, 10093, Collegno, Italy
Tel.: (39) 01141031
Web Site:
https://www.primaindustrie.com
Year Founded: 1977
PRI—(ITA)
Rev.: $408,958,475
Assets: $604,738,703
Liabilities: $405,193,920
Net Worth: $199,544,783
Earnings: ($9,106,171)
Emp.: 1,735
Fiscal Year-end: 12/31/20
Laser Machines & Lasers Mfr
N.A.I.C.S.: 333248
Gianfranco Carbonato *(Chm)*

Subsidiaries:

FINN-POWER Oy (1)
Metallitie 4, PO Box 38, 62201, Kauhava, Finland
Tel.: (358) 10 278 7111
Web Site: http://www.finn-power.com
Industrial Machinery Mfr
N.A.I.C.S.: 333248
Timo Laurinen *(Mgr-Corp Comm)*

Finn-Power Italia Srl (1)
Viale Artigianato 9, 37044, Cologna Veneta, Verona, Italy
Tel.: (39) 0442 413 111
Web Site: http://www.primapower.com
Emp.: 200
Bending Machinery Mfr
N.A.I.C.S.: 333248

Finn-Power Oy (1)
Office Bldg 2 Office 2F-49 Hamriya Free Zone, PO Box 49624, Sharjah, United Arab Emirates
Tel.: (971) 65 26 1796
Web Site: http://www.finn-power.com
Industrial Machinery Mfr
N.A.I.C.S.: 333248

MATRA-Werke GmbH (1)
Dieselstrasse 6, Hainburg, 63512, Germany
Tel.: (49) 618278331
Web Site: http://www.matra.de
Sales Range: $25-49.9 Million
Emp.: 80
Hydropumps, Hydrocylinders, Telescopic Cylinders
N.A.I.C.S.: 333914

OOO Prima Industrie (1)
Ordzhonikidze Street 11 bld 1A, 115419, Moscow, Russia
Tel.: (7) 495 730 36 88
Web Site: http://www.finn-power.com
Sales Range: $25-49.9 Million
Emp.: 20
Industrial Machinery Mfr
N.A.I.C.S.: 333248

OOO Prima Power (1)
Ordzhonikidze Street 11 Bld 1A, 115419, Moscow, Russia
Tel.: (7) 4957303688
Industrial Machinery Mfr
N.A.I.C.S.: 333248

OSAI-USA LLC (1)
711 E Main St, Chicopee, MA 01020
Tel.: (413) 592-4805
Web Site: http://www.osai-usa.com
Industrial Control Mfr
N.A.I.C.S.: 335314

Subsidiary (Non-US):

OSAI-UK Ltd. (2)
Mount House Bond Avenue, Bletchley, MK1 1SF, Milton Keynes, United Kingdom
Tel.: (44) 1908 642687
Web Site: http://www.osai.co.uk
Sales Range: $25-49.9 Million
Emp.: 5
Industrial Automation Controllers Mfr
N.A.I.C.S.: 333248
Derek Morgan *(Mgr-Applications)*

PRIMA FINN-POWER CANADA Ltd. (1)
1040 Martingrove Rd Unit 11, Toronto, M9W 4W4, ON, Canada
Tel.: (416) 242-4431
Web Site: http://www.finn-power.com
Industrial Machinery Mfr
N.A.I.C.S.: 333248

PRIMA FINN-POWER CENTRAL EUROPE Spzoo (1)
Jana Masaryka 16, 58601, Jihlava, Czech Republic
Tel.: (420) 606200959
Web Site: http://www.finn-power.com
Industrial Machinery Mfr
N.A.I.C.S.: 333248
Karel Kalenda *(Gen Mgr)*

PRIMA FINN-POWER FRANCE S.A.R.L. (1)
Espace Green Parc Route de Villepecle, 91280, Saint-Pierre-du-Perray, France
Tel.: (33) 1 60 79 97 00
Web Site: http://www.primafinnpower.fr
Sales Range: $25-49.9 Million
Emp.: 20
Industrial Machinery Distr
N.A.I.C.S.: 423830
Serraila Goen *(Mgr-Sls)*

PRIMA FINN-POWER GmbH (1)
Lise-Meitner-Strasse 5, 63128, Dietzenbach, Germany
Tel.: (49) 6074 4070 0
Web Site: http://www.finn-power.de
Industrial Machinery Mfr
N.A.I.C.S.: 333248

PRIMA FINN-POWER Iberica S.L. (1)
Carrer del Primer de Maig 13-15, 08908, L'Hospitalet de Llobregat, Barcelona, Spain
Tel.: (34) 902 302 111
Web Site: http://www.finn-power.es
Emp.: 35
Metal Cutting Machinery Mfr
N.A.I.C.S.: 333517
Enrique Tallon *(Mng Dir)*

PRIMA FINN-POWER NV (1)
Leenstraat 5, Nazareth, 9810, Belgium
Tel.: (32) 9 382 9030
Web Site: http://www.finn-power.com
Machine Tool Distr
N.A.I.C.S.: 423830

PRIMA FINN-POWER UK LTD (1)
Unit 1 Phoenix Park Bayton Road, Coventry, CV7 9QN, United Kingdom
Tel.: (44) 844 499 6241
Web Site: http://www.primafinnpower.co.uk
Industrial Machinery Mfr
N.A.I.C.S.: 333248

PRIMA INDUSTRIE (BEIJING) Co. Ltd. (1)
Rm 206 Twr 1 Wainjing, Chaoyang District, Beijing, 100028, China
Tel.: (86) 10 64603085
Industrial Machinery Mfr
N.A.I.C.S.: 333248

Prima Electro Suzhou Co. Ltd. (1)
459 Xingrui Rd, Eco-Tech Devepment Zone Wujiang District, Suzhou, China
Tel.: (86) 1868 848 8605
Electronic Components Mfr
N.A.I.C.S.: 334419

Prima Electronics S.p.A. (1)
Strada Carignano 48-2, 10024, Moncalieri, Italy (100%)
Tel.: (39) 0116827211
Web Site: http://www.primaelectronics.com
Electrical Apparatus & Equipment Wiring Supplies & Construction Material Whslr
N.A.I.C.S.: 423610

Prima Finn-Power Sweden AB (1)
Moldnalsvagen 30 C, SE-41263, Gothenburg, Sweden (100%)
Tel.: (46) 31834470
Web Site: http://www.primaindustrie.com
Industrial Machinery & Equipment Whslr
N.A.I.C.S.: 423830

Prima Industrie UK Ltd. (1)
Unit 1 Phoenix Park Bayton Road, Coventry, CV7 9QN, United Kingdom (100%)
Tel.: (44) 2476 645 588
Web Site: http://www.primapower.com
Sales Range: $25-49.9 Million
Industrial Machinery & Equipment Whslr
N.A.I.C.S.: 423830

Prima North America Inc. (1)
711 E Main St, Chicopee, MA 01020 (100%)
Tel.: (413) 598-5200
Web Site: http://www.prima-na.com
Sales Range: $25-49.9 Million
Emp.: 90
Electrical Contractor
N.A.I.C.S.: 238210
Terry Vaderwert *(Head-Laserdyne)*

Prima Power Central Europe Sp. z o.o. (1)
Dutch Str 6 05-152, Czosnow, Poland
Tel.: (48) 22 201 1346
Sheet Metal Work Mfg
N.A.I.C.S.: 332322

Prima Power China Co. Ltd. (1)
Room 2006 Unit C Tower 1 Wangjing Soho, Chaoyang District, Beijing, 100028, China
Tel.: (86) 10 64603085
Web Site: http://www.prima-power.cn
Industrial Machinery Mfr
N.A.I.C.S.: 333248

Prima Power France Sarl (1)
Espace Green Parc Route de Villepecle, 91280, Saint-Pierre-du-Perray, France
Tel.: (33) 16 079 9700
Sheet Metal Work Mfg
N.A.I.C.S.: 332322

Prima Power GmbH (1)
Am Gfild 9, 85375, Neufahrn, Germany (100%)
Tel.: (49) 816579940
Web Site: http://www.primapower.com
Sales Range: $25-49.9 Million
Electrical Apparatus & Equipment Wiring Supplies & Construction Material Whslr
N.A.I.C.S.: 423610

Prima Power Iberica S.L. (1)
Poligono Gran Via Sur Calle Primer de Maig 13-15, 08908, L'Hospitalet de Llobregat, Barcelona, Spain
Tel.: (34) 90 230 2111
Sheet Metal Work Mfg
N.A.I.C.S.: 332322

Prima Power India Pvt. Ltd. (1)
Plot No A-54/55 H Block MIDC, Pimpri, Pune, 411018, Maharashtra, India
Sheet Metal Work Mfg
N.A.I.C.S.: 332322

Prima Power Laserdyne LLC (1)
8600 109th Ave N Ste 400, Champlin, MN 55316
Tel.: (763) 433-8700
Web Site: http://www.prima-na.com

INTERNATIONAL PUBLIC

Sales Range: $25-49.9 Million
Emp.: 40
Industrial Machinery Mfr
N.A.I.C.S.: 333248

Prima Power Makina Ticaret Limited Sirketi (1)
Soganlik Yeni Mah Balikesir Cad Uprise Elite Teras Evleri Gul, Blok B2A Daire 4 Kartal, Istanbul, Türkiye
Tel.: (90) 216 594 7701
Sheet Metal Work Mfg
N.A.I.C.S.: 332322

Prima Power Mexico S de R.L. de C.V. (1)
Campo Real 121 - Valle Real, 25198, Coahuila, Mexico
Tel.: (52) 1814 160 0303
Sheet Metal Work Mfg
N.A.I.C.S.: 332322

Prima Power South America Ltda (1)
Av Fuad Lutfalla 1 182 Freguesia do O, Sao Paulo, 02968-000, Brazil
Tel.: (55) 113 978 4648
Sheet Metal Work Mfg
N.A.I.C.S.: 332322

Prima Power Suzhou Co. Ltd. (1)
No 459 Xingrui Road, Wujiang Economic and Technological Development Zone, Suzhou, Jiangsu, China
Tel.: (86) 5126 322 1411
Sheet Metal Work Mfg
N.A.I.C.S.: 332322

Prima Power UK Ltd. (1)
Unit 1 Phoenix Park Bayton Road, Coventry, CV79QN, United Kingdom
Tel.: (44) 247 664 5588
Sheet Metal Work Mfg
N.A.I.C.S.: 332322

PRIMA INDUSTRIES LIMITED
Door No V/679C Industrial Development Area, Edayar, Cochin, 683 110, India
Tel.: (91) 4842551533
Web Site:
https://www.primaindustries.in
Year Founded: 1994
531246—(BOM)
Rev.: $948,603
Assets: $3,043,539
Liabilities: $353,617
Net Worth: $2,689,923
Earnings: $53,523
Emp.: 26
Fiscal Year-end: 03/31/23
Edible Oil Refinery Services
N.A.I.C.S.: 311225
Sajjan Kumar Gupta *(Mng Dir)*

PRIMA MARINE PCL
80 Soi Bangna-Trad 30 Debaratna Road, Bangna Tai Sub-District Bangna District, Bangkok, 10260, Thailand
Tel.: (66) 20160190
Web Site:
https://www.primamarine.co.th
Year Founded: 1987
PRM—(THA)
Rev.: $236,073,214
Assets: $604,740,763
Liabilities: $253,311,597
Net Worth: $351,429,166
Earnings: $64,630,817
Emp.: 1,391
Fiscal Year-end: 12/31/23
Petroleum Product Transportation Services
N.A.I.C.S.: 486910
Bowon Vongsinudom *(Chm)*

Subsidiaries:

BSC Management Seafarer Recruitment Company Limited (1)
80 Soi Bangna-Trad 30 Debaratna Rd, Bangna Tai Bangna, Bangkok, 10260, Thailand

Tel.: (66) 27469981
Web Site: https://bangkokshipcrews.com
Emp.: 12
Ticket Agency Services
N.A.I.C.S.: 561599

Big Sea Company Limited (1)
454 Rama III Rd, Bang Klo Sub- District
Bang Kho Laem District, Bangkok, 10120,
Thailand
Tel.: (66) 22922761
Web Site: https://www.bigsea.co.th
Petroleum Transportation Services
N.A.I.C.S.: 486110

N.T.L. Marine Company Limited (1)
80 Soi Bangna-Trad 30 Debaratna Road,
Bangna Tai Sub-District Bangna District,
Bangkok, 10260, Thailand
Tel.: (66) 201601904
Petroleum Transportation Services
N.A.I.C.S.: 486110

Nathalin Shipping Pte. Ltd. (1)
6 Temasek Boulevard 32-03 Suntec Tower
Four, Singapore, 038986, Singapore
Tel.: (65) 63610379
Web Site:
https://www.nathalinshipping.com.sg
Storage Tanker Transportation Services
N.A.I.C.S.: 484110

Thaioil Marine Co., Ltd. (1)
2 84 Moo 15 Old Railway Rd, Bangchak
Phrakanong, Bangkok, 10260, Thailand
Tel.: (66) 23310080
Petroleum Transportation Services
N.A.I.C.S.: 486910

PRIMA MEAT PACKERS LTD.
Shinagawa Seaside West Tower
4-12-2 Higashi-Shinagawa,
Shinagawa-Ku, Tokyo, 140-8529,
Japan
Tel.: (81) 363861800
Web Site:
https://www.primaham.co.jp
Year Founded: 1948
2281—(TKS)
Rev.: $2,964,115,690
Assets: $1,618,081,730
Liabilities: $757,373,800
Net Worth: $860,707,930
Earnings: $49,502,290
Emp.: 1,126
Fiscal Year-end: 03/31/24
Meat Product Mfr & Whlsr
N.A.I.C.S.: 311612
Naofumi Sakai *(Corp Auditor-Standing)*

Subsidiaries:

Akita Prima Foods Co., Ltd. (1)
7000 W 60th St, Chicago, IL 60638
Tel.: (773) 847-6618
Web Site: http://www.akitafoods.com
Food Distr
N.A.I.C.S.: 445110

Clean Farm Co., Ltd. (1)
400-10 Four Seasons Place, Etobicoke,
M9B 6H7, ON, Canada
Web Site: http://www.cleanfarms.ca
Environmental Services
N.A.I.C.S.: 541620

Essen House Co., Ltd. (1)
4-3-20 Kaminofukita Shingu-cho, Kasuya-gun, Fukuoka, 811-0123, Japan
Tel.: (81) 929631039
Web Site: https://www.essenhouse.co.jp
Emp.: 79
Meat Product Whlsr
N.A.I.C.S.: 424470

Hokkaido Prima Meat Packers, Ltd. (1)
17-32 Chuo 1-jo 7-chome, Atsubetsu-ku,
Sapporo, 004-8629, Hokkaido, Japan
Tel.: (81) 118924586
Web Site: https://www.hokkaido-primaham.co.jp
Emp.: 75
Meat Product Whlsr
N.A.I.C.S.: 424470

Pacific Ocean Breeding Co., Ltd. (1)
Shinagawa Seaside West Tower 7F 4-12-2
Higashishinagawa, Shinagawa-ku, Tokyo,
140-0002, Japan
Tel.: (81) 363861870
Web Site: https://taiheiyo-breeding.jp
Pork Distr
N.A.I.C.S.: 424470

Prima Management Service Co., Ltd. (1)
No 50 Sri Jayawardenapura Mw, Rajagiriya,
Colombo, Sri Lanka
Tel.: (94) 112864580
Web Site: https://www.pms.prima.com.lk
Network Services
N.A.I.C.S.: 513199

Prima System Development Co., Ltd. (1)
2F Shinagawa Seaside South Tower 4-12-1
Higashi-Shinagawa, Shinagawa-ku, Tokyo,
140-0002, Japan
Tel.: (81) 354959365
Web Site: https://www.prima-system.co.jp
Emp.: 56
Meat Product Whlsr
N.A.I.C.S.: 424470

Primaham (Thailand) Co., Ltd. (1)
Major Tower 12 Floor Soi Thonglor 10, Kh-long Tan Nuea Watthana, Bangkok, 10110,
Thailand
Tel.: (66) 21367991
Web Site: https://www.primaham-thai.com
Meat Product Whlsr
N.A.I.C.S.: 424470

Primaham Foods (Thailand) Co., Ltd. (1)
99/1 Moo 6 Bangna-Trad KM 35 Klongniyo-myatra, Bang Bo, Samut Prakan, 10560,
Thailand
Tel.: (66) 270553005
Web Site: https://www.primahamfoods-thai.com
Emp.: 500
Frozen Food Mfr
N.A.I.C.S.: 311412

Prime Delica Co., Ltd. (1)
1-7-1 Asamizodai, Minami-ku, Sagamihara,
252-0328, Kanagawa, Japan
Tel.: (81) 427020011
Web Site: https://www.primedelica.com
Emp.: 760
Grocery Product Distr
N.A.I.C.S.: 424490

Prime Foods Co., Ltd. (1)
885 American Way, Boonville, IN 47601
Tel.: (812) 897-3783
Web Site: https://www.primefoods.us
Egg Distr
N.A.I.C.S.: 424440

Primetech Corporation (1)
Koishikawa Daikoku Building 2F 1-3-25 Koi-shikawa, Bunkyo-ku, Tokyo, 112-0002, Japan
Tel.: (81) 338160851
Web Site: https://www.primetech.co.jp
Emp.: 55
Communication Equipment Technology Services
N.A.I.C.S.: 541512
Ryosuke Ogihara *(CEO)*

Swine Genetics International, Ltd. (1)
30805 595th Ave, Cambridge, IA 50046
Tel.: (515) 383-4386
Web Site: https://www.swinegenetics.com
Pig Breeding Services
N.A.I.C.S.: 112210
Nick Berry *(Pres & CEO)*

Tsukuba Food Evaluation Center Co., Ltd. (1)
635 Nakamukaihara, Tsuchiura, 300-0841,
Ibaraki, Japan
Tel.: (81) 298424953
Emp.: 38
Food Service
N.A.I.C.S.: 624210

PRIMA MODA S.A.
Ul Parafialna 27, 52-233, Wroclaw,
Poland
Tel.: (48) 713448481
Web Site:
https://www.primamoda.com.pl
Year Founded: 2007
PMA—(WAR)
Sales Range: Less than $1 Million
Footwear Whlsr
N.A.I.C.S.: 424340
Dariusz Plesiak *(CEO)*

PRIMA PLASTICS LTD.
41 National House Opp Ansa A Bldg
Saki Vihar Road, Powai, Mumbai,
400 072, India
Tel.: (91) 2228574768
Web Site:
https://www.primaplastics.com
Year Founded: 1993
530589—(BOM)
Rev.: $23,032,648
Assets: $24,985,277
Liabilities: $8,397,338
Net Worth: $16,587,938
Earnings: $2,014,412
Emp.: 342
Fiscal Year-end: 03/31/23
Plastics Product Mfr
N.A.I.C.S.: 326199
Bhaskar M. Parekh *(Chm)*

PRIMAG AG
Hansaallee 228, 40547, Dusseldorf,
Germany
Tel.: (49) 21187575820
Web Site: http://www.primag.de
Year Founded: 1998
P9R—(DEU)
Rev.: $3,807,544
Assets: $25,301,744
Liabilities: $19,406,192
Net Worth: $5,895,552
Earnings: ($982,592)
Emp.: 5
Fiscal Year-end: 03/30/20
Real Estate Services
N.A.I.C.S.: 531390
Gerd Esser *(Member-Mgmt Bd)*

PRIMARINDO ASIA INFRA-STRUCTURE TBK
Gedung Dana Pensiun-Bank Mandiri
Lt 3 A Jl Tanjung Karang No 3-4 A,
Jakarta, 10230, Indonesia
Tel.: (62) 213148331
Web Site:
https://www.primarindo.co.id
BIMA—(INDO)
Rev.: $3,993,563
Assets: $15,664,704
Liabilities: $13,602,533
Net Worth: $2,062,171
Earnings: ($2,206,374)
Emp.: 1,050
Fiscal Year-end: 12/31/20
Sport Shoe Mfr
N.A.I.C.S.: 316210
Bambang Setiyono *(Chm)*

PRIMARY CAPITAL LIMITED
Augustine House Austin Friars, London, EC2N 2HA, United Kingdom
Tel.: (44) 2079204800
Web Site:
http://www.primaryeurope.com
Sales Range: $25-49.9 Million
Emp.: 13
Privater Equity Firm
N.A.I.C.S.: 523999
Neil Wallace *(Mng Partner)*

Subsidiaries:

Guralp Systems Limited (1)
Midas House Calleva Park, Reading, Aldermaston, RG7 8EA, United Kingdom
Tel.: (44) 118 981 9056
Web Site: http://www.guralp.com
Seismological Instruments Mfr

N.A.I.C.S.: 334516
Mark Volanthen *(Mng Dir-Oil & Gas)*

Paperchase Products Limited (1)
12 Alfred Place, London, WC1E 7EB,
United Kingdom
Tel.: (44) 2074676200
Web Site: http://www.paperchase.co.uk
Sales Range: $75-99.9 Million
Stationery Products & Greeting Cards Retailer
N.A.I.C.S.: 459410
Timothy Melgund *(CEO)*

Primary Capital Partners LLP (1)
Clarence House Clarence Street, Manchester, M2 4DW, United Kingdom
Tel.: (44) 161 641 1000
Web Site: http://www.primaryeurope.com
Emp.: 15
Investment Management Service
N.A.I.C.S.: 523940
Emma-Jane Burley *(Office Mgr)*

Thompson & Morgan (UK) Limited (1)
Poplar Lane, Ipswich, IP8 3BU, Suffolk,
United Kingdom
Tel.: (44) 333 400 0033
Web Site: http://www.thompson-morgan.com
Agriculture Product Distr
N.A.I.C.S.: 424910
Paul Hansord *(Mng Dir)*

PRIMARY HEALTH PROPERTIES PLC
Fifth floor 15-16 Buckingham Street
Burdett House, London, WC2N 6DU,
United Kingdom
Tel.: (44) 2038241841
Web Site:
https://www.phpgroup.co.uk
PHP—(LSE)
Rev.: $197,684,032
Assets: $3,873,710,932
Liabilities: $1,837,266,704
Net Worth: $2,036,444,228
Earnings: $190,216,572
Emp.: 62
Fiscal Year-end: 12/31/21
Holding Company; Hospitals
N.A.I.C.S.: 551112
Harry Hyman *(CEO)*

Subsidiaries:

MedicX Fund Limited (1)
Regency Court Glategny Esplanade, Saint
Peter Port, GY1 1WW, Guernsey
Tel.: (44) 1481 732450
Web Site: http://www.medicxfund.com
Investment Fund Services
N.A.I.C.S.: 523999
David Staples *(Chm)*

Nexus Group Holdings Ltd. (1)
Alexandra House, Alexandra Terrace, Guildford, Surrey, United Kingdom
Tel.: (44) 1483306912
Web Site: http://www.nexusgroup.org.uk
Sales Range: $50-74.9 Million
Emp.: 8
Holding Company
N.A.I.C.S.: 551112

Subsidiary (Domestic):

Nexus Corporate Finance LLP (2)
Greener House, 66-68 Haymarket, London,
SW1Y 4RF, United Kingdom
Tel.: (44) 2075209067
Web Site: http://www.nexuscf.com
Emp.: 6
Corporate Financial Advisory Services
N.A.I.C.S.: 523940
Tony Brown *(Partner)*

Nexus PHP Management Limited (2)
2nd Floor Griffin House West Street, Woking, GU21 6BS, Surrey, United Kingdom
Tel.: (44) 1483749020
Web Site: http://www.phpgroup.co.uk
Sales Range: $50-74.9 Million
Real Estate Acquisition & Property Management Services

PRIMARY HEALTH PROPERTIES PLC

Primary Health Properties Plc—(Continued)
N.A.I.C.S.: 531312
Harry Hyman *(Mng Dir)*

PRIMARY OPINION LIMITED
30 Alan Turing Road Surrey Research Park, Guildford, GU2 7AA, Surrey, United Kingdom
Tel.: (44) 1483 478320
Web Site:
    http://www.primaryopinion.com
Sales Range: $1-9.9 Million
Online Legal Publisher & Marker
N.A.I.C.S.: 541613
Chantale Millard *(CEO)*

Subsidiaries:
Carbuddy Pty. Ltd. (1)
347 Flinders Ln, Melbourne, 3000, VIC, Australia
Tel.: (61) 395840118
Web Site: http://www.carbuddy.com.au
Online Car Market Services
N.A.I.C.S.: 238990

Plutolife AS (1)
Hovfaret 17B, 0275, Oslo, Norway
Tel.: (47) 23294800
Web Site: http://www.plutolife.com
Mobile Phone Applications Provider
N.A.I.C.S.: 513210
Erik Neraal *(CEO)*

PRIMAS FREEMAN FISHER LIMITED
The Whitehouse Wilderspool Business Park, Greenalls Avenue, Manchester, M3 3BZ, United Kingdom
Tel.: (44) 1928248672
Web Site: http://www.primaslaw.co.uk
Year Founded: 2013
Law firm
N.A.I.C.S.: 541110
Adam Kerr *(Mng Partner)*

PRIMAVERA CAPITAL GROUP LTD.
48/F China World Tower 3 1 Jian Guo Men Wai Avenue, Beijing, 100004, China
Tel.: (86) 10 8559 8988
Web Site: http://www.primavera-capital.com
Privater Equity Firm
N.A.I.C.S.: 523999

PRIMAX ELECTRONICS LTD.
No 669 Ruiguang Road, Neihu District, Taipei, 11492, Taiwan
Tel.: (886) 227989008 TW
Web Site: https://www.primax.com.tw
Year Founded: 1984
4915—(TAI)
Rev.: $1,978,102,610
Assets: $1,522,388,510
Liabilities: $897,888,844
Net Worth: $624,499,666
Earnings: $86,120,831
Emp.: 11,985
Fiscal Year-end: 12/31/23
Computer Peripherals, Cell Phone Spare Parts & Office Equipment Mfr & Distr
N.A.I.C.S.: 334118
Yung-Tai Pan *(Bd of Dirs & Gen Mgr/Gen Mgr-Bus Dept)*

Subsidiaries:
Polaris Electronics Inc. (1)
7020 Koll Center Pkwy Ste 136, Pleasanton, CA 94566
Tel.: (925) 249-2260
Web Site: http://www.primax.com.tw
Sales Range: $1-9.9 Million
Emp.: 15
Computer Peripheral Equipment Mfr
N.A.I.C.S.: 334118

Primax Electronics (Thailand) Co., Ltd. (1)
888/8 Moo 7, Klongkiew Sub-district Banbueng District, Chon Buri, Thailand
Tel.: (66) 924726313
Information Technology Services
N.A.I.C.S.: 541511

Primax Industries (Hong Kong) Ltd. (1)
Room 1520-21 15/F Block A Hi-Tech Industrial Centre 5-21, Pak Tin Par Street Tsuen Wan, Hong Kong, 999077, China (Hong Kong)
Tel.: (852) 2787 1192
Computer Peripheral Equipment Mfr
N.A.I.C.S.: 334118

Tymphany Acoustic Technology Europe, s.r.o. (1)
Prumyslovy Park 305, Koprivnice, 74221, Czech Republic
Tel.: (420) 556 880 500
Audio Equipment Mfr
N.A.I.C.S.: 334310
Pavel Merhout *(Mng Dir)*

PRIME ACQUISITION CORP.
No 322 Zhongshan East Road, Shijiazhuang, 050011, Hebei, China
Tel.: (86) 408 621 8345 Ky
Web Site: http://www.primeacq.com
Year Founded: 2010
PACQF—(OTCIQ)
Sales Range: $1-9.9 Million
Emp.: 2
Investment Services
N.A.I.C.S.: 523999
Diana Chia-Huei Liu *(Chm)*

PRIME ADVERTISING
Unit 13 120 West Beaver Creek Road, Richmond Hill, L4B 1L2, ON, Canada
Tel.: (416) 591-7331
Web Site: http://www.primead.com
Year Founded: 1988
Sales Range: $10-24.9 Million
Emp.: 20
Advertising Agencies
N.A.I.C.S.: 541810

PRIME ASSET VENTURES, INC.
Under Ground Floor Worldwide Corporate Center, 684-694 Shaw Boulevard, Mandaluyong, 1552, Philippines
Tel.: (63) 2 571 3902
Web Site: http://pavi.com.ph
Holding Company
N.A.I.C.S.: 551112
Manuel Villar *(Chm)*

Subsidiaries:
TVI Resource Development Phils. Inc (1)
22nd Fl Equitable PCI Bank Tower 8751 Paseo de Roxas, Makati, Metro Manila, Philippines
Tel.: (63) 27288491
Web Site: http://www.vird.com.ph
Sales Range: $50-74.9 Million
Emp.: 25
Mining Exploration Development Services
N.A.I.C.S.: 213114
Eugene T. Mateo *(Pres)*

PRIME BANK PLC.
Adamjee Court Annexe Building-2 119-120 Motijheel C/A, Dhaka, 1000, Bangladesh
Tel.: (880) 9567265
Web Site:
    https://www.primebank.com.bd
PRIMEBANK—(DHA)
Rev.: $182,733,407
Assets: $4,545,753,287
Liabilities: $4,200,822,844
Net Worth: $344,930,443
Earnings: $37,695,555
Emp.: 2,997
Fiscal Year-end: 12/31/21
Commercial, Corporate & Personal Banking Services
N.A.I.C.S.: 522110
Mohammed Shahadat Hossain *(Vice Chm)*

Subsidiaries:
PBL Exchange (UK) Ltd. (1)
16 Brick Ln, London, E1 6RF, United Kingdom
Tel.: (44) 2076500005
Web Site: http://www.pblexchange.co.uk
Money Transmission Services
N.A.I.C.S.: 522390

PBL Finance (Hong Kong) Limited (1)
Unit 1201 12/F Taurus Building No 21A and 21B Granville Road, Tsim Sha Tsui, Kowloon, China (Hong Kong)
Tel.: (852) 25292710
Web Site: http://www.pblfinance.com.hk
Commercial Banking Services
N.A.I.C.S.: 522110
Masud Uddin Ahmed *(Ops Mgr)*

Prime Bank Investment Limited (1)
Tajwar Center 5th Floor House 34 Road No 19/A, Banani, Dhaka, 1213, Bangladesh
Tel.: (880) 248810315
Web Site: https://www.pbil.com.bd
Investment Banking Services
N.A.I.C.S.: 523150
Tabarak Hossain Bhuiyan *(CEO & Mng Dir)*

Prime Bank Securities Limited (1)
Peoples Insurance Bhaban 11th Floor 36 Dilkusha C/A, Dhaka, 1000, Bangladesh
Tel.: (880) 29513396
Web Site: http://www.pbsl.com.bd
Commercial Banking Services
N.A.I.C.S.: 522110
Mortuza Ahmed *(CEO & Mng Dir)*

Prime Exchange Co. Pte Ltd. (1)
2A Desker Road 2nd Floor, Singapore, Singapore
Tel.: (65) 63924996
Web Site: http://www.primexchange.com.sg
Banking & Remittance Services
N.A.I.C.S.: 522110
Tanjil Chowdhury *(Chm)*

PRIME CAPITAL MARKET LIMITED
Plot No-18A BJB Nagar, Bhubaneswar, 751 014, Orissa, India
Tel.: (91) 674310659
Web Site:
    https://www.primecapitalmarket.com
Year Founded: 1994
Assets: $2,652,929
Liabilities: $930,201
Net Worth: $1,722,727
Earnings: ($356,373)
Fiscal Year-end: 03/31/18
Non Banking Financial Services
N.A.I.C.S.: 523999
Sushil Kumar Purohit *(Chm & Mng Dir)*

PRIME CAR MANAGEMENT S.A.
ul Polanki 4, 80 308, Gdansk, Poland
Tel.: (48) 58 340 44 00
Web Site: http://www.primecar.pl
Rev.: $141,459,335
Assets: $426,901,145
Liabilities: $316,924,573
Net Worth: $109,976,572
Earnings: $8,939,426
Emp.: 240
Fiscal Year-end: 12/31/16
Passenger Car Leasing & Rental
N.A.I.C.S.: 532112
Tomasz Jablonski *(Chm-Mgmt Bd)*

PRIME CARCARE GROUP, INC.

INTERNATIONAL PUBLIC

8400 Lawson Road Unit 1, Milton, L9T 0J8, ON, Canada
Tel.: (905) 604-7739
Web Site: http://www.speedy.com
Holding Services
N.A.I.C.S.: 551112
David Lush *(Pres & CEO)*

Subsidiaries:
Minute Muffler & Brake (1)
1600 3rd Avenue south, Lethbridge, T1J 0L2, AB, Canada
Tel.: (403) 328-8888
Web Site: http://www.minutemuffler.com
Sales Range: $25-49.9 Million
Emp.: 6
Automotive Repair Services
N.A.I.C.S.: 811198

PRIME CITY ONE CAPITAL CORP.
333 Bay St Ste 1700, Toronto, M5H 2R2, ON, Canada
Tel.: (647) 300-1581
Financial Management Services
N.A.I.C.S.: 522310
Chen Ying *(CFO)*

PRIME COMMERCIAL BANK LTD.
Kamalpokhari, Kathmandu, Nepal
Tel.: (977) 4523254 NP
Web Site:
    https://www.primebank.com.np
Year Founded: 2007
PCBL—(NEP)
Rev.: $173,551,741
Assets: $1,654,848,676
Liabilities: $1,451,215,344
Net Worth: $203,633,332
Earnings: $7,702,913
Emp.: 1,639
Fiscal Year-end: 07/16/23
Commericial Banking
N.A.I.C.S.: 522110
Rajendra Das Shrestha *(Chm)*

PRIME DRINK GROUP CORP.
901 rue des Forges, Terrebonne, Montreal, J6Y 1V2, QC, Canada
Tel.: (514) 375-5172
Web Site: https://www.prime-group.ca
Year Founded: 2015
PRME—(CNSX)
Assets: $4,195,453
Liabilities: $237,457
Net Worth: $3,957,996
Earnings: ($4,244,092)
Fiscal Year-end: 12/31/20
Holding Company
N.A.I.C.S.: 551112
Germain Turpin *(Pres & CEO)*

PRIME ELECTRONICS & SATELLITICS INC.
No 3 Ziqiang 1st Rd Zhongli Industrial Park, Chung-Li District, Taoyuan, 32063, Taiwan
Tel.: (886) 34615000
Web Site: https://www.pesi.com.tw
Year Founded: 1995
6152—(TAI)
Rev.: $71,593,215
Assets: $90,884,362
Liabilities: $41,551,717
Net Worth: $49,332,645
Earnings: ($723,340)
Emp.: 768
Fiscal Year-end: 12/31/23
Digital Satellite Communication & Wireless Consumer Electronic Products Mfr
N.A.I.C.S.: 334220
Ching-Hui Hsu *(Chm)*

PRIME ENERGY P.E. LTD.

Lehi 2 5th Floor Rishon LeZion, Tel Aviv, Israel
Tel.: (972) 793002914
Web Site: https://www.prime-nergy.com
Year Founded: 2013
PRIM—(TAE)
Rev.: $2,769,915
Assets: $75,264,357
Liabilities: $61,710,591
Net Worth: $13,553,766
Earnings: ($5,698,444)
Fiscal Year-end: 06/30/23
Renewable Energy Services
N.A.I.C.S.: 221114
Yaron Kikoz *(Chm)*

PRIME FINANCE & INVESTMENT LIMITED
PFI Tower 5th 6th floor 5657 Dilkusha Commercial Area, Dhaka, 1000, Bangladesh
Tel.: (880) 29563883
Web Site: https://www.primefinancebd.com
PRIMEFIN—(CHT)
Rev.: $5,627,267
Assets: $119,476,008
Liabilities: $86,868,438
Net Worth: $32,607,570
Earnings: ($1,640,230)
Emp.: 82
Fiscal Year-end: 12/31/21
Financial Services
N.A.I.C.S.: 522291
Mohammad Ahsan Kabir Khan *(Mng Dir)*

Subsidiaries:

Prime Finance Capital Management Limited
PFI Tower 7th Floor 56-57 Dilkusha C/A, Dhaka, 1000, Bangladesh
Tel.: (880) 29584874
Web Site: http://www.primefincap.com
Investment Banking Services
N.A.I.C.S.: 523150
Ahsan Kabir Khan *(Chm)*

PRIME FINANCIAL GROUP LIMITED
Level 17 HWT Tower 40 City Road, Southbank, 3006, VIC, Australia
Tel.: (61) 398276999 AU
Web Site: https://www.primefinancial.com.au
PFG—(ASX)
Rev.: $27,226,411
Assets: $54,833,218
Liabilities: $19,614,725
Net Worth: $35,218,492
Earnings: $2,282,768
Emp.: 190
Fiscal Year-end: 06/30/24
Financial Services & Investment Advice
N.A.I.C.S.: 523940
Simon Madder *(Co-Founder, CEO & Mng Dir)*

Subsidiaries:

Aintree Group Financial Services Pty Ltd (1)
Level 1 273 Camberwell Road, Camberwell, 3124, VIC, Australia
Tel.: (61) 39 851 7999
Web Site: https://www.aintreegroup.com.au
Accounting Services
N.A.I.C.S.: 541219
Andrea McKenna *(Dir-Communications-Marketing)*

Primestock Securities Ltd (1)
Level 17 HWT Tower40 City Road, PO Box 6105, South Yarra, Southbank, 3006, VIC, Australia
Tel.: (61) 1800317005
Web Site: https://www.primefinancial.com.au

Sales Range: $50-74.9 Million
Emp.: 25
Financial Advisory Services
N.A.I.C.S.: 523940
Mark Johnson *(Partner)*

PRIME FOCUS LIMITED
Prime Focus House Linking Road, Khar West, Mumbai, 400052, India
Tel.: (91) 2267155000
Web Site: https://www.primefocus.com
532748—(NSE)
Rev.: $356,303,220
Assets: $732,138,225
Liabilities: $684,843,705
Net Worth: $47,294,520
Earnings: ($7,663,110)
Emp.: 246
Fiscal Year-end: 03/31/21
Post-Production & Visual Effects Services
N.A.I.C.S.: 512191
Namit Malhotra *(Co-Founder)*

Subsidiaries:

DNEG North America Inc. (1)
2255 N Ontario St Ste 230, Burbank, CA 91504
Tel.: (323) 461-7887
Video Production Services
N.A.I.C.S.: 512110

DNEG PLC (1)
160 Great Portland St, Fitzrovia, London, United Kingdom
Tel.: (44) 2072685000
Video Production Services
N.A.I.C.S.: 512110

Double Negative Canada Productions Limited (1)
149 W 4th Ave False Creek, Vancouver, V5Y 4A6, BC, Canada
Tel.: (778) 372-9000
Video Production Services
N.A.I.C.S.: 512110

Prime Focus Academy of Media and Entertainment Studies Private Limited (1)
Linking Road, Khar West, Mumbai, 400054, Maharashtra, India
Tel.: (91) 8291885860
Web Site: https://www.pfames.com
Video Production Services
N.A.I.C.S.: 512110

Prime Focus London plc (1)
64 Dean Street, London, W1D 4QQ, United Kingdom (59.96%)
Tel.: (44) 2075651000
Web Site: http://www.pflplc.com
Sales Range: $25-49.9 Million
Emp.: 235
Media & Communications Services
N.A.I.C.S.: 512191
Yuval Tori *(Exec VP-Tech-EMEA)*

Subsidiary (Domestic):

Amazing Spectacles Ltd. (2)
37 Dean Street, London, W1D 4PT, United Kingdom
Tel.: (44) 2074402948
Web Site: http://www.amazingspectacles.com
Animation Post-production Services
N.A.I.C.S.: 512191

Prime Focus Visual Entertainment Services Ltd. (2)
58 Old Compton Street, London, W1D 4UF, United Kingdom
Tel.: (44) 2074372626
Sales Range: $25-49.9 Million
Emp.: 100
Motion Picture & Video Production Services
N.A.I.C.S.: 512110

VTR Media Investments Ltd. (2)
64 Dean Street, London, W1D 4QQ, United Kingdom
Tel.: (44) 20 7437 0026
Web Site: http://www.vtr.co.uk

Special Effects & Creative Design for Commercials, Music Videos & Feature Films
N.A.I.C.S.: 512110
Anshul Doshi *(Mng Dir)*

Prime Focus North America Inc. (1)
Prime Focus House 1800 N Vine St, Hollywood, CA 90028
Tel.: (323) 461-7887
Movie Post Production Services
N.A.I.C.S.: 512191

Prime Focus VFX Pacific Inc (1)
177 West 7th Avenue Unit 200, Vancouver, V5Y 1L8, BC, Canada
Tel.: (604) 733-7030
Web Site: http://www.primefocus.com
Emp.: 100
Post Production Services
N.A.I.C.S.: 512110
Rohan Desai *(CEO)*

PRIME FRESH LTD.
102 Sanskar-2 Near Ketav Petrol Pump Polytechnic Road Ambawadi, Ahmedabad, 380 015, India
Tel.: (91) 7940320244
Web Site: https://primefreshlimited.com
Year Founded: 2007
540404—(BOM)
Rev.: $11,952,701
Assets: $4,823,272
Liabilities: $1,146,202
Net Worth: $3,677,070
Earnings: $614,699
Emp.: 637
Fiscal Year-end: 03/31/23
Agro Product Mfr & Distr
N.A.I.C.S.: 311411
Jinen Ghelani *(Founder, Chm, Mng Dir & CFO)*

PRIME GLOBAL CAPITAL GROUP INCORPORATED
E-5-2 Megan Avenue 1 Block E Jalan Tun Razak, 50400, Kuala Lumpur, Malaysia
Tel.: (60) 321620773 NV
Web Site: http://www.pgcg.cc
PGCG—(OTCBB)
Rev.: $1,918,139
Assets: $44,473,281
Liabilities: $17,631,705
Net Worth: $26,841,576
Earnings: ($268,058)
Emp.: 9
Fiscal Year-end: 10/31/19
Holding Company; E-Commerce & Internet
N.A.I.C.S.: 551112
Muhamad Bin Othman Zakaria *(CEO, Interim CFO & Sec)*

PRIME HOLDING
2 Wadi El Nil St Liberty Tower, Mohandeseen, Giza, Egypt
Tel.: (20) 233005700
Web Site: https://primeholdingco.com
Year Founded: 1992
PRMH.CA—(EGX)
Sales Range: $1-9.9 Million
Investment Banking Services
N.A.I.C.S.: 523150
Mohamed Maher *(Vice Chm & CEO)*

PRIME INDUSTRIES LIMITED
Master Chambers 3rd Floor SCO 19 Feroze Gandhi Market, Ludhiana, 141 001, Punjab, India
Tel.: (91) 1615043500
Web Site: https://www.primeindustries.com
519299—(BOM)
Rev.: $923,093
Assets: $3,225,746
Liabilities: $779,871
Net Worth: $2,445,875
Earnings: $188,191

Emp.: 8
Fiscal Year-end: 03/31/23
Industrial Machinery Mfr
N.A.I.C.S.: 333248
Rajinder Kumar Singhania *(Mng Dir & Compliance Officer)*

PRIME INSURANCE COMPANY LIMITED
Unique Heights 9th Floor 117, Kazi Nazrul Islam Avenue, Dhaka, 1000, Bangladesh
Tel.: (880) 255138659
Web Site: https://www.prime-insurance.net
Year Founded: 1996
PRIMEINSUR—(CHT)
Rev.: $2,018,136
Assets: $18,394,753
Liabilities: $8,320,580
Net Worth: $10,074,173
Earnings: $907,143
Emp.: 976
Fiscal Year-end: 12/31/23
Insurance Services
N.A.I.C.S.: 524298
Enamul Haque Khan *(Sec & Sr Exec VP)*

PRIME INTELLIGENCE SOLUTIONS GROUP LIMITED
Unit A 6/F TLP 132 Nos 132-134 Tai Lin Pai Road, Kwai Chung New Territories, Hong Kong, China (Hong Kong)
Tel.: (852) 29911112 Ky
Web Site: https://primeintelligence.com.hk
Year Founded: 1999
8379—(HKG)
Rev.: $5,931,403
Assets: $12,523,442
Liabilities: $1,920,770
Net Worth: $10,602,672
Earnings: ($915,887)
Emp.: 71
Fiscal Year-end: 03/31/21
Security System Services
N.A.I.C.S.: 561621

PRIME ISLAMI LIFE INSURANCE LIMITED
Gause Pak Bhaban 13 th floor Motijheel C/A, 28/G/1 Toyenbee Circular Road, Dhaka, 1000, Bangladesh
Tel.: (880) 41070180
Web Site: https://www.primeislamilife.com
Year Founded: 2000
PRIMELIFE—(CHT)
Rev.: $14,249,599
Assets: $85,443,157
Liabilities: $11,716,149
Net Worth: $73,727,008
Earnings: $71,940,930
Fiscal Year-end: 12/31/22
Insurance Services
N.A.I.C.S.: 524298
Abdullah Zabir *(Exec VP-Underwriting & Reinsurance)*

PRIME LIFE INSURANCE COMPANY LTD.
Hattisar, PO Box No 25979, Kathmandu, Nepal
Tel.: (977) 14441414
Web Site: http://www.primelifenepal.com
Year Founded: 2007
PLIC—(NEP)
Sales Range: Less than $1 Million
Emp.: 214
Insurance Services
N.A.I.C.S.: 524298
Mandil Adhikari *(Head-IT)*

PRIME MATERIAL HANDLING EQUIPMENT LIMITED — INTERNATIONAL PUBLIC

Prime Material Handling Equipment Limited—(Continued)

PRIME MATERIAL HANDLING EQUIPMENT LIMITED
1 Canal Street, Dartmouth, B2Y 2W1, NS, Canada
Tel.: (902) 468-1210
Web Site:
https://www.primematerial.com
Year Founded: 1993
Rev.: $14,713,600
Emp.: 100
Material Handling Equipment & Service Supplier
N.A.I.C.S.: 423830

PRIME MERIDIAN RESOURCES CORP.
2110 - 650 West Georgia Street, Vancouver, V6B 4N9, BC, Canada
Tel.: (604) 862-4184
Web Site:
https://www.primemerician.com
DYD0—(DEU)
Assets: $408,592
Liabilities: $2,100,283
Net Worth: ($1,691,692)
Earnings: ($1,022,560)
Fiscal Year-end: 12/31/23
Metal Exploration Services
N.A.I.C.S.: 213114
Brian E. B. Leeners (CEO)

PRIME MINING CORP.
710 - 1030 West Georgia St, Vancouver, V6E 2Y3, BC, Canada
Tel.: (604) 428-6128
Web Site:
https://www.primeminingcorp.ca
PRYM—(OTCIQ)
Rev.: $31
Assets: $8,104,585
Liabilities: $1,458,156
Net Worth: $6,646,429
Earnings: ($8,509,490)
Fiscal Year-end: 04/30/20
Gold Mining Services
N.A.I.C.S.: 212220
Daniel J. Kunz (Pres & CEO)

PRIME OFFICE A/S
Sonder alle 6 2nd floor, 8000, Arhus, Denmark
Tel.: (45) 87338989
Web Site: https://www.primeoffice.dk
PRIMOF—(CSE)
Rev.: $27,299,562
Assets: $549,083,359
Liabilities: $373,162,015
Net Worth: $175,921,344
Earnings: $15,774,623
Emp.: 3
Fiscal Year-end: 12/31/22
Real Estate Development & Management Services
N.A.I.C.S.: 531390
Mogens Vinther Moeller (CEO)

PRIME OIL CHEMICAL SERVICE CORPORATION
5F No 131 Sec 3 Min Sheng E Rd, Taipei, 105, Taiwan
Tel.: (886) 227174347
Web Site: https://www.pocs.com.tw
Year Founded: 1978
2904—(TAI)
Rev.: $14,438,601
Assets: $63,041,268
Liabilities: $23,404,885
Net Worth: $39,636,383
Earnings: $2,132,934
Emp.: 68
Fiscal Year-end: 12/31/23
Oil Field Operating Services
N.A.I.C.S.: 213112
Yung-Chin Chen (Dir)

PRIME PEOPLE PLC
2 Harewood Place Hanover Square, London, W1S 1BX, United Kingdom
Tel.: (44) 2076297220 UK
Web Site: http://www.prime-people.co.uk
PRP—(LSE)
Rev.: $32,800,905
Assets: $14,730,232
Liabilities: $5,718,489
Net Worth: $9,011,743
Earnings: $3,205,086
Emp.: 95
Fiscal Year-end: 03/31/23
Training & Recruitment Services
N.A.I.C.S.: 561311
Peter Moore (Mng Dir)

Subsidiaries:

Macdonald & Company Property Limited (1)
True Hardword Hannover Sq, London, W1S 1BX, United Kingdom
Tel.: (44) 2076297220
Web Site:
http://www.macdonaldandcompany.com
Sales Range: $25-49.9 Million
Emp.: 50
Recruitment Consulting Services
N.A.I.C.S.: 541612
Julie Teague (Dir-South Africa)

PRIME PROPERTY BG REIT
14 Antim I Str, 1303, Sofia, Bulgaria
Tel.: (359) 28119050
Web Site:
http://www.primepropertybg.com
PPBG—(BUL)
Sales Range: Less than $1 Million
Real Estate Investment Trust Services
N.A.I.C.S.: 525990
Sava Choroleev (Chm & Co-CEO)

PRIME PROPERTY DEVELOPMENT CORPORATION LTD
501 Soni House Plot No 34 Gulmohar Road No 1 J V P D Scheme, Vile Parle W, Mumbai, 400 049, India
Tel.: (91) 2226242144
Web Site: https://www.ppdcl.com
530695—(BOM)
Rev.: $174,210
Assets: $9,873,057
Liabilities: $358,618
Net Worth: $9,514,440
Earnings: ($2,879,763)
Emp.: 9
Fiscal Year-end: 03/31/21
Real Estate Services
N.A.I.C.S.: 531210
Vishal P. Soni (Exec Dir)

PRIME ROAD POWER PUBLIC COMPANY LIMITED
1 TP & T Tower 22nd Floor Soi Vibhavadi Rangsit 19, Vibhavadi Rangsit Road Chatuchak, Bangkok, 10900, Thailand
Tel.: (66) 21058686
Web Site:
https://www.primeroadpower.com
Year Founded: 2003
PRIME—(THA)
Rev.: $30,077,859
Assets: $269,672,470
Liabilities: $201,121,230
Net Worth: $68,551,240
Earnings: ($26,046,477)
Fiscal Year-end: 12/31/23
Solar Power Plant Project
N.A.I.C.S.: 221114
Somprasong Panjalak (CEO)

PRIME SECURITIES LIMITED
1109 / 1110 Maker Chambers V, Nariman Point, Mumbai, 400021, India
Tel.: (91) 2261842525
Web Site: https://www.primesec.com
PRIMESECU—(BOM)
Rev.: $6,180,720
Assets: $11,113,830
Liabilities: $3,304,665
Net Worth: $7,809,165
Earnings: $1,120,665
Emp.: 19
Fiscal Year-end: 03/31/21
Investment Banking Services
N.A.I.C.S.: 523150
Pradip Dubhashi (Chm)

Subsidiaries:

Prime Research & Adviosry Limited (1)
1109 / 1110 11th Floor Maker Chambers V, Nariman Point, Mumbai, 400021, Maharashtra, India
Tel.: (91) 2261842525
Web Site: https://www.primeadvisory.in
Investment Banking Services
N.A.I.C.S.: 523150

PRIME STRATEGY CO., LTD.
Ogawa Bldg 10F 1-2-2 Uchikanda, Chiyoda-ku, Tokyo, 1010047, Japan
Tel.: (81) 365512995
Web Site: https://www.prime-strategy.co.jp
Year Founded: 2002
5250—(TKS)
Rev.: $6,217,930
Assets: $10,649,180
Liabilities: $1,446,360
Net Worth: $9,202,820
Earnings: $1,311,650
Fiscal Year-end: 11/30/23
Software Development Services
N.A.I.C.S.: 541511
Kengyu Nakamura (Pres)

PRIME SYSTEM KZ LTD.
Office 2805 Emerald Towers 10 Kunayev Str, Nur-Sultan, 010000, Kazakhstan
Tel.: (7) 7172610117
Web Site: http://www.primesystem.kz
Year Founded: 2012
Construction & Engineering Services
N.A.I.C.S.: 237990

Subsidiaries:

Todini Costruzioni Generali S.p.A. (1)
Via Aurelia 477, 00165, Rome, Italy (100%)
Tel.: (39) 06909721
Web Site: http://www.todini.it
Construction & Engineering Services
N.A.I.C.S.: 237990
Roberto Converti (CEO)

PRIME URBAN DEVELOPMENT INDIA LIMITED
Door No 164/18 Maruthachalapuram Main Road Opp Ration Office, 60 Feet Road, Tirupur, 641603, Tamil Nadu, India
Tel.: (91) 4214242062
Web Site: https://www.ptlonline.com
Year Founded: 1936
521149—(BOM)
Rev.: $1,573,838
Assets: $2,972,280
Liabilities: $3,177,495
Net Worth: ($205,216)
Earnings: ($57,143)
Emp.: 5
Fiscal Year-end: 03/31/23
Cotton Yarn & Woven Fabric Mfr
N.A.I.C.S.: 313110
Purusottam Das Patodia (Chm & Mng Dir)

PRIME US REIT
1 Raffles Place No 40-01, Singapore, 048616, Singapore
Tel.: (65) 69518090 SG
Web Site:
https://www.primeusreit.com
Year Founded: 2018
OXMU—(SES)
Rev.: $159,803,000
Assets: $1,444,110,000
Liabilities: $730,455,000
Net Worth: $713,655,000
Earnings: ($115,837,000)
Emp.: 6
Fiscal Year-end: 12/31/23
Real Estate Investment Trust Services
N.A.I.C.S.: 531190
Goo Liang Yin (Controller-Fin)

PRIMECH HOLDINGS LTD.
23 Ubi Crescent, Singapore, 408579, Singapore
Tel.: (65) 62861868 SG
Web Site:
https://www.primechholdings.com
Year Founded: 2020
PMEC—(NASDAQ)
Rev.: $72,524,000
Assets: $45,509,000
Liabilities: $30,450,000
Net Worth: $15,059,000
Earnings: ($3,223,000)
Emp.: 2,744
Fiscal Year-end: 03/31/24
Holding Company
N.A.I.C.S.: 551112
Kin Wai Ho (Chm)

PRIMECITY INVESTMENT PLC
Artemidos and Nikou Dimitriou 54 B, 6027, Larnaca, Cyprus
Tel.: (357) 30887088192
Web Site: http://www.prime-city.com
ALPCI—(EUR)
Sales Range: $50-74.9 Million
Real Estate Support Services
N.A.I.C.S.: 531390
Philipp von Bodman (CEO)

PRIMEDIA LIMITED
Primedia Place 6th Floor 5 Gwen Lane, Sandown, Sandton, 2196, South Africa
Tel.: (27) 115063000
Web Site: http://www.primedia.co.za
Year Founded: 1994
Sales Range: $300-349.9 Million
Emp.: 2,605
Media Advertising & Content Services
N.A.I.C.S.: 541840
Phumzile Langeni (Chm)

Subsidiaries:

Book4golf (Pty) Ltd (1)
Primovie House, 185 Katherine Street, Eastgate Ext 4, Sandton, South Africa
Tel.: (27) 114457999
Web Site: http://www.book4golf.co.za
Call-Center & Online Golf Reservation Services
N.A.I.C.S.: 561599

ComutaNet (Pty) Ltd. (1)
ComutaNet House Maxwell Drive, Cnr Witkoppen Road, Sandton, 2193, South Africa (100%)
Tel.: (27) 118072111
Web Site: http://www.comutanet.co.za
Sales Range: $25-49.9 Million
Emp.: 150
Media Advertising Services
N.A.I.C.S.: 541840

MEGAPRO Marketing (Pty) Ltd (1)
Media City 1st floor 2 Pybus Road, 2196, Sandton, South Africa (100%)
Tel.: (27) 113059800
Web Site: http://www.megapro.co.za

Sales Range: $25-49.9 Million
Emp.: 30
Sports Marketing Company
N.A.I.C.S.: 541613
George Rautenbach *(Chm)*

PrimeTalent Pty Limited (1)
5 Gwen Lane, Sandton, South Africa
Tel.: (27) 115063163
Web Site: http://www.primedia.co.za
Human Resource Consulting Services
N.A.I.C.S.: 541612

Primedia Broadcasting (1)
Suit 7D Somerset Square Highfield Rd,
Cape Town, 8001, South Africa
Tel.: (27) 21 446 4700
Radio Broadcasting Services
N.A.I.C.S.: 516210
Karl Gostner *(Gen Mgr)*

Primedia Limited - Spectrum Division (1)
Unit 3 15 Indianapolis Street Kyalami Business Park, Kyalami, Johannesburg, South Africa
Tel.: (27) 116916900
Web Site: http://www.spectrum.tv
Emp.: 20
Advertising Services
N.A.I.C.S.: 541850

Primedia Online (Pty) Ltd (1)
Upper East Side Phase 2 6th Floor 31 Brickfield Road, Woodstock, 7925, Cape Town, South Africa
Tel.: (27) 214866900
Web Site: http://www.primediaonline.co.za
Emp.: 32
Digital Publishing Services
N.A.I.C.S.: 323111
Tanja Lategan *(CEO)*

Primedia Outdoor (Pty) Limited (1)
Entrance 5 4th Floor Falconview House Constantia Office Park, Roodepoort, 1709, South Africa (75%)
Tel.: (27) 114751419
Web Site: http://www.primeoutdoor.co.za
Sales Range: $25-49.9 Million
Emp.: 200
Outdoor Advertising Services
N.A.I.C.S.: 541890
Dave Roberts *(CEO)*

Primedia Unlimited (1)
Media City 2 Pybus Road, Sandton, South Africa
Tel.: (27) 115626666
Web Site: http://www.primedia-unlimited.co.za
Emp.: 100
Advertising Services
N.A.I.C.S.: 541850
Ryan Williams *(CEO)*

Ster-Kinekor Theatres (1)
185 Katherine Street Eastgate Ext 4, Sandton, South Africa
Tel.: (27) 861668437
Web Site: http://www.sterkinekor.com
Emp.: 1,300
Theater Operator
N.A.I.C.S.: 512131
Bradley Knowles *(Gen Mgr-Mktg)*

WideOpen Platform (Pty) Limited (1)
148 Bree Street Mirial Makeea St, Newtown Precinct, 2001, Johannesburg, South Africa (100%)
Tel.: (27) 118322800
Web Site: http://www.wideopenplatform.com
Sales Range: $25-49.9 Million
Emp.: 50
Outdoor Advertiser
N.A.I.C.S.: 541850

XProcure Ltd. (1)
Media City, 2 Fl 2 Pybus Rd, Sandton, 2146, South Africa
Tel.: (27) 115626500
Web Site: http://www.xprocure.co.za
Emp.: 30
Pharmaceutical Industry Electronic Procurement & Advertising
N.A.I.C.S.: 541890

PRIMELINE ENERGY HOLDINGS INC.
Parkview House Fourteen South Audley Street, Mayfair, London, W1K 1HN, United Kingdom
Tel.: (44) 560 372 0861
Web Site: http://www.primelineenergy.com
Year Founded: 1993
PEH—(TSXV)
Sales Range: $50-74.9 Million
Emp.: 21
Oil & Gas Exploration Services
N.A.I.C.S.: 213114
Victor Hwang *(Chm & Pres)*

Subsidiaries:

Primeline Energy China Limited (1)
Suite 1209 Tower 3 Chang Ning Raffles City 1193 Changning Road, Shanghai, 200051, China
Tel.: (86) 2164686462
Construction Services
N.A.I.C.S.: 236220

PRIMEMOVERS EQUITY (S) PTE. LTD.
Six Battery Road 03-01, Singapore, 049909, Singapore
Tel.: (65) 96164484
Web Site:
https://www.primemoversequity.com
Privater Equity Firm
N.A.I.C.S.: 523999

Subsidiaries:

Eng Teknologi Holdings Bhd. (1)
Plot 69-70 Pesara Kampung Jawa Bayan Lepas Industrial Zone, 11900, Bayan Lepas, Penang, Malaysia
Tel.: (60) 46166122
Web Site: http://www.engtek.com
Sales Range: $150-199.9 Million
Emp.: 2,400
Engineering Solutions & Services
N.A.I.C.S.: 541330
Sook Fun Thum *(Sec)*

Subsidiary (Non-US):

Altum Precision Co., Ltd. (2)
146 Moo 1 Hi-Tech Industrial Estate Asia-Nakornsawan Road T.Banlane, A.Bangpa-in, Ayutthaya, 13160, Thailand (100%)
Tel.: (66) 35729100
Web Site: http://www.engtek.com
Automotive Mechanical Components Mfr
N.A.I.C.S.: 336310

Subsidiary (Domestic):

Altum Precision Sdn. Bhd. (2)
Plo 185 Jalan Siber 9 Kawasan Perindustrian Senai IV, 81400, Senai, Johor, Malaysia
Tel.: (60) 75989928
Web Site: http://www.altumjb.com.my
Automated Die Castings Mfr
N.A.I.C.S.: 331523

Eng Teknologi Sdn. Bhd. (2)
Plot 69-70 Pesara Kampung Jawa Bayan Lepas Industrial Zone, 11900, Bayan Lepas, Penang, Malaysia (100%)
Tel.: (60) 46166122
Web Site: http://www.engtek.com
Precision Components Mfr & Distr
N.A.I.C.S.: 332721
YS Teh *(Mng Dir)*

Subsidiary (Non-US):

Engtek (Thailand) Co., Ltd. (2)
2/6 Moo 5 Rojana Industrial Park Rojana Road, Ayutthaya, 13210, Thailand
Tel.: (66) 35719579
Electronic Components Mfr
N.A.I.C.S.: 334416

Engtek International Limited (2)
16/F Flat 1612 Cheung Fung Industrial Building, 23-39 Pak Tin Par Street, Tsuen Wan, China (Hong Kong)
Tel.: (852) 24024618
Precision Machined Components Mfr
N.A.I.C.S.: 339999

Engtek Precision Philippines, Inc. (2)
L10 Phase II-A Special Export Processing Zone II, Carmelray Industrial Park I, Calamba, 4027, Laguna, Philippines
Tel.: (63) 495491748
Precision Engineering Components Mfr
N.A.I.C.S.: 335999

Subsidiary (Domestic):

Selekta Inovatif (M) Sdn. Bhd. (2)
800 Jalan Perindustrian Bukit Minyak, Kawasan Perindustrian, Bukit Mertajam, 14000, Penang, Malaysia
Tel.: (60) 45023688
Sales Range: $25-49.9 Million
Emp.: 50
Magnet Plates Mfr
N.A.I.C.S.: 332999

PRIMEPULSE SE
Promenadeplatz 12, 80333, Munich, Germany
Tel.: (49) 89 24 881 4280
Web Site: http://www.primepulse.de
Holding Company
N.A.I.C.S.: 551112
Klaus Weinmann *(Co-Founder & CEO)*

Subsidiaries:

AL-KO Kober SE (1)
Ichenhauser Str 14, 89359, Kotz, Germany
Tel.: (49) 822135510
Web Site: http://www.al-ko.com
Sales Range: $750-799.9 Million
Emp.: 4,000
Chassis & Trailer Automotive Conversion for Motor Home Industrial Trailer Caravan Accessory & Garden Care Accessory Distr
N.A.I.C.S.: 423830
Stefan Kober *(Chm-Supervisory Bd)*

Subsidiary (Domestic):

AL-KO AIR Technology Co. Ltd. (2)
Hauptstrasse 248 - 250, 89343, Jettingen, Germany
Tel.: (49) 8225390
Automobile Parts Distr
N.A.I.C.S.: 423120

Subsidiary (Non-US):

AL-KO Automotive Parts Manufacturing (Ningbo) Co. Ltd. (2)
Room 1005 10th floor 81 Nanshan Road, 315500, Fenghua, Zhejiang, China
Tel.: (86) 51253996666
Automobile Parts Mfr
N.A.I.C.S.: 336320

AL-KO ESPANA S.A.U. (2)
Autovia de Logrono Km 13 Pol Ind El Aguila, Utebo, 50180, Zaragoza, Spain
Tel.: (34) 976462280
Automobile Parts Distr
N.A.I.C.S.: 423120

AL-KO KOBER AB (2)
Stalverksgatan 20, Box 9088, 400 92, Gothenburg, Sweden
Tel.: (46) 578280
Automobile Parts Distr
N.A.I.C.S.: 423120
Johan Widbom *(Mgr-Sls)*

AL-KO KOBER G.m.b.H./S.r.l. (2)
Via G Verdi 23, Vandoies, 37060, Bolzano, Italy
Tel.: (39) 0399329311
Automobile Parts Distr
N.A.I.C.S.: 423120

AL-KO KOBER Ltd. (2)
South Warwickshire Business Park Kineton Road, Southam, CV47 0AL, Warwickshire, United Kingdom
Tel.: (44) 1926818500
Automobile Parts Distr
N.A.I.C.S.: 423120

AL-KO KOBER SIA (2)
Viskalu iela 11, 1026, Riga, Latvia
Tel.: (371) 26568757
Automobile Parts Distr
N.A.I.C.S.: 423120

AL-KO KOBER Slovakia Spol. S.R.O. (2)
Horny dvor 2/1514, 900 27, Bernolakovo, Slovakia
Tel.: (421) 245994112
Automobile Parts Distr
N.A.I.C.S.: 423120

AL-KO KOBER Sp.z.o.o. (2)
Wysogotowo ul Bukowska 10, 62-081, Przezmierowo, Poland
Tel.: (48) 618161925
Automobile Parts Distr
N.A.I.C.S.: 423120

AL-KO Kft. (2)
Haraszti u 122/a, 2351, Alsonemedi, Hungary
Tel.: (36) 29537050
Automobile Parts Distr
N.A.I.C.S.: 423120
Zsolt Baranyai *(Mng Dir)*

AL-KO Record S.A. (2)
Ctra Durango - Elorrio 25, 48220, Abadiano, Biscay, Spain
Tel.: (34) 946215740
Automobile Parts Distr
N.A.I.C.S.: 423120

AL-KO S.A.S. (2)
365 rue des industries, BP 99, Branges, 71501, Louhans, Cedex, France
Tel.: (33) 385763500
Automobile Parts Distr
N.A.I.C.S.: 423120

AL-KO TRAILCO (Pty.) Ltd. (2)
67-91 Nathan Road, Dandenong South, 3175, VIC, Australia
Tel.: (61) 397673700
Automobile Parts Distr
N.A.I.C.S.: 423120
Ralf Dreithaler *(Mng Dir)*

AL-KO Teknoloji ve Arac Ltd. Sti. (2)
Barbaros Mah Kayacan Sok No 10/A Yenisahra, Atasehir, 34746, Istanbul, Turkiye
Tel.: (90) 2164700070
Automobile Parts Distr
N.A.I.C.S.: 423120

Subsidiary (US):

AL-KO USA, Inc. (2)
21611 Protecta Dr, Elkhart, IN 46516-9543
Tel.: (574) 294-6651
Web Site: http://www.al-ko.us
Axles & Brakes Mfr
N.A.I.C.S.: 336350
Micha Harzenetter *(Pres)*

OOO AL-KO KOBER (2)
21608 Protecta Dr, Elkhart, IN 46516
Tel.: (574) 294-6651
Automobile Parts Distr
N.A.I.C.S.: 423120

Subsidiary (Non-US):

ZAO AL-KO St. Petersburg GmbH (2)
ul Krylenko 3 korp 2 lit Ja, 193230, Saint Petersburg, Russia
Tel.: (7) 8124461075
Automobile Parts Distr
N.A.I.C.S.: 423120

PRIMESERV GROUP LIMITED
25 Rudd Road Illovo, Sandton, 2196, South Africa
Tel.: (27) 116918000
Web Site:
https://www.primeserv.co.za
PMV—(JSE)
Rev.: $42,519,408
Assets: $13,064,143
Liabilities: $3,742,752
Net Worth: $9,321,391
Earnings: $1,003,496
Fiscal Year-end: 03/31/23
Education, Business Training & Employment Services
N.A.I.C.S.: 561311
David L. Rose *(Chm)*

Subsidiaries:

Primeserv ABC Recruitment (Proprietary) Limited (1)

PRIMESERV GROUP LIMITED

Primeserv Group Limited—(Continued)

Suite 316 First Floor Block 3 Island Office Park 37 Island Circle, Riverhorse Valley, Durban, 4098, Kwazulu-Natal, South Africa
Tel.: (27) 312632249
Web Site:
 http://www.primeservoutsourcing.co.za
Recruitment Services
N.A.I.C.S.: 561311
James W. Fulton (Branch Mgr)

Primeserv Denverdraft (Proprietary) Limited (1)
25 Rudd Road, Illovo, Sandton, 2196, Gauteng, South Africa
Tel.: (27) 116918000
Web Site: http://www.primeserv.co.za
Emp.: 75
Human Resource Consulting Services
N.A.I.C.S.: 541612
Ric Pedlar (Dir)

Primeserv Staff Dynamix (Proprietary) Limited (1)
25 Rudd Road, Illovo, Sandton, 2196, South Africa
Tel.: (27) 116918000
Web Site: http://www.primeserv.co.za
Recruitment Services
N.A.I.C.S.: 561311

PRIMETON INFORMATION TECHNOLOGIES, INC.
4F No 456 Bibo Road, Pilot Free Trade Zone, Shanghai, 200120, China
Tel.: (86) 2158331900
Web Site: http://www.primeton.com
Year Founded: 2003
688118—(SHG)
Rev.: $59,720,053
Assets: $143,322,693
Liabilities: $21,088,712
Net Worth: $122,233,981
Earnings: $170,993
Fiscal Year-end: 12/31/22
Information Technology Services
N.A.I.C.S.: 541512
Yadong Liu (Chm & Gen Mgr)

PRIMETOWN PROPERTY GROUP INC
UNIT 2807 Century Citadel Inn Makati 5007 P Burgos St, Makati, Philippines
Tel.: (63) 751 1957
Year Founded: 1989
Real Estate Services
N.A.I.C.S.: 531390
Gilbert Y. Yap (Treas)

PRIMEWEST MORTGAGE INVESTMENT CORPORATION
307 Jessop Avenue, Saskatoon, S7N 1Y5, SK, Canada
Tel.: (306) 955-1002
Web Site: http://www.primewest.ca
Mortgage Banking Services
N.A.I.C.S.: 522310
Marlene Kaminsky (CEO & CFO)

PRIMEWEST PTY. LTD.
Level 1 307 Murray Street, Perth, WA, Australia
Tel.: (61) 08 93217133
Web Site: http://www.primewest.biz
Real Estate Property Fund Manager
N.A.I.C.S.: 531390
John Bond (Exec Dir)

Subsidiaries:

Primewest Agrichain Management Pty Ltd (1)
Level 1 307 Murray Street, Perth, 6000, WA, Australia (100%)
Tel.: (61) 893217133
Manager of Trust
N.A.I.C.S.: 525920

PRIMEX CORPORATION
Ground Floor Richbelt Terraces 19 Annapolis Street, Green Hills, San Juan, 1502, Manila, Philippines
Tel.: (63) 7228078 PH
Web Site: https://www.primex.ph
Year Founded: 1986
PRMX—(PHI)
Rev.: $12,651,216
Assets: $60,462,515
Liabilities: $27,170,922
Net Worth: $33,291,593
Earnings: $3,096,830
Fiscal Year-end: 12/31/20
Real Estate Services
N.A.I.C.S.: 531390
Ernesto O. Ang (Chm & Pres)

PRIMIX B.V.
Nijverheidsweg 17-f, 3641 RP, Mijdrecht, Netherlands
Tel.: (31) 297287778
Web Site: http://www.primix.com
Hardware Product Mfr
N.A.I.C.S.: 332510
D. Bleeker (Gen Dir)

PRIMO MECHANICAL INC.
15 253 Jevlan Drive, Woodbridge, L4L 7Z6, ON, Canada
Tel.: (905) 851-6718
Web Site:
 http://www.primomechanical.com
Year Founded: 1975
Rev.: $20,795,000
Emp.: 80
Residential Mechanical Contractor
N.A.I.C.S.: 623990
Leo Agozzino (Pres)

PRIMO NUTRACEUTICALS, INC.
Suite 440 890 West Pender St, Vancouver, V6C 1J9, BC, Canada
Cannabis Product Mfr
N.A.I.C.S.: 325411
Richard Cindric (Founder & CEO)

PRIMOCO UAV SE
Vypadova 1563/29f, 15300, Prague, Czech Republic
Tel.: (420) 603469606
Web Site: https://www.uav-stol.com
Year Founded: 2015
PRIUA—(PRA)
Rev.: $26,719,402
Assets: $17,572,183
Liabilities: $2,234,912
Net Worth: $15,337,271
Earnings: $10,216,963
Emp.: 56
Fiscal Year-end: 12/31/23
Aircraft Mfr
N.A.I.C.S.: 336411
Ladislav Semetkovsky (Co-Founder, Chm & CEO)

PRIMORSKO CLUB PLC
Tel.: (359) 55030008
PRMC—(BUL)
Sales Range: Less than $1 Million
Resort Operator
N.A.I.C.S.: 721110
Elena Atanasova (Dir-Investor Relations)

PRIMORUS INVESTMENTS PLC
48 Chancery Lane, London, WC2A 1JF, United Kingdom
Tel.: (44) 2081547909 UK
Web Site:
 https://www.primorusinvestment.com
PRIM—(AIM)
Rev.: $117,395
Assets: $9,664,226
Liabilities: $138,854
Net Worth: $9,525,372
Earnings: ($1,873,264)
Emp.: 3
Fiscal Year-end: 12/31/22
Investment Services
N.A.I.C.S.: 523999
Rupert Labrum (Chm)

PRIMSOTSBANK PJS SCBP
D 44 Guerrilla Avenue, 690106, Vladivostok, Russia
Tel.: (7) 4232424242
Web Site: http://www.pskb.com
Year Founded: 1993
Sales Range: Less than $1 Million
Mortgage Banking Services
N.A.I.C.S.: 522292

PRIMUS FINANCIAL HOLDINGS LTD.
1101 Nine Queen's Road Central, Central, China (Hong Kong)
Tel.: (852) 28100299 HK
Web Site: http://www.primus.com
Sales Range: $25-49.9 Million
Emp.: 21
Privater Equity Firm
N.A.I.C.S.: 523999
Robert R. Morse (Chm, Co-CEO & Mng Dir)

PRINCE GEORGE MOTORS LTD
1331 Central St W, Prince George, V2M 3E2, BC, Canada
Tel.: (250) 562-9374
Web Site: http://www.pgmotors.ca
Sales Range: $50-74.9 Million
Emp.: 85
Automobile Dealers
N.A.I.C.S.: 441110
Bob Cassie (Mgr-Fleet & Comml)

PRINCE HOUSING & DEVELOPMENT CORP.
8F No 398 Sec 1 Zhonghua E Rd, East Dist, T'ainan, 701, Taiwan
Tel.: (886) 62821155
Web Site: https://www.prince.com.tw
2511—(TAI)
Rev.: $277,485,486
Assets: $1,512,503,687
Liabilities: $663,014,462
Net Worth: $849,489,225
Earnings: $19,130,350
Emp.: 1,757
Fiscal Year-end: 12/31/23
Office Building & Housing Construction
N.A.I.C.S.: 236220
Bryan Jun-Liang Lin (CFO)

Subsidiaries:

Ta-Chen Construction & Engineering Corp. (1)
7F-1 No 560 Sector 4 Jhongsiao East Road Sinyi District, Taipei, 110, Taiwan
Tel.: (886) 227588687
Web Site: http://www.ta-chen.com.tw
Architectural Design Services
N.A.I.C.S.: 541310

PRINCE OF WALES COUNTRY CLUB S.A.
Las Aranas 1901, PO Box 13281 C-21, La Reina, Santiago, Chile
Tel.: (56) 227575700
Web Site: https://www.pwcc.cl
Year Founded: 1925
COUNTRY-A—(SGO)
Sales Range: Less than $1 Million
Sports & Recreation Activity Services
N.A.I.C.S.: 713940
Juan Carlos Castro Silva (CEO)

INTERNATIONAL PUBLIC

PRINCE RESOURCE CORP.
115 1925-18th Avenue N. E., Calgary, T2E 7T8, AB, Canada
Tel.: (403) 230-3089
PNR.H—(TSX)
Sales Range: Less than $1 Million
Fuel Oil Distr
N.A.I.C.S.: 457210
Tammy Ho (CEO)

PRINCE RUPERT PORT AUTHORITY
200-215 Cow Bay Rd, Prince Rupert, V8J 1A2, BC, Canada
Tel.: (250) 627-8899
Web Site: http://www.rupertport.com
Sales Range: $1-9.9 Million
Emp.: 76
Port Operations
N.A.I.C.S.: 488310
Bud Smith (Chm)

Subsidiaries:

Prince Rupert Grain Limited (1)
1300 Ridley Island Rd, Prince Rupert, V8J 1A2, BC, Canada
Tel.: (250) 627-8777
Web Site: http://www.rupertport.com
Grain Shipping Terminal Operator
N.A.I.C.S.: 493130
Richard Forssell (Superintendent)

PRINCESS AUTO LTD
475 Panet Rd, Winnipeg, R3C 2W7, MB, Canada
Tel.: (204) 667-4630
Web Site:
 http://www.princessauto.com
Sales Range: $200-249.9 Million
Emp.: 1,500
Automobile Products Retailer
N.A.I.C.S.: 441330
Bob Tallman (Pres)

PRINCESS PRIVATE EQUITY HOLDING LIMITED
Tudor House Le Bordage, Saint Peter Port, GY1 1BT, Guernsey
Tel.: (44) 1481730946 GY
Web Site: https://www.princess-privateequity.net
Year Founded: 1999
PEYA—(DEU)
Rev.: $51,048,681
Assets: $1,153,367,922
Liabilities: $1,080,963,683
Net Worth: $72,404,239
Earnings: $51,029,915
Emp.: 1,951
Fiscal Year-end: 12/31/23
Investment Management Service
N.A.I.C.S.: 523940
Richard Battey (Chm)

PRINCETON HOLDINGS LIMITED
705 Fountain Street North, PO Box 1510, Cambridge, N1R 5T2, ON, Canada
Tel.: (519) 650-6363
Web Site:
 https://www.princetonholdings.com
Holding Company; Insurance & Risk Management Services
N.A.I.C.S.: 551112
Maureen Cowan (Chm)

PRINCIPAL CAPITAL COMPANY PUBLIC COMPANY LIMITED
23rd Floor Bangkok Business Center Building 29 Sukhumvit 63, Klongton Nua Wattana, Bangkok, 10110, Thailand
Tel.: (66) 20092015

AND PRIVATE COMPANIES

Web Site:
https://www.principalcapital.co.th
Year Founded: 2000
PRINC—(THA)
Rev.: $148,227,566
Assets: $522,055,271
Liabilities: $242,758,569
Net Worth: $279,296,701
Earnings: ($21,319,116)
Emp.: 3,922
Fiscal Year-end: 12/31/23
Real Estate Development Services
N.A.I.C.S.: 531390
Krittavith Lertutsahakul *(Chm, Vice Chm & Mng Dir)*

Subsidiaries:

Principal Healthcare Co., Ltd.   (1)
29 Bangkok Business Center Building 23rd Floor Sukhumvit Soi 63, Sukhumvit Road Khlong Tan Nuea Subdistrict Watthana District, Bangkok, 10110, Thailand
Tel.: (66) 27142173
Web Site: https://www.princhealth.com
Healthcare Services
N.A.I.C.S.: 621610

Subsidiary (Domestic):

Pitsanuloke Medical Co., Ltd.   (2)
211 Khun Phirenthorathep Road, Nai Muang Subdistrict Muang Phitsanulok District, Amphur Muang, 65000, Phitsanulok, Thailand
Tel.: (66) 55909000
Hospital Services
N.A.I.C.S.: 622110

PRINCIPAL TECHNOLOGIES INC.
700 W Georgia Street Ste 2500, Vancouver, V7Y 1B3, BC, Canada
Tel.: (587) 225-2599
Web Site: https://principal-technologies.com
Year Founded: 2018
JO7—(DEU)
Rev.: $14,650
Assets: $1,103,647
Liabilities: $322,544
Net Worth: $781,104
Earnings: ($1,152,580)
Fiscal Year-end: 07/31/24
Business Consulting Services
N.A.I.C.S.: 541611
Peter Mckeown *(CFO)*

PRINOTH FRANCE
Parc D'' Activites D Alpespace Voie Galilee, PO Box 16, Francin, 73800, Montmelian, France
Tel.: (33) 479847676
Web Site: http://www.fr.prinoth.com
Rev.: $28,400,000
Emp.: 31
Professional Equipment
N.A.I.C.S.: 423490
Denis Ribot *(Gen Mgr)*

PRINSIRI PUBLIC COMPANY LIMITED
244 Watcharon Road Tharang Subdistrict, Bangkhen, Bangkok, 10230, Thailand
Tel.: (66) 202289889
Web Site: https://projecta.prinsiri.com
Year Founded: 2000
PRIN—(THA)
Rev.: $66,764,371
Assets: $359,257,693
Liabilities: $205,002,653
Net Worth: $154,255,040
Earnings: $7,449,499
Fiscal Year-end: 12/31/23
Real Estate Agents & Brokerage Services
N.A.I.C.S.: 531210
Woraphat Tothanakasem *(Chm)*

PRINT MAIL LOGISTICS LIMITED
33 Innovation Drive, Dowsing Point, Hobart, 7010, TAS, Australia
Tel.: (61) 3 6220 8444
Web Site: http://www.pml.com.au
Rev.: $4,769,010
Assets: $3,170,913
Liabilities: $3,542,360
Net Worth: ($371,447)
Earnings: ($387,150)
Emp.: 35
Fiscal Year-end: 06/30/17
Mailing, Digital Printing, Data Management & Off-Set Printing Services
N.A.I.C.S.: 561431
Nigel B. Elias *(Mng Dir)*

PRINT N ETCH PTE. LTD.
996 Bendemeer Road 07 06, Singapore, 339944, Singapore
Tel.: (65) 6291 0698
Web Site: http://www.pne.com.sg
Year Founded: 2000
Holding Company
N.A.I.C.S.: 551112
Kong Heng Tan *(Chm)*

Subsidiaries:

PNE Benelux BV   (1)
Industrieweg Oost 21, 6662 NE, Elst, Netherlands
Tel.: (31) 481 365 665
Web Site: http://www.pne-benelux.nl
Electronic Components Distr
N.A.I.C.S.: 423690
Alex Aalmers *(Mng Dir)*

PNE Industries Ltd   (1)
996 Bendemeer Road 07-06, Singapore, 339944, Singapore
Tel.: (65) 62910698
Web Site: https://www.pne.com.sg
Rev.: $40,542,301
Assets: $62,462,319
Liabilities: $9,968,946
Net Worth: $52,493,373
Earnings: $570,325
Emp.: 776
Fiscal Year-end: 09/30/2023
Contract Manufacturing & Trading Services
N.A.I.C.S.: 236115
Koon Chwee Tan *(Exec Mng Dir)*

Subsidiary (Non-US):

Hong Nam Industry (M) Sdn Bhd   (2)
Plot 97 Jalan PKNK 1/6 Rancang Industrial Park Taman Ria Raya, 08000, Sungai Petani, Kedah, Malaysia
Tel.: (60) 44421807
Sales Range: $75-99.9 Million
Emp.: 400
Metal Products Mfr
N.A.I.C.S.: 332119
Pua Kai Chek *(Gen Mgr)*

PNE Electric Sdn Bhd   (2)
Lot 119 Jalan Firma 1 Kawasan Perindustrian Tebrau, 81100, Johor Bahru, Johor, Malaysia
Tel.: (60) 73544999
Sales Range: $100-124.9 Million
Emp.: 400
Electronic & Electrical Appliances Mfr
N.A.I.C.S.: 238990

PNE Precision Sdn Bhd   (2)
27-29 Jalan Gemilang 3 Taman Perindustrian Cemerlang, Ulu Tiram, 81800, Johor Bahru, Malaysia
Tel.: (60) 78616823
Web Site: http://www.pne.com.sg
Metal Stamping Mfr
N.A.I.C.S.: 332119

PNE Systems Sdn Bhd   (2)
No 3 Jalan SS26/13 Taman Mayang Jaya, Petaling Jaya, 47301, Selangor, Malaysia
Tel.: (60) 3 7803 7488
Web Site: http://www.pnesys.com.my
Emp.: 20
Lighting Product Distr
N.A.I.C.S.: 423610

Subsidiary (Domestic):

PNE Translite Pte Ltd   (2)
996 Bendemeer Road 07-06, Singapore, 339944, Singapore
Tel.: (65) 62910698
Web Site: http://www.pne.com.sg
Sales Range: $25-49.9 Million
Emp.: 20
Lighting Fixtures Whslr
N.A.I.C.S.: 423220

PNE International LLC   (1)
15220 NW Laidlaw Rd Ste 200, Portland, OR 97229
Tel.: (503) 439-6400
Electronic Components Distr
N.A.I.C.S.: 423690

Sen Yue Holdings Limited   (1)
3 Jalan Pesawat, Singapore, 619361, Singapore
Tel.: (65) 62689593
Web Site: https://www.senyueholdings.com
Rev.: $132,199,777
Assets: $46,135,462
Liabilities: $40,157,609
Net Worth: $5,977,852
Earnings: ($3,378,323)
Fiscal Year-end: 09/30/2020
Metal & Electrical Components Mfr & Distr
N.A.I.C.S.: 334419
Gim Kiong Neo *(CEO)*

Subsidiary (Non-US):

PNE Micron (Kuala Lumpur) Sdn Bhd   (2)
Lot 19 Jln Jaya Setia 26/3 Sector 26 Hicom Ind, Shah Alam, 40400, Malaysia
Tel.: (60) 3 5191 3236
Metal Plating Services
N.A.I.C.S.: 332812

Subsidiary (Domestic):

PNE Micron Engineering Pte Ltd   (2)
996 Bendemeer Road 07-06, Singapore, Singapore
Tel.: (65) 62910698
Web Site: http://www.pne.com.sg
Metal Stamping Mfr
N.A.I.C.S.: 332119

Subsidiary (Non-US):

PNE Micron Engineering Sdn Bhd   (2)
16 Jalan Mahir 5 Taman Perindustrian Cemerlang, Ulu Tiram, Johor Bahru, 81800, Johor, Malaysia
Tel.: (60) 78616823
Web Site: http://www.senyueholdings.com
Sales Range: $25-49.9 Million
Emp.: 100
Industrial Engineering Services
N.A.I.C.S.: 541330

PRINTNET, INC.
10-7 Jonancho, Kagoshima, 892-0835, Japan
Tel.: (81) 5037346495
Web Site: https://printnet.jp
Year Founded: 1968
7805—(TKS)
Printing Product Distr
N.A.I.C.S.: 424110
Yoichi Odawara *(Chm & Pres)*

PRINTUS FACHVERTRIEB FUR BUROBEDARF GMBH
Carl-Zeiss-Strasse 1, 77656, Offenburg, Germany
Tel.: (49) 781 607 130
Web Site: http://www.printus.de
Sales Range: $200-249.9 Million
Emp.: 800
Officer Supplies Retailer & Electronic Shopping
N.A.I.C.S.: 424120
Hans R. Schmid *(Member-Mgmt Bd)*

PRINTWORKS LTD.
3850 98 Street, Edmonton, T6E 3L2, AB, Canada
Tel.: (780) 452-8921
Web Site: http://www.printworksprint.com
Year Founded: 1984
Rev.: $20,020,524
Emp.: 80
Printing Services
N.A.I.C.S.: 323111
Darryl Smith *(Pres)*

PRINX CHENGSHAN HOLDINGS LTD.
No 98 Nanshan North Road, Rongcheng, Shandong, China
Tel.: (86) 4006188899   Ky
Web Site: http://www.prinxchengshan.com
Year Founded: 1976
1809—(HKG)
Rev.: $1,144,534,061
Assets: $1,401,998,317
Liabilities: $776,955,910
Net Worth: $625,042,408
Earnings: $55,292,609
Emp.: 6,144
Fiscal Year-end: 12/31/22
Automobile Parts Mfr & Distr
N.A.I.C.S.: 326211
Baozhen Che *(CEO)*

PRINZ VON PREUSSEN CAPITAL LTD. AD
Ulitsa Graf Ignatiev 24 1st Floor, Sofia, 1000, Bulgaria
Tel.: (359) 29801251
Web Site: http://www.pvp-capital.com
Real Estate Services
N.A.I.C.S.: 531210

PRIO-VNESHTORGBANK PAO
Ul Esenina D 82/26, 390023, Ryazan, Russia
Tel.: (7) 4912244900
Web Site: http://www.priovtb.com
Year Founded: 1989
Sales Range: Less than $1 Million
Mortgage Banking Services
N.A.I.C.S.: 522292
Ganishin Roman Viktorovich *(Chm-Mgmt Bd)*

PRIORTECH LTD.
PO Box 631, Migdal, 2310502, Israel
Tel.: (972) 46544300   II
Web Site: http://www.priortech.co.il
Sales Range: $100-124.9 Million
Emp.: 450
Holding Company
N.A.I.C.S.: 551112
Rafi Amit *(Chm & Pres)*

Subsidiaries:

Camtek Ltd.   (1)
Ramat Gavriel Ind Zone, PO Box 544, Migdal Ha'Emeq, 23150, Israel   (61.9%)
Tel.: (972) 46048100
Web Site: https://www.camtek.com
Rev.: $320,909,000
Assets: $677,087,000
Liabilities: $292,985,000
Net Worth: $384,102,000
Earnings: $79,949,000
Emp.: 446
Fiscal Year-end: 12/31/2022
Automated Optical Inspection System Mfr
N.A.I.C.S.: 333310
Rafi Amit *(Chm & CEO)*

Subsidiary (Non-US):

Camtek Europe SA   (2)
Avenue Reine Astrid 59, 1780, Wemmel, Belgium
Tel.: (32) 27328808
Web Site: http://www.camtek.co.il
Automated Optical Inspection Systems & Related Products Sales & Service
N.A.I.C.S.: 333310

Camtek Hong Kong Ltd.   (2)

PRIORTECH LTD.

Priortech Ltd.—(Continued)

4404 Bldg Hopewell, Wanchai, China (Hong Kong)
Tel.: (852) 26327645
Web Site: http://www.priortech.co.il
Sales Range: $25-49.9 Million
Emp.: 14
Automated Optical Inspection Systems & Related Products Sales & Service
N.A.I.C.S.: 333310

Camtek Imaging Technology (Su-zhou) Co., Ltd (2)
No A Factory Building Kezhi Road 1 Zhongxin Technology Block, 215000, Suzhou, Jiangsu, China
Tel.: (86) 512 6288 3033
Optical Inspection System Distr
N.A.I.C.S.: 423460
Jenny Wang (Deputy Gen Mgr)

Camtek Japan Ltd. (2)
5F-48 Sanno Bridge 2-5-6 Sanno, Ota-ku, Tokyo, 143-0023, Japan
Tel.: (81) 337745066
Web Site: http://www.camtek.co.il
Automated Optical Inspection System & Related Product Mfr
N.A.I.C.S.: 333310

Camtek Korea Co., Ltd. (2)
1101 103dong SK Ventium 522 Dangjung dong, Gunpo, 15850, Kyungki do, Korea (South)
Tel.: (82) 314518440
Web Site: http://www.camtek.co.il
Emp.: 20
Automated Optical Inspection Systems & Related Products Sales & Service
N.A.I.C.S.: 333310
Y. S. Kang (Dir-Sls)

Camtek South East Asia Pte Ltd. (2)
77 Science Park Dr Ste 04-09/10 CINTECH III, Singapore Science Park 1, Singapore, 118256, Singapore
Tel.: (65) 67733317
Web Site: http://www.camtek.co.il
Sales Range: $25-49.9 Million
Emp.: 7
Automated Optical Inspection Systems & Related Products Sales & Service
N.A.I.C.S.: 333310

Camtek Taiwan Ltd. (2)
5F-6 No 66 Section 2 Nan Kan Road, Luzhu Shiang, Taoyuan, 338, Taiwan
Tel.: (886) 33113532
Web Site: http://www.camtek.co.il
Emp.: 32
Automated Optical Inspection Systems & Related Products Sales & Service
N.A.I.C.S.: 333310

Subsidiary (US):

Camtek USA, Inc. (2)
2000 Wyatt Dr Ste 4, Santa Clara, CA 95054
Tel.: (408) 986-9954
Web Site: http://www.camtek.com
Sales Range: $25-49.9 Million
Emp.: 30
Semiconductor & Related Devices Mfr & Distr
N.A.I.C.S.: 334413
Tommy Weiss (VP-Sls & Mktg-Microelectronics & Pkg Div)

PRISM CONSTRUCTION LTD.

201 - 1525 Cliveden Avenue, Delta, V3M 6L2, BC, Canada
Tel.: (604) 526-3731
Web Site:
  https://www.prismconstruction.ca
Construction Services
N.A.I.C.S.: 236220
Alex Manzi (Project Mgr)

PRISM FINANCE LTD.

301 Iscon Mall above Star India Bazar Satellite Road, Ahmedabad, 380015, Gujarat, India
Tel.: (91) 7926763503
Web Site:
  https://www.prismfinance.in

Year Founded: 1994
531735—(BOM)
Rev.: $173,383
Assets: $2,202,494
Liabilities: $46,496
Net Worth: $2,155,998
Earnings: ($479,743)
Emp.: 2
Fiscal Year-end: 03/31/23
Financial Services
N.A.I.C.S.: 523999
Palak D. Parekh (Compliance Officer & Sec)

PRISM JOHNSON LIMITED

305 Laxmi Niwas Apartments, Ameerpet, Hyderabad, 500016, India
Tel.: (91) 4023400218
Web Site:
  https://www.prismjohnson.in
Year Founded: 1992
500338—(NSE)
Rev.: $866,227,635
Assets: $881,383,230
Liabilities: $663,592,020
Net Worth: $217,791,210
Earnings: $5,999,175
Emp.: 5,170
Fiscal Year-end: 03/31/22
Cement Mfr
N.A.I.C.S.: 327310
Aneeta S. Kulkarni (Sec)

Subsidiaries:

Raheja QBE General Insurance Company Limited (1)
Ground Floor P & G Plaza Cardinal Gracious Road Chakala, Andheri East, Mumbai, 400 099, Maharashtra, India
Tel.: (91) 2241715050
Web Site: http://www.rahejaqbe.com
General Insurance Services
N.A.I.C.S.: 524126

PRISM MEDICO & PHARMACY LIMITED

Suketi Road, Sirmour, Kala Amb, 173030, Himachal Pradesh, India
Tel.: (91) 01725020762
Web Site:
  http://www.prismmedico.com
Year Founded: 2002
512217—(BOM)
Rev.: $2,288,228
Assets: $2,940,491
Liabilities: $1,176,100
Net Worth: $1,764,391
Earnings: ($17,746)
Fiscal Year-end: 03/31/21
Medical Equipment Distr
N.A.I.C.S.: 423450
Gursimran Singh (CFO)

PRISM RESOURCES, INC.

3552 West 41st Avenue, PO Box 71030, Vancouver, V6N 4J9, BC, Canada
Tel.: (604) 803-4883
Web Site:
  https://www.prismresourcesinc.com
Year Founded: 1969
PRS—(TSXV)
Assets: $88,274
Liabilities: $1,722,551
Net Worth: ($1,634,277)
Earnings: ($330,656)
Fiscal Year-end: 12/31/20
Metal Exploration Services
N.A.I.C.S.: 213114
Robert William Baxter (Pres & CEO)

PRISM SOUND LIMITED

The Old School High Street, Stretham, CB6 3LD, Cambridgeshire, United Kingdom
Tel.: (44) 1353648888

Web Site:
  http://www.prismsound.com
Year Founded: 1987
Sales Range: $10-24.9 Million
Emp.: 50
Audio Equipment Mfr
N.A.I.C.S.: 334310
Graham Boswell (Co-Founder)

Subsidiaries:

Prism Media Products Inc (1)
45 Pine St Ste 1, Rockaway, NJ 07866
Tel.: (973) 983-9577
Web Site: http://www.prismsound.com
Emp.: 4
Audio Equipment Distr
N.A.I.C.S.: 423990
Janice Norton (Gen Mgr)

Studio Audio & Video Ltd (1)
The Old School, High Street, Stretham, CB6 3LD, Cambridgeshire, United Kingdom
Tel.: (44) 1353648888
Web Site: http://www.sadie.com
Audio Equipment Mfr
N.A.I.C.S.: 334310
Graham Boswell (Dir-Sls & Mktg)

PRISMA CAPITAL LTDA.

Avenida Brigadeiro Faria Lima 2601 11th andar, Jardim Paulistano, CEP 01452-000, Sao Paulo, SP, Brazil
Tel.: (55) 11 4858 3744 BR
Web Site:
  http://www.prismacapital.com.br
Year Founded: 2017
Alternative Investment Private Equity Firm
N.A.I.C.S.: 523999

PRISMA EXPLORATION INC.

750 West Pender Street Suite 401, Vancouver, V6C 2T7, BC, Canada
Tel.: (604) 428-7050 BC
Year Founded: 2018
PMS—(CNSX)
Assets: $261,205
Liabilities: $16,639
Net Worth: $244,566
Earnings: ($47,908)
Fiscal Year-end: 12/31/21
Mineral Exploration Services
N.A.I.C.S.: 212220
Brent Hahn (CEO)

PRISMAFLEX INTERNATIONAL SA

309 Route de Lyon CS 50001, Haute Rivoire, 69610, Lyon, France
Tel.: (33) 474706800 FR
Web Site:
  https://www.prismaflex.com
Year Founded: 1988
ALPRI—(EUR)
Sales Range: $25-49.9 Million
Outdoor Media Products; Printing Services
N.A.I.C.S.: 541850
Pierre-Henri Bassouls (Co-Founder)

Subsidiaries:

DISTEC GmbH (1)
Gladbacher Strasse 65, 52525, Heinsberg, Germany
Tel.: (49) 2452964724
Digital Printing Services
N.A.I.C.S.: 323111

Prismaflex AB (1)
Vastanvagen, 245 42, Staffanstorp, Sweden
Tel.: (46) 406646300
Digital Printing Services
N.A.I.C.S.: 323111

Prismaflex Canada Inc. (1)
1645 Queensway E, Mississauga, L4X 3A3, ON, Canada
Tel.: (905) 279-9793
Digital Printing Services
N.A.I.C.S.: 323111

Prismaflex Iberica SA (1)
Avda Sierra de Grazalema 21, 28691, Villanueva de Gallego, Spain
Tel.: (34) 918155853
Digital Printing Services
N.A.I.C.S.: 323111

Prismaflex RSA (Pty) Ltd. (1)
4 Herman Pieters Street Hughes, Boksburg, 1459, Gauuteng, South Africa
Tel.: (27) 118235008
Digital Printing Services
N.A.I.C.S.: 323111

Prismaflex UK Ltd (1)
Units 1 and 2, Newhaven Industrial Park Beach Road, Newhaven, BN9 0BX, East Sussex, United Kingdom
Tel.: (44) 1273611172
Digital Printing Services
N.A.I.C.S.: 323111

Prismaflex USA, Inc. (1)
113 W Broad St, Elizabethtown, NC 28337
Tel.: (910) 862-3550
Digital Printing Services
N.A.I.C.S.: 323111

PRISMASTAR LIMITED

St John's Innovation Centre Cowley Road, Cambridge, CB4 0WS, United Kingdom
Tel.: (44) 1223 776116
Web Site: http://www.prismastar.com
Sales Range: $10-24.9 Million
Emp.: 12
Consumer Guidance Software
N.A.I.C.S.: 513210
Joshua A. Tabin (Founder)

Subsidiaries:

StarDev, s.r.o. (1)
Rimska 12, 120 00, Prague, Czech Republic
Tel.: (420) 226 258 568
Consumer Guidance Software
N.A.I.C.S.: 513210

PRISMI S.P.A.

Via Aldo Moro snc, 20055, Vimodrone, Italy
Tel.: (39) 0593167411
Web Site: https://www.prismi.net
PRM—(ITA)
Sales Range: $10-24.9 Million
Emp.: 98
Internet Marketing & Software
N.A.I.C.S.: 513210
Alessandro Reggiani (Chm, Pres & CEO)

Subsidiaries:

3Ding Consulting s.r.l. (1)
Via Donaudi 21, 12037, Saluzzo, 12037, CN, Italy (71.01%)
Tel.: (39) 0175 41107
Web Site: http://www.3dingconsulting.com
Medical Consulting Services
N.A.I.C.S.: 541840

Crearevalore S.p.A. (1)
Via Sirolo 24, 61122, Pesaro, Italy
Tel.: (39) 0721 169 5149
Web Site: http://www.crearevalore.it
Marketing Consulting Services
N.A.I.C.S.: 541613
Pietro Malerba (Project Mgr)

PRISMO METALS, INC.

1110-1111 Melville Street, Vancouver, V6E 3V6, BC, Canada
Tel.: (587) 225-2599
Web Site:
  https://www.prismometals.com
PMOMF—(OTCQB)
Assets: $3,562,217
Liabilities: $204,755
Net Worth: $3,357,462
Earnings: ($739,151)
Fiscal Year-end: 12/31/22
Mineral Exploration Services
N.A.I.C.S.: 213115

AND PRIVATE COMPANIES

Craig Gibson *(Pres & CEO)*

PRISMX GLOBAL VENTURES LTD.
2nd Floor Purva Building Tejpal SchemeRoadNo 3 Vile Parle East, Mumbai, 400057, India
Tel.: (91) 2223010771
Web Site:
  https://www.kamalakshi.word.com
Year Founded: 1973
501314—(BOM)
Rev.: $2,538,685
Assets: $14,783,574
Liabilities: $762,964
Net Worth: $14,020,610
Earnings: $495,234
Emp.: 8
Fiscal Year-end: 03/31/23
Management Consulting Services
N.A.I.C.S.: 541618
Pratiksha Pankaj Mashkariya *(CFO)*

PRISTA OIL HOLDING EAD
20 Zlaten Rog St, 1407, Sofia, Bulgaria
Tel.: (359) 29620110
Web Site: http://www.prista-oil.com
Year Founded: 1993
Sales Range: $75-99.9 Million
Emp.: 250
Holding Company Oil Production & Product Mfr
N.A.I.C.S.: 324191
Hristo Savchev *(Gen Mgr)*

Subsidiaries:

PRISTA OIL LLC (1)
10A Naberezhno Khreschatytska St, 04070, Kiev, Ukraine
Tel.: (380) 445940892
Web Site: http://www.prista-oil.com
Lubricating Oil Mfr & Distr
N.A.I.C.S.: 324191

Prista Oil AD Beograd (1)
Bul Zorana Djindjica 71, 11070, Belgrade, Serbia
Tel.: (381) 114075571
Web Site: http://www.prista-oil.rs
Emp.: 550
Lubricating Oil Distr
N.A.I.C.S.: 424720
Nenad Vasovic *(Exec Dir)*

Prista Oil Czech Republic S.R.O. (1)
Spitalska 885/2a 190 00, Prague, Czech Republic
Tel.: (420) 266799150
Lubricating Oil Mfr & Distr
N.A.I.C.S.: 324191
Pavel Herynk *(Country Mgr)*

Prista Oil Romania SA (1)
Str Costache Negri Nr 2 etaj 2 3 Sector 3, Bucharest, Romania
Tel.: (40) 214115517
Web Site: http://www.prista-oil.ro
Lubricating Oil Mfr & Distr
N.A.I.C.S.: 324191

Prista Oil Yag Sanayi ve Ticaret Limited Sirketi (1)
Dunya Ticaret Merkezi A 1 Blok K 12 No 391, Yesilkoy, 34149, Istanbul, Turkiye
Tel.: (90) 2124652403
Lubricating Oil Mfr & Distr
N.A.I.C.S.: 324191

Prista Oil Yag-Sanayi ve Ticaret Limited Sirketi - Lubricant Blending Plant (1)
Istanbul Atalar Mahallesi Islav Sokak No 4, Istanbul, Turkiye
Tel.: (90) 2625288616
Lubricating Oil Mfr
N.A.I.C.S.: 324191

Prista Oil-Hungary Kft. (1)
Puskas Tivadar u 1, H-2040, Budaors, Hungary
Tel.: (36) 23814648
Lubricating Oil Mfr & Distr
N.A.I.C.S.: 324191

PRISTINE CAPITAL PLC
Meridien House 42 Upper Berkeley Street, London, W1H 5QL, United Kingdom
Tel.: (44) 2039880227 UK
Web Site:
  https://www.pristinecapitalplc.com
Year Founded: 2021
TMOR—(LSE)
Assets: $899,817
Liabilities: $50,959
Net Worth: $848,858
Earnings: ($585,581)
Emp.: 2
Fiscal Year-end: 10/31/23
Investment Management Service
N.A.I.C.S.: 523999
Neil Sinclair *(Exec Chm)*

PRISTOP D.O.O.
Trubarjeva cesta 79, 1000, Ljubljana, Slovenia
Tel.: (386) 1 23 91 200 SI
Web Site: http://www.pristop.si
Year Founded: 1991
Sales Range: $50-74.9 Million
Emp.: 200
Communications Management & Business Consultancy Services
N.A.I.C.S.: 541810
Ula Spindler *(Member-Mgmt Bd, Partner & Head-Entertainment)*

Subsidiaries:

IDEA Plus Communications Doo (1)
Bulevar Milutina Milankovica 136 Ulaz A/I, Belgrade, 11000, Serbia
Tel.: (381) 11 71 51 730
Business Consulting Services
N.A.I.C.S.: 541618

Nastop Plus (1)
Trubarjeva cesta 79, 1000, Ljubljana, Slovenia
Tel.: (386) 1 23 91 470
Web Site: http://www.pristop.si
Emp.: 250
N.A.I.C.S.: 541820
Leon Magdalenc *(Mng Dir)*

Premisa (1)
Heinzelova 62a, 10 000, Zagreb, Croatia
Tel.: (385) 1 23 57 800
Web Site: http://www.premisa.hr
Sales Range: $25-49.9 Million
Emp.: 18
N.A.I.C.S.: 541820
Violeta Colic *(Deputy Mng Dir)*

Pristop BG (1)
Trg Nikole Pasica 3/V, 11 000, Belgrade, Serbia
Tel.: (381) 113234272
Public Relations Agency
N.A.I.C.S.: 541820

PRITHVI EXCHANGE (INDIA) LIMITED
2nd Floor Door no 2 Mc Nichalos Road, Chetpet, Chennai, 600 031, India
Tel.: (91) 4443434250
Web Site: https://www.prithvifx.com
Year Founded: 1992
531688—(BOM)
Foreign Currency Exchange Services
N.A.I.C.S.: 522390
K. N. Dheenadayalan *(Chm)*

PRITHVI SOLUTIONS LIMITED
Prithvi House 2-56/2/19 Khanamet Madhapur, Hyderabad, 500 081, India
Tel.: (91) 4044856019
Web Site:
  http://www.prithvisolutions.com
Year Founded: 1998
Sales Range: $150-199.9 Million
Emp.: 2,050
Software Development Services

N.A.I.C.S.: 541511
Satish Kumar Vuppalapati *(Mng Dir)*

PRITI INTERNATIONAL LTD.
Plot no F-43 1st Phase, Basni, Jodhpur, India
Tel.: (91) 9314225699
Web Site: https://pritihome.com
Year Founded: 2011
PRITI—(NSE)
Rev.: $7,203,279
Assets: $3,420,827
Liabilities: $780,095
Net Worth: $2,640,732
Earnings: $524,552
Emp.: 67
Fiscal Year-end: 03/31/22
Furniture Product Mfr
N.A.I.C.S.: 337121
G. D. Lohiya *(Co-Founder)*

PRITIKA AUTO INDUSTRIES LIMITED
C 94 Phase VII Industrial Area, SAS Nagar Mohali, Chandigarh, 160055, India
Tel.: (91) 1725008900 In
Web Site:
  https://www.pritikaautoindustry.com
Year Founded: 1980
PRITIKAUTO—(NSE)
Rev.: $38,088,237
Assets: $39,627,028
Liabilities: $20,652,300
Net Worth: $18,974,729
Earnings: $1,966,665
Emp.: 366
Fiscal Year-end: 03/31/22
Industrial Engineering Services
N.A.I.C.S.: 541330
Raminder Singh Nibber *(Chm)*

PRITIKA AUTOCAST LTD.
C-94 Industrial Area Phase-VII, S A S Nagar, Mohali, 160 055, Punjab, India
Tel.: (91) 1725008900
Web Site:
  http://www.pritikagroup.com
Year Founded: 2007
Rev.: $12,720,200
Assets: $12,134,589
Liabilities: $9,374,888
Net Worth: $2,759,701
Earnings: $216,297
Fiscal Year-end: 03/31/16
Industrial Machinery Equipment Mfr
N.A.I.C.S.: 333248
Raminder Singh Nibber *(Chm)*

PRITISH NANDY COMMUNICATIONS LIMITED
87/88 Mittal Chambers Nariman Point, Mumbai, 400 021, India
Tel.: (91) 2242130000
Web Site:
  https://www.pritishnandycom.com
Year Founded: 1993
532387—(BOM)
Rev.: $2,257,311
Assets: $11,066,243
Liabilities: $2,414,567
Net Worth: $8,651,676
Earnings: ($468,233)
Emp.: 19
Fiscal Year-end: 03/31/23
Movie Production Services
N.A.I.C.S.: 512110
Pritish Nandy *(Founder & Chm)*

PRIVAS DISTRIBUTION
Boulevard De Paste, 07000, Privas, Ardeche, France
Tel.: (33) 475293685
Sales Range: $10-24.9 Million
Emp.: 20

Supermarket
N.A.I.C.S.: 445110
Perrine Amilien *(Gen Mgr)*

PRIVASIA TECHNOLOGY BERHAD
C-21-02 3Two Square No 2 Jalan 19/1, 46300, Petaling Jaya, Selangor Darul Ehsan, Malaysia
Tel.: (60) 379679600 MY
Web Site: https://www.privasia.com
Year Founded: 2008
PRIVA—(KLS)
Rev.: $8,534,068
Assets: $18,782,628
Liabilities: $6,304,649
Net Worth: $12,477,979
Earnings: ($274,625)
Emp.: 141
Fiscal Year-end: 12/31/22
Investment Holding Services
N.A.I.C.S.: 551112
Andre Anthony *(Co-Founder & Deputy CEO)*

PRIVAT-BRAUEREI HEINRICH REISSDORF GMBH & CO. KG
Emil Hoffmann Str 4 10, D-50996, Cologne, Germany
Tel.: (49) 223696550
Web Site: http://www.reissdorf.de
Year Founded: 1894
Rev.: $39,666,000
Emp.: 80
Beer Mfr
N.A.I.C.S.: 312120
Michael von Rieff *(Mng Dir)*

PRIVATBRAUEREI ERDINGER WEISSBRAU WERNER BROMBACH GMBH
Lange Zeile 1 und 3, 85435, Erding, Germany
Tel.: (49) 81224090
Web Site: http://www.erdinger.de
Year Founded: 1886
Rev.: $21,938,403
Emp.: 450
Breweries Services
N.A.I.C.S.: 312120
Werner Brombach *(Mng Dir)*

PRIVATE EQUITY HOLDING AG
Bahnhofstrasse 13, CH-8001, Zug, Switzerland
Tel.: (41) 445157080
Web Site: https://www.peh.ch
PEHN—(SWX)
Rev.: $1,863,636
Assets: $252,944,568
Liabilities: $49,598,670
Net Worth: $203,345,898
Earnings: ($1,043,237)
Fiscal Year-end: 03/31/23
Holding Company
N.A.I.C.S.: 551112
Hans Baumgartner *(Chm)*

PRIVATE EQUITY MANAGERS S.A.
1 Europejski Sq, 00-844, Warsaw, Poland
Tel.: (48) 697 888 110
Web Site:
  http://www.privateequitymanagers.pl
PEM—(WAR)
Private Equity
N.A.I.C.S.: 523999
Tomasz Czechowicz *(Pres & Mng Partner)*

PRIVATINVESTOR VERMOGENSMANAGEMENT GMBH
Ritterstrasse 3, 77652, Offenburg, Germany

PRIVATINVESTOR VERMOGENSMANAGEMENT GMBH

Privatinvestor Vermogensmanagement GmbH—(Continued)
Tel.: (49) 781 919 3280
Web Site: http://www.privatinvestor-vm.de
Year Founded: 2002
Sales Range: $50-74.9 Million
Emp.: 9
Privater Equity Firm
N.A.I.C.S.: 523999
Christian Meier (Gen Mgr)

PRIVATIZATION HOLDING COMPANY K.S.C.C.
Floor 23 Dar Al Awadi Towers Ahmed Al Jaber St, Sharq, Kuwait, Kuwait
Tel.: (965) 22322190
Web Site: http://www.phc.com.kw
Year Founded: 1994
KPPC—(KUW)
Rev.: $23,516,874
Assets: $382,421,284
Liabilities: $166,120,189
Net Worth: $216,301,095
Earnings: ($23,955,663)
Emp.: 20
Fiscal Year-end: 12/31/22
Business Consulting, Financial, Investment & Real Estate Services
N.A.I.C.S.: 541611
Reyadh S. Ali Al-Edrissi (Chm)

Subsidiaries:

Daytona Production Company-W.L.L. (1)
Khalid Bin Al-Waleed St Mazaya Towers Tower 3 Floor 20, Merqab, Kuwait, Kuwait
Tel.: (965) 22211600
Web Site: http://www.daytonamedia.tv
Entertainment Services
N.A.I.C.S.: 711120

ELogics System Company-S.P.C. (1)
Floor 23 Dar Al Awadi Towers Ahmed Al Jaber Street, Al-Sharq, Kuwait
Tel.: (965) 22322190
Web Site: http://www.elogicssystems.com
Cloud Data Services
N.A.I.C.S.: 518210

Fairy Hub General Trading Company-W.L.L. (1)
Al Kaadhmi Building, Al-Sharq, Kuwait
Tel.: (965) 22070777
Web Site: http://www.fairyhub.com
Trading Services
N.A.I.C.S.: 425120

Skills Entertainment Company-W.L.L. (1)
Sahab Tower Floor 18, Salhiya, Kuwait
Tel.: (965) 22273888
Web Site: http://www.skillsent.com
Entertainment Services
N.A.I.C.S.: 561920

PRIVEQ ADVISORY AB
Humlegardsgatan 20, PO Box 5295, 102 46, Stockholm, Sweden
Tel.: (46) 84596760   SE
Web Site: http://www.priveq.se
Year Founded: 1983
Sales Range: $25-49.9 Million
Emp.: 13
Privater Equity Firm
N.A.I.C.S.: 523999
Magnus Hardmeier (Chm & Partner)

PRIVI SPECIALITY CHEMICALS LIMITED
Privi House A-71 TTC Thane Belapur Road, Near Kopar khairane Railway Station, Navi Mumbai, 400 709, India
Tel.: (91) 2233043500   In
Web Site: https://www.privi.com
530117—(NSE)
Rev.: $176,975,280
Assets: $210,239,075
Liabilities: $111,615,231
Net Worth: $98,623,844

Earnings: $15,956,932
Emp.: 718
Fiscal Year-end: 03/31/21
Specialty Chemicals Mfr
N.A.I.C.S.: 325998
Nahoosh J. Jariwala (Mng Dir)

Subsidiaries:

Privi Organics India Limited (1)
Privi House A-71 Thane Belapur Road, TTC Industrial Area Kopar Khairane, Navi Mumbai, 400 709, Maharastra, India
Tel.: (91) 2227783040
Aroma Chemical Mfr
N.A.I.C.S.: 325199

Subsidiary (US):

Privi Organics USA Corporation (2)
51 Distribution Blvd, Edison, NJ 08817
Tel.: (732) 960-4513
Web Site: http://priviorganicsusacorp.business.site
Aroma Chemical Mfr
N.A.I.C.S.: 325199

PRIVILEGE SAS
998 Avenue Jean Monnet, 83190, Ollioules, France
Tel.: (33) 498002903   FR
Web Site: http://www.privilege-discount.fr
Sales Range: $25-49.9 Million
Emp.: 127
Online Electronics & Appliances Retailer
N.A.I.C.S.: 449210
Jean-Christophe Claie (Chm)

PRIVOZ
Montefiore 54 #3, Holon, Israel
Tel.: (972) 3 5053720   NV
Year Founded: 2013
Delivery Shipping Services
N.A.I.C.S.: 488510
Mark Milman (Pres, CEO, CFO, Principal Acctg Officer, Treas & Sec)

PRIVREDNA BANKA SARAJEVO D.D. SARAJEVO
Obala Kulina bana 18 Drvenija, 71000, Sarajevo, Bosnia & Herzegovina
Tel.: (387) 3 327 8520   BA
Web Site: http://www.pbs.ba
Year Founded: 1995
BORBRK3—(SARE)
Rev.: $7,648,926
Assets: $392,456,711
Liabilities: $359,881,781
Net Worth: $32,574,930
Earnings: $2,952,719
Emp.: 181
Fiscal Year-end: 12/31/20
Commercial Banking Services
N.A.I.C.S.: 522110
Hamid Prses (Chm-Mgmt Bd)

PRIYA LIMITED
4th Floor Kimatrai Building 77-79 Maharshi Karve Marg Marine Lines E, Mumbai, 400002, India
Tel.: (91) 2222013672
Web Site: https://www.priyaltd.com
Year Founded: 1986
524580—(BOM)
Rev.: $70,202
Assets: $353,685
Liabilities: $4,815,502
Net Worth: ($4,461,816)
Earnings: ($753,890)
Emp.: 5
Fiscal Year-end: 03/31/21
Computer Technology Products Distr
N.A.I.C.S.: 423430
A. K. Bhuwania (Chm)

Subsidiaries:

Priya International Limited (1)
Shahu Nagar E-13/8 Jasmin Mill Road Mahim E, Mumbai, 400017, Maharashtra, India
Tel.: (91) 9820212819
Web Site: https://www.priyainternational.com
Computer System Design Services
N.A.I.C.S.: 541512

PRIYADARSINI LTD.
Satyanarayan Enclave Icon Block 2nd Floor, Madinaguda, Hyderabad, 500 049, India
Tel.: (91) 40 40153333
Sales Range: $25-49.9 Million
Spun Yarn Mfr
N.A.I.C.S.: 313110
Kowsalendra Rao Cherukuri (Vice Chm)

PRIZMA PRES MATBAACILIK YAYINCILIK SANAYI VE TICARET AS
Ataturk Organized Industrial Zone 75 Year Street No 21 Hadimkoy, Arnavutkoy, Istanbul, Turkiye
Tel.: (90) 2127714636
Web Site: http://www.prizmapress.com
Year Founded: 1978
PRZMA—(IST)
Printing Services
N.A.I.C.S.: 323117
Metin Kuru (Chm)

PRNJAVOR EKSPRES A.D.
Zivojina Preradovica 2, 78430, Prnjavor, Bosnia & Herzegovina
Tel.: (387) 51660620
Year Founded: 2001
PEKS—(BANJ)
Sales Range: $200-249.9 Million
Emp.: 18
Land Transportation Services
N.A.I.C.S.: 485999
Dragutin Jankovic (Chm-Mgmt Bd & Pres)

PRO 2000 CO., LTD.
4FL B-dong Gunpo IT Valley Dangjeong-dong 411 17 148, Gosanro, Gunpo, Gyeonggi-do, Korea (South)
Tel.: (82) 23686296
Web Site: https://www.pro-2000.co.kr
Year Founded: 2006
321260—(KRS)
Rev.: $29,293,174
Assets: $28,052,480
Liabilities: $3,009,284
Net Worth: $25,043,197
Earnings: $3,495,035
Emp.: 111
Fiscal Year-end: 12/31/22
Semiconductor Device Mfr & Distr
N.A.I.C.S.: 334413
Jung Yong Seung (Mng Dir)

PRO CLB GLOBAL LIMITED
5 Pusa Road Ist Floor, New Delhi, 110005, India
Tel.: (91) 1147177000
Web Site: https://www.provestment.net
Year Founded: 1994
540703—(BOM)
Rev.: $417,956
Assets: $2,971,817
Liabilities: $1,324,042
Net Worth: $1,647,775
Earnings: $59,187
Fiscal Year-end: 03/31/21
Management Consulting Services
N.A.I.C.S.: 541618
Praveen Bhatia (Exec Dir)

INTERNATIONAL PUBLIC

PRO DV AG
Hauert 12, 44227, Dortmund, Germany
Tel.: (49) 23197920
Web Site: https://www.prodv.com
Year Founded: 1979
PDA—(DEU)
Rev.: $4,967,436
Assets: $3,002,539
Liabilities: $1,589,579
Net Worth: $1,412,959
Earnings: $419,472
Emp.: 30
Fiscal Year-end: 12/31/23
Information Technology Services
N.A.I.C.S.: 541512
Uwe Osterkamp (Chm)

PRO FIN CAPITAL SERVICES LIMITED
B-503 Western Edge 2 Western Express Highway Borivali East, Mumbai, 400 066, India
Tel.: (91) 2228702070
Web Site: https://www.profincapital.co.in
511557—(BOM)
Rev.: $2,463,198
Assets: $41,895,798
Liabilities: $37,183,694
Net Worth: $4,712,104
Earnings: $66,711
Emp.: 14
Fiscal Year-end: 03/31/23
Financial Services
N.A.I.C.S.: 523999
Anupam Narain Gupta (Co-Mng Dir)

PRO GALVANO MIKROMETAL A.D.
Marka Nikolica 9, Zemun, Serbia
Tel.: (381) 11 316 0 216
Web Site: http://www.progalvano.com
Year Founded: 1989
Sales Range: $1-9.9 Million
Hardware Product Whslr
N.A.I.C.S.: 423710
Petar Dordevic (Exec Dir)

PRO KAPITAL GRUPP AS
Sojakooli 11, 11316, Tallinn, Estonia
Tel.: (372) 6144920
Web Site: https://www.prokapital.com
Year Founded: 1994
PKG1T—(RSE)
Rev.: $23,623,968
Assets: $219,913,916
Liabilities: $208,158,430
Net Worth: $11,755,485
Earnings: ($73,026,237)
Emp.: 84
Fiscal Year-end: 12/31/20
Real Estate Development Services
N.A.I.C.S.: 531390
Paolo Michelozzi (CEO)

Subsidiaries:

Pro Kapital Eesti AS (1)
Sojakooli 11, 11316, Tallinn, Estonia
Tel.: (372) 6144920
Real Estate Services
N.A.I.C.S.: 531390

Pro Kapital Latvia JSC (1)
Strelnieku Street 1-8, Riga, LV-1010, Latvia
Tel.: (371) 67039669
Real Estate Services
N.A.I.C.S.: 531390

Pro Kapital Vilnius Real Estate UAB (1)
Aguonu str 12, LT-03213, Vilnius, Lithuania
Tel.: (370) 52660800
Real Estate Services
N.A.I.C.S.: 531390

PRO MEDICUS LIMITED

450 Swan Street, Richmond, 3121, VIC, Australia
Tel.: (61) 394298800   AU
Web Site: https://www.promed.com.au
Year Founded: 1983
PMCUF—(OTCIQ)
Rev.: $111,066,372
Assets: $171,892,360
Liabilities: $46,539,797
Net Worth: $125,352,564
Earnings: $55,284,455
Fiscal Year-end: 06/30/24
Custom Computer Programming Services
N.A.I.C.S.: 541511
Sam Aaron Hupert (Co-Founder, CEO & Mng Dir)

PRO METALURGIA SA
Av Tegula 888 - Bloco F / Mod 17e18 / Sala 1, 12952820, Atibaia, SP, Brazil
Tel.: (55) 11 4417 7800
Web Site: http://www.pmet.com.br
Year Founded: 1898
Sales Range: $1-9.9 Million
Emp.: 78
Bicycle Mfr & Whslr
N.A.I.C.S.: 336991
Luiz Augusto Trindade (Dir-IR)

PRO REAL ESATE INVESTMENT TRUST
2000 Mansfield Street Suite 1000, Montreal, H3A 2Z7, QC, Canada
Tel.: (514) 933-9552   ON
Web Site: https://www.proreit.com
Year Founded: 2010
PRV.UN—(TSX)
Rev.: $54,610,967
Assets: $496,344,144
Liabilities: $306,092,865
Net Worth: $190,251,278
Earnings: $16,484,204
Fiscal Year-end: 12/31/20
Real Estate Investment Trust
N.A.I.C.S.: 531390
James W. Beckerleg (Pres & CEO)

PRO REAL ESTATE INVESTMENT TRUST
2000 Mansfield Street Suite 1000, Montreal, H3A 2Z7, QC, Canada
Tel.: (514) 933-9552   Ca
Web Site: http://www.proreit.com
Year Founded: 2014
PRV.UN—(TSXV)
Rev.: $54,610,967
Assets: $496,344,144
Liabilities: $306,092,865
Net Worth: $190,251,278
Earnings: $16,484,204
Fiscal Year-end: 12/31/20
Commercial Real Estate Services
N.A.I.C.S.: 531210
James W. Beckerleg (Pres & CEO)

PRO TEKO A.D.
Ive Lole Ribara 5, Kovin, Serbia
Tel.: (381) 64 500 7529
Year Founded: 2005
Sales Range: Less than $1 Million
Emp.: 7
Building Construction Services
N.A.I.C.S.: 236220

PRO-BEAM AG & CO. KGAA
Zeppelinstr 26, 82205, Gilching, Germany
Tel.: (49) 898992330
Web Site: http://www.pro-beam.com
Year Founded: 1974
Rev.: $27,588,000
Emp.: 300
Engineeering Services
N.A.I.C.S.: 541330

Nicolas von Wolff (Chm)

Subsidiaries:
pro-beam electron beam technology Suzhou Co. Ltd   (1)
22 Zhongfeng Street SND, Suzhou, Shanghai, China
Tel.: (86) 51268783270105
Engineeering Services
N.A.I.C.S.: 541330

PRO-DATA INC.
1560 St James Street, Winnipeg, R3H 0L2, MB, Canada
Tel.: (204) 779-9960
Web Site: http://www.pro-data.com
Year Founded: 1987
Rev.: $27,603,880
Emp.: 40
Computer & Parts Mfr
N.A.I.C.S.: 423430
Ron Aebig (Mgr-Mktg)

PRO-HAWK CORPORATION
No 8 Wu-Chuan 3Rd Road, New Taipei Industrial Park, New Taipei City, 24891, Taiwan
Tel.: (886) 289904567
Web Site: https://www.prohawk.com.tw
Year Founded: 1976
8083—(TPE)
Rev.: $52,341,838
Assets: $61,676,047
Liabilities: $22,875,715
Net Worth: $38,800,331
Earnings: $11,312,322
Emp.: 150
Fiscal Year-end: 12/31/22
Mechanical Component Mfr
N.A.I.C.S.: 333613
Victor Liao (VP)

PRO-LOGISTIK-TEAM INTERNATIONALE SPEDITIONS GMBH
Carl Hagen Str 2, 83080, Rosenheim, Germany
Tel.: (49) 803392680
Web Site: http://www.pro-logistik.com
Year Founded: 1992
Rev.: $24,139,500
Emp.: 33
Truck Transportation Services
N.A.I.C.S.: 484121
Stefan Steinbach (Mng Dir)

PRO-MART INDUSTRIAL PRODUCTS LTD.
1147 Vanier Rd, PO Box 2226, Sarnia, N7T 7L7, ON, Canada
Tel.: (519) 336-4471
Web Site: http://www.promart.ca
Rev.: $10,801,512
Emp.: 50
Structural Steel Mfr
N.A.I.C.S.: 332312

PRO-PAC PACKAGING LIMITED
83-85 Banbury Road, PO Box 441, Reservoir, 3073, VIC, Australia
Tel.: (61) 394744200   AU
Web Site: https://www.ppgaust.com.au
PPG—(ASX)
Rev.: $197,100,694
Assets: $158,476,896
Liabilities: $104,329,594
Net Worth: $54,147,302
Earnings: ($35,900,107)
Emp.: 520
Fiscal Year-end: 06/30/24
Paper & Paper Products Industry
N.A.I.C.S.: 322130
Kathleen Forbes (Sec)

Subsidiaries:
Bev Cap Pty. Ltd.   (1)
7 Binney Road, Kings Park, 2148, NSW, Australia
Tel.: (61) 298313566
Emp.: 30
Plastic Injection Moulded Products Designer & Mfr
N.A.I.C.S.: 326160

Ctech Closures Pty. Ltd.   (1)
7 Binney Road, Kings Park, 2148, NSW, Australia
Tel.: (61) 29 831 3566
Web Site: https://www.cltech.com.au
Sales Range: $25-49.9 Million
Emp.: 10
Plastic Injection Moulded Products Mfr
N.A.I.C.S.: 326160

Integrated Recycling Pty. Ltd.   (1)
316 Etiwanda Ave, Mildura, VIC, Australia
Tel.: (61) 1300729253
Web Site: https://www.integratedrecycling.com.au
Polytensilate Product Mfr
N.A.I.C.S.: 326199

Perfection Packaging Pty. Ltd.   (1)
19-25 Nathan Road, Dandenong South, VIC, Australia
Tel.: (61) 397067355
Web Site: https://www.perfectionpackaging.com.au
Food Packaging Services
N.A.I.C.S.: 561910

Pro-Pac Packaging (Aust) Pty. Ltd.   (1)
Building 1 147-151 Newton Road, Wetherill Park, 2164, NSW, Australia
Tel.: (61) 130 077 6722
Web Site: https://www.pro-pac.com.au
Emp.: 100
Packaged Products Mfr & Distr
N.A.I.C.S.: 322220

Pro-Pac Packaging Manufacturing (Melb) Pty. Ltd.   (1)
9 Dandenong Industrial Estate 5-11 Progress St, Dandenong, 3175, VIC, Australia
Tel.: (61) 395451111
Web Site: http://www.pro-pac.com.au
Sales Range: $25-49.9 Million
Emp.: 35
Packaged Plastic Products Mfr & Distr
N.A.I.C.S.: 326199
Raoul Linossiel (Gen Mgr)

Speciality Products and Dispensers Pty. Ltd.   (1)
Warehouse B 3 Burilda Close, Wetherill Park, 2164, NSW, Australia
Tel.: (61) 287871900
Web Site: https://www.pbpackaging.com.au
Sales Range: $25-49.9 Million
Emp.: 4
Dispenser Product Mfr
N.A.I.C.S.: 333914

PRO-SHIP INCORPORATED
Sumitomo Fudosan Iidabashi ekimae Bldg 3-8-5 Iidabashi, Chiyoda-ku, Tokyo, 102-0072, Japan
Tel.: (81) 5017913000
Web Site: https://www.proship.co.jp
Year Founded: 1969
3763—(TKS)
Rev.: $45,027,320
Assets: $64,308,690
Liabilities: $14,337,090
Net Worth: $49,971,600
Earnings: $8,916,890
Emp.: 276
Fiscal Year-end: 03/31/24
Commercial Application Development & Sales
N.A.I.C.S.: 541511
Katsuyoshi Suzuki (Chm & CEO)

Subsidiaries:
Proship Information System (Dalian) Co., Ltd.   (1)
Software Park 17 201-C NO 267 Wuyi Road, Dalian, 116-023, China

Tel.: (86) 41184784783
Asset Management Services
N.A.I.C.S.: 541611

PRO.GES. SOCIETA COOPERATIVA
Via Colorno 63, 43122, Parma, Italy
Tel.: (39) 0521 600 111   IT
Web Site: http://www.proges.it
Year Founded: 2010
Emp.: 4,200
Holding Company
N.A.I.C.S.: 551112
Antonio Costantino (Dir Gen)

Subsidiaries:
Pro.Ges. Societa Cooperativa Sociale   (1)
Via Colorno 63, 43122, Parma, Italy
Tel.: (39) 0521 600 611
Web Site: http://www.proges.it
Personal & Social Services
N.A.I.C.S.: 813212
Giancarlo Anghinolfi (Mng Dir)

PRO2 ANLAGENTECHNIK GMBH
Schmelzerstrasse 25, Willich, 47877, Germany
Tel.: (49) 21544880   De
Web Site: http://www.pro2.com
Rev.: $45,531,150
Emp.: 30
Bio Energy System Mfr
N.A.I.C.S.: 335929
Otto Eichhorn (Mng Dir)

PROA CAPITAL DE INVERSIONES SGEIC, S.A.
Calle Zurbano 76 6 planta, 28010, Madrid, Spain
Tel.: (34) 913911309   ES
Web Site: https://proacapital.com
Privater Equity Firm
N.A.I.C.S.: 523999
Carlos Gordillo (Founder & Partner)

Subsidiaries:
Amara, S.A.   (1)
C/Trespaderne 29 2 Planta Edificio Barajas I, 28042, Madrid, Spain
Tel.: (34) 917224000
Web Site: http://www.amara.es
Environmental Consulting Services
N.A.I.C.S.: 541620
Pablo Arnus (Chm)

PROACT IT GROUP AB
Tel.: (46) 841066600   SE
Web Site: https://www.proact.eu
Year Founded: 1994
PACT—(OMX)
Rev.: $445,533,077
Assets: $397,301,788
Liabilities: $310,812,423
Net Worth: $86,489,365
Earnings: $17,940,000
Emp.: 1,253
Fiscal Year-end: 12/31/22
Information Technology Services
N.A.I.C.S.: 541512
Eva Elmstedt (Chm)

Subsidiaries:
Proact Belgium B.V.B.A.   (1)
Park Lane Culliganlaan 2H - Floor 3, 1831, Diegem, Belgium
Tel.: (32) 27254518
Software Development Services
N.A.I.C.S.: 541511

Proact Czech Republic,s.r.o.   (1)
Tel.: (420) 272072600
Web Site: http://www.proact.eu
Sales Range: $25-49.9 Million
Emp.: 20
Information Technology Consulting Services
N.A.I.C.S.: 541512

Proact Estonia AS   (1)

Proact IT Group AB—(Continued)
Tel.: (372) 6630900
Web Site: http://www.proact.ee
Emp.: 16
Information Technology Consulting Services
N.A.I.C.S.: 541512

Proact Finance AB (1)
Box 1205, 164 28, Kista, Sweden
Tel.: (46) 8 410 666 00
Sales Range: $100-124.9 Million
Emp.: 200
Financial Management Services
N.A.I.C.S.: 523999

Proact Finland OY (1)
Linnoitustie 7, 02600, Espoo, Finland
Tel.: (358) 207919200
Web Site: http://www.proact.fi
Information Technology Consulting Services
N.A.I.C.S.: 541512

Proact IT Latvia SIA (1)
Duntes iela 23A, Riga, 1005, LV, Latvia
Tel.: (371) 67819444
Web Site: http://www.proact.lv
Sales Range: $25-49.9 Million
Emp.: 17
Information Technology Consulting Services
N.A.I.C.S.: 541512

Proact IT Norge AS (1)
Sognsveien 75 D 4 etg, PO Box 3983, Ullevål Stadion, 0805, Oslo, Norway
Tel.: (47) 22892389
Web Site: http://www.proact.no
Sales Range: $25-49.9 Million
Emp.: 75
Information Technology Consulting Services
N.A.I.C.S.: 541512

Proact IT Sweden AB (1)
Kistagangen 2, Kista, 16440, Sweden
Tel.: (46) 8 410 666 00
Web Site: http://www.proact.se
Sales Range: $25-49.9 Million
Emp.: 200
Information Technology Consulting Services
N.A.I.C.S.: 541512

Proact IT UK Ltd. (1)
Grayson House Venture Way Dunston Technology Park Dunston Road, Chesterfield, S41 8NE, United Kingdom
Tel.: (44) 1246266300
Web Site: http://www.proact.eu
Sales Range: $75-99.9 Million
Emp.: 130
IT Services
N.A.I.C.S.: 541512

Proact Lietuva UAB (1)
J Jasinskio g 16F, 01112, Vilnius, Lithuania
Tel.: (370) 5 252 6140
Web Site: http://www.proact.lt
Information Technology Consulting Services
N.A.I.C.S.: 541512

Proact Netherlands B.V. (1)
Boerhaavelaan 11-13, Zoetermeer, 2713 HA, Netherlands
Tel.: (31) 79 3619765
Web Site: http://www.proact.nl
Emp.: 105
Information Technology Consulting Services
N.A.I.C.S.: 541512

Proact Systems A/S (1)
Delta Park 46 ground floor, 2665, Vallensbaek, Denmark
Tel.: (45) 7 010 1132
Web Site: http://www.proact.dk
Information Technology Consulting Services
N.A.I.C.S.: 541512

PROAM EXPLORATIONS CORPORATION
867 West 3rd Street, North Vancouver, V7P 1E2, BC, Canada
Tel.: (604) 988-3306
Year Founded: 1970
PMX—(TSXV)
Rev.: $4,707
Assets: $468,960
Liabilities: $93,784
Net Worth: $375,175
Earnings: ($164,852)
Fiscal Year-end: 12/31/23

Oil & Gas Production Services
N.A.I.C.S.: 213112
Donald L. MacDonald (CEO)

PROAX TECHNOLOGIES LTD.
6700 Millcreek Dr Unit 3, Mississauga, L5N 8B3, ON, Canada
Tel.: (866) 592-1240
Web Site: https://proax.ca
Year Founded: 1962
Emp.: 189
Software Development
N.A.I.C.S.: 513210

Subsidiaries:

Systematic Fluid Power Ltd. (1)
405 Maple Grove Rd #13,, Cambridge, N3E 1B6, ON, Canada
Tel.: (800) 895-8005
Industrial Equipment Distr
N.A.I.C.S.: 423830

PROBANKA, D.D.
Trg Leona Stuklja 12, 2000, Maribor, Slovenia
Tel.: (386) 22520500   SI
Web Site: http://www.probanka.si
Year Founded: 1991
Sales Range: $25-49.9 Million
Emp.: 227
Banking Services
N.A.I.C.S.: 522110
Bernard Cvikl (Exec Dir-IT Div)

Subsidiaries:

PROleasing d.o.o. (1)
Prolaz MK Kozulic 2, 51000, Rijeka, Croatia
Tel.: (385) 51356020
Web Site: http://www.probanka.si
Sales Range: $50-74.9 Million
Emp.: 3
Financial Lending Services
N.A.I.C.S.: 523999
Branimir Cvitanovic (Mgr)

Probanka Leasing d.o.o. (1)
Trg Leona Stuklja 12, 2000, Maribor, Slovenia
Tel.: (386) 22520706
Sales Range: $50-74.9 Million
Emp.: 6
Financial Management Services
N.A.I.C.S.: 522920
Joze Dover (Gen Mgr)

Probanka upravljanje premozenja d.o.o. (1)
Trg Leona Stuklja 12, 2000, Maribor, Slovenia
Tel.: (386) 22520800
Web Site: http://www.probanka-upravljanje.si
Sales Range: $50-74.9 Million
Emp.: 20
Mutual Fund Management Services
N.A.I.C.S.: 525910

PROBE METALS INC.
56 Temperance Street Suite 1000, Toronto, M5H 3V5, ON, Canada
Tel.: (416) 777-6703   ON
Web Site: https://probegold.com
Year Founded: 2015
PROBF—(OTCQB)
Rev.: $434,408
Assets: $31,926,632
Liabilities: $5,754,195
Net Worth: $26,172,436
Earnings: ($3,795,003)
Fiscal Year-end: 12/31/19
Gold Exploration Services
N.A.I.C.S.: 213114
Marco Gagnon (Exec VP)

PROBRAND LIMITED
37-55 Camden St, Birmingham, B1 3BP, United Kingdom
Tel.: (44) 1216051000
Web Site: http://www.probrand.co.uk
Year Founded: 1992
Sales Range: $75-99.9 Million

Emp.: 180
IT Products Distr
N.A.I.C.S.: 423430
Peter Robbins (Mng Dir)

PROCAD S.A.
Ul Kartuska 215, 80-122, Gdansk, Poland
Tel.: (48) 58 739 68 00
Web Site: http://www.procad.pl
PRD—(WAR)
Sales Range: Less than $1 Million
Information Technology Services
N.A.I.C.S.: 519290
Jaroslaw Jarzynski (Chm)

PROCAM INTERNATIONAL INC.
2035 Dagenais Boulevard West Suite 200, Laval, H7L 5V1, QC, Canada
Tel.: (450) 963-4442
Web Site: http://www.protransport.ca
Year Founded: 1988
Rev.: $12,740,333
Emp.: 10
Freight Transportation Services
N.A.I.C.S.: 488510
Francois Guy (Pres)

PROCAM TELEVISION LTD.
Unit 1 Wave Trade Park Concord Road Acton, London, W3 0BF, United Kingdom
Tel.: (44) 20 7622 9888
Web Site: http://www.procam.tv
Year Founded: 1989
Camera Rental Services
N.A.I.C.S.: 532210
Paul Sargeant (COO)

Subsidiaries:

HotCam New York Inc. (1)
The Arts Building 336 W 37th St Ste 750, New York, NY 10018-0000
Tel.: (212) 633-1888
Web Site: http://www.hotcamny.com
Camera Rental Services
N.A.I.C.S.: 532210
Sean Smith (VP-Ops)

True Lens Services Ltd (1)
19/20 Bank Terrace, Barwell, Leicester, LE9 8GG, United Kingdom
Tel.: (44) 1455848411
Web Site: http://www.truelens.co.uk
Lens Mfr
N.A.I.C.S.: 333310

PROCAP HOLDINGS S.A.
Zone Industrielle de Wiltz, BP 49, Wiltz, 9401, Luxembourg
Tel.: (352) 950550
Web Site: http://www.procap.com
Sales Range: $75-99.9 Million
Emp.: 350
Plastic Closure Mfr
N.A.I.C.S.: 326199
Benoit Henckes (CEO)

Subsidiaries:

PROCAP DUNA IPARI ZRT. (1)
51 - es ut 26 5 Km, 2336, Dunavarsany, Hungary
Tel.: (36) 245 21 020
Web Site: http://www.procap.hu
Plastics Product Mfr
N.A.I.C.S.: 326199

PROCAP LLAGOSTERA SAU (1)
C/Industria n 8 Apartado 29, 17240, Llagostera, Spain
Tel.: (34) 972 83 00 25
Plastic Product Distr
N.A.I.C.S.: 424610

PROCAP Schwerin GmbH (1)
Werkstrasse 122, 19061, Schwerin, Germany
Tel.: (49) 385 440004 0
Plastic Product Distr
N.A.I.C.S.: 424610

Procap Hoboken NV (1)
Schroeilaan 15, Hoboken, 2660, Antwerp, Belgium
Tel.: (32) 3 830 40 00
Plastics Product Mfr
N.A.I.C.S.: 326199
Benoit Henckes (CEO)

Procap Messia S.A.S. (1)
Rte De Chilly, 39570, Messia-sur-Sorne, Jura, France
Tel.: (33) 384870200
Web Site: http://www.procap.com
Rev.: $23,800,000
Emp.: 100
N.A.I.C.S.: 326199
Eric Badon (Mgr-Tech)

Procap Wicklow Plastics Ltd. (1)
IDA Business park Charlesland Greystones Co, Newtownmountkennedy, Wicklow, Ireland
Tel.: (353) 12872652
Web Site: http://www.procap.com
Sales Range: $10-24.9 Million
Emp.: 40
Plastic Packaging Closures & Measuring Spoons Mfr
N.A.I.C.S.: 326199
Paul Gorry (Plant Mgr)

PROCAPS GROUP, S.A.
9 Rue De Bitbourg, L-1273, Luxembourg, Luxembourg
Tel.: (352) 79956138   LU
Web Site: https://www.procapsgroup.com
Year Founded: 2021
PROC—(NASDAQ)
Rev.: $409,920,000
Assets: $460,187,000
Liabilities: $462,065,000
Net Worth: ($1,878,000)
Earnings: $42,540,000
Emp.: 5,500
Fiscal Year-end: 12/31/22
Pharmaceutical Product Mfr & Distr
N.A.I.C.S.: 325412
Ruben Minski (Chm)

PROCHEM S.A.
Lopuszanska Street 95, 02-457, Warsaw, Poland
Tel.: (48) 223260100
Web Site: https://prochem.com.pl
PRM—(WAR)
Rev.: $71,304,624
Assets: $40,594,512
Liabilities: $23,575,965
Net Worth: $17,018,547
Earnings: ($6,185,976)
Fiscal Year-end: 12/31/23
Engineeering Services
N.A.I.C.S.: 541330
Marek Garlinski (Chm-Supervisory Bd)

Subsidiaries:

ATUTOR I.C. Sp. z o.o (1)
ul Powazkowska 44c, 01-797, Warsaw, Poland
Tel.: (48) 223260385
Web Site: http://www.atutor.pl
Sales Range: $25-49.9 Million
Emp.: 5
Documentation Services
N.A.I.C.S.: 519210
Mariusz Szlon (Pres)

ELEKTROMONTAZ KRAKOW S.A (1)
ul Armii Krajowej 25, 30-150, Krakow, Poland
Tel.: (48) 126334044
Web Site: https://elektromontaz.krakow.pl
Electrical System Installation Services
N.A.I.C.S.: 238210
Krzysztof Nowicki (CEO)

ELMONT Inwestycje Sp. z o.o. (1)
ul Czysta 7, 31-121, Krakow, Poland
Tel.: (48) 12 633 44 44
Financial Investment Services
N.A.I.C.S.: 523940

AND PRIVATE COMPANIES

ELPRO Sp. z o.o. (1)
ul Stefczyka 32, 20-151, Lublin, Poland
Tel.: (48) 817406506
Web Site: http://www.elpro.enterpol.pl
Energy Consulting Services
N.A.I.C.S.: 541690

IRYD Sp. z o.o. (1)
Ekonomiczna 5, 19-500, Goldap, Poland
Tel.: (48) 876150572
Web Site: http://www.iryd.pl
Sales Range: $150-199.9 Million
Wood & Metal Product Mfr
N.A.I.C.S.: 321114

IRYDION Sp. z o.o. (1)
Powazkowska 44c, 01-797, Warsaw, Poland
Tel.: (48) 223260100
Web Site: http://www.prochem.com
Sales Range: $10-24.9 Million
Emp.: 50
Building Maintenance Services
N.A.I.C.S.: 561790

ITEL Sp. z o.o. (1)
Krzywoustego 12, 81-035, Gdynia, Poland
Tel.: (48) 586296655
Telecommunication Servicesb
N.A.I.C.S.: 517810
Robert Dyzal *(Pres)*

PKI PREDOM Sp. z o.o. (1)
Wybrzeze J Slowackiego 12 14, 50-411, Wroclaw, Poland
Tel.: (48) 713471001
Web Site: https://www.predom.biz.pl
Sales Range: $25-49.9 Million
Emp.: 300
Architectural Design & Engineering Services
N.A.I.C.S.: 541310
Witold Kordecki *(Dir-Design)*

PRO-ORGANIKA S.A. (1)
Krasinskiego 69, Warsaw, 01-755, Poland
Tel.: (48) 223260950
Web Site: http://www.proorganika.com.pl
Engineeering Services
N.A.I.C.S.: 541330
Andrzej Zelazo *(Office Mgr)*

PROCHEM SERWIS Sp. z o.o. (1)
ul Powazkowska 44 C, 01-797, Warsaw, Poland
Tel.: (48) 223260360
Web Site: http://www.prochemserwis.com.pl
Sales Range: $50-74.9 Million
Emp.: 2
Property Management Services
N.A.I.C.S.: 531312
Wojciech Szymanczuk *(Mng Dir)*

PROMIS Sp. z o.o. (1)
ul Sobieskiego 14, 40-082, Katowice, Poland
Tel.: (48) 322068411
Web Site: http://www.promis.pl
Electric Appliances Mfr
N.A.I.C.S.: 327110

PROCOM CONSULTANTS GROUP LTD
2200 Yonge Street Suite 700, Toronto, M4S 2C6, ON, Canada
Tel.: (416) 483-0766
Web Site: http://www.procom.ca
Year Founded: 1978
Sales Range: $10-24.9 Million
Staffing & Contract Workforce Services
N.A.I.C.S.: 541612
Frank McCrea *(Pres & CEO)*

PROCOMMERCEBANK LTD.
Timiryazevskaya Str 1, 127422, Moscow, Russia
Tel.: (7) 4956442525
Web Site: http://www.procombank.ru
Year Founded: 2006
Sales Range: Less than $1 Million
Commercial Banking Services
N.A.I.C.S.: 522110
Sipahi Haktanir *(Pres & Member-Mgmt Bd)*

PROCOOK GROUP PLC
10 St Modwen Park Junction 12, Gloucester, GL10 3EX, United Kingdom UK
Web Site: https://www.procookgroup.co.uk
Year Founded: 1996
PROC—(LSE)
Rev.: $93,891,769
Assets: $69,394,427
Liabilities: $51,186,044
Net Worth: $18,208,383
Earnings: ($10,427,290)
Emp.: 683
Fiscal Year-end: 04/03/22
Household Product Mfr & Distr
N.A.I.C.S.: 335220
Dan Walden *(CFO)*

PROCORP SAB DE CV
Adolfo Lopez Mateos Boulevard 2009 Office 303, 01010, Mexico, DF, Mexico
Tel.: (52) 91728506
Web Site: https://procorp-sab.mx
Year Founded: 1986
PROCORP—(MEX)
Sales Range: Less than $1 Million
Financial Investment Services
N.A.I.C.S.: 523999
Rafael Terrazas Zuniga *(Fin Dir & Dir-Administration & Legal)*

PROCREDIT HOLDING AG & CO. KGAA
Rohmerplatz 33-37, 60486, Frankfurt am Main, Germany
Tel.: (49) 699514370 De
Web Site: https://www.procredit-holding.com
Year Founded: 1998
PCZ—(DEU)
Assets: $10,761,595,514
Liabilities: $9,675,619,247
Net Worth: $1,085,976,267
Earnings: $125,145,742
Emp.: 3,834
Fiscal Year-end: 12/31/23
Bank Holding Company
N.A.I.C.S.: 551111
Claus-Peter Zeitinger *(Chm-Supervisory Bd)*

Subsidiaries:

Administracion y Recuperacion de Cartera Michoacan S. A. de C. V., Sofom, E. N. R (1)
Ecuador 20-E Las Americas Morelia, Michoacan, Mexico
Tel.: (52) 14432041445
Web Site: http://www.ardec.mx
Special Vehicle Services
N.A.I.C.S.: 525990

Banco ProCredit S.A. (1)
Avenida Jean Paul Genie, Managua, Nicaragua
Tel.: (505) 22557676
Web Site: http://www.procredit.com.ni
Finance & Banking Services
N.A.I.C.S.: 522110

Banco ProCredit S.A. (1)
1 Calle Poniente No 3538 Boulevard Constitucion Colonia Escalon, San Salvador, El Salvador
Tel.: (503) 22237676
Web Site: http://www.bancoprocredit.com.sv
Finance & Banking Services
N.A.I.C.S.: 522110

Banco ProCredit S.A. (1)
Av Amazonas Y Atahuapa Esq Edificio Banco Procredit 3Rd Floor, Quito, Ecuador
Tel.: (593) 800100400
Web Site: https://www.bancoprocredit.com.ec
Finance & Banking Services
N.A.I.C.S.: 522110

Banco Pyme Los Andes ProCredit S.A. (1)
Av 16 de Julio 1486 Zona Central El Prado, La Paz, Bolivia
Tel.: (591) 222313133
Web Site: http://www.losandesprocredit.com
Finance & Banking Services
N.A.I.C.S.: 522110

JSC ProCredit Bank (1)
21 Al Kazbegi Ave, 0160, Tbilisi, Georgia
Tel.: (995) 322202222
Web Site: https://www.procreditbank.ge
Banking Services
N.A.I.C.S.: 522110

ProConfianza S.A. de C.V (1)
Av de la Luz 244, 76110, Queretaro, Mexico
Tel.: (52) 4422980322
Finance & Banking Services
N.A.I.C.S.: 522110

ProCredit Academy GmbH (1)
Hammelbacherstrasse 2, 64658, Furth, Germany
Tel.: (49) 625320080
Professional Training Services
N.A.I.C.S.: 611430

ProCredit Bank (Bulgaria) E.A.D. (1)
26 Todor Aleksandrov Blvd, 1303, Sofia, Bulgaria
Tel.: (359) 70017070
Web Site: https://www.procreditbank.bg
Finance & Banking Services
N.A.I.C.S.: 522110
Rumyana Todorova *(Member-Mgmt Bd)*

ProCredit Bank AD (1)
Manapo no 7, 1000, Skopje, North Macedonia
Tel.: (389) 22446000
Web Site: https://www.pcb.mk
Sales Range: $10-24.9 Million
Banking Services
N.A.I.C.S.: 522110
Emilija Spirovska *(Member-Mgmt Bd)*

ProCredit Bank CJSC (1)
105/1 Teryan street area 11 Citadel Business Centre, Yerevan, 0009, Armenia
Tel.: (374) 11202020
Web Site: http://www.procreditbank.am
Finance & Banking Services
N.A.I.C.S.: 522110
Avtandil Gogoli *(Exec Dir)*

ProCredit Bank Congo S.A.R.L. (1)
4b Avenue des Aviateurs, Kinshasa, Gombe, Congo, Democratic Republic of
Tel.: (243) 818302700
Web Site: http://www.equitybank.cd
Finance & Banking Services
N.A.I.C.S.: 522110
Celestin Mukeba Muntuabu *(CEO)*

ProCredit Bank S.A. (1)
62-64 Buzesti Street nr 62 - 64 sector 1, Bucharest, Romania
Tel.: (40) 212016000
Web Site: https://www.procreditbank.ro
Finance & Banking Services
N.A.I.C.S.: 522110

ProCredit Bank S.A. (1)
65 Stefan cel Mare si Sfant Ave office 901, MD-2001, Chisinau, Moldova
Tel.: (373) 22270707
Web Site: http://www.procreditbank.md
Finance & Banking Services
N.A.I.C.S.: 522110
Olga Bulat *(Chm-Mgmt Bd)*

ProCredit Bank Sh.a (1)
Tel.: (383) 38555555
Web Site: https://www.procreditbank-kos.com
Finance & Banking Services
N.A.I.C.S.: 522110

ProCredit Bank a.d. (1)
17 Milutina Milankovica Street, 11070, Novi Beograd, Serbia
Tel.: (381) 112057000
Web Site: http://www.procreditbank.rs
Finance & Banking Services
N.A.I.C.S.: 522110
Svetlana Tolmaceva Dingarac *(Co-Chm-Exec Bd)*

ProCredit Bank d.d. Sarajevo (1)
Franca Lehara bb, 71000, Sarajevo, Bosnia & Herzegovina
Tel.: (387) 33250950
Web Site: https://www.procreditbank.ba
Rev.: $8,710,660
Assets: $316,627,006
Liabilities: $288,510,465
Net Worth: $28,116,541
Earnings: ($892,652)
Emp.: 167
Fiscal Year-end: 12/31/2019
Banking Services
N.A.I.C.S.: 521110
Amir Salkanovic *(Pres)*

ProCredit Bank sh.a (1)
Rr Dritan Hoxha Nd 92 H 15 Njesia Bashkiake Nr 11, PO Box 1026, Tirana, 1026, Albania
Tel.: (355) 42389389
Web Site: https://www.procreditbank.com.al
Finance & Banking Services
N.A.I.C.S.: 522110

Quipu GmbH (1)
Konigsberger Strasse 1, 60487, Frankfurt, Germany
Tel.: (49) 695069900
Information Technology Consulting Services
N.A.I.C.S.: 541512

PROCUDAN A/S
Bronzevej 1, 6000, Kolding, Denmark
Tel.: (45) 75508000 DK
Web Site: http://www.procudan.dk
Year Founded: 1901
Sales Range: $50-74.9 Million
Emp.: 100
Food, Pharmaceutical & Health Product Ingredients & Packaging Supplies Distr
N.A.I.C.S.: 425120
Tommy H. Pedersen *(Owner & Mng Dir)*

PROCURITAS PARTNERS AB
Biblioteksgatan 3 4th Floor, 111 46, Stockholm, Sweden
Tel.: (46) 8506 143 00 SE
Web Site: http://www.procuritas.com
Year Founded: 1986
Emp.: 15
Investment Management Service
N.A.I.C.S.: 523940
Hans Wikse *(Mng Partner)*

Subsidiaries:

Calorex Heat Pumps Ltd (1)
The Causeway, Maldon, CM9 4XD, Essex, United Kingdom
Tel.: (44) 1621856611
Web Site: http://www.calorex.com
Emp.: 500
Heat Pump Mfr
N.A.I.C.S.: 333914
Richard Carrington *(Mng Dir)*

Contex A/S (1)
2 Svanevang, 3450, Allerod, Denmark
Tel.: (45) 48 14 11 22
Web Site: http://www.contex.com
Sales Range: $25-49.9 Million
Printing Imaging & Scanning Equipment Mfr
N.A.I.C.S.: 333248
Aage Snorgaard *(CEO)*

Subsidiary (US):

Contex Americas Inc. (2)
6010 Executive Blvd Ste 702, Rockville, MD 20852
Tel.: (703) 964-9850
Web Site: http://www.contex.com
Printing, Imaging & Scanning Equipment Mfr
N.A.I.C.S.: 333248
Steve Blanken *(Gen Mgr)*

Dantherm HVAC Holding A/S (1)
Marienlystvej 65, PO Box 502, 7800, Skive, Denmark
Tel.: (45) 96143700
Web Site: http://www.dantherm.com
Emp.: 360

PROCURITAS PARTNERS AB

Procuritas Partners AB—(Continued)

Holding Company; Air Dehumidification, Heating, Air Conditioning, Ventilation & Electronics Cooling Equipment Design, Mfr & Installation Services
N.A.I.C.S.: 551112
Jesper Holm Thorstensen (Mng Dir)

Subsidiary (Non-US):

Dantherm AB (2)
Virkesgatan 5, 614 31, Soderkoping, Sweden
Tel.: (46) 121 130 40
Web Site: http://www.dantherm.com
Ventilation Equipment Distr
N.A.I.C.S.: 444180

Dantherm AS (2)
Lokkeasveien 26, Skallestad, 3138, Tonsberg, Norway
Tel.: (47) 33 35 16 00
Web Site: http://www.dantherm.com
Dehumidifiers & Ventilation Equipments Distr
N.A.I.C.S.: 423720
Vidar Rui (Gen Mgr)

Subsidiary (Domestic):

Dantherm Air Handling A/S (2)
Marienlystvej 65, 7800, Skive, Denmark
Tel.: (45) 96143700
Web Site: http://www.dantherm.com
Climate Control Systems Mfr
N.A.I.C.S.: 333415
Jesper Thorstensen (Mng Dir)

Subsidiary (Non-US):

Dantherm Air Handling Ltd. (2)
12 Windmill Business Park Windmill Road, Clevedon, BS21 6SR, North Somerset, United Kingdom
Tel.: (44) 1275 87 68 51
Web Site: http://www.dantherm.com
Climate Control & Air Handling Systems Distr
N.A.I.C.S.: 423730
Ian K. Furmidge (Mng Dir)

Polarn O. Pyret AB (1)
Drottninggatan 33 4TR, 111 51, Stockholm, Sweden
Tel.: (46) 841052210
Web Site: http://www.polarnopyret.se
Sales Range: $25-49.9 Million
Baby, Children's & Maternity Wear Retailer
N.A.I.C.S.: 458110

Procuritas Partners GmbH (1)
Niederfelbenweg 9, CH-8702, Zollikon, Switzerland
Tel.: (41) 798 87 54 74
Web Site: http://www.procuritas.ch
Financial Investment Services
N.A.I.C.S.: 523940
Erik Fougner (Partner)

PRODAPT SOLUTIONS PRIVATE LIMITED
No 283/4 4th Floor Prince Infocity II Rajiv Gandhi Salai Kandancha, Old Mahabalipuram Road, Chennai, Tamil Nadu, India
Tel.: (91) 4449033088
Web Site: http://www.prodapt.com
Year Founded: 1999
Telecommunication Servicesb
N.A.I.C.S.: 517121
Vedant Jhaver (Founder & Chm)

PRODIA SAS
93bis rue de Curembourg, 45440, Fleury-les-Aubrais, France
Tel.: (33) 238619090
Web Site: http://www.prodia.fr
Year Founded: 1998
Sales Range: $25-49.9 Million
Emp.: 400
Pet Food Mfr
N.A.I.C.S.: 311111
Bernard Lafay (CEO)

Subsidiaries:

Prodia - CUISEAUX PLANT (1)
chemin Ronde, 71480, Cuiseaux, Bresse, France
Tel.: (33) 3 85 72 76 63
Recyclable Material Distr
N.A.I.C.S.: 423930

Prodia - SAINTE FLORENCE Plant (1)
les Hauteurs, 85140, Sainte-Florence, France
Tel.: (33) 2 51 66 13 76
Recyclable Material Distr
N.A.I.C.S.: 423930

PRODIALOG 2000 MARKETING & COMMUNICATION GMBH
Helmtrudenstrasse 8, 80805, Munich, Germany
Tel.: (49) 894194990
Web Site: http://www.prodialog2000.com
Year Founded: 1995
Sales Range: $25-49.9 Million
Emp.: 13
Advertising Agencies
N.A.I.C.S.: 541810
Karl-Heinz Langhans (Chm & CEO)

PRODIGY PUBLIC COMPANY LIMITED
7/3 Moo 3, Bang Krabao Subdistrict Nakhon Chai Si District, Nakhon Pathom, 73120, Thailand
Tel.: (66) 34332611
Web Site: https://www.prodigy.co.th
Year Founded: 1992
PDG—(THA)
Rev.: $18,519,792
Assets: $20,471,587
Liabilities: $3,107,492
Net Worth: $17,364,095
Earnings: $843,550
Emp.: 270
Fiscal Year-end: 12/31/23
Plastics Bottle Mfr
N.A.I.C.S.: 326160
Prayoon Boonpraserd (Chm)

PRODIGY VENTURES, INC.
TD Canada Trust Tower 161 Bay Street Suite 4420, PO Box 125, Toronto, M5J 2S1, ON, Canada
Tel.: (416) 488-7700 Ca
Web Site: http://www.prodigy.ventures
Year Founded: 2008
GNFI—(TSXV)
Rev.: $1,517,618
Assets: $2,765,648
Liabilities: $512,192
Net Worth: $2,253,456
Earnings: $1,042,547
Fiscal Year-end: 12/31/23
Computer System Design Services
N.A.I.C.S.: 541512
Tom Beckerman (Founder, Chm & CEO)

Subsidiaries:

Ficanex Technology Inc. (1)
80 Richmond St W Suite 1401, Toronto, M5H 2A3, ON, Canada
Tel.: (905) 829-4343
Web Site: https://tunl.ca
Investment Banking & Financial Services
N.A.I.C.S.: 522320

IDVerifact Inc. (1)
1 University Ave Suite 1603, Toronto, M5J 2P1, ON, Canada
Tel.: (416) 488-7700
Web Site: https://idverifact.com
Digital Identity & Entertainment Services
N.A.I.C.S.: 518210

TCB Corporation (1)

PRODOR A.D.
Masarikova br 4, Novi Sad, Serbia
Tel.: (381) 21 528063
Year Founded: 1989
Sales Range: Less than $1 Million
Emp.: 6
Structural Metal Product Mfr
N.A.I.C.S.: 332312

PRODUCT SHIPPING LIMITED
88 Vouliagmenis Avenue, Elliniko, 16777, Athens, Greece
Tel.: (30) 211 10 24 000 MH
Year Founded: 2014
Sales Range: $25-49.9 Million
Petroleum Products Shipping Services
N.A.I.C.S.: 488510
Stamatis Molaris (Chm & CEO)

PRODUCTIVE TECHNOLOGIES COMPANY LIMITED
Room 5507 55/Floor The Center 99 Queens Road, Central, China (Hong Kong)
Tel.: (852) 39031327 BM
Web Site: http://www.idgenergyinv.com
Year Founded: 1992
0650—(HKG)
Rev.: $17,841,287
Assets: $370,573,212
Liabilities: $36,069,515
Net Worth: $334,503,697
Earnings: ($54,952,445)
Emp.: 101
Fiscal Year-end: 03/31/22
Holding Company: Energy Assets Investment & Management
N.A.I.C.S.: 551112
Jingbo Wang (Chm & CEO)

PRODUCTOS ALIMENTICIOS PASCUAL, S.A.
Way Jose Agustin Arango and Transfer, Section 0823-05837, Aquilino de la Guardia and 5 B South Ave, Panama, Panama
Tel.: (507) 217 2233
PASC—(PAN)
Sales Range: Less than $1 Million
Cookie Product Mfr
N.A.I.C.S.: 311821
Juan Carlos Jaramillo Arias (Pres & Gen Mgr)

PRODUCTOS DAMEL, S.L.
Paseo de la Estacion S/N Pol Ind I-4 Parc 19 Apdo 207, 03330, Crevillente, Spain
Tel.: (34) 965 406 410 ES
Web Site: http://www.damel.com
Year Founded: 1860
Confectionery & Snack Mfr & Whslr
N.A.I.C.S.: 311340
Silverio Lopez (Dir-Indus & Products)

Subsidiaries:

Productos Damel, S.L. - Nuts & Snacks Division (1)
Calle Ciudad de Barcelona 20, Pol Ind Fuente del Jarro, 46988, Paterna, Spain
Tel.: (34) 961 324 777
Web Site: http://www.damel.com
Snack Mfr & Whslr
N.A.I.C.S.: 311919
Margarita Pato Esteban (Dir-HR)

Productos Damel, S.L. - Valladolid Plant (1)
Calle TopacioNo 7 Poligono de San Cristobal, 47012, Valladolid, Spain
Tel.: (34) 902363522
Emp.: 70
Food Mfr
N.A.I.C.S.: 311999

INTERNATIONAL PUBLIC

PRODUCTOS DE CONCRETO S.A.
San Rafael DeAla Juela, Apartado 362, 1000, San Jose, Costa Rica
Tel.: (506) 2587 1400
Web Site: http://www.pc.co.cr
Sales Range: $300-349.9 Million
Emp.: 850
Concrete Pipe Mfr
N.A.I.C.S.: 327332

PRODUCTOS TOLEDANO, S.A.
Zone 9A, PO Box 0834-00174, Panama, Panama
Tel.: (507) 290 8200
Web Site: http://www.toledano.com
Year Founded: 1954
TOLE—(PAN)
Sales Range: Less than $1 Million
Poultry Processing Services
N.A.I.C.S.: 311615
Richard R. M. Toledano (Pres)

PRODUITS PHOENICIA INC.
2605 Pitfiled Boulevard, Saint Laurent, H4S 1T2, QC, Canada
Tel.: (514) 389-6363
Web Site: http://www.phoeniciagroup.com
Year Founded: 1989
Rev.: $12,958,000
Emp.: 100
Food Product Whslr
N.A.I.C.S.: 424420
Jimmy CheaibPres (Pres)

PRODUTORES ENERGETICOS DE MANSO S.A.
Rua Jardim Botanico n 674 Sala 316 - Jardim Botanico, Rio de Janeiro, 22461-000, RJ, Brazil
Tel.: (55) 988683168
Web Site: https://www.promanmt.com.br
Year Founded: 1997
PRMN3B—(BRAZ)
Rev.: $1,794,539
Assets: $3,220,814
Liabilities: $3,354,353
Net Worth: ($133,539)
Earnings: ($105,100)
Fiscal Year-end: 12/31/23
Eletric Power Generation Services
N.A.I.C.S.: 221118

PRODVINALCO S.A.
Calea Baciului nr 2-4, Cluj, Cluj-Napoca, Romania
Tel.: (40) 372641910
Web Site: https://www.prodvinalco.ro
Year Founded: 1932
VAC—(BUC)
Rev.: $15,591,690
Assets: $23,715,888
Liabilities: $6,527,605
Net Worth: $17,188,283
Earnings: $3,802,352
Emp.: 104
Fiscal Year-end: 12/31/23
Alcoholic Beverages Mfr
N.A.I.C.S.: 312130

PRODVINALCO SA
Bd George Cosbuc Nr 257, Galati, Romania
Tel.: (40) 236 461955
Sales Range: $1-9.9 Million
Emp.: 93
Wine Mfr
N.A.I.C.S.: 312130

PRODWARE SA
45 quai de la Seine, 75019, Paris, France
Tel.: (33) 979999799 FR

Web Site:
https://www.prodwaregroup.com
Year Founded: 1989
ALPRO—(EUR)
Rev.: $203,195,554
Assets: $380,243,902
Liabilities: $271,571,336
Net Worth: $108,672,566
Earnings: $17,144,399
Emp.: 1,100
Fiscal Year-end: 12/31/22
Computer & Information Technology Services
N.A.I.C.S.: 541512
Philippe Bouaziz (Founder & Chm)

Subsidiaries:

CKL Software GmbH (1)
Luruper Chaussee 125 House 6, 22761, Hamburg, Germany
Tel.: (49) 40533009990
Web Site: http://www.ckl-kore.de
Information Technology Services
N.A.I.C.S.: 541519
Thorsten Behrens (Mng Dir)

Prodware (UK) Limited (1)
Waterfold Business Park, Bury, BL9 7BR, Lancashire, United Kingdom
Tel.: (44) 1617056000
Web Site: http://www.prodwaregroup.com
Sales Range: $25-49.9 Million
Computer System Design Services
N.A.I.C.S.: 541512
Alain Conrard (CEO)

Prodware Belgium SA (1)
Waterloo Office Park Dreve Richelle 161 / L, 1410, Waterloo, Belgium
Tel.: (32) 490455103
System Integration Services
N.A.I.C.S.: 541512
Said Hammani (Project Mgr)

Prodware Belux (1)
Waterloo Office Park Dreve Richelle 161 / L, 1410, Waterloo, Belgium
Tel.: (32) 490455103
Web Site: http://www.prodware.be
Sales Range: $10-24.9 Million
System Integration Design Services
N.A.I.C.S.: 541512

Prodware Czech Republic, sro (1)
Videnska 4, 779 00, Olomouc, Czech Republic
Tel.: (420) 585 242 854
Web Site: http://www.prodwaregroup.com
Information Technology Consulting Services
N.A.I.C.S.: 541512
George Knap (Mng Dir)

Prodware Deutschland AG (1)
Notkestrasse 7, 22607, Hamburg, Germany
Tel.: (49) 40899580
Web Site: http://www.prodwaregroup.com
Sales Range: $25-49.9 Million
Computer System Design Services
N.A.I.C.S.: 541512

Prodware Israel Ltd. (1)
Rappaport Street 3 Kfar Saba Green Mall 16th Floor, PO Box 59, Kfar Saba, 4465142, Israel
Tel.: (972) 732770000
Information Technology Services
N.A.I.C.S.: 541519
Elad Bracha (CFO)

Prodware Luxembourg Sarl (1)
24 Rue Robert Krieps, 4702, Petange, Luxembourg
Tel.: (352) 26 65 25 55
Information Technology Consulting Services
N.A.I.C.S.: 541512

Prodware Maroc S.A.R.L (1)
71 Boulevard d'Anfa, 20000, Casablanca, Morocco
Tel.: (212) 522260565
Information Technology Services
N.A.I.C.S.: 541512
Abdelfettah Chouyab (Project Mgr)

Prodware Netherlands B.V. (1)
Van Voordenpark 1a, 5301 KP, Zaltbommel, Netherlands
Tel.: (31) 418 68 3500

Emp.: 5
Computer System Design Services
N.A.I.C.S.: 541512

Prodware Spain, S.A. (1)
Avenida del General Peron 38 Edificio Masters I Planta 10, 28020, Madrid, Spain
Tel.: (34) 918316970
Web Site: http://www.prodwaregroup.com
Information Technology Consulting Services
N.A.I.C.S.: 541512

Prodware Tunisie (1)
44 Rue IBN Charaf-2eme etage, Belvedere, 1002, Tunis, Tunisia
Tel.: (216) 71 287 538
Web Site: http://www.prodware.tn
Information Technology Consulting Services
N.A.I.C.S.: 541512

PROEL A.D.
Draze Markovica 25, Pozarevac, Serbia
Tel.: (381) 12 221 955
Year Founded: 2002
PRSPO—(BEL)
Sales Range: Less than $1 Million
Electric Device Mfr
N.A.I.C.S.: 334419
Vesna Milosevic (Exec Dir)

PROFARMA DISTRIBUIDORA DE PRODUTOS FARMACEUTICOS S.A.
Av Ayrton Senna 2 150 Bloco P 3rd floor, Barra da Tijuca, Rio de Janeiro, 22775-900, Brazil
Tel.: (55) 2140090200
Web Site:
https://www.profarma.com.br
Year Founded: 1961
PFRM3—(BRAZ)
Rev.: $1,548,371,279
Assets: $882,702,467
Liabilities: $607,586,727
Net Worth: $275,115,740
Earnings: $13,917,877
Emp.: 7,904
Fiscal Year-end: 12/31/23
Pharmaceutical Products Distr
N.A.I.C.S.: 424210
Maximiliano Guimaraes Fischer (CFO)

PROFESSIONAL COMPUTER TECHNOLOGY LIMITED
5F No 75 Sec 1 Xintai 5Th, Xizhi Dist, New Taipei City, 221, Taiwan
Tel.: (886) 26980098
Web Site: https://www.pct.com.tw
Year Founded: 1992
6270—(TPE)
Rev.: $144,031,329
Assets: $82,338,430
Liabilities: $33,228,465
Net Worth: $49,109,965
Earnings: $5,213,051
Fiscal Year-end: 12/31/22
Electronic Components Distr
N.A.I.C.S.: 423690
Tim Fu (Chm)

PROFESSIONAL IMO PARTNERS S.A.
Str Ziduri Mosi nr 23 Cladirea Centrului Comercial Veranda Mall, Biroul 3 Sector 2 Mun, Bucharest, Romania
Tel.: (40) 212521077
Web Site:
https://www.prodplastimobiliare.ro
PPLI—(BUC)
Rev.: $283,274
Assets: $47,511,697
Liabilities: $28,756
Net Worth: $47,482,941
Earnings: $37,339
Emp.: 3
Fiscal Year-end: 12/31/22
Real Estate Development Services

N.A.I.C.S.: 531390
Mihaela Ramona Popescu (Pres)

PROFESSIONAL MEDICAL EXPERTISE COMPANY
Office 503 Floor 5 Rawdah Bussiness Center Prince Saud-AlFaisal Street, Ar Rawdah, Jeddah, 23434, Saudi Arabia
Tel.: (966) 126124949
Web Site: https://www.promedex.com
Year Founded: 2010
9574—(SAU)
Rev.: $46,949,086
Assets: $53,108,831
Liabilities: $33,596,452
Net Worth: $19,512,379
Earnings: $5,083,433
Emp.: 168
Fiscal Year-end: 12/31/22
Medical Device Distr
N.A.I.C.S.: 423690
Samir Sulaiman Abdullah Alumran (Chm)

PROFESSIONAL SYSTEMS (PVT) LTD
22 - A Main Service Road Sector I - 8/2, Islamabad, 44000, Pakistan
Tel.: (92) 514939045 PK
Web Site:
http://www.professionalsystems.pk
Year Founded: 2000
Analytical Laboratory Instrument Mfr
N.A.I.C.S.: 334516
Saeed Ahmed Khawaja (CEO)

PROFESSIONAL WASTE TECHNOLOGY (1999) PUBLIC COMPANY LIMITED
1184/38-39 Soi Paholyothin 32 Paholyothin Road, Chandrakaserm Sub-district Chatuchak District, Bangkok, 10900, Thailand
Tel.: (66) 9429480
Web Site: https://www.prowaste.co.th
Year Founded: 1999
Sales Range: $10-24.9 Million
Industrial Waste Management Services
N.A.I.C.S.: 562998
Vilailuck Skulpakdee (CEO)

PROFIDATA GROUP AG
In Der Luberzen 40, CH 8902, Urdorf, Switzerland
Tel.: (41) 447364747 CH
Web Site:
http://www.profidatagroup.com
Year Founded: 1985
Sales Range: $10-24.9 Million
Emp.: 140
Holding Company; Asset Management Software Publisher
N.A.I.C.S.: 551112
Roger Wildi (Co-CEO)

Subsidiaries:

Profidata AG (1)
In der Luberzen 40, Urdorf, 8902, Switzerland
Tel.: (41) 44 736 4747
Asset Management Software Publisher
N.A.I.C.S.: 513210

Profidata Services AG (1)
Stefan Straws 3, 60313, Frankfurt, Germany
Tel.: (49) 69 29 72 89 50
Web Site: http://www.profidatagroup.com
Investment & Wealth Management Software Publisher
N.A.I.C.S.: 513210
Gunther Glabbatz (Reg Dir)

itechx GmbH (1)
Innovationsring 20, 66115, Saarbrucken, Germany
Tel.: (49) 681 7 61 87 0

Web Site: http://www.itechx.de
Asset Management Services
N.A.I.C.S.: 523940
Volker Braunberger (Mng Dir)

PROFILAGE OUEST
Zone Indust R Hautiere, L Hermitage, 35590, Rennes, France
Tel.: (33) 299640000
Web Site: http://www.spo1.com
Rev.: $26,900,000
Emp.: 40
Cold Finishing Of Steel Shapes
N.A.I.C.S.: 331221
Laurent Thouvignon (Dir)

PROFILE SYSTEMS & SOFTWARE S.R.L.
199 Syngrou Ave, 171 21, Athens, Greece
Tel.: (30) 2109301200
Web Site: https://www.profilesw.com
Year Founded: 1990
PROF—(ATH)
Rev.: $33,224,880
Assets: $61,590,206
Liabilities: $26,392,667
Net Worth: $35,197,539
Earnings: $4,252,414
Emp.: 193
Fiscal Year-end: 12/31/23
Banking & Investment Software Development Services
N.A.I.C.S.: 541511
Babis P. Stasinopoulos (Chm, Chm, Pres & Pres)

Subsidiaries:

Centevo Ab (1)
Kammakargatan 9 A, 11140, Stockholm, Sweden
Tel.: (46) 841014210
Web Site: https://centevo.se
Information Technology Services
N.A.I.C.S.: 541512

Global Soft SA (1)
199 Syggrou Ave, 17121, Nea Smyrni, Greece
Tel.: (30) 2109301200
Web Site: http://www.globalsoft.gr
Information Technology Development Services
N.A.I.C.S.: 541519

Login S.A. (1)
56 Boulevard de la Mission Marchand, 92418, Courbevoie, Cedex, France
Tel.: (33) 141168800
Web Site: http://www.login-sa.com
Information Technology Development Services
N.A.I.C.S.: 541519
Evangelos Angelides (Pres)

Profile Digital Services S.A. (1)
199 Syngrou Street, 17121, Nea Smyrni, Greece
Tel.: (30) 9301200
Web Site: https://www.profileds.gr
Information Technology Services
N.A.I.C.S.: 541512

Profile Software (UK) Ltd. (1)
92/93 Great Russell Street, Marylebone, London, WC1B 3PS, United Kingdom
Tel.: (44) 2039411941
Information Technology Development Services
N.A.I.C.S.: 541519

Profile Systems & Software (Cyprus) Ltd. (1)
2 Kritis str Office 401, 1060, Nicosia, Cyprus
Tel.: (357) 22458050
Information Technology Development Services
N.A.I.C.S.: 541519

PROFILGRUPPEN AB
Ostra Industrivagen, 364 31, Aseda, Sweden

PROFILGRUPPEN AB

ProfilGruppen AB—(Continued)
Tel.: (46) 47455000
Web Site: http://www.profilgruppen.se
PROF-B—(OMX)
Rev.: $252,568,678
Assets: $138,113,837
Liabilities: $87,976,622
Net Worth: $50,137,215
Earnings: $8,710,557
Emp.: 525
Fiscal Year-end: 12/31/22
Customized Aluminum Extrusions & Components Mfr
N.A.I.C.S.: 331318
Ulrika Svensson *(CFO-Acting & Mgr-HR)*

Subsidiaries:

ProfilGruppen Extrusions AB (1)
Ostra Industrivagen, 364 31, Aseda, Kronoberg, Sweden
Tel.: (46) 47455000
Web Site: http://www.profilGruppen.se
Sales Range: $100-124.9 Million
Emp.: 466
Aluminum Extrusions Mfr
N.A.I.C.S.: 331314

Subsidiary (Non-US):

ProfilGruppen Ltd (2)
Unit 26 Basepoint Business Ctr Isidore Rd, Bromsgrove, B60 3ET, Worcestershire, United Kingdom
Tel.: (44) 1527834640
Web Site: http://www.profilgruppen.com
Aluminum Extrusions Mfr
N.A.I.C.S.: 331314

ProfilGruppen Norge AS (2)
Enebakkveien 304, 1188, Oslo, Akershus, Norway
Tel.: (47) 9 139 2604
Web Site: https://www.profilgruppen.se
Emp.: 2
Aluminum Extrusions Mfr
N.A.I.C.S.: 333514

ProfilGruppen Manufacturing AB (1)
Ostra Industriomradet, Aseda, 36070, Sweden
Tel.: (46) 47455000
Web Site: http://www.profilgruppen.se
Sales Range: $25-49.9 Million
Emp.: 45
Engineeering Services
N.A.I.C.S.: 541330

PROFIMEDIA.CZ A.S.
K Vinici 1256, Pardubice, 530 02, Czech Republic
Tel.: (420) 466 897 100   CZ
Web Site: http://www.profimedia.cz
Year Founded: 2000
Marketing Photo & Illustration Publisher & Lessor
N.A.I.C.S.: 541890
Pavel Macku *(CEO)*

PROFIT BUILDING INDUSTRIES LTD.
3 Hayezira Street, Ramat Gan, 52521, Israel
Tel.: (972) 37518115
Year Founded: 1990
Sales Range: $1-9.9 Million
Real Estate Manangement Services
N.A.I.C.S.: 531390
Guy Itzhaki *(CEO)*

PROFIT CULTURAL & CREATIVE GROUP CO., LTD.
No1 Chuangye Road HiTech Zone, Fuzhou, 350108, China
Tel.: (86) 59187820088
Web Site: https://www.profit-cc.com
Year Founded: 1995
300640—(CHIN)
Rev.: $101,560,554
Assets: $128,861,299
Liabilities: $13,585,997
Net Worth: $115,275,302
Earnings: $3,715,299
Fiscal Year-end: 12/31/23
Household Product Mfr & Distr
N.A.I.C.S.: 316990
Wu Tifang *(Chm)*

PROFORM SA
8 Route Du Caillou, Chaponost, 69630, Lyon, France
Tel.: (33) 472671300
Web Site: http://www.proform.fr
Rev.: $28,500,000
Emp.: 172
Industrial Valves
N.A.I.C.S.: 332911
Gerard Poichot *(CHM)*

PROFOTO HOLDING AB
Landsvagen 57, 172 65, Sundbyberg, Sweden
Tel.: (46) 84475300
Web Site: https://www.profoto.com
Year Founded: 1968
PRFO—(OMX)
Rev.: $80,875,800
Assets: $73,531,800
Liabilities: $37,638,000
Net Worth: $35,893,800
Earnings: $17,809,200
Emp.: 135
Fiscal Year-end: 12/31/22
Holding Company
N.A.I.C.S.: 551112
Anders Hedebark *(Pres)*

Subsidiaries:

Profoto AB (1)
Landsvagen 57, SE-172 65, Sundbyberg, Sweden
Tel.: (46) 84475300
Web Site: https://www.profoto.com
Glass Product Mfr & Distr
N.A.I.C.S.: 327215

Profoto B.V. (1)
Kinderhuissingel 6A, 2013 AS, Haarlem, Netherlands
Tel.: (31) 237200901
Glass Product Mfr & Distr
N.A.I.C.S.: 327215

Profoto KK (1)
HSB Teppozu Bldg 3F 1-1-12, Minato Chuo-ku, Tokyo, 104-0043, Japan
Tel.: (81) 332061861
Glass Product Mfr & Distr
N.A.I.C.S.: 327215

Profoto US Inc. (1)
220 Park Ave Ste 120, Florham Park, NJ 07932
Tel.: (973) 822-1300
Glass Product Mfr & Distr
N.A.I.C.S.: 327215

PROFOUND MEDICAL CORP.
2400 Skymark Avenue Unit 6, Mississauga, L4W 5K5, ON, Canada
Tel.: (647) 476-1350   ON
Web Site: https://www.profoundmedical.com
Year Founded: 2014
PROF—(NASDAQ)
Rev.: $6,681,000
Assets: $64,421,000
Liabilities: $12,417,000
Net Worth: $52,004,000
Earnings: ($28,669,000)
Emp.: 131
Fiscal Year-end: 12/31/22
Investment Services
N.A.I.C.S.: 523999
Arun Swarup Menawat *(Chm & CEO)*

Subsidiaries:

Profound Medical GmbH (1)
Kehrwieder 9, 20547, Hamburg, Germany
Tel.: (49) 40808093342
Medical Technologies Development Services

N.A.I.C.S.: 541714
Hartmut Warnken *(Mng Dir & VP-Sls-Intl)*

PROGEN HOLDINGS LIMITED
28 Riverside Road 04-01 Progen Building, Singapore, 739085, Singapore
Tel.: (65) 67527787   SG
Year Founded: 1996
583—(CAT)
Rev.: $3,264,913
Assets: $24,223,046
Liabilities: $4,696,554
Net Worth: $19,526,491
Earnings: ($823,268)
Fiscal Year-end: 12/31/23
Holding Company
N.A.I.C.S.: 551112
Lee Ee *(Founder & Mng Dir)*

PROGER S.P.A.
Via Valadier 42, 00193, Rome, Italy
Tel.: (39) 06448771
Web Site: http://www.proger.it
Sales Range: $25-49.9 Million
Emp.: 129
Engineeering Services
N.A.I.C.S.: 541330
Claudio Recchi *(Chm)*

PROGILITY PLC
7th Floor 95 Aldwych, London, WC2B 4JF, United Kingdom
Tel.: (44) 207 751 7108
Web Site: http://www.progility.com
Year Founded: 2000
Rev.: $93,635,545
Assets: $62,004,931
Liabilities: $59,220,263
Net Worth: $2,784,668
Earnings: ($560,444)
Emp.: 674
Fiscal Year-end: 06/30/17
Business Training & Development Products & Services
N.A.I.C.S.: 611430
Wayne Malcom Bos *(Chm & CEO-Interim)*

Subsidiaries:

TFPL Limited (1)
2nd Floor Strand Bridge House 138-142 The Strand, London, WC2R 1HH, United Kingdom
Tel.: (44) 77517169
Web Site: http://www.tfpl.com
Sales Range: $1-9.9 Million
Emp.: 80
Human Resource Consulting Services
N.A.I.C.S.: 541612

PROGRES A.D.
Karadordeva 10, 74000, Doboj, Bosnia & Herzegovina
Tel.: (387) 53241844
Web Site: https://progres-doboj.com
PRGS—(BANJ)
Sales Range: $1-9.9 Million
Emp.: 105
Waste Treatment Services
N.A.I.C.S.: 562219
Maden Spasojevic *(Chm-Supervisory Bd)*

PROGRES A.D.
Ulica Zmaj Jovina broj 8-10, 11000, Belgrade, Serbia
Tel.: (381) 112620192
Web Site: https://www.progres.rs
Year Founded: 1952
PRGS—(BEL)
Sales Range: Less than $1 Million
Emp.: 22
Fuel Products Whslr
N.A.I.C.S.: 457210
Radanovic Zivko *(Mng Dir & Gen Mgr)*

INTERNATIONAL PUBLIC

PROGRESS VULFIX LIMITED
Unit 24 Spring Valley Industrial Estate, Braddan, IM2 2QR, Isle of Man
Tel.: (44) 1624676030
Web Site: http://www.progress-vulfix.com
Year Founded: 1954
Sales Range: $10-24.9 Million
Emp.: 15
Shaving Brushes Mfr & Distr
N.A.I.C.S.: 339994
Mark Watterson *(Mng Dir)*

PROGRESSIO SGR S.P.A.
Corso Venezia 37, 20121, Milan, Italy
Tel.: (39) 02 87 061 1
Web Site: http://www.progressiosgr.it
Year Founded: 2005
Privater Equity Firm
N.A.I.C.S.: 523999
Filippo Gaggini *(Mng Partner)*

Subsidiaries:

Gelit Srl (1)
Via Ninfina km 2700, Doganella di Ninfa, 04013, Latina, Italy
Tel.: (39) 06 961051
Web Site: http://gelit.it
Frozen Food Products & Snacks Mfr & Marketer
N.A.I.C.S.: 311412
Giulio Panella *(Sls Mgr)*

PROGRESSIVE BUILDING SOCIETY
Progressive House 33-37 Wellington Place, Belfast, BT1 6HH, United Kingdom
Tel.: (44) 28 90244926
Web Site: http://www.theprogressive.com
Year Founded: 1914
Rev.: $55,392,803
Assets: $2,410,728,670
Liabilities: $2,247,622,028
Net Worth: $163,106,641
Earnings: $7,873,535
Emp.: 131
Fiscal Year-end: 12/31/19
Mortgage Lending & Other Financial Services
N.A.I.C.S.: 522310

PROGRESSIVE FINANCE LIMITED
Tinkune, PO Box 10390, Kathmandu, Nepal
Tel.: (977) 15199664
Web Site: https://www.pfltd.com.np
PROFL—(NEP)
Rev.: $3,389,976
Assets: $46,862,772
Liabilities: $40,199,685
Net Worth: $6,663,088
Earnings: $90,530
Emp.: 155
Fiscal Year-end: 07/16/22
Financial Services
N.A.I.C.S.: 523999

PROGRESSIVE IMPACT CORPORATION BERHAD
Suite 5 02 MERCU PICORP Lot 10 Jalan Astaka U8/84 Bukit Jelutong, 40150, Shah Alam, Selangor Darul Ehsan, Malaysia
Tel.: (60) 378456566   MY
Web Site: https://www.picorp.com.my
PICORP—(KLS)
Rev.: $19,107,879
Assets: $37,193,828
Liabilities: $19,474,296
Net Worth: $17,719,532
Earnings: ($1,096,003)
Emp.: 589
Fiscal Year-end: 12/31/22
Environmental Consulting Services

N.A.I.C.S.: 541620
Zaidah Mohd Salleh *(Co-Sec)*

Subsidiaries:

Alam Sekitar Eco-Technology Sdn. Bhd. (1)
Suite 5 01B Mercu PICORP Lot 10 Jalan Astaka U8/84, Bukit Jelutong, 40150, Shah Alam, Selangor, Malaysia
Tel.: (60) 37 840 0375
Web Site: https://www.asetsb.com.my
Construction Services
N.A.I.C.S.: 236220
Mus'ab Zainal *(Engr-Process)*

Alam Sekitar Malaysia Sdn. Bhd. (1)
Suite 5 01 A Mercu PICORP Jalan Astaka U8/84, Bukit Jelutong, 40150, Shah Alam, Selangor, Malaysia
Tel.: (60) 378454566
Web Site:
   http://www.enviromalaysia.com.my
Entertainment Services
N.A.I.C.S.: 541620
Azman Sulaiman *(Mgr)*

Saudi ASMA Environmental Solution LLC (1)
No 35 Level 1 Quraysh Business Center Quraysh Street Al Bawadi, Jeddah, 23531, Saudi Arabia
Tel.: (966) 126067724
Web Site: http://www.saudi-asma.com
Entertainment Services
N.A.I.C.S.: 541620

PROGRESSIVE INSURANCE COMPANY LIMITED
505-507 5th Floor Japan Plaza MA Jinnah Road, Karachi, Pakistan
Tel.: (92) 21 2750940
Insurance Management Services
N.A.I.C.S.: 524298

PROGRESSIVE LIFE INSURANCE COMPANY LIMITED
National Scout Bhaban 70/1 Inner Circular Road, Kakrail, Dhaka, 1000, Bangladesh
Tel.: (880) 1815097202
Web Site:
   https://www.progressivelife.com.bd
Year Founded: 2000
PROGRESLIF—(CHT)
Rev.: $6,120,146
Assets: $39,302,701
Liabilities: $5,253,116
Net Worth: $34,049,585
Earnings: $32,626,351
Fiscal Year-end: 12/31/19
Insurance Services
N.A.I.C.S.: 524298
Gulam Mostafa Ahmed *(Vice Chm)*

PROGRESSIVE PATH GROUP HOLDINGS LIMITED
Unit 1108 11/F Tuen Mun Central Square 22 Hoi Wing Road, Tuen Mun, New Territories, China (Hong Kong)
Tel.: (852) 2 617 2831   Ky
Web Site: http://www.ppgh.com.hk
1581—(HKG)
Rev.: $56,182,914
Assets: $50,268,278
Liabilities: $25,506,827
Net Worth: $24,761,451
Earnings: $482,127
Emp.: 512
Fiscal Year-end: 03/31/21
Construction Machinery Rental Services
N.A.I.C.S.: 532412

PROGRESSIVE PLANET SOLUTIONS INC.
724 East Sarcee Street, Kamloops, V2H 1E7, BC, Canada
Tel.: (604) 683-3995   BC
Web Site:
   https://progressiveplanet.com
Year Founded: 2006
ARB3—(DEU)
Rev.: $14,498,339
Assets: $19,432,287
Liabilities: $9,831,662
Net Worth: $9,600,625
Earnings: ($290,193)
Fiscal Year-end: 04/30/24
Mineral Exploration Company
N.A.I.C.S.: 212390
Stephen Harpur *(CEO)*

PROGRESSIVE STAR FINANCE PRIVATE LIMITED
Ground Floor, Flat No. 02, 36A, Elgin Road, Kolkata, 700 020, India
Tel.: (91) 3346020842
Year Founded: 1991
Real Estate
N.A.I.C.S.: 531390

PROGREX VENTURES LTD.
Shri Mohan Parisar Zone-I, Maharana Pratap Nagar, Bhopal, 400 011, Madhya Pradesh, India
Tel.: (91) 7552558656
Web Site:
   http://www.progressivecorp.net
Year Founded: 1981
531265—(BOM)
Rev.: $1,709
Assets: $1,050,410
Liabilities: $141,267
Net Worth: $909,143
Earnings: ($12,982)
Emp.: 2
Fiscal Year-end: 03/31/23
Edible Oil Mfr & Distr
N.A.I.C.S.: 424490
Rakesh Bhatia *(Compliance Officer)*

PROIECT BUCOVINA SA
B-dul 1 Decembrie 1918 No 10, Suceava, Romania
Tel.: (40) 230523254
Web Site:
   http://www.proiectbucovina.ro
Architectural & Engineering Services
N.A.I.C.S.: 541310

PROJECT COORDINATION (AUSTRALIA) PTY LTD
20 Napier Close, Deakin, 2600, ACT, Australia
Tel.: (61) 262851555   AU
Web Site:
   http://www.projectcoord.com.au
Year Founded: 1975
Construction Company
N.A.I.C.S.: 236115
Paul Murphy *(Mng Dir & Mgr-ACT)*

PROJECT DEVELOPMENT INTERNATIONAL LIMITED
PDi House 137 Gallowgate, Aberdeen, AB25 1BU, United Kingdom
Tel.: (44) 1224269060
Web Site: http://www.pdi-ltd.com
Year Founded: 2003
Sales Range: $1-9.9 Million
Emp.: 90
Oil & Gas Industry Engineering Support Services
N.A.I.C.S.: 213112
N. Ramachandran *(Chm)*

Subsidiaries:

Project Development International Limited (1)
PDi House 137 Gallowgate, Aberdeen, AB25 1BU, United Kingdom
Tel.: (44) 1224 269060
Web Site: http://www.pdi-ltd.com
Emp.: 5
Oil & Gas Industry Project Management & Specialized Engineering Support Services
N.A.I.C.S.: 213112

Project Development International Limited (1)
6, Extension Palestine Street, New Maadi, Cairo, Egypt
Tel.: (20) 2 270 270 29
Oil & Gas Industry Project Management & Specialized Engineering Support Services
N.A.I.C.S.: 213112

PROJECT PLANNING SERVICE PUBLIC COMPANY LIMITED
381/6 Soi Rama IX 58 Soi 7 Seree 7 Rama IX Road, Suanluang, Bangkok, 10250, Thailand
Tel.: (66) 27182785
Web Site: https://www.pps.co.th
Year Founded: 1987
PPS—(THA)
Rev.: $12,084,271
Assets: $18,029,266
Liabilities: $8,947,366
Net Worth: $9,081,901
Earnings: ($545,717)
Emp.: 351
Fiscal Year-end: 12/31/23
Construction Management & Engineering Services
N.A.I.C.S.: 236220
Nopparat Narin *(Deputy Mng Dir-Bus Dev Dept)*

Subsidiaries:

Ensemble Equity Pte., Ltd. (1)
10 Anson Road 31-01 International Plaza, Singapore, 079903, Singapore
Tel.: (65) 97428370
Engineering Consulting Services
N.A.I.C.S.: 541330

PPS Innovation Co., Ltd. (1)
103 3rd Floor Soi Rama IX 60 Soi 7 Seri 7 Rama IX Road, Phatthanakan Suanluang, Bangkok, 10250, Thailand
Tel.: (66) 271827859
Media & Advertising Services
N.A.I.C.S.: 541810

PPS Oneworks Co., Ltd. (1)
101 3rd Floor Phongtheerathon Building Soi Rama IX 60 Soi 7 Seri 7, Rama IX Road Phatthanakan Suanluang, Bangkok, 10250, Thailand
Tel.: (66) 271827859
Engineering Consulting Services
N.A.I.C.S.: 541330

PROJECT/029 MEDIA & COMMUNICATIONS KFT.
Lajos u 78 IV em, 1036, Budapest, Hungary
Tel.: (36) 1 577 4301   HU
Web Site: http://www.project029.com
Sales Range: $10-24.9 Million
Emp.: 30
Information & Communication Technology Trade Magazine Publisher
N.A.I.C.S.: 513120
Marton Viragh *(CEO)*

PROJEKT A.D.
Veselina Maslese 1/4, 78000, Banja Luka, Bosnia & Herzegovina
Tel.: (387) 51211516
Web Site: https://www.projektad.com
Year Founded: 1951
PROJ—(BANJ)
Sales Range: $1-9.9 Million
Emp.: 68
Technical Consulting Services
N.A.I.C.S.: 541690

PROJEKTBIRO A.D.
ul Veljka Dugosevica br 46, Belgrade, Serbia
Tel.: (381) 11 2411 757
Web Site: http://www.projektbiro.co.rs
Year Founded: 1991
Sales Range: Less than $1 Million
Emp.: 8
Building Architectural Design Services
N.A.I.C.S.: 541310

PROJEKTENGAGEMANG SWEDEN AB
Hantverkargatan 25 A, PO Box 47146, 100 74, Stockholm, Sweden
Tel.: (46) 105160000
Web Site: https://www.pe.se
Year Founded: 2006
PENG.B—(OMX)
Rev.: $142,472,609
Assets: $138,374,628
Liabilities: $70,272,666
Net Worth: $68,101,962
Earnings: $4,528,069
Emp.: 984
Fiscal Year-end: 12/31/20
Civil Engineering Services
N.A.I.C.S.: 541330
Per Hedeback *(Chm)*

PROJEKTINVEST A.D.
Bulevar Cara Lazara 3, Novi Sad, Serbia
Tel.: (381) 21 459 184
Year Founded: 1989
PRIV—(BEL)
Sales Range: Less than $1 Million
Emp.: 6
Architectural Designing Services
N.A.I.C.S.: 541310
Marina Dosenovic *(Exec Dir)*

PROJEKTOMONTAZA AD BELGRADE
Poenkareova 20, 11000, Belgrade, Serbia
Tel.: (381) 112765022
Sales Range: $25-49.9 Million
Emp.: 414
Water Supply Systems Design & Construction Services
N.A.I.C.S.: 221310
Sinisa Zoric *(Chm & CEO)*

PROKUPAC A.D.
Kumodraska 263-a, Belgrade, Serbia
Tel.: (381) 11 2460 799
Year Founded: 2008
Sales Range: $1-9.9 Million
Emp.: 245
Distillery Operator
N.A.I.C.S.: 312140
Milan Randic *(Exec Dir)*

PROLAB TECHNOLOGIES INC.
4531 Rue Industrielle, Thetford Mines, G6H 2J1, QC, Canada
Tel.: (418) 423-2777   QC
Web Site: http://www.prolab-technologies.com
Year Founded: 1985
Sales Range: $1-9.9 Million
Emp.: 30
Lubricant & Grease Mfr
N.A.I.C.S.: 324191
Geam-Framcois Iabbe *(Mgr-R&D & Tech & Production)*

Subsidiaries:

New Life Motors, S.A de C.V. (1)
Av Nader MZ 98-1 5 LT 117, Supermanzana 3 Ctr, Cancun, 77500, Quintana Roo, Mexico
Tel.: (52) 9988877559
Web Site: http://www.newlifemotors.com.mx
Lubricant Mfr
N.A.I.C.S.: 324191

Prolab Technolub Inc (1)
4531 Rue Industrielle, Thetford Mines, G6H 2J1, QC, Canada

PROLAB TECHNOLOGIES INC.

Prolab Technologies Inc.—(Continued)
Tel.: (418) 423-2777
Web Site: http://www.prolab-technologies.com
Lubricant Mfr
N.A.I.C.S.: 324191
Chantal Grenier *(Gen Mgr)*

PROLACOM SA
Manolesti Deal, Botosani, Romania
Tel.: (40) 231 514724
Sales Range: Less than $1 Million
Dairy Products Mfr
N.A.I.C.S.: 311513

PROLETER A.D.
Milinko Kusic 108, 32250, Ivanjica, Serbia
Tel.: (381) 695504055
Web Site: https://www.proleter.rs
Year Founded: 1961
PRLI—(BEL)
Rev.: $7,582,176
Assets: $7,299,540
Liabilities: $7,035,273
Net Worth: $264,267
Earnings: ($943,473)
Emp.: 343
Fiscal Year-end: 12/31/21
Hosiery Products Mfr
N.A.I.C.S.: 315120
Katarina Mandic *(CEO)*

PROLETER A.D. - ARILJE
Svetolika Lazarevica 14, 31230, Arilje, Serbia
Tel.: (381) 31 892 455   RS
Web Site: http://www.proleter-arilje.co.rs
PRLA—(BEL)
Sales Range: Less than $1 Million
Vehicle Parts Mfr
N.A.I.C.S.: 336390

PROLETER BEACEJ A.D.
Trg oslobodenja 5, Becej, Serbia
Tel.: (381) 21 691 1909
Web Site: http://www.proleteradbecej.co.rs
Year Founded: 1998
Sales Range: Less than $1 Million
Emp.: 16
Printing Services
N.A.I.C.S.: 323111

PROLIFE INDUSTRIES LIMITED
Plot No 213 GIDC, Panoli Industrial Estate Dist Bharuch, Ankleshwar, 394116, Gujarat, India
Tel.: (91) 2646272490
Web Site: https://www.prolifeindustries.in
Year Founded: 1994
PROLIFE—(NSE)
Rev.: $9,651,436
Assets: $4,934,608
Liabilities: $1,054,565
Net Worth: $3,880,043
Earnings: $828,871
Emp.: 62
Fiscal Year-end: 03/31/23
Chemical Products Mfr
N.A.I.C.S.: 325199
Manindersingh Satnamsingh Jolly *(Chm & Mng Dir)*

PROLIFIC TECHNOLOGY INC.
7F No 48 Sec 3 Nan Kang Rd, Nan Kang, Taipei, 115, Taiwan
Tel.: (886) 226546363
Web Site: https://www.prolific.com.tw
Year Founded: 1997
6233—(TPE)
Rev.: $11,789,855
Assets: $39,211,451
Liabilities: $3,509,892
Net Worth: $35,701,559
Earnings: $94,575
Emp.: 86
Fiscal Year-end: 12/31/23
Electronic Components Mfr
N.A.I.C.S.: 334419
Ching-Tang Chang *(Chm)*

Subsidiaries:

Prolific Technology Co., Ltd.   (1)
No 10-2 Lixing 1st Rd, Hsinchu Science Park, Hsinchu, 300, Taiwan
Tel.: (886) 3 578 2011
Integrated Circuit Mfr & Distr
N.A.I.C.S.: 334413

PROLIGHT DIAGNOSTICS AB
Gasverksgatan 3A, 222 29, Lund, Sweden
Tel.: (46) 735823987
Web Site: https://prolightdx.com
Year Founded: 1999
Biomedical Device Mfr
N.A.I.C.S.: 339112
Jon Andre Lokke *(CEO)*

PROLIGHT OPTO TECHNOLOGY CORP.
No 89 Xiyuan Rd, Zhongli Dist, Taoyuan, 320, Taiwan
Tel.: (886) 34618618
Web Site: https://www.prolightopto.com
Year Founded: 2004
5277—(TAI)
Packaging Equipment Mfr
N.A.I.C.S.: 333993
Feng-Ming Chen *(Chm & CEO)*

PROLINK MICROSYSTEMS CORP.
6F 349 Sunshine Street, Neihu District, Taipei, Taiwan
Tel.: (886) 226591588
Year Founded: 1989
Multimedia Product Mfr
N.A.I.C.S.: 334310
Hsiao Teng-Po *(Chm)*

PROLOGIC PLC
Redwood House, Berkhamsted, HP4 2DH, Herts, United Kingdom
Tel.: (44) 1442876277   UK
Web Site: http://www.prologic.com
Sales Range: $10-24.9 Million
Emp.: 78
Business Software Suppliers
N.A.I.C.S.: 541511
Sam Jackson *(CTO)*

PROLOGUE S.A.
101 Avenue Laurent Cely, 92230, Gennevilliers, France
Tel.: (33) 141477000
Web Site: http://www.prologue.fr
Year Founded: 1976
PROL—(EUR)
Sales Range: $75-99.9 Million
Computer Software Designer
N.A.I.C.S.: 513210

Subsidiaries:

O2i S.A.   (1)
101 Avenue Laurent Cely, 92230, Gennevilliers, France
Tel.: (33) 1 4147 7000   (68.67%)
Web Site: http://www.groupeo2i.com
Sales Range: $50-74.9 Million
Computer Engineering Services & Solutions
N.A.I.C.S.: 541512

Subsidiary (Domestic):

M2i Formation   (2)
146-148 rue de Picpus, 75012, Paris, France
Tel.: (33) 1 44 53 36 00
Web Site: http://www.m2iformation.fr
Computer Course Training Services

N.A.I.C.S.: 611420
Thuy Trang NGuyen *(Deputy CEO)*

M2i Formation Dipl SA   (2)
146/148 rue de Picpus, 75012, Paris, France
Tel.: (33) 144533600
Web Site: http://www.diplome.m2iformation.fr
Professional Training Services
N.A.I.C.S.: 611430

M2i Location SA   (2)
146/148 rue de Picpus, 75012, Paris, France
Tel.: (33) 144533600
Web Site: http://www.m2ilocation.fr
Training Room Rental Services
N.A.I.C.S.: 812990

M2i Tech SASU   (2)
20 rue Athènes, Paris, 75009, France
Tel.: (33) 1 45 80
Computer Training Services
N.A.I.C.S.: 611420

Subsidiary (Domestic):

Bull SAS   (3)
Rue Jean Jaures, PO Box 68, Les Clayes-sous-Bois, 78340, France
Tel.: (33) 130807000
Software Development Services
N.A.I.C.S.: 541511

Subsidiary (Domestic):

Serviware S.A.S   (4)
Le Parc Aux Vignes 13/17 Allee des Vendanges, 77183, Croissy-Beaubourg, France
Tel.: (33) 164620900
Sales Range: $25-49.9 Million
Emp.: 5
Information Technology & Data Storage Services
N.A.I.C.S.: 541512
Olivier Jean *(Pres)*

Subsidiary (Domestic):

O2i Ingenierie SAS   (2)
101 avenue Laurent Cely, 92230, Gennevilliers, France
Tel.: (33) 141477000
Web Site: http://o2i-ingenierie.com
Information Technology Services
N.A.I.C.S.: 541519

PROMACT IMPEX LIMITED
12th Floor-1201 City Center-2 B/s Heer Party Plot, Nr Shukan Mall Cross Road Science City Road Sola, Ahmedabad, 380060, India
Tel.: (91) 7926583479
Web Site: https://promactimpex.com
Year Founded: 1985
526494—(BOM)
Rev.: $191,559
Assets: $877,441
Liabilities: $535,268
Net Worth: $342,174
Earnings: $62,394
Fiscal Year-end: 03/31/23
Textile Product Mfr & Whslr
N.A.I.C.S.: 314910
Jayantilal S. Patel *(CEO)*

PROMAN SAS
Zone Industrielle Saint Maurice, 04100, Manosque, France
Tel.: (33) 492728401   FR
Web Site: http://www.proman-emploi.fr
Year Founded: 1990
Management Consulting & Staffing Services
N.A.I.C.S.: 541612
Roland Gomez *(Dir)*

Subsidiaries:

Proman Staffing LLC   (1)
1200 Shermer Rd, Northbrook, IL 60062
Tel.: (847) 559-0676
Web Site: http://www.paramountstaffing.com
Professional, Scientific & Technical Services

INTERNATIONAL PUBLIC

N.A.I.C.S.: 541990
Anthony Hegarty *(VP-Sales)*

Subsidiary (Domestic):

PeopleShare, LLC   (2)
1566 Medical Dr Ste 102, Pottstown, PA 19464
Tel.: (610) 326-0700
Web Site: http://www.peoplesharework s.com
Sales Range: $10-24.9 Million
Emp.: 500
Temporary, Contract & Permanent Staff Positions
N.A.I.C.S.: 561311
Ryan Clark *(CEO & Co-Founder)*

Subsidiary (Domestic):

PeopleShare Cherry Hill   (3)
36 Kresson Rd Ste A, Cherry Hill, NJ 08034   (100%)
Tel.: (856) 685-7706
Emp.: 4
Temporary Staffing
N.A.I.C.S.: 561311
Tom Scull *(Owner)*

PeopleShare Delaware   (3)
200 Continental Dr Ste 214 2nd Fl, Newark, DE 19713   (100%)
Tel.: (302) 455-1300
Web Site: http://www.peoplesharework s.com
Temporary Staffing Services
N.A.I.C.S.: 561311

PROMATE ELECTRONIC CO., LTD.
4F No 32 Section1 Huan Shan Road Nei, Taipei, 11442, Taiwan
Tel.: (886) 226590303
Web Site: https://www.promate.com.tw
6189—(TAI)
Rev.: $965,169,721
Assets: $559,461,701
Liabilities: $369,720,317
Net Worth: $189,741,384
Earnings: $30,717,321
Emp.: 217
Fiscal Year-end: 12/31/23
Semiconductor Product Distr
N.A.I.C.S.: 423620
Cheer Du *(COO)*

Subsidiaries:

East Profit International Ltd.   (1)
Rm 902 12F Cheung Fung Industrial Bldg No 23-39, Tsuen Wan, New Territories, China (Hong Kong)
Tel.: (852) 36222339
Web Site: http://www.eastprofit.com.hk
Sales Range: $50-74.9 Million
Emp.: 1
Consumer Electronics Distr
N.A.I.C.S.: 423620

Happy On Supply Chain Management Ltd.   (1)
3F East Wing Cheung Fung Industrial Building 23-39 Pak Tin Par Street, Tsuen Wan, New Territories, China (Hong Kong)
Tel.: (852) 34282229
General Freight Trucking Services
N.A.I.C.S.: 484110

Picoway Technology Inc.   (1)
2F No 34 Sec 1 Huanshan Road, Neihu District, Taipei, 114, Taiwan
Tel.: (886) 226592355
Web Site: http://www.picoway.com
Sales Range: $25-49.9 Million
Emp.: 35
Software Programming Services
N.A.I.C.S.: 541511

Promate Electronic (Shanghai) Co., Ltd.   (1)
3F Block 10 Lane 1555 Jinshajiang West Rd, Jiading District, Shanghai, 201803, China
Tel.: (86) 2160822688
Semiconductor & Electronic Components Distr

N.A.I.C.S.: 423690

Promate Electronic (Shenzhen) Co., Ltd. (1)
Room 1409-1416 14/F FuChun-DongFang Building No 7006 Shennan Road, Shenzhen, Guangdong, China
Tel.: (86) 75525573919
Semiconductor & Electronic Diodes Mfr
N.A.I.C.S.: 333242

Promate Electronics Company (1)
14712 Franklin Ave Unit H, Tustin, CA 92780
Tel.: (714) 200-0209
Semiconductor & Electronic Components Distr
N.A.I.C.S.: 423690

PROMATE SOLUTIONS CORPORATION
1F No 30 Section 1 Huanshan Road, Nei-Hu Dist, Taipei, 11442, Taiwan
Tel.: (886) 226590606
Web Site: https://www.promate.com
Year Founded: 1986
6577—(TPE)
Rev.: $58,967,639
Assets: $54,362,411
Liabilities: $19,886,659
Net Worth: $34,475,753
Earnings: $6,070,225
Fiscal Year-end: 12/31/22
Computer Peripheral Equipment Distr
N.A.I.C.S.: 423430
Cheer Du *(Chm & CEO)*

Subsidiaries:

Promate Japan Co., Ltd. (1)
3F Biz Smart Kayabacho 1-3-21 Shinkawa, Chuo-ku, Tokyo, 104-0033, Japan
Tel.: (81) 36 868 8524
Computer Hardware Mfr
N.A.I.C.S.: 334111

PROMATERIS S.A.
SOS Bucharest-Targoviste nr 1 Buftea Ilfov, 030352, Bucharest, Romania
Tel.: (40) 212523578
Web Site: https://www.promateris.com
Year Founded: 1957
PPL—(BUC)
Rev.: $25,500,454
Assets: $38,308,840
Liabilities: $19,589,139
Net Worth: $18,719,701
Earnings: ($886,106)
Emp.: 135
Fiscal Year-end: 12/31/23
Plastics Product Mfr
N.A.I.C.S.: 326199

PROMAX POWER LIMITED
150A & 151 1St Floor Tribhuvan Complex Ishwar Nagar Mathura Road, New Delhi, 110065, India
Tel.: (91) 6280362075
Web Site: https://www.promax.co.in
Year Founded: 2004
543375—(BOM)
Emp.: 32
Construction Services
N.A.I.C.S.: 236220
Vishal Bhardwaj *(Founder & Mng Dir)*

PROMAX S.R.L.
Via Newton 5G, Castelfiorentino, 50051, Florence, Italy
Tel.: (39) 0571684620   IT
Web Site: http://www.promax.it
Year Founded: 1991
Automation Product Mfr
N.A.I.C.S.: 334512

PROMEDICAL PERSONNEL LTD.
Regent House Hubert Road Great Warley, Brentwood, CM14 4JE, United Kingdom
Tel.: (44) 1277 212 797
Web Site: http://www.promedical.co.uk
Year Founded: 2008
Sales Range: $10-24.9 Million
Emp.: 22
Employee Recuirement Services
N.A.I.C.S.: 561311
Altin Biba *(Co-Founder)*

PROMENERGOLAB LLC
Str Tkatskaya 1, 105318, Moscow, Russia
Tel.: (7) 4952211208   RU
Web Site: http://www.czl.ru
Laboratory Equipment Distr
N.A.I.C.S.: 423490

PROMET FROUP A.S.
Vaclavska 2027/11, Marianske Hory, 709 00, Ostrava, Czech Republic
Tel.: (420) 596 621 472
Web Site: http://www.prometgroup.eu
Year Founded: 2001
Holding Company
N.A.I.C.S.: 551112
Radek Strouhal *(CFO)*

Subsidiaries:

KOFING, a.s. (1)
Kirilovova 628, 739 21, Paskov, Czech Republic
Tel.: (420) 558411811
Web Site: http://www.kofing.cz
Steel Products Mfr
N.A.I.C.S.: 331511

PROMET CZECH s.r.o. (1)
28 rijna3138/41, 702 00, Ostrava, Czech Republic
Tel.: (420) 596621472
Web Site: http://www.prometczech.cz
Raw Material Distr
N.A.I.C.S.: 423930

PROMET FOUNDRY a.s. (1)
Jiraskova 1327, 755 01, Vsetin, Czech Republic
Tel.: (420) 571412250
Web Site: http://www.prometfoundry.cz
Raw Material Mfr & Distr
N.A.I.C.S.: 331511
Miroslav Snasel *(Chm & Exec Dir)*

PROMET LOGISTICS a.s. (1)
Vaclavska 11/2027, 709 00, Ostrava, Czech Republic
Tel.: (420) 597089381
Web Site: http://www.prometlogistics.cz
Logistics Consulting Servies
N.A.I.C.S.: 541614
Jan Tesar *(CEO)*

PROMET SLOVAKIA s.r.o. (1)
Radlinskeho 1730, 026 01, Dolny Kubin, Slovakia
Tel.: (421) 435864808
Web Site: http://www.prometslovakia.sk
Raw Material Distr
N.A.I.C.S.: 423930
Pavol Konecny *(CEO)*

Tawesco s.r.o (1)
Areal Tatry 1449/6, 742 21, Koprivnice, Czech Republic
Tel.: (420) 556493332
Web Site: http://www.tawesco.cz
Sales Range: $200-249.9 Million
Emp.: 700
Stamping Tools, Metal Stampings & Weldments for the Automotive Industries
N.A.I.C.S.: 336370

PROMET TP A.D.
Svetog Save 23, 78430, Prnjavor, Bosnia & Herzegovina
Tel.: (387) 51860737
Year Founded: 1962
PROM-R-A—(BANJ)
Rev.: $258,331
Assets: $7,312,787
Liabilities: $1,720,175
Net Worth: $5,592,612
Earnings: ($27,081)
Emp.: 16
Fiscal Year-end: 12/31/12
Grocery Store Operator
N.A.I.C.S.: 445110
Ognjen Jugovic *(Chm-Mgmt Bd)*

PROMETHEAN INVESTMENTS LLP
7-10 Chandos Street, London, W1G 9DQ, United Kingdom
Tel.: (44) 2072483425   UK
Web Site: http://www.promethean.com
Year Founded: 2005
Privater Equity Firm
N.A.I.C.S.: 523999
Alexander Flockhart *(Partner)*

Subsidiaries:

Envirogen Group S.A. (1)
Bromyard Road Trading Estate, Bromyard Road, Ledbury, HR8 1NS, Heref, United Kingdom
Tel.: (44) 1531 636 328
Web Site: http://www.envirogengroup.com
Holding Company; Water Filtration & Treatment Solutions
N.A.I.C.S.: 551112
Andrea Davi *(CEO)*

Subsidiary (US):

Envirogen Group North America, Inc. (2)
2627 Chestnut Ridge Rd Ste 260, Kingwood, TX 77339
Holding Company; Regional Managing Office; Water Filtration & Treatment Solutions
N.A.I.C.S.: 551112
Michael M. Stark *(Chm-Envirogen Technologies)*

Subsidiary (Domestic):

Envirogen Technologies, Inc. (3)
2627 Chestnut Ridge Rd Ste 260, Kingwood, TX 77339
Web Site: http://www.envirogen.com
Water Treatment Systems Design & Process Engineering Services
N.A.I.C.S.: 221310
Robert Stark *(VP-Chemicals & Refining)*

Subsidiary (Domestic):

Envirogen Group UK Limited (2)
Bromyard Road Trading Estate, Bromyard Road, Ledbury, HR8 1NS, Heref, United Kingdom
Tel.: (44) 1531 636 328
Web Site: http://www.envirogengroup.com
Holding Company; Regional Managing Office; Water Filtration & Treatment Solutions
N.A.I.C.S.: 551112
David Hayes *(Sls Dir)*

Subsidiary (Domestic):

Envirogen Water Technologies Ltd. (3)
Bromyard Road Trading Estate, Bromyard Road, Ledbury, HR8 1NS, Heref, United Kingdom
Tel.: (44) 1531 636 328
Web Site: http://www.envirogenwater.co.uk
Water Filtration & Treatment Solutions
N.A.I.C.S.: 221310

Produce Investments Limited (1)
Floods Ferry Road, Doddington, March, PE15 0UW, Cambs, United Kingdom
Tel.: (44) 1890 819503
Web Site: http://www.produceinvestments.co.uk
Sales Range: $250-299.9 Million
Investment Management Service
N.A.I.C.S.: 523940
Angus Armstrong *(CEO)*

Subsidiary (Domestic):

Greenvale AP Limited (2)
7 The Forum Minerva Business Park, Peterborough, PE2 6FT, Cambridgeshire, United Kingdom
Tel.: (44) 1733 372500
Web Site: http://www.greenvale.co.uk
Potato Distr
N.A.I.C.S.: 424480
Brian MacDonald *(Dir-Fin)*

Rowe Farming Limited (2)
Trenethick Farm, Wendron, Helston, TR13 0LR, Cornwall, United Kingdom
Tel.: (44) 1326 565588
Potato Farming Services
N.A.I.C.S.: 111211

Subsidiary (Non-US):

The Jersey Royal Company Limited (2)
Southfork Rue du Trot, Saint Saviour, JE2 7JQ, Jersey
Tel.: (44) 1534 852444
Web Site: http://www.jerseyroyal.co.uk
Potato Farming Services
N.A.I.C.S.: 111211
David Rankin *(Mng Dir)*

Subsidiary (Domestic):

The Kent Potato Company Limited (2)
The Pack House Wantsum Way, Saint Nicholas-at-Wade, CT7 0NE, Kent, United Kingdom
Tel.: (44) 1843 847269
Web Site: http://www.kentpotato.co.uk
Potato Farming Services
N.A.I.C.S.: 111211
Matt Maughan *(Gen Mgr)*

PROMETHERA BIOSCIENCES S.A./N.V.
Watson & Crick Hill Rue Granbonpre 11, 1435, Mont-Saint-Guibert, Belgium
Tel.: (32) 1039 4300   BE
Web Site: http://www.promethera.com
Biopharmaceutical Research & Development
N.A.I.C.S.: 325412
John Tchelingerian *(Chm & CEO)*

PROMIGAS S.A. E.S.P.
Calle 66 6-123, Barranquilla, Colombia
Tel.: (57) 53713444
Natural Gas Distr
N.A.I.C.S.: 486210
Eric Flesch *(Pres)*

PROMIMIC AB
Entreprenorsstraket 10, 431 53, Molndal, Sweden
Tel.: (46) 31160860
Web Site: https://www.promimic.com
Year Founded: 2004
PRO—(OMX)
Rev.: $2,691,147
Assets: $9,219,827
Liabilities: $1,603,828
Net Worth: $7,615,999
Earnings: ($1,248,635)
Fiscal Year-end: 12/31/23
Biotechnology Research & Development Services
N.A.I.C.S.: 541714

PROMINENCE ENERGY LTD.
Level 2 30 Richardson Street, West Perth, 6005, WA, Australia
Tel.: (61) 893219886   AU
Web Site: http://www.prominenceenergy.com
PRM—(ASX)
Rev.: $467,557
Assets: $1,568,310
Liabilities: $345,568
Net Worth: $1,222,742
Earnings: ($5,232,742)
Fiscal Year-end: 06/30/24
Oil & Gas Exploration Services
N.A.I.C.S.: 213112

PROMINENCE ENERGY LTD.

Prominence Energy Ltd.—(Continued)
Alexander Parks (CEO & Mng Dir)

PROMINENT DOSIERTECHNIK GMBH
Im Schuhmachergewann 5-11, 69123, Heidelberg, Germany
Tel.: (49) 62218420
Web Site: http://www.prominent.com
Sales Range: $400-449.9 Million
Emp.: 2,099
Chemical Fluid Handling & Water Treatment Solutions
N.A.I.C.S.: 334514
Andreas Dulger (Pres & CEO)

Subsidiaries:
Bombas Boyser, S.L. (1)
C/ Narcis Monturiol 24 Pol Ind Can Magre, Sta Eulalia de Roncana, 08187, Barcelona, Spain
Tel.: (34) 93 844 77 78
Web Site: http://www.boyser.com
Industrial Pump Mfr
N.A.I.C.S.: 333914
Ricard Montsant Herraiz (Mgr-Sls)

ProMinent Dosiertechnik Ges.m.b.H (1)
Gewerbepark 4, Rosenau, 3332, Sonntagberg, Austria
Tel.: (43) 7448 3040
Web Site: http://www.prominent.at
Emp.: 15
Industrial Pump Distr
N.A.I.C.S.: 423830

ProMinent Fluid Controls Ltd. (1)
Finisklin Industrial Estate, Sligo, Ireland
Tel.: (353) 71 91 51 222
Web Site: http://www.prominent.ie
Industrial Pump Distr
N.A.I.C.S.: 423830

ProMinent Fluid Controls Ltd. (1)
BT 7-12 Bulebel Industrial Estate, Zejtun, Malta
Tel.: (356) 21 69 36 77
Web Site: http://www.prominent.com.mt
Industrial Pump Distr
N.A.I.C.S.: 423830

ProMinent Iberia, SA (1)
Pol Ind Can Portella 16, Argelaguer, 17853, Girona, Spain
Tel.: (34) 972 28 70 11
Web Site: http://www.prominent.es
Industrial Pump & Motor Mfr
N.A.I.C.S.: 333914

ProMinent Juffali FZC (1)
Sharjah Airport Free Zone P6-074, PO Box 8090, Sharjah, United Arab Emirates
Tel.: (971) 165 572 626
Web Site: http://www.prominent-juffali.ae
Industrial Pump Distr
N.A.I.C.S.: 423830
Suresh Joboy (Mgr-Sls)

ProMinent Trading (Dalian) Co., Ltd (1)
No 14-B Road Liaohexisan Dalian Economic & Technical Development Zone, 116600, Dalian, China
Tel.: (86) 411 8731 5733
Industrial Pump Distr
N.A.I.C.S.: 423830
Steve Wang (Mng Dir)

ProMinent Verder B.V. (1)
Utrechtseweg 4A, 3451 GG, Vleuten, Netherlands
Tel.: (31) 30 677 92 80
Web Site: http://www.prominent.nl
Industrial Pump Distr
N.A.I.C.S.: 423830

Syclope Electronique (1)
Rue de Bruscos, 64230, Sauvagnon, France
Tel.: (33) 5 59 33 70 36
Web Site: http://www.syclope.fr
Industrial Pump Distr
N.A.I.C.S.: 423830
Georges Breton (Chm-Mgmt Bd)

Voney AG (1)
Dorfstrasse 23, 3032, Bern, Switzerland
Tel.: (41) 31 992 21 67
Web Site: http://www.voney-ag.ch
Waste Water Treatment Services
N.A.I.C.S.: 221320

PROMINEX RESOURCE CORP.
7548 192nd Street, Surrey, V4N 6B2, BC, Canada
Tel.: (778) 574-6163
Web Site: http://www.prominex.ca
Metal Exploration Services
N.A.I.C.S.: 213114

PROMINUS VASTGOED BV
Hessenbergweg 109-119, 1101 BS, Amsterdam, Netherlands
Tel.: (31) 205650020
Web Site: http://www.prominus.nl
Real Estate Property Management Services
N.A.I.C.S.: 531312
Rutger Schenk (Mng Dir)

PROMIS NEUROSCIENCES, INC.
1920 Yonge Street Suite 200, Toronto, M4S 3E2, ON, Canada
Tel.: (416) 341-5783
Web Site: https://promisneurosciences.com
PMN—(NASDAQ)
Rev.: $920
Assets: $1,586,831
Liabilities: $1,282,173
Net Worth: $304,658
Earnings: ($5,659,913)
Emp.: 1
Fiscal Year-end: 12/31/19
Neurodegenerative Diseases Diagnosis & Treatment Products Developer & Mfr
N.A.I.C.S.: 339112
Johanne Kaplan (Chief Dev Officer)

PROMISE TECHNOLOGY, INC.
2F 30 Industry E Rd IX Hsinchu Science Park, Hsinchu, Taiwan
Tel.: (886) 35782395
Web Site: https://www.promise.com
3057—(TAI)
Rev.: $19,115,144
Assets: $38,870,956
Liabilities: $14,856,666
Net Worth: $24,014,290
Earnings: ($4,689,689)
Emp.: 11
Fiscal Year-end: 12/31/23
Computer Storage Device Control Cards Mfr & Distr
N.A.I.C.S.: 334112
H. C. Chang (COO & Gen Mgr-Asia Pacific)

PROMISIA HEALTHCARE LIMITED
Level 5 50 Customhouse Quay, Wellington, 6011, New Zealand
Tel.: (64) 212451801 NZ
Web Site: https://www.promisia.co.nz
Year Founded: 1983
PHL—(NZX)
Rev.: $14,282,895
Assets: $42,919,258
Liabilities: $30,904,904
Net Worth: $12,014,354
Earnings: $413,876
Emp.: 335
Fiscal Year-end: 03/31/23
Therapeutic Natural Product Mfr
N.A.I.C.S.: 621511
Stephen Underwood (Chm)

Subsidiaries:
EMAC Holdings Limited (1)
2A/40 Mt Eden Road, Mount Eden, Auckland, New Zealand
Tel.: (64) 96307125
Web Site: https://www.emacsltd.co.nz
Construction Services
N.A.I.C.S.: 236220

Ranfurly Manor Limited (1)
6 Monmouth Street, Feilding, New Zealand
Tel.: (64) 63235050
Residential Services
N.A.I.C.S.: 531311

PROMOCION Y OPERACION S.A. DE C.V.
Bahia de Chachalacas #7 Colonia Veronica Anzures, Hidalgo, CP 11300, Mexico City, Mexico
Tel.: (52) 5552681515
Web Site: https://www.prosamexico.mx
Emp.: 100
Financial Transaction Processing & Payment Services
N.A.I.C.S.: 522320

PROMORE PHARMA AB
Fogdevreten 2, 171 65, Solna, Sweden
Tel.: (46) 812454859
Web Site: http://www.promorepharma.com
Year Founded: 2002
PROMO—(OMX)
Rev.: $9,273
Assets: $1,967,462
Liabilities: $657,319
Net Worth: $1,310,143
Earnings: ($2,493,186)
Emp.: 1
Fiscal Year-end: 12/31/22
Pharmaceuticals Product Mfr
N.A.I.C.S.: 325412
Jonas Ekblom (Pres & CEO)

PROMOS TECHNOLOGIES INC.
No 19-1 Li-Hsin Rd Hsinchu Science Park, Hsin-chu, 30078, Taiwan
Tel.: (886) 35798308
Web Site: http://www.promos.com.tw
Year Founded: 1996
Sales Range: $1-4.9 Billion
Emp.: 5,000
Semiconductor Mfr
N.A.I.C.S.: 334413
Jessie Peng (VP-G&A & Fin Grp)

Subsidiaries:
United Memories Inc. (1)
4815 List Dr Ste 109, Colorado Springs, CO 80919 (100%)
Tel.: (719) 594-4238
Web Site: http://www.unimem.com
Specialized Design Services
N.A.I.C.S.: 541490
Matt Manning (Engr-Design)

PROMOTICA S.P.A.
Via Monte Baldo 111, Desenzano del Garda, 25015, Brescia, Italy
Tel.: (39) 030911801
Web Site: https://www.promotica.it
Year Founded: 2003
PMT—(EUR)
Promotional Service
N.A.I.C.S.: 561990
Diego Toscan (Chm)

PROMOTION & DEVELOPMENT LIMITED
8th Floor Dias Pier Le Caudan Waterfront, Port Louis, Mauritius
Tel.: (230) 2119500 MU
Web Site: https://www.promotion.com
Year Founded: 1984
PAD—(MAU)
Rev.: $15,691,393
Assets: $381,879,637
Liabilities: $53,355,986

INTERNATIONAL PUBLIC

Net Worth: $328,523,651
Earnings: $14,830,870
Fiscal Year-end: 06/30/23
Investment Management Service
N.A.I.C.S.: 523999
Rene Leclezio (Mng Dir)

Subsidiaries:
Caudan Development Limited (1)
Dias Pier Le Caudan Waterfront, Port Louis, Mauritius (53.13%)
Tel.: (230) 2119430
Web Site: https://www.caudan.com
Rev.: $11,796,972
Assets: $131,703,755
Liabilities: $25,339,420
Net Worth: $106,364,335
Earnings: $4,189,731
Fiscal Year-end: 06/30/2022
Industrial Building Rental Services
N.A.I.C.S.: 531120
Rene Leclezio (Exec Dir)

PROMOTORA AMBIENTAL S.A.B DE C.V.
Blvd Antonio L Rodriguez 1884 Torre 1 Piso 8 Col Santa Maria, 64650, Monterrey, Nuevo Leon, Mexico
Tel.: (52) 8119667900
Web Site: https://www.pasa.mx
Year Founded: 1991
PASA—(MEX)
Sales Range: $200-249.9 Million
Emp.: 5,136
Integral Waste Management Services
N.A.I.C.S.: 325998

Subsidiaries:
Altya, S.A. de C.V. (1)
Boulevard Jesus Kumate Rodriguez, Culiacan, 8150, Sinaloa, Mexico
Tel.: (52) 6677613958
Sales Range: $10-24.9 Million
Emp.: 35
Trash Collection Services
N.A.I.C.S.: 562111

Environmental Management Group, Inc. (1)
5066R W Chester Pike Ste, Edgemont, PA 19028 (100%)
Tel.: (800) 673-7830
Web Site: http://www.emgpa.com
Environmental Consulting Services
N.A.I.C.S.: 541620
Ron Spencer (Pres)

Gen Industrial, S.A. de C.V. (1)
Avenue Churubusco No 3890 Norte, Coyoacan, Monterrey, 64510, Nuevo Leon, Mexico
Tel.: (52) 8181442200
Trash Collection Services
N.A.I.C.S.: 562111

Pasa Cuernavaca, S.A. de C.V. (1)
Mineria No 42 Loma Bonita, Cuernavaca, 62080, Morelos, Mexico
Tel.: (52) 7772293200
Web Site: http://www.pasacuernavaca.com
Waste Collection Services
N.A.I.C.S.: 562111

Professional Recycling, S.A. de C.V. (1)
Xochimilco No 2283, Mexicali, 21380, Baja California, Mexico
Tel.: (52) 6865801010
Sales Range: $75-99.9 Million
Emp.: 60
Waste Management Services
N.A.I.C.S.: 221320
Eduardo Lopez (Gen Mgr)

Promotora Ambiental de la Laguna, S.A. de C.V. (1)
Carretera Torreon San Pedro No 100 Aeropuerto, Torreon, 27016, Coahuila, Mexico
Tel.: (52) 8717218655
Waste Management Services
N.A.I.C.S.: 562998

Reciclajes Ecologicos Maritimos, S.A. de C.V. (1)
Oficinas en el Parque Torre 1 Piso 8, Santa

AND PRIVATE COMPANIES

PROMOTORA DE INFORMACIONES S.A.

Maria, Monterrey, 64650, Nuevo Leon, Mexico
Tel.: (52) 81 1366 4600
Web Site: http://www.ecomaronline.com
Hazardous Waste Treatment Services
N.A.I.C.S.: 562112

Servicio Ambiental Nacional, S.A. de C.V. (1)
Avenue Churubusco Norte No 3890 Piso 1, Coyoacan, Monterrey, 64510, Nuevo Leon, Mexico
Tel.: (52) 8182123330
Web Site: http://www.basa.mx
Sales Range: $25-49.9 Million
Emp.: 15
Waste Collection Services
N.A.I.C.S.: 562111
Ricardo Aguerre *(Mgr)*

Subsidiary (Domestic):

Biotecnologia Aplicada al Saneamiento Ambiental, S.A. de C.V. (2)
Avenue Churubsco Norte 3890, Colonia Coyoacan, Monterrey, 64510, Nuevo Leon, Mexico
Tel.: (52) 818212 3330
Web Site: http://www.basa.mx
Waste Management Services
N.A.I.C.S.: 562111

PROMOTORA DE INFORMACIONES S.A.
Gran Via 32, Tres Cantos, 28013, Madrid, Spain
Tel.: (34) 913301000   ES
Web Site: https://www.prisa.com
Year Founded: 1972
GPOPF—(OTCEM)
Rev.: $1,226,862,623
Assets: $1,760,603,577
Liabilities: $2,221,542,432
Net Worth: ($460,938,855)
Earnings: ($204,148,238)
Emp.: 8,951
Fiscal Year-end: 12/31/19
Media Holding Company
N.A.I.C.S.: 551112
Manuel Mirat Santiago *(CEO)*

Subsidiaries:

Aguilar Chilena de Ediciones, S.A. (1)
Doctor Anibal Ariztia 1444, Santiago, Providencia, Chile
Tel.: (56) 55 6402544
Newspaper Publishing Services
N.A.I.C.S.: 513110

Antena 3 de Radio de Melilla, S.A. (1)
Gran Via 32, 28013, Madrid, Spain
Tel.: (34) 913477936
Emp.: 46
Radio Broadcasting Services
N.A.I.C.S.: 516210
Salvador Villanueva Rodriguez *(Mng Dir)*

Caracol, S.A. (1)
Calle 67 N 7-37 Piso 7, Bogota, Colombia
Tel.: (57) 1348 76 00
Web Site: http://www.caracol.com.co
Radio Broadcasting Services
N.A.I.C.S.: 516210

Centro de Asistencia Telefonica, S.A. (1)
C/ Campezo 1 Edificio 5, 28022, Madrid, Telf, Spain
Tel.: (34) 902 33 40 33
Web Site: http://www.cat.es
Contact Management Services
N.A.I.C.S.: 541611

Distribuciones Aliadas, S.A. (1)
Calle Rio Viejo No 60, Poligono Industrial La Isla, 41703, Dos Hermanas, Sevile, Spain
Tel.: (34) 95 493 0168
Web Site: https://www.distasa.es
Commercial Printing Services
N.A.I.C.S.: 811310

Ediciones Grazalema, S.L. (1)
Poligono Industrial Carretera Amarilla Rafael Beca Mateos 1 Local 2, Seville, 41007, Spain
Tel.: (34) 954999724
Newspaper Publishing Services
N.A.I.C.S.: 513110

Ediciones Santillana Inc. (1)
1506 Roosevelt Ave, Guaynabo, PR 00968
Tel.: (787) 781-9800
Newspaper Publishing Services
N.A.I.C.S.: 513110

Ediciones Santillana, S.A. (1)
Av Leandro N Alem 720, C1001AAP, Buenos Aires, Argentina
Tel.: (54) 11 4119 5000
Web Site: http://www.santillana.com.ar
Books Publishing Services
N.A.I.C.S.: 513130

Ediciones Santillana, S.A. (1)
Juan Manuel Blanes 1132, 11200, Montevideo, Uruguay
Tel.: (598) 2410 7342
Web Site: http://www.santillana.com.uy
Books Publishing Services
N.A.I.C.S.: 513130

Edicions Obradoiro, S.L. (1)
Ruela de Entrecercos 2 2 B, 15705, Santiago de Compostela, Spain
Tel.: (34) 981552740
Web Site: http://www.santina.es
Emp.: 6
Newspaper Publishing Services
N.A.I.C.S.: 513110
Ana Derra *(Gen Mgr)*

Edicions Voramar, S.A. (1)
Valencia 44 Picanya, 46210, Valencia, Spain
Tel.: (34) 961 59 44 10
Web Site: http://www.santillana.es
Educational Books Publishing Services
N.A.I.C.S.: 513130

Editora Moderna, Ltda. (1)
Av Luis Viana 2192, Imbui, Salvador, 41720-200, Bahia, Brazil
Tel.: (55) 713 111 2300
Web Site: https://www.moderna.com.br
Books Publishing Services
N.A.I.C.S.: 513130

Editora Objetiva Ltda. (1)
Rua Cosme Velho 103, 22241-090, Rio de Janeiro, Brazil
Tel.: (55) 21 2199 7824
Web Site: http://www.objetiva.com.br
Books Publishing Services
N.A.I.C.S.: 513130

Editorial Santillana, S.A. (1)
Cra 11A 98-50 Oficina 501, Bogota, Colombia
Tel.: (57) 1 635 12 00
Books Publishing Services
N.A.I.C.S.: 513130

Editorial Santillana, S.A. (1)
26 Av 2-20 zona 14, Guatemala, Guatemala
Tel.: (502) 2429 4300
Web Site: http://www.santillana.com.gt
Books Publishing Services
N.A.I.C.S.: 513130

Editorial Santillana, S.A. (1)
Juan Sanchez Ramirez No 9, Gazcue, Santo Domingo, Dominican Republic
Tel.: (809) 809 682 1382
Web Site: http://www.santillana.com.do
Books Publishing Services
N.A.I.C.S.: 513130

Editorial Santillana, S.A. (1)
Romulo Gallegos Av Building Zulia PB Montercristo Boleita 1071 Sector, Sucre Municipality, Caracas, Venezuela
Tel.: (58) 212 280 94 00
Web Site: http://www.santillana.com.ve
Books Publishing Services
N.A.I.C.S.: 513130

Editorial Santillana, S.A. de C.V. (1)
San Salvador calle Siemenes numero 48 zona industrial Santa Elena, Antiguo Cuscatlan, El Salvador
Tel.: (503) 25058920
Web Site: http://www.santillana.com.sv
Books Publishing Services
N.A.I.C.S.: 513130

Educactiva, S.A.C. (1)
Av Primavera 2160, Santiago de Surco, 15023, Lima, Peru
Tel.: (51) 1 437 5656
Web Site: https://www.edicionesnorma.com
Books Publishing Services
N.A.I.C.S.: 513130

Estructura, Grupo de Estudios Economicos, S.A. (1)
Miguel Yuste 42, Madrid, 28037, Spain
Tel.: (34) 915386100
Web Site: http://www.cincodias.com
Emp.: 60
Newspaper Publishing Services
N.A.I.C.S.: 513110
Jose Luis Gomez *(Gen Mgr)*

GLR Networks, LLC (1)
4770 BiScayne Blvd Ste 700, Miami, FL 33137
Tel.: (305) 644-6641
Emp.: 580
Radio Broadcasting Services
N.A.I.C.S.: 516210
Melissa Fuentes *(Acct Mgr)*

Kapelusz Editora, S.A. (1)
Av Leandro N Alem 720 Piso 6, C1001AAP, Buenos Aires, Argentina
Tel.: (54) 112 152 5113
Web Site: https://www.editorialkapelusz.com
Books Publishing Services
N.A.I.C.S.: 513130

LS4 Radio Continental, S.A (1)
Rivadavia 835, Buenos Aires, Argentina
Tel.: (54) 1143384250
Radio Broadcasting Services
N.A.I.C.S.: 516210
Nicholas Shoka *(Gen Mgr)*

Lacoproductora, S.L. (1)
Calle del Cardenal Cisneros 74, 28010, Madrid, Spain
Tel.: (34) 910616087
Web Site: https://lacoproductora.com
Media Entertainment Services
N.A.I.C.S.: 541840

Lanza, S.A. de C.V. (1)
Avenida Rio Mixcoac 274 Col Acacias, Mexico, 03100, Mexico
Tel.: (52) 5554207530
General Management Consulting Services
N.A.I.C.S.: 541611

Multimedia, S.A. (1)
Rua de Santo Amaro a Estrela N 17 A, 1249-028, Lisbon, Portugal
Tel.: (351) 943431537
Journal Publishing Services
N.A.I.C.S.: 513120

Pleno Internacional, SPA (1)
Avenida Andres Bello 2299 8th Floor, Providencia, Chile
Tel.: (56) 22 246 6604
Web Site: https://www.pleno.digital
Computer System Integration & Design Services
N.A.I.C.S.: 541512

Plural Entertainment Portugal, S.A. (1)
Estrada da Verdelha do Ruivo, 2625-700, Vialonga, Portugal
Tel.: (351) 219 528 500
Web Site: http://www.pluralportugal.pt
Video Device Rental Services
N.A.I.C.S.: 532282

Subsidiary (Domestic):

Empresa Portuguesa de Cenarios, Lda. (2)
Quinta Melos Bucelas, 2615-341, Vialonga, Portugal
Tel.: (351) 219 527 500
Decoration Services
N.A.I.C.S.: 541410

Empresa de Meios Audiovisuais, Lda. (2)
Quinta Do Olival Das Minas Lote 9, Vialonga, 2625-577, Portugal
Tel.: (351) 219527050
Emp.: 80
Television Broadcasting Services
N.A.I.C.S.: 516120
Nuno Mendonca *(Mgr)*

Prisa Brand Solutions USA, Inc. (1)
2100 Coral Way Ste 200, Miami, FL 33145
Tel.: (305) 285-1260
Web Site: https://www.prisabrandsolutions.us
Media Advertising Services
N.A.I.C.S.: 541810

Prisa Media Mexico, S.A. de C.V. (1)
Tlalpan 3000 Col Espartaco, 04870, Mexico, Mexico
Tel.: (52) 5553272000
Media Entertainment Services
N.A.I.C.S.: 541840

Prisa Media USA, Inc. (1)
2100 Coral Way Ste 200, Miami, FL 33145
Tel.: (305) 644-6620
Media Entertainment Services
N.A.I.C.S.: 541840

Prisa Radio, S.A. (1)
Gran Via 32, 28013, Madrid, Spain
Tel.: (34) 91 330 1000
Web Site: https://www.prisa.com
Books Publishing Services
N.A.I.C.S.: 513130

Productora Extremena de Television, S.A. (1)
J M R Azorin Edificio Zeus Poligono La Corchera Merida, 06800, Badajoz, Spain
Tel.: (34) 92 437 0252
Television Broadcasting Services
N.A.I.C.S.: 516120

Promotora Audiovisual de Colombia PACSA, S.A. (1)
Calle 70 N 4-60, Bogota, Colombia
Tel.: (57) 13462011
Telecommunication Servicesb
N.A.I.C.S.: 517111

Promotora General de Revistas, S.A. (1)
Valentin Beato 48, Madrid, 28037, Spain
Tel.: (34) 91 538 6104
Magazine Publishing Services
N.A.I.C.S.: 513130

Subsidiary (Domestic):

Meristation Magazine, S.L. (2)
Calle Almogavers 12 Llagostera, Gerona, 17240, Spain
Tel.: (34) 972 80 56 65
Web Site: http://www.meristation.com
Documentation Provision Services
N.A.I.C.S.: 519210

Promotora de Actividades Audiovisuales de Colombia, Ltda. (1)
Calle 80 10 23, Bogota, Colombia
Tel.: (57) 16396000
Television Broadcasting Services
N.A.I.C.S.: 516120

RLM, S.A. (1)
Puerto de Santa Maria 65, 28043, Madrid, Spain
Tel.: (34) 91 721 64 40
Web Site: http://www.rlm.es
Event Management Services
N.A.I.C.S.: 711310

Radio 30, S.A. (1)
Radio Murcia 4, Murcia, Spain
Tel.: (34) 968220005
Radio Broadcasting Services
N.A.I.C.S.: 516210

Radio Reloj, S.A.S. (1)

Richmond Publishing, S.A. de C.V. (1)
Av Rio Mixcoac 274, Col Acacias, 03240, Mexico, Mexico
Tel.: (52) 555 420 0500
Web Site: https://www.richmond.com.mx
Books Publishing Services
N.A.I.C.S.: 513130

Santillana Canarias, S.L. (1)
Urbanizacion El Mayorazgo Parcela 14 2-7B, Santa Cruz de Tenerife, Spain
Tel.: (34) 928821523
Books Publishing Services

5995

PROMOTORA DE INFORMACIONES S.A.

Promotora de Informaciones S.A.—(Continued)
N.A.I.C.S.: 513130

Santillana Costa Rica (1)
100 metros oeste del edificio de Migracion y Extrangeria, San Jose, Costa Rica
Tel.: (506) 2520 0505
Web Site: http://www.santillana.cr
Books Publishing Services
N.A.I.C.S.: 513130

Santillana Educacao, Ltda. (1)
Rua Padre Adelino 758 Quarta Parada, Sao Paulo, 03303-000, SP, Brazil
Tel.: (55) 8007703004
Web Site: https://www.santillanaeducacao.com.br
Educational Institute Services
N.A.I.C.S.: 611699

Santillana USA Publishing Co. Inc. (1)
2023 NW 84th Ave, Doral, FL 33122
Tel.: (800) 245-8584
Web Site: http://www.santillanausa.com
Books Publishing Services
N.A.I.C.S.: 513130
Arturo Castillon *(Dir-Natl Sls)*

Santillana de Ediciones, S.A. (1)
Calle 13 N 8078 Zona de Calacoto, La Paz, Bolivia
Tel.: (591) 2442252
Books Publishing Services
N.A.I.C.S.: 513130

Santillana, S.A. (1)
Av Primavera 2160, Santiago de Surco, Lima, Peru
Tel.: (51) 21 202 942
Web Site: http://www.santillana.com.pe
Books Publishing Services
N.A.I.C.S.: 513130

Santillana, S.A. (1)
Calle De Las Higueras 118 and Julio Arellano, Quito, Ecuador
Tel.: (593) 23350418
Web Site: https://www.santillana.com.ec
Books Publishing Services
N.A.I.C.S.: 513130
Edgar Vizcaino *(Dir-Commi)*

Santillana, S.A. (1)
Avda Venezuela 276, Asuncion, Paraguay
Tel.: (595) 21 202 942
Web Site: http://www.santillana.com.py
Books Publishing Services
N.A.I.C.S.: 513130

Vertix SGPS SA (1)
Estrada Outurela 118, Carnaxide, 2790-114, Portugal
Tel.: (351) 351214347500
Holding Company
N.A.I.C.S.: 551112

Subsidiary (Domestic):

Grupo Media Capital, SGPS, S.A. (2)
Rua Mario Castelhano 40 Queluz de Baixo, 2734 502, Barcarena, Portugal
Tel.: (351) 214347603
Web Site: https://www.mediacapital.pt
Rev.: $184,911,283
Assets: $280,456,619
Liabilities: $181,101,519
Net Worth: $99,355,099
Earnings: ($61,288,818)
Emp.: 1,127
Fiscal Year-end: 12/31/2019
Audio & Video Broadcasting
N.A.I.C.S.: 516210
Mario Nuno dos Santos Ferreira *(Chm)*

W3 Comm Inmobiliaria, S.A. de C.V. (1)
Crr Libre Tijuana-ensenada 38 S/N Cuenca Diaz, Rosarito, 22710, Mexico
Tel.: (52) 661 612 1810
Real Estate Development Services
N.A.I.C.S.: 531210

Wemass Media Audience Safe Solutions, S.L. (1)

PROMOTORA Y OPERADORA DE INFRAESTRUCTURA, S.A.B. DE C.V.

Bosques de Cidros 173, Col Bosques de las Lomas, CP 05120, Mexico, DF, Mexico
Tel.: (52) 5527890200
Web Site: https://www.pinfra.com.mx
Year Founded: 1969
PUODY—(OTCIQ)
Rev: $915,146,200
Assets: $4,531,575,209
Liabilities: $1,162,086,828
Net Worth: $3,369,488,380
Earnings: $430,797,173
Emp.: 3,374
Fiscal Year-end: 12/31/23
Heavy Construction Services
N.A.I.C.S.: 237990
Luis Fernando Valle Alvarez *(Chief Investment Officer)*

Subsidiaries:

Cobro Electronico de Peaje S.A. de C.V. (1)
Radiat Forest Exterior No Sn Ground Floor Colonia Bosques de las Lomas, Cuajimalpa de Morelos, 05120, Mexico, Mexico
Tel.: (52) 554 624 3540
Web Site: https://www.viapass.com.mx
Tele Toll Services
N.A.I.C.S.: 561421

Construcciones y Drenajes Profundos S.A. de C.V. (1)
Canada 110 Tercer Piso Parque San Andres, 04040, Mexico, Mexico
Web Site: https://www.cdpsacv.net
Construction Equipment Maintenance Services
N.A.I.C.S.: 811310

Grupo Corporativo Interestatal, S.A. de C.V. (1)
Ave Jacarandas S N Cont Pirul Colonia Valle Verde, Ixtapaluca, 56570, Mexico
Tel.: (52) 5551478210
Asphalt Concretes Mfr
N.A.I.C.S.: 327390

Mexicana de Cales, S.A. de C.V. (1)
Blvd Adolfo Lopez Mateos 103, C-11 Zacatecas Centro, Zacatecas, 98000, Mexico
Tel.: (52) 4929252100
Web Site: http://www.mexicanadecales.com
Sales Range: $25-49.9 Million
Emp.: 35
Concrete Mfr
N.A.I.C.S.: 327999

Mexicana de Gestion de Agua S.A. de C.V. (1)
Manuel Dublan 37 Col Tacubaya, Miguel Hidalgo, 11870, Mexico, Mexico
Tel.: (52) 1556 730 0400
Web Site: https://www.aguademexico.com.mx
Waste Treatment Services
N.A.I.C.S.: 237110

Operadora de La Sultana, S.A. de C.V. (1)
Carretera a Monterrey Km 192 140 Autopista Monterrey, Nuevo Laredo Mpio, 85295, Nuevo Laredo, Tamaulipas, Mexico
Tel.: (52) 811 107 0215
Web Site: https://www.operadoradelasultana.com.mx
Toll Road Operation Services
N.A.I.C.S.: 488490

Pinfra US, LLC (1)
7220 Trade St Ste 360, San Diego, CA 92121
Tel.: (858) 757-8020
Web Site: https://www.pinfraus.com
Highway Construction Services
N.A.I.C.S.: 237310

PROMPRYLAD. RENOVATION

Akademika Sakharova Street 23, Ivano-Frankivs'k, 76000, Ukraine
Tel.: (380) 682302302
Web Site: http://www.promprylad.ua
Emp.: 150
Business Consulting Services
N.A.I.C.S.: 541611
Yuriy Fylyuk *(CEO)*

PROMPT PARTICIPACOES S.A.

Av Presidente Antonio Carlos No 5 10th Floor, Center, Rio de Janeiro, 20020-010, RJ, Brazil
Tel.: (55) 2138043700   BR
Web Site: http://www.promptparticipacoes.com
Year Founded: 1998
PRPT3—(BRAZ)
Sales Range: Less than $1 Million
Financial Management Services
N.A.I.C.S.: 523999
Norberto Aguiar Tomaz *(Dir-Investor Relations)*

PROMSVYAZ CAPITAL B.V

Prins Bernhardplein Street Bldg 200, Amsterdam, 1097, Netherlands
Tel.: (31) 20 521 47 77
Investment Services
N.A.I.C.S.: 525990

PROMSVYAZCAPITAL B.V.

7 Building 4 Derbenevskaya Embankment, 115114, Moscow, Russia
Tel.: (7) 495 649 70 10   NL
Web Site: http://www.pscapital.ru
Privater Equity Firm
N.A.I.C.S.: 523999
Alexey Ananiev *(Co-Owner)*

Subsidiaries:

OJSC Promsvyazbank (1)
10/22 Smirnovskaya Street, Moscow, 109052, Russia
Tel.: (7) 800 555 2020
Web Site: http://www.psbank.ru
Rev.: $1,628,832,900
Assets: $14,094,264,120
Liabilities: $19,033,268,340
Net Worth: ($4,939,004,220)
Earnings: ($7,032,254,340)
Fiscal Year-end: 12/31/2017
Banking Services
N.A.I.C.S.: 522110

PROMTRAKTOR OAO

Ul Khuzangaya 26B, 428028, Cheboksary, Chuvashskaya, Russia
Tel.: (7) 8352307514
Web Site: http://www.promtractor.ru
Year Founded: 1972
Sales Range: $100-124.9 Million
Emp.: 14,045
Industrial Tractor Mfr
N.A.I.C.S.: 333120
Mikhail Bolotin *(Gen Dir)*

Subsidiaries:

Promtractor Service JSC (1)
101 Traktorostroitelei Prospekt, 428033, Cheboksary, Russia
Tel.: (7) 8352307953
Web Site: http://www.promtractor.ru
Maintenance & Repair of Motor Vehicles
N.A.I.C.S.: 811111

PRONAL S.A.S.

Zi Roubaix Est, PO Box 18, Leers, 59115, Lille, France
Tel.: (33) 320997500   FR
Web Site: http://www.pronal.com
Sales Range: $125-149.9 Million
Emp.: 100
Fabricated Rubber Products
N.A.I.C.S.: 326299
Francois Despatures *(Chm)*

Subsidiaries:

PRONAL ASIA MANUFACTURING Sdn Bhd (1)
PT 9891 2738 Off Jalan Baru Kampung Baru Sungai Buloh Seksyen U4, 40160, Shah Alam, Selangor, Malaysia
Tel.: (60) 361 401860
Web Site: http://www.pronalasia.com
Polymer Product Mfr
N.A.I.C.S.: 325211

Pronal-USA, Inc. (1)
3000 Opportunity Ct Ste A, South Daytona, FL 32119
Tel.: (386) 310-1558
Web Site: http://www.pronal-usa.com
Polymer Product Mfr
N.A.I.C.S.: 325211

PRONEXUS INC.

5th Floor Shiodome Building 1-2-20 Kaigan, Minato-ku, Tokyo, 105-0022, Japan
Tel.: (81) 357773111   JP
Web Site: http://www.pronexus.co.jp
Year Founded: 1947
7893—(TKS)
Rev.: $199,073,370
Assets: $255,040,240
Liabilities: $85,936,610
Net Worth: $169,103,630
Earnings: $11,759,190
Emp.: 255
Fiscal Year-end: 03/31/24
Corporate Data Processing & Printing Services
N.A.I.C.S.: 323111
Takeshi Ueno *(Pres)*

Subsidiaries:

ASP Communications Co., Ltd. (1)
10-8 Shimahongo Toyama Innovation Park, Fuchucho, Toyama, 939-2708, Japan   (100%)
Tel.: (81) 764917511
Web Site: https://www.asp-communications.co.jp
Sales Range: $100-124.9 Million
Emp.: 280
Data Processing & Information Security Services
N.A.I.C.S.: 518210

eol, Inc. (1)
Shiodome Bldg 5th Floor 1-2-20 Kaigan, Minato-ku, Tokyo, 105-0022, Japan   (100%)
Tel.: (81) 357761101
Web Site: http://www.eol.db.com
Online Corporate Financial Data Services
N.A.I.C.S.: 518210
Takeshi Ueno *(Pres)*

PRONGHORN CONTROLS LTD.

101 4919 72 Ave SE, Calgary, T2C 3H3, AB, Canada
Tel.: (403) 720-2526
Web Site: https://www.pronghorn.ca
Year Founded: 1981
Rev.: $30,430,733
Emp.: 125
Industrial Equipment Services
N.A.I.C.S.: 423830
Yves Tremblay *(Pres & CEO)*

PRONTO EUROPE S.A.R.L.

12 Avenue Des Morillons, 95140, Garges-les-Gonesse, France
Tel.: (33) 139933310   FR
Sales Range: $10-24.9 Million
Emp.: 11
Desktop Computer Whslr
N.A.I.C.S.: 423430
Lacroix Auielien *(Chm)*

PROODEFTIKH TECHNICAL COMPANY S.A.

Spyrou Trikoupi 60, 11473, Athens, Greece
Tel.: (30) 2108837210
Web Site: https://www.proodeftiki.gr
Year Founded: 1960
Emp.: 3
Construction Services

AND PRIVATE COMPANIES / PROPELL HOLDINGS LIMITED

N.A.I.C.S.: 237310
Anthony George *(Dir-Fin)*

PROOFID LTD.
Lancastrian Office Centre, Talbot Road, Old Trafford, Manchester, M32 0FP, United Kingdom
Tel.: (44) 161 906 1002
Web Site: http://www.proofid.co.uk
Identity & Access Management Services
N.A.I.C.S.: 541613
Tom Eggleston *(CEO)*

PROPAK SYSTEMS LTD.
440 East Lake Road NE, Airdrie, T4A 2J8, AB, Canada
Tel.: (403) 912-7000   AB
Web Site: https://www.propaksystems.com
Year Founded: 1976
Sales Range: $100-124.9 Million
Emp.: 675
Engineering, Construction, Fabrication, Equipment Leasing; Oil & Gas Production Equipment
N.A.I.C.S.: 541330
Rod McPike *(Pres)*

Subsidiaries:

Innovative Steam Technologies   (1)
549 Conestoga Blvd, Cambridge, N1R 7P5, ON, Canada
Tel.: (519) 740-0757
Web Site: http://www.otsg.com
Steam Generators Mfr & Distr
N.A.I.C.S.: 333611

PHK Engineering Limited   (1)
18/F Fortune House 61 Connaught Road, Hong Kong, China (Hong Kong)
Tel.: (852) 2815 6782
Construction Engineering Services
N.A.I.C.S.: 541330

Propak Oil & Gas Equipment (Shenzhen) CO., Ltd.   (1)
508 Zhaoshang Building Zhaoshang Road Shekou, Nanshan, Shenzhen, 518067, Guangdong, China
Tel.: (86) 755 26688908
Web Site: http://www.propaksystems.com
Emp.: 70
Oil & Gas Plant Construction Services
N.A.I.C.S.: 237990
Larry Wang *(Office Mgr)*

Propak Systems Argentina S.A.   (1)
Florida 234 - 4to piso, Buenos Aires, Capital Federal, Argentina
Tel.: (54) 2964430355
Web Site: http://www.propaksystems.com
N.A.I.C.S.: 541330

PROPANC BIOPHARMA, INC.
302/6 Butler Street, Camberwell, 3124, VIC, Australia
Tel.: (61) 398820780   DE
Web Site: https://www.propanc.com
Year Founded: 2010
PPCB—(OTCIQ)
Rev.: $60
Assets: $72,365
Liabilities: $3,851,424
Net Worth: ($3,779,059)
Earnings: ($1,820,528)
Emp.: 1
Fiscal Year-end: 06/30/24
Cancer & Other Disease Treatments Research Services
N.A.I.C.S.: 541715
James Nathanielsz *(Chm, CEO & CFO)*

PROPEL FUNERAL PARTNERS LIMITED
Level 18 03 135 King Street, Sydney, 2000, NSW, Australia
Tel.: (61) 285148600   AU
Web Site: https://www.propelfuneral.com.au
Year Founded: 2017
PFP—(ASX)
Rev.: $139,715,544
Assets: $417,053,951
Liabilities: $182,188,835
Net Worth: $234,865,117
Earnings: $11,893,697
Emp.: 800
Fiscal Year-end: 06/30/24
Funeral Home Management Services
N.A.I.C.S.: 812210
Albin Kurti *(Co-Founder & Mng Dir)*

Subsidiaries:

Charles Berry & Son Pty. Ltd.   (1)
198-204 Magill Road, Norwood, 5067, SA, Australia
Tel.: (61) 883322088
Web Site: https://www.berryfunerals.com.au
Funeral & Memorial Services
N.A.I.C.S.: 812210

Eagars Funerals Limited   (1)
172-174 Lemon St Strandon, New Plymouth, 4312, New Zealand
Tel.: (64) 67592200
Web Site: https://www.eagars.co.nz
Funeral Arrangement Services
N.A.I.C.S.: 812210

F.W. Barnes Funeral Services Pty Ltd   (1)
701 Darling St, Redan, Ballarat, 3350, VIC, Australia
Tel.: (61) 353361211
Web Site: https://www.fwbarnes.com.au
Funeral Services
N.A.I.C.S.: 812210

Glenelg Funerals Pty. Ltd.   (1)
261/263 Brighton Rd, Somerton, 5044, SA, Australia
Tel.: (61) 872219980
Web Site: https://glenelgfunerals.com.au
Funeral Arrangement Services
N.A.I.C.S.: 812210

Grahams Funeral Services Limited   (1)
West St, Tuakau, 2121, Auckland, New Zealand
Tel.: (64) 92368919
Web Site: https://www.grahamsfunerals.co.nz
Funeral Services
N.A.I.C.S.: 812210
Mark Graham *(Gen Mgr)*

Gregson & Weight Pty Ltd   (1)
5 Gregson Place, Caloundra, Sunshine Coast, 4551, QLD, Australia
Tel.: (61) 754911559
Web Site: https://www.gregsonweight.com.au
Funeral Services
N.A.I.C.S.: 812210

Gympie Funeral Services Pty Ltd   (1)
236 Brisbane Road, Gympie, 4570, QLD, Australia
Tel.: (61) 754828400
Web Site: https://www.gympiefunerals.com.au
Funeral Services
N.A.I.C.S.: 812210

Hall Funeral Services Pty Ltd   (1)
15 Station Street, Diamond Creek, Melbourne, 3080, VIC, Australia
Tel.: (61) 394385416
Web Site: https://www.hallsfunerals.com.au
Funeral Services
N.A.I.C.S.: 812210

Handley Funerals Pty Ltd   (1)
24 Anderson Street, Leongatha, 3953, VIC, Australia
Tel.: (61) 356622717
Web Site: https://www.handleyfuneralservices.com
Funeral Services
N.A.I.C.S.: 812210

Integrity Funeral Services Pty Ltd   (1)
18 Tonga Place, Parkwood, 4214, QLD, Australia
Tel.: (61) 755764545
Web Site: http://www.integrityfunerals.com.au
Funeral Services
N.A.I.C.S.: 812210
Rowan Steer *(Gen Mgr)*

Latrobe Valley Funeral Services Pty Ltd   (1)
6 Ollerton Avenue, Moe, Latrobe, 3825, VIC, Australia
Tel.: (61) 351261111
Web Site: https://www.latrobevalleyfunerals.com.au
Funeral Services
N.A.I.C.S.: 812210
David Hastie *(Gen Mgr)*

Manning Great Lakes Memorial Gardens Pty Ltd   (1)
183 Pampoolah Road, Taree, 2430, NSW, Australia
Tel.: (61) 265500755
Web Site: https://www.mglmg.com.au
Funeral Services
N.A.I.C.S.: 812210

Morleys Funerals Pty Ltd   (1)
Cnr Hugh Street and Martinez Avenue The Lakes, Townsville, 4810, QLD, Australia
Tel.: (61) 747794744
Web Site: https://www.morleys.net.au
Funeral Services
N.A.I.C.S.: 812210

Newhaven Funerals (North Queensland) Pty Ltd   (1)
218 Harbour Road, MacKay, 4740, QLD, Australia
Tel.: (61) 749531200
Web Site: https://www.newhavenfuneralsnq.com.au
Funeral Services
N.A.I.C.S.: 812210
David Clayton *(Gen Mgr)*

PFP (NZ) Limited   (1)
Level 6 35 High St, Auckland, 1010, New Zealand
Tel.: (64) 93090868
Web Site: https://www.pfpltd.co.nz
Marketing Consulting Services
N.A.I.C.S.: 541613

Pets RIP Pty. Ltd.   (1)
Office 12 Rocla Court Glenvale, Toowoomba, 4350, QLD, Australia
Tel.: (61) 746330290
Web Site: https://petsrip.com.au
Pet Cremation Services
N.A.I.C.S.: 812220

Phillip Stephens Funeral Services Pty Ltd   (1)
25 Electra Place, Mornington, 7018, TAS, Australia
Tel.: (61) 62450544
Web Site: https://www.psfunerals.com
Funeral Services
N.A.I.C.S.: 812210

Quinn Funeral Services Pty Ltd   (1)
15 Skene Street, Colac, 3250, VIC, Australia
Tel.: (61) 352312052
Web Site: https://www.quinnfunerals.com.au
Funeral Services
N.A.I.C.S.: 812210

Riverina Funeral Services Pty Ltd   (1)
453 Harfleur St, Deniliquin, 2710, NSW, Australia
Tel.: (61) 358815111
Web Site: https://www.riverinafunerals.com.au
Funeral Services
N.A.I.C.S.: 812210

WT Howard Funeral Services Pty Ltd   (1)
5 Flett Street, Taree, 2430, NSW, Australia
Tel.: (61) 265521057
Web Site: https://www.wthowardfunerals.com.au
Funeral Services
N.A.I.C.S.: 812210
Lloyd Ninham *(Dir-Funeral)*

PROPEL GLOBAL BERHAD
Level 12 Mercu 3 Jalan Bangsar KL Eco City, 59200, Kuala Lumpur, Malaysia
Tel.: (60) 322022820
Web Site: https://www.propelglobal.com.my
PGB—(KLS)
Rev.: $23,758,095
Assets: $40,760,847
Liabilities: $21,695,026
Net Worth: $19,065,820
Earnings: $1,695,238
Emp.: 186
Fiscal Year-end: 06/30/23
Oil & Gas Exploration Services
N.A.I.C.S.: 211120
Thean Shiang Lim *(Chm)*

Subsidiaries:

Daya Polymer Sdn. Bhd.   (1)
1744 Jalan Industri Dua Taman Industri Bukit Panchor, 14300, Nibong Tebal, Penang, Malaysia
Tel.: (60) 45938811
Web Site: http://www.dmb.com.my
Sales Range: $25-49.9 Million
Emp.: 63
Polymer Compound Mfr
N.A.I.C.S.: 325991

Daya Proffscorp Sdn. Bhd.   (1)
Lot 606-A Kawasan Industri Teluk Kalong, 24007, Kemaman, Terengganu, Malaysia
Tel.: (60) 98633000
Sales Range: $25-49.9 Million
Emp.: 100
Crane & Forklifts Hiring Services
N.A.I.C.S.: 238990
Nasir Ismail *(Sr Mgr-Procurement & Purchasing)*

PT Daya Secadyme Indonesia   (1)
Kompleks Wijaya Grand Centre Blok 'H' No 12-B Lantai 3 JL Wijawa II, Kebayoran Baru, Jakarta, 12160, Indonesia
Tel.: (62) 217206696
Sales Range: $50-74.9 Million
Emp.: 10
Petrochemical Distr
N.A.I.C.S.: 424690

Propel Chemicals Sdn. Bhd.   (1)
Suite B-5-2 Setiawangsa Business Suites Jalan Setiawangsa 11, 54200, Kuala Lumpur, Selangor, Malaysia   (55%)
Tel.: (60) 362053170
Web Site: http://www.dmb.com.my
Sales Range: $50-74.9 Million
Emp.: 8
Chemical Distr
N.A.I.C.S.: 424690

PROPEL HOLDINGS INC.
69 Yonge St 1500, Toronto, M5E 1K3, ON, Canada
Tel.: (647) 776-5479   ON
Year Founded: 2011
PRL—(TSX)
Rev.: $226,850,634
Assets: $256,680,546
Liabilities: $175,039,871
Net Worth: $81,640,675
Earnings: $15,127,447
Emp.: 419
Fiscal Year-end: 12/31/22
Holding Company
N.A.I.C.S.: 551112
Kinross Clive *(CEO)*

PROPELL HOLDINGS LIMITED
Level 11 82 Eagle Street, Brisbane, 4000, QLD, Australia
Tel.: (61) 1300804091   AU
Web Site: https://www.propell.investor.com.au
Year Founded: 2016
PHL—(ASX)
Rev.: $1,149,504
Assets: $2,170,600
Liabilities: $5,325,527
Net Worth: ($3,154,927)

Propell Holdings Limited—(Continued)

Earnings: ($2,921,689)
Emp.: 4
Fiscal Year-end: 06/30/23
Holding Company
N.A.I.C.S.: 551112
Adam Gallagher (Sec)

Subsidiaries:

Propell Services Pty. Ltd. (1)
Level 2 307 Queen St, Brisbane, 4000, QLD, Australia
Tel.: (61) 1300804091
Web Site: https://propell.au
Cash & Financial Services
N.A.I.C.S.: 541611

PROPERST CO., LTD.
1-10-10 Azabu-Juban Joule A 7F, Minato-ku, Tokyo, 106-0045, Japan
Tel.: (81) 366853100
Web Site: https://www.properst.co.jp
Year Founded: 1987
3236—(TKS)
Sales Range: $15-24.9 Billion
Real Estate Development Services
N.A.I.C.S.: 531390
Shunichi Mori (CEO)

PROPERTY ACQUISITION & MANAGEMENT LIMITED
TSB House Le Truchot Street, Saint Peter Port, GY1 4AE, Guernsey
Tel.: (44) 1481 731987
Web Site: http://www.cncpfm.co.uk
Sales Range: $25-49.9 Million
Emp.: 23
Property Management Services
N.A.I.C.S.: 531312

PROPERTY AGENT INC.
6F Shinjuku Island Tower 6-5-1 Nishi-Shinjuku, Shinjuku-ku, Tokyo, 163-1306, Japan
Tel.: (81) 36 302 3011
Web Site: http://www.propertyagent.co.jp
Year Founded: 2004
3464—(TKS)
Rev.: $340,600,480
Assets: $309,585,760
Liabilities: $230,016,160
Net Worth: $79,569,600
Earnings: $11,780,560
Fiscal Year-end: 03/31/22
Real Estate Development & Property Management
N.A.I.C.S.: 531390
Sei Nakanishi (Founder, Chm & Pres)

PROPERTY CONNECT HOLDINGS LIMITED
Level 26 1 Bligh St, Sydney, 2000, NSW, Australia
Tel.: (61) 2 8226 8516 AU
Web Site: http://www.propertyconnect.com
Rev.: $154,675
Assets: $696,046
Liabilities: $31,138
Net Worth: $664,908
Earnings: ($1,251,922)
Emp.: 60
Fiscal Year-end: 06/30/18
Investment Services
N.A.I.C.S.: 523999
David Nolan (Sec)

Subsidiaries:

Conquest Crop Protection Pty. Ltd. (1)
Level 1 4 Collingwood Street, Osborne Park, 6017, WA, Australia
Tel.: (61) 8 9347 0500
Web Site: http://www.conquestag.com.au
Crop Protection Products Distr
N.A.I.C.S.: 424910

PROPERTY DATA BANK, INC.
Hamamatsucho Square 1-30-5 Hamamatsucho, Minato-ku, Tokyo, 105-0013, Japan
Tel.: (81) 357773468
Web Site: https://www.propertydbk.com
Year Founded: 2000
4389—(TKS)
Rev.: $16,630,760
Assets: $25,745,950
Liabilities: $3,952,780
Net Worth: $21,793,170
Earnings: $1,969,780
Fiscal Year-end: 03/31/24
Real Estate Development Services
N.A.I.C.S.: 531311
Toshimasa Itaya (Pres)

PROPERTY FOR INDUSTRY
Level 4 Hayman Kronfeld Building 15 Galway Street, Auckland, 1010, New Zealand
Tel.: (64) 93039450
Web Site: https://www.propertyforindustry.com
PFI—(NZX)
Rev.: $154,114,942
Assets: $1,023,388,755
Liabilities: $314,981,027
Net Worth: $708,407,727
Earnings: $118,480,058
Fiscal Year-end: 12/31/19
Industrial Property Investment, Development & Management
N.A.I.C.S.: 525990
Anthony Beverley (Chm)

PROPERTY PERFECT PUBLIC COMPANY LIMITED
17th Flr Vorasombat Bldg 100/1 Rama IX Road Huaykwang, Bangkok, 10310, Thailand
Tel.: (66) 22456640
Web Site: http://www.pf.co.th
Year Founded: 1985
PF—(THA)
Rev.: $315,984,976
Assets: $1,553,641,044
Liabilities: $1,129,282,339
Net Worth: $424,358,705
Earnings: ($19,150,808)
Emp.: 957
Fiscal Year-end: 12/31/23
Property Development Services
N.A.I.C.S.: 531190
Chainid Adhyanasakul (CEO & Member-Exec Bd)

Subsidiaries:

Perfect Sport Club Co., Ltd. (1)
134 Kanlapaphruek Rd, Bang Wah Phasi Charoen, Bangkok, 10160, Thailand
Tel.: (66) 22456640
Sports Club Operator
N.A.I.C.S.: 711211

Share Group Co., Ltd. (1)
30-3 Sarugaku-Cho A-702, Shibuya-ku, Tokyo, 150-0033, Japan
Tel.: (81) 3 3463 6013
Real Estate Development Services
N.A.I.C.S.: 531390
Hajime Mori (Mng Dir)

U & I Construction Bangkok Co., Ltd. (1)
Unit D2-04 2nd FL Metro Town 212/3 Kanlapaphruek Rd, Bang Wah Phasi Charoen, Bangkok, 10160, Thailand
Tel.: (66) 24961869
Real Estate Development Services
N.A.I.C.S.: 531390

We Retail Public Company Limited (1)
Unit D2-03 2nd FL Metro Town 212/3 Kanlapaphruek Rd, Bang Wah Phasi Charoen, Bangkok, 10160, Thailand
Tel.: (66) 24961896

Sales Range: $1-9.9 Million
Shopping Mall Operator
N.A.I.C.S.: 531120
Chainid Adhyanasakul (Vice Chm & Acting CEO)

PROPERTY TECHNOLOGIES INC.
12F Sumitomo Fudosan Nishi-Shinjuku Building No 6 3-12-1 Honmachi, Shibuya-ku, Tokyo, 151-0071, Japan
Tel.: (81) 353085050
Web Site: https://www.pptc.co.jp
Year Founded: 2020
5527—(TKS)
Rev.: $262,081,850
Assets: $269,951,750
Liabilities: $219,470,950
Net Worth: $50,480,800
Earnings: $4,686,490
Emp.: 383
Fiscal Year-end: 11/30/23
Real Estate Investment Services
N.A.I.C.S.: 531190
Takehiro Hamanaka (Pres)

PROPERTYGURU GROUP LIMITED
Paya Lebar Quarter 1 Paya Lebar Link 12-01/04, Singapore, 408533, Singapore
Tel.: (65) 62385971 Ky
Web Site: https://www.propertygurugroup.com
Year Founded: 2007
PGRU—(NYSE)
Rev.: $100,788,388
Assets: $548,262,876
Liabilities: $77,959,086
Net Worth: $470,303,790
Earnings: ($95,816,630)
Emp.: 1,711
Fiscal Year-end: 12/31/22
Digital Marketing Services
N.A.I.C.S.: 541810
Hari V. Krishnan (CEO)

PROPERTYLINK (HOLDINGS) LIMITED
Level 12 135 King Street, Sydney, 2000, NSW, Australia
Tel.: (61) 291864700 AU
Web Site: https://www.esr.com
Real Estate Investment Trust
N.A.I.C.S.: 525990
Tony Groth (CFO)

PROPHECY DEFI INC.
87 Scollard Street Suite 100, Toronto, M5R 1G4, ON, Canada
Tel.: (416) 786-9031
V8M—(DEU)
Merchant Banking Services
N.A.I.C.S.: 522110
John A. McMahon (CEO)

PROPHECY INTERNATIONAL HOLDINGS LIMITED
Level 5 60 Waymouth Street, Adelaide, 5000, SA, Australia
Tel.: (61) 882131200 AU
Web Site: https://www.prophecynational.com
Year Founded: 1980
PRO—(ASX)
Rev.: $15,272,575
Assets: $16,581,231
Liabilities: $11,171,205
Net Worth: $5,410,027
Earnings: ($2,824,094)
Emp.: 100
Fiscal Year-end: 06/30/24
Software Development Services
N.A.I.C.S.: 541511
Edwin Reynolds (Chm)

Subsidiaries:

Prophecy Americas Inc (1)
8480 E Orchard Rd Ste 4350, Greenwood Village, CO 80111
Software Development Services
N.A.I.C.S.: 541511

Prophecy Europe Limited (1)
5 Brooklands Place, Sale, M33 3SD, Berkshire, United Kingdom
Tel.: (44) 8707702864
Software Development Services
N.A.I.C.S.: 541511

Prophecy International Pty Ltd (1)
1990 Logan Road, Mount Gravatt, 4122, QLD, Australia
Tel.: (61) 738495811
Software Development Services
N.A.I.C.S.: 541511

PROPNEX LIMITED
480 Lorong 6 Toa Payoh HDB HUB East Wing 10-01, Singapore, 310480, Singapore
Tel.: (65) 68208000
Web Site: https://www.propnex.com
Year Founded: 2000
OYY—(SES)
Rev.: $634,779,974
Assets: $259,837,158
Liabilities: $164,233,129
Net Worth: $95,604,029
Earnings: $37,574,794
Emp.: 161
Fiscal Year-end: 12/31/23
Real Estate Development Services
N.A.I.C.S.: 531390
Mohamed Ismail Gafoore (Founder, Chm & CEO)

Subsidiaries:

Life Mastery Academy Pte. Ltd (1)
Blk 190 Lor 6 Toa Payoh 02-510, Singapore, 310190, Singapore
Tel.: (65) 62556083
Web Site: https://www.lma.com.sg
CPD Training & Development Services
N.A.I.C.S.: 611430

PropNex Property Management Consultants Pte. Ltd. (1)
480 Lorong 6 Toa Payoh HDB HUB East Wing 10-01, Singapore, 310480, Singapore
Tel.: (65) 63919300
Web Site: http://www.ppmc.com.sg
Property Maintenance Services
N.A.I.C.S.: 561790

PropNex Realty (Vietnam) Company Limited (1)
5th Floor Twins Tower 11 Building 85 Cach Mang Thang Tam str, Ben Thanh Ward District 1, Ho Chi Minh City, Vietnam
Tel.: (84) 907099588
Web Site: http://www.prop.vn
Real Estate Development Services
N.A.I.C.S.: 531210
Aidan Wee (Exec Dir)

PROQR THERAPEUTICS N.V.
Zernikedreef 9, 2333 CK, Leiden, Netherlands
Tel.: (31) 881667000 NI
Web Site: https://www.proqr.com
Year Founded: 2012
PRQR—(NASDAQ)
Rev.: $6,514,000
Assets: $137,883,000
Liabilities: $96,493,000
Net Worth: $41,390,000
Earnings: ($27,735,000)
Emp.: 157
Fiscal Year-end: 12/31/23
Pharmaceuticals Mfr
N.A.I.C.S.: 325412
Daniel A. de Boer (Co-Founder & CEO)

PRORED PARTNERS CO., LTD.

AND PRIVATE COMPANIES

Sumitomo Fudosan Onarimon Tower 7F 1 1 1 Shibakoen, Minato-Ku, Tokyo, 105-0012, Japan
Tel.: (81) 364356581
Web Site: https://www.prored-p.com
7034—(TKS)
Rev.: $19,249,350
Assets: $84,924,020
Liabilities: $13,556,080
Net Worth: $71,367,940
Earnings: $5,799,620
Emp.: 167
Fiscal Year-end: 10/31/23
Management Consulting Services
N.A.I.C.S.: 541618
Susumu Satani *(CEO)*

PROROUTE MARUMITSU CO., LTD.
2-1-3 Kitakyuhoji-cho, Chuo-ku, Osaka, 541-0057, Japan
Tel.: (81) 66 262 0303
Web Site: http://www.proroute.co.jp
Year Founded: 1900
8256—(JAS)
Rev.: $41,517,520
Assets: $45,321,760
Liabilities: $34,683,440
Net Worth: $10,638,320
Earnings: ($5,817,680)
Emp.: 90
Fiscal Year-end: 03/31/22
Apparel Product Whslr
N.A.I.C.S.: 458110

Subsidiaries:

Sunmar Corporation (1)
Yokoyama-cho 6-16, Nihonbashi Chuo-ku, Tokyo, 103-0003, Japan
Tel.: (81) 336638988
Web Site: http://www.e-kenthouse.com
Apparel Distr
N.A.I.C.S.: 458110
Yoshio Maeda *(Chm)*

PROSAFE SE
Forusparken 2, N-4031, Stavanger, Norway
Tel.: (47) 51642500
Web Site: https://www.prosafe.com
PRS—(OSL)
Rev.: $97,700,000
Assets: $492,700,000
Liabilities: $458,900,000
Net Worth: $33,800,000
Earnings: ($67,800,000)
Emp.: 255
Fiscal Year-end: 12/31/23
Holding Company; Floatel Fleet Owner & Operator
N.A.I.C.S.: 551112
Ryan Stewart *(COO)*

Subsidiaries:

Prosafe Offshore AS (1)
Forusparken 2, PO Box 39, Stavanger, 4064, Norway
Tel.: (47) 51642500
Oil & Gas Well Drilling Services
N.A.I.C.S.: 213111

Subsidiary (Domestic):

Prosafe Offshore Norge AS (2)
Nedre Holmeg 30-34, 4006, Stavanger, Norway
Tel.: (47) 51642500
Sales Range: $50-74.9 Million
Emp.: 10
Drilling Rigs Operation Services
N.A.I.C.S.: 213111

Prosafe Offshore B.V. (1)
Prins Bernhardplein 200, 1097 JB, Amsterdam, North Holland, Netherlands
Tel.: (31) 205214777
Drilling Rigs Operation Services
N.A.I.C.S.: 213111

Prosafe Offshore Employment Company Pte Ltd (1)
1 International Business Park 09-03 The Synergy, Singapore, 609917, Singapore
Tel.: (65) 65591980
Web Site: http://www.prosafe.com
Sales Range: $50-74.9 Million
Emp.: 13
Offshore Support Services
N.A.I.C.S.: 213112

Prosafe Offshore Ltd. (1)
Pavilion 5 Kingshill Park Venture Drive Arnhall Business Park, Westhill, Aberdeen, AB32 6FL, United Kingdom
Tel.: (44) 1224406900
Web Site: http://www.offshore.prosafe.com
Sales Range: $50-74.9 Million
Emp.: 60
Oil & Gas Well Drilling Services
N.A.I.C.S.: 213111
John Rune Hellevik *(VP-Contracts & Risk Mgmt)*

Prosafe Offshore Pte Ltd (1)
1 International Business Park 09-03 The Synergy, Singapore, 609917, Singapore
Tel.: (65) 65591980
Sales Range: $50-74.9 Million
Emp.: 15
Oil & Gas Well Drilling Services
N.A.I.C.S.: 213111
Ryan Stewart *(Chief Comml Officer)*

Prosafe Rigs Pte. Ltd. (1)
1 International Business Park 09-03 The Synergy, Singapore, 609917, Singapore
Tel.: (65) 65591980
Marine Accommodation Vessel Services
N.A.I.C.S.: 488330

Prosafe Services Maritimos Ltda. (1)
Praia de Botafogo 228 - Suites 409 e 410, Botafogo, Rio de Janeiro, CEP 22250-906, RJ, Brazil
Tel.: (55) 21995813159
Marine Accommodation Vessel Services
N.A.I.C.S.: 488330

PROSEGUR CASH SA
Calle Pajaritos 24, 28007, Madrid, 28007, Spain
Tel.: (34) 915588021
Web Site: https://www.prosegurcash.com
Year Founded: 2016
CASH—(BIL)
Rev.: $2,054,617,508
Assets: $2,196,226,957
Liabilities: $2,026,073,518
Net Worth: $170,153,439
Earnings: $69,361,960
Emp.: 45,590
Fiscal Year-end: 12/31/23
Investment Management Service
N.A.I.C.S.: 523940
Christian Gut Revoredo *(Chm)*

Subsidiaries:

Change Group Sweden AB (1)
Drottninggatan 65, 11136, Stockholm, Sweden
Tel.: (46) 84111222
Web Site: https://se.changegroup.com
Foreign Currency Exchange Services
N.A.I.C.S.: 541611

Compliofficer SLU (1)
San Maximo 3, 28041, Madrid, Spain
Tel.: (34) 910059414
Web Site: http://www.compliofficer.com
Law firm
N.A.I.C.S.: 541199

Netijam Technologies SL (1)
Pajaritos 24, 28008, Madrid, Spain
Tel.: (34) 915222478
Web Site: http://www.sisnet360.com
Information Technology Services
N.A.I.C.S.: 541511

Precinct Hub Pty. Limited (1)
Level 1 65 Epping Road, Macquarie Park, 2113, NSW, Australia
Tel.: (61) 1300661773
Web Site: https://www.precinct.com.au
Finance & Banking Services
N.A.I.C.S.: 541611

The Change Group Corporation Ltd. (1)
353 Oxford Street, London, W1C 2JG, United Kingdom
Tel.: (44) 2036758200
Web Site: http://www.changegroup.com
Sales Range: $600-649.9 Million
Emp.: 526
Foreign Currency Exchange Services
N.A.I.C.S.: 523160
Sacha Alexander Zackariya *(CEO)*

The Change Group France, S.A.S. (1)
49 Avenue de L Opera, 75002, Paris, France
Tel.: (33) 158183480
Web Site: https://fr.changegroup.com
Foreign Currency Exchange Services
N.A.I.C.S.: 541611

The Change Group Helsinki OY (1)
Pohjoisesplanadi 21, 00100, Helsinki, Finland
Tel.: (358) 405587681
Web Site: https://fi.changegroup.com
Foreign Currency Exchange Services
N.A.I.C.S.: 541611

The Change Group International PLC (1)
353 Oxford Street, London, W1C 2JG, United Kingdom
Tel.: (44) 2036758200
Web Site: https://corp.changegroup.com
Emp.: 160,000
Foreign Currency Exchange Services
N.A.I.C.S.: 541611

The Change Group London Limited (1)
353 Oxford Street, London, W1C 2JG, United Kingdom
Tel.: (44) 2070167941
Web Site: https://uk.changegroup.com
Foreign Currency Exchange Services
N.A.I.C.S.: 541611

The Change Group Spain, S.A. (1)
Calle Gran Via 49, CP 28013, Madrid, Spain
Tel.: (34) 810583232
Web Site: https://es.changegroup.com
Foreign Currency Exchange Services
N.A.I.C.S.: 541611

PROSEGUR COMPANIA DE SEGURIDAD S.A.
Calle Pajaritos 24, 28007, Madrid, Spain
Tel.: (34) 915898347
Web Site: https://www.prosegur.com
Year Founded: 1976
PSG—(MAD)
Rev.: $4,757,731,538
Assets: $4,464,610,885
Liabilities: $3,672,535,600
Net Worth: $792,075,284
Earnings: $86,665,195
Emp.: 153,584
Fiscal Year-end: 12/31/23
Security Services
N.A.I.C.S.: 561612
Helena Irene Revoredo Delvecchio *(Chm)*

Subsidiaries:

Beagle Watch Armed Response Proprietary Limited (1)
Unison House 190 Smit Street, Fairland, Johannesburg, 2195, South Africa
Tel.: (27) 116781972
Web Site: https://www.beaglewatch.co.za
Security Services
N.A.I.C.S.: 561612

Cipher S.A. (1)
Av Ermano Marchetti 1435 8 andar, Sao Paulo, 05038-001, Brazil
Tel.: (55) 1145016600
Information Technology Services
N.A.I.C.S.: 541511

Compania Transportadora de Valores Prosegur de Colombia SA (1)
B 76, CL 19 68, Bogota, Colombia
Tel.: (57) 13444420
Security Guarding Services
N.A.I.C.S.: 561612

Focal Investigation & Security Agency Pte. Ltd. (1)
5001 Beach Road 04-22 Golden Mile Complex, Singapore, 199588, Singapore
Tel.: (65) 62210110
Web Site: https://www.prosegur-focal.sg
Emp.: 250
Security Services
N.A.I.C.S.: 561612

Formacion, Seleccion y Consultoria, S.A. (1)
Santa Sabina 8, Madrid, Spain
Recruitment Services
N.A.I.C.S.: 561311

Juncadella Prosegur Internacional SA (1)
Tres Arroyos 2835, Buenos Aires, C1416DDU, Argentina
Tel.: (54) 11 4585 8200
Web Site: http://www.prosegur.com
Security Guarding Services
N.A.I.C.S.: 561612

Prosegur Brasil SA Transportadora de Valores e Seguranca (1)
Avenida Guarata no 633 Bairro do Prado, Belo Horizonte, 30411-018, Minas Gerais, Brazil
Tel.: (55) 3121262400
Web Site: https://www.prosegur.com.br
Security Guarding Services
N.A.I.C.S.: 561612

Prosegur Services Group, Inc. (1)
512 Herndon Pkwy Ste A, Herndon, VA 20170
Tel.: (703) 464-4735
Web Site: http://www.commandsecurity.com
Security Services for Commercial, Industrial & Governmental Clients
N.A.I.C.S.: 561612
Gary Crivelli *(VP-SE Region)*

Prosegur Singapore Pte. Ltd. (1)
11 Lorong 3 Toa Payoh Jackson Square Block B 03-26, Singapore, 319579, Singapore
Tel.: (65) 63895187
Web Site: https://www.prosegur.com.sg
Security Services
N.A.I.C.S.: 561612

Prosegur, S.A. (1)
Societa di vigilanza Via Brentani 11, 6904, Lugano, Switzerland
Tel.: (41) 919733210
Web Site: https://www.prosegur.ch
Security Guarding Services
N.A.I.C.S.: 561612

Tapia Seguridad, S.L. (1)
Parque Tecnologico De Asturias Parcela 32, 33420, Llanera, Spain
Tel.: (34) 98 524 0963
Web Site: https://www.tapiaseguridad.es
Fire Protection Equipments Distr
N.A.I.C.S.: 423990

PROSIEBENSAT.1 MEDIA SE
Medienallee 7, D-85774, Unterfohring, Germany
Tel.: (49) 89950710
Web Site: https://www.prosiebensat1.com
PBSFF—(OTCIQ)
Rev.: $4,252,124,959
Assets: $6,517,275,638
Liabilities: $4,773,153,770
Net Worth: $1,744,121,868
Earnings: ($147,919,196)
Emp.: 5,980
Fiscal Year-end: 12/31/23
Holding Company; Television, Radio & Internet Broadcasting Services
N.A.I.C.S.: 551112
Ralf Peter Gierig *(Deputy CFO & Exec VP-Fin & IR)*

Subsidiaries:

44 Blue Productions, Inc. (1)

PROSIEBENSAT.1 MEDIA SE

ProSiebenSat.1 Media SE—(Continued)

3900 W Alameda Ave Suite 700, Burbank, CA 91505 **(65%)**
Tel.: (818) 760-4442
Web Site: http://www.44blue.com
Sales Range: $10-24.9 Million
Emp.: 30
Motion Picture & Video Production
N.A.I.C.S.: 512110
Rasha Drachkovitch *(Co-Owner & CEO)*

ATV Privat TV GmbH & Co KG (1)
Media Quarter Marx 3 2 Maria-Jacobi-Gasse 1, 1030, Vienna, Austria
Tel.: (43) 136877660
Web Site: https://www.atv.at
Web Hosting Services
N.A.I.C.S.: 518210

CPL Productions Limited (1)
8 Gate Street, London, WC2A 3HP, United Kingdom
Tel.: (44) 2072408101
Web Site: https://www.cplproductions.co.uk
Television & Radio Broadcasting Services
N.A.I.C.S.: 516120
Danielle Lux *(Mng Dir)*

Fabrik Entertainment, LLC (1)
6320 Sunset Blvd Ste 250, Los Angeles, CA 90028
Tel.: (323) 785-5600
Web Site: https://www.fabelentertainment.com
Emp.: 8
Television Broadcasting Services
N.A.I.C.S.: 516120
Henrick Bastin *(CEO)*

Fortitude Production Services, LLC (1)
39 W 19th St Fl 9, New York, NY 10011
Tel.: (212) 967-6170
Film & Video Production Services
N.A.I.C.S.: 512120

Glomex GmbH (1)
Dieselstrasse 1, 85774, Unterfohring, Germany
Tel.: (49) 89950710
Web Site: https://www.glomex.com
Emp.: 50
Online Media Services
N.A.I.C.S.: 513199
Michael Sandbichler *(CEO)*

Gravitas Ventures LLC (1)
209 Richmond St, El Segundo, CA 90245
Tel.: (310) 648-8430
Web Site: http://www.gravitasventures.com
Sales Range: $10-24.9 Million
Emp.: 8
Worldwide Distr of Entertainment Products, Videos & Films
N.A.I.C.S.: 512120
Nolan Gallagher *(Founder & CEO)*

Hip Trips GmbH (1)
Muhldorf Strasse 8, 81671, Munich, Germany
Tel.: (49) 89606089482
Web Site: http://www.hip-trips.com
Tour Operating Services
N.A.I.C.S.: 561520

Joyn GmbH (1)
Tel.: (49) 8004395696
Web Site: https://www.joyn.de
Television Broadcasting Services
N.A.I.C.S.: 516120
Alexandar Vassilev *(CEO & Mng Dir)*

Subsidiary (Domestic):

maxdome GmbH (2)
Medienallee 7, 85774, Unterfohring, Germany
Tel.: (49) 89 9507 8320
Web Site: http://www.maxdome.de
Online Television Broadcasting Services
N.A.I.C.S.: 516120

Kinetic Content LLC (1)
11755 Wilshire Blvd Ste 2000, Los Angeles, CA 90025-1525
Tel.: (310) 883-7000
Web Site: http://www.kineticcontent.com
Television Broadcasting Services
N.A.I.C.S.: 516120
Chris Coelen *(Founder & CEO)*

MMP Event GmbH (1)
Widderdorfer Str 190 Altes Gaswerk, 50825, Cologne, Germany
Tel.: (49) 2219405770
Web Site: https://www.mmpevent.de
Event Management Services
N.A.I.C.S.: 711310

MMP Event GmbH (1)
Widderdorfer Str 190 Altes Gaswerk, 50825, Cologne, Germany
Tel.: (49) 221 940 5770
Web Site: https://www.mmpevent.de
Event Management Services
N.A.I.C.S.: 561920

MTM-TV2 Befektetesi Kft. (1)
Rona Utca 174, Budapest, 1145, Hungary
Tel.: (36) 14676400
Television Broadcasting Services
N.A.I.C.S.: 516120

MyVideo Broadband S.R.L. (1)
Calea Victoriei nr 54 et 1 ap 6 sector 1, 010082, Bucharest, Romania
Tel.: (40) 314101911
Web Site: http://www.myvideo.de
Online Community Portal Operator
N.A.I.C.S.: 519290
Andrei Gherghina *(Project Mgr)*

NUCOM GROUP SE (1)
Medienallee 7, 85774, Unterfohring, Germany **(74.9%)**
Tel.: (49) 8995078680
Web Site: http://www.nucom.group
Rev.: $958,288,000
Investment Firm
N.A.I.C.S.: 523940
Claas van Delden *(Co-CEO & Member-Exec Bd)*

Subsidiary (Domestic):

Jochen Schweizer Mydays Holding GmbH (2)
Muhldorfstrasse 8, 81671, Munich, Germany
Tel.: (49) 8921129080
Web Site: https://partner.jsmd-group.com
Tour Operator
N.A.I.C.S.: 561520

Subsidiary (Domestic):

Jochen Schweizer GmbH (3)
Muhldorfstrasse 8, 81671, Munich, Germany
Tel.: (49) 8970809090
Web Site: https://www.jochen-schweizer.de
Gift Retailer
N.A.I.C.S.: 459420

Subsidiary (Domestic):

PARSHIP ELITE Group GmbH (2)
Speersort 10, 20095, Hamburg, Germany **(50%)**
Tel.: (49) 40 460026 590
Web Site: http://www.parshipelite.com
Emp.: 230
Online Dating Services
N.A.I.C.S.: 812990
Herbert Murschenhofer *(CMO)*

Subsidiary (Domestic):

EliteMedianet GmbH (3)
Speersort 10, 20095, Hamburg, Germany
Tel.: (49) 40 46 9785 26
Web Site: http://www.elitepartner.de
Emp.: 100
Online Dating Services
N.A.I.C.S.: 516210
Beatrice Bartsch *(Mgr-PR & Content)*

PE Digital Gmbh (3)
Speersort 10, 20095, Hamburg, Germany
Tel.: (49) 4063790491
Web Site: https://www.parship.de
Online Dating Services
N.A.I.C.S.: 516210
Tim Schiffers *(CEO & Mng Dir)*

Subsidiary (US):

eHarmony.com, Inc. (3)
401 Colorado Ave Ste A200, Santa Monica, CA 90404
Tel.: (626) 795-4814
Web Site: http://www.eharmony.com

Sales Range: $10-24.9 Million
Emp.: 130
Internet Dating Services
N.A.I.C.S.: 812990
Neil Clark Warren *(Founder & Chm)*

PS Event GmbH (1)
Hauptstrasse 51, 9053, Teufen, Switzerland
Tel.: (41) 79 689 3182
Web Site: https://www.psevents.ch
Event Management Services
N.A.I.C.S.: 561920

PULS 4 TV GmbH & Co KG (1)
Maria Jacobi Gasse 1, 1030, Vienna, Austria
Tel.: (43) 136877660
Web Site: https://www.puls24.at
Web Hosting Services
N.A.I.C.S.: 518210

PULS4 Shopping GmbH (1)
Maria Jacobi Alley 1 Media Quarter Marx 3 3, 1030, Vienna, Austria
Tel.: (43) 1230603205
Web Site: http://www.4shoppingdays.com
Web Hosting Services
N.A.I.C.S.: 518210

Parship Group GmbH (1)
Speersort 10, 20095, Hamburg, Germany
Tel.: (49) 40460026590
Online Dating Services
N.A.I.C.S.: 812990

Petobel GmbH (1)
Ritterstrasse 12-14, 10969, Berlin, Germany
Tel.: (49) 800 55 55 66 0
Web Site: http://www.petobel.de
Pet Food Distr
N.A.I.C.S.: 459910
Marcel Rangnow *(Sr Mgr-SEO)*

ProSieben (Schweiz) AG (1)
Fahnlibrunnenstrasse 5, 8700, Kusnacht, Switzerland
Tel.: (41) 44 914 84 00
Web Site: http://www.prosieben.ch
Television Broadcasting Services
N.A.I.C.S.: 516120
Andrea Haemmerli *(Mng Dir)*

ProSieben Television GmbH (1)
Medienallee 7, D-85774, Unterfohring, Germany **(100%)**
Tel.: (49) 8995077700
Web Site: http://www.prosieben.de
Sales Range: $1-4.9 Billion
Emp.: 300
Television Broadcasting Network
N.A.I.C.S.: 517111

ProSiebenSat.1 Accelerator GmbH (1)
Medienallee 4, 85774, Unterfohring, Germany
Tel.: (49) 89950710
Web Site: http://www.p7s1accelerator.com
Private Equity Firm Services
N.A.I.C.S.: 551112

ProSiebenSat.1 Advertising Platform Solutions GmbH (1)
Medienallee 4, 85774, Unterfohring, Germany
Tel.: (49) 8995078934
Advertising Services
N.A.I.C.S.: 327910

Subsidiary (Domestic):

Kairion GmbH (2)
Mainzer Landstrasse 61, 60329, Frankfurt am Main, Germany
Tel.: (49) 69902839041
Web Site: https://www.kairion.de
Information Technology & Services
N.A.I.C.S.: 541511

esome Advertising Technologies GmbH (2)
Hohe Bleichen 11, 20354, Hamburg, Germany
Tel.: (49) 40600288100
Web Site: https://www.esome.com
Emp.: 130
Advertising Services
N.A.I.C.S.: 541810
Falk Bielesch *(Mng Dir)*

ProSiebenSat.1 Digital Data GmbH (1)

INTERNATIONAL PUBLIC

Ein Unternehmen der ProSiebenSat.1 Media SE Medienallee 7, 85774, Unterfohring, Germany
Tel.: (49) 89950710
Web Site: https://www.7pass.de
Private Equity Firm Services
N.A.I.C.S.: 551112

ProSiebenSat.1 Games GmbH (1)
Medienallee 19, 85774, Unterfohring, Germany
Tel.: (49) 8995078857
Web Site: http://www.prosiebensat1games.com
Online Game Development Services
N.A.I.C.S.: 541511

ProSiebenSat.1 Licensing GmbH (1)
Medienallee 4, 85774, Unterfohring, Germany
Tel.: (49) 8995078600
Web Site: http://www.prosiebensat1licensing.com
Emp.: 2,000
License Issuing Services
N.A.I.C.S.: 561990

Subsidiary (Non-US):

Merchandising Prague, s.r.o. (2)
Petrohradska 37, 101 00, Prague, Czech Republic
Tel.: (420) 77 499 4925
Web Site: https://www.merchandising.cz
License Service Provider
N.A.I.C.S.: 561990
Pavel Lipavsky *(Mng Dir)*

ProSiebenSat.1 Produktion GmbH (1)
Medienallee 7, 85774, Unterfohring, Germany **(100%)**
Tel.: (49) 89950760
Web Site: http://www.prosiebensat1produktion.de
Sales Range: $200-249.9 Million
Emp.: 1,000
Television Industry Production, Transmission & Other Technical Services
N.A.I.C.S.: 512191
Martin Emele *(Mng Dir)*

ProSiebenSat.1 Welt GmbH (1)
Medienallee 7, 85774, Unterfohring, Germany **(100%)**
Tel.: (49) 8 995 0710
Web Site: https://www.prosiebensat1welt.com
Television Broadcasting Network
N.A.I.C.S.: 517111

ProSiebenSat.1Puls 4 GmbH (1)
Media Quarter Marx 3 3 Maria Jacobi Gasse 1, 1030, Vienna, Austria
Tel.: (43) 136877660
Web Site: https://www.prosiebensat1puls4.com
Television Broadcasting Services
N.A.I.C.S.: 516120

Producers at work GmbH (1)
Alt Nowawes 116-118, 14482, Potsdam, Germany
Tel.: (49) 331 7494 200
Web Site: http://www.producersatwork.de
Television Broadcasting Services
N.A.I.C.S.: 516120
Christian Popp *(Founder & CEO)*

Subsidiary (Domestic):

Magic Flight Film GmbH (2)
Pienzenauer Str 6, 81679, Munich, Germany
Tel.: (49) 89 540434 45
Web Site: http://www.magicflightfilm.de
Television Broadcasting Services
N.A.I.C.S.: 516120
Christian Rohde *(CEO)*

Red Arrow Entertainment Limited (1)
73-75 Mortimer Street, London, W1W 7SQ, United Kingdom
Tel.: (44) 207 043 0080
Web Site: http://www.redarrowuk.tv
Motion Picture Production Services
N.A.I.C.S.: 512110
Tim Gerhartz *(Sr VP-Global Sls-Munich)*

Subsidiary (Domestic):

Endor Productions Limited (2)

8 Gate Street, London, WC2A 3HP, United Kingdom
Tel.: (44) 2078511300
Web Site:
https://www.endorproductions.co.uk
Film & Video Production Services
N.A.I.C.S.: 512120

New Entertainment Research and Design Limited (2)
73-75 Mortimer Street, London, W1W 7SQ, United Kingdom
Tel.: (44) 207 043 0080
Web Site: http://www.nerdtv.co.uk
Emp.: 9
Television Production Services
N.A.I.C.S.: 512120
John Farrar (Founder & Dir-Creative)

RedSeven Entertainment GmbH (1)
Medienallee 7, 85774, Unterfohring, Germany
Tel.: (49) 8995077000
Web Site: https://www.redseven.de
Emp.: 400
Internet Services
N.A.I.C.S.: 517121

Regiondo GmbH (1)
Muhldorfstrasse 8, 81671, Munich, Germany
Tel.: (49) 8921094737
Web Site: https://pro.regiondo.com
Travel Management Services
N.A.I.C.S.: 561599

Regiondo Software S.R.L. (1)
Strada Bahluiului 1, Sibiu, 557260, Romania
Tel.: (40) 8921094737
Travel Management Services
N.A.I.C.S.: 561599

SAM Sports - Starwatch Artist Management GmbH (1)
Medienallee 4, 85774, Unterfohring, Germany
Tel.: (49) 8995072667
Web Site: http://www.sam-sports.com
Event Management Services
N.A.I.C.S.: 561920
Thomas Eichin (Mng Dir)

Sat.1 Satelliten Fernsehen GmbH (1)
Gutenbergstr 3, D 85774, Unterfohring, Germany (100%)
Tel.: (49) 89950710
Web Site: http://www.sat1.de
Sales Range: $1-4.9 Billion
Emp.: 250
Television Broadcasting Network
N.A.I.C.S.: 517111
Matthias Alberti (Chm-Mgmt Bd)

Subsidiary (Domestic):

SAT.1 Norddeutschland GmbH (2)
Goseriede 9, 30159, Hannover, Germany
Tel.: (49) 51112123443
Web Site: https://www.sat1regional.de
Emp.: 15
Television Broadcasting Services
N.A.I.C.S.: 516120
Michael Grahl (Mng Dir & Mgr-Program)

Joint Venture (Non-US):

Sat.1 Schweiz AG (2)
Fahnlibrunnenstrasse 5, Kusnacht, 8700, Zurich, Switzerland (50%)
Tel.: (41) 449148400
Web Site: http://www.sat1.ch
Sales Range: $25-49.9 Million
Television Advertising & Program Services
N.A.I.C.S.: 541890

Seven.One Entertainment Group GmbH (1)
Medienallee 7, 85774, Unterfohring, Germany
Tel.: (49) 89950710
Web Site: https://www.seven.one
Television Broadcasting Services
N.A.I.C.S.: 516120

SevenOne AdFactory GmbH (1)
Medienallee 4, 85774, Unterfohring, Germany
Tel.: (49) 8995074599
Web Site: http://www.sevenone-adfactory.de
Online Media Services
N.A.I.C.S.: 513199

SevenOne Media GmbH (1)
Medienallee 4, 85774, Unterfohring, Germany
Tel.: (49) 89950740
Web Site: http://www.sevenonemedia.de
Advertising Services
N.A.I.C.S.: 541810
Thomas Wagner (Chm & Mng Dir)

Subsidiary (Domestic):

marktguru Deutschland GmbH (2)
Sendlinger Strasse 23, 80331, Munich, Germany
Tel.: (49) 8945242360
Web Site: https://www.marktguru.de
Magazine Publisher
N.A.I.C.S.: 459210

SevenVentures GmbH (1)
Medienallee 6, 85774, Unterfohring, Germany
Tel.: (49) 8995074599
Web Site: https://www.sevenventures.de
Investment Services
N.A.I.C.S.: 523999

Sonoma Internet GmbH (1)
Wattstrasse 11-13, 13355, Berlin, Germany
Tel.: (49) 3020847388
Web Site: http://www.jobs.amorelie.de
Ecommerce Services
N.A.I.C.S.: 541219

Studio 71 GmbH (1)
Stralauer Allee 8, 10245, Berlin, Germany
Tel.: (49) 3031988085800
Web Site: https://www.studio71.com
Online Video Publishing Services
N.A.I.C.S.: 516210

Stylight GmbH (1)
Muhldorfstrasse 8, 81671, Munich, Germany
Tel.: (49) 8912228950
Web Site: https://www.stylight.com
Ecommerce Services
N.A.I.C.S.: 541219

Sultan Sushi B.V. (1)
Wilgenweg 10 B/C/D, 1031 HV, Amsterdam, Netherlands
Tel.: (31) 20 200 90 02
Web Site: http://www.sultansushi.nl
Television Broadcasting Services
N.A.I.C.S.: 516120
Jan Kooyman (Dir-Creative)

Subsidiary (Non-US):

July August Communications and Productions Ltd. (2)
6 Beit Hilel St 3 F, Tel Aviv, 67017, Israel
Tel.: (972) 35100223
Web Site: http://www.julyaugust.co.il
Television Broadcasting Services
N.A.I.C.S.: 516120

Sultan Sushi CVBA (1)
Schalienhoevedreef 1B, 2800, Mechelen, Belgium
Tel.: (32) 15 40 08 40
Web Site: http://www.sultansushi.be
Emp.: 40
Television Broadcasting Services
N.A.I.C.S.: 516120
Filip Van Lint (Mgr-Fin)

Verivox GmbH (1)
Max-Jarecki-Strasse 21, 69115, Heidelberg, Germany
Tel.: (49) 62217961100
Web Site: https://www.verivox.de
Information Technology & Services
N.A.I.C.S.: 541511

Subsidiary (Domestic):

Maximilian Online Media GmbH (2)
Siemensstrasse 32, 35440, Linden, Germany
Tel.: (49) 64036098159
Web Site: http://www.m-o-m.de
Internet Services
N.A.I.C.S.: 517121

i12 GmbH (2)
Siemensstrasse 32, 35440, Linden, Germany
Tel.: (49) 6403609810
Web Site: http://www.i12.de
Magazine Publisher
N.A.I.C.S.: 459210

moebel.de Einrichten & Wohnen AG (1)
Gertrudenstrasse 3, 20095, Hamburg, Germany
Tel.: (49) 4021 091 0710
Web Site: https://www.moebel.de
Emp.: 1,000
Homeware Product Retailer
N.A.I.C.S.: 449129

mydays Event GmbH (1)
Rosenheimer Strasse 145 E-F, 81671, Munich, Germany
Tel.: (49) 8926 209 5410
Web Site: https://www.mydays-erlebniswerk.de
Online Shopping Services
N.A.I.C.S.: 455219

mydays GmbH (1)
Muhldorfstrasse 8, 81671, Munich, Germany
Tel.: (49) 8921129020
Web Site: https://b2b.mydays.de
Business Management Services
N.A.I.C.S.: 541611

wetter.com AG (1)
Werner-von-Siemens-Str 22, 78224, Singen, Germany
Tel.: (49) 7731 8380
Web Site: http://www.wetter.com
Online Weather Forecasting Service
N.A.I.C.S.: 519290

wetter.com GmbH (1)
Reichenaustrasse 19a, 78467, Konstanz, Germany
Tel.: (49) 75311274400
Web Site: https://www.wetter.com
Online Weather Services
N.A.I.C.S.: 541620

PROSLIDE TECHNOLOGY INC.
150-2650 Queensview Dr, Ottawa, K2B 8H6, ON, Canada
Tel.: (613) 526-5522
Web Site: http://www.proslide.com
Year Founded: 1986
Sales Range: $25-49.9 Million
Water Park Designer & Water Slides Mfr
N.A.I.C.S.: 333310
Andreas J. Tanzer (Dir-Research & Design)

PROSMART ENTERPRISES INC.
302-1353 Ellis Street, Kelowna, V1Y 1Z9, BC, Canada
Tel.: (844) 927-6278
Web Site:
http://www.prosmartinc.com
Year Founded: 2009
Assets: $7,825,970
Liabilities: $357,553
Net Worth: $7,468,417
Earnings: $1,819,204
Fiscal Year-end: 09/30/17
Metal Mining
N.A.I.C.S.: 212290
Roger He (CEO)

PROSOL LACKE + FARBEN GMBH
Schneidmuhlweg 12, 63741, Aschaffenburg, Germany
Tel.: (49) 6021 3480 0
Web Site: http://www.prosol-farben.de
Paints Mfr
N.A.I.C.S.: 325510
Dieter Prosch (Mng Dir)

Subsidiaries:

PROSOL Lacke + Farben GmbH - Oldenburg (1)
Gerhard-Stalling-Str 9a, 26135, Oldenburg, Germany
Tel.: (49) 441 205478 0
Paints Mfr
N.A.I.C.S.: 325510

PROSOURCE.IT (UK) LTD.
Hilldowntree Business Centre Banchory Devenick, Aberdeen, AB12 5YL, United Kingdom
Tel.: (44) 1224 877782
Web Site: http://www.prosource.it
Year Founded: 1999
Sales Range: $50-74.9 Million
Emp.: 557
Information Technology Services
N.A.I.C.S.: 541511
Rachael Jaypalan (Mgr-HR)

Subsidiaries:

prosource.it DMCC (1)
Mazaya AA1 Unit 2608 Jumeirah Lake Towers, Dubai, United Arab Emirates
Tel.: (971) 551150340
Information Technology Consulting Services
N.A.I.C.S.: 541512

PROSPECH LIMITED
Level 2 66 Hunter Street, Sydney, 2000, NSW, Australia
Tel.: (61) 293003333
Web Site:
https://www.prospech.com.au
Year Founded: 2014
PRS—(ASX)
Rev.: $21,155
Assets: $7,604,706
Liabilities: $398,944
Net Worth: $7,205,763
Earnings: ($1,090,260)
Fiscal Year-end: 12/31/23
Other Nonmetallic Mineral Mining & Quarrying
N.A.I.C.S.: 212390
Jason M. Beckton (Mng Dir)

PROSPECT COMMODITIES LIMITED
417 Orbit Behind Rajpath Club Rajpath Rangoli Road PLR Colony, Bodakdev, Ahmedabad, 3800054, Gujarat, India
Tel.: (91) 7948000696
Web Site:
https://www.prospectcommodity.com
Year Founded: 2015
543814—(BOM)
Rev.: $1,521,851
Assets: $1,648,894
Liabilities: $343,421
Net Worth: $1,305,473
Earnings: $65,548
Emp.: 8
Fiscal Year-end: 03/31/23
Food Products Mfr
N.A.I.C.S.: 311412
Vimal Mishra (CEO)

PROSPECT PARK CAPITAL CORP.
Suite 6000, 1 First Canadian Place 100 King Street West, Toronto, M5X 1E2, ON, Canada
Tel.: (416) 369-5265   ON
Year Founded: 2012
PPK—(TSXV)
Rev.: $9,355
Assets: $807,735
Liabilities: $24,212
Net Worth: $783,524
Earnings: ($216,605)
Fiscal Year-end: 09/30/21
Investment Services
N.A.I.C.S.: 523999
Kyle Appleby (CFO)

PROSPECT RESOURCES LIMITED

Prospect Resources Limited—(Continued)

PROSPECT RESOURCES LIMITED
Level 2 33 Richardson Street, West Perth, 6005, WA, Australia
Tel.: (61) 405524960
Web Site:
  https://www.prospectresources.com
Year Founded: 2007
5E8—(DEU)
Rev.: $534,856
Assets: $18,237,847
Liabilities: $700,454
Net Worth: $17,537,393
Earnings: ($4,638,755)
Emp.: 4
Fiscal Year-end: 06/30/24
Metal Mining Services
N.A.I.C.S.: 212290
Duncan Greaves *(Exec Dir)*

PROSPECT RIDGE RESOURCES CORPORATION
701 West Georgia Street Suite 1500, Vancouver, V7Y 1C6, BC, Canada
Tel.: (604) 670-7818   BC
Web Site:
  https://www.prospectridge.com
Year Founded: 2020
PRRSF—(OTCQB)
Assets: $6,461,146
Liabilities: $447,601
Net Worth: $6,013,546
Earnings: ($3,064,594)
Fiscal Year-end: 08/31/22
Gold Exploration & Mining Services
N.A.I.C.S.: 212220
Jasmine Lau *(CFO)*

PROSPECTIUNI S.A.
1 Caransebes Street, 012271, Bucharest, Romania
Tel.: (40) 214042800   RO
Web Site: http://www.prospectiuni.ro
Sales Range: $100-124.9 Million
Emp.: 1,978
Geophysical Engineering Services
N.A.I.C.S.: 541330
Mihail Mitroi *(COO)*

PROSPECTOR METALS CORP.
1020 - 800 West Pender Street, Vancouver, V6C 2V6, BC, Canada
Tel.: (604) 354-2491   BC
Web Site:
  https://prospectormetalscorp.com
ECC—(OTCIQ)
Rev.: $85,401
Assets: $3,313,734
Liabilities: $863,377
Net Worth: $2,450,357
Earnings: ($4,894,858)
Fiscal Year-end: 12/31/19
Gold Mining Services
N.A.I.C.S.: 212220
Craig Roberts *(Co-Pres & CEO)*

PROSPER GOLD CORP.
330 - 890 West Pender Street, Vancouver, V6C 1J9, BC, Canada
Tel.: (604) 638-3663   ON
Web Site:
  https://www.prospergoldcorp.com
Year Founded: 2007
PGXFF—(OTCQB)
Rev.: $221,269
Assets: $1,656,425
Liabilities: $231,204
Net Worth: $1,425,222
Earnings: ($4,321,180)
Fiscal Year-end: 10/31/22
Gold Exploration Services
N.A.I.C.S.: 212220
Peter Bernier *(Chm, Pres & CEO)*

PROSPER ONE INTERNA-

TIONAL HOLDINGS COMPANY LIMITED
Level 43 AIA Tower 183 Electric Road, North Point, China (Hong Kong)
Tel.: (852) 36110358   Ky
Web Site:
  http://www.prosperoneintl.com
Year Founded: 2014
1470—(HKG)
Rev.: $5,292,525
Assets: $25,703,618
Liabilities: $23,554,860
Net Worth: $2,148,758
Earnings: ($338,768)
Emp.: 55
Fiscal Year-end: 04/30/23
Electronic Device Distr
N.A.I.C.S.: 423940
Meng Guangyin *(Chm & CEO)*

Subsidiaries:

City Great Limited   (1)
Room01-02 15/F Port 33 No 33 Tseuk Luk St, San Po Kong, Kowloon, China (Hong Kong)
Tel.: (852) 28319920
Web Site: https://www.citygreat.com.hk
Watch Distr
N.A.I.C.S.: 423940

PROSPERA ENERGY INC.
Suite 730 444 - 7th Av, Calgary, T2P 0X8, AB, Canada
Tel.: (403) 454-9010
Web Site:
  https://www.prosperaenergy.com
Year Founded: 2003
PEI—(OTCIQ)
Rev.: $2,562,364
Assets: $4,286,876
Liabilities: $18,867,858
Net Worth: ($14,580,982)
Earnings: ($9,172,669)
Fiscal Year-end: 12/31/20
Oil & Gas Exploration Services
N.A.I.C.S.: 213112
Savi Franz *(CFO)*

PROSPERITY DIELECTRICS CO., LTD.
No 220-1 Sec 2 Nanshan Rd, Lujhu, Taoyuan, 33860, Taiwan
Tel.: (886) 33224471
Web Site: https://www.pdc.com.tw
Year Founded: 1990
6173—(TPE)
Rev.: $129,518,369
Assets: $273,043,617
Liabilities: $73,628,303
Net Worth: $199,415,314
Earnings: $15,309,539
Emp.: 546
Fiscal Year-end: 12/31/22
Ceramic Chip Product Mfr
N.A.I.C.S.: 327110
Yu-Heng Chiao *(Chm)*

Subsidiaries:

Dongguan Frontier Electronics Co., Ltd.   (1)
No 638 Mei Jing West Road Xiniupo Administrative Zone, Dalang Town, Dongguan, 523799, China
Tel.: (86) 76985550979
Selling Chip Component Mfr & Distr
N.A.I.C.S.: 332999

PROSPERITY INTERNATIONAL HOLDINGS (H.K.) LIMITED
Suite 1801-6 18/F Tower 2 The Gateway 25 Canton Road Tsim Sha Tsui, Kowloon, China (Hong Kong)
Tel.: (852) 3187 2618   HK
Web Site: http://www.pihl-hk.com
Rev.: $297,641,304
Assets: $964,642,533
Liabilities: $850,112,519
Net Worth: $114,530,013
Earnings: ($247,041,332)
Emp.: 240
Fiscal Year-end: 03/31/19
Cement Clinker Trading Services
N.A.I.C.S.: 327310
David Ben Koon Wong *(Founder & Chm)*

Subsidiaries:

Prosperity Cement (Asia) Limited   (1)
Rm 1801-6 18 Fl The Gateway Harbour City Tower 2 25 Canton Rd, Tsim Sha Tsui, Kowloon, China (Hong Kong)
Tel.: (852) 27592618
Web Site: http://www.pihl-hk.com
Sales Range: $50-74.9 Million
Emp.: 80
Cement Whslr
N.A.I.C.S.: 423320

PROSPERITY INVESTMENT HOLDINGS LIMITED
Suite 305 Shui On Centre 6-8 Harbour Road, Wanchai, China (Hong Kong)
Tel.: (852) 31063939   BM
Web Site:
  https://www.prosperityinvestment.hk
0310—(HKG)
Rev.: $544,553
Assets: $7,601,040
Liabilities: $1,953,938
Net Worth: $5,647,103
Earnings: ($612,893)
Emp.: 8
Fiscal Year-end: 12/31/22
Holding Company
N.A.I.C.S.: 551112
Hairong Cheng *(Chm & Mng Dir)*

PROSPERITY RESOURCES LIMITED
100 Parry Street, Perth, 6000, WA, Australia
Tel.: (61) 893227575   AU
Web Site:
  http://www.prosperity.net.au
Sales Range: Less than $1 Million
Emp.: 10
Metals Industry
N.A.I.C.S.: 212220
Sebastian Hempel *(Chm)*

PROSPEROUS FUTURE HOLDINGS LIMITED
17/F Fung House Nos19-20 Connaught Road Central, Central, China (Hong Kong)
Tel.: (852) 38926000   Ky
Web Site: http://www.fd-holdings.com
1259—(HKG)
Rev.: $64,943,273
Assets: $116,462,325
Liabilities: $32,420,700
Net Worth: $84,041,625
Earnings: ($12,851,745)
Emp.: 84
Fiscal Year-end: 12/31/22
Holding Company
N.A.I.C.S.: 551112
Wallen Tsai *(Chm)*

Subsidiaries:

Frog Prince (China) Daily Chemicals Co., Limited   (1)
No 8 Wuqiao North Road Lantian Industrials Development Zone, Zhangzhou, Fujian, China
Tel.: (86) 5962118635
Web Site: http://www.qwwz-bodycare.com
Body Care & Skin Care Product Mfr
N.A.I.C.S.: 325620

Queen's Finance Limited   (1)
Flat B 20/F Kiu Fu Commercial Building No

INTERNATIONAL PUBLIC

300-306 Lockhart Road, Wanchai, China (Hong Kong)
Tel.: (852) 36118468
Web Site: https://www.queensfinance.hk
Mortgage & Investment Services
N.A.I.C.S.: 522310

PROSPEROUS INDUSTRIAL (HOLDINGS) LIMITED
Unit 1-2 1/F Join-In Hang Sing Centre 71-75 Container Port Road, Kwai Chung, New Territories, China (Hong Kong)
Tel.: (852) 24243326   Ky
Web Site: https://www.pihl.hk
Year Founded: 1970
1731—(HKG)
Rev.: $218,188,000
Assets: $189,831,000
Liabilities: $48,213,000
Net Worth: $141,618,000
Earnings: $10,345,000
Emp.: 7,500
Fiscal Year-end: 12/31/22
Luggage Product Mfr & Distr
N.A.I.C.S.: 316990
Shu Kin Yeung *(Chm, CEO & Exec Dir)*

PROSPEROUS PRINTING COMPANY LIMITED
Flat H 4/F Yip Cheung Centre 10 Fung Yip Street, Chai Wan, China (Hong Kong)
Tel.: (852) 28730663   HK
Web Site: http://www.prosperous-printing-group.com.hk
Year Founded: 1992
8385—(HKG)
Rev.: $24,840,443
Assets: $38,313,623
Liabilities: $30,943,485
Net Worth: $7,370,138
Earnings: ($7,606,013)
Emp.: 459
Fiscal Year-end: 12/31/22
Book Labeling Services
N.A.I.C.S.: 561990
Sam Ming Lam *(Chm & CEO)*

Subsidiaries:

Great Wall Printing Co., Ltd.   (1)
3/F Yip Cheung Centre 10 Fung Yip Street, Chaiwan, Hong Kong, China (Hong Kong)
Tel.: (852) 28971083
Printing Machinery & Equipment Mfr
N.A.I.C.S.: 333248

Printplus Limited   (1)
Flat H 4/F Yip Cheung Centre 10 Fung Yip Street, Chaiwan, Hong Kong, China (Hong Kong)
Tel.: (852) 31889990
Printing Machinery & Equipment Mfr
N.A.I.C.S.: 333248

Prosperous Printing (Shenzhen) Co., Ltd.   (1)
Ci Chang Road No 8 101 Bao An Community Yuan Shan Jie Dao, Long Gang District, Shenzhen, 518115, China
Tel.: (86) 75528672512
Printing Machinery & Equipment Whslr
N.A.I.C.S.: 423830

PROSPEX ENERGY PLC
Office 506 Tintagel House 92 Albert Embankment, London, SE1 7TY, United Kingdom
Tel.: (44) 2039481619
Web Site:
  http://www.prospexoilandgas.com
PXEN—(AIM)
Assets: $27,775,770
Liabilities: $4,709,595
Net Worth: $23,066,175
Earnings: $8,600,130
Fiscal Year-end: 12/31/22
Oil & Gas Exploration Services
N.A.I.C.S.: 211120

Edward Roland Dawson *(CEO & Mng Dir)*

PROSTALUND AB
Scheelevagen 19, 223 63, Lund, Sweden
Tel.: (46) 46120908
Web Site: https://www.prostalund.se
Year Founded: 1991
Medical Equipment Mfr
N.A.I.C.S.: 339113
Hans Ostlund *(CEO & VP-Global Sls)*

PROSTAR CAPITAL (AUSTRALIA) PTY LTD
Level 19 Governor Macquarie Tower, 1 Farrer Place, Sydney, 2000, NSW, Australia
Tel.: (61) 2 8705 1290
Web Site:
  http://www.prostarcapital.com
Year Founded: 2012
Privater Equity Firm
N.A.I.C.S.: 523999
Steve Bickerton *(Sr Mng Dir)*

PROSTAR HOLDINGS INC.
2080 777 Hornby Street, Vancouver, V6Z 1S4, BC, Canada
Tel.: (604) 662-3692   BC
Web Site:
  http://www.doxaenergy.com
Year Founded: 2007
DXA—(OTCIQ)
Sales Range: $350-399.9 Million
Oil Exploration Services
N.A.I.C.S.: 211120
John D. Harvison *(Pres & CEO)*

PROSTATYPE GENOMICS AB
Gustaf IIIs Boulevard 34, 169 73, Solna, Sweden
Tel.: (46) 8208700
Web Site:
  https://www.prostatypegenomic.com
Year Founded: 2007
PROGEN—(OMX)
Rev.: $354,698
Assets: $4,610,226
Liabilities: $2,299,212
Net Worth: $2,311,014
Earnings: ($3,880,881)
Emp.: 7
Fiscal Year-end: 12/31/23
Biotechnology Research & Development Services
N.A.I.C.S.: 541714
Anders Lundberg *(Chm)*

PROSUS N.V.
Symphony Offices Gustav Mahlerplein 5, 1082 MS, Amsterdam, Netherlands
Tel.: (31) 202999777   NI
Web Site: https://www.prosus.com
Year Founded: 1997
PRX—(JSE)
Rev.: $5,467,000,000
Assets: $61,821,000,000
Liabilities: $20,529,000,000
Net Worth: $41,292,000,000
Earnings: $6,860,000,000
Emp.: 21,048
Fiscal Year-end: 03/31/24
Investment Management Service
N.A.I.C.S.: 523940
Basil Sgourdos *(Fin Dir)*

Subsidiaries:

Frontier Car Group Inc.   (1)
Karl-Liebknecht-Strasse 29 12 OG, 10178, Berlin, Germany
Tel.: (49) 15222717423
Web Site: http://www.frontiercargroup.com
Vehicle Financing Services
N.A.I.C.S.: 522220
Andreas Riexinger *(Mng Dir)*

Iyzi Odeme ve Elektronik Para Hizmetleri Anonim Sirketi   (1)
Altunizade Mah inci Cikmazi Sokak No 3 ic Kapi No 10, Uskudar, Istanbul, Turkiye
Tel.: (90) 2165990100
Web Site: https://www.iyzico.com
Emp.: 130
E-commerce Payment Services
N.A.I.C.S.: 522320
Barbaros Ozbugutu *(CEO)*

PayU Payments Private Limited   (1)
9th Floor Bestech Business Tower Sohna Road Sector-48, Gurgaon, 122004, Haryana, India
Tel.: (91) 1246624800
Web Site: https://payu.in
Online Payment Services
N.A.I.C.S.: 522320
Mohit Chawla *(Sr Mgr)*

Red Dot Payment Private Limited   (1)
143 Cecil Street 21-01 GB Building, Singapore, 069542, Singapore
Tel.: (65) 68160963
Web Site: https://www.reddotpayment.com
Ecommerce Services
N.A.I.C.S.: 522320
Randy Tan *(CEO)*

Selency   (1)
1 rue de Chateaudun, 75009, Paris, France
Tel.: (33) 972493222
Web Site: https://www.selency.fr
Hand Furniture & Decor Product Distr
N.A.I.C.S.: 449110
Laura Armengaud *(Sr Mgr-Selection)*

The Car Trader Proprietary Limited   (1)
154 Bram Fischer Drive, Randburg, 2194, Gauteng, South Africa
Tel.: (27) 860605050
Web Site: http://www.autotrader.co.za
Car Distr
N.A.I.C.S.: 441110
George Mienie *(CEO)*

PROSVETA A.D.
Knez Mihaila 12, Belgrade, Serbia
Tel.: (381) 112639714
Web Site: https://www.prosveta.rs
Year Founded: 1901
PRSB—(BEL)
Rev.: $2,828
Assets: $2,342,989
Liabilities: $907,533
Net Worth: $1,435,057
Earnings: ($126,161)
Emp.: 2
Fiscal Year-end: 12/31/23
Books Publishing Services
N.A.I.C.S.: 513130
Dragan Milenkovic *(Dir)*

PROTAN SA
Strada Tabacarilor 6-10 Sectorul 4, 040298, Bucharest, Romania
Tel.: (40) 213303001
Web Site: http://www.protansa.ro
Sales Range: $10-24.9 Million
Emp.: 230
Non-Hazardous Waste Collection
N.A.I.C.S.: 562219

PROTASCO BERHAD
Unipark Suria Jalan Ikram Uniten, 43000, Kajang, Selangor, Malaysia
Tel.: (60) 387383388
Web Site:
  https://www.protasco.com.my
Year Founded: 2001
PRTASCO—(KLS)
Rev.: $187,077,884
Assets: $176,986,878
Liabilities: $107,599,788
Net Worth: $69,387,090
Earnings: ($5,126,349)
Emp.: 652
Fiscal Year-end: 12/31/22

Construction Contracts & Engineering Services
N.A.I.C.S.: 237310
Fei San Seow *(Co-Sec)*

Subsidiaries:

HCM Engineering Sdn Bhd   (1)
GRD 1st Floor Jalan Ikram-Uniten, Corporate Block De Centrum City, 43000, Kajang, Selangor Darul Ehsan, Malaysia
Tel.: (60) 387383388
Web Site: https://www.hcme.com.my
Road Construction Services
N.A.I.C.S.: 237310

Subsidiary (Domestic):

Empayar Indera Sdn Bhd   (2)
No 2 Jalan Meru Bestari, D1 Kompleks Perdagangan DWJ Meru, 30020, Ipoh, Perak, Malaysia
Tel.: (60) 55262222
Road Maintenance Services
N.A.I.C.S.: 237310

Permint Granite-HCM Sdn Bhd   (2)
Lot PT 28533 28534 Taman Desa Solehah Jalan Kelantan, 21060, Kuala Terengganu, Malaysia
Tel.: (60) 96671373
Road Construction Services
N.A.I.C.S.: 237310

Roadcare (M) Sdn Bhd   (2)
No 87-1 Jalan Kampung Pandan Wilayah Persekutuan, 55100, Kuala Lumpur, Malaysia
Tel.: (60) 392852257
Web Site: https://www.roadcare.com.my
Road Construction & Maintenance Services
N.A.I.C.S.: 237310
Sharifuddin Uyop *(Mgr-Safety & Health)*

Ikram Works Sdn. Bhd.   (1)
Block 5 Unipark Suria Jalan Ikram Uniten, 43000, Kajang, Selangor, Malaysia
Tel.: (60) 387383381
Web Site: https://www.ikram.com.my
Engineering Consulting Services
N.A.I.C.S.: 541330

Kumpulan Ikram Sdn Bhd   (1)
Block 5 Unipark Suria Jalan Ikram Uniten, 43000, Kajang, Selangor, Malaysia
Tel.: (60) 387383381
Web Site: https://www.ikram.com.my
Road Construction & Maintenance Services
N.A.I.C.S.: 237310
Mohd Kamsatul Aidi *(Head-Fin)*

Subsidiary (Domestic):

Ikram QA Services Sdn Bhd   (2)
Block 5 Level 1 Unipark Suria Jalan Ikram-Uniten, 43000, Kajang, Selangor, Malaysia
Tel.: (60) 387383204
Web Site: https://www.ikramqa.com.my
Product Certification & Testing Services
N.A.I.C.S.: 541380
Muhammad Shafiq Jalil *(Head-Evaluation)*

Kumpulan Ikram (Sabah) Sdn Bhd   (2)
Lot 10 Fortuna Commercial Centre Lorong Seroja 2, 88200, Kota Kinabalu, Sabah, Malaysia
Tel.: (60) 88318511
Web Site: https://ikramsabah.com.my
Geotechnical Engineering Services
N.A.I.C.S.: 541330

Kumpulan Ikram (Sarawak) Sdn Bhd   (2)
1st Floor Off Lot 9900 SL4 and SL5 Mendu Commercial Centre Jalan Mendu, 93200, Kuching, Sarawak, Malaysia
Tel.: (60) 387383363
Geotechnical Engineering Services
N.A.I.C.S.: 541330

Protasco Development Sdn Bhd   (1)
Ground 1st Floor Corporate Block De Centrum City Jalan Ikram-Uniten, 43000, Kajang, Selangor, Malaysia
Tel.: (60) 387383368
Web Site:
  https://www.protascodevelopment.com
Property Development Services
N.A.I.C.S.: 531390

Subsidiary (Domestic):

De Centrum Development Sdn Bhd   (2)
Corporate Block Unipark Suria Jalan Ikram-Uniten, 43000, Kajang, Selangor, Malaysia
Tel.: (60) 387383391
Property Development Services
N.A.I.C.S.: 531390

Protasco Trading Sdn Bhd   (1)
No 37G Jalan PJS 5/30 Pusat Dagangan Petaling Jaya Selatan, 46150, Petaling Jaya, Selangor, Malaysia
Web Site:
  http://www.protascotrading.com.my
Construction Building Material Mfr
N.A.I.C.S.: 327120
Ronnie Yap Kee Tian *(Exec Dir)*

i2 Energy Sdn Bhd   (1)
2nd Floor Corporate Block Unipark Suria Jalan Ikram-Unite, 43000, Kajang, Selangor, Malaysia
Tel.: (60) 387383388
Web Site: https://www.i2energy.my
Solar Energy Services
N.A.I.C.S.: 221114

PROTEAK UNO SAB DE CV
Av Paseo de la Reforma No 540 Colonia Lomas de Chapultepec, 11000, Mexico, Mexico
Tel.: (52) 5562351504
Web Site: https://proteak.com
Year Founded: 2000
TEAK—(MEX)
Emp.: 1,451
Construction Services
N.A.I.C.S.: 236220
Hector Eduardo Bonilla Castaneda *(Chm)*

PROTEAN ENERGY LTD.
Level 3 101 St Georges Tce, Perth, 6000, WA, Australia
Tel.: (61) 865580886
Web Site:
  https://www.proteanenergy.com
POWDB—(DEU)
Rev.: $13,445
Assets: $291,115
Liabilities: $122,808
Net Worth: $168,307
Earnings: ($318,405)
Fiscal Year-end: 06/30/24
Wave Energy Conversion Technology Developer
N.A.I.C.S.: 221118
Bevan Tarratt *(Chm)*

Subsidiaries:

Protean Wave Energy Inc.   (1)
391 S Court St, Los Osos, CA 93402
Tel.: (707) 731-9261
Wave Energy Technology Developer
N.A.I.C.S.: 221118
William Toman *(Pres)*

PROTEC CO., LTD.
1114 Simindaero 327beongil, Dongan-gu, Anyang, Gyeonggi-do, Korea (South)
Tel.: (82) 314700700
Web Site: https://www.protec21.co.kr
Year Founded: 1997
053610—(KRS)
Rev.: $152,458,442
Assets: $266,531,296
Liabilities: $32,948,328
Net Worth: $233,582,967
Earnings: $33,374,552
Emp.: 254
Fiscal Year-end: 12/31/22
Semiconductor Equipment Mfr
N.A.I.C.S.: 334413
Seung-Hwan Choi *(Pres & CEO)*

PROTEC MEMS TECHNOLOGY INC

PROTEC MEMS TECHNOLOGY INC

Protec Mems Technology Inc—(Continued)

77-20 Yeonamyulgeum-ro, Eumbongmyeon, Asan, Chungcheongnam-do, Korea (South)
Tel.: (82) 414230200 KR
Web Site: https://pmt23.com
Year Founded: 2004
147760—(KRS)
Rev.: $29,333,509
Assets: $48,221,339
Liabilities: $7,591,485
Net Worth: $40,629,854
Earnings: ($3,007,517)
Emp.: 179
Fiscal Year-end: 12/31/22
Probe Card Mfr & Distr
N.A.I.C.S.: 334515
Byung-Ho Jo (CEO)

PROTECH BIOSYSTEMS PVT. LTD.

145-146 Pace City I Sector 37, Gurgaon, 122001, Haryana, India
Tel.: (91) 124 4055030 DE
Web Site:
    http://www.protechbiosystem.com
Sales Range: $1-9.9 Million
Emp.: 150
Pharmaceutical Ingredient Mfr
N.A.I.C.S.: 325412
Sanjiw Kumar Singh (Chm & Mng Dir)

PROTECH CHEMICALS LTD.

7600 Henri-Bourassa West, Montreal, H4S 1W3, QC, Canada
Tel.: (514) 745-0200
Web Site:
    http://www.protechpowder.com
Year Founded: 1976
Thermoset & Thermoplastic Powder Coatings
N.A.I.C.S.: 325510
David Ades (Mng Dir)

Subsidiaries:

Oxyplast Belgium NV (1)
Hulsdonk 35, Mendonk, 9042, Gent, Belgium
Tel.: (32) 93267920
Web Site: http://www.oxyplast.be
Paint Distr
N.A.I.C.S.: 424950
Karl Pint (Mgr-Sls & Mktg)

Oxyplast UK Limited (1)
Units 37/37A Bradley Hall Trading Estate Bradley Lane, Standish, Wigan, WN6 0XQ, Lancashire, United Kingdom
Tel.: (44) 1257473924
Web Site: http://www.oxyplastuk.com
Paints Mfr
N.A.I.C.S.: 325510

PT Oxyplast Indonesia (1)
Jl Raya Beji Bangil Km 4 Desa Cangkringmalan Kec Beji, 67154, Pasuruan, Jawa Timur, Indonesia
Tel.: (62) 343656886
Paints Mfr
N.A.I.C.S.: 325510

Protech Chemicals Ltd. - Gulf Powder Polyester & Epoxy Coating Factory (1)
2nd Industrial Area, PO Box 6416, 11442, Riyadh, Saudi Arabia
Tel.: (966) 12651977
Paints Mfr
N.A.I.C.S.: 325510

Protech Mexicana S.A. de C.V. (1)
Av Mexico No 700 Int No 115 Col San Jeronimo Lidice, Delegacion Magdelena Contreras, Mexico, 10400, Mexico
Tel.: (52) 5147450200
Plastic Product Distr
N.A.I.C.S.: 424610

Protech Oxyplast CZ, s.r.o. (1)
Janska 18, 746 01, Opava, Czech Republic
Tel.: (420) 553615901

Paints Mfr
N.A.I.C.S.: 325510

Protech Oxyplast Poland sp. z o.o. (1)
Ul Elektroniczna 2, 05-500, Piaseczno, Poland
Tel.: (48) 227029313
Paint Distr
N.A.I.C.S.: 424950
Pawel Mlynik (Dir-Sls)

Protech Powder Coatings Inc. (1)
21 Audrey Place, Fairfield, NJ 07004
Tel.: (862) 702-3537
Thermoplastic Mfr
N.A.I.C.S.: 325211

Siam Oxyplast Co. Ltd. (1)
38/9 Moo 4 Prachautis Soi 33 Rd Bangmod, Thungkru, Bangkok, 10140, Thailand
Tel.: (66) 2 427 9995 7
Web Site: http://www.oxyplast.co.th
Paints Mfr
N.A.I.C.S.: 325510

Subsidiary (Non-US):

Oxyplast Maroc s.a.r.l. (2)
Lot 111 Zone Industrielle Route de Ttouan, Tangiers, Morocco
Tel.: (212) 9351276
Paint Distr
N.A.I.C.S.: 424950

Oxyplast Taiwan Co. Ltd. (2)
No 25 Min Chih Road Tung Lo Industrial Park, Miao-li, Taiwan
Tel.: (886) 37984586
Paint Distr
N.A.I.C.S.: 424950

PROTECTA SA

Av Domingo Orue N 165 8vo piso, Surquillo, Peru
Tel.: (51) 3913030
Web Site:
    http://www.protectasecurity.pe
Year Founded: 2007
PROTECC1—(LIM)
Rev.: $147,010,229
Assets: $1,025,792,783
Liabilities: $947,270,666
Net Worth: $78,522,117
Earnings: $13,710,361
Fiscal Year-end: 12/31/23
Fire Insurance Services
N.A.I.C.S.: 524113
Alfredo Juan Jochamowitz Stafford (Chm)

PROTECTOR FORSIKRING ASA

Stoperigata 2, 0250, Oslo, Norway
Tel.: (47) 24131700
Web Site:
    http://www.protectorforsikring.no
PR4—(DEU)
Rev.: $604,196,933
Assets: $1,842,728,154
Liabilities: $1,524,537,502
Net Worth: $318,190,652
Earnings: $78,081,286
Emp.: 418
Fiscal Year-end: 12/31/22
Insurance Services
N.A.I.C.S.: 524126
Sverre Bjerkeli (CEO)

PROTEGRA INC.

67 Scurfield Boulevard, Winnipeg, R3Y 1G4, MB, Canada
Tel.: (204) 956-2727
Web Site: http://www.protegra.com
Year Founded: 1997
Sales Range: $1-9.9 Million
Emp.: 55
It Consulting
N.A.I.C.S.: 541690
Wadood Ibrahim (Founder & CEO)

PROTEK OAO

2 ul Chermyanskaya, 127282, Moscow, Russia
Tel.: (7) 495 730 78 28
Web Site: http://www.protek-group.ru
Year Founded: 1990
PRTK—(RUS)
Sales Range: $1-4.9 Billion
Emp.: 14,000
Holding Company; Pharmaceutical Mfr & Distr
N.A.I.C.S.: 551112
Yakunin Vadim Sergeyevich (Chm)

Subsidiaries:

CV Protek (1)
2 ul Chermyanskaya, 127282, Moscow, Russia (99.5%)
Tel.: (7) 495 737 3500
Web Site: http://www.protek.ru
Pharmaceutical Products Distr
N.A.I.C.S.: 424210

OOO Firm PROTEX-SVM (1)
22 Kashirskoye Shosse korp 4, 115201, Moscow, Russia
Tel.: (7) 495 231 28 61
Web Site: http://www.protek-svm.ru
Pharmaceutical Products Distr
N.A.I.C.S.: 424210

OOO Promopharm (1)
Ul Rusakova Estate 1 Bldg 4, 141200, Pushkino, Moscow, Russia
Tel.: (7) 495 787 55 53
Web Site: http://www.promopharm.ru
Pharmaceutical Products Distr
N.A.I.C.S.: 424210

OOO Transservice Customs Warehouse (1)
Anrdropova prospekt 22, 115533, Moscow, Russia
Tel.: (7) 499 618 07 92
Web Site: http://www.ts-farm.ru
Logistics Consulting Servies
N.A.I.C.S.: 541614
Nikolay Yakovlev (Gen Dir)

Protein Contour Company Ltd. (1)
Domostroitelnaya street 4, Saint Petersburg, Russia
Tel.: (7) 812 332 0903
Web Site: http://www.protc.spb.ru
Pharmaceutical Product Mfr & Distr
N.A.I.C.S.: 325412

ZAO Sotex Pharm Firm (1)
22/4 build 7 Kashirskoye Schosse, Moscow, Russia
Tel.: (7) 4952311512
Web Site: http://www.sotex.ru
Pharmaceuticals Product Mfr
N.A.I.C.S.: 325412
Vitaliy Smerdov (Gen Dir)

PROTEKTOR S.A.

ul Vetterow 24A-24B, 20-277, Lublin, Poland
Tel.: (48) 815322231
Web Site: https://www.protektorsa.pl
PRT—(WAR)
Rev.: $25,359,248
Assets: $21,037,093
Liabilities: $12,312,754
Net Worth: $8,724,339
Earnings: ($1,723,577)
Fiscal Year-end: 12/31/23
Footwear Mfr
N.A.I.C.S.: 316210
Tomasz Malicki (Chm-Mgmt Bd)

PROTEOME SCIENCES PLC

Coveham House Downside Bridge Road, Cobham, KT11 3EP, Surrey, United Kingdom
Tel.: (44) 2070432116 UK
Web Site:
    https://www.proteomics.com
Year Founded: 1994
PRM—(LSE)
Rev.: $6,963,746
Assets: $13,638,297
Liabilities: $17,405,970

INTERNATIONAL PUBLIC

Net Worth: ($3,767,673)
Earnings: $97,756
Emp.: 27
Fiscal Year-end: 12/31/21
Applied Protein Research Services
N.A.I.C.S.: 541715
Ian Pike (Chief Scientific Officer)

Subsidiaries:

Electrophoretics Ltd. (1)
Hamilton House Mabledon Place, London, WC1H 9BB, United Kingdom (100%)
Tel.: (44) 1932865065
Web Site: http://www.proteomics.com
Sales Range: $50-74.9 Million
Emp.: 5
Space Research & Technology
N.A.I.C.S.: 927110
Victoria Birse (Sec & Office Mgr)

Proteome Sciences R&D GmbH & Co. KG (1)
Altenhoferallee 3, Frankfurt am Main, 60438, Germany
Tel.: (49) 69509866
Emp.: 22
Protein Research Services
N.A.I.C.S.: 541715
Ian Pike (CEO)

PROTEOMETECH, INC.

A-702 401 Yangcheon-ro, Gangseogu, Seoul, 07573, Korea (South)
Tel.: (82) 23238342
Web Site: https://www.protia.co.kr
Year Founded: 2001
Medicinal Product Mfr
N.A.I.C.S.: 339113
Kook-Jin Lim (CEO)

PROTEOMICS INTERNATIONAL LABORATORIES LTD.

QEII Medical Centre 6 Verdun Street Nedlands, Perth, 6009, WA, Australia
Tel.: (61) 893891992
Web Site:
    https://www.proteomics.com.au
Year Founded: 2001
PIQ—(ASX)
Rev.: $2,381,155
Assets: $7,261,693
Liabilities: $1,085,687
Net Worth: $6,176,006
Earnings: ($4,328,134)
Emp.: 4,500
Fiscal Year-end: 06/30/24
Life Science Research & Development Services
N.A.I.C.S.: 541715
Terry Sweet (Chm)

PROTEOR SAS

6 Rue de la Redoute, 21850, Saint Apollinaire, France
Tel.: (33) 380 784 242 FR
Web Site: http://www.proteor.com
Year Founded: 1913
Emp.: 740
Prosthetics Leg & Orthotic Components Mfr
N.A.I.C.S.: 339113
Edouard Archambeaud (COO & Member-Mgmt Bd)

Subsidiaries:

PROTEOR USA, LLC (1)
1236 W Southern Ave Ste 101, Tempe, AZ 85282
Web Site: http://www.proteorusa.com
Prosthetic Legs & Prosthetic Components Mfr
N.A.I.C.S.: 339112
Matt Swiggum (Pres & CEO)

Subsidiary (Domestic):

Freedom Innovations, LLC (2)
3 Morgan, Irvine, CA 92618
Tel.: (949) 672-0032

Web Site: http://www.freedom-innovations.com
Prosthetic Device Developer & Mfr
N.A.I.C.S.: 339112
Maynard Carkhuff *(Chm)*

PROTERIAL, LTD.
Shinagawa Season Terrace 2-70 Konan 1-chome, Minato-ku, Tokyo, 108-8224, Japan
Tel.: (81) 367743001 JP
Web Site: https://www.proterial.com
Year Founded: 1956
Sales Range: Less than $1 Million
Emp.: 400
Steel & Special Steels, Forged & Cast Steel Products & Pipe Fittings Mfr
N.A.I.C.S.: 332919
Kazuyuki Komishi *(Pres & CEO)*

Subsidiaries:

Baosteel Hitachi Rolls (Nantong) Ltd. (1)
No 152 Jianghai Rd Nantong Economic & Technology Developing Area, Nantong, 226017, Jiangsu, China
Tel.: (86) 513 8599 6700
Steel Pole Mfr
N.A.I.C.S.: 331221

HCAS Thai Trading Co., Ltd. (1)
388 Exchange Tower Level 20 Room 2004 Sukhumvit Road Kwaeng Klongtoei, Khate Klongtoei, Bangkok, 10110, Thailand
Tel.: (66) 2 260 6310
Web Site: http://www.hitachi.co.th
Wiring Supplies Distr
N.A.I.C.S.: 423610

Hitachi Cable (China) Trading Co., Ltd. (1)
Room 1401 Maxdo Center No 8 Xingyi Road Hong Qiao Development Zone, Shanghai, 200336, China
Tel.: (86) 21 6278 7752
Wiring Supplies Distr
N.A.I.C.S.: 423610

Hitachi Cable (Johor) Sdn Bh (1)
Plot 40 Kawasan Perindustrian Senai, 81400, Senai, Johor Darul Takzim, Malaysia
Tel.: (60) 75994350
Web Site: http://www.hitachi-cable.com.my
Electric Cable Mfr & Distr
N.A.I.C.S.: 335931

Hitachi Cable (Suzhou) Co., Ltd. (1)
No 18 Shijin Road Xujiang Industrial Park Xukon, Wuzhong, Suzhou, Jiangsu, China
Tel.: (86) 512 6621 0777
Electronic Wire Mfr & Distr
N.A.I.C.S.: 335929

Hitachi Cable Trading (Dalian F.T.Z.) Co., Ltd. (1)
Room 1102 Yoma IFC No 128 Jinma Road Dalian Development Area, Dalian, 116600, China
Tel.: (86) 411 8733 2112
Web Site: http://www.hitachi-cable.com
Wiring Supplies Distr
N.A.I.C.S.: 423610

Hitachi Cable Vietnam Co., Ltd. (1)
Plot CN 6 1-2 Tan Truong Industrial Zone, Cam Giang District, Hai Duong, Vietnam
Tel.: (84) 3203 570 280
Electronic Wire Mfr & Distr
N.A.I.C.S.: 335931

Hitachi Ferrite Electronics, Ltd. (1)
70-2 Naneicho, Tottori, 689-1121, Japan
Tel.: (81) 857536460
Web Site: https://www.hfe.co.jp
Electronic Component Mfr & Distr
N.A.I.C.S.: 334419

Hitachi Metals (Dong Guan) Specialty Steel Co., Ltd. (1)
Chashan Industrial Park, Chashan Town, Dongguan, 522300, Guangdong, China
Tel.: (86) 769 8640 6726
Web Site: http://www.hitachi-metals-ds.com.cn
Steel Products Mfr & Distr
N.A.I.C.S.: 331110

Hitachi Metals (India) Pvt. Ltd. (1)
Plot No 94 & 95 Sector 8 IMT Manesar, Gurgaon, 122050, Haryana, India
Tel.: (91) 124 4124800
Emp.: 10
Metal Product Whslr
N.A.I.C.S.: 423510
Sanjay Seit *(Mng Dir)*

Hitachi Metals (Shanghai) Ltd. (1)
11F Chong Hing Finance Center No 288 Nanjing Road West, Shanghai, 200003, China
Tel.: (86) 21 3366 3000
Metal Products Mfr
N.A.I.C.S.: 332999

Hitachi Metals (Suzhou) Technology, Ltd. (1)
220 Xing Ming Street Suzhou Industrial Park, Suzhou, 215021, Jiangsu, China
Tel.: (86) 512 6256 7880
Metal Products Mfr & Distr
N.A.I.C.S.: 331110

Division (Domestic):

Hitachi Metals (Suzhou) Technology, Ltd. - Specialty Steel Division (2)
88 Xing lin Street Suzhou Industrial Park, Suzhou, 215027, Jiangsu, China
Tel.: (86) 512 6790 2106
Steel Products Mfr
N.A.I.C.S.: 331110
Masuga Yoshiki *(Gen Mgr)*

Hitachi Metals Admet, Ltd. (1)
Shuwa-Higashi Yaesu Bldg 9-1 Hatchobori 2-chome, Chuo-ku, Tokyo, 104-0032, Japan
Tel.: (81) 3 3555 5311
Web Site: http://www.hitachi-m-admet.com
Rev.: $908,191,000
Emp.: 183
Semiconductor Devices Mfr
N.A.I.C.S.: 334413
Ken Ichihashi *(Pres)*

Hitachi Metals America, Ltd. (1)
2 Manhattanville Rd Ste 301, Purchase, NY 10577-2103
Tel.: (914) 694-9200
Web Site: http://www.hitachimetals.com
Metal Products Mfr & Distr
N.A.I.C.S.: 332999

Subsidiary (Domestic):

Hitachi Cable America, Inc. (2)
2 Manhattanville Rd Ste 301, Purchase, NY 10577
Tel.: (914) 694-9200
Web Site: http://www.hca.hitachi-cable.com
Electrical Cable Distr
N.A.I.C.S.: 423610
Tomoyuki Hatano *(Chm & CEO)*

Plant (Domestic):

Hitachi Cable America, Inc. - Florida Plant (3)
9101 Ely Rd, Pensacola, FL 32514
Tel.: (850) 476-0907
Web Site: http://www.hca.hitachi-cable.com
Automobile Cable Mfr
N.A.I.C.S.: 336320

Hitachi Cable America, Inc. - Indiana Plant (3)
5300 Grant Line Rd, New Albany, IN 47150
Tel.: (812) 945-9011
Web Site: http://www.hca.hitachi-cable.com
Automobile Cable Mfr
N.A.I.C.S.: 336320
Patrick Houghlin *(CEO)*

Hitachi Cable America, Inc. - Manchester Plant (3)
900 Holt Ave E Industrial Park, Manchester, NH 03109
Tel.: (603) 669-4347
Web Site: http://www.hca.hitachi-cable.com
Sales Range: $25-49.9 Million
Emp.: 170
Wire & Cable Mfr
N.A.I.C.S.: 335929
Stephen L. Porach *(Dir-Mktg)*

Subsidiary (Domestic):

Hitachi Metals Automotive Components, USA, LLC (2)

1500 Heartland Blvd, Effingham, IL 62401
Tel.: (217) 347-0600
Web Site: http://www.hmacusa.com
Sales Range: $50-74.9 Million
Emp.: 130
Automotive Metal Product Whslr
N.A.I.C.S.: 423510
Bob Harter *(Gen Mgr)*

Plant (Domestic):

Hitachi Metals Automotive Components USA, LLC - Lawrenceville Facility (3)
18986 Route 287, Tioga, PA 16946
Tel.: (570) 638-2100
Web Site: http://www.hitachimetals.com
Sales Range: $75-99.9 Million
Automobile Parts Mfr
N.A.I.C.S.: 336390

Subsidiary (Domestic):

Hitachi Metals North Carolina, Ltd. (2)
1 Hitachi Metals Dr, China Grove, NC 28023-9461
Tel.: (704) 855-2800
Web Site: http://www.hitachimetals.com
Metal Products Mfr
N.A.I.C.S.: 332999

Metglas, Inc (2)
440 Allied Dr, Conway, SC 29526
Tel.: (843) 349-7319
Web Site: http://www.metglas.com
Sales Range: $25-49.9 Million
Emp.: 200
Electrical Metal Ribbon Mfr
N.A.I.C.S.: 335999

Subsidiary (Non-US):

Hitachi Metglas (India) Pvt. Ltd. (3)
Plot No 94 & 95 Sector 8 IMT Manesar, Gurgaon, 122 050, India
Tel.: (91) 1 244 812300
Electronic Components Mfr
N.A.I.C.S.: 334419

Hitachi Metals Europe GmbH (1)
Immermannstrasse 14-16, 40210, Dusseldorf, Germany
Tel.: (49) 211 16009 11
Electrical & Electronic Products, Information Technologies, Communication Systems & Industrial Machinery Mfr & Whslr
N.A.I.C.S.: 334419
Kazuhiro Akitomo *(Gen Mgr)*

Hitachi Metals FineTech, Ltd. (1)
2 Daifuku, Kuwana, 511-0834, Mie-ken, Japan
Tel.: (81) 594 22 2200
Metal Products Mfr
N.A.I.C.S.: 332999

Hitachi Metals Hong Kong Ltd. (1)
Suits 706-11 7th Floor South Tower World Finance Centre Harbour City, Tsimshatsui, Kowloon, China (Hong Kong)
Tel.: (852) 2724 4183
Web Site: http://www.hitachi.com.hk
Soft Ferrite Core Component Mfr
N.A.I.C.S.: 327110

Plant (Non-US):

Hitachi Metals Hong Kong Ltd. - Panyu Factory (3)
Jiu Shui Ji Pan Yu, Economy Industry Development Area, Guangzhou, Guang Dong, China
Tel.: (86) 20 3456 7456
Web Site: http://www.hitachi.com.hk
Metal Products Mfr
N.A.I.C.S.: 332999

Hitachi Metals MMC Superalloy, Ltd. (1)
1230 Kamihideya, Okegawa, 363-8510, Saitama, Japan
Tel.: (81) 48 786 3321 (51%)
Copper Alloy Mfr & Distr
N.A.I.C.S.: 423510

Hitachi Metals Neomaterial, Ltd. (1)
19-1 Minami-Suita 2-chome, Suita, Osaka, 564-0043, Japan
Tel.: (81) 66 381 9151 (100%)

Web Site: https://www.hitachi-metals-neomaterial.co.jp
Emp.: 1,100
Electronic Components Metal Materials & Processed Products Mfr
N.A.I.C.S.: 332999
Masafumi Araki *(Pres)*

Hitachi Metals Precision, Ltd. (1)
Shinagawa Season Terrace 2-70 Konan 1-chome, Minato-ku, Tokyo, 108-0075, Japan
Tel.: (81) 367743910
Web Site: http://www.hmp-ltd.co.jp
Precision Casting Metal Mfr & Distr
N.A.I.C.S.: 332999

Plant (Domestic):

Hitachi Metals Precision, Ltd. - Yasugi Works (2)
1240-2 Hashima-Cho, Yasugi, 692-0014, Shimane, Japan
Tel.: (81) 854 23 1122
Metal Products Mfr
N.A.I.C.S.: 332999

Hitachi Metals Singapore Pte Ltd. (1)
12 Gul Avenue, Singapore, 629656, Singapore
Tel.: (65) 6861 7711
Emp.: 70
Seal Products Distr
N.A.I.C.S.: 423510
Kawabata Hiro *(Mng Dir)*

Hitachi Metals Tool Steel, Ltd. (1)
Shinagawa Season Terrace 23rd Floor 2-70 Konan, Minato-ku, Tokyo, 108-0075, Japan
Tel.: (81) 367743900
Web Site: http://www.hitachi-metals-ts.co.jp
Emp.: 438
Metal Products Mfr
N.A.I.C.S.: 332999

Hitachi Metals Wakamatsu, Ltd. (1)
1-9-1 Kitahama, Wakamatsu-ku, Kitakyushu, 808-0023, Fukuoka, Japan
Tel.: (81) 93 761 4488
Web Site: https://www.hmw.co.jp
Emp.: 514
Cast Rolls Mfr
N.A.I.C.S.: 331110
Eiji Nakano *(Pres)*

Hitachi Metals, Ltd. - Kumagaya Division (1)
5200 Mikajiri, Kumagaya, 360-8577, Saitama-ken, Japan
Tel.: (81) 48 531 1200
Metal Products Mfr
N.A.I.C.S.: 332999
Masato Masuda *(Gen Mgr)*

Hitachi Metals, Ltd. - Kuwana Works (1)
2 Daifuku, Kuwana, 511-8511, Mie-ken, Japan
Tel.: (81) 594 24 2000
Web Site: http://www.hitachi-metals.co.jp
Piping Equipment Mfr
N.A.I.C.S.: 332919

Hitachi Metals, Ltd. - Metglas Yasugi Works (1)
1240-2 Hashima-cho, Yasugi, 692-8601, Shimane-ken, Japan
Tel.: (81) 854 22 1988
Amorphous Metal Mfr
N.A.I.C.S.: 332999

Hitachi Metals, Ltd. - Moka Works (1)
13 Kinugaoka, Mooka, 321-4367, Tochigi-ken, Japan
Tel.: (81) 285 80 3111
Emp.: 20
Automotive Parts & Construction Machinery Mfr
N.A.I.C.S.: 336390
Yoshimasa Fujii *(Pres)*

Hitachi Metals, Ltd. - Saga Works (1)
282 Fukumo Omachi-cho, Kishimagun, Saga, 849-2102, Japan
Tel.: (81) 952 71 4614
Emp.: 100
Metal Products Mfr

PROTERIAL, LTD.

Proterial, Ltd.—(Continued)
N.A.I.C.S.: 332999
Ao Masahiro (Mgr-Factory)

Hitachi Metals, Ltd. - Tottori Works (1)
70-2 Naneicho, Tottori, 689-1121, Japan
Tel.: (81) 857 53 6000
Web Site: http://www.hitachi-metals.co.jp
Electromagnetic Material Mfr
N.A.I.C.S.: 335314

Hitachi Valve, Ltd. (1)
200 Obuke Asahicho, Mie-gun, Mie, 510-8102, Japan
Tel.: (81) 593 77 4711
Web Site: http://www.hitachi-valve.co.jp
Emp.: 20
Metal Valve Mfr
N.A.I.C.S.: 332919
Hirukawa Takashi (Gen Mgr)

J-Power Systems Corporation (1)
5-1-1 Hidaka-cho, Hitachi, 319-1414, Ibaraki, Japan
Tel.: (81) 364062792
Web Site: https://www.jpowers.co.jp
Sales Range: $700-749.9 Mill on
Emp.: 900
Electric Power Cables & Accessories, Overhead Power Transmission Lines & Related Systems Research, Development & Mfr
N.A.I.C.S.: 423610
Tomoki Osawa (Pres)

Affiliate (Non-US):

Thai Sumiden Engineering and Construction Co., Ltd. (2)
164 166 168 Srinakarin Road Hua Mak, Bangkapi, Bangkok, 10240, Thailand
Tel.: (66) 27316647
Web Site: http://www.thaisumiden.com
Sales Range: $25-49.9 Million
Emp.: 40
Power Cable Installation Services
N.A.I.C.S.: 238210
Veeraphong Jiraphanphong (Pres & Mng Dir)

PT. NX Indonesia (1)
Jl Eropa III Kav N2 Kawasan KIEC, Cilegon, Banten, Indonesia
Tel.: (62) 254 393 100
Drying Kiln & Rotary Cooler Mfr
N.A.I.C.S.: 333415

Thai Hitachi Enamel Wire Co., Ltd. (1)
171 Moo 12 Bangna-Trad Road Km 43, Tambol Bangwua Amphur Bangpakong, Chachoengsao, 24110, Thailand
Tel.: (66) 3 853 2471
Web Site: https://www.theco.co.th
Emp.: 350
Wiring Supplies Distr
N.A.I.C.S.: 423610
Hitoshi Kato (Pres)

PROTHENA CORPORATION PLC

77 Sir John Rogerson s Quay Block C, Grand Canal Docklands, Dublin, D02 T804, Ireland
Tel.: (353) 12362500   IE
Web Site: https://www.prothena.com
Year Founded: 2012
PRTA—(NASDAQ)
Rev.: $53,905,000
Assets: $758,035,000
Liabilities: $135,993,000
Net Worth: $622,042,000
Earnings: ($116,949,000)
Emp.: 127
Fiscal Year-end: 12/31/22
Holding Company; Biopharmaceutical Developer
N.A.I.C.S.: 551112
Gene G. Kinney (Pres & CEO)

Subsidiaries:

Prothena Biosciences Limited (1)
Alexandra House The Sweepstakes, Ballsbridge, Dublin, 4, Ireland
Tel.: (353) 1 902 3519

Web Site: http://www.prothena.com
Biopharmaceutical Research & Development Services
N.A.I.C.S.: 325412
Gene G. Kinney (Chief Scientific Officer & Head-R&D)

Subsidiary (US):

Prothena Biosciences Inc. (2)
331 Oyster Point Blvd, South San Francisco, CA 94080
Tel.: (650) 837-8550
Web Site: http://www.prothena.com
Pharmaceutical Research & Development Services
N.A.I.C.S.: 541715

Prothena Switzerland GmbH (1)
Baarerstrasse 135, 6300, Zug, Switzerland
Tel.: (41) 5615481
Pharmaceuticals Product Mfr
N.A.I.C.S.: 325412
Peter Klein (Head-Mktg-Europe)

Prothena Therapeutics Limited (1)
Alexandra House The Sweepstakes Ballsbridge, Dublin, Ireland
Tel.: (353) 19023519
Biotechnology Research & Development Services
N.A.I.C.S.: 541714

PROTHERMIC

Z I Le Brezet 24 Rue Louis Bleriot, 63100, Clermont-Ferrand, Puy De Dome, France
Tel.: (33) 473919024
Rev.: $31,600,000
Emp.: 95
N.A.I.C.S.: 423720
Francois Espinasse (Dir)

PROTO CORPORATION

23-14 Aoi-1-chome, Naka-ku, Nagoya, 460-0006, Aichi, Japan
Tel.: (81) 529342000
Web Site: https://www.proto-g.co.jp
Year Founded: 1979
4298—(TKS)
Rev.: $763,772,280
Assets: $440,252,440
Liabilities: $125,193,400
Net Worth: $315,059,040
Earnings: $36,163,310
Emp.: 1,523
Fiscal Year-end: 03/31/24
Advertising Services
N.A.I.C.S.: 541890
Kenji Kamiya (Pres)

Subsidiaries:

AUTOWAY Co., Ltd (1)
3787-62 Kamata, Kamata-cho, Kyoto, 800-0365, Fukuoka, Japan
Tel.: (81) 934364800
Web Site: http://www.autoway.co.jp
Wheel Distr
N.A.I.C.S.: 423120
Akira Sakamoto (Dir-Sls Dept)

Bike Bros. Inc. (1)
Suido-Bashi Nishiguti Kaikan 4F 2-20-7 Misaki-Cho Chiyoda-Ku, Tokyo, Japan
Tel.: (81) 352125022
Web Site: http://www.bikebros.co.jp
Magazine Publisher
N.A.I.C.S.: 513120

CAR CREDO Co., Ltd. (1)
Sumitomo Fudosan Shinjuku Central Park Tower 23rd Floor, 6-18-1 Nishi-Shinjuku Shinjuku-ku, Tokyo, 160-0023, Japan
Tel.: (81) 333444600
Web Site: https://www.car-credo.jp
Vehicle Inspection Services
N.A.I.C.S.: 811198

Kings Auto Co., Ltd. (1)
PROTO Hamamatsu Bldg 543-16 Maruzuka-cho, Higashi-ku, Hamamatsu, 435-0046, Shizuoka, Japan
Tel.: (81) 534687338
Web Site: http://www.kingsautojapan.com
Emp.: 22
New & Used Car Whslr

N.A.I.C.S.: 423110
Toshihiro Inaba (Pres)

PROTO Malaysia Sdn. Bhd (1)
Suite 12 02 Level 12 Centrepoint South Mid Valley City, Lingkaran Syed Putra, 59200, Kuala Lumpur, Malaysia
Tel.: (60) 320928888
Web Site: http://www.motortrader.com.my
Magazine Publisher
N.A.I.C.S.: 513120

Proto Medical Care Co., Ltd. (1)
Daiwa Jimbocho Building 8F 2-4 Kanda Jimbocho, Chiyoda-ku, Tokyo, 101-0051, Japan
Tel.: (81) 3 3222 1800
Web Site: http://www.proto-mc.co.jp
Human Resource Consulting Services
N.A.I.C.S.: 541612

Proto Rios Inc. (1)
2nd floor Urban Ace Kitahama Building 2-3-7 Hiranocho, Chuo-ku, Osaka, 541-0046, Japan
Tel.: (81) 662275662
Web Site: https://www.proto-rios.co.jp
Emp.: 114
Magazine Publisher
N.A.I.C.S.: 513120

TIRE WORLD KAN BEST CO., LTD. (1)
2-6-5 Kutake, Miyagino-ku, Sendai, 983-0036, Miyagi, Japan
Tel.: (81) 222313411
Web Site: https://tireworldkan.com
Emp.: 140
Wheel Distr
N.A.I.C.S.: 423120

PROTO DEVELOPERS & TECHNOLOGIES LIMITED

59/15 3rd Floor Satyam House Guru Ravi Dass Marg Kalkaji, New Delhi, 110019, India
Tel.: (91) 1140528751
Web Site: http://www.protodevelopers.co.in
Year Founded: 1994
530069—(BOM)
Sales Range: $25-49.9 Million
Construction Engineering Services
N.A.I.C.S.: 541330
D. D. Mangar (Exec Dir)

PROTO RESOURCES & INVESTMENTS LTD.

Unit 2 70 Shaw Street, Beaconsfield, 7270, TAS, Australia
Tel.: (61) 2 9225 4000
Web Site: http://www.protoresources.com.au
Sales Range: $1-9.9 Million
Metal Mining
N.A.I.C.S.: 212230
Andrew Kenneth Bruce Mortimer (Mng Dir)

PROTON MOTOR POWER SYSTEMS PLC

Benzstrasse 7, 82178, Puchheim, Germany
Tel.: (49) 8912762650   UK
Web Site: https://www.proton-motor.de
Year Founded: 2006
PPS—(AIM)
Rev.: $2,639,029
Assets: $10,877,149
Liabilities: $137,256,066
Net Worth: ($126,378,918)
Earnings: ($23,892,821)
Fiscal Year-end: 12/31/22
Fuel Cell System Mfr
N.A.I.C.S.: 336390
Faiz Francois Nahab (CEO)

Subsidiaries:

Proton Motor Fuel Cell GmbH (1)
Benzstrasse 7, 82178, Puchheim, Germany
Tel.: (49) 8912762650

INTERNATIONAL PUBLIC

Web Site: https://www.proton-motor.de
Electric Motor & Generator Mfr
N.A.I.C.S.: 335312
Francois Faiz Nahab (Mng Dir)

SPower GmbH (1)
Benzstrasse 7, 82178, Puchheim, Germany
Tel.: (49) 5931883880
Web Site: http://www.s-power.de
Solar Thermal Vacuum Tube Mfr
N.A.I.C.S.: 333414

PROTOPIA GLOBAL HOLDINGS INC.

Room 408 B&C 4th Floor Lippo Sun Plaza No 28 Canton Road, Tsim Sha Tsui, Kowloon, China (Hong Kong)
Tel.: (852) 66860563   Ky
Year Founded: 2022
Assets: $130,854
Liabilities: $40,599
Net Worth: $90,255
Earnings: ($78,848)
Fiscal Year-end: 06/30/24
Holding Company
N.A.I.C.S.: 551112

PROTREADZ LTD

4230 Fountain St N, Cambridge, N3H 4R6, ON, Canada
Tel.: (519) 650-4380
Web Site: http://www.protreadz.com
Tire Sales & Services
N.A.I.C.S.: 441340
Joe McLeod (Pres)

PROUD REAL ESTATE PUBLIC COMPANY LIMITED

No 548 One City Centre Building 19th Floor Ploenchit Road Lumphini, Pathumwan, Bangkok, 10330, Thailand
Tel.: (66) 20350999
Web Site: https://www.proudrealestate.co.th
Year Founded: 1989
PROUD—(THA)
Rev.: $104,849
Assets: $132,885,385
Liabilities: $113,029,532
Net Worth: $19,855,853
Earnings: ($3,239,944)
Emp.: 43
Fiscal Year-end: 12/31/21
Construction Services
N.A.I.C.S.: 236210
Anuwat Maytheewibulwut (Chm)

PROUDS JEWELLERS PTY. LTD.

12-28 Parramatta Road, Summer Hill, 2130, NSW, Australia
Tel.: (61) 295816999
Web Site: http://www.prouds.com.au
Year Founded: 1903
Jewelry Product Mfr & Distr
N.A.I.C.S.: 339910
Terence Edmond Johnstone (Sec)

PROVARIS ENERGY LTD

Level 14 234 George St, Sydney, 2000, NSW, Australia
Tel.: (61) 291278250   AU
Web Site: https://www.provaris.energy
PV1—(ASX)
Rev.: $228,464
Assets: $819,507
Liabilities: $666,887
Net Worth: $152,620
Earnings: ($4,096,255)
Fiscal Year-end: 06/30/24
Coal, Oil & Gas Exploration Services
N.A.I.C.S.: 213112
Garry Triglavcanin (Chief Dev Officer)

PROVATI INSURANCE COMPANY LIMITED
Khan Mension 11th Floor 107
Motijheel C/A, Dhaka, 1000, Bangladesh
Tel.: (880) 471311
Web Site: https://www.provati-insurance.com
Year Founded: 1996
PROVATIINS—(CHT)
Rev.: $25,865
Assets: $14,997,400
Liabilities: $7,202,847
Net Worth: $7,794,552
Earnings: $1,309,552
Emp.: 848
Fiscal Year-end: 12/31/22
Insurance Services
N.A.I.C.S.: 524298
Shakhawat Hossain Mamun *(Mng Dir)*

PROVEN GROWTH & INCOME VCT PLC
39 Earlham Street, London, WC2H 9LT, United Kingdom
Tel.: (44) 2078457820 UK
Web Site: http://www.provenvcts.co.uk
PGOO—(LSE)
Rev.: $24,126,684
Assets: $186,238,452
Liabilities: $461,625
Net Worth: $185,776,828
Earnings: $19,619,054
Fiscal Year-end: 02/28/21
Financial Investment Services
N.A.I.C.S.: 523999

PROVEN VCT PLC
39 Earlham Street, London, WC2H 9LT, United Kingdom
Tel.: (44) 2078457820 UK
Web Site: http://www.provenvcts.co.uk
PVN—(LSE)
Rev.: $24,412,811
Assets: $121,333,493
Liabilities: $8,095,195
Net Worth: $113,238,298
Earnings: $13,569,814
Fiscal Year-end: 02/28/19
Investment Management Service
N.A.I.C.S.: 523940

PROVENANCE GOLD CORP.
885 West Georgia St Suite 2200, Vancouver, V6C 3E8, BC, Canada
Tel.: (250) 516-2455
Web Site: https://www.provenancegold.com
Year Founded: 2016
PVGDF—(OTCQB)
Assets: $325,475
Liabilities: $306,651
Net Worth: $18,825
Earnings: ($345,995)
Fiscal Year-end: 12/31/20
Mineral Exploration Services
N.A.I.C.S.: 213115
Rauno Perttu *(Co-Founder, Chm & CEO)*

PROVENTURE CAPITAL INC.
203-100 Queens Street East, Toronto, M5C 1S6, ON, Canada
Tel.: (437) 888-3102
Web Site: http://www.proventure-gold.com
Gold Exploration & Mining Services
N.A.I.C.S.: 212220
Mauricio Gonzalez *(CEO)*

PROVENTUS AB
Katarinavagen 15, 111 87, Stockholm, Sweden
Tel.: (46) 87233100 SE
Web Site: http://www.proventus.se
Year Founded: 1980
Sales Range: $400-449.9 Million
Emp.: 24
Investment Services
N.A.I.C.S.: 523940
Robert Weil *(Founder & Chm)*

Subsidiaries:

Superia N.V. (1)
Torhoutsesteenweg 222, 8210, Zedelgem, Belgium
Tel.: (32) 50209221
Web Site: http://www.superia.be
Mfr of Lawn Mowers, Gas Heaters & Radiators
N.A.I.C.S.: 333112

PROVENTUS AGROCOM LIMITED
515 Wing C 215 Atrium Andheri-Kurla Road Andheri East, Mumbai, 400052, India
Tel.: (91) 2262110900
Web Site: https://www.proventusagro.com
Year Founded: 2015
PROV—(NSE)
Rev.: $50,396,835
Assets: $12,221,749
Liabilities: $4,616,929
Net Worth: $7,604,820
Earnings: $440,237
Emp.: 16
Fiscal Year-end: 03/31/23
Investment Management Service
N.A.I.C.S.: 523999
Ranganathan Subramanian *(Chm)*

Subsidiaries:

Prov Foods Private Limited (1)
Unit 515 5th Floor C Wing 21 Atrium Andheri Kurla Road, Andheri E, Mumbai, 400069, Maharashtra, India
Tel.: (91) 2262110900
Web Site: https://provfoods.in
Food Product Whslr
N.A.I.C.S.: 445298

PROVEXIS PLC
2 Blagrave Street, Reading, RG1 1AZ, Berkshire, United Kingdom
Tel.: (44) 7490391888 UK
Web Site: https://www.provexis.com
Year Founded: 1999
PXS—(AIM)
Rev.: $484,198
Assets: $1,050,553
Liabilities: $233,877
Net Worth: $816,676
Earnings: ($480,721)
Emp.: 2
Fiscal Year-end: 03/31/23
All Other Miscellaneous Food Manufacturing
N.A.I.C.S.: 311999
Ian Ford *(CEO, CFO & Sec)*

PROVIDENCE GOLD MINES INC.
Tel.: (778) 952-2660 BC
Web Site: https://www.providencegold.com
Year Founded: 2010
PHD—(OTCIQ)
Assets: $2,299,037
Liabilities: $57,175
Net Worth: $2,241,862
Earnings: ($581,392)
Fiscal Year-end: 12/31/20
Gold & Metal Mining
N.A.I.C.S.: 212220
Ronald Allan Coombes *(Pres & CEO)*

Subsidiaries:

Providence Gold Mines (US) Inc. (1)
Suite 501 - 595 Howe Street, Vancouver, V6C 3B6, BC, Canada
Tel.: (604) 724-2369
Gold Mining Services
N.A.I.C.S.: 212220
Ronald Allan Coombes *(Pres & CEO)*

PROVINCIAL MEDICAL SUPPLIES LTD.
51 Pippy Place, Saint John's, A1B 4B7, NL, Canada
Tel.: (709) 754-3033
Web Site: https://www.provincialmedical.com
Sales Range: $10-24.9 Million
Emp.: 15
Medical Supplies Distr
N.A.I.C.S.: 423450
Robert Grady *(Pres)*

PROVIRON HOLDING N.V.
G Gilliotstraat 60, 2620, Hemiksem, Belgium
Tel.: (32) 3 870 8820
Web Site: http://www.proviron.com
Year Founded: 1977
Rev.: $78,046,403
Assets: $93,646,053
Liabilities: $51,180,962
Net Worth: $42,465,091
Earnings: ($1,039,230)
Fiscal Year-end: 12/31/19
Holding Company; Chemical Products Mfr
N.A.I.C.S.: 551112
Wim Michiels *(CEO)*

Subsidiaries:

Proviron America, Inc. (1)
62 Industrial Park Rd, Friendly, WV 26146 (100%)
Tel.: (304) 652-6932
Web Site: http://www.proviron.com
Sales Range: $50-74.9 Million
Emp.: 9
Mfr of Chemicals
N.A.I.C.S.: 424690

Proviron Fine Chemicals N.V. (1)
Stationstraat 123, PO Box 2, 8400, Oostende, Belgium (100%)
Tel.: (32) 59562100
Web Site: http://www.proviron.com
Sales Range: $50-74.9 Million
Emp.: 300
Chemicals Mfr
N.A.I.C.S.: 325998
Wim Michiels *(Mng Dir)*

Proviron Industries N.V. (1)
G Gilliotstraat 60, 2620, Hemiksem, Belgium (100%)
Tel.: (32) 38708820
Web Site: http://www.proviron.com
Sales Range: $25-49.9 Million
Emp.: 40
Chemicals Mfr
N.A.I.C.S.: 325998

Zhejiang Pu Wei Lun Chemicals Co., Ltd. (1)
No 529 Chunxiao Rd, Binjiang District, 310051, Hangzhou, Zhejiang, China
Tel.: (86) 57186633286
Chemical Products Distr
N.A.I.C.S.: 424690

PROWINKO NEDERLAND B.V.
Bella Donna 2, 1181 RM, Amstelveen, Netherlands
Tel.: (31) 206735045 NL
Web Site: https://prowinko.com
Year Founded: 1990
Commercial Property Investment & Leasing Services
N.A.I.C.S.: 531120
Max Vorst *(CEO)*

Subsidiaries:

Prowinko Belgie B.V. (1)
Louizalaan 32 b15 Av Louise, 1050, Brussels, Belgium
Tel.: (32) 24691513
Web Site: https://prowinko.com
Commercial Property Investment & Leasing Services
N.A.I.C.S.: 531120
Philip van Perlstein *(Mng Dir)*

Prowinko Canada Ltd. (1)
1200 Bay Street Suite 813, Toronto, M5R 2A5, ON, Canada
Tel.: (416) 637-4651
Web Site: https://prowinko.com
Commercial Property Investment & Leasing Services
N.A.I.C.S.: 531120

Prowinko Portugal SA (1)
Avenida da Liberdade 180 - 9a, 1250-146, Lisbon, Portugal
Tel.: (351) 308800800
Web Site: https://prowinko.com
Commercial Property Investment & Leasing Services
N.A.I.C.S.: 531120

PROXIMANIA S.A.
5 rue de Marignan, 75008, Paris, France
Tel.: (33) 156594000
Web Site: http://www.proximania.com
Sales Range: $150-199.9 Million
Internet Services
N.A.I.C.S.: 517121
Laurent Troude *(Chm)*

PROXIMAR SEAFOOD AS
Edvard Griegs vei 3c, 5059, Bergen, Norway
Tel.: (47) 99477599
Web Site: https://www.proximarseafood.com
Year Founded: 2015
PROXI—(OSL)
Rev.: $3,233
Assets: $128,202,660
Liabilities: $93,807,316
Net Worth: $34,395,345
Earnings: ($8,622,298)
Emp.: 24
Fiscal Year-end: 12/31/23
Seafood Product Mfr & Distr
N.A.I.C.S.: 311710
Dharma Rajeswaran *(COO)*

Subsidiaries:

Proximar Ltd. (1)
Industry & Trade Center 3F 2, Yamashita-cho Naka-ku, Yokohama, Kanagawa, Japan
Tel.: (81) 453056570
Farm Construction Services
N.A.I.C.S.: 236220

PROXIMUS PLC
Koning Albert II-laan 27, B - 1030, Brussels, Belgium
Tel.: (32) 22054000 BE
Web Site: https://www.proximus.com
Year Founded: 1994
PROX—(EUR)
Sales Range: $5-14.9 Billion
Telecommunication Servicesb
N.A.I.C.S.: 517111
Nancy Goossens *(Dir-IR)*

Subsidiaries:

Belgacom Group International Services SA (1)
Koning Albert II laan 27, 1030, Brussels, Belgium
Tel.: (32) 22026040
Web Site: http://www.Belgacom.be
Integrated Telecom Services
N.A.I.C.S.: 541618

Belgacom International Carrier Services SA (1)
Boulevard du Roi Albert II 27, 1030, Brussels, Belgium (57.6%)
Tel.: (32) 2 547 5210
Web Site: https://www.bics.com
Global Wireless Service Providers
N.A.I.C.S.: 517112
Frederic Salmon *(CFO)*

PROXIMUS PLC

Proximus PLC—(Continued)

Subsidiary (US):

TeleSign Corporation (2)
13274 Fiji Way Ste 600, Marina Del Rey, CA 90292
Tel.: (310) 740-9700
Web Site: http://www.telesign.com
Account Security; PhoneID Fraud Prevention, Mobile App-Based Authentication & Communications Platform as a Service (CPaaS)
N.A.I.C.S.: 541990
Philipp Gast *(CFO)*

Belgacom Mobile S.A (1)
Rue Du Progres 55, 1210, Brussels, Belgium
Tel.: (32) 22054000
Web Site: http://www.proximus.be
Sales Range: $5-14.9 Billion
Emp.: 2,100
Mobile Telecommunications Services
N.A.I.C.S.: 517112
Jan Van Acoleyen *(Chief HR Officer)*

Connectimmo SA (1)
Koning Albert II Laan 27, 1030, Schaarbeek, Belgium
Tel.: (32) 2 202 2749
Web Site: https://www.connectimmo.be
Sales Range: $25-49.9 Million
Emp.: 50
Real Estate Manangement Services
N.A.I.C.S.: 531210

ICTS Hungary Kft (1)
Petzval József u 52, 1119, Budapest, Hungary
Tel.: (36) 1 465 8040
Web Site: https://www.ictshungary.hu
Sales Range: $25-49.9 Million
Emp.: 6
Information Technology Services
N.A.I.C.S.: 541512

ISit BV (1)
Krommeweteing 7, Utrecht, 3543, Netherlands
Tel.: (31) 302477711
Web Site: http://www.telindus.nl
Sales Range: $25-49.9 Millicn
Emp.: 200
Computer Software Consulting Services
N.A.I.C.S.: 541512

ISit Education & Support BV (1)
Krommewetering, Utrecht, 3543AP, Netherlands
Tel.: (31) 302477711
Sales Range: $25-49.9 Million
Emp.: 200
Computer Software Consulting Services
N.A.I.C.S.: 541512

Route Mobile Ltd. (1)
4th Dimension 3Rd Floor Mind Space, Malad West, Mumbai, 400064, India   (82.7%)
Tel.: (91) 2240337676
Web Site: https://www.routemobile.com
Rev.: $432,663,509
Assets: $345,942,090
Liabilities: $126,723,818
Net Worth: $219,218,272
Earnings: $39,938,853
Emp.: 404
Fiscal Year-end: 03/31/2023
Telecommunication Servicesb
N.A.I.C.S.: 517810
Sandipkumar Gupta *(Chm)*

Subsidiary (Non-US):

Route Mobile UK Limited (2)
Tel.: (44) 2088111188
Telecommunication Servicesb
N.A.I.C.S.: 517810

Scarlet NV (1)
Carlistraat 2, 1140, Evere, Belgium
Tel.: (32) 2275 3311
Web Site: http://www.scarlet.be
Holding Company; Telecommunications Services
N.A.I.C.S.: 551112

Subsidiary (Non-US):

Scarlet B.V. (2)

Liska Building Schottegatweg Oost 191A, Willemstad, Curacao
Tel.: (599) 9766 0000
Web Site: http://www.scarlet.cw
Internet Service Provider
N.A.I.C.S.: 517810

Subsidiary (Domestic):

Scarlet Belgium NV (2)
Carle street 2, Evere, 1140, Flemish Brabant, Belgium
Tel.: (32) 22753311
Web Site: http://www.scarlet.be
Emp.: 90
Integrated Telecommunication Services
N.A.I.C.S.: 517810
Bruno Delhaise *(CEO)*

Subsidiary (Domestic):

Scarlet Business NV (3)
Belgicastraat 5, 1930, Zaventem, Flemish Brabant, Belgium
Tel.: (32) 22753311
Web Site: http://www.scarletbusiness.be
Sales Range: $150-199.9 Million
Integrated Telecom Services
N.A.I.C.S.: 541618

Scarlet Telecom BVBA (3)
Belgicastraat 5, 1930, Zaventem, Flemish Brabant, Belgium
Tel.: (32) 80084111
Integrated Telecom Services
N.A.I.C.S.: 541618

Tango S.A. (1)
Rue de Luxembourg 177, 8077, Bertrange, Luxembourg
Tel.: (352) 691700777
Web Site: http://www.tango.lu
Sales Range: $25-49.9 Million
Emp.: 100
Telecommunication Servicesb
N.A.I.G.S.: 517112
Jean-Francois Willame *(CEO)*

Subsidiary (Domestic):

Tango Mobile SA (2)
Rue de Luxembourg 177, 8077, Bertrange, Luxembourg
Tel.: (352) 27777101
Web Site: http://www.tango.lu
Sales Range: $25-49.9 Million
Emp.: 100
Integrated Telecom Services
N.A.I.C.S.: 541618

Tango SA (2)
Rue de Luxembourg 177, 8077, Bertrange, Luxembourg
Tel.: (352) 27777101
Web Site: http://www.tango.lu
Sales Range: $125-149.9 Million
Emp.: 100
Integrated Telecom Services
N.A.I.C.S.: 541618

Telectronics SA (1)
81 Rte Arlon, Esch-sur-Alzette, 8009, Luxembourg
Tel.: (352) 508373
Web Site: http://www.telindus.lu
Sales Range: $125-149.9 Million
Emp.: 330
Telecommunication Equipment Distr
N.A.I.C.S.: 423690
Hoffman Gerard *(Gen Mgr)*

Telindus BV (1)
Krommewetering 7, Postbus 9559, 3543 AP, Utrecht, Netherlands
Tel.: (31) 30 247 7711
Web Site: https://www.telindus.nl
Information Technology Consulting Services
N.A.I.C.S.: 541690

Telindus France SA (1)
10 Ave de Norvege, 91140, Villebon-sur-Yvette, Essonne, France
Tel.: (33) 169183232
Web Site: http://www.telindus.fr
Sales Range: $600-649.9 Million
Emp.: 2,700
Information Technology Consulting Services
N.A.I.C.S.: 541512
Henri Juin *(Mng Dir)*

Telindus International BV (1)

Krommewetering 7, 3543 AP, Utrecht, Netherlands
Tel.: (31) 302477711
Information Technology Consulting Services
N.A.I.C.S.: 541690

Telindus Limited (1)
Unit No 1106 11th Fl Prosperity Ctr, Kowloon, China (Hong Kong)
Tel.: (852) 28022126
Web Site: http://www.telindus.com
Sales Range: $25-49.9 Million
Emp.: 100
Information Technology Services
N.A.I.C.S.: 541512

Subsidiary (Non-US):

Yunnan Telindus Technology Co. Ltd. (2)
Room C22-23 Innovation Park No 3 Jinkai Road, Kunming Econ & Tech Devel Zone, Kunming, Yunnan, China
Tel.: (86) 8717270668
Information Technology Services
N.A.I.C.S.: 541512

Telindus PSF SA (1)
Rue des Mines 2, 4244, Esch-sur-Alzette, Luxembourg
Tel.: (352) 5328201
Internet Software Development Services
N.A.I.C.S.: 541511

Telindus SA (1)
Route d'Arlon 81-83, 8009, Strassen, Luxembourg
Tel.: (352) 4509151
Web Site: http://www.telindus.lu
Emp.: 100
Internet Software Development Services
N.A.I.C.S.: 541511

PROYA COSMETICS CO., LTD.

PROYA Building No 588 Xixi Road, Xihu District, Hangzhou, 310023, China
Tel.: (86) 57188931111
Web Site: https://www.proya-group.com
Year Founded: 2003
603605—(SHG)
Rev.: $896,517,377
Assets: $811,241,281
Liabilities: $314,615,129
Net Worth: $496,626,151
Earnings: $114,762,988
Emp.: 3,177
Fiscal Year-end: 12/31/22
Cosmetic Product Mfr & Distr
N.A.I.C.S.: 325620
Hou Juncheng *(Chm)*

PROZONE REALTY LTD.

105/106 Ground Floor Dream Square Dalia Industrial Estate, Off New Link Road Andheri West, Mumbai, 400 053, India
Tel.: (91) 2268239000   In
Web Site: https://prozonerealty.com
534675—(BOM)
Rev.: $7,994,737
Assets: $221,610,958
Liabilities: $115,137,422
Net Worth: $106,473,535
Earnings: ($5,694,357)
Emp.: 12
Fiscal Year-end: 03/31/21
Shopping Center Leasing Services
N.A.I.C.S.: 531120
Nikhil Chaturvedi *(Mng Dir)*

PRUDENT CORPORATE ADVISORY SERVICES LIMITED

Prudent House Panjrapole Cross Road, Nr Polytechnic Ambawadi, Ahmedabad, 380015, Gujarat, India
Tel.: (91) 7940209600
Web Site: https://www.prudentcorporate.com
Year Founded: 2000

INTERNATIONAL PUBLIC

543527—(BOM)
Rev.: $62,594,082
Assets: $54,597,871
Liabilities: $22,163,655
Net Worth: $32,434,215
Earnings: $10,966,137
Emp.: 822
Fiscal Year-end: 03/31/22
Investment Management Service
N.A.I.C.S.: 523999

Subsidiaries:

Prudent Broking Services Private Limited (1)
401 Sears Tower Off C G Road Gulbai Tekra Ambawadi, Ahmedabad, 380006, Gujarat, India
Tel.: (91) 7961600900
Web Site: https://www.prudentbroking.com
Intermediary Broking Services
N.A.I.C.S.: 523150

PRUDENTIAL DISCOUNT & GUARANTEE HOUSE LTD.

707 Ibrahim Trade Tower Plot 1 Block 7&8 SMCHS, Shahrah-e-Faisal, Karachi, Pakistan
Tel.: (92) 21 34327557
Investment Banking Services
N.A.I.C.S.: 523150

PRUDENTIAL GUARANTEE & ASSURANCE INC.

Coyiuto House 119 Carlos Palanca St, Legaspi Village, Makati, 1229, Philippines
Tel.: (63) 810 4916   PH
Web Site: http://www.prudentialguarantee.com
Sales Range: $25-49.9 Million
Property & Casualty Insurance Providing Services
N.A.I.C.S.: 524126
James G. Coyiuto *(Treas & Sr VP)*

Subsidiaries:

PGA Sompo Insurance Corporation (1)
5th Floor Corinthian Plaza 121 Paseo de Roxas, Legaspi Village, Makati, 1229, Manila, Philippines
Tel.: (63) 28113417
Web Site: https://www.pgasompo.com.ph
Property & Casualty Insurance Products & Services
N.A.I.C.S.: 524126
Yuichiro Funabashi *(Pres & COO)*

PRUDENTIAL INVESTMENT BANK LIMITED

26-D 1st Floor Kashmir Plaza Jinnah Avenue Blue Area, Islamabad, Pakistan
Tel.: (92) 51 282 9776
Investment Banking Services
N.A.I.C.S.: 523150

PRUDENTIAL PLC

1 Angel Court, London, EC2R 7AG, United Kingdom
Tel.: (44) 2039779720   UK
Web Site: https://www.prudentialplc.com
Year Founded: 1848
PUK—(NYSE)
Rev.: $9,371,000,000
Assets: $174,066,000,000
Liabilities: $156,083,000,000
Net Worth: $17,983,000,000
Earnings: $1,712,000,000
Emp.: 15,030
Fiscal Year-end: 12/31/23
Investment Management Service
N.A.I.C.S.: 551112
Al-Noor Gulamali Abdulla Ramji *(Chief Digital Officer-Grp)*

AND PRIVATE COMPANIES — PRUKSA HOLDING PUBLIC COMPANY LIMITED

Subsidiaries:

Eastspring Al-Wara' Investments Berhad (1)
Level 22 Menara Prudential Persiaran TRX Barat Tun Razak Exchange, No 5 Jalan Bangsar Utama 1, 55188, Kuala Lumpur, Malaysia
Tel.: (60) 32 778 3888
Investment Management Service
N.A.I.C.S.: 523940
Khadijah Sairah Ibrahim *(Exec Dir & CEO)*

Eastspring Asset Management Korea Co. Ltd. (1)
22F One IFC 10 Gukjegeumyung-ro, Yeongdeungpo-gu, Seoul, 07326, Korea (South)
Tel.: (82) 22 126 3500
Investment Management Service
N.A.I.C.S.: 523940
Cheon Woong Park *(CEO)*

Eastspring Investment (Singapore) Ltd. (1)
10 Marina Boulevard 32-01, MBFC Tower 2, Singapore, 018983, Singapore
Tel.: (65) 63499100
Web Site: https://www.eastspring.com
Investment Company
N.A.I.C.S.: 523999
Bernard Teo *(Chm)*

Subsidiary (Non-US):

TMB Asset Management Co., Ltd. (2)
No 990 Abdulrahim Place Building Floor 32, Rama 4 Road Silom Bang Kak, Bangkok, 10500, Thailand **(65%)**
Tel.: (66) 2838100
Web Site: http://www.tmbameastspring.com
Mutual Fund Management Services
N.A.I.C.S.: 523940
Thida Chotiyanon *(Deputy Mng Dir-Corp Bus Support & Registration Dept)*

Eastspring Investment Management (Shanghai) Company Limited (1)
Units 306-308 3rd Floor Azia Center 1233 Lujiazui Ring Road, Shanghai, 200120, China
Tel.: (86) 215 053 1200
Investment Management Service
N.A.I.C.S.: 523940

Eastspring Investments (Hong Kong) Limited (1)
13th Floor One International Finance Centre 1 Harbour View Street, Central, China (Hong Kong)
Tel.: (852) 2 918 6300
Investment Management Service
N.A.I.C.S.: 523940

Eastspring Investments (Luxembourg) S.A. (1)
26 Boulevard Royal, 2449, Luxembourg, Luxembourg
Tel.: (352) 229 999 5763
Investment Management Service
N.A.I.C.S.: 523940

Eastspring Investments Berhad (1)
Level 22 Menara Prudential Persiaran TRX Barat Tun Razak Exchange, 55188, Kuala Lumpur, Malaysia
Tel.: (60) 32 778 3888
Investment Management Service
N.A.I.C.S.: 523940
Lilian Tham *(Chm)*

Eastspring Investments Fund Management Limited Liability Company (1)
23rd Floor-Saigon Trade Center 37 Ton Duc Thang Street, District 1, Ho Chi Minh City, Vietnam
Tel.: (84) 283 910 2848
Investment Management Service
N.A.I.C.S.: 523940
Xavier Bernard Maurice Meyer *(Chm)*

Eastspring Investments Incorporated
203 N LaSalle St Ste 2100, Chicago, IL 60601
Tel.: (312) 730-9540
Web Site: https://www.eastspring.com

Investment Management Service
N.A.I.C.S.: 523940

Eastspring Investments Limited (1)
Marunouchi Park Building 5F 2-6-1 Marunouchi, Chiyoda-ku, Tokyo, 100-6905, Japan
Tel.: (81) 35 224 3400
Investment Management Service
N.A.I.C.S.: 523940
Yasuhisa Nitta *(CEO)*

Eastspring Securities Investment Trust Co., Ltd.
4F No 1 Songzhi Road, Taipei, 110, Taiwan
Tel.: (886) 28 758 6688
Investment Management Service
N.A.I.C.S.: 523940
Polly Wang *(CEO)*

ICICI Prudential Asset Management Company Limited (1)
One BKC 13th Floor Bandra Kurla Complex, Mumbai, 400 051, Bandra, India
Tel.: (91) 2226525000
Web Site: https://www.icicipruamc.com
Sales Range: $100-124.9 Million
Emp.: 140
Financial Services
N.A.I.C.S.: 523999
Sankaran Naren *(Chief Investment Officer)*

ICICI Prudential Life Insurance Company Ltd. (1)
ICICI PruLife Towers 1089 Appasaheb Marathe Marg, Prabhadevi, Mumbai, 400025, India
Tel.: (91) 40391600
Web Site: https://www.iciciprulife.com
Life Insurance Services; Joint Venture Between ICICI Bank Limited & Prudential Plc
N.A.I.C.S.: 524113
Puneet Nanda *(Deputy Mng Dir)*

P.T. Prudential Life Assurance (1)
Prudential Tower Jl Jend Sudirman kav 79, Jakarta, 12910, Indonesia
Tel.: (62) 150 0085
Web Site: https://www.prudential.co.id
Fire Insurance Services
N.A.I.C.S.: 524113

Prudential (Cambodia) Life Assurance Plc (1)
VTrust Tower 3rd Floor 24 Street 169 Tchecoslovaquie Blvd, PO Box 417, Sangkat Vealvong Khan 7 Makara, 12253, Phnom Penh, Cambodia
Tel.: (855) 2 396 4222
Web Site: https://www.prudential.com.kh
Fire Insurance Services
N.A.I.C.S.: 524113
Sanjay Chakrabarty *(CEO)*

Prudential Assurance Company Singapore (Pte) Limited (1)
7 Straits View 06-01 Marina One East Tower, Singapore, 018936, Singapore
Tel.: (65) 63330333
Web Site: https://www.prudential.com.sg
Emp.: 600
Insurance Management Services
N.A.I.C.S.: 524298

Prudential Assurance Malaysia Berhad (1)
Ground Floor Menara Prudential Persiaran TRX Barat Tun Razak Exchange, 55188, Kuala Lumpur, Malaysia
Tel.: (60) 32 778 3888
Web Site: https://www.prudential.com.my
Fire Insurance Services
N.A.I.C.S.: 524113
Abdul Khalil Abdul Hamid *(Chm)*

Prudential Assurance Uganda Limited (1)
9th Floor Zebra Plaza Kampala Road, PO Box 2660, Kampala, Uganda
Tel.: (256) 41 434 3909
Web Site: https://www.prudential.ug
Insurance Services
N.A.I.C.S.: 524298
Wilf Blackburn *(CEO)*

Prudential BeLife Insurance S.A. (1)
Abidjan Plateau Avenue Nogues Immeuble Woodin Center 1er etage 01, BP5173, Abidjan, Cote d'Ivoire
Tel.: (225) 272 031 1470

Web Site: https://www.prubelife.com
Insurance Services
N.A.I.C.S.: 524298

Prudential Beneficial General Insurance Cameroon S.A. (1)
Beneficial Insurance building Rue Lotin Same, BP 2328, Douala, Cameroon
Tel.: (237) 23 342 2344
Web Site: https://www.prubeneficial.cm
Fire Insurance Services
N.A.I.C.S.: 524113

Prudential Beneficial Life Insurance Togo S.A. (1)
2963 Rue De La Chance, BP 1115, Agbalepedogan District, Lome, Togo
Tel.: (228) 2 251 0607
Web Site: https://www.prubeneficial.tg
Fire Insurance Services
N.A.I.C.S.: 524113

Prudential Capital Plc (1)
Governors House 5 Laurence Pountney Hill, London, EC4R0HH, United Kingdom
Tel.: (44) 2072207588
Financial Management Services
N.A.I.C.S.: 523999

Prudential Corporation Asia (1)
13th Fl 1 International Finance Ctr 1 Harbour View St, Central, Hong Kong, China (Hong Kong) **(100%)**
Tel.: (852) 29186300
Web Site: http://www.prudentialcorporationasia.com
Sales Range: $100-124.9 Million
Emp.: 200
Insurance & Asset Management Services
N.A.I.C.S.: 524298
Nic Nicandrou *(CEO)*

Prudential Corporation Holdings Limited (1)
Governors House 5 Laurence Pountney Hill, London, EC4R 0HH, United Kingdom
Tel.: (44) 2072207588
Web Site: http://www.pru.co.uk
Investment Management Service
N.A.I.C.S.: 523999

Prudential Financial Advisers Singapore Pte. Ltd. (1)
Prudential Scotts 51 Scotts Road 01-01, Singapore, Singapore
Tel.: (65) 63330333
Web Site: https://www.prudentialfa.sg
Financial Advisory Services
N.A.I.C.S.: 522320

Prudential International Assurance Plc (1)
Montague House Adelaide Rd, Dublin, Ireland
Tel.: (353) 14765000
Web Site: http://www.prudential-international.com
Insurance Management Services
N.A.I.C.S.: 524298

Prudential Life Assurance (Lao) Company Limited (1)
5th Floor Vientiane Center Office Building, Nongchan Village Sisattanak District, Vientiane, Lao People's Democratic Republic
Tel.: (856) 2 121 1123
Web Site: https://www.prudential.la
Fire Insurance Services
N.A.I.C.S.: 524113
Veejay Madhavan *(CEO)*

Prudential Life Assurance (Thailand) Public Company Limited (1)
944 Mitrtown Office Tower 10th 29th-31st Floor Rama 4 Road, Wangmai Pathumwan, Bangkok, 10330, Thailand
Tel.: (66) 2 353 4700
Web Site: https://www.prudential.co.th
Fire Insurance Services
N.A.I.C.S.: 524113
Lilian Ng *(Chm)*

Prudential Life Assurance Kenya Limited (1)
Ground Floor Vienna Court State House Crescent off State House Avenue, Nairobi, Kenya
Tel.: (254) 71 907 5000
Web Site: https://www.prudentiallife.co.ke

Fire Insurance Services
N.A.I.C.S.: 524113
Titus Naikuni *(Chm)*

Prudential Life Assurance Zambia Limited (1)
Plot Number 32256 Prudential House Thabo Mbeki Road, Lusaka, Zambia
Tel.: (260) 21 138 9710
Web Site: https://www.prudential.co.zm
Insurance Services
N.A.I.C.S.: 524298

Prudential Life Insurance Ghana Limited (1)
64 Motorway Extension George W Bush Highway N1 Road, Dzorwulu, Accra, Ghana
Tel.: (233) 30 220 8877
Web Site: https://www.prudential.com.gh
Fire Insurance Services
N.A.I.C.S.: 524113
Agyeman Badu Akosa *(Chm)*

Prudential Myanmar Life Insurance Limited (1)
15-01 15th Floor Sule Square 221 Sule Pagoda Road, Kyauktada Township, Yangon, Myanmar
Tel.: (95) 977 011 0010
Web Site: https://www.prudential.com.mm
Fire Insurance Services
N.A.I.C.S.: 524113

Prudential Property Investment Managers Limited (1)
City Place House 55 Basinghall Street, London, EC2V 5DU, United Kingdom
Tel.: (44) 2075486600
Web Site: http://www.prupim.com
Sales Range: $75-99.9 Million
Emp.: 200
Real Estate Investment Services
N.A.I.C.S.: 531390

Prudential Vietnam Assurance Private Limited (1)
25th Floor Saigon Trade Center Building 37 Ton Duc Thang, Ho Chi Minh City, Vietnam
Tel.: (84) 2839101660
Insurance Services
N.A.I.C.S.: 524298

Pulse EcoSystems Pte. Ltd. (1)
1 Wallich Street 19-01 Guoco Tower, Singapore, 078881, Singapore
Tel.: (65) 6 704 4522
Web Site: https://www.wedopulse.com
Health Care Srvices
N.A.I.C.S.: 622110
Lilian Ng *(CEO-Insurance)*

The Prudential Assurance Company Limited (1) **(100%)**
Web Site: http://www.pru.co.uk
Life Insurance Products & Services
N.A.I.C.S.: 524113

PRUDENTIAL SUGAR CORPORATION LIMITED

Plot No 144 Akash Ganga 3rd Floor Sri Nagar Colony, Hyderabad, 500073, Andhra Pradesh, India
Tel.: (91) 40 23746451
Sales Range: $10-24.9 Million
Sugar Mfr
N.A.I.C.S.: 311314
Vinod Baid *(Chm & Mng Dir)*

PRUKSA HOLDING PUBLIC COMPANY LIMITED

1177 24 Floor Pearl Bangkok Building Phaholyothin Road, Phayathai, Bangkok, 10400, Thailand
Tel.: (66) 20801739   TH
Web Site: https://www.psh.co.th
Year Founded: 2016
PSH—(THA)
Rev.: $762,847,774
Assets: $2,001,048,676
Liabilities: $663,036,077
Net Worth: $1,338,012,599
Earnings: $68,292,353
Emp.: 908
Fiscal Year-end: 12/31/23

PRUKSA HOLDING PUBLIC COMPANY LIMITED

Pruksa Holding Public Company Limited—(Continued)

Holding Company
N.A.I.C.S.: 551112
Thongma Vijitpongpun *(CEO)*

Subsidiaries:

Kaysorn Construction Company Limited (1)
1177 21 Floor Pearl Bangkok Building Phaholyothin Road, Samsennai Phayathai, Bangkok, 10400, Thailand
Tel.: (66) 20801739
Construction & Decoration Services
N.A.I.C.S.: 541410

Pruksa Overseas Company Limited (1)
1177 23rd Floor Pearl Bangkok Building Phaholyothin Road, Phayathai Sub-district Phayathai District, Bangkok, 10400, Thailand
Tel.: (66) 20801739
Stock Investment Services
N.A.I.C.S.: 523150

Vimut Hospital Company Limited (1)
1177 17th Floor Pearl Bangkok Building Phaholyothin Road, Samsennai Phayathai, Bangkok, 10400, Thailand
Tel.: (66) 20801739
Hospital Operator
N.A.I.C.S.: 622110

Vimut Hospital Holding Co., Ltd. (1)
1177 17th Floor Pearl Bangkok Building Phaholyothin Road, Samsennai Phayathai, Bangkok, 10400, Thailand
Tel.: (66) 20801739
Investment Holding Services
N.A.I.C.S.: 551112

PRUKSA REAL ESTATE PUBLIC COMPANY LIMITED

27-30 Floor SM Tower 979/83 Paholyothin Rd Samsennai, Phayathai, Bangkok, 10400, Thailand
Tel.: (66) 2298 0101   TH
Web Site: http://www.pruksa.com
Year Founded: 1993
Sales Range: $800-899.9 Million
Emp.: 2,737
Real Estate Development Services
N.A.I.C.S.: 531390
Pisit Leeahtam *(Chm)*

Subsidiaries:

Phanalee Estate Co., Ltd. (1)
30th Floor SM Tower 979/97 Phaholyothin Road Samsennai, Phaya Thai, Bangkok, 10400, Thailand
Tel.: (66) 2298 0010
Real Estate Development Services
N.A.I.C.S.: 531390

Pruksa India Housing Private Limited (1)
Ferns Icon Unit No 7 1st Floor Marathahalli Outer Ring Road, Next to Akme Ballet, Bengaluru, 560 037, India
Tel.: (91) 80 4340 9300
Web Site: http://www.pruksa.co.in
Emp.: 60
Real Estate Development Services
N.A.I.C.S.: 531390

Pruksa Real Estate Public Company Limited - PS Precast Factory (1)
54/1 Moo 4 Lamlookka Road, Tambon Ladsawai Amphur Lamlookka, Pathumthani, Thailand
Tel.: (66) 2532 8124 32
Precast Concrete Mfr
N.A.I.C.S.: 327390

Putthachart Estate Co., Ltd. (1)
30th Floor SM Tower 979/97 Phaholyothin Road Samsennai, Phaya Thai, Bangkok, 10400, Thailand
Tel.: (66) 2298 0820
Real Estate Development Services
N.A.I.C.S.: 531390

PRVA GROUP PLC

Fajfarjeva Ulica 33, 1000, Ljubljana, Slovenia
Tel.: (386) 12345801
Web Site: http://www.prvagroup.eu
Year Founded: 2000
Rev.: $26,239,796
Assets: $406,779,830
Liabilities: $360,428,601
Net Worth: $46,351,228
Earnings: $4,351,469
Emp.: 150
Fiscal Year-end: 12/31/18
Holding Company; Insurance & Pension Products & Services
N.A.I.C.S.: 551112
Nicholas Andrew Lindsay Stuart *(Chm-Supervisory Bd)*

Subsidiaries:

DDOR Garant A.D. (1)
Marsala Birjuzova br 3-5, 11000, Belgrade, Serbia
Tel.: (381) 113036142
Web Site: http://www.garant-penzije.eu
Pension Fund Management Services
N.A.I.C.S.: 525110
Milos Skrbic *(Mgr-Exec)*

Fondi Slloveno- Kosovar i Pensioneve Sh.A. (1)
Str Ukshin Hoti 45/10, 10000, Pristina, Kosovo, Serbia
Tel.: (381) 38220031
Web Site: http://www.fondipensional.com
Pension Fund Management Services
N.A.I.C.S.: 523940
Bajram Bajrami *(Mng Dir)*

KB Prvo penzisko društvo AD (1)
Orce Nikolov 3, PO Box 563, 1000, Skopje, North Macedonia
Tel.: (389) 23168168
Web Site: http://www.kb.com.mk
Pension Fund Management Services
N.A.I.C.S.: 525110
Hari Kostov *(CEO)*

PRVA STRATEGICKA AS

Trnavska Cesta 27/B, 831 04, Bratislava, Slovakia
Tel.: (421) 258246202
Web Site: https://www.prvastrategicka.sk
Year Founded: 1996
1PRV001E—(BRA)
Sales Range: Less than $1 Million
Financial Investment Services
N.A.I.C.S.: 523999
Vladimir Balanik *(Supervisory Board of Directors & Chm-Mgmt Bd)*

PRVI PARTIZAN EMO A.D.

Milosa Obrenovica 2, Uzice, Serbia
Tel.: (381) 31 563 442
Web Site: http://prvipartizan.com
Year Founded: 2001
PPEMO—(BEL)
Sales Range: Less than $1 Million
Emp.: 1
Metal Structure Mfr
N.A.I.C.S.: 331110
Jelena Bujic *(Exec Dir)*

PRYCE CORPORATION

17th Floor Pryce Center 1179 Chino Roces Avenue Cor Bagtikan Street, Makati, Philippines
Tel.: (63) 288994401   PH
Web Site: https://www.pryce.com.ph
Year Founded: 1989
PPC—(PHI)
Rev.: $347,715,154
Assets: $443,227,176
Liabilities: $138,900,976
Net Worth: $304,326,200
Earnings: $42,555,794
Emp.: 4,737
Fiscal Year-end: 12/31/23
Property Holding & Real Estate Development Company

N.A.I.C.S.: 531311
Simeon S. Umandal *(Sec)*

PRYKARPATTYAOBLENERGO PJSC

St Industrialna 34, 76014, Ivano-Frankivs'k, Ukraine
Tel.: (380) 342594020
Web Site: https://www.oe.if.ua
Year Founded: 1930
Eletric Power Generation Services
N.A.I.C.S.: 221118

PRYMUS S.A.

Ul Turynska 101, 43-100, Tychy, Poland
Tel.: (48) 322169644
Web Site: https://www.prymussa.pl
Year Founded: 1994
Chemical Products Distr
N.A.I.C.S.: 424690
Ewa Kobosko *(Pres)*

PRYSMIAN S.P.A.

Via Chiese 6, 20126, Milan, Italy
Tel.: (39) 0264491   IT
Web Site: https://www.prysmian.com
Year Founded: 2007
PRY—(ITA)
Rev.: $16,077,661,600
Assets: $14,758,531,840
Liabilities: $10,964,498,480
Net Worth: $3,794,033,360
Earnings: $380,754,400
Emp.: 29,763
Fiscal Year-end: 12/31/21
Energy & Telecommunications Cables & Systems
N.A.I.C.S.: 335929
Pier Francesco Facchini *(CFO)*

Subsidiaries:

Associated Cables Pvt. Ltd. (1) (60%)
Tel.: (91) 2240563400
Web Site: https://www.aclcables.com
Sales Range: $25-49.9 Million
Emp.: 55
Instrumentation Cable Mfr
N.A.I.C.S.: 335921

Cableries de Valenciennes SAS (1)
Zone Industrielle, PO Box 119, 59490, Somain, France
Tel.: (33) 327950418
Sales Range: $10-24.9 Million
Emp.: 70
Cable Mfr
N.A.I.C.S.: 335929

Draka Belgium N.V. (1)
Jan van Rijswijcklaan 158, 2018, Antwerp, Belgium
Tel.: (32) 32572563
Web Site: http://www.drakakabel.be
Installation Wire & Cable Mfr
N.A.I.C.S.: 335929

Draka Cables (Hong Kong) Limited (1)
6th Floor MTL warehouse Phase II Berth One, Kwai Chung Container Terminal, Kwai Chung, New Territories, China (Hong Kong)
Tel.: (852) 24109229
Power Cable Mfr
N.A.I.C.S.: 335929

Draka Comteq Germany GmbH & Co. KG (1)
Piccolominstrasse 2, 51063, Cologne, Germany
Tel.: (49) 2216770
Power Cable Mfr
N.A.I.C.S.: 335929

Draka Distribution Aberdeen Limited (1)
Unit 3 Peterseat Drive, Altens Industrial Estate, Aberdeen, AB12 3HT, United Kingdom
Tel.: (44) 1224244800
Power Cable Mfr
N.A.I.C.S.: 335929

INTERNATIONAL PUBLIC

Draka Kabel Sverige AB (1)
Vallgatan 5 Tuvegatan, 571 41, Nassjo, Sweden
Tel.: (46) 380554000
Web Site: http://www.draka.se
Sales Range: $25-49.9 Million
Emp.: 175
Cable Installation & Connection Services
N.A.I.C.S.: 238210

Draka Kabely s.r.o. (1)
Trebicska 777/99, Velke Mezirici, Czech Republic
Tel.: (420) 566501511
Web Site: http://www.cz.prysmiangroup.com
Telecommunication Cable Supply Services
N.A.I.C.S.: 517111

Draka UK Ltd. (1)
Chickenhall Lane, Eastleigh, SO50 6YU, Hampshire, United Kingdom
Tel.: (44) 2380295016
Web Site: http://www.drakauk.com
Emp.: 19,000
Power Cable Distr
N.A.I.C.S.: 423610

EHC Global, Inc. (1)
1287 Boundary Rd, Oshawa, L1J 6Z7, ON, Canada
Tel.: (905) 432-3200
Web Site: http://www.ehc-global.com
Mfr & Distr of Escalator & Elevator Components, Escalator Handrail Advertising, Escalator Handrail Field Services & Custom Engineered Polyurethane Products
N.A.I.C.S.: 333921
Jeno Eppel *(Pres)*

Plant (Non-US):

EHC Global - Baesweiler Plant (2)
Peter-Debye-Strasse 1, Baesweiler, Germany
Tel.: (49) 2401916011
Elevator Component Mfr
N.A.I.C.S.: 333921

EHC Global - Shanghai Plant (2)
215 Ma Lu Industrial Park No 58 Chenbao Road, Jiading, Shanghai, 201801, China
Tel.: (86) 2169153231
Elevator Component Mfr
N.A.I.C.S.: 333921

Eksa Sp. Z.o.o (1)
Ul Sasiedzka 1g, 05-806, Sokolow, Poland
Tel.: (48) 22 846 4234
Web Site: https://www.eksa.eu
Sales Range: $50-74.9 Million
Emp.: 1
Electrical Cable Distr
N.A.I.C.S.: 423610
Boleslaw Uryga *(Pres)*

Encore Wire Corporation (1)
1329 Millwood Rd, McKinney, TX 75069
Tel.: (972) 562-9473
Web Site: https://www.encorewire.com
Rev.: $2,567,722,000
Assets: $1,967,912,000
Liabilities: $220,335,000
Net Worth: $1,747,577,000
Earnings: $372,399,000
Emp.: 1,629
Fiscal Year-end: 12/31/2023
Copper Rolling, Drawing, Extruding & Alloying
N.A.I.C.S.: 331420

General Cable Corporation (1)
4 Tesseneer Dr, Highland Heights, KY 41076-9753
Tel.: (859) 572-8000
Web Site: http://www.generalcable.com
Rev.: $3,837,200,000
Assets: $2,235,300,000
Liabilities: $2,103,500,000
Net Worth: $131,800,000
Earnings: ($56,600,000)
Emp.: 8,500
Fiscal Year-end: 12/31/2017
Wire, Cable & Associated Products Mfr
N.A.I.C.S.: 331491
Roberto A. Sacasa *(Chief Compliance Officer & Sr VP)*

Subsidiary (Non-US):

ACM Mexico, S.A. de C.V. (2)
Ave Ferrocarril No 162-1 Col Fortin de las

AND PRIVATE COMPANIES — PRYSMIAN S.P.A.

Flores, Tijuana, 22114, Baja California, Mexico
Tel.: (52) 6642506797
Web Site: http://www.acmdemexico.com
Building Materials Distr
N.A.I.C.S.: 444180

Alcap Comercial, S.A. (2)
Cl 4 La Loceria, Panama, Panama
Tel.: (507) 2360923
Electric Conductors Distr
N.A.I.C.S.: 423610

Cobre Cerrillos, S.A. (2)
Tel.: (56) 224222200
Web Site: https://chile.prysmian.com
Cable & Wire Mfr & Distr
N.A.I.C.S.: 332618

Colada Continua Chilena S.A. (2)
Av Las Esteras Sur 2850, Quilicura, Santiago, Metropolitan, Chile
Tel.: (56) 229649070
Web Site: https://www.coladacontinua.cl
Emp.: 38
Copper Rod Mfr
N.A.I.C.S.: 331491

Subsidiary (Domestic):

Diversified Contractors, Inc. (2)
15915 Highland Dr, McKenzie, TN 38201
Tel.: (731) 352-7996
Construction & Demolition Services
N.A.I.C.S.: 541330

Subsidiary (Non-US):

Dominion Wire and Cables Ltd. (2)
Lot 3 King's Road, PO Box 1562, Yalalevu, Ba, Fiji
Tel.: (679) 6675244
Web Site: https://www.dominioncables.com
Emp.: 50
Cable & Wire Mfr
N.A.I.C.S.: 332618

Dongguan Keystone Electric Wire & Cable Co, Ltd. (2)
110 D D 83 Kwan Ti North Village Fanling Post Office Fanling, PO Box 376, Hong Kong, China (Hong Kong)
Tel.: (852) 26917183
Web Site: http://www.keystonecable.com
Cable & Wire Mfr & Distr
N.A.I.C.S.: 332618

Subsidiary (Domestic):

GK Technologies, Inc. (2)
204 5th St E, Halstad, MN 56548
Tel.: (855) 458-3244
Web Site: http://www.geektechforag.com
Software Package Services
N.A.I.C.S.: 513210

Subsidiary (Non-US):

General Cable (China) Company Limited (2)
Unit 4902 Wheelock Square 1717 Nanjing West Rd, Shanghai, 200040, China
Tel.: (86) 2160871588
Web Site: http://www.generalcable.com.cn
Cable & Wire Mfr & Distr
N.A.I.C.S.: 332618
Ting He (Mgr-Comm)

General Cable (Jiangyin) Co. Ltd. (2)
B4 2 Qingtong Rd, Qingyang Industrial Park, Jiangyin, Jiangsu, China
Tel.: (86) 510 6508358
Web Site: http://www.generalcable.com.cn
Cable & Wire Products Mfr
N.A.I.C.S.: 333248

General Cable Automotiva Brasil Fabricacao de Cabos Eletricos Ltda. (2)
Est Samuel Aizemberg 1100 Cooperativa Sao Bernardo do Campo, Sao Paulo, 09851-550, Brazil
Tel.: (55) 1143432100
Cable & Wire Mfr & Distr
N.A.I.C.S.: 332618

General Cable Brasil Industria e Comercio de Condutores Eletricos Ltda. (2)
Av Francisco Matarazzo 1400 Edificio Milano 7 Andar, Agua Branca, 05001-903, Brazil
Tel.: (55) 1134570300
Cable & Wire Mfr & Distr
N.A.I.C.S.: 335929

General Cable Celcat, Energia e Telecomunicacoes SA (2)
Avenida Marques De Pombal 36/38, Pombal, 2715-055, Pero Pinheiro, Portugal
Tel.: (351) 219678500
Cable & Wire Products Mfr
N.A.I.C.S.: 333248

General Cable Condel, Cabos de Energia e Telecomunicacoes SA (2)
5 Av N 9 Zona Industrial do Cazenga, 3043, Luanda, Angola
Tel.: (244) 917651707
Web Site: http://www.generalcable.es
Cable & Wire Mfr & Distr
N.A.I.C.S.: 332618

Plant (Domestic):

General Cable Corp. - Franklin Plant (2)
20 Forge Pkwy, Franklin, MA 02038-3134
Tel.: (508) 541-7100
Web Site: http://www.generalcable.com
Rev: $10,500,000
Emp.: 120
Fiber Optic Cables, Electronics Cables, Data Communications Cables & Coaxial Cables Mfr
N.A.I.C.S.: 335929

General Cable Corp. - Jackson Plant (2)
19 Bobrick Dr, Jackson, TN 38305
Tel.: (731) 422-3700
Web Site: http://www.generalcable.com
Cable & Wire Products Mfr
N.A.I.C.S.: 333248
Joe Brown (Plant Mgr)

General Cable Corp. - Willimantic Plant & Tech Center (2)
1600 W Main St, Willimantic, CT 06226-1128
Tel.: (860) 456-8000
Web Site: http://www.generalcable.com
Sales Range: $125-149.9 Million
Emp.: 300
Production of Electronic Wire & Cable Products for the Computer, Military, Aerospace, Automotive, Industrial & Local Area Network Markets
N.A.I.C.S.: 332618

Subsidiary (Non-US):

General Cable Holdings (Spain) S.L. (2)
Calle Del Metall 4, 08630, Barcelona, Spain
Tel.: (34) 937734880
Web Site: http://www.generalcable.com
Cable & Wire Products Mfr
N.A.I.C.S.: 333248

General Cable Italia, Sarl (2)
Via Da Volpedo 20, Cinisello Balsamo, Milan, 20092, Lombardia, Italy
Tel.: (39) 0266049494
Cable & Wire Distr
N.A.I.C.S.: 423610
Roberto Salvaneschi (Gen Mgr)

General Cable Maroc Sarl (2)
Abdelmoumen center Angle bd My Abdelmoumen et Anoual Office N 307, Casablanca, Morocco
Tel.: (212) 522865300
Cable & Wire Mfr & Distr
N.A.I.C.S.: 332618
Mohammed Zegzouti (Gen Mgr)

General Cable Nordic A/S (2)
Randemveien 17, PO Box 113, 1541, Vestby, Norway
Tel.: (47) 64955900
Cable & Wire Mfr & Distr
N.A.I.C.S.: 332618
Jan Kristian Ruud (Gen Mgr)

General Cable Norge A/S (2)
Randemveien 17, Vestby, 1541, Norway
Tel.: (47) 64955900
Web Site: http://www.generalcable.no
Cable & Wire Products Mfr
N.A.I.C.S.: 333248

General Cable Oman, LLC (2)
PC 102 Al Qurum, PO Box 60, Muscat, Oman
Tel.: (968) 24667625
Cable & Wire Mfr & Distr
N.A.I.C.S.: 332618
Sulaya Premjit (Gen Mgr & Dir-Sls-Middle East)

General Cable Peru S.A.C. (2)
Av Manuel Olguin Nro 335 oficina 706, Santiago de Surco, Lima, 33, Peru
Tel.: (51) 14154030
Web Site: http://www.generalcable.com
Cable & Wire Products Mfr
N.A.I.C.S.: 333248

General Cable Services Europe Limited (2)
15 Chesney Ave, Chadderton, Oldham, OL9 8DR, Lancashire, United Kingdom
Tel.: (44) 1616849188
Sales Range: $10-24.9 Million
Emp.: 1
Cable & Wire Products Mfr
N.A.I.C.S.: 333248
Paul Mullender (Mgr-Sls-Europe)

General Cable de Mexico del Norte, S.A. de C.V. (2)
Parque Industrial No 18, Piedras Negras, 26060, Coahuila, Mexico
Tel.: (52) 8787834057
Sales Range: $75-99.9 Million
Emp.: 40
Cable & Wire Products Mfr
N.A.I.C.S.: 333248

KTG Kabeltrommel GmbH & Co. KG (2)
Camp-Spich-Str 55/59, 53842, Troisdorf, Germany
Tel.: (49) 22 412 5240
Web Site: https://www.kabeltrommel.de
Logistics Consulting Servies
N.A.I.C.S.: 541614
Manfred Schlenter (Mng Dir)

NSW Technology Limited (2)
Unit G8 The Enterprise Centre Exploration Drive Bridge Of Don, Aberdeen, AB23 8GX, United Kingdom
Tel.: (44) 1224339880
Web Site: http://www.nsw.com
Sales Range: $25-49.9 Million
Electrical Products Supplier
N.A.I.C.S.: 423510

Norddeutsche Seekabelwerke GmbH (2)
Kabelstrasse 9-11, 26954, Nordenham, Germany
Tel.: (49) 4731820
Web Site: https://www.nsw.com
Sales Range: $100-124.9 Million
Emp.: 470
Cable & Wire Products Mfr
N.A.I.C.S.: 333248
Heiko Dirks (Mng Dir)

Nostag GmbH & Co. KG (2)
Ammerlander Heerstrasse 368, 26129, Oldenburg, Germany
Tel.: (49) 4419704500
Cable & Wire Products Mfr
N.A.I.C.S.: 335921

PD Energy International Corporation (2)
Luisita Industrial Park San Miguel, Tarlac, 2301, Philippines
Tel.: (63) 459851090
Web Site: http://www.phelpsdodge.com
Emp.: 190
Cable & Wire Products Mfr
N.A.I.C.S.: 333248
Albert Joseph Reyes (Mgr-HR)

Subsidiary (Domestic):

Phelps Dodge International Corporation (2)
9850 Nw 41st St Ste 200, Doral, FL 33178-2987
Tel.: (305) 648-7721
Web Site: http://www.generalcable.com
Sales Range: $1-9.9 Million
Emp.: 30
Power, Construction, Oil, Gas & Mining Equipment
N.A.I.C.S.: 213114

Subsidiary (Non-US):

Electroconductores de Honduras, S.A. (3)
Km 7 Carretera al Primer Batallon, Colonia Inestroza Comayaguela MDC, Tegucigalpa, Honduras
Tel.: (504) 22899300
Web Site: http://cdn.generalcable.com
Insulated Aluminum Cable Mfr
N.A.I.C.S.: 332618

Keystone Electric Wire & Cable Co. Ltd. (3)
110 DD 83, PO Box 376, Kwan Ti North Village Fanling Post Office, Fanling, New Territories, China (Hong Kong)
Tel.: (852) 2 691 7183
Web Site: https://www.keystonecable.com
Sales Range: $10-24.9 Million
Copper & Aluminum Cable & Wire Mfr
N.A.I.C.S.: 332618
Ching Sum Yu (Founder)

Plant (Domestic):

Dongguan Keystone Electric Wire & Cable Co. Ltd. (4)
#110 D D 83 Kwan Ti North Village, PO Box Box 376 Fanling Post Office, Shatin, Fanling, China (Hong Kong)
Tel.: (852) 2691 7183
Web Site: http://www.keystonecable.com
Copper & Aluminum Cable & Wire Mfr
N.A.I.C.S.: 332618

Subsidiary (Non-US):

Metal Fabricators of Zambia Ltd. (3)
1400 Figov Road, PO Box 15692, Luanshya, Copperbelt, Zambia
Tel.: (260) 212512637
Web Site: https://www.zamefa.com
Copper Rod, Cable & Wire Mfr
N.A.I.C.S.: 331420

Phelps Dodge International (Thailand) Limited (3)
Maneeya Center Building 16th Floor 518/5 Ploenchit Road, Lumpinee Pathumwan, Bangkok, 10330, Thailand
Tel.: (66) 26805800
Web Site: https://www.pdcable.com
Copper & Aluminum Wire & Cable Mfr
N.A.I.C.S.: 331420

Phelps Dodge Yantai Cable Co., Ltd. (3)
No. 11 Nenjiag Rd, E&T Development Zone, Yantai, 264006, Shandong, China
Tel.: (86) 5356371293
Web Site: http://www.pdic.com
Copper & Aluminum Wire & Cable Mfr
N.A.I.C.S.: 331420
Zhang Gongli (Gen Mgr)

Subsidiary (Non-US):

Phelps Dodge International Philippines, Inc. (3)
2nd Floor BCS PRIME Bldg 2297 Chino Roces Ave Ext, Makati, 1231, Philippines
Tel.: (63) 288132529
Web Site: https://www.phelpsdodge.com.ph
Emp.: 60
Cable & Wire Products Mfr
N.A.I.C.S.: 333248

Subsidiary (Domestic):

Phelps Dodge National Cables Corporation (2)
4 Tesseneer Dr, Highland Heights, KY 41076
Tel.: (859) 572-8000
Cable & Wire Products Mfr
N.A.I.C.S.: 333248

Subsidiary (Non-US):

Phelps Dodge Philippines Energy Products Corporation (2)
2nd Floor BCS PRIME Holding Bldg, Pasong Tamo Ext, Makati, 1200, Philippines
Tel.: (63) 28132529
Cable & Wire Products Mfr

PRYSMIAN S.P.A.

Prysmian S.p.A.—(Continued)
N.A.I.C.S.: 333248
Alex Ignasio *(Mgr)*

Silec Cable, S.A.S. (2)
Rue de Varennes prolongee, 77130, Montereau, France
Tel.: (33) 160573000
Web Site: http://www.sileccable.com
Sales Range: $200-249.9 Million
Emp.: 120
Cable & Wire Products Mfr
N.A.I.C.S.: 333248

Hohn GmbH (1)
Detlev Hohn Gruner Weg 18, Wildeshausen, 27793, Oldenburg, Germany
Tel.: (49) 443192094
Web Site: https://www.zimmerei-hohn.de
Roofing Construction & Window Roofing Services
N.A.I.C.S.: 238160

Kabeltrommel Gesellschaft mbH & CO.KG (1)
Camp-Spich-Str 55/59, 53842, Troisdorf, Germany
Tel.: (49) 2241 2524 0
Wooden Drum Mfr
N.A.I.C.S.: 321920

Limited Liability Company Rybinskelektrokabel (1)
Ul Tolbukhina d 33, Rybinsk, 152914, Russia
Tel.: (7) 4855288288
Sales Range: $100-124.9 Million
Emp.: 300
Electrical Wire Mfr
N.A.I.C.S.: 335931

Nantong Haixum Draka Elevator Products Co., Ltd. (1)
No 18 Donghai Road, Hai'an, Nantong, 226600, Jiangsu, China
Tel.: (86) 51369889859
Web Site: https://haixun-draka.com.cn
Elevator Mfr
N.A.I.C.S.: 333921

Nantong Haixum Draka Elevator Products Co. (1)
No 18 Donghai Road, Hai'an, Nantong, 226600, Jiangsu, China
Tel.: (86) 51369889859
Web Site: https://www.haixun-draka.com.cn
Elevator Parts Mfr
N.A.I.C.S.: 333921

Oman Cables Industries SAOG (1)
Plot No 206 Road No 2, Rusayl, 124, Muscat, 124, Oman (51%)
Tel.: (968) 24443100
Web Site: https://www.omancables.com
Rev.: $589,272,766
Assets: $391,068,759
Liabilities: $108,749,400
Net Worth: $282,319,360
Earnings: $15,476,892
Emp.: 313
Fiscal Year-end: 12/31/2021
Electric Equipment Mfr
N.A.I.C.S.: 335999
Fabio Ignazio Romeo *(Chm)*

Subsidiary (Domestic):

Oman Aluminium Processing Industries LLC (1)
Plot 606 Phase 6, Sohar Industrial Estate, Falaj Al Qabail, Oman
Tel.: (968) 26827347
Web Site: https://www.oapil.com
Aluminium Rod & Overhead Line Conductor Mfr
N.A.I.C.S.: 331313
Fawzi Mubarak *(Gen Mgr-Acting)*

P.T.Prysmian Cables Indonesia (1)
Gedung BRI II Suite 1502 Jln Jend Sudirman No 44-46, Jakarta, 10210, Indonesia
Tel.: (62) 264351222
Fiber Optic Cable Mfr
N.A.I.C.S.: 335921

Parimetal
Zone Industrielle No 1 Rue Vulcain, 27000, Evreux, France
Tel.: (33) 32240080
N.A.I.C.S.: 334220

Power Cables Malaysia Sdn Bhd (1)
Lot 2 Jalan Kawat 15/18, PO Box 7065, Seksyen 15, 40200, Shah Alam, Selangor, Malaysia
Tel.: (60) 355185000
Web Site: https://powercables.my
Voltage Power Cable Mfr
N.A.I.C.S.: 335929
Azman Yusoff *(CEO)*

Prysmian Australia Pty. Ltd. (1)
1 Heathcote Rd, Liverpool, 2170, NSW, Australia
Tel.: (61) 1300300304
Web Site: https://www.prysmiancable.com.au
Telecommunication Cable Mfr
N.A.I.C.S.: 335921

Prysmian Cable (Shanghai) Co., Ltd. (1)
Room 1505 Tower A City of Shanghai No 100 Zunyi Rd, Changning District, Shanghai, 200093, China
Tel.: (86) 2162371411
Sales Range: $25-49.9 Million
Emp.: 4
Fiber Optic Cable Mfr
N.A.I.C.S.: 335921

Prysmian Cable Holding B.V. (1)
Schieweg 2, Delft, 2627 AN, Netherlands
Tel.: (31) 152605260
Web Site: http://www.prysmiangroup.com
Investment Management Service
N.A.I.C.S.: 523999

Subsidiary (Domestic):

Prysmian (Dutch) Holdings B.V. (2)
Schieweg 9, Delft, 2627 AN, Netherlands
Tel.: (31) 152605260
Web Site: http://www.prysmiangroup.com
Investment Management Service
N.A.I.C.S.: 523999

Prysmian Cable Systems Pte. Ltd. (1)
No 4 Tuas Ave 12 3rd Story, Singapore, 639047, Singapore
Tel.: (65) 68629866
Sales Range: Less than $1 Million
Emp.: 10
Distr of Energy & Telecommunications Cables & Systems
N.A.I.C.S.: 335929

Branch (Non-US):

Prysmian Cable Systems Pte Ltd. (2)
555 RASA Tower 23th Floor Phaholyothin Road Lardyao C, Chatuchak, Bangkok, 10900, Thailand
Tel.: (66) 29370316
Distr of Energy & Telecommunications Cables & Systems
N.A.I.C.S.: 335929

Prysmian Cables & Systems B.V. (1)
Schieweg 9, Delft, 2600 AL, Netherlands
Tel.: (31) 152605260
Web Site: http://www.prysmiangrup.com
Sales Range: $50-74.9 Million
Emp.: 200
Energy & Telecommunications Cables & Systems Distr
N.A.I.C.S.: 335929

Prysmian Cables & Systems Limited (1)
Leigh Road, PO Box 6, Eastleigh, SO50 9YE, Hampshire, United Kingdom
Tel.: (44) 2380295555
N.A.I.C.S.: 331318

Subsidiary (Domestic):

Prysmian Cables Limited (2)
Chickenhall Lane, Eastleigh, SO50 6YU, United Kingdom
Tel.: (44) 8705 133143
Fiber Optic Cable Mfr
N.A.I.C.S.: 335921

Prysmian Cables and Systems International Ltd. (2)
Chickenhall Lane, Eastleigh, SO50 6YU, Hampshire, United Kingdom
Tel.: (44) 2380295555
Web Site: http://www.prysmiangroup.com
Sales Range: $75-99.9 Million
Electric Power & Telecommunication Cable Mfr
N.A.I.C.S.: 335929

Prysmian Metals Limited (2)
Chickenhall Lane, Eastleigh, Hampshire, United Kingdom
Tel.: (44) 87 0513 3143
Risk Managemeng Srvices
N.A.I.C.S.: 523940
Steve Price *(Plant Mgr)*

Prysmian Telecom Cables and Systems Uk Ltd. (2)
Chickenhall Lane, Eastleigh, SO50 6YU, Hampshire, United Kingdom
Tel.: (44) 2380295555
Web Site: http://www.prysmiangroup.com
Fiber Optic Cable Mfr
N.A.I.C.S.: 335921

Prysmian Cables & Systems Oy (1)
Kaapelitie 68, PO Box 13, FIN 02401, Pikkala, Finland
Tel.: (358) 1077551
Web Site: http://www.en.prysmian.fi
Sales Range: $50-74.9 Million
Emp.: 120
Energy & Telecommunications Cables & Systems Distr
N.A.I.C.S.: 335929
Aija Virtanan *(Dir-HR)*

Subsidiary (Non-US):

Prysmian Group Baltics AS (2)
Tel.: (372) 6747466
Web Site: https://baltics.prysmian.com
Electrical Cables Mfr
N.A.I.C.S.: 335929

Prysmian Cables & Systems S.A. (1)
Via Cantonale Centro Galleria 2, CH-6928, Manno, Switzerland
Tel.: (41) 9161 09192
Sales Range: $50-74.9 Million
Emp.: 4
N.A.I.C.S.: 331318

Prysmian Cables Asia-Pacific Pte Ltd. (1)
20 Jurong Port Road Jurong Town, Singapore, 619094, Singapore
Tel.: (65) 62650707
Fiber Optic Cable Mfr
N.A.I.C.S.: 335921

Prysmian Cables et Systemes France S.A.S. (1)
23 Boulevard Aristide Briand, Sens, 89100, France
Tel.: (33) 386955656
Web Site: http://www.prysmian.com
Sales Range: $50-74.9 Million
Emp.: 200
Electrical Wire Mfr
N.A.I.C.S.: 335931

Subsidiary (Non-US):

Eurelectric Tunisie S.A. (2)
Rue Borj Allam Rte De Korbous, Soliman, Nabeul, 8020, Tunisia
Tel.: (216) 72333337
Electronic Cable Mfr
N.A.I.C.S.: 335931

Prysmian Cables y Sistemas S.A. (1)
Carretera C-15 Km 2 Poligon Masia d en Notari, 08800, Vilanova i la Geltru, Barcelona, Spain
Tel.: (34) 902 146 006
Fiber Optic Cable Mfr
N.A.I.C.S.: 335921

Subsidiary (Domestic):

Fercable S.L. (2)
Avenida Torrelles 15 - 23, Sant Vicenc dels Horts, 8620, Spain
Tel.: (34) 936569050
Fiber Optic Cable Mfr
N.A.I.C.S.: 335921

INTERNATIONAL PUBLIC

Prysmian Cabluri Si Sisteme S.A. (1)
28 Draganesti Str, Slatina, 230002, Romania
Tel.: (40) 249430285
Sales Range: $100-124.9 Million
Emp.: 50
Fiber Optic Cable Mfr
N.A.I.C.S.: 335921

Prysmian Cavi e Sistemi Energia S.r.l. (1)
Via Artigianato 65, 57121, Livorno, Milan, Italy
Tel.: (39) 0586448111
Web Site: http://www.prysmian.it
Sales Range: $50-74.9 Million
Emp.: 110
Energy Wire Mfr
N.A.I.C.S.: 335929

Subsidiary (Non-US):

Prysmian Cables et Systemes France S.A.S (2)
23 Avenue Aristide Briand Paron, BP 801, 89108, Sens, France
Tel.: (33) 386957600
Web Site: http://fr.prysmiangroup.com
Energy & Telecommunications Cables & Systems Distr
N.A.I.C.S.: 335929

Plant (Domestic):

Prysmian Energie Cables et Systemes France S.A. (3)
19 Avenue de la Paix, BP 712, Paron, Sens, 89100, France
Tel.: (33) 386957769
Web Site: http://www.prysmian.com
Emp.: 300
Energy & Telecommunications Cables & Systems Distr
N.A.I.C.S.: 335929
Pierre Trijemini *(Mgr)*

Subsidiary (Non-US):

SICABLE - Societe Ivoirienne de Cables S.A (3)
Z I Vridi rue du Textile 15, BP 35, Abidjan, Cote d'Ivoire
Tel.: (225) 21213502
Web Site: https://www.sicable.ci
Domestic Wire & Cable Mfr

Subsidiary (Domestic):

Prysmian Cavi e Sistemi Italia S.r.l. (2)
Viale Sarca 222, Milan, 20126, Italy
Tel.: (39) 0264491
Web Site: http://www.prysmian.com
Sales Range: $25-49.9 Million
Emp.: 20
Electric Cable Wire Mfr
N.A.I.C.S.: 335921
Agusti Valls *(Gen Mgr)*

Subsidiary (Non-US):

Ravin Cables Limited (3)
302 3rd Floor Akruti Trade Centre Road No 7 MIDC, Andheri E, Mumbai, 400 093, India
Tel.: (91) 2230816666
Web Site: https://www.ravincables.com
Power Cable Mfr
N.A.I.C.S.: 327910
Murli Velayudhan *(Mgr-IT)*

Subsidiary (Non-US):

Power Plus Cable Co LLC (4)
Office-217 Sheikha Mohra Bldg Al Qusais-2, PO Box 84977, Dubai, United Arab Emirates
Tel.: (971) 42577888
Web Site: https://www.powerpluscable.com
Power Cable Mfr
N.A.I.C.S.: 335929

Subsidiary (Non-US):

Prysmian Energia Cables y Sistemas de Argentina S. A. (2)
Fabrica La Rosa Av da Argentina 6784, 1439, Buenos Aires, Argentina
Tel.: (54) 1146302000

Web Site: http://www.prysmian.com.ar
Sales Range: $1-9.9 Million
Emp.: 350
Energy & Telecommunications Cables & Systems Distr
N.A.I.C.S.: 335929

Prysmian Energia Cabos e Sistemas do Brasil S.A. (2)
Av Alexandre de Gusmao 145, 09110 900, Santo Andre, SP, Brazil
Tel.: (55) 1149984000
Web Site: http://www.prysmian.com.br
Sales Range: $75-99.9 Million
Energy & Telecommunications Cables & Systems Distr
N.A.I.C.S.: 335929

Group (US):

Prysmian Power Cables & Systems - North America (2)
700 Industrial Dr, Lexington, SC 29072-3755
Tel.: (803) 951-4800
Regional Managing Office; Power Cables Mfr & Services
N.A.I.C.S.: 551114

Subsidiary (Domestic):

Prysmian Power Cables & Systems USA, LLC (3)
700 Industrial Dr, Lexington, SC 29072
Tel.: (803) 951-4800
Web Site: http://www.prysmianusa.com
Emp.: 100
Energy & Telecommunications Cables & Systems Mfr
N.A.I.C.S.: 335929
Martin Hanchard *(Pres & CEO)*

Plant (Domestic):

Prysmian Power Cables & Systems USA, LLC (4)
569 Hwy 28 By Pass, Abbeville, SC 29620
Tel.: (864) 366-1220
Web Site: http://www.us.prysmian.com
Energy Cable Mfr
N.A.I.C.S.: 335931

Division (Domestic):

Prysmian Power Cables & Systems-High Voltage Systems & Installation Division (4)
5 Hollywood Ct, South Plainfield, NJ 07080
Tel.: (908) 791-2828
Web Site: http://www.prysmianusa.com
Sales Range: $300-349.9 Million
Emp.: 1,144
Energy Cables & Systems Distr & Installation Services
N.A.I.C.S.: 237130

Subsidiary (Non-US):

Prysmian Power Cables & Systems Australia Pty. Limited (2)
1 Heathcote Road, Liverpool, 2170, NSW, Australia
Tel.: (61) 1300300304
Web Site: http://www.prysmiangroup.com
Energy & Telecommunications Cables & Systems Distr
N.A.I.C.S.: 335929

Subsidiary (Non-US):

Prysmian Power Cables & Systems New Zealand Ltd. (2)
30 Binsted Road, New Lynn, Auckland, 600, New Zealand
Tel.: (64) 98273109
Web Site: http://www.prysmiancable.co.nz
Sales Range: $25-49.9 Million
Emp.: 30
Fiber Optic Cable Mfr
N.A.I.C.S.: 335921
Mark Beckham *(Gen Mgr)*

Subsidiary (Domestic):

Prysmian PowerLink S.r.l. (2)
Viale Sarca 222, Milan, 20126, Italy
Tel.: (39) 0264491
Fiber Optic Cable Mfr
N.A.I.C.S.: 335921

Prysmian Cavi e Sistemi Telecom S.r.l. (1)
Viale Sarca 222, 20126, Milan, Italy
Tel.: (39) 02 6449 1
Electric Wiring Supplies Distr
N.A.I.C.S.: 423610

Subsidiary (US):

Prysmian Communications Cables & Systems USA, LLC (2)
700 Industrial Dr, Lexington, SC 29072-3741
Tel.: (803) 951-4800
Web Site: http://www.prysmianusa.com
Fiber Optics & Communications Cables Mfr & Distr
N.A.I.C.S.: 335921

Subsidiary (Non-US):

Prysmian Telecom Cables & Systems Australia Pty Ltd. (2)
1 Heathcote Rd, Liverpool, 2170, NSW, Australia
Tel.: (61) 1300300304
Web Site: https://www.prysmiancable.com.au
Fiber Optic Cable Mfr
N.A.I.C.S.: 335921

Prysmian Electronics S.r.l. (1)
Viale Sarca 222, 20126, Milan, Italy
Tel.: (39) 0264491
Web Site: https://pry-cam.com
Transmission & Power Generation Services
N.A.I.C.S.: 221118

Prysmian Group Denmark A/S (1)
Roskildevej 22, 2620, Albertslund, Denmark
Tel.: (45) 60392700
Web Site: https://dk.prysmian.com
Multimedia Cable Mfr & Whslr
N.A.I.C.S.: 335929

Prysmian Group Finland Oy (1)
PL 13, 02401, Pikkala, Finland
Tel.: (358) 105661
Web Site: https://fi.prysmian.com
N.A.I.C.S.: 335921

Prysmian Group Norge AS (1)
PB 369 Bragernes, 3001, Drammen, Norway
Tel.: (47) 32249000
Web Site: https://no.prysmian.com
Telecommunication Cable Mfr
N.A.I.C.S.: 335921

Prysmian Group Sverige AB (1)
Vallgatan 5, 57141, Nassjo, Sweden
Tel.: (46) 380554000
Web Site: https://se.prysmian.com
Telecommunication Cable Mfr
N.A.I.C.S.: 335921

Prysmian Hong Kong Holding Ltd. (1)
Fl 15 Rm 1511 Lu Plaza 2 Wing Yip Street, Kwun Tong, Kowloon, China (Hong Kong)
Tel.: (852) 28278308
Sales Range: $50-74.9 Million
Emp.: 14
Investment Management Service
N.A.I.C.S.: 523999
Alvin Wong *(Mgr-Sls)*

Prysmian Kabel und Systeme GmbH (1)
Alt-Moabit 91D, 10559, Berlin, Germany
Tel.: (49) 30367540
Web Site: https://de.prysmian.com
Sales Range: $75-99.9 Million
Energy & Telecommunications Cables & Systems for Mfr & Distr
N.A.I.C.S.: 335929

Prysmian Kabely S.r.o. (1)
Trebicska 777/99, 594 01, Velke Mezirici, Czech Republic
Tel.: (420) 566501511
Web Site: https://cz.prysmian.com
N.A.I.C.S.: 335921

Prysmian Kabler og Systmer AS (1)
PO Box 1384, Ski, Norway
Tel.: (47) 64 915713
Energy & Telecommunications Cables & Systems Distr
N.A.I.C.S.: 335929

Prysmian Kablo s.r.o (1)
Trnavska cesta 50B, 821 02, Bratislava, Slovakia
Tel.: (421) 249491212
Web Site: https://sk.prysmian.com
Sales Range: $25-49.9 Million
Emp.: 50
Energy & Telecommunications Cables & Systems Distr
N.A.I.C.S.: 335929

Prysmian MKM Magyar Kabel Muvek Kft (1)
Neumann J U 1/E, H-1117, Budapest, Hungary
Tel.: (36) 13822222
Web Site: https://hu.prysmian.com
Sales Range: $200-249.9 Million
Energy & Telecommunications Cables & Systems Distr
N.A.I.C.S.: 335929

Prysmian OEKW GmbH (1)
Lemboeckgasse 47a, 1230, Vienna, Austria
Tel.: (43) 186677500
Web Site: http://at.prysmiangroup.com
Sales Range: $50-74.9 Million
Energy & Telecommunications Cables & Systems Distr
N.A.I.C.S.: 335929

Prysmian Tianjin Cables Co. Ltd. (1)
Tel.: (86) 2227539679
Sales Range: $100-124.9 Million
Emp.: 300
Energy & Telecommunications Cables & Systems Distr
N.A.I.C.S.: 335929

Prysmian Treasury S.r.l. (1)
Viale Sarca 222, Milan, 20126, Italy
Tel.: (39) 0264421
Fiber Optic Cable Mfr
N.A.I.C.S.: 335929

Prysmian Wuxi Cable Co. Ltd. (1)
No 54-56 Xinan Rd Taihu Town, Binhu District, Wuxi, 214125, Jiangsu, China
Tel.: (86) 51085180316
Sales Range: $50-74.9 Million
Emp.: 21
Telecommunication Cable Mfr
N.A.I.C.S.: 332618

Sindutch Cable Manufacturer Sdn. Bhd. (1)
38 Jalan Industri 11 Alor Gajah Industrial Estate, 78000, Alor Gajah, Melaka, Malaysia
Tel.: (60) 65563833
Web Site: http://www.draka.com.my
Sales Range: $10-24.9 Million
Emp.: 80
Cable Mfr
N.A.I.C.S.: 335929

Singapore Cables Manufacturers Pte. Ltd. (1)
No 20 Jurong Port Road, Jurong, 619094, Singapore
Tel.: (65) 62650707
Web Site: http://www.prysmiangroup.com
Sales Range: $25-49.9 Million
Emp.: 100
N.A.I.C.S.: 334220

Sociedade Produtora de Fibras Opticas S.A. (1)
Pirelli 1 100 Bloco C, Sorocaba, 18103-085, Brazil
Tel.: (55) 1532359000
Sales Range: $25-49.9 Million
Emp.: 51
Fiber Optic Cable Mfr
N.A.I.C.S.: 335921

Suzhou Draka Cable Co. Ltd. (1)
No 88 Kangyuan Road Xiangcheng Economic Development Zone, 215131, Suzhou, China
Tel.: (86) 51265789888
Web Site: http://www.draka.com.cn
Sales Range: $75-99.9 Million
Emp.: 300
Cable Mfr
N.A.I.C.S.: 335929

Turk Prysmian Kablo Ve Sistemleri A.S. (1)
Omerbey Mah Bursa Asfalti Cad No 51 Mudanya, 16941, Bursa, Turkiye
Tel.: (90) 2242703000
Web Site: https://tr.prysmian.com
Energy & Telecommunications Cables & Systems
N.A.I.C.S.: 335929

Voltimum Brasil (1)
Av Das Nacoes Unidas 18605, Sao Paulo, 04753-100, Brazil
Tel.: (55) 1121655448
Web Site: http://www.voltimum-interactive.com
Electrical Equipment Installation Services
N.A.I.C.S.: 238210

Voltimum GmbH (1)
Bergheimer Strasse 147, 69115, Heidelberg, Germany
Tel.: (49) 6221589870
Web Site: http://www.voltimum.de
Electrical Equipment Installation Services
N.A.I.C.S.: 238210

Voltimum Portugal (1)
Estrada Da Alagoa 96, Carcavelos, 2775-716, Cascais, Portugal
Tel.: (351) 214 548 800
Web Site: http://www.voltimum.com
Electrical Equipment Installation Services
N.A.I.C.S.: 238210

Yangtze Optical Fibre & Cable Joint Stock Limited Company (1)
No 9 Optics Valley Avenue, Wuhan, 430073, China
Tel.: (86) 2768789088
Web Site: http://www.yofc.com
Rev.: $1,259,622,143
Assets: $2,429,236,476
Liabilities: $991,280,957
Net Worth: $1,437,955,519
Earnings: $83,297,213
Emp.: 7,000
Fiscal Year-end: 12/31/2020
Fiber Optic Cable Mfr
N.A.I.C.S.: 335921
Frank Franciscus Dorjee *(Exec Dir)*

PRZEDSIEBIORSTWO HANDLU ZAGRANICZNEGO BALTONA S.A.
Ul Dzialkowa 115, 02-234, Warsaw, Poland
Tel.: (48) 22 519 20 00
Web Site: http://www.baltona.pl
Duty Free Retail Store Operator
N.A.I.C.S.: 459999
Piotr Kazimierski *(Chm-Mgmt Bd)*

PRZEDSIEBIORSTWO HYDRAULIKI SILOWEJ HYDROTOR S.A.
ul Chojnicka 72, 89-500, Tuchola, Poland
Tel.: (48) 523363600
Web Site: https://hydrotor.pl
Year Founded: 1991
HDR—(WAR)
Rev.: $31,948,425
Assets: $46,512,957
Liabilities: $17,024,644
Net Worth: $29,488,313
Earnings: ($572,917)
Fiscal Year-end: 12/31/23
Gear Pumps Mfr
N.A.I.C.S.: 333914

Subsidiaries:

Agromet Zehs Luban S.A. (1)
Ul Esperantystow 2, Luban, 59-800, Warsaw, Poland
Tel.: (48) 757222081
Web Site: https://www.zehs.com.pl
Agricultural Machinery Mfr
N.A.I.C.S.: 333111

PRZEDSIEBIORSTWO PRODUKCYJNO HANDLOWE KOMPAP S.A.
56 Parkowa Street, 86-130, Laskowice, Poland
Tel.: (48) 525108800

PL

PRZEDSIEBIORSTWO PRODUKCYJNO HANDLOWE KOMPAP S.A.

Przedsiebiorstwo Produkcyjno Handlowe Kompap S.A.—(Continued)

Web Site: https://www.kompap.pl
Year Founded: 1989
KMP—(WAR)
Rev.: $7,300,305
Assets: $8,466,972
Liabilities: $1,278,455
Net Worth: $7,188,516
Earnings: $424,035
Fiscal Year-end: 12/31/23
Commercial Printing Services
N.A.I.C.S.: 323111
Marek Gluchowski *(Chm-Supervisory Bd)*

Subsidiaries:

BZGraf S.A. (1)
Aleja 1000-lecia PP 2, 15-111, Bialystok, Poland
Tel.: (48) 856752906
Web Site: http://www.bzgraf.pl
Printing Services
N.A.I.C.S.: 323113

Ozgraf S.A. (1)
ul Towarowa 2, 10-417, Olsztyn, Poland
Tel.: (48) 895334380
Web Site: http://www.ozgraf.com.pl
Printing Services
N.A.I.C.S.: 323113
Miroslaw Jachemek *(Production Mgr)*

PRZEDSIEBIORSTWO PRZEMYSLU SPOZYWCZEGO PEPEES S.A.

ul Poznanska 121, 18-402, Lomza, Poland
Tel.: (48) 862155878
Web Site: https://www.pepees.pl
PPS—(WAR)
Rev.: $56,457,825
Assets: $96,161,839
Liabilities: $50,354,929
Net Worth: $45,806,910
Earnings: $931,911
Fiscal Year-end: 12/31/23
Potato Starch Mfr
N.A.I.C.S.: 111211
Wojciech Faszczewski *(Chm-Mgmt Bd & Pres)*

Subsidiaries:

CHP Energia Sp z o.o. (1)
Wojny Wawrzynce 1, Szepietowo, 18-210, Bialystok, Poland
Tel.: (48) 732876121
Web Site: http://www.chpenergia.pl
Biomass Electric Power Generation Services
N.A.I.C.S.: 221117

PPZ Bronislaw S.A. (1)
Bronislaw 41, Strzelno, 88-320, Inowroclaw, Poland
Tel.: (48) 523189390
Web Site: http://www.ppzbronislaw.com.pl
Potato Production Services
N.A.I.C.S.: 111211

ZPZ Lublin Sp. z o.o. (1)
ul Betonowa 9, 20-402, Lublin, Poland
Tel.: (48) 815327071
Web Site: http://www.zpzlublin.eu
Potato Farming Services
N.A.I.C.S.: 111211

PS GROUP HOLDINGS LTD

9 Tampines Industrial Drive 01-03, Singapore, 528543, Singapore
Tel.: (65) 6747 7080
Web Site: http://www.psfasteners.com
Rev.: $8,103,875
Assets: $11,126,068
Liabilities: $3,037,876
Net Worth: $8,088,193
Earnings: $46,973
Emp.: 27
Fiscal Year-end: 12/31/18
Fastener Importer & Exporter

N.A.I.C.S.: 423510

PS INTERNATIONAL GROUP LTD.

Un. 1002, 10/f, Join-in Hang Sing Ctr., #2-16 Kwai Fung Crescent, Kwai Chung, Hong Kong, F4 00000, China (Hong Kong)
Tel.: (852) 27543320   Ky
Web Site: https://psi-groups.com
Year Founded: 1993
PSIG—(NASDAQ)
Integrated Freight & Logistics
N.A.I.C.S.: 488510
Hok Wai Ko *(CEO)*

Subsidiaries:

AIB Acquisition Corporation (1)
875 3rd Ave Ste M204A, New York, NY 10022
Tel.: (212) 380-8128
Web Site: https://www.aibspac.com
Rev.: $1,413,075
Assets: $88,637,755
Liabilities: $91,716,281
Net Worth: ($3,078,526)
Earnings: $588,411
Emp.: 2
Fiscal Year-end: 12/31/2022
Investment Services
N.A.I.C.S.: 523999
Eric Chen *(CEO)*

PS IT INFRASTRUCTURE & SERVICES LTD.

Office no 308 B2B Agarwal Centre 3rd Floor Near Malad Industrial Estat, Kanchpada Malad West, Mumbai, 400064, Maharashtra, India
Tel.: (91) 2269400303
Web Site: https://www.psitinfrastructure.co.in
Year Founded: 1982
Rev.: $28,100,374
Assets: $8,868,641
Liabilities: $151,814
Net Worth: $8,716,827
Earnings: ($31,505)
Fiscal Year-end: 03/31/18
Investment Services
N.A.I.C.S.: 523999
Kawarlal Kanhaiyalal Ojha *(Chm, CEO & Mng Dir)*

PS TEC CO., LTD.

46 Wangsimni-ro, Seongdong-gu, Seoul, 04773, Korea (South)
Tel.: (82) 234081700
Web Site: https://www.pstec.co.kr
Year Founded: 1948
002230—(KRS)
Rev.: $54,438,970
Assets: $119,081,042
Liabilities: $17,412,857
Net Worth: $101,668,185
Earnings: ($3,554,686)
Emp.: 137
Fiscal Year-end: 12/31/22
Electric Power Equipment & Automobile Parts Mfr
N.A.I.C.S.: 334515
Sun-Tae Hwang *(Chm)*

PSA CORPORATION PTE LTD.

460 Alexandra Road, Singapore, 119963, Singapore
Tel.: (65) 62747111
Web Site: http://www.singaporepsa.com
Sales Range: $800-899.9 Million
Emp.: 7,000
Worldwide Integrated Port & Logistics Services
N.A.I.C.S.: 541614
Caroline Lim *(Global Head-HR & Corp Affairs)*

Subsidiaries:

CWT Distribution Ltd. (1)
38 Tankong Penjuru CWT Logistics Hub 1, Singapore, 609039, Singapore
Tel.: (65) 62626888
Web Site: http://www.cwtlimited.com
Sales Range: $25-49.9 Million
Emp.: 400
Warehousing, Distr, Transporation, International Freight Services, Container Freight Stations, Container Depots & Engineering
N.A.I.C.S.: 493110
Lynda Goh *(CFO)*

Subsidiary (Non-US):

MRI TRADING AG (2)
Baarerstrasse 53, Zug, 6304, Switzerland
Tel.: (41) 41 727 2800
Web Site: http://www.mri-trading.com
Commodity Trading
N.A.I.C.S.: 523160
Axel Krueger *(Head-Structured Fin)*

Subsidiary (Domestic):

Sinsenmoh Transportation Pte. Ltd. (2)
32 Tanjung Penjuru, Jurong Town, Singapore, 609028, Singapore
Tel.: (65) 62648488
Sales Range: $1-9.9 Million
Freight Forwarding Services
N.A.I.C.S.: 488510

PSA Marine (Pte) Ltd (1)
70 West Coast Ferry Road, Singapore, 126800, Singapore
Tel.: (65) 67772288
Web Site: http://www.psamarine.com
Marine Engineering Services
N.A.I.C.S.: 541330
Boon Chew Toh *(Sr Mgr-IT)*

PSB INDUSTRIES SA

Route de la bouvarde, Park Nord Immeuble Les Pleiades n21, 74370, Metz, France
Tel.: (33) 450090002   FR
Web Site: http://www.psbindus.com
Year Founded: 1904
PSB—(EUR)
Rev.: $298,100,013
Assets: $307,675,936
Liabilities: $136,933,121
Net Worth: $170,742,814
Earnings: $13,344,252
Emp.: 1,939
Fiscal Year-end: 12/31/19
Packaging & Chemical Mfr
N.A.I.C.S.: 322220
Francois-Xavier Entremont *(Pres & CEO)*

Subsidiaries:

Baikowski International Corporation (1)
6601 Northpark Blvd Ste H, Charlotte, NC 28216-0092
Tel.: (704) 587-7100
Web Site: http://www.baikowski.com
Specialty Chemicals Mfr
N.A.I.C.S.: 325998

Baikowski Malakoff Inc. (1)
1631 W Royall Blvd, Malakoff, TX 75148
Tel.: (903) 489-1910
Sales Range: $25-49.9 Million
Emp.: 30
Alumina Powders Mfr
N.A.I.C.S.: 325180
Tom Lassanske *(Plant Mgr)*

Baikowski SAS (1)
1046 route de, BP 501, Poisy, 74330, Chaumont, France
Tel.: (33) 4 50 22 69 02
Web Site: http://www.baikowski.com
Alumina Powders Mfr
N.A.I.C.S.: 325180

Subsidiary (Domestic):

Baikowski Chimie (2)

INTERNATIONAL PUBLIC

PO Box 501, Annecy, 74339, France **(63.35%)**
Tel.: (33) 450226912
Web Site: http://www.baikowskichimie.com
Sales Range: $1-9.9 Million
Emp.: 100
Fine Mineral Products Mfr
N.A.I.C.S.: 331313
Greg Cousin *(Mgr-Comml)*

Lecot SAS (1)
6 Rue Du Tanay, 74960, Cran-Gevrier, France
Tel.: (33) 4 50 69 36 36
Packaging Products Mfr
N.A.I.C.S.: 322220

Mar-Lee Companies, Inc. (1)
180 Authority Dr, Fitchburg, MA 01420
Tel.: (978) 751-5772
Plastic Bell Mfr
N.A.I.C.S.: 326199

Mar-Lee Mold (1)
55 Marshall St, Leominster, MA 01453
Tel.: (978) 534-8305
Web Site: http://dev.mar-leecompanies.com
Precision Injection Molded Tools
N.A.I.C.S.: 332721

Mar-Lee Packaging and Consumer Products (1)
180 Authority Dr, Fitchburg, MA 01420
Tel.: (978) 343-9600
Injection Molding Machine Mfr
N.A.I.C.S.: 333248

Plastibell SAS (1)
150-400 ZI La Plaine, 01580, Izernore, France
Tel.: (33) 474491346
Web Site: http://www.plastibell.com
Plastic Bell Mfr
N.A.I.C.S.: 326199

Quadpack Industries SA (1)
Plaza Europa 9-11 Planta 11, Catalonia, 08908, L'Hospitalet de Llobregat, 08908, Spain
Tel.: (34) 935322790
Web Site: https://www.quadpack.com
Rev.: $141,958,274
Assets: $119,660,007
Liabilities: $83,784,082
Net Worth: $35,875,924
Earnings: ($1,324,650)
Emp.: 592
Fiscal Year-end: 01/31/2024
Packaging Services
N.A.I.C.S.: 561910

Rose SAS (1)
Zone d'activites les 2B, 01360, Bressolles, France
Tel.: (33) 472251919
Web Site: http://www.standards-de-rose.com
Emp.: 63
Screw Top Product Mfr
N.A.I.C.S.: 332722

Texen Group (1)
ZI Le Pognat, BP77, 01460, Brion, France
Tel.: (33) 474767160
Web Site: http://www.texen.com
Sales Range: $200-249.9 Million
Emp.: 1,500
Injection Molding for the Cosmetics & Perfumes Industries
N.A.I.C.S.: 326199
Oliver Salaun *(Pres-Interim)*

Subsidiary (Domestic):

C.C.M. SAS (2)
ZI Ouest Sur Champagne, 01580, Izernore, France **(80%)**
Tel.: (33) 4 7449 1430
Sales Range: $25-49.9 Million
Emp.: 120
Injection Molding for the Cosmetics & Perfumes Industries
N.A.I.C.S.: 326199
Bruno Cornet *(Dir Gen)*

CMSI Conception et Moulage au Service de l'Industrie SAS (2)
Parc d'Activites Bourg Nord, PO Box 10, 01340, Attignat, France **(80%)**
Tel.: (33) 474259900

AND PRIVATE COMPANIES

Sales Range: $50-74.9 Million
Emp.: 135
Injection Molding for the Cosmetics & Perfumes Industries
N.A.I.C.S.: 326199
Frederic Perdrix *(Mgr-Comml)*

Subsidiary (Non-US):

Ceica Plasticos de Mexico (2)
Av Santa Rosa Lote 8 Manzana 16, Parque Industrial De Lerma, 52000, Lerma, Mexico
Tel.: (52) 7282822541
Sales Range: $50-74.9 Million
Injection Molding for the Cosmetics & Perfumes Industries
N.A.I.C.S.: 326199

Subsidiary (Domestic):

Mayet Pierre de Bresse (2)
1 Ave De Beauregard, 71270, Pierre-de-Bresse, France (80%)
Tel.: (33) 385768910
Injection Molding for Cosmetics & Perfumes Mfr
N.A.I.C.S.: 326199
Bernard Jean Luc *(Gen Mgr)*

Rose SA (2)
Zone D Activites Les 2 B, 01360, Bressolles, France (100%)
Tel.: (33) 472251919
Web Site: http://www.standards-de-rose.com
Sales Range: $25-49.9 Million
Emp.: 50
Injection Molding for the Cosmetics & Perfumes Industries
N.A.I.C.S.: 326199

Sr2p (2)
ZI Le Pognat, PO Box 62, 01460, Bron, France (80%)
Tel.: (33) 474767820
Web Site: http://www.healthsolutionsint.com
Sales Range: $25-49.9 Million
Emp.: 100
Injection Molding for the Cosmetics & Perfumes Industries
N.A.I.C.S.: 326199

Texen - Ceica (2)
ZI Le Pognat, BP77, 01460, Brion, France
Tel.: (33) 474767160
Web Site: http://www.texen.com
Injection Molding for the Cosmetics & Perfumes Industries
N.A.I.C.S.: 326199

Texen Services (1)
Zone Industrielle Du Pognat, Brion, 01460, France
Tel.: (33) 474767160
Sales Range: $25-49.9 Million
Emp.: 70
Packaging Products Mfr
N.A.I.C.S.: 322220
Tesla Tristram *(Mng Dir)*

PSC CORPORATION LTD.
348 Jalan Boon Lay, Singapore, 619529, Singapore
Tel.: (65) 62684822
Web Site:
  https://www.psccorporation.com
Year Founded: 1974
DM0—(SES)
Rev.: $365,174,581
Assets: $432,742,558
Liabilities: $126,709,839
Net Worth: $306,032,720
Earnings: $22,602,439
Emp.: 848
Fiscal Year-end: 12/31/23
Investment Management Services; Consumer Products Mfr
N.A.I.C.S.: 541611
John Seow Phun Chen *(Deputy Chm)*

Subsidiaries:

Alliance Entertainment Singapore Pte. Ltd (1)
Asia Media Centre 39 MacTaggart Road, Singapore, 368084, Singapore
Tel.: (65) 68410939
Web Site: http://www.all-entertainment.com.sg
Entertainment Video Distr
N.A.I.C.S.: 423990

Fortune Food Manufacturing Pte Ltd (1)
348 Jalan Boon Lay, Singapore, 619529, Singapore
Tel.: (65) 6 266 4188
Web Site: https://www.fortunefood.com.sg
Emp.: 25
Food Products Mfr
N.A.I.C.S.: 311520

Fortune Food Marketing Pte Ltd (1)
PSC 348 Jalan Boon Lay, Singapore, 619529, Singapore
Tel.: (65) 62664188
Web Site: http://www.topseller.com.sg
Emp.: 30
Fresh Food Retailer
N.A.I.C.S.: 424480

Health Solutions (Malaysia) Sdn. Bhd (1)
Suite 11 1 & 11 2 Level 6 1 Menara Genesis 33 Jalan Sultan Ismail, Kuala Lumpur, 50250, Malaysia
Tel.: (60) 321424143
Web Site: http://www.healthsolutionsint.com
Sales Range: $25-49.9 Million
Emp.: 30
Health Care Consultancy Services
N.A.I.C.S.: 541611

Subsidiary (Domestic):

Health Solutions Services Sdn. Bhd (2)
Level 6 1 Ste 11-01 Menara Genesis 33 Jalan Sultan Ismail, Kuala Lumpur, 50250, Malaysia
Tel.: (60) 321424143
Web Site: http://www.healthsolutionsint.com
Sales Range: $10-24.9 Million
Emp.: 30
Hospital Management Services
N.A.I.C.S.: 561110
Dato'Seri Siew *(Exec Dir)*

InnoForm Media Pte Ltd (1)
39 MacTaggart Road Asia Media Centre, 368084, Singapore, Singapore
Tel.: (65) 68481212
Sales Range: $25-49.9 Million
Emp.: 100
Entertainment Video Distr
N.A.I.C.S.: 423990

Subsidiary (Domestic):

InnoForm Entertainment Pte. Ltd (2)
39 Mactaggart Road Asia Media Centre, Singapore, 368084, Singapore
Tel.: (65) 68468118
Entertainment Video Distr
N.A.I.C.S.: 423990
Steven Tan *(Mng Dir)*

Subsidiary (Non-US):

InnoForm Media (HK) Limited (2)
Flat B 8 F Sing Tao News Corp Building 3 Tung Wong Road, Shau Kei Wan, Hong Kong, China (Hong Kong)
Tel.: (852) 34223852
Web Site: http://www.innokidz.com.hk
Educational Videos Disk Distr
N.A.I.C.S.: 423990

InnoForm Media (M) Sdn. Bhd (2)
Ste 10-08 10th fl Wisma Zelan No1 Jln Tasik Permaisuri 2, Bandar Tun Razak, Kuala Lumpur, 56000, Bandar Tun Razak, Malaysia
Tel.: (60) 391711866
Web Site: http://www.innoform.com.my
Emp.: 25
Children Entertainment Videos Distr
N.A.I.C.S.: 423990

PSC Investment Pte Ltd (1)
PSC 348 Jalan Boon Lay, Singapore, 619529, Singapore
Tel.: (65) 62684822
Consumer Products Distr
N.A.I.C.S.: 423990

Socma Trading (M) Sendirian Berhad (1)
Lot 805 Jalan Subang 5 Taman Perindustrian Subang, 47600, Subang Jaya, Selangor, Malaysia
Tel.: (60) 356233633
Web Site: http://www.socma.com.my
Grocery Product Distr
N.A.I.C.S.: 424490
Karen Vanden Driesen *(Sr Mgr-Natl Sls)*

Tat Seng Packaging Group Ltd. (1)
28 Senoko Drive, Singapore, 758214, Singapore
Tel.: (65) 68919030
Web Site: https://www.tspg.sg
Rev.: $249,339,756
Assets: $228,290,054
Liabilities: $82,221,969
Net Worth: $146,068,085
Earnings: $15,702,004
Emp.: 1,081
Fiscal Year-end: 12/31/2022
Corrugated Paper Packaging Products Mfr
N.A.I.C.S.: 322211
John Seow Phun Chen *(Deputy Chm)*

Subsidiary (Non-US):

Hefei Dansun Packaging Co., Ltd (2)
No 105 Zipeng Road, Economic and Technological Development Zone, Hefei, 230601, Anhui, China
Tel.: (86) 55163810166
Packaging Products Mfr & Distr
N.A.I.C.S.: 322211

Nantong Hengcheng Paper Industry Co., Ltd. (2)
Xin Sheng Gang Zong He Industrial Park, Shizhuang, Rugao, 226531, Jiangsu, China
Tel.: (86) 513 6816 3612
Packaging Products Mfr
N.A.I.C.S.: 322211

Nantong Tat Seng Packaging Co., Ltd. (2)
Ting Nan Heng Road, Xiting, Nantong, 226301, Jiangsu, China
Tel.: (86) 513 8653 8888
Packaging Products Mfr
N.A.I.C.S.: 322211

Tat Seng Packaging (Suzhou) Co., Ltd (2)
No 88 Wendu Road, Wangting Town Xiangcheng District, Suzhou, 215155, Jiangsu, China (100%)
Tel.: (86) 5126 538 0538
Web Site: https://www.tatseng-packaging.com.cn
Paper Packaging Products Mfr & Whslr
N.A.I.C.S.: 322299

Tianjin Dansun Packaging Co., Ltd. (2)
257 Jing Yi Road Airport Economic Zone, Tianjin, 300303, China (67%)
Tel.: (86) 22 5809 7080
Web Site: http://www.tspg.sg
Packaging Products Mfr
N.A.I.C.S.: 322211

Subsidiary (Domestic):

United Packaging Industries Pte. Ltd (2)
28 Senoko Drive, Singapore, 758214, Singapore
Tel.: (65) 6 862 0123
Web Site: https://www.upi.sg
Packaging Products Mfr
N.A.I.C.S.: 326112

Tipex Trading Pte Ltd (1)
348 Jalan Boon Lay, Singapore, 619529, Singapore
Tel.: (65) 62687600
Web Site: http://www.tipex.com.sg
Emp.: 300
Paper Products Mfr & Distr
N.A.I.C.S.: 322120

Tips Industry (M) Sdn. Bhd (1)
MLO 1101 Jalan Air Hitam Batu 31 3/4 Bukit Batu, 81000, Kulai, Johor, Malaysia
Tel.: (60) 76563758
Emp.: 250
Consumer Paper Products Mfr
N.A.I.C.S.: 322120

PSC INSURANCE GROUP LIMITED

PSC INSURANCE GROUP LIMITED
96 Wellington Parade, Melbourne, 3002, VIC, Australia
Tel.: (61) 385938333   AU
Web Site:
  http://www.pscinsurancegroup.com
PSI—(ASX)
Rev.: $172,077,080
Assets: $681,038,708
Liabilities: $415,625,129
Net Worth: $265,413,579
Earnings: $31,202,322
Fiscal Year-end: 06/30/21
Insurance Brokerage Services
N.A.I.C.S.: 524210
Paul Robert Dwyer *(Deputy Chm)*

Subsidiaries:

AWIB Pty. Ltd. (1)
40 Argyle Street, Traralgon, VIC, Australia
Tel.: (61) 351775500
Web Site: https://awib.com.au
Insurance Brokerage Services
N.A.I.C.S.: 524210

Abaco Insurance Brokers Limited (1)
1 Lewis Court Grove Park, Enderby, LE19 1SD, Leicester, United Kingdom
Tel.: (44) 116 281 5960
Web Site: https://www.abacoinsurance.co.uk
Insurance Brokerage Services
N.A.I.C.S.: 524210

Absolute Insurance Brokers Limited (1)
Airport House Purley Way, Croydon, CR0 0XZ, Surrey, United Kingdom
Tel.: (44) 208 915 1022
Web Site:
  https://www.absoluteinsurancebrokers.com
Insurance Brokerage Services
N.A.I.C.S.: 524210

Alsford Page & Gems Limited (1)
75 King William Street, London, EC4N 7BE, United Kingdom
Tel.: (44) 207 456 0500
Web Site: https://www.apg.net
Insurance Brokerage Services
N.A.I.C.S.: 524210
David Pratt *(CEO)*

Assured Cover Pty Ltd (1)
Level 12 189 Kent Street, Sydney, 2000, NSW, Australia
Tel.: (61) 414521519
Web Site: http://www.assuredcover.com.au
Insurance Consulting Services
N.A.I.C.S.: 524298

Breeze Underwriting Limited (1)
42-43 Broomfield House Lanswoodpark Business Centre Broomfield Rd, Elmstead Market, Colchester, CO7 7FD, United Kingdom
Tel.: (44) 207 645 4600
Web Site: https://www.breezeuw.co.uk
Underwriting Services
N.A.I.C.S.: 524126
Ian Hamilton *(Dir-Underwriting)*

Breeze Underwriting Pty Ltd (1)
Level 1 68 Clarke Street, Southbank, 3006, VIC, Australia
Tel.: (61) 130 055 6826
Web Site: https://www.breezeuw.com.au
Insurance Brokerage Services
N.A.I.C.S.: 524210
Shane Upton *(Mng Principal)*

Certus Life Pty Ltd (1)
2/47-59 Ashmore Road, Bundall, 4217, QLD, Australia
Tel.: (61) 75 539 0088
Web Site: https://www.certuslife.com.au
Fire Insurance Services
N.A.I.C.S.: 524113

Charter Gilman Insurance Holdings Limited (1)
3rd Floor Prosperity Millennia Plaza 663 King's Road, North Point, China (Hong Kong)
Tel.: (852) 2 866 9311
Web Site: https://www.charter-gilman.com.hk

PSC INSURANCE GROUP LIMITED

PSC Insurance Group Limited—(Continued)
Insurance Brokerage Services
N.A.I.C.S.: 524210
Hei Wong *(Mng Dir)*

Connect Life Pty Ltd (1)
Level 1 96 Wellington Parade, Melbourne, 3002, VIC, Australia
Tel.: (61) 39 862 6528
Web Site: https://www.connectlife.net.au
Fire Insurance Services
N.A.I.C.S.: 524113
Joanne Rowling *(Founder)*

Easy Broking Online Ltd. (1)
42-43 Broomfield House Lanswood Park Business Centre Broomfied Road, Market Elmstead, London, CO7 7FD, United Kingdom
Tel.: (44) 207 283 5324
Web Site: https://www.easybroking.net
Underwriting Insurance Services
N.A.I.C.S.: 524126

Ensurance UK Limited (1)
3rd Floor 24 Chiswell Street, London, EC1Y 4YX, United Kingdom
Tel.: (44) 2039417700
Web Site: http://www.ensuranceuk.com
Construction Insurance Services
N.A.I.C.S.: 524298
Tim James *(CEO)*

Fenchurch Insurance Risk Management Limited (1)
24 Parklands Great Linford, Milton Keynes, MK14 5DZ, Buckinghamshire, United Kingdom
Tel.: (44) 2081332112
Web Site: http://www.fenchurchins.com
Insurance Brokerage Services
N.A.I.C.S.: 524210
Simon Lonnergan *(Dir-Broking)*

JHR Corporate Risk Pty Ltd (1)
Level 3 10 William St, Perth, 6000, WA, Australia
Tel.: (61) 89 328 5399
Web Site: https://www.jhr.com.au
Insurance Brokerage Services
N.A.I.C.S.: 524210
Tim Drinkwater *(Acct Exec)*

Medisure Indemnity Australia Pty Ltd (1)
Level 8 145 Eagle Street, Brisbane, 4000, QLD, Australia
Tel.: (61) 73 184 5300
Web Site: https://www.medisure.com.au
Insurance Brokerage Services
N.A.I.C.S.: 524210

PSC Coastwide Newcastle Pty Ltd (1)
Suite 3 Level 2 426 King Street, Newcastle, 2300, NSW, Australia
Tel.: (61) 249259800
Web Site: https://www.pscinsurance.com.au
Insurance Brokerage Services
N.A.I.C.S.: 524210

PSC Connect Life NZ Ltd. (1)
Level 3 139 Quay Street, Auckland, New Zealand
Tel.: (64) 9 523 5822
Web Site: https://www.pscconnectlife.co.nz
Insurance Brokerage Services
N.A.I.C.S.: 524210

PSC Connect NZ Ltd (1)
Level 3 139 Quay Street, Auckland, New Zealand
Tel.: (64) 9 358 1186
Web Site: https://www.pscconnect.co.nz
Insurance Brokerage Services
N.A.I.C.S.: 524210

PSC Insurance Brokers (Brisbane) Pty Ltd (1)
Corporate House Level 3/52 McDougall Street, Milton, Brisbane, 4064, QLD, Australia
Tel.: (61) 732293294
Web Site: https://www.pscinsurance.com.au
Insurance Brokerage Services
N.A.I.C.S.: 524210

PSC Insurance Brokers (Darwin) Pty Ltd (1)
Level 1 14 Shepherd Street, Darwin, 0800, NT, Australia
Tel.: (61) 889817777
Web Site: https://www.pscinsurance.com.au
Insurance Brokerage Services
N.A.I.C.S.: 524210

PSC Insurance Brokers (Wagga) Pty Ltd (1)
37 Trail Street, Wagga Wagga, 2650, NSW, Australia
Tel.: (61) 269218174
Web Site: https://www.pscinsurance.com.au
Insurance Brokerage Services
N.A.I.C.S.: 524210

PSC Insurance Brokers Adelaide Pty Ltd (1)
Level 1 267 Melbourne Street North, Adelaide, 5006, SA, Australia
Tel.: (61) 884183900
Web Site: https://www.pscinsurance.com.au
Insurance Brokerage Services
N.A.I.C.S.: 524210

PSC McKenna Hampton Insurance Brokers Pty Ltd (1)
Level 3 10 William Street, Perth, 6000, WA, Australia
Tel.: (61) 861420000
Web Site: http://www.mcham.com.au
Insurance Brokerage Services
N.A.I.C.S.: 524210
Rod Tonzing *(Mng Principal & Reg Mgr)*

PSC National Franchise Insurance Brokers Pty Ltd (1)
10 William St, Perth, 6000, WA, Australia
Tel.: (61) 1800776747
Web Site: http://www.mynfib.com.au
Insurance Brokerage Services
N.A.I.C.S.: 524210

PSC Reliance Franchise Partners Pty Ltd (1)
96 Wellington Parade, East Melbourne, Melbourne, 3002, VIC, Australia
Tel.: (61) 1300403386
Web Site: http://www.reliancepartners.com.au
Insurance Brokerage Services
N.A.I.C.S.: 524210
David Wyner *(Mng Dir)*

Paragon Brokers (Bermuda) Ltd. (1)
LOM Building 27 Reid Street, Hamilton, HM 11, Bermuda
Tel.: (441) 292 0875
Insurance Brokerage Services
N.A.I.C.S.: 524210
Spenser Lee *(Partner)*

Paragon International Insurance Brokers Ltd. (1)
140 Leadenhall Street, London, EC3V 4QT, United Kingdom
Tel.: (44) 207 280 8200
Web Site: https://www.paragonbrokers.com
Insurance Brokerage Services
N.A.I.C.S.: 524210
James Kalbassi *(Co-CEO, Co-Founder & Partner)*

Reliance Workplace Solutions Pty Ltd (1)
10 William Street, Perth, 6056, WA, Australia
Tel.: (61) 893827888
Insurance Brokerage Services
N.A.I.C.S.: 524210

Trust Insurance Services Limited (1)
Trust House Scirocco Close Moulton Park, Northampton, NN3 6AP, United Kingdom
Tel.: (44) 160 449 2644
Web Site: https://www.trustinsurance.co.uk
Insurance Brokerage Services
N.A.I.C.S.: 524210

UK Facilities Limited (1)
Barnett House, Bolton, BL3 2RR, United Kingdom
Tel.: (44) 1204394080
Insurance Brokerage Services
N.A.I.C.S.: 524210

PSC TAIF
80 Puskina Str, 420015, Kazan, Tatarstan, Russia
Tel.: (7) 8432779402
Web Site: http://en.taif.ru
Sales Range: $5-14.9 Billion
Emp.: 43,000
Holding Company
N.A.I.C.S.: 551112
Rustem N. Sulteev *(Deputy Gen Dir-Production & Sls & First Deputy Gen Dir)*

Subsidiaries:

NMU-3 (1)
POB 188, Nizhnekamsk, 423570, Russia
Tel.: (7) 8555 37 78 13
Building Construction Services
N.A.I.C.S.: 236220

Nizhnekamskneftekhim OAO (1)
Office 129 23 Sobolekovskaya Street, Nizhnekamsk Municipal District Republic of Tatarstan, 423574, Nizhnekamsk, Russia
Tel.: (7) 8555377009
Web Site: http://www.nknh.ru
Rev.: $2,887,108,700
Assets: $3,472,756,740
Liabilities: $1,120,793,050
Net Worth: $2,351,963,690
Earnings: $387,587,770
Emp.: 30,000
Fiscal Year-end: 12/31/2019
Chemical & Petrochemical Producer
N.A.I.C.S.: 325110
Ruslan A. Shigabutdinov *(Chm)*

Subsidiary (Non-US):

Nizhex Scandinavia Ltd Oy (2)
Wavulinintie 10, Helsinki, 00210, Finland (50%)
Tel.: (358) 96824700
Web Site: http://www.nizhex.fi
Sales Range: $25-49.9 Million
Emp.: 12
Petroleum & Petroleum Products Whslr
N.A.I.C.S.: 424720
Anneli Matikainen *(Controller)*

PJSC Kazanorgsintez (1)
101 Belomorskaya Str, 420051, Kazan, Russia
Tel.: (7) 8435339809
Web Site: http://www.kazanorgsintez.ru
Chemical Products Mfr
N.A.I.C.S.: 325411
Rinat T. Zaripov *(Deputy Gen Dir-Production)*

TAIF-NK (1)
Nizhnekamsk - 11, PO Box 20, Republic of Tatarstan, 423570, Kazan, Russia
Tel.: (7) 8555381616
Web Site: http://en.taifnk.ru
Oil & Gas Exploration Services
N.A.I.C.S.: 211120
Alla V. Evstafeva *(Deputy Gen Dir-Economy & Fin)*

Taif-Invest OOO (1)
6 Ul vishnevskogo, Republic of Tatarstan, 420043, Kazan, Russia
Tel.: (7) 8432363342
Web Site: http://www.taif-invest.ru
Financial Advisory Services
N.A.I.C.S.: 523940

PSD GROUP PLC
62 Queen Street, London, EC4R 1EB, United Kingdom
Tel.: (44) 2079709700
Web Site: http://www.psdgroup.com
Sales Range: $50-74.9 Million
Emp.: 286
Recruitment Services
N.A.I.C.S.: 541612
Francesca Robinson *(Chm)*

Subsidiaries:

Hoggett Bowers (1)
62 Queen Street, London, EC4R 1EB, United Kingdom
Tel.: (44) 2079649100
Web Site: http://www.hoggett-bowers.com
Sales Range: $25-49.9 Million
Emp.: 25
Executive Search Service
N.A.I.C.S.: 541612

Karen Wilson *(CEO)*

PSD Group GmbH (1)
Sendlinger strasse 7, Munich, 80333, Germany
Tel.: (49) 891898570
Web Site: http://www.munichpsdgroup.com
Emp.: 2
Other Management Consulting Services
N.A.I.C.S.: 541618
Oliver Tonner *(Mng Dir)*

PSD Group Limited (1)
5107 Central Plaza No 18 Harbour Road, Wanchai, China (Hong Kong)
Tel.: (852) 2531 2200
Web Site: http://www.psdgroup.com.hk
Recruitment Consulting Services
N.A.I.C.S.: 541612
Francesca Robinson *(Chm)*

PSD Group SA (1)
94 rue de Provence, 75009, Paris, France
Tel.: (33) 155279000
Web Site: http://www.psdgroup.com
Sales Range: $25-49.9 Million
Emp.: 10
Other Management Consulting Services
N.A.I.C.S.: 541618

PSG GROUP LIMITED
2nd Floor Ou Kollege 35 Church Street, Stellenbosch, 7600, South Africa
Tel.: (27) 218879602   ZA
Web Site:
    https://www.psggroup.co.za
Year Founded: 1995
PSG—(JSE)
Rev.: $960,262,240
Assets: $7,528,265,360
Liabilities: $5,328,808,240
Net Worth: $2,199,457,120
Earnings: $238,820,960
Emp.: 21,915
Fiscal Year-end: 02/29/20
Investment Holding Company
N.A.I.C.S.: 551112
Wynand L. Greeff *(CFO)*

Subsidiaries:

HeyCarter (Pty.) Ltd. (1)
65 Corlett Dr, Birnam, Johannesburg, South Africa
Tel.: (27) 100452682
Web Site: https://www.heycarter.co.za
Car Dealership Operator
N.A.I.C.S.: 441110

Optimi Holdings (Pty.) Ltd. (1)
Irene Link Office Park Building B 7 Impala Avenue, Doringkloof, Centurion, Gauteng, South Africa
Tel.: (27) 874052233
Web Site: https://www.optimi.co.za
Accessible Training & Learning Solution Services
N.A.I.C.S.: 611710

Ou Kollege Beleggings Ltd (1)
35 Kerk St 1st Ou College, Stellenbosch, 7600, Western Cape, South Africa
Tel.: (27) 218879602
Web Site: http://www.psggroup.co.za
Sales Range: $50-74.9 Million
Emp.: 40
Insurance Agencies
N.A.I.C.S.: 524126
Piet Mouton *(CEO)*

PSG Financial Services Limited (1)
1 Old College Building 35 Church Street, Stellenbosch, 7600, Western Cape, South Africa
Tel.: (27) 218832250
Web Site: http://www.psg.co.za
Rev.: $312,101,726
Assets: $6,026,103,800
Liabilities: $5,753,093,636
Net Worth: $273,010,165
Earnings: $59,028,981
Emp.: 3,199
Fiscal Year-end: 04/29/2024
Financial Planning Services
N.A.I.C.S.: 523940
Francois Gouws *(CEO)*

AND PRIVATE COMPANIES

Subsidiary (Domestic):

PSG Corporate Services (Pty) Ltd (2)
1st Fl O College Bldg 35 Kerk St, Stellenbosch, 7600, Western Cape, South Africa
Tel.: (27) 218879602
Web Site: http://www.psggroup.co.za
Sales Range: $10-24.9 Million
Emp.: 40
Business Management Services
N.A.I.C.S.: 541611
Wynand Greeff *(Dir-Fin & Gen Mgr)*

PSG Konsult Limited (1)
4th Floor The Edge 3 Howick Close, Tyger Waterfront, Bellville, 7530, South Africa (61.7%)
Tel.: (27) 219187800
Web Site: http://www.psg.co.za
Rev.: $101,323,683
Assets: $4,660,854,783
Liabilities: $4,411,011,946
Net Worth: $249,842,837
Earnings: $54,291,131
Emp.: 3,074
Fiscal Year-end: 02/28/2023
Asset & Wealth Management, Financial Planning & Consulting Services
N.A.I.C.S.: 523940
Willem Theron *(Co-Founder)*

PSI SOFTWARE SE
Dircksenstrasse 42-44, 10178, Berlin, Germany
Tel.: (49) 3028010
Web Site: https://www.psi.de
Year Founded: 1969
PSAN—(MUN)
Rev.: $297,923,474
Assets: $312,560,790
Liabilities: $189,225,395
Net Worth: $123,335,395
Earnings: $353,238
Emp.: 2,281
Fiscal Year-end: 12/31/23
Software Publisher
N.A.I.C.S.: 513210
Harald Schrimpf *(CEO)*

Subsidiaries:

MOVEO Software GmbH (1)
Berliner Strasse 74, 14467, Potsdam, Germany
Tel.: (49) 331909730
Web Site: http://www.moveo-software.com
Computer Software Services
N.A.I.C.S.: 541519

Nentec GmbH (1)
Greschbachstrasse 12, Karlsruhe, 76229, Germany
Tel.: (49) 721942490
Web Site: http://www.nentec.de
Sales Range: $25-49.9 Million
Emp.: 18
Telecommunication Network Equipments Mfr
N.A.I.C.S.: 238210

OOO PSI (1)
Bolschoj Savvinkij Pereulok 12 str 16, 119435, Moscow, Russia
Tel.: (7) 4992727779
Sales Range: $25-49.9 Million
Emp.: 11
Software System Distr
N.A.I.C.S.: 423430

PSI AG (1)
Santisstrasse 2, 9500, Wil, Switzerland
Tel.: (41) 448325700
Software Services
N.A.I.C.S.: 541519

PSI AG Schweiz (1)
Santisstrasse 2, Postfach, 9500, Wil, Switzerland
Tel.: (41) 448325700
Web Site: http://www.psi-automotive-industry.de
Solutions For Production Industry & Service Companies
N.A.I.C.S.: 541720

PSI Automotive & Industry Austria GmbH (1)
Technologiering 13 17, 4060, Leonding, Austria
Tel.: (43) 7326706700
Computer Software Services
N.A.I.C.S.: 541519

PSI Busing und Buchwald GmbH (1)
Boschweg 6, 63741, Aschaffenburg, Germany
Tel.: (49) 60213660
Web Site: http://www.psi-bub.de
Energy Management Services
N.A.I.C.S.: 333414
Michael Wolf *(Mng Dir)*

PSI Energy Markets GmbH (1)
Kriegerstrasse 1E, 30161, Hannover, Germany
Tel.: (49) 5116101890
Web Site: https://www.psi-energymarkets.de
Energy Distribution Services
N.A.I.C.S.: 221122

PSI FLS Fuzzy Logik & Neuro Systeme GmbH (1)
Joseph-von-Fraunhofer-Str 20, 44227, Dortmund, Germany
Tel.: (49) 2319700921
Web Site: https://www.fuzzy.de
Information Technology Services
N.A.I.C.S.: 519290

PSI Information Technology Co., Ltd. (1)
1212 South Building Raycom InfoTech Park Tower C KeXueYuanNanLu No 2, Haidian District, Beijing, 100190, China
Tel.: (86) 1062800698
Web Site: http://www.psiproduction.com
Sales Range: $25-49.9 Million
Production Management Services
N.A.I.C.S.: 541613

PSI Logistics GmbH (1)
Dircksenstrasse 42-44, 10178, Berlin, Germany
Tel.: (49) 3028012850
Web Site: https://www.psilogistics.com
Sales Range: $25-49.9 Million
Emp.: 220
Logistic Services
N.A.I.C.S.: 541614
Giovanni Prestifilippo *(Mng Dir & Dir-Transportation Grp)*

PSI Metals Austria GmbH (1)
Bahnhofguertel 77 79, 8020, Graz, Austria
Tel.: (43) 31626974710
Information Technology Services
N.A.I.C.S.: 519290

PSI Metals Belgium NV (1)
Researchdreef 65, 1070, Brussels, Belgium
Tel.: (32) 25585260
Information Technology Services
N.A.I.C.S.: 519290

PSI Metals Brazil Ltda. (1)
Av Presidente Wilson 231 9 andar-parte, 20030-021, Rio de Janeiro, Brazil
Tel.: (55) 2135785520
Information Technology Services
N.A.I.C.S.: 519290

PSI Metals GmbH (1)
Parsevalstrasse 7a, 40468, Dusseldorf, Germany
Tel.: (49) 21160219271
Web Site: https://www.psimetals.de
Sales Range: $25-49.9 Million
Standard Software Metals Mfr
N.A.I.C.S.: 513210
Thomas Quinet *(Mng Dir)*

PSI Metals Non Ferrous GmbH (1)
Campus Boulevard 57, 52074, Aachen, Germany
Tel.: (49) 2419278800
Information Technology Services
N.A.I.C.S.: 519290
Gunther Schober *(Sls Mgr)*

PSI Metals North America Inc. (1)
Park West Two Ste 600 2000 Cliff Mine Rd, Pittsburgh, PA 15275
Tel.: (412) 747-9900
Information Technology Services
N.A.I.C.S.: 519290
Mike Redilla *(Mgr-Div)*

PSI Metals UK Ltd. (1)
Suite 9 Building 6, Croxley Park, Watford, WD18 8YH, United Kingdom
Tel.: (44) 1923652000
Information Technology Services
N.A.I.C.S.: 519290

PSI Mines & Roads GmbH (1)
Weichertstrasse 5, 63741, Aschaffenburg, Germany
Tel.: (49) 60213660
Web Site: http://www.psi-minesandroads.de
Emp.: 2,000
Software Services
N.A.I.C.S.: 541519
Elmar Jaeker *(Mng Dir)*

PSI Neplan AG (1)
Oberwachtstrasse 2, Zurich, CH-8700, Kusnacht, Switzerland
Tel.: (41) 449143666
Web Site: https://www.neplan.ch
Heating & Cooling System Mfr
N.A.I.C.S.: 333415

PSI Polska Sp. z o.o. (1)
ul Towarowa 37, 61-896, Poznan, Poland
Tel.: (48) 616556550
Web Site: http://www.psi.pl
Emp.: 330
Information Technology Services
N.A.I.C.S.: 519290

PSI Production GmbH (1)
Dircksenstrabe 42-44, 10178, Berlin, Germany
Tel.: (49) 3028010
Web Site: http://www.psi-production.de
Sales Range: $10-24.9 Million
Emp.: 500
Production Management Services
N.A.I.C.S.: 561110

PSI Transcom GmbH (1)
Dircksenstrasse 42-44, 10178, Berlin, Germany
Tel.: (49) 3028011610
Web Site: http://www.psitrans.de
Sales Range: $25-49.9 Million
Transport Related Telecommunication Services
N.A.I.C.S.: 517810
Torsten Vogel *(Mng Dir)*

PSI inControl Sdn. Bhd. (1)
No 15 Jalan BRP 9/1D Perusahaan Bukit Rahman Putra, 47000, Sungai Buloh, Selangor, Malaysia
Tel.: (60) 361578050
Web Site: http://www.psi-incontrol.com
Sales Range: $50-74.9 Million
Emp.: 200
Automation System Mfr
N.A.I.C.S.: 334512
Azhar Abd Aziz *(COO)*

PSIAG Scandinavia AB (1)
Horst Heimberg Ostra Torggatan 2C, 65224, Karlstad, Sweden
Tel.: (46) 4960213660
Oil & Energy Distribution Services
N.A.I.C.S.: 519290

PSIPENTA Software Systems GmbH (1)
Dircksenstr 42-44, 10178, Berlin, Germany
Tel.: (49) 3028012000
Web Site: http://www.psipenta.de
Sales Range: $150-199.9 Million
Emp.: 500
Software Products Developers
N.A.I.C.S.: 541511

Time-Steps AG (1)
Bergstrasse 9, 8910, Zurich, Switzerland
Tel.: (41) 447761430
Web Site: https://www.time-steps.com
Computer Software Services
N.A.I.C.S.: 541519

inControl Tech Co. Ltd (1)
1023 TPS Building Pattanakarn Road, Suan Luang Sub-district Suan Luang District, Bangkok, 10250, Thailand
Tel.: (66) 27178118
Sales Range: $25-49.9 Million
Automation Systems
N.A.I.C.S.: 541512

PSINAPTIC INC.
583 Woodpark Cr Southwest, Calgary, T2W 2S1, AB, Canada
Tel.: (403) 775-2236   AB
Year Founded: 1999
Sales Range: Less than $1 Million
Software Products & Services
N.A.I.C.S.: 513210
Aaron Dagan *(Pres & CEO)*

PSK, INC.
75 Geumto-ro, Sujeong-gu, Seongnam, 13453, Gyeonggi-do, Korea (South)
Tel.: (82) 316608703   KS
Web Site: https://www.psk-inc.com
Year Founded: 1990
031980—(KRS)
Rev.: $54,028,913
Assets: $243,776,996
Liabilities: $34,332,185
Net Worth: $209,444,811
Earnings: $30,252,463
Emp.: 91
Fiscal Year-end: 12/31/22
Semiconductor & LCD Equipment Mfr
N.A.I.C.S.: 334413

Subsidiaries:

Psk Inc (1)
F23-07 New Columbus Plaza No 282 Changjiang N Road, Binhu, Wuxi, 214000, Jiangsu Sheng, China
Tel.: (86) 51085222744
Web Site: http://www.psk-inc.com
Semiconductor Product Mfr
N.A.I.C.S.: 334413

Psk Tech America Inc (1)
1006 E Yager Ln Ste 108, Austin, TX 78753
Tel.: (512) 507-7589
Semiconductor Devices Mfr
N.A.I.C.S.: 334413
Kook Jeon Jin *(Gen Mgr)*

PSL HOLDINGS LIMITED
37 Jalan Pemimpin 07-16 Mapex, Singapore, 577177, Singapore
Tel.: (65) 63637622   SG
Year Founded: 1997
BLL—(SES)
Rev.: $1,233,998
Assets: $26,041,436
Liabilities: $6,728,069
Net Worth: $19,313,367
Earnings: ($948,659)
Fiscal Year-end: 12/31/19
Investment Holding Company; Engineering Services, Construction & Marine Logistics
N.A.I.C.S.: 551112
Stephen Leong *(Vice Chm)*

Subsidiaries:

Resource Hardware and Trading Pte Ltd (1)
18 Boon Lay Way Unit 09-96 TradeHub 21, Singapore, 609966, Singapore
Tel.: (65) 63637622
Sales Range: $25-49.9 Million
Emp.: 26
Hardware Whslr
N.A.I.C.S.: 423710

PSP PROJECTS LIMITED
PSP House Opp Celesta Courtyard Opposite lane of Vikram Nagar Colony, Iscon- Ambali Road, Ahmedabad, 380 058, India
Tel.: (91) 7926936200   In
Web Site: https://www.pspprojects.com
Year Founded: 2008
540544—(BOM)
Rev.: $235,334,440
Assets: $211,665,751
Liabilities: $115,629,243
Net Worth: $96,036,509
Earnings: ($323,722)
Emp.: 1,836

PSP PROJECTS LIMITED

PSP Projects Limited—(Continued)
Fiscal Year-end: 03/31/23
Civil Engineering Services
N.A.I.C.S.: 541330
Prahaladbhai S. Patel *(Chm, CEO & Mng Dir)*

PSP SWISS PROPERTY LTD.
Kolinplatz 2, CH-6300, Zug, Switzerland
Tel.: (41) 417280404   CH
Web Site: https://www.psp.info
Year Founded: 1999
PSPSF—(OTCIQ)
Rev.: $228,863,799
Assets: $11,631,685,337
Liabilities: $5,426,881,412
Net Worth: $6,204,803,925
Earnings: $246,725,696
Emp.: 90
Fiscal Year-end: 12/31/23
Real Estate Holding Company
N.A.I.C.S.: 551112
Luciano Gabriel *(Chm)*

Subsidiaries:

PSP Group Services Ltd. (1)
South African Airways 353, 8038, Zurich, Switzerland
Tel.: (41) 44 625 59 00
Sales Range: $25-49.9 Million
Emp.: 60
Corporate Services
N.A.I.C.S.: 561499
Luciano Gabriel *(CEO)*

PSP Management Ltd. (1)
Seestrasse 353, 8038, Zurich, Switzerland
Tel.: (41) 446255757
Web Site: http://www.psp.info
Sales Range: $50-74.9 Million
Real Estate Management Services
N.A.I.C.S.: 531312

PSP Properties Ltd. (1)
Brandschenkestrasse 150, 8027, Zurich, Switzerland   (100%)
Tel.: (41) 446255757
Web Site: http://www.psp.info
Sales Range: $75-99.9 Million
Real Estate Agents & Brokers
N.A.I.C.S.: 531210

PSP Real Estate Ltd. (1)
Brandschenkestrasse 150, 8027, Zurich, Switzerland   (100%)
Tel.: (41) 446255757
Web Site: http://www.psp.info
Sales Range: $75-99.9 Million
Emp.: 80
Real Estate Agents & Brokers
N.A.I.C.S.: 531210

PSV COMPANY S.A.
8-10 Calea Grivitei Ave Section 1, 010731, Bucharest, Romania
Tel.: (40) 212089325
Year Founded: 1997
Sales Range: $1-4.9 Billion
Emp.: 3,000
Oil & Gas Machinery, Equipment & Services
N.A.I.C.S.: 333132
Sorin Mihai *(Pres)*

PSV HOLDINGS LIMITED
Stoneridge Office Park 8 Greenstone Place, Building C 2nd Floor Greenstone Hill, Johannesburg, 1609, South Africa
Tel.: (27) 860778778   ZA
Web Site:
   http://www.psvholdings.com
PSV—(JSE)
Rev.: $16,444,389
Assets: $7,137,895
Liabilities: $5,264,820
Net Worth: $1,873,075
Earnings: ($1,751,169)
Emp.: 59
Fiscal Year-end: 02/28/19

Industrial Holding Company
N.A.I.C.S.: 551112
Anthony de la Rue *(Chm)*

Subsidiaries:

Engineered Linings (Pty) Limited (1)
8 Station Road Montague Gardens, Milnerton, Cape Town, 7441, Western Cape, South Africa
Tel.: (27) 215512430
Web Site: http://www.englining.co.za
Emp.: 20
Geosynthetic Liners Distribution & Installation Services
N.A.I.C.S.: 237990

Groupline Projects (Pty) Limited (1)
17 Grader Road Spartan Kempton park, Garden View Jetpark, 1620, Johannesburg, Gauteng, South Africa
Tel.: (27) 113874600
Web Site: http://www.groupline.co.za
Sales Range: $25-49.9 Million
Emp.: 25
Construction Engineering Services
N.A.I.C.S.: 541330

Rand Air & Gas Installations (Pty) Limited (1)
Cnr North Reef and Serenade Roads Henville Ext, Elandsfontein, Gauteng, South Africa
Tel.: (27) 118221333
Web Site: http://www.ragi.co.za
Sales Range: $25-49.9 Million
Emp.: 14
Liquefied Gas Storage Equipment Mfr & Distr
N.A.I.C.S.: 332420
Alan Sparrow *(Mng Dir)*

PSYCHED WELLNESS LTD.
3000 - 77 King Street West, Toronto, M5K 1G8, ON, Canada
Tel.: (416) 364-7256
Web Site: https://www.psyched-wellness.com
PSYCF—(OTCQB)
Rev.: $11,166
Assets: $2,589,959
Liabilities: $154,948
Net Worth: $2,435,012
Earnings: ($3,360,365)
Fiscal Year-end: 11/30/22
Metal Exploration Services
N.A.I.C.S.: 213114
Del Mahabadi *(Mktg Mgr-Intl)*

PSYENCE BIOMEDICAL LTD.
121 Richmond Street West Penthouse Suite 1300, Toronto, M5H 2K1, ON, Canada
Tel.: (416) 477-1708   Ca
Web Site: https://www.psyence.com
Year Founded: 2020
PBM—(NASDAQ)
Rev.: $879,344
Assets: $1,132,159
Liabilities: $12,104,699
Net Worth: ($10,972,540)
Earnings: ($51,159,048)
Emp.: 10
Fiscal Year-end: 03/31/24
Biotechnology Research & Development Services
N.A.I.C.S.: 541714

PSYKEY, INC.
190 Norseman St Suite 100, Toronto, M8Z 2R4, ON, Canada
Web Site: https://psykeyworld.com
CEOS—(OTCIQ)
Rev.: $19,000
Assets: $574,000
Liabilities: $1,389,000
Net Worth: $814,000
Earnings: ($497,000)
Emp.: 4
Fiscal Year-end: 12/31/22
Software Development Services
N.A.I.C.S.: 541511

Robert Gardiner *(Pres)*

PT ABM INVESTAMA TBK.
Gedung TMT 1 18th Fl Suite 1802 Jl Cilandak KKO No 1, Jakarta, 12560, Indonesia
Tel.: (62) 2129976767   Id
Web Site: https://www.abm-investama.com
Year Founded: 1970
ABMM—(INDO)
Rev.: $1,492,998,856
Assets: $2,156,687,895
Liabilities: $1,397,760,928
Net Worth: $758,926,967
Earnings: $315,623,893
Emp.: 114
Fiscal Year-end: 12/31/23
Business Management Consulting Services
N.A.I.C.S.: 541618
Adrian Erlangga Sjamsul *(COO)*

Subsidiaries:

P.T. Multi Harapan Utama (1)
TCC Batavia Tower One 41st Floor JI KH Mas Mansyur No 126, Karet Tengsin Tanah Abang, Jakarta Pusat, 10220, Indonesia
Tel.: (62) 2122513676
Web Site: https://www.mhucoal.com
Coal Mining Services
N.A.I.C.S.: 532412

PT Cipta Krida Bahari (1)
Gedung TMT 1 7th Floor Suite 701 Jl Cilandak KKO No 1, Jakarta, 12560, Indonesia
Tel.: (62) 212 997 6777
Web Site: https://www.ckb.co.id
Logistic Services
N.A.I.C.S.: 541614
Iman Sjafei *(Pres)*

Subsidiary (Domestic):

PT Alfa Trans Raya (2)
Gedung TMT 1 Lantai 8 Jl Cilandak KKO No 1, Jakarta, 12560, Indonesia
Tel.: (62) 2129976673
Mining Services
N.A.I.C.S.: 213114

PT Baruna Dirga Dharma (2)
TMT 1 Building 8th Floor Suite 801 Jl Cilandak KKO No 1, South Jakarta, 12560, Indonesia
Tel.: (62) 2129976673
Web Site: http://www.bdd.co.id
Mining Services
N.A.I.C.S.: 213114

PT Dianta Daya Embara (2)
Gedung TMT 2 2nd Floor Jl Cilandak KKO No 1, Jakarta, 12560, Indonesia
Tel.: (62) 2129976673
Web Site: https://dde.co.id
Mining Services
N.A.I.C.S.: 213114
Rully Fahreza *(Ops Mgr)*

PT Pelabuhan Buana Reja (2)
Gedung TMT 1 Lantai 9 Suite 1802 Jl Cilandak KKO No 1, Jakarta, 12560, Indonesia
Tel.: (62) 2129976777
Fuel Procuring Services
N.A.I.C.S.: 221112

PT Cipta Kridatama (1)
Gedung TMT 2 3rd Floor Jl Cilandak KKO No 1, Jakarta, 12560, Indonesia
Tel.: (62) 2129976866
Web Site: https://www.ciptakridatama.co.id
Mining Services
N.A.I.C.S.: 213114
Yonathan Sarira *(Mgr-QSHE)*

PT Mifa Bersaudara (1)
Jl Meulabouh-Tapak Tuan Km 8 Desa Peunaga Cut Ujong, Meurebo, Jakarta Barat, 23615, Aceh, Indonesia
Tel.: (62) 212 997 6756
Web Site: https://www.mifacoal.co.id
Mining Services
N.A.I.C.S.: 213114

PT Prima Wiguna Parama (1)
Gedung TMT 1 18th Floor Suite 1802 Jl

INTERNATIONAL PUBLIC

Cilandak KKO No 1, Jakarta, 12560, Indonesia
Tel.: (62) 2129976767
Fuel Procuring Services
N.A.I.C.S.: 221112

PT Reswara Minergi Hartama (1)
Gedung TMT 1 9th Fl Suite 901 Jl Cilandak KKO No 1, Jakarta, 12560, Indonesia
Tel.: (62) 212 997 6733
Web Site: https://www.reswara.co.id
Coal Mining Services
N.A.I.C.S.: 213113

Subsidiary (Domestic):

PT Bara Energi Lestari (2)
10th Floor Treasury Tower District 8 - SCBD Lot 28, Jl Jend Sudirman Kav 52 -53 Jakarta Selatan, Jakarta, 12190, Indonesia
Tel.: (62) 2129976733
Web Site: https://belcoal.co.id
Mining Services
N.A.I.C.S.: 213114

PT Sanggar Sarana Baja (1)
Gedung TMT I 5th Floor Suite 501 Jl Cilandak KKO No 1, Jakarta, 12560, Indonesia
Tel.: (62) 2129976830
Web Site: https://www.ptssb.co.id
Construction & Mining Machinery Mfr
N.A.I.C.S.: 333120

PT Sumberdaya Sewatama (1)
Gedung TMT 2 1st Floor Jl Cilandak KKO No 1, Jakarta Selatan, 12560, Indonesia
Tel.: (62) 2129976712
Web Site: http://www.sewatama.com
Electric Power Generation Services
N.A.I.C.S.: 221118

PT ACE HARDWARE INDONESIA TBK.
Gedung Kawan Lama Jalan Puri Kencana No 1 Kembangan, Jakarta, 11610, Indonesia
Tel.: (62) 215822222
Web Site:
   https://www.acehardware.co.id
Year Founded: 1995
ACES—(INDO)
Rev.: $494,314,582
Assets: $503,497,313
Liabilities: $101,752,640
Net Worth: $401,744,672
Earnings: $49,606,133
Emp.: 13,673
Fiscal Year-end: 12/31/23
Commercial & Industrial Products Retailer
N.A.I.C.S.: 444140
Prabowo Widyakrisnadi *(Chm)*

Subsidiaries:

PT Toys Games Indonesia (1)
Gedung Kawan Lama Lt 7 Jl Puri Kencana No 1, Kembangan, Jakarta Barat, Indonesia
Tel.: (62) 2158358155
Web Site: http://www.toyskingdom.co.id
Baby Doll Mfr
N.A.I.C.S.: 339930

PT ACE OLDFIELDS TBK
Jl Raya Cileungsi Jonggol Km 22.5 Mekarsari, Cileungsi, Bogor, Indonesia
Tel.: (62) 218232202
Web Site:
   https://www.aceoldfields.com
KUAS—(INDO)
Rev.: $10,498,246
Assets: $17,167,497
Liabilities: $7,007,317
Net Worth: $10,160,180
Earnings: $617,315
Emp.: 78
Fiscal Year-end: 12/31/23
Painting & Construction Equipment Mfr
N.A.I.C.S.: 333120
Josef Kandiawan *(Pres)*

PT ADARO ENERGY INDONESIA TBK
Menara Karya 23rd floor JL H R Rasuna Said Block X-5 Kav 1-2, Jakarta, 12950, Indonesia
Tel.: (62) 2125533000
Web Site: http://www.adaro.com
Year Founded: 1991
ADRO—(INDO)
Rev.: $6,517,556,000
Assets: $10,472,711,000
Liabilities: $3,063,961,000
Net Worth: $7,408,750,000
Earnings: $1,854,878,000
Emp.: 14,189
Fiscal Year-end: 12/31/23
Coal Mining Services
N.A.I.C.S.: 212114
Ah Hoo Chia *(COO)*

Subsidiaries:

Kestrel Coal Resources Pty. Ltd. (1)
Level 22 10 Eagle Street, Brisbane, 4000, QLD, Australia
Tel.: (61) 73 557 3000
Web Site: https://kestrelcoal.com
Emp.: 600
Coal Mining Services
N.A.I.C.S.: 213113
Peter Smith *(CEO)*

PT Alam Tri Abadi (1)
Menara Karya Building Jl Hr Rasuna Said Kav 1-2 Block X-5, Kuningan, Jakarta, Indonesia
Tel.: (62) 215211265
Coal Mining Services
N.A.I.C.S.: 213113
Garibaldi Thohir *(Pres)*

Subsidiary (Non-US):

Coaltrade Services International Pte Ltd (2)
8 Shenton Way Unit 21-01, Singapore, 068811, Singapore
Tel.: (65) 63232033
Emp.: 20
Coal Distr
N.A.I.C.S.: 423520
Clement Woon *(Mgr)*

Orchard Maritime Logistics Pte Ltd (2)
237 Alexandria Road 06-05, 159929, Singapore, Singapore
Tel.: (65) 63230054
Freight Transportation Services
N.A.I.C.S.: 481212
Pepen Handianto Danuatmadja *(Chm)*

Subsidiary (Domestic):

PT Adaro Indonesia (2)
Menara Karya 22nd Floor Jln H R Rasuna Said Blok X-5 Kav 1-2, Jakarta, 12950, Indonesia
Tel.: (62) 215211265
Web Site: http://www.adaroindonesia.com
Emp.: 1,000
Coal Mining Services
N.A.I.C.S.: 213113
Garibaldi Thohir *(Pres)*

PT Indonesia Bulk Terminal (2)
Jl HR Rasuna Said Blok X-5 Kav 1-2 Menara Karya 22nd Floor, Jakarta, Indonesia
Tel.: (62) 215229250
Web Site: http://www.ptibt.com
Terminal Operation Services
N.A.I.C.S.: 488310

PT Bhakti Energi Persada (1)
Tempo Scan Tower 29th Floor Jalan HR Rasuna Said Kav 3-4, Jakarta, 12950, Indonesia
Tel.: (62) 2125533000
Web Site: http://www.bepcoal.com
Coal Mining Services
N.A.I.C.S.: 213113

PT Bhimasena Power Indonesia (1)
Menara Karya Building 29th Floor Unit F G H Jl HR Rasuna Said, Kav 1-2 Blok X-5, South Jakarta, 12950, Indonesia
Tel.: (62) 218 065 9988
Web Site: https://www.bhimasenapower.co.id
Electricity Supply Services
N.A.I.C.S.: 221122

PT Makmur Sejahtera Wisesa (1)
Menara Karya 18th Floor Jl HR Rasuna Said Blok X5 Kav 1-2, Jakarta, 12950, Indonesia
Tel.: (62) 2125533095
Web Site: http://www.adaro.com
Eletric Power Generation Services
N.A.I.C.S.: 221118

PT ADARO MINERALS INDONESIA TBK
Cyber 2 Tower Lt 34 Jl Rasuna Said Blok X-5 No13 Kel Kuningan Timur, Kec Setiabudi Kota Adm, Jakarta Selatan, 129502, Indonesia
Tel.: (62) 2125533060
Web Site: https://www.adarominerals.id
Year Founded: 2007
ADMR—(INDO)
Rev.: $1,085,961,921
Assets: $1,695,419,616
Liabilities: $657,370,421
Net Worth: $1,038,049,195
Earnings: $440,843,141
Emp.: 387
Fiscal Year-end: 12/31/23
Mining Services
N.A.I.C.S.: 212290
Christian Ariano Rachmat *(Pres)*

PT ADHI KARYA (PERSERO) TBK
South Building Pasar Minggu Highway KM 18, South Jakarta, 12510, Indonesia
Tel.: (62) 217975312
Web Site: https://adhi.co.id
ADHI—(INDO)
Rev.: $1,303,540,193
Assets: $2,629,552,468
Liabilities: $2,030,884,091
Net Worth: $598,668,377
Earnings: $18,824,970
Emp.: 1,458
Fiscal Year-end: 12/31/23
High Rise Building & Bridge Construction Services
N.A.I.C.S.: 236116
Ki Syahgolang Permata *(Sec & Dir-HR & Fin)*

Subsidiaries:

Adhi Multipower Pte. Ltd. (1)
20 Mactaggart Road 07-02, Singapore, Singapore
Tel.: (65) 62851749
Sales Range: $25-49.9 Million
General Trading Services
N.A.I.C.S.: 238990

P.T. Aneka Dharma Persada (1)
Jl Retno Dumilah No 37A Rejowinangun, Kecamatan Kotagede, Yogyakarta, Daerah Istimewa, Indonesia
Tel.: (62) 2744436733
Web Site: https://ptadp.co.id
Water Resources Development & Management Services
N.A.I.C.S.: 924110

P.T. Ciriajasa E C (1)
Komplek Golden Plaza Fatmawati Blok J6 Jl RS Fatmawati No 15, Gandaria selatan, Jakarta Selatan, Indonesia
Tel.: (62) 217947723
Web Site: https://www.ciriajasa-ec.com
Building Consultant Services
N.A.I.C.S.: 531120

P.T. Dumai Tirta Persada (1)
Gedung Kompeten Competent Building Jl Raya Pasar Minggu Km 18, Jakarta, Indonesia
Tel.: (62) 217975312
Drinking Water & Mineral Water Supply Services
N.A.I.C.S.: 523910

P.T. Hutama Karya (1)
HK Tower Jl Letjen MT Haryono Kav 8 Cawang, East Jakarta, Indonesia
Tel.: (62) 218193708
Web Site: https://www.hutamakarya.com
Asphalt & Steel Mfr
N.A.I.C.S.: 332111

P.T. Jalintim Adhi Abipraya (1)
Gedung Harmonis Lantai 3 Harmonis Building 3rd Floor Jl, Raya Pasar Minggu Km 18, Jakarta, Indonesia
Tel.: (62) 217975312
Construction Association Contractor Services
N.A.I.C.S.: 237990

P.T. Nindya Karya (1)
Jl Letjend MT Haryono Kav 22, Jakarta, Indonesia
Tel.: (62) 218093276
Web Site: https://www.nindyakarya.co.id
Construction Engineering Services
N.A.I.C.S.: 541330

PT Adhi Karya (Persero) Tbk - EPC Division (1)
Jl Iskandarsyah I No 8, Kebayoran Baru, Jakarta, 12160, Indonesia
Tel.: (62) 21 7279 6567
Web Site: http://www.adhi.co.id
Commercial Building Construction Services
N.A.I.C.S.: 236220

PT Adhi Karya (Persero) Tbk - International Division (1)
South Building Jl Raya Pasar Minggu Km 18, Jakarta, 12510, Indonesia
Tel.: (62) 21 797 5312
Web Site: http://www.adhi.co.id
Commercial Building Construction Services
N.A.I.C.S.: 236220

PT Adhi Persada Realti (1)
Jl Raya Hankam Exit Toll Jorr KM 37 Tower Arlington Lt G, Gedung Grand Dhika City Jatiwarna, Jakarta, 17113, Indonesia
Tel.: (62) 82653404
Web Site: http://www.adhipersadaproperti.com
Real Estate Development Services
N.A.I.C.S.: 531311

PT ADI SARANA ARMADA TBK
Samudera Kirana Building 6th Floor Jl Yos Sudarso No 88, Jakarta Utara, 14350, Indonesia
Tel.: (62) 2165308811
Web Site: https://assarent.co.id
Year Founded: 2003
ASSA—(INDO)
Rev.: $288,237,639
Assets: $476,386,698
Liabilities: $307,381,889
Net Worth: $169,004,810
Earnings: $1,261,795
Emp.: 1,385
Fiscal Year-end: 12/31/23
Transportation & Logistics; Car Rental Services
N.A.I.C.S.: 488999
Hindra Tanujaya *(Sec, Head-IR Dept & Dir-Fin)*

Subsidiaries:

P.T. Autopedia Sukses Gadai (1)
UG-56 Floor Karet Kuningan, Kuningan City Setiabudi, South Jakarta, Indonesia
Tel.: (62) 87875523572
Car Rental Services
N.A.I.C.S.: 532111

P.T. Autopedia Sukses Lestari Tbk (1)
Lantai UG56 Jl Prof DR Satrio No Kav 18, Kuningan City, Jakarta Selatan, 12940, Indonesia
Tel.: (62) 2150862055
Web Site: https://autopedia.id
Automotive Component Mfr & Distr
N.A.I.C.S.: 336390

P.T. Caroline Karya Teknologi (1)
Jl Tipar Cakung No 8 RT 009 RW 02, Cilincing Sukapura, Jakarta Utara, Indonesia
Tel.: (62) 2175810888
Software Development Services
N.A.I.C.S.: 541519

P.T. Kargo Bersama Teknologi (1)
Jl Kuningan City Mll UG-01B Jalan Prof Dr Satrio Kav 18, South Jakarta, Indonesia
Tel.: (62) 2150683333
Software Development Services
N.A.I.C.S.: 541519

P.T. Krida Gawai Abadi (1)
Mall Building 7th Floor Jalan ProfDr Satrio Kav 18, Kuningan City, South Jakarta, Indonesia
Tel.: (62) 2150603333
Communication Equipment Repair Services
N.A.I.C.S.: 811210

PT Adi Sarana Investindo (1)
Jl Tipar Cakung No 8, Jakarta Utara, Indonesia
Tel.: (62) 214418888
Transportation Services
N.A.I.C.S.: 485999
Jan Bastian Sunarjanto *(CEO)*

PT Adi Sarana Logistik (1)
Jl Tipar Cakung No 8, Jakarta, Indonesia
Tel.: (62) 214 4837277
Freight Transportation Services
N.A.I.C.S.: 488510
Hindra Tanujaya *(Pres)*

PT Duta Mitra Solusindo (1)
Jl Tipar Cakung No 8, Jakarta Utara, Indonesia
Tel.: (62) 214418888
Driver Provision Services
N.A.I.C.S.: 561990
Hindra Tanujaya *(Pres)*

PT JBA Indonesia (1)
Jalan Sosial, No 4 Wijaya Kusuma, Grogol Petamburan, Jakarta Barat, Indonesia
Tel.: (62) 1500369
Web Site: https://www.jba.co.id
Vehicle Distr
N.A.I.C.S.: 423110
Kazuhiro Shioyama *(CEO)*

PT Tri Adi Bersama (1)
Menara Kadin Indonesia Lt 23 Jl HR Rasuna Said Blok X-5 Kav 2-3, Karet Kuningan Setiabudi, Jakarta Selatan, Indonesia
Tel.: (62) 21 527 4323
Transportation Services
N.A.I.C.S.: 485999
Tjoeng Suyanto *(CEO)*

PT AESLER GRUP LNTERNASIONAL
Noble House 36-11 Dr Ide Anak Agung Gde Agung Kav E4 2, No 2 Mega Kuningan, Jakarta Selatan, 12950, Indonesia
Tel.: (62) 2129183111
Web Site: http://www.aeslergroup.com
Year Founded: 2010
RONY—(INDO)
Rev.: $317,169
Assets: $568,438
Liabilities: $260,991
Net Worth: $307,446
Earnings: $6,674
Emp.: 27
Fiscal Year-end: 12/31/23
Architectural Services
N.A.I.C.S.: 541310
Dewi Sustiwi *(Sec)*

PT AGRO BAHARI NUSANTARA TBK
Ruko Shibuya Unit SHC 012-PIK 2 Jl Marina Indah Raya No 1, Teluknaga, Tangerang, 15510, Banten, Indonesia
Tel.: (62) 87881011234
Web Site: https://abn.farm
Year Founded: 2019
UDNG—(INDO)
Rev.: $268,100
Assets: $484,208

PT AGRO BAHARI NUSANTARA TBK

PT Agro Bahari Nusantara Tbk—(Continued)
Liabilities: $54,378
Net Worth: $429,830
Earnings: ($1,111)
Fiscal Year-end: 12/31/22
Seafood Product Distr
N.A.I.C.S.: 424460
Vincent Lukito *(Pres)*

PT AGRO YASA LESTARI
Gedung Gondangdia Lama 25 Lt 3 Jl R P Soeroso No 25, Jakarta, 10330, Indonesia
Tel.: (62) 213918838
Web Site: https://agroyasalestari.com
AYLS—(INDO)
Rev.: $242,833
Assets: $2,990,584
Liabilities: $103,390
Net Worth: $2,887,194
Earnings: ($122,579)
Emp.: 3
Fiscal Year-end: 12/31/23
Construction Materials Distr
N.A.I.C.S.: 423320
Indra Jaya David Pardosi *(Pres)*

PT AIRASIA INDONESIA TBK
AirAsia Redhouse Jl Marsekal Suryadharma No 1 Selapajang Jaya, Neglasari, Tangerang, 15127, Banten, Indonesia
Tel.: (62) 21298508888
Web Site: https://ir.aaid.co.id
Year Founded: 2017
Commercial Air Transportation Services
N.A.I.C.S.: 481219
Indah Permatasari Saugi *(Bd of Dirs & Sec)*

PT AKASHA WIRA INTERNATIONAL TBK
Simatupang Kav 89 RT C1 RW 02, TB Simatupang Kav 88, Jakarta, 12530, Indonesia
Tel.: (62) 2127545000
Web Site: https://www.akashainternational.com
Year Founded: 1985
ADES—(INDO)
Rev.: $99,062,398
Assets: $135,411,719
Liabilities: $23,077,988
Net Worth: $112,333,732
Earnings: $25,703,122
Emp.: 433
Fiscal Year-end: 12/31/23
Water Bottle Mfr
N.A.I.C.S.: 312112
Wihardjo Hadiseputro *(Chm)*

PT AKR CORPORINDO TBK
AKR Tower JL Panjang No 5 Kebon Jeruk, Jakarta Barat, 11530, Indonesia
Tel.: (62) 215311110 Id
Web Site: https://www.akr.co.id
PKCPY—(OTCIQ)
Rev.: $2,733,126,691
Assets: $1,964,735,225
Liabilities: $1,052,785,564
Net Worth: $911,949,661
Earnings: $199,915,822
Emp.: 2,011
Fiscal Year-end: 12/31/23
Petroleum & Chemicals Distr
N.A.I.C.S.: 424720
Haryanto Adikoesoemo *(Chm)*

Subsidiaries:

AKR (Guigang) Transshipment Port Co Ltd (1)
Maoershan, Guigang, 537100, Guangxi, China
Tel.: (86) 7754204372

Port Operation Services
N.A.I.C.S.: 488310

Guangxi (Guigang) AKR Container Port Co Ltd (1)
No 33 Nannping Road, Guigang, 537100, Guangxi, China
Tel.: (86) 7754281373
Web Site: http://www.akrchina.com
Cargo Transportation Services
N.A.I.C.S.: 488320

Khalista (Liuzhou) Chemical Industries Ltd (1)
No 38 Jinglan Road, Liuzhou, 545006, Guangxi, China
Tel.: (86) 7723160960
Web Site: http://www.khalista.com.cn
Chemicals Mfr
N.A.I.C.S.: 325199

P.T. Anugerah Kimia Indonesia (1)
Jalan Panjang No 5 Lantai 21, Kebon Jeruk, Jakarta, 11530, Indonesia
Tel.: (62) 2059366
Web Site: https://pt-anugerah-kimia-indonesia.business.site
Goods & Chemical Whslr
N.A.I.C.S.: 424690

PT AKR Niaga Indonesia (1)
Wisma Akr Jl Panjang No 5, Jakarta, Indonesia
Tel.: (62) 215311110
Chemical Distr
N.A.I.C.S.: 423830

PT AKR Sea Transport (1)
AKR Tower Lt 26 Jl Panjang No 5, Jakarta Barat, 11530, Indonesia
Tel.: (62) 215311145
Domestic Shipping Services
N.A.I.C.S.: 488330

PT Anugerah Krida Retailindo (1)
AKR Tower Lt 25 Jl Panjang No 5, Jakarta Barat, 11530, Indonesia
Tel.: (62) 215311110
Trading Services
N.A.I.C.S.: 522299
Nery Polim *(Pres)*

Subsidiary (Domestic):

PT Anugerah Lubrindo Raya (2)
AKR Tower 26th Floor Jl Panjang No 5, Kebon Jeruk, Jakarta, 11530, Indonesia
Tel.: (62) 215311110
Web Site: https://www.alr.co.id
Chemical Distr
N.A.I.C.S.: 424690

PT Anugrah Karya Raya (1)
AKR Tower Lt 26 Jl Panjang No 5, Jakarta Barat, 11530, Indonesia
Tel.: (62) 215311145
Coal Trading & Mining Services
N.A.I.C.S.: 213113

PT Arjuna Utama Kimia (1)
Jl Rungkut Industri I No 18-22, Surabaya, 60292, East Java, Indonesia
Tel.: (62) 318431646
Web Site: https://www.aruki.co.id
Emp.: 150
Adhesive Mfr & Distr
N.A.I.C.S.: 325520
Surojit Ghosh *(CEO)*

PT Jakarta Tank Terminal (1)
Jalan Timur Raya No 2 Tanjung Priok, Pelindo II Area KOJA - Tanjung Priok, Jakarta Utara, 14310, Indonesia
Tel.: (62) 2143904002
Storage Tank Whslr
N.A.I.C.S.: 424710

PT Terminal Nilam Utara (1)
Jl Nilam Utara No 1 Perak Utara Pabean Cantikan, Surabaya, 60165, Indonesia
Tel.: (62) 319 909 4737
Web Site: https://www.tnu.co.id
Logistic Services
N.A.I.C.S.: 541614

PT Usaha Era Pratama Nusantara (1)
Tel.: (62) 313284727
Logistics Consulting Servies
N.A.I.C.S.: 541614

Subsidiary (Domestic):
PT Berkah Kawasan Manyar Sejahtera (2)
Jl Raya Manyar Km 11, Manyar-Gresik, Surabaya, 61151, East Java, Indonesia
Tel.: (62) 3198540999
Web Site: https://www.jiipe.com
Real Estate Manangement Services
N.A.I.C.S.: 531210

PT AKSARA GLOBAL DEVELOPMENT TBK
Gedung Office 8 Lt 5 Unit F SCBD Lot 28Jl Jend Sudirman Kav 52-53, Banten, 12190, Indonesia
Tel.: (62) 2129333521 Id
Web Site: http://www.agd.co.id
Year Founded: 2003
GAMA—(INDO)
Rev.: $2,818,505
Assets: $98,352,413
Liabilities: $22,159,743
Net Worth: $76,192,670
Earnings: ($926,677)
Emp.: 41
Fiscal Year-end: 12/31/20
Building Construction Services
N.A.I.C.S.: 236116
Denny Nandar Haulian *(Dir)*

PT ALFA ENERGI INVESTAMA TBK
Plaza 5 Pondok Indah Blok D-12 Jl Margaguna Raya RT03/RW11, Gandaria Utara Kebayoran Baru, Jakarta Selatan, Indonesia
Tel.: (62) 217246966
Web Site: https://www.alfacentra.com
Year Founded: 2015
FIRE—(INDO)
Rev.: $17,167,829
Assets: $27,197,698
Liabilities: $13,331,672
Net Worth: $13,866,026
Earnings: ($33,524)
Emp.: 96
Fiscal Year-end: 12/31/23
Oil & Gas Mining Services
N.A.I.C.S.: 213112
Aris Munandar *(Pres)*

PT ALKINDO NARATAMA TBK
Terusan Pasirkoja 273C, Bandung, 40211, Indonesia
Tel.: (62) 226011220
Web Site: https://www.alkindo.co.id
Year Founded: 1989
ALDO—(INDO)
Rev.: $107,313,113
Assets: $113,755,565
Liabilities: $61,158,215
Net Worth: $52,597,350
Earnings: $157,958
Emp.: 165
Fiscal Year-end: 12/31/23
Converted Paper Product Mfr & Distr
N.A.I.C.S.: 322299
Herwanto Sutanto *(Chm)*

Subsidiaries:

PT Alfa Polimer Indonesia (1)
Jl Industri Cimareme II no 5, Padalarang, Bandung, 40553, Indonesia
Tel.: (62) 22 686 6951
Web Site: https://www.alfa-polimer.com
Chemical Products Mfr
N.A.I.C.S.: 325998

PT Eco Paper Indonesia (1)
Kp Padaasih RT 009 RW 004 Padaasih Cibogo, Subang, East Javan, Indonesia
Tel.: (62) 2607426000
Web Site: https://www.ecopaper.co.id
Paper Mfr & Distr
N.A.I.C.S.: 322120

PT ALLO BANK INDONESIA TBK

Menara Bank Mega Lantai 5-6, Jakarta, 12790, Indonesia
Tel.: (62) 79184705
Web Site: http://bankbhi.co.id
BBHI—(INDO)
Rev.: $86,301,544
Assets: $828,013,221
Liabilities: $380,896,394
Net Worth: $447,116,828
Earnings: $28,870,125
Emp.: 223
Fiscal Year-end: 12/31/23
Banking Services
N.A.I.C.S.: 522110
Barlian Halim *(Chm)*

Subsidiaries:

PT BPR Cahaya Wiraputra (1)
Jalan Adisucipto No 71, Sungai Raya Kubu Raya, Kalimantan, Kalimantan Barat, Indonesia
Tel.: (62) 561722101
Web Site: http://www.bprcahayawiraputra.com
Banking Services
N.A.I.C.S.: 522110

PT ALUMINDO LIGHT METAL INDUSTRY TBK
Jalan Kembang Jepun No 38-40, Surabaya, 60162, Indonesia
Tel.: (62) 313530333 Id
Web Site: https://www.alumindo.com
Year Founded: 1978
ALMI—(INDO)
Rev.: $56,737,863
Assets: $57,287,046
Liabilities: $34,413,825
Net Worth: $22,873,221
Earnings: ($10,684,884)
Emp.: 692
Fiscal Year-end: 12/31/23
Flat Rolled Aluminium Mfr
N.A.I.C.S.: 332312
Alim Markus *(Chm)*

Subsidiaries:

PT Alumindo Light Metal Industry Tbk - Gedangan Factory (1)
Desa Sawotratap Gedangan, Sidoarjo, 61254, Indonesia
Tel.: (62) 318531531
Aluminum Mfr
N.A.I.C.S.: 331524

PT AMMAN MINERAL INTERNASIONAL TBK
Menara Karya Lantai 6 Unit A, B, C, H Jl. H.R. Rasuna Said Blok X-5 Kav 1-2, Jakarta, 12950, Indonesia
Tel.: (62) 215799460
Web Site: https://www.amman.co.id
AMMN—(INDO)
Rev.: $2,033,365,000
Assets: $9,097,053,000
Liabilities: $4,461,508,000
Net Worth: $4,635,545,000
Earnings: $258,889,000
Emp.: 1,349
Fiscal Year-end: 12/31/23
Holding Company ; Mining
N.A.I.C.S.: 551112
Alexander Ramlie *(Pres)*

PT ANABATIC TECHNOLOGIES TBK
Graha Anabatic Jl Scientia Boulevard Kav U2 Summarecon, Serpong, Tangerang, Banten, Indonesia
Tel.: (62) 2180636010
Web Site: https://www.anabatic.com
ATIC—(INDO)
Rev.: $662,844,199
Assets: $353,120,851
Liabilities: $327,576,297
Net Worth: $25,544,553
Earnings: $22,244,253

Emp.: 1,585
Fiscal Year-end: 12/31/23
It Consulting
N.A.I.C.S.: 541690
Harry Surjanto Hambali *(Chm)*

Subsidiaries:

Anabatic Technologies Philippines Inc. (1)
Unit 1408 14th Floor The Trade and Financial Tower 7th Avenue Corner, 32nd Bonifacio Global City, Taguig, 1634, Philippines
Tel.: (63) 2 886 7088
Banking Services
N.A.I.C.S.: 522110

Computrade Technology Malaysia Sdn. Bhd. (1)
Unit 7-1 Surian Tower 1 Jalan PJU 7/3, Mutiara Damansara, 47810, Petaling Jaya, Selangor, Malaysia
Tel.: (60) 376613000
Web Site:
https://www.computradetech.com.my
Information Technology Services
N.A.I.C.S.: 541511

Computrade Technology Philippines Inc. (1)
2202C Equitable Bank Tower 8751 Paseo de Roxas, Makati, 1226, Philippines
Tel.: (63) 279567121
Web Site:
https://www.computradetech.com.ph
Information Technology Services
N.A.I.C.S.: 541511

P.T. Egeroo Inovasi Teknologi (1)
Scientia Business ParkTower 2, Lt 2 Jl Boulevard Gading Serpong Blok 0/2, Tangerang, 15810, Banten, Indonesia
Tel.: (62) 2121885359
Web Site: https://egeroo.ai
Software Development Services
N.A.I.C.S.: 541519

P.T. Equine Global (1)
Satrio Tower Building 20th Floors Jl Prof DR Satrio Kav C4 RT7/RW2, Kota Jakarta Selatan DKI Jakarta, Kuningan, 12950, Indonesia
Tel.: (62) 2127883570
Web Site: https://www.equine.co.id
Information Technology Services
N.A.I.C.S.: 541519

P.T. Virtus Technology Indonesia (1)
Centennial Tower 12th Floor Jl Gatot Subroto Kav 24-25, Jakarta, 12930, Indonesia
Tel.: (62) 2180622288
Web Site: https://www.virtusindonesia.com
Information Technology Services
N.A.I.C.S.: 541519

PT Aristi Jasadata (1)
Graha Anabatic 4th Floor Jalan Scientia Boulevard Kav U2, Summarecon Serpong, Tangerang, 15811, Banten, Indonesia
Tel.: (62) 2180636010
Web Site: http://www.aristi.co.id
Information Technology Consulting Services
N.A.I.C.S.: 541512

PT Blue Power Technology (1)
Centennial Tower 12th Floor Jl Jend Subroto Kav 24 - 25, Jakarta, 12930, Indonesia
Tel.: (62) 2180622278
Web Site:
https://www.bluepowertechnology.com
Information Technology Consulting Services
N.A.I.C.S.: 541512
Lugas M. Satrio *(Pres)*

PT Central Data Technology (1)
Centennial Tower 12th Floor Jl Jend Gatot Subroto Kav 24-25 RT 2/RW 2, Kuningan Karet Semanggi Setiabudi, South Jakarta, 12950, Jakarta, Indonesia
Tel.: (62) 218 062 2200
Web Site: https://www.centraldatatech.com
Information Technology Services
N.A.I.C.S.: 541511
Lugas Mondo Satrio *(Pres)*

PT Defender Nusa Semesta (1)
Graha BIP 6th Floor Jalan Jend Gatot Subroto Kav 23, Jakarta, 12930, Indonesia
Tel.: (62) 2129023055
Web Site: https://www.defenxor.com
Information Technology Services
N.A.I.C.S.: 541511

PT IKI Karunia Indonesia (1)
Graha Anabatic 11th Floor Jl Scientia Boulevard Kav U2, Summarecon Serpong Kec Kelapa Dua, Tangerang, 15810, Banten, Indonesia
Tel.: (62) 81211117359
Web Site: https://www.ikimodal.com
Remittance Agent Services
N.A.I.C.S.: 522390

PT Inovasi Informatika Indonesia (1)
Jl Jenderal Gatot Subroto Kav 23 Graha BIP 6th Floor RT 02 RT 2/RW 2, Karet Semanggi Kecamatan Setiabudi, Jakarta Selatan, 12930, Jakarta, Indonesia
Tel.: (62) 2129023393
Web Site: https://www.i-3.co.id
Information Technology Services
N.A.I.C.S.: 541511

PT JEDI Global Teknologi (1)
Centennial Tower 26th Floor Jl Jendral Gatot Subroto kav 24-25, South Jakarta, 12930, Indonesia
Tel.: (62) 2180622255
Web Site: https://www.jedi.id
Emp.: 100
Information Technology Services
N.A.I.C.S.: 541511
Elsa Mayasari *(Pres)*

PT Jaga Nusantara Satu (1)
Jl Scientia Boulevard Kav U2, Summarecon Serpong Curug Sangereng Klp Dua, Tangerang, 15810, Banten, Indonesia
Tel.: (62) 2180636812
Web Site: https://www.jn1.co.id
Security Guard Services
N.A.I.C.S.: 561612
D. Vita Karuna Budhiwati *(Chm)*

PT Karyaputra Suryagemilang (1)
Graha BIP 9th Floor Jl Gatot Subroto Kav 23, Jakarta, 12930, Indonesia
Tel.: (62) 215229910
Web Site: https://kpsg.com
Human Resource Consulting Services
N.A.I.C.S.: 541612
Bennydictus Dharma *(CFO)*

Subsidiary (Domestic):

PT Technetindo Utama (2)
Jl Jatinegara Barat 166, 13330, Jakarta, Indonesia
Tel.: (62) 218194919
Software Distr
N.A.I.C.S.: 423430

PT Mahacitta Teknologi (1)
Graha BIP 6th Floor Jl Jend Gatot Subroto, Jakarta, 12930, Indonesia
Tel.: (62) 215202911
Web Site: http://www.mahacitta.com
Software Development Services
N.A.I.C.S.: 541511

PT Mega Buana Teknologi (1)
Graha BIP 9th Floor Jl Jend Gatot Subroto kav 23, Jakarta, 12930, Indonesia
Tel.: (62) 2180622286
Web Site: https://www.megabuana.id
Information Technology Services
N.A.I.C.S.: 541511

PT Optima Data International (1)
Tel.: (62) 2127883570
Web Site: https://www.optima-data.com
Software Development Services
N.A.I.C.S.: 541511
Johnson Tan *(Dir-Business Development-Information Technology-Operations)*

PT Q2 Technologies (1)
Satrio Tower Building 17th Fl Jl Prof Dr Satrio Kav C4, Mega Kuningan, Jakarta Selatan, 12950, DKI Jakarta, Indonesia
Tel.: (62) 2180636010
Web Site: https://www.q2.co.id
Information Technology Security Services
N.A.I.C.S.: 561621

PT Smartnet Magna Global (1)
Graha BIP 5th Floor Jl Gatot Subroto Kav 23, Karet Semanggi Kecamatan Setiabudi, Jakarta Selatan, 12930, Jakarta, Indonesia
Tel.: (62) 2180622280
Web Site: https://www.magnaglobal.id
Information Technology Security Services
N.A.I.C.S.: 561621

PT XDCI Indonesia (1)
Komplek Ketapang Business Center Blok D2-3 Jl Kyai H Zainul Arifin, RT 8/RW 7 Krukut Kec Taman Sari, Jakarta Barat, 11140, Jakarta, Indonesia
Tel.: (62) 216348020
Web Site: https://xdc-indonesia.com
Information Technology Services
N.A.I.C.S.: 541511

PT Xsis Mitra utama (1)
Satrio Tower Building 25th Floor Jl Prof Dr Satrio Kav 1-4 Blok C4, RT 7/RW 2 Kuningan East Kuningan Setiabudi, South Jakarta, 12950, Jakarta, Indonesia
Tel.: (62) 2127883570
Web Site: https://www.xsis.co.id
Emp.: 500
Information Technology Managed Services
N.A.I.C.S.: 541513
Sutanto Tanuwijaya *(Pres)*

PT. Helios Informatika Nusantara (1)
Centennial Tower 12th Floor Jl Jend Gatot Subroto Kav 24-25, Jakarta, 12930, Indonesia
Tel.: (62) 2180622220
Web Site: https://www.helios.id
Computer Peripheral Equipment Distr
N.A.I.C.S.: 423430
Deddy Sudja *(Pres)*

PT. Niagaprima Paramitra (1)
The City Center Batavia Tower One Lt 33 Jalan K H Mas Mansyur, Kav 126 Karet Tengsin, Jakarta, 10250, Indonesia
Tel.: (62) 2129678261
Web Site: http://www.npp-asia.com
Information Technology Consulting Services
N.A.I.C.S.: 541512
Surya Isjwara *(Pres)*

PT. XDC Indonesia (1)
Komplek Ketapang Business Center Blok D2-D3 Jl KH Zainul Arifin No 20, Jakarta, 11140, Indonesia
Tel.: (62) 216348020
Web Site: http://xdc-indonesia.com
Computer Peripheral Equipment Distr
N.A.I.C.S.: 423430

PT ANCORA INDONESIA RESOURCES TBK.

Equity Tower 41st Floor SuiteB Sudirman Central Business District SCBD, Jl Jend Sudirman Kav 52-53 Lot 9, Jakarta, 12190, Indonesia
Tel.: (62) 2129035011 Id
Web Site: https://www.ancorair.com
Year Founded: 2017
OKAS—(INDO)
Rev.: $185,090,463
Assets: $184,061,742
Liabilities: $142,326,865
Net Worth: $41,734,877
Earnings: $8,378,898
Emp.: 509
Fiscal Year-end: 12/31/23
Ammonium Nitrate Mfr
N.A.I.C.S.: 325180
Rolaw Parlindungan Samosir *(Chm)*

Subsidiaries:

PT Bormindo Nusantara (1)
Equity Tower 41th floor SCBD Lot 9, Jl Jenderal Sudirman Kav 52 - 53, Jakarta, 12190, Indonesia
Tel.: (62) 2129035033
Web Site: https://www.bormindo.com
Oil Field Drilling Services
N.A.I.C.S.: 213111

PT. Multi Nitrotama Kimia (1)
Equity Tower 41th Floor Suite E, Sudirman Central Business District Jl Jend Sudirman Kav 52-53 Lot 9, Jakarta, 12190, Indonesia
Tel.: (62) 2129035022
Web Site: https://mnk.co.id
Sales Range: $150-199.9 Million
Emp.: 500
Explosives Mfr & Mining Support Services
N.A.I.C.S.: 325920

Plant (Domestic):

PT. Multi Nitrotama Kimia - Plant (2)
Kawasan Industri Kujang Cikampek, Jl Jend A Yani Dawuan, Cikampek, 41373, Jawa Barat, Indonesia
Tel.: (62) 264313700
Web Site: http://www.mnk.co.id
Nitric Acid & Ammonium Nitrate Mfr
N.A.I.C.S.: 325998

PT ANDALAN PERKASA ABADI TBK

Jalan Raya Cendrawasih No 88A Kerobokan Kelod, Kabupaten Badung Kuta Utara, Bali, Indonesia
Tel.: (62) 3618499595
Web Site:
https://www.ayanaland.com
Year Founded: 2014
NASA—(INDO)
Rev.: $969,022
Assets: $73,111,602
Liabilities: $3,108,885
Net Worth: $70,002,717
Earnings: $411,735
Emp.: 3
Fiscal Year-end: 12/31/23
Real Estate Development Services
N.A.I.C.S.: 237210

PT ANDALAN SAKTI PRIMAINDO TBK

Sona Topas Tower 5th Floor Jl Jenderal Sudirman No Kav 26 Rw 2, Kuningan Karet Kuningan Kecamatan Setiabudi Kota Daerah Khusus Ibukota, Jakarta, 12920, Indonesia
Tel.: (62) 212506789
Web Site: https://www.ansa-land.com
Year Founded: 2012
ASPI—(INDO)
Rev.: $545,235
Assets: $6,205,496
Liabilities: $1,604,001
Net Worth: $4,601,495
Earnings: ($160,202)
Emp.: 13
Fiscal Year-end: 12/31/23
Real Estate Services
N.A.I.C.S.: 531210
Suwandi Notopradono *(Pres)*

PT ANDIRA AGRO TBK

Meta Epsi Building Jl Mayjen D I Panjaitan Kav 2, Jakarta Timur, 13350, Indonesia
Tel.: (62) 218564955
Web Site:
https://www.andiraagro.com
Year Founded: 1995
ANDI—(INDO)
Rev.: $14,283,058
Assets: $24,556,090
Liabilities: $12,688,997
Net Worth: $11,867,093
Earnings: ($3,633,993)
Emp.: 94
Fiscal Year-end: 12/31/23
Palm Oil Mfr
N.A.I.C.S.: 311225

PT ANEKA GAS INDUSTRI TBK

UGM Samator Pendidikan Building A 5th and 6th Floor, Jl Dr Sahardjo No 83 Manggarai - Tebet, Jakarta Selatan, 12850, Indonesia
Tel.: (62) 2183709111
Web Site: https://samatorgas.com
Year Founded: 1916
AGII—(INDO)
Rev.: $183,309,060
Assets: $506,386,469
Liabilities: $264,280,668
Net Worth: $242,105,801

PT ANEKA GAS INDUSTRI TBK

PT Aneka Gas Industri Tbk—(Continued)
Earnings: $11,027,721
Emp.: 1,492
Fiscal Year-end: 12/31/23
Industrial Gas Mfr
N.A.I.C.S.: 325120
Rachmat Harsono *(Chm)*

PT ANEKA TAMBANG (PERSERO) TBK
Gedung Aneka Tambang Tower A Jl Letjen T B Simatupang No 1, Lingkar Selatan Tanjung Barat, Jakarta, 12530, Indonesia
Tel.: (62) 217891234
Web Site: https://www.antam.com
Year Founded: 1968
ANTM—(INDO)
Rev.: $2,665,637,183
Assets: $2,782,765,305
Liabilities: $758,866,695
Net Worth: $2,023,898,610
Earnings: $199,862,461
Emp.: 2,724
Fiscal Year-end: 12/31/23
Metal Exploration Services
N.A.I.C.S.: 213114

Subsidiaries:

P.T. Emas Antam Indonesia (1)
Gedung Aneka Tambang Tower B Lantai Mz Jalan Letjen TB Simatupang No 1, Kelurahan Tanjung Barat Kecamatan Jagakarsa, Jakarta Selatan, 12530, DKI Jakarta, Indonesia
Tel.: (62) 2131151848
Web Site: https://www.emasantam.id
Precious Metal Distr
N.A.I.C.S.: 423940

PT Feni Haltim (1)
Antam Building 4th Floor Jl TB Simatupang No 1, West Tanjung Jagakarsa, South Jakarta, 12530, Indonesia
Tel.: (62) 217812751
Web Site: http://www.fht-antam.com
Port Services
N.A.I.C.S.: 488310

PT ANTAM (PERSERO) TBK
Gedung Aneka Tambang Jl Letjen TB Simatupang No 1 Lingkar Selatan, Tanjung Barat, Jakarta, 12530, Indonesia
Tel.: (62) 217891234 Id
Web Site: http://www.antam.co.id
Year Founded: 1968
Rev.: $885,753,344
Assets: $2,100,999,142
Liabilities: $806,670,895
Net Worth: $1,294,328,246
Earnings: $9,555,229
Emp.: 2,616
Fiscal Year-end: 12/31/17
Ore Mining
N.A.I.C.S.: 212230
Tri Hartono *(Gen Mgr-Unit Geomin & Tech Dev)*

Subsidiaries:

PT Antam Resourcindo (1)
(99.98%)
Tel.: (62) 217891234
Web Site: http://www.antam.com
Sales Range: $50-74.9 Million
Emp.: 12
Metal Ore Mining
N.A.I.C.S.: 212290

PT Borneo Edo International (1)
Jl Budi Karya No B4, Pontianak, 78121, West Kalimantan, Indonesia
Tel.: (62) 2187784206
Web Site: http://www.borneoedo.com
Sales Range: $50-74.9 Million
Emp.: 9
Bauxite Mining Services
N.A.I.C.S.: 212290

PT Indonesia Coal Resources (1)
Gd Aneka Tambang Lt 2 Jl TB Simatupang No 1, Tanjung Barat, Jakarta, 12530, Indonesia
Tel.: (62) 217891234
Web Site: http://www.icr-antam.com
Sales Range: $50-74.9 Million
Emp.: 14
Coal Mining & Exploration Services
N.A.I.C.S.: 213113

PT ANUGERAH KAGUM KARYA UTAMA TBK
Jl Otista Raya No 60, Jakarta, 13330, Indonesia
Tel.: (62) 217205426 Id
Web Site: http://www.anugerahkagum.com
AKKU—(INDO)
Rev.: $458,141
Assets: $72,639,971
Liabilities: $29,201,135
Net Worth: $43,438,836
Earnings: ($3,575,603)
Emp.: 6
Fiscal Year-end: 12/31/22
Chemical Products Mfr
N.A.I.C.S.: 325180

PT ANUGERAH SPAREPARTS SEJAHTERA TBK
Jln Raya Soekarno-Hatta No 134, Losari Kidul Losari, Cirebon, 45192, West Java, Indonesia
Tel.: (62) 231831035
Web Site: https://www.aegisfilter.co.id
Year Founded: 2015
AEGS—(INDO)
Rev.: $1,964,571
Assets: $4,808,003
Liabilities: $395,815
Net Worth: $4,412,188
Earnings: $62,303
Fiscal Year-end: 12/31/23
Automobile Parts Mfr & Distr
N.A.I.C.S.: 336390
Jeihan Sumawi Putra *(Sec)*

PT ARCHI INDONESIA TBK
Rajawali Place 27th Floor Jl H R Rasuna Said Kav, Setiabudi, South Jakarta, 12950, Indonesia
Tel.: (62) 215761719
Web Site: https://www.archiindonesia.com
Year Founded: 2010
ARCI—(INDO)
Rev.: $249,630,768
Assets: $803,580,181
Liabilities: $540,950,196
Net Worth: $262,629,985
Earnings: $14,759,124
Emp.: 674
Fiscal Year-end: 12/31/23
Mining Services
N.A.I.C.S.: 212220
Kenneth Ronald Kennedy Crichton *(Pres)*

PT ARKADIA DIGITAL MEDIA
Sahid Sudirman Center 19F B-C Jend Sudirman, Karet Tengsin Tanah Abang, Jakarta, 12120, Indonesia
Tel.: (62) 50101239
Web Site: https://www.arkadiacorp.com
DIGI—(INDO)
Rev.: $3,759,623
Assets: $1,222,407
Liabilities: $1,742,080
Net Worth: ($519,673)
Earnings: ($266,611)
Emp.: 145
Fiscal Year-end: 12/31/23
Digital Marketing Services
N.A.I.C.S.: 541890
Stephen Kurniawan Sulistyo *(Pres & Commissioner)*

PT ARKHA JAYANTI PERSADA TBK
Jl Lanbau No 8 Kampung Gudang RT 06 RW 09 Kelurahan Karang Asam Barat, Kecamatan Citeureup, Bogor, 16810, Indonesia
Tel.: (62) 2187918903
Web Site: https://www.arkhajayanti.co.id
Year Founded: 2000
ARKA—(INDO)
Rev.: $11,889,812
Assets: $29,410,477
Liabilities: $22,186,560
Net Worth: $7,223,916
Earnings: $659,790
Emp.: 88
Fiscal Year-end: 12/31/23
Heavy Equipment Component Mfr
N.A.I.C.S.: 336120
Doddy Prasetio Nugroho *(Sec)*

PT ARMADA BERJAYA TRANS
Green Sedayu Bizpark Cakung Gs 7 No 19, Cakung Timur, Jakarta, Indonesia
Tel.: (62) 2165310675
Web Site: https://armadaberjaya.com
Year Founded: 2012
JAYA—(INDO)
Rev.: $5,507,291
Assets: $10,828,343
Liabilities: $2,929,432
Net Worth: $7,898,911
Earnings: $664,476
Emp.: 29
Fiscal Year-end: 12/31/23
Freight Forwarding & Logistics Consulting Services
N.A.I.C.S.: 488510
Darmawan Suryadi *(Pres)*

PT ARPENI PRATAMA OCEAN LINE TBK
Jl Abdul Muis No 50, Jakarta, 10160, Indonesia
Tel.: (62) 21 350 5350 Id
Web Site: http://www.apol.co.id
Sales Range: $25-49.9 Million
Emp.: 763
Marine Shipping Services
N.A.I.C.S.: 488330
Surjono Abdullah Suharsono *(Chm)*

PT ARSY BUANA TRAVELINDO TBK.
Ruko Harvest Bintaro No 3 Jl Merpati Raya, Sawah Lama Ciputat, Tangerang, 15413, Banten, Indonesia
Tel.: (62) 217422898
Web Site: https://abttravel.id
Year Founded: 2016
HAJJ—(INDO)
Rev.: $32,569,596
Assets: $12,298,705
Liabilities: $2,775,025
Net Worth: $9,523,680
Earnings: $293,770
Fiscal Year-end: 12/31/23
Travel Agency Services
N.A.I.C.S.: 561510
Saipul Bahri *(Chm)*

PT ARTHAVEST TBK
Sahid Sudirman Center Floor 55th Jl Jend Sudirman no 86, Jakarta Pusat, 10220, Indonesia
Tel.: (62) 2131116101 Id
Web Site: https://www.arthavest.com
Year Founded: 1992
ARTA—(INDO)
Rev.: $5,049,050
Assets: $18,865,538
Liabilities: $1,195,971
Net Worth: $17,669,567
Earnings: $153,388

Emp.: 2
Fiscal Year-end: 12/31/23
Financial Services
N.A.I.C.S.: 523999
Tsun Tien Wen Lie *(Sec)*

Subsidiaries:

PT Sentral Pembayaran Indonesia (1)
Gedung Sahid Sudirman Center lt 55 Jl Jendral Sudirman 86, Jakarta Pusat, 10220, Indonesia
Tel.: (62) 2131116109
Web Site: http://www.spin-ku.com
Digital Payment Services
N.A.I.C.S.: 522320
Caecilia Candra *(Dir-Payment Svcs)*

PT ARWANA CITRAMULIA TBK
Sentra Niaga Puri Indah Blok T2 No 24 Kembangan Selatan, Jakarta, 11610, Indonesia
Tel.: (62) 2158302363 Id
Web Site: https://www.arwanacitra.com
Year Founded: 1993
ARNA—(INDO)
Rev.: $158,936,886
Assets: $170,174,728
Liabilities: $49,708,661
Net Worth: $120,466,067
Earnings: $29,163,263
Emp.: 1,493
Fiscal Year-end: 12/31/23
Ceramic Tile Mfr & Distr
N.A.I.C.S.: 327110
Tandean Rustandy *(Founder & CEO)*

Subsidiaries:

PT Primagraha Keramindo (1)
Sentra Niaga Puri Indah Blok T5 No 16-17, Kembangan Selatan, Jakarta Barat, 11610, Indonesia
Tel.: (62) 215 835 8118
Web Site: https://www.primagrahakeramindo.com
Financial Marketing Services
N.A.I.C.S.: 523999
Restian Saardillah *(Mgr-IT)*

PT ASIA PACIFIC FIBERS TBK
The East 35th Floor Units 5-6-7 Jl DR Ide Anak Agung Gde Agung, Kav E3 2 No 1, Jakarta, 12950, Indonesia
Tel.: (62) 2157938555
Web Site: https://www.asiapacificfibers.com
Year Founded: 1984
POLY—(INDO)
Rev.: $291,198,704
Assets: $211,215,567
Liabilities: $1,166,388,998
Net Worth: ($955,173,431)
Earnings: ($11,213,407)
Emp.: 2,236
Fiscal Year-end: 12/31/23
Polyester Mfr
N.A.I.C.S.: 313110
Vasudevan Ravi Shankar *(Chm)*

PT ASIA PACIFIC INVESTAMA TBK
No 62 Gandasari Jl Pajajaran 14, Jatiuwung, Tangerang, 15137, Indonesia
Tel.: (62) 55668888
Web Site: https://www.apinvestama.co.id
Year Founded: 1987
MYTX—(INDO)
Rev.: $78,386,347
Assets: $242,128,790
Liabilities: $274,179,732
Net Worth: ($32,050,942)
Earnings: ($22,863,491)
Emp.: 1,265
Fiscal Year-end: 12/31/23

AND PRIVATE COMPANIES

Garment & Textile Product Mfr
N.A.I.C.S.: 315990
Johnny Pesik (Chm)

PT ASIA SEJAHTERA MINA TBK
Jl Dr Makaliwe Raya No 16 B Kelurahan Grogol, Kecamatan Grogol Petamburan, Jakarta Barat, 11450, Indonesia
Tel.: (62) 2121192523
Web Site: https://www.asiamina.com
Year Founded: 2008
AGAR—(INDO)
Rev.: $353,124,124
Assets: $12,787,654
Liabilities: $5,841,296
Net Worth: $6,946,357
Earnings: $1,119
Emp.: 9
Fiscal Year-end: 12/31/23
Seaweed Farming Services
N.A.I.C.S.: 112519
Indra Widyadharma (Pres)

PT ASIAPLAST INDUSTRIES TBK
Jl K H E Z Muttaqien No 94 Kel Gembor Kec Periuk Kota, Tangerang, 15133, Banten, Indonesia
Tel.: (62) 215901465
Web Site: http://www.engine8.asiaplast.co.id
Year Founded: 1992
APLI—(INDO)
Rev.: $30,465,872
Assets: $31,853,519
Liabilities: $10,173,344
Net Worth: $21,680,175
Earnings: $3,273,014
Emp.: 425
Fiscal Year-end: 12/31/23
Plastic Film Mfr & Distr
N.A.I.C.S.: 326113
Wilson Agung Pranoto (Pres)

PT ASTRA AGRO LESTARI TBK
Jl Puloayang Raya Blok OR-I Kawasan Industri Pulogadung, Jakarta Timur, 13930, Indonesia
Tel.: (62) 214616555
Web Site: https://www.astra-agro.co.id
Year Founded: 1988
AAGRY—(OTCIQ)
Rev.: $1,347,211,017
Assets: $1,873,275,020
Liabilities: $407,838,591
Net Worth: $1,465,436,430
Earnings: $70,665,760
Emp.: 30,057
Fiscal Year-end: 12/31/23
Palm Oil Producer
N.A.I.C.S.: 311224
Joko Supriyono (Vice Chm & Chief Comm & Sustainability Officer)

PT ASTRA INTERNATIONAL TBK
Menara Astra 59 floor Jl Jenderal Sudirman Kav 5-6, Jakarta, 10250, Indonesia
Tel.: (62) 2150843888
Web Site: https://www.astra.co.id
Year Founded: 1957
ASII—(INDO)
Rev.: $20,557,731,100
Assets: $28,942,394,260
Liabilities: $12,680,249,340
Net Worth: $16,262,144,920
Earnings: $2,889,894,940
Emp.: 201,553
Fiscal Year-end: 12/31/23
Holding Company; Automobile Mfr
N.A.I.C.S.: 551112

Gita Tiffani Boer (Gen Counsel & Sec)

Subsidiaries:

P.T. Astra Digital Arta (1)
Menara Astra Lantai 56 Jalan Jenderal Sudirman Kav 5-6, RT 10 RW 11 Karet Tengsin Tanah Abang DKI Jakarta, Jakarta Pusat, 10220, Indonesia
Tel.: (62) 211500793
Web Site: https://www.astrapay.com
Fire Insurance Services
N.A.I.C.S.: 524113

P.T. Astra Isuzu Casting Company (1)
Lot N6-9 Jl Toll Jakarta Cikampek KM 47, Karawang International Industry City, Karawang, 41361, Indonesia
Tel.: (62) 218904590
Web Site: http://www.aicc.co.id
Automobile Manufacturing
N.A.I.C.S.: 336110

P.T. Astra Juoku Indonesia (1)
Kawasan Industri Mitra karawang Jl Mitra Timur II Blok D no 6, Parangmulya Ciampel, Karawang, 17520, Jawa Barat, Indonesia
Tel.: (62) 2678638064
Web Site: https://astra-juoku-indonesia.com
Automotive Lamp Mfr & Distr
N.A.I.C.S.: 336320

P.T. Astra Land Indonesia (1)
Menara Astra 10th Floor Jl Jendral Sudirman Kav 5-6, Jakarta, 10220, Indonesia
Tel.: (62) 2155958888
Web Site: https://astra-land.co.id
Property Investment Services
N.A.I.C.S.: 531390

P.T. Astra Nippon Gasket Indonesia (1)
Jl Maligi III Lot N-1 Karawang International Industrial City, Karawang Barat, Karawang, 41361, Jawa Barat, Indonesia
Tel.: (62) 218904404
Web Site: https://www.angi.co.id
Cylinder Head Gasket Mfr & Distr
N.A.I.C.S.: 339991

P.T. Asuransi Jiwa Astra (1)
Pondok Indah Office Tower 3 Lt 1 Jl Sultan Iskandar Muda Kav V-TA, Pondok Indah, Jakarta Selatan, 12310, Indonesia
Tel.: (62) 89521500282
Web Site: https://www.astralife.co.id
Fire Insurance Services
N.A.I.C.S.: 524113

P.T. Bhumi Jati Power (1)
Summitmas I 15th Floor Jl Jend Sudirman Kav 61-62, Jakarta, 12190, Indonesia
Tel.: (62) 212522281
Web Site: https://www.bhumi-jati.co.id
Electricity Power Plants Services
N.A.I.C.S.: 562213

P.T. Kreasi Mandiri Wintor Indonesia (1)
Jl Raya Bekasi Km 25 Ujung menteng, Cakung, East Jakarta, 13960, Indonesia
Tel.: (62) 2129844323
Web Site: https://www.kmwi-astra.com
Automotive Component Mfr & Distr
N.A.I.C.S.: 336390

P.T. Lintas Marga Sedaya (1)
Menara Astra Tower 12 Floor Jl Jendral Sudirman Kav 5-6, Jakarta, 10220, Indonesia
Tel.: (62) 2150821986
Web Site: https://www.lintasmarga.com
Highway Construction Services
N.A.I.C.S.: 541370

P.T. Pantja Motor (1)
Jl Gaya Motor III No 5 Sunter II, Jakarta, 14330, Indonesia (20%)
Tel.: (62) 216501000
Sales Range: $50-74.9 Million
Emp.: 200
Commercial Vehicles & RVs Import, Assembly & Distr
N.A.I.C.S.: 333310

P.T. Surya Cakra Anugerah Nusantara (1)

PT ASTRA INTERNATIONAL TBK

Jl TB Simatupang No 18 RW 1 Kebagusan Kec Ps Minggu, Daerah Khusus Ibukota Jakarta, Jakarta Selatan, 12520, Indonesia
Tel.: (62) 81998811818
Web Site: https://www.scanina.com
Truck & Equipment Rental Services
N.A.I.C.S.: 532120

P.T. Suryaraya Rubberindo Industries (1)
Kawasan Industri Menara Permai Jl Raya Narogong KM 23 8, Cileungsi, Bogor, 16820, West Java, Indonesia
Tel.: (62) 218230555
Web Site: https://fdrtire.com
Motor Bike Tire Mfr & Distr
N.A.I.C.S.: 336991

P.T. Toyofuji Logistics Indonesia (1)
Grha SERA 7th Floor Jl Mitra Sunter Boulevard Kav 90/C2 Sunter, Jakarta, 14350, Indonesia
Tel.: (62) 2165304788
Domestic Marine Transport Services
N.A.I.C.S.: 522320

P.T. Toyofuji Serasi Indonesia (1)
Grha SERA 7th Floor Jl Mitra Sunter Boulevard Kav 90/C2 Sunter, Jakarta, 14350, Indonesia
Tel.: (62) 2165304788
Domestic Marine Transport Services
N.A.I.C.S.: 522320

PT Astra Digital Internasional (1)
Altira Business Park Jl Yos Sudarso No Kav 85 RW 11, Sunter Jaya Kec Tanjung Priok, Jakarta Utara, Indonesia
Tel.: (62) 21882358
Web Site: https://www.astradigital.id
Artificial Intelligence Services
N.A.I.C.S.: 541511
Wiwie Yudiantyo (Head-Mobility Solutions Div)

PT Astra Nissan Diesel Indonesia (1)
Jl Danau Sunter Selatan Blok O/5 Sunter, Jakarta, Indonesia
Tel.: (62) 216507150
Web Site: http://www.astra-nissandiesel.co.id
Sales Range: $25-49.9 Million
Emp.: 80
Diesel Trucks Mfr & Spare Parts Distr
N.A.I.C.S.: 333120

PT Astra Nusa Perdana (1)
Menara Astra 11th Floor Jalan Jenderal Sudirman Kav 5-6, Jakarta, 10220, Indonesia
Tel.: (62) 2150821982
Toll Road Services
N.A.I.C.S.: 488490

PT Astra Sedaya Finance (1)
Jl MH Thamrin 150 Karangkidul, Semarang, 50241, Central Java, Indonesia
Tel.: (62) 24 8415351
Automobile Finance Leasing Services
N.A.I.C.S.: 522220

PT Astra Tol Nusantara (1)
Menara Astra 11th Floor Jalan Jenderal Sudirman Kav 5-6, Jakarta, 10220, Indonesia
Tel.: (62) 2150821982
Toll Road Services
N.A.I.C.S.: 488490

PT Astratel Nusantara (1)
Setiabudi Atrium Building 3rd Floor Suite 303 Jalan HR, Rasuna Said Kav, Jakarta, 12920, Astratel, Indonesia
Tel.: (62) 21 5210440
Web Site: http://www.astratel.co.id
Emp.: 60
Telecommunications Installation Services
N.A.I.C.S.: 238210

PT Asuransi Astra Buana (1)
Jl TB Simatupang Kav 15, Lebak Bulus Cilandak, Jakarta Selatan, 12440, Indonesia
Tel.: (62) 1500112
Web Site: https://www.asuransiastra.com
General Insurance Services
N.A.I.C.S.: 524130

Subsidiary (Domestic):

PT Samadista Karya (2)

Menara FIF Lt 18 Jl TB Simatupang Kav 15, Jakarta Selatan, Jakarta, 12520, Indonesia
Tel.: (62) 21 75900800
Office Building Construction Services
N.A.I.C.S.: 236220

PT Brahmayasa Bahtera (1)
Jl Casablanca Kav 12 Apartemen Casablanca Menteng Dlm Tebet, Jakarta, 12870, Indonesia
Tel.: (62) 2183704425
Sales Range: $25-49.9 Million
Emp.: 2
Luxury Apartments Construction Services
N.A.I.C.S.: 236116

PT Federal International Finance (1)
Menara FIF Jl Tb Simatupang Kav 15 Cilandak, Jakarta, 12440, Indonesia
Tel.: (62) 217698899
Automobile Finance Leasing Services
N.A.I.C.S.: 522220

PT Fuji Technica Indonesia (1)
Jl Maligi Raya Lot A-6 7 Klic Sukaluyu Industrial Area Telukjambe East, Karawang International Industrial City, Karawang, 41361, West Java, Indonesia
Tel.: (62) 218902550
Auto Parts Stamping & Die Mfr
N.A.I.C.S.: 336370

PT Inti Ganda Perdana (1)
Jl. Pegangsaan Dua Km 1 6 Kelapa Gading, Jakarta, 14250, Indonesia
Tel.: (62) 214602755
Web Site: http://www.igpgroup.astra.co.id
Automobile Body Mfr
N.A.I.C.S.: 336211

PT Marga Mandalasakti (1)
Karawaci Office Park Blok H No 65-68 Lippo Karawaci, Tangerang, 15811, Banten, Indonesia
Tel.: (62) 254207878
Web Site: http://www.margamandala.co.id
Toll Road Services
N.A.I.C.S.: 488490
Agung Prasetyo (Head-Maintenance Div)

PT Menara Astra (1)
Jl Jendral Sudirman Kav 5-6, Jakarta, 10220, Indonesia
Tel.: (62) 81299920889
Web Site: https://www.menara-astra.co.id
Commercial Property Services
N.A.I.C.S.: 531312

PT Sedaya Pratama (1)
Jl RS Fatmawati 9 Ged ACC Lt 2 Gandaria Selatan Cilandak, Jakarta, 12420, Indonesia
Tel.: (62) 217509000
Property Management Services
N.A.I.C.S.: 531311

PT Serasi Autoraya (1)
Grha Sera Jl Mitra Sunter Boulevard Kav 90/C2, Sunter Jaya, Jakarta Utara, 14350, Indonesia
Tel.: (62) 2126605333
Web Site: https://www.sera.astra.co.id
Transportation Services
N.A.I.C.S.: 485999
Firman Yosafat Siregar (Pres)

PT Serasi Logistics Indonesia (1)
Jl Mitra Sunter Boulevard Kav 90/C2 Sunter Jaya, Jakarta, 14350, Utara, Indonesia
Tel.: (62) 21 26605333
Sales Range: $50-74.9 Million
Emp.: 20
Automobile Leasing Services
N.A.I.C.S.: 532112

PT Serasi Transportasi Nusantara (1)
Jl Wonorejo Tmr 99 Wonorejo Rungkut, Surabaya, 60296, East Java, Indonesia
Tel.: (62) 318711818
General Freight Trucking Services
N.A.I.C.S.: 484110
Erawan Gusmardana (Head-Sls & Mktg)

PT Staco Estika Sedaya Finance (1)
Jl Letjen TB Simatupang No 90 Tanjung Barat Indah, Jakarta Selatan, Jakarta, 12530, Indonesia
Tel.: (62) 21 78859000
Automobile Finance Leasing Services

PT ASTRA INTERNATIONAL TBK

PT Astra International Tbk—(Continued)
N.A.I.C.S.: 522220

PT Stacomitra Graha (1)
Jl Boulevard Brt Raya Bl XB/7 Lt 1 Kelapa Gading Barat Kelapa Gading, Jakarta, 14240, Indonesia
Tel.: (62) 21 4509000
Web Site: http://www.acc.co.id
Real Estate Property Investment Services
N.A.I.C.S.: 523999

PT Surya Artha Nusantara Finance (1)
18 Office Park 23rd Floor Jl T B Simatupang No 18, Jakarta, 12520, Indonesia
Tel.: (62) 217817555
Investment Financing Services
N.A.I.C.S.: 523999
Davin Susanto (Sec)

PT Suryaraya Prawira (1)
Jl Casablanca Kav 12, Jakarta, 12870, Indonesia
Tel.: (62) 218310046
Web Site: http://www.apartment-casablanca.co.id
Sales Range: $25-49.9 Million
Emp.: 18
Luxury Apartments Construction Services
N.A.I.C.S.: 236116

PT Swadharma Bhakti Sedaya Finance (1)
Jl Sumantri Brojonegoro 96 Kenali Besar, Kota Baru, Jambi, 36129, Indonesia
Tel.: (62) 741 60137
Sales Range: $50-74.9 Million
Emp.: 60
Automobile Finance Leasing Services
N.A.I.C.S.: 522220

PT Tjahja Sakti Motor (1)
Jl Gaya Motor Selatan II No 1 Sunter II, Jakarta, 14330, Indonesia
Tel.: (62) 216509330
Automobiles Import & Assembling Services
N.A.I.C.S.: 336110

PT ASTRA OTOPARTS TBK

Jl Raya Pegangsaan Dua Km 2 2 Kelapa Gading, Jakarta, 14250, Indonesia
Tel.: (62) 214603550   Id
Web Site: https://www.astra-otoparts.com
Year Founded: 1976
AUTO—(INDO)
Rev.: $1,211,070,281
Assets: $1,273,671,012
Liabilities: $329,461,336
Net Worth: $944,209,677
Earnings: $130,704,868
Emp.: 20,672
Fiscal Year-end: 12/31/23
Automobile Parts Mfr
N.A.I.C.S.: 333310
Hamdhani Dzulkarnaen Salim (Chm)

Subsidiaries:

PT Ardendi Jaya Sentosa (1)
Jl Raya Pegangsaan Dua Km 2 2 Kelapa Gading, Jakarta Utara, 14250, Indonesia
Tel.: (62) 214603550
Automobile Parts Mfr
N.A.I.C.S.: 336110

PT Astra Daido Steel Indonesia (1)
Kawasan Industri Green Land Cluster Batavia Blok AG/12 Cikarang Pusat, Bekasi, 17530, Indonesia
Tel.: (62) 2189973241
Automobile Parts Mfr
N.A.I.C.S.: 336110

PT Astra Komponen Indonesia (1)
Jl Raya Mayor Oking KM 2 2 Karangasem Barat, Citeureup, Bogor, Indonesia
Tel.: (62) 2187919119
Automobile Parts Mfr
N.A.I.C.S.: 336110

PT Autoplastik Indonesia (1)
Jl Mitra Barat I Blok GB Kawasan Industri Mitra Karawang, Karawang, 41361, Indonesia

Jl E 5 Simpangan No
Tel.: (62) 2678634072
Automobile Parts Mfr
N.A.I.C.S.: 336110

PT Century Batteries Indonesia (1)
Jl Raya Bekasi Km 25 Cakung, Jakarta, 13960, Indonesia
Tel.: (62) 21 460 0880
Web Site: https://www.cbi-astra.com
Lead Acid Battery Mfr
N.A.I.C.S.: 335910
P. Wahyu Indrianto (Head-Mktg)

PT Federal Izumi Manufacturing (1)
Komplek Industri Menara Permai Jl Narogong Raya Km 23 8, Cileungsi, Bogor, 16820, Indonesia
Tel.: (62) 218230355
Web Site: https://www.fim.co.id
Automobile Parts Mfr
N.A.I.C.S.: 336110
Rokhmatul Wakhidah (Mgr-HRD)

PT Indokarlo Perkasa (1)
Jl Raya Jakarta-Bogor Km 47 Nanggewer Mekar, Bogor, 16912, Indonesia
Tel.: (62) 218754146
Automobile Parts Mfr
N.A.I.C.S.: 336110

PT KMW Indonesia (1)
Jl Pahlawan Km 1 5 Kp Kambing RT 003/007, Desa Karang Asem Timur Citeureup Kab, Bogor, 16810, Jawa Barat, Indonesia
Tel.: (62) 21 875-4293
Web Site: https://www.kmwi-astra.com
Mechanical Equipment Mfr
N.A.I.C.S.: 333613

PT Menara Terus Makmur (1)
Jl Jababeka XI Blok H-3 No 12, Bekasi, 17530, Jawa Barat, Indonesia
Tel.: (62) 218934504
Web Site: http://www.mtm.astra.co.id
Mechanical Jack & Forging Part Mfr
N.A.I.C.S.: 332111

PT Nusa Keihin Indonesia (1)
Jl Selayar II Blok D7 No 1, Kawasan Industri MM 2100 Cikarang Barat, Bekasi, 17845, Indonesia
Tel.: (62) 2189844945
Automobile Parts Mfr
N.A.I.C.S.: 336110

PT Pakoakuina (1)
Jl Gaya Motor Raya Sunter II, Jakarta Utara, 14330, Indonesia
Tel.: (62) 216511228
Automobile Parts Mfr
N.A.I.C.S.: 336110
Nini Tjandrasa (Dir-Fin)

PT Palingda Nasional (1)
Jl Gaya Motor Raya Sunter II, Jakarta Utara, 14330, Indonesia
Tel.: (62) 216511228
Automobile Parts Mfr
N.A.I.C.S.: 336110

PT Senantiasa Makmur (1)
Jl Raya Pegangsaan Dua Km 2 2, Kelapa Gading, Jakarta Utara, 14250, Indonesia
Tel.: (62) 214603550
Automobile Parts Mfr
N.A.I.C.S.: 336110

PT ASTRINDO NUSANTARA INFRASTRUKTUR TBK

Sopo Del Office Tower B 21st Floor, Jl Mega Kuningan Barat III Lot 10 1-6, Jakarta, 12950, Indonesia
Tel.: (62) 2150815252
Web Site:
https://astrindonusantara.com
Year Founded: 2007
BIPI—(INDO)
Rev.: $42,280
Assets: $114,125
Liabilities: $76,864
Net Worth: $37,261
Earnings: $953
Emp.: 332
Fiscal Year-end: 12/31/23
Oil & Gas Exploration & Production Services

N.A.I.C.S.: 211120

Subsidiaries:

PT Suluh Ardhi Engineering (1)
Garden Centre Building Suite 3&7 Fl -02 Cilandak Commercial Estate, Jl Raya Cilandak KKO, Jakarta, 12560, Indonesia
Tel.: (62) 217803339
Web Site: http://www.sae-engineering.com
Sales Range: $25-49.9 Million
Emp.: 200
Construction Engineering Services
N.A.I.C.S.: 541330

PT ASURANSI JASA TANIA TBK

Gedung Agro Plaza Lantai 9 Jl HR Rasuna Said Kav X2 No 1, Jakarta Selatan, 12950, Indonesia
Tel.: (62) 215262529
Web Site: https://www.jastan.co.id
Year Founded: 1979
ASJT—(INDO)
Rev.: $7,610,559
Assets: $32,387,080
Liabilities: $11,322,242
Net Worth: $21,064,838
Earnings: $261,030
Emp.: 136
Fiscal Year-end: 12/31/23
Insurance Brokerage Services
N.A.I.C.S.: 524210
Hasbi Ashsiddiqi (Sec & Dir-Technical)

PT ASURANSI JIWA SYARIAH JASA MITRA ABADI TBK

Graha Kospin Jasa Lantai 5 Jl Jend Gatot Soebroto Kav 1, Jakarta Selatan, 12870, Indonesia
Tel.: (62) 2182470083
Web Site: https://jmasyariah.com
Year Founded: 2014
JMAS—(INDO)
Rev.: $4,717,560
Assets: $19,681,466
Liabilities: $11,875,259
Net Worth: $7,806,207
Earnings: $164,099
Emp.: 55
Fiscal Year-end: 12/31/23
Insurance Services
N.A.I.C.S.: 524210
Basuki Agus (Pres)

PT ASURANSI MAXIMUS GRAHA PERSADA TBK

Gedung Graha Kirana 6th and 10th Fl, Jl Yos Sudarso No 88 Sunter, Jakarta, 14350, Indonesia
Tel.: (62) 2165311150
Web Site:
https://www.asuransimaximus.com
Year Founded: 1956
ASMI—(INDO)
Rev.: $24,825,342
Assets: $62,411,436
Liabilities: $37,380,831
Net Worth: $25,030,605
Earnings: $491,529
Emp.: 170
Fiscal Year-end: 12/31/23
Property, Casualty, Life, Marine Cargo, Fire & Engineering Insurance
N.A.I.C.S.: 524126
Pepe Arinata (Chm)

PT ASURANSI RAMAYANA TBK

Jl Kebon Sirih No 49, Jakarta, 10340, Indonesia
Tel.: (62) 2131937148
Web Site:
https://www.ramayanatbk.com
Year Founded: 1956
ASRM—(INDO)
Rev.: $138,266,502

INTERNATIONAL PUBLIC

Assets: $120,188,940
Liabilities: $76,128,513
Net Worth: $44,060,426
Earnings: $5,766,555
Emp.: 1,175
Fiscal Year-end: 12/31/23
Insurance Services
N.A.I.C.S.: 524298
Jiwa Anggara (Dir-Mktg)

PT ASURANSI TUGU PRATAMA INDONESIA TBK

Wisma Tugu I Jalan H R Rasuna Said Kav C8-9, Jakarta, 12920, Indonesia
Tel.: (62) 2152961777
Web Site: https://www.tugu.com
Year Founded: 1981
TUGU—(INDO)
Rev.: $500,656,493
Assets: $1,632,457,993
Liabilities: $964,884,000
Net Worth: $667,573,994
Earnings: $84,558,456
Emp.: 353
Fiscal Year-end: 12/31/23
Insurance Services
N.A.I.C.S.: 524210
Indra Baruna (Chm)

Subsidiaries:

PT Tugu Reasuransi Indonesia (1)
Tugure Building Gedung Tugure Jl Raden Saleh no 50, Menteng, Jakarta Pusat, 10330, Indonesia
Tel.: (62) 213140267
Web Site: https://www.tugure.id
Insurance Services
N.A.I.C.S.: 524210
Adi Pramana (Pres)

YHT & Company Limited (1)
Regency Court Glategny Esplanade, Saint Peter Port, GY1 3AP, Guernsey
Tel.: (44) 1481711521
Brokerage Services
N.A.I.C.S.: 523150

PT ATELIERS MECANIDUQES D'INDONESIE TBK

Jl Sei Belumai Km 2 4 No 3038 Desa, Dagang Kelambir Tanjung Morawa, Sumatera Barat, 20362, North Sumatra, Indonesia
Tel.: (62) 617947751
Web Site:
https://www.atmindoboiler.com
AMIN—(INDO)
Rev.: $12,752,911
Assets: $21,804,775
Liabilities: $11,552,018
Net Worth: $10,252,757
Earnings: $267,572
Emp.: 291
Fiscal Year-end: 01/31/22
Electric Equipment Mfr
N.A.I.C.S.: 335999

PT ATLAS RESOURCES TBK

Sampoerna Strategic Square South Tower Level 18 Jl Jend. Sudirman Kav 45-46, Jakarta, 12930, Indonesia
Tel.: (62) 217193343   Id
Web Site: https://www.atlas-coal.co.id
Year Founded: 2007
ARII—(INDO)
Rev.: $280,609,000
Assets: $527,750,000
Liabilities: $456,697,000
Net Worth: $71,053,000
Earnings: $728,000
Emp.: 240
Fiscal Year-end: 12/31/23
Coke Mfr
N.A.I.C.S.: 213113
Andre Abdi (Chm)

AND PRIVATE COMPANIES

PT BANK ALADIN SYARIAH TBK

PT AUSTINDO NUSANTARA JAYA TBK.
Menara BTPN 40 Floor Jl Dr Ide Anak Agung Gde Agung Kav 5 5-5 6, Kawasan Mega Kuningan, Jakarta, 12950, Indonesia
Tel.: (62) 2129651777
Web Site: https://www.anj-group.com
ANJT—(INDO)
Rev.: $236,511,703
Assets: $614,072,260
Liabilities: $188,746,577
Net Worth: $425,325,683
Earnings: $1,901,654
Emp.: 9,272
Fiscal Year-end: 12/31/23
Holding Company; Palm Oil; Renewable Energy
N.A.I.C.S.: 551112
Istini Tatiek Siddharta (Chm)

PT AVIA AVIAN TBK
Jalan Surabaya-Sidoarjo Km 19 Kelurahan Wadungasih Kecamatan Buduran, Sidoarjo, 61252, Jawa Timur, Indonesia
Tel.: (62) 318968000
Web Site:
https://www.avianbrands.com
Year Founded: 1978
AVIA—(INDO)
Rev.: $455,676,317
Assets: $725,184,136
Liabilities: $80,882,640
Net Worth: $644,301,496
Earnings: $111,988,965
Emp.: 8,477
Fiscal Year-end: 12/31/23
Paint & Printing Inks Mfr
N.A.I.C.S.: 325910
Ruslan Tanoko (VP)

PT AVIANA SINAR ABADI TBK
Jl Alaydrus Lt 3 No 66 BC, Petojo Utara Gambir, Jakarta Pusat, 10130, Indonesia
Tel.: (62) 216317523
Web Site: https://www.aviana.co.id
Year Founded: 2010
IRSX—(INDO)
Rev.: $16,157,779
Assets: $10,909,960
Liabilities: $256,825
Net Worth: $10,653,135
Earnings: ($150,737)
Emp.: 45
Fiscal Year-end: 12/31/23
Software Development Services
N.A.I.C.S.: 541511
Fajar Indrayanto D. (Sec)

PT BAKRIE & BROTHERS TBK
Bakrie Tower 35th-37th Floor Rasuna Epicentrum Complex, Jalan HR Rasuna Said, Jakarta, 12940, Indonesia
Tel.: (62) 2129912222
Web Site: https://www.bakrie-brothers.com
Year Founded: 1942
BNBR—(INDO)
Rev.: $244,140,891
Assets: $461,178,294
Liabilities: $288,394,838
Net Worth: $172,783,455
Earnings: $17,173,903
Emp.: 1,668
Fiscal Year-end: 12/31/23
Pipe, Corrugated Steel, Building Materials, Cast Iron Auto Parts Mfr & Whslr; Engineering, Wireless Telecommunications & Other Infrastructure Services; Plantations Operator
N.A.I.C.S.: 541330
Dody Taufiq Wijaya (Chief Risk Officer)

Subsidiaries:

P.T. Vktr Teknologi Mobilitas Tbk (1)
Bakrie Tower 35 Floor Rasuna Epicentrum Jl H R Rasuna Said, Jakarta, 12940, Indonesia
Tel.: (62) 2129912222
Web Site: https://www.vktr.id
Electric Vehicle Parts Mfr & Distr
N.A.I.C.S.: 336211

PT Bakrie Autoparts (1)
Jl Raya Bekasi KM 27 Pondok Ungu, Bekasi, 17132, Indonesia
Tel.: (62) 218 897 6601
Web Site: https://www.bakrie-autoparts.com
Automobile Parts Mfr
N.A.I.C.S.: 336390
Dino Ahmad Ryandi (Pres)

Subsidiary (Domestic):

PT Bakrie Steel Industries (2)
Jl Raya Bekasi KM 27 Pondokungu, 17132, Bekasi, Indonesia
Tel.: (62) 21889766013
Web Site: http://www.bakriesteel.com
Automotive & Heavy Industry Component Mfr
N.A.I.C.S.: 336390

PT Bina Usaha Mandiri Mizusawa (2)
Jl KH EZ Muttaqien Kec, Jatiuwung Kel Alam Jaya, Tangerang, 15133, Banten, Indonesia
Tel.: (62) 2159 024 8889
Web Site: https://www.bumm.co.id
Automotive & Heavy Industry Component Mfr
N.A.I.C.S.: 336390
Bapak Kamal (Mgr-Sls & PPIC)

PT Bakrie Building Industries (1)
Jl Daan Mogot Km 17 3, Jakarta, 11850, Indonesia
Tel.: (62) 216190208
Web Site: http://www.bakrie-building.com
Sales Range: $200-249.9 Million
Industrial Building Construction Services
N.A.I.C.S.: 236220

PT Bakrie Communications (1)
Wisma Bakrie 2nd floor, Jl HR Rasuna Said Kav B-2, Jakarta, 12920, Indonesia
Tel.: (62) 219160016
Telecommunications Solutions
N.A.I.C.S.: 517112

PT Bakrie Construction (1)
Komplek Rasuna Epicentrum Bakrie Tower Lantai 35, Jakarta, 12940, Indonesia
Tel.: (62) 2129912222
Web Site: https://bakrieconstruction.com
Construction Services
N.A.I.C.S.: 236220
Rachmat Harimurti (Chief Comml Officer)

PT Bakrie Indo Infrastructure (1)
Bakrie Tower 34th Floor Kompleks Rasuna Epicentrum Jl HR Rasuna Said, Jakarta, 12940, Indonesia
Tel.: (62) 2129912345
Construction Engineering Services
N.A.I.C.S.: 541330

Subsidiary (Domestic):

PT Bakrie Oil & Gas Infrastructure (2)
Gd Wisma Bakrie 1Lt 1 Jl HR Rasuna Said Kav B-1, Jakarta Selatan, Jakarta, 12920, Indonesia
Tel.: (62) 2152920266
Oil & Gas Field Engineering Services
N.A.I.C.S.: 213112

PT Bakrie Metal Industries (1)
Jl Raya Kaliabang Bungur No 86 RT 004 RW 002 Kelurahan Harapan, Jaya Kecamatan, Bekasi, 17124, West Java, Indonesia
Tel.: (62) 2188958673
Sales Range: $100-124.9 Million
Emp.: 400
Fabricated Metal Products Mfr
N.A.I.C.S.: 331410

PT Bakrie Pipe Industries (1)
Wisma Bakrie 2 Bldg, Jl HR Rasuna Said Kav B-1, Jakarta, 12920, Indonesia
Tel.: (62) 8871135
Steel Pole Mfr
N.A.I.C.S.: 331210

PT Bakrie Power (1)
Bakrie Tower 34th 37th Floor Rasuna Epicentrum Jl H R Rasuna Said, Jakarta, 12940, Indonesia
Tel.: (62) 2129912060
Web Site: https://bakriepower.co.id
Electric Power Generation Services
N.A.I.C.S.: 221118
Anindra Ardiansyah Bakrie (Commissioner)

PT Bakrie Tosanjaya (1)
JL Raya Bekasi Km 27, Pondok Ungu, Bekasi, 17132, Indonesia
Tel.: (62) 2188976601
Web Site: http://www.bakrie-tosanjaya.co.id
Sales Range: $200-249.9 Million
Emp.: 510
Automotive Components Mfr
N.A.I.C.S.: 333618

PT Multi Kontrol Nusantara (1)
Wisma Bakrie HR Rasuna Said Kav B1, Jakarta, 12920, Selatan, Indonesia
Tel.: (62) 215205476
Web Site: https://mkncorp.com
Sales Range: $25-49.9 Million
Telecommunication System & Network Integration Services
N.A.I.C.S.: 541512
Didit Ardyanto (Chm)

Subsidiary (Domestic):

PT Graha Multimedia Nusantara (2)
Rasuna Office Park 3 4th Fl-Unit UO-11nd Jl HR Rasuna Said, Jakarta, 12950, Indonesia
Tel.: (62) 212 994 1010
Web Site: https://www.zumstar.co.id
Internet Broadcasting Services
N.A.I.C.S.: 517111

PT Southeast Asia Pipe Industries (1)
Bakrie Tower 7th Floor Rasuna Epicentrum Jl H R Rasuna Said, Jakarta Selatan, 12940, Indonesia
Tel.: (62) 212 994 1270
Web Site: https://www.seapi.co.id
Steel Pole Mfr
N.A.I.C.S.: 331210
R. Atok Hendrayanto (CEO)

PT System Energi Nusantara (1)
Kompleks Golden Plaza J33 Jl RS Fatmawati Raya No 15, Jakarta, 12420, Indonesia
Tel.: (62) 215205476
Web Site: https://www.sen-indonesia.co.id
Oil & Gas Services
N.A.I.C.S.: 213112
Anto Reksoprodjo (VP-Bus Dev)

PT BAKRIE SUMATERA PLANTATIONS TBK
Kompleks Rasuna Epicentrum Bakrie Tower 19th Floor, Jl H R Rasuna Said, Jakarta, 12960, Indonesia
Tel.: (62) 2129941286
Web Site:
https://www.bakriesumatera.com
Year Founded: 1911
UNSP—(INDO)
Rev.: $156,190,636
Assets: $296,108,542
Liabilities: $681,389,119
Net Worth: ($385,280,578)
Earnings: $1,697,337
Emp.: 7,510
Fiscal Year-end: 12/31/23
Rubber Plantation & Farming Services
N.A.I.C.S.: 115112
C. S. Seshadri (Dir-Compliance & Internal Control Audit)

Subsidiaries:

PT Agrowiyana (1)
Jl Besar WKS Km11 Desa Tebing Tinggi Kecamatan Tungkal Ulu, Kabupaten Tanjung Jabung, Jambi, Indonesia
Tel.: (62) 741444763
Oil Operation Services
N.A.I.C.S.: 213112

PT Bakrie Pasaman Plantations (1)
Nagari Sungai Aua Kecamatan, Sungai Aur Kabupaten Pasaman Barat, Sumatera Barat, Indonesia
Tel.: (62) 75347055
Oil Operation Services
N.A.I.C.S.: 213112
Edy Susanto (Commissioner)

PT Flora Sawita Chemindo (1)
Jl Raya Medan - Lubuk Pakam Km 20, Sarana Tamora Permai Industrial Estate Tanjung Moraw, Medan, 20362, Indonesia
Tel.: (62) 617944974
Chemical Products Mfr
N.A.I.C.S.: 325199
Darrell Tan (Co-Pres & Commissioner)

PT Sawitmas Agro Perkasa (1)
Kompleks Rasuna Epicentrum Bakrie Tower 18th-19th Floor, Jl HR Rasuna Said, Jakarta, 12960, Indonesia
Tel.: (62) 2129941286
Chemical Products Mfr
N.A.I.C.S.: 325199
Darrell Tan (Co-Pres & Commissioner)

PT Sumbertama Nusapertiwi (1)
Kompleks Rasuna Epicentrum Bakrie Tower 19th Floor Jl HR Rasuna Said, Jakarta, 12960, Indonesia
Tel.: (62) 2129941286
Oil Operation Services
N.A.I.C.S.: 213112

PT BALI BINTANG SEJAHTERA TBK
Jl Pararaton Off Sunset Road, Legian Kuta, Bali, 80361, Indonesia
Tel.: (62) 3619609893
Web Site: https://www.baliutd.com
Year Founded: 2014
BOLA—(INDO)
Rev.: $23,595,187
Assets: $52,672,468
Liabilities: $5,448,327
Net Worth: $47,224,142
Earnings: ($113,247)
Emp.: 52
Fiscal Year-end: 12/31/23
Football Club Operator
N.A.I.C.S.: 711211
Yabes Tanuri (Pres)

PT BALI TOWERINDO SENTRA TBK
The Autograph Tower Lantai 77 Jl M H Thamrin No 10, Thamrin Nine Complex, Jakarta, 10230, Indonesia
Tel.: (62) 2157905788
Web Site: https://www.balitower.co.id
Year Founded: 2015
BALI—(INDO)
Rev.: $62,034,689
Assets: $358,378,913
Liabilities: $195,047,556
Net Worth: $163,331,358
Earnings: $9,773,603
Emp.: 565
Fiscal Year-end: 12/31/23
Telecommunication Tower Leasing Services
N.A.I.C.S.: 531190
Jap Owen Ronadhi (Chm)

PT BANK ALADIN SYARIAH TBK
Millennium Centennial Center 7th Floor Jl Jenderal Sudirman Kav 25, South Jakarta, 12920, Indonesia
Tel.: (62) 2185500947
Web Site: https://www.aladinbank.id
Year Founded: 1994
BANK—(INDO)
Rev.: $21,722,560
Assets: $460,562,273
Liabilities: $260,206,722
Net Worth: $200,355,551
Earnings: ($14,724,366)
Emp.: 279
Fiscal Year-end: 12/31/23

PT BANK ALADIN SYARIAH TBK

PT Bank Aladin Syariah Tbk—(Continued)
Bank Holding Company
N.A.I.C.S.: 551111
Dyota Marsudi (Pres)

PT BANK AMAR INDONESIA TBK
Jl Basuki Rachmad No 109, Kel Embong Kaliasin Kec Genteng Kota, Surabaya, Jawa Timur, Indonesia
Tel.: (62) 3199015959
Web Site:
https://www.amarbank.co.id
Year Founded: 1991
AMAR—(INDO)
Rev.: $64,065,323
Assets: $284,399,340
Liabilities: $70,391,583
Net Worth: $214,007,757
Earnings: $11,557,502
Emp.: 395
Fiscal Year-end: 12/31/23
Bank Holding Company
N.A.I.C.S.: 551111
Tuk Yulianto (Dir-Compliance)

PT BANK ARTHA GRAHA INTERNASIONAL TBK
Jalan Jendral Sudirman Kaveling 52 - 53, Jakarta Selatan, 12190, Indonesia
Tel.: (62) 215152168 Id
Web Site:
https://www.arthagraha.com
Year Founded: 1973
INPC—(INDO)
Rev.: $96,419,860
Assets: $1,695,168,498
Liabilities: $1,424,301,615
Net Worth: $270,866,883
Earnings: $9,530,140
Fiscal Year-end: 12/31/23
Non Financial Banking Services
N.A.I.C.S.: 522110
Andy Kasih (Chm)

PT BANK BTPN SYARIAH TBK.
Menara BTPN lt 12 CBD Mega Kuningan Jl Dr Ide Anak Agung Gde Agung, Kav 5 5 5 6, Jakarta Selatan, 12950, Indonesia
Tel.: (62) 2130026400
Web Site:
https://www.btpnsyariah.com
Year Founded: 2014
BTPS—(INDO)
Rev.: $373,157,059
Assets: $1,392,012,668
Liabilities: $822,025,651
Net Worth: $569,987,017
Earnings: $70,173,385
Emp.: 3,612
Fiscal Year-end: 12/31/23
Commercial Banking Services
N.A.I.C.S.: 522110
Hadi Wibow (Chm)

Subsidiaries:

P.T. BTPN Syariah Ventura (1)
Jl Radio Dalam No 100 Gandaria Utara, Kebayoran Baru, South Jakarta, Indonesia
Tel.: (62) 2127099533
Web Site:
https://www.btpnsyariahventura.com
Venture Capital Funding Services
N.A.I.C.S.: 523910

PT BANK CAPITAL INDONESIA TBK
Menara BP Jamsostek Lt 1 & 6 Jl Jend Gatot Subroto Kav 38, Jakarta Selatan, 12710, Indonesia
Tel.: (62) 2127938989 Id
Web Site:
https://www.bankcapital.co.id
Year Founded: 1989
BACA—(INDO)
Rev.: $54,474,270
Assets: $1,250,691,604
Liabilities: $1,030,524,223
Net Worth: $220,167,381
Earnings: $6,608,749
Emp.: 707
Fiscal Year-end: 12/31/23
Commercial Banking Services
N.A.I.C.S.: 522110
Wahyu Dwi Aji (Chm)

PT BANK GANESHA TBK
Wisma Hayam Wuruk Jl Hayam Wuruk No 8, Jakarta, 10120, Indonesia
Tel.: (62) 2129109900 Id
Web Site:
https://www.bankganesha.co.id
Year Founded: 1990
BGTG—(INDO)
Rev.: $38,493,315
Assets: $610,585,946
Liabilities: $399,907,469
Net Worth: $210,678,478
Earnings: $6,751,487
Emp.: 266
Fiscal Year-end: 12/31/23
Banking Services
N.A.I.C.S.: 522110
Sugiarto Surjadi (Dir-Compliance)

PT BANK INA PERDANA TBK.
Wisma BSG Jl Abdul Muis No 40, Jakarta, 10160, Pusat, Indonesia
Tel.: (62) 213859050
Web Site: http://www.bankina.co.id
Year Founded: 1990
BINA—(INDO)
Rev.: $112,125,729
Assets: $1,583,534,625
Liabilities: $1,352,597,725
Net Worth: $230,936,901
Earnings: $13,499,467
Emp.: 448
Fiscal Year-end: 12/31/23
Banking Services
N.A.I.C.S.: 522110
Edy Kuntardjo (Pres)

PT BANK JAGO TBK
Menara BTPN Lt 46 Jl Dr Ide Anak Agung Gde Agung Kav 5 5 - 5 6, Jakarta Selatan, 40171, Indonesia
Tel.: (62) 2130000746
Web Site:
https://www.bankartos.co.id
Year Founded: 1992
ARTO—(INDO)
Rev.: $105,125,586
Assets: $1,382,951,850
Liabilities: $840,261,777
Net Worth: $542,690,072
Earnings: $4,699,188
Emp.: 454
Fiscal Year-end: 12/31/23
Banking Services
N.A.I.C.S.: 522110
Bambang Setiawan (Dir-Compliance)

PT BANK JTRUST INDONESIA TBK.
Sahid Sudirman Center Lt 33 Jl Jend Sudirman No 86, Jakarta, 10220, Indonesia
Tel.: (62) 29261111 Id
Web Site:
https://www.jtrustbank.co.id
BCIC—(INDO)
Rev.: $163,991,034
Assets: $2,547,876,221
Liabilities: $2,303,719,290
Net Worth: $244,156,931
Earnings: $1,811,956
Emp.: 745
Fiscal Year-end: 12/31/23
Commercial Banking Services
N.A.I.C.S.: 522110
Felix Istyono Hartadi Tiono (Dir-Compliance)

Subsidiaries:

J Grand Co., Ltd. (1)
7th floor Ebisu Garden Place Tower 4-20-3 Ebisu, Shibuya-ku, Tokyo, 150-0013, Japan
Tel.: (81) 366349998
Web Site: https://www.j-grand.co.jp
Real Estate Brokerage Services
N.A.I.C.S.: 531210

J Trust Global Securities Co., Ltd. (1)
7F Ebisu Garden Place Tower 4-20-3 Ebisu, Shibuya-ku, Tokyo, 150-6007, Japan
Tel.: (81) 345600200
Web Site: https://www.jtg-sec.co.jp
Financial Investment Services
N.A.I.C.S.: 523940

JT Chinae Saving Bank, Ltd. (1)
15-17F Pine Avenue B Bldg 100 Eulji-ro, Jung-gu, Seoul, Korea (South)
Tel.: (82) 15990060
Web Site: https://www.jtchinae-bank.co.kr
Emp.: 423
Banking Services
N.A.I.C.S.: 522320

Liverent Co., Ltd. (1)
1F Wako Building 5-65-4 Nakano, Nakano-ku, Tokyo, 164-0001, Japan
Tel.: (81) 359133199
Web Site: https://www.c21-live.co.jp
Real Estate Investment Services
N.A.I.C.S.: 531210

Nexus Card Co., Ltd. (1)
4-17 Chigusa-cho, Miyazaki, 880-0006, Japan
Tel.: (81) 985621123
Web Site: https://www.nexuscard.co.jp
Real Estate Financial Services
N.A.I.C.S.: 522292

Nihon Honshou Co., Ltd. (1)
7th floor Ebisu Garden Place Tower 4-20-3 Ebisu, Shibuya-ku, Tokyo, 150-6007, Japan
Tel.: (81) 368308100
Web Site: https://www.nihon-hoshou.co.jp
Real Estate Financial Services
N.A.I.C.S.: 522292

P.T. Jtrust Investments Indonesia (1)
Gedung Sahid Sudirman Center 36th Floor Jl Jenderal Sudirman Kav 86, Jakarta Pusat, 10220, Indonesia
Tel.: (62) 2127889238
Web Site: https://www.jtii.co.id
Financial Investment Services
N.A.I.C.S.: 523940

P.T. Turnaround Asset Indonesia (1)
35F Sahid Sudirman Center Building Jl Gen Sudirman No 86, Central Jakarta, Jakarta, Indonesia
Tel.: (62) 2124101005
Web Site: https://www.ta-asset.co.id
Emp.: 84
Asset Management Services
N.A.I.C.S.: 523999

Partir Service Co., Ltd. (1)
7-17-3 Nishigotanda, Shinagawa-ku, Tokyo, 141-0031, Japan
Tel.: (81) 343309988
Web Site: https://partir-servicer.jp
Emp.: 197
Real Estate Financial Services
N.A.I.C.S.: 522292

PT BANK KB BUKOPIN TBK
Jl MT Haryono Kav 50-51, Jakarta, 12770, Indonesia
Tel.: (62) 217988266 Id
Web Site: https://www.kbbank.co.id
Year Founded: 1970
BBKP—(INDO)
Rev.: $412,867,000
Assets: $8,999,535,200
Liabilities: $7,877,874,700
Net Worth: $1,121,660,500
Earnings: ($503,250,400)
Emp.: 2,833

INTERNATIONAL PUBLIC

Fiscal Year-end: 12/31/22
Financial Services
N.A.I.C.S.: 523999
Mikrowa Kirana (Dir-Comml)

Subsidiaries:

P.T. KB Bukopin Finance (1)
Jl Melawai Raya No 66 Kramat Pela Kec, Kebayoran Baru, South Jakarta, 12160, Jakarta, Indonesia
Tel.: (62) 2127936558
Web Site: https://www.bukopinfinance.co.id
Financial Services
N.A.I.C.S.: 523999

PT Bank Syariah Bukopin (1)
Kantor Pusat Jl Salemba Raya No 55, Jakarta Pusat, 10440, Indonesia
Tel.: (62) 212300912
Web Site: http://www.syariahbukopin.co.id
Commercial Banking Services
N.A.I.C.S.: 522110

PT Bukopin Finance (1)
Jl Melawai No 66 Kramat Pela Kec, Kebayoran Baru, Jakarta Selatan, 12160, Indonesia
Tel.: (62) 2172789683
Web Site: http://www.bukopinfinance.co.id
Commercial Banking Services
N.A.I.C.S.: 522110

PT BANK MANDIRI (PERSERO) TBK.
Jenderal Gatot Subroto Street Kav 36-38, Jakarta, 12190, Indonesia
Tel.: (62) 2152997777 Id
Year Founded: 1998
BMRI—(INDO)
Rev.: $13,254,447,000
Assets: $217,421,944,900
Liabilities: $188,672,448,700
Net Worth: $28,749,496,200
Earnings: $6,005,187,000
Emp.: 34,363
Fiscal Year-end: 12/31/23
Financial Investment Services
N.A.I.C.S.: 523999
Hery Gunardi (Dir-Consumer & Retail Transaction)

Subsidiaries:

Bank Mandiri (Europe) Limited (1)
4 Thomas More Square, London, E1W 1YW, United Kingdom
Tel.: (44) 2075538688
Web Site: https://www.bkmandiri.co.uk
Banking Services
N.A.I.C.S.: 522110
Mahendra Siregar (Chm)

Mandiri International Remittance Sendirian Berhad (1)
Ground Mezzanine Floor No29 31 Jalan Ipoh, 51200, Kuala Lumpur, Malaysia
Tel.: (60) 192619200
Web Site:
https://www.mandiriremittance.com
Remittance Services
N.A.I.C.S.: 522320
Mohd Fodli Hamzah (Dir)

Mandiri Securities Pte. Ltd. (1)
12 Marina View 19-06 Asia Square Tower 2, Singapore, 018961, Singapore
Tel.: (65) 65893880
Investment Bank & Broker Services
N.A.I.C.S.: 523999

P.T. FitAja Digital Nusantara (1)
Menara Palma Lantai 7 Jl H R Rasuna Said Blok X2 Kav 6, Jakarta Selatan, 12950, Indonesia
Tel.: (62) 89525306216
Web Site: https://fitaja.id
Information Technology Services
N.A.I.C.S.: 541519

P.T. Mandiri Capital Indonesia (1)
Menara Mandiri II lantai 14 Jl Jend Sudirman No 54-55, Jakarta, 12190, Indonesia
Tel.: (62) 215266661
Web Site: https://mandiri-capital.co.id
Investment Finance Services

AND PRIVATE COMPANIES

N.A.I.C.S.: 524298

PT AXA Mandiri Financial Services (1)
AXA Tower 9th Floor Jl Prof Dr Satrio Kav 18 Kuningan City, Kav 36-38, Jakarta, 12940, Indonesia
Tel.: (62) 2130058888
Financial Services; Joint Venture Owned 51% by AXA S.A. & 49% PT Bank Mandiri (Persero) Tbk.
N.A.I.C.S.: 523999

PT Asuransi Jiwa Inhealth Indonesia (1)
Mandiri Inhealth Tower lt 9 JL Prof Dr Satrio Kav E-IV, No 6 Kel Karet Kuningan Kec Setiabudi, Jakarta, 12920, Indonesia
Tel.: (62) 2125095000
Web Site: https://www.inhealth.co.id
Commercial Health Insurance Services
N.A.I.C.S.: 524114
Yusak Labanta Sudena Silalahi (Pres & Commissioner)

PT Bank Mandiri Taspen (1)
Graha Mantap Proklamasi street No 31, Menteng District, Jakarta, 10320, Indonesia
Tel.: (62) 2121231772
Web Site: https://www.bankmandiritaspen.co.id
Banking Services
N.A.I.C.S.: 522110
Elmamber P. Sinaga (Pres)

PT Bank Syariah Mandiri (1)
Wisma Mandiri I Jl MH Thamrin No 5, Jakarta, 10340, Indonesia
Tel.: (62) 212300509
Web Site: http://www.mandirisyariah.co.id
Banking Services
N.A.I.C.S.: 522110
Toni Eko Boy Subari (Chm)

PT Mandiri AXA General Insurance (1)
AXA Tower Lantai Dasar Jl Prof Dr Satrio Kav 18, Kuningan, 12940, Jakarta, Indonesia
Tel.: (62) 150 0803
Web Site: https://www.axa-mandiri.co.id
Financial Investment Services
N.A.I.C.S.: 523999
Handojo Gunawan Kusuma (Pres)

PT Mandiri Manajemen Investasi (1)
Tel.: (62) 215263505
Investment Portfolio Management Services
N.A.I.C.S.: 523940
Aliyahdin Saugi (Co-Pres)

PT Mandiri Sekuritas (1)
JL Jenderal Sudirman Kav 54-55, Jakarta, 12190, Indonesia
Tel.: (62) 215263445
Sales Range: $100-124.9 Million
Emp.: 200
Financial Services
N.A.I.C.S.: 522299

PT Mandiri Tunas Finance (1)
Graha Mandiri Lt 3A Jl Imam Bonjol No 61, Jakarta, 10310, Indonesia
Tel.: (62) 212305608
Web Site: https://www.mtf.co.id
Financial Investment Services
N.A.I.C.S.: 523999

PT Mandiri Utama Finance (1)
Menara Mandiri 1 Floor 26-27 Jl Jendral Sudirman Kav 54-55, Jakarta, 12190, Indonesia
Tel.: (62) 1500824
Web Site: https://www.muf.co.id
Vehicle Financing Services
N.A.I.C.S.: 525990

PT Mitra Transaksi Indonesia Kepemilika (1)
Millennium Centennial Center 17th Floor Jl Jend Sudirman Kav 25, Jakarta Selatan, 12920, Indonesia
Tel.: (62) 2180628787
Web Site: https://www.yokke.co.id
Financial Investment Services
N.A.I.C.S.: 523999
Niniek Rahardja (Pres)

PT Usaha Gedung Bank Dagang Negara (1)
Jalan MH Thamrin No 5, PO Box 2802, 10340, Jakarta, Indonesia (99%)
Tel.: (62) 212300800
Web Site: http://www.ptugbdn.com
Commercial Banking Services
N.A.I.C.S.: 522110

PT BANK MASPION INDONESIA TBK
Jl Embong Malang No 21-31 Pakuwon Tower Tunjungan Plaza 6 Lt 32 & 33, Surabaya, 60262, Indonesia
Tel.: (62) 3198588789
Web Site: http://www.bankmaspion.co.id
BMAS—(INDO)
Rev.: $78,141,951
Assets: $1,277,107,635
Liabilities: $840,538,256
Net Worth: $436,569,379
Earnings: $4,107,676
Emp.: 795
Fiscal Year-end: 12/31/23
Banking Services
N.A.I.C.S.: 522110
Herman Halim (Chm)

PT BANK MAYAPADA INTERNASIONAL TBK.
Mayapada Tower Ground Floor-3rd Floor Jl Jend Sudirman Kav 28, Jakarta, 12920, Indonesia
Tel.: (62) 215212288
Web Site: https://www.bankmayapada.com
MAYA—(INDO)
Rev.: $569,139,225
Assets: $9,188,295,400
Liabilities: $8,157,852,352
Net Worth: $1,030,443,048
Earnings: $1,435,369
Emp.: 2,605
Fiscal Year-end: 12/31/23
Banking Services
N.A.I.C.S.: 521110
Hariyono Tjahjarijadi (Chm)

PT BANK MEGA TBK
Menara Bank Mega 15th Floor Jl Kapten P Tendean No 12-14A, Jakarta, 12790, Indonesia
Tel.: (62) 2179175000
Web Site: https://www.bankmega.com
Year Founded: 1969
MEGA—(INDO)
Rev.: $663,526,528
Assets: $8,575,300,440
Liabilities: $7,162,501,971
Net Worth: $1,412,798,468
Earnings: $227,982,910
Emp.: 4,729
Fiscal Year-end: 12/31/23
Bank Holding Company
N.A.I.C.S.: 551111
Kostaman Thayib (Pres)

PT BANK MESTIKA DHARMA TBK
Jl H Zainul Arifin No 118, Medan, 20112, Indonesia
Tel.: (62) 614525800
Web Site: https://www.bankmestika.com
Year Founded: 1955
BBMD—(INDO)
Rev.: $129,174,627
Assets: $1,658,399,093
Liabilities: $1,203,169,297
Net Worth: $455,229,795
Earnings: $52,310,388
Emp.: 1,085
Fiscal Year-end: 12/31/22
Banking Services
N.A.I.C.S.: 522110
Achmad Suherman Kartasasmita (Chm)

PT BANK MITRANIAGA TBK
Wisma 77 Jl Letjen S Parman Kav 77, Slipi, Jakarta, Indonesia
Tel.: (62) 21 5481877
Web Site: http://www.bankmitraniaga.co.id
Rev.: $15,132,280
Assets: $161,935,726
Liabilities: $147,060,794
Net Worth: $14,874,932
Earnings: $627,266
Emp.: 139
Fiscal Year-end: 12/31/18
Commericial Banking
N.A.I.C.S.: 522110
Paberd Leonard Hutagaol (Dir-Operation)

PT BANK MNC INTERNASIONAL TBK
MNC Financial Center Lantai 8 Jalan Kebon Sirih No 21-27, Jakarta, 10340, Indonesia
Tel.: (62) 2129805555
Web Site: https://mncbank.co.id
Year Founded: 1989
BABP—(INDO)
Rev.: $85,268,883
Assets: $1,178,490,727
Liabilities: $945,522,763
Net Worth: $232,967,964
Earnings: $6,819,934
Emp.: 735
Fiscal Year-end: 12/31/23
Commercial Banking Services
N.A.I.C.S.: 522110
Rita Montagna (Dir-Funding & Operation)

PT BANK MULTIARTA SENTOSA TBK
Grha Bank Mas Jl Setiabudi Selatan Kav 7-8, 12920, Jakarta Selatan, 12920, Indonesia
Tel.: (62) 2157906006
Web Site: https://www.bankmas.co.id
Year Founded: 1992
MASB—(INDO)
Rev.: $95,972,829
Assets: $1,778,479,749
Liabilities: $1,539,337,479
Net Worth: $239,142,271
Earnings: $15,836,059
Emp.: 799
Fiscal Year-end: 12/31/23
Bank Holding Company
N.A.I.C.S.: 551111
Ho Danny Hartono (Pres)

PT BANK NATIONALNOBU TBK
Plaza Semanggi Jl Jend Sudirman Kav 50, Jakarta, 12930, Indonesia
Tel.: (62) 57974066
Web Site: http://www.nobubank.com
NOBU—(INDO)
Rev.: $97,356,684
Assets: $1,728,855,539
Liabilities: $1,512,279,665
Net Worth: $216,575,874
Earnings: $9,191,348
Emp.: 935
Fiscal Year-end: 12/31/23
Banking Services
N.A.I.C.S.: 522110
Suhaimin Djohan (Chm)

PT BANK NEGARA INDONESIA (PERSERO) TBK
Gedung Grha BNI Jl Jenderal Sudirman Kav 1, Jakarta Pusat, 10220, Indonesia
Tel.: (62) 212511946
Web Site: https://www.bni.co.id
Year Founded: 1946
BBNI—(INDO)
Rev.: $6,147,169,600
Assets: $108,666,398,600
Liabilities: $93,193,146,600
Net Worth: $15,473,252,000
Earnings: $2,110,622,800
Emp.: 25,460
Fiscal Year-end: 12/31/23
Financial Investment Services
N.A.I.C.S.: 523999
Rico Rizal Budidarmo (Mng Dir-Risk Mgmt)

Subsidiaries:

BNI Remittance Limited (1)
Flat/RM5 on GF nos 1-7 Keswick Street, Causeway Bay, China (Hong Kong)
Tel.: (852) 2890 8082
Banking Services
N.A.I.C.S.: 522110

BNI Securities Pte. Ltd. (1)
Prudential Tower 30 Cecil Street 17-08, Singapore, 049712, Singapore
Tel.: (65) 69113750
Web Site: https://bnisecurities.com.sg
Investment Banking Services
N.A.I.C.S.: 523150

Bank Negara Indonesia (1)
1 Exchange Plz 5th Fl 55 Broadway, New York, NY 10006
Tel.: (212) 943-4750
Web Site: https://www.bankbniny.com
Sales Range: Less than $1 Million
Banking Services
N.A.I.C.S.: 522110

P.T. Bank Mayora (1)
Jl Tomang Raya Kav 21-23, Jakarta Barat, 11440, Indonesia
Tel.: (62) 215655287
Web Site: https://www.bankmayora.com
Banking Services
N.A.I.C.S.: 522110

PT BNI Life Insurance (1)
Centennial Tower 9th Floor Jl Gatot Subroto Kav 24-25, Jakarta, 12930, Indonesia
Tel.: (62) 1500045
Web Site: https://www.bni-life.co.id
Fire Insurance Services
N.A.I.C.S.: 524113

PT BNI Multifinance (1)
Graha Binakarsa Lt 11 Lot E - F dan Lt 12, Jl H R Rasuna Said Kav C-18 kuningan, Jakarta, 12940, Indonesia
Tel.: (62) 2129022555
Web Site: https://www.bnimultifinance.co.id
Consumer Finance Services
N.A.I.C.S.: 522291

PT BNI Securities (1)
Sudirman Plaza Indofood Tower Lantai 16, Jl Jend Sudirman Kav 76-78, Jakarta, 12910, Indonesia
Tel.: (62) 2125543946
Web Site: http://www.bnisecurities.co.id
Securities Brokerage Services
N.A.I.C.S.: 523150

PT BNI Syariah (1)
Gedung Tempo Pavilion 1 Jl HR Rasuna Said Kav 10-11 Lt 3-8, Jl Jend Sudirman Kav 1, Jakarta, Indonesia
Tel.: (62) 2129701946
Web Site: http://www.bnisyariah.co.id
Banking Services
N.A.I.C.S.: 522110

PT BANK NEO COMMERCE TBK
Gedung Gozco Jl Raya Pasar Minggu Kav 32, Jakarta Selatan, Indonesia
Tel.: (62) 2129752975
Web Site: https://www.yudhabhakti.co.id
Year Founded: 1990
BBYB—(INDO)
Rev.: $249,827,362
Assets: $1,179,929,993
Liabilities: $964,131,840
Net Worth: $215,798,153

PT BANK NEO COMMERCE TBK

PT Bank Neo Commerce Tbk—(Continued)
Earnings: ($37,222,309)
Emp.: 579
Fiscal Year-end: 12/31/23
Banking Services
N.A.I.C.S.: 522110
Tjandra Gunawan (Chm)

PT BANK OKE INDONESIA TBK
Jl Ir H Juanda No 12, Jakarta, 10120, Pusat, Indonesia
Tel.: (62) 212312633
Web Site: https://www.okbank.co.id
Year Founded: 1990
DNAR—(INDO)
Rev.: $64,964,873
Assets: $719,220,311
Liabilities: $486,443,822
Net Worth: $232,776,490
Earnings: $1,860,647
Emp.: 302
Fiscal Year-end: 12/31/23
Commercial Banking Services
N.A.I.C.S.: 522110

PT BANK PEMBANGUNAN DAERAH BANTEN TBK
Jl Sudirman Lingkungan Kemang Ruko Sembilan No 8b 9a, Kelurahan Sumur Pecung, Serang, Indonesia
Tel.: (62) 547917346
Web Site: https://www.bankbanten.co.id
Year Founded: 1992
BEKS—(INDO)
Rev.: $29,402,169
Assets: $441,645,316
Liabilities: $333,256,235
Net Worth: $108,389,081
Earnings: $1,726,820
Emp.: 829
Fiscal Year-end: 12/31/23
Commercial Banking Services
N.A.I.C.S.: 522110
Fahmi Bagus Mahesa (Chm)

PT BANK PEMBANGUNAN DAERAH JAWA TIMUR TBK
Jalan Basuki Rachmad No 98-104, Surabaya, 60271, Indonesia
Tel.: (62) 315310090   Id
Web Site: https://www.bankjatim.co.id
Year Founded: 1961
BJTM—(INDO)
Rev.: $477,782,023
Assets: $6,744,328,959
Liabilities: $5,955,238,538
Net Worth: $789,090,421
Earnings: $95,468,619
Emp.: 4,225
Fiscal Year-end: 12/31/23
Commercial Banking Services
N.A.I.C.S.: 522110

PT BANK RAKYAT INDONESIA (PERSERO) TBK
Gedung BRI Jl Jenderal Sudirman Kav 44-46, Jakarta, 10210, Indonesia
Tel.: (62) 621500017   Id
Web Site: http://www.ir-bri.com
Year Founded: 1895
BBRI—(INDO)
Rev.: $8,185,275,840
Assets: $105,826,323,960
Liabilities: $89,484,239,320
Net Worth: $16,342,084,640
Earnings: $1,306,227,510
Emp.: 62,388
Fiscal Year-end: 12/31/20
Financial Investment Services
N.A.I.C.S.: 523999
Haru Koesmahargyo (Dir-Fin)

Subsidiaries:

BRI Remittance Co. Ltd.   (1)
Shop 3 G/F Bayview Mansion Shopping Arcade 33 Moreton Terrace, Causeway Bay, China (Hong Kong)
Tel.: (852) 28902709
Money Transfer Services
N.A.I.C.S.: 522320

P.T. BRI Danareksa Sekuritas   (1)
Gedung BRI II lt 23 Jl Jend Sudirman Kav 44-46, Jakarta, 10210, Indonesia
Tel.: (62) 1500688
Web Site: https://www.bridanareksasekuritas.co.id
Financial Advisory Services
N.A.I.C.S.: 522320

P.T. Danareksa Investment Management   (1)
Gedung BRI II Lantai 22 Jl Jend Sudirman Kav 44-46, Jakarta, 10210, Indonesia
Tel.: (62) 2129555789
Web Site: https://www.danareksainvestment.co.id
Financial Investment Management Services
N.A.I.C.S.: 525110

P.T. Pegadaian   (1)
Jl Kramat Raya 162, Jakarta Pusat, 10430, Indonesia
Tel.: (62) 213155550
Web Site: https://www.pegadaian.co.id
Pawn Shops Services
N.A.I.C.S.: 561720

PT BRI Multifinance Indonesia   (1)
Brilliant Tower Fl 121 and 22 Jl Gatot Subroto Kav 64 No 117A, Menteng Dalam Tebet, Jakarta, 10220, Indonesia
Tel.: (62) 215745333
Web Site: https://www.brifinance.co.id
Financial Lending Services
N.A.I.C.S.: 522220

PT BRI Ventura Investama   (1)
District 8 Office Prosperity Tower Lt 16 Unit F SCBD Lot 28 Jl Jend, Sudirman Kav 52-53 Senayan Kebayoran Baru, Jakarta, 12190, Indonesia
Tel.: (62) 2150928500
Investment Banking Services
N.A.I.C.S.: 523150
William Gozali (VP-Investment)

PT Bank Raya Indonesia Tbk   (1)
Gedung Bank RAYA Jl Warung Jati Barat No 139, Jakarta, 12740, Indonesia
Tel.: (62) 2180667667
Web Site: https://bankraya.co.id
Rev.: $57,858,853
Assets: $807,895,307
Liabilities: $585,784,274
Net Worth: $222,111,033
Earnings: $1,581,356
Emp.: 702
Fiscal Year-end: 12/31/2023
Retail & Commercial Banking
N.A.I.C.S.: 522110
Ebeneser Girsang (Chm-Acting)

PT Bank Syariah Indonesia Tbk   (1)
Kantor Pusat Gedung The Tower, Jl Gatot Subroto, Kecamatan Setiabudi, Jakarta Selatan, 12930, Indonesia
Tel.: (62) 81584114040
Web Site: https://www.bankbsi.co.id
Retail Banking Services
N.A.I.C.S.: 522110

PT Danareksa Sekuritas   (1)
Gedung BRI II lt 23 Jl Jend Sudirman Kav 44-46, Jakarta, 10210, Indonesia
Tel.: (62) 2150914100
Web Site: http://www.danareksasekuritas.com
Investment Security Services
N.A.I.C.S.: 523150
Venny Tri Handayani (Mgr-Human Capital)

PT Kustodian Sentral Efek Indonesia   (1)
Jakarta Stock Exchange Building Tower 1 5th Fl, Jl Jenderal Sudirman Kav 52-53, Jakarta, 12190, Indonesia
Tel.: (62) 2152991099
Sales Range: $50-74.9 Million
Emp.: 76
Security & Commodity Services

N.A.I.C.S.: 523999

PT BANK SINARMAS TBK.
Sinar Mas Land Plaza Tower I Lt 1 & 2 Jl MH Thamrin Kav 51, Jakarta, 10350, Indonesia
Tel.: (62) 2131990101   Id
Web Site: https://www.banksinarmas.com
Year Founded: 1989
BSIM—(INDO)
Rev.: $230,496,997
Assets: $3,418,116,640
Liabilities: $2,909,846,326
Net Worth: $508,270,314
Earnings: $4,922,192
Emp.: 4,685
Fiscal Year-end: 12/31/23
Commercial Banking Services
N.A.I.C.S.: 522110
Loa Johnny Mailoa (Dir-Enterprise & Retail Banking)

PT BANK TABUNGAN NEGARA (PERSERO) TBK
Menara Bank BTN Jl Gajah Mada No 1, Jakarta, 10130, Indonesia
Tel.: (62) 216336789
Web Site: http://www.btn.co.id
Year Founded: 1897
BBTN—(INDO)
Rev.: $1,836,584,505
Assets: $28,492,407,856
Liabilities: $24,752,821,916
Net Worth: $3,739,585,940
Earnings: $227,354,161
Emp.: 11,270
Fiscal Year-end: 12/31/23
Commercial Banking Services
N.A.I.C.S.: 522110
Nixon L. P. Napitupulu (Dir-Fin, Treasury & Strategy)

PT BANK VICTORIA INTERNATIONAL TBK
Gedung Graha BIP lt 10 Jl Gatot Subroto Kav 23, Jakarta Selatan, 12930, Indonesia
Tel.: (62) 215228888   Id
Web Site: http://www.victoriabank.co.id
BVIC—(INDO)
Rev.: $119,255,240
Assets: $1,923,798,173
Liabilities: $1,675,416,634
Net Worth: $248,381,539
Earnings: $6,611,953
Emp.: 410
Fiscal Year-end: 12/31/23
Commercial Banking Services
N.A.I.C.S.: 522110
Claudia Audrey (Head-Acctg & Fin Div)

Subsidiaries:

PT Bank Victoria Syariah   (1)
BIP Graha Building 5th Floor Jl Gatot Subroto Kav 23, Exo Karet Semanggi Kec Setiabudi, South Jakarta, Indonesia
Tel.: (62) 215600467
Web Site: http://www.bankvictoriasyariah.co.id
Financial Bank Services
N.A.I.C.S.: 522110
Lydia Sabarudin (Branch Mgr)

PT BANK WOORI SAUDARA INDONESIA 1906 TBK
Treasury Tower Lantai 26 dan 27 District 8 SCBD Lot 28, Jl Jend Sudirman Kav 52-53, Jakarta, 12190, Indonesia
Tel.: (62) 2150871906
Web Site: https://www.bankwoorisaudara.com
SDRA—(INDO)
Rev.: $241,528,142

Assets: $3,560,152,434
Liabilities: $2,893,018,489
Net Worth: $667,133,945
Earnings: $45,319,288
Emp.: 1,217
Fiscal Year-end: 12/31/23
Banking Services
N.A.I.C.S.: 521110
Madyantoro Purbo (Deputy Chm)

PT BARA JAYA INTERNASIONAL TBK.
AXA Tower 29th Floor Suite 01 Kuningan City, Jl Prof Dr Satrio Kav 18 Setiabudi, Jakarta, 12940, Indonesia
Tel.: (62) 2130056388   Id
Web Site: http://www.atpkresources.co.id
Year Founded: 1988
Sales Range: $50-74.9 Million
Emp.: 1,064
Holding Company; Coal Mining, Oil & Gas Exploration, Energy Investment & Resource Trading Services
N.A.I.C.S.: 551112

PT BARAMULTI SUKSESSARANA TBK
Graha Baramulti Jl Suryopranoto No 2 Komplek Harmoni Blok 8A, Jakarta Pusat 10131 Indonesia, Jakarta, 10131, Indonesia
Tel.: (62) 63853228
Web Site: https://www.bssr.co.id
BSSR—(INDO)
Rev.: $1,134,336,606
Assets: $408,454,573
Liabilities: $165,971,113
Net Worth: $242,483,460
Earnings: $162,269,459
Emp.: 1,095
Fiscal Year-end: 12/31/23
Coal Mining
N.A.I.C.S.: 212115
Anand Agarwal (Vice Chm)

PT BARITO PACIFIC TBK
Wisma Barito Pacific II 23rd Floor Jl Let Jend S Parman Kav 60, Jakarta, 11410, Indonesia
Tel.: (62) 215306711   Id
Web Site: https://www.barito-pacific.com
BRPT—(INDO)
Rev.: $2,760,359,000
Assets: $10,149,666,000
Liabilities: $6,037,737,000
Net Worth: $4,111,929,000
Earnings: $99,776,000
Emp.: 3,026
Fiscal Year-end: 12/31/23
Plastic Resin Mfr
N.A.I.C.S.: 325211
Agus Salim Pangestu (Chm)

Subsidiaries:

PT Chandra Asri Pacific Tbk   (1)
Wisma Barito Pacific Tower A 7th Floor Jl Let Jend S Parman Kav 62-63, Jakarta, 11410, Indonesia   (34.63%)
Tel.: (62) 215307950
Web Site: https://www.chandra-asri.com
Rev.: $2,159,932,000
Assets: $5,614,452,000
Liabilities: $2,620,552,000
Net Worth: $2,993,900,000
Earnings: ($31,547,000)
Emp.: 1,943
Fiscal Year-end: 12/31/2023
Petrochemical Mfr & Distr
N.A.I.C.S.: 325110
Erwin Ciputra (CEO)

Star Energy Geothermal ("SEG") Pte. Ltd.   (1)
17th-21st Floor Jl Letjen S Parman Kav 60, Jakarta, 11410, Indonesia
Tel.: (62) 2129180800

PT BARITO RENEWABLES ENERGY TBK
Wisma Barito Pacific II 23rd Floor Jl Let Jend S Parman Kav 60, Jakarta, 11410, Indonesia
Tel.: (62) 215306711
Web Site:
 https://www.baritorenewables.co.id
Year Founded: 2018
BREN—(INDO)
Rev.: $38,289
Assets: $228,058
Liabilities: $198,826
Net Worth: $29,232
Earnings: $11,596
Fiscal Year-end: 12/31/22
Renewable Energy Services
N.A.I.C.S.: 221210
Hendra Soetjipto Tan *(Pres)*

PT BATAVIA PROSPERINDO INTERNASIONAL TBK
Chase Plaza 12th Floor Jl Jend Sudirman Kav 21, Jakarta, 12920, Indonesia
Tel.: (62) 215200180
Web Site:
 https://www.bpinternasional.com
Year Founded: 1998
BPII—(INDO)
Rev.: $63,071,984
Assets: $270,299,241
Liabilities: $163,117,882
Net Worth: $107,181,359
Earnings: $9,014,159
Emp.: 380
Fiscal Year-end: 12/31/23
Management Consulting Services
N.A.I.C.S.: 541613
Rudi Setiadi Tjahjono *(Chm)*

Subsidiaries:

PT Batavia Prosperindo Aset Manajemen (1)
Gedung Chase Plaza Lantai 12 Jl Jend Sudirman Kav 21, Jakarta, 12920, Indonesia
Tel.: (62) 215208390
Web Site: http://www.bpam.co.id
Asset Management Services
N.A.I.C.S.: 523940
M. Arie Armand *(Commissioner)*

PT Batavia Prosperindo Trans Tbk (1)
Gd Chase Plaza Lt 12 Jl Jend Sudirman Kav 21, Jakarta, 12920, Indonesia
Tel.: (62) 2153191717 (74.95%)
Web Site: https://www.bataviarent.com
Rev.: $11,381,731
Assets: $37,529,379
Liabilities: $22,234,887
Net Worth: $15,294,491
Earnings: $567,578
Fiscal Year-end: 12/31/2019
Freight Forwarding & Logistics Consulting Services
N.A.I.C.S.: 488510
Paulus Handigdo *(Pres)*

PT BATULICIN NUSANTARA MARITIM TBK
Jl Pelabuhan Ferry No 69 Kelurahan Batulicin, Kecamatan Batulicin Kabupaten Tanah Bumbu, Kalimantan, 72271, Indonesia
Tel.: (62) 51870069
Web Site:
 https://www.batulicinnusantara.com
Year Founded: 2011
BESS—(INDO)
Rev.: $23,621,352
Assets: $44,795,831
Liabilities: $7,615,200
Net Worth: $37,180,631
Earnings: $5,159,485
Fiscal Year-end: 12/31/23
Marine Transportation Services
N.A.I.C.S.: 488320

PT BAYU BUANA TBK
Jl Ir H Juanda III No 2, Jakarta, 10120, Indonesia
Tel.: (62) 2123509999
Web Site:
 https://www.bayubuanatravel.com
Year Founded: 1972
BAYU—(INDO)
Rev.: $141,225,727
Assets: $57,377,034
Liabilities: $28,039,259
Net Worth: $29,337,775
Earnings: $4,595,043
Emp.: 398
Fiscal Year-end: 12/31/23
Travel Management Services
N.A.I.C.S.: 561599
Agustinus Kasjaya Pake Seko *(Chm)*

Subsidiaries:

P.T. Duta Buana Express (1)
Jl Ir H Juanda III No 2, Jakarta, 10120, Indonesia
Tel.: (62) 34831525
Airline Ticket Booking Services
N.A.I.C.S.: 561599

PT BERAU COAL ENERGY TBK
Jl Pemuda No 40, PO Box 114, 77311, Tanjung Redeb, 77311, Kalimantan Timur, Indonesia
Tel.: (62) 55423400
Web Site:
 https://beraucoalenergy.co.id
Coal Mining Services
N.A.I.C.S.: 212115
Gandi Sulistiyanto Soeherman *(Pres)*

PT BERDIKARI PONDASI PERKASA TBK
Jl Bandengan Utara No 32B RT 008/RW 011 Kel Pekojan Kec Tambora, Jakarta Barat, 11240, Indonesia
Tel.: (62) 215662756
Web Site: https://www.ptbppid.com
Year Founded: 1984
BDKR—(INDO)
Rev.: $39,838,203
Assets: $100,543,455
Liabilities: $49,602,754
Net Worth: $50,940,700
Earnings: $5,150,366
Emp.: 98
Fiscal Year-end: 12/31/23
Construction Services
N.A.I.C.S.: 236210
John Tanuwijaya Tan *(Founder)*

PT BERKAH BETON SADAYA TBK
Jl Raya Sembung Pagaden KM 9 5 Gunungsari Pagaden Subang, Kabupaten Subang, Jakarta Barat, 41252, Indonesia
Tel.: (62) 2604551571
Web Site:
 https://www.berkahbeton.com
Year Founded: 2019
BEBS—(INDO)
Rev.: $26,100,055
Assets: $58,469,803
Liabilities: $5,502,921
Net Worth: $52,966,881
Earnings: $2,845,439
Emp.: 25
Fiscal Year-end: 12/31/23
Construction Materials Distr
N.A.I.C.S.: 423320
Hasan Muldhani *(Pres)*

PT BERKAH PRIMA PERKASA TBK
Jln Mangga Besar 1 No 82, Jakarta, 11180, Indonesia
Tel.: (62) 216259975
Web Site:
 https://www.primaperkasaal.com
BLUE—(INDO)
Rev.: $9,291,827
Assets: $6,753,272
Liabilities: $863,214
Net Worth: $5,890,058
Earnings: $1,086,667
Emp.: 38
Fiscal Year-end: 12/31/23
Aluminium Product Distr
N.A.I.C.S.: 423510
Vini Hardianti *(Sec)*

PT BERLIAN LAJU TANKER TBK
Jl Abdul Muis No 40, Jakarta, 10160, Indonesia
Tel.: (62) 2130060300
Web Site: https://www.blt.co.id
BLTA—(INDO)
Rev.: $39,025,697
Assets: $93,000,230
Liabilities: $35,379,853
Net Worth: $57,620,377
Earnings: $15,616,876
Emp.: 61
Fiscal Year-end: 12/31/23
Fleet Operation Services
N.A.I.C.S.: 532112
Siana Anggraeni Surya *(Chm)*

Subsidiaries:

Gold Bridge Shipping Ltd. (1)
Room 2205-2206 China Insurance Group Bldg 141 Des Voeux Road C, Hong Kong, China (Hong Kong)
Tel.: (852) 28542318
Web Site: https://www.gbship.com
Ship Management Services
N.A.I.C.S.: 483111
Muhammed Jalal Uddin *(Dir)*

Indigo Pacific Corporation (1)
Unit A-35-10 Level 35 Tower A No 5 Jalan Bangsar Utama 1, Menara UOA Bangsar, 59000, Kuala Lumpur, Malaysia
Tel.: (60) 322833676
Document Preparation Services
N.A.I.C.S.: 561410

PT Buana Lintas Lautan Tbk (1)
Jl Mega Kuningan Timur Blok C6 Kav 12A, Mega Kuningan, South Jakarta, 12950, Indonesia
Tel.: (62) 2130485700
Web Site: https://www.bull.co.id
Rev.: $101,451,071
Assets: $550,843,358
Liabilities: $267,850,212
Net Worth: $282,993,146
Earnings: $23,269,848
Emp.: 159
Fiscal Year-end: 12/31/2019
Marine Shipping Services
N.A.I.C.S.: 488330
Kevin Wong *(Bd of Dirs & Chm)*

PT BETONJAYA MANUNGGAL TBK
Jl Raya Krikilan No 434 Km 28, Kecamatan Driyorejo, Gresik, 61177, Indonesia
Tel.: (62) 317507303
Web Site: https://www.bjm.co.id
Year Founded: 1995
BTON—(INDO)
Rev.: $9,062,325
Assets: $23,483,153
Liabilities: $6,777,731
Net Worth: $16,705,422
Earnings: $1,138,428
Emp.: 53
Fiscal Year-end: 12/31/23
Metal Bar Mfr
N.A.I.C.S.: 331221
Jenny Tanujaya *(Dir-Fin)*

PT BHAKTI AGUNG PROPERTINDO TBK
Jl Raden Fatah No 62, Ciledug, Tangerang, 15151, Indonesia
Tel.: (62) 2122797778
Web Site:
 https://www.bhaktiagung.com
Year Founded: 2012
BAPI—(INDO)
Rev.: $142,608
Assets: $43,682,849
Liabilities: $15,991,674
Net Worth: $27,691,175
Earnings: ($85,891)
Emp.: 4
Fiscal Year-end: 12/31/23
Real Estate Services
N.A.I.C.S.: 531210
H. Agung Hadi Tjahjanto *(Chm)*

PT BHAKTI MULTI ARTHA TBK
Tifa Building Lt 8 Kuningan Barat Street No 26, South Jakarta, 12710, Indonesia
Tel.: (62) 27097677
Web Site:
 https://www.bhaktimultiartha.co.id
Year Founded: 2017
BHAT—(INDO)
Rev.: $12,188,833
Assets: $72,391,964
Liabilities: $36,841,747
Net Worth: $35,550,218
Earnings: $223,871
Emp.: 40
Fiscal Year-end: 12/31/23
Financial Services
N.A.I.C.S.: 523150
Dimas Teguh Mulyanto *(Pres)*

Subsidiaries:

PT Asuransi Jiwa Nasional (1)
Gedung Menara Jamsostek Menara Utara Lt 3A, Jl Jenderal Gatot Subroto No 38, Jakarta Selatan, 12710, Indonesia
Tel.: (62) 2129181999
Web Site: https://www.nasionallife.co.id
Fire Insurance Services
N.A.I.C.S.: 524113

PT Bhakti Cahaya Utama (1)
Sona Topas Tower Lt 9 Jl Jenderal Sudirman Kav 26 Kel Karet Kec, Setiabudi, Jakarta Selatan, Jakarta, Indonesia
Tel.: (62) 212506210
Management Consulting Services
N.A.I.C.S.: 541611

PT Bhakti Fintek Indonesia (1)
Sona Topas Tower Lt 9 Jl Jenderal Sudirman Kav 26 Kel Karet Kec, Setiabudi, Jakarta Selatan, Jakarta, Indonesia
Tel.: (62) 212506210
Management Consulting Services
N.A.I.C.S.: 541611

PT Nasional Investindo Perkasa (1)
Office 8 Lt 18A SCBD Jl Jenderal Sudirman Kav 52-53 Kel Senayan Kec, Kebayoran Baru, Jakarta Selatan, Jakarta, Indonesia
Tel.: (62) 2129222999
Management Consulting Services
N.A.I.C.S.: 541611

PT BIMA SAKTI PERTIWI TBK
Jalan Jend Sudirman No 123 E, Kota Tinggi, Pekanbaru, 28112, Riau, Indonesia
Tel.: (62) 761853888
Web Site:
 https://www.bimasaktipertiwi.com
Year Founded: 1980
PAMG—(INDO)
Rev.: $3,342,914
Assets: $37,836,440
Liabilities: $10,352,143
Net Worth: $27,484,297
Earnings: $27,755

PT BIMA SAKTI PERTIWI TBK

PT Bima Sakti Pertiwi TBK—(Continued)
Emp.: 72
Fiscal Year-end: 12/31/23
Real Estate Services
N.A.I.C.S.: 531210
Christopher Sumasto *(Pres)*

PT BINAKARYA JAYA ABADI TBK
Mall Taman Palem Lantai 3 Jl Kamal Raya Outer Ring Road, Cengkareng, Jakarta, 11730, Indonesia
Tel.: (62) 2154360381
Web Site: https://www.bpg.id
BIKA—(INDO)
Rev.: $17,525,555
Assets: $189,275,032
Liabilities: $213,418,956
Net Worth: ($24,143,924)
Earnings: ($2,868,834)
Emp.: 152
Fiscal Year-end: 12/31/23
Property Developer
N.A.I.C.S.: 236220
Budianto Halim *(Chm)*

PT BINTANG MITRA SEMESTARAYA TBK
Graha BIP Lt 2 Jl Jend Gatot Subroto Kav 23 Selatan, Jakarta, 12930, Indonesia
Tel.: (62) 212522586
Web Site:
https://www.bintangmitra.com
Year Founded: 2008
Rev.: $203,697,512
Assets: $43,543,601
Liabilities: $32,968,929
Net Worth: $10,574,672
Earnings: $363,448
Emp.: 59
Fiscal Year-end: 12/31/19
Chemical & Rice Distr
N.A.I.C.S.: 424690
Fajri Rahmawati *(Sec)*

Subsidiaries:

PT. Binatek Reka Kruh (1)
Graha BIP Jl Jend Gatot Subroto Kav 23, Jakarta Selatan, 12930, Indonesia
Tel.: (62) 212522586
Real Estate Services
N.A.I.C.S.: 531390

PT BINTANG OTO GLOBAL TBK
S Supriadi Street No 19-22 Sukun, Malang, East Java, Indonesia
Tel.: (62) 341363499   Id
Web Site:
https://www.bintangotoglobal.com
Year Founded: 2011
BOGA—(INDO)
Rev.: $58,565,455
Assets: $53,590,975
Liabilities: $21,956,500
Net Worth: $31,634,475
Earnings: $486,160
Emp.: 200
Fiscal Year-end: 12/31/23
New Car Retailer
N.A.I.C.S.: 441110
Arif Andi Wihatmanto *(Chm)*

PT BINTANG SAMUDERA MANDIRI LINES TBK
Aminta Plaza Floor 04 Jl TB Sirnatupang Kar I0, Menteng Atas Setiabudi, Jakarta Selatan, 12310, Indonesia
Tel.: (62) 2176634850
Web Site: https://bsmlines.com
Year Founded: 2007
BSML—(INDO)
Rev.: $20,589,611
Assets: $16,572,766
Liabilities: $8,550,084
Net Worth: $8,022,682
Earnings: $1,108,643
Emp.: 19
Fiscal Year-end: 12/31/23
Marine Transportation Services
N.A.I.C.S.: 488390
Pramayari Hardian Doktrianto *(Sec)*

PT BINTRACO DHARMA TBK
Jl Sunburst CBD LOT II No 3 BSD City Serpong, Lengkong Gudang Serpong Sub-District, Tangerang, 15321, Indonesia
Tel.: (62) 2122356800
Web Site:
https://www.bintracodharma.com
Year Founded: 1969
CARS—(INDO)
Rev.: $421,137,266
Assets: $251,247,734
Liabilities: $194,307,360
Net Worth: $56,940,373
Earnings: $13,073,437
Emp.: 2,726
Fiscal Year-end: 12/31/23
Automobile Financing Services
N.A.I.C.S.: 522220
Sebastianus Harno Budi *(Chm)*

Subsidiaries:

PT Meka Adipratama (1)
Jl Puspowaro Tengah No 7-13 salamamirnloyo, Semarang Barat, Semarang, 50143, Barat Jawa Tengah, Indonesia
Tel.: (62) 247603001
Web Site: https://www.meka.co.id
Spare Parts Distr
N.A.I.C.S.: 423120
Joko Trisanyoto *(Pres)*

PT Mitra Oto Prima (1)
Jalan Sunburst CBD Lot II No 3 Lengkong Gudang BSD City, Serpong, Tangerang, 15321, Banten, Indonesia
Tel.: (62) 2122356808
Web Site: http://pt-mitra-oto-prima.business.site
Truck Retailer
N.A.I.C.S.: 441120

PT Ulticar Oto Galeri (1)
Jl Sunburst CBD LOT II No 3 BSD City Carsworld Building Ground Floor, Serpong, Tangerang, 15321, Selatan, Indonesia
Tel.: (62) 81216816882
Web Site: http://www.ulticar.co.id
Car Distr
N.A.I.C.S.: 423110

PT BISI INTERNATIONAL TBK
Jl Raya Surabaya Mojokerto Km 19 Desa Bringinbendo Kecamatan Taman, Kabupaten Sidoarjo, Bandung, Jawa Timur, Indonesia
Tel.: (62) 317882528
Web Site: http://www.bisi.co.id
Rev.: $158,593,050
Assets: $193,550,700
Liabilities: $31,855,600
Net Worth: $161,695,100
Earnings: $28,270,900
Emp.: 702
Fiscal Year-end: 12/31/18
Hybrid Seed Mfr & Distr
N.A.I.C.S.: 111130
Agus Saputra Wijaya *(Pres & Dir)*

Subsidiaries:

PT Tanindo Intertraco (1)
Jl Raya Surabaya Mojokerto Km 19 Taman, Sidoarjo, 61257, East Java, Indonesia
Tel.: (62) 31 7882528
Web Site: http://www.tanindo.com
Pesticide Mfr
N.A.I.C.S.: 325320

PT BLISS PROPERTI INDONESIA, TBK
Millenium Centennial Center Lt 1 Unit A & H Jl Jend Sudirman Kav 25, Karet Setiabudi, Jakarta Selatan, 12920, Indonesia
Tel.: (62) 2139737007
Web Site:
https://www.blissproperti.com
Year Founded: 2010
POSA—(INDO)
Rev.: $3,723,840
Assets: $50,832,696
Liabilities: $69,309,764
Net Worth: ($18,477,069)
Earnings: ($9,503,088)
Emp.: 41
Fiscal Year-end: 12/31/23
Hotel Operator
N.A.I.C.S.: 721110
Rasyiid John Siwu *(Sec)*

PT BLUE BIRD TBK
Jl Mampang Prapatan Raya No 60, Jakarta, 12790, Indonesia
Tel.: (62) 217989000
Web Site:
https://www.bluebirdgroup.com
BIRD—(INDO)
Rev.: $287,195,332
Assets: $492,259,747
Liabilities: $126,554,163
Net Worth: $365,705,584
Earnings: $30,071,636
Emp.: 3,054
Fiscal Year-end: 12/31/23
Taxi & Charter Bus Services
N.A.I.C.S.: 485310
Ayati Purnomo *(Chm)*

Subsidiaries:

P.T. Layanan Pusaka Prima (1)
Jl Mampang Prapatan Raya No 60 Kel Tegal Parang Kec, Mampang Prapatan, Jakarta Selatan, Indonesia
Tel.: (62) 217989000
Car Rental Services
N.A.I.C.S.: 532111

PT Balai Lelang Caready (1)
Jl Raya Narogong No 37 RT 002/RW 007 Bojong Menteng Kec Rawalumbu, Bojong Menteng Rawalumbu Bojong Menteng, Bekasi, 17117, Jawa Barat, Indonesia
Tel.: (62) 2182621611
Web Site: https://www.caready.co.id
Vehicle Auction Services
N.A.I.C.S.: 561990

PT Big Bird Pusaka (1)
Jl Bojong Indah Raya No 6A, Kel Rawa Buaya Kec Cengkareng, Jakarta Barat, Indonesia
Tel.: (62) 215453350
Car Rental Services
N.A.I.C.S.: 532111

PT Blue Bird Pusaka (1)
Jl Bojong Indah Raya No 6A, Kel Rawa Buaya Kec Cengkareng, Jakarta Barat, Indonesia
Tel.: (62) 2154394000
Car Rental Services
N.A.I.C.S.: 532111

PT Lombok Taksi Utama (1)
Jl Koperasi No 102 Ampenan Lombok Barat, Tenggarong, Nusa Tenggara Barat, Indonesia
Tel.: (62) 370627000
Car Rental Services
N.A.I.C.S.: 532111

PT Silver Bird (1)
Jl Mampang Prapatan Raya No 60, Kel Tegal Parang Kec Mampang Prapatan, Jakarta Selatan, Indonesia
Tel.: (62) 217989000
Car Rental Services
N.A.I.C.S.: 532111

PT BORNEO LUMBUNG ENERGI & METAL TBK.
Jl Budi Kemulian I No 2, Jakarta, 10110, Indonesia
Tel.: (62) 2129573737   Id
Web Site: http://www.borneo.co.id

Sales Range: $100-124.9 Million
Emp.: 3,264
Coal Mining Services
N.A.I.C.S.: 212115
Kenneth Raymond Allan *(Sec)*

PT BORNEO OLAH SARANA SUKSES TBK
Wisma 77 Building Tower 1 8th Floor Letjen S Parman No 77 West, Jakarta, 11410, Indonesia
Tel.: (62) 215359777
Web Site: https://www.bosscoal.com
BOSS—(INDO)
Rev.: $30,693,672
Assets: $46,980,072
Liabilities: $49,626,627
Net Worth: ($2,646,554)
Earnings: $2,622,685
Emp.: 60
Fiscal Year-end: 12/31/22
Mineral Exploration Services
N.A.I.C.S.: 213114
Widodo Nurly Sumady *(CFO)*

PT BOSTON FURNITURE INDUSTRIES TBK
Jl Milenium 15 Blok I-2 No 5A, Panongan, Tangerang, Banten, Indonesia
Tel.: (62) 2129159118
Web Site: https://www.boston-industries.com
Year Founded: 2012
SOFA—(INDO)
Rev.: $3,028,992
Assets: $4,151,992
Liabilities: $1,202,803
Net Worth: $2,949,189
Earnings: $7,046
Emp.: 73
Fiscal Year-end: 12/31/23
Furniture Mfr
N.A.I.C.S.: 337122
Hardy Satya *(Pres)*

PT BUANA ARTHA ANUGERAH TBK
BCA tower 45th floor Jl MH Thamrin No 1, Jakarta, 10310, Indonesia
Tel.: (62) 2123585612
Web Site:
https://buanaarthaanugerah.co.id
Year Founded: 2008
STAR—(INDO)
Rev.: $307,698
Assets: $33,270,984
Liabilities: $96,406
Net Worth: $33,174,578
Earnings: $177,297
Emp.: 12
Fiscal Year-end: 12/31/23
Petrochemical Mfr
N.A.I.C.S.: 325110
Asep Mulyana *(Chm & Sec)*

PT BUANA FINANCE TBK.
Tokopedia Tower Ciputra World 2 Lt 38 Unit A-F, Jl Prof Dr Satrio Kav 11, Jakarta Selatan, 12950, Indonesia
Tel.: (62) 2150806969
Web Site:
https://www.buanafinance.co.id
Year Founded: 1982
BBLD—(INDO)
Rev.: $47,131,893
Assets: $375,977,728
Liabilities: $285,403,572
Net Worth: $90,574,156
Earnings: $6,819,544
Emp.: 563
Fiscal Year-end: 12/31/23
Financial Services
N.A.I.C.S.: 522291
Herman Lesmana *(Dir-Fin Lease)*

PT BUDI STARCH & SWEETENER TBK
Wisma Budi Lt 8-9 Jl HR Rasuna Said Kav C-6, Jakarta, 12940, Indonesia
Tel.: (62) 215213383
Web Site: https://budistarchsweetener.com
Year Founded: 1947
BUDI—(INDO)
Rev.: $256,185,248
Assets: $216,110,319
Liabilities: $112,769,544
Net Worth: $103,340,775
Earnings: $6,659,077
Emp.: 1,921
Fiscal Year-end: 12/31/23
Citric Acid & Tapioca Starch Mfr
N.A.I.C.S.: 325199
Tasmin Sudarno *(Vice Chm)*

Subsidiaries:

PT Associated British Budi (1)
Jl Hr Rasuna Said Kav C-6 Wisma Budi Lt 8-9, Karet Kuningan Setia Budi, Jakarta, 12940, Indonesia
Tel.: (62) 215213383
Sugar & Sugar Syrups Mfr3
N.A.I.C.S.: 311313

PT Budi Lumbung Ciptatani (1)
Keron Rt 24/13 Jatipuro/Wisma Budi Lt 9-9 Jl Hr Rasuna Said Kav C-6, Jakarta Selatan, Jakarta, Indonesia
Tel.: (62) 215213383
Cassava Starch Mfr
N.A.I.C.S.: 311221

PT BUKAKA TEKNIK UTAMA TBK
Bukaka Industrial Estate Jl Raya Narogong - Bekasi Km 19 5 Cileungsi, Bogor, 16820, Indonesia
Tel.: (62) 218232323
Web Site: https://www.bukaka.com
Year Founded: 1978
BUKK—(INDO)
Rev.: $299,488,040
Assets: $425,851,937
Liabilities: $129,088,901
Net Worth: $296,763,036
Earnings: $44,957,403
Emp.: 514
Fiscal Year-end: 12/31/23
Engineering Construction Services
N.A.I.C.S.: 541330
Saptiastuti Hapsari *(Dir-Operational I)*

PT BUKIT ASAM (PERSERO) TBK
Jl Parigi No 1 Tanjung Enim, 31716, Palembang, 31716, South Sumatera, Indonesia
Tel.: (62) 734451096 Id
Web Site: https://www.ptba.co.id
Year Founded: 1981
PTBA—(INDO)
Rev.: $2,499,467,023
Assets: $2,517,411,374
Liabilities: $1,117,097,425
Net Worth: $1,400,313,948
Earnings: $40,863,625
Emp.: 1,561
Fiscal Year-end: 12/31/23
Coal Mining & Exploration Services
N.A.I.C.S.: 212114
Joko Pramono *(Dir-HR)*

Subsidiaries:

P.T. Bukit Asam Prima (1)
Menara Kadin LT 26 No Kav 2-3, South Jakarta, Indonesia
Tel.: (62) 2157944522
Web Site: https://baprima.co.id
Exploration & Coal Mining Services
N.A.I.C.S.: 532412

P.T. Bukit Energi Servis Terpadu (1)
Menara Kadin Lantai 11 Jalan Rasuna Said Blok X-5 Kav 2-3, Jakarta, 12950, Indonesia
Tel.: (62) 2129675136
Web Site: https://bestpower1.co.id
Power Plant Operation & Maintenance Services
N.A.I.C.S.: 532411

P.T. Pelabuhan Bukit Prima (1)
Building Jalan Soekarno Hatta Km 15, Bandar Lampung, Indonesia
Tel.: (62) 7213400003
Web Site: https://pelabuhanbukitprima.co.id
Dock & Tugboat Services
N.A.I.C.S.: 531120

PT Bukit Asam (Persero) Tbk - Briquette (1)
Jl Falatehan Raya No 1A Blok, Kebayoran Baru, Jakarta, 12160, Indonesia
Tel.: (62) 2172796115
Coal Mining Services
N.A.I.C.S.: 213113

PT Bukit Asam (Persero) Tbk - Gresik (1)
Jl Raya Manyar Km 6 Manyar, Gresik, 61151, Jawa Timur, Indonesia
Tel.: (62) 313950288
Coal Mining Services
N.A.I.C.S.: 213113

PT Bukit Asam (Persero) Tbk - Lampung (1)
Jl Raya Natar Km 16, Natar, Lapung, Indonesia
Tel.: (62) 721783558
Coal Mining Services
N.A.I.C.S.: 213113

PT Bukit Asam (Persero) Tbk - Semarang (1)
Kawasan Industri Terboyo, Blok O No 1, Semarang, Jawa Tengah, Indonesia
Tel.: (62) 24 6595 185
Coal Mining Services
N.A.I.C.S.: 213113

PT Bukit Pembangkit Innovative (1)
Graha Surveyor Indonesia Building Floor 17 Suite 1703, Jl Jend Gatot Subroto Kav 56, South Jakarta, 12950, Indonesia
Tel.: (62) 215212463
Web Site: http://www.bpi-ipp.com
Coal & Oil Services
N.A.I.C.S.: 327910
Dadan Ruswandana *(Pres)*

PT BUKIT ULUWATU VILLA TBK
Sequis Center Lantai 9 Jl Jend Sudirman 71 Kebayoran Baru, Jakarta, 12190, Indonesia
Tel.: (62) 215256516
Web Site: https://www.buvagroup.com
Year Founded: 2000
BUVA—(INDO)
Rev.: $24,111,232
Assets: $110,933,717
Liabilities: $48,834,295
Net Worth: $62,099,422
Earnings: $1,111,915
Emp.: 307
Fiscal Year-end: 12/31/23
Hotel & Resort Operator
N.A.I.C.S.: 721120
Franky Tjahyadikarta *(Chm)*

Subsidiaries:

P.T. Bukit Lagoi Villa (1)
Town Ship Bintan Resort Housing Type A Blok 819 Unit 2100 Kota Kapur, Kawasan Pariwisata Lagoi Teluk Sebong kabupaten, Bintan, 29115, Indonesia
Tel.: (62) 770691087
Hotel & Resort Operator
N.A.I.C.S.: 721110

P.T. Bukit Lentera Sejahtera (1)
Kawasan SCBD Lot 11A Jl Jend Sudirman kav 52-53, Senayan Kebayoran Baru, Jakarta, Indonesia
Tel.: (62) 215155061
Food & Beverage Distr
N.A.I.C.S.: 424410

PT Culina Global Utama (1)
Talavera Office Park 10th Floor Jl Letjend T B Simatupang kav 22-26, Jakarta, 12430, Indonesia
Tel.: (62) 2175924475
Casino Hotel Operator
N.A.I.C.S.: 721120

PT BUMI BENOWO SUKSES SEJAHTERA TBK
Jl W R Supratman No 19 Kel Dr Soetomo Kec Tegalsari, Surabaya, Indonesia
Tel.: (62) 315612227
Web Site: https://www.bumibenowo.com
Year Founded: 1987
BBSS—(INDO)
Rev.: $29,259
Assets: $16,344,853
Liabilities: $268,644
Net Worth: $16,076,209
Earnings: ($78,654)
Emp.: 11
Fiscal Year-end: 12/31/23
Construction Services
N.A.I.C.S.: 236220
Direktur Utama *(Chm)*

PT BUMI CITRA PERMAI TBK
Jl Kramat Raya No 32-34 Senen, Jakarta Pusat, 10450, Indonesia
Tel.: (62) 213916338
Web Site: https://www.bumicitrapermai.com
Year Founded: 2000
BCIP—(INDO)
Rev.: $6,124,036
Assets: $59,136,478
Liabilities: $27,900,408
Net Worth: $31,236,070
Earnings: $1,122,875
Emp.: 143
Fiscal Year-end: 12/31/23
Industrial Construction Services
N.A.I.C.S.: 236220

PT BUMI RESOURCES TBK
Bakrie Tower Building 12th Fl Kompleks Rasuna Epicentrum, Jalan HR Rasuna Said, Jakarta, 12940, Indonesia
Tel.: (62) 2157942080 Id
Web Site: https://www.bumiresources.com
BUMI—(INDO)
Rev.: $109,096
Assets: $272,923
Liabilities: $92,729
Net Worth: $180,194
Earnings: $2,106
Emp.: 64
Fiscal Year-end: 12/31/23
Coal, Oil & Natural Gas Exploration & Production Services
N.A.I.C.S.: 212115
Dileep Srivastava *(Sec)*

Subsidiaries:

Gallo Oil (Jersey) Ltd. (1)
Western Ring Road Al Senay Street, Sana'a, Yemen
Tel.: (967) 1202132
Oil & Gas Exploration Services
N.A.I.C.S.: 213112

Herald Resources Limited (1)
Level 1 17 Ord St, West Perth, 6005, WA, Australia (84%)
Tel.: (61) 892263188
Web Site: http://www.herald.net.au
Metal Ore Mining
N.A.I.C.S.: 212290

PT Arutmin Indonesia (1)
Wisma Bakrie II 10th Floor Jl HR Rasuna Said Kav B2, Jakarta, 12920, Indonesia (70%)
Tel.: (62) 2157945700
Web Site: http://www.arutmin.com

Coal Mining & Distr
N.A.I.C.S.: 213113
Faisal Firdaus *(CEO)*

PT Bumi Resources Minerals Tbk (1)
Bakrie Tower Lt 6 And Lt 10 Rasuna Epicentrum Complex Jl IH R Rasuna, said Kuningan, Jakarta, 12940, Indonesia
Tel.: (62) 2157945698
Web Site: https://www.bumiresourcesminerals.com
Rev.: $46,637,766
Assets: $1,104,867,719
Liabilities: $135,516,460
Net Worth: $969,351,259
Earnings: $14,188,051
Emp.: 843
Fiscal Year-end: 12/31/2023
Mining Exploration Services
N.A.I.C.S.: 213114
Makin Perdana Kusuma *(Chief HR Officer)*

PT Fajar Bumi Sakti (1)
Wisma Bakrie 2 11th Floor Jl HR Rasuna Said Kav B-2, Jakarta, 12920, Indonesia
Tel.: (62) 215200428
Web Site: http://www.fajarbumisakti.co.id
Sales Range: $50-74.9 Million
Emp.: 100
Coal Mining Services
N.A.I.C.S.: 212114

PT Kaltim Prima Coal (1)
KPC Mine Site M1 Building, Sangatta, 75611, East Kalimantan, Indonesia
Tel.: (62) 549521402
Web Site: http://www.kaltimprimacoal.co.id
Emp.: 5,000
Coal Mining Services
N.A.I.C.S.: 212114
Ashok Mitra *(CFO)*

PT BUMI TEKNOKULTURA UNGGUL TBK
Permata Senayan Complex Rukan Block No 37-38, Jl Tentara Pelajar, Jakarta, 12210, Indonesia
Tel.: (62) 215300700 Id
Web Site: https://www.btek.co.id
Year Founded: 2001
BTEK—(INDO)
Rev.: $12,771,631
Assets: $263,380,464
Liabilities: $191,501,974
Net Worth: $71,878,489
Earnings: ($7,406,263)
Emp.: 267
Fiscal Year-end: 12/31/23
Forest Conservation Services
N.A.I.C.S.: 115310
Ari Sutanto *(Dir-Comml)*

Subsidiaries:

PT Golden Harvest Cocoa Indonesia (1)
Gedung Meta Epsi Lt 1 Jl DI Panjaitan Kav 2 RT 09/RW 09, Rawa Bunga Jatinegara, Jakarta Timur, 13350, Jakarta, Indonesia
Tel.: (62) 218192989
Web Site: https://www.ghcocoa.com
Cocoa Product Distr
N.A.I.C.S.: 424490

PT BUNDAMEDIK TBK
Jl Teuku Cik Ditiro No 28, Menteng, Jakarta Pusat, 10350, Indonesia
Tel.: (62) 1500799
Web Site: https://www.bmhs.co.id
Year Founded: 1973
BMHS—(INDO)
Rev.: $96,643,545
Assets: $200,220,543
Liabilities: $83,326,211
Net Worth: $116,894,332
Earnings: $1,053,939
Emp.: 1,401
Fiscal Year-end: 12/31/23
Hospital & Health Care Services
N.A.I.C.S.: 622110
Mesha Rizal Sini *(Pres)*

PT BUNDAMEDIK TBK

PT Bundamedik Tbk—(Continued)

Subsidiaries:

PT Bunda Global Pharma (1)
Jalan Margonda Raya No 18A RT 03/RW 01 Kelurahan Pondok Cina, Kecamatan Beji, Depok, 16424, Jawa Barat, Indonesia
Tel.: (62) 2178880909
Web Site: https://www.bundaglobalpharma.com
Pharmaceutical Products Distr
N.A.I.C.S.: 424210

PT Emphi Pharma Sejahtera (1)
BIC 2 Building 3rd Floor Jl Teuku Cik Ditiro No 12, Menteng, Jakarta Pusat, Indonesia
Tel.: (62) 8132 700 0671
Web Site: https://www.empipharma.co.id
Pharmaceutical Products Distr
N.A.I.C.S.: 424210
Dian Rizki (VP)

PT Morula IVF Padang (1)
RSU Citra BMC Padang Jl Proklamasi No 37, Padang, 2521, Sumatera Barat, Indonesia
Tel.: (62) 7 512 3164
Fertility Clinic Services
N.A.I.C.S.: 621410

PT Morula Indonesia (1)
THE BIC Jalan Teuku Cik Ditiro No 12-14 RT 8/RW 2 Gondangdia Kec, Menteng Kota, Jakarta Pusat, 10350, DKI Jakarta, Indonesia
Tel.: (62) 150483
Web Site: https://www.morulaivf.co.id
Fertility Clinic Services
N.A.I.C.S.: 621410

PT BURSA EFEK INDONESIA

Indonesia Stock Exchange Building 1st Tower Jl Jend Sudirman Kav 52-53, Jakarta, 12190, Selatan, Indonesia
Tel.: (62) 215150515   Id
Web Site: http://www.idx.co.id
Year Founded: 1912
Sales Range: $75-99.9 Million
Stock Exchange
N.A.I.C.S.: 523210
Inarno Djajadi (Chm)

Subsidiaries:

PT Penilai Harga Efek Indonesia (1)
Menara Global Lantai 19 Jl Gatot Subroto Kavling 27, Jakarta, Indonesia
Tel.: (62) 21 527 0179
Web Site: http://www.ibpa.co.id
Bond Brokerage Services
N.A.I.C.S.: 523150
Ignatius Girendroheru (Pres)

PT BUYUNG POETRA SEMBADA TBK

Pasar Induk Cipinang Blok K No 17 Cipinang, Pulo Gadung, East Jakarta, 13240, Indonesia
Tel.: (62) 87738885401
Web Site: https://www.topikoki.com
Year Founded: 2003
HOKI—(INDO)
Rev.: $83,416,112
Assets: $67,939,642
Liabilities: $24,977,052
Net Worth: $42,962,590
Earnings: ($218,901)
Emp.: 240
Fiscal Year-end: 12/31/23
Rice Distr
N.A.I.C.S.: 424510
Victor Reinhard Lanes (Sec)

PT CAHAYA BINTANG MEDAN FURNITURE TBK

Kp Patumbak Jl Pertahanan No 111 Rt 004 / Rw 006, Ds V Desa Patumbak Kab Deli Serdang, Medan, 20361, Sumatera Utara, Indonesia
Tel.: (62) 617852277

Web Site: http://www.cbm-furniture.com
Year Founded: 2012
CBMF—(INDO)
Rev.: $1,516,710
Assets: $23,484,969
Liabilities: $7,460,750
Net Worth: $16,024,220
Earnings: ($101,913)
Emp.: 56
Fiscal Year-end: 12/31/22
Furniture Mfr & Distr
N.A.I.C.S.: 337121
Felicia Kweesly (Sec)

PT CAHAYAPUTRA ASA KERAMIK TBK

Bellezza Office Tower Lantai 21 Unit 01-02 Jalan Letjen Soepeno No 34, Kebayoran Lama, Jakarta Selatan, 12210, Indonesia
Tel.: (62) 2125675721
Web Site: https://www.kaisar-ceramics.com
Year Founded: 1997
CAKK—(INDO)
Rev.: $13,548,815
Assets: $30,263,521
Liabilities: $17,231,689
Net Worth: $13,031,832
Earnings: ($2,213,888)
Emp.: 145
Fiscal Year-end: 12/31/23
Flooring Tile Mfr
N.A.I.C.S.: 327120

PT CAHAYASAKTI INVESTINDO SUKSES TBK

Jl Kaum Sari No 1 RT 001 RW 005 Kelurahan Cibuluh, Kecamatan Bogor Utara, Bogor, 16151, Jawa Barat, Indonesia
Tel.: (62) 2518666873
Web Site: https://csis.co.id
Year Founded: 1995
CSIS—(INDO)
Rev.: $3,635,675
Assets: $35,633,207
Liabilities: $15,109,515
Net Worth: $20,523,691
Earnings: $351,082
Emp.: 19
Fiscal Year-end: 12/31/23
Interior Design Services
N.A.I.C.S.: 541410
Reza Purnama (Fin Dir)

Subsidiaries:

P.T. Bogorindo Cemerlang (1)
Jl Olympic Raya Kav B Commercial Area Sentul, Bogor, 16810, Indonesia
Tel.: (62) 21876346869
Web Site: https://olympic-kis.com
Residential Property Leasing Services
N.A.I.C.S.: 531311

PT CAKRA BUANA RESOURCES ENERGI TBK

Sahid Sudirman Centre Floor 42 Unit B Jl Jend Sudirman No 86, Jakarta Pusat, 10220, Indonesia
Tel.: (62) 212528444
Web Site: https://www.cbre.co.id
Year Founded: 2016
CBRE—(INDO)
Rev.: $2,774,767
Assets: $22,921,586
Liabilities: $11,967,319
Net Worth: $10,954,267
Earnings: $58,735
Emp.: 6
Fiscal Year-end: 12/31/23
Coal Mining Services
N.A.I.C.S.: 213113
Suminto Husin Giman (Chm)

PT CAKRA MINERAL, TBK.

Jl Cideng Timur Raya No 12A Petojo Utara, Gambir Kodepos, Jakarta Pusat, 10130, Indonesia
Tel.: (62) 2163852596   Id
Web Site: http://www.ckra.co.id
Year Founded: 1990
Rev.: $38
Assets: $10,277,747
Liabilities: $1,157,055
Net Worth: $9,120,692
Earnings: ($159,200)
Emp.: 16
Fiscal Year-end: 12/31/19
Mineral Ore Mining Services
N.A.I.C.S.: 212290
Boelio Muliadi (Chm & Mng Dir)

PT CAMPINA ICE CREAM INDUSTRY TBK

Jl Raya Rungkut Industri II No 15 Kec Kota SBY, Tenggilis Mejoyo, Surabaya, 60292, Jawa Timur, Indonesia
Tel.: (62) 318432247
Web Site: https://www.campina.co.id
Year Founded: 1972
CAMP—(INDO)
Rev.: $73,758,234
Assets: $70,701,879
Liabilities: $8,837,485
Net Worth: $61,864,394
Earnings: $8,275,075
Emp.: 477
Fiscal Year-end: 12/31/23
Ice Cream Mfr
N.A.I.C.S.: 311520
Samudera Prawirawidjaja (Chm)

PT CAPITAL FINANCIAL INDONESIA TBK

Gedung Menara Jamsostek 5th floor North Tower Jl Gatot Subroto No 3, Jakarta, Indonesia
Tel.: (62) 2127082002   Id
Web Site: https://www.capitalfinancial.co.id
CASA—(INDO)
Rev.: $493,314,632
Assets: $2,000,635,673
Liabilities: $1,440,742,800
Net Worth: $559,892,873
Earnings: $6,287,816
Emp.: 938
Fiscal Year-end: 12/31/23
Fire Insurance Services
N.A.I.C.S.: 524210
Hengky Setiono (Chm)

Subsidiaries:

PT Capital Asset Management (1)
Gedung Menara Jamsostek Menara Utara Lantai 5 Jl Gatot Subroto No 38, Jakarta, 12710, Indonesia
Tel.: (62) 212 277 3900
Web Site: https://www.capital-asset.co.id
Financial Investment Services
N.A.I.C.S.: 523999

PT Capital Life Indonesia (1)
Menara Jamsostek Gedung Menara Utara Lt 5 Jl Gatot Subroto No 38, Jakarta Selatan, 12710, Indonesia
Tel.: (62) 212 277 3899
Web Site: https://www.capitallife.co.id
Financial Investment Services
N.A.I.C.S.: 523999

PT Capital Life Syariah (1)
Jamsostek Tower 5th Floor North Tower Building Jl Gatot Subroto No 38, South Jakarta, 12710, Jakarta, Indonesia
Tel.: (62) 2122773108
Web Site: https://www.capitallifesyariah.co.id
Financial Investment Services
N.A.I.C.S.: 523999

PT CAPITALINC INVESTMENT TBK

INTERNATIONAL PUBLIC

Jl Radio Dalam Raya No 2 Gandaria Utara, Kebayoran baru, Jakarta, Indonesia
Tel.: (62) 27517000   Id
Web Site: https://www.capitalinc-investment.com
Year Founded: 1983
MTFN—(INDO)
Rev.: $27,324,074
Assets: $35,663,886
Liabilities: $60,236,561
Net Worth: ($24,572,675)
Earnings: $21,954,188)
Emp.: 10
Fiscal Year-end: 12/31/23
Investment Management Service
N.A.I.C.S.: 523940
Abas Soeriawidjaja (Chm)

Subsidiaries:

PT Cahaya Batu Raja Blok (1)
Menara Jamsostek Menara Utara Lt 19 Jl Jend Gatot Subroto No 38, Jakarta Selatan, 12710, Indonesia
Tel.: (62) 2129660976
Oil & Gas Services
N.A.I.C.S.: 213112

PT Indogas Kriya Dwiguna (1)
Jl Radio Dalam Raya No 2 Gandaria Utara Kebayoran Baru, Jakarta, 12140, Indonesia
Tel.: (62) 2127517000
Web Site: https://www.indogas.co.id
Oil & Gas Services
N.A.I.C.S.: 213112
Henry Siahaan (Pres)

PT CAPITOL NUSANTARA INDONESIA TBK.

Pangeran Suriansyah No 30-34, Samarinda, 75113, East Kalimantan, Indonesia
Tel.: (62) 541732893
Web Site: https://cani.co.id
Year Founded: 2004
CANI—(INDO)
Rev.: $3,604,390
Assets: $14,650,279
Liabilities: $44,481,063
Net Worth: ($29,830,784)
Earnings: ($3,555,616)
Emp.: 23
Fiscal Year-end: 06/30/23
Ship Chartering & Management Services
N.A.I.C.S.: 488390
Ang Ah Nui (Chm, Pres & Dir)

PT CAPRI NUSA SATU PROPERTI TBK

Multipiranti Graha Lt 4 Jl Raden Inten II No 2 Duren Sawit, Jakarta, 13440, Indonesia
Tel.: (62) 218632722
Web Site: https://www.caprinusa.com
CPRI—(INDO)
Rev.: $249,075
Assets: $14,854,449
Liabilities: $1,930,418
Net Worth: $12,924,031
Earnings: ($270,937)
Emp.: 19
Fiscal Year-end: 12/31/21
Architectural Design & Engineering Services
N.A.I.C.S.: 541310
Jansen Surbakti (Chm)

PT CARSURIN TBK

Neo Soho Capital 28th Floor Jl Letjen S Parman Kav 28, Grogol Petamburan, Jakarta Barat, 11470, Indonesia
Tel.: (62) 2150226868
Web Site: https://www.carsurin.com
Year Founded: 1968
CRSN—(INDO)
Rev.: $28,861,194

Assets: $19,874,583
Liabilities: $6,038,222
Net Worth: $13,836,361
Earnings: $1,805,348
Emp.: 903
Fiscal Year-end: 12/31/23
Mineral Mining Services
N.A.I.C.S.: 213115
Flora Regina Regian *(Chm)*

PT CASHLEZ WORLDWIDE INDONESIA TBK
Podomoro Avenue Garden Shopping Arcade Blok Beauford No 8 BA, Jl Letjen S Parman Kec Grogol Petamburan, Jakarta Barat, 11470, Indonesia
Tel.: (62) 2129860750
Web Site: https://www.cashlez.com
Year Founded: 2015
CASH—(INDO)
Rev.: $1,492,562
Assets: $10,107,323
Liabilities: $2,551,431
Net Worth: $7,555,892
Earnings: $1,695,480
Emp.: 92
Fiscal Year-end: 12/31/23
Financial Technological Services
N.A.I.C.S.: 522320
Djayanto Suseno *(Chief Revenue Officer)*

Subsidiaries:

PT Softorb Technology Indonesia (1)
Kompleks Mutiara Taman Palem Blok A11 No 8 Cengkareng, Jakarta Barat, 11730, Indonesia
Tel.: (62) 2129668601
Web Site: https://www.softorb.co.id
Hardware Products Distr
N.A.I.C.S.: 423710

PT CATUR SENTOSA ADIPRANA TBK
Jl Daan Mogot Raya No 234, Jakarta, 11510, Indonesia
Tel.: (62) 215668801
Web Site: https://www.csahome.com
CSAP—(INDO)
Rev.: $1,068,538,264
Assets: $734,833,697
Liabilities: $507,433,550
Net Worth: $227,400,147
Earnings: $13,416,182
Emp.: 9,268
Fiscal Year-end: 12/31/23
Paint & Building Material Distr
N.A.I.C.S.: 423310
Budyanto Totong *(Chm)*

Subsidiaries:

PT Catur Hasil Sentosa (1)
Kawasan Pergudangan Kuala Ketapang Jl Ki Agus Anang No 28, Bandar Lampung, 35227, Indonesia
Tel.: (62) 72132057
Building Materials Distr
N.A.I.C.S.: 444180

PT Catur Karda Sentosa (1)
Jl Yos Sudarso Km 10 Kawasan Industri Xi No 2, Medan, 20242, North Sumatra, Indonesia
Tel.: (62) 616851010
Building Materials Distr
N.A.I.C.S.: 444180

PT Catur Logamindo Sentosa (1)
Jl Ring Road Timur, Bantul, Yogyakarta, 55197, Indonesia
Tel.: (62) 274452010
Sales Range: $25-49.9 Million
Emp.: 100
Building Materials Distr
N.A.I.C.S.: 444180

PT Catur Mitra Sejati Sentosa (1)
Boulevard Gading Serpong Blok Mitra10 Summarecon Serpong, Kalimalang, Tangerang, 15310, Banten, Indonesia
Tel.: (62) 2184599747
Building Materials Distr
N.A.I.C.S.: 444180

Subsidiary (Domestic):

PT Mitra Bali Indah (2)
JL Gatot Subroto Barat No 405, Denpasar, Denpasar, Indonesia
Tel.: (62) 361418148
Building Materials Distr
N.A.I.C.S.: 444180

PT Catur Sentosa Anugerah (1)
Jl Daan Mogot Raya Km 14 RT 006/011, Cengkareng, Jakarta, 11730, Indonesia
Tel.: (62) 216191232
Building Materials Distr
N.A.I.C.S.: 424950

PT Catur Sentosa Berhasil (1)
House of Blessing Jl Lingkar Luar Barat No 108, Kembangan Selatan, Jakarta, 11610, Kalimantan Selatan, Indonesia
Tel.: (62) 215800757
Building Materials Distr
N.A.I.C.S.: 424950
Bondan Pramudita *(Mgr-Retail Store)*

PT Caturaditya Sentosa (1)
Jl Rawa Sumur II Bl BB/7 Kawasan Industri, Pulogadung, Jakarta, 13920, Indonesia
Tel.: (62) 2146826455
Building Materials Distr
N.A.I.C.S.: 444180

PT Kusuma Kemindo Sentosa (1)
Komp Greenville Maisonette Blok FA No 12A, Jakarta, 11510, Indonesia
Tel.: (62) 215653736
Web Site: https://www.kks-chemicals.com
Sales Range: $75-99.9 Million
Emp.: 113
Chemical Distr
N.A.I.C.S.: 424690
Kiki Sadrach *(Pres)*

PT Satya Galang Kemika (1)
Green Ville Maisonette Complex Block FA No 12-A Duri Kepa, Jakarta, 11510, Indonesia
Tel.: (62) 21 5653736
Chemical Products Distr
N.A.I.C.S.: 424690

PT CATURKARDA DEPO BANGUNAN TBK
Jl Raya Serpong Km 2 Pakulonan Serpong, Tangerang, 15325, Indonesia
Tel.: (62) 2153120808
Web Site: https://www.depobangunan.co.id
Year Founded: 1996
DEPO—(INDO)
Rev.: $174,120,690
Assets: $134,908,273
Liabilities: $54,333,720
Net Worth: $80,574,553
Earnings: $5,561,883
Emp.: 2,890
Fiscal Year-end: 12/31/23
Building Material Retailer
N.A.I.C.S.: 444180
Erwan Irawan Noer *(Sec)*

PT CEMINDO GEMILANG TBK
Gama Tower Lt 43 Jl HR Rasuna Said Kav C-22, Jakarta Selatan, 12940, Indonesia
Tel.: (62) 2121889999
Web Site: https://www.cemindo.com
Year Founded: 2011
CMNT—(INDO)
Rev.: $624,258,284
Assets: $1,166,061,601
Liabilities: $907,486,042
Net Worth: $258,575,559
Earnings: $10,344,422
Emp.: 3,234
Fiscal Year-end: 12/31/23
Cement Mfr
N.A.I.C.S.: 327310
Tony Liu *(Pres)*

Subsidiaries:

Chinfon Cement Corporation (1)
No 288 Bach Dang Street, Minh Duc Town Thuy Nguyen District, Haiphong, Vietnam
Tel.: (84) 225 387 5480
Web Site: https://www.cfc.vn
Cement Mfr
N.A.I.C.S.: 327310

PT CENTRAL OMEGA RESOURCES TBK
Plaza Asia 6th Floor Jl Jenderal Sudirman Kav 59, Jakarta, 12190, Indonesia
Tel.: (62) 215153533
Web Site: https://www.centralomega.com
Year Founded: 1995
DKFT—(INDO)
Rev.: $52,709,140
Assets: $166,746,029
Liabilities: $139,550,615
Net Worth: $27,195,414
Earnings: $1,992,152
Emp.: 111
Fiscal Year-end: 12/31/23
Nickel Mining Services
N.A.I.C.S.: 212230
Kiki Hamidjaja *(Chm)*

Subsidiaries:

PT Macrolink Omega Adiperkasa (1)
Plaza Asia 8th Floor Jl Jend Sudirman Kav 59, South Jakarta, Indonesia
Tel.: (62) 21515353
Nickel Refining Product Mfr
N.A.I.C.S.: 331410

PT CENTRAL PROTEINAPRIMA TBK
Treasury Tower Lt 8 District 8 SCBD Lot 28 Jl Jend Sudirman Kav 52 53, Senayan Kebayoran Baru DKI, Jakarta, 12190, Indonesia
Tel.: (62) 2150191788
Web Site: https://www.cpp.co.id
Year Founded: 1980
CPRO—(INDO)
Rev.: $586,231,303
Assets: $445,250,590
Liabilities: $223,175,077
Net Worth: $222,075,513
Earnings: $26,091,204
Emp.: 1,794
Fiscal Year-end: 12/31/23
Poultry Farming & Sales Services
N.A.I.C.S.: 112340
Saleh Yu *(Vice Chm)*

PT CENTRATAMA TELEKOMUNIKASI INDONESIA TBK
TCC Batavia Tower One 16th 19th Floor Jl KH Mas Mansyur Kav 126 J, Jakarta, 10220, Indonesia
Tel.: (62) 29529404
Web Site: https://www.centratama.com
CENT—(INDO)
Rev.: $163,839,983
Assets: $1,301,455,851
Liabilities: $1,396,655,229
Net Worth: ($95,199,377)
Earnings: ($54,835,206)
Emp.: 311
Fiscal Year-end: 12/31/23
Telecommunications Equipment Mfr
N.A.I.C.S.: 334210

Subsidiaries:

P.T. Centratama Menara Indonesia (1)
TCC Batavia Tower One 16th 19th Floor Jl KH Mas Mansyur Kav 126, Jakarta Pusat, 10220, DKI Jakarta, Indonesia
Tel.: (62) 2129529404
Web Site: https://www.centratama.com
Telecommunication Tower Infrastructures Services
N.A.I.C.S.: 517810

P.T. EPID Menara AssetCo (1)
TCC Batavia Tower One Lt 16 Jl KH Mas Mansyur Kav 126, Jakarta, 10220, Indonesia
Tel.: (62) 2129529404
Telecommunications Network Facilities Services
N.A.I.C.S.: 517810

P.T. Network Quality Indonesia (1)
TCC Batavia Tower One Lt 16 Jl KH Mas Mansyur Kav 126, Jakarta, 10220, Indonesia
Tel.: (62) 2129529404
Telecommunication Servicesb
N.A.I.C.S.: 517410

PT Fastel Sarana Indonesia (1)
TCC Batavia Tower One 16th & 19th Floor Jl KH Mas Mansyur Kav 126, Jakarta Pusat, 10220, Jakarta, Indonesia
Tel.: (62) 2129529404
Antenna System Product Distr
N.A.I.C.S.: 423690

PT MAC Sarana Djaya (1)
TCC Batavia Tower One 16th 19th Floor Jl KH Mas Mansyur Kav 126, Jakarta Pusat, 10220, DKI Jakarta, Indonesia
Tel.: (62) 212 952 9404
Web Site: https://www.macsaranadjaya.co.id
Construction Services
N.A.I.C.S.: 236220

PT CHAMPION PACIFIC INDONESIA TBK
Jl Raya Sultan Agung Km 28 5, Bekasi, 17133, Indonesia
Tel.: (62) 218840040
Web Site: https://www.champion.co.id
IGAR—(INDO)
Rev.: $55,703,913
Assets: $59,017,978
Liabilities: $4,998,523
Net Worth: $54,019,456
Earnings: $3,678,427
Emp.: 546
Fiscal Year-end: 12/31/23
Pharmaceutical Preparation Mfr
N.A.I.C.S.: 325412
Antonius Muhartoyo *(Pres)*

Subsidiaries:

P.T. Avesta Continental Pack (1)
Jl Raya Bekasi Km 28 5 Kota Baru, Bekasi Barat Kota, Bekasi, 17133, Indonesia
Tel.: (62) 218841088
Web Site: https://avesta.co.id
Medical Equipment Mfr & Distr
N.A.I.C.S.: 339112

PT CHARLIE HOSPITAL SEMARANG TBK
Jl Ngabean Gowok Ngabean, Boja, Kendal, 51381, Central Java, Indonesia
Tel.: (62) 2486005000
Web Site: https://www.charliehospital.co.id
Year Founded: 2019
RSCH—(INDO)
Rev.: $2,219,828
Assets: $6,114,457
Liabilities: $3,590,334
Net Worth: $2,524,123
Earnings: ($494,228)
Fiscal Year-end: 12/31/22
Information Technology Services
N.A.I.C.S.: 541512

PT CHAROEN POKPHAND INDONESIA TBK
Jl Ancol VIII/1, Jakarta, 14430, Indonesia
Tel.: (62) 216919999
Web Site: http://www.cp.co.id
Year Founded: 1972

PT CHAROEN POKPHAND INDONESIA TBK

PT Charoen Pokphand Indonesia Tbk—(Continued)
CPIN—(INDO)
Rev.: $4,001,333,299
Assets: $2,660,643,752
Liabilities: $905,396,207
Net Worth: $1,755,247,545
Earnings: $150,536,635
Emp.: 9,564
Fiscal Year-end: 12/31/23
Poultry Feed Mfr
N.A.I.C.S.: 311119
Tjiu Thomas Effendy *(Chm)*

PT CHITOSE INTERNASIONAL TBK

Jl Industri III No 5 Leuwigajah Cimahi, Bandung, 40533, West Java, Indonesia
Tel.: (62) 226031900
Web Site: https://www.chitose-indonesia.com
Year Founded: 1979
CINT—(INDO)
Rev.: $29,671,712
Assets: $28,916,726
Liabilities: $9,949,945
Net Worth: $18,966,781
Earnings: $380,574
Emp.: 445
Fiscal Year-end: 12/31/23
Furniture Mfr
N.A.I.C.S.: 321999
Dedie Suherlan *(Chm)*

Subsidiaries:

PT Chitose C-Engineering Indonesia (1)
Jl HMS Mintareja Sarjana Hukum Baros Cimahi Tengah, Cimahi, Bandung, 40251, Jawa Barat, Indonesia
Tel.: (62) 2220664777
Web Site: http://www.c-pro.co.id
Mattress Mfr
N.A.I.C.S.: 337910

PT Delta Furindotama (1)
Jl Marsekal Surya Dharma Komp Pergudangan Bandara Mas Blok A2 No 2, Neglasari, Tangerang, Jakarta, Indonesia
Tel.: (62) 215594488
Furniture Product Retailer
N.A.I.C.S.: 449110

PT Mega Inti Mandiri (1)
Jl Gambir No 90 Pasar VIII Tembung Percut Sei Tuan Deli, Serdang, Medan, Sumatera Utara, Indonesia
Tel.: (62) 85101489777
Household Appliance Retailer
N.A.I.C.S.: 449210

PT Sejahtera Bali Furindo (1)
Tel.: (62) 361419884
Furniture Product Retailer
N.A.I.C.S.: 449110

PT Sejahtera Palembang Furindo (1)
Jln Kenten Villa Kencana Damai F-31 Sukamaju Sako, Palembang, Sumatera Utara, Indonesia
Tel.: (62) 7115704141
Furniture Product Retailer
N.A.I.C.S.: 449110

PT Sejahtera Samarinda Furindo (1)
Komplek Pergudangan Jl IR Sutami Blok K No 3 Propinsi, Samarinda, Indonesia
Tel.: (62) 5412771884
Furniture Product Retailer
N.A.I.C.S.: 449110

PT Sejahtera Wahana Gemilang (1)
Ruko Rich Palace R 28-30 Jl MayJend Sungkono No 151, Surabaya, Jawa Timur, Indonesia
Tel.: (62) 315622677
Household Appliance Retailer
N.A.I.C.S.: 449210

PT Sinar Sejahtera Mandiri (1)
Jl Walisongo No 43, Semarang, Jawa Tengah, Indonesia
Tel.: (62) 247618137

Household Appliance Retailer
N.A.I.C.S.: 449210
Dedy Ruswandi *(Mgr-Plant Ops)*

PT Trijati Primula (1)
Jl Ibu Inggit Garnasih No 158B, Bandung, 40525, Indonesia
Tel.: (62) 225227007
Web Site: https://www.trijatiprimula.com
Furniture Product Distr
N.A.I.C.S.: 423210
Setiawan Huang *(Exec Dir)*

PT CIKARANG LISTRINDO TBK

World Trade Centre 1 17th Floor Jl Jend Sudirman Kav 29-31, Jakarta, 12920, Indonesia
Tel.: (62) 215228122
Web Site: https://www.listrindo.com
Year Founded: 1992
POWR—(INDO)
Rev.: $546,079,025
Assets: $1,324,229,288
Liabilities: $620,104,942
Net Worth: $704,124,346
Earnings: $76,976,795
Emp.: 796
Fiscal Year-end: 12/31/23
Electric Power Generation & Distribution Services
N.A.I.C.S.: 221118
Andrew K. Labbaika *(Chm & CEO)*

Subsidiaries:

Listrindo Capital B.V. (1)
Strawinskylaan 3127 8th Floor, 1077 ZX, Amsterdam, Netherlands
Tel.: (31) 885609950
Electric Power Distribution Services
N.A.I.C.S.: 221118

PT Bahtera Listrindo Jaya (1)
World Trade Centre 1 17th Floor Jl Jend Sudirman Kav 29-31, Jakarta Selatan, 12920, Indonesia
Tel.: (62) 215228120
Electric Power Distribution Services
N.A.I.C.S.: 221118

PT CIPTA SELERA MURNI TBK

Menara Imperium Lantai Lower Ground No 04, Selatan, Jakarta, 12980, Indonesia
Tel.: (62) 213140411
Web Site: http://www.ciptaseleramurni.co.id
Year Founded: 1983
CSMI—(INDO)
Rev.: $3,472,470
Assets: $5,021,471
Liabilities: $4,195,180
Net Worth: $826,290
Earnings: ($580,090)
Emp.: 160
Fiscal Year-end: 12/31/22
Restaurant Services
N.A.I.C.S.: 722511
Radino Miharjo *(Pres)*

PT CIPUTRA DEVELOPMENT TBK

Ciputra World 1 DBS Bank Tower 39th Floor Jl Prof Dr Satrio Kav 3-5, Jakarta, 12940, Indonesia
Tel.: (62) 2129885858
Web Site: https://www.ciputradevelopment.com
Year Founded: 1981
CTRA—(INDO)
Rev.: $600,372,378
Assets: $2,864,842,062
Liabilities: $1,395,593,005
Net Worth: $1,469,249,057
Earnings: $123,972,084
Emp.: 3,457
Fiscal Year-end: 12/31/23
Real Estate Services
N.A.I.C.S.: 531312

Tulus Santoso Brotosiswojo *(Sec)*

Subsidiaries:

PT Ciputra Graha Mitra (1)
Ciputra World 1 DBS Bank Tower 38th Floor-Suite 3802 Jl Prof DR Satrio, Kav 3-5, Jakarta, 12940, Indonesia
Tel.: (62) 2129885858
Web Site: http://www.ciputragrahamitra.com
Real Estate Development Services
N.A.I.C.S.: 531210
Danisworo Danisworo *(Head-Mktg)*

PT Ciputra Property Tbk (1)
Ciputra World 1 DBS Bank Tower 38th Floor Jl Prof Dr Satrio Kav 3-5, Jakarta, 12940, Indonesia (56.3%)
Tel.: (62) 2129888898
Web Site: http://www.ciputradevelopment.com
Emp.: 150
Real Estate Services
N.A.I.C.S.: 531311
Candra Ciputra *(Pres)*

PT CISADANE SAWIT RAYA TBK

Jl Pluit Selatan Raya Komplek Cbd Pluit Blok R2 B-25, Jakarta, 14440, Indonesia
Tel.: (62) 2166673312
Web Site: https://www.csr.co.id
Year Founded: 1983
CSRA—(INDO)
Rev.: $56,855,777
Assets: $119,675,175
Liabilities: $47,255,934
Net Worth: $72,419,241
Earnings: $9,490,266
Emp.: 1,567
Fiscal Year-end: 12/31/23
Palm Oil-Based Soap Mfr
N.A.I.C.S.: 311225
Gita Sapta Adi *(Pres)*

PT CISARUA MOUNTAIN DAIRY TBK

Jl Komp Rukan Taman Meruya No N/27-28 Rt 16/Rw 7, Meruya Utara Kec Kembangan Kota Jakarta Barat Daerah Khusus Ibukota, Jakarta, 11620, Indonesia
Tel.: (62) 215874630
Web Site: https://www.cimory.com
Year Founded: 2004
CMRY—(INDO)
Rev.: $504,772,775
Assets: $457,622,894
Liabilities: $71,793,053
Net Worth: $385,829,840
Earnings: $80,641,193
Emp.: 4,686
Fiscal Year-end: 12/31/23
Dairy Products Mfr
N.A.I.C.S.: 311512
Yerki Teguh *(Dir-Supply Chain & Ops)*

Subsidiaries:

PT. Java Egg Specialities (1)
Taman Meruya Shophouse Block N1-2, Jakarta, 11620, Indonesia
Tel.: (62) 215874630
Web Site: https://www.javaegg.com
Mayonnaise & Sauce Preparation Egg Product Mfr
N.A.I.C.S.: 311941

PT CITRA BUANA PRASIDA TBK

Komplek Paskal Hyper Square Blok G Lantai 2 No 206, 208 Jl H O S Cokroaminoto No 25-27 dh Jl Pasirkaliki No 25-27, Bandung, 40181, Indonesia
Tel.: (62) 2286061108
Web Site: https://www.citrabuanaprasida.co.id
Year Founded: 2000

INTERNATIONAL PUBLIC

CBPE—(INDO)
Rev.: $5,508,762
Assets: $19,543,765
Liabilities: $4,832,101
Net Worth: $14,711,665
Earnings: $2,687,424
Emp.: 46
Fiscal Year-end: 12/31/23
Real Estate Development Services
N.A.I.C.S.: 531390
R. Asep Eddy *(Chm)*

PT CITRA MARGA NUSAPHALA PERSADA TBK.

Jl Yos Sudarso Kav 28, Jakarta, 14350, Indonesia
Tel.: (62) 2165306930
Web Site: https://id.citramarga.com
Year Founded: 1987
CMNP—(INDO)
Rev.: $496,772,303
Assets: $1,401,143,137
Liabilities: $556,199,148
Net Worth: $844,943,990
Earnings: $68,544,340
Emp.: 737
Fiscal Year-end: 12/31/23
Toll Road Operation Services
N.A.I.C.S.: 488490
Shadik Wahono *(Chm)*

Subsidiaries:

P.T. Citra Marga Lintas Jabar (1)
Muara Street No 1 RT 001 RW 011, Kopo Village Kutawaringin District, Bandung, 40911, Indonesia
Tel.: (62) 2254416358
Web Site: https://cmlj.co.id
Highway Toll System Mfr
N.A.I.C.S.: 334220

P.T. Citra Margatama Surabaya (1)
Graha CMS Jl Wisata Menanggal 21, Surabaya, 60234, Indonesia
Tel.: (62) 318497777
Web Site: https://www.cms.co.id
Highway Toll System Mfr
N.A.I.C.S.: 334220

P.T. Citra Persada Infrastruktur (1)
Jl Angkasa No 20 RT 12/RW 2 Gn Sahari Sel, Kec Kemayoran Kota Jakarta Pusat Daerah Khusus Ibukota, Jakarta, 10610, Indonesia
Tel.: (62) 214213333
Web Site: https://citrapersada.net
Highway Toll System Mfr
N.A.I.C.S.: 334220

P.T. Girder Indonesia (1)
Jl Yos Sudarso Kav 28 CMNP Building lt 2 Sunter, Jakarta Utara, 14350, Indonesia
Tel.: (62) 2165306930
Web Site: https://girder-indonesia.com
Civil Construction Services
N.A.I.C.S.: 541330

PT CITRA PUTRA REALTY TBK

The City Tower 18 th Floor Jl MH Thamrin No 81, Jakarta, 10310, Indonesia
Tel.: (62) 2131996270
Web Site: https://cpr.co.id
Year Founded: 2009
CLAY—(INDO)
Rev.: $14,583,198
Assets: $36,868,654
Liabilities: $36,480,763
Net Worth: $387,891
Earnings: $407,486
Emp.: 267
Fiscal Year-end: 12/31/23
Hotel & Restaurant Operator
N.A.I.C.S.: 721110
Firman M. Silalahi *(Chm)*

PT CITY RETAIL DEVELOPMENTS TBK

Gedung Menara Jamsostek Menara Utara Lt 8 Jl Jend, Gatot Subroto No 38, Jakarta Selatan, 12710, Indonesia
Tel.: (62) 2150842878 Id
Web Site:
  https://www.citydevelopments.com
Year Founded: 2003
NIRO—(INDO)
Rev.: $74,386,488
Assets: $882,203,139
Liabilities: $505,104,055
Net Worth: $377,099,085
Earnings: ($20,313,594)
Emp.: 160
Fiscal Year-end: 12/31/23
Commercial Property Development Services
N.A.I.C.S.: 531312

Subsidiaries:

P.T. Cella Management Logistik (1)
Ruko ICE Business Park Block G12-15 Jl BSD Grand Boulevard, Pagedangan, Tangerang, 15339, Banten, Indonesia
Tel.: (62) 8122484556
Web Site: https://www.cella.co.id
Logistics & Warehousing Services
N.A.I.C.S.: 541614

PT COMETA INTERNATIONAL

Jl Muara Karang Block S No 1, Pluit Penjaringan, Jakarta Utara, 14450, Indonesia
Tel.: (62) 216603800
Web Site: http://www.cometa-international.com
Year Founded: 1953
Industrial Supplies Distr
N.A.I.C.S.: 423840
Zaini Cometa (Gen Mgr)

PT COMMUNICATION CABLE SYSTEMS INDONESIA TBK

Grand Slipi Tower 45th Floor Jl Letjen S Parman No Kav 22-24, Palmerah, Jakarta, Indonesia
Tel.: (62) 2129865963
Web Site: https://www.ptccsi.my.id
Year Founded: 1996
CCSI—(INDO)
Rev.: $22,696,598
Assets: $48,831,872
Liabilities: $22,256,281
Net Worth: $26,575,591
Earnings: ($1,453,136)
Emp.: 154
Fiscal Year-end: 12/31/23
Fiber Cable Mfr
N.A.I.C.S.: 335921
Sudarno Khou (VP)

PT COTTONINDO ARIESTA TBK

Jl Raya Cipendeuy Dusun III/ No 414 RT 0001/RW 001 Cipendeuy, Kabupaten Subang, Jakarta, 41272, Jawa Barat, Indonesia
Tel.: (62) 2286066517
Web Site: http://www.cottonindo.com
Year Founded: 1994
KPAS—(INDO)
Rev.: $4,627,287
Assets: $17,830,784
Liabilities: $7,551,845
Net Worth: $10,278,939
Earnings: ($344,776)
Emp.: 211
Fiscal Year-end: 12/31/20
Cotton Product Mfr
N.A.I.C.S.: 314999
Fransiskus Toni (Vice Chm, Fin Dir & Dir)

PT COWELL DEVELOPMENT TBK.

Graha Atrium Lt 6 Jl Senen Raya No 135, Jakarta, 10410, Indonesia
Tel.: (62) 213867868
Web Site: http://www.cowelldev.com
Real Estate Property Development Services
N.A.I.C.S.: 531311
Irwan Susanto (Pres)

PT CT CORPORA

Menara Bank Mega 24th Floor Jl Kapt P Tendean Kav 12-14A, Jakarta, 12790, Indonesia
Tel.: (62) 21 7917 5533
Web Site: http://www.ctcorpora.com
Year Founded: 1984
Sales Range: $5-14.9 Billion
Emp.: 60,000
Holding Company
N.A.I.C.S.: 551112
Chairul Tanjung (Chm)

Subsidiaries:

PT Mega Asset Management (1)
Menara Bank Mega 7 th Floor Jl Kapten P Tendean Kav 12-14A, Jakarta, 12790, Indonesia
Tel.: (62) 2179175924
Web Site: http://www.mega-asset.co.id
Asset Management Services
N.A.I.C.S.: 531390

PT Mega Capital Investama (1)
Menara Bank Mega Lt 6 Jalan Kapten Tendean Kav 12-14A, Jakarta Selatan, 12790, Indonesia
Tel.: (62) 79186999
Web Site: http://www.megainvestama.co.id
Investment Management Service
N.A.I.C.S.: 523940

PT Trans Retail Indonesia (1)
Gedung Carrefour Jl Lebak Bulus Raya No 8, Jakarta, 12310, Indonesia
Tel.: (62) 21 27585800
Web Site: http://www.carrefour.co.id
Grocery & Convenience Stores Operator
N.A.I.C.S.: 445110

PT DAFAM PROPERTY INDONESIA TBK

Jl Raung No 15, Semarang, 50134, Jawa Tengah, Indonesia
Tel.: (62) 248312735
Web Site:
  https://www.dafamproperty.com
Year Founded: 2011
DFAM—(INDO)
Rev.: $4,502,861
Assets: $16,093,341
Liabilities: $13,611,896
Net Worth: $2,481,445
Earnings: ($1,064,440)
Emp.: 192
Fiscal Year-end: 12/31/23
Property Management Services
N.A.I.C.S.: 531311
Billy Dahlan (Pres)

PT DAMAI SEJAHTERA ABADI TBK

Jl Kertajaya 149 Kel Airlangga Kec, Gubeng, Surabaya, 60286, Jawa Timur, Indonesia
Tel.: (62) 315037745
UFOE—(INDO)
Rev.: $57,261,638
Assets: $29,287,397
Liabilities: $15,598,734
Net Worth: $13,688,663
Earnings: $847,628
Emp.: 246
Fiscal Year-end: 12/31/23
Furniture Retailer
N.A.I.C.S.: 449110
Tedy Suronoto (Sec)

PT DANA BRATA LUHUR TBK

Treasury Tower 15th Fl Unit H District 8 Scbd Lot 28, Jl Jend Sudirman Kav 52-53, Jakarta, 12190, Indonesia
Tel.: (62) 2150106300
Web Site: https://www.tebe.co.id
Year Founded: 2008
TEBE—(INDO)
Rev.: $41,057,199
Assets: $74,739,488
Liabilities: $4,143,892
Net Worth: $70,595,596
Earnings: $14,397,951
Emp.: 290
Fiscal Year-end: 12/31/23
Investment Management Service
N.A.I.C.S.: 523999
Dian Heryandi (Pres)

Subsidiaries:

P.T. Talenta Bumi (1)
km 21 5 Pleihari Department No 16 RT 12 RW 03, Ulin Selatan Platform Liang Anggang Banjarbaru, Kalimantan, 70722, Indonesia
Tel.: (62) 5116747241
Web Site: https://www.talentabumi.co.id
Mining Infrastructure Services
N.A.I.C.S.: 212321

PT DANASUPRA ERAPACIFIC TBK

Tower B Lantai 3 18 Parc Place SCBD Jl Jend Sudirman Kav 52-53, Jakarta, 12190, Indonesia
Tel.: (62) 2151401157 Id
Web Site:
  https://www.danasupra.com
Year Founded: 1995
DEFI—(INDO)
Rev.: $108,639
Assets: $2,729,565
Liabilities: $26,248
Net Worth: $2,703,317
Earnings: ($212,175)
Emp.: 7
Fiscal Year-end: 12/31/23
Loan Mortgage Services
N.A.I.C.S.: 522310

PT DARMA HENWA TBK

Bakrie Tower 8th Floor Rasuna Epicentrum Jl HR Rasuna Said, Kuningan, Jakarta, 12940, Indonesia
Tel.: (62) 2129912350
Web Site: https://www.ptdh.co.id
Year Founded: 1991
DEWA—(INDO)
Rev.: $478,781,089
Assets: $528,456,981
Liabilities: $314,848,872
Net Worth: $213,608,109
Earnings: $2,292,037
Emp.: 2,986
Fiscal Year-end: 12/31/23
Integrated Mining Services
N.A.I.C.S.: 213113
Agus Efendi (COO)

PT DARMI BERSAUDARA TBK

Nginden Intan Barat V Blok C410, Surabaya, 60118, East Java, Indonesia
Tel.: (62) 315967274
Web Site:
  https://www.darbewood.com
KAYU—(INDO)
Rev.: $1,526,206
Assets: $7,028,084
Liabilities: $1,630,332
Net Worth: $5,397,751
Earnings: $119,544
Emp.: 10
Fiscal Year-end: 12/31/22
Wood Product Distr
N.A.I.C.S.: 423310

PT DATA SINERGITAMA JAYA TBK

The Manhattan Square Tower Lt 22 unit FJI TB Simatupang RT 3/RW 3, East Cilandak Pasar Minggu Jakarta, South Jakarta, 12560, Indonesia
Tel.: (62) 217511004
Web Site: https://www.elitery.com
Year Founded: 2011
ELIT—(INDO)
Rev.: $11,467,595
Assets: $7,686,771
Liabilities: $4,175,073
Net Worth: $3,511,698
Earnings: $618,871
Fiscal Year-end: 12/31/22
Information Technology Services
N.A.I.C.S.: 541512
Astrid Erawan (Sec)

PT DAYAMITRA TELEKOMUNIKASI TBK

Telkom Landmark Tower Lantai 25-27 Jl Gatot Subroto Kav 52, Jakarta, 12710, Indonesia
Tel.: (62) 2127933363
Web Site: https://www.mitratel.co.id
Year Founded: 2008
MTEL—(INDO)
Rev.: $558,128,778
Assets: $3,702,237,712
Liabilities: $1,491,835,384
Net Worth: $2,210,402,328
Earnings: $130,550,700
Emp.: 537
Fiscal Year-end: 12/31/23
Telecommunication Servicesb
N.A.I.C.S.: 517810
Theodorus Ardi Hartoko (CEO)

PT DCI INDONESIA TBK

Equity Building 17th Floor Suite F Lot 9 Jl Jend Sudirman Kav 52-53, Sudirman Center Business District, Jakarta, 12190, Indonesia
Tel.: (62) 2129037500
Web Site: https://www.dci-indonesia.com
Year Founded: 2011
DCII—(INDO)
Rev.: $84,801,639
Assets: $238,750,871
Liabilities: $95,431,538
Net Worth: $143,319,333
Earnings: $33,410,786
Emp.: 101
Fiscal Year-end: 12/31/23
Data Processing Services
N.A.I.C.S.: 518210
Toto Sugiri (Founder & CEO)

PT DELTA DUNIA MAKMUR TBK

Pacific Century Place 38 F SCBD Lot 10, Jl Jend Sudirman Kav 52 53, Jakarta, 12190, Indonesia
Tel.: (62) 30432080 VN
Web Site:
  https://www.deltadunia.com
Year Founded: 1990
DOID—(INDO)
Rev.: $1,833,320,502
Assets: $1,874,599,404
Liabilities: $1,601,994,468
Net Worth: $272,604,936
Earnings: $36,010,191
Emp.: 16,628
Fiscal Year-end: 12/31/23
Coal Mining & Production
N.A.I.C.S.: 212115
Hagianto Kumala (Pres)

Subsidiaries:

PT Bukit Makmur Mandiri Utama (1)
Tel.: (62) 216613636
Emp.: 12,000
Coal Mining Services
N.A.I.C.S.: 238910
Ronald Sutardja (Pres)

PT DESTINASI TIRTA NUSANTARA TBK

PT Delta Dunia Makmur Tbk—(Continued)

PT DESTINASI TIRTA NUSANTARA TBK
Panorama Building 5th floor Jl Tomang Raya no 63, Jakarta, 11440, Indonesia
Tel.: (62) 80820600
Web Site: https://www.panorama-destination.com
Year Founded: 1999
PDES—(INDO)
Rev.: $23,931,155
Assets: $17,268,526
Liabilities: $12,585,817
Net Worth: $4,682,709
Earnings: $2,295,819
Emp.: 171
Fiscal Year-end: 12/31/23
Tourism Operator
N.A.I.C.S.: 561520
Renato Domini *(Chm)*

Subsidiaries:

PT Buaya Travel Indonesia (1)
Jl By Pass Ngurah Rai No 620 Suwung, Denpasar, 80228, Bali, Indonesia
Tel.: (62) 361726800
Travel Agency Services
N.A.I.C.S.: 561510

PT Destinasi Garuda Wisata (1)
Jl Laksda Adi Sucipto KM9 Gudeg bu Tjitro Airport, Yogyakarta, Indonesia
Tel.: (62) 274488663
Travel Agency Services
N.A.I.C.S.: 561510

PT Graha Destinasi (1)
Panorama Building 4th Floor Jl Tomang Raya No 63, Jakarta, 11440, Indonesia
Tel.: (62) 2125565000
Travel Agency Services
N.A.I.C.S.: 561510

Panorama Destination (Vietnam) Jv Ltd.
Level 6 Anh Minh Tower 56 Nguyen Dinh Chieu, District 01, Ho Chi Minh City, Vietnam
Tel.: (84) 2871099228
Tourism & Travel Services
N.A.I.C.S.: 561510

PT DEWATA FREIGHT INTERNATIONAL TBK
Kirana Two Office Tower 12nd Floor, Jl Boulevard Timur No 88 Kelapa Gading, Jakarta Utara, 14240, Indonesia
Tel.: (62) 2129688899
Web Site: https://www.dfilogistics.id
Year Founded: 1995
DEAL—(INDO)
Rev.: $4,979,930
Assets: $19,828,904
Liabilities: $14,544,701
Net Worth: $5,284,203
Earnings: ($3,618,316)
Emp.: 98
Fiscal Year-end: 12/31/20
Transportation Services
N.A.I.C.S.: 485999
Nur Hasanah *(Sec)*

PT DHARMA POLIMETAL TBK
Jl Angsana Raya Blok A9 No 8 Delta Silicon 1, Cikarang, 17550, Indonesia
Tel.: (62) 218974637
Web Site: https://www.dharmagroup.co.id
Year Founded: 1989
DRMA—(INDO)
Rev.: $359,843,624
Assets: $219,857,069
Liabilities: $88,007,612
Net Worth: $131,849,457
Earnings: $40,620,534
Emp.: 2,252
Fiscal Year-end: 12/31/23
Automotive Components Mfr
N.A.I.C.S.: 336390
Irianto Santoso *(Pres)*

PT DHARMA SATYA NUSANTARA TBK
Jl Rawa Gelam V Kav OR/3B, Kawasan Industri Pulogadung, Jakarta, 13930, Indonesia
Tel.: (62) 214618135
Web Site: https://www.dsn.co.id
Year Founded: 1980
DSNG—(INDO)
Rev.: $616,848,760
Assets: $1,050,617,373
Liabilities: $473,337,919
Net Worth: $577,279,454
Earnings: $54,657,725
Emp.: 19,509
Fiscal Year-end: 12/31/23
Palm Oil & Wood Processing
N.A.I.C.S.: 311224
Andrianto Oetomo *(Chm & CEO)*

Subsidiaries:

P.T. Tanjung Kreasi Parquet Industry (1)
Jl Rawa Gelam V Kav Or/3B Kawasan Industri, Pulo Gadung, Jakarta, 13930, Indonesia
Tel.: (62) 214606979
Web Site: https://tekaparquet.com
Wooden Floor Mfr
N.A.I.C.S.: 316210

PT Mandiri Cahaya Abadi (1)
Jl Raya Enggano Perk Enggano Megah 7-E, Tanjung priok, Jakarta, 14310, Indonesia
Tel.: (62) 21 43937439
Palm Oil Mfr
N.A.I.C.S.: 311224

PT DIAGNOS LABORATORIUM UTAMA TBK
Bic-1 Rsia Bunda Jakarta Jl Teuku Cik Ditiro 1 No 12, Jakarta Pusat, 10350, Indonesia
Tel.: (62) 85881500799
Web Site: https://www.diagnos.co.id
Year Founded: 2009
DGNS—(INDO)
Rev.: $9,461,499
Assets: $17,629,595
Liabilities: $4,927,953
Net Worth: $12,701,642
Earnings: ($886,808)
Emp.: 93
Fiscal Year-end: 12/31/23
Medical Laboratory Services
N.A.I.C.S.: 621511
Fanfan Riksani *(Sec)*

PT DIAMOND CITRA PROPERTINDO TBK
Jl Palakali Raya, Kukusan, Depok, 16425, West Java, Indonesia
Tel.: (62) 2129302135
Web Site: https://diamondland.co.id
Year Founded: 2014
DADA—(INDO)
Rev.: $1,948,666
Assets: $42,888,033
Liabilities: $20,513,271
Net Worth: $22,374,762
Earnings: $57,810
Fiscal Year-end: 12/31/23
Real Estate Services
N.A.I.C.S.: 531210
Muhammad Reza *(Sec)*

PT DIAMOND FOOD INDONESIA TBK
Gedung Tcc Batavia Tower One Lantai 15 Unit 03 & 05, Jl Kh Mas Mansyur Kav 126, Jakarta Pusat, 10220, Indonesia
Tel.: (62) 2128649888
Web Site: https://diamondfoodindonesia.com
DMND—(INDO)
Rev.: $600,040,794
Assets: $465,417,187
Liabilities: $86,704,511
Net Worth: $378,712,676
Earnings: $20,720,925
Emp.: 6,805
Fiscal Year-end: 12/31/23
Food Retail & Distr
N.A.I.C.S.: 424490
Philip Min Lih Chen *(Pres)*

Subsidiaries:

P.T. Diamondfair Ritel Indonesia (1)
MM 2100 Industrial Estate Jl Halmahera Blok EE-02 West Cikarang, Bekasi, 17520, Indonesia
Tel.: (62) 2128649800
Web Site: https://www.diamondfair.co.id
Dairy Product Mfr & Distr
N.A.I.C.S.: 311920

P.T. Sukanda Djaya (1)
JL Irian Blok FF-2, MM 2100 INDUSTRIAL TOWN Cibitung, Bekasi, 17520, Indonesia
Tel.: (62) 2129812788
Web Site: https://sukandadjaya.com
Food & Beverage Distr
N.A.I.C.S.: 424490

PT DIAN SWASTATIKA SENTOSA TBK
Sinar Mas Land Plaza Tower II 24th floor Jl M H Thamrin No 51, Jakarta, 10350, Indonesia
Tel.: (62) 2131990258
Web Site: https://www.dss.co.id
DSSA—(INDO)
Rev.: $5,014,659,972
Assets: $3,063,273,017
Liabilities: $1,342,457,831
Net Worth: $1,720,815,186
Earnings: $865,313,519
Emp.: 1,840
Fiscal Year-end: 12/31/23
Coal Mining & Power Generation Services
N.A.I.C.S.: 237990
Lay Krisnan Cahya *(Chm)*

Subsidiaries:

PT Dian Semesta Sentosa (1)
Ruko Rungkut Megah Raya Blok E 18-19 Jalan Kalirungkut No 5, Surabaya, 60293, Indonesia
Tel.: (62) 318720041
Web Site: https://www.ptdiansentosa.com
Construction Services
N.A.I.C.S.: 236220

PT Dwikarya Sejati Utama (1)
Sinar Mas Land Plaza Tower II 6th Floor Jl MH Thamrin No 51, Jakarta, 10350, Indonesia
Tel.: (62) 215 018 6888
Venture Capital Management Services
N.A.I.C.S.: 523940

PT Eka Mas Republik (1)
Jl KH Abdullah syafei gudang peluru blok A No 27B samping Bank BCA, Jakarta, Indonesia
Tel.: (62) 150 0818
Web Site: https://www.myrepublic.co.id
Internet Communication Services
N.A.I.C.S.: 517810

PT Energi Mas Anugerah Semesta (1)
Wisma BCA Wing A Zona 5 and 6 3rd Floor, Jl Kapten Soebijanto Djojohadikusumo, Tangerang, Indonesia
Tel.: (62) 2129004378
Fertilizer & Chemical Product Distr
N.A.I.C.S.: 424910

PT Golden Energy Mines Tbk (1)
Sinar Mas Land Plaza Tower II 6th floor Jl MH Thamrin no 51, Jakarta, Indonesia
Tel.: (62) 2150186888

INTERNATIONAL PUBLIC

Web Site: https://www.goldenenergymines.com
Rev.: $2,901,836,296
Assets: $1,312,042,245
Liabilities: $648,930,158
Net Worth: $663,112,087
Earnings: $528,748,412
Emp.: 491
Fiscal Year-end: 12/31/2023
Mineral Mining Services
N.A.I.C.S.: 213115
Kumar Krishnan *(CFO)*

PT Rolimex Kimia Nusamas (1)
ITC Cempaka Mas Office Tower Lt 11 Jl Letjen Suprapto Kav 1, Sumur Batu Kemayoran, Jakarta, 10640, Indonesia
Tel.: (62) 2142887070
Web Site: https://www.rolimex.co.id
Fertilizer & Chemical Product Distr
N.A.I.C.S.: 424910

PT Wahana Alam Lestari (1)
Jl Sei Silau No 93, Padang Bulan Selayang I Kec Medan Selayang, Medan, 20154, Sumatera Utara, Indonesia
Tel.: (62) 6142404227
Web Site: https://www.wahanaalamlestari.co.id
Environmental Consulting Services
N.A.I.C.S.: 541620

PT DIGITAL MEDIATAMA MAXIMA TBK
Mangkuluhur City Tower One 18th Floor, Jl Jend Gatot Subroto Kav 1-3, South Jakarta, 12930, Indonesia
Tel.: (62) 2127883335
Web Site: https://dmmgroup.id
Year Founded: 2015
DMMX—(INDO)
Rev.: $126,311,919
Assets: $56,366,969
Liabilities: $12,611,363
Net Worth: $43,755,606
Earnings: ($17,350,999)
Emp.: 35
Fiscal Year-end: 12/31/23
Digital Marketing Services
N.A.I.C.S.: 541870
Budiasto Kusuma *(Pres)*

PT DISTRIBUSI VOUCHER NUSANTARA TBK
Axa Tower 7th Floor Suite 5 Jln Prof Dr Satrio Kav 18, Setiabudi Jakarta Selatan, Kuningan, 12940, Indonesia
Tel.: (62) 2130480712
Web Site: https://www.ptdvn.com
Year Founded: 2004
DIVA—(INDO)
Rev.: $250,242,228
Assets: $65,812,346
Liabilities: $8,898,687
Net Worth: $56,913,659
Earnings: ($82,665,801)
Emp.: 106
Fiscal Year-end: 12/31/23
Data Processing Services
N.A.I.C.S.: 518210
Raymond Loho *(Chm)*

Subsidiaries:

PT Surprise Indonesia (1)
JL Majapahit No 26 Rukan Golden Centrum Blok D-E, Jakarta, 10160, Indonesia
Tel.: (62) 2121880588
Web Site: http://www.surprise.co.id
Online Marketing Services
N.A.I.C.S.: 541613

PT DJASA UBERSAKTI TBK
Bona Indah Plaza Blok A2/B8 Jl Karang Tengah Raya, South Jakarta, 12440, Indonesia
Tel.: (62) 217660114
Web Site: https://www.djasaubersakti.co.id
Year Founded: 1971
PTDU—(INDO)
Rev.: $7,701,708

AND PRIVATE COMPANIES

Assets: $13,646,780
Liabilities: $11,346,920
Net Worth: $2,299,860
Earnings: ($2,193,758)
Emp.: 15
Fiscal Year-end: 12/31/23
Construction Services
N.A.I.C.S.: 236220
Heru Putranto (Pres)

PT DMS PROPERTINDO TBK
Gedung Graha Mampang Jl Mampang Prapatan Raya No 100 Lantai 2, Jakarta Selatan, 12760, Indonesia
Tel.: (62) 217940671
Web Site:
https://www.dmspropertindo.com
Year Founded: 2011
KOTA—(INDO)
Rev.: $1,810,468
Assets: $98,927,400
Liabilities: $20,114,620
Net Worth: $78,812,780
Earnings: ($1,602,532)
Emp.: 22
Fiscal Year-end: 12/31/23
Real Estate Services
N.A.I.C.S.: 531210
Mohamad Prapanca (Founder, Pres & CEO)

PT DUA PUTRA UTAMA MAKMUR TBK.
Jl Raya Pati-Juwana No km 7 Pondohan Purworejo, Kec Pati Kabupaten Pati, Semarang, 59119, Jawa Tengah, Indonesia
Tel.: (62) 2954199011
Web Site: https://www.duaputra.co.id
Year Founded: 2012
DPUM—(INDO)
Rev.: $59,745,254
Assets: $77,942,078
Liabilities: $49,985,116
Net Worth: $27,956,962
Earnings: ($9,240,865)
Emp.: 89
Fiscal Year-end: 12/31/23
Seafood Product Processing
N.A.I.C.S.: 311710

PT DUTA ANGGADA REALTY TBK
Plaza Chase Lantai 21 Jl Jend Sudirman Kav 21, Jakarta, 12920, Indonesia
Tel.: (62) 215208000   Id
Web Site:
https://www.dutaanggadarealty.com
Year Founded: 1983
DART—(INDO)
Rev.: $28,132,040
Assets: $410,224,008
Liabilities: $297,323,928
Net Worth: $112,900,080
Earnings: ($22,326,212)
Emp.: 283
Fiscal Year-end: 12/31/23
Real Estate Development Services
N.A.I.C.S.: 531390
Ventje Chandraputra Suardana (Chm)

PT DUTA INTIDAYA TBK
EightyEight Kasablanka Tower A 28th and 37th Floor, Jl Casablanca Raya Kav 88 Kelurahan Menteng Dalam Kecamatan Tebet, South Jakarta, 12870, Indonesia
Tel.: (62) 2121283001
Web Site: https://www.watsons.biz.id
Year Founded: 2005
DAYA—(INDO)
Rev.: $100,397,256
Assets: $44,791,927
Liabilities: $43,648,462
Net Worth: $1,143,464
Earnings: ($1,051,313)
Emp.: 997
Fiscal Year-end: 12/31/23
Beauty Product Distr
N.A.I.C.S.: 424210
Sukarnen Suwanto (Sec)

PT DUTA PERTIWI NUSANTARA TBK
Jl Tanjung pura no 263 D, Pontianak, 78122, kalimantan barat, Indonesia
Tel.: (62) 561736406   Id
Web Site: https://www.dpn.co.id
Year Founded: 1982
DPNS—(INDO)
Rev.: $7,546,063
Assets: $22,537,349
Liabilities: $992,399
Net Worth: $21,544,950
Earnings: $1,043,947
Emp.: 86
Fiscal Year-end: 12/31/23
Chemical & Adhesive Mfr
N.A.I.C.S.: 325520
Siang Hadi Widjaja (Chm)

PT DWI GUNA LAKSANA TBK
Jl Pramuka No 18A Pemurus Luar, Banjarmasin, Kalimantan, 70249, Selatan, Indonesia
Tel.: (62) 5116127021
Web Site:
https://www.dwigunalaksana.co.id
Year Founded: 1986
DWGL—(INDO)
Rev.: $211,781,271
Assets: $119,764,908
Liabilities: $109,607,296
Net Worth: $10,157,612
Earnings: $1,015,498
Emp.: 44
Fiscal Year-end: 12/31/23
Coal Mining Services
N.A.I.C.S.: 213113
Herman Fasikhin (Chm)

PT DYANDRA MEDIA INTERNATIONAL TBK
Jl Johar no 9 Menteng, Jakarta Pusat, 10310, Indonesia
Tel.: (62) 2131996077
Web Site:
https://www.dyandramedia.com
Year Founded: 1994
DYAN—(INDO)
Rev.: $86,313,163
Assets: $78,164,546
Liabilities: $39,701,088
Net Worth: $38,463,458
Earnings: $4,551,889
Emp.: 355
Fiscal Year-end: 12/31/23
Holding Company
N.A.I.C.S.: 551112
Mirna Gozal (Head-IR & Strategic Mgmt)

Subsidiaries:

PT Dyandra Promosindo   (1)
Gedung Dyandra Promosindo Jalan Gelora VII No 15 RT 4/RW 2 Gelora, Palmerah Selatan, Jakarta Pusat, 10270, Indonesia
Tel.: (62) 2131996077
Web Site: https://www.dyandra.com
Events Services
N.A.I.C.S.: 561920
Hendra Saleh (Co-Pres)

Subsidiary (Domestic):

PT Debindo Mitra Tama   (2)
Jl Kalibokor Selatan No 66, Surabaya, 60283, Indonesia
Tel.: (62) 315010177
Web Site: http://www.debindomitratama.com
Events Services
N.A.I.C.S.: 561920

PT Dyandra Communication   (2)
Jalan Johar No 9 Menteng, Jakarta Pusat, 10350, Indonesia
Tel.: (62) 213100705
Web Site: https://www.dyacomm.com
Events Services
N.A.I.C.S.: 561920

PT Dyandra Global Edutainment   (2)
Jl Gelora 7 No 15 Palmerah, Jakarta Pusat, Indonesia
Tel.: (62) 2153672758
Web Site: http://www.dyandraglobal.com
Entertainment Services
N.A.I.C.S.: 711110

PT Fasen Creative Quality   (2)
Jl Bangka Raya No 98 Pela Mampang, Mampang Prapatan, Jakarta Selatan, 12720, Indonesia
Tel.: (62) 2171792480
Web Site: http://www.quadevent.com
Events Services
N.A.I.C.S.: 561920
Michael Bayu A. Sumarijanto (Pres)

PT Samudra Dyan Praga   (1)
Gedung Graha Inti 5th Floor Jl Raya Kalimalang No 87, Jakarta, 13430, Indonesia
Tel.: (62) 218604622
Web Site: http://www.samudra.co.id
Construction Services
N.A.I.C.S.: 236220
Hariman T. Zagloel (Pres)

PT Sinar Dyandra Abadi   (1)
Jl Raden Saleh No 41 Karang Mulya, Karang Tengah, Tangerang, 15157, Banten, Indonesia
Tel.: (62) 2122546991
Web Site: http://www.sda-indonesia.com
Events Services
N.A.I.C.S.: 561920

PT DYNAPLAST TBK.
Dynapack Tower Test Road Name, Lippo Karawaci, Tangerang, Banten, Indonesia
Tel.: (62) 215463111
Web Site: http://www.dynaplast.co.id
Sales Range: $10-24.9 Million
Plastic Mfr
N.A.I.C.S.: 325211
Tirtadjaja Hambali (Pres)

Subsidiaries:

Berli Dynaplast Co., Ltd.   (1)
Berli Jucker House 13th Floor 99 Soi Rubia Sukhumvit 42 Road, Prakanong Klongtoey, Bangkok, 10110, Thailand
Tel.: (66) 23815088
Web Site: http://www.berlidynaplast.com
Packaging Plastics Products Mfr
N.A.I.C.S.: 326160

PT Sanpak Unggul   (1)
Jl Pancasila 4 Cicadas Raya Km 9, Gunung Putri, Bogor, 16964, West Java, Indonesia
Tel.: (62) 218670839
Web Site: http://www.sanpak.co.id
Food Packaging Products Mfr
N.A.I.C.S.: 327213

PT EAGLE HIGH PLANTATIONS TBK
Rajawali Place 28th Floor Jl HR Rasuna Said Kav B/4, Kawasan Mega Kuningan, Jakarta, 12910, Indonesia
Tel.: (62) 2186658828   Id
Web Site:
https://eaglehighplantations.com
Year Founded: 2000
BWPT—(INDO)
Rev.: $273,047,503
Assets: $661,317,139
Liabilities: $518,997,882
Net Worth: $142,319,257
Earnings: $10,388,452
Emp.: 7,203
Fiscal Year-end: 12/31/23
Crude Palm Oil Mfr
N.A.I.C.S.: 324110
Henderi Djunaidi (CFO)

PT EASPARC HOTEL TBK
Jl Kapas No 1 Ngentak Caturtunggal Depok Sleman Daerah Istimewa, Yogyakarta, 55281, Indonesia
Tel.: (62) 2744932000
Web Site: https://www.eastparc.co.id
Year Founded: 2011
EAST—(INDO)
Rev.: $6,906,660
Assets: $31,396,415
Liabilities: $1,383,439
Net Worth: $30,012,976
Earnings: $2,496,274
Emp.: 116
Fiscal Year-end: 12/31/23
Hotel Operator
N.A.I.C.S.: 721110
Muhammad Anis (Sec)

PT EKADHARMA INTERNATIONAL TBK
Pasar Kemis Industrial Area Blok C1 Jl Raya Pasar Kemis, Tangerang, 15560, Banten, Indonesia
Tel.: (62) 215900160
Web Site:
https://www.ekadharma.com
EKAD—(INDO)
Rev.: $33,662,229
Assets: $80,997,434
Liabilities: $6,461,834
Net Worth: $74,535,601
Earnings: $4,809,889
Emp.: 469
Fiscal Year-end: 12/31/23
Adhesive Tape Mfr
N.A.I.C.S.: 322220
Lie Phing (Sec)

Subsidiaries:

Visko industries Sdn. Bhd.   (1)
Menara Mitraland D-09-3A No 13A Jalan PJU 5/1 Kota Damansara PJU 5, 47810, Petaling Jaya, Selangor, Malaysia
Tel.: (60) 37 499 0080
Web Site: https://www.visko-malaysia.com
Self Adhesive Tape Packaging Mfr
N.A.I.C.S.: 322220

PT ELDERS INDONESIA
Jl Letjen TB Simatupang Kav 1 Cilandak Timur, Pasar Minggu, Jakarta Selatan, 12560, Indonesia
Tel.: (62) 2178840708
Web Site: http://elders.co.id
Year Founded: 2001
Chilled & Frozen Beef Distr
N.A.I.C.S.: 424470
Jason Hatchett (Pres)

PT ELNUSA TBK
Graha Elnusa 16th Floor Jl TB Simatupang Kav 1 B, Jakarta, 12560, Indonesia
Tel.: (62) 2178830850
Web Site: http://www.elnusa.co.id
ELSA—(INDO)
Rev.: $815,931,552
Assets: $623,520,241
Liabilities: $336,740,785
Net Worth: $286,779,456
Earnings: $32,673,327
Emp.: 871
Fiscal Year-end: 12/31/23
Oil & Gas Drilling Services
N.A.I.C.S.: 211120
Hery Setawan (Dir-Fin)

Subsidiaries:

P.T. KSO Elnusa - RAGA   (1)
Graha Elnusa 2nd floor Jl TB Simatupang Kav 1B, Jakarta, 12560, Indonesia
Tel.: (62) 2178830850
Technical Maintenance Services
N.A.I.C.S.: 811310

PT Elnusa Fabrikasi Konstruksi   (1)
Graha Elnusa Lantai 10 Jalan TB Simatu-

PT ELNUSA TBK

PT Elnusa Tbk—(Continued)
pang Kav 1B, Jakarta Selatan, 12560, Indonesia
Tel.: (62) 2178845519
Web Site: http://www.elnusa-konstruksi.co.id
Oil & Gas Services
N.A.I.C.S.: 213112

PT Elnusa Geosains Indonesia (1)
Graha Elnusa 15th floor Jl TB Simatupang Kav 1B, Jakarta, 12560, Indonesia
Tel.: (62) 2178830850
Oil & Gas Services
N.A.I.C.S.: 213112

PT Elnusa Oilfield Services (1)
Graha Elnusa 11th Floor Jl TB Simatupang Kav 1B, Jakarta, 12560, Indonesia
Tel.: (62) 2178830850
Oil & Gas Services
N.A.I.C.S.: 213112

PT Elnusa Petrofin (1)
Graha Elnusa 14th Floor Jl TB Simatupang Kav 1B, Cilandak, Jakarta Selatan, 12560, Indonesia
Tel.: (62) 2178830860
Web Site: https://www.elnusapetrofin.co.id
Oil & Gas Services
N.A.I.C.S.: 213112

PT Elnusa Trans Samudera (1)
Gedung Elnusa Trans Samudera Jl TB Simatupang Kav 1B, Jakarta, 12560, Indonesia
Tel.: (62) 2178846667
Web Site: https://www.etsa.co.id
Oil & Gas Services
N.A.I.C.S.: 213112
Didik Purwanto (Co-Pres)

PT Patra Nusa Data (1)
Graha Elnusa Lt 10 Jl TB Simatupang Kav 1B, Jakarta Selatan, 12560, Indonesia
Tel.: (62) 217816770
Web Site: https://www.patranusa.com
Oil & Gas Services
N.A.I.C.S.: 213112

PT Sigma Cipta Utama (1)
Graha Elnusa Jl TB Simatupang KAV 1B 2nd Floor, Jakarta, Indonesia
Web Site: http://www.scu.co.id
Oil & Gas Services
N.A.I.C.S.: 213112

PT EMDEKI UTAMA TBK
Jl Raya Krikilan Nomor 294 RT 011 RW 005, Driyorejo, Gresik, 61177, Jawa Timur, Indonesia
Tel.: (62) 317507001
Web Site: https://www.emdeki.co.id
Year Founded: 1981
MDKI—(INDO)
Rev.: $30,567,258
Assets: $69,131,682
Liabilities: $6,470,492
Net Worth: $62,661,190
Earnings: $3,143,551
Emp.: 221
Fiscal Year-end: 12/31/23
Calcium Carbide & Ferro Alloy Mfr
N.A.I.C.S.: 331110

PT ENERGI MEGA PERSADA TBK
Bakrie Tower 27th-31th and 32nd Floor Rasuna Epicentrum, Jl HR Rasuna Said, Jakarta, 12960, Selatan, Indonesia
Tel.: (62) 2129941500   Id
Web Site: https://www.emp.id
Year Founded: 2001
ENRG—(INDO)
Rev.: $420,775,224
Assets: $1,368,757,121
Liabilities: $783,652,104
Net Worth: $585,105,017
Earnings: $68,175,457
Emp.: 519
Fiscal Year-end: 12/31/23
Oil & Gas Production Services
N.A.I.C.S.: 211120
Imam P. Agustino (Co-Chm)

Subsidiaries:

Malacca Brantas Finance, B.V (1)
Prins Bernhardplein 200, Amsterdam, 1097 JB, Noord-Holland, Netherlands
Tel.: (31) 203200330
Financial Investment Services
N.A.I.C.S.: 541611

PT ENVY TECHNOLOGIES INDONESIA TBK
Satrio Tower Lantai 24 Jl Prof Dr Satrio, No 4-C Kav 1 Kuningan, Jakarta Selatan, 12950, Indonesia
Tel.: (62) 2121684097
Web Site: https://www.envytech.co.id
Year Founded: 2004
ENVY—(INDO)
Rev.: $161,899
Assets: $1,002,094
Liabilities: $3,724,084
Net Worth: ($2,721,990)
Earnings: ($1,972,674)
Emp.: 9
Fiscal Year-end: 12/31/23
Information Technology Services
N.A.I.C.S.: 541519
Nadzaruddin Abd Hamid (Pres)

PT EQUITY DEVELOPMENT INVESTMENT TBK
Wisma Hayam Wuruk 3rd Floor Jl Hayam Wuruk No 8, Jakarta, 10120, Indonesia
Tel.: (62) 2180632550
Web Site: https://www.theequityone.com
Year Founded: 1982
GSMF—(INDO)
Rev.: $58,718,683
Assets: $374,195,190
Liabilities: $209,797,502
Net Worth: $164,397,688
Earnings: ($3,647,680)
Emp.: 582
Fiscal Year-end: 12/31/23
Financial Services
N.A.I.C.S.: 523999
Muhamad Zulkifli Abusuki (Chm)

Subsidiaries:

PT Equity Finance Indonesia (1)
Wisma Hayam Wuruk 8th Floor Jalan Hayam Wuruk No 8, Jakarta, 10120, Indonesia
Tel.: (62) 2180632888
Web Site: http://www.equityfinance.co.id
Multi Financing Services
N.A.I.C.S.: 522299

PT Equity Life Indonesia (1)
Sahid Sudirman Center 20th Floor Jl Jend Sudirman No 86, Jakarta, 10220, Indonesia
Tel.: (62) 2180868000
Web Site: http://www.equity.co.id
Fire Insurance Services
N.A.I.C.S.: 524113
Caroline Sutedja (Sec)

PT Lumbung Sari (1)
Komp Mangga Dua Plaza Blok N-2 Jl Mangga Dua Raya, Jakarta, 10730, Indonesia
Tel.: (62) 216124363
Web Site: https://lumbungs.com
Insurance Broker Services
N.A.I.C.S.: 524210
Iva Susanti (Officer-Mktg)

PT Mediacom Prima (1)
Rukan Artha Gading Niaga B No 15 A Jl Boulevard Artha Gading, Kelapa Gading Barat, Jakarta Utara, 14240, Indonesia
Tel.: (62) 2145856775
Web Site: http://www.medicomprima.co.id
Health & Clinical Care Services
N.A.I.C.S.: 621999

PT ERA DIGITAL MEDIA TBK.
Jl Cikini Raya No 72 RT 14 RW 05 Kel Cikini, Kec Menteng Kota Jakarta Pusat, Jakarta, 10330, Indonesia
Tel.: (62) 2139720720
Web Site: https://www.ptedm.com
Year Founded: 2015
AWAN—(INDO)
Rev.: $2,064,607
Assets: $6,345,572
Liabilities: $415,405
Net Worth: $5,930,166
Earnings: $40,581
Emp.: 34
Fiscal Year-end: 12/31/23
Digital Marketing Services
N.A.I.C.S.: 541810
Shaane Harjani (Chief Innovation Officer)

PT ERA MANDIRI CEMERLANG TBK
Ruko Lodan Center Jl Lodan Raya No 2 Blok F2-7 Ancol, Jakarta Utara, 14430, Indonesia
Tel.: (62) 216930017
Web Site: https://www.indonesiaseafood.net
Year Founded: 2000
IKAN—(INDO)
Rev.: $9,338,771
Assets: $9,168,769
Liabilities: $4,383,589
Net Worth: $4,785,180
Earnings: $60,670
Emp.: 80
Fiscal Year-end: 12/31/23
Seafood Mfr
N.A.I.C.S.: 311710
Johan Rose (Pres)

PT ERA MEDIA SEJAHTERA TBK.
Kantor Fatmawati Mas Blok III No 205, Jakarta, 12430, Indonesia
Tel.: (62) 217659237
Web Site: https://www.sspace.id
Year Founded: 2021
DOOH—(INDO)
Rev.: $11,206,072
Assets: $15,226,886
Liabilities: $1,142,438
Net Worth: $14,084,448
Earnings: $28,291
Fiscal Year-end: 12/31/23
Advertising Agency Services
N.A.I.C.S.: 541840
Devi Nisa Suhartono (Sec)

PT ERAJAYA SWASEMBADA TBK
Erajaya Plaza Jl Bandengan Selatan No 19-20 Pekojan - Tambora, Jakarta Barat, 11240, Indonesia
Tel.: (62) 216905788
Web Site: https://www.erajaya.com
Year Founded: 1996
ERAA—(INDO)
Rev.: $3,905,453,005
Assets: $1,327,857,514
Liabilities: $799,845,075
Net Worth: $528,012,439
Earnings: $55,644,538
Emp.: 5,337
Fiscal Year-end: 12/31/23
Telecommunication Device Distr
N.A.I.C.S.: 423690
Budiarto Halim (Chm)

Subsidiaries:

CG Computers Sdn. Bhd. (1)
1-07-01 Menara IJM Land Lebuh Tengku Kudin 3, Gelugor, 11700, Pulau Penang, Malaysia
Tel.: (60) 42023972
Web Site: https://shop.switch.com.my
Information Technology Services
N.A.I.C.S.: 541519

Era Tech Communication Pte. Ltd. (1)
150 Kampong Ampat 06-06 KA Centre, Singapore, 368324, Singapore
Tel.: (65) 129250
Web Site: https://eratech.sg
Information Technology Services
N.A.I.C.S.: 541519

Erajaya Digital Retail Pte. Ltd. (1)
No 170-03-09/10/11/12/12A 3 Temasek Boulevard 1-327/328, Suntec City Mall, Singapore, 38983, Singapore
Tel.: (65) 64623688
Web Site: https://www.switch.sg
Information Technology Services
N.A.I.C.S.: 541519

P.T. Era Blu Elektronik (1)
Citicon Tower 15th Floor Jl Letjen S Parman No Kav 72 4 RT 4/RW 3, Kec Palmerah Daerah Khusus Ibukota Jakarta, Jakarta Barat, 11410, Slipi, Indonesia
Tel.: (62) 2130200946
Web Site: https://www.erablue.id
Household Appliance Retailer
N.A.I.C.S.: 423620

PT Urogen Advanced Solutions (1)
Jl Gedong Panjang no 29-31 Pekojan, Tambora, Jakarta Barat, 11240, Indonesia
Tel.: (62) 216509090
Web Site: http://www.urogen.co.id
Medical Device Distr
N.A.I.C.S.: 423840

Switch Concept Sdn. Bhd. (1)
1-07-01 Menara IJM Land Lebuh Tengku Kudin 3, 11700, Gelugor, Pulau Pinang, Malaysia
Tel.: (60) 42023972
Web Site: https://www.switchconcept.com.my
Phone Whslr
N.A.I.C.S.: 423840

PT ERATEX DJAJA TBK
Spazio Building 3rd Floor Unit 319-321 Graha Festival Kav 3, Graha Family Jl Mayjend Yono Soewoyo, Surabaya, 60226, Indonesia
Tel.: (62) 3199001101   Id
Web Site: https://www.eratexco.com
Year Founded: 1972
ERTX—(INDO)
Rev.: $120,703,132
Assets: $79,764,350
Liabilities: $54,691,859
Net Worth: $25,072,491
Earnings: $2,730,844
Emp.: 5,193
Fiscal Year-end: 12/31/23
Clothing Apparel Distr
N.A.I.C.S.: 458110
Sekertaris Perusahaan (Co-Sec)

PT ESSA INDUSTRIES INDONESIA TBK.
DBS Bank Tower 18th Floor, Jl Prof Dr Satrio Kav 3-5, Jakarta, 12940, Indonesia
Tel.: (62) 2129885600
Web Site: https://essa.id
Year Founded: 2006
ESSA—(INDO)
Rev.: $344,961,625
Assets: $695,442,247
Liabilities: $197,698,606
Net Worth: $497,743,641
Earnings: $46,723,437
Emp.: 382
Fiscal Year-end: 12/31/23
Liquefied Petroleum Refining Services
N.A.I.C.S.: 324110
Chander Vinod Laroya (Chm)

Subsidiaries:

PT SEPCHEM (1)
Gedung Menara Kadin Lt 16 Jl H R Rasuna Said Blok X-5 Kav 2-3, Jakarta, 12950, Indonesia
Tel.: (62) 21 5790 3701
General Management Consulting Services
N.A.I.C.S.: 541611

PT ESTA MULTI USAHA TBK
Gedung Wisma D Esta Komplek Komersil Sekt Ii Blok Ah 2 No 7A Bsd, Rawabuntu Serpong Kota, Tangerang, 15318, Banten, Indonesia
Tel.: (62) 2160834569
Web Site: http://www.estamultiusaha.co.id
ESTA—(INDO)
Rev.: $616,112
Assets: $5,193,323
Liabilities: $1,088,372
Net Worth: $4,104,951
Earnings: $120,361
Emp.: 33
Fiscal Year-end: 12/31/20
Hotel Operator
N.A.I.C.S.: 721110
Lukman Nelam *(Chm)*

PT ESTIKA TATA TIARA TBK
Equity Tower Lantai 22 Suite A Sudirman Central Business Dist Lot 9, Jl Jend Sudirman Kav 52-53, Jakarta, 12190, Indonesia
Tel.: (62) 2151402094
Web Site: https://www.kibif.com
BEEF—(INDO)
Rev.: $39,728,436
Assets: $44,830,065
Liabilities: $35,703,483
Net Worth: $9,126,582
Earnings: $3,706,192
Emp.: 219
Fiscal Year-end: 12/31/23
Financial Consulting Services
N.A.I.C.S.: 541611
Yustinus Sadmoko *(Chm)*

PT ETERINDO WAHANATAMA TBK
Wisma Slipi 8th floor Jl Let Jend S Parman Kav 12, Jakarta, 11480, Indonesia
Tel.: (62) 215307218 Id
Web Site: http://www.eterindo.com
Year Founded: 1992
ETWA—(INDO)
Rev.: $3,101,298
Assets: $57,472,126
Liabilities: $83,027,857
Net Worth: ($25,555,732)
Earnings: ($18,154,130)
Emp.: 29
Fiscal Year-end: 12/31/22
Bio Diesel Mfr & Distr
N.A.I.C.S.: 457210
Azwar Alinuddin *(Sec)*

PT EVER SHINE TEX TBK
Jl H Fachruddin No 16, Jakarta, 10250, DKI Jakarta, Indonesia
Tel.: (62) 213160238
Web Site: https://www.evershinetex.com
Year Founded: 1974
ESTI—(INDO)
Rev.: $22,330,314
Assets: $48,714,670
Liabilities: $32,899,468
Net Worth: $15,815,202
Earnings: $1,303,481
Emp.: 793
Fiscal Year-end: 12/31/23
Synthetic Yarns & Fabric Mfr
N.A.I.C.S.: 313110
Sung Pui Man *(Chm)*

Subsidiaries:

PT Primarajuli Sukses (1)
Jl Arya Jaya Santika Kampung Bolang RT002 RW001, Desa Pasir Bolang Tigaraksa, Tangerang, 15720, Banten, Indonesia
Tel.: (62) 215991612
Synthetic Yarn & Fabric Mfr
N.A.I.C.S.: 325220

PT EXPLOITASI ENERGI INDONESIA TBK
Sinarmas MSIG Tower 9th Floor Jl Jend Sudirman Kav 21, Jakarta, 12930, Indonesia
Tel.: (62) 2180511130
Web Site: https://www.energiindonesia.com
Year Founded: 1999
Oil & Gas Exploration Services
N.A.I.C.S.: 213112
Benny Wirawansa *(Chm)*

PT FAP AGRI TBK
Gedung Gold Coast Tower Liberty Lt 16 A- H, Jl Pantai Indah Kapuk Rt 6 Rw 2 Kamal Muara Penjaringan, Jakarta, 14470, Indonesia
Tel.: (62) 2150205811
Web Site: https://www.fap-agri.com
Year Founded: 1994
FAPA—(INDO)
Rev.: $978,142,108
Assets: $560,694,262
Liabilities: $296,800,897
Net Worth: $263,893,365
Earnings: $10,499,434
Emp.: 16,143
Fiscal Year-end: 12/31/23
Palm Oil Mfr
N.A.I.C.S.: 311225
Ricky Tjandra *(Pres)*

PT FAST FOOD INDONESIA TBK
Jl Let Jend Haryono MT Kav 7, Jakarta, 12810, Indonesia
Tel.: (62) 218301133
Web Site: https://kfcku.com
Year Founded: 1978
FAST—(INDO)
Rev.: $385,419,205
Assets: $253,950,746
Liabilities: $206,942,143
Net Worth: $47,008,603
Earnings: ($27,158,714)
Emp.: 10,052
Fiscal Year-end: 12/31/23
Restaurant Operating Services
N.A.I.C.S.: 722511
Ricardo Gelael *(Chm)*

PT FIMPERKASA UTAMA TBK
Graha Fim Lt 5 Jl Teuku Cik Ditiro No 37 Kel Menteng Kec Menteng, Jakarta, Indonesia
Tel.: (62) 213100074
Web Site: https://www.fimperkasautama.co.id
Year Founded: 1993
FIMP—(INDO)
Rev.: $464,321
Assets: $2,253,594
Liabilities: $260,762
Net Worth: $1,992,832
Earnings: $41,678
Emp.: 8
Fiscal Year-end: 12/31/23
Construction Services
N.A.I.C.S.: 236220
Mohamad Mulky Thalib *(Pres)*

PT FIRST INDO AMERICAM LEASING TBK
Jalan Batu Ceper No36, Jakarta Pusat, 10120, Indonesia
Tel.: (62) 0212312088
Rev.: $12,144,511
Assets: $33,861,615
Liabilities: $29,702,025
Net Worth: $4,159,590
Earnings: ($16,764,128)
Fiscal Year-end: 12/31/19
Financing & Rental Leasing Services
N.A.I.C.S.: 522220
Sumartono Mardjuki *(Chm)*

PT FIRST MEDIA TBK
BeritaSatu plaza 4th Floor Suite 401 Jl Jend Gatot Subroto Kav 35-36, Jakarta, 12950, Indonesia
Tel.: (62) 215278811
Web Site: https://www.firstmedia.co.id
Year Founded: 1994
KBLV—(INDO)
Rev.: $7,371,989
Assets: $66,852,158
Liabilities: $104,931,611
Net Worth: ($38,079,452)
Earnings: ($5,073,373)
Emp.: 187
Fiscal Year-end: 12/31/23
Telecommunication Servicesb
N.A.I.C.S.: 517112
Harianda Noerlan *(Chm)*

Subsidiaries:

PT Jakarta Globe Media (1)
BeritaSatu Plaza 11th Floor Suite 1102 Jl Jend Gatot Subroto Kav 35-36, Jakarta, 12650, Indonesia
Tel.: (62) 2129957500
Web Site: http://www.jakartaglobe.id
Newspaper Printing Services
N.A.I.C.S.: 513110
Theo L. Sambuaga *(Pres)*

PT MSH Niaga Telecom Indonesia (1)
Graha Cempaka Mas Blok C 06 Jl Letjen Suprapto Kav 3, Jakarta Pusat, 10640, Indonesia
Tel.: (62) 21 424 2000
Web Site: https://www.msh-niagatelecom.com
Telecommunication Servicesb
N.A.I.C.S.: 517810

PT FKS FOOD SEJAHTERA TBK
Menara Astra Lantai 29 Jl Jend Sudirman Kav 5-6, Karet Tengsin - Tanah Abang, Jakarta, 10220, Indonesia
Tel.: (62) 2125521698
Web Site: https://www.fksfs.co.id
Year Founded: 1990
AISA—(INDO)
Rev.: $110,658,604
Assets: $120,139,260
Liabilities: $57,264,482
Net Worth: $62,874,778
Earnings: $1,220,612
Emp.: 1,004
Fiscal Year-end: 12/31/23
Food Products Mfr
N.A.I.C.S.: 311999
Lim Aun Seng *(Chm)*

PT FKS MULTI AGRO TBK
Sampoerna Strategic Square The Function Room Anggerik 5 North Tower, lantai 3A Jl Jend Sudirman Kav 45-46, Jakarta, 12930, Indonesia
Tel.: (62) 2150889889
Web Site: https://www.fksmultiagro.com
Year Founded: 1992
FISH—(INDO)
Rev.: $1,241,611,453
Assets: $444,042,774
Liabilities: $273,002,418
Net Worth: $171,040,356
Earnings: $24,184,606
Emp.: 862
Fiscal Year-end: 12/31/23
Food Products Distr
N.A.I.C.S.: 445298
Indarto Gondo Po *(Chm)*

PT FORMOSA INGREDIENT FACTORY TBK
Berlian 88 Biz Estate Jl Diklat Pemda Bojong Nangka Kabupaten, Tangerang, 15810, Banten, Indonesia
Tel.: (62) 8118133788
Web Site: https://www.formosa.id
BOBA—(INDO)
Rev.: $9,986,255
Assets: $11,405,117
Liabilities: $1,595,862
Net Worth: $9,809,256
Earnings: $971,404
Emp.: 37
Fiscal Year-end: 12/31/23
Packaged Food Product Mfr
N.A.I.C.S.: 311412
Yunita Sugiarto *(Pres)*

PT FORTUNE MATE INDONESIA TBK
Gedung Gozco Lantai 3 Jl Raya Darmo No 54-56, Surabaya, 60265, Indonesia
Tel.: (62) 315612818 Id
Web Site: https://www.fmiindo.com
Year Founded: 1989
FMII—(INDO)
Rev.: $2,765,155
Assets: $50,804,862
Liabilities: $7,339,311
Net Worth: $43,465,550
Earnings: $1,127,538
Emp.: 47
Fiscal Year-end: 12/31/23
Real Estate Development Services
N.A.I.C.S.: 531390
Tjandra Mindharta Gozali *(Chm)*

PT FORZA LAND INDONESIA TBK
Wisma 77 Tower 1 Lt 8 Jln Jend S Parman Kav 77, Jakarta, 11410, Indonesia
Tel.: (62) 2153669777
Web Site: http://www.forzaland.com
Year Founded: 2011
FORZ—(INDO)
Rev.: $4,074,339
Assets: $50,793,990
Liabilities: $30,785,785
Net Worth: $20,008,205
Earnings: $87,778
Emp.: 38
Fiscal Year-end: 12/31/19
Real Estate Manangement Services
N.A.I.C.S.: 531390
Patris Jasur *(Chm)*

PT FUJI FINANCE INDONESIA TBK
Menara Sudirman 8th Floor Jl Jend Sudirman Kav 60, Jakarta, 12190, Indonesia
Tel.: (62) 215226509
Web Site: https://www.fujifinance.com
Year Founded: 1982
FUJI—(INDO)
Rev.: $620,141
Assets: $10,695,178
Liabilities: $218,173
Net Worth: $10,477,005
Earnings: $251,693
Emp.: 17
Fiscal Year-end: 12/31/23
Financial Services
N.A.I.C.S.: 523150
Anita Marta *(Pres)*

PT GALVA TECHNOLOGIES TBK
Jalan Hayam Wuruk 27 Gambir, Jakarta Pusat, 10120, Indonesia
Tel.: (62) 213456650
Web Site: https://www.gtc.co.id
Year Founded: 1991
GLVA—(INDO)
Rev.: $133,880,174
Assets: $60,505,832

PT GALVA TECHNOLOGIES TBK

PT Galva Technologies Tbk—(Continued)
Liabilities: $35,021,233
Net Worth: $25,484,599
Earnings: $5,087,140
Emp.: 279
Fiscal Year-end: 12/31/23
Electronic Product Distr
N.A.I.C.S.: 423690
Oki Widjaja (Pres)

PT GARDA TUJUH BUANA TBK

Gedung Menara Hijau 5th Floor Suite 501A, Jl MT Haryono Kav 33, Jakarta, 12770, Indonesia
Tel.: (62) 217943947
Web Site: https://www.gtb.co.id
Year Founded: 1996
GTBO—(INDO)
Rev.: $58,797,005
Assets: $66,303,542
Liabilities: $16,602,529
Net Worth: $49,701,013
Earnings: $4,152,251
Emp.: 130
Fiscal Year-end: 12/31/23
Coal Mining Services
N.A.I.C.S.: 213113
Ratendra Kumar Srivastva (Chm)

PT GARUDA INDONESIA (PERSERO) TBK

Management Building Soekarno Hatta International Airport, Tangerang, 15111, Garuda, Indonesia
Tel.: (62) 2125601201
Web Site: http://www.garuda-indonesia.com
Year Founded: 1949
GIAA—(INDO)
Rev.: $2,936,631,094
Assets: $6,727,645,053
Liabilities: $8,010,372,227
Net Worth: ($1,282,727,174)
Earnings: $251,996,580
Emp.: 4,401
Fiscal Year-end: 12/31/23
Oil Transportation Services
N.A.I.C.S.: 481111
Iwan Joeniarto (Dir-Maintenance & Svcs)

Subsidiaries:

Garuda Indonesia Holiday France S.A.S (1)
255 rue Saint Honore, 75001, Paris, France
Tel.: (33) 186215223
Web Site: https://www.garudaholiday.fr
Tour Operating Services
N.A.I.C.S.: 561520

P.T. Aero Wisata (1)
Aerowisata Building Jalan Prajurit KKO Usman dan Harun No 3, Jakarta Pusat, 10410, Indonesia
Tel.: (62) 212310002
Web Site: https://www.aerowisata.com
Home Management Services
N.A.I.C.S.: 721110

PT Aero Systems Indonesia (1)
Gedung Garuda 1st Floor Jl Gunung Sahari Raya No 52, Kemayoran, Jakarta, 10610, Indonesia
Tel.: (62) 2129356070
Web Site: https://www.asyst.co.id
Information Technology Development Services
N.A.I.C.S.: 541511
Achmad Royhan (Pres & CEO)

PT Aerojasa Cargo (1)
Jl Prof Dr Soepomo SH No 45, Tebet, Jakarta Selatan, Indonesia
Tel.: (62) 2183702563
Web Site: https://www.aeroexpress.co.id
Air Cargo Services
N.A.I.C.S.: 481212
Istiadi Hanafiah (Mgr-Comml)

PT Aerotrans Services Indonesia (1)
Jl Husein Sastranegara No 2, Tangerang, 15124, Indonesia
Tel.: (62) 8129563182
Web Site: https://www.aerotrans.co.id
Emp.: 2,000
Ground Transportation Services
N.A.I.C.S.: 485999
Baskara Adhitama (VP-Fin & Acctg)

PT Citilink Indonesia (1)
Bandara Soekarno Hatta Cengkareng, Tangerang, Jakarta, 19120, Banten, Indonesia
Tel.: (62) 8041080808
Web Site: https://www.citilink.co.id
Airline Transportation Services
N.A.I.C.S.: 488190
Juliandra Nurtjahjo (Pres)

PT GIH Indonesia (1)
Garuda Indonesia Building 7th Floor Jl Gunung Sahari Raya No 52, Jakarta, 10610, Indonesia
Tel.: (62) 2129553100
Web Site: http://www.gih-indonesia.com
Tour Operating Services
N.A.I.C.S.: 561520
Erik Kurnia (Mgr-Leisure)

PT Garuda Maintenance Facility AeroAsia (1)
Tel.: (62) 215508609
Web Site: http://www.gmf-aeroasia.co.id
Automotive Mechanical & Electrical Repair & Maintenance
N.A.I.C.S.: 811114
Asep Kurnia (Dir-Human Capital & Corp Affairs)

PT Sabre Travel Network Indonesia (1)
Jl Mampang Prapatan Raya No 93, South Jakarta, 12790, Indonesia
Tel.: (62) 2127535399
Web Site: https://www.sabretn.co.id
National Marketing Services
N.A.I.C.S.: 541613

P.T. Aerowisata International (1)
Aerowisata Building Jalan Prajurit KKO Usman dan Harun No 32 Pusat, Jakarta, 10410, Indonesia
Tel.: (62) 212310002
Web Site: http://www.aerowisata.com
Sales Range: $25-49.9 Million
Travel Arrangement & Reservation Services
N.A.I.C.S.: 561599

P.T. Gapura Angkasa (1)
Dapenra Building Floor 1 2 and 3 Jl Angkasa Blok B-12 Kav 8 Kota Baru, Bandar Kemayoran, Jakarta, 10610, Indonesia
Tel.: (62) 216545410
Web Site: http://www.gapura.co.id
Sales Range: $25-49.9 Million
Emp.: 100
Transit & Ground Passenger Transportation
N.A.I.C.S.: 485999

PT GARUDA MAINTENANCE FACILITY AERO ASIA TBK

GMF Management Building 3rd Floor Soekarno Hatta International Airport, PO Box 1303, Cengkareng, Tangerang, 15125, Indonesia
Tel.: (62) 215508717
Web Site: https://gmf-aeroasia.co.id
Year Founded: 1949
GMFI—(INDO)
Rev.: $373,206,984
Assets: $450,021,103
Liabilities: $761,183,005
Net Worth: ($311,161,902)
Earnings: $20,168,689
Emp.: 4,348
Fiscal Year-end: 12/31/23
Aircraft Services
N.A.I.C.S.: 488190
Andi Fahrurrozi (CEO)

PT GARUDA METALINDO TBK

Jl Kapuk Kamal Raya No 23, Jakarta, 14470, Indonesia
Tel.: (62) 215553963
Web Site: https://garudametalindo.co.id
Year Founded: 1966
BOLT—(INDO)
Rev.: $95,169,414
Assets: $87,294,916
Liabilities: $30,687,172
Net Worth: $56,607,744
Earnings: $7,561,601
Emp.: 1,044
Fiscal Year-end: 12/31/23
Fastener & Bolt Mfr
N.A.I.C.S.: 339993
Ervin Wijaya (Chm)

Subsidiaries:

PT Garuda Metal Utama (1)
Blok AE No 23, Jl Industri Raya III Jatake, Tangerang, 15710, Indonesia
Tel.: (62) 215902114
Automobile Parts Mfr
N.A.I.C.S.: 336330

PT Indo Kida Plating (1)
Jl Selayar Blok D5 1, kawasan industri MM2100 DS Mekar Wangi Cibitung, Bekasi, 17520, Cikarang Barat, Indonesia
Tel.: (62) 2189983923
Alkaline Zinc Plating Mfr
N.A.I.C.S.: 332813

PT Indo Nesian Tooling Technology (1)
JL Selayar Blok D5 No 1, kawasan industri MM2100, Bekasi, 17550, Cikarang Barat, Indonesia
Tel.: (62) 2189983923
Web Site: http://www.pt-itt.com
Emp.: 30
Superior Precision Tooling Mfr
N.A.I.C.S.: 332721
Christian Engel (Comml Dir-Technical)

PT Mega Pratama Ferindo (1)
Blok AB No 5, Jl Industri Raya III Jatake, Tangerang, 15710, Indonesia
Tel.: (62) 215901927
Steel Wire & Bar Mfr
N.A.I.C.S.: 331221

PT GAYA ABADI SEMPURNA TBK

Jalan Raya Serang Km 14 2 No 8 Pasir Gadung Cikupa, Balaraja, Tangerang, Banten, Indonesia
Tel.: (62) 22597464
Web Site: https://www.gaya-slis.com
Year Founded: 1996
SLIS—(INDO)
Rev.: $29,376,711
Assets: $30,753,850
Liabilities: $8,276,203
Net Worth: $22,477,647
Earnings: $1,381,270
Emp.: 205
Fiscal Year-end: 12/31/23
Electric Bicycle Mfr
N.A.I.C.S.: 336991
Edi Hanafiah Kwanto (Pres)

Subsidiaries:

PT Juara Bike (1)
Jl Raya Serang No 88 RT/Rw 004 Pasir Gadung Kec, Cikupa, Tangerang, 15710, Banten, Indonesia
Tel.: (62) 2129382938
Web Site: https://www.selis.co.id
Electric Vehicle Mfr
N.A.I.C.S.: 336320

PT GEMA GRAHASARANA TBK

South78 Jl Boulevard Gading Serpong Blok O No 7 & 8, Pagedangan Medang, Tangerang, 15334, Banten, Indonesia
Tel.: (62) 2150986988
Web Site: http://www.ggs-interior.com
Year Founded: 1984
GEMA—(INDO)
Rev.: $74,543,839

INTERNATIONAL PUBLIC

Assets: $73,560,876
Liabilities: $47,242,274
Net Worth: $26,318,601
Earnings: $46,911
Emp.: 574
Fiscal Year-end: 12/31/22
Furniture Mfr
N.A.I.C.S.: 337211
Dedy Rochimat (Chm, Pres & Commissioner)

Subsidiaries:

P.T. Aida Rattan Industry (1)
Block Duku Setu Desa Bodesari Plumbon Cirebon West Java, Cirebon, Indonesia
Tel.: (62) 231324556
Web Site: https://www.aida-rattan.co.id
Rattan Furniture Mfr
N.A.I.C.S.: 321999

P.T. Laminatech Kreasi Sarana (1)
South78 9th-11th Floor Jln Boulevard, Gading Serpong Blok O No 7 & 8, Tangerang, 15334, Indonesia
Tel.: (62) 2150986988
Web Site: https://www.wilsonart.id
Furniture Components Mfr
N.A.I.C.S.: 321999

P.T. Prasetya Gemamulia (1)
South78 Jl Boulevard Gading Serpong Blok O No 7-8, Medang Kec Pagedangan Selatan, Tangerang, 15334, Indonesia
Tel.: (62) 2150986988
Furniture Components Distr
N.A.I.C.S.: 423210

P.T. Vinotindo Grahasarana (1)
South78 10th Floor Jl Boulevard, Gading Serpong Blok O No 7 & 8, Tangerang, 15334, Indonesia
Tel.: (62) 2150986988
Web Site: https://www.vinoti.com
Office Furniture Mfr
N.A.I.C.S.: 337214

P.T. Vivere Multi Kreasi (1)
South78 9th-11th Floor Jln Boulevard, Gading Serpong Blok O No 7 & 8, Tangerang, 15334, Indonesia
Tel.: (62) 50986988
Web Site: https://www.vivere.co.id
Home Furniture Mfr
N.A.I.C.S.: 321999

PT GEOPRIMA SOLUSI TBK

Rukan Artha Gading Niaga Blok D-9, Kelapa Gading, Jakarta Utara, 14240, Indonesia
Tel.: (62) 2145850667
Web Site: http://www.geoprima.co.id
Year Founded: 1997
GPSO—(INDO)
Rev.: $1,049,188
Assets: $4,063,555
Liabilities: $741,646
Net Worth: $3,321,910
Earnings: $1,869
Emp.: 16
Fiscal Year-end: 12/31/23
Electronic Product Distr
N.A.I.C.S.: 423690
Daniel Gunawan (Sec)

PT GINTING JAYA ENERGI TBK

Jln Tanjung Api-Api Km 8 Kelurahan Gasing, Kecamatan Talang Kelapa Banyuasin, Palembang, 30961, Sumatera Selatan, Indonesia
Tel.: (62) 7115735399
Web Site: https://www.gj-energi.co.id
Year Founded: 2011
WOWS—(INDO)
Rev.: $7,952,447
Assets: $43,264,466
Liabilities: $9,304,016
Net Worth: $33,960,449
Earnings: ($646,763)
Emp.: 26
Fiscal Year-end: 12/31/23
Oil & Gas Support Services

N.A.I.C.S.: 213112
Jimmy Hidayat *(Pres)*

PT GLOBAL MEDIACOM TBK.
MNC Tower 26th Floor Jalan Kebon Sirih No 17 - 19, Jakarta Pusat, 10340, Indonesia
Tel.: (62) 213900065
Web Site:
https://www.mediacom.co.id
Year Founded: 1981
BMTR—(INDO)
Rev.: $659,995,416
Assets: $2,290,323,532
Liabilities: $494,732,142
Net Worth: $1,795,591,390
Earnings: $69,339,165
Emp.: 7,686
Fiscal Year-end: 12/31/23
Television Broadcasting & Production Services
N.A.I.C.S.: 516120
Hary Tanoesoedibjo *(Chm)*

Subsidiaries:

PT MNC Sky Vision Tbk (1)
Jl Raya Panjang Z / III Green Garden, Jakarta, 11520, Indonesia
Tel.: (62) 5828000
Web Site: https://www.mncvision.id
Rev.: $48,123,722
Assets: $196,994,776
Liabilities: $69,958,433
Net Worth: $127,036,342
Earnings: ($17,847,265)
Emp.: 463
Fiscal Year-end: 12/31/2023
Television Broadcasting Services
N.A.I.C.S.: 516120

PT GLOBAL SUKSES SOLUSI TBK
Grha Run System Jl Pakuningratan No 15 Cokrodiningratan Jetis, Daerah Istimewa Yogyakarta, Yogyakarta, 55233, Indonesia
Tel.: (62) 2745306454
Web Site: https://runsystem.id
Year Founded: 2013
RUNS—(INDO)
Rev.: $1,799,898
Assets: $6,262,566
Liabilities: $1,773,514
Net Worth: $4,489,052
Earnings: ($308,645)
Emp.: 38
Fiscal Year-end: 12/31/23
Software Development Services
N.A.I.C.S.: 541511
Sony Rachmadi Purnomo *(Pres)*

PT GOLDEN EAGLE ENERGY TBK
The Suites Tower 17th Floor Jl Boulevard Pantai Indah Kapuk, No 1 Kav OFS North Jakarta, Jakarta, 14470, Indonesia
Tel.: (62) 215761815
Web Site: https://www.go-eagle.co.id
Year Founded: 1980
SMMT—(INDO)
Rev.: $65,996,385
Assets: $65,450,663
Liabilities: $13,529,589
Net Worth: $51,921,074
Earnings: $16,622,990
Emp.: 57
Fiscal Year-end: 12/31/23
Mineral Mining Services
N.A.I.C.S.: 213115
Roza Permana Putra *(Chm)*

Subsidiaries:

PT PRIMA BUANA KARUNIA (1)
Menara Rajawali Lantai 27 Jl Dr Ide Anak Agung Gde Agung Lot, 5 1 kawasan Mega Kuningan, Jakarta, 12950, Indonesia
Tel.: (62) 215761815
Coal Mining Services
N.A.I.C.S.: 213113

PT Rajawali Resources (1)
Menara Rajawali Lantai 27 Jl Dr Ide Anak Agung Gde Agung Lot, 5 1 kawasan Mega Kuningan, Jakarta, 12950, Indonesia
Tel.: (62) 215760808
Coal & Mining Services
N.A.I.C.S.: 213113

Subsidiary (Domestic):

PT MEGA RAYA KUSUMA (2)
Menara Rajawali Lantai 27 Jl Dr Ide Anak Agung Gde Agung Lot, 5 1 kawasan Mega Kuningan, Jakarta, 12950, Indonesia
Tel.: (62) 215760808
Coal Mining Services
N.A.I.C.S.: 213113

PT TRIARYANI (1)
Menara Rajawali Lantai 27 Jl Dr Ide Anak Agung Gde Agung Lot, 5 1 kawasan Mega Kuningan, Jakarta, 12950, Indonesia
Tel.: (62) 215761815
Coal Mining Services
N.A.I.C.S.: 213113
Jajang Safaat *(Head-Fin Acctg & Asset Mgmt)*

PT GOLDEN FLOWER TBK
Jl Karimunjawa, Gedanganak Ungaran, Semarang, 50519, Central Jawa, Indonesia
Tel.: (62) 246921228
Web Site:
https://www.goldenflower.co.id
Year Founded: 1980
POLU—(INDO)
Rev.: $5,688,939
Assets: $12,349,189
Liabilities: $4,456,892
Net Worth: $7,892,297
Earnings: ($971,964)
Emp.: 850
Fiscal Year-end: 12/31/23
Garment Product Mfr
N.A.I.C.S.: 315210
Handojo Koentoro Setyadi *(Pres)*

PT GOLDEN PLANTATION TBK
Gedung Plaza Mutiara Lantai 16 Jalan DR Ide Agung Gede Agung Kav, E1 2 No 1 & 2 Jalan Lingkar Mega Kuningan Kecamatan Setiabudi, Jakarta, 12950, Indonesia
Tel.: (62) 2157956768
Web Site:
https://www.goldenplantation.com
GOLL—(INDO)
Rev.: $264,635
Assets: $33,544,623
Liabilities: $27,542,896
Net Worth: $6,001,727
Earnings: ($27,255,238)
Emp.: 11
Fiscal Year-end: 12/31/20
Crude Palm Oil & Palm Kernel Production & Cultivation
N.A.I.C.S.: 115112
Budhi Istanto Suwito *(Pres)*

PT GOTO GOJEK TOKOPEDIA TBK
Gedung Pasaraya Blok M lantai 6-7 Jl Iskandarsyah II No 2, Jakarta, 12160, Indonesia
Tel.: (62) 2129101072 Id
Web Site:
https://www.gotocompany.com
Year Founded: 2009
GOTO—(INDO)
Rev.: $960,169,850
Assets: $3,513,075,805
Liabilities: $1,193,419,005
Net Worth: $2,319,656,800
Earnings: ($5,878,286,066)
Emp.: 7,522
Fiscal Year-end: 12/31/23
Holding Company
N.A.I.C.S.: 551112
Andre Soelistyo *(CEO, Co-Founder & Chm)*

Subsidiaries:

GoPay Vietnam Payment Services Company Limited (1)
Tang 7 Toa nha Richy Tower so 35 duong Mac Thai To, Phuong Yen Hoa quan Cau Giay, Hanoi, Vietnam
Tel.: (84) 1900636153
Web Site: https://gopay.com.vn
Financial Transaction & Payment Technology Services
N.A.I.C.S.: 522320

Lotus Pay Joint Stock Company (1)
9-9A No Trang Long street, Ward 07 Binh Thanh District, Ho Chi Minh City, Vietnam
Tel.: (84) 2873099920
Web Site: https://lotusgroup.com.vn
Emp.: 2,500
Food Product Mfr & Distr
N.A.I.C.S.: 311919

P.T. Midtrans (1)
Pasaraya Blok M Building B 4th Floor Jl Iskandarsyah II No 2, South Jakarta, 12160, Indonesia
Tel.: (62) 8041401099
Web Site: https://midtrans.com
Emp.: 100
Financial Transaction & Payment Technology Services
N.A.I.C.S.: 522320

PT GOWA MAKASSAR TOURISM DEVELOPMENT TBK
Jl Metro Tanjung Bunga Mall GTC GA-9 No 1B Tanjung Bunga, Makassar, 90134, Sulawesi Selatan, Indonesia
Tel.: (62) 4118113456
Web Site:
https://www.tanjungbunga.com
Year Founded: 1991
GMTD—(INDO)
Rev.: $27,866,992
Assets: $78,183,572
Liabilities: $32,966,879
Net Worth: $45,216,693
Earnings: $8,378,190
Emp.: 83
Fiscal Year-end: 12/31/23
Real Estate Development Services
N.A.I.C.S.: 531390
Siek Citra Yohandra *(Vice Chm)*

PT GOZCO PLANTATIONS TBK
Gedung Gozco Jl Raya Darmo 54-56 Lt 5, Surabaya, 60265, Indonesia
Tel.: (62) 315612818 Id
Web Site: https://www.gozco.com
Year Founded: 2001
GZCO—(INDO)
Rev.: $55,472,100
Assets: $204,540,600
Liabilities: $89,286,400
Net Worth: $115,254,200
Earnings: $7,581,800
Emp.: 881
Fiscal Year-end: 12/31/22
Oil Palm Farming Services
N.A.I.C.S.: 111191
Andrew Michael Vincent *(Dir-Plantations & Technique)*

PT GRAHA LAYAR PRIMA TBK
Gedung AIA Central Lt 26 Jl Jend Sudirman Kav 48A Kel Karet Semanggi, Kec Setiabudi, Jakarta, 12930, Indonesia
Tel.: (62) 2129200100 Id
Web Site: https://cgv.id
BLTZ—(INDO)
Rev.: $68,932,460
Assets: $138,933,960
Liabilities: $109,186,686
Net Worth: $29,747,273
Earnings: ($885,789)
Emp.: 352
Fiscal Year-end: 12/31/23
Cinema Operator
N.A.I.C.S.: 512131

PT GRAHA MITRA ASIA TBK
Sovereign Plaza Fl 5A Kav 36 Jl TB Simatupang RT 1/RW 2, Cilandak, South Jakarta, 12430, Indonesia
Tel.: (62) 2129400139
Web Site: https://www.relifeasia.com
Year Founded: 2018
RELF—(INDO)
Rev.: $2,949,618
Assets: $19,257,106
Liabilities: $4,382,040
Net Worth: $14,875,066
Earnings: $678,730
Emp.: 7
Fiscal Year-end: 12/31/23
Real Estate Development Services
N.A.I.C.S.: 531390
Edy Abdul Malik *(Sec)*

PT GRAHA PRIMA MENTARI TBK
Jl Tuparev No 87A, Cirebon, West Java, Indonesia
Tel.: (62) 231233500
Web Site:
https://www.grahaprimamentari.co.id
Year Founded: 2016
GRPM—(INDO)
Rev.: $19,883,433
Assets: $4,772,052
Liabilities: $188,893
Net Worth: $4,583,159
Earnings: $288,578
Emp.: 148
Fiscal Year-end: 12/31/23
Beverage Product Distr
N.A.I.C.S.: 424820
Agus Susant *(Sec)*

PT GRAHAMAS CITRAWISATA TBK
Medco Building II-4th Floor Jl Ampera Raya No 20, Jakarta, 12560, Indonesia
Tel.: (62) 21 7892013
Restaurant Operating Services
N.A.I.C.S.: 722511
Ngakan Putu Adhiriana *(Sec)*

PT GRAHAPRIMA SUKSESMANDIRI TBK
Graha 55 Lt 3 Jl Tanah Abang II/57, Petojo Selatan & Gambir, Jakarta Pusat, 10160, Indonesia
Tel.: (62) 2134832477
Web Site:
https://www.grahatrans.com
Year Founded: 2005
GTRA—(INDO)
Rev.: $22,398,894
Assets: $61,128,747
Liabilities: $42,805,180
Net Worth: $18,323,566
Earnings: $2,171,085
Emp.: 149
Fiscal Year-end: 12/31/23
Transportation Services
N.A.I.C.S.: 541614
Naomy Herdhianti *(Sec)*

PT GRAND HOUSE MULIA TBK
Kawasan Parkville Serpong Jl Raya Pengasinan No 99 Lingkar Luar Bsd, Serpong, Jakarta, Indonesia
Tel.: (62) 2175871688
Web Site:
https://www.granddevelopment.id

PT GRAND HOUSE MULIA TBK

PT Grand House Mulia Tbk—(Continued)
Year Founded: 2006
HOMI—(INDO)
Rev.: $4,109,381
Assets: $14,441,269
Liabilities: $5,920,046
Net Worth: $8,521,223
Earnings: $279,515
Emp.: 10
Fiscal Year-end: 12/31/23
Real Estate Services
N.A.I.C.S.: 531210
T. Velliana (Pres)

PT GRAND KARTECH TBK
Jl Rawa Gelam III No 1 Pulogadung Industrial Estate, Jakarta, 13930, Indonesia
Tel.: (62) 214600228
Web Site:
  http://www.grandkartech.com
Year Founded: 1921
Rev.: $18,190,244
Assets: $42,423,894
Liabilities: $38,314,778
Net Worth: $4,109,116
Earnings: ($4,671,195)
Emp.: 934
Fiscal Year-end: 12/31/18
Boiler Mfr
N.A.I.C.S.: 332410
Johanes Budi Kartika (Mng Dir, Mng Dir & Sec)

PT GREENWOOD SEJAHTERA TBK
TCC Batavia Tower One lantai 35 Jl KH Mas Mansyur Kav 126, Jakarta, 10220, Indonesia
Tel.: (62) 2125984969
Web Site:
  https://www.greenwood.com
Year Founded: 1990
GWSA—(INDO)
Rev.: $4,662,874
Assets: $511,027,246
Liabilities: $50,768,696
Net Worth: $460,258,550
Earnings: $3,990,321
Emp.: 34
Fiscal Year-end: 12/31/23
Real Estate Development Services
N.A.I.C.S.: 531390
Paulus Indra Intan (Chm)

PT GRHA 165 TBK
Jl Tb Simatupang Kav 1 Cilandak Timur Pasar Minggu, Jakarta Selatan, 12560, Indonesia
Tel.: (62) 217825165
Web Site: http://www.grha165.co.id
Year Founded: 2005
GRHA—(INDO)
Real Estate Services
N.A.I.C.S.: 531390
Wishnumurti Darmawan (Sec)

PT GTSI TBK
Mangkuluhur City Tower One 26th Floor Jl Jend Gatot Subroto Kav 1-3, Jakarta, 12930, Indonesia
Tel.: (62) 2150933163
Web Site: https://www.gtsi.co.id
Year Founded: 1986
GTSI—(INDO)
Rev.: $32,160,145
Assets: $107,840,328
Liabilities: $46,209,885
Net Worth: $61,630,443
Earnings: $7,799,177
Emp.: 20
Fiscal Year-end: 12/31/23
Natural Gas Distr
N.A.I.C.S.: 221210
Kemal Imam Santoso (Pres)

PT GUARDIAN PHARMATAMA
Komplek Green Ville Maisonette Blok FA 18-19, Jakarta, 11510, Indonesia
Tel.: (62) 215656253
Web Site:
  http://www.guardianpharma.com
Year Founded: 1993
Pharmaceuticals Mfr
N.A.I.C.S.: 325412
Djoko Bongso (Pres)

PT GUDANG GARAM TBK
Jl Semampir II/1, Kediri, 64121, Indonesia
Tel.: (62) 3546820917
Web Site:
  http://www.gudanggaramtbk.com
Year Founded: 1958
GGRM—(INDO)
Rev.: $8,013,411,770
Assets: $5,473,398,630
Liabilities: $1,376,825,870
Net Worth: $4,096,572,760
Earnings: $535,341,030
Emp.: 30,940
Fiscal Year-end: 12/31/20
Tobacco Mfr
N.A.I.C.S.: 312230
Susilo Wonowidjojo (Chm)

Subsidiaries:
P.T. Surya Air (1)
Jl Mataram No 1 Kel, Semampir Kediri, East Java, 64121, Indonesia
Tel.: (62) 3546582091
Web Site: https://www.suryaair.co.id
Air Transport Services
N.A.I.C.S.: 561720

PT Surya Pamenang (1)
Jl Raya Kediri - Kertosono KM 7, PO Box 154, Kediri, 64182, Indonesia
Tel.: (62) 354681360
Web Site: https://www.suryapamenang.com
Emp.: 1,000
Pulp Product Mfr
N.A.I.C.S.: 322110

PT GUNA TIMUR RAYA TBK
Jl R E Martadinata No 8 Block A1 Ancol, Jakarta, 14430, Indonesia
Tel.: (62) 216910618
Web Site:
  https://www.gunatimurraya.com
Year Founded: 1980
TRUK—(INDO)
Rev.: $2,816,710
Assets: $4,247,283
Liabilities: $927,336
Net Worth: $3,319,947
Earnings: ($224,997)
Emp.: 43
Fiscal Year-end: 12/31/23
Transportation Services
N.A.I.C.S.: 485999
Budi Gunawan (Chm)

PT GUNAWAN DIANJAYA STEEL
Jl Margomulyo No 29A Tambak Sarioso Asemrowo, Surabaya, 60184, East Java, Indonesia
Tel.: (62) 317490598
Web Site:
  https://www.gunawansteel.com
Year Founded: 1989
Sales Range: $600-649.9 Million
Emp.: 600
Steel Plate Mfr, Importer & Distr
N.A.I.C.S.: 331110
Tetsuro Okano (Pres)

PT GUNUNG RAJA PAKSI TBK
Jl Perjuangan No 8 Sukadanau Cikarang Barat, Bekasi, 17530, West Java, Indonesia
Tel.: (62) 218900111
Web Site:
  https://www.gunungrajapaksi.com
Year Founded: 1970
GGRP—(INDO)
Rev.: $709,839,048
Assets: $1,228,574,394
Liabilities: $304,123,933
Net Worth: $924,450,461
Earnings: $37,827,714
Emp.: 3,725
Fiscal Year-end: 12/31/23
Steel Mfrs
N.A.I.C.S.: 331110
Abednedju Giovano Warani Sangkaeng (Pres)

PT HALONI JANE TBK
Jl Raya Serang KM 13 8 Cikupa, Cikupa kabupaten, Tangerang, 15710, Banten, Indonesia
Tel.: (62) 2130008777
Web Site:
  https://www.halonijane.co.id
Year Founded: 2001
HALO—(INDO)
Rev.: $15,006,852
Assets: $17,031,694
Liabilities: $6,012,649
Net Worth: $11,019,045
Earnings: $1,103,725
Emp.: 76
Fiscal Year-end: 12/31/23
Medicinal Product Mfr
N.A.I.C.S.: 339112
Yakub Indra Kusuma (Sec)

PT HANSON INTERNATIONAL TBK
Mayapada Tower Lantai 11 Jl Jend Sudirman Kav 28, Jakarta, 12920, Indonesia
Tel.: (62) 215213555
Web Site: http://www.hanson.co.id
Year Founded: 1971
MYRX—(INDO)
Sales Range: $50-74.9 Million
Real Estate Development Services
N.A.I.C.S.: 531390
Rony Agung Suseno (Board of Directors & Sec)

PT HARAPAN DUTA PERTIWI TBK
Kawasan Industri Kencana Alam Jl Raya Serang, Km 18 8 Kav 23E Cikupa Talaga Kec Cikupa, Tangerang, 15710, Banten, Indonesia
Tel.: (62) 2159408707
Web Site: https://www.hope.co.id
Year Founded: 2005
HOPE—(INDO)
Rev.: $2,526,367
Assets: $11,817,080
Liabilities: $4,345,785
Net Worth: $7,471,295
Earnings: $466,484
Emp.: 70
Fiscal Year-end: 12/31/23
Steel Mfrs
N.A.I.C.S.: 331110
Rista Widya Saputri (Sec)

PT HARTADINATA ABADI TBK
Jl Kopo Sayati No 165 kab, Bandung, 40228, Indonesia
Tel.: (62) 225402326
Web Site:
  https://hartadinataabadi.co.id
Year Founded: 1989
HRTA—(INDO)
Rev.: $834,935,445
Assets: $326,613,358
Liabilities: $198,513,607
Net Worth: $128,099,751
Earnings: $19,889,080
Emp.: 701

INTERNATIONAL PUBLIC

Fiscal Year-end: 12/31/23
Golden Jewellery Product Distr
N.A.I.C.S.: 458310
Sandra Sunanto (Chm)

Subsidiaries:
P.T. Aurum Digital Internusa (1)
88Kasabalanka 18th Floor Tower A Jl Raya Kasabalanka Kav 88, Kelurahan Menteng Dalam Kecamatan Tebet, Jakarta Selatan, Indonesia
Tel.: (62) 2129607612
E-Commerce Trading Services
N.A.I.C.S.: 523999

P.T. Gadai Cahaya Abadi Mulia (1)
Jl Gunung Mutis No 05, Kelurahan Todekisar Kecamatan Kota Lama, Kupang, Indonesia
Tel.: (62) 8139350359
Investment Finance Services
N.A.I.C.S.: 523999

P.T. Gadai Cahaya Dana Abadi (1)
Jl Katapang Andir Kompleks Topaz Residence No B9, Desa Rancamanyar Kec Baleendah Kab, Bandung, Indonesia
Tel.: (62) 2285939389
Pawn Shop Operator
N.A.I.C.S.: 459510

P.T. Gadai Cahaya Terang Abadi (1)
Jl Raya Mandalika Depan Terminal Renteng, Kecamatan Praya, Kabupaten Lombok Tengah, Nusa Tenggara Barat, Indonesia
Tel.: (62) 3706502297
Pawn Shop Operator
N.A.I.C.S.: 459510

P.T. Gadai Hartadinata Terang Sejati (1)
Jl Abdullah Daeng Sirua No 66 Rt 01 Rw 05, Kelurahan Masale Kecamatan Panakukang, Makassar, Indonesia
Tel.: (62) 8114448703
Investment Finance Services
N.A.I.C.S.: 523999

P.T. Gadai Terang Abadi Mulia (1)
Jl KH Wahid Hasyim No 44 Rw X Gn Sekar, Kec Sampang Kabupaten Sampang, East Java, 69216, Indonesia
Tel.: (62) 82333377605
Investment Finance Services
N.A.I.C.S.: 523999

P.T. Gemilang Hartadinata Abadi (1)
Ruko Topaz No B9 Jl Katapang Andir Rt 03 RW 01 Ds, Rancamanyar Kec Baleendah Kab, Bandung, Jawa Barat, Indonesia
Tel.: (62) 816600778
Web Site: https://gadaihartadinataabadi.com
Investment Finance Services
N.A.I.C.S.: 523999

PT HARUM ENERGY TBK.
Deutsche Bank Building 9th Floor Jl Imam Bonjol No 80, Jakarta Pusat, 10310, Indonesia
Tel.: (62) 2139831288
Web Site:
  https://www.harumenergy.com
Year Founded: 1995
HRUM—(INDO)
Rev.: $925,520,340
Assets: $1,633,107,192
Liabilities: $458,386,742
Net Worth: $1,174,720,450
Earnings: $195,672,112
Emp.: 447
Fiscal Year-end: 12/31/23
Thermal Coal Mining Services
N.A.I.C.S.: 212114
Ray Antonio Gunara (Chm)

Subsidiaries:
PT Karya Usaha Pertiwi (1)
Coal Mining Services
N.A.I.C.S.: 212114

PT Layar Lintas Jaya (1)
Jl Jimbaran Blok 3A No 1, Jakarta, 11840, Indonesia
Coal Mining Services
N.A.I.C.S.: 212114

AND PRIVATE COMPANIES

Riky Kurniawan *(Mgr-Acctg)*

PT Mahakam Sumber Jaya (1)
Deutsche Bank Building lt 8 Jl Imam Bonjol No 80, Jakarta, 10310, Indonesia
Coal Mining Services
N.A.I.C.S.: 212114
Didied Sulistiyono *(Mgr-Ops)*

PT Santan Batubara (1)
Deutsche Bank Building Lantai 10 Jl Imam Bonjol No 80, Jakarta, 10310, Indonesia
Tel.: (62) 213903708
Coal Mining Services
N.A.I.C.S.: 212114

PT Tambang Batubara Harum (1)
Jl Alaydrus No 82, Jakarta, 11840, Indonesia
Tel.: (62) 2170968682
Coal Mining Services
N.A.I.C.S.: 212114

PT HASNUR INTERNASIONAL SHIPPING TBK
Jl Senopati No 8B Kelurahan Senayan Kecamatan Kebayoran Baru, Jakarta Selatan, 12190, Indonesia
Tel.: (62) 2129343888
Web Site: https://www.pthis.id
Year Founded: 1996
HAIS—(INDO)
Rev.: $61,167,492
Assets: $59,386,672
Liabilities: $16,127,573
Net Worth: $43,259,100
Earnings: $10,228,872
Emp.: 80
Fiscal Year-end: 12/31/23
Marine Transportation Services
N.A.I.C.S.: 488320
Dwita Amelia Lestari *(Sec)*

PT HASSANA BOGA SEJAHTERA TBK
Multipurpose Warehouse Area Taman Tekno 2 Block L2 No 35 BSD, Selatan, Tangerang, Banten, Indonesia
Tel.: (62) 81319496469
Web Site: https://www.hassana.co.id
Year Founded: 2009
NAYZ—(INDO)
Rev.: $3,117,440
Assets: $4,855,794
Liabilities: $287,475
Net Worth: $4,568,319
Earnings: $19,952
Emp.: 56
Fiscal Year-end: 12/31/23
Packaged Food Product Distr
N.A.I.C.S.: 424420
Mohamad Zulkarnain *(Sec)*

PT HATTEN BALI TBK
Jl Bypass Ngurah Rai No 393, Sanur, Bali, 80227, Indonesia
Tel.: (62) 3614721377
Web Site:
   https://www.hattenbali.co.id
WINE—(INDO)
Rev.: $16,473,919
Assets: $24,966,608
Liabilities: $7,641,897
Net Worth: $17,324,711
Earnings: $2,763,175
Emp.: 93
Fiscal Year-end: 12/31/23
Alcoholic Beverage Mfr & Distr
N.A.I.C.S.: 312140

PT HENSEL DAVEST INDONESIA TBK
Eighty Eight Kasablanka Tower Lt 28C Jl Raya Casablanca Kav 88, Jakarta Selatan, 12870, Indonesia
Tel.: (62) 2122831619
Web Site: https://www.hdi.co.id
Year Founded: 2013

HDIT—(INDO)
Rev.: $139,915,139
Assets: $22,601,198
Liabilities: $3,851,269
Net Worth: $18,749,928
Earnings: ($2,737,784)
Emp.: 5
Fiscal Year-end: 12/31/23
Online Shopping Operator
N.A.I.C.S.: 236220
Hendra David *(CEO)*

Subsidiaries:

PT Doeku Peduli Indonesia (1)
Business Park A5/05 Jl Citraland Boulevard Mariso, Makassar, 90122, South Sulawesi, Indonesia
Tel.: (62) 4116000808
Web Site: https://doeku.id
Loan Services
N.A.I.C.S.: 522390

PT Emposh Sinergi Asia (1)
JL Casablanca Raya Kav 88, Jakarta Selatan, Indonesia
Tel.: (62) 8228 858 9333
Web Site: https://emposh.com
Ecommerce Services
N.A.I.C.S.: 423690

PT Motransfer Otoritas Internasional (1)
Travellers Phinisi Lt 12 Jl Lamadukelleng Buntu No 59, Makassar, 90113, South Sulawesi, Indonesia
Tel.: (62) 212 283 1619
Web Site: https://motransfer.com
Money Transfer Services
N.A.I.C.S.: 522320

PT Starlink Solusi (1)
Gedung Graha Pena Lt 17 Kav 1701 Jalan Urip Sumoharjo No 20, Makassar, 90234, South Sulawesi, Indonesia
Tel.: (62) 41 143 9012
Web Site: https://www.starlink-solusi.net
Ecommerce Services
N.A.I.C.S.: 518210

PT HEXINDO ADIPERKASA TBK
Kawasan Industri Pulo Gadung Jalan Pulo, Kambing II Kav I-II No 33, Jakarta, 13930, Indonesia
Tel.: (62) 214611688
Web Site: https://www.hexindo-tbk.co.id
Year Founded: 1988
HEXA—(INDO)
Rev.: $612,326,209
Assets: $409,431,521
Liabilities: $230,246,983
Net Worth: $179,184,538
Earnings: $55,711,878
Emp.: 1,822
Fiscal Year-end: 03/31/24
Hydraulic Excavator & Heavy Equipment Sales Services
N.A.I.C.S.: 423120

PT HILLCON TBK
Taman Modern Blok R2 No19 Cakung, PO Box 1016, Jakarta Timur, 13960, Indonesia
Tel.: (62) 214618458
Web Site: https://www.hillcon.co.id
Year Founded: 1995
HILL—(INDO)
Rev.: $262,730,875
Assets: $323,230,668
Liabilities: $204,001,867
Net Worth: $119,228,801
Earnings: $28,505,738
Emp.: 1,947
Fiscal Year-end: 12/31/23
Mining Services
N.A.I.C.S.: 213113
Hersan Qiu *(Chm)*

PT HIMALAYA ENERGI PERKASA TBK

Jl Soebagjono Tjondrokoesoemo Kp Perbalan RT 001 RW 008 Gunung Pati, Semarang, 50229, Jawa Tengah, Indonesia
Tel.: (62) 2476921635   Id
Web Site:
   https://himalayaenergi.co.id
Year Founded: 1989
Rev.: $252,556
Assets: $1,250,059
Liabilities: $155,462
Net Worth: $1,094,596
Earnings: ($3,867,290)
Fiscal Year-end: 12/31/19
Financial Advisory Services
N.A.I.C.S.: 523940
Ismayati Solihat *(Commissioner)*

PT HK METALS UTAMA
Jl Rose Garden 1 No 52 RT 002/RW 017 Kel Jaka Setia Kec, Bekasi, 17147, Jawa, Indonesia
Tel.: (62) 182758384
Web Site: http://www.hyamn.com
Year Founded: 1995
HKMU—(INDO)
Rev.: $12,731,138
Assets: $32,271,592
Liabilities: $30,758,444
Net Worth: $1,513,148
Earnings: ($14,255,617)
Emp.: 233
Fiscal Year-end: 12/31/22
Fabricated Metal Mfr
N.A.I.C.S.: 332312
Ngasidjo Achmad *(Chm)*

Subsidiaries:

PT Dantool Karya Teknik Utama (1)
Jl Kayu Putih Tengah I blok B No 7-8 Rt 011/007, Kec Pulo Gadung, East Jakarta, Indonesia
Tel.: (62) 214704360
Aluminum Distr
N.A.I.C.S.: 423510

PT Hakaru Metalindo Perkasa (1)
Jl Pejuang No 9 RT 010 / RW 009 d/h Raya Kaliabang Kel Harapan Jaya, Kec Bekasi Utara, Bekasi, Indonesia
Tel.: (62) 2188871866
Aluminum Distr
N.A.I.C.S.: 423510

PT Handal Aluminium Sukses (1)
Jl Nyi Gede Cangkring Wadas Tegalsar Plered Kab, Cirebon, Jawa Barat, Indonesia
Tel.: (62) 2318821137
Aluminum Distr
N.A.I.C.S.: 423510

PT Metalutama Perkasa Jaya (1)
Jl HS Kampung Kedep RT 002/023 Desa Tlajung Udik, kec Gunung Putri, Bogor, Indonesia
Tel.: (62) 2186863139
Steel Distr
N.A.I.C.S.: 423510

PT Rasa Langgeng Wira (1)
Kp Cibugis RT 005 RW 006 Desa, Klapanunggal, Bogor, 16710, Jawa Barat, Indonesia
Tel.: (62) 8111686755
Aluminum Distr
N.A.I.C.S.: 423510

PT HOFFMEN CLEANINDO TBK
Jl Raya Jembatan Tiga No 8, Jakarta Utara, 14440, Indonesia
Tel.: (62) 216628126
Web Site: https://www.hoffmen.co.id
Year Founded: 2008
KING—(INDO)
Rev.: $13,839,198
Assets: $9,560,385
Liabilities: $3,490,575
Net Worth: $6,069,810
Earnings: $165,368
Emp.: 125
Fiscal Year-end: 12/31/23

Waste Management Services
N.A.I.C.S.: 562998
Meliza Laudy Oktaviani *(Sec)*

PT HOTEL MANDARINE REGENCY TBK
The Bellezza - Gapura Prima Office Tower Lt 10 Unit 2 3 5 dan 6, Jl Letjen Soepeno No 34, Jakarta, 29432, Indonesia
Tel.: (62) 2130485536
Web Site: http://www.hmr.co.id
Year Founded: 1986
HOME—(INDO)
Rev.: $1,743,615
Assets: $173,234,876
Liabilities: $24,102,118
Net Worth: $149,132,757
Earnings: ($3,290,518)
Emp.: 170
Fiscal Year-end: 12/31/19
Restaurant Operating Services
N.A.I.C.S.: 722511
Bayu Widia Prakoso *(Chm, Pres & Dir)*

PT HOTEL SAHID JAYA INTERNATIONAL TBK
Jenderal Sudirman Kav 86, Po Box 1041, Jakarta, 10220, Indonesia
Tel.: (62) 215704444
Web Site: https://www.pthsji.com
Year Founded: 2012
SHID—(INDO)
Rev.: $8,643,827
Assets: $82,094,370
Liabilities: $32,765,090
Net Worth: $49,329,280
Earnings: ($1,527,508)
Emp.: 179
Fiscal Year-end: 12/31/23
Home Management Services
N.A.I.C.S.: 721110
H. Hariyadi B. Sukamdani *(Chm)*

Subsidiaries:

PT Sahid International Hotel Mangement & Consultants (1)
SAHID Annex Building South Wing 3rd Floor Jl Jendral Sudirman No 86, Jakarta, 10220, Indonesia
Tel.: (62) 215702329
Web Site: http://www.sahidhotels.com
Hotel Services
N.A.I.C.S.: 721110

PT HUMPUSS INTERMODA TRANSPORTASI TBK
Jl Jend Gatot Subroto Kav 1-3, Jakarta, 12950, Indonesia
Tel.: (62) 50933155   Id
Web Site: https://www.hits.co.id
HITS—(INDO)
Rev.: $112,471,989
Assets: $271,820,404
Liabilities: $164,026,920
Net Worth: $107,793,484
Earnings: $9,241,846
Emp.: 169
Fiscal Year-end: 12/31/23
Liquefied Natural Gas Transportation Services
N.A.I.C.S.: 211130

Subsidiaries:

P.T. Humpuss Maritim Internasional (1)
Mangkuluhur City Tower One 27th Floor Jl Jend Gatot Subroto Kav 1-3, Jakarta, 12930, Indonesia
Tel.: (62) 2150933159
Web Site: https://www.humi.co.id
Port & Human Resources Development Services
N.A.I.C.S.: 541612

PT Humpuss Transportasi Kimia (1)
Granadi Building 9th Floor Jl HR Rasuna

PT HUMPUSS INTERMODA TRANSPORTASI TBK

PT Humpuss Intermoda Transportasi Tbk—(Continued)
Said Blok X-1 Kav 8-9, Kuningan, Jakarta, 12950, Indonesia
Tel.: (62)-2152963460
Web Site: http://www.humpuss.co.id
Shipping & Logistics Services
N.A.I.C.S.: 541614
Yulianti Khaenur *(Asst Mgr-Acctg)*

PT MISI Hutama International (1)
Granadi Building 8th Floor North Wing Jl HR Rasuna Said Blok X-1, Kav 8-9, Jakarta, 12950, Indonesia
Tel.: (62) 212524114
Dredging Services
N.A.I.C.S.: 237990

PT ICTSI JASA PRIMA TBK
Graha Kirana Building 7th Floor Suite 701 Jl Yos Sudarso No 88, Jakarta Utara, Indonesia
Tel.: (62) 2165314710
Web Site: https://www.ijp.co.id
Year Founded: 1978
KARW—(INDO)
Rev.: $6,783,708
Assets: $12,433,920
Liabilities: $44,764,090
Net Worth: ($32,330,170)
Earnings: $1,201,795
Emp.: 69
Fiscal Year-end: 12/31/23
Marine Terminal Operator
N.A.I.C.S.: 488310
Wesly Ezra Parlindungan Situmeang *(Sec)*

PT IDEA INDONESIA AKADEMI TBK
18 Office Park Lantai 10 Jalan Tb Simatupang Kav 18 Rw 1, Kebagusan Pasar Minggu, Jakarta Selatan, 12520, Indonesia
Tel.: (62) 217872288
Web Site: https://www.ideaindonesia.com
IDEA—(INDO)
Rev.: $1,317,031
Assets: $5,152,617
Liabilities: $1,125,361
Net Worth: $4,027,256
Earnings: $61,629
Emp.: 3
Fiscal Year-end: 12/31/23
Educational Support Services
N.A.I.C.S.: 611710
Dody Arifianto *(Sec)*

PT IFISHDECO TBK
Jl Jend Sudirman Kav 7-8 Gd Wisma Nugra Santana Lt 8 Suite 802, Jakarta, 10220, Indonesia
Tel.: (62) 215704988
Web Site: https://www.ifishdeco.com
Year Founded: 1971
IFSH—(INDO)
Rev.: $93,073,138
Assets: $69,647,098
Liabilities: $18,611,723
Net Worth: $51,035,376
Earnings: $14,310,088
Emp.: 199
Fiscal Year-end: 12/31/23
Mining Services
N.A.I.C.S.: 213113
Oei Harry Fong Jaya *(Pres)*

Subsidiaries:

PT Bintang Smelter Indonesia (1)
Wisma Nugra Santana Lt 8 Suite 802 Jalan Jenderal Sudirman Kav 7-8, Jakarta Pusat, 10220, Indonesia
Tel.: (62) 21 570 4988
Nickel Mining Services
N.A.I.C.S.: 213114

PT IMAGO MULIA PERSADA TBK
Jalan Simprug Golf Ii Vip 3, Jakarta Selatan, 12220, Indonesia
Tel.: (62) 217210240
Web Site: https://www.imago-int.com
Year Founded: 2014
LFLO—(INDO)
Rev.: $5,243,387
Assets: $7,195,446
Liabilities: $3,678,773
Net Worth: $3,516,673
Earnings: $575,923
Emp.: 16
Fiscal Year-end: 12/31/23
Furniture Distr
N.A.I.C.S.: 423210
Erlangga Ksatria *(Pres)*

PT IMPACK PRATAMA INDUSTRI TBK
Altira Office Tower Lantai 38 Altira Business Park Jl Yos Sudarso, Kav 85, Jakarta, 14350, Indonesia
Tel.: (62) 2121882000
Web Site: https://www.impack-pratama.com
Year Founded: 1981
IMPC—(INDO)
Rev.: $185,753,609
Assets: $233,591,871
Liabilities: $72,043,891
Net Worth: $161,547,980
Earnings: $28,608,861
Emp.: 1,733
Fiscal Year-end: 12/31/23
Plastics Product Mfr
N.A.I.C.S.: 326199
Haryanto Tjiptodihardjo *(Chm)*

Subsidiaries:

Impack Vietnam Co. Ltd. (1)
Factory No 17-18 Road No 6, Long Thanh Industrial Park, Long Thanh, Dong Nai, Vietnam
Tel.: (84) 2513514919
Web Site: https://www.impackvietnam.com
Corrugated Sheet Mfr
N.A.I.C.S.: 322211

ImpackOne Sdn Bhd (1)
No 3 Jalan TPP5, Taman Perindustrian Putra, 47100, Puchong, Selangor, Malaysia
Tel.: (60) 380665933
Web Site: https://impackone.com.my
Polymer Sheet Mfr
N.A.I.C.S.: 327390

Mulford Plastics (M) Sdn Bhd (1)
No 3 Jalan TPP 5, Taman Perindustrian Putra, 47100, Puchong, Selangor, Malaysia
Tel.: (60) 380663298
Web Site: https://www.mulford-malaysia.com
Plastic Sheet Mfr
N.A.I.C.S.: 326113

PT INDAH PRAKASA SENTOSA TBK
Jl Sunder Garden Raya Blok D8 N0 3G-3H, Jakarta Utara, 14350, Indonesia
Tel.: (62) 2165837620
Web Site: http://www.inprasegroup.co.id
INPS—(INDO)
Rev.: $18,040,520
Assets: $19,045,996
Liabilities: $17,688,923
Net Worth: $1,357,073
Earnings: $7,827
Emp.: 154
Fiscal Year-end: 12/31/23
Passenger Transportation Services
N.A.I.C.S.: 485999
Eddy Purwanto Winto *(Chm)*

PT INDAL ALUMINIUM INDUSTRY TBK
Kompleks Maspion Unit-1 Sawotratap, Sidoarjo, Surabaya, 61254, Indonesia
Tel.: (62) 318531531
Web Site: https://www.indalcorp.com
Year Founded: 1971
INAI—(INDO)
Rev.: $82,041,541
Assets: $95,908,122
Liabilities: $78,119,494
Net Worth: $17,788,628
Earnings: ($3,755,908)
Emp.: 707
Fiscal Year-end: 12/31/23
Aluminium Product Mfr & Distr
N.A.I.C.S.: 332999
Alim Markus *(Chm)*

Subsidiaries:

PT Indal Aluminium Industry Tbk - East Java Factory (1)
Desa Sawotratap Gedangan, Sidoarjo, 61254, Indonesia
Tel.: (62) 318536993
Aluminium Products Mfr
N.A.I.C.S.: 332999

PT Indalex (1)
Maspion Plaza 15-17th Floor Jl Gunung Sahari Raya No 18, Kota Tua Pademangan Jakarta Utara, Jakarta, Indonesia
Tel.: (62) 21 647 0100
Web Site: https://www.indalex.co.id
Construction Services
N.A.I.C.S.: 236220
Ryan Robinson *(Mgr-Project)*

PT INDIKA ENERGY TBK
Graha Mitra 3rd Floor Jl Jend Gatot Subroto Kav 21, Jakarta, 12930, Indonesia
Tel.: (62) 2125579888
Web Site: https://www.indikaenergy.co.id
INDY—(INDO)
Rev.: $3,026,839,190
Assets: $3,113,102,390
Liabilities: $1,735,964,940
Net Worth: $1,377,137,450
Earnings: $151,043,091
Emp.: 13,673
Fiscal Year-end: 12/31/23
Holding Company; Coal Production; Energy Infrastructure Engineering & Construction; Electric Power Generation
N.A.I.C.S.: 551112
P. M. Arsjad Rasjid *(Chm)*

Subsidiaries:

Indika Power Investments Pte. Ltd. (1)
9 Temasek Boulevard Suntec Tower Two Unit 30-01/02/03, Singapore, 038989, Singapore
Tel.: (65) 62387870
Web Site: http://www.indikaenergy.com
Sales Range: $50-74.9 Million
Emp.: 15
Energy & Coal Production Services
N.A.I.C.S.: 213113

P.T. Electra Distribusi Indonesia (1)
Indy Bintaro Office Park Building A Floor 5th, Jl Boulevard Bintaro Jaya Blok B7/A6, Tangerang, 15424, Indonesia
Tel.: (62) 150590
Web Site: https://www.alvaauto.com
Motorcycle Mfr & Distr
N.A.I.C.S.: 336991

PT Interport Mandiri Utama (1)
Graha Mitra Lantai 7 Jl Jend Gatot Subroto Kav 21, Jakarta, 12930, Indonesia
Engineeering Services
N.A.I.C.S.: 541330
Agus Cahyadi *(Mgr-Internal Audit)*

PT POSB Reksabumi Indonesia (1)
Indy Bintaro Office Park Building B Jl Boulevard, Bintaro Jaya Blok B7/A6 Sektor VII CBD Bintaro, Tangerang, 15224, Indonesia
Tel.: (62) 2129770999

INTERNATIONAL PUBLIC

Web Site: https://www.petrosea.com
Hazardous Waste Management Services
N.A.I.C.S.: 562211
Richard Bruce Ness *(VP)*

PT Petrosea Tbk (1)
Indy Bintaro Office Park Building B Sektor VII CBD Bintaro Jaya, Jl Boulevard Bintaro Jaya Blok B7/A6, Tangerang, 15224, Indonesia
Tel.: (62) 2129770999
Web Site: https://www.petrosea.com
Rev.: $577,617,000
Assets: $727,945,000
Liabilities: $492,315,000
Net Worth: $235,630,000
Earnings: $12,438,000
Emp.: 4,655
Fiscal Year-end: 12/31/2023
Contract Engineering, Construction & Mining Services
N.A.I.C.S.: 237990
Indradjaya Hanifa *(Chm)*

PT Tripatra Engineering Indonesia (1)
Jl Boulevard Bintaro Jaya Blok B7/A6 Sektor VII CBD Bintaro Jaya, Selatan, Tangerang, 15224, Indonesia
Tel.: (62) 2129770700
Web Site: http://www.tripatra.com
Sales Range: $150-199.9 Million
Emp.: 600
Engineering Consulting Services
N.A.I.C.S.: 541330

PT Tripatra Engineers & Constructors Indonesia (1)
Jl RA Kartini 34, Outer Ring Rd, Jakarta, Indonesia
Tel.: (62) 217500701
Web Site: http://www.tripatra.com
Sales Range: $25-49.9 Million
Emp.: 20
Administrative Management Services
N.A.I.C.S.: 541611

PT Xapiens Teknologi Indonesia (1)
Indy Bintaro Office Park, Building F Jl Boulevard Bintaro Jaya Blok B7/A6, Tangerang, 15224, Selatan, Indonesia
Tel.: (62) 2129770900
Web Site: https://staging.xapiens.id
Information Technology Services
N.A.I.C.S.: 541511

PT. Kideco Jaya Agung (1)
Batu Sopang Kabupaten Paser, Desa Batu Kajang Kecamatan, 76252, Kalimantan, Timur, Indonesia (91%)
Tel.: (62) 5 432 2522
Web Site: https://www.kideco.co.id
Coal Mining & Distribution Services
N.A.I.C.S.: 213113

PT INDO ACIDATAMA TBK
Graha Kencana 9th Floor-Suite A Jl Raya Perjuangan 88, Jakarta Barat, 11530, Indonesia
Tel.: (62) 2153660777
Web Site: https://www.acidatama.co.id
Year Founded: 1983
SRSN—(INDO)
Rev.: $66,674,252
Assets: $60,829,158
Liabilities: $14,683,605
Net Worth: $46,145,554
Earnings: $3,767,699
Emp.: 297
Fiscal Year-end: 12/31/23
Agrochemical Mfr
N.A.I.C.S.: 325199
Budhi Moeljono *(Chm)*

PT INDO KOMODITI KORPORA TBK
Centennial Tower Jl Jenderal Gatot Subroto Kav 24 25, Floor21 Unit H, Jakarta, 12930, Indonesia
Tel.: (62) 2122958323
Web Site: https://indokomoditikorpora.com
Year Founded: 1982

INCF—(INDO)
Rev.: $13,133,638
Assets: $28,979,103
Liabilities: $19,434,322
Net Worth: $9,544,781
Earnings: $138,928
Emp.: 208
Fiscal Year-end: 12/31/23
Rubber Mfr & Distr
N.A.I.C.S.: 325998

PT INDO KORDSA TBK
Jalan Pahlawan Desa Karang Asem Timur, Citeureup, Bogor, 16810, Indonesia
Tel.: (62) 218752115
Web Site:
https://www.indokordsa.com
Year Founded: 1981
BRAM—(INDO)
Rev.: $16,362
Assets: $19,408
Liabilities: $4,730
Net Worth: $14,678
Earnings: $1,133
Emp.: 1,076
Fiscal Year-end: 12/31/23
Tire Cord Fabric Mfr
N.A.I.C.S.: 314994
Ibrahim Ozgur Yildirim *(Pres)*

Subsidiaries:

Thai Indo Kordsa Co., Ltd. (1)
Rojana Industrial Park 1/61 Moo 5, Khanham Subdistrict Uthai District, Ayutthaya, 13210, Thailand
Tel.: (66) 35330221
Tire Cord Fabric Mfr
N.A.I.C.S.: 314994

PT INDO OIL PERKASA
Jl Raya Perning Km 39 Jetis, Mojokerto, East Java, Indonesia
Tel.: (62) 3213671741
Web Site:
https://www.indooilperkasa.com
Year Founded: 2016
OILS—(INDO)
Rev.: $38,986,835
Assets: $12,982,020
Liabilities: $7,495,487
Net Worth: $5,486,532
Earnings: $203,291
Emp.: 27
Fiscal Year-end: 12/31/23
Coconut Oil Distr
N.A.I.C.S.: 311225
Johan Widakdo Liem *(Pres)*

PT INDO STRAITS TBK.
Graha Kirana Building 15th Floor Suite 1501, Jl Yos Sudarso Kav88, Jakarta, 14350, Indonesia
Tel.: (62) 2165311285
Web Site:
https://www.indostraits.co.id
PTIS—(INDO)
Rev.: $13,983,917
Assets: $37,747,188
Liabilities: $17,086,914
Net Worth: $20,660,274
Earnings: $1,021,862
Emp.: 167
Fiscal Year-end: 12/31/23
Marine Engineering Services
N.A.I.C.S.: 541330
Tan Kim Leng *(Chm)*

Subsidiaries:

PT Pelayaran Straits Perdana (1)
Graha Kirana Building 15th Floor Suite 1501 Jl Yos Sudarso Kav 88, Jakarta, 14350, Indonesia
Tel.: (62) 2165311285
Emp.: 320
Marine Engineering & Logistic Services
N.A.I.C.S.: 488390
Tan Kim Leng *(Co-Pres)*

PT INDO TAMBANGRAYA MEGAH TBK.
Pondok Indah Office Tower III 3rd Floor Jalan Sultan Iskandar Muda, Pondok Indah Kav V-TA, Jakarta, 12310, Selatan, Indonesia
Tel.: (62) 2129328100
Web Site: https://www.itmg.co.id
ITMG—(INDO)
Rev.: $2,374,315,000
Assets: $2,187,847,000
Liabilities: $399,307,000
Net Worth: $1,788,540,000
Earnings: $499,620,000
Emp.: 1,883
Fiscal Year-end: 12/31/23
Coal Mining & Related Services
N.A.I.C.S.: 212114
A. H. Bramantya Putra *(Deputy Chm)*

Subsidiaries:

P.T. Graha Panca Karsa (1)
Pondok Indah Office Tower 3 3rd Floor, Jalan Sultan Iskandar Muda Kav V-TA, Jakarta, 12310, Indonesia
Tel.: (62) 2129328100
Coal Whslr
N.A.I.C.S.: 423520

P.T. ITM Bhinneka Power (1)
Pondok Indah Office Tower 3 3rd Floor, Jalan Sultan Iskandar Muda Kav V-TA, Jakarta, 12310, Indonesia
Tel.: (62) 2129328100
Coal Whslr
N.A.I.C.S.: 423520

PT Jorong Barutama Greston (1)
Jl A Yani km 104 Desa Swarangan RT 07 No 286 Kecamatan Jorong, PO Box 141, Kabupaten Tanah Laut Pelahari, Kalimantan, 70882, Kalimantan Selatan, Indonesia
Tel.: (62) 29328100
Coal Mining Services
N.A.I.C.S.: 213113
W. Widianto *(Head-Fin Acctg)*

PT Kitadin (1)
Desa Embalut Kecamatan Tenggarong Seberang Kabupaten Kutai Kertanegara, Kalimantan, 75572, Indonesia
Tel.: (62) 29328100
Coal Mining Services
N.A.I.C.S.: 213113
Daniel Tobing *(Head-Mine Ops)*

PT Tambang Raya Usaha Tama (1)
Jl Poros Bontang-Samarinda Km 10, Bontang, 75300, Kalimantan Timur, Indonesia
Tel.: (62) 29328100
Coal Mining Services
N.A.I.C.S.: 213113
Anhar Al Ala *(Mgr-HSEC)*

PT INDOCEMENT TUNGGAL PRAKARSA TBK
Citeureup Factory Mayor Oking Jayaatmaja Street, Bogor, 16810, Indonesia
Tel.: (62) 218752812
Web Site:
https://www.indocement.co.id
Year Founded: 1975
INTP—(INDO)
Rev.: $1,165,657,155
Assets: $1,925,447,946
Liabilities: $563,687,902
Net Worth: $1,361,760,044
Earnings: $126,650,274
Emp.: 2,973
Fiscal Year-end: 12/31/23
Cement Mfr
N.A.I.C.S.: 325520
Christian Kartawijaya *(Chm)*

Subsidiaries:

PT Mandiri Sejahtera Sentra (1)
Kp Cikakak RT/RW 009/005 Kelurahan Sukamulya Kecamatan Tegalwaru, Purwakarta, Indonesia
Tel.: (62) 264700288
Web Site: http://www.indocement.co.id
Cement Mfr
N.A.I.C.S.: 327310

PT Mineral Industri Sukabumi (1)
Jl Diponegoro No 7 Kel Gunung Puyuh, Sukabumi, Indonesia
Tel.: (62) 266223408
Cement Mfr
N.A.I.C.S.: 327310

PT INDOFARMA (PERSERO) TBK
Jalan Indofarma No 1 Cikarang Barat, Bekasi, 17530, Indonesia
Tel.: (62) 2188323975
Web Site: http://www.indofarma.id
Year Founded: 1918
INAF—(INDO)
Rev.: $34,002,525
Assets: $49,343,294
Liabilities: $101,564,941
Net Worth: ($52,221,648)
Earnings: ($47,137,980)
Emp.: 621
Fiscal Year-end: 12/31/23
Pharmaceuticals Product Mfr
N.A.I.C.S.: 325412
Arie Genipa Suhendi *(Sec)*

Subsidiaries:

PT Indofarma Global Medika (1)
Kompleks Infinia Park Blok B-86 Street Dr Saharjo No 45, Jakarta Selatan, 12850, Jakarta, Indonesia
Tel.: (62) 2183781166
Pharmaceutical Product & Medical Device Distr
N.A.I.C.S.: 424210

PT INDOFOOD CBP SUKSES MAKMUR TBK.
Sudirman Plaza Indofood Tower 23th Floor, Jl Jend Sudirman Kav 76-78, Jakarta, 12910, Indonesia
Tel.: (62) 2157938822
Web Site:
https://www.indofoodcbp.com
Year Founded: 1982
ICBP—(INDO)
Rev.: $4,410,068,971
Assets: $7,745,203,915
Liabilities: $3,712,168,012
Net Worth: $4,033,035,903
Earnings: $549,725,088
Emp.: 29,162
Fiscal Year-end: 12/31/23
Packaged Food Product Mfr
N.A.I.C.S.: 311999
Anthoni Salim *(Chm)*

Subsidiaries:

Indofood (M) Food Industries Sdn. Bhd. (1)
Lot 26 Jalan Tasek Tasek Industrial Estate, 31400, Ipoh, Perak, Malaysia
Tel.: (60) 55451706
Food Product Mfr & Distr
N.A.I.C.S.: 311991

P.T. Indofood Comsa Sukses Makmu (1)
Sudirman Plaza Indofood Tower 25th Floor Jl Jend Sudirman Kav 76-78, Jakarta, 12910, Indonesia
Tel.: (62) 2157958822
Food & Beverage Mfr
N.A.I.C.S.: 311999

PT Buana Distrindo (1)
Jl Sunter Agung Brt Kompl Sunter Agung Podomoro Bl A-2/12 Sunter Agung, Tanjung Priok, Jakarta, 14350, Indonesia
Tel.: (62) 2165832904
Beverages Mfr
N.A.I.C.S.: 312120

PT Indokuat Sukses Makmur (1)
Cyber 2 Tower 12th Floor Jl HR Rasuna Said Blok X-5 No 13, Jakarta, 12950, Indonesia
Tel.: (62) 2129961100
Food Products Mfr
N.A.I.C.S.: 311919

PT Indolakto (1)
Jl Raya Siliwangi, Cicurug, Sukabumi, 43359, Indonesia
Tel.: (62) 266732870
Food Products Mfr
N.A.I.C.S.: 311919
Taufik Wiraatmadja *(Pres)*

PT Surya Rengo Containers (1)
Jl KH Agus Salim No 4, Tangerang, 15141, Indonesia
Tel.: (62) 21 552 3542
Web Site: http://www.rengo.co.id
Emp.: 250
Corrugated Packaging Box Mfr
N.A.I.C.S.: 322211
Taufik Wiraatmadja *(Pres)*

Plant (Domestic):

PT Surya Rengo Containers - Karawang Factory (2)
Jl Maligi Raya Lot Q 5 Kawasan Industri KIIC, Karawang, 41361, Indonesia
Tel.: (62) 2189114325
Corrugated Packaging Box Mfr
N.A.I.C.S.: 322211

PT Surya Rengo Containers - Semarang Factory (2)
Jl Raya Semarang-Demak Km 13 5, Semarang, 59563, Indonesia
Tel.: (62) 246585000
Corrugated Packaging Box Mfr
N.A.I.C.S.: 322211

PT Surya Rengo Containers - Surabaya Factory (2)
Jl Raya Bypass Krian Km 29 4 Krian Sidoarjo, East Java, Indonesia
Tel.: (62) 318982499
Corrugated Packaging Box Mfr
N.A.I.C.S.: 322211

PT INDOINTERNET TBK
Rempoa Raya No 11, Ciputat, Tangerang, 15412, Indonesia
Tel.: (62) 2173882525
Web Site: https://www.indonet.co.id
Year Founded: 1994
EDGE—(INDO)
Rev.: $61,719,560
Assets: $176,855,843
Liabilities: $81,306,958
Net Worth: $95,548,885
Earnings: $16,447,029
Emp.: 226
Fiscal Year-end: 12/31/23
Information Technology Services
N.A.I.C.S.: 541519
Karla Winata *(CEO)*

Subsidiaries:

Fast Speed Network Pte. Ltd. (1)
20 Cross Street 02-18 Cross Street Exchange, Singapore, 048422, Singapore
Tel.: (65) 65387488
Tire Cord Fabric Mfr
N.A.I.C.S.: 314994

PT Ekagrata Data Gemilang (1)
Gedung Cyber Lantai 8 Jl Kuningan Barat Raya No 8, Mampang Prapatan, Jakarta Selatan, 12710, Indonesia
Tel.: (62) 215 296 0202
Data Processing Services
N.A.I.C.S.: 518210

PT Wiratapura Indo Parahyangan (1)
Ruko Wangsaniaga Wetan No 16, Tatar Wangsakerta Kota Baru Parahyangan, Bandung, Indonesia
Tel.: (62) 2221102888
Computer System Design Services
N.A.I.C.S.: 541512

PT INDOMOBIL MULTI JASA TBK
Indomobil Tower 11th Floor Jl MT Haryono Kav 11, Jakarta, 13330, Indonesia
Tel.: (62) 2129185400

PT INDOMOBIL MULTI JASA TBK

PT Indomobil Multi Jasa Tbk—(Continued)

Web Site:
https://indomobilmultijasa.com
Year Founded: 1997
IMJS—(INDO)
Rev.: $334,724,731
Assets: $1,864,528,772
Liabilities: $1,556,856,848
Net Worth: $307,671,924
Earnings: $17,507,931
Emp.: 2,321
Fiscal Year-end: 12/31/23
Consumer Finance & Vehicle Rental Services
N.A.I.C.S.: 522220
Maureen Oktarita (Sec)

Subsidiaries:

P.T. Hino Finance Indonesia (1)
Indomobil Tower 17th Floor Jl Letjen MT Haryono Kav 11 Bidara Cina, Jatinegara, Jakarta Timur, 13330, Indonesia
Tel.: (62) 2129827960
Web Site: https://www.hinofinance.co.id
Financial Services
N.A.I.C.S.: 522220

P.T. Indomobil Bussan Trucking (1)
Indomobil Tower Lt 5 Jl MT Haryono Kav 11, Jakarta, 13330, Indonesia
Tel.: (62) 218564569
Web Site: https://www.indopenske.co.id
Vehicle Rental Services
N.A.I.C.S.: 532120

PT INDOMOBIL SUKSES INTERNASIONAL TBK

Wisma Indomobil 1 6th Floor Jl MT Haryono Kav 8, Jakarta, 13330, Indonesia
Tel.: (62) 218564850   Id
Web Site: https://www.indomobil.com
Year Founded: 1976
IMAS—(INDO)
Rev.: $1,876,266,871
Assets: $4,085,539,438
Liabilities: $3,080,836,918
Net Worth: $1,004,702,520
Earnings: $50,480,589
Emp.: 7,468
Fiscal Year-end: 12/31/23
Automotive Distr
N.A.I.C.S.: 423110
Jusak Kertowidjojo (Chm & Mktg Dir)

Subsidiaries:

PT Central Sole Agency (1)
Wisma Indoparts Jl Gatot Subroto Km 8 Kav 8 No 18 Manis Jaya, Jatiuwung, Tangerang, 15136, Indonesia
Tel.: (62) 215 565 0101
Web Site: https://www.indoparts.id
Automotive Spare Parts Distr
N.A.I.C.S.: 441330
Emil Wardana (Mgr-HRD & GA)

Subsidiary (Domestic):

PT Furukawa Indomobil Battery Sales (2)
Wisma Indopart Jl Raya Gatot Subroto Kav 8 No 18 Km 8 Jatake, Tangerang, 15111, Indonesia
Web Site: http://www.furukawa-battery.co.id
Battery Product Mfr
N.A.I.C.S.: 335910
R. Dedi (Mgr-Direct Sls)

PT Data Arts Xperience (1)
Wisma Indomobil Lt 8 Mt Haryono Kav 8, East Jakarta, 13330, Indonesia
Tel.: (62) 21 856 9126
Web Site: https://dax.co.id
Digital Advertising & Marketing Services
N.A.I.C.S.: 541810
Eisuke Okamoto (Mgr-DMP)

PT Eka Dharma Jaya Sakti (1)
Kanto A 18 Mega Glodok Kemayoran Jl Angkasa Kav-B6, Kota Baru Bandar Kemayoran, Jakarta Pusat, 10610, Indonesia
Tel.: (62) 218 591 8444

Web Site: https://www.ekadharma.co.id
Automobile Product Distr
N.A.I.C.S.: 441110
Sari Rahmawati (Mgr-Personnel)

PT Indo Traktor Utama (1)
Green Sedayu Biz Park Unit GS1/015-017 Jl Timur Raya, Cakung Cilincing, Jakarta, 13910, Indonesia
Tel.: (62) 212 983 2112
Web Site: https://www.indotraktor-utama.co.id
Emp.: 222
Automobile Product Distr
N.A.I.C.S.: 441110
Teguh Yahya (Head-Aftermarket Div)

PT Indomobil Finance Indonesia (1)
Indomobil Tower Lantai 8 Jl MT Haryono Kav 11, Jakarta, 13330, Indonesia
Tel.: (62) 212 918 5400
Web Site: https://www.indomobilfinance.com
Automobile Financing Services
N.A.I.C.S.: 522220
Edy Handojo (Sec)

PT Indomobil Wahana Trada (1)
Jl Mt Haryono Kav 10 Bidara Cina - Jatinegara, Desa/Kelurahan Bidara Cinam Jatinegara Kota Adm Jakarta Timur, Jakarta, 13330, Indonesia
Tel.: (62) 218565959
Web Site: https://www.indomobilnissan.com
Automobile Product Distr
N.A.I.C.S.: 441110

PT Indotruck Utama (1)
Jl Raya Cakung Cilincing KAV 3A, Semper Timur, Jakarta Utara, 14130, Indonesia
Tel.: (62) 21 441 2168
Web Site: https://www.indotruck-utama.co.id
Automotive Equipment Distr
N.A.I.C.S.: 423120
Antonius Panggabean (Head-Sls)

PT Jasa Logistik Utama (1)
Gd Perum Bulog lt 16 Jl Gatot Subroto kav 49, Kuningan, Jakarta Selatan, Jakarta, Indonesia
Tel.: (62) 215203020
Web Site: https://www.jplogistics.co.id
Transportation Logistics Services
N.A.I.C.S.: 541614

PT Wahana Sun Motor Semarang (1)
Jl Madukoro 4-5 Komp PRPP Fax Kota, Semarang, Jawa Tengah, Indonesia
Tel.: (62) 247615200
Automobile Product Distr
N.A.I.C.S.: 441110

PT INDONESIA ASAHAN ALUMINIUM (PERSERO)

Kuala Tanjung Office Kuala Tanjung, PO Box 1, Sei Suka District Batu Bara Regency, Sumatra Utara, Indonesia
Tel.: (62) 622 31311
Web Site: http://www.inalum.id
Energy Distr
N.A.I.C.S.: 221118
Orias P. Moedak (CEO)

PT INDONESIA FIBREBOARD INDUSTRY

Wisma Adr Lt 3 Jl Pluit Raya I No 1, Penjaringan, Jakarta Utara, 14440, Indonesia
Tel.: (62) 216615555
Web Site: https://www.pt-ifi.com
Year Founded: 2007
IFII—(INDO)
Rev.: $64,095,114
Assets: $123,021,587
Liabilities: $43,735,277
Net Worth: $79,286,309
Earnings: $6,552,640
Emp.: 625
Fiscal Year-end: 12/31/23
Wood Products Mfr
N.A.I.C.S.: 321999
Heffy Hartono (Pres)

PT INDONESIA PONDASI RAYA TBK.

JL Pegangsaan Dua KM 4 5, Kelapa Gading, Jakarta Utara, 14250, Indonesia
Tel.: (62) 214603253
Web Site: https://www.indopora.com
IDPR—(INDO)
Rev.: $83,745,515
Assets: $109,023,414
Liabilities: $66,121,907
Net Worth: $42,901,506
Earnings: $2,154,567
Emp.: 731
Fiscal Year-end: 12/31/23
Engineeering Services
N.A.I.C.S.: 237990
Heribertus Herry Putranto (Dir-Operational)

Subsidiaries:

PT Rekagunatek Persada (1)
Ruko Fluorite Blok FR No 28-29 Jalan Gading.Serpong Boulevard, Pakulonan Bar Klp Dua, Tangerang, 15138, Banten, Indonesia
Tel.: (62) 2154220450
Web Site: https://www.rekagunatek.com
Concrete Products Mfr
N.A.I.C.S.: 327390

PT INDONESIA POWER

Jl Jend Gatot Subroto Kav 18, Jakarta, 12950, Indonesia
Tel.: (62) 215267666
Web Site:
http://www.indonesiapower.co.id
Sales Range: $1-4.9 Billion
Emp.: 3,800
Power Distr & Generation
N.A.I.C.S.: 221122
Sripeni Inten Cahyani (Pres)

Subsidiaries:

PT Cogindo DayaBersama (1)
Building 9th Floor Gatot Subroto Street Kav 18, Jakarta, 12950, Indonesia
Tel.: (62) 215214515
Web Site: http://www.cogindo.co.id
Power Plant Maintenance Services
N.A.I.C.S.: 561730
Mangampin Saragi (Pres & Dir)

PT Rajamandala Electric Power (1)
No 65 Jl Wijaya Timur Raya No 1 Kby Baru Kota Jakarta Selatan Daerah, Khusus Ibukota, Jakarta, 12170, Indonesia
Tel.: (62) 217265145
Web Site: http://www.rajamandala-power.com
Power Supplies Distr
N.A.I.C.S.: 423610

PT Tangkuban Parahu Geothermal Power (1)
PT Indonesia Power Building 7th Floor Jalan Gatot Subroto Kav 18, Jakarta, Indonesia
Tel.: (62) 215267666
Power Distribution Services
N.A.I.C.S.: 221122

PT INDONESIA PRIMA PROPERTY TBK

Jl Jend Sudirman Kav 34 RT 03/RW 02, Karet Tengsin Subdistrict Tanah Abang District, Jakarta, 10220, Indonesia
Tel.: (62) 2150913988
Web Site: https://www.ipp.co.id
Year Founded: 1983
OMRE—(INDO)
Rev.: $4,635,036
Assets: $260,706,907
Liabilities: $26,714,561
Net Worth: $233,992,347
Earnings: ($10,678,810)
Emp.: 208
Fiscal Year-end: 12/31/23
Property Development Services
N.A.I.C.S.: 531312

Husni Ali (Chm)

PT INDONESIAN PARADISE PROPERTY TBK

Centennial Tower 30th Floor Jl Gatot Subroto Kav 24-25, Jakarta, 12930, Indonesia
Tel.: (62) 2129880466   Id
Web Site:
https://paradiseindonesia.com
Year Founded: 1996
INPP—(INDO)
Rev.: $71,739,927
Assets: $606,880,578
Liabilities: $221,894,635
Net Worth: $384,985,942
Earnings: $12,007,202
Emp.: 511
Fiscal Year-end: 12/31/23
Property Development Services
N.A.I.C.S.: 531312
Anthony Prabowo Susilo (Chm)

PT INDONESIAN TOBACCO TBK

Jl Letjend S Parman No 92, Malang, 65122, East Java, Indonesia
Tel.: (62) 341491017
Web Site:
https://www.indonesiantobacco.com
Year Founded: 1955
ITIC—(INDO)
Rev.: $19,737,099
Assets: $36,389,345
Liabilities: $10,547,692
Net Worth: $25,841,653
Earnings: $1,751,018
Emp.: 302
Fiscal Year-end: 12/31/23
Tobacco Mfr
N.A.I.C.S.: 312230
Djonny Saksono (Pres)

PT INDOPOLY SWAKARSA INDUSTRY TBK

Wisma Indosemen 5th Floor Jl Jenderal Sudirman Kav 70 - 71, Jakarta, 12910, Indonesia
Tel.: (62) 212510088
Web Site: https://www.ilenefilms.com
Year Founded: 1995
IPOL—(INDO)
Rev.: $193,862,822
Assets: $284,075,431
Liabilities: $107,102,928
Net Worth: $176,972,503
Earnings: $432,323
Emp.: 962
Fiscal Year-end: 12/31/23
Packaging Material Mfr & Distr
N.A.I.C.S.: 326130
Henry Halim (Chm)

Subsidiaries:

Ilene Inc. (1)
200 S Frontage Rd Ste 102, Burr Ridge, IL 60527
Tel.: (630) 891-3142
Plastic Film & Sheet Distr
N.A.I.C.S.: 424610

Suzhou Kunlene Film Industries Co., Ltd. (1)
368 Xing Long Road, Suzhou Industrial Park, Suzhou, 215126, Jiangsu, China
Tel.: (86) 51262833030
Plastic Film & Sheet Distr
N.A.I.C.S.: 424610

Subsidiary (Domestic):

Yunnan Kunlene Film Industries Co., Ltd. (2)
No 10 Kun Ling Road, Kunming National Economic and Technological Development Zone, Kunming, 650217, Yunnan, China
Tel.: (86) 87167266661
Plastic Film & Sheet Distr
N.A.I.C.S.: 424610

AND PRIVATE COMPANIES

Hermanto Rudy *(Mgr)*

PT INDORITEL MAKMUR INTERNASIONAL TBK
Wisma Indocement Lt 10 Jl Jendral Sudirman Kav 70-71, Jakarta, 12910, Indonesia
Tel.: (62) 2129410709   Id
Web Site: https://www.indoritel.co.id
Year Founded: 1995
DNET—(INDO)
Rev.: $90,273,419
Assets: $1,344,963,248
Liabilities: $495,966,522
Net Worth: $848,996,727
Earnings: $51,097,519
Emp.: 198
Fiscal Year-end: 12/31/23
Holding Company
N.A.I.C.S.: 551112
Kiki Yanto Gunawan *(Sec)*

Subsidiaries:

PT Indoritel Persada Nusantara   (1)
Gedung Wisma Indocement Lantai 10 Jl Jendral Sudirman Kav 79-71, Jakarta, 12910, Indonesia
Tel.: (62) 2129410709
Consumer Product Retailer
N.A.I.C.S.: 532289

PT Mega Akses Persada   (1)
Cyber 2 Tower Lt 3 Jl H R Rasuna Said Blok X-5 No 13, Jakarta, 12950, Selatan, Indonesia
Tel.: (62) 2180621200
Consumer Product Retailer
N.A.I.C.S.: 532289

PT INDOSPRING TBK
Jl Mayjend Sungkono No 10 Desa Segoromadu, Gresik, 61123, Indonesia
Tel.: (62) 313981135
Web Site: https://www.indospring.co.id
Year Founded: 1978
INDS—(INDO)
Rev.: $246,938,456
Assets: $289,592,249
Liabilities: $62,900,502
Net Worth: $226,691,747
Earnings: $12,372,452
Emp.: 2,713
Fiscal Year-end: 12/31/23
Automotive Spring Mfr
N.A.I.C.S.: 332613
Wiranto Nurhadi *(Pres)*

Subsidiaries:

P.T. MK Prima Indonesia   (1)
Ji mayjend Sungkono 16, Desa Segoromadu, Gresik, East-Java, Indonesia
Tel.: (62) 313984761
Web Site: https://mkpi.indoprima-group.com
Meld & Dies Mfr
N.A.I.C.S.: 333511

PT Indobaja Prima Murni   (1)
Jl Mayjend Sungkono No 90 Karangtanjung Giri Kec Kebomas, Gresik, 61124, East Java, Indonesia
Tel.: (62) 31 397 2857
Web Site: https://www.indobaja.co.id
Farm Machinery & Equipment Mfr
N.A.I.C.S.: 333111
Widjijono Nurhadi *(Pres)*

PT Indonesia Prima Spring   (1)
JL Mayjen Sungkono KM 3 1 Desa Segoromadu Kecamatan Kebomas, East Java, Gresik, Indonesia
Tel.: (62) 315 116 7501
Automotive Spring Mfr
N.A.I.C.S.: 332613

PT Sinar Indra Nusa Jaya   (1)
JL Mayjen Sungkono No 1 Desa Segoromadu Kecamatan Kebomas, Gresik, Jawa Timur, Indonesia
Tel.: (62) 313986221
Office Equipment Whslr

N.A.I.C.S.: 424120

PT INDOSTERLING TECHNOMEDIA TBK
Jl Jenderal Sudirman Kav 1, Gelora Tanah Abang Kec Kebayoran Baru, Jakarta, 10220, Indonesia
Tel.: (62) 217228893
Web Site: http://www.indosterlingtechno.com
Year Founded: 2007
TECH—(INDO)
Rev.: $1,244,296
Assets: $4,834,362
Liabilities: $568,791
Net Worth: $4,265,571
Earnings: $185,885
Fiscal Year-end: 12/31/23
Information Technology Services
N.A.I.C.S.: 541511
Billy Andrian *(Pres)*

Subsidiaries:

PT Technomedia Multi Sejahtera   (1)
Jl Kramat Pela No 81 Gandaria Utara, Kebayoran Baru, Jakarta Selatan, Indonesia
Tel.: (62) 212 972 1008
Web Site: https://kawn.co.id
Information Technology Services
N.A.I.C.S.: 541519

PT INDUSTRI JAMU DAN FARMASI SIDO MUNCUL TBK
Office Sido Muncul Lt 1 Gedung Hotel Tentrem Jl Gajahmada No 123, Semarang, 50134, Indonesia
Tel.: (62) 2476928811
Web Site: https://www.sidomuncul.co.id
Year Founded: 1940
SIDO—(INDO)
Rev.: $231,571,494
Assets: $252,662,448
Liabilities: $32,779,439
Net Worth: $219,883,009
Earnings: $61,735,081
Emp.: 3,487
Fiscal Year-end: 12/31/23
Medicinal Herbs, Energy Drinks, Sweets & Other Beverages Mfr
N.A.I.C.S.: 325411
David Hidayat *(Chm)*

Subsidiaries:

PT Berlico Mulia Farma   (1)
Jl Jogja-Solo KM 10 6 Juwangan Kalasan, Yogyakarta, Central Java, Indonesia
Tel.: (62) 2744986829
Web Site: https://www.berlico.co.id
Pharmaceutical Mfr & Distr
N.A.I.C.S.: 325412

PT Semarang Herbal Indo Plant   (1)
Jalan Soekarno Hatta KM 28, District Bergas, Semarang, 50552, Central Java, Indonesia
Tel.: (62) 298525580
Web Site: https://www.semarangherbal.co.id
Botanical Extract Mfr & Distr
N.A.I.C.S.: 325412

PT INFORMASI TEKNOLOGI INDONESIA TBK.
Jl Mampang Prapatan Raya No 3, Jakarta Selatan, 12790, Indonesia
Tel.: (62) 1845675
Web Site: https://www.jatismobile.com
Year Founded: 2002
JATI—(INDO)
Rev.: $14,774,731
Assets: $18,981,279
Liabilities: $8,416,418
Net Worth: $10,564,861
Earnings: $4,677
Fiscal Year-end: 06/30/23
Pharmaceutical Product Mfr & Distr
N.A.I.C.S.: 325412
Erik Rivai Ridzal *(CEO)*

PT INFRATECH INDONESIA
Wisma Tugu II 6th Floor Jalan H R Rasuna, Jakarta, 15111, Indonesia
Tel.: (62) 21 5210338   Id
Sales Range: $1-9.9 Million
Telecommunications Structure Construction Services
N.A.I.C.S.: 237130

PT INGRIA PRATAMA CAPITALINDO TBK
Pondok Cabe Mutiara Shop House Block C No 27, Kecamatan Pamulang, Tangerang, 15418, Banten, Indonesia
Tel.: (62) 2174636691
Web Site: https://www.ingriagroup.com
Year Founded: 2013
GRIA—(INDO)
Rev.: $3,114,762
Assets: $30,910,305
Liabilities: $5,943,013
Net Worth: $24,967,292
Earnings: $222,941
Fiscal Year-end: 12/31/23
Real Estate Development Services
N.A.I.C.S.: 531190
Irwansyah Hakim Noor *(Mng Dir)*

PT INOCYCLE TECHNOLOGY GROUP TBK
Pasar Kemis Industrial Estate Jl Putera Utama No 10, Tangerang, 15560, Banten, Indonesia
Tel.: (62) 215903307
Web Site: https://www.inocycle.com
Year Founded: 2001
INOV—(INDO)
Rev.: $38,977,660
Assets: $64,818,349
Liabilities: $47,621,470
Net Worth: $17,196,879
Earnings: ($1,789,533)
Emp.: 265
Fiscal Year-end: 12/31/23
Polyester Product Mfr
N.A.I.C.S.: 325220
Jae-Hyuk Choi *(Pres)*

PT INTANWIJAYA INTERNASIONAL TBK
Wisma IWI 5th Floor Jl Arjuna Selatan Kav 75, West Jakarta, Jakarta, 11530, Indonesia
Tel.: (62) 215308637
Web Site: https://www.intanwijaya.com
Year Founded: 1982
INCI—(INDO)
Rev.: $24,555,249
Assets: $31,987,358
Liabilities: $3,634,606
Net Worth: $28,352,752
Earnings: $1,136,378
Emp.: 154
Fiscal Year-end: 12/31/23
Chemical Resin Mfr
N.A.I.C.S.: 325211
Tazran Tanmizi *(Chm)*

PT INTEGRA INDOCABINET TBK
Jalan Raya Betro 678 Sedati, Sidoarjo, 61253, East Java, Indonesia
Tel.: (62) 31891043436
Web Site: https://integragroup-indonesia.com
Year Founded: 1989
WOOD—(INDO)
Rev.: $141,961,042
Assets: $497,630,099
Liabilities: $217,617,874
Net Worth: $280,012,225
Earnings: $6,142,962
Emp.: 1,544

PT INTIKERAMIK ALAMASRI INDUSTRI TBK

Fiscal Year-end: 12/31/23
Furniture Mfr
N.A.I.C.S.: 321999

Subsidiaries:

P.T. Intera Indonesia   (1)
Jl Raya Betro 678, Sedati, Sidoarjo, 61253, East Java, Indonesia
Tel.: (62) 318910434
Wood Product Mfr & Distr
N.A.I.C.S.: 321211

P.T. Interkraft   (1)
Jl Raya Babat Jombang 678, Ds Dradah Kec Kedungpring Babat Lamongan, East Java, 62272, Indonesia
Tel.: (62) 318910434
Wood Product Mfr & Distr
N.A.I.C.S.: 321211

P.T. Intertrend Utama   (1)
Jl Industri 28 Buduran, Sidoarjo, 61252, East Java, Indonesia
Tel.: (62) 31894949192
Wood Product Mfr & Distr
N.A.I.C.S.: 321211

PT INTERNATIONAL DEVELOPMENT CORPORATION LTD.
Suites 3412-3413 34/F China Merchants Tower Shun Tak Centre, 168-200 Connaught Road, Central, China (Hong Kong)
Tel.: (852) 2 207 9500
Web Site: http://www.ptcorp.com.hk
0372—(HKG)
Rev.: $189,370,629
Assets: $101,769,992
Liabilities: $9,530,203
Net Worth: $92,239,789
Earnings: $21,469,108
Emp.: 35
Fiscal Year-end: 03/31/21
Investment Management
N.A.I.C.S.: 523940
Louis Man Chun Ching *(Chm & Mng Dir)*

Subsidiaries:

Cupral Group Ltd.   (1)
2 Berners Lee Way TeesAMP Riverside Park West, Middlesbrough, TS2 1ED, United Kingdom
Tel.: (44) 1642989739
Web Site: https://www.cupralgroup.com
Copper Products Mfr & Distr
N.A.I.C.S.: 331420

PT INTI BANGUN SEJAHTERA TBK
Jalan Riau No 23 Menteng, Jakarta Pusat, 10350, Indonesia
Tel.: (62) 2131935919
Web Site: https://www.ibstower.com
Year Founded: 2006
IBST—(INDO)
Rev.: $72,067,553
Assets: $643,712,587
Liabilities: $235,926,139
Net Worth: $407,786,449
Earnings: $2,486,885
Emp.: 298
Fiscal Year-end: 12/31/23
Telecommunication Servicesb
N.A.I.C.S.: 517810
Andrie Tjioe *(Chm)*

PT INTIKERAMIK ALAMASRI INDUSTRI TBK
Bidakara Tower 2 1st Floor Gatot Subroto Street Kav 71-73, Jakarta, 12870, Indonesia
Tel.: (62) 2183700435
Web Site: https://intikeramik.com
Year Founded: 1991
IKAI—(INDO)
Rev.: $13,533,061

PT INTIKERAMIK ALAMASRI INDUSTRI TBK

PT Intikeramik Alamasri Industri Tbk—(Continued)
Assets: $76,909,041
Liabilities: $27,933,042
Net Worth: $48,975,999
Earnings: $438,709
Emp.: 41
Fiscal Year-end: 12/31/23
Ceramic Product Mfr & Distr
N.A.I.C.S.: 327110
Teuku Johas Raffli *(Chm)*

Subsidiaries:

PT Hotel Properti Internasional (1)
Jl Salak No 38-40, Bogor, 16128, Jawa barat, Indonesia
Tel.: (62) 2517565111
Hotel Operator
N.A.I.C.S.: 721110

PT INTILAND DEVELOPMENT TBK.

Intiland Tower Penthouse Floor Jl Jend Sudirman 32, Jakarta, 10220, Indonesia
Tel.: (62) 215701912
Web Site: https://www.intiland.com
DILD—(INDO)
Rev.: $253,709,306
Assets: $948,377,795
Liabilities: $523,723,353
Net Worth: $424,654,442
Earnings: $49,226,362
Emp.: 987
Fiscal Year-end: 12/31/23
Property Development Services
N.A.I.C.S.: 531312
Utama Gondokusumo *(Vice Chm & Chief Comm & Svcs Officer)*

Subsidiaries:

P.T. Mutiara Raga Indah (1)
JL Pantai Mutiara Pluit Dki Jakarta, Pejagalan Penjaringan, Jakarta Utara, 14450, Indonesia
Tel.: (62) 216697146
Fitness Center Services
N.A.I.C.S.: 713940

P.T. Perkasalestari Permai (1)
Jl Marsekal Suryadharma Blok A No 1, Tangerang, 15129, Banten, Indonesia
Tel.: (62) 2155913456
Web Site: https://aeropolis.co.id
Real Estate Property Services
N.A.I.C.S.: 531190

P.T. Perkebunan dan Industri Segajung (1)
Jalan Raya Tulis-Bandar Tulis, Batang Regency, 51261, Central Java, Indonesia
Tel.: (62) 81908310111
Web Site: https://www.batangindustrialpark.com
Real Estate Investment Services
N.A.I.C.S.: 531190

P.T. Sinar Cemerlang Gemilang (1)
Spazio 8th Floor Jl Mayjend Yono Soewoyo Kav 3, Surabaya, 60226, Indonesia
Tel.: (62) 3199000980
Web Site: https://grahagolf.com
Real Estate Services
N.A.I.C.S.: 531190

PT Gandaria Permai (1)
Jl KH M Syafi i Hadzami No 1, Jakarta, 12240, Indonesia
Tel.: (62) 217237878
Property Development Services
N.A.I.C.S.: 531390

PT Grande Family View (1)
Boulevard Famili Utara Graha Famili Blok O, Jl Mayjend Sungkono Kav B5, Surabaya, 60227, East Java, Indonesia
Tel.: (62) 3199020888
Sales Range: $25-49.9 Million
Emp.: 50
Property Development Services
N.A.I.C.S.: 531390
Sinarto Darmawan *(Mng Dir)*

PT INTINUSA SELAREKSA TBK

Wisma Indocement 6th Floor Jl Jend Sudirman Kav 70-71, Jakarta, 12910, Indonesia
Tel.: (62) 218754761
Web Site: http://www.intinusa.com
Year Founded: 2002
INSA—(INDO)
Granite & Marble Distr
N.A.I.C.S.: 444180
Martinus Murdianto *(Sec)*

PT INTRACO PENTA TBK

Jl Raya Cakung Cilincing Km 3 5, Jakarta, 14130, Indonesia
Tel.: (62) 214401408
Web Site: https://intracopenta.com
Year Founded: 1970
INTA—(INDO)
Rev.: $66,130,900
Assets: $218,667,800
Liabilities: $405,345,000
Net Worth: ($186,677,200)
Earnings: ($9,892,300)
Emp.: 386
Fiscal Year-end: 12/31/22
Construction Equipment Mktg Services
N.A.I.C.S.: 238910
Petrus Halim *(Chm)*

Subsidiaries:

P.T. Inta Sarana Infrastruktur (1)
Jl Raya Cakung Cilincing Km 35, Jakarta, 14130, Indonesia
Tel.: (62) 214401408
Real Estate Manangement Services
N.A.I.C.S.: 531311

P.T. Pratama Wana Motor (1)
Jl MT Haryono No 30, Damai Kec Kota Balikpapan, Balikpapan, Kalimantan Timur, Indonesia
Tel.: (62) 5428709582
Real Estate Manangement Services
N.A.I.C.S.: 531311

PT Intan Baru Prana Tbk (1)
Jl Raya Cakung Cilincing KM 3 5, Jakarta, 14130, Indonesia
Tel.: (62) 214401408
Web Site: http://www.ibf.co.id
Rev.: $3,242,096
Assets: $52,180,706
Liabilities: $108,515,021
Net Worth: ($56,334,315)
Earnings: ($4,150,638)
Emp.: 12
Fiscal Year-end: 12/31/2022
Consumer Financial Services
N.A.I.C.S.: 522291
Carolina Dina Rusdiana *(Chm)*

PT ISLAND CONCEPTS INDONESIA TBK

Jimbaran HUB Jl Karangmas, Badung, Kuta, 80361, Bali, Indonesia
Tel.: (62) 3616202424
Web Site: https://islandconcepts.id
Year Founded: 2001
ICON—(INDO)
Rev.: $11,778,370
Assets: $23,361,644
Liabilities: $9,384,263
Net Worth: $13,977,381
Earnings: ($335,235)
Emp.: 45
Fiscal Year-end: 12/31/23
Tourism & Accommodation Management Services
N.A.I.C.S.: 561520
Dodi Prawira Amtar *(Chm)*

PT ITAMA RANORAYA TBK

Mt Haryono Square Lt I Unit 101 Jl Otto Iskandardinata Raya No 390, Jakarta Timur, 13330, Indonesia
Tel.: (62) 2129067207
Web Site: https://www.itama.co.id
Year Founded: 2000

IRRA—(INDO)
Rev.: $45,217,968
Assets: $68,764,073
Liabilities: $38,943,546
Net Worth: $29,820,527
Earnings: $337,585
Emp.: 106
Fiscal Year-end: 12/31/23
Medical Device Distr
N.A.I.C.S.: 423450
Heru Firdausi Syarif *(Pres)*

PT ITSEC ASIA TBK

Noble House Level 11, Jakarta, 12950, Indonesia
Tel.: (62) 2129783050
Web Site: https://www.itsec.asia
Year Founded: 2010
CYBR—(INDO)
Rev.: $12,567,763
Assets: $11,425,773
Liabilities: $13,962,063
Net Worth: ($2,536,290)
Earnings: ($729,421)
Emp.: 270
Fiscal Year-end: 12/31/22
Information Technology Services
N.A.I.C.S.: 541512
Joseph Edi Hut Lumban Gaol *(Pres)*

PT JABABEKA TBK

Mayfair Building Jl Wahidin Sudirohusodo Kav Oasis Blok E, Kota Jababeka Cikarang, Bekasi, 17550, West Java, Indonesia
Tel.: (62) 218934580
Web Site: https://www.jababeka.com
KIJA—(INDO)
Rev.: $213,775,413
Assets: $840,806,450
Liabilities: $390,682,812
Net Worth: $450,123,638
Earnings: $34,328,799
Emp.: 736
Fiscal Year-end: 12/31/23
Property Development Services
N.A.I.C.S.: 531312
T. Budianto Liman *(Chm)*

Subsidiaries:

P.T. Infrastuktur Cakrawala Telekomunikasi (1)
Jl Jababeka IV Blok B No 12 Jababeka Industrial Estate Cikarang, Bekasi, Indonesia
Tel.: (62) 8118056321
Web Site: https://www.ictel.co.id
Fiber Optic Network Technology Services
N.A.I.C.S.: 517111

P.T. Mitra Pengembang Kawasan (1)
Jababeka Center Hollywood Plaza No 10-12 Jl H Usmar Ismail, Indonesia Movieland Kota Jababeka Cikarang, Bekasi, 17550, West Java, Indonesia
Tel.: (62) 218934580
Web Site: https://www.mpkindonesia.com
Civil Construction Services
N.A.I.C.S.: 518210

PT. Graha Buana Cikarang (1)
Jl H Usmar Ismail Hollywood Plaza No 10-12, Cikarang Kabupaten, Bekasi, 17550, West Java, Indonesia
Tel.: (62) 218934350
Web Site: http://www.jababeka.com
Emp.: 300
Real Estate Development Services
N.A.I.C.S.: 531311
Febi Yanti *(Mgr-Sls)*

Subsidiary (Domestic):

PT. Padang Golf Cikarang (2)
Lemahabang Cibarusah Street, PO Box 17, Cikarang Baru, Bekasi, 17530, West Java, Indonesia
Tel.: (62) 218936148
Web Site: https://www.jababekagolf.co.id
Emp.: 700
Golf Course Operation Services
N.A.I.C.S.: 713910

INTERNATIONAL PUBLIC

PT. Jababeka Infrastruktur (1)
Tel.: (62) 218934580
Indoor Recreational Services
N.A.I.C.S.: 236220

PT. Metropark Condominium Indah (1)
Jl Niaga Raya Blok CC No 2, Cikarang Baru, Bekasi, 17550, West Java, Indonesia
Tel.: (62) 2189840550
Web Site: http://www.jababeka.com
Residential Property Development Services
N.A.I.C.S.: 236117
Doddy Siagian *(Mgr-Ops)*

PT JAKARTA INTERNATIONAL HOTELS & DEVELOPMENT TBK

Artha Graha Building 15th Floor Jl Jendral Sudirman Kav 5253, Jakarta, 12190, Indonesia
Tel.: (62) 215152555
Web Site: https://www.jihd.co.id
JIHD—(INDO)
Rev.: $63,438,480
Assets: $470,356,110
Liabilities: $128,865,450
Net Worth: $341,490,660
Earnings: ($4,377,870)
Emp.: 1,715
Fiscal Year-end: 12/31/20
Home Management Services
N.A.I.C.S.: 561110
Hartono Tjahjadi Adiwana *(Co-Chm)*

Subsidiaries:

P.T. Pacific Place Jakarta (1)
Jl Jend Sudirman No 52-53, Senayan Kebayoran Baru, Jakarta Selatan, 12190, DKI Jakarta, Indonesia
Tel.: (62) 2151402828
Web Site: https://pacificplace.co.id
Civil Construction Services
N.A.I.C.S.: 518210

PT Artha Telekomindo (1)
Control Building Jl Jend Sudirman kav 52-53 RT 5/RW 3, Sudirman Central Business Dist Senayan Kby Baru Kota Jakarta Selatan, Jakarta, 12190, Indonesia
Tel.: (62) 2125525100
Web Site: https://www.arthatel.co.id
Information Technology Services
N.A.I.C.S.: 541511

PT Danayasa Arthatama Tbk (1)
12th Floor Artha Graha Building Jl Jendral Sudirman kav 52-53, Jakarta, 12190, Indonesia
Tel.: (62) 215152390
Web Site: https://www.scbd.com
Rev.: $72,680,617
Assets: $404,828,467
Liabilities: $103,074,257
Net Worth: $301,754,210
Earnings: $15,842,944
Emp.: 714
Fiscal Year-end: 12/31/2017
Real Estate Development Services
N.A.I.C.S.: 531390
Tuan Santoso Gunara *(Chm)*

PT JAKARTA KYOEI STEEL WORKS TBK

Jalan Rawa Terate II No 1 Kawasan Industri Pulo Gadung, Jakarta, 13930, Indonesia
Tel.: (62) 4602832
Year Founded: 1975
JKSW—(INDO)
Rev.: $759,997
Assets: $10,295,678
Liabilities: $42,368,288
Net Worth: ($32,072,611)
Earnings: ($5,443)
Emp.: 4
Fiscal Year-end: 12/31/23
Steel Mfr & Distr
N.A.I.C.S.: 331221
H. Sumedi *(Commissioner)*

PT JAKARTA SETIABUDI IN-

AND PRIVATE COMPANIES

TERNASIONAL TBK
Setiabudi 2 Building 3A Floor Jl H R Rasuna Said Kav 62, Jakarta, 12920, Indonesia
Tel.: (62) 215220568
Web Site: https://www.jsi.co.id
Year Founded: 1975
JSPT—(INDO)
Rev.: $115,261,828
Assets: $407,421,787
Liabilities: $236,123,119
Net Worth: $171,298,668
Earnings: $15,243,347
Emp.: 1,911
Fiscal Year-end: 12/31/23
Real Estate Development Services
N.A.I.C.S.: 531390
Jefri Darmadi *(Chm)*

Subsidiaries:

P.T. Skyline Building (1)
Jl M H Thamrin No 9, Jakarta, 10340, Indonesia
Tel.: (62) 213141708
Real Estate Investment Services
N.A.I.C.S.: 531190

PT Hotel Cikini Realty (1)
Mercure Conventon Centre Jl Pantai Indah Taman Impian Jaya Ancol, Jakarta, Indonesia
Tel.: (62) 216406000
Real Estate Manangement Services
N.A.I.C.S.: 531210
Andi Sofyan *(Pres)*

PT Puri Prima Development (1)
Maisonete Mega Kebon Jeruk Unit 1-4 Jl Raya Joglo No 48, Jakarta, 11640, Indonesia
Tel.: (62) 215870077
Real Estate Manangement Services
N.A.I.C.S.: 531210

PT Skyline Building (1)
Jl M H Thamrin No 9, Jakarta, 10340, Indonesia
Tel.: (62) 213141708
Real Estate Manangement Services
N.A.I.C.S.: 531210
Masaaki Tajima *(Pres)*

PT JANU PUTRA SEJAHTERA TBK.
Casa Grande Shophouse No 35 North Ring Road Maguwoharjo, Sleman Daerah, Depok, Yogyakarta, Indonesia
Tel.: (62) 274871163
Web Site:
https://www.januputrasejahtera.com
Year Founded: 2007
AYAM—(INDO)
Poultry Farming Product Distr
N.A.I.C.S.: 424440
Sri Mulyani *(Pres & CEO)*

PT JAPFA COMFEED INDONESIA TBK
Wisma Millenia Lt 7 Jl M T Haryono Kav 16, Jakarta, 12810, Indonesia
Tel.: (62) 2128545680
Web Site:
https://www.japfacomfeed.co.id
Year Founded: 1971
JPFA—(INDO)
Rev.: $3,323,362,816
Assets: $2,215,066,449
Liabilities: $1,295,047,702
Net Worth: $920,018,747
Earnings: $61,428,175
Emp.: 30,372
Fiscal Year-end: 12/31/23
Animal Feed Mfr; Chicken Breeding; Poultry Processing; Aquaculture Farming
N.A.I.C.S.: 311611
Handojo Santosa *(Chm)*

Subsidiaries:

Japfa Ltd (1)
391B Orchard Road 18-08, Ngee Ann City Tower B, Singapore, 238874, Singapore
Tel.: (65) 67350031
Web Site: https://www.japfa.com
Rev.: $4,428,948,000
Assets: $3,083,821,000
Liabilities: $1,891,284,000
Net Worth: $1,192,537,000
Earnings: ($5,966,000)
Emp.: 37,000
Fiscal Year-end: 12/31/2023
Food Mfr Including Milk, Poultry & Beef Products
N.A.I.C.S.: 311999
Yong Nang Tan *(CEO)*

P.T. Vaksindo Satwa Nusantara (1)
Wisma Milenia M T Haryono Kav 16, Jakarta, 12810, Indonesia
Tel.: (62) 2128545680
Web Site: https://www.vaksindo.co.id
Animal Pharmaceutical Mfr & Distr
N.A.I.C.S.: 325412

PT Agrinusa Jaya Santosa (1)
Kedoya Elok Plaza DE-12 Jalan Panjang RT19 RW04 South Kedoya, Kebon Jeruk, Jakarta, 11520, Indonesia
Tel.: (62) 215812819
Web Site: https://www.agrinusa.com
Poultry Farm Operator
N.A.I.C.S.: 112390

PT Ciomas Adisatwa (1)
Grha Praba Samanta, Jl Daan Mogot Km 12 No 9, 11730, Jakarta, Indonesia
Tel.: (62) 215455665
Poultry Processing
N.A.I.C.S.: 311615

PT Indopell Raya (1)
Jl Ir Sutami Km 18 2 Way Gubak, Panjang, 35244, Indonesia
Tel.: (62) 721350181
Sales Range: $25-49.9 Million
Emp.: 45
Animal Feed Mfr
N.A.I.C.S.: 311119

PT Japfa Comfeed Indonesia Tbk - WISMA JCI Division
Jl HRM Mangundiprojo Km 3 5, Sidoarjo, 61252, East Java, Indonesia
Tel.: (62) 318921961
Animal Feed Mfr
N.A.I.C.S.: 311119

PT Japfafood Nusantara (1)
Graha Praba Samanta Jl Daan Mogot Km 12 No 9 Cengkareng, 11730, Jakarta, Indonesia
Tel.: (62) 21 5448710
Web Site: http://www.japfacomfeed.co.id
Poultry Processing & Hatcheries
N.A.I.C.S.: 311615

PT Karya Ciptanyata Wisesa (1)
Wisma Millenia lt 7 Jl M.T. Haryono Kav 16, 12810, Jakarta, Indonesia
Tel.: (62) 21 285 45640
Web Site: http://www.japfacomfeed.co.id
Poultry Processing & Feed
N.A.I.C.S.: 311615

PT Multibreeder Adirama Indonesia Tbk (1)
Grha Praba Samanta Jl Daan Mogot Km 12 No 9, Cengkareng, 11730, Jakarta, Indonesia
Tel.: (62) 215448710
Web Site: http://www.japfacomfeed.co.id
Poultry Processing
N.A.I.C.S.: 311615

PT Supra Sumber Cipta (1)
Graha Praba Samanta Jl Daan, Mogot Km 12 No 9, 11730, Jakarta, Indonesia
Tel.: (62) 215448648
Agricultural Marketing & Commodities regulation
N.A.I.C.S.: 926140

PT Suri Tani Pemuka (1)
46/100 Jl Raya Situbondo Yos Sudarso, Kalipuro, Banyuwangi, Indonesia
Tel.: (62) 333423255
Animal Feed Mfr
N.A.I.C.S.: 311119

Vaksindo Animal Health Pvt. Ltd. (1)
H No8-7-89/C/P-II/125 Ground Floor, Chaitanya Nagar Kharmanghat beside Sampoorna Hotel lane Saroomagar, Telangana, 500070, India
Tel.: (91) 4035858744
Web Site: https://www.vaksindo-india.com
Animal Pharmaceutical Mfr & Distr
N.A.I.C.S.: 325412

PT JASA ARMADA INDONESIA TBK
Gedung Rukindo Jl Raya Ancol Baru Ancol Timur, Jakarta, 14430, Indonesia
Tel.: (62) 214306789
Web Site:
https://www.ipcmarine.co.id
Year Founded: 1960
IPCM—(INDO)
Rev.: $73,936,624
Assets: $98,847,424
Liabilities: $18,288,072
Net Worth: $80,559,352
Earnings: $10,238,570
Emp.: 788
Fiscal Year-end: 12/31/23
Marine Shipping Services
N.A.I.C.S.: 488510
Amri Yusuf *(Pres)*

PT JASA BERDIKARI LOGISTICS TBK
Jln Kopi No 4D Lt 2 Roa Malaka, Tambora, Jakarta Barat, 11230, Indonesia
Tel.: (62) 216912287
Web Site:
https://www.jasaberdikari.co.id
Year Founded: 2007
LAJU—(INDO)
Rev.: $10,831,019
Assets: $11,777,728
Liabilities: $3,401,967
Net Worth: $8,375,761
Earnings: $830,054
Emp.: 107
Fiscal Year-end: 12/31/23
Logistic Services
N.A.I.C.S.: 541614

PT JASNITA TELEKOMINDO TBK
E-Trade Building Lt 5 Jl K H Wahid Hasyim No 55, Kebon Sirih, Jakarta Pusat, 10350, Indonesia
Tel.: (62) 2128565288
Web Site: https://www.jasnita.com
Year Founded: 1996
JAST—(INDO)
Rev.: $4,300,182
Assets: $7,986,609
Liabilities: $4,077,857
Net Worth: $3,908,753
Earnings: ($562,876)
Fiscal Year-end: 12/31/20
Software Development Services
N.A.I.C.S.: 541511
Yentoro Hadiwibowo *(Pres)*

PT JAYA AGRA WATTIE TBK
Gedung Graha Dinamika 25th Floor Jl Tanah Abang II No 49 - 51, Jakarta, 10160, Indonesia
Tel.: (62) 213505906
Web Site: https://www.jawattie.com
Year Founded: 1921
JAWA—(INDO)
Rev.: $58,196,096
Assets: $237,435,357
Liabilities: $173,691,432
Net Worth: $63,743,925
Earnings: ($19,732,232)
Emp.: 7,148
Fiscal Year-end: 12/31/23
Rubber Oil Palm Farming Services
N.A.I.C.S.: 111120
Harli Wijayadi *(Sec & Dir-Fin)*

PT JAYA TRISHINDO TBK

PT JAYA BERSAMA INDO TBK
Business Park Kebon Jeruk Blok C2 No 1 Jalan Meruya Ilir, No 88 Kelurahan Meruya Utara, Jakarta, Kembangan, Indonesia
Tel.: (62) 2158901633
Web Site: https://www.ptjbi.id
Year Founded: 2003
DUCK—(INDO)
Rev.: $51,575,782
Assets: $101,921,072
Liabilities: $38,757,034
Net Worth: $63,164,038
Earnings: $10,523,709
Emp.: 1,988
Fiscal Year-end: 12/31/19
Restaurant Operators
N.A.I.C.S.: 722511
Limpa Itsin Bachtiar *(CEO)*

PT JAYA PARI STEEL TBK
Jl Margomulyo No 4, Po Box 1092, Tandes, Surabaya, 60183, Indonesia
Tel.: (62) 31 7491288
Web Site:
http://www.jayaparisteel.co.id
Year Founded: 1973
Rev.: $17,102,708
Assets: $25,018,290
Liabilities: $4,635,368
Net Worth: $20,382,922
Earnings: ($1,042,593)
Emp.: 250
Fiscal Year-end: 12/31/17
Steel Product Mfr & Distr
N.A.I.C.S.: 331110
Yurnalis Ilyas *(Dir-Fin & HR)*

PT JAYA SUKSES MAKMUR SENTOSA TBK
Jl Central Square C3 Shophouse Jl Ahmad Yani 41-43, Gedangan Village Gedangan District, Sidoarjo, 60189, Indonesia
Tel.: (62) 318544400
RISE—(INDO)
Rev.: $31,978,235
Assets: $271,216,095
Liabilities: $41,074,484
Net Worth: $230,141,611
Earnings: $3,584,576
Emp.: 441
Fiscal Year-end: 12/31/22
Real Estate Manangement Services
N.A.I.C.S.: 531390
Belinda Natalia *(Chm, Pres & Dir)*

PT JAYA SWARASA AGUNG TBK
Jalan Parung Panjang Raya No 68, Legok Kemuning, Tangerang, 15820, Banten, Indonesia
Tel.: (62) 213457591
Web Site:
https://www.taysbakers.com
Year Founded: 1998
TAYS—(INDO)
Rev.: $16,598,462
Assets: $26,737,601
Liabilities: $18,638,910
Net Worth: $8,098,691
Earnings: ($1,264,141)
Emp.: 150
Fiscal Year-end: 12/31/23
Snack Food Mfr & Distr
N.A.I.C.S.: 311919
Alexander Anwar *(Pres)*

PT JAYA TRISHINDO TBK
Perkantoran Grand Aries Niaga Jl Taman Aries Blok E1/1A, Jakarta Barat, 11620, Indonesia
Tel.: (62) 2158900022
HELI—(INDO)
Rev.: $4,486,177
Assets: $13,286,564

PT JAYA TRISHINDO TBK

PT Jaya Trishindo Tbk—(Continued)
Liabilities: $9,677,755
Net Worth: $3,608,809
Earnings: $43,103
Emp.: 3
Fiscal Year-end: 12/31/23
Oil Transportation Services
N.A.I.C.S.: 481112
Gouw Erene Goetama *(Pres & Commissioner)*

Subsidiaries:

P.T. Komala Indonesia (1)
Rukan Grand Aries Niaga Jl Taman Aries Blok E1 No 1A, Kembangan Kota Jakarta Barat DKI, Jakarta, 11620, Indonesia
Tel.: (62) 2158900300
Web Site: https://www.flykomala.com
Aircraft Engine Mfr & Distr
N.A.I.C.S.: 336412

PT JOBUBU JARUM MINAHASA TBK

Jl Prapanca Raya No 41 RT 2/RW 5 Pulo Kec Kby Baru, Kota Jakarta Selatan Daerah Khusus Ibukota, Jakarta, 12160, Indonesia
Tel.: (62) 2129307799
Web Site: https://www.jobubu.com
Year Founded: 2018
BEER—(INDO)
Rev.: $5,850,180
Assets: $16,113,494
Liabilities: $973,462
Net Worth: $15,140,033
Earnings: $1,059,474
Emp.: 49
Fiscal Year-end: 12/31/23
Beverage Product Mfr
N.A.I.C.S.: 312111
Audy Charles Lieke *(Chm)*

PT KABELINDO MURNI TBK.

Jl Rawa Girang No 2 Kawasan Industri Pulogadung, Jakarta, 13930, Indonesia
Tel.: (62) 214609065
Web Site: https://www.kabelindo.co.id
Year Founded: 1972
KBLM—(INDO)
Rev.: $107,054,809
Assets: $103,737,911
Liabilities: $21,605,104
Net Worth: $82,132,807
Earnings: $1,997,942
Emp.: 274
Fiscal Year-end: 12/31/23
Wire & Cable Mfr
N.A.I.C.S.: 335921
Elly Soepono *(Chm)*

PT KALBE FARMA TBK.

Gedung Kalbe Jl Let Jend Suprapto Kav 4, PO Box 3105, Jakarta, 10510, Indonesia
Tel.: (62) 2142873888
Web Site: https://www.kalbe.co.id
Year Founded: 1966
KLBF—(INDO)
Rev.: $1,977,366,767
Assets: $1,757,118,478
Liabilities: $255,704,248
Net Worth: $1,501,414,229
Earnings: $180,429,609
Emp.: 13,205
Fiscal Year-end: 12/31/23
Pharmaceutical & Nutritional Product Mfr
N.A.I.C.S.: 325412
Bernadus Karmin Winata *(Sec)*

Subsidiaries:

Innogene Kalbiotech Pte Ltd (1)
21 Bukit Batok Cresent #28-79 WCEGA Tower, Singapore, 658065, Singapore
Tel.: (65) 65010400
Web Site: http://www.innogene-kalboitech.com
Pharmaceuticals Mfr & Distr
N.A.I.C.S.: 325412

Kalbe International Pte. Ltd. (1)
21 Bukit Batok Crescent 27-79 WCEGA Tower, Singapore, 658065, Singapore
Tel.: (65) 65010419
Web Site: http://www.kalbeinternational.com
Pharmaceuticals Distr
N.A.I.C.S.: 424210

Kalbe Malaysia Sdn. Bhd. (1)
Suite 2A 3-2 Block 2A Plaza Sentral, Jalan Stesen Sentral 5, 50470, Kuala Lumpur, Malaysia
Tel.: (60) 129211588
Web Site: https://kalbe.com.my
Pharmaceutical & Medical Product Whslr
N.A.I.C.S.: 424210

Kalbe Vision Pte. Ltd. (1)
21 Bukit Batok Crescent 27-79 WCEGA Tower, Singapore, 658065, Singapore
Tel.: (65) 65010419
Ophthalmic Product Distr
N.A.I.C.S.: 423460

P.T. Agroveta Husada Dharma (1)
Kalbe Business Innovation Center Lt 4 Jl Pulogadung No 23 Kav II G5, Kawasan Industri Pulogadung, Jakarta Timur, 13930, Indonesia
Tel.: (62) 2150867668
Web Site: https://agroveta.co.id
Pharmaceutical Mfr & Distr
N.A.I.C.S.: 325412

P.T. Emos Global Digital (1)
Enseval III Building 1st Floor Unit 1 K Jalan Pulo Lentut number 12, Village/Kelurahan Rawa Terate Kec Cakung City of Adm, East Jakarta, 13920, DKI Jakarta, Indonesia
Tel.: (62) 2146822422
Web Site: https://www.emos.id
Health Product Distr
N.A.I.C.S.: 424210

P.T. Forsta Kalmedic Global (1)
Pulogadung Street No 23 Kav No II G 5 Lt 2 Unit 2A, Jakarta Industrial Estate Pulogadung Jatinegara Subdistrict Cakung District, East Jakarta, 13930, DKI Jakarta, Indonesia
Tel.: (62) 2150867788
Web Site: https://www.forsta.co.id
Medical & Diagnostic Device Mfr
N.A.I.C.S.: 334510

P.T. Global Parama Medika (1)
Jl Jend A Yani No 2 Pulomas, Jakarta Timur, 13210, Indonesia
Tel.: (62) 214757777
Pharmaceutical Product Mfr & Distr
N.A.I.C.S.: 325412

P.T. Global Usadha Arana (1)
Jl Jend A Yani No 2 Pulomas, Jakarta Timur, 13210, Indonesia
Tel.: (62) 214757777
Pharmaceutical Product Mfr & Distr
N.A.I.C.S.: 325412

P.T. Kalbe Morinaga Indonesia (1)
Kawasan Industri Indotaisei Sektor 1A Blok Q1, Kalihurip Cikampek, Karawang, 41373, West Java, Indonesia
Tel.: (62) 2165311234
Nutritional Product Mfr
N.A.I.C.S.: 325412
Irawati Setiady *(Pres)*

P.T. Mostrans Global Digilog (1)
Jl Pulo lentut no 12 Kawasan Industri Pulo Gadung, Jakarta, 13920, Indonesia
Tel.: (62) 2146823130
Web Site: https://mostrans.co.id
Sea Transportation Services
N.A.I.C.S.: 541614

PT Bifarma Adiluhung (1)
Jl Jend A Yani No 2 Pulomas, Jakarta Timur, 13210, Indonesia
Tel.: (62) 214202939
Health Screening Services
N.A.I.C.S.: 621999

Subsidiary (Domestic):

PT Kalgen DNA (2)
Jl Jend A Yani No 2 Pulomas, Jakarta Timur, 13210, Indonesia
Tel.: (62) 2147860173
Health Screening Services
N.A.I.C.S.: 621999

PT Bintang Toedjoe (1)
Jl Jend Ahmad Yani No 2 Pulomas, Jakarta Timur, Jakarta, 13210, Indonesia
Tel.: (62) 214757777
Web Site: https://www.bintang7.com
Energy Drinks Distr
N.A.I.C.S.: 424490

PT Dankos Farma (1)
Jalan Rawa Gatel Block III S Kav 37-38, Jatinegara Cakung Kota, Jakarta, Indonesia
Tel.: (62) 215951630
Pharmaceuticals Product Mfr
N.A.I.C.S.: 325412

PT Enseval Putera Megatrading Tbk. (1)
Jl Pulo Lentut No 10 Kawasan Industri Pulo Gadung, Jakarta, 13920, Indonesia (58.19%)
Tel.: (62) 2146822422
Web Site: https://www.enseval.com
Rev.: $2,802,748,822
Assets: $1,040,235,685
Liabilities: $326,473,096
Net Worth: $713,762,589
Earnings: $84,259,088
Emp.: 4,118
Fiscal Year-end: 12/31/2022
Pharmaceutical Distribution & Logistics Services
N.A.I.C.S.: 424210
Handi Halim *(Dir-IT, Ops & Legal)*

Subsidiary (Domestic):

PT Enseval Medika Prima (2)
Jl Pulo lentut No 12 INDUSTRIAL ESTATE JIEP RW 3 Rw Terate RW 3, Rawa Terate Cakung, Jakarta, 13920, Indonesia
Tel.: (62) 2146823234
Web Site: https://emp.co.id
Sales Range: $100-124.9 Million
Emp.: 400
Pharmaceuticals Product Mfr
N.A.I.C.S.: 325412
Taruna Widjaja *(Pres)*

PT Global Chemindo Megatrading (2)
Jl Pulokambing Raya Kav II E No 8 Kawasan Industri Pulogadung, Jakarta Timur, Jakarta, 13920, Indonesia
Tel.: (62) 2146830028
Pharmaceutical Products Distr
N.A.I.C.S.: 424210

PT Millenia Dharma Insani (2)
Kawasan Industri Pulo Gadung, Jl Pulo Lentut No 12, Jakarta Timur, 13920, Indonesia
Tel.: (62) 2180625506
Web Site: http://www.mitrasana.co.id
General Medical Services
N.A.I.C.S.: 621111

Subsidiary (Non-US):

PT Renalmed Tiara Utama (2)
Tel.: (62) 214609046
Web Site: http://www.renalmed.co.id
Sales Range: $10-24.9 Million
Emp.: 20
Hemodialysis Services
N.A.I.C.S.: 621492

Subsidiary (Domestic):

PT Tri Sapta Jaya (2)
Enseval III Building Jalan Pulolentut Industrial Area No12 RW 3, Rw Terate District Pulo Gadung, Jakarta, 13930, Indonesia
Tel.: (62) 214618737
Web Site: https://www.trisaptajaya.co.id
Pharmaceutical Products Distr
N.A.I.C.S.: 424210

PT Finusolprima Farma Internasional (1)
Jl Raya Bekasi Km 28 5 Kalibaru, Bekasi, West Java, Indonesia
Tel.: (62) 218842253
Pharmaceuticals Product Mfr
N.A.I.C.S.: 325412

INTERNATIONAL PUBLIC

Poo Shyue Shyong *(Pres)*

PT Global Onkolab Farma (1)
Gedung Dankos Jl Rawa Gatel Blok IIIS Kav 36, Kawasan Industri Pulo Gadung, Jakarta Timur, Indonesia
Tel.: (62) 214600158
Pharmaceuticals Mfr
N.A.I.C.S.: 325412

PT Hale International (1)
Jl Raya Pemuda Kav 88A Desa Curug Gn Sindur, Bogor, Indonesia
Tel.: (62) 2518604691
Health Drink Mfr
N.A.I.C.S.: 312111

PT Hexpharm Jaya Laboratories (1)
Kem Tower Jalan Selangit RW 10, South Gunung Sahari, Jakarta, 10510, Indonesia
Tel.: (62) 2165704100
Web Site: http://www.hexpharmjaya.com
Pharmaceuticals Product Mfr
N.A.I.C.S.: 325412

PT Kalbe Farma Tbk. - Bekasi Factory (1)
Jl M H Thamrin Blok A3-1, Kawasan Industri Delta Sillicon Lippo Cikarang, Bekasi, 17550, Indonesia
Tel.: (62) 2189907333
Pharmaceuticals Mfr
N.A.I.C.S.: 325412

PT Kalbe Genexine Biologics (1)
Plaza Property Lt 3 Komplek Pertokoan Pulomas Blok VIII No 1, Jl Perintis Kemerdekaan Pulogadung, Jakarta Timur, 13210, Indonesia
Tel.: (62) 2147860033
Pharmaceuticals Mfr
N.A.I.C.S.: 325412

PT Kalbe Milko Indonesia (1)
Jl Mayjend HR Edi Sukma KM 15, Ciherang Pondok - Caringin - Kab, Bogor, 16730, West Java, Indonesia
Tel.: (62) 2518291600
Web Site: https://www.kalbemilko.com
Food Service
N.A.I.C.S.: 722330

PT Kalbio Global Medika (1)
Delta Silicon 3 Industrial Zone Jl Soka Blok F19 No 002, Cicau - Central Cikarang Kab, Bekasi, 17530, West Java, Indonesia
Tel.: (62) 250943200
Web Site: https://kalbio.co.id
Pharmaceuticals Mfr
N.A.I.C.S.: 325412

PT Pharma Metric Laboratories (1)
Gedung Indra Sentral Unit R & T Jl Let Jend Suprapto No 60, Cempaka Putih, Jakarta Pusat, 10520, Indonesia
Tel.: (62) 214265310
Web Site: https://www.pharmametriclabs.com
Pharmaceutical Lab Services
N.A.I.C.S.: 621511
Marini Indarjanto *(Mgr-Mktg & BD)*

PT Saka Farma Laboratories (1)
Jl Jend A Yani No 2 Pulomas, Jakarta Timur, 13210, Indonesia
Tel.: (62) 2147866556
Pharmaceuticals Mfr
N.A.I.C.S.: 325412

PT Sanghiang Perkasa (1)
Gedung Graha Kirana Lt 5 Suite 501 Jl Yos Sudarso Kav 88, Jakarta, 14350, Utara, Indonesia
Tel.: (62) 2165311234
Web Site: https://kalbenutritionals.com
Nutritional Product Mfr
N.A.I.C.S.: 325412

Subsidiary (Domestic):

PT Karsa Lintas Buwana (2)
Gedung Tridana Lt 8 Jl Pulomas Selatan Kav 22, Jakarta Timur, 13210, Indonesia
Tel.: (62) 2129574880
E-Commerce Online Services
N.A.I.C.S.: 519290

Subsidiary (Domestic):

PT Cakra Radha Mustika (3)
Graha ganesha Lt 1 Jl Raya Bekasi KM 17

No 5, Jakarta Timur, Indonesia
Tel.: (62) 2146836226
Digital Marketing Services
N.A.I.C.S.: 541613

PT Karya Hasta Dinamika (3)
Gedung Cementaid Lt 3 Jl Raya Bekasi KM 17 No 5, Jakarta Timur, Indonesia
Tel.: (62) 2146000968
Home Delivery Services
N.A.I.C.S.: 492110

PT. Global Karsa Medika (1)
Jl Rawa Gelam IV No 6 Gedung A Lt 3, Kawasan Industri Pulo Gadung, Jakarta, 13930, Indonesia
Tel.: (62) 2146825686
Medical Device Distr
N.A.I.C.S.: 423450

PT KAPUAS PRIMA COAL TBK
Ruko Elang Laut Boulevard Blok A No 32-33 Jl Pantai Indah Selatan 1, Pantai Indah Kapuk, Jakarta Utara, 14460, Indonesia
Tel.: (62) 2129676236
Web Site:
  https://www.kapuasprima.co.id
Year Founded: 2005
ZINC—(INDO)
Rev.: $30,609,052
Assets: $169,052,888
Liabilities: $120,707,200
Net Worth: $48,345,688
Earnings: ($1,730,860)
Emp.: 392
Fiscal Year-end: 12/31/23
Metal Exploration Services
N.A.I.C.S.: 213114
Hendra Susanto William (CFO)

PT KARYA BERSAMA ANUGERAH TBK
Pam Tower 8th Floor Balikpapan Superblock, Jalan Jendral Sudirman No 47, Balikpapan, 76114, Indonesia
Tel.: (62) 811590878
Web Site: https://www.kbag.co.id
Year Founded: 2014
KBAG—(INDO)
Rev.: $3,066,220
Assets: $27,589,510
Liabilities: $2,872,566
Net Worth: $24,716,944
Earnings: ($610,891)
Emp.: 26
Fiscal Year-end: 12/31/23
Real Estate Services
N.A.I.C.S.: 531210
Nicholas Sumasto (Pres)

PT KEDAWUNG SETIA INDUSTRIAL TBK
Jl Mastrip 862 Warugunung Karangpilang, Surabaya, 60221, Indonesia
Tel.: (62) 317661971
Web Site:
  https://www.kedawungsetia.com
Year Founded: 1973
KDSI—(INDO)
Rev.: $138,171,007
Assets: $73,286,018
Liabilities: $22,350,618
Net Worth: $50,935,400
Earnings: $5,160,533
Emp.: 1,402
Fiscal Year-end: 12/31/23
Metal Kitchenware Mfr
N.A.I.C.S.: 332215
Ali Sugiharto Wibisono (Chm)

Subsidiaries:

PT KedawungSetia Corrugated Carton Box Industrial (1)
Jl Mastrip 862 Warugunung Karangpilang, Surabaya, East Java, Indonesia
Tel.: (62) 3176619716
Web Site: https://www.ksccb.com
Corrugated Carton Box & Egg Tray Mfr
N.A.I.C.S.: 322211

PT KEDOYA ADYARAYA TBK
Rs Grha Kedoya Jalan Panjang Arteri No 26, Kedoya Utara Kebon Jeruk, Jakarta Barat, 11520, Indonesia
Tel.: (62) 150789
RSGK—(INDO)
Rev.: $24,248,588
Assets: $53,822,035
Liabilities: $5,041,543
Net Worth: $48,780,492
Earnings: $1,629,518
Fiscal Year-end: 12/31/23
Hospital & Health Care Services
N.A.I.C.S.: 622110
Liem Kian Hong (Pres)

PT KENCANA ENERGI LESTARI TBK
Kencana Tower 11th floor Business Park kebon Jeruk Jl, Meruya Ilir Raya No 88, Jakarta, 11620, Indonesia
Tel.: (62) 2158900791
Web Site:
  http://www.kencanaenergy.com
Electrical Energy Distr
N.A.I.C.S.: 221122
Albert Maknawi (Pres)

PT KERTAS BASUKI RACHMAT INDONESIA TBK
Gedung GKM Green Tower Lantai 19 unit 1908 Jl TB, Simatupang Kav 89G RT010-02, Jakarta Selatan, 12530, Indonesia
Tel.: (62) 2127872466
Web Site: http://www.kbri.co.id
Year Founded: 1978
KBRI—(INDO)
Sales Range: Less than $1 Million
Paper Mfr & Distr
N.A.I.C.S.: 322299

PT KIAN SANTANG MULIATAMA TBK.
RT 001/RW 009 Jatiluhur Jatiasih, Bekasi, 17425, West Java, Indonesia
Tel.: (62) 2182748249
Web Site: https://www.kianmulia.com
Year Founded: 2018
RGAS—(INDO)
Oil & Gas Support Services
N.A.I.C.S.: 213112
Edy Nurhamid Amin (Pres)

PT KING TIRE INDONESIA TBK.
Jl Raya Serang KM 68 Desa Nambo Ilir, Kecamatan Kibin, Serang, 42185, Banten, Indonesia
Tel.: (62) 254402675
Web Site: https://www.kingland.co.id
Year Founded: 2020
TYRE—(INDO)
Rev.: $34,032,262
Assets: $24,513,509
Liabilities: $11,750,503
Net Worth: $12,763,007
Earnings: $1,482,820
Emp.: 178
Fiscal Year-end: 12/31/22
Tire Product Mfr & Distr
N.A.I.C.S.: 326211
Harris Muliawan (Chm)

PT KINO INDONESIA TBK.
Kino Tower Lt 17 JL Jalur Sutera Boulevard No 1, Alam Sutera, Tangerang, 15143, Indonesia
Tel.: (62) 2180821100
Web Site: https://www.kino.co.id
Year Founded: 1999
KINO—(INDO)
Rev.: $268,603,643
Assets: $301,735,840
Liabilities: $196,615,484
Net Worth: $105,120,356
Earnings: $5,016,206
Emp.: 2,283
Fiscal Year-end: 12/31/23
Personal & Home Care Product Manufacturing
N.A.I.C.S.: 339999
Harry Sanusi (Pres & CEO)

Subsidiaries:

PT Kino Food Indonesia (1)
Kino Tower Lt 12 JL Jalur Sutera Boulevard No 1, Alam Sutera, Tangerang, 15143, Indonesia
Tel.: (62) 2180821188
Web Site: http://www.kinofood.co.id
Food Products Mfr
N.A.I.C.S.: 311999

PT KIOSON KOMERSIAL INDONESIA TBK
Axa Tower Lt 42 Suite 02 03 dan 05 Jl Prof Dr Satrio Kav 18, Karet Kuningan, Jakarta Selatan, 12940, Indonesia
Tel.: (62) 2130056255
Web Site: https://www.kioson.app
Year Founded: 2015
KIOS—(INDO)
Rev.: $36,387,267
Assets: $18,016,351
Liabilities: $1,129,396
Net Worth: $16,886,955
Earnings: $81,911
Emp.: 10
Fiscal Year-end: 12/31/22
Financial Payment Services
N.A.I.C.S.: 522320
Roby Tan (Founder)

PT KIRANA MEGATARA TBK
Menara The East 21st Floor Jl Dr Ide Anak Agung Gde, Agung Kav E3 2 No 1, Jakarta, 12950, Indonesia
Tel.: (62) 2157947988
Web Site:
  https://www.kiranamegatara.com
Year Founded: 1991
KMTR—(INDO)
Rev.: $593,522,126
Assets: $297,609,746
Liabilities: $174,306,333
Net Worth: $123,303,413
Earnings: ($4,775,522)
Emp.: 3,796
Fiscal Year-end: 12/31/23
Rubber Products Mfr
N.A.I.C.S.: 326299
Martinus Sinarya (Pres)

Subsidiaries:

PT Kirana Permata (1)
Jl Prabumulih - Baturaja Crossing Km 44, Aur Village Lubai District, Sumatera Barat, 31173, South Sumatra, Indonesia
Tel.: (62) 713325159
Rubber Products Mfr
N.A.I.C.S.: 326291
Amiruddin Isra (Mgr-Factory)

PT Kirana Prima (1)
Jl Raya Tayan - Meliau km 8, Begijan Village District Tayan Hilir-Sanggau, Kalimantan, Indonesia
Tel.: (62) 811573534
Rubber Product Distr
N.A.I.C.S.: 423990
Adhe Mourpie (Mgr-Factory)

PT Kirana Triputra Persada (1)
The East Building Floor 21 Jl Dr Ide Anak Agung Gde Agung, formerly Jl Lingkar Mega Kuningan Kav E3 2 No 1, Jakarta, 12950, Indonesia
Tel.: (62) 2157947988
Crumb Rubber Mfr
N.A.I.C.S.: 326291

PT New Kalbar Processors (1)
Jl Adi Sucipto KM 11 3, Sei Raya, Pontianak, 78391, Indonesia
Tel.: (62) 561721959
Rubber Products Mfr
N.A.I.C.S.: 326291

PT Pantja Surya (1)
Jl Kuala Tanjung, Simalungun, Sumatera Barat, 21184, North Sumatera, Indonesia
Tel.: (62) 62296414
Rubber Products Mfr
N.A.I.C.S.: 326291

PT Tirta Sari Surya (1)
Jl Pasir Jaya Km 6, Rengat, Riau Islands, 29315, Riau, Indonesia
Tel.: (62) 769323060
Rubber Products Mfr
N.A.I.C.S.: 326291
Rizky Tomi Rezhandi (Officer-Safety Health & Environmental)

PT KLIK EAT INDONESIA
Graha Tirtadi Jl Wolter Monginsidi No 71, Kebayoran Baru, Jakarta Selatan, 12110, Indonesia
Tel.: (62) 2954 5050
Web Site: http://foodspot.co.id
Online Food Distr
N.A.I.C.S.: 424490
Kenichi Aoyagi (CEO)

PT KMI WIRE & CABLE TBK.
Jl Raya Bekasi Km 23 1-Cakung, Jakarta, 13910, Indonesia
Tel.: (62) 214601733
Web Site: https://www.kmiwire.com
Year Founded: 1972
KBLI—(INDO)
Rev.: $179,507,943
Assets: $193,287,880
Liabilities: $24,765,239
Net Worth: $168,522,640
Earnings: $7,440,417
Emp.: 582
Fiscal Year-end: 12/31/23
Power Cable Mfr
N.A.I.C.S.: 335921
Gabriela Lili (Vice Chm)

Subsidiaries:

P.T. KMI Electric Solution (1)
Jl Raya Bekasi Km 23 1, Cakung, Jakarta Timur, 13910, DKI Jakarta, Indonesia
Tel.: (62) 214614952
Electrical Engineering Services
N.A.I.C.S.: 541330

PT Langgeng Bajapratama (1)
Jl Sumba Block A2, Bekasi Fajar Industrial Estate MM2100 Industrial Town Cibitung, Bekasi, 17520, Indonesia
Tel.: (62) 218980236
Web Site: http://www.lbp.co.id
Steel Pole Mfr
N.A.I.C.S.: 331222
Wijaya Chandra (Plant Mgr)

PT KOKA INDONESIA TBK
Jl Sultan Iskandar Muda no 7C Kebayoran Lama Utara, Jakarta Selatan, 12240, Indonesia
Tel.: (62) 217226172
Web Site: https://www.koka.co.id
Year Founded: 2011
KOKA—(INDO)
Rev.: $12,291,674
Assets: $5,479,084
Liabilities: $1,084,038
Net Worth: $4,395,045
Earnings: $1,300,263
Emp.: 26
Fiscal Year-end: 12/31/22
Engineeering Services
N.A.I.C.S.: 237310
Gao Jing (Pres)

PT KOTA SATU PROPERTI TBK
Jl MT Haryono Ruko The Amaya CA

PT KOTA SATU PROPERTI TBK

PT Kota Satu Properti Tbk—(Continued)
1-3, Ungaran, 50511, Semarang, 50511, Indonesia
Tel.: (62) 2476901000
Web Site:
https://www.kotasatuproperti.com
Year Founded: 2012
SATU—(INDO)
Rev.: $1,817,744
Assets: $14,959,199
Liabilities: $11,241,099
Net Worth: $3,718,100
Earnings: ($251,418)
Emp.: 107
Fiscal Year-end: 12/31/23
Real Estate Investment Services
N.A.I.C.S.: 531390
Johan Prasetyo Santosa *(Chm)*

PT KRAKATAU STEEL (PERSERO) TBK
Jl Industri No 5, PO Box 14, Cilegon, 42435, Banten, Indonesia
Tel.: (62) 254392159
Web Site:
https://www.krakatausteel.com
Year Founded: 1970
PKRKY—(OTCEM)
Rev.: $1,453,968,000
Assets: $2,849,189,000
Liabilities: $2,352,388,000
Net Worth: $496,801,000
Earnings: ($132,724,000)
Emp.: 1,301
Fiscal Year-end: 12/31/23
Steel & Other Metal Products Mfr
N.A.I.C.S.: 331513
Ogi Rulino *(Dir-Logistic)*

Subsidiaries:

P.T. Krakatau Argo Logistics (1)
Jl Afrika No 02 Kawasan PT Krakatau Posco Kel Semang Raya, Kec Citangkil, Cilegon, 42443, Indonesia
Tel.: (62) 254383339
Web Site: https://www.krakatau-argologistics.com
Warehouse Management Services
N.A.I.C.S.: 541511

P.T. Krakatau Jasa Industri (1)
Jl Sulawesi No1 Ramanuju, Kec Purwakarta, Cilegon, 42431, Banten, Indonesia
Tel.: (62) 254392433
Web Site:
https://www.krakataujasaindustri.com
Industrial Management Services
N.A.I.C.S.: 541611

P.T. Krakatau Jasa Samudera (1)
Jl Brigadier General Katamso Cigading No 11, Cilegon, 42445, Banten, Indonesia
Tel.: (62) 254601472
Web Site: https://www.kjscompany.co.id
Logistics Management Services
N.A.I.C.S.: 541614

P.T. Krakatau Konsultan (1)
Jl Industri No 5 Ramanuju, Kec Purwakarta, Cilegon, 42441, Banten, Indonesia
Tel.: (62) 2543202202
Web Site:
https://www.krakataukonsultan.com
Emp.: 40
Business Consulting Services
N.A.I.C.S.: 541611

P.T. Krakatau Niaga Indonesia (1)
Centrum Blok 26 AB Jl Majapahit No 26, Petojo Selatan Gambir, Jakarta Pusat, 10160, Indonesia
Tel.: (62) 213501118
Web Site: https://krakatauniaga.co.id
Steel Product Distr
N.A.I.C.S.: 423510

P.T. Krakatau Perbengkelan dan Perawatan (1)
Jl Raya anyer kav A-0/1 kawasan industri Krakatau Warnasari, Citangkil, Cilegon, 42443, Banten, Indonesia
Tel.: (62) 254386464
Web Site: https://kpdp.id
Machine Repair & Maintenance Services
N.A.I.C.S.: 811310

P.T. Krakatau Pipe Industries (1)
Krakatau Steel Building 7th Floor Jl Jend Gatot Subroto Kav 54, Jakarta, 12950, Indonesia
Tel.: (62) 215254140
Web Site: https://www.krakataupipe.com
Steel Pole Mfr
N.A.I.C.S.: 331110

P.T. Krakatau Sarana Properti (1)
Jl KH Yasin Beji No 6, Kota, Cilegon, 42435, Banten, Indonesia
Tel.: (62) 83890600919
Web Site: https://krakatauproperti.com
Property Management Services
N.A.I.C.S.: 531190

P.T. Krakatau Tirta Operasi dan Pemeliharaan (1)
Krakatau Industrial Estate Cilegon Jl Raya Anyer Kav A/01 Warnasari, Citangkil Gedung KTOP lt 2-Area PT KPdP, Cilegon, 42443, Indonesia
Tel.: (62) 2547843089
Web Site: https://www.ktop.co.id
Water Treatment Plant Maintenance Services
N.A.I.C.S.: 221310

PT KHI Pipe Industries (1)
Krakatau Steel Bldg 7th Fl, Jl Gatot Subroto 54, Jakarta, 12950, Indonesia
Tel.: (62) 215254140
Web Site: http://www.khi.co.id
Sales Range: $50-74.9 Million
Emp.: 250
Steel Pole Mfr
N.A.I.C.S.: 332996
Nizar Achmad *(Dir-Production & Tech)*

PT Krakatau Bandar Samudera (1)
Jl Raya Anyer Km 13 Cigading, Cilegon, Banten, Indonesia
Tel.: (62) 254311121
Web Site:
https://www.krakatauinternationalport.co.id
Bulk Cargo Transportation Services
N.A.I.C.S.: 484230

PT Krakatau Daya Listrik (1)
Jl Amerika I Kawasan Industri Krakatau, Cilegon, 42443, Banten, Indonesia
Tel.: (62) 254315001
Web Site: http://www.kdl.co.id
Electric Power Generation Services
N.A.I.C.S.: 221118
Nandang Hariana *(Pres)*

PT Krakatau Engineering (1)
Gedung KS 7th Floor JL Jend Gatot Subroto Kav 54, PO Box 174, Jakarta, 12950, Indonesia
Tel.: (62) 215221246
Web Site: https://www.krakataueng.co.id
Engineeering Services
N.A.I.C.S.: 541330

PT Krakatau Industrial Estate Cilegon (1)
Jl KH Yasin Beji No 6 Kota, Cilegon, 42435, Banten, Indonesia
Tel.: (62) 254393232
Web Site: https://www.kiec.co.id
Iron & Steel Product Mfr
N.A.I.C.S.: 331110

PT Krakatau Information Technology (1)
Gedung Krakatau IT Jl Raya Anyer Km 3, Cilegon, 42441, Banten, Indonesia
Tel.: (62) 254817021
Web Site: http://www.krakatau-it.co.id
Steel Products Mfr
N.A.I.C.S.: 332312

PT Krakatau Jasa Logistics (1)
Jl Mayjend S Parman KM 13, Cilegon, 42445, Banten, Indonesia
Tel.: (62) 2543111121
Web Site: http://krakataujasalogistik.co.id
Distribution & Logistic Services
N.A.I.C.S.: 541614

PT Krakatau Medika (1)
Jl Semang Raya, Cilegon, 42435, Banten, Indonesia
Tel.: (62) 254 396333
Web Site: http://www.krakataumedika.com
Health Care Srvices
N.A.I.C.S.: 621999

PT Krakatau Wajatama (1)
Jl Industri No 5, Cilegon, Indonesia
Tel.: (62) 254391485
Web Site:
http://www.krakatauwajatama.co.id
Steel Products Mfr
N.A.I.C.S.: 332312
Hendro Martowardojo *(Pres & Commissioner)*

PT Meratus Jaya Iron & Steel (1)
ADB Krakatau Steel Jl Industry No 5, Cilegon, 42435, Banten, Indonesia
Tel.: (62) 254372069
Web Site: https://www.meratusjaya.co.id
Iron & Steel Product Mfr
N.A.I.C.S.: 331110

PT KRIDA JARINGAN NUSANTARA TBK
Jl Kramat Vi No 2, Jakarta Pusat, 10430, Indonesia
Tel.: (62) 2131901010
Web Site: https://www.kjn.id
Year Founded: 1998
KJEN—(INDO)
Rev.: $505,543
Assets: $4,318,765
Liabilities: $274,903
Net Worth: $4,043,862
Earnings: $1,484
Emp.: 32
Fiscal Year-end: 12/31/23
Express Delivery Services
N.A.I.C.S.: 492110
Farida Sulistyorini *(Sec)*

PT KURNIAMITRA DUTA SENTOSA TBK
Jl Komplek Pergudangan Multi Guna T8 No 16, Serpong Utara, Tangerang, 15325, Banten, Indonesia
Tel.: (62) 2122353388
Web Site: https://www.kmds.co.id
Year Founded: 2000
KMDS—(INDO)
Rev.: $21,969,026
Assets: $15,920,326
Liabilities: $2,437,967
Net Worth: $13,482,359
Earnings: $3,327,519
Emp.: 60
Fiscal Year-end: 12/31/23
Food & Beverage Services
N.A.I.C.S.: 722511
Sarrah Jessica Hidayat *(Sec)*

PT LADANG BAJA MURNI TBK
Rukan Sunter Permai Blok D-8, Jakarta Utara, Indonesia
Tel.: (62) 216511595
Web Site:
http://www.ladangbajamurni.com
LABA—(INDO)
Rev.: $721,537
Assets: $3,806,463
Liabilities: $253,611
Net Worth: $3,552,852
Earnings: ($255,784)
Emp.: 31
Fiscal Year-end: 12/31/23
Steel Distr
N.A.I.C.S.: 423510
Yohanes Fernandes *(Sec)*

PT LAMICITRA NUSANTARA TBK
Kantor Pusat Jembatan Merah Plaza Lt 5, Jl Taman Jayengrono No 2-4, Surabaya, 60175, Indonesia
Tel.: (62) 31355 6400
Web Site: http://www.lamicitra.com
Year Founded: 1988
Real Estate Development Services

INTERNATIONAL PUBLIC

N.A.I.C.S.: 531390
Laksmono Kartika *(Chm)*

PT LANCARTAMA SEJATI TBK
Graha Pakubuwono Jl Pakubuwono VI No 71, Gunung Kby Baru, South Jakarta, 12120, Indonesia
Tel.: (62) 217392222
Web Site:
https://lancartamasejati.com
Year Founded: 1990
TAMA—(INDO)
Rev.: $1,842,483
Assets: $12,600,304
Liabilities: $9,161,451
Net Worth: $3,438,853
Earnings: ($414,014)
Emp.: 10
Fiscal Year-end: 12/31/23
Construction Services
N.A.I.C.S.: 236220
Alex Widjaja *(Pres)*

PT LANGGENG MAKMUR INDUSTRI TBK
No 256 Letjen Sutoyo, Waru, Sidoarjo, 61256, East Java, Indonesia
Tel.: (62) 318533688
Web Site:
https://www.langgengmakmur.com
Year Founded: 1972
LMPI—(INDO)
Rev.: $35,389,552
Assets: $43,377,957
Liabilities: $31,882,816
Net Worth: $11,495,142
Earnings: ($1,813,849)
Emp.: 844
Fiscal Year-end: 12/31/23
Plastic Houseware Mfr
N.A.I.C.S.: 326199
Hidayat Alim *(Chm)*

Subsidiaries:

PT Langgeng Makmur Industri Tbk - Trosobo Factory (1)
Raya Surabaya Mojokerto KM 19 Desa Bringinbendo Kec Taman Trosobo, Sidoarjo, 61257, East Java, Indonesia
Tel.: (62) 317871478
Plastics Product Mfr
N.A.I.C.S.: 326199
Sun Lie Lie *(Mgr-IT)*

PT LAVENDER BINA CENDIKIA TBK
Office Suite Taman Melati lantai 5 Jalan Margonda Raya No 525A Beji, Depok, Jawa Barat, Indonesia
Tel.: (62) 2129503963
Web Site:
https://lavenderbinacendikia.id
Year Founded: 2013
BMBL—(INDO)
Rev.: $1,121,341
Assets: $5,336,765
Liabilities: $202,111
Net Worth: $5,134,654
Earnings: $5,695
Emp.: 7
Fiscal Year-end: 12/31/23
Educational Support Services
N.A.I.C.S.: 611710
Muhammad Ilhanul Hakim *(Sec & Dir-Human Resources)*

PT LCK GLOBAL KEDATON TBK
Cempaka Mas Office Complex Blok M No 64, RW 007 Kel Sumur Batu Kec Kemayoran, Jakarta Pusat, Indonesia
Tel.: (62) 2121475967
Web Site: https://www.lckglobal.co.id
LCKM—(INDO)
Rev.: $953,700
Assets: $9,180,733

Liabilities: $343,093
Net Worth: $8,837,640
Earnings: $4,641
Emp.: 5
Fiscal Year-end: 12/31/23
Building Construction Services
N.A.I.C.S.: 236210
Lim Kah Hock *(Chm)*

PT LEYAND INTERNATIONAL TBK

Panin Tower Lantai 11 Senayan City Jl Asia Afrika Lot 19, Jakarta, 10270, Indonesia
Tel.: (62) 2172781895
Web Site: https://www.leyand.co.id
Year Founded: 1990
LAPD—(INDO)
Rev.: $11,289,229
Assets: $13,221,785
Liabilities: $10,385,728
Net Worth: $2,836,056
Earnings: ($269,838)
Emp.: 30
Fiscal Year-end: 12/31/23
Electric Power Generation & Distr
N.A.I.C.S.: 221111
Risming Andyanto *(Chm)*

PT LIMA DUA LIMA TIGA TBK

DWB Tower 5th floor Jalan Kebagusan 1 Kav 6, Jakarta Selatan, 12520, Indonesia
Tel.: (62) 81319867542
Web Site: https://lucy-group.com
LUCY—(INDO)
Rev.: $6,551,826
Assets: $6,881,718
Liabilities: $3,952,898
Net Worth: $2,928,820
Earnings: $37,262
Emp.: 450
Fiscal Year-end: 12/31/23
Restaurant Operators
N.A.I.C.S.: 721110
Ratna Sari Ismianti *(Sec)*

PT LIMAS INDONESIA MAKMUR TBK

Plaza Asia 22nd Floor Jl Jend Sudirman Kav 59, Jakarta, 12190, Indonesia
Tel.: (62) 215155168   Id
Web Site: http://www.limas.com
Year Founded: 1996
LMAS—(INDO)
Rev.: $7,188,997
Assets: $24,288,230
Liabilities: $15,593,047
Net Worth: $8,695,183
Earnings: ($268,695)
Emp.: 38
Fiscal Year-end: 12/31/20
Information Technology Consulting Services
N.A.I.C.S.: 541512
Baso Amir *(Sec)*

PT LINK NET TBK.

Centennial Tower Lantai 26 Unit D Jl Jend Gatot Subroto Kav 24-25, kuningan timur, Jakarta, 12930, Indonesia
Tel.: (62) 2155777755
Web Site: http://www.link.net.id
LINK—(INDO)
Rev.: $254,927,230
Assets: $820,600,088
Liabilities: $540,312,164
Net Worth: $280,287,924
Earnings: ($34,611,916)
Emp.: 846
Fiscal Year-end: 12/31/23
Internet Services
N.A.I.C.S.: 518210
Marlo Budiman *(Chm)*

Subsidiaries:

PT Infra Solusi Indonesia   (1)
Human Resource Consulting Services
N.A.I.C.S.: 541612

PT LION MENTARI AIRLINES

Lion Air Tower, Jl Gajah Mada No 7, Jakarta, Indonesia
Tel.: (62) 80 4177 8899   Id
Web Site: http://www.lionair.co.id
Air Travel Services
N.A.I.C.S.: 488999
Rusdi Kirana *(Pres)*

PT LIPPO CIKARANG TBK

Easton Commercial Centre Jl Gunung Panderman Kav 05, Lippo Cikarang, Bekasi, 17550, Indonesia
Tel.: (62) 218972488
Web Site: https://www.lippo-cikarang.com
LPCK—(INDO)
Rev.: $126,772,500
Assets: $934,961,300
Liabilities: $265,444,200
Net Worth: $669,517,100
Earnings: $30,281,400
Emp.: 254
Fiscal Year-end: 12/31/22
Real Estate Brokerage Services
N.A.I.C.S.: 531210

PT LIPPO GENERAL INSURANCE TBK

Lippo Kuningan Building Lt 27 Unit A and F Jl HR Rasuna Said Kav B-12, Jakarta Selatan, 12940, Indonesia
Tel.: (62) 215256161
Web Site: https://www.lippoinsurance.com
Year Founded: 1963
LPGI—(INDO)
Rev.: $225,483,345
Assets: $179,846,662
Liabilities: $125,053,881
Net Worth: $54,792,781
Earnings: $1,616,053
Emp.: 359
Fiscal Year-end: 12/31/23
Insurance Management Services
N.A.I.C.S.: 524298
Agus Benjamin *(Chm)*

Subsidiaries:

PT Lippo Life Insurance   (1)
Berita Satu Plaza Lantai 2 Jl Jend Gatot Subroto Kav 35-36, Jakarta, 12950, Indonesia
Tel.: (62) 215224460
Web Site: http://www.lippolife.co.id
Fire Insurance Services
N.A.I.C.S.: 524113
Budi Tampubolon *(CEO)*

PT LIPPO KARAWACI TBK

Menara Matahari 22nd Floor7 Boulevard Palem Raya, Lippo Karawaci Central, Tangerang, 15811, Banten, Indonesia
Tel.: (62) 2125669000
Web Site: https://www.lippokarawaci.co.id
Year Founded: 1990
LPKR—(INDO)
Rev.: $1,103,336,704
Assets: $3,219,129,311
Liabilities: $1,945,887,681
Net Worth: $1,273,241,629
Earnings: $42,451,213
Emp.: 15,549
Fiscal Year-end: 12/31/23
Property Development Services
N.A.I.C.S.: 531311
Ketut Budi Wijaya *(Chm)*

Subsidiaries:

PT Almaron Perkasa   (1)
Jl Kemang 1 B RT 012 RW 01, Mampang Prapatan, Jakarta, Indonesia
Tel.: (62) 217191777
Property Development Services
N.A.I.C.S.: 531311

PT Bellanova Country Mall   (1)
Jl MH Thamrin No 8, Sentul, Bogor, 16810, West Java, Indonesia
Tel.: (62) 2187923888
Shopping Center Management Services
N.A.I.C.S.: 531120

PT Jagat Pertala Nusantara   (1)
Jl Margonda Raya 1 Depok Town Square Lt Upper Ground Pondok Cina, Beji, Jakarta, 16424, Indonesia
Tel.: (62) 2178884330
Real Estate Manangement Services
N.A.I.C.S.: 531312

PT Kemang Village   (1)
36 P Antasari, Kemang, Jakarta, 12150, Indonesia
Tel.: (62) 217255999
Web Site: https://www.kemangvillage.com
Property Management Services
N.A.I.C.S.: 531312

PT Panca Permata Pejaten   (1)
Jl Warung Buncit Raya Pejaten, Pasar Minggu, Jakarta, 12780, Indonesia
Tel.: (62) 217822611
Web Site: http://www.lippokarawaci.co.id
Emp.: 33
Real Estate Manangement Services
N.A.I.C.S.: 531311
Fatija Wivama *(Mgr-Ops)*

PT Shimatama Graha   (1)
Jl Prapatan No 44-48 Hotel Aryaduta Ground Floor, Jakarta Pusat, Jakarta, 10110, Indonesia
Tel.: (62) 213844926
Restaurant Management Services
N.A.I.C.S.: 722511
Darmawan Iwan *(Gen Mgr)*

PT Siloam International Hospitals Tbk   (1)
Gedung Fak Kedokteran UPH Lt 32 Jl Boulevard Jend Sudirman No 15, Lippo Village, Tangerang, 15810, Indonesia
Tel.: (62) 2125668000
Web Site: https://www.siloamhospitals.com
Rev.: $164,163,255
Assets: $713,175,106
Liabilities: $190,561,624
Net Worth: $522,613,482
Earnings: $80,983,037
Emp.: 13,851
Fiscal Year-end: 12/31/2023
Hospital
N.A.I.C.S.: 622110
Caroline Riady *(Vice Chm)*

PT LOGINDO SAMUDRAMAKMUR TBK

Graha Corner Stone Jl Rajawali Selatan II No 1, Jakarta, 10720, Pusat, Indonesia
Tel.: (62) 2164713088
Web Site: https://www.logindo.co.id
LEAD—(INDO)
Rev.: $32,772,228
Assets: $129,522,421
Liabilities: $105,702,020
Net Worth: $23,820,401
Earnings: ($5,407,151)
Emp.: 179
Fiscal Year-end: 12/31/23
Marine Services For the Oil & Gas Industry
N.A.I.C.S.: 488390
Eddy Kurniawan Logam *(Chm)*

PT LOGISTICSPLUS INTERNATIONAL TBK

SAV Building Jl Kav Polri No 20 RT 4/RW 6 Jagakarsa Kec, Jagakarsa Kota Jakarta Selatan Daerah Khusus Ibukota, Jakarta, 12550, Indonesia
Tel.: (62) 217883279
Web Site: https://www.logisticsplus.co.id
Year Founded: 2013
LOPI—(INDO)
Rev.: $4,800,172
Assets: $2,473,462
Liabilities: $1,103,766
Net Worth: $1,369,696
Earnings: $129,447
Emp.: 500
Fiscal Year-end: 12/31/22
Logistics Consulting Servies
N.A.I.C.S.: 541614
Ari Purwanti *(Commissioner)*

PT LOTTE CHEMICAL TITAN NUSANTARA

Mangkuluhur City Tower One 32nd Floor Jln Jenderal Gatot Subroto Kav, 1-3 karet semanggi Setiabudi, Jakarta Selatan, 12930, Indonesia
Tel.: (62) 2127883355
Web Site: http://www.lottechem.co.id
Year Founded: 1987
Chemical Products Mfr
N.A.I.C.S.: 325998
Jongwon Kang *(Pres)*

PT LOVINA BEACH BREWERY TBK

Jl Tukad Banyu Poh 110X, Sesetan, Denpasar, 80223, Indonesia
Tel.: (62) 361255600
Web Site: https://www.lovinabeachbrewery.com
Year Founded: 2010
STRK—(INDO)
Beverage Product Distr
N.A.I.C.S.: 424820
Febriana Veronika Adam *(Sec)*

PT LUPROMAX PELUMAS INDONESIA TBK

Ruko Graha Boulevard Blok A No 15 Jl Raya Boulevard, Gading Serpong Curug Sangereng Kec Kelapa Dua, Tangerang, 15810, Banten, Indonesia
Tel.: (62) 2155680515
Web Site: https://www.lupromax.co.id
Year Founded: 2017
LMAX—(INDO)
Rev.: $2,958,194
Assets: $4,469,956
Liabilities: $1,273,525
Net Worth: $3,196,430
Earnings: $77,644
Fiscal Year-end: 12/31/23
Lubricating Oil Product Distr
N.A.I.C.S.: 424710

PT M CASH INTEGRASI TBK

Mangkuluhur City 7th floor Jalan Jendral Gatot Subroto Kav 1-3, Karet Semanggi Daerah Khusus Ibukota, Jakarta, 12930, Indonesia
Tel.: (62) 2180623767
Web Site: https://www.mcash.id
Year Founded: 2010
MCAS—(INDO)
Rev.: $759,612,608
Assets: $129,228,955
Liabilities: $53,252,871
Net Worth: $75,976,084
Earnings: $185,971
Emp.: 207
Fiscal Year-end: 12/31/23
Management Consulting Services
N.A.I.C.S.: 541618
Martin Suharlie *(Chm)*

Subsidiaries:

P.T. DAM Korporindo Digital   (1)
Mangkuluhur City 7th Floor Jl Gatot Subroto Kav 1 - 3, Jakarta Selatan, 12930, Indonesia
Tel.: (62) 81119593111
Web Site: https://damcorp.id
What Sapp Business Application Services
N.A.I.C.S.: 518210

PT M CASH INTEGRASI TBK

PT M Cash Integrasi Tbk—(Continued)

P.T. Edukasi Atlit Internet Digital (1)
Mangkuluhur City Office Tower One Lt 18 Jl Gatot Subroto No Kav. 2-3 RT 1/RW 4 Karet Semanggi Setiabudi, Jakarta, 12930, Indonesia
Tel.: (62) 88971795845
Web Site: https://esportsacademy.id
Emp.: 523
Sports Ecosystem Services
N.A.I.C.S.: 611620

P.T. Volta Indonesia Semesta (1)
Jl Roxy Mas Pertokoan 2-7 Rt 6/Rw 5 Cideng, Kecamatan Gambir, Jakarta, 10150, Indonesia
Tel.: (62) 81119595777
Web Site: https://voltaindonesia.com
Electric Motorcycle Mfr
N.A.I.C.S.: 336320

PT MADUSARI MURNI INDAH
Equity Tower 19th Floor SCBD Jl Jend Sudirman Kav 52-53, Jakarta Selatan, 12190, Indonesia
Tel.: (62) 2129035431
MOLI—(INDO)
Rev.: $94,047,966
Assets: $131,174,204
Liabilities: $43,465,736
Net Worth: $87,708,467
Earnings: $6,113,317
Emp.: 422
Fiscal Year-end: 12/31/23
Fuel Oil Distr
N.A.I.C.S.: 457210

Subsidiaries:

P.T. Molindo Inti Gas (1)
Jl Sumberwaras No 273, Lawang Kalirejo, Malang, 65216, Jawa Timur, Indonesia
Tel.: (62) 341425370
Web Site: https://www.molindointigas.co.id
Chemical Product Mfr & Distr
N.A.I.C.S.: 325998

P.T. Molindo Raya Industrial (1)
Jl Sumber Waras no 255, Lawang, Malang, 65216, Indonesia
Tel.: (62) 341426681
Web Site: https://molindo.co.id
Chemical Product Mfr & Distr
N.A.I.C.S.: 325998

P.T. Sumber Kita Indah (1)
Kawasan Industri MM2100 Blok LL 2 5, Cikarang Barat Kabupaten, Bekasi, 17520, Indonesia
Tel.: (62) 2189982904
Web Site: https://www.sumberkitaindah.co.id
Chemical Product Mfr & Distr
N.A.I.C.S.: 325998

PT MAHA PROPERTI INDONESIA TBK
Mayapada Tower 2 20th Floor Jl Jenderal Sudirman Kav 27, Jakarta, 12920, Selatan, Indonesia
Tel.: (62) 212500608
Web Site: https://mahaproperti.co.id
Year Founded: 2004
MPRO—(INDO)
Rev.: $354,445
Assets: $111,060,247
Liabilities: $27,512,714
Net Worth: $83,547,533
Earnings: ($2,529,817)
Emp.: 10
Fiscal Year-end: 12/31/23
Real Estate Services
N.A.I.C.S.: 531390
Raymond Budhin (Chm)

Subsidiaries:

PT Creative Softhouse (1)
Mayapada Complex Tower II Lantai 3 A Jl Mayjend Sungkono No 178, Surabaya, Indonesia
Tel.: (62) 315674188
Real Estate Services
N.A.I.C.S.: 531210

PT Trixindo Selaras (1)
Mayapada Tower 2 Lantai 20 Jl Jenderal Sudirman Kav 27 RT/RW 014/001, Kel Karet Kec Setiabudi Kota Administrasi, Jakarta Selatan, Indonesia
Tel.: (62) 212500608
Real Estate Services
N.A.I.C.S.: 531210

PT MAHAKA MEDIA TBK
Sahid Office Boutique Blok G Jl Jend Sudirman Kav 86, Jakarta, 10220, Indonesia
Tel.: (62) 215739203
Web Site: https://www.mahakax.com
Year Founded: 1992
ABBA—(INDO)
Rev.: $13,038,376
Assets: $17,607,603
Liabilities: $24,477,742
Net Worth: ($6,870,139)
Earnings: ($3,403,545)
Fiscal Year-end: 12/31/23
Internet Publishing & Broadcasting Services
N.A.I.C.S.: 513140
Adrian Syarkawie (Chm)

PT MAHAKA RADIO INTEGRA TBK.
Menara Imperium Lt P7 Metropolitan Kuningan Super Blok Kav No 1, Jl HR Rasuna Said, Jakarta, 12980, Indonesia
Tel.: (62) 2183707171
Web Site: https://www.mari.co.id
MARI—(INDO)
Rev.: $5,600,143
Assets: $31,138,810
Liabilities: $26,908,184
Net Worth: $4,230,626
Earnings: ($6,707,986)
Fiscal Year-end: 12/31/23
Radio Broadcasting Group
N.A.I.C.S.: 516210
Maria Natalina Sindhikara (Sec)

PT MAHARAKSA BIRU ENERGI TBK
Treasury Tower Suite A B M N -Lt 15 District 8 -SCBD Lot 28 Jl, Jendral Sudirman Kav 52-53, Jakarta Selatan, 12190, Indonesia
Tel.: (62) 2150105555
Web Site: https://maharaksabiru.com
Year Founded: 2006
OASA—(INDO)
Rev.: $2,867,189
Assets: $49,379,617
Liabilities: $6,088,071
Net Worth: $43,291,546
Earnings: $166,427
Emp.: 38
Fiscal Year-end: 12/31/23
Telecommunication Tower Construction Services
N.A.I.C.S.: 237130
Caroline Feliciany Seikka (Head-Internal Audit)

PT MAHKOTA GROUP TBK
Grand Jati Junction Complex 27th Floor, Jalan Perintis Kemerdekaan No 3 -A, Medan, 20239, North Sumatra, Indonesia
Tel.: (62) 6142009810
Web Site: https://mahkotagroup.com
Year Founded: 2011
MGRO—(INDO)
Rev.: $352,330,545
Assets: $174,052,590
Liabilities: $140,214,652
Net Worth: $33,837,937
Earnings: ($11,187,467)
Emp.: 991
Fiscal Year-end: 12/31/23
Farm Management Services

N.A.I.C.S.: 115116
Mily Mily (Pres)

PT MAKMUR BERKAH AMANDA TBK
Apl Tower Ot/35/T5 Podomoro City, Jl S Parman Kav 28 Tanjung Duren Selatan, Jakarta Barat, 11470, Indonesia
Tel.: (62) 2121192888
Web Site: https://www.mbagroup.id
Year Founded: 1996
AMAN—(INDO)
Rev.: $11,576,741
Assets: $70,488,503
Liabilities: $24,410,998
Net Worth: $46,077,505
Earnings: $3,702,175
Emp.: 139
Fiscal Year-end: 12/31/23
Real Estate Services
N.A.I.C.S.: 531210
Adi Saputra Tedja Surya (Pres)

PT MAKNA PRAKARSA UTAMA
Jalan MH Thamrin Niaga Bukit Sentul Plaza Bl A/3, Bogor, 16869, West Java, Indonesia
Tel.: (62) 2187961560
Beverage Product Mfr
N.A.I.C.S.: 312112

Subsidiaries:

PT Mitra Tirta Buwana Tbk (1) (73.2%)
Jl Waru No 74 Sambilegi Baru RT 001 RW 003 Maguwoharjo, Depok Sleman, Yogyakarta, 55282, Indonesia
Tel.: (62) 2742802707
Web Site: https://www.hexsoul.co.id
Rev.: $312,707
Assets: $2,751,034
Liabilities: $213,692
Net Worth: $2,537,343
Earnings: ($211,175)
Fiscal Year-end: 12/31/2023
Beverage Product Mfr & Distr
N.A.I.C.S.: 312112
Andri Yunan Nugroho (Sec)

PT MAMING ENAM SEMBILAN MINERAL TBK.
District 8 Treasury Tower Level 52 lot 28 Jl Jendral Sudirman Kav, 52-53 Senayan Kebayoran Baru, Jakarta Selatan, 12190, Indonesia
Tel.: (62) 2150105769
Web Site: http://www.mesmineral.co.id
AKSI—(INDO)
Assets: $2,858,733
Liabilities: $1,805,983
Net Worth: $1,052,750
Earnings: ($187,214)
Emp.: 8
Fiscal Year-end: 12/31/22
Investment Management Service
N.A.I.C.S.: 525990
Doddy Hermawan (Chm)

PT MANDIRI HERINDO ADIPERKASA TBK
Office 8 Fl 31 Senopati Raya No 8B SCBD Lot 28, Jakarta, 12190, Indonesia
Tel.: (62) 2172120273
Web Site: https://www.mha.co.id
Year Founded: 1994
MAHA—(INDO)
Rev.: $110,337,489
Assets: $107,959,612
Liabilities: $31,551,887
Net Worth: $76,407,725
Earnings: $33,708,917
Fiscal Year-end: 12/31/22
Mineral Mining Services
N.A.I.C.S.: 213115
Yenny Hamidah Koean (Chm)

INTERNATIONAL PUBLIC

PT MARGA ABHINAYA ABADI TBK
ITS Tower Lantai 3 Niffaro Park Jalan Raya Pasar Minggu No 18, Jakarta, 12510, Indonesia
Tel.: (62) 2122790880
Web Site: http://www.mabaindonesia.com
Year Founded: 2009
MABA—(INDO)
Rev.: $3,181,408
Assets: $155,775,954
Liabilities: $135,897,679
Net Worth: $19,878,275
Earnings: ($18,595,559)
Fiscal Year-end: 12/31/19
Hotel & Restaurant Operator
N.A.I.C.S.: 721110
Dwi Yudha Permata Adhi (Sec)

Subsidiaries:

PT Dream Food (1)
ITS Tower 3rd Fl - Nifarro Park Jl Raya Pasar Minggu No 18, Jakarta Selatan, 12510, Indonesia
Tel.: (62) 2122790880
Web Site: http://www.dream-food.com
Restaurant Services
N.A.I.C.S.: 722511

PT MARK DYNAMICS INDONESIA TBK
Jl Utama Dusun I Desa Dalu Sepuluh, A Tanjung Morawa, Sumatra Utara, 20362, Deli Serdang, Indonesia
Tel.: (62) 617940715
Web Site: https://www.markdynamicsindo.com
MARK—(INDO)
Rev.: $36,331,915
Assets: $61,793,704
Liabilities: $7,237,510
Net Worth: $54,556,194
Earnings: $10,133,156
Emp.: 525
Fiscal Year-end: 12/31/23
Pharmaceuticals Product Mfr
N.A.I.C.S.: 325412
Ridwan Goh (Pres)

Subsidiaries:

P.T. Agro Dynamics Indo (1)
Pelita Raya I Block F No 20 Tanjung Morawa B, Tanjung Morawa Kab Deli Serdang, Medan, 20362, Sumatra Utara, Indonesia
Tel.: (62) 617943721
Web Site: https://agrodynamicsindo.com
Agriculture Product Distr
N.A.I.C.S.: 423820

P.T. Berjaya Dynamics Indonesia (1)
Jl Utama Dusun I Desa Dalu Sepuluh A Tanjung Morawa Deli Serdang, Sumatera Utara, 20362, Indonesia
Tel.: (62) 82277023166
Web Site: https://berjayadynamicsindo.com
Building Materials Distr
N.A.I.C.S.: 423390

PT MARTINA BERTO TBK
Jl Pulo Kambing II no 1 Kawasan Industri Pulogadung, Jakarta, 13930, Indonesia
Tel.: (62) 214603909
Web Site: https://www.martinaberto.co.id
Year Founded: 1977
MBTO—(INDO)
Rev.: $27,179,276
Assets: $43,720,943
Liabilities: $19,748,597
Net Worth: $23,972,346
Earnings: ($2,073,378)
Emp.: 213
Fiscal Year-end: 12/31/23
Cosmetic Product Mfr & Distr
N.A.I.C.S.: 325620
Samuel Eduard Pranata (Dir-Mktg)

AND PRIVATE COMPANIES — PT MEGALESTARI EPACK SENTOSARAYA TBK

Subsidiaries:

PT Cedefindo (1)
Jl Raya Narogong Km 4, Bekasi, 17116, Jawa Barat, Indonesia
Tel.: (62) 218215710
Web Site: http://www.cedefindo.co
Cosmetic Product Distr
N.A.I.C.S.: 456120
Kunto W. Widarto (Pres)

PT MAS MURNI INDONESIA TBK
Jl Yos Sudarso, Jawa Timur, Surabaya, Indonesia
Tel.: (62) 315320951
Web Site: https://www.masmurniindonesia.com
Year Founded: 1970
MAMI—(INDO)
Rev.: $2,984,975
Assets: $124,626,478
Liabilities: $35,799,853
Net Worth: $88,826,625
Earnings: ($2,582,421)
Emp.: 88
Fiscal Year-end: 12/31/21
Hotel Operator
N.A.I.C.S.: 722511
Djaja Santoso (Chm)

PT MASKAPAI REASURANSI INDONESIA TBK
Plaza Marein 18th Floor Jl Jend Sudirman Kav 76-78, Jakarta Selatan, 12910, Indonesia
Tel.: (62) 2157936588
Web Site: https://www.marein-re.co
Year Founded: 1953
MREI—(INDO)
Rev.: $197,262,196
Assets: $309,937,881
Liabilities: $215,971,742
Net Worth: $93,966,140
Earnings: $3,984,516
Emp.: 143
Fiscal Year-end: 12/31/23
Reinsurance Services
N.A.I.C.S.: 524298
Robby Loho (Chm)

PT MASTERSYSTEM INFOTAMA TBK.
Sudirman 7 8 Tower 1 25th Floor Jl Jend Sudirman Kav 7-8, Jakarta Pusat, Indonesia
Tel.: (62) 2139731111
Web Site: https://www.mastersystem.co.id
Year Founded: 1994
MSTI—(INDO)
Rev.: $234,380,210
Assets: $155,729,708
Liabilities: $73,108,989
Net Worth: $82,620,719
Earnings: $26,637,359
Fiscal Year-end: 12/31/22
Information Technology Services
N.A.I.C.S.: 541512

PT MATAHARI DEPARTMENT STORE TBK
Menara Matahari 12th floor Jl Boulevard Palem Raya No 7, Lippo Karawaci 1200, Tangerang, 15811, Indonesia
Tel.: (62) 215475333
Web Site: https://matahari.com
Year Founded: 1958
LPPF—(INDO)
Rev.: $424,615,775
Assets: $381,872,916
Liabilities: $379,876,791
Net Worth: $1,996,126
Earnings: $43,857,878
Emp.: 4,769
Fiscal Year-end: 12/31/23
Departmental Store Operator
N.A.I.C.S.: 455110
Bunjamin J. Mailool (Chm)

PT MATAHARI PUTRA PRIMA TBK
Hypermart Cyberpark Upper Ground Floor Jl sultan Falatehan Lippo, Karawaci Utara, Tangerang, 15138, Indonesia
Tel.: (62) 2150813000   Id
Web Site: https://www.hypermart.co.id
Year Founded: 1986
MPPA—(INDO)
Rev.: $449,047,242
Assets: $236,476,283
Liabilities: $219,646,757
Net Worth: $16,829,526
Earnings: ($16,582,429)
Emp.: 4,125
Fiscal Year-end: 12/31/23
Fashion & Household Grocery Retailer
N.A.I.C.S.: 523999
Iwan Goenadi (Dir-IT)

PT MAXINDO KARYA ANUGERAH TBK
Sentul Industrial Estate Jl Cahaya Raya Kav H5 Kec Citeureup, Bogor, 16810, West Java, Indonesia
Tel.: (62) 2139721616
Web Site: https://www.maxisnacks.com
Year Founded: 1977
MAXI—(INDO)
Rev.: $5,375,761
Assets: $12,272,168
Liabilities: $2,644,606
Net Worth: $9,627,562
Earnings: ($192,347)
Emp.: 210
Fiscal Year-end: 12/31/23
Food Products Mfr
N.A.I.C.S.: 311919
Sarkoro Handajani (Chm & Pres)

PT MD PICTURES TBK
MD Place Tower 1 8th Floor Jl Setia Budi Selatan No 7 RT 5/RW 1, Kuningan Kota Jakarta Selatan, Jakarta, 12910, Indonesia
Tel.: (62) 2129855777
Web Site: https://www.mdpictures.com
Year Founded: 2002
FILM—(INDO)
Rev.: $23,998,259
Assets: $111,235,939
Liabilities: $5,432,762
Net Worth: $105,803,177
Earnings: $6,187,358
Emp.: 73
Fiscal Year-end: 12/31/23
Motion Picture Production Services
N.A.I.C.S.: 512110
Manoj Dhamoo Punjabi (Chm)

PT MEDCO ENERGI INTERNASIONAL TBK
The Energy 53rd Fl SCBD Lot 11A Jl Jend Sudirman Kav 52-53, Jakarta, 12910, Indonesia
Tel.: (62) 2129953000   Id
Web Site: https://www.medcoenergi.com
MEDC—(INDO)
Rev.: $2,249,337,578
Assets: $7,468,316,269
Liabilities: $5,440,720,277
Net Worth: $2,027,595,992
Earnings: $388,187,052
Emp.: 3,317
Fiscal Year-end: 12/31/23
Oil & Gas Exploration Services
N.A.I.C.S.: 211120
Hilmi Panigoro (Pres Dir)

Subsidiaries:

Ophir Energy plc (1)
Level 4 123 Victoria Street, London, SW1E 6DE, United Kingdom
Tel.: (44) 2078112400
Web Site: http://www.ophir-energy.com
Rev.: $378,480,139
Assets: $2,178,626,887
Liabilities: $1,295,807,743
Net Worth: $882,819,143
Earnings: $991,954,863
Emp.: 386
Fiscal Year-end: 12/31/2018
Oil & Gas Exploration
N.A.I.C.S.: 211120

Subsidiary (Non-US):

Ophir Energy Indonesia (2)
15th Floor Indonesia Stock Exchange Building #15-02 Tower II, Jln Jenderal Sudirman Kav 52-53, Jakarta, 12190, Indonesia
Tel.: (62) 21 5291 2900
Web Site: http://www.ophir-energy.com
Oil & Gas Exploration
N.A.I.C.S.: 211120

Ophir Services Pty Limited (2)
Level 3 38 Station Street, Subiaco, 6008, WA, Australia
Tel.: (61) 8 9212 9600
Web Site: http://www.ophir-energy.com
Oil & Gas Exploration Services
N.A.I.C.S.: 213112

PT Amman Mineral Nusa Tenggara (1)
Energy Building 28th Floor SCBD Lot 11A Jalan Jend Sudirman Kav 52-53, Kebayoran Baru, Jakarta, 12190, Indonesia
Tel.: (62) 2157994600
Web Site: http://www.amnt.co.id
Gold & Copper Mining Services
N.A.I.C.S.: 212290

PT Exspan Petrogas Intranusa (1)
Gedung MEDCO III lantai 3 Jalan Ampera Raya No 18-20, Cilandak, Jakarta Selatan, 12560, Indonesia
Tel.: (62) 7828667
Web Site: https://ptepi.co.id
Drilling Rig Rental Services
N.A.I.C.S.: 532412
Andon Suwito (Mgr-Drilling)

PT Medco E&P Indonesia (1)
The Energy 33-39th Floor SCBD Lot 11A Jl Jend Sudirman, Jakarta, 12190, Indonesia
Tel.: (62) 2129954000
Oil & Gas Extraction Services
N.A.I.C.S.: 211130

PT Medco Power Indonesia (1)
Tel.: (62) 2129953300
Web Site: http://www.medcopower.co.id
Electricity Power Supply Services
N.A.I.C.S.: 221118
Eka Satria (Pres)

Subsidiary (Domestic):

Sarulla Operation Ltd. (2)
The Energy Building 7th Floor SCBD Lot 11A, Jl Jend Sudirman Kav 52-53, Jakarta, 12190, Indonesia
Tel.: (62) 2127830000
Web Site: http://www.sarullaoperations.com
Geothermal Power Resource Services
N.A.I.C.S.: 221116
Hisao Nakano (CEO)

PT TJB Power Services (1)
Tanjung Jati B Power Plant Unit 1 & 2 Desa Tubanan, Kecamatan Kembang, Semarang, 59542, Kabupaten Jepara, Indonesia
Tel.: (62) 291771566
Web Site: http://www.tjbservices.com
Eletric Power Generation Services
N.A.I.C.S.: 221118

PT MEDIKALOKA HERMINA TBK
Hermina Tower 7th Floor Jl Selangit B-10 Kav 4 Kemayoran, Jakarta Pusat, 10610, Indonesia
Tel.: (62) 2139702525
Web Site: https://www.herminahospitals.com
Year Founded: 1999
HEAL—(INDO)
Rev.: $375,618,545
Assets: $571,644,156
Liabilities: $234,064,866
Net Worth: $337,579,290
Earnings: $36,319,903
Emp.: 16,676
Fiscal Year-end: 12/31/23
Healtcare Services
N.A.I.C.S.: 621999
Paulus Kusuma Gunawan (Pres & Commissioner)

Subsidiaries:

P.T. Medikaloka Pasteur (1)
Jl Dr Djunjunan 107 Pasteur, Bandung, 40173, West Java, Indonesia
Tel.: (62) 226072525
Healtcare Services
N.A.I.C.S.: 621610

PT Medikaloka Husada (1)
Jl Raya Siliwangi No 50, Pancoran Mas, Depok, 16436, West Java, Indonesia
Tel.: (62) 2177202525
Healtcare Services
N.A.I.C.S.: 621999

PT MEGA MANUNGGAL PROPERTY TBK
GRHA INTIRUB 2nd Floor Intirub Business Park IBP Jl Cililitan, Besar No 454, Jakarta Timur, 13650, Indonesia
Tel.: (62) 2129379058
Web Site: https://mmproperty.com
MMLP—(INDO)
Rev.: $22,621,782
Assets: $435,875,469
Liabilities: $140,465,243
Net Worth: $295,410,226
Earnings: $7,361,181
Emp.: 114
Fiscal Year-end: 12/31/23
Warehouse Mfr & Leasing
N.A.I.C.S.: 493110

PT MEGA PERINTIS TBK
JL Karet Pedurenan No 240, Karet Kuningan, Jakarta Selatan, 12940, Indonesia
Tel.: (62) 2152904379
Web Site: https://www.megaperintis.co.id
ZONE—(INDO)
Rev.: $47,760,264
Assets: $48,897,000
Liabilities: $24,473,736
Net Worth: $24,423,264
Earnings: $3,050,411
Emp.: 576
Fiscal Year-end: 12/31/23
Online Clothing Fashion Retailer
N.A.I.C.S.: 458110
Fx Afat Adinata (Pres & CEO)

PT MEGALESTARI EPACK SENTOSARAYA TBK
Pergudangan 19 Blok A1 No 1, Pakuhaji, Tangerang, 15570, Banten, Indonesia
Tel.: (62) 2129667017
Web Site: https://www.epack.co.id
Year Founded: 2013
EPAC—(INDO)
Rev.: $7,226,971
Assets: $18,420,067
Liabilities: $12,842,108
Net Worth: $5,577,959
Earnings: ($1,855,501)
Emp.: 79
Fiscal Year-end: 12/31/23
Plastic Packaging Mfr & Distr
N.A.I.C.S.: 326112

PT MEGALESTARI EPACK SENTOSARAYA TBK

PT Megalestari Epack Sentosaraya Tbk—(Continued)

Bahar Ghazali (Pres)

Subsidiaries:

PT Epac Flexibles Indonesia (1)
Pergudangan Bandaramas Blok A 10 No 18 Jl Marsekal Surya Dharma, Selapajang Jaya Neglasari, Tangerang, Indonesia
Tel.: (62) 2155727606
Real Estate Services
N.A.I.C.S.: 531210

PT MEGAPOLITAN DEVELOPMENTS, TBK

The Bellagio Residence & Mall Jl Kawasan Mega Kuningan Barat, Kav E4 No 3 Kuningan Timur, Jakarta, 12950, Indonesia
Tel.: (62) 2130019938
Web Site: https://www.megapolitan-group.com
EMDE—(INDO)
Rev.: $10,038,918
Assets: $228,540,435
Liabilities: $140,354,500
Net Worth: $88,185,936
Earnings: ($17,635,404)
Emp.: 98
Fiscal Year-end: 12/31/23
Real Estate Development Services
N.A.I.C.S.: 531390

PT MEGAPOWER MAKMUR TBK

Galeri Niaga Mediterania 2 Blok M8 I-J Jalan Pantai Indah Utara 2, Pantai Indah Kapuk, Jakarta Utara, 14460, Indonesia
Tel.: (62) 215883595
Web Site: https://www.megapowermakmur.id
MPOW—(INDO)
Rev.: $1,871,369
Assets: $11,687,476
Liabilities: $3,838,334
Net Worth: $7,849,142
Earnings: ($217,519)
Emp.: 27
Fiscal Year-end: 12/31/23
Electric Power Distribution Services
N.A.I.C.S.: 221122
Kang Jimmi (Chm)

PT MENN TEKNOLOGI INDONESIA TBK.

Mal Ambasador Lantai 5 No 9F Jl Prof Dr Satrio, Kuningan DKI Jakarta, Jakarta Selatan, 12940, Indonesia
Tel.: (62) 2157939508
Web Site: https://www.menngroup.id
Year Founded: 2014
MENN—(INDO)
Rev.: $401,769
Assets: $927,410
Liabilities: $115,370
Net Worth: $812,040
Earnings: $61,198
Emp.: 3
Fiscal Year-end: 12/31/22
Information Technology Services
N.A.I.C.S.: 541512
Edrick Pramana (CMO)

PT MENTENG HERITAGE REALTY TBK

Jalan Cilacap No 1, Menteng, Jakarta Pusat, 10310, Jakarta, Indonesia
Tel.: (62) 2157951819
Web Site: https://hrme.co.id
Year Founded: 2007
HRME—(INDO)
Rev.: $7,130,352
Assets: $59,712,514
Liabilities: $18,094,152
Net Worth: $41,618,362

Earnings: ($1,541,722)
Emp.: 77
Fiscal Year-end: 12/31/23
Hotel & Restaurant Operator
N.A.I.C.S.: 721110
Herry Wijaya (Pres & Commissioner)

PT MERDEKA BATTERY MATERIALS TBK.

Treasury Tower 69th Floor, District 8 SCBD Lot 28 Jalan Jenderal Sudirman Kav 52-53, Jakarta Selatan, 12190, Indonesia
Tel.: (62) 2139525581   Id
Web Site: https://www.merdekabattery.com
Year Founded: 2010
MBMA—(INDO)
Rev.: $455,737,485
Assets: $2,421,567,874
Liabilities: $862,177,954
Net Worth: $1,559,389,920
Earnings: $37,848,159
Emp.: 1,443
Fiscal Year-end: 12/31/22
Battery Mfr
N.A.I.C.S.: 335910
Devin Antonio Ridwan (Chm)

PT MERDEKA COPPER GOLD TBK

Treasury Tower 67th-68th Floor District 8 SCBD Lot 28, Jl Jenderal Sudirman Kav 52-53, Jakarta, 12190, Indonesia
Tel.: (62) 2139525580
Web Site: https://www.merdekacoppergold.id
Year Founded: 2012
MDKA—(INDO)
Rev.: $1,706,782,227
Assets: $4,964,258,915
Liabilities: $2,200,203,593
Net Worth: $2,764,055,322
Earnings: $5,665,022
Emp.: 6,528
Fiscal Year-end: 12/31/23
Copper & Gold Mining
N.A.I.C.S.: 212230
Adi Adriansyah Sjoekri (Sec)

Subsidiaries:

PT Bumi Suksesindo (1)
Tel.: (62) 333710368
Web Site: http://www.bumisuksesindo.com
Emp.: 1,500
Gold Mining Services
N.A.I.C.S.: 212220

PT META EPSI TBK

Jl Mayjen Di Panjaitan Kav 2, Jakarta, 13350, Timur, Indonesia
Tel.: (62) 218564955
Web Site: https://www.metaepsi.com
Year Founded: 1975
MTPS—(INDO)
Rev.: $55,442
Assets: $6,292,358
Liabilities: $3,130,585
Net Worth: $3,161,773
Earnings: ($1,032,003)
Emp.: 9
Fiscal Year-end: 12/31/23
Engineeering Services
N.A.I.C.S.: 541330
Kahar Anwar (Chm)

PT METRO HEALTHCARE INDONESIA TBK

Jl Raya Serang Km 16 8 Rt/Rw 005/001 Kel Sukamulya Kec Cikupa Kab, Tangerang, 15710, Indonesia
Tel.: (62) 2159647937
Web Site: https://www.metrohealthcare.co.id
Year Founded: 2015

CARE—(INDO)
Rev.: $15,759,691
Assets: $268,657,186
Liabilities: $67,490,989
Net Worth: $201,166,197
Earnings: ($7,188,135)
Emp.: 729
Fiscal Year-end: 12/31/23
Hospital & Health Care Services
N.A.I.C.S.: 622110
Henry Kembaren (Pres)

Subsidiaries:

P.T. Bintang Langit (1)
Jl Moch Toha KM 2 No 1 Kel, Nambo Jaya Kota, Tangerang, Indonesia
Tel.: (62) 2142883061
Hospital Services
N.A.I.C.S.: 622110

P.T. Bunda Mulia Medika (1)
Jl Raya Imam Bonjol No 80 RT 08/RW 08 Kp Warung Bangkok Kel, Sukadanau Kec Cikarang Barat Kab, Bekasi, Indonesia
Tel.: (62) 218900579
Health Care & Training Centre Services
N.A.I.C.S.: 621610

P.T. Cahaya Usaha Bersama (1)
Gedung Menara APL Central Park Lt 19 Unit T 7 Jl, Letjen S Parman RT 012/RW 006 Kel Tanjung Duren Selatan, Jakarta, Indonesia
Tel.: (62) 215669411
Health Care Development Services
N.A.I.C.S.: 541715

P.T. Sinergi Serasi Prima (1)
Cengkareng Business City Lt 5 CBC Gallery Jl Atang Sanjaya No 21, Tangerang, Banten, Indonesia
Tel.: (62) 215504289
Health Care & Training Centre Services
N.A.I.C.S.: 621610

PT Metro Hospitals Indonesia (1)
JL Raya Serang KM 16 8, Sukamulya, Tangerang, Cikupa, Indonesia
Tel.: (62) 21 596 2790
Integrated Health Services
N.A.I.C.S.: 622110

PT Rumah Sakit Bunda Sejahtera (1)
Perumahan Pondok Makmur Jl Puri Agung No 3 Kuta Baru Kec Ps Kemis, Tangerang, Banten, Indonesia
Tel.: (62) 21 592 5889
Integrated Health Services
N.A.I.C.S.: 622110

PT METRO REALTY TBK

Gedung Metro Pasar Baru Lantai 10Jl H Samanhudi, Pasar Baru, Jakarta, 10710, Indonesia
Tel.: (62) 3441222
Web Site: https://ptmetrorealty.co.id
Year Founded: 1980
MTSM—(INDO)
Rev.: $1,657,081
Assets: $3,585,972
Liabilities: $1,691,470
Net Worth: $1,894,503
Earnings: ($472,107)
Emp.: 69
Fiscal Year-end: 12/31/23
Grocery Product Distr
N.A.I.C.S.: 445110

PT METROPOLITAN KENTJANA TBK

Plaza Pondok Indah 2 Jl Metro Duta Niaga Blok B5 Pondok Indah, South Jakarta, 12310, Indonesia
Tel.: (62) 217505757   Id
Web Site: https://www.pondokindahgroup.co.id
Year Founded: 1972
MKPI—(INDO)
Rev.: $151,129,195
Assets: $544,764,666
Liabilities: $99,839,248
Net Worth: $444,925,419

Earnings: $54,838,405
Emp.: 543
Fiscal Year-end: 12/31/23
Building Construction Services
N.A.I.C.S.: 236116
Jeffri Sandra Tanudjaja (Vice Chm)

PT METROPOLITAN LAND TBK

M Gold Tower Lantai 15, Jl Letkol M Moeffreni Moe'min Pekayon Jaya Bekasi Selatan, Bekasi, 17148, Indonesia
Tel.: (62) 2128087777
Web Site: https://www.metropolitanland.com
Year Founded: 1994
MTLA—(INDO)
Rev.: $110,722,440
Assets: $468,912,972
Liabilities: $134,527,691
Net Worth: $334,385,281
Earnings: $32,009,575
Emp.: 427
Fiscal Year-end: 12/31/23
Real Estate Development Services
N.A.I.C.S.: 531390
Thomas Johannes Angfendy (Chm)

Subsidiaries:

P.T. Sumber Selera Indonesia (1)
Karawaci Office Park Blok I No 50 Ruko Pinangsia, Karawaci, Tangerang, 15138, Banten, Indonesia
Tel.: (62) 2155778453
Web Site: https://www.sumberselera.com
Meat Product Mfr & Distr
N.A.I.C.S.: 311615

PT Agus Nusa Penida (1)
Jl Arjuna Double Six Street Seminyak Kuta Badung, Bali, 80361, Indonesia
Tel.: (62) 361730733
Real Estate Services
N.A.I.C.S.: 531390

PT Fajarputera Dinasti (1)
Generali Tower Gran Rubina Business Park Building 22nd Floor Unit B, Jl Kuningan Raya, Jakarta Selatan, Indonesia
Tel.: (62) 2128087777
Real Estate Services
N.A.I.C.S.: 531390

PT Kembang Griya Cahaya (1)
Jl HR Rasuna Said Brass Rubber, Grand Rubina Business Park, Jakarta Selatan, 12940, Indonesia
Tel.: (62) 2128087777
Real Estate Services
N.A.I.C.S.: 531390

PT Metropolitan Deta Graha (1)
Jl Siliwangi No 61 RT 03 RW 07, Kel Kesenden Kec Kejaksan Kota, Cirebon, Indonesia
Tel.: (62) 231200222
Real Estate Services
N.A.I.C.S.: 531390

PT Metropolitan Graha Management (1)
Jl Arjuna GG Raja No 1 Kel Seminyak Kec Kuta Kab Badung, Bali, Indonesia
Tel.: (62) 2128087777
Real Estate Services
N.A.I.C.S.: 531390

PT Metropolitan Karyadeka Ascendas (1)
Menara Kadin Building Lt 20 Jl HR, Rasuna Said blok X-5 Kav 2-3 Kuningan, Jakarta Selatan, Indonesia
Tel.: (62) 2157903888
Real Estate Services
N.A.I.C.S.: 531390

PT Metropolitan Karyadeka Development (1)
Generali Tower Gran Rubina Business Park 22 Unit B Jl Epicentrum Kav 11 RW 5 Kel Karet Kuningan Kec Setia Budi Kota Administrasi, Jakarta Selatan, Indonesia
Tel.: (62) 2128087777
Real Estate Services

AND PRIVATE COMPANIES

PT MITRA PEMUDA TBK.

N.A.I.C.S.: 531390

PT Metropolitan Permata Development (1)
Mgold Tower Building 15th Floor Jl KH Noer Alie RT 007 RW 003, Pekayon Jaya, Bekasi, Indonesia
Tel.: (62) 2128087777
Real Estate Services
N.A.I.C.S.: 531390

PT MIDI UTAMA INDONESIA TBK
Gedung Alfa Tower Lantai 12 Kav 7-9 Jl Jalur Sutera Barat, Alam Sutera, Tangerang, 15143, Banten, Indonesia
Tel.: (62) 2180821618 Id
Web Site: https://www.alfamidiku.com
Year Founded: 2007
MIDI—(INDO)
Rev.: $1,126,783,811
Assets: $505,629,918
Liabilities: $251,556,454
Net Worth: $254,073,464
Earnings: $33,529,691
Emp.: 12,793
Fiscal Year-end: 12/31/23
Convenience Store Operator
N.A.I.C.S.: 445131
Maria Theresia Velina Yulianti *(Mng Dir)*

PT MINNA PADI INVESTAMA SEKURITAS TBK
Equity Tower 11th Fl SCBD lot 9, Jl Jend Sudirman Kav 52-53, Jakarta, Indonesia
Tel.: (62) 215255555
Web Site:
  https://www.minnapadi.com
Year Founded: 1998
PADI—(INDO)
Rev.: $676,460
Assets: $15,500,616
Liabilities: $4,734,636
Net Worth: $10,765,981
Earnings: ($1,578,855)
Emp.: 50
Fiscal Year-end: 12/31/23
Security Brokerage Services
N.A.I.C.S.: 523150
Djoko Joelijanto *(Chm)*

PT MITRA ENERGI PERSADA TBK
Graha Krama Yudha Lantai 2, Jl Warung Jati Barat No 43, Jakarta, 122760, Selatan, Indonesia
Tel.: (62) 217945838
Web Site:
  https://www.mitraenergipersada.com
Year Founded: 1981
KOPI—(INDO)
Rev.: $11,759,605
Assets: $22,419,924
Liabilities: $15,897,783
Net Worth: $6,522,142
Earnings: $157,887
Emp.: 28
Fiscal Year-end: 12/31/23
Oil, Gas & Power Distr
N.A.I.C.S.: 486210
Ivo Wongkaren *(Chm)*

PT MITRA INTERNATIONAL RESOURCES TBK.
Grha Mitra Jl Pejaten Barat No 6, Jakarta, 12510, Indonesia
Tel.: (62) 218671237
Web Site:
  https://www.mitrarajasa.com
Year Founded: 1979
MIRA—(INDO)
Rev.: $5,014,356
Assets: $15,795,195
Liabilities: $5,291,545
Net Worth: $10,503,650

Earnings: ($661,030)
Emp.: 92
Fiscal Year-end: 12/31/23
Oil & Gas Production Support Services
N.A.I.C.S.: 213112
Wirawan Halim *(Chm)*

Subsidiaries:

PT Apexindo Pratama Duta Tbk (1)
Office 8 Building 20-21 Fl SCBD Lot 28, Jl Jend Sudirman Kav 52-53 Kebayoran Baru, Jakarta, 12190, Indonesia **(98.14%)**
Tel.: (62) 2129333000
Web Site: https://www.apexindo.com
Rev.: $62,274,932
Assets: $257,247,269
Liabilities: $192,309,209
Net Worth: $64,938,060
Earnings: ($1,346,561)
Emp.: 1,242
Fiscal Year-end: 12/31/2023
Oil & Gas Well Drilling Services
N.A.I.C.S.: 213111
Zainal Abidinsyah Siregar *(Chm)*

PT Pulau Kencana Raya (1)
Medco Building 2nd & 3rd Floor 20 Jl Ampera Raya, Jakarta, 12560, Indonesia
Tel.: (62) 217800840
Oil & Gas Exploration Services
N.A.I.C.S.: 213112

PT MITRA INVESTINDO TBK
Jl Menteng Raya No 72, Jakarta, 12950, Indonesia
Tel.: (62) 29079558 Id
Web Site: https://www.mitra-investindo.com
Year Founded: 1993
MITI—(INDO)
Rev.: $19,936,258
Assets: $32,138,026
Liabilities: $3,837,430
Net Worth: $28,300,597
Earnings: $3,109,895
Emp.: 187
Fiscal Year-end: 12/31/23
Coal Mining Services
N.A.I.C.S.: 212115
Sugi Handoko *(Chm)*

Subsidiaries:

P.T. Karya Abdi Luhur (1)
Jl Melati No 123, Koja, Jakarta, 14230, Indonesia
Tel.: (62) 214303831
Web Site: https://www.karyaabdiluhur.com
Shipping Agencies & Leasing Services
N.A.I.C.S.: 532420

P.T. Karyatama Inti Lestari (1)
Pondok Cilegon Indah Blok B18 No 15 Kedaleman, Desa Cibeber Kecamatan Cibeber, Cilegon, Banten, Indonesia
Tel.: (62) 254396982
Transport & Storage Warehouse Services
N.A.I.C.S.: 532411

P.T. Pelayaran Karana Line (1)
Jl Melati No 123, Koja Tanjung Priok, Jakarta Utara, 14230, Indonesia
Tel.: (62) 2143934356
Web Site: https://karanaline.com
Ship Transport Services
N.A.I.C.S.: 532411

P.T. Perusahaan Bongkar Muat Berkah Sarana Inti (1)
Jl Perak Barat Barat 143, Surabaya, Indonesia
Tel.: (62) 313297160
Web Site: https://www.berkahsaranainti.com
Ship Transport Services
N.A.I.C.S.: 532411

P.T. Wasesa Line (1)
Jl Melati No 123, Tanjung Priok, Jakarta, 14230, Indonesia
Tel.: (62) 143932282
Web Site: https://www.wasesaline.com
Oil & Gas Services
N.A.I.C.S.: 532412

PT MITRA KELUARGA KARYASEHAT TBK
Jl Pengasinan Jl Rw Semut Raya, Margahayu, Bekasi, 17113, Indonesia
Tel.: (62) 218817777
Web Site:
  https://www.mitrakeluarga.com
Year Founded: 1989
MIKA—(INDO)
Rev.: $276,922,292
Assets: $476,714,314
Liabilities: $48,124,390
Net Worth: $428,589,924
Earnings: $64,696,906
Emp.: 8,745
Fiscal Year-end: 12/31/23
Hospital Operations
N.A.I.C.S.: 622110
Rustiyan Oen *(Chm)*

Subsidiaries:

P.T. Alpen Agung Raya (1)
Jl Satelit Indah 2 Darmo Satelit, Surabaya, 60187, Indonesia
Tel.: (62) 317345333
Hospital & Health Care Services
N.A.I.C.S.: 524114

P.T. Bina Husada Gemilang (1)
Jl Oking Jaya Atmaja KM1 No 101, Cibinong, Bogor, 16917, Indonesia
Tel.: (62) 2187911000
Hospital & Health Care Services
N.A.I.C.S.: 524114

P.T. Kasih Abdi Dharma (1)
Jl Pulasaren No 7 Kesepuhan, Cirebon, 45114, Indonesia
Tel.: (62) 231203873
Hospital & Health Care Services
N.A.I.C.S.: 524114

P.T. Kinarya Loka Buana (1)
Kp Cakung RT 01/12, Jatiasih, Bekasi, 17425, Indonesia
Tel.: (62) 2185511333
Hospital & Health Care Services
N.A.I.C.S.: 524114

P.T. Mitra Brayan Indonesia (1)
Jl Bukit Gading Raya Kav 2, Kelapa Gading, Jakarta, 14240, Indonesia
Tel.: (62) 2145852700
Hospital & Health Care Services
N.A.I.C.S.: 524114

P.T. Sehat Digital Nusantara (1)
Jl Bintaro Utama 3 Pondok Aren, Tangerang, 15225, Indonesia
Tel.: (62) 212971211
Hospital & Health Care Services
N.A.I.C.S.: 524114

PT Bina Ilma Husada (1)
Jl Raya Cisaat No 595, Sukabumi, 43152, Indonesia
Tel.: (62) 266224128
Hospital Operator
N.A.I.C.S.: 622110

PT Citra Mandiri Prima (1)
Jl Sipelem No 4, Kemandungan, Tegal, 52114, Indonesia
Tel.: (62) 283340999
Hospital Operator
N.A.I.C.S.: 622110

PT Ekamita Arahtegar (1)
Jl Bukit Gading Raya Kav 2 Kelapa Gading, Jakarta, 14240, Indonesia
Tel.: (62) 2145852700
Hospital Operator
N.A.I.C.S.: 622110

PT Kartika Parama Medika (1)
Jalan Jendral A Yani No 18 A, Sukabumi, 43131, Indonesia
Tel.: (62) 266625090205
Hospital Operator
N.A.I.C.S.: 622110

PT Karunia Bunda Setia (1)
Jl Raya Jatiwaringin No 133 Pondok Gede, Bekasi, 17411, Indonesia
Tel.: (62) 218461970
Hospital Operator
N.A.I.C.S.: 622110

PT Pondok Karya Medika (1)
Jl Ciputat Baru Raya No 10 Ciputat Selatan, Tangerang, 15413, Indonesia
Tel.: (62) 2174706020
Hospital Operator
N.A.I.C.S.: 622110

PT Proteindo Karyasehat (1)
Jl Jend A Yani Kayuringin Jaya, Bekasi, 17144, Indonesia
Tel.: (62) 218853333
Hospital Operator
N.A.I.C.S.: 622110

PT Ragamsehat Multifita (1)
Jl Margonda Raya Pancoranmas, Depok, 16431, Indonesia
Tel.: (62) 2177210700
Hospital Operator
N.A.I.C.S.: 622110

PT Sumber Kasih (1)
Jl Siliwangi No 135, Cirebon, 45124, Indonesia
Tel.: (62) 231203815
Hospital Operator
N.A.I.C.S.: 622110

PT MITRA KOMUNIKASI NUSANTARA TBK
Axa Tower Lt 42 Suite 02 03 dan 05 Jl Prof Dr Satrio Kav 18, Jakarta Selatan, 12940, Indonesia
Tel.: (62) 2130056255
Web Site: https://www.mknt.id
Year Founded: 2008
MKNT—(INDO)
Rev.: $137,378,343
Assets: $29,066,216
Liabilities: $31,365,020
Net Worth: ($2,298,804)
Earnings: ($2,972,866)
Emp.: 57
Fiscal Year-end: 12/31/22
Telecommunication Product Distr
N.A.I.C.S.: 423690
Jefri Junaedi *(Chm)*

Subsidiaries:

PT Graha Planet Nusantara (1)
Ruko Victoria Jalan Imam Bonjol Kota, Karawaci, Tangerang, 15115, Banten, Indonesia
Tel.: (62) 2155734355
Web Site: http://www.pt-graha-planet-nusantara.business.site
Telecommunication Equipment Distr
N.A.I.C.S.: 423690

PT MITRA PACK TBK
Jl Pangeran Jayakarta No 135 Blok C12-15, Jakarta, 10730, Indonesia
Tel.: (62) 216240170
Web Site:
  https://www.mitrapack.co.id
Year Founded: 2000
PTMP—(INDO)
Rev.: $9,935,231
Assets: $16,693,107
Liabilities: $5,597,294
Net Worth: $11,095,813
Earnings: $545,856
Emp.: 70
Fiscal Year-end: 12/31/23
Industrial Machinery Mfr
N.A.I.C.S.: 333310
Ardi Kusuma *(Chm)*

Subsidiaries:

P.T. Master Print (1)
Ruko Grand Boulevard Blok D1 No 42-43 Duta Garden, Jurumudi, Tangerang, 15124, Indonesia
Tel.: (62) 29863066
Web Site: https://masterprint.co.id
Packaging Machinery Distr
N.A.I.C.S.: 423840

PT MITRA PEMUDA TBK.
Komplek Ruko Permata Kota blok E11 & E12. Jl. P., Tubagus Angke

PT MITRA PEMUDA TBK.

PT Mitra Pemuda Tbk.—(Continued)
No.170, Jakarta, 14450, Indonesia
Tel.: (62) 1 66671549
Heavy Constructions & Engineering Services
N.A.I.C.S.: 236220
Novel Maraden Firdaus Simatupang *(Mgr-Ops)*

PT MITRA PINASTHIKA MUSTIKA TBK

Lippo Kuningan 26th Floor Jl HR Rasuna Said Kav B-12, Kuningan, Jakarta, 12940, Indonesia
Tel.: (62) 2129710170
Web Site:
   https://www.mpmgroup.co.id
MPMX—(INDO)
Rev.: $900,008,071
Assets: $558,420,748
Liabilities: $161,513,118
Net Worth: $396,907,630
Earnings: $34,010,961
Emp.: 1,353
Fiscal Year-end: 12/31/23
Motor Cycle Distr
N.A.I.C.S.: 441227
Titien Supeno *(Dir-HR)*

Subsidiaries:

PT Asuransi Mitra Pelindung Mustika (1)
Wisma Slipi Lt 5 Jl Letjen S Parman Kav 12, Jakarta, 11480, Indonesia
Tel.: (62) 21 53661958
Web Site: http://www.mpm-insurance.com
Motor Vehicle Insurance Services
N.A.I.C.S.: 524126
Alexander H. Setokusumo *(Chm)*

PT Grahamitra Lestarijay (1)
Jl Kh Hasyim Ashari No 42, Jakarta, 10140, Indonesia
Tel.: (62) 217418971
Automobile Rental Services
N.A.I.C.S.: 522220

PT Mitra Pinasthika Mulia (1)
Jl Simpang Dukuh No 42-44, Surabaya, 60275, Indonesia
Tel.: (62) 31 532 4000
Motor Cycle Distr
N.A.I.C.S.: 441227
Ratna Tri Hartati *(Head-Internal Trng Section)*

PT Mitra Pinasthika Mustika Auto (1)
Jl Agung Karya IV Blok B No 19, Sunter Podomoro, Jakarta, 14340, Indonesia
Tel.: (62) 21 651 0789
Web Site: http://www.mpm-auto.com
New Car Dealers
N.A.I.C.S.: 441110
Ricky Ngani *(Mgr-Mktg)*

PT Mitra Pinasthika Mustika Finance (1)
Lippo Kuningan 26th Floor Jl H R Rasuna Said Kav B-12, Jakarta, 12910, Indonesia
Tel.: (62) 21 29710100
Web Site: http://www.mpm-finance.com
Automobile Financing Services
N.A.I.C.S.: 522220

PT Mitra Pinasthika Mustika Rent (1)
Sunburst CBD Lot II No 10 Jl Kapten Soebijanto Djojohadikusumo, BSD City, Tangerang, 15322, Indonesia
Tel.: (62) 215 315 7668
Web Site: https://www.mpm-rent.com
Automobile Rental Services
N.A.I.C.S.: 532111

PT Putra Mustika Prima (1)
Gedung MPM Auto Lt 5 Jl Jalur Sutera Kav 9A, Alam Sutera, Tangerang, 15144, Banten, Indonesia
Tel.: (62) 213 042 9910
Web Site: https://www.mpm-parts.com
Automobile Parts Distr
N.A.I.C.S.: 441330

PT Sasana Artha Finance (1)
Komp Puri Mutiara Blok D No 20-21 Jl Griya Utama, Kel Sunter Agung Kec Tanjung Priok, Jakarta, Indonesia
Tel.: (62) 21 6531 3967
Automobile Financing Services
N.A.I.C.S.: 522220

PT MITRABAHTERA SEGARA SEJATI TBK

Autograph Tower Thamrin Nine Complex Jl MH Thamrin No 10, Kuningan, Jakarta, 10230, Indonesia
Tel.: (62) 50603688
Web Site: https://www.mbss.co.id
Year Founded: 1994
MBSS—(INDO)
Rev.: $63,186,783
Assets: $247,068,111
Liabilities: $36,253,325
Net Worth: $210,814,786
Earnings: $24,638,813
Emp.: 127
Fiscal Year-end: 12/31/23
Logistics Consulting Servies
N.A.I.C.S.: 541614
Lucas Djunaidi *(Vice Chm)*

Subsidiaries:

PT Transship Teknik Solusi (1)
Gedung Menara Karya Lantai 10 Jl H R Rasuna Said Block X-5 Kav, Kuningan, Jakarta, 12950, Indonesia
Tel.: (62) 2157944755
Consultancy Services
N.A.I.C.S.: 541618

PT MITRABARA ADIPERDANA TBK

Graha Baramulti Jl Suryopranoto No 2 Komplek Harmoni Blok 8A, Jakarta Pusat, 10130, Indonesia
Tel.: (62) 2163856211
Web Site:
   https://www.mitrabaraadiperdana.id
Year Founded: 1992
MBAP—(INDO)
Rev.: $224,087,006
Assets: $229,500,650
Liabilities: $56,712,853
Net Worth: $172,787,797
Earnings: $21,686,927
Emp.: 441
Fiscal Year-end: 12/31/23
Coal Mining Services
N.A.I.C.S.: 213113
Hidefumi Kodama *(Vice Chm)*

Subsidiaries:

P.T. Mitra Alam Bahari Sentosa (1)
Grha Baramulti Jl Suryopranoto No 2 Komplek Harmoni Plaza Blok A-8, Jakarta Pusat, 10130, Indonesia
Tel.: (62) 2163856211
Coal Mining Services
N.A.I.C.S.: 561730

P.T. Mitradelta Bahari Pratama (1)
Grha Baramulti Jl Suryopranoto No 2 Komplek Harmoni Plaza Blok A-8, Jakarta Pusat, 10130, Indonesia
Tel.: (62) 2163856211
Coal Mining Services
N.A.I.C.S.: 561730

PT Baradinamika Mudasukses (1)
Graha Baramulti Jl Suryopranoto No 2 Komplek Harmoni Blok 8A, Jakarta Pusat, 10130, Indonesia
Tel.: (62) 2163856211
Coal Mining Services
N.A.I.C.S.: 213113

PT MITRAIS INDOSERVICES

Jalan By Pass Ngurah Rai Gang Mina Utama No 1, Bali, 80223, Indonesia
Tel.: (62) 3618497952
Web Site: http://www.mitrais.com
Year Founded: 2000
Sales Range: $75-99.9 Million
Emp.: 400
Software & IT Services
N.A.I.C.S.: 513210
David Magson *(CEO)*

Subsidiaries:

PT Mitrais Indoservices - Jakarta (1)
Plaza Kuningan Menara Selatan Ste 502, Jl HR Rasuna Said, Jakarta, 12940, Indonesia
Tel.: (62) 215201655
Web Site: http://www.mitrais.com
Software & IT Services
N.A.I.C.S.: 513210
Daicc Matson *(CEO)*

PT MIZUHO LEASING INDONESIA TBK

Komp Rukan Red Top Blok A No 3-3A Jl Pecenongan 72, Jakarta Pusat, 10120, Jakarta, Indonesia
Tel.: (62) 3524243
Web Site: https://mizuho-ls.co.id
Year Founded: 1993
VRNA—(INDO)
Rev.: $26,063,061
Assets: $181,415,205
Liabilities: $132,678,720
Net Worth: $48,736,485
Earnings: $3,971,070
Emp.: 563
Fiscal Year-end: 12/31/23
Consumer Financing & Leasing Services
N.A.I.C.S.: 523999
Konosuke Mizuta *(Chm)*

PT MNC DIGITAL ENTERTAINMENT TBK

Jl Raya Perjuangan No 1 RT005RW010, Kebon Jeruk, Jakarta Barat, 11530, Indonesia
Tel.: (62) 29709700
Web Site: https://mncdigital.com
Year Founded: 2000
MSIN—(INDO)
Rev.: $351,780,800
Assets: $653,708,400
Liabilities: $442,650,000
Net Worth: $211,058,400
Earnings: $(207,769,500)
Emp.: 1,040
Fiscal Year-end: 12/31/22
Video Production Services
N.A.I.C.S.: 512110
Ella Kartika *(Pres)*

PT MNC ENERGY INVESTMENTS TBK

MNC Tower 22th Floor Jl Kebon Sirih No 17-19, Jakarta, 10340, Indonesia
Tel.: (62) 213912935
Web Site: https://mncenergy.com
Year Founded: 1968
IATA—(INDO)
Rev.: $170,071,936
Assets: $245,446,279
Liabilities: $142,305,447
Net Worth: $103,140,832
Earnings: $26,392,992
Emp.: 181
Fiscal Year-end: 12/31/23
Transportation Services
N.A.I.C.S.: 485999
Henry Suparman *(Chm)*

Subsidiaries:

P.T. Indonesia Air Transport (1)
MNC Tower 22nd floor MNC Center Jl Kebon Sirih No 17-19, Jakarta Pusat, 10340, Indonesia
Tel.: (62) 213912935
Web Site: https://indonesia-air.com
Aircraft Transport Services
N.A.I.C.S.: 532411

P.T. Suma Sarana (1)
MNC Tower 21/F MNC Center Jl Kebon

INTERNATIONAL PUBLIC

Sirih No 17-19, Jakarta Pusat, 10340, Indonesia
Tel.: (62) 213912935
Web Site: https://sumasarana.com
Oil & Gas Drilling Services
N.A.I.C.S.: 811310

PT MNC INVESTAMA TBK

MNC Bank Tower 21/F MNC Center Jl Kebon Sirih Kav 21-27, Jakarta, 10340, Pusat, Indonesia
Tel.: (62) 2129709700
Web Site: https://www.mncgroup.com
Year Founded: 1989
BHIT—(INDO)
Rev.: $1,016,993,065
Assets: $4,572,356,953
Liabilities: $1,884,928,114
Net Worth: $2,687,428,839
Earnings: $80,101,737
Emp.: 11,423
Fiscal Year-end: 12/31/23
Financial Services
N.A.I.C.S.: 523999
Darma Putra *(Chm)*

Subsidiaries:

PT MNC Kapital Indonesia Tbk (1)
MNC Financial Center 21/F MNC Center Jalan Kebon Sirih Kav 21-27, Jakarta, 10340, Indonesia
Tel.: (62) 2129709700
Web Site:
   https://www.mncfinancialservices.com
Rev.: $191,851,982
Assets: $1,679,595,951
Liabilities: $1,224,821,521
Net Worth: $454,774,430
Earnings: $5,038,370
Emp.: 1,590
Fiscal Year-end: 12/31/2023
Financial Brokerage Services
N.A.I.C.S.: 522310
Wito Mailoa *(Chm)*

PT. Global Informasi Bermutu (1)
MNC Studios Tower 3 Jl Lapangan Bola, Kebon Jeruk, Jakarta, 11520, Indonesia
Tel.: (62) 215303555
Web Site: https://www.gtv.id
Marketing Research Service
N.A.I.C.S.: 327910
Henry Supermon *(Pres)*

PT. Infokom Elektrindo (1)
Gedung MNC Tower Lantai 25 Jl Kebon Sirih Raya Kav 17-19, Menteng, Jakarta Pusat, 10340, Indonesia
Tel.: (62) 2165831110
Web Site: https://www.infokom.id
Integrated Communications Technology Services
N.A.I.C.S.: 541512
Widhy Nugroho *(Mng Dir)*

Subsidiary (Domestic):

PT. Flash Mobile (2)
MNC Tower Lt 10 Jl No 17-19, Kebon Sirih, Jakarta, 10340, Indonesia
Tel.: (62) 213925544
Web Site: http://www.flashmobile.co.id
Switching Equipment Mfr
N.A.I.C.S.: 334210

PT. MNC Asset Management (1)
MNC Financial Center Lt 9 Jl No 21-27, Kebon Sirih, Jakarta, 10340, Indonesia
Tel.: (62) 2129709696
Web Site: https://www.mncasset.com
Asset Management Services
N.A.I.C.S.: 523940
Frery Kojongian *(Pres)*

PT. MNC Asuransi Indonesia (1)
MNC Financial Center 11th Fl Jl no 21 - 27, Kebon Sirih, Jakarta Pusat, 10340, Indonesia
Tel.: (62) 2129701234
Web Site: https://www.mnc-insurance.com
Insurance Services
N.A.I.C.S.: 524210
Wito Mailoa *(Co-Pres)*

PT. MNC Finance (1)
MNC Financial Center lt 12 Jl No 21-27,

Kebon Sirih, Jakarta Pusat, 10340, Indonesia
Tel.: (62) 2129701100
Web Site: http://www.mncfinance.com
Financial Investment Services
N.A.I.C.S.: 523999

PT. MNC Life Assurance (1)
MNC Financial Center 18th Floor Jl No 21-27, Kebon Sirih Gondangdia, Jakarta, 10340, Indonesia
Tel.: (62) 2129704288
Web Site: http://www.mnclife.com
Insurance Services
N.A.I.C.S.: 524210

PT. MNC Networks (1)
MNC Tower Lt 15 Jalan Kebon Sirih No 17, Jakarta, 10340, Indonesia
Tel.: (62) 213923555
Web Site: http://www.mncnetworks.com
Radio Broadcasting Services
N.A.I.C.S.: 516210

Subsidiary (Domestic):

PT. Radio Suara Monalisa (2)
MNC News Center Lantai 5 Jl K H Wahid Hasyim No 28 Kelurahan, Kebon Sirih Kecamatan Menteng, Jakarta Pusat, 10340, Indonesia
Tel.: (62) 213923555
Radio Station Operating Services
N.A.I.C.S.: 516110

PT. MNC Sekuritas (1)
MNC Financial Center Lt 15-16 Jl No 21-27, Kebon Sirih, Jakarta Pusat, 10340, Indonesia
Tel.: (62) 2129803111
Web Site: https://www.mncsekuritas.id
Comprehensive Security Services
N.A.I.C.S.: 523150
Susy Meilina (Co-Pres)

PT. MNC Televisi Network (1)
iNews Tower Lt 7 MNC Center Jl Kebon Sirih No 17-19, Jakarta, 10340, Indonesia
Tel.: (62) 2123567600
Web Site: http://www.tv.inews.id
Internet Protocol Television Services
N.A.I.C.S.: 517311
Gregorius Marihot (Gen Mgr-Legal)

PT. Rajawali Citra Televisi Indonesia (1)
Mnc Studios Ji Raya Pejuangan, Kebon Jeruk, Jakarta, 11530, Indonesia
Tel.: (62) 215303555
Web Site: https://www.rcti.tv
Television Broadcasting Services
N.A.I.C.S.: 516120

PT MNC LAND TBK
MNC Tower 17/F MNC Center Jalan Kebon Sirih Kav 17-19, Jakarta, 10340, Indonesia
Tel.: (62) 213929828
Web Site: https://www.mncland.com
Year Founded: 1990
KPIG—(INDO)
Rev.: $92,280,158
Assets: $2,173,875,550
Liabilities: $436,476,589
Net Worth: $1,737,398,960
Earnings: $22,411,186
Emp.: 367
Fiscal Year-end: 12/31/23
Real Estate Development Services
N.A.I.C.S.: 531390
Hary Tanoesoedibjo (Chm)

Subsidiaries:

PT Global Jasa Sejahtera (1)
MNC Tower Mezzanine Floor MNC Center Jl Kebon Sirih Kav 17-19, Jakarta, 10340, Indonesia
Tel.: (62) 213911456
Web Site: https://www.gjs.co.id
Emp.: 500
Building Management Services
N.A.I.C.S.: 531311
Hary Tanoesoedibjo (Co-Pres)

PT MNC VISION NETWORKS TBK
Mnc Tower Lantai 27 Jl Kebon Sirih No 17-19 Rt/Rw 015/007, Kel Kebon Sirih Kec Menteng, Jakarta Pusat, 10340, Indonesia
Tel.: (62) 213909211
Web Site:
https://mncvisionnetworks.com
IPTV—(INDO)
Rev.: $135,041,171
Assets: $615,527,621
Liabilities: $114,319,532
Net Worth: $501,208,089
Earnings: ($6,164,170)
Emp.: 891
Fiscal Year-end: 12/31/23
Broadband Services
N.A.I.C.S.: 519290
Syafril Nasution (Pres)

Subsidiaries:

P.T. MNC Kabel Mediacom (1)
MNC Tower Jl Kebon Sirih Kav 17-19, Kebon Sirih Menteng, Jakarta Pusat, 10340, Indonesia
Tel.: (62) 1500121
Web Site: https://mncplay.id
Network Information Services
N.A.I.C.S.: 541511

PT MODERN INTERNASIONAL TBK
Jln Sultan Iskandar Muda No 29, Jakarta Selatan, Jakarta, 12240, Indonesia
Tel.: (62) 2127937489 Id
Web Site:
Year Founded: 1971
MDRN—(INDO)
Rev.: $3,196,075
Assets: $13,589,066
Liabilities: $33,911,912
Net Worth: ($20,322,846)
Earnings: $758,582
Emp.: 43
Fiscal Year-end: 12/31/23
Convenience Store Operator
N.A.I.C.S.: 445131
Sungkono Honoris (Chm)

Subsidiaries:

P.T. Modern Data Solusi (1)
Jl Sultan Hasanuddin Dalam No 72 RW 1 Melawai Kec Kby New, Special Capital Region, Jakarta, 12160, Indonesia
Tel.: (62) 2127937489
Web Site:
https://www.moderndatasolusi.com
Emp.: 130
Information Technology Services
N.A.I.C.S.: 541512

PT MODERNLAND REALTY TBK
Green Central City Commercial Area 5th Floor Jl Gajah Mada no 188, Jakarta Barat, 11120, Indonesia
Tel.: (62) 2129365888 Id
Web Site:
https://www.modernland.co.id
Year Founded: 1983
MDLN—(INDO)
Rev.: $74,830,859
Assets: $888,959,627
Liabilities: $621,612,906
Net Worth: $267,346,721
Earnings: ($6,808,383)
Emp.: 411
Fiscal Year-end: 12/31/23
Real Estate Development Services
N.A.I.C.S.: 531390
William Honoris (Chm)

Subsidiaries:

JGC Ventures Pte. Ltd. (1)
1 Marina Boulevard 28-00 One Marina Boulevard, Singapore, Singapore
Tel.: (65) 68907129

Real Estate Development Services
N.A.I.C.S.: 531390

PT Bagasasi Inti Pratama (1)
Jl Marunda Makmur No 8 Desa Segara Makmur Kec Tarumajaya, Bekasi, Indonesia
Tel.: (62) 2188990888
Real Estate Development Services
N.A.I.C.S.: 531390
Tatang Gunawan (Mgr-HR)

PT Golden Surya Makmur (1)
Perum Cikande Permai Blok B RT 1/RW 4 Desa Situterate Kec Cikande, Serang, Indonesia
Tel.: (62) 254401932
Real Estate Development Services
N.A.I.C.S.: 531390
Iswan Wahid (Mgr-Mktg)

PT Mitra Mutiara Makmur (1)
Jl Gajah Mada No 188 Tamansari, Jakarta Barat, Indonesia
Tel.: (62) 2129367777
Real Estate Development Services
N.A.I.C.S.: 531390

PT Mitra Sindo Makmur (1)
Jl Cakung Cilincing KM 05, Kel Cakung Timur Kec Cakung, Jakarta Timur, Indonesia
Tel.: (62) 2129061500
Real Estate Development Services
N.A.I.C.S.: 531390

PT Mitra Sindo Sukses (1)
Jl Cakung Cilincing KM 05, Kel Cakung Timur Kec Cakung, Jakarta Timur, Indonesia
Tel.: (62) 2129061500
Real Estate Development Services
N.A.I.C.S.: 531390
Albertus Kurniawan (Mgr-Pur)

PT Modern Industrial Estat (1)
Jl Raya Jakarta-Serang km 68 Cikande, Serang, 42186, Banten, Indonesia
Tel.: (62) 254401605
Web Site: https://www.modern-cikande.co.id
Real Estate Development Services
N.A.I.C.S.: 531390

Subsidiary (Domestic):

PT Bekasi Development (2)
Jl Marunda Makmur No 8 Desa Segara Makmur Kec Tarumajaya, Bekasi, Indonesia
Tel.: (62) 2129365888
Real Estate Development Services
N.A.I.C.S.: 531390

PT Mega Agung Nusantara (2)
Jl Marunda Makmur No 8 RT 10/RW 3 Kel Segaramakmur Kec Tarumajaya, Bekasi, Indonesia
Tel.: (62) 2188990888
Real Estate Development Services
N.A.I.C.S.: 531390

PT Modern Panel Indonesia (1)
Modern Cikande Industrial Estate, Jalan Modern Industri XXIV Blok BF No 02, Serang, 42186, Banten, Indonesia
Tel.: (62) 2547950500
Web Site: https://www.mpanelindonesia.com
Readymix Concrete Mfr
N.A.I.C.S.: 327320

PT MORENZO ABADI PERKASA TBK
Desa Gajah Rt 002/ Rw 003 Kel Gajah Kec, Gajah Kab Demak, Semarang, 59581, Jawa Tengah, Indonesia
Tel.: (62) 2916910185
Web Site: https://www.morenzo.co.id
Year Founded: 2013
ENZO—(INDO)
Rev.: $33,203,743
Assets: $23,097,936
Liabilities: $12,975,493
Net Worth: $10,122,444
Earnings: ($261,094)
Emp.: 125
Fiscal Year-end: 12/31/23
Frozen & Seafood Distr
N.A.I.C.S.: 424460
Markus Silitonga (CEO)

PT MPX LOGISTICS INTERNATIONAL TBK.
Jl Soekarno Hatta No 16 A Kampung Baru Raya, Labuhan Ratu, Bandar Lampung, 35148, Lampung, Indonesia
Tel.: (62) 2150111701
Year Founded: 2017
MPXL—(INDO)
Rev.: $9,108,370
Assets: $10,072,916
Liabilities: $4,261,881
Net Worth: $5,811,035
Earnings: $612,437
Emp.: 17
Fiscal Year-end: 12/31/23
Transportation Services
N.A.I.C.S.: 541614
Budi Chandra (Commissioner)

PT MSIG LIFE INSURANCE INDONESIA TBK
Sinarmas MSIG Tower 6th Floor Jl Gen Sudirman Kav 21, Kebayoran Baru, South Jakarta, 12190, Indonesia
Tel.: (62) 2150609999
Web Site: https://www.msiglife.co.id
Year Founded: 1985
LIFE—(INDO)
Rev.: $352,114,700
Assets: $1,553,644,200
Liabilities: $785,187,200
Net Worth: $768,457,000
Earnings: $36,777,300
Emp.: 430
Fiscal Year-end: 12/31/22
Fire Insurance Services
N.A.I.C.S.: 524113

PT MULIA BOGA RAYA TBK
Blugreen Office Unit A Green Lantai Gf, Jalan Lingkar Luar Barat No88 Kembangan, Jakarta Barat, 11610, Indonesia
Tel.: (62) 2156943299
Web Site: https://www.prochiz.com
Year Founded: 2006
KEJU—(INDO)
Rev.: $66,217,357
Assets: $53,794,890
Liabilities: $10,234,894
Net Worth: $43,559,996
Earnings: $5,217,436
Emp.: 359
Fiscal Year-end: 12/31/23
Dairy Products Mfr
N.A.I.C.S.: 311511
Bobby K. Gandasaputra (Pres)

PT MULIA INDUSTRINDO TBK
Jalan Raya Tegal Gede No 1 Lemahabang Sukaresmi Cikarang Selatan, Bekasi, 17550, Jawa Barat, Indonesia
Tel.: (62) 218935728 Id
Web Site:
https://www.muliaindustrindo.com
Year Founded: 1986
MLIA—(INDO)
Rev.: $312,128,350
Assets: $455,698,359
Liabilities: $133,713,874
Net Worth: $321,984,485
Earnings: $36,537,107
Emp.: 3,231
Fiscal Year-end: 12/31/23
Ceramic Products Mfr
N.A.I.C.S.: 327211
Henry Bun (Sec & Dir-Fin & Acctg)

PT MULTI AGRO GEMILANG PLANTATION TBK
PT Multi Agro Gemilang Plantation Tbk Jalan Kudus nomor 6 Menteng, Jakarta Pusat, 10310, Indonesia
Tel.: (62) 213106145 Id

PT MULTI AGRO GEMILANG PLANTATION TBK

PT Multi Agro Gemilang Plantation Tbk—(Continued)
Web Site: https://mag-plantation.com
Year Founded: 2005
MAGP—(INDO)
Rev.: $11,689,265
Assets: $81,428,129
Liabilities: $69,972,551
Net Worth: $11,455,578
Earnings: ($15,163,787)
Fiscal Year-end: 12/31/20
Oil Palm Plantation Services
N.A.I.C.S.: 111191
Ade Moesthafa *(Chm)*

PT MULTI GARAM UTAMA TBK

Prosperity Tower Jl Jend Sudirman Kav 52-53 No 5 RW 3 S, Senayan Kec Kebayoran Baru DKI Jakarta, South Jakarta, 12190, Indonesia
Tel.: (62) 2150123124
Web Site: https://www.folkgroup.co
Year Founded: 2019
FOLK—(INDO)
Rev.: $2,703,968
Assets: $5,111,063
Liabilities: $231,834
Net Worth: $4,879,229
Earnings: $349,530
Fiscal Year-end: 12/31/22
Management Consulting Services
N.A.I.C.S.: 541618
Ardilla Juli Kristantie *(Sec)*

PT MULTI MAKMUR LEMINDO TBK.

Jl Sultan Iskandar Muda No 70 Kedaung Baru, Neglasari, Tangerang, 15128, Banten, Indonesia
Tel.: (62) 2155916300
Web Site: https://www.multilemindo.com
Year Founded: 2012
PIPA—(INDO)
Rev.: $2,084,321
Assets: $11,709,934
Liabilities: $2,213,122
Net Worth: $9,496,812
Earnings: $32,699
Emp.: 58
Fiscal Year-end: 12/31/23
Building Material Mfr & Distr
N.A.I.C.S.: 327120
Immanuel Kevin Mayola *(Fin Dir)*

PT MULTI PRIMA SEJAHTERA TBK

Karawaci Office Park Blok M39-50 Lippo Karawaci, 15139, Tangerang, 15139, Indonesia
Tel.: (62) 215589767
Web Site:
 https://multiprimasejahtera.net
Year Founded: 1987
LPIN—(INDO)
Rev.: $8,923,524
Assets: $22,119,540
Liabilities: $1,490,513
Net Worth: $20,629,027
Earnings: $1,231,620
Emp.: 104
Fiscal Year-end: 12/31/23
Automobile Parts Mfr
N.A.I.C.S.: 336390
Eddy Harsono Handoko *(Chm)*

PT MULTIFILING MITRA INDONESIA TBK

Delta Silicon Industrial Park Jl Akasia II Blok A7 - 4A Lippo Cikarang, Bekasi, 17550, Indonesia
Tel.: (62) 2189907636
Web Site: https://www.mmi.co.id
Year Founded: 1992
MFMI—(INDO)
Rev.: $11,059,974
Assets: $23,015,569
Liabilities: $14,625,173
Net Worth: $8,390,397
Earnings: $1,827,770
Emp.: 176
Fiscal Year-end: 12/31/23
Data Management Services
N.A.I.C.S.: 518210
Sylvia Lestariwati F. Kertawihardja *(Chm & CEO)*

PT MULTIPOLAR TBK

Menara Matahari Lantai 20-21 Jl Boulevard Palem Raya No 7, Lippo Karawaci 1100, Tangerang, 15811, Banten, Indonesia
Tel.: (62) 215468888
Web Site: https://www.multipolar.com
Year Founded: 1975
MLPL—(INDO)
Rev.: $711,925,726
Assets: $850,013,752
Liabilities: $544,857,380
Net Worth: $305,156,372
Earnings: $2,249,976
Emp.: 291
Fiscal Year-end: 12/31/23
Departmental Store Operator
N.A.I.C.S.: 455110
Agus Arismunandar *(Chief Bus Dev & IR Officer)*

Subsidiaries:

P.T. Digital Daya Teknologi (1)
Lippo Kuningan 17th floor Jl HR Rasuna Said Kav B-12, Setiabudi, Jakarta, 12940, Indonesia
Tel.: (62) 150813084
Web Site: http://www.digdayatech.id
Emp.: 90
Information Technology Services
N.A.I.C.S.: 561621

PT Air Pasifik Utama (1)
Lippo Cyberpark Boulevard Gajah Mada No 2096-2110, Kel Panunggangan Barat Kec Cibodas Kota, Tangerang, Indonesia
Tel.: (62) 215777911
Aircraft Part Mfr
N.A.I.C.S.: 336413

PT Graha Teknologi Nusantara (1)
Tower B Lantai 18 Jl Mega Kuningan Barat III Lot 10 1-6, Kawasan Lingkar Mega Kuningan Kuningan Timur, Jakarta Selatan, 12950, Indonesia
Tel.: (62) 21 546 0011
Web Site: https://www.gtndatacenter.com
Software Development Services
N.A.I.C.S.: 541519
Wahyudi Chandra *(Pres & CEO)*

PT Mega Duta Persada (1)
Perkantoran Gading Bukit Indah Jl Bukit Gading Raya Blok W-5 lt 3, Kelapa Gading, Jakarta Utara, Indonesia
Tel.: (62) 2129376210
Web Site:
 http://www.dutamegahpersada.com
Construction Services
N.A.I.C.S.: 236220

PT Multipolar Technology Tbk (1)
Boulevard Gajah Mada No 2025 Lippo Cyber Park Lippo Village, Tangerang, 15811, Indonesia
Tel.: (62) 2155777000
Web Site: https://www.multipolar.com
Rev.: $214,121,532
Assets: $202,717,288
Liabilities: $156,366,428
Net Worth: $46,350,860
Earnings: $14,577,017
Emp.: 901
Fiscal Year-end: 12/31/2023
Information Technology Services
N.A.I.C.S.: 541512
Wahyudi Chandra *(Chm & Sec)*

PT Visionet Data Internasional (1)
Jalan Boulevard Gajah Mada no 2120 Lippo Cyber Park, Lippo Village, Tangerang, 15811, Indonesia
Tel.: (62) 2155777678
Web Site: https://www.visionet.co.id
Information Technology Managed Services
N.A.I.C.S.: 541519

PT MULTISARANA INTAN EDUKA TBK

Jl Raya Kedung Baruk No 112-114 Penjaringan Sari, Kec Rungkut, Surabaya, 60298, East Java, Indonesia
Tel.: (62) 318709595
Web Site: https://msie.co.id
Year Founded: 2011
MSIE—(INDO)
Rev.: $249,424
Assets: $6,223,495
Liabilities: $827,520
Net Worth: $5,395,974
Earnings: $4,554,575
Fiscal Year-end: 12/31/22
Investment Management Service
N.A.I.C.S.: 523999
Catharina Siena Nesti D. U. Sunaryo *(Sec)*

PT MURNI SADAR TBK

Jl Jawa No 2 LK II Gg, Buntu Kec Medan Timur, Medan, 20231, Sumatera Utara, Indonesia
Tel.: (62) 6180501888
Web Site:
 https://www.rsmurniteguh.com
Year Founded: 2010
MTMH—(INDO)
Rev.: $40,557,228
Assets: $106,942,656
Liabilities: $26,720,469
Net Worth: $80,222,187
Earnings: $1,473,058
Emp.: 1,334
Fiscal Year-end: 12/31/23
Health Care Srvices
N.A.I.C.S.: 621610
Anton Sudjarot *(Sec)*

Subsidiaries:

P.T. Rumah Sakit Ibu dan Anak Rosiva (1)
Jalan Bangka No 15 Gg Buntu Medan Timur, Medan, 20212, North Sumatera, Indonesia
Tel.: (62) 614538201
Healtcare Services
N.A.I.C.S.: 622110

PT MUTUAGUNG LESTARI TBK

aya Bogor No 19 KM 33 5, Cimanggis, Depok, 16453, Indonesia
Tel.: (62) 218740202
Web Site:
 https://www.mutucertification.com
Year Founded: 1990
MUTU—(INDO)
Rev.: $18,938,100
Assets: $10,717,039
Liabilities: $5,742,024
Net Worth: $4,975,015
Earnings: $2,471,876
Fiscal Year-end: 12/31/22
Medical Laboratory Services
N.A.I.C.S.: 541380

PT NANOTECH INDONESIA GLOBAL TBK

Gedung Nanoplex Jl Puspiptek Komplek Batan Lama A12, Kota Tangerang Selatan Kode Pos, Tangerang, 15314, Banten, Indonesia
Tel.: (62) 2175665177
Web Site: https://nig.co.id
Year Founded: 2005
NANO—(INDO)
Rev.: $5,443,298
Assets: $13,171,260
Liabilities: $2,221,749
Net Worth: $10,949,511

INTERNATIONAL PUBLIC

Earnings: $51,164
Emp.: 21
Fiscal Year-end: 12/31/23
Engineeering Services
N.A.I.C.S.: 541330
Ahmad Fathoni *(Sec)*

PT NATURA CITY DEVELOPMENTS TBK

Sentul International Convention Center SICC Tower 3rd Floor Jl Jendral, Sentul City Bogor, Sentul, Jawa Barat, Indonesia
Tel.: (62) 2187953448
Web Site: https://www.naturacity.co.id
Year Founded: 2011
CITY—(INDO)
Rev.: $5,797,028
Assets: $63,169,040
Liabilities: $7,476,453
Net Worth: $55,692,586
Earnings: $124,994
Emp.: 37
Fiscal Year-end: 12/31/23
Property Management Services
N.A.I.C.S.: 531311
James Frederick Kumala *(Pres)*

PT NFC INDONESIA TBK

Mangkuluhur City 7th floor Jalan Jendral Gatot Subroto Kav 1-3, Karet Semanggi Daerah Khusus Ibukota, Jakarta, 12930, Indonesia
Tel.: (62) 80623767
Web Site: https://nfcindonesia.id
Year Founded: 2013
NFCX—(INDO)
Rev.: $618,625,055
Assets: $102,466,262
Liabilities: $44,538,645
Net Worth: $57,927,617
Earnings: ($31,025,571)
Emp.: 144
Fiscal Year-end: 12/31/23
Data Processing Services
N.A.I.C.S.: 518210
Abraham Theofilus *(Chm)*

PT NIPPON INDOSARI CORPINDO TBK

Kawasan Industri MM2100 Jl Selayar Blok A9 Desa Mekarwangi, Cikarang Barat, Bekasi, 17530, Jawa Barat, Indonesia
Tel.: (62) 2189844959
Web Site: https://www.sariroti.com
Year Founded: 1995
ROTI—(INDO)
Rev.: $248,105,389
Assets: $256,092,087
Liabilities: $100,662,640
Net Worth: $155,429,446
Earnings: $21,644,529
Emp.: 5,666
Fiscal Year-end: 12/31/23
Baked Goods Mfr
N.A.I.C.S.: 311812
Wendy Yap *(Chm & CEO)*

Subsidiaries:

P.T. Indosari Niaga Nusantara (1)
Wisma GKBI Lantai 12 Jl Jendral Sudirman No 28 Bendungan Hilir, Tanah Abang DKI Jakarta, Jakarta Pusat, 10210, Indonesia
Tel.: (62) 2157907777
Bakery Products Mfr
N.A.I.C.S.: 311824

P.T. Mitra New Grain (1)
Wisma GKBI Lt 12 Jl Jendral Sudirman No 28 Bendungan Hilir, Tanah Abang DKI Jakarta, Jakarta Pusat, 10210, Indonesia
Tel.: (62) 2157907777
Bakery Products Mfr
N.A.I.C.S.: 311824

PT Prima Top Boga (1)
Cikarang Technopark Lt 5 Jl Inti 1 Blok C1

No 7, Lippo Cikarang, Bekasi, 17550, Indonesia
Tel.: (62) 2189905061
Web Site: http://www.primatopboga.com
Bakery Product Mfr & Retailer
N.A.I.C.S.: 311812

PT NORTHCLIFF CITRANUSA INDONESIA TBK
Graha Mampang Lantai 2 Suite LPA Jl Mampang Prapatan Raya No 100, Jakarta, 12760, Indonesia
Tel.: (62) 217975947
Web Site: http://www.skybee.com
Year Founded: 1995
SKYB—(INDO)
Sales Range: Less than $1 Million
Telecommunication Products Mfr
N.A.I.C.S.: 334220
Sugiono Wiyono Sugialam (Chm)

PT NORTHSTAR PACIFIC CAPITAL
Cyber 2 Tower Floor 28, Jalan HR Rasuna Said, Blok X-5 No. 13, Jakarta, 12950, Indonesia
Tel.: (62) 21 2554 2000
Private Equity Firm
N.A.I.C.S.: 523999
Patrick Walujo (Founder)

PT NUSA KONSTRUKSI ENJINIRING TBK
ITS Tower Niffaro Park 20th floor, Jl KH Guru Amin No 18, Jakarta, 12160, Indonesia
Tel.: (62) 217221003
Web Site: https://www.nusakonstruksi.com
DGIK—(INDO)
Rev.: $30,052,828
Assets: $59,480,109
Liabilities: $18,461,390
Net Worth: $41,018,720
Earnings: $1,633,105
Emp.: 263
Fiscal Year-end: 12/31/23
Construction & Engineering Services
N.A.I.C.S.: 541330
Djoko Eko Suprastowo (Chm)

PT NUSA PALAPA GEMILANG TBK
Jl Raya Surabaya Mojokerto Km 39 Desa Bakung Temenggungan, Kecamatan Balongbendo, Sidoarjo, East Java, Indonesia
Tel.: (62) 318982405
Web Site: http://www.ptnpg.com
Year Founded: 2001
NPGF—(INDO)
Rev.: $3,395,481
Assets: $17,681,537
Liabilities: $2,587,198
Net Worth: $15,094,339
Earnings: $3,905,147
Emp.: 26
Fiscal Year-end: 12/31/23
Fertilizer Mfr
N.A.I.C.S.: 325314
Uus Sudianto (Pres)

PT NUSANTARA ALMAZIA TBK
Kantor Marketing Ckm City Jl Raya Citra Kebun Mas Kav 1, Karawang, 41371, Indonesia
Tel.: (62) 267432851
Web Site: https://www.nusantara-almazia.com
Year Founded: 2007
NZIA—(INDO)
Rev.: $2,928,544
Assets: $39,484,976
Liabilities: $6,756,786
Net Worth: $32,728,190

Earnings: ($569,293)
Emp.: 19
Fiscal Year-end: 12/31/23
Real Estate Services
N.A.I.C.S.: 531210
Deddy Indrasetiawan (Pres)

PT NUSANTARA INTI CORPORA TBK
Gedung Menara Palma Jl H Rasuna Said Blok X2, Setiabudi, Jakarta, 12950, Indonesia
Tel.: (62) 2129391242
Web Site: https://www.nusantaraintcorp.com
Year Founded: 1988
Securities Brokerage Services
N.A.I.C.S.: 523150
Prianto Paseru (Chm & Sec)

PT NUSANTARA PELABUHAN HANDAL TBK
NPH Building Jl Kebon Bawang I No 45 Tanjung Priok, Jakarta, 14320, Indonesia
Tel.: (62) 2122435010
Web Site: https://www.nusantaraport.id
Year Founded: 2003
PORT—(INDO)
Rev.: $74,287,959
Assets: $111,778,154
Liabilities: $48,307,473
Net Worth: $63,470,681
Earnings: $4,243,409
Emp.: 672
Fiscal Year-end: 12/31/23
Marine Transportation Services
N.A.I.C.S.: 541614
Paul Krisnadi (Chm)

Subsidiaries:

PT Mustika Alam Lestari (1)
Jalan Bitung Ujung No 1 Tanjung Priok Harbour, Jakarta, 14310, Indonesia
Tel.: (62) 214374370
Web Site: https://www.malt300.com
Water Transportation Services
N.A.I.C.S.: 488390
Paul Krisnadi (Pres)

PT Parvi Indah Persada (1)
Jl Kebon Bawang I No 45 Tanjung Priok, Jakarta Utara, 14320, Indonesia
Tel.: (62) 2122435910
Web Site: http://www.pipte.com
Logistic Services
N.A.I.C.S.: 488510

Suksawat Terminal Co., Ltd. (1)
88/1 M 4 Suksawat Rd Phrapradang, Bangkok, 10130, Samutprakarn, Thailand
Tel.: (66) 246320614
Web Site: http://www.ssw.co.th
Logistic Services
N.A.I.C.S.: 488510

PT NUSANTARA SAWIT SEJAHTERA TBK
MENARA IMPERIUM Lt 20 Suite C Jl HR Rasuna Said Kav, 1 Kel Guntur Kec Setiabudi Kota Adm, Jakarta Selatan, 12980, Indonesia
Tel.: (62) 218354045
Web Site: https://www.nssgroup.id
Year Founded: 2008
NSSS—(INDO)
Rev.: $76,926,671
Assets: $238,481,508
Liabilities: $169,567,777
Net Worth: $68,913,731
Earnings: $135,939
Emp.: 163
Fiscal Year-end: 12/31/23
Agricultural Management Consulting Services
N.A.I.C.S.: 541690
Teguh Patriawan (Pres)

PT NUSANTARA SEJAHTERA RAYA TBK
14 Jl K H Wahid Hasyim No 96 RT 14/RW 3 Kb Sirih Kec Menteng, Kota Jakarta Pusat Daerah Khusus Ibukota, Jakarta, 10340, Indonesia
Tel.: (62) 818392121
Web Site: https://www.cinema21.co.id
Year Founded: 1987
CNMA—(INDO)
Rev.: $295,750,560
Assets: $454,241,491
Liabilities: $275,983,478
Net Worth: $178,258,013
Earnings: $33,904,752
Fiscal Year-end: 12/31/22
Theater Operating Services
N.A.I.C.S.: 512131
Suryo Suherman (Pres)

PT OBM DRILCHEM
Dipo Business Center 7th Floor Suite 7E Jl Gatot Subroto Kav 50-52, Jakarta, 10260, Indonesia
Tel.: (62) 2130051341
Web Site: https://www.drilchem.com
Year Founded: 1996
OBMD—(INDO)
Rev.: $10,032,488
Assets: $11,438,710
Liabilities: $2,652,571
Net Worth: $8,786,139
Earnings: $1,583,631
Emp.: 25
Fiscal Year-end: 12/31/23
Drilling Fluid Mfr & Distr
N.A.I.C.S.: 333132
Ryanto Husodo (Pres)

PT ONIX CAPITAL TBK
Deutsche Bank Building 1504 Jl Imam Bonjol No 80, Jakarta, 10310, Indonesia
Tel.: (62) 2139831376
Web Site: https://www.ocap.co.id
OCAP—(INDO)
Rev.: $6,715
Assets: $239,326
Liabilities: $15,472,551
Net Worth: ($15,233,225)
Earnings: ($2,128,953)
Emp.: 32
Fiscal Year-end: 12/31/22
Securities Brokerage Services
N.A.I.C.S.: 523150
Tjie Ping Astono Setiadi (Dir-Operational)

Subsidiaries:

PT Onix Sekuritas (1)
Deutsche Bank Building 15-04 Jl Imam Bonjol No 80 DKI Jaya, Jakarta Pusat, 10350, Indonesia
Tel.: (62) 2131901777
Web Site: http://www.onix.co.id
Financial Banking Services
N.A.I.C.S.: 522110
Bagus Hananto (Commissioner)

PT OPTIMA PRIMA METAL SINERGI TBK
Jl Margomulyo Permai Blok Ac No 10, Surabaya, East Java, Indonesia
Tel.: (62) 317495673
Web Site: https://www.opms.co.id
Year Founded: 2012
OPMS—(INDO)
Rev.: $592,069
Assets: $5,792,804
Liabilities: $115,996
Net Worth: $5,676,808
Earnings: ($308,565)
Emp.: 4
Fiscal Year-end: 12/31/23
Metal Scrap Distr
N.A.I.C.S.: 423930

PT PAKUAN TBK
Jl Raya Muchtar Sawangan Rt 002 / Rw 007 Kel Sawangan Kec, Sawangan, Depok, 16517, Indonesia
Tel.: (62) 215154126
Web Site: https://www.ptpakuan.com
UANG—(INDO)
Rev.: $35,005,335
Assets: $96,684,502
Liabilities: $80,985,756
Net Worth: $15,698,746
Earnings: $16,963,993
Emp.: 75
Fiscal Year-end: 12/31/23
Sports Club Operator
N.A.I.C.S.: 711211
Erick Wihardja (Pres)

PT PALMA SERASIH TBK
Graha Arda Building 7th Floor Zone B Jl H R Rasuna Said Kav, B-6 Setiabudi, Jakarta, 12910, Indonesia
Tel.: (62) 5277715
Web Site: https://www.palmaserasih.co.id
Year Founded: 2008
PSGO—(INDO)
Rev.: $133,093,740
Assets: $271,526,074
Liabilities: $126,247,456
Net Worth: $145,278,618
Earnings: $35,667,906
Emp.: 3,317
Fiscal Year-end: 12/31/23
Palm Oil Processing Services
N.A.I.C.S.: 311225
Budiono Tanbun (Pres)

PT PANASIA INDO RESOURCES TBK
Jl Moh Toha KM 6, Bandung, 40256, Indonesia
Tel.: (62) 225202930
Web Site: https://www.panasiagroup.co.id
Year Founded: 1973
HDTX—(INDO)
Rev.: $1,812
Assets: $15,535,057
Liabilities: $21,558,061
Net Worth: ($6,023,004)
Earnings: ($972,787)
Emp.: 1
Fiscal Year-end: 12/31/23
Textile Products Mfr
N.A.I.C.S.: 314999
Enrico Haryono (Chm)

PT PANCA ANUGRAH WISESA TBK
Jalan Kemang Raya Nomor 17 RT 006 RW 005 Kelurahan Bangka, Kecamatan Mampang Prapatan, Jakarta Pusat, 10260, Indonesia
Tel.: (62) 217180349
Web Site: https://www.pancaanugrahtbk.com
Year Founded: 1990
MGLV—(INDO)
Rev.: $134,357,611
Assets: $19,224,643
Liabilities: $11,028,748
Net Worth: $8,195,895
Earnings: $1,061,741
Emp.: 36
Fiscal Year-end: 12/31/23
Home Furnishing Product Mfr
N.A.I.C.S.: 337121
Dennis Rahardja (Pres)

Subsidiaries:

PT Megah Sumber Sejahtera (1)
Jl Regenttown Gold J1/8, Tangerang, Jakarta, Banten, Indonesia
Tel.: (62) 315021677
Web Site: https://megahsejahtera.com
Lab Equipment Distr

PT PANCA ANUGRAH WISESA TBK

PT Panca Anugrah Wisesa Tbk—(Continued)
N.A.I.C.S.: 423450

PT PANCA BUDI IDAMAN
Kawasan Pusat Niaga Terpadu Jl
Daan Mogot Raya Km 19,
Tangerang, 15122, Indonesia
Tel.: (62) 2154365555
Web Site:
https://www.pancabudi.com
PBID—(INDO)
Rev.: $305,427,389
Assets: $207,571,141
Liabilities: $36,744,875
Net Worth: $170,826,265
Earnings: $24,416,476
Emp.: 4,350
Fiscal Year-end: 12/31/23
Plastic Packaging Products Mfr
N.A.I.C.S.: 326112

PT PANCA GLOBAL KAPITAL TBK
Indonesia Stock Exchange Tower I
Suite 1711 Jl Jend, Sudirman Kav
52-53, Jakarta, 12190, Indonesia
Tel.: (62) 215150196   Id
Web Site:
https://www.pancaglobal.co.id
Year Founded: 1999
PEGE—(INDO)
Rev.: $4,628,690
Assets: $16,227,210
Liabilities: $2,434,201
Net Worth: $13,793,009
Earnings: ($4,750,388)
Emp.: 6
Fiscal Year-end: 12/31/23
Securities Brokerage Services
N.A.I.C.S.: 523150
Justy Intan (Chm)

PT PANCA MITRA MULTIPERDANA TBK
Jl Bubutan Raya 16-22 Kav A No 1-2,
Surabaya, 60174, Indonesia
Tel.: (62) 315462539
Web Site:
https://www.pancamitra.com
Year Founded: 2004
PMMP—(INDO)
Rev.: $187,877,008
Assets: $299,724,702
Liabilities: $218,399,372
Net Worth: $81,325,330
Earnings: $81,247
Emp.: 673
Fiscal Year-end: 12/31/23
Shrimp Distr
N.A.I.C.S.: 424460
Martinus Soesilo (Pres)

PT PANINVEST TBK
Panin Bank Plaza Lt 6 Jl Palmerah
Utara No 52, Jakarta, 11480, Indonesia
Tel.: (62) 215481974
Web Site: https://www.paninvest.co.id
PNIN—(INDO)
Rev.: $918,054,442
Assets: $15,345,413,176
Liabilities: $11,207,581,257
Net Worth: $4,137,831,919
Earnings: $230,027,286
Emp.: 346
Fiscal Year-end: 12/31/23
General Insurance Services
N.A.I.C.S.: 524113
Syamsul Hidayat (Vice Chm)

Subsidiaries:

PT Panin Dai-ichi Life   (1)
Panin Life Center 5th Floor Jl Letjend S
Parman Kav 91, Jakarta, 11420, Indonesia
Tel.: (62) 2125566788
Web Site: https://www.panindai-ichilife.co.id

Insurance Services
N.A.I.C.S.: 524210

PT Panin Financial Tbk   (1)
Panin Life Center 7th Floor Jl Letjend S
Parman Kav 91, Jakarta, 11420, Indonesia
Tel.: (62) 2125566822
Web Site: https://www.paninfinancial.co.id
Financial Management Consulting Services
N.A.I.C.S.: 541611

PT PANORAMA SENTRAWISATA TBK
Panorama Building 6th floor Jl Tomang Raya No 63, Jakarta, 11440,
Indonesia
Tel.: (62) 2125565000
Web Site: https://www.panorama-sentrawisata.com
Year Founded: 1995
PANR—(INDO)
Rev.: $185,655,737
Assets: $106,248,479
Liabilities: $60,400,801
Net Worth: $45,847,678
Earnings: $8,019,425
Emp.: 706
Fiscal Year-end: 12/31/23
Leisure & Travel Services
N.A.I.C.S.: 561510
Budijanto Tirtawisata (Chm)

Subsidiaries:

P.T. Pameran Masa Kini   (1)
Jalan Tanjung Selor No 17A RT 11 RW 6
Kel Cideng Kec Gambir, DKI Jakarta, Jakarta Pusat, 10150, Indonesia
Tel.: (62) 81990962288
Web Site: https://www.panoramamedia.co.id
Media Advertising Services
N.A.I.C.S.: 541840

P.T. Panorama Aplikasi Nusantara   (1)
Panorama Building 2nd Floor Jl Tomang
Raya No 63 RT 2/RW 13 Tomang Kec,
Grogol Petamburan DKI Jakarta, Jakarta
Barat, 11440, Indonesia
Tel.: (62) 81510305555
Web Site: https://www.panorama.id
Online Travel Ticketing Services
N.A.I.C.S.: 561599

PT PANTAI INDAH KAPUK DUA TBK
Agung Sedayu Group Tower 8th and
10th Floor, Jl Marina Raya Kamal
Muara Penjaringan, Jakarta, 11470,
Indonesia
Tel.: (62) 2139734100
Web Site:
https://www.pratamaabadi.com
Year Founded: 2000
PANI—(INDO)
Rev.: $140,198,479
Assets: $2,189,257,637
Liabilities: $949,615,674
Net Worth: $1,239,641,963
Earnings: $46,978,925
Emp.: 294
Fiscal Year-end: 12/31/23
Chemical Products Mfr
N.A.I.C.S.: 325998
Prilli Budi Pasravita Soetantyo
(Owner, Chm & Sec)

PT PAPEROCKS INDONESIA TBK
Ruko Cibubur Times Square Blok C 1
N0 23 Jl Alternatif Cibubur, Transyogi
RT 001/RW 010 Jatikarya Kec Jatisampurna, Bekasi, 17435, Jawa Barat, Indonesia
Tel.: (62) 2122816962
Web Site:
https://www.paperocks.co.id
Year Founded: 2011
PPRI—(INDO)
Rev.: $6,923,983

Assets: $7,023,720
Liabilities: $1,127,515
Net Worth: $5,896,205
Earnings: $146,246
Emp.: 24
Fiscal Year-end: 12/31/23
Food Packaging Product Mfr & Distr
N.A.I.C.S.: 322219

PT PARAMITA BANGUN SARANA TBK
Plaza Paramita Lt 8-9 Jl KH Hasyim
Ashari No 39, Jakarta Pusat, 10130,
Indonesia
Tel.: (62) 2163864358   Id
Web Site: https://www.paramita.co.id
Year Founded: 2002
PBSA—(INDO)
Rev.: $37,195,258
Assets: $51,667,725
Liabilities: $12,888,223
Net Worth: $38,779,502
Earnings: $12,516,700
Emp.: 95
Fiscal Year-end: 12/31/23
Construction Contractor Services
N.A.I.C.S.: 236115
Yonggi Tanuwidjaja (Chm & CEO)

PT PELABUHAN INDONESIA II
Jl Pasoso No 1 Tanjung Priok, 14310,
Jakarta, Indonesia
Tel.: (62) 21 4367505   Id
Web Site:
http://www.indonesiaport.co.id
Port Services
N.A.I.C.S.: 488310
Richard Joost Lino (Mng Dir)

Subsidiaries:

PT Indonesia Kendaraan Terminal   (1)
Jl Sindang Laut No 100, Cilincing, Jakarta
Utara, 14110, Indonesia
Tel.: (62) 2143932251
Web Site: https://indonesiacarterminal.co.id
Port Handling Services
N.A.I.C.S.: 488310

PT Integrasi Logistik Cipta Solusi   (1)
Plaza Telkom Lantai 4 Jalan Yos Sudarso
no 23-24, Jakarta Utara, Indonesia
Tel.: (62) 11500950
Web Site: http://www.ilcs.co.id
Logistic Services
N.A.I.C.S.: 541614

PT Pengerukan Indonesia   (1)
Jalan Raya Ancol Baru Ancol Timur, Jakarta, Indonesia
Tel.: (62) 214301521
Web Site: http://www.rukindo.co.id
Port Handling Services
N.A.I.C.S.: 488310
Yayat Supriyatna (Mgr-Mktg)

PT PELANGI ARJUNA
Jl Embong Malang Raya 39-43, Kedungdoro, Surabaya, Indonesia
Tel.: (62) 31 5346088
Property Investment Services
N.A.I.C.S.: 531390

Subsidiaries:

PT Sentral Supel Perkasa   (1)
Jl Bubutan 1-7, Surabaya, Indonesia
Tel.: (62) 31 547 2333
Real Estate Development Services
N.A.I.C.S.: 531390

PT PELAT TIMAH NUSANTARA TBK.
Gedung Krakatau Steel Lantai 3 Jl
Gatot Subroto Kav 54, Jakarta,
12950, Indonesia
Tel.: (62) 215209883   Id
Web Site: https://www.latinusa.co.id
Year Founded: 1982

INTERNATIONAL PUBLIC

NIKL—(INDO)
Rev.: $171,087,110
Assets: $135,817,817
Liabilities: $80,056,950
Net Worth: $55,760,867
Earnings: ($3,666,646)
Emp.: 230
Fiscal Year-end: 12/31/23
Tin Plate Mfr
N.A.I.C.S.: 331110
Ardhiman Trikaryawan Akanda (Chm)

PT PELAYARAN KURNIA LAUTAN SEMESTA TBK
Rukan Grand Puri Niaga Jalan Puri
Kencana Blok K6 No 3-O, Kel Kembangan Selatan Kec Kembangan,
Jakarta Barat, 11610, Indonesia
Tel.: (62) 2158351606
Web Site:
https://www.pelayarankls.co.id
Year Founded: 2011
KLAS—(INDO)
Rev.: $5,519,959
Assets: $18,098,050
Liabilities: $3,797,096
Net Worth: $14,300,953
Earnings: $2,078,736
Emp.: 53
Fiscal Year-end: 12/31/23
Transportation Services
N.A.I.C.S.: 484220

PT PELAYARAN NASIONAL BINA BUANA RAYA TBK
TCC Batavia Tower one 8th Floor
Suite 08-09, Jl KH Mas Mansyur Kav
126, Jakarta, 10220, Indonesia
Tel.: (62) 2129529461
Web Site: https://www.bbr.co.id
Year Founded: 1998
BBRM—(INDO)
Rev.: $10,545,555
Assets: $34,786,295
Liabilities: $5,022,539
Net Worth: $29,763,756
Earnings: $4,040,076
Emp.: 11
Fiscal Year-end: 12/31/23
Ship Owning & Chartering; Freight
Transportation
N.A.I.C.S.: 488510

PT PELAYARAN NELLY DWI PUTRI TBK
Jln Majapahit No 28 A, Jakarta,
10160, Indonesia
Tel.: (62) 213859649
Web Site:
https://www.nellydwiputri.co.id
NELY—(INDO)
Rev.: $33,921,479
Assets: $53,851,750
Liabilities: $6,428,829
Net Worth: $47,422,921
Earnings: $14,870,303
Emp.: 70
Fiscal Year-end: 12/31/23
Shipping Transportation Services
N.A.I.C.S.: 488510
Tjahya Tjugiarto (Chm)

PT PELAYARAN TAMARIN SAMUDRA TBK
Jalan Alaydrus No 78 C, Petojo
Utara-Gambir, Jakarta, 10130, Indonesia
Tel.: (62) 216342275
Web Site: https://www.tamarin.co.id
TAMU—(INDO)
Rev.: $11,220,746
Assets: $56,199,678
Liabilities: $30,261,389
Net Worth: $25,938,289
Earnings: ($4,998,297)
Emp.: 10

Fiscal Year-end: 12/31/23
Marine Shipping Services
N.A.I.C.S.: 488320
Kardja Rahardjo (Pres)

PT PELITA TEKNOLOGI GLOBAL TBK
Gd RPX Center Lt 8 Jl Ciputat Raya No 99 Pondok Pinang, Pondok Pinang Jakarta Selatan - DKI Jakarta, Jakarta Selatan, 12310, Indonesia
Tel.: (62) 217694639
Web Site:
https://www.pelitateknologi.com
CHIP—(INDO)
Rev.: $21,238,540
Assets: $7,397,436
Liabilities: $3,517,524
Net Worth: $3,879,912
Earnings: $799,173
Emp.: 17
Fiscal Year-end: 12/31/23
Telecommunication Servicesb
N.A.I.C.S.: 517810

PT PEMBANGUNAN JAYA ANCOL .TBK
Jl Lodan Timur No 7, Taman Impian Jaya Ancol, Jakarta Utara, 14430, Indonesia
Tel.: (62) 2129222222
Web Site:
https://www.korporat.ancol.com
Year Founded: 1992
PJAA—(INDO)
Rev.: $95,101,876
Assets: $286,714,046
Liabilities: $136,166,301
Net Worth: $150,547,745
Earnings: $16,312,395
Emp.: 344
Fiscal Year-end: 12/31/19
Real Estate Consulting Service
N.A.I.C.S.: 531210
Teuku Sahir Syahali (Chm)

PT PENTA VALENT TBK
Jl Kedoya Raya No 33, Kedoya Utara Kebon Jeruk, Jakarta Barat, 11520, Indonesia
Tel.: (62) 215673891
Web Site:
https://www.pentavalent.co.id
Year Founded: 1968
PEVE—(INDO)
Rev.: $161,354,836
Assets: $58,883,661
Liabilities: $43,803,958
Net Worth: $15,079,703
Earnings: $2,348,994
Emp.: 954
Fiscal Year-end: 12/31/23
Pharmaceutical Product Mfr & Distr
N.A.I.C.S.: 325412
Hadi Kartono (Sec)

PT PERDANA BANGUN PUSAKA TBK
Gedung Konica Lantai 6-7 Jl Gunung Sahari No 78, Gn Sahari Sel Kemayoran, Jakarta Pusat, 10610, Indonesia
Tel.: (62) 214221888   Id
Web Site:
https://www.perdanabangun.co.id
Year Founded: 1987
KONI—(INDO)
Rev.: $16,299,514
Assets: $10,432,929
Liabilities: $1,550,866
Net Worth: $8,882,063
Earnings: $1,286,448
Emp.: 151
Fiscal Year-end: 12/31/23
Photographic Product Mfr
N.A.I.C.S.: 325992

PT PERDANA GAPURA PRIMA TBK
Office Walk 2nd Floor The Bellezza Permatas Hijau Jl Arteri, Soepeno No 34, Jakarta Selatan, 12210, Indonesia
Tel.: (62) 2153668360
Web Site:
https://www.gapuraprima.com
Year Founded: 1987
GPRA—(INDO)
Rev.: $29,841,885
Assets: $126,907,788
Liabilities: $44,540,552
Net Worth: $82,367,236
Earnings: $6,265,319
Emp.: 221
Fiscal Year-end: 12/31/23
Real Estate Development Services
N.A.I.C.S.: 531390
Rinny Febrianty Mustikasari (Sec)

PT PERDANA KARYA PERKASA TBK
Jl Letnan Jendral Soepeno No 34 Arteri Permata Hijau, Jakarta Selatan, 12210, Kalimantan Timur, Indonesia
Tel.: (62) 2129181077   Id
Web Site: https://www.pkpk-tbk.co.id
Year Founded: 1983
PKPK—(INDO)
Rev.: $3,754,382
Assets: $16,312,950
Liabilities: $509,026
Net Worth: $15,803,924
Earnings: ($396,958)
Emp.: 10
Fiscal Year-end: 12/31/23
Coal Mining Services
N.A.I.C.S.: 212114
Soerjadi Soedarsono (Chm)

PT PERINTIS TRINITI PROPERTI TBK
Brooklyn Premium Office JL Sutera Boulevard Kav 22-26, Alam Sutera Selatan, Tangerang, 15320, Indonesia
Tel.: (62) 2130066688
Web Site: https://www.trinitiland.com
Year Founded: 2009
TRIN—(INDO)
Rev.: $5,345,700
Assets: $143,682,339
Liabilities: $103,239,926
Net Worth: $40,442,413
Earnings: $9,510,513
Emp.: 119
Fiscal Year-end: 12/31/23
Property Management Services
N.A.I.C.S.: 531311
Ishak Chandra (Chm)

Subsidiaries:

P.T. Puri Triniti Batam   (1)
Lantai 18A/J Jl Senopati Raya, District 8 SCBD Prosperity Tower Senayan, Jakarta Selatan, Indonesia
Tel.: (62) 81275619998
Web Site: https://www.marcsboulevard.com
Real Estate Services
N.A.I.C.S.: 531390

PT PERMA PLASINDO TBK
Jl Raya Boulevard Barat Blok Lc Vi No 23 Kelapa Gading Barat, Jakarta Utara, 14240, DKI, Indonesia
Tel.: (62) 214507929
Web Site: https://permaplasindo.co.id
Year Founded: 1992
BINO—(INDO)
Rev.: $23,688,512
Assets: $35,283,088
Liabilities: $6,564,875
Net Worth: $28,718,213
Earnings: $285,071
Emp.: 584

Fiscal Year-end: 12/31/23
Real Estate Services
N.A.I.C.S.: 531390
Lie Fonda (Board of Directors & Sec)

PT PERTAMINA (PERSERO)
Jl Medan Merdeka Timur 1 A, Jakarta, 10110, Indonesia
Tel.: (62) 213815111
Web Site: http://www.pertamina.com
Year Founded: 1968
Sales Range: $1-4.9 Billion
Emp.: 22,000
Oil & Gas Drilling Services
N.A.I.C.S.: 213111
Dwi Subjipbo (CEO)

Subsidiaries:

Etablissements Maurel & Prom S.A.   (1)
51 rue d Anjou, 75008, Paris, France   (72.65%)
Tel.: (33) 153831600
Web Site: https://www.maureletprom.fr
Rev.: $676,480,000
Assets: $1,677,664,000
Liabilities: $807,199,000
Net Worth: $870,465,000
Earnings: $205,889,000
Emp.: 707
Fiscal Year-end: 12/31/2022
Oil & Gas Exploration Services
N.A.I.C.S.: 213112
Philippe Corlay (COO)

Subsidiary (Non-US):

Wentworth Resources Plc   (2)
4th Floor St Pauls Gate 22-24 New Street, Saint Helier, Jersey
Tel.: (44) 1182062982
Web Site: https://www.wentplc.com
Rev.: $23,818,000
Assets: $111,203,000
Liabilities: $4,468,000
Net Worth: $106,735,000
Earnings: $6,067,000
Emp.: 16
Fiscal Year-end: 12/31/2021
Natural Gas Distribution Services
N.A.I.C.S.: 221210

PT Indopelita Aircraft Service   (1)
Hangar IV Bandara Pondok Cabe Hilir, Ciputat, Tangerang, 15418, Indonesia
Tel.: (62) 21 7429310
Web Site: http://www.indopelita.co.id
Sales Range: $50-74.9 Million
Emp.: 200
Aircraft Maintenance Services
N.A.I.C.S.: 488190

PT Patra Drilling Contractor   (1)
Jl Mampang Prapatan Raya 139 Graha Mobisel Lt 5 Mampang, Jakarta, 12790, Indonesia
Tel.: (62) 21 7987974
Oil & Gas Well Drilling Services
N.A.I.C.S.: 213111

PT Patra Teknik   (1)
Jl Otto Iskandardinata Raya No 66, Jakarta, 13330, Indonesia
Tel.: (62) 21 857 1145
Web Site: http://www.patrateknik.com
Engineering Consulting Services
N.A.I.C.S.: 541330

PT Pertamina (Persero) - Unit II   (1)
Jl Raya Kilang Putri Tujuh, Dumai, 28815, Indonesia
Tel.: (62) 765 31244
Oil, Gas & Consumable Fuel Mfr
N.A.I.C.S.: 311224

PT Pertamina (Persero) - Unit V   (1)
Jl Kom L Yos Sudarso No 1, PO Box 626, Balikpapan, 76111, East Kalimantan, Indonesia
Tel.: (62) 542 733011
Oil, Gas & Consumable Fuel Mfr
N.A.I.C.S.: 311224

PT Pertamina Dana Ventura   (1)
Jl Merdeka Timur No 11, Jakarta, Indonesia
Tel.: (62) 21 34833887
Oil, Gas & Consumable Fuel Mfr
N.A.I.C.S.: 311224

Subsidiary (Domestic):

PT Mitra Tour & Travel   (2)
Jl Abdul Muis No 68, Jakarta, 10160, Indonesia
Tel.: (62) 21 3852621
Web Site: http://www.mitratour.com
Sales Range: $25-49.9 Million
Emp.: 100
Travel Arrangement & Ticket Reservation Services
N.A.I.C.S.: 561599

PT Pertamina Drilling Services Indonesia   (1)
Jl Matraman Raya No 87, Jakarta, 13140, Indonesia
Tel.: (62) 21 2936 0730
Oil & Gas Well Drilling Services
N.A.I.C.S.: 213111

PT Pertamina EP   (1)
Standard Chartered Tower 21st-29thFloor Jl Prof Dr Satrio No 164, Jakarta, 12950, Indonesia
Tel.: (62) 21 5797 4000
Web Site: http://www.pertamina-ep.com
Oil & Gas Exploration Services
N.A.I.C.S.: 213112
Syamsu Alam (Pres)

PT Pertamina EP Cepu   (1)
Patra Jasa Tower Level 6th-8th Jl Gatot Subroto Kav 32-34, Jakarta, 12950, Indonesia
Tel.: (62) 21 52900900
Oil, Gas & Consumable Fuel Mfr
N.A.I.C.S.: 311224

PT Pertamina Hulu Energi Jambi Merang   (1)
Jl Jend Sudirman Kav 54-55, Jakarta, 12190, Indonesia
Tel.: (62) 21 526 0909
Oil, Gas & Consumable Fuel Mfr
N.A.I.C.S.: 311224

PT Pertamina Hulu Energi West Madura Offshore   (1)
PHE Tower Lt 20 Jl Letjen T B Simatupang Kav 99, Jakarta, 12520, Indonesia
Tel.: (62) 21 2954 7500
Web Site: http://www.phe-wmo.com
Oil & Gas Exploration Services
N.A.I.C.S.: 213112

PT Pertamina Retail Indonesia   (1)
Wisma Tugu Wahid Hasyim Jl Wahid Hasyim No 100-102, 10340, Jakarta, Indonesia
Tel.: (62) 21 3926772
Web Site: http://web.pertaminaretail.com
Fuel Retailer
N.A.I.C.S.: 424710

PT Pertamina Trans Kontinental   (1)
Jl Kramat Raya No 29, Jakarta, 10450, Indonesia
Tel.: (62) 21 31923005
Web Site: http://www.ptk-shipping.com
Marine Shipping Services
N.A.I.C.S.: 488510
Ahmad Bambang (Pres)

Subsidiary (Domestic):

PT Peteka Karya Gapura   (2)
Gedung PT Pertamina Trans Kontinental Area Logistic Pertamina Jl Yos, Sudarso Sunter Tanjung Priok, Jakarta, Indonesia
Tel.: (62) 21 65307031
Web Site: http://www.pekage.com
Freight Forwarding Services
N.A.I.C.S.: 488510

PT Peteka Karya Jala   (2)
Jl Kom L Yos Sudarso Ged Pertamina Tongkang Sunter Agung, Tanjung Priok, Jakarta, 14350, Indonesia
Tel.: (62) 21 6516054
Water Distribution Services
N.A.I.C.S.: 221310

PT Peteka Karya Samudera   (2)
Jl Raya Pelabuhan Kabil, Batam, 29437, Indonesia
Tel.: (62) 778 711543

PT PERTAMINA (PERSERO)

PT Pertamina (Persero)—(Continued)
Sales Range: $25-49.9 Million
Emp.: 25
Cargo Handling Services
N.A.I.C.S.: 488119

PT Peteka Karya Tirta (2)
Jl Raya Anyer Km 119 Ciwandan, Cilegon, Banten, Indonesia
Tel.: (62) 254 601146
Web Site: http://www.petekakaryatirta.com
Water Distribution Services
N.A.I.C.S.: 221310

PT Tugu Pratama Indonesia (1)
Wisma Tugu I Jalan H R Rasuna Said Kav C 8-9, Jakarta, 12920, Indonesia
Tel.: (62) 21 529 61 777
Web Site: http://www.tugu.com
Sales Range: $200-249.9 Million
Emp.: 280
General Insurance & Risk Management Services
N.A.I.C.S.: 524298
Yasril Rasyid (CEO)

Subsidiary (Domestic):

PT Synergy Risk Management Consultants (2)
Jl Bukit Hijau VIII No 31 Pondok Indah, Jakarta, 12310, Selatan, Indonesia
Tel.: (62) 2127811486
Web Site: https://www.synergy.co.id
Sales Range: $25-49.9 Million
Emp.: 25
Risk Management Consulting Services
N.A.I.C.S.: 541618

PT Tugu Pratama Interindo
Gedung Wisma Tugu II Lantai 8 Jalan HR Rasuna Said Kavling C 7, Kuningan, Jakarta Selatan, 12920, Indonesia
Tel.: (62) 215212279
Web Site: https://www.tuguholding.com
General Insurance & Risk Management Services
N.A.I.C.S.: 524298

Subsidiary (Domestic):

PT Pratama Mitra Sejati (3)
Wisma Tugu Raden Saleh Jl Raden Saleh No 44, Jakarta, 10330, Indonesia
Tel.: (62) 213911770
Web Site: https://www.pratamamitra.co.id
Office Space Rental Services
N.A.I.C.S.: 531120
Etom Katamsi (Dir)

PT. Asuransi Staco Mandiri (3)
Wisma Tugu Raden Saleh Lantai 3 dan 4 Jl Raden Saleh No 44, Jakarta, 10330, Indonesia
Tel.: (62) 21 391 1840
Web Site: http://www.stacoinsurance.com
General Insurance Services
N.A.I.C.S.: 524298

Subsidiary (Non-US):

TRB (London) Ltd. (2)
83-85 Mansell Street, London, E1 8AN, United Kingdom
Tel.: (44) 2074819442
General Insurance & Risk Management Services
N.A.I.C.S.: 524298

Tugu Insurance Company Limited (2)
28/F United Asia Finance Centre 333 Lockhart Road, Wanchai, China (Hong Kong)
Tel.: (852) 28242939
Web Site: https://www.tuguhk.com
General Insurance Services
N.A.I.C.S.: 524298

Pertamina Energy Trading Limited (1)
44/F Office Tower Convention Plaza 1 Harbour Road, Wanchai, China (Hong Kong)
Tel.: (852) 28667712
Web Site: http://www.pnatrade.com.sg
Sales Range: $50-74.9 Million
Emp.: 2
Crude Oil Distr
N.A.I.C.S.: 424720

Subsidiary (Non-US):

Pertamina Energy Services Pte. Limited (2)
391A Orchard Road 10-04 Ngee Ann City Tower A, Singapore, 238873, Singapore
Tel.: (65) 6736 1977
Sales Range: $25-49.9 Million
Crude Oil Whslr
N.A.I.C.S.: 424720

Pertamina Hulu Energi Australia Pty. Ltd. (1)
L 27 50 Bridge St, Sydney, 2000, NSW, Australia
Tel.: (61) 2 9230 0808
Oil, Gas & Consumable Fuel Mfr
N.A.I.C.S.: 311224

Pertamina Trans Kontinental (1)
Jl Kramat Raya No 29, Jakarta, 10450, Indonesia
Tel.: (62) 21-31923005
Web Site: http://www.petekashipping.com
Marine Shipping Services
N.A.I.C.S.: 488510

PT PERTAMINA GEOTHERMAL ENERGY TBK

Jalan Medan Merdeka Timur No 11-13, Grha Pertamina Tower Pertamax Lantai 7, Jakarta Pusat, 10110, Indonesia
Tel.: (62) 2139833222
Web Site: https://www.pge.pertamina.com
Year Founded: 2006
PGEO—(INDO)
Rev.: $406,288,000
Assets: $2,964,141,000
Liabilities: $992,885,000
Net Worth: $1,971,256,000
Earnings: $163,570,000
Emp.: 502
Fiscal Year-end: 12/31/23
Eletric Power Generation Services
N.A.I.C.S.: 221111
Muhammad Baron (Sec)

Subsidiaries:

P.T. Geothermal Energi Seulawah (1)
Grha Pertamina-Tower Pertamax 9th Floor, Jl Medan Merdeka Timur No 11- 13 Gambir, Central Jakarta, 10110, Indonesia
Tel.: (62) 2139833222
Geothermal Electric Power Generation Services
N.A.I.C.S.: 562213

P.T. Pertamina Geothermal Energy Kotamobagu (1)
Grha Pertamina-Tower Pertamax 9th Floor, Jl Medan Merdeka Timur No 11- 13 Gambir, Central Jakarta, 10110, Indonesia
Tel.: (62) 2139833222
Geothermal Electric Power Generation Services
N.A.I.C.S.: 562213

P.T. Pertamina Hulu Energi Ogan Komering (1)
Main Building 5th Floor Jl Merdeka Timur 1A, Jakarta Pusat, 10110, Indonesia
Tel.: (62) 213815709
Web Site: https://www.pertamina.com
Oil & Gas Distr
N.A.I.C.S.: 486110

PT PERUSAHAAN GAS NEGARA (PERSERO) TBK

Jl K H Zainul Arifin No 20, Jakarta, 11140, Indonesia
Tel.: (62) 216334838 Id
Web Site: https://www.pgn.co.id
PPAAY—(OTCIQ)
Rev.: $3,646,304,165
Assets: $6,599,238,469
Liabilities: $3,058,835,090
Net Worth: $3,540,403,379
Earnings: $376,615,901
Emp.: 3,318

Fiscal Year-end: 12/31/23
Gas & Energy Distr
N.A.I.C.S.: 424720
Dilo Seno Widagdo (Comml Dir)

Subsidiaries:

PT Gagas Energi Indonesia (1)
Jl K H Zainul Arifin No 20 Perkantoran PGN Gedung B 9th-10th Floor, Jakarta Barat, 11140, Indonesia
Tel.: (62) 2129071415
Natural Gas Transportation & Distr
N.A.I.C.S.: 486210

Subsidiary (Domestic):

PT Widar Mandripa Nusantara (2)
Komplek Perkantoran PT Perusahaan Gas Negara Tbk Jl KH, Zainul Arifin No 20, Jakarta, 11140, Indonesia
Tel.: (62) 212 984 5050
Web Site: https://www.wmnusantara.co.id
Power Generation Services
N.A.I.C.S.: 221118
Rizal Wibisono (CEO)

PT PGAS Solution
Komplek Perkantoran PGN Gedung C Jl K H Zainul Arifin No 20, Jakarta Barat, 11140, Indonesia
Tel.: (62) 216 385 4572
Web Site: https://www.pgn-solution.co.id
Emp.: 2,672
Oil & Gas Pipeline Construction Services
N.A.I.C.S.: 237120
Erning Laksmi (Dir-Fin)

PT PGAS Telekomunikasi Nusantara (1)
Wisma 77 Lantai 19, Jl S Parman Kav 77-78, Jakarta, Indonesia
Tel.: (62) 2153660444
Web Site: http://www.pgascom.co.id
Sales Range: $25-49.9 Million
Emp.: 1
Telecommunication Servicesb
N.A.I.C.S.: 517810
Dwika Agustianto (Pres)

PT PGN LNG Indonesia (1)
Jl K H Zainul Arifin No 20, Jakarta, 11140, Indonesia
Tel.: (62) 212 903 7505
Web Site: https://www.pgnlng.co.id
Natural Gas Transportation Services
N.A.I.C.S.: 486210
Jeffry Hotman Simanjuntak (Pres)

PT Permata Graha Nusantara (1)
Komplek Perkantoran PGN Gedung B Lantai 6 - 8 Jl KH Zainul Arifin, No 20 Jakarta Barat, Jakarta Barat, 11140, Indonesia
Tel.: (62) 21 633 1180
Web Site: https://pgnmas.co.id
Real Estate Manangement Services
N.A.I.C.S.: 531390
Bayu Nurcahyono (Gen Mgr-Ops)

Subsidiary (Domestic):

PT Kalimantan Jawa Gas (2)
Jl K H Zainul Arifin No 20 Perkantoran PGN Gedung B 2nd Floor, Jakarta Barat, 11140, Indonesia
Tel.: (62) 2163854534
Web Site: https://www.kalijagas.co.id
Natural Gas Transportation Services
N.A.I.C.S.: 486210
Agus Iskandar (Dir-Engrg & Ops)

PT Permata Karya Jasa (1)
Jl K H Zainul Arifin No 20 Perkantoran PGN Gedung A 4th Floor, Jakarta Barat, 11140, Indonesia
Tel.: (62) 2163850047
Natural Gas Transportation Services
N.A.I.C.S.: 486210
Moh Zulfa (Sr Mgr)

PT Pertamina Gas (1)
Grha Pertamina Pertamax Tower Lantai 20-23, Jl Medan Merdeka Timur No 11-13, Jakarta, 10110, Indonesia
Tel.: (62) 213 190 6825
Web Site: https://www.pertagas.pertamina.com
Oil & Gas Exploration Services
N.A.I.C.S.: 327910
Wiko Migantoro (Pres)

INTERNATIONAL PUBLIC

Subsidiary (Domestic):

PT Perta Arun Gas (2)
Gedung Patra Jasa Lantai 1 Jl Jend Gatot Subroto Kav 32-34, Jakarta Selatan, Indonesia
Tel.: (62) 215251005
Oil & Gas Exploration Services
N.A.I.C.S.: 213112
Gusti Azis (Dir-Ops & Technical)

PT Perta Daya Gas (2)
Tanjung Emas Harbor Complex Jl Ronggowarsito No 1, Semarang Tengah, Semarang, 50134, Central Java, Indonesia
Tel.: (62) 248 657 0237
Web Site: https://www.pertadayagas.co.id
Natural Gas Transportation Services
N.A.I.C.S.: 486210
Tutut Sandewan (Mgr-Unit)

PT Perta Kalimantan Gas (2)
Oil Centre Building 2nd 3rd Floor Jl MH Thamrin Kav 55, Jakarta, 10350, Indonesia
Tel.: (62) 2131906825
Oil & Gas Exploration Services
N.A.I.C.S.: 213112

PT Pertagas Niaga (2)
Gedung Patra Jasa Lantai 16 Jl Jend Gatot Subroto Kav 32-34, Jakarta Selatan, Indonesia
Tel.: (62) 215203088
Oil & Gas Exploration Services
N.A.I.C.S.: 213112
Wildan Rizanjaya (Mgr-Comml-LNG)

PT Perusahaan Gas Negara (Persero) Tbk - Strategic Business Unit Region I (1)
Jl M I Ridwan Rais No 8, Jakarta, 10110, Indonesia
Tel.: (62) 213452147
Web Site: http://www.pgn.co.id
Sales Range: $25-49.9 Million
Emp.: 150
Business Management Consulting Services
N.A.I.C.S.: 541611

PT Perusahaan Gas Negara (Persero) Tbk - Strategic Business Unit Region II (1)
Jl Pemuda No 56-58, Surabaya, 60271, East Java, Indonesia
Tel.: (62) 31 5490555
Web Site: http://www.pgn.co.id
Business Management Services
N.A.I.C.S.: 561499

PT Perusahaan Gas Negara (Persero) Tbk - Strategic Business Unit Sumatera-Java Transmission (1)
Wisma 77 Lantai 3 Jl S Parman Slipi, Jakarta Barat, Jakarta, 11410, Indonesia
Tel.: (62) 215363069
Web Site: http://www.pgn.co.id
Natural Gas Transmission Services
N.A.I.C.S.: 486210

PT Saka Energi Indonesia (1)
The Manhattan Square 26th Floor Jl TB Simatupang Kav 1S, Jakarta, 12560, Indonesia
Tel.: (62) 212 995 1000
Web Site: https://www.sakaenergi.com
Oil & Gas Exploration Services
N.A.I.C.S.: 213112
Gigih Prakoso (Pres)

PT Solusi Energi Nusantara (1)
Daan Mogot gang Macan Rt 3 Rw 5, Duri Kepa Kebon Jeruk, Jakarta, 11510, Indonesia
Tel.: (62) 212 119 1988
Web Site: https://www.pt-sena.co.id
Oil & Gas Exploration Services
N.A.I.C.S.: 213112
Leo Kapmas Sinambela (Mgr-Engrg)

PT Telemedia Dinamika Sarana (1)
Gedung C Lantai 1 Komplek PT Perusahaan Gas Negara Jl KH, Zainul Arifin No 20, Jakarta, 11140, Indonesia
Tel.: (62) 213 001 0645
Web Site: https://www.gasnet.id
Internet Services
N.A.I.C.S.: 517121

PT Transportasi Gas Indonesia (1)
Jalan Kebon Sirih Raya No 1, Jakarta,

10340, Indonesia
Tel.: (62) 213158929
Web Site: http://www.tgi.co.id
Natural Gas Pipeline Transportation Services
N.A.I.C.S.: 486210

PT PETRINDO JAYA KREASI TBK
Wisma Barito Pacific Tower B Lantai 3, 3rd Floor Jl Let Jend S Parman Kav 62-63, Jakarta, 11410, Indonesia
Tel.: (62) 215308520
Web Site: https://www.petrindo.co.id
Year Founded: 2008
CUAN—(INDO)
Rev.: $97,028,531
Assets: $230,318,086
Liabilities: $109,482,420
Net Worth: $120,835,666
Earnings: $15,107,361
Emp.: 80
Fiscal Year-end: 12/31/23
Coal Mining Services
N.A.I.C.S.: 213113

PT PHAPROS TBK
Menara Rajawali Lantai 17 Jl Dr Ide Anak Agung Gde Agung, Mega Kuningan, Jakarta, 12950, Indonesia
Tel.: (62) 215762709
Web Site: https://www.phapros.co.id
Year Founded: 1954
PEHA—(INDO)
Rev.: $65,857,583
Assets: $114,676,740
Liabilities: $64,651,690
Net Worth: $50,025,051
Earnings: $390,427
Emp.: 1,050
Fiscal Year-end: 12/31/23
Pharmaceuticals Product Mfr
N.A.I.C.S.: 325412
Syamsul Huda (Dir)

PT PIKKO LAND DEVELOPMENT TBK
The Office Sahid Sudirman Residence 3rd Floor Jend Sudirman 86, Sahid City, Jakarta, 10220, Indonesia
Tel.: (62) 2152970288
Web Site: https://www.pikkoland.com
Year Founded: 1984
RODA—(INDO)
Rev.: $6,894,835
Assets: $220,851,414
Liabilities: $79,392,443
Net Worth: $141,458,972
Earnings: ($2,245,148)
Emp.: 151
Fiscal Year-end: 12/31/23
Real Estate Manangement Services
N.A.I.C.S.: 531390
Nio Yantony (Chm)

PT PINAGO UTAMA TBK
Jalan Jend Basuki Rahmat No 23, Pantai Indah Kapuk Kel Kamal Muara Kec Penjaringan, Palembang, 30127, Indonesia
Tel.: (62) 2155966133
Web Site: https://pinagoutama.com
PNGO—(INDO)
Rev.: $132,301,255
Assets: $96,705,342
Liabilities: $44,958,440
Net Worth: $51,746,903
Earnings: $12,446,677
Emp.: 1,886
Fiscal Year-end: 12/31/23
Agricultural Product Mfr
N.A.I.C.S.: 333111
Raymon Wahab (Dir-Processing & Industry)

PT PIONEERINDO GOURMET INTERNATIONAL TBK
Graha Cfc Centre Jl Palmerah Utara No 100, Jakarta, 11480, Indonesia
Tel.: (62) 53668999
Web Site: http://www.cfcindonesia.com
Year Founded: 1983
PTSP—(INDO)
Rev.: $40,519,361
Assets: $21,361,035
Liabilities: $11,564,732
Net Worth: $9,796,303
Earnings: $1,143,267
Fiscal Year-end: 12/31/23
Restaurant Operators
N.A.I.C.S.: 722511
Henkie Sutjieawan (Chm)

PT PLANET PROPERINDO JAYA TBK
Jl Otto Iskandar Dinata No 3 Babakan Ciamis, Ciamis District, Bandung, 40117, West Java, Indonesia
Tel.: (62) 224266288
Web Site: https://www.planetproperindo.com
PLAN—(INDO)
Rev.: $707,392
Assets: $5,729,486
Liabilities: $1,770,195
Net Worth: $3,959,292
Earnings: ($141,284)
Fiscal Year-end: 12/31/23
Hotel Services
N.A.I.C.S.: 721110
Antonyo Hartono Tanujaya (Pres & Dir)

PT PLATINUM WAHAB NUSANTARA TBK
Ruko Golden Square Blok GS No 2 Jl Ciater Raya Kel Mekarjaya, Kec Serpong, Tangerang, 15321, Banten, Indonesia
Tel.: (62) 2153160311
Web Site: https://www.teguk.co.id
Year Founded: 2018
TGUK—(INDO)
Rev.: $8,607,407
Assets: $13,030,254
Liabilities: $1,520,071
Net Worth: $11,510,183
Earnings: $381,392
Emp.: 4
Fiscal Year-end: 12/31/23
Beauty Product Mfr
N.A.I.C.S.: 325620
Akhmad Riski Rasyid (Sec)

PT PLAZA INDONESIA REALTY TBK
The Plaza Office Tower 10th Floor Jl MH Thamrin Kav 28 - 30, Jakarta, 10350, Indonesia
Tel.: (62) 2129920000
Web Site: https://www.plazaindonesia.com
Year Founded: 1983
PLIN—(INDO)
Rev.: $84,373,694
Assets: $795,028,866
Liabilities: $87,880,668
Net Worth: $707,148,198
Earnings: $39,825,559
Emp.: 369
Fiscal Year-end: 12/31/23
Real Estate Lending Services
N.A.I.C.S.: 531190
Rosano Barack (Chm)

PT PLN (PERSERO)
Jl Trunojoyo Blok M I No 135, Kebayoran Baru, Jakarta, 12160, Indonesia
Tel.: (62) 21 7251234
Web Site: http://www.pln.co.id
Year Founded: 1961
Rev.: $19,102,841,940
Assets: $104,474,142,150
Liabilities: $39,555,172,160
Net Worth: $64,918,969,990
Earnings: $810,302,920
Emp.: 54,124
Fiscal Year-end: 12/31/18
Eletric Power Generation Services
N.A.I.C.S.: 221118
Supangkat Iwan Santoso (Reg Dir-Bus-East Java)

Subsidiaries:

PT Bangun Persada Jambi Energi (1)
Komp Citra Land NGK B-07 Walk Plaza Alegro Mayang Mangurai, Kota Baru, Jambi, 36129, Indonesia
Tel.: (62) 7413073008
Electricity Power Generation Services
N.A.I.C.S.: 221118

PT Haleyora Power (1)
Kindo Square Blok A15-16 JL Duren Tiga Raya No 101 Duren Tiga, South Jakarta, 12760, Indonesia
Tel.: (62) 2179192517
Web Site: http://www.haleyorapower.co.id
Electricity Power Generation Services
N.A.I.C.S.: 221118

PT Indo Raya Tenaga (1)
Sentra Senayan II Lt 17 Jl Asia Afrika Lot 8, Jakarta Pusat, 10270, Jakarta, Indonesia
Tel.: (62) 2157900202
Web Site: http://www.irt.co.id
Electricity Power Generation Services
N.A.I.C.S.: 221118
Peter Wijaya (Co-Pres)

PT Indo Tenaga Hijau (1)
PT PLN (Persero) Building Complex Jl Jend Gatot Subroto Kav 18, Setiabudi, South Jakarta, 12950, Indonesia
Tel.: (62) 212523005
Web Site: http://www.indotenagahijau.co.id
Renewable Energy Services
N.A.I.C.S.: 221111

PT Mitra Karya Prima (1)
Juanda Business Center JBC Blok A No 4 5 and 6 Jl Raya Juanda No 1, Sidoarjo, 61253, Indonesia
Tel.: (62) 318548595
Web Site: http://www.mitrakaryaprima.com
Electricity Power Generation Services
N.A.I.C.S.: 221118
Abu Hasan (Dir-Mktg & Ops)

PT PJB Investasi (1)
Bidakara Tower-2 8th Fl Gatot Subroto St Kav 71-73, South Jakarta, 12870, Indonesia
Tel.: (62) 2183708760
Web Site: http://www.pjbinvest.com
Electricity Power Generation Services
N.A.I.C.S.: 221118
Eni Wulansari (Co-Pres & Commissioner)

PT PJB Services (1)
Jl Raya Juanda No 17, Sidoarjo, 61253, East Java, Indonesia
Tel.: (62) 318548391
Web Site: http://www.pjbservices.com
Electricity Power Generation Services
N.A.I.C.S.: 221118
Supangkat Iwan Satoso (Co-Pres & Commissioner)

PT PLN Batubara (1)
Jalan Warung Buncit Raya No 10, Keluran Kalibata Kecamatan Pancoran, Jakarta Selatan, 12740, Indonesia
Tel.: (62) 2129122118
Web Site: http://www.plnbatubara.co.id
Coal Distr
N.A.I.C.S.: 423520

PT PLN Gas dan Geothermal (1)
KMO Building 8th Floor Jalan Kyai Maja No 1, Kebayoran Baru, South Jakarta, 12120, Jakarta, Indonesia
Tel.: (62) 2129721019
Web Site: http://www.plngg.com
Gas & Geothermal Electricity Services
N.A.I.C.S.: 221115

PT PLN Suku Cadang (1)
Recapital Building 3rd Floor Jl Adityawarman No 55, South Jakarta, 12160, Jakarta, Indonesia
Tel.: (62) 217246184
Web Site: http://www.plnsc.co.id
Electricity Power Generation Services
N.A.I.C.S.: 221118

PT Paguntaka Cahaya Nusantara Balikpapan (1)
JL RE Martadinata RT 52 No 35 Kec Central, Balikpapan, 76113, East Kalimantan, Indonesia
Tel.: (62) 5428507238
Web Site: http://www.pcn-balikpapan.com
Labor Providing Services
N.A.I.C.S.: 561320

PT Pelayanan Listrik Nasional Batam (1)
Jl Engku Putri No 3 Center, Batam, Indonesia
Tel.: (62) 778463150
Web Site: http://www.plnbatam.com
Electricity Power Generation Services
N.A.I.C.S.: 221118

PT Pelayanan Listrik Nasional Tarakan (1)
Jl MT Haryono Komplek Balikpapan Baru Nomor 1-5, Balikpapan, Kalimantan Timur, Indonesia
Tel.: (62) 5428506674
Web Site: http://www.pln-t.co.id
Electricity Power Generation Services
N.A.I.C.S.: 221118

PT Pembangkitan Jawa Bali (1)
Jl Ketintang Baru No 11, Surabaya, 60231, Indonesia
Tel.: (62) 318283180
Web Site: http://www.ptpjb.com
Electricity Power Generation Services
N.A.I.C.S.: 221118
Benny M. M. Marbun (Commissioner)

PT Prima Layanan Nasional Enjiniring (1)
Jl Ciputat Raya No 123, Kebayoran Lama, Jakarta Selatan, 12310, Indonesia
Tel.: (62) 2127510363
Web Site: http://www.plne.co.id
Construction Services
N.A.I.C.S.: 236220
Ahmad Rofik (Commissioner)

PT Prima Power Nusantara (1)
Menara Engineering Jalan Ciputat Raya No 123, Pondok Pinang-Kebayoran Lama, Jakarta, 12310, Indonesia
Tel.: (62) 2122768719
Web Site: http://www.primapowernusantara.co.id
Power Plant Construction Services
N.A.I.C.S.: 237130

PT Rekadaya Elektrika (1)
Building 18 Office Park Lt 18 Jl T B Simatupang No 18, Pasar Minggu, South Jakarta, 12520, Indonesia
Tel.: (62) 2127871818
Web Site: http://www.rekadaya.co.id
Electricity Power Generation Services
N.A.I.C.S.: 221118
Vernon Sapalatua Tampubolon (Dir-Mktg & Bus Dev)

PT Rekadaya Elektrika Consult (1)
Wisma 46 Kota BNI Lt 17 Jl Jend Sudirman Kav 1, Jakarta, 10220, Indonesia
Tel.: (62) 215721375
Web Site: http://www.reconsult.co.id
Business Consulting Services
N.A.I.C.S.: 541611

PT Sertifikasi Kompetensi Pembangkitan Tenaga Listrik (1)
Jl Tebet Raya No 44D, South Jakarta, Indonesia
Tel.: (62) 2122831822
Web Site: http://www.ptskp.id
Electricity Power Generation Services
N.A.I.C.S.: 221118

PT POLARIS INVESTAMA TBK
Mayapada Tower Lt 11 Jl Jend Sudirman Kav 28, Jakarta, 12920, Indonesia
Tel.: (62) 2152897418

PT POLARIS INVESTAMA TBK

PT Polaris Investama Tbk—(Continued)
Web Site:
https://www.polarisinvestama.co.id
Rev.: $1,881,839
Assets: $13,348,312
Liabilities: $2,491,507
Net Worth: $10,856,805
Earnings: $28,925
Emp.: 34
Fiscal Year-end: 12/31/18
Investment Management Service
N.A.I.C.S.: 523940
Khaeruman Nasruddinnillah *(Chm)*

Subsidiaries:

PT Polaris Indonesia (1)
JL Gunawarman No 16, Kel Selong Kec
Kebayoran Baru, South Jakarta, 12110,
Indonesia
Tel.: (62) 2172787110
Web Site: http://www.polaris.id
Body Recovery & Beauty Care Services
N.A.I.C.S.: 812199

PT POLLUX HOTELS GROUP TBK

Noble House 36Dr Ide Anak Agung
Gde Agung Kav E4 2 No 2 Mega
Kuningan, Jakarta Selatan, 12950,
Indonesia
Tel.: (62) 2129183111
Web Site: https://pollux.co.id
POLI—(INDO)
Rev.: $23,434,784
Assets: $210,742,535
Liabilities: $80,821,654
Net Worth: $129,920,882
Earnings: $5,999,948
Emp.: 451
Fiscal Year-end: 12/31/23
Real Estate Manangement Services
N.A.I.C.S.: 531210

Subsidiaries:

P.T. Widya Bhakti (1)
Jl Moh Toha 77, Bandung, 40253, Jawa
Barat, Indonesia
Tel.: (62) 2288885401
Web Site: https://widyabhakti.co.id
Property Management & Development Services
N.A.I.C.S.: 531311

PT POLLUX PROPERTI INDONESIA TBK

Noble House 36 Dr Ide Anak Agung
Gde Agung Kav E4 2 No 2, Mega
Kuninga, Jakarta Selatan, 12950,
Indonesia
Tel.: (62) 29183111
Web Site: https://www.pollux.co.id
POLL—(INDO)
Rev.: $21,785,458
Assets: $311,051,398
Liabilities: $202,031,039
Net Worth: $109,020,360
Earnings: $30,092,224
Emp.: 144
Fiscal Year-end: 12/31/22
Real Estate Development Services
N.A.I.C.S.: 237210
R. M. Suryo Atmanto *(Chm)*

PT POLYCHEM INDONESIA TBK

Gedung Wisma 46 - Kota BNI Lt 20
Jl Jend Sudirman Kavling 1, RT 010
RW 009 Karet Tengsin Tanah Abang
Kota Adm, Jakarta, 10220, Indonesia
Tel.: (62) 215744848   Id
Web Site:
https://www.polychemindo.com
Year Founded: 1986
ADMG—(INDO)
Rev.: $104,802,680
Assets: $158,715,638
Liabilities: $32,716,223
Net Worth: $125,999,415
Earnings: ($19,119,581)
Emp.: 565
Fiscal Year-end: 12/31/23
Polyester Resin Mfr
N.A.I.C.S.: 325211
Gautama Hartarto *(Chm)*

PT POOL ADVISTA FINANCE TBK

5th-6th floor 11 Hwangsaeul-ro
359beon-gil, South Jakarta, 12210,
Indonesia
Tel.: (62) 2180626300
Web Site: https://www.paf.co.id
Year Founded: 2001
POLA—(INDO)
Rev.: $1,254,319
Assets: $15,934,032
Liabilities: $576,239
Net Worth: $15,357,794
Earnings: ($1,081,515)
Emp.: 34
Fiscal Year-end: 12/31/23
Financial Investment Services
N.A.I.C.S.: 523999
Mujoko Yandri Panjaitan *(Pres)*

PT POOL ADVISTA INDONESIA TBK

Jl Letjen Soepono Blok CC6 No 9-10,
Arteri Permata Hijau, Jakarta, 12210,
Selatan, Indonesia
Tel.: (62) 2180626300   Id
Web Site:
http://www.pooladvista.com
Year Founded: 1958
POOL—(INDO)
Holding Company; Investment Management & Development Services
N.A.I.C.S.: 551112
Bima Aranta *(Commissioner)*

PT PP (PERSERO) TBK

Plaza PP - Wisma Subiyanto Jl
Letjend TB Simatupang No 57 Pasar
Rebo, Jakarta, 13760, Indonesia
Tel.: (62) 218403883
Web Site: https://www.ptpp.co.id
Year Founded: 1953
PTPP—(INDO)
Rev.: $1,199,066,153
Assets: $3,670,736,265
Liabilities: $2,687,324,432
Net Worth: $983,411,833
Earnings: $8,253,193
Emp.: 1,707
Fiscal Year-end: 12/31/23
Construction Services
N.A.I.C.S.: 237990
Lukman Hidayat *(Co-Chm)*

Subsidiaries:

P.T. PP Krakatau Tirta (1)
Tegalsari Hamlet RT 11 RW 06, Sidomukti
Village Bungah District Gresik Regency,
East Java, 61152, Indonesia
Tel.: (62) 31313000900
Web Site: https://pp-krakatautirta.co.id
Water Treatment Plant Services
N.A.I.C.S.: 237110

P.T. Pekanbaru Permai Propertindo (1)
Gandaria 8 Office Tower Lantai 3 unit F Jl
Sultan Iskandar Muda, Kebayoran Lama,
Jakarta Selatan, 12240, DKI Jakarta, Indonesia
Tel.: (62) 2129304047
Residential Services
N.A.I.C.S.: 531210

P.T. Presisi Sumber Anugerah (1)
Plaza PP - Wisma Robinson Building, 3rd
Floor Jl TB Simatupang No 57 Gedong
Pasar Rebo DKI Jakarta, East Jakarta,
13760, Indonesia
Tel.: (62) 218230353
Waste Water Treatment Services
N.A.I.C.S.: 924110

P.T. Ultra Mandiri Telekomunikasi (1)
Plaza PP Jl Letjend TB Simatupang No 57
Pasar Rebo, Jakarta, 13760, Indonesia
Tel.: (62) 87879555652
Web Site: https://um-tel.co.id
Telecommunication Infrastructure Services
N.A.I.C.S.: 561520

PT Griyaton Indonesia (1)
Jl Kaliabang RT 001/RW 018 Harapan Jaya
Kec, Bekasi Utara, Bekasi, 17124, Jawa
Barat, Indonesia
Tel.: (62) 2188958629
Web Site: http://www.griyaton.com
Construction Equipment Mfr
N.A.I.C.S.: 333120

PT Lancarjaya Mandiri Abadi (1)
Jl Raya Narogong KM 12 5 No 18, Bekasi,
17152, Jawa Barat, Indonesia
Tel.: (62) 218250365
Web Site: https://lmacontractor.com
Construction Equipment Services
N.A.I.C.S.: 532412

PT PP Energi (1)
Plaza PP 7th Floor Jl TB Simatupang No
57 DKI Jakarta, Jakarta Timur, 13760, Indonesia
Tel.: (62) 218403988
Web Site: http://www.pp-energi.com
Renewable Energy Services
N.A.I.C.S.: 221114
Ario Setyawan *(Pres)*

PT PP Infrastruktur (1)
Plaza PP 4th Floor Jl Letjend TB Simatupang No 57 Pasar Rebo, Jakarta Timur,
13760, Indonesia
Tel.: (62) 218414449
Web Site: http://www.pp-infrastructure.com
Real Estate Services
N.A.I.C.S.: 531390

PT PP Presisi Tbk (1)
Plaza PP Wisma Robinson Lt 1 Jl TB Simatupang No 57 Pasar rebo, Jakarta Timur,
13760, Indonesia
Tel.: (62) 218414119
Web Site: https://www.pp-presisi.co.id
Construction Equipment Services
N.A.I.C.S.: 532412
Nur Rochmad *(Pres & Commissioner)*

PT PP Urban (1)
Plaza PP Lt 2 Jl TB Simatupang No 57
Pasar Rebo, Jakarta, 13760, Indonesia
Tel.: (62) 21840393334
Construction Services
N.A.I.C.S.: 236220

PT PPRO BIJB Aerocity Development (1)
Jalan Soekarno - Hatta No 522 Batununggal, Bandung, 40266, Jawa Barat West
Java, Indonesia
Tel.: (62) 227569921
Web Site: http://www.pprobijbaerocity.com
Real Estate Services
N.A.I.C.S.: 531390

PT PP LONDON SUMATRA INDONESIA TBK

Ariobimo Sentral 12th Floor Jl HR
Rasuna Said Blok X2 Kav 5, Jakarta,
12950, Indonesia
Tel.: (62) 2180657388
Web Site:
https://www.londonsumatra.com
PPLFF—(OTCIQ)
Rev.: $272,091,846
Assets: $812,672,343
Liabilities: $75,769,524
Net Worth: $736,902,819
Earnings: $49,398,105
Emp.: 14,110
Fiscal Year-end: 12/31/23
Palm Oil Production & Development Services
N.A.I.C.S.: 311225
Benny Tjoeng *(Chm)*

Subsidiaries:

PT Wushan Hijau Lestari (1)

INTERNATIONAL PUBLIC

Sudirman Plaza Indofood Tower 11th Floor
Jl Jend Sudirman Kav 76-78, Jakarta,
12910, Indonesia
Tel.: (62) 2157958822
Agriculture & Forestry Development Services
N.A.I.C.S.: 115310

Sumatra Bioscience Pte., Ltd. (1)
8 Eu Tong Sen Street 16-96/97 The Central, Singapore, 059818, Singapore
Tel.: (65) 65572389
Bioscience Marketing & Research Services
N.A.I.C.S.: 541715

PT PP PROPERTI TBK

Plaza PP - Lantai 7 Jl Letjend TB
Simatupang No 57 Pasar Rebo, Jakarta, 13760, Indonesia
Tel.: (62) 2187792734
Web Site: https://www.pp-properti.com
Year Founded: 2013
PPRO—(INDO)
Rev.: $63,869,230
Assets: $1,278,888,648
Liabilities: $1,065,446,221
Net Worth: $213,442,428
Earnings: ($83,389,754)
Emp.: 529
Fiscal Year-end: 12/31/23
Property Developer
N.A.I.C.S.: 236115
I. Gede Upeksa Negara *(Chm)*

PT PRATAMA WIDYA TBK

Widya Griya Jl Kelapa Buaran Pln No
92 A-D, Cikokol, Tangerang, 15117,
Indonesia
Tel.: (62) 2155782407
Web Site:
https://www.pratamawidya.com
Year Founded: 1981
PTPW—(INDO)
Rev.: $25,684,972
Assets: $45,470,756
Liabilities: $6,454,886
Net Worth: $39,015,869
Earnings: $6,677,556
Emp.: 7
Fiscal Year-end: 12/31/24
Heavy Construction Services
N.A.I.C.S.: 237990
Henny Farida *(Sec)*

Subsidiaries:

P.T. Pratama Beton Nusantara (1)
Widya Griya Kelapa Buaran PLN No 92 A-D
Cikokol, Tangerang, 15117, Banten, Indonesia
Tel.: (62) 2155782407
Building Material Mfr & Distr
N.A.I.C.S.: 321992

PT PRIMA ALLOY STEEL UNIVERSAL TBK

Jl Muncul No 1 Gedangan, Sidoarjo,
61254, Jawa Timur, Indonesia
Tel.: (62) 318537088
Web Site: http://www.pantherwheels.net
Year Founded: 1984
PRAS—(INDO)
Rev.: $6,163,191
Assets: $105,968,568
Liabilities: $80,806,349
Net Worth: $25,162,219
Earnings: ($6,089,273)
Emp.: 427
Fiscal Year-end: 12/31/22
Aluminium Wheel Mfr
N.A.I.C.S.: 336390
Djoko Sutrisno *(Chm & Pres)*

PT PRIMA ANDALAN MANDIRI

Office 8 Senopati Fl 28 Jenderal
Sudirman Kav 52-53, Jakarta, 12190,
Indonesia
Tel.: (62) 2129333189

Web Site:
https://www.mandiricoal.co.id
Year Founded: 1989
MCOL—(INDO)
Rev.: $376,647,657
Assets: $470,176,708
Liabilities: $158,049,088
Net Worth: $312,127,620
Earnings: $129,116,411
Fiscal Year-end: 09/30/21
Coal Mining Services
N.A.I.C.S.: 213113
Handy Glivirgo *(Pres)*

PT PRIMA CAKRAWALA ABADI TBK
Jl KRT Wongsonegoro No 39, Keluruhan Wonosari Kecamatan Ngaliyan, Semarang, 50186, Indonesia
Tel.: (62) 248661860
Web Site: https://www.pcafoods.com
PCAR—(INDO)
Rev.: $17,789,789
Assets: $6,789,660
Liabilities: $2,449,578
Net Worth: $4,340,082
Earnings: $597,715
Emp.: 79
Fiscal Year-end: 12/31/23
Fishery Product Distr
N.A.I.C.S.: 424460
Raditya Wardhana *(Chm)*

PT PRIMA GLOBALINDO LOGISTIK
Rukan Puri Mutiara Jl Griya utama Blok BC-8 Sunter Agung, T Priok, Jakarta Utara, 14350, Indonesia
Tel.: (62) 2122651324
Web Site: https://www.pgl-logistic.com
Year Founded: 2015
PPGL—(INDO)
Rev.: $11,962,591
Assets: $12,918,340
Liabilities: $3,449,665
Net Worth: $9,468,675
Earnings: $1,132,067
Emp.: 28
Fiscal Year-end: 12/31/23
Freight Forwarding Services
N.A.I.C.S.: 488510
Darmawan Suryadi *(Pres)*

PT PRODIA WIDYAHUSADA TBK
Jl Kramat Raya 150, Jakarta, 10430, Indonesia
Tel.: (62) 213144182 Id
Web Site: https://www.prodia.co.id
Year Founded: 1973
PRDA—(INDO)
Rev.: $144,326,942
Assets: $175,861,157
Liabilities: $22,563,208
Net Worth: $153,297,948
Earnings: $16,840,501
Emp.: 2,966
Fiscal Year-end: 12/31/23
Health Care Testing Services
N.A.I.C.S.: 621511
Dewi Muliaty *(Chm)*

Subsidiaries:

P.T. Prodia Digital Indonesia (1)
Jalan Kramat Raya No 148 ABC, Jakarta Pusat, 10430, Indonesia
Tel.: (62) 213144142
Web Site: https://prodiadigital.com
Diagnostic Research Services
N.A.I.C.S.: 621511

PT PROVIDENT INVESTASI BERSAMA TBK
The Convergence Indonesia Building 21st Floor, Kawasan Rasuna Epicentrum Jl HR Rasuna Said, Jakarta, 12940, Indonesia
Tel.: (62) 2121572008
Web Site: https://www.provident-investasi.com
Year Founded: 2006
PALM—(INDO)
Rev.: $199,034
Assets: $571,860,833
Liabilities: $412,081,337
Net Worth: $159,779,496
Earnings: ($214,579,126)
Emp.: 1,651
Fiscal Year-end: 12/31/23
Palm Plantations
N.A.I.C.S.: 111120
Tri Boewono *(Chm)*

PT PUDJIADI & SONS TBK
Jl Hayam Wuruk No 126 Hotel The Jayakarta Sp Lantai 21, Jakarta, 11180, Indonesia
Tel.: (62) 216593626
Web Site: https://pudjiadiandsons.co.id
Year Founded: 1970
PNSE—(INDO)
Rev.: $14,391,941
Assets: $23,912,293
Liabilities: $10,897,577
Net Worth: $13,014,716
Earnings: $1,633,121
Emp.: 601
Fiscal Year-end: 12/31/23
Hotel Operator
N.A.I.C.S.: 721110
Budhi Liman *(Chm)*

PT PUDJIADI PRESTIGE TBK
Hotel Jayakarta 21 Jalan Hayam Wuruk 126, Jakarta Barat, 11180, Indonesia
Tel.: (62) 216241030
Web Site: https://www.pudjiadiprestige.co.id
PUDP—(INDO)
Rev.: $2,443,814
Assets: $34,570,838
Liabilities: $1,021,186
Net Worth: $33,549,652
Earnings: $23,836
Emp.: 94
Fiscal Year-end: 12/31/23
Real Estate Development Services
N.A.I.C.S.: 531390
Damian Pudjiadi *(Chm)*

PT PURI GLOBAL SUKSES TBK
Komplek Ruko Mahkota Raya Blok D No 12A, Batam Centre, Batam, Indonesia
Tel.: (62) 7784801509
Web Site: https://www.puriglobalsukses.com
Year Founded: 2015
PURI—(INDO)
Rev.: $4,260,614
Assets: $22,394,916
Liabilities: $14,072,572
Net Worth: $8,322,344
Earnings: $71,367
Emp.: 21
Fiscal Year-end: 12/31/23
Real Estate Services
N.A.I.C.S.: 531390
Eko Saputro Wijaya *(Pres)*

PT PUTRA MANDIRI JEMBAR TBK
Dipo Tower Lt 17 JL Jend Gatot Subroto Kav 51, Jakarta, 10260, Indonesia
Tel.: (62) 2130060000
Web Site: https://ptpmj.co.id
Year Founded: 2003
PMJS—(INDO)
Rev.: $684,500,839
Assets: $279,435,248
Liabilities: $106,827,080
Net Worth: $172,608,168
Earnings: $13,680,273
Emp.: 1,933
Fiscal Year-end: 12/31/21
Vehicle Rental Services
N.A.I.C.S.: 532111
Fritz Gunawan *(Pres)*

Subsidiaries:

P.T. Dipo Angkasa Motor (1)
Jl Pluit Selatan No 1 C, Penjaringan, Jakarta Utara, 14440, Indonesia
Tel.: (62) 216611111
Automotive Mfr & Distr
N.A.I.C.S.: 336211

P.T. Dipo Internasional Pahala Otomotif (1)
Jl Sisingamangaraja Km 7 No 34 Medan Amplas Harjosari II, Medan, 20147, Sumatera Utara, Indonesia
Tel.: (62) 617866868
Web Site: https://www.dipo.co.id
Vehicle Maintenance Services
N.A.I.C.S.: 811198

P.T. Global Pahala Rental (1)
Dipo Tower Jl Gatot Subroto Rw 5 Petamburan, Kecamatan Tanah Abang Daerah Khusus Ibu Kota Jakarta, Jakarta Pusat, 10260, Indonesia
Tel.: (62) 2130060066
Web Site: https://www.gprrent.co.id
Motor Vehicle Rental Services
N.A.I.C.S.: 532112

PT PUTRA RAJAWALI KENCANA TBK
Jl Rungkut Industri Raya No 1F Ruko Sectionone Blok F7-F11, Kendangsari Tenggilis Mejoyo, Surabaya, 60292, Indonesia
Tel.: (62) 3199013573
Web Site: https://www.puratrans.com
Year Founded: 2012
PURA—(INDO)
Rev.: $12,539,727
Assets: $37,657,860
Liabilities: $5,302,590
Net Worth: $32,355,270
Earnings: $272,676
Emp.: 24
Fiscal Year-end: 12/31/23
Transportation Services
N.A.I.C.S.: 484110
Ratna Hidayati *(Sec)*

PT QUANTUM CLOVERA INVESTAMA TBK
Kresna Tower 6th Floor 18 Parc Place SCBD Jalan Jend, Sudirman Kav 52-53, Jakarta, 12190, Indonesia
Tel.: (62) 215152889
Web Site: https://quantumclovera.com
Year Founded: 1999
KREN—(INDO)
Rev.: $782,733,812
Assets: $233,156,332
Liabilities: $40,985,559
Net Worth: $192,170,773
Earnings: $(16,828,541)
Emp.: 271
Fiscal Year-end: 12/31/20
Financial Investment Services
N.A.I.C.S.: 523999
Michael Steven *(Founder & CEO)*

Subsidiaries:

PT Emitama Wahana Mandiri (1)
Mal Ambasador Lt 5 No 5 Jl Prof Dr Satrio Kav 8, Jakarta, 12940, Indonesia
Tel.: (62) 2180623812
Web Site: http://www.ewm-indonesia.com
Human Resource Consulting Services
N.A.I.C.S.: 541612

PT Indonesia Persada Gemilang (1)
Jl Utan Kayu No 20, Jakarta Timur, Indonesia
Tel.: (62) 2185912730
Web Site: http://www.indonesiaachievers.com
Educational Support Services
N.A.I.C.S.: 611710

PT Kresna Asset Management (1)
18 Parc Kresna Tower 10th Floor Jl Jend Sudirman Kav 52-53, Jakarta, 12190, Indonesia
Tel.: (62) 2129391800
Web Site: http://www.kresna-am.com
Asset Management Services
N.A.I.C.S.: 523940

PT Kresna Sekuritas (1)
Kresna Tower 6th Floor 18 Parc Place SCBD Jalan Jendral, Sudirman Kavling 52-53, Jakarta, 12190, Indonesia
Tel.: (62) 2125557000
Web Site: http://www.kresnasecurities.com
Financial Investment Services
N.A.I.C.S.: 523940
Octavianus Budiyanto *(Pres)*

PT RADANA BHASKARA FINANCE TBK
Cibis Nine Building 11th Floor Unit W 16 JL TB Simatupang No 2 RT 001, RW 005 Kelurahan Cilandak Timur Pasar Minggu, Jakarta, 12560, Indonesia
Tel.: (62) 2150991088 Id
Web Site: https://www.radanafinance.co.id
Year Founded: 1972
HDFA—(INDO)
Rev.: $16,856,604
Assets: $159,763,162
Liabilities: $119,776,212
Net Worth: $39,986,950
Earnings: $(3,707,619)
Emp.: 99
Fiscal Year-end: 12/31/23
Financial Services
N.A.I.C.S.: 522320
Evy Indahwaty *(Chm)*

PT RADIANT UTAMA INTERISCO TBK.
Radiant Group Building Jl Kapten Tendean No 24 Mampang Prapatan, Jakarta, 12720, Indonesia
Tel.: (62) 217191020
Web Site: https://www.radiant.co.id
Year Founded: 1984
RUIS—(INDO)
Rev.: $115,587,180
Assets: $87,131,902
Liabilities: $51,448,934
Net Worth: $35,682,968
Earnings: $921,397
Emp.: 745
Fiscal Year-end: 12/31/23
Oil & Gas Exploration Services
N.A.I.C.S.: 211120
Sofwan Farisyi *(Chm)*

PT RAJAWALI CORPORATION
Jl Mega Kuningan Lot 5 1 Menara Rajawali Lt 27 28, Kuningan Timur Setia Budi, Jakarta, 12950, Indonesia
Tel.: (62) 215760808 Id
Year Founded: 1984
Holding Company; Hotels, Retail & Department Stores, Transportation & Telecommunications
N.A.I.C.S.: 551112
Peter Sondakh *(Founder, Owner & Pres)*

Subsidiaries:

PT Express Transindo Utama Tbk (1)
Jl Sukarjo Wiryopranoto No 11, Jakarta, 11160, Indonesia
Tel.: (62) 2126507000

PT RAJAWALI CORPORATION

PT Rajawali Corporation—(Continued)
Web Site: https://www.expressgroup.co.id
Rev.: $315,005
Assets: $4,470,114
Liabilities: $749,605
Net Worth: $3,720,509
Earnings: ($262,977)
Emp.: 3
Fiscal Year-end: 12/31/2023
Taxi Service
N.A.I.C.S.: 485310
Megawati Affan *(Sec)*

PT RAMAYANA LESTARI SENTOSA TBK
Jln KH Wahid Hasyim No 220 A-B Tanah Abang, Jakarta, 10250, Indonesia
Tel.: (62) 213920480
Web Site: https://www.ramayana.co.id
RALS—(INDO)
Rev.: $144,318,020
Assets: $369,965,260
Liabilities: $109,653,180
Net Worth: $260,312,080
Earnings: ($9,721,180)
Emp.: 5,501
Fiscal Year-end: 12/31/20
Apparels & Clothes Retailer
N.A.I.C.S.: 458110

PT RATU PRABU ENERGI TBK
Tel.: (62) 2178836836
Web Site: http://www.ratuprabuenergi.com
Year Founded: 1993
ARTI—(INDO)
Rev.: $4,926,236
Assets: $41,341,333
Liabilities: $51,827,839
Net Worth: ($10,486,506)
Earnings: ($3,880,633)
Emp.: 74
Fiscal Year-end: 12/31/22
Oil & Gas Field Operating Services
N.A.I.C.S.: 213112
Julius Simbolon *(Mgr-Acctg)*

PT RED PLANET INDONESIA TBK
15A Floor Sona Topas Tower Jl Jend Sudirman Kav 26, Jakarta, 12920, Indonesia
Tel.: (62) 2129498800
Web Site: https://redplanetindonesia.co.id
Year Founded: 2010
PSKT—(INDO)
Rev.: $3,528,551
Assets: $25,969,692
Liabilities: $3,880,347
Net Worth: $22,089,345
Earnings: ($692,283)
Emp.: 136
Fiscal Year-end: 12/31/23
Hotel & Resort Operator
N.A.I.C.S.: 721110
Florent Humeau *(Dir-Ops)*

Subsidiaries:

PT Red Planet Hotel Bekasi (1)
Jl Chairil Anwar No 26-37 Kav 28 - 36 Timur, Bekasi, 17113, Indonesia
Tel.: (62) 2129689222
Hotel Services
N.A.I.C.S.: 721110

PT Red Planet Hotel Makassar (1)
Jl DR Sam Ratulangi 136A, Makassar, 90112, Indonesia
Tel.: (62) 4118117421
Hotel Services
N.A.I.C.S.: 721110

PT Red Planet Hotel Palembang (1)
Jl Jend Sudirman KM 3 5, Palembang, 30129, Indonesia
Tel.: (62) 711315222
Hotel Services
N.A.I.C.S.: 721110

PT Red Planet Hotel Pekanbaru (1)
Jl Tengku Zainal Abidin No 23, Pekanbaru, 28112, Indonesia
Tel.: (62) 761851008
Hotel Services
N.A.I.C.S.: 721110

PT Red Planet Hotel Surabaya (1)
Jl Arjuna No 64 - 66, Surabaya, 60251, Indonesia
Tel.: (62) 315358500
Hotel Services
N.A.I.C.S.: 721110

PT Red Planet Hotels Solo (1)
Jl Dr Soepomo No 49, Surakarta, 57139, Central Java, Indonesia
Tel.: (62) 2717889333
Hotel Services
N.A.I.C.S.: 721110

PT RELIANCE CAPITAL MANAGEMENT
Menara Batavia Lt 27 Jl K H Mas Mansyur Kav 126, Jakarta, Indonesia
Tel.: (62) 21 5793 0008
Web Site: http://www.relianceindonesia.com
Year Founded: 2003
Financial Services
N.A.I.C.S.: 523999
Anton Budidjaja *(Founder & Chm)*

Subsidiaries:

PT Reliance Securities Tbk (1)
Soho West Point Kota Kedoya Jl Macan Kav 4-5 Kedoya Utara, Kebon Jeruk DKI, Jakarta, 11520, Indonesia
Tel.: (62) 2129520558
Web Site: https://www.reliancesekuritas.com
Rev.: $4,468,314
Assets: $49,276,996
Liabilities: $8,372,842
Net Worth: $40,904,154
Earnings: $2,343,527
Emp.: 78
Fiscal Year-end: 12/31/2023
Financial Services & Stock Brokerage Services
N.A.I.C.S.: 523150
Rendy Miftah Ananda *(Officer-Internal Audit)*

Subsidiary (Domestic):

PT Reliance Asset Management (2)
Menara Batavia Lt 27 Jl KH Mas Mansyur Kav 126, Jakarta, 10220, Indonesia
Tel.: (62) 21 57930008
Sales Range: $50-74.9 Million
Emp.: 11
Investment Management Service
N.A.I.C.S.: 523940

PT REPOWER ASIA INDONESIA TBK
Graha Repower Jl Warung Buncit Raya No 65 Rt 6/Rw 5, Kalibata Kec Pancoran, Jakarta Selatan, 12740, Indonesia
Tel.: (62) 2125033198
Web Site: https://www.repowerasia.co.id
Year Founded: 2011
REAL—(INDO)
Rev.: $543,415
Assets: $22,919,539
Liabilities: $80,999
Net Worth: $22,838,540
Earnings: $11,544
Emp.: 3
Fiscal Year-end: 12/31/23
Real Estate Services
N.A.I.C.S.: 531390
Rully Muliarto *(Sec)*

PT RESOURCE ALAM INDONESIA TBK
Bumi Raya Group Building Jl Pembangunan I No 3, Jakarta, 10130, Pusat, Indonesia
Tel.: (62) 216333036   Id
Web Site: https://www.raintbk.com
Year Founded: 1981
KKGI—(INDO)
Rev.: $294,672,016
Assets: $200,536,560
Liabilities: $61,195,903
Net Worth: $139,340,657
Earnings: $26,802,561
Emp.: 402
Fiscal Year-end: 12/31/23
Coal Mining Services
N.A.I.C.S.: 212114
Pintarso Adijanto *(Chm)*

PT RICKY PUTRA GLOBALINDO TBK
Jl Sawah Lio II No 29-37 Jembatan Lima, Tambora, Jakarta Barat, 11250, Indonesia
Tel.: (62) 216342330   Id
Web Site: https://www.rpg.co.id
Year Founded: 1987
RICY—(INDO)
Rev.: $56,399,295
Assets: $100,465,578
Liabilities: $89,301,322
Net Worth: $11,164,256
Earnings: ($3,939,900)
Emp.: 3,596
Fiscal Year-end: 12/31/23
Textile Products Mfr
N.A.I.C.S.: 314999
Paulus Gunawan *(Chm)*

Subsidiaries:

P.T. Ricky Arta Jaya (1)
Jl Andir No 70 Ciroyom, Bandung, 40182, West Java, Indonesia
Tel.: (62) 226002846
Apparel Mfr & Distr
N.A.I.C.S.: 315990

P.T. Ricky Jaya Sakti (1)
Jl Tanjung Sari III Komplek Pergudangan Blok A10, Surabaya, 60188, East Java, Indonesia
Tel.: (62) 317492231
Apparel Mfr & Distr
N.A.I.C.S.: 315990

P.T. Ricky Kobayashi (1)
Jl Industri No 54 Tarikolot, Citeureup, Bogor, 16810, Indonesia
Tel.: (62) 2187941141
Web Site: https://www.rickykobayashi.co.id
Apparel Mfr & Distr
N.A.I.C.S.: 315990

P.T. Ricky Mumbul Daya (1)
Jl Rejosari V/22 Gg Buntu, Semarang, 50125, Central Java, Indonesia
Tel.: (62) 243551212
Apparel Mfr & Distr
N.A.I.C.S.: 315990

P.T. Ricky Musi Wijaya (1)
Jl Perintis Kemerdekaan No 49, Palembang, 30116, South Sumatera, Indonesia
Tel.: (62) 711714788
Apparel Mfr & Distr
N.A.I.C.S.: 315990

PT RIMO INTERNATIONAL LESTARI TBK
Ambassade Residence Lt1, Jl Denpasar Raya Kav 5-7, Jakarta, 12950, Selatan, Indonesia
Tel.: (62) 212522702
Web Site: http://www.rimointernational.com
RIMO—(INDO)
Sales Range: $25-49.9 Million
Departmental Store Operator
N.A.I.C.S.: 455110
R. Ade Tutut Tunggal *(Sec)*

PT RMK ENERGY TBK
Wisma Rmk 2Nd Floor Jalan Puri Kencana Blok M4 No 1 Kembangan, Jakarta Barat, Jakarta, 11610, Indonesia

INTERNATIONAL PUBLIC

Tel.: (62) 215822555
Web Site: https://www.rmkenergy.com
Year Founded: 2009
RMKE—(INDO)
Rev.: $165,798,721
Assets: $145,965,312
Liabilities: $49,540,289
Net Worth: $96,425,023
Earnings: $20,062,522
Emp.: 59
Fiscal Year-end: 12/31/23
Coal Logistic Services
N.A.I.C.S.: 484220
Tony Saputra *(Pres)*

PT ROCKFIELDS PROPERTI INDONESIA TBK
Noble House Floor 35 No 2 Jl Dr Ide Anak Agung Gede Agung Kav E 4 2, Jakarta, 12950, Indonesia
Tel.: (62) 2129783000
Web Site: https://www.rockfields.co.id
Year Founded: 2013
ROCK—(INDO)
Rev.: $6,943,948
Assets: $63,613,948
Liabilities: $12,174,708
Net Worth: $51,439,240
Earnings: $760,935
Emp.: 25
Fiscal Year-end: 12/31/23
Real Estate Services
N.A.I.C.S.: 531390
Po Wiwiek Purnomo *(Mng Dir)*

Subsidiaries:

PT Graha Lestari Internusa (1)
Jl Dr Ide Anak Agung Gede Agung Kav E 4 2 No 2, Jakarta, 12950, Indonesia
Tel.: (62) 2129783000
Web Site: https://noblehouse.co.id
Real Estate Services
N.A.I.C.S.: 531210

PT ROYAL PRIMA TBK
Jl Raden Wijaya RT 35 Kebun Kopi, Jambi, Indonesia
Tel.: (62) 88813182
Web Site: https://www.royalprima.com
Year Founded: 2012
PRIM—(INDO)
Rev.: $17,230,980
Assets: $66,939,414
Liabilities: $3,226,571
Net Worth: $63,712,843
Earnings: ($180,003)
Emp.: 736
Fiscal Year-end: 12/31/23
Educational Consulting Services
N.A.I.C.S.: 611710
Tommy Leonard *(Pres)*

Subsidiaries:

PT Royal Prima Jambi (1)
Jl Raden Wijaya RT 35 Kebun Kopi, Jambi, Indonesia
Tel.: (62) 74141010
Healtcare Services
N.A.I.C.S.: 621999

PT RUKUN RAHARJA TBK
Office Park Thamrin Residences Blok A No 01-05 Jl Thamrin Boulevard, Kebon Melati Tanah Abang, Jakarta, 10230, Indonesia
Tel.: (62) 2129291053
Web Site: https://www.raja.co.id
Year Founded: 1993
RAJA—(INDO)
Rev.: $203,745,960
Assets: $328,648,128
Liabilities: $174,105,842
Net Worth: $154,542,286

Earnings: $27,149,480
Emp.: 198
Fiscal Year-end: 12/31/23
Gas & Fuel Distribution Services
N.A.I.C.S.: 221210
Djauhar Maulidi (Chm)

Subsidiaries:

P.T. Artha Prima Energy (1)
Jalan Tegar Beriman No 1 C-17 Cibinong Center C-17, Cibinong City, 16915, Jawa Barat, Indonesia
Tel.: (62) 2183728052
Web Site: https://pt-artha-prima-energy.business.site
Compressed Natural Gas Commerce Services
N.A.I.C.S.: 561790

P.T. Artifisial Teknologi Persada (1)
Office Park Thamrin Residences A01-05 Jl Thamrin Boulevard, Kebon Melati Tanah Abang, Jakarta, 10220, Indonesia
Tel.: (62) 2123579802
Oil & Gas Services
N.A.I.C.S.: 532412

P.T. Bravo Delta Persada (1)
Office Park Thamrin Residence B07-08 Jl Thamrin Boulevard, Kel Kebon Melati Kec Tanah Abang, Jakarta Pusat, 10230, Indonesia
Tel.: (62) 2123579802
Clean Water Distr
N.A.I.C.S.: 487210

P.T. Heksa Energi Mitraniaga (1)
Office Park Thamrin Residence B07-08 Jl Thamrin Boulevard, Kel Kebon Melati Kec Tanah Abang, Jakarta Pusat, 10230, Indonesia
Tel.: (62) 2123579802
Liquefied Petroleum Gas Distr
N.A.I.C.S.: 424720

P.T. Majuko Utama Indonesia (1)
Office Park Thamrin Residences Blok A 01-05 Jl Thamrin, Residence Boulevard Tanah Abang, Jakarta, 10220, Indonesia
Tel.: (62) 23579930
Web Site: https://majuko.co.id
Pipeline Operating Services
N.A.I.C.S.: 541990

P.T. Petrotech Penta Nusa (1)
Office Park Thamrin Residences A01-05 Jl Thamrin Boulevard, Kebon Melati Tanah Abang, Jakarta, 10220, Indonesia
Tel.: (62) 2123579802
Oil & Gas Services
N.A.I.C.S.: 532412

P.T. Raharja Energi Cepu (1)
Office Park Thamrin Residence A01-05 Jl Thamrin Boulevard, Kel Kebon Melati Kec Tanah Abang, Jakarta Pusat, 10230, Indonesia
Tel.: (62) 2123579812
Business Management Consulting Services
N.A.I.C.S.: 541611

PT Energasindo Heksa Karya (1)
Office Park Thamrin Residences Blok A 01-05 Jl Thamrin Residence, Boulevard Tanah Abang, Jakarta, 10230, Indonesia
Web Site: http://www.energasindo.com
Gas & Fuel Distr
N.A.I.C.S.: 221210
Agustinus Hendrayana (Pres)

PT SAMINDO RESOURCES TBK
Equity Tower 30th Floor SCBD, Jl Jenderal Sudirman Kav No 52-53 Lot 9, Jakarta Selatan, 12190, Indonesia
Tel.: (62) 2129037723
Web Site:
https://www.samindoresources.com
Year Founded: 2000
MYOH—(INDO)
Rev.: $134,187,479
Assets: $236,712,430
Liabilities: $69,507,184
Net Worth: $167,205,246
Earnings: $18,495,084
Emp.: 1,452
Fiscal Year-end: 12/31/23
Coal & Mining Services
N.A.I.C.S.: 213113
Weon Son Baek (Chm)

Subsidiaries:

PT Transkon Jaya Tbk (1)
Jl Mulawarman No 21 Rt 23 Manggar, Balikpapan, 76116, Kalimantan, Indonesia (74%)
Tel.: (62) 542770401
Web Site: http://www.transkon-rent.com
Rev.: $48,300,134
Assets: $87,344,313
Liabilities: $52,331,524
Net Worth: $35,012,790
Earnings: $3,648,023
Emp.: 263
Fiscal Year-end: 12/31/2022
Vehicle Rental Services
N.A.I.C.S.: 532120
Lexi Roland Rompas (Pres)

PT SAMPOERNA AGRO TBK.
Jln Basuki Rahmat 788, Palembang, 30128, South Sumatra, Indonesia
Tel.: (62) 711813388
Web Site:
https://www.sampoernaagro.com
SGRO—(INDO)
Rev.: $364,995,465
Assets: $653,785,593
Liabilities: $295,809,882
Net Worth: $357,975,711
Earnings: $28,624,188
Emp.: 8,996
Fiscal Year-end: 12/31/23
Palm Kernel & Palm Oil Mfr
N.A.I.C.S.: 311224
Eris Ariaman (Sec & Head-Affairs & Legal)

Subsidiaries:

PT Hutan Ketapang Industri (1)
Jl DI Panjaitan No 76, Ketapang, 78800, Kalimantan Barat, Indonesia
Tel.: (62) 5 343 3456
Web Site: https://www.hki-indonesia.com
Industrial Forestry Management Services
N.A.I.C.S.: 115310
Hero Djajakusumah (CEO)

PT SAMUDERA INDONESIA TBK
Samudera Indonesia Building Jl Letjen S Parman Kav 35, Jakarta, 11480, Indonesia
Tel.: (62) 215480088
Web Site: https://www.samudera.id
SMDR—(INDO)
Rev.: $772,404,229
Assets: $1,256,963,375
Liabilities: $571,449,588
Net Worth: $685,513,787
Earnings: $109,996,540
Emp.: 1,963
Fiscal Year-end: 12/31/23
Cargo & Logistics Transportation Services
N.A.I.C.S.: 336611
Masli Mulia (Chm)

Subsidiaries:

Foremost Maritime Pte., Ltd. (1)
6 Raffles Quay 25-01, Singapore, 048580, Singapore
Tel.: (65) 65323688
Freight Transportation & Cargo Services
N.A.I.C.S.: 488510

Ocean Technologies Pte., Ltd. (1)
ICON IBP 3A International Business Park 09-14, Singapore, Singapore
Tel.: (65) 66599669
Web Site: https://www.weficgroup.com
Ship & Tanker Repairing Services
N.A.I.C.S.: 561599

PT Adib Cold Logistic (1)
Jl Pangkalan 2 Km 12 5 Narogong Bantar Gebang Bekasi, Jakarta, 17151, Jawa barat, Indonesia
Tel.: (62) 2122114933
Web Site: http://www.adibcoldlogistics.com
Freight Transportation & Cargo Services
N.A.I.C.S.: 488510
Irene Natasha (Head-Comml Div)

PT Cumawis (1)
Jl Perak Tmr 400, Surabaya, 60165, East Java, Indonesia
Tel.: (62) 313291394
Logistics Management Services
N.A.I.C.S.: 541614

PT Masaji Prayasa Cargo (1)
Kirana Three Building 12th Floor Jl Boulevard Raya Kav 1, Kelapa Gading, Jakarta, 14240, Indonesia
Tel.: (62) 212 245 8101
Web Site: https://samudera.id
Sales Range: $50-74.9 Million
Emp.: 200
Freight Services
N.A.I.C.S.: 483111

PT Samudera Agencies Indonesia (1)
Samudera Indonesia Building 3rd Fl Jl Letjen S Parman Kav 35, Jakarta, 11480, Indonesia
Tel.: (62) 215300580
Freight Transportation & Cargo Services
N.A.I.C.S.: 488510

PT Samudera Daya Mitra (1)
Gedung Samudera Indonesia 7th Fl Jl Letjen S Parman Kav 35, Jakarta, 11480, Indonesia
Tel.: (62) 215307875
Freight Transportation & Cargo Services
N.A.I.C.S.: 488510

PT Samudera Indonesia Ship Management (1)
Jl Kali Besar Barat No 39, Jakarta, 11230, Indonesia
Tel.: (62) 216907130
Web Site: http://www.sism.co.id
Sales Range: $50-74.9 Million
Ship Management Services
N.A.I.C.S.: 532411

PT Samudera Perdana (1)
Jl Walisongo No 60 Tugurejo Tugu, Semarang, 50151, Central Java, Indonesia
Tel.: (62) 24 760 3573
Web Site: https://samudera.id
Sales Range: $25-49.9 Million
Emp.: 44
Transportation Services
N.A.I.C.S.: 484110

PT Samudera Properti Indonesia (1)
Samudera Indonesia Building 3Ath Fl Jl Letjen S Parman Kav 35, Jakarta, 11480, Indonesia
Tel.: (62) 2153675606
Freight Transportation & Cargo Services
N.A.I.C.S.: 488510

PT Samudera Sarana Logistik (1)
Jl Raya Cakung No 15 Semper Timur, Jakarta Utara, 144130, Indonesia
Tel.: (62) 214401592
Freight Transportation & Cargo Services
N.A.I.C.S.: 488510

Subsidiary (Domestic):

PT Masaji Kargosentra Tama (2)
Blok E 7 No A and B Jl Marunda Makmur, Industrial Estate and Warehousing Marunda Center, Bekasi, 17211, Indonesia
Tel.: (62) 2129088220
Freight Transportation & Cargo Services
N.A.I.C.S.: 488510

PT Samudera Shipping Services (1)
Samudera Indonesia Building 1st Floor Jl Letjen S Parman Kav 35, Jakarta, 11480, Indonesia
Tel.: (62) 215328566
Freight Transportation & Cargo Services
N.A.I.C.S.: 488510
Tarmizi Amir (Mng Dir)

PT Samudera Terminal Indonesia (1)
Samudera Indonesia Building Jl Letjen S Parman Kav 35, Jakarta, 11480, Indonesia
Tel.: (62) 215480088
Freight Transportation & Cargo Services
N.A.I.C.S.: 327910

Subsidiary (Domestic):

PT Prima Nur Panurjwan (2)
Komplek Perkantoran Yos Sudarso Megah Jl Yos Sudarso No 1 Blok B/19-20, Tanjung Priok, Jakarta, 14320, Indonesia
Tel.: (62) 2143904610
Freight Transportation & Cargo Services
N.A.I.C.S.: 488510

PT Samudera Sarana Terminal Indonesia (2)
Kom Yos Sudarso Megah No 1 Blok A1-7 Jl Yos Sudarso Tanjung Priok, Jakarta, 14320, Indonesia
Tel.: (62) 2143904610
Freight Transportation & Cargo Services
N.A.I.C.S.: 488510

PT Silkargo Indonesia (1)
Alamanda Tower Lt 16 Jl TB Simatupang Kav 23-24, Cilandak Barat, Jakarta, 12430, Indonesia
Tel.: (62) 216919901
Freight Transportation & Cargo Services
N.A.I.C.S.: 488510

PT Tangguh Samudera Jaya (1)
Jl Yos Sudarso No 1 Blok A1-A7 Tanjung Priok, Jakarta, 14320, Indonesia
Tel.: (62) 21 436 8247
Web Site: https://samudera.id
Cargo Handling Services
N.A.I.C.S.: 488320

Samudera Logistics DWC LLC (1)
A5 - 416 Dubai Aviation Logistics City Dubai World Central, PO Box 644269, Dubai, United Arab Emirates
Tel.: (971) 42257363
Web Site: https://samudera.ae
Cargo Transportation Services
N.A.I.C.S.: 488490

Samudera Shipping Line (India) Pvt., Ltd. (1)
402 6th floor Rustomjee Aspire Everard Nagar Road, Off Eastern Express Highway Sion, Mumbai, 400022, India
Tel.: (91) 2266594700
Freight Transportation & Cargo Services
N.A.I.C.S.: 488510

Samudera Shipping Line Ltd. (1)
6 Raffles Quay 25-01, Singapore, 048580, Singapore
Tel.: (65) 64031687
Web Site: http://www.samudera.id
Rev.: $990,594,000
Assets: $888,337,000
Liabilities: $315,394,000
Net Worth: $572,943,000
Earnings: $323,099,000
Emp.: 154
Fiscal Year-end: 12/31/2022
Marine Offshore Operation Services
N.A.I.C.S.: 488320
Hermawan Fridiana Herman (Exec Dir-Fin)

Silkargo Logistics (Singapore), Pte., Ltd. (1)
6 Raffles Quay 24-02, Singapore, 048580, Singapore
Tel.: (65) 62243633
Freight Transportation & Cargo Services
N.A.I.C.S.: 488510

PT SANURHASTA MITRA TBK
Equity Tower Lt 11 Unit 11D Sudirman Central Business, Lot 9Jl Jend Sudirman Kav 52-53, Jakarta, 12190, Indonesia
Tel.: (62) 2129035620
Web Site:
https://www.sanurhastamitra.com
MINA—(INDO)
Rev.: $758,145
Assets: $6,843,720
Liabilities: $566,004
Net Worth: $6,277,716
Earnings: ($189,055)
Emp.: 16
Fiscal Year-end: 12/31/23
Real Estate Manangement Services

PT SANURHASTA MITRA TBK

PT Sanurhasta Mitra Tbk—(Continued)
N.A.I.C.S.: 531390
Edy Suwarno *(Pres & Commissioner)*

Subsidiaries:

PT Radhia Nitya Pratama (1)
Apartment Pavilion Retail Arcade JL KH Mas Mansyur Kav 24, Jakarta, 10220, Indonesia
Tel.: (62) 216281087
Web Site: http://www.radhiacruise.com
Diving Services
N.A.I.C.S.: 561990

PT SAPTAUSAHA GEMILANG-INDAH TBK

Jl Kramat Raya No 3234 Senen, DKI Jakarta, Jakarta Pusat, 10450, Indonesia
Tel.: (62) 213916338
Web Site: https://www.saptagroup.com
Year Founded: 1992
SAGE—(INDO)
Rev.: $1,426,298
Assets: $20,725,250
Liabilities: $2,034,113
Net Worth: $18,691,137
Earnings: $309,922
Fiscal Year-end: 12/31/23
Property Management Services
N.A.I.C.S.: 531311
Cindy Veronica Jong *(Sec)*

PT SARANA MEDITAMA METROPOLITAN TBK

Jl Pulomas Barat VI No 20, Jakarta Timur, 13210, Indonesia
Tel.: (62) 21297799999
Web Site: https://www.emc.id
Year Founded: 1984
SAME—(INDO)
Rev.: $99,724,430
Assets: $348,388,689
Liabilities: $89,692,502
Net Worth: $258,696,187
Earnings: $1,152,184
Emp.: 2,613
Fiscal Year-end: 12/31/23
Health Care Srvices
N.A.I.C.S.: 621491
Hassan Themas *(Sec)*

PT SARANA MENARA NUSANTARA TBK

Jl Jend A Yani No 19A Kudus, Jakarta, Indonesia
Tel.: (62) 291431691
Web Site: https://www.ptsmn.co.id
SMNUF—(OTCIQ)
Rev.: $762,418,004
Assets: $4,443,126,353
Liabilities: $3,370,858,893
Net Worth: $1,072,267,460
Earnings: $214,538,511
Emp.: 1,551
Fiscal Year-end: 12/31/23
Telecommunications Towers Construction
N.A.I.C.S.: 237130
Adam Gifari *(Vice Chm)*

Subsidiaries:

PT Solusi Tunas Pratama Tbk (1)
Menara BCA 49th Floor Jl M H Thamrin No 1, Jakarta, 10310, Indonesia **(94.03%)**
Tel.: (62) 2123585555
Web Site: www.stptower.com
Rev.: $122,872,000
Assets: $641,969,695
Liabilities: $271,055,209
Net Worth: $370,914,486
Earnings: $73,274,265
Emp.: 168
Fiscal Year-end: 12/31/2023
Communication Tower Construction Services
N.A.I.C.S.: 237130

Nobel Tanihaha *(Chm)*

Subsidiary (Domestic):

PT Platinum Teknologi (2)
Perkantoran Permata Senayan Blok C23 3rd Floor Jl Tentara Pelaja, Jakarta, 12210, Indonesia
Tel.: (62) 2157940688
Communication Tower Construction Services
N.A.I.C.S.: 237130

Subsidiary (Domestic):

PT Broadband Wahana Asia (3)
Perkantoran Permata Senayan Blok F8-9 Jl Tentara Pelajar, Jakarta, 12210, Indonesia
Tel.: (62) 2157940966
Communication Tower Construction Services
N.A.I.C.S.: 237130

Subsidiary (Domestic):

PT Rekajasa Akses (4)
Perkantoran Permata Senayan Blok F8-9 Jl Tentara Pelajar, Jakarta, 12210, Indonesia
Tel.: (62) 2157940680
Web Site: http://acsata.com
Data Communication Services
N.A.I.C.S.: 517810

Subsidiary (Domestic):

PT Gema Dwimitra Persada (3)
Perkantoran Permata Senayan Blok C1 Jl Tentara Pelajar, Jakarta, 12210, Indonesia
Tel.: (62) 2157940688
Communication Tower Construction Services
N.A.I.C.S.: 237130

Subsidiary (Domestic):

PT BIT Teknologi Nusantara (4)
Perkantoran Permata Senayan Blok C1 Jl Tentara Pelajar, Senayan, Jakarta, 12210, Indonesia
Tel.: (62) 2157940680
Web Site: http://www.bit-teknologi.com
Network Infrastructure Services
N.A.I.C.S.: 518210

Subsidiary (Domestic):

PT Sarana Inti Persada (2)
Jl Ibrahim Adjie No 402 Kiaracondong, Bandung, 40275, West Java, Indonesia
Tel.: (62) 227333328
Communication Tower Construction Services
N.A.I.C.S.: 237130

Protelindo Towers B.V. (1)
Hardwareweg 4, 3821 BM, Amersfoort, Netherlands
Tel.: (31) 33 4546600
Telecommunication Tower Construction Services

PT SARANA MITRA LUAS TBK.

Jl GemalapikPasirsari Cikarang Selatan Bekasi, Pasirsari Cikarang Selatan, Bekasi, 17530, Jawa Barat, Indonesia
Tel.: (62) 2189902188
Web Site: https://www.sml.co.id
Year Founded: 1996
SMIL—(INDO)
Rev.: $23,183,436
Assets: $56,956,315
Liabilities: $12,341,314
Net Worth: $44,615,001
Earnings: $5,412,512
Emp.: 44
Fiscal Year-end: 12/31/23
Equipment Rental Services
N.A.I.C.S.: 532490
Hadi Suhermin *(Chm)*

PT SARANA MULTIGRIYA FINANSIAL (PERSERO) TBK

Grha SMF Jl Panglima Polim I No 1 Melawai Kebayoran Baru, Jakarta, 12160, Indonesia
Tel.: (62) 212700400
Web Site: http://www.smf-indonesia.co.id
Year Founded: 2005
Mortgage Financing Services
N.A.I.C.S.: 522292
Ananta Wiyogo *(Chm)*

PT SARANA TIRTA REJEKI

Jl Joseph Martadilaga No 25 Attack, Serang, Banten, Indonesia
Tel.: (62) 254 206813
Sales Range: $1-9.9 Million
Water Supply, Treatment & Management Services
N.A.I.C.S.: 221310

PT SARANACENTRAL BAJATAMA TBK

Gedung Baja Tower B Lantai 6 Jl Pangeran Jayakarta No 55, Jakarta, 10730, Indonesia
Tel.: (62) 216288647
Web Site: https://www.saranacentral.com
Year Founded: 1996
BAJA—(INDO)
Rev.: $61,722,496
Assets: $47,153,680
Liabilities: $39,944,617
Net Worth: $7,209,063
Earnings: ($84,213)
Emp.: 137
Fiscal Year-end: 12/31/23
Steel Product Mfr & Distr
N.A.I.C.S.: 331110

PT SARASWANTI ANUGERAH MAKMUR TBK

AMG Tower 20th Floor Jl Dukuh Menanggal 1-A, Gedangan, Surabaya, 60234, Jawa Timur, Indonesia
Tel.: (62) 3182516888
Web Site: https://www.saraswantifertilizer.com
Year Founded: 1998
SAMF—(INDO)
Rev.: $289,860,209
Assets: $181,420,573
Liabilities: $91,798,386
Net Worth: $89,622,187
Earnings: $27,279,826
Emp.: 482
Fiscal Year-end: 12/31/23
Fertilizer Mfr & Distr
N.A.I.C.S.: 325311
Dadang Suryanto *(Sec)*

Subsidiaries:

P.T. Anugerah Pupuk Lestari (1)
AMG Tower Lantai 20 Jl Dukuh Menanggal 1- A Gayungan, Surabaya, 60234, Jawa Timur, Indonesia
Tel.: (62) 3182516888
Web Site: https://www.pupukindonesia.id
Compound Fertilizer Mfr & Distr
N.A.I.C.S.: 325311

P.T. Anugerah Pupuk Makmur (1)
AMG Tower Lantai 20 Jl Dukuh Menanggal 1- A Gayungan, Surabaya, 60234, Jawa Timur, Indonesia
Tel.: (62) 3182516888
Web Site: https://www.pupuknpk.id
Compound Fertilizer Mfr & Distr
N.A.I.C.S.: 325311

P.T. Dupan Anugerah Lestari (1)
AMG Tower Lt 20 Jl Dukuh Menanggal 1-A Gayungan, Surabaya, 60234, Jawa Timur, Indonesia
Tel.: (62) 3182516888
Web Site: https://www.pupindo.id
Compound Fertilizer Mfr & Distr
N.A.I.C.S.: 325311

PT SARASWATI GRIYA LESTARI TBK

Bellezza Shopping Arcade Suite GF 30-31 Jl Arteri Permata Hijau 34 4, RT 4/RW 2 Grogol Utara Kec Kby Lama Kota Jakarta Selatan, Jakarta, 12210, Indonesia
Tel.: (62) 2125675505
Web Site: https://ptsgl.com
Year Founded: 2006
HOTL—(INDO)
Rev.: $4,405,630
Assets: $91,768,956
Liabilities: $70,720,547
Net Worth: $21,048,409
Earnings: ($2,317,679)
Emp.: 267
Fiscal Year-end: 12/31/21
Restaurant Operators
N.A.I.C.S.: 722511

PT SARATOGA INVESTAMA SEDAYA TBK.

Menara Karya 15th Floor Jl HR Rasuna Said Block X-5 Kav 1-2, Jakarta, 12950, Indonesia
Tel.: (62) 2157944355
Web Site: https://www.saratoga-investama.com
SRTG—(INDO)
Rev.: $182,353,598
Assets: $3,308,376,093
Liabilities: $140,068,826
Net Worth: $3,168,307,267
Earnings: ($659,228,085)
Emp.: 61
Fiscal Year-end: 12/31/23
Investment Holding Company
N.A.I.C.S.: 551112
Edwin Soeryadjaya *(Founder)*

Subsidiaries:

PT Pelayaran Antarbuwana Pertala (1)
Ruko Mega Grossir Cempaka Mas Block H12, Jakarta, Indonesia
Tel.: (62) 2142906883
Financial Investment Services
N.A.I.C.S.: 523150

PT Wana Bakti Sukses Mineral (1)
Tower Cyber 2 29th R JL HR Rausana Said Block x5 No 13, Jakarta, 12950, Indonesia
Tel.: (62) 2129021700
Financial Investment Services
N.A.I.C.S.: 523150

PT SARIGUNA PRIMATIRTA TBK

Jl Raya A Yani No 41-43 Komplek Central Square Blok C1, Sidoarjo, 61254, Indonesia
Tel.: (62) 318544400
Web Site: https://www.tanobel.com
Year Founded: 2003
CLEO—(INDO)
Rev.: $135,732,126
Assets: $149,117,028
Liabilities: $50,759,876
Net Worth: $98,357,152
Earnings: $21,046,544
Emp.: 807
Fiscal Year-end: 12/31/23
Bottled Water Distr
N.A.I.C.S.: 424490
Hermanto Tanoko *(Owner)*

PT SARIMELATI KENCANA TBK

Jl Jend Gatot Subroto Kav 1 000, Selatan, Jakarta, 12870, Indonesia
Tel.: (62) 2150966789
Web Site: https://www.sarimelatikencana.co.id
Year Founded: 1987
PZZA—(INDO)
Rev.: $230,146,251

Assets: $152,446,212
Liabilities: $82,552,847
Net Worth: $69,893,365
Earnings: ($6,248,840)
Emp.: 5,021
Fiscal Year-end: 12/31/23
Pizza & Pasta Product Mfr
N.A.I.C.S.: 311991
Hadian Iswara *(Pres & Commissioner)*

PT SAT NUSAPERSADA TBK
Jl Pelita VI No 99, Batam, 29443, Kepri, Indonesia
Tel.: (62) 7785708888
Web Site: https://www.satnusa.com
Year Founded: 1990
PTSN—(INDO)
Rev.: $126,588,110
Assets: $152,134,921
Liabilities: $43,261,335
Net Worth: $108,873,586
Earnings: $11,168,318
Emp.: 3,165
Fiscal Year-end: 12/31/23
Printed Circuit Board Mfr
N.A.I.C.S.: 334412
Bidin Yusuf *(Dir/Dir-Operational)*

PT SATRIA ANTARAN PRIMA TBK
Jl Komodor Halim Perdana Kusuma No 28 Halim Perdana Kusuma, Makassar, 13610, Indonesia
Tel.: (62) 2122806611
Web Site: https://www.sap-express.id
Year Founded: 2014
SAPX—(INDO)
Rev.: $40,404,472
Assets: $21,051,029
Liabilities: $9,552,392
Net Worth: $11,498,637
Earnings: $75,037
Emp.: 205
Fiscal Year-end: 12/31/23
Courier Service
N.A.I.C.S.: 492110
Budiyanto Darmastono *(Pres)*

PT SATRIA MEGA KENCANA TBK
Panin Tower 9th Floor Jl Asia Afrika Lot 19, Senayan City, Jakarta Pusat, 10270, Indonesia
Tel.: (62) 2172781782
Web Site:
https://www.satriakencana.com
SOTS—(INDO)
Rev.: $1,466,687
Assets: $25,790,267
Liabilities: $10,981,685
Net Worth: $14,808,583
Earnings: ($888,102)
Emp.: 85
Fiscal Year-end: 12/31/23
Hotel & Restaurant Operator
N.A.I.C.S.: 721110
Ivo Wongkaren *(Chm)*

PT SATYAMITRA KEMAS LESTARI TBK
Kawasan Industri Benua Permai Lestari Jl Raya Serang Km 25 6, Desa Cisereh Tigaraksa, Tangerang, 15720, Indonesia
Tel.: (62) 215950988
Web Site:
https://www.satyamitra.com
Year Founded: 2001
SMKL—(INDO)
Rev.: $112,950,172
Assets: $122,798,095
Liabilities: $62,595,742
Net Worth: $60,202,353
Earnings: $769,330
Emp.: 1,007

Fiscal Year-end: 12/31/23
Corrugated Box Mfr
N.A.I.C.S.: 322211
Kinardo Ang *(Pres)*

PT SAWIT SUMBERMAS SARANA TBK
Jl H Udan Said No 47, Pangkalan Bun, 74113, Kalimantan Tengah, Indonesia
Tel.: (62) 53221297
Web Site: https://ssms.co.id
Year Founded: 1995
SSMS—(INDO)
Rev.: $695,079,565
Assets: $766,970,274
Liabilities: $637,742,138
Net Worth: $129,228,136
Earnings: $22,340,375
Emp.: 833
Fiscal Year-end: 12/31/23
Palm Oil
N.A.I.C.S.: 111120
Vallauthan Subraminam *(Chm & CEO)*

PT SEJAHTERA BINTANG ABADI TEXTILE TBK
Jalan Raya Cicalengka-Majalaya Km 5 Desa Srirahayu, Kecamatan Cikancung, 40396, Bandung, 40396, West Java, Indonesia
Tel.: (62) 227947100
Web Site: http://www.sbatextile.com
Year Founded: 2003
SBAT—(INDO)
Rev.: $11,198,981
Assets: $65,765,726
Liabilities: $48,625,356
Net Worth: $17,140,369
Earnings: ($8,762,341)
Emp.: 294
Fiscal Year-end: 12/31/22
Yarn Mfr & Distr
N.A.I.C.S.: 313110
Jefri Junaedi *(Pres)*

PT SEJAHTERARAYA ANUGRAHJAYA TBK
Jl Honoris Raya Kav 6 Kota Modern Modernland, Banten, Tangerang, 15117, Indonesia
Tel.: (62) 2155781888
Web Site:
https://www.mayapadahospital.com
Year Founded: 1991
SRAJ—(INDO)
Rev.: $162,556,120
Assets: $364,072,538
Liabilities: $243,449,280
Net Worth: $120,623,258
Earnings: ($2,488,046)
Emp.: 3,243
Fiscal Year-end: 12/31/23
Health Care Srvices
N.A.I.C.S.: 621491
Grace Dewi Riady *(Chm)*

PT SEKAR BUMI TBK
Plaza Asia 21st Floor Jl Jend Sudirman Kav 59, Jakarta, 12190, Indonesia
Tel.: (62) 2151401122
Web Site:
https://www.sekarbumi.com
Year Founded: 1968
Frozen Food Product Distr
N.A.I.C.S.: 424420
Harry Lukmito *(Pres, CEO & Dir)*

PT SELAMAT SEMPURNA TBK
Wisma ADR Jl Pluit Raya I No 1, Jakarta, 14440, Indonesia
Tel.: (62) 216610033
Web Site: https://www.smsm.co.id

SMSM—(INDO)
Rev.: $331,218,158
Assets: $297,087,057
Liabilities: $61,352,714
Net Worth: $235,734,343
Earnings: $67,312,518
Emp.: 3,076
Fiscal Year-end: 12/31/23
Automobile Spare Parts Mfr
N.A.I.C.S.: 332510
Ang Andri Pribadi *(Dir-Fin)*

Subsidiaries:

Bradke Synergies Sdn. Bhd. (1)
No 21 Jalan SBC-5 Taman Sri Batu Caves, 68100, Batu Caves, Selangor, Malaysia
Tel.: (60) 361862288
Automotive Filter Product Distr
N.A.I.C.S.: 423120

Filton Industries Sdn. Bhd. (1)
Lot 9869 4 Miles Jalan Sellathevan Kg Jawa, 41000, Klang, Selangor Darul Ehsan, Malaysia
Tel.: (60) 351611482
Web Site: https://filton.com.my
Filter Mfr
N.A.I.C.S.: 336390

PT Hydraxle Perkasa (1)
Jl Raya Curug No 88 Desa Kadujaya - Bitung, Tangerang, Banten, Indonesia
Tel.: (62) 215980160
Dump Truck Leasing Services
N.A.I.C.S.: 532120
Johan Setiawan *(Head-Production)*

PT Posco Indonesia Jakarta Processing Center (1)
Jl Permata Raya Lot FF 3 Kawasan Industri KIIC, Karawang, 41361, Jawa Barat, Indonesia
Tel.: (62) 2189118989
Web Site: http://www.ptijpc.co.id
Steel Fabrication Product Mfr
N.A.I.C.S.: 332312

PT Prapat Tunggal Cipta (1)
Jl Karang Anyar No 55 Blok A1 No 1, Jakarta Pusat, Indonesia
Tel.: (62) 216288835
Automobile Parts Mfr
N.A.I.C.S.: 336390
Agus S. Salinata *(Mgr-Mktg)*

PT Selamat Sempana Perkasa (1)
Jl Raya Curug No 88 Desa Kadujaya - Bitung, Tangerang, Banten, Indonesia
Tel.: (62) 215980224
Automobile Parts Mfr
N.A.I.C.S.: 336390

Powerfil Auto Parts Sdn. Bhd. (1)
21 Jalan SBC-5 Taman Sri, 68100, Batu Caves, Selangor, Malaysia
Tel.: (60) 361862288
Web Site: https://www.powerfil.com.my
Filter Mfr & Distr
N.A.I.C.S.: 336390

SS Auto Sdn. Bhd. (1)
Lot 38 39 40 & 41 Jalan Samudra Barat 2 Taman Samudra, 68100, Batu Caves, Selangor West, Malaysia
Tel.: (60) 361851818
Web Site: http://www.ssauto.com.my
Automotive Component Mfr & Distr
N.A.I.C.S.: 336390

PT SELARAS CITRA NUSANTARA PERKASA TBK
Office & Plant Site Raya Narogong Km 19 Dusun Pasir Angin, Rt/Rw 003/004 Cileungsi, Bogor, 16820, Indonesia
Tel.: (62) 218233320
Web Site: https://www.scnp.co.id
Year Founded: 2000
SCNP—(INDO)
Rev.: $45,686,760
Assets: $26,601,186
Liabilities: $3,648,892
Net Worth: $22,952,294
Earnings: $1,339,029
Emp.: 150

Fiscal Year-end: 12/31/23
Electrical Appliance Mfr
N.A.I.C.S.: 335210
Hendrik Nursalim *(Co-CEO)*

PT SENTRA FOOD INDONESIA TBK
Equity Tower 29th Floor Unit E SCBD Lot9 Jl Jendral Sudirman Kav 52-53, Jakarta Selatan, 12190, Indonesia
Tel.: (62) 2129035295
Web Site:
https://www.sentrafood.co.id
Year Founded: 2004
FOOD—(INDO)
Rev.: $5,038,633
Assets: $3,311,544
Liabilities: $1,920,092
Net Worth: $1,391,452
Earnings: ($1,323,537)
Emp.: 93
Fiscal Year-end: 12/31/23
Food Products Mfr
N.A.I.C.S.: 311999
Karina Larasati Putri *(Sec)*

Subsidiaries:

PT Kemang Food Industries (1)
Equity Tower 29th Floor Unit E SCBD Lot 9 Jl Jendral Sudirman, Kav 52-53, Jakarta Selatan, 12190, Indonesia
Tel.: (62) 2129035295
Food Products Distr
N.A.I.C.S.: 424490
Rheza R. R. Susanto *(Co-Pres)*

PT SENTRAL MITRA INFORMATIKA TBK
Graha Mas Fatmawati Block A 27-29 Jln RS Fatmawati No 71 Daerah Khusus, Ibukota, Jakarta, 12150, Indonesia
Tel.: (62) 2172800110
Web Site: https://www.sentral.co.id
Year Founded: 2008
LUCK—(INDO)
Rev.: $6,929,034
Assets: $11,338,948
Liabilities: $2,468,487
Net Worth: $8,870,461
Earnings: $10,465
Emp.: 60
Fiscal Year-end: 12/31/23
Financial Investment Services
N.A.I.C.S.: 523999
Teddy Pohan *(Sec)*

Subsidiaries:

P.T. Sentral Kreasi Inovas (1)
Graha Mas Fatmawati Blok A 28 Jln RS Fatmawati No 71, Jakarta Selatan, 12150, Indonesia
Tel.: (62) 81958567889
Web Site: https://www.sentralinovasi.co.id
Software Development Services
N.A.I.C.S.: 541511

PT SENTUL CITY TBK.
Sentul City Building Jl MH Thamrin Kav 8 Sentul City, Bogor, 16811, Indonesia
Tel.: (62) 2187926555
Web Site: https://www.sentulcity.co.id
BKSL—(INDO)
Rev.: $111,707,229
Assets: $1,291,453,850
Liabilities: $308,191,903
Net Worth: $983,261,947
Earnings: $20,639,845
Emp.: 352
Fiscal Year-end: 12/31/23
Commercial & Non Commercial Building Construction Services
N.A.I.C.S.: 236220
David Partono *(Chm)*

PT SENTUL CITY TBK.

PT Sentul City Tbk.—(Continued)

Subsidiaries:

PT. Gununggeulis Elok Abadi (1)
Taman Budaya Sentul City, Sentul City, Bogor, 16810, West Java, Indonesia
Tel.: (62) 2187961579
Web Site: http://www.tamanbudaya.co.id
Emp.: 65
Park Management Servies
N.A.I.C.S.: 712190

PT. Sukaputra Grahacemerlang (1)
Ruko Plaza Niaga I Blok C No 25 and 27, Sentul City, Bogor, 16810, Indonesia
Tel.: (62) 2187961557
Web Site: https://www.townmanagementsgc.com
Real Estate Services
N.A.I.C.S.: 531390

PT SEPEDA BERSAMA INDONESIA TBK

Jl Boulevard Alam Sutera No 12A, North Serpong South Tangerang, Banten, 15325, Indonesia
Tel.: (62) 2130052633
Web Site: https://www.sepedabersama.co.id
Year Founded: 2017
BIKE—(INDO)
Rev.: $27,942,389
Assets: $16,703,542
Liabilities: $8,344,395
Net Worth: $8,359,148
Earnings: $1,250,872
Emp.: 10
Fiscal Year-end: 12/31/23
Bicycle Product Distr
N.A.I.C.S.: 423910
Marina Pratiwi Sanjaya (Sec)

PT SHIELD-ON SERVICE TBK

Graha Dinamika Lantai 3 Jl Tanah Abang II No 49-51, Jakarta Pusat, 10160, Indonesia
Tel.: (62) 213505919
Web Site: https://www.sos.co.id
SOSS—(INDO)
Rev.: $115,616,119
Assets: $29,944,634
Liabilities: $10,835,657
Net Worth: $19,108,977
Earnings: $2,243,784
Emp.: 20
Fiscal Year-end: 12/31/23
Security System Services
N.A.I.C.S.: 561621

PT SIDOMULYO SELARAS TBK

Jl Gunung Sahari II No 12 A, Jakarta, 10610, Indonesia
Tel.: (62) 214266002
Web Site: https://www.sidomulyo.com
SDMU—(INDO)
Rev.: $5,963,278
Assets: $9,665,276
Liabilities: $7,291,834
Net Worth: $2,373,442
Earnings: $2,072,193
Emp.: 153
Fiscal Year-end: 12/31/23
Transportation Services
N.A.I.C.S.: 488490
Tjoe Mien Sasminto (Chm)

PT SIGMA ENERGY COMPRESSINDO TBK

GKM Green Tower 10th Floor Jl TB Simatupang Kav 89 G, Jakarta Selatan, 12520, Indonesia
Tel.: (62) 2127878099
Web Site: https://www.sinerco.co.id
Year Founded: 2007
SICO—(INDO)
Rev.: $6,499,002
Assets: $8,992,744
Liabilities: $1,372,525
Net Worth: $7,620,219
Earnings: $754,171
Emp.: 52
Fiscal Year-end: 12/31/23
Oil & Gas Production Services
N.A.I.C.S.: 237120
Aris Marisi Napitupulu (Dir-Operations-Development)

PT SILLO MARITIME PERDANA TBK

GHJ Suite Lt 5 dan 6 Jl Tanah Abang III No 18, Petojo Selatan Gambir, Jakarta Pusat, 10160, Indonesia
Tel.: (62) 213863861
Web Site: https://www.sillomaritime.com
Year Founded: 1989
SHIP—(INDO)
Rev.: $163,631,548
Assets: $432,180,554
Liabilities: $236,710,174
Net Worth: $195,470,380
Earnings: $25,763,464
Emp.: 128
Fiscal Year-end: 12/31/23
Offshore Shipping Services
N.A.I.C.S.: 211130
Dina Chardina (Mgr-Mktg)

Subsidiaries:

PT Eastern Jason (1)
Gedung Wirausaha 3rd Floor Jl HR Rasuna Said Kav C5 Karet Kuningan, Selatan Setiabudi, Jakarta, Indonesia
Tel.: (62) 215213605
Offshore Shipping Services
N.A.I.C.S.: 488390

PT Pratama Unggul Lestari (1)
Gedung Wirausaha 2nd Floor Jl HR Rasuna Said Kav C-5 Karet Kuningan, Selatan Setiabudi, Jakarta, Indonesia
Tel.: (62) 215279080
Offshore Shipping Services
N.A.I.C.S.: 488390

PT Suasa Benua Sukses (1)
The City Tower TCT Building 17th Floor Jl MH Thamrin No 81, Jakarta Pusat, 10310, Indonesia
Tel.: (62) 2131997332
Offshore Shipping Services
N.A.I.C.S.: 488390

PT SINAR MAS GROUP

Sinar Mas Land Plaza Tower II 33/F, Jalan MH Thamrin 51, Jakarta, 10350, Indonesia
Tel.: (62) 213929266
Web Site: http://www.sinarmas.com
Holding Company
N.A.I.C.S.: 551112
Rudy Halim (Chm & CEO)

Subsidiaries:

Asia Pulp & Paper (1)
BII Plaza 2nd Tower 15th & 18th Floors, Jl MH Thamrin No 51, Jakarta, 10350, Indonesia
Tel.: (62) 21 3929266
Web Site: http://www.asiapulppaper.com
Holding Company; Pulp & Paper Mills
N.A.I.C.S.: 551112

Holding (Domestic):

PT. Indah Kiat Pulp & Paper Tbk. (2)
Serang Mill Jl Raya Serang Km 76 Kragilan, Serang, Banten, 42184, Indonesia (67%)
Tel.: (62) 254280088
Web Site: https://www.ikserang.com
Rev.: $3,479,018,000
Assets: $10,125,138,000
Liabilities: $4,125,086,000
Net Worth: $6,000,052,000
Earnings: $411,423,000
Emp.: 11,000
Fiscal Year-end: 12/31/2023

Paper Mfr
N.A.I.C.S.: 322120
Lan Cheng Ting (Vice Chm)

PT Bumi Serpong Damai Tbk (1)
Sinar Mas Land Plaza Jl Grand Boulevard, BSD City, Tangerang, 15345, Indonesia
Tel.: (62) 2150368368
Web Site: https://www.bsdcity.com
Rev.: $749,351,833
Assets: $4,339,787,493
Liabilities: $1,664,156,485
Net Worth: $2,675,631,008
Earnings: $146,729,127
Emp.: 2,230
Fiscal Year-end: 12/31/2023
Real Estate Development Services
N.A.I.C.S.: 531390
Franciscus Xaverius Ridwan Darmali (Chm)

Subsidiary (Domestic):

PT Duta Pertiwi Tbk (2)
Sinar Mas Land Plaza Jl Grand Boulevard, BSD City, Tangerang, 15345, Banten, Indonesia
Tel.: (62) 2150368368
Web Site: https://dutapertiwi.com
Rev.: $250,825,825
Assets: $982,638,895
Liabilities: $238,368,880
Net Worth: $744,270,015
Earnings: $83,464,874
Emp.: 1,167
Fiscal Year-end: 12/31/2023
Real Estate Development Services
N.A.I.C.S.: 531390

PT Suryamas Dutamakmur Tbk (2)
16Th Floor Jl Jend Sudirman Kav 76-78, Sudirman Plaza Business Complex Plaza Marein, Jakarta Selatan, 12910, Indonesia (92%)
Tel.: (62) 2157936733
Web Site: https://rancamayagolf.com
Rev.: $32,242,574
Assets: $229,536,198
Liabilities: $30,927,972
Net Worth: $198,608,226
Earnings: $6,319,280
Emp.: 289
Fiscal Year-end: 12/31/2023
Real Estate Services
N.A.I.C.S.: 531210
Ferry Suhardjo (Sec)

Paper Excellence B.V. (1)
Beechavenue 54-80, Schiphol-Rijk, 1119 PW, Netherlands
Tel.: (31) 206586002
Holding Company
N.A.I.C.S.: 551112

Subsidiary (Non-US):

Paper Excellence Canada Holdings Corporation (2)
2nd Floor 3600 Lysander Lane, Richmond, V7B 1C3, BC, Canada
Tel.: (604) 247-4400
Web Site: http://www.paperexcellence.com
Emp.: 2,300
Holding Company; Paper & Pulp Mills Operator
N.A.I.C.S.: 551112
Joe Ragan (CFO)

Subsidiary (Domestic):

Catalyst Paper Corporation (3)
2nd Floor 3600 Lysander Lane, Richmond, V7B 1C3, BC, Canada
Tel.: (604) 247-4400
Web Site: http://www.catalystpaper.com
Emp.: 2,600
Paper & Pulp Products Mfr & Mill Operator
N.A.I.C.S.: 322120
Matthew Stapleton (Interim Sr VP-Sls & Mktg)

Plant (US):

Catalyst Paper Corporation - Biron (4)
621 N Biron Dr, Wisconsin Rapids, WI 54494-1843
Tel.: (715) 422-2236
Web Site: http://www.catalystpaper.com
Emp.: 425
Paper Mfr

INTERNATIONAL PUBLIC

N.A.I.C.S.: 322120

Catalyst Paper Corporation - Rumford (4)
35 Hartford St, Rumford, ME 04276
Tel.: (207) 364-4521
Web Site: http://www.catalystpaper.com
Emp.: 640
Paper Mfr
N.A.I.C.S.: 322120
Randy Chicoine (VP & Gen Mgr)

Subsidiary (US):

Domtar Corporation (3)
234 Kingsley Park Dr, Fort Mill, SC 29715
Tel.: (803) 802-7500
Web Site: https://www.domtar.com
Rev.: $6,936,000,000
Assets: $7,531,000,000
Liabilities: $4,956,000,000
Net Worth: $2,575,000,000
Earnings: $288,000,000
Emp.: 13,000
Fiscal Year-end: 12/31/2023
Pulp & Paper Products Mfr
N.A.I.C.S.: 322120
Daniel Buron (CFO & Exec VP)

Subsidiary (Domestic):

Associated Hygienic Products LLC (4)
3400 River Green Ct Ste 600, Duluth, GA 30096
Tel.: (770) 497-9800
Web Site: http://www.ahp-dsg.com
Sales Range: $300-349.9 Million
Emp.: 621
Disposable Diaper Mfr
N.A.I.C.S.: 322291

Subsidiary (Non-US):

Attends AB (4)
Jarnvagsgatan 4, 578 33, Aneby, Sweden
Tel.: (46) 20778000
Web Site: http://www.attends.se
Sanitary Product Mfr & Distr
N.A.I.C.S.: 325620

Attends AS (4)
Klingenberggata 7, 0125, Oslo, Norway
Tel.: (47) 80032090
Cosmetic & Sanitary Product Mfr
N.A.I.C.S.: 325620

Attends BVBA (4)
Haachtsebaan 119, 3140, Keerbergen, Belgium
Tel.: (32) 15509595
Web Site: http://www.attends.be
Sanitary Product Mfr & Distr
N.A.I.C.S.: 325620

Attends Europe GmbH (4)
Baslerstrasse 15, 4310, Rheinfelden, Switzerland
Tel.: (41) 618333091
Web Site: http://www.attends.ch
Emp.: 4
Sanitary Product Mfr & Distr
N.A.I.C.S.: 325620

Attends GmbH (4)
Am Kronberger Hang 3, 65824, Schwalbach am Taunus, Germany
Tel.: (49) 619650893
Web Site: http://www.attends.se
Sanitary Product Mfr & Distr
N.A.I.C.S.: 325620

Attends GmbH (4)
Baslerstrasse 15, 4310, Rheinfelden, Switzerland
Tel.: (41) 618333091
Web Site: http://www.attends.ch
Sanitary Product Mfr & Distr
N.A.I.C.S.: 325620

Attends Healthcare AB (4)
Jarnvagsgatan 4, Box 173, 578 24, Aneby, Sweden
Tel.: (46) 3 804 7500
Web Site: https://www.attends.se
Sanitary Product Mfr & Distr
N.A.I.C.S.: 325620

Attends Healthcare Group Ltd. (4)
3rd Floor The Old Post Office St Nicholas

AND PRIVATE COMPANIES

Street, Newcastle upon Tyne, NE1 1RH,
United Kingdom
Tel.: (44) 1912427128
Web Site: http://www.attendshealthcare.com
Sales Range: $125-149.9 Million
Emp.: 413
Paper & Sanitary Product Distr
N.A.I.C.S.: 424130

Attends Healthcare Ltd (4)
Unit 10 Mariner Court, Calder Park, Wakefield, WF4 3FL, Yorkshire, United Kingdom
Tel.: (44) 8456013272
Web Site: http://www.attends.co.uk
Health Care Srvices
N.A.I.C.S.: 621111

Subsidiary (Domestic):

Attends Healthcare Products, Inc. (4)
8020 Arco Corporate Dr Ste 200, Raleigh, NC 27617
Tel.: (252) 752-1100
Web Site: http://www.attends.com
Incontinence Products Mfr & Distr
N.A.I.C.S.: 322291

Subsidiary (Domestic):

Attends Healthcare Products, Inc. (5)
1941 N White Ave, La Verne, CA 91750
Tel.: (909) 392-1200
Web Site: http://www.attends.com
Incontinence Products Mfr & Distr
N.A.I.C.S.: 322291

Subsidiary (Non-US):

Attends Ltd (4)
Unit 10 Mariner Court Calder Park, Wakefield, WF4 3FL, Yorkshire, United Kingdom
Tel.: (44) 8456013272
Web Site: http://www.attends.co.uk
Emp.: 16
Sanitary Product Mfr & Distr
N.A.I.C.S.: 325620

Attends OY (4)
Sinikalliontie 11, 02630, Espoo, Finland
Tel.: (358) 102791383
Web Site: http://www.attends.fi
Paper & Sanitary Product Distr
N.A.I.C.S.: 424130

Subsidiary (Domestic):

Domtar A.W. LLC (4)
285 Hwy 71 S, Ashdown, AR 71822
Tel.: (870) 898-2711
Uncoated Freesheet Paper Mfr
N.A.I.C.S.: 322220

Subsidiary (Non-US):

Domtar Asia Limited (4)
Millennium City Kwun Tong, Hong Kong, China (Hong Kong)
Tel.: (852) 37176888
Pulp Mill
N.A.I.C.S.: 322110

Plant (Non-US):

Domtar Corporation - Kamloops Mill
2005 Mission Flats Road, Kamloops, V2C 1A9, BC, Canada
Tel.: (250) 434-6000
Pulp Product Mfr
N.A.I.C.S.: 322110

Domtar Corporation - Windsor Mill (4)
609 Rang 12, PO Box 1010, Windsor, J1S 2L9, QC, Canada
Sales Range: $250-299.9 Million
Emp.: 800
Paper & Pulp Mfr
N.A.I.C.S.: 322120

Subsidiary (Domestic):

Domtar Paper Company, LLC (4)
234 Kingsley Park Dr, Fort Mill, SC 29715
Tel.: (803) 802-7500
Web Site: http://www.domtar.com
Paper Mfr & Distr
N.A.I.C.S.: 322299

Plant (Domestic):

Domtar Industries (5)
301 Point Basse Ave, Nekoosa, WI 54457
Tel.: (715) 887-5806
Sales Range: $400-449.9 Million
Emp.: 1,100
Paper Mill Mfr
N.A.I.C.S.: 322299

Domtar Industries-Ashdown Mill (5)
285 Hwy 71 S, Ashdown, AR 71822 (100%)
Tel.: (870) 898-2711
Web Site: http://www.domtar.com
Sales Range: $450-499.9 Million
Emp.: 1,260
Paper Mills
N.A.I.C.S.: 322110

Subsidiary (Non-US):

Domtar Pacific Papers ULC (5)
395 de Maisonneuve Blvd West, Montreal, H3A 1L6, QC, Canada
Tel.: (514) 848-5555
Web Site: http://www.domtar.com
Sales Range: $125-149.9 Million
Emp.: 500
Paper Pulp Mills
N.A.I.C.S.: 322110

Subsidiary (Domestic):

Domtar, Inc. (6)
395 De Maisonneuve Blvd West, Montreal, H3A 1L6, QC, Canada (100%)
Tel.: (514) 848-5555
Web Site: http://www.domtar.com
Sales Range: $25-49.9 Million
Emp.: 17
Mfr of Paper Products
N.A.I.C.S.: 322211

Subsidiary (Non-US):

Domtar Personal Care Europe, S.L.U. (5)
Paseo Club Deportivo 18 Pozuelo De Alarcon Comunidad De Madrid, 28223, Madrid, Spain
Tel.: (34) 915096000
Tape Distr
N.A.I.C.S.: 424110
Victor J. Puente (Pres)

Plant (Domestic):

Domtar-Hawesville (5)
Hwy 1406 58 Wescor Rd, Hawesville, KY 42348
Tel.: (270) 927-6961
Web Site: http://www.domtar.com
Sales Range: $100-124.9 Million
Emp.: 450
Paper & Pulp Mill
N.A.I.C.S.: 322120

Domtar-Johnsonburg (5)
100 Center St, Johnsonburg, PA 15845
Tel.: (814) 965-2521
Web Site: http://www.domtor.com
Sales Range: $100-124.9 Million
Emp.: 400
Paper Mills
N.A.I.C.S.: 322120

Domtar-Kingsport (5)
100 Clinchfield St, Kingsport, TN 37660
Tel.: (423) 247-7111
Web Site: http://www.domtar.com
Sales Range: $100-124.9 Million
Emp.: 332
Paper Mills
N.A.I.C.S.: 322120

Domtar-Marlboro (5)
585 Willamette Rd, Bennettsville, SC 29512
Tel.: (843) 479-0200
Web Site: http://www.domtar.com
Sales Range: $100-124.9 Million
Emp.: 300
Paper & Pulp Mill
N.A.I.C.S.: 322120

Domtar-Plymouth (5)
Hwy 149, Plymouth, NC 27962
Tel.: (252) 793-8111
Web Site: http://www.domtar.com
Paper & Pulp Mill
N.A.I.C.S.: 322120

Domtar-Rothschild (5)
200 N Grand Ave, Rothschild, WI 54474
Tel.: (715) 359-3101
Web Site: http://www.domtar.com
Sales Range: $100-124.9 Million
Emp.: 400
Paper Mills
N.A.I.C.S.: 322120

Subsidiary (Domestic):

Domtar Personal Care Absorbent Hygiene Inc. (4)
160 Greentree Dr Ste 101, Dover, DE 19904
Tel.: (514) 848-5151
Paper Mill Operator
N.A.I.C.S.: 322110

EAM Corporation (4)
2075 Sunset Blvd, Jesup, GA 31545 (100%)
Tel.: (912) 588-2600
Web Site: http://www.eam-corp.com
Sales Range: $10-24.9 Million
Emp.: 70
Absorbent Material for Diapers Mfr
N.A.I.C.S.: 322291

Subsidiary (Domestic):

Palmetto Enterprises LLC (5)
11190 Eagle Watch, Smithfield, VA 23430
Tel.: (757) 357-7244
Management Consulting Services
N.A.I.C.S.: 541618

Subsidiary (Domestic):

Home Delivery Incontinent Supplies Co., Inc. (4)
9385 Dielman Ind Dr, Olivette, MO 63132 (100%)
Tel.: (314) 997-8771
Web Site: http://www.hdis.com
Sales Range: $50-74.9 Million
Emp.: 240
Incontinence Products Mail-Order Services
N.A.I.C.S.: 456199

Iconex LLC (4)
3237 Satellite Blvd Ste 550, Duluth, GA 30096
Web Site: https://www.iconex.com
Print Label Solutions Services
N.A.I.C.S.: 561910
Mike Vigunas (VP-Bus Dev-Global)

Subsidiary (Domestic):

Max International Converters, Inc. (5)
2360 Dairy Rd, Lancaster, PA 17601
Tel.: (717) 898-0147
Web Site: http://www.maxintl.com
Rev: $7,800,000
Emp.: 25
Coated & Laminated Paper Mfr
N.A.I.C.S.: 322220

Subsidiary (Non-US):

Laboratorios Indas, S.A.U. (4)
Paseo Del Club Deportivo N1 Edif 18 Parque Empresarial La Finca, Pozuelo, 28223, Madrid, Spain
Tel.: (34) 902760600
Web Site: http://www.indas.com
Sales Range: $200-249.9 Million
Emp.: 453
Sanitary & Hygienic Products Mfr & Distr
N.A.I.C.S.: 325620

Subsidiary (Domestic):

Algodones del Bages, S.A.U. (5)
C/ Frederic Mompou s/n, PO Box 121, 08295, Sant Vicenc de Castellet, Barcelona, Spain
Tel.: (34) 938748444
Web Site: http://www.albasa.com
Emp.: 50
Cosmetic & Sanitary Product Mfr
N.A.I.C.S.: 325620

Subsidiary (Non-US):

Indas EURL (5)
8 Rue Joseph Cugnot, CS 92004, 38307, Bourgoin-Jallieu, Cedex, France
Tel.: (33) 664212371

PT SINAR MAS GROUP

Paper Products Mfr
N.A.I.C.S.: 322299

Subsidiary (Domestic):

Prisma Renewable Composites, LLC (4)
9125 Cross Park Dr Ste 150, Knoxville, TN 37923
Tel.: (865) 394-9638
Web Site: http://www.prismacomposites.com
Renewable Composite Biotechnology Services
N.A.I.C.S.: 541713
Adam McCall (Pres & CEO)

Reassure, LLC (4)
9385 Dielman Ind Dr, Olivette, MO 63132
Web Site: http://www.reassure.com
Sanitary Paper Product Mfr
N.A.I.C.S.: 322291

Subsidiary (Non-US):

Resolute Forest Products Inc. (4)
1010 De La Gauchetière Street West Suite 400, Montreal, H3B 2N2, QC, Canada
Tel.: (514) 875-2160
Web Site: http://www.resolutefp.com
Rev.: $3,664,000,000
Assets: $3,538,000,000
Liabilities: $2,021,000,000
Net Worth: $1,517,000,000
Earnings: $307,000,000
Emp.: 6,900
Fiscal Year-end: 12/31/2021
Newsprint & Uncoated Groundwood Papers Mfr
N.A.I.C.S.: 322120
Bradley P. Martin (Vice Chm)

Subsidiary (US):

Apache Railway Company (5)
PO Box 857, Snowflake, AZ 85937
Tel.: (928) 536-4696
Common Carrier Railroad
N.A.I.C.S.: 482111

Atlas Paper Mills, LLC (5)
3301 NW 107th St, Miami, FL 33167 (100%)
Tel.: (305) 636-5740
Web Site: http://www.atlaspapermills.com
Emp.: 8,000
Tissue & Recycled Waste Paper Mfr & Whslr
N.A.I.C.S.: 423930

Subsidiary (Domestic):

Accurate Paper Holdings, LLC (6)
5500 E Giddens Ave, Tampa, FL 33610
Tel.: (813) 622-8328
Web Site: http://accuratepaper.com
Paper Recycling Services
N.A.I.C.S.: 423930

Subsidiary (US):

Fibrek Recycling U.S. Inc. (5)
702 Afr Dr, Fairmont, WV 26554
Recycled Product Distr
N.A.I.C.S.: 423930

Resolute FP US Inc. (5)
5020 Hwy 11 S, Calhoun, TN 37309
Tel.: (423) 336-2211
Web Site: http://www.resolutefp.com
Emp.: 416
Holding Company; Regional Managing Office
N.A.I.C.S.: 551112

Subsidiary (Domestic):

AbiBow Recycling LLC (6)
15600 JFK Blvd Ste 600, Houston, TX 77032
Tel.: (281) 372-7010
Pulp & Paper Mfr
N.A.I.C.S.: 322299

Resolute FP Augusta LLC (6)
2434 Doug Barnard Pkwy, Augusta, GA 30906 (100%)
Tel.: (706) 798-3440
Newsprint Paper Mfr
N.A.I.C.S.: 322299
Derrick Lindgren (Plant Mgr)

PT SINAR MAS GROUP — INTERNATIONAL PUBLIC

PT Sinar Mas Group—(Continued)

Unit (Domestic):

Resolute FP US Inc. - Coosa Pines (6)
17589 Plant Rd, Coosa Pines, AL 35044-0555
Tel.: (256) 378-5541
Web Site: http://www.resolutefp.com
Emp.: 289
Newsprint; Groundwood Printing Papers; Kraft Pulp; Lumber
N.A.I.C.S.: 322120

Resolute FP US Inc. - Grenada (6)
1000 Papermill Rd, Grenada, MS 38901
Tel.: (662) 227-7900
Web Site: http://www.resolutefp.com
Newsprint Mill
N.A.I.C.S.: 322120

Subsidiary (Non-US):

Fibre Excellence Saint-Gaudens SAS (3)
President Saragat St, PO Box 149, 31803, Saint-Gaudens, Cedex, France
Tel.: (33) 561947575
Web Site: http://www.fibre-excellence.fr
Sales Range: $150-199.9 Million
Emp.: 255
N.A.I.C.S.: 322120

Fibre Excellence Tarascon SAS (3)
13156 Tarascon cedex, PO Box 8, 13156, Tarascon, France
Tel.: (33) 490910300
Web Site: http://www.fibre-excellence.fr
Sales Range: $150-199.9 Million
Emp.: 273
N.A.I.C.S.: 322120
Alexandre Razgonnikoff (Plant Mgr)

Subsidiary (Domestic):

Howe Sound Pulp & Paper Corporation (3)
3838 Port Mellon Highway Bentall Postal Station, Port Mellon, V0N 2S0, BC, Canada (100%)
Tel.: (604) 884-5223
Web Site: http://www.hspp.ca
Sales Range: $250-299.9 Million
Emp.: 540
Pulp & Paper Mfr
N.A.I.C.S.: 322110
Fred Fominoff (CFO)

Northern Resources Nova Scotia Corporation (3)
260 Granton Abercrombie Branch Road, Abercrombie, New Glasgow, B2H 5C6, NS, Canada
Tel.: (902) 752-8461
Emp.: 230
Holding Company; Wood Pulp Mills Operator; Forestry & Timber Tract Operations
N.A.I.C.S.: 551112
Don Breen (Gen Mgr-Northern Pulp Nova Scotia)

Subsidiary (Domestic):

Northern Pulp Nova Scotia Corporation (4)
260 Granton Abercrombie Branch Road, Abercrombie, New Glasgow, B2H 5C6, NS, Canada
Tel.: (902) 752-8461
Web Site: http://www.northernpulp.ca
Sales Range: $150-199.9 Million
Emp.: 230
Wood Pulp Mills Operator
N.A.I.C.S.: 322110

Plant (Domestic):

Paper Excellence Canada - Skookumchuck NBSK Pulp Mill (3)
4501 Farstad Way, Skookumchuck, V0B 2E0, BC, Canada
Tel.: (250) 422-3261
Sales Range: $125-149.9 Million
Emp.: 300
Chemical Pulp Mill
N.A.I.C.S.: 322110
Curtis Jeffrey (Mgr-HR)

PT SINAR MAS MULTIARTHA TBK
Menara Tekno Lt 7, Jakarta, 10250, Indonesia
Tel.: (62) 213925660
Web Site: https://www.smma.co.id
Year Founded: 1982
SMMA—(INDO)
Rev.: $1,748,843,941
Assets: $7,400,952,689
Liabilities: $5,788,586,912
Net Worth: $1,612,365,777
Earnings: $6,204,497
Emp.: 9,039
Fiscal Year-end: 12/31/23
Financial Consulting Services
N.A.I.C.S.: 541611
Doddy Susanto (Chm)

Subsidiaries:

P.T. Artha Bina Usaha (1)
Menara Tekno Lt 7 Jl Fachruddin No 19, Jakarta Pusat, 10250, Indonesia
Tel.: (62) 213925660
Real Estate & Finance Services
N.A.I.C.S.: 531190

P.T. Arthamas Informatika (1)
Menara Tekno Lt 7 Jl Fachruddin No 19, Jakarta Pusat, 10250, Indonesia
Tel.: (62) 213925660
Information Technology Services
N.A.I.C.S.: 541512

P.T. Arthamas Solusindo (1)
Menara Tekno Lt 7 Jl Fachruddin No 19, Kampung Bali Tanah Abang DKI Jakarta, Jakarta Pusat, 10250, Indonesia
Tel.: (62) 2150102388
Web Site: https://www.amsconsult.com
Information Technology Services
N.A.I.C.S.: 541519

P.T. Balai Lelang Sinarmas (1)
Jl KH Fachrudin No 4 RT 009/ RW 005, Kampung Bali Tanah Abang, Jakarta Pusat, 10250, Indonesia
Tel.: (62) 2129189812
Web Site: https://balailelangsimas.id
Motor Vehicle Mfr & Distr
N.A.I.C.S.: 336211

P.T. Data Opal Terpadu (1)
Menara Tekno Lt 7 Jl Fachruddin No 19, Jakarta Pusat, 10250, Indonesia
Tel.: (62) 213925660
Financial Services
N.A.I.C.S.: 522291

P.T. Digital Solusindo Nusantara (1)
Menara Tekno Lt 7 Jl Fachruddin No 19, Jakarta Pusat, 10250, Indonesia
Tel.: (62) 213925660
Financial Services
N.A.I.C.S.: 522291

P.T. Pasar Gadai Digital (1)
Menara Tekno Lt 7 Jl Fachruddin No 19, Jakarta Pusat, 10250, Indonesia
Tel.: (62) 213925660
Real Estate & Finance Services
N.A.I.C.S.: 531190

P.T. Sinar Artha Inforindo (1)
Menara Tekno Lt 7 Jl Fachruddin No 19, Jakarta Pusat, 10250, Indonesia
Tel.: (62) 213925660
Information Technology Services
N.A.I.C.S.: 541512

P.T. Sinar Artha Solusindo (1)
Menara Tekno Lt 7 Jl Fachruddin No 19, Jakarta Pusat, 10250, Indonesia
Tel.: (62) 213925660
Real Estate & Finance Services
N.A.I.C.S.: 531190

P.T. Sinar Artha Trading (1)
Menara Tekno Lt 7 Jl Fachruddin No 19, Jakarta Pusat, 10250, Indonesia
Tel.: (62) 213925660
Real Estate & Finance Services
N.A.I.C.S.: 531190

P.T. Sistem Loka Triprima (1)
Menara Tekno Lt 7 Jl Fachruddin No 19, Jakarta Pusat, 10250, Indonesia
Tel.: (62) 213925660

Financial Services
N.A.I.C.S.: 522291

P.T. Zimba Onix Mustika (1)
Menara Tekno Lt 7 Jl Fachruddin No 19, Jakarta Pusat, 10250, Indonesia
Tel.: (62) 213925660
Property & Real Estate Services
N.A.I.C.S.: 531190

PT AB Sinar Mas Multifinance (1)
Sinar Mas Land Plaza Tower 1 9th Floor Jln MH Thamrin No 51, Jakarta, 10350, Indonesia
Tel.: (62) 213925660
Web Site: http://www.absimasfinance.co.id
Financial Services
N.A.I.C.S.: 523999

PT Asuransi Simas Insurtech (1)
Gedung Menara Tekno Lt 5 Jl K H Fachrudin No19, Tanah Abang, Jakarta Pusat, 10250, Indonesia
Tel.: (62) 2129189888
Web Site: https://www.simasinsurtech.com
Financial Services
N.A.I.C.S.: 523999

PT Asuransi Simas Jiwa (1)
Jl Lombok no 73, Jakarta Pusat, 10350, Indonesia
Tel.: (62) 2128547999
Web Site: https://www.simasjiwa.co.id
Insurance Services
N.A.I.C.S.: 524210

PT Asuransi Sinar Mas (1)
Plaza Simas Jl Fachrudin No 18 Tanah Abang, Jakarta, 10250, Indonesia
Tel.: (62) 2129189999
Web Site: http://www.sinarmas.co.id
Financial Services
N.A.I.C.S.: 523999

PT Asuransi Sumit Oto (1)
Plaza Simas Lantai 6 Jl Fachrudin No 18, Jakarta, 10250, Indonesia
Tel.: (62) 2129189898
Web Site: http://www.aso.co.id
Financial Services
N.A.I.C.S.: 523999

PT Bima Multi Finance (1)
Jl Cideng Barat No 471, Jakarta Pusat, 10150, Indonesia
Tel.: (62) 2163858555
Web Site: http://www.bimafinance.co.id
Financial Services
N.A.I.C.S.: 523999

PT Century Tokyo Leasing Indonesia (1)
Menara Astra 25th Floor Jl Jend Sudirman Kav 5, Jakarta, 10220, Indonesia
Tel.: (62) 2130404080
Leasing Services
N.A.I.C.S.: 532490
Tatsuyoshi Ogino (Co-Pres)

PT Dana Pinjaman Inklusif (1)
Sinar Mas Land Plaza Tower I 9th Floor Jl MH Thamrin No 51, Jakarta, 10350, Indonesia
Tel.: (62) 2130033039
Web Site: http://www.pinjamango.co.id
Loan Services
N.A.I.C.S.: 522390

PT Dana Saham Bersama (1)
Roxy Square Lantai 1 Blok A No 01 Jalan Kyai Tapa No 1, Tomang Grogol Petamburan, Jakarta Barat, 11440, Indonesia
Tel.: (62) 2156954551
Web Site: https://www.danasaham.co.id
Financial Services
N.A.I.C.S.: 523999

PT Jakarta Teknologi Utama (1)
Jl Raya Bekasi KM 20 Rawa Terate, Cakung, Jakarta, 13920, Indonesia
Tel.: (62) 2150556789
Web Site: https://www.teknobodyrepair.id
Vehicle Maintenance Services
N.A.I.C.S.: 811121

PT KB Insurance Indonesia (1)
Sinar Mas Land Plaza Tower 2 Lantai 25 Suite 2501 Jl M H Thamrin 51, Jakarta, 10350, Indonesia
Tel.: (62) 213913101
Web Site: http://www.kbinsure.co.id

Insurance Services
N.A.I.C.S.: 524210
Indra Widjaja (Co-Pres)

PT Oto Multiartha (1)
Gedung Summitmas II Lt 7 Jl Jendral Sudirman Kav 61-62, Jakarta, 12910, Indonesia
Tel.: (62) 215226410
Financial Services
N.A.I.C.S.: 523999

PT Rizky Lancar Sentosa (1)
Roxy Square Jl Kyai Tapa No 1, Jakarta Barat, Indonesia
Tel.: (62) 215693500
Financial Services
N.A.I.C.S.: 523999

PT SGMW Multifinance Indonesia (1)
Sinarmas MSIG Tower Lt 43 Jl Jendral Sudirman No Kav 21 RT 10 RW 01, Kuningan Karet Kec Setiabudi, Jakarta Selatan, 12920, Indonesia
Tel.: (62) 2122535050
Web Site: http://www.wulingfinance.co.id
Financial Services
N.A.I.C.S.: 523999
Nathan Sun (CEO)

PT Shinta Utama (1)
Sinar Mas Land Plaza JI MH Thamrin No 51, Jakarta, 10350, Indonesia
Tel.: (62) 213925660
Financial Services
N.A.I.C.S.: 523999

PT Simas Money Changer (1)
Sinar Mas Land Plaza Jl MH Thamrin No 51, Jakarta, 10350, Indonesia
Tel.: (62) 2131934590
Financial Services
N.A.I.C.S.: 523999

PT Sinar Mas Multifinance (1)
Jl Lombok No 71 Gondangdia Menteng Central, Jakarta, 10350, Indonesia
Tel.: (62) 8001588588
Web Site: https://www.simasfinance.co.id
Financial Services
N.A.I.C.S.: 523999

PT Sinar Mas Ventura (1)
Roxy Square Lt 1 Blok B 08 No 1 Jl Kyai Tapa No 1, Tomang Grogol Petamburan, Jakarta Barat, 11440, Indonesia
Tel.: (62) 2156954451
Financial Services
N.A.I.C.S.: 523999

PT Sinarmas Asset Management (1)
Sinar Mas Land Plaza Menara 3 Lt 7 Jl M H Thamrin No 51, Jakarta, 10350, Indonesia
Tel.: (62) 2150507000
Web Site: https://www.sinarmas-am.co.id
Financial Services
N.A.I.C.S.: 523999
Alex Setyawan WK (Pres)

PT Sinarmas Sekuritas (1)
Sinar Mas Land Plaza Menara 3 Lt 5 JI MH Thamrin No 51, Jakarta, 10350, Indonesia
Web Site: http://www.sinarmassekuritas.co.id
Investment Services
N.A.I.C.S.: 523999
Hermawan Hosein (Pres)

PT SINERGI INTI ANDALAN PRIMA TBK
Gedung Cyber 1 Lantai 10 Jl Kuningan Barat No 8, Jakarta Selatan, 12710, Jakarta, Indonesia
Tel.: (62) 215265943
Web Site: https://www.siapnetworks.co.id
Year Founded: 2016
INET—(INDO)
Rev.: $1,876,076
Assets: $14,541,233
Liabilities: $609,073
Net Worth: $13,932,160
Earnings: $56,867
Emp.: 20
Fiscal Year-end: 12/31/23

Information Technology Services
N.A.I.C.S.: 541512
Muhammad Arif (CEO)

PT SINERGI INTI PLASTINDO TBK
Simprug Garden Office No 9D Jl Teuku Nyak Arief Simprug, Kebayoran Lama, South Jakarta, 12220, Indonesia
Tel.: (62) 2127515411
Web Site:
https://www.sinergiplastama.co.id
Year Founded: 2001
ESIP—(INDO)
Rev.: $4,031,629
Assets: $6,533,890
Liabilities: $278,926
Net Worth: $6,254,964
Earnings: $56,986
Emp.: 18
Fiscal Year-end: 12/31/23
Plastic Packaging Mfr & Distr
N.A.I.C.S.: 326112
Sherlie Asih Atmaja (Sec)

PT SINERGI MEGAH INTERNUSA TBK
Jl Ring Road Utara No 409 Caturtunggal Depok Sleman, Catur Tunggal Daerah Istimewa, Yogyakarta, Indonesia
Tel.: (62) 2742924777
Web Site:
http://www.sinergimegahtbk.com
Year Founded: 2014
Hotel & Restaurant Operator
N.A.I.C.S.: 721110
Rizky Karunia Putra (Head-Audit Internal)

PT SINGARAJA PUTRA TBK
Jalan Galeria Singaraja Blok C No 16-17, Lippo Cikarang, Bekasi, 17550, Indonesia
Tel.: (62) 218974309
Web Site:
https://www.singarajaputra.com
Year Founded: 2005
SINI—(INDO)
Rev.: $19,313,902
Assets: $38,735,170
Liabilities: $79,229,944
Net Worth: ($40,494,774)
Earnings: ($624,802)
Emp.: 308
Fiscal Year-end: 12/31/23
Accommodation Operator
N.A.I.C.S.: 721199
Erick Tonny Tjandra (Sec)

PT SKY ENERGY INDONESIA TBK
Graha Mas Fatmawati B10 Jln RS Fatmawati No 71 RT/RW 002/005 Kel, Cipete Utara Kec Kebayoran Baru, Jakarta, Jawa Barat, Indonesia
Tel.: (62) 217262081
Web Site: http://www.sky-energy.co.id
Year Founded: 2008
JSKY—(INDO)
Rev.: $10,380,612
Assets: $27,117,509
Liabilities: $15,873,002
Net Worth: $11,244,506
Earnings: ($5,094,033)
Emp.: 26
Fiscal Year-end: 12/31/21
Solar Energy Equipment Distr
N.A.I.C.S.: 423690
Yusuf Woro Widhi Firmanto (Sec)

PT SLJ GLOBAL TBK.
Capital Place Lantai 28 Jl Jend Gatot Subroto Kav 18, PO Box 3396, Kel Kec Mampang PrapatanJakarta Selatan -12710, Jakarta, 12950, Indonesia
Tel.: (62) 215761188   Id
Web Site: https://www.sljglobal.com
Year Founded: 1980
SULI—(INDO)
Rev.: $15,510,443
Assets: $53,030,906
Liabilities: $44,067,401
Net Worth: $8,963,505
Earnings: ($14,128,571)
Emp.: 118
Fiscal Year-end: 12/31/23
Hardwood Veneer & Plywood Mfr; Forest Management Services
N.A.I.C.S.: 321211
Amir Sunarko (Chm)

PT SMARTFREN TELECOM TBK
Jl H Agus Salim No 45 Menteng, Jakarta Pusat, 10340, Indonesia
Tel.: (62) 2150538888
Web Site: https://www.smartfren.com
Year Founded: 2002
FREN—(INDO)
Rev.: $756,921,678
Assets: $2,925,209,377
Liabilities: $1,907,427,161
Net Worth: $1,017,782,216
Earnings: ($7,075,343)
Emp.: 2,431
Fiscal Year-end: 12/31/23
Mobile Communications Services
N.A.I.C.S.: 517112
Merza Fachys (Chm)

PT SMR UTAMA TBK
Rukan Puri Mutiara Blok A12 A15 Jl Griya Utama Sunter Agung, Jakarta Utara, 14350, Indonesia
Tel.: (62) 2165310818   Id
Web Site: https://www.smrutama.com
Year Founded: 2003
SMRU—(INDO)
Rev.: $20,880,730
Assets: $53,796,711
Liabilities: $46,565,105
Net Worth: $7,231,606
Earnings: ($5,285,128)
Emp.: 156
Fiscal Year-end: 12/31/23
Mining Services
N.A.I.C.S.: 212210
Gani Bustan (Chm)

Subsidiaries:

PT Ricobana   (1)
Puri Mutiara A12 and A15 Jl Griya Utama, Sunter Agung, Jakarta, 14350, Indonesia
Tel.: (62) 2165310818
Web Site: https://www.ricobana.co.id
Mining Services
N.A.I.C.S.: 213115

PT. Adikarsa Alam Resources   (1)
5th Floor Suite 501 Jl Yos Sudarso Kav 89, Jakarta, 14350, Indonesia
Tel.: (62) 216508133
Coal Mining Services
N.A.I.C.S.: 213113

PT. Ricobana Abadi   (1)
Web Site: http://www.ricobana.co.id
Coal Mining Services
N.A.I.C.S.: 213113

PT. Troposfir Pancar Sejati   (1)
Sentral Senayan II Lantai 16 Jl Asia Afrika No 8, Kelurahan Gelora Kecamatan Tanah Abang, Jakarta Pusat, 10270, Indonesia
Tel.: (62) 2157974410
Coal Mining Services
N.A.I.C.S.: 213113

PT SOECHI LINES TBK
Sahid Sudirman Center 51st Floor Jl Jend Sudirman Kav 86, Jakarta Pusat, 10220, Indonesia
Tel.: (62) 2180861000   Id
Web Site: https://www.soechi.com
Year Founded: 1977
SOCI—(INDO)
Rev.: $169,963,708
Assets: $604,303,565
Liabilities: $221,780,720
Net Worth: $382,522,845
Earnings: $8,931,190
Emp.: 222
Fiscal Year-end: 12/31/23
Marine Freight Transportation & Shipyard Operations
N.A.I.C.S.: 483111
Go Darmadi (Chm)

Subsidiaries:

PT Lintas Samudra Maritim   (1)
Gama Tower 29th Floor Jl H R Rasuna Said Kav C-22 RT 2/RW 5, Karet Kuningan Kecamatan Setiabudi, Jakarta, 12940, Indonesia
Tel.: (62) 212527161
Web Site: https://www.lintasmaritim.com
Cargo Transportation Services
N.A.I.C.S.: 484110

PT SOFYAN HOTELS TBK
Jl Cut Meutia No 09, Menteng, Jakarta, 10330, Indonesia
Tel.: (62) 213160125
Web Site:
http://www.sofyanhotel.co.id
SPOT—(INDO)
Hotel Services
N.A.I.C.S.: 721110
Ratna Suci Apriani (Sec)

PT SOHO GLOBAL HEALTH TBK
Jl Rawa Sumur Ii Kav Bb No 3 Kawasan Industri Pulogadung, Kel Jatinegara Kec Cakung, Jakarta Timur, Indonesia
Tel.: (62) 29858888
Web Site:
https://www.sohoglobalhealth.com
Year Founded: 1946
SOHO—(INDO)
Rev.: $532,362,210
Assets: $308,267,582
Liabilities: $152,470,158
Net Worth: $155,797,424
Earnings: $24,114,885
Emp.: 2,500
Fiscal Year-end: 12/31/23
Pharmaceutical Mfr & Distr
N.A.I.C.S.: 325412
Rogelio Paulino Jr. (Pres)

PT SOLUSI KEMASAN DIGITAL TBK
JL Jababeka 2 Blok C/11-D Kawasan Industri Jababeka Utara Kabupaten, Cikarang, Bekasi, 17530, Jawa Barat, Indonesia
Tel.: (62) 2129918991
Web Site: https://www.flexypack.com
Year Founded: 2019
PACK—(INDO)
Rev.: $3,437,387
Assets: $5,008,787
Liabilities: $1,454,396
Net Worth: $3,554,391
Earnings: $148,634
Emp.: 93
Fiscal Year-end: 12/31/23
Packaging Products Mfr
N.A.I.C.S.: 322220
Denny Winoto (Chm)

PT SOLUSI SINERGI DIGITAL TBK
Kantor Fatmawati Mas Blok III 328 329 Jl RS Fatmawati No 20, Jakarta, 12430, Indonesia
Tel.: (62) 217659228
Web Site: https://www.surge.co.id
Year Founded: 2012
WIFI—(INDO)
Rev.: $28,529,854
Assets: $101,581,071
Liabilities: $53,353,642
Net Worth: $48,227,430
Earnings: $3,783,191
Emp.: 85
Fiscal Year-end: 12/31/23
Advertising Agency Services
N.A.I.C.S.: 541810
Gilman Pradana Nugraha (Sec)

Subsidiaries:

PT Integrasi Jaringan Ekosistem   (1)
Kantor Fatmawati Mas Blok III No 328-329 Jl RS Fatmawati No 20, Jakarta, 12430, Indonesia
Tel.: (62) 217659228
Web Site: https://weave.co.id
Telecommunication Servicesb
N.A.I.C.S.: 517810

PT SONA TOPAS TOURISM INDUSTRY TBK
Sudirman Tower 20th floor Jl Jend Sudirman Kav 60, Jakarta, 12190, Indonesia
Tel.: (62) 215213056   Id
Web Site:
https://www.sonatopas.co.id
Year Founded: 1978
SONA—(INDO)
Rev.: $45,964,840
Assets: $58,412,850
Liabilities: $19,943,866
Net Worth: $38,468,984
Earnings: ($643,706)
Emp.: 732
Fiscal Year-end: 12/31/23
Travel Agency Services
N.A.I.C.S.: 561599
Wong Budi Setiawan (Chm & Sec)

PT SREEYA SEWU INDONESIA TBK
Sequis Tower Lt 40 Jl Jendral Sudirman Kav 71, Jakarta Selatan, 12190, Indonesia
Tel.: (62) 2150991599   Id
Web Site:
https://www.sreeyasewu.com
Year Founded: 1985
SIPD—(INDO)
Rev.: $395,571,749
Assets: $213,098,727
Liabilities: $135,622,125
Net Worth: $77,476,602
Earnings: ($1,124,436)
Emp.: 1,984
Fiscal Year-end: 12/31/23
Poultry Mfr
N.A.I.C.S.: 112340
Soh Ching Kher (Vice Chm)

Subsidiaries:

PT Belfoods Indonesia   (1)
Citra Indah Kav 1 & 2 Jl Raya Jonggol Km 23 2, Sukamaju Jongg, Bogor, 16830, Jawa Bara, Indonesia
Tel.: (62) 2189931234
Frozen Product Distr
N.A.I.C.S.: 424420
Dicky Saelan (Mng Dir)

PT Dwipa Mina Nusantara   (1)
Dusun Ketapang Desa Pengambengan, Negara Jembrana, Bali, Indonesia
Tel.: (62) 36542147
Fish Meal Mfr
N.A.I.C.S.: 311710

PT Sierad Industries   (1)
Jl Modern Industri I No 24 Kawasan Industri Modern, Cikande, Serang, 42186, Banten, Indonesia

PT SREEYA SEWU INDONESIA TBK

PT Sreeya Sewu Indonesia Tbk—(Continued)
Tel.: (62) 254402536
Poultry Farming Services
N.A.I.C.S.: 112990

PT SRIWAHANA ADITYAKARTA TBK
Jl Solo-Jogja Km16 Bendosari Sawit, Boyolali, Indonesia
Tel.: (62) 2717687170
Web Site: https://www.sriwahana.id
Year Founded: 1990
SWAT—(INDO)
Rev.: $15,927,702
Assets: $41,174,932
Liabilities: $28,028,692
Net Worth: $13,146,240
Earnings: ($1,630,634)
Emp.: 261
Fiscal Year-end: 12/31/23
Packaging Product Services
N.A.I.C.S.: 561910
Edi Cahyono (Mgr-Investments)

PT STAR PACIFIC TBK
Graha Lippo Lantai LG Jl Boulevard Diponegoro No 101, Lippo Village, Tangerang, 15810, Banten, Indonesia
Tel.: (62) 2155777111   Id
Web Site: https://www.star-pacific.co.id
Year Founded: 1983
LPLI—(INDO)
Rev.: $1,366,338
Assets: $109,337,335
Liabilities: $4,387,541
Net Worth: $104,949,794
Earnings: $20,661,051
Emp.: 5
Fiscal Year-end: 12/31/23
Newspaper Publishing Services
N.A.I.C.S.: 513110
Samuel Tahir (Co-Chm)

PT STEEL PIPE INDUSTRY OF INDONESIA TBK
Jl Kalibutuh No 189-191, East Java, Surabaya, 60173, Indonesia
Tel.: (62) 315320921
Web Site: https://www.spindo.com
Year Founded: 1971
ISSP—(INDO)
Rev.: $419,209,065
Assets: $517,682,718
Liabilities: $217,767,328
Net Worth: $299,915,389
Earnings: $32,343,951
Emp.: 920
Fiscal Year-end: 12/31/23
Steel Pole Mfr
N.A.I.C.S.: 331210
Ibnu Susanto (Chm)

PT SUGIH ENERGY TBK
Anugerah Tower 10th Floor Jl Dr, Ide Anak Agung Gde Lot 86-87 Office Park E33 Mega Kuningan Area, Jakarta, 12950, Indonesia
Tel.: (62) 2157948877
Web Site: http://www.sugihenergy.com
SUGI—(INDO)
Sales Range: Less than $1 Million
Emp.: 49
Energy Services
N.A.I.C.S.: 213112
Handy Eko Saputro (Sec)

PT SUMBER ALFARIA TRIJAYA TBK
Alfa Tower 12th Floor Jl Jalur Sutera Barat Kav 9 Kota, Tangerang, 151143, Banten, Indonesia
Tel.: (62) 211500959
Web Site: https://www.alfamart.co.id
Year Founded: 1989
AMRT—(INDO)
Rev.: $6,944,987,714
Assets: $2,223,947,124
Liabilities: $1,204,051,436
Net Worth: $1,019,895,688
Earnings: $226,252,584
Emp.: 55,131
Fiscal Year-end: 12/31/23
Convenience Store Operator
N.A.I.C.S.: 445131
Anggara Hans Prawira (Chm)

Subsidiaries:

P.T. Global Loyalty Indonesia   (1)
Alfa Tower 24th Floor Jl Jalur Sutera Bar No Kav 7-9, Alam Sutera, Tangerang, Indonesia
Tel.: (62) 2180821510
Web Site: https://gli.id
Business Management Consulting Services
N.A.I.C.S.: 541611

PT SUMBER ENERGI ANDALAN TBK
Sopo Del Office & Lifestyle Tower B Lantai 21, Jl Mega Kuningan Barat III Lot 10 1-6 Kawasan Mega Kuningan, Jakarta, 12950, Indonesia
Tel.: (62) 2150815254
Web Site: https://www.energi-andalan.co.id
Year Founded: 1987
ITMA—(INDO)
Rev.: $245,643
Assets: $226,695,921
Liabilities: $15,091,389
Net Worth: $211,604,532
Earnings: $2,087,099
Emp.: 36
Fiscal Year-end: 12/31/23
Mining Industry & Construction Services
N.A.I.C.S.: 541330
Rocky Oktanso Sugih (Chm)

PT SUMBER GLOBAL ENERGY TBK
Graha Bip 2Nd Floor Jl Gatot Subroto Kav 23 Karet Semanggi, Setiabudi, Jakarta, Indonesia
Tel.: (62) 212500120
Web Site: https://www.sumberglobalenergy.id
Year Founded: 2008
SGER—(INDO)
Rev.: $799,597,241
Assets: $297,220,558
Liabilities: $200,994,557
Net Worth: $96,226,001
Earnings: $44,244,044
Emp.: 46
Fiscal Year-end: 12/31/23
Coal Distr
N.A.I.C.S.: 423520
Michael H. Harold (Sec)

PT SUMBER MAS KONSTRUKSI TBK
Gedung Graha Mustika Ratu Lantai 5, Jalan Jenderal Gatot Subrto Kav 74 75, Jakarta Selatan, Indonesia
Tel.: (62) 2182850095
Web Site: https://www.konstruksimas.co.id
Year Founded: 1981
SMKM—(INDO)
Rev.: $8,443,925
Assets: $13,487,519
Liabilities: $13,264,528
Net Worth: $222,992
Earnings: $629,993
Fiscal Year-end: 12/31/23
Construction Services
N.A.I.C.S.: 237990
Budiman Pramono Sidi (Sec)

PT SUMBER TANI AGUNG RESOURCES TBK
Office Tower Cambridge City Square LT 3 JL S Parman No 217, Medan, 20152, Sumatra Utara, Indonesia
Tel.: (62) 614156262
Web Site: https://www.sta.co.id
Year Founded: 1970
STAA—(INDO)
Rev.: $343,220,953
Assets: $433,874,725
Liabilities: $121,923,876
Net Worth: $311,950,849
Earnings: $50,799,445
Emp.: 10,922
Fiscal Year-end: 12/31/23
Agriculture Product Distr
N.A.I.C.S.: 424910
Mosfly Ang (Chm)

PT SUMMARECON AGUNG TBK
Plaza Summarecon Jl Perintis Kemerdekaan No 42 Pulo Gadung, Jakarta, 13210, Indonesia
Tel.: (62) 214714567
Web Site: https://www.summarecon.com
Year Founded: 1975
SMRA—(INDO)
Rev.: $432,421,346
Assets: $2,024,074,278
Liabilities: $1,225,113,440
Net Worth: $798,960,838
Earnings: $68,686,519
Emp.: 2,537
Fiscal Year-end: 12/31/23
Real Estate Development Services
N.A.I.C.S.: 531390
Liliawati Rahardjo (Mng Dir)

Subsidiaries:

P.T. Satu Summarecon Sukses   (1)
Plaza Summarecon Serpong Jalan Boulevard Gading Serpong Block M 5 No 3, Gading Serpong Block M 5 No 3 Pakulonan Barat Kelapa Dua, Tangerang, 15810, Banten, Indonesia
Tel.: (62) 214531101
Web Site: https://www.satusummarecon.com
Online Shopping Services
N.A.I.C.S.: 531120

PT SUNINDO ADIPERSADA TBK
Komplek Industri Bostinco Jalan Raya Cileungsi-Bekasi, Kilometer 22 5 Cileungsi, Bogor, 16820, Indonesia
Tel.: (62) 218230272
Web Site: https://www.sunindo.id
TOYS—(INDO)
Rev.: $3,924,677
Assets: $23,176,583
Liabilities: $7,093,784
Net Worth: $16,082,799
Earnings: ($884,684)
Emp.: 60
Fiscal Year-end: 12/31/23
Toy Mfr
N.A.I.C.S.: 339930
Gusnaidi Hetminado (Sec)

PT SUNINDO PRATAMA TBK
Jl Prof Dr Soepomo SH No 48 Tebet, Jakarta Selatan, 12870, Indonesia
Tel.: (62) 2183785773
Web Site: https://www.sunindogroup.com
Year Founded: 2002
SUNI—(INDO)
Rev.: $49,511,875
Assets: $51,231,475
Liabilities: $13,027,745
Net Worth: $38,203,730
Earnings: $6,549,838
Emp.: 60

INTERNATIONAL PUBLIC

Fiscal Year-end: 12/31/23
Chemical Product Mfr & Distr
N.A.I.C.S.: 325998
Andy Gunawan (Sec)

PT SUNSON TEXTILE MANUFACTURER TBK
Jl Raya Rancaekek Km 25 5 Sumedang Regency, Bandung, Indonesia
Tel.: (62) 227798289   Id
Web Site: https://www.sunson.co.id
Year Founded: 1972
Rev.: $24,787,978
Assets: $36,033,601
Liabilities: $22,009,176
Net Worth: $14,024,425
Earnings: ($1,138,671)
Fiscal Year-end: 12/31/19
Textile Products Mfr
N.A.I.C.S.: 314999
Purnawan Suriadi (Board of Directors & Chm)

PT SUNTER LAKESIDE HOTEL TBK
Jl Danau Permai Raya Blok C1 Sunter, Jakarta, 14350, Indonesia
Tel.: (62) 6509969
Web Site: https://www.sunlakehotel.com
SNLK—(INDO)
Rev.: $3,068,285
Assets: $14,132,448
Liabilities: $3,114,586
Net Worth: $11,017,861
Earnings: $188,103
Emp.: 186
Fiscal Year-end: 12/31/23
Hotel & Motel Services
N.A.I.C.S.: 721110
Lenny Triana (Sec)

PT SUPARMA TBK
Jl Raya Mastrip No 856 Warugunung Karang Pilang, Surabaya, 60221, Indonesia
Tel.: (62) 317666666   Id
Web Site: https://www.ptsuparmatbk.com
Year Founded: 1976
SPMA—(INDO)
Rev.: $172,644,353
Assets: $214,556,728
Liabilities: $63,933,660
Net Worth: $150,623,068
Earnings: $11,602,073
Emp.: 779
Fiscal Year-end: 12/31/23
Paper Products Mfr
N.A.I.C.S.: 322120
Hendro Luhur (Co-Sec)

PT SUPER ENERGY TBK
Equity Tower 29th Floor Unit E SCBD Lot 9 Jl Jend Sudirman Kav 52-53, Sudirman Central Business District, Jakarta Selatan, 12190, Indonesia
Tel.: (62) 2129035295
Web Site: https://www.superenergy.co.id
Year Founded: 2011
SURE—(INDO)
Rev.: $19,777,905
Assets: $63,886,642
Liabilities: $33,788,783
Net Worth: $30,097,859
Earnings: ($9,243,635)
Emp.: 194
Fiscal Year-end: 12/31/23
Oil & Gas Distribution Services
N.A.I.C.S.: 221210
Rheza R. R. Susanto (Pres & Commissioner)

PT SUPERKRANE MITRA UTAMA TBK

Raya Cakung Cilincing 9B, Jakarta Utara, 14130, Indonesia
Tel.: (62) 214413455
Web Site:
https://www.superkrane.com
Year Founded: 1996
SKRN—(INDO)
Rev.: $58,020,791
Assets: $190,007,352
Liabilities: $133,984,904
Net Worth: $56,022,448
Earnings: $14,103,820
Emp.: 495
Fiscal Year-end: 12/31/23
Equipment Rental Services
N.A.I.C.S.: 532490
Yafin Tandiono Tan *(Chm)*

PT SUPRA BOGA LESTARI TBK
Jl Pesanggrahan Raya No 2, Kembangan, Jakarta, 11610, Indonesia
Tel.: (62) 2158351999
Web Site:
https://www.ranchmarket.co.id
Year Founded: 1997
RANC—(INDO)
Rev.: $182,105,712
Assets: $80,992,380
Liabilities: $61,562,925
Net Worth: $19,429,455
Earnings: ($7,860,855)
Emp.: 2,885
Fiscal Year-end: 12/31/23
Supermarket Operator
N.A.I.C.S.: 445110
Harman Siswanto *(Dir-Supply Chain)*

PT SURYA BIRU MURNI ACETYLENE TBK
Jl Jendral Sudirman No 5-6 Rt 16, Klandasan Ilir, Balikpapan, Indonesia
Tel.: (62) 542743555
Web Site:
https://www.suryabirumurni.co.id
Year Founded: 1980
SBMA—(INDO)
Rev.: $7,362,229
Assets: $17,935,124
Liabilities: $3,943,864
Net Worth: $13,991,260
Earnings: $307,336
Emp.: 226
Fiscal Year-end: 12/31/23
Industrial Gas Mfr
N.A.I.C.S.: 325120
Rini Dwiyanti *(Pres)*

PT SURYA DUMAI INDUSTRI TBK
Jl Jend Sudirman No 395, Pekanbaru, Riau, Indonesia
Tel.: (62) 76132888
Web Site: http://www.sdg.co.id
SUDI—(INDO)
Plywood Mfr
N.A.I.C.S.: 321211
Heru Subagio *(Chm)*

PT SURYA FAJAR CAPITAL TBK
Satrio Tower Building Lt 14 Unit 5 Jalan Prof Dr Satrio Blok C4/5, Kuningan, 12950, Indonesia
Tel.: (62) 2122513339
Web Site: https://www.sfcapital.co.id
Year Founded: 2016
SFAN—(INDO)
Rev.: $946,751
Assets: $21,087,501
Liabilities: $6,339,909
Net Worth: $14,747,592
Earnings: ($1,118,686)
Emp.: 96
Fiscal Year-end: 12/31/23
Financial Consulting Services

N.A.I.C.S.: 541611
Hary Herdiyanto *(CEO)*
Subsidiaries:

PT Bursa Akselerasi Indonesia (1)
Satrio Tower Lantai 14 unit 6 Jalan Prof DR Satrio Kav 1-4 Blok C4 Kel, Kuningan Timur Kec Setiabudi, Jakarta Selatan, 12950, Indonesia
Tel.: (62) 2125982507
Web Site: https://indofund.id
Loan Services
N.A.I.C.S.: 522390
Ryan Filbert *(CEO & Founder)*

PT Mareco Prima Mandiri (1)
Satrio Tower Lt 14 Unit 2 Jl Prof DR Satrio No 7 RT 7/RW 2, Kuningan Tim Kecamatan Setiabudi Kota Jakarta Selatan, 12950, Indonesia
Tel.: (62) 8119956595
Web Site: https://dipay.id
Electronic Payment Services
N.A.I.C.S.: 522320
Novi Setiawati *(COO)*

PT Surya Fajar Equity Fund (1)
Satrio Tower Jalan Prof Dr Satrio Blok Building Lt 6 Unit 5 C4/5, Kuningan, Jakarta, 12950, Indonesia
Tel.: (62) 21 252 5099
Web Site: https://sfund.id
Administrative Management Services
N.A.I.C.S.: 541611
Hary Herdiyanto *(Pres)*

PT Surya Fajar Sekuritas (1)
Satrio Tower Building Lt 9 Unit B Jalan Prof Dr Satrio Blok C4/5, Kuningan, Jakarta, 12950, Indonesia
Tel.: (62) 2127883989
Web Site: https://www.sfsekuritas.co.id
Administrative Management Services
N.A.I.C.S.: 541611
Steffen Fang *(Pres)*

PT SURYA INTRINDO MAKMUR TBK
Gedung Gozco Lantai 6 Jl Raya Darmo No 54-56, Surabaya, 60265, Indonesia
Tel.: (62) 315612818
Web Site: http://www.simtbk.co.id
Year Founded: 1996
SIMM—(INDO)
Rev.: $1,293,463
Assets: $15,899,484
Liabilities: $1,577,288
Net Worth: $14,322,196
Earnings: $689,201
Emp.: 42
Fiscal Year-end: 12/31/23
Footwear Mfr
N.A.I.C.S.: 316210
Sasra Adhiwana *(Pres)*

PT SURYA PERMATA ANDALAN TBK
Jl Sarinande No 20 Seminyak, Bali, Indonesia
Tel.: (62) 361738163
Web Site:
https://suryapermataandalan.co.id
Year Founded: 2015
NATO—(INDO)
Rev.: $810,035
Assets: $52,163,436
Liabilities: $188,461
Net Worth: $51,974,975
Earnings: $43,492
Emp.: 37
Fiscal Year-end: 12/31/23
Appraisal Services
N.A.I.C.S.: 531320
Gede Putu Adnawa *(Chm)*

PT SURYA PERTIWI TBK
Wisma 81 TOTO Office Building JL Letjen S Parman Kav 81, Jakarta Barat, 11420, Indonesia
Tel.: (62) 2129298585

Web Site:
https://www.suryapertiwi.co.id
Year Founded: 1968
SPTO—(INDO)
Rev.: $169,200,452
Assets: $210,253,367
Liabilities: $65,463,594
Net Worth: $144,789,773
Earnings: $17,855,354
Emp.: 471
Fiscal Year-end: 12/31/23
Sanitary Ware & Bathroom Fitting Distr
N.A.I.C.S.: 423720
Tjahjono Alim *(Chm)*

PT SURYA SEMESTA INTERNUSA TBK
Tempo Scan Tower 20th Floor Jl HR Rasuna Said, Kav 3-4 Kuningan, Jakarta, 12950, Indonesia
Tel.: (62) 215262121
Web Site:
https://www.suryainternusa.com
Year Founded: 1971
SSIA—(INDO)
Rev.: $294,675,240
Assets: $546,585,247
Liabilities: $258,027,320
Net Worth: $288,557,927
Earnings: $15,036,582
Emp.: 1,846
Fiscal Year-end: 12/31/23
Property Development Services
N.A.I.C.S.: 531311
The Jok Tung *(Dir-Fin)*
Subsidiaries:

PT Batiqa Hotel Manajemen (1)
Tempo Scan Tower 20th Floor Jl HR Rasuna Said Kav 3-4, Kuningan, Jakarta Selatan, 12950, Indonesia
Tel.: (62) 2129023111
Web Site: https://www.batiqa.com
Hotel Operator
N.A.I.C.S.: 721110
Amir Michael Tjahaja *(VP)*

PT Sitiagung Makmur (1)
Gran Melia Jakarta Jl H R Rasuna Said Kav X-0, Kuningan, Jakarta, 12950, Indonesia
Tel.: (62) 2152777788
Residential Property Management Services
N.A.I.C.S.: 531311

PT Surya Energi Parahita (1)
Gedung 18 Office Park Lt 25 Suite A2 Jl TB Simatupang No 18, Kebagusan Pasar Minggu, Jakarta Selatan, Indonesia
Tel.: (62) 2175914724
Web Site:
https://www.suryaenergiparahita.com
Natural Gas Distribution Services
N.A.I.C.S.: 221210

PT Surya Internusa Hotels (1)
Tempo Scan Tower 20th Floor Jl HR Rasuna Said Kav 3-4 RT 5/RW 4, Kuningan, Jakarta, 12950, Indonesia
Tel.: (62) 215276682
Hotel Operator
N.A.I.C.S.: 721110

PT Ungasan Semesta Resort (1)
Jl Melasti Banjar Kelod Ungasan, Bali, 80364, Indonesia
Tel.: (62) 215276688
Hotel Operator
N.A.I.C.S.: 721110

PT. Nusa Raya Cipta tbk (1)
Gedung Graha Cipta, Jl D I Panjaitan No 40, Jakarta, 13350, Indonesia
Tel.: (62) 218193526
Web Site: https://www.nusarayacipta.com
Rev.: $188,034,242
Assets: $151,717,105
Liabilities: $73,902,891
Net Worth: $77,814,214
Earnings: $6,462,104
Fiscal Year-end: 12/31/2023
Construction Engineering Services

N.A.I.C.S.: 541330
Hadi Winarto Christanto *(Chm)*

PT. Suryacipta Swadaya (1)
The Manor Building Suryacipta City of Industry Jalan Surya Utama Kav, C-1 Suryacipta Square, Karawang, 41363, Jawa Barat, Indonesia
Tel.: (62) 267440088
Web Site: https://www.suryacipta.com
Industrial Parks Development & Management Services
N.A.I.C.S.: 531312

PT. Suryalaya Anindita International (1)
Graha Surya Internusa 11th Floor Jl HR Rasuna Said, Kav X-0 Kuningan, Jakarta, 12950, Indonesia
Tel.: (62) 215262121
Web Site:
Home Management Services
N.A.I.C.S.: 721110

PT. TCP Internusa (1)
Gedung Hotel Gran Melia Jakarta Jl H R Rasuna Said, Kav X-0 Kav 4 Kuningan Timur, Jakarta, 12950, Indonesia
Tel.: (62) 215277788
Web Site: https://tcpinternusa.com
Construction Engineering Services
N.A.I.C.S.: 541330

PT SURYAINTI PERMATA TBK
Wisma Permata Jl Panglima Sudirman 55, 60271, Surabaya, Indonesia
Tel.: (62) 315481666
Web Site: http://www.suryainti.com
Sales Range: $1-9.9 Million
Real Estate & Property Development Services
N.A.I.C.S.: 531311
Jusuf Wangsaredja *(Dir-Ops)*

PT TANAH LAUT TBK
Grha HRH 2nd Floor Jl Lebak Bulus Raya No 20, Jakarta, 12440, Indonesia
Tel.: (62) 2127812154
Web Site: https://www.tanahlaut.co.id
INDX—(INDO)
Rev.: $94,571
Assets: $3,388,900
Liabilities: $942,365
Net Worth: $2,446,534
Earnings: ($415,460)
Emp.: 8
Fiscal Year-end: 12/31/23
Logistic Services
N.A.I.C.S.: 488510
Harun Halim Rasip *(Chm)*

PT TBS ENERGI UTAMA TBK
Treasury Tower Level 33 District 8 SCBD Lot 28, Jl Jend Sudirman Kav 52-52, Jakarta, 12190, Indonesia
Tel.: (62) 2150200353
Web Site: https://www.tbsenergi.com
Year Founded: 2007
TOBA—(INDO)
Rev.: $501,262,751
Assets: $947,837,728
Liabilities: $524,150,083
Net Worth: $423,687,645
Earnings: $20,846,270
Emp.: 885
Fiscal Year-end: 12/31/23
Coal Mining & Production
N.A.I.C.S.: 212115
Justarina Sinta Marisi Naiborhu *(Chm)*
Subsidiaries:

PT Adimitra Baratama Nusantara (1)
Level 37 District 8 SCBD Lot 28 Jl Jend Sudirman Kav 52-53, Prosperity Tower Senayan Kebayoran baru, Jakarta, 12190, Indonesia
Tel.: (62) 215020070608
Web Site: https://www.adimitra-baratama.co.id

PT TBS ENERGI UTAMA TBK

PT TBS Energi Utama Tbk—(Continued)
Mining Services
N.A.I.C.S.: 213114

PT Indomining
Gedung Wisma Bakrie 2 Lantai 11 Jl. HR Rasuna Said Kav B-2, Jakarta, 12920, Indonesia
Tel.: (62) 2157930579
Web Site: https://www.indomining.co.id
Mining Services
N.A.I.C.S.: 213114

PT Perkebunan Kaltim Utama I (1)
Treasury Tower Level 33 Office District 8 SCBD Lot 28 Jl, Jakarta, 12190, Indonesia
Coal Underground Mining Services
N.A.I.C.S.: 212115

PT Trisensa Mineral Utama (1)
Treasury Tower Level 33 Office District 8 SCBD Lot 28 Jl, Jend Sudirman Kav 52-52, Jakarta, 12190, Indonesia
Coal Underground Mining Services
N.A.I.C.S.: 212115

PT TEKNOLOGI KARYA DIGITAL NUSA TBK
Central 88 Blok G1 No 826 Jl Trembesi Desa, Kelurahan Pademangan Timur Kec Pademangan Kota Adm, Jakarta Utara, 14410, Jakarta, Indonesia
Tel.: (62) 2126054109
Web Site: https://www.tkdn.co.id
Year Founded: 2011
TRON—(INDO)
Rev.: $12,176,360
Assets: $16,050,649
Liabilities: $2,337,088
Net Worth: $13,713,560
Earnings: $1,173,978
Emp.: 64
Fiscal Year-end: 12/31/23
Information Technology Services
N.A.I.C.S.: 541512
Wendy Jolanda Waas (Sec)

PT TELADAN PRIMA AGRO TBK
Beltway Office Park Tower B 7th Floor Jl TB Simatupang No 41, Jakarta Selatan, 12550, Indonesia
Tel.: (62) 2129600300
Web Site: https://www.teladanprima.com
Year Founded: 2004
TLDN—(INDO)
Rev.: $260,219,922
Assets: $352,221,533
Liabilities: $192,581,025
Net Worth: $159,640,507
Earnings: $29,339,485
Emp.: 10,262
Fiscal Year-end: 12/31/23
Agriculture Product Distr
N.A.I.C.S.: 424910
Unggul Santoso (Sec)

PT TELEFAST INDONESIA TBK
Mall Ambasador Lt 5 No 5 Jl Prof Dr Satrio No 65, Jakarta, 12940, Indonesia
Tel.: (62) 2157933556
Web Site: https://www.telefast.co.id
Year Founded: 2008
TFAS—(INDO)
Rev.: $41,134,107
Assets: $16,630,325
Liabilities: $4,072,127
Net Worth: $12,558,198
Earnings: $57,847
Fiscal Year-end: 12/31/23
Supply Chain Management Services
N.A.I.C.S.: 541614
Jody Hedrian (Founder, Pres & CEO)

Subsidiaries:

PT Logitek Digital Nusantara (1)
AXA Tower Kuningan City Lt 7 Jalan Prof Dr Satrio Kav 18, Setiabudi, Jakarta Selatan, 12940, Indonesia
Tel.: (62) 218 062 3812
Web Site: https://logitek.id
Logistic Services
N.A.I.C.S.: 541614

PT Logitek Digital Nusantara (1)
AXA Tower Kuningan City Lt 7 Jalan Prof Dr Satrio Kav 18, Setiabudi, Jakarta Selatan, 12940, Indonesia
Tel.: (62) 81110575252
Web Site: https://logitek.id
Logistics Delivery Services
N.A.I.C.S.: 492110

PT TEMAS TBK
Jl Yos Sudarso Kav 33 Sunter Jaya, Jakarta Utara, 14350, Indonesia
Tel.: (62) 214302388
Web Site: http://www.temasline.com
Year Founded: 1987
TMAS—(INDO)
Rev.: $327,796,627
Assets: $295,939,526
Liabilities: $146,382,835
Net Worth: $149,556,691
Earnings: $95,008,570
Emp.: 505
Fiscal Year-end: 12/31/22
Shipping Services
N.A.I.C.S.: 483111
Sutikno Khusumo (Chm)

Subsidiaries:

PT Temas Bulker (1)
Temasline Building Jl Yos Sudarso Kav 33, Jakarta Utara, 14350, Indonesia
Tel.: (62) 214302388
Web Site: https://www.temasbulker.com
Cargo Transportation Services
N.A.I.C.S.: 484110

PT TEXMACO PERKASA ENGINEERING TBK
Centennial Tower Lt 15 Unit F Jln Jend Gatot Subroto Kav 24-25, Karet Semanggi Setiabudi, Jakarta, 12930, Indonesia
Tel.: (62) 212526220
Web Site: http://www.perkasaengineering.co.id
TPEN—(INDO)
Industrial Machinery Mfr
N.A.I.C.S.: 333248
Bala Krisna (Pres)

PT TIGARAKSA SATRIA TBK
Menara Duta Lantai 2 & 4 Jl H R Rasuna Said Kav B-9, Jakarta Selatan, 12910, Indonesia
Tel.: (62) 2527300
Web Site: http://www.tigaraksa.co.id
Year Founded: 1919
TGKA—(INDO)
Rev.: $922,806,167
Assets: $296,516,430
Liabilities: $153,625,571
Net Worth: $142,890,859
Earnings: $28,644,969
Emp.: 1,746
Fiscal Year-end: 12/31/23
Food & Health Care Product Whslr
N.A.I.C.S.: 424420
Lianne Widjaja (Chm)

Subsidiaries:

P.T. Gramedia Digital Nusantara (1)
Menara Kompas Lt 17-18 Jl Palmerah Selatan No 21, Desa Kelurahan Gelora Kec Kota Adm Tanah Abang Provinsi DKI Jakarta, Jakarta Pusat, Indonesia
Tel.: (62) 2102122807040
E-Commerce Trading Services
N.A.I.C.S.: 523999

PT Blue Gas Indonesia (1)
Gedung Tigaraksa Jl Raya Pulo Gebang Km 3, Cakung, Jakarta Timur, 13950, Indonesia
Tel.: (62) 8071000861
Web Site: http://www.bluegaz.co.id
Gas Stove & Regulator Mfr
N.A.I.C.S.: 335220
P. Alfian Dani (Sr Mgr-HR)

PT TIMAH TBK.
Jalan Jenderal Sudirman No 51, Pangkal Pinang, 33121, Bangka, Indonesia
Tel.: (62) 7174258000
Web Site: https://www.timah.com
Year Founded: 1976
TINS—(INDO)
Rev.: $840,288,758
Assets: $878,100,787
Liabilities: $404,884,906
Net Worth: $473,215,882
Earnings: $69,993,034
Emp.: 4,249
Fiscal Year-end: 12/31/22
Tin Mining Services
N.A.I.C.S.: 212290
Mochtar Riza Pahlevi Tabrani (Chm)

Subsidiaries:

Indometal (London) Ltd. (1)
326a City Rd, London, EC1V 2PT, United Kingdom
Tel.: (44) 2078375344
Business Services
N.A.I.C.S.: 561439

PT TIMAH Investasi Mineral (1)
Jl Teuku Cik Ditiro No 56A Menteng, Jakarta Pusat, 10310, Indonesia
Tel.: (62) 2123528000
Web Site: http://www.pttim.co.id
Investment Company Services
N.A.I.C.S.: 523999
Firman Pratama (Gen Mgr-Fin Admin)

PT TIMAH Karya Persada Properti (1)
Jl Gatot Subroto Kompleks ex Timah No 21, South Jakarta, 12820, Indonesia
Tel.: (62) 218306844
Web Site: http://www.timahproperti.co.id
Property Development Services
N.A.I.C.S.: 531390
Yonas Kristian (Mgr-Fin)

PT Tambang Timah (1)
Jalan Jenderal Sudirman 51, Pangkal Pinang, 33121, Indonesia
Tel.: (62) 71 743 1335
Coal Mining Services
N.A.I.C.S.: 213113

Timah International Investment Pte. Ltd. (1)
Jl Jendral Sudirman No 51, Pangkal Pinang, Kep Bangka Belitung, Indonesia
Tel.: (62) 81319777979
Web Site: http://www.tinves.com
Investment Company Services
N.A.I.C.S.: 523999

PT TIPHONE MOBILE INDONESIA TBK
Jl Gajah Mada No 27A Taman Sari Kota, Jakarta Barat, 11140, Indonesia
Tel.: (62) 2129999999
Web Site: http://www.tiphone.co.id
Year Founded: 2008
Rev.: $2,054,014,760
Assets: $583,735,950
Liabilities: $311,531,360
Net Worth: $272,204,590
Earnings: $31,103,730
Emp.: 1,322
Fiscal Year-end: 12/31/18
Mobile Phone Distr
N.A.I.C.S.: 423690
Lie Pin Tan (Chm)

PT TIRTA MAHAKAM RESOURCES TBK

INTERNATIONAL PUBLIC

Gapura Prima Office Tower The Bellezza Lt 20, Jl Let Jend Soepeno No 34 Arteri Permata Hijau, Jakarta Selatan, 12210, Indonesia
Tel.: (62) 2125675717
Web Site: https://www.tirtamahakam.com
Year Founded: 1981
TIRT—(INDO)
Rev: $1,452
Assets: $14,038,889
Liabilities: $55,313,744
Net Worth: ($41,274,855)
Earnings: ($2,166,312)
Emp.: 49
Fiscal Year-end: 12/31/23
Plywood Products Mfr
N.A.I.C.S.: 321211
Djohan Surjaputra (Chm & Sec)

PT TOTAL BANGUN PERSADA TBK
Jl Letjen S Parman Kav 106, Jakarta Barat, 11440, Indonesia
Tel.: (62) 215666999
Web Site: https://www.totalbp.com
Year Founded: 1970
TOTL—(INDO)
Rev.: $227,681,579
Assets: $299,042,731
Liabilities: $175,025,177
Net Worth: $124,017,553
Earnings: $9,164,667
Emp.: 518
Fiscal Year-end: 12/31/22
Building Construction & Other Related Services
N.A.I.C.S.: 236220
Janti Komadjaja (Chm)

Subsidiaries:

PT Inti Propertindo Jaya (1)
CV Citra Maju Cemerlang Ruko Rich Palace No 36-40 Blok A9 Jl Meruya, Ilir Raya Kembangan, Jakarta Barat, Indonesia
Tel.: (62) 2122545665
Web Site: https://www.intipropertindo.com
Real Estate Services
N.A.I.C.S.: 531390
Ivonne Anggraini (Founder)

PT TOTALINDO EKA PERSADA TBK
Jl Tebet Raya No 14A, Jakarta Selatan, 12810, Indonesia
Tel.: (62) 2183792192
Web Site: http://www.totalindo.co.id
TOPS—(INDO)
Rev.: $22,298,739
Assets: $103,293,461
Liabilities: $75,443,205
Net Worth: $27,850,256
Earnings: ($21,157,646)
Emp.: 40
Fiscal Year-end: 12/31/23
Construction Services
N.A.I.C.S.: 236220

PT TOURINDO GUIDE INDONESIA TBK
Lt 9 Unit B Satrio Tower Building Jl Prof Dr Satrio No 5 Rt 7/Rw 2, Kuningan, Jakarta Selatan, 12950, Indonesia
Tel.: (62) 82246598802
Web Site: https://www.pigijo.com
PGJO—(INDO)
Rev.: $62,785
Assets: $1,546,256
Liabilities: $44,464
Net Worth: $1,501,792
Earnings: ($736,225)
Emp.: 11
Fiscal Year-end: 12/31/21
Travel & Tourism Services
N.A.I.C.S.: 561510
Adi Putera Widjaja (Pres)

PT TOWER BERSAMA INFRASTRUCTURE TBK
The Convergence Indonesia 11th Floor, Kawasan Rasuna Epicentrum Jl HR Rasuna Said, Jakarta Selatan, 12940, Indonesia
Tel.: (62) 2129248900
Web Site: https://www.tower-bersama.com
PTFRF—(OTCIQ)
Rev.: $431,243,486
Assets: $3,050,002,302
Liabilities: $2,247,277,209
Net Worth: $802,725,093
Earnings: $105,312,808
Emp.: 741
Fiscal Year-end: 12/31/23
Communication Tower Construction
N.A.I.C.S.: 237130
Herman Setya Budi *(Chm & COO)*

Subsidiaries:

PT Gihon Telekomunikasi Indonesia Tbk (1)
Taman Tekno Blok J2 No 1 BSD Sektor IX, Tangerang, 15314, Indonesia
Tel.: (62) 2175880519
Web Site: https://www.gihon-indonesia.com
Telecommunication Tower Services
N.A.I.C.S.: 237130
Rudolf P. Nainggolan *(Pres)*

PT Permata Karya Perdana (1)
Mutiara Building 2nd Floor R 201 Jalan Mampang Prapatan No 10, Mampang Prapatan, Jakarta Selatan, 12790, Indonesia
Tel.: (62) 217975207
Web Site: http://www.pekape.com
Communication Network Services
N.A.I.C.S.: 517810

PT United Towerindo (1)
The Convergence Indonesia 11th Floor Jl Epicentrum West Boulevard, Rasuna Epicentrum Area, Jakarta, 12940, Indonesia
Tel.: (62) 2180629300
Web Site: http://www.lamongankab.go.id
Telecommunication Tower Services
N.A.I.C.S.: 237130

PT Visi Telekomunikasi Infrastruktur Tbk (1)
Menara Imperium 18th floor Suite C Jl H R Rasuna Said No 1, Jakarta, 12980, Indonesia
Tel.: (62) 2183707370
Web Site: https://www.ptvti.co.id
Telecommunication Tower Services
N.A.I.C.S.: 237130

PT TRADA ALAM MINERA TBK
Graha Iskandarsyah 5th Floor Kebayoran Baru, Jakarta Selatan, 12160, Indonesia
Tel.: (62) 2172783708
Web Site: http://www.tram.co.id
Year Founded: 2000
TRAM—(INDO)
Rev.: $252,736,028
Assets: $384,341,321
Liabilities: $290,367,063
Net Worth: $93,974,259
Earnings: ($79,204,649)
Fiscal Year-end: 12/31/20
Marine Transportation Services
N.A.I.C.S.: 483211
Soebianto Hidayat *(Chm)*

PT TRANS POWER MARINE TBK
Centennial Tower Building 26th fl Suite A-B Karet Semanggi-Setiabudi, Jl Gatot Subroto Kav 24-25, Jakarta Selatan, 12930, Indonesia
Tel.: (62) 2122958999
Web Site: https://www.transpowermarine.com
Year Founded: 2005
TPMA—(INDO)
Rev.: $66,582,357
Assets: $117,406,903
Liabilities: $24,882,851
Net Worth: $92,524,052
Earnings: $19,695,773
Emp.: 91
Fiscal Year-end: 12/31/23
Marine Cargo Services
N.A.I.C.S.: 488320
Ronny Kurniawan *(Chm)*

Subsidiaries:

PT Trans Logistik Perkasa (1)
Centennial Tower Lantai 26 Unit A and B Jl Gatot Subroto Kav 24-25, Jakarta, Indonesia
Tel.: (62) 2122958888
Marine Transportation Services
N.A.I.C.S.: 488390

PT TRANSCOAL PACIFIC TBK
Bakrie Tower 9th Floor Rasuna Epicentrum Complex, Jl HR Rasuna Said Karet Kuningan Setiabudi, Jakarta, 12940, Indonesia
Tel.: (62) 2129941389
Web Site: https://www.transcoalpacific.com
Year Founded: 2007
TCPI—(INDO)
Rev.: $118,553,425
Assets: $227,890,890
Liabilities: $91,780,546
Net Worth: $136,110,344
Earnings: $12,252,749
Emp.: 76
Fiscal Year-end: 12/31/23
Freight Transportation Services
N.A.I.C.S.: 488510
Dirc Richard Talumewo *(Chm)*

Subsidiaries:

PT Berkah Daya Mandiri (1)
Bakrie Tower 9th Floor Rasuna Epicentrum Complex Jl, HR Rasuna Said Kuningan, Jakarta, 12940, Indonesia
Tel.: (62) 29941466
Stone Whslr
N.A.I.C.S.: 423320

PT TRI BANYAN TIRTA TBK
Kp Pasir Dalem RT RW 002/002 Babakan Pari Cidahu Sukabumi, Jakarta Barat, 43158, Indonesia
Tel.: (62) 266735813
Web Site: https://www.altospringswater.com
Year Founded: 1997
ALTO—(INDO)
Rev.: $18,615,312
Assets: $63,854,732
Liabilities: $42,829,375
Net Worth: $21,025,357
Earnings: ($1,683,100)
Emp.: 1,047
Fiscal Year-end: 12/31/23
Mineral Water Mfr
N.A.I.C.S.: 312112
Bhakti Salim *(Chm)*

PT TRIDOMAIN PERFORMANCE MATERIALS TBK
Mayapada Tower II 8th Floor Jl Jend Sudirman Kav 27, Jakarta, 12920, Indonesia
Tel.: (62) 215712998
Web Site: https://tianrongchemicalindustry.com
Year Founded: 2003
TDPM—(INDO)
Rev.: $63,482,303
Assets: $146,631,100
Liabilities: $126,372,809
Net Worth: $20,258,291
Earnings: ($52,613,572)
Emp.: 89
Fiscal Year-end: 12/31/22
Chemical Products Mfr
N.A.I.C.S.: 325998
Choi Choon Ha *(Pres)*

Subsidiaries:

PT Eterindo Nusa Graha (1)
Jl Prof Dr Moh Yamin SH, Gresik, 61118, Jawa Timur, Indonesia
Tel.: (62) 313950838
Resin Mfr
N.A.I.C.S.: 325211

PT Eternal Buana Chemical Industries (1)
Jl Raya Serang KM 14 RT 003 RW 001 Kampung Lamporan Desa Dukuh, Kecamatan Cikupa Kabupaten, Tangerang, Banten, Indonesia
Tel.: (62) 215960680
Resin Mfr
N.A.I.C.S.: 325211

PT Petronika (1)
Jl Prof Dr Moh Yamin SH, Gresik, 61119, Jawa Timur, Indonesia
Tel.: (62) 313951956
Plasticizer Mfr
N.A.I.C.S.: 325199

PT Tridomain Chemicals (1)
Jl Raya Merak Km 117 Kel Gerem, Kec Grogol Cilegon, Banten, 42438, Indonesia
Tel.: (62) 254570142
Chemical Products Mfr
N.A.I.C.S.: 325998

PT TRIMEGAH BANGUN PERSADA TBK.
Gedung Bank Panin Lt 2 Jalan Jendral Sudirman Kav 1, Jakarta Pusat, 10270, Indonesia
Tel.: (62) 215722924
Web Site: https://www.tbpnickel.com
Year Founded: 2004
NCKL—(INDO)
Rev.: $669,756,849
Assets: $2,422,328,812
Liabilities: $1,426,289,495
Net Worth: $996,039,317
Earnings: $321,216,299
Emp.: 2,571
Fiscal Year-end: 12/31/22
Nickel Ore Mining Services
N.A.I.C.S.: 212210
Roy Arman Arfandy *(Chm)*

PT TRIMEGAH KARYA PRATAMA TBK
Jl Tebet Barat Ix No 35Bb, Tebet Barat, Jakarta Selatan, 12810, Indonesia
Tel.: (62) 2122008385
Year Founded: 2017
UVCR—(INDO)
Rev.: $122,216,927
Assets: $10,912,629
Liabilities: $1,962,299
Net Worth: $8,950,331
Earnings: $1,188,566
Emp.: 39
Fiscal Year-end: 12/31/22
Digital Marketing Services
N.A.I.C.S.: 541870
Ayu Kusuma Trisyani *(Sec)*

PT TRIMEGAH SEKURITAS INDONESIA TBK.
Gedung Artha Graha 18th & 19th Floor Jl Jend Sudirman Kav 52-53, Jakarta, 12190, Indonesia
Tel.: (62) 2129249088
Web Site: https://www.trimegah.com
Year Founded: 1990
TRIM—(INDO)
Rev.: $46,299,368
Assets: $186,588,627
Liabilities: $107,502,288
Net Worth: $79,086,339
Earnings: $10,553,670
Emp.: 277
Fiscal Year-end: 12/31/23
Equity Brokerage & Market Lending Services
N.A.I.C.S.: 522310
Stephanus Turangan *(Pres)*

Subsidiaries:

PT Trimegah Asset Management (1)
Gedung Artha Graha Lt 19 Jl Jend Sudirman Kav 52-53, Jakarta, 12190, Indonesia
Tel.: (62) 2129248030
Web Site: http://www.trimegah-am.com
Financial Services
N.A.I.C.S.: 523999
Antony Dirga *(CEO)*

PT TRIMITRA PRAWARA GOLDLAND TBK
Jl Taman Cimanggu Selatan No 12A Rt 006 Rw 009, Kedung Waringin Tanah Sareal, Bogor, 16163, Indonesia
Tel.: (62) 2518574836
Web Site: https://www.trimitraprawaraland.co.id
Year Founded: 2015
ATAP—(INDO)
Rev.: $1,536,056
Assets: $7,388,397
Liabilities: $2,219,802
Net Worth: $5,168,595
Earnings: $10,574
Emp.: 7
Fiscal Year-end: 12/31/23
Real Estate Services
N.A.I.C.S.: 531210
H. J. Indriati *(Pres)*

PT TRIMITRA PROPERTINDO TBK
Jl Raya Serpong No 89 Cilenggang Kec Serpong Kota Tangerang Selatan, Tangerang, Indonesia
Tel.: (62) 215389388
Web Site: https://www.trimitraland.com
Year Founded: 2012
LAND—(INDO)
Rev.: $3,347,785
Assets: $50,168,247
Liabilities: $12,239,346
Net Worth: $37,928,902
Earnings: $204,849
Emp.: 8
Fiscal Year-end: 12/31/19
Residential Property Investment Services
N.A.I.C.S.: 531311
Suryadi Tan *(Chm)*

PT TRINITAN METALS & MINERALS TBK
Jl Parung Tanjung No 89, Gunung Putri, Bogor, 16964, Indonesia
Tel.: (62) 218678999
Web Site: http://www.trinitanmetals.co.id
PURE—(INDO)
Rev.: $9,542,040
Assets: $48,652,198
Liabilities: $44,390,691
Net Worth: $4,261,507
Earnings: ($6,912,347)
Emp.: 110
Fiscal Year-end: 12/31/20
Metal & Mineral Services
N.A.I.C.S.: 212390
Desfrina Novita Sinaga *(Sec)*

PT TRIPAR MULTIVISION PLUS TBK.
Multivision Tower Lt 21-23 Jl Kuningan Mulia Lot 9B, Kuningan, Jakarta Selatan, 12980, Indonesia

PT TRIPAR MULTIVISION PLUS TBK.

PT Tripar Multivision Plus Tbk.—(Continued)
Tel.: (62) 2129380700
Web Site: https://www.mvpworld.com
Year Founded: 1990
RAAM—(INDO)
Rev.: $4,393,245,263
Assets: $15,080,056,141
Liabilities: $2,620,232,345
Net Worth: $12,459,823,797
Earnings: $1,191,593,817
Emp.: 148
Fiscal Year-end: 12/31/22
Film Production Services
N.A.I.C.S.: 512120

PT TRIPUTRA AGRO PERSADA TBK

The East Building 23th Floor Jl Dr Ide Anak Agung Gde Agung, Kav E 3 2 No 1 Kelurahan Kuningan Timur, Jakarta Selatan, 12950, Indonesia
Tel.: (62) 2157944737
Web Site: https://www.tap-agri.com
Year Founded: 2005
TAPG—(INDO)
Rev.: $540,683,102
Assets: $900,548,112
Liabilities: $164,158,384
Net Worth: $736,389,728
Earnings: $107,882,095
Emp.: 14,295
Fiscal Year-end: 12/31/23
Palm Oil Processing Services
N.A.I.C.S.: 311225
Tjandra Karya Hermanto (Pres)

PT TRISULA INTERNATIONAL TBK

Trisula Center Jl Lingkar Luar Barat Blok A No 1 Rawa Buaya, Cengkareng, Jakarta, 11740, Indonesia
Tel.: (62) 2158357377 Id
Web Site: https://www.trisula.co.id
Year Founded: 1968
TRIS—(INDO)
Rev.: $95,647,281
Assets: $75,952,803
Liabilities: $28,888,492
Net Worth: $47,064,311
Earnings: $4,427,400
Emp.: 3,233
Fiscal Year-end: 12/31/23
Textile Products Mfr
N.A.I.C.S.: 314999
Kartono Budiman (Dir-Intl Mktg)

Subsidiaries:

Mido Uniforms Pte. Ltd. (1)
Blk 7 Kallang Place 07-01/02, Kallang Basin Ind Est, Singapore, 339153, Singapore
Tel.: (65) 62927111
Web Site: http://www.midouniforms.com.sg
Fashion Accessory Mfr
N.A.I.C.S.: 315990

P.T. Bina Citra Sento S.A. (1)
Jl Pierre Tendean No 14, Semarang, Jawa Tengah, Indonesia
Tel.: (62) 243563311
Textile Product Mfr & Distr
N.A.I.C.S.: 313210

P.T. Cakra Kencana (1)
Ruko Textile Mangga Dua JL Mangga Dua Raya Blok C6 No 12, Utara, Jakarta, Indonesia
Tel.: (62) 216016055
Textile Product Mfr & Distr
N.A.I.C.S.: 313210

P.T. Mido Indonesia (1)
Jl Abdul Wahab No 38 RT 1/RW 4 Kedaung, Sawangan, Depok, Jawa Barat, Indonesia
Tel.: (62) 2122794268
Web Site: https://www.mido-uniform.com
Textile Product Mfr & Distr
N.A.I.C.S.: 313210

P.T. Permata Busana Mas (1)
Ruko Textile Mangga Dua JL Mangga Dua Raya Blok D2 No 22, Utara, Jakarta, Indonesia
Tel.: (62) 216128064
Textile Product Mfr & Distr
N.A.I.C.S.: 313210

P.T. Savana Lestari (1)
Ruko Textile Mangga Dua JL Mangga Dua Raya Blok C4 No 12, Utara, Jakarta, Indonesia
Tel.: (62) 216019122
Textile Product Mfr & Distr
N.A.I.C.S.: 313210

P.T. Sinar Abadi Citranusa (1)
Ruko Textile Mangga Dua Jl Mangga Dua Raya Blok C2 No 31, Utara, Jakarta, Indonesia
Tel.: (62) 216013301
Fabric & Garment Whslr
N.A.I.C.S.: 424310

PT Trimas Sarana Garment Industry (1)
Jl Raya Kopo KM 7 No 82 Desa Sayati Margahayu, Bandung, Indonesia
Tel.: (62) 225400488
Textile Products Mfr
N.A.I.C.S.: 314999

PT Tritirta Saranadamai (1)
Jl Lingkar Luar Barat Blok A No 1 RT 014/RW 004, Rawa Buaya Cengkareng, Jakarta Barat, 11740, Indonesia
Tel.: (62) 2158357377
Textile Products Mfr
N.A.I.C.S.: 314999

Trisco Tailored and Woven International Ltd. (1)
175 N 27th St Ste 800, Billings, MT 59101
Tel.: (406) 869-4514
Textile Product Mfr & Distr
N.A.I.C.S.: 313210

PT TRIWIRA INSANLESTARI TBK

Jl Guntur No 45 Ps Manggis, Jakarta, 12970, Indonesia
Tel.: (62) 216399195
Web Site: http://www.triwirainsanlestari.com
Automobile Equipment Mfr
N.A.I.C.S.: 336110
Tommy Lybianto (Chm)

PT TUNAS ALFIN TBK

Jalan K H Agus Salim No 9 Poris Plawad Cipondoh, Banten, Tangerang, 15119, Indonesia
Tel.: (62) 215526268
Web Site: https://www.tunasalfin.com
Year Founded: 1977
TALF—(INDO)
Rev.: $82,012,484
Assets: $112,597,352
Liabilities: $33,542,604
Net Worth: $79,054,749
Earnings: $2,497,021
Emp.: 670
Fiscal Year-end: 12/31/23
Packaging Products Mfr
N.A.I.C.S.: 326199
John Tika (Chm)

Subsidiaries:

PT Dharma Anugerah (1)
Jl Margomulyo No 7, Tandes, Surabaya, 60186, Indonesia
Tel.: (62) 317491508
Web Site: http://www.daiprint.com
Printing & Packaging Services
N.A.I.C.S.: 561910

PT TUNAS BARU LAMPUNG TBK

Floor 8-9 Wisma Budi HRRasuna Said Rd Lot C-6, Jakarta, 12940, Indonesia
Tel.: (62) 215213383 Id
Web Site: http://www.tunasbarulampung.com
Year Founded: 1973
TBLA—(INDO)
Rev.: $1,114,173,312
Assets: $1,590,868,877
Liabilities: $1,131,742,752
Net Worth: $459,126,125
Earnings: $53,856,768
Emp.: 2,776
Fiscal Year-end: 12/31/22
Agricultural Product Mfr
N.A.I.C.S.: 811310
Sudarmo Tasmin (Deputy Chm)

Subsidiaries:

PT Solusi Jaya Perkasa (1)
Jl Jend Pol RS Soekanto No 34, Duren Sawit Kota, Jakarta Timur, 13460, Indonesia
Tel.: (62) 2186612083
Web Site: https://www.solusijaya.com
Emp.: 25
Pump Distr
N.A.I.C.S.: 423830

PT ULTRA JAYA MILK INDUSTRY TBK

Jl Raya Cimareme 131 Padalarang, Bandung, 40552, Indonesia
Tel.: (62) 2286700700
Web Site: http://www.ultrajaya.co.id
Year Founded: 1971
ULTJ—(INDO)
Rev.: $539,180,001
Assets: $488,605,703
Liabilities: $54,354,001
Net Worth: $434,251,702
Earnings: $77,029,295
Emp.: 1,013
Fiscal Year-end: 12/31/23
Food & Beverage Mfr
N.A.I.C.S.: 311423
Sabana Prawirawidjaja (Founder & Chm)

Subsidiaries:

PT Nikos Intertrade (1)
Jln Rawa Terate I No 5, Kawasan Industri Pulogadung, Jakarta Timur, Indonesia
Tel.: (62) 214600973
Milk Product Mfr
N.A.I.C.S.: 311511

PT UNGGUL INDAH CAHAYA TBK

Wisma UIC Lt 2 Jl Jend Gatot Subroto Kav 6-7, Jakarta Selatan, 12930, Indonesia
Tel.: (62) 2157905100
Web Site: https://www.uic.co.id
Year Founded: 1983
UNIC—(INDO)
Rev.: $339,302,689
Assets: $335,210,659
Liabilities: $44,840,780
Net Worth: $290,369,879
Earnings: $21,385,503
Emp.: 256
Fiscal Year-end: 12/31/23
Alkylbenzene Producer
N.A.I.C.S.: 325611
Yani Alifen (Chm)

Subsidiaries:

Albright & Wilson (Australia) Limited (1)
21-22 Davis Road, PO Box 6787, Wetherill Park, 2164, NSW, Australia
Tel.: (61) 297570280
Web Site: https://www.albright.com.au
Sales Range: $50-74.9 Million
Phosphate Mfr
N.A.I.C.S.: 325998
Denise van Gessel (Mng Dir & CFO)

Subsidiary (Non-US):

Albright & Wilson New Zealand Ltd. (2)
Tel.: (64) 94147448
Web Site: http://www.albright.com.au

INTERNATIONAL PUBLIC

Sales Range: $25-49.9 Million
Emp.: 2
Surfactants & Phosphate Mfr
N.A.I.C.S.: 325998
Peter Bickle (Mgr-Sls)

PT Petrocentral (1)
Jl Raya Roomo, PO Box 53, Propinsi Jawa Timur, Gresik, 61151, East Java, Indonesia
Tel.: (62) 313981736
Web Site: http://www.petrocentral.co.id
Sales Range: $125-149.9 Million
Emp.: 205
Sodium Tripolyphosphate Mfr
N.A.I.C.S.: 325998

PT Wiranusa Grahatama (1)
UIC Homestead 2nd fl Jl General, Gatot Subroto Kav 6-7, Jakarta, 12930, Indonesia
Tel.: (62) 2157905100
Web Site: http://www.pearlgardenjakarta.com
Sales Range: $25-49.9 Million
Emp.: 12
Office & Resort Infrastructure Development Services
N.A.I.C.S.: 541490

Universal Interchemicals Corp. Pte., Ltd. (1)
75 Bukit Timah Road, 05-01/02 Boon Siew Building, Singapore, 229833, Singapore
Tel.: (65) 63377515
Sales Range: $25-49.9 Million
Emp.: 4
Trading & Investment Services
N.A.I.C.S.: 238990
Yani Alifen (Gen Mgr)

PT UNITED TRACTORS TBK

Jl Raya Bekasi Km 22, Cakung, Jakarta Timur, 13910, Indonesia
Tel.: (62) 2124579999 Id
Web Site: https://www.unitedtractors.com
Year Founded: 1972
UNTR—(INDO)
Rev.: $8,350,197,164
Assets: $10,002,594,425
Liabilities: $4,545,324,964
Net Worth: $5,457,269,461
Earnings: $1,437,128,434
Emp.: 26,254
Fiscal Year-end: 12/31/23
Holding Company; Construction Machinery Mfr & Whslr; Coal Mining; Mining Contractor
N.A.I.C.S.: 551112
Edhie Sarwono (Dir-Human Capital Mgmt, CORPU, ESRSGA & Comm)

Subsidiaries:

P.T. Granif Konsultan (1)
21st Floor Unit C D Office 8 Building Jl Jend Sudirman Kav 52-53, Lot 28 SCBD, Jakarta, 12190, Indonesia
Tel.: (62) 2129333288
Web Site: https://granif.com
Engineering Consulting Services
N.A.I.C.S.: 541330

P.T. Uway Energi Perdana (1)
Jl Raya Bekai KM 22 jk, Bekasi, 13910, Indonesia
Tel.: (62) 46823539
Web Site: https://uway.node3.id
Power Generator Distr
N.A.I.C.S.: 221114

PT Acset Indonusa Tbk. (1)
Acset Bldg Jl Majapahit No 26 Petojo Selatan, Gambir, Jakarta, 10160, Indonesia
Tel.: (62) 213511961
Web Site: https://www.acset.co
Rev.: $152,585,492
Assets: $169,414,303
Liabilities: $143,694,362
Net Worth: $25,719,942
Earnings: $(17,964,872)
Emp.: 373
Fiscal Year-end: 12/31/2023
Civil & Structural Engineering
N.A.I.C.S.: 237990
Ronnie Tiam Seng Tan (Vice Chm)

Subsidiary (Non-US):

Acset Indonusa Co. Ltd. (2)

3rd Floor C2 Thuy Loi Building No 301 D1 Street, Binh Thanh, Vietnam
Tel.: (84) 822103915
Civil Engineering Services
N.A.I.C.S.: 237990

Subsidiary (Domestic):

PT ATMC Pump Services (2)
Jl Majapahit No 26 Petojo Selatan, Gambir Kota, Jakarta Pusat, 10160, Indonesia
Tel.: (62) 81513442755
Web Site: http://www.atmc.co.id
Construction Equipment Rental Services
N.A.I.C.S.: 532412

PT Innotech Systems (2)
ACSET Building Jalan Majapahit No 26, Petojo Selatan-Gambir, Jakarta, 10160, Indonesia
Tel.: (62) 213511961
Civil Engineering Services
N.A.I.C.S.: 237990

PT Aneka Raya Konstruksi Mesindo (1)
Acset Building Blok K dan L Jl Majapahit No 26 RT 14/RW 8 Petojo Sel, Gambir Kota, Jakarta Pusat, Jakarta, Indonesia
Tel.: (62) 81296795634
Web Site: https://arkm.co.id
Construction Equipment Rental Services
N.A.I.C.S.: 532412

PT Bina Pertiwi Energi (1)
Jl Raya Bekasi Km 22, Jakarta, 13910, Indonesia
Web Site: http://www.binapertiwi.co.id
Industrial Equipment Whsr
N.A.I.C.S.: 423830

PT Bintai Kindenko Engineering Indonesia (1)
Komplek Golden Centrum Jl Majapahit No 26 Blok S T, Kelurahan Petojo Selatan Kecamatan Gambir, Jakarta Pusat, 10160, Indonesia
Tel.: (62) 216304945
Web Site: https://www.binkei-indo.com
Electrical & Plumbing Services
N.A.I.C.S.: 238220

PT Komatsu Remanufacturing Asia (1)
J1 Jenderal Sudirman No 844, 76114, Balikpapan, Indonesia (51%)
Tel.: (62) 542760110
Web Site: http://www.komatsu-remanufacturing-asia.com
Sales Range: $250-299.9 Million
Emp.: 700
Business to Business Electronic Markets
N.A.I.C.S.: 425120

PT Pamapersada Nusantara (1)
Jl Rawagelam I No 9, Kawasan Industri Pulogadung, Jakarta, 13930, Indonesia
Tel.: (62) 214602015
Web Site: https://www.pamapersada.com
Emp.: 22,281
Heavy Equipment Distr
N.A.I.C.S.: 423830
Frans Kesuma (Pres)

Subsidiary (Domestic):

PT Energia Prima Nusantara (2)
Jl Rawagelam 1 No 9, Pulogadung Industrial Estate, Jakarta, 13930, Indonesia
Tel.: (62) 214602015
Web Site: http://www.epnusantara.com
Power Station Services
N.A.I.C.S.: 221118
Chinthya Theresa (Chm)

PT Kalimantan Prima Persada (2)
JL Rawa Gelam I No9, Kawasan Industri Pulogadung, Jakarta Timur, Indonesia
Tel.: (62) 2146827706
Web Site: http://www.kppmining.com
Industrial Mining Services
N.A.I.C.S.: 212390

PT United Tractors Pandu Engineering (1)
Jl Jababeka XI Blok H 30-40, Kawasan Industri Jababeka, Cikarang, 17530, Indonesia
Tel.: (62) 218935016
Web Site: https://www.patria.co.id
Heavy Equipment Mfr
N.A.I.C.S.: 336120

Subsidiary (Domestic):

PT Patria Maritim Perkasa (2)
Kav 20 Dapur 12 Sei Lekop Sagulung, Batam, Indonesia
Tel.: (62) 7787367111
Web Site: https://www.patriashipyard.com
Ship Building & Repairing Services
N.A.I.C.S.: 336611

PT Patria Maritime Industry (2)
Jl Sei Jingah Besar Kec Tabunganen Kab, Kuala Kencana, Kalimantan Selatan, Indonesia
Tel.: (62) 5116715999
Web Site: http://www.pami.co.id
Ship Building & Repairing Services
N.A.I.C.S.: 336611

PT Patria Maritime Lines (2)
Jl Jababeka XI Blok H30-40, Kawasan Industri Jababeka, Cikarang, 17530, Indonesia
Tel.: (62) 218935016
Web Site: http://www.pml.co.id
Energy Transportation Services
N.A.I.C.S.: 486210

PT Patria Perikanan Lestari Indonesia (2)
Wings Area 5th Floor Jl Raya Bekasi KM22, Cakung - East, Jakarta, Indonesia
Tel.: (62) 2124579999
Web Site: http://www.patriafishery.co.id
Ship Building & Repairing Services
N.A.I.C.S.: 336611

PT Universal Tekno Reksajaya (1)
Jl Raya Bekasi Km 22, Cakung, Jakarta, 13910, Indonesia
Tel.: (62) 2124576818
Web Site: http://www.utr.co.id
Heavy Equipment Mfr
N.A.I.C.S.: 336120
Yayat Supriatna (Dir-Ops)

PT URBAN JAKARTA PROPERTINDO TBK

District 8 Treasury Tower-Lt 19 F-G-SCBD Lot 28 Jl Jendral Sudirman, Kav 52-53, Jakarta Selatan, 12190, Indonesia
Tel.: (62) 2140111717
Web Site: https://www.urbanjakarta.co.id
Year Founded: 1995
URBN—(INDO)
Rev.: $14,385,876
Assets: $268,543,144
Liabilities: $135,343,422
Net Worth: $133,199,723
Earnings: $1,618,689
Emp.: 12
Fiscal Year-end: 12/31/23
Real Estate Development Services
N.A.I.C.S.: 531390

PT VASTLAND INDONESIA TBK

Jl Tembesu no 8A Campang Raya Sukabumi, Bandar Lampung, 35122, Lampung, Indonesia
Tel.: (62) 7218030075
Web Site: https://www.vastland.co.id
Year Founded: 2011
VAST—(INDO)
Rev.: $1,667,999
Assets: $33,863,615
Liabilities: $10,177,145
Net Worth: $23,686,470
Earnings: $6,415,766
Emp.: 8
Fiscal Year-end: 12/31/23
Real Estate Development Services
N.A.I.C.S.: 531390
Trisna Wisanta (Sec)

PT VICTORIA CARE INDONESIA TBK

Puri Indah Financial Tower 10th-11th Floor, Jl Puri Lingkar Dalam Block T No 8 Kembangan Puri Indah, Jakarta Barat, 11610, Indonesia
Tel.: (62) 2154368111
Web Site: https://www.vci.co.id
Year Founded: 2007
VICI—(INDO)
Rev.: $80,717,157
Assets: $69,845,790
Liabilities: $17,334,812
Net Worth: $52,510,978
Earnings: $12,409,311
Emp.: 557
Fiscal Year-end: 12/31/21
Cosmetics Products Mfr
N.A.I.C.S.: 325620
Billy Hartono Salim (Pres)

PT VICTORIA INVESTAMA TBK

Graha BIP lantai 3A Jl Jend Gatot Subroto Kav 23, Jl Asia Afrika Lot 19, Jakarta, 12930, Indonesia
Tel.: (62) 2130008870
Web Site: https://www.victoriainvestama.co.id
Year Founded: 1989
VICO—(INDO)
Rev.: $67,174,803
Assets: $2,142,203,767
Liabilities: $1,816,709,760
Net Worth: $325,494,007
Earnings: $7,164,905
Emp.: 567
Fiscal Year-end: 12/31/23
Financial Services
N.A.I.C.S.: 522320
Aldo Jusuf Tjahaja (Chm)

Subsidiaries:

P.T. Victoria Alife Indonesia (1)
Graha BIP Lantai 3A Jalan Gatot Subroto Kavling 23, South Jakarta, 12930, Indonesia
Tel.: (62) 2130008872
Web Site: https://www.victorialife.co.id
Life Insurance & Financial Services
N.A.I.C.S.: 524113

P.T. Victoria Manajemen Investasi (1)
Graha BIP Lantai 3A Jl Gatot Subroto Kavling 23, South Jakarta, Indonesia
Tel.: (62) 2130008873
Web Site: https://vmi.co.id
Financial Investment Management Services
N.A.I.C.S.: 523999

P.T. Victoria Sekuritas Indonesia (1)
Graha Bip Jl Gatot Subroto No 3A RT 2/RW 2 Karet Semanggi, Setiabudi South Jakarta, Jakarta, 12930, Indonesia
Tel.: (62) 2130008898
Web Site: https://victoria-sekuritas.co.id
Investment Bank Services
N.A.I.C.S.: 523150

PT Victoria Insurance Tbk (1)
Graha BIP 3rd Floor Jl Jend Gatot Subroto Kav 22-23, Setiabudi, South Jakarta, 12930, Indonesia
Tel.: (62) 2130055555
Web Site: https://victoriainsurance.co.id
Rev.: $8,137,797
Assets: $15,776,215
Liabilities: $5,799,513
Net Worth: $9,976,702
Earnings: $420,750
Emp.: 27
Fiscal Year-end: 12/31/2023
Insurance Services
N.A.I.C.S.: 524210
Suwandi Suharto (Chm & Pres)

PT VISI MEDIA ASIA TBK

Wisma Bakrie 4th Floor JL HR Rasuna Said Kav B-1, Jakarta, 12920, Setiabudi, Indonesia
Tel.: (62) 215225057
Web Site: https://www.vivagroup.co.id
Year Founded: 2004
VIVA—(INDO)
Rev.: $114,147,233
Assets: $596,277,858
Liabilities: $702,749,192
Net Worth: ($106,471,334)
Earnings: ($115,549,631)
Emp.: 1,885
Fiscal Year-end: 12/31/22
Media Advertising Services
N.A.I.C.S.: 541840
Anindya Novyan Bakrie (Chm)

Subsidiaries:

PT Cakrawala Andalas Televisi (1)
Kawasan Rasuna Epicentrum Jl HR Rasuna Said RT 1/RW 3Karet Kuningan, Setiabudi, Jakarta Selatan, 12940, Indonesia
Tel.: (62) 2129912155
Web Site: https://www.antvklik.com
Television Broadcasting Services
N.A.I.C.S.: 516120
A. Ardiansyah Bakrie (Co-Pres & Commissioner)

PT Lativi Mediakarya (1)
Jl Rawa Terate II No 2, Pulogadung Industrial Estate, East Jakarta, 13260, Indonesia
Tel.: (62) 214613545
Web Site: http://www.tvonenews.com
Television Broadcasting Services
N.A.I.C.S.: 516120
Ria Dwi Mahardina (Chief Sls & Mktg Officer)

PT VISI TELEKOMUNIKASI INFRASTRUKTUR TBK

Menara Imperium 18th floor Suite C Jl HR Rasuna Said No 1, Jakarta, 12980, Indonesia
Tel.: (62) 2183707370
Web Site: https://ptvti.co.id
Year Founded: 1995
Supermarket Operator
N.A.I.C.S.: 445110
Helmy Yusman Santoso (Commissioner)

PT WAHANA INTERFOOD NUSANTARA TBK

Holis Regency Blok M55, Bandung, 40222, West Java, Indonesia
Tel.: (62) 226011375
Web Site: https://www.wahana-interfood.com
Year Founded: 2006
COCO—(INDO)
Rev.: $11,108,638
Assets: $34,350,645
Liabilities: $24,570,482
Net Worth: $9,780,163
Earnings: ($3,275,565)
Emp.: 264
Fiscal Year-end: 12/31/23
Cocoa & Chocolate Product Mfr
N.A.I.C.S.: 311351
Reinald Siswanto (Chm)

PT WAHANA INTI MAKMUR TBK

Jalan Prof Dr Latumenten No 35 I/J, Angke Tambora, Jakarta Barat, 11290, Banten, Indonesia
Tel.: (62) 216316994
Web Site: https://www.wahanaintimakmur.com
Year Founded: 2015
NASI—(INDO)
Rev.: $5,085,157
Assets: $4,760,504
Liabilities: $908,370
Net Worth: $3,852,134
Earnings: $23,248
Emp.: 11
Fiscal Year-end: 12/31/22
Rice Mfr & Distr
N.A.I.C.S.: 311212
Piero Mustafa (Pres)

PT WASKITA KARYA (PERSERO) TBK

PT Waskita Karya (Persero) Tbk—(Continued)

PT WASKITA KARYA (PERSERO) TBK
Waskita Building MT Haryono Kav No 10, Cawang, Jakarta, 13340, Indonesia
Tel.: (62) 218508510
Web Site: https://www.waskita.co.id
Year Founded: 1961
WSKT—(INDO)
Rev.: $711,397,766
Assets: $6,207,997,581
Liabilities: $5,454,595,421
Net Worth: $753,402,160
Earnings: ($260,946,130)
Emp.: 1,435
Fiscal Year-end: 12/31/23
Civil Construction
N.A.I.C.S.: 237990
Bambang Rianto *(Dir-Operation II)*

Subsidiaries:

P.T. Pemalang Batang Toll Road (1)
Jalan Tol Pemalang Batang KM 344A Candiareng, Warungasem Batang, Central Java, 51252, Indonesia
Tel.: (62) 2853974560
Web Site: http://pbtr.co.id
Toll Road Construction Services
N.A.I.C.S.: 926120

PT Waskita Beton Precast Tbk (1)
Jl MT Haryono Kav No 10A, Jakarta Timur, 13340, Indonesia
Tel.: (62) 2122892999
Web Site: http://www.waskitaprecast.co.id
Rev.: $96,603,956
Assets: $290,486,083
Liabilities: $333,638,329
Net Worth: ($43,152,246)
Earnings: $409,140
Emp.: 332
Fiscal Year-end: 12/31/2023
Concrete Mfr
N.A.I.C.S.: 327320
Agus Wantoro *(Mktg Dir)*

PT Waskita Karya (Persero) Tbk - Pasuruan Plant (1)
Jl Eks Tol Lama Porong Desa Panggreh Kecamatan Jabon, Sidoarjo, Indonesia
Tel.: (62) 34 3659476
Precast Building Material Mfr
N.A.I.C.S.: 327390

PT Waskita Karya (Persero) Tbk - Pusri Plant (1)
Jl Mayor Zein Kompleks Pusri, Palembang, Indonesia
Tel.: (62) 711 37 63 85
Precast Building Material Mfr
N.A.I.C.S.: 327390

PT Waskita Toll Road (1)
Gedung Waskita Rajawali Tower 7th Floor Jl MT Haryono Kav No 12-13, Kel Bidara Cina Jatinegara, Jakarta Timur, 13340, Indonesia (81.48%)
Tel.: (62) 2122892048
Web Site: https://www.wtr.co.id
Engineering & Construction Services
N.A.I.C.S.: 541330
Rudi Purnomo *(Dir-Fin & HR)*

PT WEHA TRANSPORTASI INDONESIA TBK
Grha White Horse Jl Husein Sastranegara No 111 RT 5/RW 8, Rawa Bokor Benda, Tangerang, 15125, Banten, Indonesia
Tel.: (62) 2129675555
Web Site: https://www.whitehorse.co.id
WEHA—(INDO)
Rev.: $17,349,924
Assets: $22,847,121
Liabilities: $8,031,668
Net Worth: $14,815,452
Earnings: $2,061,041
Emp.: 216
Fiscal Year-end: 12/31/23
Transportation Services
N.A.I.C.S.: 485999
Angreta Chandra *(Chm)*

Subsidiaries:

P.T. Day Trans (1)
Jl Deplu Raya No 43, Bintaro Pesanggrahan, South Jakarta, 12320, Indonesia
Tel.: (62) 2130296767
Web Site: https://www.daytrans.co.id
Transportation & Goods Delivery Services
N.A.I.C.S.: 532210

PT WIDIANT JAYA KRENINDO TBK
Jl Teh no 4 lt 3 Pinangsia Taman Sari, Jakarta Barat, 11110, Indonesia
Tel.: (62) 2122692232
Web Site: https://www.ptwidi.com
Year Founded: 2016
WIDI—(INDO)
Rev.: $483,445
Assets: $3,266,953
Liabilities: $222,836
Net Worth: $3,044,117
Earnings: $81,487
Emp.: 11
Fiscal Year-end: 12/31/23
Heavy Equipment Rental Services
N.A.I.C.S.: 238910
Bernard Widianto *(Chm)*

PT WIDJAJATUNGGAL SEJAHTERA
Menara Duta Building, Jl HR Rasuna Said Kav B-9, 12910, Jakarta, Kuningan, Indonesia
Tel.: (62) 21 522 5090
Web Site: http://www.sintesagroup.com
Year Founded: 1992
Sales Range: $800-899.9 Million
Emp.: 5,000
Holding Company
N.A.I.C.S.: 551112
Johnny Widjaja *(Founder & Chm)*

Subsidiaries:

Sintesa Group (1)
Menara Duta Building 3rd Floor Jl H R Rasuna Said Kav B-9, Jakarta, 12910, Indonesia
Tel.: (62) 21 522 5090
Web Site: http://www.sintesagroup.com
Profitable investment Services
N.A.I.C.S.: 523999
Shinta Widjaja Kamdani *(CEO)*

PT WIDODO MAKMUR PERKASA TBK
Jl Raya Cilangkap No 58 Cilangkap, Cipayung, Jakarta Timur, 13870, Indonesia
Tel.: (62) 2184306787
Web Site: https://www.widodomakmur.co.id
Year Founded: 1995
WMPP—(INDO)
Rev.: $58,915,268
Assets: $325,131,238
Liabilities: $246,021,673
Net Worth: $79,109,564
Earnings: ($57,205,826)
Fiscal Year-end: 12/31/23
Meat Mfr
N.A.I.C.S.: 311612
Teddy Mulyawan Subekti *(Chief Bus Dev Officer)*

PT WIDODO MAKMUR UNGGAS TBK
Jl Raya Cilangkap No 58 Cilangkap, Cipayung, East Jakarta, 13870, Indonesia
Tel.: (62) 2184306787
Web Site: https://www.widodomakmur.co.id
Year Founded: 2015
WMUU—(INDO)
Rev.: $21,864,320
Assets: $160,324,938
Liabilities: $96,855,400
Net Worth: $63,469,538
Earnings: ($14,330,262)
Fiscal Year-end: 12/31/23
Poultry Processing & Distr
N.A.I.C.S.: 311615
Ali Masadi *(CEO)*

PT WIJAYA CAHAYA TIMBER TBK
Puri Indah Financial Tower 27th Floor, Jl Puri Lingkar Dalam Blok T8 RT 001/RW 002, Jakarta Barat, 11610, Indonesia
Tel.: (62) 2122585789
Web Site: https://www.wijayacahaya.com
Year Founded: 2017
FWCT—(INDO)
Rev.: $61,586,249
Assets: $36,841,931
Liabilities: $18,366,895
Net Worth: $18,475,035
Earnings: $2,692,597
Fiscal Year-end: 12/31/23
Timber Product Mfr
N.A.I.C.S.: 321114
Mareci Susi Afrisca Sembiring *(Sec)*

PT WIJAYA KARYA (PERSERO) TBK.
Jl D I Panjaitan Kav 9-10, Jakarta, 13340, Indonesia
Tel.: (62) 2180679200
Web Site: https://www.wika.co.id
Year Founded: 1960
WIKA—(INDO)
Rev.: $1,463,121,305
Assets: $4,284,821,459
Liabilities: $3,663,240,908
Net Worth: $621,580,551
Earnings: ($508,125,562)
Emp.: 2,269
Fiscal Year-end: 12/31/23
Construction Services
N.A.I.C.S.: 236220
Destiawan Soewardjono *(Dir-Ops III)*

Subsidiaries:

P.T. Hotel Indonesia Propertiy (1)
Tamansari Hive Office Lantai 12-15 Jl DI Panjaitan Kav 2 RT 7/RW 11, Cipinang Cempedak Kecamatan Jatinegara Daerah Khusus Ibukota Jakarta, East Jakarta, 13340, Indonesia
Tel.: (62) 2121011200
Web Site: https://www.wikarealty.co.id
Tourism & Hospitality Services
N.A.I.C.S.: 721110

P.T. Kurnia Realty Jaya (1)
Tamansari Hive Lantai 2 Jl D I Panjaitan Kav 3-4, Cawang, Jakarta Timur, 13340, Indonesia
Tel.: (62) 213513339
Property Management Services
N.A.I.C.S.: 531311

P.T. Navigate Energy (1)
Green Office Park Green Office Park 9 Lt 5 Wing B Zona 8-15, Jl Grand Boulevard BSD City Sampora Cisauk, Tangerang, 15345, Banten, Indonesia
Tel.: (62) 2139700900
Web Site: https://navigat.com
Energy Power Plants Services
N.A.I.C.S.: 541690

P.T. Wijaya Karya Komponen Beton (1)
Kawasan Industri Surya Cipta Jl Surya Madya 3 Kav I-28Q, Karawang, Indonesia
Tel.: (62) 2678630417
Web Site: https://wikakobe.com
Concrete Construction Services
N.A.I.C.S.: 541310

P.T. Wijaya Karya Krakatau Beton (1)
Gedung KE JL Asia Raya Kav O 3, P.O. Box 147, Cilegon, 42435, Indonesia
Tel.: (62) 254394100
Precast Concrete Product Mfr & Distr
N.A.I.C.S.: 327390

PT Balai Pustaka (1)
Jl Bunga No 8-8A, Matraman Jakarta timur, Jakarta, 13140, Indonesia
Tel.: (62) 218583369
Web Site: http://balaipustaka.co.id
Books Publishing Services
N.A.I.C.S.: 513130

PT Citra Lautan Teduh (1)
Jl Hang Jebat Km 1 Batu Besar, Kota Batam, Batam, 29432, Indonesia
Tel.: (62) 778761185
Industrial & Building Construction Services
N.A.I.C.S.: 236210
Aan Sutiana *(Mktg Mgr)*

PT Wijaya Karya Beton Tbk. (1)
WIKA Tower 1 Lt 2-4 Jl D I Panjaitan Kav 9-10, Jakarta, 13340, Indonesia (60%)
Tel.: (62) 218192802
Web Site: https://www.wika-beton.co.id
Rev.: $272,953,902
Assets: $495,600,693
Liabilities: $260,121,110
Net Worth: $235,479,583
Earnings: $1,286,901
Emp.: 1,163
Fiscal Year-end: 12/31/2023
Precast Concrete Mfr
N.A.I.C.S.: 327390
Hadian Pramudita *(Chm)*

PT Wijaya Karya Bitumen (1)
Wika Building Tower 1 6th Floor Jl D I Panjaitan Kav 9 cawang, Jakarta, 13340, Indonesia
Tel.: (62) 2185909416
Web Site: https://www.wikabitumen.co.id
Asphalt Exploration Services
N.A.I.C.S.: 213112
Agung Budi Waskito *(Co-Pres & Commissioner)*

PT Wijaya Karya Gedung Pracetak (1)
Menara MTH MT Haryono St No Kav 2, West Tebet, Jakarta, 12810, Indonesia
Tel.: (62) 2122894529
Web Site: https://www.wikapracetak.co.id
Precast Concrete Mfr
N.A.I.C.S.: 327390

PT Wijaya Karya Industri dan Konstruksi (1)
Tamansari HIVE Office Jl DIPanjaitan Kav 2, East Jakarta, 13340, Indonesia
Tel.: (62) 2121013545
Web Site: http://wikaikon.co.id
Steel Mfrs
N.A.I.C.S.: 331513
Dwi Johardian *(Co-Pres)*

PT Wijaya Karya Realty Tbk (1)
Tamansari Hive Office Lantai 12 Jl D I Panjaitan Kav 2, Cawang, Jakarta Timur, 13340, Indonesia
Tel.: (62) 2121011200
Web Site: https://www.wikarealty.co.id
Property Development Services
N.A.I.C.S.: 531390
Puji Hariyadi *(Commissioner)*

PT Wijaya Karya Rekayasa Konstruksi (1)
JL DI Panjaitan Kav 2 Tamansari Hive Office Lt 5 Kel, Cipinang Cempedak Kec Jatinegara, Jakarta Timur, 13340, Indonesia
Tel.: (62) 2122864446
Web Site: https://www.wikarekon.co.id
Power Plant Construction Services
N.A.I.C.S.: 237130
Hendra Jayusman *(Pres)*

Subsidiary (Domestic):

PT Wijaya Karya Industri Energi (2)
PT Wijaya Karya Building 7th Floor Jln DI Panjaitan Kavling 9, Jakarta, 13340, Indonesia
Tel.: (62) 218508650
Web Site: http://www.wikaenergi.com
Renewable Energy Services
N.A.I.C.S.: 221118
Andi Nugraha *(Pres)*

PT Wika Industri Manufaktur (2)
Jl Raya Narogong Km 26 Cileungsi, Kawasan Industri WIKA, Bogor, 16820, Indonesia
Tel.: (62) 2186863102
Web Site: http://wima.co.id
Electric Motorcycle Part Mfr
N.A.I.C.S.: 336991

PT Wijaya Karya Serang Panimbang (1)
Tamansari Hive Office Tower Head Office 3rd Fl Jl IN Panjaitan Kav 2, RT 11 / RW 11 Kel Cipinang Cempedak Kec Jatinegara, East Jakarta, Indonesia
Tel.: (62) 2122807100
Web Site: http://wikaserangpanimbang.com
Road & Highway Construction Services
N.A.I.C.S.: 237310
Rendy Dwiandika (Mgr-Legal)

PT WIJAYA KARYA BANGUNAN GEDUNG TBK
WIKA Tower 1 8th-10th Floor JL D I Panjaitan Kav 9, Jakarta Timur, 13340, Indonesia
Tel.: (62) 2185909003
Web Site:
  http://www.wikagedung.co.id
Year Founded: 2008
WEGE—(INDO)
Rev.: $258,442,664
Assets: $361,166,007
Liabilities: $195,000,971
Net Worth: $166,165,036
Earnings: $3,019,720
Emp.: 525
Fiscal Year-end: 12/31/23
Building Construction Services
N.A.I.C.S.: 236220

PT WILMAR CAHAYA INDONESIA TBK
Jl Industri Selatan 3 Blok GG1, Kawasan Industri Jababeka Pasirsari Cikarang Selatan, Bekasi, 17550, Jawa Barat, Indonesia
Tel.: (62) 2189830003
Web Site:
  https://www.wilmarcahaya.co.id
CEKA—(INDO)
Rev.: $411,552,615
Assets: $122,967,838
Liabilities: $16,317,807
Net Worth: $106,650,031
Earnings: $9,973,146
Emp.: 417
Fiscal Year-end: 12/31/23
Oil & Food Product Mfr
N.A.I.C.S.: 311225
Erry Tjuatja (Chm)

PT WILTON MAKMUR INDONESIA TBK
Komplek Harco Mangga Dua Agung Sedayu Block C No 5, Jl Mangga dua Raya, Jakarta, 10730, Indonesia
Tel.: (62) 216125585
Web Site: https://www.wilton.id
Year Founded: 2009
SQMI—(INDO)
Rev.: $259,083
Assets: $33,057,797
Liabilities: $26,254,502
Net Worth: $6,803,295
Earnings: ($3,633,012)
Fiscal Year-end: 12/31/23
Coal Mining Services
N.A.I.C.S.: 213113
Vishwanath Mathur (Pres & Commissioner)

PT WINTERMAR OFFSHORE MARINE TBK
Jl Kebayoran Lama No 155, Jakarta, 11560, Indonesia
Tel.: (62) 215305201
Web Site: https://www.wintermar.com
Year Founded: 1995
WINS—(INDO)
Rev.: $72,561,169
Assets: $194,795,420
Liabilities: $32,875,918
Net Worth: $161,919,502
Earnings: $6,630,627
Emp.: 1,065
Fiscal Year-end: 12/31/23
Offshore Marine Services
N.A.I.C.S.: 483211
Sugiman Layanto (Mng Dir)

Subsidiaries:

Abbeypure Pte Ltd (1)
100 Jalan Sultan 09-04 Sultan Plaza, Singapore, 199001, Singapore
Tel.: (65) 64622883
Offshore Marine Services
N.A.I.C.S.: 483211

Florissa Pte Ltd (1)
24 Raffles Place 18-00 Clifford Centre, Singapore, 048621, Singapore
Tel.: (65) 65332323
Offshore Marine Services
N.A.I.C.S.: 483211

P.T. Azureus Simulator Asia (1)
Daan Mogot No 345A, Jakarta Barat, 11460, Indonesia
Tel.: (62) 2122563805
Web Site:
  https://azureusoffshoretraining.com
Marine Shipping Services
N.A.I.C.S.: 541370

P.T. Fast Offshore Indonesia (1)
Jalan Muhajar No 1B RT 001/RW 002, Kel Sukabumi Selatan Kec Kebon Jeruk, Jakarta Barat, 11560, Indonesia
Tel.: (62) 215305201
Ship Transport Services
N.A.I.C.S.: 532411

P.T. Hammar Marine Offshore (1)
Jalan Kebayoran Lama No 155, Jakarta Barat, 11560, Indonesia
Tel.: (62) 215305201
Ship Transport Services
N.A.I.C.S.: 532411

P.T. Nusa Maritim Jaya (1)
Jalan Muhajar No 1B RT 001/RW 002, Kel Sukabumi Selatan Kec Kebon Jeruk, Jakarta Barat, 11560, Indonesia
Tel.: (62) 215305201
Ship Transport Services
N.A.I.C.S.: 532411

P.T. PSV Indonesia (1)
Jalan Kebayoran Lama No 155, Jakarta Barat, 11560, Indonesia
Tel.: (62) 215305201
Ship Transport Services
N.A.I.C.S.: 532411

P.T. Sentosasegara Mulia Shipping (1)
Jalan Muhajar No 1B RT 001/RW 002 Kel Sukabumi Selatan Kec Kebon Jeruk, Jakarta Barat, 11560, Indonesia
Tel.: (62) 215305201
Marine Shipping Services
N.A.I.C.S.: 541370

P.T. WM Offshore (1)
Jalan Kebayoran Lama No 155, Jakarta Barat, 11560, Indonesia
Tel.: (62) 215305201
Ship Transport Services
N.A.I.C.S.: 532411

P.T. Win Maritim (1)
Jalan Kebayoran Lama No 155, Jakarta Barat, 11560, Indonesia
Tel.: (62) 215305201
Ship Transport Services
N.A.I.C.S.: 532411

P.T. Win Offshore (1)
Jalan Kebayoran Lama No 155, Jakarta Barat, 11560, Indonesia
Tel.: (62) 215305201
Ship Transport Services
N.A.I.C.S.: 532411

P.T. Winpan Offshore (1)
Jalan Kebayoran Lama No 155, Jakarta Barat, 11560, Indonesia
Tel.: (62) 215305201
Ship Transport Services
N.A.I.C.S.: 532411

P.T. Wintermar (1)
Jalan Kebayoran Lama No 155, Jakarta Barat, 11560, Indonesia
Tel.: (62) 215305201
Marine Shipping Services
N.A.I.C.S.: 541370

P.T. Wintermar Asia (1)
Jalan Kebayoran Lama No 155, Jakarta Barat, 11560, Indonesia
Tel.: (62) 215305201
Marine Shipping Services
N.A.I.C.S.: 541370

P.T. Wintermar Geo Offshore (1)
Jalan Kebayoran Lama No 155, Jakarta Barat, 11560, Indonesia
Tel.: (62) 215305201
Geophysical Investigation Services
N.A.I.C.S.: 541360

PT Arial Niaga Nusantara (1)
Lorong BDN No 571/I-A9 Kelurahan 16 Ilir Kecamatan ILIR Timur I, Palembang, 30122, Indonesia
Tel.: (62) 711 373388
Emp.: 20
Offshore Marine Services
N.A.I.C.S.: 483211
Johnson Williang Sutjipto (Gen Mgr)

PT WIR ASIA TBK
No 71 Level 9 Senayan Kebayoran Baru, Jeruk Kota Jakarta Barat Daerah Khusus Ibukota, Jakarta, 11530, Indonesia
Tel.: (62) 2153678064
Web Site: https://www.wirglobal.com
Year Founded: 2009
WIRG—(INDO)
Rev.: $161,804,312
Assets: $73,164,981
Liabilities: $26,722,260
Net Worth: $46,442,721
Earnings: $4,448,706
Emp.: 234
Fiscal Year-end: 12/31/23
Information Technology Services
N.A.I.C.S.: 541512
Michel Budi (Chm)

PT WIRA GLOBAL SOLUSI TBK
The Breeze Bsd City L81-82 Jln Grand Boulevard, Tangerang, 15345, Indonesia
Tel.: (62) 2129580058
Web Site: https://www.wgshub.com
Year Founded: 2015
WGSH—(INDO)
Rev.: $2,152,593
Assets: $3,770,440
Liabilities: $126,531
Net Worth: $3,643,908
Earnings: $289,526
Emp.: 2
Fiscal Year-end: 12/31/23
Information Technology Services
N.A.I.C.S.: 541519
Edwin Pramana (CEO)

PT YANAPRIMA HASTAPERSADA TBK
Gedung Graha Irama Lantai 2-E Jl HR Rasuna Said Blok X-1 Kav 1-2, Kuningan Timur, Jakarta, 12950, Indonesia
Tel.: (62) 215261172
Web Site:
  https://www.yanaprima.com
Year Founded: 1995
YPAS—(INDO)
Rev.: $22,501,558
Assets: $17,899,340
Liabilities: $9,560,304
Net Worth: $8,339,036
Earnings: $534,260
Emp.: 111
Fiscal Year-end: 12/31/23
Plastic Bag Mfr & Distr
N.A.I.C.S.: 314910

PT YELOOO INTEGRA DATANET TBK
Jl Alaydrus No 66 B/C Petojo Utara Gambir, Jakarta Pusat, 10150, Indonesia
Tel.: (62) 2122066286
Web Site: https://www.passpod.com
YELO—(INDO)
Rev.: $2,624,719
Assets: $5,847,057
Liabilities: $116,551
Net Worth: $5,730,506
Earnings: $91,120
Emp.: 54
Fiscal Year-end: 12/31/19
Leisure & Tourism Services
N.A.I.C.S.: 561510
Hiro Whardana (Chm)

PT YULIE SEKURITAS INDONESIA TBK
7th Floor Suite 701 Dr Ide Anak Agung Gde Agung st Kav E 1 2 No 1&2, East Kuningan-Setiabudi, Jakarta, 12950, Indonesia
Tel.: (62) 2120392025
Web Site:
  https://www.yuliesekurindo.com
Year Founded: 1989
YULE—(INDO)
Rev.: $3,241,637
Assets: $36,767,722
Liabilities: $2,628,312
Net Worth: $34,139,410
Earnings: $1,762,072
Emp.: 36
Fiscal Year-end: 12/31/23
Financial Services
N.A.I.C.S.: 523999
Vera Marlinata Widjaya (Chm)

PT ZEBRA NUSANTARA TBK.
23Th Fl Satrio Tower Jl.Prof.DR.satrio C4 RT.7/RW.2 Mega Kuningan Setiabudi Kuningan Timur, Kota Jakarta Selatan, DKI Jakarta, Indonesia
Tel.: (62) 2127883900
Web Site: https://www.dnr.id
Year Founded: 1987
ZBRA—(INDO)
Rev.: $1,099,212
Assets: $390,429
Liabilities: $1,026,472
Net Worth: ($636,043)
Earnings: ($69,600)
Emp.: 32
Fiscal Year-end: 12/31/19
Transportation Services
N.A.I.C.S.: 485310

PT ZYREXINDO MANDIRI BUANA TBK
Jl Daan Mogot No 59 RT 5 /RW 1 North Duren Street, Grogol Petamburan District, Jakarta, 11470, Indonesia
Tel.: (62) 215653311
Web Site: https://zyrex.com
Year Founded: 1996
ZYRX—(INDO)
Rev.: $18,808,787
Assets: $31,888,250
Liabilities: $13,091,446
Net Worth: $18,796,804
Earnings: $2,139,961
Emp.: 44
Fiscal Year-end: 12/31/23
Computer Mfr
N.A.I.C.S.: 334111
Evan Jordan (Sec)

PT. ALAKASA INDUSTRINDO, TBK

PT Zyrexindo Mandiri Buana Tbk—(Continued)

PT. ALAKASA INDUSTRINDO, TBK
Jl Pulogadung no 4 Kawasan Industri Pulogadung, Jakarta, 13920, Indonesia
Tel.: (62) 214608855
Web Site: https://www.ai.alakasa.co.id
Year Founded: 1967
ALKA—(INDO)
Rev.: $122,806,333
Assets: $22,062,961
Liabilities: $8,532,186
Net Worth: $13,530,774
Earnings: $2,728,226
Emp.: 26
Fiscal Year-end: 12/31/23
Aluminium Products Mfr
N.A.I.C.S.: 331315
Peng Tjoan *(Chm & Sec)*

Subsidiaries:

PT. Alakasa Extrusindo (1)
Jl Pulogadung no 4, KawasanIndustri Pulogadung, Jakarta Timur, Indonesia
Tel.: (62) 214608855
Web Site: https://www.alakasa.co.id
Aluminum Extrusions Mfr
N.A.I.C.S.: 333514

PT. ALAM SUTERA REALTY TBK
Wisma Argo Manunggal 18th Floor Jl Jend Gatot Subroto, Kav 22, Jakarta, 12930, Indonesia
Tel.: (62) 212523838   Id
Web Site: https://www.alamsuterarealty.co.id
Year Founded: 1993
ASRI—(INDO)
Rev.: $256,903,650
Assets: $1,444,021,222
Liabilities: $712,070,419
Net Worth: $731,950,803
Earnings: $41,408,332
Emp.: 921
Fiscal Year-end: 12/31/23
Property Management Services
N.A.I.C.S.: 531311
Tony Rudiyanto *(Sec)*

PT. ALTAVINDO INDONESIA
Centennial Tower 35th Floor Jl Jend Gatot Subroto Kav 24-25, Jakarta, 12930, Indonesia
Tel.: (62) 21 2953 9505
Web Site: http://www.altavindo.com
Year Founded: 2010
Information Technology Services
N.A.I.C.S.: 519290
Kevin Yaphon Sanjoto *(CEO)*

Subsidiaries:

PT. V-cube Indonesia (1)
Epi Walk Building 3rd Floor Unit A/306-307 Jl HR Rasuna Said, No 306 RT 2/RW 5 Karet Kuningan Setia Budi, South Jakarta, 12940, Indonesia (95%)
Tel.: (62) 2129941363
Telecube Planning Development & Provision Services
N.A.I.C.S.: 541330
Gisca Syalindri *(Mgr-Asst Solutions)*

PT. ARTHA MAHIYA INVESTAMA TBK
Jl Cipaku 1 No 3 RT/RW 002/004 Petogogan Kebayoran Baru, Jakarta Pusat, 12170, Indonesia
Tel.: (62) 217221279
Web Site: http://www.aims.co.id
AIMS—(INDO)
Rev.: $633,561
Assets: $252,417
Liabilities: $134,196
Net Worth: $118,220
Earnings: ($893,560)
Emp.: 4
Fiscal Year-end: 12/31/23
Coal Distr
N.A.I.C.S.: 324199
Ramono Sukadis *(Chm)*

PT. ASTRA GRAPHIA TBK.
Jl Kramat Raya No 43, Jakarta, 10450, Indonesia
Tel.: (62) 213909190
Web Site: https://www.astragraphia.co.id
ASGR—(INDO)
Rev.: $290,997,200
Assets: $267,765,100
Liabilities: $98,442,900
Net Worth: $169,322,200
Earnings: $9,707,100
Emp.: 1,302
Fiscal Year-end: 12/31/22
Business Document Solution Providing Services
N.A.I.C.S.: 561410
Harijadi Halim *(Co-Chm)*

Subsidiaries:

PT Astragraphia Xprins Indonesia (1)
Jl Kramat Raya No 43, Jakarta, 10450, Indonesia
Tel.: (62) 213925977
Web Site: https://www.axi.co.id
Office Related Services
N.A.I.C.S.: 561990
Widi Triwibowo *(Pres)*

PT. ASURANSI BINTANG TBK
Jl RS Fatmawati No 32, Jakarta, 12430, Indonesia
Tel.: (62) 2175902777   Id
Web Site: https://www.asuransibintang.com
Year Founded: 1955
ASBI—(INDO)
Rev.: $24,565,536
Assets: $63,016,377
Liabilities: $37,839,346
Net Worth: $25,177,031
Earnings: $378,405
Emp.: 327
Fiscal Year-end: 12/31/23
Insurance Management Services
N.A.I.C.S.: 524298
Margi Widodo Hartanto *(Chm)*

PT. ASURANSI HARTA AMAN PRATAMA TBK.
Wisma 46 Lantai 33 Kota BNI Jl Jend Sudirman Kav 1, Jakarta, 10220, Indonesia
Tel.: (62) 215702060
Web Site: https://www.asuransi-harta.co.id
Year Founded: 1982
AHAP—(INDO)
Rev.: $67,999,130
Assets: $93,327,945
Liabilities: $72,321,218
Net Worth: $21,006,726
Earnings: ($746,938)
Emp.: 226
Fiscal Year-end: 12/31/22
Insurance & Reinsurance Services
N.A.I.C.S.: 524113
Roy S. Wiradharma *(Chm)*

PT. BAKRIELAND DEVELOPMENT, TBK.
Wisma Bakrie 1 6th & 7th floor Jl HR Rasuna Said Kav B-1, Jakarta, 12920, Indonesia
Tel.: (62) 215257835
Web Site: https://www.bakrieland.com
KJ6—(DEU)
Sales Range: $75-99.9 Million
Emp.: 5,114
Property Development Services
N.A.I.C.S.: 531390
Ambono Janurianto *(Chm & CEO)*

Subsidiaries:

PT Graha Andrasentra Propertindo (1)
Jl Dreded Pahlawan, Bogor, 16132, Indonesia
Tel.: (62) 251211290
Real Estate Development Services
N.A.I.C.S.: 531390

PT Hotel Elty Tenggarong (1)
Jl Pahlawan Timbau, Kutai Kartanegara, Tenggarong, Indonesia
Tel.: (62) 541 664703
Web Site: http://www.grandelty.com
Hotel Operator
N.A.I.C.S.: 721110

PT Jasa Boga Raya (1)
Plaza Amsterdam D/50 JL MH Thamrin Sentul City, Citaringgul Babakan Madang, Bogor, 16810, Jawa Barat, Indonesia
Tel.: (62) 218 796 2194
Web Site: https://www.jasabogaraya.com
Food & Beverage Services
N.A.I.C.S.: 722310

PT Mitra Langgeng Sejahtera (1)
Grha Mitra Jl Bintaro Raya No 19 A, Jakarta, 12250, Indonesia
Tel.: (62) 217 289 5689
Web Site: https://www.mitralanggeng.com
Real Estate Development Services
N.A.I.C.S.: 531390

PT Sanggraha Pelita Sentosa (1)
Ktr Pemasaran Kompl Taman Kebayoran Bl A-4/1, Duren Jaya Bekasi Timur, Bekasi, 17111, Jawa Barat, Indonesia
Tel.: (62) 21 8811685
Real Estate Development Services
N.A.I.C.S.: 531390

PT. BAKTI TANI NUSANTARA
Tunas Industrial Park Type 6F-6G, Jl Engku Putri, Batam, 29400, Kepulauan Riau, Indonesia
Tel.: (62) 778471271   Id
Web Site: http://www.btnindo.com
Emp.: 80
Oil Palm Seed Engineering & Processing Services
N.A.I.C.S.: 111120
Peng Boong Ching *(Mgr)*

PT. BANK PAN INDONESIA TBK
Jl Jendral Sudirman Senayan Kav 1, Jakarta, 10270, Indonesia
Tel.: (62) 212700545   Id
Web Site: https://www.panin.co.id
PNBN—(INDO)
Rev.: $947,369,462
Assets: $14,417,332,647
Liabilities: $10,955,219,871
Net Worth: $3,462,112,776
Earnings: $195,179,508
Emp.: 7,376
Fiscal Year-end: 12/31/23
Banking Services
N.A.I.C.S.: 521110
Gunawan Santoso *(Dir-Treasury)*

Subsidiaries:

PT Bank Panin Dubai Syariah Tbk. (1)
Gedung Panin Life Center, Jl Letjen S Parman Kav 91Slipi, Jakarta, 11420, Indonesia (67.3%)
Tel.: (62) 2156956100
Web Site: https://pdsb.co.id
Rev.: $72,746,300
Assets: $1,126,270,451
Liabilities: $945,183,773
Net Worth: $181,086,679
Earnings: $15,890,199
Emp.: 486
Fiscal Year-end: 12/31/2023
Banking Services

INTERNATIONAL PUBLIC

N.A.I.C.S.: 522110
Bratha Widjaja *(Chm)*

PT Clipan Finance Indonesia Tbk (1)
Wisma Slipi Lantai 6 Jl Let Jend S Parman Kav 12, Jakarta Barat, 11480, Indonesia
Tel.: (62) 215308005
Web Site: https://www.clipan.co.id
Rev.: $149,127,101
Assets: $643,636,844
Liabilities: $284,729,150
Net Worth: $358,907,694
Earnings: $52,926,450
Emp.: 1,496
Fiscal Year-end: 12/31/2023
Financial Lending Services
N.A.I.C.S.: 522220
Gita Puspa Kirana Darmawan *(Chm)*

PT. BANK PEMBANGUNAN DAERAH JAWA BARAT & BANTEN, TBK.
Bank bjb Jl Naripan No 12-14, Bandung, 40111, Indonesia
Tel.: (62) 224234868   Id
Web Site: https://www.bankbjb.co.id
Year Founded: 1961
BJBR—(INDO)
Rev.: $925,928,092
Assets: $12,227,908,991
Liabilities: $11,224,649,762
Net Worth: $1,003,259,229
Earnings: $109,175,634
Emp.: 7,300
Fiscal Year-end: 12/31/23
Commercial Banking Services
N.A.I.C.S.: 522110
Nia Kania *(Dir-Fin)*

Subsidiaries:

P.T. Bjb Sekuritas (1)
Jl Teuku Umar No 10 Lebakgede Kecamatan Coblong, Bandung, 40132, West Java, Indonesia
Tel.: (62) 224211415
Web Site: https://bjbsekuritas.co.id
Banking Education Services
N.A.I.C.S.: 522110

PT. BAYAN RESOURCES TBK.
Gedung Office 8 Lantai 37 Unit A - H Jalan Senopati No 8B Senayan, Kebayoran Baru Kota Adm, Jakarta Selatan, 12190, DKI Jakarta, Indonesia
Tel.: (62) 2129356888   Id
Web Site: http://www.bayan.com.sg
BYAN—(INDO)
Rev.: $3,581,375,403
Assets: $3,444,319,816
Liabilities: $1,465,501,614
Net Worth: $1,978,818,202
Earnings: $1,279,580,842
Emp.: 1,194
Fiscal Year-end: 12/31/23
Coal Mining Services
N.A.I.C.S.: 212114
David Yi Ngo Low *(Dir-Sls & Mktg)*

Subsidiaries:

Kangaroo Resources Limited (1)
Level 2 Suite 9 389 Oxford Street, Mount Hawthorn, Perth, 6016, WA, Australia (100%)
Tel.: (61) 893814320
Web Site: https://www.kangarooresources.com
Rev.: $1,631,251
Assets: $154,005,201
Liabilities: $66,197,396
Net Worth: $87,807,805
Earnings: ($2,504,663)
Emp.: 3
Fiscal Year-end: 12/31/2017
Mineral Exploration & Development Services
N.A.I.C.S.: 423520
Paul Mario Jurman *(Sec)*

PT. BEKASI FAJAR INDUSTRIAL ESTATE TBK.

Jl Sumatera Kawasan Industri MM2100, Cikarang Barat, Bekasi, 17520, Indonesia
Tel.: (62) 218980133
Web Site: https://befa.id
BEST—(INDO)
Rev.: $35,347,808
Assets: $385,750,376
Liabilities: $102,105,586
Net Worth: $283,644,790
Earnings: $2,566,960
Emp.: 149
Fiscal Year-end: 12/31/23
Industrial Real Estate Developer
N.A.I.C.S.: 237210
Yoshihiro Kobi *(Chm)*

PT. BERLINA TBK

Jl Jababeka Raya Blok E 12 17 Kawasan Industri Jababeka Cikarang, Desa Wangunharja Kecamatan Cikarang Utara, Bekasi, 17520, Indonesia
Tel.: (62) 2189830160
Web Site: https://www.berlina.co.id
BRNA—(INDO)
Rev.: $64,953,309
Assets: $111,793,991
Liabilities: $70,057,802
Net Worth: $41,736,189
Earnings: ($5,264,517)
Emp.: 911
Fiscal Year-end: 12/31/23
Plastics & Fibre Glass Mfr
N.A.I.C.S.: 314910

Subsidiaries:

Berlina Pte. Ltd. (1)
190 Middle Road 14-05 Fortune Center, Singapore, 188979, Singapore
Tel.: (65) 63392838
Plastic Tank Mfr
N.A.I.C.S.: 326122

Hefei Paragon Plastic Packaging Co. Ltd. (1)
No 28 Shanghai Road, Baohe Industrial Zone, Hefei, 230051, China
Tel.: (86) 55166105708
Plastic Tank Mfr
N.A.I.C.S.: 326122

PT Natura Plastindo (1)
Dusun Baran Desa Winong Gempol, Pasuruan, 67155, Indonesia
Tel.: (62) 343659460
Plastic Fabrication Mfr
N.A.I.C.S.: 326199

PT Quantex (1)
Jl Gatot Subroto Km 6 Kampung Cikoneng Ilir No 8 Gandasari, Jatiuwung, Tangerang, 15137, Indonesia
Tel.: (62) 2155666584
Plastic Tank Mfr
N.A.I.C.S.: 326122
Winda Rismawati *(Mgr-Pur)*

PT. Lamipak Primula Indonesia (1)
Jl Sawunggaling 26 Gilang Taman, Sidoarjo, 61257, Indonesia
Tel.: (62) 317881418
Web Site: http://www.lamipak.co.id
Plastic Tank Mfr
N.A.I.C.S.: 326122

PT. BFI FINANCE INDONESIA TBK.

BFI Tower Sunburst CBD Lot 1 2 Jl Kapt, Soebijanto Djojohadikusumo BSD City, Tangerang, 15322, Indonesia
Tel.: (62) 2129650500 Id
Web Site: https://www.bfi.co.id
Year Founded: 1982
BFIN—(INDO)
Rev.: $412,571,158
Assets: $1,558,003,789
Liabilities: $941,087,037
Net Worth: $616,916,752
Earnings: $106,748,307
Emp.: 11,207
Fiscal Year-end: 12/31/23
Financial Services
N.A.I.C.S.: 523999
Francis Lay Sioe Ho *(Chm & CEO)*

PT. BHUWANATALA INDAH PERMAI TBK

Graha BIP Lt 6 Jl Gatot Subroto Kav 23, Jakarta, 12930, Indonesia
Tel.: (62) 212522535 Id
Web Site: https://www.bipp.co.id
Year Founded: 1968
BIPP—(INDO)
Rev.: $17,148,380
Assets: $126,329,332
Liabilities: $57,919,739
Net Worth: $68,409,593
Earnings: ($290,476)
Emp.: 273
Fiscal Year-end: 12/31/23
Real Estate Development Services
N.A.I.C.S.: 531390
Arianto Sjarief *(Chm & Sec)*

Subsidiaries:

P.T. Magna Investama Mandiri Tbk (1)
Jl Biak Block B No 2 C Cideng, Gambir, Jakarta Pusat, Indonesia
Tel.: (62) 2157940936
Web Site: https://www.magnainvestamamandiri.co.id
Investment Management Service
N.A.I.C.S.: 541611

PT Asri Kencana Gemilang (1)
Jl Gatot Subroto Kav 23, Jakarta, 12930, Indonesia
Tel.: (62) 212520318
Office Space Rental Services
N.A.I.C.S.: 531120
Eddy Widjaja *(Mgr-Building)*

PT BIP Sentosa (1)
Jl Martimbang Raya No 9, Kebayoran Baru, South Jakarta, Indonesia
Tel.: (62) 212522535
Apartment Rental Services
N.A.I.C.S.: 531110

PT Studio One (1)
Jl Talang Betutu No 15, Jakarta Pusat, Indonesia
Tel.: (62) 213140777
Hotel Room & Accommodation Services
N.A.I.C.S.: 721110

PT. BUKIT DARMO PROPERTY TBK.

Jalan Tanah Abang 3 no 6, Jakarta, 10160, Indonesia
Tel.: (62) 213517007 Id
Web Site: http://www.bukitdarmoproperty.com
Year Founded: 1989
BKDP—(INDO)
Rev.: $1,369,112
Assets: $55,358,812
Liabilities: $21,665,649
Net Worth: $33,693,164
Earnings: ($2,173,508)
Emp.: 98
Fiscal Year-end: 12/31/20
Property Management Services
N.A.I.C.S.: 531311
Iefenn Adrianne Sumampow *(Vice Chm)*

PT. CARDIG AERO SERVICES TBK

Menara Cardig 3rd Floor Jl Raya Halim Perdanakusuma, Jakarta, 13650, Indonesia
Tel.: (62) 2180875050 Id
Web Site: https://www.casgroup.co.id
Year Founded: 2011
CASS—(INDO)
Rev.: $142,817,152
Assets: $124,646,031
Liabilities: $57,600,156
Net Worth: $67,045,874
Earnings: $27,728,796
Emp.: 2,581
Fiscal Year-end: 12/31/23
Aviation Services
N.A.I.C.S.: 488119
Radianto Kusumo *(Vice Chm, Mng Dir & COO)*

Subsidiaries:

PT Cardig Anugra Sarana Bersama (1)
Menara Cardig 3rd Floor Jl Raya Halim Perdanakusuma, Jakarta, 13650, Indonesia
Tel.: (62) 2180875050
Facility Management Services
N.A.I.C.S.: 561210
L. Hendro Gunawan *(Mgr-Operational)*

PT Cardig Anugrah Sarana Catering (1)
Menara Cardig 3rd Floor Jl Raya Halim Perdanakusuma, Jakarta, 13650, Indonesia
Tel.: (62) 2180875050
Food Service
N.A.I.C.S.: 722310

PT JAS Aero Engineering Services (1)
Tel.: (62) 215591167173
Web Site: http://www.jas-aero.com
Engineering Services
N.A.I.C.S.: 541330
Indra Waskita *(Mgr-Mktg)*

PT Jakarta Aviation Training Centre (1)
PT Jakarta Aviation Training Center Kawasan Pergudangan Bandara, Mas J/5 Kav 20-23 Jl Marsekal Suryadharma, Tangerang, 15127, Indonesia
Tel.: (62) 2129215731
Web Site: http://www.jatc.aero
Training Center Services
N.A.I.C.S.: 611519

PT Jasa Angkasa Semesta Tbk (1)
Wisma Soewarna 1st Floor Soewama Business Park Soekarno Hatta, International Airport, Jakarta, 15126, Indonesia
Tel.: (62) 2155912988
Web Site: http://www.ptjas.co.id
Logistic Services
N.A.I.C.S.: 488510
Nurhadijono Nurjadin *(Commissioner)*

PT Purantara Mitra Angkasa Dua (1)
Purantara Building Soekarno-Hatta International Airport, PO Box 1126, Jakarta, 15000, Indonesia
Tel.: (62) 2155915001
Flight Catering Services
N.A.I.C.S.: 722320

PT. CITATAH TBK

Jl Tarum Timur No 64 Desa Tamelang Kecamatan Purwasari, Karawang, 41373, Indonesia
Tel.: (62) 264317577 Id
Web Site: https://www.citatah.co.id
Year Founded: 1974
CTTH—(INDO)
Rev.: $6,444,623
Assets: $48,811,097
Liabilities: $35,090,235
Net Worth: $13,720,862
Earnings: ($638,223)
Emp.: 576
Fiscal Year-end: 12/31/23
Marble Handicraft Mfr & Distr
N.A.I.C.S.: 339930
Taufik Johannes *(Chm)*

PT. DHARMA SAMUDERA FISHING INDUSTRIES, TBK

Jl Laksamana R E Martadinata Tj Priok, Jakarta, 14310, Indonesia
Tel.: (62) 214301001 Id
Web Site: https://www.dsfi.id
Year Founded: 1973
DSFI—(INDO)
Rev.: $36,340,180
Assets: $26,747,566
Liabilities: $10,480,023
Net Worth: $16,267,543
Earnings: $784,983
Emp.: 69
Fiscal Year-end: 12/31/23
Fish Farming Services
N.A.I.C.S.: 112511
Herman Sutjiamidjaja *(Chm)*

PT. EKA SARI LORENA TRANSPORT TBK.

Jl RA Kartini No 16, Cilandak, Jakarta, 12430, Indonesia
Tel.: (62) 217506655
Web Site: https://www.lorena-transport.com
Year Founded: 1970
LRNA—(INDO)
Rev.: $6,036,732
Assets: $23,298,079
Liabilities: $3,388,814
Net Worth: $19,909,265
Earnings: ($50,472)
Emp.: 198
Fiscal Year-end: 12/31/23
Transportation Services
N.A.I.C.S.: 485210

PT. ELANG MAHKOTA TEKNOLOGI TBK.

SCTV Tower 18th Floor Senayan City Jl Asia Afrika Lot 19, Jakarta, 10270, Indonesia
Tel.: (62) 2172782066 Id
Web Site: https://www.emtek.co.id
Year Founded: 1983
EMTK—(INDO)
Rev.: $600,137,774
Assets: $2,785,357,809
Liabilities: $293,495,686
Net Worth: $2,491,862,124
Earnings: ($16,006,423)
Emp.: 7,153
Fiscal Year-end: 12/31/23
Media & Telecommunication Services
N.A.I.C.S.: 517810
Sutanto Hartono *(Vice Chm)*

Subsidiaries:

P.T. Bitnet Komunikasindo (1)
Jl RP Soeroso No 37 RT 2/RW 2 Gondangdia, Menteng Kota Jakarta Pusat Daerah Khusus Ibukota, Jakarta, 10350, Indonesia
Tel.: (62) 213910123
Web Site: https://bitnet.net.id
Information Technology Services
N.A.I.C.S.: 541512

P.T. Indopay Merchant Services (1)
Jl KH Mas Mansyur No Kav 126 Karet Tengsin, Kecamatan Tanah Abang Kota Jakarta Pusat Daerah Khusus Ibukota, Jakarta, 10220, Indonesia
Tel.: (62) 215746711
Web Site: https://www.indopay.com
Electronic Payment Services
N.A.I.C.S.: 522320

P.T. Sakalaguna Semesta (1)
Jl Mega Kuningan Barat III Lot 10 RT 3 / RW 3 Tower B 16th Floor, Kuningan Kuningan Timur Kota Jakarta Selatan, Jakarta, 12950, Indonesia
Tel.: (62) 2150815222
Web Site: https://www.sakalaguna.co.id
Telecommunication Servicesb
N.A.I.C.S.: 517810

P.T. Screenplay Produksi (1)
SCTV Tower - Senayan City Lt 11 Jl Asia Afrika Lot 19, Jakarta, 10270, Indonesia
Tel.: (62) 2172782063
Film & Video Production Services
N.A.I.C.S.: 512120

P.T. Sinemart Indonesia (1)
Komplek Ruko Plaza Kedoya Elok Blok DE 19-20 Jl Panjang Kedoya, Jakarta, 11520, Indonesia
Tel.: (62) 2158300098
Web Site: https://www.sinemart.com
Film & Video Production Services

PT. ELANG MAHKOTA TEKNOLOGI TBK.

PT. Elang Mahkota Teknologi Tbk.—(Continued)
N.A.I.C.S.: 512120

P.T. Tangara Mitrakom (1)
Jl R P Soeroso No 37, Jakarta, 10350, Indonesia
Tel.: (62) 213903939
Web Site: https://www.mitrakom.co.id
Telecommunication Servicesb
N.A.I.C.S.: 517810

P.T. Utama Pratama Medika (1)
Jl KH Hasyim Ashari No 24 Buaran Indah, Tangerang, 15119, Banten, Indonesia
Tel.: (62) 2155752575
Medical Research & Development Services
N.A.I.C.S.: 524114

PT Abhimata Citra Abadi (1)
Menara Batavia Lt 24 Jl KH Mas Mansyur No 126, Jakarta, 10220, Indonesia
Tel.: (62) 2157930304
Trading & Telecommunication Services
N.A.I.C.S.: 517810

PT Binary Ventura Indonesia (1)
SCTV Tower Lt 18 Senayan City JL Asia Afrika Lot 19, Jakarta, 10270, Indonesia
Tel.: (62) 212793555
Media & Telecommunication Services
N.A.I.C.S.: 517810

PT Kreatif Media Karya (1)
Tel.: (62) 217229690
Web Site: http://www.kmkonline.co.id
Emp.: 1,700
Online Publishing Services
N.A.I.C.S.: 513199

PT Mediatama Anugrah Citra (1)
SCTV Tower-Senayan City Lt 15 Jl Asia Afrika Lot 19, Jakarta, 10270, Indonesia
Tel.: (62) 2127935600
Pay TV Operator
N.A.I.C.S.: 516210

PT Omni Intivision (1)
SCTV Tower-Senayan City Lt 16 Jl Asia Afrika Lot 19, Jakarta, 10270, Indonesia
Tel.: (62) 2172782200
Media & Telecommunication Services
N.A.I.C.S.: 517810

PT. ELECTRONIC CITY INDONESIA TBK

Jl Jend Sudirman Kav-52-53 Lot 22, Sudirman Central Business District SCBD, Jakarta, 12190, Indonesia
Tel.: (62) 215151177
Web Site:
https://www.corp.electronic-city.com
Year Founded: 2002
ECII—(INDO)
Rev.: $160,354,882
Assets: $110,211,489
Liabilities: $34,077,759
Net Worth: $76,133,730
Earnings: $847,293
Emp.: 702
Fiscal Year-end: 12/31/23
Electronics Stores
N.A.I.C.S.: 449210

PT. GLOBAL PUTRA INTERNATIONAL GROUP

Jl Ir H Juanda III No 26 A-B, Jakarta, 10120, Indonesia
Tel.: (62) 21 380 7882
Web Site: http://www.gpi-g.com
Year Founded: 1981
Emp.: 1,700
Logistics & Supply Chain Services
N.A.I.C.S.: 541614
Sumadi Kusuma (CEO)

Subsidiaries:

PT Ocean Global Shipping (1)
Jl Ir H Juanda III No 23 C-D-E, Jakarta, 10120, Indonesia
Tel.: (62) 21 381 0338
Web Site: http://www.gpi-g.com
Freight Deep Sea Transportation Services
N.A.I.C.S.: 483111

PT. INFINITT INDONESIA

Lt 2 J Musi No 37 RT 13/RW 2, Cideng Gambir, Jakarta Pusat, 10150, Jakarta, Indonesia
Tel.: (62) 2138900342
Health Care Srvices
N.A.I.C.S.: 621610

PT. INTERMEDIA CAPITAL TBK.

The Convergence Indonesia Building 27th Floor, Kawasan Rasuna Epicentrum Jl H R Rasuna Said Karet Kuninga, Jakarta, 12940, Indonesia
Tel.: (62) 2129912182
Web Site: https://www.imc.co.id
Year Founded: 2008
MDIA—(INDO)
Rev.: $85,072,543
Assets: $523,108,279
Liabilities: $325,164,980
Net Worth: $197,943,299
Earnings: $2,086,517
Emp.: 632
Fiscal Year-end: 12/31/22
Television Broadcasting
N.A.I.C.S.: 516120
Arief Yahya (Chm & Pres)

PT. JASA MARGA (PERSERO) TBK

Plaza Tol Taman Mini Indonesia Indah, Jakarta, 13550, Indonesia
Tel.: (62) 218413630
Web Site:
https://www.jasamarga.com
JSMR—(INDO)
Rev.: $1,384,430,209
Assets: $8,397,520,566
Liabilities: $5,870,626,848
Net Worth: $2,526,893,718
Earnings: $438,311,816
Emp.: 5,022
Fiscal Year-end: 12/31/23
Highway & Toll Management Services
N.A.I.C.S.: 488490
Mohammad Sofyan (Fin Dir)

Subsidiaries:

P.T. Jasamarga Related Business (1)
Gedung Jagorawi Lantai 2 Plaza Tol Taman Mini Indonesia Indah, RT 8/RW 2 Dukuh Kec Kramat jati Kota Timur Daerah Khusus Ibukota, Jakarta, 13550, Indonesia
Tel.: (62) 2122093560
Web Site: https://www.jmrb.co.id
Asset Management Services
N.A.I.C.S.: 531390

PT Cinere Serpong Jaya (1)
Ruko City Market Pondok Cabe Blok D2 No 07 Jln Pondok Cabe Raya, Kelurahan Pondok Cabe Udik Kecamatan Pamulang Selatan, Tangerang, 15418, Banten, Indonesia
Tel.: (62) 2174166620
Food Transportation Services
N.A.I.C.S.: 236220

PT Jalantol Lingkarluar Jakarta (1)
Plaza Tol Jatiasih, Bekasi, 17423, Indonesia
Tel.: (62) 218223232
Food Transportation Services
N.A.I.C.S.: 236220

PT Jasamarga Bali Tol (1)
Tel.: (62) 361725326
Food Transportation Services
N.A.I.C.S.: 236220

PT Jasamarga Balikpapan Samarinda (1)
Web Site: http://www.ptjbs.co.id
Food Transportation Services
N.A.I.C.S.: 236220

PT Jasamarga Gempol Pasuruan (1)
Pandaan Toll Road 3rd Floor, Pasuruan, 67156, East Java, Indonesia
Tel.: (62) 3436741324
Web Site: http://www.jmgempas.co.id

Food Transportation Services
N.A.I.C.S.: 236220

PT Jasamarga Jalanlayang Cikampek (1)
Plaza Tol Jagorawi Jln Raya Taman Mini Indonesia Indah DKI, Jakarta Timur, 13550, Jakarta, Indonesia
Tel.: (62) 2122819658 (60%)
Food Transportation Services
N.A.I.C.S.: 236220

PT Jasamarga Japek Selatan (1)
Kel Pinang Ranti Kec Makassar, Jakarta Timur, 13560, Indonesia
Tel.: (62) 2122854389
Web Site:
http://www.jasamargajapekselatan.co.id
Food Transportation Services
N.A.I.C.S.: 236220

PT Jasamarga Kualanamu Tol (1)
Jln Tengku Raja Muda No 10 Deli Serdang, Lubuk Pakam, Medan, 20511, Sumatera Utara, Indonesia (55%)
Tel.: (62) 617955941
Food Transportation Services
N.A.I.C.S.: 236220

PT Jasamarga Kunciran Cengkareng (1)
Business Park Tangerang City Blok A No 19 Jl Jend Sudirman, No 1 Cikokol, Tangerang, 15117, Banten, Indonesia (88.67%)
Tel.: (62) 2155782453
Web Site: http://www.jkc.co.id
Food Transportation Services
N.A.I.C.S.: 236220

PT Jasamarga Manado Bitung (1)
Perumahan Taman Sari Metropolitan Cluster Siladen Blok C3 No 6/7, Manado, Indonesia
Tel.: (62) 4317242780
Web Site: http://www.jmmanadobitung.com
Food Transportation Services
N.A.I.C.S.: 236220

PT Jasamarga Pandaan Malang (1)
Plaza Tol Singosari, Singosari, Malang, 65153, Jawa Timur, Indonesia
Tel.: (62) 3414366666
Food Transportation Services
N.A.I.C.S.: 236220

PT Jasamarga Pandaan Tol (1)
Plaza Tol Pandaan Pandaan, Pasuruan, 67156, Jawa Timur, Indonesia
Tel.: (62) 3435650727
Food Transportation Services
N.A.I.C.S.: 236220

PT Jasamarga Probolinggo Banyuwangi (1)
Jln Bina Marga No 42B RT 002/06 Keluruhan Cipayung Kecamatan DKI, Cipayung, Jakarta Timur, 13840, Jakarta, Indonesia
Tel.: (62) 2184341752
Food Transportation Services
N.A.I.C.S.: 236220

PT Jasamarga Properti (1)
Graha Simatupang Tower 2B Lt 3 Jl TB Simatupang Kav 38 Jati Padang, Pasar Minggu, Jakarta Selatan, 12540, Indonesia
Tel.: (62) 217829422
Web Site: http://www.jmrb.co.id
Food Transportation Services
N.A.I.C.S.: 236220

PT Jasamarga Surabaya Mojokerto (1)
Tel.: (62) 317879994
Food Transportation Services
N.A.I.C.S.: 236220

PT Jasamarga Tollroad Maintenance (1)
Building C Graha Service Provider 1st Floor, PT Jasa Marga Tbk Head Office Taman Mini Indonesia Indah Toll Plaza, Jakarta, 13550, Indonesia
Tel.: (62) 2129835858
Web Site: https://www.jmtm.co.id
Food Transportation Services
N.A.I.C.S.: 236220

PT Jasamarga Tollroad Operator (1)
Tel.: (62) 2122984722
Web Site: http://www.jmto.co.id

Food Transportation Services
N.A.I.C.S.: 236220

PT Jasamarga Transjawa Tol (1)
Kawasan Kantor Pusat Jasa Marga Gedung Cabang Jagorawi, Lt 3-4 Plaza Tol Taman Mini Indonesia Indah DKI Jakarta, Jakarta Timur, 13550, Indonesia
Tel.: (62) 2122094724
Food Transportation Services
N.A.I.C.S.: 236220

PT Marga Lingkar Jakarta (1)
PT Marga Lingkar Jakarta JORR W2 Utara - Plaza Tol Meruya, Jalan Raya Meruya Utara No1 Kembangan, Jakarta Barat, Indonesia
Tel.: (62) 2158908462
Web Site:
https://www.margalingkarjakarta.co.id
Food Transportation Services
N.A.I.C.S.: 236220

PT Marga Sarana Jabar (1)
Tel.: (62) 2129255000
Food Transportation Services
N.A.I.C.S.: 236220

PT Marga Trans Nusantara (1)
Astra Biz Centre Commercial Park Barat Lot I No 11 Jln BSD Raya Utama, BSD City, Tangerang, 15331, Banten, Indonesia
Tel.: (62) 2130450666
Food Transportation Services
N.A.I.C.S.: 236220

PT Trans Marga Jateng (1)
Web Site: http://www.transmargajateng.co.id
Food Transportation Services
N.A.I.C.S.: 236220

PT. JAYAMANDIRI GEMASEJATI

jl. BKR no. 5, Bandung, West Java, 40265, Indonesia
Tel.: (91) 0227318755
Web Site: https://jgmotor.co.id
Year Founded: 1994
Emp.: 144
Retail Services
N.A.I.C.S.: 459999

Subsidiaries:

PT. Mandala Multifinance Tbk (1)
Jl Menteng Raya No 24 A-B, Jakarta Pusat, 10340, Indonesia
Tel.: (62) 2129259955
Web Site: https://www.mandalafinance.com
Rev.: $143,703,063
Assets: $432,732,625
Liabilities: $212,168,461
Net Worth: $220,564,164
Earnings: $27,463,775
Emp.: 5,765
Fiscal Year-end: 12/31/2023
Consumer Financial Services
N.A.I.C.S.: 522291
Harryjanto Lasmana (Chm)

PT. KERETA API INDONESIA

Jalan Perintis Kemerdekaan No 1, 40117, Bandung, Indonesia
Tel.: (62) 22 4230031
Web Site: http://www.kereta-api.co.id
Emp.: 1,000
Railcar & Locomotive Mfr
N.A.I.C.S.: 336510
Edi Sukmoro (Pres)

Subsidiaries:

PT KA Logistik (1)
Jl Kh Wahid Hasyim No 11 A, Jakarta, 10340, Indonesia
Tel.: (62) 2131922299
Web Site: http://www.kalogistics.co.id
Container Transportation Services
N.A.I.C.S.: 484110
Army Hani (VP-Ops)

PT KA Properti Manajemen (1)
Stasiun Sawah Besar Lt Dasar Jl K H Samanhudi, Jakarta, 10710, Indonesia
Tel.: (62) 213451040
Web Site: http://www.kapm.co.id
Railway Freight Transportation Services
N.A.I.C.S.: 482111

Andry Gumilar *(Asst Mgr)*

PT KAI Commuter Jabodetabek (1)
Stasiun Juanda Jl Ir H Juanda 1, Jakarta, 10120, Indonesia
Tel.: (62) 213453535
Web Site: http://www.krl.co.id
Railway Freight Transportation Services
N.A.I.C.S.: 482111
Sondang Manullang *(Mgr-Strategic Plng)*

PT Railink (1)
Kantor Pusat Jakarta Jl Ir H Uanda 1B No8 3rd fl, Jakarta, 10120, Indonesia
Tel.: (62) 213502963
Web Site: http://www.railink.co.id
Tour Operator
N.A.I.C.S.: 561599

PT Reska Multi Usaha (1)
Gedung Stasiun Mangga Besar Lantai 1 Jl Karang Anyar No 1, Jakarta, 11740, Indonesia
Tel.: (62) 2162302540
Web Site: http://www.reska.co.id
Emp.: 5,000
Restaurant Management Services
N.A.I.C.S.: 722511
Arjo Pamantjar *(Gen Mgr-Logistic)*

PT. KIMIA FARMA (PERSERO) TBK.
Jl Veteran No 9, Jakarta, 10110, Indonesia
Tel.: (62) 213847709
Web Site:
https://www.kimiafarma.co.id
Year Founded: 1971
KAEF—(INDO)
Rev.: $647,129,246
Assets: $1,141,989,225
Liabilities: $726,846,941
Net Worth: $415,142,284
Earnings: ($117,024,742)
Emp.: 6,257
Fiscal Year-end: 12/31/23
Pharmaceuticals
N.A.I.C.S.: 325412
Verdi Budidarmo *(Chm)*

Subsidiaries:

PT Kimia Farma Apotek (1)
Jl Budi Utomo 1, Jakarta, 10710, Indonesia
Tel.: (62) 21 3857245
Web Site: http://www.kimiafarmaapotek.com
Pharmacy, Clinic & Laboratory Operator
N.A.I.C.S.: 456110

PT Kimia Farma Diagnostika (1)
Jl Budi Utomo No 1, Sawah Besar, Jakarta, 10710, Indonesia
Tel.: (62) 213857245
Web Site: http://www.labkimiafarma.co.id
Medical Laboratories Operator
N.A.I.C.S.: 621511

PT Kimia Farma Sungwun Pharmacopia
Jl Angsana Raya Blok A06-001, Sukaresmi Cikarang Sel Kabupaten, Bekasi, 17530, Jawa Barat, Indonesia
Tel.: (62) 2189916857
Web Site: https://kfsp.co.id
Pharmaceuticals Product Mfr
N.A.I.C.S.: 325412
Randy Kelana *(Ops Mgr)*

PT Kimia Farma Trading & Distribution (1)
Jl Budi Utomo No 1 Ps Baru, Kecamatan Sawah Besar, Jakarta, 10710, Khusus Ibukota, Indonesia
Tel.: (62) 213456959
Web Site: https://www.kftd.co.id
Pharmaceuticals Distr
N.A.I.C.S.: 424690

PT Sinkona Indonesia Lestari (1)
Jl Raya Ciater Km 171, Subang, Bandung, 41281, West Java, Indonesia (56%)
Tel.: (62) 260470918
Web Site: http://www.sinkona-indonesia.com
Quinine Salt Mfr
N.A.I.C.S.: 325998

PT. KOBEXINDO TRACTORS TBK
Kobexindo Tower Jl Pasir Putih Raya Blok E-5-D, Ancol Pademangan, Jakarta Utara, 14430, Indonesia
Tel.: (62) 2164700800
Web Site:
https://www.kobexindo.com
Year Founded: 2002
KOBX—(INDO)
Rev.: $127,430,746
Assets: $227,580,226
Liabilities: $196,406,962
Net Worth: $31,173,265
Earnings: ($5,509,061)
Emp.: 1,069
Fiscal Year-end: 12/31/23
Tractor Distr
N.A.I.C.S.: 423820
Humas Soputro *(Founder & Chm)*

Subsidiaries:

P.T. Khatulistiwa Prima Sejahtera (1)
Kobexindo Tower Jl Pasir Puth Raya Blok E-5-D Ancol LT 7, Pademangan, Jakarta Utara, 14430, Indonesia
Tel.: (62) 2164700800
Machinery Equipment Mfr
N.A.I.C.S.: 333248

P.T. Kobexindo Konstruksi Indonesia (1)
Kobexindo Tower Jl Pasir Puth Raya Blok E-5-D Ancol LT 6, Pademangan, Jakarta Utara, 14430, Indonesia
Tel.: (62) 2164700800
Machinery Equipment Mfr
N.A.I.C.S.: 333248

PT Kobexindo Equipment (1)
Jl Pasir Putih Raya Blok E-5-D Ancol LT 1, Pademangan, Jakarta Utara, 14430, Indonesia
Tel.: (62) 214220808
Web Site: http://www.kobexindo-equipment.com
Garden Machinery & Equipment Merchant Whslr
N.A.I.C.S.: 423820

Subsidiary (Domestic):

PT Eurotruk Transindo (2)
Jl Ampera No 1 RT 22 Kelurahan Simpang Pasir Kecamatan Palaran, Seberang, Samarinda, Kalimantan Timur, Indonesia
Tel.: (62) 5417270088
Web Site:
https://www.eurotruktransindo.com
Garden Machinery & Equipment Merchant Whslr
N.A.I.C.S.: 423820

PT. LAUTAN LUAS TBK
Graha Indramas Jl AIP II KS Tubun Raya No 77, Jakarta, 11410, Indonesia
Tel.: (62) 2180660777
Web Site: https://www.lautan-luas.com
Year Founded: 1951
LTLS—(INDO)
Rev.: $475,159,616
Assets: $365,517,388
Liabilities: $172,446,871
Net Worth: $193,070,516
Earnings: $10,873,878
Emp.: 2,749
Fiscal Year-end: 12/31/23
Industrial Chemicals Mfr & Distr
N.A.I.C.S.: 325998
Indrawan Masrin *(Chm)*

Subsidiaries:

Lautan Luas Singapore Pte Ltd (1)
75 Bukit Timah Road, 05-14 Boon Siew Building, Singapore, 229833, Singapore
Tel.: (65) 68831173
Web Site: https://www.lautan-luas.com
Sales Range: $50-74.9 Million
Emp.: 39
Chemical & Allied Products Whslr
N.A.I.C.S.: 424690

P.T. Lautan Mitra Kreasi (1)
Jl Mojosari-Pacet Km 4 Kutorejo, Mojokerto, East Java, Indonesia
Tel.: (62) 321599778
Web Site: https://lmk.co.id
Food & Beverage Retailer
N.A.I.C.S.: 445298

PT Cipta Mapan Logistik (1)
The Bellezza Gapuraprima Office Tower 2nd Floor 217-222 225-226 SA, Jl Letjen Soepeno No 34 Arteri Permata Hijau, Jakarta Selatan, 12210, Indonesia
Tel.: (62) 2150880200
Web Site: https://www.lincgrp.com
Sales Range: $125-149.9 Million
Emp.: 1,006
Freight Transportation Arrangement
N.A.I.C.S.: 488510

PT Dunia Kimia Jaya (1)
Kawasan Industri Greenland Batavia Blok BD No1, Kota Deltamas Sukamahi Cikarang Pusat, Bekasi, 17530, Indonesia
Tel.: (62) 2189970430
Web Site: https://www.duniakimiajaya.com
Emp.: 331
Chemical Product & Preparation Mfr
N.A.I.C.S.: 325998

PT Dunia Kimia Utama (1)
Jalan Raya Palembang KM 24, Komplek Ilir Barat Permai, 30134, Palembang, Indralaya, Indonesia
Tel.: (62) 711311772
Web Site: https://duniakimiautama.id
Emp.: 103
Chemical Product & Preparation Mfr
N.A.I.C.S.: 325998

PT Indonesian Acids Industry Limited (1)
Graha Indramas Lantai 2 Jl AIP II K S Tubun Raya No 77, Kelurahan Slipi Kecamatan Palmerah, Jakarta Barat, 11410, Indonesia
Tel.: (62) 2153671281
Emp.: 151
Chemical Product & Preparation Mfr
N.A.I.C.S.: 325998
Sandjjaja Shajadi *(Mng Dir)*

PT Lautan Jasaindo (1)
Jl Manis II No 9 Zona Industri Manis, Desa Kadu Kecamatan Curug, Tangerang, Banten, Indonesia
Tel.: (62) 215918838
Sales Range: $25-49.9 Million
Emp.: 35
Chemical Product & Preparation Mfr
N.A.I.C.S.: 325998

PT Lautan Sulfamat Lestari (1)
Jl Raya Bekasi KM 21, Cakung, 13920, Jakarta, Indonesia
Tel.: (62) 214603875
Web Site: http://www.lautan-sulfamat-lestari.com
Sales Range: $50-74.9 Million
Emp.: 200
Sulfamic Acid Production
N.A.I.C.S.: 325998
Indrawan Masrin *(Pres)*

PT Metabisulphite Nusantara (1)
Desa Sukomulyo KM 24 Manyar Gresik, Jl AIP II KS Tubun Raya No 77, 61151, East Java, Indonesia
Tel.: (62) 31 395 8500
Web Site:
https://metabisulphite.lookchem.com
Chemical Product & Preparation Mfr
N.A.I.C.S.: 325998

PT Pacinesia Chemical Industry (1)
Graha Indramas Bldg, Jl AIP II KS Tubun Raya No 77, 11410, Jakarta, Indonesia
Tel.: (62) 2153673277
Chemical Product & Preparation Mfr
N.A.I.C.S.: 325998

PT Strategic Partner Solution (1)
The Bellezza Shopping Arcade 2nd Floor Unit SA15-16, Jl Arteri Permata Hijau Kec Kby Lama DKI, Jakarta, 12210, Indonesia
Tel.: (62) 81287000879
Web Site: https://www.myspsolution.com
Sales Range: $25-49.9 Million
Emp.: 47
Management Consulting Services
N.A.I.C.S.: 541618

PT White Oil Nusantara (1)
Raya Sukomulyo KM 24, Sukomulyo-Manya, Gresik, 61151, Indonesia
Tel.: (62) 31 395 8686
Web Site:
https://whiteoilnusantara.lookchem.com
Barium & Sodium Petroleum Sulfonates Production
N.A.I.C.S.: 324110

PT. LIPPO SECURITIES, TBK
Ruko Pinangsia Karawaci Office Park Lantai 3 Blok M No 39-50, Lippo Karawaci, Tangerang, 15139, Indonesia
Tel.: (62) 215589810
Web Site:
https://www.lipposecurities.com
Year Founded: 1989
Emp.: 11
Investment Management Service
N.A.I.C.S.: 523940
Agustinus Benawar *(Sec)*

Subsidiaries:

PT Bank Nobunalnobu Tbk (1)
Plaza Semanggi Jl Jend Sudirman Kav 50, Jakarta, 12930, Indonesia
Tel.: (62) 21 255 351 28
Web Site: http://www.nobubank.com
Commercial Banking Services
N.A.I.C.S.: 522110
Martysen Lie *(Bus Mgr-Card)*

PT. MACROCHEMA PRATAMA
Jalan Kedoya Raya No22 Kebon Jeruk Kota Jakarta Barat, Daerah Khusus Ibukota, Jakarta, 15520, Indonesia
Tel.: (62) 215823233   Id
Web Site:
http://www.macrochema.com
Year Founded: 1986
Chemical Mfr & Distr
N.A.I.C.S.: 325199
Arus Sutantino *(Pres & Dir)*

Subsidiaries:

PT. Moresco Macro Adhesive (1)
APL Office Tower Central Park 23rd Floor Unit 8, Jalan Let Jend S Parman Kav 28, Jakarta, 11470, Indonesia (49%)
Tel.: (62) 2129119026
Hotmelt Adhesive Mfr & Distr
N.A.I.C.S.: 325520
Motohiza Morozumi *(Pres & Dir)*

PT. MAYORA INDAH TBK
Mayora Building Jl Tomang Raya Kav 21 - 23 West, Jakarta, 11440, Indonesia
Tel.: (62) 2180637704
Web Site:
https://www.mayoraindah.co.id
Year Founded: 1977
D7V—(DEU)
Rev.: $1,991,671,224
Assets: $1,446,613,876
Liabilities: $613,128,841
Net Worth: $833,485,034
Earnings: $127,935,991
Emp.: 6,328
Fiscal Year-end: 12/31/23
Food & Beverage Product Mfr & Whslr
N.A.I.C.S.: 311821
Wardhana Atmadja *(Gen Dir-Operations)*

PT. MEDIA NUSANTARA CITRA TBK
MNC Tower Lantai 26 Jalan Kebon Sirih Kav 17-19, Pusat, Jakarta, 10340, Indonesia
Tel.: (62) 213900885
Web Site: https://www.mnc.co.id
MNCN—(INDO)
Rev.: $556,936,660

PT. MEDIA NUSANTARA CITRA TBK

PT. MEDIA NUSANTARA CITRA Tbk—(Continued)
Assets: $1,324,626,450
Liabilities: $312,292,960
Net Worth: $1,012,333,490
Rev.: $130,971,960
Emp.: 6,516
Fiscal Year-end: 12/31/20
Television Channel Programming Services
N.A.I.C.S.: 512110
David Fernando Audy *(Chm)*

Subsidiaries:

PT. Mediate Indonesia
MNC News Center Building 5th Floor Jl K H Wahid Hasim No 28, Kebon Sirih, Jakarta Pusat, 10340, Jakarta, Indonesia
Tel.: (62) 2131900001
Web Site: https://www.mediate.co.id
Investment Services
N.A.I.C.S.: 523999

PT. Star Media Nusantara (1)
RCTI - Gedung Annex Lt 4 Jalan Raya Perjuangan No 1, Kebon Jeruk, Jakarta Barat, 11530, Indonesia
Tel.: (62) 215303587
Web Site:
 https://www.starmedianusantara.com
Entertainment Services
N.A.I.C.S.: 711130
Liliana Tanoesoedibjo *(Commissioner)*

PT. METRODATA ELECTRONICS, TBK.

APL Tower 37th Floor Suite 3 Jl Letjen S Parman Kav 28, Jakarta, 11470, Indonesia
Tel.: (62) 2129345888 Id
Web Site:
 https://www.metrodata.co.id
Year Founded: 1983
MTDL—(INDO)
Rev.: $1,434,290,167
Assets: $658,918,256
Liabilities: $331,741,704
Net Worth: $327,176,552
Earnings: $61,050,354
Emp.: 1,981
Fiscal Year-end: 12/31/23
System Integration Services
N.A.I.C.S.: 541512

Subsidiaries:

PT Metrodata E Bisnis (1)
Wisma Metropolitan 16th Floor Jl Jend Sudirman Kav 29-31, Jakarta, 12920, Indonesia
Tel.: (62) 21 5705998
Sales Range: $150-199.9 Million
Emp.: 500
Computers & Laptops Distr
N.A.I.C.S.: 423430

PT Mitra Integrasi Informatika (1)
Information Technology Services
N.A.I.C.S.: 541512

PT Soltius Indonesia (1)
15th Floor Suite SC - 1503-05 Jl Letjen S Parman Kav 28, Tanjung Duren Selatan Grogol Petamburan, Jakarta Barat, 11470, Indonesia
Tel.: (62) 2129345900
Web Site: https://www.soltius.co.id
Emp.: 200
Information Technology Services
N.A.I.C.S.: 541512
Budi L. Halim *(Pres)*

Soltius Australia Pty. Ltd. (1)
Suite 103 Level 1 90 Mount Street, North Sydney, 2060, NSW, Australia
Tel.: (61) 289230000
Customized Software Development Services
N.A.I.C.S.: 541511

PT. MITRA ADIPERKASA TBK

29th Floor Sahid Sudirman Center Jl Jend Sudirman Kav 86, Jakarta, 10220, Indonesia
Tel.: (62) 215745808 Id
Web Site: https://www.map.co.id
Year Founded: 1995
MAPI—(INDO)
Rev.: $2,163,723,586
Assets: $1,786,944,823
Liabilities: $980,929,025
Net Worth: $806,015,798
Earnings: $152,303,327
Emp.: 11,002
Fiscal Year-end: 12/31/23
Apparel Retailer
N.A.I.C.S.: 458110
Susiana Latif *(CFO)*

Subsidiaries:

Map Active (Thailand) Ltd. (1)
43 Thai CC Tower 156-7 Rm 15 FL Sathorn, Yannawa, Bangkok, 10120, Thailand
Tel.: (66) 2056085660
Web Site: https://www.mapactive.co.th
Sports & Fashion Toy Distr
N.A.I.C.S.: 423910
Cholruk Sayawatana *(CFO)*

PT Map Aktif Adiperkasa Tbk (1)
26th Floor Sahid Sudirman Center-Sahid City Jl Jend Sudirman Kav 86, Jakarta, 10220, Indonesia
Tel.: (62) 2180648488
Web Site: www.mapactive.id
Sports & Fashion Toy Distr
N.A.I.C.S.: 423910

PT Map Boga Adiperkasa Tbk (1)
27th Floor Sahid Sudirman Center Jl Jend Sudirman Kav 86, Jakarta, 10220, Indonesia
Tel.: (62) 215746501
Web Site: https://www.mbai.co.id
Food & Beverage Services
N.A.I.C.S.: 722513
Anthony Valentine McEvoy *(Pres)*

PT. PAKUWON JATI TBK

Gandaria 8 Office Tower 32nd Floor Jl Sultan Iskandar Muda 8, Gandaria Kebayoran Lama, Jakarta Selatan, 12240, Indonesia
Tel.: (62) 2129008000
Web Site:
 https://www.pakuwonjati.com
PWON—(INDO)
Rev.: $402,656,470
Assets: $2,124,238,507
Liabilities: $643,909,493
Net Worth: $1,480,329,014
Earnings: $154,678,589
Emp.: 1,940
Fiscal Year-end: 12/31/23
Property Development Services
N.A.I.C.S.: 531190
Alexander Stefanus Ridwan Suhendra *(Chm)*

Subsidiaries:

PT Artisan Wahyu (1)
Jl Sultan Iskandar Muda, Kebayoran Lama, Jakarta Selatan, 12240, Indonesia
Tel.: (62) 2129052888
Web Site: http://www.gandariacity.co.id
Real Estate Services
N.A.I.C.S.: 531210

PT Dwijaya Manunggal (1)
Jl Ahmad Yani No 16-18, Surabaya, 60231, Indonesia
Tel.: (62) 318270898
Web Site:
 https://www.royalplazasurabaya.com
Real Estate Services
N.A.I.C.S.: 531210

PT Elite Prima Hutama (1)
Jl Casablanca Raya Kav 88, South Jakarta, 12870, Indonesia
Tel.: (62) 2129465000
Web Site: https://www.kotakasablanka.co.id
Real Estate Services
N.A.I.C.S.: 531210

PT Grama Pramesi Siddhi (1)
Gandaria 8 Office Tower 32nd Floor Jl Sultan Iskandar Muda 8, Jakarta Selatan, 12240, Indonesia
Tel.: (62) 2129008000
Real Estate Services
N.A.I.C.S.: 531210

PT Pakuwon Permai (1)
Jl Kejawan Putih Mutiara No 17, Surabaya, 60123, East Java, Indonesia
Tel.: (62) 317393888
Web Site: https://www.pakuwonmall.com
Real Estate Services
N.A.I.C.S.: 531210

PT Pakuwon Sentosa Abadi (1)
Plaza Blok M 7th Floor Jl Bulungan No 76, Jakarta Selatan, 12130, Indonesia
Tel.: (62) 217209288
Real Estate Services
N.A.I.C.S.: 531210

PT Pakuwon Sentra Wisata (1)
Jl Basuki Rakhmat 8-12, Surabaya, 60261, Indonesia
Tel.: (62) 315311088
Real Estate Services
N.A.I.C.S.: 531210

PT Permata Berlian Realty (1)
Jl Permata Berlian V Permata Hijau, Jakarta, 12210, Indonesia
Tel.: (62) 3153668888
Real Estate Services
N.A.I.C.S.: 531210

Pakuwon Jati Finance, B.V. (1)
Locatellikade 1, Amsterdam, 1076, Noord-Holland, Netherlands
Tel.: (31) 203013600
Financial Management Services
N.A.I.C.S.: 523940

PT. PAN BROTHERS TBK.

Jl Siliwangi No 178 Jatiuwung, Tangerang, 15133, Banten, Indonesia
Tel.: (62) 215900718 Id
Web Site:
 https://www.panbrotherstbk.com
Year Founded: 1980
PBRX—(INDO)
Rev.: $581,615,182
Assets: $696,766,629
Liabilities: $363,112,480
Net Worth: $333,654,149
Earnings: ($4,336,274)
Emp.: 27,038
Fiscal Year-end: 12/31/23
Men's & Women's Apparel Designer, Mfr & Distr
N.A.I.C.S.: 315250
Ludijanto Setijo *(Chm)*

Subsidiaries:

PT. Pancaprima Ekabrothers (1)
Jl Siliwangi No 178 A, Desa Alam Jaya Jatiuwung, Tangerang, 15133, Banten, Indonesia
Tel.: (62) 215900755
Garments Mfr & Distr
N.A.I.C.S.: 315210
Budiman Kartono *(Mgr-Consumption Saving)*

PT. PANIN SEKURITAS TBK

Indonesia Stock Exchange Building Tower II Suite 1705, Jl Jendral Sudirman Kav 52-53 South, Jakarta Selatan, 12190, Indonesia
Tel.: (62) 215153055
Web Site: https://www.pans.co.id
Year Founded: 1989
PANS—(INDO)
Rev.: $25,759,262
Assets: $145,149,248
Liabilities: $43,441,173
Net Worth: $101,708,076
Earnings: $8,962,608
Emp.: 265
Fiscal Year-end: 12/31/23
Stock Exchange Security & Brokerage Services
N.A.I.C.S.: 523150
Rosmini Lidarjono *(Vice Chm)*

INTERNATIONAL PUBLIC

Subsidiaries:

PT Panin Asset Management (1)
Stock Exchange Building Tower II Lt 11 Suite 1104 Jl Jend Sudirman, Kav 52-53, Jakarta, 12190, Indonesia
Tel.: (62) 1500726
Web Site: http://www.panin-am.co.id
Asset Management Services
N.A.I.C.S.: 523940

PT. PEMBANGUNAN GRAHA LESTARI INDAH, TBK.

Jl Listrik No 15, Medan, 20112, Indonesia
Tel.: (62) 614535888 Id
Web Site: https://ptpgli.co.id
Year Founded: 1994
PGLI—(INDO)
Rev.: $1,261,069
Assets: $2,946,553
Liabilities: $1,857,276
Net Worth: $1,089,276
Earnings: ($3,337,530)
Emp.: 113
Fiscal Year-end: 12/31/23
Hotel Operating Services
N.A.I.C.S.: 721110
Nicholas Spassky Hutapea *(Chm)*

PT. PERMATA PRIMA SAKTI TBK

Equity Tower Building 27th Floor Sudirman Central Business District, Lot 9, Jl Jendral Sudirman Kav 52-53, Jakarta, 12190, Indonesia
Tel.: (62) 21 515 0055
Web Site:
 http://www.permatacoal.com
Sales Range: $125-149.9 Million
Emp.: 250
Coal Producer & Distr
N.A.I.C.S.: 324199
Yanto Yanto *(Chm)*

PT. SEMEN INDONESIA (PERSERO) TBK

South Quarter Tower A Lt 19-20 Jl RA Kartini Kav 8 Cilandak Barat, Jakarta, 12430, Selatan, Indonesia
Tel.: (62) 215261174
Web Site:
 http://www.semenindonesia.com
Year Founded: 1957
PSGTF—(OTCIQ)
Rev.: $2,444,641,718
Assets: $5,574,912,806
Liabilities: $2,400,427,814
Net Worth: $3,174,484,992
Earnings: $167,938,378
Emp.: 10,047
Fiscal Year-end: 12/31/22
Cement Mfr
N.A.I.C.S.: 327310
Budi Waseso *(Pres & Commissioner)*

Subsidiaries:

P.T. Baturaja Multi Usaha (1)
Jalan K H Bastari Perumahan Ogan Permata Indah Jakabaring, Poros OPI Blok DA 21D 21E 21F RT 63 seberang ulu 1 15 Ulu, Palembang, Indonesia
Tel.: (62) 7115541379
Web Site: https://baturajamultiusaha.com
Cement Distr
N.A.I.C.S.: 423320

P.T. Semen Indonesia Internasional (1)
The East Floor 18 Lingkar Mega Kuningan, RT 5/RW 2 Kuningan Kuningan Tim Setiabudi District Jakarta, South Jakarta, 12950, Indonesia
Tel.: (62) 2157853977
Web Site:
 https://www.semenindonesianational.com
Cement Building Material Mfr
N.A.I.C.S.: 327310

PT Bima Sepaja Abadi (1)

AND PRIVATE COMPANIES

Komplek Perkantoran Enggano Megah Blok A No 5 Q Jl Enggano Raya, Tanjung Priok, Jakarta Utara, Jakarta, Indonesia
Tel.: (62) 214372337
Web Site:
https://www.bimasepajaabadi.co.id
Building Materials Mfr
N.A.I.C.S.: 327390

PT Eternit Gresik (1)
Jl Indro 1, Gresik, Indonesia
Tel.: (62) 313981091
Web Site: http://www.eternit.com
Sales Range: $25-49.9 Million
Emp.: 30
Nonmetallic Mineral Product Mfr
N.A.I.C.S.: 327999

PT Industri Kemasan Semen Gresik (1)
Desa Socorejo Kecamatan Jenu, Kabupaten Tuban, Gresik, 62352, Jawa Timur, Indonesia
Tel.: (62) 356491200
Web Site: https://www.iksg.co.id
Sales Range: $125-149.9 Million
Emp.: 300
Cement Bag Mfr
N.A.I.C.S.: 327310

PT Kawasan Industri Gresik (1)
Jl Tri Dharma No 3, Kel Kebomas Kec Kebomas, Gresik, East Java, Indonesia
Tel.: (62) 313984707
Web Site: https://www.kig.co.id
Cement Mfr
N.A.I.C.S.: 327310

PT Krakatau Semen Indonesia (1)
Kawasan Industri Krakatau Bandar Samudera Jalan Mayjend S Parman KM 13, Ciwandan, Cilegon, 42445, Banten, Indonesia
Tel.: (62) 2547960092
Web Site:
http://www.krakatausemenindonesia.com
Cement Mfr
N.A.I.C.S.: 327310
Bambang Tridoso Oktanto (Pres)

PT Semen Baturaja (Persero) Tbk (1)
Jl Abikusno Cokrosuyoso Kertapati, Palembang, 30258, Indonesia
Tel.: (62) 711511261
Web Site: http://www.semenbaturaja.co.id
Rev.: $132,521,720
Assets: $315,396,088
Liabilities: $110,029,029
Net Worth: $205,367,058
Earnings: $7,894,918
Emp.: 880
Fiscal Year-end: 12/31/2023
Cement Mfr
N.A.I.C.S.: 327310
Dede Parasade (Mktg Dir)

PT Semen Indonesia Beton (1)
Gedung Graha Irama Lt 11 Jl H R Rasuna Said Blok X-1 No 1-2 RT 6/RW 4, Kuningan Timur Setia budi, Jakarta Selatan, 12950, Indonesia
Tel.: (62) 2127821910
Web Site: https://semenindonesiabeton.id
Readymix Concrete Mfr
N.A.I.C.S.: 327320

PT Semen Indonesia Distributor (1)
Jl DR Wahidin Sudirohusodo 728A, Gresik, Jawa Timur, Indonesia
Tel.: (62) 3199101004
Web Site: https://www.sidistributor.com
Building Materials Distr
N.A.I.C.S.: 423390

PT Semen Indonesia Logistik (1)
Jl Veteran 129, Gresik, 61122, East Java, Indonesia
Tel.: (62) 313981463
Web Site: https://www.silog.co.id
Cement Distr
N.A.I.C.S.: 423320

PT Semen Padang (1)
Indarung, Padang, 25237, Sumatera Barat, Indonesia
Tel.: (62) 751815250
Web Site: https://www.semenpadang.co.id
Cement Mfr
N.A.I.C.S.: 327310
Benny Wendry (Pres)

PT Semen Tonasa (1)
Jl Tonasa 2 Biring Ere, PO Box 114, District Bungoro Pangkajene and Islands Regency, Sulawesi, Indonesia
Tel.: (62) 410312345
Web Site: https://www.sementonasa.co.id
Cement Mfr
N.A.I.C.S.: 327310

PT Sepatim Batamtama (1)
Jl Dolphin No 1 Batam, Riau Islands, 29432, Kepulauan Riau, Indonesia
Tel.: (62) 778412979
Web Site:
https://www.sepatimbatamtama.com
Ready Mix Concrete Distr
N.A.I.C.S.: 423320

PT Sinergi Informatika Semen Indonesia (1)
Graha Aktiva 11th Floor Jl H R Rasuna Said Kav 3, Kav 1-2, Jakarta Selatan, 12950, Indonesia
Tel.: (62) 2129410371
Web Site: https://www.sisi.id
Software Programming Services
N.A.I.C.S.: 541511

PT Sinergi Mitra Investama (1)
Jl Awikoen A-7 Segunting Gresik, East Javan, Jawa Timur, Indonesia
Tel.: (62) 313970374
Web Site:
http://www.sinergimitrainvestama.com
Residential Property Management Services
N.A.I.C.S.: 531311
A. Mirza (Officer-Asset Mgmt)

PT Solusi Bangun Indonesia Tbk (1)
Zurcherstrasse 156, 8645, Jona, Switzerland (80.6%)
Tel.: (41) 588585858
Web Site: http://www.lafargeholcim.com
Rev.: $803,394,365
Assets: $1,442,105,631
Liabilities: $630,055,998
Net Worth: $812,049,633
Earnings: $58,098,246
Emp.: 1,935
Fiscal Year-end: 12/31/2023
Cement, Aggregates & Ready-Mixed Concrete Mfr
N.A.I.C.S.: 327310

PT Swadaya Graha (1)
Jl R A Kartini 25, 61112, Gresik, Indonesia
Tel.: (62) 313984477
Web Site: http://www.swadayagraha.com
Plate Work Mfr
N.A.I.C.S.: 332313

PT United Tractors Semen Gresik (1)
Sumberarum Kerek, Tuban, East Javan, 62356, Indonesia
Tel.: (62) 356711800
Web Site: http://www.utsg.co.id
Ready Mix Concrete Distr
N.A.I.C.S.: 423320

PT Varia Usaha Bahari (1)
Jl Veteran No 171 A, Gresik, Jawa Timur, Indonesia
Tel.: (62) 313987927
Cement Distr
N.A.I.C.S.: 423320

PT Varia Usaha Beton (1)
Komplek The Royal Business Park Blok F 02-F 03 Jalan H Anwar Hamzah, Tambak Oso Kec Waru Kabupaten, Sidoarjo, 61256, Jawa Timur, Indonesia
Tel.: (62) 3199841300
Web Site: https://www.variabeton.com
Ready Mix Concrete Distr
N.A.I.C.S.: 423320

PT Varia Usaha Dharma Segara (1)
Veteran No 171 A, Gresik, 61123, Jawa Timur, Indonesia
Tel.: (62) 313973413
Freight Forwarding Services
N.A.I.C.S.: 483111

PT Varia Usaha Lintas Segara (1)
Jl Veteran No 171 A, Gresik, Indonesia
Tel.: (62) 313978204
Cement Distr
N.A.I.C.S.: 423320

PT. SRI REJEKI ISMAN TBK

Jl KH Samanhudi 88 Jetis Sukoharjo, Solo, Semarang, Central Java, Indonesia
Tel.: (62) 271593188
Web Site: https://www.sritex.co.id
SRIL—(INDO)
Rev.: $325,081,656
Assets: $648,988,075
Liabilities: $1,603,813,550
Net Worth: ($954,825,475)
Earnings: ($174,840,395)
Emp.: 4,052
Fiscal Year-end: 12/31/23
Textile Products
N.A.I.C.S.: 314999
Iwan Setiawan Lukminto (Vice Chm)

Subsidiaries:

PT Bitratex Industries (1)
The Energy Building 20th Floor Jl Jendral Sudirman, Kav 52-53 Lot 11A-SCBD, Jakarta, 12190, Indonesia
Tel.: (62) 2129951619
Web Site: http://www.bitratex.com
Spun Yarn-Woven & Knitted Fabric Mfr
N.A.I.C.S.: 313310

PT Primayudha Mandirijaya (1)
Tel.: (62) 2157903640
Web Site: http://primayudha.com
Spun Yarn-Woven & Knitted Fabric Mfr
N.A.I.C.S.: 313310
K. K. Agrawal (Pres)

PT. TEAMWORX INDONESIA

Beltway Office Park Building C Groundfloor, Jl TB Simatupang No 41, Cilandak, Jakarta, 12550, Indonesia
Tel.: (62) 217800940   Id
Web Site:
http://www.teamworx.com.id
Year Founded: 2003
Engineering Consultancy Services
N.A.I.C.S.: 541690
Joop G. van Keulen (Pres)

PT. TERREGRA ASIA ENERGY TBK

Lippo Puri Tower 0905 St Moritz Jl Puri Indah Raya Blok U1, Jakarta Barat, 11610, Indonesia
Tel.: (62) 2130497777
Web Site:
https://investor.terregra.co.id
Year Founded: 1995
TGRA—(INDO)
Rev.: $63,431
Assets: $30,652,328
Liabilities: $8,937,862
Net Worth: $21,714,466
Earnings: ($554,643)
Emp.: 16
Fiscal Year-end: 12/31/23
Solar Power Generation Services
N.A.I.C.S.: 221114
Christin Soewito (Deputy Chm, Sec & VP)

PT. TIRA AUSTENITE TBK

Kawasan Industri Pulo Gadung, PO Box 1010/JAT, Jl Pulo Ayang Kav R-1, Jakarta, 13930, Indonesia
Tel.: (62) 214602594   Id
Web Site:
https://www.tiraaustenite.com
TIRA—(INDO)
Rev.: $28,515,442
Assets: $35,109,143
Liabilities: $18,368,691
Net Worth: $16,740,451
Earnings: $222,272
Emp.: 380
Fiscal Year-end: 12/31/22
Electronic & Consumer Goods Mfr
N.A.I.C.S.: 333992
Selo Winardi (Chm)

PT. TRIKOMSEL OKE TBK.

Subsidiaries:

P.T. Alpha Austenite (1)
Kawasan Industri Menara Permai Jl Raya Narogong km-23 8 Kabupaten, Bogor, Jawa Barat, Indonesia
Tel.: (62) 82110100411
Web Site: https://www.alphaaustenite.com
Centrifugal Casting Moulding Equipment Mfr
N.A.I.C.S.: 333914

P.T. Genta Laras Semesta (1)
Kawasan Industri Pulogadung Jl Pulo Ayang Kav R-1 JAT, PO Box 1010, Jakarta, 13930, Indonesia
Tel.: (62) 214602594
Welding Machine Whslr
N.A.I.C.S.: 423830

P.T. Tira Stahlindo Indonesia (1)
Gedung PT Alpha Austenite Kawasan Industri Menara Permai, Jl Raya Narogong Km 28 85 Komplek Menara Permai Cileungsi, Bogor, 16820, Indonesia
Tel.: (62) 218235630
Welding Machine Whslr
N.A.I.C.S.: 423830

P.T. Tira Austenite Tbk - Bandung Filling Station & Plant (1)
Komplek Cikawao Permai Kav 26 - 27 No 55, Bandung, 40251, West Java, Indonesia
Tel.: (62) 224202280
Web Site: http://www.tiraaustenite.com
Sales Range: $50-74.9 Million
Gas Refilling Services
N.A.I.C.S.: 213112

P.T. Tira Austenite Tbk - Banyuwangi Filling Station & Plant (1)
Jl Gatot Subroto Km 06, Ketapang, Banyuwangi, Indonesia
Tel.: (62) 333413678
Web Site: http://www.tiraaustenite.com
Sales Range: $25-49.9 Million
Gas Refilling Services
N.A.I.C.S.: 424690

P.T. Tira Austenite Tbk - Cikarang Filling Station & Plant (1)
Kawasan Industri Jababeka Jl Jababeka V Blok F 1-3, Cikarang, Bekasi, 17530, West Java, Indonesia
Tel.: (62) 2170723122
Gas Refilling Services
N.A.I.C.S.: 213112

P.T. Tira Austenite Tbk - Gresik Filling Station & Plant (1)
Jl Alpha Maspion Lot L-12 Kawasan Industri Maspion, Desa Manyar, Gresik, 61151, East Java, Indonesia
Tel.: (62) 313930045
Web Site: http://www.tiraaustenite.com
Sales Range: $50-74.9 Million
Gas Refilling Services
N.A.I.C.S.: 424710

P.T. Tira Austenite Tbk - Makassar Filling Station & Plant (1)
Jl Sultan Alauddin No 246 Samping Terminal Malengkeri Gunung Sari, Sulawesi, 90221, Selatan, Indonesia
Tel.: (62) 411885333
Sales Range: $50-74.9 Million
Emp.: 26
Gas Refilling Services
N.A.I.C.S.: 213112

P.T. Tira Austenite Tbk - Semarang Filling Station & Plant (1)
Lingkungan Industri Kecil Banjardowo Kav A-9, Kel Banjardowo Kec Genuk, Semarang, 50117, Central Java, Indonesia
Tel.: (62) 246584197
Gas Refilling Services
N.A.I.C.S.: 213112

PT. TRIKOMSEL OKE TBK.

Jl Kebon Sirih No 63, Jakarta Pusat, 10340, Indonesia
Tel.: (62) 2131905997   Id
Web Site:
https://www.trikomseloke.com
Year Founded: 1996
TRIO—(INDO)
Rev.: $49,006,938
Assets: $6,803,186

PT. TRIKOMSEL OKE TBK.

PT. Trikomsel Oke Tbk.—(Continued)

Liabilities: $256,059,658
Net Worth: ($249,256,471)
Earnings: ($7,866,104)
Emp.: 66
Fiscal Year-end: 12/31/23
Electronic Components Distr
N.A.I.C.S.: 423690

Subsidiaries:

P.T. Globe Kita Terang Tbk (1)
Jl Kebon Sirih Raya No 63, Jakarta Pusat, Indonesia
Tel.: (62) 2131905997
Web Site: https://www.globekitaterang.co.id
Telecommunication Support Services
N.A.I.C.S.: 541618

PT Global Teleshop Tbk (1)
Gedung Graha Bimasaki, Jl Mampang Prapatan Raya No 151, Jakarta, 12760, Indonesia
Tel.: (62) 21 799 0708
Web Site: http://www.globalteleshop.com
Sales Range: $300-349.9 Million
Telecommunication Retailers
N.A.I.C.S.: 517121
Evy Soenarjo *(Chm)*

PT. VOKSEL ELECTRIC TBK

Menara Karya 3rd Floor Suite D Jl HR Rasuna Said Block X-5 Kav 1-2, Jakarta, 12950, Indonesia
Tel.: (62) 215794462
Web Site: https://www.voksel.co.id
Year Founded: 1971
VOKS—(INDO)
Rev.: $198,420,403
Assets: $170,347,029
Liabilities: $122,559,085
Net Worth: $47,787,944
Earnings: $1,170,092
Emp.: 915
Fiscal Year-end: 12/31/23
Power & Telecommunication Cable Mfr
N.A.I.C.S.: 331420
David Lius *(Chm)*

Subsidiaries:

PT Bangun Prima Semesta (1)
Menara Kadin Indonesia Lantai 26 Suite A-B Jl HR Rasuna Said, Blok X-5 Kav 3, Jakarta, 12950, Indonesia
Tel.: (62) 215274709
Web Site: https://www.bangunprimasemesta.com
Telecommunication Equipment & Accessory Mfr
N.A.I.C.S.: 334290
Stanley Natanael *(Controller-Project)*

PT Cendikia Global Solusi (1)
Menara Karya 3rd Floor Suite D Kav 1-2, Jakarta, 12950, Indonesia
Tel.: (62) 2157944622
Web Site: https://www.cgs.co.id
Fiber Optic Cable Mfr
N.A.I.C.S.: 335921
Tjong Denny *(Head-Ops)*

PT Cipta Karya Teknik (1)
Komplek Perkantoran Bonagabe Blok B17 Jl Jatinegara Timur No 101, Balimester Jatinegara, Jakarta, Timur, Indonesia
Tel.: (62) 2121011698
Web Site: https://citratel.net
Fiber Optic Cable Mfr
N.A.I.C.S.: 335921

PT Prima Mitra Elektrindo (1)
Jl Raya Leuwinanggung No 83 Tapos, Depok, 16457, Indonesia
Tel.: (62) 2122853137
Fiber Optic Cable Mfr
N.A.I.C.S.: 335921

PT. WAHANA OTTOMITRA MULTIARTHA TBK.

Altira Office Tower Floor 32 33 35 Jl Yos Sudarso Kav 85, Kelurahan Sunter Jaya Kecamatan Tanjung Priok, Jakarta Utara, 14350, Indonesia
Tel.: (62) 2121882400
Web Site: http://www.wom.co.id
WOMF—(INDO)
Rev.: $129,581,925
Assets: $430,923,332
Liabilities: $320,790,157
Net Worth: $110,133,175
Earnings: $15,352,271
Emp.: 2,198
Fiscal Year-end: 12/31/23
Vehicle Finance Services
N.A.I.C.S.: 522220
Djaja Suryanto Sutandar *(Chm)*

Subsidiaries:

PT Bank Maybank Indonesia Finance (1)
Gedung Wisma Eka Jiwa Lt 10 Jl Mangga Dua Raya, Mangga Dua Selatan Sawah Besar, Jakarta Pusat, Indonesia
Tel.: (62) 2162300088
Web Site: http://www.maybankfinance.co.id
Car Financial Services
N.A.I.C.S.: 522220

PT. WISMILAK INTI MAKMUR TBK.

Grha Wismilak Jl Dr Sutomo No 27, Surabaya, 60264, Indonesia
Tel.: (62) 312952899 Id
Web Site: https://www.wismilak.com
Year Founded: 1962
WIIM—(INDO)
Rev.: $316,568,514
Assets: $167,269,657
Liabilities: $47,304,547
Net Worth: $119,965,111
Earnings: $32,127,713
Emp.: 3,166
Fiscal Year-end: 12/31/23
Tobacco Mfr
N.A.I.C.S.: 312230
Ronald Walla *(Chm)*

PTB GROUP LIMITED

22 Orient Avenue, PO Box 90, Pinkenba, 4008, QLD, Australia
Tel.: (61) 736377000 AU
Web Site: http://www.pacificturbine.com.au
PTB—(ASX)
Rev.: $65,309,269
Assets: $114,464,955
Liabilities: $42,712,794
Net Worth: $71,752,161
Earnings: $9,808,764
Emp.: 30
Fiscal Year-end: 06/30/21
Aerospace & Defense Industry
N.A.I.C.S.: 336412
Craig Louis Baker *(Chm)*

Subsidiaries:

IAP Group Australia Pty. Ltd. (1)
5A Jubilee Ave, Warriewood, 2102, NSW, Australia
Tel.: (61) 299978166
Web Site: http://www.iapgroup.com.au
Sales Range: $25-49.9 Million
Emp.: 20
Aircraft Engine Repair Services
N.A.I.C.S.: 811198
Andy Nicodemo *(Mgr-Engine Sls)*

Pacific Turbine USA, LLC (1)
12005 SW 130th St Unit 301, Miami, FL 33186
Tel.: (786) 409-0011
Aircraft Maintenance & Overhaul
N.A.I.C.S.: 488190

Prime Turbines LLC (1)
1615 Diplomat Dr Ste 120, Carrollton, TX 75006
Tel.: (972) 406-2100
Web Site: https://www.primeturbines.com
Aircraft Maintenance & Repairing Services
N.A.I.C.S.: 488190

John Waldrop *(VP & Gen Mgr)*

PTC INDIA LIMITED

2nd Floor NBCC Tower 15 Bhikaji Cama Place, New Delhi, 110066, India
Tel.: (91) 1141659500
Web Site: https://www.ptcindia.com
PTC—(BOM)
Rev.: $1,918,651,160
Assets: $1,993,837,300
Liabilities: $1,289,621,725
Net Worth: $704,215,575
Earnings: $60,805,707
Emp.: 104
Fiscal Year-end: 03/31/23
Electric Power Distr
N.A.I.C.S.: 221122
Rajiv Maheshwari *(Officer-Compliance & Sec)*

Subsidiaries:

PTC India Financial Services Limited (1)
7th Floor Telephone Exchange Building 8 Bhikaji Cama Place, New Delhi, 110066, India (77.6%)
Tel.: (91) 1126737300
Web Site: https://www.ptcfinancial.com
Rev.: $155,535,512
Assets: $1,574,128,319
Liabilities: $1,284,815,982
Net Worth: $289,312,337
Earnings: $3,494,823
Emp.: 48
Fiscal Year-end: 03/31/2021
Investment & Financial Services
N.A.I.C.S.: 523999
Pawan Singh *(CEO & Mng Dir)*

PTC INDUSTRIES LIMITED

Advanced Manufacturing and Technology Centre NH-25 A Sarai Sahjadi, Sahjadi Kanpur Road, Lucknow, 227 101, India
Tel.: (91) 5227111017
Web Site: https://www.ptcil.com
Year Founded: 1963
PTCIL—(NSE)
Rev.: $27,184,797
Assets: $66,292,488
Liabilities: $29,524,405
Net Worth: $36,768,083
Earnings: $3,095,150
Emp.: 519
Fiscal Year-end: 03/31/23
Industrial Machinery Parts Mfr
N.A.I.C.S.: 333248
Sachin Agarwal *(Chm & Mng Dir)*

PTFC REDEVELOPMENT CORPORATION

802 A Bonifacio Street, Quezon City, Philippines
Tel.: (63) 23306955
Web Site: https://www.ptfc-brc.com
Year Founded: 1951
TFC—(PHI)
Rev.: $3,705,292
Assets: $11,086,434
Liabilities: $1,218,563
Net Worth: $9,867,872
Earnings: $1,767,473
Fiscal Year-end: 08/31/23
Real Estate Lending Services
N.A.I.C.S.: 531110
Albert C. Eufemio *(Officer-IR, Treas & VP)*

PTG ENERGY PUBLIC COMPANY LIMITED

90 CW Tower A 33rd Floor Ratchadaphisek Road, Huai Khwang Subdistrict Huai Khwang District, Bangkok, 10310, Thailand
Tel.: (66) 21683377
Web Site: https://www.ptgenergy.co.th

INTERNATIONAL PUBLIC

Year Founded: 1988
PTG—(THA)
Rev.: $5,803,686,613
Assets: $1,370,033,509
Liabilities: $1,109,472,289
Net Worth: $260,561,219
Earnings: $28,192,160
Emp.: 21,954
Fiscal Year-end: 12/31/23
Fuel Retailer & Distr
N.A.I.C.S.: 457210
Soontorn Saikwan *(Chm)*

Subsidiaries:

Alpine Oil Co., Ltd. (1)
90 CW Tower A 33rd Floor Ratchadaphisek Road, Huaykwang, Bangkok, 10310, Thailand
Tel.: (66) 2168337788
Petroleum Product Distr
N.A.I.C.S.: 424720

BPTG Co., Ltd. (1)
90 CW Tower A 33rd Floor Ratchadaphisek Road, Huaykwang, Bangkok, 10310, Thailand
Tel.: (66) 2168337788
Petroleum Product Distr
N.A.I.C.S.: 424720

Empire Service Solution Co., Ltd. (1)
9/15 Moo 6 Sawaipracharaj Road, Lumlukka, Pathumthani, 12150, Thailand
Tel.: (66) 20485942
Web Site: https://www.empireservice.co.th
Fuel Dispenser & Other Equipment Distr
N.A.I.C.S.: 423830

GFA Corporation (Thailand) Co., Ltd. (1)
90 CW Tower A 33rd Floor Ratchadaphisek Road, Huaykwang, Bangkok, 10310, Thailand
Tel.: (66) 2168337788
Food & Beverage Product Distr
N.A.I.C.S.: 424490

Innotech Green Energy Co., Ltd. (1)
90 CW Tower A 33rd Floor Ratchadaphisek Road, Huaykwang, Bangkok, 10310, Thailand
Tel.: (66) 2168337788
Ethanol & Biomass Power Distr
N.A.I.C.S.: 221117

Jitramas Catering Co., Ltd. (1)
36/29 Moo 13 Bueng Kham Phroi, Lam Luk Ka District, Pathumthani, 12150, Thailand
Tel.: (66) 849100100
Food & Beverage Product Distr
N.A.I.C.S.: 424490

Jitramas Co., Ltd. (1)
36/29 Village No 13 Bueng Kham Phroi, Lam Luk Ka, Pathumthani, 12150, Thailand
Tel.: (66) 849100100
Herbal Product & Food Supplement Distr
N.A.I.C.S.: 424480

Max Card Co., Ltd. (1)
90 CW Tower A Building 33rd Floor Ratchadaphisek Road, Huai Khwang Subdistrict Huai Khwang District, Bangkok, 10310, Thailand
Tel.: (66) 26183377
Web Site: https://www.maxcard.co.th
Fuel Distr
N.A.I.C.S.: 424720

Max Me Corp Co., Ltd. (1)
90 CW Tower A Building 33rd Floor Ratchadaphisek Road, Huai Khwang Subdistrict Huai Khwang District, Bangkok, 10310, Thailand
Tel.: (66) 26183377
Web Site: https://www.maxme.co.th
Fuel Distr
N.A.I.C.S.: 424720

Palangngan Pattana Co., Ltd. (1)
62/45 Asia Road Tambon Ban Phut Amphoe, Hat Yai, 90250, Songkhla, Thailand
Tel.: (66) 74216342
Electric Power Distr
N.A.I.C.S.: 221122

PTK PANONONIJA A.D.

AND PRIVATE COMPANIES / PTT PUBLIC COMPANY LIMITED

Trg Lenjina br 1, Panonija, 24330, Serbia
Tel.: (381) 24725002
Web Site: http://www.ptkpanonija.rs
Year Founded: 1998
PAPA—(BEL)
Rev.: $15,961,061
Assets: $20,766,043
Liabilities: $11,256,787
Net Worth: $9,509,256
Earnings: $120,523
Emp.: 38
Fiscal Year-end: 12/31/22
Grain Farming Services
N.A.I.C.S.: 111191
Igor Ivanisevic *(CEO)*

PTL ENTERPRISES LTD.
3rd floor Areekal Mansion Near Manorama Junction Panampilly Nagar, Kochi, 682036, Kerala, India
Tel.: (91) 4844012046
Web Site:
  https://www.ptlenterprise.com
Year Founded: 1959
PTL—(NSE)
Rev.: $9,635,317
Assets: $117,162,618
Liabilities: $35,897,589
Net Worth: $81,265,029
Earnings: $9,561,088
Emp.: 632
Fiscal Year-end: 03/31/21
Healtcare Services
N.A.I.C.S.: 621999
Onkar S. Kanwar *(Chm)*

PTS PLAST-BOX S.A.
ul Lutosawskiego 17a, 76-200, Slupsk, Poland
Tel.: (48) 598400880
Web Site: http://www.plast-box.com
Year Founded: 1983
PLX—(WAR)
Sales Range: Less than $1 Million
Plastics Product Mfr
N.A.I.C.S.: 326199

Subsidiaries:

Suwary S.A. (1)
ul Piotra Skargi 45/47, 95-200, Pabianice, Poland
Tel.: (48) 422252200
Web Site: http://www.suwary.com.pl
Plastic Packaging Services
N.A.I.C.S.: 326160
Walter Tymon Kuskowski *(CEO)*

PTT GLOBAL CHEMICAL PUBLIC COMPANY LIMITED
555/1 Energy Complex Building A 18th Floor Vibhavadi Rangsit Road, Chatuchak, Bangkok, 10900, Thailand
Tel.: (66) 22658400   TH
Web Site:
  https://www.pttgcgroup.com
Year Founded: 2011
PTTGC—(OTCIQ)
Sales Range: $5-14.9 Billion
Chemical Products Mfr
N.A.I.C.S.: 551112
Varit Namwong *(COO-Value Added Products)*

Subsidiaries:

Bangkok Polyethylene Public Company Limited (1)
Vibhavadi Rangsit Road 555/1 Energy Complex Building A 15th Floor, Chatuchak, Bangkok, 10900, Thailand
Tel.: (66) 2265 8400
Polymer Product Marketing
N.A.I.C.S.: 325998

Cognis Oleochemicals (Malaysia) Sdn. Bhd. (1)
Level 9 Building A Peremba Square, Saujana Resort Section U2, 40150, Shah Alam, Selangor, Malaysia
Tel.: (60) 3 7845 3000
Sales Range: $450-499.9 Million
Emp.: 1,100
Oleochemical Products Mfr; Owned 50% by Sime Darby Berhad & 50% by PTT Chemical Public Company Limited
N.A.I.C.S.: 325199

GC Glycol Company Limited (1)
555/1 Energy Complex Building A 15th Floor Vibhavadi Rangsit Road, Chatuchak, Bangkok, 10900, Thailand
Tel.: (66) 2 265 8400
Web Site: https://www.gcglycol.com
Chemical Products Mfr
N.A.I.C.S.: 325998

GC International Corporation (1)
3009 Post Oak Blvd Ste 998, Houston, TX 77056
Web Site: https://gcinternational.com
Export & Import Management Services
N.A.I.C.S.: 488510

GC Logistics Solutions Company Limited (1)
555/1 Energy Complex Building A 8th Floor Vibhavadi Rangsit Road, Chatuchak, Bangkok, 10900, Thailand
Tel.: (66) 2 140 3700
Web Site: https://www.gc-logistic.com
Integrated Logistics Services
N.A.I.C.S.: 541614
Pornsak Mongkoltrirat *(Chm)*

GC Maintenance & Engineering Company Limited (1)
22/2 Pakorn Songkhraorat Road, Tambon Map Ta Phut Amphur Muang Rayong, Rayong, 21150, Thailand
Tel.: (66) 3 897 7800
Web Site: https://www.gcme.co.th
Maintenance & Engineering Services
N.A.I.C.S.: 541330

GC Marketing Solutions Company Limited (1)
555/1 Energy Complex Building A 9th Fl Vibhavadi Rangsit Road, Chatuchak, Bangkok, 10900, Thailand
Tel.: (66) 2 140 4488
Web Site: https://www.gcmgrp.com
Chemical Product Mfr & Distr
N.A.I.C.S.: 325998
Patiparn Sukorndhaman *(Chm)*

GC Marketing Solutions Myanmar Co., Ltd. (1)
192 Kaba Aye Pagoda Road Unit 05 14th Floor Tower 1, Myanmar Centre Tower Bahan Township, Yangon, Myanmar
Tel.: (95) 19 345 4112
Chemical Product Mfr & Distr
N.A.I.C.S.: 325998

GC Marketing Solutions Vietnam Co., Ltd. (1)
Unit 5 02 5 03 and 5 04 5th Floor Deutsches Haus Ho Chi Minh-Stadt, No 33 Le Duan Street Ben Nghe Ward District 1, Ho Chi Minh City, Vietnam
Tel.: (84) 283 823 3611
Polymer Product Distr
N.A.I.C.S.: 424610

GC Polyols Company Limited (1)
555/1 Energy Complex Building A 6th Floor Vibhavadi Rangsit Road, Chatuchak, Bangkok, 10900, Thailand
Tel.: (66) 2 140 8844
Web Site: https://www.gcpolyols.com
Chemical Products Distr
N.A.I.C.S.: 424690
Patiparn Sukorndhaman *(Chm)*

GC-M PTA Company Limited (1)
8 Soi G-2 Prakornsongkror Road Eastern Industrial Estate Huai Pong, Muang, Rayong, 21150, Thailand (49%)
Tel.: (66) 38685100
Purified Terephthalic Acid Mfr & Sales
N.A.I.C.S.: 325998

GCM Polymer Trading DMCC (1)
Unit 406 Indigo Tower Plot No JLT-PH1-D1A Jumeirah Lakes Towers, Dubai, United Arab Emirates
Tel.: (971) 4 423 0774
Chemical Product Mfr & Distr
N.A.I.C.S.: 325998

Myriant Corporation (1)
1 Pine Hill Dr Batterymarch Park II 3rd Fl, Quincy, MA 02169 (72.62%)
Tel.: (617) 657-5200
Web Site: http://www.myriant.com
Sales Range: $10-24.9 Million
Emp.: 64
Biochemical Mfr
N.A.I.C.S.: 325998
Susan Hager *(Sr VP-Corp Comm & Govt Affairs)*

NPC S&E Security Guard Company Limited (1)
20/9 Pakorn Songkhraorat Road, Tambon Map Ta Phut Amphur Muang Rayong, Rayong, 21150, Thailand
Tel.: (66) 3 897 7777
Security Guard Services
N.A.I.C.S.: 561612

NPC Safety and Environmental Service Co., Ltd. (1)
555/1 Energy Complex Building A 15th Floor Vibhavadi Rangsit Road, Chatuchak, Bangkok, 10900, Thailand (100%)
Tel.: (66) 2 265 8110
Web Site: https://www.npc-se.co.th
Safety & Environmental Management Services, Including Fire Fighting & Fire Prevention Training, Safety Standards Compliance, Sea Rescue Training & Other Related Programs
N.A.I.C.S.: 922190

NatureWorks LLC (1)
15305 Minnetonka Blvd, Minnetonka, MN 55343 (50%)
Tel.: (952) 742-0400
Web Site: http://www.natureworksllc.com
Sales Range: $25-49.9 Million
Emp.: 25
Biopolymer Mfr
N.A.I.C.S.: 325414
Steve Davies *(Dir-Comml)*

PTT Maintenance and Engineering Company Limited (1)
22/2 Pakornsongkhraorat Road Tambon Map Ta Phut, Amphoe Muang Rayong, Rayong, 21150, Thailand (60%)
Tel.: (66) 3897 7800
Web Site: http://www.pttme.co.th
Maintenance, Engineering & Construction & Plant Inspection Service
N.A.I.C.S.: 236210

PTT Phenol Company Limited (1)
123 Suntowers Building B 36th Floor Vibhavadi Rangsit Road, Comphon Chatuchak, Bangkok, 10900, Thailand (60%)
Tel.: (66) 2273 8800
Web Site: http://www1.pttchem.com
Phenol & Phenol By-Products Mfr & Marketer
N.A.I.C.S.: 325998

PTT Polyethylene Co., Ltd. (1)
555/1 Energy Complex Building A 15th Floor, Vibhavadi Rangsit Road, Chatuchak Bangkok, 10900, Thailand (100%)
Tel.: (66) 22658300
Web Site: http://www.pttchem.com
Sales Range: $25-49.9 Million
Emp.: 100
Polyethylene Mfr
N.A.I.C.S.: 325110

PTT Polymer Logistics Co., Ltd (1)
555/1 A Building Energy Complex 8 Fl Vibhavadi Rangsit Rd, Chatuchak, Bangkok, 10900, Thailand (50%)
Tel.: (66) 2 140 3700
Web Site: https://www.pttpls.com
Logistic Services
N.A.I.C.S.: 541614
Pitipan Tepartimargorn *(Chm)*

PTT Polymer Marketing Co., Ltd (1)
Energy Complex Building A 9th Fl 555/1 Vibhavadi Rangsit Road, Chatuchak, Bangkok, 10900, Thailand (50%)
Tel.: (66) 2 140 4488
Web Site: http://www.pttpm.com
Sales Range: $75-99.9 Million
Emp.: 180
Polymer Distr
N.A.I.C.S.: 424690
Pitipan Tepartimargorn *(Chm)*

PTT Utility Company Limited (1)
555 15th Floor Vibhavadi Rangsit Road, Lard Yao Chatuchak, Bangkok, 10900, Thailand (60%)
Tel.: (66) 2537 3074
Web Site: http://www1.pttchem.com
Steam & Electricity Production
N.A.I.C.S.: 221118

Solution Creation Company Limited (1)
123 Suntowers Building A 18th Floor Vibhavadi Rangsit Road, Chomphon Chatuchak, Bangkok, 10900, Thailand (100%)
Tel.: (66) 2265 8100
Choline Chloride Mfr & Marketer
N.A.I.C.S.: 325998

TOC Glycol Company Limited (1)
18th Floor Suntowers A Building 123 Vibhavadi Ransit Road, Chormphol Chatuchak, Bangkok, 10900, Thailand (100%)
Tel.: (66) 2265 8100
Web Site: http://www.glycol.co.th
Ethylene Oxide & Ethylene Glycol Mfr
N.A.I.C.S.: 325998

Thai Ethanolamines Co., Ltd. (1)
123 Suntowers Building A 18th Floor Vibhavadi Rangsit Road, Chomphon Chatuchak, Bangkok, 10900, Thailand (100%)
Tel.: (66) 2265 8100
Web Site: http://www1.pttchem.com
Ethanolamines Mfr & Marketer
N.A.I.C.S.: 325998

Thai Oleochemicals Company Limited (1)
123 Suntowers Building A 18th Floor Vibhavadi Rangsit Road, Chomphon Chatuchak, Bangkok, 10900, Thailand (100%)
Tel.: (66) 2265 8100
Web Site: http://www.thaioleochemicals.com
Organic Chemicals Mfr & Marketer
N.A.I.C.S.: 325199

Thai Tank Terminal Limited (1)
19 I-1 Road Map Ta Phut, Chomphon Chatuchak, Muang Rayong, 21150, Rayong, Thailand (51%)
Tel.: (66) 38673500
Web Site: http://www.thaitank.com
Storage & Transport Services for Liquid Chemicals, Oil & Gas
N.A.I.C.S.: 493190

PTT OIL & RETAIL BUSINESS PUBLIC COMPANY LIMITED
555/2 Energy Complex Building B 12th Floor Vibhavadi Rangsit Rd, Chatuchak, Bangkok, 10900, Thailand
Tel.: (66) 21965959   TH
Web Site: https://www.pttor.com
Year Founded: 1978
OR—(THA)
Rev.: $22,455,156,805
Assets: $6,429,110,820
Liabilities: $3,232,362,898
Net Worth: $3,196,747,923
Earnings: $323,926,672
Emp.: 1,856
Fiscal Year-end: 12/31/23
Petroleum Product Distr
N.A.I.C.S.: 486910
Terdkiat Prommool *(Sr Exec VP-Organization Mgmt & Sustainability & Dir)*

PTT PUBLIC COMPANY LIMITED
555 Vibhavadi Rangsit Road Chatuchak, Bangkok, 10900, Thailand
Tel.: (66) 25372000   TH
Web Site: https://www.pttplc.com
Year Founded: 2001
PTT—(THA)
Rev.: $86,476,661,126
Assets: $95,164,367,526
Liabilities: $50,476,761,854

PTT PUBLIC COMPANY LIMITED

PTT Public Company Limited—(Continued)

Net Worth: $44,687,605,672
Earnings: $4,270,280,262
Fiscal Year-end: 12/31/23
Oil & Gas Distribution Services
N.A.I.C.S.: 213112
Kris Imsang *(COO-Downstream Petroleum Bus Grp)*

Subsidiaries:

Al and Robotics Ventures Company Limited (1)
Bhiraj Tower at Sathorn Building C 33 31 31/1 S Sathorn Road, Yannawa Sathorn, Bangkok, Thailand
Tel.: (66) 20784000
Web Site: https://arv.co.th
Industrial Automation Products Mfr
N.A.I.C.S.: 334512

Business Professional Solutions Recruitments Co., Ltd. (1)
555/6 Energy Complex Building F 2nd Floor, Vibhavadi Rangsit Road Chatuchak, Bangkok, Thailand
Tel.: (66) 2140315859
Web Site: https://bpsthailand.com
Recruitment Services
N.A.I.C.S.: 561312

Delta Gas Transportation Limited (1)
2 Sei-Myaung Yeiktha Lane 8 Mile Road, Mayangone Township, Yangon, Myanmar
Tel.: (95) 1652700
Web Site: https://www.deltagasmm.com
Energy Support Services
N.A.I.C.S.: 541690

Global Power Synergy Public Company Limited (1)
555/2 Energy Complex Building B 5th Floor Vibhavdi - Rangsit Road, Chatuchak, Bangkok, 10900, Thailand
Tel.: (66) 21404600
Web Site: https://www.gpscgroup.com
Rev.: $2,623,187,587
Assets: $8,223,468,583
Liabilities: $4,792,687,496
Net Worth: $3,430,781,087
Earnings: $140,386,939
Emp.: 800
Fiscal Year-end: 12/31/2023
Electric Power Distr
N.A.I.C.S.: 221122
Wanida Boonpiraks *(CFO)*

Glow Energy Public Company Limited (1)
Empire Tower 38th Floor-Park Wing, No 1 South Sathorn Road Yannawa Sathorn, Bangkok, 10120, Thailand (69.11%)
Tel.: (66) 26701500
Web Site: http://www.glow.co.th
Rev.: $1,669,076,312
Assets: $3,566,979,082
Liabilities: $2,131,843,455
Net Worth: $1,435,135,626
Earnings: $258,004,815
Fiscal Year-end: 12/31/2019
Power Generation & Steam & Water Distr
N.A.I.C.S.: 221118
Prateep Puthamrugsa *(VP-Supply Chain Mgmt)*

Subsidiary (Domestic):

Glow Co., Ltd. (2)
38th Floor Empire Tower - Park Wing No 1 South Sathorn Road, Yannawa Sathorn, Bangkok, 10120, Thailand
Tel.: (66) 2670150033
Web Site: http://www.glow.co.th
Electric Power Generation & Distribution Services
N.A.I.C.S.: 221118
Pajongwit Pongsinvapai *(CEO)*

Glow IPP Company Limited (2)
195 Empire Tower South Sathorn Rd, Yannawa Sathorn, Bangkok, 10120, Thailand
Tel.: (66) 26701500
Web Site: http://www.glow.co.th
Electricity Generation
N.A.I.C.S.: 221118

Glow SPP 3 Co., Ltd. (2)
11 I - 5 Road Map Ta Phut Industrial Estate,
Map Ta Phut, 21150, Rayong, Thailand
Tel.: (66) 3869840010
Web Site: http://www.glow.co.th
Electric Power Generation & Distribution Services
N.A.I.C.S.: 221118

Subsidiary (Non-US):

Houay Ho Power Company Limited (2)
Nong Bon Road, PO Box 5464, Bane Fai, Vientiane, Xaysettha District, Lao People's Democratic Republic
Tel.: (856) 214149323
Web Site: http://www.houayho.com
Electric Power Distr
N.A.I.C.S.: 221118

Innobic (Asia) Company Limited (1)
555/6 EnCo F Building 2Fl Vibhavadi-Rangsit Rd, Chatuchak, Bangkok, Thailand
Tel.: (66) 25373623
Web Site: https://innobicasia.com
Life Sciences Research & Development Services
N.A.I.C.S.: 541715

International Coal Holdings Limited (1)
Level 1 35 Ventnor Avenue, West Perth, 6005, WA, Australia
Tel.: (61) 894800500
Sales Range: $250-299.9 Million
Emp.: 1,707
Coal Mining Services
N.A.I.C.S.: 212115
Milan Jerkovic *(CEO)*

Subsidiary (Non-US):

Sakari Resources Limited (2)
391B Orchard Road Ngee Ann City Tower B 17-01, Singapore, 238874, Singapore (60.37%)
Tel.: (65) 64994100
Web Site: https://www.sakariresources.com
Rev.: $496,560,000
Assets: $853,024,000
Liabilities: $158,071,000
Net Worth: $694,953,000
Earnings: $59,056,000
Emp.: 722
Fiscal Year-end: 12/31/2019
Coal Mining Services
N.A.I.C.S.: 324199
Mike Koay *(CFO)*

Subsidiary (Non-US):

PT Bahari Cakrawala Sebuku (3)
Graha Kirana Building 15th Floor, Suite 1204 Jl Yos Sudarso Kav, 14350, Jakarta, Indonesia
Tel.: (62) 2129987900
Web Site: http://www.Sebuku.com
Coal Mining
N.A.I.C.S.: 213113

Subsidiary (Domestic):

Tiger Energy Trading Pte. Ltd. (3)
391B Orchard Road Ngee Ann City Tower B 17-05, Tower 15, Singapore, 238874, Singapore (100%)
Tel.: (65) 64994101
Web Site: https://www.tiger-et.com
Coal & Mineral & Ore Whslr
N.A.I.C.S.: 423520

JSKEM Private Limited (1)
24 Sin Ming Lane 06-97 Midview City, Singapore, 573970, Singapore
Tel.: (65) 66591073
Web Site: https://www.jskem.com.sg
Chemical Equipment Distr
N.A.I.C.S.: 423830

Mekha Technology Co., Ltd. (1)
555/1 Energy Complex A Vibhavadi Rangsit Rd, Chatuchak, Bangkok, Thailand
Tel.: (66) 869795515
Web Site: https://www.mekhatech.com
Software Development Services
N.A.I.C.S.: 541511

Orange Energy Limited (1)
Khwang Chatuchak, Khet Chatuchak, Bangkok, Thailand
Tel.: (66) 27376000
Web Site: https://orange-ep.com
Oil & Gas Services
N.A.I.C.S.: 213112

PTT (Cambodia) Co., Ltd (1)
No 320 Kampuchea Krom Blvd 128 corner of Street 171, Sangkat Mittapheap Khan 7 Makara, Phnom Penh, Cambodia
Tel.: (855) 23300018
Web Site: https://www.ptt.com.kh
Petroleum Product Distr
N.A.I.C.S.: 424720

PTT Energy Resources Co., Ltd. (1)
555/2 Energy Complex Building B 14th Floor Vibhavadi Rangsit Road, Chatuchak, Bangkok, 10900, Thailand
Tel.: (66) 2 140 4800
Web Site: https://www.ptt-er.com
Coal & Mining Services
N.A.I.C.S.: 212115

PTT Exploration & Production Public Co., Ltd. (1)
555/1 Energy Complex Building A 6th 19th-36th Floor, Vibhavadi-Rangsit Road Chatuchak Chatuchak, Bangkok, 10900, Thailand (65.29%)
Tel.: (66) 25374000
Web Site: http://www.pttep.com
Rev.: $9,057,333,000
Assets: $26,380,337,000
Liabilities: $11,786,668,000
Net Worth: $14,593,669,000
Earnings: $2,207,767,000
Emp.: 1,975
Fiscal Year-end: 12/31/2023
Petroleum Exploration & Production Services
N.A.I.C.S.: 324110
Phongsthorn Thavisin *(CEO)*

Subsidiary (Non-US):

Murphy Sarawak Oil Co., Ltd. (2)
Level 26 27 28 31 Tower 2 Petronas Twin Towers, Kuala Lumpur, 50088, Malaysia
Tel.: (60) 374907400
Crude Petroleum & Natural Gas Extraction Servcies
N.A.I.C.S.: 211120

Partex Oil & Gas (Holdings) Corp. (2)
Rua Ivone Silva 6-1, 1050-124, Lisbon, Portugal
Tel.: (351) 217912900
Web Site: http://www.partex-oilgas.com
Sales Range: $550-599.9 Million
Emp.: 45
Holding Company
N.A.I.C.S.: 551112

Subsidiary (Non-US):

PMO Services, SA (3)
Pflugstrasse 20, Vaduz, 9490, Liechtenstein
Tel.: (423) 2375680
Sales Range: $25-49.9 Million
Emp.: 4
Petroleum & Coal Products Mfr
N.A.I.C.S.: 324199
Fernando Moraira *(Gen Mgr)*

Partex (Oman) Corporation (3)
Icaza Gonzalez-Ruiz Y Aleman Abogados (Igra), 507, Panama, Panama
Tel.: (507) 2635555
Sales Range: $25-49.9 Million
Emp.: 50
Holding Company
N.A.I.C.S.: 551112

Partex Brasil Ltda. (3)
Av Rui Barbosa 1363 Salas 101/104, Gracas-Recife, Recife, Brazil
Tel.: (55) 8134268128
Web Site: http://www.partexbrazil.com
Sales Range: $50-74.9 Million
Emp.: 2
Holding Company
N.A.I.C.S.: 551112

Partex Brasil Servicos Petroliferos Ltd (3)
av rui barbosa 1 363, Recife, 52011-040, Pernambuco, Brazil
Tel.: (55) 8134268128
Emp.: 20
Oil & Gas Field Engineering Services
N.A.I.C.S.: 333132

INTERNATIONAL PUBLIC

Alvaro Ribeiro *(Mng Dir)*

Partex Gas Corporation (3)
Sheikh Khalifa St Blue Tower 6th Fl 604, PO Box 46065, Abu Dhabi, United Arab Emirates
Tel.: (971) 26271395
Oil & Gas Operations Services
N.A.I.C.S.: 213112

Subsidiary (Domestic):

Partex Services Portugal, S.A. (3)
Rua Ivone Silva 6 - 1, Lisbon, 1050-124, Portugal
Tel.: (351) 217912900
Web Site: http://www.partex-oilgas.com
Emp.: 50
Holding Company
N.A.I.C.S.: 551112

Joint Venture (Non-US):

Petroleum Development Oman LLC (3)
Mina Alfahal, Postal Office Box 81, Muscat, 100, Oman
Tel.: (968) 24678111
Web Site: https://www.pdo.co.om
Sales Range: $1-4.9 Billion
Emp.: 8,000
Petroleum Refiner
N.A.I.C.S.: 324110
Mohammed Saif Al Rumhy *(Chm)*

PTT International Company Limited (1)
555 2 Energy Complex Building B 5th Floor Vibhavadi Rangsit Road, Chatuchak, Bangkok, 10900, Thailand
Tel.: (66) 2140 4800
Web Site: http://www.ptt-international.com
Energy Resource Investment Services
N.A.I.C.S.: 523999

PTT International Trading London Limited (1)
Suite 7 5th Floor Berkeley Square House, London, W1J 6BU, United Kingdom
Tel.: (44) 203 912 1824
Web Site: https://www.pttitldn.com
Oil Mfr
N.A.I.C.S.: 324191

PTT International Trading Pte. Ltd. (1)
391A Orchard Road 12-01/05 and 12-10 Ngee Ann City Tower A, Singapore, 238873, Singapore
Tel.: (65) 67346540
Web Site: https://www.ptt-trading.com
Crude Oil & Petroleum Product Trading Services
N.A.I.C.S.: 424720
Supasachi Hongsinlark *(Mng Dir)*

PTT LNG Co., Ltd. (1)
3rd Floor Energy Complex Building A 555/1 Vibhavadi Rangsit Road, Chatuchak, Bangkok, 10900, Thailand
Tel.: (66) 2 140 1555
Web Site: https://www.pttlng.com
Oil & Gas Exploration Services
N.A.I.C.S.: 213112
Pitak Janyapong *(Chm)*

PTT MEA Ltd. (1)
Unit 9 5th Floor of Al Khatem Tower Abu Dhabi Global Market, ADGM Square, Abu Dhabi, United Arab Emirates
Tel.: (971) 24455951
Petroleum Product Mfr & Distr
N.A.I.C.S.: 325110

PTT Natural Gas Distribution Co., Ltd. (1)
3rd Floor Building A Energy Complex 555/1 Vibhavadi - Rangsit Road, Chatuchak, Bangkok, 10900, Thailand (58%)
Tel.: (66) 2 140 1500
Web Site: https://www.pttngd.co.th
Sales Range: $75-99.9 Million
Emp.: 80
Natural Gas Distr
N.A.I.C.S.: 221210
Somnuek Phangwapee *(Co-Chm)*

PTT Polymer Logistics Co., Ltd (1)
555/1 A Building Energy Complex 8 Fl Vibhavadi Rangsit Rd, Chatuchak, Bangkok,

10900, Thailand
Tel.: (66) 2 140 3700
Web Site: http://www.pttpls.com
Logistic Services
N.A.I.C.S.: 541614
Pitipan Tepartimargorn (Chm)

PTT Polymer Marketing Co., Ltd (1)
Energy Complex Building A 9th Fl 555/1 Vibhavadi Rangsit Road, Chatuchak, Bangkok, 10900, Thailand (50%)
Tel.: (66) 2 140 4488
Web Site: http://www.pttpm.com
Sales Range: $75-99.9 Million
Emp.: 180
Polymer Distr
N.A.I.C.S.: 424690
Pitipan Tepartimargorn (Chm)

PTT Retail Management Company Limited
1010 Vibhavadi Rangsit Road, Chatuchak Subdistrict Chatuchak District, Bangkok, 10900, Thailand (100%)
Tel.: (66) 20300444
Web Site: https://www.pttrm.com
Sales Range: $75-99.9 Million
Emp.: 400
Petroleum Refining
N.A.I.C.S.: 324110

PTTEP Australia Perth Pty Limited (1)
Level 5 225 St Georges Terrace, Perth, 6000, WA, Australia
Tel.: (61) 894839483
Web Site: https://www.au.pttep.com
Petroleum Product Distr
N.A.I.C.S.: 424720

PTTEP Indonesia Company Limited (1)
Pondok Indah Office Tower 2 4th Floor, Jl Iskandar Muda 'Kav V-T, Jakarta Selatan, Indonesia
Tel.: (62) 217697437
Web Site: https://www.pttep-indonesia.co.id
Petroleum Product Distr
N.A.I.C.S.: 424720

PTTOR China (Shanghai) Co., Ltd. (1)
Room No 112 13th Floor No 1000 Lujiazui Ring Road, New Pudong Area, Shanghai, China
Tel.: (86) 2150783298
Web Site: https://en.pttorcn.com
Oil & Gas Distr
N.A.I.C.S.: 424720

PTTOR International Holdings (Singapore) Pte. Ltd. (1)
391A Orchard Road 12-01/04 Ngee Ann City, Singapore, 238873, Singapore
Tel.: (65) 64342601
Petroleum Product Distr
N.A.I.C.S.: 424720

PTTOR Singapore Pte. Ltd. (1)
391A Orchard Road 12-01/05 & 12-10 Ngee Ann City Tower A, Singapore, 238873, Singapore
Tel.: (65) 66947028
Oil & Gas Distr
N.A.I.C.S.: 424720

Peaberry Thai Company Limited (1)
123/17 Nontri Rd, Chongnonsri Yanawa, Bangkok, Thailand
Tel.: (66) 26812424
Web Site: https://www.peaberryltd.com
Coffee Mfr & Distr
N.A.I.C.S.: 311920

REACC Co., Ltd. (1)
555/1 Energy Complex Building A G Floor Vibhavadi Rangsit Road, Chatuchak Subdistrict Chatuchak District, Bangkok, Thailand
Tel.: (66) 878165652
Web Site: https://reacc.io
Solar Electric Power Generation Services
N.A.I.C.S.: 221114

Sapthip Green Energy Co., Ltd. (1)
68 Soi Santipharb Siphraya, Bangrak, Bangkok, Thailand
Tel.: (66) 223304445
Web Site: https://www.sapthip.com
Ethanol Mfr & Distr

N.A.I.C.S.: 325193

PTT SYNERGY GROUP
No 63-1A 1B and 1C Jalan Anggerik Vanilla T31/T Kota Kemuning, Section 31, 40460, Shah Alam, Selangor Darul Ehsan, Malaysia
Tel.: (60) 350372822
Web Site:
https://www.pttgroup.com.my
PTT—(KLS)
Rev.: $34,585,100
Assets: $89,390,177
Liabilities: $67,787,153
Net Worth: $21,603,024
Earnings: $465,784
Emp.: 204
Fiscal Year-end: 06/30/23
Property Development Services
N.A.I.C.S.: 531312
Chee Jing Kan (Co-Sec)

Subsidiaries:

Grand Hoover Property Sdn. Bhd. (1)
No 63 G Jalan Anggerik Vanilla T31/T Kota Kemuning Section 31, Shah Alam, Selangor, Malaysia
Tel.: (60) 351228702
Property Development & Investment Services
N.A.I.C.S.: 531390

Heap Wah Barakah Sdn. Bhd. (1)
No 40 and 46 Jalan 18/2, 46000, Petaling Jaya, Selangor, Malaysia
Tel.: (60) 377829436
Web Site: https://www.heap-wah.com
Sanitary Ware & Plumbing Services
N.A.I.C.S.: 423720

Heap Wah Enterprise Sdn. Bhd. (1)
No 40 and 46 Jalan 18/2, 46000, Petaling Jaya, Selangor, Malaysia
Tel.: (60) 377829436
Web Site: https://www.heap-wah.com
Sales Range: $50-74.9 Million
Emp.: 10
Sanitary Wares & Tapwares Distr
N.A.I.C.S.: 423720

Hoover Management Sdn. Bhd. (1)
49 Jalan Sultan Ismail, 20200, Kuala Terengganu, Terengganu, Malaysia
Tel.: (60) 96233833
Web Site: http://www.hoover.com
Sales Range: $50-74.9 Million
Emp.: 20
Investment Management Service
N.A.I.C.S.: 523999
Lee Hen Hee (Gen Mgr)

Hoover Tiling Trading Sdn. Bhd. (1)
No 51 Jalan 17/45, 46400, Petaling Jaya, Selangor, Malaysia
Tel.: (60) 379581212
Sales Range: $25-49.9 Million
Emp.: 8
Ceramic Tiles & Marbles Distr
N.A.I.C.S.: 444180

PTT Infra Sdn. Bhd. (1)
2A-1-1 B Bangunan PTT Space U8 No 6, Persiaran Pasak Bumi Taman Bukit Jelutong Seksyen U8, 40150, Shah Alam, Selangor, Malaysia
Tel.: (60) 350372822
Construction & Infrastructure Services
N.A.I.C.S.: 541370

PTT Property Sdn. Bhd. (1)
2A-1-1 B Bangunan PTT Space U8 No 6, Persiaran Pasak Bumi Taman Bukit Jelutong Seksyen U8, 40150, Shah Alam, Selangor, Malaysia
Tel.: (60) 350372822
Building Construction Services
N.A.I.C.S.: 541330

PTW ENERGY SERVICES LTD.
2308 8th Street, Nisku, T9E 7Z2, AB, Canada
Tel.: (780) 955-2988
Web Site: http://www.ptwenergy.com
Year Founded: 2014

Emp.: 5,000
Engineeering Services
N.A.I.C.S.: 541330
Don Basenett (Pres & CEO)

Subsidiaries:

Pyramid Corporation (1)
Bow Valley Square II, 205 5 Ave SW #3300,, Calgary, T2P 2V7, AB, Canada
Tel.: (403) 205-3880
Electrical Instrumentaion & Maintenance Services
N.A.I.C.S.: 811114

Tarpon Energy Services Ltd. (1)
7020 - 8st Street SE, Calgary, T2C 5B8, AB, Canada
Tel.: (403) 234-8647
Web Site: http://www.tarponenergy.com
Sales Range: $150-199.9 Million
Emp.: 1,050
Electrical & Instrumentation Services
N.A.I.C.S.: 238210
Rick Wickland (Sr VP-Electric & Controls Div)

Subsidiary (US):

Tarpon Energy Services LLC (2)
9164 Marshall Pl, Westminster, CO 80031
Tel.: (303) 412-9955
Building Construction Services
N.A.I.C.S.: 236220
Birk Bablitz (Gen Mgr-Ops)

Subsidiary (Non-US):

Tarpon International Energy Services LLC (2)
604 Zarouni Building Barsha First Sheikh Zayed Road, PO Box 454737, Dubai, United Arab Emirates
Tel.: (971) 43957708
Building Construction Services
N.A.I.C.S.: 236220

PTW FREIBURG GMBH
Lorracher Strasse 7, 79115, Freiburg, Germany
Tel.: (49) 761490550
Web Site: http://www.ptw.de
Year Founded: 1922
Rev.: $40,315,724
Emp.: 200
Medical Equipment Mfr & Distr
N.A.I.C.S.: 423450
Christian Pychlau (Mng Partner)

Subsidiaries:

PTW Dosimetria Iberia S. L. U. (1)
Calle Profesor Beltran Baguena 4 - 312E, 46009, Valencia, Spain
Tel.: (34) 963462854
Medical Equipment Distr
N.A.I.C.S.: 423450
Jose Luis Bonet Sancho (Mgr-Sls)

PTW Dosimetry India Pvt. Ltd. (1)
ACE Towers 2nd Floor 73/75 Dr Radhakrishnan Road, Mylapore, Chennai, 600004, India
Tel.: (91) 4442079999
Medical Equipment Distr
N.A.I.C.S.: 423450
Bala Viswanathan (Mng Dir)

PTW-Asia Pacific Ltd. (1)
11th Floor Valiant Industrial Centre Nos 2-12 Au Pui Wan Street, Fo Tan, Hong Kong, New Territories, China (Hong Kong)
Tel.: (852) 23699234
Medical Equipment Distr
N.A.I.C.S.: 423450

PTW-Beijing Ltd (1)
Room 712 JinYiYe Building No 2 Sheng Gu Zhong Lu, ChaoYang District, 100029, Beijing, China
Tel.: (86) 1064430746
Medical Equipment Distr
N.A.I.C.S.: 423450
Pierpaolo Piracci (Reg Mgr-Sls)

PTW-France SARL (1)
41 Chemin de la Cerisaie, 91620, La Ville-du-Bois, France
Tel.: (33) 164499858

Medical Equipment Distr
N.A.I.C.S.: 423450

PTW-New York Corporation (1)
140 58th St Ste 5H3, Brooklyn, NY 11220
Tel.: (516) 827-3181
Medical Equipment Distr
N.A.I.C.S.: 423450
Lance Wilson (Mgr-Ops)

PTW-UK Ltd. (1)
Old School House Station Road East, Grantham, NG31 6HX, Lincolnshire, United Kingdom
Tel.: (44) 1476577503
Medical Equipment Distr
N.A.I.C.S.: 423450

PTX METALS INC.
The Exchange Tower 130 King St W Suite 3680, Toronto, M5X 1B1, ON, Canada
Tel.: (416) 270-5042 ON
Web Site: https://ptxmetals.com
Year Founded: 1998
PANXF—(OTCQB)
Assets: $2,575,803
Liabilities: $574,513
Net Worth: $2,001,290
Earnings: ($1,051,543)
Emp.: 5
Fiscal Year-end: 12/31/22
Mineral Exploration Services
N.A.I.C.S.: 213114
James R. Trusler (Founder, Chm, Pres & CEO)

PUBALI BANK PLC
26 Dilkusha Commercial Area, GPO Box Number 853, Dhaka, 1000, Bangladesh
Tel.: (880) 2223381614
Web Site:
https://www.pubalibangla.com
Year Founded: 1959
PUBALIBANK—(DHA)
Rev.: $215,879,804
Assets: $6,561,860,845
Liabilities: $6,113,001,932
Net Worth: $448,858,913
Earnings: $42,999,062
Emp.: 8,118
Fiscal Year-end: 12/31/20
Commercial Banking Services
N.A.I.C.S.: 522110
Md. Abdul Halim Chowdhury (CEO & Mng Dir)

Subsidiaries:

Pubali Bank Securities Limited (1)
A-A Bhaban 7th Floor 23 Motijheel C/A, Dhaka, 1000, Bangladesh
Tel.: (880) 29576147
Web Site: http://www.pubalibangla.com
Banking Services
N.A.I.C.S.: 522110
Moniruddin Ahmed (Chm)

PUBANG LANDSCAPE ARCHITECTURE CO., LTD.
34F Building A1 Fortune Century Plaza No 13 Hai'an Road, Tianhe District, Guangzhou, 510627, Guangdong, China
Tel.: (86) 2087526515
Web Site:
http://www.pblandscape.com
Year Founded: 1995
002663—(SSE)
Rev.: $346,873,644
Assets: $799,607,484
Liabilities: $368,697,420
Net Worth: $430,910,064
Earnings: ($34,812,180)
Emp.: 1,400
Fiscal Year-end: 12/31/22
Landscape Architectural & Engineering Services
N.A.I.C.S.: 541320

Pubang Landscape Architecture Co., Ltd.—(Continued)
Shanzhong Tu (Chm)

PUBLIC BANK BERHAD
27th Floor Menara Public Bank 146 Jalan Ampang, 50450, Kuala Lumpur, Malaysia
Tel.: (60) 321638888   MY
Web Site: http://www.pbebank.com
PBBANK—(KLS)
Rev.: $4,534,799,153
Assets: $104,394,235,979
Liabilities: $93,489,303,069
Net Worth: $10,904,932,910
Earnings: $1,305,741,164
Emp.: 19,188
Fiscal Year-end: 12/31/22
Banking Services
N.A.I.C.S.: 522110
Hong Piow Teh (Founder)

Subsidiaries:

Cambodian Public Bank Limited (1)
Campu Bank Building No 23 Kramuon Sar Avenue Street No 114, Sangkat Phsar Thmey 2 Khan Daun Penh, Phnom Penh, Cambodia   (100%)
Tel.: (855) 23428100
Web Site: http://www.cpbebank.com
Sales Range: $200-249.9 Million
Emp.: 500
Banking Services
N.A.I.C.S.: 522110

Campu Securities Plc
6th Floor Campu Bank Building No 23 Kramuon Sar Avenue, Street No 114 Sangkat Phsar Thmey II Khan Daun Penh, Phnom Penh, Cambodia
Tel.: (855) 23999880
Web Site: https://www.campusecurities.com.kh
Security Services
N.A.I.C.S.: 561612

PB Trust (L) Ltd. (1)
Level 8 Main Office Tower Financial Park Labuan Jalan Merdeka, Jalan Merdeka, 87000, Labuan, FT, Malaysia
Tel.: (60) 87412336
Web Site: https://www.pbtrust.com.my
Trust Management Services
N.A.I.C.S.: 541618

PB Trustee Services Berhad (1)
17th Floor Menara Public Bank 146 Jalan Ampang, 50450, Kuala Lumpur, Malaysia
Banking Services
N.A.I.C.S.: 522110
Idzwan Rossli (Asst Mgr)

PB Venture Capital Sdn. Bhd. (1)
27th Floor Menara Public Bank 146 Jalan Ampang, 50450, Kuala Lumpur, Malaysia
Tel.: (60) 321638899
Web Site: http://www.publicbank.com
Investment Management Service
N.A.I.C.S.: 523940
Tay Ah Lek (Mng Dir)

Public Bank (L) Ltd. (1)
Level 8 A&B Main Office Tower Financial Park Labuan, Jalan Merdeka, 87000, Labuan, Wilayah Persekutuan, Malaysia
Tel.: (60) 87411898
Sales Range: $50-74.9 Million
Emp.: 14
Private Banking Services
N.A.I.C.S.: 522110
Alexander Wong (Gen Mgr)

Public Bank (Nominees) Limited (1)
7F Public Bank Center 120 Des Voeux Road, Central, China (Hong Kong)
Tel.: (852) 25419222
Web Site: http://www.publicbank.com.hk
Banking Services
N.A.I.C.S.: 521110

Public Bank Lao Limited (1)
No 100/1-4 Khun Bu Lom Road, PO Box 6614, Hatsady Tai Village Chanthabouly District, Vientiane, Laos
Tel.: (856) 21216614
Web Site: https://www.publicbank.com.la

Banking & Financial Services
N.A.I.C.S.: 522110

Public Financial Holdings Limited (1)
2/F Public Bank Centre 120 Des Voeux Road Central, Central, China (Hong Kong)
Tel.: (852) 25419222
Web Site: http://www.publicfinancial.com.hk
Rev.: $191,356,590
Assets: $5,344,536,203
Liabilities: $4,242,352,253
Net Worth: $1,102,183,950
Earnings: $41,908,868
Emp.: 1,207
Fiscal Year-end: 12/31/2022
Financial Services
N.A.I.C.S.: 522299
Yoke Kong Tan (CEO & Co-Sec)

Subsidiary (Domestic):

Winton Holdings (Bermuda) Limited (2)
Room 1101-1110 11th Floor Phase 1 Argyle Centre, 688 Nathan Rd Mongkok, Kowloon, China (Hong Kong)
Tel.: (852) 23919388
Web Site: http://www.wintongroup.com.hk
Sales Range: $25-49.9 Million
Emp.: 20
Financial Holding Company
N.A.I.C.S.: 551112

Public Financial Limited (1)
Room 1105-07 Wing On House 71 Des Voeux Road, Central, China (Hong Kong)
Tel.: (852) 25259351
Banking & Financial Services
N.A.I.C.S.: 521110

Subsidiary (Domestic):

Public Securities Limited (2)
Room 1101-1103 Wing On House 71 Des Voeux Road, Central, China (Hong Kong)
Tel.: (852) 3 929 2800
Web Site: https://www.publicsec.com.hk
Securities Trading Services
N.A.I.C.S.: 523150

Public Financial Securities Limited (1)
10th Fl Public Bank Ctr Desvoeux Rd, Central, China (Hong Kong)
Tel.: (852) 81070818
Sales Range: $50-74.9 Million
Emp.: 20
Securities Brokerage Services
N.A.I.C.S.: 523150

Public Holdings Sdn. Bhd. (1)
8th Floor Menara Public Bank 146 Jalan Ampang, 50450, Kuala Lumpur, Malaysia
Tel.: (60) 321766000
Sales Range: $50-74.9 Million
Emp.: 33
Investment Management Service
N.A.I.C.S.: 523940
Cheong Kien Meng (Mng Dir)

Public Invest Nominees (Tempatan) Sdn. Bhd. (1)
27th Floor Bangunan Public Bank 6 Jalan Sultan Sulaiman, 50000, Kuala Lumpur, Malaysia
Tel.: (60) 322683000
Investment Services
N.A.I.C.S.: 523999

Public Investment Bank Berhad (1)
Level 27 Menara Public Bank 2 No 78 Jalan Raja Chulan, PO Box 12154, 50200, Kuala Lumpur, Malaysia
Tel.: (60) 320362800
Web Site: https://www.publicinvestbank.com
Sales Range: $100-124.9 Million
Emp.: 150
Investment Banking Services
N.A.I.C.S.: 521110

Subsidiary (Domestic):

Public Invest Nominees (Asing) Sdn. Bhd. (2)
27th Fl Bangunan Public Bank 6 Jalan Sultan Sulaiman, 50000, Kuala Lumpur, Malaysia
Tel.: (60) 320313011
Web Site: http://www.publicinvestbank.com

Sales Range: $75-99.9 Million
Emp.: 200
Commercial Banking Services
N.A.I.C.S.: 522110

Public Islamic Bank Berhad (1)
Menara Public Bank 146 Jalan Ampang, 50450, Kuala Lumpur, Malaysia
Tel.: (60) 321766000
Web Site: http://www.publicislamicbank.com.my
Banking Services
N.A.I.C.S.: 522110
Syamsul Azuan Ahmad Fauzi (CEO)

Public Mutual Berhad (1)
Menara Public Bank 2 No 78 Jalan Raja Chulan, 50200, Kuala Lumpur, Malaysia
Tel.: (60) 362796800
Web Site: http://www.publicmutual.com.my
Sales Range: $200-249.9 Million
Emp.: 300
Trust Services
N.A.I.C.S.: 523991

Public Nominees (Tempatan) Sdn. Bhd. (1)
6th Floor Menara Public Bank 146 Jalan Ampang, 50450, Kuala Lumpur, Malaysia
Tel.: (60) 321626077
Sales Range: $50-74.9 Million
Emp.: 15
Commercial Banking Services
N.A.I.C.S.: 522110
Raymond Paul Lei (Mgr)

Public Securities (Nominees) Limited (1)
Room 1108 Wing On House 71 Des Voeux Road, Central, China (Hong Kong)
Tel.: (852) 28778622
Securities Brokerage Services
N.A.I.C.S.: 523150

VID Public Bank (1)
7th Floor Prime Centre Building 53 Quang Trung, Hanoi, Vietnam   (50%)
Tel.: (84) 49438999
Web Site: http://www.vidpublicbank.com.vn
Sales Range: $50-74.9 Million
Emp.: 50
Banking Services
N.A.I.C.S.: 522110

PUBLIC INTELLIGENCE APS
Billedskaerervej 17, 5230, Odense, Denmark
Tel.: (45) 30708593   DK
Web Site: http://www.publicintelligence.dk
Management Consulting Services
N.A.I.C.S.: 541618
Peter Julius (Founder, CEO & Partner)

PUBLIC INVESTMENT CORPORATION (SOC) LIMITED
Menlyn Maine Central Square Corner Aramist Avenue & Corobay Avenue, Waterkloof Glen Extension 2, Pretoria, 0181, South Africa
Tel.: (27) 12 742 3400
Web Site: http://www.pic.gov.za
Year Founded: 1911
Investment Management
N.A.I.C.S.: 523999
Matshepo More (CFO)

Subsidiaries:

Daybreak Farms (Pty) Ltd. (1)
1 Main Road, Sundra, Delmas, 2200, Mpumalanga, South Africa
Tel.: (27) 136611063
Web Site: http://www.daybreakfarms.co.za
Frozen Chicken Products Distr
N.A.I.C.S.: 424440

Efora Energy Ltd. (1)
2nd Floor Building 11 Leslie Avenue, Design Quarter District, Fourways, 2191, Gauteng, South Africa
Tel.: (27) 105912260
Web Site: https://www.eforaenergy.com
Rev.: $82,177,781
Assets: $12,750,208

Liabilities: $21,418,216
Net Worth: ($8,668,007)
Earnings: ($36,921,982)
Emp.: 102
Fiscal Year-end: 02/28/2021
Oil & Gas Exploration Services
N.A.I.C.S.: 211120

Subsidiary (Non-US):

MENA International Petroleum Company Limited (2)
5 Hassan Havez Street, Saraia El Qoba, Cairo, Egypt   (100%)
Tel.: (20) 2 2452 8282
Oil & Gas Exploration & Extraction Services
N.A.I.C.S.: 213112

PUBLIC JOINT STOCK COMPANY ACRON
World Trade Center Krasnopresnenskaya embankment 12, Moscow, 123610, Russia
Tel.: (7) 4954115594   RU
Web Site: https://www.acron.ru
AKRN—(MOEX)
Rev.: $1,614,568,080
Assets: $2,964,598,830
Liabilities: $2,037,822,420
Net Worth: $926,776,410
Earnings: $51,670,920
Emp.: 11,429
Fiscal Year-end: 12/31/20
Mineral Fertilizer Mfr
N.A.I.C.S.: 212390
Alexander Popov (Chm & Sr VP)

Subsidiaries:

AS DBT (1)
Narva mnt 7d, 10117, Tallinn, Estonia
Tel.: (372) 6646500
Web Site: http://www.dbt.eu
Logistic & Supply Chain Services
N.A.I.C.S.: 541614

Acron Argentina S.R.L. (1)
Avda Cervino 4678 4th Floor, Buenos Aires, 1425, Argentina
Tel.: (54) 1147730084
Mineral Fertilizer Producer Mfr
N.A.I.C.S.: 325998

Acron Brasil Ltda. (1)
1455 Av Presidente Juscelino Kubitschek Office 403, Sao Paulo, 04543-011, Brazil
Tel.: (55) 9544555600
Mineral Fertilizer Producer Mfr
N.A.I.C.S.: 325998

Acron France SAS (1)
21 rue Saint Pierre, 92200, Neuilly-sur-Seine, France
Tel.: (33) 143333326
Mineral Fertilizer Producer Mfr
N.A.I.C.S.: 325998

Acron Switzerland AG (1)
4 Lindenstrasse, Baar, 6340, Switzerland
Tel.: (41) 415606565
Mineral Fertilizer Producer Mfr
N.A.I.C.S.: 325998

Acron USA Inc. (1)
20803 Biscayne Blvd Ste 505, Aventura, FL 33180
Tel.: (954) 455-5600
Mineral Fertilizer Producer Mfr
N.A.I.C.S.: 325998

Beijing Yong Sheng Feng AMP Co., Ltd. (1)
182-8 Haier Road Ban Dao International Mansion 14 Floor Room 1405, Laoshan District, Qingdao, 266100, Shandong, China
Tel.: (86) 53280995768
Mineral Fertilizer Producer Mfr
N.A.I.C.S.: 325998

JSC Agronova (1)
12 Krasnopresnenskaya Naberezhnaya, 123610, Moscow, Russia
Tel.: (7) 4992451145
Mineral Fertilizer Producer Mfr
N.A.I.C.S.: 325998
Vladimir Kharin (Gen Dir)

LLC Andrex (1)

AND PRIVATE COMPANIES

1 5th Prichalnaya Street, 236035, Kaliningrad, Russia
Tel.: (7) 4012632186
Mineral Fertilizer Producer Mfr
N.A.I.C.S.: 325998

North Atlantic Potash Inc. (1)
Suite 701 Midtown Tower 201-1st Avenue South, Saskatoon, S7K 1J5, SK, Canada
Tel.: (306) 975-0210
Web Site:
https://www.northatlanticpotash.com
Mineral Exploration Services
N.A.I.C.S.: 213114
David Waugh (CEO)

North-Western Phosphorous Company (1)
26 Koashva Settlement, 184227, Kirovsk, Murmansk region, Russia
Tel.: (7) 8155527189
Web Site: http://www.szfk.ru
Emp.: 2,000
Apatite Ore Mining Services
N.A.I.C.S.: 212390
Evgeni Sozinov (CEO)

PJSC Dorogobuzh (1)
Dorogobuzh Industrial Site Dorogobuzh, Dorogobuzh district, 215753, Smolensk, Russia
Tel.: (7) 4814468207
Chemical Fertilizer Mfr & Distr
N.A.I.C.S.: 325998

Verkhnekamsk Potash Company (1)
10 Gagarin St Prem krai, 618419, Berezniki, Russia **(80.01%)**
Tel.: (7) 3424255180
Web Site:
http://www.verkhnekamskpotashco.ru
Potassium & Magnesium Salt Mineral Mfr
N.A.I.C.S.: 325180
Alexander Pupov (CEO)

PUBLIC JOINT STOCK COMPANY CHELINDBANK

Karla Marksa Street 80, Chelyabinsk, 454091, Russia
Tel.: (7) 3512397777 RU
Web Site: https://www.chelindbank.ru
Year Founded: 1990
Emp.: 100
Commercial Banking Services
N.A.I.C.S.: 522110
Mikhail I. Bratishkin (Chm-Mgmt Bd & Gen Dir)

PUBLIC JOINT STOCK INSURANCE COMPANY ENERGOGARANT

23 Sadovnicheskaya Emb, 115035, Moscow, Russia
Tel.: (7) 4957370330 RU
Web Site:
https://www.energogarant.ru
Year Founded: 1992
Rev.: $10,341,812
Assets: $255,743,291
Liabilities: $187,235,326
Net Worth: $68,507,964
Earnings: $2,350,977
Fiscal Year-end: 12/31/18
Life Insurance Products & Services
N.A.I.C.S.: 524113
Sergey Vasiliev (Gen Dir)

PUBLIC PACKAGES HOLDINGS BERHAD

Wisma Public Packages Lintang Kampung Jawa Bayan Lepas Industrial Park, 11900, Penang, Malaysia
Tel.: (60) 46444777
Web Site: https://www.pph.com.my
Year Founded: 1976
PPHB—(KLS)
Rev.: $47,349,630
Assets: $83,740,952
Liabilities: $11,511,111
Net Worth: $72,229,841
Earnings: $8,145,608
Emp.: 827

Fiscal Year-end: 12/31/22
Corrugated Box Mfr
N.A.I.C.S.: 322211
Teng Liang Koay (Exec Dir)

Subsidiaries:

PPH Printing & Packaging (Kulim) Sdn. Bhd. (1)
Plot 75 Kulim Industrial Estate, 09000, Kulim, Kedah, Malaysia
Tel.: (60) 44891294
Packaging Products Mfr
N.A.I.C.S.: 326112

PPH Printing & Packaging (Penang) Sdn. Bhd. (1)
Plot 468 482 Jalan Perusahaan Baru, Prai Inudstrial Estate, 13600, Penang, Malaysia
Tel.: (60) 43901501
Packaging Products Mfr
N.A.I.C.S.: 326112

Public Packages (NT) Sdn. Bhd. (1)
No 3779 MK11, Nibong Tebal Seberang Prai Selatan, 14300, Penang, Malaysia
Tel.: (60) 45936888
Packaging Products Mfr
N.A.I.C.S.: 326112

Public Packages (Shah Alam) Sdn. Bhd. (1)
No 33 Jalan Utas 15/7 Seksyen 15, 40200, Shah Alam, Selangor Darul Ehsan, Malaysia
Tel.: (60) 355112099
Packaging Products Mfr
N.A.I.C.S.: 326112

Public Packages Asia (S) Pte. Ltd. (1)
3791 Jalan Bukit Merah 07-03 E-Centre At Redhill, Singapore, 159471, Singapore
Tel.: (65) 62749768
Packaging Products Mfr
N.A.I.C.S.: 326112

Public Packages Sdn. Bhd. (1)
Plot 67 72 Lintang Kampong Jawa, Bayan Lepas Industrial Park, 11900, Bayan Lepas, Penang, Malaysia
Tel.: (60) 46444777
Packaging Products Mfr
N.A.I.C.S.: 326112

PUBLIC POWER CORPORATION S.A.

30 Chalkokondyli St, 104 32, Athens, Greece
Tel.: (30) 21052930301 GR
Web Site: http://www.dei.gr
PU8—(DEU)
Rev.: $12,144,514,354
Assets: $21,074,050,291
Liabilities: $16,023,467,516
Net Worth: $5,050,582,776
Earnings: ($9,621,196)
Emp.: 12,755
Fiscal Year-end: 12/31/22
Electric Power Distr; Telecommunications Services
N.A.I.C.S.: 221122
Vasileios Germanopoulos (Officer)

Subsidiaries:

EDS DOO Belgrade (1)
Tel.: (381) 112451570
Web Site: https://www.eds.rs
Hydro Electric Power Services
N.A.I.C.S.: 221118

EDS DOO Skopje (1)
Boulevard St Kliment Ohridski 30, 1000, Skopje, North Macedonia
Tel.: (389) 25514100
Web Site: http://www.eds.mk
Hydro Electric Power Services
N.A.I.C.S.: 221118

Hedno S.A (1)
Perraivou 20 and Kallirrois 5, 117 43, Athens, Greece
Tel.: (30) 2111900500
Web Site: https://www.deddie.gr
Electric Power Distr
N.A.I.C.S.: 221122

Lignitiki Megalopolis S.A. (1)
57 Veranzerou, 10437, Athens, Greece
Tel.: (30) 279 102 5045
Web Site: https://www.lignitiki-megalopolis.gr
Electric Power & Fuel Services
N.A.I.C.S.: 221112

PPC Bulgaria JSCo (1)
2 Pozitano Square Floor 7, Triaditsa District, Sofia, 1000, Bulgaria
Tel.: (359) 24008088
Web Site: https://www.ppc-bg.com
Electric Power Services
N.A.I.C.S.: 221122
Alexandra Payrri (Chm & Exec Dir)

PPC Elektrik Tedaric Ve Ticaret A.S. (1)
Maslak Mah Bilim Sk No 5 Sun Plaza Kat 13, Maslak, 34398, Istanbul, Turkiye
Tel.: (90) 2123674963
Web Site: https://www.ppc.com.tr
Electric Power Services
N.A.I.C.S.: 221122

PPC Renewables S.A. (1)
3 Kapodistriou, Ag Paraskevi, 153 43, Athens, Greece **(100%)**
Tel.: (30) 2112118000
Web Site: https://www.ppcr.gr
Sales Range: $50-74.9 Million
Emp.: 75
Management of Renewable Energy Sources
N.A.I.C.S.: 221122

Subsidiary (Non-US):

Land Power srl (2)
251-253 Mamaia Avenue, 900559, Constanta, Romania
Tel.: (40) 341432770
Web Site: https://www.landpower.ro
Wind Power Generation Services
N.A.I.C.S.: 221115

PUBLIC SECTOR PENSION INVESTMENT BOARD

1250 Rene-Levesque Boulevard West Suite 1400, Montreal, H3B 5E9, QC, Canada
Tel.: (514) 937-2772 Ca
Web Site: http://www.investpsp.com
Year Founded: 1999
Rev.: $25,492,940,640
Assets: $182,109,308,040
Liabilities: $22,290,286,320
Net Worth: $159,819,021,720
Earnings: $24,705,184,680
Emp.: 897
Fiscal Year-end: 03/31/21
Pension Fund Investment Management Services
N.A.I.C.S.: 524292
Martin J. Glynn (Chm)

Subsidiaries:

Aerostar Airport Holdings, LLC (1)
Terminal D Arrivals Ave, Carolina, PR 00979 **(40%)**
Tel.: (787) 289-7240
Web Site: https://www.aerostarairports.com
Holding Company; Airport Operator
N.A.I.C.S.: 551112
Maria Fuentes (Coord-Quality)

AlixPartners, LLP (1)
909 3rd Ave, New York, NY 10022
Tel.: (212) 490-2500
Web Site: http://www.alixpartners.com
Emp.: 2,000
Management Consulting Services
N.A.I.C.S.: 541618
Fred Crawford (Mng Dir)

Subsidiary (Non-US):

AlixPartners Argentina SRL (2)
Avenida Corrientes 1750 Piso 12, C1042AAQ, Buenos Aires, Argentina
Tel.: (54) 11 5031 2900
Financial Advisory Services
N.A.I.C.S.: 523940

AlixPartners UK LLP (2)

PUBLIC SECTOR PENSION INVESTMENT BOARD

6 New Street Square, London, EC4A 3BF, United Kingdom
Tel.: (44) 20 7098 7400
Financial Advisory Services
N.A.I.C.S.: 523940
Nick Wood (Mng Dir-Merger & Acq Services Practice-EMEA)

Angel Trains Limited (1)
123 Victoria Street, London, SW1E 6DE, United Kingdom
Tel.: (44) 20 7592 0500
Web Site: http://www.angeltrains.co.uk
Emp.: 145
Rolling Stock Leasing Services
N.A.I.C.S.: 532411
Malcolm Brown (CEO)

AviAlliance GmbH (1)
Alfredstrasse 236, Essen, 45133, Germany
Tel.: (49) 201 824 1249
Web Site: http://www.avialliance.com
Sales Range: $25-49.9 Million
Emp.: 59
Holding Company; Airport Investment & Portfolio Management
N.A.I.C.S.: 551112
Holger Linkweiler (Mng Dir & Member-Mgmt Bd)

Subsidiary (Domestic):

AviAlliance Capital Verwaltungs GmbH & Co. KG (2)
Alfredstrasse 236, Essen, 45133, Germany **(100%)**
Tel.: (49) 201 824 1415
Web Site: http://www.avialliance-capital.com
Airport Investment & Portfolio Management Services
N.A.I.C.S.: 523940
Holger Linkweiler (Mng Dir)

Affiliate (Domestic):

Flughafen Dusseldorf GmbH (2)
Flughafenstrasse 120, D 40474, Dusseldorf, Germany **(20%)**
Tel.: (49) 2114210
Web Site: http://www.dus-int.de
Airport
N.A.I.C.S.: 488119
Thomas Schnalke (Dir-Fin)

Flughafen Hamburg GmbH (2)
Flughafenstr 1 - 3, 22335, Hamburg, Germany **(34.8%)**
Tel.: (49) 4050750
Web Site: http://www.hamburg-airport.de
Airport Services
N.A.I.C.S.: 488119

Galderma Holding S.A. (1)
Avenue de Gratta Paille 2, 1018, Lausanne, Switzerland
Tel.: (41) 21 642 7800
Web Site: http://www.galderma.com
Holding Company; Skin Health Products Mfr & Whslr
N.A.I.C.S.: 551112
Janusz Czernielewski (VP-Medical Affairs)

Subsidiary (US):

ALASTIN Skincare, Inc (2)
3129 Tiger Run Ct Ste 109, Carlsbad, CA 92010
Web Site: http://www.alastin.com
Skin Care Product Mfr
N.A.I.C.S.: 325620
Cam L. Garner (Co-Founder)

Subsidiary (Domestic):

Galderma Pharma S.A. (2)
Avenue de Gratta Paille 2, 1018, Lausanne, Switzerland
Tel.: (41) 21 642 78 00
Web Site: http://www.galderma.com
Holding Company; Dermatology Products Developer, Mfr & Marketer
N.A.I.C.S.: 551112

Subsidiary (Non-US):

Galderma Brasil Ltda. (3)
Edifico E Tower Ruafunchal 418 6 Andar, 04551-060, Sao Paulo, SP, Brazil
Tel.: (55) 1135246300
Web Site: http://www.galderma.com.br

PUBLIC SECTOR PENSION INVESTMENT BOARD

Public Sector Pension Investment Board—(Continued)
Sales Range: $25-49.9 Million
Emp.: 50
Dermatology Products Sales & Marketing
N.A.I.C.S.: 424210

Galderma Canada, Inc. (3)
55 Commerce Valley Dr W 400, Thornhill, L3T 7V9, ON, Canada
Tel.: (905) 762-2500
Web Site: http://www.galderma.com
Sales Range: $25-49.9 Million
Emp.: 25
Dermatology Product Mfr
N.A.I.C.S.: 325412

Galderma International SAS (3)
Tour Europlaza La Defense 4 20 Avenue Andre Prothin, La Defense, 92927, Paris, Cedex, France
Tel.: (33) 158864545
Web Site: http://www.galderma.com
Sales Range: $125-149.9 Million
Emp.: 300
Dermatology Products Sales & Marketing
N.A.I.C.S.: 424210

Subsidiary (US):

Galderma Laboratories, L.P. (3)
14501 N Fwy, Fort Worth, TX 76177-3304
Tel.: (817) 961-5000
Web Site: http://www.galdermausa.com
Sales Range: $50-74.9 Million
Emp.: 250
Dermatology Product Mfr
N.A.I.C.S.: 325412
Kelly Huang *(VP & Gen Mgr-Aesthetic & Corrective Bus)*

Subsidiary (Non-US):

Galderma Laboratorium GmbH (3)
Toulouser Allee 23a, 40211, Dusseldorf, Germany
Tel.: (49) 2115860100
Web Site: http://www.galderma.de
Sales Range: $50-74.9 Million
Emp.: 200
Dermatology Product Mfr
N.A.I.C.S.: 325412
Marion Bock *(Mng Dir, Head-DACH & Gen Mgr)*

Galderma Production Canada Inc. (3)
19400 Transcanada Highway, Baie-d'Urfe, H9X 3S4, QC, Canada
Tel.: (514) 457-3366
Web Site: http://www.galderma.com
Sales Range: $50-74.9 Million
Emp.: 220
Dermatology Product Mfr
N.A.I.C.S.: 325412

Laboratoires Galderma SAS (3)
Zone Industrielle Touviere, 74540, Alby-sur-Cheran, France
Tel.: (33) 158864545
Sales Range: $50-74.9 Million
Emp.: 200
Dermatology Product Mfr
N.A.I.C.S.: 325412

Q-Med AB (3)
Seminariegatan 21, 752 28, Uppsala, 75228, Sweden
Tel.: (46) 184790000
Web Site: http://www.q-med.com
Sales Range: $200-249.9 Million
Emp.: 636
Biotechnology & Medical Devices
N.A.I.C.S.: 339112

Subsidiary (Non-US):

Q-Med (Sweden) Australia Pty Ltd. (4)
37 Belmore Street, Surry Hills, 2010, Sydney, NSW, Australia
Tel.: (61) 292817727
Web Site: http://www.revitaliseyourskin.com.au
Sales Range: $25-49.9 Million
Emp.: 20
Pharmaceutical Preparation Mfr
N.A.I.C.S.: 325412

Q-Med Brasil Comercio e Importacao de Produtos Medicos Ltda (4)
Rua Alexandre Dumas 2100 conjunto 22, Chacara Santo Antonio, 04717-004, Sao Paulo, SP, Brazil
Tel.: (55) 1151855589
Web Site: http://www.q-med.com
Sales Range: $50-74.9 Million
Emp.: 8
Medical Dental & Hospital Equipment & Supplies Whslr
N.A.I.C.S.: 423450

Q-Med ICT S.r.l. (4)
Via M Borsa 11, Codogno, 26845, Lodi, Italy
Tel.: (39) 0377436091
Web Site: http://www.q-med.com
Sales Range: $25-49.9 Million
Emp.: 50
Toilet Preparation Mfr
N.A.I.C.S.: 325620

Q-Med International Ltd (4)
39 Healthy Street East, Kodak House II Rm 2207-08 22nd, North Point, China (Hong Kong)
Tel.: (852) 25165002
Surgical & Medical Instrument Mfr
N.A.I.C.S.: 339112

Q-Med International Trading (Shanghai) Ltd (4)
Room 2017 No 1 Ji Long Road, Waigaoqiao Free Trade Zone, Shanghai, 200131, China
Tel.: (86) 1085321642
Web Site: http://www.q-med.com
Drugs & Druggists Sundries Whslr
N.A.I.C.S.: 424210

Q-Med Mexico S.A de C.V. (4)
Lglesia 2 Torre E Despacho 503, Colonia Tizapan San Angel, 1090, Mexico, Mexico
Tel.: (52) 5556168292
Web Site: http://www.q-med.com
Sales Range: $25-49.9 Million
Emp.: 18
Surgical Appliance & Supplies Mfr
N.A.I.C.S.: 339113

Q-Med Polska SP. Z.o.o (4)
Nowy Swiat 47, 00-042, Warsaw, Poland
Tel.: (48) 228929120
Web Site: http://www.q-med.com
Sales Range: $25-49.9 Million
Emp.: 15
Surgical & Medical Instrument Mfr
N.A.I.C.S.: 339112

Q-Med S.a.r.l. (4)
49 Rue de Lisbonne, 75008, Paris, France
Tel.: (33) 156434300
Web Site: http://www.q-med.com
Drugs & Druggists Sundries Whslr
N.A.I.C.S.: 424210

Q-Med Spain S.L. (4)
Agustin Foxa 29 Planta Baja, Modulo 1 C-Jose Echegaray 8, 28036, Madrid, Spain
Tel.: (34) 916369205
Web Site: http://www.q-med.com
Sales Range: $25-49.9 Million
Emp.: 30
Drugs & Druggists Sundries Whslr
N.A.I.C.S.: 424210

H2O Power Limited Partnership (4)
560 King Street West Unit 2, Oshawa, L1J 7J1, ON, Canada
Tel.: (905) 438-8539
Web Site: http://www.h2opower.ca
Holding Company; Hydroelectric Power Plants Operator
N.A.I.C.S.: 551112
Francis DeBay *(Ops Mgr-Oshawa Operating Center)*

Subsidiary (US):

FirstLight Power Resources, Inc. (2)
111 S Bedford St Ste 103, Burlington, MA 01803
Tel.: (781) 359-9601
Web Site: http://www.firstlightpower.com
Hydroelectric Power Generation Plant Operator
N.A.I.C.S.: 561110
Peter Rider *(VP-Comml)*

Subsidiary (Domestic):

FirstLight Hydro Generating Company (3)
111 S Bedford St Ste 103, Burlington, MA 01803
Tel.: (781) 359-9601
Hydroelectric Power Generation Plant Operator
N.A.I.C.S.: 221111

Homeplus Co., Limited (1)
398 Hwagokoro, Gangseo-gu, Seoul, 135-080, Korea (South)
Tel.: (82) 234598000
Web Site: http://www.homeplus.co.kr
Hypermarkets, Supermarkets & Convenience Stores Operator & Franchisor
N.A.I.C.S.: 445110
Sang Hyun Kim *(CEO)*

Radius Global Infrastructure, Inc. (1)
3 Bala Plz E Ste 502, Bala Cynwyd, PA 19004
Tel.: (610) 660-4910
Web Site: https://www.radiusglobal.com
Rev.: $135,456,000
Assets: $2,453,490,000
Liabilities: $1,770,696,000
Net Worth: $682,794,000
Earnings: ($60,687,000)
Emp.: 399
Fiscal Year-end: 12/31/2022
Holding Company
N.A.I.C.S.: 551112
Richard I. Goldstein *(COO)*

Subsidiary (Domestic):

AP WIP Investments Holdings, LP (2)
9373 Towne Ctr Dr Ste 200, San Diego, CA 92121
Web Site: http://www.apwip.com
Holding Company
N.A.I.C.S.: 551112
Dan Hasselman *(Co-Founder & Pres)*

Subsidiary (Domestic):

APWireless Infrastructure Partners, LLC (3)
4250 Executive Sq Ste 900, La Jolla, CA 92037
Web Site: https://www.apwip.com
Real Estate Credit
N.A.I.C.S.: 522292
Scott E. Langeland *(CEO)*

Subsidiary (Non-US):

AP Wireless (UK) Limited (2)
2nd Floor 16-18 Conduit Street, Lichfield, WS13 6JR, Staffordshire, United Kingdom
Tel.: (44) 1543547901
Web Site: https://www.apwireless.co.uk
Tower Infrastructure Services
N.A.I.C.S.: 517810
Thomas Evans *(Exec VP-Global Asset Mgmt)*

AP Wireless Australia Pty Ltd (2)
64 York Street, Sydney, 2000, NSW, Australia
Tel.: (61) 1800983402
Web Site: http://www.apwireless.com.au
Wireless Telecommunication Services
N.A.I.C.S.: 517112

AP Wireless Belgium, BVBA (2)
Suikerui 16, 2000, Antwerp, Belgium
Tel.: (32) 35470115
Web Site: https://www.apwbelgium.be
Wireless Telecommunication Services
N.A.I.C.S.: 517112
Thomas Evans *(Exec VP-Global Asset Mgmt)*

AP Wireless Canada, ULC (2)
3080 Yonge Street Suite 6060, Toronto, M4N 3N1, ON, Canada
Web Site: https://www.apwip.ca
Wireless Telecommunication Services
N.A.I.C.S.: 517112
Jeanne Lagueux *(Dir-Acquisitions & Site Dev)*

AP Wireless Ireland Investments Ltd. (2)
Gray Office Park Galway Retail Park Head-ford Road, Galway, Ireland
Tel.: (353) 91457880
Web Site: https://www.apwireless.ie
Tower Infrastructure Services
N.A.I.C.S.: 517810
Linda Evans *(Mgr-Site Acquisition & Dev)*

APWPT II Investimentos, S.A. (2)
Rua Luciano Cordeiro 123 - 5E, 1050 139, Lisbon, Portugal
Tel.: (351) 210200105
Web Site: https://www.apwportugal.pt
Tower Infrastructure Services
N.A.I.C.S.: 517810
Fernando Alves *(Country Mgr)*

Cell: CM Ltd. (2)
16-18 Conduit Street, Lichfield, WS13 6JR, Staffordshire, United Kingdom
Tel.: (44) 1926298187
Web Site: https://www.cellcm.com
Wireless Telecommunication Services
N.A.I.C.S.: 517112
Marc Blake *(Mgr-Accounts)*

Dacia Antena, S.R.L. (2)
General David Praporgescu Street no 1-5 Sector 2, Bucharest, Romania
Tel.: (40) 312294646
Web Site: https://www.daciaantena.ro
Tower Infrastructure Services
N.A.I.C.S.: 517810

Pannon Antenna, Kft (2)
Bencyur utca 47 1 em 313, 1068, Budapest, Hungary
Tel.: (36) 15507374
Web Site: https://www.pannonantenna.hu
Tower Infrastructure Services
N.A.I.C.S.: 517810

Telecom Iberica De Inversiones, S.L. (2)
Parque Empresarial Via Norte Calle Quintanavides No 15, Building 2 PB Module D Door A, 28050, Madrid, Spain
Tel.: (34) 900838542
Web Site: http://www.telecomiberica.es
Tower Infrastructure Services
N.A.I.C.S.: 517810

Telecom Vastgoed, B.V. (2)
Bisonspoor 3002-C801, 3605 LT, Maarssen, Netherlands
Tel.: (31) 733690553
Web Site: https://www.apwnetherlands.nl
Tower Infrastructure Services
N.A.I.C.S.: 517810
Thomas Evans *(Exec VP-Global Asset Mgmt)*

Revera Inc. (1)
5015 Spectrum Way Suite 600, Mississauga, L4W 0E4, ON, Canada (100%)
Tel.: (289) 360-1200
Web Site: https://www.reveraliving.com
Sales Range: $800-899.9 Million
Emp.: 6,000
Senior Citizen Health Care Services & Facilities Operator
N.A.I.C.S.: 623311
Thomas G. Wellner *(Pres & CEO)*

Subsidiary (US):

CPL Subacute LLC (2)
538 Preston Ave Ste 270, Meriden, CT 06450
Tel.: (203) 608-6100
Continuing Care Retirement Communities
N.A.I.C.S.: 623311

Sunrise Senior Living Management, Inc. (2)
7902 Westpark Dr, McLean, VA 22102 (65%)
Tel.: (703) 273-7500
Web Site: http://www.sunriseseniorliving.com
Assisted Living, Continuing Care & Nursing Care Facilities Management Services
N.A.I.C.S.: 561110
Teresa M. Klaassen *(Co-Founder)*

Subsidiary (Domestic):

Sunrise Senior Living, LLC (3)
7900 Westpark Dr, McLean, VA 22102
Tel.: (703) 273-7500
Web Site: http://www.sunriseseniorliving.com

AND PRIVATE COMPANIES

Emp.: 31,600
Holding Company; Assisted Living, Continuing Care & Nursing Care Facilities
N.A.I.C.S.: 551112
Teresa M. Klaassen *(Co-Founder)*

Subsidiary (Non-US):

Sunrise Senior Living Limited **(4)**
Sunrise House Post Office Lane, Beaconsfield, HP9 1FN, Buckinghamshire, United Kingdom
Tel.: (44) 8081599314
Web Site: http://www.sunrise-care.co.uk
Assisted Living, Continuing Care & Nursing Care Facilities Management Services
N.A.I.C.S.: 561110
Amanda Scott *(Mng Dir)*

TDF S.A.S. **(1)**
Tel.: (33) 155951000
Web Site: http://www.tdf.fr
Television, Radio, Telecommunications & Satellite Communications Infrastructure Operator
N.A.I.C.S.: 517810
Olivier Huart *(Chm & CEO)*

TimberWest Forest Corp. **(1)**
Suite 2000 1055 W Hastings St, Vancouver, V6E 2E9, BC, Canada
Tel.: (604) 654-4600
Web Site: http://www.timberwest.com
Sales Range: $250-299.9 Million
Emp.: 80
Logging & Lumbermill Services
N.A.I.C.S.: 113310
Rick Jaccard *(VP-Mktg & Sls)*

Webster Limited **(1)**
61 Kurrajong Avenue, Leeton, 2705, NSW, Australia
Tel.: (61) 2 6951 3000
Web Site: http://www.websterltd.com.au
Rev.: $113,376,319
Assets: $593,518,938
Liabilities: $202,115,690
Net Worth: $391,403,247
Earnings: $21,139,572
Fiscal Year-end: 09/30/2018
Holding Company; Walnut & Onion Farming, Processing & Whslr
N.A.I.C.S.: 551112
Derek C. Goullet *(Gen Mgr-Ops-Walnuts)*

Subsidiary (Domestic):

Walnuts Australia Pty. Ltd. **(2)**
349 Forth Road, PO Box 417, Devonport, 7310, TAS, Australia
Tel.: (61) 3 6427 5000
Web Site: http://www.websterltd.com.au
Sales Range: $25-49.9 Million
Emp.: 50
Walnut Farming, Processing & Whslr
N.A.I.C.S.: 111335
Derek Goullet *(Gen Mgr-Horticulture)*

PUBLIC SERVICE PROPERTIES INVESTMENT LIMITED

St Peters House Rue des Brehauts, Saint Peter Port, GY7 9RT, Guernsey
Tel.: (44) 1481 266 777   GY
Web Site: http://www.pspiltd.com
Year Founded: 1988
Sales Range: $10-24.9 Million
Real Estate Investment Services
N.A.I.C.S.: 531390

PUBLICIDAD FERRER Y ASOCIADOS, S.A. DE C.V.

Montes Urales 750 IV Seccion, Lomas de Chapultepec, Mexico, 11000, Mexico
Tel.: (52) 5554801400   MX
Web Site: http://www.grupoferrer.com
Year Founded: 1960
Emp.: 60
Advertising Agency Services
N.A.I.C.S.: 541810
Juan Cristobal Ferer *(Pres)*

Subsidiaries:

Ferrer USA **(1)**
9911 W Pico Blvd Ste 826, Los Angeles, CA 90035
Tel.: (310) 284-2692
Web Site: http://www.grupoferrer.com
Advertising Agency
N.A.I.C.S.: 541810

PUBLICIS GROUPE S.A.

133 Avenue des Champs-Elysees, 75008, Paris, France
Tel.: (33) 144437000   FR
Web Site:
    https://www.publicisgroupe.com
Year Founded: 1926
PGPEF—(OTCQX)
Sales Range: $75-99.9 Million
Emp.: 1,000
Fiscal Year-end: 12/31/21
Holding Company; Advertising Agency
N.A.I.C.S.: 551112
Jean-Michel Etienne *(CFO, Member-Mgmt Bd & Exec VP)*

Subsidiaries:

3 Share Inc. **(1)**
40 Water St 8th Fl, Boston, MA 02109
Web Site: http://www.3sharecorp.com
Marketing & Advertising Services
N.A.I.C.S.: 541810

Ambience Publicis Advertising Pvt. Ltd. **(1)**
Viva Ctr 126 Mathuradas Mills Compoud, N M Joshi Marg Lower Parel W, Mumbai, 400 013, India
Tel.: (91) 222482 9000
Web Site: http://www.publicis.com
Advetising Agency
N.A.I.C.S.: 541810
Paritosh Srivastava *(COO)*

Arc Amsterdam **(1)**
Cronenburg 2, 1081 GN, Amsterdam, Netherlands
Tel.: (31) 20 669 44 44
Sales Range: $25-49.9 Million
Emp.: 45
N.A.I.C.S.: 541810

BOZ Paris **(1)**
22 rue de Courcelles, 75008, Paris, France
Tel.: (33) 1 44 95 99 00
Sales Range: $25-49.9 Million
Emp.: 30
N.A.I.C.S.: 541810

Bartle Bogle Hegarty Limited **(1)**
60 Kingly Street, London, W1B 5DS, United Kingdom   **(100%)**
Tel.: (44) 20 7734 1677
Web Site:
    http://www.bartleboglehegarty.com
Sales Range: $1-4.9 Billion
Emp.: 500
Advetising Agency
N.A.I.C.S.: 541810
Sarah Watson *(Chief Strategy Officer)*

Branch (Non-US):

BBH Mumbai **(2)**
Amiye 2nd Floor Linking Road, Santacruz (West), Mumbai, 400054, India
Tel.: (91) 22 3992 9000
Web Site: http://www.bbh.co.uk
N.A.I.C.S.: 541810
Subhash Kamath *(CEO)*

Branch (US):

BBH New York **(2)**
32 Ave of the Americas 19th Fl, New York, NY 10013
Tel.: (212) 812-6600
Web Site:
    http://www.bartleboglehegarty.com
Sales Range: $25-49.9 Million
Emp.: 175
Advertising Services
N.A.I.C.S.: 541810
Hugo Bierschenk *(Copywriter & Art Dir)*

Branch (Non-US):

BBH Singapore **(2)**
5 Magazine Road 03 03 Central Mall, Singapore, 059571, Singapore
Tel.: (65) 6500 3000

PUBLICIS GROUPE S.A.

Web Site: http://www.bbh.co.uk
Emp.: 100
Advertising Services
N.A.I.C.S.: 541810
Charles Wigley *(Chm-Asia)*

Subsidiary (US):

Domani Studios LLC **(2)**
45 Main St Ste 206, Brooklyn, NY 11201
Tel.: (718) 797-4470
Web Site: http://www.domanistudios.com
Sales Range: $1-9.9 Million
Emp.: 9
Digital Marketing Services
N.A.I.C.S.: 541890
Evan Stark *(CTO)*

Beehive Communications Pvt. Ltd. **(1)**
3rd Floor Trust House 35 Dr E Borges Road, Parel, Mumbai, 400 012, India
Tel.: (91) 22 4315 2000
Web Site:
    http://www.beehivecommunications.com
Emp.: 120
Advetising Agency
N.A.I.C.S.: 541810

Big Fuel Communications LLC **(1)**
32 Avenue of the Americas 19th Fl, New York, NY 10013
Tel.: (212) 616-6300
Web Site: http://www.bigfuel.com
Emp.: 32
Advetising Agency
N.A.I.C.S.: 541810
Mike McGraw *(Mng Partner)*

Brand Pharm **(1)**
79 Madison Ave 3rd Fl, New York, NY 10016
Tel.: (212) 684-0909
Sales Range: $125-149.9 Million
Advertising Services
N.A.I.C.S.: 541890

Bromley Communications, LLC **(1)**
401 E Houston St, San Antonio, TX 78205-2615
Tel.: (210) 244-2000
Sales Range: $25-49.9 Million
Emp.: 180
Marketing & Advertising Agency
N.A.I.C.S.: 541810
Ernest W. Bromley *(CEO)*

CNC AG **(1)**
Dammstrasse 54, 33824, Werther, Germany
Tel.: (49) 520397480
Web Site: http://www.cnc-ag.de
3D Printing & Prototype Construction Services
N.A.I.C.S.: 323111

Capital Advertising **(1)**
UGF Tower A Building No 8, Cyber City DLF Phase II, Gurgaon, 122002, India
Tel.: (91) 124 4568100
Web Site: http://www.adcapital.com
Advertising Services
N.A.I.C.S.: 541810

Carmi & Ubertis Design S.R.L. **(1)**
2 Via Savio Alessandro, 15033, Casale Monferrato, Italy
Tel.: (39) 014271686
Sales Range: $25-49.9 Million
Emp.: 21
N.A.I.C.S.: 541810
Elio Carmi *(Dir-Art)*

Carre Noir **(1)**
24 rue Salmon de Rothschild, 92288, Suresnes, Cedex, France
Tel.: (33) 1 57 32 85 00
Web Site: http://www.carrenoir.com
Sales Range: $25-49.9 Million
Emp.: 150
N.A.I.C.S.: 541810
Christophe Fillatre *(Pres)*

Carre Noir Barcelona **(1)**
Duana 3-2, Barcelona, 08003, Spain
Tel.: (34) 933 016 500
Web Site: http://www.carrenoir.es
Sales Range: Less than $1 Million
Emp.: 6
N.A.I.C.S.: 541810
Joan Ricart *(Dir Gen)*

Carre Noir London **(1)**
82 Baker Street, London, W1U 6AE, United Kingdom
Tel.: (44) 207 830 3039
N.A.I.C.S.: 541810

Carre Noir Turino **(1)**
Corso Re Umberto 87, 10128, Turin, Italy
Tel.: (39) 011 56 21 937
Web Site: http://www.carrenoir.com
Sales Range: $25-49.9 Million
Emp.: 20
N.A.I.C.S.: 541810

Carre Noir Warszaw **(1)**
Ul Ordynacka 14/10, 00-358, Warsaw, Poland
Tel.: (48) 22 826 35 38
Web Site: http://www.soulcommpublicis.com
Sales Range: $25-49.9 Million
Emp.: 2
N.A.I.C.S.: 541810

Champs Medias **(1)**
36 Rue Vivienne, 75002, Paris, France
Tel.: (33) 1 56 21 20 00
Sales Range: $25-49.9 Million
Emp.: 11
Public Relations
N.A.I.C.S.: 541820

Chemistry Communications Group, Plc **(1)**
Melbray Mews, 158 Hurlingham Rd, London, SW6 3NG, United Kingdom
Tel.: (44) 20 7736 5355
Web Site: http://www.chemistrygroup.co.uk
Sales Range: $25-49.9 Million
Emp.: 160
Digital/Interactive, Email, Media Relations, Outdoor, Radio, Sales Promotion
N.A.I.C.S.: 541810
Laura Holme *(Head-New Bus)*

Ciszewski Public Relations Sp. z o.o. **(1)**
Bobrowiecha 1A, 00728, Warsaw, Poland
Tel.: (48) 22 488 41 50
Web Site: http://www.ciszewskipr.pl
Sales Range: $25-49.9 Million
Emp.: 45
N.A.I.C.S.: 541820
Jerzy Ciszewski *(Owner)*

Compasso Mundocom **(1)**
Prof WH Keeflan 12, 1185 LN, Amstelveen, Netherlands
Tel.: (31) 20 517 1580
Web Site: http://www.compasso.nl
Sales Range: $25-49.9 Million
Emp.: 45
N.A.I.C.S.: 541810

Denuo **(1)**
35 W Wacker Dr, Chicago, IL 60601
Tel.: (312) 220-5959
Sales Range: $25-49.9 Million
Emp.: 25
Advertising Services
N.A.I.C.S.: 541810
Dan Buczaczer *(Sr VP & Mng Dir)*

Branch (Domestic):

Denuo **(2)**
6500 Wilshire Blvd, Los Angeles, CA 90048
Tel.: (323) 658-4122
Advertising Services
N.A.I.C.S.: 541810

Digitas Inc. **(1)**
40 Water St, Boston, MA 02109
Tel.: (617) 867-1000
Web Site: http://www.digitas.com
Sales Range: $150-199.9 Million
Marketing Consulting Services
N.A.I.C.S.: 541613
David W. Kenny *(Founder)*

Branch (Non-US):

Digitas Greater China **(2)**
7/F Jing An Modern Industry Tower, 68 Changping Rd, Shanghai, 200041, China
Tel.: (86) 21 6120 5688
Sales Range: $25-49.9 Million
Emp.: 200
Advertising Services
N.A.I.C.S.: 541810

PUBLICIS GROUPE S.A.

Publicis Groupe S.A.—(Continued)

Branch (Domestic):

Digitas Health (2)
355 Park Ave S, New York, NY 10010
Tel.: (212) 610-5000
Web Site: http://www.digitashealth.com
Digital/Interactive, Health Care
N.A.I.C.S.: 541810

Digitas Health (2)
100 Penn Sq E 11th Fl, Philadelphia, PA 19107
Tel.: (215) 545-4444
Web Site: http://www.digitashealth.com
Sales Range: $25-49.9 Million
Emp.: 300
Direct Response Marketing, Health Care, Internet/Web Design, Pharmaceutical
N.A.I.C.S.: 541810
Eric Muller *(Pres)*

Branch (Non-US):

Digitas Health London (2)
82 Baker Street, London, W1U 6AE, United Kingdom (100%)
Tel.: (44) 2079354426
Web Site: http://www.digitashealth.com
Sales Range: $25-49.9 Million
Emp.: 100
Advertising Services
N.A.I.C.S.: 541810
June Dawson *(Mng Dir)*

Branch (Domestic):

Digitas Inc (2)
4 Stamford Plaza, 107 Elm St Ste 900, Stamford, CT 06902
Tel.: (203) 905-2200
Web Site: http://www.digitas.com
N.A.I.C.S.: 541810

Digitas Inc (2)
1230 Peachtree St Ste 500, Atlanta, GA 30309
Tel.: (404) 460-1010
Emp.: 70
N.A.I.C.S.: 541810

Branch (Non-US):

Digitas London (2)
23 Howland Street, London, W1A 4AY, United Kingdom
Tel.: (44) 207 8749 400
Web Site: http://www.digitas.com
Sales Range: $25-49.9 Million
Emp.: 100
Interactive Agencies, Internet/Web Design
N.A.I.C.S.: 541810
James Whatley *(Partner-Strategy)*

Branch (Domestic):

Digitas, Inc. (2)
180 N La Salle St Ste 1100, Chicago, IL 60601-2608
Tel.: (312) 729-0100
Web Site: http://www.digitas.com
Sales Range: $75-99.9 Million
Emp.: 285
Digital/Interactive
N.A.I.C.S.: 541810
Douglas Ryan *(Pres-North America)*

DigitasLBi - New York (2)
375 Hudson St 16th Fl, New York, NY 10014
Tel.: (212) 610-5000
Web Site: http://www.digitaslbi.com
Digital Media Advertising Services
N.A.I.C.S.: 541810
David W. Kenny *(Co-Founder)*

Branch (Non-US):

LBi International N.V. (2)
Joop Geesinkweg 209, 1114 AB, Amsterdam, Netherlands
Tel.: (31) 204061200
Web Site: http://www.digitaslbi.com
Sales Range: $250-299.9 Million
Digital Marketing Services
N.A.I.C.S.: 541890
Anthony Lye *(Pres-Digital Platforms & Channel)*

Subsidiary (Domestic):

DigitasLBi (3)
Joop Geesinkweg 209, 1096 AV, Amsterdam, Netherlands
Tel.: (31) 20 460 4500
Web Site: http://www.digitaslbi.com
Sales Range: $75-99.9 Million
Emp.: 150
Digital Marketing Services
N.A.I.C.S.: 541613
Lauren Ahearn *(Dir-Bus-Singapore)*

Branch (Non-US):

DigitasLBi France (3)
36/40 rue Raspail, 92300, Levallois-Perret, France
Tel.: (33) 1 49 68 12 12
Web Site: http://www.digitaslbi.com
Sales Range: $25-49.9 Million
Emp.: 8
Advertising Services
N.A.I.C.S.: 541810

DigitasLBi Spain (3)
Avda del Partenon 12-14, 28042, Madrid, Spain
Tel.: (34) 915767072
Web Site: http://www.digitaslbi.com
Search Engine Optimization Services
N.A.I.C.S.: 519290

LBI Nordic Holding A/S (3)
Vermundsgade 40A, 2100, Copenhagen, Denmark
Tel.: (45) 3916 2929
Web Site: http://www.lbi.com
Sales Range: $25-49.9 Million
Emp.: 75
Marketing Consulting Services
N.A.I.C.S.: 541613

Drugstore Champs-Elysees SNC (1)
133 Avenue des Champs-Elysees, 75008, Paris, France
Tel.: (33) 144437507
Web Site: http://www.publicisdrugstore.com
Ecommerce Services
N.A.I.C.S.: 456199
Jacques Terzian *(Mgr-Publication)*

Duval Guillaume Corporate (1)
Rue Picardstraat 7, mailbox 205, 1000, Brussels, Belgium
Tel.: (32) 26207030
Web Site: http://www.duvalguillaume.com
Sales Range: Less than $1 Million
Advertising Agency
N.A.I.C.S.: 541810

Branch (Domestic):

Duval Guillaume Antwerp (2)
Uitbreidingsstraat 2-8, 2600, Berchem, Belgium
Tel.: (32) 3 609 09 00
Web Site: http://www.duvalguillaume.com
N.A.I.C.S.: 541810

Duval Guillaume Brussels (2)
Antwerpselaan 40, B-1000, Brussels, Belgium
Tel.: (32) 2 412 08 88
N.A.I.C.S.: 541810

Epsilon Data Management, LLC (1)
6021 Connection Dr, Irving, TX 75039
Tel.: (972) 582-9600
Web Site: http://www.epsilon.com
Sales Range: $100-124.9 Million
Emp.: 9,000
Advertising Agency
N.A.I.C.S.: 541810
Bryan Kennedy *(CEO)*

Subsidiary (Domestic):

Aspen Marketing Services, LLC (2)
1240 N Ave, West Chicago, IL 60185
Tel.: (630) 293-9600
Web Site: http://www.epsilon.com
Sales Range: $10-24.9 Million
Advertising Agency
N.A.I.C.S.: 541810
Gust Kouvaris *(Pres-Events)*

Branch (Domestic):

Aspen Marketing Services (3)
9700 W Higgins Rd Ste 600, Rosemont, IL 60018-4776
Tel.: (847) 318-9010
Rev.: $50,000,000
Emp.: 50
Advertising Agency
N.A.I.C.S.: 541810
Cathy Lang *(Pres)*

Aspen Marketing Services (3)
205 N 10th St, Boise, ID 83702
Tel.: (208) 342-6403
Full Service
N.A.I.C.S.: 541810

Aspen Marketing Services (3)
4469 Fairmont Dr, Pinson, AL 35126-5307
Tel.: (205) 591-0760
Direct Marketing
N.A.I.C.S.: 541810

Aspen Marketing Services, Inc. - Atlanta (3)
6 Concourse Pkwy Ste 2500, Atlanta, GA 30328
Tel.: (770) 752-7011
Emp.: 55
Advetising Agency
N.A.I.C.S.: 541810

Aspen Marketing Services, Inc. - Auburn Hills (3)
2455 Featherstone Rd, Auburn Hills, MI 48326-2810
Tel.: (248) 364-6600
Emp.: 60
Advetising Agency
N.A.I.C.S.: 541810

Aspen Marketing Services, Inc. - Costa Mesa (3)
3070 Bristol St Ste 300, Costa Mesa, CA 92626
Tel.: (949) 477-1266
Advertising Agency
N.A.I.C.S.: 541810

Aspen Marketing Services, Inc. - Irving (3)
6021 Connection Dr, Irving, TX 75039
Tel.: (972) 582-9600
Emp.: 500
Advertising Agency
N.A.I.C.S.: 541810

Aspen Marketing Services, Inc. - New York (3)
16 W 20th St 9th Fl, New York, NY 10011
Tel.: (212) 457-7000
Emp.: 10
Advetising Agency
N.A.I.C.S.: 541810

Aspen Marketing Services, Inc. - Parsippany (3)
1 Gatehall Dr Ste 309, Parsippany, NJ 07960-4558
Tel.: (973) 775-6700
Sales Range: $10-24.9 Million
Emp.: 100
Advetising Agency
N.A.I.C.S.: 541810

Aspen Marketing Services, Inc. - Saint Petersburg (3)
150 2nd Ave N Ste 670, Saint Petersburg, FL 33701-3340
Tel.: (727) 827-4200
Emp.: 25
Advetising Agency
N.A.I.C.S.: 541810

Aspen Marketing Services, Inc. - San Diego (3)
10431 Water Ridge Cir Ste 200, San Diego, CA 92121
Tel.: (858) 346-5000
Web Site: http://www.aspenmarketingservices.com
Emp.: 75
Advetising Agency
N.A.I.C.S.: 541810

Subsidiary (Domestic):

Newgen Results Corporation (4)
10243 Genetic Ctr Dr, San Diego, CA 92121
Tel.: (858) 346-5000
Web Site: http://www.newgen.com

INTERNATIONAL PUBLIC

Marketing Services for Car Dealerships
N.A.I.C.S.: 561422

Branch (Domestic):

Aspen Marketing Services, Inc. - Scottsdale (3)
7231 E Princess Blvd Ste 202, Scottsdale, AZ 85255
Emp.: 5
Advetising Agency
N.A.I.C.S.: 541810

Subsidiary (Domestic):

Conversant, LLC (2)
30699 Russell Ranch Rd Ste 250, Westlake Village, CA 91362
Tel.: (818) 575-4500
Web Site: http://www.conversantmedia.com
Emp.: 200
Electronic Media
N.A.I.C.S.: 541613
Ric Elert *(Pres)*

Subsidiary (Domestic):

CJ Affiliate (3)
530 E Montecito St, Santa Barbara, CA 93103
Tel.: (805) 730-8000
Web Site: http://www.cj.com
Online Advertising & Marketing Solutions
N.A.I.C.S.: 541613
Paul Tibbitt *(Pres)*

Subsidiary (Non-US):

CJ Affiliate-London (3)
Oxford House 180 Upper Richmond Road, London, SW15 2SH, United Kingdom
Tel.: (44) 208 785 5870
Web Site: http://www.cj.com
Online Advertising & Marketing Solutions
N.A.I.C.S.: 541810

Subsidiary (Domestic):

CJ Affiliate-Westborough (3)
4 Technology Dr Ste 200A, Westborough, MA 01581
Tel.: (508) 480-4000
Web Site: http://www.cj.com
Online Advertising, Marketing & Publishing Solutions
N.A.I.C.S.: 541810

Commission Junction (3)
425 6th Ave Ste 2000, Pittsburgh, PA 15219
Tel.: (412) 471-7500
N.A.I.C.S.: 541810

Subsidiary (Non-US):

Conversant Europe Ltd. (3)
Oxford House 182 Upper Richmond Road, Putney, London, SW15 2SH, United Kingdom
Tel.: (44) 20 8785 5800
Web Site: http://www.conversantmedia.eu
Advertising Agency
N.A.I.C.S.: 541810
Oded Benyo *(Pres)*

Conversant-Germany (3)
Rosenheimer Str 145 e-f, Munich, D-81671, Germany
Tel.: (49) 89 66 54 79 0
Web Site: http://www.conversantmedia.com
Emp.: 30
Advertising Agency
N.A.I.C.S.: 541810
David Allen *(CEO)*

Subsidiary (Domestic):

Conversant-New York (3)
565 5th Ave Fl 6, New York, NY 10017-2457
Tel.: (646) 439-2600
Web Site: http://www.valueclickmedia.com
Emp.: 150
Advetising Agency
N.A.I.C.S.: 541810

Conversant-San Francisco (3)
160 Spear St 15th Fl, San Francisco, CA 94105
Tel.: (415) 644-1400
Advertising Agency
N.A.I.C.S.: 541810

AND PRIVATE COMPANIES — PUBLICIS GROUPE S.A.

Conversant-Santa Barbara (3)
530 E Montecito St, Santa Barbara, CA 93103
Tel.: (805) 879-1600
Sales Range: $25-49.9 Million
Emp.: 25
Advetising Agency
N.A.I.C.S.: 541810

Mediaplex, Inc. (3)
160 Spear St 15th Fl, San Francisco, CA 94105
Tel.: (415) 644-1400
Web Site: http://www.mediaplex.com
Sales Range: $25-49.9 Million
Emp.: 40
Advertising Technology Solutions
N.A.I.C.S.: 541810

Branch (Domestic):

Mediaplex (4)
150 East 52nd St.14th Fl, New York, NY 10022
Tel.: (212) 471-9600
N.A.I.C.S.: 541810

Branch (Non-US):

Mediaplex (4)
Cambridge House, 180 Upper Richmond Rd, London, SW15 2SH, United Kingdom
Tel.: (44) 20 8785 5830
N.A.I.C.S.: 541810

Branch (Domestic):

Mediaplex East Coast Sales & Support (4)
150 E 52nd St, New York, NY 10022-6017
Tel.: (212) 471-9573
N.A.I.C.S.: 541810

Mediaplex Systems, Inc. Home Office (4)
5111 Commerce Crossing Dr, Ste 200, Louisville, KY 40229
Tel.: (502) 810-5000
N.A.I.C.S.: 541810

Subsidiary (Domestic):

Pricerunner.com (3)
30699 Russell Ranch Rd Ste 250, Westlake Village, CA 91361
Tel.: (818) 575-4500
N.A.I.C.S.: 541810

Subsidiary (Non-US):

ValueClick AB (3)
Sveavagen 38, Stockholm, 111 34, Sweden
Tel.: (46) 856210350
Custom Computer Programming Services
N.A.I.C.S.: 541511

Subsidiary (Domestic):

ValueClick Brands, Inc. (3)
30699 Russell Ranch Rd Ste 50, Westlake Village, CA 91362
Tel.: (626) 408-9100
Web Site: http://www.conversantmedia.com
Emp.: 200
Advertisement Services
N.A.I.C.S.: 541810

ValueClick Media (3)
30699 Russell Ranch Rd Ste 250, Westlake Village, CA 91362
Tel.: (818) 575-4500
Sales Range: $25-49.9 Million
Emp.: 100
N.A.I.C.S.: 541810
Bill Todd (Pres)

Subsidiary (Non-US):

ValueClick SARL (3)
4 rue du Faubourg Montmartre, 75 009, Paris, France
Tel.: (33) 146514071
Data Processing & Related Services
N.A.I.C.S.: 518210

Branch (Domestic):

Epsilon (2)
199 Water St, New York, NY 10038
Tel.: (212) 457-7000
Web Site: http://www.epsilon.com
Sales Range: $10-24.9 Million
Emp.: 15
Interactive Services
N.A.I.C.S.: 541519
Jerzy Szlosarek (CEO)

Epsilon (2)
1 American Eagle Plz, Earth City, MO 63045
Tel.: (314) 344-3380
Web Site: http://www.epsilon.com
Sales Range: $50-74.9 Million
Emp.: 150
Marketing & Advertising Services
N.A.I.C.S.: 541613

Epsilon (2)
2550 Crescent Dr, Lafayette, CO 80026
Tel.: (303) 410-5100
Web Site: http://www.ads.com
Sales Range: $75-99.9 Million
Emp.: 400
Marketing & Advertising Services
N.A.I.C.S.: 541613

Epsilon (2)
601 Edgewater Dr, Wakefield, MA 01880-6235
Tel.: (781) 685-6000
Web Site: http://www.epsilon.com
Sales Range: $50-74.9 Million
Marketing & Advertising Services
N.A.I.C.S.: 541613

Epsilon (2)
1100 N Glebe Rd Ste 1000, Arlington, VA 22201
Tel.: (703) 312-0509
Web Site: http://www.epsilon.com
Sales Range: Less than $1 Million
Emp.: 7
Marketing & Advertising Services
N.A.I.C.S.: 541613

Epsilon (2)
445 Lake Forest Dr Ste 200, Cincinnati, OH 45242
Tel.: (513) 248-2882
Web Site: http://www.epsilon.com
Rev.: $50,000,000
Emp.: 100
Marketing & Advertising Services
N.A.I.C.S.: 541613

Epsilon (2)
1100 E Woodfield Rd Ste 500, Schaumburg, IL 60173
Tel.: (847) 330-1313
Web Site: http://www.epsilon.com
Sales Range: $25-49.9 Million
Emp.: 85
Marketing & Advertising Services
N.A.I.C.S.: 541613

Subsidiary (Domestic):

Epsilon International, LLC (2)
6021 Connection Dr, Irving, TX 75039
Tel.: (972) 582-9600
Web Site: http://www.epsilon.com
Sales Range: $25-49.9 Million
Emp.: 20
Holding Company
N.A.I.C.S.: 551112

Division (Non-US):

Abacus (UK) Ltd. (3)
Teddington House 67 Broad Street, Teddington, TW11 8QZ, Mddx, United Kingdom
Tel.: (44) 2089438000
Web Site: http://www.abacus.epsilon.com
Marketing & Advertising Services
N.A.I.C.S.: 541613
Jim Ktori (Dir-Strategic Dev)

Branch (Non-US):

Epsilon Data Management, LLC. - Toronto (3)
20 Dundas St W 9th Fl, Toronto, M5G 2C2, ON, Canada
Tel.: (416) 369-1100
Web Site: http://www.welcometoepsilon.com
Marketing & Advertising Services
N.A.I.C.S.: 541613

Epsilon International (3)
Hansaallee 247b, 40549, Dusseldorf, Germany
Tel.: (49) 211913870

Web Site: http://www.epsilon.com
Sales Range: $50-74.9 Million
Emp.: 80
Marketing & Advertising Services
N.A.I.C.S.: 541613

Epsilon International (3)
Room 2502 25 Floor Hopewell Center 183 Queen's Road E, Wanchai, China (Hong Kong)
Tel.: (852) 35896300
Web Site: http://www.epsilon.com
Sales Range: $50-74.9 Million
Emp.: 13
Marketing & Advertising Services
N.A.I.C.S.: 541613

Epsilon International (3)
Room 2019 20/F Tian Qi Yi HongXiang Building, 611 Tian He Bei Road, Guangzhou, China
Tel.: (86) 20 3847 3736
Web Site: http://www.epsilon.com
Sales Range: $50-74.9 Million
Marketing & Advertising Services
N.A.I.C.S.: 541613

Epsilon International (3)
8 Eu Tong Sen St #18-98 Office 1, The Central, Singapore, 059818, Singapore
Tel.: (65) 6728 1274
Web Site: http://www.epsilon.com
Sales Range: $50-74.9 Million
Marketing & Advertising Services
N.A.I.C.S.: 541613

Epsilon International (3)
88 Cumberland St Suite 22 Level 1, The Rocks, Sydney, 2000, NSW, Australia
Tel.: (61) 292715400
Web Site: http://www.epsilon.com
Sales Range: $50-74.9 Million
Marketing & Advertising Services
N.A.I.C.S.: 541613

Epsilon International (3)
Teddington House 67 Broad St, Teddington, Middlesex, TW11 8QZ, United Kingdom
Tel.: (44) 2088341011
Web Site: http://www.epsilon.com
Sales Range: $10-24.9 Million
Emp.: 30
Marketing & Advertising Services
N.A.I.C.S.: 541613

Epsilon International (3)
55 quai de Grenelle, Paris, 75015, France
Tel.: (33) 17300550
Web Site: http://www.epsilon-france.com
Marketing & Advertising Services
N.A.I.C.S.: 541613

Epsilon International (3)
Rm 1507 15/F Wantong Ctr Block C 6A Chaoyangmen Wai Ave, Beijing, 100020, China
Tel.: (86) 1059073001
Web Site: http://www.epsilon.com
Sales Range: $50-74.9 Million
Marketing & Advertising Services
N.A.I.C.S.: 541613

Epsilon International (3)
Ste 103 Block D Red Town, 570 Huai Hai Rd W, Shanghai, 200052, China
Tel.: (86) 21 6132 3890
Web Site: http://www.epsilon.com
Sales Range: $50-74.9 Million
Marketing & Advertising Services
N.A.I.C.S.: 541613

Expicient Inc. (1)
26 Chestnut St Ste 1D, Andover, MA 01810
Tel.: (978) 662-0498
Web Site: http://www.expicient.com
Software Publisher
N.A.I.C.S.: 513210
Darpan Seth (Founder & Mng Partner)

Fallon Worldwide (1)
901 Marquette Ave Ste 2400, Minneapolis, MN 55402
Tel.: (612) 758-2345
Web Site: http://www.fallon.com
Sales Range: $200-249.9 Million
Emp.: 120
Advertising Services
N.A.I.C.S.: 541810
Mike Buchner (Chm)

Branch (Non-US):

Fallon London (2)
40 Chancery Ln, London, WC2A 1JA, United Kingdom
Tel.: (44) 20 7494 9120
Web Site: http://www.fallon.co.uk
Sales Range: $25-49.9 Million
Emp.: 120
Advertising Services
N.A.I.C.S.: 541810

Fallon Tokyo (2)
4-9-3 Jingumae, Shibuyaku, Tokyo, 150-0001, Japan
Tel.: (81) 3 5774 1255
Advertising Services
N.A.I.C.S.: 541810

Freud Communications (1)
1 Stephen Street, London, W1T 1AL, United Kingdom
Tel.: (44) 20 3003 6300
Web Site: http://www.freud.com
Sales Range: $25-49.9 Million
Emp.: 250
Advertising Services
N.A.I.C.S.: 541810
Matthew Freud (Founder & Chm)

Subsidiary (US):

Brew Media Relations (2)
2110 Main St Ste 201, Santa Monica, CA 90405
Tel.: (310) 464-6348
Web Site: http://www.brewpr.com
Public Relations Services
N.A.I.C.S.: 541820
Brooke Hammerling (Founder)

Geller Nessis D'Arcy (1)
7 Achim Bejerano, Ramat Gan, Israel
Tel.: (972) 36 25 4777
Web Site: http://www.publicis.co.il
Sales Range: $25-49.9 Million
Emp.: 17
Full Service
N.A.I.C.S.: 541810

GroupeConnect LLC (1)
40 Water St, Boston, MA 02109
Tel.: (617) 867-1785
Web Site: http://www.groupeconnect.com
Marketing & Advertising Services
N.A.I.C.S.: 541810
Andre Ferla (Mgr-Digital Product)

Hanmer & Partners (1)
Rehem Mansion - 1 3rd Floor 42 Shahih Bhagat Singh Road, Colaba, Mumbai, 400 001, India
Tel.: (91) 22 6633 5969
Sales Range: $25-49.9 Million
Emp.: 150
Public Relations Services
N.A.I.C.S.: 541820

Hepta Group Publicis (1)
vulica Niamiha 5, Minsk, 220030, Belarus
Tel.: (375) 17 289 1009
Web Site: http://www.hepta.net
Sales Range: $75-99.9 Million
Emp.: 160
N.A.I.C.S.: 541810

Impact (1)
3 Avenue Jugurtha, 1002, Tunis, Belvedere, Tunisia
Tel.: (216) 98 286 000
Web Site: http://www.impact.com.tn
N.A.I.C.S.: 541810

Kekst & Co. (1)
437 Madison Ave, New York, NY 10022
Tel.: (212) 521-4800
Web Site: http://www.kekst.com
Sales Range: $25-49.9 Million
Emp.: 70
Advertising Services
N.A.I.C.S.: 541810
Jeffrey Z. Taufield (Vice Chm & Mng Dir)

Kredo R (1)
P Zadeikos g 1B, 06319, Vilnius, Lithuania
Tel.: (370) 5 213 1023
Web Site: http://www.kredor.lt
Sales Range: Less than $1 Million
Advetising Agency
N.A.I.C.S.: 541810

LPT Publicis (1)
Bulevar Zorana Djindjica 144, 11070, Belgrade, Serbia

PUBLICIS GROUPE S.A.

Publicis Groupe S.A.—(Continued)
Tel.: (381) 112090200
Web Site: http://www.publicis.com
N.A.I.C.S.: 541810

Leo Burnett Worldwide, Inc. (1)
35 W Wacker Dr, Chicago, IL 60601-1723
Tel.: (312) 220-5959
Web Site: http://www.leoburnett.com
Sales Range: $800-899.9 Million
Emp.: 6,844
Advetising Agency
N.A.I.C.S.: 541810
Mark Tutssel *(Chm)*

Subsidiary (Non-US):

AMA Leo Burnett (2)
2005C Corniche El Nil St Ramlet Beaulec, Nile City Towers N Tower, 11221, Cairo, Egypt
Tel.: (20) 2 2461 8000
Advertising Services
N.A.I.C.S.: 541810
Amr Darwish *(Mng Dir)*

Access Leo Burnett (2)
Bishops Garden Towers 4th Floor, PO Box 42379, Nairobi, 00100, Kenya
Tel.: (254) 2 719 501
Web Site: http://www.leoburnett.com
Sales Range: $10-24.9 Million
Emp.: 30
Advertising Services
N.A.I.C.S.: 541810
Raul Martyres *(Chm)*

Ads Limited
Ad House No 2A 31 Awundoma Roundabout, PO Box 14858, Accra, Ghana
Tel.: (233) 21 226 926
Sales Range: $25-49.9 Million
Emp.: 20
Advertising Services
N.A.I.C.S.: 541810

Airlock Limited (2)
Reeds Wharf 33 Mill St, London, SE1 2AX, United Kingdom
Tel.: (44) 20 7173 0600
Web Site: http://www.airlock.com
Sales Range: $10-24.9 Million
Emp.: 50
Advertising Services
N.A.I.C.S.: 541810

Subsidiary (Domestic):

Arc Worldwide (2)
35 W Wacker Dr 15th Fl, Chicago, IL 60601
Tel.: (312) 220-3200
Web Site: http://www.arcww.com
Sales Range: $300-349.9 Million
Emp.: 1,100
Advertising Services
N.A.I.C.S.: 541810
Melinda Roenisch *(Assoc Dir-Creative)*

Branch (Non-US):

Arc Italia (3)
Viale Jenner 19, 20159, Milan, Italy
Tel.: (39) 02 63541
Web Site: http://www.arcww.it
Advertising Services
N.A.I.C.S.: 541810

Arc Middle East (3)
Dubai Media City, PO Box 7534, Dubai, United Arab Emirates
Tel.: (971) 4 367 2622
Advertising Services
N.A.I.C.S.: 541810
Sarah Anani *(Dir-Creative)*

Branch (Domestic):

Arc Worldwide (3)
1675 Broadway 7th Fl, New York, NY 10019
Tel.: (646) 756-8950
Web Site: http://www.arcww.com
Advertising Services
N.A.I.C.S.: 541810

Branch (Non-US):

Arc Worldwide (3)
175 Bloor St E N Twr 12th Fl, Toronto, M4W 3R9, ON, Canada
Tel.: (416) 925-3343

Web Site: http://www.leoburnett.ca
Advertising Services
N.A.I.C.S.: 541810

Arc Worldwide (3)
20 rue des Jardins, 92600, Asnieres, France
Tel.: (33) 1 55 20 26 44
Web Site: http://www.leoburnett.com
Advertising Services
N.A.I.C.S.: 541810

Arc Worldwide (3)
6 Patroklou & Andromachis St, 151 25, Maroussi, Greece
Tel.: (30) 210 9011 255
Web Site: http://www.arcww.com
Sales Range: $10-24.9 Million
Emp.: 35
Advertising Services
N.A.I.C.S.: 541810

Arc Worldwide (3)
Platinum Bus Park, Ul Woloska 9, 02-583, Warsaw, Poland
Tel.: (48) 22 448 9600
Web Site: http://www.arcww.com.pl
Sales Range: $25-49.9 Million
Emp.: 100
Advertising Services
N.A.I.C.S.: 541810

Arc Worldwide (3)
Rua Gonzalves Zarco 14, Lisbon, 1449 013, Portugal
Tel.: (351) 213 244 570
Web Site: http://www.arcww.pt
Sales Range: $25-49.9 Million
Emp.: 30
Advertising Services
N.A.I.C.S.: 541810
Antony Gibson *(Pres)*

Arc Worldwide (3)
Karolenska 650, Danube House, 186-00, Prague, Czech Republic
Tel.: (420) 251 171 911
Advertising Services
N.A.I.C.S.: 541810

Arc Worldwide (3)
3/F Sindhorn Tower 1, 130-132 Wireless Road Patunwan, Bangkok, 10330, Thailand
Tel.: (66) 2 684 5555
Web Site: http://www.leoburnett.co.th
Advertising Services
N.A.I.C.S.: 541810

Arc Worldwide (3)
RHQ 6/F Cityplaza, 3 14 Taikoo Wan Road, Hong Kong, China (Hong Kong)
Tel.: (852) 2567 4333
Advertising Services
N.A.I.C.S.: 541810
Simon Holt *(Reg Dir)*

Arc Worldwide (3)
Menara Thamrin 26th Fl, Jl M H Thamrin Kav 3, Jakarta, 10250, Indonesia
Tel.: (62) 21 3983 0118
Web Site: http://www.arcww.com
Advertising Services
N.A.I.C.S.: 541810

Arc Worldwide (3)
24 Floor Tower 2 The Enterprise Centre, 6766 Ayala Ave, Corner Paseo de Roxas, Makati, 12, Philippines
Tel.: (63) 2 884 8413
Web Site: http://www.arcww.com
Sales Range: $25-49.9 Million
Emp.: 100
Advertising Services
N.A.I.C.S.: 541810

Arc Worldwide (3)
10th Floor 16 Nanjing East Road, Sec 4, Taipei, Taiwan
Tel.: (886) 622577 1211
Advertising Services
N.A.I.C.S.: 541810

Arc Worldwide (3)
Carrera 13 No 90-21, Oficina 406, Bogota, Colombia
Tel.: (57) 1 628 5959
Web Site: http://www.arcww.com
Advertising Services
N.A.I.C.S.: 541810

Arc Worldwide (3)

Olga Cossenttini 1545 2nd Fl, C1107 CEK, Buenos Aires, Argentina
Tel.: (54) 11 4819 5959
Advertising Services
N.A.I.C.S.: 541810

Arc Worldwide (3)
Rua Brejo Alegre 99, 04557-050, Sao Paulo, Brazil
Tel.: (55) 11 5504 1300
Advertising Services
N.A.I.C.S.: 541810

Branch (Domestic):

Arc Worldwide (3)
35 West Wacker Dr, Chicago Park, IL 60601
Tel.: (312) 220-1177
Web Site: http://www.arcww.com
Sales Range: $10-24.9 Million
Emp.: 50
Advertising Services
N.A.I.C.S.: 541810
Katie Newman *(Chief Mktg Officer)*

Branch (Non-US):

Arc Worldwide (3)
7th Fl Gwanhun Bldg Gwanhun-dong, Jongno-ku Seoul, 110-704, Seoul, Korea (South)
Tel.: (82) 2 2000 3600
Advertising Services
N.A.I.C.S.: 541810

Arc Worldwide, Asia Pacific (3)
Level 5 Menara Olympia, 8 Jalan Raja Chulan, Kuala Lumpur, 50200, Malaysia
Tel.: (60) 3 2031 0998
Web Site: http://www.leoburnett.com.my
Sales Range: $25-49.9 Million
Emp.: 200
Advertising Services
N.A.I.C.S.: 541810

Arc Worldwide, Europe, Middle East & Africa (3)
Warwick Building Kensington Village Avonmore Road, London, W14 8HQ, United Kingdom
Tel.: (44) 20 7751 1800
Web Site: http://www.arcww.co.uk
Sales Range: $25-49.9 Million
Emp.: 110
Advertising Services
N.A.I.C.S.: 541810

Branch (Domestic):

Arc Worldwide, North America (3)
35 W Wacker 15th Fl, Chicago, IL 60601
Tel.: (312) 220-3200
Web Site: http://www.arcww.com
Advertising Services
N.A.I.C.S.: 541810

Branch (Non-US):

Publicis (3)
Boulevard d'Anvers 40, Brussels, 1000, Belgium
Tel.: (32) 2645 3511
Web Site: http://www.publicis.be
Sales Range: $25-49.9 Million
Emp.: 50
Advertising Services
N.A.I.C.S.: 541810
Jeannette Westerhout *(Mng Partner & Dir-Client Svc)*

Publicis Grupo K (3)
Calle Ramirez de Arellano, 21 planta 3, Madrid, 28043, Spain
Tel.: (34) 91 590 23 60
Web Site: http://www.publicis.es
Sales Range: $25-49.9 Million
Emp.: 122
Communication Service
N.A.I.C.S.: 541810
Manuel Amat *(Gen Mgr-Client Svcs)*

Subsidiary (Non-US):

Ark Amsterdam (2)
Danzigerkade 23c, Amsterdam, 1013AP, Netherlands
Tel.: (31) 205046161
Sales Range: $25-49.9 Million
Emp.: 15
Advertising Services

INTERNATIONAL PUBLIC

N.A.I.C.S.: 541810
Jan Uitendaal *(Dir-Fin)*

Beacon Communications K.K. (2)
JR Tokyo Maguro Building 3-1-1 Kami-Osaki, Shinagawa-ku, Tokyo, 141-0021, Japan
Tel.: (81) 354377200
Web Site: http://www.beaconcom.co.jp
Sales Range: $1-9.9 Million
Emp.: 400
Advertising Services
N.A.I.C.S.: 541810
Sayori Kato *(Exec Dir-HR)*

Bitopi Advertising Ltd. (2)
Plot 180 Block B Basundhara r/a, Dhaka, 1229, Bangladesh
Tel.: (880) 2 805 3418
Web Site: http://www.bitopi.com
Advertising Services
N.A.I.C.S.: 541810

Blackwood Communications Group (2)
75 France Street, Newton, Auckland, New Zealand
Tel.: (64) 9 379 9007
Web Site: http://www.bcg2.com
Emp.: 30
Advertising Services
N.A.I.C.S.: 541810

EmporioAsia Leo Burnett (2)
Unit 5C Jin Min Building 8 Zun Yi Road South, Shanghai, 200335, China
Tel.: (86) 21 6275 8802
Web Site: http://www.emporioasia.com
Emp.: 120
Advertising Services
N.A.I.C.S.: 541810
Angie Wong *(Mng Dir)*

H&C, Leo Burnett (2)
Sofil Center 5th Floor Achrafieh, PO Box 55369, Beirut, Lebanon
Tel.: (961) 1201090
Web Site: http://leoburnett.com
Sales Range: $25-49.9 Million
Advertising Services
N.A.I.C.S.: 541810

Holler Digital Ltd. (2)
13-19 Vine Hill, London, EC1R 5DW, United Kingdom
Tel.: (44) 207 209 2690
Web Site: http://www.holler.co.uk
Advertising Services
N.A.I.C.S.: 541810

Huella Publicidad (2)
Villa Fontana Edificio Discover I, Managua, Nicaragua
Tel.: (505) 22704100
Web Site: http://huella.com.ni
Sales Range: $10-24.9 Million
Advertising Services
N.A.I.C.S.: 541810

Innovation Leo Burnett (2)
21 Akademias Avenue KEMA Building 6th Floor Aglantzia, Nicosia, 2107, Cyprus
Tel.: (357) 22 378 828
Web Site: http://leoburnett.com.cy
Sales Range: $25-49.9 Million
Advertising Services
N.A.I.C.S.: 541810
Vasso Vassiliou *(Mng Dir)*

Kitchen Leo Burnett (2)
Nedre Slottsgate 13-15 3 etasje, 0157, Oslo, Norway
Tel.: (47) 90634400
Web Site: http://www.kitchen.no
Sales Range: $100-124.9 Million
Advertising Services
N.A.I.C.S.: 541810
Bendik Romstad *(Copywriter)*

Kontuur-Leo Burnett (2)
Laeva 2 4th floor, 10111, Tallinn, Estonia
Tel.: (372) 5040295
Web Site: http://www.kontuur.ee
Sales Range: $25-49.9 Million
Advertising Services
N.A.I.C.S.: 541810
Urmas Villmann *(Dir-Creative)*

Subsidiary (Domestic):

Lapiz (2)

AND PRIVATE COMPANIES

PUBLICIS GROUPE S.A.

35 W Wacker Dr 12th Fl, Chicago, IL 60601
Tel.: (312) 220-5000
Web Site: http://www.lapizusa.com
Sales Range: $10-24.9 Million
Emp.: 40
Consumer Marketing Services
N.A.I.C.S.: 541810
Luciana Cani *(Sr Exec VP & Exec Dir-Creative)*

Subsidiary (Non-US):

Leo Burnett & Target SA (2)
13 Nicolae Iorga Str, Bucharest, 010432, Romania
Tel.: (40) 21 201 6100
Web Site: http://www.leoburnett.ro
Sales Range: $25-49.9 Million
Emp.: 100
Advertising Services
N.A.I.C.S.: 541810

Subsidiary (Domestic):

Leo Burnett - Los Angeles (2)
6500 Wilshire Blvd Ste 1950, Los Angeles, CA 90048
Tel.: (323) 866-6020
Web Site: http://www.leoburnett.com
Sales Range: $10-24.9 Million
Emp.: 5
Advertising Services
N.A.I.C.S.: 541810

Subsidiary (Non-US):

Leo Burnett Advertising S.R.O. (2)
Jankovcova 23, 17000, Prague, 8, Czech Republic
Tel.: (420) 257310506
Web Site: http://www.leoburnett.com
Sales Range: $75-99.9 Million
Emp.: 84
Advertising Services
N.A.I.C.S.: 541810

Leo Burnett Annonsbyra (2)
Kungstensgatan 21B, PO Box 476, Stockholm, 113 57, Sweden
Tel.: (46) 84125000
Web Site: http://www.leoburnett.se
Sales Range: $25-49.9 Million
Emp.: 20
Advertising Services
N.A.I.C.S.: 541810

Leo Burnett Associates (2)
46 Wellington Rd Ballsbridge, Dublin, 4, Ireland
Tel.: (353) 1 668 9627
Web Site: http://www.leoburnett.com
Sales Range: $25-49.9 Million
Emp.: 25
Advertising Services
N.A.I.C.S.: 541810

Leo Burnett Belgium (2)
18 Place Eugene Flageyplien, Box 17, 1050, Brussels, Belgium
Tel.: (32) 27756540
Web Site: http://www.leoburnett.be
Sales Range: $10-24.9 Million
Emp.: 32
Advertising Services
N.A.I.C.S.: 541810

Leo Burnett Budapest (2)
Becsi Ut 49, H-1036, Budapest, Hungary
Tel.: (36) 14371300
Sales Range: $25-49.9 Million
Emp.: 80
Advertising Services
N.A.I.C.S.: 541810

Subsidiary (Domestic):

Leo Burnett Business (2)
300 Park Ave S Fl 7, New York, NY 10010-5355
Tel.: (646) 840-8350
Web Site: http://www.leoburnettbusiness.com
Sales Range: $25-49.9 Million
Emp.: 30
Communication Service
N.A.I.C.S.: 541810

Subsidiary (Non-US):

Leo Burnett Casablanca (2)
Villa Oasis 14 rue Mohamed Benbrahim, Abderrahim Bouabid - Quartier Oasis, Casablanca, Morocco
Tel.: (212) 522989291
Web Site: http://www.leoburnett.com
Sales Range: $25-49.9 Million
Advertising Services
N.A.I.C.S.: 541810
Kamal El Allam *(Dir-Comm)*

Leo Burnett Chile (2)
Av Apoquindo 6550 Piso 4, Las Condes, Santiago, Chile
Tel.: (56) 27573030
Web Site: http://www.leoburnett.cl
Sales Range: $25-49.9 Million
Emp.: 25
Advertising Services
N.A.I.C.S.: 541810

Leo Burnett Co. S.r.l. (2)
Via Dell'Arsenale 5, 10121, Turin, Italy
Tel.: (39) 011 560 1911
Web Site: http://www.leoburnett.com
Sales Range: $25-49.9 Million
Advertising Services
N.A.I.C.S.: 541810
Romeo Repetto *(CEO)*

Leo Burnett Co., S.r.l. (2)
Viale Edoardo Jenner 19, 20159, Milan, MI, Italy
Tel.: (39) 0263541
Web Site: http://www.leoburnett.it
Sales Range: $25-49.9 Million
Advertising Services
N.A.I.C.S.: 541810
Giorgio Brenna *(Chm & CEO-Western Europe)*

Leo Burnett Colombia, S.A. (2)
Carrera 13 N 89-59, Bogota, DC, Colombia
Tel.: (57) 16285959
Web Site: http://www.col-leoburnett.com
Sales Range: $25-49.9 Million
Emp.: 150
Advertising Services
N.A.I.C.S.: 541810
Olga Lucia Villegas *(Pres)*

Leo Burnett Company Ltd. (2)
175 Bloor Street East North Tower, Toronto, M4W 3R9, ON, Canada
Tel.: (416) 925-5997
Web Site: https://www.leoburnett.ca
Sales Range: $25-49.9 Million
Emp.: 100
Advertising Services
N.A.I.C.S.: 541810

Leo Burnett Comunica, S.A. (2)
5a Av 6-39 Zona 14, Condominio Las Plazas, Colonia El Campo, Guatemala, 01014, Guatemala
Tel.: (502) 2285 7676
Advertising Services
N.A.I.C.S.: 541810
Andres Mazuera *(Gen Mgr)*

Leo Burnett Del Peru S.A. (2)
Av Angamos Oeste 1270, Miraflores, Lima, 18, Peru
Tel.: (51) 1617 9292
Web Site: http://www.leoburnett.com
Rev.: $21,718,000
Emp.: 75
Advertising Services
N.A.I.C.S.: 541810

Subsidiary (Domestic):

Leo Burnett Detroit, Inc. (2)
3310 W Big Beaver Rd Ste 107, Troy, MI 48084-2809
Tel.: (248) 458-8300
Web Site: http://www.leoburnett.com
Sales Range: $75-99.9 Million
Communication Service
N.A.I.C.S.: 541810

Subsidiary (Non-US):

Leo Burnett GmbH (2)
Otto-Messmer-Strasse 1, Frankfurt am Main, 60314, Germany
Tel.: (49) 69780770
Web Site: http://www.leoburnett.de
Emp.: 200
Advertising Services
N.A.I.C.S.: 541810
Andreas Pauli *(Chief Creative Officer)*

Leo Burnett Inc. (2)
Prolongacion Arabia 13 Altos de Arroyo Hondo, Santo Domingo, Dominican Republic
Tel.: (809) 5650558
Web Site: http://www.leoburnett.com
Sales Range: $10-24.9 Million
Advertising Services
N.A.I.C.S.: 541810

Subsidiary (Domestic):

Leo Burnett Inc. (2)
A-16 Calle Genova Ext Villa Caparra, Guaynabo, PR 00918
Tel.: (787) 754-7760
Web Site: http://www.leoburnett.com
Sales Range: $25-49.9 Million
Emp.: 55
Advertising Services
N.A.I.C.S.: 541810
Wanda Reichard *(Gen Mgr)*

Subsidiary (Non-US):

Leo Burnett Inc., Sucursal Argentina (2)
Sucre 865, 1428, Buenos Aires, Argentina
Tel.: (54) 1148195959
Web Site: http://www.leoburnett.com
Advertising Services
N.A.I.C.S.: 541810

Leo Burnett India (2)
36 Big Apple Dr Shirodkar Road, Mumbai, 400 012, India
Tel.: (91) 2266634444
Web Site: http://leoburnett.co.in
Sales Range: $25-49.9 Million
Advertising Services
N.A.I.C.S.: 541810
Rajdeepak Das *(Chief Creative, Officer/Mng Dir & South Asia)*

Branch (Domestic):

Leo Burnett India (3)
Big Apple 315 Udyog Vihar Phase - IV, New Delhi, 122 015, India
Tel.: (91) 8880194334
Web Site: http://leoburnett.co.in
Sales Range: $10-24.9 Million
Advertising Services
N.A.I.C.S.: 541810

Orchard Advertising (3)
4 2nd Floor Meanee Avenue Road, Ulsoor, Bengaluru, 560 042, India
Tel.: (91) 8880194334
Web Site: http://leoburnett.co.in
Sales Range: $10-24.9 Million
Advertising Services
N.A.I.C.S.: 541810

Subsidiary (Non-US):

Leo Burnett Jordan (2)
18 Al Mutanabi Street 3rd Cicle, PO Box 2013, Amman, 11181, Jordan
Tel.: (962) 646 44142
Web Site: http://www.leoburnett.com
Sales Range: $25-49.9 Million
Advertising Services
N.A.I.C.S.: 541810
Youssef Naaman *(Reg Mng Dir)*

Leo Burnett Kiev (2)
St Boulevard-Kudryavskaya 24 Bldg 2 Renaissance Business Center, 01054, Kiev, Ukraine
Tel.: (380) 44 490 9060
Web Site: http://www.leoburnett.ua
Sales Range: $10-24.9 Million
Emp.: 50
Advertising Services
N.A.I.C.S.: 541810

Leo Burnett Korea (2)
7th Floor Gwanhun Bldg 198-42 Gwanhundong, Chongro-ku, Seoul, 110-300, Korea (South)
Tel.: (82) 220003611
Web Site: http://www.leoburnett.co.kr
Sales Range: $25-49.9 Million
Emp.: 50
Advertising Services
N.A.I.C.S.: 541810

Leo Burnett Kreasindo Indonesia (2)
Noble House 15th Floor Jl Dr Ide Anak Agung Gede Agung Kav E4 2, No 2 Kuningan Timur, Jakarta, 12950, Indonesia
Tel.: (62) 2139830118
Web Site: http://leoburnett.co.id
Sales Range: $25-49.9 Million
Advertising Services
N.A.I.C.S.: 541810

Leo Burnett Manila (2)
The Enterprise Center 6766 Ayala Avenue Corner, Paseo de Roxas, Makati, 1200, Manila, Philippines
Tel.: (63) 28848001
Web Site: http://leoburnett.com
Sales Range: $25-49.9 Million
Advertising Services
N.A.I.C.S.: 541810
Raymond Arrastia *(Mng Dir)*

Leo Burnett Melbourne (2)
Level 7 28 Fresh Water Supply South Bank, Melbourne, 3006, VIC, Australia
Tel.: (61) 392511300
Web Site: http://www.leoburnett.com.au
Sales Range: $10-24.9 Million
Emp.: 88
Advertising Services
N.A.I.C.S.: 541810
Patrick Rowe *(Gen Mgr)*

Leo Burnett Mexico S.A. de C.V. (2)
Javier Barros Sierra 540 Park Plaza Torre 1 Piso 6, Mexico, 01210, DF, Mexico
Tel.: (52) 5552465900
Web Site: http://www.leoburnett.com.mx
Rev.: $148,765,000
Emp.: 100
Advertising Services
N.A.I.C.S.: 541810
Spadge Arteaga *(Gen Dir-ARC Mexico)*

Leo Burnett Moscow (2)
15 Bld 1 Leningradskiy Prospect, 125040, Moscow, Russia
Tel.: (7) 4959692030
Web Site: http://www.leoburnett.ru
Sales Range: $25-49.9 Million
Emp.: 200
Advertising Services
N.A.I.C.S.: 541810
Vladimir Tkachev *(Chm & CEO-Eastern Europe & Russia)*

Leo Burnett Panama, S.A. (2)
Avenue Balboa Edf Balboa Piso 7, Panama, Panama
Tel.: (507) 2252542
Web Site: http://www.leoburnett.com
Sales Range: $25-49.9 Million
Emp.: 20
Advertising Services
N.A.I.C.S.: 541810

Leo Burnett Publicidade, Ltda. (2)
Rua Brejo Alegre 99, Sao Paulo, 04557-050, Brazil
Tel.: (55) 1155041300
Web Site: http://www.leoburnett.com.br
Advertising Services
N.A.I.C.S.: 541810

Leo Burnett Publicidade, Ltda. (2)
Rua das Flores 7, 1200-193, Lisbon, Portugal
Tel.: (351) 213260800
Web Site: http://www.leoburnett.pt
Sales Range: $25-49.9 Million
Emp.: 57
Advertising Services
N.A.I.C.S.: 541810

Leo Burnett Rome (2)
Via Delle Sette Chiese 142, 00145, Rome, Italy
Tel.: (39) 06 684 321
Web Site: http://www.leoburnett.it
Sales Range: $10-24.9 Million
Advertising Services
N.A.I.C.S.: 541810
Romeo Repetto *(CEO)*

Leo Burnett Shanghai Advertising Co., Ltd. (2)
Suite 1201 Henderson 688 688 Nanjing West Road, Jingan, Shanghai, 200041, China
Tel.: (86) 2160283100
Web Site: http://leoburnett.com.cn
Advertising Services
N.A.I.C.S.: 541810

Leo Burnett Solutions Inc. (2)

PUBLICIS GROUPE S.A.

Publicis Groupe S.A.—(Continued)

379 R A de Mel Mawatha, Colombo, 3, Sri Lanka
Tel.: (94) 11 237 2080
Web Site: http://www.leoburnett.lk
Sales Range: $25-49.9 Million
Emp.: 80
Advertising Services
N.A.I.C.S.: 541810
Ransley Burrows (Chief Creative Officer)

Leo Burnett Sydney (2)
26 Windmill Road, McMahons Point, Sydney, 2000, NSW, Australia
Tel.: (61) 299253555
Web Site: http://www.leoburnett.com.au
Sales Range: $25-49.9 Million
Emp.: 160
Advertising Services
N.A.I.C.S.: 541810
Emma Montgomery (CEO)

Subsidiary (Domestic):

Leo Burnett USA (2)
35 W Wacker Dr, Chicago, IL 60601-1723
Tel.: (312) 220-5959
Web Site: http://www.leoburnett.us
Sales Range: $150-199.9 Million
Emp.: 1,000
Advertising Services
N.A.I.C.S.: 541810
Marcello Magalhaes (Chief Strategy Officer)

Subsidiary (Non-US):

Leo Burnett Vilnius (2)
Birutes 1D, Vilnius, 08117, Lithuania
Tel.: (370) 5 264 7505
Web Site: http://www.leoburnett.lt
Sales Range: $25-49.9 Million
Emp.: 10
Advertising Services
N.A.I.C.S.: 541810
German Lapin (Dir-Fin)

Leo Burnett Warsaw SP.Z.O.O. (2)
Platinum Business Park ul Woloska 9, 02-583, Warsaw, Poland
Tel.: (48) 224489800
Web Site: http://www.leoburnett.com
Sales Range: $25-49.9 Million
Advertising Services
N.A.I.C.S.: 541810
Hanna Jackowska (Mng Dir)

Leo Burnett Werbeagentur GmbH & Co. KG (2)
Gottfried Keller Gasse 2/28, Vienna, 1030, Austria
Tel.: (43) 1 713 73 95 0
Web Site: http://www.leoburnett.at
Sales Range: $25-49.9 Million
Emp.: 20
Advertising Services
N.A.I.C.S.: 541810
Rudolf Reisner (Mng Dir)

Subsidiary (Domestic):

Leo Burnett Worldwide - Latin America (2)
806 Douglas Rd Ste 700, Coral Gables, FL 33134-3129
Tel.: (305) 448-5959
Web Site: http://www.leoburnett.com
Sales Range: $10-24.9 Million
Emp.: 30
Hispanic Marketing
N.A.I.C.S.: 541810

Subsidiary (Non-US):

Leo Burnett, Ltd. (2)
40 Chancery Lane, Avonmore Road, London, WC2A 1JA, United Kingdom
Tel.: (44) 2077511800
Web Site: http://www.leoburnett.co.uk
Sales Range: $75-99.9 Million
Advertising Services
N.A.I.C.S.: 541810
Chaka Sobhani (Chief Creative Officer)

Leo Burnett-Beijing (2)
Room 1308 China World Tower 2 No 1 Jian Guo Meri Wai Avenue, Beijing, 100020, China
Tel.: (86) 10 6505 8838
Web Site: http://www.leoburnett.com
Advertising Services
N.A.I.C.S.: 541810
Carol Lam (Pres/Chief Creative Officer-Greater China)

Leo Burnett-Guangzhou (2)
5/F North Tower Poly International Plaza, Yue Jiang Zhong Road, Guangzhou, 510308, China
Tel.: (86) 2028360333
Web Site: http://www.leoburnett.com
Sales Range: $25-49.9 Million
Emp.: 60
Advertising Services
N.A.I.C.S.: 541810

Leo Burnett-Hong Kong (2)
6th Floor AIA Kowloon Tower 100 How Ming Street, Kwun Tong, China (Hong Kong)
Tel.: (852) 25674333
Web Site: http://leoburnett.hk
Advertising Services
N.A.I.C.S.: 541810

Manhattan Communications (Pvt) Ltd. (2)
Suite 322, Eden Center, 43 Jail Road, Lahore, Pakistan
Tel.: (92) 42 753 8851
Sales Range: $25-49.9 Million
Emp.: 20
Advertising Services
N.A.I.C.S.: 541810

Manhattan Communications Pvt. Ltd. (2)
Manhattan Centre 6A/45 DCHS Dr Mahmood Hussain Road, Karachi, 74800, Pakistan
Tel.: (92) 21 453 9972
Sales Range: $25-49.9 Million
Emp.: 80
Advertising Services
N.A.I.C.S.: 541810

Markom/Leo Burnett (2)
Buyukdere Cad 26/6 Beytem Plaza, Sisli, 34360, Istanbul, Turkiye
Tel.: (90) 2122342728
Web Site: http://www.leoburnett.com.tr
Sales Range: $10-24.9 Million
Emp.: 65
Advertising Services
N.A.I.C.S.: 541810

Mass Publicidad S.R.L. (2)
Estados Unidos 961 3rd Floor, Asuncion, Paraguay
Tel.: (595) 21 451 031
Web Site: http://www.mass.com.py
Rev.: $5,313,000
Emp.: 34
Advertising Services
N.A.I.C.S.: 541810
Pascual Rubiani (Mng Dir)

Metro Leo Burnett Advertising (2)
Velanas St 5, Riga, 1010, Latvia
Tel.: (371) 67 333 375
Web Site: http://www.leoburnett.lv
Sales Range: $10-24.9 Million
Emp.: 34
Advertising Services
N.A.I.C.S.: 541810
Peteris Puritis (Dir-Creative)

Radius Leo Burnett (2)
Dubai Media City Bldg No 11, PO Box 7534, Dubai, 7534, United Arab Emirates
Tel.: (971) 43672600
Web Site: http://www.leoburnettmena.com
Sales Range: $25-49.9 Million
Emp.: 225
Advertising Services
N.A.I.C.S.: 541810
Raja Trad (CEO)

Subsidiary (Non-US):

AMA Leo Burnett (3)
21 Ahmed Orabi Street Al Nahda Tower 7th Floor, Sahafeyeen, 11511, Giza, Egypt
Tel.: (20) 23047901
Web Site: http://www.leoburnett.com
Sales Range: $10-24.9 Million
Emp.: 38
Advertising Services
N.A.I.C.S.: 541810

Subsidiary (Non-US):

Red Rabbit Leo Burnett (2)
Hopsen Str 23, 20359, Hamburg, Germany
Tel.: (49) 40 43 19700
Web Site: http://www.red-rabbit.de
Sales Range: $10-24.9 Million
Emp.: 30
Advertising Services
N.A.I.C.S.: 541810
Jochen Matzer (Owner)

Rosabel Advertising Ltd. (2)
Rosabel Court 31 Aromire Ave, Ikeja, Lagos, Nigeria
Tel.: (234) 1 740 6265
Sales Range: $25-49.9 Million
Emp.: 61
Advertising Services
N.A.I.C.S.: 541810
Mikhail Ojediran (Head-Fin)

Spillmann/Felser/Leo Burnett (2)
Stadelhoferstrasse 25, PO Box 8040, 8001, Zurich, Switzerland
Tel.: (41) 433112525
Web Site: http://www.leoburnett.ch
Sales Range: $25-49.9 Million
Emp.: 70
Advertising Services
N.A.I.C.S.: 541810
Martin Spillmann (Exec Dir-Creative)

Styx & Leo Burnett (2)
38 Tulebayev St, Almaty, 050004, Kazakhstan
Tel.: (7) 3272 501 502
Sales Range: $10-24.9 Million
Emp.: 50
Advertising Services
N.A.I.C.S.: 541810

Targets/Leo Burnett (2)
Al Faisalah Tower 7th Floor King Fahad Road, PO Box 295797, Riyadh, 11351, Saudi Arabia
Tel.: (966) 112737070
Web Site: http://www.leoburnett.com
Sales Range: $10-24.9 Million
Advertising Services
N.A.I.C.S.: 541810

Targets/Leo Burnett Advertising (2)
Diners Square Building 4th Floor Near SABB Bank Al-Malek Road, PO Box 6093, Jeddah, 21442, Saudi Arabia
Tel.: (966) 26905722
Web Site: http://www.leoburnett.com
Sales Range: $10-24.9 Million
Advertising Services
N.A.I.C.S.: 541810

Votan Leo Burnett (2)
Ob Ljublanici 12, 1000, Ljubljana, Slovenia
Tel.: (386) 1 236 40 50
Sales Range: $10-24.9 Million
Emp.: 14
Advertising Services
N.A.I.C.S.: 541810
Samo Bobnar (Acct Dir)

Wiktor/Leo Burnett, s.r.o. (2)
Leskova 5, Bratislava, 81104, Slovakia
Tel.: (421) 2 5249 7250
Web Site: http://www.wlb.sk
Sales Range: $10-24.9 Million
Emp.: 50
Advertising Services
N.A.I.C.S.: 541810

masius London (2)
3rd Floor 81 Whitfield Street, London, W1T 4HG, United Kingdom
Tel.: (44) 20 7307 9170
Rev.: $35,000,000
Emp.: 26
Advertising Services
N.A.I.C.S.: 541810

Loeb et Associes (1)
36 Rue Vivenne, 75008, Paris, France
Tel.: (33) 1 44 43 47 70
Sales Range: $25-49.9 Million
Emp.: 10
N.A.I.C.S.: 541810
Koubi Jacques (Dir-Creative)

M.I.T.A. (2)
Trg Solidarnofpi 2A, 71000, Sarajevo, Bosnia & Herzegovina
Tel.: (387) 33 768 895
Web Site: http://www.mita.ba
Sales Range: $25-49.9 Million
Emp.: 20
Media Buying Services

INTERNATIONAL PUBLIC

N.A.I.C.S.: 541810

MMS Communications (Finland) Oy (1)
Mannerheimintie 15, 00260, Helsinki, Finland
Tel.: (358) 9 4257 9660
Web Site: http://www.reputation.fi
Advetising Agency

MRY US LLC (1)
299 W Houston St 11th Fl, New York, NY 10014
Tel.: (212) 274-0470
Web Site: http://www.mry.com
Marketing & Advertising Services
N.A.I.C.S.: 541810
James Wood (Grp Dir-Creative)

MSL China (1)
12F 01-03 Prosper Center West 5 Guanghua Road, Beijing, 100020, China
Tel.: (86) 10 8573 0688
Web Site: http://www.eastweimsl.com
Sales Range: $25-49.9 Million
Emp.: 200
Public Relations Services
N.A.I.C.S.: 541820
Lusha Niu (Dir-Corp Comm & Pub Affairs)

MSL Group London Ltd. (1)
82 Baker St, London, W1U 6AE, United Kingdom
Tel.: (44) 2032198700
Web Site: http://www.mslgroup.co.uk
Management Consulting Services
N.A.I.C.S.: 541618
Chris Mccaffer (CEO)

MSLGroup (1)
375 Hudson St 14th Fl, New York, NY 10014
Tel.: (646) 500-7600
Web Site: http://www.mslgroup.com
Sales Range: $450-499.9 Million
Emp.: 1,300
Public Relations
N.A.I.C.S.: 541810
Jim Fingeroth (Pres)

Branch (Non-US):

20:20 MSL (2)
A/12 1st Floor Vikas Center, S V Road, Santa Cruz West, Mumbai, 400054, India
Tel.: (91) 22 3965 1700
Web Site: http://www.2020india.com
Sales Range: $75-99.9 Million
Emp.: 300
Public Relations
N.A.I.C.S.: 541820

Branch (Domestic):

20:20 MSL (3)
17/B 1st Floor Jamals, Jagannathan Street Nungabakkam, Chennai, 00034, India
Tel.: (91) 44 2826 0145
Sales Range: $25-49.9 Million
Emp.: 16
Public Relations
N.A.I.C.S.: 541820

20:20 MSL (3)
4th Fl Srinivasa Plz, 6-3-850/3 Ameerpet, Hyderabad, 500016, India
Tel.: (91) 40 23416882
Web Site: http://www.2020india.com
Sales Range: $25-49.9 Million
Emp.: 5
Public Relations
N.A.I.C.S.: 541820

20:20 MSL (3)
604 Sacred World Opp Sacred Heart Town, Wanoworie, Pune, 411040, India
Tel.: (91) 20 4005 3004
Web Site: http://www.2020india.com
Public Relations
N.A.I.C.S.: 541820

20:20 MSL (3)
16/6 Raintree Hall 2nd Fl Rhenius St, Richmond Town, Bengaluru, 560 025, India
Tel.: (91) 80 212 3112
Public Relations
N.A.I.C.S.: 541820

Branch (Non-US):

Andreoli/MS&L (2)

AND PRIVATE COMPANIES

Av Ibirapuera 2332 Torre 1 - 14 andar, Moema, 04028-002, Sao Paulo, SP, Brazil
Tel.: (55) 11 3169 9300
Web Site: http://www.andreolimsl.com.br
Sales Range: $10-24.9 Million
Emp.: 30
Public Relations
N.A.I.C.S.: 541820

Capital MS&L (2)
55 Whitfield Street, London, W1T 4AH, United Kingdom
Tel.: (44) 207 307 5330
Web Site: http://www.capitalmsl.com
Sales Range: $50-74.9 Million
Emp.: 19
Public Relations
N.A.I.C.S.: 541820

De Maruri Publicidad DMP
Avenida Raul Gomez Lince Av 32 N-O 640 Edificio MCG, Bajo el Mirador de Urdenor, Guayaquil, Ecuador
Tel.: (593) 4 2888 120
Sales Range: $10-24.9 Million
Emp.: 50
Advertising Services
N.A.I.C.S.: 541810
Fausto Maruri (Gen Mgr)

Hollander en Van der Mey/MS&L (2)
Floris Grijpstraat 2, 2596 XE, Hague, Netherlands
Tel.: (31) 70 354 90 00
Web Site: http://www.hvdm.nl
Sales Range: $25-49.9 Million
Emp.: 50
Public Relations
N.A.I.C.S.: 541810

JKL Copenhagen (2)
Esplanaden 34A 1st Floor 1256, DK-1256, Copenhagen, Denmark
Tel.: (45) 33 38 56 80
Sales Range: $25-49.9 Million
Emp.: 11
Public Relations
N.A.I.C.S.: 541820

JKL Goteborg (2)
Vastra Hamngatan 24-26, Gothenburg, 41117, Sweden
Tel.: (46) 31 708 91 00
Sales Range: $25-49.9 Million
Emp.: 10
Public Relations
N.A.I.C.S.: 541820

JKL Helsinki (2)
Mannerheimintie 15 B, 00260, Helsinki, Finland
Tel.: (358) 9 6869 790
Sales Range: $25-49.9 Million
Emp.: 9
Public Relations
N.A.I.C.S.: 541820

JKL Oslo (2)
Drammensveien 127, PO Box 114, Skoyen, 0212, Oslo, Norway
Tel.: (47) 24 10 38 00
Sales Range: $25-49.9 Million
Emp.: 18
Public Relations
N.A.I.C.S.: 541820

JKL Stockholm (2)
Sveavagen 24-26, PO Box 1405, Stockholm, 11157, Sweden
Tel.: (46) 8 696 12 00
Sales Range: $25-49.9 Million
Emp.: 57
Public Relations
N.A.I.C.S.: 541820
Maria Grimberg Bostrom (CEO-JKL Grp & Partner)

MS&L (2)
Room 1716 Tower 1 Bright China Chang An Building No 7, Jian Guo Men Nei Da Jie, Beijing, 100005, China
Tel.: (86) 10 5108 8238
Public Relations
N.A.I.C.S.: 541820

MS&L (2)
6/F Cityplaza 3, 14 Taikoo Wan Rd, Hong Kong, China (Hong Kong)
Tel.: (852) 2886 5523
Sales Range: $25-49.9 Million
Emp.: 20
Public Relations
N.A.I.C.S.: 541820
Glen Osaki (Pres-Asia)

MS&L (2)
Suite 500 358 Rue Beaubien Ouest Montreal, Montreal, H2V 4S6, QC, Canada
Tel.: (514) 842-1077
Web Site: http://www.mslgroup.com
Sales Range: $25-49.9 Million
Emp.: 5
Public Relations
N.A.I.C.S.: 541820

Branch (Domestic):

MS&L Digital (2)
115 W Liberty Ste 200, Ann Arbor, MI 48104
Tel.: (212) 468-4200
Sales Range: $25-49.9 Million
Emp.: 20
Public Relations
N.A.I.C.S.: 541820

Branch (Non-US):

MS&L Dubai (2)
Dubai Media City Building No 11, PO Box 7534, Dubai Media City 2nd Floor, Dubai, United Arab Emirates
Tel.: (971) 43676150
Sales Range: $25-49.9 Million
Emp.: 20
Public Relations
N.A.I.C.S.: 541820
Ajit Ramaswami (COO-MENA)

MS&L France (2)
15 rue Bleue, 75341, Paris, Cedex 09, France
Tel.: (33) 155334300
Sales Range: $25-49.9 Million
Emp.: 25
Public Relations
N.A.I.C.S.: 541820

MS&L Italia (2)
Viale Vittorio Veneto 22, 20124, Milan, Italy
Tel.: (39) 027733661
Sales Range: $10-24.9 Million
Emp.: 50
Public Relations
N.A.I.C.S.: 541810
Adriana Mavellia (Founder)

Affiliate (Domestic):

Chiappe Revello Associati (3)
Via Domenico Fiasella 1/13, 16121, Genoa, Italy
Tel.: (39) 010566334
Web Site: http://www.chiapperevello.com
Advertising Services
N.A.I.C.S.: 541810
Rossana Revello (Founder & Pres)

Branch (Non-US):

MS&L Japan (2)
14F JR Tokyu Meguro Blg, 3-1-1 Kami-Osaki Shinagawa-ku, Tokyo, 141-0021, Japan
Tel.: (81) 3 5719 8901
Emp.: 30
Public Relations
N.A.I.C.S.: 541820
Eric Hess (Mng Dir)

MS&L Shanghai (2)
Room F 15/F No755 Huai Hai Zhong Road, Shanghai, 200020, China
Tel.: (86) 21 5465 8488
Public Relations
N.A.I.C.S.: 541820
Glenn Osaki (Pres-Asia)

MS&L South Africa (2)
Building 1 Silver Stream Business Park 10 Muswell Road, Sunninghill, Bryanston, 2191, Johannesburg, South Africa
Tel.: (27) 872550500
Web Site: http://www.mslgroup.co.za
Sales Range: $25-49.9 Million
Emp.: 15
Public Relations
N.A.I.C.S.: 541820
Gavin Etheridge (Mng Dir)

MS&L Sweden (2)
Sveavagen 24-26, SE-111 84, Stockholm, Sweden

Tel.: (46) 855051100
Web Site: http://www.mslpr.se
Sales Range: $25-49.9 Million
Emp.: 20
Public Relations
N.A.I.C.S.: 541820
Jan Lindow (Mng Dir)

Branch (Domestic):

MS&L Worldwide (2)
1201 Connecticut Ave NW Ste 500, Washington, DC 20036
Tel.: (202) 467-6600
Web Site: http://www.mslgroup.com
Sales Range: $10-24.9 Million
Emp.: 26
Public Relations
N.A.I.C.S.: 541820

MSLGROUP - Atlanta (2)
1170 Peachtree St NE Ste 1600, Atlanta, GA 30309
Tel.: (404) 875-1444
Web Site: http://northamerica.mslgroup.com
N.A.I.C.S.: 541820
Doug Busk (Mng Dir)

Branch (Non-US):

MSLGroup Germany GmbH (2)
Leibnizstr 65, 10629, Berlin, Germany
Tel.: (49) 3082082543
Web Site: http://www.mslgroup.de
Sales Range: $25-49.9 Million
Public Relations Agency
N.A.I.C.S.: 541820
Philip Maravilla (Mng Dir)

Branch (Domestic):

Manning Selvage & Lee (2)
33 Arch St 8th Fl, Boston, MA 02110
Tel.: (617) 437-7722
Sales Range: $25-49.9 Million
Emp.: 15
Public Relations
N.A.I.C.S.: 541820

Manning Selvage & Lee (2)
2001 The Embarcadero, San Francisco, CA 94133
Tel.: (415) 293-2800
Sales Range: $25-49.9 Million
Emp.: 25
Public Relations
N.A.I.C.S.: 541820

Manning Selvage & Lee (2)
222 Merchandise Mart Plz Ste 4 150, Chicago, IL 60654
Tel.: (312) 861-5200
Sales Range: $10-24.9 Million
Emp.: 26
Public Relations
N.A.I.C.S.: 541820
Nancy Glick (Sr VP)

Manning Selvage & Lee (2)
2029 Century Park E Ste 1750, Los Angeles, CA 90067-3036
Tel.: (323) 866-6000
Sales Range: $10-24.9 Million
Emp.: 28
Public Relations
N.A.I.C.S.: 541820

Branch (Non-US):

Manning Selvage & Lee London (2)
Pembroke Building Kensington Village Avonmore Road, London, W14 8DG, United Kingdom
Tel.: (44) 44207 878 3000
Web Site: http://www.mslpr.co.uk
Sales Range: $25-49.9 Million
Emp.: 110
Public Relations
N.A.I.C.S.: 541820

Muchnik, Alurralde, Jasper & Assoc./MS&L (2)
Callao 1046 Piso 4, Buenos Aires, C1023AAQ, Argentina
Tel.: (54) 11 5031 1300
Sales Range: $10-24.9 Million
Emp.: 45
Public Relations
N.A.I.C.S.: 541820

PUBLICIS GROUPE S.A.

Publicis Dialog Malaysia (2)
Level 5 Menara Olympia, 8 Jalan Raja Chulan, Kuala Lumpur, 50200, Malaysia
Tel.: (60) 3 2031 0998
Web Site: http://www.leoburnett.com.my
Sales Range: $25-49.9 Million
Emp.: 250
Advertising Services
N.A.I.C.S.: 541810

Subsidiary (Domestic):

Qorvis Communications, LLC (2)
1201 Connecticut Ave NW Ste 500, Washington, DC 20036
Tel.: (202) 496-1000
Web Site: http://www.qorvis.com
Emp.: 100
Public Relations Agency
N.A.I.C.S.: 541820
Michael J. Petruzzello (Founder & CEO)

Branch (Domestic):

TMG Strategies (2)
2300 Clarendon Blvd Ste 901, Arlington, VA 22201
Tel.: (703) 312-0140
Web Site: http://www.tmgstrategies.com
Sales Range: $10-24.9 Million
Emp.: 30
Advertising Services
N.A.I.C.S.: 541810

Market Forward (1)
427 S LaSalle St, Chicago, IL 60605
Tel.: (312) 220-1700
Web Site: http://www.marketforward.com
Sales Range: $25-49.9 Million
Emp.: 50
N.A.I.C.S.: 541870

Marketway Ltd. (1)
Marketway Building 20 Karpenisiou Street, Nicosia, 1071, Cyprus
Tel.: (357) 22 391000
Web Site: http://www.marketway.com.cy
Sales Range: $25-49.9 Million
Emp.: 38
N.A.I.C.S.: 541810
Barbara Petropoulou Lillikas (CEO)

Match Media Australia Ltd. (1)
Ground Floor 63-73 Ann Street Surry Hills, Sydney, 2010, NSW, Australia
Tel.: (61) 286443000
Web Site: http://www.matchmedia.com.au
Marketing & Advertising Services
N.A.I.C.S.: 541810

Media Solutions GmbH (1)
Osterwaldstr 10/G19, 80805, Munich, Germany
Tel.: (49) 893066990
Web Site: http://media-solutions.de
Marketing & Advertising Services
N.A.I.C.S.: 541810

Medicus Life Brands (1)
1675 Broadway 5th Fl, New York, NY 10019-5820
Tel.: (212) 468-3100
Sales Range: $200-249.9 Million
Emp.: 598
Communication Service
N.A.I.C.S.: 541820
Josh Hoekstra (Acct Dir)

Mikado S.A. (1)
38 route d'Esch, Luxembourg, 1470, Luxembourg
Tel.: (352) 45 75 45 1
Web Site: http://www.mikado.lu
Sales Range: $25-49.9 Million
Emp.: 15
N.A.I.C.S.: 541810
Jean-Luc Mines (Chm)

Mr. Youth (1)
225 Park Ave S 16th Fl, New York, NY 10003
Tel.: (212) 779-8700
Web Site: http://www.mryouth.com
Sales Range: $25-49.9 Million
Emp.: 120
Advertising Services
N.A.I.C.S.: 541810
Matt Britton (Founder)

Multi Market Services France Holdings SAS (1)

PUBLICIS GROUPE S.A.

Publicis Groupe S.A.—(Continued)
133 Avenue des Champs Elysees, Paris, 75008, France
Tel.: (33) 144437000
Data Science & Technology Consulting Services
N.A.I.C.S.: 541690
Veronique Weill *(Gen Mgr)*

Subsidiary (Domestic):

Soft Computing SA (2)
55 quai de Grenelle, 75015, Paris, France (82.99%)
Tel.: (33) 1 73 00 55 00
Web Site: http://www.softcomputing.com
Management Consulting Services
N.A.I.C.S.: 541611
Gilles Venturi *(CEO)*

Neogama BBH (1)
Av Mofarrej 1174, Vila Leopoldina, Sao Paulo, 05311 000, SP, Brazil
Tel.: (55) 11 2184 1200
Web Site: http://www.neogamabbh.com.br
Sales Range: $50-74.9 Million
Emp.: 270
Advetising Agency
N.A.I.C.S.: 541810
Alexandre Gama *(Founder, CEO & Dir-Creative)*

Nurun Inc. (1)
358 Beaubien West Suite 500, Montreal, H2V 4S6, QC, Canada
Tel.: (514) 392-1900
Web Site: http://www.nurun.com
Advetising Agency
N.A.I.C.S.: 541810
Christian Ayotte *(Pres)*

Branch (Non-US):

Nurun China (2)
501 Li Yuan Road A7 5th Floor, Shanghai, 200023, China
Tel.: (86) 21 2326 6800
Web Site: http://www.nurun.com
Advetising Agency
N.A.I.C.S.: 541810
Julie Marchesseault *(VP & Gen Mgr)*

Branch (Domestic):

Nurun Inc. (2)
111 Queen Street East, Toronto, M5C 1S2, ON, Canada
Tel.: (416) 925-5260
Web Site: https://www.nurun.com
Advetising Agency
N.A.I.C.S.: 541810

Branch (Non-US):

Nurun Spain (2)
C/ Ramirez De Arellano 21 3, 28043, Madrid, Spain
Tel.: (34) 91 358 49 59
Web Site: http://www.nurun.com
Advetising Agency
N.A.I.C.S.: 541810
Xabier Olazabal *(CEO)*

Subsidiary (US):

Odopod, Inc. (2)
391 Grove St, San Francisco, CA 94102
Tel.: (415) 436-9980
Web Site: http://www.odopod.com
Advertising, Digital/Interactive, Internet/Web Design
N.A.I.C.S.: 541430

Branch (Non-US):

Publicis Nurun (2)
133 Avenue Des Champs Elysees, 75008, Paris, Cedex, France
Tel.: (33) 1 44 43 78 00
Web Site: http://www.publicisnurun.fr
Emp.: 550
Advetising Agency
N.A.I.C.S.: 541810
Jean-Guy Saulou *(Gen Mgr)*

OnPoint Consulting, Inc. (1)
2107 Wilson Blvd Ste 510, Arlington, VA 22201
Tel.: (703) 841-5500
Web Site: http://www.onpointcorp.com

Information Technology Consulting Services
N.A.I.C.S.: 541512
Tim Smith *(Pres)*

Ove Design & Communications Ltd. (1)
164 Merton St, Toronto, M4S 3A8, ON, Canada
Tel.: (416) 423-6228
Web Site: http://www.ovedesign.com
Sales Range: $25-49.9 Million
Emp.: 25
N.A.I.C.S.: 541810

PBJS, Inc. (1)
2226 3rd Ave, Seattle, WA 98121
Tel.: (206) 464-8392
Web Site: http://www.pbjs.com
Sales Range: $25-49.9 Million
Emp.: 26
Digital/Interactive
N.A.I.C.S.: 541810

Payer Sciences LLC (1)
240 Headquarters Plz E Tower-10th Fl, Morristown, NJ 07960
Tel.: (973) 998-7501
Web Site: http://www.payersciences.com
Marketing & Advertising Services
N.A.I.C.S.: 541810
Laura Fields *(VP-Client Engagement)*

Performics (1)
180 N LaSalle Ste 1100, Chicago, IL 60601
Tel.: (312) 739-0222
Web Site: http://www.performics.com
Sales Range: $50-74.9 Million
Emp.: 140
Performance-Based Online Marketing Services & Technologies
N.A.I.C.S.: 541613
Scott Shamberg *(Pres-USA)*

Phonevalley (1)
30-34 rue Du Chemin Vert, 75011, Paris, France
Tel.: (33) 172632400
Web Site: http://www.phonevalley.com
Sales Range: $25-49.9 Million
Emp.: 60
Advetising Agency
N.A.I.C.S.: 541810

Poke London Ltd. (1)
Biscuit Bldg 10 Redchurch St, E2 7DD, London, United Kingdom - England
Tel.: (44) 20 7749 5353
Web Site: http://www.pokelondon.com
Emp.: 75
Advertising Services
N.A.I.C.S.: 541810
Pete Beech *(Partner)*

Protishabda Communications (1)
26 Kemal Ata Turk Ave 3rd Floor, Banani Commercial Area, Dhaka, 1213, Bangladesh
Tel.: (880) 2 881 7147
Sales Range: $25-49.9 Million
Emp.: 25
N.A.I.C.S.: 541810

Proximedia SA (1)
Boulevard de l'Humanite 237, 1620, Drogenbos, Belgium
Tel.: (32) 23492343
Web Site: http://www.proximedia.be
Internet Services
N.A.I.C.S.: 517121

Publicis (1)
111 Queen Street East Suite 200, Toronto, M5C 1S2, ON, Canada
Tel.: (416) 925-7733
Web Site: http://www.publicis.ca
Sales Range: $75-99.9 Million
Advetising Agency
N.A.I.C.S.: 541810

Publicis (Beijing) (1)
Rm 1510 15/F Zhuzong Tower No 25 Dong San Huan Zhong Rd, Chaoyang District, Beijing, 100020, China
Tel.: (86) 10 6594 5180
Web Site: http://www.publicis-bj.com.cn
Sales Range: $25-49.9 Million
Emp.: 104
N.A.I.C.S.: 541810
David Gompel *(CEO-Greater China)*

Publicis (Malaysia) Sdn. Bhd. (1)

M1 Mezanine Fl Wisme LYL, 46100, Petaling Jaya, Selangor, Malaysia
Tel.: (60) 3 7952 2222
Web Site: http://www.publicis.com.my
Sales Range: $25-49.9 Million
Emp.: 100
N.A.I.C.S.: 541810
Dean Branhan *(CEO)*

Publicis (Thailand) Ltd. (1)
Empire Tower 47th Fl, Yannawa, 10120, Bangkok, Thailand
Tel.: (66) 2 659 5959
Web Site: http://www.publicisapac.com
Advetising Agency
N.A.I.C.S.: 541810

Publicis Activ Annecy (1)
Park Nord Les Pleiades No 26, 74370, Metz-Tessy, France
Tel.: (33) 4 50 52 64 94
Web Site: http://www.publicis-annecy.fr
Advetising Agency
N.A.I.C.S.: 541810

Publicis Activ Lyon (1)
22 Rue Seguin, 69002, Lyon, France
Tel.: (33) 472416484
Web Site: http://www.publicisactiv-lyon.fr
Emp.: 80
Advetising Agency
N.A.I.C.S.: 541810

Publicis Ariely (1)
7 Achim Bezerano St, 52711, Ramat Gan, Israel
Tel.: (972) 3 611 9999
N.A.I.C.S.: 541810

Publicis Arredondo de Haro (1)
Prolongacion Paseo de la Reforma, 1015 5 piso Col Desarrollo, Mexico, CP 01310, DF, Mexico
Tel.: (52) 5 9177 5600
N.A.I.C.S.: 541810

Publicis Asia/Pacific Pte. Ltd. (1)
80 Anson Road 33-00, Fuji Xerox Twrs, Singapore, 079907, Singapore
Tel.: (65) 6 836 3488
Web Site: http://www.publicis.com
Emp.: 100
N.A.I.C.S.: 541810

Publicis Asociados (1)
Los Eucaliptos 245 San Isidro, Lima, 27, Peru
Tel.: (51) 1 215 5500
Sales Range: $25-49.9 Million
Emp.: 80
N.A.I.C.S.: 541810

Publicis Atlantique (1)
Espace Grand Large Quai de la Douane, BP 918191, 44018, Brest, Cedex 1, France
Tel.: (33) 2 40 35 85 10
Web Site: http://www.publicisgroupe.com
Sales Range: Less than $1 Million
Emp.: 13
N.A.I.C.S.: 541810

Publicis Brand/Design (1)
111 Queen St E Ste 200, Toronto, M5C 1S2, ON, Canada
Tel.: (416) 925-7733
Web Site: http://www.publicis.ca
Emp.: 350
N.A.I.C.S.: 541810

Publicis Brasil Communicao (1)
Av Presidente Juscelino Kubitschek 1 909 - 12 Andar, Torre Norte Vila Nova Conceicao, Sao Paulo, 04543-907, SP, Brazil
Tel.: (55) 1145609000
Web Site: http://www.publicis.com.br
Sales Range: $75-99.9 Million
Emp.: 390
Brand Development, New Product Development, Sales Promotion
N.A.I.C.S.: 541810

Branch (Domestic):

Publicis Brasil Communicao (2)
Praca Pio X 15 8 andar, 20040 020, Rio de Janeiro, Brazil
Tel.: (55) 21 3981 0300
Web Site: http://www.publicis.com.br
Sales Range: $25-49.9 Million
Emp.: 55
Marketing & Advertising

INTERNATIONAL PUBLIC

N.A.I.C.S.: 541613

Publicis Brasil Communicao (2)
SCN Quadra 04 Bloco B Petala B Sala 404 B, Ed Centro Empress, 70714 906, Brasilia, DF, Brazil
Tel.: (55) 61 362 2040
Web Site: http://www.publicis.com.br
Sales Range: $10-24.9 Million
Emp.: 30
Advetising Agency
N.A.I.C.S.: 541810
Monica Rebello *(Dir)*

Publicis Canada Inc. (1)
358 Rue Beaubien Ouest Bureau 500, Montreal, H2X 4S6, QC, Canada
Tel.: (514) 285-1414
Web Site: http://www.publicis.ca
Marketing & Advertising Services
N.A.I.C.S.: 541810

Publicis Caribbean (1)
55 Dundonald Str Port, Port of Spain, Trinidad & Tobago
Tel.: (868) 627 4040
Web Site: http://www.publicis.com
Sales Range: $25-49.9 Million
Emp.: 50
N.A.I.C.S.: 541810

Publicis Caribbean Dominicana (1)
Av Bolivar 217, Segundo Livel, 1080, Santo Domingo, Dominican Republic
Tel.: (809) 920 0404
Sales Range: $25-49.9 Million
Emp.: 20
N.A.I.C.S.: 541810

Publicis Casadevall Pedreno & PRG (1)
Avenida Diagonal 579 2nd Fl, 08014, Barcelona, Spain
Tel.: (34) 93 418 51 18
Web Site: http://www.publicis.es
Sales Range: $25-49.9 Million
Emp.: 9
N.A.I.C.S.: 541810

Publicis Chile SA (1)
Rapallo, 4322, Las Condes, 755-0306, Santiago, Chile
Tel.: (56) 2 757 3000
Sales Range: $25-49.9 Million
Emp.: 20
N.A.I.C.S.: 541810

Publicis Communications Schweiz AG (1)
Stadelhoferstrasse 25, 8001, Zurich, Switzerland
Tel.: (41) 442653111
Web Site: http://www.publicis.ch
Marketing & Advertising Services
N.A.I.C.S.: 541810
Peter Van der Touw *(COO)*

Publicis Conseil (1)
133 Avenue des Champs Elysees, 75008, Paris, France
Tel.: (33) 144437000
Sales Range: $25-49.9 Million
Emp.: 500
Advetising Agency
N.A.I.C.S.: 541810
Fabrice Delacourt *(Dir-Creative)*

Publicis Constellation (1)
36 rue Divienne, 75002, Paris, France
Tel.: (33) 1 56 21 20 62
Sales Range: $75-99.9 Million
Emp.: 486
N.A.I.C.S.: 541810

Publicis Consultants (1)
133 av des Champs Elysees, 75380, Paris, France
Tel.: (33) 1 44 43 7100
Web Site: http://www.publicis-consultants.fr
Sales Range: $25-49.9 Million
Emp.: 200
N.A.I.C.S.: 541810

Publicis Dialog (1)
111 Queen St E Ste 200, Toronto, M5C 1S2, ON, Canada
Tel.: (416) 925-5260
Web Site: http://www.publicis.ca
Sales Range: $75-99.9 Million
Emp.: 300
N.A.I.C.S.: 541810

AND PRIVATE COMPANIES / PUBLICIS GROUPE S.A.

Publicis Dialog (1)
133 Avenue des Champs Elysees, 75008, Paris, CEDEX, France
Tel.: (33) 1 44 43 78 00
Web Site: http://www.publicis-dialog.fr
Sales Range: $25-49.9 Million
Emp.: 150
N.A.I.C.S.: 541810

Publicis Dialog & Interactive-Montreal (1)
358 Beaubien Street West Office 500, Montreal, H2V 4S6, QC, Canada
Tel.: (514) 285-1414
Web Site: http://www.publicismontreal.ca
Sales Range: $75-99.9 Million
N.A.I.C.S.: 541810

Publicis Drum PR (1)
Textile Ctr 4th Fl Kenwyn St & St Georges Bay Rd, PO Box 9235, Parnell, Auckland, New Zealand
Tel.: (64) 9 915 3786
Web Site: http://www.publicismojo.co.nz
Sales Range: $25-49.9 Million
Emp.: 20
N.A.I.C.S.: 541820

Publicis Et Nous (1)
36 rue des Jeuneurs, 75012, Paris, France
Tel.: (33) 1 55 35 90 90
Web Site: http://www.publicisgroupe.com
Sales Range: $25-49.9 Million
Emp.: 35
N.A.I.C.S.: 541810

Publicis Fergo, S.A. (1)
Calle 50 y Calle 67 San Francisco Building 3rd Fl, Panama, Panama
Tel.: (507) 2708811
Rev.: $8,500,000
Emp.: 51
Advertising Services
N.A.I.C.S.: 541810

Publicis Full Player (1)
36 Rue Vivienne, Paris, 75002, France
Tel.: (33) 1 58 36 46 10
Sales Range: $25-49.9 Million
Emp.: 60
N.A.I.C.S.: 541810

Publicis Graffiti S.A. (1)
Armenia 1528, C1414DKH, Buenos Aires, Argentina
Tel.: (54) 1155563500
Web Site: http://www.publicis.com.ar
Advertising Services
N.A.I.C.S.: 541810
Paula Katz *(Dir Gen-Accounts)*

Publicis Graphics (1)
Ashrafieh Quantum Tower 9th Floor Charles Malek Street, 55369, Beirut, Lebanon
Tel.: (961) 1201090
Web Site: http://www.publicis.com
Sales Range: $25-49.9 Million
N.A.I.C.S.: 541810

Publicis Graphics (1)
10 Saeed Abu Javer St Um Uthaina, Po Box 17992, Amman, 11195, Jordan
Tel.: (962) 655 28174
N.A.I.C.S.: 541810

Publicis Graphics (1)
Salmiya Salem Al Mubarak Street Danda Center Blld 2nd & 5th Floor, Kuwait City, Kuwait, 13011, Kuwait
Tel.: (965) 5712 598
N.A.I.C.S.: 541810

Publicis Group Media Kazakhstan (Metro) (1)
A6 h 162, Dostyk Ave, Almaty, 50051, Kazakhstan
Tel.: (7) 727 258 13 13
Web Site: http://www.pgm.kz
Sales Range: $25-49.9 Million
Emp.: 25
N.A.I.C.S.: 541810
Victoria Poklonova *(Chm)*

Publicis Guangzhou (1)
6F One Bravo 1 Jinsui Road, Zhu Jiang New Town Tianhe District, Guangzhou, 510623, China
Tel.: (86) 2038791228
Web Site: http://www.publicisgroupe.com
Sales Range: $25-49.9 Million
N.A.I.C.S.: 541810

Publicis Health LLC (1)
1675 Broadway, New York, NY 10019
Tel.: (212) 771-5500
Web Site: http://www.publicishealth.com
Marketing & Advertising Services
N.A.I.C.S.: 541810
Alexandra Von Plato *(CEO)*

Publicis Hellas (1)
3-5 Menandrou Street, Kifissia, Athens, 14561, Greece
Tel.: (30) 210 628 1000
Web Site: http://www.publicis.gr
Sales Range: $25-49.9 Million
Emp.: 50
N.A.I.C.S.: 541810
Niki Akrioti *(Chm-Greece)*

Publicis Hong Kong (1)
33/F AIA Kowloon Tower Landmark East 100 How Ming Street, Kowloon, China (Hong Kong)
Tel.: (852) 2590 5888
Web Site: http://www.publicis.com
Sales Range: $25-49.9 Million
N.A.I.C.S.: 541810

Publicis Hourra! (1)
20-22 rue Basse, Lille, 59000, France
Tel.: (33) 3 28 36 70 00
Web Site: http://www.publicis-hourra.fr
Sales Range: $10-24.9 Million
Emp.: 60
N.A.I.C.S.: 541810
Hubert Van Robias *(Pres)*

Publicis Impetu (1)
Ciudad De Paris 5969, 11400, Montevideo, Uruguay
Tel.: (598) 26054799
Web Site: http://www.publicisimpetu.com.uy
Sales Range: $25-49.9 Million
Emp.: 30
Advertising Services
N.A.I.C.S.: 541810
Jorge Caponi *(Pres)*

Publicis India Communications Pvt. Ltd. (1)
126 Mathuradas Mills Compound N M Joshi Marg, Off Senapati Bapat Marg Lower, 400 013, Mumbai, India
Tel.: (91) 22 2482 9000
Sales Range: $25-49.9 Million
Emp.: 160
N.A.I.C.S.: 541810
Hemant Misra *(CEO-Capital)*

Branch (Domestic):

Publicis India Communications Pvt. Ltd. (2)
90 D Sector 18 Udyog Vihar Phase IV, Delhi, 122015, India
Tel.: (91) 124 412 1000
Emp.: 70
N.A.I.C.S.: 541810
Mohit Tomar *(Dir-Creative)*

Publicis Indonesia (1)
Menara Jamsostek South Tower 17th Floor, Jl Jend Gatot Subroto Kav 38, 12710, Jakarta, Indonesia
Tel.: (62) 2129026500
Web Site: http://www.publicis.co.id
Sales Range: $25-49.9 Million
Emp.: 90
Advertising Services
N.A.I.C.S.: 541810
Brian Capel *(CEO)*

Publicis JimenezBasic (1)
14/F Solaris One Bldg 130 Dela Rosa St, Legaspi Village, Makati, Philippines
Tel.: (63) 2 811 5098
N.A.I.C.S.: 541810
Bebot Ngo *(CEO)*

Publicis Knut (1)
Nove Zahrady 1/13A, 82105, Bratislava, Slovakia
Tel.: (421) 248 2356 41
Web Site: http://www.publicis.sk
Sales Range: $25-49.9 Million
Emp.: 40
N.A.I.C.S.: 541810

Publicis Koufra (1)
1 rue du Dome, 67000, Strasbourg, France
Tel.: (33) 388143536
Web Site: http://www.publicis-activ.fr
Sales Range: $25-49.9 Million
Emp.: 20
N.A.I.C.S.: 541810
Franck Barelles *(Mng Dir)*

Publicis Koufra (1)
13 rue Here, PO Box 90666, Nancy, 54063, France
Tel.: (33) 3 83 17 04 86
Web Site: http://www.publicisactiv-nancy.fr
Sales Range: $25-49.9 Million
Emp.: 10
Advetising Agency
N.A.I.C.S.: 541810

Publicis Manila (1)
6766 Ayala Avenue Corner Paseo De Roxas Legaspi Village, Makati, 1229, Philippines
Tel.: (63) 288125466
Web Site: http://www.publicis.com
Sales Range: $25-49.9 Million
Full Service
N.A.I.C.S.: 541810

Publicis Media GmbH (1)
Toulouser Allee 3, 40211, Dusseldorf, Germany
Tel.: (49) 211175407
Web Site: http://www.publicismedia.de
Marketing & Advertising Services
N.A.I.C.S.: 541810

Publicis Montreal (1)
358 Rue Beaubien Ouest, Montreal, H2V 4S6, QC, Canada
Tel.: (514) 285-1414
Web Site: http://www.publicis.ca
Sales Range: $25-49.9 Million
Emp.: 150
Advetising Agency
N.A.I.C.S.: 541810
Maxime Merchez *(Dir-Art)*

Publicis NetWorks (1)
111 Queen St E Suite 200, Toronto, M5C 1S2, ON, Canada
Tel.: (416) 925-7733
Web Site: http://www.publicis.ca
Sales Range: $10-24.9 Million
N.A.I.C.S.: 541810

Publicis Pixelpark GmbH (1)
Heidi-Kabel-Platz 2, 20099, Hamburg, Germany
Tel.: (49) 40341010
Web Site: http://www.digitaspixelpark.com
Marketing & Advertising Services
N.A.I.C.S.: 541810

Publicis Shanghai (1)
6/F Building A 98 Yan Ping Road, Shanghai, 200042, China
Tel.: (86) 21 2208 3888
Sales Range: $25-49.9 Million
Emp.: 120
N.A.I.C.S.: 541810
C. H. Yang *(Mng Dir)*

Publicis Singapore (1)
80 Anson Road, 33-00 Fuji Xerox Twrs, Singapore, 79907, Singapore
Tel.: (65) 6836 3488
Web Site: http://www.publicis.com.sg
Sales Range: $25-49.9 Million
Emp.: 100
N.A.I.C.S.: 541810
Ajay Vikram *(Chief Creative Officer-Global Clients)*

Publicis Singapore (1)
80 Anson Road 33-00 Fuji Xerox Towers, 79907, Singapore, Singapore
Tel.: (65) 6732 3212
Web Site: http://www.publicis.com.sg
Emp.: 120
Advetising Agency
N.A.I.C.S.: 541810
Sharim Gubbels *(Dir-Creative-Social)*

Publicis Soleil (1)
23 Rue Vacon, Marseilles, 13001, France
Tel.: (33) 4 91 10 79 70
Sales Range: $25-49.9 Million
Emp.: 45
N.A.I.C.S.: 541810

Publicis Soleil (1)
12 Boulevard Victor Hugo, 34000, Montpellier, France
Tel.: (33) 4 67 92 16 36
Sales Range: $25-49.9 Million
Emp.: 10
N.A.I.C.S.: 541810

Publicis Sp. z.o.o. (1)
ul Woloska 9A, 02-583, Warsaw, Poland
Tel.: (48) 223193550
Web Site: http://www.publicis.pl
Sales Range: $25-49.9 Million
Advertising Services
N.A.I.C.S.: 541810
Marek Gargala *(Mng Dir)*

Publicis Taiwan (1)
7F NO6 Sec 4 Xin Yi RD, 106, Taipei, Taiwan
Tel.: (886) 2 2742 5656
Interactive Agencies, Sales Promotion
N.A.I.C.S.: 541810

Publicis Technology (1)
4-6 Louis Philippe Passage, 75011, Paris, France
Tel.: (33) 1 49 29 66 00
Web Site: http://www.publicis-technology.com
Sales Range: $10-24.9 Million
Emp.: 100
N.A.I.C.S.: 541810

Publicis Toronto (1)
111 Queen St E Suite 200, Toronto, M5C 1S2, ON, Canada
Tel.: (416) 925-7733
Web Site: http://www.publicis.ca
Rev.: $23,611,000
Emp.: 270
N.A.I.C.S.: 541810
Brett McIntosh *(Pres)*

Publicis United (1)
lenim gragsky paoprospek bldg 15 ste 1, Moscow, 125040, Russia
Tel.: (7) 4959373300
Web Site: http://www.publicisunited.com
Sales Range: $25-49.9 Million
Emp.: 200
N.A.I.C.S.: 541810
Nazim Valimahomed *(Exec Chm)*

Publicis Venezuela (1)
Avenida Casanova CC El Recreo Torre Norte Piso 11, Caracas, 1050, Venezuela
Tel.: (58) 212 400 4500
Web Site: http://www.publicis.com.ve
Sales Range: $25-49.9 Million
Emp.: 70
Advetising Agency
N.A.I.C.S.: 541810

Publicis WebImage (1)
7, Achim Bezerano, Ramat Gan, Israel
Tel.: (972) 3 611 9770
N.A.I.C.S.: 541810

Publicis WellCare (1)
133 av des Champs Elysees, 75008, Paris, France
Tel.: (33) 1 44 43 78 00
Web Site: http://www.publicisgroup.com
Sales Range: $150-199.9 Million
Emp.: 1,000
N.A.I.C.S.: 541810
Maurice Levey *(Pres)*

Publicis d.o.o. (1)
Heinzelova 33, 10000, Zagreb, Croatia
Tel.: (385) 1 23 09 100
Web Site: http://www.publicis.hr
Sales Range: $25-49.9 Million
Emp.: 40
N.A.I.C.S.: 541810

Publicis, Inc. (1)
4 Herald Sq 950 6th Ave, New York, NY 10001
Tel.: (212) 279-5550
Advertising Services
N.A.I.C.S.: 541810

Group (Domestic):

Publicis & Hal Riney (2)
2001 The Embarcadero, San Francisco, CA 94133-5200
Tel.: (415) 293-2001
Web Site: http://www.hrp.com
Rev.: $821,200,000
Emp.: 253
Advertising Services

PUBLICIS GROUPE S.A.

Publicis Groupe S.A.—(Continued)
N.A.I.C.S.: 541810
Dave Whetstone (Head-Mobile Mktg Practice)

Publicis Consultants (2)
1675 Broadway 3rd Fl, New York, NY 10019
Tel.: (212) 527-8895
Sales Range: $10-24.9 Million
Emp.: 40
Public Relations Services
N.A.I.C.S.: 541820

Subsidiary (Non-US):

Argyle Communications (3)
175 Bloor Street East Suite 1007 South Tower, Toronto, M4W 3R8, ON, Canada
Tel.: (416) 968-7311
Web Site: https://argylepr.com
Public Relations
N.A.I.C.S.: 541820
Daniel Tisch Echevarria (Pres)

Subsidiary (Domestic):

Comstat/Rowland (3)
1504 Ave Roosevelt, San Juan, PR 00920
Tel.: (787) 622-1075
Public Relations Services
N.A.I.C.S.: 541820

Branch (Domestic):

Publicis Consultants (3)
424 2nd Ave W, Seattle, WA 98119-4013
Tel.: (206) 285-5522
Advertising Services
N.A.I.C.S.: 541810
Steve Bryant (Exec VP-USA)

Subsidiary (Non-US):

Saatchi & Saatchi Simko (3)
Stadelhoferstrasse 25, 8001, Zurich, Switzerland
Tel.: (41) 442981818
Web Site: http://saatchi.ch
Communications
N.A.I.C.S.: 541820

The Rowland Company (3)
ul Sw Bonifacego 112, 02-909, Warsaw, Poland
Tel.: (48) 22 593 9100
Sales Range: $10-24.9 Million
Emp.: 17
Public Relations
N.A.I.C.S.: 541820

Branch (Domestic):

Publicis Dallas (2)
7300 Lonestar Dr, Plano, TX 75024
Tel.: (972) 628-7500
Sales Range: $10-24.9 Million
Emp.: 125
Advertising Services
N.A.I.C.S.: 541810

Group (Domestic):

Publicis Healthcare Communications Group, Inc. (2)
1675 Broadway 8th Fl, New York, NY 10019
Tel.: (212) 468-4033
Web Site: http://www.publicishealthcare.com
Sales Range: $10-24.9 Million
Emp.: 25
Advertising Services
N.A.I.C.S.: 541810
Nicholas Colucci (Chm)

Branch (Domestic):

NCI Consulting Inc. (3)
820 Matlack Dr Ste 101, Moorestown, NJ 08057
Tel.: (856) 866-1133
Web Site: http://www.nciconsulting.net
Advertising Services
N.A.I.C.S.: 541613
Susan L. Coleman (Pres)

Branch (Non-US):

Publicis Healthcare Communications Group Limited (3)
Pembroke Building Kensington Village, Avonmore Road, London, W14 8DG, United Kingdom
Tel.: (44) 20 7173 4000
Web Site: http://www.publicislifebrands.co.uk
Healthcare Advertising Services
N.A.I.C.S.: 541810

Publicis Life Brands (3)
4F Shinanomachi Rengakan 35 Shinano-Machi, Shinjuku-ku, Tokyo, 160-0016, Japan
Tel.: (81) 3 5361 2750
Advertising Services
N.A.I.C.S.: 541810

Publicis Life Brands (3)
Via Pontaccio 14, 20121, Milan, Italy
Tel.: (39) 02 88 586 330
Advertising Services
N.A.I.C.S.: 541810

Publicis Life Brands Canada (3)
Web Site: http://www.publicis.ca.com
Advertising Services
N.A.I.C.S.: 541810

Publicis Life Brands Madrid (3)
Avda Partenon 12 14, 28032, Madrid, Spain
Tel.: (34) 91 768 4700
Web Site: http://www.publicislifebrands.es
Sales Range: $10-24.9 Million
Advertising Services
N.A.I.C.S.: 541810

Publicis Life Brands Osaka (3)
6F Hiranomachi Yasui Bldg 6-8 Hiranomachi 1-chome, Chuo-ku, Osaka, 541-0046, Japan
Tel.: (81) 6 6208 0020
Advertising Services
N.A.I.C.S.: 541810

Publicis Life Brands Paris (3)
43-47 Av de la Grande Armee, 75116, Paris, France
Tel.: (33) 1 53 65 63 33
Sales Range: $10-24.9 Million
Advertising Services
N.A.I.C.S.: 541810

Branch (Domestic):

Publicis Selling Solutions (3)
1000 Floral Vale Blvd Ste 400, Morrisville, PA 19067-5570
Tel.: (609) 896-4700
Web Site: http://www.psellingsolutions.com
Sales Range: $10-24.9 Million
Marketing Consulting Services
N.A.I.C.S.: 541613

Publicis Touchpoint Solutions (3)
1000 Floral Vale Blvd Ste 400, Yardley, PA 19067
Tel.: (215) 525-6026
Web Site: http://www.touchpointsolutions.com
Sales Range: Less than $1 Million
Marketing Consulting Services
N.A.I.C.S.: 541611
Andrew Adams (Pres)

Verilogue, Inc. (3)
300 Welsh Rd Bldg 1 Ste 225, Horsham, PA 19044
Tel.: (215) 394-0300
Web Site: http://www.verilogue.com
Sales Range: $1-9.9 Million
Emp.: 45
Research & Marketing Training to Pharmaceutical Companies
N.A.I.C.S.: 611430
Jamison Barnett (CTO & VP)

Group (Domestic):

Publicis Modem (2)
2001 The Embarcadero, San Francisco, CA 94133
Tel.: (415) 293-2570
Sales Range: $75-99.9 Million
Emp.: 279
Advertising Services
N.A.I.C.S.: 541810
Jean-Philippe Maheu (CEO)

Branch (Non-US):

Portfolio Publicis Modem (3)
3rd 8th Fl Samwha & Sansu Bldg 6 Yang-Jae Dong, SeoCho-Gu, Seoul, Korea (South)
Tel.: (82) 2 2057 6981
Sales Range: $75-99.9 Million
Emp.: 70
Advertising Services
N.A.I.C.S.: 541810

Publicis Modem (3)
80 Anson Road, #33-00 Fuji Xerox Towers, Singapore, 079907, Singapore
Tel.: (65) 6732 3212
Advertising Services
N.A.I.C.S.: 541810
Ajay Thrivikraman (Dir-Creative)

Branch (Domestic):

Publicis Modem (3)
One Selleck St 2nd Fl, Norwalk, CT 06855
Tel.: (203) 295-0615
Sales Range: $50-74.9 Million
Emp.: 100
Advertising Services
N.A.I.C.S.: 541810

Branch (Non-US):

Publicis Modem France (3)
133 avenue des Champs Elisees, 75008, Paris, France
Tel.: (33) 1 42 47 83 83
Sales Range: $25-49.9 Million
Emp.: 100
Advertising Services
N.A.I.C.S.: 541810

Group (Domestic):

Publicis Modem & Dialog (2)
2001 The Enbarcadero, San Francisco, CA 94133
Tel.: (415) 293-2570
Sales Range: $25-49.9 Million
Emp.: 85
Advertising Services
N.A.I.C.S.: 541810
Ted Barton (Chm, CEO & Chief Creative Officer)

Subsidiary (Domestic):

Publicis Dialog (3)
6500 Wilshire Blvd Ste 1900, Los Angeles, CA 90048
Tel.: (323) 782-5160
Sales Range: $25-49.9 Million
Emp.: 10
N.A.I.C.S.: 541810

Branch (Domestic):

Publicis Dialog Boise (4)
168 N 9th St Ste 250, Boise, ID 83702
Tel.: (208) 395-8300
Sales Range: $10-24.9 Million
Digital/Interactive
N.A.I.C.S.: 541810
Christal Gammill (Mng Dir)

Branch (Domestic):

Publicis Modem & Dialog, East (3)
85 10th Ave Fl 3, New York, NY 10011-4752
Tel.: (212) 336-3300
Sales Range: $25-49.9 Million
Advertising Services
N.A.I.C.S.: 541810

Branch (Domestic):

Publicis New York (2)
4 Herald Sq 950 6th Ave, New York, NY 10001
Tel.: (212) 279-5550
Sales Range: $75-99.9 Million
Emp.: 350
Advertising Services
N.A.I.C.S.: 541810
Mick McCabe (Global Chief Strategy Officer)

Publicis West (2)
424 2nd Ave W, Seattle, WA 98119-4013
Tel.: (206) 285-2222
Web Site: http://www.publicisseattle.com
Sales Range: $25-49.9 Million
Emp.: 200
Advertising Services
N.A.I.C.S.: 541810

INTERNATIONAL PUBLIC

Bob Moore (Dir-Creative)

Publicis in Mid America (2)
200 S Meridian St Ste 500, Indianapolis, IN 46225-1076
Tel.: (317) 639-5135
Sales Range: $25-49.9 Million
Emp.: 38
Advertising Services
N.A.I.C.S.: 541810
Jay Schemanske (Gen Mgr)

re:Sources USA (2)
79 Madison Ave 4th Fl, New York, NY 10016
Tel.: (212) 213-7000
Advertising Services
N.A.I.C.S.: 541810

Publicis-CB (1)
Calle 82 No 6-51, 11001, Bogota, Colombia
Tel.: (57) 16341810
Web Site: http://www.publiciscolombia.com
Sales Range: $25-49.9 Million
Emp.: 60
N.A.I.C.S.: 541810
Fernando Marcelo (Pres)

Publicis-Dialog (1)
4th Fl Pilgrim Bldg, 111 Aguirre St Legaspi Village, Quezon City, 1229, Philippines
Tel.: (63) 2 818 3678
Sales Range: $25-49.9 Million
Emp.: 20
N.A.I.C.S.: 541810

Publicis-Graphics (1)
Shaikh Mubarak Bldg 203 Rm 502 5th Floor, PO Box 1004, 30 Government Road, Manama, Bahrain
Tel.: (973) 22 87 37
N.A.I.C.S.: 541810

Publicis-Graphics (1)
3 El Mansour Mohamed St 5th Fl Ste 502, Zamalek, 11211, Cairo, Egypt
Tel.: (20) 2 7353 994
N.A.I.C.S.: 541810

Publicis-Graphics (1)
Villa No 20 Al Kanan Street, Al Mirqab, 22582, Doha, Qatar
Tel.: (974) 435 7663
Sales Range: Less than $1 Million
Emp.: 20
N.A.I.C.S.: 541810

Publicis-Graphics (1)
Jewelry Centre Tahlia Road, 21462, Jeddah, Saudi Arabia
Tel.: (966) 2 665 7514
N.A.I.C.S.: 541810

Publicis-Graphics (1)
1st Floor Mutabagani Headqarters Bldg, Tahlia Street, Riyadh, 11515, Saudi Arabia
Tel.: (966) 1 465 2707
Sales Range: $10-24.9 Million
Emp.: 40
N.A.I.C.S.: 541810

Publicis-Graphics (1)
Office Tower 10th Fl Ste 1036, Al Ghurair Ctr, Dubai, 11853, United Arab Emirates
Tel.: (971) 4 222 2231
Sales Range: $75-99.9 Million
Emp.: 420
N.A.I.C.S.: 541810

Publicis-Mojo Group (1)
Level 4 Textile Centre Kenwyn St, Parnell, Auckland, 1011, New Zealand
Tel.: (64) 9915 6656
Web Site: http://www.publicismojo.co.nz
Sales Range: $25-49.9 Million
Emp.: 50
Advertising Services
N.A.I.C.S.: 541810

Publicis-Mojopartners (1)
Bond Store 3 30 Windmill St, Walsh Bay, Sydney, 2000, NSW, Australia
Tel.: (61) 2 9258 9000
Web Site: http://www.publicismojo.com.au
Sales Range: $75-99.9 Million
Emp.: 300
N.A.I.C.S.: 541810
Graeme Wills (Grp Chm)

Publicis-Mojopartners Brisbane (1)
Level 2 99 melbourne Street, PO Box 3204,

AND PRIVATE COMPANIES / PUBLICIS GROUPE S.A.

Brisbane, 4101, QLD, Australia
Tel.: (61) 73121 6666
Web Site: http://www.publicis.com.au
Sales Range: $25-49.9 Million
Emp.: 75
N.A.I.C.S.: 541810
Ian de Raat *(Dir-Art)*

Publicis-Mojopartners Melbourne (1)
Level 6 28 Freshwater place, Melbourne, 3006, VIC, Australia
Tel.: (61) 3 9685 3444
Web Site: http://www.publicismojo.com.au
Sales Range: $25-49.9 Million
Emp.: 60
N.A.I.C.S.: 541810
Ryan Petie *(Dir-Creative)*

Publicis.Net (1)
133 Ave des Champs Elysees, 75002, Paris, France
Tel.: (33) 1 55 34 44 44
Sales Range: $25-49.9 Million
Emp.: 60
N.A.I.C.S.: 541810

Rauxa Direct LLC (1)
275 A McCormick Ave, Costa Mesa, CA 92626
Tel.: (714) 427-1271
Sales Range: $50-74.9 Million
Emp.: 170
Direct Marketing Services
N.A.I.C.S.: 541860
Jill Gwaltney *(Founder)*

Razorfish (1)
424 2nd Ave W, Seattle, WA 98119
Tel.: (206) 816-8800
Web Site: http://www.razorfish.com
Rev.: $312,000,000
Emp.: 350
Digital Advertising Services
N.A.I.C.S.: 541810
Ray Velez *(CTO)*

Branch (Domestic):

Razorfish Atlanta (2)
730 Peachtree St NE Ste 1100, Atlanta, GA 30303
Tel.: (678) 538-6000
Web Site: http://www.razorfish.com
Sales Range: $25-49.9 Million
Emp.: 60
Digital Advertising Services
N.A.I.C.S.: 541810

Razorfish Chicago (2)
600 W Fulton St 4th Fl, Chicago, IL 60661
Tel.: (312) 696-5000
Web Site: http://www.razorfish.com
Sales Range: $25-49.9 Million
Emp.: 250
Digital Advertising Services
N.A.I.C.S.: 541810

Razorfish New York (2)
375 Hudson St, New York, NY 10018
Tel.: (212) 798-6600
Web Site: http://www.razorfish.com
Sales Range: $75-99.9 Million
Digital Advertising Services
N.A.I.C.S.: 541810
Pete Stein *(Global CEO)*

Razorfish Philadelphia (2)
100 Penn S, Philadelphia, PA 19017
Tel.: (267) 295-7100
Web Site: http://www.razorfish.com
Sales Range: $25-49.9 Million
Emp.: 135
Interactive Agencies
N.A.I.C.S.: 541810
Matthew Comstock *(VP-Customer Insight Grp)*

Razorfish San Francisco (2)
2001 The Embarcadero 1st Fl, San Francisco, CA 94133
Tel.: (415) 369-6300
Web Site: http://www.razorfish.com
Sales Range: $25-49.9 Million
Emp.: 250
Digital Advertising Services
N.A.I.C.S.: 541810
Holly Perkins *(Dir-Creative Svcs)*

Unit (Domestic):

Razorfish Technology Platforms (2)
7750 Paragon Rd, Dayton, OH 45459
Tel.: (937) 723-2300
Emp.: 150
Software Services for Content-Enabled Applications
N.A.I.C.S.: 541519
Mark Kennedy *(Co-Founder & Pres)*

Branch (Non-US):

Razorfish UK (2)
2022 Great Pitch Field St, London, W1W 8BE, United Kingdom
Tel.: (44) 207 907 4545
Web Site: http://www.razorfish.com
Emp.: 150
Digital Advertising Services
N.A.I.C.S.: 541810
William Lidstone *(CMO)*

Relaxnews SA (1)
30/34 rue de Chemin Vert, 75545, Paris, Cedex 11, France
Tel.: (33) 1 53 19 89 50
Web Site: http://www.relaxnews.com
Emp.: 40
Online Leisure News Publisher
N.A.I.C.S.: 516210
Jerome Doncieux *(Co-Pres & Dir-Publication)*

Relay Worldwide (1)
222 Merchandise Mart Plz Ste 4-160-B, Chicago, IL 60654
Tel.: (312) 297-1400
Sales Range: $25-49.9 Million
Emp.: 30
N.A.I.C.S.: 541810
Marco Lopez *(Sr Dir-Hispanic Mktg)*

Relay Worldwide (1)
1435 S 18th St Apt 142, Saint Louis, MO 63104-2500
Tel.: (314) 569-1977
Sales Range: $25-49.9 Million
Emp.: 103
Event Marketing, Exhibit/Trade Shows
N.A.I.C.S.: 541810

Reputation (1)
Bredgade 15, 1260, Copenhagen, Denmark
Tel.: (45) 3338 5070
Web Site: http://www.reputationcph.com
Sales Range: $25-49.9 Million
Emp.: 36
N.A.I.C.S.: 541810
Mikkel Jonsson *(Exec Dir-Creative)*

Rosetta Marketing Group, LLC (1)
100 American Metro Blvd, Hamilton, NJ 08619
Tel.: (609) 689-6100
Web Site: http://www.rosetta.com
Sales Range: $250-299.9 Million
Emp.: 1,100
Advetising Agency
N.A.I.C.S.: 541810
David Worth *(Partner-Tech & Telecom)*

Subsidiary (Domestic):

Level, a Rosetta Co. (2)
4800 Morabito Pl, San Luis Obispo, CA 93401-7363
Tel.: (805) 781-0546
Web Site: http://www.rosetta.com
Sales Range: $25-49.9 Million
Emp.: 215
Internet Development Specializing in Technology-Enabled Customer Relationship Management
N.A.I.C.S.: 541512
Alex Mahernia *(Chief Creative Officer)*

Branch (Domestic):

Rosetta (2)
629 euclit ave, Cleveland, OH 44122
Tel.: (216) 896-8900
Web Site: http://www.rosetta.com
Sales Range: $1-9.9 Million
Emp.: 80
N.A.I.C.S.: 541890

Rosetta (2)
190 S Lasalle, Chicago, IL 60603
Tel.: (312) 568-7010
Web Site: http://www.rosetta.com
Advetising Agency
N.A.I.C.S.: 541810

Rosetta (2)
375 Hudson St, New York, NY 10013
Tel.: (646) 502-3100
Web Site: http://www.rosetta.com
Sales Range: $25-49.9 Million
Emp.: 150
N.A.I.C.S.: 541810
Joe Lozito *(CTO)*

Rosetta (2)
275 Grove St Ste 2-400, Newton, MA 02466
Tel.: (617) 244-8800
N.A.I.C.S.: 541810

Saatchi & Saatchi Group Ltd. (1)
40 Chancery Lane, London, WC2A 1JA, United Kingdom
Tel.: (44) 2076365060
Web Site: http://www.saatchi.co.uk
Marketing & Advertising Services
N.A.I.C.S.: 541810
Magnus Djaba *(CEO)*

Saatchi & Saatchi Worldwide, Inc. (1)
375 Hudson St, New York, NY 10014-3660
Tel.: (212) 463-2000
Web Site: http://www.saatchi.com
Sales Range: $1-4.9 Billion
Emp.: 6,709
Advertising Agency
N.A.I.C.S.: 541810
Monet Lacock *(Dir-Art)*

Subsidiary (Non-US):

AAC Saatchi & Saatchi (2)
29 Front Street, Hamilton, HM-11, Bermuda
Tel.: (441) 295 2626
Web Site: http://www.aac.bm
Sales Range: $25-49.9 Million
Emp.: 10
Advertising Services
N.A.I.C.S.: 541810
Peter Hebberd *(VP & Gen Mgr)*

AW Nazca Saatchi & Saatchi (2)
Edificio ABA 4th Fl, Las Mercedes, Caracas, Venezuela
Tel.: (58) 212 400 4430
Web Site: http://www.saatchi.com
Sales Range: $25-49.9 Million
Emp.: 61
Advetising Agency
N.A.I.C.S.: 541810

Ace Saatchi & Saatchi (2)
Saatchi House 2296 Don Chino Roces Avenue Pasong Tamo Extension, Kayamanan C, Makati, Philippines
Tel.: (63) 2 857 4900
Web Site: http://www.acesaatchi.com.ph
Sales Range: $25-49.9 Million
Emp.: 160
Full Service
N.A.I.C.S.: 541810
Mio Chongson *(Pres & COO)*

Unit (Domestic):

Badillo Saatchi & Saatchi (2)
A-16 Calle Genova Ext Villa Caparra, Guaynabo, PR 00066-1729
Tel.: (787) 622-1000
Web Site: http://www.saatchi.com
Advetising Agency
N.A.I.C.S.: 541810

Conill Advertising, Inc. (2)
800 Brickell Ave Ste 1115, Miami, FL 33131
Tel.: (305) 351-2901
Web Site: http://www.conill.com
Sales Range: $10-24.9 Million
Emp.: 180
Advertising Agencies
N.A.I.C.S.: 541810
Carlos Martinez *(Pres)*

Branch (Domestic):

Conill Advertising, Inc. - Torrance (3)
2101 Rosecrans Ave, El Segundo, CA 90245
Tel.: (424) 290-4400
Web Site: http://www.conill.com
Advertising Services
N.A.I.C.S.: 541810
Carlos Martinez *(Pres)*

Subsidiary (Non-US):

Creacion Nazca Saatchi & Saatchi (2)
7A Avenida 14-57 Zona 10, Guatemala, Guatemala
Tel.: (502) 2429 1111
Sales Range: $10-24.9 Million
Emp.: 30
Full Service
N.A.I.C.S.: 541810

Cumbre Nazca Saatchi & Saatchi (2)
Jose Contreras No 14 Gazcue, Apartado 872, Santo Domingo, Dominican Republic
Tel.: (809) 687 5181
Web Site: http://www.saatchi.com
Advertising Services
N.A.I.C.S.: 541810

Del Campo Nazca Saatchi & Saatchi (2)
Bogota 973, Martinez, 1640, Buenos Aires, Argentina
Tel.: (54) 11 4836 0800
Web Site: http://www.delcampo-ss.com
Sales Range: $10-24.9 Million
Emp.: 80
N.A.I.C.S.: 541810
Pablo Del Campo *(Founder)*

F/Nazca Saatchi & Saatchi (2)
Av Republica do Libano 253, Sao Paulo, 04501-000, SP, Brazil
Tel.: (55) 11 3059 4800
Web Site: http://www.fnazca.com.br
Advertising Services
N.A.I.C.S.: 541810
Fabio Fernandes *(Founder, Mng Partner & Mng Dir-Creative)*

F/Nazca Saatchi & Saatchi (2)
Rua Humaita 275 54 andar, Rio de Janeiro, 22210-030, Humaita, Brazil
Tel.: (55) 21 3284 3700
Web Site: http://www.fnazca.com.br
Sales Range: $25-49.9 Million
Emp.: 64
Full Service
N.A.I.C.S.: 541810

Law & Kenneth Saatchi & Saatchi Private Limited (2)
203 Neelam Centre A Wing 2nd Floor, Hind Cycle Road, Mumbai, 4010030, India
Tel.: (91) 22 61460000
Web Site: http://www.lawkenneth.in
Emp.: 120
Advetising Agency
N.A.I.C.S.: 541810
Chandan Mahimkar *(Chief Creative Officer-Design)*

Division (Domestic):

Digital Law & Kenneth (3)
203 A Wing Neelam Ctr, Hind Cycle Road Worli, Mumbai, 400 030, India
Tel.: (91) 22 24955545
Web Site: http://www.lkdigi.com
Advetising Agency
N.A.I.C.S.: 541810

Subsidiary (Non-US):

Mass Nazca Saatchi & Saatchi (2)
Edif Metropolis Torre 2 Local 22016 Blvd, 11101, Tegucigalpa, Honduras
Tel.: (504) 22759995
Web Site: http://www.saatchi.com
Sales Range: $25-49.9 Million
Full Service
N.A.I.C.S.: 541810

Nazca Saatchi & Saatchi (2)
San Sebastian 2909 Oficina 101, Los Condes, 7550118, Santiago, Chile
Tel.: (56) 2 756 4500
Web Site: http://www.nazcasaatchi.com
Sales Range: $25-49.9 Million
Emp.: 20
N.A.I.C.S.: 541810
Jose Fuentes *(Dir-Fin)*

Unit (Domestic):

Nazca Saatchi & Saatchi (2)
800 Brickell Ave Ste 400, Miami, FL 33131
Tel.: (305) 351-2900

PUBLICIS GROUPE S.A.

Publicis Groupe S.A.—(Continued)
Web Site: http://www.saatchi.com
Sales Range: $25-49.9 Million
Emp.: 40
N.A.I.C.S.: 541810

Subsidiary (Non-US):

Nazca Saatchi & Saatchi (2)
Juan Salvador Agraz 65 Piso 15, Lomas de Santa Fe, 01376, Mexico, Mexico
Tel.: (52) 55 1084 1900
Web Site: http://www.saatchi.com
Full Service
N.A.I.C.S.: 541810
Gabriela Fenton *(CEO)*

P&P Link Saatchi & Saatchi (2)
D Seetulsingh St, Port Louis, Mauritius
Tel.: (230) 211 4429
Web Site: http://www.saatchi.com
Full Service
N.A.I.C.S.: 541810

Perwanal Saatchi & Saatchi (2)
No 2 Jalan Dr Ide Anak Agung Gde Agung Kav E 4-2, Kuningan, 12950, Indonesia
Tel.: (62) 21 5297 1500
N.A.I.C.S.: 541810
Jaswinder Kaur *(Head-Media)*

Publicitas Nazca Saatchi & Saatchi (2)
Primero de Mayo 812 Entre Los Rios Esmareldas, 11446, Guayaquil, Ecuador
Tel.: (593) 42 283 300
Web Site: http://www.saatchi.com
Full Service
N.A.I.C.S.: 541810

Quorum Nazca Saatchi & Saatchi (2)
Avenue Angamos Oeste 1218, Miraflores, Lima, 18, Peru
Tel.: (51) 1 421 2313
Web Site: http://www.saatchi.com
Sales Range: $10-24.9 Million
Emp.: 40
Advertising Services
N.A.I.C.S.: 541810

Saatchi & Saatchi (2)
101-103 Courtenay Pl, Te Aro, Wellington, 6011, New Zealand
Tel.: (64) 4 385 6524
Web Site: http://www.saatchi.com
Sales Range: $10-24.9 Million
Emp.: 40
N.A.I.C.S.: 541810

Saatchi & Saatchi (2)
111 Queen St East 300, Toronto, M5C 1S2, ON, Canada
Tel.: (416) 359-9595
Web Site: http://www.saatchi.ca
Sales Range: $25-49.9 Million
Emp.: 70
Advertising Agency
N.A.I.C.S.: 541810
John McCarter *(Mng Dir & Exec VP)*

Saatchi & Saatchi (2)
27/F Tai Tung Building Fleming Road, Wanchai, China (Hong Kong)
Tel.: (852) 2 582 3333
Web Site: http://www.saatchi.com
Emp.: 80
Full Service
N.A.I.C.S.: 541810

Saatchi & Saatchi (2)
3D River Valley Rd 03-01 Clarke quay, Singapore, S179023, Singapore
Tel.: (65) 6339 4733
Web Site: http://www.saatchi.com
Sales Range: $25-49.9 Million
Emp.: 80
Full Service
N.A.I.C.S.: 541810

Saatchi & Saatchi (2)
123 - 125 The Strand Parnell, Auckland, 1010, New Zealand
Tel.: (64) 9 3555 000
Web Site: http://www.saatchi.co.nz
Sales Range: $25-49.9 Million
Advetising Agency
N.A.I.C.S.: 541810
Paul Wilson *(Mng Dir)*

Saatchi & Saatchi (2)
7F 6 Xinyi Road, Taipei, Taiwan
Tel.: (886) 2 2703 9057
Sales Range: $25-49.9 Million
Emp.: 60
Advertising Services
N.A.I.C.S.: 541810

Saatchi & Saatchi (2)
3-5F Gold Sun Building 109 Ti Yu Xi Road, Guangzhou, 510620, China
Tel.: (86) 20 3879 1228
Web Site: http://www.saatchi.com
Sales Range: $25-49.9 Million
Emp.: 100
Full Service
N.A.I.C.S.: 541810

Saatchi & Saatchi (2)
36/F Central International Trade Centre Tower C, 6A Jianguomen Wai Avenue, Beijing, 100022, China
Tel.: (86) 10 6563 3600
Web Site: http://www.saatchi.com.cn
Emp.: 80
Full Service
N.A.I.C.S.: 541810
Michael Lee *(CEO)*

Saatchi & Saatchi (2)
29 F Lippo Plaza, 222 Huai Hai Zhong Road, Shanghai, 200021, China
Tel.: (86) 21 5396 5586
Web Site: http://www.saatchi.com.cn
Sales Range: $25-49.9 Million
Full Service
N.A.I.C.S.: 541810
Michael Lee *(CEO-Greater China)*

Saatchi & Saatchi (2)
Sitaram Mills Compound 1st Floor NM Joshi Marg, Delisle Road, Mumbai, 400 011, India
Tel.: (91) 22 6610 3002
Web Site: http://www.saatchi.com
Full Service
N.A.I.C.S.: 541810

Saatchi & Saatchi (2)
170 Nguyen Van Huong, Thao Dien Ward District 2, Ho Chi Minh City, Vietnam
Tel.: (84) 838241207
Web Site: http://www.saatchi.com
N.A.I.C.S.: 541810
Mai Huong *(CEO)*

Saatchi & Saatchi (2)
37-6 Aga Abbas Ali Road, Bengaluru, 560 042, India
Tel.: (91) 80 4149 9174
Web Site: http://www.saatchi.com
Full Service
N.A.I.C.S.: 541810

Unit (Domestic):

Saatchi & Saatchi (2)
5285 SW Meadows Rd Ste 232, Lake Oswego, OR 97035
Tel.: (503) 333-9088
Sales Range: Less than $1 Million
Emp.: 5
N.A.I.C.S.: 541810
Wes Alexander *(Dir-Mgmt)*

Saatchi & Saatchi Advertising (2)
375 Hudson St 9th Fl, New York, NY 10014-3658
Tel.: (212) 463-3400
Web Site: http://www.saatchihealthcare.com
Sales Range: $25-49.9 Million
Emp.: 200
Advertising Services
N.A.I.C.S.: 541810

Subsidiary (Non-US):

Saatchi & Saatchi Australia (2)
70 George Street, The Rocks, Sydney, 2000, NSW, Australia
Tel.: (61) 2 8264 1111
Web Site: http://www.saatchi.com
Sales Range: $25-49.9 Million
Emp.: 180
Advertising Services
N.A.I.C.S.: 541810
Mike Spirkovski *(Chief Creative Officer)*

Saatchi & Saatchi Direct (2)
37/6 Aga Abbas Ali Road off Ulsoor Road, Bengaluru, 560 042, India
Tel.: (91) 80 4149 9181

Web Site: http://www.saatchifocus.com
Emp.: 60
Direct Marketing
N.A.I.C.S.: 541810

Saatchi & Saatchi EMEA Region Headquarters (2)
80 Charlotte St, London, W1A 1AQ, United Kingdom
Tel.: (44) 207 636 5060
Web Site: http://www.saatchi.co.uk
Sales Range: $75-99.9 Million
Emp.: 500
N.A.I.C.S.: 541810
Magnus Djaba *(CEO)*

Subsidiary (Non-US):

Adel Saatchi & Saatchi (3)
15 Tsiklitira Street, Iraklio Attikis, 141 21, Athens, Greece
Tel.: (30) 210 27 83 000
Web Site: http://www.adel.gr
Sales Range: $25-49.9 Million
Emp.: 70
Advertising Agency
N.A.I.C.S.: 541810

Adell Saatchi & Saatchi (3)
5 Noliktavas Street, Riga, 1010, Latvia
Tel.: (371) 7 320 263
Web Site: http://www.saatchi.com
Sales Range: $25-49.9 Million
Emp.: 22
Full Service
N.A.I.C.S.: 541810

Akeel/Saatchi & Saatchi (3)
Al Mas Center 5th Floor King Fahd Hwy, Olaya, Riyadh, 11476, Saudi Arabia
Tel.: (966) 1 201 30 10
Web Site: http://www.satchi.com
Sales Range: $10-24.9 Million
Emp.: 36
Advertising Agency
N.A.I.C.S.: 541810

BBR Saatchi & Saatchi (3)
6 Hachilason Street, Ramat Gan, 52522, Israel
Tel.: (972) 3755 2626
Web Site: http://www.bbr.co.il
Advetising Agency
N.A.I.C.S.: 541810
Yoram Baumann *(Chm)*

Business Active (3)
53 Boulevard Ornano, 93200, Saint Denis, France
Tel.: (33) 1 40 88 40 00
Web Site: http://www.saatchi.fr
Full Service
N.A.I.C.S.: 541810

DV.8 Saatchi & Saatchi (3)
84 Frans Indongo St, Windhoek, Namibia
Tel.: (264) 61 239 757
Sales Range: $25-49.9 Million
Emp.: 13
Full Service
N.A.I.C.S.: 541810

Guzel Sanatlar Saatchi & Saatchi (3)
Gazeteciler Mahallesi Hikaye Sokak No 13 4U Plaza, Esentepe, 34394, Istanbul, Turkiye
Tel.: (90) 212 354 08 00
Web Site: http://www.gs-saatchi.com
Sales Range: $25-49.9 Million
Emp.: 60
Full Service
N.A.I.C.S.: 541810

IAL Saatchi & Saatchi (3)
72-C 13th Commercial Street Phase II Ext DHA, Karachi, Pakistan
Tel.: (92) 21531 2231
Sales Range: $25-49.9 Million
Emp.: 110
Full Service
N.A.I.C.S.: 541810

Ideo Saatchi & Saatchi (3)
Abacus business center 118 Bulgaria Blvd, 1504, Sofia, Bulgaria
Tel.: (359) 2 439 50 81
Sales Range: $25-49.9 Million
Emp.: 15
Full Service

N.A.I.C.S.: 541810

Lonsdale Saatchi & Saatchi (3)
13 Alcazar Street, PO Box 1251, Port of Spain, Trinidad & Tobago
Tel.: (868) 622 6480
Web Site: http://www.e-lonsdale.com
Sales Range: $25-49.9 Million
Emp.: 75
Advetising Agency
N.A.I.C.S.: 541810

MCL Saatchi & Saatchi (3)
Ideas House Muthithi Road Museum Hill, Westlands, Nairobi, Kenya
Tel.: (254) 20 374 8868
Web Site: http://www.saatchi.com
Sales Range: $10-24.9 Million
Emp.: 30
Advertising Services
N.A.I.C.S.: 541810

MITA Group Saatchi & Saatchi/Publicis (3)
Trg solidarnosti 2A, Sarajevo, 71 000, Bosnia & Herzegovina
Tel.: (387) 33 768 895
Web Site: http://www.mita.ba
N.A.I.C.S.: 541810

Origin8 Saatchi & Saatchi (3)
32 Amugi Avenue Behind O'Reilly Sec School, Adabraka, Accra, Ghana
Tel.: (233) 21 247 330
Web Site: http://www.origin8saatchi.com
Full Service
N.A.I.C.S.: 541810

Primary Saatchi & Saatchi (3)
Kazarmenny Lane 4 Office 1, Minsk, 220030, Belarus
Tel.: (375) 17 328 62 11
Sales Range: $25-49.9 Million
Emp.: 25
N.A.I.C.S.: 541810

QG Saatchi & Saatchi (3)
21 Bukoto Street, Kampala, Uganda
Tel.: (256) 41 263 333
Sales Range: $10-24.9 Million
Emp.: 35
N.A.I.C.S.: 541810

SO&U Saatchi & Saatchi (3)
2 Oyetula Street Off Ajanaku Street via Thomas Ajufo Street Opebi, Ikeja, Lagos, Nigeria
Tel.: (234) 1 497 9361
Sales Range: $25-49.9 Million
Emp.: 15
Communications
N.A.I.C.S.: 541810

Saatchi & Saatchi (3)
Jankovcova 23, 170 00, Prague, 7, Czech Republic
Tel.: (420) 234 721 222
Sales Range: $10-24.9 Million
Emp.: 30
Full Service
N.A.I.C.S.: 541810

Saatchi & Saatchi (3)
Heinzelova 33, 10000, Zagreb, Croatia
Tel.: (385) 1 23 09 500
Sales Range: $10-24.9 Million
Emp.: 50
Full Service
N.A.I.C.S.: 541810

Saatchi & Saatchi (3)
Drottninggatan 95 A 2nd Floor, 113 60, Stockholm, Sweden
Tel.: (46) 8 5057 1700
Web Site: http://www.saatchi.se
Sales Range: $25-49.9 Million
N.A.I.C.S.: 541810

Saatchi & Saatchi (3)
Place du Temple 15, Carouge, 1227, Switzerland
Tel.: (41) 22 307 2727
Web Site: http://www.saatchi.com.ch
Sales Range: $25-49.9 Million
Emp.: 85
N.A.I.C.S.: 541810

Saatchi & Saatchi (3)
Poslovna Stavba Slovenijales III Nadstopje, Dunajska Cesta 22, 1000, Ljubljana, Slovenia

AND PRIVATE COMPANIES **PUBLICIS GROUPE S.A.**

Tel.: (386) 1 23 43 550
Web Site: http://www.saatchi.si
Sales Range: $10-24.9 Million
Emp.: 30
N.A.I.C.S.: 541810

Saatchi & Saatchi (3)
Louis-Pasteur-Platz 3, 40211, Dusseldorf, Germany
Tel.: (49) 21117810
Web Site: http://www.saatchi.de
Sales Range: $25-49.9 Million
Advertising Services
N.A.I.C.S.: 541810

Saatchi & Saatchi (3)
53 Boulevard Ornano, 93200, Seine-Saint-Denis, 93200, France
Tel.: (33) 1 48 13 40 00
Web Site: http://www.saatchi.fr
Sales Range: $75-99.9 Million
Emp.: 100
Consumer Marketing
N.A.I.C.S.: 541810

Saatchi & Saatchi (3)
Danzigerkabe 23C, 1013 AP, Amsterdam, Netherlands
Tel.: (31) 20 5431 543
Web Site: http://www.saatchi.nl
Sales Range: $10-24.9 Million
Emp.: 40
Advertising Services
N.A.I.C.S.: 541810

Saatchi & Saatchi (3)
Calle Ramirez de Arellano 21 Floor 0, 28001, Madrid, Spain
Tel.: (34) 91 151 20 00
Web Site: http://www.saatchi.com
Sales Range: $25-49.9 Million
Emp.: 50
Advertising Services
N.A.I.C.S.: 541810

Unit (Domestic):

Saatchi & Saatchi (3)
80 Charlotte Street, London, W1A 1AQ, United Kingdom
Tel.: (44) 20 7636 5060
Web Site: http://www.saatchi.co.uk
Sales Range: $75-99.9 Million
Emp.: 500
Full Service
N.A.I.C.S.: 541810
Kate Stanners *(Chm & Chief Creative Officer-Global)*

Subsidiary (Non-US):

Saatchi & Saatchi (3)
Esplanaden 34A 1 sal, 1263, Copenhagen, Denmark
Tel.: (45) 33 937980
Web Site: http://www.saatchi.dk
Sales Range: $10-24.9 Million
Emp.: 10
Advertising Services
N.A.I.C.S.: 541810

Saatchi & Saatchi (3)
Keppenbrueckengasse 16, 1040, Vienna, Austria
Tel.: (43) 1588090
Web Site: http://www.saatchi.at
Sales Range: $10-24.9 Million
Emp.: 40
Advertising Services
N.A.I.C.S.: 541810

Saatchi & Saatchi (3)
Bldg 11 Leslie Ave E Fourways, Fourways, Johannesburg, 2190, South Africa
Tel.: (27) 11 548 6000
Web Site: http://www.saatchi.com
Sales Range: $10-24.9 Million
Emp.: 70
Advertising Agency
N.A.I.C.S.: 541810

Saatchi & Saatchi (3)
Montevideo 6, 1022, Budapest, Hungary
Tel.: (36) 1 345 9300
Web Site: http://www.saatchi.com
Sales Range: $10-24.9 Million
Emp.: 50
Advertising Services
N.A.I.C.S.: 541810

Saatchi & Saatchi (3)
Ul Domaniewska 42, 02-672, Warsaw, Poland
Tel.: (48) 22 345 21 00
Web Site: http://www.saatchi.pl
Sales Range: $25-49.9 Million
Emp.: 80
Advertising Services
N.A.I.C.S.: 541810

Saatchi & Saatchi (3)
The Foundry Ebenezer Road, Greenpoint, Cape Town, 8001, South Africa
Tel.: (27) 21 413 7500
Web Site: http://www.saatchi.com
Sales Range: $25-49.9 Million
Emp.: 30
Advertising Services
N.A.I.C.S.: 541810

Saatchi & Saatchi (3)
Central Business Park Cladirea D+E Parter Calea Serban Voda nr 133, Sector 4, 040205, Bucharest, Romania
Tel.: (40) 31 7300 600
Web Site: http://www.saatchi.com
Sales Range: $25-49.9 Million
Emp.: 100
Full Service
N.A.I.C.S.: 541810
Radu Florescu *(CEO)*

Saatchi & Saatchi (3)
27 28 & 29 Beach Villas Jumeira Beach Rd, Jumeira 1, Dubai, United Arab Emirates
Tel.: (971) 4 344 4346
Sales Range: $10-24.9 Million
Emp.: 50
Full Service
N.A.I.C.S.: 541810

Saatchi & Saatchi (3)
Franklin Ruzvelt 37, 1000, Skopje, North Macedonia
Tel.: (389) 2 3297 688
Web Site: http://www.saatchi.com
Sales Range: $25-49.9 Million
Emp.: 15
Full Service
N.A.I.C.S.: 541810
Aleksandra Dilevska Simova *(CEO & Reg Mgr)*

Saatchi & Saatchi (3)
Quantum Tower 9th Floor Charles Malek Avenue Saint Nicolas St, Beirut, Achrafieh, Lebanon
Tel.: (961) 1 204 060
Full Service
N.A.I.C.S.: 541810

Saatchi & Saatchi A/S (3)
Storgata 33, 0184, Oslo, Norway
Tel.: (47) 23 32 70 00
Web Site: http://www.saatchi.no
Sales Range: $10-24.9 Million
Emp.: 16
Advertising Services
N.A.I.C.S.: 541810

Saatchi & Saatchi Brussels (3)
Uitbreidingstraat 228, Berchem, 2600, Belgium
Tel.: (32) 2 247 1711
Web Site: http://www.saatchi.be
Sales Range: $10-24.9 Million
Emp.: 20
N.A.I.C.S.: 541810

Saatchi & Saatchi Dusseldorf (3)
Schirmerstrasse 76, 40211, Dusseldorf, Germany
Tel.: (49) 21116870
Sales Range: $25-49.9 Million
Emp.: 120
Full Service
N.A.I.C.S.: 541810
Claus Lieck *(Dir-Creative)*

Saatchi & Saatchi Egypt (3)
19 Soliman Abaza Street, Mohandesseen, Cairo, Egypt
Tel.: (20) 23 761 0076
Web Site: http://www.saatchi.com
Sales Range: $10-24.9 Million
Emp.: 30
Full Service Advertising Agency
N.A.I.C.S.: 541810

Unit (Domestic):

Saatchi & Saatchi Healthcare Connection (3)

67-69 Whitfield Street, London, W1P 4HR, United Kingdom
Tel.: (44) 207 462 7474
Web Site: http://www.saatchi.co.uk
Sales Range: $25-49.9 Million
Emp.: 25
N.A.I.C.S.: 541810

Subsidiary (Non-US):

Saatchi & Saatchi Milan (3)
Via Bernina 32, 20122, Milan, Italy
Tel.: (39) 0277011
Web Site: http://www.saatchi.com
Sales Range: $25-49.9 Million
Emp.: 7
Advetising Agency
N.A.I.C.S.: 541810

Branch (Domestic):

Saatchi & Saatchi (4)
Via della Vite 13, 00187, Rome, Italy
Tel.: (39) 06 362 201
Web Site: http://www.saatchi.com.it
Advertising Services
N.A.I.C.S.: 541810
Camilla Pollice *(CEO)*

Division (Domestic):

Saatchi & Saatchi Health (4)
Corso Monforte 52/54, 20122, Milan, Italy
Tel.: (39) 02 77012
Web Site: http://www.saatchi-health.it
Sales Range: $10-24.9 Million
Full Service, Health & Wellness Campaigns
N.A.I.C.S.: 541810

Subsidiary (Non-US):

Saatchi & Saatchi Russia (3)
Bldg 14 Leningradsky Prospekt 15, BC Bolshevik, 125040, Moscow, Russia
Tel.: (7) 4956638777
Web Site: http://saatchi.ru
Full Service
N.A.I.C.S.: 541810

Saatchi Barcelona (3)
Diagonal 579 2nd Fl, 08006, Barcelona, Spain
Tel.: (34) 93 241 9150
Web Site: http://www.saatchi-healthcare.es
Sales Range: $10-24.9 Million
Emp.: 35
N.A.I.C.S.: 541810

Unit (Domestic):

Team Saatchi (3)
23 Howland Street, London, WNT 4AY, United Kingdom
Tel.: (44) 207 436 6636
Web Site: http://www.teamsaatchi.co.uk
Rev.: $16,755,000
Emp.: 18
Advertising Services
N.A.I.C.S.: 541810

Subsidiary (Non-US):

Tengri CA Saatchi & Saatchi (3)
30A Satpayev St Tengiz Towers Bldng 1 3rd Fl, Almaty, 0500040, Kazakhstan
Tel.: (7) 727 2 954 860
Web Site: http://www.saatchi.com
Emp.: 30
Full Service
N.A.I.C.S.: 541810

The Boz Group (3)
Charlotte Saint-Marcq, Paris, France
Tel.: (33) 1 44 95 99 41
Full Service, Health Care
N.A.I.C.S.: 541810

Unit (Domestic):

The Outside Line Ltd. (3)
80 Charlotte St, London, W1A 1AQ, United Kingdom
Tel.: (44) 20 7462 7400
Web Site: http://www.outsideline.co.uk
Advertising Services
N.A.I.C.S.: 541810

Subsidiary (Non-US):

Saatchi & Saatchi Fallon Tokyo (2)
4-9-3 Jingumae, Shibuya-ku, Tokyo, 150-0001, Japan
Tel.: (81) 3 6438 1255
Web Site: http://www.ssftokyo.co.jp
Sales Range: $10-24.9 Million
Emp.: 40
Advertising Services
N.A.I.C.S.: 541810

Unit (Domestic):

Saatchi & Saatchi Healthcare Advertising (2)
375 Hudson St, New York, NY 10014
Tel.: (212) 463-3400
Web Site: http://www.saatchihealthcare.com
Sales Range: $25-49.9 Million
Emp.: 180
N.A.I.C.S.: 541810
Dave Merek *(Exec VP & Mng Dir)*

Saatchi & Saatchi Healthcare Innovations (2)
1000 Floral Vale Blvd Ste 400, Morrisville, PA 19067-5570
Tel.: (215) 497-8400
Web Site: http://www.saatchihealthcare.com
Sales Range: $25-49.9 Million
Emp.: 62
N.A.I.C.S.: 541810

Saatchi & Saatchi Los Angeles (2)
3501 Sepulveda Blvd, Torrance, CA 90505-2538 (100%)
Tel.: (310) 214-6000
Web Site: http://www.saatchila.com
Sales Range: $75-99.9 Million
Emp.: 342
Advetising Agency
N.A.I.C.S.: 541810
Chuck Maguy *(COO-US)*

Subsidiary (Non-US):

Saatchi & Saatchi Malaysia (2)
A-16-2 Tower A Northpoint Offices MidValley City, 1 Medan Syed Putra Utara, Kuala Lumpur, 59200, Malaysia
Tel.: (60) 3 2287 2200
Web Site: http://www.saatchi.com
Sales Range: $25-49.9 Million
Emp.: 45
Advertising Agencies
N.A.I.C.S.: 541810

Unit (Domestic):

Saatchi & Saatchi New York (2)
375 Hudson St, New York, NY 10014-3660
Tel.: (212) 463-2000
Web Site: http://www.saatchiny.com
Sales Range: $150-199.9 Million
Emp.: 515
Advertising Services
N.A.I.C.S.: 541810
Lynne Collins *(VP & Dir-Comm)*

Subsidiary (Non-US):

Saatchi & Saatchi Singapore (2)
16 Collyer Quay, Income at the Raffles 03-00, Singapore, 049318, Singapore
Tel.: (65) 62066260
Web Site: http://www.saatchi.com
N.A.I.C.S.: 541810
Lou Dela Pena *(CEO)*

Saatchi & Saatchi Thailand (2)
12th Floor Sindhom Tower 3 130-132 Wireless Road Kwaeng Lumpini, Khet Pathumwan, Bangkok, 10330, Thailand
Tel.: (66) 2 640 4700
Web Site: http://www.saatchi.com
Advetising Agency
N.A.I.C.S.: 541810

Unit (Domestic):

Saatchi & Saatchi Wellness (2)
375 Hudson St, New York, NY 10014
Tel.: (212) 463-2578
Web Site: http://www.saatchiwellness.com
Advertising Agency
N.A.I.C.S.: 541810

Saatchi & Saatchi X (2)
375 Hudson St, New York, NY 10014-3660
Tel.: (212) 463-2000
Web Site: http://www.saatchix.com
Sales Range: $25-49.9 Million
Emp.: 25
N.A.I.C.S.: 541810

PUBLICIS GROUPE S.A.

Publicis Groupe S.A.—(Continued)

Saatchi & Saatchi X (2)
605 Lakeview Dr, Springdale, AR 72764
Tel.: (479) 575-0200
Web Site: http://www.saatchix.com
Sales Range: $25-49.9 Million
Emp.: 125
N.A.I.C.S.: 541810
Jessica Hendrix (Pres & CEO)

Division (Domestic):

Team One (2)
1960 E Grand Ave, El Segundo, CA 90245-5059
Tel.: (310) 615-2000
Web Site: http://www.teamone-usa.com
Sales Range: $75-99.9 Million
Emp.: 290
Advertising Agency
N.A.I.C.S.: 541860
Julie Michael (Pres)

Branch (Domestic):

Team One Advertising (3)
1 Tower Ste 3120 Oak Brook Ter, Oak Brook, IL 60181
Tel.: (630) 684-0317
Sales Range: Less than $1 Million
Emp.: 6
N.A.I.C.S.: 541810
Kamerin Elsasser (Office Mgr)

Team One Advertising (3)
375 Hudson St, New York, NY 10014
Tel.: (212) 463-3201
Sales Range: $75-99.9 Million
Emp.: 12
N.A.I.C.S.: 541810

Team One Advertising (3)
1170 Peachtree St NE Ste 1600, Atlanta, GA 30309
Tel.: (404) 870-6805
Web Site: http://www.teamone-usa.com
Sales Range: $25-49.9 Million
N.A.I.C.S.: 541810

Team One Advertising (3)
2300 Clarendon Blvd Ste 255, Arlington, VA 22201-3392
Tel.: (202) 223-8945
N.A.I.C.S.: 541810
Nick Terr (Mng Dir)

Subsidiary (Non-US):

Team Saatchi/Saatchi & Saatchi Healthcare (2)
70 George Street, The Rocks, Sydney, 2000, NSW, Australia
Tel.: (61) 2 8264 1111
Web Site: http://www.saatchi.com.au
Sales Range: $25-49.9 Million
Emp.: 160
N.A.I.C.S.: 541810

Tribu/Nazca Saatchi & Saatchi (2)
150 Sur del Gimnasio Nacional, Sabana Sur, San Jose, Costa Rica
Tel.: (506) 2209 7700
Web Site: http://www.tribu.co.cr
Emp.: 180
Full Service
N.A.I.C.S.: 541810

Umbrella Graphics Ltd. (2)
2 Bloor St E Ste 600, Toronto, M4W 1A8, ON, Canada
Tel.: (416) 359-9595
Web Site: http://www.saatchi.ca
Sales Range: $25-49.9 Million
Emp.: 3
Advertising Services
N.A.I.C.S.: 541810

Sapient Corporation (1)
40 Water St, Boston, MA 02109
Tel.: (617) 621-0200
Web Site: http://www.publicis.sapient.com
Sales Range: $1-4.9 Billion
Consultancy & Interactive Marketing Services
N.A.I.C.S.: 541613

Subsidiary (Domestic):

Corra Technology, Inc (2)
11 S Fullerton Ave Ste 2, Montclair, NJ 07042-3382
Tel.: (973) 783-2783
Web Site: http://www.corra.com
Custom Computer Programming Services
N.A.I.C.S.: 541511
Ron Bongo (Pres)

Sapient (m)PHASIZE (2)
15 Ketchum St, Westport, CT 06881
Tel.: (203) 557-0000
Web Site: http://www.sapient.com
Emp.: 5,001
Global Analytics & Marketing Investments
N.A.I.C.S.: 541613
Sunil Garga (Founder & Principal)

Subsidiary (Non-US):

Sapient Canada Inc. (2)
134 Peter Street 12th Floor, Toronto, M5V 2H2, ON, Canada (100%)
Tel.: (416) 645-1500
Web Site: http://www.sapien.com
Sales Range: $50-74.9 Million
Emp.: 325
Business Consulting, Technology & Services
N.A.I.C.S.: 541512

Branch (Domestic):

Sapient Corporation - Atlanta (2)
3630 Peachtree Rd NE Ste 1600, Atlanta, GA 30326
Tel.: (770) 407-3400
Sales Range: $25-49.9 Million
Emp.: 103
Advertising Agency & Interactive Marketing
N.A.I.C.S.: 541810
Alan M. Wexler (CEO-SapientNitro)

Sapient Corporation - Chicago (2)
35 W Wacker Dr, Chicago, IL 60601
Tel.: (312) 696-5000
Web Site: http://www.sapientglobalmarkets.com
Sales Range: $10-24.9 Million
Interactive Marketing & Consulting Services
N.A.I.C.S.: 541613

Sapient Corporation - Houston (2)
1111 Bagby St Ste 1950, Houston, TX 77002
Tel.: (713) 493-6880
Web Site: http://www.sapientglobalmarkets.com
Interactive Marketing, Advertising & Consulting Services
N.A.I.C.S.: 541810
Alan J. Herrick (Pres & CEO)

Sapient Corporation - Los Angeles (2)
3211 Olympic Blvd, Santa Monica, CA 90404
Tel.: (310) 264-6900
Sales Range: $25-49.9 Million
Emp.: 120
Interactive Marketing, Advertising & Technology Services
N.A.I.C.S.: 541810
Debbie Blevins (Mng Dir & VP)

Sapient Corporation - Miami/Falls (2)
2911 Grand Ave Suite 100, Coconut Grove, FL 33133
Tel.: (305) 253-0100
Sales Range: $25-49.9 Million
Emp.: 40
Advertising & Interactive Marketing
N.A.I.C.S.: 541810
Alan M. Wexler (CEO-SapientNitro)

Sapient Corporation - New York (2)
40 Fulton St 2nd Fl, New York, NY 10038
Tel.: (212) 560-5700
Sales Range: $50-74.9 Million
Emp.: 200
Interactive Marketing, Advertising & Technology Solutions
N.A.I.C.S.: 541810
Amy Junger (Dir)

Sapient Corporation - San Francisco (2)
30 Hotaling Place 2nd Fl, San Francisco, CA 94111
Tel.: (415) 655-7400
Rev: $50,000,000
Emp.: 40
Advertising, Consulting & Interactive Marketing
N.A.I.C.S.: 541810
Sonia Acosta (Art Dir)

Sapient Corporation - Washington, DC (2)
1515 N Courthouse Rd 4th Fl, Arlington, VA 22201-2909
Tel.: (703) 908-2400
Web Site: http://www.sapientglobalmarkets.com
Sales Range: $25-49.9 Million
Interactive Marketing & Consulting Services
N.A.I.C.S.: 541810
Alan Herrick (Pres & CEO)

Subsidiary (Non-US):

Sapient Corporation Private Limited (2)
Unitech Infospace Ground Floor Tower A Building 2 Sector 21 Old Delhi, Gurgaon Rd Dundahera, Gurgaon, 122026, Haryana, India (100%)
Tel.: (91) 124 499 6000
Web Site: http://www.sapientindiacareers.com
Computer & Design Consulting Services
N.A.I.C.S.: 541511
Sanjay Menon (Mng Dir)

Branch (Domestic):

Sapient Corporation Pvt. Ltd. - Bengaluru (3)
Bagmane Constellation Business Park 2870 Bldg Virgo Outer Ring Road, Doddanekundi Circle Marathahalli Post, Bengaluru, 560037, Karnataka, India
Tel.: (91) 080 6128 0000
Web Site: http://www.sapientnitro.com
Interactive Marketing Services
N.A.I.C.S.: 541613

Sapient Corporation Pvt. Ltd. - Noida (3)
Oxygen Tower C Ground -3rd Floor Plot No 7 Sector 144 Expressway, Noida, 201304, Uttar Pradesh, India
Tel.: (91) 120 479 5000
Web Site: http://www.sapientindiacareers.com
Business, Marketing & Technology Agency Services
N.A.I.C.S.: 541810

Subsidiary (Non-US):

Sapient GmbH (2)
Arnulfstrasse 60, 80335, Munich, Germany (100%)
Tel.: (49) 895529870
Web Site: http://www.sapient.com
Sales Range: $50-74.9 Million
Interactive Marketing & Consulting Services
N.A.I.C.S.: 541613

Subsidiary (Domestic):

Sapient Government Services, Inc. (2)
131 Dartmouth St 3rd Fl, Boston, MA 02116
Tel.: (617) 621-0200
Web Site: http://www.publicissapient.com
Administrative Management & General Management Consulting Service
N.A.I.C.S.: 541611

Subsidiary (Non-US):

Sapient Italy S.r.l. (2)
Via Bernina 34, 20158, Milan, Italy
Tel.: (39) 02 831 371
Web Site: http://www.sapientglobalmarkets.com
Marketing Analytics & Consulting Services
N.A.I.C.S.: 541613

Sapient Limited (2)
63 Turnmill Street, London, EC1M 5RR, United Kingdom (100%)
Tel.: (44) 2077864500
Web Site: http://www.sapient.com
Sales Range: $75-99.9 Million
Emp.: 400

INTERNATIONAL PUBLIC

Marketing, Technology, Advertising & Consulting Services
N.A.I.C.S.: 541511

Group (Domestic):

SapientNitro Limited (3)
Eden House 8 Spital Square, London, E1 6DU, United Kingdom
Tel.: (44) 2077864500
Web Site: http://www.sapientnitro.com
Sales Range: $25-49.9 Million
Emp.: 700
Advertising Agency
N.A.I.C.S.: 541810
Damien O'Donohoe (Global CFO)

Subsidiary (Domestic):

Digital and Direct Communications Limited (4)
The Glassmill 1 Battersea Bridge Road, London, SW11 3BZ, United Kingdom
Tel.: (44) 2073269191
Sales Range: $50-74.9 Million
Emp.: 200
Marketing Consulting Services
N.A.I.C.S.: 541613
John Foenander (VP)

Subsidiary (Non-US):

SapientNitro Hong Kong Limited (4)
22/F Chinachem Exchange Square 1 1 Hoi Wan Street, Quarry Bay, China (Hong Kong)
Tel.: (852) 3102 4512
Web Site: http://www.sapientnitro.com
N.A.I.C.S.: 541810

SapientNitro Pty. Ltd. (4)
Level 1 359-361 City Road, Southbank, 3006, VIC, Australia
Tel.: (61) 395370488
Web Site: http://www.sapientnitro.com
Sales Range: $25-49.9 Million
Emp.: 20
N.A.I.C.S.: 541810

Subsidiary (US):

SapientNitro USA, Inc. (4)
40 Fulton St 2nd Floor, New York, NY 10038-1603
Tel.: (212) 560-5700
Web Site: http://www.sapientnitro.com
Advertising Agency
N.A.I.C.S.: 541810
Michael Howatson (Exec Dir-Creative-Toronto)

Subsidiary (Domestic):

La Comunidad (5)
6400 Biscayne Blvd, Miami, FL 33138
Tel.: (305) 865-9600
Web Site: http://www.lacomunidad.com
Sales Range: $25-49.9 Million
Emp.: 100
Advertising Services
N.A.I.C.S.: 541810
Jose Molla (Co-Founder & Chief Creative Officer)

Branch (Non-US):

La Comunidad (6)
Virrey Arredondo 3464, C1426EAN CABA, Buenos Aires, Argentina
Tel.: (54) 11 4552 0350
Web Site: http://www.lacomunidad.com
Emp.: 30
Advertising Agency
N.A.I.C.S.: 541810
Joaquin Molla (Co-Founder & Co-Chief Ideas Officer)

Branch (Domestic):

SapientNitro Atlanta (5)
384 Northyards Blvd NW Ste 300, Atlanta, GA 30313
Tel.: (770) 407-3400
Web Site: http://www.sapient.com
Brand & Digital Marketing
N.A.I.C.S.: 541810

Subsidiary (Domestic):

Second Story, Inc. (5)

AND PRIVATE COMPANIES

PUBLICIS GROUPE S.A.

1330 Norwest 14th Ave, Portland, OR 97209
Tel.: (503) 827-7155
Web Site: http://www.secondstory.com
Sales Range: $25-49.9 Million
Emp.: 30
Advetising Agency
N.A.I.C.S.: 541890
Julie Beeler *(Co-Founder)*

Subsidiary (Non-US):

Shanghai Nitro Advertising Co., Limited (4)
31/F Lan Sheng Building 2-8 Huai Hai Zhong Road, Shanghai, 200021, China
Tel.: (86) 2163910011
Web Site: http://www.sapientnitro.com
Emp.: 50
Digital Marketing & Advertising Services
N.A.I.C.S.: 541810

Subsidiary (Non-US):

Sapient Netherlands B.V. (2)
Damrak 70, 1012 LM, Amsterdam, Netherlands
Tel.: (31) 20 330 0011
Web Site: http://www.sapient.com
Advetising Agency
N.A.I.C.S.: 541810

Sapient Sweden AB (2)
Ljusslingan 26 3rd Floor, 120 31, Stockholm, Sweden
Tel.: (46) 841032700
Web Site: http://www.sapient.com
Sales Range: Less than $1 Million
Interactive Marketing, Advertising & Consulting Services
N.A.I.C.S.: 541810

Sapient Switzerland GmbH (2)
Seefeldstrasse 35, 8008, Zurich, Switzerland   (100%)
Tel.: (41) 58 206 0600
Web Site: http://www.sapient.com
Interactive Marketing, Advertising & Consulting Services
N.A.I.C.S.: 541810

The Derivatives Consulting Group Limited (2)
26 Old Bailey Hillgate House, London, EC4M 7HW, United Kingdom
Tel.: (44) 2076531470
Web Site: http://www.publicis.sapient.com
Emp.: 500
Risk Management Consulting Services
N.A.I.C.S.: 541618

iThink Comunicacao e Publicidade LTDA (2)
4800 Avenida Magalhaes de Castro Torre 2 15 andar, Sao Paulo, CEP 05502-001, SP, Brazil
Tel.: (55) 1132017400
Web Site: http://www.ithink.com.br
Emp.: 13,000
Digital Media Communication & Publishing Services
N.A.I.C.S.: 517810
Raffael Mastrocola *(Mng Dir)*

Skanaali (1)
Tammasaarenkatu 1, 00180, Helsinki, Finland
Tel.: (358) 207 758 758
Web Site: http://www.tamaonskandaali.com
Sales Range: $25-49.9 Million
Emp.: 100
N.A.I.C.S.: 541810

Starcom MediaVest Group (1)
35 W Wacker Dr, Chicago, IL 60601-1723
Tel.: (312) 220-3535
Web Site: http://www.starcomworldwide.com
Sales Range: $1-4.9 Billion
Emp.: 7,300
Advertising Services
N.A.I.C.S.: 541810
John Muszynski *(Chief Investment Officer)*

Branch (Domestic):

42 Degrees (2)
1675 Broadway, New York, NY 10019
Tel.: (212) 468-4000
Web Site: http://www.mediavestww.com
Media Buying Services

N.A.I.C.S.: 541830

Halogen Response Media (2)
1675 Broadway, New York, NY 10019
Tel.: (212) 468-3627
Web Site: http://www.halogenresponse.com
Sales Range: $25-49.9 Million
Emp.: 14
Direct Marketing
N.A.I.C.S.: 541810
David Mead *(COO)*

Branch (Non-US):

LBiQ GmbH (2)
Leibnizstrasse 65, 10629, Berlin, Germany
Tel.: (49) 3031804490
Web Site: http://www.lbiq.de
Digital Marketing Services
N.A.I.C.S.: 541613
Leif Seemann *(Mng Dir)*

Branch (Domestic):

Liquid Thread (2)
1675 Broadway, New York, NY 10019
Tel.: (212) 468-4000
Web Site: http://www.liquidthread.com
Sales Range: $10-24.9 Million
Emp.: 50
Advertising Services
N.A.I.C.S.: 541810
Olivier Gers *(Global Pres)*

Liquid Thread (2)
35 West Wacker Dr, Chicago, IL 60601
Tel.: (312) 220-3591
Advertising Agencies
N.A.I.C.S.: 541810
John Doyle *(Mng Dir & Sr VP)*

Branch (Non-US):

M, C & A MediaVest (2)
Via Borsi 9, 20154, Milan, Italy
Tel.: (39) 0200640500
Web Site: http://www.mediavestww.com
Emp.: 40
Advertising Services
N.A.I.C.S.: 541810

MediaVest (Manchester) Ltd. (2)
117-119 Portland St, Manchester, M1 6ED, United Kingdom
Tel.: (44) 161 228 3909
Web Site: http://www.mvmediagroup.co.uk
Sales Range: $25-49.9 Million
Emp.: 200
Media Buying Services
N.A.I.C.S.: 541830
David Lucas *(Mng Partner)*

MediaVest UK London (2)
63 Turnmill Street, London, EC1M 5RR, United Kingdom
Tel.: (44) 20 7190 8000
Web Site: http://www.smvgroup.co.uk
Sales Range: $1-4.9 Billion
Emp.: 350
Media Buying Services
N.A.I.C.S.: 541830
Aimee Stokes *(Acct Mgr-Starcom MediaVest Grp)*

Branch (Domestic):

MediaVest USA (2)
1675 Broadway, New York, NY 10019
Tel.: (212) 468-4000
Web Site: http://www.mediavestww.com
Sales Range: $75-99.9 Million
Emp.: 500
Media Buying Services, Planning & Consultation
N.A.I.C.S.: 541830
Christine Merrifield *(Pres-Video Investment)*

MediaVest USA (2)
6500 Wilshire Blvd Ste 1100, Los Angeles, CA 90046
Tel.: (323) 658-4500
Media Buying Services
N.A.I.C.S.: 541830

Branch (Non-US):

MediaVest Worldwide (2)
175 Bloor Street E N Tower 10th Floor, Toronto, M4W 3Rp, ON, Canada
Tel.: (416) 927-3300
Advetising Agency

N.A.I.C.S.: 541810

MediaVest Worldwide (2)
Via San Quintino 28, 10121, Turin, Italy
Tel.: (39) 0115601980
Media Buying Services
N.A.I.C.S.: 541830
Julie Goldstein *(VP-Activation)*

MetaDesign AG (2)
Leibnizstrasse 65, Berlin, 10629, Germany
Tel.: (49) 305900540
Web Site: http://www.metadesign.de
Emp.: 200
Graphic Design Services
N.A.I.C.S.: 541430

MetaDesign China Limited (2)
Unit 2601 Zhongyu Plaza A6 Gongti North Road, 100027, Beijing, China
Tel.: (86) 1085235788
Web Site: http://www.metadesign.cn
Sales Range: $25-49.9 Million
Emp.: 20
Graphic Design Services
N.A.I.C.S.: 541430

Branch (Domestic):

Relay (2)
22 Merchandise Mart Plz, Chicago, IL 60654
Tel.: (312) 297-1212
Web Site: http://www.relayworldwide.com
Rev: $5,000,000
Advertising Services
N.A.I.C.S.: 541810

SMG Directory Marketing (2)
3000 Lakeside Dr Ste 305S, Bannockburn, IL 60015
Tel.: (847) 615-6800
Web Site: http://www.smgdirectorymarketing.com
Sales Range: $25-49.9 Million
Emp.: 45
Advertising Services
N.A.I.C.S.: 541870

SMG United (2)
1675 Broadway, New York, NY 10019
Tel.: (212) 468-4000
Emp.: 4,000
Advertising Services
N.A.I.C.S.: 541810
Diane Kenny *(Office Mgr)*

SMG/P&G (2)
35 W Wacker Dr, Chicago, IL 60601
Tel.: (312) 220-3535
Advertising Services
N.A.I.C.S.: 541810

Branch (Non-US):

Sandberg Starcom (2)
Solbjergvej 3 3 sal, 2000, Copenhagen, N, Denmark
Tel.: (45) 3 520 0080
Web Site: http://www.starcomww.com
Media Buying Services
N.A.I.C.S.: 541830

Branch (Domestic):

Spark Communications (2)
222 Merchandise Mart Plz Ste 550, Chicago, IL 60654-1032
Tel.: (312) 970-8400
Web Site: http://www.sparksmg.com
Sales Range: $25-49.9 Million
Emp.: 70
Media Buying Services
N.A.I.C.S.: 541810
Anne Nomellini *(Dir-LIG Media)*

Branch (Non-US):

Starcom (2)
Eriksgatan 46C, PO Box 21007, 100 31, Stockholm, Sweden
Tel.: (46) 85 626 6660
Sales Range: $25-49.9 Million
Emp.: 100
Media Buying Services
N.A.I.C.S.: 541830
Liv Sandberg *(CEO)*

Starcom (2)
Beethoven 15 Planta 5, Barcelona, 8021, Spain
Tel.: (34) 933 9677 00

Sales Range: $10-24.9 Million
Emp.: 28
Media Buying Services
N.A.I.C.S.: 541830
Rita Gutierrez *(Mng Dir-Starcom Barcelona)*

Starcom Adplus AG (2)
Heinrichstrasse 225, 8005, Zurich, Switzerland
Tel.: (41) 433666161
Web Site: http://www.adplus.ch
Sales Range: $25-49.9 Million
Emp.: 7
Media Buying Services
N.A.I.C.S.: 541830

Starcom Beijing (2)
Rm 1507 15/F Bright China Chang An Tower One, 7 Jianguomen Nei Ave, Beijing, 100005, China
Tel.: (86) 10 8519 9699
Media Buying Services
N.A.I.C.S.: 541830

Starcom Guangzhou (2)
2&3A/F SanXin Plz No 33 W Huangpu Ave, Guangzhou, 510620, China
Tel.: (86) 20 3820 1900
Media Buying Services
N.A.I.C.S.: 541830

Starcom Hong Kong (2)
11th Fl Warwick House Taikoo Place 979 King's Road, Quarry Bay, China (Hong Kong)
Tel.: (852) 2539 1683
Media Buying Services
N.A.I.C.S.: 541830
Margaret Ho *(Deputy Gen Mgr)*

Starcom Jakarta (2)
Mega Plz Bldg 4th Fl, Jl HR Rasuna Said Kav C-3, Jakarta, 12920, Indonesia
Tel.: (62) 21 5212 955
Advertising Services
N.A.I.C.S.: 541810

Branch (Domestic):

Starcom Latin America Regional Headquarters (2)
806 Douglas Rd Ste 700, Coral Gables, FL 33134-3129
Tel.: (305) 648-2122
Sales Range: $10-24.9 Million
Emp.: 40
Media Buying Services
N.A.I.C.S.: 541830

Branch (Non-US):

Starcom Media S.R.L. (2)
13 Nicolae Iorga Street, Bucharest, Romania
Tel.: (40) 21 201 6140
Sales Range: $25-49.9 Million
Emp.: 172
Advertising Services
N.A.I.C.S.: 541810
Carmen Chipuc *(Mng Dir)*

Starcom MediaVest (2)
16 Sir John Rogersons Quay, Dublin, Ireland
Tel.: (353) 1 649 6445
Sales Range: $10-24.9 Million
Emp.: 32
Media Buying Services
N.A.I.C.S.: 541830
Alan Cox *(CEO)*

Branch (Domestic):

Starcom MediaVest (2)
150 W Jefferson Ste 400, Detroit, MI 48226
Tel.: (313) 237-8200
Media Buying Services
N.A.I.C.S.: 541810
Molly Marchese *(VP & Dir-Media)*

Starcom MediaVest (2)
35 W Wacker, Chicago, IL 60601
Tel.: (312) 970-8400
Web Site: http://www.sparksmg.com
Emp.: 275
Advertising Services
N.A.I.C.S.: 541810
Sam Chadha *(Exec VP & Mng Dir-USA)*

Branch (Non-US):

Starcom MediaVest Group (2)

PUBLICIS GROUPE S.A.

Publicis Groupe S.A.—(Continued)
Quintanavides 19 Building 4, 28050, Madrid, Spain
Tel.: (34) 911 872 100
Web Site: http://www.starcomww.com
Sales Range: $25-49.9 Million
Emp.: 100
Media Buying Services
N.A.I.C.S.: 541830

Starcom MediaVest Group (2)
175 Bloor St E N Tower 10th Fl, Toronto, M4W 3R9, ON, Canada
Tel.: (416) 928-3636
Media Buying Services
N.A.I.C.S.: 541830
Jeff Thibodeau *(Sr VP-Digital Media)*

Starcom Mediavest Group Moscow (2)
15 Leningradsky Prospekt Bld 1, 194021, Moscow, Russia
Tel.: (7) 4959692010
Sales Range: $25-49.9 Million
Emp.: 110
Media Buying Services
N.A.I.C.S.: 541830
Jeff Chalmers *(CEO)*

Starcom Medios (2)
Avenida Apoquindo 3000, Las Condes Piso 7, Santiago, 6760341, Chile
Tel.: (56) 236 25803
Sales Range: $25-49.9 Million
Emp.: 20
Media Buying Services
N.A.I.C.S.: 541830

Starcom Middle East & Egypt Regional Headquarters (2)
Dubai Media City Bldg No 11, PO Box 7534, Dubai, United Arab Emirates
Tel.: (971) 4 367 6401
Media Buying Services
N.A.I.C.S.: 541830

Starcom Motive Partnership London (2)
83-89 Whitfield Street, London, W1T 4HQ, United Kingdom
Tel.: (44) 207 453 4444
Web Site: http://www.smg.com
Sales Range: $75-99.9 Million
Emp.: 350
Media Buying Services
N.A.I.C.S.: 541830

Starcom Norway (2)
Tollbugata 17, 0152, Oslo, Norway
Tel.: (47) 90637700
Web Site: http://www.starcom.no
Emp.: 48
Media Buying Services
N.A.I.C.S.: 541830
Catharine Mitlid *(Dir-Strategy)*

Starcom Pakistan (2)
Suit No 401-A 4th Floor Panorama Centre-II Raja Ghazanfar Ali, Saddar, Karachi, Pakistan
Tel.: (92) 2135661550
Web Site: http://www.starcom.com.pk
Advertising Services
N.A.I.C.S.: 541810

Starcom Shanghai (2)
3/F 900 HuaiHai Middle Rd, Shanghai, 200020, China
Tel.: (86) 21 6133 8518
Media Buying Services
N.A.I.C.S.: 541830

Starcom Sp. z o.o. (2)
Domaniewska 44A Platinium V, Warsaw, 02-672, Poland
Tel.: (48) 22 493 99 99
Web Site: http://www.starcom.com.pl
Sales Range: $25-49.9 Million
Emp.: 90
Media Buying Services
N.A.I.C.S.: 541830
Jakub Benke *(Pres & CEO)*

Starcom Taipei (2)
8/F No 6 Sec 4 Xin Yi Road, Taipei, 106, Taiwan
Tel.: (886) 2 2704 2211
Media Buying Services
N.A.I.C.S.: 541830

Scarlett Shih *(Mng Dir)*

Branch (Domestic):

Starcom USA (2)
35 W Wacker Dr, Chicago, IL 60601
Tel.: (312) 220-3535
Sales Range: $25-49.9 Million
Emp.: 100
Advertising Services
N.A.I.C.S.: 541830
Gina Jacobson *(Mng Dir & Exec VP)*

Branch (Non-US):

Starcom WW (2)
Rui Gonzalves Zarco 14, 1449-013, Lisbon, Portugal
Tel.: (351) 217818100
Sales Range: $10-24.9 Million
Emp.: 26
Media Buying Services, Out-of-Home Media
N.A.I.C.S.: 541830
Adrian Gustia *(Mng Dir)*

Starcom Worldwide (2)
24F Tower 2 Enterprise Center 6766 Ayala Avenue Corner, Paseo de Roxas, Makati, 1200, Philippines
Tel.: (63) 2 884 8025
Media Buying Services
N.A.I.C.S.: 541830
Jack Klues *(Chm)*

Starcom Worldwide (2)
6th Floor Kwanhoon Building 198-42 Kwanhoon Dong, Chongro-Ku, Seoul, 110-300, Korea (South)
Tel.: (82) 2 2000 3682
Media Buying Services
N.A.I.C.S.: 541830

Starcom Worldwide (2)
Silver Stream Business Park, 10 Muswell Road, 2191, Bryanston, South Africa
Tel.: (27) 11 235 4011
Sales Range: $10-24.9 Million
Emp.: 25
Media Buying Services
N.A.I.C.S.: 541830
Kate Carlisle *(Mng Dir)*

Starcom Worldwide (2)
19 Mayis Cad Nova Baran Plaza Kat 18, Sisli, 24360, Istanbul, Türkiye
Tel.: (90) 212 219 62 29
Sales Range: $25-49.9 Million
Emp.: 20
Media Buying Services
N.A.I.C.S.: 541830
Bosko Spasojevic *(Mng Dir)*

Starcom Worldwide (2)
Szepvolgyi Business Park Cepulet Bldg 1V Emelet Fl, Budapest, 1037, Hungary
Tel.: (36) 1 801 3300
Sales Range: $25-49.9 Million
Emp.: 20
Media Buying Services
N.A.I.C.S.: 541830

Starcom Worldwide (2)
6 Patroklou & Adromachis Str, Marousi, 151 25, Athens, Greece
Tel.: (30) 2 10 8112 811
Media Buying Services
N.A.I.C.S.: 541830

Branch (Domestic):

Starcom Worldwide (2)
5200 Lankershim Blvd Ste 600, North Hollywood, CA 91601
Tel.: (818) 753-7200
Emp.: 100
Media Buying Services
N.A.I.C.S.: 541830
Kathy O. Ring *(CEO)*

Branch (Non-US):

Starcom Worldwide (2)
Bond Store 2 28 Windmill St Walsh Bay, Sydney, 2000, NSW, Australia
Tel.: (61) 2 8666 8000
Rev.: $355,000,000
Emp.: 100
Media Buying Services
N.A.I.C.S.: 541830
Toby Barbour *(CEO)*

Branch (Domestic):

Starcom Melbourne (3)
Level 6 28 Freshwater Place Southbank, Southbank, Melbourne, 3006, VIC, Australia
Tel.: (61) 3 9673 7000
Web Site: http://www.starcomworldwide.com.au
Emp.: 85
Media Buying Services
N.A.I.C.S.: 541830
Yvonne Mayer *(Chief Digital Officer)*

Starcom Worldwide (3)
Level 2 99 Melbourne St, Brisbane, 4101, QLD, Australia
Tel.: (61) 7 3329 1000
Web Site: http://www.starcomworldwide.com.au
Emp.: 25
Media Buying Services
N.A.I.C.S.: 541810
Caleb Watson *(Gen Mgr)*

Starcom Worldwide-Adelaide (3)
53-57 Glen Osmond Road, Eastwood, 5063, SA, Australia
Tel.: (61) 8 8291 0000
Sales Range: $25-49.9 Million
Emp.: 15
Media Buying Services
N.A.I.C.S.: 541830
Mark Clemow *(Gen Mgr)*

Branch (Non-US):

Starcom Worldwide (2)
15 Rue du Dome, 92100, Boulogne-Billancourt, France
Tel.: (33) 1 55 20 33 00
Media Buying Services
N.A.I.C.S.: 541830

Starcom Worldwide India (2)
Big Apple 26 Dr L Shirodkar Road, Mumbai, 400 012, India
Tel.: (91) 22 42164411
Advertising Services
N.A.I.C.S.: 541810
Hanley King *(Chm)*

Starcom Worldwide Northeast Asia HQ (2)
1063 King's Road Room 1405, Room 602-608, Quarry Bay, China (Hong Kong)
Tel.: (852) 2539 1688
Media Buying Services
N.A.I.C.S.: 541830
Pushkar Sane *(Gen Mgr-Asia-Starcom IP)*

Starcom Worldwide Southeast Asia HQ (2)
137 Telok Ayer St #06-01, Singapore, 068602, Singapore
Tel.: (65) 6435 7101
Media Buying Services
N.A.I.C.S.: 541830
Ian Loon *(Mng Dir)*

Branch (Domestic):

Tapestry Partners (2)
806 Douglas Rd Ste 700, Coral Gables, FL 33134
Tel.: (305) 461-6832
Sales Range: $25-49.9 Million
Emp.: 5
Advertising Services
N.A.I.C.S.: 541810

Tapestry Partners (2)
35 W Wacker Dr, Chicago, IL 60601
Tel.: (312) 220-3535
Advertising Services
N.A.I.C.S.: 541830
Monica Gadsby *(CEO)*

Telenext Media (2)
825 8th Ave, New York, NY 10019
Tel.: (212) 474-5888
Sales Range: $25-49.9 Million
Emp.: 25
Advertising Services
N.A.I.C.S.: 541810

Starcom Worldwide SA de CV (1)
Bosque de Duraznos 47 - 4 Col Bosques de las Lomas, Miguel Hidalgo CDMX, 11700, Mexico, Mexico
Tel.: (52) 5552465800
Marketing & Advertising Services

INTERNATIONAL PUBLIC

N.A.I.C.S.: 541810

Taterka (1)
Avenida Sao Gualter 766, Praca Sao Marcos, Sao Paulo, Brazil
Tel.: (55) 11 3026 9595
Web Site: http://www.taterka.com.br
Emp.: 200
N.A.I.C.S.: 541810

The Creative Counsel Pty. Ltd. (1)
Unit 6 and Unit 9 22 Witkoppen Road, Cambridge Commercial Park West Paulshof, Johannesburg, 2191, Gauteng, South Africa
Tel.: (27) 872551050
Web Site: http://www.creativecounsel.co.za
Marketing & Advertising Services
N.A.I.C.S.: 541810
M. Sevana *(Sr Mgr-Content)*

The Kaplan Thaler Group (1)
825 8th Ave 34th Fl, New York, NY 10019
Tel.: (212) 474-5000
Sales Range: $25-49.9 Million
Emp.: 240
Advertising Services
N.A.I.C.S.: 541810
Gerry Killeen *(Mng Dir-Creative Svcs)*

Translate Plus UK Limited (1)
82 Baker Street, London, W1U 6AE, United Kingdom
Tel.: (44) 2073240950
Web Site: http://www.translateplus.com
Translation & Localization Services
N.A.I.C.S.: 541930
Adrian Metcalf *(Dir-Technical)*

Turner Duckworth Limited (1)
Voysey House Barley Mow Passage, London, W4 4PH, United Kingdom
Tel.: (44) 20 8994 7190
Web Site: http://www.turnerduckworth.com
Advetising Agency
N.A.I.C.S.: 541810
Bruce Duckworth *(Co-Founder)*

Subsidiary (US):

Turner Duckworth, LLC (2)
831 Montgomery St, San Francisco, CA 94133
Tel.: (415) 675-7777
Web Site: http://www.turnerduckworth.com
Advetising Agency
N.A.I.C.S.: 541810

Verbe (1)
24 rue Salomon de Rothschild, 92288, Suresnes, France
Tel.: (33) 157328900
Web Site: http://www.verbe.fr
Sales Range: $25-49.9 Million
Emp.: 1,000
N.A.I.C.S.: 541810
Yannick Le Bourdonnec *(Gen Dir)*

Vigilante Advertising (1)
345 Hudson Street, New York, NY 10014
Tel.: (212) 545-2850
Rev.: $154,000,000
Emp.: 25
Advertising Services
N.A.I.C.S.: 541810

Winner & Associates (1)
2029 Century Park E Ste 1750, Los Angeles, CA 90067
Tel.: (818) 385-1900
Web Site: http://www.winnerandassociates.com
Sales Range: $25-49.9 Million
Emp.: 25
N.A.I.C.S.: 541810
Charles Winner *(Pres)*

ZenithOptimedia Ltd. (1)
5th Floor 2 Television Centre 101 Wood Lane, London, W12 7FR, United Kingdom
Tel.: (44) 207 961 1000
Advetising Agency
N.A.I.C.S.: 541810
Natalie Cummins *(CEO)*

Subsidiary (Domestic):

Meridian Outdoor Advertising (2)
24 Percey Street, London, W1T 2BS, United Kingdom
Tel.: (44) 207 961 1000

AND PRIVATE COMPANIES

Sales Range: $25-49.9 Million
Emp.: 25
N.A.I.C.S.: 541810

Zenith Optimedia International Limited (2)
24 Percy Street, London, W1T 2BS, United Kingdom
Tel.: (44) 2079611000
Emp.: 75
Holding Company
N.A.I.C.S.: 551112
Rob Gold *(Mng Partner)*

Subsidiary (Non-US):

IUM Oy (3)
Peramiehenkatu 12 E 4 Krs, 00150, Helsinki, Finland
Tel.: (358) 207 426 700
Web Site: http://www.ium.fi
Advetising Agency
N.A.I.C.S.: 541810
Marja Uski *(Head-Client Unit)*

Interactive ZenithOptimedia (3)
Quintanavides 13, Torre Europa - Plta 20, 28046, Madrid, Spain
Tel.: (34) 911319860
Web Site: http://www.zointeractive.com
Sales Range: $25-49.9 Million
Emp.: 10
N.A.I.C.S.: 541810

Metrix (3)
Quintanavides 13 Building 1 4th Floor, 28046, Madrid, Spain
Tel.: (34) 913233028
Web Site: http://www.zenithmedia.es
Sales Range: $25-49.9 Million
Emp.: 19
N.A.I.C.S.: 541810

New Cast (3)
8/F Bright China Chang An Tower Two 7 Jiangguomen Nei Avenue, Beijing, 100005, China
Tel.: (86) 10 6510 2277
N.A.I.C.S.: 541810

Optimedia (3)
26 Tran Cao Van Str - Ward 6 District 3, District 1, Ho Chi Minh City, Vietnam
Tel.: (84) 8 3827 6002
Sales Range: $10-24.9 Million
Emp.: 50
N.A.I.C.S.: 541810

Optimedia (3)
Bosques de Duraznos No. 47 Piso 2, Bosque de los Lomas, Mexico, 11700, Mexico
Tel.: (52) 5530881500
Sales Range: $25-49.9 Million
Emp.: 25
Advetising Agency
N.A.I.C.S.: 541810

Optimedia (3)
Armenia 1528, C1414 DKH, Buenos Aires, Argentina
Tel.: (54) 11 5556 3500
Web Site: http://www.zenithoptimedia.com.ar
Sales Range: $25-49.9 Million
Emp.: 5
N.A.I.C.S.: 541810

Optimedia (3)
Gumpendorfer Strasse 21, 1060, Vienna, Austria
Tel.: (43) 1 716 370
Web Site: http://www.zenithoptimedia.at
Sales Range: $25-49.9 Million
Emp.: 10
N.A.I.C.S.: 541810
Ervin Vaskovich *(CEO)*

Optimedia (3)
Via Norte Edificio 3 Calle Quintanavides 17, Torre Europa, 28046, Madrid, Spain
Tel.: (34) 913080540
Web Site: http://www.optimedia.es
Sales Range: $25-49.9 Million
Emp.: 60
N.A.I.C.S.: 541810
Fernando Rodriguez *(CEO)*

Optimedia (3)
Avda Diagonal 512 Bajos, Barcelona, 8006, Spain

Tel.: (34) 93 415 0880
Web Site: http://www.optimedia.es
Sales Range: $10-24.9 Million
Emp.: 30
N.A.I.C.S.: 541810

Optimedia (3)
3-5 Menandrou Street 145 61, 145 61, Kifissia, Athens, Greece
Tel.: (30) 21 0 623 5000
Sales Range: $25-49.9 Million
Emp.: 25
N.A.I.C.S.: 541810

Optimedia (3)
Ul 11 Oktomvri br 3/4, 1000, Skopje, North Macedonia
Tel.: (389) 2 3297 670
Sales Range: Less than $1 Million
Emp.: 5
N.A.I.C.S.: 541810
Igor Celebic *(Mng Dir)*

Optimedia (3)
Omar Saab Building Verdun Rachid Karame Street 2nd Fl, Beirut, Lebanon
Tel.: (961) 1 738 644
Sales Range: $25-49.9 Million
Emp.: 9
N.A.I.C.S.: 541810

Optimedia (3)
Al Ghurair City Office Tower 9th Floor Office #940, Dubai, United Arab Emirates
Tel.: (971) 4 227 6773
Sales Range: $25-49.9 Million
Emp.: 25
N.A.I.C.S.: 541810

Optimedia (3)
Panonska cesta 7, Bratislava, 85104, Slovakia
Tel.: (421) 2 32 15 35 01
Web Site: http://www.unimedia.com
Sales Range: $25-49.9 Million
Emp.: 3
N.A.I.C.S.: 541810
Gurag Matus *(Dir)*

Optimedia (3)
Country Club Estate, Building B, 21 Woodlands Dr, Sandton, 2191, South Africa
Tel.: (27) 112354401
Sales Range: $25-49.9 Million
Emp.: 7
N.A.I.C.S.: 541810

Optimedia (3)
Rua Goncalves Zarco 14 R C, 1449-013, Lisbon, Portugal
Tel.: (351) 21 391 3400
Sales Range: $10-24.9 Million
Emp.: 28
N.A.I.C.S.: 541810

Optimedia Gesellschaft fur Media-Services mbH (3)
Toulouser-Allee 1, 40211, Dusseldorf, Germany
Tel.: (49) 211 390 30
Web Site: http://www.optimedia.de
Sales Range: $10-24.9 Million
Emp.: 45
N.A.I.C.S.: 541810
Ulrike Hefter *(Member-Mgmt Bd)*

Optimedia Peru (3)
950 Avenida Santa Cruz Miraflores, Lima, 18, Peru
Tel.: (51) 1 610 8484
Sales Range: $10-24.9 Million
Emp.: 15
N.A.I.C.S.: 541810

Zenith BR Media (3)
Luis Vives 6, Valencia, 46005, Spain
Tel.: (34) 96 315 3600
Web Site: http://www.zenithmedia.es
Emp.: 24
N.A.I.C.S.: 541810
Jose-Maria Rubert *(Mgr)*

Zenith Gestion de Medios (3)
Plaza de Zaragoza 1, CP 20007, San Sebastian, Spain
Tel.: (34) 943 430 000
Web Site: http://www.zenithmedia.es
Sales Range: $25-49.9 Million
Emp.: 10
N.A.I.C.S.: 541810
Matias Jiminez *(Mgr)*

Zenith Media (3)
landmarket 10, 1119, Copenhagen, Denmark
Tel.: (45) 33 33 00 67
Sales Range: $25-49.9 Million
N.A.I.C.S.: 541810

Zenith Media (3)
3 Chilason St, Ramat Gan, 52522, Israel
Tel.: (972) 3 755 2655
Sales Range: $25-49.9 Million
Emp.: 20
N.A.I.C.S.: 541810
Alon Hochdorf *(CEO)*

Zenith Media (3)
ul Domaniewska 42, 02-672, Warsaw, Poland
Tel.: (48) 22 345 21 40
Web Site: http://www.zenithmedia.pl
Sales Range: $75-99.9 Million
Media Buying Services
N.A.I.C.S.: 541810

Zenith Media (3)
Avenida Del Partenon 12-14, 28042, Madrid, Spain
Tel.: (34) 91 567 4600
Web Site: http://www.zenithmedia.es
Sales Range: $25-49.9 Million
Emp.: 75
Media Buying Services
N.A.I.C.S.: 541810
Valentin Ruiz *(Dir-Media)*

Zenith Media (3)
Avenida Diagonial 512, Barcelona, 8006, Spain
Tel.: (34) 93 342 6970
Web Site: http://www.zenithmedia.es
Sales Range: $25-49.9 Million
Emp.: 22
N.A.I.C.S.: 541810
Philipp Furst *(Mgr)*

Zenith Media (3)
Buyukdere Cad No 193, Istanbul, 34394, Turkiye
Tel.: (90) 2123159999
Sales Range: $10-24.9 Million
N.A.I.C.S.: 541810
Esin Alptekin *(Mng Dir)*

ZenithOptimedia (3)
Bond Store 3 30 Windmill Street, Walsh Bay, Sydney, 2000, NSW, Australia
Tel.: (61) 292589100
Sales Range: $25-49.9 Million
Communications, Media Buying Services
N.A.I.C.S.: 541810

ZenithOptimedia (3)
1404-06 14/F 1063 Kings Road, Quarry Bay, China (Hong Kong)
Tel.: (852) 2236 9000
N.A.I.C.S.: 541810

ZenithOptimedia (3)
1-4/F900 Huai Hai Zhong Road, Shanghai, China
Tel.: (86) 21 6133 8399
N.A.I.C.S.: 541810
Steven Chang *(CEO-China)*

ZenithOptimedia (3)
68 bis rue Marjolin, 92685, Levallois-Perret, CEDEX, France
Tel.: (33) 1 58 74 86 00
Sales Range: $75-99.9 Million
N.A.I.C.S.: 541810
Pascale Miguet *(Pres)*

ZenithOptimedia (3)
Toulouser Allee 1, 40211, Dusseldorf, Germany
Tel.: (49) 2115280999
Media Services
N.A.I.C.S.: 541810
Dirk Lux *(CEO)*

ZenithOptimedia (3)
1 WML, Dublin, D02 F206, Ireland
Tel.: (353) 16496420
Sales Range: $25-49.9 Million
N.A.I.C.S.: 541810
Craig Farrell *(Mng Dir)*

ZenithOptimedia (3)
Via G Borsi nr 9, 20143, Milan, Italy
Tel.: (39) 02 75299 1

PUBLICIS GROUPE S.A.

Sales Range: $25-49.9 Million
N.A.I.C.S.: 541810

ZenithOptimedia (3)
Piazza G Marçoni 15, 00144, Rome, Italy
Tel.: (39) 06 32803730
Sales Range: $25-49.9 Million
Emp.: 8
N.A.I.C.S.: 541810

ZenithOptimedia (3)
8 Jalan Raja Chulan, 50200, Kuala Lumpur, Malaysia
Tel.: (60) 320592600
N.A.I.C.S.: 541810

ZenithOptimedia (3)
Prof WH Keesomlaan 12, 1183 DG, Amstelveen, Netherlands
Tel.: (31) 20 46 22 760
Web Site: http://www.zenithoptimediagroep.nl
Sales Range: $25-49.9 Million
Emp.: 80
N.A.I.C.S.: 541810
Linda Boks *(CEO)*

ZenithOptimedia (3)
Dronningensgate 15, 0105, Oslo, Norway
Tel.: (47) 91805010
Sales Range: $10-24.9 Million
N.A.I.C.S.: 541810

ZenithOptimedia (3)
60 Anson Road 07-01/02/03/04 Mapletree Anson, Singapore, 079914, Singapore
Tel.: (65) 69142600
Sales Range: $25-49.9 Million
N.A.I.C.S.: 541810

ZenithOptimedia (3)
Kapellgrand 7, Box 2100, 116 25, Stockholm, Sweden
Tel.: (46) 856266850
Web Site: http://www.zenithmedia.se
Sales Range: $25-49.9 Million
Emp.: 12
Advertising Services
N.A.I.C.S.: 541810

ZenithOptimedia (3)
8FL 6 Xin Yi Road Section 4, Taipei, 106, Taiwan
Tel.: (886) 2 2700 3151
N.A.I.C.S.: 541810
Irene Chang *(Mng Dir)*

ZenithOptimedia (3)
Sindhorn Tower 1 6th Floor 130/132 Wireless Road, Lumpini Patumwan, Bangkok, 10330, Thailand
Tel.: (66) 2 627 3370
Advetising Agency
N.A.I.C.S.: 541810
Chanida Vibulkitvorakul *(Gen Mgr)*

Subsidiary (US):

ZenithOptimedia (3)
299 W Houston St 11th Fl, New York, NY 10014
Tel.: (212) 859-5100
Emp.: 100
Digital/Interactive, Direct Response Marketing
N.A.I.C.S.: 541810
Philippe Seignol *(Head-Digital-Latin America)*

Subsidiary (Domestic):

Optimedia International U.S., Inc. (4)
375 Hudson St 7th Fl, New York, NY 10014
Tel.: (212) 820-3200
Web Site: http://www.optimedia-us.com
Sales Range: $25-49.9 Million
Emp.: 200
Media Buying Agency
N.A.I.C.S.: 541830
Dave Ehlers *(Pres & CEO)*

Branch (Domestic):

Optimedia-Dallas (5)
7300 Lone Star Dr Ste 200, Plano, TX 75024
Tel.: (469) 366-2550
Web Site: http://www.optimedia-us.com
Sales Range: $75-99.9 Million
Emp.: 20
Media Buying Services

PUBLICIS GROUPE S.A.

Publicis Groupe S.A.—(Continued)
N.A.I.C.S.: 541830

Optimedia-Indianapolis (5)
200 S Meridian St Ste 500, Indianapolis, IN 46225-1076
Tel.: (317) 639-5135
Web Site: http://www.optimedia-us.com
Sales Range: $75-99.9 Million
Emp.: 11
Media Buying Services
N.A.I.C.S.: 541830
Jay Schemanske *(VP & Dir-Strategic Comm)*

Optimedia-San Francisco (5)
2001 The Embarcadero, San Francisco, CA 94133
Tel.: (415) 398-2669
Web Site: http://www.optimedia-us.com
Media Buying Services
N.A.I.C.S.: 541830

Optimedia-Seattle (5)
424 2nd Ave W, Seattle, WA 98119-4013
Tel.: (206) 272-2300
Web Site: http://www.optimedia-us.com
Sales Range: $50-74.9 Million
Emp.: 26
Media Buying Services
N.A.I.C.S.: 541830
Rudy Grahn *(VP-Analytics)*

Subsidiary (Domestic):

Zenith Media Services, Inc. (4)
299 W Houston St 11th Fl, New York, NY 10014-4806
Tel.: (212) 859-5100
Sales Range: $50-74.9 Million
Media Buying Agency
N.A.I.C.S.: 541830

Subsidiary (Domestic):

Engauge Marketing, LLC (5)
375 N Front St Ste 400, Columbus, OH 43215
Tel.: (614) 573-1010
Web Site: http://www.engauge.com
Sales Range: $200-249.9 Million
Emp.: 300
Advetising Agency
N.A.I.C.S.: 541810
Nick Bandy *(CEO)*

Branch (Domestic):

Engauge Marketing, LLC - Atlanta (6)
1230 Peachtree St NE Promenade 2 Ste 1700, Atlanta, GA 30309
Tel.: (404) 601-4321
Web Site: http://www.engauge.com
Sales Range: Less than $1 Million
Emp.: 7
Advetising Agency
N.A.I.C.S.: 541810

Engauge Marketing, LLC - Orlando (6)
904 N Orange Ave, Orlando, FL 32801-1017
Tel.: (407) 649-8101
Web Site: http://www.engauge.com
Emp.: 20
Advetising Agency
N.A.I.C.S.: 541810

Engauge Marketing, LLC - Pittsburgh (6)
437 Grant St, Pittsburgh, PA 15219
Tel.: (412) 471-5300
Web Site: http://www.engauge.com
Advetising Agency
N.A.I.C.S.: 541810

Subsidiary (Domestic):

Moxie Interactive Inc. (5)
The Northyards 384 Northyards Blvd NW Ste 290, Atlanta, GA 30313-2440
Tel.: (404) 601-4500
Web Site: http://www.moxieinteractive.com
Rev.: $38,000,000
Emp.: 300
Advetising Agency
N.A.I.C.S.: 541810
Matt Wernsman *(Mgr-Ops)*

Branch (Domestic):

Moxie Interactive (6)
Century Plz Towers 2049 Century Pk E Ste 1300, Los Angeles, CA 90067-3115
Tel.: (310) 551-3500
N.A.I.C.S.: 541810
Lane Soelberg *(Sr VP-Bus Dev & Client Svcs)*

Moxie Interactive (6)
375 Hudson St 11th Fl, New York, NY 10014-3658
Tel.: (212) 859-5100
Web Site: http://www.moxieusa.com
Emp.: 40
N.A.I.C.S.: 541810

Branch (Domestic):

Zenith Media (5)
2049 Century Park E Ste 1300, Los Angeles, CA 90067
Tel.: (310) 551-3500
Sales Range: $50-74.9 Million
Emp.: 107
Media Buying Services
N.A.I.C.S.: 541830
Marti Grimsley *(Sr VP)*

Zenith Media (5)
701 5th Ave Ste 1220, Seattle, WA 98104
Tel.: (206) 386-5301
Sales Range: $75-99.9 Million
Emp.: 15
Media Buying Services
N.A.I.C.S.: 541830

Zenith Media (5)
1777 Harrison St Ste 303, Denver, CO 80210-3928
Tel.: (303) 758-4730
Sales Range: $75-99.9 Million
Emp.: 4
Media Buying Services, Out-of-Home Media, Outdoor
N.A.I.C.S.: 541830
Linda Vorenkamp *(VP & Assoc Dir-Media)*

Zenith Media (5)
Ste 4 - 160A 222 Merchandise Mart Plz, Chicago, IL 60654
Tel.: (312) 980-7140
Sales Range: $50-74.9 Million
Emp.: 34
N.A.I.C.S.: 541810

Zenith Media (5)
384 Northyards Blvd NW Ste 290, Atlanta, GA 30318
Tel.: (404) 601-4500
Web Site: http://www.moxieusa.com
Sales Range: $50-74.9 Million
Emp.: 8
N.A.I.C.S.: 541810

Zenith Media Services (5)
5285 SW Meadows Rd Ste 232, Lake Oswego, OR 97035-5291
Tel.: (503) 639-9003
Web Site: http://www.zenithmedia.com
Media Buying Services
N.A.I.C.S.: 541830

Zenith Media Services (5)
2001 The Embarcadero, San Francisco, CA 94133
Tel.: (415) 293-2440
N.A.I.C.S.: 541830

Subsidiary (Non-US):

ZenithOptimedia (3)
Vorovskogo 24, Kiev, 01054, Ukraine
Tel.: (380) 44 492 9980
Sales Range: $10-24.9 Million
Emp.: 50
N.A.I.C.S.: 541810

ZenithOptimedia (3)
Level 6 28 Freshwater Place, Southbank, Melbourne, 3006, VIC, Australia
Tel.: (61) 292 589100
Sales Range: $10-24.9 Million
Emp.: 30
N.A.I.C.S.: 541810
Nickie Scriven *(CEO)*

ZenithOptimedia (3)
Gatot Subroto No 38 Jamsostek Tower 22nd floor, PO Box 4515, Slipi, Jakarta, 11480, Indonesia
Tel.: (62) 21 530 6219
N.A.I.C.S.: 541810
Ernita Ariestanty *(CEO)*

ZenithOptimedia (3)
7 rue Picardstraat, 1000, Brussels, Belgium
Tel.: (32) 26207000
Web Site: http://www.publicis.com
Sales Range: $10-24.9 Million
Advertising Services
N.A.I.C.S.: 541810
Davy Caluwaerts *(Mng Dir)*

ZenithOptimedia (3)
Abacus Business Building fl 5, 118 Bulgaria Blvd, Sofia, 1618, Bulgaria
Tel.: (359) 2 43 40 710
Sales Range: $25-49.9 Million
Emp.: 12
N.A.I.C.S.: 541810
Alexander Birtsoev *(Mng Dir)*

ZenithOptimedia (3)
Heinzelova 33, Zagreb, 10000, Croatia
Tel.: (385) 1 23 09 300
Sales Range: $25-49.9 Million
Emp.: 15
N.A.I.C.S.: 541810

ZenithOptimedia (3)
Amereskah 100, Ljubljana, 1000, Slovenia
Tel.: (386) 1 23 43 500
Sales Range: $25-49.9 Million
Emp.: 12
N.A.I.C.S.: 541810
Jasna Spelko Smerajc *(Mng Dir)*

ZenithOptimedia (3)
ul Domaniewska 42, 02-672, Warsaw, Poland
Tel.: (48) 22 345 21 40
Web Site: http://www.zenithoptimedia.pl
Sales Range: $25-49.9 Million
Emp.: 170
N.A.I.C.S.: 541810
Iwona Jaskiewicz *(Dir-Media Buying)*

ZenithOptimedia (3)
Leningradsky prospekt 15 bldg 14 2nd Fl, Bolshevik Business Center, 125040, Moscow, Russia
Tel.: (7) 4959373377
Web Site: http://www.zenithoptimedia.ru
Sales Range: $25-49.9 Million
Emp.: 70
N.A.I.C.S.: 541810
Svetlana Shupe *(Gen Dir)*

ZenithOptimedia (3)
The Textile Centre 4th Fl Kenwyn St, Parnell, Auckland, 1071, New Zealand
Tel.: (64) 9 914 6784
Web Site: http://www.zenithoptimedia.co.nz
Sales Range: $10-24.9 Million
Emp.: 13
N.A.I.C.S.: 541810

ZenithOptimedia (3)
4/F Zaragoza Building 102 Gamboa Street, Legaspi Village, Makati, 1227, Metro Manila, Philippines
Tel.: (63) 2 815 0871
Sales Range: $25-49.9 Million
N.A.I.C.S.: 541810

ZenithOptimedia AG (3)
Stadelhoferstrasse 25, 8001, Zurich, Switzerland
Tel.: (41) 43 499 21 21
Web Site: http://zenithmedia.ch
Sales Range: $10-24.9 Million
Advertising Services
N.A.I.C.S.: 541810

ZenithOptimedia Canada Inc. (3)
3530 St-laurent Boulevard Suite 400, Montreal, H2X 2V1, QC, Canada
Tel.: (416) 925-7277
Web Site: https://www.zenithmedia.com
Sales Range: $25-49.9 Million
N.A.I.C.S.: 541810

ZenithOptimedia Canada Inc. (3)
111 Queen St E Ste 200, Toronto, M5C 1S2, ON, Canada
Tel.: (416) 925-7277
Sales Range: $25-49.9 Million
Emp.: 90
N.A.I.C.S.: 541810

INTERNATIONAL PUBLIC

ZenithOptimedia India (3)
10th Floor Vatika Towers, Tower B, Sector 54, Gurgaon, 122002, Haryana, India
Tel.: (91) 124 4195 100
Sales Range: $10-24.9 Million
Emp.: 30
N.A.I.C.S.: 541810

ZenithOptimedia Interactive Direct (3)
Via vorsi 98, 20134, Milan, Italy
Tel.: (39) 02752991
Sales Range: $25-49.9 Million
Emp.: 5
N.A.I.C.S.: 541810

Zenithmedia Dusseldorf GmbH (1)
Toulouser Allee 1, 40211, Dusseldorf, Germany
Tel.: (49) 2115280999137
Marketing & Advertising Services
N.A.I.C.S.: 541810
Olivier Korte *(Mng Dir)*

PUBLIGAS

Ravensteingalerij 4 bus 2, 1000, Brussels, 1000, Belgium
Tel.: (32) 25483602
Web Site: http://www.publigas.be
Year Founded: 1996
Holding Company
N.A.I.C.S.: 551112

Subsidiaries:

Fluxys SA (1)
Avenue des Arts 31, B-1040, Brussels, Belgium (77.7%)
Tel.: (32) 2282 7211
Web Site: http://www.fluxys.com
Sales Range: $1-4.9 Billion
Holding Company; Natural Gas Transmission, Storage & Distribution Services
N.A.I.C.S.: 551112
Pascal De Buck *(CEO)*

Joint Venture (Non-US):

Dunkerque LNG SAS (2)
30 Rue Lhemitte Centre Tértiaire Des Trois Ponts, 59140, Dunkerque, France (30.39%)
Tel.: (33) 328241663
Web Site: http://dunkerquelng.com
Liquefied Natural Gas Terminal Operator
N.A.I.C.S.: 424710

Subsidiary (Non-US):

FluxSwiss SAGL (2)
Via della Posta 2, 6900, Lugano, Switzerland
Tel.: (41) 91 910 93 00
Natural Gas Pipeline Transportation Services
N.A.I.C.S.: 486210

Subsidiary (Domestic):

Fluxys Belgium SA (2)
Avenue des Arts 31, B-1040, Brussels, Belgium (89.97%)
Tel.: (32) 22827211
Web Site: http://www.fluxys.com
Rev.: $984,846,752
Assets: $3,676,419,167
Liabilities: $2,981,818,476
Net Worth: $694,600,691
Earnings: $90,360,458
Emp.: 784
Fiscal Year-end: 12/31/2022
Holding Company; Natural Gas Transmission, Storage & Terminal Operation Services
N.A.I.C.S.: 551112
Pascal De Buck *(CEO & Mng Dir)*

Subsidiary (Domestic):

Fluxys LNG SA (3)
Rue Guimard 4, 1040, Brussels, Belgium
Tel.: (32) 22827211
Web Site: http://www.fluxyslng.net
Sales Range: $75-99.9 Million
Emp.: 200
Natural Gas Terminal Operator
N.A.I.C.S.: 424710
Gontran Soumoy *(Mgr-Fin)*

AND PRIVATE COMPANIES

Subsidiary (Non-US):

Fluxys TENP GmbH (2)
Elisabethstrasse 11, 40217, Dusseldorf, Germany
Tel.: (49) 211 42 09 09 0
Natural Gas Pipeline Transportation Services
N.A.I.C.S.: 486210

Gas Management Services Limited (2)
Clarendon House, Clarendon Road, Cambridge, CB2 2BH, United Kingdom
Tel.: (44) 8456442724
Web Site: http://www.gmsl.co.uk
Sales Range: $50-74.9 Million
Emp.: 50
Natural Gas Operational Support Services
N.A.I.C.S.: 221210
George Wyth *(Gen Mgr)*

Subsidiary (Domestic):

Huberator SA (2)
Avenue des Arts 31, Brussels, 1040, Belgium
Tel.: (32) 25569897
Web Site: http://www.huberator.com
Natural Gas Hub Services
N.A.I.C.S.: 221210
Rudy Van Buerden *(Mng Dir)*

Subsidiary (Non-US):

Interconnector (UK) Limited (2)
4th Floor 10 Furnival Street, London, EC4A 1AB, United Kingdom **(76%)**
Tel.: (44) 20 3621 7800
Web Site: http://www.interconnector.com
Natural Gas Pipeline Transportation Services
N.A.I.C.S.: 486210
Danielle Stoves *(Mgr-Comml)*

PUBLISHER'S INTERNATIONALE
Level 1 97 Pacific Highway, North Sydney, 2060, NSW, Australia
Tel.: (61) 2 9252 3476
Web Site: http://www.pubintl.com.au
Year Founded: 1989
Sales Range: $25-49.9 Million
Emp.: 30
Media Representatives
N.A.I.C.S.: 541840
Charlton D'Silva *(CEO)*

PUBLITY AG
Bockenheimer Landstrasse 24, 60306, Frankfurt, Germany
Tel.: (49) 69695973500   De
Web Site: https://www.publity.org
Year Founded: 1999
PBY—(DEU)
Rev.: $7,583,619
Assets: $280,836,737
Liabilities: $131,460,426
Net Worth: $149,376,311
Earnings: ($261,474,777)
Emp.: 17
Fiscal Year-end: 12/31/23
Trust Management Services
N.A.I.C.S.: 541618
Thomas Olek *(Co-Founder & Member-Exec Bd)*

PUC BERHAD
C-2-01 Level 2 Capital 3 Oasis Square No 2 Jalan PJU 1A/7A, Ara Damansara, 47301, Petaling Jaya, Selangor Darul Ehsan, Malaysia
Tel.: (60) 327191018   MY
Web Site: https://www.puc.com
Year Founded: 1997
PUC—(KLS)
Rev.: $4,073,090
Assets: $38,323,814
Liabilities: $2,168,995
Net Worth: $36,154,819
Earnings: ($11,336,155)
Emp.: 80

Fiscal Year-end: 12/31/22
Investment Holding Services
N.A.I.C.S.: 551112
Chia Chou Cheong *(CEO-Grp & Mng Dir-Grp)*

Subsidiaries:

Enovax Pte. Ltd. (1)
33 Ubi Avenue 3 02-02/03 Vertex, Singapore, 408868, Singapore
Tel.: (65) 69081875
Web Site: https://www.enovax.com
Emp.: 30
Software Development Services
N.A.I.C.S.: 541511
Erwin Foo *(CEO & Chm)*

Greentech Malaysia Founder Sdn. Bhd. (1)
No 6 8 10 Jalan Bk 3/2 Bandar Kinrara, Puchong, 47100, Selangor, Malaysia
Tel.: (60) 380709933
Renewable Energy Services
N.A.I.C.S.: 221118

PUCARA GOLD LTD.
2110-650 West Georgia St, Vancouver, V6B 4N9, BC, Canada
Tel.: (604) 687-9931
Web Site: https://www.pucaragold.com
Year Founded: 2011
MML.P—(TSX)
Assets: $5,332,308
Liabilities: $611,131
Net Worth: $4,721,177
Earnings: ($4,311,256)
Fiscal Year-end: 12/31/20
Asset Management Services
N.A.I.C.S.: 541611

Subsidiaries:

Pucara Resources S.A.C. (1)
Av Dos de Mayo 1321, San Isidro, Lima, Peru
Tel.: (51) 1 448 1866
Mineral Exploration Services
N.A.I.C.S.: 213114

PUCCINI HOLDING GMBH
Karlstr 35, 80333, Munich, Germany
Tel.: (49) 89 444 5565 0
Web Site: http://www.puccini-group.de
Rev.: $707,900,000
Emp.: 2,600
Holding Company
N.A.I.C.S.: 551112
Georg Nolting-Hauff *(Chm-Mgmt Bd)*

Subsidiaries:

Elegance GmbH (1)
Lukasstrasse 10, 52070, Aachen, Germany
Tel.: (49) 241 43 90
Web Site: http://www.elegance.de
Sales Range: $75-99.9 Million
Emp.: 10
Clothing & Accessories Retailer, Mail Order & Electronic Shopping
N.A.I.C.S.: 458110
Silvia Leister *(Mng Dir)*

PUDA COAL, INC.
426 Xuefu Street, Taiyuan, Shanxi, China
Tel.: (86) 351 228 1302   DE
Year Founded: 2001
Coal Production
N.A.I.C.S.: 324199
Liping Zhu *(Pres & CEO)*

PUDITEC CO., LTD.
3 Soi Petchkasaem 77-4-13, Nongkangphlu Nongkam, Bangkok, 10160, Thailand
Tel.: (66) 21019494   TH
Web Site: http://www.puditec.com
Analytical Laboratory Instrument Mfr
N.A.I.C.S.: 334516

PUDO INC.
6600 Goreway Dr D, Mississauga, L4V 1S6, ON, Canada
Tel.: (905) 507-5232   ON
Web Site: https://pudopoint.com
Year Founded: 1945
PDPTF—(OTCQB)
Rev.: $2,999,300
Assets: $479,053
Liabilities: $445,219
Net Worth: $33,834
Earnings: ($256,441)
Fiscal Year-end: 02/28/23
Holding Company; Courier Services
N.A.I.C.S.: 551112
Frank Coccia *(Founder & CEO)*

Subsidiaries:

My Courier Depot Inc. (1)
400 Brunel Road, Mississauga, L4Z 2C2, ON, Canada
Web Site: http://www.mycourierdepot.com
Courier Service
N.A.I.C.S.: 492110
Frank Coccia *(CEO)*

PUEBLA RESOURCES CORP.
Apartada Postal 3-3, Pitillal, Jalisco, CP 48290, Mexico
Tel.: (52) 702 475 5278   NV
Year Founded: 2016
Mineral Exploration Services
N.A.I.C.S.: 213115
Alejandro Vargas *(Pres, CEO & CFO)*

PUEQU CO., LTD.
2-1-12 Minamizao-cho, Fukuyama, 721-0973, Japan
Tel.: (81) 849228551
Web Site: https://www.puequ.co.jp
9264—(TKS)
Rev.: $52,067,620
Assets: $71,262,540
Liabilities: $45,014,140
Net Worth: $26,248,400
Earnings: $1,872,220
Emp.: 263
Fiscal Year-end: 08/31/24
Air-Conditioning Equipment Mfr & Distr
N.A.I.C.S.: 333415

PUERTAS PUIG OLIVER, S.L.U.
Oscar Espla 14, E 03330, Crevillente, Alicante, Spain
Tel.: (34) 965406464
Web Site: http://www.luvipol.com
Year Founded: 1960
Sales Range: $25-49.9 Million
Emp.: 300
Internal & External Wooden Doors Mfr & Exporter
N.A.I.C.S.: 321911
Luis Puig Oliver *(Co-Founder)*

PUERTO VENTANAS S.A.
El Trovador 4253 2nd floor Las Condes, Santiago, Chile
Tel.: (56) 228372900
Web Site: https://www.puertoventanas.cl
Year Founded: 1966
VENTANAS—(SGO)
Sales Range: Less than $1 Million
Cargo Transportation Services
N.A.I.C.S.: 488310
Juan Eduardo Errazuriz Ossa *(Chm)*

PUHUI WEALTH INVESTMENT MANAGEMENT CO., LTD.
Room 801 802 8th Floor W1 Office Building, Oriental Commerce Tower No 1 Chang An Street Dong Cheng District, Beijing, 100006, China
Tel.: (86) 105 360 5158   Ky

Web Site: http://www.puhuiwealth.com
Year Founded: 2013
PHCF—(NASDAQ)
Rev.: $2,031,016
Assets: $8,429,465
Liabilities: $5,169,849
Net Worth: $3,259,616
Earnings: ($4,735,800)
Emp.: 40
Fiscal Year-end: 06/30/21
Wealth Investment Management Services
N.A.I.C.S.: 523940
Zhe Ji *(Founder, Chm & CEO)*

PUIG BRANDS S.A.
Puig Tower T1 46-48 Placa Europa, 08902, Barcelona, Spain
Tel.: (34) 934007000
Web Site: https://www.puig.com
PUIG—(MAD)
Rev.: $4,751,150,238
Assets: $8,512,294,956
Liabilities: $7,453,448,505
Net Worth: $1,058,846,451
Earnings: $551,813,666
Emp.: 9,612
Fiscal Year-end: 12/31/23
Fashion Brands & Perfume Products Retailers
N.A.I.C.S.: 456120

Subsidiaries:

Puig S.L. (1)
Plaza Europa 46/48, L Hospitalet de Llobregat, 08902, Barcelona, Spain
Tel.: (34) 934007000
Web Site: http://www.puig.com
Sales Range: $1-4.9 Billion
Emp.: 5,000
Perfume Cosmetic Toiletries Soap & Fashion Marketer Mfr
N.A.I.C.S.: 325620
Manuel Puig *(Vice Chm)*

Subsidiary (Domestic):

Antonio Puig, S.A. (2)
Plaza Europa 46 48 L Hospitalet de Llobregat, 08902, Barcelona, Spain
Tel.: (34) 934007000
Web Site: https://www.puig.com
Sales Range: $50-74.9 Million
Emp.: 600
Mfr of Toiletries
N.A.I.C.S.: 325620
Marc Puig *(Gen Mgr)*

Affiliate (US):

Carolina Herrera Ltd (2)
501 7th Ave, New York, NY 10018-5911
Tel.: (212) 944-5757
Web Site: https://www.carolinaherrera.com
Sales Range: $50-74.9 Million
Emp.: 125
Clothing Designer & Mfr & Cologne & Fragrance Distr
N.A.I.C.S.: 315250
Damion Nelson *(Supvr-Ops)*

Subsidiary (Non-US):

Parfums Nina Ricci (2)
55-57 Ave Des Champs Elysees, 92200, Paris, France **(100%)**
Tel.: (33) 17170454
Web Site: https://www.ninaricci.fr
Sales Range: $125-149.9 Million
Emp.: 300
Mfr of Perfumes & Cosmetics
N.A.I.C.S.: 325620

Puig Prestige Beauty (2)
6 Blvd Du Parc, Neuilly-sur-Seine, 92523, Neuilly Sur, France **(100%)**
Tel.: (33) 140884545
Web Site: https://www.pacorabanne.fr
Sales Range: $125-149.9 Million
Emp.: 300
Mfr of Perfumes & Fasion Accessories
N.A.I.C.S.: 325620

Puig Brands S.A.—(Continued)

PUJIANG INTERNATIONAL GROUP
Floor 16 518 Shancheng Road, Shanghai, 200120, China
Web Site: http://www.pji-group.com
2060—(SHG)
Bridge Cables & Prestressed Materials Mfr
N.A.I.C.S.: 335921
Liang Tang *(Chm)*

Subsidiaries:

Ossen Innovation Co. Ltd. (1)
518 Shangcheng Road Floor 17, Shanghai, 200120, China (100%)
Tel.: (86) 2168888886
Web Site: http://www.osseninnovation.com
Rev.: $138,577,870
Assets: $203,305,181
Liabilities: $52,193,902
Net Worth: $151,111,279
Earnings: $11,075,863
Emp.: 171
Fiscal Year-end: 12/31/2020
Prestressed Steel Materials Producer
N.A.I.C.S.: 332111
Liang Tang *(Chm)*

PULAI SPRINGS BERHAD
Pulai Springs Jalan1 PJS 5.30, Petaling Jaya Selatan, Petaling Jaya, 46150, Selangor, Malaysia
Tel.: (60) 377817220
Web Site: http://www.pulaigroup.com
Sales Range: $10-24.9 Million
Hospitality & Property Development Services
N.A.I.C.S.: 531312
Azmi Sharuddin *(Gen Mgr-Pulai Desaru Beach Resort & Spa)*

PULDIN HOLDING SA
No 176 Brezovsko shosse Str, Plovdiv, Bulgaria
Tel.: (359) 32953271
Web Site: https://www.puldinjsc.ideabg.com
Year Founded: 1996
Financial Services
N.A.I.C.S.: 523999
Georgi Staykov Stoychev *(Co-Chm & Exec Mgr)*

PULDIN PROPERTIES INVEST REIT
ul Vladimir Vazov 83, 1839, Sofia, Bulgaria
Tel.: (359) 9634461
Web Site: http://www.rodnazemya.bg
PLG—(BUL)
Sales Range: Less than $1 Million
Real Estate Investment Services
N.A.I.C.S.: 531210

PULIKE BIOLOGICAL ENGINEERING INC.
No 5 Lingbo Road HighTech Development Zone, Luoyang, 471025, Henan, China
Tel.: (86) 37969902166
Web Site: https://www.pulikeglobal.com
Year Founded: 1995
603566—(SHG)
Rev.: $172,413,517
Assets: $475,474,260
Liabilities: $82,565,000
Net Worth: $392,909,260
Earnings: $24,445,549
Fiscal Year-end: 12/31/22
Veterinary Biological Product Mfr & Distr
N.A.I.C.S.: 325414

Subsidiaries:

Luoyang Huizhong Animal Medicine Co., Ltd. (1)
No 15 Zhenghe Road, Luolong District, Luoyang, Henan, China
Tel.: (86) 37961123578
Web Site: http://www.huizhongsy.cn
Veterinary Medicine Mfr
N.A.I.C.S.: 325412

Luoyang Huizhong Biological Technology Co., Ltd. (1)
No 25 Yuwenkai Street, Luolong District, Luoyang, China
Tel.: (86) 69981188
Web Site: https://en.huizhongbio.com
Veterinary Biological Product Mfr
N.A.I.C.S.: 325414

Luoyang Huizhong Biotechnology Co., Ltd. (1)
Mudan dadao 18, Luolong Area, Luoyang, Henan, China
Tel.: (86) 37965610020
Web Site: http://www.en.huizhongbio.com
Biological Product Mfr
N.A.I.C.S.: 325414

PULMUONE CO., LTD.
280 Gwangpyeong-ro, Gangnam-gu, Seoul, Korea (South)
Tel.: (82) 80220085
Web Site: https://www.pulmuone.co.kr
Year Founded: 1984
017810—(KRS)
Rev.: $2,176,979,061
Assets: $1,571,750,018
Liabilities: $1,152,471,945
Net Worth: $419,278,073
Earnings: ($28,354,066)
Emp.: 507
Fiscal Year-end: 12/31/22
Holding Company; Food Mfr & Distr
N.A.I.C.S.: 551112
Seung-Woo Nam *(Chm)*

Subsidiaries:

Pulmuone Foods USA, Inc. (1)
2315 Moore Ave, Fullerton, CA 92833
Web Site: http://www.pulmuonefoodsusa.com
Food Products Mfr & Distr
N.A.I.C.S.: 311999
Jerry Henry *(Sls Dir-Organic Plant Based Protein)*

Subsidiary (Domestic):

Nasoya Food USA LLC (2)
1 New England Way, Ayer, MA 01432
Web Site: https://www.nasoya.com
Soy Products & Other Asian Style Foods Producer & Distr
N.A.I.C.S.: 424490
Ross Gatta *(CEO)*

Pulmuone Wildwood Inc. (2)
2315 Moore Ave, Fullerton, CA 92833
Tel.: (714) 578-2800
Rev.: $11,000,000
Emp.: 100
Tofu & Other Soy Products Mfr
N.A.I.C.S.: 424490
John Breen *(COO)*

Subsidiary (Domestic):

Monterey Gourmet Foods, Inc. (3)
1528 Moffett St, Salinas, CA 93905-3342
Tel.: (831) 753-6262
Web Site: http://www.montereygourmetfoods.com
Sales Range: $75-99.9 Million
Gourmet Pasta & Sauce Producer & Marketer
N.A.I.C.S.: 311824

PULOON TECHNOLOGY INC.
23-10 Hyoryeong-ro 60 gil, Seocho-gu, Seoul, 137-866, Korea (South)
Tel.: (82) 269594700
Web Site: https://www.puloon.co.kr
Year Founded: 1997
094940—(KRS)
Rev.: $26,141,603
Assets: $32,565,300
Liabilities: $7,561,078
Net Worth: $25,004,222
Earnings: $147,584
Emp.: 134
Fiscal Year-end: 12/31/22
Computer & Peripheral Equipment Mfr
N.A.I.C.S.: 334118
Hyun-Chul Ham *(Pres & CEO)*

Subsidiaries:

Puloon Technology Inc. - Chungju Factory (1)
46 Gieopdosi-ro Gageum-myeon, Chungju, 380-871, Chungcheongbuk-do, Korea (South)
Tel.: (82) 43 724 9126
Metal Plate Mfr
N.A.I.C.S.: 332999

Puloon Technology Inc. - Gasan Factory (1)
A-601 371-51 Gasan-dong, Geumcheon-gu, Seoul, Korea (South)
Tel.: (82) 2 6959 4300
Computer Peripheral Equipment Mfr
N.A.I.C.S.: 334118

PULSAR GROUP
The Johnson Building 79 Hatton Garden, London, EC1N 8AW, United Kingdom
Tel.: (44) 2034264070 UK
Web Site: https://www.pulsargroup.com
Year Founded: 2017
PULS—(AIM)
Rev.: $89,215,781
Assets: $130,986,037
Liabilities: $49,015,050
Net Worth: $81,970,987
Earnings: ($5,692,920)
Emp.: 1,077
Fiscal Year-end: 11/30/22
Software & Computer Services
N.A.I.C.S.: 541511
Joanna Arnold *(CEO)*

Subsidiaries:

Access Intelligence Media & Communications Ltd. (1)
3rd Floor Welken House 10-11 Charterhouse Square, London, EC1M 6EH, United Kingdom
Tel.: (44) 8436593480
Web Site: http://www.aimediacomms.com
Sales Range: $25-49.9 Million
Emp.: 20
Software Support Services
N.A.I.C.S.: 541511
Charlie O'Rourke *(Mng Dir)*

ResponseSource Ltd. (1)
The Johnson Building 79 Hatton Garden, London, EC1N 8AW, United Kingdom
Tel.: (44) 203 426 4007
Web Site: https://www.responsesource.com
Journalist Enquiry Services
N.A.I.C.S.: 516210

Solcara Limited (1)
The Long Rm Coppermill Lock, Harefield, UB9 6JA, Middlesex, United Kingdom
Tel.: (44) 1895820950
Web Site: http://www.solcara.com
Sales Range: $25-49.9 Million
Emp.: 15
Software Development Services
N.A.I.C.S.: 541511

iSentia Group Limited (1)
Level 3 219-241 Cleveland Street, Strawberry Hills, Sydney, 2012, NSW, Australia
Tel.: (61) 1300136806
Web Site: http://www.isentia.com
Rev.: $85,722,134
Assets: $99,055,305
Liabilities: $58,340,316
Net Worth: $40,714,989
Earnings: ($24,017,752)
Emp.: 1,200
Fiscal Year-end: 06/30/2019
Media Intelligence Services
N.A.I.C.S.: 519290
Francoise Dixon *(Dir-IR)*

Subsidiary (Non-US):

Isentia (M) Sdn. Bhd. (2)
Unit 27-1 Level 27 Tower A Vertical Business Suite Avenue 3, Bangsar South No 8 Jalan Kerinchi, 59200, Kuala Lumpur, Malaysia
Tel.: (60) 327301600
IT Services
N.A.I.C.S.: 541519

Isentia Limited (2)
Level 4 78 Victoria Street, Wellington, 6011, New Zealand
Tel.: (64) 800607000
IT Services
N.A.I.C.S.: 541519

Isentia Pte Limited (2)
72 Bendemeer Road 05-28 Luzerne, Singapore, 339941, Singapore
Tel.: (65) 65939888
IT Services
N.A.I.C.S.: 541519

Isentia Vietnam Co. Investment (2)
3rd Floor Robot Tower 308-308C Dien Bien Phu Street, District 3, Ho Chi Minh City, Vietnam
Tel.: (84) 2862638610
IT Services
N.A.I.C.S.: 541519

Subsidiary (Domestic):

King Content Pty Ltd (2)
534 Church St, Richmond, 3121, VIC, Australia
Tel.: (61) 1300766552
Web Site: http://www.kingcontent.com.au
Marketing & Advertising Services
N.A.I.C.S.: 541810
Robert Tadros *(Founder & CEO)*

Subsidiary (Non-US):

PT Isentia Jakarta (2)
Jagat Office Building Jl Tomang Raya No 28 Jatipulo Kec, Palmerah Kota Jakarta Barat Daerah Khusus Ibukota, Jakarta, 11430, Indonesia
Tel.: (62) 2150912188
IT Services
N.A.I.C.S.: 541519

PULSAR INTERNACIONAL S.A. DE C.V.
Colonia Valle del Campestre San Pedro, Avenida Roble 565 Oriente, Garza Garcia, 66265, NL, Mexico
Tel.: (52) 8183995600 MX
Web Site: http://www.pulsar.com.mx
Year Founded: 1981
Holding Company
N.A.I.C.S.: 551112
Alfonso Romo Garza *(Chm & CEO)*

Subsidiaries:

Bionova Holding Corporation (1)
Martin de Zavala 840 Mirador, Nuevo Leon, 64070, Mexico (80%)
Tel.: (52) 81 8343 3063
Sales Range: $25-49.9 Million
Emp.: 211
Developer of Plant Science Capabilities to Improve Quality & Agronomic Traits of Fruits & Vegetables
N.A.I.C.S.: 541715

Subsidiary (Domestic):

Agrobionova, S.A. de C.V. (2)
Km 9 Carretera A El Dorado, Culiacan, 80150, Mexico (98.6%)
Tel.: (52) 6677605001
Whlsr of Fruits & Vegetables
N.A.I.C.S.: 445230

Subsidiary (Domestic):

Comercialzadora Premier, S.A. de C.V. (3)
Avda Roble 565, Col Valle del Campestre, Garza Garcia, 66265, NL, Mexico (100%)
Tel.: (52) 8183995600
Whlsr of Fruits & Vegetables
N.A.I.C.S.: 445230

Subsidiary (US):

International Produce Holding Company (2)
4121 N 10th St Ste 284, McAllen, TX 78504 (100%)
Tel.: (956) 782-0926
Holding Company
N.A.I.C.S.: 445230

PULSAR INTERNATIONAL LIMITED
Adarsh Laxmi Building Officer No 3 Sai Babanagar Navghar Road, Bhayandar, Thane, 401101, Maharashtra, India
Tel.: (91) 2222660520
Web Site: https://pulsarinternational.com
512591—(BOM)
Rev.: $44,206
Assets: $613,488
Net Worth: $613,488
Earnings: $15,814
Emp.: 4
Fiscal Year-end: 03/31/23
Financial Services
N.A.I.C.S.: 523999
Mahesh Ratilal Shah *(Mng Dir)*

PULSE INVESTMENTS LIMITED
38a Trafalgar Road, Kingston, 10, Jamaica
Tel.: (876) 9681089
Web Site: https://www.pulseinvestments.com
PULS—(JAM)
Rev.: $6,206,233
Assets: $74,425,095
Liabilities: $15,105,226
Net Worth: $59,319,869
Earnings: $10,288,417
Fiscal Year-end: 06/30/23
Media Production Services
N.A.I.C.S.: 512110
Romae Gordon *(Sec)*

PULSE SEISMIC INC.
Suite 2700 421 7th Avenue SW, Calgary, T2P 4K9, AB, Canada
Tel.: (403) 237-5559 Ca
Web Site: https://www.pulseseismic.com
Year Founded: 1985
PSD—(OTCIQ)
Rev.: $38,449,062
Assets: $41,381,830
Net Worth: $34,530,621
Earnings: $16,829,972
Emp.: 16
Fiscal Year-end: 12/31/21
Oil & Gas Data Services
N.A.I.C.S.: 519290
Wayne McKinnon *(Mgr-Ops)*

PULSENMORE LTD.
8 Omarim St, Omer, Israel
Tel.: (972) 544499606
Web Site: https://www.pulsenmore.com
Year Founded: 2015
PULS—(TAE)
Rev.: $1,677,783
Assets: $48,779,350
Liabilities: $12,926,631
Net Worth: $35,852,719
Earnings: ($15,879,562)
Fiscal Year-end: 06/30/23
Medical Device Mfr & Distr
N.A.I.C.S.: 339112
Jonathan Adereth *(Chm)*

PULSTEC INDUSTRIAL CO LTD
7000-35 Nakagawa Hosoe-cho, Kita-ku, Hamamatsu, 4311304, Shizuoka, Japan
Tel.: (81) 535223611
Web Site: https://www.pulstec.co.jp
6894—(TKS)
Rev.: $17,265,320
Assets: $34,253,020
Liabilities: $9,967,880
Net Worth: $24,285,140
Earnings: $2,161,470
Emp.: 156
Fiscal Year-end: 03/31/24
Electronic Equipments Mfr & Sales
N.A.I.C.S.: 335312
Yukihiro Suzuki *(Pres & CEO)*

Subsidiaries:

Pulstec USA Inc. (1)
28175 Haggerty Rd Ste 140, Novi, MI 48377
Tel.: (310) 316-8185
Sales Range: $50-74.9 Million
Emp.: 2
Electronic Components Mfr
N.A.I.C.S.: 423690
Yukihiro Suzuki *(Pres)*

PULZ ELECTRONICS LTD.
Plot 10A Kailashpati Veera Desai Road Andheri W, Mumbai, 400 053, India
Tel.: (91) 2249702172
Web Site: https://www.pulz.co.in
PULZ—(NSE)
Rev.: $1,347,382
Assets: $2,647,330
Liabilities: $881,467
Net Worth: $1,765,864
Earnings: ($44,335)
Fiscal Year-end: 03/31/21
Electronic Components Mfr
N.A.I.C.S.: 334419

Subsidiaries:

R&S Electronics Systems India Private Limited (1)
Plot 10A Kailashpati Veera Desai Road, Andheri W, Mumbai, 400053, India
Tel.: (91) 2249702172
Web Site: https://www.rns.asia
Audio & Video Product Distr
N.A.I.C.S.: 423410

PUMA ALPHA VCT PLC
Cassini House 57 St Jamess Street, London, SW1A 1LD, United Kingdom
Tel.: (44) 2074084070 UK
Web Site: https://www.pumainvestments.co.uk
Year Founded: 2019
PUAL—(LSE)
Rev.: $5,508,270
Assets: $24,244,806
Liabilities: $887,949
Net Worth: $23,356,857
Earnings: $4,115,249
Fiscal Year-end: 02/28/22
Miscellaneous Financial Investment Activities
N.A.I.C.S.: 523999
Paul Frost *(Sec)*

PUMA EXPLORATION INC.
175 rue Legare, Rimouski, G5L 3B9, QC, Canada
Tel.: (418) 724-0901 AB
Web Site: https://www.explorationpuma.com
Year Founded: 2000
PUMXF—(OTCQB)
Assets: $10,338,183
Liabilities: $219,142
Net Worth: $10,119,041
Earnings: $951,081
Fiscal Year-end: 02/28/23
Exploratory Mining
N.A.I.C.S.: 212220
Marcel Robillard *(Chm, Pres & CEO)*

PUMA SE
Puma Way 1, 91074, Herzogenaurach, Germany
Tel.: (49) 9132810
Web Site: https://www.puma.com
Year Founded: 1948
PUMSY—(OTCIQ)
Rev.: $9,495,158,579
Assets: $7,330,138,348
Liabilities: $4,511,516,690
Net Worth: $2,818,621,658
Earnings: $336,569,963
Emp.: 18,023
Fiscal Year-end: 12/31/23
Athletic Apparel, Footwear, Athletic Equipment & Accessories Mfr
N.A.I.C.S.: 339920
Thore Ohlsson *(Deputy Chm)*

Subsidiaries:

Austria PUMA Dassler GmbH (1)
Siezenheimer Strasse 39A, Salzburg, 5020, Austria
Tel.: (49) 9132810
Web Site: https://il.puma.com
Sales Range: $50-74.9 Million
Emp.: 130
Sport Shoes, Bags & Clothing
N.A.I.C.S.: 424340
Martyn Bowen *(Gen Mgr)*

Cobra Golf Incorporated (1)
1818 Aston Ave, Carlsbad, CA 92008
Web Site: https://www.cobragolf.com
Sporting & Athletic Goods Mfr
N.A.I.C.S.: 339920

P.T. Puma Sports Indonesia (1)
Gedung Dea Tower II LT 5 Unit 503, Kawasan Mega Kuningan Jl Mega Kuningan Barat Kav E4 3 No 1-2, Jakarta Selatan, Indonesia
Tel.: (62) 8001401947
Web Site: https://id.puma.com
Sporting Goods & Equipment Mfr
N.A.I.C.S.: 339999

PUMA ASIA PACIFIC Ltd (1)
6/F Tower 2 The Gateway 25 Canton Rd, Tsim Sha Tsui, Kowloon, China (Hong Kong)
Tel.: (852) 39605200
Web Site: https://about.puma.com
Sports Goods Mfr
N.A.I.C.S.: 339920

PUMA BENELUX BV (1)
Plesmanstraat 4, 3833LA, Leusden, Netherlands
Tel.: (31) 334320060
Web Site: http://www.puma.com
Sales Range: $25-49.9 Million
Emp.: 5
Athletic Goods Mfr & Distr
N.A.I.C.S.: 339920

PUMA CANADA, Inc. (1)
165 Galaxy Blvd Suite 201, Toronto, M9W 0C8, ON, Canada
Tel.: (514) 738-9474
Web Site: https://ca.puma.com
Emp.: 100
Sports Goods Retailer
N.A.I.C.S.: 459110
Rich Benford *(Gen Mgr)*

PUMA CHINA LTD (1)
20F The Headquarters Building No168 Xi-Zang Road M, Shanghai, China
Tel.: (86) 2123306666
Web Site: https://about.puma.com
Sports Goods Mfr
N.A.I.C.S.: 339920

PUMA ITALIA S.R.L. (1)
Via Roggia Bartolomea 9, Assago, 20057, Milan, Italy
Tel.: (39) 0236013500
Sales Range: $25-49.9 Million
Emp.: 199
Sport Footwear Whslr
N.A.I.C.S.: 424340

PUMA KOREA Ltd (1)
6th Floor 100 Eulji-ro, Jung-gu, Seoul, Korea (South)
Tel.: (82) 800820888
Web Site: https://kr.puma.com
Footwear Product Distr
N.A.I.C.S.: 424340

PUMA NORWAY AS (1)
Rolfsbuktveien 4B, Fornebu, 1364, Norway
Tel.: (47) 67111140
Web Site: https://about.puma.com
Emp.: 24
Footwear & Apparel Mfr
N.A.I.C.S.: 315990

PUMA Sprint GmbH (1)
Wurzburger Str 13, Herzogenaurach, 91074, Germany
Tel.: (49) 0302238993
Web Site: https://eu.puma.com
Sales Range: $150-199.9 Million
Emp.: 800
Shoe Retailer
N.A.I.C.S.: 458210

PUMA TAIWAN SPORTS Ltd (1)
6F No 302 Ruiguang Rd, Neihu District, Taipei, 114, Taiwan
Tel.: (886) 7010123688
Footwear & Accessories Mfr & Distr
N.A.I.C.S.: 424340

PUMA UKRAINE LIMITED LIABILITY COMPANY (1)
str Bolsunovska, 13-15 BC IQ Business Center, Kiev, 01014, Ukraine
Tel.: (380) 800211948
Web Site: https://ua.puma.com
Sporting Goods Retailer
N.A.I.C.S.: 459110

PUMA-RUS o.o.o. (1)
Leningradskoe shosse 16 building 1 Metropolis Business Center, 125171, Moscow, Russia
Tel.: (7) 84957832552
Web Site: https://ru.puma.com
Sports Footwear Distr
N.A.I.C.S.: 424340

Puma Australia Pty. Ltd. (1)
111 Keys Road, Moorabbin, 3189, VIC, Australia
Tel.: (61) 345145262
Web Site: https://au.puma.com
Athletic Apparel & Footwear Mfr & Distr
N.A.I.C.S.: 339920

Puma Chile S.p.A. (1)
Av Kennedy 5454 Office 102, Vitacura, Santiago, Chile
Tel.: (56) 23696800
Web Site: https://cl.puma.com
Sport Footwear Mfr
N.A.I.C.S.: 424340

Puma Czech Republic s.r.o. (1)
Vyskocilova 1481/4 Michle, 140 00, Prague, Czech Republic
Tel.: (420) 225996011
Web Site: http://www.puma.com
Sports Goods Distr
N.A.I.C.S.: 459110

Puma Denmark AS (1)
Ankersgade 12E 1 th, 8000, Aarhus, Denmark
Tel.: (45) 86524100
Web Site: https://about.puma.com
Emp.: 34
Sporting Goods Distr
N.A.I.C.S.: 459110

Puma France SAS (1)
4A Pl Adrien Zeller, 67000, Strasbourg, France
Tel.: (33) 388653838
Web Site: https://us.puma.com
Emp.: 300
Sport Footwear Mfr & Distr
N.A.I.C.S.: 316210

Puma New Zealand Limited (1)
43 Bath Street Parnell, Auckland, 1052, New Zealand
Tel.: (64) 800447278
Web Site: https://nz.puma.com
Sport Footwear Whslr
N.A.I.C.S.: 424340

Puma Nordic AB (1)
Garnisonsgatan 51, 254 66, Helsingborg, Sweden
Tel.: (46) 42197100

PUMA SE

Puma SE—(Continued)
Web Site: http://www.puma.com
Footwear Whslr
N.A.I.C.S.: 424340

Puma North America, Inc. (1)
455 Grand Union Blvd, Somerville, MA 02145
Tel.: (978) 698-1000
Web Site: http://www.puma.com
Casual & Athletic Shoes Whslr
N.A.I.C.S.: 424340
Allison Giorgio *(VP-Mktg)*

Puma Polska Sp. z o.o. (1)
Burakowska 14, 01 066, Warsaw, Poland
Tel.: (48) 222330440
Web Site: http://www.puma.com
Sport Footwear Whslr
N.A.I.C.S.: 424340

Puma Retail AG (1)
Östringstrasse 17, Oensingen, 4702, Switzerland
Tel.: (41) 623963708
Web Site: http://about.puma.com
Sporting Goods Mfr & Distr
N.A.I.C.S.: 339920

Puma Sports Goods Sdn Bhd (1)
Menara Mustapha Kamal Block A Level 10 PJ Trade Centre, No 8 Jalan PJU 8/8A Bandar Damansara Perdana, 47820, Petaling Jaya, Selangor, Malaysia
Tel.: (60) 377260003
Web Site: https://my.puma.com
Sports Product Mfr
N.A.I.C.S.: 339920
Leow Chee Eng *(Head-Retail)*

Puma United Kingdom Ltd. (1)
70 Scalley Way, Rounds, NN9 6RJ, United Kingdom
Tel.: (44) 203326548
Web Site: http://www.puma.com
Sport Footwear
N.A.I.C.S.: 424340

Stichd Italy Srl (1)
Via Roggia Bartolomea 9, 20090, Assago, MI, Italy
Tel.: (39) 028261514
Web Site: https://stichd.com
Textile Products Distr
N.A.I.C.S.: 424310

Stichd Southeast Asia Sdn. Bhd. (1)
Penthouse Level Level 27 Centrepoint South Tower, Mid Valley City Lingkaran Syed Putra, 59200, Kuala Lumpur, Malaysia
Tel.: (60) 320969580
Apparel Mfr & Distr
N.A.I.C.S.: 315990

Stichd Trading (Shanghai) Co., Ltd. (1)
Room 03-05 19FL The Headquarters building 168 Xizang Middle Road, Shanghai, China
Tel.: (86) 236210406
Apparel Mfr & Distr
N.A.I.C.S.: 315990

stichd group B.V. (1)
De Waterman 2, 5215 MX, 's-Hertogenbosch, Netherlands
Tel.: (31) 736889393
Web Site: https://www.stichd.com
Emp.: 700
Textile Products Distr
N.A.I.C.S.: 424310
Esmee Brok *(Product Mgr)*

PUMACY TECHNOLOGIES AG
Liebknechtstrasse 24, 06406, Bernburg, Germany
Tel.: (49) 3471346390
Web Site: http://www.pumacy.de
Year Founded: 2000
Information Technology Services
N.A.I.C.S.: 541511
Toralf Kahlert *(Co-Chm)*

PUMPIRAN
Second Eskan Tower 1st Floor Mirdamad Junction Vali-EAsr Ave, Tehran, Iran
Tel.: (98) 21886548114
Web Site: https://www.pumpiran.co
Year Founded: 1973
PIRN1—(THE)
Sales Range: Less than $1 Million
Pump Product Mfr
N.A.I.C.S.: 333996

PUMTECH KOREA CO., LTD.
46 Bupyeong-daero 329 beon-gil, Bupyeong-Gu, Incheon, Korea (South)
Tel.: (82) 327247542
Web Site: https://www.pum-tech.co.kr
Year Founded: 2001
251970—(KRS)
Rev.: $181,505,184
Assets: $244,074,627
Liabilities: $46,374,444
Net Worth: $197,700,183
Earnings: $15,366,317
Emp.: 657
Fiscal Year-end: 12/31/22
Cosmetic Dispenser Mfr
N.A.I.C.S.: 327213
Kang-Seok Seo *(Gen Mgr)*

PUNAMUSTA MEDIA OYJ
Kosti Aaltosen Tie 9, 80141, Joensuu, 80141, Finland
Tel.: (358) 102308400
Web Site: https://www.pkkoyj.com
PUMU—(HEL)
Rev.: $144,118,282
Assets: $127,401,252
Liabilities: $86,455,860
Net Worth: $40,945,392
Earnings: ($5,816,965)
Emp.: 756
Fiscal Year-end: 12/31/22
Newspaper Printing & Publishing Services
N.A.I.C.S.: 323111

PUNCAK NIAGA HOLDINGS BERHAD
10th Floor Wisma Rozali No 4 Persiaran Sukan Seksyen 13, 40100, Shah Alam, Selangor Darul Ehsan, Malaysia
Tel.: (60) 355228428 MY
Web Site: https://www.puncakniaga.com.my
Year Founded: 1997
PUNCAK—(KLS)
Rev.: $46,757,249
Assets: $626,520,000
Liabilities: $347,742,222
Net Worth: $278,777,778
Earnings: ($4,070,053)
Emp.: 622
Fiscal Year-end: 12/31/22
Investment Holding Company; Water, Wastewater & Environmental Solutions
N.A.I.C.S.: 551112
Bee Lian Tan *(Sec & Exec Dir-Corp Svcs Div)*

Subsidiaries:

Puncak Niaga (M) Sdn. Bhd. (1)
Wisma Rozali No 4 Persiaran Sukan Seksyen 13, 40100, Shah Alam, Selangor Darul Ehsan, Malaysia (100%)
Tel.: (60) 3 5522 8589
Web Site: http://www.puncakniaga.com.my
Water Treatment Facilities Operator
N.A.I.C.S.: 221310

Puncak Niaga Infrastructures & Projects Private Limited (1)
No 12 1st Fl 9th main Rd Kasthuri Bai nagar Adayar, Mylapore, Chennai, 600020, Tamil Nadu, India (99.99%)
Tel.: (91) 44 4210 2058

Infrastructure Engineering & Construction Services
N.A.I.C.S.: 237990

Puncak Oil & Gas Sdn. Bhd. (1)
Unit 12-1 Level 12 No 11 Jalan 16/11, Pusat Dagang Seksyen 16, 46350, Petaling Jaya, Selangor Darul Ehsan, Malaysia (100%)
Tel.: (60) 3 7958 5533
Petroleum & Natural Gas Exploration, Development & Support Services
N.A.I.C.S.: 213112

Subsidiary (Domestic):

Global Offshore (Malaysia) Sdn. Bhd. (2)
Level 17 Tower 1 Etiqa Twin Towers, No 11 Jalan Pinang, Kuala Lumpur, 50450, Malaysia (100%)
Tel.: (60) 3 2166 0522
Offshore Oil & Gas Well & Pipeline Support Services
N.A.I.C.S.: 213112

KGL, Ltd. (2)
c/o Level 15(A1) Main Office Tower, Financial Park Labuan, Labuan, 87000, FT, Malaysia (100%)
Tel.: (60) 87443118
Petroleum & Gas Pipeline-Laying Barge Operator & Leasing Services
N.A.I.C.S.: 532411

Sino Water Pte. Ltd. (1)
80 Robinson Road 02-00, Singapore, 068898, Singapore (98.65%)
Tel.: (65) 6 236 3333
Web Site: http://www.sino-water.com.my
Emp.: 4,000
Holding Company; Water & Wastewater Services
N.A.I.C.S.: 551112
Danial Ariffin *(Chm)*

Subsidiary (Non-US):

Sino Water Environmental Consultancy (Shanghai) Co., Ltd. (2)
Unit 301 No 398 City Gateway Caoxi North Road, Xuhui District, Shanghai, 200030, China (100%)
Tel.: (86) 21 6090 5282
Water & Wastewater Project Consultancy Services
N.A.I.C.S.: 541620

Syarikat Bekalan Air Selangor Sdn. Bhd. (1)
Jalan Pantai Baharu, 59990, Kuala Lumpur, Malaysia (70%)
Tel.: (60) 320885400
Web Site: http://www.syabas.com.my
Treated Water Supply Distr
N.A.I.C.S.: 221310

TRIplc Berhad (1)
Wisma Rozali No 4 Persiaran Sukan Seksyen 13, 40100, Shah Alam, Selangor Darul Ehsan, Malaysia
Tel.: (60) 355228589
Web Site: https://www.triplc.com.my
Property Development Services
N.A.I.C.S.: 531312
Mohd Khalid Mohammed Yusuf *(COO)*

Subsidiary (Domestic):

Central Challenger (M) Sdn. Bhd. (2)
6 & 8 1st Floor Jalan Appolo SH U5/CH Bandar Pinggiran Subang, 40150, Shah Alam, Selangor, Malaysia
Tel.: (60) 378451011
Residential Property Development Services
N.A.I.C.S.: 531210

Insa Alliance Sdn. Bhd. (2)
PLO64 & PLO 65 Jln Kejuruteraan 4 Kaw Perindustrian Jln Genuang, 85000, Segamat, Johor, Malaysia
Tel.: (60) 79434585
Web Site: http://www.insa-alliance.com
Bulker Bags Mfr
N.A.I.C.S.: 314910

PUNCH INDUSTRY CO., LTD.
Omori Bellport E 5F 6-22-7 Minami-

INTERNATIONAL PUBLIC

oi, Shinagawa ku, Tokyo, 140-0013, Japan
Tel.: (81) 368938007
Web Site: https://www.punch.co.jp
Year Founded: 1975
6165—(TKS)
Rev.: $253,453,840
Assets: $195,979,890
Liabilities: $72,042,390
Net Worth: $123,937,500
Earnings: ($3,813,970)
Emp.: 3,575
Fiscal Year-end: 03/31/24
Mold & Die Components Mfr
N.A.I.C.S.: 333511
Yasuhiro Sanada *(Co-COO & Mng Exec Officer)*

Subsidiaries:

Cenel Development Corporation (1)
9A Valero Tower 122 Valero Street, Salcedo Village, Makati, Philippines
Tel.: (63) 2 810 9051
Web Site: https://www.cenelph.com
Plastic Mold Parts Distr
N.A.I.C.S.: 424610

Daewoong Engineering Co., Ltd. (1)
9 Saneom-ro, Ojeong-gu, Bucheon, Gyeonggi-do, Korea (South)
Tel.: (82) 32 682 6060
Web Site: https://www.daewoongeng.co.kr
Plastic Mold Parts Mfr & Distr
N.A.I.C.S.: 333511
Jung-Woo Cheong *(CEO)*

Hales Australia Pty. Ltd. (1)
45 Woodlands Drive, Braeside, 3195, VIC, Australia
Tel.: (61) 38 587 1600
Web Site: https://www.hales.com.au
Plastic Mold Parts Mfr & Distr
N.A.I.C.S.: 333511

Kansei Co., Ltd. (1)
3300/114-115 22nd Flr Elephant Tower B Phaholyothin Rd, Chomphon Chatuchak, Bangkok, 10900, Thailand
Tel.: (66) 29 373 3814
Web Site: https://www.kansei.co.th
Mold & Die Component Mfr & Distr
N.A.I.C.S.: 333511
Kuntalee Srinual *(Pres)*

PT Punch Industry Indonesia (1)
Komplek Griya Inti Sentosa Jl Griya Agung No 3, Sunter Agung, Jakarta, 14350, Indonesia
Tel.: (62) 216410730
Industrial Mold Distr
N.A.I.C.S.: 423830

PT.Somagede Indonesia (1)
Komplek Griya Inti Sentosa Jl Griya Agung Blok M No 3, Sunter Agung, Jakarta Utara, 14350, Indonesia
Tel.: (62) 21 641 0730
Web Site: https://www.somagede.com
Machining Product Distr
N.A.I.C.S.: 423830

PUNCH INDUSTRY (Dalian) CO., LTD (1)
No 5 Jinzhou Street Dalian Economy and Technology Development Zone, Dalian, Liaoning, China
Tel.: (86) 41187613087
Web Site: https://enlink.punch.com.cn
Industrial Mold Distr
N.A.I.C.S.: 423830

PUNCH INDUSTRY (Dongguan) CO., LTD. (1)
No 5 Yongji Road, Yongtou Village Chang'an Town, Dongguan, Guangdong, China
Tel.: (86) 76985070387
Industrial Mold Distr
N.A.I.C.S.: 423830

PUNCH INDUSTRY INDIA PVT. LTD. (1)
No 97/A-1 SIDCO Nagar 4th Street, Villivakkam, Chennai, 600 049, India
Tel.: (91) 4442699644
Industrial Mold Distr
N.A.I.C.S.: 423830

AND PRIVATE COMPANIES

PUNCH INDUSTRY SINGAPORE PTE. LTD. (1)
33 Ubi Avenue 3 06-10 Vertex Lobby B, Singapore, 408868, Singapore
Tel.: (65) 65334151
Industrial Mold Distr
N.A.I.C.S.: 423830
Jessie Peck (Mgr-Sls)

PUNCH INDUSTRY VIETNAM CO. LTD. (1)
8th Floor PTS Office Building 118 Huynh Tan Phat Street, Tan Thuan Tay ward District 7, Ho Chi Minh City, Vietnam
Tel.: (84) 2838720087
Industrial Mold Distr
N.A.I.C.S.: 423830

Pintec Corporation (1)
2-2-26 Zao Matsugaoka, Yamagata, 990-2338, Japan
Tel.: (81) 236881770
Web Site: https://www.pintec.co.jp
Emp.: 80
Printed Circuit Board Mold-Related Parts Mfr
N.A.I.C.S.: 334418
Koichi Koga (CEO)

Punch Industry (Wafangdian) Co., Ltd. (1)
No 153 North Gongji Street, Dalian Wafangdian, Wafangdian, Liaoning, China
Tel.: (86) 41185508785
Industrial Mold Distr
N.A.I.C.S.: 423830

Punch Industry (Wuxi) Co., Ltd. (1)
Building 2 No 77 South Tongyun Road, Xishan Economy and Technology Development Zone, Wuxi, Jiangsu, China
Tel.: (86) 51088264838
Web Site: http://www.punch.co.jp
Industrial Mold Distr
N.A.I.C.S.: 423830

Punch Industry Co., Ltd. - Hyogo Plant (1)
922-202 Aza-Higashihata, Tsuneyoshi-cho, Kasai, 679-2102, Hyogo, Japan
Tel.: (81) 790 47 8077
Web Site: http://www.punch.co.jp
Emp.: 100
Industrial Mold Mfr
N.A.I.C.S.: 333511
Kenji Haga (Mgr)

Punch Industry Co., Ltd. - Kitakami Plant (1)
21-26-17 Murasakino, Kitakami, 024-0004, Iwate, Japan
Tel.: (81) 197683087
Industrial Mold Mfr
N.A.I.C.S.: 333511

Punch Industry Co., Ltd. - Miyako Plant (1)
29-1 Matsuyama, Matsuyama, Miyako, 027-0037, Iwate, Japan
Tel.: (81) 193628007
Industrial Mold Mfr
N.A.I.C.S.: 333511

Punch Industry Malaysia Sdn. Bhd. (1)
Nagasari Industrial Park No 3061 Jalan Nagasari1 Prai Industry Zone, 13600, Prai, Penang, Malaysia
Tel.: (60) 43984826
Industrial Mold Distr
N.A.I.C.S.: 423830

Punch Industry Manufacturing Vietnam Co., Ltd. (1)
Lot B 6E1 CN, My Phuoc 3 Industrial Park Thoi Hoa ward, Ben Cat, Binh Duong, Vietnam
Tel.: (84) 274 380 3100
Mold & Die Component Mfr
N.A.I.C.S.: 333511

Punch Industry USA Inc. (1)
1055 Hawthorn Dr, Itasca, IL 60143
Tel.: (630) 625-8080
Mold & Die Component Distr
N.A.I.C.S.: 423830

RSH GmbH (1)
Bretonischer Ring 11, 85630, Grasbrunn, Germany
Tel.: (49) 89 452 2070
Web Site: https://www.rsh-gmbh.de
Motor Vehicle Parts Distr
N.A.I.C.S.: 423120

PUNCH PUNK SA
Al Tadeusza Kosciuszki 80/82 lok 301, 90-437, Lodz, Poland
Tel.: (48) 514340927
Year Founded: 2011
PPG—(WAR)
Software Development Services
N.A.I.C.S.: 541511

PUNCTUAL TRADING LIMITED
411 Floor-4 Plot-207 Embassy Centre Jamnalal Bajaj Marg, Nariman Point, Mumbai, 400021, Maharashtra, India
Tel.: (91) 2261155300 In
Web Site: https://punctualtrading.com
Year Founded: 1986
512461—(BOM)
Rev.: $107,288
Assets: $1,930,009
Liabilities: $121,550
Net Worth: $1,808,459
Earnings: $10,228
Emp.: 3
Fiscal Year-end: 03/31/21
Financial Investment Services
N.A.I.C.S.: 523999
Sonia Omprakash Chhajer (Sec)

PUNE STOCK EXCHANGE LIMITED
Shivleela Chambers 1st Floor, 752 Sadashiv Peth, RB Kumathekar Marg, Pune, 411030, India
Tel.: (91) 20 244 600 84
Stock Exchange Services
N.A.I.C.S.: 523210
S. L. Joshi (Chm)

PUNGGUK ALCOHOL INDUSTRIAL CO., LTD
72 Seongseo-ro, Dalseo-Gu, Daegu, Korea (South)
Tel.: (82) 535832071
Web Site: http://www.punggguk.com
Year Founded: 1953
023900—(KRS)
Rev.: $118,109,146
Assets: $146,309,417
Liabilities: $18,810,400
Net Worth: $127,499,016
Earnings: $4,203,046
Emp.: 59
Fiscal Year-end: 12/31/22
Ethyl Alcohol Mfr
N.A.I.C.S.: 325193

Subsidiaries:

Hwashin Chemical Co., Ltd (1)
15-42 Bonsan 2-ro, Jinyeong-eup, Kimhae, Gyeongnam, Korea (South)
Tel.: (82) 55 342 5447
Web Site: http://www.hwasinchem.com
Specialty Chemicals Distr
N.A.I.C.S.: 424690

SUNDO Industrial Co., Ltd. (1)
618 Bongeunsa-ro, Gangnam-gu, Seoul, Korea (South)
Tel.: (82) 220582611
Web Site: http://www.sundoind.co.kr
Industrial Gas Mfr & Distr
N.A.I.C.S.: 325120
Seong-cheol Lee (CEO)

PUNGKANG CO., LTD
745 Namyangman-ro Ujeong-eup, Hwaseong, Gyeonggi-do, Korea (South)
Tel.: (82) 313593600
Web Site: https://pungkang.com
Year Founded: 1974
093380—(KRS)
Rev.: $72,237,710
Assets: $67,541,959
Liabilities: $13,084,565
Net Worth: $54,457,394
Earnings: $4,175,152
Emp.: 249
Fiscal Year-end: 08/31/23
Automobile Parts Mfr
N.A.I.C.S.: 332722

Subsidiaries:

PK Mechatronic Co., Ltd. (1)
745 Namyangman-ro, Ujeong-eup, Hwaseong, 18572, Gyeonggi-do, Korea (South)
Tel.: (82) 313583610
Automation Equipment Mfr
N.A.I.C.S.: 333998

SPM AUTO PARTS S.A. de C.V. (1)
Av International No 240, Vynmsa Escobedo Industrial Park, CP66053, Escobedo, Mexico
Tel.: (52) 18186472775
Web Site: https://www.spmautoparts.com
Automotive Nuts & Bolts Mfr
N.A.I.C.S.: 332722

PUNIT COMMERCIALS LIMITED
AW 2022 Bharat Diamond Bourse, Bandra Kurla complex Bandra East, Mumbai, 400 051, India
Tel.: (91) 2242106999
Web Site: https://www.punitcommercials.com
Year Founded: 1984
512099—(BOM)
Rev.: $596,007
Assets: $341,658
Liabilities: $90,426
Net Worth: $251,232
Earnings: $62,910
Emp.: 4
Fiscal Year-end: 03/31/23
Diamond Product Mfr & Distr
N.A.I.C.S.: 339910
Nirav P. Mehta (Chm & Mng Dir)

PUNJ LLOYD LTD.
78 Institutional Area Sector 32, Gurgaon, 122 001, India
Tel.: (91) 1242620123 In
Web Site: https://www.punjlloydgroup.com
532693—(BOM)
Engineering & Construction
N.A.I.C.S.: 541330
Atul Punj (Chm & Mng Dir)

Subsidiaries:

Construction Technology Pte Ltd (1)
107 Bukit Batok West Avenue 3, 659167, Singapore, Singapore
Tel.: (65) 65673647
Precast Material Mfr
N.A.I.C.S.: 327390

Jurubina Sembawang (M) Sdn Bhd (1)
Suite 1006 10 Floor Menara Amcorp, 46200, Petaling Jaya, Selangor, Malaysia
Tel.: (60) 379555293
Construction Engineering Services
N.A.I.C.S.: 541330

PL Engineering Limited (1)
95 Institutional Area Sector 32, Gurgaon, 122 001, Haryana, India
Tel.: (91) 1242620769
Construction Engineering Services
N.A.I.C.S.: 541330

PLN Construction Ltd (1)
Corporate Office II 95 Institutional Area Sector 32, Gurgaon, 122001, Haryana, India
Tel.: (91) 1242620769
Web Site: http://www.punjlloyd.com
Emp.: 400
Construction Engineering Services
N.A.I.C.S.: 213111
Raman Chadha (Mgr-Mktg)

PT Punj Lloyd Indonesia (1)
Wisma GKBI 17th Floor Suite 1708 Jl Jend Sudirman No 28, 10210, Jakarta, Indonesia
Tel.: (62) 21 5785 1944
Construction Engineering Services
N.A.I.C.S.: 541330

PT Sempec Indonesia (1)
Wisma GKBI 17 Floor Suite 1209 Jl Jend Sudirman No 28, 10210, Jakarta, Indonesia
Tel.: (62) 215741128
Emp.: 50
Construction Engineering Services
N.A.I.C.S.: 541330

Punj Lloyd Construction Contracting Company Limited (1)
Tanami Tower 8th Floor Prince Turki Street Near Corniche, PO Box 31909, Al Khobar, 31952, Saudi Arabia
Tel.: (966) 38969241
Construction Engineering Services
N.A.I.C.S.: 541330

Punj Lloyd Delta Renewables Pvt Ltd (1)
Corporate Office I 78 Institutional Area Sector 32, 122001, Gurgaon, Haryana, India
Tel.: (91) 1242620123
Sales Range: $25-49.9 Million
Emp.: 52
Construction Engineering Services
N.A.I.C.S.: 541330
J. P. Chalanas (Mgr-Production)

Punj Lloyd Kazakhstan LLP (1)
Plot No 7 A Atyrau Dossor Highway, DSK Area, Atyrau, 060000, Kazakhstan
Tel.: (7) 7122395021
Web Site: http://www.punjlloyd.com
Emp.: 30
Construction Engineering Services
N.A.I.C.S.: 541330
Amit Jain (Mng Dir)

Punj Lloyd Pte Ltd (1)
60 Alexandra Terrace 09-01, 118 502, Singapore, Singapore
Tel.: (65) 6309 9040
Construction Engineering Services
N.A.I.C.S.: 237120

Punjlloyd Oil & Gas (Malaysia) Sdn. Bhd. (1)
Lot No 6 05 Level 6 KPMG Tower 8 First Avenue, Bandar Utma, 47800, Petaling Jaya, Selangor, Malaysia
Tel.: (60) 79555293
Construction Engineering Services
N.A.I.C.S.: 541330

Sembawang (Tianjin) Construction Engineering Co Ltd (1)
Unit 1106 The Exchange 189 Nanjing Road, Helping District, 300051, Tianjin, China
Tel.: (86) 22 8319 1198
Web Site: http://www.sembawangenc.com
Construction Engineering Services
N.A.I.C.S.: 541330

Sembawang Engineers and Constructors Middle East FZE (1)
Unit 251 Lob 15 Jebel Air Free Zone, Sheikh Zayed Road, Dubai, United Arab Emirates
Tel.: (971) 4 8815 165
Web Site: http://www.sembawangenc.com
Sales Range: $25-49.9 Million
Emp.: 4
Construction Engineering Services
N.A.I.C.S.: 541330

Sembawang Engineers and Constructors Pte Ltd. (1)
AXA Tower 8 Shenton Way 50-01, Singapore, 068811, Singapore
Tel.: (65) 67095604
Web Site: http://www.sembawangenc.com
Construction Engineering Services
N.A.I.C.S.: 541330
Chuan Ooi Hock (VP-Contracts)

Sembawang UAE Pte Ltd. (1)
501-504 Al Gaith Tower Hamdan Street, PO Box 28907, Abu Dhabi, 17188, United Arab Emirates
Tel.: (971) 48815165
Web Site: http://www.sembawangenc.com
Sales Range: $25-49.9 Million
Emp.: 15
Construction Engineering Services

PUNJ LLOYD LTD.

Punj Lloyd Ltd.—(Continued)
N.A.I.C.S.: 237130
Mohamed Arafa (Gen Mgr)

PUNJAB & SIND BANK
21 Rajendra Place, New Delhi, 110008, India
Tel.: (91) 1125720849
Web Site:
 https://www.punjabsindbank.com
Year Founded: 1908
PSB—(BOM)
Rev.: $1,099,533,271
Assets: $16,525,720,084
Liabilities: $671,572,233
Net Worth: $15,854,147,850
Earnings: $141,830,953
Emp.: 8,725
Fiscal Year-end: 03/31/22
Banking Services
N.A.I.C.S.: 522110
Fareed Ahmed (Exec Dir)

PUNJAB ALKALIES & CHEMICALS LIMITED.
SCO 125-127 Sector 17-B, Chandigarh, 160 017, India
Tel.: (91) 1724072543
Web Site: https://primochemicals.in
Year Founded: 1975
506852—(BOM)
Rev.: $38,415,809
Assets: $33,537,982
Liabilities: $20,347,577
Net Worth: $13,190,405
Earnings: $1,124,310
Emp.: 338
Fiscal Year-end: 03/31/21
Industrial Chemicals Mfr
N.A.I.C.S.: 325998
Sugandha Kukreja (Compliance Officer & Sec)

PUNJAB CHEMICALS & CROP PROTECTION LIMITED
Oberoi Chambers II 5th Floor 645/646 New Link Road, Andheri West, Mumbai, 400053, India
Tel.: (91) 2226747900
Web Site:
 https://www.punjabchemicals.com
Year Founded: 1975
506618—(BOM)
Rev.: $127,544,235
Assets: $76,065,990
Liabilities: $45,268,860
Net Worth: $30,797,130
Earnings: $11,392,290
Emp.: 1,213
Fiscal Year-end: 03/31/22
Chemical Products Mfr
N.A.I.C.S.: 325998
Shalil Shashikumar Shroff (Mng Dir)

Subsidiaries:

Agrichem B.V (1)
Industrial Area Weststad Koopvaardijweg 9, 4906 CV, Oosterhout, Netherlands
Tel.: (31) 162431931
Web Site: http://www.uplbenelux.nl
Emp.: 45
Crop Protection Chemical Mfr
N.A.I.C.S.: 325320
Jeroen Coorbraak (Gen Mgr)

Agrichem Helvetia GmbH (1)
Alpenstrasse 15, Zug, Switzerland
Tel.: (41) 417268200
Specialty Chemicals Mfr
N.A.I.C.S.: 325998

Punjab Chemicals & Crop Protection Limited - Excel Phospho Chem Unit (1)
Site No I & II HA Ltd Compound Pimpri, Pune, 400 018, India
Tel.: (91) 20 27425647
Industrial Chemicals Mfr
N.A.I.C.S.: 325998

Punjab Chemicals & Crop Protection Limited - Pharma Division (1)
Alpha Drug village Kolimajra & Samalheri Po Lalru Distt, Lalru Distt, Mohali, 140 501, Punjab, India
Tel.: (91) 1762 275519
Web Site: http://www.punjabchemicals.com
Sales Range: $50-74.9 Million
Emp.: 200
Pharmaceuticals Product Mfr
N.A.I.C.S.: 325412
Jain Prakash (Sr VP)

PUNJAB COMMUNICATIONS LIMITED
B-91 Phase-VIII Industrial Area SAS Nagar, Chandigarh, 160 071, India
Tel.: (91) 1722237101
Web Site: https://www.puncom.com
500346—(BOM)
Rev.: $2,231,581
Assets: $9,466,267
Liabilities: $7,231,197
Net Worth: $2,235,070
Earnings: ($1,873,341)
Emp.: 153
Fiscal Year-end: 03/31/23
Communication Equipment Mfr & Distr
N.A.I.C.S.: 334290
Alok Shekhar (Chm)

PUNJAB NATIONAL BANK
Plot No 4 Sector -10 Dwarka, New Delhi, 110075, India
Tel.: (91) 18001800
Web Site: https://www.pnbindia.in
Year Founded: 1859
532461—(BOM)
Rev.: $11,879,968,827
Assets: $179,083,860,680
Liabilities: $166,748,808,824
Net Worth: $12,335,051,855
Earnings: $705,831,785
Emp.: 104,120
Fiscal Year-end: 03/31/23
Commercial Banking Services
N.A.I.C.S.: 522110
Agyey Kumar Azad (Exec Dir)

Subsidiaries:

JSC Tengri Bank (1)
Abay Ave 42 1st Floor, 050000, Almaty, Kazakhstan
Tel.: (7) 727 244 3434
Web Site: http://www.tengribank.kz
Banking Services
N.A.I.C.S.: 522110

PNB Gilts Ltd. (1)
5 Sansad Marg, New Delhi, 110001, India
Tel.: (91) 1123325759
Web Site: https://www.pnbgilts.com
Rev.: $143,635,401
Assets: $1,657,066,811
Liabilities: $1,477,381,979
Net Worth: $179,684,833
Earnings: $61,986,943
Emp.: 41
Fiscal Year-end: 03/31/2021
Brokerage Services
N.A.I.C.S.: 523150
Vikas Goel (CEO, CEO, Mng Dir & Mng Dir)

PNB Housing Finance Ltd. (1)
9th Floor Antriksh Bhavan 22 Kasturba Gandhi Marg, Near Connaught Place, 110001, New Delhi, 110001, India
Tel.: (91) 1123445200
Web Site: https://www.pnbhousing.com
Rev.: $846,399,645
Assets: $8,972,091,765
Liabilities: $7,624,614,270
Net Worth: $1,347,477,495
Earnings: $114,179,520
Emp.: 1,549
Fiscal Year-end: 03/31/2022
Investment Banking & Securities Dealing
N.A.I.C.S.: 523150
Sanjay Jain (Compliance Officer, Sec & Head-Compliance)

PNB International Ltd (1)
1 Moorgate, London, EC2R 6JH, United Kingdom
Tel.: (44) 8008499229
Web Site: https://www.pnbint.com
Rev.: $46,348,000
Assets: $1,061,590,000
Liabilities: $844,721,000
Net Worth: $216,869,000
Earnings: $8,318,000
Emp.: 148
Fiscal Year-end: 03/31/2019
Commercial Banking Services
N.A.I.C.S.: 523150
Atul Kumar Goel (Mng Dir)

PNB Investment Services Ltd (1)
10 Rakeshdeep Bulding Yusuf Sarai Commercial Complex, Gulmohar Enclave, New Delhi, 110049, India
Tel.: (91) 1149495050
Web Site: http://www.pnbisl.com
Banking Services
N.A.I.C.S.: 522110
K. R. Kamath (Chm)

United Bank of India (1)
11 Hemanta Basu Sarani, Kolkata, 700 001, India
Tel.: (91) 3322487472
Web Site: http://www.unitedbankofindia.com
Sales Range: $1-4.9 Billion
Banking Services
N.A.I.C.S.: 522110
Sunanda Basu (Gen Mgr-Premises, Branch Expansion/Consolidation & Stationery Dep)

PUNJAB OIL MILLS LIMITED
19-A/1 Block E-II Gulberg III, Lahore, Pakistan
Tel.: (92) 4235761585
Web Site:
 https://www.punjaboilmills.com
Year Founded: 1983
POML—(PSX)
Rev.: $39,520,345
Assets: $15,786,086
Liabilities: $6,864,987
Net Worth: $8,921,099
Earnings: $770,973
Emp.: 239
Fiscal Year-end: 06/30/19
Edible Oil Mfr
N.A.I.C.S.: 311225
Izaz Ilahi Malik (CEO & Mng Dir)

PUNTER SOUTHALL GROUP LIMITED
11 Strand, London, WC2N 5HR, United Kingdom
Tel.: (44) 20 3327 5000 UK
Web Site:
 http://www.puntersouthall.com
Year Founded: 1988
Holding Company; Actuarial, Benefits & Investment Consulting Services; Pension Administration Services
N.A.I.C.S.: 551112
Jonathan Punter (Co-Founder & CEO)

Subsidiaries:

CAMRADATA Analytical Services Ltd (1)
Marlow House Lloyd's Avenue, London, EC3N 3AA, United Kingdom
Tel.: (44) 2033275600
Web Site: http://www.camradata.com
Data Processing Services
N.A.I.C.S.: 518210
Martin Hughes (Mng Dir)

PS Independent Trustees Limited (1)
1 Colmore Row, Birmingham, B3 2BJ, United Kingdom
Tel.: (44) 1212301900
Web Site: http://www.psitl.com
Pensoin Management Services
N.A.I.C.S.: 523940
Ann Geer (Mgr-Schene)

INTERNATIONAL PUBLIC

Psigma Investment Management Limited (1)
6th Floor 1 Colmore Row, Birmingham, B3 2BJ, United Kingdom
Tel.: (44) 1212301937
Web Site: http://www.psigma.com
Investment Management Service
N.A.I.C.S.: 523940
Adam Side (Mng Dir)

Punter Southall Financial Management Ltd (1)
1st Floor 7 Castle Street, Edinburgh, EH2 3AH, United Kingdom
Tel.: (44) 1312300300
Web Site: http://www.psfm.com
Financial Consulting Services
N.A.I.C.S.: 541611
Geoff Tressman (Chm)

Punter Southall Health & Protection Consulting Limited (1)
11 Strand, London, WC2N 5 HR, United Kingdom
Tel.: (44) 20 3327 5700
Employee Healthcare & Protection Insurance Services
N.A.I.C.S.: 523940
John Dean (Mng Dir)

Subsidiary (Domestic):

The Private Health Partnership Ltd (2)
Butterfield Park, Otley Road, Bradford, BD17 7HE, West Yorkshire, United Kingdom
Tel.: (44) 1274588862
Web Site: http://www.php.co.uk
Emp.: 75
Direct Health & Medical Insurance Carriers
N.A.I.C.S.: 524114
Jan Lawson (Exec Dir)

PUNTO APARTE
Calle 54 Ave Ricardo Arango Ovarrio, Zona 1, Panama, Panama
Tel.: (507) 2692133 Pa
Web Site:
 http://www.puntoaparte.com
Year Founded: 1991
Sales Range: $25-49.9 Million
Emp.: 25
Full Service
N.A.I.C.S.: 541810
Stephan Proano (CEO)

PUPIN TELECOM AD
Batajnicki put 23 Zemun, 11080, Belgrade, Zemun, Serbia
Tel.: (381) 11 3070 500
Web Site:
 http://www.pupintelecom.co.rs
Year Founded: 1947
PTLK—(BEL)
Sales Range: Less than $1 Million
Telecommunications Equipment Mfr
N.A.I.C.S.: 339999
Vladimir Lazovic (Gen Dir & Member-Exec Bd)

PURABI GENERAL INSURANCE COMPANY LIMITED
Sandhani Life Tower 2nd Floor 34 Banglamotor, Dhaka, 1000, Bangladesh
Tel.: (880) 1714044146
Web Site:
 https://www.purabiinsurance.org
Year Founded: 1988
PURABIGEN—(DHA)
Rev.: $998,054
Assets: $13,257,622
Liabilities: $6,924,975
Net Worth: $6,332,646
Earnings: $940,830
Emp.: 62
Fiscal Year-end: 12/31/23
Insurance Agency Services
N.A.I.C.S.: 524210

PURAPHARM CORPORATION LIMITED
Romm 201 207 2nd Fl Wireless Centre Phase One, Hong Kong Science Park, Tai Po, Pak Shek Kok, China (Hong Kong)
Tel.: (852) 28401840 Ky
Web Site: http://www.purapharm.com
Year Founded: 2015
1498—(HKG)
Rev.: $57,128,798
Assets: $129,603,368
Liabilities: $96,671,520
Net Worth: $32,931,848
Earnings: ($15,327,285)
Emp.: 663
Fiscal Year-end: 12/31/22
Pharmaceutical Product Mfr & Distr
N.A.I.C.S.: 325412
Abraham Yu Ling Chan *(Founder, Chm & CEO)*

Subsidiaries:

Kan Herb Company, Inc. (1)
380 Encinal St Ste 100, Santa Cruz, CA 95060
Tel.: (831) 438-9450
Web Site: http://www.kanherb.com
Herbal Product Mfr & Distr
N.A.I.C.S.: 325412

Nong's Healthcare 16 Limited (1)
Plaza 168, Sheung Wan, China (Hong Kong)
Tel.: (852) 24550900
Medical Diagnostic Services
N.A.I.C.S.: 621511

PuraPharm Australia Pty Ltd (1)
Suite 1 Level 2 75 Elizabeth Street, Sydney, 2000, NSW, Australia
Tel.: (61) 283206196
Healthcare Product Distr
N.A.I.C.S.: 424210

PuraPharm Canada Corporation (1)
Suite 303 80 Acadia Ave, Markham, L3R 9V1, ON, Canada
Tel.: (905) 881-4299
Healthcare Product Distr
N.A.I.C.S.: 424210

PuraPharm Japan Corporation (1)
Room 406 4th Fl Joho Bldg Takata-527, Toyama, 930-0866, Japan
Tel.: (81) 764321101
Medical Product Research & Development Services
N.A.I.C.S.: 541715
Norimoto Hisayoshi *(Chief R&D Officer & Gen Mgr)*

SODX Co., Ltd. (1)
1-3-14 Techno Stage, Izumi, 594-1144, Osaka, Japan
Tel.: (81) 725531100
Web Site: https://www.sodx.co.jp
Healthy Food Mfr
N.A.I.C.S.: 311999

PURAVANKARA LTD.
130/1 Ulsoor Road, Bengaluru, 560 042, India
Tel.: (91) 8025599000
Web Site:
https://www.puravankara.com
Year Founded: 1975
532891—(BOM)
Rev.: $143,845,065
Assets: $1,152,323,445
Liabilities: $891,749,040
Net Worth: $260,574,405
Earnings: $637,455
Emp.: 494
Fiscal Year-end: 03/31/21
Real Estate Developers
N.A.I.C.S.: 236117
Ravi Puravankara *(Founder & Chm)*

Subsidiaries:

Propmart Technologies Limited (1)
21 Haudin Rd Halasuru Yellappa Chetty Layout Sivanchetti Gardens, Bengaluru, 560042, Karnataka, India
Tel.: (91) 8044559966
Web Site: https://propmart.com
Real Estate Services
N.A.I.C.S.: 531390

Provident Housing Limited (1)
Tel.: (91) 8044555544
Web Site: http://www.providenthousing.com
Sales Range: $25-49.9 Million
Emp.: 30
Housing Services
N.A.I.C.S.: 236117

Purvaland Private Limited (1)
Tel.: (91) 8044555525
Web Site: https://www.purvaland.com
Real Estate Development Services
N.A.I.C.S.: 531390

Starworth Infrastructure & Construction Limited (1)
Tel.: (91) 8069388520
Web Site: https://www.starworthinfra.com
Real Estate Development Services
N.A.I.C.S.: 531390
Ravi Puravankara *(Chm)*

PURCARI WINERIES PUBLIC COMPANY LIMITED
Strada Lampousas Nr 1, 1095, Nicosia, Cyprus
Tel.: (357) 22856035
Web Site: http://www.purcari.wine
WINE—(BUC)
Rev.: $65,699,411
Assets: $123,751,268
Liabilities: $57,037,940
Net Worth: $66,713,329
Earnings: $15,074,151
Emp.: 800
Fiscal Year-end: 12/31/22
Beverage Product Mfr & Distr
N.A.I.C.S.: 312130
Victor Bostan *(Founder & CEO)*

Subsidiaries:

Angel's Estate SA (1)
Bul Simeonovsko Shose N 110B Floor 4 Office 22, Sofia, Bulgaria
Tel.: (359) 884246619
Web Site: https://angelsestate.bg
Wine Beverage Distr
N.A.I.C.S.: 424820

Crama Ceptura SRL (1)
Str Dr Iacob Felix 17-19 et 4 sector 1 Sat Ceptura de Jos, Comuna Ceptura Jud Prahova, Bucharest, Romania
Tel.: (40) 372771038
Web Site: https://www.crama-ceptura.eu
Beverages Mfr
N.A.I.C.S.: 312111

Ecosmart Union SA (1)
Strada Nerva Traian Nr 3 Etaj 6 Biroul 18, Cladirea City Business Center Sector 3, 031041, Bucharest, Romania
Tel.: (40) 720437497
Web Site: https://ecosmart-union.eu
Environmental Management Services
N.A.I.C.S.: 541620

Vinaria Bardar SA (1)
Str Calea Iesilor 10B, Chisinau, MD2069, Moldova
Tel.: (373) 22856022
Web Site: http://www.bardar.md
Beverages Mfr
N.A.I.C.S.: 312111

Vinaria Bostavan SRL (1)
8 Calea Iesilor Street, Chisinau, MD2069, Moldova
Tel.: (373) 22856022
Web Site: https://www.bostavan.md
Beverages Mfr
N.A.I.C.S.: 312111

PURDEL, COOPERATIVE AGRO-ALIMENTAIRE
155 Saint Jean Baptiste, Bic, G0L 1B0, QC, Canada
Tel.: (418) 736-4363 QC
Web Site: http://www.purdel.qc.ca
Year Founded: 1928
Sales Range: $25-49.9 Million
Emp.: 125
Seafood, Agricultural Machinery, Biological Fertilizers, Feeds & Seeds
N.A.I.C.S.: 333111
Jean Paul Theriault *(Dir Gen)*

PURDICOM LIMITED
Mitchell House Unit 4 Woolley Barns Woolley, Wantage, OX12 8TA, Oxon, United Kingdom
Tel.: (44) 845 331 6169
Web Site: http://www.purdi.com
Year Founded: 2005
Sales Range: $10-24.9 Million
Emp.: 22
Wireless Telecommunication Services
N.A.I.C.S.: 517112
Hugh Garrod *(Founder & Mng Dir)*

PURDY MOTOR S.A.
Frente a Compania Nacional de Fuerza y Luz, La Uruca, 10107, San Jose, Costa Rica
Tel.: (506) 2519 7777 CR
Web Site:
 http://www.purdyusados.com
Year Founded: 1957
Automobile Distr & Dealerships
Owner & Operator
N.A.I.C.S.: 441110

PURDYS CHOCOLATIER
8330 Chester St, Vancouver, V5X 3Y7, BC, Canada
Tel.: (604) 454-2777
Web Site: http://www.purdys.com
Year Founded: 1907
Sales Range: $50-74.9 Million
Chocolate Mfr
N.A.I.C.S.: 311351
Karen Flavelle *(Co-Owner & CEO)*

PURE BIOLOGICS SA
Szczytnicka 11, 50-382, Wroclaw, Poland
Tel.: (48) 795611811
Web Site: https://purebiologics.com
Year Founded: 2010
PUR—(WAR)
Pharmaceuticals Product Mfr
N.A.I.C.S.: 325412
Filip Jelen *(Founder)*

PURE ENERGY MINERALS LIMITED
1111 Melville Street Suite 1100, Vancouver, V6E 3V6, BC, Canada
Tel.: (604) 608-6611
Web Site:
 https://www.pureenergyminerals.com
Year Founded: 1999
PEMIF—(OTCQB)
Assets: $25,775,981
Liabilities: $336,651
Net Worth: $25,439,331
Earnings: ($755,253)
Fiscal Year-end: 06/30/19
Mineral Exploration Services
N.A.I.C.S.: 213114
Dianne Szigety *(Sec)*

PURE GLOBAL CANNABIS INC.
418 - 2095 Lake Shore Blvd West, Toronto, M8V 4G4, ON, Canada
Tel.: (289) 206-1552 BC
Web Site: http://pureglobal.com
Year Founded: 2011
PURE—(TSXV)
Sales Range: Less than $1 Million
Pure Cannabis Products Mfr
N.A.I.C.S.: 111419
Malay Panchal *(Pres & CEO)*

Subsidiaries:

PureSinse Inc. (1)
Greater Toronto Area, Toronto, L6T 3Y9, ON, Canada (100%)
Tel.: (866) 899-7873
Web Site: http://puresinse.com
Soil-less Indoor Horticulture Technologies
N.A.I.C.S.: 115112
Malay Panchal *(Founder, Chm & CEO)*

PURE HYDROGEN CORPORATION LIMITED
119 Willoughby Road, Locked Bag 2000, Crows Nest, 2065, NSW, Australia
Tel.: (61) 299554008 BC
Web Site:
 https://purehydrogen.com.au
PH2—(ASX)
Rev.: $1,409,589
Assets: $21,670,673
Liabilities: $3,216,480
Net Worth: $18,454,193
Earnings: ($2,276,309)
Emp.: 7
Fiscal Year-end: 06/30/24
Crude Petroleum Extraction Services
N.A.I.C.S.: 211120
Tim Hoops *(Pres, CEO & Mng Dir)*

Subsidiaries:

Real Energy Corporation Limited (1)
Level 3 32 Walker Street, North Sydney, 2060, NSW, Australia (100%)
Tel.: (61) 2 9955 4008
Web Site: http://www.realenergy.com.au
Oil & Gas Exploration
N.A.I.C.S.: 211120
Scott Brown *(CEO & Exec Dir)*

PURE INTERNATIONAL LIMITED
Concept House Home Park Road, Kings Langley, WD4 8UD, Herts, United Kingdom
Tel.: (44) 1923623099 UK
Web Site: http://www.pure.com
Year Founded: 2016
Digital Radio Mfr
N.A.I.C.S.: 423620
Mario Tuta *(CEO)*

Subsidiaries:

PURE Digital Limited (1)
Concept House Home Park Estate, Kings Langley, WD4 8UD, Herts, United Kingdom
Tel.: (44) 1923623099
Web Site: http://www.pure.com
Digital Radio Mfr
N.A.I.C.S.: 334220
Steven Paul Smith *(Dir)*

Subsidiary (Non-US):

PURE Australasia Pty Ltd (2)
49 Babbage Dr, Dandenong, 3115, VIC, Australia
Tel.: (61) 3 87806800
Web Site: http://www.pure.com
Radio Communication Equipments Mfr
N.A.I.C.S.: 334290

PURE IRON PLANT OJSC
75 Arcakhi Ave, 0053, Yerevan, Armenia
Tel.: (374) 11474260
Web Site:
 http://www.pureironplant.am
MQER—(ARM)
Sales Range: $1-9.9 Million
Molybdenum Metal Mining Services
N.A.I.C.S.: 212290

PURE RECRUITMENT GROUP LTD.
20 St Dunstans Hill, London, EC3R 8HL, United Kingdom
Tel.: (44) 20 7429 4400
Web Site: http://www.puresearch.com

PURE RECRUITMENT GROUP LTD.

Pure Recruitment Group Ltd.—(Continued)
Year Founded: 1999
Executive Search Service
N.A.I.C.S.: 561312
Charles Ferguson (Co-CEO)
Subsidiaries:
Correlate UK Search Ltd. (1)
107 Queen Victoria Street, London, EC4V 4BF, United Kingdom
Tel.: (44) 203 440 5220
Web Site: http://www.puresearch.com
Sales Range: $25-49.9 Million
Emp.: 35
Finance Executive Search Services
N.A.I.C.S.: 561312
Gavin Bonnet (Mng Dir & Head-Bus Mgmt & Controls-EMEA)

Pure Search International Limited (1)
Level 61 Unit 09 The Center 99 Queens Rd, Central, China (Hong Kong)
Tel.: (852) 24991611
Executive Search Service
N.A.I.C.S.: 561312
Liam Richardson (Mng Dir)

Pure Search International Singapore Pte Ltd (1)
Asia Square 8 Marina View 07-04 Asia Square Tower 1, Singapore, 018960, Singapore
Tel.: (65) 64071200
Executive Search Service
N.A.I.C.S.: 561312
Andrew Wallace (Mng Dir)

PURE RESOURCES LIMITED
22 Townsend Road, Subiaco, 6008, WA, Australia
Tel.: (61) 893880051
Web Site: https://www.pureresources.com.au
Year Founded: 2021
PR1—(ASX)
Rev.: $42,292
Assets: $1,914,095
Liabilities: $96,323
Net Worth: $1,817,772
Earnings: ($601,712)
Fiscal Year-end: 06/30/24
Exploration & Mining Services
N.A.I.C.S.: 213115
Patric Glovac (Chm)

PURE TO PURE BEAUTY INC.
Suite 650 1231 Pacific Blvd, Vancouver, V6Z 0E2, BC, Canada
Tel.: (604) 339-0339
Web Site: https://www.p2pbrands.com
Year Founded: 2014
PPB—(CNSX)
Rev.: $20,119
Assets: $276,389
Liabilities: $81,028
Net Worth: $195,362
Earnings: ($157,953)
Fiscal Year-end: 09/30/22
Cosmetic Product Distr
N.A.I.C.S.: 456120
Simon Cheng (CEO)

PUREGOLD PRICE CLUB, INC.
No 900 Romualdez Street, Paco, Manila, 1007, Philippines
Tel.: (63) 5233055
Web Site: http://www.puregold.com.ph
Year Founded: 1998
PGCMF—(OTCIQ)
Rev.: $3,413,796,574
Assets: $2,900,223,190
Liabilities: $1,330,322,552
Net Worth: $1,569,900,638
Earnings: $170,144,453
Emp.: 11,647
Fiscal Year-end: 12/31/21
Supermarket Owner & Operator
N.A.I.C.S.: 445110
Lucio L. Co (Bd of Dirs & Chm)
Subsidiaries:
Puregold Junior Supermarket, Inc. (1)
Aguirre Street Corner Kyoto Street Bf Homes, Paranaque, 1720, Philippines
Tel.: (63) 28200060
Supermarkets Operation Services
N.A.I.C.S.: 445110

PUREPOINT URANIUM GROUP INC
120 Adelaide St W Suite 2500, Toronto, M5H 1T1, ON, Canada
Tel.: (416) 603-8368
Web Site: http://www.purepoint.ca
Uranium Exploration Services
N.A.I.C.S.: 212290
Chris Frostad (Pres & CEO)

PUREPROFILE LIMITED
263 Riley Street, Surry Hills, 2010, NSW, Australia
Tel.: (61) 293339700
Web Site: https://www.pureprofile.com
Year Founded: 2000
PPL—(ASX)
Rev.: $32,097,306
Assets: $16,969,446
Liabilities: $13,270,403
Net Worth: $3,699,043
Earnings: $71,479
Fiscal Year-end: 06/30/24
Application Hosting Services
N.A.I.C.S.: 518210
Martin Filz (CEO & Mng Dir)
Subsidiaries:
Cohort Global Limited (1)
Level 5 Audley House 13 Palace Street, London, SW1E 5HX, United Kingdom
Tel.: (44) 2036370023
Digital Marketing Services
N.A.I.C.S.: 541613

Funbox India Private Limited (1)
197 HM Rochester 3rd Floor Indiranagar Double Road HAL 2nd Stage, Bengaluru, 560038, India
Tel.: (91) 8044021200
Web Site: http://www.funbox.com
Advertising Services
N.A.I.C.S.: 541810

PUREPROMOTER LTD
Unit A-E Level 3 South New England House, New England Street, Brighton, BN1 4GH, East Sussex, United Kingdom
Tel.: (44) 1273 648 822
Web Site: http://www.pure360.com
Year Founded: 2001
Sales Range: $1-9.9 Million
Emp.: 60
Email Marketing Software
N.A.I.C.S.: 513210
Stuart Dawson (Mng Dir)

PUREUN MUTUAL SAVINGS BANK
Blue Bldg 581 Gangnam-daero, Seocho-gu, Seoul, 137904, Korea (South)
Tel.: (82) 25459000
Web Site: https://www.prsb.co.kr
Year Founded: 1971
007330—(KRS)
Rev.: $50,805,116
Assets: $1,112,910,227
Liabilities: $868,483,541
Net Worth: $244,426,686
Earnings: $15,864,451
Fiscal Year-end: 12/31/22
Banking Services
N.A.I.C.S.: 522110
Myeong-Gu Song (CEO)

PURIFLOH LIMITED
Level 3 2-4 Ross Place, South Melbourne, 3205, VIC, Australia
Tel.: (61) 396739690
Web Site: https://www.purifloh.com
Year Founded: 2007
PUFLF—(OTCIQ)
Rev.: $13
Assets: $107,460
Liabilities: $925,698
Net Worth: ($818,237)
Earnings: ($2,365,980)
Fiscal Year-end: 06/30/21
Waste Treatment Services
N.A.I.C.S.: 924110
Adam Gallagher (Sec)

PURIT CO., LTD.
21 Sabak-gil, Angang-eup, Gyeongju, Gyeongsangbuk-do, Korea (South)
Tel.: (82) 547603200
Web Site: https://www.purit.co.kr
Year Founded: 2010
445180—(KRS)
Chemical Products Mfr
N.A.I.C.S.: 325998

PURITY FACTORIES LIMITED
96 Blackmarsh Road, Saint John's, A1C 5M9, NL, Canada
Tel.: (709) 579-2035
Web Site: https://www.purity.nf.ca
Year Founded: 1924
Sales Range: $10-24.9 Million
Emp.: 60
Biscuits, Confectionery, Jams & Fruit Syrups Mfr
N.A.I.C.S.: 311821
Douglas Spurrell (Gen Mgr)

PURITY FLEX PACK LTD.
At Vanseti Tajpura Road Near Baska, Dist Panchmahal, Halol, 389 350, Gujarat, India
Tel.: (91) 8758752215
Web Site: https://www.purityflexpack.com
Year Founded: 1988
523315—(BOM)
Rev.: $13,870,116
Assets: $9,079,216
Liabilities: $5,172,436
Net Worth: $3,906,780
Earnings: $115,892
Fiscal Year-end: 03/31/23
Packaging Services
N.A.I.C.S.: 561910
Anil Patel (Chm & Mng Dir)

PUROHIT CONSTRUCTION LTD.
Purohit House Opp Stadium, Navarangpura, Ahmedabad, 380 009, India
Tel.: (91) 7965214001
Web Site: https://www.purohitconstruction.com
538993—(BOM)
Rev.: $19,874
Assets: $880,261
Liabilities: $337,797
Net Worth: $542,465
Earnings: ($256,019)
Emp.: 5
Fiscal Year-end: 03/31/21
Commercial Building Construction Services
N.A.I.C.S.: 236220
Narendrabhai Purohit (Founder, Chm & Co-Mng Dir)

PURPLE BIOTECH LTD.
4 Oppenheimer Street, Science Park, Rehovot, 7670104, Israel
Tel.: (972) 39333121
Web Site: https://www.purple-biotech.com
Year Founded: 1968
PPBT—(NASDAQ)
Assets: $44,302,000
Liabilities: $10,005,000
Net Worth: $34,297,000
Earnings: ($19,977,000)
Emp.: 20
Fiscal Year-end: 12/31/23
Holding Company;Pharmaceutical Products Mfr & Distr
N.A.I.C.S.: 551112
Isaac Israel (CEO)

PURPLE ENTERTAINMENT LIMITED
30-B 3rd floor Ajanta complex Income Tax Ashram Road, Ahmedabad, 380 009, India
Tel.: (91) 7940069097
Web Site: http://www.purpleentertainment.co.in
540159—(BOM)
Rev.: $93,172
Assets: $2,462,934
Liabilities: $1,301,553
Net Worth: $1,161,381
Earnings: $19,879
Fiscal Year-end: 03/31/23
Entertainment Services
N.A.I.C.S.: 512110

PURPLE GROUP LIMITED
WeWork The Link 173 Oxford Rd, Rosebank, Johannesburg, 2196, South Africa
Tel.: (27) 879406000
Web Site: https://www.purplegroup.co.za
Year Founded: 1998
PPE—(JSE)
Rev.: $13,972,003
Assets: $51,550,426
Liabilities: $20,974,448
Net Worth: $30,575,978
Earnings: $4,956,568
Fiscal Year-end: 08/31/21
Financial Services
N.A.I.C.S.: 525990
Charles Savage (CEO)
Subsidiaries:
First World Trader (Pty) Limited (1)
16th floor 25 Owl Street Braamfontein Werf, Johannesburg, 2092, Gauteng, South Africa
Tel.: (27) 879406000
Web Site: http://www.easyequities.co.za
Sales Range: $50-74.9 Million
Emp.: 55
Securities Trading Services
N.A.I.C.S.: 523150

PURPLE VENTURES CO., LTD.
No 101 Ratchadaphisek Corner Property Tower RCPGround floor Ratchadaphisek Rd Jatujak, Bangkok, 10900, Thailand
Tel.: (66) 27777564
Web Site: https://www.robinhood.co.th
Investment Services
N.A.I.C.S.: 523999

PURPLE WIFI LTD
11 Northampton Rd, Arbeta, Ste 2.5, Manchester, M40 5BP, United Kingdom
Tel.: (44) 3330165290
Web Site: http://www.purple.ai
Year Founded: 2012
Cloud Based Solutions
N.A.I.C.S.: 513210
Gavin Wheeldon (CEO)

Subsidiaries:

LogicJunction Inc. (1)
23950 Commerce Park Rd, Beachwood, OH 44122-0000
Custom Computer Programming Services
N.A.I.C.S.: 541511

PURPOSE ETHER STAKING CORP. ETF
130 Adelaide Street West Suit 3100, Toronto, M5H 3P5, ON, Canada
Tel.: (416) 583-3850 ON
Web Site: https://www.ethcap.co
Year Founded: 2009
ETHC—(OTCIQ)
Rev.: $73,471
Assets: $7,134,320
Liabilities: $242,625
Net Worth: $6,891,695
Earnings: ($1,125,388)
Emp.: 2
Fiscal Year-end: 12/31/19
Home Entertainment Creator & Producer
N.A.I.C.S.: 512110
Som Seif *(Chm & Co-Chief Investment Officer)*

PURPOSE FLOATING RATE INCOME FUND
130 Adelaide St W Ste 3100, PO Box 109, Toronto, M5H 3P5, ON, Canada
Tel.: (416) 583-3850
FLOT.B—(TSX)
Investment Management Service
N.A.I.C.S.: 525990
Norman Milner *(Mgr-Fund)*

PURPOSE INVESTMENTS INC.
130 Adelaide St West Suite 1700, PO Box 83, Toronto, M5H 3P5, ON, Canada
Tel.: (416) 583-3850
Web Site: http://www.purposeinvest.com
Year Founded: 2013
Investment Fund Asset Management Services
N.A.I.C.S.: 523940
Greg Taylor *(Chief Investment Officer)*

Subsidiaries:

Limited Duration Investment Grade Preferred Securities Fund (1)
130 Adelaide St West Suite 1700, PO Box 83, Toronto, M5K 3P5, ON, Canada
Tel.: (416) 583-3850
Web Site: http://www.purposeinvest.com
Rev.: $5,341,098
Assets: $55,384,040
Liabilities: $18,232,785
Net Worth: $37,151,254
Earnings: $4,169,570
Fiscal Year-end: 12/31/2017
Closed-End Investment Fund
N.A.I.C.S.: 525990
Som Seif *(Founder & CEO)*

Purpose Global Financials Income Fund (1)
130 Adelaide St West Suite 3100, PO Box 83, Toronto, M5H 3P5, ON, Canada
Tel.: (416) 583-3850
Web Site: http://www.purposeinvest.com
Sales Range: $25-49.9 Million
Closed-End Investment Trust
N.A.I.C.S.: 525990
Darren N. Cabral *(CEO)*

PURPOSE SILVER BULLION FUND
130 Adelaide Street West Suite 1700, Toronto, M5H 3P5, ON, Canada
Tel.: (416) 583-3857 ON
Web Site: http://www.silverbulliontrust.com
Year Founded: 2009
SBT.B—(TSX)
Sales Range: Less than $1 Million

Investment Trust Services
N.A.I.C.S.: 523991
Scott Bartholomew *(CFO & COO)*

PURSHOTTAM INVESTOFIN LTD.
L-7 Menz Floor Green Park Extension, New Delhi, 110 016, India
Tel.: (91) 1146067802
Web Site: https://www.purshottaminvestofin.in
538647—(BOM)
Rev.: $1,900,881
Assets: $10,021,018
Liabilities: $6,703,447
Net Worth: $3,317,571
Earnings: $44,674
Emp.: 8
Fiscal Year-end: 03/31/23
Financial Support Services
N.A.I.C.S.: 523999
Sahib Singh Gusain *(Mng Dir)*

PURSO GROUP OY
Alumiinitie 1, 37200, Siuro, Finland
Tel.: (358) 3 3404 111
Web Site: http://www.purso.fi
Year Founded: 1959
Sales Range: $75-99.9 Million
Emp.: 240
Aluminum Profile & Component Mfr
N.A.I.C.S.: 331315
Jussi Aro *(Mng Dir)*

Subsidiaries:

Fennosteel Oy (1)
Fennokatu 1, 39700, Parkano, Finland
Tel.: (358) 344100
Web Site: http://www.fennosteel.com
Aluminium Products Mfr
N.A.I.C.S.: 331315
Antti Poussa *(Mng Dir-Sls-Domestic)*

Nordisk Profil A/S (1)
Nannasgade 28, DK 2200, Copenhagen, Denmark
Tel.: (45) 45166100
Web Site: http://www.nordisk-profil.dk
Emp.: 4
Industrial Supplies Whslr
N.A.I.C.S.: 423840
John Bitsch *(Gen Mgr)*

Purso-Tools Oy (1)
Koivukummuntie 2, 28760, Pori, Finland
Tel.: (358) 26287400
Web Site: http://www.purso-tools.fi
Emp.: 80
Diesel Engine Mfr
N.A.I.C.S.: 333618
Harri Heikkila *(CEO)*

Veme Oy (1)
Papinsaarentie 1, 23800, Laitila, Finland
Tel.: (358) 285921
Web Site: http://www.veme.fi
Emp.: 155
Metal Component Mfr
N.A.I.C.S.: 332510
Lasse Aaltonen *(Mng Dir)*

PURSUIT GOLD CORP.
Suite 409 221 West Esplanade, Vancouver, V7M 3J3, BC, Canada
Tel.: (604) 506-3325 BC
Year Founded: 2020
PUGS—(CNSX)
Assets: $67,038
Liabilities: $23,286
Net Worth: $43,752
Earnings: ($226,474)
Fiscal Year-end: 11/30/22
Mineral Exploration Services
N.A.I.C.S.: 212220
Kostantinos Sakarellos *(Pres)*

PURSUIT MINERALS LIMITED
Suite 4 246-250 Railway Parade, West Leederville, 6007, WA, Australia
Tel.: (61) 865003271

Web Site:
https://www.pursuitminerals.com.au
PUR—(ASX)
Rev.: $11,713
Assets: $33,693,552
Liabilities: $275,462
Net Worth: $33,418,089
Earnings: ($1,406,189)
Emp.: 10
Fiscal Year-end: 06/30/24
Iron, Uranium, Base & Precious Metals Exploration & Mining Services
N.A.I.C.S.: 212210

PURWANCHAL GRAMEEN BIKASH BANK LIMITED
Bata Road, Biratnagar, Nepal
Tel.: (977) 21 521703
Web Site: http://www.pgbb.org.np
Sales Range: Less than $1 Million
Emp.: 271
Banking Services
N.A.I.C.S.: 522110

PUSAN CAST IRON CO., LTD.
10 Shinso Property group 1 of jangan-eup, Busan, Korea (South)
Tel.: (82) 517805980
Web Site: https://www.pci21c.com
Year Founded: 1967
005030—(KRS)
Rev.: $176,831,433
Assets: $178,366,284
Liabilities: $160,706,532
Net Worth: $17,659,752
Earnings: ($6,218,310)
Emp.: 261
Fiscal Year-end: 12/31/22
Automotive Components Mfr
N.A.I.C.S.: 336340
Chang Se Hoon *(CEO)*

PUSHFOR TECH INC.
9648-128th Street Suite 210, Surrey, V3T 2X9, BC, Canada
Tel.: (604) 357-4730 BC
Web Site: https://www.pushfortech.com
PUSOF—(OTCIQ)
Assets: $136,421
Liabilities: $113,844
Net Worth: $22,577
Earnings: ($178,981)
Fiscal Year-end: 09/30/23
Real Estate Services
N.A.I.C.S.: 531390

PUSHPANJALI REALMS & INFRATECH LTD.
Orchid Park Khasra No 11 Tarla Nagal, Near Helipad Sahastradhara-Rajpur Link Road, Dehradun, 248001, Uttarakhand, India
Tel.: (91) 8979333888
Web Site: http://www.pushpanjali.co
Rev.: $1,916,881
Assets: $12,946,222
Liabilities: $8,911,501
Net Worth: $4,034,721
Earnings: ($533,170)
Emp.: 42
Fiscal Year-end: 03/31/19
Real Estate Manangement Services
N.A.I.C.S.: 531390
Deepak Mittal *(Mng Dir)*

PUSHPSONS INDUSTRIES LTD.
B-40 Okhla Industrial Area, Phase -1, New Delhi, 110020, India
Tel.: (91) 01141610121 In
Web Site: https://www.pushpsons.com
Year Founded: 1993
Rev.: $374,616
Assets: $548,917

Liabilities: $24,104
Net Worth: $524,813
Earnings: $25,368
Emp.: 6
Fiscal Year-end: 03/31/19
Home Furnishing Product Distr
N.A.I.C.S.: 449129
Pankaj Jain *(Chm & CEO)*

PUT A.D.
Dositejeva 1/II, Zajecar, Serbia
Tel.: (381) 19 422 830
Year Founded: 2001
Sales Range: $1-9.9 Million
Emp.: 76
Road Construction Services
N.A.I.C.S.: 237310

PUTEVI A.D.
Ul 600 br 2, Cacak, Serbia
Tel.: (381) 11 222 1719
Year Founded: 1991
Sales Range: $1-9.9 Million
Emp.: 102
Road Construction Services
N.A.I.C.S.: 237310
Dragan Rsumovic *(CEO)*

PUTEVI A.D.
Nikole Pasica 38, Uzice, Serbia
Tel.: (381) 31512822
Web Site: https://www.puteviuzice.com
Year Founded: 1991
PUPO—(BEL)
Rev.: $6,513,339
Assets: $2,971,818
Liabilities: $3,387,590
Net Worth: ($415,772)
Earnings: $231,509
Emp.: 173
Fiscal Year-end: 12/31/23
Road Construction Services
N.A.I.C.S.: 237310
Branko Bojovic *(Dir)*

PUTIAN COMMUNICATION GROUP LTD.
No 8899 Changdong Avenue, Nanchang National High-tech Development Zone, Nanchang, Jiangxi, China
Tel.: (86) 15079843096 Ky
Web Site: http://www.potel-group.com
Year Founded: 2001
1720—(HKG)
Rev.: $90,733,921
Assets: $165,893,972
Liabilities: $85,808,128
Net Worth: $80,085,845
Earnings: $3,465,072
Emp.: 585
Fiscal Year-end: 12/31/22
Optical Fiber Cable Mfr & Distr
N.A.I.C.S.: 335921
Qiuping Wang *(Founder, Chm & CEO)*

PUTNIK A.D.
Prote Nikole Kostica 20, 78000, Banja Luka, Bosnia & Herzegovina
Tel.: (387) 51304605
PUTN-R-A—(BANJ)
Rev.: $40,272
Assets: $579,539
Liabilities: $71,427
Net Worth: $508,112
Earnings: ($5,726)
Emp.: 2
Fiscal Year-end: 12/31/12
Restaurant Management Services
N.A.I.C.S.: 722511
Dijana Milasinovic *(Chm-Mgmt Bd)*

PUTNIK A.D.

PUTNIK A.D.

Putnik a.d.—(Continued)
Ilije Ognjanovica 24, 21000, Novi Sad, Serbia
Tel.: (381) 216615778
Web Site: https://www.putnikns.rs
Year Founded: 1991
PUNS—(BEL)
Sales Range: Less than $1 Million
Emp.: 56
Home Management Services
N.A.I.C.S.: 721110
Milos Tutunovic *(Exec Dir)*

PUTPROP LIMITED
91 Protea Road, Chislehurston Sandton, Johannesburg, 2196, South Africa
Tel.: (27) 118838650 ZA
Web Site: https://www.putprop.co.za
Year Founded: 1971
PPR—(JSE)
Rev.: $6,782,866
Assets: $65,307,196
Liabilities: $29,187,201
Net Worth: $36,119,995
Earnings: $488,229
Emp.: 8
Fiscal Year-end: 06/30/23
Property Investment Services
N.A.I.C.S.: 523999
Bruno Carleo *(CEO)*

PUTRAJAYA PERDANA BERHAD
2nd & 3rd Floor No 5 Jalan P16 Precinct 16, 62150, Putrajaya, Malaysia
Tel.: (60) 388868888 MY
Web Site: http://www.p-perdana.com
Year Founded: 1998
Sales Range: $200-249.9 Million
Construction & Property Development Services
N.A.I.C.S.: 236116

PUTSCH GMBH & CO. KG
Frankfurter Strasse 5-21, 58095, Hagen, Germany
Tel.: (49) 23313990
Web Site: http://www.en.putsch.com
Year Founded: 1871
Sales Range: $450-499.9 Million
Emp.: 5,000
Holding Company
N.A.I.C.S.: 551112
Carl Christian Radinger *(Member-Exec Bd)*

Subsidiaries:

Fontaine & Co. GmbH (1)
Gruner Weg 31, 52070, Aachen, Germany
Tel.: (49) 241918630
Web Site: http://de.fontaine.putsch.he-hosting.de
Sugar Mfr
N.A.I.C.S.: 311313
Manuel Martin *(Dir-Sls)*

OOO Putsch (1)
Lane 4th Lesnoy House 4 Prom I Room 91 Office 421, 125047, Moscow, Russia
Tel.: (7) 9191800214
Customer Care Services
N.A.I.C.S.: 541613

Putsch & Company Inc. (1)
PO Box 5128, Asheville, NC 28813-5128
Tel.: (828) 684-0671
Web Site: http://www.putschusa.com
Sugar Mfr
N.A.I.C.S.: 311313
Jon DeBuvitz *(Office Mgr-Sls)*

Putsch CST GmbH (1)
Industriestrasse 14 - 22, 27404, Zeven, Germany
Tel.: (49) 4281950191
Crop Farming Services
N.A.I.C.S.: 111219

Putsch Meniconi S. p. A. (1)
Via Irlanda 1, Poggibonsi, 53036, Siena, Italy
Tel.: (39) 057790311
Web Site: http://www.putschmeniconi.com
Wood & Plastic Product Mfr
N.A.I.C.S.: 337215
Marco Ammannati *(Area Mgr)*

Putsch Nerva S.A. (1)
C/ Vazquez de Menchaca 7 - Poligono de Argales, 47008, Valladolid, Spain
Tel.: (34) 983272208
Web Site: http://www.putschnerva.com
Industrial Machinery Mfr
N.A.I.C.S.: 333241

Putsch Stord s.r.o. (1)
Senetarov 183, 679 06, Jedovnice, Czech Republic
Tel.: (420) 725868966
Web Site: http://www.putsch-stord.cz
Industrial Machinery Mfr
N.A.I.C.S.: 333241

RECARO GmbH & Co. (1)
Stuttgarter Strasse 73, 73230, Kirchheim, Germany (100%)
Tel.: (49) 7021935000
Web Site: http://www.recaro-automotive.com
Sales Range: $100-124.9 Million
Emp.: 300
Mfr of Automotive Seats.
N.A.I.C.S.: 336360

Division (Domestic):

RECARO Aircraft Seating GmbH & Co. (2)
Daimler Strasse 21, Schwabisch Hall, 74523, Germany (100%)
Tel.: (49) 7915037000
Web Site: http://www.recaro-as.com
Sales Range: $75-99.9 Million
Mfr of Automotive Seats.
N.A.I.C.S.: 336360
Joachim Ley *(VP-Supply Chain)*

Subsidiary (US):

RECARO Aircraft Seating Inc. (3)
2275 Eagle Pkwy, Fort Worth, TX 76177-2312
Tel.: (817) 490-9160
Web Site: http://www.recaro-as.com
Sales Range: $50-74.9 Million
Emp.: 110
Mfr of Automotive Seats.
N.A.I.C.S.: 336360
Chris Buckner *(Dir-Product Mgmt)*

Stord International A.S. (1)
Kokstadflaten 17, PO Box 4, Kokstad, 5863, Bergen, Norway
Tel.: (47) 55984020
Web Site: http://www.stordinternational.no
Industrial Machinery Distr
N.A.I.C.S.: 423830
Anica Samleit *(Mgr-Admin)*

PUXIN LIMITED
5/F Building 4 Dingjun Building 75 Suzhou Street, Haidian District, Beijing, 100080, China
Tel.: (86) 10 8260 5578 Ky
Web Site: http://www.pxjy.com
NEW—(NYSE)
Rev.: $444,908,817
Assets: $707,461,577
Liabilities: $643,247,742
Net Worth: $64,213,835
Earnings: ($4,934,281)
Emp.: 9,650
Fiscal Year-end: 12/31/20
Educational Support Services
N.A.I.C.S.: 611710

Subsidiaries:

Global Education & Technology Group Limited (1)
9F Floor Block D Beijing International No 18, South Street Zhongguancun, Beijing, 100081, Haidian, China (100%)
Tel.: (86) 1062125800
Web Site: http://www.gedu.org

Sales Range: $50-74.9 Million
Educational Facilities & Services
N.A.I.C.S.: 611710

PUXING ENERGY LTD.
Room 706 7th Floor Albion Plaza 2-6 Granville Road, Tsim Sha Tsui, Kowloon, China (Hong Kong)
Tel.: (852) 23699080
Web Site: http://www.pxcleanenergy.com
0090—(HKG)
Rev.: $105,764,303
Assets: $249,871,284
Liabilities: $145,291,536
Net Worth: $104,579,748
Earnings: $7,290,972
Emp.: 290
Fiscal Year-end: 12/31/22
Power Generation Services
N.A.I.C.S.: 221112
Genyong Gu *(Gen Mgr)*

PUYANG HUICHENG ELECTRONIC MATERIAL CO., LTD.
West section of Shengli Road, Puyang, 457001, Henan, China
Tel.: (86) 3938910800
Web Site: https://www.huichengchem.com
300481—(CHIN)
Rev.: $194,260,517
Assets: $397,439,149
Liabilities: $52,936,670
Net Worth: $344,502,480
Earnings: $33,116,962
Fiscal Year-end: 12/31/23
Organic Chemical Product Mfr & Distr
N.A.I.C.S.: 325199
Wang Zhongzhong *(Chm)*

Subsidiaries:

Shandong Qingyang New Material Co., Ltd. (1)
Taiwan east road Heze development zone, Shandong, 274000, China
Tel.: (86) 3938910800
Web Site: https://www.qingyangchemical.com
Chemical Product Mfr & Distr
N.A.I.C.S.: 325199

PUYANG REFRACTORIES GROUP CO., LTD.
Middle West Circle Road, Puyang, 457100, Henan, China
Tel.: (86) 3938776666
Web Site: https://en.punai.com
Year Founded: 1988
002225—(SSE)
Rev.: $693,004,572
Assets: $1,056,625,128
Liabilities: $586,155,960
Net Worth: $470,469,168
Earnings: $32,240,052
Fiscal Year-end: 12/31/22
Refractory Material Mfr
N.A.I.C.S.: 212323
Liu Baikuan *(Chm)*

Subsidiaries:

Haicheng Huayin High-Tech Materials Co., Ltd. (1)
Xiangtang Area, Huangling County, Haicheng, 114200, Liaoning, China
Tel.: (86) 4123388009
Mineral Mining Services
N.A.I.C.S.: 212323

Maanshan Yushan Metallurgy New Materials Co., Ltd. (1)
181 Yongqing Road, Yushan Industrial Park, Ma'anshan, 243000, Anhui, China
Tel.: (86) 5552106018
Metal Work Mfr
N.A.I.C.S.: 332323

PRCO America, Inc. (1)

INTERNATIONAL PUBLIC

8150 Perry Hwy Ste 303, Pittsburgh, PA 15237
Tel.: (412) 837-2798
Web Site: http://www.prco-america.com
Mineral Mining Services
N.A.I.C.S.: 212323
Joan Taylor *(Mgr-Logistics)*

PRCO Functional Refractories Co., Ltd. (1)
West Huanghe Road, Puyang, 457000, Henan, China
Tel.: (86) 3938728044
Mineral Mining Services
N.A.I.C.S.: 212323

PRCO Yingkou Magnesia Refractories Co., Ltd. (1)
129 Nanhai Road, Xishi District, Yingkou, 115104, Liaoning, China
Tel.: (86) 4174892860
Mineral Mining Services
N.A.I.C.S.: 212323

Shanghai Baoming Refractories Co., Ltd. (1)
No 2319 Fujin Road, Yang Yang Industrial Park, Shanghai, 201901, China
Tel.: (86) 2131160021
Mineral Mining Services
N.A.I.C.S.: 212323

Suzhou Baoming Refractories Co., Ltd. (1)
No 6 Jin Road Fen Lake Economic Development Zone, Wujiang, Suzhou, 215200, Jiangsu, China
Tel.: (86) 2131195666
Mineral Mining Services
N.A.I.C.S.: 212323

Zhengzhou Huite Refractories Co., Ltd. (1)
Yuanzhuang Industrial Park, Xinmi, 452370, Henan, China
Tel.: (86) 37169831588
Mineral Mining Services
N.A.I.C.S.: 212323

PV CRYSTALOX SOLAR PLC
Innovation Centre 99 Park Drive Milton Park, Abingdon, OX14 4RY, United Kingdom
Tel.: (44) 1235437160
Web Site: http://www.pvcrystalox.com
Year Founded: 1982
PVCS—(LSE)
Rev.: $594,646
Assets: $10,161,610
Liabilities: $1,770,499
Net Worth: $8,391,111
Earnings: ($2,553,281)
Emp.: 23
Fiscal Year-end: 12/31/19
Solar Power System Component Mfr
N.A.I.C.S.: 335999
Iain Dorrity *(CEO)*

Subsidiaries:

Crystalox Ltd (1)
BrookHouse 174 Milton Park Avingdon, Wantage, OX14 4ST, Oxon, United Kingdom
Tel.: (44) 1235437160
Web Site: http://www.crystalox.com
Sales Range: $25-49.9 Million
Emp.: 50
Glass Products Mfr
N.A.I.C.S.: 327215
Iain Dorrity *(CEO)*

PV Crystalox Solar GmbH (1)
Wilhelm-Wolff-Strasse 25, 99099, Erfurt, Germany
Tel.: (49) 36160085900
Sales Range: $25-49.9 Million
Emp.: 45
Silicone Mfr
N.A.I.C.S.: 334413
Hubert Aulich *(Exec Dir)*

PV Crystalox Solar KK (1)
Tokyo Opera City Tower 29F 3-20-2, Nishi-Shinjuku Shinjuku-ku, Tokyo, 163-1429, Japan
Tel.: (81) 353545520

Web Site: http://www.pvcrystalox.com
Electronic Components Mfr
N.A.I.C.S.: 334419

PV Silicon Forschungs und Produktions GmbH (1)
Wilhelm Wolff Strasse 25, Erfurt, Germany
Tel.: (49) 36160085150
Web Site: http://www.pvcrystalox.com
Sales Range: $50-74.9 Million
Emp.: 130
Silicon Materials Mfr
N.A.I.C.S.: 327910
Iain Dorrity *(CEO)*

Silicon Products Research Engineering Production GmbH (1)
Alu-Strasse 5, Wolfen, 06749, Bitterfeld, Germany
Tel.: (49) 34933456100
Web Site: http://www.silicon-products-gmbh.com
Sales Range: $50-74.9 Million
Emp.: 125
Silicone Mfr
N.A.I.C.S.: 325199

PV2 INVESTMENT JSC
No 1 Pham Van Bach Yen Hoa Ward, Cau Giay District, Hanoi, Vietnam
Tel.: (84) 462732659
Web Site: https://www.pv2.com.vn
Year Founded: 2007
PV2—(HNX)
Rev.: $527,739
Assets: $11,272,055
Liabilities: $1,846,126
Net Worth: $9,425,929
Earnings: $509,997
Fiscal Year-end: 12/31/19
Real Estate Investment & Development Services
N.A.I.C.S.: 531390
Xuan Vu Han *(Gen Dir & Member-Mgmt Bd)*

PVA TEPLA AG
Im Westpark 10-12, 35435, Wettenberg, Germany
Tel.: (49) 641686900
Web Site: https://www.pvatepla.com
TPE—(MUN)
Rev.: $290,814,552
Assets: $337,077,743
Liabilities: $196,422,628
Net Worth: $140,655,115
Earnings: $26,956,505
Emp.: 717
Fiscal Year-end: 12/31/23
Industrial Material & Equipment Mfr
N.A.I.C.S.: 332313
Alexander Von Witzleben *(Chm-Supervisory Bd)*

Subsidiaries:

OKOS Solutions, LLC (1)
7036 Tech Cir, Manassas, VA 20109
Tel.: (703) 880-3039
Web Site: https://www.okos.com
Measure Electricity Instrument Mfr
N.A.I.C.S.: 334513

PVA Control GmbH (1)
Im Westpark 17, 35435, Wettenberg, Germany
Tel.: (49) 64168690775
Sales Range: $25-49.9 Million
Emp.: 10
Electrical Motors & Generators Mfr
N.A.I.C.S.: 335312

PVA Crystal Growing Systems GmbH (1)
Im Westpark 10-12, 35435, Wettenberg, Germany
Tel.: (49) 641686900
Web Site: http://www.pvatepla-cgs.com
Semiconductor Mfr
N.A.I.C.S.: 334413

PVA Industrial Vacuum Systems GmbH (1)
Im Westpark 10-12, 35435, Wettenberg, Germany
Tel.: (49) 641686900
Web Site: https://www.pvatepla-ivs.com
Vacuum Furnaces Mfr
N.A.I.C.S.: 333994
Udo Broich *(Mng Dir)*

PVA Italy S.R.L. (1)
Via Vicenza 13, 36030, San Vito di Leguzzano, VI, Italy
Tel.: (39) 03316618977
Web Site: http://www.pva-italy.com
Vacuum Chamber Mfr
N.A.I.C.S.: 333914

PVA Lot- und Werkstofftechnik GmbH (1)
Im Westpark 17, 35435, Wettenberg, Germany
Tel.: (49) 64168690750
Web Site: http://www.pva-lwt-gmbh.de
Sales Range: $25-49.9 Million
Emp.: 14
Vacuum Brazing Services
N.A.I.C.S.: 332811

PVA SPA Software Entwicklungs GmbH (1)
Seifartshofstrasse 12 - 14, 96450, Coburg, Germany
Tel.: (49) 956179470
Web Site: http://www.pvatepla-spa.com
Semiconductor Mfr
N.A.I.C.S.: 334413
Kevin Fredriksen *(Sls Mgr)*

PVA Semiconductor Systems Xi'an Ltd. (1)
No 385 Hangtian Zhong Road Zhongchuang Plaza 1103, Xi'an, 710100, China
Tel.: (86) 2989687501
Semiconductor Mfr
N.A.I.C.S.: 334413

PVA TePla (China) Ltd. (1)
Bldg B/1F Dachen Park No 10 Jingyuan St BDA, Beijing, 100176, China
Tel.: (86) 1065814049
Semiconductor Mfr
N.A.I.C.S.: 334413
Hongzhi Wang *(Mgr-Sls Vacuum Furnace)*

PVA TePla America Inc. (1)
251 Corporate Ter, Corona, CA 92879-6000
Tel.: (951) 371-2500
Web Site: http://www.pvateplaamerica.com
Emp.: 21
Gas Plasma Systems Mfr
N.A.I.C.S.: 333517

PVA TePla Analytical Systems GmbH. (1)
Gartenstrasse 133, 73430, Aalen, Baden-Wurttemberg, Germany
Tel.: (49) 73613765230
Web Site: http://www.pva-analyticalsystems.com
Sales Range: $25-49.9 Million
Emp.: 20
Acoustic Instruments Designing & Mfr
N.A.I.C.S.: 541330

PVA TePla Singapore Pte. Ltd. (1)
12 New Industrial Road 05-03 Morningstar Centre, Singapore, 536202, Singapore
Tel.: (65) 96314005
Semiconductor Mfr
N.A.I.C.S.: 334413
Rolf Paul Mueller *(Mgr-Svc & Commissioning)*

PVA Vakuum Anlagenbau Jena GmbH. (1)
Am Nasstal 6/8, Maua, 07751, Jena, Germany
Tel.: (49) 3641613890
Web Site: http://www.pvatepla-jena.com
Sales Range: $25-49.9 Million
Emp.: 100
Vacuum Systems Mfr
N.A.I.C.S.: 335314

PlaTeG GmbH (1)
Park 10-12, 57076, Wettenberg, Nordrhein-Westfalen, Germany
Tel.: (49) 271772410
Web Site: http://www.plateg.com
Sales Range: $25-49.9 Million
Emp.: 25
Metal Cutting Machines & Tools Mfr

N.A.I.C.S.: 333517
Reinar Gruen *(Pres)*

Plasma Systems GmbH. (1)
Hans Riedl Str 5, Feldkirchen, 85622, Germany
Tel.: (49) 89905030
Web Site: http://www.pvatepla.com
Sales Range: $25-49.9 Million
Emp.: 35
Plasma Systems Mfr
N.A.I.C.S.: 325414

PVGASCITY JOIN STOCK COMPANY
4th floor No 167 Trung Kinh Yen Hoa ward, Cau Giay District, Hanoi, Vietnam
Tel.: (84) 437346858
Web Site: https://www.pvgascity.com.vn
PCG—(HNX)
Rev.: $15,712,381
Assets: $10,194,215
Liabilities: $3,462,465
Net Worth: $6,731,750
Earnings: $156,654
Fiscal Year-end: 12/31/21
Petroleum & Industrial Gas Mfr
N.A.I.C.S.: 325120

PVI HOLDINGS
PVI Tower Lot VP2 Pham Van Bach Street Yen Hoa Ward, Cau Giay District, Hanoi, Vietnam
Tel.: (84) 2437342299
Web Site: https://www.pvi.com.vn
Year Founded: 1996
PVI—(HNX)
Rev.: $670,934,000
Assets: $2,694,267,900
Liabilities: $1,884,330,300
Net Worth: $809,937,600
Earnings: $95,713,000
Emp.: 2,482
Fiscal Year-end: 12/31/23
Insurance Agency Services
N.A.I.C.S.: 524210
Bui Van Thuan *(CEO & Member-Mgmt Bd)*

Subsidiaries:

Hanoi Reinsurance Joint Stock Corporation (1)
25th Floor PVI Tower 01 Pham Van Bach Street, Cau Giay Dist, Hanoi, Vietnam
Tel.: (84) 2437342828
Web Site: https://www.hanoire.com
Reinsurance Services
N.A.I.C.S.: 524130

PVI Asset Management Joint Stock Company (1)
25th Floor PVI Tower No 1 Pham Van Bach Street, Cau Giay District, Hanoi, Vietnam
Tel.: (84) 2432565555
Web Site: https://www.pviam.com.vn
Insurance Brokerage Services
N.A.I.C.S.: 524210
Nguyen Xuan Hoa *(Chm)*

Subsidiary (Domestic):

Vietnam Asset Development Joint Stock Company (2)
25th Floor PVI Tower 1 Pham Van Bach Str Yen Hoa, Cau Giay Dist, Hanoi, Vietnam
Tel.: (84) 2438582626
Web Site: http://www.vad.vn
Asset Management Services
N.A.I.C.S.: 531390

PVI Insurance Corporation (1)
24th Floor PVI Tower 01 Pham Van Bach Street, Cau Giay District, Hanoi, Vietnam
Tel.: (84) 2437335588
Web Site: https://www.pvi.com.vn
Insurance Brokerage Services
N.A.I.C.S.: 524210

PVR LIMITED
61 Basant Lok Vasant Vihar, New Delhi, 110057, India
Tel.: (91) 1244708100
Web Site: https://www.pvrcinemas.com
Year Founded: 1995
532689—(BOM)
Rev.: $102,286,275
Assets: $1,024,099,440
Liabilities: $773,840,340
Net Worth: $250,259,100
Earnings: ($102,073,335)
Emp.: 7,763
Fiscal Year-end: 03/31/21
Film Production & Distribution Services; Motion Picture Theaters
N.A.I.C.S.: 512110
Ajay Bijli *(Co-Founder, Chm & Co-Mng Dir)*

Subsidiaries:

Cinemax India Limited (1)
215 Atrium 10th Fl Opp Divine School, JB Nagar Andheri Kurla Road, Andheri East, Mumbai, 400059, Maharashtra, India (93%)
Tel.: (91) 22 6726 8888
Web Site: http://www.cinemax.co.in
Sales Range: $25-49.9 Million
Movie Theaters
N.A.I.C.S.: 512131
Mayur Parekh *(VP-Accts & Fin)*

PVS-KUNSTSTOFFTECHNIK GMBH & CO. KG
Salzstrasse 20, 74676, Niedernhall, Germany
Tel.: (49) 794091260
Web Site: http://www.pvs-plastics.net
Year Founded: 1976
Rev.: $41,382,000
Emp.: 192
Electric Motor Component Mfr
N.A.I.C.S.: 334419
Juergen Frank *(Gen Mgr-Engrg & Sls)*

Subsidiaries:

PVS Plastics Technology (Shanghai) Co., Ltd. (1)
No 31 Building No 289 Xuanzhong Road Nanhui Industrial Zone, 201300, Shanghai, China
Tel.: (86) 2120307497
Electric Motor Component Distr
N.A.I.C.S.: 423610

PVS Plastics Technology Corp. (1)
6290 Executive Blvd, Huber Heights, OH 45424
Tel.: (937) 233-4376
Electric Motor Component Distr
N.A.I.C.S.: 423610
Tony Rockas *(Project Mgr)*

PVS-Hungary Kft. (1)
Epitok utja 8a, 9500, Celldomolk, Hungary
Tel.: (36) 95424118
Electric Motor Component Distr
N.A.I.C.S.: 423610

PVT PORTAFOLIO DE VALORES S.A.
Calle Porta 643, Miraflores, Lima, Peru
Tel.: (51) 1 471 7172
PVTBC1—(LIM)
Sales Range: Less than $1 Million
Investment Brokerage & Other Financial Investment Services
N.A.I.C.S.: 921130

PVV INFRA LIMITED
Plot No 42 D No 54-28/3-5 Opp Gurudwara, Behind OBC Bank Gurunanak Colony, Vijayawada, 520008, Andhra Pradesh, India
Tel.: (91) 8662544224
Web Site: https://www.pvvinfra.com
Year Founded: 2000

PVV Infra Limited—(Continued)
536659—(BOM)
Rev.: $292,670
Assets: $1,815,164
Liabilities: $9,982
Net Worth: $1,805,182
Earnings: $156,994
Fiscal Year-end: 03/31/21
Civil Engineering Services
N.A.I.C.S.: 237990
K. Sambasiva Rao (CEO)

PW MEDTECH GROUP LIMITED
Building 1 Courtyard 23 Panlong West Road Mafang Industrial Park, Pinggu District, Beijing, China
Tel.: (86) 10 84783617 Ky
Web Site: http://www.pwmedtech.com
1358—(HKG)
Sales Range: $25-49.9 Million
Emp.: 1,079
Medical Device Mfr & Distr
N.A.I.C.S.: 339112
Yue'e Zhang (Chm & CEO)

Subsidiaries:
Beijing Fert Technology Co., Ltd. (1)
Block A Pioneer Park Badachu Science and Technology Park, Shijingshan District, Beijing, 100041, China
Tel.: (86) 10 88795658
Web Site: http://www.china-fert.com
Medical Filter Product Mfr & Distr
N.A.I.C.S.: 339112

Shenzhen Bone Medical Device Co., Ltd. (1)
A1/C Building 3/F Tefalonger Industrial Park Longgang, Central City, Shenzhen, 518172, China
Tel.: (86) 75589724646
Web Site: http://www.bone-med.com
Orthopedic Product Mfr & Distr
N.A.I.C.S.: 339113

Tianjin Walkman Biomaterial Co., Ltd. (1)
No 19 Technology Road Jinghai Economic Development Zone, Tianjin, China
Tel.: (86) 2268660775
Web Site: http://www.walkman.com.cn
Surgical Instrument Mfr & Distr
N.A.I.C.S.: 339112

Xuzhou Yijia Medical Appliance Co., Ltd. (1)
Hongda Road South & Jiankang Road East, Xinyi, Gangtou Jiangsu, China
Tel.: (86) 51688584333
Infusion Product Mfr
N.A.I.C.S.: 339112

PWC ASESORES EMPRESARIALES CIA. LTDA.
Urb Parque Empresarial Colon Mz 275 Solar 1 Edif Metropark, Guayaquil, Guayas, Ecuador
Tel.: (593) 4 3700 220 EC
Sales Range: $10-24.9 Million
Accounting Tax Preparation Risk Management Business Assurance Regulatory & Advisory Services
N.A.I.C.S.: 541211

Subsidiaries:
PricewaterhouseCoopers del Ecuador Cia. Ltda. (1)
Carchi No 702 y 9 de Octubre 2o piso, Guayaquil, Ecuador
Tel.: (593) 4 3700 200
Corporate Auditing Services
N.A.I.C.S.: 541219

PWC OSTERREICH GMBH WIRTSCHAFTSPRUFUNGSGESELLSCHAFT
Donau-City-Strasse 7, 1220, Vienna, Austria
Tel.: (43) 1 501 88 0 AT
Web Site: http://www.pwc.at
Accounting, Tax & Business Consulting Services
N.A.I.C.S.: 541211
Aslan Milla (Sr Partner)

Subsidiaries:
PricewaterhouseCoopers Salzburg Wirtschaftsprufung und Steuerberatung GmbH (1)
Wilhelm-Spazier-Strasse 2a, 5020, Salzburg, Austria
Tel.: (43) 662 21950
Emp.: 32
Auditing & Tax Preparation Services
N.A.I.C.S.: 541219
Horst Bernegger (Mgr)

PricewaterhouseCoopers Tirol Wirtschaftsprufungsgesellschaft mbH (1)
AndreasHofer-Strasse 43, 6020, Innsbruck, Austria
Tel.: (43) 512 567 565
Business Consulting Services
N.A.I.C.S.: 541611

PricewaterhouseCoopers Vorarlberg Wirtschaftsprufungs GmbH (1)
Marktstrassse 30, 6850, Dornbirn, Austria
Tel.: (43) 5572 39 40 32
Auditing & Tax Preparation Services
N.A.I.C.S.: 541219

PwC Burgenland Wirtschaftsprufung und Steuerberatung GmbH (1)
Colmarplatz 1 3 floor, 7000, Eisenstadt, Austria
Tel.: (43) 2682 62660
Business Consulting Services
N.A.I.C.S.: 541611

PwC Karnten Wirtschaftsprufung und Steuerberatung GmbH (1)
Neuer Platz 5, 9020, Klagenfurt, Austria
Tel.: (43) 463 50 7905
Emp.: 8
Auditing & Tax Preparation Services
N.A.I.C.S.: 541219

PwC Oberosterreich Wirtschaftsprufung und Steuerberatung GmbH (1)
Hafenstrasse 2a, 4020, Linz, Austria
Tel.: (43) 732 611 750
Emp.: 35
Auditing & Tax Preparation Services
N.A.I.C.S.: 541219

PwC Steiermark Wirtschaftsprufung und Steuerberatung GmbH (1)
Conrad-von-Hoetzendorf-Strasse 37a/II, 8010, Graz, Austria
Tel.: (43) 316 825 300 0
Emp.: 30
Auditing & Tax Preparation Services
N.A.I.C.S.: 541219

PWE HOLDINGS PLC
1210 Parkview Arlington Business Park Theale, Reading, RG7 4TY, United Kingdom
Tel.: (44) 1184620252
Year Founded: 2013
Holding Company
N.A.I.C.S.: 551112
Sean Fitzpatrick (CEO)

PWF CORPORATION BHD.
Plot 127 Jalan Perindustrian Bukit Minyak 7, Taman Perindustrian Bukit Minyak, 14100, Bukit Mertajam, Penang, Malaysia
Tel.: (60) 45081088
Web Site: https://www.pwf.com.my
Year Founded: 1997
PWF—(KLS)
Rev.: $102,905,191
Assets: $111,390,098
Liabilities: $42,898,872
Net Worth: $68,491,226
Earnings: $3,149,688
Fiscal Year-end: 12/31/22
Poultry Farming Services
N.A.I.C.S.: 311615
Lay Hoon Ch'ng (Sec)

Subsidiaries:
PWF Feeds Sdn. Bhd. (1)
Plot 31 Lorong Perindustrian Bukit Minyak 9, Taman Perindustrian Bukit Minyak, 14100, Bukit Mertajam, S P T Penang, Malaysia
Tel.: (60) 45081099
Poultry Food Mfr
N.A.I.C.S.: 311615

PWF Foods Sdn. Bhd. (1)
No 8 & 9 Jalan PS 3 Taman Prima Selayang, 68100, Batu Caves, Selangor, Malaysia
Tel.: (60) 361206041
Web Site: http://www.pwf.com.my
Processed Food Whslr
N.A.I.C.S.: 424420

PWM GMBH & CO. KG
Kolner Strasse 120, 51702, Bergneustadt, Germany
Tel.: (49) 226140960
Web Site: http://www.pwm.com
Year Founded: 1806
Sales Range: $10-24.9 Million
Emp.: 100
Electric Equipment Mfr
N.A.I.C.S.: 335999
Max-Ferdinand Krawinkel (Pres)

Subsidiaries:
PWM Electronic Price Signs, Inc. (1)
221 Barren Springs Dr Ste 1, Houston, TX 77090
Tel.: (713) 290-0626
Electronic Equipment Distr
N.A.I.C.S.: 423690
Wolfgang Manz (Pres)

PWO AG
Industriestrasse 8, 77704, Oberkirch, Germany
Tel.: (49) 7802840 De
Web Site: https://www.pwo-group.com
PWO—(DEU)
Rev.: $572,804,878
Assets: $431,988,992
Liabilities: $268,686,596
Net Worth: $163,302,396
Earnings: $16,415,929
Emp.: 2,820
Fiscal Year-end: 12/31/22
Air Pump Manufacturer
N.A.I.C.S.: 333912
Georg Hengstberger (Deputy Chm-Supervisory Bd)

Subsidiaries:
PWO Canada Inc. (1)
255 McBrine Dr, Kitchener, N2R 1G7, ON, Canada
Tel.: (519) 893-6880
Web Site: https://www.pwo-group.com
Rev.: $17,504,370
Emp.: 250
Metal Components Mfr & Supplier
N.A.I.C.S.: 332722

PWO Czech Republic A.S. (1)
Palackeho 1261, 757 01, Valasske Mezirici, Czech Republic
Tel.: (420) 571878411
Advanced Metal Component Mfr
N.A.I.C.S.: 332312
Bernd Bartmann (Chm)

PWO High-Tech Metal Components (Suzhou) Co., Ltd. (1)
33 Tian edang Rd Wuzhong Econ Dev Zone, Suzhou, Jiangsu, China
Tel.: (86) 51266379721
Rev.: $292,540
Emp.: 80
Metal Components Mfr & Distr
N.A.I.C.S.: 333517

PWO High-Tech Tool Trading (Suzhou) Co., Ltd. (1)
Tianedang Rd Wangshan Indus Park Wuzhong Econ Dev Zone, Suzhou, 215104, Jiangsu, China
Tel.: (86) 51266379721
Machine Tool Distr
N.A.I.C.S.: 423830

PWO UNITOOLS CZ a.s. (1)
Palackeho 1261, PO Box 180, 757 11, Valasske Mezirici, Czech Republic
Tel.: (420) 571 878 411
Web Site: http://www.pwo-unitools.cz
Sales Range: $125-149.9 Million
Emp.: 300
Dies & Sheet Metal Pressed Parts Mfr
N.A.I.C.S.: 333517
Jiri Safarik (Mgr-Quality)

PWO de Mexico S.A. de C.V. (1)
Carril Norte De San Cristobal S n Autopista Puebla-Orizaba Km14 5, Parque Industrial Chachapa, Puebla, 72990, Mexico
Tel.: (52) 222 2238600
Web Site: http://www.pwo-mexico.com.mx
Rev.: $18,850,860
Emp.: 279
Metallic Components Mfr
N.A.I.C.S.: 333517

PWR HOLDINGS LIMITED
103 Lahrs Road, Ormeau, 4208, QLD, Australia
Tel.: (61) 755471600
Web Site: https://www.pwr.com.au
PWH—(ASX)
Rev.: $77,440,356
Assets: $75,489,636
Liabilities: $16,955,019
Net Worth: $58,534,617
Earnings: $15,969,698
Emp.: 451
Fiscal Year-end: 06/30/22
Custom Automobile Components
N.A.I.C.S.: 336310
Kees Cornelius Weel (CEO & Mng Dir)

Subsidiaries:
C&R Racing Inc. (1)
6950 Guion Rd, Indianapolis, IN 46268
Tel.: (317) 293-4100
Web Site: http://www.crracing.com
Cooling System Mfr
N.A.I.C.S.: 333415

PWR Europe Limited (1)
1141 Silverstone Park Buckingham Road, Silverstone, Towcester, NN12 8FU, Northants, United Kingdom
Tel.: (44) 1327362940
Web Site: http://www.pwreurope.com
Automotive Radiator Mfr
N.A.I.C.S.: 333414

PYC THERAPEUTICS LIMITED
Suite 8 7 The Esplanade, Mount Pleasant, 6153, WA, Australia
Tel.: (61) 893169100
Web Site: https://www.pyctx.com
PYC—(ASX)
Rev.: $2,483,734
Assets: $44,393,703
Liabilities: $3,077,473
Net Worth: $41,316,230
Earnings: ($14,274,120)
Emp.: 5
Fiscal Year-end: 06/30/21
Biopharmaceutical Mfr & Researcher
N.A.I.C.S.: 325412
Kevin Hart (Sec)

PYE MOTORS LTD
Ovangle Road, Morecambe, LA3 3PF, Lancashire, United Kingdom
Tel.: (44) 1524598598
Web Site: http://www.pyemotors.co.uk
Year Founded: 1925
Sales Range: $25-49.9 Million
Emp.: 132

AND PRIVATE COMPANIES / PYRIDAM FARMA TBK

New & Used Car Dealers
N.A.I.C.S.: 441110
Gary Williams *(Mgr-IT)*

PYEONG HWA AUTOMOTIVE CO., LTD
392 Seongseo 4-cha Cheomdan-ro, Dalseo-gu, Daegu, 704-801, Korea (South)
Tel.: (82) 533506114
Web Site: https://www.phakr.com
Year Founded: 1985
043370—(KRS)
Rev.: $785,742,003
Assets: $751,565,692
Liabilities: $235,298,304
Net Worth: $516,267,388
Earnings: $21,676,405
Emp.: 682
Fiscal Year-end: 12/31/22
Automobile Parts Mfr
N.A.I.C.S.: 336390
Sang Tae Kim *(Chm & Principal)*

Subsidiaries:

AST Co., Ltd. (1)
649-3 Naksan-ri Chilgok-gun, Waegwan, Gyeongsangbuk-do, Korea (South)
Tel.: (82) 549791114
Automobile Parts Mfr
N.A.I.C.S.: 336390

PHA Body Systems, LLC (1)
139 Folmar Pkwy, Montgomery, AL 36105
Tel.: (334) 284-9972
Emp.: 137
Automobile Parts Mfr
N.A.I.C.S.: 336390

PHA Czech s.r.o (1)
Tel.: (420) 558774400
Emp.: 201
Automobile Parts Mfr
N.A.I.C.S.: 336390

PHA E&E Inc. (1)
205-2 Paho-dong Dalseo-gu, Daegu, Korea (South)
Tel.: (82) 535802600
Automobile Parts Mfr
N.A.I.C.S.: 336390

PHA Edscha Ltd. (1)
21-12 Asan-ro 1233, Asan, Chungcheongnam-do, Korea (South)
Tel.: (82) 415422620
Automobile Parts Mfr
N.A.I.C.S.: 336390

PHA India (Pvt), Ltd. (1)
C-16 and C-25 SIPCOT Industrial Park Irrungatukottai, Sriperumbudur Taluk Kanchipuram District, 602 105, Chennai, Tamil Nadu, India
Tel.: (91) 4427156036
Web Site: http://phauto.co.in
Automotive Parts Mfr & Distr
N.A.I.C.S.: 336320
Chakara Varthy *(Asst Gen Mgr)*

PHA Slovakia s.r.o. (1)
Tel.: (421) 414250100
Emp.: 156
Automobile Parts Mfr
N.A.I.C.S.: 336390

PHA USA, LLC (1)
765 Standard Pkwy, Auburn Hills, MI 48326-1448
Tel.: (248) 244-2019
Automobile Parts Mfr
N.A.I.C.S.: 336390
Eugene Paik *(Pres & CEO)*

Pyeong Hwa Automotive Beijing Co., Ltd. (1)
1 Secondary and Tertiary Industry Base Nachaizhen Shunyi, Beijing, China
Tel.: (86) 1089475001
Emp.: 262
Automobile Parts Mfr
N.A.I.C.S.: 336390

Pyeong Hwa Automotive Co., Ltd - Asan Plant (1)
59-3 Wolseon-ri Yeongin-myeon, 336-821, Asan, Chungcheongnam-do, Korea (South)
Tel.: (82) 415429880
Automobile Parts Mfr
N.A.I.C.S.: 336390

Pyeong Hwa Automotive Co., Ltd - Ihyeon Plant (1)
1055 Jungri-dong Seo-gu, 703-833, Daegu, Korea (South)
Tel.: (82) 536056251
Automobile Parts Mfr
N.A.I.C.S.: 336390

Pyeong Hwa Automotive Co., Ltd - Oedong Plant (1)
5b Oedong Industrial Complex Oedong-Eup, 780-826, Gyeongju, Gyeongsangbuk-do, Korea (South)
Tel.: (82) 547409800
Automobile Parts Mfr
N.A.I.C.S.: 336390

Pyeong Hwa Automotive Co., Ltd - Seongseo Plant (1)
587-4 Daecheon-dong Dalseo-gu, 704-801, Daegu, Korea (South)
Tel.: (82) 535929881
Automobile Parts Mfr
N.A.I.C.S.: 336390

Pyeong Hwa Automotive Taicang Co., Ltd. (1)
Emp.: 295
Automobile Parts Mfr
N.A.I.C.S.: 336390

Pyeong Hwa Automotive Yangcheng Co., Ltd. (1)
No 28-6 Xiangjiang Road Economic-Technical Development Zone, Yancheng, Jiangsu, China
Tel.: (86) 51589850260
Emp.: 126
Automobile Parts Mfr
N.A.I.C.S.: 336390

PYEONG SAN CO., LTD.
1658-7 Songjeong dong, Kangseo gu, Busan, 618-819, Korea (South)
Tel.: (82) 51 9703000
Web Site: http://www.psminc.co.kr
Year Founded: 1986
Sales Range: $250-299.9 Million
Emp.: 320
Wind Turbine Components, Forgings & Electrical Power Generating Equipment Mfr
N.A.I.C.S.: 333611
Dong-soo Shin *(CEO)*

Subsidiaries:

Jahnel-Kestermann Getriebewerke GmbH & Co. KG (1)
Hunscheidtstrasse 116, 44789, Bochum, Germany
Tel.: (49) 2343390
Web Site: http://www.jake-gear.com
Sales Range: $25-49.9 Million
Emp.: 295
Transmission Systems Mfr
N.A.I.C.S.: 333612

PYI CORPORATION LIMITED
33/F Paul Y Centre 51 Hung To Road, Kwun Tong, Kowloon, China (Hong Kong)
Tel.: (852) 28318328   BM
Web Site: http://www.pyicorp.com
Rev.: $678,111,152
Assets: $979,189,871
Liabilities: $301,210,112
Net Worth: $677,979,759
Earnings: $8,217,618
Emp.: 1,343
Fiscal Year-end: 03/31/19
Ports & Infrastructure Development & Investment Company
N.A.I.C.S.: 336611
June Wai Au *(Exec Dir)*

Subsidiaries:

PYI Management Limited (1)
33 F Paul Y Ctr 51 Hung To Rd, Kwun Tong, Kowloon, China (Hong Kong)
Tel.: (852) 28318338
Real Estate Property Management Services
N.A.I.C.S.: 531311

PYLON PUBLIC COMPANY LIMITED
252 SPE Tower Building 14th Floor Phaholyothin Road, Sam Sen Nai Subdistrict Phayathai District, Bangkok, 10400, Thailand
Tel.: (66) 26151259
Web Site: https://www.pylon.co.th
Year Founded: 2002
PYLON—(THA)
Rev.: $43,282,034
Assets: $37,039,028
Liabilities: $6,499,367
Net Worth: $30,539,661
Earnings: $3,104,139
Emp.: 564
Fiscal Year-end: 12/31/23
Construction Services
N.A.I.C.S.: 236210
Seri Chintanaseri *(Co-Chm)*

Subsidiaries:

Excelon Co., Ltd. (1)
Maurice Pitot Lane Curepipe Road, Curepipe, Mauritius
Tel.: (230) 52533121
Web Site: http://www.excelon.co
General Management Consulting Services
N.A.I.C.S.: 541618

PYLON TECHNOLOGIES CO., LTD.
No 300 Miaoqiao Road, Kangqiao Town Pudong New Area, Shanghai, 201315, China
Tel.: (86) 2131590029
Web Site: http://www.pylontech.com.cn
Year Founded: 2009
688063—(SHG)
Rev.: $844,249,742
Assets: $1,135,771,248
Liabilities: $530,652,246
Net Worth: $605,119,002
Earnings: $178,691,152
Fiscal Year-end: 12/31/22
Energy Distribution Services
N.A.I.C.S.: 221122
Zaisheng Wei *(Chm)*

PYNE GOULD CORPORATION LIMITED
Sarnia House Le Truchot, Le Truchot, Saint Peter Port, GY1 4NA, Guernsey
Tel.: (44) 1481737600   GY
Web Site: http://www.pgc.co.nz
Rev.: $52,756,926
Assets: $193,181,832
Liabilities: $150,903,789
Net Worth: $42,278,043
Earnings: $7,453,883
Fiscal Year-end: 06/30/22
Wealth Management Services
N.A.I.C.S.: 523999
George Kerr *(Mng Dir)*

PYRAMID AG
Sendlinger Tor Platz 8, 80336, Munich, Germany
Tel.: (49) 89244192200
Web Site: https://pyramid-ag.com
Year Founded: 2006
M3B—(DEU)
Rev.: $895,888
Assets: $2,687,664
Liabilities: $1,007,874
Net Worth: $1,679,790
Earnings: ($1,679,790)
Fiscal Year-end: 12/30/19
Financial Investment Services
N.A.I.C.S.: 523940

PYRAMID TECHNOPLAST LIMITED
Office No 2 Second Floor Shah Trade Center Rani Sati Marg, Near W E Highway Malad East, Mumbai, 400097, India
Tel.: (91) 2242761500
Web Site: https://www.pyramidtechnoplast.com
Year Founded: 1997
543969—(BOM)
Rev.: $58,614,532
Assets: $27,455,018
Liabilities: $14,413,382
Net Worth: $13,041,636
Earnings: $3,862,101
Emp.: 493
Fiscal Year-end: 03/31/23
Plastics Product Mfr
N.A.I.C.S.: 326199
Bijaykumar Agarwal *(Chm)*

PYRAMISA HOTELS & RESORTS
60 Giza St Pyramisa Hotel, Giza, Egypt
Tel.: (20) 233360791
Web Site: http://www.pyramisaegypt.com
Year Founded: 1994
PHTV.CA—(EGX)
Sales Range: Less than $1 Million
Home Management Services
N.A.I.C.S.: 721110
Mohamed Azab *(Chm & Mng Dir)*

PYRIDAM FARMA TBK
Sinarmas MSIG Tower Lantai 12 Jl Jend Sudirman Kav 21 RT 10 RW 01, Kuningan Karet, Jakarta, 12920, Indonesia
Tel.: (62) 2150991067
Web Site: https://www.pyridam.com
Year Founded: 1976
PYFA—(INDO)
Rev.: $45,592,271
Assets: $98,788,849
Liabilities: $75,601,392
Net Worth: $23,187,457
Earnings: ($5,534,607)
Emp.: 880
Fiscal Year-end: 12/31/23
Pharmaceuticals Product Mfr
N.A.I.C.S.: 325412
Kuntoro W. Nurtanio *(Dir-Ops)*

Subsidiaries:

PYFA Australia Pty Ltd. (1)
Level 16 80 Collins Street South Tower, Melbourne, 3000, VIC, Australia
Tel.: (61) 396793000
Pharmaceuticals Product Mfr
N.A.I.C.S.: 325412

Subsidiary (Domestic):

PROBIOTEC LIMITED (2)
83 Cherry Lane, Laverton North, Melbourne, 3026, VIC, Australia
Tel.: (61) 392787555
Web Site: https://www.probiotec.com.au
Rev.: $92,331,164
Assets: $176,894,648
Liabilities: $124,323,867
Net Worth: $52,570,781
Earnings: $3,712,981
Emp.: 42
Fiscal Year-end: 06/30/2021
Biotechnology Industry
N.A.I.C.S.: 325411
Jared Stringer *(CFO & Sec)*

Subsidiary (Domestic):

Milton Australia Pty. Ltd. (3)
83 Cherry Ln, Laverton N, Melbourne, 3026, VIC, Australia
Tel.: (61) 392787555
Web Site: http://www.miltonpharma.com
Pharmaceutical Products Mfr & Sales
N.A.I.C.S.: 325412

PYRIDAM FARMA TBK

Pyridam Farma Tbk—(Continued)

Probiotec (QLD) Pty. Ltd. (3)
83 Cherry Ln, Laverton N, Melbourne, 3026, VIC, Australia
Tel.: (61) 392787555
Web Site: http://www.probiotec.com.au
Sales Range: $50-74.9 Million
Emp.: 200
Pharmaceuticals Product Mfr
N.A.I.C.S.: 325412

Probiotec Nutritionals Pty. Ltd. (3)
83 Cherry Ln, Laverton N, Melbourne, 3026, VIC, Australia
Tel.: (61) 392787565
Web Site: http://www.probiotec.com.au
Sales Range: $150-199.9 Million
Pharmaceutical Products Mfr & Sales
N.A.I.C.S.: 325412

Probiotec Pharma Pty. Ltd. (3)
83 Cherry Lane, Laverton North, Melbourne, 3026, VIC, Australia
Tel.: (61) 39 278 7555
Web Site: https://probiotecpharma.com.au
Sales Range: $50-74.9 Million
Emp.: 300
Pharmaceuticals Product Mfr
N.A.I.C.S.: 325412
Wayne Stringer (CEO)

PYROGENESIS CANADA INC.
1744 William St Suite 200, Montreal, H3J 1R4, QC, Canada
Tel.: (514) 937-0002
Web Site: https://www.pyrogenesis.com
PYR—(NASDAQ)
Rev.: $14,873,883
Assets: $37,288,745
Liabilities: $24,092,521
Net Worth: $13,196,224
Earnings: ($25,163,622)
Emp.: 116
Fiscal Year-end: 12/31/22
Waste Mangement Services
N.A.I.C.S.: 333310
Massimo Dattilo (VP-Sls)

PYROLL GROUP OY
Malminsuontie 6, Siltakyla, 49220, Broby, Finland
Tel.: (358) 306242400
Web Site: http://www.pyroll.com
Year Founded: 1973
Paper & Paper Products Mfr
N.A.I.C.S.: 322120
Reino Uusitalo (Chm & CEO)

Subsidiaries:

Stora Enso Baienfurt GmbH (1)
Fabrikstrasse 1, 88255, Baienfurt, Germany
Tel.: (49) 7514040
Paper Sheeting Services
N.A.I.C.S.: 322230
Oliver Spraul (Gen Mgr)

PYRUM INNOVATIONS AG
Dieselstrasse 8, 66763, Dillingen, Germany
Tel.: (49) 6831959480
Web Site: https://www.pyrum.net
Year Founded: 2008
PYRUM—(OSL)
Rev.: $20,579,629
Assets: $53,806,786
Liabilities: $19,389,198
Net Worth: $34,417,588
Earnings: ($8,426,625)
Emp.: 63
Fiscal Year-end: 12/31/22
Recycling Equipment Mfr
N.A.I.C.S.: 333310
Michael Kapf (Deputy Chm)

PYUNG HWA HOLDINGS CO., LTD.
597 Nongong-ro Nongong-eup, Dalseong-gun, Daegu, Korea (South)
Tel.: (82) 536108500

Web Site: https://www.phhc.co.kr
Year Founded: 1950
010770—(KRS)
Rev.: $567,757,181
Assets: $428,270,108
Liabilities: $334,319,831
Net Worth: $93,950,278
Earnings: ($10,785,835)
Emp.: 82
Fiscal Year-end: 12/31/22
Holding Company
N.A.I.C.S.: 551112
Jong-Suk Kim (Chm)

Subsidiaries:

Pyung Hwa Industrial Co., Ltd. (1)
597 Nongong-ro Nongong-eup, Dalseong-gun, Daegu, Korea (South)
Tel.: (82) 536108500
Web Site: https://www.ph.co.kr
Rev.: $398,788,033
Assets: $181,472,665
Liabilities: $149,694,089
Net Worth: $31,778,575
Earnings: $4,665,941
Emp.: 809
Fiscal Year-end: 12/31/2022
Automobile Parts Mfr
N.A.I.C.S.: 336991
Jong Suk Kim (Chm)

PYX RESOURCES LIMITED
Level 5 56 Pitt Street, Sydney, 2000, NSW, Australia
Tel.: (61) 2 8823 3177
Web Site: http://www.southpacificlimited.com
Sales Range: Less than $1 Million
Oil & Gas Exploration
N.A.I.C.S.: 211120

PYXIS TANKERS INC.
K Karamanli 59, 15125, Maroussi, Greece
Tel.: (30) 2106380200
Web Site: https://www.pyxistankers.com
Year Founded: 2015
PXS—(NASDAQ)
Rev.: $45,468,000
Assets: $166,313,000
Liabilities: $65,454,000
Net Worth: $100,859,000
Earnings: $36,836,000
Fiscal Year-end: 12/31/23
Freight Transportation Services
N.A.I.C.S.: 488510
Valentios Valentis (Founder, Chm & CEO)

Subsidiaries:

Maritime Technologies Corp. (1)
3530 S Hanover St 2, Baltimore, MD 21225-1732
Tel.: (443) 842-4357
Web Site: http://www.martechnocorp.com
Dredging Services
N.A.I.C.S.: 237990

PZ CORMAY S.A.
ul Wiosenna 22, 05-092, Lomianki, Poland
Tel.: (48) 227517910
CRM—(WAR)
Rev.: $20,884,146
Assets: $23,856,707
Liabilities: $9,705,285
Net Worth: $14,151,423
Earnings: ($1,143,293)
Fiscal Year-end: 12/31/23
Diagnostic Reagents Mfr & Laboratory Equipment Distr
N.A.I.C.S.: 423450
Flavio Finotello (CEO)

PZ CUSSONS PLC
1 Hardman Square, Manchester, M3 3EB, United Kingdom

Tel.: (44) 1612452500 UK
Web Site: https://www.pzcussons.com
Year Founded: 1860
PZC—(OTCIQ)
Rev.: $777,279,360
Assets: $1,234,232,560
Liabilities: $645,110,400
Net Worth: $589,122,160
Earnings: $59,528,480
Fiscal Year-end: 05/31/22
Soap & Other Detergent Manufacturing
N.A.I.C.S.: 325611
Jonathan Myers (CEO)

Subsidiaries:

Charles Worthington Hair and Beauty Ltd. (1)
1 Exchange Place, London, EC2M2QT, United Kingdom (100%)
Tel.: (44) 2076380802
Web Site: http://www.charlesworthington.com
Sales Range: $25-49.9 Million
Emp.: 18
Cosmetics Beauty Supplies & Perfume Stores
N.A.I.C.S.: 456120
Charles Worthington (Mng Dir)

FC Ltd. (1)
Cromwell Rd, Ellesmere Port, CH654DP, Cheshire, United Kingdom (100%)
Tel.: (44) 1513558234
Soap & Detergent Mfr
N.A.I.C.S.: 325611

PT PZ Cussons Indonesia (1)
Cyber Bldg 9th Floor, JL Kuningan Barat No 8, Jakarta, 12710, Indonesia (100%)
Tel.: (62) 215269227
Web Site: http://www.pzcussons.com
Sales Range: $450-499.9 Million
Emp.: 100
Store Retailers
N.A.I.C.S.: 459999
Panos Mouchteros (Mng Dir)

PZ Coolworld Limited (1)
45-47 Town Planning Way, Ilupeju Industrial Estate, Lagos, Nigeria
Tel.: (234) 70026 659 6753
Web Site: https://www.coolworld.com.ng
Electrical Products Distr
N.A.I.C.S.: 449210

PZ Cussons (Holdings) Ltd. (1)
PZ Cussion House, Bird Hall Lane, Stockport, SK3 0XN, Cheshire, United Kingdom (100%)
Tel.: (44) 1614918000
Holding Company
N.A.I.C.S.: 551112

Subsidiary (Non-US):

PZ Cussons Nigeria Plc. (2)
45/47 Town Planning Way Ilupeju Industrial Estate, PMB 21132, Ikeja, Lagos, Nigeria (73.27%)
Tel.: (234) 17000180
Web Site: http://www.pzcussons.com.ng
Rev.: $828,452,411
Assets: $1,247,664,731
Liabilities: $714,844,736
Net Worth: $532,819,995
Earnings: $58,571,068
Emp.: 2,600
Fiscal Year-end: 05/31/2023
Pharmaceuticals & Cosmetics Mfr & Distr
N.A.I.C.S.: 325412
Joyce Folake Coker (Dir-HR & Admin)

PZ Cussons (International) Ltd. (1)
Manchester Business Park, 3500 Aviator Way, Manchester, M22 5TG, Cheshire, United Kingdom (100%)
Tel.: (44) 1614918000
Soap & Detergent Mfr
N.A.I.C.S.: 325611

PZ Cussons (Thailand) Ltd. (1)
TST Tower Building 16th Floor Chomphon Chatuchak, 21 Vibhavadee Rangsit Road, 10900, Bangkok, Thailand (100%)
Tel.: (66) 22738161

INTERNATIONAL PUBLIC

Sales Range: $25-49.9 Million
Emp.: 50
Soap & Detergent Mfr
N.A.I.C.S.: 325611

PZ Cussons Australia Pty Ltd (1)
Building A Level 1 13-15 Compark Circuit, Mulgrave, Melbourne, 3170, VIC, Australia
Tel.: (61) 3 8545 2700
Web Site: http://www.pzcussons.com.au
Sales Range: $75-99.9 Million
Emp.: 170
Household Detergent Products Mfr & Distr
N.A.I.C.S.: 325611
Rob Spence (Dir-Bus Unit)

PZ Cussons Ghana Limited (1)
Plot 27/3-27/7 Sanyo Road Tema Heavy Industrial Area, PO Box 628, Tema, Ghana (90%)
Tel.: (233) 303 302701
Web Site: http://www.pzcussonsghana.com
Sales Range: $500-549.9 Million
Emp.: 500
Soap, Detergent & Cosmetics Mfr
N.A.I.C.S.: 325611

PZ Cussons India Pvt. Ltd. (1)
321 Sai Commercial Bldg, BKS Devshi Marg Govandi East, Mumbai, 400088, MH, India
Tel.: (91) 2261477300
Web Site: http://www.imperialleather.in
Sales Range: $25-49.9 Million
Emp.: 6
Soap & Detergent Mfr
N.A.I.C.S.: 325611
Nitin Thacker (Gen Mgr)

PZ Cussons Middle East and South Asia FZE (1)
Jebel Ali, PO Box 17233, Dubai, 17233, United Arab Emirates (100%)
Tel.: (971) 48814230
Web Site: http://www.pzcussons.com
Sales Range: $25-49.9 Million
Emp.: 15
Soap & Detergent Mfr
N.A.I.C.S.: 325611
Abdul Rab (Gen Mgr)

PZ Cussons Polska S.A. (1)
Ul Chocimska 17, 00-791, Warsaw, Poland (100%)
Tel.: (48) 5272364701
Web Site: http://www.pzcussons.com.pl
Sales Range: $125-149.9 Million
Emp.: 440
Soap & Detergent Mfr
N.A.I.C.S.: 325611

PZ Cussons UK Ltd (1)
PZ Cussons House Bird Hall Lane, Stockport, SK3 0XN, Cheshire, United Kingdom (100%)
Tel.: (44) 614918000
Web Site: http://www.pzcussons.com
Sales Range: $800-899.9 Million
Emp.: 300
Mfr & Marketing of Soap, Toiletries & Other Household Products
N.A.I.C.S.: 325611

St Tropez Holdings Ltd (1)
Unit, 4c Tissington Close Chilwell, Nottingham, NG9 6QG, Nottinghamshire, United Kingdom
Tel.: (44) 1159 836363
Web Site: http://www.st-tropez.com
Emp.: 5
Investment Management Service
N.A.I.C.S.: 523999
Selma Terzic (Mng Dir)

St Tropez Inc (1)
27334 Muirfield Ln, Valencia, CA 91355
Tel.: (800) 366-6383
Web Site: http://www.sttroperztan.com
Cosmetics Products Mfr
N.A.I.C.S.: 325620
Michelle Feeney (CEO)

The Sanctuary City Spas Ltd (1)
Saint Nicholas Close, Borehamwood, WD6 3EW, Hertfordshire, United Kingdom
Tel.: (44) 20 8334 9999
Beauty Spa Operating Services
N.A.I.C.S.: 812112

The Sanctuary Spa Holdings Ltd (1)

AND PRIVATE COMPANIES — Q&M DENTAL GROUP (SINGAPORE) LIMITED

Sanctuary House Swallowdale Lane, Hemel Hempstead, HP2 7EA, Hertfordshire, United Kingdom
Tel.: (44) 1442 430300
Investment Management Service
N.A.I.C.S.: 523999

The Sanctuary at Covent Garden Ltd (1)
12 Floral Street Covent Garden, London, WC2E 9DH, United Kingdom
Tel.: (44) 844 875 8443
Web Site: http://www.thesanctuary.co.uk
Beauty Center & Spa Operating Services
N.A.I.C.S.: 812112

PZP ZAJECAR A.D.
Generala Gambete 68, Zajecar, Serbia
Tel.: (381) 19 422 528
Web Site: http://www.pzpzajecar.rs
Year Founded: 1961
Sales Range: $10-24.9 Million
Emp.: 200
Road Construction Services
N.A.I.C.S.: 237310
Bojan Aleksic *(Exec Dir)*

Q ACOUSTICS LIMITED
Units 7 & 8 Stortford Hall Industrial Park, Dunmow Road, Bishop's Stortford, CM23 5GZ, Herts, United Kingdom
Tel.: (44) 1279 501 111   UK
Web Site:
    http://www.qacoustics.co.uk
Year Founded: 2014
Sales Range: $10-24.9 Million
Holding Company; Home Entertainment Electronics & Accessories Mfr & Distr
N.A.I.C.S.: 551112
George Dexter *(CEO)*

Subsidiaries:

Armour Home Electronics Limited (1)
Units 7 & 8 Stortford Hall Industrial Park, Dunmow Road, Bishop's Stortford, CM23 5GZ, Herts, United Kingdom
Tel.: (44) 1279 501 111
Web Site: http://www.armourhome.co.uk
Sales Range: $10-24.9 Million
Emp.: 90
Specialist Hi-Fi & Home Entertainment Equipment Designer, Mfr & Distr
N.A.I.C.S.: 334220
Steve Reichert *(Mgr-PR)*

Armour Hong Kong Limited (1)
HKI Building 1st Floor 56 Hung To Road, Kwun Tong, Kowloon, China (Hong Kong)
Tel.: (852) 28106886
Web Site: http://www.armourasia.com
Home Audio Equipment & Related Furniture Whslr
N.A.I.C.S.: 423620
Darrell Huggins *(Mng Dir)*

Q ASSOCIATES LTD.
Langley Business Court, Beedon, Newbury, RG20 8RY, Berks, United Kingdom
Tel.: (44) 1635248181
Web Site:
    http://www.qassociates.co.uk
Year Founded: 1985
IT Services
N.A.I.C.S.: 541512
David M. Cue *(Mng Dir)*

Q CAPITAL PARTNERS CO., LTD
11F KAIT Tower 306 Teheran-ro, Gangnam-Gu, Seoul, 06290, Korea (South)
Tel.: (82) 25382411
Web Site: https://www.qcapital.co.kr
Year Founded: 1982
016600—(KRS)

Sales Range: $25-49.9 Million
Emp.: 26
Venture Investment Services
N.A.I.C.S.: 523910
Hee Yeon Hwang *(CEO)*

Subsidiaries:

Doosan Engineering & Construction Co., Ltd. (1)
726 Eonju-ro, Gangnam-gu, Seoul, 135-714, Korea (South)
Tel.: (82) 25103114
Web Site: https://www.doosanenc.com
Rev.: $1,532,520,000
Assets: $2,003,800,000
Liabilities: $1,516,180,000
Net Worth: $487,620,000
Earnings: ($64,500,000)
Emp.: 1,328
Fiscal Year-end: 12/31/2019
Construction Industry
N.A.I.C.S.: 236116
Jeongwon Park *(Chm & CEO-Doosan Grp)*

Subsidiary (Non-US):

Doosan Cuvex Co., Ltd. (2)
Tel.: (82) 332601114
Golf Club & Resort Management Operator
N.A.I.C.S.: 721110

Plant (Non-US):

Doosan Engineering & Construction Co., Ltd. - Doosan Vina (CPE Plant) (2)
Dung Quat Econ Zone Binh Thuan, Binh Soon, Quang Ngai, Vietnam
Tel.: (84) 553618900
Chemical Process Equipment Mfr
N.A.I.C.S.: 333248

Q L LIGHT SOURCE COMPANY LIMITED
200 Nanxu Avenue, Henjiang High-Tech Dev Zone, Zhenjiang, 212000, Jiangsu, China   HK
Holding Company; LED Light Bulb Mfr
N.A.I.C.S.: 551112
Solomon Yan *(Chm)*

Subsidiaries:

Quality Light Source LLC (1)
300 Lena Dr, Aurora, OH 44202
Tel.: (330) 954-3072
Web Site: http://www.qlightsource.com
LED Light Bulb Distr
N.A.I.C.S.: 423610

TCP International Holdings Ltd. (1)
325 Campus Dr, Aurora, OH 44202
Tel.: (330) 995-6111
Web Site: http://www.tcpi.com
Holding Company; Light Bulb Mfr
N.A.I.C.S.: 551112
Tom Keaty *(CFO)*

Subsidiary (Domestic):

Technical Consumer Products, Inc. (2)
325 Campus Dr, Aurora, OH 44202
Tel.: (330) 995-6111
Web Site: http://www.tcpi.com
Lighting Fittings & Accessories
N.A.I.C.S.: 335139
Ellis Yan *(CEO)*

Subsidiary (Non-US):

TCP Solutions B.V. (3)
Keizersgracht 268, 1016 EV, Amsterdam, Netherlands
Tel.: (31) 206757162
Web Site: http://www.tcpsolutions.com
Payroll Processing Services
N.A.I.C.S.: 541214

Q P GROUP HOLDINGS LIMITED
Flat J 21/F Kings Wing Plaza 2 No 1 On Kwan Street, Shek Mun, Sha Tin, New Territories, China (Hong Kong)
Tel.: (852) 23426168   Ky

Web Site: http://www.qpp.com
Year Founded: 1985
1412—(HKG)
Rev.: $162,739,980
Assets: $150,352,463
Liabilities: $42,890,235
Net Worth: $107,462,228
Earnings: $16,171,973
Emp.: 2,280
Fiscal Year-end: 12/31/22
Holding Company
N.A.I.C.S.: 551112
Wan Wai Cheng *(Co-Founder, Chm & CEO)*

Subsidiaries:

DPI Laboratory Services Limited (1)
Flat J 21/F Kings Wing Plaza 2 No 1 On Kwan Street, Shek Mun, Sha Tin, New Territories, China (Hong Kong)
Tel.: (852) 31023179
Laboratory Operator
N.A.I.C.S.: 621511

Dongguan Zensee Printing Limited (1)
Dongshan Industrial District, Aobeiwei Zhangmutou, Dongguan, 523619, China
Tel.: (86) 76987712112
Paper Products Mfr
N.A.I.C.S.: 322299

Shenzhen Zen See Information Technology Co., Ltd. (1)
2406 VIA Technology Building No 9966 Shennan Avenue, Shenzhen, 518000, China
Tel.: (86) 75526001990
Paper Products Mfr
N.A.I.C.S.: 322299

Taunus Printing (Heshan) Company Limited (1)
New Material Industrial Base Zone, Gonghe Town, Heshan, 529728, Guangdong, China
Tel.: (86) 7508306888
Paper Products Mfr
N.A.I.C.S.: 322299

Q RESOURCES PLC
43/45 La Motte Street, Saint Helier, JE4 8SD, Jersey
Tel.: (44) 1534 702800
Investment Services
N.A.I.C.S.: 523999
Ivan Murphy *(Chm)*

Q TECHNOLOGY (GROUP) COMPANY LIMITED
3 Taihong Road Hi-tech Industrial Development Zone, Kunshan, Jiangsu, China
Tel.: (86) 51236687999
Web Site:
    http://www.qtechglobal.com
1478—(HKG)
Rev.: $1,931,787,468
Assets: $1,724,880,830
Liabilities: $1,055,537,168
Net Worth: $669,343,662
Earnings: $23,900,292
Emp.: 7,780
Fiscal Year-end: 12/31/22
Camera Module Mfr
N.A.I.C.S.: 334310
Ningning He *(Chm)*

Subsidiaries:

Chengdu Q Technology Limited (1)
6F C12 Tianfu Software Park, Chengdu, Sichuan, China
Tel.: (86) 2885325022
Camera Module Mfr
N.A.I.C.S.: 333310

Kunshan Q Technology Limited (1)
No 3 Taihong Road Hi-tech Industrial Development Zone, Kunshan, Jiangsu, China
Tel.: (86) 51257109980
Camera Module Mfr & Distr
N.A.I.C.S.: 333310
He Ningning *(Founder)*

Q TECHNOLOGY GROUP LIMITED
5 435 Williamstown Road, Port Melbourne, 3207, VIC, Australia
Tel.: (61) 3 9676 7054   AU
Web Site:
    http://www.qtechnologygroup.com.au
Rev.: $10,051,931
Assets: $3,668,303
Liabilities: $4,348,110
Net Worth: ($679,807)
Earnings: ($1,601,565)
Emp.: 40
Fiscal Year-end: 06/30/18
Security System & Locksmith Services
N.A.I.C.S.: 561621
Andrew Phillips *(Sec)*

Subsidiaries:

QRSciences Security Pty. Ltd. (1)
Unit 5 435 Williamstown Rd, Port Melbourne, 3207, Victoria, Australia
Tel.: (61) 396469016
Web Site:
    http://www.qsecuritysystems.com.au
Sales Range: $10-24.9 Million
Security System Monitoring Services
N.A.I.C.S.: 561621
Rob Rosa *(CEO)*

Q&M DENTAL GROUP (SINGAPORE) LIMITED
2 Clementi Loop 04-01 Logis Hub Clementi, Singapore, 129809, Singapore
Tel.: (65) 67059888   SG
Web Site: https://www.qandm.com.sg
Year Founded: 1996
QC7—(SES)
Rev.: $138,395,062
Assets: $195,855,487
Liabilities: $117,910,323
Net Worth: $77,945,164
Earnings: $8,386,730
Emp.: 707
Fiscal Year-end: 12/31/23
Holding Company; Dental Healthcare Services
N.A.I.C.S.: 551112
Raymond Ee Peng Ang *(COO)*

Subsidiaries:

AR Dental Supplies Sdn. Bhd. (1)
No 28 Jalan Kartunis U1/47, Temasya Industrial Park Seksyen U1, 40150, Shah Alam, Selangor Darul Ehsan, Malaysia
Tel.: (60) 355252581
Web Site: https://www.ardental.com.my
Dental Care Services
N.A.I.C.S.: 621210
Carey Chua *(Mng Dir)*

Bright Smile Dental Surgery (Buangkok MRT) Pte. Ltd. (1)
10 Sengkang Central 01-02, MRT Station Exit A, Singapore, 545061, Singapore
Tel.: (65) 62429132
Dental Services
N.A.I.C.S.: 621210

Bright Smile Dental Surgery Pte. Ltd. (1)
18 Jalan Membina 01-05, Singapore, 164018, Singapore
Tel.: (65) 62746800
Dental Services
N.A.I.C.S.: 621210

Killiney Dental Centre Pte. Ltd. (1)
91 Killiney Road, Singapore, 239535, Singapore
Tel.: (65) 62351638
Dental Healthcare Providing Services
N.A.I.C.S.: 621210

Q & M College of Dentistry Pte. Ltd. (1)
180 Kitchener Rd B1-13/14/15 City Square Mall, Singapore, 208539, Singapore
Tel.: (65) 67059888
Web Site: https://www.qandm.edu.sg

Q&M DENTAL GROUP (SINGAPORE) LIMITED — INTERNATIONAL PUBLIC

Q&M Dental Group (Singapore) Limited—(Continued)
Dental Education Training Services
N.A.I.C.S.: 611710
Razak Ahmad (Mgr-Course)

Q & M Dental Centre (Balestier) Pte. Ltd. (1)
627 Balestier Road, Singapore, 329916, Singapore
Tel.: (65) 69965816
Dental Health Care Services
N.A.I.C.S.: 621210

Q & M Dental Centre (Kim Seng) Pte. Ltd. (1)
1 Kim Seng Promenade 03-117 Great World, Singapore, 237994, Singapore
Tel.: (65) 67340603
Dental Health Care Services
N.A.I.C.S.: 621210

Q & M Dental Centre (North Bridge) Pte. Ltd. (1)
107 North Bridge Road B1-37/38 Funan Mall, Singapore, 179105, Singapore
Tel.: (65) 69799296
Dental Health Care Services
N.A.I.C.S.: 621210

Q & M Dental Centre (Orchard) Pte. Ltd. (1)
181 Orchard Road 04-14/19 04-16 Orchard Central, Singapore, 238896, Singapore
Tel.: (65) 67322633
Dental Healthcare Providing Services
N.A.I.C.S.: 621210

Q & M Dental Centre (Raffles Place) Pte. Ltd. (1)
20 Malacca Street 01-00, Singapore, 048979, Singapore
Tel.: (65) 62253033
Dental Healthcare Providing Services
N.A.I.C.S.: 621210

Q & M Dental Surgery (Admiralty) Pte. Ltd. (1)
Blk 717 Woodlands Drive 70 01-114, Singapore, 730717, Singapore
Tel.: (65) 63653903
Dental Healthcare Providing Services
N.A.I.C.S.: 621210

Q & M Dental Surgery (Alexandra Road) Pte. Ltd. (1)
370 Alexandra Road B1-42 Anchorpoint Shopping Centre, Singapore, 159953, Singapore
Tel.: (65) 60161008
Dental Health Care Services
N.A.I.C.S.: 621210

Q & M Dental Surgery (Aljunied) Pte. Ltd. (1)
Blk 113 Aljunied Avenue 2 01-11, Singapore, 380113, Singapore
Tel.: (65) 67487730
Dental Health Care Services
N.A.I.C.S.: 621210

Q & M Dental Surgery (Ang Mo Kio Central) Pte. Ltd. (1)
Blk 710A Ang Mo Kio Avenue 8 01-2629, Singapore, 561710, Singapore
Tel.: (65) 65543363
Dental Healthcare Providing Services
N.A.I.C.S.: 621210

Q & M Dental Surgery (Austin) Sdn. Bhd. (1)
No 29 Ground Floor Jalan Mutiara Emas 10/19 Taman Mount Austin, 81100, Johor Bahru, Malaysia
Tel.: (60) 73614789
Dental Care Services
N.A.I.C.S.: 621210

Q & M Dental Surgery (Bandar Melaka) Sdn. Bhd. (1)
No 230 Jalan Gajah Berang, 75200, Melaka, Malaysia
Tel.: (60) 62811811
Dental Care Services
N.A.I.C.S.: 621210

Q & M Dental Surgery (Bandar Puteri Puchong) Sdn. Bhd. (1)
No 06-01 1st Floor Jalan Puteri 1/1 Bandar Puteri, 47100, Puchong, Kuala Lumpur, Malaysia
Tel.: (60) 380669011
Dental Care Services
N.A.I.C.S.: 621210

Q & M Dental Surgery (Bedok Reservoir) Pte. Ltd. (1)
Blk 632 Bedok Reservoir Road 01-842, Singapore, 470632, Singapore
Tel.: (65) 69803902
Dental Health Care Services
N.A.I.C.S.: 621210

Q & M Dental Surgery (Boon Lay MRT) Pte. Ltd. (1)
301 Boon Lay Way 01-05 Boon Lay MRT Station, Next to Jurong Point Shopping Centre, Singapore, 649846, Singapore
Tel.: (65) 67913323
Dental Healthcare Providing Services
N.A.I.C.S.: 621210

Q & M Dental Surgery (Braddell) Pte. Ltd. (1)
Blk 111 Lorong 1 Toa Payoh 01-360, Singapore, 310111, Singapore
Tel.: (65) 63581098
Dental Healthcare Providing Services
N.A.I.C.S.: 621210

Q & M Dental Surgery (Bukit Batok) Pte. Ltd. (1)
Blk 151 Bukit Batok St 11 01-252, Singapore, 650151, Singapore
Tel.: (65) 66654233
Dental Healthcare Providing Services
N.A.I.C.S.: 621210

Q & M Dental Surgery (Bukit Panjang) Pte. Ltd. (1)
Blk 257 Bangkit Road 01-47, Singapore, 670257, Singapore
Tel.: (65) 67663363
Dental Healthcare Providing Services
N.A.I.C.S.: 621210

Q & M Dental Surgery (Bukit Timah) Pte. Ltd. (1)
3A Cheong Chin Nam Rd Opposite Beauty World, Singapore, 599728, Singapore
Tel.: (65) 64663393
Dental Healthcare Providing Services
N.A.I.C.S.: 621210

Q & M Dental Surgery (Choa Chu Kang) Pte. Ltd. (1)
21 Choa Chu Kang Avenue 4 B1-06 Lot One Shoppers Mall, Singapore, 689812, Singapore
Tel.: (65) 60129338
Dental Health Care Services
N.A.I.C.S.: 621210

Q & M Dental Surgery (Clementi Central) Pte. Ltd. (1)
Blk 450 Clementi Ave 3 01-291 Next to DBS Bank, Singapore, 120450, Singapore
Tel.: (65) 68723633
Dental Healthcare Providing Services
N.A.I.C.S.: 621210

Q & M Dental Surgery (Clementi) Pte. Ltd. (1)
321 Clementi Ave 3 02-02 321 Clementi, Singapore, 129905, Singapore
Tel.: (65) 67782768
Dental Healthcare Providing Services
N.A.I.C.S.: 621210

Q & M Dental Surgery (Elias Mall) Pte. Ltd. (1)
Blk 625 Elias Rd 02-308 Elias Mall, Singapore, 510625, Singapore
Tel.: (65) 65848793
Dental Healthcare Providing Services
N.A.I.C.S.: 621210

Q & M Dental Surgery (Gombak MRT) Pte. Ltd. (1)
802 Bukit Batok West Ave 5 01-09 Bukit Gombak MRT Station, Singapore, 659083, Singapore
Tel.: (65) 65621161
Dental Healthcare Providing Services
N.A.I.C.S.: 621210

Q & M Dental Surgery (Gombak) Pte. Ltd. (1)
Blk 371 Bukit Batok St 31 01-302, Singapore, 650371, Singapore
Tel.: (65) 65693120
Dental Healthcare Providing Services
N.A.I.C.S.: 621210

Q & M Dental Surgery (Hougang Central) Pte. Ltd. (1)
Blk 810 Hougang Central 01-230/232, Singapore, 530810, Singapore
Tel.: (65) 63862663
Dental Healthcare Providing Services
N.A.I.C.S.: 621210

Q & M Dental Surgery (Hougang Mall) Pte. Ltd. (1)
90 Hougang Ave 10 04-07 Hougang Mall, Singapore, 538766, Singapore
Tel.: (65) 62825500
Dental Healthcare Providing Services
N.A.I.C.S.: 621210

Q & M Dental Surgery (Jelapang) Pte. Ltd. (1)
Blk 524A Jelapang Road 02-15 Greenridge Shopping Centre, Singapore, 671524, Singapore
Tel.: (65) 68912668
Dental Healthcare Providing Services
N.A.I.C.S.: 621210

Q & M Dental Surgery (Jurong East Central) Pte. Ltd. (1)
50 Jurong Gateway Road 03-24 Jem, Singapore, 608549, Singapore
Tel.: (65) 64250398
Dental Healthcare Providing Services
N.A.I.C.S.: 621210

Q & M Dental Surgery (Kallang MRT) Pte. Ltd. (1)
4 Lorong 1 Geylang, Singapore, 389116, Singapore
Tel.: (65) 65471833
Dental Healthcare Providing Services
N.A.I.C.S.: 621210

Q & M Dental Surgery (Khatib) Pte. Ltd. (1)
Blk 846 Yishun Ring Road 01-3613 Opposite Khatib MRT Station, Singapore, 760846, Singapore
Tel.: (65) 68523363
Dental Healthcare Providing Services
N.A.I.C.S.: 621210

Q & M Dental Surgery (Kim Tian) Pte. Ltd. (1)
Blk 126 Kim Tian Road 01-03 Kim Tian Green, Singapore, 160126, Singapore
Tel.: (65) 69797668
Dental Health Care Services
N.A.I.C.S.: 621210

Q & M Dental Surgery (Kovan) Pte. Ltd. (1)
Blk 203 Hougang Street 21 01-87, Singapore, 530203, Singapore
Tel.: (65) 62463956
Dental Services
N.A.I.C.S.: 621210

Q & M Dental Surgery (Marsiling) Pte. Ltd. (1)
Blk 304 Woodlands St 31 01-121/123, Singapore, 730304, Singapore
Tel.: (65) 63656500
Dental Healthcare Providing Services
N.A.I.C.S.: 621210

Q & M Dental Surgery (Molek) Sdn. Bhd. (1)
No 43 Jalan Molek 1/29, Taman Molek, 81100, Johor Bahru, Johor, Malaysia
Tel.: (60) 73558989
Dental Services
N.A.I.C.S.: 621210

Q & M Dental Surgery (Old Airport Rd) Pte. Ltd. (1)
Blk 39 Jalan Tiga 01-03, Singapore, 390039, Singapore
Tel.: (65) 64479033
Dental Healthcare Providing Services
N.A.I.C.S.: 621210

Q & M Dental Surgery (Pasir Ris) Pte. Ltd. (1)
1 Pasir Ris Central St 3 05-08 White Sands, Singapore, 518457, Singapore
Tel.: (65) 65830298
Dental Healthcare Providing Services
N.A.I.C.S.: 621210

Q & M Dental Surgery (Redhill MRT) Pte. Ltd. (1)
920 Tiong Bahru Road 01-10 Redhill MRT Station, Singapore, 158792, Singapore
Tel.: (65) 62724858
Dental Healthcare Providing Services
N.A.I.C.S.: 621210

Q & M Dental Surgery (Sembawang MRT) Pte. Ltd. (1)
11 Canberra Rd 02-01 Sembawang MRT Station, Singapore, 759775, Singapore
Tel.: (65) 67523093
Dental Healthcare Providing Services
N.A.I.C.S.: 621210

Q & M Dental Surgery (Serangoon Central) Pte. Ltd. (1)
Blk 264 Serangoon Central 01-235, Singapore, 550264, Singapore
Tel.: (65) 63831763
Dental Healthcare Providing Services
N.A.I.C.S.: 621210

Q & M Dental Surgery (Serangoon North) Pte. Ltd. (1)
Blk 153 Serangoon North Ave 1 01-536, Singapore, 550153, Singapore
Tel.: (65) 62828597
Dental Healthcare Providing Services
N.A.I.C.S.: 621210

Q & M Dental Surgery (Serangoon) Pte. Ltd. (1)
Blk 261 Serangoon Central Drive 01-29, Singapore, 550261, Singapore
Tel.: (65) 63430398
Dental Healthcare Providing Services
N.A.I.C.S.: 621210

Q & M Dental Surgery (Taman Merdeka) Sdn. Bhd. (1)
No 13 Jalan M1 Taman Merdeka, 75350, Batu Berendam, Melaka, Malaysia
Tel.: (60) 63320411
Dental Care Services
N.A.I.C.S.: 621210

Q & M Dental Surgery (Tanjong Katong) Pte. Ltd. (1)
11 Tanjong Katong Road B1-13 Kinex Shopping Mall, Singapore, 437157, Singapore
Tel.: (65) 62416562
Dental Services
N.A.I.C.S.: 621210

Q & M Dental Surgery (Toa Payoh Central) Pte. Ltd. (1)
Blk 177 Toa Payoh Central 01-150, Singapore, 310177, Singapore
Tel.: (65) 62563633
Dental Healthcare Providing Services
N.A.I.C.S.: 621210

Q & M Dental Surgery (Toa Payoh) Pte. Ltd. (1)
Blk 125 Lorong 1 Toa Payoh 01-547, Singapore, 310125, Singapore
Tel.: (65) 69901822
Dental Healthcare Providing Services
N.A.I.C.S.: 621210

Q & M Dental Surgery (Woodlands) Pte. Ltd. (1)
Blk 573 Woodlands Drive 16 01-07, Singapore, 730573, Singapore
Tel.: (65) 63690047
Dental Services
N.A.I.C.S.: 621210

Q & M Dental Surgery (Yishun Central) Pte. Ltd. (1)
Blk 743 Yishun Avenue 5 01-540, Singapore, 760743, Singapore
Tel.: (65) 68516789
Dental Healthcare Providing Services
N.A.I.C.S.: 621210

Q & M Medical & Aesthetic Clinic (Farrer Park) Pte. Ltd. (1)
180 Kitchener Road B1-13/15 City Square Mall, Singapore, 208539, Singapore
Tel.: (65) 65099558

Dental Healthcare Providing Services
N.A.I.C.S.: 621210

Q & M Medical & Aesthetic Clinic (Tampines Central) Pte. Ltd. (1)
10 Tampines Central 1 04-18/19 Tampines 1, Singapore, 529536, Singapore
Tel.: (65) 65883233
Dental Healthcare Providing Services
N.A.I.C.S.: 621210

Q & M Medical Clinic (Buangkok Mrt) Pte. Ltd. (1)
10 Sengkang Central 01-02, Singapore, 545061, Singapore
Tel.: (65) 62429133
Medical Healthcare Services
N.A.I.C.S.: 621610

Q & M Medical Clinic (Bukit Batok) Pte. Ltd. (1)
Blk 151 Bukit Batok Street 11 01-252, Singapore, 650151, Singapore
Tel.: (65) 66654233
Medical Healthcare Services
N.A.I.C.S.: 621498

Q & M Medical Clinic (Serangoon Central) Pte. Ltd. (1)
23 Serangoon Central 04-25 Nex, Singapore, 556083, Singapore
Tel.: (65) 65098858
Dental Healthcare Providing Services
N.A.I.C.S.: 621210

Quantumleap Healthcare Pte. Ltd. (1)
2 Clementi Loop 01-01 01-02 02-01 02-02, Singapore, 129809, Singapore
Tel.: (65) 63685488
Web Site: https://www.quantumleaphc.sg
Dental Healthcare Providing Services
N.A.I.C.S.: 621210

Specialist Oral Surgeons Pte. Ltd. (1)
09-25 Novena Medical Centre 10 Sinaran Dr, Singapore, 307506, Singapore
Tel.: (65) 63976638
Web Site: https://specialistoralsurgeons.com.sg
Dental Services
N.A.I.C.S.: 621210

TP Dental Surgeons Pte. Ltd. (1)
The Penthouse 391B Orchard Road 26-01 Ngee Ann City Tower B, Singapore, 238874, Singapore
Tel.: (65) 6567379011
Web Site: https://www.tpdental.com.sg
Dental Healthcare Providing Services
N.A.I.C.S.: 621210

Q-LINE TRUCKING LTD.
101 Wurtz Ave RR No 4 Corman Industrial Park, Saskatoon, S7K 3J7, SK, Canada
Tel.: (306) 651-3540
Web Site: http://www.qlinetrucking.com
Sales Range: $10-24.9 Million
Transportation Services
N.A.I.C.S.: 484121

Q-LINEA AB
Dag Hammarskjolds Vag 52 A, 752 37, Uppsala, Sweden
Tel.: (46) 706001520 SE
Web Site: https://www.qlinea.com
Year Founded: 2008
QLINEA—(OMX)
Rev.: $1,197,748
Assets: $21,534,369
Liabilities: $6,249,684
Net Worth: $15,284,685
Earnings: ($25,166,390)
Emp.: 151
Fiscal Year-end: 12/31/22
Medical Device Mfr
N.A.I.C.S.: 339113
Mats Gullberg (VP & Dir-Res)

Q-TECH ENGINEERING LTD & CO.
Batthyany u 8, 1161, Budapest, Hungary
Tel.: (36) 14053338 HU
Motion Controller Distr
N.A.I.C.S.: 423610

Q.B. INDUSTRIAS, S.A. DE C.V.
Bosques De Ciruelos 304-9 Bosques De Las Lomas, 11700, Mexico, CDMX, Mexico
Tel.: (52) 5585036400
Year Founded: 1954
QBINDUS—(MEX)
Sales Range: Less than $1 Million
Chemical Product Mfr & Whslr
N.A.I.C.S.: 325998
Aroldo de Rienzo Betancourt (Chm)

Q.BEYOND AG
Richard-Byrd-Str 4, 50829, Cologne, Germany
Tel.: (49) 2216698000 De
Web Site: https://qbeyond.de
QBY—(MUN)
Rev.: $208,940,514
Assets: $170,371,296
Liabilities: $62,357,616
Net Worth: $108,013,679
Earnings: ($19,295,648)
Emp.: 1,111
Fiscal Year-end: 12/31/23
Broadband Telecommunication Services
N.A.I.C.S.: 517810
Bernd Schlobohm (Co-Founder & Chm-Supervisory Bd)

Subsidiaries:

010090 GmbH (1)
Mathias Bruggen Str 55, Cologne, 50829, Germany
Tel.: (49) 2216698000
Web Site: http://www.qsc.de
Emp.: 700
Voice Telephony Products
N.A.I.C.S.: 517810
Christof Sommerberg (Mng Dir)

Q-loud GmbH (1)
Mathias-Bruggen-Str 55, 50829, Cologne, Germany
Tel.: (49) 2216698411
Web Site: http://www.q-loud.de
Information Technology Services
N.A.I.C.S.: 513210
Myriam Jahn (CEO)

SIA q.beyond (1)
Brivibas Iela 40-19, Riga, 1050, Latvia
Tel.: (371) 24971074
Web Site: https://qbeyond.lv
Information Technology Services
N.A.I.C.S.: 541519

Ventelo GmbH (1)
Mathias-Bruggen Str 55, Gebaude der QSC AG, 50829, Cologne, Germany
Tel.: (49) 2216698010
Web Site: http://www.ventelo.de
Sales Range: $1-4.9 Billion
Emp.: 100
Telecommunication Services Provider
N.A.I.C.S.: 517112

q.beyond Data Solutions GmbH (1)
Ballindamm 3, 20095, Hamburg, Germany
Tel.: (49) 40209345950
Web Site: https://www.qbeyond-data-solutions.de
Software Development Services
N.A.I.C.S.: 541511

q.beyond iberica Sociedad Limitada (1)
Avenida Tio Pepe 8, 11407, Cadiz, Cadiz, Spain
Tel.: (34) 956751809
Web Site: https://qbeyond.es
Information Technology Services
N.A.I.C.S.: 541519

q.beyond logineer GmbH (1)
Flughafenstrasse 52b, 22335, Hamburg, Germany
Tel.: (49) 4080904210
Web Site: https://www.logineer.com
Emp.: 150
Information Technology Services
N.A.I.C.S.: 541519

Q/MEDIA SOLUTIONS CORPORATION
Unit 120 1231 Burdette St, Richmond, V6V 2Z2, BC, Canada
Tel.: (604) 303-6630 BC
Web Site: http://www.qmscorp.com
Year Founded: 1986
Sales Range: $25-49.9 Million
Emp.: 55
Software & Documentation Kits for Technology Customers
N.A.I.C.S.: 541519
Robert M. Lawrie (Pres & CEO)

Subsidiaries:

Q-Media Solutions (1)
4095 Oceanside Blvd Ste K, Oceanside, CA 92056
Tel.: (760) 216-6400
Web Site: http://www.qmedia.com
Prepackaged Software
N.A.I.C.S.: 323111

Q2 METALS CORP.
625 Howe Street Suite 488, Vancouver, V6C 2T6, BC, Canada
Tel.: (604) 653-8052 BC
Web Site: http://minfocus.com
Year Founded: 2010
QUEXF—(OTCQB)
Assets: $3,741,449
Liabilities: $158,111
Net Worth: $3,583,338
Earnings: ($1,761,220)
Fiscal Year-end: 02/28/22
Investment Services
N.A.I.C.S.: 523999
Kenneth B. de Graff (CEO)

Subsidiaries:

Orefox Exploration Pty. Ltd. (1)
Old Mineral House Level 3 Two Edward Street, Brisbane, 4000, QLD, Australia
Tel.: (61) 437177556
Web Site: https://orefox.com
Mineral Exploration & Mining Services
N.A.I.C.S.: 212312

Q_PERIOR AG
Bavariaring 28, 80336, Munich, Germany
Tel.: (49) 89 45599 0 De
Web Site: http://www.q-perior.com
Year Founded: 2011
Sales Range: $100-124.9 Million
Emp.: 430
Management Consulting Services
N.A.I.C.S.: 541611
Karsten Hoppner (CEO)

Subsidiaries:

FIS-SST Sp. z o.o. (1)
Ul Bojkowska 37C, 44-101, Gliwice, Poland
Tel.: (48) 327201260
Software Development Services
N.A.I.C.S.: 541511

QAF LIMITED
150 South Bridge Road 09-03 Fook Hai Building, Singapore, 058727, Singapore
Tel.: (65) 65382866 SG
Web Site: https://www.qaf.com.sg
Year Founded: 1958
Q01—(SES)
Rev.: $476,096,341
Assets: $506,824,206
Liabilities: $136,846,171
Net Worth: $369,978,035
Earnings: $20,888,434
Emp.: 9,992
Fiscal Year-end: 12/31/23
Bakery & Confectionery Whslr & Food Retailer
N.A.I.C.S.: 311812
Andree Halim (Vice Chm)

Subsidiaries:

Bakers Maison Australia Pty Ltd. (1)
98 Milperra Road, Revesby, 2212, NSW, Australia (100%)
Tel.: (61) 28 707 7777
Web Site: https://www.bakersmaison.com.au
Emp.: 200
Frozen Cakes Pies & Other Pastries Mfr
N.A.I.C.S.: 311813
Pascal Chaneliere (Gen Mgr)

Bakers Maison Pte Ltd (1)
150 South Bridge Road 09-04 Fook Hai Building, Singapore, 58727, Singapore
Tel.: (65) 65382866
Emp.: 30
Food Products Mfr
N.A.I.C.S.: 311999

Bakers Maison Pty Ltd. (1)
98 Milperra Road, Revesby, 2212, NSW, Australia (100%)
Tel.: (61) 287077777
Web Site: https://www.bakersmaison.com.au
Frozen Cakes Pies & Pastries Mfr
N.A.I.C.S.: 311813

Ben Foods (East Malaysia) Sdn Bhd (1)
B1 Hock Lee Centre Jln Datuk Abang Abdul Rahim, 93450, Kuching, Malaysia (100%)
Tel.: (60) 82348639
Grocery & Products Whslr
N.A.I.C.S.: 424490

Ben Foods (S) Pte Ltd. (1)
1 Fishery Port Road, 128417, Singapore, Singapore (100%)
Tel.: (65) 67786655
Web Site: http://www.benfoods.com
Dry Condensed & Evaporated Dairy Product Mfr
N.A.I.C.S.: 311514

Bonjour Bakery Pte Ltd. (1)
150 South Bridge Road 09-04 Fook Hai Building, Singapore, 058727, Singapore (100%)
Tel.: (65) 68980983
Web Site: https://www.bonjour.sg
Emp.: 300
Frozen Cakes Pies & Other Pastries Mfr
N.A.I.C.S.: 311813
Ng Cher Siang (Gen Mgr)

Delicia Sdn. Bhd. (1)
No 5 Jalan Belati Kawasan Perindustrian Maju Jaya, 81300, Johor Bahru, Johor, Malaysia
Tel.: (60) 75584399
Sales Range: $25-49.9 Million
Emp.: 150
Mfr of Breads & Bakery Products
N.A.I.C.S.: 311812

Diamond Valley Pork Pty Ltd. (1)
13-15 Thomas Road, Laverton, 3050, VIC, Australia
Tel.: (61) 383692250
Web Site: http://www.diamondvalleypork.com.au
Sales Range: $25-49.9 Million
Emp.: 10
Meat Markets
N.A.I.C.S.: 445240
Allen Bittisnich (Gen Mgr)

Farmland Central Bakery (S) Pte Ltd. (1)
224 Pandan Loop, Singapore, 128411, Singapore (100%)
Tel.: (65) 68732344
Web Site: http://www.gardenia.com.sg
Commercial Equipment Whslr
N.A.I.C.S.: 423440

Gardenia Bakeries (KL) Sdn Bhd (1)
Lot 3 Jalan Pelabur 23/1, 40300, Shah Alam, Selangor, Malaysia
Tel.: (60) 35 542 3228

QAF LIMITED

QAF Limited—(Continued)
Web Site: https://www.gardenia.com.my
Emp.: 800
Frozen Cakes Pies & Other Pastries Mfr
N.A.I.C.S.: 311813

Gardenia Bakeries (Philippines) Inc. (1)
Gardenia Centre Star Avenue Mamplasan, Laguna International Industrial Park LIIP, Binan, 4024, Laguna, Philippines **(100%)**
Tel.: (63) 9209114606
Web Site: http://www.gardenia.com.ph
Commercial Bakeries
N.A.I.C.S.: 311812

Gardenia Foods Pte Ltd. (1)
150 South Bridge Road 09-04 Fook Hai Building, Singapore, 058727, Singapore **(100%)**
Tel.: (65) 67785666
Web Site: https://www.gardenia.com.sg
Emp.: 300
Bakery Products Mfr
N.A.I.C.S.: 311812
Kong King Tan *(Grp Mng Dir & Exec Dir)*

Gardenia Sales & Distribution Sdn Bhd (1)
Lot 3 Jalan Pelabur 23/1, 40300, Shah Alam, Selangor, Malaysia **(70%)**
Tel.: (60) 355423228
Web Site: http://www.gardenia.com.my
Sales Range: $100-124.9 Million
Emp.: 300
Retail Bakeries
N.A.I.C.S.: 311811

Hamsdale Australia Pty Ltd. (1)
Redlands Road, Corowa, Albury, 2646, NSW, Australia **(100%)**
Tel.: (61) 260338333
Web Site: http://www.rivalea.com.au
Emp.: 1,000
Investment Advice
N.A.I.C.S.: 523940
Mick Hewat *(Gen Mgr)*

Millif Industries Sdn Bhd (1)
No 17 Jln Seruling 57 Kaw 3 Taman Klang Jaya, 41200, Kelang, Selangor, Malaysia **(65%)**
Tel.: (60) 333241703
Web Site: http://www.gardenia.com.my
Sales Range: $25-49.9 Million
Emp.: 30
Fresh & Frozen Seafood Processing
N.A.I.C.S.: 311710
Muhammad Ali *(Mgr-Production)*

NCS Cold Stores (S) Pte Ltd (1)
1 Fishery Port Rd, Jurong Town, Singapore, 619729, Singapore
Tel.: (65) 62675013
Web Site: https://www.ncscold.sg
Emp.: 35
Food Preservation Cold Storage Services
N.A.I.C.S.: 493190
Philip Lee *(CEO)*

QAF Fruits Cold Store Pte Ltd. (1)
230A Pandan Loop, Singapore, 138416, Singapore **(100%)**
Tel.: (65) 67755729
Web Site: http://www.qaf.com.sg
Refrigerated Warehousing & Storage
N.A.I.C.S.: 493120
C. Goh *(Mgr-Operations)*

Shaanxi Hengxing Fruit Juice Co., Ltd. (1)
9/F Hi-Tech International Business Center, No 55 Keji Road, Xi'an, 710075, Shaanxi, China **(46.5%)**
Tel.: (86) 2988337509
Web Site: http://www.fruitjuice-china.com
Food Mfr
N.A.I.C.S.: 311999

Subsidiary (Domestic):

Jingchuan Hengxing Fruit Juice Co., Ltd. (2)
industrial park of hot spring, Jingchuan, 744300, Gansu, China
Tel.: (86) 9333332325
Web Site: http://www.fruitjuice-china.com
Sales Range: $25-49.9 Million
Emp.: 108
Fresh & Frozen Seafood Processing
N.A.I.C.S.: 311710

Linyi Hengxing Fruit Juice Co., Ltd. (2)
Linjin Village, Linyi, 044102, Shaanxi, China
Tel.: (86) 3594216618
Web Site: http://www.fruitjuice-china.com
All Other Miscellaneous Food Mfr
N.A.I.C.S.: 311999

Qixian Hengxing Fruit Juice Co., Ltd. (2)
East Road of The North Ring, Qixian, 030900, Shanxi, China
Tel.: (86) 354 524 6160
Web Site: http://www.fruitjuice-china.com
Frozen Fruit Juice & Vegetable Mfr
N.A.I.C.S.: 311411

Shinefoods Pte Ltd. (1)
10-01 Fook Hai Bldg, 150 S Bridge Rd, Singapore, 058727, Singapore
Tel.: (65) 65332993
Web Site: http://www.shinefoods.com
Sales Range: $50-74.9 Million
Emp.: 3
Goods Whslr
N.A.I.C.S.: 423990
Chen Unice *(Mgr)*

Spices International Pte Ltd. (1)
263 Pandan Loop, Singapore, 128437, Singapore **(100%)**
Tel.: (65) 67788800
Web Site: http://www.spices.com.sg
Sales Range: $25-49.9 Million
Emp.: 15
Food Mfr
N.A.I.C.S.: 311991

QANBAR DYWIDAG PRECAST CONCRETE CO. LTD.

PO Box 515, Al Jubayl, 31051, Saudi Arabia
Tel.: (966) 33401234   SA
Web Site: http://www.qdc.com.sa
Year Founded: 1981
Precast Concrete Structural Contractor & Products Mfr
N.A.I.C.S.: 238120
Mohammed Qanbar Al Ansari *(Owner & CEO)*

QANTAS AIRWAYS LIMITED

10 Bourke Road, Qantas, Mascot, 2020, NSW, Australia
Tel.: (61) 296913636   AU
Web Site: https://www.qantas.com
Year Founded: 1934
QABSY—(OTCIQ)
Passenger & Freight Air Transportation Services
N.A.I.C.S.: 481111
Andrew Finch *(Gen Counsel & Sec)*

Subsidiaries:

Australian Air Express Pty. Ltd. (1)
440 Elizabeth St Level 7, Melbourne, 3000, Australia **(50%)**
Tel.: (61) 386333100
Web Site: http://www.aae.com.au
Freight Air Transportation Services
N.A.I.C.S.: 481112

Holiday Tours & Travel Pte. Ltd (1)
15 Cairnhill Road 07-05 Cairnhill Place, Singapore, 229650, Singapore
Tel.: (65) 67347091
Travel Tour Operating Agencies
N.A.I.C.S.: 561520

Subsidiary (Non-US):

Holiday Tours & Travel (Korea) Limited (2)
8F 97 Toegye-ro, Jung-Gu, Seoul, 100731, Korea (South)
Tel.: (82) 27776871
Web Site: http://www.toureast.net
Sales Range: $25-49.9 Million
Emp.: 11
Travel Tour Operating Agencies
N.A.I.C.S.: 561520
Orin Kwon *(Gen Mgr)*

Subsidiary (Domestic):

Holiday Tours & Travel (Singapore) Pte. Ltd (2)
541 Orchard Road 15-01 Liat Towers, Singapore, 238881, Singapore
Tel.: (65) 67347091
Web Site: http://www.holidaytours-sin.com
Sales Range: $150-199.9 Million
Emp.: 150
Travel Tour Operating Agencies
N.A.I.C.S.: 561520

Subsidiary (Non-US):

Holiday Tours & Travel Limited (2)
Rm 1202 12th Floor Excel Centre 483 Castle Peak Road, Tsim Sha Tsui, Kowloon, China (Hong Kong)
Tel.: (852) 27376798
Web Site: http://www.jetabout.com.hk
Tour Operating Services
N.A.I.C.S.: 561520
Raymond Lam *(Gen Mgr)*

Holiday Tours & Travel Ltd (2)
Rm 1307 13 Floor No 96 Sec 2 Zhongshan N Rd, Zhongshan Dist, Taipei, 104217, Taiwan
Tel.: (886) 225095111
Web Site: http://www.holidaytours.net
Tours & Travel Management Services
N.A.I.C.S.: 561520
Iris Lee *(Gen Mgr)*

PT Pacto Holiday Tours (2)
Lagoon Tower Level B1 The Sultan Hotel Jl Jend, Gatot Subroto, Jakarta, 12730, Indonesia
Tel.: (62) 215705800
Sales Range: $25-49.9 Million
Emp.: 100
Travel Tour Operating Agencies
N.A.I.C.S.: 561520

Jetconnect Limited (1)
1 Lenard Isitt Drive, Auckland, 2150, New Zealand
Tel.: (64) 92567634
Web Site: http://www.qantas.com.au
Emp.: 480
Oil Transportation Services
N.A.I.C.S.: 488190
Shelley Musk *(Gen Mgr)*

Jetstar Airways Pty. Ltd. (1)
222 Bourke Street, Melbourne, 3001, VIC, Australia **(100%)**
Tel.: (61) 131538
Web Site: https://www.jetstar.com
Passenger & Freight Air Transportation Services
N.A.I.C.S.: 481111
Xu Haibing *(Gen Mgr-Greater China & Southeast Asia)*

Q Catering Riverside Pty Limited (1)
300 Coward St, Mascot, 2020, NSW, Australia
Tel.: (61) 299348000
Web Site: http://www.quatas.com
Sales Range: $50-74.9 Million
Emp.: 400
Catering Services
N.A.I.C.S.: 722320

Qantas Airways - USA (1)
6080 Ctr Dr Ste 400, Los Angeles, CA 90045
Tel.: (310) 726-1400
Web Site: http://www.qantas.com.au
Sales Range: $300-349.9 Million
Emp.: 45
Operator of Airlines
N.A.I.C.S.: 541820

Qantas Catering Group Limited (1) **(100%)**
Tel.: (61) 296910880
Web Site: http://www.qantas.com.au
Airline Food Service Contractor
N.A.I.C.S.: 722320

Subsidiary (Non-US):

Q Catering Cairns Pty Limited (2)
Tel.: (61) 740423900
Sales Range: $25-49.9 Million
Emp.: 130
Catering Services

INTERNATIONAL PUBLIC

N.A.I.C.S.: 722320

Q Catering Limited (2)
Tel.: (61) 296910880
Web Site: http://www.qantas.com.au
Sales Range: $400-449.9 Million
Emp.: 3,500
Catering Services
N.A.I.C.S.: 722320

Qantas Flight Training (1)
Qantas Flight Training Centre Building S148 Qantas Jet Base, Qantas Drive, Mascot, 2020, NSW, Australia
Tel.: (61) 296917900
Web Site: https://www.qantastraining.com
Aircraft Training Services
N.A.I.C.S.: 611512

Qantas Foundation Trustee Limited (1)
C/o Georgina Gaussen Qantas Centre QCA8 203 Coward Street, Mascot, 2020, NSW, Australia
Tel.: (61) 2 9691 4284
Oil Transportation Services
N.A.I.C.S.: 488190

Qantas Freight Enterprises Limited (1)
Qantas Freight Domestic Terminal T2 Link Road, 203 Coward Street, Mascot, 2020, NSW, Australia
Tel.: (61) 299529753
Web Site: https://freight.qantas.com
Freight Air Transportation Services
N.A.I.C.S.: 481112

Subsidiary (Domestic):

Express Freighters Australia Pty Limited (2)
Bldg A L 9 203 Coward St, Mascot, 2020, NSW, Australia
Tel.: (61) 296913636
Web Site: http://www.qantasfreight.com
Sales Range: $50-74.9 Million
Emp.: 150
Oil Transportation Services
N.A.I.C.S.: 488190

Qantas Courier Limited (2)
Unit 3/55 Kent Rd, Mascot, 2020, NSW, Australia
Tel.: (61) 283378900
Web Site: http://www.qantascourier.com.au
Air Freight Courier Services
N.A.I.C.S.: 492110

Qantas Information Technology Ltd. (1)
Qantas Centre 203 Coward Street, Mascot, 2020, NSW, Australia **(100%)**
Tel.: (61) 296913636
Web Site: http://www.qantas.com
Sales Range: $25-49.9 Million
Emp.: 10
Corporate Information Technology Services
N.A.I.C.S.: 541513

Qantas Superannuation Limited (1)
GPO Box 4303, Melbourne, 3001, VIC, Australia
Tel.: (61) 1300362967
Web Site: https://www.qantassuper.com.au
Oil Transportation Services
N.A.I.C.S.: 488190
Michael Clancy *(CEO)*

QantasLink (1)
10 Bourke road, Mascot, 2020, NSW, Australia **(100%)**
Tel.: (61) 296913636
Sales Range: $200-249.9 Million
Emp.: 650
Regional Airline Operations
N.A.I.C.S.: 481111
Allen Joycey *(CEO)*

Snap Fresh Pty Limited (1)
90 Magnesium Drive, Crestmead, 4132, QLD, Australia
Tel.: (61) 738039700
Sales Range: $25-49.9 Million
Emp.: 130
Ice Cream & Frozen Dessert Mfr
N.A.I.C.S.: 311520
Tim Knopke *(Gen Mgr)*

Southern Cross Insurances Pte Limited (1)

PWC Building 11-00 8 Cross Street, Singapore, 048424, Singapore
Tel.: (65) 62208141
General Insurance Services
N.A.I.C.S.: 524210

QASSIM CEMENT CO.
Building No 4266 Unit Number 1, Buraidah, 52271 - 6735, Saudi Arabia
Tel.: (966) 163165555
Web Site: https://www.qcc.com.sa
Year Founded: 1976
3040—(SAU)
Rev.: $180,897,538
Assets: $513,645,617
Liabilities: $69,764,314
Net Worth: $443,881,302
Earnings: $34,798,709
Emp.: 667
Fiscal Year-end: 12/31/22
Cement Mfr
N.A.I.C.S.: 327310
Omar Abdullah Al-Omar (CEO)

Subsidiaries:

Hail Cement Company (1)
King Abdullah Rd, PO Box 1008, Second industrial city, Hail, 81431, Saudi Arabia
Tel.: (966) 165344444
Web Site: https://www.hailcement.com
Rev.: $97,444,066,391
Assets: $305,030,733,236
Liabilities: $22,134,329,023
Net Worth: $282,896,404,213
Earnings: $4,376,611,385
Emp.: 450
Fiscal Year-end: 12/31/2022
Cement Mfr & Distr
N.A.I.C.S.: 327310

QATAR CENTRAL BANK
PO Box 1234, Doha, Qatar
Tel.: (974) 4456456
Web Site: http://www.qcb.gov.qa
Banking Services
N.A.I.C.S.: 521110
Abdullah Saud Al-Thani (Chm)

QATAR CINEMA AND FILM DISTRIBUTION COMPANY QSC
Office No 3 Building No 105 Street No 320 Najman Street Zone No 26, PO BOX 1970, Doha, Qatar
Tel.: (974) 44671625
Web Site: https://www.qatarcinemas.com
Year Founded: 1970
QCFS—(QE)
Rev.: $5,688,428
Assets: $42,130,297
Liabilities: $5,924,191
Net Worth: $36,206,106
Earnings: $1,201,502
Emp.: 72
Fiscal Year-end: 12/31/23
Motion Picture Importer & Distr; DVD Rental Services; Movie Theater Owner & Operator
N.A.I.C.S.: 512120
Ali Ishaq Hussein Al Ishaq (Mng Dir)

QATAR ELECTRICITY & WATER COMPANY Q.S.C.
Qatar Navigation Tower in Al-Dafna Area Floor 48 Maysaloun Street, PO Box 22046, Building No 11 Street No 860 Zone 63, Doha, Qatar
Tel.: (974) 44858585
Web Site: https://www.qewc.com
Year Founded: 1990
QEWS—(QE)
Rev.: $704,701,400
Assets: $4,673,073,417
Liabilities: $1,957,541,279
Net Worth: $2,715,532,138
Earnings: $322,263,186
Emp.: 1,256
Fiscal Year-end: 12/31/20
Power Generation & Water Desalination Plant Operator
N.A.I.C.S.: 335311
Abdul Rahman Mohammed Saeed Nasrallah (CEO-Ras Abu Fontas Station)

Subsidiaries:

Ras Laffan Operating Company W.L.L. (1)
Ras Laffan Power Company Building 1st Floor Salwa Rd, PO Box 22237, Ras Laffan Industrial City, Doha, Qatar
Tel.: (974) 44672723
Eletric Power Generation Services
N.A.I.C.S.: 221111

QATAR ENGINEERING & CONSTRUCTION COMPANY W.L.L.
Al Shamal Road Exit 66 West Side Support Service Area, PO Box 24491, Wosail Street Plot No SI-08 CA-50, Mesaieed, Qatar
Tel.: (974) 44587200
Web Site: http://www.qcon.com.qa
Year Founded: 1975
Sales Range: $600-649.9 Million
Emp.: 5,000
Industrial Engineering & Construction Services
N.A.I.C.S.: 237990
Mazen Abu Naba'a (Gen Mgr)

QATAR EXCHANGE
Hamad Grant Street, PO Box 22114, Doha, Qatar
Tel.: (974) 4333666
Web Site: http://www.dsm.com.qa
Year Founded: 1997
Stock Exchange Services
N.A.I.C.S.: 523210
Ahmad Muhammad Al Sayed (Vice Chm)

QATAR FUEL COMPANY Q.S.C.
WOQOD Tower West Bay, PO Box 7777, Doha, Qatar
Tel.: (974) 40217777
Web Site: https://www.woqod.com.qa
Year Founded: 2002
QFLS—(QE)
Rev.: $5,321,942,030
Assets: $3,626,191,633
Liabilities: $1,125,507,795
Net Worth: $2,500,683,838
Earnings: $273,140,219
Emp.: 374
Fiscal Year-end: 12/31/21
Refined Petroleum Products Distr
N.A.I.C.S.: 424720
Ahmed Ali Mirza (Chief Support Svcs Officer)

Subsidiaries:

WOQOD Vehicle Inspection Co. (Fahes) W.L.L. (1)
Almazrooah, PO Box 22298, Doha, Qatar
Tel.: (974) 40218800
Web Site: http://www.fahes.com.qa
Vehicle Technical Inspection Services
N.A.I.C.S.: 926120

QATAR GAS TRANSPORT COMPANY LIMITED (NAKILAT) Q.S.C.
Shoumoukh Towers B C Ring Road, PO Box 22271, Doha, Qatar
Tel.: (974) 44998111 QA
Web Site: https://www.nakilat.com.qa
Year Founded: 2004
QGTS—(QE)
Rev.: $1,275,912,527
Assets: $8,769,124,418
Liabilities: $5,453,646,543
Net Worth: $3,315,477,875
Earnings: $427,481,423
Emp.: 794
Fiscal Year-end: 12/31/23
Gas Transport Services
N.A.I.C.S.: 213112
Mohammed Saleh Al Sada (Chm)

QATAR GENERAL INSURANCE AND REINSURANCE COMPANY S.A.Q.
No 880 Zone 4 building 23 Al Areeq St, PO Box 4500, Doha, Qatar
Tel.: (974) 44282222 QA
Web Site: https://www.qgirco.com
Year Founded: 1979
QGRI—(QE)
Rev.: $210,757,748
Assets: $1,543,613,429
Liabilities: $633,189,843
Net Worth: $910,423,586
Earnings: $(442,491,628)
Fiscal Year-end: 12/31/23
General Insurance Services
N.A.I.C.S.: 524210
Mohammad Hamad Al-Mana (Chm)

Subsidiaries:

General Real Estate Company S.P.C. (1)
PO Box 4500, Doha, Qatar
Tel.: (974) 44282222
Real Estate Investment Services
N.A.I.C.S.: 531390

General Takaful Company S.P.C. (1)
C Ring Road Al Salatah Al Jadedah Interchange, PO Box 23990, Doha, Qatar
Tel.: (974) 4 449 9999
Web Site: https://www.g-takaful.net
General Insurance Services
N.A.I.C.S.: 524210
Mohamed Veera (Mgr-Technical)

Qatar General Holding Company S.P.C. (1)
PO Box 4500, Doha, Qatar
Tel.: (974) 44282222
Investment Management Service
N.A.I.C.S.: 523940

QATAR INDUSTRIAL MANUFACTURING COMPANY (S.A.Q.)
PO Box 16875, Doha, Qatar
Tel.: (974) 44344222 QA
Web Site: https://www.qimc.com.qa
Year Founded: 1990
QIMD—(QE)
Rev.: $108,020,763
Assets: $749,035,538
Liabilities: $299,678,693
Net Worth: $449,356,846
Earnings: $22,280,239
Emp.: 21
Fiscal Year-end: 12/31/20
Industrial Manufacturing & Development Services
N.A.I.C.S.: 561499
Nasser Rashid Sraiya Al-Kaabi (Vice Chm)

Subsidiaries:

National Food Company (1)
PO Box 30100, Doha, Qatar (50%)
Tel.: (974) 4684981
Web Site: http://www.hassad.com
Sales Range: $25-49.9 Million
Emp.: 22
Mfr & Producer of Food & Agricultural Products
N.A.I.C.S.: 311423
Ahamad Saad Alsaad (Mng Dir)

Affiliate (Domestic):

Qatar Tunisian Food Company (2)
Central Market Qatar, PO Box 30100, Doha, 30100, Qatar (51%)
Tel.: (974) 4684981
Sales Range: $1-9.9 Million
Emp.: 20
Bottler of Olive Oil & Processed Food Products
N.A.I.C.S.: 311225

National Paper Industries Company (1)
Salwa Industrial Area Street No 2 Block No 215, PO Box 40631, Doha, Qatar (100%)
Tel.: (974) 44600567
Web Site: http://www.napico.com.qa
Sales Range: $1-9.9 Million
Emp.: 30
Mfr of Facial Tissues, Female Sanitary Pads, Toilet Rolls, Kitchen & Hospital Rolls & Other Related Products
N.A.I.C.S.: 322291

Qatar Acids Company (1)
Mesaieed Industrial City, PO Box 50229, Doha, Qatar (100%)
Tel.: (974) 44760340
Sales Range: $1-9.9 Million
Emp.: 26
Sulfuric Acid & Other Chemicals Mfr
N.A.I.C.S.: 325998

Qatar Clay Bricks Company (1)
52 Industrial Ave, PO Box 1569, Doha, 1569, Qatar (100%)
Tel.: (974) 4603487
Web Site: http://www.qcbc.com.qa
Sales Range: $1-9.9 Million
Emp.: 125
Mfr of Building Materials
N.A.I.C.S.: 333120
Abdul Rehman (Gen Mgr)

Qatar Jet Fuel Company (1)
Doha International Airport, PO Box 22244, Doha, Qatar (40%)
Tel.: (974) 40107274
Web Site: http://www.qjet.com.qa
Sales Range: $50-74.9 Million
Emp.: 160
Provider of Aviation Fuel; Joint Venture of Qatar Petroleum (60%) & Qatar Industrial Manufacturing Company (S.A.Q.)
N.A.I.C.S.: 324110

Qatar Metal Coating Company WLL (1)
PO Box 50090, Mesaieed, Qatar
Tel.: (974) 4778415
Web Site: http://www.qcoat.com.qa
Sales Range: $25-49.9 Million
Emp.: 72
Provider of Epoxy Coating of Steel Bars; Joint Venture of Qatar Industrial Manufacturing Company (S.A.Q.) (50%) & Qatar Steel Company Ltd. (50%)
N.A.I.C.S.: 332812
Mohammed Nasser Al-Hajiri (Vice Chm & Gen Mgr)

Qatar Nitrogen Company (1)
16th Bldg 7 St Qatar, PO Box 16875, Mesaieed Industrial Area, Doha, 16875, Qatar (100%)
Tel.: (974) 586 3604
Sales Range: $10-24.9 Million
Emp.: 22
Producer of Gaseous & Liquid Nitrogen; Joint Venture of Qatar Industrial Manufacturing Company (S.A.Q.) (50%) & Qatar Petroleum (50%)
N.A.I.C.S.: 221210

Qatari Saudi Gypsum Inds. Company (1)
PO Box 22052, Doha, Qatar
Tel.: (974) 4602165
Sales Range: $25-49.9 Million
Emp.: 55
Producer of Gypsum Powder; Joint Venture of Qatar Industrial Manufacturing Company (S.A.Q.) (33.375%), Qatar National Cement Co. (33.25%) & National Gypsum Co., Jeddah (33.375%)
N.A.I.C.S.: 327420

QATAR INSURANCE COMPANY S.A.Q.
Tamin Street West Bay, PO Box 666, Doha, Qatar
Tel.: (974) 44962311 QA
Web Site: https://qic-group.com
Year Founded: 1964

QATAR INSURANCE COMPANY S.A.Q.

Qatar Insurance Company S.A.Q.—(Continued)
QATI—(QE)
Rev.: $1,730,843,057
Assets: $7,868,937,103
Liabilities: $5,463,702,831
Net Worth: $2,405,234,272
Earnings: $168,817,008
Emp.: 243
Fiscal Year-end: 12/31/23
Insurance Services
N.A.I.C.S.: 524298
Sunil Talwar *(Deputy Pres)*

Subsidiaries:

Antares Global Management Limited (1)
21 Lime Street, London, United Kingdom
Tel.: (44) 2079591900
Web Site: https://www.antaresglobal.com
Underwriting & Claim Services
N.A.I.C.S.: 524291

Antares Managing Agency Limited (1)
21 Lime Street, London, EC3M 7HB, United Kingdom
Tel.: (44) 207 959 1900
Web Site: https://www.antaresunderwriting.com
Insurance Services
N.A.I.C.S.: 524298

Subsidiary (Non-US):

Antares Underwriting Asia Pte. Limited (2)
138 Market Street 04-04 CapitaGreen, Singapore, 048946, Singapore
Tel.: (65) 69112790
Insurance Services
N.A.I.C.S.: 524298

Epicure Investment Management LLC (1)
3rd Floor QIC Annex Building Tamin Street West Bay, Doha, Qatar
Tel.: (974) 44962233
Web Site: https://eim.com.qa
Investment Management Service
N.A.I.C.S.: 523999

Oman Qatar Insurance Company S.A.O.G. (1)
4th Floor Al Nawras Commercial Center Building Near HSBC, PO Box 3660, Al Khuwair, 112, Ruwi, Oman
Tel.: (968) 24765333
Web Site: https://www.oqic.com
Fire Insurance Services
N.A.I.C.S.: 524210
Navin Kumar *(CEO)*

QIC International L.L.C. (1)
10th Floor Al Fardan Office Tower, PO Box 12713, Doha, Qatar
Tel.: (974) 4491 0505
General Insurance Services
N.A.I.C.S.: 524130

Subsidiary (Non-US):

Kuwait Qatar Insurance Company K.S.C.C (2)
Burj Jasim 8th Floor Al Soor Street Mirgab, PO Box 25137, Kuwait, 13112, Kuwait
Tel.: (965) 22960131
Property Reinsurance Services
N.A.I.C.S.: 524298

QLM Life & Medical Insurance W.L.L. (1)
QLM Building Tameen Street West Bay, PO Box 12713, Doha, Qatar
Tel.: (974) 4 404 0600
Web Site: https://www.qlm.com.qa
Insurance Services
N.A.I.C.S.: 524298
Salem Khalaf Al Mannai *(CEO)*

Qatar Insurance Company - Abu Dhabi (1)
Al Manara Bldg Muroor Road, Abu Dhabi, United Arab Emirates (100%)
Tel.: (971) 800 4742
Web Site: https://www.qicuae.com
Sales Range: $50-74.9 Million
Emp.: 10
Insurance Services
N.A.I.C.S.: 524298

Qatar Insurance Company - Al Khobar (1)
PO Box 3381, Al Khobar, 31952, Eastern, Saudi Arabia (100%)
Tel.: (966) 38873006
Sales Range: $50-74.9 Million
Emp.: 10
Insurance Services
N.A.I.C.S.: 524298

Qatar Insurance Company - Dubai (1)
Office 210 Al Dana Centre Al Maktoum Road, PO Box 4066, Deira, Dubai, United Arab Emirates (100%)
Tel.: (971) 800 4742
Web Site: https://www.qicuae.com
Sales Range: $50-74.9 Million
Emp.: 75
Insurance Services
N.A.I.C.S.: 524298

Qatar Reinsurance Company Limited (1)
71 Pitts Bay Road, Pembroke, HM 08, Bermuda
Tel.: (441) 400 5000
Web Site: https://www.qatarreinsurance.com
Insurance Services
N.A.I.C.S.: 524298
Michael Van Der Straaten *(CEO)*

Subsidiary (Non-US):

QIC Europe Limited (2)
Pendergardens Business Centre Level One, Saint Julian's, STJ 1901, Malta
Tel.: (356) 2 092 8888
Web Site: https://www.qiceuropeltd.com
Reinsurance Services
N.A.I.C.S.: 524130
Pantelis Koulovasilopoulos *(CEO)*

Qatar Reinsurance Services LLC (2)
8th Floor QIC Building Tamin Street, PO Box 24938, West Bay Area, Doha, Qatar
Tel.: (974) 4033777
Insurance Services
N.A.I.C.S.: 524298

QATAR INTERNATIONAL ISLAMIC BANK Q.S.C.
Grand Hamad Ave, Doha, Qatar
Tel.: (974) 44840000
Web Site: https://www.qiib.com.qa
Year Founded: 1991
QIIK—(QE)
Rev.: $667,637,580
Assets: $16,706,748,257
Liabilities: $6,709,249,972
Net Worth: $9,997,498,285
Earnings: $255,506,676
Emp.: 269
Fiscal Year-end: 12/31/20
Banking Services
N.A.I.C.S.: 522110
Khalid Thani A. Al-Thani *(Chm & Mng Dir)*

QATAR INVESTMENT AUTHORITY
PO Box 23224, Doha, Qatar
Tel.: (974) 4499 5900
Web Site: http://www.qia.qa
Year Founded: 2005
Investment Holding Company
N.A.I.C.S.: 551112
Mansoor Bin Ebrahim Al Mahmoud *(CEO)*

Subsidiaries:

Canary Wharf Group PLC (1)
One Canada Square Canary Wharf, London, E14 5AB, United Kingdom
Tel.: (44) 2074182000
Web Site: https://group.canarywharf.com
Emp.: 1,000
Holding Company; Property Investors & Leasors

N.A.I.C.S.: 551112
George Iacobescu *(Chm)*

Hassad Food Co. (1)
840 Al Corniche St, Doha, 25566, Qatar
Tel.: (974) 44079292
Web Site: http://www.hassad.com
Food Mfr
N.A.I.C.S.: 311999
Nasser Mohamed Al Hajri *(Chm)*

Qatar Airways Company (1)
Qatar Airways Tower 1 Next to Al Manna Building Airport Road, Doha, Qatar
Tel.: (974) 40226000
Web Site: http://www.qatarairways.com
Sales Range: $1-4.9 Billion
Emp.: 46,000
Airline Services
N.A.I.C.S.: 481111
Akbar Al Baker *(CEO)*

Subsidiary (Domestic):

Doha International Airport (2)
PO Box 24659, Doha, Qatar
Tel.: (974) 4465 6666
Web Site: http://www.dohahamadairport.com
Airport Operator
N.A.I.C.S.: 488119
Akbar Al Baker *(CEO)*

Internal Media Services (2)
PO Box 22550, Doha, Qatar
Tel.: (974) 44621407
Airport Advertising Services
N.A.I.C.S.: 541850

Qatar Airways Cargo (2)
D Ring Road Beside Airport Opp Family Food Center, Doha, Qatar
Tel.: (974) 44235077
Web Site: http://www.qrcargo.com
Air Freight Transportation Services
N.A.I.C.S.: 481112
Kirsten de Bruijn *(Sr VP-Cargo Sls & Network Plng)*

Qatar Aviation Services (2)
Doha International Airport, PO Box 383, Doha, Qatar
Tel.: (974) 4462 6531
Web Site: http://www.qataraviation.com
Sales Range: $1-4.9 Billion
Emp.: 5,000
Aviation Services
N.A.I.C.S.: 488119
Clive Sauve-Hopkins *(VP)*

Qatar Executive (2)
Khawla Garden Villa 5 34 Kaab Bin Omair St Area 42 Al Hilal, PO Box 22550, Doha, Qatar
Tel.: (974) 4445 3800
Web Site: http://www.qatarexec.com.qa
Jet Aircraft Charter Services
N.A.I.C.S.: 481219
Tilmann Gabriel *(Exec VP)*

QATAR ISLAMIC BANK (S.A.Q.)
Grand Hamad Street, PO Box 559, Doha, Qatar
Tel.: (974) 44020020
Web Site: https://www.qib.com.qa
Year Founded: 1982
QIBK—(QE)
Rev.: $3,048,408,337
Assets: $51,873,604,552
Liabilities: $43,641,837,653
Net Worth: $8,231,766,900
Earnings: $1,175,902,098
Emp.: 998
Fiscal Year-end: 12/31/23
Commercial Banking Services
N.A.I.C.S.: 522110
Jassim Hamad Jassim Jaber Al Thani *(Chm)*

Subsidiaries:

Arab Finance House (AFH) S.A.L. (1)
Corniche El-Mazraa Saeb Salam Avenue Arab Finance House Tower, Beirut, Lebanon

INTERNATIONAL PUBLIC

Tel.: (961) 170 8100
Web Site: https://www.afh.com.lb
Banking Services
N.A.I.C.S.: 522110

Panmure Gordon & Co. Limited (1)
One New Change, London, EC4M 9AF, United Kingdom
Tel.: (44) 207 886 2500
Web Site: http://www.panmure.com
Sales Range: $10-24.9 Million
Holding Company; Corporate Finance, Securities Brokerage, Institutional Trading, Equity Research & Market Maker Services
N.A.I.C.S.: 551112
Barrie Cornes *(Head-Res)*

Subsidiary (Domestic):

Panmure Gordon (Broking) Limited (2)
Moorgate Hall 155 Moorgate, London, EC2M 6XB, United Kingdom
Tel.: (44) 2074593600
Web Site: http://www.panmuregordon.com
Sales Range: $50-74.9 Million
Emp.: 90
Stock Brokerage Services
N.A.I.C.S.: 523150

Panmure Gordon (UK) Limited (2)
Moorgate Hall 155 Moorgate, London, EC2M 6XB, United Kingdom
Tel.: (44) 2074593600
Web Site: http://www.panmuregordon.com
Stock Brokerage Services
N.A.I.C.S.: 523150

QIB (UK) plc (1)
43 Grosvenor Street, Berkeley Square, London, W1K 3HL, United Kingdom (100%)
Tel.: (44) 207 268 7200
Web Site: https://www.qib-uk.com
Sales Range: $50-74.9 Million
Emp.: 30
Investment Advisory & Management Services
N.A.I.C.S.: 523940

QInvest LLC (1)
Tornado Tower 39th Floor West Bay, PO Box 26222, Doha, Qatar (47.15%)
Tel.: (974) 4405 6666
Web Site: http://www.qinvest.com
Rev.: $63,516,000
Assets: $903,231,000
Liabilities: $344,215,000
Net Worth: $559,016,000
Earnings: ($14,436,000)
Fiscal Year-end: 12/31/2019
Investment Banking
N.A.I.C.S.: 523150
Jassim Hamad Jassim Jaber Al Thani *(Chm)*

QATAR ISLAMIC INSURANCE COMPANY Q.S.C.
C Ring Road-Opposite Gulf Cinema, PO Box 22676, Doha, Qatar
Tel.: (974) 44658888
Web Site: https://www.qiic.com.qa
QISI—(QE)
Rev.: $36,168,891
Assets: $308,454,165
Liabilities: $135,541,846
Net Worth: $172,912,319
Earnings: $21,828,496
Fiscal Year-end: 12/31/21
General Insurance Services
N.A.I.C.S.: 524210
Abdullah Thani Al-Thani *(Chm)*

QATAR NATIONAL BANK S.A.Q.
PO Box 1000, Doha, Qatar
Tel.: (974) 44252444 QA
Web Site: http://www.qnb.com
QNBK—(QE)
Rev.: $14,550,482,124
Assets: $258,969,978,034
Liabilities: $233,004,612,510
Net Worth: $25,965,365,524
Earnings: $3,964,139,104
Emp.: 29,000
Fiscal Year-end: 12/31/19
Commercial Banking Services

N.A.I.C.S.: 522110
Mira Al-Attiyah *(CEO-QNB Capital)*

Subsidiaries:

Al-Mansour Investment Bank (1)
Karradah Khaarej Mahallah 925 Street 18 Building 140, Infront of Abu Rafel Sweets store, Baghdad, Iraq
Tel.: (964) 7805444666
Web Site: https://mbi.iq
Commercial Bank Services
N.A.I.C.S.: 522110

Mansour Bank for Investment (1)
AL Wihda Quarter-Street 14-Bldg 51, Baghdad, Iraq (50.8%)
Tel.: (964) 1 7175568
Web Site: http://www.mansourbank.com
Investment Banking Services
N.A.I.C.S.: 523150

PT Bank QNB Indonesia Tbk (1)
Revenue Tower 8th Floor District 8 SCBD Lot 13, Jl Jenderal Sudirman Kav 52-53, Jakarta, 12190, Indonesia
Tel.: (62) 215155155
Web Site: https://www.qnb.co.id
Rev: $61,348,883
Assets: $763,271,316
Liabilities: $458,608,618
Net Worth: $304,662,698
Earnings: $4,497,030
Emp.: 379
Fiscal Year-end: 12/31/2023
Banking Services
N.A.I.C.S.: 522110
Windiartono Tabingin *(Dir-Compliance)*

QNB (India) Private Limited (1)
G-1A Ground Floor 4 North Avenue Maker Maxity Bandra Kurla Complex, Bandra East, Mumbai, 400 051, India
Tel.: (91) 2262296300
Web Site: http://www.qnb.com
Commercial & Private Banking
N.A.I.C.S.: 522110
Gaurav Gupta *(CEO)*

QNB Alahli Bank S.A.E. (1)
5 Champollion Street, Down Town, 11111, Cairo, Egypt
Tel.: (20) 227707777
Emp.: 6,700
Commercial Banking Services
N.A.I.C.S.: 522110
Mohamed Osman El Dib *(Chm & Mng Dir)*

QNB Banque Privee (Suisse) SA (1)
Quai du Mont-Blanc 1, Geneva, 1201, Switzerland
Tel.: (41) 229077070
Emp.: 15
Private Banking Services
N.A.I.C.S.: 523150
Ramzi Zuraikat *(COO)*

QNB Capital LLC (1)
Sikkat Alwadi Street Mshereib Downtown Building No 4 Street No 800, PO Box 1000, Zone No 03, Doha, Qatar
Tel.: (974) 44963888
Web Site: https://www.qnb.com.qa
Sales Range: $25-49.9 Million
Emp.: 12
Financial Management Services
N.A.I.C.S.: 541611
Mira Al-Attiyah *(CEO)*

QNB Finansbank A.S. (1)
Esentepe Mahallesi Buyukdere Caddesi, Kristal Kule Binasi No 215, Sisli, 34385, Istanbul, Turkiye (99.88%)
Tel.: (90) 2123185000
Web Site: https://www.qnbfinansbank.com
Rev: $2,069,336,844
Assets: $19,185,613,010
Liabilities: $17,818,031,598
Net Worth: $1,367,581,412
Earnings: $532,075,798
Emp.: 11,427
Fiscal Year-end: 12/31/2022
Commericial Banking
N.A.I.C.S.: 522110
Temel Guzeloglu *(CEO)*

Subsidiary (Domestic):

Finans Finansal Kiralama A.S. (2)
Esentepe Mahallesi Buyukdere Caddesi, Kristal Kule Binasi No 215 Kat 22 Sisli, 34394, Istanbul, Turkiye (99.4%)
Tel.: (90) 2123491111
Web Site: http://www.qnbfl.com
Emp.: 200
Financial Lending Services
N.A.I.C.S.: 523999
Metin Karabiber *(Gen Mgr)*

Finans Portfoy Yonetimi A.S. (2)
Esentepe Mahallesi Buyukdere Caddesi, Kristal Kule Binasi No 215 Kat 27 Sisli, 34394, Istanbul, Turkiye (100%)
Tel.: (90) 2123367171
Web Site: http://www.qnbfp.com
Financial Investment Services
N.A.I.C.S.: 523999
Bahar Cakan *(Sr Portfolio Mgr)*

Finans Yatirim Menkul Degerler A.S. (2)
Esentepe Mahallesi Buyukdere Caddesi, Kristal Kule Binasi, No 215 Kat 6-7 Sisli, 34394, Istanbul, Turkiye (100%)
Tel.: (90) 212 336 7000
Web Site: http://www.qnbfi.com
Emp.: 500
Commericial Banking
N.A.I.C.S.: 522110
Ipek Hekimoglu *(Exec VP-Investment Banking)*

IBTECH Uluslararasi Bilisim ve Iletisim Teknolojileri Arastirma, Gelistirme Danismanlik Destek San Ve Tic A.S. (2)
Tubitak Mam Teknoloji Serbest Bolgesi Baris Mah 5003 SK No 6, 41470, Gebze, Kocaeli, Turkiye (99%)
Tel.: (90) 2626791500
Web Site: https://www.ibtech.com.tr
Emp.: 600
Investment Banking & Securities Dealing
N.A.I.C.S.: 523510
Kursat Demirkol *(CIO)*

QNB Suisse S.A. (1)
Quai du Mont Blanc 1, 1201, Geneva, Switzerland
Tel.: (41) 229077070
Commercial Banking Services
N.A.I.C.S.: 522110
Ghadeer Abu Hijleh *(CEO)*

Qatar National Bank Alahli (1)
Champollion 5 Champollion St Downtown, 11111, Cairo, Egypt (97.13%)
Tel.: (20) 2277070000
Web Site: https://www.qnbalahli.com
Rev: $1,628,593,173
Assets: $13,259,954,493
Liabilities: $11,854,623,312
Net Worth: $1,405,331,181
Earnings: $342,241,313
Emp.: 7,209
Fiscal Year-end: 12/31/2023
Commericial Banking
N.A.I.C.S.: 522110
Mohamed Osman El-Dib *(Chm & Mng Dir)*

Qatar National Bank-Syria (1)
Al Abbassiyeen Square, PO Box 33000, Damascus, Syria (50.8%)
Tel.: (963) 1122901000
Web Site: https://www.qnb.com
Rev: $26,648,375,066
Assets: $337,718,793,360
Liabilities: $307,483,651,249
Net Worth: $30,235,142,112
Earnings: $4,297,750,304
Fiscal Year-end: 12/31/2023
Commercial Banking Services
N.A.I.C.S.: 522110

QATAR NATIONAL CEMENT CO Q.S.C.
Zone No 55 St No 340 Salwa Road Building No 316 Office No 25 to 28, PO Box 1333, Doha, Qatar
Tel.: (974) 44693800
Web Site: https://www.qatarcement.com
Year Founded: 1965
QNCD—(QE)
Rev: $126,415,961
Assets: $936,157,528
Liabilities: $88,311,525
Net Worth: $847,846,003
Earnings: $56,268,947
Emp.: 1,254
Fiscal Year-end: 12/31/23
Cement Mfr
N.A.I.C.S.: 327310
Salem Butti Al-Naimi *(Chm)*

QATAR NAVIGATION (MILAHA) Q.P.S.C.
East Industrial Road Umm Al Saneem Area Street No 523 Zone 56, PO Box 153, Doha, Qatar
Tel.: (974) 44949666
Web Site: https://www.milaha.com
Year Founded: 1957
QNNS—(QE)
Rev: $617,801,806
Assets: $4,635,437,389
Liabilities: $886,552,917
Net Worth: $3,748,884,472
Earnings: $16,136,811
Emp.: 1,799
Fiscal Year-end: 12/31/20
Marine Transportation Services
N.A.I.C.S.: 488390
Jassim Hamad Jassim Jaber Al-Thani *(Chm)*

Subsidiaries:

Halul Offshore Services Company W.L.L. (1)
PO Box 24600, Doha, Qatar (50%)
Tel.: (974) 4339111
Web Site: http://www.haluloffshore.com
Offshore Support Services
N.A.I.C.S.: 213112
Ismail Ali Abdulla Al-Emadi *(CEO)*

Qatar Shipping Company S.P.C. (1)
Abdulla Ben Jaissm Corniche, PO Box 22180, Doha, Qatar
Tel.: (974) 4315500
Web Site: http://www.qship.com
Sales Range: $125-149.9 Million
Shipping & Transportation Services
N.A.I.C.S.: 488510
Joseph Coutinho *(CEO)*

QATAR OMAN INVESTMENT COMPANY Q.S.C.
C-Ring Road Financial Square Building next to Muntazah Signal, PO Box 37048, Building 1 - first floor - office 2, Doha, Qatar
Tel.: (974) 44914886 QA
Web Site: https://www.qatar-oman.com
Year Founded: 2007
QOIS—(QE)
Rev: $664,815
Assets: $85,596,608
Liabilities: $22,190,568
Net Worth: $63,406,039
Earnings: ($2,237,648)
Fiscal Year-end: 12/31/23
Financial Investment Services
N.A.I.C.S.: 523999
Abdul Rahman Mohammed Jabor Al Thani *(Chm)*

QATAR PETROLEUM
World Trade Center Corniche Road, Doha, Qatar
Tel.: (974) 40134895
Web Site: http://www.qp.com.qa
Year Founded: 1974
Sales Range: $1-4.9 Billion
Emp.: 7,492
Crude Petroleum & Natural Gas Mfr
N.A.I.C.S.: 211120
Abdulla Hamad Al Attiya *(Chm & Mng Dir)*

Subsidiaries:

Amwaj Catering Services Limited (1)
Old Salata Area Museum Street, PO Box 23904, Doha, Qatar
Tel.: (974) 44912009
Web Site: http://www.amwajcatering.com.qa
Catering Services
N.A.I.C.S.: 722320

Gulf Helicopter Company (1)
PO Box 811, Doha, Qatar (100%)
Tel.: (974) 44333888
Web Site: http://www.gulfhelicopters.com
Sales Range: $125-149.9 Million
Emp.: 340
Helicopter Services
N.A.I.C.S.: 481111

Industries Qatar Q.S.C. (1)
6th Floor Tower 10, PO Box 3212, Doha, Qatar (70%)
Tel.: (974) 40132080
Web Site: http://www.iq.com.qa
Rev: $3,220,631,290
Assets: $11,806,558,344
Liabilities: $843,623,749
Net Worth: $10,962,934,595
Earnings: $1,295,156,726
Emp.: 3,764
Fiscal Year-end: 12/31/2023
Holding Company
N.A.I.C.S.: 551112

Subsidiary (Domestic):

Qatar Fertiliser Company (S.A.Q.) (2)
Po Box 50001, Mesaieed, Qatar (75%)
Tel.: (974) 442 28888
Web Site: http://www.qafco.com
Sales Range: $300-349.9 Million
Emp.: 840
Mfr of Urea & Ammonia
N.A.I.C.S.: 212390
Abdulaziz Bin Ahmed Al-Malki *(Chm)*

Joint Venture (Domestic):

Qatar Petrochemical Company Ltd. (2)
PO Box 756, Doha, Qatar
Tel.: (974) 40338000
Web Site: http://www.qapco.com
Sales Range: $300-349.9 Million
Mfr of Petrochemicals; Owned 80% by Qatar Petroleum & 20% by Total S.A.
N.A.I.C.S.: 325110
Abdulaziz Jassim M. Al-Muftah *(Chm)*

Affiliate (Domestic):

Qatar Plastic Products Company W.L.L. (3)
Nike Industrial Area, PO Box 50174, Mesaieed, 50174, Qatar
Tel.: (974) 4770815
Web Site: https://www.qppc.net
Emp.: 38
N.A.I.C.S.: 326199

Mesaieed Petrochemical Holding Company Q.S.C. (1)
Doha State of Qatar, PO Box 3212, Doha, Qatar
Tel.: (974) 40132080
Web Site: https://www.mphc.com.qa
Rev: $38,465,843
Assets: $4,811,544,538
Liabilities: $124,815,637
Net Worth: $4,686,728,901
Earnings: $297,034,291
Fiscal Year-end: 12/31/2023
Holding Company
N.A.I.C.S.: 551112
Ahmad Saif Al-Sulaiti *(Chm)*

Qatar Chemical Company Ltd. (1)
Amwal Tower Omar Al Mukhtar St, PO Box 24646, Al Dafna, Doha, Qatar (51%)
Tel.: (974) 44847111
Web Site: http://www.qchem.com.qa
Chemicals Mfr
N.A.I.C.S.: 325998
Abdulrahman M. Al-Suwaidi *(Chm)*

Qatar Fuel Additives Company Ltd. (1)
PO Box 22700, Doha, Qatar
Tel.: (974) 44766777
Web Site: http://www.qafac.com.qa
Operator of Production Facility of Methanol & Methyl Tertiary Butyl Ether Mfr
N.A.I.C.S.: 325998

Qatar Intermediate Industries Company Ltd. (1)

QATAR PETROLEUM

Qatar Petroleum—(Continued)
Al Dana Tower 15th - 20th Floors Street
837 West Bay Area 61, PO Box 28882,
Doha, Qatar
Tel.: (974) 40208888
Web Site: http://www.alwaseeta.com
Construction Engineering Services
N.A.I.C.S.: 541330

Qatar Jet Fuel Company (1)
Doha International Airport, PO Box 22244,
Doha, Qatar
Tel.: (974) 40107274
Web Site: http://www.qjet.com.qa
Sales Range: $50-74.9 Million
Emp.: 160
Provider of Aviation Fuel; Joint Venture of
Qatar Petroleum (60%) & Qatar Industrial
Manufacturing Company (S.A.Q.)
N.A.I.C.S.: 324110

**Qatar Liquefied Gas Company
Ltd.** (1)
PO Box 22666, Doha, Qatar (65%)
Tel.: (974) 4736000
Sales Range: $500-549.9 Million
Emp.: 1,000
Liquefied Natural Gas
N.A.I.C.S.: 221210
Sheikh Khalid Bin Khalifa Al-Thani *(CEO)*

Qatar Nitrogen Company (1)
16th Bldg 7 St Qatar, PO Box 16875, Mesaieed Industrial Area, Doha, 16875, Qatar
Tel.: (974) 586 3604
Sales Range: $10-24.9 Million
Emp.: 22
Producer of Gaseous & Liquid Nitrogen;
Joint Venture of Qatar Industrial Manufacturing Company (S.A.Q.) (50%) & Qatar
Petroleum (50%)
N.A.I.C.S.: 221210

**Qatar Vinyl Company Limited
Q.S.C.** (1)
PO Box 24440, Doha, Qatar (55.2%)
Tel.: (974) 4765888
Web Site: http://www.qatarvinyl.com
Sales Range: $200-249.9 Million
Emp.: 200
Vinyl Products Mfr
N.A.I.C.S.: 325211

**Ras Laffan Liquefied Natural Gas
Company Ltd.** (1)
PO Box 24200, Doha, Qatar (70%)
Tel.: (974) 44738435
Web Site: http://www.rasgas.com
Sales Range: $500-549.9 Million
Emp.: 850
Mfr of Natural Gas
N.A.I.C.S.: 221210

QATAR STEEL COMPANY
PO Box 50090, Mesaieed Industrial
City, Mesaieed, Qatar
Tel.: (974) 44778778
Web Site:
  http://www.qatarsteel.com.qa
Sales Range: $250-299.9 Million
Emp.: 1,400
Mfr of Steel Products
N.A.I.C.S.: 331513
Ali Hassan Al Muraikhi *(Mng Dir &
Gen Mgr)*

Subsidiaries:

Qatar Metal Coating Company
WLL (1)
PO Box 50090, Mesaieed, Qatar
Tel.: (974) 4778415
Web Site: http://www.qcoat.com.qa
Sales Range: $25-49.9 Million
Emp.: 72
Provider of Epoxy Coating of Steel Bars;
Joint Venture of Qatar Industrial Manufacturing Company (S.A.Q.) (50%) & Qatar
Steel Company Ltd. (50%)
N.A.I.C.S.: 332812
Mohammed Nasser Al-Hajiri *(Vice Chm &
Gen Mgr)*

Qatar Steel Company FZE (1)
PO Box 18255, Jebel Ali Free Zone, Dubai,
United Arab Emirates
Tel.: (971) 48053111

Steel Products Mfr
N.A.I.C.S.: 331511
Jeena Manzoor *(Head-HR)*

QATARI DIAR REAL ESTATE INVESTMENT COMPANY
PO Box 23175, Lusail, Doha, Qatar
Tel.: (974) 44974444
Web Site: http://www.qataridiar.com
Sales Range: $200-249.9 Million
Emp.: 700
Real Estate Investment Services
N.A.I.C.S.: 531390
Abdullah Hamad Al-Attiyah *(CEO)*

Subsidiaries:

Qatari Diar Real Estate Investment
Co. Moroco S.A.R.L (1)
Residence Borj Khalij Tanja Av Mohammed
VI 5eme etage no 196 & 197, Tangiers,
Morocco
Tel.: (212) 539 34 34 14
Real Estate Investment Services
N.A.I.C.S.: 531390

QATARI GERMAN COMPANY FOR MEDICAL DEVICES Q.S.C.
Street Number 54 Building Number
136, PO Box 22556, Abu Hamour,
22556, Doha, Qatar
Tel.: (974) 44581201
Web Site: https://www.qgmd.com
Year Founded: 2000
QGMD—(QE)
Rev.: $7,637,864
Assets: $55,102,824
Liabilities: $45,220,940
Net Worth: $9,881,884
Earnings: $366,374
Emp.: 6
Fiscal Year-end: 12/31/23
Medical Syringe Mfr
N.A.I.C.S.: 339112
Eisa Khalid Al-Maslamani *(Mng Dir)*

QATARI INVESTORS GROUP Q.S.C.
QIG Tower Lusail 1st Floor Zone No
69 Street No 303, PO Box 22504,
Doha, Qatar
Tel.: (974) 44747000 QA
Web Site:
  https://www.qatariinvestors.com
Year Founded: 2006
QIGD—(QE)
Rev.: $190,953,735
Assets: $1,284,240,739
Liabilities: $500,817,465
Net Worth: $783,423,274
Earnings: $24,478,399
Emp.: 600
Fiscal Year-end: 12/31/20
Investment Services; Cement Mfr
N.A.I.C.S.: 523999
Abdulla Nasser Al Misnad *(Chm)*

QAYEN CEMENT COMPANY
No 14 Sh Bahram Naderi St Keshavarz Blvd, Tehran, 14166 33531, Iran
Tel.: (98) 21 88956455
Year Founded: 1981
SGEN1—(THE)
Sales Range: Less than $1 Million
Emp.: 313
Cement Mfr
N.A.I.C.S.: 327310

QAZAQ BANKI JSC
279 Furmanov str, 050059, Almaty,
Kazakhstan
Tel.: (7) 727 250 55 77
Web Site: http://www.qazaqbanki.kz
Commercial Banking Services
N.A.I.C.S.: 522110

QAZAQGAZ AIMAQ JSC
12 Alihan Bokeihan st, Yesil district,
Nur-Sultan, 010000, Kazakhstan
Tel.: (7) 172558960
Web Site: https://www.aimaq.kz
Year Founded: 2002
KTGA—(KAZ)
Rev.: $46,178,855
Assets: $946,633,543
Liabilities: $494,001,387
Net Worth: $452,632,156
Earnings: $16,527,136
Fiscal Year-end: 12/31/19
Natural Gas Distribution Services
N.A.I.C.S.: 221210
Tasybaev Manas Mukhitovich *(Co-Chm & Gen Dir)*

QB NET HOLDINGS CO., LTD.
7F Totate Nagai Building 2-12-24
Shibuya, Shibuya-Ku, Tokyo, 150-0002, Japan
Tel.: (81) 364189190
Web Site: https://qbnet.jp
Year Founded: 1995
6571—(TKS)
Rev.: $153,988,540
Assets: $200,887,340
Liabilities: $112,749,940
Net Worth: $88,137,400
Earnings: $8,092,220
Emp.: 2,700
Fiscal Year-end: 06/30/24
Hair Salon Services
N.A.I.C.S.: 812112
Yasuo Kitano *(Pres & CEO)*

Subsidiaries:

QB House(Hong Kong) Ltd. (1)
Unit No 1122 Floor 11 Star House No 3
Salisbury Road Tsim Sha Tsui, Kowloon,
China (Hong Kong)
Tel.: (852) 23593300
Emp.: 232
Hair Stylist Services
N.A.I.C.S.: 812112

QBE INSURANCE GROUP LIMITED
Level 18 388 George Street, Sydney,
2000, NSW, Australia
Tel.: (61) 293754444 AU
Web Site: https://www.qbe.com
Year Founded: 1921
QBE—(OTCIQ)
Rev.: $20,826,000,000
Assets: $42,108,000,000
Liabilities: $32,155,000,000
Net Worth: $9,953,000,000
Earnings: $1,364,000,000
Emp.: 13,479
Fiscal Year-end: 12/31/23
Investment Management Service
N.A.I.C.S.: 551111
John M. Green *(Deputy Chm)*

Subsidiaries:

British Marine Managers Limited (1)
Plantation Place 30 Fenchurch Street, London, EC3M 3BD, United Kingdom
Tel.: (44) 2071055555
Web Site: http://www.britishmarine.com
Sales Range: $200-249.9 Million
Emp.: 500
Marine Insurance Services
N.A.I.C.S.: 524126

Elders Insurance (Underwriting
Agency) Pty Limited (1)
Level 9 400 King William Street, Adelaide,
5000, SA, Australia
Tel.: (61) 135622
Web Site:
  https://www.eldersinsurance.com.au
Property & Motor Insurance Services
N.A.I.C.S.: 524126

Equator Reinsurances Limited (1)
Clarendon House Church Street, Hamilton,
HM1234, Bermuda
Tel.: (441) 292 5105

INTERNATIONAL PUBLIC

Emp.: 18
Insurance Management Services
N.A.I.C.S.: 524298
James Fiore *(Gen Mgr)*

Limit Corporate Members
Limited (1)
88 Leadenhall Street, London, EC3A 3BP,
United Kingdom
Tel.: (44) 2078986000
General Insurance Services
N.A.I.C.S.: 524210

Limit Holdings Limited (1)
88 Leadenhall Street, London, EC3A 3BP,
United Kingdom
Tel.: (44) 20 7898 6000
Financial Investment Services
N.A.I.C.S.: 523999

National Credit Insurance (Brokers)
NZ Limited (1)
Level 1 1 Stokes Road, Mount Eden, Auckland, 1024, New Zealand
Tel.: (64) 9 520 5790
Web Site: http://www.ncinz.co.nz
Credit Insurance Management Services
N.A.I.C.S.: 524298
Phil Ashby *(Gen Mgr-NZ)*

National Credit Insurance (Brokers)
Pty Limited (1)
Level 2 165 Grenfell Street, Adelaide, 5000,
SA, Australia
Tel.: (61) 8 8228 4800
Web Site: http://www.nci.com.au
Insurance Brokerage Services
N.A.I.C.S.: 524210
Kirk Cheesman *(Mng Dir)*

QBE Americas, Inc. (1)
Wall Street Plaza 88 Pine St, New York, NY
10005
Tel.: (212) 422-1212
Web Site: http://www.qbeusa.com
Sales Range: $400-449.9 Million
Property, Casualty & Specialty Insurance
Services
N.A.I.C.S.: 524126
Joe Bielawski *(VP-Underwriting-Chicago)*

Subsidiary (Domestic):

Blue Ridge Indemnity Company (2)
One General Dr, Sun Prairie, WI 53596
Tel.: (860) 651-1065
Insurance Management Services
N.A.I.C.S.: 524298

North Pointe Financial Services,
Inc. (2)
28819 Franklin Rd, Southfield, MI 48034
Tel.: (248) 358-1171
Web Site: http://www.npic.com
Holding Company; Financial & Insurance
Services
N.A.I.C.S.: 551112

Subsidiary (Domestic):

North Pointe Casualty Insurance
Company (3)
28819 Franklin Rd, Southfield, MI 48034-1656
Tel.: (248) 358-1171
Insurance Management Services
N.A.I.C.S.: 524298

North Pointe Insurance
Company (3)
28819 Franklin Rd, Southfield, MI 48034
Tel.: (248) 358-1171
Web Site: http://www.npic.com
Sales Range: $50-74.9 Million
Emp.: 3
Property & Casualty Insurance Services
N.A.I.C.S.: 524126
Brent Leonard *(Office Mgr)*

Subsidiary (Domestic):

Praetorian Financial Group, Inc. (2)
Wall St Plz 88 Pine St, New York, NY
10005
Tel.: (212) 805-9700
Specialty Insurance Services
N.A.I.C.S.: 524126
Solange Charas *(Chief HR Officer)*

Subsidiary (Domestic):

Praetorian Insurance Company (3)

AND PRIVATE COMPANIES — QBE INSURANCE GROUP LIMITED

1 Pierce Pl Ste 650, Itasca, IL 60143
Tel.: (630) 250-5511
Web Site: http://www.qbeamericas.com
Sales Range: $50-74.9 Million
Emp.: 32
Reinsurance Carriers
N.A.I.C.S.: 524130

Subsidiary (Domestic):

General Casualty (4)
8500 Keystone Crossing Ste 200, Indianapolis, IN 46240-7336
Tel.: (317) 722-3838
Sales Range: $50-74.9 Million
Emp.: 72
Property & Casualty Insurance Services
N.A.I.C.S.: 524126

Branch (Domestic):

General Casualty Co. of Illinois (5)
2900 W Pearl City Rd, Freeport, IL 61032
Tel.: (815) 235-8900
Property & Liability Damage Insurance
N.A.I.C.S.: 524126

Subsidiary (Domestic):

General Casualty (Southern Guaranty) Insurance Co. (4)
1 General Dr, Sun Prairie, WI 53596
Tel.: (336) 412-3300
Sales Range: $50-74.9 Million
Emp.: 65
Property & Casualty Insurance Services
N.A.I.C.S.: 524126

Branch (Domestic):

General Casualty (Southern Guaranty) Insurance (5)
100 Creasent Ctr Ste 800, Tucker, GA 30084-7009
Tel.: (770) 493-1931
Property & Casualty Insurance Services
N.A.I.C.S.: 524210

Subsidiary (Domestic):

General Casualty Insurance (4)
82 Hopmeadow St, Simsbury, CT 06089
Tel.: (860) 651-1065
Sales Range: $100-124.9 Million
Emp.: 160
Property, Casualty & Commercial Insurance Services
N.A.I.C.S.: 524210

Unigard Insurance Group (4)
15800 Northup Way, Bellevue, WA 98008-2537
Tel.: (425) 641-4321
Web Site: http://www.qbena.com
Sales Range: $150-199.9 Million
Emp.: 360
Insurance Services
N.A.I.C.S.: 524126

Subsidiary (Domestic):

QBE Agri (2)
1 General Dr, Sun Prairie, WI 53590
Tel.: (866) 265-8685
Web Site: http://www.qbeagri.com
Rev.: $85,700,000
Agricultural Insurance Services
N.A.I.C.S.: 524128
Jim Henry (Pres)

QBE Financial Institution Risk Services, Inc. (2)
210 Interstate N Pkwy, Atlanta, GA 30339
Tel.: (770) 690-8400
Web Site: http://www.qbefirst.com
Property, Casualty & Specialty Insurance Services
N.A.I.C.S.: 524126
Mark Amacher (CMO)

Subsidiary (Domestic):

Seattle Specialty Insurance Services, Inc. (3)
332 Sw Everett Mall Way Bldg A, Everett, WA 98204
Tel.: (425) 609-3555
Web Site: http://www.seattlespecialty.com
Sales Range: $25-49.9 Million
Emp.: 50
Insurance Services

N.A.I.C.S.: 327910

Subsidiary (Domestic):

QBE Investments (North America) Inc (2)
1 General Dr, Sun Prairie, WI 53590-9334
Tel.: (608) 837-4440
Financial Investment Services
N.A.I.C.S.: 523999

QBE Regional Insurance (2)
1 General Dr, Sun Prairie, WI 53596
Tel.: (608) 837-4440
Insurance Holding Company
N.A.I.C.S.: 551112

QBE Reinsurance Corporation (2)
55 Water St, New York, NY 10041
Tel.: (212) 422-1212
Web Site: http://www.qbere.com
Reinsurance Management Services
N.A.I.C.S.: 524130

QBE Specialty Insurance Company (2)
Wall St Plz 88 Pine St 16th Fl, New York, NY 10005
Tel.: (212) 422-1212
General Insurance Services
N.A.I.C.S.: 524210

Regent Insurance Company (2)
1 General Dr, Sun Prairie, WI 53590-9334
Tel.: (608) 837-4440
Insurance Management Services
N.A.I.C.S.: 524298

SIU LLC (2)
700 N Brand Blvd Ste 300, Glendale, CA 91203
Tel.: (818) 547-1333
Web Site: http://www.siumanagers.com
Sales Range: $50-74.9 Million
Emp.: 17
Insurance Underwriting Services
N.A.I.C.S.: 524126
Guillermo E. Gonzalez (Pres)

Sterling National Insurance Agency Inc (2)
210 Interstate N Pkwy, Atlanta, GA 30339-2230
Tel.: (770) 690-8400
Web Site: http://www.qbefirst.com
Sales Range: $150-199.9 Million
Emp.: 317
Insurance Agency Services
N.A.I.C.S.: 524210

QBE Corporate Limited (1)
Plantation Place 30 Fenchurch Street, London, EC3 M3BD, United Kingdom
Tel.: (44) 2071054000
Insurance Management Services
N.A.I.C.S.: 524298

QBE European Operations
30 Fenchurch St, London, EC3M 3BD, United Kingdom
Tel.: (44) 2071054000
Web Site: http://www.qbeeurope.com
Sales Range: $200-249.9 Million
Emp.: 500
Insurance & Underwriting Services
N.A.I.C.S.: 524298
David Winkett (CFO)

QBE European Underwriting Services (Australia) Pty Limited (1)
Se 2 L 3 60-70 Elizabeth St, Sydney, 2000, NSW, Australia
Tel.: (61) 292102400
Web Site: http://www.qbeeuropre.com
Emp.: 20
Insurance Brokerage Services
N.A.I.C.S.: 524298

QBE Holdings (Europe) Limited (1)
Plantation Place 30 Fenchurch Street, London, EC3M 3BD, United Kingdom
Tel.: (44) 2078986000
Insurance Management Services
N.A.I.C.S.: 524298

QBE Holdings (UK) Limited (1)
Plantation Place 30 Fenchurch Street, London, EC3M 3BD, United Kingdom
Tel.: (44) 20 7105 4000
Insurance Brokerage Services
N.A.I.C.S.: 524210

QBE Insurance (Australia) Limited (1)
Level 5 2 Park Street, Sydney, 2000, NSW, Australia
Tel.: (61) 282759999
Web Site: http://www.qbe.com.au
General Insurance Services
N.A.I.C.S.: 524298
Jon Fox (Chief Claims Officer)

QBE Insurance (Europe) Limited (1)
Plantation Place 30 Fenchurch Street, London, EC3M 3BD, United Kingdom
Tel.: (44) 20 7105 4827
Insurance Management Services
N.A.I.C.S.: 524298

QBE Insurance (International) Limited (1)
1 Wallich Street, Singapore, 78881, Singapore (100%)
Tel.: (65) 62246633
Web Site: http://www.qbe.com.sg
Sales Range: $100-124.9 Million
Emp.: 130
N.A.I.C.S.: 522210

QBE Insurance (Malaysia) Berhad
No 638 Level 6 Block B1 Pusat Dagang Setia Jaya No 9 Jalan PJS 8/9, 46150, Petaling Jaya, Selagor Darul Ehsan, Malaysia
Tel.: (60) 378618400
Web Site: http://www.qbe.com.my
Sales Range: $50-74.9 Million
Emp.: 100
Insurance Management Services
N.A.I.C.S.: 524298

QBE Insurance (PNG) Limited (1)
QBE Building Musgrave Street, PO Box 814, Port Moresby, Papua New Guinea
Tel.: (675) 321 2144
Insurance Management Services
N.A.I.C.S.: 524298

QBE Insurance (Singapore) Pte. Ltd. (1)
1 Wallich Street 35-01 Guoco Tower, Singapore, 078881, Singapore
Tel.: (65) 6 224 6633
Reinsurance Services
N.A.I.C.S.: 524130

QBE Insurance (Vietnam) Company Limited (1)
Unit 1302A Metropolitan Tower 235 Dong Khoi Street, District 1, Ho Chi Minh City, 84, Vietnam
Tel.: (84) 8 3 824 5050
Web Site: http://www.qbe.com.vn
Sales Range: $50-74.9 Million
Emp.: 16
Insurance Management Services
N.A.I.C.S.: 524298

QBE International (Investments) Pty Limited (1)
Level 1 60 Station St Parramatta, Sydney, 2150, NSW, Australia (100%)
Tel.: (61) 293754444
Web Site: http://www.group.qbe.com
Sales Range: $700-749.9 Million
Emp.: 2,000
Investment Services
N.A.I.C.S.: 523999

QBE Lenders Mortgage Insurance Limited (1)
Level 21 50 Bridge St, Sydney, 2000, NSW, Australia
Tel.: (61) 2 9231 7777
Web Site: http://www.qbelmi.com
Mortgage Insurance Services
N.A.I.C.S.: 524298
Michael Savery (CFO)

QBE Marine and Energy Services Pte Limited (1)
60 Anson Road 11-0-1 Mapletree Anson, Singapore, 079914, Singapore
Tel.: (65) 62246633
Marine Insurance Services
N.A.I.C.S.: 524126

QBE Mortgage Insurance (Asia) Limited (1)
19/F Oxford House Taikoo Place 979 Kings Road Quarry Bay, Central, Hong Kong, China (Hong Kong)

Tel.: (852) 2295 0040
Web Site: http://www.qbemiasia.com
Emp.: 7
Residential Mortgage Insurance Services
N.A.I.C.S.: 524298
Wendy Tsang (Head-Risk Mgmt)

QBE Nordic Aviation Insurance A/S (1)
Vester Farimagsgade 7, 1606, Copenhagen, Denmark
Tel.: (45) 33450300
Sales Range: $50-74.9 Million
Emp.: 18
Aviation Insurance Services
N.A.I.C.S.: 524298
Claus Bang Hansen (Country Mgr)

QBE Reinsurance (Europe) Limited (1)
Riverside Two 43-49 Sir John Rogersons Quay, Dublin, Ireland
Tel.: (353) 16053800
Web Site: http://www.qbeeurope.com
Sales Range: $50-74.9 Million
Emp.: 90
Insurance Management Services
N.A.I.C.S.: 524298

Branch (Non-US):

QBE Re (Europe) Ltd. - Secura Branch (2)
Boulevard du Regent 37, Brussels, BE-1000, Belgium
Tel.: (32) 25048211
Web Site: http://www.qbere.com
Sales Range: $50-74.9 Million
Emp.: 90
Insurance Services
N.A.I.C.S.: 524210

QBE Reinsurance (UK) Limited (1)
Plantation Place 30 Fenchurch Street, London, EC3M 3BD, United Kingdom
Tel.: (44) 2071054000
General Insurance Services
N.A.I.C.S.: 524298

QBE Services Inc (1)
Bay-Adelaide Centre 333 Bay Street Suite 520, Toronto, M5H 2R2, ON, Canada
Tel.: (416) 682-5930
Web Site: http://www.qbecanada.com
Sales Range: $50-74.9 Million
Emp.: 40
Insurance Management Services
N.A.I.C.S.: 524298

QBE Underwriting Limited (1)
30 Fenchurch Street, London, EC3M 3BD, United Kingdom
Tel.: (44) 20 7105 4000
Web Site: http://www.qbeeurope.com
Emp.: 2,000
General Insurance Services
N.A.I.C.S.: 524210

QBE Underwriting Services (Ireland) Limited (1)
6-10 Suffolk Street, Dublin, 2, Ireland
Tel.: (353) 1 605 3640
Web Site: http://www.qbeeurope.com
Sales Range: $50-74.9 Million
Emp.: 90
Insurance Underwriting Services
N.A.I.C.S.: 524113

QBE Underwriting Services Limited (1)
Plantation Place 30 Fenchurch Street, London, EC3M 3BD, United Kingdom
Tel.: (44) 1179 809260
Insurance Management Services
N.A.I.C.S.: 524298

QBE Workers Compensation (NSW) Limited (1)
Level 27 8 Chifley Square, Sydney, 2000, NSW, Australia
Tel.: (61) 293754444
Web Site: http://www.qbe.com.au
Workers Insurance Compensation Services
N.A.I.C.S.: 524126

QBE Workers Compensation (SA) Limited (1)
400 King William Street Level 9, Adelaide, 5000, SA, Australia
Tel.: (61) 882022300

QBE INSURANCE GROUP LIMITED

QBE Insurance Group Limited—(Continued)
Worker Compensation Insurance Management Services
N.A.I.C.S.: 524126

QBE Workers Compensation (VIC) Limited (1)
Level 2 628 Bourke St, Melbourne, 3000, VIC, Australia
Tel.: (61) 3 9246 2444
Web Site: http://www.qbe.com
Insurance Brokerage Services
N.A.I.C.S.: 524210

Qbe Insurance (Fiji) Limited (1)
QBE Centre 18 Victoria Parade, GPO Box 101, Suva, Fiji
Tel.: (679) 331 5455
Sales Range: $50-74.9 Million
Emp.: 30
Insurance Management Services
N.A.I.C.S.: 524298
Darryl Williamson (Gen Mgr)

Raheja QBE General Insurance Company Limited (1)
Ground Floor P & G Plaza Cardinal Gracious Road Chakala, Andheri East, Mumbai, 400 099, Maharashtra, India
Tel.: (91) 2241715050
Web Site: http://www.rahejaqbe.com
General Insurance Services
N.A.I.C.S.: 524126

The MiniBus & Coach Club Limited (1)
Mill Court Mill Street, Stafford, ST16 2AX, United Kingdom
Tel.: (44) 845 609 0323
Web Site: http://www.minibusclub.co.uk
Vehicle Insurance Management Services
N.A.I.C.S.: 524298

Universal Underwriting Agencies Pty Limited (1)
L 4 85 Harrington St, Sydney, 2001, NSW, Australia
Tel.: (61) 2 8275 9999
Web Site: http://www.usu.com.au
Security Brokerage Services
N.A.I.C.S.: 523150

QBRICK AB
Farogatan 33, 164 51, Kista, Sweden
Tel.: (46) 84599000
Web Site: https://www.qbrick.com
Year Founded: 1999
2A8—(DEU)
Software Development Services
N.A.I.C.S.: 541511
Magnus Ingvarsson (Chm)

QC COPPER & GOLD INC.
55 University Avenue Suite 1805, Toronto, M5J 2H7, ON, Canada
Tel.: (416) 644-1567 BC
Web Site: https://qccopper.com
Year Founded: 2018
QCCU—(TSXV)
Metal Exploration Services
N.A.I.C.S.: 213114
Stephen Stewart (CEO)

QC COPPER & GOLD, INC.
55 University Avenue Suite 1805, Toronto, M5J 2H, ON, Canada
Tel.: (416) 644-1567 BC
Web Site: http://www.qccopper.com
Year Founded: 2018
QCCUF—(OTCQB)
Rev.: $227,771
Assets: $9,350,302
Liabilities: $198,043
Net Worth: $9,152,259
Earnings: ($5,529,156)
Emp.: 6
Fiscal Year-end: 10/31/23
Gold Mining Services
N.A.I.C.S.: 212220
Stephen Stewart (CEO)

QC SOLAR (SUZHOU) CO., LTD.
No 31 Xinfa Road SIP, Suzhou, 215028, Jiangsu, China
Tel.: (86) 51262603391
Web Site: https://www.quick-contact.com
Year Founded: 2005
301278—(CHIN)
Rev.: $177,917,465
Assets: $233,039,502
Liabilities: $68,714,569
Net Worth: $164,324,934
Earnings: $26,806,699
Fiscal Year-end: 12/31/23
Electronic Component Mfr & Distr
N.A.I.C.S.: 334419
Zhenggang Duan (Chm)

QCX GOLD CORP.
217 Queen Street West Suite 401, Toronto, M5V 0R2, ON, Canada
Tel.: (416) 361-2832
Web Site: https://www.qcxgold.com
Year Founded: 2007
QCX—(OTCIQ)
Assets: $2,941,600
Liabilities: $293,845
Net Worth: $2,647,755
Earnings: ($612,838)
Fiscal Year-end: 12/31/20
Mineral Exploration Services
N.A.I.C.S.: 213114

Subsidiaries:

Cornelius Exploration S. de R.L. de C.V. (1)
Avenida Santa Margarita 4140 2nd Floor 22b, Colonia Santa Margarita, Zapopan, 45140, Jalisco, Mexico
Tel.: (52) 33 31655553
Gold Mining Services
N.A.I.C.S.: 212220
Arturo Garcia (Office Mgr)

QD LASER, INC.
Keihin Building 1st Floor 1-1 Minamiwatarida-Cho, Kawasaki-Ku, Kawasaki, 210-0855, Kanagawa, Japan
Tel.: (81) 443333338
Web Site: https://www.qdlaser.com
Year Founded: 2006
6613—(TKS)
Telecommunication Servicesb
N.A.I.C.S.: 517810
Mitsuru Sugawara (Founder, Pres, CEO & Superintendent)

QD SYSTEM AB
Rasundavagen 166, 169 36, Solna, Sweden
Tel.: (46) 856256200
Web Site: http://www.qd.se
Sales Range: $10-24.9 Million
Emp.: 20
Information Technology Services
N.A.I.C.S.: 541512
Macus Lovenstad (CEO)

QDM INTERNATIONAL INC.
Room 707 Soho T2 Tianshan Plaza, Changning District, Shanghai, 200051, China
Tel.: (86) 34886893
Year Founded: 2020
QDMI—(OTCQB)
Rev.: $6,366,154
Assets: $5,776,289
Liabilities: $2,358,329
Net Worth: $3,417,960
Earnings: $1,564,538
Emp.: 5
Fiscal Year-end: 03/31/24
Health Care Srvices
N.A.I.C.S.: 621112
Huihe Zheng (Chm, Pres & CEO)

QEEKA HOME(CAYMAN), INC.
Building 6 No 3131 Jinshajiang Road, Jiading District, Shanghai, China
Tel.: (86) 2169108711 Ky
Web Site: http://www.qeeka.com
Year Founded: 2007
1739—(HKG)
Rev.: $122,953,194
Assets: $254,455,625
Liabilities: $90,112,792
Net Worth: $164,342,833
Earnings: ($19,693,346)
Emp.: 755
Fiscal Year-end: 12/31/22
Industrial Construction & Interior Design Services
N.A.I.C.S.: 541410
Huajin Deng (Chm & CEO)

QEM LIMITED
Suite 6A 50 Appel St, Surfers Paradise, 4217, QLD, Australia
Tel.: (61) 756469553 AU
Web Site: https://www.qldem.com.au
Year Founded: 2014
QEM—(ASX)
Rev.: $295,624
Assets: $2,209,759
Liabilities: $417,231
Net Worth: $1,792,528
Earnings: ($2,974,062)
Fiscal Year-end: 06/30/23
Exploration & Mining Services
N.A.I.C.S.: 213115
Gavin Loyden (Mng Dir)

QES GROUP BHD
No 2 Jalan Jururancang U1/21 Hicom Seksyen U1, Glenmarie Industrial Park, 40150, Shah Alam, Selangor, Malaysia
Tel.: (60) 358826668
Web Site: https://www.qesnet.com
Automated Handling Equipment Mfr
N.A.I.C.S.: 333924
Chew Ne Weng (Mng Dir)

Subsidiaries:

QES (Asia-Pacific) Sdn. Bhd. (1)
HICOM Glenmarie Industrial Park No 9 Jalan Juruukur U1/19 Seksyen U1, Shah Alam, 40150, Selangor, Malaysia
Tel.: (60) 358826668
Inspection, Test & Measurement Equipment Distr
N.A.I.C.S.: 334513

QEX LOGISTICS LTD.
70 Richard Pearse Drive Airport Oaks, Auckland, 2022, New Zealand
Tel.: (64) 98388681
Web Site: http://www.qex.co.nz
QEX—(NZX)
Rev.: $39,953,062
Assets: $12,435,009
Liabilities: $4,757,053
Net Worth: $7,677,956
Earnings: $1,318,641
Fiscal Year-end: 03/31/19
Freight Forwarding & Logistics Consulting Services
N.A.I.C.S.: 488510
Ronnie Xue (CEO)

QGO FINANCE LIMITED
3rd Floor A-514 TTC Industrial Area, MIDC Mahape, Navi Mumbai, 400701, India
Tel.: (91) 8657400776
Web Site: https://www.qgofinance.com
Year Founded: 1993
538646—(BOM)
Rev.: $711,523
Assets: $5,933,122
Liabilities: $4,518,257
Net Worth: $1,414,865

INTERNATIONAL PUBLIC

Earnings: $87,628
Emp.: 8
Fiscal Year-end: 03/31/21
Financial Consulting Services
N.A.I.C.S.: 523940
Rachana Abhishek Singi (Mng Dir)

QGOG CONSTELLATION S.A.
40 avenue Monterey, L-2163, Luxembourg, Luxembourg
Tel.: (352) 20 20 2401 LU
Web Site: http://www.qgogconstellation.com
Sales Range: $800-899.9 Million
Emp.: 2,370
Offshore Oil & Gas Contract Drilling
N.A.I.C.S.: 213111
Antonio Augusto de Queiroz Galvao (Chm)

Subsidiaries:

Queiroz Galvao Oleo e Gas S.A. (1)
Av Presidente Antonio Carlos 51 - 5 6 e 7 floors Centro, Rio de Janeiro, 20020-010, Brazil
Tel.: (55) 2132312500
Oil & Gas Exploration Services
N.A.I.C.S.: 213111

QGOLD PTY. LTD.
Level 15 40 Creek Street, Brisbane, 4000, QLD, Australia
Tel.: (61) 730022900
Web Site: https://www.qcoal.com.au
Emp.: 100
Mineral Exploration & Development Services
N.A.I.C.S.: 212210

Subsidiaries:

Carawine Resources Limited (1) (100%)
Tel.: (61) 892092703
Web Site: https://www.carawine.com.au
Rev.: $1,473
Assets: $14,364,914
Liabilities: $543,259
Net Worth: $13,821,655
Earnings: ($1,272,615)
Fiscal Year-end: 06/30/2022
Mineral Exploration & Development Services
N.A.I.C.S.: 213115
David Boyd (Mng Dir)

QHD GOLD LIMITED
242 Angas Street, Adelaide, 5000, SA, Australia
Tel.: (61) 2 9283 6662
Web Site: http://www.qhdgold.com.au
Gold Mining
N.A.I.C.S.: 212220
Liangzhong Chen (Chm, CEO & Mng Dir)

QI AN XIN TECHNOLOGY GROUP, INC.
QAX Security Center No 1 26 of Xizhimenwai South Road, Xicheng, Beijing, 100000, China
Tel.: (86) 1057836300
Web Site: https://www.qianxin.com
Year Founded: 2014
688561—(SHG)
Rev.: $873,679,463
Assets: $1,931,699,269
Liabilities: $532,029,387
Net Worth: $1,399,669,881
Earnings: $8,004,372
Fiscal Year-end: 12/31/22
Cyber Security Product Mfr & Distr
N.A.I.C.S.: 334290
Xiangdong Qi (Chm)

QI LTD.
Unit F 26/F MG Tower 133 Hoi Bun Road Kwun Tong, Kowloon, China (Hong Kong)

AND PRIVATE COMPANIES   **QIAGEN N.V.**

Tel.: (852) 2263 9010
Web Site: http://www.qigroup.com
Sales Range: $400-449.9 Million
Holding Company
N.A.I.C.S.: 551112
Vijay Eswaran (Chm)

Subsidiaries:

QI Philippines Inc. (1)
Unit 3D Strata 2000 Building F Ortigas Jr Road Ortigas Centre, Pasig, 1605, Philippines
Tel.: (63) 6262200
Telecommunication Servicesb
N.A.I.C.S.: 517112

QI Services (M) Sdn Bhd (1)
QI Tower PJ8 No 23 Jalan Barat Section 8, 46050, Petaling Jaya, Selangor, Malaysia
Tel.: (60) 79679888
Telecommunication Servicesb
N.A.I.C.S.: 517112
Iona Anthony (Head-Internal Audit & Corp Governance)

QI Services (TH) Ltd. (1)
540 Mercury Tower 20th Floor Ploenchit Road, Lumpini Pathum Wan, Bangkok, 10330, Thailand
Tel.: (66) 22073888
Telecommunication Servicesb
N.A.I.C.S.: 517112

Wawasan QI Properties Sdn Bhd (1)
Level 11 QI Tower PJ8No. 23 Jalan Barat Section 846050, Petaling Jaya, Malaysia
Tel.: (60) 7967 9898
Construction & Property Development Services
N.A.I.C.S.: 236220

Subsidiary (Domestic):

Kami Builders Sdn Bhd (2)
2nd Floor Wisma IJM, Jalan Yong Shook Lin, Petaling Jaya, 46050, Malaysia
Tel.: (60) 379558122
Heavy & Civil Engineering Construction
N.A.I.C.S.: 237990

QI-HOUSE HOLDINGS LIMITED

28/F Horizon Plaza 2 Lee Wing Street Ap Lei Chau, Hong Kong, China (Hong Kong)
Tel.: (852) 28701582   Ky
Web Site: http://www.treeholdings.com
8395—(HKG)
Rev.: $9,969,735
Assets: $12,723,353
Liabilities: $6,134,280
Net Worth: $6,589,073
Earnings: ($1,408,875)
Emp.: 72
Fiscal Year-end: 03/31/23
Furniture Product Mfr & Distr
N.A.I.C.S.: 337121
Mary Kathleen Babington (Exec Dir)

Subsidiaries:

Hong Kong Italiving International Co., Limited (1)
Room 1801 18/F Lee Garden Five 18 Hysan Avenue, Causeway Bay, China (Hong Kong)
Tel.: (852) 1057626048
Web Site: http://www.hkitaliving.com
Furniture Product Distr
N.A.I.C.S.: 423210
Marco Corti (Creative Dir)

QIAGEN N.V.

Hulsterweg 8, 5912 PL, Venlo, Netherlands
Tel.: (31) 773556600   Nl
Web Site: http://www.qiagen.com
Year Founded: 1984
QGEN—(NYSE)
Rev.: $1,965,311,000
Assets: $6,115,190,000
Liabilities: $2,307,426,000
Net Worth: $3,807,764,000
Earnings: $341,303,000
Emp.: 6,000
Fiscal Year-end: 12/31/23
Holding Company; Medical Supplies Distr
N.A.I.C.S.: 551112
Thomas Schweins (Sr VP-Life Science Bus Area)

Subsidiaries:

Cellestis Ltd. (1)
Office Tower 2 Chadstone Centre, PO Box 169, Chadstone Centre, Chadstone, 3148, VIC, Australia
Tel.: (61) 395713500
Web Site: http://www.cellestis.com
Sales Range: $25-49.9 Million
Emp.: 75
Developer of Medical Diagnosis & Scientific Research Technologies
N.A.I.C.S.: 339112

Subsidiary (Non-US):

Cellestis GmbH (2)
Robert Bosch St 7, 64293, Darmstadt, Germany
Web Site: http://www.cellestis.com
Sales Range: $25-49.9 Million
Emp.: 15
Pharmaceuticals Product Mfr
N.A.I.C.S.: 325412

Subsidiary (US):

Cellestis Inc. (2)
28358 Constellation Rd No 698, Valencia, CA 91355
Tel.: (661) 775-7480
Web Site: http://www.cellestis.com
Sales Range: $25-49.9 Million
Emp.: 25
Laboratory Equipment Suppliers
N.A.I.C.S.: 423490

DxS Ltd. (1)
(100%)
Web Site: http://www.qiagen.com
Sales Range: $10-24.9 Million
Emp.: 150
Molecular Diagnostic Services
N.A.I.C.S.: 334516

Exiqon A/S (1)
Skelstedet 16, 2950, Vedbaek, Denmark
Tel.: (45) 45660888
Web Site: http://www.exiqon.com
Pharmaceuticals Product Mfr
N.A.I.C.S.: 325412
Kim Sorensen (VP & Gen Mgr-Life Sciences Bus Area)

NeuMoDx Inc. (1)
1250 Eisenhower Pl, Ann Arbor, MI 48108
Tel.: (734) 477-0111
Web Site: https://www.neumodx.com
Clinical Diagnostic Services
N.A.I.C.S.: 621511

QAIGEN GmbH (1)
QIAGEN Strasse 1, 40724, Hilden, Germany
Tel.: (49) 2103 291 2000
Bio Technology Services
N.A.I.C.S.: 541714

QIAGEN AB (1)
Torshamnsgatan 35, 16440, Kista, Sweden
Tel.: (46) 2 079 0282
Bio Technology Services
N.A.I.C.S.: 541714

QIAGEN AG (1)
Elisabeth St House 3, 4010, Basel, Switzerland   (100%)
Tel.: (41) 613193030
Web Site: http://www.qiagen.com
Sales Range: $25-49.9 Million
Emp.: 8
Technologies & Products for the Separation, Purification & Handling of Nucleic Acids
N.A.I.C.S.: 325414

Joint Venture (Domestic):

PreAnalytiX GmbH (2)
Feldbachstrasse, 8634, Hombrechtikon, Switzerland   (50%)
Tel.: (41) 614852222
Web Site: http://www.preanalytix.com
Sales Range: $75-99.9 Million
Nucleic Acids Molecular Diagnostic Testing Services
N.A.I.C.S.: 541380

QIAGEN Aarhus A/S (1)
Silkeborgvej 2, 8000, Aarhus, Denmark
Tel.: (45) 8 082 0167
Bio Technology Services
N.A.I.C.S.: 541714

QIAGEN Biotecnologia Brasil Ltda (1)
Tel.: (55) 1150794000
Web Site: http://www1.qiagen.com
Sales Range: $800-899.9 Million
Emp.: 3,000
Medical Diagnostic Products & Testing Equipment Mfr & Distr
N.A.I.C.S.: 334515

QIAGEN Business Services S.p.z.o.o. (1)
ul Powstancow Slaskich 95, 53-332, Wroclaw, Poland
Tel.: (48) 717107893
Emp.: 6,000
Pharmaceutical Research & Development Services
N.A.I.C.S.: 541714

QIAGEN China (Shanghai) Co., Ltd. (1)
Block 20 Landscape Park 88 Da Er Wen Road Zhangjiang Hi-Tech Park, Pudong, Shanghai, 201203, China
Tel.: (86) 2138653865
Web Site: http://www.qiagen.com
Sales Range: $25-49.9 Million
Emp.: 80
Diagnostic Product Distr
N.A.I.C.S.: 456110

QIAGEN Deutschland Holding GmbH (1)
Qiagen Str 1, 40724, Hilden, Germany
Tel.: (49) 21032912000
Investment Management Service
N.A.I.C.S.: 523999

QIAGEN France S.A.S. (1)
3 avenue du Canada LP 809, 91974, Courtaboeuf, France
Tel.: (33) 16 092 0926
Bio Technology Services
N.A.I.C.S.: 541714

QIAGEN GmbH (1)
Qiagen Strasse 1, 40724, Hilden, Germany   (100%)
Tel.: (49) 2103290
Sales Range: $350-399.9 Million
Emp.: 1,400
Assay Products & Solutions Mfr
N.A.I.C.S.: 541715

QIAGEN Iberia, S.L. (1)
Baldiri Reixac 4, 808028, Barcelona, Spain
Tel.: (34) 916307050
Sales Range: $25-49.9 Million
Emp.: 11
Diagnostic Health Care Products Distr
N.A.I.C.S.: 424210
Eugenio Pinel (Gen Mgr)

QIAGEN India Pvt. Ltd. (1)
Corporate One Plot No 5, District Center Jasola, New Delhi, India
Tel.: (91) 1147128301
Pharmaceutical Research & Development Services
N.A.I.C.S.: 541715

QIAGEN Instruments Ag (1)
Garstligweg 8, 8634, Hombrechtikon, Switzerland
Tel.: (41) 800897470
Medical & Surgical Apparatus Mfr
N.A.I.C.S.: 339112

QIAGEN K.K. (1)
Forefront Tower II 13-1 Kachidoki 3-chome, Chuo-ku, Tokyo, 104-0054, Japan   (100%)
Tel.: (81) 368907320
Sales Range: $25-49.9 Million
Emp.: 50
Provider of Technologies & Products for the Separation, Purification & Handling of Nucleic Acids
N.A.I.C.S.: 325414

QIAGEN Korea Ltd. (1)
5th Fl Seoul Square 416 Hangang-daero, Jung-gu, Seoul, 4637, Korea (South)
Tel.: (82) 800007146
Diagnostics Products Distr
N.A.I.C.S.: 424210

QIAGEN Ltd. (1)
Fleming Way, Crawley, RH10 9NQ, W Sussex, United Kingdom   (100%)
Tel.: (44) 293422900
Web Site: http://www1.qiagen.com
Sales Range: $25-49.9 Million
Emp.: 40
Provider of Technologies & Products for the Separation, Purification & Handling of Nucleic Acids
N.A.I.C.S.: 325414

QIAGEN Nordic (1)
PL 3810, 2, Helsinki, Finland
Tel.: (358) 800914416
Diagnostics Products Distr
N.A.I.C.S.: 424210
Thorbjorn Senson (Gen Mgr)

QIAGEN North American Holdings, Inc. (1)
27220 Turnberry Ln Ste 200, Valencia, CA 91355
Tel.: (661) 702-3000
Web Site: http://qiagen.com
Sales Range: $50-74.9 Million
Emp.: 80
Pharmaceutical Holding Company
N.A.I.C.S.: 551112

Subsidiary (Domestic):

QIAGEN Inc. (2)
27220 W Turnberry Ln Ste 200, Valencia, CA 91355
Tel.: (661) 702-3000
Web Site: http://www1.qiagen.com
Sales Range: $25-49.9 Million
Emp.: 80
Medical Testing & Diagnostic Equipment Mfr & Distr
N.A.I.C.S.: 423450

QIAGEN Pty. Ltd. (1)
Level 2 Office Tower 2, PO Box 641, Doncaster, Chadstone, 3148, VIC, Australia   (100%)
Tel.: (61) 398409800
Web Site: http://www.qiagen.com
Sales Range: $25-49.9 Million
Emp.: 20
Assay Technologies & Products Mfr
N.A.I.C.S.: 325414

QIAGEN Redwood City Inc. (1)
1001 Marshall St Ste 200, Redwood City, CA 94063
Tel.: (650) 381-5100
Biotechnology Research & Development Services
N.A.I.C.S.: 541714

QIAGEN S.A. (1)
3 Avenue du Canada, LP 809, 91974, Courtaboeuf, Cedex, France   (100%)
Tel.: (33) 160920926
Sales Range: $25-49.9 Million
Emp.: 40
Provider of Technologies & Products for the Separation, Purification & Handling of Nucleic Acids
N.A.I.C.S.: 325414

QIAGEN S.A.S. (1)
3 Avenue du Canada, LP 809, 91974, Courtaboeuf, Cedex, France
Tel.: (33) 160920926
Diagnostics Products Distr
N.A.I.C.S.: 424210

QIAGEN S.p.A. (1)
(100%)
Web Site: http://www1.qiagen.com
Sales Range: $25-49.9 Million
Emp.: 12
Provider of Technologies & Products for the Separation, Purification & Handling of Nucleic Acids
N.A.I.C.S.: 334516

QIAGEN S.r.l. (1)
Tel.: (39) 02334304811

QIAGEN N.V.

QIAGEN N.V.—(Continued)
Web Site: http://www.qiagen.com
Diagnostics Products Distr
N.A.I.C.S.: 424210

QIAGEN Shenzhen Co. Ltd. (1)
6 7F R3-B High-Tech Industrial Park, Nanshan District, Shenzhen, 518063, China
Tel.: (86) 75586366188
Pharmaceutical Products Mfr & Distr
N.A.I.C.S.: 325412

QIAGEN Singapore Pte. Ltd. (1)
8 Commonwealth Lane 02-02, Singapore, 149555, Singapore
Tel.: (65) 18007424362
Diagnostic Health Care Products Distr
N.A.I.C.S.: 424210

QIAGEN Taiwan Co Ltd (1)
5F No 100 Sec 2 Roosevelt Rd, Zhongzheng Dist, Taipei, 100, Taiwan
Tel.: (886) 2 89781000
Diagnostics Products Distr
N.A.I.C.S.: 424210

QIAGEN, Inc. (1)
181 Bay Street Suite 4400, Toronto, M5J 2T3, ON, Canada (100%)
Tel.: (905) 821-1702
Web Site: http://www1.qiagen.com
Sales Range: $25-49.9 Million
Emp.: 10
Provider of Technologies & Products for the Separation, Purification & Handling of Nucleic Acids
N.A.I.C.S.: 325414

Qiagen Lake Constance GmbH (1)
Jacques-Schiesser-Strasse 3, 78315, Stockach, Germany
Tel.: (49) 777191660
Sales Range: $25-49.9 Million
Emp.: 45
Optical Measurement Device Mfr
N.A.I.C.S.: 333310
Joerg Schickedanz (Gen Mgr)

Qiagen Manchester Ltd. (1)
4 Skelton House Lloyd Street North, Manchester, M15 6SH, United Kingdom
Tel.: (44) 16 1204 1100
Web Site: http://www.qiagen.com
Sales Range: $75-99.9 Million
Emp.: 15
Pharmaceutical Products Distr
N.A.I.C.S.: 424210

Qiagen Marseille S.A. (1)
Luminy Biotech Entreprises 163 avenue de Luminy, Case 923, 13288, Marseilles, Cedex 9, France
Tel.: (33) 491293090
Web Site: http://www.qiagenmarseille.com
Emp.: 74
Diagnostic Test Developer & Mfr
N.A.I.C.S.: 541715
Helene Peyro-Saint-Paul (Chief Medical Officer)

Subsidiary (US):

Ipsogen Inc. (2)
700 Canal St, Stamford, CT 06902
Tel.: (203) 504-8585
Sales Range: $10-24.9 Million
Emp.: 15
Health Care Srvices
N.A.I.C.S.: 621491

QIAN HU CORPORATION LIMITED

71 Jalan Lekar Sungei Tengah, Singapore, 698950, Singapore
Tel.: (65) 67667087
Web Site: https://www.qianhu.com
Year Founded: 1998
BCV—(SES)
Rev.: $53,255,917
Assets: $44,635,948
Liabilities: $13,028,262
Net Worth: $31,607,686
Earnings: ($6,912,281)
Emp.: 555
Fiscal Year-end: 12/31/23
Ornamental Fish Breeding Services
N.A.I.C.S.: 112511

Kenny Kim Lee Yap (Chm & Mng Dir)

Subsidiaries:

Beijing Qian Hu Aquarium & Pets Co., Ltd. (1)
Dong Fish Farm, Bei Ma Fang Village Jin Zhan Town Chao Yang District, Beijing, 100018, China
Tel.: (86) 1084312255
Ornamental Fish Product Distr
N.A.I.C.S.: 424490

Guangzhou Qian Hu Aquarium & Pets Accessories Manufacturing Co., Ltd. (1)
No 12 Dongfeng Avenue Tanbu Town, Huadu District, Guangzhou, Guangdong, China
Tel.: (86) 2066856928
Aquarium Supplies Mfr & Distr
N.A.I.C.S.: 712130

Guangzhou Qian Hu Aquarium & Pets Co., Ltd. (1)
No 12 Dongfeng Avenue, Tanbu Town Huadu District, Guangzhou, China
Tel.: (86) 2066856928
Aquarium Accessory Mfr & Distr
N.A.I.C.S.: 332999

P.T. Qian Hu Joe Aquatic Indonesia (1)
JL Raya Brantamulya-Tengsaw No 9 Tarik Kolot, Kecamatan Citeureup, Bogor, 16810, Jawa Barat, Indonesia
Tel.: (62) 2187942020
Web Site: https://www.qianhu.co.id
Ornamental Fish Product Distr
N.A.I.C.S.: 424490

Qian Hu Aquarium & Pets (M) Sdn Bhd (1)
Block E Lot 6212 Kg Baru Balakong, 43300, Balakong, Selangor Darul Ehsan, Malaysia
Tel.: (60) 389615142
Web Site: http://www.qianhu.com
Sales Range: $25-49.9 Million
Pet & Aquarium Supplies Retailer
N.A.I.C.S.: 459910
Thomas Wah Hong Ng (Mng Dir)

Qian Hu Marketing Co Ltd (1)
30/23 Moo 8 Klongnung, Klongluang, Pathumthani, 12120, Thailand
Tel.: (66) 290264479
Web Site: http://www.qianhu.com
Sales Range: $25-49.9 Million
Pet & Aquarium Supplies Retailer
N.A.I.C.S.: 459910

Qian Hu Tat Leng Plastic Pte Ltd (1)
2 Woodlands Sector 1 03-35 Woodlands Spectrum 1, Singapore, 738068, Singapore
Tel.: (65) 67527258
Web Site: https://www.tatleng.com
Plastic Bags Mfr & Distr
N.A.I.C.S.: 326111

Qian Hu The Pet Family (M) Sdn Bhd (1)
Block E Lot 6212 Kampung Baru Balakong, 43300, Balakong, Selangor Darul Ehsan, Malaysia
Tel.: (60) 389615142
Web Site: http://www.thepetfamily.com
Emp.: 100
Pet Supplies Retailer
N.A.I.C.S.: 459910

Shanghai Qian Hu Aquarium and Pets Co., Ltd. (1)
No 688 Jin Hui Road Zhu Di Town, Min Hang District, Shanghai, 201103, China
Tel.: (86) 2162217181
Pet & Aquarium Supplies Retailer
N.A.I.C.S.: 459910

Thai Qian Hu Company Limited (1)
30/25 Moo 8 Klongnung, Klongluang, Pathumthani, 12120, Thailand
Tel.: (66) 25161155
Web Site: http://www.qianhu.com
Sales Range: $25-49.9 Million
Aquarium Supplies Retailer
N.A.I.C.S.: 712130
Jimmy Tan Kim (Mng Dir)

QIANHE CONDIMENT AND FOOD CO., LTD.

Minjiadu Chengnan, Dongpo District, Meishan, 620010, Sichuan, China
Tel.: (86) 2838568229
Web Site: http://www.qianhefood.com
Year Founded: 2012
603027—(SHG)
Rev.: $342,080,627
Assets: $445,291,685
Liabilities: $114,927,270
Net Worth: $330,364,415
Earnings: $48,291,001
Fiscal Year-end: 12/31/22
Food Additive Mfr & Distr
N.A.I.C.S.: 311941
Wu Chao Qun (Chm & Pres)

QIANJIANG WATER RESOURCES DEVELOPMENT CO., LTD.

No 3 Santaishan Road, Hangzhou, 310013, Zhejiang, China
Tel.: (86) 57187974386
Web Site: http://www.qjwater.com
Year Founded: 1998
600283—(SHG)
Rev.: $256,562,257
Assets: $967,897,832
Liabilities: $566,842,283
Net Worth: $401,055,548
Earnings: $24,208,414
Fiscal Year-end: 12/31/22
Water Supply Services
N.A.I.C.S.: 221310
Xue Zhiyong (Chm)

QIANJIANG YONGAN PHARMACEUTICAL CO., LTD.

No 2 Guangze Avenue Qianjiang Economic Development Zone, Wuhan, 433132, Hubei, China
Tel.: (86) 2786202727
Web Site: http://www.chinataurine.com
Year Founded: 2006
002365—(SSE)
Rev.: $205,327,980
Assets: $340,354,872
Liabilities: $45,092,268
Net Worth: $295,262,604
Earnings: $19,705,140
Emp.: 500
Fiscal Year-end: 12/31/22
Pharmaceuticals Mfr
N.A.I.C.S.: 325412
Chen Yong (Chm)

QIANJIN PHARMACEUTICAL CO., LTD.

No 801 Zhuzhou Avenue, Tianyuan District, Zhuzhou, 412000, Hunan, China
Tel.: (86) 18774834452
Web Site: https://www.qjyy.com
Year Founded: 1966
600479—(SHG)
Rev.: $565,289,515
Assets: $648,925,388
Liabilities: $253,519,016
Net Worth: $395,406,372
Earnings: $42,628,978
Emp.: 8,000
Fiscal Year-end: 12/31/22
Pharmaceutic Product Mfr & Distr
N.A.I.C.S.: 325412
Duanyu Jiang (Chm & Sec-Party)

QIAO XING UNIVERSAL RESOURCES, INC.

Qiao Xing Science Industrial Park, Tang Quan, Huizhou, 516023, Guangdong, China
Tel.: (86) 752 2820268
Year Founded: 1992
Sales Range: $150-199.9 Million
Emp.: 457

Telecommunication Terminals & Equipment Mfr & Sales
N.A.I.C.S.: 334210

Subsidiaries:

Qiao Xing Mobile Communication Co., Ltd. (1)
30th Floor Tower A Eagle Run Plaza, No 26 Xiaoyun Road, Chaoyang District, Beijing, 100016, China
Tel.: (86) 10 62501728
Web Site: http://www.qxmc.com
Sales Range: $125-149.9 Million
Emp.: 278
Mobile Phone Handsets Mfr
N.A.I.C.S.: 334220

QIAOYIN CITY MANAGEMENT CO., LTD.

QiaoYin Building No 9 Baihesha Road, Liwan District, Guangzhou, 510145, Guangdong, China
Tel.: (86) 2022283188
Web Site: http://www.gzqiaoyin.com
Year Founded: 2001
002973—(SSE)
Rev.: $555,252,516
Assets: $966,105,036
Liabilities: $665,182,908
Net Worth: $300,922,128
Earnings: $44,169,840
Emp.: 60,000
Fiscal Year-end: 12/31/22
Management Consulting Services
N.A.I.C.S.: 541613
Guo Beihua (Chm & Gen Mgr)

QIAQIA FOOD CO., LTD.

Lianhua Rd Economic And Technological Development Zone, Xuhui District, Hefei, 230601, Anhui, China
Tel.: (86) 55162227008
Web Site: http://cnqiaqia.waimaotong.com
Year Founded: 2001
002557—(SSE)
Rev.: $966,425,148
Assets: $1,200,042,324
Liabilities: $459,923,724
Net Worth: $740,118,600
Earnings: $137,030,400
Emp.: 8,000
Fiscal Year-end: 12/31/22
Roasted Nuts & Seeds Mfr
N.A.I.C.S.: 311911
Xianbao Chen (Chm, Pres & Gen Mgr)

QIBU CO., LTD.

11th Floor Husheng Building No 555 Renhuangshan Street, Wuxing, Huzhou, 313099, Zhejiang, China
Tel.: (86) 5722693037
Web Site: http://www.twabc.com.cn
Year Founded: 2009
603557—(SHG)
Rev.: $49,348,438
Assets: $229,657,096
Liabilities: $131,570,104
Net Worth: $98,086,992
Earnings: ($84,629,610)
Fiscal Year-end: 12/31/22
Child Product Mfr & Distr
N.A.I.C.S.: 316210
Chen Lihong (Chm)

QIC LIMITED

Level 5 66 Eagle Street, GPO Box 2242, Brisbane, 4001, QLD, Australia
Tel.: (61) 0733603800
Web Site: http://www.qic.com
Investment Services
N.A.I.C.S.: 523999
Melissa Schulz (Gen Mgr-Sustainability)

AND PRIVATE COMPANIES — QINETIQ GROUP PLC

Subsidiaries:

Nexus Day Hospitals Holdings Pty Ltd (1)
Level 8 601 Pacific Highway, St Leonards, 2065, NSW, Australia (70%)
Tel.: (61) 292956800
Holding Company
N.A.I.C.S.: 551112

Subsidiary (Domestic):

Nexus Day Hospitals Pty Ltd (2)
601 Pacific Highway, St Leonards, 2065, NSW, Australia
Tel.: (61) 292956800
Web Site: https://www.nexushospitals.com.au
Medical & Surgical Services
N.A.I.C.S.: 622110

Subsidiary (Domestic):

Montserrat Healthcare Pty. Ltd. (3)
32 Morrow Street, Taringa, 4068, Australia
Tel.: (61) 738336701
Web Site: https://www.montserrat.com.au
Medical & Surgical Services
N.A.I.C.S.: 622110

Pacific Energy Limited (1)
338 Gnangara Road, Landsdale, Perth, 6065, WA, Australia
Tel.: (61) 8 9303 8888
Web Site: http://www.pacificenergy.com.au
Rev.: $53,133,418
Assets: $246,689,474
Liabilities: $112,812,805
Net Worth: $133,876,669
Earnings: $5,292,503
Fiscal Year-end: 06/30/2018
Power Generation & Development Services
N.A.I.C.S.: 221111
James Cullen (CEO)

Subsidiary (Domestic):

Kalgoorlie Power Systems (2)
338 Gnangara Road, Landsdale, Perth, 6065, WA, Australia
Tel.: (61) 893038800
Web Site: http://www.kpspg.com.au
Sales Range: $75-99.9 Million
Emp.: 23
Electric Power Distribution Services
N.A.I.C.S.: 221122
Darius Zimnoch (Mgr-Queensland & New South Wales)

QICOMM LIMITED
Network House 15 High Street, Hampton Hill, London, TW12 1NB, United Kingdom
Tel.: (44) 20 8635 5555
Web Site: http://www.qicomm.com
Year Founded: 2005
Sales Range: $125-149.9 Million
Emp.: 100
Telecommunication Servicesb
N.A.I.C.S.: 517810
Pat Nabhan (Founder & CEO)

QIFENG NEW MATERIAL CO., LTD.
No 22 Qifeng Road Zhutai Town, Linzi District, Zibo, 255432, Shandong, China
Web Site: http://www.qifeng.cn
Year Founded: 1976
002521—(SSE)
Rev.: $437,857,056
Assets: $664,632,540
Liabilities: $166,427,352
Net Worth: $498,205,188
Earnings: $1,190,592
Emp.: 1,800
Fiscal Year-end: 12/31/22
Decorative Paper Mfr
N.A.I.C.S.: 322120
Li Xuefeng (Chm)

QIFU TECHNOLOGY, INC.
7/F Lujiazui Finance Plaza No 1217 Dongfang Road, Pudong New Area, Shanghai, 200122, China
Tel.: (86) 2158357668 Ky
Web Site: https://ir.360shuke.com
Year Founded: 2016
QFIN—(NASDAQ)
Rev.: $2,536,227,615
Assets: $6,180,977,076
Liabilities: $3,280,513,062
Net Worth: $2,900,464,013
Earnings: $616,543,545
Emp.: 2,199
Fiscal Year-end: 12/31/22
Online Financial Information Services
N.A.I.C.S.: 541511
Hongyi Zhou (Chm)

QIIWI GAMES AB
Stora Torget 3, 441 30, Alingsas, Sweden
Tel.: (46) 322635000
Web Site: https://www.qiiwi.com
Year Founded: 2005
QIIWI—(OMX)
Rev.: $2,560,208
Assets: $3,516,191
Liabilities: $448,707
Net Worth: $3,067,485
Earnings: ($2,783,569)
Emp.: 16
Fiscal Year-end: 12/31/23
Software Development Services
N.A.I.C.S.: 541511
Erik Dale Rundberg (CEO)

QIJING MACHINERY CO., LTD
No 1 Sanxing East Road, Ninghai, Ningbo, 315609, Zhejiang, China
Tel.: (86) 57465310999
Web Site: http://www.qijing-m.com
Year Founded: 1996
603677—(SHG)
Rev.: $253,303,896
Assets: $282,079,900
Liabilities: $125,378,099
Net Worth: $156,701,802
Earnings: $8,989,798
Fiscal Year-end: 12/31/22
Precision Equipment Mfr & Distr
N.A.I.C.S.: 332721
Mei Xuhui (Chm)

QILIAN INTERNATIONAL HOLDING GROUP LIMITED
No 152 Hongliang East 1st Street No 1703, Tianfu New District, Chengdu, 610200, China
Tel.: (86) 2864775652 Ky
Web Site: https://bgm.ltd
Year Founded: 2019
QLI—(NASDAQ)
Rev.: $64,855,025
Assets: $64,526,617
Liabilities: $9,563,081
Net Worth: $54,963,536
Earnings: $1,076,693
Emp.: 344
Fiscal Year-end: 09/30/22
Holding Company
N.A.I.C.S.: 551112
Chen Xin (CEO)

QILU BANK CO., LTD.
Shuangjin Building, Block B No. 10817, Jingshi Road Lixia District, Jinan, 250014, China
Tel.: (86) 53186075850
Web Site: https://www.qlbchina.com
Year Founded: 1996
601665—(SHG)
Rev.: $1,654,832,466
Assets: $83,741,690,851
Liabilities: $77,950,888,624
Net Worth: $5,790,802,226
Earnings: $586,197,247
Fiscal Year-end: 12/31/23
Financial Services
N.A.I.C.S.: 522110
Hua Zhang (Vice Chm & Pres)

QILU EXPRESSWAY COMPANY LIMITED
Room 2301 Block 4 Zone 3 Hanyu Financial and Business Centre, No 7000 Jingshi East Road High-tech Zone, Jinan, Shandong, China
Tel.: (86) 53187207088 CN
Web Site: http://www.qlecl.com
Year Founded: 2004
1576—(HKG)
Rev.: $411,553,678
Assets: $1,461,923,705
Liabilities: $657,713,909
Net Worth: $804,209,796
Earnings: $109,519,862
Emp.: 693
Fiscal Year-end: 12/31/22
Expressway Management Services
N.A.I.C.S.: 561730
Gang Li (Chm)

QIMING VENTURE PARTNERS
Room 3906 Jinmao Tower 88 Century Boulevard, Shanghai, 200121, China
Tel.: (86) 21 6101 6522
Web Site: http://www.qimingventures.com
Year Founded: 2006
Venture Capital Firm
N.A.I.C.S.: 523999
Gary Rieshel (Founder & Mng Partner)

QINCHUAN MACHINE TOOL & TOOL GROUP SHARE CO., LTD.
No 22 Jiangtan Road, Baoji, 721009, Shaanxi, China
Tel.: (86) 9173670665
Web Site: https://www.qinchuan.com
Year Founded: 1998
000837—(SSE)
Rev.: $575,793,036
Assets: $1,196,330,148
Liabilities: $617,722,092
Net Worth: $578,608,056
Earnings: $38,610,000
Fiscal Year-end: 12/31/22
Machine Tools Mfr
N.A.I.C.S.: 333517
Ma Xuyao (Chm & Sec-Party)

Subsidiaries:

Baoji Machine Tool Group Co., Ltd. (1)
Web Site: http://www.bjmtw.com
Emp.: 3,500
Metal Cutting Machine Tool Mfr & Distr
N.A.I.C.S.: 333517

Subsidiary (Domestic):

Shaanxi Guanzhong Tool Manufacturing Co., Ltd. (2)
No 34 Guanzhong Road, Fengxiang, Baoji, 721400, Shaanxi, China
Tel.: (86) 9177222139
Web Site: https://en.gztool.com.cn
Cutting Tool Mfr & Distr
N.A.I.C.S.: 333515

QC American, LLC (1)
575 S Mansfield St, Ypsilanti, MI 48197
Tel.: (734) 961-0300
Web Site: https://www.qcamerican.com
Grinding Machine Mfr & Distr
N.A.I.C.S.: 333248
Fran Mao (Mng Dir)

Qinchuan Machine Tool Group Baoji Instrument Co., ltd. (1)
No 14 Qingjiang E 2 Rood, Baoji, 721006, Shaanxi, China
Tel.: (86) 9173617300
Web Site: http://www.qcbjyb.com
Pressure Gauge Mfr & Distr
N.A.I.C.S.: 334513

QINETIQ GROUP PLC
Cody Technology Park, Farnborough, GU14 0LX, Hampshire, United Kingdom
Tel.: (44) 1252392000 UK
Web Site: https://www.qinetiq.com
Year Founded: 2001
QQ—(LSE)
Rev.: $1,792,733,488
Assets: $2,385,106,724
Liabilities: $968,461,676
Net Worth: $1,416,645,048
Earnings: $122,194,800
Emp.: 6,915
Fiscal Year-end: 03/31/22
Holding Company; Defense Technology & Security Solutions
N.A.I.C.S.: 551112
David Smith (CFO)

Subsidiaries:

Boldon James Ltd. (1)
Cody Technology Park Ively Road, Farnborough, GU14 0LX, Hampshire, United Kingdom
Tel.: (44) 1270507800
Web Site: http://www.boldonjames.com
Sales Range: $10-24.9 Million
Emp.: 72
Formal Messaging Security Software & Services
N.A.I.C.S.: 513210
Martin Sugden (CEO)

Graphics Research Corporation Ltd. (1)
Baker Building, Haslar Marine Technology Park, Gosport, PO12 2AG, Hampshire, United Kingdom
Tel.: (44) 2392334003
Web Site: http://www.grc-ltd.co.uk
Sales Range: $25-49.9 Million
Emp.: 15
Naval Architecture Software, Consulting & Research Services
N.A.I.C.S.: 336999
Vittorio Vagliani (Mng Dir)

HVR Consulting Services Limited (1)
Selborne House Mill Lane, Alton, GU34 2QJ, Hampshire, United Kingdom
Tel.: (44) 00142087977
Web Site: http://www.hvr-csl.co.uk
Sales Range: $25-49.9 Million
Emp.: 100
Risk Management Consulting Services
N.A.I.C.S.: 541611

Inzpire Limited (1)
Unit 1B Alpha Court Business Park Kingsley Road, Lincoln, LN6 3TA, Lincolnshire, United Kingdom
Tel.: (44) 152 268 8231
Web Site: https://www.inzpire.com
Military Aviation Training Services
N.A.I.C.S.: 611512
Hugh Griffiths (CEO)

Newman & Spurr Consultancy Ltd. (1)
River View 2 Meadows Business Park, Camberley, GU17 9AB, Surrey, United Kingdom
Tel.: (44) 127 667 8867
Web Site: https://www.nsc.co.uk
Management Consultancy Services
N.A.I.C.S.: 541611

OptaSense Limited (1)
Bldg A8 Rm 1005 Cody Technology Park Ively Road, Farnborough, GU14 0LX, Hampshire, United Kingdom (100%)
Tel.: (44) 1252 392000
Web Site: http://www.optasense.com
Emp.: 140
Acoustic Sensing Technology Developer & Mfr
N.A.I.C.S.: 334413
Jamie Pollard (CEO)

Subsidiary (US):

Redfern Integrated Optics, Inc. (2)

QINETIQ GROUP PLC

QinetiQ Group plc—(Continued)

3350 Scott Blvd Bldg 1, Santa Clara, CA 95054
Tel.: (408) 970-3500
Web Site: https://www.rio-lasers.com
Sales Range: $1-9.9 Million
Emp.: 22
Optical Sources & Subsystems Developer & Mfr
N.A.I.C.S.: 334413
Yves LeMaitre *(Pres)*

QinetiQ GmbH
Flughafenstrasse 65, 41066, Monchengladbach, Germany
Tel.: (49) 2161 830 3290
Aviation Training Services
N.A.I.C.S.: 611512
Christian Zeppenfeld *(Head)*

QinetiQ Group Canada Inc. (1)
Suite 260 99 Bank Street, Ottawa, K1P 6B9, ON, Canada
Tel.: (613) 680-8011
Aviation Training Services
N.A.I.C.S.: 611512

QinetiQ Limited (1)
Cody Technology Park Ively Road, Farnborough, GU14 0LX, Hampshire, United Kingdom
Tel.: (44) 1252 392000
Web Site: http://www.qinetiq.com
Defense Research & Development Services
N.A.I.C.S.: 927110

QinetiQ Nanomaterials Ltd (1)
Cody Technology Park Y25 Building, Ively Road, Farnborough, GU14 0LX, Hants, United Kingdom
Tel.: (44) 1252393000
Sales Range: $25-49.9 Million
Emp.: 70
Gas Producer
N.A.I.C.S.: 325120

QinetiQ North America, Inc. (1)
350 2nd Ave/Bldg 1, Waltham, MA 02451 **(100%)**
Tel.: (781) 684-4000
Web Site: http://www.qinetiq-na.com
Sales Range: $75-99.9 Million
Emp.: 2
Holding Company; Engineering, Technology & Information Security Services
N.A.I.C.S.: 551112
Richard Wiesman *(Exec VP)*

Subsidiary (Domestic):

Foster-Miller, Inc. (2)
350 2nd Ave, Waltham, MA 02451
Tel.: (781) 684-4000
Sales Range: $100-124.9 Million
Emp.: 250
Government & Commercial Research & Special Machinery, Products & Systems Developer
N.A.I.C.S.: 541330
Andrew Rogers *(Pres)*

QinetiQ Inc. (2)
4100 Fairfax Dr Ste 800, Arlington, VA 22203-1666
Tel.: (703) 741-0300
Sales Range: $10-24.9 Million
Security System Services
N.A.I.C.S.: 561621
Daniela Walrath *(Chief People Officer)*

QinetiQ US Holdings, Inc. (2)
7918 Jones Branch Dr Ste 350, McLean, VA 20120-1969
Tel.: (703) 752-9595
Holding Company
N.A.I.C.S.: 551112

SimAuthor, Inc. (2)
890 Explorer Blvd NW, Huntsville, AL 35806
Tel.: (256) 922-6300
Web Site: http://www.simauthor.com
Sales Range: $10-24.9 Million
Flight Data Analysis & Visualization Software Developer & Publisher
N.A.I.C.S.: 513210
Fairfax O'Riley *(VP-Sls & Mktg)*

Westar Aerospace & Defense Group, Inc. (2)

4 Research Park Dr, Saint Charles, MO 63304-5685
Tel.: (636) 300-5000
Web Site: http://www.westar.com
Holding Company; Aerospace & Defense Products Mfr
N.A.I.C.S.: 551111
Randall Tieszen *(COO & Exec VP)*

Subsidiary (Domestic):

Westar Display Technologies, Inc. (3)
4 Research Park Dr, Saint Charles, MO 63304-5685
Tel.: (636) 300-5100
Web Site: https://www.westardisplaytechnology.com
LCD Contoller, Video Processor, Optical Instrument & Display Measurement Systems & Components Mfr
N.A.I.C.S.: 334419

QinetiQ Novare Pty. Ltd. (1)
Level 5 30 Makerston Street, Brisbane, 4000, QLD, Australia
Tel.: (61) 73 031 0200
Aviation Training Services
N.A.I.C.S.: 611512

QinetiQ Pty. Ltd. (1)
Level 3 12 Brindabella Circuit Brindabella Business Park, Canberra Airport, Canberra, 2609, ACT, Australia
Tel.: (61) 226002600
Web Site: http://www.qinetiq.com
Sales Range: $1-4.9 Billion
Emp.: 6,000
Holding Company
N.A.I.C.S.: 551112
Rodney Smith *(CFO)*

Subsidiary (Domestic):

QinetiQ Consulting Pty Ltd (2)
Unit 5 Level 1 no 8 Brindabella Circuit Brindabella Business Park, Canberra, 2612, ACT, Australia
Tel.: (61) 262002600
Web Site: http://www.qinetiq.com.au
Sales Range: $10-24.9 Million
Emp.: 150
Consulting & Professional Services
N.A.I.C.S.: 541611
Rob Hawketts *(Mng Dir)*

QinetiQ Solutions Sdn. Bhd. (1)
L4-E-2 Level 4 Enterprise 4 Technology Park, Bukit Jalil, 57000, Kuala Lumpur, Malaysia
Tel.: (60) 38 996 6788
Web Site: https://www.qinetics.net
Information Technology Services
N.A.I.C.S.: 541511

QinetiQ Sweden AB (1)
The Flight Physiological Centre Nobymalmsvagen 5, PO Box 1541, 581 15, Linkoping, Sweden
Tel.: (46) 1 324 3060
Aviation Training Services
N.A.I.C.S.: 611512

QinetiQ Target Systems Limited (1)
The Boulevard Orbital Park Roundabout, Willesborough, Ashford, TN26 0GA, Kent, United Kingdom
Tel.: (44) 123 350 5600
Management Consultancy Services
N.A.I.C.S.: 541611

cueSim Ltd (1)
Units 2-4 Highfield Parc Highfield Rd, Oakley, Bedford, MK43 7TA, United Kingdom
Tel.: (44) 1234828000
Web Site: http://www.cuesim.com
Sales Range: $10-24.9 Million
Emp.: 4
Simulation Services
N.A.I.C.S.: 611430
Hassina Maycroft *(Mng Dir)*

QINGCI GAMES INC.
33 Wang Hai Road Xiamen Software Park II, Xiamen, 361008, China
Web Site: https://www.qcplay.com
Year Founded: 2012
6633—(HKG)
Rev.: $125,406,652

Assets: $276,753,988
Liabilities: $35,440,851
Net Worth: $241,313,137
Earnings: ($5,206,026)
Emp.: 656
Fiscal Year-end: 12/31/23
Software Development Services
N.A.I.C.S.: 541511
Xiangshuo Zeng *(COO)*

QINGCLOUD TECHNOLOGIES CORP.
Room 601 6F Building 16 Yard No 36 Chuangyuan Road, Chaoyang, Beijing, 100073, China
Tel.: (86) 1083051688
Web Site: http://www.qingcloud.com
Year Founded: 2012
688316—(SHG)
Rev.: $42,817,928
Assets: $84,282,597
Liabilities: $37,956,915
Net Worth: $46,325,682
Earnings: ($34,290,706)
Fiscal Year-end: 12/31/22
Information Technology Services
N.A.I.C.S.: 541512
Yunsong Huang *(Chm & Gen Mgr)*

QINGDAO AINNOVATION TECHNOLOGY GROUP CO., LTD.
8F Tower A Ding Hao Building No 3 Haidian St, Haidian District, Beijing, China
Tel.: (86) 1082169566
Web Site:
https://www.ainnovation.com
Year Founded: 2018
2121—(HKG)
Rev.: $238,646,484
Assets: $500,758,765
Liabilities: $139,340,205
Net Worth: $361,418,560
Earnings: ($55,333,324)
Emp.: 728
Fiscal Year-end: 12/31/22
Information Technology Services
N.A.I.C.S.: 541512
Tao He *(Chief Revenue Officer)*

Subsidiaries:

EPSA Himatic GmbH (1)
Humboldtstrasse 25A 2 OG, 21509, Glinde, Germany
Tel.: (49) 4033485600
Web Site: https://www.epsahimatic.de
Industrial Equipment Mfr & Distr
N.A.I.C.S.: 333413

QINGDAO BAHEAL MEDICAL INC.
88 Kaifeng Road, Shibei, Qingdao, 266042, Shandong, China
Tel.: (86) 53266756688
Web Site: https://www.baheal.cn
Year Founded: 2005
301015—(CHIN)
Rev.: $1,054,350,648
Assets: $706,240,080
Liabilities: $386,137,908
Net Worth: $320,102,172
Earnings: $70,493,436
Fiscal Year-end: 12/31/22
Pharmaceutical Product Mfr & Distr
N.A.I.C.S.: 325412
Gang Fu *(Pres)*

QINGDAO CHOHO INDUSTRIAL CO., LTD.
No 112 Hongkong Road, Pingdu, Qingdao, 266705, China
Tel.: (86) 53255578019
Web Site:
https://www.chohogroup.com
Year Founded: 1999

INTERNATIONAL PUBLIC

003033—(SSE)
Rev.: $225,611,568
Assets: $244,854,792
Liabilities: $92,211,912
Net Worth: $152,642,880
Earnings: $23,856,768
Emp.: 1,900
Fiscal Year-end: 12/31/22
Automobile Parts Mfr
N.A.I.C.S.: 336390
Yumo Jin *(Chm & Pres)*

QINGDAO CITYMEDIA CO., LTD.
No 182 Haier Road, Laoshan District, Qingdao, 266061, Shandong, China
Tel.: (86) 53268068888
Web Site: http://www.qdjy.com
Year Founded: 1958
600229—(SHG)
Rev.: $358,639,936
Assets: $574,791,928
Liabilities: $152,088,244
Net Worth: $422,703,684
Earnings: $47,164,530
Emp.: 1,800
Fiscal Year-end: 12/31/22
Chemical Product Mfr & Distr
N.A.I.C.S.: 325998
Jia Qingpeng *(Chm)*

QINGDAO COPTON TECHNOLOGY COMPANY LIMITED
No 18 Shenzhen Road, Laoshan District, Qingdao, 266101, China
Tel.: (86) 4001639006
Web Site: https://www.copton.com.cn
Year Founded: 1989
603798—(SHG)
Rev.: $111,140,865
Assets: $184,479,535
Liabilities: $26,712,027
Net Worth: $157,767,508
Earnings: $5,554,772
Fiscal Year-end: 12/31/22
Automotive Lubricating Oil Mfr
N.A.I.C.S.: 324191
Zhu Lei *(Chm)*

QINGDAO DOUBLESTAR CO., LTD.
No 666 Lianghe Road, Huangdao District, Qingdao, 266400, Shandong, China
Tel.: (86) 53267710729
Year Founded: 1921
000599—(SSE)
Rev.: $549,020,160
Assets: $1,384,812,936
Liabilities: $1,050,232,716
Net Worth: $334,580,220
Earnings: ($84,510,972)
Fiscal Year-end: 12/31/22
Holding Company; Tire Mfr & Whslr; Rubber & Plastic Machinery Mfr & Whslr
N.A.I.C.S.: 551112

Subsidiaries:

Doublestar Tire, Inc. (1)
No 5 Wendling Rd, Laoshan Distric, Qingdao, 266400, China
Tel.: (86) 53280958024
Tire Mfr & Whslr
N.A.I.C.S.: 326211

Qingdao Doublestar Rubber & Plastic Machinery Co., Ltd. (1)
No 768 Taishan Road, Jiaonan, Qingdao, 266400, China
Tel.: (86) 532 8616 4073
Web Site: http://en.doublestar.cc
Industrial Machinery Mfr & Whslr
N.A.I.C.S.: 333248

QINGDAO EAST STEEL TOWER STOCK CO., LTD.
No 318 Guangzhou North Road, Ji-

aozhou, Qingdao, 266300, Shandong, China
Tel.: (86) 53288056092
Web Site: http://www.qddftt.cn
Year Founded: 1982
002545—(SSE)
Rev.: $507,701,844
Assets: $1,830,278,268
Liabilities: $641,345,796
Net Worth: $1,188,932,472
Earnings: $115,759,800
Emp.: 2,700
Fiscal Year-end: 12/31/22
Steel Structure & Iron Tower Construction Services
N.A.I.C.S.: 237130
Fangru Han *(Chm)*

QINGDAO EASTSOFT COMMUNICATION TECHNOLOGY CO., LTD.
16A Shangqing Road, Shibei District, Qingdao, 266023, Shandong, China
Tel.: (86) 53283676959
Web Site: http://www.eastsoft.com.cn
Year Founded: 1993
300183—(CHIN)
Rev.: $131,396,148
Assets: $502,799,076
Liabilities: $60,331,284
Net Worth: $442,467,792
Earnings: $22,921,704
Emp.: 150
Fiscal Year-end: 12/31/22
Low Voltage Power Line Carrier Communication Products Mfr
N.A.I.C.S.: 237130
Jian Cui *(Chm)*

QINGDAO FOODS CO., LTD.
No 2 Siliu Middle Branch Road, Licang District, Qingdao, 266041, Shandong, China
Tel.: (86) 53284633589
Web Site: https://www.qdfood.com
Year Founded: 1997
001219—(SSE)
Rev.: $69,330,924
Assets: $142,952,472
Liabilities: $13,347,828
Net Worth: $129,604,644
Earnings: $12,836,772
Fiscal Year-end: 12/31/22
Food Product Mfr & Distr
N.A.I.C.S.: 333241
Xiangwei Cheng *(CFO)*

QINGDAO GAOCE TECHNOLOGY CO., LTD.
No 66 Chongsheng Road High Tech Industrial Development Zone, High & New Tech Development Zone, Qingdao, 266114, Shandong, China
Tel.: (86) 53287903188
Web Site: https://www.gaoce.cc
Year Founded: 2006
688055—(SHG)
Rev.: $501,306,554
Assets: $792,749,632
Liabilities: $502,542,116
Net Worth: $290,207,516
Earnings: $110,721,125
Fiscal Year-end: 12/31/22
Cutting Tool Mfr
N.A.I.C.S.: 333515
Xu Zhang *(Chm)*

Subsidiaries:
Changzhi Gaoce New Material Technology Co., Ltd. (1)
Xiwang Village, Huangxian Town Luzhou District, Changzhi, Shanxi, China
Tel.: (86) 3557737812
Cutting Equipment Mfr & Distr
N.A.I.C.S.: 333517

Huguan Gaoce New Material Technology Co., Ltd. (1)
Beihuang Village, Jidian Township Huguan County, Changzhi, Shanxi, China
Tel.: (86) 3557737812
Industrial Equipment Whsr
N.A.I.C.S.: 423830

Leshan Gaoce New Energy Technology Co., Ltd. (1)
Floors 1-2 Building 101 No 100 Yongxiang Road, Zhugen Town Wutongqiao District, Leshan, Sichuan, China
Tel.: (86) 8333302835
Industrial Equipment Whsr
N.A.I.C.S.: 423830

Luoyang Gaoce Precision Machinery Co., Ltd. (1)
Dongda Science & Technology Industrial Park Luoxin Industrial Cluster, Luoyang, Henan, China
Tel.: (86) 37963008073
Industrial Equipment Whsr
N.A.I.C.S.: 423830

Yancheng Gaoce New Energy Technology Co., Ltd. (1)
South of Tianyi Company East of G343 National Road, Jianhu High-Tech Zone, Jiangsu, China
Tel.: (86) 53287903188
Cutting Equipment Mfr & Distr
N.A.I.C.S.: 333515

Yibin Gaoce New Energy Technology Co., Ltd. (1)
Building 72 Jinrun Industrial Park Gaoxin Community, Gaochang Town Xuzhou District, Yibin, Sichuan, China
Tel.: (86) 53287903188
Construction Services
N.A.I.C.S.: 236210

QINGDAO GON TECHNOLOGY CO., LTD.
No 2 Road Qingda Industrial Park Jihongtan Street, Chengyang District, Qingdao, 266109, China
Tel.: (86) 53289082888
Web Site: https://qdgon.com
Year Founded: 2000
002768—(SSE)
Rev.: $1,882,264,176
Assets: $1,790,536,644
Liabilities: $961,985,700
Net Worth: $828,550,944
Earnings: $93,100,644
Fiscal Year-end: 12/31/22
Electrical & Electronic Equipment Distr
N.A.I.C.S.: 423690

QINGDAO GREENSUM ECOLOGY CO., LTD.
No 6 Youyun Road, Laoshan, Qingdao, 266100, Shandong, China
Tel.: (86) 53258820001
Web Site: https://www.greensum.com.cn
Year Founded: 2000
300948—(SSE)
Rev.: $63,650,340
Assets: $185,622,840
Liabilities: $67,481,856
Net Worth: $118,140,984
Earnings: $7,894,692
Fiscal Year-end: 12/31/22
Engineeering Services
N.A.I.C.S.: 541330
Chunlin Li *(Chm)*

QINGDAO GUOLIN TECHNOLOGY GROUP CO., LTD.
No 188 Zhuzhou Road, Shibei, Qingdao, 266031, Shandong, China
Tel.: (86) 53284992168
Web Site: https://www.china-guolin.com
Year Founded: 1994

300786—(SSE)
Rev.: $41,085,252
Assets: $239,724,576
Liabilities: $63,533,808
Net Worth: $176,190,768
Earnings: $2,528,604
Fiscal Year-end: 12/31/22
Environmental Equipment Mfr
N.A.I.C.S.: 334512

Subsidiaries:
Qingdao Lontec Electronic Technology Co., Ltd. (1)
Tel.: (86) 4009982567
Electric Device Mfr
N.A.I.C.S.: 334419

QINGDAO HAIER BIOMEDICAL CO., LTD.
Haier Biomedical Emerging Industrial Park No 280 Fengyuan Road, High-tech Zone, Qingdao, 266000, Shandong, China
Tel.: (86) 53288935566
Web Site: http://www.haiermedical.com
Year Founded: 2005
688139—(SHG)
Rev.: $402,111,862
Assets: $770,655,010
Liabilities: $188,226,614
Net Worth: $582,428,396
Earnings: $84,351,099
Fiscal Year-end: 12/31/22
Medical Product Mfr & Distr
N.A.I.C.S.: 339112
Peter Pedersen *(Dir-Intl Bus)*

QINGDAO HANHE CABLE CO., LTD.
No 628 Jiushui East Road, Laoshan District, Qingdao, 266102, Shandong, China
Tel.: (86) 53288817759
Web Site: http://www.hanhe-cable.com
Year Founded: 2007
002498—(SSE)
Rev.: $1,381,806,972
Assets: $1,383,705,180
Liabilities: $374,661,612
Net Worth: $1,009,043,568
Earnings: $110,309,472
Fiscal Year-end: 12/31/22
Electric Wires & Cables Mfr
N.A.I.C.S.: 335921
Wang Zhengzhuang *(Sec)*

Subsidiaries:
Changzhou Bayi Cable Co., Ltd. (1)
No 18 Science and Technology Avenue, Electronic Technology Industrial Park Changzhou High-tech Zone, Jiangsu, 213031, China
Tel.: (86) 51985480080
Web Site: https://www.en.81cable.com
Communication & Energy Wire Mfr
N.A.I.C.S.: 335929

Qingdao Hanhe Cable Co., Ltd. - Hanhe Cable -American Branch (1)
37 E Huntington Dr, Arcadia, CA 91006
Tel.: (626) 699-2239
Communication & Energy Wire Mfr
N.A.I.C.S.: 335929

QINGDAO HI-TECH MODULDS & PLASTICS TECHNOLOGY CO., LTD.
No 66 Jinsheng 2nd Road Jihongtan street, Chengyang, Qingdao, 266111, Shandong, China
Tel.: (86) 53289086869
Web Site: https://www.hitechmoulds.cn
Year Founded: 2003
301022—(CHIN)
Rev.: $80,625,112

Assets: $260,612,351
Liabilities: $118,908,239
Net Worth: $141,704,112
Earnings: $3,279,831
Fiscal Year-end: 12/31/22
Plastic Product Mfr & Distr
N.A.I.C.S.: 326199
Wenqiang Sun *(Chm)*

QINGDAO HIRON COMMERCIAL COLD CHAIN CO., LTD.
No 1817 Yinzhushan Road, Huangdao District, Qingdao, 266400, China
Tel.: (86) 53258762777
Web Site: https://www.chinahiron.com
Year Founded: 2006
603187—(SHG)
Rev.: $407,810,951
Assets: $718,747,825
Liabilities: $202,432,778
Net Worth: $516,315,047
Earnings: $41,026,593
Fiscal Year-end: 12/31/22
Commercial Refrigeration Product Mfr & Distr
N.A.I.C.S.: 333413
Shao Wei *(Chm & Gen Mgr)*

QINGDAO HOLDINGS INTERNATIONAL LIMITED
Unit No 8 26th Floor Tower 1 Admiralty Centre No 18 Harcourt Road, Hong Kong, China (Hong Kong)
Tel.: (852) 31582138   BM
Web Site: http://www.qingdaohi.com
0499—(HKG)
Rev.: $7,946,780
Assets: $154,502,057
Liabilities: $98,567,399
Net Worth: $55,934,658
Earnings: ($9,665,276)
Emp.: 119
Fiscal Year-end: 12/31/22
Investment Management Service
N.A.I.C.S.: 523940
Luzheng Xing *(Chm)*

QINGDAO HUICHENG ENVIRONMENTAL TECHNOLOGY GROUP CO., LTD.
No 57 Huaihe East Road, Qingdao Economic & Technological Development Zone, Qingdao, 266000, Shandong, China
Tel.: (86) 53258657750
Web Site: https://en.hcpect.com
Year Founded: 2006
300779—(SSE)
Rev.: $50,997,492
Assets: $359,355,204
Liabilities: $252,060,120
Net Worth: $107,295,084
Earnings: $346,788
Fiscal Year-end: 12/31/22
Chemical Products Mfr
N.A.I.C.S.: 325520
Sheng Bo *(CFO & Deputy Gen Mgr)*

Subsidiaries:
Forland Petrochemical Technology LLC (1)
20333 TX-249 Ste 200, Houston, TX 77070
Tel.: (281) 606-3456
Web Site: https://www.forlandtech.com
Chemical Additive Distr
N.A.I.C.S.: 424690

QINGDAO HUIJINTONG POWER EQUIPMENT CO., LTD.
Eastern Industrial Zone Puji Town Jiaozhou City, Qingdao, Shandong, China
Tel.: (86) 53255595161

QINGDAO HUIJINTONG POWER EQUIPMENT CO., LTD.

Qingdao Huijintong Power Equipment Co., Ltd.—(Continued)
Web Site: https://www.hjttower.com
603577—(SHG)
Rev.: $506,751,855
Assets: $833,201,891
Liabilities: $581,826,600
Net Worth: $251,375,291
Earnings: $5,641,749
Emp.: 1,700
Fiscal Year-end: 12/31/22
Galvanized Steel Mfr & Distr
N.A.I.C.S.: 331110
Subsidiaries:
HJT Steel Tower (Australia) Pty, Ltd. (1)
Unit 6 54 Portrush Rd, Payneham, 5070, SA, Australia
Tel.: (61) 435936232
Web Site: http://www.hjttower.com.au
Iron & Steel Mfr
N.A.I.C.S.: 331110

QINGDAO KINGKING APPLIED CHEMISTRY CO., LTD.
15-16F Building T3 Shangshi Center
No 195 Hong Kong East Road, Laoshan District, Qingdao, 266071, Shandong, China
Tel.: (86) 53285779728
Web Site: http://www.chinakingking.com
Year Founded: 1997
002094—(SSE)
Rev.: $414,366,732
Assets: $454,328,784
Liabilities: $248,399,892
Net Worth: $205,928,892
Earnings: ($113,570,964)
Fiscal Year-end: 12/31/22
Wax Product Mfr
N.A.I.C.S.: 325998
Chen Suobin (Chm)

QINGDAO KUTESMART CO., LTD.
No 17 Hongling Street, Jimo, Qingdao, 266200, Shandong, China
Tel.: (86) 53288598088
Web Site: http://www.kutesmart.com
Year Founded: 2007
300840—(SSE)
Rev.: $86,539,752
Assets: $222,265,836
Liabilities: $70,510,284
Net Worth: $151,755,552
Earnings: $11,980,332
Fiscal Year-end: 12/31/22
Clothing Apparel Mfr & Distr
N.A.I.C.S.: 315250
Lanlan Zhang (Chm, Pres & Gen Mgr)

QINGDAO NOVELBEAM TECHNOLOGY CO., LTD.
No 100 Keyuanweisi Rd, Qingdao, 266100, China
Tel.: (86) 53288705269
Web Site: https://www.novelbeam.com
Year Founded: 2003
688677—(SHG)
Rev.: $66,945,711
Assets: $195,652,258
Liabilities: $24,015,237
Net Worth: $171,637,020
Earnings: $25,632,772
Fiscal Year-end: 12/31/22
Optical Instrument Mfr & Distr
N.A.I.C.S.: 333310
Anmin Zheng (Chm)

QINGDAO PORT INTERNATIONAL CO., LTD.
7 Ganghua Road, City North District, Qingdao, 266011, Shandong, China
Tel.: (86) 53282983083   CN
Web Site: http://www.qingdao-port.com
Year Founded: 2013
6198—(HKG)
Rev.: $2,704,492,203
Assets: $8,069,617,815
Liabilities: $2,274,338,506
Net Worth: $5,795,279,308
Earnings: $736,659,447
Emp.: 10,286
Fiscal Year-end: 12/31/22
Port Operations
N.A.I.C.S.: 488310
Xinze Wang (Exec Dir)
Subsidiaries:
Mercuria Logistics Co., Ltd. (1)
2/22 Iyara Tower Unit306 Chan rd Thungwatdon Sathon, Bangkok, 10120, Thailand
Tel.: (66) 2 287 4454
Web Site: https://www.mercurial.co.th
Freight Management Services
N.A.I.C.S.: 488510

QINGDAO RICHEN FOOD CO., LTD.
No 20 Jifa Longshan Road, Qingdao Environmental Protection Industrial Park Jimo District, Qingdao, 266200, Shandong, China
Tel.: (86) 53287520888
Web Site: https://www.richen-qd.cn
Year Founded: 2001
603755—(SHG)
Rev.: $43,324,056
Assets: $129,426,448
Liabilities: $33,030,153
Net Worth: $96,396,295
Earnings: $7,168,894
Fiscal Year-end: 12/31/22
Food Products Mfr
N.A.I.C.S.: 311421
Huajun Zhang (Chm & Gen Mgr)

QINGDAO RISO FOODS CO., LTD.
Food Industry Park Landi Town, 266734, Pingdu, Shandong, China
Tel.: (86) 532 82342033
Web Site: http://www.risofoods.com
Year Founded: 2002
Emp.: 1,000
Mfr of Prepared Foods & Miscellaneous Food Specialties
N.A.I.C.S.: 311999

QINGDAO RURAL COMMERCIAL BANK
No 6 QinLing Road, Laoshan District, Qingdao, 266061, China
Tel.: (86) 4001196668
Web Site: https://www.qrcb.com.cn
Year Founded: 2012
002958—(SSE)
Rev.: $1,396,123,560
Assets: $61,044,701,328
Liabilities: $55,922,538,672
Net Worth: $5,122,162,656
Earnings: $325,326,456
Emp.: 5,000
Fiscal Year-end: 12/31/22
Commercial Banking Services
N.A.I.C.S.: 522110

QINGDAO SENTURY TIRE CO., LTD.
No 5 Tianshan Third Road, Daxin Town Jimo, Qingdao, 266229, Shandong, China
Tel.: (86) 53268968896
Web Site: https://www.senturytire.com
Year Founded: 2007
002984—(SSE)
Rev.: $883,423,476
Assets: $1,560,624,624
Liabilities: $490,261,356
Net Worth: $1,070,363,268
Earnings: $112,440,744
Fiscal Year-end: 12/31/22
Tire Mfr & Distr
N.A.I.C.S.: 326211
Long Qin (Chm)

QINGDAO TGOOD ELECTRIC CO., LTD.
No 336 Songling Road, Laoshan District, Qingdao, 266104, Shandong, China
Tel.: (86) 53280938126
Web Site: http://www.qdtgood.com
Year Founded: 2004
300001—(CHIN)
Rev.: $2,056,629,854
Assets: $3,363,058,647
Liabilities: $2,279,132,753
Net Worth: $1,083,925,894
Earnings: $69,177,985
Fiscal Year-end: 12/31/23
Power Transmission Product Mfr & Distr
N.A.I.C.S.: 333612
Yu Dexiang (Chm)
Subsidiaries:
TGOOD Africa (Pty) Ltd. (1)
21 Roan Crescent Unit 2 Sultana Park Corporate Park North, Midrand, 1683, South Africa
Tel.: (27) 100105706
Electrical Apparatus & Equipment Whslr
N.A.I.C.S.: 423610
Kobus Coetzer (CEO)
TGOOD Australia Pty Ltd. (1)
Unit 1 4 Henry Street, Loganholme, 4129, QLD, Australia
Tel.: (61) 1300061299
Electrical Apparatus & Equipment Whslr
N.A.I.C.S.: 423610
TGOOD Central Asia LLP (1)
7th Floor BC Pioneer-2 Dostyk Avenue No 134, Medeo District, 050051, Almaty, Kazakhstan
Tel.: (7) 7273130168
Electrical Apparatus & Equipment Whslr
N.A.I.C.S.: 423610
Altay Toiganbayev (CEO)
TGOOD Germany GmbH (1)
Daimler street 2, 41836, Huckelhoven, Germany
Tel.: (49) 2433525662
Electrical Apparatus & Equipment Whslr
N.A.I.C.S.: 423610
Raimund Buhl (CEO)
TGOOD Latin America SAS (1)
Calle 116 15b-26 of 407, Bogota, Colombia
Tel.: (57) 17444663
Electrical Apparatus & Equipment Whslr
N.A.I.C.S.: 423610
Blanca Ruiz (CEO)
TGOOD Middle East General Trading LLC (1)
Emirates Concorde - Office Tower Suite 1302, PO Box 413884, Al Maktoom Street Rigat Al Buteen Deira, Dubai, United Arab Emirates
Tel.: (971) 43454596
Electrical Apparatus & Equipment Whslr
N.A.I.C.S.: 423610
Eihab F. A. Al Sarabi (CEO)
TGOOD North America Inc. (1)
3-1101 Main Street, Penticton, V2A 5E6, BC, Canada
Tel.: (778) 476-5833
Electrical Apparatus & Equipment Whslr
N.A.I.C.S.: 423610
TGOOD Russia Ltd. (1)
Technique Museum Building 8 Office 302 4 km of Ilyinsky Highway, P O Arkhangelskoe Krasnogorsk District, 143420, Moscow, Russia

INTERNATIONAL PUBLIC

Tel.: (7) 9681747725
Electrical Apparatus & Equipment Whslr
N.A.I.C.S.: 423610

QINGDAO TIANNENG HEAVY INDUSTRIES CO LTD
No 7 Haishuo Road Ligezhuang Town, Jiaozhou, Shandong, China
Tel.: (86) 53258829926
Web Site: https://en.qdtnp.com
300569—(CHIN)
Rev.: $596,567,513
Assets: $1,808,884,027
Liabilities: $1,005,683,592
Net Worth: $803,200,435
Earnings: $35,417,352
Fiscal Year-end: 12/31/23
Wind Turbine Tower Mfr & Distr
N.A.I.C.S.: 333611

QINGDAO TOPSCOMM COMMUNICATION CO., LTD.
Topscomm Industry Park 858 Huaguan Rd, Hi-tech District, Qingdao, China
Tel.: (86) 75586728920
Web Site: https://www.topsmetering.com
Year Founded: 2008
603421—(SHG)
Rev.: $437,343,332
Assets: $795,169,594
Liabilities: $328,507,737
Net Worth: $466,661,857
Earnings: $16,662,756
Emp.: 3,000
Fiscal Year-end: 12/31/22
Electric Communication Product Mfr & Distr
N.A.I.C.S.: 334515

QINGDAO VICTALL RAILWAY CO., LTD.
No 3 Xinghai Branch Rd, Huanhai Economic & Technical Developing Zone Chengyang, Qingdao, 266108, China
Tel.: (86) 53281108080
Web Site: https://www.victall.com
Year Founded: 2007
605001—(SHG)
Rev.: $111,878,751
Assets: $624,097,361
Liabilities: $271,460,185
Net Worth: $352,637,176
Earnings: ($15,976,228)
Emp.: 3,000
Fiscal Year-end: 12/31/22
Railroad Equipment Mfr
N.A.I.C.S.: 336510
Hanben Sun (Chm)
Subsidiaries:
Qingdao Victall Precision Moulds Co., Ltd. (1)
West Section of Songshan Road Liuting Street, Chengyang District, Qingdao, 266108, Shandong, China
Tel.: (86) 18660287118
Web Site: https://www.victallmould.com
Precision Mold Mfr
N.A.I.C.S.: 333511
Victall Transportation (Canada) Co., Ltd. (1)
69 boul Clairevue Ouest, Saint-Bruno-de-Montarville, J3V 1P9, QC, Canada
Tel.: (514) 800-0877
Web Site: https://victall.weebly.com
Railway Equipment Mfr
N.A.I.C.S.: 336510

QINGDAO VLAND BIOTECH, INC.
Vland Innovation Park 596-1 Jiushui East Rd, Qingdao, 266100, Shandong, China
Tel.: (86) 53288966607

AND PRIVATE COMPANIES

Web Site:
https://www.vlandgroup.com
Year Founded: 2005
603739—(SHG)
Sales Range: $100-124.9 Million
Emp.: 1,300
Biotechnology Research & Development Services
N.A.I.C.S.: 541714

Subsidiaries:

Qingdao Vland Biotech Group Co., Ltd. (1)
596-1 East Jiushui Road, Qingdao, 266102, China
Tel.: (86) 53288966607
Biotechnology Research & Development Services
N.A.I.C.S.: 541714
Rong Jin (Mgr-Technical-Overseas)

QINGDAO WEFLO VALVE CO., LTD.
789 Chunyang Road, Qingdao, 266000, China
Tel.: (86) 53287905017
Web Site:
https://www.weflovalve.com
Year Founded: 1995
002871—(SSE)
Rev.: $75,835,656
Assets: $139,553,388
Liabilities: $31,260,060
Net Worth: $108,293,328
Earnings: $19,123,884
Emp.: 700
Fiscal Year-end: 12/31/22
Valve Product Mfr & Distr
N.A.I.C.S.: 332911
Fan Qingwei (Chm)

QINGDAO WEST COAST DEVELOPMENT (GROUP) CO., LTD.
1777 Binhai Avenue, Qingdao, China
Tel.: (86) 053267791500   CN
Web Site: http://www.xhafz.com
Year Founded: 2012
Infrastructure Construction & Investment Services
N.A.I.C.S.: 523999

Subsidiaries:

Prosper Construction Holdings Ltd. (1)
Rm 504-505 K Wah Centre 191 Java Road, North Point, China (Hong Kong)
Tel.: (852) 31508330
Web Site: http://www.prosperch.com
Rev.: $368,232,638
Assets: $625,910,474
Liabilities: $546,064,330
Net Worth: $79,846,144
Earnings: $1,347,743
Emp.: 638
Fiscal Year-end: 12/31/2022
Marine Construction Services
N.A.I.C.S.: 237990
Qi Cui (CEO)

QINGDAO ZHONGZI ZHONGCHENG GROUP CO., LTD.
Airport Industrial Cluster West Side Shuangyuan Road, Liuting Subdistrict Chengyang District, Qingdao, 266108, Shandong, China
Tel.: (86) 53266962326
Web Site:
http://www.qdhengshun.com
Year Founded: 1998
300208—(CHIN)
Rev.: $64,645,939
Assets: $448,344,790
Liabilities: $499,042,452
Net Worth: ($50,697,662)
Earnings: ($163,356,407)
Fiscal Year-end: 12/31/23

Electric Power Transmission & Control Equipment Mfr
N.A.I.C.S.: 221121
Quanchen Jia (Chm)

QINGHAI HUADING INDUSTRIAL CO., LTD.
No 24 Jing 2nd Road North Section, Chengbei District, Xining, 810000, Qinghai, China
Tel.: (86) 9717111668
Web Site: http://www.qhhdsy.com
Year Founded: 1998
600243—(SHG)
Rev.: $75,129,542
Assets: $192,842,531
Liabilities: $65,367,755
Net Worth: $127,474,776
Earnings: ($21,438,167)
Fiscal Year-end: 12/31/22
Mechanical Product Mfr
N.A.I.C.S.: 333998
Wang Feng (Chm)

QINGHAI HUZHU TIANYOUDE HIGHLAND BARLEY SPIRIT CO., LTD.
No 6 West Street, Weiyuan Town Huzhu County, Haidong, 810500, Qinghai, China
Tel.: (86) 4009969969
Web Site: https://www.002646.com
002646—(SSE)
Rev.: $137,573,748
Assets: $448,910,748
Liabilities: $64,798,812
Net Worth: $384,111,936
Earnings: $10,567,908
Fiscal Year-end: 12/31/22
Barley Wine Mfr
N.A.I.C.S.: 312130
Li Yinhui (Chm)

QINGHAI JINRUI MINERAL DEVELOPMENT CO., LTD.
No 36 Xinning Road, Xining, 810008, Qinghai, China
Tel.: (86) 9716321653
600714—(SHG)
Rev.: $52,222,187
Assets: $112,473,878
Liabilities: $10,587,241
Net Worth: $101,886,637
Earnings: $7,685,552
Fiscal Year-end: 12/31/22
Coal Poduct Mfr & Distr
N.A.I.C.S.: 212114
Gan Chenxia (Sec)

QINGHAI SALT LAKE INDUSTRY CO., LTD.
No 41 West Qilian Road, Xining, 810003, Qinghai, China
Tel.: (86) 9715502673   CN
Web Site: http://www.qhsalt.com.cn
000792—(SSE)
Rev.: $2,987,719,373
Assets: $6,425,466,216
Liabilities: $1,622,257,477
Net Worth: $4,803,208,739
Earnings: $1,095,704,281
Emp.: 1,200
Fiscal Year-end: 12/31/23
Salt Mining
N.A.I.C.S.: 212390
Qiuping Yu (VP)

QINGHAI SPRING MEDICINAL RESOURCES TECHNOLOGY CO., LTD.
No 1 Dongxin Road Xining Economic and Technological Development Zone, Xining, 810000, Qinghai, China
Tel.: (86) 9718816171
600381—(SHG)
Rev.: $22,489,005

Assets: $218,915,780
Liabilities: $3,692,380
Net Worth: $215,223,400
Earnings: ($40,371,866)
Fiscal Year-end: 12/31/22
Investment Services
N.A.I.C.S.: 523999
Chen Ding (Sec)

QINGLING MOTORS (GROUP) CO. LTD.
1 Xiexingcun Zhongliangshan, Chongqing, 400052, JiuLongpo, China
Tel.: (86) 23 65262277
Web Site: http://www.qingling.com.cn
Sales Range: $750-799.9 Million
Emp.: 2,813
Automobile & Truck Mfr
N.A.I.C.S.: 336110
Keiicgiro Maegaki (Vice Chm)

Subsidiaries:

Chongqing Qingling Casting Co., Ltd (1)
No 1 Sanxikou, Beibei District, Chongqing, 400707, China
Tel.: (86) 23 68 305018
Web Site: http://www.qingling.com.cn
Fabricated Structural Metal Mfr
N.A.I.C.S.: 332312

QINGMU DIGITAL TECHNOLOGY CO., LTD.
Building 1 Haizhu Tech Park II No 189 Dunhe Road, Haizhu District, Guangzhou, 510310, Guangdong, China
Tel.: (86) 2089558888
Web Site:
https://www.qingmutec.com
Year Founded: 2009
301110—(SSE)
Rev.: $118,866,852
Assets: $225,049,968
Liabilities: $25,422,228
Net Worth: $199,627,740
Earnings: $9,159,696
Emp.: 2,200
Fiscal Year-end: 12/31/22
Digital Marketing Services
N.A.I.C.S.: 541810
Lv Bin (Chm)

QINGYAN ENVIRONMENTAL TECHNOLOGY CO., LTD.
Room C527 5F Research Institute of Tsinghua University, South Zone of Nanshan District Science Park, Shenzhen, 518000, Guangdong, China
Tel.: (86) 75526556300
Web Site:
https://www.tsinghuan.com.cn
Year Founded: 2014
301288—(CHIN)
Water Distribution Services
N.A.I.C.S.: 221310
Shujie Liu (Chm)

QINHONG INTERNATIONAL GROUP
Block 1 Unit 2 Suite 1705 Poly Center 7 Consulate Road, Wuhou District, Chengdu, 610000, Sichuan, China
Tel.: (86) 288 140 3245   Ky
Year Founded: 2019
Rev.: $2,132,477
Assets: $3,427,407
Liabilities: $495,169
Net Worth: $2,932,238
Earnings: $1,672,426
Emp.: 10
Fiscal Year-end: 06/30/21
Holding Company
N.A.I.C.S.: 551112

Xu Jiang (CEO & Chm)

QINHUANGDAO ASANO CEMENT CO., LTD.
Du Zhuang Nan Funing County, Qinhuangdao, 066326, Hebei, China
Tel.: (86) 3356087518
Web Site: http://www.qhd-asano.com
Cement Mfr
N.A.I.C.S.: 327310

QINHUANGDAO PORT CO., LTD.
35 Habin Road, Qinhuangdao, 066002, Hebei, China
Tel.: (86) 3353099676
Web Site: https://www.portqhd.com
3369—(HKG)
Rev.: $971,486,713
Assets: $3,922,874,151
Liabilities: $1,364,073,435
Net Worth: $2,558,800,716
Earnings: $190,531,883
Emp.: 10,583
Fiscal Year-end: 12/31/22
Port Terminal Operations
N.A.I.C.S.: 488310
Xiping Ma (VP)

QINHUANGDAO TIANQIN EQUIPMENT MANUFACTURING CO., LTD.
No 5 Xueshan Road, Economic & Technological Development Zone, Qinhuangdao, 066004, Hebei, China
Tel.: (86) 3358501157
Web Site: https://www.tianqin.net.cn
Year Founded: 1996
300922—(SSE)
Rev.: $20,766,564
Assets: $130,167,648
Liabilities: $8,584,056
Net Worth: $121,583,592
Earnings: $3,775,356
Fiscal Year-end: 12/31/22
Plastic Product Mfr & Distr
N.A.I.C.S.: 326199
Jinsuo Song (Chm)

QINIU LIMITED
Floor 1-5 Building Q No 66 Boxia Road, PuDong New District, Shanghai, 201203, China
Tel.: (86) 2120703999   VG
Year Founded: 2011
Rev.: $166,878,477
Assets: $146,705,010
Liabilities: $500,570,010
Net Worth: ($353,865,000)
Earnings: ($26,217,295)
Emp.: 528
Fiscal Year-end: 12/31/20
Holding Company
N.A.I.C.S.: 551112
Shiwei Xu (Co-Founder, Chm & CEO)

QINQIN FOODSTUFFS GROUP (CAYMAN) COMPANY LIMITED
Wuli Industrial Area, Jinjiang, Fujian, China
Tel.: (86) 59588162612   Ky
Web Site: http://www.fjqinqin.com
Year Founded: 1990
1583—(HKG)
Rev.: $134,442,688
Assets: $288,765,313
Liabilities: $115,413,714
Net Worth: $173,351,599
Earnings: ($248,227)
Emp.: 2,600
Fiscal Year-end: 12/31/22
Food Product Mfr & Distr
N.A.I.C.S.: 311911

QISDA CORPORATION
No 157 Shanying Road Guishan Dis-

QISDA CORPORATION

Qisda Corporation—(Continued)
trict, Taoyuan, 333, Taiwan
Tel.: (886) 33598800
Web Site: https://www.qisda.com
2352—(TAI)
Rev.: $6,657,993,175
Assets: $6,161,863,693
Liabilities: $4,065,864,165
Net Worth: $2,095,999,528
Earnings: $147,685,628
Emp.: 11,545
Fiscal Year-end: 12/31/23
Electronic Products Mfr
N.A.I.C.S.: 334510
Joe Huang *(Sr VP-IT Products Grp)*

Subsidiaries:

BenQ Asia Pacific Corp. (1)
12 Jihu Road Neihu, Taipei, 00114, Taiwan
Tel.: (886) 227278899
Projector & Monitor Distr
N.A.I.C.S.: 423430
Jeffery Liang *(Pres)*

Subsidiary (Non-US):

BenQ (M.E.) FZE (2)
Business Cluster Building 2 Office 502, Umm Ramool, Dubai, United Arab Emirates
Tel.: (971) 42991000
Projector & Monitor Mfr.
N.A.I.C.S.: 333310
Deepak Singh *(Mgr-Bus Dev)*

BenQ Australia Pty. Ltd. (2)
Unit 7 175 Briens Road, Northmead, 2152, NSW, Australia
Tel.: (61) 289886500
Web Site: https://www.benq.com
Projector & Monitor Mfr
N.A.I.C.S.: 333310

BenQ India Private Ltd. (2)
3rd Floor 9B Building DLF Cyber City DLF Phase 3, Gurgaon, 122 002, Haryana, India
Tel.: (91) 1244501400
Web Site: https://www.benq.com
Projector & Monitor Mfr
N.A.I.C.S.: 333310
Rajeev Singh *(Mng Dir)*

BenQ Singapore Pte. Ltd. (2)
8 Burn Road 11-07 Trivex, Singapore, 369977, Singapore
Tel.: (65) 63968800
Projector & Monitor Mfr
N.A.I.C.S.: 333310
Daren Low *(Sr Mgr-Product)*

BenQ Deutschland GmbH (1)
Essener Str 5, 46047, Oberhausen, Germany
Tel.: (49) 208409420
Web Site: https://www.benq.eu
Projector & Monitor Mfr
N.A.I.C.S.: 333310
Jennifer Sommer *(Mgr-Bus Line)*

BenQ Dialysis Technology Corp. (1)
No 159-1 Shanying Road, Guishan District, Taoyuan, 333-41, Taiwan
Tel.: (886) 3 329 2071
Web Site: https://www.benqdialysistech.com
Dialysis Related Product Mfrs
N.A.I.C.S.: 621492
Nicole C. L. Wang *(Dir-Laboratory)*

Expert Alliance Systems & Consultancy (HK) Company Limited (1)
Unit 1103 11/F Orient International Tower 1018 Tai Nan W St, Cheung Sha Wan, Kowloon, China (Hong Kong)
Tel.: (852) 39983710
Web Site: https://www.easc-asia.com
Information Technology Services
N.A.I.C.S.: 518210

Mainteq Europe B.V. (1)
Ekkersrijt 4134, 5692 DC, Son, Netherlands
Tel.: (31) 499750200
Web Site: http://www.mainteq-eu.com
LED Panel & Monitor Mfr
N.A.I.C.S.: 335139

Partner Tech Corp. (1)
10F No 233-1 Baoqiao Rd, New Taipei City, 231018, Taiwan
Tel.: (886) 229188500
Web Site: https://www.partnertechcorp.com
Hardware Product Mfr
N.A.I.C.S.: 332510
Pao-Hsin Wang *(Pres)*

Partner Tech UK Corp., Ltd. (1)
Unit 8 Berkeley Court Manor Park, Runcorn, Cheshire, United Kingdom
Tel.: (44) 1928579707
Web Site: https://www.partnertechcorp.com
Point Of Sale Terminals Mfr & Distr
N.A.I.C.S.: 334118

Qisda (Shanghai) Co., Ltd. (1)
No 669 Taihua Road South Area, Shanghai, 201201, China
Tel.: (86) 2161098899
Consumer Electronics Distr
N.A.I.C.S.: 423620

Qisda Electronics (Suzhou) Co. Ltd. (1)
No 169 Zhujiang Road, 215015, Suzhou, Jiangsu, China
Tel.: (86) 51266651888
Sales Range: $1-4.9 Billion
Consumer Electronics Distr
N.A.I.C.S.: 423620

Qisda Electronics Corp. (1)
157 Shanying Road, Kuei Shan Hsiang, Taoyuan, 33341, Taiwan
Tel.: (886) 33598800
Sales Range: $250-299.9 Million
Emp.: 800
Consumer Electronics Distr
N.A.I.C.S.: 423620

Qisda Japan Co., Ltd. (1)
Akimoto Soko 3A 5F 3-30-1, Minato-Ku, Tokyo, 108-0022, Japan
Tel.: (81) 354445901
Web Site: https://qisda.co.jp
Sales Range: $25-49.9 Million
Emp.: 20
Computer Hardware Whslr
N.A.I.C.S.: 423430

Qisda Mexicana S.A. De C.V. (1)
Venustiano Carranza No 88 Plutarco Elias Calles, Mexicali, 21376, Baja California, Mexico
Tel.: (52) 6869068800
Liquid Crystal Display Mfr
N.A.I.C.S.: 334419

Qisda Vietnam Co., Ltd. (1)
Lot CN12 Dong Van IV Industrial Park, Tan Commune Dai Cuong Commune, Kim Bang, Ha Nam, Vietnam
Tel.: (84) 2263638800
Web Site: https://www.qisda.com
Information Technology Services
N.A.I.C.S.: 541511

Yan Ying Hao Trading (ShenZhen) Co., Ltd. (1)
1819 18F Hongyu Building Longguan Road Shitouling Yucui Community, Longhua Street Longhua District, Shenzhen, China
Tel.: (86) 75523729390
Motherboard & Computer Panel Mfr
N.A.I.C.S.: 334111

QITIAN TECHNOLOGY GROUP CO., LTD.
1st Floor Building 36 No 1-42 Lane 83Hongxiang North Road, Lin-gang Special Area Pilot Free Trade Zone, Shanghai, 200070, China
Tel.: (86) 18918300078
Web Site: https://www.conantoptical.com
Year Founded: 1996
300061—(CHIN)
Rev.: $137,313,792
Assets: $230,046,713
Liabilities: $119,706,978
Net Worth: $110,339,735
Earnings: ($69,782,330)
Fiscal Year-end: 12/31/23
Optical Lens Mfr
N.A.I.C.S.: 333310
Lin Sio Ngo *(Co-Sec)*

Subsidiaries:

Conant Optical INC. (1)
2255 Sewell Mill Rd, Marietta, GA 30062
Tel.: (770) 509-7860
Web Site: http://www.conantoptical.com
Optical Lens Mfr
N.A.I.C.S.: 333310

QIWI PLC
12 Kennedy Avenue Kennedy Business Centre 2nd Floor, 1087, Nicosia, Cyprus
Tel.: (357) 22653390 CY
Web Site: https://www.qiwi.com
Year Founded: 2007
QIWI—(NASDAQ)
Rev.: $693,731,940
Assets: $1,507,643,220
Liabilities: $727,797,570
Net Worth: $779,845,650
Earnings: $185,279,850
Emp.: 2,118
Fiscal Year-end: 12/31/22
Payment Processing Services
N.A.I.C.S.: 522320
Sergey N. Solonin *(Founder & Chm)*

QKL STORES, INC.
4 Nanreyuan Street Dongfeng Road, Sartu District, 163300, Daqing, China
Tel.: (86) 4594607987 DE
Web Site: http://www.qklstoresinc.com
Sales Range: $250-299.9 Million
Emp.: 5,207
Super Markets & Department Stores Owner & Operator
N.A.I.C.S.: 445110
Zhuangyi Wang *(Chm, CEO & CFO)*

QL RESOURCES BERHAD
16A Jalan Astaka U8/83 Bukit Jelutong, 40150, Shah Alam, Selangor Darul Ehsan, Malaysia
Tel.: (60) 378012288 MY
Web Site: https://www.ql.com.my
QL—(KLS)
Rev.: $1,295,922,128
Assets: $1,226,871,113
Liabilities: $557,035,380
Net Worth: $669,835,733
Earnings: $58,296,398
Emp.: 5,896
Fiscal Year-end: 03/31/22
Marine Products Mfr
N.A.I.C.S.: 311119
Mak Hooi Chia *(Exec Dir)*

Subsidiaries:

QL Endau Marine Products Sdn. Bhd. (1)
11 Jalan Merlimau, Endau, 86900, Mersing, Malaysia
Tel.: (60) 77943814
Web Site: http://www.qlendau.com.my
Fish Meat Product Mfr
N.A.I.C.S.: 311710

QL Figo (Johor) Sdn. Bhd. (1)
Jalan Harmoni 1 Taman Harmoni, 81000, Kulai, Johor, Malaysia
Tel.: (60) 76637388
Web Site: http://www.figofoods.com.my
Seafood Product Mfr
N.A.I.C.S.: 311710

QL Fishmeal Sdn. Bhd. (1)
Lot 164 2647 3314 Jalan Tepi Sungai, Hutan Melintang, 36400, Perak, Malaysia
Tel.: (60) 56412752
Web Site: https://www.qlfishmeal.com
Fish Meat Product Mfr
N.A.I.C.S.: 311710

QL Foods Sdn. Bhd. (1)
Lot 9120 and 9121 Jalan Tepi Sungai, Hutan Melintang, 36400, Perak, Malaysia
Tel.: (60) 56415805
Web Site: http://www.qlfoods.com
Fish Meat Product Mfr
N.A.I.C.S.: 311710

QL Lian Hoe Sdn. Bhd. (1)
No 4 Jalan Penaga 9 Kota Putri, Kawasan Perindustrian, Masai, Johor, Malaysia
Tel.: (60) 73875745
Web Site: http://www.lian-hoefood.com.my
Seafood Product Mfr
N.A.I.C.S.: 311710

QL Marine Products Sdn. Bhd. (1)
PO Box 502, Tuaran, 89208, Kampung Dengkil, Sabah, Malaysia
Tel.: (60) 88791833
Web Site: http://www.qlmarine.com.my
Seafood Product Mfr
N.A.I.C.S.: 311710

QL Poultry Farms Sdn. Bhd. (1)
16A Jalan Astaka U8/83, Bukit Jelutong, 40150, Shah Alam, Selangor, Malaysia
Tel.: (60) 378012288
Web Site: http://www.qleggs.com
Chicken Egg Production Services
N.A.I.C.S.: 112310

QLEANAIR AB
Torggatan 13, Po Box 1178, 171 54, Solna, Sweden
Tel.: (46) 854578800
Web Site: https://www.qleanair.com
Year Founded: 1988
QAIR—(OMX)
Rev.: $47,160,452
Assets: $62,008,579
Liabilities: $41,843,641
Net Worth: $20,164,939
Earnings: $4,061,742
Emp.: 109
Fiscal Year-end: 12/31/23
Sports Club Operator
N.A.I.C.S.: 713120
Bengt Engstrom *(Chm)*

QLOSR GROUP AB
Medborgarplatsen 4 8 tr, Stockholm, Sweden
Tel.: (46) 851784400
Web Site: https://www.qlosrgroup.se
Year Founded: 2013
Y57—(DEU)
Information Technology Services
N.A.I.C.S.: 541512
Jonas Norberg *(CEO)*

QLS HOLDINGS CO., LTD.
3rd Floor Namba Muromachi Building 1-12-5 Namba-naka, Naniwa-ku, Osaka, 556-0011, Japan
Tel.: (81) 665759845
Web Site: https://www.qlshd.co.jp
Year Founded: 2019
7075—(TKS)
Rev.: $54,575,840
Assets: $45,670,240
Liabilities: $40,452,720
Net Worth: $5,217,520
Earnings: $125,840
Fiscal Year-end: 03/31/22
Holding Company
N.A.I.C.S.: 551112
Takeshi Ameda *(Pres & CEO)*

QLUCORE AB
Scheelevagen 17, Ideon Science Park, 223 70, Lund, Sweden
Tel.: (46) 462863110
Web Site: https://www.qlucore.com
Year Founded: 2007
QLUCORE—(OMX)
Rev.: $1,426,529
Assets: $8,935,414
Liabilities: $1,082,058
Net Worth: $7,853,356
Earnings: ($1,556,575)
Emp.: 22
Fiscal Year-end: 12/31/23
Software Development Services
N.A.I.C.S.: 541511
Carl-Johan Ivarsson *(Co-Founder & CEO)*

QMC CO., LTD.

41-8 Burim-ro 170beon-gil, Dongan-gu, Anyang, 431-804, Gyeonggi-do, Korea (South)
Tel.: (82) 314270710
Web Site: https://www.iqmc.co.kr
Year Founded: 2003
Semiconductor Equipment Mfr
N.A.I.C.S.: 334413

QMC QUANTUM MINERALS CORP.
Suite 540 1100 Melville Street, Vancouver, V6E 4A6, BC, Canada
Tel.: (604) 601-2018 BC
Web Site:
   https://www.qmcminerals.com
Year Founded: 2003
QMCQF—(OTCIQ)
Assets: $4,371,928
Liabilities: $1,661,033
Net Worth: $2,710,895
Earnings: ($2,273,897)
Fiscal Year-end: 08/31/21
Metal Mining Services
N.A.I.C.S.: 212290
Balraj Mann (Pres & CEO)

QMINES LIMITED
Suite J 34 Suakin Drive, PO Box 36, Mosman, Mosman, 2088, NSW, Australia
Tel.: (61) 95048420 AU
Web Site:
   https://www.qmines.com.au
Year Founded: 2020
QML—(ASX)
Rev.: $22,197
Assets: $10,689,430
Liabilities: $296,738
Net Worth: $10,392,692
Earnings: ($3,716,002)
Fiscal Year-end: 06/30/23
Gold Exploration Services
N.A.I.C.S.: 212220
Andrew Sparke (Exec Chm)

QMP PUBLICIS
Level 4 The Observatory 7-11 Sir John Rogersons Quay, Dublin, 2, Ireland
Tel.: (353) 16496500 IE
Web Site: http://www.publicis.ie
Year Founded: 1973
Sales Range: $100-124.9 Million
Emp.: 120
N.A.I.C.S.: 541810
Dave Wright (Dir-Production)

Subsidiaries:

Pembroke Communications (1)
16 Sir John Rogersons Quay, Dublin, 2, Ireland
Tel.: (353) 1 649 6486
Emp.: 10
N.A.I.C.S.: 541810
Michael O'Keeffe (Mng Dir)

Publicis Direct Ltd. (1)
16 Sir John Rogersson Quay, Dublin, 2, Ireland
Tel.: (353) 16496400
N.A.I.C.S.: 518210
Josh Joyce (Mng Dir)

QNB FINANS FAKTORING A.S.
Esentepe mahallesi Buyukdere Caddesi Kristal Kule Binasi No 215 Kat 21, Sisli, Istanbul, Turkiye
Tel.: (90) 2123713800
Web Site: http://www.qnbff.com
QNBFF—(IST)
Rev.: $49,238,869
Assets: $300,990,101
Liabilities: $282,954,117
Net Worth: $18,035,984
Earnings: $9,721,456
Emp.: 136
Fiscal Year-end: 12/31/22
Banking Services
N.A.I.C.S.: 522110
Sinan Sahinbas (Chm)

Subsidiaries:

QNB Finans Leasing A.S. (1)
Esentepe Mahallesi Buyukdere cad, Kristal Kule Binasi No 215 Kat 22, 34394, Istanbul, Turkiye
Tel.: (90) 2123491111
Web Site: https://www.qnbfl.com
Finance Leasing Services
N.A.I.C.S.: 522220

QNB Finansinvest AS (1)
Esentepe Mah Buyukdere Cad Kristal Kule Binasi No 215 Kat 6-7, Sisli, 34394, Istanbul, Turkiye
Tel.: (90) 2123367000
Web Site: https://www.qnbfi.com
Investment Banking Services
N.A.I.C.S.: 523150

QNB Finansportfoy A.S. (1)
Esentepe Mah Buyukdere Cad Crystal Tower Building No 215 Floor 6, Sisli, 34394, Istanbul, Turkiye
Tel.: (90) 2123367171
Web Site: https://www.qnbfp.com
Investment Services
N.A.I.C.S.: 523999

QNB Finansvarlik A.S. (1)
Esentepe Mahallesi Buyukdere Cad No 215/1, Sisli, Istanbul, Turkiye
Tel.: (90) 2123367000
Web Site: https://www.qnbfv.com
Investment Services
N.A.I.C.S.: 523999

QNB Sigorta A.S. (1)
Barbaros Mah Kardelen St Palladium TowerNo 2 Floor 28, Atasehir, 2934746, Istanbul, Turkiye
Tel.: (90) 2164680300
Web Site: https://www.qnbsigorta.com
Investment Services
N.A.I.C.S.: 523999

QNB eFinans A.S. (1)
Esentepe Mahallesi Buyukdere Caddesi Kristal Kule Binasi No 215/1, Sisli, 34394, Istanbul, Turkiye
Tel.: (90) 2123704200
Financial Investment Services
N.A.I.C.S.: 523999

QNB FINANS FINANSAL KIRALAMA A.S.
2 Kisim A Blok No 443 Hava Limani, Bakirkoy, Istanbul, 34158, Turkiye
Tel.: (90) 2123491111
Web Site: https://www.qnbfl.com
Year Founded: 1990
QNBFL—(IST)
Rev.: $89,943,023
Assets: $989,566,859
Liabilities: $838,668,137
Net Worth: $150,898,721
Earnings: $15,287,746
Fiscal Year-end: 12/31/19
Financial Lending Services
N.A.I.C.S.: 533110
Metin Karabiber (Gen Mgr)

QNB FINANS VARLIK KIRALAMA A.S.
Esentepe Mahallesi Buyukdere Cad No 215/1, Sisli, Istanbul, Turkiye
Tel.: (90) 2123367000
Web Site: http://www.qnbfv.com
QNBVK—(IST)
Sales Range: Less than $1 Million
Financial Lending Services
N.A.I.C.S.: 533110
Bulent Yurdalan (Chm)

Subsidiaries:

Cigna Saglik Hayat ve Emeklilik A.S. (1)
Barbaros Mah Kardelen Sok Palladium Tower No 2 Kat 28-29, Atasehir, 34746, Istanbul, Turkiye
Tel.: (90) 2164680300
Web Site: http://www.cigna.com.tr
Health Insurance Services
N.A.I.C.S.: 524114

QOL HOLDINGS CO., LTD.
37F Shiroyama Trust Tower 4-3-1 Toranomon, Minato-ku, Tokyo, 105-8452, Japan
Tel.: (81) 354059011
Web Site: https://www.qolhd.co.jp
Year Founded: 1992
3034—(TKS)
Rev.: $1,190,143,720
Assets: $778,519,190
Liabilities: $429,266,620
Net Worth: $349,252,570
Earnings: $32,256,800
Emp.: 5,856
Fiscal Year-end: 03/31/24
Holding Company; Pharmacy & BPO Businesses
N.A.I.C.S.: 551112
Takashi Nakamura (Pres)

Subsidiaries:

APO PLUS STATION Co., Ltd. (1)
Front Place Nihonbashi 2-14-1 Nihonbashi, Chuo-ku, Tokyo, 103-0027, Japan (100%)
Tel.: (81) 358005827
Emp.: 790
Pharmaceutical Products Distr
N.A.I.C.S.: 424210

Alpharm Co., Ltd. (1)
2nd Floor Qol Bldg 2-8-12, Chuo, Mito, 310-0805, Ibaraki, Japan
Tel.: (81) 292915011
Medical Healthcare Services
N.A.I.C.S.: 621999

Apo Plus Station (Thailand) Co., Ltd. (1)
No 308 Charasanitwong Soi 67 Kwaeng Bangplad, Bangkok, Thailand
Tel.: (66) 28810209
Web Site: http://www.apoplus.co.th
Consulting Training Services
N.A.I.C.S.: 611430

Fujinaga Pharm Co., Ltd. (1)
9F Front Place Nihonbashi 2-14-1 Nihonbashi, Chuo-ku, Tokyo, 103-0027, Japan
Tel.: (81) 345331100
Web Site: https://www.fujinaga-pharm.co.jp
Emp.: 140
Pharmaceuticals Product Mfr
N.A.I.C.S.: 325412

Life Plan Co., Ltd. (1)
3F No 10 Lane 9 Sec 1 Jhonghua Rd, Jhongjheng District, Taipei, 10043, Taiwan
Tel.: (886) 2 23810185
Medical Healthcare Services
N.A.I.C.S.: 621999

Medical Qol Co., Ltd. (1)
9F Front Place Nihonbashi 2-14-1 Nihonbashi, Chuo-ku, Tokyo, 103-0027, Japan
Tel.: (81) 363698700
Medical Adverting Services
N.A.I.C.S.: 541810

Moriyama Co., Ltd. (1)
1-1 Kamihoshigawa 3-chome, Hodogaya-ku, Yokohama, 240-0042, Hyogo, Japan
Tel.: (81) 453712341
Web Site: https://www.moriyama-inc.co.jp
Sales Range: $25-49.9 Million
Emp.: 70
Machine Tools Mfr
N.A.I.C.S.: 333517

Qol Assist Co., Ltd. (1)
9F Front Place Nihonbashi 2-14-1 Nihonbashi, Chuo-ku, Tokyo, 103-0027, Japan
Tel.: (81) 335100485
Consulting Training Services
N.A.I.C.S.: 611430

Qol Co., Ltd. (1)
Shiroyama Trust Tower 37F 4-3-1, Toranomon Minato-ku, Tokyo, 105-8452, Japan
Tel.: (81) 354059011
Web Site: https://www.qol-net.co.jp
Emp.: 7,729
Pharmacy Services
N.A.I.C.S.: 524292

Suzukyu Yakuhin Co., Ltd. (1)
7-12-11 Ueno, Taito-Ku, Tokyo, 110-0005, Japan
Tel.: (81) 338444521
Medical Healthcare Services
N.A.I.C.S.: 621999

QOO10 PTE. LTD
50 Beach Road #18-01 Gateway West, Singapore, 189720, Singapore
Tel.: (65) 65004440
Web Site: https://www.qoo10.sg
Emp.: 100
Online Retail & eCommerce Services
N.A.I.C.S.: 519290

QPL INTERNATIONAL HOLDINGS LIMITED
Unit H 24/ Golden Bear Industrial Center 66-82 Chai Wan Kok Street, Tsuen Wan, New Territories, China (Hong Kong)
Tel.: (852) 24065111 BM
Web Site: https://www.qpl.com
Year Founded: 1982
0243—(HKG)
Rev.: $39,898,320
Assets: $67,544,528
Liabilities: $18,146,565
Net Worth: $49,397,963
Earnings: ($4,375,673)
Emp.: 870
Fiscal Year-end: 04/30/23
Integrated Circuit Mfr & Distr
N.A.I.C.S.: 334413
Tung Lok Li (Founder, Chm & CEO)

Subsidiaries:

Dongguan Changan QPL Electronics Manufacturing Company Limited (1)
No 9 Mu Lin Road, Chang An Town, Dongguan, 523860, Guangdong, China
Tel.: (86) 76985391118
Integrated Circuit Product Mfr & Distr
N.A.I.C.S.: 334413

QPL (US) Inc. (1)
2795 E Bidwell St Ste 100 333, Folsom, CA 95630
Tel.: (510) 656-7411
Electronic Parts & Equipment Distr
N.A.I.C.S.: 423690

QPL Limited (1)
8th Floor Hale Weal Industrial Building 22-28 Tai Chung Road, Tsuen Wan, New Territories, China (Hong Kong)
Tel.: (852) 24065111
Web Site: https://www.qpl.com
Semiconductor Devices Mfr
N.A.I.C.S.: 334413

Subsidiary (Non-US):

QPL (Pte) Limited (2)
14-02A 150 Cecil Street, Singapore, 069543, Singapore
Tel.: (65) 62233878
Electronic Parts & Equipment Distr
N.A.I.C.S.: 423690

Plant (Non-US):

QPL Limited - Dongguan Chang An QPL Electronics Factory (2)
No 1 Pin Zhi Lu Xin An Industrial Park, Chang An Town, Dongguan, 523860, Guangdong, China
Tel.: (86) 76985391118
Electronic Parts & Equipment Distr
N.A.I.C.S.: 423690

QPR SOFTWARE PLC
Huopalahdentie 24, 00350, Helsinki, Finland
Tel.: (358) 290001150
Web Site: https://www.qpr.com
Year Founded: 1991
QPR1V—(HEL)
Rev.: $8,442,694
Assets: $8,031,513

QPR SOFTWARE PLC

QPR Software Plc—(Continued)
Liabilities: $7,505,936
Net Worth: $525,577
Earnings: ($3,095,187)
Emp.: 85
Fiscal Year-end: 12/31/22
Software Services
N.A.I.C.S.: 513210
Vesa-Pekka Leskinen (Chm)

Subsidiaries:

QPR CIS Oy (1)
Huopalahdentie 24, 00350, Helsinki, Finland
Tel.: (358) 290001150
Web Site: https://www.qpr.com
Computer Software Development Services
N.A.I.C.S.: 541511

QRF COMM. VA
Gaston Crommenlaan 8, 9050, Gent, Belgium
Tel.: (32) 92962163
Web Site: https://www.qrf.be
QRF—(EUR)
Rev.: $15,635,280
Assets: $278,942,488
Liabilities: $147,692,902
Net Worth: $131,249,586
Earnings: ($2,710,012)
Emp.: 7
Fiscal Year-end: 12/31/23
Real Estate Investment Services
N.A.I.C.S.: 523999
Inge Boets (Chm)

QSI CO., LTD.
17 Cheonheung 8-gil Seonggeo-eup, Seobukgu, Cheonan, 31044, Chungcheongnam-do, Korea (South)
Tel.: (82) 424105000
Web Site: https://www.qsilaser.com
Year Founded: 2000
066310—(KRS)
Rev.: $17,410,479
Assets: $65,953,265
Liabilities: $3,623,054
Net Worth: $62,330,211
Earnings: $5,375,422
Emp.: 105
Fiscal Year-end: 12/31/22
Semiconductor Laser Diode Mfr
N.A.I.C.S.: 334413
Cheong-Dai Lee (CEO)

QST GROUP
Unit No 10 05 10th Floor Menara K1 No 1 Lorong 3/137C Batu 5 Off, Jalan Kelang Lama, 58000, Kuala Lumpur, Malaysia
Tel.: (60) 377733197
Web Site: http://www.qsttech.com
Year Founded: 2005
Medical Equipment Distr
N.A.I.C.S.: 423450

Subsidiaries:

QST Technologies (HK) Co. Ltd. (1)
Unit C 17/F Ford Glory Plaza No 37 Wing Hong Street, Lai Chi Kok, Kowloon, China (Hong Kong)
Tel.: (852) 26260512
Medical Equipment Distr
N.A.I.C.S.: 423450

QST Technologies Pte. Ltd. (1)
196 Pandan Loop 04-29 Pantech Business Hub, Singapore, 128384, Singapore
Tel.: (65) 62706260
Web Site: https://www.qsttech.com
Medical Equipment Distr
N.A.I.C.S.: 423450

QT GROUP PLC
Bertel Jungin Aukio D3A, 02600, Espoo, Finland
Tel.: (358) 988618040
Web Site: https://www.qt.io

QTCOM—(HEL)
Rev.: $167,621,412
Assets: $192,210,231
Liabilities: $98,613,210
Net Worth: $93,597,021
Earnings: $37,018,131
Emp.: 603
Fiscal Year-end: 12/31/22
Software Development Services
N.A.I.C.S.: 541511
Robert Ingman (Chm)

Subsidiaries:

Axivion GmbH (1)
Nobelstrasse 15, 70569, Stuttgart, Germany
Tel.: (49) 71162043780
Web Site: https://www.axivion.com
Software Development Services
N.A.I.C.S.: 541511

The Qt Company AS (1)
Sandakerveien 116, 0484, Oslo, Norway
Tel.: (47) 21080430
Software Development Services
N.A.I.C.S.: 541511
Lars Knoll (CTO)

The Qt Company GmbH (1)
Erich-Thilo-Strasse 10, 12489, Berlin, Germany
Tel.: (49) 30403656411
Software Development Services
N.A.I.C.S.: 541511
Axel Fersen (Sr Mgr-Acct)

The Qt Company LLC (1)
311 ABN Building 331 Pangyo-ro, Bundang-gu, Seongnam, 13488, Gyeonggi-do, Korea (South)
Tel.: (82) 317120045
Software Development Services
N.A.I.C.S.: 541511
Hollis Kim (Project Mgr-Technical & Professional Svcs)

The Qt Company Ltd. (1)
701-1 and 701-2 Shimen No 1 Road, Jing an District, Shanghai, China
Tel.: (86) 2151748525
Software Development Services
N.A.I.C.S.: 541511
Jane Zheng (Mktg Mgr-APAC)

QTC ENERGY PUBLIC COMPANY LIMITED
2/2 Soi Krunthep Kritha 8 5 Krunthep Kritha Rd Haumark, Bangkapi, Bangkok, 10240, Thailand
Tel.: (66) 23793089
Web Site: https://www.qtc-energy.com
Year Founded: 1966
QTC—(THA)
Rev.: $39,033,057
Assets: $54,361,217
Liabilities: $8,178,895
Net Worth: $46,182,323
Earnings: $1,952,540
Emp.: 254
Fiscal Year-end: 12/31/23
Transformer Mfr
N.A.I.C.S.: 335311
Poonphiphat Tantanasin (CEO)

QTONE EDUCATION GROUP GUANGDONG LTD.
Floor 18-20 Building 5 Shangfeng Financial Business Center, No 88 Zhongshan 4th Road East District, Zhongshan, 528400, Guangdong, China
Tel.: (86) 76088368596
Web Site: http://www.qtone.cn
Year Founded: 2005
300359—(CHIN)
Rev.: $84,922,344
Assets: $163,825,740
Liabilities: $50,570,676
Net Worth: $113,255,064
Earnings: $1,767,636
Emp.: 2,197

Fiscal Year-end: 12/31/22
Family Education Information Services
N.A.I.C.S.: 611710
Mao Jianbo (Chm)

QUA GRANITE HAYAL YAPI VE URUNLERI SANAYI TICARET A.S.
Soke Organized Industrial Zone District 4 Street No 1, Soke, 09260, Aydin, Turkiye
Tel.: (90) 8508880708
Web Site: https://www.qua.com.tr
Year Founded: 2016
QUAGR—(IST)
Rev.: $263,476,087
Assets: $490,618,328
Liabilities: $227,611,870
Net Worth: $263,006,458
Earnings: $14,203,188
Emp.: 1,378
Fiscal Year-end: 12/31/23
Ceramic Wall Mfr
N.A.I.C.S.: 327120
Ali Ercan (Chm)

QUADIENT SA
42-46 avenue Aristide Briand, 92220, Bagneux, France
Tel.: (33) 892892111   FR
Web Site: https://www.quadient.com
Year Founded: 1924
NPACF—(OTCIQ)
Rev.: $1,166,846,536
Assets: $2,856,248,651
Liabilities: $1,689,078,351
Net Worth: $1,167,170,300
Earnings: $17,051,586
Emp.: 4,900
Fiscal Year-end: 01/31/23
Mailing & Logistics Services
N.A.I.C.S.: 541614
Geoffrey Godet (CEO)

Subsidiaries:

Neopost AG (1)
Hertistrasse 25, 8304, Wallisellen, Switzerland
Tel.: (41) 523543800
Web Site: http://www.neopost.ch
Mail Handling Machinery Whslr
N.A.I.C.S.: 423830

Neopost Australia Pty Ltd (1)
Unit 1 Block Q Regents Park Estate, Princes Road East, Regents Park, 2143, NSW, Australia
Tel.: (61) 297384000
Web Site: http://www.neopost.com.au
Emp.: 200
Business Mailing & Document Finishing Solutions
N.A.I.C.S.: 323120
Stuart MacDonald (Mng Dir)

Neopost BV (1)
Tel.: (31) 365496300
Web Site: http://www.neopost.nl
Sales Range: $10-24.9 Million
Emp.: 63
Mailing & Document Systems Sales & Distribution
N.A.I.C.S.: 323120

Neopost BVBA (1)
Ikaroslaan 37, 1930, Zaventem, Belgium
Tel.: (32) 27095330
Web Site: http://www.neopost.be
Sales Range: $50-74.9 Million
Emp.: 80
Postage Supplies Distr
N.A.I.C.S.: 423420
Benoit Berson (Gen Mgr)

Neopost Canada Limited (1)
150 Steelcase Road West, Markham, L3R 3J9, ON, Canada   (100%)
Tel.: (905) 475-3722
Web Site: http://www.neopost.ca
Rev.: $10,000,000
Emp.: 50

INTERNATIONAL PUBLIC

Shipping Room Products, Gummed Tape Dispensing Machinery, Case Tape Machinery, Scales & Postal Meter Bases, Mailroom Furniture, Inserters, Mailroom Equipment Mfr; Parking Systems, Carpark Management
N.A.I.C.S.: 339940
Lou Gizzarelli (Pres)

Neopost Danmark A/S (1)
Valhojs Alle 176, 2610, Rodovre, Denmark
Tel.: (45) 36709088
Web Site: http://www.neopost.dk
Software Solutions Services
N.A.I.C.S.: 541511
Jesper Koch (Sls Mgr)

Neopost Finland Oy (1)
Konalantie 47 A, 00390, Helsinki, Finland
Tel.: (358) 925320200
Web Site: http://www.neopost.fi
Software Solutions Services
N.A.I.C.S.: 541511
Pasi Tiainen (Mng Dir)

Neopost GmbH & Co (1)
Landsberger Strasse 154, 80339, Munich, Germany
Tel.: (49) 895168910
Web Site: http://www.neopost.de
Sales Range: $75-99.9 Million
Emp.: 150
Postage Supplies Distr
N.A.I.C.S.: 423420

Neopost GmbH & Co (1)
Schonbrunner Strasse 131 Top 1-03, Vienna, 1050, Austria
Tel.: (43) 18939494
Web Site: http://www.neopost.at
Sales Range: $50-74.9 Million
Emp.: 5
Postage Supplies Distr
N.A.I.C.S.: 423420

Neopost Ireland Ltd. (1)
Unit 16 Fonthill Retail Industrial Park Fonthill Road, Clondalkin, D22 F2P1, Dublin, 22, Ireland
Tel.: (353) 16250900
Software Solutions Services
N.A.I.C.S.: 541511

Neopost Italia S.R.L (1)
Via Sirtori 34, Passione di Rhode, 20017, Rho, Milan, Italy
Tel.: (39) 0293158611
Web Site: http://www.neopost.it
Postage Supplies Distr
N.A.I.C.S.: 423420

Neopost Japan Inc. (1)
23 1 Oyama Cho, Itabashi Ku, Tokyo, 173 0023, Japan   (100%)
Tel.: (81) 359950880
Web Site: http://www.neopost.co.jp
Sales Range: $1-9.9 Million
Emp.: 20
Mfr of Tape Dispensing Equipment
N.A.I.C.S.: 333310

Neopost Limited (1)
Neopost House, South Street, Romford, RM1 2AR, Essex, United Kingdom
Tel.: (44) 1708746000
Web Site: http://www.neopost.co.uk
Sales Range: $100-124.9 Million
Emp.: 500
Supplier of Telecommunications Equipment & Mail Handling Equipment
N.A.I.C.S.: 517111
Erwan Kernevez (Dir-Digital Solutions)

Subsidiary (US):

Neopost Inc. (2)
26250 Eden Landing Rd, Hayward, CA 94544-7005
Tel.: (510) 266-3000
Web Site: http://www.neopostusa.com
Commercial Machinery
N.A.I.C.S.: 333310

Subsidiary (Non-US):

Neopost Industrie AG (3)
Brunnenstrasse 66, 3108, Bern, Switzerland   (100%)
Tel.: (41) 9995754
Sales Range: $50-74.9 Million
Emp.: 193
N.A.I.C.S.: 334290

AND PRIVATE COMPANIES

Neopost Luxembourg (1)
183 Rue de Luxembourg, Bertrange, 8007, Luxembourg
Tel.: (352) 245 27 441
Web Site: http://www.neopost.lu
Mail Handling Machinery Whslr
N.A.I.C.S.: 423440
Evan Sens *(Dir-Sls)*

Neopost Norge AS (1)
Jerikoveien 18, 1067, Oslo, Norway
Tel.: (47) 22901400
Web Site: http://www.neopost.no
Sales Range: $25-49.9 Million
Emp.: 35
Office Equipments Mfr
N.A.I.C.S.: 333248
Eric Thorhallsson *(Gen Mgr)*

Neopost Sverige AB (1)
Rontgenvagen 5, Box 1126, 171 22, Solna, Sweden
Tel.: (46) 84459780
Web Site: http://www.neopost.se
Sales Range: $25-49.9 Million
Emp.: 100
Office Equipments Mfr
N.A.I.C.S.: 333310
Joachim Alestam *(Gen Mgr)*

Parcel Pending Inc. (1)
210 Progress Ste 100, Irvine, CA 92618
Web Site: https://www.parcelpending.com
Packaging & Labeling Services
N.A.I.C.S.: 561910
Lori Torres *(Founder & CEO)*

ProShip Inc. (1)
400 N Executive Dr Ste 210, Brookfield, WI 53005
Tel.: (414) 302-2929
Web Site: https://www.proshipinc.com
Software Services
N.A.I.C.S.: 541511
Justin Cramer *(Head-Sls)*

Quadient Australia Pty. Ltd. (1)
Suite 303b Level 3 31 Market Street, Sydney, 2000, NSW, Australia
Tel.: (61) 282841022
Software Solutions Services
N.A.I.C.S.: 541511

Quadient China Ltd. (1)
Rm 1006 Tower A Eton Plaza No 69 Dangfang Rd, Pudong New District, Shanghai, 200120, China
Tel.: (86) 2158771899
Software Solutions Services
N.A.I.C.S.: 541511

Quadient Data UK Ltd. (1)
Suite 24 Second Floor 250 South Oak Way, Reading, RG2 6UG, United Kingdom
Tel.: (44) 8458800000
Application Software Services
N.A.I.C.S.: 541511

Quadient Denmark Aps (1)
22-24 Rodager Alle, 2610, Rodovre, Denmark
Tel.: (45) 36709088
Software Solutions Services
N.A.I.C.S.: 541511

Quadient France SAS (1)
7 rue Henri Becquerel, CS 30129, 92565, Rueil-Malmaison, Cedex, France
Tel.: (33) 892892111
Application Software Services
N.A.I.C.S.: 541511

Quadient Germany GmbH (1)
Richard-Reitzner-Allee 1, 85540, Haar, Germany
Tel.: (49) 89454553230
Web Site: http://www.de.quadient.com
Software Solutions Services
N.A.I.C.S.: 541511
Mina Smolej *(Mktg Mgr)*

Quadient Hungary Kft. (1)
61 Lehel utca, 1135, Budapest, Hungary
Tel.: (36) 12888575
Software Solutions Services
N.A.I.C.S.: 541511

Quadient Poland Sp. z.o.o. (1)
27 Orzycka, 02-695, Warsaw, Poland
Tel.: (48) 224871111
Software Solutions Services

N.A.I.C.S.: 541511

Quadient Singapore Pte. Ltd. (1)
20 Cecil Street 17-02, Singapore, 049705, Singapore
Tel.: (65) 66531400
Software Solutions Services
N.A.I.C.S.: 541511

Quadient Software Brazil Ltda. (1)
Rua Iguatemi 192 Cj 192, Sao Paulo, 01451-010, SP, Brazil
Tel.: (55) 1123377746
Software Solutions Services
N.A.I.C.S.: 541511

Quadient Switzerland AG (1)
Hertistrasse 25, 8304, Wallisellen, Switzerland
Tel.: (41) 848231231
Software Solutions Services
N.A.I.C.S.: 541511
Karl-Heinz Fuchs *(Sls Mgr)*

Quadient s.r.o (1)
Hornopolni 3322/34 Moravska, 702 00, Ostrava, Czech Republic
Tel.: (420) 770149481
Software Solutions Services
N.A.I.C.S.: 541511
Boris Letocha *(Head-Dept)*

icon Systemhaus GmbH (1)
Hauptstatter Strasse 70, 70178, Stuttgart, Germany
Tel.: (49) 7118060980
Web Site: https://www.icongmbh.de
Software Solutions Services
N.A.I.C.S.: 541511
Thomas Jurgens *(Mng Dir)*

QUADPRO ITES LIMITED
S-3 Second Floor 53 to 58 Sri Chakravarthy Complex, V V Puram Sajjan Rao Circle, Bengaluru, 560004, Karnataka, India
Tel.: (91) 8049118300
Web Site: https://www.quadpro.co.in
Year Founded: 2010
QUADPRO—(NSE)
Rev.: $1,125,292
Assets: $2,347,317
Liabilities: $141,610
Net Worth: $2,205,707
Earnings: $95,330
Emp.: 92
Fiscal Year-end: 03/31/23
Information Technology Services
N.A.I.C.S.: 541512

QUADRANT PRIVATE EQUITY PTY. LTD.
Level 30 126 Phillip Street, Sydney, 2000, NSW, Australia
Tel.: (61) 292213044   AU
Web Site: https://www.quadrantpe.com.au
Year Founded: 1996
Privater Equity Firm
N.A.I.C.S.: 523999
Chris Hadley *(Exec Chm)*

Subsidiaries:

Fitness and Lifestyle Management Health Clubs Pty. Ltd. (1)
Level 8 60 Miller Street, Milsons Point, 2060, NSW, Australia
Tel.: (61) 294093670
Web Site: https://www.fitlg.com
Health Club Management Services
N.A.I.C.S.: 713940

Grays eCommerce Group Limited (1)
376 Newbridge Road, Moorebank, 2170, NSW, Australia
Tel.: (61) 279081700
Web Site: https://www.grays.com
Holding Company; eCommerce Services
N.A.I.C.S.: 551112

Great Southern Rail Limited (1)
Adelaide Parklands Terminal, Keswick, 5035, SA, Australia   (70%)
Tel.: (61) 882134444

Web Site: http://www.greatsouthernrail.com.au
Holding Company; Railway Passenger Transportation & Tour Services
N.A.I.C.S.: 551112
Russell Westmoreland *(Gen Mgr-Rail Ops & Dir-Special Projects)*

Subsidiary (Domestic):

Great Southern Rail Travel Pty. Limited (2)
Adelaide Parklands Terminal, Keswick, 5035, SA, Australia
Tel.: (61) 882134444
Web Site: http://www.greatsouthernrail.com.au
Sales Range: $25-49.9 Million
Emp.: 50
Railway Passenger Transportation & Tour Services
N.A.I.C.S.: 482112
Chris Tallent *(CEO)*

QMS Media Limited (1)
214 Park Street, South Melbourne, 3205, VIC, Australia
Tel.: (61) 392687000
Web Site: http://www.qmsmedia.com
Sales Range: $50-74.9 Million
Outdoor Media Advertising
N.A.I.C.S.: 541850
Nick Errey *(Head-Comm)*

Subsidiary (US):

TGI Systems Corp (2)
188 North Wells Ste 202, Chicago, IL 60606
Tel.: (312) 977-1800
Web Site: http://www.worldwidetgi.com
Marketing & Advertising Services
N.A.I.C.S.: 541890
Pat Vendrely *(Founder & Pres)*

Serendipity (WA) Pty Ltd (1)
58 Ord Street, West Perth, 6005, WA, Australia
Tel.: (61) 8 9463 1300
Web Site: http://apm.net.au
Employment & Health Care & Injury Management Services
N.A.I.C.S.: 561311

Superior Food Group Pty Ltd (1)
33-59 Clarinda Rd, South Oakleigh, Melbourne, 3167, VIC, Australia
Tel.: (61) 0395380800
Web Site: http://superiorfs.com.au
Food Services & Sea Food Distr
N.A.I.C.S.: 722310
Carolina Moore *(VP-Ops)*

Subsidiary (Domestic):

Sealanes (1985) Pty Ltd (2)
178 Marine Terrace, South Fremantle, Perth, 6162, WA, Australia
Tel.: (61) 894328888
Web Site: http://www.sealanes.com.au
Food Services & Sea Food Distr
N.A.I.C.S.: 311710

TEEG Australia Pty. Ltd. (1)
491B River Valley Road Unit 10-01/2 Valley Point, Singapore, 248373, Singapore
Tel.: (65) 65139650
Web Site: https://teeg.com
Bowling Center Operator
N.A.I.C.S.: 713950
Scott Blume *(Mng Dir)*

QUADRANT TELEVENTURES LIMITED
Plot no 196 Flat no 6 Dinkar Appartment Ulkanagri, Behind Gayakwad Classes, Aurangabad, 431005, Maharashtra, India
Tel.: (91) 2402320754
Web Site: https://www.connectzone.in
Year Founded: 1946
511116—(BOM)
Rev.: $48,320,484
Assets: $18,473,221
Liabilities: $304,439,902
Net Worth: ($285,966,681)
Earnings: ($12,590,228)

QUADRAVEST CAPITAL MANAGEMENT INC.
Emp.: 1,050
Fiscal Year-end: 03/31/23
Telecom Solutions Provider
N.A.I.C.S.: 517810
Munish Bansal *(CFO)*

QUADRAVEST CAPITAL MANAGEMENT INC.
200 Front Street West Suite 2510, PO Box 51, 77 King Street West, Toronto, M5V 3K2, ON, Canada
Tel.: (416) 304-4440
Web Site: http://www.quadravest.com
Sales Range: $25-49.9 Million
Emp.: 5
Investment Management
N.A.I.C.S.: 523940
Laura L. Johnson *(Mng Dir & Portfolio Mgr)*

Subsidiaries:

Canadian Banc Corp. (1)
200 Front Street West Suite 2510, PO Box 51, Toronto, M5V 3K2, ON, Canada
Tel.: (416) 304-4443
Web Site: http://www.quadravest.com
Rev: $5,348,900
Assets: $276,237,335
Liabilities: $132,024,158
Net Worth: $144,213,177
Earnings: ($4,083,184)
Fiscal Year-end: 11/30/2022
Closed-End Investment Fund
N.A.I.C.S.: 525990

Canadian Life Companies Split Corp. (1)
200 Front Street West Suite 2510, PO Box 51, Toronto, M5V 3K2, ON, Canada
Tel.: (416) 304-4443
Web Site: http://www.quadravest.com
Closed-End Investment Fund
N.A.I.C.S.: 525990
S. Wayne Finch *(Chm, Pres, CEO, Chief Investment Officer & Sec)*

Dividend 15 Split Corp. (1)
200 Front Street West Suite 2510, PO Box 51, Toronto, M5V 3K2, ON, Canada
Tel.: (416) 304-4443
Web Site: http://www.quadravest.com
Rev.: $59,073,858
Assets: $1,357,875,101
Liabilities: $845,902,232
Net Worth: $511,972,870
Earnings: ($1,332,504)
Fiscal Year-end: 11/30/2022
Closed-End Investment Fund
N.A.I.C.S.: 525990
Laura L. Johnson *(Sec)*

Dividend 15 Split Corp. II (1)
200 Front Street West Suite 2510, PO Box 51, Toronto, M5V 3K2, ON, Canada
Tel.: (416) 304-4443
Web Site: http://www.quadravest.com
Rev.: $124,211
Assets: $708,804,450
Liabilities: $462,871,536
Net Worth: $245,932,914
Earnings: ($75,792,633)
Fiscal Year-end: 11/30/2020
Closed-End Investment Fund
N.A.I.C.S.: 525990
S. Wayne Finch *(Chm, Pres, CEO, Chief Investment Officer & Sec)*

Dividend Select 15 Corp. (1)
200 Front Street West Suite 2510, PO Box 51, Toronto, M5V 3K2, ON, Canada
Tel.: (416) 304-4443
Web Site: http://www.quadravest.com
Rev.: $1,768,591
Assets: $40,663,991
Liabilities: $513,874
Net Worth: $40,150,118
Earnings: ($936,902)
Fiscal Year-end: 11/30/2023
Closed-End Investment Fund
N.A.I.C.S.: 525990

Financial 15 Split Corp. (1)
200 Front Street West Suite 2510, PO Box 51, Toronto, M5V 3K2, ON, Canada
Tel.: (416) 304-4443

QUADRAVEST CAPITAL MANAGEMENT INC.

Quadravest Capital Management Inc.—(Continued)
Web Site: http://www.quadravest.com
Rev.: $1,241,322
Assets: $524,850,475
Liabilities: $282,419,474
Net Worth: $242,431,001
Earnings: ($21,205,158)
Fiscal Year-end: 11/30/2022
Closed-End Investment Fund
N.A.I.C.S.: 525990
S. Wayne Finch *(Chm, Pres & CEO)*

Income Financial Trust (1)
200 Front Street West Suite 2510, PO Box 51, Toronto, M5V 3K2, ON, Canada
Tel.: (416) 304-4443
Web Site: http://www.quadravest.com
Rev.: $3,132,554
Assets: $14,793,821
Liabilities: $194,797
Net Worth: $14,599,024
Earnings: $2,828,566
Fiscal Year-end: 12/31/2019
Closed-End Investment Fund
N.A.I.C.S.: 525990
S. Wayne Finch *(Chm, Pres, CEO, Chief Investment Officer & Sec)*

M Split Corp. (1)
200 Front Street West Suite 2510, PO Box 51, Toronto, M5V 3K2, ON, Canada
Tel.: (416) 304-4443
Web Site: http://www.quadravest.com
Assets: $11,295,533
Liabilities: $11,295,532
Net Worth: $1
Earnings: $2,210,475
Fiscal Year-end: 11/30/2020
Closed-End Investment Fund
N.A.I.C.S.: 525990

North American Financial 15 Split Corporation (1)
200 Front Street West Suite 2510, PO Box 51, Toronto, M5V 3K2, ON, Canada
Tel.: (416) 304-4443
Web Site: https://www.quadravest.com
Rev.: $1,414,571
Assets: $635,552,371
Liabilities: $419,551,131
Net Worth: $216,001,241
Earnings: ($35,991,541)
Fiscal Year-end: 11/30/2022
Closed-End Investment Fund
N.A.I.C.S.: 525990

Prime Dividend Corp. (1)
200 Front Street West Suite 2510, PO Box 51, Toronto, M5V 3K2, ON, Canada
Tel.: (416) 304-4443
Web Site: http://www.quadravest.com
Assets: $10,646,722
Liabilities: $6,840,152
Net Worth: $3,806,570
Earnings: ($984,911)
Fiscal Year-end: 11/30/2022
Closed-End Investment Fund
N.A.I.C.S.: 525990

TDb Split Corp. (1)
200 Front Street West Suite 2510, PO Box 51, Toronto, M5V 3K2, ON, Canada
Tel.: (416) 304-4443
Web Site: http://www.quadravest.com
Rev.: $1,955,501
Assets: $70,205,744
Liabilities: $51,343,705
Net Worth: $18,862,040
Earnings: ($1,452,447)
Fiscal Year-end: 11/30/2022
Closed-End Investment Fund
N.A.I.C.S.: 525990

US Financial 15 Split Corp. (1)
200 Front Street West Suite 2510, PO Box 51, Toronto, M5V 3K2, ON, Canada
Tel.: (416) 304-4443
Rev.: $968,052,322
Assets: $12,473,607,901
Liabilities: $137,978,129
Net Worth: $12,335,629,773
Earnings: $689,774,327
Fiscal Year-end: 11/30/2019
Closed-End Investment Fund
N.A.I.C.S.: 525990

QUADRIA CAPITAL INVESTMENT MANAGEMENT PTE LTD

Level 2 The Crescent Lado Sarai Mehrauli, New Delhi, 110 030, India
Tel.: (91) 11 4953 9900
Web Site: http://www.quadriacapital.com
Healtcare Services
N.A.I.C.S.: 621999
Abrar Mir *(Mng Partner)*

Subsidiaries:

Strand Life Sciences Pvt. Ltd. (1)
5th Floor Kirloskar Bus Park Bellary Rd, Bengaluru, 560024, India
Tel.: (91) 8040787263
Web Site: http://www.strandls.com
Clinical Diagnostics
N.A.I.C.S.: 621511
Ramesh Hariharan *(Founder & CEO)*

QUADRIGA CAPITAL BETEILIGUNGSBERATUNG GMBH

Hamburger Allee 4, 60486, Frankfurt, Germany
Tel.: (49) 69 795 000 0 De
Web Site: http://www.quadriga-capital.de
Emp.: 30
Privater Equity Firm
N.A.I.C.S.: 523999
Max Walter Romer *(Founder & Partner)*

Subsidiaries:

Ipsen International Holding GmbH (1)
Flutstrasse 78, D 47533, Kleve, Germany
Tel.: (49) 28218040
Web Site: http://www.ipsen.de
Sales Range: $150-199.9 Million
Holding Company; Thermal Technology Products Mfr
N.A.I.C.S.: 551112
Hendrik Grobler *(CEO)*

Subsidiary (Non-US):

Ipsen Industries Nordiska AB (2)
Smedjevagen 1, 16732, Bromma, Kungsholmen, Sweden
Tel.: (46) 87606210
Web Site: http://www.ipseninternational.com
Sales Range: $25-49.9 Million
Emp.: 2
Thermal Technology Products Mfr
N.A.I.C.S.: 334513

Subsidiary (Domestic):

Ipsen International GmbH (2)
Flutstrasse 78, D-47533, Kleve, Germany
Tel.: (49) 28218040
Web Site: http://www.ipsen.de
Thermal Technology Products Mfr
N.A.I.C.S.: 334519
Geoffrey Somary *(CEO)*

Subsidiary (US):

Ipsen International, Inc. (2)
984 Ipsen Rd, Cherry Valley, IL 61016
Tel.: (815) 332-4941
Web Site: http://www.ipsenusa.com
Sales Range: $75-99.9 Million
Mfr of Production Heat Treating & Brazing Equipment, Vacuum Furnaces; Industrial Furnaces; Parts & Service
N.A.I.C.S.: 333994
Mark Heninger *(Product Mgr)*

Palmers Textil AG (1)
Ares Tower Donau-City-Strasse 11, 1220, Vienna, Austria (70%)
Tel.: (43) 13570000
Web Site: http://www.palmers-shop.com
Sales Range: $250-299.9 Million
Lingerie, Swimwear & Hosiery Mfr & Retailer
N.A.I.C.S.: 315250

QUADRISE PLC

Eastcastle House 27-28 Eastcastle Street, London, W1W 8DH, United Kingdom
Tel.: (44) 2070317321 UK
Web Site: https://www.quadrisefuels.com
QED—(LSE)
Rev.: $40,445
Assets: $8,503,539
Liabilities: $556,117
Net Worth: $7,947,422
Earnings: ($3,614,762)
Emp.: 9
Fiscal Year-end: 06/30/24
Emulsion Fuel Producer
N.A.I.C.S.: 324110
Jason Miles *(CEO)*

QUADRIVIO SGR S.P.A.

Via G Mazzini 2, 20123, Milan, Italy
Tel.: (39) 0272147767 IT
Web Site: http://www.quadriviosgr.com
Year Founded: 2000
Investment Management Service
N.A.I.C.S.: 523940

QUADRO RESOURCES LTD.

1400 - 1040 West Georgia Street, Vancouver, V6E 4H1, BC, Canada
Tel.: (778) 373-6734
Web Site: https://www.quadroresources.com
QDROD—(OTCIQ)
Assets: $3,357,880
Liabilities: $260,670
Net Worth: $3,097,210
Earnings: ($626,588)
Fiscal Year-end: 07/31/21
Mineral Exploration Services
N.A.I.C.S.: 213114
T. Barry Coughlan *(Chm, Pres & CEO)*

QUAESTIO HOLDING S.A.

5 Allee Scheffer, 2520, Luxembourg, Luxembourg
Tel.: (352) 4767 5655
Web Site: http://www.quaestiocapital.com
Holding Company
N.A.I.C.S.: 551112
Francesco Ceci *(CEO)*

Subsidiaries:

Quaestio Capital Management SGR S.p.A. (1)
Corso Como 15, 20154, Milan, Italy
Tel.: (39) 02 3676 5200
Asset Management
N.A.I.C.S.: 523999
Alessandro Penati *(Pres)*

QUAKESAFE TECHNOLOGIES CO., LTD.

Plot D-2-4-1 D-2-4-2 Kunming International Printing and Packaging City, Guandu District Industrial Park, Kunming, 650000, Yunnan, China
Tel.: (86) 87163356306
300767—(CHIN)
Rev.: $97,757,055
Assets: $372,406,907
Liabilities: $151,097,838
Net Worth: $221,309,069
Earnings: ($5,793,752)
Fiscal Year-end: 12/31/23
Vibration Isolation Product Mfr
N.A.I.C.S.: 334519

QUALFON SA DE CV

Avenida Insurgentes Sur 2453 Piso 7, Mexico, Mexico
Tel.: (52) 55 2122 9700
Web Site: http://www.qualfon.com
Year Founded: 1996
Emp.: 10,000

INTERNATIONAL PUBLIC

Business Process Outsourcing & Call Center Services
N.A.I.C.S.: 561499
Michael P. Marrow *(CEO)*

Subsidiaries:

Inter-Media Marketing, LLC (1)
204 Carter Dr, West Chester, PA 19382
Tel.: (610) 696-4646
Sales Range: $25-49.9 Million
Telemarketing Services
N.A.I.C.S.: 561422
Paul Santry *(CEO)*

Qualfon Guyana, Inc. (1)
64 Industrial Site Beterverwagting East Coast Demarara, Georgetown, Guyana
Tel.: (592) 2200401
Business Management Services
N.A.I.C.S.: 561110
Scott Warner *(VP & Gen Mgr)*

Qualfon Philippines Inc. (1)
9th Floor Skyrise 3 Qualfon Bldg Asiatown IT Park Apas, Cebu, 6000, Philippines
Tel.: (63) 4799976
Business Management Services
N.A.I.C.S.: 561110
Steven Brown *(VP & Gen Mgr)*

QUALI-SMART HOLDINGS LTD.

Workshop C 19th Floor TML Tower No 3 Hoi Shing Road, Tsuen Wan, Hong Kong, New Territories, China (Hong Kong)
Tel.: (852) 25568822 Ky
Web Site: https://main.quali-smart.com.hk
Year Founded: 1996
1348—(HKG)
Rev.: $57,867,522
Assets: $49,206,773
Liabilities: $23,577,157
Net Worth: $25,629,616
Earnings: ($12,172,359)
Emp.: 48
Fiscal Year-end: 03/31/22
Toy Mfr
N.A.I.C.S.: 339930
Kam Seng Ng *(Exec Dir)*

Subsidiaries:

Crosby Securities Limited (1)
5th Floor Capital Centre 151 Gloucester Road, Wan Chai, Hong Kong, China (Hong Kong)
Tel.: (852) 34762700
Web Site: http://www.crosby.com
Financial Services
N.A.I.C.S.: 523940
Raymond Chu *(CEO & Head-Equities)*

Pulse Mediatech Limited (1)
Workshop C2 6/F TML Tower 3 Hoi Shing Road, Tsuen Wan, New Territories, China (Hong Kong)
Tel.: (852) 28388218
Web Site: http://www.pulsedna.com
Software Development Services
N.A.I.C.S.: 513210
Leonard Chan *(CEO)*

QUALICORP CONSULTORIA E CORRETORA DE SEGUROS S.A.

Rua Doutor Pinio Barreto, 365 1 andar, Bela Vista, 01313-020, Sao Paulo, Brazil
Tel.: (55) 1131913829
Web Site: http://www.qualicorp.com.br
Year Founded: 1997
QUAL3—(BRAZ)
Rev.: $312,812,777
Assets: $806,085,855
Liabilities: $576,284,284
Net Worth: $229,801,571
Earnings: ($13,474,017)
Emp.: 1,459
Fiscal Year-end: 12/31/23

AND PRIVATE COMPANIES

Health Care Insurance Services
N.A.I.C.S.: 524114

QUALIFIED METAL FABRICATORS LTD
55 Steinway Blvd, Toronto, M9W 6H6, ON, Canada
Tel.: (416) 675-7777
Web Site: http://www.qmf.com
Year Founded: 1969
Rev.: $11,998,403
Emp.: 95
Metal Fabricating Services
N.A.I.C.S.: 332119
Bryan Haryott *(Pres & CEO)*

QUALIPOLY CHEMICAL CORPORATION
No 2 Yong Gong 5th Rd, Yeong An Dist, Kaohsiung, 82841, Taiwan
Tel.: (886) 76236199
Web Site: https://www.qualipoly.com
Year Founded: 1978
4722—(TAI)
Rev.: $112,979,263
Assets: $151,984,657
Liabilities: $57,510,446
Net Worth: $94,474,211
Earnings: $5,462,114
Emp.: 142
Fiscal Year-end: 12/31/23
Chemical & Resin Mfr & Distr
N.A.I.C.S.: 325998

QUALIS INNOVATIONS, INC.
Yuan Xing Technology Building 8th Floor South Block, Shenzhen, 518041, China
Tel.: (86) 75582718088
QLIS—(OTCIQ)
Assets: $295,461
Liabilities: $71,507
Net Worth: $223,954
Earnings: ($920,515)
Fiscal Year-end: 12/31/22
Software Development Services
N.A.I.C.S.: 541511
Xiangfeng Lin *(Chm, Pres & CEO)*

QUALITAS LIMITED
Level 38 120 Collins Street, Melbourne, 3000, VIC, Australia
Tel.: (61) 396123900
Web Site:
https://www.qualitas.com.au
Year Founded: 2008
QAL—(ASX)
Rev.: $47,860,077
Assets: $482,440,503
Liabilities: $246,372,172
Net Worth: $236,068,331
Earnings: $14,695,834
Emp.: 80
Fiscal Year-end: 06/30/23
Real Estate Investment Services
N.A.I.C.S.: 531190
Andrew Fairley *(Chm)*

QUALITAS MEDICAL GROUP LIMITED
Amcorp Trade Centre Menara PJ 18 Persiaran Barat Suite 301, 46050, Petaling Jaya, Selangor, Malaysia
Tel.: (60) 379646363
Web Site:
http://www.qualitas.com.my
Year Founded: 1997
Sales Range: $25-49.9 Million
Emp.: 500
Healtcare Services
N.A.I.C.S.: 621491
Noorul Ameen Mohd Ishack *(Chm & Mng Dir)*

Subsidiaries:

Qualitas Healthcare Corporation Sdn. Bhd. (1)
Unit 301 Level 3 Menara PJ Amcorp Trade Centre 18, Jalan Persiaran, Petaling Jaya, 46050, Selangor, Malaysia
Tel.: (60) 3 7964 6363
Web Site: http://www.qualitas.com.my
Sales Range: $50-74.9 Million
Emp.: 35
Investment Management Service
N.A.I.C.S.: 523999

Subsidiary (Domestic):

Daya X-Ray Centre Sdn. Bhd. (2)
25G Jalan Bandar Sepuluh, Pusat Bandar, 41700, Puchong, Selangor, Malaysia
Tel.: (60) 358824655
General Medical & X Ray Laboratories
N.A.I.C.S.: 621512
Mohan Singh *(Mng Dir)*

Klinik Anis Sdn. Bhd. (2)
17 Jalan Bunga Melur 2/18, 40000, Shah Alam, Selangor, Malaysia
Tel.: (60) 355103840
Sales Range: $10-24.9 Million
Emp.: 30
General Medical Services
N.A.I.C.S.: 622110

Klinik Catterall, Khoo and Raja Malek Sdn. Bhd. (2)
Suite 3B-3-6 Level 3 Block 3B Plaza Sentral, Jalan Stesen Sentral, 50470, Kuala Lumpur, Malaysia
Tel.: (60) 322730344
Web Site: http://www.qualitas.com.my
Emp.: 7
General Medical Services
N.A.I.C.S.: 622110
Chua Su Boi *(Gen Mgr)*

Klinik Daiman Sdn. Bhd. (2)
105 Jalan Keris Satu, Taman Sri Tebrau, 80050, Johor Bahru, Johor, Malaysia
Tel.: (60) 73325531
Sales Range: $10-24.9 Million
Emp.: 4
General Medical Services
N.A.I.C.S.: 622110

Klinik Dhas Sdn. Bhd. (2)
7A Lorong 1, 81400, Senai, Johor, Malaysia
Tel.: (60) 75995 058
Sales Range: $10-24.9 Million
Emp.: 6
General Medical Services
N.A.I.C.S.: 622110
Mohan Dhas *(Dir-Medical)*

Klinik Dr Nur Ainita Sdn. Bhd. (2)
No 12 A-1 Ground Fl Jalan USJ 9/5Q, Subang Business Ctr, 47620, Subang Jaya, Selangor, Malaysia
Tel.: (60) 380244844
General Medical Services
N.A.I.C.S.: 622110

Klinik JJ (Johor) Sdn. Bhd. (2)
Permas Mall G-5 Block A 3 Jalan Permas Utara, Baru Permas Jaya, 81750, Masai, Johor, Malaysia
Tel.: (60) 73874929
Web Site: http://www.qualitas.com.my
Sales Range: $10-24.9 Million
Emp.: 6
General Medical Services
N.A.I.C.S.: 622110
Thulasi Kannan *(Branch Mgr)*

Klinik Ludher Sdn. Bhd. (2)
No 4-1 Commerce One Lorong 2/137C Off, Jalan Kelang Lama, 58200, Kuala Lumpur, Federal Territory, Malaysia
Tel.: (60) 379819542
Sales Range: $10-24.9 Million
Emp.: 3
General Medical Services
N.A.I.C.S.: 622110

Klinik Pantai Sdn. Bhd. (2)
875 Taman Mewah 1st Mile, Jalan Pantai, Port Dickson, 71000, Negeri Sembilan, Malaysia
Tel.: (60) 66473695
Sales Range: $10-24.9 Million
Emp.: 5
General Medical

N.A.I.C.S.: 622110
Narayanan Nair *(Mgr)*

Klinik Port Dickson Sdn. Bhd. (2)
75C Jalan Dato K Pathmanaban, Port Dickson, 71000, Negeri Sembilan, Malaysia
Tel.: (60) 66472800
Web Site: http://www.qualitas.com.my
Sales Range: $10-24.9 Million
Emp.: 6
General Medical Services
N.A.I.C.S.: 622110
Sivapatham Tharmalingam *(Dir-Medical)*

Klinik Salak (Selangor) Sdn. Bhd. (2)
Lot No 1 Pusat Komersil Uniten KM 7, Jalan Kajang, 43009, Puchong, Selangor, Malaysia
Tel.: (60) 389251477
Sales Range: $10-24.9 Million
Emp.: 3
General Medical Services
N.A.I.C.S.: 622110
Noorul Ameen Mohamed Ishack *(Gen Mgr)*

Klinik Salak Sdn. Bhd. (2)
4703 Jalan TS 1/1 Taman Semarak, 71800, Nilai, Negeri Sembilan, Malaysia
Tel.: (60) 67992201
Web Site: http://www.qualitas.com.my
Emp.: 12
General Medical Services
N.A.I.C.S.: 622110

Klinik Syed Alwi dan Chandran (Penang) Sdn. Bhd. (2)
3 Jalan Todak 5 Bandar Seberang Jaya Pera, 13700, Perai, Penang, Malaysia
Tel.: (60) 43901464
General Medical Services
N.A.I.C.S.: 622110

Klinik Thomas Sdn. Bhd. (2)
58 Persiaran Silibin Utara, Silibin, Ipoh, 30020, Perak, Malaysia
Tel.: (60) 55264667
Sales Range: $10-24.9 Million
Emp.: 3
General Medical Services
N.A.I.C.S.: 622110

Kumpulan Medic (K.L.) Sdn. Bhd. (2)
No 71 M Jalan Mamanda 1, Taman Dato Ahmad Razali, 68000, Ampang, Selangor, Malaysia
Tel.: (60) 342528216
Sales Range: $10-24.9 Million
Emp.: 5
General Medical Services
N.A.I.C.S.: 622110

Kumpulan Medic (Selangor) Sdn. Bhd. (2)
78 Jalan SS 21/35 Damansara Utama, Petaling Jaya, 47400, Selangor, Malaysia
Tel.: (60) 377284955
Sales Range: $10-24.9 Million
Emp.: 7
General Medical Services
N.A.I.C.S.: 622110
Ravindren M. G. Nair *(Mng Dir)*

Poliklinik Central & Surgeri Sdn. Bhd. (2)
No 20 Jalan Suria Setapak Batu 4 1/2, Gombak, 53000, Kuala Lumpur, Malaysia
Tel.: (60) 340234390
Sales Range: $10-24.9 Million
Emp.: 10
General Medical Services
N.A.I.C.S.: 622110
A. S. Kumar *(Mgr)*

Poliklinik Puteri dan Surgeri Sdn. Bhd. (2)
SH-100 Jalan Sawah Pekan Nenas, Pontian, 81500, Johor Bahru, Johor, Malaysia
Tel.: (60) 76993790
Web Site: http://www.qualitas.com.my
Emp.: 5
General Medical Services
N.A.I.C.S.: 622110
Winnni Lim Peewei *(Mgr)*

Poliklinik Simpang Pulai Sdn. Bhd. (2)
No 63 Persiaran Sengat Baru 2 Taman Bersatu, Kampung Kepayang, 31300, Perak, Malaysia
Tel.: (60) 53575929
General Medical Services
N.A.I.C.S.: 622110

Qualitas Healthcare International Sdn. Bhd. (2)
No 20 Jalan Pjs 7/17 Taman, Bandar Sunway, 46150, Petaling Jaya, Selangor, Malaysia
Tel.: (60) 356316486
General Medical Services
N.A.I.C.S.: 621491

Subsidiary (Non-US):

Dr Marcus Cooney & Associates Pte Ltd (3)
1 Orchard Boulevard 14-02 Camden Medical Centre, Singapore, 248649, Singapore
Tel.: (65) 68340877
Web Site: http://www.smilefocus.com.sg
Sales Range: $10-24.9 Million
Emp.: 42
Dental Care Services
N.A.I.C.S.: 621210
Suzanne Broderick *(Gen Mgr)*

Subsidiary (Domestic):

Qualitas Pharma Sdn. Bhd. (2)
20 & 22 Jalan PJS 7/17, Bandar Sunway, 46150, Petaling Jaya, Selangor, Malaysia
Tel.: (60) 356380923
Sales Range: $10-24.9 Million
Emp.: 7
General Medical Services
N.A.I.C.S.: 622110

Reddy Clinic Sdn. Bhd. (2)
No 121 Jln Ipoh, 51200, Kuala Lumpur, Malaysia
Tel.: (60) 34041 2611
Web Site: http://www.qualitashealth.com
Sales Range: $10-24.9 Million
Emp.: 12
General Medical Services
N.A.I.C.S.: 622110
Yin Leong Soong *(Mng Dir)*

QUALITAS SEMICONDUCTOR CO., LTD.
8 Seongnam-daero 331 beon-gil, Bundang-gu, Seongnam, 13558, Gyeonggi-do, Korea (South)
Tel.: (82) 25553305
Web Site: https://www.q-semi.com
Year Founded: 2017
432720—(KRS)
Electronic Products Mfr
N.A.I.C.S.: 334419

QUALITAU, LTD.
Kiryat Weizmann Industrial Science Park, PO Box 4047, Ness Ziona, 70400, Israel
Tel.: (972) 89404427
Web Site: https://www.qualitau.com
Year Founded: 1994
QLTU—(TAE)
Rev.: $41,112,000
Assets: $47,354,000
Liabilities: $7,372,000
Net Worth: $39,982,000
Earnings: $12,300,000
Fiscal Year-end: 12/31/23
Instrument Manufacturing for Measuring & Testing Electricity & Electrical Signals
N.A.I.C.S.: 334515
Nava Ben-Yehuda *(VP-Fin & Control)*

QUALITECH PUBLIC COMPANY LIMITED
213 Banplong Road, Maptaphut Muang, Rayong, 21150, Thailand
Tel.: (66) 3869140810
Web Site:
https://www.qualitechplc.com
QLT—(THA)
Rev.: $12,482,252
Assets: $11,434,949

QUALITECH PUBLIC COMPANY LIMITED

Qualitech Public Company Limited—(Continued)
Liabilities: $2,802,983
Net Worth: $8,631,966
Earnings: ($4,120,047)
Emp.: 451
Fiscal Year-end: 12/31/23
Non-Destructive Testing & Engineering Services
N.A.I.C.S.: 334515
Sannpat Rattakham *(Chm)*

Subsidiaries:

QLT International Company Limited (1)
21/3 Banplong Road, Maptaphut Muang, Rayong, 21150, Thailand
Tel.: (66) 3869140810
Safety Engineering Services
N.A.I.C.S.: 541330
Weerachon Chaipim *(Asst Mgr-Engrg)*

Qualitech Solution Energy Company Limited (1)
83/50 Moo 10, Nongkham, Si Racha, 20230, Chonburi, Thailand
Tel.: (66) 974153539
Engineeering Services
N.A.I.C.S.: 541330

QUALITEX SUPPLIES LTD.
Unit 3b Deacon Trading Estate, Aylesford, ME20 7SP, United Kingdom
Tel.: (44) 1622790011
Web Site: http://www.qualitex.co.uk
Year Founded: 1990
Rev.: $25,771,108
Emp.: 96
Bathroom Accessories Distr
N.A.I.C.S.: 423220
Duncan Andrews *(Founder & Mng Dir)*

QUALITY & RELIABILITY S.A.
11 B Konitsis str, 151 52, Maroussi, Greece
Tel.: (30) 2108029409
Web Site: https://www.qnr.com.gr
Year Founded: 1992
QUAL—(ATH)
Sales Range: Less than $1 Million
Emp.: 31
All Other Computer Related Services
N.A.I.C.S.: 541519
Apostolos Tourkantonis *(Chm)*

Subsidiaries:

Digibooks4all S.A. (1)
eBookStore SaaS Platform, Athens, Greece
Tel.: (30) 2108029409
Web Site: http://www.digibooks4all.com
Computer Software Development Services
N.A.I.C.S.: 541511

Greenovative S.A. (1)
Konitsis 11B, 15125, Maroussi, Greece
Tel.: (30) 2108029409
Web Site: http://www.greenovative.gr
Building Automation Services
N.A.I.C.S.: 236220

QUALITY COMPONENTS EUROPE
Technology House 20 Grove Place, Bedford, MK40 3JJ, United Kingdom
Tel.: (44) 1234364406   **UK**
Web Site: http://www.qceuk.com
Sales Range: $25-49.9 Million
Emp.: 100
Electronic Components Distr
N.A.I.C.S.: 423690
John Hislop *(Mng Dir)*

Subsidiaries:

QCE, LLC (1)
5908 Littlestone Ct, North Fort Myers, FL 33903-4925   **(100%)**
Tel.: (239) 541-1986
Web Site: http://www.qceusa.com

Sales Range: $1-9.9 Million
Emp.: 5
Stock Distribution of Electronic Components
N.A.I.C.S.: 449210

QUALITY CONCRETE HOLDINGS BERHAD
209 Level 2 Wisma Bukit Mata Kuching Jalan Tunku Abdul Rahman, 93100, Kuching, Sarawak, Malaysia
Tel.: (60) 82206600
Web Site: https://www.qchb.com.my
QUALITY—(KLS)
Rev.: $44,124,021
Assets: $57,126,984
Liabilities: $35,840,212
Net Worth: $21,286,772
Earnings: ($523,598)
Emp.: 500
Fiscal Year-end: 01/31/23
Readymix Concrete Mfr
N.A.I.C.S.: 327320
Puay Huang Yeo *(Co-Sec)*

Subsidiaries:

Polyflow Pipes Sdn. Bhd. (1)
Lot 626 Block 4 Muara Tebas Land District Jalan Bako, 93050, Kuching, Sarawak, Malaysia
Tel.: (60) 82432217
Web Site: https://www.polyflowpipes.com.my
Pipe Product Mfr
N.A.I.C.S.: 326122

QUALITY ELASTICS LIMITED
9800 Clark Street, Montreal, H3L 2R3, QC, Canada
Tel.: (514) 381-9955
Web Site: http://www.qualityelastics.com
Rev.: $10,694,229
Emp.: 100
Elastics & Fabric Mfr
N.A.I.C.S.: 313220
Steve Ayoub *(Pres)*

QUALITY HOUSES PUBLIC CO., LTD.
No 1 Q House Lumpini Building 7th floor South Sathorn Road, Tungmahamek Sathorn, Bangkok, 10120, Thailand
Tel.: (66) 26777000
Web Site: https://www.qh.co.th
Year Founded: 1983
QH—(THA)
Rev.: $269,646,313
Assets: $1,268,160,364
Liabilities: $439,910,324
Net Worth: $828,250,040
Earnings: $73,056,517
Emp.: 911
Fiscal Year-end: 12/31/23
Real Estate Manangement Services
N.A.I.C.S.: 531210
Pravit Choatewattanaphan *(Mng Dir)*

Subsidiaries:

Q.H. International Co., Ltd. (1)
100 Center Point Witthayu Witthayu Khwang, Lumphini Khet Pathumwan, Bangkok, 10330, Thailand
Tel.: (66) 26595373
Emp.: 40
Residential Building Leasing Services
N.A.I.C.S.: 531110

QUALITY MEAT PACKERS LIMITED
2 Tecumseh Street, Toronto, M5V 2R5, ON, Canada
Tel.: (416) 703-7675
Year Founded: 1931
Emp.: 700
Animal Slaughterhouse Operator
N.A.I.C.S.: 311611
Sheldon Garfinkle *(VP)*

QUALITY ONLINE EDUCATION GROUP INC.
#306-650 HIGHWAY 7 EAST, RICHMOND HILL, Ontario, Canada
Tel.: (647) 776-8618   **DE**
Web Site: https://www.qualityonline.education
Year Founded: 2007
QOEG—(OTCIQ)
Sales Range: $1-9.9 Million
Emp.: 30
Financial Consulting Services
N.A.I.C.S.: 541611

QUALITY PLATES & PROFILES LIMITED.
20 Nicholas Beaver Road, Puslinch, N0B 2J0, ON, Canada
Tel.: (519) 837-4000
Web Site: http://www.qualityplates.com
Year Founded: 1981
Rev.: $11,978,417
Emp.: 40
Steel Whslr
N.A.I.C.S.: 423510
Joe Freitas *(Pres)*

Subsidiaries:

Quality Plates & Profiles Limited. - Sarnia Division (1)
1018 Prescott Dr, Sarnia, N7T 7H3, ON, Canada
Tel.: (519) 332-6666
Steel Products Mfr
N.A.I.C.S.: 331222
Jeff Freitas *(Mgr)*

QUALITY RELIABILITY TECHNOLOGY INC.
2091 Gyeongchung-daero, Bubaleup, Icheon, 17336, Gyeonggi-do, Korea (South)
Tel.: (82) 3180948211
Web Site: https://www.qrtkr.com
Year Founded: 1983
405100—(KRS)
Information Technology Services
N.A.I.C.S.: 541512
Kim Young-Boo *(CEO)*

QUALITY RO INDUSTRIES LIMITED
Plot No 09 Por Industrial Park NH 08 Behind Sahyog Hotel Por, Vadodara, 391243, Gujarat, India
Tel.: (91) 9099309361
Web Site: https://www.qualityro.in
Year Founded: 2021
543460—(BOM)
Industry Machinery Mfr
N.A.I.C.S.: 333310
Vivek Dholiya *(Mng Dir & Chm)*

QUALITY SOFTWARE S.A.
Av Rio Branco 114-4th & 6th floors Center, Rio de Janeiro, 20040-001, Brazil
Tel.: (55) 2131473000   **BR**
Web Site: http://www.quality.com.br
QUSW3—(BRAZ)
Rev.: $12,106,886
Assets: $40,768,043
Liabilities: $26,016,097
Net Worth: $14,751,946
Earnings: $3,533,776
Fiscal Year-end: 12/31/23
Information Technology Services
N.A.I.C.S.: 541512
Caio Nogueira *(Dir-Ops)*

QUALITY STEEL WORKS LIMITED
D/22 SITE Manghopir Road, Karachi, Pakistan
Tel.: (92) 2572072

INTERNATIONAL PUBLIC

Steel Products Mfr
N.A.I.C.S.: 331110

QUALIUM INVESTISSEMENT
41 avenue de Friedland, 75008, Paris, France
Tel.: (33) 1 8180 4700   **FR**
Web Site: http://www.qualium-investissement.com
Year Founded: 1998
Privater Equity Firm
N.A.I.C.S.: 523999
Jean Eichenlaub *(Mng Partner)*

QUALTEC CO., LTD.
4-230 Sanpo-cho, Sakai-ku, Sakai, 590-0906, Osaka, Japan
Tel.: (81) 722267175
Web Site: https://www.qualtec.co.jp
Year Founded: 1993
9165—(TKS)
Emp.: 220
Electrical Equipment Mfr & Distr
N.A.I.C.S.: 333414
Tomohiro Yamaguchi *(Pres)*

QUALTER HALL & COMPANY LIMITED
Johnson Street, PO Box 8, Barnsley, S75 2BY, South Yorkshire, United Kingdom
Tel.: (44) 1226 205 761
Web Site: http://www.qualterhall.co.uk
Year Founded: 1860
Construction Engineering Services
N.A.I.C.S.: 237990
Wayne Bowser *(Chm)*

QUAM PLUS INTERNATIONAL FINANCIAL LIMITED
18th & 19th Floors China Building 29 Queen's Road, Central, China (Hong Kong)
Tel.: (852) 22172888   **BM**
Web Site: http://www.tonghaifinancial.com
0952—(HKG)
Rev.: $142,473,243
Assets: $1,281,664,200
Liabilities: $521,815,031
Net Worth: $759,849,169
Earnings: $13,317,185
Emp.: 249
Fiscal Year-end: 12/31/20
Financial Services
N.A.I.C.S.: 523999
Kenneth Kin Hing Lam *(CEO)*

Subsidiaries:

China Tonghai Asset Management Limited (1)
5/F Wing On Centre 111 Connaught Road, Central, China (Hong Kong)
Tel.: (852) 29229555
Web Site: https://www.quamam.com
Asset Management Services
N.A.I.C.S.: 523940

China Tonghai Capital Limited (1)
5/F Wing On Centre 111 Connaught Road, Central, China (Hong Kong)
Tel.: (852) 31848600
Web Site: https://www.quamcap.com
Finance & Advisory Services
N.A.I.C.S.: 523940

China Tonghai Communications Limited (1)
5/F Wing On Centre 111 Connaught Road, Central, China (Hong Kong)
Tel.: (852) 22172753
Financial Investment Services
N.A.I.C.S.: 523999

Hong Kong Quam Securities Company Limited (1)
26/F Zhonghan Bld 124 Huigong Street, Shenhe District, Shenyang, China
Tel.: (86) 24 2351 5222

Web Site: http://www.oceanwsec.com
Securities Brokerage Services
N.A.I.C.S.: 523150

Oceanwide Securities Company Limited (1)
18/F China Building 29 Queen's Road, Central, China (Hong Kong)
Tel.: (852) 2847 2222
Web Site: http://www.oceanwsec.com
Securities Brokerage Services
N.A.I.C.S.: 523150
Kenneth Lam *(Mng Dir)*

Subsidiary (Non-US):

Quam Investment Advisory (Hangzhou) Company Limited (2)
Room 1407 Winning Bldg 100 Min Xin Road Hangzhou Qianjiang New City, Jiang Gan District, Hangzhou, Zhejiang, China
Tel.: (86) 571 2899 9520
Web Site: http://www.oceanwsec.com
Investment Advisory Services
N.A.I.C.S.: 523940

QUANG NAM MINERAL INDUSTRY CORPORATION
Ha Lam-Cho Duoc IZ, Thang Binh District, Hanoi, Quang Nam, Vietnam
Tel.: (84) 510 3665022
Web Site: http://www.minco.com.vn
Mineral Products Mfr
N.A.I.C.S.: 212390
Nguyen Dinh Chinh *(Gen Dir)*

Subsidiaries:

Dai Loc Feldspar Company Limited (1)
Ban Tan, Dai Dong, Quang Nam, Vietnam
Tel.: (84) 510 3846935
Mineral Products Mfr
N.A.I.C.S.: 212390

QUANG NAM RUBBER INVESTMENT JOINT STOCK COMPANY
Lot 4 Dien Nam IDZ, Dien Ngoc, Quang Nam, Vietnam
Tel.: (84) 510 394 6345
Sales Range: $1-9.9 Million
Investment Services
N.A.I.C.S.: 523999

QUANG NAM TRANSPORTATION CONSTRUCTION JSC
No 10 Nguyen Du Street, Tam Ky, Quang Nam, Vietnam
Tel.: (84) 5103851734
QTC—(HNX)
Rev.: $8,998,500
Assets: $5,985,100
Liabilities: $1,929,600
Net Worth: $4,055,500
Earnings: $220,700
Fiscal Year-end: 12/31/22
Construction Services
N.A.I.C.S.: 236220
Nguyen Anh Tuan *(Gen Mgr)*

QUANG NINH BOOK & EDUCATIONAL EQUIPMENT JSC
No 10 Long Tien Bach Dang Ward, Ha Long, Quang Ninh, Vietnam
Tel.: (84) 333826331
Web Site: https://www.sachquangninh.vn
Year Founded: 1983
QST—(HNX)
Rev.: $5,481,488
Assets: $3,128,614
Liabilities: $1,511,611
Net Worth: $1,617,003
Earnings: $232,751
Fiscal Year-end: 12/31/21
Books Publishing Services
N.A.I.C.S.: 513130
Vu The Ban *(Chm-Mgmt Bd)*

QUANG NINH CONSTRUCTION & CEMENT COMPANY
Cai Lan Industrial zone - Bai Chay ward, Ha Long, Quang Ninh, Vietnam
Tel.: (84) 33841648
Web Site: http://www.qncc.vn
QNC—(HNX)
Rev.: $149,129,600
Assets: $167,070,000
Liabilities: $106,071,200
Net Worth: $60,998,800
Earnings: $8,955,400
Fiscal Year-end: 12/31/22
Construction & Cement Mfr
N.A.I.C.S.: 327310

QUANG VIET ENTERPRISE CO., LTD.
6F No 607 Ruiguang Rd, Neihu Dist, Taipei, 114, Taiwan
Tel.: (886) 227989169
Web Site: https://www.qve.com.tw
Year Founded: 1996
4438—(TAI)
Rev.: $541,313,038
Assets: $513,159,011
Liabilities: $188,028,509
Net Worth: $325,130,502
Earnings: $29,575,721
Emp.: 21,828
Fiscal Year-end: 12/31/23
Garment Mfr & Distr
N.A.I.C.S.: 321999
Charles Wu *(Chm)*

Subsidiaries:

Joykey Industrial (Pinghu) Limited (1)
No 2000 Xingping 2nd Road Pinghu Economic Development Zone, Pinghu, China
Tel.: (86) 57389179328
Web Site: https://www.joykeyss.com
Medical Equipment Mfr & Distr
N.A.I.C.S.: 334510

King Hamm Industrial Co., Ltd. (1)
4F No 312 Sec 2 New Taipei Blvd, Xinzhuang Dist, New Taipei City, 242, Taiwan
Tel.: (886) 285212588
Garment & Swimwear Mfr
N.A.I.C.S.: 315990

QUANTA COMPUTER, INC.
No 211 Wenhua 2nd Rd, Guishan Dist, Taoyuan, 333, Taiwan
Tel.: (886) 33272345
Web Site: https://www.quantatw.com
Year Founded: 1988
2382—(TAI)
Rev.: $33,943,377,794
Assets: $21,577,714,567
Liabilities: $15,515,358,753
Net Worth: $6,062,355,814
Earnings: $1,265,940,844
Emp.: 40,359
Fiscal Year-end: 12/31/23
Electric Equipment Mfr
N.A.I.C.S.: 334111
Barry Lam *(Founder & Chm)*

Subsidiaries:

QCG Computer GmbH (1)
Indeland Str 2 4, 52249, Eschweiler, Germany
Tel.: (49) 2403 884 3100
Web Site: http://www.quantade.com
Sales Range: $50-74.9 Million
Emp.: 200
Computer & Electronic Products Mfr
N.A.I.C.S.: 334118

QCT (Beijing) Co., Ltd. (1)
Building 2 Runcheng Center No 12 Dongdaqiao Road, Chaoyang District, Beijing, China
Tel.: (86) 1059207600
Information Technology Services
N.A.I.C.S.: 541519

QCT LLC (1)
1010 Rincon Cr, San Jose, CA 95131
Tel.: (510) 270-6111
Notebook Computer & Other Electronic Hardware Mfr
N.A.I.C.S.: 334111
Mike Yang *(Pres)*

Subsidiary (Non-US):

QCT Korea Inc. (2)
10th floor Kyobo Securities Building 97 Uisadang-daero, Yeongdeungpo-gu, Seoul, 07327, Korea (South)
Tel.: (82) 1053971412
Notebook Computer & Other Electronic Hardware Mfr
N.A.I.C.S.: 334111

Quanta Cloud Technology Germany GmbH (1)
Hamborner Str 55, 40472, Dusseldorf, Germany
Tel.: (49) 24213863400
Notebook Computer & Other Electronic Hardware Mfr
N.A.I.C.S.: 334111
Chyan-Hwa Yang *(Mng Dir)*

Quanta Cloud Technology Inc. (1)
1F No 211 Wenhua 2nd Rd, Guishan District, Taoyuan, 33377, Taiwan
Tel.: (886) 32860707
Notebook Computer & Other Electronic Hardware Mfr
N.A.I.C.S.: 334111

Quanta Cloud Technology Japan Inc. (1)
3-1-3 Minami - Aoyama, Minato-ku, Tokyo, 107-0062, Japan
Tel.: (81) 357770818
Notebook Computer & Other Electronic Hardware Mfr
N.A.I.C.S.: 334111

Quanta Cloud Technology USA LLC (1)
1010 Rincon Cir, San Jose, CA 95131
Tel.: (510) 270-6111
Computer Peripheral Distr
N.A.I.C.S.: 423430

Quanta Computer Nashville LLC (1)
1621 Heil Quaker Blvd, La Vergne, TN 37086
Tel.: (615) 501-7500
Notebook Computer & Other Electronic Hardware Mfr
N.A.I.C.S.: 334111
Richard Bixenman *(Sr Mgr-Fin & Acct)*

Quanta Computer USA, Inc (1)
45630 Northport Loop E, Fremont, CA 94538
Tel.: (510) 226-1001
Web Site: https://www.quantatw.com
Computer & Electronic Products Mfr
N.A.I.C.S.: 334118

Quanta Computer, Inc. (1)
9F No 116 Hougang St, Shilin Dist, Taipei, 111, Taiwan
Tel.: (886) 22 882 1612
Web Site: http://www.quantatw.com
Computer & Electronic Products Mfr
N.A.I.C.S.: 334118

Quanta Manufacturing Inc. (1)
45630 Northport Loop E, Fremont, CA 94538
Tel.: (510) 226-1000
Computer Peripheral Equipment Mfr
N.A.I.C.S.: 334118
Alan Lam *(Pres)*

Quanta Microsystems Inc. (1)
188 Wenhwa 2nd Road Kueishan TaoYuan, 333, Taipei, Taiwan
Tel.: (886) 33979000
Web Site: http://www.qmitw.com
Sales Range: $25-49.9 Million
Emp.: 18
Wireless Networking Services
N.A.I.C.S.: 517112

Quanta Shanghai Manufacture City (1)
No 68 Sanzhuang Road, Songjiang District, Shanghai, 201613, China
Tel.: (86) 213 781 8168

Web Site: https://quantacn.zhiye.com
Sales Range: $1-4.9 Billion
Emp.: 15,000
Computer & Electronic Products Mfr
N.A.I.C.S.: 334118

Tech-Com (Shanghai) Computer Co., Ltd. (1)
No 1 Lane 58 Sanzhuang Road Songjiang Export Processing Zone, Shanghai, 202400, China
Tel.: (86) 2137818168
Computer Peripheral Equipment Mfr
N.A.I.C.S.: 334111

Tech-Front (Chongqing) Computer Co., Ltd. (1)
18 Zongbao Road, Shapingba District, Chongqing, China
Tel.: (86) 2388118168
Notebook Computer & Other Electronic Hardware Mfr
N.A.I.C.S.: 334111

Tech-Front (Shanghai) Computer Co., Ltd. (1)
No 2 Lane 58 SanZhuang Road Songjiang Export Processing Zone, Shanghai, 201613, China
Tel.: (86) 2137818268
Computer Peripheral Equipments Mfr & Distr
N.A.I.C.S.: 334118

Tech-Full (Changshu) Computer Co., Ltd. (1)
No 8 Jingzhou Rd High-Tech Industrial Park, Economic Development Zone, Changshu, Jiangsu, China
Tel.: (86) 5125 236 0888
Web Site: http://www.quanta.com
Sales Range: $800-899.9 Million
Emp.: 5,000
Computer & Electronic Products Mfr
N.A.I.C.S.: 334118

Tech-Full Computer (Changshu) Co., Ltd. (1)
No 8 Jingzhou Rd, Changshu Economic Development Zone High-Tech Industrial Park, Changshu, Jiangsu, China
Tel.: (86) 51252360888
Notebook Computer & Other Electronic Hardware Mfr
N.A.I.C.S.: 334111

Tech-Lead (Shanghai) Computer Co., Ltd. (1)
No 68 Rongjiang Road Songjiang Export Processing Zone, Songjia, Shanghai, 201613, China
Tel.: (86) 2137740168
Computer Peripherals Mfr & Whslr
N.A.I.C.S.: 334118

Tech-Trend (Shanghai) Computer Co., Ltd. (1)
No 8 DongJing Road Songjiang Export Processing Zone, Shanghai, 201613, China
Tel.: (86) 2137814567
Computer Peripheral Equipment Whslr
N.A.I.C.S.: 423430

Techman Electronics (Thailand) Co., Ltd. (1)
40/10-12 40/28 Rojana Industrial Park, Uthai District, Phra Nakhon Si Ayutthaya, 13210, Thailand
Tel.: (66) 35902682
Web Site: https://techman-electronics-thailand-coltd.business.site
Computer Storage Device Mfr & Distr
N.A.I.C.S.: 334112

Techman Robot (Shanghai) Ltd. (1)
Room 402 Building 6 No 1158 Zhongxin Rd, Songjiang District, Shanghai, 201600, China
Tel.: (86) 13621868920
Industrial Collaborative Robot Distr
N.A.I.C.S.: 423830

Techman Robot Inc. (1)
5F No 58-2 Huaya 2nd Rd, Guishan Dist, Taoyuan, 333411, Taiwan
Tel.: (886) 33288350
Web Site: https://www.tm-robot.com
Industrial Collaborative Robot Mfr & Distr
N.A.I.C.S.: 333998

QUANTA STORAGE, INC.

Quanta Storage, Inc.—(Continued)

QUANTA STORAGE, INC.
6F No 58-2 Huaya 2nd Rd, Guishan Dist, Taoyuan, 333411, Taiwan
Tel.: (886) 33288090
Web Site: https://www.qsitw.com
Year Founded: 1999
6188—(TPE)
Rev.: $378,904,230
Assets: $439,344,245
Liabilities: $148,168,902
Net Worth: $291,175,343
Earnings: $35,021,011
Emp.: 444
Fiscal Year-end: 12/31/22
Electronic Components Mfr
N.A.I.C.S.: 334419
Shih-Chih Ho (Pres)

QUANTAFUEL ASA
Lilleakerveien 2C, 0283, Oslo, Norway
Web Site:
https://www.quantafuel.com
Year Founded: 2015
QFUEL—(EUR)
Rev.: $6,236,380
Assets: $172,889,071
Liabilities: $47,042,757
Net Worth: $125,846,314
Earnings: ($44,860,187)
Emp.: 56
Fiscal Year-end: 12/31/22
Recycling Services
N.A.I.C.S.: 325991
Lars Rosenlv (CEO)

QUANTAMATRIX INC.
16F Bldg B Byc Highcity 131 Gasan Digital 1-Ro, Geumcheon-Gu, Seoul, 08506, Korea (South)
Tel.: (82) 27638820
Web Site:
https://www.quantamatrix.com
Year Founded: 2010
317690—(KRS)
Rev.: $986,311
Assets: $34,973,045
Liabilities: $4,385,481
Net Worth: $30,587,565
Earnings: ($14,754,954)
Emp.: 113
Fiscal Year-end: 12/31/22
Pharmaceutical Preparation Mfr & Distr
N.A.I.C.S.: 325412
Sunghoon Kwon (Pres & CEO)

QUANTASING GROUP LIMITED
2/F Building D Ronsin Technology Center, Chaoyang District, Beijing, 100102, China
Tel.: (86) 1064937857
Web Site: https://quantasing.com
Year Founded: 2022
QSG—(NASDAQ)
Rev.: $522,247,755
Assets: $196,224,050
Liabilities: $125,154,463
Net Worth: $71,069,588
Earnings: $53,049,552
Emp.: 827
Fiscal Year-end: 06/30/24
Educational Support Services
N.A.I.C.S.: 611710
Dong Xie (CFO)

QUANTEC GEOSCIENCE LTD.
146 Sparks Avenue, Toronto, M2H 2S4, ON, Canada
Tel.: (416) 306-1941
Web Site:
http://www.quantecgeo.com
Year Founded: 1986
Rev.: $25,909,595
Emp.: 200
Geophysical Services
N.A.I.C.S.: 541360
Roger Sharpe (VP-Technical)

Subsidiaries:

Quantec Geoscience (Peru) S.A.C.   (1)
Pj Malecon Socabaya Nro 109, Arequipa, Peru
Tel.: (51) 54 288 686
Web Site:
http://www.quantecgeoscience.com
Emp.: 12
Geophysical Services
N.A.I.C.S.: 541360
Cercado Arequipa (Mgr)

Quantec Geoscience Chile Ltda.   (1)
Avda Gertrudis Echenique 470, Santiago, Chile
Tel.: (56) 2 2368 4564
Geophysical Services
N.A.I.C.S.: 541360
Chris Jones (Gen Mgr)

QUANTRILL CHEVROLET BUICK GMC CADILLAC
265 Peter Street, Port Hope, L1A 3Z4, ON, Canada
Tel.: (905) 885-4573
Web Site:
http://www.quantrillchev.com
Year Founded: 1986
Sales Range: $10-24.9 Million
New & Used Car Dealers
N.A.I.C.S.: 441110
Dave Parker (Sls Mgr)

QUANTS INC.
3F Madre Matsuda Building 4-13 Kioi-cho, Chiyoda-ku, Tokyo, 102-0094, Japan
Tel.: (81) 355496411
Web Site: http://www.quants.co.jp
Year Founded: 1935
Sales Range: $25-49.9 Million
Venture Capital Financing Services
N.A.I.C.S.: 523999
Kyota Yamada (Chm)

QUANTUM BATTERY METALS CORP.
400-837 West Hastings Street, Vancouver, V6C 3N6, BC, Canada
Tel.: (604) 283-1722   BC
Web Site:
http://www.quantumcobalt.com
Year Founded: 2010
QBAT—(DEU)
Assets: $701,360
Liabilities: $1,693,634
Net Worth: ($992,274)
Earnings: ($6,584,580)
Fiscal Year-end: 01/31/22
Metal Mining Services
N.A.I.C.S.: 212290
Greg Burns (CEO)

QUANTUM BLOCKCHAIN TECHNOLOGIES LTD.
1250 639-5th Avenue SW Suite 1250, Calgary, T2P 0M9, AB, Canada
Tel.: (403) 650-7718
QBC.P—(TSXV)
Assets: $200,375
Liabilities: $7,368
Net Worth: $193,007
Earnings: ($27,344)
Fiscal Year-end: 12/31/19
Business Consulting Services
N.A.I.C.S.: 522299

QUANTUM BLOCKCHAIN TECHNOLOGIES PLC
First Floor 1 Chancery Lane, London, WC2A 1LF, United Kingdom
Tel.: (44) 7795168157   UK

Web Site:
https://www.quantumblock.co.uk
Year Founded: 1999
QBT—(AIM)
Assets: $6,531,405
Liabilities: $10,008,634
Net Worth: ($3,477,229)
Earnings: ($5,424,131)
Emp.: 4
Fiscal Year-end: 12/31/22
Investment Management Service
N.A.I.C.S.: 523940
Francesco Gardin (Chm & CEO)

Subsidiaries:

Mediapolis S.p.A.   (1)
via della Rocca 21, 10123, Turin, Italy
Tel.: (39) 011 8127837
Real Estate Investment Services
N.A.I.C.S.: 531210

You Can Group S.r.l.   (1)
via Farini 9, 40124, Bologna, Italy
Tel.: (39) 051 0362351
Web Site: http://youcangroup.it
Event Management Services
N.A.I.C.S.: 711310
Andrea Magelli (Co-Founder)

QUANTUM BUILD-TECH LIMITED
8-1-405/A/66 Dreamvalley Shaikpet, Hyderabad, 500 008, India
Tel.: (91) 4023568766
Web Site:
https://www.quantumbuild.com
Year Founded: 1998
538596—(BOM)
Assets: $728,985
Liabilities: $335,867
Net Worth: $393,118
Earnings: ($47,251)
Fiscal Year-end: 03/31/23
Civil Engineering Services
N.A.I.C.S.: 237990
Guduru Satyanarayana (Mng Dir)

QUANTUM CAPITAL PARTNERS AG
Ludwigstr 10, 80539, Munich, Germany
Tel.: (49) 89 45 213 29 0 0
Web Site: http://www.quantum-capital-partners.com
Year Founded: 2008
Privater Equity Firm
N.A.I.C.S.: 523999
Steffen Gorig (CEO)

Subsidiaries:

Leichtmetall Aluminium Giesserei Hannover GmbH   (1)
Gottinger Chaussee 12-14, 30453, Hannover, Germany
Tel.: (49) 51189878393
Web Site: http://www.leichtmetall.eu
Aluminum Casting Mfr
N.A.I.C.S.: 331523
Thomas Witte (Mng Dir)

QUANTUM CAPITAL, INC.
Room 1105 11/F Hip Kwan Commercial Building No 38 Pitt, Yau Ma Tei, Kowloon, China (Hong Kong)
Tel.: (852) 29803711   NV
QTCI—(OTCIQ)
Rev.: $826,000
Assets: $208,000
Liabilities: $253,000
Net Worth: ($45,000)
Earnings: $239,000
Emp.: 8
Fiscal Year-end: 06/30/23
Information Technology Services
N.A.I.C.S.: 513210
Jie Ming Kui (Pres & Sec)

INTERNATIONAL PUBLIC

QUANTUM DEVELOPMENTS REIT
Konstantin Petkanov Str, Lozenets region, 1700, Sofia, 1700, Bulgaria
Tel.: (359) 29398888
Web Site: https://www.quantum-bg.com
QUAD—(BUL)
Sales Range: Less than $1 Million
Real Estate Investment Services
N.A.I.C.S.: 531210
Stanislav Ananiev (Exec Dir)

QUANTUM DIGITAL VISION (INDIA) LIMITED
143 Athipattu Village, Ponneri - Taluk, Chennai, 601 203, Tamil Nadu, India
Tel.: (91) 2226846530
530281—(BOM)
Rev.: $44,434
Assets: $547,078
Liabilities: $180,097
Net Worth: $366,980
Earnings: $2,146
Fiscal Year-end: 03/31/23
Automotive Parts Mfr & Distr
N.A.I.C.S.: 332613
Himalay Pannalal Dassani (Mng Dir)

QUANTUM EMOTION INC.
2300 Alfred Nobel Blvd Suite 209, Montreal, H4S 2A4, QC, Canada
Tel.: (438) 858-8873
Web Site:
https://www.quantumemotion.com
Year Founded: 2012
QNC—(TSXV)
Rev.: $45,109
Assets: $1,242,738
Liabilities: $171,270
Net Worth: $1,071,468
Earnings: ($1,802,302)
Emp.: 2
Fiscal Year-end: 12/31/23
Investment Services
N.A.I.C.S.: 523999
Pierre C. Miron (CFO)

QUANTUM FOODS HOLDINGS LTD.
11 Main Road, PO Box 1183, Wellington, 7654, Western Cape, South Africa
Tel.: (27) 218648600
Web Site:
http://www.quantumfoods.co.za
Year Founded: 2013
QFH—(JSE)
Rev.: $378,637,234
Assets: $159,765,381
Liabilities: $49,977,506
Net Worth: $109,787,875
Earnings: ($1,937,360)
Emp.: 1,821
Fiscal Year-end: 09/30/23
Holding Company
N.A.I.C.S.: 551112
Wouter Andre Hanekom (Chm)

QUANTUM GENOMICS SA
6 rue Cambaceres, 75008, Paris, France
Tel.: (33) 185347770
Web Site: https://www.quantum-genomics.com
ALQGC—(EUR)
Rev.: $3,854,217
Assets: $26,090,274
Liabilities: $14,216,878
Net Worth: $11,873,396
Earnings: ($21,321,018)
Emp.: 11
Fiscal Year-end: 12/31/21
Pharmaceutical Researcher, Developer & Mfr
N.A.I.C.S.: 325412

AND PRIVATE COMPANIES

Lionel Segard *(Founder & Chm)*

QUANTUM GRAPHITE LIMITED
349 Collins Street, Melbourne, 3000, VIC, Australia
Tel.: (61) 386148414   AU
Web Site:
https://quantumgraphite.wp.com
Sales Range: Less than $1 Million
Graphite Mining
N.A.I.C.S.: 212290
Brunio Ruggiero *(Chm)*

QUANTUM HEALTHCARE LIMITED
745 Lorong 5 Toa Payoh, 01-00 Singapore, Singapore, 319455, Singapore
Tel.: (65) 65890588
Web Site: http://www.qtvascular.com
V8Y—(SES)
Rev.: $9,368,000
Assets: $14,909,000
Liabilities: $16,537,000
Net Worth: ($1,628,000)
Earnings: ($8,633,000)
Emp.: 76
Fiscal Year-end: 12/31/22
Medical Device Mfr
N.A.I.C.S.: 339112
Eitan Konstantino *(Founder & CEO)*

Subsidiaries:

TriReme Medical, LLC   (1)
7060 Koll Ctr Pkwy Ste 300, Pleasanton, CA 94566
Tel.: (925) 931-1300
Medical Instrument Mfr & Distr
N.A.I.C.S.: 339112
Eitan Konstantino *(Founder)*

QUANTUM HI-TECH (CHINA) BIOLOGICAL CO., LTD.
28th Floor Exchange Plaza No 268 Dongfeng Middle Road, Yuexiu District, Guangzhou, 510031, Guangdong, China
Tel.: (86) 2066811798
Web Site: http://www.qht.cc
Year Founded: 2000
300149—(CHIN)
Sales Range: $25-49.9 Million
Prebiotics Products Mfr
N.A.I.C.S.: 325414
Woo Swee Lian *(Chm & CEO)*

QUANTUM SOFTWARE S.A.
ul Walerego Slawka 3A, 30-633, Krakow, Poland
Tel.: (48) 126469800
Web Site: https://www.quantum-software.com
QNT—(WAR)
Rev.: $10,488
Assets: $6,606
Liabilities: $1,383
Net Worth: $5,223
Earnings: $872
Emp.: 100
Fiscal Year-end: 12/31/21
Software Development & Design Services
N.A.I.C.S.: 513210

Subsidiaries:

Quantum Qguar Sp. z o.o.   (1)
Ul Walerego Slawka 3A, 30-633, Krakow, Poland
Tel.: (48) 126469800
Web Site: https://www.quantum-software.com
Software Services
N.A.I.C.S.: 541511
Tomasz Polonczyk *(Product Mgr-WMS)*

QUANTUM SOLAR POWER CORP.
Suite 300 1055 West Hastings Street, Vancouver, V6E 2E9, BC, Canada
Tel.: (604) 681-7311   NV
Year Founded: 2004
Solar Power Generato
N.A.I.C.S.: 221122
Graham R. Hughes *(CFO, Treas & Sec)*

QUANTUM SOLUTIONS CO., LTD.
Gran Tokyo South Tower 11F 1-9-2 Marunouchi, Chiyoda-ku, Tokyo, 100-6611, Japan
Tel.: (81) 353608998
Web Site: https://www.quantum-s.co.jp
Year Founded: 1999
2338—(TKS)
Rev.: $1,453,450
Assets: $8,146,410
Liabilities: $8,018,790
Net Worth: $127,620
Earnings: ($6,395,180)
Emp.: 52
Fiscal Year-end: 02/29/24
Engineering Consulting Services
N.A.I.C.S.: 541330
Junichi Kimura *(Pres)*

QUANTUM THINKING LIMITED
Room 1403 14/F Capital Centre 151 Gloucester Road, Wanchai, China (Hong Kong)
Tel.: (852) 2 967 9020   Ky
Web Site: http://www.8050hk.com
8050—(HKG)
Rev.: $4,230,544
Assets: $7,507,539
Liabilities: $7,088,225
Net Worth: $419,314
Earnings: ($2,826,597)
Emp.: 34
Fiscal Year-end: 03/31/22
System Integration Services
N.A.I.C.S.: 541512
Xiaoqi Wang *(Exec Dir)*

QUANTUMA ADVISORY LIMITED
High Holborn House 52-54 High Holborn, London, WC1V 6RL, United Kingdom
Tel.: (44) 2038566720   UK
Web Site: https://www.quantuma.com
Year Founded: 2020
Corporate Advisory & Accounting Services
N.A.I.C.S.: 561499
Gavin Pearson *(Mng Dir & Head-Forensic Acctg-Investigations)*

QUANTUMCTEK CO., LTD.
Science Park No 777 Huatuo Lane, High-tech Industrial Development Zone, Hefei, 230088, Anhui, China
Tel.: (86) 55166180898
Web Site: https://www.quantum-info.com
Year Founded: 2009
688027—(SHG)
Rev.: $18,915,741
Assets: $272,758,660
Liabilities: $41,729,070
Net Worth: $231,029,590
Earnings: ($12,102,494)
Fiscal Year-end: 12/31/22
Plastics Product Mfr
N.A.I.C.S.: 326199
Feng Lei *(Chm-Supervisory Bd)*

Subsidiaries:

QuantumCTek (Shangai) Co., Ltd.   (1)

611 Chengzhi Plaza No 3801 Pusan Road, Pudong New Area, Shanghai, 201319, China
Tel.: (86) 2158011666
Web Site: http://www.quantum-sh.com
Information Technology Services
N.A.I.C.S.: 541511

Shandong Institute of Quantum Science & Technology Co., Ltd.   (1)
Tel.: (86) 53166680088
Web Site: http://www.quantum-sd.com
Communication Technology Research & Development Services
N.A.I.C.S.: 541715

QUANZHOU HUIXIN MICRO-CREDIT CO., LTD.
12/F Former Finance Building No 361 Feng Ze Street, Quanzhou, Fujian, China
Tel.: (86) 59522731777   CN
Web Site: http://www.qzhuixin.net
Year Founded: 2010
1577—(HKG)
Rev.: $19,445,654
Assets: $186,163,901
Liabilities: $12,163,629
Net Worth: $174,000,272
Earnings: $10,169,082
Emp.: 51
Fiscal Year-end: 12/31/22
Financial Services
N.A.I.C.S.: 522291
Yongwei Zhou *(Chm & Exec Dir)*

QUARK TECHNOLOGY GLOBAL INC.
80 D Leitchcroft Cr, Thornhill, L3T 7W1, ON, Canada
Tel.: (416) 417-4588
Web Site: http://quarktech.co
Year Founded: 2003
QTGI—(NASDAQ)
Liabilities: $54,000
Net Worth: ($54,000)
Earnings: ($6,000)
Fiscal Year-end: 02/29/20
Software Services
N.A.I.C.S.: 513210

QUARRY INTEGRATED COMMUNICATIONS
1440 King Street North, 7th Fl Allen Sq, Saint Jacobs, N0B 2N0, ON, Canada
Tel.: (519) 664-2999
Web Site: http://www.quarry.com
Year Founded: 1973
Sales Range: $10-24.9 Million
Emp.: 100
Public Relations Agency
N.A.I.C.S.: 541820
Richard Hill *(Mng Dir-Demand Generation)*

QUARTERHILL INC.
200 Bay Street North Tower Suite 1200, Toronto, M5J 2J2, ON, Canada
Tel.: (416) 247-9652   Ca
Web Site: https://www.quarterhill.com
Year Founded: 1992
QTRH—(NASDAQ)
Rev.: $146,731,898
Assets: $250,759,494
Liabilities: $107,244,408
Net Worth: $143,515,087
Earnings: ($33,075,766)
Emp.: 449
Fiscal Year-end: 12/31/23
Wireless Communications Products & Technologies
N.A.I.C.S.: 517112
James Douglas Skippen *(Vice Chm)*

Subsidiaries:

Electronic Transaction Consultants, LLC   (1)

QUARTERHILL INC.

1600 N Collins Blvd Ste 4000, Richardson, TX 75080
Tel.: (214) 615-2302
Web Site: http://www.etcc.com
System Integration & Maintenance Services
N.A.I.C.S.: 541519
Bret Kidd *(CEO)*

International Road Dynamics Inc.   (1)
702-43rd Street East, Saskatoon, S7K 3T9, SK, Canada
Tel.: (306) 653-6600
Web Site: https://www.irdinc.com
Traffic Management, Monitoring & Enforcement Systems Developer & Mfr
N.A.I.C.S.: 333310
Randy Hanson *(Pres & CEO)*

Subsidiary (Non-US):

Global Industrial Ltda.   (2)
Cr 25 39-66 of 401, Bogota, Distrito Capital, Colombia
Tel.: (57) 16097241
Sales Range: $25-49.9 Million
Emp.: 6
Traffic Management Products Mfr
N.A.I.C.S.: 334290

IRD South Asia Pvt. Ltd.   (2)
Villa-13 Ground Fl Block-5 Charmwood Vlg, Surajkund Rd, 121004, Faridabad, Haryana, India
Tel.: (91) 1294116986
Sales Range: $25-49.9 Million
Emp.: 20
Traffic Management Products Mfr
N.A.I.C.S.: 334290

Subsidiary (US):

IRD U.S. Corp.   (2)
2402 Spring Ridge Dr Ste E, Spring Grove, IL 60081
Tel.: (815) 675-1430
Sales Range: $25-49.9 Million
Emp.: 3
Traffic Management Products Mfr
N.A.I.C.S.: 334290

International Road Dynamics Corp   (2)
2402 Spring Ridge Dr Ste E, Spring Grove, IL 60081
Tel.: (815) 675-1430
Traffic Management Products Mfr
N.A.I.C.S.: 334290

Subsidiary (Non-US):

PAT Traffic Ltda.   (2)
Rua Maria Luisa, Santander, 0360, Santiago, Chile
Tel.: (56) 2 25802900
Web Site: http://www.pat-traffic.cl
Traffic Management Products Mfr
N.A.I.C.S.: 334290

PAT Traffic Sistemas de Transporte Inteligente Ltda   (2)
Rua Doutor Jesuino Macie 1175, Sao Paulo, 04615-003, SP, Brazil
Tel.: (55) 1138072297
Emp.: 30
Traffic Management Products Mfr
N.A.I.C.S.: 334290
Wagner Madeira *(Gen Mgr)*

Pat-Kruger Traffic B.V.   (2)
Manganese 6, 5234 GD, 's-Hertogenbosch, Netherlands
Tel.: (31) 736443366
Web Site: http://www.pat-kruger.nl
Sales Range: $25-49.9 Million
Traffic Management Products Mfr
N.A.I.C.S.: 334290

Joint Venture (Non-US):

Xuzhou PAT Control Technology Co., Ltd.   (2)
No 1 Industrial Zone Development Zone, Jinshan Bridge, Xuzhou, 221004, Jiangsu, China
Tel.: (86) 51687737991
Web Site: http://www.xzpat.com
Traffic Management Products Mfr
N.A.I.C.S.: 334290
Jong Zheng Shi *(Mgr-Sls)*

Wi-LAN V-Chip Corp.   (1)

QUARTERHILL INC.

Quarterhill Inc.—(Continued)
515 Consumers Road Ste 210, Toronto, M2J 4Z2, ON, Canada
Tel.: (416) 640-7330
Web Site: http://www.tri-vision.ca
Sales Range: $1-9.9 Million
Emp.: 45
Cable Television & Multimedia Software & Hardware Developer, Designer & Mfr
N.A.I.C.S.: 513210

QUARTIERS PROPERTIES AB
Strandvagen 7 A, 114 56, Stockholm, Sweden
Tel.: (46) 952157222
Web Site:
 https://www.quartiersproperties.com
Year Founded: 2015
QUART.PREF—(OMX)
Rev.: $6,812,064
Assets: $79,808,091
Liabilities: $45,410,708
Net Worth: $34,397,383
Earnings: ($8,253,096)
Emp.: 68
Fiscal Year-end: 12/31/20
Real Estate Investment Services
N.A.I.C.S.: 531390
Jorgen Cederholm *(Chm)*

QUARTIX TECHNOLOGIES PLC
No 9 Journey Campus Castle Park, Cambridge, CB3 0AX, United Kingdom
Tel.: (44) 1686806663
Web Site: http://www.quartix.com
Year Founded: 2001
QTX—(AIM)
Rev.: $34,734,915
Assets: $37,999,243
Liabilities: $11,619,541
Net Worth: $26,379,702
Earnings: $6,363,292
Emp.: 189
Fiscal Year-end: 12/31/22
Vehicle Tracking Systems Software
N.A.I.C.S.: 513210
Andy Walters *(Chm & CEO)*

Subsidiaries:

Quartix Inc. (1)
875 N Michigan Ave Ste 3100, Chicago, IL 60611
Web Site: https://www.quartix.com
Software Services
N.A.I.C.S.: 513210

QUARTZ MOUNTAIN RESOURCES LTD.
14th Floor 1040 West Georgia Street, Vancouver, V6E 4H1, BC, Canada
Tel.: (604) 684-6365
Web Site:
 https://www.quartzmountain.com
Year Founded: 1982
QZM—(TSXV)
Rev.: $18,341
Assets: $2,203,410
Liabilities: $243,470
Net Worth: $1,959,941
Earnings: ($1,781,424)
Fiscal Year-end: 07/31/24
Gold & Silver Mining Services
N.A.I.C.S.: 212290
Trevor Thomas *(Chm, Pres, CEO & Sec)*

QUARTZELEC LTD.
Castel Mound Way Central Park, Rugby, CV23 0WB, Warwickshire, United Kingdom
Tel.: (44) 1788512512
Web Site: http://www.quartzelec.com
Sales Range: $75-99.9 Million
Emp.: 650
Electrical Engineering Design, Manufacturing, Installation & Maintenance Services
N.A.I.C.S.: 238210
Daniel Laval *(Mng Dir)*

Subsidiaries:

Maser and Quartzelec Service Sdn. Bhd.
Lot 55631 Jalan Sellathevan Seksyen 36, Shah Alam, 40450, Kuala Lumpur, Selangor, Malaysia
Tel.: (60) 351666612
Electrical Contracting Services
N.A.I.C.S.: 238210
Upkar Singh *(Mgr-Sls)*

Quartzelec Ltd (1)
501 Room 2 Old Al Masaood Building Najda Street, PO Box 109891, Abu Dhabi, United Arab Emirates
Tel.: (971) 26418489
Electrical Contracting Services
N.A.I.C.S.: 238210

Quartzteq GmbH (1)
Technopark Aargau Dorfstrasse 69, 5210, Windisch, Switzerland
Tel.: (41) 565602064
Electrical Contracting Services
N.A.I.C.S.: 238210
Vitaliy Touriantchyk *(Mgr-Intl Sls Dev)*

TS Metals Ltd (1)
Mill Road West, Rugby, CV21 1BZ, United Kingdom
Tel.: (44) 1788540019
Fabricated Metal Products Mfr
N.A.I.C.S.: 332999

QUARZWERKE GMBH
Kaskadenweg 40, 50226, Frechen, Germany
Tel.: (49) 2234 101 0
Web Site:
 http://www.quarzwerke.com
Industrial Mineral Mining & Processing Services
N.A.I.C.S.: 212323
Robert Lindemann-Berk *(Mng Partner)*

Subsidiaries:

Kaolin AD (1)
8 Dabrava Str, Ruse, 1092, Senovo, Bulgaria
Tel.: (359) 84612500
Web Site: http://www.kaolin.bg
Sales Range: $800-899.9 Million
Emp.: 1,400
Non-Metallic Materials Mining & Processing
N.A.I.C.S.: 212323
Dimitar Angelov *(Exec Dir)*

Provodinske pisky a.s. (1)
Provodin 165, 471 67, Provodin, Czech Republic
Tel.: (420) 487 809 911
Web Site: http://www.pisky.cz
Industrial Sand Mining
N.A.I.C.S.: 212322
Jiri Vacek *(Mgr-Sls & Mktg)*

Quarzwerke GmbH Haltern Plant (1)
Quarzwerkstrasse 160, 45721, Haltern, Germany
Tel.: (49) 23649640
Construction & Mining Equipment Mfr
N.A.I.C.S.: 333120

Quarzwerke GmbH St. Georgen Plant (1)
Knierublerstrasse 18, 4222, Sankt Georgen an der Gusen, Austria
Tel.: (43) 723724490
Ground Mineral Mfr
N.A.I.C.S.: 327992

Quarzwerke Osterreich GmbH (1)
Wachbergstrasse 1, A 3390, Vienna, Austria
Tel.: (43) 2752 500 40 0
Web Site: http://www.quarzwerke.at
Industrial Sand Mining
N.A.I.C.S.: 212322

QUASAR INDIA LIMITED
305 Third Floor Aggarwal Plaza, Sector- 14 Rohini, New Delhi, 110 085, India
Tel.: (91) 119873037413
Web Site: http://www.quasarindia.in
Year Founded: 1979
538452—(BOM)
Rev.: $521,066
Assets: $1,138,610
Liabilities: $377,554
Net Worth: $761,057
Earnings: $121,406
Emp.: 1
Fiscal Year-end: 03/31/23
Textile Products Distr
N.A.I.C.S.: 424310
Sachin Chandrakant Gawant *(Exec Dir)*

QUASEM INDUSTRIES LIMITED
Icon Centre Plot No 57/4 Pragoti Sarani North Baridhara, Dhaka, 1212, Bangladesh
Tel.: (880) 9677008888
Web Site:
 https://www.quasemindustries.com
Year Founded: 1980
QUASEMIND—(CHT)
Rev.: $10,804,885
Assets: $36,808,001
Liabilities: $18,128,107
Net Worth: $18,679,894
Earnings: $201,560
Emp.: 2,400
Fiscal Year-end: 06/30/23
Battery Mfr
N.A.I.C.S.: 335910
Tasvir Ul Islam *(CEO & Mng Dir)*

QUASER MACHINE TOOLS, INC.
3 Gong 6th Road, Youshih Industrial Park Dajia Dist, Taichung, 43768, Taiwan
Tel.: (886) 426821277
Web Site: https://www.quaser.com
Year Founded: 1991
4563—(TPE)
Rev.: $80,791,577
Assets: $122,216,427
Liabilities: $82,105,994
Net Worth: $40,110,434
Earnings: $3,404,340
Fiscal Year-end: 12/31/22
Tool Machinery Product Mfr
N.A.I.C.S.: 333517
Jui-Mu Hsieh *(Chm)*

Subsidiaries:

600SA Machine Tools (PTY.) Ltd. (1)
284 Dekema Road Unit C5 Dekema Park Wadeville, Germiston, 1428, South Africa
Tel.: (27) 721576003
Web Site: https://mt600sa.co.za
Computer Numerical Control Machine Tool Mfr & Distr
N.A.I.C.S.: 333517

All Tech Machinery & Supply Company (1)
10650 County Rd 81 Ste 216, Maple Grove, MN 55369
Tel.: (763) 370-4670
Web Site: https://www.alltechmachinery.com
Computer Numerical Control Machine Tool Mfr & Distr
N.A.I.C.S.: 333517

BOST - stroje, s.r.o. (1)
Suvoz 1/1594, 911 01, Trencin, Slovakia
Tel.: (421) 944625586
Web Site: https://www.bost-stroje.sk
Computer Numerical Control Machine Tool Mfr & Distr
N.A.I.C.S.: 333517

Buscotrade d.o.o. (1)
Gmajna 3, 1236, Trzin, Slovenia
Tel.: (386) 15621834

INTERNATIONAL PUBLIC

Web Site: https://www.buscotrade.si
Polishing & Clamping Tool Mfr
N.A.I.C.S.: 332813

CNC Direct Ltd. (1)
17 Mahunga Drive Mangere Bridge, Auckland, 2022, New Zealand
Tel.: (64) 96222169
Web Site: https://www.cncdirect.co.nz
Computer Numerical Control Machine Tool Mfr & Distr
N.A.I.C.S.: 333517

CNC Force ApS (1)
Smedegade 14, DK-7130, Juelsminde, Denmark
Tel.: (45) 25791280
Web Site: https://cncforce.dk
Computer Numerical Control Machine Tool Mfr & Distr
N.A.I.C.S.: 333517

Camex Machinery Inc. (1)
4732 Boul Thimens, Montreal, H4R 2B2, QC, Canada
Tel.: (514) 903-6447
Web Site: https://camexmachinery.com
Computer Numerical Control Machine Tool Mfr & Distr
N.A.I.C.S.: 333517

Cnc-Inaxes S.R.O. (1)
Nadrazni 219, 549 01, Nove Mesto nad Metuji, Czech Republic
Tel.: (420) 494530967
Web Site: https://www.cnc-inaxes.cz
Computer Numerical Control Machine Tool Mfr & Distr
N.A.I.C.S.: 333517

Cron - Tek Oy (1)
Ormuspellontie 7, PO Box 122, 00700, Helsinki, Finland
Tel.: (358) 95494660
Web Site: https://www.crontek.fi
Grinding & Spark Machine Mfr & Whslr
N.A.I.C.S.: 333517

Direc Machine Tool LLC (1)
20711 Watertown Rd Unit E, Waukesha, WI 53186
Tel.: (414) 509-5107
Web Site: https://direcmachinetool.com
Computer Numerical Control Machine Tool Mfr & Distr
N.A.I.C.S.: 333517

Dynamic Machinery Ltd. (1)
12 Visoker st, Petach Tikva, 4900857, Israel
Tel.: (972) 528387720
Web Site:
Quasar Machine Tool Mfr & Whslr
N.A.I.C.S.: 333517

ELBE Leading Technology Solutions Ltd. (1)
5B Atir Yeda St, Kfar Saba, 4464305, Israel
Tel.: (972) 99720202
Web Site: https://www.elbe.co.il
Computer Numerical Control Machine Tool Mfr & Distr
N.A.I.C.S.: 333517

Empire of Metals Ltd. (1)
88 Grigorovskoe shosse, Kharkiv, Ukraine
Tel.: (380) 577196211
Web Site: https://imperija.com
Metal Cutting Tool Mfr
N.A.I.C.S.: 333517

EverGreen Machine Tools Pte. Ltd. (1)
39 Woodlands Close 04-19 Mega Woodland, Singapore, 737856, Singapore
Tel.: (65) 96345617
Web Site:
 https://www.evergreenmachinetools.com
Computer Numerical Control Machine Tool Mfr & Distr
N.A.I.C.S.: 333517

Evolent Technische Handel B.V. (1)
Flevolaan 23, 1382 JX, Weesp, Netherlands
Tel.: (31) 294450540
Web Site: https://evolent.nl
Quasar Machine Repair & Maintenance Services
N.A.I.C.S.: 423430

Glomato Technologies Sdn. Bhd. (1)
3E Lorong Delima 1 Greenlane, 11600, Penang, Malaysia

AND PRIVATE COMPANIES

Tel.: (60) 46570520
Web Site: http://www.glomato-tech.com
Computer Numerical Control Machine Tool Mfr & Distr
N.A.I.C.S.: 333517

Hanuman Machine Tools Corporation (1)
84/C 17th D Main 6th Block Koramangala, Bengaluru, 560095, India
Tel.: (91) 9731929444
Web Site: https://hmtcorp.in
Boring & Milling Tool Services
N.A.I.C.S.: 811310

Hommel GmbH (1)
Donatusstrasse 24 Pesch, 50767, Cologne, Germany
Tel.: (49) 22159890
Web Site: https://www.hommel-gruppe.de
Emp.: 200
Milling Machine Mfr & Whslr
N.A.I.C.S.: 333517

Istanbul Makina A.S. (1)
IMES Sanayi Sitesi B Blok 203 Sok No 7 Umraniye, 34776, Istanbul, Turkiye
Tel.: (90) 2165266500
Web Site: https://www.istmak.com
Computer Numerical Control Machine Tool Mfr & Distr
N.A.I.C.S.: 333517

Kunshan Quaser Machine Tools, Inc. (1)
B No 287 Kangzhuang Road, Zhoushi, Kunshan, China
Tel.: (86) 51282627139
Quasar Machine Tool Mfr & Whslr
N.A.I.C.S.: 333517

LM Innovative Technologies Centre LLC (1)
Fuchika street Office 18, 49000, Dnepropetrovsk, Ukraine
Tel.: (380) 567674033
Quasar Machine Tool Mfr & Whslr
N.A.I.C.S.: 333517

Mexpol-Trading Sp. z.o.o. (1)
ul Chelmska 21, 00-724, Warsaw, Poland
Tel.: (48) 228413903
Quasar Machine Tool Mfr & Whslr
N.A.I.C.S.: 333517

P.Meidell AS (1)
Stalfjaera 16 Kalbakken, N-0975, Oslo, Norway
Tel.: (47) 22202025
Web Site: https://www.meidell.no
Computer Numerical Control Machine Tool Mfr & Distr
N.A.I.C.S.: 333517

Pan Machine Import and Export Trade (1)
Avenida Eurico Ambrogi Santos 1300 Piracangagua, Taubate, Sao Paulo, 12042-010, Brazil
Tel.: (55) 1236270004
Web Site: https://panmachine.com.br
Computer Numerical Control Machine Tool Mfr & Distr
N.A.I.C.S.: 333517

Quality Cutting Tools, Inc. (1)
620 56th St E, Saskatoon, S7K 8G5, SK, Canada
Tel.: (306) 664-8410
Computer Numerical Control Machine Tool Mfr & Distr
N.A.I.C.S.: 333517

Quaser America Machine Tools Inc. (1)
3049 Southcross Blvd Ste 104, Rock Hill, SC 29730
Tel.: (803) 324-7125
Industrial Machinery Mfr
N.A.I.C.S.: 333248

Rieckermann (Singapore) Pte. Ltd. (1)
06-30/31 Interlocal Centre 100G Pasir Panjang Rd, Singapore, 118523, Singapore
Tel.: (65) 62581990
Quasar Machine Tool Mfr & Whslr
N.A.I.C.S.: 333517

SFG Baltika LLC (1)
3-Y Verkhniy Pereulok 10E, Saint Petersburg, 194 292, Russia
Tel.: (7) 8124413655
Web Site: https://sfg-baltika.ru
Engineering & Automation Services
N.A.I.C.S.: 541330

Sc Holcz Stile S.R.L. (1)
Str Ilarie Chendi Nr 21, Satu-Mare, Romania
Tel.: (40) 742995785
Web Site: https://www.hsmachinetools.ro
Milling & Drilling Machine Tool Services
N.A.I.C.S.: 811310

Tecnor Macchine S.p.A. (1)
Strada 3 - Palazzo B 4 Milanofiori, 20057, Assago, Italy
Tel.: (39) 028242851
Web Site: https://www.tecnormacchine.it
Machinery Mfr
N.A.I.C.S.: 333248

QUASH PRODUCTS PLC
15a Ives Street, London, SW3 2ND, United Kingdom
Tel.: (44) 20 7594 4949
Year Founded: 2009
Hand Sanitizer Mfr
N.A.I.C.S.: 325611
Ben Fisher *(CEO)*

QUATTRO EXPLORATION & PRODUCTION LTD.
Suite 4110 825 - 8th Avenue SW, Calgary, T2P 2T3, AB, Canada
Tel.: (403) 984-3917
Web Site: http://www.qxp-petro.com
Year Founded: 1997
Oil & Gas Exploration Services
N.A.I.C.S.: 213112

QUATTROR SGR S.P.A.
Via Borgonuovo 14, 20121, Milan, Italy
Tel.: (39) 02 3679 9670
Web Site: http://www.quattror.com
Year Founded: 2016
Financial Investment Services
N.A.I.C.S.: 523999
Andrea Morante *(Chm & Pres)*

Subsidiaries:

Gruppo Ceramiche Ricchetti S.p.A. (1)
Via Statale 118/m, S. Antonino di Casalgrande, 42013, Casalgrande, Reggio Emilia, Italy **(64.8%)**
Tel.: (39) 0536992511
Web Site: http://www.ricchetti-group.com
Interior & Exterior Glazed Ceramic & Stoneware Tile Mfr
N.A.I.C.S.: 327120

Subsidiary (Non-US):

Bellegrove Ceramics Plc (2)
Watling Street Bellegrove House, Salisbury Road, Dartford, DA2 6EJ, United Kingdom **(100%)**
Tel.: (44) 1322277877
Web Site: http://www.bellegroveceramics.co.uk
Sales Range: $200-249.9 Million
Emp.: 550
Hobby Toy & Game Stores
N.A.I.C.S.: 459120
Andrea Zannoni *(Mng Dir)*

Subsidiary (Domestic):

Biztiles Italia S.p.A. (2)
Via Statale 118, Casalgrande, 42013, Bologna, Italy **(99.98%)**
Tel.: (39) 0536992711
Web Site: http://www.biztiles.com
Ceramic Wall & Floor Tile Mfr
N.A.I.C.S.: 327120

Subsidiary (Non-US):

CC Hoganas Byggkeramik AB (2)
PO Box 501, Ekeby, 26051, Orebro, Sweden **(100%)**
Tel.: (46) 42173900
Web Site: http://www.cchoganas.se
Sales Range: $50-74.9 Million
Emp.: 60
Construction Materials Whslr
N.A.I.C.S.: 423390

Subsidiary (US):

Casa Reale Ceramic Inc (2)
913 W N Carrier Pkwy, Grand Prairie, TX 75050 **(100%)**
Tel.: (972) 641-1817
Sales Range: $50-74.9 Million
Emp.: 7
Brick Stone & Related Construction Material Whslr
N.A.I.C.S.: 423320

Subsidiary (Non-US):

Cinca Companhia Industrial de Ceramica S.A. (2)
Rua Principal 39, Apartado 12 Fiaes VFR, 4509-908, Aveiro, Portugal **(100%)**
Tel.: (351) 227476400
Web Site: http://www.cinca.pt
Sales Range: $200-249.9 Million
Emp.: 700
Brick & Structural Clay Tile Mfr
N.A.I.C.S.: 327120
Gosa Gosenunesamaral *(Mng Dir)*

Delefortrie SARL (2)
Le Cornu Za, Rochetoirin, 38110, La Tour-du-Pin, France **(100%)**
Tel.: (33) 474974140
Grain & Field Bean Whslr
N.A.I.C.S.: 424510

Evers AS (2)
Ejby Industrivej 2, PO Box 1402, 2600, Glostrup, Denmark **(100%)**
Tel.: (45) 43434315
Web Site: http://www.evers.dk
Sales Range: $25-49.9 Million
Emp.: 20
Carpentry Contractor
N.A.I.C.S.: 238350

Hoganas Ceramiques France SA (2)
12 Impasse Gutenberg, 38110, Isere, France **(100%)**
Tel.: (33) 474835590
Web Site: http://www.hoganas-france.com
Sales Range: $50-74.9 Million
Emp.: 10
Construction Materials Whslr
N.A.I.C.S.: 423390

Klingenberg Dekoramik GmbH (2)
Trennfurter Str 33, 63911, Klingenberg, Germany **(100%)**
Tel.: (49) 93721310
Web Site: http://www.dekoramik.de
Sales Range: $50-74.9 Million
Emp.: 120
Ceramic Wall & Floor Tile Mfr
N.A.I.C.S.: 327120
Georg Richerzhagen *(Mng Dir)*

OY Pukkila AB (2)
Pitkamaenkatu 9, Turku Mail PL 29, Turku, 20250, Finland **(100%)**
Tel.: (358) 207219600
Web Site: http://www.pukkila.com
Emp.: 50
Ceramic Wall & Floor Tile Mfr
N.A.I.C.S.: 327120
Johan Westerlund *(Gen Mgr)*

Subsidiary (US):

Ricchetti Ceramic Inc. (2)
2425 Pineapple Ave Ste 308, Melbourne, FL 00032-935 **(100%)**
Tel.: (321) 259-0894
Web Site: http://www.ricchetti.it
Sales Range: $50-74.9 Million
Emp.: 10
Brick Stone & Related Construction Material Whslr
N.A.I.C.S.: 423320

QUAY MARINAS LTD.
A & W Building The Docks, Bristol, BS20 7DF, North Somerset, United Kingdom
Tel.: (44) 1275841188   UK
Web Site: http://www.quaymarinas.com
Sales Range: $10-24.9 Million
Emp.: 70
Marinas Development & Management Services
N.A.I.C.S.: 713930
Keith Berry *(Mgr-Portishead Quays)*

QUAYLE MUNRO HOLDINGS LIMITED
102 West Port, Edinburgh, EH3 9EP, United Kingdom
Tel.: (44) 1312222600   UK
Web Site: http://www.quaylemunro.com
Year Founded: 1983
Sales Range: $1-9.9 Million
Emp.: 48
Holding Company; Corporate Banking, Financial Advisory & Investment Management Services
N.A.I.C.S.: 551112
Andrew D. Adams *(CEO)*

QUBA NEW MEDIA
Belgravia House 115 Rockingham St, Sheffield, S1 4EB, United Kingdom
Tel.: (44) 114 279 7779
Web Site: http://www.quba.co.uk
Sales Range: $10-24.9 Million
Emp.: 25
Digital/Interactive, E-Commerce, Graphic Design, Internet/Web Design, Local Marketing, Strategic Planning/Research
N.A.I.C.S.: 541810
Matthew Williams *(Co-Founder & Mng Dir)*

QUBE HOLDINGS LIMITED
Level 27 45 Clarence Street, Sydney, 2000, NSW, Australia
Tel.: (61) 290801900   AU
Web Site: https://www.qube.com.au
QUB—(ASX)
Rev.: $1,503,954,351
Assets: $4,781,868,409
Liabilities: $2,573,478,972
Net Worth: $2,208,389,437
Earnings: $70,336,242
Emp.: 6,500
Fiscal Year-end: 06/30/21
Offices of Other Holding Companies
N.A.I.C.S.: 551112
Paul Lewis *(CFO)*

Subsidiaries:

AAT Port Kembla Pty. Ltd. (1)
Yampi Way Off Tom Thumb Road, PO Box 144, Port Kembla, 2505, NSW, Australia
Tel.: (61) 24 221 0900
Terminal Services
N.A.I.C.S.: 488310
Evan Wissell *(Mgr)*

Asciano Limited (1)
Level 4 476 St Kilda Road, Melbourne, 3004, VIC, Australia
Tel.: (61) 3 92487000
Web Site: http://www.asciano.com.au
Sales Range: $1-4.9 Billion
Ports & Rail Assets Management
N.A.I.C.S.: 485112
Roger Burrows *(CFO)*

Joint Venture (Non-US):

C3 Limited (2)
58 Cross Road Sulphur Point, Tauranga, 3110, New Zealand
Tel.: (64) 75728972
Web Site: https://www.c3.co.nz
Emp.: 800
Marine Cargo Handling Services
N.A.I.C.S.: 488320
Chris Sutherland *(Gen Mgr-Logistics-New Zealand)*

Australian Amalgamated Terminals Pty. Ltd. (1)

QUBE HOLDINGS LIMITED

Qube Holdings Limited—(Continued)
Level 27 45 Clarence Street, Sydney, 2000, NSW, Australia
Tel.: (61) 28 346 2300
Web Site: https://www.aaterminals.com.au
Terminal Services
N.A.I.C.S.: 488310
Antony Perkins (Mng Dir)

BOMC Pte. Ltd. (1)
8 Jurong Town Hall Road 26-03 The JTC Summit, Singapore, Singapore
Tel.: (65) 6 221 6875
Web Site: http://www.bomc.com.sg
Offshore Marine Services
N.A.I.C.S.: 488390

ISO Ltd. (1)
Level 2/161 Tasman Quay, Mount Maunganui, 3116, Tauranga, New Zealand
Tel.: (64) 7 577 7600
Web Site: https://www.iso.co.nz
Marine Logistics & Cargo Handling Services
N.A.I.C.S.: 488320
Paul Cameron (CEO)

K Line Auto Logistics Pty. Ltd. (1)
570 St Kilda Rd, Melbourne, 3004, VIC, Australia
Tel.: (61) 3 9944 3000
Vehicle Transport Services
N.A.I.C.S.: 488510

Joint Venture (Domestic):

PrixCar Services Pty. Ltd. (2)
Gate 3 120-124 Foundation Road, Altona North, Truganina, 3029, VIC, Australia (50%)
Tel.: (61) 1300660616
Automobile Transport, Logistics & Storage Services
N.A.I.C.S.: 541614

Subsidiary (Domestic):

PrixCar Transport Services Pty. Ltd. (3)
810-848 Kororoit Creek Road, Altona North, Melbourne, 3025, VIC, Australia
Tel.: (61) 1300 660 616
Web Site: http://www.prixcartransport.com.au
Automobile Transport Services
N.A.I.C.S.: 541614

Kalari Pty Ltd (1)
183 Fitzgerald Road, Laverton, 3026, VIC, Australia
Tel.: (61) 393694722
Web Site: http://www.kalari.com.au
Sales Range: $50-74.9 Million
Emp.: 100
Inventory Management, Bulk Storage, General Freight Handling, Raw Materials Transport & Logistics Management
N.A.I.C.S.: 484110
Peter O'Shannessy (Mng Dir)

LCR Group Pty Ltd (1)
494 Nudgee Road, Hendra, 4011, QLD, Australia
Tel.: (61) 733320000
Web Site: https://lcrcranes.com.au
Mining & Industrial Services
N.A.I.C.S.: 238990
Colin Partington (CEO & Mng Partner)

P&O Wharf Management Pty Ltd (1)
U 2 31 Sabre Dr, Melbourne, 3207, VIC, Australia
Tel.: (61) 396731600
Logistics Consulting Servies
N.A.I.C.S.: 541614

Qube Logistics (Aust) Pty Ltd (1)
19-43 Enterprize Road, Melbourne, 3003, VIC, Australia (100%)
Tel.: (61) 3 9680 1200
Web Site: http://qube.com.au
Freight Transportation Services
N.A.I.C.S.: 488510
Paul Lewis (CFO)

Subsidiary (Domestic):

Chalmers Limited (2)
20-28 Cawley Road, PO Box 50, Yarraville, 3013, VIC, Australia
Tel.: (61) 3 9316 2011

Web Site: http://www.chalmers.net.au
Sales Range: $50-74.9 Million
Container Handling, Warehousing, Distribution & Transport Services
N.A.I.C.S.: 493110
Gary W. Chalmers (Dir-Container Parks)

Subsidiary (Domestic):

Chalmers Industries (Brisbane) Pty. Ltd (3)
1 Bingera Drive, Brisbane, 4178, QLD, Australia
Tel.: (61) 738959500
Web Site: http://www.chalmers.net.au
Sales Range: $50-74.9 Million
Emp.: 150
Water Transportation Services
N.A.I.C.S.: 483211

Chalmers Industries Pty. Ltd (3)
19-43 Enterprize Road, Melbourne, 3003, VIC, Australia
Tel.: (61) 396801200
Web Site: http://www.chalmers.net.au
Water Transportation Services
N.A.I.C.S.: 483211

Subsidiary (Domestic):

Macarthur Intermodal Shipping Terminal Pty Ltd (2)
9 Stonny Batter Road, Minto, 2566, NSW, Australia
Tel.: (61) 2 9603 0960
Web Site: http://www.qube.com.au
Logistics Consulting Servies
N.A.I.C.S.: 541614
Craig Mckay (Gen Mgr)

Qube Logistics (H&S) Pty Ltd (2)
1 Rous Head Road, North Fremantle, Fremantle, 6159, WA, Australia
Tel.: (61) 8 9430 2900
Web Site: http://www.qube.com.eu
Logistics Consulting Servies
N.A.I.C.S.: 541614

Qube Logistics (Qld) Pty Ltd (2)
1 Bingera Drv, Brisbane, 4178, QLD, Australia
Tel.: (61) 738959500
Logistics Consulting Servies
N.A.I.C.S.: 541614

Qube Logistics (SA) Pty Ltd (2)
Coghlan Rd, Outer Harbor, Victoria, 5018, SA, Australia
Tel.: (61) 8 8248 0655
Emp.: 194
Logistics Management Services
N.A.I.C.S.: 541614
Alby Gluyas (Gen Mgr)

Qube Logistics (WA1) Pty Ltd (2)
16 Irene St, Fremantle, 6159, WA, Australia
Tel.: (61) 8 9335 6788
Logistics Consulting Servies
N.A.I.C.S.: 541614

Qube Ports & Bulk (2)
Level 27 45 Clarence Street, Sydney, 2000, NSW, Australia
Tel.: (61) 290051100
Web Site: https://qube.com.au
Emp.: 100
Freight Shipping Services
N.A.I.C.S.: 488310

Subsidiary (Domestic):

Continental Freight Services (Aust.) Pty. Ltd (2)
Unit 11/41 Sabre Drive, Port Melbourne, 3207, VIC, Australia
Tel.: (61) 3 9646 7044
Web Site: http://www.continentalfreight.com.au
Freight Forwarding & Logistics Consulting Services
N.A.I.C.S.: 488510
Ken Colwell (Mgr-Ops)

Giacci Bros. Pty Ltd (2)
Goulds Rd, Narngulu, Geraldton, 6532, WA, Australia
Tel.: (61) 8 99233653
Web Site: http://www.qube.com.au
Logistics Management Services
N.A.I.C.S.: 541614

Giacci Holdings Pty Ltd (2)
South Western Highway, Picton, 6229, WA, Australia
Tel.: (61) 897249500
Web Site: http://www.giacci.com.au
Emp.: 400
Container Haulage Services
N.A.I.C.S.: 484121
Mike Batchelar (Grp Mgr-Bus Dev)

QUBEGB LTD.
Enterprise House Gala Bank Business Park, Galashiels, TD1 1PR, United Kingdom
Tel.: (44) 333 240 1806
Web Site: http://www.qubegb.com
Year Founded: 2007
Sales Range: $25-49.9 Million
Emp.: 434
Telecommunication Servicesb
N.A.I.C.S.: 517112
John Munnelly (Officer-Quality Assurance)

QUDIAN INC.
Tower A AVIC Zijin Plaza, Siming District, Xiamen, 361000, Fujian, China
Tel.: (86) 5925911580   Ky
Web Site: https://www.qudian.com
Year Founded: 2014
QD—(NYSE)
Rev.: $88,477,758
Assets: $1,952,881,366
Liabilities: $107,817,428
Net Worth: $1,845,063,937
Earnings: ($55,456,523)
Emp.: 215
Fiscal Year-end: 12/31/22
Online Shopping Services
N.A.I.C.S.: 459999
Min Luo (CEO, Founder & Chm)

QUEBEC NICKEL CORP.
1100 - 1111 Melville Street, Vancouver, V6E 3V6, BC, Canada   BC
Web Site: https://www.quebecnickel.com
Year Founded: 2020
QNICF—(OTCQB)
Rev.: $31,549
Assets: $13,190,333
Liabilities: $3,811,586
Net Worth: $9,378,746
Earnings: ($1,412,689)
Fiscal Year-end: 03/31/23
Mineral Mining Services
N.A.I.C.S.: 213115

QUEBEC PRECIOUS METALS CORPORATION
1080 Cote du Beaver Hall Suite 2101, Montreal, H2Z 1S8, QC, Canada
Tel.: (514) 871-1258   BC
Web Site: https://www.qpmcorp.ca
Year Founded: 1984
CJCFF—(OTCQB)
Rev.: $1,627,135
Assets: $2,745,531
Liabilities: $902,219
Net Worth: $1,843,311
Earnings: $2,979,985
Fiscal Year-end: 01/31/22
Metal Exploration Services
N.A.I.C.S.: 212290
Jean-Francois Meilleur (Pres)

QUEBEC RARE EARTH ELEMENTS CORP
217 Queen Street West Suite 401, Toronto, M5V 0R2, ON, Canada
Tel.: (604) 446-6440   BC
Web Site: https://qree.ca
Year Founded: 1987
41K—(DEU)
Rev.: $3,382
Assets: $2,336,020

INTERNATIONAL PUBLIC

Liabilities: $100,439
Net Worth: $2,235,581
Earnings: ($6,462,723)
Fiscal Year-end: 04/30/23
Mineral Exploration Services
N.A.I.C.S.: 213114
Paul Teniere (CEO)

Subsidiaries:

FortyTwo Metals Inc. (1)
490-1122 Mainland Street, Vancouver, V6B 5L1, BC, Canada (100%)
Tel.: (604) 684-2900
Web Site: http://www.fortytwometals.com
Mineral Mining Services
N.A.I.C.S.: 212390

QUEBECOR INC.
612 Saint-Jacques St, Montreal, H3C 4M8, QC, Canada
Tel.: (514) 380-1999   QC
Web Site: http://www.quebecor.com
Year Founded: 1950
QBR.A—(OTCIQ)
Rev.: $3,285,787,512
Assets: $7,442,647,716
Liabilities: $6,622,233,912
Net Worth: $820,413,804
Earnings: $503,757,492
Emp.: 10,038
Fiscal Year-end: 12/31/19
Multimedia Holding Company
N.A.I.C.S.: 551112
M. Brian Mulroney (Chm)

Subsidiaries:

CEC Publishing Inc. (1)
9001 Louis-H La Fontaine Boulevard, Anjou, H1J 2C5, QC, Canada
Tel.: (514) 351-6010
Web Site: https://www.editionscec.com
Books Publishing Services
N.A.I.C.S.: 513130

Quebecor Media Inc. (1)
612 St-Jacques Street, Montreal, H3C 4M8, QC, Canada (75.4%)
Tel.: (514) 380-1999
Web Site: http://www.quebecor.com
Rev.: $2,787,119,726
Assets: $6,569,412,053
Liabilities: $5,613,527,411
Net Worth: $955,884,642
Earnings: $355,366,332
Emp.: 9,172
Fiscal Year-end: 12/31/2021
Printing & Media Services
N.A.I.C.S.: 516210
M. Brian Mulroney (Chm)

Subsidiary (Domestic):

JPL Production II, Inc. (2)
1600 De Maisonneuve Blvd E, Montreal, H2L 4P2, QC, Canada (100%)
Tel.: (514) 526-2881
Web Site: http://www.tva.camoe.com
Sales Range: $25-49.9 Million
Emp.: 20
Television Program Production Company
N.A.I.C.S.: 512110

Les Editions CEC, Inc. (2)
9001 Blvd Louis-H-Lafontaine, Ville d'Anjou, H1J 2C5, QC, Canada (100%)
Tel.: (514) 351-6010
Web Site: http://www.editionscec.com
Sales Range: $25-49.9 Million
Emp.: 70
Textbook Publisher; Owned by Quebecor, Inc. & by Livres SA
N.A.I.C.S.: 513130

Les Editions Quebec-Livres (2)
4545 rue Frontenac 3rd Floor, Montreal, H2H 2R7, QC, Canada
Tel.: (514) 270-1746
Web Site: http://www.quebec-livres.com
Sales Range: $25-49.9 Million
Emp.: 10
Book Publishers
N.A.I.C.S.: 513130

Les Editions du Trecarre, Inc. (2)
La Tourelle 1055 boulevard Rene-Levesque

Est Bureau 800, Montreal, H2L 4S5, QC, Canada
Tel.: (514) 849-5259
Web Site: http://www.quebecor.com
Rev.: $267,834
Emp.: 20
Non-Fiction Book Publisher
N.A.I.C.S.: 513130

Librairie Paragraphe Bookstore (2)
2220 McGill College Avenue, Montreal, H3A 3P9, QC, Canada (100%)
Tel.: (514) 845-5811
Web Site: https://www.paragraphbooks.com
Sales Range: $25-49.9 Million
Emp.: 15
Book Stores
N.A.I.C.S.: 459210

SETTE (2)
1500 Papineau Avenue Suite 100, Montreal, H2K 4L9, QC, Canada (100%)
Tel.: (514) 525-1245
Web Site: https://sette.com
Sales Range: $25-49.9 Million
Emp.: 80
Television Broadcasting & Post Production Services
N.A.I.C.S.: 516120
Benoit Delpech *(Mgr-Described Video)*

TVA Group, Inc. (2)
1600 de Maisonneuve Boulevard East, Montreal, H2L 4P2, QC, Canada
Tel.: (514) 526-9251
Web Site: http://www.tva.canoe.ca
Rev.: $397,510,888
Assets: $460,912,335
Liabilities: $216,356,744
Net Worth: $244,555,591
Earnings: $25,280,943
Emp.: 1,330
Fiscal Year-end: 12/31/2020
Network Television Broadcasting & Multimedia Publishing Services
N.A.I.C.S.: 516120
France Lauziere *(Pres & CEO)*

Subsidiary (Domestic):

TVA Films (3)
1600 Blvd De Maisonneuv, Montreal, H2L 4P2, QC, Canada
Tel.: (514) 284-2525
Web Site: https://tvafilms.ca
Sales Range: $10-24.9 Million
Emp.: 20
Television, Feature Film & Multimedia Producer
N.A.I.C.S.: 512110

TVA Publications Inc. (3)
1010 Rue de Serigny 4e etage, Longueuil, J4K 5G7, QC, Canada
Tel.: (514) 848-7000
Web Site: http://www.tvapublications.com
Sales Range: $50-74.9 Million
Emp.: 30
Magazine Publishing Services
N.A.I.C.S.: 513120
Claudio Mendez *(VP)*

TVA Publications, Inc. (3)
7 Bates Road, Outremont, H2V 4V7, QC, Canada (100%)
Tel.: (514) 848-7000
Web Site: http://www.tvapublications.com
Emp.: 250
Book & Magazine Publisher
N.A.I.C.S.: 513130

Subsidiary (Domestic):

Videotron Ltd. (2)
612 Saint-Jacques Street 17th floor North Tower, Montreal, H3C 4M8, QC, Canada (100%)
Tel.: (514) 281-1232
Web Site: https://www.videotron.com
Rev.: $2,285,678,064
Assets: $5,450,011,165
Liabilities: $5,657,037,909
Net Worth: ($207,026,744)
Earnings: $424,334,450
Emp.: 5,841
Fiscal Year-end: 12/31/2021
Cable TV, Internet & Wireless Telephone Services
N.A.I.C.S.: 516210
Jean-Francois Pruneau *(Pres & CEO)*

QUECHEN SILICON CHEMICAL CO., LTD.
New Materials Industrial Park, Donggang Town Xishan District, Wuxi, 214196, Jiangsu, China
Tel.: (86) 51088793288
Web Site: https://www.quechen.com
Year Founded: 2003
605183—(SHG)
Rev.: $245,204,697
Assets: $433,651,416
Liabilities: $60,496,029
Net Worth: $373,155,387
Earnings: $53,416,879
Fiscal Year-end: 12/31/22
Chemical Product Mfr & Distr
N.A.I.C.S.: 325520
Weidong Que *(Chm & Gen Mgr)*

QUECLINK WIRELESS SOLUTIONS CO., LTD.
No 30 Lane 500 Xinlong Road, Minhang District, Shanghai, 201101, China
Tel.: (86) 2151082965
Web Site: https://www.queclink.com
Year Founded: 2009
300590—(CHIN)
Rev.: $143,069,852
Assets: $285,552,388
Liabilities: $36,881,572
Net Worth: $248,670,816
Earnings: $20,669,484
Fiscal Year-end: 12/31/23
Terminal Mfr & Distr
N.A.I.C.S.: 335931

QUECTEL WIRELESS SOLUTIONS CO., LTD.
Building 5 Phase III Area B No 1016 Tianlin Road, Shanghai Business Park Minhang, Shanghai, 200233, China
Tel.: (86) 2151086236
Web Site: https://www.quectel.com
Year Founded: 2010
603236—(SHG)
Rev.: $1,997,926,609
Assets: $1,442,353,517
Liabilities: $920,105,279
Net Worth: $522,248,239
Earnings: $87,443,703
Fiscal Year-end: 12/31/22
Wireless Communication Product Mfr
N.A.I.C.S.: 334220
Patrick Qian *(CEO)*

QUEEN SOUTH TEXTILE MILLS LTD.
Plot No 85-88 Extension Area Dhaka Export Processing Zone Savar, Dhaka, Bangladesh
Tel.: (880) 27790219
Web Site: https://www.qstmills.com
QUEENSOUTH—(CHT)
Rev.: $41,598,138
Assets: $49,513,202
Liabilities: $24,745,686
Net Worth: $24,767,516
Earnings: $1,904,286
Emp.: 865
Fiscal Year-end: 06/30/21
Textile Products Mfr
N.A.I.C.S.: 313310
Wong Kwok Chuen *(Chm)*

QUEEN'S ROAD CAPITAL INVESTMENT LTD.
Suite 1240-1140 West Pender St, Vancouver, V6E 4G1, BC, Canada
Tel.: (604) 365-6681 BC
Web Site: http://www.lithionenergycorp.com
Year Founded: 2011
BRSGF—(OTCIQ)
Rev.: $23,197,239
Assets: $282,856,142
Liabilities: $32,858,227
Net Worth: $249,997,915
Earnings: $18,035,391
Fiscal Year-end: 08/31/24
Gold & Copper Mining
N.A.I.C.S.: 212220

Subsidiaries:

PT East Asia Minerals Indonesia (1)
Wisma 46 Kota BNI 11th Floor Suite 11 01, Jl Jend Sudirman Kav 1, Jakarta, Indonesia
Tel.: (62) 21 5749118
Gold & Copper Exploration Services
N.A.I.C.S.: 212220

QUEEN'S ROAD CAPITAL INVESTMENT LTD.
Cheung Kong Centre Suite 2006 2 Queens Road Central, Hong Kong, China (Hong Kong)
Tel.: (852) 27592022
Web Site: https://www.queensrdcapital.com
QRC—(TSX)
Rev.: $71,391,730
Assets: $149,224,629
Liabilities: $172,712
Net Worth: $149,051,917
Earnings: $67,024,933
Fiscal Year-end: 08/31/21
Asset Management Services
N.A.I.C.S.: 523940
Warren Gilman *(Chm & CEO)*

QUEENCO LEISURE INTERNATIONAL LTD.
16 Bar-Kochva St Noa House 9 Flr, Bnei Brak, 5126107, Israel
Tel.: (972) 37566585
Web Site: http://www.queenco.com
Year Founded: 2007
Sales Range: $10-24.9 Million
Emp.: 2,670
Casino Operator
N.A.I.C.S.: 721120
Yigal Zilkha *(Founder & Chm)*

Subsidiaries:

Club Hotel Loutraki S.A. (1)
48 Posidonos Str, 20300, Loutraki, Greece
Tel.: (30) 744060333
Web Site: http://www.clubhotelloutraki.gr
Casinos Services
N.A.I.C.S.: 721120

QUEENS LANE CAPITAL PTY LTD
10 Queens Road Level 13, Melbourne, 3004, VIC, Australia
Tel.: (61) 03 9092 2634
Web Site: http://www.qlcapital.com.au
Privater Equity Firm
N.A.I.C.S.: 523999
Larry Kestelman *(Chm)*

Subsidiaries:

The PAS Group Pty Ltd (1)
Level 1 Building 8 658 Church Street, Richmond, 3121, VIC, Australia
Tel.: (61) 3 9902 5555
Web Site: http://www.thepasgroup.com.au
Clothing Mfr & Distr
N.A.I.C.S.: 315250
Eric Morris *(CEO & Mng Dir)*

Subsidiary (Domestic):

Designworks Clothing Company Pty. Ltd. (2)
Level 1 Building 8 658 Church Street, Richmond, 3121, VIC, Australia
Tel.: (61) 398229888
Web Site: http://www.designwcc.com.au
Clothing Design Services
N.A.I.C.S.: 541490

JETS Swimwear Pty. Ltd. (2)
34 The Mill 41-43 Bourke Road, Alexandria, 2015, NSW, Australia
Tel.: (61) 1300575620
Web Site: http://www.jets.com.au
Clothing Distr
N.A.I.C.S.: 424350

Subsidiary (US):

PAS US, Inc. (2)
2010 W 15th St, Washington, NC 27889
Tel.: (252) 974-5500
Web Site: http://www.pas-net.biz
Emp.: 100
Cable Mfr
N.A.I.C.S.: 335921

Subsidiary (Domestic):

Review Australia Pty. Ltd. (2)
Level 1 Building 8 658 Church St, Richmond, 3121, VIC, Australia
Tel.: (61) 399025400
Web Site: http://www.review-australia.com
Clothing Distr
N.A.I.C.S.: 424350

White Runway Pty. Ltd. (2)
Suite 22 21 Collins Street, Alexandria, 2015, NSW, Australia
Tel.: (61) 1300133839
Web Site: http://www.whiterunway.com
Clothing Distr
N.A.I.C.S.: 424350

Yarra Trail Pty. Ltd. (2)
PO Box 4398, Mulgrave, 3170, VIC, Australia
Tel.: (61) 800001399
Web Site: http://www.yarratrail.com.au
Clothing Distr
N.A.I.C.S.: 424350

QUEENSLAND RAIL LIMITED
Level 14 Rail Centre 1 305 Edward Street, Brisbane, 4000, QLD, Australia
Tel.: (61) 7 3072 2222 AU
Web Site: http://www.queenslandrail.com.au
Rev.: $1,334,360,946
Assets: $4,752,398,467
Liabilities: $2,788,759,208
Net Worth: $1,963,639,259
Earnings: $154,456,172
Emp.: 5,778
Fiscal Year-end: 06/30/15
Passenger Rail Services
N.A.I.C.S.: 485112
Martin Ryan *(Exec Gen Mgr-Customer Svc)*

QUEENSLAND TREASURY CORPORATION
Level 31 111 Eagle Street, GPO Box 1096, Brisbane, 4001, QLD, Australia
Tel.: (61) 738424600
Web Site: http://www.qtc.com.au
Year Founded: 1988
XQL—(ASX)
Rev.: $73,956,490
Assets: $129,526,019,305
Liabilities: $129,100,474,314
Net Worth: $425,544,991
Earnings: ($27,762,128)
Emp.: 201
Fiscal Year-end: 06/30/22
Financial Advisory Services
N.A.I.C.S.: 523940
Gerard Bradley *(Chm)*

QUEENSWAY GROUP LIMITED
3rd Floor 247-249 Cromwell Road, London, SW5 9GA, United Kingdom
Tel.: (44) 20 7244 4100 UK
Web Site: http://www.queensway.com
Year Founded: 1973
Emp.: 900
Hospitality Real Estate Investment & Franchise Management Services
N.A.I.C.S.: 531390
Naushad Jivraj *(CEO)*

Queensway Group Limited—(Continued)

QUEMCHI SA
Hendaya N 60 Oficina N 1502, Las Condes, Santiago, Chile
Tel.: (56) 224413790
Web Site: https://www.quemchi.cl
QUEMCHI—(SGO)
Sales Range: Less than $1 Million
Holding Company
N.A.I.C.S.: 551112
Luis Rafael Grez Jordan (CEO)

QUENDALE CAPITAL CORP.
2000 350 - 7th Avenue S W, Calgary, T2P 3N9, AB, Canada
Tel.: (403) 774-2900
QOC.P—(TSXV)
Rev.: $15,076
Assets: $81,800,673
Liabilities: $29,502,908
Net Worth: $52,297,765
Earnings: ($14,909,475)
Fiscal Year-end: 12/31/20
Asset Management Services
N.A.I.C.S.: 523940
Richard A. Graham (CEO & CFO)

QUERCUS TOWARZYSTWO FUNDUSZY INWESTYCYJNYCH S.A.
Nowy Swiat 6/12, 00-400, Warsaw, Poland
Tel.: (48) 222053000
Web Site: https://www.quercustfi.pl
Year Founded: 2007
QRS—(WAR)
Rev.: $3,009,654
Assets: $51,952,744
Liabilities: $25,297,002
Net Worth: $26,655,742
Earnings: $8,057,927
Fiscal Year-end: 12/31/23
Miscellaneous Financial Investment Activities
N.A.I.C.S.: 523999
Sebastian Buczek (Chm-Mgmt Bd)

QUESS CORP LIMITED
Quess House 3/3/2 Bellandur Gate Sarjapur Road, Bengaluru, 560103, Karnataka, India
Tel.: (91) 8061056001
Web Site: https://www.quesscorp.com
Year Founded: 2007
539978—(BOM)
Rev.: $2,060,394,701
Assets: $733,621,605
Liabilities: $406,206,942
Net Worth: $327,414,663
Earnings: $26,726,096
Emp.: 2,534
Fiscal Year-end: 03/31/23
Staffing Services
N.A.I.C.S.: 561320
Ajit Isaac (Chm & Mng Dir)

Subsidiaries:

Allsectech Manila Inc. (1)
3/F Market Market Mall Bonifacio Global City, Taguig, Metro Manila, Philippines
Tel.: (63) 288565386
Web Site: https://allsec-astig.com
Outsourcing Services
N.A.I.C.S.: 541612

Conneqt Business Solutions Ltd. (1) (100%)
Tel.: (91) 8061056001
Web Site: https://www.conneqtbusiness.com
Business Process Outsourcing Services
N.A.I.C.S.: 561499
A. S. Krishnan (CFO)

Subsidiary (Domestic):

Allsec Technologies Limited (2)
46C Velachery Main Road Velachery, Chennai, 600 042, India (73.38%)
Tel.: (91) 4442997070
Web Site: https://www.allsectech.com
Rev.: $38,265,045
Assets: $43,603,560
Liabilities: $7,414,680
Net Worth: $36,188,880
Earnings: $4,793,880
Emp.: 3,805
Fiscal Year-end: 03/31/2021
Business Process Outsourcing Services
N.A.I.C.S.: 561499
R. Vaithiyanathan (Sr VP-Ops & HR)

Subsidiary (US):

Retreat Capital Management, Inc. (3)
6306 Commerce Dr Ste 120, Irving, TX 75063
Tel.: (800) 551-2827
Web Site: http://www.allsecfin.com
Mortgage Solutions Services
N.A.I.C.S.: 561499

Golden Star Facilities & Services Private Limited (1)
Plot No 25 and 26 No 1-98/9/3/9 & 10 Image Gardens Road, Madhapur, Hyderabad, 500081, India
Tel.: (91) 404 240 8000
Web Site: https://www.goldenstarfacilities.com
Facility Management Services
N.A.I.C.S.: 561210

Greenpiece Landscapes India Private Limited (1)
435 18th Main Rd IMAD building 6th Block, Koramangala, Bengaluru, 560095, Karnataka, India
Tel.: (91) 8025525129
Web Site: https://www.greenpiece.in
Building Maintenance Services
N.A.I.C.S.: 561790

Mindwire Systems Limited (1)
Carling Executive Park 1545 Carling Avenue Suite 308, Ottawa, K1Z 8P9, ON, Canada
Tel.: (613) 789-7000
Web Site: https://www.mindwire.ca
Software Development Services
N.A.I.C.S.: 541511
Marc Bolduc (COO)

Quess Corp Lanka (Private) Limited (1)
Level 7 BOC Merchant Tower No 28 St Michaels Road, 03, Colombo, Sri Lanka
Tel.: (94) 112392269
Staffing & Recruiting Services
N.A.I.C.S.: 561311

Quess Corp NA LLC (1)
201 Littleton Rd Ste 250, Morris Plains, NJ 07950
Tel.: (973) 906-8985
Web Site: https://www.quessgts.com
Information Technology Services
N.A.I.C.S.: 541511

Quesscorp Management Consultancies (1)
2204 Al Shafar Tower 1 Barsha Heights, PO Box 32936, Dubai, United Arab Emirates
Tel.: (971) 44329777
Web Site: https://www.quesscorpme.com
Human Resource Outsourcing Services
N.A.I.C.S.: 541612

Quessglobal (Malaysia) Sdn. Bhd. (1)
Unit 25-13A Level 25 Q Sentral JalanStesenSentral 2, Kuala Lumpur Sentral, 50470, Kuala Lumpur, Malaysia
Tel.: (60) 327136670
Staffing & Recruiting Services
N.A.I.C.S.: 561311

Terrier Security Services (India) Private Limited (1)
Tel.: (91) 18003099177
Web Site: https://www.terrier.co.in
Security Guard Services
N.A.I.C.S.: 561612
Guruprasad Srinivasan (COO)

Vedang Cellular Services Private Limited (1)
Office No-3B 3rd Floor B Wing Times Square Andheri Kurla Road, Marol Naka Near Marol Naka Metro Station Andheri East, Mumbai, 400059, Maharashtra, India
Tel.: (91) 2240022930
Web Site: https://www.vedangcellular.com
Emp.: 2,200
Design & Build Services
N.A.I.C.S.: 541310
Ashish Kapoor (CEO)

QUEST CAPITAL MARKETS LTD.
Mayfair Towers 2 Palm Avenue, Kolkata, 700019, West Bengal, India
Tel.: (91) 46022160
Web Site: https://www.bnkcapital.com
Year Founded: 1986
500069—(BOM)
Rev.: $5,342,228
Assets: $117,052,476
Liabilities: $5,556,492
Net Worth: $111,495,985
Earnings: $3,002,631
Emp.: 3
Fiscal Year-end: 03/31/22
Investment Banking Services
N.A.I.C.S.: 523150
Ajit Khandelwal (Chm & Mng Dir)

Subsidiaries:

BNK Commodities Pvt Ltd. (1)
Mayfair Towers 2 Palm Avenue, Kolkata, 700 019, India
Tel.: (91) 3322810560
Web Site: http://www.bnkcomdex.com
Commodity Exchange Services
N.A.I.C.S.: 523210

QUEST CO., LTD.
Msb Tamachi - Tamachi Station Tower N 14F 3-1-1 Shibaura, Minato-ku, Tokyo, 108-0023, Japan
Tel.: (81) 334531181
Web Site: https://www.quest.co.jp
Year Founded: 1965
2332—(TKS)
Rev.: $94,020,640
Assets: $62,530,600
Liabilities: $17,668,530
Net Worth: $44,862,070
Earnings: $4,600,560
Emp.: 1,052
Fiscal Year-end: 03/31/24
Information Services
N.A.I.C.S.: 519290
Kazuro Sato (Chm)

QUEST FOR GROWTH NV
Lei 19 bus 3, B-3000, Leuven, Belgium
Tel.: (32) 16284128
Web Site: https://www.questforgrowth.com
Year Founded: 1998
QFG—(EUR)
Rev.: $86,125
Assets: $155,404,773
Liabilities: $44,282
Net Worth: $155,364,491
Earnings: ($3,890,341)
Fiscal Year-end: 12/31/23
Investment Services
N.A.I.C.S.: 523999
Antoon De Proft (Chm)

QUEST HOLDINGS S.A.
2A Argyroupoleos str, 176 76, Athens, Greece
Tel.: (30) 2119991000
Web Site: https://www.quest.gr
Year Founded: 1981
QUEST—(ATH)
Rev.: $1,113,605,655
Assets: $746,024,174
Liabilities: $488,281,891
Net Worth: $257,742,284
Earnings: $45,327,002
Emp.: 2,599
Fiscal Year-end: 12/31/22
Telecom & Software Application & Development Services
N.A.I.C.S.: 334220
Eftychia Koutsoureli (Vice Chm)

Subsidiaries:

ISQUARE S.A. (1)
27 Al Pantou str, Kallithea, 17671, Athens, Greece
Tel.: (30) 2119997500
Web Site: http://www.isquare.gr
Sales Range: $25-49.9 Million
Emp.: 50
Electronic Product Distr
N.A.I.C.S.: 423690

UNISYSTEMS S.A. (1)
19-23 Al Pantou str, Kallithea, 17671, Athens, Greece
Tel.: (30) 2119997000
Web Site: http://www.unisystems.gr
Sales Range: $150-199.9 Million
Emp.: 549
Business Management Software Development Services
N.A.I.C.S.: 541511
Loumakis Ioannis (Chm & Mng Dir)

Subsidiary (Non-US):

Uni Systems Romania SRL (2)
17C Sevastopol Street 1st Floor apartment no 4, 1st District, Bucharest, 10991, Romania
Tel.: (40) 212244197
Web Site: http://www.unisystems.gr
Sales Range: $25-49.9 Million
Emp.: 2
Business Software Development Services
N.A.I.C.S.: 541511

Unisystems Belgium S.A. (2)
38-40 Square de Meeus Rue du Luxembourg, Brussels, 1000, Belgium
Tel.: (32) 24016878
Sales Range: $25-49.9 Million
Emp.: 4
Business Software Development Services
N.A.I.C.S.: 541511

Uni Systems Bulgaria LTD (1)
Office III-A2 Section III Floor 5 81 Bulgaria Boulevard, 1404, Sofia, Bulgaria
Tel.: (359) 29506450
Web Site: http://www.unisystems.gr
Sales Range: $25-49.9 Million
Emp.: 2
Business Software Development Services
N.A.I.C.S.: 541511

Unisystems Information Technology Systems SRL (1)
Str Sevastopol 17c Sectorul 1, Bucharest, 10991, Romania
Tel.: (40) 212244197
Web Site: http://www.unisystems.com
Sales Range: $25-49.9 Million
Emp.: 4
Information Technology Support Services
N.A.I.C.S.: 519290

QUEST PHARMATECH INC.
4342 97 Street, Edmonton, T6E 5R9, AB, Canada
Tel.: (780) 448-1400
Web Site: https://www.questpharmatech.com
QPTFF—(OTCIQ)
Rev.: $11,868
Assets: $18,482,164
Liabilities: $998,855
Net Worth: $17,483,308
Earnings: ($2,278,957)
Fiscal Year-end: 01/31/24
Pharmaceutical Products Research & Development
N.A.I.C.S.: 325412

QUEST RARE MINERALS LTD.
1200 Avenue McGill College Ste 1100, Montreal, H3B 4G7, QC, Canada
Tel.: (514) 228-0377

Year Founded: 2007
Sales Range: Less than $1 Million
Metal Mining Services
N.A.I.C.S.: 212290
Alan D. Wilson *(CFO & VP)*

QUEST WATER GLOBAL, INC.
828 Harbourside Drive Suite 209,
North Vancouver, V7P 3R9, BC,
Canada
Tel.: (604) 565-1103   DE
Web Site:
   https://www.questwaterglobal.com
Year Founded: 2010
QWTR—(OTCIQ)
Assets: $2,199
Liabilities: $1,837,103
Net Worth: ($1,834,904)
Earnings: ($596,013)
Emp.: 2
Fiscal Year-end: 12/31/23
Water Purification Systems
N.A.I.C.S.: 221310
John Balanko *(Chm, Pres & CEO)*

QUESTBACK GROUP AS
Bogstadveien 54, 0366, Oslo, Norway
Tel.: (47) 21027070
Web Site:
   https://www.questback.com
Year Founded: 2000
QUEST—(EUR)
Rev.: $144,812,290
Assets: $512,269,100
Liabilities: $492,781,870
Net Worth: $19,487,230
Earnings: ($33,840,100)
Emp.: 51
Fiscal Year-end: 12/31/21
Software Development Services
N.A.I.C.S.: 541511
Niklas Olsson *(COO)*

QUESTE COMMUNICATIONS LIMITED
Suite 1 Level 1 680 Murray Street,
West Perth, 6005, WA, Australia
Tel.: (61) 892149777   AU
Web Site: https://www.queste.com.au
Year Founded: 1998
QUE—(ASX)
Rev.: $28,889
Assets: $2,634,162
Liabilities: $603,205
Net Worth: $2,030,957
Earnings: ($3,209,692)
Emp.: 8
Fiscal Year-end: 06/30/22
Business Services
N.A.I.C.S.: 518210
Farooq Khan *(Chm & Mng Dir)*

QUESTEL SAS
1 Boulevard de la Madeleine, 75001,
Paris, France
Tel.: (33) 155045200   FR
Web Site: http://www.questel.com
Software Services
N.A.I.C.S.: 513210
Antonia Rodgers *(Mng Dir-Foreign Filings)*

QUESTERRE ENERGY CORPORATION
1650 AMEC Place 801 Sixth Avenue
SW, Calgary, T2P 3W2, AB, Canada
Tel.: (403) 777-1185   AB
Web Site: https://www.questerre.com
Year Founded: 1971
QEC—(TSX)
Rev.: $23,784,441
Assets: $144,146,042
Liabilities: $27,616,831
Net Worth: $116,529,211
Earnings: ($3,364,586)
Emp.: 8

Fiscal Year-end: 12/31/21
Oil & Gas Exploration & Production
N.A.I.C.S.: 211120
John Brodylo *(VP-Exploration)*

QUESTFIRE ENERGY CORP.
1100 350 - 7th Ave SW, Calgary, T2P
3N9, AB, Canada
Tel.: (403) 263-6658   AB
Web Site: http://www.questfire.ca
Year Founded: 2010
Rev.: $24,503,473
Assets: $72,255,295
Liabilities: $62,573,467
Net Worth: $9,681,828
Earnings: ($5,732,214)
Emp.: 20
Fiscal Year-end: 12/31/16
Oil & Gas Exploration
N.A.I.C.S.: 211120
Richard H. Dahl *(Pres & CEO)*

QUESTOR TECHNOLOGY INC.
140 4 Avenue SW Suite 2240, Calgary, T2P 3N3, AB, Canada
Tel.: (403) 571-1530   AB
Web Site:
   https://www.questortech.com
QUTIF—(OTCIQ)
Rev.: $4,305,352
Assets: $27,417,236
Liabilities: $3,571,714
Net Worth: $23,845,522
Earnings: ($3,120,034)
Emp.: 12
Fiscal Year-end: 12/31/21
Oil & Gas Environmental Solutions
N.A.I.C.S.: 213112
Audrey Mascarenhas *(Chm, Pres & CEO)*

Subsidiaries:

ClearPower Systems Inc. (1)
15330 Flight Path Dr, Brooksville, FL 34604
Tel.: (352) 442-8651
Web Site:
   https://www.clearpowersystems.com
Power Generator Product Mfr
N.A.I.C.S.: 335312

Questor Solutions & Technology Inc. (1)
15330 Flight Path Dr, Brooksville, FL 34604
Waste Gas Incinerator System Distr
N.A.I.C.S.: 423830

QUESTUS LIMITED
Unit 1 5 Bramall Street, Perth, 6004,
WA, Australia
Tel.: (61) 8 6311 8332
Web Site: http://www.questus.com.au
Rev.: $1,245,344
Assets: $7,209,105
Liabilities: $5,835,184
Net Worth: $1,373,921
Earnings: ($1,457,253)
Emp.: 10
Fiscal Year-end: 06/30/18
Securities Services
N.A.I.C.S.: 525910
David James Somerville *(Chm)*

Subsidiaries:

Questus Capital Solutions Pty. Ltd. (1)
105 Railway Road, Subiaco, 6008, WA, Australia
Tel.: (61) 863105020
Web Site: http://www.questus.com.au
Sales Range: $50-74.9 Million
Emp.: 12
Property & Investment Management Services
N.A.I.C.S.: 531311

Questus Funds Management Limited (1)
Level 3 47 Kishorn Rd, PO Box 1346, Applecross, 6153, WA, Australia
Tel.: (61) 863105040

Web Site: http://www.questus.com.au
Sales Range: $50-74.9 Million
Emp.: 12
Fund Management Services
N.A.I.C.S.: 525910

QUETTA GROUP OF COMPANIES LLC
Nadir House Ground Floor I I Chundrigar Road, Karachi, Pakistan
Tel.: (92) 2132414334
Web Site:
   http://www.quettagroup.com
Sales Range: $200-249.9 Million
Manages & Operates Various Manufacturing Companies
N.A.I.C.S.: 551112

Subsidiaries:

Elegant Footwear Limited (1)
17-J Gulberg III, Lahore, 54660, Pakistan
Tel.: (92) 425858720
Leather Footwear
N.A.I.C.S.: 811430

Nabeel Limited (1)
33 KM G T Road Khori, 39000, Sheikhupura, Pakistan
Tel.: (92) 427991912
Produces Glue, Gelatine, Ossein & Decalcium Phospate
N.A.I.C.S.: 316110

National Tanneries of Pakistan Limited (1)
17-J Gulberg-III, Lahore, 54660, Pakistan
Tel.: (92) 425858717
Machinery Used to Produce Leather & Leather Garments
N.A.I.C.S.: 316110

Nova Leathers (Pvt.) Ltd. (1)
Plot 30 Sector 15 Korangi Industrial Area, Karachi, Pakistan
Tel.: (92) 215061716
Web Site: http://www.novaleathers.com
Leather Mfr
N.A.I.C.S.: 316990

Quetta Power Generation Limited (1)
Nadir House Ground Fl, I.I Chundrigar Rd, Karachi, Pakistan
Tel.: (92) 212414334
Sales Range: $75-99.9 Million
Emp.: 65
Distributes Electric Power
N.A.I.C.S.: 221122

Quetta Textile Mills Limited (1)
Nadir House Ground Floor I I Chundrigar Road, Karachi, 74000, Pakistan
Tel.: (92) 2132414334
Web Site: https://quettagroup.com
Rev.: $12,206,217
Assets: $54,001,333
Liabilities: $39,656,498
Net Worth: $14,344,835
Earnings: ($3,543,787)
Emp.: 2,542
Fiscal Year-end: 06/30/2023
Textile Mfr
N.A.I.C.S.: 313310
Tariq Iqbal *(CEO)*

QUHUO LIMITED
3F Building A Xinanmen No 1 South
Bank Huihe South Street, Chaoyang
District, Beijing, 100020, China
Tel.: (86) 1085765328   Ky
Web Site: https://quhuo.cn
Year Founded: 2019
QH—(NASDAQ)
Rev.: $585,320,113
Assets: $161,731,081
Liabilities: $85,497,308
Net Worth: $76,233,772
Earnings: ($2,011,647)
Emp.: 495
Fiscal Year-end: 12/31/22
Holding Company
N.A.I.C.S.: 551112
Leslie Yu *(Founder, Chm & CEO)*

QUI! GROUP S.P.A.
Via XX Settembre 29/7, 16121,
Genoa, Italy
Tel.: (39) 010 576751
Web Site: http://www.quigroup.it
Year Founded: 1989
Sales Range: $700-749.9 Million
Emp.: 1,000
Electronic Financial Payment Services
N.A.I.C.S.: 522320
Gregorio Fogliani *(Founder & Pres)*

Subsidiaries:

PayBay Networks Srl (1)
Via XX Settembre 98/G, 00187, Rome, Italy
Tel.: (39) 064883188
Web Site: http://www.paybay.it
Emp.: 60
Software Development Services
N.A.I.C.S.: 541511

Welfare Company Srl (1)
Piazza della Repubblica 32, 20124, Milan, Italy
Tel.: (39) 0220245494
Web Site: http://www.welfarecompany.it
Management Support Services
N.A.I.C.S.: 523940

QUIAPEG PHARMACEUTICALS HOLDING AB
Uppsala Business Park Virdings Alle
32 B, 754 50, Uppsala, Sweden
Tel.: (46) 706931253
Web Site: https://www.quiapeg.com
Year Founded: 2004
99B—(DEU)
Holding Company
N.A.I.C.S.: 551112
Per S. Thoresen *(Chm)*

QUICE FOOD INDUSTRIES LIMITED
WS7 Madina Palace Mezzanine Floor
Faran Co-operative Society, Dhoraji
Colony, Karachi, Pakistan
Tel.: (92) 213485717780
Web Site: https://www.quice.com.pk
Year Founded: 1980
QUICE—(PSX)
Rev.: $1,475,964
Assets: $4,825,492
Liabilities: $1,681,119
Net Worth: $3,144,373
Earnings: ($182,402)
Emp.: 37
Fiscal Year-end: 06/30/21
Food Products Mfr
N.A.I.C.S.: 311999
Muhammad Atif *(CEO)*

QUICK CO., LTD.
Osaka Fukoku Seimei Bldg 2-4
Komatsubaracho, Kita-ku, Osaka,
530-0018, Japan
Tel.: (81) 663660919
Web Site: https://www.919.jp
Year Founded: 1980
4318—(TKS)
Rev.: $194,909,070
Assets: $145,697,620
Liabilities: $37,161,420
Net Worth: $108,536,200
Earnings: $23,168,050
Emp.: 1,925
Fiscal Year-end: 03/31/24
Human Resource & Information Services
N.A.I.C.S.: 519290
Tsutomu Wano *(Chm & CEO)*

Subsidiaries:

QUICK USA, INC. (1)
8 W 38th St Ste 802, New York, NY 10018
Tel.: (212) 692-0850
Web Site: https://www.919usa.com
Human Resource Consulting Services

QUICK CO., LTD.

QUICK CO., LTD.—(Continued)
N.A.I.C.S.: 541612
Shoichi Yamanaka *(COO & Gen Mgr)*

QUICK VIETNAM CO., LTD. (1)
4F IBC Building 1A Cong Truong Me Linh Street, Dist 1, Ho Chi Minh City, 71050, Vietnam
Tel.: (84) 283 823 6001
Web Site: https://www.919vn.com
Human Resource Consulting Services
N.A.I.C.S.: 541612
Takeo Furuya *(Pres)*

Shanghai Quick Myts Mingsheng HR-Consulting Service CO., LTD. (1)
2601 1 Grand Gateway No 1 Hongqiao Road, Shanghai, 200030, China
Tel.: (86) 21 6407 1919
Web Site: http://www.919myts.com.cn
Human Resource Consulting Services
N.A.I.C.S.: 541612

QUICK HEAL TECHNOLOGIES (P) LTD.
Marvel Edge Office No 7010 C & D 7th Floor Viman Nagar, Pune, 411014, Maharashtra, India
Tel.: (91) 2066813232
Web Site: http://www.quickheal.co.in
Year Founded: 1995
Sales Range: $75-99.9 Million
Emp.: 450
Security Software Development Services
N.A.I.C.S.: 513210
Kailash Katkar *(CEO & Mng Dir)*

Subsidiaries:

Quick Heal Japan KK. (1)
10 F 5 Sankyou Building Shinkawa 1-2-8, Chuo-ku, Tokyo, 104-0033, Japan
Tel.: (81) 362283983
Software Development Services
N.A.I.C.S.: 541511

Quick Heal Technologies (MENA) FZE (1)
Office 122B Business Center 4, Ras al Khaimah, United Arab Emirates
Tel.: (971) 72031025
Software Development Services
N.A.I.C.S.: 541511

Quick Heal Technologies Africa Ltd. (1)
Office Suite No D1 Showroom No 4 Winsford Industrial Park Off, Baba Dogo Road, Nairobi, Kenya
Tel.: (254) 733120621
Software Development Services
N.A.I.C.S.: 541511

Quick Heal Technologies America Inc (1)
1 Courthouse Ln Unit 7, Chelmsford, MA 01824
Tel.: (347) 338-2630
Software Development Services
N.A.I.C.S.: 541511

QUICK INTELLIGENT EQUIPMENT CO., LTD.
No 11 Fengxiang Road Wujin High-Tech Development Zone, Southern District, Changzhou, 213167, Jiangsu, China
Tel.: (86) 51986225678
Web Site: https://www.quick-global.com
Year Founded: 2006
603203—(SHG)
Rev.: $126,558,062
Assets: $263,649,887
Liabilities: $62,884,584
Net Worth: $200,765,303
Earnings: $38,382,566
Fiscal Year-end: 12/31/22
Electronic Equipment Mfr & Distr
N.A.I.C.S.: 333992
Jin Chun *(Chm)*

QUICK RESTAURANTS S.A.
Parc des Portes de Paris batiment n 123 50 avenue du President Wilson, 93214, Saint Denis, Cedex, France
Tel.: (33) 33149516464 BE
Web Site: http://www.quick.fr
Year Founded: 1970
Fast Food Restaurant Operator & Franchisor
N.A.I.C.S.: 722511
Luc Thibaud *(VP-Ops)*

QUICKFEE LIMITED
Suite 4 07 10 Century Circuit, Norwest, Sydney, 2153, NSW, Australia
Tel.: (61) 280907700
Web Site: https://www.quickfee.com
Year Founded: 2009
QFE—(ASX)
Rev.: $9,627,698
Assets: $31,370,542
Liabilities: $25,538,241
Net Worth: $5,832,301
Earnings: ($5,265,697)
Fiscal Year-end: 06/30/23
Payment Management Services
N.A.I.C.S.: 522320
Simon Yeandle *(Sec)*

Subsidiaries:

Franchise Payment Services Pty. Ltd. (1)
Suite 4 07 10 Century Cct, Norwest, Sydney, 2153, NSW, Australia
Tel.: (61) 285998413
Web Site: https://franchisepaymentservices.com
Financial Payment Services
N.A.I.C.S.: 522320

QuickFee Group LLC (1)
8605 Santa Monica Blvd Ste 83260, West Hollywood, CA 90069-4109
Web Site: https://quickfee.com
Online Payment & Financing Services
N.A.I.C.S.: 522220

QUICKLIZARD LTD.
Hashiloah 4, Petah Tikva, Israel
Tel.: (972) 37428800
Web Site: https://www.quicklizard.com
Year Founded: 2010
QLRD—(TAE)
Rev.: $5,729,353
Assets: $7,622,146
Liabilities: $2,701,318
Net Worth: $4,920,829
Earnings: ($2,890,841)
Fiscal Year-end: 06/30/23
Information Technology Services
N.A.I.C.S.: 541519
Yossi Cohen *(Co-Founder & CTO)*

QUICKSILVER TRANSLATE
Girona 17 Esc A 1 2, Sant Cugat del Valles, 08172, Barcelona, Spain
Tel.: (34) 93 590 7140
Web Site: http://www.quicksilvertranslate.com
Year Founded: 2004
Sales Range: $1-9.9 Million
Emp.: 10
Translation Services
N.A.I.C.S.: 561499
Stephen Whiteley *(Mng Dir-Bus Dev)*

QUICKSTEP HOLDINGS LIMITED
361 Milperra Road, Bankstown, 2200, NSW, Australia
Tel.: (61) 297740300
Web Site: https://www.quickstep.com.au
QHL—(ASX)
Rev.: $59,408,387
Assets: $49,342,949
Liabilities: $40,765,892

Net Worth: $8,577,057
Earnings: ($721,822)
Emp.: 200
Fiscal Year-end: 06/30/24
Industrial Machinery
N.A.I.C.S.: 322219
Jaime Pinto *(Sec)*

Subsidiaries:

Quickstep Technologies Pty. Ltd. (1)
136 Cockburn Rd, N Coogee, Perth, 6166, Western Australia, Australia
Tel.: (61) 894323200
Web Site: http://www.quickstep.com.au
Sales Range: $25-49.9 Million
Emp.: 25
Aerospace Composite Components Mfr
N.A.I.C.S.: 334511
David Marino *(CEO & Mng Dir)*

QUICKTOUCH TECHNOLOGIES LIMITED
Office No 203 2nd Floor D-Mall Netaji Subhash Place, Pitampura, Delhi, 110034, India
Tel.: (91) 8929593668
Web Site: https://www.quicktouch.co.in
Year Founded: 2013
QUICKTOUCH—(NSE)
Rev.: $10,535,726
Assets: $5,633,931
Liabilities: $4,074,683
Net Worth: $1,559,248
Earnings: $766,240
Emp.: 53
Fiscal Year-end: 03/31/23
Information Technology Services
N.A.I.C.S.: 541512
Gaurav Jindal *(Mng Dir)*

QUIETUDE PROMOTION
Rue Jean Perrin, 17000, La Rochelle, Charente Maritime, France
Tel.: (33) 546310313
Web Site: http://www.quietude.fr
Rev.: $23,900,000
Emp.: 28
Property Promotion & Leasehold
N.A.I.C.S.: 551112
Denis Cormenier *(Gen Mgr)*

QUIK-RUN COURIER LTD
3190 Caravelle Drive, Mississauga, L4V 1K9, ON, Canada
Tel.: (905) 791-9004
Web Site: http://www.qrclogistics.com
Sales Range: $50-74.9 Million
Emp.: 100
Courier & Warehousing Distribution Provider
N.A.I.C.S.: 541614
Larry Bain *(Mgr-HR)*

QUIKR INDIA PVT LTD.
1st Floor Raghuvanshi Mansion Senapati Bapat Marg Lower Parel, Mumbai, India
Tel.: (91) 22 67290000
Web Site: http://www.quikr.com
Sales Range: $50-74.9 Million
Online Classified Advertising Services
N.A.I.C.S.: 541870

QUILICURA S.A.
Malaga 89 Piso 5 Las Condes, Santiago, Chile
Tel.: (56) 4111700
Web Site: https://www.quilicurasa.cl
QUILICURA—(SGO)
Sales Range: Less than $1 Million
Holding Company
N.A.I.C.S.: 551112
Gonzalo Garcia Bustamante *(CEO)*

QUILLER & BLAKE

INTERNATIONAL PUBLIC

6 Lansing Sq Ste 218, Toronto, M2J 1T5, ON, Canada
Tel.: (416) 502-0591
Web Site: http://www.quillerandblake.com
Sales Range: $10-24.9 Million
Emp.: 18
N.A.I.C.S.: 541613
Chris Lindley *(Founder)*

Subsidiaries:

Quiller & Blake (1)
737 Main St Ste 250, Buffalo, NY 14203
Tel.: (716) 842-1900
Web Site: http://www.quillerandblake.com
Sales Range: $10-24.9 Million
Emp.: 6
N.A.I.C.S.: 541810
Todd Mecca *(Dir-Creative)*

QUILTER PLC
Senator House 85 Queen Victoria Street, London, EC4V 4AB, United Kingdom
Tel.: (44) 2070027016
Web Site: https://plc.quilter.com
Year Founded: 2007
QLTE—(JSE)
Rev.: $5,839,434,486
Assets: $67,337,793,486
Liabilities: $65,420,348,397
Net Worth: $1,917,445,090
Earnings: $53,016,915
Emp.: 3,014
Fiscal Year-end: 12/31/23
Health Care Srvices
N.A.I.C.S.: 523940
John-Paul Crutchley *(Head-IR)*

Subsidiaries:

AAM Advisory Pte. Ltd. (1)
138 Market Street Capitagreen 06-01, Singapore, 048946, Singapore
Tel.: (65) 6 653 6600
Web Site: https://www.aam-advisory.com
Financial Advisory Services
N.A.I.C.S.: 523940
Eryk Lee *(CEO)*

Intrinsic Financial Services Limited (1)
Wiltshire Court Farnsby Street, Swindon, SN1 5AH, United Kingdom (100%)
Tel.: (44) 793 647400
Web Site: http://www.intrinsicfs.com
Financial Advice & Services
N.A.I.C.S.: 523999
Andy Thompson *(CEO)*

Subsidiary (Domestic):

Lighthouse Group PLC (2)
26 Throgmorton Street, London, EC2N 2AN, United Kingdom
Tel.: (44) 2070655640
Web Site: http://www.lighthousegroup.plc.uk
Sales Range: $50-74.9 Million
Wealth Management Services
N.A.I.C.S.: 523940
Malcolm Streatfield *(CEO)*

Subsidiary (Domestic):

Deverill Black & Company Limited (3)
23 Westfield Park, Redland, Bristol, BS6 6LT, United Kingdom
Tel.: (44) 1179744321
Web Site: http://www.deverillblack.co.uk
Sales Range: $50-74.9 Million
Emp.: 5
Financial Advisory Services
N.A.I.C.S.: 523999
Iain Black *(Mng Dir)*

Financial Services Advice and Support Limited (3)
No 5 Castle Court Carnegie Campus, Dunfermline, KY11 8PB, Scotland, United Kingdom
Tel.: (44) 1383841155
Web Site: http://www.fsas-scotland.co.uk

Sales Range: $50-74.9 Million
Emp.: 7
Financial Advisory Services
N.A.I.C.S.: 523999

Lighthouse Advisory Services Limited (3)
Rydon House Pynes Hill, Exeter, EX2 5AZ, Devon, United Kingdom
Tel.: (44) 8701977400
Web Site: http://www.lighthouseadvisory.co.uk
Financial Advisory Services
N.A.I.C.S.: 523999

Division (Domestic):

Lighthouse Carrwood (3)
Highbank House Exchange St, Stockport, SK3 0ET, United Kingdom
Tel.: (44) 1618192525
Web Site: http://www.lighthousecarrwood.uk
Sales Range: $50-74.9 Million
Emp.: 50
Wealth Management Services
N.A.I.C.S.: 523940
Mark Dallas (Mng Dir)

Lighthouse Express (3)
26 Throgmorton Street, London, EC2N 2AN, United Kingdom
Tel.: (44) 2070655640
Web Site: http://www.lighthouseplc.uk
Sales Range: $50-74.9 Million
Emp.: 40
Wealth Management Services
N.A.I.C.S.: 523940

Subsidiary (Domestic):

Lighthouse GP Limited (3)
9b Harewood Yard Harewood House Estate, Leeds, LS17 9LF, West Yorkshire, United Kingdom
Tel.: (44) 1132886622
Sales Range: $50-74.9 Million
Emp.: 15
Financial Advisory Services
N.A.I.C.S.: 523999

Division (Domestic):

Lighthouse Wealth (3)
26 Throgmorton Street, London, EC2N 2AN, United Kingdom
Tel.: (44) 2070655640
Web Site: http://www.lighthousewealth.co.uk
Sales Range: $350-399.9 Million
Emp.: 1,000
Wealth Management Services
N.A.I.C.S.: 523940

Subsidiary (Domestic):

LighthouseGEB Limited. (3)
Highbank House Exchange Street, Stockport, SK3 0ET, Greater Manchester, United Kingdom
Tel.: (44) 1618194940
Web Site: http://www.lighthousegroup.plc.uk.com
Financial Advisory Services
N.A.I.C.S.: 523940

The Falcon Group Plc (3)
Falcon Court Triangle West, Clifton, BS8 1ER, Bedfordshire, United Kingdom
Tel.: (44) 1179291012
Web Site: http://www.falcon-ifa.com
Financial Consulting Services
N.A.I.C.S.: 523999
Will Nagle (CEO)

Quilter Cheviot Europe Limited (1)
Hambleden House 19-26 Lower Pembroke Street, Dublin, D02 WV96, Ireland
Tel.: (353) 1 799 6900
Web Site: https://www.quiltercheviot.com
Financial Advisory Services
N.A.I.C.S.: 523940
Brian Weber (CEO)

Quilter International Isle of Man Limited (1)
King Edward Bay House King Edward Road, IM99 1NU, Onchan, Isle of Man
Tel.: (44) 162 465 5555
Financial Advisory Services
N.A.I.C.S.: 523940

Quilter International Middle East Limited (1)
7 and 8 Level 2 Gate Village 7 Dubai International Financial Centre, PO Box 482062, Dubai, United Arab Emirates
Tel.: (971) 4 304 5800
Financial Advisory Services
N.A.I.C.S.: 523999
Peter Winder (Head-Sales)

Quilter International Trust Company Limited (1)
King Edward Bay House King Edward Road, PO Box 142, IM99 3DJ, Onchan, Isle of Man
Tel.: (44) 162 465 5456
Trust Services
N.A.I.C.S.: 523991

Quilter Investors Limited (1)
Senator House 85 Queen Victoria Street, London, EC4V 4AB, United Kingdom
Tel.: (44) 207 167 3500
Web Site: https://www.quilterinvestors.com
Financial Advisory Services
N.A.I.C.S.: 523940
Owain Kember (Dir-Investments)

Quilter Private Client Advisers Limited (1)
Senator House 85 Queen Victoria Street, London, EC4V 4AB, United Kingdom
Tel.: (44) 207 562 5856
Web Site: https://www.quilterpca.co.uk
Financial Advisory Services
N.A.I.C.S.: 523940
Kevin Speake (Reg Dir)

QUILVEST S.A.
3 Boulevard Royal, L-2449, Luxembourg, Luxembourg
Tel.: (352) 473885   FR
Web Site: http://www.quilvest.com
Year Founded: 1888
Rev.: $149,317,000
Assets: $4,036,386,000
Liabilities: $2,845,181,000
Net Worth: $1,191,205,000
Earnings: $94,832,000
Emp.: 452
Fiscal Year-end: 12/31/18
Investment Company
N.A.I.C.S.: 523999
Jean-Benoit Lachaise (CFO)

Subsidiaries:

CBP Quilvest S.A. (1)
48 rue Charles Martel, 2134, Luxembourg, Luxembourg
Tel.: (352) 27 027 1
Web Site: http://www.cbpquilvest.com
Sales Range: $50-74.9 Million
Emp.: 90
Private Banking Services
N.A.I.C.S.: 522180
Marc Hoffmann (CEO)

Quilvest (Switzerland) Ltd. (1)
Stockerstrasse 23, 8027, Zurich, Switzerland
Tel.: (41) 442244444
Web Site: http://www.quilvest.com
Emp.: 80
Wealth Planning Trust Services & Investment Solution & Hedge Fund Investing Services
N.A.I.C.S.: 523999
Philippe Monti (Mng Dir)

Quilvest Dubai Ltd. (1)
Gate Village 4 Office 105 DIFC, PO Box 506724, Dubai, United Arab Emirates
Tel.: (971) 4323 1664
Web Site: http://www.quilvest.com
Sales Range: $50-74.9 Million
Emp.: 5
Investment Advisory Services
N.A.I.C.S.: 523940
Jamal Al-Husseini (Gen Mgr)

Quilvest France S.A.S. (1)
243 Boulevard Saint Germain, 75007, Paris, France
Tel.: (33) 140620762
Sales Range: $50-74.9 Million
Emp.: 25
Investment Management Service

N.A.I.C.S.: 523999
Michel Abouchalache (CEO)

Subsidiary (Domestic):

Quilvest Banque Privee S.A. (2)
243 Boulevard Saint Germain, 75007, Paris, France
Tel.: (33) 1 40 62 07 62
Web Site: http://www.quilvestbanqueprivee.com
Sales Range: $100-124.9 Million
Emp.: 150
Asset Management, Private Banking & Trust Services
N.A.I.C.S.: 523150
Stephane Chretien (Chm-Mgmt Bd)

Quilvest Hong Kong Ltd. (1)
21 F ICBC Tower Suite 2111 Citibank Plaza 3 Garden Road, Central, China (Hong Kong)
Tel.: (852) 2273 5525
Web Site: http://www.quilvest.com
Investment Management Service
N.A.I.C.S.: 523999

Quilvest UK Ltd. (1)
46 Albemarle Street, London, W1S 4JN, United Kingdom
Tel.: (44) 2072901710
Web Site: http://www.quilvest.com
Investment Advisory Services
N.A.I.C.S.: 523940

Quilvest USA, Inc. (1)
527 Madison Ave 11th Fl, New York, NY 10022
Tel.: (212) 920-3830
Web Site: http://www.quilvest.com
Sales Range: $50-74.9 Million
Emp.: 40
Private Equity & Venture Capital Investment Services
N.A.I.C.S.: 523999
Michele Kinner (Partner)

QUIMBAYA GOLD INC.
100 King street W Suite, Toronto, MFX 1E2, ON, Canada
Tel.: (647) 576-7135   Ca
Web Site: https://www.quimbayagold.com
Year Founded: 2020
QIM—(CNSX)
Rev.: $756
Assets: $1,058,189
Liabilities: $53,513
Net Worth: $1,004,676
Earnings: ($628,056)
Fiscal Year-end: 12/31/21
Gold Exploration Services
N.A.I.C.S.: 212220
Olivier Berthiaume (CFO)

QUIMPAC S.A.
Av Nestor Gambeta 8585, PO Box 3741, 3741, Callao, Peru
Tel.: (51) 6142000
Web Site: http://www.quimpac.com.pe
Year Founded: 1964
QUIMPAC1—(LIM)
Rev.: $429,080,000
Assets: $879,714,000
Liabilities: $451,992,000
Net Worth: $427,722,000
Earnings: $31,860,000
Fiscal Year-end: 12/31/23
Chemical Products Mfr
N.A.I.C.S.: 325998
Fernando Carranza (Mgr-Comml)

QUINARY S.P.A.
via Mario Bianchini 60, IT-00142, Rome, Italy
Tel.: (39) 065159141   IT
Web Site: http://www.quinary.com
Commercial Information Technology Services
N.A.I.C.S.: 541519
Mauro Botta (Dir-Govt & Corp Bus)

QUINCAILLERIE TERRASSIER
Avenue De Limoges Avenue Zac, Sauze-Vaussais, 79190, Deux Sevres, France
Tel.: (33) 549076001
Web Site: http://www.terrassier.fr
Rev.: $15,400,000
Emp.: 62
Garden, Materials & Household Equipment
N.A.I.C.S.: 459120
Christophe Terrassier (Pres)

QUINENCO S.A.
Enrique Foster Sur 20 15th floor, Las Condes, Santiago, Chile
Tel.: (56) 27507100   CL
Web Site: https://www.quinenco.cl
Year Founded: 1957
QUINENCO—(SGO)
Rev.: $4,990,087,967
Assets: $70,981,533,074
Liabilities: $56,696,562,386
Net Worth: $14,284,970,687
Earnings: $6,340,123,447
Emp.: 74,700
Fiscal Year-end: 12/31/22
Financial Investment Services
N.A.I.C.S.: 551112
Andronico Luksic Craig (Chm)

Subsidiaries:

Aerosan Airport Services S.A. (1)
Captain Manuel Avalos Prados Street NOS 1656/1720/1860, Santiago, Chile
Tel.: (56) 22 230 5900
Web Site: https://www.aerosan.com
Airline Services
N.A.I.C.S.: 481111

Banco de Chile (1)
Paseo Ahumada 251, Santiago, Chile   (100%)
Tel.: (56) 226533535
Web Site: https://portales.bancochile.cl
Rev.: $4,610,918,100
Assets: $63,518,566,740
Liabilities: $56,585,149,440
Net Worth: $6,933,417,300
Earnings: $1,566,390,780
Emp.: 12,550
Fiscal Year-end: 12/31/2023
Banking Services
N.A.I.C.S.: 522110
Eduardo Ebensperger Orrego (CEO)

Division (Domestic):

Banco Edwards del Banco de Chile (2)
Huerfanos 740, Santiago, Chile
Tel.: (56) 24683000
Web Site: http://www.banedwards.cl
Sales Range: $600-649.9 Million
Emp.: 2,500
Banking Services
N.A.I.C.S.: 522320

Dicomac Ltda. (1)
Lira 1818, Santiago, Chile
Tel.: (56) 99 158 0453
Web Site: https://www.dicomac.cl
Hardware & Furniture Fitting Distr
N.A.I.C.S.: 423990

Ecuaestibas S.A. (1)
Av 9 de Octubre y Malecon Edif Previsora piso 25 of 03, Guayaquil, Ecuador
Tel.: (593) 4 251 7360
Marine Towage Services
N.A.I.C.S.: 488330

Empresa Nacional de Energia ENEX S.A. (1)
Av Del Condor Sur 520 Business City, Huechuraba, Santiago, Chile
Tel.: (56) 600 350 2000
Web Site: https://www.enex.cl
Fuel & Lubricant Distr
N.A.I.C.S.: 424720

Inmobiliaria Norte Verde S.A. (1)
Av Los Dominicos 8630 of 806, Las Condes, Santiago, Chile
Tel.: (56) 22 838 6300

QUINENCO S.A.

Quinenco S.A.—(Continued)
Web Site: https://www.norte-verde.cl
Real Estate Services
N.A.I.C.S.: 531390

Inversiones y Rentas S.A. (1)
CCU Corporate Building Vitacura 2670 23rd Fl, PO Box 33, Santiago, Chile (50%)
Tel.: (56) 24273000
Holding Company
N.A.I.C.S.: 551112

Holding (Domestic):

Compania Cervecerias Unidas S.A. (2)
Bandera 84 Sixth Floor, Santiago, Chile (61.56%)
Tel.: (56) 224273000
Web Site: http://www.ccu.cl
Rev.: $3,796,008,927
Assets: $5,033,110,571
Liabilities: $3,022,753,896
Net Worth: $2,010,356,674
Earnings: $189,678,233
Emp.: 9,354
Fiscal Year-end: 12/31/2022
Alcoholic Beverages Producer, Marketer & Distr
N.A.I.C.S.: 312120
Andronico Luksic Craig *(Chm)*

Subsidiary (Non-US):

CCU Argentina S.A. (3)
Edison 2659, Martinez, 1640, Argentina
Tel.: (54) 1151672300
Web Site: http://www.ccu.com.ar
Sales Range: $350-399.9 Million
Emp.: 543
Producer & Distr of Beer & Mineral Water
N.A.I.C.S.: 312120
Fernando Sanchis *(Mng Dir)*

Subsidiary (Domestic):

CCU Chile Ltda. (3)
Av Pdte Eduardo Frei Montalva 8000, Quilicura, Santiago, Chile
Tel.: (56) 24278200
Web Site: http://www.ccu.cl
Sales Range: $75-99.9 Million
Emp.: 1,389
Producer & Distributor of Beer & Other Beverages
N.A.I.C.S.: 312120

Embotelladoras Chilenas Unidas S.A.
Av Presidente Eduardo Frei Montalva 1500, Renca, Santiago, Chile
Tel.: (56) 24274000
Web Site: http://www.ccu-sa.com
Sales Range: $150-199.9 Million
Emp.: 100
Producer & Distributor of Soft Drinks, Mineral Water, Juices & Other Beverages
N.A.I.C.S.: 312112

Vina San Pedro S.A. (3)
Betacura 4380 Pisso 6, Betacura, Santiago, Chile (82.01%)
Tel.: (56) 24775300
Web Site: http://www.sanpedro.cl
Sales Range: $50-74.9 Million
Emp.: 100
Producer & Distributor of Wine
N.A.I.C.S.: 312130
Alejandro Jorquera Rojas *(Comptroller)*

Subsidiary (Non-US):

Finca La Celia S.A. (4)
Ave San Martin 972 3F, 5500, Mendoza, Argentina
Tel.: (54) 2614134400
Web Site: http://www.fincalacelia.com.ar
Sales Range: $10-24.9 Million
Vineyards; Winery
N.A.I.C.S.: 312130

Invexans Limited (1)
3rd Floor 11-12 ST James s Square, London, SW1Y 4LB, United Kingdom
Tel.: (44) 203 709 5285
Web Site: https://www.invexans.co.uk
Cable Mfr
N.A.I.C.S.: 335929
Francisco Perez Mackenna *(Chm)*

Invexans S.A. (1)
San Francisco 4760 San Miguel, Santiago, Chile (98.33%)
Tel.: (56) 25201000
Web Site: http://www.invexans.cl
Sales Range: Less than $1 Million
Emp.: 2,930
Holding Company; Copper & Aluminum Cable & Wire Products Mfr
N.A.I.C.S.: 551112
Francisco Perez Mackenna *(Chm)*

Iquique Terminal Internacional S.A. (1)
Esmeralda 340 Office 720 Edificio Esmeralda, Iquique, Chile
Tel.: (56) 57 239 6000
Web Site: https://www.iti.cl
Emp.: 400
Port Terminal Services
N.A.I.C.S.: 488310
Ricardo Cordova *(CEO)*

KIOS S.A. (1)
Zabala 1584/501, Montevideo, Uruguay
Tel.: (598) 2 915 0942
Marine Towage Services
N.A.I.C.S.: 488330

SAAM Guatemala S.A. (1)
17 Avenida 19-70 Zona 10 Edificio Centro de Negocios Torino, Oficina 807, Guatemala, Guatemala
Tel.: (502) 2 337 4328
Tugboat Services
N.A.I.C.S.: 488330

SAAM Remolcadores Colombia S.A.S. (1)
Av Miramar 23-05, Cartagena, Colombia
Tel.: (57) 320 715 3830
Marine Towage Services
N.A.I.C.S.: 488330

SAAM Towage Brasil S.A. (1)
Rua de Assembleia 100 - 15 andar Centro, Rio de Janeiro, 20011-000, Brazil
Tel.: (55) 212 121 1000
Marine Towage Services
N.A.I.C.S.: 488330
Bruno Lessa *(Mgr & Officer)*

SAAM Towage Canada Inc. (1)
411-1930 Pandora Street, Vancouver, V5C 0C7, BC, Canada
Tel.: (604) 250-7354
Marine Towage Services
N.A.I.C.S.: 488330

SAAM Towage Panama Inc. (1)
Terrazas de Albrook Ave Omar Torrijos Herrera Nivel D oficina D11, Panama, Panama
Tel.: (507) 6 983 1077
Marine Towage Services
N.A.I.C.S.: 488330

Tech Pack S.A. (1)
Enrique Foster Sur N20 Piso 12 Of 1202, Las Condes, Santiago, Chile (65.92%)
Tel.: (56) 228605800
Web Site: http://www.techpack.com
Holding Company
N.A.I.C.S.: 551112
Francisco Perez Mackenna *(Pres)*

Subsidiary (Non-US):

Aluflex S.A. (2)
Suipacha 1067, Buenos Aires, 1008, Argentina (75%)
Tel.: (54) 1157890000
Web Site: http://www.aluflex.com.ar
Sales Range: $50-74.9 Million
Emp.: 155
Flexible Packaging Mfr
N.A.I.C.S.: 322220
Ricardo Illias Grbich *(Plant Mgr)*

Subsidiary (Domestic):

Indalum S.A. (2)
Ave La Divisa 1100 Sanderlando, Santiago, San Bernardo, Chile
Tel.: (56) 27510600
Web Site: http://www.indalum.cl
Sales Range: $100-124.9 Million
Emp.: 300
Mfr & Distr of Aluminum Profiles
N.A.I.C.S.: 331318

Subsidiary (Domestic):

Alumco S.A. (3)
Ureta Cox 745, San Miguel, Santiago, Chile
Tel.: (56) 27510800
Web Site: http://www.indalum.cl
Sales Range: $25-49.9 Million
Emp.: 10
Aluminum Extrusion Mfr & Distr
N.A.I.C.S.: 331318

PVTEC S.A. (3)
Av La Divisa 1100, San Bernardo, Santiago, Chile
Tel.: (56) 2 956 3500
Web Site: http://www.pvtec.cl
Sales Range: $25-49.9 Million
Emp.: 20
Door & Window Distr
N.A.I.C.S.: 423310

Subsidiary (Non-US):

Peruplast S.A. (2)
Jr Felipe Santiago Salaverry 227 Urb El Pino, San Luis, Lima, Peru
Tel.: (51) 1 319 2200
Web Site: http://www.peruplast.com.pe
Packaging Products Mfr
N.A.I.C.S.: 322220

Terminal Maritima Mazatlan S.A. de C.V. (1)
Av Emilio Barragan S/N Col Centro Interior Recinto Fiscalizado, 82000, Mazatlan, Sinaloa, Mexico
Tel.: (52) 669 915 6670
Web Site: https://www.tmaz.com.mx
Marine Cargo Handling Services
N.A.I.C.S.: 488320

Transportes TPG S.A. (1)
Estrada Redondela - Airport 118 Villar de Infesta, 36815, Redondela, Pontevedra, Spain
Tel.: (34) 98 622 3268
Web Site: https://www.transportesportuarios.com
Container Transportation Services
N.A.I.C.S.: 484110

QUINN RADIATORS LIMITED
Imperial Park, Newport, NP10 8FS, United Kingdom
Tel.: (44) 1633 657271 UK
Web Site: http://www.quinn-radiators.com
Emp.: 150
Radiators Mfr & Distr
N.A.I.C.S.: 333414
Nick Whitwell *(Mng Dir)*

Subsidiaries:

Quinn Radiators NV (1)
Van Doornelaan 2A, B 2440, Geel, Belgium (100%)
Tel.: (32) 14500011
Web Site: http://www.quinn-radiators.net
Sales Range: $25-49.9 Million
Emp.: 20
Radiators Mfr
N.A.I.C.S.: 333414
Eddy Van Dijck *(Gen Mgr)*

QUINSAM CAPITAL CORPORATION
77 King Street West Suite 2905, PO Box 121, Toronto Dominion Centre, Toronto, M5K 1H1, ON, Canada
Tel.: (905) 330-7948 Ca
Web Site: https://www.quinsamcapital.com
Year Founded: 2004
0Q4—(DEU)
Rev.: $682,864
Assets: $10,973,258
Liabilities: $206,694
Net Worth: $10,766,565
Earnings: ($11,461,470)
Fiscal Year-end: 12/31/22
Merchant Banking Services
N.A.I.C.S.: 523150
Roger Dent *(CEO)*

INTERNATIONAL PUBLIC

QUINT DIGITAL MEDIA LIMITED
403 Prabhat Kiran 17 Rajendra Place, Lower Parel West, New Delhi, 110008, Maharashtra, India
Tel.: (91) 1204751818
Web Site: https://quintdigitalmedia.com
539515—(BOM)
Rev.: $9,666,375
Assets: $33,792,710
Liabilities: $11,223,788
Net Worth: $22,568,923
Earnings: ($3,378,143)
Emp.: 150
Fiscal Year-end: 03/31/23
Ship Dismantling Services
N.A.I.C.S.: 336611
Raghav Bahl *(CEO)*

QUINT GROUP LTD
Cottage Street Mill Cottage Street, Macclesfield, SK11 8DZ, United Kingdom
Tel.: (44) 1625 505 464 UK
Web Site: http://www.quint.co.uk
Year Founded: 2009
Emp.: 100
Financial Management Services
N.A.I.C.S.: 523999
Gregory Cox *(Founder & CEO)*

QUINTAIN STEEL CO., LTD.
4th Floor No 47 Xinjian Road, Nan District, T'ainan, 702, Taiwan
Tel.: (886) 62643888
Web Site: https://www.quintain.com.tw
Year Founded: 1973
2017—(TAI)
Rev.: $99,015,562
Assets: $361,481,395
Liabilities: $144,819,217
Net Worth: $216,662,178
Earnings: ($6,727,918)
Emp.: 290
Fiscal Year-end: 12/31/23
Galvanized Wire Mfr
N.A.I.C.S.: 331110
Cheng-Cheng Shieh *(Pres)*

Subsidiaries:

Quintain Steel Co., Ltd. - Kuan-Tien Plant (1)
5F No 307 Sec 2 Minsheng Road, West Central District, T'ainan, 70054, Taiwan
Tel.: (886) 62261917
Rolled Steel Wire Mfr
N.A.I.C.S.: 331110

Quintain Steel Co., Ltd. - Ma-Tou Plant (1)
No 307 5 Section 2 Minsheng Road, West Central District, T'ainan, 70054, Taiwan
Tel.: (886) 6 2261919
Spheroidize Annealed Wire Mfr
N.A.I.C.S.: 331110

Quintain Steel Co., Ltd. - Yung-Kung Plant (1)
5F No 307 Sec 2 Minsheng Road, West Central District, T'ainan, 70054, Taiwan
Tel.: (886) 62261922
Sales Range: $100-124.9 Million
Emp.: 300
Galvanized Wire Mfr
N.A.I.C.S.: 331110

QUINTANA SHIPPING LTD.
5 Xenias Street 6th Floor, 14562, Kifissia, Greece
Tel.: (30) 2106235900 MH
Web Site: http://www.quintanashipping.com
Year Founded: 2010
Sales Range: $25-49.9 Million
Marine Transportation Services
N.A.I.C.S.: 483111
Paul J. Cornell *(CFO)*

QUINTEGRA SOLUTIONS LTD.
Wescare Towers 3rd Floor No 16
Cenotaph Road, Teynampet, Chennai, 600018, Tamil Nadu, India
Tel.: (91) 4424328395
Web Site:
https://www.quintegrasolutions.com
Sales Range: Less than $1 Million
Emp.: 1
Software Services
N.A.I.C.S.: 541511

Subsidiaries:

Quintegra Solutions GmbH (1)
Stromberger Str 2, 55545, Bad Kreuznach, Germany
Tel.: (49) 671 920 275 1
Web Site:
http://www.quintegrasolutions.com
Software Development Services
N.A.I.C.S.: 541511

QUINTESSENTIALLY (UK) LTD
29 Portland Place, London, W1B 1QB, United Kingdom
Tel.: (44) 845 269 8585
Web Site:
http://www.quintessentially.com
Year Founded: 2000
Sales Range: $400-449.9 Million
Emp.: 1,500
Private Club Operator
N.A.I.C.S.: 713910
Emma Sherrard Matthew *(CEO)*

QUINTIS LIMITED
The Old Swan Brewery Level 2
Mounts Bay Road, Perth, 6000, WA, Australia
Tel.: (61) 8 9215 3000 AU
Web Site: http://www.quintis.com.au
Year Founded: 1997
Rev.: $76,025,189
Assets: $681,674,503
Liabilities: $434,142,880
Net Worth: $247,531,623
Earnings: ($328,924,242)
Emp.: 210
Fiscal Year-end: 06/30/17
Sandalwood Product Mfr & Distr
N.A.I.C.S.: 321999
Alistair Stevens *(CFO)*

Subsidiaries:

Viroxis Corporation (1)
12621 Silicon Dr Ste 100, San Antonio, TX 78249
Tel.: (210) 558-8896
Web Site: http://www.viroxis.com
Chemicals Mfr
N.A.I.C.S.: 325412
Gary E. Frashier *(Pres)*

QUINTO REAL CAPITAL CORPORATION
777 de la Commune West Suite 100, Montreal, H3C 1Y1, QC, Canada
Tel.: (514) 303-7895 Ca
Web Site: http://www.quintocorp.com
Year Founded: 2010
QIT.P—(TSXV)
Sales Range: Less than $1 Million
Investment Services
N.A.I.C.S.: 523999
Marcel Bergeron *(CFO)*

QUINVIR INVESTMENT INC.
5F J Tower 139 Dosandae ro, Gangnam gu, 06036, Seoul, Korea (South)
Tel.: (82) 2 6205 4627
Web Site: http://www.quinvir.com
Financial Advisory & Placement Services Firm
N.A.I.C.S.: 523999
Andrew O Kwon *(Founder & Exec Mng Dir)*

QUINYX AB
Vattugatan 17, Stockholm, 11152, Sweden
Tel.: (46) 86115020
Web Site: https://www.quinyx.com
Year Founded: 2005
Emp.: 100
Software Devolepment
N.A.I.C.S.: 513210
Erik Fjellborg *(Founder & CEO)*

Subsidiaries:

Concrete Media, Inc. (1)
601 W 26th St Fl 8, New York, NY 10001
Tel.: (212) 937-3800
Sales Range: $1-9.9 Million
Emp.: 75
Internet Service Provider
N.A.I.C.S.: 517810
Aaron Cohen *(CEO)*

QUIRIN PRIVATBANK AG
Kurfuerstendamm 119, 10711, Berlin, 10711, Germany
Tel.: (49) 3089021300
Web Site:
https://www.quirinprivatbank.de
Investment Banking Services
N.A.I.C.S.: 523150
Karl Matthaeus Schmidt *(Chm-Mgmt Bd)*

QUISITIVE TECHNOLOGY SOLUTIONS, INC.
6 Antares Drive Phase 3 Suite 200, Ottawa, K2E 8A9, ON, Canada
Tel.: (613) 232-4295
Web Site: https://www.quisitive.com
Year Founded: 2016
QUIS—(TSXV)
Rev.: $91,538,667
Assets: $177,146,621
Liabilities: $88,409,450
Net Worth: $88,737,172
Earnings: ($9,666,291)
Emp.: 525
Fiscal Year-end: 12/31/23
Information Technology Services
N.A.I.C.S.: 541512
Mike Reinhart *(CEO)*

Subsidiaries:

Catapult Systems, Inc. (1)
1221 S Mopac Expy 3 Barton Skyway Ste 350, Austin, TX 78746
Tel.: (512) 328-8181
Web Site: http://www.catapultsystems.com
Sales Range: $10-24.9 Million
Emp.: 230
It Consulting
N.A.I.C.S.: 541511
Sam Goodner *(Founder)*

LedgerPay, Inc. (1)
1431 Greenway Dr Ste 1000, Irving, TX 75038
Tel.: (972) 573-0995
Web Site: https://www.ledgerpay.com
Computer Software Development Services
N.A.I.C.S.: 541511
Mike Reinhart *(CEO)*

Mazik Global, Inc. (1)
2604 Dempster St Ste 410, Park Ridge, IL 60068
Tel.: (847) 768-9353
Web Site: https://www.mazikglobal.com
Software Services
N.A.I.C.S.: 518210

Menlo Technologies, Inc. (1)
520 S El Camino Real Ste 518, San Mateo, CA 94402
Tel.: (408) 736-8100
Web Site: http://www.menlo-technologies.com
Information Technology Services
N.A.I.C.S.: 541512
Gary Prioste *(CEO)*

QUIXANT PLC
Aisle Barn 100 High Street, Balsham, Cambridge, CB21 4EP, United Kingdom
Tel.: (44) 1223892696 UK
Web Site: https://www.quixant.com
Year Founded: 2005
NXQ—(AIM)
Rev.: $119,870,000
Assets: $95,970,000
Liabilities: $23,760,000
Net Worth: $72,210,000
Earnings: $10,990,000
Fiscal Year-end: 12/31/22
Computer System Design Services
N.A.I.C.S.: 541512
Nicholas Jarmany *(Vice Chm)*

Subsidiaries:

Densitron Technologies Limited (1)
16 South Park, Sevenoaks, TN13 1AN, Kent, United Kingdom (100%)
Tel.: (44) 2076484200
Web Site: http://www.densitron.com
Sales Range: $25-49.9 Million
Information Display Systems Designer & Mfr
N.A.I.C.S.: 334118
Bruno Recaldini *(Gen Mgr-EMEA)*

Subsidiary (US):

Densitron Corporation (2)
2330 Pomona Rd, Corona, CA 92878
Tel.: (951) 284-7600
Web Site: https://www.densitron.com
Information Display Systems Design & Marketing
N.A.I.C.S.: 423430
Allen Chong *(Pres-DCA)*

Subsidiary (Non-US):

Densitron Corporation of Japan (2)
2F 1-26-2 Omorikita, Ota-ku, Tokyo, Japan
Tel.: (81) 33 767 9701
Web Site: https://www.densitron.com
Information Display Systems Sales & Customer Support Services
N.A.I.C.S.: 423430
Shinji Mihashi *(Mng Dir)*

Densitron Display Taiwan Limited (2)
12F No 150 Jianyi Road, Zhonghe District, Taipei, 23511, Taiwan
Tel.: (886) 282268168
Web Site: http://www.densitron.com
Emp.: 70
Information Display Systems Sales & Customer Support Services
N.A.I.C.S.: 423430
Pablo Lin *(Assoc VP)*

Subsidiary (Domestic):

Densitron Europe Limited (2)
16 South Park, Sevenoaks, TN13 1AN, Kent, United Kingdom
Tel.: (44) 2076484200
Web Site: https://www.densitron.com
Information Display Systems Designer, Mfr & Marketer
N.A.I.C.S.: 334118

Subsidiary (Non-US):

Densitron Deutschland GmbH (3)
Romerstrasse 7, Forstinning, 85661, Ebersberg, Germany
Tel.: (49) 8121975940
Web Site: http://www.densitron.com
Information Display Systems Sales & Customer Support Services
N.A.I.C.S.: 423430
Marc Corrigan *(Mng Dir)*

Densitron France (3)
3 rue de Tasmanie Espace com Bat B, 44115, Basse-Goulaine, France
Tel.: (33) 25 171 0158
Web Site: http://www.densitron.com
Information Display Systems Sales & Customer Support Services
N.A.I.C.S.: 423430
Christophe Desage *(Mng Dir)*

Densitron Nordic Oy (3)
Jauhokuja 3, 00920, Helsinki, Finland
Tel.: (358) 400421448

Web Site: http://www.densitron.com
Information Display Systems Sales & Customer Support Services
N.A.I.C.S.: 423430
Jukka-Pekka Paakkonen *(Mng Dir)*

Quixant Deutschland GmbH (1)
Prinzregentenstr 20, 83022, Rosenheim, Germany
Tel.: (49) 8121975940
Computer System Design Services
N.A.I.C.S.: 541512

Quixant Italia srl (1)
Case Bruciate 1, Poggio Mirteto, 00060, Roma, Italy
Tel.: (39) 0765 030023
Web Site: http://www.quixant.com
Emp.: 20
Oil & Gas Exploration Services
N.A.I.C.S.: 213112

Quixant USA Inc (1)
2147 Pama Ln Bldg 6, Las Vegas, NV 89119
Tel.: (702) 522-7849
Web Site: http://www.quixant.com
Oil & Gas Exploration Services
N.A.I.C.S.: 213112

QUIZ PLC
61 Hydepark Street, Glasgow, G3 8BW, United Kingdom
Tel.: (44) 1415691544 JE
Web Site:
https://www.quizgroup.co.uk
Year Founded: 1993
QUIZ—(AIM)
Rev.: $53,905,557
Assets: $41,472,915
Liabilities: $18,904,893
Net Worth: $22,568,022
Earnings: $8,434,157
Emp.: 1,249
Fiscal Year-end: 03/31/21
Apparel Product Retailer
N.A.I.C.S.: 458110
Tarak Ramzan *(Founder & CEO)*

QUIZAM MEDIA CORPORATION
609 Granville Street Suite 650, PO Box 10381, Vancouver, V7Y 1G6, BC, Canada
Tel.: (604) 683-0020 BC
Web Site: https://www.on-track.com
Year Founded: 2000
QQQFF—(OTCQB)
Rev.: $3,179,289
Assets: $1,617,769
Liabilities: $978,302
Net Worth: $639,467
Earnings: ($1,513,952)
Fiscal Year-end: 05/31/21
Educational Software Publisher
N.A.I.C.S.: 513210
Russ Rossi *(Founder, Pres & CEO)*

Subsidiaries:

On-Track Computer Training Ltd. (1)
Suite 401 885 West Georgia Street, PO Box 1052, Vancouver, V6C 3E8, BC, Canada
Tel.: (604) 683-0020
Web Site: http://www.on-track.com
Sales Range: $10-24.9 Million
Emp.: 10
Computer Training Services
N.A.I.C.S.: 611420
David Lee *(Gen Mgr)*

On-Track Corporate Training Ltd. (1)
Suite 650 - 609 Granville Street, PO Box 10381, Vancouver, V7Y 1G6, BC, Canada
Tel.: (604) 683-0020
Web Site: https://www.on-track.com
Computer Training Services
N.A.I.C.S.: 611420

Quizam Entertainment LLC (1)
Suite 401 885 West Georgia Street, Box 1052, Vancouver, V6C 3E8, BC, Canada
Tel.: (604) 683-0020

QUIZAM MEDIA CORPORATION

Quizam Media Corporation—(Continued)
Web Site:
https://www.quizamentertainment.com
Media Entertainment Services
N.A.I.C.S.: 516210

QUMAK S.A.
ul Szyszkowa 20, PL 02-285, Warsaw, Poland
Tel.: (48) 225190800   PL
Web Site: http://www.qumak.pl
Year Founded: 1988
Sales Range: $100-124.9 Million
Information & Communication Technology Services
N.A.I.C.S.: 541512
Monika Ponarad *(Dir-Mgmt Office)*

QUMEI HOME FURNISHINGS GROUP CO., LTD.
No 217 Shunhuang Road, Chaoyang District, Beijing, 100103, China
Tel.: (86) 1084482500
Web Site: http://www.qumei.com
Year Founded: 1993
603818—(SHG)
Rev.: $681,291,211
Assets: $1,070,666,813
Liabilities: $741,014,520
Net Worth: $329,652,292
Earnings: $5,188,805
Fiscal Year-end: 12/31/22
Home Furnisher Mfr & Distr
N.A.I.C.S.: 337121
Ruihai Zhao *(Founder, Chm & Gen Mgr)*

Subsidiaries:

Ekornes ASA   (1)
Industrivegen 1, N-6222, Ikornnes, Norway   **(90.5%)**
Tel.: (47) 70255200
Web Site: http://www.ekornes.com
Rev.: $374,573,986
Assets: $275,855,655
Liabilities: $145,450,735
Net Worth: $130,404,921
Earnings: $24,393,195
Emp.: 2,140
Fiscal Year-end: 12/31/2017
Furniture Mfr
N.A.I.C.S.: 337126
Arve Ekornes *(Dir-Product Dev)*

Subsidiary (Non-US):

Ekornes Asia Pte Ltd   (2)
10 Eunos Road 8, Singapore, 408600, Singapore   **(100%)**
Tel.: (65) 68424000
Web Site: http://www.ekornes.com
Sales Range: $300-349.9 Million
Emp.: 1,500
All Other Business Support Services
N.A.I.C.S.: 561499

Subsidiary (Domestic):

Ekornes Fetsund AS   (2)
J A Ekornes 22, Fetsund, Fet, 1900, Norway   **(100%)**
Tel.: (47) 63883300
Web Site: http://www.svane.no
Sales Range: $25-49.9 Million
Emp.: 130
Other Knit Fabric & Lace Mills
N.A.I.C.S.: 313240
Jon Erlend Alstad *(Mng Dir)*

Subsidiary (Non-US):

Ekornes Iberica SL   (2)
Calle Roger De Lluria, Barcelona, Spain   **(100%)**
Tel.: (34) 559802510
Other Miscellaneous Durable Goods Merchant Whslr
N.A.I.C.S.: 423990

Subsidiary (US):

Ekornes Inc.   (2)
615 Pierce St, Somerset, NJ, 08873   **(100%)**
Tel.: (732) 302-0097
Web Site: http://www.ekornes.com
Sales Range: $25-49.9 Million
Emp.: 44
Nonupholstered Wood Household Furniture Mfr
N.A.I.C.S.: 337122
Peter Bjerregaard *(Pres)*

Subsidiary (Non-US):

Ekornes KK   (2)
Daiki Bldg 3rd Floor, 3-11-1 Hatchobori, 104-003, Tokyo, Japan   **(100%)**
Tel.: (81) 362223511
Web Site: http://www.ekornes.jp
Theater Companies & Dinner Theaters
N.A.I.C.S.: 711110

Ekornes Latin America Ltda   (2)
Rue General Almerio de Moura 780, Morumbi, 05690-080, Sao Paulo, Brazil
Tel.: (55) 11 3755 1075
Sales Range: $25-49.9 Million
Emp.: 5
Office Furniture Mfr
N.A.I.C.S.: 337214

Ekornes Ltd   (2)
Kings Court No 2-16 Goodge St, W1T2QA, London, United Kingdom   **(100%)**
Tel.: (44) 2074620440
Web Site: http://www.ekornes.co.uk
Sales Range: $25-49.9 Million
Emp.: 17
Household Furniture (except Wood & Metal) Mfr
N.A.I.C.S.: 337126
James Tate *(Gen Mgr)*

Ekornes Moebelvertriebs GmbH   (2)
Am Stadtrand 56, Hamburg, Germany   **(100%)**
Tel.: (49) 406969800
Web Site: http://www.ekornes.de
Sales Range: $25-49.9 Million
Emp.: 30
Institutional Furniture Mfr
N.A.I.C.S.: 337127

Ekornes S.A.R.L.   (2)
Centre dAffaires Activa, Allees Condorcet, 64011, Pau, France   **(100%)**
Tel.: (33) 559842510
Web Site: http://www.ekornes.fr
Sales Range: $25-49.9 Million
Emp.: 40
Other Miscellaneous Durable Goods Whslr
N.A.I.C.S.: 423990

Subsidiary (Domestic):

Ekornes Skandinavia AS   (2)
Industrivegen 1, 6222, Ikornnes, Norway
Tel.: (47) 70 25 52 00
Household Furniture Mfr
N.A.I.C.S.: 337121

Subsidiary (Non-US):

Ekornes Sp. z.o.o.   (2)
AL Jana Pawla II 80, 00-175, Warsaw, Poland   **(100%)**
Tel.: (48) 224354756
Other Miscellaneous Nondurable Goods Whslr
N.A.I.C.S.: 424990

Subsidiary (Domestic):

J.E. Ekornes AS   (2)
Industrivegen 1, Ikornnes, 6222, Norway
Tel.: (47) 70255200
Web Site: http://www.ekornes.no
Sales Range: $200-249.9 Million
Emp.: 800
Household Furniture Mfr
N.A.I.C.S.: 337121
Ola Arne Ramstad *(Dir-Production)*

Subsidiary (Non-US):

J.E. Ekornes Aps   (2)
Svendborgvej 83, 5000, Odense, Denmark
Tel.: (45) 40754272
Web Site: http://www.ekornes.dk
Sales Range: $25-49.9 Million
Emp.: 4
Other Knit Fabric & Lace Mills
N.A.I.C.S.: 313240
Peter Hjelmholm *(Mng Dir)*

Oy Ekornes AB   (2)
Asemantie 10 PL 109, 03100, Nummela, Finland   **(100%)**
Tel.: (358) 92242800
Web Site: http://www.ekornes.no
Sales Financing
N.A.I.C.S.: 522220

Subsidiary (Domestic):

Stay AS   (2)
Tveten vn 44, 0666, Oslo, Norway
Tel.: (47) 23194600
Web Site: http://www.stay.no
Sales Range: $25-49.9 Million
Emp.: 7
Home Interior Design Services
N.A.I.C.S.: 541410

QUNXING PAPER HOLDINGS COMPANY LIMITED
Level 22 The Center 99 Queen's Road, Central, China (Hong Kong)
Tel.: (852) 23059333
Web Site: http://www.qxpaper.com
Sales Range: $250-299.9 Million
Emp.: 1,700
Base Paper Products Mfr
N.A.I.C.S.: 322120
Shu Guang Sun *(Head-Fin & Deputy Gen Mgr)*

QUOC CUONG GIA LAI JOINT STOCK COMPANY
Nguyen Chi Thanh, Tra Ba Ward, Pleiku, Gia Lai, Vietnam
Tel.: (84) 2839300046
Web Site:
https://www.quoccuonggialai.com
Year Founded: 1994
QCG—(HOSE)
Rev.: $1,781,298
Assets: $394,166,003
Liabilities: $215,283,555
Net Worth: $178,882,448
Earnings: $131,346
Fiscal Year-end: 12/31/23
Wood Products Whslr
N.A.I.C.S.: 423310
Nguyen Thi Nhu Loan *(Member-Mgmt Bd & Gen Dir)*

QUONIA SOCIMI SA
C/Villarroel 216-218 5 4, 08036, Barcelona, Spain
Tel.: (34) 932692071
Web Site: https://www.quonia.com
YQUO—(MAD)
Sales Range: Less than $1 Million
Real Estate Investment Services
N.A.I.C.S.: 531390
Eduard Mercader *(CEO)*

QUORUM INFORMATION TECHNOLOGIES INC.
B28 6020 2nd Street SE, Calgary, T2H 2L8, AB, Canada   AB
Tel.: (403) 777-0036
Web Site:
https://quoruminformation.com
Year Founded: 2000
QIFTF—(OTCIQ)
Rev.: $30,403,795
Assets: $34,605,644
Liabilities: $14,171,323
Net Worth: $20,434,321
Earnings: $176,660
Fiscal Year-end: 12/31/23
Automobile Computer Systems Design & Related Services
N.A.I.C.S.: 541511
Maury Marks *(Founder, Pres & CEO)*

Subsidiaries:

Accessible Accessories Ltd.   (1)
B28 6020 2nd ST SE, Calgary, T2H 2L8, AB, Canada
Web Site: https://acc-acc.com
Vehicle Accessory Mfr & Distr

INTERNATIONAL PUBLIC

N.A.I.C.S.: 336390

Quorum Information Systems   (1)
300 10655 S Port Rd, Calgary, T2W 4Y1, AB, Canada   **(100%)**
Tel.: (403) 777-0035
Automotive Dealership Management Software
N.A.I.C.S.: 541512

QUOTABLE VALUE LIMITED
Level 1 22 Nevis St, Petone, 5014, New Zealand
Tel.: (64) 45764630
Web Site: http://www.qv.co.nz
Sales Range: $25-49.9 Million
Emp.: 250
Real Estate Valuation & Information Services
N.A.I.C.S.: 531390
Jacquie Barker *(COO)*

Subsidiaries:

Darroch Limited   (1)
Level 1 kencarrow 58 W 56 Jervosis, Private Bag 39818, Wellington Mail Centre, Wellington, New Zealand
Tel.: (64) 4 472 3529
Web Site: http://www.darroch.co.nz
Emp.: 30
Property Valuation Services
N.A.I.C.S.: 531320

QUOTIENT LIMITED
B1 Business Park Terre Bonne Route de Crassier 13, 1262, Eysins, Switzerland
Tel.: (41) 114122 716 9800   JE
Web Site: http://www.quotientbd.com
Year Founded: 2012
QTNT—(NASDAQ)
Rev.: $38,514,000
Assets: $193,989,000
Liabilities: $338,087,000
Net Worth: ($144,098,000)
Earnings: ($125,130,000)
Emp.: 436
Fiscal Year-end: 03/31/22
Transfusion Diagnostics
N.A.I.C.S.: 621511
Heino von Prondzynski *(Chm)*

QUOTIUM TECHNOLOGIES S.A
84/88 bd de la Mission Marchand, 92411, Courbevoie, France
Tel.: (33) 149047070
Web Site: http://www.quotium.fr
Year Founded: 1981
Sales Range: $1-9.9 Million
Communication Software Development Services
N.A.I.C.S.: 541511

Subsidiaries:

Quotium Corporation   (1)
575 Madison Ave 25th Fl, New York, NY 10022
Tel.: (212) 935-9760
Web Site: http://www.quotium.com
Emp.: 25
Software Development Services
N.A.I.C.S.: 541511
Michele Maturo *(Dir-Bus Dev & Sls)*

Quotium Technologies Ltd   (1)
20 Garrick Street, London, WC2E 9BT, United Kingdom
Tel.: (44) 203 178 3681
Software Development Services
N.A.I.C.S.: 541511
Michel Tiberini *(Pres)*

QURATIS INC.
9th Floor Daeryeong Seocho Tower 327 Gangnam-daero, Seocho-gu, Seoul, 06627, Korea (South)
Tel.: (82) 28660604
Web Site: https://www.quratis.com
Year Founded: 2016

348080—(KRS)
Rev.: $6,450,045
Assets: $49,466,114
Liabilities: $68,741,470
Net Worth: ($19,275,355)
Earnings: ($27,426,743)
Emp.: 158
Fiscal Year-end: 12/31/22
Biotechnology Research & Development Services
N.A.I.C.S.: 541714

QURI-MAYU DEVELOPMENTS LTD.
Suite 1000-1285 West Pender Street, Vancouver, V6E 4B1, BC, Canada
Tel.: (604) 309-6340 BC
Year Founded: 2017
QURI—(TSXV)
Assets: $1,230,000
Liabilities: $414,126
Net Worth: $815,873
Earnings: ($258,609)
Fiscal Year-end: 10/31/22
Mineral Mining Services
N.A.I.C.S.: 213115
Braydon Hobbs (CFO)

QURIENT CO., LTD.
C-dong 801 242 Pangyo-ro Bundang-gu, Seongnam, 13487, Gyeonggi-do, Korea (South)
Tel.: (82) 3180601600
Web Site: http://www.qurient.com
Year Founded: 2008
115180—(KRS)
Rev.: $6,495,380
Assets: $29,461,747
Liabilities: $2,512,235
Net Worth: $26,949,512
Earnings: ($20,799,585)
Emp.: 33
Fiscal Year-end: 12/31/22
Pharmaceuticals Mfr
N.A.I.C.S.: 325412
Kiyean Nam (CEO & Chief Scientific Officer)

QUTOUTIAO INC.
Building No 8 Shanghai Pudong Software Park 519 Yi De Road, Pudong New Area, Shanghai, 200124, China
Tel.: (86) 2158890398 Ky
Web Site: http://www.qutoutiao.net
Year Founded: 2016
QTT—(NASDAQ)
Rev.: $103,228,428
Assets: $57,240,114
Liabilities: $383,206,275
Net Worth: ($325,966,161)
Earnings: ($25,658,091)
Emp.: 370
Fiscal Year-end: 12/31/23
Mobile Entertainment Application Development Services
N.A.I.C.S.: 541511
Eric Siliang Tan (Co-Founder, Chm & CEO)

QUVA NV
Pottelberg Engelse Wandeling 2 Building K19 & K20, 8500, Kortrijk, Belgium
Web Site: http://www.quva.com
Investment Company
N.A.I.C.S.: 523940
Pascal Vanhalst (Founder)

QUZHOU XIN'AN DEVELOPMENT CO., LTD
11th Floor Xinhu Business Building No 128 Xixi Road, Hangzhou, 310007, Zhejiang, China
Tel.: (86) 5732080040
Web Site: http://www.600208.net
Year Founded: 1993
600208—(SHG)
Rev.: $1,811,021,060
Assets: $17,479,393,739
Liabilities: $11,586,852,099
Net Worth: $5,892,541,640
Earnings: $260,848,472
Fiscal Year-end: 12/31/22
Real Estate Manangement Services
N.A.I.C.S.: 531110
Lin Junbo (Vice Chm & Pres)

QV EQUITIES LIMITED
Level 24 25 Bligh Street, Sydney, 2000, NSW, Australia
Tel.: (61) 1300552895
Web Site: http://www.qvequities.com
Year Founded: 2014
QVE—(ASX)
Rev.: $7,559,899
Assets: $192,975,884
Liabilities: $6,695,129
Net Worth: $186,280,755
Earnings: $4,711,072
Fiscal Year-end: 06/30/22
Equity Investments
N.A.I.C.S.: 523150
Peter McKillop (Chm)

QWAMPLIFY S.A
9 Pl Marie-Jeanne Bassot, 92300, Levallois-Perret, France
Tel.: (33) 486914143
Web Site: https://www.qwamplify.com
Year Founded: 1997
ALQWA—(EUR)
Sales Range: $25-49.9 Million
Marketing Solutions
N.A.I.C.S.: 541613
Cedric Reny (Chm & CEO)

QWICK MEDIA INC.
104-8331 Eastlake Dr, Burnaby, V5A 4W2, BC, Canada
Tel.: (778) 370-1715 Ky
Web Site: http://www.qwickmedia.com
Year Founded: 2000
Rev.: $154,313
Assets: $361,737
Liabilities: $1,664,634
Net Worth: ($1,302,897)
Earnings: ($622,615)
Emp.: 5
Fiscal Year-end: 12/31/18
Media Services
N.A.I.C.S.: 541840
Ross J. Tocher (Pres, CEO, Treas & Sec)

QYOU MEDIA, INC.
100 University Ave 8th Floor, Toronto, M5J 2Y1, ON, Canada
Tel.: (416) 263-9200
Web Site: https://www.qyoumedia.com
QYOU—(OTCIQ)
Assets: $12,805,001
Liabilities: $4,149,413
Net Worth: $8,655,588
Earnings: ($5,716,474)
Emp.: 110
Fiscal Year-end: 06/30/21
Media Advertising Services
N.A.I.C.S.: 541840
G. Scott Paterson (Co-Founder & Chm)

Subsidiaries:

Maxamtech Digital Ventures Private Limited (1)
Spring Valley 902 Lavender Magarpatta City Road, Hadapsar, Pune, 411028, Maharashtra, India
Tel.: (91) 9175544454
Web Site: https://maxamventures.com
Online Game Development Services
N.A.I.C.S.: 541511

R & C TOURS JAPAN INC.
3-18-11 Hatchabori Chuo-ku, 104-0032, Tokyo, Japan
Tel.: (81) 3 3297 3633
Web Site: http://www.rctours.co.jp
Year Founded: 1985
Sales Range: $150-199.9 Million
Emp.: 12,000
Tour & Hotel Operations
N.A.I.C.S.: 561520
Tajima Sachio (Pres & CEO)

Subsidiaries:

R & C Tours Guam Inc (1)
200 Chichirica St, Tamuning, GU 96913-4217
Tel.: (671) 647-3333
Web Site: http://www.rcguam.com
Tour Operator
N.A.I.C.S.: 561520
Tajima Sachio (Pres & Gen Mgr)

R & G PHARMASTUDIES CO., LTD.
Floor 11 North Tower Building B Huatong Plaza No 19, Chegongzhuang West Road Haidian District, Beijing, 100048, China
Tel.: (86) 1088918650
Web Site: https://www.rg-pharma.com
Year Founded: 2008
301333—(CHIN)
Rev.: $99,879,971
Assets: $287,136,700
Liabilities: $44,191,114
Net Worth: $242,945,586
Earnings: $22,503,918
Emp.: 2,000
Fiscal Year-end: 12/31/23
Biotechnology Research & Development Services
N.A.I.C.S.: 541714
Jie Wu (Chm & Gen Mgr)

R ALKAN & CIE
Rue Du 8 Mai 1945, 94460, Valenton, Val De Marne, France
Tel.: (33) 145108600
Web Site: http://www.alkan.fr
Sales Range: $25-49.9 Million
Carriage, Release & Ejection Systems Mfr
N.A.I.C.S.: 336411
Armand Carlier (Pres)

R ENERGY 1 S.A.
32 A Theodorou Diligianni Street, Kifisia, 14562, Athens, Greece
Tel.: (30) 2108081241
Web Site: http://www.r-energy.gr
Investment Services
N.A.I.C.S.: 523940
Georgios M. Rokas (Chm & CEO)

R J BIO-TECH LIMITED
Siddharth Arcade Railway Station Road, Aurangabad, 431 005, Maharashtra, India
Tel.: (91) 2402354912
Web Site: https://www.rjbiotech.com
Year Founded: 2005
536456—(BOM)
Rev.: $1,746,987
Assets: $230,023
Liabilities: $6,265,666
Net Worth: ($6,035,643)
Earnings: ($1,098,002)
Emp.: 51
Fiscal Year-end: 03/31/22
Agricultural Services
N.A.I.C.S.: 111998
Dilip Rajput (Coord-Sls)

R M DRIP & SPRINKLERS SYSTEMS LTD.
Gut No 475 Village Gonde, Tal Sinnar Dist, Nashik, 422 103, India
Tel.: (91) 9226509809
Web Site: https://www.rmdrip.com
RMDRIP—(NSE)
Rev.: $1,656,967
Assets: $3,457,544
Liabilities: $1,930,581
Net Worth: $1,526,963
Earnings: $3,470
Emp.: 49
Fiscal Year-end: 03/31/23
Electronic Design & Testing Services
N.A.I.C.S.: 541420
Vijay H. Kshirsagar (Chm)

R P MARTIN HOLDINGS LIMITED
Cannon Bridge 25 Dowgate Hill, London, EC4R 2BB, United Kingdom
Tel.: (44) 2074699000
Web Site: http://www.martin-brokers.com
Sales Range: $10-24.9 Million
Emp.: 355
Stock Broking & Money Exchange Services
N.A.I.C.S.: 523150
David S.M. Caplin (CEO)

Subsidiaries:

Martin Brokers (UK) Ltd (1)
26-28 Frederick St, Edinburgh, EH2 2JR, United Kingdom
Tel.: (44) 1312267401
Web Site: http://www.martin-brokers.com
Securities Brokerage Services
N.A.I.C.S.: 523150

R P Martin LLC (1)
44 Wall St 21st Fl, New York, NY 10005
Tel.: (646) 688-7585
Brokerage Services
N.A.I.C.S.: 523150

RP Martin (Austria) AG (1)
Riemergasse 14/20/21, 1010, Vienna, Austria
Tel.: (43) 15373831
Web Site: http://www.martin-brokers.com
Brokerage Services
N.A.I.C.S.: 523150

R R KABEL LIMITED
Ram Ratna House Utopia City P B Marg Worli, Mumbai, 400013, Maharashtra, India
Tel.: (91) 2224949009
Web Site: https://rrkabel.com
Year Founded: 1995
543981—(BOM)
Rev.: $685,050,685
Assets: $319,851,776
Liabilities: $147,613,475
Net Worth: $172,238,301
Earnings: $22,973,706
Emp.: 3,036
Fiscal Year-end: 03/31/23
Electronic Components Mfr
N.A.I.C.S.: 334419
Rajesh Jain (CFO)

R S SOFTWARE INDIA LTD
A-2 FMC Fortuna 234/3A AJC Bose Road, Kolkata, 700020, India
Tel.: (91) 3322810106
Web Site: https://www.rssoftware.com
Year Founded: 1987
RSSOFTWARE—(NSE)
Rev.: $5,086,563
Assets: $9,768,158
Liabilities: $2,003,615
Net Worth: $7,764,543
Earnings: ($2,891,316)
Emp.: 150
Fiscal Year-end: 03/31/21
Computer Software Development Services
N.A.I.C.S.: 541511

R S SOFTWARE INDIA LTD

R S Software India Ltd—(Continued)
Raj Jain *(Chm & Mng Dir)*

R&A TELECOMMUNICATION GROUP BERHAD
No 2 Jalan Pengacara U1/48 Section U1 Temasya Industrial Park, 40150, Shah Alam, Selangor Darul Ehsan, Malaysia
Tel.: (60) 355691801   MY
Web Site: http://www.ratelecomm.com.my
Year Founded: 1993
Telecommunication Support Services
N.A.I.C.S.: 541618
Sim Keng Siong *(CEO)*

R&B DENIMS LTD
Plot No 467 Palsana Sachin-Palsana Highway Road, Surat, 394315, Gujarat, India
Tel.: (91) 9601281648
Web Site: https://www.rnbdenims.com
538119—(BOM)
Rev.: $31,799,269
Assets: $18,464,205
Liabilities: $8,937,066
Net Worth: $9,527,139
Earnings: $1,855,560
Emp.: 346
Fiscal Year-end: 03/31/23
Textile Mfr
N.A.I.C.S.: 314999
Rajkumar Mangilal Borana *(Chm & Mng Dir)*

Subsidiaries:

RB Industries Ltd. (1)
No 206 Elango Nagar South, KR Puram Avarampalayam, Coimbatore, 641006, Tamil Nadu, India
Tel.: (91) 8047631026
Web Site: https://www.rbindustries.net
Emp.: 10
Soft Drink Making Machine Mfr
N.A.I.C.S.: 333310
S. Rajesh *(CEO)*

R&B FOOD SUPPLY PUBLIC COMPANY LIMITED
3395 Soi Ladprao 101, Klongchan Bangkapi, Bangkok, 10240, Thailand
Tel.: (66) 2946681221   TH
Web Site: https://www.rbfoodsupply.co.th
Year Founded: 1989
RBF—(THA)
Rev.: $129,060,768
Assets: $167,851,582
Liabilities: $26,677,771
Net Worth: $141,173,811
Earnings: $18,955,743
Emp.: 1,675
Fiscal Year-end: 12/31/23
Food Product Mfr & Distr
N.A.I.C.S.: 311423
Somchai Ratanapoompinyo *(Vice Chm & CEO)*

Subsidiaries:

Best Odour Co., Ltd. (1)
3 Soi Phokaew 3 Yaek 17 Klongchan Bangkapi, Bangkok, 10240, Thailand
Tel.: (66) 26717000
Web Site: https://bestodour.webflow.io
Chemical Product Mfr & Distr
N.A.I.C.S.: 325998

Premium Foods Co., Ltd. (1)
258 M 3 Chiang Mai-Phrao Rd Km 27 T Maefak A Sansai, Chiang Mai, 50290, Thailand
Tel.: (66) 53849761
Web Site: https://www.premium-foods.com
Frozen Food Product Mfr
N.A.I.C.S.: 311412

Thai Flavor & Fragrance Company Limited (1)
3 Soi Phokaew 3 Yaek 17 Klongchan, Bangkapi, Bangkok, 10240, Thailand
Tel.: (66) 26717000
Web Site: http://www.tff.co.th
Chemical Product Mfr & Distr
N.A.I.C.S.: 325998

R&D COMPUTER CO., LTD.
MS Shibaura Building 4-13-23 Shibaura, Minato-ku, Tokyo, 108-0023, Japan
Tel.: (81) 352323040
Web Site: https://www.rand.co.jp
Year Founded: 1971
3924—(TKS)
Rev.: $90,768,520
Assets: $57,586,320
Liabilities: $19,426,790
Net Worth: $38,159,530
Earnings: $8,150,130
Emp.: 583
Fiscal Year-end: 03/31/24
Computer System Consulting
N.A.I.C.S.: 541512
Hideo Tamura *(Chm)*

R&D NICKERSON FISH PRODUCTS LTD.
5163 Highway 3 Shag Harbour, Shelburne, B0W 3B0, NS, Canada
Tel.: (902) 723-2028
Web Site: http://www.rdnickerson.com
Year Founded: 1977
Sales Range: $10-24.9 Million
Emp.: 20
Fishery Products Whslr
N.A.I.C.S.: 424460
Tyler D. Nickerson *(Pres)*

R&M INTERNATIONAL GMBH
Schellerdamm 22-24, 21079, Hamburg, Germany
Tel.: (49) 40 752444 0   De
Web Site: http://www.rm-group.com
Year Founded: 1887
Holding Company
N.A.I.C.S.: 551112
Vollrath Schuster *(CEO)*

Subsidiaries:

R&M Romania (1)
Str Herastrau nr 1 Sector 1, 11981, Bucharest, Romania
Tel.: (40) 31 7100 164
Network Cable Installation Services
N.A.I.C.S.: 238210

R&M Ship Technologies GmbH (1)
Petridamm 11c, 18146, Rostock, Germany
Tel.: (49) 381 6584 100
Web Site: http://www.rm-group.com
Ship Building Services
N.A.I.C.S.: 336611

R&Q INSURANCE HOLDINGS LTD.
FB Perry Building 40 Church Street, PO Box HM2062, Hamilton, HM HX, Bermuda
Tel.: (441) 2390020   BM
Web Site: http://www.rqih.com
Year Founded: 1991
RQIHF—(OTCEM)
Rev.: $1,908,700,000
Assets: $5,914,900,000
Liabilities: $5,729,700,000
Net Worth: $185,200,000
Earnings: ($297,000,000)
Emp.: 330
Fiscal Year-end: 12/31/22
Holding Company; Insurance Products & Services
N.A.I.C.S.: 551112
Alan K. Quilter *(CEO-Grp)*

Subsidiaries:

A.M. Associates Insurance Services Ltd. (1)
2425 Matheson Blvd E 8th Floor, Mississauga, L4W 5K4, ON, Canada
Tel.: (778) 433-2510
Web Site: https://www.amassociates.ca
Property Insurance Services
N.A.I.C.S.: 524126

Accredited Insurance Holdings Inc. (1)
4798 New Broad St Ste 200, Orlando, FL 32814
Tel.: (407) 629-2562
Web Site: https://accreditedinsurance.com
Holding Company; Property & Casualty Insurance Products & Services
N.A.I.C.S.: 551112
Neil McConachie *(Chief Risk Officer & Chief Capital Officer)*

Subsidiary (Domestic):

Accredited Holding Corporation (2)
4798 New Broad St Ste 200, Orlando, FL 32814
Web Site: http://www.accredited-inc.com
Holding Company
N.A.I.C.S.: 551112
Deborah Snow *(Pres)*

Subsidiary (Domestic):

Accredited Group Agency, Inc. (3)
4798 New Broad St Ste 200, Orlando, FL 32814
Tel.: (407) 629-2562
Web Site: http://www.accredited-inc.com
Investment Banking & Securities Dealing
N.A.I.C.S.: 523150

Accredited Surety and Casualty Company Inc. (3)
4798 New Broad St Ste 200, Orlando, FL 32814
Web Site: https://www.accredited-inc.com
Surety & Casualty Insurance Carrier; Bail Bond Services
N.A.I.C.S.: 524126
Deborah Snow Jallad *(Chm & Pres)*

John Heath & Company Inc (1)
950 S Tamiami Trl Ste 102, Sarasota, FL 34236
Tel.: (941) 955-5005
Web Site: https://www.jheathco.com
Health Insurance Services
N.A.I.C.S.: 524114
John Heath *(Pres)*

Principle Insurance Company Limited (1)
Citygate 2 Cross Street Sale, Manchester, M33 7JR, United Kingdom
Tel.: (44) 8081787923
Web Site: http://www.principalinsurance.co.uk
Vehicle Insurance Services
N.A.I.C.S.: 524126

R&Q Captive Management LLC (1)
13253 N La Montana Dr Ste 203, Fountain Hills, AZ 85268
Tel.: (480) 816-5609
Web Site: http://www.rqquestusa.com
Insurance Consulting Services
N.A.I.C.S.: 524298
Jeff Kenneson *(Pres)*

R&Q Central Services Limited (1)
71 Fenchurch Street, London, EC3M 4BS, United Kingdom
Tel.: (44) 2077805850
Insurance Services
N.A.I.C.S.: 524210

R&Q Insurance Management (Gibraltar) Limited (1)
Eurosuites 4 3 03 Block 4 Eurotowers, PO Box 371, Europort Avenue, Gibraltar, Gibraltar
Tel.: (350) 200 45 578
Web Site: http://www.rqgib.gi
Emp.: 4
Insurance Consulting Services
N.A.I.C.S.: 524298
Richard Wood *(Dir-Ops)*

INTERNATIONAL PUBLIC

R&Q Quest Management Services Limited (1)
F B Perry Building 40 Church Street, PO Box HM2062, Hamilton, HM HX, Bermuda
Tel.: (441) 295 2185
Web Site: https://www.rqquestbermuda.com
Reinsurance Services
N.A.I.C.S.: 524130
Nicholas Dove *(Chm)*

R&Q Solutions LLC (1)
1 Logan Sq Ste 320, Philadelphia, PA 19103
Tel.: (267) 675-3400
Web Site: http://www.rsi-solutions.com
Insurance Consulting Services
N.A.I.C.S.: 524298

Randall & Quilter Underwriting Management Holdings Limited (1)
Tel.: (44) 2077805850
Holding Company
N.A.I.C.S.: 551112

Subsidiary (Domestic):

R&Q MGA Limited (2)
London Underwriting Centre 3 Minster Court, Mincing Lane, London, EC3R 7DD, United Kingdom
Tel.: (44) 20 7780 5974
Insurance Underwriting Services
N.A.I.C.S.: 524113

Reinsurance Solutions Limited (1)
Mayland House Floor 2 Mayland Road, Witham, CM8 2FR, Essex, United Kingdom
Tel.: (44) 1376 507500
Web Site: http://www.rsl-solutions.co.uk
Reinsurance Services
N.A.I.C.S.: 524130
Yvonne Eatwell *(Head-Bus Dev)*

Risk Transfer Underwriting Inc (1)
Tel.: (212) 220-9280
Web Site: http://www.risk-transfer.com
Emp.: 3
Insurance Underwriting Services
N.A.I.C.S.: 524113

Southern Illinois Land Company (1)
1660 Carrier Mills Rd, Harrisburg, IL 62946
Tel.: (618) 994-2311
Property Insurance Services
N.A.I.C.S.: 524126

Syndicated Services Company Inc (1)
1000 Elm St Ste 1900, Manchester, NH 03101
Tel.: (603) 622-4220
Insurance Brokerage Services
N.A.I.C.S.: 524210

R&R REAL ESTATE INVESTMENT TRUST
5090 Explorer Drive Suite 500, Mississauga, L4W 4T9, ON, Canada
Tel.: (905) 206-7100   ON
Year Founded: 2014
RRR.UN—(TSXV)
Rev.: $30,646,700
Assets: $115,501,764
Liabilities: $96,369,740
Net Worth: $19,132,024
Earnings: $357,259
Fiscal Year-end: 12/31/20
Real Estate Asset Management Services
N.A.I.C.S.: 531390
Lakha Irfan *(CEO)*

R&T PLUMBING TECHNOLOGY CO.,LTD
No 18 Houxiang Road, Haicang District, Xiamen, 361028, China
Tel.: (86) 5926539788
Web Site: http://www.rtplumbing.com
Year Founded: 1999
002790—(SSE)
Rev.: $275,126,436
Assets: $341,204,292
Liabilities: $70,647,876
Net Worth: $270,556,416
Earnings: $29,615,976

R&W METAL FABRICATING & DESIGN INC.
54 Spalding Dr, PO Box 8, Brantford, N3T 5M3, ON, Canada
Tel.: (519) 753-2407
Web Site: http://www.rwmetal.com
Year Founded: 1988
Rev.: $11,408,600
Emp.: 70
Metal Products Mfr
N.A.I.C.S.: 332312
Randal Huszczo (Pres)
Fiscal Year-end: 12/31/22
Bathroom Accessory Mfr & Distr
N.A.I.C.S.: 327110

R-BIOPHARM AG
An der neuen Bergstrasse 17, Darmstadt, 64297, Germany
Tel.: (49) 61 51 81 02 0
Web Site: http://www.r-biopharm.com
Year Founded: 1988
Sales Range: $75-99.9 Million
Emp.: 270
Test Kit Mfr
N.A.I.C.S.: 339113
Ralf M. Dreher (Chm)

Subsidiaries:

Multimetrix GmbH (1)
Maassstrasse 30, 69123, Heidelberg, Baden-Wurttemberg, Germany
Tel.: (49) 6221752060
Sales Range: $25-49.9 Million
Emp.: 5
Diagnostic Test Systems Mfr
N.A.I.C.S.: 334510
Brigitte Weins (Mng Dir)

PROGEN Biotechnik Gesellschaft mit beschrankter Haftung (1)
Maassstrasse 30, Heidelberg, 69123, Baden-Wurttemberg, Germany
Tel.: (49) 622182780
Web Site: http://www.progen.de
Sales Range: $25-49.9 Million
Emp.: 19
Diagnostic Test Kits Mfr
N.A.I.C.S.: 339113
Brigitte Weins (Gen Mgr)

R-Biopharm Analysis Systems Trading (Beijing) Co. Ltd. (1)
Suite 1601 tower F phoenix place Jia-No 5 Shuguang Xili, Chaoyang, Beijing, 100028, China
Tel.: (86) 1084583218
Healthcare Product Distr
N.A.I.C.S.: 424210

R-Biopharm Australia (1)
Serenity Cove Corporate Park Unit 7 260 Captain Cook Drive, Kurnell, 2231, NSW, Australia
Tel.: (61) 296680600
Healthcare Product Distr
N.A.I.C.S.: 424210

R-Biopharm Brasil Ltda. (1)
Rua Jose Bonifacio 768 - Jardim Flamboyant, Campinas, Sao Paulo, 13050-800, Brazil
Tel.: (55) 1933057351
Healthcare Product Distr
N.A.I.C.S.: 424210

R-Biopharm Espana S.A. (1)
Los Manzanos 4, San Sebastian de los Reyes, 28700, Madrid, Spain
Tel.: (34) 902903355
Healthcare Product Distr
N.A.I.C.S.: 424210
Elsa Munoz (Gen Dir)

R-Biopharm France (1)
5a rue Claude Chappe Parc daffaires de Crecy, Saint-Didier-au-Mont-d'Or, 69370, France
Tel.: (33) 478643200
Healthcare Product Distr
N.A.I.C.S.: 424210

R-Biopharm Inc. (1)
870 Vossbrink Dr, Washington, MO 63090
Tel.: (877) 789-3033
Healthcare Product Distr
N.A.I.C.S.: 424210

R-Biopharm Italia srl (1)
Via Morandi 10, 20077, Melegnano, Italy
Tel.: (39) 0298233330
Healthcare Product Distr
N.A.I.C.S.: 424210
Luca Losito (Mgr-Sls)

R-Biopharm Latinoamerica S.A. (1)
Vuelta de Obligado 2943, C1429AVC, Buenos Aires, Argentina
Tel.: (54) 1147016262
Healthcare Product Distr
N.A.I.C.S.: 424210
Dan Kaplan (Pres)

R-Biopharm Neugen Pvt. Ltd. (1)
2nd Floor Udai Square Ida Industrial Area Phase V Cherlapally, Hyderabad, 500 051, Andhra Pradesh, India
Tel.: (91) 4027266002
Healthcare Product Distr
N.A.I.C.S.: 424210
Sindhe Rao (Area Mgr-Sls)

R-Biopharm Rhone Ltd. (1)
Block 10 Todd Campus West of Scotland Science Park Acre Road, Glasgow, G20 0XA, United Kingdom
Tel.: (44) 1419452924
Medical Diagnostic Equipment Distr
N.A.I.C.S.: 423450

R-PHARM CJSC
Leninsky Prospekt 111 k 1, 119421, Moscow, Russia
Tel.: (7) 4959567937
Web Site: http://www.r-pharm.com
Year Founded: 2001
Sales Range: $1-4.9 Billion
Emp.: 2,800
Pharmaceutical Supplies & Equipment Mfr
N.A.I.C.S.: 325412
Alexey Repik (Chm)

Subsidiaries:

JSC Ecostil (1)
St Stachek 63, 150002, Yaroslavl, Russia
Tel.: (7) 4852459805
Web Site: http://www.ecostyle76.ru
Medical Equipment Mfr
N.A.I.C.S.: 339112

R-Pharm Germany GmbH (1)
Heinrich-Mack-Str 35, 89257, Illertissen, Germany
Tel.: (49) 7303120
Web Site: http://www.germany.r-pharm.com
Pharmaceuticals Product Mfr
N.A.I.C.S.: 325412
Vasily Ignatiev (CEO)

R-Pharm-Us LLC (1)
PO Box 3096, Princeton, NJ 08543
Tel.: (609) 512-1739
Web Site: http://www.rpharm-us.com
Pharmaceuticals Product Mfr
N.A.I.C.S.: 325412
Demetrios Kydonieus (Pres)

R. N. SPINNING MILLS LIMITED
House 11 5th Floor Unit 5-B Road 12, Niketon Gulshan-1, Dhaka, 1212, Bangladesh
Tel.: (880) 29335879
Web Site: https://www.rnspinningmills.com
Year Founded: 2004
RNSPIN—(DHA)
Rev.: $15,822
Assets: $3,310,372
Liabilities: $3,398,319
Net Worth: ($87,947)
Earnings: ($287,031)
Emp.: 15
Fiscal Year-end: 06/30/23
Textile Products Mfr
N.A.I.C.S.: 314999
Al-Haj Mohammad Abdul Kader Faruk (Founder)

R. STAHL AG
Am Bahnhof 30, 74638, Waldenburg, Germany
Tel.: (49) 79429430
Web Site: https://r-stahl.com
Year Founded: 1876
RSL2—(DUS)
Rev.: $364,895,267
Assets: $299,568,241
Liabilities: $224,990,783
Net Worth: $74,577,457
Earnings: $220,774
Emp.: 1,798
Fiscal Year-end: 12/31/23
Printing & Publishing Industry
N.A.I.C.S.: 333248
Heike Dannenbauer (Deputy Chm-Supervisory Bd)

Subsidiaries:

E.M. Stahl B.V. (1)
Jan Tinberganstraat 193, 7556 MZ, Hengelo, Overijssel, Netherlands
Tel.: (31) 742472472
Web Site: http://www.electromach.com
Sales Range: $50-74.9 Million
Emp.: 200
Electric Plugs & Terminal Boxes Mfr
N.A.I.C.S.: 334513
Peter Boers (Gen Mgr)

Electromach B.V. (1)
Jan Tinbergenstraat 193, 7559 SP, Hengelo, Netherlands
Tel.: (31) 742472472
Web Site: https://www.zone-atex.nl
Sales Range: $75-99.9 Million
Emp.: 150
Electronic Components Distr
N.A.I.C.S.: 423690

Gesellschaft fur Grundstucksvermietung und Finanzierungsvermittlung mbH (1)
Am Bahnhof 30, Waldenburg, 74638, Baden-Wurttemberg, Germany
Tel.: (49) 7942 943 0
Web Site: http://www.stahl.de
Emp.: 1,500
Switchboards & Connectors Whslr
N.A.I.C.S.: 423690
Martin Schomaker (Gen Mgr)

Industrias Stahl S.A. (1)
Planta 1a Calle de Julian Camarillo 53, 28037, Madrid, Spain
Tel.: (34) 916615500
Web Site: http://www.stahl.es
Sales Range: $50-74.9 Million
Emp.: 15
Electric Component Whslr
N.A.I.C.S.: 423690

OOO R. STAHL (1)
Presnenskaya Embankment 6 Bldg 2 Empire Tower Floor 12 Office 15, 122112, Moscow, Russia
Tel.: (7) 4959898007
Web Site: http://www.stahl.ru.com
Sales Range: $50-74.9 Million
Switchboards & Connectors Whslr
N.A.I.C.S.: 423690

R Stahl, Inc. (1)
13259 N Promenade Blvd, Stafford, TX 77477
Tel.: (713) 792-9300
Web Site: http://www.rstahl.com
Sales Range: $25-49.9 Million
Electrical Plugs & Terminal Boxes Mfr
N.A.I.C.S.: 335999

R. STAHL Engineering & Manufacturing SDN. BHD. (1)
Lot 1912 Jalan KBP 9 Kawasan Perindustrian Kg Bahru, Balakong, 43300, Seri Kembangan, Selangor Darul Ehsan, Malaysia
Tel.: (60) 389621889
Web Site: http://www.stahl.de
Sales Range: $25-49.9 Million
Emp.: 15
Electronic Components Mfr
N.A.I.C.S.: 334513

R. STAHL JAPAN Kabushiki Kaisha (1)
Level 32 Shinjuku Nomura Building 1-26-2, Nishi-Shinjuku Shinjuku-ku, Tokyo, 163-0532, Japan
Tel.: (81) 353222064
Electrical Instrumentation Mfr & Distr
N.A.I.C.S.: 334515

R. Stahl (P) Limited (1)
Plot No 5 Malrosapuram Main Road, Sengundram Ind Area Singaperumal Koil, Chennai, 603 204, Tamil Nadu, India
Tel.: (91) 4467300600
Web Site: http://r-stahl.com
Sales Range: $50-74.9 Million
Electric Component Whslr
N.A.I.C.S.: 423690

R. Stahl Australia Pty. Ltd. (1)
848 Old Princes Highway, Sutherland, 2232, NSW, Australia
Tel.: (61) 242544777
Web Site: http://www.stahl.com.au
Electric & Electronic Component Mfr
N.A.I.C.S.: 335999
John Zagame (Mng Dir)

R. Stahl Co. Ltd. (1)
Suite 1107 Kolon Digital Tower 1 4 Gil 25 Sungsoo-il-ro, Sungdong-gu, Seoul, 04781, Korea (South)
Tel.: (82) 24892736
Web Site: https://r-stahl.com
Sales Range: $50-74.9 Million
Emp.: 18
Electronic Accessories Distr
N.A.I.C.S.: 423690

R. Stahl Ex-Proof (Shanghai) Co., Ltd. (1)
Unit D 9th Floor Building No 4 889 Yishan Road, Shanghai, 200233, China
Tel.: (86) 2164850011
Electric & Electronic Component Mfr
N.A.I.C.S.: 335999
Benjamin Liang (Mng Dir)

R. Stahl France S.A.S. (1)
Immeuble Naxos 56 Rue des Hautes Patures, 92737, Nanterre, France
Tel.: (33) 141194858
Web Site: http://www.stahl.fr
Sales Range: $25-49.9 Million
Emp.: 13
Electronic Components Distr
N.A.I.C.S.: 423690

R. Stahl Gulf FZCO (1)
Office 832 6WB Building Dubai Airport Free Zone, PO Box 371697, Dubai, United Arab Emirates
Tel.: (971) 45257400
Electric & Electronic Component Mfr
N.A.I.C.S.: 335999
Ashish Sharma (Sls Dir)

R. Stahl HMI Systems GmbH (1)
Adolf-Grimme-Allee 8, 50829, Cologne, Germany
Tel.: (49) 221768061200
Web Site: http://www.stahl-hmi.de
Sales Range: $25-49.9 Million
Emp.: 80
Surveillance & Monitoring Systems Mfr
N.A.I.C.S.: 334511
Alain Schellings (Dir-Sls)

R. Stahl Kabushiki Kaisha (1)
1-1-1 Manpukuji, Asao-ku, Kawasaki, 215-0004, Kanagawa, Japan
Tel.: (81) 449592612
Web Site: http://www.rstahl.com
Sales Range: $50-74.9 Million
Emp.: 6
Electric Component Whslr
N.A.I.C.S.: 423690

R. Stahl LLP (1)
Terenozek St 26, 060000, Atyrau, Kazakhstan
Tel.: (7) 7777390086
Electric & Electronic Component Mfr
N.A.I.C.S.: 335999

R. Stahl Ltd. (1)
STAHL House 43 Elmdon Trading Estate Bickenhill Ln, Birmingham, B37 7HE, West Midlands, United Kingdom
Tel.: (44) 1217676400

R. STAHL AG

R. STAHL AG—(Continued)
Web Site: http://www.rstahl.co.uk
Sales Range: $25-49.9 Million
Emp.: 25
Explosion Protection Equipments Mfr
N.A.I.C.S.: 335314
Matt Withington *(Product Mgr-Process Automation)*

R. Stahl Ltd. (1)
8925-51 Avenue NW Unit 303, Edmonton, T6E 5J3, AB, Canada
Web Site: https://r-stahl.com
Sales Range: $25-49.9 Million
Electronic Parts Mfr
N.A.I.C.S.: 423690

R. Stahl Middle East FZE (1)
Jebel Ali Free Zone, PO Box 17784, Dubai, United Arab Emirates
Tel.: (971) 48835855
Web Site: http://www.stahl.ae
Electrical Plugs & Terminal Boxes Mfr
N.A.I.C.S.: 423690
Andreas Kaufmann *(Mng Dir)*

R. Stahl Norge AS (1)
Luhrtoppen 2 N - 1470, 1081, Lorenskog, Norway
Tel.: (47) 24084410
Web Site: http://www.stahl-syberg.no
Sales Range: $25-49.9 Million
Emp.: 20
Electronic Parts Whslr
N.A.I.C.S.: 423690
Fredrik Syberg *(Gen Mgr)*

R. Stahl Private Limited (1)
Plot No 5 Malrosapuram Main Road, Sengundram Ind Area Singaperumal Koil, Chengalpattu, 603204, Tamil Nadu, India
Tel.: (91) 4467300600
Electric & Electronic Component Mfr
N.A.I.C.S.: 335999
Thomas Wittek *(Mng Dir)*

R. Stahl S.R.L. (1)
Via Achille Grandi 27, 20068, Peschiera Borromeo, MI, Italy
Tel.: (39) 0255308024
Web Site: http://www.stahl.it
Electric & Electronic Component Mfr
N.A.I.C.S.: 335999
Alberto Digiuni *(Mng Dir)*

R. Stahl Schaltgerate GmbH (1)
Heidenkampsweg 100, 20097, Hamburg, Germany
Tel.: (49) 407360540
Web Site: http://www.stahl.de
Sales Range: $25-49.9 Million
Emp.: 15
Electrical Plugs & Terminal Boxes Mfr
N.A.I.C.S.: 335999
Herbert Schober *(Dir-Sls)*

Subsidiary (Non-US):

R. Stahl Pte. Ltd. (2)
Tel.: (65) 62719595
Web Site: http://www.rstahl.com.sg
Cables & Switches Mfr.
N.A.I.C.S.: 331420

R. Stahl Services GmbH (1)
Am Bahnhof 30, 74638, Waldenburg, Germany
Tel.: (49) 79429434196
Electric & Electronic Component Mfr
N.A.I.C.S.: 335999

R. Stahl South Africa (Pty) Ltd. (1)
61 Ronald Ave Linbro Park, Sandton, 2090, South Africa
Tel.: (27) 116083120
Electric & Electronic Component Mfr
N.A.I.C.S.: 335999
Roman Panis *(Mng Dir)*

R. Stahl Svenska AB (1)
Skarprattarvagen 1a Room 9, 176 77, Jarfalla, Stockholm, Sweden
Tel.: (46) 8389100
Web Site: http://www.rstahl.se
Monitoring Systems & Alarm Mfr
N.A.I.C.S.: 334290

R. Stahl Switzerland AG (1)
Bruelstrasse 26, 4312, Magden, Switzerland

Tel.: (41) 618554060
Web Site: http://en.stahl-schweiz.ch
Electric & Electronic Component Mfr
N.A.I.C.S.: 335999

R. Stahl Tranberg As (1)
Strandsvingen 6, N-4032, Stavanger, Norway
Tel.: (47) 51578900
Web Site: https://stahl-tranberg.com
Emp.: 62
Heat Tracing Equipment Mfr & Distr
N.A.I.C.S.: 333414

R. Stahl do Brasil Ltda. (1)
Cond Network Business Tower-Park Tower Alameda Terracota 185-sl 1302, Sao Caetano do Sul, 09531-190, Sao Paulo, Brazil
Tel.: (55) 1136370557
Web Site: http://www.rstahl.com.br
Electric & Electronic Component Mfr
N.A.I.C.S.: 335999

Stahl N.V. (1)
Sint-Gillislaan 6 bus 3, Dendermonde, 9200, Belgium
Tel.: (32) 52211351
Web Site: http://www.stahl.be
Sales Range: $50-74.9 Million
Emp.: 5
Explosion Protection Components Distr
N.A.I.C.S.: 423690
Peter Boers *(Mng Dir)*

Stahl-Syberg AS (1)
Luhrtoppen 2, 1081, Lorenskog, Norway
Tel.: (47) 24084410
Web Site: http://www.stahl-syberg.no
Sales Range: $25-49.9 Million
Emp.: 35
Explosion & Dust Protection Components Distr
N.A.I.C.S.: 423690
Fredrik Syberg *(Gen Mgr)*

Tranberg AS (1)
Strandsvingen 6, PO Box 8033, 4032, Stavanger, Norway
Tel.: (47) 51578900
Web Site: http://www.tranberg.com
Sales Range: $25-49.9 Million
Emp.: 70
Electromechanical Products Mfr & Distr
N.A.I.C.S.: 334514

R. T. BRISCOE (NIGERIA) PLC
18 Fatai Atere Way Matori Oshodi, Lagos, Nigeria
Tel.: (234) 14537694
Web Site: https://www.rtbriscoe.com
Year Founded: 1957
Motor Vehicle Parts Distr
N.A.I.C.S.: 441330
Seyi Onajide *(CEO & Mng Dir-Grp)*

Subsidiaries:

Briscoe Properties Limited (1)
18 Fatai Atere Way Matori Oshodi, Lagos, Nigeria
Tel.: (234) 9099241592
Web Site: http://www.briscoeproperties.com
Engineeering Services
N.A.I.C.S.: 541330
Seyi Onajide *(Chm)*

R.C.CORE CO., LTD.
6F Mansard Daikanyama 10-1 Sarugakucho, Shibuya-ku, Tokyo, 150-0033, Japan
Tel.: (81) 359904070
Web Site: https://www.rccore.co.jp
Year Founded: 1985
7837—(TKS)
Rev.: $80,258,620
Assets: $52,113,240
Liabilities: $32,488,150
Net Worth: $19,625,090
Earnings: $14,019,810
Emp.: 213
Fiscal Year-end: 03/31/24
Real Estate Development Services
N.A.I.C.S.: 531390

R.E.A HOLDINGS PLC
The Pavilions Bridgewater Road, Bristol, BS99 6ZZ, United Kingdom
Tel.: (44) 2074367877 UK
Web Site: https://www.rea.co.uk
Year Founded: 1906
RE—(LSE)
Rev.: $208,780,000
Assets: $561,300,000
Liabilities: $303,770,000
Net Worth: $257,530,000
Earnings: $32,890,000
Fiscal Year-end: 12/31/22
Holding Company
N.A.I.C.S.: 551111
David J. Blackett *(Chm)*

Subsidiaries:

R.E.A. Services Limited (1)
First Floor 32-36 Great Portland Street, London, W1W 8QX, United Kingdom
Tel.: (44) 2074367877
Palm Oil Mfr
N.A.I.C.S.: 311225

R.E.D. GRANITI S.P.A.
Via Dorsale 12, 54100, Massa, Massa and Carrara, Italy
Tel.: (39) 058588471 IT
Web Site: http://www.redgraniti.com
Sales Range: $200-249.9 Million
Emp.: 1,000
Granite Production Services
N.A.I.C.S.: 212313
Massimo Pezzana *(Mgr-Accts)*

Subsidiaries:

Finska Stenindustri AB (1)
Vinkkilantie 5, 23200, Vinkkila, Finland
Tel.: (358) 24377711
Web Site: http://www.finskastone.fi
Sales Range: $50-74.9 Million
Emp.: 4
Granite Exporter; Granite Quarries Owner
N.A.I.C.S.: 212313
Pirjo Herrala *(Controller)*

R.E.D GRANITI XIAMEN CO., LTD (1)
A6 10F Xiangyu Building Xiangyu Bonded area, 361009, Xiamen, China
Tel.: (86) 592 6027438
Granite Distr
N.A.I.C.S.: 423320

R.E.D. GRANITI BRASIL Ltda. (1)
Avenida Joao Baptista Parra n 673 sala 501 Ed Enseada Tower, 29052-123, Vitoria, Espirito Santo, Brazil
Tel.: (55) 27 3223 9111
Granite Distr
N.A.I.C.S.: 423320
Fabrizio Ponzanelli *(Pres)*

R.E.D. GRANITI DEUTSCHLAND Gmbh (1)
Pfalzring 94, 67112, Mutterstadt, Germany
Tel.: (49) 6234 9275250
Granite Distr
N.A.I.C.S.: 423320

R.E.D. GRANITI ESPANA SL (1)
Ines Perez de Ceta 3 8 B, 36201, Vigo, Spain
Tel.: (34) 986224175
Granite Distr
N.A.I.C.S.: 423320

R.E.D. GRANITI MADAGASCAR Sarl (1)
Lot II-M46KB Androhibe, 101, Antananarivo, Madagascar
Tel.: (261) 202243522
Granite Mfr
N.A.I.C.S.: 327991

R.E.D. GRANITI MINERACAO Ltda (1)
Estrada Nova Venecia a Luzilandia KM 11 5, Nova Venecia, Espirito Santo, Brazil
Tel.: (55) 27 3752 8150
Granite Mfr
N.A.I.C.S.: 327991

R.E.D. GRANITI QUARRIES & BLOCKS INDIA Pvt Ltd (1)
1/21 Sathyam 10th Main II Cross Rajmahal Vilas Extension, 560 080, Bengaluru, India
Tel.: (91) 9902059032
Granite Distr
N.A.I.C.S.: 423320

R.E.D. GRANITI SA SOUTH AFRICA Pty Ltd. (1)
Menlyn Corporate Park 3rd Floor Block C 175 Corobay Road, Waterkloof Glen, 10, Pretoria, South Africa
Tel.: (27) 12 348 4195
Web Site: http://www.redgraniti.co.za
Granite Mfr
N.A.I.C.S.: 327991
Motsoasele Emily *(Mgr-HR)*

Red Graniti Poland Sp. z o.o. (1)
ul Pocztowa 1, 66-400, Gorzow Wielkopolski, Poland
Tel.: (48) 95 782 12 21
Web Site: http://www.redgraniti.pl
Granite Distr
N.A.I.C.S.: 423320

R.H. AMAR & CO. LTD.
Turnpike Way, High Wycombe, HP12 3TF, Bucks, United Kingdom
Tel.: (44) 1494530200
Web Site: http://www.rhamar.com
Emp.: 70
Fine Foods Importer & Distr
N.A.I.C.S.: 445298
Henry Amar *(Chm)*

R.J. BURNSIDE & ASSOCIATES LIMITED
15 Townline, Orangeville, L9W 3R4, ON, Canada
Tel.: (519) 941-5331
Web Site: http://www.rjburnside.com
Year Founded: 1970
Rev.: $160,000,000
Emp.: 200
Engineeering Services
N.A.I.C.S.: 541330
Dave Bannister *(Exec VP-Pub Sector)*

R.J. SHAH & COMPANY LIMITED
Mahul Road Antop Hill, Mumbai, 400037, Maharashtra, India
Tel.: (91) 2224105159
Web Site: https://rjshahandco.com
509845—(BOM)
Rev.: $275,019
Assets: $4,394,509
Liabilities: $211,196
Net Worth: $4,183,313
Earnings: $71,234
Fiscal Year-end: 03/31/21
Civil Engineering Construction Services
N.A.I.C.S.: 237990
Kalindi R. Shah *(Chm & Co-Mng Dir)*

R.M. WILLIAMS PTY. LTD.
121 Frost Road, Sailsbury, Adelaide, 5108, SA, Australia
Tel.: (61) 882591007
Web Site: http://www.rmwilliams.com.au
Year Founded: 1932
Apparel & Accessory Distr
N.A.I.C.S.: 424350
Ravinder Singh Thakran *(Chm)*

R.R. SECURITIES LIMITED
1 Rushil Bungalow Sterling City Village Bopal CT Taluka Dascroi, Ahmedabad, 380058, Gujarat, India
Tel.: (91) 7940041301 In
Web Site: http://www.rrsecurities.com
Year Founded: 1993
530917—(BOM)
Rev.: $38,403
Assets: $642,081
Liabilities: $28,629

Net Worth: $613,453
Earnings: $23,662
Emp.: 1
Fiscal Year-end: 03/31/21
Financial Investment Services
N.A.I.C.S.: 523999
Rajendra Babulal Shah *(Chm & Officer-Compliance)*

R.T. EXPORTS LIMITED
508 Dalamal House Jamnalal Bajaj Marg, Nariman Point, Mumbai, 400 021, India
Tel.: (91) 2240812000
Web Site: https://www.rtexports.com
512565—(BOM)
Rev.: $401,133
Assets: $3,455,989
Liabilities: $2,192,654
Net Worth: $1,263,335
Earnings: ($6,921)
Emp.: 2
Fiscal Year-end: 03/31/21
Export Trading Services
N.A.I.C.S.: 522299
Bhavik R. Bhimjyani *(Chm & Mng Dir)*

R12 KAPITAL FUND I AB
Riddargatan 12, PO Box 55720, 114 83, Stockholm, Sweden
Tel.: (46) 8 622 36 00   SE
Web Site: http://www.r12kapital.se
Private Investment Firm
N.A.I.C.S.: 523999
Per Hesselmark *(Co-Owner)*

Subsidiaries:

Nimbus Boats AB   (1)
GKSS Harbour, Langedrag, Vastra Frolunda, Sweden   **(100%)**
Tel.: (46) 317267700
Web Site: http://www.nimbus.se
Sales Range: $125-149.9 Million
Emp.: 600
Boat Mfr
N.A.I.C.S.: 336612

Subsidiary (Non-US):

Paragon Yachts Oy   (2)
Kortelaaksontie 34 B, 65280, Vaasa, Finland
Tel.: (358) 440 668 765
Web Site: http://www.paragonyachts.com
Sales Range: $25-49.9 Million
Emp.: 30
Boat Mfr
N.A.I.C.S.: 336612

R3D GLOBAL LIMITED
Level 12 210 George Street, Sydney, 2000, NSW, Australia
Tel.: (61) 2 8880 3688
Web Site: http://www.r3d.com.au
R3D—(ASX)
Sales Range: Less than $1 Million
Financial Services
N.A.I.C.S.: 523999
Daniel Yeo *(Chm)*

R8 CAPITAL INVESTMENTS PLC
Finsgate 5-7 Cranwood Street, London, EC1V 9EE, United Kingdom UK
Web Site: https://www.modeplc.com
Year Founded: 2019
MODE—(LSE)
Rev.: $1,364,554
Assets: $1,346,882
Liabilities: $3,293,360
Net Worth: ($1,946,478)
Earnings: ($8,095,178)
Emp.: 39
Fiscal Year-end: 12/31/22
Holding Company
N.A.I.C.S.: 551112
Jonathan Rowland *(Chm)*

RA INTERNATIONAL GROUP PLC
One Fleet Place, London, EC4M 7WS, United Kingdom
Tel.: (44) 2032866229   UK
Web Site: https://www.ragrpplc.co.uk
Year Founded: 2004
RAI—(AIM)
Rev.: $62,917,000
Assets: $53,068,000
Liabilities: $28,200,000
Net Worth: $24,868,000
Earnings: ($13,166,000)
Emp.: 1,368
Fiscal Year-end: 12/31/22
Construction Services
N.A.I.C.S.: 236220

RAA INSURANCE LIMITED
101 Richmond Road Mile End, GPO Box 1499, Adelaide, 5031, SA, Australia
Tel.: (61) 882024500   AU
Web Site: http://www.raa.com.au
Year Founded: 1903
Sales Range: $50-74.9 Million
Emp.: 500
Insurance Services
N.A.I.C.S.: 524126

RAAJ MEDISAFE INDIA LIMITED
75/2 and 3 Industrial Area, Maksi Road, Ujjain, 456010, Madhya Pradesh, India
Tel.: (91) 7342518989
Web Site: https://www.raajmedisafeindia.com
Year Founded: 1989
524502—(BOM)
Rev.: $4,633,458
Assets: $3,089,775
Liabilities: $2,191,648
Net Worth: $898,126
Earnings: $399,230
Emp.: 111
Fiscal Year-end: 03/31/23
Medical Disposable Device Mfr
N.A.I.C.S.: 339113
Arpit Bangur *(Chm)*

RAASI REFRACTORIES LTD.
15-145/9 Kodandaram Nagar, Saroornagar Near Sarada Talkies, Hyderabad, 500060, India
Tel.: (91) 4024054462
Web Site: https://www.raasi.in
502271—(BOM)
Rev.: $2,862,378
Assets: $4,965,251
Liabilities: $7,097,871
Net Worth: ($2,132,619)
Earnings: $47,938
Fiscal Year-end: 03/31/21
Refractory Brick Mfr
N.A.I.C.S.: 327120
Sistla Subrahmanya Sastry *(CFO)*

RAB CAPITAL LIMITED
1 Adam Street, London, WC2N 6LE, United Kingdom
Tel.: (44) 2073897000   UK
Web Site: http://www.rabcap.com
Sales Range: $10-24.9 Million
Emp.: 20
Investment Services
N.A.I.C.S.: 523999
Michael Alen-Buckley *(Chm)*

RABA AUTOMOTIVE HOLDING PLC
Martin u 1, H-9027, Gyor, Hungary
Tel.: (36) 304449500   HU
Web Site: https://www.raba.hu
RABA—(BUD)
Rev.: $156,023,646

Assets: $151,725,474
Liabilities: $71,165,885
Net Worth: $80,559,588
Earnings: $4,311,512
Emp.: 1,380
Fiscal Year-end: 12/31/21
Holding Company; Heavy-Duty Commercial Vehicles & Related Parts Mfr
N.A.I.C.S.: 551112
Istvan Lepsenyi *(Chm-Supervisory Bd)*

RABAUD
Bellevue, 85110, Sainte-Cecile, Vendee, France
Tel.: (33) 251485151
Web Site: http://www.rabaud.com
Sales Range: $10-24.9 Million
Emp.: 126
Agriculture, Building & Construction (PW), Garden & Landscape Businesses Equipments Mfr
N.A.I.C.S.: 333111
Claude Rabaud *(Pres)*

RABEN MANAGEMENT SERVICES SP. Z O.O.
Zbozowa 1, Robakowo, 62-023, Poznan, Poland
Tel.: (48) 618988800   PL
Web Site: http://www.raben-group.com
Sales Range: $700-749.9 Million
Emp.: 5,200
Logistic Services
N.A.I.C.S.: 541614

Subsidiaries:

Fresh Logistics Polska sp. z o.o.   (1)
Ul Poznanska 71, Gadki k, 62-023, Poznan, Poland
Tel.: (48) 618988400
Logistics Consulting Servies
N.A.I.C.S.: 541614

Raben Eesti OU   (1)
Parnu mnt 388B, 10612, Tallinn, Estonia
Tel.: (372) 60 70 077
Logistics Consulting Servies
N.A.I.C.S.: 541614

Raben Latvia SIA   (1)
Plienciema iela 16, Marupe, 2167, Riga, Latvia
Tel.: (371) 6 738 29 11
Logistics Consulting Servies
N.A.I.C.S.: 541614

Raben Lietuva UAB   (1)
Liepkalnio 85a, 2120, Vilnius, Lithuania
Tel.: (370) 5 232 18 13
Logistics Consulting Servies
N.A.I.C.S.: 541614

Raben Logistics Czech s.r.o.   (1)
K Plevnu 338, 26 801, Horovice, Czech Republic
Tel.: (420) 222 802 111
Logistics Consulting Servies
N.A.I.C.S.: 541614
Jakub Trnka *(Mng Dir)*

Raben Logistics Polska sp. z o.o.   (1)
Poznanska 71, Gadki k, 62-023, Poznan, Poland
Tel.: (48) 618988100
Logistics Consulting Servies
N.A.I.C.S.: 541614

Raben Logistics Slovakia s.r.o. (1)
Areal Prologis DC5 Dial'nicna cesta 14/A, 903 01, Senec, Slovakia
Tel.: (421) 249 110 609
Logistics Consulting Servies
N.A.I.C.S.: 541614

Raben Netherlands B.V.   (1)
Vorstengrafdonk 81, 5342 LW, Oss, Netherlands
Tel.: (31) 88 772 0000
Web Site: http://www.raben-group.com
Emp.: 100
Logistics Consulting Servies

N.A.I.C.S.: 541614
Serge Claesen *(Mng Dir)*

Raben Trans European Germany GmbH   (1)
Regioparkring 8, 41199, Monchengladbach, Germany
Tel.: (49) 2166 520 0
Logistics Consulting Servies
N.A.I.C.S.: 541614

Raben Transport sp. z o.o.   (1)
Ul Poznanska 71, Gadki k, 62-023, Poznan, Poland
Tel.: (48) 618988500
Logistics Consulting Servies
N.A.I.C.S.: 541614

Raben Ukraine   (1)
150 Brovars'ka str Velyka Dymerka, Brovarskiy district, Kiev, 7442, Ukraine
Tel.: (380) 44 459 72 00
Web Site: http://www.ukraine.raben-group.com
Logistics Consulting Servies
N.A.I.C.S.: 541614
Boris Khruslov *(Mng Dir)*

RABIGH REFINING AND PETROCHEMICAL COMPANY
PO Box 101, Rabigh, 21911, Saudi Arabia
Tel.: (966) 124250390
Web Site: http://www.petrorabigh.com
Year Founded: 2005
2380—(SAU)
Rev.: $5,824,033,727
Assets: $18,825,814,597
Liabilities: $17,173,827,074
Net Worth: $1,651,987,523
Earnings: ($1,006,914,386)
Emp.: 3,500
Fiscal Year-end: 12/31/20
Hydrocarbon & Petrochemical Production Services
N.A.I.C.S.: 211130
Noriaki Takeshita *(Deputy Chm)*

RABITEBANK OJSC
28 May Str 33, AZ1010, Baku, Azerbaijan
Tel.: (994) 125984488
Web Site: http://www.rabitabank.com
Year Founded: 1993
Commercial Banking Services
N.A.I.C.S.: 522110
Elchin Gadimov *(Member-Mgmt Bd)*

RACCOON HOLDINGS, INC.
1-14-14 Nihonbashi-Kakigaracho, Chuo-ku, Tokyo, 103-0014, Japan
Tel.: (81) 356521692
Web Site: https://www.raccoon.ne.jp
Year Founded: 1995
3031—(TKS)
Rev.: $38,390,880
Assets: $101,675,020
Liabilities: $69,074,500
Net Worth: $32,600,520
Earnings: $2,148,250
Emp.: 239
Fiscal Year-end: 04/30/24
Holding Company; Sales Channels & Other Business Transaction Services
N.A.I.C.S.: 551112
Isao Ogata *(Pres)*

Subsidiaries:

Raccoon Rent, Inc.   (1)
1-14-14 Nihonbashi-Kakigaracho, Chuo-ku, Tokyo, 103-0014, Japan
Tel.: (81) 353407861
Apparel Retailer
N.A.I.C.S.: 424310

RACE ECO CHAIN LTD.
56/33 Site - IV Industrial Area, Sahibabad, Ghaziabad, 201 010, UP, India

RACE ECO CHAIN LTD.

Race Eco Chain Ltd.—(Continued)
Tel.: (91) 9821002515
Web Site: https://raceecochain.com
Year Founded: 1999
RACE—(NSE)
Rev.: $32,363,971
Assets: $5,896,517
Liabilities: $3,430,262
Net Worth: $2,466,255
Earnings: $156,441
Emp.: 56
Fiscal Year-end: 03/31/23
Home Textile Products
N.A.I.C.S.: 314999
Anshu Agarwal *(CFO)*

RACING FORCE S.P.A.
Via E Bazzano 5, Ronco Scrivia, 16019, Genoa, Italy
Tel.: (39) 01096501
Web Site:
https://www.racingforce.com
ALRFG—(EUR)
Rev.: $57,327,283
Assets: $79,724,676
Liabilities: $42,979,213
Net Worth: $36,745,464
Earnings: $5,118,898
Emp.: 413
Fiscal Year-end: 12/31/21
Sports Equipment Mfr
N.A.I.C.S.: 339920

RACING VICTORIA LIMITED
400 Epsom Road, Flemington, 3031, VIC, Australia
Tel.: (61) 392584258
Web Site: http://www.rv.racing.com
Rev.: $291,970,615
Assets: $145,714,216
Liabilities: $44,555,316
Net Worth: $101,158,900
Earnings: $6,189,039
Emp.: 3,518
Fiscal Year-end: 06/30/19
Horse Racing Track Owner & Operator
N.A.I.C.S.: 711212
Greg Carpenter *(Exec Gen Mgr-Racing)*

RACKLA METALS INC.
Suite 650 200 Burrard Street, Vancouver, V6C 3L6, BC, Canada
Tel.: (604) 801-5432   BC
Web Site:
https://www.racklametals.com
Year Founded: 2011
RLH1—(DEU)
Rev.: $67,878
Assets: $2,057,263
Liabilities: $377,757
Net Worth: $1,679,506
Earnings: ($3,661,602)
Fiscal Year-end: 12/31/23
Gold Mining Services
N.A.I.C.S.: 212220
Simon T. P. Ridgway *(CEO)*

RACL GEARTECH LTD.
15th Floor Eros Corporate Tower
Nehru Place, New Delhi, 110 019, India
Tel.: (91) 1166155129
Web Site: https://raclgeartech.com
520073—(BOM)
Rev.: $28,355,145
Assets: $37,038,647
Liabilities: $22,292,661
Net Worth: $14,745,986
Earnings: $3,206,412
Emp.: 473
Fiscal Year-end: 03/31/21
Automotive Gears Mfr
N.A.I.C.S.: 333612
Gursharan Singh *(Chm & Mng Dir)*

RACO-ELEKTRO-MASCHINEN GMBH
Jesinghauser Str 56-64, D-58332, Schwelm, Germany
Tel.: (49) 233640090
Web Site: http://www.raco.de
Year Founded: 1994
Sales Range: $1-9.9 Million
Emp.: 73
Electromechanical System Mfr
N.A.I.C.S.: 335999
Reinhard Wilke *(Pres & CEO)*

RACONTEUR GLOBAL RESOURCES LIMITED
503 5th Floor Plot 461D A Wing Parshvanath Gardens Bhaudaji Road, King Circle Matunga, Mumbai, 400019, Maharashtra, India
Tel.: (91) 8104449343
Web Site:
https://www.ganeshfilms.com
Year Founded: 1985
541703—(BOM)
Rev.: $22,594
Assets: $2,251,397
Liabilities: $529,269
Net Worth: $1,722,129
Earnings: ($119,605)
Emp.: 6
Fiscal Year-end: 03/31/21
Film Distribution & Promotion Services
N.A.I.C.S.: 512110
Rupesh Prakash Kamble *(CFO)*

RAD A.D.
Decanska 12, Belgrade, Serbia
Tel.: (381) 63249224
Year Founded: 2004
RBGD—(BEL)
Rev.: $178,331
Assets: $4,313,662
Liabilities: $305,138
Net Worth: $4,008,523
Earnings: $5,149
Emp.: 4
Fiscal Year-end: 12/31/23
Books Publishing Services
N.A.I.C.S.: 513130
Radosav Gocmanac *(Gen Mgr)*

RAD A.D.
Vrnjci bb, Vrnjaacka Banja, Serbia
Tel.: (381) 36 632 862
Year Founded: 2000
RDVB—(BEL)
Sales Range: $1-9.9 Million
Emp.: 20
Heavy Construction Services
N.A.I.C.S.: 237990
Soka Dmitrasinovic *(Exec Dir)*

RAD A.D. TESLIC
Kralja Petra I bb, 74270, Teslic, Bosnia & Herzegovina
Tel.: (387) 53 431 499
Web Site: http://www.vodovod-teslic.com
Year Founded: 1974
RDTS—(BANJ)
Sales Range: Less than $1 Million
Emp.: 4,200
Water Supply & Purification Services
N.A.I.C.S.: 488390
Aleksandar Lazetic *(Chm-Supervisory Bd)*

RAD GROUP
24 Raoul Wallenberg St, Tel Aviv, 69719, Israel
Tel.: (972) 36458181
Web Site: http://www.rad.com
Sales Range: $150-199.9 Million
Emp.: 1,000

Voice & Data Communications Technologies & Services
N.A.I.C.S.: 518210

Subsidiaries:

Bynet Data Communications Ltd. (1)
HaNehoshet St 8, Tel Aviv, 69710, Israel
Tel.: (972) 778985000
Web Site: http://www.bynet.co.il
Emp.: 350
Telecommunication Network Integration Services
N.A.I.C.S.: 541990
Alon Ben-zur *(CEO)*

Subsidiary (Domestic):

Bynet Electronics Ltd. (2)
27 Habarzel Street, Tel Aviv, 69710, Israel
Tel.: (972) 3 768 4999
Web Site: http://www.bynete.co.il
Emp.: 17
Electronic Test & Monitoring Systems Developer & Mfr
N.A.I.C.S.: 334515
Avi Barel *(CEO)*

Bynet Software Systems Ltd. (2)
27 Habarzel Street, Tel Aviv, 69710, Israel
Tel.: (972) 3 766 8940
Web Site: http://www.bynetsoft.co.il
Emp.: 70
Enterprise System Software Developer
N.A.I.C.S.: 513210
Eyal Zaslavsky *(CEO)*

Bynet Systems Applications Ltd. (2)
24 Raoul Wallenberg, Tel Aviv, 69719, Israel
Tel.: (972) 3 645 5333
Web Site: http://www.bynet-sys.com
Communication Infrastructure, Security & Control Systems Integration Solutions
N.A.I.C.S.: 541990
Tzachi Itach *(Project Mgr-Defense Comm Div)*

PacketLight Networks Ltd. (1)
27 Habarzel Street, Tel Aviv, 69710, Israel
Tel.: (972) 3 768 7888
Web Site: http://www.packetlight.com
Emp.: 24
Telecommunications Technologies & Software Developer
N.A.I.C.S.: 334290
Koby Reshef *(CEO)*

RAD DATA COMMUNICATIONS IBERIA, SL (1)
Avenida de Europa 14, 28108, Alcobendas, Madrid, Spain
Tel.: (34) 91 189 0500
Communication Networking Services
N.A.I.C.S.: 517810

RAD Data Australia Pty. LTD. (1)
Level 7 Suite 2 100 Walker St, North Sydney, 2060, NSW, Australia
Tel.: (61) 2 9922 7581
Communication Networking Services
N.A.I.C.S.: 517810

RAD Data Communications, Inc. (1)
24 Raoul Wallenberg St, Ramat Hahael, Tel Aviv, 69719, Israel
Tel.: (972) 36458181
Web Site: http://www.rad.com
Sales Range: $200-249.9 Million
Access Equipment for Data Communication & Telecommunication Application Mfr
N.A.I.C.S.: 334290

Subsidiary (Non-US):

RAD America Latina S.A. (2)
Gorgostiaga 1664 1A Floor, Buenos Aires, Argentina (100%)
Tel.: (54) 1147791117
Web Site: http://www.rad-espanol.com
Sales Range: $25-49.9 Million
Emp.: 3
N.A.I.C.S.: 518210

RAD Data Communications GmbH (2)
Otto Hahn St 28 30, Ottobrunn, 85521, Riemerling, Germany (100%)
Tel.: (49) 896659270
Web Site: http://www.rad.com

INTERNATIONAL PUBLIC

Sales Range: $25-49.9 Million
Emp.: 7
N.A.I.C.S.: 518210
Volker Bendzuweit *(VP-Sls-Europe)*

Subsidiary (US):

RAD Data Communications Inc. (2)
900 Corprate Dr, Mahwah, NJ 07430
Tel.: (201) 529-1100
Web Site: http://www.radusa.com
Sales Range: $25-49.9 Million
Emp.: 50
N.A.I.C.S.: 518210
Uri Zilberman *(Pres)*

Subsidiary (Non-US):

RAD Data Communications Ltd. (UK) (2)
PO Box 318, Romsey, SO51 1AS, United Kingdom (100%)
Tel.: (44) 1794514220
Web Site: http://www.raddata.co.uk
Sales Range: $25-49.9 Million
Emp.: 3
N.A.I.C.S.: 518210

RAD Far East Ltd. (2)
Ste A 26th Fl 1 Capital Pl 18 Luard Rd, Wanchai, Hong Kong, China (Hong Kong) (100%)
Tel.: (852) 25270101
Web Site: http://www.radvoip.com
Sales Range: $25-49.9 Million
Emp.: 7
N.A.I.C.S.: 518210

RAD France (2)
Immeuble lEuropeen 98 Alle Des Champs Elysees, 91042, Evry, Cedex, France (100%)
Tel.: (33) 60878500
Web Site: http://www.rad-france.fr
Sales Range: $25-49.9 Million
Emp.: 4
N.A.I.C.S.: 518210

RAD do Brasil Ltda. (2)
Edificio Diamond Tower Rua Maestro Cardim, 1 191 13 andar CJ 135, 01323-001, Sao Paulo, SP, Brazil (100%)
Tel.: (55) 11 3171 2940
Web Site: http://www.rad.com
Sales Range: $25-49.9 Million
Emp.: 35
Data Communications Wireless Multiplexer Services
N.A.I.C.S.: 518210
Oscar Calderon Prager *(Mgr-Acct Sls)*

RAD West Africa Limited (1)
6B Bendel Close Off Bishop Aboyade Cole St Victoria Island, Lagos, Nigeria
Tel.: (234) 813 554 9343
Communication Networking Services
N.A.I.C.S.: 517810

RADCOM Ltd. (1)
24 Raoul Wallenberg Street, Tel Aviv, 69719, Israel
Tel.: (972) 36455055
Web Site: http://www.radcom.com
Rev.: $46,051,000
Assets: $101,004,000
Liabilities: $28,221,000
Net Worth: $72,783,000
Earnings: ($2,257,000)
Emp.: 284
Fiscal Year-end: 12/31/2022
Network Test Equipment Mfr
N.A.I.C.S.: 334118
Eyal Harari *(CEO)*

Subsidiary (Domestic):

Continual Ltd. (2)
10 Topaz St, Caesarea, 30889, Israel
Tel.: (972) 46363142
Web Site:
http://www.continualexperience.com
Rev.: $186,000
Assets: $1,193,000
Liabilities: $616,000
Net Worth: $577,000
Earnings: $1,985,000
Fiscal Year-end: 06/30/2023
Software Development Services
N.A.I.C.S.: 541511
Greg Snipper *(CEO)*

AND PRIVATE COMPANIES — RADIALL S.A.

Subsidiary (US):

RADCOM Equipment, Inc. (2)
6 Forest Ave, Paramus, NJ 07652
Tel.: (201) 518-0033
Web Site: http://www.radcom.com
Network Test Equipment Mfr
N.A.I.C.S.: 334118

RADWIN Ltd. (1)
27 Habarzel Street, Tel Aviv, 6971039, Israel
Tel.: (972) 3 766 2900
Web Site: http://www.radwin.com
Emp.: 170
Wireless Telecommunication Services
N.A.I.C.S.: 517112
Sharon Sher (Pres & CEO)

RADiFlow Ltd. (1)
4 Hanehoshet Street, Tel Aviv, 69710, Israel
Tel.: (972) 3 767 4860
Web Site: http://www.radiflow.com
Industrial Ethernet Switches Mfr
N.A.I.C.S.: 335313
Ilan Barda (Co-Founder & CEO)

Radware Ltd. (1)
22 Raoul Wallenberg Street, Tel Aviv, 6971917, Israel (50%)
Tel.: (972) 37668666
Web Site: http://www.radware.com
Rev.: $261,292,000
Assets: $571,916,000
Liabilities: $248,642,000
Net Worth: $323,274,000
Earnings: ($21,590,000)
Emp.: 1,218
Fiscal Year-end: 12/31/2023
Enhanced Information Access by Optimal Utilization of Server Resources
N.A.I.C.S.: 561499
Yehuda Zisapel (Co-Founder & Chm)

Division (US):

Radware Inc. (2)
575 Corporate Dr Ste 205, Mahwah, NJ 07430-2330
Tel.: (201) 512-9771
Web Site: http://www.radware.com
Sales Range: $25-49.9 Million
Emp.: 10
Networking Equipment, Load Balancing Switches, Internet Traffic Management Device Mfr
N.A.I.C.S.: 541512
Yehuda Zisapel (Chm)

Silicom Ltd. (1)
14 Atir Yeda Street, Kfar Saba, 4464323, Israel
Tel.: (972) 97644555
Web Site: http://www.silicom.co.il
Rev.: $150,582,000
Assets: $216,197,000
Liabilities: $36,902,000
Net Worth: $179,295,000
Earnings: $18,306,000
Emp.: 309
Fiscal Year-end: 12/31/2022
Networking Solutions Services
N.A.I.C.S.: 541512
Shaike Orbach (Pres & CEO)

Subsidiary (US):

ADI Engineering, Inc. (2)
1758 Worth Park, Charlottesville, VA 22911
Tel.: (434) 978-2888
Web Site: http://www.adiengineering.com
Sales Range: $1-9.9 Million
Emp.: 30
Computer Related Solutions
N.A.I.C.S.: 541519
Steven W. Yates (Pres)

Silicom Connectivity Solutions Inc. (2)
6 Forest Ave, Paramus, NJ 07652
Tel.: (201) 843-1175
Web Site: http://www.silicom-usa.com
Sales Range: $25-49.9 Million
Emp.: 10
Networking Solutions Services
N.A.I.C.S.: 334210
Shaike Orbach (CEO)

Subsidiary (Domestic):

Silicom Connectivity Solutions Ltd. (2)

8 Hanagar St, PO Box 2164, Kfar Saba, 44000, Israel (100%)
Tel.: (972) 97644555
Web Site: http://www.silicom.co.il
Sales Range: $25-49.9 Million
Emp.: 100
Networking Solutions Services
N.A.I.C.S.: 541511
David Hendel (VP-R&D)

RAD LABUD A.D.
Valterova 141, Prijepolje, Serbia
Tel.: (381) 33 31 178
Year Founded: 1948
Sales Range: Less than $1 Million
Emp.: 37
Building Construction Services
N.A.I.C.S.: 236220

RADA ELECTRONIC INDUSTRIES LTD.
7 Giborei Israel Street, Netanya, 4250407, Israel
Tel.: (972) 76 538 6200
Web Site: http://www.rada.com
Year Founded: 1970
RADA—(NASDAQ)
Rev.: $117,236,000
Assets: $203,843,000
Liabilities: $47,777,000
Net Worth: $156,066,000
Earnings: $25,074,000
Emp.: 242
Fiscal Year-end: 12/31/21
Aircraft Electronics Test Equipment Mfr
N.A.I.C.S.: 334515
Oleg Kiperman (CTO)

Subsidiaries:

RADA Sensors Inc. (1)
20300 Seneca Meadows Pkwy Ste 310, Germantown, MD 20876
Tel.: (240) 261-6277
Electric & Electronic Appliance Distr
N.A.I.C.S.: 423620
Max Cohen (CEO)

Subsidiary (Domestic):

RADA Technologies LLC (2)
20511 Seneca Meadows Pkwy Ste 100, Germantown, MD 20876
Tel.: (240) 503-3395
Web Site: http://www.radausa.com
Missile Product Mfr
N.A.I.C.S.: 336414

RADAAN MEDIAWORKS INDIA LIMITED
No 14 Jayammal Street Teynampet, Chennai, 600018, Tamil Nadu, India
Tel.: (91) 4424313001
Web Site: https://www.radaan.tv
Year Founded: 1999
590070—(BOM)
Rev.: $1,278,390
Assets: $3,928,932
Liabilities: $4,719,410
Net Worth: ($790,478)
Earnings: ($1,008,705)
Emp.: 64
Fiscal Year-end: 03/31/21
Motion Picture Production & Distribution Services
N.A.I.C.S.: 512110
R. Radikaa Sarathkumar (Chm & Mng Dir)

RADE KONCAR A.D.
Zemunski put 3, Novi Beograd, Serbia
Tel.: (381) 112139523
Year Founded: 1990
RDKN—(BEL)
Rev.: $296,325
Assets: $268,291
Liabilities: $50,795
Net Worth: $217,496
Earnings: $1,554
Emp.: 13
Fiscal Year-end: 12/31/22
Motor Vehicle Repair & Maintenance Services
N.A.I.C.S.: 811198
Aleksandar Miljus (Exec Dir)

RADE KONCAR-APARATNA TEHNIKA AD
Bulevar 3-ta Makedonska Brigada BB, Skopje, North Macedonia
Tel.: (389) 22402481
Web Site: http://www.radekoncar-ad.com.mk
RADE—(MAC)
Rev.: $50,247
Assets: $6,286,738
Liabilities: $150,398
Net Worth: $6,136,340
Earnings: $545,339
Fiscal Year-end: 12/31/23
Electrical Component Mfr
N.A.I.C.S.: 335999

RADHA MADHAV CORPORATION LIMITED
50/A Daman Industrial Estate, Village Kadaiya, Daman, 396210, UT, India
Tel.: (91) 2606619000
Web Site: https://www.rmclindia.co.in
Year Founded: 1994
RMCL—(NSE)
Sales Range: $75-99.9 Million
Packaging Services
N.A.I.C.S.: 561910
Mitesh Anil Agrawal (Mng Dir)

RADHAGOBIND COMMERCIAL LIMITED
40 Metcalfe Street 3rd Floor Room No 339, Kolkata, 700 013, India
Tel.: (91) 7736100361
Web Site: https://www.radhagobindcomm.com
Year Founded: 1981
539673—(BOM)
Rev.: $16,959
Assets: $894,163
Liabilities: $431,842
Net Worth: $462,321
Earnings: ($26,332)
Emp.: 2
Fiscal Year-end: 03/31/21
Textile Goods Distr
N.A.I.C.S.: 424310
Pratik Jain (Chm)

RADHI BIDHYUT CO., LTD.
Bluestar Complex Tripureshwor-11, PO Box 4995, Kathmandu, Nepal
Tel.: (977) 5332750
Web Site: https://www.radhibidyut.com.np
Year Founded: 2005
RADHI—(NEP)
Rev.: $1,135,054
Assets: $18,942,811
Liabilities: $11,821,484
Net Worth: $7,121,327
Earnings: $439,663
Fiscal Year-end: 07/16/22
Hydroelectric Power Generation Services
N.A.I.C.S.: 221111
Bimesh Man Pati (Chm)

Subsidiaries:

Kasuwa Khola Hydropower Limited (1)
Tripura Marg, Kathmandu, Nepal
Tel.: (977) 14101140
Web Site: https://www.kasuwakhola.com.np
Hydroelectric Power Distr
N.A.I.C.S.: 221111

RADHIKA JEWELTECH LIMITED
3-4-5 Raj Shrungi Complex Palace Road, Rajkot, 360 001, Gujarat, India
Tel.: (91) 02812225056
Web Site: https://www.radhikajeweltech.com
Year Founded: 1987
RADHIKAJWE—(NSE)
Rev.: $37,723,530
Assets: $31,063,318
Liabilities: $5,240,957
Net Worth: $25,822,361
Earnings: $3,559,847
Emp.: 124
Fiscal Year-end: 03/31/23
Jewellery Product Mfr & Distr
N.A.I.C.S.: 339910
Ashokkumar Mathurdas Zinzuwadia (Mng Dir)

RADIAL CAPITAL PARTNERS GMBH & CO. KG
Hackenstr 5A, 80331, Munich, Germany
Tel.: (49) 12 22 34 750
Web Site: http://www.radialcapital.com
Year Founded: 2014
Financial Investment Services
N.A.I.C.S.: 523999
Ulrich Radlmayr (Mng Dir)

Subsidiaries:

Van der Molen GmbH (1)
Industriestr 34a, 86438, Kissing, Germany
Tel.: (49) 823 37 92 70
Web Site: http://www.van-der-molen.com
Emp.: 65
Beverage Products Machinery Mfr
N.A.I.C.S.: 333241
Andreas Mayr (Mng Dir)

RADIAL RESEARCH CORP.
Suite 600-1090 West Georgia Street, Vancouver, V6E 3V7, BC, Canada
Tel.: (778) 999-7030
Web Site: https://radial-research.com
Year Founded: 2013
RAD—(CNSX)
Rev.: $7,340
Assets: $992,218
Liabilities: $411,957
Net Worth: $580,261
Earnings: ($511,071)
Fiscal Year-end: 05/31/21
Software Development Services
N.A.I.C.S.: 541511
Chris Haill (CEO)

RADIALL S.A.
25 Rue Madeleine Vionnet, Aubervilliers Paris, Paris, 93300, France
Tel.: (33) 149353535
Web Site: http://www.radiall.com
Year Founded: 1952
Rev.: $331,794,837
Assets: $352,736,068
Liabilities: $106,510,803
Net Worth: $246,225,265
Earnings: $36,846,125
Emp.: 2,957
Fiscal Year-end: 12/31/16
Interconnect Products & Components Mfr
N.A.I.C.S.: 334220
Pierre Gattaz (Chm-Exec Bd)

Subsidiaries:

Acetec Inc. (1)
6540 Lusk Blvd Ste C-146, San Diego, CA 92121
Tel.: (858) 784-0900
Web Site: http://www.acetec.com
Construction Engineering Services
N.A.I.C.S.: 541330
Mike Hsiao (Engr-Field Sls)

RADIALL S.A.

Radiall S.A.—(Continued)

Eclipse Marketing Group, Inc. (1)
13657 NE 126th Pl, Kirkland, WA 98034
Tel.: (425) 885-6991
Web Site: http://www.eclipsemarketing.com
General Marketing Services
N.A.I.C.S.: 541613
Chris Gastelum *(Pres)*

Nihon Radiall K.K. (1)
1-3-10 Higashi Nihonbashi, Chuuok-ku, Tokyo, 103-0004, Japan (100%)
Tel.: (81) 338662390
Electrical Apparatus & Equipment Wiring Supplies & Construction Material Whslr
N.A.I.C.S.: 423610

Radiall AB (1)
Sjoangsvagen 2, 19272, Sollentuna, Sweden (100%)
Tel.: (46) 84443410
Web Site: http://www.radiall.com
Sales Range: $50-74.9 Million
Emp.: 4
Electrical Apparatus & Equipment Wiring Supplies & Construction Material Whslr
N.A.I.C.S.: 423610
Pierre Gattaz *(Chm)*

Radiall Do Brasil Componentes Electronicos Ltda (1)
Largo do Machado 54 Sala 706, 22221-020, Rio de Janeiro, Brazil (99%)
Tel.: (55) 2125580576
Web Site: http://www.radiall.com.br
Sales Range: $25-49.9 Million
Emp.: 50
Electronic Components Mfr
N.A.I.C.S.: 334419

Radiall Electronics (Asia) Ltd. (1)
Fret D 6th Floor Ford Glory Plaza, 37-39 Wing Hong Street, Kowloon, China (Hong Kong) (55%)
Tel.: (852) 29593833
Web Site: http://www.radiall.com
Sales Range: $50-74.9 Million
Emp.: 10
Electronic Parts & Equipment Whslr
N.A.I.C.S.: 423690
Fabian Oltino *(Gen Mgr)*

Radiall Elettronica Srl (1)
Via Concordia 5 Assago, 20090, Milan, Italy (100%)
Tel.: (39) 024885121
Web Site: http://www.radiall.com
Sales Range: $50-74.9 Million
Emp.: 7
Electrical Apparatus & Equipment Wiring Supplies & Construction Material Whslr
N.A.I.C.S.: 423610
Capsone Guarcaero *(Mgr)*

Radiall GmbH (1)
Carl Zeiss Strasse 10, PO Box 200143, Rodermark, 63322, Germany (100%)
Tel.: (49) 607491070
Web Site: http://www.radiall.com
Sales Range: $25-49.9 Million
Emp.: 14
Electronic Components Mfr
N.A.I.C.S.: 334419
Pierre Gattaz *(Chm)*

Radiall India Pvt. Ltd. (1)
25 D II phase Peenya Industrial Area, 560058, Bengaluru, India (51%)
Tel.: (91) 8023720989
Web Site: http://www.radiall.com
Emp.: 20
Electronic Components Mfr & Sales
N.A.I.C.S.: 334419
Arun Parasnis *(Mng Dir)*

Radiall Ltd. (1)
Radiall Ltd 3Rd Fl Profile West 950 Great West Road, Brentford, TW8 9ES, Middlesex, United Kingdom (100%)
Tel.: (44) 1895425000
Sales Range: $25-49.9 Million
Emp.: 6
Current-Carrying Wiring Device Mfr
N.A.I.C.S.: 335931
Savio Cotta *(Mgr-Acctg)*

Radiall Nederland B.V. (1)
Hogebrinkerweg 15b, Hoevelaken, 3871, Netherlands (100%)
Tel.: (31) 332534009
Web Site: http://www.radiall.nl
Sales Range: $50-74.9 Million
Emp.: 5
Electrical Apparatus & Equipment Wiring Supplies & Construction Material Whslr
N.A.I.C.S.: 423610
Golanda Meinen *(Mng Dir)*

Radiall SF (1)
PO Box 202, 90101, Oulu, Finland
Tel.: (358) 407522412
Electrical & Electronic Mfr
N.A.I.C.S.: 336320

Radiall Systems SA (1)
101 Rue Philibert Hoffmann, Rosny Sous Bois, 93116, Saint Denis, France (90%)
Tel.: (33) 149353535
Web Site: http://www.radiallsystems.com
Sales Range: $25-49.9 Million
Emp.: 100
Engineeering Services
N.A.I.C.S.: 541330

Radiall USA, Inc. (1)
8950 S 52nd St ste 401, Tempe, AZ 85284
Tel.: (480) 682-9400
Web Site: http://www.radiall.com
Antennas, RF Coaxial Connectors, Cable Assemblies, Microwave Passive Components & Fiber Optic Connectors Mfr.
N.A.I.C.S.: 334417
Maite Tristan *(Gen Mgr)*

Subsidiary (Domestic):

RADIALL USA Inc. - New Haven (2)
104 John W Murphy Dr, New Haven, CT 06513
Tel.: (203) 776-2813
Web Site: http://www.radiall.com
Subminiature Coaxial Connectors & Cable Assemblies Mfr
N.A.I.C.S.: 334417
William Neale *(VP)*

Timbercon, Inc. (2)
20245 SW 95th Ave, Tualatin, OR 97062
Tel.: (503) 827-8141
Web Site: http://www.timbercon.com
Sales Range: $1-9.9 Million
Emp.: 80
Product Development & Manufacturing of Fiber Optic Solutions
N.A.I.C.S.: 335921
Eric Meslow *(Co-Founder, Pres & CEO)*

Radiall Usa, Inc. (1)
8950 S 52th St Ste 401, Tempe, AZ 85284
Tel.: (480) 682-9400
Web Site: http://www.radiall.com
Sales Range: $1-9.9 Million
Emp.: 36
Current-Carrying Wiring Device Mfr
N.A.I.C.S.: 335931
Maite Tristan *(Gen Mgr)*

Radiall Ventures Capital SA (1)
25 Rue Madeleine Vionnet, 93300, Aubervilliers, France (80%)
Tel.: (33) 149353535
Web Site: http://www.radiall.com
Sales Range: $50-74.9 Million
Emp.: 85
Open-End Investment Funds
N.A.I.C.S.: 525910
Pierre Gattaz *(Chm)*

Shanghai Radiall Electronic Co., Ltd. (1)
390 Yong He Road, Shanghai, 200072, China
Tel.: (86) 2166523788
Electrical & Electronic Mfr
N.A.I.C.S.: 336320
Chris Shi *(Mgr-Mfr Engrg)*

Shanghai Radiall Electronics Co. Ltd. (1)
N 390 Yong He Road, 200072, Shanghai, China (80%)
Tel.: (86) 2166523788
Web Site: http://www.radiall-sh.com.cn
Sales Range: $50-74.9 Million
Emp.: 200
Electronic Connector Mfr
N.A.I.C.S.: 336320
Andre Hartmann *(Mng Dir)*

RADIAN GROUP LIMITED
Collins House Bishopstoke Road, Eastleigh, SO50 6AD, Hampshire, United Kingdom
Tel.: (44) 300 123 1567
Web Site: http://www.radian.co.uk
Rev.: $212,832,420
Assets: $2,091,574,653
Liabilities: $1,770,414,878
Net Worth: $321,159,775
Earnings: $39,589,617
Emp.: 770
Fiscal Year-end: 03/31/19
Housing Services
N.A.I.C.S.: 925110
Andrew Newberry *(Dir-Fin)*

Subsidiaries:

Drum Housing Association Limited (1)
Drum Court The Spain, Petersfield, GU32 3NG, Hampshire, United Kingdom
Tel.: (44) 3001231567
Home Care Services
N.A.I.C.S.: 623210

Radian Support Limited (1)
14 Drayton Road, Newton Longville, Milton Keynes, MK17 0BJ, Buckinghamshire, United Kingdom
Tel.: (44) 1908649592
Home Care Services
N.A.I.C.S.: 623210

Windsor and District Housing Association Limited (1)
Parkside House 33-39 Sheet Street, Windsor, SL4 1BY, United Kingdom
Tel.: (44) 1753777400
Home Care Services
N.A.I.C.S.: 623210

RADIANCE HOLDINGS GROUP COMPANY LIMITED
42/F Radiance Plaza Qiyang Road, Wangjing Chaoyang District, Beijing, China Ky
Web Site: https://www.weareradiance.com
Year Founded: 1996
9993—(HKG)
Rev.: $4,742,008,889
Assets: $17,968,817,568
Liabilities: $12,991,372,259
Net Worth: $4,977,445,309
Earnings: ($60,082,936)
Emp.: 1,432
Fiscal Year-end: 12/31/23
Holding Company
N.A.I.C.S.: 551112
Junquan Huang *(Sr VP)*

RADIANT CASH MANAGEMENT SERVICES LIMITED
28 Vijay Building Vijayaragava Road T Nagar, Chennai, 600017, India
Tel.: (91) 4449044904
Web Site: https://www.radiantcashservice.com
Year Founded: 2005
RADIANTCMS—(NSE)
Rev.: $42,860,980
Assets: $33,434,207
Liabilities: $5,865,835
Net Worth: $27,568,371
Earnings: $7,520,772
Emp.: 2,174
Fiscal Year-end: 03/31/23
Logistic Services
N.A.I.C.S.: 541614
David Devasahayam *(Mng Dir)*

RADIANT GEMS INTERNATIONAL PLC
Gatahetta, Dehigahapitiya, Sri Lanka
Tel.: (94) 362230616
Web Site: http://www.radiantgems.lk
Year Founded: 1987

INTERNATIONAL PUBLIC

RGEM.N0000—(COL)
Rev.: $745,323
Assets: $562,306
Liabilities: $329,640
Net Worth: $232,666
Earnings: $129,929
Fiscal Year-end: 12/31/23
Gemstones Cutting Services
N.A.I.C.S.: 339910

RADIANT GLOBALTECH BERHAD
Unit 03-06 & 03-07 Level 3 Tower B Vertical Business Suite Avenue 3, Bangsar South No 8 Jalan Kerinchi, 59200, Kuala Lumpur, Malaysia
Tel.: (60) 322422059
Web Site: https://www.rgtech.com.my
Year Founded: 2003
0202—(KLS)
Rev.: $29,500,424
Assets: $24,180,700
Liabilities: $8,082,622
Net Worth: $16,098,078
Earnings: $1,783,973
Fiscal Year-end: 12/31/23
Software Development Services
N.A.I.C.S.: 541511
Ban Foo Yap *(Mng Dir)*

Subsidiaries:

Grand-Flo Spritvest Sdn. Bhd. (1)
L1-1 Wisma Ehsan Bina No 3 Jalan Kuchai Maju 12 Jalan 1/11 6C, Kuchai Entrepreneurs Park, Kuala Lumpur, 58200, Malaysia (80%)
Tel.: (60) 379808580
Data Management Services
N.A.I.C.S.: 518210
Cheng Peng Liong *(CEO)*

RADIANT GROWTH INVESTMENTS LIMITED
Queensway House Hilgrove Street, Saint Helier, JE1 1ES, Jersey
Tel.: (44) 8707020009 JE
Web Site: http://www.radgltd.com
Sales Range: Less than $1 Million
Investment Services
N.A.I.C.S.: 523999
Alex Chee Teong Teh *(Chm)*

RADIANT INNOVATION, INC.
1F No 3 Industrial E 9th Rd, Science-Based Industrial Park, Hsinchu, 300, Taiwan
Tel.: (886) 36111666
Web Site: https://www.radiantek.com.tw
Year Founded: 2000
3373—(TPE)
Rev.: $17,651,721
Assets: $34,915,987
Liabilities: $2,977,082
Net Worth: $31,938,905
Earnings: $896,226
Fiscal Year-end: 12/31/22
Medical Equipment & Device Mfr
N.A.I.C.S.: 339112
Chih-Yuan Chou *(Chm)*

Subsidiaries:

Kunshan Radiant Innovation Co., Ltd. (1)
No 20 TaiHong Road WuSongJiang Development Zone, YuShan Town, Kunshan, 215300, JiangSu, China
Tel.: (86) 51286165995
Medical Infrared Thermometer Mfr & Distr
N.A.I.C.S.: 339112

RADIANT OPTO-ELECTRONICS CORPORATION
No 1 Central 6th Rd Qianzhen Dist, Kaohsiung, Taiwan
Tel.: (886) 78216151

AND PRIVATE COMPANIES
RADICI PARTECIPAZIONI S.P.A.

Web Site: https://www.radiant.com.tw
Year Founded: 1995
6176—(TAI)
Rev.: $1,441,792,679
Assets: $1,993,082,432
Liabilities: $870,189,215
Net Worth: $1,122,893,218
Earnings: $172,535,492
Emp.: 867
Fiscal Year-end: 12/31/23
Optical Product Mfr
N.A.I.C.S.: 333310
Pen-Jan Wang *(Chm & CEO)*

Subsidiaries:

Radiant Opto-Electronics Corporation
- Guangzhou Factory (1)
No 11 Xinrui Road, Science City of High-tech Industrial Development Zone,
Guangzhou, China
Tel.: (86) 2028203000
Electronic Components Mfr
N.A.I.C.S.: 334419

Radiant Opto-Electronics Corporation
- Nanjing Factory (1)
No 35 Hengtong Avenue, Xingang Developing Area, Nanjing, China
Tel.: (86) 2568905000
Electronic Components Mfr
N.A.I.C.S.: 334419

Radiant Opto-Electronics Corporation
- Wujiang Factory (1)
No 1621 JiangXing East RD, Economic Developing Area, Wujiang, Jiangsu, China
Tel.: (86) 51263400666
Electronic Components Mfr
N.A.I.C.S.: 334419

RADICI PARTECIPAZIONI S.P.A.
Via Ugo Foscolo 152, 24024, Bergamo, Gandino, Italy
Tel.: (39) 035715411   IT
Web Site: http://www.radicigroup.com
Sales Range: $1-4.9 Billion
Emp.: 5,068
Chemicals, Plastics, Fibers, Textiles & Energy Products & Services
N.A.I.C.S.: 325998
Angelo Radici *(Pres)*

Subsidiaries:

Caucasian PET Co. (1)
Mshvidoba St 12, Rustavi, 3700, Tbilisi, Georgia
Tel.: (995) 34155496
Web Site: http://www.radipol.com
Chemicals Mfr
N.A.I.C.S.: 325199

Cordonsed Argentina S.A. (1)
Luis Maria Campos 1061 3er Piso Frente, C 1426 BOI, Buenos Aires, Argentina
Tel.: (54) 11 5778 2531
Broadwoven Fabric Mills
N.A.I.C.S.: 313210

GeoEnergie SpA (1)
Via Ca' Antonelli 55, Gandino, 24024, Bergamo, Italy
Tel.: (39) 035715811
Electric Power & Natural Gas Distr
N.A.I.C.S.: 423610

Geogreen SpA (1)
Via Provinciale 36, Lallio, 24040, Bergamo, Italy
Tel.: (39) 035209280
Web Site: http://www.radicigroup.com
Electric Power Services
N.A.I.C.S.: 221122

Gorispac S.p.A (1)
Via Asola 6, 46040, Casalmoro, Italy
Tel.: (39) 0376739710
Web Site: http://www.radicigroup.com
Yarn Spinning Mills
N.A.I.C.S.: 313110

Hotel San Marco Srl (1)
Via Garibaldi 6, Servigliano, Ascoli Piceno, 63839, Italy   (100%)
Tel.: (39) 0734750761

Hotels & Motels
N.A.I.C.S.: 721110

Itema Holding SpA (1)
Via Cav Gianni Radici 4, 24020, Colzate, Italy   (75%)
Tel.: (39) 0357283224
Web Site: http://www.itemagroup.com
Holding Company
N.A.I.C.S.: 551112
Mario Bertocchi *(Gen Mgr)*

Subsidiary (Domestic):

Itema S.p.A. (2)
Via Cav Gianni Radici 4, 24020, Colzate, BG, Italy
Tel.: (39) 0357283224
Web Site: http://www.itemagroup.com
Sales Range: $350-399.9 Million
Mfr of Textiles & Textile Machinery
N.A.I.C.S.: 313210
Carlo Rogora *(CEO)*

Subsidiary (US):

Itema America, Inc. (3)
PO Box 5332, Spartanburg, SC 29304-5332   (100%)
Tel.: (864) 585-5255
Web Site: http://www.itemausa.com
Sales Range: $25-49.9 Million
Emp.: 75
Textile Machinery Mfr
N.A.I.C.S.: 333248
Werner Mendler *(Mgr-Sls)*

Logit s.r.o. (1)
Hlubany 119, 44101, Podborany, Czech Republic
Tel.: (420) 41523791
Cotton Yarn Mfr
N.A.I.C.S.: 313110

Noyfil SA (1)
Via gaggiolo 31, 6855, Stabio, Switzerland
Tel.: (41) 916416141
Polyester Filament Mfr
N.A.I.C.S.: 325220

Noyfil SpA (1)
Via Orobie 4, Andalo Valtellino, 23014, Sondrio, Italy
Tel.: (39) 0342699111
Polyester Fiber & Filament Yarn Mfr
N.A.I.C.S.: 325220

Pratrivero S.p.A. (1)
Fr Pratrivero 51, 13835, Biella, Italy
Tel.: (39) 015 7388880
Web Site: http://www.pratrivero.com
Printed Fabric Mfr
N.A.I.C.S.: 313320
Stefano Piana *(Sls Mgr)*

Division (US):

Pratrivero U.S.A. Inc. (2)
50 Commerce Ctr, Greenville, SC 29615
Tel.: (864) 234-0322
Web Site: http://www.pratrivero.com
Printed Fabric Mfr
N.A.I.C.S.: 313320
Alberto Amosso *(Gen Mgr)*

Radici Chem (Shanghai) Co., Ltd. (1)
Room 1322 Yunsun Tower No 2025 West Zhongshan Rd, Xuhui, Shanghai, 200235, China
Tel.: (86) 2164389210
Chemical Products Distr
N.A.I.C.S.: 424690
Sun Bin *(Gen Mgr)*

Radici Chemiefaser GmbH (1)
Hofer Strasse 23, 95152, Selbitz, Germany
Tel.: (49) 9280981030
Fiber Yarn Mfr & Distr
N.A.I.C.S.: 325199

Radici Chimica Deutschland GmbH (1)
Dr Bergius - Strasse 6, Troglitz, 6729, Halle, Germany
Tel.: (49) 34418298122
Web Site: http://www.radicichemicagroup.com
Sales Range: $125-149.9 Million
Emp.: 200
Chemicals Mfr

N.A.I.C.S.: 325199
Jens Metzner *(Mgr)*

Radici Chimica S.p.A. (1)
Via G Fauser 50, 28100, Novara, Italy
Tel.: (39) 0321693111
Web Site: http://www.radicigroup.com
Sales Range: $125-149.9 Million
Emp.: 300
Chemicals Mfr
N.A.I.C.S.: 325199
Angelo Radicei *(Pres)*

Branch (Non-US):

Radici Chimica S.p.A. - Mendrisio Branch (2)
Via Lavizzari 4, Mendrisio, 6850, Switzerland
Tel.: (41) 916400750
Web Site: http://www.radicigroup.com
Sales Range: $25-49.9 Million
Emp.: 15
Chemicals Mfr
N.A.I.C.S.: 325199
Andrea Adembri *(Mgr-Sls)*

Radici Energie Srl (1)
Via Provinciale 36, Lallio, 24040, Bergamo, Italy
Tel.: (39) 035209280
Web Site: http://www.radicigroup.com
Electrical Equipment & Component Mfr
N.A.I.C.S.: 335999

Radici Fil S.p.A. (1)
Via Europa 41, Casnigo, 24020, Gandino, Bergamo, Italy
Tel.: (39) 035 736000
Web Site: http://www.radicigroup.com
Production & Sale of Yarns for Carpeting, Raw, Space Dyed & Solution Dyed Yarns
N.A.I.C.S.: 313110

Radici Holding Meccanotessile S.p.A. (1)
Via Ugo Foscolo 152, IT-24024, Gandino, BG, Italy   (50%)
Tel.: (39) 035 715411
Web Site: http://www.radicigroup.com
Sales Range: $25-49.9 Million
Emp.: 25
Holding Company
N.A.I.C.S.: 551112

Radici Immobiliare S.p.A. (1)
Via Ugo Foscolo 152, Gandino, Bergamo, 24024, Italy
Tel.: (39) 0357154411
Web Site: http://www.radicigroup.com
Holding Company
N.A.I.C.S.: 551112
Alessandro Manzoni *(Mgr-Fin)*

Radici Novacips S.p.A. (1)
Via Provinciale 1331, Villa d Ogna, 24020, Bergamo, Italy
Tel.: (39) 034622453
Web Site: http://www.radicigroup.com
Plastics Product Mfr
N.A.I.C.S.: 326199
Angelo Radici *(Pres)*

Radici Plastics (Suzhou) Co., Ltd. (1)
No 49 Ping Sheng Road Sip - 215126, 215126, Suzhou, Jiangsu, China
Tel.: (86) 51262952290
Engineering Plastic Mfr & Distr
N.A.I.C.S.: 325211
Elisa Gelmi *(Mgr-HR)*

Radici Plastics France SA (1)
65 Rue du Dauphine, Saint Priest, 69800, France
Tel.: (33) 472782090
Web Site: http://www.radicigroup.com
Industrial Machinery & Equipment Whslr
N.A.I.C.S.: 423830

Radici Plastics GmbH & Co. KG (1)
Glockengiesserwall 2, 20095, Hamburg, Germany
Tel.: (49) 403095410
Web Site: http://www.radicigroup.com
Sales Range: $50-74.9 Million
Emp.: 6
Chemical & Allied Products Merchant Whslr
N.A.I.C.S.: 424690
Cesare Clausi *(Gen Mgr)*

Radici Plastics Iberica SL (1)
Ave De La Ilustracion 20 3rd Fl, 23200, Jaen, La Carolina, Spain
Tel.: (34) 953685021
Sales Range: $50-74.9 Million
Emp.: 4
Plastics Materials & Basic Forms & Shapes Merchant Whslr
N.A.I.C.S.: 424610
Luis Garcia *(Mgr)*

Radici Plastics India Pvt. Ltd. (1)
C-5 1st Floor Amar Colony Market-Lajpat Nagar-IV, 110 018, Delhi, India
Tel.: (91) 1141638170
Engineering Plastic Mfr & Distr
N.A.I.C.S.: 325211

Radici Plastics Ltda. (1)
Rua Giuseppe Marchiori 497, Aracariguama, 18147-970, Sao Paulo, Brazil
Tel.: (55) 1141366500
Sales Range: $50-74.9 Million
Emp.: 60
Chemical & Products Whslr
N.A.I.C.S.: 424690
Jenny Campos *(Gen Mgr)*

Radici Plastics Mexico S. de R.L. de C.V. (1)
Av Francisco Zarco 2688 C P Col Loma Bonita, Ocotlan, 47810, Jalisco, Mexico
Tel.: (52) 3929232390
Engineering Plastic Mfr & Distr
N.A.I.C.S.: 325211

Radici Plastics UK Ltd. (1)
Hampstead High Street, High Hill House 6A, London, NW3 1PR, United Kingdom
Tel.: (44) 2074314554
Sales Range: $50-74.9 Million
Emp.: 4
Piece Goods Notions & Dry Goods Merchant Whslr
N.A.I.C.S.: 424310
John Rae *(Mng Dir)*

Radici Plastics USA, LLC (1)
960 Seville Rd, Wadsworth, OH 44281
Tel.: (330) 336-7611
Web Site: http://www.mdayinc.com
Plastics Product Mfr
N.A.I.C.S.: 326199
Aaron Howell *(Dir-Mgmt Info Sys)*

Radici Spandex Corp. (1)
3145 NW Blvd, Gastonia, NC 28052
Tel.: (704) 864-5495
Web Site: http://www.radicispandex.com
Sales Range: $25-49.9 Million
Emp.: 50
Yarn Spinning Mills
N.A.I.C.S.: 313110
Marty Moran *(CEO)*

Radici Yarn S.p.A. (1)
Via Provinciale 1125, Villa d'Ogna, Bergamo, 24020, Italy
Tel.: (39) 0346 89111
Web Site: http://www.radicigroup.com
Yarn Mill
N.A.I.C.S.: 313110
Oscar Novali *(Mng Dir)*

Radicifibras Industria e Comercio Ltda (1)
Rua Pedro Rachid 846, 12211-180, Sao Jose dos Campos, Brazil
Tel.: (55) 1239096300
Web Site: http://www.radicifibras.com.br
Yarn Spinning Mills
N.A.I.C.S.: 313110

Radicifibras Industria e Comercio Ltda (1)
Rua Pedro Rachid 846, 12211-180, Sao Jose dos Campos, Brazil
Tel.: (55) 1239096412
Chemical Product Mfr & Distr
N.A.I.C.S.: 325199

Radicifin S.p.A. (1)
Via Paleocapa 9, 24122, Bergamo, Italy   (100%)
Tel.: (39) 035477011
Web Site: http://www.radicigroup.com
Holding Company
N.A.I.C.S.: 551112

S.C. Yarnea S.R.L. (1)

RADICI PARTECIPAZIONI S.P.A.

Radici Partecipazioni S.p.A.—(Continued)

5 Gheorghe Caranfil str, Savinesti, Bacau, 617351, Romania
Tel.: (40) 233205000
Web Site: http://www.yarnea.ro
Sales Range: $100-124.9 Million
Emp.: 400
Broadwoven Fabric Mills
N.A.I.C.S.: 313210
Alessandro Bagnini *(Gen Mgr)*

Societa Elettrica Radici SpA (1)
Via Ugo Foscolo 152, Gandino, 24024, Bergamo, Italy
Tel.: (39) 035715411
Chemical Products Distr
N.A.I.C.S.: 424690

RADICI PIETRO INDUSTRIES & BRANDS S.P.A.
Via Cavalier Pietro Radici 19, Cazzano Sant Andrea, 24026, Bergamo, Italy
Tel.: (39) 035724242
Web Site: https://www.radici.it
Year Founded: 1950
RAD—(ITA)
Sales Range: Less than $1 Million
Flooring Installation Services
N.A.I.C.S.: 238330
Palmiro Radici *(Vice Chm)*

RADICO KHAITAN LIMITED
Bareilly Road, Rampur, 244901, UP, India
Tel.: (91) 5952350601
Web Site: https://www.radicokhaitan.com
Year Founded: 1943
RADICO—(NSE)
Rev.: $1,417,884,864
Assets: $370,510,386
Liabilities: $125,777,379
Net Worth: $244,733,007
Earnings: $36,931,931
Emp.: 1,179
Fiscal Year-end: 03/31/21
Liquor Mfr & Sales
N.A.I.C.S.: 339999
Dilip K. Banthiya *(CFO)*

Subsidiaries:

Radico Khaitan Limited - Plant 1 (1)
Rampur Distillery Bareilly Road, Rampur, 244 901, Uttar Pradesh, India
Tel.: (91) 595 2350601
Sales Range: $100-124.9 Million
Emp.: 400
Liquor Mfr
N.A.I.C.S.: 312140

RADIENT TECHNOLOGIES INC.
4035 101 St NW, Edmonton, T6E 0A4, AB, Canada
Tel.: (780) 465-1318
Web Site: https://www.radientinc.com
RDDTF—(OTCIQ)
Rev.: $2,701,849
Assets: $20,689,968
Liabilities: $28,243,799
Net Worth: $(7,553,831)
Earnings: $(9,645,765)
Emp.: 74
Fiscal Year-end: 03/31/22
Pharmaceutical Product Developer
N.A.I.C.S.: 325412
Denis Taschuk *(Pres & CEO)*

RADIKO HOLDINGS CORP.
639-5 Avenue Southwest Suite 1250, Calgary, T2P 0M9, AB, Canada
Tel.: (303) 474-4383
GEATF—(OTCIQ)
Sales Range: Less than $1 Million
Cannabis Product Mfr
N.A.I.C.S.: 325411
Steve Gormley *(CEO)*

RADIO FRANCE
116 Ave du President Kennedy 75220, 75220, Paris, Cedex 16, France
Tel.: (33) 156402222
Web Site: http://www.radiofrance.fr
Year Founded: 1984
Sales Range: $700-749.9 Million
Emp.: 3,000
Radio Broadcasting & Publishing
N.A.I.C.S.: 516110
Jean-Luc Hees *(Dir-Publ & Pres)*

RADIO JAMAICA LIMITED
32 Lyndhurst Road, Kingston, 5, Jamaica
Tel.: (876) 9261100   JM
Web Site: https://www.rjrgleanergroup.com
RJR—(JAM)
Rev.: $34,956,740
Assets: $43,215,773
Liabilities: $13,502,447
Net Worth: $29,713,326
Earnings: $1,263,611
Emp.: 342
Fiscal Year-end: 03/31/23
Media Holding Company; Radio Broadcasting & Television Stations Operator; Newspaper Publisher
N.A.I.C.S.: 551112
Gary Allen *(CEO & Mng Dir)*

Subsidiaries:

Jamaica News Network (1)
32 Lyndhurst Road, Kingston, Jamaica
Tel.: (876) 9261100
Web Site: http://www.jamaicanewsnetwork.com
National 24/7 All-News Cable Network
N.A.I.C.S.: 516210
Gary Allen *(Mng Dir)*

Multi-Media Jamaica Limited (1)
32 Lyndhurst road, Kingston, Jamaica   (100%)
Tel.: (876) 9261100
Web Site: https://www.multimediajamaica.com
Commercial & Technology Solutions
N.A.I.C.S.: 541840
Gary Allen *(Mng Dir & Dir-Media)*

Television Jamaica Limited (1)
32 Lyndhurst Road, Kingston, Jamaica
Tel.: (876) 9261100
Web Site: https://www.televisionjamaica.com
Sales Range: $100-124.9 Million
Emp.: 500
Television Broadcasting Services
N.A.I.C.S.: 516120
Gary Allen *(Mng Dir)*

The Gleaner Company (Media) Limited (1)
7 North Street, PO Box 40, Kingston, Jamaica
Tel.: (876) 9223400
Web Site: https://www.jamaica-gleaner.com
Holding Company; Radio Broadcasting Stations Operator & Newspaper Publisher
N.A.I.C.S.: 551112
Garfield Grandison *(Gen Mgr-Acting)*

Subsidiary (Non-US):

GV Media Group Limited (2)
6th Floor Northern and Shell Tower 4 Selsdon Way, London, E14 9GL, United Kingdom
Tel.: (44) 20 7510 0340
Web Site: http://www.voice-online.co.uk
Newspaper Publishing Services
N.A.I.C.S.: 513110
Rodney Hinds *(Editor-Sports & Features)*

Subsidiary (US):

The Gleaner Company (USA) Limited (2)
92-05 172nd St 2nd Fl, Jamaica, NY 11433
Tel.: (718) 657-0788
Web Site: https://www.jamaica-gleaner.com
Newspaper Publishing & Advertising Services
N.A.I.C.S.: 541890

The Gleaner Company (UK) Limited (1)
Milnfield, Morayshire, Elgin, IV30 1UU, United Kingdom
Tel.: (44) 800833534
Web Site: https://www.gleaner.co.uk
Agricultural Fuel & Heating Oil Supply Services
N.A.I.C.S.: 561710

RADIO TV PODRINJE A.D.
Kneza Milosa 3, Loznica, Serbia
Tel.: (381) 15 889 567
Year Founded: 1965
Sales Range: Less than $1 Million
Emp.: 16
Television Broadcasting Services
N.A.I.C.S.: 516120

RADIOPHARM THERANOSTICS LIMITED
Tel.: (61) 398245254   AU
Web Site: https://www.radiotheranostics.com
Year Founded: 2021
RAD—(ASX)
Biotechnology Research & Development Services
N.A.I.C.S.: 541714
Paul Hopper *(Founder)*

RADISSON MINING RESOURCES INC.
Tel.: (819) 763-9969
Web Site: https://www.radissonmining.com
RDS—(TSXV)
Sales Range: Less than $1 Million
Gold Exploration Services
N.A.I.C.S.: 213114
Denis Lachance *(Chm, Interim Pres & Interim CEO)*

RADIUM DEVELOPMENT BERHAD
No 7-2 PV7 Jalan Melati Utama 2 Taman Melati Utama, Setapak Wilayah Persekutuan, 53100, Kuala Lumpur, Malaysia
Tel.: (60) 341618218
Web Site: https://www.radiumdevelop.com
Year Founded: 2013
5313—(KLS)
Rev.: $27,919,243
Assets: $199,591,207
Liabilities: $27,064,867
Net Worth: $172,526,340
Earnings: $3,888,333
Fiscal Year-end: 12/31/23
Property Management Services
N.A.I.C.S.: 531311
Sam Yan Li *(CFO)*

RADIUM LIFE TECH CO., LTD.
103 14th Floor No 209 Section 1 Citizen Avenue, Datong Dist, Taipei, 103, Taiwan
Tel.: (886) 277338888
Web Site: https://www.radium.com.tw
2547—(TAI)
Rev.: $244,655,604
Assets: $1,974,426,296
Liabilities: $1,589,309,695
Net Worth: $385,116,601
Earnings: $(542,235)
Emp.: 208
Fiscal Year-end: 12/31/23
Construction Services
N.A.I.C.S.: 236220

Subsidiaries:

Jing-Jan Retail Business Co., Ltd. (1)

INTERNATIONAL PUBLIC

No 1 Sec 1 Chengde Rd, Datong Dist, Taipei, 103, Taiwan
Tel.: (886) 221828888
Web Site: https://qsquare.com.tw
All Consumer Good Retailer
N.A.I.C.S.: 455110
Samantha Lin *(Chm)*

Rih Ding Water Enterprise Co., Ltd. (1)
No 177 Section 1 Fuhua Road, Luzhu District, Taoyuan, Taiwan
Tel.: (886) 33229688
Web Site: https://www.rihding.com.tw
Sewage Treatment Services
N.A.I.C.S.: 562219

RADIUS GOLD INC.
Suite 650 200 Burrard Street, Vancouver, V6C 3L6, BC, Canada
Tel.: (604) 801-5432   BC
Web Site: https://www.radiusgold.com
RDU—(TSXV)
Rev.: $7,353
Assets: $2,741,534
Liabilities: $188,144
Net Worth: $2,553,390
Earnings: $794,972
Emp.: 5
Fiscal Year-end: 12/31/22
Gold Mining Services
N.A.I.C.S.: 212220
Simon T. P. Ridgway *(Founder & Chm)*

RADIX INDUSTRIES (INDIA) LIMITED
4-243 Chivatam Near NH-5 Road, West Godavari District, Tanuku, 534 211, Andhra Pradesh, India
Tel.: (91) 4064523706
Web Site: https://radixindustries.in
Year Founded: 1993
531412—(BOM)
Rev.: $3,149,595
Assets: $2,492,884
Liabilities: $306,289
Net Worth: $2,186,596
Earnings: $183,286
Emp.: 9
Fiscal Year-end: 03/31/23
Hair Product Mfr & Distr
N.A.I.C.S.: 325620
G. Raghu Rama Raju *(Chm & Mng Dir)*

RADIXWEB
30/B Adarsh Society Near Kaashi Parekh Complex, Swastik Char Rasta CG Road, Ahmedabad, 380009, Gujarat, India
Tel.: (91) 79 26400685
Web Site: http://www.radixweb.com
Sales Range: $25-49.9 Million
Emp.: 250
IT Outsourcing Services
N.A.I.C.S.: 541519
Naresh Bordia *(VP)*

RADLEY YELDAR
24 Charlotte Rd, London, EC2A 3PB, United Kingdom
Tel.: (44) 20 7033 0700
Year Founded: 1986
Emp.: 120
Brand Development & Integration, Communications, Digital/Interactive, Investor Relations, Local Marketing, Media Relations
N.A.I.C.S.: 541810
Carl Radley *(Co-Founder)*

RADNIK A.D.

Branka Bajica 79, Backa Palanka, Serbia
Tel.: (381) 21 6141 423
Year Founded: 1989
Sales Range: Less than $1 Million
Emp.: 45
Building Construction Services
N.A.I.C.S.: 236220

RADPOL S.A.
ul Batorego 14, 77-300, Czluchow, Poland
Tel.: (48) 598342271
Web Site: http://www.radpol.com.pl
RDL—(WAR)
Sales Range: $10-24.9 Million
Emp.: 300
Plastic Shrink-Wrap Products Mfr
N.A.I.C.S.: 322220

RADVIEW SOFTWARE LTD.
13 Haamal St Park Afek, Rosh Ha'Ayin, 4809249, Israel
Tel.: (972) 39157060
Web Site: https://www.radview.com
Year Founded: 1993
RDVWF—(OTCEM)
Sales Range: $1-9.9 Million
Emp.: 13
Software Tools Mfr for Performance Testing & Analysis
N.A.I.C.S.: 334610
Yochai Hacohen (Chm)

Subsidiaries:

RadView Software Inc. (1)
991 Hwy 22 W Ste 200, Bridgewater, NJ 08807
Tel.: (908) 526-7756
Web Site: www.radview.com
Performance & Load Testing Software Developer
N.A.I.C.S.: 449210
Konstantin Ostrovski (Mgr-Sls)

RAEMONGRAEIN CO., LTD.
19 Hakdong-ro 25-gil, Gangnam-gu, Seoul, 137-745, Korea (South)
Tel.: (82) 27619978
Web Site: https://www.raemongraein.co.kr
Year Founded: 2007
Television Broadcasting Services
N.A.I.C.S.: 512110
Dong-Lea Kim (CEO)

RAFAEL ADVANCED DEFENSE SYSTEMS LTD.
Tel.: (972) 733354444
Web Site: https://www.rafael.co.il
Year Founded: 1948
Software Development Services
N.A.I.C.S.: 541511
Einat Gilady (Mgr-Talent Acq)

Subsidiaries:

Aeronautics Ltd. (1)
Nahal Snir 10 St, Yavne, 81101, Israel
Tel.: (972) 8 9433600
Web Site: http://www.aeronautics-sys.com
Unmanned Aerial Systems Mfr
N.A.I.C.S.: 334511
Moshe Elazar (CEO)

Rafael USA, Inc. (1)
Ste 850 6903 Rockledge Dr, Bethesda, MD 20817
Tel.: (240) 482-0240
Web Site: https://www.rafael-usa.com
Defense, Cyber & Security Systems
N.A.I.C.S.: 561621
Azarel Ram (Pres & CEO)

Subsidiary (Domestic):

PVP Advanced EO Systems, Inc. (2)
14312 Franklin Ave, Tustin, CA 92780
Tel.: (714) 508-2740
Web Site: http://www.pvpaeo.com

Sales Range: $1-9.9 Million
Emp.: 36
Optical Instrument & Lens Mfr
N.A.I.C.S.: 333310
Bruce Ferguson (Pres & CEO)

RAFAEL MICROELECTRONICS, INC.
Ideon Science Park Beta 6 Scheelevagen 17, 223 70, Lund, Sweden
Tel.: (46) 462863840
Web Site: http://www.quickcool.se
Year Founded: 2003
6568—(TPE)
Rev.: $40,744,646
Assets: $58,696,870
Liabilities: $12,099,303
Net Worth: $46,597,567
Earnings: $3,803,489
Fiscal Year-end: 12/31/22
Hardware Product Mfr
N.A.I.C.S.: 332510
Fredrik Radencrantz (CEO)

RAFAELLA RESOURCES LTD.
Level 8 175 Eagle Street, Brisbane, 4000, QLD, Australia
Tel.: (61) 94810389
Web Site: http://www.rafaellaresources.com.au
PVT—(ASX)
Rev.: $36,285
Assets: $8,914,656
Liabilities: $207,593
Net Worth: $8,707,063
Earnings: ($1,248,585)
Fiscal Year-end: 06/30/24
Mineral Exploration Services
N.A.I.C.S.: 213114
Steven Turner (Mng Dir)

RAFAMET S.A.
Staszica 1, Kuznia Raciborska, 47420, Warsaw, Silesian, Poland
Tel.: (48) 327213300
Web Site: https://www.rafamet.com
Year Founded: 1846
RAF—(WAR)
Rev.: $30,342,480
Assets: $64,150,660
Liabilities: $40,394,309
Net Worth: $23,756,352
Earnings: ($1,828,506)
Fiscal Year-end: 12/31/23
Industrial Machinery Mfr
N.A.I.C.S.: 333248
Piotr Regulski (Deputy Chm)

RAFFAELLO CAPITAL LIMITED
Unit 1701 17/F Low Block Grand Millennium Plaza, 181 Queen's Road Central Sheung Wan, Hong Kong, China (Hong Kong)
Tel.: (852) 3102 3363
Web Site: http://www.raffaellocap.com
Corporate Finance Activities
N.A.I.C.S.: 525990

RAFFLES EDUCATION CORPORATION LIMITED
Raffles Education Square 51 Merchant Road, Singapore, 058283, Singapore
Tel.: (65) 63385288
Web Site: https://raffles.education
Year Founded: 1990
RFLFY—(OTCIQ)
Rev.: $82,171,916
Assets: $852,196,369
Liabilities: $336,579,474
Net Worth: $515,616,895
Earnings: ($6,666,914)
Emp.: 2,500
Fiscal Year-end: 06/30/23
College Operator

N.A.I.C.S.: 611310
Hua Seng Chew (Founder, Chm & CEO)

Subsidiaries:

PT Raffles Design Institute (1)
Lippo Thamrin Mezzanine Floor JL M H Thamrin No 20, Menteng, Jakarta Pusat, 10350, Indonesia
Sales Range: $10-24.9 Million
Emp.: 20
Fashion Designing Educational Services
N.A.I.C.S.: 611710
Ken Chan (Mgr)

Raffles College of Higher Education Sdn. Bhd. (1)
No 1 Lorong Damai 3 Off Jalan Aman, 55000, Kuala Lumpur, Malaysia
Tel.: (60) 321641059
Web Site: https://www.raffles.edu.my
Education Services
N.A.I.C.S.: 611710
David Liew (Dir-College)

Raffles Design Institute Pte Ltd (1)
99 Beach Rd, Singapore, 189701, Singapore
Tel.: (65) 63385288
Web Site: http://www.raffles-education.edu.sg
Sales Range: $10-24.9 Million
Emp.: 80
Fashion Designing Education Support Services
N.A.I.C.S.: 611710
Kai How Ong (Principal)

Raffles Design International (Thailand) Limited (1)
2 Silom Road 5th Floor Silom Center Suriyawong, Bangrak, Bangkok, 10500, Thailand
Tel.: (66) 26327666
Web Site: http://www.raffles.ac.th
Sales Range: $10-24.9 Million
Emp.: 30
Fashion Designing Education Support Services
N.A.I.C.S.: 611710
Low Lip Keong (Dir-Program-Fashion Mktg)

Raffles International College (HK) Ltd (1)
1/F Centre Point 181-185 Gloucester Road, Wanchai, China (Hong Kong)
Tel.: (852) 25206838
Web Site: http://www.raffles.edu.hk
Sales Range: $10-24.9 Million
Emp.: 35
Educational Support Services
N.A.I.C.S.: 611710

RAFFLES FINANCIAL GROUP LIMITED
3 Fraser Street 08-21, Singapore, 189352, Singapore
Tel.: (65) 68281483 SG
Web Site: http://www.rafflesfinancial.co
RICH—(CNSX)
Rev.: $6,571,445
Assets: $25,740,518
Liabilities: $2,596,238
Net Worth: $23,144,280
Earnings: ($315,154)
Fiscal Year-end: 06/30/20
Financial Advisory Services
N.A.I.C.S.: 523940
Charlie In (Chm)

RAFFLES INTERIOR LIMITED
59 Sungei Kadut Loop, Singapore, 729490, Singapore
Tel.: (65) 63899888 Ky
Web Site: https://www.rafflesinterior.com
Year Founded: 1986
1376—(HKG)
Rev.: $69,060,819
Assets: $33,494,660
Liabilities: $24,132,394
Net Worth: $9,362,266

Earnings: $1,062,637
Emp.: 391
Fiscal Year-end: 12/31/23
Construction Management Services
N.A.I.C.S.: 236116
Boon Par Chua (Chm & CEO)

RAFFLES MEDICAL GROUP LTD
Raffles Hospital 585 North Bridge Road Raffles Hospital, Singapore, 188770, Singapore
Tel.: (65) 63111111
Web Site: https://www.rafflesmedicalgroup.com
BSL—(SES)
Rev.: $548,082,254
Assets: $1,157,486,934
Liabilities: $366,869,651
Net Worth: $790,617,284
Earnings: $68,991,896
Emp.: 2,892
Fiscal Year-end: 12/31/23
Hospital Management Services
N.A.I.C.S.: 621491
Choon Yong Loo (Founder & Chm)

Subsidiaries:

AEA International SOS (Cambodia) Ltd. (1)
93 Floor 2 BG Serviced Office Preah Sihanouk Boulevard, Phnom Penh, Cambodia
Tel.: (855) 23216928
Hospital & Health Care Services
N.A.I.C.S.: 622110
I. N. Udom (Mgr-IT)

International Medical Insurers Pte Ltd (1)
25 Tannery Lane, Singapore, 347786, Singapore
Tel.: (65) 6 286 2866
Web Site: https://www.raffleshealthinsurance.com
Sales Range: $50-74.9 Million
Emp.: 50
Medical Insurance Services
N.A.I.C.S.: 524114

PT Raffles Medika Indonesia (1)
The East Tower JL DR Ide Anak Agung Gde Agung Lot E3 2 No 1, Kuningan, Jakarta, 12950, Indonesia
Tel.: (62) 2129527102
Web Site: https://www.rafflleshospital.co.id
Sales Range: $10-24.9 Million
General Medical Services
N.A.I.C.S.: 622110

PeopleSolve Pte. Ltd. (1)
585 North Bridge Road 11-00, Singapore, Singapore
Tel.: (65) 96457147
Web Site: https://www.peoplesolve.com.sg
Emp.: 6,000
Healthcare Professional Services
N.A.I.C.S.: 621399

Raffles Chinese Medicine Pte Ltd (1)
585 North Bridge Road Level 2 Raffles Hospital, Singapore, 188770, Singapore
Tel.: (65) 63112388
General Medical Services
N.A.I.C.S.: 622110
Lawrence Lim (Dir)

Raffles Diagnostica Pte Ltd (1)
Level 2 Raffles Hosptial 585 North Bridge Road, Singapore, 188770, Singapore
Tel.: (65) 63111289
Laboratory Testing Services
N.A.I.C.S.: 621512
Lawrence Lim (Dir-Corp Dev)

Raffles Health Insurance Pte. Ltd. (1)
25 Tannery Lane, Singapore, 347786, Singapore
Tel.: (65) 62862866
Web Site: https://www.rafflleshealthinsurance.com
Health Insurance Services
N.A.I.C.S.: 524210
Zoey Leong (Acct Mgr)

RAFFLES MEDICAL GROUP LTD

Raffles Medical Group Ltd—(Continued)

Raffles Health Pte Ltd (1)
585 North Bridge Road Level 1, Singapore, 188770, Singapore
Tel.: (65) 6 311 1108
Web Site: https://www.raffleshealth.com
Emp.: 100
General Medical Services
N.A.I.C.S.: 622110

Raffles Hospital Beijing Co., Ltd. (1)
Room 105 Building 1 Kunsha Center No 15, Xinyuanli Chaoyang District, Beijing, China
Tel.: (86) 1064629112
Web Site: https://www.rafflesmedicalchina.com
Medical Devices
N.A.I.C.S.: 621999

Raffles Hospital Pte Ltd (1)
585 North Bridge Road, Singapore, 188770, Singapore
Tel.: (65) 63111111
Web Site: https://www.rafflesmedicalgroup.com
General Medical Services
N.A.I.C.S.: 622110

Raffles Hospital Shanghai Co. Ltd. (1)
200 Yuan Zhao Road, Pudong New District, Shanghai, China
Tel.: (86) 2161293000
Hospital Operator
N.A.I.C.S.: 622110

Raffles Japanese Clinic Pte Ltd (1)
585 North Bridge Road Raffles Hospital 02-00, Singapore, 188770, Singapore
Tel.: (65) 63111190
Web Site: https://www.rafflesj-clinic.com
Emp.: 50
General Medical Services
N.A.I.C.S.: 622110

Raffles Medical Group (Hong Kong) Limited (1)
6T-104 Level 6 Terminal 1 Hong Kong International Airport, Chek Lap Kok, Hong Kong, China (Hong Kong)
Tel.: (852) 22612626
General Medical Services
N.A.I.C.S.: 622110

Raffles SurgiCentre Pte. Ltd. (1)
Level 13 Raffles Specialist Centre 585 North Bridge Road, Singapore, 188770, Singapore
Tel.: (65) 63111140
Hospital Services
N.A.I.C.S.: 622110
Walter Tan Tiang Lee *(Dir-Medical)*

RAFFLES UNITED HOLDINGS LTD.

5 Changi South Street 3, Singapore, 486117, Singapore
Tel.: (65) 62875866 SG
Web Site: http://www.rafflesunited.com.sg
Year Founded: 1956
Rev.: $50,055,104
Assets: $102,479,018
Liabilities: $38,025,292
Net Worth: $64,453,726
Earnings: $1,369,800
Fiscal Year-end: 12/31/18
Investment Holding Company
N.A.I.C.S.: 551114
Teng Beng Teo *(Mng Dir)*

Subsidiaries:

Acee Electric Pte. Ltd. (1)
51 Ubi Ave 1 03-22 Paya Ubi Industrial Park, Singapore, 408933, Singapore
Tel.: (65) 68412788
Web Site: http://www.kncomedia.com
Hardware Whslr
N.A.I.C.S.: 423710

RAFINA INNOVATIONS INC.

Kintyre House 209 Govan Road, Glasgow, G51 1HJ, Scotland, United Kingdom
Tel.: (44) 1413700321 NV
Web Site: http://www.rafina-innovations.com
Year Founded: 2007
VICA—(OTCIQ)
Rev.: $3,262,000
Assets: $7,713,000
Liabilities: $3,675,000
Net Worth: $4,038,000
Earnings: ($879,000)
Emp.: 4
Fiscal Year-end: 12/31/21
Medical Device Mfr
N.A.I.C.S.: 339112
Georgios Thrapsaniotis *(Treas)*

RAFINARIA ASTRA ROMANA S.A.

Tel.: (40) 745109539
Web Site: https://www.astrarom.ro
Year Founded: 1880
ASP—(BUC)
Sales Range: $1-9.9 Million
Emp.: 85
Petroleum Refinery Operator
N.A.I.C.S.: 324199
Marcela Elena Patrascu *(CFO)*

RAFINERIJA NAFTE A.D

Pancevacki put br 83, 11210, Belgrade, Serbia
Tel.: (381) 112711433
Web Site: https://www.rnb.rs
RNAF-R-A—(BANJ)
Sales Range: Less than $1 Million
Petroleum Product Mfr
N.A.I.C.S.: 324199

RAG-STIFTUNG

Im Welterbe 10, 45141, Essen, Germany
Tel.: (49) 2013783333
Web Site: http://www.rag-stiftung.de
Year Founded: 2007
Emp.: 15
Mining, Chemicals & Energy Regulation Organization
N.A.I.C.S.: 926130
Barbel Bergerhoff-Wodopia *(Member-Exec Bd)*

Subsidiaries:

Dorsch Holding GmbH (1)
Berliner Strasse 74-76, 63065, Offenbach, Germany
Tel.: (49) 691302570
Web Site: http://www.dorsch.de
Emp.: 2,000
Engineering Consulting Services
N.A.I.C.S.: 541330
Olaf Hoffmann *(CEO & Member-Mgmt Bd)*

Subsidiary (Domestic):

BDC Dorsch Consult Ingenieurgesellschaft mbH (2)
Storkower Strasse 207A 3 Stock, 10369, Berlin, Germany (100%)
Tel.: (49) 302639240
Web Site: http://www.bdc-dorsch.de
Emp.: 90
Engineeering Services
N.A.I.C.S.: 541330
Andreas Rienecker *(Mng Dir)*

Subsidiary (Non-US):

Dorsch Consult (India) Private Ltd. (2)
236 Oshiwara Industrial Centre Opp Goregaon Bus Depot, Off New Link Road Goregaon West, Mumbai, 400 104, India
Tel.: (91) 22 2878 9116
Web Site: http://www.dorsch.de
Emp.: 2,000
Engineeering Services
N.A.I.C.S.: 541330
Nirmal G. Humbad *(Mng Dir)*

Dorsch Consult Abu Dhabi (2)
Salam Street, PO Box 26417, Abu Dhabi, 26417, United Arab Emirates
Tel.: (971) 26721923
Web Site: http://www.dorsch.de
Emp.: 800
Engineeering Services
N.A.I.C.S.: 541330

Dorsch Consult Asia Co., Ltd. (2)
1168/45 Lumpini Tower-18th Floor Rama 4 Road Tungmahamek, Sathon, Bangkok, 10120, Thailand
Tel.: (66) 2 679 89 00
Web Site: http://www.dorsch.de
Construction Engineering Services
N.A.I.C.S.: 541330
Juergen Supik *(CEO)*

Subsidiary (Domestic):

Dorsch International Consultants GmbH (2)
Landsberger Str 368, 80687, Munich, Germany
Tel.: (49) 89 57 97 0
Web Site: http://di.dorsch.de
Emp.: 240
Construction Engineering Services
N.A.I.C.S.: 541330
Andreas Rienecker *(Mng Dir)*

Subsidiary (Non-US):

Dorsch Qatar LLC (2)
Al Salam Tower Sheraton Roundabout, PO Box 23593, Doha, Qatar
Tel.: (974) 4 480 2097
Web Site: http://www.dorsch.de
Construction Engineering Services
N.A.I.C.S.: 541330
Hany Labib *(Dir-External Ops-PMO & Bus Dev)*

Evonik Industries AG (1)
Rellinghauser Strasse 1-11, 45128, Essen, Germany (56.9%)
Tel.: (49) 20117701
Web Site: https://www.evonik.com
Rev.: $16,476,365,206
Assets: $21,519,533,779
Liabilities: $11,821,713,792
Net Worth: $9,697,819,987
Earnings: ($487,804,878)
Emp.: 33,409
Fiscal Year-end: 12/31/2023
Chemical Products Mfr
N.A.I.C.S.: 511112
Christian Kullmann *(Chm-Exec Bd)*

Subsidiary (Non-US):

Cosmoferm B.V. (2)
Alexander Fleminglaan 1, 2613 AX, Delft, Netherlands
Tel.: (31) 0152792162
Web Site: http://www.cosmoferm.com
Sales Range: $25-49.9 Million
Emp.: 5
Development, Production & Trade of Cosmetics Ingredients
N.A.I.C.S.: 325620

Joint Venture (Non-US):

Daicel-Evonik Ltd. (2)
Shinjuku Monolith 13F 2-3-1 Nishi-shinjuku, Shinjuku-ku, Tokyo, 163-0913, Japan (50%)
Tel.: (81) 353246331
Web Site: https://www.pp-evonik.com
Sales Range: $25-49.9 Million
Polymers Mfr & Distr
N.A.I.C.S.: 325211

Subsidiary (Non-US):

Evonik Antwerpen N.V. (2)
Tijsmanstunnel West, 2040, Antwerp, Belgium
Tel.: (32) 35603211
Web Site: http://www.corporate.evonik.be
Emp.: 1,000
Methionine, Silica & Hydrogen Peroxide Mfr
N.A.I.C.S.: 325998

Subsidiary (US):

Evonik Corporation (2)
379 Interpace Pkwy, Parsippany, NJ 07054-1115
Tel.: (973) 541-8230
Web Site: http://www.degussa-bk.com

INTERNATIONAL PUBLIC

Sales Range: $1-4.9 Billion
Specialty Chemicals Mfr
N.A.I.C.S.: 325199
Bonnie Tully *(Pres)*

Unit (Domestic):

Evonik Degussa - Birmingham Labs (3)
750 Lakeshore Pkwy, Birmingham, AL 35211
Tel.: (205) 917-2200
Web Site: http://biomaterials.evonik.com
Sales Range: $25-49.9 Million
Drug Delivery Systems Research & Development
N.A.I.C.S.: 541715

Subsidiary (Non-US):

Evonik Degussa Canada Inc. (3)
235 Orenda Rd, Brampton, L6T 1E6, ON, Canada
Tel.: (905) 451-3810
Web Site: http://www.evonik.com
Sales Range: $25-49.9 Million
Mfr of Colorants & Driers
N.A.I.C.S.: 325510

Plant (Domestic):

Evonik Degussa Corp. - Lockland (3)
620 Shepherd Dr, Cincinnati, OH 45215-2104
Tel.: (513) 733-5111
Web Site: http://www.degussa-nafta.com
Sales Range: $25-49.9 Million
Colorants Mfr
N.A.I.C.S.: 325110
Tom Tindera *(Plant Mgr)*

Evonik Degussa Corp. - Mobile (3)
4201 Degussa Rd, Theodore, AL 36582
Tel.: (251) 443-4000
Web Site: http://www.evonik.com
Sales Range: $200-249.9 Million
Mfr of Organic Chemical Intermediates, Silanes, Microelectronic Chemicals
N.A.I.C.S.: 325110

Subsidiary (Domestic):

Evonik Stockhausen, LLC (3)
2401 Doyle St, Greensboro, NC 27406-2911
Tel.: (336) 333-7956
Sales Range: $125-149.9 Million
Chemicals Mfr
N.A.I.C.S.: 325199
Janice Lanier *(Mgr-HR)*

Subsidiary (Domestic):

Evonik Stockhausen, LLC - Garyville (4)
3606 Hwy 44, Garyville, LA 70051
Tel.: (985) 535-6700
Web Site: http://www.stockhausen.com
Sales Range: $10-24.9 Million
Chemical Distr
N.A.I.C.S.: 424690
Daniel Fricker *(Mgr-Site)*

Subsidiary (Non-US):

Evonik Degussa (China) Co., Ltd. (2)
16/F Beijing Sunflower Tower 37 Maizidian Street, Chao Yang District, 100026, Beijing, China
Tel.: (86) 1085 27 64 00
Web Site: http://www.degussa.com
Chemical Producer & Distr
N.A.I.C.S.: 325998

Subsidiary (Non-US):

Evonik Taiwan Ltd. (3)
9F 133 Min Sheng E Road Sector 3, Taipei, 105, Taiwan
Tel.: (886) 227171242
Sales Range: $25-49.9 Million
Chemical Distr
N.A.I.C.S.: 325998

Subsidiary (Domestic):

Evonik Goldschmidt GmbH (2)
Goldschmitstrasse 100, Essen, 45127, Germany

AND PRIVATE COMPANIES — RAG-STIFTUNG

Tel.: (49) 20117301
Web Site: http://www.evonik.com
Sales Range: $10-24.9 Million
Mfr of Chemicals Additives for Personal Care Products & Cleaning Products
N.A.I.C.S.: 325998

Subsidiary (US):

Evonik Goldschmidt Corporation (3)
914 E Randolph Rd, Hopewell, VA 23860
Tel.: (804) 541-8658
Web Site: http://www.degussa-nafta.com
Emp.: 125
Industrial Organic Chemicals Mfr
N.A.I.C.S.: 325199
Philip Munson (Mgr-Site)

Subsidiary (Domestic):

Evonik Immobilien GmbH (2)
Rellinghauser Strasse 7, 45128, Essen, Germany
Tel.: (49) 20117706
Sales Range: $50-74.9 Million
Real Estate Trust
N.A.I.C.S.: 525990

Subsidiary (Domestic):

Auguste Victoria GmbH (3)
Victoriastrasse 43, 45772, Marl, Germany
Tel.: (49) 2365400
Web Site: http://www.dsk.de
General Contractors Residential Buildings
N.A.I.C.S.: 236118

Gesellschaft fur Wohnen Datteln mbH (3)
Zechenstrasse 6, 45711, Datteln, Germany
Tel.: (49) 236397080
Web Site: http://www.gewo-datteln.de
Building Svcs
N.A.I.C.S.: 236118

Rhein Lippe Wohnen GmbH (3)
Hufstrasse 27, 47166, Duisburg, Germany
Tel.: (49) 20354480
Web Site: http://www.vivawest.de
Sales Range: $75-99.9 Million
Provider of Real Estate Services
N.A.I.C.S.: 531210

Unit (Domestic):

Evonik Industries AG - Feed Additives (2)
Rodenbacher Chaussee 4, Hanau-Wolfgang, D-63457, Hanau, Germany
Tel.: (49) 6181596766
Web Site: http://www.feed-additives.evonik.com
Mfr of Amino Acid-Based Feed Additives
N.A.I.C.S.: 311119
Christian Schmid (Head-Corp Comm)

Plant (Domestic):

Evonik Industries AG - Hanau-Wolfgang Catalysts Plant (2)
Rodenbacher Chaussee 4 Building 097, 63457, Hanau, Germany
Tel.: (49) 6181 59 01
Web Site: http://corporate.evonik.com
Ligands & Metal Complex Catalysts Mfr
N.A.I.C.S.: 325998

Evonik Industries AG - Krefeld Plant (2)
Bakerpfad 25, 47805, Krefeld, Germany
Tel.: (49) 21513801
Sales Range: $200-249.9 Million
Personal Care Industry Chemicals & Specialty Polymers Mfr
N.A.I.C.S.: 325998

Evonik Industries AG - Marl Coatings & Additives Plant (2)
Paul Baumann Strasse 1, 45764, Marl, Germany
Tel.: (49) 2365 49 9449
Web Site: http://www.evonik.com
Sales Range: $600-649.9 Million
Crosslinkers, Polyesters, Performance Resins & Colorants Mfr
N.A.I.C.S.: 325211

Branch (Non-US):

Evonik Industries Japan Co., Ltd. - Osaka Office (2)
Kintetsu Shin Namba Bldg 12F 1-4-38 Minato-machi, Naniwa-ku, Osaka, 556 0017, Japan
Tel.: (81) 666441512
Web Site: http://japan.evonik.com
Sales Range: $150-199.9 Million
Chemical Distr
N.A.I.C.S.: 325998

Subsidiary (Domestic):

Evonik Oxeno GmbH (2)
Paul Baumann Strasse 1, 45772, Marl, Germany
Tel.: (49) 23654903
Sales Range: $125-149.9 Million
Mfr of Specialty Chemical Additives
N.A.I.C.S.: 325998

Evonik Rohm GmbH (2)
Kirschenallee, Darmstadt, 64293, Germany
Tel.: (49) 61511801
Web Site: http://www.evonik.com
Sales Range: $1-4.9 Billion
Polymers Mfr
N.A.I.C.S.: 325180

Subsidiary (US):

Evonik Cyro LLC (3)
299 Jefferson Rd, Parsippany, NJ 07054
Tel.: (973) 541-8000
Web Site: http://www.cyro.com
Sales Range: $200-249.9 Million
Acrylic Sheets & Films & Methyl Methacrylates Producer
N.A.I.C.S.: 325211

Rohm America LLC (3)
2 Turner Pl, Piscataway, NJ 08854-3839
Tel.: (732) 981-5000
Web Site: http://www.roehm.com
Mfr of Methacrylate Monomers
N.A.I.C.S.: 325180

Subsidiary (Domestic):

Knipping System-Technik GmbH (2)
Angerstrasse 18, 06118, Halle, Saale, Germany
Tel.: (49) 34552161590
Web Site: http://www.knipping-systemtechnik.de
Sales Range: $25-49.9 Million
Emp.: 2
Mfr of Windows & Doors
N.A.I.C.S.: 332321

Kroger Greifertechnik GmbH Co. & KG (2)
Steinheide 1-9, Sonsbeck, 47665, Germany
Tel.: (49) 2838370
Web Site: http://www.kroeger-greifertechnik.de
Hydraulic Motors Mfr
N.A.I.C.S.: 333996
Norbert Bollen (Mgr-Technical)

Subsidiary (US):

PeroxyChem LLC (2)
1 Commerce Sq 2005 Market St Ste 3200, Philadelphia, PA 19103-7501
Tel.: (267) 422-2400
Web Site: http://www.peroxychem.com
Specialty Oxidative Chemicals Mfr & Distr
N.A.I.C.S.: 325180
Mark Valentino (CFO)

HAHN Automation GmbH (1)
Liebshausener Strasse 3, 55494, Rheinbollen, Germany (51%)
Tel.: (49) 676490220
Web Site: http://www.hahnautomation.com
Automated Assembly Equipment & Machine Mfr, Design & Installation Services
N.A.I.C.S.: 333248
Thomas Hahn (Gen Mgr)

Subsidiary (Non-US):

HAHN Automation (Kunshan) Co. Ltd. (2)
No 329 Jujin Road Zhangpu Township, 215321, Kunshan, China
Tel.: (86) 512 3662 51 02
Molding Machine Mfr
N.A.I.C.S.: 333511

HAHN Automation AG (2)
La Praye 1, 2608, Courtelary, Switzerland
Tel.: (41) 31 734 31 11
Molding Machine Mfr
N.A.I.C.S.: 333511

HAHN Automation d.o.o. (2)
Sveti Duh 123, 10000, Zagreb, Croatia
Tel.: (385) 3370 339
Molding Machine Mfr
N.A.I.C.S.: 333511
Daniel Zima (Engr-Automation)

HAHN Automation, s.r.o. (2)
Klostermannova 1000, 250 82, Prague, Czech Republic
Tel.: (420) 281 012 572
Molding Machine Mfr
N.A.I.C.S.: 333511

Subsidiary (Domestic):

HAHN ENERSAVE GmbH (2)
Fritz-Kotz-Str 1, 51674, Wiehl, Germany
Tel.: (49) 6764 9022 0
Molding Machine Mfr
N.A.I.C.S.: 333511

Subsidiary (Non-US):

HAHN OTOMASYON Ltd. Sti. (2)
Hadimkoy Mah Ataturk Sanayi Niyaz Sokak No 12, Hadimkoy Arnavutkoy, Istanbul, Turkiye
Tel.: (90) 212 549 99 82
Molding Machine Mfr
N.A.I.C.S.: 333511

Subsidiary (Domestic):

Hahn Automation Components GmbH (2)
Darmstadter Strasse 72, D-64354, Reinheim, Germany
Tel.: (49) 61628040
Web Site: http://www.haehn-automation.de
Sales Range: $50-74.9 Million
Molding Machine Mfr
N.A.I.C.S.: 333511

Subsidiary (Non-US):

Hahn Automation San ve Tic. Ltd. Sti. (3)
Eskoop San St, A3 Blok No 131-132, Istanbul, Turkiye
Tel.: (90) 2125491199
Web Site: http://www.hahnautomation.com
Sales Range: $25-49.9 Million
Emp.: 4
Molding Machine Mfr
N.A.I.C.S.: 333511
Mehmet Uzunkok (Gen Mgr)

Subsidiary (US):

Hahn Automation, Inc. (3)
3012 Kustom Dr, Hebron, KY 41048
Tel.: (859) 283-1820
Web Site: http://www.hahnautomation.com
Machine Assembly, Design & Integration Services
N.A.I.C.S.: 541420
John Baines (Pres)

RAG Aktiengesellschaft (1)
Im Welterbe 10, 45141, Essen, Germany (100%)
Tel.: (49) 2013780
Web Site: https://www.rag.de
Sales Range: $900-999.9 Million
Coal Mining & Processing
N.A.I.C.S.: 212114
Michael Kalthoff (CFO)

Subsidiary (Domestic):

RAG Deutsche Steinkohle AG (2)
Shamrockring 1, 44623, Herne, Germany
Tel.: (49) 2323150
Web Site: http://www.rag-deutsche-steinkohle.de
Sales Range: $650-699.9 Million
Coal Mining
N.A.I.C.S.: 212114
Bernd Toenjes (Chm-Mgmt Bd)

RAG Verkauf GmbH (2)
Shamrockring 1, 44623, Herne, Germany (100%)
Tel.: (49) 2323 15 0
Web Site: http://www.rag-verkauf.de

Hard Coal, Coke & Carbon Byproducts Marketing, Transportation & Distribution
N.A.I.C.S.: 423520
Manfred Muller (Chm-Mgmt Bd)

RSBG SE (1)
Baumstrasse 25, 45128, Essen, Germany
Tel.: (49) 20156578010
Web Site: https://www.rsbg.com
Financial Services
N.A.I.C.S.: 523999

TK Elevator GmbH (1)
thyssenkrupp Allee 1, 45143, Essen, Germany
Tel.: (49) 2018440
Web Site: http://www.thyssenkrupp-elevator.com
Sales Range: $5-14.9 Billion
Emp.: 39,501
Holding Company; Elevator & Lift Developr, Mfr & Distr
N.A.I.C.S.: 551112
Uday Yadav (CEO)

Subsidiary (US):

Braun Thyssenkrupp Elevator, LLC (2)
2829 Royal Ave, Madison, WI 53713
Tel.: (608) 221-4400
Web Site: http://www.braun-corp.com
Sales Range: $1-9.9 Million
Emp.: 100
Building Equipment Contractors
N.A.I.C.S.: 238290
Darrell Braun (CEO)

O'Keefe Elevator Company Inc. (2)
1402 Jones St, Omaha, NE 68102
Tel.: (402) 345-4056
Web Site: http://www.okeefe-elevator.com
Sales Range: $10-24.9 Million
Elevators
N.A.I.C.S.: 423830
Denny B. Wychulis (CEO)

Subsidiary (Non-US):

Sun Rhine Enterprises Ltd. (2)
10F-1 No 18 Sec 1 Chang-An E Road, Taipei, 104, Taiwan
Tel.: (886) 2 25618310
Web Site: http://www.thyssenkrupp-elevator.com.tw
Sales Range: $25-49.9 Million
Emp.: 100
Lift Repair & Installation Services
N.A.I.C.S.: 238290

TK Elevator (2)
Andropov Ave 18 bldg 7, 115432, Moscow, Russia
Tel.: (7) 4959358517
Web Site: http://tkelevator.ru
Sales Range: $50-74.9 Million
Emp.: 150
Elevator Mfr
N.A.I.C.S.: 333921

ThyssenKrupp Accessibility B.V. (2)
Van Utrechtweg 99, 2921 LN, Krimpen aan de Ijssel, Netherlands
Tel.: (31) 180 530 900
Web Site: http://www.tkacc.nl
Elevator & Stair Lift Mfr
N.A.I.C.S.: 333921

Subsidiary (Domestic):

ThyssenKrupp Accessibility Holding GmbH (2)
Hatzper Strasse 36, 45149, Essen, Germany
Tel.: (49) 2017995911
Web Site: http://www.tk-access4all.com
Sales Range: $25-49.9 Million
Emp.: 11
Holding Company; Wheel Chair Lift Mfr
N.A.I.C.S.: 551112

ThyssenKrupp Aufzuge GmbH (2)
Bernhaeuser Strasse 45, PO Box 230370, 73765, Neuhausen, Germany
Tel.: (49) 711652220
Web Site: http://www.thyssenkrupp-elevator.com
Sales Range: $1-4.9 Billion
Emp.: 3,000
Elevator Mfr

RAG-Stiftung—(Continued)
N.A.I.C.S.: 331513

Subsidiary (Non-US):

ThyssenKrupp Elevadores S.A. (2)
Fonrouge 1561, C1440CYO, Buenos Aires, Argentina
Tel.: (54) 1146301600
Web Site: http://www.thyssenkrupp.com
Elevator Mfr
N.A.I.C.S.: 333921

ThyssenKrupp Elevadores S.A. (2)
Carrera 85K 46 A 66 Torre 2 of 401, Centro Logistico San Cayetano 666 Santa Fe, Bogota, Colombia
Tel.: (57) 16700070
Web Site: http://www.thyssenkrupp.com
Sales Range: $100-124.9 Million
Emp.: 270
Elevator Mfr
N.A.I.C.S.: 333921

ThyssenKrupp Elevadores S.A. (2)
Via Porras San Francisco Local 65, Panama, Panama
Tel.: (507) 3881111
Web Site: http://www.thyssenkrupp.com
Elevator Mfr
N.A.I.C.S.: 333921

ThyssenKrupp Elevadores S.A. (2)
Alcantara 200 Piso 6, Las Condes, Santiago, Chile
Tel.: (56) 2 370 2932
Elevator Mfr
N.A.I.C.S.: 333921

ThyssenKrupp Elevadores S.A.C. (2)
Av San Borja Sur 1180 - 1182, San Borja, Lima, Peru
Tel.: (51) 16250400
Web Site: http://www.thyssenkrupp.com
Elevator Mfr
N.A.I.C.S.: 333921

ThyssenKrupp Elevadores, S.A. (2)
Sintra Business Park Building 4 2B, 2710-089, Sintra, Portugal
Tel.: (351) 21 430 81 00
Sales Range: $100-124.9 Million
Emp.: 500
Elevator & Escalator Installation Services
N.A.I.C.S.: 238290
Ricardo Malheiro *(CEO)*

ThyssenKrupp Elevadores, S.A. (2)
4th avenue 17-09 - zone 14, Guatemala, Guatemala
Tel.: (502) 2 368 2020
Web Site: http://www.thyssenkrupp.com
Sales Range: $25-49.9 Million
Emp.: 40
Elevator Mfr
N.A.I.C.S.: 333921

ThyssenKrupp Elevadores, S.A. (2)
Rua Santa Maria 1000, 92500-000, Guaiba, Portoalegre, Brazil
Tel.: (55) 51 2129 7241
Elevator Mfr
N.A.I.C.S.: 333921

ThyssenKrupp Elevadores, S.A. de C.V. (2)
General Mendez 19 Col Daniel Garza Extension, 11840, Mexico, Mexico
Tel.: (52) 55 5344 4571
Web Site: http://www.thyssenkrupp.com
Sales Range: $25-49.9 Million
Emp.: 100
Elevator Mfr
N.A.I.C.S.: 333921

ThyssenKrupp Elevadores, S.L. (2)
Calle Cifuentes s / n, 28021, Madrid, Spain
Tel.: (34) 901020909
Web Site: http://www.thyssenkrupp-elevator.com
Installation, Modernization & Maintenance of Elevators, Escalators, Moving Walks, Platform & Scenic Equipment
N.A.I.C.S.: 333921

ThyssenKrupp Elevadores, S.R.L. (2)
Democracia N 1893, 11800, Montevideo, Uruguay
Tel.: (598) 51 48 07 206
Elevator Mfr
N.A.I.C.S.: 333921

ThyssenKrupp Elevator & Escalator (Shanghai) Co.Ltd. (2)
Room 2603 Wisdom Plaza 518 Wuning South Road, Shanghai, 200042, China
Tel.: (86) 21 5298 8958
Web Site: http://www.thyssenkrupp-elevator.com.cn
Elevator Mfr
N.A.I.C.S.: 333921

ThyssenKrupp Elevator (BD) Pvt. Ltd. (2)
AncAnchor Tower 7th Floor 108 Bir Uttam C R Dutta Road, 1205, Dhaka, Bangladesh
Tel.: (880) 2448620013
Web Site: http://www.thyssenkrupp-elevator.com.bd
Sales Range: $25-49.9 Million
Emp.: 70
Elevator Mfr
N.A.I.C.S.: 333921

ThyssenKrupp Elevator (HK) Ltd. (2)
31st Floor Enterprise Plaza 3 39 Wang Chiu Road, Kowloon Bay, Kowloon, China (Hong Kong)
Tel.: (852) 2766 0218
Web Site: http://www.thyssenkrupp-elevator.com.hk
Emp.: 250
Elevator Mfr
N.A.I.C.S.: 333921

ThyssenKrupp Elevator (India) Private Limited (2)
A-24 Vardhan House Street no 3 MIDC, Andheri East, Mumbai, 400 093, Maharashtra, India
Tel.: (91) 2266902300
Web Site: http://www.thyssenkrupp-elevator.com
Sales Range: $100-124.9 Million
Emp.: 500
Elevator Mfr
N.A.I.C.S.: 333921

ThyssenKrupp Elevator (Korea) Ltd. (2)
201 Mokdongseo-ro, Yangcheon-gu, Seoul, 158-719, Korea (South)
Tel.: (82) 2 2610 7777
Web Site: http://www.thyssenkrupp-elevator.co.kr
Elevator Mfr
N.A.I.C.S.: 333921

Plant (Domestic):

ThyssenKrupp Elevator (Korea) Ltd. - Cheonan Plant (3)
115-24 Sindu-ri Ipjang-myeon, Seobuk-gu, Cheonan, 330-826, Chungcheongnam-do, Korea (South)
Tel.: (82) 41 589 4000
Web Site: http://www.thyssenkrupp-elevator.co.kr
Emp.: 1,000
Elevator Mfr
N.A.I.C.S.: 333921

Subsidiary (Non-US):

ThyssenKrupp Elevator (Singapore) Pte.Ltd. (2)
3 International Business Park 06-01 Nordic European Centre, Singapore, 609927, Singapore
Tel.: (65) 68901640
Web Site: http://www.thyssenkrupp-elevator.com.sg
Emp.: 70
Elevator & Escalator Installation Services
N.A.I.C.S.: 238290

ThyssenKrupp Elevator A/S (2)
Erhvervsvej 4, 2600, Glostrup, Denmark
Tel.: (45) 70130808
Web Site: http://www.thyssenkrupp-elevator.dk
Sales Range: $25-49.9 Million
Emp.: 231
Elevator Mfr
N.A.I.C.S.: 333921

ThyssenKrupp Elevator A/S (2)
Brobekkveien 38, PO Box 6877, Rodelokka, 504, Oslo, Norway
Tel.: (47) 23173700
Sales Range: $25-49.9 Million
Emp.: 30
Elevator Mfr
N.A.I.C.S.: 333921

ThyssenKrupp Elevator Almoayyed W.L.L. (2)
Suite 2703 Almoayyed Tower Building 2504 Road 2832, PO Box 60059, Al Seef District, 428, Manama, Bahrain
Tel.: (973) 17311515
Web Site: http://www.thyssenkrupp-elevator-seame.com
Elevator Installation & Maintenance Services
N.A.I.C.S.: 811310

Subsidiary (US):

ThyssenKrupp Elevator Americas Corp. (2)
2500 Northwinds Pkwy, Alpharetta, GA 30004
Tel.: (678) 319-3245
Web Site: http://www.thyssenkruppelevator.com
Elevator & Lift Product Mfr & Maintenance
N.A.I.C.S.: 333921

Subsidiary (Domestic):

Computerized Elevator Control Corp. (3)
24 Empire Blvd, Moonachie, NJ 07074-1303
Tel.: (201) 508-2300
Web Site: http://www.swiftcec.com
Sales Range: $25-49.9 Million
Emp.: 85
Elevators & Equipment Mfr
N.A.I.C.S.: 333921

National Wheel-O-Vator Co. Inc. (3)
509 W Font St, Roanoke, IL 61561
Tel.: (309) 923-7803
Web Site: http://www.wheelovator.com
Sales Range: $25-49.9 Million
Emp.: 150
Wheelchair Lift & Home Elevator Mfr & Distr
N.A.I.C.S.: 333921

Plant (Domestic):

ThyssenKrupp Elevator (3)
1650 Shelby Oaks Dr N Ste 6, Memphis, TN 38134
Tel.: (901) 377-1993
Web Site: http://www.thyssenkruppelevator.com
Sales Range: $25-49.9 Million
Emp.: 100
Passenger & Freight Elevators & Stage Lifts Mfr
N.A.I.C.S.: 333921

ThyssenKrupp Elevator (3)
700 Hicksville Rd, Bethpage, NY 11714
Tel.: (631) 491-3111
Web Site: http://www.thyssenkruppelevator.com
Sales Range: $50-74.9 Million
Emp.: 215
Elevator Installation & Conversion
N.A.I.C.S.: 238290

Subsidiary (Domestic):

ThyssenKrupp Elevator Capital Corp. (3)
3965 Mendenhall Rd Ste 10, Memphis, TN 38115
Tel.: (901) 365-5100
Web Site: http://www.thyssenkrupp.com
Elevator Mfr
N.A.I.C.S.: 333921

ThyssenKrupp Elevator Corp. (3)
15141 E Whittier Blvd Ste 505, Whittier, CA 90603
Tel.: (901) 365-5600
Web Site: http://www.thyssenkrupp.com
Elevator Mfr
N.A.I.C.S.: 333921

ThyssenKrupp Elevator Inc. (3)
1650 Shelby Oaks Dr Ste 6, Memphis, TN 38134
Tel.: (901) 377-1993
Web Site: http://www.thyssenkrupp.com
Elevator Mfr
N.A.I.C.S.: 333921

ThyssenKrupp Elevator Manufacturing Inc. (3)
9280 Crestwyn Hills Dr, Collierville, TN 38125
Tel.: (901) 261-1800
Elevator Mfr
N.A.I.C.S.: 333921

Subsidiary (Non-US):

ThyssenKrupp Elevator Asia Pacific Ltd. (2)
7/F Sun Hung Kai Center 30 Habour Road, Wanchai, China (Hong Kong)
Tel.: (852) 3511 0688
Web Site: http://www.thyssenkrupp-elevator-ap.com
Sales Range: $25-49.9 Million
Emp.: 40
Elevator Installation & Maintenance Services
N.A.I.C.S.: 811310

ThyssenKrupp Elevator B.V. (2)
Fascinatio Boulevard 806-808, 2909 VA, Capelle aan den IJssel, Netherlands
Tel.: (31) 88 4479 200
Web Site: http://www.thyssenkruppliften.nl
Sales Range: $25-49.9 Million
Emp.: 60
Elevator Installation Services
N.A.I.C.S.: 238290

ThyssenKrupp Elevator Canada Ltd. (2)
2075 Kennedy Rd Suite 600, Scarborough, M1T 3V3, ON, Canada
Tel.: (416) 291-2000
Sales Range: $25-49.9 Million
Emp.: 1,800
Elevator & Lift Mfr & Distr
N.A.I.C.S.: 333921

ThyssenKrupp Elevator Holding France S.A.S. (2)
8 Rue Parmentier, 92816, Puteaux, France
Tel.: (33) 1 573265 58
Web Site: http://www.thyssenkrupp.com
Elevator Installation & Maintenance Services
N.A.I.C.S.: 811310

ThyssenKrupp Elevator Innovation Center, S.A. (2)
La Laboral Ciudad de la Cultura, 33203, Gijon, Asturias, Spain
Tel.: (34) 98 519 67 92
Elevator Mfr
N.A.I.C.S.: 333921

ThyssenKrupp Elevator Ireland, Ltd. (2)
Unit 11 Seatown Business Campus Seatown Road, Swords, Dublin, Ireland
Tel.: (353) 1 8956903
Web Site: http://www.thyssenkrupp.com
Sales Range: $25-49.9 Million
Emp.: 20
Elevator Installation Services
N.A.I.C.S.: 238290

ThyssenKrupp Elevator Italia S.p.A. (2)
Via A Volta 16, 20093, Cologno Monzese, Italy
Tel.: (39) 02 89 69 63 00
Web Site: http://www.thyssenkrupp-elevator.com
Elevator Installation Services
N.A.I.C.S.: 238290

ThyssenKrupp Elevator Malaysia Sdn. Bhd. (2)
Level 18 The Pinnacle Persiaran Lagoon Bandar Sunway, 46150, Petaling Jaya, Selangor Darul Ehsen, Malaysia
Tel.: (60) 356229988
Web Site: http://www.thyssenkrupp-elevator.com.my
Emp.: 200
Elevator Installation & Maintenance Services
N.A.I.C.S.: 811310

ThyssenKrupp Elevator Manufacturing France S.A.S. (2)

AND PRIVATE COMPANIES

Rue de Champfleur Z I Saint-Barthelemy,
BP 10746, 49007, Angers, France
Tel.: (33) 2 41 33 36 75
Web Site: http://www.thyssenkrupp-
  ascenseurs.fr
Elevator & Escalator Mfr
N.A.I.C.S.: 333921

ThyssenKrupp Elevator Manufacturing Spain S.L. (2)
C/ Federico Cantero Villamil 4 Parque
Tecnologico, 28935, Mostoles, Madrid,
Spain
Tel.: (34) 91 481 7700
Web Site: http://www.thyssenkrupp-elevator-
  manufacturing-spain.com
Elevator Mfr
N.A.I.C.S.: 333921
Elena Mozo (Mgr-Comm)

ThyssenKrupp Elevator Queensland Pty. Ltd. (2)
303 Cleveland Street, PO Box 16, Surry
Hills, 2010, NSW, Australia
Tel.: (61) 2 8303 9000
Web Site: http://www.thyssenkrupp.com
Elevator Installation Services
N.A.I.C.S.: 238290

ThyssenKrupp Elevator SRL (2)
Preciziei no 11 floor 3 sector 6, 6th District,
Bucharest, 62202, Romania
Tel.: (40) 21 3180879
Web Site: http://www.thyssenkrupp-elevator-
  romania.com
Sales Range: $25-49.9 Million
Emp.: 32
Elevator Installation Services
N.A.I.C.S.: 238290

ThyssenKrupp Elevator Saudi Co. Ltd. (2)
Salah Eddin Al-Ayoubi Street, PO Box
9812, Jarir District Al Bawani Tower 6th
Floor, 11423, Riyadh, Saudi Arabia
Tel.: (966) 114868900
Web Site: http://www.thyssenkrupp.com
Elevator Installation & Maintenance Services
N.A.I.C.S.: 811310

ThyssenKrupp Elevator Southern Europe, Africa & Middle East, S.L.U. (2)
Paseo de la Castellana 259C Floor 23, Madrid, 28046, Spain
Tel.: (34) 912028000
Web Site: http://www.thyssenkrupp-elevator-
  seame.com
Elevator Mfr
N.A.I.C.S.: 333921

ThyssenKrupp Elevator Sp. z o.o. (2)
Aleje Jerozolimskie 179, 02-222, Warsaw,
Poland
Tel.: (48) 22 530 99 00
Web Site:
  http://www.thyssenkruppelevator.pl
Emp.: 50
Elevator Installation & Maintenance Services
N.A.I.C.S.: 811310

ThyssenKrupp Elevator Sverige AB (2)
Storsatragrand 12, 127 39, Skarholmen,
Sweden
Tel.: (46) 8 449 2250
Web Site: http://www.thyssenkrupp.com
Sales Range: $25-49.9 Million
Emp.: 100
Elevator Installation Services
N.A.I.C.S.: 238290

ThyssenKrupp Elevator UK Ltd. (2)
4 Bull Close Road, Nottingham, NG7 2UL,
United Kingdom
Tel.: (44) 115 986 8213
Web Site: http://www.thyssenkrupp-
  elevator.com
Elevator Installation Services
N.A.I.C.S.: 238290

ThyssenKrupp Elevator Vietnam Co., Ltd. (2)
198 Truong Chinh, Khuong Thuong Ward
Dong Da District, 10200, Hanoi, Vietnam
Tel.: (84) 437282116

Web Site: http://www.thyssenkrupp.com.vn
Elevator Installation Services
N.A.I.C.S.: 238290

ThyssenKrupp Elevatori d.o.o. (2)
Bulevar Mihaila Pupina 10z/1, Belgrade,
11000, Serbia
Tel.: (381) 11 21 29 612
Web Site: http://www.thyssenkrupp-
  elevator.rs
Sales Range: $25-49.9 Million
Emp.: 20
Elevator Installation & Maintenance Services
N.A.I.C.S.: 811310
Igor Tanaskovic (Mng Dir)

ThyssenKrupp Elevators (Shanghai) Co., Ltd. (2)
No 2 Xunye Rd Sheshan Subarea Songjiang Industrial Area, Shanghai, 201602, China
Tel.: (86) 2157076888
Web Site: http://www.thyssenkrupp-
  elevator.com.cn
Elevator Mfr
N.A.I.C.S.: 333921

ThyssenKrupp Elevators Hellas S.A. (2)
37 Sepolion Str, 104 45, Athens, Greece
Tel.: (30) 210 825 2766
Web Site: http://www.thyssenkrupp.com
Sales Range: $25-49.9 Million
Emp.: 52
Elevator Installation Services
N.A.I.C.S.: 238290

ThyssenKrupp Northern Elevator Ltd. (2)
410 Passmore Avenue Unit 1, Scarborough,
M1V 5C3, ON, Canada
Tel.: (416) 291-2000
Sales Range: $75-99.9 Million
Emp.: 300
Elevator Mfr
N.A.I.C.S.: 333921

Subsidiary (Domestic):

Thyssen Dover Elevator (Canada) Ltd. (3)
410 Passmore Ave, Scarborough, M1V
5C3, ON, Canada
Tel.: (416) 291-2000
Web Site: http://www.thyssenkrupp.com
Elevator Mfr
N.A.I.C.S.: 333921

Subsidiary (Non-US):

ThyssenKrupp Tailored Blanks (Wuhan) Ltd. (2)
Yinguang Av Guannan Industry Park,
430074, Wuhan, China
Tel.: (86) 27 8756 1616
Web Site: http://www.thyssenkrupp.com
Automotive Tailored Blank Mfr
N.A.I.C.S.: 336390

Vivawest GmbH (1)
Nordsternplatz 1, 45899, Gelsenkirchen,
Germany
Tel.: (49) 2093800
Web Site: https://www.vivawest.de
Apartment Rental Services
N.A.I.C.S.: 531110

RAGDOLL PRODUCTIONS LIMITED
9 Timothy's Bridge Road Stratford
Enterprise Park, Stratford-upon-Avon,
CV37 9NQ, United Kingdom
Tel.: (44) 1789404100 UK
Web Site: http://www.ragdoll.co.uk
Year Founded: 1984
Sales Range: $50-74.9 Million
Emp.: 10
Television Shows, Videos & Motion
Pictures Producer; Books, Audio, Music & Theatre Publisher
N.A.I.C.S.: 512110
Anne Wood (Founder & Dir-Creative)

RAGHAV PRODUCTIVITY ENHANCERS LTD.
409 Alankar Palaza, Vidhyadhar Nagar, Jaipur, 302023, Rajasthan, India
Tel.: (91) 1412235760 In
Web Site:
  https://www.rammingmass.com
Year Founded: 2009
539837—(BOM)
Rev.: $16,525,028
Assets: $19,288,928
Liabilities: $3,316,684
Net Worth: $15,972,244
Earnings: $3,023,548
Emp.: 145
Fiscal Year-end: 03/31/23
Industrial Material Mfr & Distr
N.A.I.C.S.: 327120
Rajesh Kabra (Mng Dir)

RAGHAVA ESTATES & PROPERTIES LIMITED
Near NTR Statue Kanuru Subbaiah
Bldgs Patamata, Patamata, Vijayawada, 520010, Andhra Pradesh,
India
Tel.: (91) 866 2478380
Web Site:
  http://www.raghavaestates.in
Year Founded: 1988
Sales Range: $1-9.9 Million
Real Estate Development Services
N.A.I.C.S.: 531390
L. Ravindra Rao (Mng Dir)

RAGHUNATH INTERNATIONAL LIMITED
6926 Jaipuria Mills Clock Tower
Subzi Mandi, Delhi, 110007, India
Tel.: (91) 1123852583
Web Site:
  https://www.raghunathintlimited.in
526813—(BOM)
Rev.: $160,182
Assets: $1,753,864
Liabilities: $133,541
Net Worth: $1,620,323
Earnings: ($34,171)
Emp.: 1
Fiscal Year-end: 03/31/23
Real Estate Development Services
N.A.I.C.S.: 531390
G. N. Choudhary (Chm)

RAGHUVANSH AGROFAMS LTD.
Cabin No 559 Third Floor Padam
Tower-I 14/113 Civil Lines, Kanpur,
208001, Uttar Pradesh, India
Tel.: (91) 9956122107
Web Site:
  https://www.raghuvanshagro.com
Year Founded: 1996
538921—(BOM)
Rev.: $1,854,453
Assets: $8,693,534
Liabilities: $1,131,733
Net Worth: $7,561,802
Earnings: $714,399
Emp.: 7
Fiscal Year-end: 03/31/23
Dairy Products Mfr
N.A.I.C.S.: 112120
Renu Agarwal (Exec Dir)

Subsidiaries:

Kanpur Organics Private Limited (1)
117/10 S-10 Sarvodaya Nagar, Kanpur, Uttar Pradesh, India
Tel.: (91) 9839330614
Web Site: http://www.kanpurorganics.com
Organic Fertilizer Mfr
N.A.I.C.S.: 325311

RAGHUVIR SYNTHETICS LIMITED
Block No 1035A Near Ayodhya Shilaj
township Shilaj Rancharda Road,

RAGUSA MINERALS LTD.

Shilaj, Ahmedabad, 380058, Gujarat,
India
Tel.: (91) 7922911015
Web Site: https://www.raghuvir.com
Year Founded: 1968
514316—(BOM)
Rev.: $24,529,637
Assets: $9,536,081
Liabilities: $5,746,432
Net Worth: $3,789,650
Earnings: $804,504
Emp.: 226
Fiscal Year-end: 03/31/21
Textile Products Mfr
N.A.I.C.S.: 313310
Sunil Raghuvirprasad Agarwal (Chm
  & Co-Mng Dir)

Subsidiaries:

Raghuvir Synthetics Limited - Ahmedabad Factory (1)
Nr Gujarat Bottling, Rakhial, Ahmedabad,
380 023, Gujarat, India
Tel.: (91) 79 2291 1015
Textile Products Mfr
N.A.I.C.S.: 314999

RAGNI SAS
Chemin du Vallon des Vaux - Le
Gueirard, 06801, Cagnes-sur-Mer,
Cedex, France
Tel.: (33) 493310548
Web Site: https://www.ragni.com
Year Founded: 1927
VICP—(OTC)
Lighting Equipment Design & Manufacturing
N.A.I.C.S.: 335132
Marcel Ragni (CEO)

Subsidiaries:

Hess GmbH Licht + Form (1)
Lantwatten Strasse 22, Villingen-
Schwenningen, 78050, Germany
Tel.: (49) 77219200
Web Site: http://www.hess.eu
Architectural Lighting Mfr
N.A.I.C.S.: 335132
Alexander Hartlieb (Mng Dir)

Subsidiary (US):

Hess America (2)
PO Box 28, Gaffney, SC 29342-0028
Tel.: (864) 487-3535
Web Site: http://www.hessamerica.com
Architectural Lighting Mfr
N.A.I.C.S.: 335132
Terry O'Toole (Gen Mgr)

RAGOLDS SUSSWAREN GMBH & CO.
Tullastrasse 62, Karlsruhe, 76131,
Germany
Tel.: (49) 7216269050
Web Site: http://www.ragolds-park.de
Year Founded: 1887
Sales Range: $25-49.9 Million
Emp.: 200
Candy & Cough Drops Mfr
N.A.I.C.S.: 311352
Jorg Schindler (Pres)

Subsidiaries:

Ragold, Inc. (1)
2201 Willton Dr, Wilton Manors, FL
33305 (100%)
Tel.: (954) 561-2090
Web Site: http://www.ragold.com
Sales Range: $1-9.9 Million
Emp.: 3
Distr of Sugarfree Mints & Filled Hard
Candy
N.A.I.C.S.: 424450

RAGUSA MINERALS LTD.
Level 2 22 Mount Street, Perth, 6000,
WA, Australia
Tel.: (61) 861818181 AU

RAGUSA MINERALS LTD.

Ragusa Minerals Ltd.—(Continued)
Web Site:
https://www.ragusaminerals.com.au
RAS—(ASX)
Rev.: $504,137
Assets: $1,638,721
Liabilities: $53,803
Net Worth: $1,584,918
Earnings: ($1,412,731)
Fiscal Year-end: 06/30/24
Investment Fund Management Services
N.A.I.C.S.: 523940
Jerko Zuvela (Chm)

RAHEJA DEVELOPERS PVT. LTD.
Rectangle One 406 4th Floor D 4 Behind Sheraton Hotel Saket, D-4 District Centre Saket, New Delhi, 110017, India
Tel.: (91) 1140611111
Web Site: http://www.raheja.com
Year Founded: 1989
Sales Range: $50-74.9 Million
Real Estate Developers
N.A.I.C.S.: 236117
Navin M, Raheja (Mng Dir)

RAHEJA UNIVERSAL LIMITED
Raheja Ctr-Point 294 CST Rd, Kalina Santa Cruz E, Mumbai, 400 098, India
Tel.: (91) 2266414141
Web Site:
http://www.rahejauniversal.com
Sales Range: $150-199.9 Million
Emp.: 800
Residental & Commercial Construction Services
N.A.I.C.S.: 236117
Ashish Reheja (Mng Dir)

RAHIM TEXTILE MILLS LIMITED
Tower-117 117/A Tejgaon Industrial Area, Dhaka, 1208, Bangladesh
Tel.: (880) 9612111177   BD
Web Site:
https://www.newasiabd.com
Year Founded: 1987
RAHIMTEXT—(DHA)
Rev.: $14,868,026
Assets: $19,933,986
Liabilities: $15,764,808
Net Worth: $4,169,178
Earnings: $394,330
Emp.: 707
Fiscal Year-end: 06/30/21
Fabric Finishing Services
N.A.I.C.S.: 313310

RAHIMA FOOD CORPORATION LIMITED
115/7/A Distillery Road Gandaria, Dhaka, 1204, Bangladesh
Tel.: (880) 9611611123
Web Site:
https://www.rahimafood.com
Year Founded: 1990
RAHIMAFOOD—(CHT)
Rev.: $2,001,947
Assets: $3,089,235
Liabilities: $1,207,943
Net Worth: $1,881,293
Earnings: $187,547
Emp.: 5
Fiscal Year-end: 06/30/23
Edible Oil & Vegetable Ghee Mfr
N.A.I.C.S.: 339999
Mohammad Zakir Hossain (Sec)

RAHUL MERCHANDISING LIMITED
H NO 1/61-B Vishwas Nagar Shahdara, New Delhi, 110032, India
Tel.: (91) 1126212295
Web Site:
https://www.rahulmerchandising.in
Year Founded: 1993
531887—(BOM)
Rev.: $8,465
Assets: $779
Liabilities: $23,620
Net Worth: ($22,840)
Earnings: ($1,079)
Emp.: 2
Fiscal Year-end: 03/31/23
Apparel Whslr
N.A.I.C.S.: 458110
Sunny Kumar (CFO)

RAI RADIOTELEVISIONE ITALIANA S.P.A.
Viale Mazzini 14, 00195, Rome, Italy
Tel.: (39) 0638781
Web Site: http://www.rai.it
Sales Range: $1-4.9 Billion
Emp.: 10,120
Television Broadcasting Stations Owner
N.A.I.C.S.: 516120
Paolo Garimberti (Pres)

Subsidiaries:

RAI Corporation   (1)
32 Ave of the Americas, New York, NY 10013
Tel.: (212) 468-2500
Sales Range: $25-49.9 Million
Emp.: 45
Television Production Services
N.A.I.C.S.: 512110

RAI WAY S.P.A.
Via Teulada 66, 00195, Rome, Italy
Tel.: (39) 0633175083
Web Site: https://www.raiway.it
RWAY—(ITA)
Rev.: $264,888,704
Assets: $477,664,883
Liabilities: $287,546,286
Net Worth: $190,118,597
Earnings: $79,527,250
Emp.: 560
Fiscal Year-end: 12/31/22
Television & Radio Broadcasting
N.A.I.C.S.: 516120
Aldo Mancino (CEO)

Subsidiaries:

Sud Engineering S.r.l.   (1)
Via Castriota n 108, 80058, Torre Annunziata, Na, Italy
Tel.: (39) 0818995113
Web Site: https://www.sudengineering.com
Railway Environmental Consulting Services
N.A.I.C.S.: 541620

RAIA DROGASIL S.A.
Av Corifeu de Azevedo Marques 3097, Butanta, Sao Paulo, 05339-900, SP, Brazil
Tel.: (55) 37695678
Web Site: https://rdsaude.com.br
Year Founded: 1905
RADL3—(BRAZ)
Rev.: $7,001,296,220
Assets: $4,141,043,163
Liabilities: $2,898,734,871
Net Worth: $1,242,308,291
Earnings: $224,037,712
Emp.: 17,000
Fiscal Year-end: 12/31/23
Pharmaceutical Product Whslr
N.A.I.C.S.: 424210
Flavio de Moraes Correia (Dir-Investor Relations)

Subsidiaries:

4Bio Medicamentos S.A.   (1)
Rua Pedroso Alvarenga 58 Cj 02, Itaim Bibi, Sao Paulo, Brazil
Tel.: (55) 1135792999
Web Site: https://www.4bio.com.br
Medicine Distr
N.A.I.C.S.: 423450

Drogaria Onofre Ltda.   (1)
Av Nsa Sra Assuncao 638, Butanta, Sao Paulo, 05359-001, SP, Brazil
Tel.: (55) 40072526
Web Site: http://www.onofre.com.br
Drug Stores & Online Retailer of Healthcare & Personal Care Products
N.A.I.C.S.: 424210

RAICO BAUTECHNIK GMBH
Gewerbegebiet Nord 2, Pfeffenhausen, 87772, Germany
Tel.: (49) 82659110
Web Site: http://www.raico.de
Year Founded: 1992
Rev.: $34,641,052
Emp.: 101
Window & Door Systems Mfr
N.A.I.C.S.: 332321
Rainer Vogele (Co-Founder & Mng Partner)

Subsidiaries:

RAICO East   (1)
Ul Bolschaja Spasskaja 12, 129090, Moscow, Russia
Tel.: (7) 4959951159
Window & Door Distr
N.A.I.C.S.: 423310

RAICO France S.a.r.l.   (1)
8a rue Icare, 67960, Entzheim, France
Tel.: (33) 388784894
Window & Door Distr
N.A.I.C.S.: 423310

RAICO Swiss GmbH   (1)
Delfterstrasse 10, 5000, Aarau, Switzerland
Tel.: (41) 627386600
Window & Door Distr
N.A.I.C.S.: 423310

RAICO UK   (1)
Unit 63 Gosport Business Centre Aerodrome Road, Gosport, PO13 0FQ, United Kingdom
Tel.: (44) 1329848175
Window & Door Distr
N.A.I.C.S.: 423310

RAIDEEP INDUSTRIES LIMITED
C-193 A Phase VI Focal Point, Ludhiana, 141 010, Punjab, India
Tel.: (91) 1612676893
Web Site:
https://www.raideepindustries.com
540270—(BOM)
Rev.: $2,753,391
Assets: $2,623,882
Liabilities: $1,712,792
Net Worth: $911,090
Earnings: $21,503
Emp.: 8
Fiscal Year-end: 03/31/21
Textile Product Mfr & Distr
N.A.I.C.S.: 313240
Paramjit Bhalla (Exec Dir)

RAIDEN RESOURCES LTD.
Suite 7 63 Shepperton Rd, Victoria Park, 6100, WA, Australia
Tel.: (61) 861589990   AU
Web Site:
https://www.raidenresources.com.au
RDN—(ASX)
Rev.: $240,299
Assets: $14,374,053
Liabilities: $605,643
Net Worth: $13,768,410
Earnings: ($2,445,529)
Fiscal Year-end: 06/30/24
Metal Exploration Services
N.A.I.C.S.: 213114
Dusko Ljubojevic (Mng Dir)

INTERNATIONAL PUBLIC

RAIFFEISEN BANK INTERNATIONAL AG
Am Stadtpark 9, A-1030, Vienna, Austria
Tel.: (43) 1717070   AT
Web Site:
https://www.rbinternational.com
RBI—(VIE)
Rev.: $5,694,120,640
Assets: $235,946,132,240
Liabilities: $216,939,118,240
Net Worth: $19,007,014,000
Earnings: $1,852,185,920
Emp.: 46,185
Fiscal Year-end: 12/31/21
Bank Holding Company
N.A.I.C.S.: 551111
Martin Grull (CFO & Member-Mgmt Bd)

Subsidiaries:

A-Leasing SpA   (1)
Piazza delle Istituzioni 27 H, 31100, Treviso, Italy
Tel.: (39) 04224097
Web Site: https://www.a-leasing.it
General Insurance Services
N.A.I.C.S.: 524126

A-SPV d.o.o.   (1)
Danijela Ozme, Sarajevo, Bosnia & Herzegovina
Tel.: (387) 61156733
Commercial Banking Services
N.A.I.C.S.: 522110

AKCENTA DE GmbH   (1)
Axel-Springer-Platz 3, 20355, Hamburg, Germany
Tel.: (49) 40210919991
Web Site: https://www.akcenta.de
Currency Exchange & Foreign Payment Services
N.A.I.C.S.: 523160

BRL Raiffeisen-Immobilien-Leasing Gesellschaft m.b.H.   (1)
Raiffeisenstrasse 1, Eisenstadt, 7000, Austria
Tel.: (43) 2682691
Commercial Banking Services
N.A.I.C.S.: 522110

Bondy Centrum, s.r.o.   (1)
cl Vaclava Klementa 1459, 293 01, Mlada Boleslav, Czech Republic
Tel.: (420) 32 621 0499
Web Site: https://www.bondycentrum.cz
Commercial Banking Services
N.A.I.C.S.: 522110

Centrotrade Commodities Malaysia Sdn Bhd   (1)
Unit 6 01 6th Floor Bangunan KWSP No 3 Changkat Raja Chulan, Off Jalan Raja Chulan, 50200, Kuala Lumpur, Malaysia
Tel.: (60) 20580188
Rubber Product Distr
N.A.I.C.S.: 424690

Centrotrade Singapore Pte. Ltd.   (1)
10 Anson Road 14-08A International Plaza, Singapore, 079903, Singapore
Tel.: (65) 65395133
Rubber Product Distr
N.A.I.C.S.: 424690
George Sulkowski (Mng Dir)

HERMIONE Raiffeisen-Immobilien-Leasing GmbH   (1)
Hollandstrasse 11-13, 1020, Vienna, Austria
Tel.: (43) 1716018355
Commercial Banking Services
N.A.I.C.S.: 522110

ICS Raiffeisen Leasing s.r.l.   (1)
Alexandru cel Bun 51, Chisinau, 2012, Moldova
Tel.: (373) 22279313
Web Site: http://www.raiffeisen-leasing.md
Automobile Leasing Services
N.A.I.C.S.: 532112

Kathrein Privatbank Aktiengesellschaft   (1)
Wipplingerstrasse 25, 1010, Vienna, Austria   (100%)

AND PRIVATE COMPANIES — RAIFFEISEN BANK INTERNATIONAL AG

Tel.: (43) 1534510
Web Site: https://www.kathrein.at
Sales Range: $50-74.9 Million
Investment Banking & Asset Management Services
N.A.I.C.S.: 523150
Stefan Neubauer *(Member-Mgmt Bd)*

OOO Raiffeisen Capital Asset Management Company (1)
Tel.: (7) 4957455210
Web Site: https://www.raiffeisen-capital.ru
Asset Management Services
N.A.I.C.S.: 531390

OOO Raiffeisen-Leasing (1)
Smolenskaya-Sennaya sq 28, Moscow, 119121, Russia
Tel.: (7) 4957219980
Web Site: https://raiffeisen-leasing.ru
Automobile Leasing Services
N.A.I.C.S.: 532112

Perun Capital GmbH & Co KG (1)
Krugerstrasse 13, 1015, Vienna, Austria
Tel.: (43) 15130474
Web Site: http://www.perun-capital.com
Portfolio Management Services
N.A.I.C.S.: 523940
Paul Thorsten *(CEO & Mng Dir)*

Priorbank JSC (1)
Tel.: (375) 172899090
Web Site: https://www.priorbank.by
Commercial Banking Services
N.A.I.C.S.: 522110

RB International Finance (USA) LLC (1)
1133 Ave of the Americas 16th Fl, New York, NY 10036
Tel.: (212) 845-4100
Web Site: http://www.usa.rbinternational.com
Financial Consulting Services
N.A.I.C.S.: 327910
Astrid Astrid *(VP-Commodity Trade Fin)*

RIRBRO ESTATE MANAGEMENT S.R.L. (1)
SkyTower Building 246C Calea Floreasca 1st floor, RO-District 1, Bucharest, Romania
Tel.: (40) 21317114030
Real Estate Manangement Services
N.A.I.C.S.: 531390
Ruxandra Grinzeanu *(Mng Dir)*

RL-NEDVISHIMOSTI EOOD (1)
55 Balgaria, Sofia, Bulgaria
Tel.: (359) 28099740
Commercial Banking Services
N.A.I.C.S.: 522110

RL-Nordic AB (1)
Drottninggatan 89 14th Floor, 113 60, Stockholm, Sweden
Tel.: (46) 734449550
Web Site: https://www.rl-nordic.com
Real Estate Management Services
N.A.I.C.S.: 531390

RSC Raiffeisen Service Center GmbH (1)
Mooslackengasse 25, 1190, Vienna, Austria
Tel.: (43) 1337010
Web Site: http://www.rsc.at
Emp.: 600
Logistics Consulting Servies
N.A.I.C.S.: 541614
Christian Nowotny *(CEO)*

RZB Sektorbeteiligung GmbH (1)
Invalidenstrasse 10, 1030, Vienna, Austria
Tel.: (43) 1717070
Commercial Banking Services
N.A.I.C.S.: 522110

Raiffeisen Apart GmbH (1)
Mooslackengasse 12, 1190, Vienna, Austria
Tel.: (43) 1716018241
Web Site: https://www.kelchsau-apart.at
Residential Property Services
N.A.I.C.S.: 531311

Raiffeisen Bank Aval, JSC (1)
4a Henerala Almazova Str, 01011, Kiev, Ukraine
Tel.: (380) 444908888
Web Site: https://raiffeisen.ua
Rev: $518,884,919
Assets: $4,961,360,102
Liabilities: $4,382,526,758
Net Worth: $578,833,344
Earnings: $125,812,158
Emp.: 5,433
Fiscal Year-end: 12/31/2023
Commercial Banking Services
N.A.I.C.S.: 522110
Volodymyr Lavrenchuk *(Chm-Mgmt Bd)*

Raiffeisen Bank Kosovo J.S.C (1)
Robert Doll Street No 99, 10000, Pristina, Kosovo
Tel.: (383) 38222222
Web Site: https://www.raiffeisen-kosovo.com
Rev.: $85,496,015
Assets: $1,168,841,289
Liabilities: $1,023,109,861
Net Worth: $145,731,428
Earnings: $20,909,625
Emp.: 870
Fiscal Year-end: 12/31/2019
Commericial Banking
N.A.I.C.S.: 522110
Anita Kovacic *(Member-Mgmt Bd-Risk Mgmt)*

Raiffeisen Bank Polska S.A. (1)
Ul Piekna 20, 00 549, Warsaw, Poland
Tel.: (48) 22 585 2001
Web Site: http://www.raiffeisenpolbank.com
Sales Range: $500-549.9 Million
Emp.: 59,000
Retail, Commercial & Investment Banking
N.A.I.C.S.: 522110
Herbert Stepic *(Chm-Supervisory Bd)*

Subsidiary (Domestic):

Polbank EFG (2)
ul Mokotowska 19, PL-00 560, Warsaw, Poland (70%)
Tel.: (48) 22 347 7000
Web Site: http://www.polbank.pl
Retail & Commercial Banking
N.A.I.C.S.: 522110
Kazimierz Stanczak *(Dir Gen)*

Raiffeisen Bank S.A. (1) (99.49%)
Tel.: (40) 213063007
Web Site: https://www.raiffeisen.ro
Rev.: $1,917,543,824
Assets: $10,250,954,733
Liabilities: $9,121,825,746
Net Worth: $1,129,128,987
Earnings: $195,105,115
Emp.: 4,845
Fiscal Year-end: 12/31/2019
Retail & Commercial Banking
N.A.I.C.S.: 522110

Raiffeisen Bank Sh.a. (1)
Tel.: (355) 42381381
Web Site: https://www.raiffeisen.al
Rev.: $156,654,392
Assets: $2,030,116,550
Liabilities: $1,769,323,656
Net Worth: $260,792,894
Earnings: $28,178,830
Emp.: 1,255
Fiscal Year-end: 12/31/2019
Retail & Commercial Banking
N.A.I.C.S.: 522110
Christian Canacaris *(CEO & Member-Mgmt Bd)*

Raiffeisen Bank Zrt. (1)
Tel.: (36) 14844400
Web Site: https://www.raiffeisen.hu
Sales Range: $900-999.9 Million
Retail & Commercial Banking
N.A.I.C.S.: 522110
Andreas Gschwenter *(Chm)*

Raiffeisen Bank d.d. Bosna i Hercegovina (1)
Zmaja od Bosne bb, 71000, Sarajevo, Bosnia & Herzegovina (100%)
Tel.: (387) 33755010
Web Site: https://www.raiffeisenbank.ba
Rev.: $90,402,854
Assets: $2,570,917,745
Liabilities: $2,237,525,166
Net Worth: $333,392,578
Earnings: $49,392,468
Emp.: 1,389
Fiscal Year-end: 12/31/2018
Retail & Commercial Banking
N.A.I.C.S.: 522110
Peter Jacenko *(Chm-Supervisory Bd)*

Raiffeisen Bausparkasse Gesellschaft m.b.H. (1)
Mooslackengasse 12, 1190, Vienna, Austria
Tel.: (43) 1546460
Web Site: https://www.bausparen.at
Financial Consulting Services
N.A.I.C.S.: 523940

Raiffeisen Capital a.d. Banja Luka (1)
St Vase Pelagi ca 2, 78000, Banja Luka, Bosnia & Herzegovina
Tel.: (387) 51231490
Commercial Banking Services
N.A.I.C.S.: 522110

Raiffeisen Centrobank AG (1)
Tegetthoffstrasse 1, 1010, Vienna, Austria
Tel.: (43) 1515200
Web Site: http://www.rcb.at
Rev.: $66,398,396
Assets: $4,972,441,002
Liabilities: $4,831,430,513
Net Worth: $141,010,489
Earnings: $12,960,345
Emp.: 195
Fiscal Year-end: 12/31/2019
Investment & Private Banking Services
N.A.I.C.S.: 523150
Heike Arbter *(Member-Mgmt Bd)*

Subsidiary (Non-US):

Centrotrade Chemicals AG (2)
Poststrasse 14, Zug, 63201, Switzerland
Tel.: (41) 417106644
Sales Range: $50-74.9 Million
Emp.: 5
Petrochemical Trade Whslr
N.A.I.C.S.: 425120
Stuart Goldsmith *(Mng Dir)*

Centrotrade Deutschland GmbH (2)
Koelner Strasse 10b, Eschborn, 65760, Germany
Tel.: (49) 6196775080
Web Site: http://www.centrotrade.net
Emp.: 20
Rubber & Latex Trade Whslr
N.A.I.C.S.: 425120
Gunter Muller *(Mng Dir)*

Subsidiary (US):

Centrotrade Minerals & Metals, Inc. (3)
1317 Executive Blvd Ste 120, Chesapeake, VA 23320
Tel.: (757) 518-2300
Web Site: http://www.centrotrade.net
Chemicals, Rubber & Latex Trade Whslr
N.A.I.C.S.: 425120
D. Thomas Marsh *(Pres)*

Subsidiary (Non-US):

Raiffeisen Investment Polska Sp. z o.o. (2)
ul Piekna 18, Warsaw, 549, Poland
Tel.: (48) 223756952
Sales Range: $75-99.9 Million
Emp.: 7
Investment & Corporate Banking Services
N.A.I.C.S.: 523150
Maciej Ptak *(Mng Dir)*

Raiffeisen Digital Bank AG (1)
Am Stadtpark 9, 1030, Vienna, Austria
Tel.: (43) 1717075560
Web Site: https://www.raiffeisendigital.com
Banking Services
N.A.I.C.S.: 522110

Raiffeisen Group IT GmbH (1)
Mooslackengasse 12, 1190, Vienna, Austria
Tel.: (43) 1906020
Web Site: https://www.raiffeisen-group-it.com
Information Technology Services
N.A.I.C.S.: 541511

Raiffeisen INVEST Sh.a. (1)
Tel.: (355) 694040481
Web Site: https://www.raiffeisen-invest.al
Investment Management Service
N.A.I.C.S.: 523940

Raiffeisen Informatik GmbH (1)
Lilienbrunngasse 7-9, 1020, Vienna, Austria
Tel.: (43) 1993990
Web Site: https://www.raiffeiseninformatik.at
Sales Range: $1-4.9 Billion
Information Technology Management, Consulting & Support Services; Owned 47.75% by Raiffeisenlandesbank Niederoesterreich-Wien AG & 47.65% by Raiffeisen Zentralbank Osterreich AG
N.A.I.C.S.: 541513
Hartmut Muller *(Mng Dir)*

Subsidiary (Non-US):

COMPAREX Deutschland AG (2)
Blochstrasse 1, D-04329, Leipzig, Germany
Tel.: (49) 3412568000
Web Site: http://www.comparex.de
Sales Range: $1-4.9 Billion
Emp.: 1,700
Holding Company; Information Technology Products & Services
N.A.I.C.S.: 551112
Wilfried Pruschak *(Chm-Supervisory Bd)*

Subsidiary (Non-US):

COMPAREX Austria GmbH (3)
Hietzinger Hauptstrasse 119, 1130, Vienna, Austria
Tel.: (43) 1878100
Web Site: http://www.comparex.at
Sales Range: $25-49.9 Million
Emp.: 65
Information Technology Asset Management, Software Licensing & License Consulting Services
N.A.I.C.S.: 541513
Peter Kampf *(Mng Dir)*

Subsidiary (Non-US):

COMPAREX Espana, S.A. (4)
Via de los Poblados, ES-28033, Madrid, Spain
Tel.: (34) 91 598 1406
Web Site: http://www.comparex.es
Sales Range: $50-74.9 Million
Emp.: 30
Information Technology Asset Management, Software Licensing & License Consulting Services
N.A.I.C.S.: 541513

COMPAREX Poland Sp. z o.o. (4)
Ulica Rownolegla 2, PL-02 231, Warsaw, Poland
Tel.: (48) 225781900
Web Site: http://www.comparex.pl
Sales Range: $50-74.9 Million
Emp.: 30
Information Technology Asset Management, Software Licensing & License Consulting Services
N.A.I.C.S.: 541513
Filip Krokowski *(Mng Dir)*

COMPAREX Slovakia spol. s.r.o. (4)
Dunajska 15, 811 08, Bratislava, Slovakia
Tel.: (421) 25 245 1020
Web Site: http://www.comparex.sk
Sales Range: $75-99.9 Million
Emp.: 10
Information Technology Asset Management, Software Licensing & License Consulting Services
N.A.I.C.S.: 541513

COMPAREX d.o.o. (4)
Smartinska cesta 53, SI-1000, Ljubljana, Slovenia
Tel.: (386) 59250300
Web Site: http://www.comparex.si
Sales Range: $75-99.9 Million
Emp.: 14
Information Technology Asset Management, Software Licensing & License Consulting Services
N.A.I.C.S.: 541513
Ales Leskosek *(Gen Mgr)*

Subsidiary (Non-US):

COMPAREX Danmark A/S (3)
Bregneroedbej 144, 3520, Birkerod, Denmark
Tel.: (45) 44889900
Web Site: http://www.comparex.dk
Sales Range: $25-49.9 Million
Emp.: 20
Software Licensing, License Consulting Services & Software Whslr

RAIFFEISEN BANK INTERNATIONAL AG

Raiffeisen Bank International AG—(Continued)
N.A.I.C.S.: 541690
Henrik Andersson *(Gen Mgr)*

COMPAREX Finland Oy (3)
Italahdenkatu 19 2 krs, PO Box 4, FI-00211, Helsinki, Finland
Tel.: (358) 968106900
Web Site: http://www.comparex.fi
Sales Range: $25-49.9 Million
Emp.: 5
Software Licensing, License Consulting Services & Software Whslr
N.A.I.C.S.: 541690
Bo Wallin *(Mng Dir)*

COMPAREX France S.A.S. (3)
Energy Park 6 3eme Etage 150-154 Bd de Verdun, 92413, Courbevoie, Cedex, France
Tel.: (33) 149 044 040
Web Site: http://www.pc-ware.fr
Sales Range: $25-49.9 Million
Emp.: 15
Software Licensing, License Consulting Services & Software Whslr
N.A.I.C.S.: 541690

COMPAREX Italia S.r.l. (3)
Via Galileo Ferraris 2, IT-21047, Saronno, Italy
Tel.: (39) 0296410300
Web Site: http://www.comparex.it
Sales Range: $10-24.9 Million
Emp.: 40
Software Licensing, License Consulting Services & Software Whslr
N.A.I.C.S.: 541690

COMPAREX Nederland B.V. (3)
Naritaweg 177, 1043 BW, Amsterdam, Netherlands
Tel.: (31) 207114800
Web Site: http://www.comparex.nl
Sales Range: $25-49.9 Million
Emp.: 85
Software Licensing, License Consulting Services & Software Whslr
N.A.I.C.S.: 541690
Marc Betgem *(Mng Dir & Gen Mgr-Benelux)*

Subsidiary (Non-US):

COMPAREX Belgium S.A./N.V. (4)
Buro & Design Center 1 Suite 317 Esplanade Heysel, BE-1160, Brussels, Belgium
Tel.: (32) 23731411
Web Site: http://www.comparex.be
Sales Range: $50-74.9 Million
Emp.: 40
Information Technology Asset Management, Software Licensing & License Consulting Services
N.A.I.C.S.: 541513
Marc Betgem *(Mng Dir & Gen Mgr-Benelux)*

Subsidiary (Domestic):

COMPAREX Software Belgium BVBA (5)
Bureau & Design Center Suite 315 Heyzel Esplanade, Box 3, Brussels, 1020, Belgium
Tel.: (32) 2405 8900
Web Site: http://www.comparex-group.com
Sales Range: $50-74.9 Million
Emp.: 40
Software Licensing, License Consulting Services & Software Whslr
N.A.I.C.S.: 541690
Marc Betgem *(Mng Dir & Gen Mgr-Benelux)*

Subsidiary (Non-US):

COMPAREX Software Luxemburg SARL (4)
La Cloche d'Or Centre d'Affaires NCI Batiment Laccolith, 20 rue Eugene Ruppert, L-2453, Luxembourg, Luxembourg
Tel.: (352) 26493500
Web Site: http://www.comparex.lu
Sales Range: $75-99.9 Million
Emp.: 6
Software Licensing, License Consulting Services & Software Whslr
N.A.I.C.S.: 541690
Marc Betgem *(Mng Dir & Gen Mgr-Benelux)*

Subsidiary (Non-US):

COMPAREX Norge AS (3)
Grensesvingen 9, 166, Oslo, Norway
Tel.: (47) 230 555 00
Web Site: http://www.comparex.no
Sales Range: $25-49.9 Million
Emp.: 13
Software Licensing, License Consulting Services & Software Whslr
N.A.I.C.S.: 541690
Erik Froystein *(Gen Mgr)*

Subsidiary (Domestic):

COMPAREX PC-Ware Deutschland GmbH (3)
Joseph-Meyer-Strasse 13-15, D-68167, Mannheim, Germany
Tel.: (49) 621 39 1747 11
Web Site: http://www.comparex.pc-ware.de
Sales Range: $300-349.9 Million
Emp.: 700
Information Technology Consulting Services
N.A.I.C.S.: 541690

Subsidiary (Non-US):

COMPAREX Solutions (Schweiz) AG (3)
Lerzenstrasse 21, Dietikon, 8953, Switzerland
Tel.: (41) 433223200
Web Site: http://www.comparex.ch
Sales Range: $25-49.9 Million
Emp.: 15
Software Licensing, License Consulting Services & Software Whslr
N.A.I.C.S.: 541690
Kurt Bylang *(Gen Mgr)*

COMPAREX Sweden AB (3)
Finlandsgatan 28, SE-164 26, Stockholm, Sweden
Tel.: (46) 854670500
Web Site: http://www.comparex.se
Sales Range: $25-49.9 Million
Emp.: 25
Software Licensing, License Consulting Services & Software Whslr
N.A.I.C.S.: 541690
Suss Vom Ahm *(Mgr-Sls)*

COMPAREX UK Limited (3)
The Powerhouse 87 West Street, Harrow-on-the-Hill, London, HA1 3EL, Mddx, United Kingdom
Tel.: (44) 8700500125
Web Site: http://www.comparex.co.uk
Sales Range: $10-24.9 Million
Emp.: 40
Software Licensing, License Consulting Services & Software Whslr
N.A.I.C.S.: 541690
Mike Chambers *(Gen Mgr)*

DIGI Trade, s.r.o. (3)
Evropska 2588, 160 00, Prague, Czech Republic
Tel.: (420) 222722739
Web Site: http://www.digi-trade.cz
Sales Range: $25-49.9 Million
Emp.: 120
Software Licensing, License Consulting Services & Software Whslr
N.A.I.C.S.: 541690
Peter Dupak *(Gen Mgr)*

PC-Ware (Beijing) Ltd. (3)
Unit 205 2nd Fl Raffles City Office Building Tower 1 DongZhiMen, NanDaJie Dongcheng District, Beijing, 100007, China
Tel.: (86) 1065180640
Web Site: http://www.pc-ware.com.cn
Sales Range: $10-24.9 Million
Emp.: 50
Software Licensing, License Consulting Services & Software Whslr
N.A.I.C.S.: 541690

PC-Ware Information Technologies (Pty) Ltd. (3)
Cardiff House 54 Peter Place, Peter Place Ofc Park Block C, Bryanston, 2191, South Africa
Tel.: (27) 11 540 0700
Web Site: http://www.pc-ware.co.za
Sales Range: $25-49.9 Million
Emp.: 20
Software Licensing, License Consulting Services & Software Whslr
N.A.I.C.S.: 541690

PC-Ware OOO (3)
6 Barklaya Street Building 3 Suite 505, 121087, Moscow, Russia
Tel.: (7) 495 982 3911
Web Site: http://www.pc-ware.ru
Software Licensing, License Consulting Services & Software Whslr
N.A.I.C.S.: 541690

Raiffeisen Leasing d.o.o. (1)
Dorda Stanojevica 16, Belgrade, Serbia
Tel.: (381) 11 220 7400
Web Site: https://www.raiffeisen-leasing.rs
Automobile Leasing Services
N.A.I.C.S.: 532112

Raiffeisen Leasing d.o.o. (1)
Zmaja od Bosne bb, 71000, Sarajevo, Bosnia & Herzegovina
Tel.: (387) 33254367
Web Site: http://www.rlbh.ba
Automobile Leasing Services
N.A.I.C.S.: 532112

Raiffeisen Property International GmbH (1)
Lehargasse 11, 1060, Vienna, Austria
Tel.: (43) 171313130
Web Site: https://www.rphinternational.com
Real Estate Manangement Services
N.A.I.C.S.: 531390

Raiffeisen Salzburg Invest Kapitalanlage GmbH (1)
Schwarzstrasse 13-15, 5020, Salzburg, Austria
Tel.: (43) 662888612500
Web Site: http://www.raiffeisen-salzburg-invest.de
Investment Management Service
N.A.I.C.S.: 523940

Subsidiary (Non-US):

Raiffeisenbank Austria d.d. (2)
Magazinska cesta 69, 10000, Zagreb, Croatia
Tel.: (385) 14566466
Web Site: https://www.rba.hr
Rev.: $149,230,080
Assets: $7,239,121,920
Liabilities: $6,351,056,640
Net Worth: $888,065,280
Earnings: $81,767,680
Emp.: 1,869
Fiscal Year-end: 12/31/2021
Retail & Commercial Banking
N.A.I.C.S.: 522110
Liana Keseric *(Member-Mgmt Bd)*

Raiffeisenbank a.s. (2)
Hvezdova 1716/2b, 140 78, Prague, 2, Czech Republic (51%)
Tel.: (420) 234405059
Web Site: https://www.rb.cz
Rev.: $365,348,319
Assets: $16,048,592,671
Liabilities: $14,741,800,117
Net Worth: $1,306,792,555
Earnings: $152,569,845
Emp.: 2,976
Fiscal Year-end: 12/31/2017
Retail & Commercial Banking
N.A.I.C.S.: 522110
Frantisek Jezek *(Head-Risk)*

Raiffeisen Tech GmbH (1)
Am Stadtpark 9, 1030, Vienna, Austria
Tel.: (43) 1717070
Web Site: https://www.raiffeisen-tech.com
Information Technology Services
N.A.I.C.S.: 541511

Raiffeisen banka a.d. (1)
Djordja Stanojevica 16, 11000, Belgrade, Serbia
Tel.: (381) 113202100
Web Site: https://www.raiffeisenbank.rs
Rev.: $99,113,444
Assets: $2,670,029,351
Liabilities: $2,090,424,406
Net Worth: $579,604,945
Earnings: $66,864,261
Emp.: 1,477
Fiscal Year-end: 12/31/2017
Retail, Commercial & Investment Banking
N.A.I.C.S.: 522110
Zoran Petrovic *(Pres)*

Raiffeisen stambena stedionica d.d. (1)

INTERNATIONAL PUBLIC

SR Njemacke 8, 10000, Zagreb, Croatia
Tel.: (385) 16006100
Commercial Banking Services
N.A.I.C.S.: 522110

Raiffeisen-Leasing Real Estate, s.r.o. (1)
Hvezdova 1716/2b, 140 00, Prague, Czech Republic
Tel.: (420) 221511611
Web Site: http://www.rl.cz
Financial Consulting Services
N.A.I.C.S.: 523940

S.A.I. Raiffeisen Asset Management S.A. (1)
Tel.: (40) 213061711
Web Site: https://www.raiffeisenfonduri.ro
Asset Management Services
N.A.I.C.S.: 531390
Adrian Negru *(Pres)*

SF Hotelerrichtungsgesellschaft m.b.H. (1)
Tel.: (43) 171690
Commercial Banking Services
N.A.I.C.S.: 522110

Tatra Leasing Broker, s.r.o. (1)
Hodzovo Namestie 3, 811 06, Bratislava, Slovakia
Tel.: (421) 259195919
Real Estate Lending Services
N.A.I.C.S.: 531110

Tatra banka, a.s. (1)
Hodzovo namestie 3, 811 06, Bratislava, Slovakia (65.77%)
Tel.: (421) 259191000
Web Site: https://www.tatrabanka.sk
Rev.: $352,206,111
Assets: $15,093,335,030
Liabilities: $13,798,674,553
Net Worth: $1,294,660,476
Earnings: $137,111,826
Emp.: 3,793
Fiscal Year-end: 12/31/2018
Retail, Commercial & Private Banking
N.A.I.C.S.: 522110
Michal Liday *(Chm-Mgmt Bd & CEO)*

Valida Holding AG (1)
Mooslackengasse 12, 1190, Vienna, Austria
Tel.: (43) 1316480
Web Site: https://www.valida.at
Holding Company
N.A.I.C.S.: 551112
Markus Kirchmair *(Chm-Supvr Bd)*

Subsidiary (Domestic):

Valida Plus AG (2)
Mooslackengasse 12, 1190, Vienna, Austria
Tel.: (43) 1 316480
Insurance & Employee Benefit Funds
N.A.I.C.S.: 525190

ZUNO BANK AG (1)
Muthgasse 26, 1190, Vienna, Austria
Tel.: (43) 907288801
Web Site: http://www.zuno.eu
Commercial Banking Services
N.A.I.C.S.: 522110
Oyvind Oanes *(CEO)*

RAIFFEISEN BANK WESERMARSCH-SUD EG

Weserstrasse 60, 26919, Brake, Germany
Tel.: (49) 44019882210 De
Web Site: http://www.raibawesermarschsued.de
Retail & Commercial Banking Services
N.A.I.C.S.: 522110
Gerd Borchardt *(Member-Exec Bd)*

Subsidiaries:

Raiffeisenbank-Immobilien GmbH (1)
Weserstrasse 60, 26919, Brake, Germany
Tel.: (49) 4401 9882 2143
Web Site: http://www.raibawesermarschsued.de
Real Estate Brokerage Services
N.A.I.C.S.: 531210

AND PRIVATE COMPANIES — RAIFFEISEN-HOLDING NIEDEROSTERREICH-WIEN REG. GEN.M.B.H.

RAIFFEISEN SCHWEIZ GENOSSENSCHAFT
Raiffeisenplatz, CH-9001, Saint Gallen, Switzerland
Tel.: (41) 712258888   CH
Web Site: http://www.raiffeisen.ch
Year Founded: 1902
Rev.: $3,126,553,670
Assets: $228,852,659,820
Liabilities: $212,115,421,984
Net Worth: $16,737,237,835
Earnings: $549,267,608
Emp.: 10,838
Fiscal Year-end: 12/31/18
Retail, Commercial & Investment Banking Services
N.A.I.C.S.: 522110

RAIFFEISEN TOURISTIK GROUP GMBH
Burghauser Str 4 a, 84503, Altotting, Germany
Tel.: (49) 8677 918 100   De
Tour Operator & Travel Agency
N.A.I.C.S.: 561520

Subsidiaries:

Thomas Cook GmbH   (1)
Thomas-Cook-Platz 1, 61440, Oberursel, Germany
Tel.: (49) 61716500
Web Site: http://www.thomascookag.com
Sales Range: $5-14.9 Billion
Emp.: 19,775
Holding Company; Travel Agencies, Tour Operator, Airline Operator & Other Travel Arrangement Services
N.A.I.C.S.: 551112
Ralf Teckentrup (CEO-Airlines-Germany & Member-Mgmt Bd)

Subsidiary (Domestic):

Thomas Cook Touristik GmbH   (2)
Thomas-Cook-Platz 1, 61440, Oberursel, Germany   (100%)
Tel.: (49) 6171 6500
Web Site: http://www.thomascook.de
Sales Range: $125-149.9 Million
Emp.: 987
Travel Agency
N.A.I.C.S.: 561510
Ralf Teckentrup (Member-Mgmt Bd)

Subsidiary (Non-US):

Neckermann Utazas Szolgaltato Kft.   (3)
Dayka Gabor Utca 5, Budapest, 1118, Hungary   (100%)
Tel.: (36) 13095900
Web Site: http://www.neckermann.hu
Sales Range: $25-49.9 Million
Emp.: 125
Travel Agency
N.A.I.C.S.: 561510
Veronika Bekefi (Mng Dir)

Thomas Cook Austria AG   (3)
Ungargasse 59-61, 1030, Vienna, Austria
Tel.: (43) 150202777
Web Site: http://www.neckermannreisen.at
Sales Range: $25-49.9 Million
Emp.: 80
Travel Agency
N.A.I.C.S.: 561510
Klaus Wriessnig (Mgr-Mktg & Sls)

RAIFFEISEN- UND VOLKS- BANKEN TOURISTIK GMBH
Amalienstrasse 9b-11, 80333, Munich, Germany
Tel.: (49) 89 2868 4800   De
Web Site: http://www.rv-touristik.de
Year Founded: 1981
Tour Operator & Travel Agency
N.A.I.C.S.: 561520
Bernhard Hofbauer (Mng Dir)

Subsidiaries:

Raiffeisen Reiseburo Ges.m.b.H.   (1)
Modecenterstrasse 16, 1030, Vienna, Austria   (100%)
Tel.: (43) 1 31375 0
Web Site: http://www.raiffeisen-reisen.at
Emp.: 40
Travel Agency
N.A.I.C.S.: 561510
Bernd Knoflach (Head-Org)

RAIFFEISEN-HOLDING NIEDEROSTERREICH-WIEN REG. GEN.M.B.H.
Friedrich-Wilhelm-Raiffeisen-Platz 1, 1020, Vienna, Austria
Tel.: (43) 1211360   AT
Web Site: http://www.rhnoew.at
Sales Range: $25-49.9 Billion
Emp.: 162,000
Investment Holding Company
N.A.I.C.S.: 551112
Erwin Hameseder (Chm-Mgmt Bd)

Subsidiaries:

Leipnik-Lundenburger Invest Beteiligungs AG   (1)
Borsegasse 9, Vienna, A-1010, Austria   (53.8%)
Tel.: (43) 15351124
Web Site: http://www.lli.at
Emp.: 15
Investment Holding Company
N.A.I.C.S.: 551112
Christian Teufl (Member-Mgmt Bd)

Division (Domestic):

GoodMills Group GmbH   (2)
F-W-Raiffeisen Platz 1, 1020, Vienna, Austria   (100%)
Tel.: (43) 1 535 1124 521
Web Site: http://www.goodmillsgroup.com
Sales Range: $50-74.9 Million
Emp.: 19
Holding Company; Flour & Rice Milling & Food Products Mfr
N.A.I.C.S.: 551112

Subsidiary (Domestic):

Erste Wiener Walzmuhle Vonwiller GmbH   (3)
Schmidgasse 3-7, 2320, Schwechat, Austria
Tel.: (43) 170776910
Web Site: http://www.vonwiller.at
Sales Range: $25-49.9 Million
Flour Milling & Food Products Mfr
N.A.I.C.S.: 311211
Peter Warnke (Head-Sls & Mktg)

Subsidiary (Non-US):

GoodMills Deutschland GmbH   (3)
Haulander Hauptdeich 2, 21107, Hamburg, Germany
Tel.: (49) 407510951
Web Site: http://www.goodmills.de
Holding Company; Flour & Rice Milling
N.A.I.C.S.: 551112
Thomas Galus (Accountant)

Subsidiary (Domestic):

Kampffmeyer Muhlen GmbH   (4)
Haulander Hauptdeich 2, D-21107, Hamburg, Germany   (100%)
Tel.: (49) 407510951
Web Site: http://www.kampffmeyer.de
Flour Milling & Food Products Mfr
N.A.I.C.S.: 311211

Subsidiary (Domestic):

Aurora Muhlen GmbH   (5)
Trettaustrasse 49, D-21107, Hamburg, Germany   (100%)
Tel.: (49) 407510902
Web Site: http://www.aurora-mehl.de
Flour Milling & Food Products Mfr
N.A.I.C.S.: 311211

Subsidiary (Non-US):

Aurora Polska Sp. z o.o.   (6)
ul Chopina 29, PL-99 300, Kutno, Poland   (60%)
Tel.: (48) 242538010
Web Site: http://www.aurorapolska.pl
Emp.: 27
Flour Milling
N.A.I.C.S.: 311211

Subsidiary (Domestic):

Kampffmeyer Food Innovation GmbH   (5)
Trettaustrasse 32-34, 21107, Hamburg, Germany
Tel.: (49) 40 75109 666
Web Site: http://www.kampffmeyer.de
Commercial-Use Flour & Baking Mixes Mfr & Whslr
N.A.I.C.S.: 311824
Michael Gusko (Gen Mgr)

Nordland Muhlen GmbH   (5)
Dampferweg 4, Jarmen, 17126, Germany
Tel.: (49) 3999710402
Web Site: http://www.nordland-muehle.de
Emp.: 25
Flour Milling
N.A.I.C.S.: 311211
Keeping Christoph (Mng Dir)

Rosenmuhle GmbH   (5)
Meisenstrasse 32, 84030, Ergolding, Germany
Tel.: (49) 871 7809 0
Web Site: http://www.rosenmehl.de
Flour Milling Mfr
N.A.I.C.S.: 311211
Herbert Pritscher (Mng Dir)

Subsidiary (Domestic):

Muller's Muhle GmbH   (4)
Am Stadthafen 42-50, D-45881, Gelsenkirchen, Germany   (100%)
Tel.: (49) 2094030
Web Site: http://www.muellers-muehle.de
Sales Range: $75-99.9 Million
Emp.: 140
Rice Milling & Packing
N.A.I.C.S.: 311212
Birgit Vosen (Mgr-Mktg)

Subsidiary (Non-US):

PannonMill Malomipari Zrt.   (3)
Klapka Gyorgy ut 40, HU-2901, Komarom, Hungary   (99.9%)
Tel.: (36) 34 540 850
Web Site: http://www.pannonmill.hu
Sales Range: $125-149.9 Million
Flour Milling, Food Product & Animal Feed Mfr
N.A.I.C.S.: 311211

Sofia Mel EAD   (3)
4 Pavlina Unufrieva Str, 1510, Sofia, Bulgaria   (100%)
Tel.: (359) 8132 700
Web Site: http://www.sofiamel.bg
Sales Range: $25-49.9 Million
Flour Milling
N.A.I.C.S.: 311211

Unimills a.s.   (3)
Ke Klicovu 56/1, CZ-190 00, Prague, 9, Czech Republic
Tel.: (420) 242454901
Web Site: http://www.unimills.cz
Flour Milling, Food Products & Bio-Products Mfr
N.A.I.C.S.: 311211

Division (Domestic):

cafe+co International Holding GmbH   (2)
Theodor-Sickel-Gasse 2, Vienna, 1100, Austria
Tel.: (43) 505200267
Web Site: http://www.cafeplusco.com
Sales Range: $150-199.9 Million
Holding Company; Coffee Vending Machine Operating Services
N.A.I.C.S.: 551112
Gerald Steeger (CEO)

NOM AG   (1)
Voslauer Strasse 109, 2500, Baden, Austria   (84.8%)
Tel.: (43) 225289581
Web Site: http://www.noem.at
Sales Range: $200-249.9 Million
Emp.: 600
Milk & Dairy Product Mfr
N.A.I.C.S.: 311511

Alfred Berger (Member-Mgmt Bd & Dir-Mktg & Sls)

Raiffeisenlandesbank Niederosterreich-Wien AG   (1)
Friedrich-Wilhelm-Raiffeisen-Platz 1, Vienna, 1020, Austria   (78.58%)
Tel.: (43) 1211360
Web Site: http://www.raiffeisenbank.at
Rev.: $740,095,405
Assets: $30,798,946,288
Liabilities: $28,118,795,629
Net Worth: $2,680,150,659
Earnings: $669,385,729
Emp.: 1,176
Fiscal Year-end: 12/31/2017
Retail & Commercial Banking
N.A.I.C.S.: 522110
Erwin Hameseder (Chm-Supervisory Bd)

Joint Venture (Domestic):

Raiffeisen Informatik GmbH   (2)
Lilienbrunngasse 7-9, 1020, Vienna, Austria
Tel.: (43) 1993990
Web Site: https://www.raiffeiseninformatik.at
Sales Range: $1-4.9 Billion
Information Technology Management, Consulting & Support Services; Owned 47.75% by Raiffeisenlandesbank Niederosterreich-Wien AG & 47.65% by Raiffeisen Zentralbank Osterreich AG
N.A.I.C.S.: 541513
Hartmut Muller (Mng Dir)

Subsidiary (Non-US):

COMPAREX Deutschland AG   (3)
Blochstrasse 1, D-04329, Leipzig, Germany
Tel.: (49) 3412568000
Web Site: http://www.comparex.de
Sales Range: $1-4.9 Billion
Emp.: 1,700
Holding Company; Information Technology Products & Services
N.A.I.C.S.: 551112
Wilfried Pruschak (Chm-Supervisory Bd)

Subsidiary (Non-US):

COMPAREX Austria GmbH   (4)
Hietzinger Hauptstrasse 119, 1130, Vienna, Austria
Tel.: (43) 1878100
Web Site: http://www.comparex.at
Sales Range: $25-49.9 Million
Emp.: 65
Information Technology Asset Management, Software Licensing & License Consulting Services
N.A.I.C.S.: 541513
Peter Kampf (Mng Dir)

Subsidiary (Non-US):

COMPAREX Espana, S.A.   (5)
Via de los Poblados, ES-28033, Madrid, Spain
Tel.: (34) 91 598 1406
Web Site: http://www.comparex.es
Sales Range: $50-74.9 Million
Emp.: 30
Information Technology Asset Management, Software Licensing & License Consulting Services
N.A.I.C.S.: 541513

COMPAREX Poland Sp. z o.o.   (5)
Ulica Rownolegla 2, PL-02 231, Warsaw, Poland
Tel.: (48) 225781900
Web Site: http://www.comparex.pl
Sales Range: $50-74.9 Million
Emp.: 30
Information Technology Asset Management, Software Licensing & License Consulting Services
N.A.I.C.S.: 541513
Filip Krokowski (Mng Dir)

COMPAREX Slovakia spol. s.r.o.   (5)
Dunajska 15, 811 08, Bratislava, Slovakia
Tel.: (421) 25 245 1020
Web Site: http://www.comparex.sk
Sales Range: $75-99.9 Million
Emp.: 10
Information Technology Asset Management, Software Licensing & License Consulting Services
N.A.I.C.S.: 541513

RAIFFEISEN-HOLDING NIEDEROSTERREICH-WIEN REG. GEN.M.B.H. — INTERNATIONAL PUBLIC

Raiffeisen-Holding Niederosterreich-Wien reg.
Gen.m.b.H.—(Continued)

COMPAREX d.o.o. (5)
Smartinska cesta 53, SI-1000, Ljubljana,
Slovenia
Tel.: (386) 59250300
Web Site: http://www.comparex.si
Sales Range: $75-99.9 Million
Emp.: 14
Information Technology Asset Management,
Software Licensing & License Consulting
Services
N.A.I.C.S.: 541513
Ales Leskosek (Gen Mgr)

Subsidiary (Non-US):

COMPAREX Danmark A/S (4)
Bregneroedbej 144, 3520, Birkerod, Denmark
Tel.: (45) 44889900
Web Site: http://www.comparex.dk
Sales Range: $25-49.9 Million
Emp.: 20
Software Licensing, License Consulting Services & Software Whslr
N.A.I.C.S.: 541690
Henrik Andersson (Gen Mgr)

COMPAREX Finland Oy (4)
Italahdenkatu 19 2 krs, PO Box 4, FI-00211,
Helsinki, Finland
Tel.: (358) 968106900
Web Site: http://www.comparex.fi
Sales Range: $25-49.9 Million
Emp.: 5
Software Licensing, License Consulting Services & Software Whslr
N.A.I.C.S.: 541690
Bo Wallin (Mng Dir)

COMPAREX France S.A.S. (4)
Energy Park 6 3eme Etage 150-154 Bd de
Verdun, 92413, Courbevoie, Cedex, France
Tel.: (33) 149 044 040
Web Site: http://www.pc-ware.fr
Sales Range: $25-49.9 Million
Emp.: 15
Software Licensing, License Consulting Services & Software Whslr
N.A.I.C.S.: 541690

COMPAREX Italia S.r.l. (4)
Via Galileo Ferraris 2, IT-21047, Saronno,
Italy
Tel.: (39) 0296410300
Web Site: http://www.comparex.it
Sales Range: $10-24.9 Million
Emp.: 40
Software Licensing, License Consulting Services & Software Whslr
N.A.I.C.S.: 541690

COMPAREX Nederland B.V. (4)
Naritaweg 177, 1043 BW, Amsterdam,
Netherlands
Tel.: (31) 207114800
Web Site: http://www.comparex.nl
Sales Range: $25-49.9 Million
Emp.: 85
Software Licensing, License Consulting Services & Software Whslr
N.A.I.C.S.: 541690
Marc Betgem (Mng Dir & Gen Mgr-Benelux)

Subsidiary (Non-US):

COMPAREX Belgium S.A./N.V. (5)
Buro & Design Center 1 Suite 317 Esplanade Heysel, BE-1160, Brussels, Belgium
Tel.: (32) 23731411
Web Site: http://www.comparex.be
Sales Range: $50-74.9 Million
Emp.: 40
Information Technology Asset Management,
Software Licensing & License Consulting
Services
N.A.I.C.S.: 541513
Marc Betgem (Mng Dir & Gen Mgr-Benelux)

Subsidiary (Domestic):

COMPAREX Software Belgium BVBA (6)
Bureau & Design Center Suite 315 Heyzel
Esplanade, Box 3, Brussels, 1020, Belgium
Tel.: (32) 2405 8900
Web Site: http://www.comparex-group.com
Sales Range: $50-74.9 Million
Emp.: 40
Software Licensing, License Consulting Services & Software Whslr
N.A.I.C.S.: 541690
Marc Betgem (Mng Dir & Gen Mgr-Benelux)

Subsidiary (Non-US):

COMPAREX Software Luxemburg SARL (5)
La Cloche d'Or Centre d'Affaires NCI Batiment Laccolith, 20 rue Eugene Ruppert,
L-2453, Luxembourg, Luxembourg
Tel.: (352) 26493500
Web Site: http://www.comparex.lu
Sales Range: $75-99.9 Million
Emp.: 6
Software Licensing, License Consulting Services & Software Whslr
N.A.I.C.S.: 541690
Marc Betgem (Mng Dir & Gen Mgr-Benelux)

Subsidiary (Non-US):

COMPAREX Norge AS (4)
Grensesvingen 9, 166, Oslo, Norway
Tel.: (47) 230 555 00
Web Site: http://www.comparex.no
Sales Range: $25-49.9 Million
Emp.: 13
Software Licensing, License Consulting Services & Software Whslr
N.A.I.C.S.: 541690
Erik Froystein (Gen Mgr)

Subsidiary (Domestic):

COMPAREX PC-Ware Deutschland GmbH (4)
Joseph-Meyer-Strasse 13-15, D-68167,
Mannheim, Germany
Tel.: (49) 621 39 1747 11
Web Site: http://www.comparex.pc-ware.de
Sales Range: $300-349.9 Million
Emp.: 700
Information Technology Consulting Services
N.A.I.C.S.: 541690

Subsidiary (Non-US):

COMPAREX Solutions (Schweiz) AG (4)
Lerzenstrasse 21, Dietikon, 8953, Switzerland
Tel.: (41) 433223200
Web Site: http://www.comparex.ch
Sales Range: $25-49.9 Million
Emp.: 15
Software Licensing, License Consulting Services & Software Whslr
N.A.I.C.S.: 541690
Kurt Bylang (Gen Mgr)

COMPAREX Sweden AB (4)
Finlandsgatan 28, SE-164 26, Stockholm,
Sweden
Tel.: (46) 854670500
Web Site: http://www.comparex.se
Sales Range: $25-49.9 Million
Emp.: 25
Software Licensing, License Consulting Services & Software Whslr
N.A.I.C.S.: 541690
Suss Vom Ahm (Mgr-Sls)

COMPAREX UK Limited (4)
The Powerhouse 87 West Street, Harrow-on-the-Hill, London, HA1 3EL, Mddx, United Kingdom
Tel.: (44) 8700500125
Web Site: http://www.comparex.co.uk
Sales Range: $10-24.9 Million
Emp.: 40
Software Licensing, License Consulting Services & Software Whslr
N.A.I.C.S.: 541690
Mike Chambers (Gen Mgr)

DIGI Trade, s.r.o. (4)
Evropska 2588, 160 00, Prague, Czech Republic
Tel.: (420) 222722739
Web Site: http://www.digi-trade.cz
Sales Range: $25-49.9 Million
Emp.: 120
Software Licensing, License Consulting Services & Software Whslr
N.A.I.C.S.: 541690
Peter Dupak (Gen Mgr)

PC-Ware (Beijing) Ltd. (4)
Unit 205 2nd Fl Raffles City Office Building
Tower 1 DongZhiMen, NanDaJie
Dongcheng District, Beijing, 100007, China
Tel.: (86) 1065180640
Web Site: http://www.pc-ware.com.cn
Sales Range: $10-24.9 Million
Emp.: 50
Software Licensing, License Consulting Services & Software Whslr
N.A.I.C.S.: 541690

PC-Ware Information Technologies (Pty) Ltd. (4)
Cardiff House 54 Peter Place, Peter Place
Ofc Park Block C, Bryanston, 2191, South Africa
Tel.: (11) 540 0700
Web Site: http://www.pc-ware.co.za
Sales Range: $25-49.9 Million
Emp.: 20
Software Licensing, License Consulting Services & Software Whslr
N.A.I.C.S.: 541690

PC-Ware OOO (4)
6 Barklaya Street Building 3 Suite 505,
121087, Moscow, Russia
Tel.: (7) 495 982 3911
Web Site: http://www.pc-ware.ru
Sales Range: $25-49.9 Million
Emp.: 20
Software Licensing, License Consulting Services & Software Whslr
N.A.I.C.S.: 541690

RAIFFEISEN-LANDESBANK STEIERMARK AG

Kaiserfeldgasse 5, 8010, Graz, Austria
Tel.: (43) 31680360 AT
Web Site: http://www.raiffeisen.at
Year Founded: 1927
Sales Range: $400-449.9 Million
Emp.: 896
Retail & Commercial Banking
N.A.I.C.S.: 522110
Martin Schaller (Chm-Mgmt Bd & CEO)

Subsidiaries:

DASAA 8010 (1)
Schwarzenbergplatz 3, 1010, Vienna, Austria
Tel.: (43) 1711700
Commercial Banking Services
N.A.I.C.S.: 522110

Grundstucksverwaltung Salzburg-Mitte GmbH (1)
Straubinger Str 25, 4600, Wels, Austria
Tel.: (43) 72426250
Commercial Banking Services
N.A.I.C.S.: 522110

HST Beteiligungs GmbH (1)
Heinrichsthaler Strasse 8, 59872, Meschede, Germany
Tel.: (49) 29199290
Commercial Banking Services
N.A.I.C.S.: 522110

HYPO Steiermark Leasing - Holding GmbH (1)
Joanneumring 20, 8010, Graz, Austria
Tel.: (43) 316400242070
Holding Company
N.A.I.C.S.: 551112

Hypo-Leasing Steiermark d.o.o. (1)
Garicgradska 18, 10000, Zagreb, Croatia
Tel.: (385) 13090400
Web Site: http://www.leasing.hypobank.at
Commercial Banking Services
N.A.I.C.S.: 522110

Landes-Hypothekenbank Steiermark Aktiengesellschaft (1)
Radetzkystrasse 15-17, 8010, Graz, Austria   (100%)
Tel.: (43) 3168051
Web Site: http://www.hypobank.at
Commercial Banking Services
N.A.I.C.S.: 522110

Raiffeisen Rechenzentrum Holding GmbH (1)
Raiffeisen Platz 1, 8074, Raaba, Austria
Tel.: (43) 31640028880

Web Site: http://www.rrz.co.at
Commercial Banking Services
N.A.I.C.S.: 522110

RAIFFEISEN-LANDESBANK TIROL AG

Adamgasse 1-7, 6020, Innsbruck, Austria
Tel.: (43) 512 5305 AT
Web Site: http://www.raiffeisen.at
Rev.: $155,976,943
Assets: $9,028,997,466
Liabilities: $8,523,040,289
Net Worth: $505,957,178
Earnings: $5,826,720
Emp.: 346
Fiscal Year-end: 12/31/18
Retail & Commercial Banking Services
N.A.I.C.S.: 522110
Reinhard Mayr (Deputy Chm & Member-Mgmt Bd)

Subsidiaries:

RACON West Software GmbH (1)
Adamgasse 28, 6020, Innsbruck, Austria   (76%)
Tel.: (43) 599936999
Web Site: http://www.racon.at
Banking Software Publisher & Support Services
N.A.I.C.S.: 513210

Raiffeisen Bau Tirol GmbH (1)
Innrain 9, Ursulinenpassage, A-6020, Innsbruck, Austria
Tel.: (43) 5125746560
Web Site: http://www.rbt.at
Residential & Commercial Real Estate Development, Construction, Property Management, Leasing & Sales
N.A.I.C.S.: 531390

RAIFFEISEN-WARENVERBAND TIROL REG. GENOSSENSCHAFT M.B.H.

Duilestrasse 20, A-6020, Innsbruck, Austria
Tel.: (43) 512599350 AT
Sales Range: $100-124.9 Million
Emp.: 300
Farm Supplies, Building Materials & Garden Products Whslr
N.A.I.C.S.: 493130

RAIFFEISENBANK JSC

Smolenskaya-Sennaya sq 28, 119002, Moscow, Russia
Tel.: (7) 4957219900
Web Site: http://www.raiffeisen.ru
Year Founded: 1996
Commercial Banking Services
N.A.I.C.S.: 522110
Sergey A. Monin (Chm-Mgmt Bd)

RAIFFEISENBANK REUTTE REG. GEN.M.B.H.

Untermarkt 3, Reutte, 6600, Austria
Tel.: (43) 567269000 AT
Web Site: http://www.rbr.at
Year Founded: 1898
Retail, Commercial, Private & Investment Banking Services
N.A.I.C.S.: 522110
Johannes Gomig (Member-Mgmt Bd)

Subsidiaries:

Bankhaus Bauer AG (1)
Zeppelin Carre Lautenschlagerstrasse 2,
Stuttgart, 70173, Germany
Tel.: (49) 7 11 1 82 99 0
Web Site: http://www.bankhausbauer.de
Sales Range: $50-74.9 Million
Emp.: 30
Private Banking Services
N.A.I.C.S.: 523150
Stefan Brugger (Mng Dir)

RAIFFEISENLANDESBANK

BURGENLAND UND REVISIONSVERBAND REG. GEN.M.B.H.
Raiffeisenstrasse 1, Eisenstadt, 7000, Austria
Tel.: (43) 26826910 AT
Web Site: http://www.raiffeisen-burgenland.at
Sales Range: $75-99.9 Million
Emp.: 1,431
Retail & Commercial Banking
N.A.I.C.S.: 522110
Julius Marhold *(Chm-Mgmt Bd & CEO)*

RAIFFEISENLANDESBANK KARNTEN-RECHENZENTRUM UND REVISIONSVERBAND, REG. GEN.M.B.H.
Raiffeisenplatz 1 Worthersee, 9020, Klagenfurt, Austria
Tel.: (43) 463993002020 AT
Web Site: http://www.raiffeisen.at
Sales Range: $150-199.9 Million
Emp.: 1,509
Retail & Commercial Banking
N.A.I.C.S.: 522110
Georg Messner *(Member-Exec Bd)*

RAIFFEISENLANDESBANK OBEROSTERREICH AKTIENGESELLSCHAFT
Europaplatz 1a, A 4020, Linz, Austria
Tel.: (43) 73265960 AT
Web Site: https://www.raiffeisen.at
Year Founded: 1992
Rev.: $1,291,224,531
Assets: $57,787,587,791
Liabilities: $52,304,258,531
Net Worth: $5,483,329,260
Earnings: $300,588,012
Emp.: 6,006
Fiscal Year-end: 12/31/18
Retail, Commercial & Investment Banking Services
N.A.I.C.S.: 522110
Michaela Keplinger-Mitterlehner *(Deputy Chm-Mgmt Bd, Deputy CEO & CMO)*

Subsidiaries:

A.C.G. Praha a.s. (1)
Janackovo nabrezi 139/57, 150 00, Prague, 5, Czech Republic
Tel.: (420) 724235379
Web Site: http://www.acg.cz
Corporate Investment Consulting Services
N.A.I.C.S.: 561499

BHG Beteiligungsmanagement und Holding GmbH (1)
Europaplatz 1a, A-4020, Linz, Austria
Tel.: (43) 732 6596 22451
Web Site: http://www.raiffeisen-invest.at
Privater Equity Firm
N.A.I.C.S.: 523999

Subsidiary (Domestic):

Invest Unternehmensbeteiligungs Aktiengesellschaft (2)
Europaplatz 5a, 4020, Linz, Austria (100%)
Tel.: (43) 73266208622451
Web Site: http://www.investag.at
Sales Range: $150-199.9 Million
Emp.: 8
Equity Investment & Private Equity Firm
N.A.I.C.S.: 523999
Andreas Szigmund *(CEO & Mng Dir)*

Holding (Domestic):

Lenzing Plastics GmbH & Co. KG (3)
Werkstrasse 2, 4860, Lenzing, Austria
Tel.: (43) 767233000
Web Site: http://www.lenzing-plastics.com
Sales Range: $150-199.9 Million
Specialty Films & Laminates Mfr
N.A.I.C.S.: 326130
Jurgen Miethlinger *(Mng Dir)*

GRZ IT Center Linz GmbH (1)
Goethestrasse 80, 4020, Linz, Austria (96.19%)
Tel.: (43) 73269290
Web Site: http://www.grz.at
Sales Range: $300-349.9 Million
Emp.: 600
Banking Data Hosting, Storage, Information Technology Products & Services
N.A.I.C.S.: 518210
Arthur Greiderer *(Mng Dir & Member-Mgmt Bd)*

Subsidiary (Domestic):

LOGIS IT Service GmbH (2)
Goethestrasse 80, 4021, Linz, Austria (76%)
Tel.: (43) 73269290
Web Site: http://www.grz.at
Information Technology Infrastructure Services
N.A.I.C.S.: 541519
Hermann Sikora *(Mng Dir)*

RACON Software GmbH (2)
Goethestrasse 80, 4021, Linz, Austria
Tel.: (43) 73269290
Web Site: http://www.racon.at
Sales Range: $50-74.9 Million
Emp.: 250
Banking Software Publisher & Support Services
N.A.I.C.S.: 513210
Hermann Sikora *(Chm-Mgmt Bd)*

Hypo Holding GmbH (1)
Europaplatz 1a, A-4020, Linz, Austria (70%)
Tel.: (43) 73265960
Bank Holding Company
N.A.I.C.S.: 551111

Joint Venture (Domestic):

HYPO Oberosterreich (2)
Landstrasse 38, 4010, Linz, Austria
Tel.: (43) 73276390
Web Site: http://www.hypo.at
Sales Range: $250-299.9 Million
Emp.: 459
Retail & Commercial Banking, Real Estate, Leasing & Other Financial Services
N.A.I.C.S.: 522110

Subsidiary (Domestic):

Salzburger Landes-Hypothekenbank AG (2)
Residenzplatz 7, 5020, Salzburg, Austria (50.02%)
Tel.: (43) 6628046
Web Site: http://www.hyposalzburg.at
Sales Range: $100-124.9 Million
Emp.: 410
Retail & Commercial Banking
N.A.I.C.S.: 522110
Reinhard Salhofer *(Chm-Exec Bd)*

KEPLER-FONDS Kapitalanlagegesellschaft m.b.H. (1)
Europaplatz 1a, 4020, Linz, Austria (64%)
Tel.: (43) 732659625314
Web Site: http://www.kepler.at
Rev.: $14,242,676,500
Emp.: 58
Portfolio Management Services
N.A.I.C.S.: 523940
Andreas Lassner-Klein *(Mng Dir & Member-Mgmt Bd)*

PRIVAT BANK AG der Raiffeisenlandesbank Oberosterreich (1)
Europaplatz 1a, A-4020, Linz, Austria (100%)
Tel.: (43) 73265967500
Web Site: http://www.privatbank.at
Sales Range: $100-124.9 Million
Emp.: 80
Investment Banking & Asset Management Services
N.A.I.C.S.: 523150
Jakob Auer *(Chm-Supervisory Bd)*

RVM Raiffeisen-Versicherungsmakler GmbH (1)
Europaplatz 1a, 4020, Linz, Austria (100%)
Tel.: (43) 732 6596 25651
Web Site: http://www.rvm.at
Sales Range: $50-74.9 Million
Emp.: 25
Insurance Brokerage Services
N.A.I.C.S.: 524210
Gunther Grossmann *(Mng Dir)*

Subsidiary (Non-US):

RPM Pojist'ovaci maklerstvi Spol. s.r.o. (2)
Dlouha Street 29799, CZ-110 00, Prague, 1, Czech Republic
Tel.: (420) 224 816 894
Web Site: http://www.rpmak.cz
Insurance Brokerage Services
N.A.I.C.S.: 524210
Gunther Grossmann *(Chm-Mgmt Bd)*

Raiffeisen-IMPULS-Leasing Gesellschaft m.b.H. (1)
Europaplatz 1a, 4020, Linz, Austria
Tel.: (43) 732659628500
Web Site: http://www.ril.at
Sales Range: $75-99.9 Million
Emp.: 50
Holding Company; Real Estate, Motor Vehicle & Equipment Leasing & Sales Financing Services
N.A.I.C.S.: 551112
Manfred Herbsthofer *(Member-Mgmt Bd)*

Subsidiary (Non-US):

IMPULS-Leasing-Austria s.r.o. (2)
Dlouha 29, Prague, 110 00, Czech Republic (100%)
Tel.: (420) 224819081
Web Site: http://www.ilaustria.cz
Sales Range: $75-99.9 Million
Emp.: 42
Real Estate, Motor Vehicle & Equipment Leasing & Sales Financing Services
N.A.I.C.S.: 522390
Ivan Kadecka *(Co-CEO)*

Raiffeisen-IMPULS-Leasing GmbH & Co. KG (2)
Dr-Emil-Brichta-Str 9, 94036, Passau, Germany (100%)
Tel.: (49) 851931830
Web Site: http://www.ril.de
Sales Range: $75-99.9 Million
Emp.: 18
Real Estate, Motor Vehicle & Equipment Leasing & Sales Financing Services
N.A.I.C.S.: 522390

Real-Treuhand Management GmbH (1)
Europaplatz 1a, 4020, Linz, Austria
Tel.: (43) 5065968058
Web Site: http://www.realtreuhand.at
Holding Company; Real Estate Acquisition, Development, Construction, Property Management & Brokerage Services
N.A.I.C.S.: 236220
Eduard Hrab *(Mng Dir)*

Subsidiary (Non-US):

Real-Treuhand Immobilien Bayern GmbH (2)
Brienner Strasse 23, 80333, Munich, Germany
Tel.: (49) 891433291811
Web Site: http://www.realtreuhand.at
Real Estate Acquisition, Development & Construction Services
N.A.I.C.S.: 531390

Subsidiary (Domestic):

Real-Treuhand Immobilien Vertriebs GmbH (2)
Europaplatz 1a, 4020, Linz, Austria (100%)
Tel.: (43) 5065968058
Web Site: http://www.realtreuhand.at
Sales Range: $50-74.9 Million
Emp.: 100
Real Estate Brokerage & Property Valuation Services
N.A.I.C.S.: 531210

Thomas Stollnberger *(Mng Dir & Member-Mgmt Bd)*

Reisewelt GmbH (1)
Europaplatz 1a, 4020, Linz, Austria
Tel.: (43) 73265966002
Web Site: http://www.reisewelt.at
Sales Range: $50-74.9 Million
Emp.: 150
Travel Agency & Tour Operator
N.A.I.C.S.: 561510
Felix Konig *(Mng Dir)*

TSC Telefon-Servicecenter GmbH (1)
Europaplatz 1a, A-4020, Linz, Austria (100%)
Tel.: (43) 73265968100
Web Site: http://www.tscooe.at
Sales Range: $25-49.9 Million
Emp.: 40
Telephone Answering & Customer Support Services
N.A.I.C.S.: 561421
Gabriele Oyrer *(Mng Dir)*

VIVATIS Holding AG (1)
Lindengasse 8, 4040, Linz, Austria (95%)
Tel.: (43) 732771933
Web Site: http://www.vivatis.at
Sales Range: $1-4.9 Billion
Emp.: 2,630
Investment Holding Company; Food & Beverage Mfr
N.A.I.C.S.: 551112
Gerald Hackl *(CEO & Member-Mgmt Bd)*

Subsidiary (Domestic):

CERNYs Fisch & Feinkost GmbH (2)
Hermann-Gebauer-Strasse 18, 1220, Vienna, Austria
Tel.: (43) 5997028000
Web Site: http://www.cernys.at
Fish & Seafood & Retail Market Operator
N.A.I.C.S.: 424460
Reinhard Fritz *(Mng Dir)*

Daily Service GmbH (2)
Gewerbestrasse 6, 4481, Asten, Austria (100%)
Tel.: (43) 722467391
Web Site: http://www.daily.at
Emp.: 170
Frozen Food Warehousing & Truck Transportation Services
N.A.I.C.S.: 484220
Bernhard Ebenberger *(Mng Dir)*

Gourmet Menu-Service GmbH & Co. KG (2)
Zdarskystrasse 3, 3106, Saint Polten, Austria (100%)
Tel.: (43) 508765000
Web Site: http://www.gourmet.at
Sales Range: $100-124.9 Million
Emp.: 350
Prepared Meal & Food Service Contractor Mfr
N.A.I.C.S.: 311991
Herbert Fuchs *(Mng Dir)*

LANDHOF GesmbH & Co. KG (2)
Lederergasse 59, 4020, Linz, Austria (100%)
Tel.: (43) 732798020
Web Site: http://www.landhof.at
Sales Range: $200-249.9 Million
Emp.: 560
Ham, Sausage & Other Pork Products Mfr
N.A.I.C.S.: 311612

Subsidiary (Domestic):

H. Loidl Wurstproduktions- und Vertriebsgesellschaft m.b.H. & Co. KG (3)
Mureckerstrasse 1, 8083, Saint Stefan-im-Rosental, Austria (100%)
Tel.: (43) 311689940
Web Site: http://www.h-loidl.at
Sales Range: $50-74.9 Million
Emp.: 117
Salami, Sausage & Other Processed Pork Products Mfr & Whslr
N.A.I.C.S.: 311612

Karnerta GmbH (3)

RAIFFEISENLANDESBANK OBEROSTERREICH AKTIENGESELLSCHAFT

Raiffeisenlandesbank Oberosterreich Aktiengesellschaft—(Continued)

Sudring 334, Klagenfurt, 9020, Austria
Tel.: (43) 5997021000 **(100%)**
Web Site: http://www.karnerta.at
Emp.: 250
Meat Processor Prepared & Frozen Meat Product Mfr
N.A.I.C.S.: 311612
Franz Tremschnig *(Mng Dir)*

Subsidiary (Domestic):

Fleisch- und Wurstwaren Trading GmbH **(4)**
Kirchengasse 53, 9020, Klagenfurt, Austria
Tel.: (43) 5997121113
Web Site: http://www.fw-trading.at
Poultry Wholesale Trade Broker
N.A.I.C.S.: 425120
Siegfried Brunner *(CEO)*

Subsidiary (Non-US):

FWT Hungaria Kft. **(5)**
Ugocsa Utca 12, Budapest, 1126, Hungary **(100%)**
Tel.: (36) 14893229
Web Site: http://www.fw-trading.at
Emp.: 3
Poultry
N.A.I.C.S.: 424440
Andras Penzes *(CEO)*

Subsidiary (Domestic):

Maresi Austria GmbH **(2)**
Hietzinger Hauptstrasse 119-121, 1130, Vienna, Austria
Tel.: (43) 1531890
Web Site: http://www.maresi.at
Sales Range: $125-149.9 Million
Emp.: 70
Milk & Food Products Mfr & Whslr; Food Wholesale Brokerage Services
N.A.I.C.S.: 311511

Subsidiary (Non-US):

Maresi Foodbroker Kft. **(3)**
Magyarorszag Budapest Homonna utca 2-4, Budapest, 1124, Hungary **(100%)**
Tel.: (36) 12483030
Web Site: http://www.maresi.hu
Sales Range: $50-74.9 Million
Emp.: 35
Food Wholesale Brokerage Services
N.A.I.C.S.: 425120

Maresi Foodbroker s.r.o. **(3)**
Hradesinska 1932/60, CZ-101 00, Prague, 10, Czech Republic **(100%)**
Tel.: (420) 233323734
Web Site: http://www.maresifoodbroker.com
Sales Range: $50-74.9 Million
Emp.: 22
Food Wholesale Brokerage Services
N.A.I.C.S.: 425120
Pavel Mestanek *(Mng Dir)*

Subsidiary (Domestic):

SENNA Nahrungsmittel GmbH & Co. KG **(2)**
Stockhammerngasse 19, 1140, Vienna, Austria **(100%)**
Tel.: (43) 1910420
Web Site: http://www.senna.at
Sales Range: $75-99.9 Million
Emp.: 130
Margarine, Fats & Oil Products, Dressings, Condiments, Baking Components & Frozen Pastries Mfr & Whslr
N.A.I.C.S.: 311225

Weinbergmaier GmbH **(2)**
Leopold-Werndl-Strasse 1, Wolfern, 4493, Steyr, Austria **(100%)**
Tel.: (43) 72537691
Web Site: http://www.weinbergmaier.at
Sales Range: $25-49.9 Million
Emp.: 65
Frozen Specialty Food Mfr
N.A.I.C.S.: 311412
Andreas Kirchner *(Mgr)*

activ factoring AG **(1)**
Briennerstrasse 23, 80333, Munich, Germany **(94%)**

Tel.: (49) 89548480
Web Site: http://www.af-ag.de
Sales Range: $50-74.9 Million
Emp.: 35
Corporate Factoring & Debt Financing Services
N.A.I.C.S.: 522299
Andreas Wagner *(Member-Mgmt Bd)*

RAIFFEISENLANDESBANK VORARLBERG WAREN- UND REVISIONSVERBAND REG. GEN.M.B.H.

Rheinstrasse 11, 6900, Bregenz, Austria
Tel.: (43) 55744050 AT
Web Site: http://www.raiba.at
Retail & Commercial Banking
N.A.I.C.S.: 522110
Wilfried Hopfner *(CEO)*

Subsidiaries:

Raiffeisen Immobilien Gesellschaft m.b.H. **(1)**
Rheinstrasse 11 6900, 6900, Bregenz, Austria **(100%)**
Tel.: (43) 5574 405 310
Web Site: http://www.raiba.at
Emp.: 7
Real Estate Brokerage Services
N.A.I.C.S.: 531210
Josef Gasser *(Mng Dir)*

RAIFFEISENVERBAND SALZBURG REG. GEN.M.B.H.

Schwarzstrasse 13-15, 5020, Salzburg, Austria
Tel.: (43) 6628886 AT
Web Site: http://www.rvs.at
Sales Range: $800-899.9 Million
Emp.: 1,692
Retail, Commercial & Investment Banking, Real Estate, Insurance & Leasing Services
N.A.I.C.S.: 522110
Gunter Reibersdorfer *(CEO)*

Subsidiaries:

Fremdenverkehrs GmbH **(1)**
Steinergasse 3-5, 5700, Zell am See, Austria
Tel.: (43) 65427850
Web Site: http://www.freizeitzentrum.at
Recreational Services
N.A.I.C.S.: 713990

Value Holdings Vermogensmanagement GmbH **(1)**
Landsbergerstr 478, 81241, Munich, Germany
Tel.: (49) 8954801970
Web Site: http://www.vhv-gmbh.de
Asset Management Services
N.A.I.C.S.: 531390

RAIGAM MARKETING SERVICES (PVT) LTD.

No 277 Koswatta, Kiriwattuduwa, 94, Sri Lanka
Tel.: (94) 115059261
Web Site: http://www.raigam.lk
Year Founded: 1996
Sales Range: $250-299.9 Million
Emp.: 1,400
Holding Company; Bakery & Other Food Products Mfr, Distr, Retailer, Marketer, Importer & Exporter
N.A.I.C.S.: 551112
Ravi Liyanage *(Co-Founder, Chm & CEO)*

Subsidiaries:

Dream Life Science (Pvt.) Limited **(1)**
School Junction, Millaniya, Paragastota, Sri Lanka
Tel.: (94) 34 7212777
Herbal Product Mfr
N.A.I.C.S.: 325411
Sisira Perera *(Mgr-R&D)*

Eastern Salt (Pvt.) Limited **(1)**
Trinco-Pulmudai Road, Periyakachchi, Kuchchaveli, Sri Lanka
Tel.: (94) 77 1061 528
Salt Refining Services
N.A.I.C.S.: 311942

Raigam Wayamba Salterns (Pvt.) Limited **(1)**
Kalpitiya Road, Palavi, Sri Lanka
Tel.: (94) 32 22 6 9468
Salt Refining Services
N.A.I.C.S.: 311942

Subsidiary (Domestic):

Southern Salt (Pvt.) Ltd. **(2)**
Kahanda Modera, Ranna, Sri Lanka
Tel.: (94) 47 2269469
Salt Refining Services
N.A.I.C.S.: 325180

Sorana Lanka (Pvt.) Ltd **(1)**
No 90 Station Road, Homagama, Sri Lanka
Tel.: (94) 11 2753341
Chemical Products Distr
N.A.I.C.S.: 424690

Venus Consolidated (Pvt.) Ltd. **(1)**
No 158 Dam Street, Colombo, Sri Lanka
Tel.: (94) 11 5843992
Food Products Distr
N.A.I.C.S.: 424490

RAIL VIKAS NIGAM LTD.

First Floor August Kranti Bhawan Bhikaji Cama Place, R K Puram, New Delhi, 110066, India
Tel.: (91) 1126738299
Web Site: https://rvnl.org
Year Founded: 2003
RVNL—(NSE)
Rev.: $2,144,835,420
Assets: $1,931,735,715
Liabilities: $1,171,855,230
Net Worth: $759,880,485
Earnings: $125,908,965
Emp.: 568
Fiscal Year-end: 03/31/22
Rail Construction Services
N.A.I.C.S.: 488210
Pradeep Gaur *(Chm & Mng Dir)*

Subsidiaries:

High Speed Rail Corporation of India Ltd. **(1)**
2nd Floor Asia Bhawan Road No 205 Sec 09, Dwarka, New Delhi, 110077, India
Tel.: (91) 1128070000
Web Site: http://www.nhsrcl.in
Railway Services
N.A.I.C.S.: 488210
Vinod Kumar Yadav *(Chm)*

RAIL VISION LTD.

15 Ha'Tidhar st, POB 2155, Ra'anana, 4366517, Israel
Tel.: (972) 99577706 Il
Web Site: https://railvision.io
Year Founded: 2016
RVSN—(NASDAQ)
Rev.: $142,000
Assets: $5,921,000
Liabilities: $3,134,000
Net Worth: $2,787,000
Earnings: ($11,148,000)
Emp.: 49
Fiscal Year-end: 12/31/23
Sensor Device Mfr
N.A.I.C.S.: 334519
Elen Katz *(Co-Founder)*

RAILCARE GROUP AB

Nasuddsvagen 10, PO Box 34, 932 21, Stockholm, Sweden
Tel.: (46) 910438800
Web Site: https://www.railcare.se
RAIL—(OMX)
Rev.: $47,980,087
Assets: $55,529,611
Liabilities: $32,667,210
Net Worth: $22,862,401

Earnings: $3,445,166
Emp.: 157
Fiscal Year-end: 12/31/22
Railway Freight Transportation Services
N.A.I.C.S.: 482111

RAILSBANK TECHNOLOGY LIMITED

1 Snowden Street, London, United Kingdom
Web Site: http://www.railsbank.com
Financial Services
N.A.I.C.S.: 523999
Nigel Verdon *(CEO)*

Subsidiaries:

Wirecard Card Solutions Ltd. **(1)**
Grainger Chambers 3-5 Hood Street, Newcastle upon Tyne, NE1 6JQ, United Kingdom
Tel.: (44) 1912275450
Web Site: http://www.wirecard-cardsolutions.co.uk
Online Payment & Processing Services
N.A.I.C.S.: 522320
Emma Ord *(Mgr-Customer Svcs)*

RAILTEL CORPORATION OF INDIA LIMITED

Plate-A 6th Floor Office Block Tower-2 East Kidwai Nagar, New Delhi, 110023, India
Tel.: (91) 1122900600
Web Site: https://www.railtel.in
Year Founded: 2000
543265—(BOM)
Rev.: $240,057,551
Assets: $400,352,497
Liabilities: $202,656,915
Net Worth: $197,695,582
Earnings: $22,668,905
Emp.: 474
Fiscal Year-end: 03/31/23
Telecommunication Servicesb
N.A.I.C.S.: 517111
Puneet Chawla *(Chm & Mng Dir)*

Subsidiaries:

RailTel Enterprises Limited **(1)**
Plate - A 6th Floor Office Block-2 East Kidwai Nagar, New Delhi, 110023, India
Tel.: (91) 1122900600
Web Site: https://www.relindia.in
Administration Network Services
N.A.I.C.S.: 518210
Puneet Chawla *(Chm)*

RAILY AESTHETIC MEDICINE INTERNATIONAL HOLDINGS LIMITED

3-5/F Minhang Tower No 290 North Zhongshan Road, Xiacheng, Hangzhou, China
Tel.: (86) 88826555 Ky
Web Site: http://www.ruilizx.com
Year Founded: 2008
2135—(HKG)
Holding Company
N.A.I.C.S.: 523999
Haishu Fu *(Founder & Chm)*

RAIMON LAND PUBLIC COMPANY LIMITED

OCC - One City Centre Level 54 Ploenchit Road, Sathorn, Bangkok, 10330, Thailand
Tel.: (66) 20291888 TH
Web Site: https://www.raimonland.com
Year Founded: 1987
RML—(THA)
Rev.: $7,924,117
Assets: $220,619,202
Liabilities: $119,368,436
Net Worth: $101,250,765
Earnings: ($24,431,741)

Emp.: 194
Fiscal Year-end: 12/31/23
Property Development Services
N.A.I.C.S.: 531190
Pleumjit Chaiya *(Chief Project Dev Officer)*
Subsidiaries:

Asangha Realty Company Limited (1)
548 One City Centre Building 54th Floor Ploenchit Road, Lumphini Pathun Wan, Bangkok, 10330, Thailand
Tel.: (66) 20291889
Web Site: https://www.asangharealty.com
Residential Property Services
N.A.I.C.S.: 531311

Baan Ying Pte. Ltd. (1)
103 Irrawaddy Road Royal Square Novena 02-07, Singapore, 329566, Singapore
Tel.: (65) 91117852
Web Site: http://www.baanying.sg
Hotel Operator
N.A.I.C.S.: 721110
Elly Lim *(Mgr-HR)*

RAIN CITY RESOURCES, INC.
757 West Hastings Street 142, Vancouver, V6C 1A1, BC, Canada
Tel.: (778) 819-3792
Web Site:
  https://raincityresources.com
Year Founded: 2015
RAIN—(CNSX)
Assets: $81,138
Liabilities: $206,103
Net Worth: ($124,965)
Earnings: ($155,831)
Fiscal Year-end: 09/30/23
Mineral Exploration Services
N.A.I.C.S.: 213115
David Shaw *(Chm)*

RAIN FOREST INTERNATIONAL, INC.
612 Pueblo Nuevo, Chincha Alta, Ica, Peru
Tel.: (51) 8334777333   DE
Year Founded: 1987
RFII—(OTCIQ)
Sales Range: Less than $1 Million
Financial Investment Services
N.A.I.C.S.: 523999

RAIN INDUSTRIES LIMITED
Rain Center 34 Srinagar Colony, Hyderabad, 500073, India
Tel.: (91) 4040401234
Web Site: https://www.rain-industries.com
500339—(BOM)
Rev.: $1,490,578,635
Assets: $2,495,378,477
Liabilities: $1,716,646,250
Net Worth: $778,732,227
Earnings: $80,293,532
Emp.: 143
Fiscal Year-end: 12/31/20
Cement, Calcined Petroleum Coke, Coal Tar Pitch & Specialty Chemicals Mfr
N.A.I.C.S.: 327310
S. Venkat Ramana Reddy *(Sec)*
Subsidiaries:

RUTGERS Germany GmbH (1)
Kekulestrasse 30, 44579, Castrop-Rauxel, Germany
Tel.: (49) 23057050
Emp.: 460
Carbon & Steel Product Mfr
N.A.I.C.S.: 335991
Bram D'hondt *(Mng Dir)*

Rain CII Carbon (India) Limited (1)
Rain Center 34 Srinagar Colony Road, Hyderabad, 500073, Telangana, India
Tel.: (91) 404 040 1234
Web Site: https://www.raincarbon.com
Petroleum Coke Mfr
N.A.I.C.S.: 324199

Plant (Domestic):

Rain CII Carbon (India) Limited - Visakhapatnam (2)
Scindia Road, Naval Base Post, Visakhapatnam, 530014, Andhra Pradesh, India
Tel.: (91) 891 282 2833
Web Site: https://www.raincarbon.com
Sales Range: $100-124.9 Million
Emp.: 300
Petroleum Coke Mfr
N.A.I.C.S.: 324199

Subsidiary (US):

Rain CII Carbon LLC (2)
1330 Greengate Dr Ste 300, Covington, LA 70433
Tel.: (985) 635-3400
Web Site: https://www.raincarbon.com
Petroleum Coke Mfr
N.A.I.C.S.: 324199
Gerard Sweeney *(Pres & CEO)*

Plant (Domestic):

Rain CII Carbon LLC - Chalmette (3)
700 Coke Plant Rd, Chalmette, LA 70043
Tel.: (504) 278-1705
Web Site: http://www.raincii.com
Sales Range: $25-49.9 Million
Emp.: 35
Coke Mfr for Aluminum & Petroleum Products
N.A.I.C.S.: 324199

Rain CII Carbon LLC - Gramercy (3)
1140 Jefferson Hwy, Gramercy, LA 70052
Tel.: (225) 869-8010
Web Site: https://www.raincarbon.com
Sales Range: $25-49.9 Million
Emp.: 28
Petroleum Coke Mfr
N.A.I.C.S.: 324199

Rain CII Carbon LLC - Lake Charles (3)
1920 Pak Tank Rd, Sulphur, LA 70665
Tel.: (337) 558-5944
Web Site: https://www.raincarbon.com
Sales Range: $25-49.9 Million
Emp.: 46
Petroleum Coke Mfr
N.A.I.C.S.: 324199

Rain CII Carbon LLC - Norco (3)
801 Prospect Ave, Norco, LA 70079
Tel.: (985) 764-3994
Web Site: https://www.raincarbon.com
Sales Range: $25-49.9 Million
Emp.: 21
Petroleum Coke Mfr
N.A.I.C.S.: 324199

Plant (Non-US):

Rain CII Carbon LLC - Purvis (3)
Tel.: (601) 794-2753
Web Site: https://www.raincarbon.com
Sales Range: $25-49.9 Million
Emp.: 8
Petroleum Coke Mfr
N.A.I.C.S.: 324199

Plant (Domestic):

Rain CII Carbon LLC - Robinson (3)
12187 E 950th Ave, Robinson, IL 62454
Tel.: (618) 544-2193
Web Site: http://www.raincarbon.com
Sales Range: $25-49.9 Million
Emp.: 28
Calcined Coke Products Mfr
N.A.I.C.S.: 324199

Subsidiary (Non-US):

Ruetgers N.V. (3)
Vredekaai 18, Zelzate, 9060, Belgium
Tel.: (32) 9 348 2191
Web Site: http://www.ruetgers-group.com
Sales Range: $1-4.9 Billion
Emp.: 180
Holding Company
N.A.I.C.S.: 551112

Subsidiary (Non-US):

Ruetgers Holding Germany GmbH (4)
Varziner Strasse 49, D-47138, Duisburg, Germany
Tel.: (49) 203 4296 02
Web Site: http://www.ruetgers-group.com
Sales Range: $1-4.9 Billion
Holding Company; Tar Chemicals Mfr & Raw Materials Supplier to Aluminum & Steel Industries
N.A.I.C.S.: 551112

Subsidiary (Non-US):

Handy Chemicals Ltd. (5)
120 Boulevard de l'Industrie, Candiac, J5R 1J2, QC, Canada
Tel.: (450) 659-9693
Web Site: http://www.handy-chemicals.com
Sales Range: $125-149.9 Million
Emp.: 125
Chemicals Mfr
N.A.I.C.S.: 325998

Subsidiary (Domestic):

RUTGERS ChemTrade GmbH (5)
Varziner Strasse 49, D 47138, Duisburg, Germany
Tel.: (49) 203 4296 02
Web Site: http://www.ruetgers-group.com
Aromatic Hydrocarbon Resins Mfr
N.A.I.C.S.: 325998

Subsidiary (Non-US):

Ruetgers Belgium N.V. (5)
Vredekaai 18, B-9060, Zelzate, Belgium
Tel.: (32) 9 342 9542
Web Site: http://www.ruetgers-group.com
Sales Range: $125-149.9 Million
Emp.: 180
Chemicals & Chemical Preparations Mfr
N.A.I.C.S.: 325998

Ruetgers Canada Inc. (5)
725 Strathearne Avenue North, Hamilton, L8H 5L3, ON, Canada
Tel.: (905) 544-2891
Web Site: http://www.ruetgers-group.com
Sales Range: $75-99.9 Million
Emp.: 75
Mfr of Chemical Raw Materials from Coal Tar
N.A.I.C.S.: 325998

Subsidiary (Domestic):

Ruetgers Novares GmbH (5)
Varziner Strasse 49, D 47138, Duisburg, Germany   (100%)
Tel.: (49) 203 4296 02
Web Site: http://www.novares.de
Sales Range: $50-74.9 Million
Emp.: 26
Coal Tar Resins Mfr
N.A.I.C.S.: 325998

Rain Carbon (Shanghai) Trading Co. Ltd. (1)
Suite 706-Equatorial Hotel Office Block No 65 Yan An Road West, Shanghai, China
Tel.: (86) 2162493327
Carbon Product Mfr & Distr
N.A.I.C.S.: 325194

Rain Carbon B.V. (1)
Vredekaai 18, 9060, Zelzate, Belgium
Tel.: (32) 94302200
Carbon Product Mfr & Distr
N.A.I.C.S.: 324199

Rain Carbon Canada Inc. (1)
725 Strathearne Avenue North, Hamilton, ON, Canada
Tel.: (905) 544-2891
Carbon Products Mfr
N.A.I.C.S.: 335991

Rain Carbon Germany GmbH (1)
Varziner Strasse 49, 47138, Duisburg, Germany
Tel.: (49) 203429602
Carbon Product Mfr & Distr
N.A.I.C.S.: 324199

Rain Carbon Inc. (1)
Ten Signal Rd, Stamford, CT 06902
Tel.: (203) 406-0535
Web Site: https://www.raincarbon.com
Carbon & Steel Product Mfr
N.A.I.C.S.: 335991
Romeo Kreinberg *(Chm)*

Rain Global Services LLC (1)
10 Signal Rd, Stamford, CT 06902
Tel.: (203) 406-0535
Web Site:
  https://www.rainglobalservices.com
Petroleum Coke Mfr
N.A.I.C.S.: 324199

Rain Holding Limited (1)

RAINBOW CHILDREN'S MEDICARE LIMITED
Road No 2 Near Hotel Park Hyatt Banjara Hills, Eye Hospital Next to Hotel Park Hyatt, Hyderabad, 500034, Telangana, India
Tel.: (91) 4044665555
Web Site:
  https://www.rainbowhospitals.in
Year Founded: 1999
543524—(BOM)
Rev.: $135,502,868
Assets: $176,869,739
Liabilities: $94,114,566
Net Worth: $82,755,173
Earnings: $18,928,865
Emp.: 2,875
Fiscal Year-end: 03/31/22
Health Care Srvces
N.A.I.C.S.: 621610
Subsidiaries:

Rainbow Children's Hospital Private Limited (1)
3/4 Sarjapur Road-Marathahalli Road, Ambalipura Village, Bengaluru, 560103, Karnataka, India
Tel.: (91) 8062261218
Medical Healthcare Services
N.A.I.C.S.: 621112

RAINBOW DENIM LTD
51-52 Free Press House Free Press Journal Marg, Nariman Point, Mumbai, 400 021, India
Tel.: (91) 2222834182
Web Site:
  http://www.rainbowdenim.com
532441—(BOM)
Rev.: $1,564,494
Assets: $4,136,244
Liabilities: $26,201,332
Net Worth: ($22,065,088)
Earnings: ($1,018,094)
Emp.: 304
Fiscal Year-end: 03/31/21
Denim Fabric Mfr
N.A.I.C.S.: 313210
D. Ramsinghani Haresh *(Chm)*

RAINBOW DIGITAL COMMERCIAL CO., LTD.
9F-14F and 17-20F Tianhong Building No 3019 Zhongixn Road, Shenzhen Bay Section Nanshan District, Shenzhen, 518052, Guangdong, China
Tel.: (86) 75523651888
Web Site: http://www.rainbow.cn
Year Founded: 2007
002419—(SSE)
Rev.: $1,702,354,212
Assets: $4,274,327,772
Liabilities: $3,705,728,832
Net Worth: $568,598,940
Earnings: $16,860,636
Emp.: 10,600
Fiscal Year-end: 12/31/22
Department Store Owner & Operator
N.A.I.C.S.: 455110
Xiao Zhanglin *(Chm)*

RAINBOW FORD SALES INC

Rainbow Ford Sales Inc—(Continued)

4312 - 42nd Avenue, PO Box 1228,
Rocky Mountain House, T4T 1A9,
AB, Canada
Tel.: (403) 845-3673
Web Site: https://www.rainbowford.ca
Year Founded: 1981
Sales Range: $10-24.9 Million
New & Used Car Dealers
N.A.I.C.S.: 441110
Greg Gordon *(Gen Mgr)*

RAINBOW FOUNDATIONS LTD.
4 Thanikachalam Road T Nagar,
Chennai, 600 017, Tamil Nadu, India
Tel.: (91) 4424344647
Web Site:
 https://www.rainbowfoundations.in
Year Founded: 1994
531694—(BOM)
Rev.: $5,463,220
Assets: $63,619,002
Liabilities: $55,345,770
Net Worth: $8,273,232
Earnings: $161,977
Emp.: 19
Fiscal Year-end: 03/31/23
Real Estate Development Services
N.A.I.C.S.: 531390
Nitesh Jain *(CFO)*

RAINBOW HOLDCO LIMITED
EDM House Village Way, Bilston,
Wolverhampton, WV14 0UJ, W Midlands, United Kingdom
Tel.: (44) 800 731 4911   UK
Web Site: http://www.edmgroup.com
Year Founded: 1974
Sales Range: $100-124.9 Million
Holding Company; Information & Records Management Services
N.A.I.C.S.: 551112

Subsidiaries:

EDM Americas, Inc.   (1)
10 E D Preate Dr Moosic, Moosic, PA 18507
Tel.: (570) 343-2300
Web Site: http://edmgroup.com
Emp.: 1,500
Records Management Solutions, Document Conversion & Database Development Technologies; Special Warehousing & Storage
N.A.I.C.S.: 518210
Jimmy Eyerman *(Pres)*

EDM Records Management
Limited   (1)
EDM House Village Way, Bilston, Wolverhampton, WV14 0UJ, W Midlands, United Kingdom
Tel.: (44) 800 731 4911
Web Site: http://www.edmgroup.co.uk
Records Management Services
N.A.I.C.S.: 518210

xit2 Limited   (1)
EDM House Village Way, Wolverhampton, WV14 0UJ, Kent, United Kingdom
Tel.: (44) 1902 406200
Web Site: http://www.xit2.com
Online Property Data Services
N.A.I.C.S.: 519290

RAINBOW PAPERS LTD
801 Avdhesh House Sarkhej - Gandhinagar Highway, Opp Shri Govind Gurudwara Thaltej, Ahmedabad, 380054, Gujarat, India
Tel.: (91) 7971797179   In
523523—(BOM)
Sales Range: Less than $1 Million
Paper Mfr
N.A.I.C.S.: 322120
Ajay Goenka *(Chm)*

Subsidiaries:

Rainbow Papers Ltd - Coating
Division   (1)
1423 Vlg Rajpur Mehsana Hwy, Kadi Taluk, Kalol, 382715, Gujarat, India
Tel.: (91) 9879605436
Web Site: http://www.rainbowpapers.com
Sales Range: $25-49.9 Million
Emp.: 35
Coated Paper Mfr
N.A.I.C.S.: 322220

Rainbow Papers Ltd - Paper & Crepe
Units   (1)
1453 Vlg Rajpur Mehsana Hwy, Kadi Taluk, Kalol, 382715, Gujarat, India
Tel.: (91) 2764278492
Web Site: http://www.rainbowpapers.com
Sales Range: $200-249.9 Million
Paper Mfr
N.A.I.C.S.: 322299

RAINBOW RARE EARTHS LTD.
Connaught House St Julian's Avenue,
Saint Peter Port, GY1 1GZ, Guernsey, United Kingdom
Tel.: (44) 2039104550
Web Site:
 https://www.rainbowrareearths.com
Rev.: $1,541,000
Assets: $7,130,000
Liabilities: $3,759,000
Net Worth: $3,371,000
Earnings: ($12,277,000)
Emp.: 206
Fiscal Year-end: 06/30/19
Metal Exploration Services
N.A.I.C.S.: 213114
George Bennett *(CEO)*

RAINBOW ROBOTICS CO., LTD.
10-19 Expo-Ro 339Beon-Gil,
Yuseong-Gu, Daejeon, 34122, Korea (South)
Tel.: (82) 427198070
Web Site: https://www.rainbow-robotics.com
Year Founded: 2011
277810—(KRS)
Rev.: $10,443,021
Assets: $58,414,312
Liabilities: $11,238,234
Net Worth: $47,176,077
Earnings: $4,430,030
Emp.: 70
Fiscal Year-end: 12/31/22
Industrial Robots Mfr
N.A.I.C.S.: 333998
Jung-Ho Lee *(CEO)*

RAINBOW TOURISM GROUP LIMITED
1 Pennefather Avenue, Harare, Zimbabwe
Tel.: (263) 242754507
Web Site: https://www.rtgafrica.com
Year Founded: 1992
RTG—(ZIM)
Sales Range: $25-49.9 Million
Emp.: 810
Tour Operating Services
N.A.I.C.S.: 561520
Tendai Madziwanyika *(CEO)*

RAINBOW TOURS S.A.
Ul Piotrkowska 270, 90-361, Lodz, Poland
Tel.: (48) 426803860
Web Site: http://www.r.pl
Year Founded: 2007
RBW—(WAR)
Rev.: $826,165,648
Assets: $228,628,556
Liabilities: $174,500,254
Net Worth: $54,128,303
Earnings: $42,432,927
Fiscal Year-end: 12/31/23
Tour Operator
N.A.I.C.S.: 561520

Grzegorz Baszczynski *(Chm-Mgmt Bd)*

RAINER KIEL KANALSANIERUNG GMBH
Blomberger Strasse 36, 32825,
Blomberg, Germany
Tel.: (49) 523596090   De
Web Site: http://www.kanalsanierung-kiel.de
Year Founded: 1988
Sales Range: $10-24.9 Million
Emp.: 45
Sewerage Renovation Services
N.A.I.C.S.: 237110
Rainer Kiel *(Founder & Co-CEO)*

RAINMAKER WORLDWIDE, INC.
271 Brock Street, Peterborough, K9H 2P8, ON, Canada
Web Site:
 https://www.rainmakerww.com
RAKR—(OTCQB)
Rev.: $20,000
Assets: $43,038
Liabilities: $10,343,413
Net Worth: ($10,300,375)
Earnings: ($1,837,611)
Fiscal Year-end: 12/31/22
Water Purification Services
N.A.I.C.S.: 221310
Michael O'Connor *(Founder, Chm & CEO)*

RAINMED MEDICAL LTD.
Building 31 Northeast District No 99
Jinji Lake Avenue, Suzhou Industrial
Park, Suzhou, 215000, Jiangsu, China
Tel.: (86) 51262622215   Ky
Web Site: https://www.rainmed.com
Year Founded: 2014
2297—(HKG)
Rev.: $10,137,766
Assets: $79,379,154
Liabilities: $7,379,265
Net Worth: $71,999,889
Earnings: ($16,208,739)
Emp.: 406
Fiscal Year-end: 12/31/23
Medical Device Mfr
N.A.I.C.S.: 339112
Liang Zhang *(CFO)*

RAINY MOUNTAIN ROYALTY CORP.
700 - 1090 West Georgia Street,
West Vancouver, V6E 3V7, BC, Canada
Tel.: (604) 922-2030   BC
Web Site: https://www.rmroyalty.com
Year Founded: 2005
RMNXF—(OTCIQ)
Assets: $2,145,734
Liabilities: $686,442
Net Worth: $1,459,292
Earnings: ($258,075)
Fiscal Year-end: 04/30/23
Mineral Exploration Services
N.A.I.C.S.: 213114
Douglas L. Mason *(Pres & CEO)*

RAISECOM TECHNOLOGY CO., LTD.
No 11 East District No 10 Xibeiwang
East Road, Haidian District, Beijing,
100094, China
Tel.: (86) 1082884499
Web Site:
 https://www.raisecom.com.cn
Year Founded: 1999
603803—(SHG)
Rev.: $302,674,166
Assets: $487,628,603
Liabilities: $213,626,406

Net Worth: $274,002,197
Earnings: $11,241,589
Emp.: 2,000
Fiscal Year-end: 12/31/22
Network Device Mfr
N.A.I.C.S.: 334210
Ren Jianhong *(Chm)*

RAISIO PLC
Raisionkaari 55, FI-21200, Raisio, Finland
Tel.: (358) 24432111
Web Site: http://www.raisio.com
Year Founded: 1939
RAIVV—(HEL)
Rev.: $264,622,918
Assets: $345,476,810
Liabilities: $41,770,778
Net Worth: $303,706,032
Earnings: $28,556,430
Emp.: 319
Fiscal Year-end: 12/31/19
Foodstuffs, Animal Feeds, Malt & Biofuel Intermediates Mfr
N.A.I.C.S.: 311423
Holger Falck *(Deputy Chm-Supervisory Bd)*

Subsidiaries:

Big Bear Group Limited   (1)
Bridge Road, Southall, UB2 4AG, Middlesex, United Kingdom
Tel.: (44) 208 574 2388
Web Site: http://www.bigbeargroup.co.uk
Food Products Mfr
N.A.I.C.S.: 311999

Carlshamn Mejeri AB   (1)
Pyramidvagen 9B, 16956, Solna, Sweden   (100%)
Tel.: (46) 87302042
Web Site: http://www.carlshamnmejeri.se
Sales Range: $25-49.9 Million
Emp.: 11
Food Products Mfr
N.A.I.C.S.: 311423
Markku Krutsin *(Pres & CEO)*

FDS Informal Foods Limited   (1)
Unit 1a Standard Road Oakwood Business Park, Park Royal, London, NW10 6EX, United Kingdom
Tel.: (44) 20 8838 3380
Web Site: http://www.informalfoods.com
Sales Range: $25-49.9 Million
Emp.: 60
Snacks & Crisps Mfr
N.A.I.C.S.: 311919

Glisten Ltd.   (1)
6a Harewood Yard Harewood Estate, Leeds, LS17 9LF, United Kingdom
Tel.: (44) 1132181950
Web Site: http://www.glistenltd.com
Sales Range: $100-124.9 Million
Emp.: 900
Confectionery & Snack Foods Mfr
N.A.I.C.S.: 311352

Subsidiary (Domestic):

Glisten Confectionery   (2)
Hill Street, Blackburn, BB1 3HG, Lancashire, United Kingdom
Tel.: (44) 1254266300
Web Site:
 http://www.glistenconfectionery.com
Sales Range: $25-49.9 Million
Emp.: 50
Confectionery Mfr
N.A.I.C.S.: 311340

Glisten Snacks Limited   (1)
Oakwood Business Park 1A Standard Road, Willesden, London, NW10 6EX, United Kingdom
Tel.: (44) 20 8838 3380
Web Site: http://www.bigthoughts.co.uk
Fresh Juice Mfr & Distr
N.A.I.C.S.: 311411

Holgates Nutritional Foods
Limited   (1)
Pendre Industrial Estate, Tywyn, Gwynedd, LL36 9LW, United Kingdom

AND PRIVATE COMPANIES — RAIZEN S.A.

Tel.: (44) 1654711171
Snack Food Distr
N.A.I.C.S.: 424420

Honey Monster Foods Limited (1)
Bridge Road, Southall, UB2 4AG, Middlesex, United Kingdom
Tel.: (44) 208 574 2388
Web Site: http://www.honeymonster.co.uk
Sales Range: $25-49.9 Million
Emp.: 14
Grain Mill Product Mfr
N.A.I.C.S.: 311919

OOO Raisio Nutrition (1)
Zemlyanov Val 66/20 Office 5C, 109004, Moscow, Russia
Tel.: (7) 495 6265560
Web Site: http://www.raisio.ru
Sales Range: $25-49.9 Million
Emp.: 25
Food Mfr
N.A.I.C.S.: 311423

P.T. Intercipta Kimia Pratama (1)
Plz BII Twr 3 Ste 903 Jl MH Thamrin No 51, Jakarta, 10350, Indonesia (50%)
Tel.: (62) 213162621
Sales Range: $25-49.9 Million
Emp.: 100
N.A.I.C.S.: 311423
Gorgon Chan (Gen Mgr)

Proteinoil Oy - Raisio Factory (1)
Raisionkaari 55, PO Box 101, Raisio, 21201, Finland
Tel.: (358) 2 443 2111
Web Site: http://www.raisio.com
Bio Lubricant Mfr
N.A.I.C.S.: 311224

Raisio Benecol Ltd. (1)
Raisionkaari 55, PO Box 101, Raisio, 21200, Finland (100%)
Tel.: (358) 24432111
Web Site: http://www.raiosio.com
Sales Range: $200-249.9 Million
Emp.: 1,000
N.A.I.C.S.: 311423

Raisio Echeveste S.A. (1)
Avenida San Sebastian 11, E 20400, Tolosa, Spain (51%)
Tel.: (34) 943651982
Web Site: http://www.cibasc.com
Sales Range: $25-49.9 Million
Emp.: 14
N.A.I.C.S.: 311423

Raisio Eesti AS (1)
Mustamae tee 44, EE-10621, Tallinn, Estonia
Tel.: (372) 5029901
Web Site: http://www.raisio.ee
Sales Range: $50-74.9 Million
Emp.: 4
Snack Food Distr
N.A.I.C.S.: 424420

Raisio Feed Ltd. (1)
Raisionkaari 55, PO Box 101, Raisio, 21200, Finland (100%)
Tel.: (358) 24432111
Web Site: http://www.raisio.com
Sales Range: $400-449.9 Million
Emp.: 1,400
N.A.I.C.S.: 311423

Plant (Domestic):

Raisioagro Ltd - Kouvola Factory (2)
Raisiontie 8, 46400, Kaipiainen, Finland
Tel.: (358) 5 812 7121
Web Site: http://www.raisio.com
Animal Feed Mfr & Distr
N.A.I.C.S.: 311119
Perttu Eerola (Mng Dir)

Raisioagro Ltd - Raisio Factory (2)
Raisionkaari 55, PO Box 101, Raisio, 21200, Finland
Tel.: (358) 2 443 2111
Web Site: http://www.raisio.com
Sales Range: $150-199.9 Million
Emp.: 600
Animal Feed Mfr
N.A.I.C.S.: 311119

Raisioagro Ltd - Ylivieska Factory (2)
Rehutie 2, Ylivieska, 84100, Finland

Tel.: (358) 44 781 8970
Web Site: http://www.raisio.com
Animal Feed Mfr
N.A.I.C.S.: 311119

Raisio Grain Starch Ltd. (1)
Raisionkaari 55, PO Box 101, Raisio, 21201, Finland (100%)
Tel.: (358) 24432111
Sales Range: $50-74.9 Million
Emp.: 60
Grain Starch
N.A.I.C.S.: 424510
Pekka Kuusniemi (Mng Dir)

Raisio Group, St. Petersburg (1)
5 Bakunina St Rm 314, 191024, Saint Petersburg, Russia (100%)
Tel.: (7) 8123322056
Web Site: http://www.raisio.ru
Sales Range: $25-49.9 Million
Emp.: 3
Food
N.A.I.C.S.: 311423
Reiter Natalio (Dir-Sls)

Raisio Malt (1)
Raisionkaari 55, PO Box 101, FIN 21201, Raisio, Finland (100%)
Tel.: (358) 24432111
Sales Range: $100-124.9 Million
Emp.: 400
Malting
N.A.I.C.S.: 311213

Raisio Nordic, Lithuania (1)
Darbininku Str 22-1, LT-3005, Kaunas, Lithuania
Tel.: (370) 37330020
Web Site: http://www.raisio.com
Sales Range: $25-49.9 Million
Emp.: 2
N.A.I.C.S.: 311423

Raisio Nutrition Ltd (1)
Raisionkaari 55, PO Box 101, 21200, Raisio, Finland
Tel.: (358) 24432111
Web Site: http://www.raisio.com
Fruits & Vegetables Farming Services
N.A.I.C.S.: 311421

Plant (Domestic):

Raisio Nutrition Ltd - Nokia Factory (2)
Rounionkatu 55, PO Box 9, 37101, Nokia, Finland
Tel.: (358) 3 282 8111
Nutritional Food Mfr
N.A.I.C.S.: 311999

Raisio Nutrition Ltd - Raisio Factory (2)
Raisionkaari 55, PO Box 101, 21201, Raisio, Finland
Tel.: (358) 2 443 2111
Emp.: 30
Nutritional Food Mfr
N.A.I.C.S.: 311999
Kim Hwa Joong (CEO)

Raisio Portugal-Produtos Quimicos, Lda. (1)
Rio Noqueira, P-4470, Noqueira Mai, Portugal (51%)
Tel.: (351) 22 960 0166
N.A.I.C.S.: 311423

Raisio Sp. z.o.o. (1)
ul Nowa 23, 05-500, Stara Iwiczna, Poland
Tel.: (48) 22 398 3 993
Snack Food Distr
N.A.I.C.S.: 424420

Raision Konsernipalvelut Oy (1)
Raisionkaari 55, 21200, Raisio, Finland
Tel.: (358) 24432111
Web Site: http://www.raisio.com
Emp.: 360
Oilseed Processing Services
N.A.I.C.S.: 311224

SIA Raisio Latvija (1)
45 Akmenu Street, Ogre, 5001, Latvia
Tel.: (371) 6504 8604
Web Site: http://www.raisio.com
Sales Range: $50-74.9 Million
Emp.: 2
Grain Products Distr
N.A.I.C.S.: 424510

TOV Raisio Ukraina (1)
V Khvoyki Str 18/14 of 308, 04080, Kiev, Ukraine
Tel.: (380) 442306051
Sales Range: $50-74.9 Million
Emp.: 5
Food Products Distr
N.A.I.C.S.: 424420
Konstantin Morgulis (Gen Mgr)

The Lindum Snack Company Limited (1)
Unit 10 Cowbridge Industrial Estate Horncastle Road, Cowbridge, Boston, PE22 7DJ, Lincolnshire, United Kingdom
Tel.: (44) 1205 350570
Sales Range: $25-49.9 Million
Emp.: 12
Snack Food Distr
N.A.I.C.S.: 424450

UAB Raisio Lietuva (1)
Savanoriu 349, 49425, Kaunas, Lithuania
Tel.: (370) 37 330 020
Web Site: http://www.raisio.com
Sales Range: $50-74.9 Million
Emp.: 1
Dairy Products Distr
N.A.I.C.S.: 424430

RAITO KOGYO CO., LTD.
4-2-35 Kudan-kita, Chiyoda-ku, Tokyo, 102-8236, Japan
Tel.: (81) 332652551   JP
Web Site: https://www.raito.co.jp
Year Founded: 1948
1926—(TKS)
Rev.: $775,511,640
Assets: $822,594,670
Liabilities: $220,463,330
Net Worth: $602,131,340
Earnings: $54,076,410
Emp.: 1,122
Fiscal Year-end: 03/31/24
Construction Company
N.A.I.C.S.: 562910
Shigeaki Funayama (Mng Dir)

Subsidiaries:

AURA CE Co., Ltd. (1)
2-18-3 Iwamotocho NBS Iwamotocho Building 6F, Chiyoda-ku, Tokyo, 101-0032, Japan
Tel.: (81) 358350291
Web Site: http://www.aurace.co.jp
Sales Range: $50-74.9 Million
Emp.: 20
Construction Materials & Equipment Sales, Leasing, Civil Engineering & Seismic Building Reinforcement Measures
N.A.I.C.S.: 237990
Masahiro Sokaku (Pres)

C.E. CREATE Co., Ltd. (1)
2F NBS Iwamoto-cho Bldg 2-18-3, Chiyoda-ku, Tokyo, 101-0032, Japan
Tel.: (81) 3 5833 8894
Civil Engineering Services
N.A.I.C.S.: 541330

ONORYO Co., Ltd. (1)
Minami-machi chome No 1 No 11, Kesennuma, 988-0017, Miyagi, Japan
Tel.: (81) 226222600
Web Site: http://www.onoryo.co.jp
Emp.: 150
Construction Services
N.A.I.C.S.: 237990

RAITO Singapore Pte. Ltd. (1)
1003 Bukit Merah Central 05-15, Singapore, 159836, Singapore
Tel.: (65) 68627441
Civil Engineering Services
N.A.I.C.S.: 541330
Norio Machida (Mng Dir)

Raito, Inc. (1)
32960 Alvarado-Niles Rd Ste 680, Union City, CA 94587
Tel.: (510) 259-9900
Sales Range: $25-49.9 Million
Emp.: 20
Geotechnical Construction Services
N.A.I.C.S.: 237990

Yasashiite Raito Co., Ltd. (1)
5-28-17 Shinkawa-cho Oak III Mansion 2nd floor, Minami-ku, Yokohama, 232-0027, Japan (100%)
Tel.: (81) 452860010
Web Site: http://www.yasashiite-raito.co.jp
Emp.: 21
Elder Care Services
N.A.I.C.S.: 623110
Sueo Miyamoto (Pres)

RAIZ INVEST LIMITED
Level 11 2 Bulletin Place, Sydney, 2000, NSW, Australia
Tel.: (61) 1300754748   AU
Web Site: https://www.raizinvest.com.au
Year Founded: 2016
RZI—(ASX)
Rev.: $14,662,126
Assets: $28,632,479
Liabilities: $4,354,968
Net Worth: $24,277,511
Earnings: ($1,016,960)
Fiscal Year-end: 06/30/24
Holding Company
N.A.I.C.S.: 551114
Brendan Malone (Mng Dir & CEO-Grp)

Subsidiaries:

Instreet Investment Limited (1)
Level 11 2 Bulletin Place, Sydney, 2000, NSW, Australia
Tel.: (61) 1300954678
Web Site: https://www.instreet.com.au
Financial Investment Services
N.A.I.C.S.: 523999
David Gordon (Chm)

RAIZEN S.A.
Av Brig Faria Lima 4100 Itaim Bibi, 04538-132, Sao Paulo, Brazil
Tel.: (55) 1123446200   BR
Web Site: https://www.raizen.com.br
RAIZ4—(BRAZ)
Rev.: $43,963,354,705
Assets: $25,562,531,028
Liabilities: $21,150,213,884
Net Worth: $4,412,317,144
Earnings: $122,471,435
Fiscal Year-end: 03/31/24
Bioenergy Services
N.A.I.C.S.: 221117

Subsidiaries:

Raizen Energia S.A. (1)
Avenida Brigadeiro Faria Lima 4100 11th floor Part V, Sao Paulo, Brazil
Tel.: (55) 8007170010
Web Site: http://www.raizen.com.br
Rev.: $5,904,115,542
Assets: $8,632,025,769
Liabilities: $7,173,198,741
Net Worth: $1,458,827,028
Earnings: $52,672,463
Emp.: 28,843
Fiscal Year-end: 03/31/2020
Food Products Mfr
N.A.I.C.S.: 311999
Guilherme Jose de Vasconcelos Cerqueira (CFO & Officer-IR)

Subsidiary (Domestic):

Biosev S.A. (2)
Av Brigadeiro Faria Lima 1355 - 11 andar, 01452-919, Sao Paulo, SP, Brazil
Tel.: (55) 1130925200
Web Site: http://www.biosev.com.br
Rev.: $1,605,095,899
Assets: $2,277,300,626
Liabilities: $2,140,066,139
Net Worth: $137,234,487
Earnings: ($308,835,931)
Emp.: 14,000
Fiscal Year-end: 03/31/2019
Sugar Mfr & Distr
N.A.I.C.S.: 311314
Michael Andrew Gorrel (Vice Chm)

Unit (Domestic):

Biosev S.A. - Continental Unit (3)
Rod Brigadeiro Faria Lima km 458 5, PO

RAIZEN S.A.

Raizen S.A.—(Continued)
Box 31, Colombia, 14795-000, Sao Paulo, Brazil
Tel.: (55) 17 3335 8000
Sugar Mfr
N.A.I.C.S.: 311314

Biosev S.A. - Cresciumal Unit (3)
Estrada Vicinal Jose de Souza Queiroz Filho s/n - Zona Rural, Leme, 13610-970, Sao Paulo, Brazil
Tel.: (55) 19 3573 7200
Sugar Mfr
N.A.I.C.S.: 311314

Biosev S.A. - Estivas Unit (3)
Vila Estivas s/n - Zona Rural, 59170-000, Ares, Rio Grande do Norte, Brazil
Tel.: (55) 84 3242 4800
Sugar Mfr
N.A.I.C.S.: 311314

Biosev S.A. - Giasa Unit (3)
Fazenda Ibura s/n - Zona Rural, 58328-000, Pedras de Fogo, Paraiba, Brazil
Tel.: (55) 83 3651 1150
Sugar Mfr
N.A.I.C.S.: 311314

Biosev S.A. - Lagoa da Prata Unit (3)
Vila Luciania s/n - Zona Rural, 35590-000, Lagoa da Prata, Minas Gerais, Brazil
Tel.: 37 3261 9300
Sugar Mfr & Distr
N.A.I.C.S.: 311314

Biosev S.A. - MB Unit (3)
Fazenda Sucuri s/n - Zona Rural, PO Box 147, Morro Agudo, 14640-000, Sao Paulo, Brazil
Tel.: (55) 16 3851 9000
Sugar Mfr
N.A.I.C.S.: 311314

Biosev S.A. - Maracaju Unit (3)
Fazenda Estrada da Agua Fria km 54 s/n - Zona Rural, 79150-000, Maracaju, Brazil
Tel.: (55) 67 3494 1600
Sugar Mfr
N.A.I.C.S.: 311314

Biosev S.A. - Passa Tempo Unit (3)
Fazenda Passa Tempo s/n - Zona Rural, 79130-000, Rio Brilhante, Mato Grosso do Sul, Brazil
Tel.: (55) 67 3408 1400
Sugar Mfr
N.A.I.C.S.: 311314

Biosev S.A. - Rio Brilhante Unit (3)
Rod BR 163 km 329 6 s/n Fazenda Santa Maria - Zona Rural, 79130-000, Rio Brilhante, Mato Grosso do Sul, Brazil
Tel.: (55) 67 3452 5700
Sugar Mfr
N.A.I.C.S.: 311314

Biosev S.A. - Santelisa Unit (3)
Rod Armando de Salles Oliveira km 346 3, PO Box 145, 14176-500, Sertaozinho, Sao Paulo, Brazil
Tel.: (55) 16 3946 3900
Sugar Mfr
N.A.I.C.S.: 311314

Biosev S.A. - Vale do Rosario Unit (3)
Fazenda Invernada s/n - Zona Rural, PO Box 146, Morro Agudo, 14640-000, Sao Paulo, Brazil
Tel.: (55) 16 3820 2000
Sugar Mfr
N.A.I.C.S.: 311314

Subsidiary (Domestic):

Crystalsev Comercio e Representacao Ltda. (3)
Av Antonio Diederichsen 400- Jardim America Edificio Metropolitan -18, Ribeirao Preto, 14020-250, Sao Paulo, Brazil
Tel.: (55) 16 2101 4400
Sugar Mfr & Distr
N.A.I.C.S.: 311314
Cicero torquato Junqueira franco *(Mgr)*

Subsidiary (Non-US):

LDC Trading & Services Co. S.A. (3)
Dr Luis Bonavita 1294 Complejo World Trade Center Free Zone Of 901, 11300, Montevideo, Uruguay
Tel.: (598) 26263300
Agricultural Goods Whslr
N.A.I.C.S.: 424310

Subsidiary (Domestic):

Louis Dreyfus Company Brasil S.A. (3)
Avenida Conselheiro Nebias 703 - 10 ao 12 andares, Boqueirao, Santos, Brazil
Tel.: (55) 1321279850
Web Site: https://www.ldc.com
Agricultural Goods Whslr
N.A.I.C.S.: 424310

Subsidiary (Non-US):

Louis Dreyfus Company Suisse S.A. (3)
29 route de l'Aeroport, 1215, Geneva, Switzerland
Tel.: (41) 586882700
Agricultural Goods Whslr
N.A.I.C.S.: 424310

Subsidiary (US):

Term Commodities Inc. (3)
175 W Jackson Blvd Ste 2130, Chicago, IL 60604
Tel.: (312) 554-4070
Agricultural Goods Whslr
N.A.I.C.S.: 424310

Subsidiary (Domestic):

Usina Estivas Ltda. (3)
Fazenda Tres Pontes, Novo Horizonte, Sao Paulo, 14960-000, Brazil
Tel.: (55) 1735429500
Web Site: http://www.estiva.com.br
Sugar Cane Mfr
N.A.I.C.S.: 311314

Subsidiary (Non-US):

Raizen Trading LLP (2)
Rue de Jargonnant 2, 1207, Geneva, Switzerland
Tel.: (41) 223170044
Biomass Electric Power Generation Services
N.A.I.C.S.: 221117

RAIZNEXT CORPORATION

27-5 Shin-Isogocho, Isogo-ku, Yokohama, 235-0017, Kanagawa, Japan
Tel.: (81) 457581950
Web Site: https://www.raiznext.co.jp
Year Founded: 2000
6379—(TKS)
Rev.: $927,819,260
Assets: $732,031,060
Liabilities: $175,978,030
Net Worth: $556,053,030
Earnings: $47,915,890
Emp.: 1,690
Fiscal Year-end: 03/31/24
Engineeering Services
N.A.I.C.S.: 541330
Yoshiji Otomo *(Vice Chm)*

Subsidiaries:

Ikeda Kiko Co., Ltd. (1)
47-2 Shinden, Saijo, 793-0028, Ehime, Japan
Tel.: (81) 897552259
Machinery Maintenance & Repair Services
N.A.I.C.S.: 811310

Kounan Tsusho Co., Ltd. (1)
27-5 Shin-Isogocho, Isogo-ku, Yokohama, 235-0017, Kanagawa, Japan
Tel.: (81) 457594020
Plant Construction Service
N.A.I.C.S.: 236210

N.S. Engineering Co., Ltd. (1)
2-17-35 Tsurumichuo, Tsurumi-ku, Yokohama, 230-0051, Japan
Tel.: (81) 45521 1621
Plant Construction Service
N.A.I.C.S.: 236210

PT. Shinko Plantech (1)
Mid Plaza Bldg II 16th Floor Jl Jenderal Sudirman Kav 10-11, Jakarta, 10220, Indonesia
Tel.: (62) 215705155
Plant Construction Service
N.A.I.C.S.: 236210

Shinko Machinery Service Co., Ltd. (1)
27-5 Shin-Isogocho, Isogo-ku, Yokohama, 235-0017, Kanagawa, Japan
Tel.: (81) 457582560
Machinery Maintenance & Repair Services
N.A.I.C.S.: 811310

Shinko Sogo Service Co., Ltd. (1)
27-5 Shin-Isogocho, Isogo-ku, Yokohama, 235-0017, Kanagawa, Japan
Tel.: (81) 457581945
Real Estate Manangement Services
N.A.I.C.S.: 531210

Tasaka Tekko Kensetsu Co., Ltd. (1)
1-6 Ishikawa-cho, Kashiwara, 582-0029, Osaka, Japan
Tel.: (81) 729771166
Tank Construction Services
N.A.I.C.S.: 237110

Tokai Engineering & Construction Co., Ltd. (1)
350-1 Imaduasayama, Ichihara, 299-0106, Chiba, Japan
Tel.: (81) 436622141
Plant Construction Service
N.A.I.C.S.: 236210

Toshin Seisakusyo Co., Ltd. (1)
6-3-13 Takihama, Niihama, 792-0893, Ehime, Japan
Tel.: (81) 897461177
Plant Construction Service
N.A.I.C.S.: 236210

Wuxi Shinko Plantech Co., Ltd. (1)
Unit F G H Floor 12 Building B Oriental Plaza No 359 Zhongshan Road, Wuxi, Jiangsu, China
Tel.: (86) 51082791353
Plant Construction Service
N.A.I.C.S.: 236210

RAJ OIL MILLS LTD.

224-230 Bellasis Road, Mumbai, 400 008, Maharashtra, India
Tel.: (91) 2223021996   In
Web Site: https://www.rajoilmillsltd.com
Year Founded: 1943
ROML—(NSE)
Rev.: $14,133,846
Assets: $4,434,087
Liabilities: $6,069,573
Net Worth: ($1,635,486)
Earnings: $555,725
Emp.: 183
Fiscal Year-end: 03/31/21
Oil Producer
N.A.I.C.S.: 311225
Sufyan Maknojia *(Mng Dir)*

RAJ PACKAGING INDUSTRIES LTD.

631247 Metro Residency Flat No 202 203 Raj Bhavan Road, Hyderabad, 500082, India
Tel.: (91) 4023392024
Web Site: https://www.rajpack.com
530111—(BOM)
Rev.: $5,660,056
Assets: $2,627,936
Liabilities: $865,188
Net Worth: $1,762,748
Earnings: ($59,805)
Emp.: 47
Fiscal Year-end: 03/31/23
Packaging Plastic Film Mfr
N.A.I.C.S.: 326112
Prem Chand Kankaria *(Mng Dir)*

RAJ RAYON INDUSTRIES LIMITED

5C/196 & 197 Akshay Mittal Mittal Industrial Estate, Sakinaka Andheri E, Mumbai, 400 059, India
Tel.: (91) 2240343434   In
Web Site: http://www.rajrayon.com
Year Founded: 1993
RAJRAYON—(NSE)
Rev.: $464,933
Assets: $26,076,755
Liabilities: $103,992,716
Net Worth: ($77,915,961)
Earnings: ($4,628,879)
Fiscal Year-end: 03/31/20
Polyester Yarn Mfr
N.A.I.C.S.: 339999
Sushil Kumar Kanodia *(CEO & CFO)*

RAJ TELEVISION NETWORK LIMITED

32 Poes Road 2nd Street, Tenyampet, Chennai, 600 018, India
Tel.: (91) 4424334150
Web Site: https://www.rajtvnet.in
Year Founded: 1994
532826—(BOM)
Rev.: $10,721,989
Assets: $27,070,055
Liabilities: $7,752,293
Net Worth: $19,317,762
Earnings: $17,999
Emp.: 338
Fiscal Year-end: 03/31/21
Television Broadcasting Services
N.A.I.C.S.: 516120
M. Raajhendhran *(Chm, CEO & Mng Dir)*

RAJA BAHADUR INTERNATIONAL LIMITED

Hamam House 3rd Floor Ambalal Doshi Marg, Fort, Mumbai, 400 001, India
Tel.: (91) 2222654278
Web Site: https://www.rajabahadur.com
Year Founded: 1926
503127—(BOM)
Rev.: $2,376,344
Assets: $19,036,772
Liabilities: $17,648,882
Net Worth: $1,387,890
Earnings: ($533,481)
Emp.: 34
Fiscal Year-end: 03/31/23
Real Estate Development Services
N.A.I.C.S.: 531390
Manoharlal M. Pittie *(Chm)*

RAJA FERRY PORT PCL

25/1 Moo 8 mittraphap road, Don Sak, Surat Thani, 84220, Thailand
Tel.: (66) 773728002
Web Site: https://www.rajaferryport.com
Year Founded: 1981
RP—(THA)
Rev.: $16,502,804
Assets: $35,209,603
Liabilities: $19,324,208
Net Worth: $15,885,394
Earnings: ($2,599,837)
Fiscal Year-end: 12/31/23
Transportation Services
N.A.I.C.S.: 485999

RAJANI, SINGHANIA & PARTNERS

204-207 Krishna Chambers 59 New Marine Lines, Mumbai, 400020, India
Tel.: (91) 22 4096 1000   In
Web Site: http://www.rsplaw.net
Year Founded: 1999
Emp.: 100
Law firm
N.A.I.C.S.: 541110
Prem Rajani *(Mng Partner)*

AND PRIVATE COMPANIES

Subsidiaries:

Rajani, Singhania & Partners (1)
RS&P House P-24 Green Park Ext, New Delhi, 110016, India
Tel.: (91) 11 4747 1414
Web Site: http://www.rsplaw.net
Emp.: 50
Law firm
N.A.I.C.S.: 541110
Ravi Singhania (Mng Partner)

RAJAPALAYAM MILLS LTD
P A C Ramasamy Raja Salai, PO Box No 1, Rajapalayam, 626117, Tamil Nadu, India
Tel.: (91) 4563235666
Web Site:
    https://www.rajapalayammills.co.in
RAJPALAYAM—(NSE)
Rev.: $104,513,015
Assets: $416,248,702
Liabilities: $147,474,024
Net Worth: $268,774,678
Earnings: $9,817,589
Emp.: 4,713
Fiscal Year-end: 03/31/23
Yarn Mfr
N.A.I.C.S.: 313110
Poosapadi Ramasubrahmaneya Rajha Venketrama Raja (Chm)

RAJASTHAN CYLINDERS & CONTAINERS LTD.
SP-825 Road No 14 Vishwakarma Industrial Area, Jaipur, 302013, Rajasthan, India
Tel.: (91) 1412331771
Web Site: https://www.bajoriagroup.in
Year Founded: 1980
538707—(BOM)
Rev.: $2,167,866
Assets: $6,446,253
Liabilities: $3,806,275
Net Worth: $2,639,978
Earnings: ($364,673)
Emp.: 19
Fiscal Year-end: 03/31/21
Gas Cylinder Mfr
N.A.I.C.S.: 332420
Preetanjali Bajoria (Exec Dir)

RAJASTHAN GASES LTD.
157-B 1st Floor Bldg No 5 Akshay Mittal Indl Estate A K Road, Marol Naka Andheri E, Mumbai, 400059, India
Tel.: (91) 2226465178
Web Site:
    http://www.rajasthangasltd.com
526873—(BOM)
Assets: $302,637
Liabilities: $2,485
Net Worth: $300,152
Earnings: ($14,758)
Fiscal Year-end: 03/31/18
Gas Filling & Distribution Services
N.A.I.C.S.: 221210
Nikhilesh Narendra Khandelwa (Chm & Mng Dir)

RAJASTHAN PETRO SYNTHETICS LTD.
S-4 Second Floor Pankaj Central Market, I P Extension Patparganj, Delhi, 110 092, India
Tel.: (91) 1141326013
Web Site: https://www.rpsl.co.in
Year Founded: 1983
506975—(BOM)
Rev.: $21,677
Assets: $1,966
Liabilities: $121,707
Net Worth: ($119,741)
Earnings: $348
Fiscal Year-end: 03/31/23
Logistics Consulting Servies
N.A.I.C.S.: 541614
Rishabh Goel (Mng Dir)

RAJASTHAN TUBE MANUFACTURING COMPANY LTD.
28-37 Banke Bihari Industrial Area Jatawali Mod Maharkala Road, Village Dehra Teh Chomu, Jaipur, 303806, India
Tel.: (91) 8875009017
Web Site: https://www.rajtube.com
530253—(BOM)
Rev.: $11,978,646
Assets: $3,434,482
Liabilities: $2,529,668
Net Worth: $904,814
Earnings: $114,621
Emp.: 20
Fiscal Year-end: 03/31/23
Steel Pipe & Tube Mfr
N.A.I.C.S.: 331210
Harish Chand Jain (Mng Dir)

RAJATH FINANCE LIMITED
208-215 Star Plaza Phulchhab Chowk, Rajkot, 360 001, Gujarat, India
Tel.: (91) 2812447800
Web Site: https://fynxcapital.com
Year Founded: 1984
507962—(BOM)
Rev.: $39,710
Assets: $899,463
Liabilities: $82,033
Net Worth: $817,430
Earnings: ($13,264)
Fiscal Year-end: 03/31/23
Financial Management Services
N.A.I.C.S.: 523999
Hiteshbhai M. Bagdai (Mng Dir)

RAJDARSHAN INDUSTRIES LIMITED
59 Moti Magri Scheme, Udaipur, 313 001, Rajasthan, India
Tel.: (91) 2942427999
Web Site:
    https://www.rajdarshanindustry.com
Year Founded: 1980
526662—(BOM)
Rev.: $293,702
Assets: $2,553,458
Liabilities: $61,973
Net Worth: $2,491,484
Earnings: $35,370
Emp.: 3
Fiscal Year-end: 03/31/23
Mineral Mining Services
N.A.I.C.S.: 327999
K. M. Murdia (CFO)

RAJESH EXPORTS LTD
No 4 Batavia Chambers Kumara Krupa Road Kumara Park East, Bengaluru, 560001, India
Tel.: (91) 8022282216
Web Site:
    https://www.rajeshindia.com
531500—(NSE)
Rev.: $35,259,071,348
Assets: $3,204,035,753
Liabilities: $1,676,347,614
Net Worth: $1,527,688,139
Earnings: $115,323,144
Emp.: 181
Fiscal Year-end: 03/31/21
Gold & Diamond Jewelry Mfr
N.A.I.C.S.: 339910
Prashant Jasvantrai Mehta (Co-Founder & Mng Dir)

RAJESHWARI CANS LIMITED
96 Mahagujarat Industrial Estate Moraiya, Sanand, Ahmedabad, 382210, Gujarat, India
Tel.: (91) 7929796584
Web Site:
    https://www.rajeshwaricans.com
543285—(BOM)
Rev.: $3,916,929
Assets: $2,302,052
Liabilities: $1,257,369
Net Worth: $1,044,683
Earnings: $127,665
Emp.: 67
Fiscal Year-end: 03/31/23
Tin Container Mfr
N.A.I.C.S.: 332431
Bharatkumar Nagindas Vora (Mng Dir)

RAJESWARI INFRASTRUCTURE LTD.
18/23 2nd Cross Street East CIT Nagar Nandanam, Chennai, 600 035, India
Tel.: (91) 4445522434
Web Site: http://www.rflindia.org
Year Founded: 1993
526823—(BOM)
Rev.: $277,981
Assets: $1,849,350
Liabilities: $1,802,662
Net Worth: $46,688
Earnings: ($10,491)
Emp.: 8
Fiscal Year-end: 03/31/22
Construction Services
N.A.I.C.S.: 236115
R. Usha (Exec Dir)

RAJKAMAL SYNTHETICS LIMITED
411 Atlanta Estate Premises Co Op Soc Ltd G M Link Road Goregaon East, Mumbai, 400063, India
Tel.: (91) 2248255368
Web Site:
    https://www.rajkamalsynthetics.com
Year Founded: 1981
514028—(BOM)
Rev.: $783
Assets: $34,191
Liabilities: $14,707
Net Worth: $19,484
Earnings: ($13,740)
Fiscal Year-end: 03/31/21
Textile Product Whslr
N.A.I.C.S.: 424990
Ankur Ajmera (Mng Dir & Compliance Officer)

RAJKOT INVESTMENT TRUST LIMITED
Shop No2 Alokik Appartment Near Mohanbhai Hall kasturba Road, Rajkot, 360003, Gujarat, India
Tel.: (91) 2813241064
Web Site: https://www.ritl.co.in
539495—(BOM)
Rev.: $28,517
Assets: $1,594,824
Liabilities: $1,052,515
Net Worth: $542,309
Earnings: $2,312
Emp.: 7
Fiscal Year-end: 03/31/23
Financial Support Services
N.A.I.C.S.: 523999
Rupesh Jain (Chm & Mng Dir)

RAJKUMAR FORGE LIMITED
Office No 511 to 513 Global Square S No 247 14B Yerawada, Pune, 411 006, Maharashtra, India
Tel.: (91) 8956616160
Web Site: https://www.kvforge.com
513369—(BOM)
Rev.: $9,773,539
Assets: $5,386,512
Liabilities: $1,163,683
Net Worth: $4,222,828
Earnings: $197,170
Emp.: 70
Fiscal Year-end: 03/31/23
Forgings & Specialized Components Mfr
N.A.I.C.S.: 332112
Nitin Shyam Rajore (Exec Dir)

RAJNANDINI METAL LTD.
Plot No 344 Sector 3 Phase II Imt Bawal, Industrial Twp 3, Rewari, 123501, Haryana, India
Tel.: (91) 1284264194
Web Site: https://rajnandinimetal.com
Year Founded: 2010
RAJMET—(NSE)
Rev.: $124,578,862
Assets: $16,771,177
Liabilities: $11,803,849
Net Worth: $4,967,328
Earnings: $1,640,189
Emp.: 156
Fiscal Year-end: 03/31/23
Waste Management Services
N.A.I.C.S.: 562998
Het Ram (Mng Dir)

RAJNISH WELLNESS LIMITED
Plot No 24 ABCD Govt Industrial Estate Near Hindustan Naka, Charkop Kandivali, Mumbai, 400 067, India
Tel.: (91) 2223065555
Web Site:
    https://www.rajnishwellness.com
Year Founded: 2015
541601—(BOM)
Rev.: $2,318,138
Assets: $4,681,362
Liabilities: $1,715,450
Net Worth: $2,965,912
Earnings: $13,615
Emp.: 20
Fiscal Year-end: 03/31/21
Personal Care Product Retailer
N.A.I.C.S.: 456199

RAJOO ENGINEERS LIMITED
Rajoo Avenue Survey No 210 Plot No 1 Industrial Area, Veraval Shapar, Rajkot, 360 024, Gujarat, India
Tel.: (91) 9712962704
Web Site: https://www.rajoo.com
522257—(BOM)
Rev.: $21,778,562
Assets: $22,040,165
Liabilities: $8,982,735
Net Worth: $13,057,431
Earnings: $1,377,471
Emp.: 288
Fiscal Year-end: 03/31/23
Blown Film Line Mfr
N.A.I.C.S.: 326113
Rajesh Nanalal Doshi (Founder, Chm & Co-Mng Dir)

RAJPUTANA INVESTMENT & FINANCE LTD.
BRD Complex NH Bypass, Konikkara, Thrissur, 680306, India
Tel.: (91) 7593818458
Web Site:
    https://www.rajputanainvestment.com
539090—(BOM)
Rev.: $136,886
Assets: $385,972
Liabilities: $4,880
Net Worth: $381,092
Earnings: $7,769
Fiscal Year-end: 03/31/23
Financial Support Services
N.A.I.C.S.: 523999
Villadath Vinitha (Compliance Officer)

RAJRATAN GLOBAL WIRE LIMITED
Rajratan House 11/2 Meera Path

RAJRATAN GLOBAL WIRE LIMITED

Rajratan Global Wire Limited—(Continued)
Dhenu Market, Indore, 452003, Madhya Pradesh, India
Tel.: (91) 731 254 6401
Web Site: http://www.rajratan.co.in
517522—(NSE)
Rev.: $122,149,755
Assets: $84,200,025
Liabilities: $37,657,620
Net Worth: $46,542,405
Earnings: $16,971,045
Emp.: 425
Fiscal Year-end: 03/31/22
Carbon Steel Wire Mfr
N.A.I.C.S.: 331222
Sunil Chordia *(Chm & Mng Dir)*

Subsidiaries:

Rajratan Thai Wire Co. Limited (1)
155/11 Moo 4 Tombol Chetsamian, Amphor Potharam, Ratchaburi, 70120, Thailand
Tel.: (66) 32375841
Carbon Steel Wire Mfr & Distr
N.A.I.C.S.: 331222

Swaraj Technocraft Pvt. Ltd. (1)
Plot-40 Sector-II, Dhar, 454 775, MP, India
Tel.: (91) 7292 407213
Web Site: http://swarajtechnocrafts.com
Sales Range: $25-49.9 Million
Emp.: 45
Wire Drawing Equipment Mfr & Whslr
N.A.I.C.S.: 423830
Rajendra Ekbote *(Mng Dir)*

RAJSANKET REALTY LIMITED
139 Seksaria Chambers 2nd Floor N M Road, Fort, Mumbai, 400023, Maharashtra, India
Tel.: (91) 22 22670717
Sales Range: $1-9.9 Million
Financial Investment Services
N.A.I.C.S.: 523999
Ketan Trivedi *(Sec)*

RAJSHREE POLYPACK LTD.
212 Lodha Supremus Building No 1 2nd Floor Road No 22, Near New Passport Office Wagle Estate, Thane, 400 604, India
Tel.: (91) 2225818200
Web Site:
https://www.rajshreepolypack.com
RPPL—(NSE)
Rev.: $30,488,963
Assets: $31,526,371
Liabilities: $15,931,491
Net Worth: $15,594,880
Earnings: $1,278,065
Emp.: 541
Fiscal Year-end: 03/31/23
Packaging Products Mfr
N.A.I.C.S.: 326112
Ramswaroop Radheshyam Thard *(Founder, Chm & Mng Dir)*

Subsidiaries:

Olive Ecopak Private Limited (1)
616 6th Floor Lodha Supremus 2 Road No 22, Wagle Estate Thane West, Thane, 400604, Maharashtra, India
Tel.: (91) 8108819000
Web Site: https://www.oliveecopak.com
Plastic Container Mfr
N.A.I.C.S.: 326160

RAJSHREE SUGARS & CHEMICALS LIMITED
The Uffizi 3388 Avanashi Road Peelamedu, Coimbatore, 641 004, Tamilnadu, India
Tel.: (91) 4222580981
Web Site:
https://www.rajshreesugars.com
Year Founded: 1987
500354—(BOM)
Rev.: $50,999,226
Assets: $92,033,583
Liabilities: $87,868,435
Net Worth: $4,165,147
Earnings: $2,287,549
Emp.: 828
Fiscal Year-end: 03/31/21
Sugar Mfr
N.A.I.C.S.: 311313
Rajshree Pathy *(Chm)*

RAJTHANEE HOSPITAL PCL
111 moo 3, Suanplu Subdistrict Phra Nakonsri Ayutthaya District, Phra Nakhon Si Ayutthaya, 13000, Thailand
Tel.: (66) 35335555
Web Site: https://www.rajthanee.com
Year Founded: 1990
RJH—(THA)
Rev.: $69,844,971
Assets: $117,356,403
Liabilities: $49,171,127
Net Worth: $68,185,276
Earnings: $12,135,127
Emp.: 1,180
Fiscal Year-end: 12/31/23
Medical Instrument Mfr
N.A.I.C.S.: 339112
Surin Prasithiran *(Mng Dir)*

Subsidiaries:

Rajthanee Rojana Hospital Co., Ltd. (1)
Rojana-Wang Noi Road 78 Village No 3, Sam Ruean Subdistrict Bang Pa-in District, Phra Nakhon Si Ayutthaya, Thailand
Tel.: (66) 35249249
Web Site: https://rajthanee-rojana.com
Health Care Srvices
N.A.I.C.S.: 621498

RAJVI LOGITRADE LIMITED
Plot No 267 Ward 12/B, Gandhidham, 370201, Gujarat, India
Tel.: (91) 9979898027
Web Site:
https://www.rajvilogitrade.com
Year Founded: 1986
Assets: $177
Liabilities: $46,630
Net Worth: ($46,453)
Earnings: ($11,142)
Fiscal Year-end: 03/31/19
Financial Services
N.A.I.C.S.: 523999
Narendrasinh D. Rana *(CFO)*

RAJVIR INDUSTRIES LIMITED
Surya Towers 1st floor 105 S P Road, Secunderabad, 500 003, India
Tel.: (91) 4027845628
Web Site:
https://www.rajvirindustries.com
Year Founded: 1962
RAJVIR—(NSE)
Rev.: $8,336,330
Assets: $27,809,089
Liabilities: $36,537,847
Net Worth: ($8,728,758)
Earnings: ($437,772)
Emp.: 235
Fiscal Year-end: 03/31/19
Yarn Mfr
N.A.I.C.S.: 339999
Upender Kumar Agarwal *(Chm)*

Subsidiaries:

Srilakshmi Enterprise (1)
Hasgul Road Syno - 205 & 206, Bhainsa, 504103, Andhra Pradesh, India
Tel.: (91) 99896 00201
Web Site:
http://www.srilaxmienterprises.com
Emp.: 20
Cotton Yarn Mfr
N.A.I.C.S.: 313110
Omprakash Agarwal *(Mng Dir)*

RAK PETROLEUM PLC
23rd Floor Festival Tower, PO Box 62042, Dubai, United Arab Emirates
Tel.: (971) 7 235 6662
Web Site:
http://www.rakpetroleum.ae
Year Founded: 2005
RAKP—(OSL)
Rev.: $971,400,000
Assets: $3,590,100,000
Liabilities: $2,125,300,000
Net Worth: $1,464,800,000
Earnings: $74,300,000
Fiscal Year-end: 12/31/19
Oil & Gas Investment Services
N.A.I.C.S.: 213112
Bijan Mossavar-Rahmani *(Chm)*

RAK PROPERTIES P.J.S.C
Julphar Towers Floor 40 41, PO Box 31113, Ras al Khaimah, United Arab Emirates
Tel.: (971) 72444432
Web Site:
https://www.rakproperties.ae
Year Founded: 2005
RAKPROP—(ABU)
Rev.: $273,588,619
Assets: $1,758,483,524
Liabilities: $586,592,702
Net Worth: $1,171,890,822
Earnings: $54,946,093
Emp.: 168
Fiscal Year-end: 12/31/23
Real Estate Manangement Services
N.A.I.C.S.: 531390
Mohammad Hassan Omran *(Chm)*

RAK UNITY PETROLEUM COMPANY PLC.
Block 5 Water Corporation Road, Ijora GRA, Lagos, Nigeria
Tel.: (234) 12704833 NG
Web Site: https://www.rakunity.com
Year Founded: 1982
RAKUNITY—(NIGE)
Rev.: $3,675,164
Assets: $1,500,609
Liabilities: $228,409
Net Worth: $1,272,200
Earnings: ($167,559)
Emp.: 13
Fiscal Year-end: 12/31/20
Petroleum Product Distr
N.A.I.C.S.: 424720
James Ogungbemi *(Mng Dir)*

RAKISA HOLDING CO.
22nd Floor Kingdom Tower, PO Box 305897, Riyadh, 11361, Saudi Arabia
Tel.: (966) 12110800
Web Site: http://www.rakisa.com
Year Founded: 1993
Investment Services
Abdullah Bin Ibrahim Al Rakhis *(Founder & Chm)*

RAKON LIMITED
8 Sylvia Park Road Mt Wellington, Auckland, 1060, New Zealand
Tel.: (64) 95735554
Web Site: https://www.rakon.com
RAK—(NZX)
Rev.: $107,855,263
Assets: $123,965,311
Liabilities: $30,147,129
Net Worth: $93,818,182
Earnings: $13,886,962
Emp.: 1,000
Fiscal Year-end: 03/31/23
Frequency Control Products Mfr
N.A.I.C.S.: 334515
Warren Robinson *(Founder)*

Subsidiaries:

Rakon America LLC (1)
7600 Dublin Blvd Ste 220, Dublin, CA 94568
Tel.: (925) 361-8808
Web Site: https://www.rakon.com
Sales Range: $50-74.9 Million
Emp.: 6
Electric Component Whslr
N.A.I.C.S.: 423690
Andrew Mccraith *(Gen Mgr)*

Rakon France SAS (1)
44 Avenue de la Glaciere, BP165, 95105, Argenteuil, Val-d'Oise, France
Tel.: (33) 139983600
Web Site: http://www.rakon.com
Electronic Parts & Equipment Whslr
N.A.I.C.S.: 423690

Subsidiary (Domestic):

Rakon Temex SA (2)
The Marco Polo Building A1 790 Avenue du Dr Maurice Donat, 06250, Mougins, France
Tel.: (33) 49 797 9797
Web Site: http://www.temex.com
Sales Range: $25-49.9 Million
Emp.: 15
High-Performance & High-Precision Frequency Equipment Mfr
N.A.I.C.S.: 334220

Rakon UK Limited (1)
Antell House Windsor Place, Harlow, CM20 2GQ, Essex, United Kingdom
Tel.: (44) 152 281 2600
Web Site: https://www.rakon.com
Frequency Control Products Mfr
N.A.I.C.S.: 334413

RAKOVINA THERAPEUTICS INC.
Suite 720 999 West Broadway, Vancouver, V5Z 1K5, BC, Canada
Tel.: (604) 619-0225
Web Site:
https://rakovinatherapeutics.com
Year Founded: 2020
RKVTF—(OTCIQ)
Rev.: $16,892
Assets: $3,887,040
Liabilities: $1,123,424
Net Worth: $2,763,615
Earnings: ($1,973,072)
Fiscal Year-end: 12/31/23
Asset Management Services
N.A.I.C.S.: 523940
Jeffrey Bacha *(Chm)*

RAKSUL, INC.
1F IK bldg 2-24-9 Kami-Osaki, Shinagawa-ku, Tokyo, 141-0021, Japan
Tel.: (81) 366294893
Web Site:
https://www.corp.raksul.com
4384—(TKS)
Rev.: $317,972,620
Assets: $272,877,620
Liabilities: $175,173,860
Net Worth: $97,703,760
Earnings: $13,173,960
Fiscal Year-end: 07/31/24
Printing Products Mfr
N.A.I.C.S.: 323111
Yasukane Matsumoto *(Founder & CEO)*

Subsidiaries:

Amida Holding Co., Ltd. (1)
1-Chome Shinmeomachi 13, Nishi-Ku, Osaka, 550-0004, Japan
Tel.: (81) 664495510
Web Site: http://www.amida.co.jp
Rev.: $29,572,400
Assets: $25,022,800
Liabilities: $3,959,120
Net Worth: $21,063,680
Earnings: $2,807,200
Fiscal Year-end: 06/30/2022
Holding Company
N.A.I.C.S.: 551112
Masaru Fujita *(Founder, Chm, Pres & CEO)*

RAKU CO., LTD.

12 Tai Seng Street 06-03, Singapore, 534118, Singapore
Tel.: (65) 62813888
Web Site: http://www.kinobiotech.com
4154—(TPE)
Rev.: $13,782,072
Assets: $26,445,799
Liabilities: $14,924,178
Net Worth: $11,521,621
Earnings: ($1,282,838)
Fiscal Year-end: 12/31/22
Beauty Product Mfr
N.A.I.C.S.: 325620
Ting Yen Hock (Chm)

RAKUMO, INC.
Kajimachi Building 3-2 Kojimachi, Chiyoda-ku, Tokyo, 102-0083, Japan
Tel.: (81) 5017469891
Web Site: https://www.rakumo.com
Year Founded: 2004
4060—(TKS)
Rev.: $9,181,550
Assets: $18,930,300
Liabilities: $9,252,450
Net Worth: $9,677,850
Earnings: $1,389,640
Emp.: 100
Fiscal Year-end: 12/31/23
Software Development Services
N.A.I.C.S.: 541511
Daisuke Mitarai (Pres & CEO)

Subsidiaries:
Rakumo Company Limited (1)
9F Etown2 364 Cong Hoa, Ward 13 Tan Binh District, Ho Chi Minh City, Vietnam
Tel.: (84) 283 812 0200
Web Site: https://rakumo.vn
Emp.: 47
Mobile Application Development Services
N.A.I.C.S.: 513210

RAKUS CO., LTD.
Link Square Shinjuku 5-27-5, Sendagaya Shibuya-ku, Tokyo, 151-0051, Japan
Tel.: (81) 663463640
Web Site: https://www.rakus.co.jp
Year Founded: 2000
3923—(TKS)
Rev.: $253,876,880
Assets: $140,356,740
Liabilities: $52,133,070
Net Worth: $88,223,670
Earnings: $27,662,850
Emp.: 2,561
Fiscal Year-end: 03/31/24
Data Storage for Businesses
N.A.I.C.S.: 518210
Takanori Nakamura (Pres)

Subsidiaries:
RAKUS Partners Co., Ltd. (1)
4-3-25 Shinjuku Tokyo Reit Shinjuku Building 8F, Shinjuku-ku, Tokyo, 160-0022, Japan
Tel.: (81) 366753638
Web Site: http://www.rakus-partners.co.jp
Emp.: 534
Staffing Services
N.A.I.C.S.: 561311

RAKUS Vietnam Co., Ltd. (1)
4th Floor Bldg QTSC 9 Street 3 Quang Trung Software City, Tan Chanh Hiep Ward District 12, Ho Chi Minh City, Vietnam
Tel.: (84) 2837153882
Web Site: https://www.rakus.com.vn
Emp.: 59
Information Technology Services
N.A.I.C.S.: 541511

RAKUTEN BANK, LTD.
2-16-5 Konan, Minato-ku,, Tokyo, Japan
Tel.: (81) 5055816910   JP
Web Site: https://www.rakuten-bank.co.jp
Year Founded: 2000
5838—(TKS)
Rev.: $911,463,240
Assets: $89,068,181,206
Liabilities: $87,220,893,979
Net Worth: $1,847,287,226
Earnings: $227,525,539
Fiscal Year-end: 03/31/24
Electronic & Mobile Banking Services
N.A.I.C.S.: 522320
Hiroyuki Nagai (Pres & CEO)

Subsidiaries:
Rakuten Bank Systems, Ltd. (1)
4-13-9 Higashishishinagawa Rakuten Tower 2 4f, Shinagawa-Ku, Tokyo, 140-0002, Japan
Tel.: (81) 357800011
Commercial Banking Technology Development & Programming Services
N.A.I.C.S.: 541519

RAKUTEN GROUP, INC.
Rakuten Crimson House 1-14-1 Tamagawa, Setagaya-ku, Tokyo, 158-0094, Japan
Tel.: (81) 5055816910   JP
Web Site: https://global.rakuten.com
Year Founded: 1997
RKUNF—(OTCIQ)
Rev.: $12,737,879,088
Assets: $135,033,353,155
Liabilities: $129,277,885,695
Net Worth: $5,755,467,460
Earnings: ($2,483,719,855)
Emp.: 32,079
Fiscal Year-end: 12/31/22
Holding Company; Online Shopping, E-Commerce, Travel Services, Financial Services & Professional Baseball Team Owner
N.A.I.C.S.: 551112
Masatada Kobayashi (Chief Well-Being Officer & Mng Exec Officer)

Subsidiaries:
Dot Commodity, Inc. (1)
1-21-8 Ebisu Cera 51 Building 6F, Shibuya-ku, Tokyo, 150-0013, Japan
Tel.: (81) 3 5447 3022
Web Site: http://www.commodity.co.jp
Online Commodity Brokerage Services
N.A.I.C.S.: 523160
Jin Funada (Pres)

Rakuten Auction, Inc. (1)
Shinagawa Seaside Rakuten Tower 4-12-3 Higashi-Shinagawa, Shinagawa-ku, Tokyo, 140-0002, Japan (60%)
Tel.: (81) 3 6387 1111
Web Site: http://auction.rakuten.co.jp
Online Auction Services
N.A.I.C.S.: 425120
Hiroshi Mikitani (Chm)

Rakuten Baseball, Inc. (1)
2-11-6 Miyagino, Miyagino-ku, Sendai, Miyagi, Japan (100%)
Tel.: (81) 222985300
Web Site: https://www.rakuteneagles.jp
Sales Range: $75-99.9 Million
Emp.: 149
Professional Baseball Club
N.A.I.C.S.: 711211
Hiroshi Miki (Chm)

Rakuten Card Co., Ltd. (1)
Rakuten Crimson House Aoyama 2-6-21 Minami Aoyama, Minato-ku, Tokyo, Japan
Tel.: (81) 367406740
Web Site: http://www.rakuten-card.co.jp
Credit Card Issuing Services
N.A.I.C.S.: 522210
Masayuki Hosaka (Pres)

Rakuten Communications Corp. (1)
Rakuten Crimson House 1-14-1 Tamagawa, Setagaya-ku, Tokyo, 158-0094, Japan (54.78%)
Tel.: (81) 5055265531
Web Site: http://comm.rakuten.co.jp
Telecommunication Servicesb

N.A.I.C.S.: 517111

Rakuten Deutschland GmbH (1)
Geisfelder Str 16, 96050, Bamberg, Germany
Tel.: (49) 95140839100
Web Site: http://www.rakuten.de
E-Commerce Online Services
N.A.I.C.S.: 423620
Breno Ribeiro (Mgr-IT)

Rakuten Direct, Inc. (1)
Tamagawa 1, Setagaya-ku, Tokyo, 158-0094, Japan
Tel.: (81) 120 22 55 66
Web Site: http://www.kenko.com
Electronic Shopping Services
N.A.I.C.S.: 456110
Noriaki Komori (Pres & CEO)

Rakuten General Insurance Co., Ltd. (1)
Tel.: (81) 120849028
Web Site: https://www.rakuten-sonpo.co.jp
Non-Life Insurance Services
N.A.I.C.S.: 524128

Rakuten Insurance Planning Co., Ltd. (1)
Rakuten Crimson House Aoyama 2-6-21 Minamiaoyama, Minato-ku, Tokyo, 102-0083, Japan
Tel.: (81) 120994294
Web Site: https://hoken.rakuten.co.jp
Human Resource Consulting Services
N.A.I.C.S.: 541614

Rakuten Life Insurance Co., Ltd. (1)
Tel.: (81) 120849019
Web Site: https://www.rakuten-life.co.jp
Insurance Services
N.A.I.C.S.: 524113

Rakuten Realty Management Co., Ltd. (1)
Shinagawa Seaside Rakuten Tower 4-12-3 Higashi-Shinagawa, Shinagawa-ku, Tokyo, 140-0002, Japan (100%)
Tel.: (81) 3 6387 1111
Real Estate Agents & Brokers Offices
N.A.I.C.S.: 531210

Rakuten Research, Inc. (1)
Shinagawa Seaside Rakuten Tower 4-12-3 Higashi-Shinagawa, Shinagawa-ku, Tokyo, 140-0002, Japan (100%)
Tel.: (81) 3 6387 1111
Web Site: http://research.rakuten.co.jp
Database Marketing Research & Consulting Services
N.A.I.C.S.: 541910
Atsushi Tamura (CEO)

Rakuten SS Insurance Co., Ltd. (1)
Tel.: (81) 5054323600
Web Site: https://small-short-ins.rakuten.co.jp
Short Term Insurance Services
N.A.I.C.S.: 524114

Rakuten Securities, Inc. (1)
(80.01%)
Tel.: (81) 366656784
Web Site: https://www.rakuten-sec.co.jp
Sales Range: $100-124.9 Million
Emp.: 598
Securities Brokerage & Dealing Services
N.A.I.C.S.: 523150
Yuji Kusunoki (Pres)

Rakuten Travel, Inc. (1)
Shinagawa Seaside Rakuten Tower 4-13-9 Higashi-Shinagawa, Shinagawa-ku, Tokyo, 140-0002, Japan (100%)
Tel.: (81) 3 6387 1111
Web Site: http://travel.rakuten.co.jp
Sales Range: $50-74.9 Million
Emp.: 200
Online Travel Service
N.A.I.C.S.: 561510

Rakuten USA, Inc. (1)
1 Cambridge Ctr Ste 9, Cambridge, MA 02142-1612 (100%)
Tel.: (617) 491-5205
Online E-Commerce Products & Services
N.A.I.C.S.: 425120
Shawn Roberts (Head-Corp Comm)

Subsidiary (Non-US):
Ebates, Inc. (2)

Tel.: (415) 908-2200
Web Site: https://www.rakuten.com
Emp.: 150
Internet Retailer
N.A.I.C.S.: 425120
Amit Patel (CEO)

Subsidiary (Domestic):
Cartera Commerce, Inc. (3)
1 Cranberry Hill, Lexington, MA 02421
Tel.: (781) 541-6800
Web Site: http://www.cartera.com
Card-Linked Marketing Solutions
N.A.I.C.S.: 541890
Marc Mazzone (Pres & CEO)

Subsidiary (Domestic):
Rakuten LinkShare Corporation (2)
215 Park Ave S 2nd Fl, New York, NY 10003
Tel.: (646) 943-8200
Web Site: http://www.rakutenmarketing.com
Online Search, Lead Generation & Affiliate Marketing Services
N.A.I.C.S.: 425120
Yasuhisa Iida (Pres)

Subsidiary (Non-US):
LinkShare Japan K.K. (3)
1-14-1 Tamagawa, Setagaya-ku, Tokyo, 158-0094, Japan
Tel.: (81) 344559099
Web Site: https://www.linkshare.ne.jp
Online Marketing Services
N.A.I.C.S.: 541613

Subsidiary (Domestic):
Rakuten Ready, Inc. (2)
800 Concar Dr Ste 175, San Mateo, CA 94402
Web Site: http://www.rakutenready.com
Software Services
N.A.I.C.S.: 541511
Jaron Waldman (Co-Founder & CEO)

Slice Technologies, Inc. (2)
431 Florence St Ste 100, Palo Alto, CA 94301
Tel.: (650) 323-9100
Web Site: http://www.slice.com
Emp.: 50
Online Shopping Services
N.A.I.C.S.: 541511

Webgistix Corporation (2)
127 East Warm Springs Rd, Las Vegas, NV 89119
Tel.: (716) 372-5211
Web Site: http://www.webgistix.com
Sales Range: $10-24.9 Million
Emp.: 105
Outsourced Order Fulfillment Services
N.A.I.C.S.: 488510
Joseph DiSorbo (Founder & CEO)

Rakuten Vissel Kobe, Inc. (1)
4F Kobe Fukoku Life Kaigandori Building 1-2-31 Kaigandori, Chuo-ku, Kobe, 650-0024, Japan
Tel.: (81) 785998077
Web Site: https://www.vissel-kobe.co.jp
Athletic Club Services
N.A.I.C.S.: 711211
Hiroshi Mikitani (Chm)

TABIMADO CO., LTD (1)
Room 1101 LT Square 500 Chengdu North Road, Shanghai, 200003, China
Tel.: (86) 21 6351 5008
Web Site: http://www.tabimado.net.cn
Travel Agency Services
N.A.I.C.S.: 561599

Viber Media Ltd. (1)
Filiou Zannetou 2 C&F Orologas Bldg 1st Floor, Katholiki, 3021, Limassol, Cyprus (100%)
Tel.: (357) 9173967488
Web Site: http://www.viber.com
Sales Range: $1-9.9 Million
Mobile Messaging & VoIP Services
N.A.I.C.S.: 517810

Voyager moins Cher S.A.S. (1)
57 Boulevard De La Villette, 75010, Paris, France
Tel.: (33) 1 42 78 94 56

RAKUTEN GROUP, INC.

Rakuten Group, Inc.—(Continued)
Web Site:
http://www.voyagermoinscher.com
Web Hosting Services
N.A.I.C.S.: 518210

World Travel System Inc. (1)
Futakotamagawa Rise Office 8th floor
2-21-1 Tamagawa, Setagaya-ku, Tokyo,
158-0094, Japan
Tel.: (81) 354918561
Web Site: https://www.wts.jp
Emp.: 48
Airline Ticket Booking Services
N.A.I.C.S.: 561599
Hirosuke Yasuda *(Chm)*

bitWallet, Inc. (1)
4-12-3 Higashishinagawa Shinagawa Sea-
side Rakuten Tower, Shinagawa-Ku, Tokyo,
140-0002, Japan
Tel.: (81) 363879800
Web Site: http://www.edy.jp
Electronic Money Transfer Services
N.A.I.C.S.: 522320

RAL YATIRIM HOLDING A.S.
Varlik Mah Yakacik Street No 11/1
Yenimahalle, Ankara, Turkiye
Tel.: (90) 3123350628
Web Site: https://www.ralyatirim.com
Year Founded: 1976
RALYH—(IST)
Rev.: $11,103,508
Assets: $25,640,037
Liabilities: $13,798,512
Net Worth: $11,841,526
Earnings: $6,928,303
Fiscal Year-end: 12/31/22
Cotton Fabric Mfr & Whslr
N.A.I.C.S.: 313210

RALAWISE LIMITED
Unit 112 Tenth Avenue Zone 3 Dee-
side Industrial Park, Deeside, CH5
2UA, Flintshire, United Kingdom
Tel.: (44) 1244 838393
Web Site: http://www.ralawise.com
Year Founded: 1978
Sales Range: $75-99.9 Million
Emp.: 600
Men & Women Apparel Mfr
N.A.I.C.S.: 315250
Jonathan Batson *(Co-Mng Dir)*

RALCO AGENCIES LTD.
Al-Mazuda St Azot Azor, Azur, Tel
Aviv, 58001 31, Israel
Tel.: (972) 36508282
Web Site: https://www.ralco.co.il
Year Founded: 1983
RLCO—(TAE)
Rev.: $75,177,786
Assets: $40,924,436
Liabilities: $14,349,772
Net Worth: $26,574,665
Earnings: $6,318,276
Emp.: 60
Fiscal Year-end: 12/31/23
Electronics & Appliance Retailers
N.A.I.C.S.: 449210
Eliyahu Amitay *(CFO)*

RALCO CORPORATION BER-HAD
10th Floor Menara Hap Seng No 1 &
3 Jalan P Ramlee, 50250, Kuala
Lumpur, Malaysia
Tel.: (60) 323824288
Web Site: http://www.ralco.net
RALCO—(KLS)
Rev.: $13,034,384
Assets: $17,885,858
Liabilities: $8,499,722
Net Worth: $9,386,136
Earnings: ($670,757)
Emp.: 214
Fiscal Year-end: 12/31/23
Plastic Container Mfr

N.A.I.C.S.: 424130
Heng Ta Tan *(Mng Dir)*

RALEC ELECTRONIC CORPORATION
8F-13 No 79 Sec 1 Hsin Tai Wu Rd,
Hsi-Chih, Taipei, Taiwan
Tel.: (886) 2 2698 9977 TW
Web Site: http://www.ralec.com
Year Founded: 1994
Sales Range: $125-149.9 Million
Resistors Mfr
N.A.I.C.S.: 334416
Chen Yi Liao *(CEO & Chm)*

Subsidiaries:

ASJ Holdings Limited (1)
514 Chai Chee Lane #05-05/06, Bedok In-
dustrial Estate, Singapore, 469029, Singa-
pore
Tel.: (65) 6412 0800
Web Site: http://www.asj.com.sg
Sales Range: $25-49.9 Million
Emp.: 310
Holding Company; Electronic Resistor Mfr &
Distr
N.A.I.C.S.: 551112
Eng Lam Seah *(CEO)*

Subsidiary (Domestic):

ASJ Pte. Ltd. (2)
514 Chai Chee Lane 05-05/06, Bedok In-
dustrial Estate, Singapore, 469029, Singa-
pore
Tel.: (65) 6412 0800
Web Site: http://www.asj.com.sg
Electronic Resistor Mfr & Distr
N.A.I.C.S.: 334416
Daren Peng Ghee Chan *(Dir-Sls & Mktg-Distr Segment)*

Ralec Electronic Corporation - China Kunshan Factory (1)
333 Huang Pujiang Road, Kunshan,
215300, Jiangsu, China
Tel.: (86) 51257709898
Web Site: http://www.ralec.com
Resistors Mfr
N.A.I.C.S.: 334416

Ralec Electronic Corporation - Taiwan Kaohsiung Factory (1)
No 1 Central 2nd Street Nantze Export Pro-
cessing Zone, Kaohsiung, 811, Taiwan
Tel.: (886) 73661067
Web Site: http://www.ralec.com
Sales Range: $50-74.9 Million
Emp.: 200
Resistors Mfr
N.A.I.C.S.: 334416
Yi Liao Chen *(Pres)*

RALF TEICHMANN GMBH
Am Stadthafen 40, Essen, 45356,
Germany
Tel.: (49) 201834550
Web Site: http://www.teichmann-krane.de
Year Founded: 1988
Rev.: $16,424,773
Emp.: 84
Crane Installations Mfr
N.A.I.C.S.: 333923
Ralf Teichmann *(Mng Dir)*

Subsidiaries:

Krantechnik Ost GmbH (1)
Camburger Str 5, 99091, Erfurt, Germany
Tel.: (49) 3616545971
Web Site: http://www.krantechnik-ost.de
Crane Mfr
N.A.I.C.S.: 333923

RALLIS INDIA LIMITED
23rd Floor Vios Tower New Cuffe Pa-
rade Off Eastern Freeway, Wadala,
Mumbai, 400 037, Maharastra, India
Tel.: (91) 2262327400
Web Site: https://www.rallis.com
500355—(BOM)
Rev.: $337,139,685
Assets: $353,346,507

Liabilities: $136,108,736
Net Worth: $217,237,771
Earnings: $31,199,355
Emp.: 1,700
Fiscal Year-end: 03/31/21
Pesticide Mfr
N.A.I.C.S.: 325320
Ravindra R. Joshi *(VP-Tech Transfer)*

Subsidiaries:

KSCMF Ltd. (1)
Building II Floor III Block Next to Hotel
Chandrika 8 Cunningham Road, Bengaluru,
560 052, India
Tel.: (91) 8022268051
Agricultural Support Services
N.A.I.C.S.: 115116

Metahelix Life Sciences Limited (1)
Plot No 3 KIADB 4th Phase Bommasandra,
Bengaluru, 560099, India
Tel.: (91) 8110420500
Agricultural Support Services
N.A.I.C.S.: 115116

RALMANA PTY. LTD.
4 5 Kirke Street, Balcatta, 6021, WA,
Australia
Tel.: (61) 893453999 AU
Web Site: http://www.rjv.com.au
Year Founded: 1955
Engineeering Services
N.A.I.C.S.: 541330
John Vincent *(Mng Dir)*

RALOS NEW ENERGIES AG
Kuhbergstrasse 28, 34131, Kassel,
Hesse, Germany
Tel.: (49) 6151951650
Sales Range: $150-199.9 Million
Emp.: 144
Engineeering Services
N.A.I.C.S.: 541330
Martin Meurer *(Chm, CFO & Member-Mgmt Bd)*

RAM CONSTRUCTION INC.
8369 River Way, Delta, V4G 1G2,
BC, Canada
Tel.: (604) 940-5265
Web Site: https://www.ramconst.com
Year Founded: 1986
Construction Services
N.A.I.C.S.: 236220
Steve Knoblauch *(Founder)*

RAM INFO LTD.
3-225/SH/401 4th Floor Sterling
Heights Mahindra Mind Space, Kavuri
Hills GB PET Phase 2 Road, Hydera-
bad, 500 033, India
Tel.: (91) 4023541894
Web Site: https://www.raminfo.com
Year Founded: 1995
530951—(BOM)
Rev.: $10,041,137
Assets: $13,103,747
Liabilities: $9,285,271
Net Worth: $3,818,476
Earnings: $699,131
Emp.: 71
Fiscal Year-end: 03/31/23
Information Technology Consulting
Services
N.A.I.C.S.: 541512
Lingamdinne Srinath Reddy *(Mng Dir)*

RAM RATNA WIRES LIMITED
Ram Ratna House Victoriamill Com-
pound Utopia City, Worli Pandurang
Budha Karm Marg, Mumbai, 400 013,
India
Tel.: (91) 2224924144
Web Site: https://www.rrshramik.com
Year Founded: 1992
RAMRAT—(NSE)
Rev.: $318,507,763
Assets: $99,357,269

Liabilities: $60,294,359
Net Worth: $39,062,910
Earnings: $5,635,106
Emp.: 842
Fiscal Year-end: 03/31/23
Copper Wires Mfr
N.A.I.C.S.: 331420
Tribhuvanprasad Kabra *(Chm & Co-Mng Dir)*

Subsidiaries:

Global Copper Private Limited (1)
Survey No 65/66 Jarod-Samlaya Road, Vil-
lage Garadiya Taluka Savli District, Vado-
dara, 391520, India
Tel.: (91) 7046051520
Web Site: https://www.globalcopper.co.in
Copper Tube Mfr
N.A.I.C.S.: 331420

RAM TECHNOLOGY CO., LTD.
285 Jubuk-ro, Yangji-myeon Cheoin-
gu, Yongin, Gyeonggi-do, Korea
(South)
Tel.: (82) 313231119
Web Site: https://www.ramtech.co.kr
Year Founded: 2001
171010—(KRS)
Rev.: $51,406,471
Assets: $63,447,691
Liabilities: $23,858,483
Net Worth: $39,589,207
Earnings: $4,647,419
Emp.: 87
Fiscal Year-end: 12/31/22
Chemicals Used In Semiconductors
N.A.I.C.S.: 325990
Jun Ing Kil *(Chm)*

RAMA PAPER MILLS LIMITED
26/6 Ground Floor East Patel Nagar,
New Delhi, 110 008, India
Tel.: (91) 1143158250
Web Site:
https://www.ramapaper.com
500357—(BOM)
Rev.: $9,713,398
Assets: $9,467,166
Liabilities: $9,367,964
Net Worth: $99,203
Earnings: ($661,987)
Emp.: 172
Fiscal Year-end: 03/31/23
Printing Paper Mfr
N.A.I.C.S.: 322299
Pramod Kumar Agarwal *(Mng Dir)*

RAMA PETROCHEMICALS LTD
51/52 Free Press House, Nariman
Point, Mumbai, 400021, India
Tel.: (91) 2222834123
Web Site:
https://www.ramapetrochemicals.com
Year Founded: 1985
500358—(BOM)
Rev.: $59,933
Assets: $300,276
Liabilities: $7,480,164
Net Worth: ($7,179,889)
Earnings: ($245,017)
Emp.: 4
Fiscal Year-end: 03/31/21
Sewage Treatment Services
N.A.I.C.S.: 221320
Deonath N. Singh *(Exec Dir)*

RAMA PHOSPHATES LTD.
51/52 Free Press House Nariman
Point, Mumbai, 400 021, India
Tel.: (91) 2222833355
Web Site:
https://www.ramaphosphates.com
Year Founded: 1984
524037—(BOM)
Rev.: $79,315,987
Assets: $42,444,934

Liabilities: $14,560,564
Net Worth: $27,884,370
Earnings: $5,747,919
Emp.: 518
Fiscal Year-end: 03/31/21
Chemical Fertiliser Mfr
N.A.I.C.S.: 325314
Haresh D. Ramsinghani (Chm & Mng Dir)

RAMA STEEL TUBES LIMITED
B-5 3rd Floor Main Road, Ghazipur, New Delhi, 110096, India
Tel.: (91) 1143446600
Web Site: https://www.ramasteel.com
Year Founded: 1974
RAMASTEEL—(NSE)
Rev.: $65,052,283
Assets: $33,791,722
Liabilities: $20,149,297
Net Worth: $13,642,424
Earnings: $1,689,611
Emp.: 85
Fiscal Year-end: 03/31/21
Steel Products Mfr
N.A.I.C.S.: 331110
Kapil Datta (Officer-Compliance & Sec)

RAMA VISION LIMITED
23 Najafgarh Road Indl Area Shivaji Marg, New Delhi, 110015, India
Tel.: (91) 1145349999
Web Site:
   https://www.ramavisionltd.com
523289—(BOM)
Rev.: $7,590,738
Assets: $3,489,759
Liabilities: $1,039,420
Net Worth: $2,450,339
Earnings: $41,824
Emp.: 111
Fiscal Year-end: 03/31/21
Babycare Products Mfr
N.A.I.C.S.: 325620
Satish Jain (Chm & Mng Dir)

RAMALLAH SUMMER RESORTS COMPANY
Arizona Bldg - Main St, PO Box 446, Ramallah, Palestine
Tel.: (970) 97222956488
Year Founded: 1945
RSR—(PAL)
Rev.: $916,171
Assets: $21,381,729
Liabilities: $1,554,178
Net Worth: $19,827,551
Earnings: $460,705
Fiscal Year-end: 12/31/23
Home Management Services
N.A.I.C.S.: 721110
Khalil Salem Khalil Hanania (Chm)

RAMASIGNS INDUSTRIES LIMITED
Unit No 3 Ground Floor, Vimala Bhavan Sharma Industrial Estate Walbhat Road Goregaon East, Mumbai, 400 063, Maharashtra, India
Tel.: (91) 2261087777
Web Site: https://www.ramasigns.in
Year Founded: 1981
515127—(BOM)
Rev.: $5,316,684
Assets: $8,169,365
Liabilities: $5,820,556
Net Worth: $2,348,809
Earnings: $36,225
Emp.: 97
Fiscal Year-end: 03/31/21
Signages & Digital Mediaconsumable Mfr
N.A.I.C.S.: 541870
Pankaj Hasmukhlal Jobalia (Exec Dir)

RAMBLER METALS & MINING PLC
3 Sheen Road Richmond Upon Thames, Richmond, TW9 1AD, Surrey, United Kingdom
Tel.: (44) 207 096 0662
Web Site:
   http://www.ramblermines.com
RMM—(LSE)
Rev.: $28,176,000
Assets: $124,320,000
Liabilities: $47,815,000
Net Worth: $76,505,000
Earnings: ($13,998,000)
Emp.: 218
Fiscal Year-end: 12/31/21
Copper & Gold Mining Services
N.A.I.C.S.: 212230
Tim Sanford (Sec & VP)

RAMBOLL GRUPPEN A/S
Hennemanns Arre 53, 2300, Copenhagen, Denmark
Tel.: (45) 45986000   DK
Web Site: http://www.ramboll.com
Year Founded: 1945
Sales Range: $550-599.9 Million
Emp.: 10,000
Engineeering Services
N.A.I.C.S.: 541330
Vidya Basarkod (Dir-Engrg Centre-India)

Subsidiaries:

DevConsultants Limited (1)
House No 69 Road No 16 Block-A, Banani, Dhaka, 1213, Bangladesh
Tel.: (880) 255035214
Web Site: https://www.devconbd.com
Management Consulting Services
N.A.I.C.S.: 541611

Henning Larsen Architects A/S (1)
Vesterbrogade 76, 1620, Copenhagen, Denmark
Tel.: (45) 82333000
Web Site: https://henninglarsen.com
Architectural Services
N.A.I.C.S.: 541310
Eva Ravnborg (Dir)

Ramboll (Thailand) Co., Ltd. (1)
92/31A 12th Floor Sathorn Thani Building 2, North Sathorn Road Silom, Bangrak, Bangkok, 10500, Thailand
Tel.: (66) 22671500
Engineeering Services
N.A.I.C.S.: 541330

Ramboll Danmark A/S (1)
Hannemanns Alle 53, 2300, Copenhagen, Denmark
Tel.: (45) 986000
Web Site: http://www.ramboll.dk
Sales Range: $350-399.9 Million
Emp.: 1,600
Engineeering Services
N.A.I.C.S.: 541330

Ramboll Eesti AS (1)
Laki 34, Tallinn, 12915, Estonia
Tel.: (372) 6645808
Web Site: http://www.ramboll.ee
Engineeering Services
N.A.I.C.S.: 541330
Kristoffer Bergholt (Mgr-Engrg)

Ramboll Environ Germany GmbH (1)
Friedrich-Ebert-Strasse 55, 45127, Essen, Germany
Tel.: (49) 201438830
Engineeering Services
N.A.I.C.S.: 541330
Chris M. Keller (Principal & Mng Dir)

Ramboll Environ, Inc. (1)
4350 N Fairfax Dr Ste 300, Arlington, VA 22203-1619
Tel.: (703) 516-2300
Web Site: http://www.ramboll-environ.com
Emp.: 2,100
Public Health & Environmental Risk Management Consulting Services

N.A.I.C.S.: 541690
Guy Lewis (Fin Dir)

Ramboll Finland Oy (1)
PL 25 Itsehallintokuja 3, PO Box 3, Espoo, 02601, Finland
Tel.: (358) 20755611
Web Site: http://www.fi.ramboll.com
Sales Range: $150-199.9 Million
Emp.: 1,000
Engineeering Services
N.A.I.C.S.: 541330
Markku Moilanen (CEO)

Ramboll Future as (1)
Sondre Kullerod 6, PO Box 1071, 3204, Sandefjord, Norway
Tel.: (47) 33487800
Engineeering Services
N.A.I.C.S.: 541330

Ramboll Hannemann og Hojlund Ingeniortut Siunnersuisarfik A/S (1)
Imaneq 32 2 sal, PO Box 850, 3900, Nuuk, Greenland
Tel.: (299) 324088
Web Site: http://www.ramboll.gl
Sales Range: $25-49.9 Million
Emp.: 25
Engineeering Services
N.A.I.C.S.: 541330

Subsidiary (Domestic):

Ramboll Hannemann og Hojlund Ingeniortut Siunnersuisarfik A/S (2)
Glahnip Aqq 15, PO Box 426, 3911, Sisimiut, Greenland
Tel.: (299) 866130
Web Site: http://www.ramboll.gl
Sales Range: $25-49.9 Million
Emp.: 15
Engineering Services
N.A.I.C.S.: 541330
Jorn Hansen (Office Mgr)

Ramboll IMS Ingenieurgesellschaft mbh (1)
Stadtdeich 7, 20097, Hamburg, Germany
Tel.: (49) 40328180
Web Site: http://www.ims-ing.de
Engineeering Services
N.A.I.C.S.: 541330
Peter Ruland (Mng Dir)

Ramboll Informatik A/S (1)
Hannemanns Alle 53, DK-2300, Copenhagen, Denmark
Tel.: (45) 45985400
Web Site: http://www.ramboll.dk
Sales Range: $700-749.9 Million
Emp.: 5,000
IT Solutions
N.A.I.C.S.: 541519
Bjarne Mann (Dir-Custom Dev)

Ramboll Management A/S (1)
Olof Palmes Alle 20, 8200, Arhus, Denmark
Tel.: (45) 89447800
Web Site: http://www.ramboll-management.com
Sales Range: $100-124.9 Million
Emp.: 400
Engineering Consulting Services
N.A.I.C.S.: 541690
Tonny Johansen (CEO & Mng Dir)

Ramboll Management Consulting GmbH (1)
Chilehaus C Burchardstrasse 13, 20095, Hamburg, Germany
Tel.: (49) 403020200
Web Site: http://www.ramboll.de
Engineeering Services
N.A.I.C.S.: 541330

Ramboll Norge AS (1)
Hoffsveien 4, 0275, Oslo, Norway
Tel.: (47) 22518000
Web Site: http://www.ramboll.no
Sales Range: $25-49.9 Million
Emp.: 250
Engineeering Services
N.A.I.C.S.: 541330
Ole-Petter Thunes (CEO)

Ramboll Nyvig Ldt. (1)
Hannemanns Alle 53, DK-2300, Copenhagen, Denmark
Tel.: (45) 45743600

Web Site: http://www.nyvig.dk
Transport Planning Services
N.A.I.C.S.: 488999

Ramboll Poland Sp. z oo (1)
ul Mlynarska 48, 01-171, Warsaw, Poland
Tel.: (48) 226310550
Web Site: http://www.ramboll.pl
Engineeering Services
N.A.I.C.S.: 541330

Ramboll Romania S.R.L. (1)
Sf Constantin Street 10, Sector 1, Bucharest, Romania
Tel.: (40) 314056027
Web Site: http://www.ramboll.ro
Sales Range: $25-49.9 Million
Emp.: 10
Engineeering Services
N.A.I.C.S.: 541330
Daniela Cancescu (Mgr-Bus Dev)

Ramboll Sverige AB (1)
Krukmakargatan 21, 118 51, Stockholm, Sweden
Tel.: (46) 10 615 6000
Web Site: http://www.se.ramboll.com
Sales Range: $200-249.9 Million
Emp.: 1,215
Engineeering Services
N.A.I.C.S.: 541330
Bent Johannesson (CEO & Mng Dir)

Ramboll Towers Sp. z o.o. (1)
ul J Uphagena 27, 80-237, Gdansk, Poland
Tel.: (48) 583484174
Construction Engineering Services
N.A.I.C.S.: 541330

Ramboll Transport Germany Ramboll IMS Ingenieurgesellschaft mbH (1)
Zur Giesserei 19-27c, 76227, Karlsruhe, Germany
Tel.: (49) 72194188830
Engineeering Services
N.A.I.C.S.: 541330
Alan Pauling (Dir-Grp Market-Transport)

Ramboll UK Holding Ltd. (1)
240 Blackfriars Road, London, SE1 8NW, United Kingdom
Tel.: (44) 2076315291
Web Site: https://uk.ramboll.com
Architectural Services
N.A.I.C.S.: 541310

Ramboll UK Limited (1)
240 Blackfriars Road, London, SE1 8NW, United Kingdom
Tel.: (44) 2076315291
Web Site: http://www.ramboll.co.uk
Engineeering Services
N.A.I.C.S.: 541330
Dan Harvey (Dir-Environment & Transport)

ZAO Ramboll Russia (1)
Mazhorov per 14 Bld 11 Business Centre ABC, 107023, Moscow, Russia
Tel.: (7) 495 259 2564
Web Site: http://ramboll.com
Engineeering Services
N.A.I.C.S.: 541330

Subsidiary (Domestic):

LLC Poyry (2)
Logovsky prospect 266 Liter V, 196084, Saint Petersburg, Russia
Tel.: (7) 812 320 8703
Web Site: http://www.poyry.ru
Sales Range: $25-49.9 Million
Emp.: 15
Construction Engineering Services
N.A.I.C.S.: 541330

Unit (Domestic):

LLC Poyry - Management Consulting (3)
Korovy Val Street 7 Office 211, 117049, Moscow, Russia
Tel.: (7) 495 937 5257
Emp.: 12
Engineering Consulting Services
N.A.I.C.S.: 541330
Jean-Paul Ternisien (Gen Mgr)

RAMCHANDRA LEASING & FINANCING LIMITED

Ramchandra Leasing & Financing Limited—(Continued)
201/1 Rudra Plaza Complex Opp VMC Gas Office, Dandia Bazar Main Road, Vadodara, 390001, Gujarat, India
Tel.: (91) 9820130029
Web Site: http://www.ramchandrafinance.com
Year Founded: 1993
538540—(BOM)
Rev.: $56,627
Assets: $863,366
Liabilities: $203,453
Net Worth: $659,912
Earnings: $1,655
Emp.: 5
Fiscal Year-end: 03/31/23
Financial Services
N.A.I.C.S.: 523999
Asmita Sanjaykumar Purohit *(Compliance Officer & Sec)*

RAMCO INDUSTRIES LIMITED
Auras Corporate Centre 98-A Dr Radhakrishnan Road Mylapore, Chennai, 600 004, Tamil Nadu, India
Tel.: (91) 4428478585
Web Site: https://www.ramcoindltd.com
Year Founded: 1938
532369—(BOM)
Rev.: $177,341,167
Assets: $535,360,434
Liabilities: $69,678,820
Net Worth: $465,681,614
Earnings: $12,725,772
Emp.: 1,704
Fiscal Year-end: 03/31/23
Cement Mfr
N.A.I.C.S.: 327310
S. Balamurugasundaram *(Officer-Compliance, Sec & Gen Mgr-Legal)*

Subsidiaries:

Ramco Industries Limited - Arakonam Factory (1)
Winterpet Post, Arakkonam, 631005, Tamil Nadu, India
Tel.: (91) 417 722 4932
Web Site: https://www.ramcoindltd.com
Fiber Cement Sheet Mfr
N.A.I.C.S.: 327390

Ramco Industries Limited - Gangaikondan Factory (1)
Plot No A-12 Sipcot Industrial Growth Centre, Gangaikondan, 627352, Tamil Nadu, India
Tel.: (91) 462 2950029
Sales Range: $25-49.9 Million
Emp.: 70
Fiber Cement Sheet Mfr
N.A.I.C.S.: 327390

Ramco Industries Limited - Kharagpur Factory (1)
Village-Dewanmaro Ayma P O Hariatara, Pachim Medinipur District, Kharagpur, 721301, West Bengal, India
Tel.: (91) 322 220 1700
Web Site: https://www.ramcoindltd.com
Cement Sheet Mfr
N.A.I.C.S.: 327390

Ramco Industries Limited - Maksi Factory (1)
Agra-Bombay Road, Shajapur District, Maksi, 456106, Madhya Pradesh, India
Tel.: (91) 736 323 3072
Web Site: https://www.ramcoindltd.com
Fiber Cement Sheet Mfr
N.A.I.C.S.: 327390

Ramco Industries Limited - Rane Bennur Factory (1)
Ranebennur Taluk, Haveri District, Ranebennuru, 581143, Karnataka, India
Tel.: (91) 8373 248756
Cement Sheet Mfr
N.A.I.C.S.: 327120

Ramco Industries Limited - Silvassa Factory (1)
Survey No 204 / 3 Silly Road Galanda Village, Dadra & Nagar Haveli, Silvassa, 396230, India
Tel.: (91) 260 6546494
Fiber Cement Sheet Mfr
N.A.I.C.S.: 327390

Sudharsanam Investments Limited (1)
47 PSK Nagar, Rajapalayam, 626 108, India
Tel.: (91) 4563235688
Financial Investment Services
N.A.I.C.S.: 523999

RAMCO SYSTEMS LIMITED
64 Sardar Patel Road, Taramani, Chennai, 600 113, India
Tel.: (91) 4422354510
Web Site: https://www.ramco.com
Year Founded: 1997
532370—(BOM)
Rev.: $87,478,892
Assets: $128,463,290
Liabilities: $39,076,947
Net Worth: $89,386,343
Earnings: $7,739,277
Emp.: 1,693
Fiscal Year-end: 03/31/21
Software Development Services
N.A.I.C.S.: 541511
P. R. Venketrama Raja *(Founder & Chm)*

Subsidiaries:

RSL Enterprise Solutions (Pty) Ltd (1)
2nd Floor Suite 56 03 102 Stephen Dlamini Road, PO No 1228, Musgrave, Durban, 4001, South Africa
Tel.: (27) 313133326
Software Services
N.A.I.C.S.: 541519

Ramco System Inc. (1)
17th Floor BDO Equitable Tower 8751 Paseo de Roxas Metro Manila, Makati, 1227, Philippines
Tel.: (63) 23101716
Software Services
N.A.I.C.S.: 541512

Ramco Systems Australia Pty Ltd (1)
Level 17 60 City Road Southbank, Melbourne, 3006, VIC, Australia
Tel.: (61) 407474906
Software Services
N.A.I.C.S.: 541519

Ramco Systems Corporation (1)
Tel.: (609) 620-4800
Software Development Services
N.A.I.C.S.: 541511

Ramco Systems FZ-LLC (1)
Suite No 210 2nd Floor BT Building EIB 04, PO Box 500189, Dubai, United Arab Emirates
Tel.: (971) 43636784
Software Services
N.A.I.C.S.: 541519

Ramco Systems Pte. Ltd. (1)
79 Anson Road 15-04/05, Singapore, 079906, Singapore
Tel.: (65) 67431513
Software Services
N.A.I.C.S.: 541519

Ramco Systems Sdn. Bhd. (1)
3B-5-3 Block 3B Level 5 Plaza Sentral Jalan Stesen Sentral 5, 50470, Kuala Lumpur, Malaysia
Tel.: (60) 322603978
Software Services
N.A.I.C.S.: 541519

RAMELIUS RESOURCES LIMITED
Level 1 130 Royal Street, Perth, 6004, WA, Australia
Tel.: (61) 892021127
Web Site: https://www.rameliusresources.com
RMS—(ASX)
Rev.: $589,324,250
Assets: $1,064,334,932
Liabilities: $176,829,593
Net Worth: $887,505,338
Earnings: $144,619,390
Emp.: 300
Fiscal Year-end: 06/30/24
Mineral Exploration Services
N.A.I.C.S.: 212390
Kevin Mark Seymour *(Gen Mgr)*

Subsidiaries:

Ramelius Milling Services Pty. Ltd. (1)
Nepean Rd, Coolgardie, Perth, 6429, WA, Australia
Tel.: (61) 890266138
Web Site: http://www.rameliusresources.com.au
Emp.: 16
Gold Mining Services
N.A.I.C.S.: 212220

Spectrum Metals Limited (1)
Suite 1/827 Beaufort Street, Mount Lawley, Inglewood, 6052, WA, Australia
Tel.: (61) 863691195
Metal Mineral Exploration Services
N.A.I.C.S.: 212290

RAMGOPAL POLYTEX LIMITED
701 Tulsiani Chambers Free Press journal Marg Nariman Point, Mumbai, 400 021, India
Tel.: (91) 2222834838
Web Site: https://www.ramgopalpolytex.com
Year Founded: 1981
Rev.: $1,187,682
Assets: $2,921,029
Liabilities: $312,426
Net Worth: $2,608,604
Earnings: ($68,732)
Emp.: 8
Fiscal Year-end: 03/31/19
Metal Product Distr
N.A.I.C.S.: 423510
Sanjay Jatia *(Chm & Mng Dir)*

RAMI LEVI CHAIN STORES HASHIKMA MARKETING 2006 LTD.
15 Haoman Street, Jerusalem, 93420, Israel
Tel.: (972) 26481843
RMLI—(TAE)
Rev.: $1,984,224,586
Assets: $1,159,457,642
Liabilities: $985,788,353
Net Worth: $173,669,289
Earnings: $56,689,045
Fiscal Year-end: 12/31/23
Supermarkets & Other Grocery Retailers (except Convenience Retailers)
N.A.I.C.S.: 445110
Rami Levi *(Board of Directors & CEO)*

RAMKHAMHAENG HOSPITAL PUBLIC COMPANY LIMITED
436 Ramkhamhaeng Hospital Rd Ramkhamhaeng Huamak Bangkapi, Bangkok, 10240, Thailand
Tel.: (66) 27439999
Web Site: http://www.ram-hosp.co.th
Year Founded: 1976
RAM—(THA)
Rev.: $301,662,089
Assets: $1,204,417,409
Liabilities: $409,763,405
Net Worth: $794,654,005
Earnings: $41,534,460
Emp.: 7,299
Fiscal Year-end: 12/31/23
Hospital Management Services
N.A.I.C.S.: 622110
Racha Somburanasin *(Chm)*

RAMKRISHNA FORGINGS LIMITED
23 Circus Avenue, Kolkata, 700 017, West Bengal, India
Tel.: (91) 3340820900
Web Site: https://www.ramkrishnaforgings.com
Year Founded: 1981
532527—(BOM)
Rev.: $176,702,226
Assets: $369,151,364
Liabilities: $248,678,512
Net Worth: $120,472,853
Earnings: $2,821,223
Emp.: 1,896
Fiscal Year-end: 03/31/21
Screw Couplings Mfr
N.A.I.C.S.: 332722
Mahabir Prasad Jalan *(Chm)*

Subsidiaries:

Ramkrishna Forgings Limited - Plant I (1)
Plot No M-6 Phase VI, Gamaria, Jamshedpur, 832108, Jharkhand, India
Tel.: (91) 657 3040700
Metal Forging Mfr
N.A.I.C.S.: 332112

Ramkrishna Forgings Limited - Plant II (1)
7/40 Duffer Street, Liluah, Howrah, 700204, West Bengal, India
Tel.: (91) 332 654 8062
Web Site: https://www.ramkrishnaforgings.com
Metal Forging Mfr
N.A.I.C.S.: 332112

Ramkrishna Forgings Limited - Plant III & IV (1)
Plot No M-15 16 & NS-26 Phase - VII, Aditypur Industrial Area, Jamshedpur, 832109, Jharkhand, India
Tel.: (91) 6572326900
Web Site: http://www.ramkrishnaforgings.com
Sales Range: $400-449.9 Million
Metal Forging Parts Mfr
N.A.I.C.S.: 332112

RAMKY GROUP
Ramky Grandiose Ramky Towers Complex, Gachibowli, Hyderabad, 500 032, India
Tel.: (91) 4023015000
Web Site: http://www.ramky.com
Year Founded: 1994
Emp.: 4,500
Holding Company
N.A.I.C.S.: 551112
Alla Ayodhya Rami Reddy *(Chm)*

Subsidiaries:

Ramky Estates and Farms Limited (1)
Ramky Grandiose 9th Floor Ramky Towers Complex, Gachibowli, Hyderabad, 500 032, India
Tel.: (91) 40 6455 7575
Web Site: http://www.ramkyestates.com
Real Estate Development Services
N.A.I.C.S.: 531210
Aparna Alla *(Head-Project)*

Ramky Infrastructure Limited (1)
Ramky Grandiose 15th Floor Sy No 1362 4, Gachibowli, Hyderabad, 500 032, Telangana, India **(67.76%)**
Tel.: (91) 4023015000
Web Site: https://www.ramkyinfrastructure.com
Rev.: $169,387,355
Assets: $598,291,649
Liabilities: $548,799,069
Net Worth: $49,492,580
Earnings: $2,657,792

Emp.: 476
Fiscal Year-end: 03/31/2021
Construction Services
N.A.I.C.S.: 237990
Alla Ayodhya Rami Reddy *(Founder & Chm)*

Subsidiary (Domestic):

Ramky Enclave Limited (2)
Near Railway Station, Warangal, India
Tel.: (91) 88974 45679
Hazardous Waste Collection Services
N.A.I.C.S.: 562112

Ramky Pharma City (India) Limited (2)
Admin Block Commercial Hub JNPC Road No 13, Parawada Mandal, Visakhapatnam, 531 019, Andhra Pradesh, India
Tel.: (91) 8924 236001
Web Site: http://www.ramky.com
Pharmaceuticals Product Mfr
N.A.I.C.S.: 325412

RAMM PHARMA CORP.
200 82 Richmond St East, Toronto, M5C 1P1, ON, Canada
Tel.: (416) 848-7744
Web Site:
   http://www.rammpharma.com
RAMM—(CNSX)
Rev.: $3,824,860
Assets: $24,390,542
Liabilities: $2,141,139
Net Worth: $22,249,403
Earnings: ($5,830,183)
Fiscal Year-end: 10/31/23
Pharmaceuticals Product Mfr
N.A.I.C.S.: 325412
Jack Burnett *(CEO)*

RAMPART DETECTION SYSTEMS, LTD.
22242 48th Avenue Suite 203, Murrayville, Langley, V3A 3N5, BC, Canada
Tel.: (604) 533-5533 Ca
Web Site: http://www.beltgard.com
Year Founded: 2009
Sales Range: Less than $1 Million
Emp.: 10
Electromagnetic Detection Equipment Mfr
N.A.I.C.S.: 334511
Kenneth F. Swaisland *(Chm & CFO)*

RAMPHASTOS INVESTMENTS MANAGEMENT BV
Grebbeweg 111, 3911 AV, Rhenen, Netherlands
Tel.: (31) 317 722 722
Web Site:
   http://www.ramphastosinvest.com
Year Founded: 1994
Privater Equity Firm
N.A.I.C.S.: 523999
Marcel Boekhoorn *(Founder)*

Subsidiaries:

Hema B.V. (1)
Ndsm St 10, Amsterdam, 1033SB, Netherlands
Tel.: (31) 203114411
Web Site: http://www.hema.nl
Sales Range: $1-4.9 Billion
Emp.: 19,000
Department Store Chain
N.A.I.C.S.: 455110
Alex Jonker *(Dir-Logistics)*

RAMSAY HEALTH CARE LIMITED
Suite 18 03 Level 18 126 Phillip Street, Sydney, 2000, NSW, Australia
Tel.: (61) 292201000 AU
Web Site:
   http://www.ramsayhealth.com
Year Founded: 1964

RHC—(OTCIQ)
Rev.: $10,215,074,937
Assets: $14,806,315,274
Liabilities: $11,319,537,822
Net Worth: $3,486,777,452
Earnings: $391,906,185
Emp.: 77,000
Fiscal Year-end: 06/30/21
Health Care Srvices
N.A.I.C.S.: 622110
Michael S. Siddle *(Chm)*

Subsidiaries:

AH Holdings Health Care Pty Limited (1)
L 9 154 Pacific Hwy, Saint Leonards, 2065, NSW, Australia
Tel.: (61) 294333444
General Medical Services
N.A.I.C.S.: 622110

Subsidiary (Domestic):

Affinity Health Pty Limited (2)
L9 154 Pacific Highway, Saint Leonards, 2065, NSW, Australia
Tel.: (61) 294333444
Web Site: http://www.ramsayhealth.com.au
Emp.: 80
General Medical Services
N.A.I.C.S.: 622110

Subsidiary (Domestic):

AME Hospitals Pty Limited (3)
L 9 154 Pacific Highway, Saint Leonards, Sydney, 2065, NSW, Australia
Tel.: (61) 294333444
General Medical Services
N.A.I.C.S.: 622110

Subsidiary (Domestic):

Attadale Hospital Property Pty Limited (4)
21 Hislop Road, Attadale, Perth, 6156, WA, Australia
Tel.: (61) 893301000
Web Site:
   https://www.attadalerehabilitation.com.au
Sales Range: $10-24.9 Million
Emp.: 60
General Medical Services
N.A.I.C.S.: 622110
Jane Case *(Mng Dir)*

Subsidiary (Domestic):

Australian Hospital Care (Latrobe) Pty Limited (3)
L 9 154 Pacific Highway, Saint Leonards, Sydney, 2065, NSW, Australia
Tel.: (61) 294333444
General Medical Services
N.A.I.C.S.: 622110

Australian Hospital Care (Masada) Pty Limited (3)
26 Balaclava Rd, Saint Kilda, 3183, VIC, Australia
Tel.: (61) 390381300
Sales Range: $25-49.9 Million
Hospital Management Services
N.A.I.C.S.: 541618
Lisa Carter *(CEO)*

Australian Hospital Care (The Avenue) Pty Limited (3)
L 9 154 Pacific Hwy, Saint Leonards, 2065, NSW, Australia
Tel.: (61) 294333435
Web Site: http://www.ranseyhealth.com.au
General Medical Services
N.A.I.C.S.: 622110
John O'Grady *(Gen Counsel)*

Caboolture Hospital Pty Limited (3)
McKean Street, PO Box 1495, Caboolture, 4510, QLD, Australia
Tel.: (61) 754959400
Web Site:
   https://www.cabooltureprivate.com.au
Sales Range: $50-74.9 Million
General Medical Services
N.A.I.C.S.: 524114

HCoA Hospital Holdings (Australia) Pty Limited (3)

L 9 154 Pacific Highway, Saint Leonards, 2065, NSW, Australia
Tel.: (61) 294333435
General Medical Services
N.A.I.C.S.: 622110

HCoA Operations (Australia) Pty Limited (3)
L 9 154 Pacific Highway, Saint Leonards, 2065, NSW, Australia
Tel.: (61) 294333444
General Medical Services
N.A.I.C.S.: 622110

Hospital Corporation Australia Pty Limited (3)
Level 5 417 St Kilda Road, Sydney, 2060, NSW, Australia
Tel.: (61) 294333444
General Medical Services
N.A.I.C.S.: 622110

Subsidiary (Non-US):

Joondalup Hospital Pty Limited (3)
Tel.: (61) 894009400
Emp.: 3,000
General Medical Services
N.A.I.C.S.: 622110
Charlene Woodbine *(Mgr-HR)*

Subsidiary (Domestic):

Port Macquarie Hospital Pty Limited (3)
86-94 Lake Road, Port Macquarie, 2444, NSW, Australia
Tel.: (61) 265829800
Web Site:
   https://www.portmacquarieprivate.com.au
General Medical Services
N.A.I.C.S.: 622110
Connie Porter *(CEO)*

AHH Holdings Health Care Pty Limited (1)
L 9 154 Pacific Highway, Saint Leonards, Sydney, 2065, NSW, Australia
Tel.: (61) 294333444
Web Site: http://www.ramseyhealth.com.au
General Medical Services
N.A.I.C.S.: 622110

Armidale Hospital Pty Limited (1)
Rusden Street, Armidale, 2350, NSW, Australia
Tel.: (61) 2 6771 4000
Web Site:
   http://www.armidaleprivate.com.au
Emp.: 60
Hospital Management Services
N.A.I.C.S.: 622110
Mary Single *(CEO)*

Australian Hospital Care (MSH) Pty Limited (1)
Level 9 154 Pacific Highway, Saint Leonards, 2065, NSW, Australia
Tel.: (61) 294333444
Healtcare Services
N.A.I.C.S.: 621491

Australian Hospital Care (Pindara) Pty Limited (1)
Allchurch Avenue, Benowa, 4217, QLD, Australia
Tel.: (61) 755889888
Web Site:
   https://www.pindaraprivate.com.au
Sales Range: $100-124.9 Million
Emp.: 700
General Medical Services
N.A.I.C.S.: 622110

Benchmark - Beleura Pty Limited (1)
925 Nepean Highway, Mornington, 3931, VIC, Australia
Tel.: (61) 359760888
Emp.: 500
General Medical Services
N.A.I.C.S.: 622110

Bowral Management Company Pty Limited (1)
99 Bowral Street, Bowral, Bowral, 2576, NSW, Australia
Tel.: (61) 248629400
Healtcare Services
N.A.I.C.S.: 621491

Dandenong Valley Private Hospital Pty Limited (1)
Corner Police Gladstone Roads Corner Gladstone Road, Mulgrave, Melbourne, 3170, VIC, Australia
Tel.: (61) 397909333
Web Site: http://www.healthycare.com.au
General Medical Services
N.A.I.C.S.: 622110

Exeter Medical Limited (1)
Admiral House Grenadier Road Exeter Business Park, Exeter, EX1 3QF, United Kingdom
Tel.: (44) 139 236 3534
Web Site: https://www.exetermedical.co.uk
Health Care Srvices
N.A.I.C.S.: 621610

Glenferrie Private Hospital Pty Limited (1)
29 Hilda Crescent, Hawthorn, 3122, VIC, Australia
Tel.: (61) 39 009 3800
Web Site:
   https://www.glenferrieprivate.com.au
Hospital Care Services
N.A.I.C.S.: 622110
Lisa McFadden *(CEO)*

Hospital Developments Pty Limited (1)
Fairfax Road, Warners Bay, Newcastle, 2282, NSW, Australia
Tel.: (61) 249584288
Web Site:
   http://www.warnersbayprivate.com.au
Healtcare Services
N.A.I.C.S.: 621491
Sherin Ruwitt *(CEO)*

Ramsay Aged Care Holdings Pty Limited (1)
L 9 154 Pacific Highway, Saint Leonards, 2065, NSW, Australia
Tel.: (61) 294333444
General Medical Services
N.A.I.C.S.: 622110

Subsidiary (Domestic):

Ramsay Aged Care Properties Pty Limited (2)
L 9 154 Pacific Highway, Saint Leonards, Saint Leonards, 2065, NSW, Australia
Tel.: (61) 294333444
Web Site: http://www.ramsayhealth.com.au
General Medical Services
N.A.I.C.S.: 622110

Ramsay Centauri Pty Limited (1)
L 9 154 Pacific Highway, Greenwich, 2065, NSW, Australia
Tel.: (61) 294333444
General Medical Services
N.A.I.C.S.: 622110

Subsidiary (Domestic):

Health Care Corporation Pty Limited (2)
L 9 154 Pacific Highway, Saint Leonards, 2525, NSW, Australia
Tel.: (61) 294333444
General Medical Services
N.A.I.C.S.: 622110

Subsidiary (Domestic):

Westmead Private Hospital Pty Limited (3)
Cnr Mons and Darcy Roads 12, PO Box 161, Westmead, 2145, NSW, Australia
Tel.: (61) 288379000
Acute Medical & Surgical Services
N.A.I.C.S.: 622110

Ramsay Generale de Sante SA (1)
39 Rue Mstislav Rostropovitch, 75017, Paris, France (50.9%)
Tel.: (33) 187862300
Web Site: http://www.ramsaygds.fr
Rev.: $5,282,660,240
Assets: $8,337,170,296
Liabilities: $6,815,749,408
Net Worth: $1,521,420,888
Earnings: $156,969,072
Emp.: 36,000
Fiscal Year-end: 06/30/2022
Hospital Healthcare Services

RAMSAY HEALTH CARE LIMITED

Ramsay Health Care Limited—(Continued)
N.A.I.C.S.: 622110
Lorenzo Pellicioli (Vice Chm)

Subsidiary (Domestic):

Clinque de la Muette SAS (2)
46-48 rue Nicolo, 75016, Paris, France
Tel.: (33) 140723333
Web Site: https://clinique-de-la-muette-paris.ramsaysante.fr
General Medical Services
N.A.I.C.S.: 622110

Subsidiary (Non-US):

La Clinique du Mousseau SAS (2)
Tel.: (33) 160901010
General Medical Services
N.A.I.C.S.: 622110

Ramsay Health Care (1)
Level 7 Tower B 7 Westbourne Street, Saint Leonards, Sydney, 2065, NSW, Australia
Tel.: (61) 29 433 3444
Web Site: http://www.ramsayhealthcare.com.au
General Medical Services
N.A.I.C.S.: 622110

Ramsay Health Care Australia Pty Limited (1)
Level 7 National Australia Bank Building 255 Adelaide Street, Brisbane, 4000, QLD, Australia
Tel.: (61) 732295188
General Medical Services
N.A.I.C.S.: 622110

Subsidiary (Domestic):

Adelaide Clinic Holdings Pty Limited (2)
33 Park Terrace, Gilberton, 5081, SA, Australia
Tel.: (61) 882698100
Web Site: https://www.ramsaymentalhealth.com.au
General Medical Services
N.A.I.C.S.: 622110
Patrick Grier (Mng Dir)

New Farm Hospitals Pty Limited (2)
22 Sargent Street, New Farm, Brisbane, 4005, QLD, Australia
Tel.: (61) 732549100
Web Site: https://www.ramsaymentalhealth.com.au
Sales Range: $25-49.9 Million
Emp.: 150
General Medical Services
N.A.I.C.S.: 622110
Mitchell Haines (Gen Mgr)

North Shore Private Hospital Pty Limited (2)
Westbourne Street, Locked Bag 1008, St Leonards Crows Nest Delivery Centre, Sydney, 2065, NSW, Australia
Tel.: (61) 284253000
General Medical Services
N.A.I.C.S.: 622110

Ramsay Health Care (Asia Pacific) Pty Limited (2)
L 9 154 Pacific Highway, Saint Leonards, Sydney, 2065, NSW, Australia
Tel.: (61) 2 94333444
Web Site: http://www.ramsayhealth.com.au
Sales Range: $25-49.9 Million
Emp.: 140
General Medical Services
N.A.I.C.S.: 622110

Ramsay Health Care (South Australia) Pty Limited (2)
33 Park Terrace, Gilberton, 5081, SA, Australia
Tel.: (61) 882698100
Web Site: http://www.ramsayhealth.com.au
Emp.: 200
General Medical Services
N.A.I.C.S.: 622110
Ian Patrick Stewart Grier (CEO)

Ramsay Health Care (Victoria) Pty Limited (2)
31 Albert Road, Melbourne, 3004, VIC, Australia

Tel.: (61) 392568311
Web Site: http://www.albertroadclinic.com.au
General Medical Services
N.A.I.C.S.: 622110

Ramsay Professional Services Pty Limited (2)
23 Piper Street, Tamworth, 2340, NSW, Australia
Tel.: (61) 267645687
Web Site: http://www.ramsayhealth.com.au
Sales Range: $10-24.9 Million
Emp.: 3
Physiotherapy Services
N.A.I.C.S.: 621399
Tony Gibson (Mgr-Practice)

Sibdeal Pty Limited (2)
72 Phillip Street, Thirroul, Wollongong, 2515, NSW, Australia
Tel.: (61) 242672811
Web Site: https://www.lawrencehargrave.com.au
Emp.: 100
Healtcare Services
N.A.I.C.S.: 621491
Lauren Sharpe (Mgr-GP Liaison)

Ramsay Health Care Investments Pty Limited (2)
L 9 154 Pacific Highway, St Leonards, Sydney, 2065, NSW, Australia
Tel.: (61) 294333444
Investment Management Service
N.A.I.C.S.: 523999

Ramsay Health Care UK (1)
1 Hassett Street, Bedford, MK40 1HA, Bedfordshire, United Kingdom
Tel.: (44) 123 427 3473
Web Site: https://www.ramsayhealth.co.uk
Sales Range: $500-549.9 Million
Emp.: 45
Healtcare Services
N.A.I.C.S.: 524114
Hiten Mehta (CFO)

Subsidiary (Domestic):

Ramsay Health Care Holdings UK Limited (2)
1 Hassett Street, Bedford, MK40 1HA, Bedfordshire, United Kingdom
Tel.: (44) 1234273473
Web Site: http://www.ramsayhealth.co.uk
Sales Range: $10-24.9 Million
General Medical Services
N.A.I.C.S.: 622110

Subsidiary (Domestic):

Ramsay Health Care UK Operations Limited (3)
Level 18 Tower 42 25 Old Broad Street, London, EC2N 1HQ, United Kingdom
Tel.: (44) 207 847 2850
Web Site: https://www.ramsayhealth.co.uk
Sales Range: $10-24.9 Million
Emp.: 7,600
General Medical Services
N.A.I.C.S.: 622110

Unit (Domestic):

The Nottingham Woodthorpe Hospital (3)
748 Mansfield Road, Woodthorpe, Nottingham, NG5 3FZ, United Kingdom
Web Site: http://www.nottinghamhospital.co.uk
Sales Range: $10-24.9 Million
Hospital Services
N.A.I.C.S.: 622110

Ramsay Hospital Holdings (Queensland) Pty Limited (1)
L 9 154 Pacific Hwy, Saint Leonards, 2065, NSW, Australia
Tel.: (61) 294333444
Web Site: http://www.ramsayhealth.com.au
Emp.: 130
General Medical Services
N.A.I.C.S.: 622110
Chris Rex (Mng Dir)

Ramsay Hospital Holdings Pty Limited (1)
Unit 9 154 Pacific Highway, Saint Leonards, 2065, NSW, Australia

Tel.: (61) 294333444
Healtcare Services
N.A.I.C.S.: 621491
Lisa Chisholm (Office Mgr)

RAMSDENS FINANCIAL LIMITED

Birchwood House Dalby Way Coulby Newham, Middlesbrough, TS8 0TW, United Kingdom
Tel.: (44) 16 4257 9975
Web Site: https://www.ramsdensforcash.co.uk
Year Founded: 1987
Sales Range: $10-24.9 Million
Emp.: 324
Foreign Currency Exchange Services
N.A.I.C.S.: 523160
Peter Kenyon (CEO)

RAMSDENS HOLDINGS PLC

Unit 16 The Parkway Centre, Coulby Newham, Middlesbrough, TS8 0TJ, United Kingdom
Tel.: (44) 1642579957 UK
Web Site: https://www.ramsdensplc.com
Year Founded: 2014
RFX—(AIM)
Rev.: $74,838,420
Assets: $77,351,904
Liabilities: $29,980,656
Net Worth: $47,371,248
Earnings: $7,461,198
Fiscal Year-end: 09/30/22
Jewelry & Silverware Manufacturing
N.A.I.C.S.: 339910
Peter Edward Kenyon (CEO)

RAMSONS PROJECTS LIMITED

Unit No 501 5th Floor SAS Tower Tower B Sector-38, Gurgaon, 122001, Haryana, India
Tel.: (91) 1244679000
Web Site: https://www.ramsonsprojects.com
Year Founded: 1994
530925—(BOM)
Rev.: $45,618
Assets: $1,314,959
Liabilities: $3,686
Net Worth: $1,311,274
Earnings: $17,772
Fiscal Year-end: 03/31/22
Financial Services
N.A.I.C.S.: 523999

RAMTECH SOFTWARE SOLUTIONS PVT. LTD.

A-6 Sector-67, Noida, 201309, India
Tel.: (91) 1206757900
Web Site: http://www.ramtech-corp.com
Year Founded: 1992
Information Management Technology & Services
N.A.I.C.S.: 541512
Manish Sanwalka (Founder & Pres)

Subsidiaries:

Analytical Surveys, Inc. (1)
106 Chestnut St E, Stillwater, MN 55082-5116
Tel.: (262) 574-9000
Sales Range: $25-49.9 Million
Emp.: 25
Data Capture & Management Services
N.A.I.C.S.: 518210

RANA GRUBER AS

Mjolanveien 29 Gullsmedvik, PO Box 434, 8601, Mo i Rana, Norway
Tel.: (47) 75137300 NO
Web Site: https://www.ranagruber.no
Year Founded: 1964

INTERNATIONAL PUBLIC

7XH—(DEU)
Rev.: $131,472,289
Assets: $133,479,217
Liabilities: $57,453,630
Net Worth: $76,025,587
Earnings: $44,728,062
Emp.: 279
Fiscal Year-end: 12/31/22
Iron Ore Mining Services
N.A.I.C.S.: 212210
Erlend Hoyen (CFO)

RANA SUGARS LIMITED

SCO 49-50 Sector 8 C Madhya Marg, Chandigarh, 160018, India
Tel.: (91) 1722540007
Web Site: https://www.ranagroup.com
Year Founded: 1992
507490—(BOM)
Rev.: $197,935,999
Assets: $175,277,537
Liabilities: $113,841,556
Net Worth: $61,435,981
Earnings: $7,601,019
Emp.: 1,194
Fiscal Year-end: 03/31/23
Sugar Mfr
N.A.I.C.S.: 311313
Rana Inder Pratap Singh (Mng Dir)

RANCHERO GOLD CORP.

910-800 West Pender Street, Vancouver, V6C 2V6, BC, Canada
Tel.: (416) 644-1217
Web Site: https://rancherogold.com
3C2—(DEU)
Assets: $865,220
Liabilities: $4,921,378
Net Worth: ($4,056,158)
Earnings: ($1,513,533)
Fiscal Year-end: 12/31/23
Financial Investment Services
N.A.I.C.S.: 523999
Martyn Buttenshaw (Chm & CEO)

RAND MINING LIMITED

Unit G1 49 Melville Parade, South Perth, 6151, WA, Australia
Tel.: (61) 894742113
Web Site: https://www.randmining.com.au
RND—(ASX)
Rev.: $23,269,792
Assets: $69,606,922
Liabilities: $3,724,020
Net Worth: $65,882,902
Earnings: $4,448,781
Fiscal Year-end: 06/30/24
Mineral Mining Services
N.A.I.C.S.: 212220
Roland Berzins (Co-Sec)

RANDGOLD & EXPLORATION COMPANY LIMITED

Suite 25 Katherine & West Building Corner Katherine & West Streets, Sandton, 2196, South Africa
Tel.: (27) 715803739
Web Site: https://www.randgoldexp.co.za
Year Founded: 1922
RNG—(JSE)
Rev.: $290,561
Assets: $5,242,134
Liabilities: $619,884
Net Worth: $4,622,250
Earnings: ($873,636)
Fiscal Year-end: 12/31/22
Gold Ore Mining Services
N.A.I.C.S.: 212220
Hilton Gischen (Exec Dir)

RANDON S.A. IMPLEMENTOS E. PARTICIPACOES.

Avenida Abramo Randon no 770 In-

terlagos, 95055-010, Caxias do Sul, 95055-010, RS, Brazil
Tel.: (55) 5432092000
Web Site: https://www.randon.com.br
Year Founded: 1949
RAPT4—(BRAZ)
Rev.: $1,946,308,202
Assets: $2,291,725,686
Liabilities: $1,595,386,704
Net Worth: $696,338,982
Earnings: $118,557,942
Fiscal Year-end: 12/31/23
Auto Parts Mfr
N.A.I.C.S.: 336390
David Abramo Randon *(Chm)*

Subsidiaries:

Fremax S.A. (1)
Rua Anaburgo 5600, Joinville, SC, Brazil
Tel.: (55) 4734616600
Web Site: http://www.fremax.com.br
Automobile Parts Mfr
N.A.I.C.S.: 336390

Randon Argentina S.A. (1)
Ruta Provincial 16 Km 4 5 AO12 Alvear, 2126, Santa Fe, 2126, Argentina
Tel.: (54) 3413177400
Web Site: https://www.randon.com.ar
Automobile Parts Mfr
N.A.I.C.S.: 336390
Diego Strafaccio *(VP)*

Randon Peru S.A.C. (1)
Av Argentina 4140, Callao, 07001, Lima, Peru
Tel.: (51) 15658513
Web Site: http://www.randon.pe
Automobile Parts Mfr
N.A.I.C.S.: 336390
Matheus Augusto Segat *(Gen Mgr)*

RANDSTAD N.V.
Diemermere 25, NL-1112 TC, Diemen, Netherlands
Tel.: (31) 205695911   NI
Web Site: https://www.randstad.com
Year Founded: 1960
RAND—(EUR)
Rev.: $26,329,888,000
Assets: $11,799,552,000
Liabilities: $6,560,294,400
Net Worth: $5,239,257,600
Earnings: $820,838,400
Emp.: 46,190
Fiscal Year-end: 12/31/21
Temporary Staffing & Permanent Placement Services
N.A.I.C.S.: 541612
Wout Dekker *(Chm-Supervisory Bd)*

Subsidiaries:

AUSY SA (1)
6 rue Troyon, 92310, Sevres, France   (94.34%)
Tel.: (33) 1 41 08 65 65
Web Site: http://www.ausy.fr
Information Technology Services
N.A.I.C.S.: 541512
Frank Ribuot *(Chm)*

Subsidiary (Non-US):

AUSY BELGIUM (2)
Esperantolaan 8, 3001, Leuven, Belgium
Tel.: (32) 16 65 20 16
Web Site: http://www.ausy.be
Information Technology Consulting Services
N.A.I.C.S.: 541512

AUSY Luxembourg PSF SA (2)
15 rue Leon Laval, 3372, Leudelange, Luxembourg
Tel.: (352) 45 39 11
Web Site: http://www.ausy.lu
Emp.: 200
Information Technology Consulting Services
N.A.I.C.S.: 541512
Marianne David *(Dir)*

AUSY SERVICIOS DE INGENIERIA S.L. (2)
Calle Principe de Vergara n 8 2 Lzda, 28001, Madrid, Spain
Tel.: (34) 91 781 75 30
Web Site: http://www.ausy.com
Information Technology Consulting Services
N.A.I.C.S.: 541512

Representative Office (Non-US):

AUSY Sweden (2)
Scheelevagen 17, 223 70, Lund, Sweden
Tel.: (46) 46 2864940
Web Site: http://www.ausy.com
Information Technology Consulting Services
N.A.I.C.S.: 541512

Subsidiary (US):

Celerity IT, LLC (2)
8405 Greensboro Dr Ste 700, McLean, VA 22102
Tel.: (703) 848-1900
Web Site: https://www.celerity.com
Emp.: 400
Corporate IT Consulting Services
N.A.I.C.S.: 541690
Kathy Hebert *(VP-Mktg)*

Subsidiary (Non-US):

ELAN-AUSY GmbH (2)
Channel 2 Harburger Schlossstr 24, 21079, Hamburg, Germany
Tel.: (49) 40 21909 0
Web Site: http://www.elan-ausy.com
Emp.: 500
Information Technology Consulting Services
N.A.I.C.S.: 541512
Mario L. Susnjar *(Mng Dir)*

PENTASYS AG (2)
Rudesheimer Strasse 9, 80686, Munich, Germany
Tel.: (49) 89 5 79 52 0
Web Site: http://www.pentasys.de
Emp.: 400
Information Technology Consulting Services
N.A.I.C.S.: 541512
Philippe Morsillo *(Chm-Supervisory Bd)*

VITM GMBH (2)
Heilbronner Strasse 86, 70191, Stuttgart, Germany
Tel.: (49) 7 119 6021 24
Web Site: http://www.ausy.com
Information Technology Consulting Services
N.A.I.C.S.: 541512

AUSY Switzerland AG (1)
Baslerstrasse 60, 8048, Zurich, Switzerland
Tel.: (41) 58 330 0400
Web Site: https://www.ausy.ch
Management Consulting Services
N.A.I.C.S.: 541611

AUSYpt Lda. (1)
Espaco Amoreiras - Centro Empresarial Rua D Joao V n 24 1 03, 1250-091, Lisbon, Portugal
Tel.: (351) 21 041 5942
Web Site: https://www.ausy.pt
Human Resource Consulting Services
N.A.I.C.S.: 541612
Frederico Costa *(Mng Dir)*

AYS Placements & Workshop s.r.o (1)
Karla Englise 11, 150 00, Prague, Czech Republic
Tel.: (420) 2222100134
Web Site: http://www.ranstad.cz
Sales Range: $25-49.9 Million
Emp.: 50
N.A.I.C.S.: 561311
Roman Ftrnad *(Mgr-Accts)*

Agensi Pekerjaan Select Appointments Malaysia (1)
Ste 1901 Central Plz Jalan Sultan Ismail, 50250, Kuala Lumpur, Malaysia
Tel.: (60) 321413166
Web Site: http://www.selectappointment.com.my
Sales Range: $25-49.9 Million
Emp.: 20
Staffing Services
N.A.I.C.S.: 561311

Arve Interim SAS (1)
15 rue Pierre Trappier, 74300, Cluses, France
Tel.: (33) 450984050
Web Site: https://www.arveinterim.fr
Temporary Staffing Services
N.A.I.C.S.: 561320

Atoll SAS (1)
Route des Moutiers, ZI Sebastopol industrial zone, 85400, Lucon, France
Tel.: (33) 251291515
Web Site: https://www.atoll-sa.fr
Industrial Sheet Metal Assembly Mfr
N.A.I.C.S.: 333517

Aurec Pty. Ltd. (1)
Suite 3 Level 24/45 Clarence Street, Sydney, 2000, NSW, Australia
Tel.: (61) 282481800
Web Site: https://www.aurec.com
Recruitment Agency Services
N.A.I.C.S.: 561311
Matthew Cossens *(Mng Dir)*

Ausy Consulting GmbH (1)
Frankenstr 3, 20097, Hamburg, Germany
Tel.: (49) 40696382930
Engineering Consultancy Services
N.A.I.C.S.: 541330

Ausy Technologies Germany AG (1)
Christoph-Rapparini-Bogen 29, 80639, Munich, Germany
Tel.: (49) 8 957 9520
Web Site: https://www.ausy-technologies.de
Information Technology Services
N.A.I.C.S.: 541511

Ausy Technologies Romania SRL (1)
11 Doamna Stanca St, Selimbar, 557260, Sibiu, Romania
Tel.: (40) 36 910 1160
Information Technology Services
N.A.I.C.S.: 541511

BMC Advies B.V. (1)
Eemnesserweg 56, 3741 GB, Baarn, Netherlands
Tel.: (31) 355430080
Web Site: https://www.bmcadvies.com
Business Management Consulting Services
N.A.I.C.S.: 541611

BMC Groep B.V. (1)
Databankweg 26 D, 3821 AL, Amersfoort, Netherlands
Tel.: (31) 334965200
Web Site: https://www.bmc.nl
Human Resource Consulting Services
N.A.I.C.S.: 541612

CapSecur Conseil (1)
62-64 cours Albert Thomas, 69008, Lyon, France
Tel.: (33) 4 37 53 24 30
Web Site: http://www.capsecur.com
Security Management Consulting Services
N.A.I.C.S.: 541618

Contact Mocambique (1)
Av Friedrich Engels 515, Maputo, Mozambique
Tel.: (258) 21 484 050
Web Site: http://www.contact.co.mz
Human Resource Management Services
N.A.I.C.S.: 541612

DB Concepts Inc. (1)
10 Presidential Way, Woburn, MA 01801
Tel.: (781) 939-1660
Web Site: http://www.dbconcepts.com
Temporary Staffing Services
N.A.I.C.S.: 561320

Dfind Consulting AS (1)
Stortingsgata 4, 0158, Oslo, Norway
Tel.: (47) 45405764
Web Site: https://www.dfindconsulting.no
Information Technology Services
N.A.I.C.S.: 541511

Digby Morgan (1)
2nd Floor 36 Queen Street, London, EC4R 1BN, United Kingdom
Tel.: (44) 2036800748
Web Site: http://www.digby-morgan.com
Sales Range: $25-49.9 Million
Emp.: 20
Human Resource Consulting Services
N.A.I.C.S.: 541612

Digby Morgan (DIFC) Limited (1)
The Gate Level 14 DIFC, International Financial Centre, Dubai, 506902, United Arab Emirates
Tel.: (971) 43622222
Web Site: https://www.difc.ae
Human Resource Consulting Services
N.A.I.C.S.: 541612

E-bridge BV (1)
Diemermere 15, 1112 TB, Diemen, Netherlands
Tel.: (31) 205695578
Web Site: http://www.ebridge.nl
Sales Range: $150-199.9 Million
Emp.: 1,000
Administrative Management Consulting Services
N.A.I.C.S.: 541611

EXPECTRA S.A.S. (1)
276 avenue du President Wilson, 93200, Saint Denis, France
Tel.: (33) 141622020
Web Site: http://www.expectra.fr
Human Resource Consulting Services
N.A.I.C.S.: 541612

Expand BV (1)
Kleine Gent 9, 5261 BS, Vught, Netherlands
Tel.: (31) 736155980
Web Site: http://www.expand.nl
Sales Range: $1-9.9 Million
Emp.: 8
Employment Agency
N.A.I.C.S.: 561311
Marc Loohuis *(Owner)*

Expedite Headhunters (1)
6th Floor 100 Grays Inn Road, London, WC1X 8AL, United Kingdom
Tel.: (44) 20 7400 6051
Web Site: http://www.expediteheadhunters.com
Executive Search Service
N.A.I.C.S.: 561311

FIRTH ROSS MARTIN ASSOCIATES LTD (1)
85 London Wall, London, EC2M 7AD, United Kingdom
Tel.: (44) 20 7786 8028
Web Site: http://www.firthrossmartin.co.uk
Sales Range: $25-49.9 Million
Emp.: 3
Human Resource Consulting Services
N.A.I.C.S.: 541612

GULP Schweiz AG (1)
Baslerstrasse 60, 8048, Zurich, Switzerland
Tel.: (41) 445118686
Web Site: https://www.gulp.ch
Staffing Services
N.A.I.C.S.: 561320

GULP Solution Services GmbH & Co. KG (1)
Breite Strasse 137-139, 50667, Cologne, Germany
Tel.: (49) 2218882250
Temporary Staffing Services
N.A.I.C.S.: 561320

Galilei Belgium (1)
Career Services & Outplacement Avenue Roger Vandendriesschelaan 18, 1150, Brussels, Belgium
Tel.: (32) 2 777 96 00
Web Site: http://www.galilei.be
Emp.: 15
Human Resource Consulting Services
N.A.I.C.S.: 541612

HR Consultancy Partners SAS (1)
39 rue saint lazare, 75009, Paris, France
Tel.: (33) 15 338 2661
Web Site: https://www.hrconsultancypartners.fr
Human Resource Consulting Services
N.A.I.C.S.: 541612

HR Partners Pty Limited (1)
Level 9 83 Clarence Street, Sydney, 2000, NSW, Australia
Tel.: (61) 290191600
Web Site: https://www.hrpartners.com.au
Recruitment Agency Services
N.A.I.C.S.: 561311
David Owens *(Founder & Mng Dir)*

Human Solutions S.A. (1)
C Mallorca 221 6 2, 8008, Barcelona, Spain

RANDSTAD N.V.   INTERNATIONAL PUBLIC

Randstad N.V.—(Continued)
Tel.: (34) 933235050
Web Site: http://www.humansolutions.es
Sales Range: $25-49.9 Million
Emp.: 15
Staffing Services
N.A.I.C.S.: 561311

Hutac Sarl (1)
Route des Jeunes 9, Les Acacias, 1227, Geneva, Switzerland
Tel.: (41) 78 667 7840
Web Site: https://www.hutaconsulting.com
Human Resource Consulting Services
N.A.I.C.S.: 541612

I-bridge bv (1)
Diemermere 25, Diemen, 1112TC, Netherlands
Tel.: (31) 20 569 1028
Web Site: http://www.ibridge.nl
Application Software Development Services
N.A.I.C.S.: 541511

JBM SAS (1)
50 avenue de la Grande Armee, 75017, Paris, France
Tel.: (33) 1 44 17 17 77
Web Site: http://www.jbm-medical.com
Temporary Staffing Services
N.A.I.C.S.: 561311
Christophe Bougeard (Dir-Publ)

L'Appel Medical (1)
23 rue Edmond Michelet, 33000, Bordeaux, France
Tel.: (33) 556483121
Web Site: http://www.appelmedical.com
Sales Range: $25-49.9 Million
Emp.: 250
Employment Agency Services
N.A.I.C.S.: 561311
Stephane Volleau (Reg Dir)

Major Players Ltd (1)
7-11 Stukeley Street, London, WC2B 5LB, Bedfordshire, United Kingdom
Tel.: (44) 20 7836 4041
Web Site: http://www.majorplayers.co.uk
Human Resource Consulting Services
N.A.I.C.S.: 541612
Jack Gratton (Chm)

Management Angels GmbH (1)
Atlantic Haus-17th Floor Bernhard-Nocht-Strasse 113, 20359, Hamburg, Germany
Tel.: (49) 4044195577
Web Site:
   http://www.managementangels.com
Sales Range: $1-9.9 Million
Emp.: 20
Interim Management Services
N.A.I.C.S.: 541618
Thorsten Becker (Head-Bus Dev)

Martin Ward Anderson B.V. (1)
Spaklerweg 52, Amsterdam, 1114 AE, Netherlands
Tel.: (31) 20 571 1520
Web Site: http://www.martinwardanderson.nl
Emp.: 15
Professional Employment Services
N.A.I.C.S.: 561320
Sieto Engelmoer (Mng Dir)

Maxon Project Support (1)
Kaezarsparash 13, 5466 AA, Veghel, Netherlands
Tel.: (31) 413353300
Web Site: http://www.maxomps.nl
Sales Range: $25-49.9 Million
Emp.: 250
Temporary Help Service
N.A.I.C.S.: 561320

Muhlenhoff + Partner GmbH (1)
Wallstrasse 16, 40213, Dusseldorf, Germany
Tel.: (49) 211 558 6760
Web Site: https://www.muehlenhoff.com
Outplacement Consulting Services
N.A.I.C.S.: 561320

Niscom Inc. (1)
1 15 21 Shibuya Ku, Tokyo, 150 0002, Japan
Tel.: (81) 337977701
Web Site: http://www.niscom.co.jp
Sales Range: $25-49.9 Million
Emp.: 100
Recruitment Agency Services

N.A.I.C.S.: 561311

Optedis SA (1)
16 Rue Jean-Jacques Rousseau, 92130, Issy-les-Moulineaux, France
Tel.: (33) 184760331
Web Site: https://www.optedis.com
Engineering Consultancy Services
N.A.I.C.S.: 541330

Otter-Westelaken Groep B.V. (1)
Keizersgracht 14, 5466 AA, Eindhoven, Netherlands
Tel.: (31) 413340440
Web Site: http://www.otterwestelaken.nl
Sales Range: $25-49.9 Million
Emp.: 15
Temporary Help Service
N.A.I.C.S.: 561320
Wilco De Vries (Gen Mgr)

P-Flex (1)
Diemermere 25, 1112 TC, Diemen, Netherlands
Tel.: (31) 203989030
Sales Range: $10-24.9 Million
Emp.: 35
Temporary Help Service
N.A.I.C.S.: 561320

Pareto Law Ltd (1)
Pareto House 49 Church Street, Wilmslow, SK9 1AX, United Kingdom
Tel.: (44) 3333556762
Web Site: https://www.pareto.co.uk
Emp.: 250
Human Resource Consulting Services
N.A.I.C.S.: 541612
Sarah Skelton (Sls Dir-Reg)

Profcore Business Services (1)
Mauritslaan 111, 6161 HT, Geleen, Netherlands
Tel.: (31) 884787778
Web Site: http://www.proforce.nl
Sales Range: $50-74.9 Million
Emp.: 350
Temporary Help Service
N.A.I.C.S.: 561320

Qualitair Aviation Group Limited (1)
Francis Court High Ditch Road, Fen Ditton, Cambridge, CB5 8TE, United Kingdom
Tel.: (44) 1223295111
Web Site: https://www.qualitair.com
Staffing Services
N.A.I.C.S.: 561320

Qualitair Aviation Holland BV (1)
Aalsmeerderweg 604a, 1437 EJ, Rozenburg, Netherlands
Tel.: (31) 206536119
Web Site: https://www.randstad.co.uk
Sales Range: $25-49.9 Million
Emp.: 6
Aircraft Maintenance Services
N.A.I.C.S.: 488190

Qualitair Aviation Services Limited (1)
Francis Court High Ditch Road, Fen Ditton, Cambridge, CB5 8TE, United Kingdom
Tel.: (44) 1223 295111
Web Site: http://www.qualitair.com
Emp.: 12
Aviation Staffing Services
N.A.I.C.S.: 561320

RANDSTAD HELLAS S.A. (1)
Athens Tower Building A 13th Floor 2 Mesogeion Ave & Sinopis St, 11527, Athens, Greece
Tel.: (30) 2166001312
Web Site: http://www.randstad.gr
Sales Range: $25-49.9 Million
Emp.: 35
Human Resource Consulting Services
N.A.I.C.S.: 541612

RANDSTAD S.A. (1)
41 Place de la Gare, 1611, Luxembourg, Luxembourg
Tel.: (352) 40 32 041
Web Site: http://www.randstad.lu
Sales Range: $25-49.9 Million
Emp.: 30
Human Resource Consulting Services
N.A.I.C.S.: 541612

RANDSTAD SA

Via de los Poblados 9, 28033, Madrid, Spain
Tel.: (34) 91 490 60 00
Web Site: http://www.randstad.es
Human Resource Consulting Services
N.A.I.C.S.: 541612
Rodrigo Martin (CEO)

RANDSTAD SA DE CV (1)
Insurgentes Sur 1524 Piso 1 Col Actipan, 3230, Mexico, Mexico
Tel.: (52) 55 5200 1800
Web Site: http://www.randstad.com.mx
Sales Range: $25-49.9 Million
Emp.: 10
Temporary Staffing Services
N.A.I.C.S.: 561320
Simone Nijssen (Gen Mgr)

RH Internacional Limitada (1)
Rua Primeiro De Marco 23 6 Andar, 20010 000, Rio de Janeiro, Brazil
Tel.: (55) 2125096323
Web Site: http://www.rhi.com.br
Sales Range: $10-24.9 Million
Emp.: 2,500
Employment Agency
N.A.I.C.S.: 561311

Randstad A/S (1)
Vester Farimagsgade 7 2, 1606, Copenhagen, Denmark
Tel.: (45) 33930800
Web Site: https://www.randstad.dk
Sales Range: $10-24.9 Million
Emp.: 30
Recruitment Services
N.A.I.C.S.: 561311
Joachim Gottschalck (Acct Dir)

Randstad AB (1)
rattarvagen 3, box 3037, solna, 169 03, Stockholm, Sweden
Tel.: (46) 201707070
Web Site: https://www.randstad.se
Sales Range: $25-49.9 Million
Emp.: 40
Human Resource Consulting Services
N.A.I.C.S.: 541612

Subsidiary (Domestic):

Antenn Consulting AB (2)
Regeringsgatan 65, Box 16057, Stockholm, 103 21, Sweden
Tel.: (46) 854516760
Web Site: http://www.antenn.se
Emp.: 200
Management Consulting Services
N.A.I.C.S.: 541618

Dfind IT AB (2)
Box 70368, 107 24, Stockholm, Sweden
Tel.: (46) 20 170 70
Web Site: http://www.dfind.se
Emp.: 600
Staffing & Recruitment Services
N.A.I.C.S.: 561311
Margareta Strandbacke (Bus Area Mgr)

Subsidiary (Domestic):

Dfind AB (3)
Ostra Hamngatan 23, 411 10, Gothenburg, Sweden
Tel.: (46) 20 170 70 70
Web Site: http://www.dfind.se
Staffing & Recruitment Services
N.A.I.C.S.: 561311
Margareta Strandbacke (Bus Area Mgr)

Subsidiary (Non-US):

Dfind AS (3)
Kristian Augusts gate 15, 0164, Oslo, Norway
Tel.: (47) 40021450
Web Site: https://www.dfind.no
Information Technology Consultancy Services
N.A.I.C.S.: 541512

Randstad AE (1)
athens tower building a 13th floor 2 mesogeion ave sinopis st, 11527, Athens, Greece
Tel.: (30) 2166001312
Web Site: https://www.randstad.gr
Temporary Staffing Services
N.A.I.C.S.: 561320

Randstad Argentina S.A. (1)

Carlos Pellegrini 1141 10th floor, 1009, Buenos Aires, Argentina
Tel.: (54) 8002200888
Web Site: https://www.randstad.com.ar
Staffing Services
N.A.I.C.S.: 561320

Randstad Austria GmbH (1)
Neubaugasse 43/1/1-2, A-1070, Vienna, Austria
Tel.: (43) 152455010
Web Site: https://www.randstad.at
Staffing Services
N.A.I.C.S.: 561320

Randstad Belgium (1)
Access Building Boulevard Charles Quint 586, 1082, Brussels, Belgium
Tel.: (32) 24746000
Web Site: https://www.randstad.be
Sales Range: $25-49.9 Million
Emp.: 300
Temporary Help Service
N.A.I.C.S.: 561320

Subsidiary (Domestic):

Randstad Professionals (2)
Chaussee Romaene 564 A, 1853, Strombeek-Bever, Belgium
Tel.: (32) 25590380
Web Site:
  http://www.randstadprofessionals.be
Sales Range: $25-49.9 Million
Emp.: 95
Temporary Help Service
N.A.I.C.S.: 561320
Dominica Hermens (Dir)

Subsidiary (Non-US):

Expectra Gestion (3)
12 Rue Boissy D'Anglas, 75008, Paris, France
Tel.: (33) 155305800
Web Site: http://www.expectra.fr
Staffing Services
N.A.I.C.S.: 561311

Expectra Technology S.A. (3)
Dr Saminhos 22, 28027, Madrid, Spain
Tel.: (34) 917434531
Web Site: http://www.expectra.es
Sales Range: $25-49.9 Million
N.A.I.C.S.: 561311

Branch (Domestic):

Randstad Espana S.L. (4)
Calle Via de los Poblados 9 Edificio B 5 planta, 28033, Madrid, Spain
Tel.: (34) 914906174
Web Site: http://www.randstad.es
Sales Range: $25-49.9 Million
Emp.: 160
Employment Services
N.A.I.C.S.: 561311

Subsidiary (Domestic):

INSEL belgium (3)
Verlorenbroodstraat 120, 9820, Merelbeke, Belgium
Tel.: (32) 9 259 12 12
Web Site: http://www.insel.be
Engineering Staff Recruitment Services
N.A.I.C.S.: 561311

Sapphire B.V. (3)
Berchem Stadionstraat 78, 2600, Berchem, Belgium
Tel.: (32) 323013939
Web Site: http://www.sapphire.be
Sales Range: $10-24.9 Million
Emp.: 45
IT Consultants & Staffing
N.A.I.C.S.: 561320

Randstad Bouw (1)
Diemermere 25, Diemen, 1112 TC, Amsterdam, Netherlands
Tel.: (31) 20 569 59 11
Web Site: http://www.randstad.nl
Construction Staff Recruitment Services
N.A.I.C.S.: 561311

Randstad Brasil Recursos Humanos Ltda (1)
Avenida Francisco Matarazzo 1350-Torre I-20th floor, Agua Branca, Sao Paulo, 05001-100, SP, Brazil

RANDSTAD N.V.

Tel.: (55) 1151805170
Web Site: https://www.randstad.com.br
Sales Range: $75-99.9 Million
Emp.: 700
Human Resource Consulting Services
N.A.I.C.S.: 541612

Randstad Callflex (1)
Diemermere 25, 1112 TC, Diemen, Netherlands
Tel.: (31) 205695911
Web Site: http://www.randstad.com
Sales Range: $25-49.9 Million
Emp.: 36,000
Temporary Help Service
N.A.I.C.S.: 561320

Randstad Canada (1)
525 Viger Avenue West Suite 501, Montreal, H2Z 1G6, QC, Canada
Tel.: (514) 350-0033
Web Site: http://www.randstad.ca
Sales Range: $10-24.9 Million
Emp.: 30
Temporary Help Service
N.A.I.C.S.: 561320

Subsidiary (Domestic):

Randstad Enginnering (2)
777 Bay Street Suite 2000, Toronto, M5H 2C9, ON, Canada
Tel.: (416) 861-1060
Web Site: http://www.randstad.ca
Sales Range: $10-24.9 Million
Employment Agencies
N.A.I.C.S.: 561311

Randstad Chile S.A. (1)
Agustinas 785 piso 5 Codigo, 7550000, Santiago, Chile
Tel.: (56) 233299370
Human Resource Consulting Services
N.A.I.C.S.: 541612

Randstad Deutschland (1)
Frankfurter Strasse 100, D-65760, Eschborn, Germany
Tel.: (49) 61964080
Web Site: https://www.randstad.de
Sales Range: $75-99.9 Million
Emp.: 300
Temporary Help Service
N.A.I.C.S.: 561320

Subsidiary (Domestic):

GULP Information Services GmbH (2)
Landsberger Strasse 187, 80687, Munich, Germany
Tel.: (49) 895003160
Web Site: http://www.gulp.de
Sales Range: $250-299.9 Million
Emp.: 180
Information Technology Staffing Services
N.A.I.C.S.: 561320
Michael Moser (CEO)

ISU Personaldienstleistungen GmbH (2)
Schwarcwald 39, Karlsruhe, 76137, Germany
Tel.: (49) 721937800
Web Site: http://www.isu-personal.de
Sales Range: $25-49.9 Million
Emp.: 113
Temporary Employment Agency Services
N.A.I.C.S.: 561311

Randstad Empleo E.T.T. (1)
Via de los Poblados 9, Edificio Trianon Bloque B, 28033, Madrid, Spain
Tel.: (34) 914906000
Web Site: http://www.randstad.es
Sales Range: $150-199.9 Million
Emp.: 150
Temporary Help Service
N.A.I.C.S.: 561320
Rodrigo Martin (Dir-Comm)

Randstad Engineering USA (1)
5975 Peachtree Pkwy Ste 5, Norcross, GA 30092
Tel.: (770) 840-9006
Web Site: http://www.randstadengineering.com
Sales Range: $25-49.9 Million
Emp.: 100
Human Resource Consulting Services

N.A.I.C.S.: 541612
Graig Paglieri (CEO-Randstad Technologies Grp & Mng Dir-Professionals-Global)

Randstad Finance & Accounting (1)
111 Anza Blvd Ste 411, Burlingame, CA 94010
Tel.: (650) 343-5111
Web Site: http://finance.randstadusa.com
Emp.: 8
Accounting Staffing Services
N.A.I.C.S.: 561320

Randstad Gezondheidszorg (1)
Diemermere 25, 1112 TC, Diemen, Netherlands
Tel.: (31) 205695888
Web Site: http://www.randstadgezondheidszorg.nl
Temporary Help Service
N.A.I.C.S.: 561320

Randstad Groep Nederland bv (1)
Juridische Zaken, Postbus 12600, 1100 AP, Amsterdam, Netherlands
Tel.: (31) 205695133
Human Resource Consulting Services
N.A.I.C.S.: 541612

Randstad Group Belgium N.V. (1)
Building Access Keizer Karellaan 586 B 8, 1082, Brussels, Belgium
Tel.: (32) 26122000
Web Site: https://www.randstadgroup.be
Staffing Services
N.A.I.C.S.: 561320

Randstad HR Solutions Limited (1)
1st Floor Randstad Court Laporte Way, Luton, LU4 8SB, United Kingdom
Tel.: (44) 1582811600
Human Resource Consulting Services
N.A.I.C.S.: 541612

Randstad HR Solutions bv (1)
Chaussee de Liege 622, Jambes, Jambes, Belgium
Tel.: (32) 2 474 60 00
Human Resource Consulting Services
N.A.I.C.S.: 541612

Randstad HR Solutions s.r.o. (1)
Jungmannova 26/15, Nove Mesto, 110 00, Prague, Czech Republic
Tel.: (420) 22 221 0013
Web Site: https://www.randstad.cz
Temporary Staffing Services
N.A.I.C.S.: 561320

Randstad Healthcare (1)
150 Presidential Way 3rd Fl, Woburn, MA 01801
Tel.: (781) 273-1472
Web Site: http://www.randstadhealthcare.com
Healthcare Staffing Services
N.A.I.C.S.: 561320

Randstad Hong Kong Limited (1)
33/F Sino Plaza 255-257 Gloucester Rd, Causeway Bay, China (Hong Kong)
Tel.: (852) 22323408
Web Site: https://www.randstad.com.hk
Professional Employment Services
N.A.I.C.S.: 561311

Randstad Hr Solutions BV. (1)
Diemermere 25, 1112 TC, Diemen, Netherlands
Tel.: (31) 205698237
Web Site: https://www.randstad.nl
Human Resource Consulting Services
N.A.I.C.S.: 541612

Randstad Human Resources United States (1)
111 Anza Blvd Ste 400, Burlingame, CA 94010
Tel.: (650) 579-1111
Human Resource Consulting Services
N.A.I.C.S.: 541612

Randstad India Private Limited (1)
Randstad House Old No 5 and 5A New No 9 Pycrofts Garden Road, Nungambakkam, Chennai, 600 006, Tamil Nadu, India
Tel.: (91) 4466227000
Web Site: https://www.randstad.in
Staffing Services
N.A.I.C.S.: 561320

Randstad Inhouse Services (1)
Diemermere, 1112 TC, Diemen, Netherlands (100%)
Tel.: (31) 205695911
Sales Range: $25-49.9 Million
Emp.: 500
Temporary Help Service
N.A.I.C.S.: 561320

Randstad Inhouse Services Ltd (1)
Unit 142 Hartlebury Trading Estate, Kidderminster, DY10 4JB, United Kingdom
Tel.: (44) 1299252317
Web Site: http://www.randstadinhouse.co.uk
Human Resource Consulting Services
N.A.I.C.S.: 541612
Sally Cleary (Mng Dir)

Randstad Inhouse Services S.A. (1)
276 Avenue du President Wilson, La Plaine, 93200, Saint Denis, France
Tel.: (33) 1 41 62 20 20
Web Site: http://www.randstad.fr
Emp.: 600
Human Resource Consulting Services
N.A.I.C.S.: 541612

Randstad Interim (1)
Place de l Hotel de Ville, Esch-sur-Alzette, 4138, Luxembourg, Luxembourg
Tel.: (352) 540004
Web Site: https://www.randstad.lu
Sales Range: $25-49.9 Million
Emp.: 25
Temporary Help Service
N.A.I.C.S.: 561320

Randstad Interim Inc. (1)
777 Bay Street Suite 2000, PO Box 128, Toronto, M5G 2C8, ON, Canada
Tel.: (416) 861-1060
Web Site: http://www.randstad.ca
Human Resource Consulting Services
N.A.I.C.S.: 541612
Marc-Etienne Julien (CEO)

Randstad Ireland Operations Limited (1)
Harcourt centre Harcourt Road, Dublin, D02 HW77, Ireland
Tel.: (353) 14029541
Recruitment Agency Services
N.A.I.C.S.: 561311

Randstad Italia SpA (1)
Via Roberto Lepetit n 8/10, 20124, Milan, Italy (100%)
Tel.: (39) 0287110730
Web Site: https://www.randstad.it
Sales Range: $150-199.9 Million
Emp.: 700
Temporary Help Service
N.A.I.C.S.: 561320

Subsidiary (Domestic):

Select Societa Difornitura Dilavoro Temporanio S.p.A. (2)
Via Lario 16, 20159, Milan, Italy
Tel.: (39) 0266814385
Web Site: http://www.selectitalia.com
Sales Range: $10-24.9 Million
Emp.: 20
Temporary Employment Agency Services
N.A.I.C.S.: 561320

Randstad KK (1)
21F New Otani Garden Court 4-1 Kioicho, Chiyoda-ku, Tokyo, 102-8578, Japan
Tel.: (81) 120502870
Web Site: https://www.randstad.co.jp
Temporary Staffing Services
N.A.I.C.S.: 561320

Randstad Managed Services NV (1)
Rue des Princes 8-10, 1000, Brussels, Belgium
Tel.: (32) 22291400
Web Site: http://www.randstad.be
Emp.: 300
Human Resource Consulting Services
N.A.I.C.S.: 541612

Randstad Managed Solutions Sdn Bhd (1)
Lot C203 2nd Fl Enterprise Bldg 1 Jalan Teknorat 3, 63000, Cyberjaya, Malaysia
Tel.: (60) 3 8319 9899
Web Site: http://www.randstad.my
Human Resource Consulting Services

N.A.I.C.S.: 541612

Randstad Middle East Limited (1)
G08 Building 1 Internet City, PO Box 500362, Dubai, United Arab Emirates
Tel.: (971) 4 360 2626
Web Site: http://www.randstadmena.com
Sales Range: $25-49.9 Million
Emp.: 46
Temporary & Permanent Employment Services
N.A.I.C.S.: 561320

Randstad Mobiliteitsdiensten (1)
Diemermere 25, 1112 TC, Diemen, Netherlands
Tel.: (31) 205698200
Web Site: http://www.randstadmobiliteitsdiensten.nl
Temporary Help Service
N.A.I.C.S.: 561320

Randstad Nederland bv (1)
Diemermere 25, 1112 TC, Diemen, Netherlands
Tel.: (31) 205695911
Human Resource Consulting Services
N.A.I.C.S.: 541612

Randstad Norway AS (1)
Kristian Augusts gate 15C, 0164, Oslo, Norway
Tel.: (47) 40021400
Web Site: https://www.randstad.no
Sales Range: $10-24.9 Million
Emp.: 35
Professional Employment Services
N.A.I.C.S.: 561320
Camilla Grana (Grp Dir-Sls & Marcom)

Randstad Outsourcing & Project Services (1)
Diemere 25, Diemen, 1112 TC, Netherlands
Tel.: (31) 205698245
Web Site: http://www.randstadrops.nl
Sales Range: $10-24.9 Million
Emp.: 50
Temporary Help Service
N.A.I.C.S.: 561320
Chris Heutenk (Mng Dir)

Randstad Outsourcing GmbH (1)
Frankfurter Strasse 100, 65760, Eschborn, Germany
Tel.: (49) 61964081150
Temporary Staffing Services
N.A.I.C.S.: 561320

Randstad Pharma, Inc. (1)
4 Pkwy N Ste 120, Deerfield, IL 60015
Tel.: (877) 335-8210
Web Site: http://pharma.randstadusa.com
Pharmaceutical Staffing Services
N.A.I.C.S.: 561311
Greg Coir (Pres & Exec VP-Pharma & Life Sciences Div)

Randstad Polska Sp. z o.o. (1)
Aleje Jerozolimskie 134, 02-305, Warsaw, Poland
Tel.: (48) 224544400
Web Site: https://www.randstad.pl
Staffing Services
N.A.I.C.S.: 561320

Randstad Professionals SA (1)
Leutschenbachstrasse 45, Zurich, 8050, Switzerland
Tel.: (41) 58 201 55 30
Sales Range: $25-49.9 Million
Emp.: 30
Human Resource Consulting Services
N.A.I.C.S.: 541612

Randstad Professionals US L.P. (1)
150 Presidential Way, Woburn, MA 01801
Tel.: (781) 213-1500
Sales Range: $25-49.9 Million
Emp.: 167
Executive Recruitment & Placement Services
N.A.I.C.S.: 541612
Jennifer Gannon (Sr VP-Strategic Sls)

Subsidiary (Domestic):

Delta Pharma (2)
4 Pkwy N Ste 120, Deerfield, IL 60015
Tel.: (847) 374-8250
Emp.: 100

RANDSTAD N.V.

INTERNATIONAL PUBLIC

Randstad N.V.—(Continued)

Clinical Research Employment Placement Services
N.A.I.C.S.: 561311
John Ebeid *(VP-Delta Outsourcing)*

Placement Pros (2)
1601 New Stine Rd Ste 130, Bakersfield, CA 93309-3697
Tel.: (661) 832-1900
Web Site: http://www.placementpros.com
Rev.: $2,200,000
Emp.: 18
Placement Consultants
N.A.I.C.S.: 561320

Sapphire Technologies (2)
10 Presidential Way, Woburn, MA 01801
Tel.: (781) 939-1709
Web Site: http://www.sapphire.com
Information Technology Staffing Services
N.A.I.C.S.: 561311

Randstad Professionals sa. (1)
Vicente Lopez Hipolito Yrigoyen 571, B1638AIE, Buenos Aires, Argentina
Tel.: (54) 8002200888
Web Site: http://www.randstadprof.com.ar
Human Resource Consulting Services
N.A.I.C.S.: 541612

Randstad Pte Ltd. (1)
50 Raffles Place Singapore Land Tower 17-02, Singapore, 048623, Singapore
Tel.: (65) 65101350
Web Site: http://www.randstad.com.sg
Sales Range: $25-49.9 Million
Emp.: 15
Temporary Personnel
N.A.I.C.S.: 561311

Randstad Pty Limited (1)
Level 8 83 Clarence Street, Sydney, 2060, NSW, Australia
Tel.: (61) 282983800
Web Site: http://www.randstad.com.au
Sales Range: $10-24.9 Million
Emp.: 27
Employment Agency
N.A.I.C.S.: 561311

Subsidiary (Non-US):

Randstad (2)
Level 2 154 Featherston Street, Wellington, 6011, New Zealand
Tel.: (64) 4736223
Web Site: http://www.randstad.co.nz
Sales Range: $10-24.9 Million
Emp.: 20
Employment Staffing Services for the Finance, Accounting & Banking Industries
N.A.I.C.S.: 561311
Sander M. van 't Noordende *(CEO)*

Randstad (2)
Level 14 120 Albert Street, Auckland, 1010, Central, New Zealand
Tel.: (64) 9 336 0399
Web Site: http://www.randstad.co.nz
Sales Range: $10-24.9 Million
Temporary Staffing Solutions
N.A.I.C.S.: 561311

Division (Domestic):

Randstad Education (2)
Level 8 83 Clarence Street, Sydney, 2060, NSW, Australia
Tel.: (61) 282380200
Web Site: http://www.randstad.com.au
Office Administration & Staffing
N.A.I.C.S.: 561110

Randstad Legal (2)
Level 18 Central Plaza 66 Eagle St, Brisbane, 4000, QLD, Australia
Tel.: (61) 731007777
Web Site: http://www.randstad.com.au
Sales Range: $10-24.9 Million
Emp.: 12
Permanent & Temporary Staffing Services in the Legal Sector
N.A.I.C.S.: 561311

Randstad Pty Limited - Melbourne (2)
Level 12 525 Collins Street, Melbourne, 3000, VIC, Australia
Tel.: (61) 383191111

Web Site: http://www.randstad.com.au
Employment Agency
N.A.I.C.S.: 561311

Randstad-IT Division (2)
Level 8 83 Clarence Street, Sydney, 2060, NSW, Australia
Tel.: (61) 282353300
Web Site: http://www.randstad.com.au
Sales Range: $10-24.9 Million
Emp.: 15
Employment Agency
N.A.I.C.S.: 561311
Alex Jones *(Natl Dir)*

Subsidiary (Non-US):

Randstad-IT Division (2)
Level 2 154 Featherston Street, PO Box 3843, Wellington, 6011, New Zealand
Tel.: (64) 4736223
Web Site: http://www.sapphireasiapac.nz.com
Sales Range: $10-24.9 Million
Emp.: 11
IT Staffing Services
N.A.I.C.S.: 561311

Randstad Recursos Humanos S.A. (1)
Avenida da Republica 26, 1069-220, Lisbon, Portugal
Tel.: (351) 210 105 400
Web Site: http://www.randstad.pt
Temporary Staffing Services
N.A.I.C.S.: 561320

Randstad Recursos Humanos, Empresa de Trabalho Temporario S.A. (1)
Avenida Republica 26, 1069-228, Lisbon, Portugal
Tel.: (351) 210161352
Web Site: https://www.randstad.pt
Emp.: 100
Human Resource Consulting Services
N.A.I.C.S.: 541612
Jose Leonardo *(Gen Mgr)*

Randstad RiseSmart AB (1)
Rattarvagen 3, 169 68, Solna, Sweden
Tel.: (46) 854516760
Web Site: https://www.randstadrisesmart.se
Outplacement Services
N.A.I.C.S.: 561320

Randstad Romania Srl (1)
Barbu Vacarescu Street No 301-311 Afi Lakeview Building 1st Floor, Sector 2, 020276, Bucharest, Romania
Tel.: (40) 213365253
Web Site: https://www.randstad.ro
Staffing Services
N.A.I.C.S.: 561320

Randstad S.A. (1)
Sarmiento 991, S2000CMO, Rosario, Argentina
Tel.: (54) 8002200888
Web Site: http://www.randstad.com.ar
Emp.: 300
Professional Employment Services
N.A.I.C.S.: 561311
Andrea Abila *(CEO)*

Randstad SA (1)
Av Apoquindo 4501 oficinas 501-502, Las Condes, Santiago, Chile
Tel.: (56) 233299370
Web Site: http://www.randstad.cl
Human Resource Consulting Services
N.A.I.C.S.: 541612

Randstad Schweiz AG (1)
Leutschenbachstrasse 45, 8050, Zurich, Switzerland
Tel.: (41) 582015900
Web Site: https://www.randstad.ch
Sales Range: $10-24.9 Million
Emp.: 50
Temporary Help Service
N.A.I.C.S.: 561320
Taco De Vries *(CEO)*

Randstad Search & Selection (1)
11 Rue Hector Malot, Paris, 75012, France
Tel.: (33) 143424440
Web Site: http://www.randstadsearchandselection.fr
Human Resource Consulting Services

N.A.I.C.S.: 541612

Randstad Search & Selection Personel Secme ve Yerlestirme Limited Sirketi (1)
apa giz plaza buyukdere street no 191 flat 2 3, Levent, 34330, Istanbul, Turkiye
Tel.: (90) 2122828212
Web Site: https://www.randstad.com.tr
Staffing Services
N.A.I.C.S.: 561320

Randstad Sourceright B.V. (1)
Diemermere 25, 1112 TC, Diemen, Netherlands
Tel.: (31) 205695050
Web Site: http://www.randstadsourceright.com
Emp.: 60
Professional Training Services
N.A.I.C.S.: 611430

Randstad Sourceright Canada (1)
60 Bloor Street West Suite 1400, Toronto, ON, Canada
Tel.: (416) 628-6557
Web Site: http://www.randstad.ca
Recruitment Process Outsourcing Services
N.A.I.C.S.: 561320

Randstad Sourceright GmbH (1)
Frankfurter Strasse 100, 65760, Eschborn, Germany
Tel.: (49) 15254506451
Staffing Services
N.A.I.C.S.: 561320

Randstad Sourceright Sdn. Bhd. (1)
A-1-17 Tower A Cyber Bistari Jalan Impact Cyber 6, 63000, Cyberjaya, Selangor, Malaysia
Tel.: (60) 327856990
Web Site: https://www.sourceright.com.my
Information Technology Services
N.A.I.C.S.: 541511

Randstad Sourceright UK (1)
1st Floor 30 Furnival Street, London, EC4A 1JQ, United Kingdom
Tel.: (44) 20 7539 2999
Web Site: http://www.randstadsourceright.co.uk
Sales Range: $25-49.9 Million
Emp.: 50
Human Resource Consulting Services
N.A.I.C.S.: 541612
Sue Ruddock *(Mng Dir-UK & Ireland)*

Randstad Sourceright US (1)
2050 Spectrum Blvd, Fort Lauderdale, FL 33309
Tel.: (954) 308-7600
Web Site: http://www.randstadsourceright.com
Human Resource Consulting Services
N.A.I.C.S.: 541612
Anthea Collier *(Mng Dir-APAC)*

Randstad Sp. z o.o. (1)
al jerozolimskie 134, 02-305, Warsaw, Poland
Tel.: (48) 222741000
Web Site: http://www.randstad.pl
Permanent & Temporary Staffing Services
N.A.I.C.S.: 561311

Randstad Sri Lanka (Pvt) Ltd. (1)
Level 7 BoC Merchant Tower 28 Saint Michael's Road, Colombo, 00300, Sri Lanka
Tel.: (94) 11 2395292
Sales Range: $25-49.9 Million
Emp.: 10
Human Resource Consulting Services
N.A.I.C.S.: 541612

Randstad Staffing (1)
1 Overton Pk 3625 Cumberland Blvd SE Ste 500, Atlanta, GA 30339
Tel.: (770) 937-7000
Web Site: https://www.randstadusa.com
Sales Range: $25-49.9 Million
Emp.: 200
Recruitment Agency Services
N.A.I.C.S.: 561311
Karen L. Fichuk *(CEO)*

Division (Domestic):

Randstad USA (2)
80 S 8th St IDS Center Ste 1500, Minneapolis, MN 55402 (60%)

Tel.: (612) 332-8700
Web Site: http://www.randstadstaffing.com
Sales Range: $25-49.9 Million
Emp.: 8
Personnel Placement Services
N.A.I.C.S.: 561320
Abigail Tremble *(Pres-Healthcare)*

Randstad Techniek (1)
Diemermere 25, 1112 TC, Diemen, Netherlands
Tel.: (31) 205695699
Sales Range: $25-49.9 Million
Emp.: 75
Temporary Help Service
N.A.I.C.S.: 561320

Randstad Technologies Inc. (1)
777 Bay Street, Toronto, M5G 2C8, ON, Canada
Tel.: (416) 962-9262
Web Site: http://www.randstadtechnologies.ca
Human Resource Consulting Services
N.A.I.C.S.: 541612

Randstad Technologies U.S. (1)
150 Presidential Way 3rd Fl, Woburn, MA 01801
Tel.: (781) 273-1472
Web Site: http://www.randstadusa.com
Human Resource Consulting Services
N.A.I.C.S.: 541612
Graig Paglieri *(CEO-Grp & Mng Dir-Professionals-Global)*

Randstad Technologies, Lda. (1)
Avenida da Republica N 26, Lisbon, 1069-228, Portugal
Tel.: (351) 210 105 400
Web Site: http://www.randstadtech.pt
Sales Range: $25-49.9 Million
Emp.: 50
Human Resource Consulting Services
N.A.I.C.S.: 541612
João Martins *(Gen Mgr)*

Randstad Transportdiensten (1)
Diemermere 25, 1112 TC, Diemen, Netherlands
Tel.: (31) 205695911
Web Site: http://www.randstadtransportdiensten.nl
Sales Range: $25-49.9 Million
Emp.: 11
Temporary Help Service
N.A.I.C.S.: 561320

Randstad UK Limited (1)
1st Floor 30 Furnival St, London, EC4A 1JQ, United Kingdom
Tel.: (44) 2075392999
Web Site: http://www.randstad.co.uk
Sales Range: $25-49.9 Million
Emp.: 30
Holding Company; Employment Placement Services
N.A.I.C.S.: 551112

Subsidiary (Domestic):

Datum Personnel Ltd. (2)
The Stabbles 348 Moorside Rd, Swincan, Manchester, United Kingdom
Tel.: (44) 1617379845
Sales Range: $25-49.9 Million
Emp.: 6
Engineering & IT Professional Employment Services
N.A.I.C.S.: 561311

Fairplace Consulting plc (2)
36-38 Cornhill, London, EC3V3PQ, United Kingdom
Tel.: (44) 2078160707
Web Site: http://www.fairplace.com
Sales Range: $10-24.9 Million
Specialist Outplacement Services
N.A.I.C.S.: 561311

Legal Appointments Ltd (2)
87 Chancery Ln, London, WC2A 1BD, United Kingdom
Tel.: (44) 2076114650
Web Site: http://www.kinseycraig.com
Sales Range: $10-24.9 Million
Emp.: 50
International Executive Search Firm
N.A.I.C.S.: 561311

Parkhouse Recruitment (2)

AND PRIVATE COMPANIES — RANDSTAD N.V.

6-7 Saint Johns Street 1st Floor, Cardiff, CF10 1GJ, United Kingdom
Tel.: (44) 2920384021
Web Site: http://www.parkhouse.com
Sales Range: $10-24.9 Million
Emp.: 50
N.A.I.C.S.: 561311

Prolaw Ltd. (2)
87 Chancery Ln, London, WC2A 1BD, United Kingdom
Tel.: (44) 2072426633
Web Site: http://www.prolaw.co.uk
Sales Range: $10-24.9 Million
Emp.: 100
N.A.I.C.S.: 561311

Randstad CPE Limited (2)
Second Floor Forum 4 Parkway, Solent Business Park, Fareham, PO15 7AD, United Kingdom
Tel.: (44) 1489560200
Web Site: http://www.randstadcpe.com
Sales Range: $25-49.9 Million
Emp.: 20
N.A.I.C.S.: 561311

Randstad Care Ltd. (2)
85 London Wall, London, EC2M 7AD, United Kingdom
Tel.: (44) 2038706355
Web Site: http://www.randstadcare.co.uk
Sales Range: $25-49.9 Million
Emp.: 50
N.A.I.C.S.: 561311

Branch (Domestic):

Randstad Care - Belfast (3)
Scottish Provident Building 7 Donegall Square West, Belfast, BT1 6JH, United Kingdom
Tel.: (44) 2890912840
Web Site: http://www.randstadcare.co.uk
Emp.: 5
Recruitment Agency Services
N.A.I.C.S.: 561311

Subsidiary (Domestic):

Randstad Education Ltd. (2)
450 Capability Green, Luton, LU1 3LU, Beds, United Kingdom
Tel.: (44) 1582811878
Web Site: http://www.randstad.co.uk
Sales Range: $10-24.9 Million
Emp.: 30
N.A.I.C.S.: 561311

Subsidiary (Non-US):

Randstad Education (3)
Level 13 120 Albert Street, Auckland, 1001, New Zealand
Tel.: (64) 9 300 7408
Employment Services
N.A.I.C.S.: 561311

Subsidiary (Domestic):

Randstad Financial & Professional Ltd. (2)
85 London Wall 5th Floor, London, EC2M 7AD, United Kingdom
Tel.: (44) 2077866914
Web Site: http://www.randstadfp.com
Sales Range: $10-24.9 Million
Emp.: 30
Employment Services
N.A.I.C.S.: 561311

Randstad Interim Executives Ltd. (2)
85 London Wall 5th Floor, London, EC2M 7AD, United Kingdom
Tel.: (44) 2077866500
Web Site: http://www.randstadinterimexecutives.com
Sales Range: $25-49.9 Million
Emp.: 15
Interim Executive & Project Managers Employment Services
N.A.I.C.S.: 561311

Randstad Technologies Ltd. (2)
450 Capability Green, Luton, LU1 3LU, Bedfordshire, United Kingdom
Tel.: (44) 2072555555
Web Site: http://www.abraxas.com
Sales Range: $10-24.9 Million
Employment Agency Services
N.A.I.C.S.: 561311

Randstad UK Holding Ltd. (2)
450 Capability Green, Luton, LU1 3LU, Bedfordshire, United Kingdom
Tel.: (44) 908660866
Web Site: https://www.randstad.co.uk
Sales Range: $25-49.9 Million
Emp.: 20
N.A.I.C.S.: 561311

Teleresources Consultancy Ltd. (2)
Kiln House 15-17 High St, Elstree, WD6 3BY, Herts, United Kingdom
Tel.: (44) 8707776012
Web Site: http://www.telesources.co.uk
Sales Range: $25-49.9 Million
Emp.: 10
Temporary Staffing
N.A.I.C.S.: 561311

Randstad Uruguay S.A. (1)
Bv Gral Artigas 2097, 11200, Montevideo, Uruguay
Tel.: (598) 24024444
Web Site: https://www.randstad.com.uy
Human Resouce Services
N.A.I.C.S.: 541612

Randstad Vikar (1)
Vester Farimagsgade 7 2 sal, 1606, Copenhagen, Denmark (100%)
Tel.: (45) 33930800
Web Site: http://www.randstad.dk
Sales Range: $10-24.9 Million
Emp.: 35
Temporary Help Service
N.A.I.C.S.: 561320
Jeroen Giel *(Mng Dir)*

Randstad s.r.o. (1)
Jungmannova 26/15, 110 00, Prague, 1, Czech Republic
Tel.: (420) 222210013
Web Site: http://www.randstad.cz
Human Resource Consulting Services
N.A.I.C.S.: 541612

Randstad, s.r.o. (1)
Apollo Business Center - Blok A Prievozska 2/A, Bratislava, 82109, Slovakia
Tel.: (421) 2 5263 2514
Web Site: http://www.randstad.sk
Emp.: 40
Human Resource Consulting Services
N.A.I.C.S.: 541612

Rowlands International S.A. (1)
18 r Glesener, 1616, Luxembourg, Luxembourg
Tel.: (352) 464135
Web Site: http://www.rowlandsonline.com
Sales Range: $25-49.9 Million
Emp.: 110
Statistical & Technology Recruiting Services
N.A.I.C.S.: 561311

SESA Select (1)
Sarmiento 991, S2000CMO, Rosario, Argentina
Tel.: (54) 3414105100
Web Site: http://www.randstad.com.ar
Sales Range: $25-49.9 Million
Emp.: 100
Staffing Services
N.A.I.C.S.: 561311
Andrea Avila *(Pres)*

SUPREME EDUCATION LTD. (1)
Randstad Court Laporte Way, Luton, LU4 8SB, United Kingdom
Tel.: (44) 1582 436 010
Web Site: http://www.supreme-education.com
Educational Consulting & Staffing Services
N.A.I.C.S.: 611710

Select AV Personeel B.V. (1)
Media Park Koos Postemalaan 2 Gateway C 1st Floor, 1217 ZC, Hilversum, Netherlands
Tel.: (31) 35 542 9966
Web Site: https://www.avpersoneel.nl
Temporary Staffing Services
N.A.I.C.S.: 561320

Select Appointments B.V. (1)
Europeanlaan 12, PO Box 2400, 5232 DC, 's-Hertogenbosch, Netherlands
Tel.: (31) 736414010
Sales Range: $25-49.9 Million
Emp.: 30
N.A.I.C.S.: 561311

Select Audio Visueel B.V. (1)
39C Sumatralaan 45, PO Box 1200, 1217 GP, Hilversum, Netherlands
Tel.: (31) 355429966
Web Site: http://www.avpersoneel.nl
Sales Range: $25-49.9 Million
Emp.: 6
N.A.I.C.S.: 561311

Select Audio Visueel Personeel BV (1)
Mediapark Koos Postemalaan 2 Hilversum Gateway C 1e verdieping, Hilversum, 1217GP, Netherlands
Tel.: (31) 35 5429966
Web Site: http://www.avpersoneel.nl
Emp.: 10
Professional Employment Services
N.A.I.C.S.: 561320

Select Recursos Humanos, S.A. (1)
Avenida da Republica 26, 1069-079, Lisbon, Portugal
Tel.: (351) 210105400
Web Site: http://www.ranstad.pt
Sales Range: $100-124.9 Million
Emp.: 120
N.A.I.C.S.: 561311

Sesa International (1)
Sarmiento 991 Piso 1, 2000, Rosario, Argentina
Tel.: (54) 3414105136
Web Site: http://www.randstad.com.ar
Sales Range: $75-99.9 Million
Emp.: 264
Staffing Services
N.A.I.C.S.: 561311

Sparq (1)
Reactorweg 47, 3542 AD, Utrecht, Netherlands
Tel.: (31) 881269914
Web Site: http://www.sparq.nl
Sales Range: $25-49.9 Million
Emp.: 15
Telecommunications
N.A.I.C.S.: 517111

Staff Planning Nederlands B.V. (1)
Stationsplein 2, 5211 AP, 's-Hertogenbosch, Netherlands
Tel.: (31) 737505000
Web Site: http://www.staffplanning.nl
Sales Range: $25-49.9 Million
Emp.: 30
N.A.I.C.S.: 561311

Talisman Software (Benelux) BV (1)
A van Leeuwenhoekweg 38 D14, Alphen aan den Rijn, 2408 AN, Netherlands
Tel.: (31) 172 766 070
Web Site: http://www.talisman-software.nl
Sales Range: $25-49.9 Million
Emp.: 15
Software Staff Recruitment Services
N.A.I.C.S.: 561311
Koen Frese *(Gen Mgr)*

Subsidiary (Domestic):

Tempo-Team IT-Flex (2)
Diemermere 15, 1112 TB, Diemen, Netherlands
Tel.: (31) 205695922
Web Site: http://www.tempoteam.nl
Temporary Help Service
N.A.I.C.S.: 561320

Tempo-Team Personeelsdiensten (2)
Diemermere 15, 1112 TB, Diemen, Netherlands
Tel.: (31) 205695922
Web Site: http://www.randstad.com
Sales Range: $125-149.9 Million
Temporary Help Service
N.A.I.C.S.: 561320

Tempo-Team Projecten (2)
Diemermere 15, Diemen, 1112 TB, Netherlands
Tel.: (31) 205695922
Web Site: http://www.tempo-team.nl
Temporary Help Service
N.A.I.C.S.: 561320

Tempo-Team Uitzenden (2)
Diemermere 15, 1112 TB, Diemen, Netherlands
Tel.: (31) 205695922
Web Site: http://www.tempo-team.nl
Employment Services
N.A.I.C.S.: 561320
Kees Stroomer *(Mng Dir)*

Tatum, LLC (1)
3715 Northside Dr NW, Atlanta, GA 30327
Tel.: (404) 841-9297
Web Site: http://www.tatumllc.com
Sales Range: $125-149.9 Million
Emp.: 50
Executive & Consulting Services
N.A.I.C.S.: 541618
Chris Shaw *(Dir-Bus Dev-Northeast & Mid-Atlantic)*

Branch (Domestic):

Tatum - Austin/San Antonio (2)
901 S MoPac Ste 200, Austin, TX 78746
Tel.: (512) 377-6550
Web Site: http://www.tatumllc.com
Sales Range: $25-49.9 Million
Executive & Consulting Services
N.A.I.C.S.: 541618

Tatum - Charlotte (2)
201 S College St Ste 2180, Charlotte, NC 28244
Tel.: (703) 917-1102
Web Site: http://www.tatumllc.com
Executive & Consulting Services
N.A.I.C.S.: 541618

Tatum - Chicago (2)
Three First National Plz 70 W Madison St Ste 470, Chicago, IL 60602
Tel.: (312) 233-2402
Web Site: http://www.tatumllc.com
Executive & Consulting Services
N.A.I.C.S.: 541618

Tatum - Houston (2)
10111 Richmond Ave Ste 100, Houston, TX 77042
Tel.: (281) 657-7260
Web Site: http://www.tatumllc.com
Executive & Consulting Services
N.A.I.C.S.: 541618

Tatum - Los Angeles (2)
300 Continental Blvd, El Segundo, CA 90245
Tel.: (310) 693-4455
Web Site: http://www.tatumllc.com
Sales Range: $10-24.9 Million
Emp.: 45
Executive & Consulting Services
N.A.I.C.S.: 541618

Tatum - Mid-Atlantic (2)
1750 Tysons Blvd, McLean, VA 22102
Tel.: (202) 470-0365
Web Site: http://www.tatumllc.com
Sales Range: $25-49.9 Million
Executive & Consulting Services
N.A.I.C.S.: 541618

Tatum - Minneapolis (2)
7701 France Ave S Ste 200, Edina, MN 55435
Tel.: (630) 291-5670
Executive & Consulting Services
N.A.I.C.S.: 541618

Tatum - New England (2)
150 Presidential Way Ste 120, Woburn, MA 01801
Tel.: (617) 340-2121
Web Site: http://www.tatum-us.com
Sales Range: $25-49.9 Million
Emp.: 5
Executive & Consulting Services
N.A.I.C.S.: 541618

Tatum - Orange County (2)
2040 Main St Ste 720, Irvine, CA 92614
Tel.: (949) 287-4022
Web Site: http://www.tatum-us.com
Sales Range: $25-49.9 Million
Executive & Consulting Services
N.A.I.C.S.: 541618

Tatum - Philadelphia (2)
1500 Market St 12th Fl, Philadelphia, PA 19102
Tel.: (215) 944-3028
Web Site: http://www.tatumllc.com
Executive & Consulting Services
N.A.I.C.S.: 541618

RANDSTAD N.V.

INTERNATIONAL PUBLIC

Randstad N.V.—(Continued)

Tatum - Portland (2)
1001 SW 5th Ave Ste 1100, Portland, OR 97204
Tel.: (206) 905-4584
Web Site: http://www.tatumllc.com
Executive & Consulting Services
N.A.I.C.S.: 541618

Tatum - Seattle (2)
601 Union St Ste 4200 176, Seattle, WA 98101
Tel.: (206) 905-4584
Web Site: http://www.tatumllc.com
Executive & Consulting Services
N.A.I.C.S.: 541618

Tatum - Tampa (2)
201 E Kennedy Blvd Ste 950, Tampa, FL 33602
Tel.: (813) 639-8369
Web Site: http://www.tatumllc.com
Executive Services & Consulting Firm
N.A.I.C.S.: 541618

Teachanywhere Ltd (1)
1A Embankment Old Boathouse, Putney, Putney, United Kingdom
Tel.: (44) 208 788 8663
Web Site: http://www.teachanywhere.com
Sales Range: $25-49.9 Million
Emp.: 10
Staffing Services
N.A.I.C.S.: 561311

Team2Venture GmbH (1)
Friedrichstr 224, 10969, Berlin, Germany
Tel.: (49) 3020 164 0340
Web Site: https://www.twago.com
Information Technology Services
N.A.I.C.S.: 541511
Thomas Jajeh (CEO, Founder & Mng Dir)

Tempo-Team (1)
Diemermere 15, 1112 TB, Diemen, Netherlands
Tel.: (31) 205695922
Web Site: http://www.tempo-team.nl
Sales Range: $25-49.9 Million
Emp.: 100
Temporary Help Service
N.A.I.C.S.: 561320
K. Stroomer (Mng Dir)

Tempo-Team GmbH (1)
Herrnrainweg 5, 63067, Offenbach, Germany
Tel.: (49) 69 91 33 45 0
Web Site: http://www.tempo-team.de
Human Resource Consulting Services
N.A.I.C.S.: 541612

Tempo-Team Group B.V. (1)
Diemermere 15, Diemen, 1112 TB, Netherlands
Tel.: (31) 205695922
Web Site: http://www.tempo-team.nl
Human Resource Consulting Services
N.A.I.C.S.: 541612

Subsidiary (Domestic):

JMW Horeca Uitzendbureau bv (2)
Overtoom 201 - 203, 1054 HT, Amsterdam, Netherlands
Tel.: (31) 204624001
Web Site: http://www.horeca-uitzendbureau.nl
Catering Staff Recruitment Services
N.A.I.C.S.: 561311

Tempo-Team HR Services SA (1)
5 Place de la Gare, 1616, Luxembourg, Luxembourg
Tel.: (352) 46 41 34
Web Site: http://www.tempo-team.lu
Human Resource Consulting Services
N.A.I.C.S.: 541612

Tempo-Team Management Holding GmbH (1)
Frankfurter Strasse 100, 65760, Eschborn, Germany
Tel.: (49) 699133450
Web Site: https://www.tempo-team.de
Staffing Services
N.A.I.C.S.: 561320

Tempo-Team SA (1)
5 Place de la Gare, 1616, Luxembourg, Luxembourg
Tel.: (352) 49 98 70
Human Resource Consulting Services
N.A.I.C.S.: 541612

Tempo-Team nv (1)
Keizer Karellaan 586, Brussels, 1082, Belgium
Tel.: (32) 2 555 16 11
Web Site: http://www.tempo-team.be
Human Resource Consulting Services
N.A.I.C.S.: 541612
Brigitte Bastin (Mgr-Sls)

The Mergis Group (1)
600 Corporate Dr Ste 240, Fort Lauderdale, FL 33334
Tel.: (954) 308-7600
Web Site: http://www.mergisgroup.com
Employment Consulting Services
N.A.I.C.S.: 561311

Top Personnel S. de R.L. de CV (1)
Insurgentes Sur 1446 piso 1, Mexico, 03230, Mexico
Tel.: (52) 55 5200 1800
Human Resource Consulting Services
N.A.I.C.S.: 541612

Uitzendbureau Otter-Westelaken b.v. (1)
Kennedylaan 1, Veghel, 5466 AA, Netherlands
Tel.: (31) 413 34 04 40
Web Site: http://www.otterwestelaken.nl
Emp.: 13
Professional Employment Services
N.A.I.C.S.: 561320
Cees Stromer (Gen Mgr)

VEXTER OUTSOURCING S.A. (1)
Via de los Poblados 9-6a Planta, 28033, Madrid, Spain
Tel.: (34) 917281370
Business Process Outsourcing Services
N.A.I.C.S.: 561499

Yacht Group (1)
Diemermere 25, 1112 TC, Diemen, Netherlands
Tel.: (31) 205197777
Web Site: http://www.yacht.nl
Sales Range: $25-49.9 Million
Emp.: 60
Temporary Help Service
N.A.I.C.S.: 561320

Subsidiary (Non-US):

YACHT TECCON (2)
Stuhrbaum 14, 28816, Stuhr, Bremen, Germany
Tel.: (49) 42156552100
Web Site: http://www.yacht-teccon.de
Temporary & Permanent Engineering & IT Staffing Services
N.A.I.C.S.: 561320

Yacht France (2)
23 Allee Lavoiser Bat R1 Entree A, 59650, Villeneuve d'Ascq, France
Tel.: (33) 320344490
Web Site: http://www.yachtgroup.com
Sales Range: $10-24.9 Million
Emp.: 50
Temporary Help Service
N.A.I.C.S.: 561320

Yacht Group Nederland B.V. (1)
Diemermere 25, 1112 TC, Diemen, Netherlands
Tel.: (31) 205197777
Web Site: https://www.yacht.nl
Temporary Staffing Services
N.A.I.C.S.: 561320

RANE HOLDINGS LIMITED
Maithri 132 Cathedral Road, Chennai, 600 086, India
Tel.: (91) 4428112472
Web Site:
  https://www.ranegroup.com
Year Founded: 1929
RANEHOLDIN—(NSE)
Rev.: $280,783,230
Assets: $311,441,130
Liabilities: $176,904,000
Net Worth: $134,537,130
Earnings: ($8,237,775)
Emp.: 91
Fiscal Year-end: 03/31/21
Automotive Components Mfr
N.A.I.C.S.: 336110
L. Ganesh (Chm & Mng Dir)

Subsidiaries:

Rane (Madras) Limited (1)
MAITHRI 132 Cathedral Road, Chennai, 600 086, India
Tel.: (91) 4428112472
Web Site: https://www.ranegroup.com
Rev.: $284,431,389
Assets: $161,731,311
Liabilities: $132,758,228
Net Worth: $28,973,083
Earnings: $3,599,305
Emp.: 1,165
Fiscal Year-end: 03/31/2023
Automobile Mfr
N.A.I.C.S.: 336110
Harish Lakshman (Vice Chm)

Rane Brake Lining Limited (1)
Plot No 30 II Main Road Ambattur Industrial Estate, Chennai, 600 058, India
Tel.: (91) 4426250566
Web Site: https://www.ranegroup.com
Rev.: $74,707,098
Assets: $51,020,286
Liabilities: $20,939,268
Net Worth: $30,081,018
Earnings: $5,238,402
Emp.: 756
Fiscal Year-end: 03/31/2019
Automotive Product Mfr
N.A.I.C.S.: 336110

Rane Engine Valve Limited (1)
Maithri 132 Cathedral Road, Chennai, 600 086, India
Tel.: (91) 4428112472
Web Site: https://www.ranegroup.com
Rev.: $41,624,310
Assets: $41,258,490
Liabilities: $26,904,150
Net Worth: $14,354,340
Earnings: ($831,285)
Emp.: 1,012
Fiscal Year-end: 03/31/2021
Valve Mfr
N.A.I.C.S.: 332911
L. Ganesh (Chm & Mng Dir)

Rane Holdings America Inc. (1)
4830 Bonnie Ct, West Bloomfield, MI 48322-4460
Tel.: (248) 979-8900
Emp.: 1
Auto Component Distr
N.A.I.C.S.: 423120
Srini Raman (Sr Mgr)

Rane Steering Systems Pvt Ltd (1)
14 Rajagopalan Salai, Vallancherry Guduvancherry, Chennai, 603 202, Tamil Nadu, India (49%)
Tel.: (91) 4447406017
Automobile Parts Mfr
N.A.I.C.S.: 336390

ZF Rane Automotive India Private Limited (1)
45 TTK Road, Alwarpet, Chennai, 600 018, Tamil Nadu, India (49%)
Tel.: (91) 4424994390
Web Site: http://ranegroup.com
Automobile Parts Distr
N.A.I.C.S.: 423120

Subsidiary (Domestic):

TRW Sun Steering Wheels Pvt. Ltd. (2)
A-47 LGF Hauz Khas, New Delhi, 110 016, India
Tel.: (91) 124 455 8500
Web Site: http://www.zf.com
Automobile Parts Distr
N.A.I.C.S.: 423120

RANG DONG LIGHT SOURCE & VACUUM FLASK JOINT STOCK COMPANY
87-89 Ha Dinh Str, Thanh Xuan Dist, Hanoi, Vietnam
Tel.: (84) 438584310
Web Site:
  https://www.rangdongvn.com
Year Founded: 1961
RAL—(HOSE)
Rev.: $342,632,466
Assets: $319,369,546
Liabilities: $196,829,539
Net Worth: $122,540,006
Earnings: $24,072,006
Emp.: 2,418
Fiscal Year-end: 12/31/23
Electric Bulb Mfr
N.A.I.C.S.: 335139
Nguyen Doan Thang (Exec Dir)

RANGE GOLD CORP.
1177 West Hastings Street Suite 2000, Vancouver, V6E 3T5, BC, Canada
Tel.: (604) 688-9600 BC
Web Site: http://www.rangegold.com
Year Founded: 2006
Gold Mining Services
N.A.I.C.S.: 212220
Garth Edgar (CFO)

RANGE INTELLIGENT COMPUTING TECHNOLOGY GROUP COMPANY LIMITED
No 84 Jinzhang Sub Road, Zhangyan Jinshan, Shanghai, China
Tel.: (86) 2157213619
Web Site: http://www.cn-pls.com
300442—(CHIN)
Rev.: $70,398,463
Assets: $206,992,838
Liabilities: $132,613,980
Net Worth: $74,378,859
Earnings: ($34,818,505)
Emp.: 760
Fiscal Year-end: 12/31/20
Packaging Machinery Mfr
N.A.I.C.S.: 333993
Weidong Jiang (Chm & Gen Mgr)

RANGE INTERNATIONAL LIMITED
Level 5 137 Bathurst Street, Sydney, 2000, NSW, Australia
Tel.: (61) 282807355
Web Site:
  https://www.rangeinternational.com
RAN—(ASX)
Rev.: $2,054,033
Assets: $5,327,762
Liabilities: $1,089,556
Net Worth: $4,238,206
Earnings: ($1,952,366)
Emp.: 300
Fiscal Year-end: 12/31/22
Industrial Truck, Tractor, Trailer & Stacker Machinery Manufacturing
N.A.I.C.S.: 333924
Richard Jenkins (Chm)

RANGER INSURANCE INC.
100 Scurfield Boulevard, Winnipeg, R3Y 1G4, MB, Canada
Tel.: (204) 925-8550
Web Site:
  http://www.rangerinsurance.ca
Year Founded: 1983
Insurance Agency Services
N.A.I.C.S.: 524210
Scott Feasey (Sr VP-Comm Sls)

RANGER METAL PRODUCTS LTD.
31 Malcolm Road, Guelph, N1K 1A7, ON, Canada
Tel.: (519) 824-7470
Web Site:
  http://www.rangermetal.com
Year Founded: 1963
Rev.: $38,168,833

Emp.: 250
Wire Product Mfr
N.A.I.C.S.: 332618
J. K. Macpherson *(VP-Mktg)*

RANGERS INTERNATIONAL FOOTBALL CLUB PLC
Ibrox Stadium 150 Edmiston Drive,
Glasgow, G51 2XD, United Kingdom
Tel.: (44) 141 580 8647   UK
Web Site:
   http://www.rangersfootballclub.com
Year Founded: 2012
Holding Company; Professional Soccer Club Owner & Operator
N.A.I.C.S.: 551112
Dougla Park *(Deputy Chm)*

Subsidiaries:

The Rangers Football Club
Limited   (1)
Ibrox Stadium 150 Edmiston Drive, Glasgow, G51 2XD, United Kingdom
Tel.: (44) 871 702 1972
Web Site: http://www.rangers.co.uk
Professional Soccer Club
N.A.I.C.S.: 711211
Derek Llambias *(CEO)*

RANGPUR DAIRY & FOOD PRODUCTS LIMITED
23 Adarsha Chayaneer 3rd Floor
Ring Road Adabor, Dhaka, 1207,
Bangladesh
Tel.: (880) 1978090829   BD
Web Site: https://www.rdmilk.com
Year Founded: 2004
RDFOOD—(CHT)
Rev.: $11,059,449
Assets: $15,635,136
Liabilities: $4,546,953
Net Worth: $11,088,183
Earnings: $958,717
Emp.: 350
Fiscal Year-end: 06/30/23
Milk Product Distr
N.A.I.C.S.: 424430
M. A. Kabir *(Founder & Mng Dir)*

RANGPUR FOUNDRY LIMITED
PRAN-RFL Center 105 Middle
Badda, Dhaka, 1212, Bangladesh
Tel.: (880) 29881792
Web Site:
   https://www.rangpurfoundry.com
RANFOUNDRY—(CHT)
Rev.: $13,120,646
Assets: $4,192,553
Liabilities: $1,224,720
Net Worth: $2,967,832
Earnings: $346,461
Emp.: 555
Fiscal Year-end: 06/30/23
Cast Iron Product Mfr
N.A.I.C.S.: 331511

RANHILL UTILITIES BERHAD
Bangunan Ranhill SAJ Jalan Garuda
Larkin, Johor Darul Takzim, 80350,
Johor Bahru, Malaysia
Tel.: (60) 72255300   MY
Web Site: http://www.ranhill.com.my
Year Founded: 1973
RANHILL—(KLS)
Rev.: $365,363,175
Assets: $690,311,958
Liabilities: $488,176,931
Net Worth: $202,135,026
Earnings: $30,098,836
Emp.: 3,015
Fiscal Year-end: 12/31/22
Engineering, Construction & Facilities Management Services
N.A.I.C.S.: 541330
Hamdan Mohamad *(Pres & CEO)*

Subsidiaries:

Ranhill Bersekutu Sdn Bhd   (1)
Level 22 Menara FELDA Platinum Park No 11 Persiaran KLCC, No 6 Jalan Kampar Off Jalan Tun Razak, 50088, Kuala Lumpur, Malaysia
Tel.: (60) 327168888
Web Site:
   https://www.ranhillbersekutu.com.my
Engineeering Services
N.A.I.C.S.: 541330

Ranhill Energy Sdn Bhd   (1)
36th Floor Empire Tower, No.182 Jalan Tun Razak, 50400, Kuala Lumpur, Malaysia
Tel.: (60) 321712020
Engineering Services
N.A.I.C.S.: 541330

Ranhill Engineers and Constructors Sdn Bhd   (1)
21st Floor Empire Tower, No 182 Jalan Tun Razak, 50400, Kuala Lumpur, Malaysia
Tel.: (60) 321712020
Sales Range: $75-99.9 Million
Emp.: 300
Engineeering Services
N.A.I.C.S.: 541330

Ranhill Power Berhad   (1)
Level 15 Wisma Perkeso, 155 Jalan Tun Razak, 50400, Kuala Lumpur, Malaysia
Tel.: (60) 26855200
Web Site: http://www.ranhill.com.my
Switchgear & Switchboard Apparatus Mfr
N.A.I.C.S.: 335313

Ranhill Powertron Sdn Bhd   (1)
32nd Floor Empire Tower, No 182 Jalan Tun Razak, 50400, Kuala Lumpur, Malaysia
Tel.: (60) 321712020
Web Site: http://www.ranhill.com.my
Electrical Contractor
N.A.I.C.S.: 238210

Ranhill Utilities Berhad   (1)
15th Floor Wisma Perkeso 155 Jalan Tun Razak, Kuala Lumpur, 50400, Malaysia
Tel.: (60) 3 2685 5200
Web Site: http://www.ranhill.com.my
Emp.: 100
Holding Company; Power Generation
N.A.I.C.S.: 551112

Subsidiary (Domestic):

Malaysian Issuing House Sdn. Bhd.   (2)
Level 6 Symphony House Pusat Dagangan Dana 1, Jalan PJU 1A 46, 47301, Petaling Jaya, Selangor, Malaysia
Tel.: (60) 378418000
Web Site: http://www.mih.com.my
Issuing House Services
N.A.I.C.S.: 561990
Ahmad Hassan *(Sr Mgr)*

Ranhill SAJ Sdn Bhd   (2)
Jalan Garuda, PO Box 262, Larkin, 80350, Johor Bahru, Johor, Malaysia
Tel.: (60) 72244040
Web Site: https://www.ranhillsaj.com.my
Sales Range: $200-249.9 Million
Emp.: 50
Water Distr
N.A.I.C.S.: 221310
Abdul Wahab Hamid *(CEO)*

Symphony Assets Sdn. Bhd.   (2)
Level 8 Symphony House Pusat Dagangan Dana 1, Jalan PJU 1A / 46, Petaling Jaya, Selangor, Malaysia
Tel.: (60) 378418000
Web Site: http://www.symphony.com.my
Investment Management Service
N.A.I.C.S.: 523999

Symphony Corporatehouse Sdn. Bhd.   (2)
02-19 19th Floor Menara Symphony, Jalan PJU 1A / 46, 46200, Petaling Jaya, Selangor, Malaysia
Tel.: (60) 376257777
Web Site: http://www.symphony.com.my
Corporate Secretarial & Accounting Services
N.A.I.C.S.: 561499

Ranhill Water Services Sdn Bhd   (1)
Level 4 Matang Building 83 Jalan Langkasuka, Larkin, 80350, Johor Bahru, Malaysia   (70%)
Tel.: (60) 72762020
Web Site: http://www.rws.com.my
Sales Range: $50-74.9 Million
Emp.: 400
Water Sewer & Pipeline Construction
N.A.I.C.S.: 237120

Ranhill WorleyParsons Sdn Bhd   (1)
Level 23 Menara AIA Cap Square No 10 Jalan Munshi Abdullah, 50100, Kuala Lumpur, Malaysia
Tel.: (60) 320399888
Sales Range: $75-99.9 Million
Emp.: 500
Engineeering Services
N.A.I.C.S.: 541330

RANI ZIM SHOPPING CENTERS LTD.
11 Redness Street, Petach Tikva,
4951794, Israel
Tel.: (972) 737962555
RANI—(TAE)
Rev.: $31,331,951
Assets: $792,646,762
Liabilities: $590,880,223
Net Worth: $201,766,539
Earnings: $24,011,051
Fiscal Year-end: 12/31/23
Industrial Building Construction
N.A.I.C.S.: 236210
Rani Zim *(Chm & CEO)*

RANIX, INC.
25 Eonju-ro 135-gil, Gangnam-Gu,
Seoul, Korea (South)
Tel.: (82) 25845516
Web Site: https://www.ranix.co.kr
Year Founded: 2003
317120—(KRS)
Rev.: $8,477,519
Assets: $41,506,212
Liabilities: $23,719,640
Net Worth: $17,786,572
Earnings: ($2,456,770)
Emp.: 72
Fiscal Year-end: 12/31/21
Semiconductor Chip Mfr
N.A.I.C.S.: 334413
Ui-Sun Park *(Mgr)*

RANJEET MECHATRONICS LTD.
Dev Aurum Block A 4th Floor 407/408
Anand Nagar Cross Road, Prahladnagar Satellite, Ahmedabad, 380015,
India
Tel.: (91) 9099053990
Web Site: https://www.ranjeet.co.in
Year Founded: 1993
541945—(BOM)
Rev.: $3,915,078
Assets: $5,375,692
Liabilities: $3,723,801
Net Worth: $1,651,891
Earnings: $11,969
Emp.: 23
Fiscal Year-end: 03/31/21
Mechanical Electronic Product Mfr
N.A.I.C.S.: 334419
Rakesh Swadia *(Chm & Mng Dir)*

RANJIT SECURITIES LIMITED
317-318 Transport Nagar Scheme no 44, Indore, 452014, Madhya Pradesh, India
Tel.: (91) 7314293747
Web Site:
   https://www.ranjitsecurities.com
Year Founded: 1994
531572—(BOM)
Rev.: $66,694
Assets: $798,750
Liabilities: $67,048
Net Worth: $731,702
Earnings: ($24,105)
Fiscal Year-end: 03/31/14
Financial Services
N.A.I.C.S.: 523999
Taranjeet Singh Hora *(Chm & Mng Dir)*

RANK GROUP LTD.
Level 9 148 Quay Street, PO Box
3515, Auckland, 1140, VIC, New Zealand
Tel.: (64) 93666259   NZ
Web Site: http://www.rankgroup.co.nz
Sales Range: $400-449.9 Million
Holding Company
N.A.I.C.S.: 551112
Graeme Hart *(CEO)*

Subsidiaries:

Rank Group Investments Ltd.   (1)
Level 9 148, PO Box 3515, Auckland, 1010, New Zealand
Tel.: (64) 93666259
Web Site: http://www.rankgroup.vo.nz
Sales Range: $50-74.9 Million
Emp.: 32
Equity Investment Firm
N.A.I.C.S.: 523999
Graeme Hart *(CEO)*

Holding (Domestic):

Carter Holt Harvey Limited   (2)
173 Captain Springs Road, Private Bag 92-106, Te Papapa, Auckland, 1142, New Zealand
Tel.: (64) 96330600
Web Site: http://www.chh.com
Sales Range: $150-199.9 Million
Paper, Pulp & Lumber Products Mfr; Hardware Store Owner
N.A.I.C.S.: 321912
Chris O'Brien *(Mgr-HR)*

Subsidiary (Domestic):

Carter Holt Harvey Building Products Group Limited   (3)
173 Captain Spring Road, Onehunga, 1061, Auckland, New Zealand
Tel.: (64) 92626000
Web Site: http://www.chh.com
Emp.: 120
Holding Company for the Building Products Segment
N.A.I.C.S.: 551112

Division (Domestic):

Carter Holt Harvey   (4)
173 Captain Springs Road, Onehunga, Auckland, 1061, New Zealand
Tel.: (64) 96331700
Web Site: http://www.chh.com
Sales Range: $25-49.9 Million
Emp.: 78
Timber, Plywood Product Mfr & Distr
N.A.I.C.S.: 321999

Subsidiary (Non-US):

Carter Holt Harvey Limited   (3)
Zenith Centre, Tower B, Level 2, 821 Pacific Highway, Chatswood, 2067, NSW, Australia
Tel.: (61) 294685700
Web Site:
   http://www.chhwoodproducts.com.au
Holding Company
N.A.I.C.S.: 551112

Subsidiary (Domestic):

Carter Holt Harvey Plastic Products Group Limited   (3)
173 Captain Springs Road, Onehunga, Auckland, 1061, New Zealand
Tel.: (64) 96331700
Web Site: http://www.chh.com
Emp.: 3,000
Holding Company for the Plastic Products & Agricultural Segments
N.A.I.C.S.: 551112
Ven Tribbe *(Controller-Fin)*

Division (Domestic):

Carter Holt Harvey Plastic
Products   (4)

RANK GROUP LTD.

Rank Group Ltd.—(Continued)

640 Great South Road, Manukau, New Zealand
Tel.: (64) 9262600
Mfr of Plastic Bottles, Jars, Flagons & Other Plastic Containers; Tamper Evident Containers; Industrial & Custom Moulded Products
N.A.I.C.S.: 326199

Carter Holt Harvey Plastic Products-Beverage Division (4)
862 Great South Rd, Manukau, New Zealand
Tel.: (64) 9 372 7200
Mfr of Plastic Carbonated Beverage Containers
N.A.I.C.S.: 326160

Subsidiary (Non-US):

Carter Holt Harvey Pty. Limited (3)
Tower B Level 2 821 Pacific Hwy, The Zenith Tower, NSW 2067, Chatswood, Australia
Tel.: (61) 294685700
Web Site: http://www.chh.com
Sales Range: $25-49.9 Million
Emp.: 50
Thermoformed Food Containers & Roll Sheet Manufacturers.
N.A.I.C.S.: 322219

Subsidiary (Domestic):

Carter Holt Harvey Timber Limited (3)
640 Great South Road, Manukau, Auckland, New Zealand
Tel.: (64) 92626000
Web Site: http://www.chh.com
Sales Range: $450-499.9 Million
Sawmilling, Timber Treatment & Wood Chip Production; Manufacture of Plywood Cladding, Doors, Timber Mouldings & Other Timber Products
N.A.I.C.S.: 321920

Carter Holt Harvey Wood Products Limited (3)
173 Captain Springs Road, PO Box 1951, Onehunga, 1061, Auckland, New Zealand
Tel.: (64) 92626000
Web Site: http://www.chh.com
Sales Range: $150-199.9 Million
Emp.: 100
Holding Company for Wood Products Segment
N.A.I.C.S.: 551112
Prafull Kesha *(CEO)*

Division (Domestic):

Carter Holt Building Supplies (4)
173 Caption Springs Road, Onahunga, Auckland, 1061, New Zealand
Tel.: (64) 92626000
Web Site: http://www.chh.com
Sales Range: $75-99.9 Million
Emp.: 300
Building Supplies & Hardware Retailer
N.A.I.C.S.: 444140
Bill Hayward *(Mgr-Mktg)*

Carter Holt Harvey (4)
195 Browns Rd, PO Box 76153, Manurewa, Manukau, Auckland, New Zealand
Tel.: (64) 92672920
Web Site: http://www.interion.co.nz
Sales Range: $25-49.9 Million
Emp.: 100
Producers of Natural Wood Veneer
N.A.I.C.S.: 321211

Carter Holt Harvey Forests Limited (4)
173 Captain Springs Road, PO Box 1951, Manukau, Auckland, New Zealand
Tel.: (64) 92626000
Web Site: http://www.chh.com
Emp.: 120
Forestry Establishment & Management
N.A.I.C.S.: 115310
Prafull Kesha *(CEO)*

Subsidiary (Non-US):

Carter Holt Harvey Woodproducts Australia Pty Ltd (4)
The Zenith Centre Tower B Level 2 821 Pacific Highway, Chatswood, 2067, NSW, Australia
Tel.: (61) 2 9468 5700
Web Site: http://www.chhwoodproducts.com.au
Emp.: 3
Timber Wood Product Mfr
N.A.I.C.S.: 321215
Des Tolan *(Mgr-Comml)*

Subsidiary (US):

Evergreen Packaging, Inc. (3)
5350 Poplar Ave, Memphis, TN 38119
Tel.: (901) 821-5350
Web Site: http://www.evergreenpackaging.com
Packaging Services
N.A.I.C.S.: 322220

Branch (Non-US):

Evergreen Packaging
503-5 8F Doowon Building Sinsa-dong, Gangnam-gu, Seoul, 135746, Korea (South)
Tel.: (82) 25405011
Web Site: http://www.evergreenpackaging.com
Sales Range: $50-74.9 Million
Emp.: 150
Beverage Packaging
N.A.I.C.S.: 488991
H. T. Lee *(Pres)*

Plant (Domestic):

Evergreen Packaging - Athens (4)
600 Dairy Park Rd, Athens, GA 30607-1118
Tel.: (706) 552-1111
Web Site: http://www.evergreenpackaging.com
Sales Range: $25-49.9 Million
Emp.: 169
Mfr of Milk & Juice Cartons
N.A.I.C.S.: 322120
Deborah Williams *(Mgr-HR)*

Evergreen Packaging - Cedar Rapids (4)
2400 6th St SW, Cedar Rapids, IA 52404-3510
Tel.: (319) 399-3200
Web Site: http://www.evergreenpackaging.com
Sales Range: $50-74.9 Million
Emp.: 250
Mfr of Packaging Machinery
N.A.I.C.S.: 322120

Evergreen Packaging - Clinton (4)
1500 S 14th St, Clinton, IA 52732-6130
Tel.: (563) 244-7334
Web Site: http://www.evergreenpackaging.com
Sales Range: $25-49.9 Million
Emp.: 145
Milk & Juice Cartons Mfr
N.A.I.C.S.: 322120

Evergreen Packaging - Olmsted Falls (4)
7920 Mapleway Dr, Olmsted Falls, OH 44138-1626
Tel.: (440) 235-7200
Web Site: http://www.evergreenpackaging.com
Sales Range: $25-49.9 Million
Emp.: 175
Mfr of Milk & Juice Cartons
N.A.I.C.S.: 322120

Evergreen Packaging - Plant City (4)
2104 Henderson Way, Plant City, FL 33566-7902
Tel.: (813) 752-2150
Web Site: http://www.evergreenpackaging.com
Sales Range: $50-74.9 Million
Emp.: 200
Manufacture Cartons
N.A.I.C.S.: 322120
Kerry Temoin *(Plant Mgr)*

Evergreen Packaging - Raleigh (4)
2215 S Wilmington St, Raleigh, NC 27603-2541
Tel.: (919) 821-8200
Web Site: http://www.evergreenpackaging.com
Sales Range: $50-74.9 Million
Emp.: 170
Packaging Facility
N.A.I.C.S.: 322219

Evergreen Packaging - Turlock (4)
1500 W Main St, Turlock, CA 95380-3704
Tel.: (209) 668-1600
Web Site: http://www.evergreenpackaging.com
Sales Range: $50-74.9 Million
Emp.: 149
Mfr Beverage Cartons
N.A.I.C.S.: 322219
Ed Burton *(Plant Mgr)*

Subsidiary (Non-US):

Holt Lloyd International Ltd (3)
Unit 100 Barton Dock Road, Stretford, M32 0YQ, Manchester, United Kingdom
Tel.: (44) 161 866 4800
Web Site: http://www.holtsauto.com
Automotive Products Mfr
N.A.I.C.S.: 336390
Kathrin Gamble *(Mgr-Channel Mktg)*

Holding (Domestic):

UCI Holdings Limited (2)
Level Nine 148 Quay Street, Auckland, 1010, New Zealand
Tel.: (64) 9 366 6259
Web Site: http://www.uciholdings.com
Rev.: $1,009,793,000
Assets: $1,360,123,000
Liabilities: $1,134,542,000
Net Worth: $225,581,000
Earnings: ($36,248,000)
Emp.: 3,900
Fiscal Year-end: 12/31/2014
Holding Company; Motor Vehicle Parts & Supplies Mfr & Distr
N.A.I.C.S.: 551112
Ricardo F. Alvergue *(CFO)*

Subsidiary (US):

UCI International, Inc. (3)
1900 W Field Ct, Lake Forest, IL 60045
Tel.: (847) 482-4335
Web Site: http://www.uci-fram.com
Sales Range: $900-999.9 Million
Emp.: 3,900
Holding Company; Motor Vehicle Aftermarket Replacement Parts
N.A.I.C.S.: 551112
Thomas Degnan *(Pres & CEO)*

Subsidiary (Domestic):

FRAM Group, LLC (4)
39 Old Ridgebury Rd, Danbury, CT 06810-5109
Tel.: (203) 830-7800
Web Site: http://www.framgrp.com
Antifreeze, Oil & Air Filters, Spark Plugs & Car Care Products Mfr
N.A.I.C.S.: 325998

Branch (Domestic):

FRAM Group, LLC - Rogers Facility (5)
200 SE 22nd St Ste 8, Bentonville, AR 72712
Tel.: (479) 271-7934
Sales Range: $25-49.9 Million
Emp.: 13
Electrical Apparatus & Equipment, Wiring Supplies & Related Equipment Merchant Whslr
N.A.I.C.S.: 423610
Issac Petersen *(Mgr-Bus Dev)*

Subsidiary (Domestic):

United Components, Inc. (4)
1900 W Field Ct, Lake Forest, IL 60045
Tel.: (847) 482-4335
Web Site: http://www.ucinc.com
Sales Range: $900-999.9 Million
Emp.: 3,900
Automotive Parts Designer, Mfr & Distr
N.A.I.C.S.: 336390

Subsidiary (Domestic):

Champion Laboratories, Inc. (5)
200 S 4th St, Albion, IL 62806-1313
Tel.: (618) 445-6011
Web Site: http://www.champlabs.com
Sales Range: $300-349.9 Million
Emp.: 1,200
Mfr of Oil, Air, Fuel, Transmission & Cabin Air Filters & Dust Collector Filters
N.A.I.C.S.: 336390

SIG Combibloc Group AG (1)
Laufengasse 18, Neuhausen am Rheinfall, 8212, Switzerland
Tel.: (41) 526746111
Web Site: http://www.sig.biz
Emp.: 5,000
Packaging Machinery Distr
N.A.I.C.S.: 423840
Rolf Stangl *(CEO)*

INTERNATIONAL PUBLIC

RANK PROGRESS S.A.
ul Zlotoryjska 63, 59-220, Legnica, Poland
Tel.: (48) 767467766
Web Site: https://www.rankprogress.pl
Year Founded: 1997
RNK—(WAR)
Rev.: $18,085,366
Assets: $225,567,581
Liabilities: $100,601,880
Net Worth: $124,965,701
Earnings: $6,096,799
Fiscal Year-end: 12/31/23
Property Investment & Development Services
N.A.I.C.S.: 531390
Jan Mroczka *(Founder, Pres & CEO)*

RANMARINE TECHNOLOGY B.V.
Galileistraat 15, 3029 AL, Rotterdam, Netherlands
Tel.: (31) 616952175
Web Site: https://www.ranmarine.io
Year Founded: 2016
RAN—(NASDAQ)
Rev.: $717,386
Assets: $3,998,687
Liabilities: $13,550,020
Net Worth: ($9,551,332)
Earnings: ($5,880,901)
Emp.: 32
Fiscal Year-end: 12/31/23
Information Technology Services
N.A.I.C.S.: 541512

RANPLAN GROUP AB
Upper Pendrill Court Ermine Street North Papworth Everar, Cambridge, CB23 3UY, United Kingdom
Tel.: (44) 1480831747
Web Site: https://www.ranplanwireless.com
RPLAN—(OMX)
Rev.: $2,718,443
Assets: $1,894,968
Liabilities: $1,817,884
Net Worth: $77,084
Earnings: ($2,500,398)
Emp.: 66
Fiscal Year-end: 12/31/22
Software Development Services
N.A.I.C.S.: 541511
Per Lindberg *(CEO)*

RAONSECURE CO. LTD
48F 108 Yeoui-daero, Yeongdeungpo-gu, Seoul, 07335, Korea (South)
Tel.: (82) 25614545
Web Site: http://www.raoncorp.com
Year Founded: 1998
042510—(KRS)
Rev.: $35,913,500
Assets: $58,975,720
Liabilities: $24,387,475
Net Worth: $34,588,244
Earnings: $6,370,147
Emp.: 202

Fiscal Year-end: 12/31/22
Security Application Development Services
N.A.I.C.S.: 541511
Jiyoung Yoo *(Gen Mgr)*

RAONTEC INC
88-4 156beon-gil Saneop-ro, Suwon, Gyeonggi-do, Korea (South)
Tel.: (82) 312010062
Web Site: https://www.raonrobot.com
Year Founded: 2000
Robot Mfr & Distr
N.A.I.C.S.: 334513
Won-Geyung Kim *(CEO)*

RAOOM TRADING CO.
The 1st Industrial City, Buraidah, Al-Qussim, Saudi Arabia
Tel.: (966) 163222999
Web Site: https://www.raoomco.com
Year Founded: 1988
9529—(SAU)
Rev.: $29,344,124
Assets: $37,044,969
Liabilities: $11,625,358
Net Worth: $25,419,611
Earnings: $6,730,804
Emp.: 302
Fiscal Year-end: 12/31/21
Glass Products Mfr
N.A.I.C.S.: 327215
Abdul-Aziz Abdul-Allah Al-Hameed *(Chm)*

RAP MEDIA LTD.
Arora House 16 Golf Link Union Park Khar West, Mumbai, 400052, India
Tel.: (91) 2226041313
Web Site: http://www.rapmedia.co.in
531583—(BOM)
Rev.: $4,964
Assets: $1,767,965
Liabilities: $325,054
Net Worth: $1,442,911
Earnings: ($126,704)
Fiscal Year-end: 03/31/21
Real Estate Services
N.A.I.C.S.: 531390
Rupinder Singh Arora *(Chm & Mng Dir)*

RAPALA VMC OYJ
Makelankatu 87, 00610, Helsinki, Finland
Tel.: (358) 97562540
Web Site: https://www.rapalavmc.com
RAP1V—(HEL)
Rev.: $296,136,413
Assets: $364,882,366
Liabilities: $214,871,573
Net Worth: $150,010,792
Earnings: $3,993,093
Emp.: 1,543
Fiscal Year-end: 12/31/22
Fishing Tackle Mfr
N.A.I.C.S.: 713990
Stanislas de Castelnau *(Exec VP & Head-Ops)*

Subsidiaries:

Dynamite Baits Ltd. (1)
Wolds Farm The Fosse, Cotgrave, Nottingham, NG12 3HG, United Kingdom
Tel.: (44) 1159892145
Emp.: 60
Fishing Accessory Mfr
N.A.I.C.S.: 339920
Duncan Lennox *(Mgr-Ops)*

Elbe Normark AS (1)
Rolfsbuktveien 4 D, PO Box 113, 1330, Fornebu, Norway
Tel.: (47) 67 16 74 00
Web Site: http://www.elbe.no
Sales Range: $25-49.9 Million
Emp.: 16
Sporting Equipment Distr

N.A.I.C.S.: 423910
Hans Coucheron Aamot *(Chm)*

KL-Teho Oy (1)
Tehotie 1, PL 21, 41801, Korpilahti, Finland
Tel.: (358) 108307300
Web Site: http://www.kl-teho.fi
Injection Molded Plastic Products Mfr
N.A.I.C.S.: 326121

Marttiini OU (1)
Suur-Joe 71, 80042, Parnu, Estonia
Tel.: (372) 4478411
Web Site: http://www.Marttiini.fi
Sales Range: $25-49.9 Million
Emp.: 20
Fishing Supplies Whslr
N.A.I.C.S.: 423910

Marttiini Oy (1)
Tehtaantie 2, 17200, Vaaksy, Finland
Tel.: (358) 403110600
Web Site: https://www.marttiini.fi
Sales Range: $25-49.9 Million
Knives Mfr
N.A.I.C.S.: 332215

NC Holdings (1)
10395 Yellow Circle Dr, Minnetonka, MN 55343-9101
Tel.: (952) 933-7060
Web Site: http://www.rapala.com
Sales Range: $50-74.9 Million
Emp.: 76
Mfr of Sporting & Recreation Goods
N.A.I.C.S.: 423910

Subsidiary (Domestic):

Rapala Mail Order Inc. (2)
10395 Yellow Circle Dr, Minnetonka, MN 55343-9101
Tel.: (952) 933-7060
Web Site: http://www.rapala.com
Sales Range: $25-49.9 Million
Emp.: 25
Fishing, Tackle & Catalog/Mail-Order Services
N.A.I.C.S.: 423910

Normark Adriatik D.o.o. (1)
Hrastovicka Ulica 19 Lucko, 10250, Zagreb, Croatia
Tel.: (385) 14107565
Web Site: www.normarkadriatik.hr
Fishing Accessory Mfr
N.A.I.C.S.: 339920

Normark Chile Ltd. (1)
C/El Robre N 731 Comuna Recoleta, 8431449, Santiago, Chile
Tel.: (56) 24017467
Fishing Accessory Mfr
N.A.I.C.S.: 339920

Normark Corporation (1)
10395 Yellow Cir Dr, Minnetonka, MN 55343
Tel.: (952) 933-7060
Fishing Lures Distr
N.A.I.C.S.: 423910
Tom MacKin *(Pres)*

Normark Denmark A/S (1)
Endelavevej 1, 8940, Randers, Denmark
Tel.: (45) 87114170
Web Site: http://www.normark.dk
Sales Range: $25-49.9 Million
Emp.: 25
Fishing & Hunting Supplies Distr
N.A.I.C.S.: 423490
Allan Magnus *(Mgr-Mktg)*

Normark Eesti OU (1)
Asula 4c, EE-11312, Tallinn, Harju, Estonia
Tel.: (372) 6117081
Sales Range: $50-74.9 Million
Emp.: 2
Fishing Equipment & Supplies Whslr
N.A.I.C.S.: 423910

Normark Hungary Ltd. (1)
Gubacsi ut 6/B, 1097, Budapest, Hungary
Tel.: (36) 12060702
Web Site: http://www.normark.hu
Sales Range: $25-49.9 Million
Emp.: 15
Fishing Accessories Distr
N.A.I.C.S.: 423490

Normark Inc.
1350 Phillip Murray Avenue, Oshawa, L1J 6Z9, ON, Canada
Tel.: (905) 571-3001
Web Site: http://www.rapala.ca
Sales Range: $25-49.9 Million
Emp.: 30
Fishing Hooks Mfr
N.A.I.C.S.: 339920

Normark Innovations, Inc. (1)
161 Lakeside View Cir, Jenkinsville, SC 29065
Tel.: (803) 945-4700
Fishing Accessory Mfr
N.A.I.C.S.: 339920

Normark Italia S.R.L. (1)
Via Audinot 4, 40134, Bologna, Italy
Tel.: (39) 03487332655
Fishing Accessory Mfr
N.A.I.C.S.: 339920

Normark Polska Sp.z.o.o. (1)
ul Dluga 30, 05-092, Mlonianki, Masovian, Poland
Tel.: (48) 600222704
Web Site: http://www.normark.pl
Sales Range: $25-49.9 Million
Fishing Equipment & Supplies Whslr
N.A.I.C.S.: 423910

Normark Portugal SA (1)
Rua Escultor Barata Feyo 70 Aldeia De Juso, 2750-020, Cascais, Portugal
Tel.: (351) 214851202
Web Site: http://www.normark.pt
Sales Range: $50-74.9 Million
Emp.: 4
Fishing Lures Distr
N.A.I.C.S.: 423910

Normark Scandinavia AB (1)
Hamnplan 11, 753 19, Uppsala, Sweden
Tel.: (46) 18142010
Web Site: http://www.normark.se
Emp.: 30
Sporting Goods Distr
N.A.I.C.S.: 423910

Normark Spain SA (1)
Camino Monte De Valdeoliva 14 Nave L1 Poligono Industrial Norte, El Raso San Agustin de Guadalix, 28750, Madrid, Spain
Tel.: (34) 918487277
Fishing Accessory Mfr
N.A.I.C.S.: 339920

Normark Suomi Oy (1)
Aholaidantie 3, 40320, Jyvaskyla, Finland
Tel.: (358) 444250500
Web Site: http://www.normark.fi
Sales Range: $25-49.9 Million
Emp.: 30
Fishing & Hunting Supplies Distr
N.A.I.C.S.: 423910
Saku Kulmala *(Mng Dir)*

Normark UAB (1)
Europos av 11, 46329, Kaunas, Lithuania
Tel.: (370) 37457144
Sales Range: $25-49.9 Million
Emp.: 13
Fishing Accessories Distr
N.A.I.C.S.: 423490
Vitas Miskinis *(Mgr)*

OOO Raptech (1)
Fabrichnaja 18 Helyla, Sortavala, 186760, Russia
Tel.: (7) 8143000000
Fishing Accessory Mfr
N.A.I.C.S.: 339920

PT Rapala Indonesia (1)
Taman Surya 5 Ruko Palm Crown Blok 001 No 11, Pegadungan Kali Deras, Jakarta Barat, 11830, Indonesia
Tel.: (62) 215504049
Fishing Accessory Mfr
N.A.I.C.S.: 339920

PT Rapala VMC Batam (1)
Jl Beringin Lot 206 BIP Muka Kuning, Batam, 29433, Kepulauan Riau, Indonesia
Tel.: (62) 42639800
Fishing Accessory Mfr
N.A.I.C.S.: 339920

PT VMC Fishing Tackle Indonesia (1)
Jalan Angsana Lot 282 BIP Muka Kuning,

Batam, 29433, Kepulauan Riau, Indonesia
Tel.: (62) 770611995
Fishing Accessory Mfr
N.A.I.C.S.: 339920

Peltonen Ski Oy (1)
Viilukatu 11, FI-18130, Heinola, Finland
Tel.: (358) 3876070
Web Site: https://www.peltonenski.fi
Sales Range: $25-49.9 Million
Emp.: 20
Skis Mfr
N.A.I.C.S.: 339920
Saku Kulmala *(Mng Dir)*

Rapala B.V. (1)
Avenue Emile Demot 19 9th floor, B-1000, Brussels, Belgium
Tel.: (32) 26260439
Fishing Accessory Mfr
N.A.I.C.S.: 339920

Rapala Eesti AS (1)
Lao 8, EE-800 10, Parnu, Estonia
Tel.: (372) 4478470
Sales Range: $50-74.9 Million
Emp.: 200
Fishing Knives & Lures Mfr
N.A.I.C.S.: 339999

Rapala Finance N.V. (1)
Avenue Emile De Mot 19, 1000, Brussels, Belgium
Tel.: (32) 26260430
Business Management Services
N.A.I.C.S.: 561110

Rapala France SAS (1)
Zone industrielle 3 rue des chenes, Bourogne, 90140, France
Tel.: (33) 384573500
Web Site: http://www.rapala.fr
Emp.: 100
Fishing Lures Distr
N.A.I.C.S.: 423910
Jean Philippe Nicolle *(Gen Mgr)*

Rapala Freetime Australia Pty. Ltd. (1)
1B Amour Street, Milperra, 2214, NSW, Australia
Tel.: (61) 297808200
Web Site: http://www.rapala.com.au
Emp.: 20
Fishing Accessory Mfr
N.A.I.C.S.: 423910

Rapala Japan K.K. (1)
7-1-4 Habucho, Kishiwada, 596-0825, Osaka, Japan
Tel.: (81) 724260767
Web Site: https://www.rapala.co.jp
Sales Range: $50-74.9 Million
Emp.: 9
Fishing Lures Distr
N.A.I.C.S.: 423910

Rapala VMC (Asia Pacific) Sdn. Bhd. (1)
Suite 12 06 12th Floor MWE Plaza No 8 Lebuh Farquhar, 10200, Penang, Malaysia
Tel.: (60) 42639800
Fishing Accessory Mfr
N.A.I.C.S.: 339920

Rapala VMC (ShenZhen) Ltd. (1)
No 3 Xin Di Road Gang Tou Village Second Street, Ban Tian Long Gang District, Shenzhen, China
Tel.: (86) 75528762318
Fishing Accessory Mfr
N.A.I.C.S.: 339920

Rapala VMC (Thailand) Co., Ltd. (1)
44/4 Moo 5 Rattanathibet Road Bang Rak Yai, Bang Bua Thong, Nonthaburi, 11110, Thailand
Tel.: (66) 98203847
Fishing Accessory Mfr
N.A.I.C.S.: 339920

Rapala VMC Australia Pty Ltd. (1)
1b Amour St, Milperra, 2214, NSW, Australia
Tel.: (61) 297808200
Fishing Accessory Mfr
N.A.I.C.S.: 339920

Rapala VMC China Co. (1)
Room 218 2nd Floor No 1 Building No 62 Yard Ba Li Zhuang Road, HaiDian District, Beijing, 100036, China

RAPALA VMC OYJ

Rapala VMC Oyj—(Continued)
Tel.: (86) 51082704801
Fishing Accessory Mfr
N.A.I.C.S.: 339920

Rapala VMC Corporation (1)
10395 Yellow Circle Dr, Minnetonka, MN 55343-9101
Tel.: (952) 933-7060
Sales Range: $25-49.9 Million
Emp.: 60
Fishing Lures, Fillet Knives & Boards; Whetstones; Sporting & Recreation Goods Mfr
N.A.I.C.S.: 311812

Subsidiary (Domestic):

Blue Fox Tackle Co. (2)
10395 Yellow Circle Dr, Minnetonka, MN 55343-9101
Tel.: (952) 933-7060
Web Site: http://www.rapala.com
Sales Range: $25-49.9 Million
Emp.: 40
Sporting Goods
N.A.I.C.S.: 339920

Rapala VMC Iceland ehf (1)
Hafnargata 21, Keflavik, 230, Reykjanesbae, Iceland
Tel.: (354) 5712001
Fishing Accessory Mfr
N.A.I.C.S.: 339920

Rapala VMC Korea Co., Ltd (1)
Room 202 2nd floor Cheongbong Building 130 Bupyeong-daero, Bupyeong-gu, Incheon, Korea (South)
Tel.: (82) 3252955612
Web Site: https://www.rapala.co.kr
Emp.: 10
Fishing Hooks & Lures Mfr
N.A.I.C.S.: 339920

Rapala VMC Mexico S. de R.L. de C.V (1)
Calle Oriente 233 No 151 2nd Floor, 08500, Mexico, Mexico
Tel.: (52) 5555587822
Fishing Accessory Mfr
N.A.I.C.S.: 339920

Rapala VMC Singapore Pte. Ltd. (1)
73 Ubi Road 1 08-49 Oxley Bizhub, Singapore, 408733, Singapore
Tel.: (65) 297808200
Fishing Accessory Mfr
N.A.I.C.S.: 339920

Rapala VMC South-Africa Distributors Pty. Ltd. (1)
1489 Zeiss Rd Laserpark Honeydew Ext 5, Johannesburg, 2040, Gauteng, South Africa
Tel.: (27) 117946950
Web Site: http://www.rapalasa.co.za
Fishing Equipment & Supplies Whslr
N.A.I.C.S.: 423910

Rapala-Fishco AG (1)
Werkstrasse 43, 8630, Rueti, Zurich, Switzerland
Tel.: (41) 552515292
Web Site: http://www.rapala-fishco.ch
Fishing Equipment & Supplies Whslr
N.A.I.C.S.: 423910

Remen Slukfabrikk AS (1)
Rolssduktveien 4 D, PO Box 113, 1361, Fornebu, Norway
Tel.: (47) 67167400
Web Site: http://www.elbe.no
Sales Range: $25-49.9 Million
Emp.: 15
Fishing Knives & Lures Mfr
N.A.I.C.S.: 339999
Morten Fredriksen (Mgr)

SC Normark Sport Romania S.r.l. (1)
Str Leordeni Nr 161S Etaj 3 Judet, Ilfov, 077105, Popesti-Leordeni, Romania
Tel.: (40) 214050007
Fishing Accessory Mfr
N.A.I.C.S.: 339920

SIA Normark Latvia (1)
Ventspils Street 50, LV-1002, Riga, Latvia
Tel.: (371) 7672275
Fishing Accessory Mfr

N.A.I.C.S.: 339920

Smokehouse LLC
400 Portway Ave, Hood River, OR 97031
Tel.: (541) 386-3811
Web Site: http://www.smokehouseproducts.com
Rev.: $11,585,454
Emp.: 18
Mfr Electric Smokers, Smoker Accessories, Insulation Blankets, Dry Rubs & Replacement Parts
N.A.I.C.S.: 335220
Levi Strayer (Pres)

VMC Peche SA (1)
12 rue Charles de Gaulle, 90120, Morvillars, France
Tel.: (33) 384573434
Web Site: https://vmc-hooks.com
Sales Range: $50-74.9 Million
Emp.: 120
Fishing Hooks Mfr & Distr
N.A.I.C.S.: 339999

VMC Waterqueen Ukraine (1)
New Petrivtsi st Vatutina 57-A, Vyshgorod, 07300, Kiev, Ukraine
Tel.: (380) 44 585 2991
Web Site: http://www.normark.com.ua
Fishing Knives & Lures Distr
N.A.I.C.S.: 423910

Willtech (PRC) Ltd. (1)
Unit 3201-3203 Tower 2 Metroplaza No 223 Hing Fong Road, Kwai Chung, New Territories, China (Hong Kong)
Tel.: (852) 24098408
Web Site: http://www.cmotion.com.hk
Stationery Product Mfr
N.A.I.C.S.: 339940

ZAO Normark (1)
28B building A 3rd floor, Balaklavsky prospect, 117452, Moscow, Russia
Tel.: (7) 4957753732
Web Site: http://www.normark.ru
Sales Range: $50-74.9 Million
Fishing Knives & Lures Distr
N.A.I.C.S.: 423910

RAPHAEL MICHEL SA
ZA Crepon Sud - Avenue de l'Aygues, BP 90025, 84420, Piolenc, Cedex, France
Tel.: (33) 4 90 34 06 07
Web Site: http://www.raphael-michel.com
Year Founded: 1899
MLRAM—(EUR)
Sales Range: $50-74.9 Million
Wine Mfr & Whslr
N.A.I.C.S.: 312130

RAPHAS CO., LTD.
62 Magokjungang 8-Ro 1-Gil, Gangseo-Gu, Seoul, 07793, Korea (South)
Tel.: (82) 23923011
Web Site: https://www.raphas.com
Year Founded: 2006
214260—(KRS)
Rev.: $18,130,919
Assets: $73,678,163
Liabilities: $39,920,231
Net Worth: $33,757,932
Earnings: ($6,616,925)
Emp.: 94
Fiscal Year-end: 12/31/22
Cosmetics Mfr
N.A.I.C.S.: 325620
Do-Hyeon Jeong (CEO)

Subsidiaries:

Raphas China Co., Ltd. (1)
781-3 Magok-dong, Gangseo-gu, Seoul, 07793, Korea (South)
Tel.: (82) 23923011
Web Site: https://www.acropass.cn
Biotechnology Research Services
N.A.I.C.S.: 541714

RAPICUT CARBIDES LIMITED

119 GIDC Industrial Area, Ankleshwar, 393002, Gujarat, India
Tel.: (91) 2646251118
Web Site: https://www.rapicutcarbides.com
Year Founded: 1977
500360—(BOM)
Rev.: $4,745,327
Assets: $4,091,289
Liabilities: $1,523,290
Net Worth: $2,568,000
Earnings: ($162,161)
Emp.: 99
Fiscal Year-end: 03/31/23
Tungsten Carbide Products Mfr
N.A.I.C.S.: 325180
Dhananjay Digambar Kanitkar (Chm)

RAPID A.D.
Studentski trg 4, 11000, Belgrade, Serbia
Tel.: (381) 113281722
Web Site: https://www.rapid.co.rs
Year Founded: 1952
RAPD—(BEL)
Sales Range: Less than $1 Million
Emp.: 23
Retail Store Operator
N.A.I.C.S.: 459999
Rade Pops-Dragic (Gen Mgr)

RAPID A.D.
Industrijska zona bb, 25260, Apatin, Serbia
Tel.: (381) 114427400
Web Site: https://www.rapid.rs
Year Founded: 1991
RPID—(BEL)
Sales Range: Less than $1 Million
Emp.: 89
Bricks Mfr
N.A.I.C.S.: 327331
Jasmina Kuga (Exec Dir & Dir)

RAPID DOSE THERAPEUTICS, INC.
1121 Walkers Line, Burlington, L7N 2G4, ON, Canada
Tel.: (416) 477-1052
Web Site: https://www.rapid-dose.com
Year Founded: 2017
RDTCF—(OTCIQ)
Rev.: $535,850
Assets: $1,676,078
Liabilities: $3,667,975
Net Worth: ($1,991,898)
Earnings: ($2,841,880)
Fiscal Year-end: 02/28/23
Pharmaceuticals Product Mfr
N.A.I.C.S.: 325412
Mark Upsdell (CEO)

RAPID ELECTRONICS LIMITED
Severalls Lane, Colchester, CO4 5JS, Essex, United Kingdom
Tel.: (44) 1206751166
Web Site: http://www.rapidonline.com
Year Founded: 1979
Sales Range: $10-24.9 Million
Emp.: 144
Electronic Components Distr
N.A.I.C.S.: 423690
James Bell (COO)

RAPID INVESTMENTS LIMITED
107 Turf Estate E Moses Road, Shakti Mill Lane Mahalaxmi, Mumbai, 400 011, India
Tel.: (91) 2249608349
Web Site: https://www.rapidinvestments.co.in
Year Founded: 1979
Rev.: $182,744

INTERNATIONAL PUBLIC

Assets: $1,182,961
Liabilities: $878,113
Net Worth: $304,848
Earnings: $17,417
Fiscal Year-end: 03/31/19
Investment Banking Services
N.A.I.C.S.: 523150
Shailendra T. Singh (CFO)

RAPID NUTRITION PLC
82 James Carter Road Suite A, Mildenhall, London, IP28 7DE, Suffolk, United Kingdom
Tel.: (44) 2032392561 UK
Web Site: https://www.rnplc.com
Year Founded: 2001
RPNRF—(EUR)
Rev.: $2,299,921
Assets: $2,007,321
Liabilities: $2,704,391
Net Worth: ($697,070)
Earnings: $182,407
Emp.: 13
Fiscal Year-end: 12/31/21
Healthcare Product Distr
N.A.I.C.S.: 423450
Simon Ledger (CEO)

RAPID SYNERGY BERHAD
161 Jalan Sungai Keluang Bayan Lepas FIZ Phase 1, 11900, Penang, Malaysia
Tel.: (60) 46439300 MY
Web Site: https://www.rapidsynergy.com.my
RAPID—(KLS)
Rev.: $9,095,238
Assets: $70,883,598
Liabilities: $36,927,407
Net Worth: $33,956,190
Earnings: $368,254
Fiscal Year-end: 06/30/23
Precision Tools, Dies & Molds Mfr
N.A.I.C.S.: 332216
Yit Chan Tai (Co-Sec)

RAPIDO PRET SA
2 Rue du Pot d Argent, 22200, Guingamp, France
Tel.: (33) 296402431
Web Site: http://www.rapidopret.fr
ML350—(EUR)
Sales Range: $1-9.9 Million
Mortgage Brokerage Services
N.A.I.C.S.: 522310
Emmanuel Aubry (Chm & CEO)

RAPIDO SAS
Rue de Bretagne RN12, 53100, Mayenne, France
Tel.: (33) 2 43 30 10 70
Web Site: https://www.rapido.fr
Motor Home Mfr
N.A.I.C.S.: 336213
Pierre Rousseau (CEO)

Subsidiaries:

Westfalia Mobil GmbH (1)
Franz Knobel Str 34, 33378, Rheda-Wiedenbruck, Germany
Tel.: (49) 5242150
Web Site: http://www.westfalia-mobil.net
Sales Range: $50-74.9 Million
Emp.: 100
Motor Home Mfr
N.A.I.C.S.: 336213
Pierre Rousseau (Mng Dir)

RAPTIS GROUP LIMITED
Level 39 Chevron Renaissance Skyline Central 23 Ferny Ave, Surfers Paradise, 4217, QLD, Australia
Tel.: (61) 7 5570 8000
Web Site: http://www.raptisgroup.com.au
Real Estate Development Services
N.A.I.C.S.: 531390

James Raptis *(Founder, Chm, CEO, Mng Dir & Co-Sec)*

RAPTOR RIG LTD.
7016-81 Street SE, Calgary, T2C 5B8, AB, Canada
Tel.: (587) 885-1505
Web Site: http://www.raptorrig.com
Drilling Services
N.A.I.C.S.: 213111
Reg Layden *(Co-Founder)*

RAQUALIA PHARMA INC.
8F Meieki Southside Square 1-21-19 Meieki Minami, Nakamura-ku, Nagoya, 450-0003, Japan
Tel.: (81) 569840700
Web Site: https://www.raqualia.com
Year Founded: 2008
4579—(TKS)
Rev.: $13,478,090
Assets: $48,715,390
Liabilities: $5,324,590
Net Worth: $43,390,800
Earnings: ($2,290,070)
Emp.: 86
Fiscal Year-end: 12/31/23
Pharmaceuticals Mfr
N.A.I.C.S.: 325412
Naoki Tani *(Pres & CEO)*

Subsidiaries:

TMRC Co., Ltd. (1)
MI Bldg 1-12-12 KitaShinjuku, Shinjuku-ku, Tokyo, 169-0074, Japan
Tel.: (81) 362791086
Web Site: https://www.tmrc.co.jp
Drug & Health Research Development Services
N.A.I.C.S.: 541713
Hirobumi Takeuchi *(CEO)*

RARE ENTERPRISES LTD.
151-155, Nariman Bhavan 15th Floor Nariman Point Mumbai,, Maharashtra, 400021, India
Tel.: (91) 2266590100
Private Equity
N.A.I.C.S.: 523999

Subsidiaries:

Inventurus Knowledge Solutions, Inc. (1)
8951 Cypress Waters Blvd Ste 100, Coppell, TX 75019
Tel.: (866) 885-5935
Web Site: https://www.ikshealth.com
Emp.: 4,670
Hospitals & Health Care
N.A.I.C.S.: 621610

Subsidiary (Domestic):

AQuity Solutions, LLC (2)
125 Edinburgh South Drive Suite 310, Cary, NC 27511
Tel.: (800) 233-3030
Web Site: https://aquitysolutions.com
Emp.: 7,000
Business Outsourcing Services
N.A.I.C.S.: 561410
Marty Serro *(CIO)*

Subsidiary (Domestic):

Acusis LLC (3)
4 Smithfield St, Pittsburgh, PA 15222
Tel.: (412) 209-1300
Web Site: http://www.acusis.com
Clinical Document Preparation Services
N.A.I.C.S.: 561410

Subsidiary (Domestic):

Cybergistics, LLC (4)
3535 Route 66 Bldg 2, Neptune, NJ 07753-2624
Tel.: (732) 918-7329
Web Site: http://www.cybergistics.com
Full-service Information Management Company
N.A.I.C.S.: 513210
Donna Pizzulli *(CEO)*

RARE FOODS AUSTRALIA LTD.
Level 3 3 Cantonment St, Fremantle, 6160, WA, Australia
Tel.: (61) 861818888   AU
Web Site: https://www.rarefoodsaustralia.com
Year Founded: 1960
RFA—(ASX)
Rev.: $5,048,039
Assets: $10,291,932
Liabilities: $3,869,214
Net Worth: $6,422,718
Earnings: ($2,810,079)
Fiscal Year-end: 06/30/24
Sea Ranching Services
N.A.I.C.S.: 114119
Bradley Adams *(Mng Dir)*

Subsidiaries:

Two Oceans Abalone Pty. Ltd. (1)
Level 3 3 Cantonment Street, Fremantle, 6160, WA, Australia
Tel.: (61) 861818888
Web Site: http://www.twooceansabalone.com.au
Seafood Distr
N.A.I.C.S.: 424460

RARE HOLDINGS LIMITED
22 Old Vereeniging Road Kliprivier, Midvaal, South Africa
Tel.: (27) 11 906 8000   ZA
Web Site: http://www.rare.co.za
Year Founded: 1975
Sales Range: $10-24.9 Million
Steel Pole Mfr
N.A.I.C.S.: 331210
Wally van Coller *(CEO)*

Subsidiaries:

RARE Construction Zambia (1)
Sensele Building Complex Room 4-5 Plot 4866 Station Rd, Mwaiseni, Zambia
Tel.: (260) 973 417 496
Pipe Fitting & Valve Distr
N.A.I.C.S.: 423720
Kelvin Mukuma *(Controller-Pipeline Svc Quality)*

RAREJOB INC.
2F Kyocera Harajuku Building 6-27-8 Jingumae, Shibuya-ku, Tokyo, 150-0001, Japan
Tel.: (81) 354687401
Web Site: https://www.rarejob.co.jp
6096—(TKS)
Rev.: $67,256,750
Assets: $41,352,160
Liabilities: $29,236,030
Net Worth: $12,116,130
Earnings: ($1,903,680)
Emp.: 253
Fiscal Year-end: 03/31/24
Education Services
N.A.I.C.S.: 611710
Tomohisa Kato *(Co-Founder)*

Subsidiaries:

RareJob Philippines, Inc. (1)
Unit 1003 10/F Coher Center 1424 Quezon Avenue, South Triangle, Quezon City, 1103, metro manila, Philippines
Tel.: (63) 284423942
Web Site: http://www.rarejob.com.ph
Educational Support Services
N.A.I.C.S.: 611710

Ripple Kids Educational Services, Inc. (1)
Tel.: (63) 325203549
Web Site: http://www.ripplekids-edu.ph
Educational Support Services
N.A.I.C.S.: 611710

RAREX LIMITED
Level 1 338 Barker Road, Subiaco, 6008, WA, Australia
Tel.: (61) 63836593   AU

Web Site: https://www.rarex.com.au
Year Founded: 2003
REE—(ASX)
Rev.: $2,491,949
Assets: $9,061,224
Liabilities: $1,732,621
Net Worth: $7,328,603
Earnings: ($8,600,624)
Fiscal Year-end: 06/30/22
Copper, Nickel, Lead & Zinc Mining
N.A.I.C.S.: 212230

RAS AL KHAIMAH CEMENT COMPANY PSC
Khor Khwair, PO Box 2499, Ras al Khaimah, United Arab Emirates
Tel.: (971) 65898870   AE
Web Site: https://www.rakcc.ae
Year Founded: 1995
APEX—(ABU)
Rev.: $196,985,298
Assets: $598,752,823
Liabilities: $69,013,068
Net Worth: $529,739,755
Earnings: ($15,909,690)
Emp.: 5,016
Fiscal Year-end: 12/31/23
Cement Mfr & Whslr
N.A.I.C.S.: 327310
Ahmed Amer Omar Saleh *(Chm)*

RAS AL KHAIMAH CERAMICS PJSC
PO Box 4714, Al Jazzera Al Hamra, Ras al Khaimah, United Arab Emirates
Tel.: (971) 72467000   AE
Web Site: https://www.rakceramics.com
Year Founded: 1989
RAKCEC—(ABU)
Rev.: $941,450,133
Assets: $1,458,585,024
Liabilities: $813,641,103
Net Worth: $644,943,921
Earnings: $87,359,781
Emp.: 12,000
Fiscal Year-end: 12/31/23
Ceramic Wall & Floor Tile & Related Products Mfr
N.A.I.C.S.: 327120
Khalid Saud Al Qasimi *(Chm)*

Subsidiaries:

Al Hamra Construction Company LLC (1)
PO Box 30019, Ras al Khaimah, United Arab Emirates
Tel.: (971) 72446955
Web Site: https://www.alhamraconstruction.org
Emp.: 5,000
Building Contractor Services
N.A.I.C.S.: 236220
Fawwaz Abdulla Al Teneiji *(Chm)*

Ceramin FZ LLC (1)
PO Box 6390, Al Jazeera, Ras al Khaimah, United Arab Emirates
Tel.: (971) 72433360
Web Site: https://www.ceramin.net
Ceramic Tile Mfr & Distr
N.A.I.C.S.: 327110

RAK Ceramics (Bangladesh) Ltd. (1)
RAK Tower 7th 8th and 9th Floors 1/A Jasimuddin Avenue Sector-3, Uttara Model Town, Dhaka, 1230, Bangladesh
Tel.: (880) 258957393
Web Site: https://www.rakceramics.com
Rev.: $61,351,433
Assets: $145,178,975
Liabilities: $63,708,554
Net Worth: $81,470,420
Earnings: $3,603,580
Emp.: 1,921
Fiscal Year-end: 12/31/2020
Ceramic Tiles & Sanitary Wares Mfr
N.A.I.C.S.: 327120

RAK Ceramics Australia Pty Limited (1)
16 Raglan Road, Auburn, Sydney, 2144, NSW, Australia
Tel.: 13002372642
Web Site:
Ceramic Tile Mfr & Distr
N.A.I.C.S.: 327110

RAK Ceramics GmbH (1)
Otto-Hahn-Strasse 7, 64579, Gernsheim, Germany
Tel.: (49) 62589418410
Ceramic Tile Mfr & Distr
N.A.I.C.S.: 327110

RAK Ceramics India Private Limited (1)
Carnival House 1st Floor Near Dindoshi Fire Station, Off Gen AK Vaidya Marg Malad East, Mumbai, 400097, India
Tel.: (91) 2226605704
Ceramic Tile Mfr & Distr
N.A.I.C.S.: 327110

RAK Ceramics Saudi LLC (1)
Southern Ring Road Al Kharjh Road Exit 19, PO Box 68647, Al Mansoura District, Riyadh, 11537, Saudi Arabia
Tel.: (966) 500310075
Sales Range: $25-49.9 Million
Emp.: 100
Floor & Wall Tile Mfr & Distr
N.A.I.C.S.: 327120

RAK Distribution Europe SARL (1)
via Ferrari Carazzoli 21, 41042, Fiorano-Modenese, MO, Italy
Tel.: (39) 05361888600
Ceramic Tile Mfr & Distr
N.A.I.C.S.: 327110

RAK Paints LLC (1)
Al Jayed Street - behind RAK Ceramics Factory, PO Box 86012, Al Jazeera Al Hamra Industrial, Ras al Khaimah, United Arab Emirates
Tel.: (971) 72444036
Web Site: https://www.rakpaint.com
Paints Mfr
N.A.I.C.S.: 325510

RAK Porcelain USA Inc. (1)
330 Crown Ct, Oakdale, PA 15071
Web Site: https://www.rakporcelain.com
Tableware Catering Product Mfr & Distr
N.A.I.C.S.: 332215
Abdallah Massaad *(CEO)*

RAK Securities & Services Private Ltd. (1)
House 15 Road 03 Sector 03, Uttara, Dhaka, 1230, Bangladesh
Tel.: (880) 24 895 1784
Web Site: https://www.raksecuritybd.com
Security Services
N.A.I.C.S.: 561612

RAK Universal Plastics Industries LLC (1)
PO Box 34815, Jazeera Al Hamra, Ras al Khaimah, United Arab Emirates
Tel.: (971) 72435189
Web Site: https://www.rakupi.net
Pipe Distr
N.A.I.C.S.: 423510

RAS AL KHAIMAH FREE TRADE ZONE
Al Nakheel, PO Box 10055, Ras al Khaimah, United Arab Emirates
Tel.: (971) 72041111
Web Site: http://www.rakftz.com
Business Services
N.A.I.C.S.: 561499
Peter Fort *(CEO)*

Subsidiaries:

RAK FTZ Business Center L.L.C (1)
Boulevard Plaza Tower 2 Floor 22 Sheikh Mohammed Bin Rashid Boulevard, Dubai, United Arab Emirates
Tel.: (971) 4 7041888
Business Consulting Services
N.A.I.C.S.: 561499

RAK Free Zone Business Promotion Centre (1)

RAS AL KHAIMAH FREE TRADE ZONE

Ras Al Khaimah Free Trade Zone—(Continued)

Fairmont Hotel RAK Businessmen & Emirates Business Centre, Dubai, United Arab Emirates
Tel.: (971) 43124300
Web Site: http://www.rakftz.com
Emp.: 6
Business Services
N.A.I.C.S.: 561499
Peter Fort (CEO)

RAK Free Zone Business Promotion Centre (1)
Twin Towers, Dubai, United Arab Emirates
Tel.: (971) 42088555
Sales Range: $75-99.9 Million
Emp.: 300
Business Services
N.A.I.C.S.: 561499

RAK Free Zone Promotion Centre (1)
Abu Dhabi Mall West Tower First Floor, Abu Dhabi, United Arab Emirates
Tel.: (971) 26994888
Sales Range: $25-49.9 Million
Emp.: 5
Business Services
N.A.I.C.S.: 561499

RAS AL KHAIMAH POULTRY & FEEDING CO.
PO Box 184, Ras al Khaimah, United Arab Emirates
Tel.: (971) 72462222 AE
Web Site: https://www.rakpoultry.com
Year Founded: 1976
RAPCO—(ABU)
Rev.: $3,129,907
Assets: $99,095,722
Liabilities: $2,314,069
Net Worth: $96,781,653
Earnings: $4,603,002
Emp.: 16
Fiscal Year-end: 12/31/23
Poultry Product Mfr & Whslr
N.A.I.C.S.: 112320
Mubarak Ali Al Shamsi (Deputy Chm)

RAS RESORTS & APART HOTELS LTD.
Rosewood Chambers 99/C Tulsiwadi Tardeo, PO Box 38, Mumbai, 400034, Maharashtra, India
Tel.: (91) 2243216600
Web Site: https://www.rrahl.com
Year Founded: 1985
507966—(BOM)
Rev.: $619,183
Assets: $4,459,777
Liabilities: $1,599,848
Net Worth: $2,859,929
Earnings: ($53,839)
Emp.: 72
Fiscal Year-end: 03/31/21
Home Management Services
N.A.I.C.S.: 721110
Pravin Vepari (Chm)

RAS TECHNOLOGY HOLDINGS LIMITED
Tel.: (61) 262884080
Web Site: https://www.racingandsports.com.au
Year Founded: 1999
RTH—(ASX)
Rev.: $8,667,275
Assets: $11,765,013
Liabilities: $3,562,626
Net Worth: $8,202,386
Earnings: ($845,667)
Fiscal Year-end: 06/30/23
Holding Company
N.A.I.C.S.: 551112
Gary Crispe (Chief Comml Officer)

Subsidiaries:

Racing and Sports Pty. Ltd. (1)
PO Box 5430, Kingston, Canberra, 2604, ACT, Australia
Tel.: (61) 262884080
Web Site: https://www.racingandsports.com.au
Racing & Sports Services
N.A.I.C.S.: 711211

RASA CORPORATION
RASA Nihonbashi Bldg 11-5 Nihonbashi-Kakigara-cho 1-chome, Chuo-ku, Tokyo, Japan
Tel.: (81) 336688231 JP
Web Site: https://www.rasaco.co.jp
Year Founded: 1939
3023—(TKS)
Rev.: $184,524,760
Assets: $215,274,480
Liabilities: $73,489,980
Net Worth: $141,784,500
Earnings: $13,200,170
Emp.: 253
Fiscal Year-end: 03/31/24
Raw Materials, Industrial Machines & Construction Equipment Wholesale Trade Distr; Environmental Technical Services
N.A.I.C.S.: 425120
Ichiro Hayakawa (Exec Officer & Gen Mgr-Fukuoka Branch)

Subsidiaries:

Izumi Co., Ltd. (1)
3-3-1 Futabanosato, Higashi-ku, Hiroshima, Japan (83.4%)
Tel.: (81) 822643211
Web Site: https://www.izumi.co.jp
Rev.: $3,340,566,940
Assets: $3,470,618,810
Liabilities: $1,384,506,840
Net Worth: $2,086,111,970
Earnings: $145,238,650
Emp.: 4,407
Fiscal Year-end: 02/29/2024
Shopping Mall Operator
N.A.I.C.S.: 531390
Toyomi Nakamura (Mng Dir & Mgr-Tenant Rels Div)

Subsidiary (Domestic):

Youme Card Co., Ltd. (2)
3-3-1 Futaba no Sato, Higashi Ward, Hiroshima, 732-8570, Japan
Tel.: (81) 822255100
Web Site: https://www.youmecard.jp
Emp.: 292
Credit Card Services
N.A.I.C.S.: 522210

RASA INDUSTRIES, LTD.
Akihabara Daibiru Building 1-18-13 Soto-Kanda, Chiyoda-ku, Tokyo, 101-0021, Japan
Tel.: (81) 332581812
Web Site: https://www.rasa.co.jp
Year Founded: 1911
4022—(TKS)
Rev.: $282,828,680
Assets: $292,975,030
Liabilities: $127,949,770
Net Worth: $165,025,260
Earnings: $15,745,020
Emp.: 620
Fiscal Year-end: 03/31/24
Chemical Products Mfr
N.A.I.C.S.: 325998
Kousaku Sakao (Pres)

Subsidiaries:

Rasa Industries, Ltd. - Hainuzuka Factory (1)
322-1 Hainuzuka, Chikugo, 833-0003, Fukuoka, Japan
Tel.: (81) 942527111
Industrial Machinery Mfr
N.A.I.C.S.: 333248

Rasa Industries, Ltd. - Isesaki Factory (1)
449-1 Kokuryo-Cho, Isesaki, 372-0853, Gunma, Japan
Tel.: (81) 270203211
Chemical Products Mfr
N.A.I.C.S.: 325998

Rasa Industries, Ltd. - Miyako Factory (1)
1-7 Koyamada, Miyako, 027-0038, Iwate, Japan
Tel.: (81) 193636809
Electronic Equipment Distr
N.A.I.C.S.: 334419

Rasa Industries, Ltd. - Noda Factory (1)
746-1 Yatsu Aza-Tamukai, Noda, 278-0046, Chiba, Japan
Tel.: (81) 471247559
Chemical Products Mfr
N.A.I.C.S.: 325998

Rasa Industries, Ltd. - Osaka Factory (1)
1-3-80 Funamachi, Taisho-Ku, Osaka, 551-0022, Japan
Tel.: (81) 665521261
Chemical Products Mfr
N.A.I.C.S.: 325998

Rasa Industries, Ltd. - Sanbongi Factory (1)
26-2 Otonashi, Aza-Yamazaki Sanbongi, Osaki, 989-6313, Miyagi, Japan
Tel.: (81) 229523811
Electronic Components Mfr
N.A.I.C.S.: 334419

RASA LAND COMPANY LIMITED
555 Rasa Tower 28th Floor, Phaholyothin Road, Chatuchak, Bangkok, 10900, Thailand
Tel.: (66) 29371200
Web Site: http://www.rasa.co.th
Sales Range: $1-9.9 Million
Emp.: 44
Property Developer
N.A.I.C.S.: 236220
Manop Bongsadadt (Chm)

RASADNIK A.D.
Ulica mira br 1, 24000, Subotica, Serbia
Tel.: (381) 24 546 007
Year Founded: 1991
RSDK—(BEL)
Sales Range: Less than $1 Million
Nursery & Tree Production Services
N.A.I.C.S.: 111421
Zdravko Cvitkovac (Dir)

RASAMNY-YOUNIS MOTOR CO., S.A.L.
RYMCO Bldg, 112737, Beirut, Lebanon
Web Site: http://www.rymco.com
Year Founded: 1957
Emp.: 250
New Cars, Trucks & Motorcycles Retailer & Distr
N.A.I.C.S.: 441110
Fadi Adib Younis (Sr Dir-Aftersales)

RASANDIK ENGINEERING INDUSTRIES INDIA LIMITED
13 14 Roz Ka Meo Industrial Area Sohna, Gurgaon, 122103, Haryana, India
Tel.: (91) 1242362646
Web Site: https://www.rasandik.com
Year Founded: 1984
522207—(BOM)
Rev.: $18,751,358
Assets: $26,985,133
Liabilities: $15,821,474
Net Worth: $11,163,659
Earnings: ($395,348)
Emp.: 97
Fiscal Year-end: 03/31/23
Sheet Metal Components Mfr
N.A.I.C.S.: 333514

INTERNATIONAL PUBLIC

Rajiv Kapoor (Founder, Chm & Mng Dir)

RASHTRIYA CHEMICALS & FERTILIZERS LTD.
Priyadarshini Building Eastern Express Highway Sion, Mumbai, 400 022, Maharashtra, India
Tel.: (91) 2225523000
Web Site: https://www.rcfltd.com
RCF—(NSE)
Rev.: $1,148,487,795
Assets: $1,040,285,610
Liabilities: $585,272,415
Net Worth: $455,013,195
Earnings: $51,228,450
Emp.: 2,845
Fiscal Year-end: 03/31/21
Fertilizer Mfr
N.A.I.C.S.: 325314
Umesh Dongre (CFO & Dir-Fin)

RASI ELECTRODES LIMITED
No A14 3rd Floor Rams Apartments Raja Annamalai Road Purasawalkam, Chennai, 600 084, India
Tel.: (91) 4426424523
Web Site: https://www.rasielectrodes.com
531233—(BOM)
Rev.: $10,663,893
Assets: $4,149,511
Liabilities: $621,677
Net Worth: $3,527,834
Earnings: $360,410
Emp.: 128
Fiscal Year-end: 03/31/23
Welding Electrode Mfr
N.A.I.C.S.: 333992
B. Popatalal Kothari (Chm & Mng Dir)

RASMALA PLC
12 Hay Hill Mayfai, London, W1J 8NR, United Kingdom
Tel.: (44) 2078479900
Web Site: http://rasmala.com
Rev.: $16,309,512
Assets: $100,571,500
Liabilities: $20,161,249
Net Worth: $80,410,250
Earnings: $2,244,936)
Emp.: 80
Fiscal Year-end: 12/31/17
Investment Management Service
N.A.I.C.S.: 523940
Haroon Ahmad (Head-Products & Sls)

RASOI LIMITED
Rasoi Court 20 Sir R N Mukherjee Road, Kolkata, 700001, India
Tel.: (91) 3322480114
Web Site: http://www.rasoigroup.in
Food Products Mfr
N.A.I.C.S.: 311999
Naresh Patangi (Compliance Officer, Sec & Exec Dir)

RASOYA PROTEINS LTD.
Rasoya House Plot 20 21Sita Nagar Kheta Layout, Near New Sneh Nagar, Nagpur, 440025, India
Tel.: (91) 07122283899 In
Web Site: http://www.rasoyaproteins.in
Year Founded: 1992
Soya Refined Oil Mfr
N.A.I.C.S.: 311224
Anil Lonkar (Mng Dir)

RASSINI S.A.B. DE C.V.
Pedregal 24 Col Molino del Rey, Alcaldia Miguel Hidalgo, 11040, Mexico, DF, Mexico
Tel.: (52) 5552295800 MX
Web Site: https://www.rassini.com

Year Founded: 1979
Rev.: $973,830,032
Assets: $709,858,584
Liabilities: $374,467,104
Net Worth: $335,391,480
Earnings: $67,657,872
Emp.: 6,500
Fiscal Year-end: 12/31/18
Auto Suspension Systems & Brake Components Mfr
N.A.I.C.S.: 336330
Eugenio Carlos Madero Pinson *(Vice Chm)*

Subsidiaries:

SANLUIS Co-Inter, S. A. (1)
Monte Pelvoux 220 Piso 8, Ciudad De, Leon, Mexico (100%)
Tel.: (52) 5552295800
Web Site: http://www.Sanluisrassene.com
Sales Range: $25-49.9 Million
Emp.: 18
Holding Company
N.A.I.C.S.: 551112

SANLUIS Rassini Autopartes, S.A. de C.V. (1)
Monte Pelvoux No 220 P 4, Lomas de Chapultepec Del Miguel Hidalgo, 11000, Mexico, Mexico (100%)
Tel.: (52) 5552295845
Sales Range: $25-49.9 Million
Emp.: 18
Motor Vehicle Parts Mfr
N.A.I.C.S.: 336390

SANLUIS Rassini S.A. de C.V. (1)
Monte Pelvoux 220 8th Fl, Lomas De Chapultepec, 11000, Mexico, Mexico (100%)
Tel.: (52) 5552295800
Sales Range: $400-449.9 Million
Emp.: 1,800
Mfr of Motor Vehicle Components & Hardware
N.A.I.C.S.: 336330
Antonio Madero Bracho *(Pres)*

RASSINI SAB DE CV
Pedregal 24 Col Molino del Rey Del, Miguel Hidalgo, Mexico, 11040, Mexico
Tel.: (52) 5552295800
Web Site: http://www.rassini.com
Commercial Vehicle Component Mfr
N.A.I.C.S.: 336390
Sergio Davila Flores *(COO-Suspension Div)*

RASTAR ENVIRONMENTAL PROTECTION MATERIALS CO., LTD.
No 37 Tongyang Road, Shantou, 515078, Guangdong, China
Tel.: (86) 75488817218
Web Site: https://www.rastarchem.cn
Year Founded: 2006
300834—(CHIN)
Rev.: $224,831,013
Assets: $488,940,153
Liabilities: $66,125,014
Net Worth: $422,815,140
Earnings: $11,284,648
Fiscal Year-end: 12/31/23
Chemical Product Mfr & Distr
N.A.I.C.S.: 327120
Chen Yueping *(Chm)*

RASTAR GROUP
24-25th Floor Rongxing Building No 30 Huangshan Road, Longhu District, Shantou, Guangdong, China
Tel.: (86) 2028123517
Web Site: https://www.rastar.com
300043—(CHIN)
Rev.: $225,473,976
Assets: $607,881,456
Liabilities: $347,214,816
Net Worth: $260,666,640
Earnings: ($43,587,180)
Fiscal Year-end: 12/31/22
Electric & Electronic Toy Cars & Plastic Toys Mfr & Distr
N.A.I.C.S.: 339930

Subsidiaries:

Rastar (HK) Industrial Co., Ltd. (1)
Unit 1 5/F Concordia Plaza No 1 Science Museum Road, TST East, Kowloon, China (Hong Kong)
Tel.: (852) 35904300
Web Site: https://www.rastar.hk
Automobile Parts Mfr
N.A.I.C.S.: 336390

RASTRIYA BEEMA COMPANY LIMITED
RBCL Building Ramshahpath, Kathmandu, Nepal
Tel.: (977) 14258866
Web Site: https://www.rbcl.gov.np
RBCL—(NEP)
Sales Range: Less than $1 Million
Insurance & Financial Services
N.A.I.C.S.: 524210
Umesh Chandra Upadhayaya *(Chm)*

RASTRIYA BEEMA SANSTHAN
R B S Building Ramshahpath, PO Box 527, Kathmandu, Nepal
Tel.: (977) 1 4262520
Web Site: http://www.beema.com.np
Year Founded: 1967
Insurance Services
N.A.I.C.S.: 524298
Mahesh Rimal *(Deputy Gen Mgr-Acting & Head-Life Accounts)*

RATANPUR STEEL RE-ROLLING MILLS LTD.
Nahar Mansion 116 C D A Avenue, Muradpur, Chittagong, Bangladesh
Tel.: (880) 316522557
Web Site: https://www.rsrmbd.com
RSRMSTEEL—(DHA)
Rev.: $16,826,638
Assets: $84,457,504
Liabilities: $31,712,743
Net Worth: $52,744,762
Earnings: ($4,405,797)
Emp.: 338
Fiscal Year-end: 06/30/21
Steel Products Mfr
N.A.I.C.S.: 331222
Maksudur Rahman *(Mng Dir)*

RATAR A.D.
Zarka Zrenjanina 76, 26000, Pancevo, Serbia
Tel.: (381) 13352176
Web Site: https://www.ratar.net
Year Founded: 1880
RTAR—(BEL)
Rev.: $2,261,704
Assets: $10,105,621
Liabilities: $2,727,358
Net Worth: $7,378,263
Earnings: ($380,616)
Emp.: 56
Fiscal Year-end: 12/31/23
Grain Mill Product Mfr
N.A.I.C.S.: 311230
Gordana Savkovic *(Dir)*

RATCH GROUP PUBLIC COMPANY LIMITED
72 Ngamwongwan Road, Bangkhen Muang, Nonthaburi, 11000, Thailand
Tel.: (66) 27949999
Web Site: https://www.ratch.co.th
RATCH—(THA)
Rev.: $1,203,833,838
Assets: $6,231,871,043
Liabilities: $3,104,434,484
Net Worth: $3,127,436,558
Earnings: $159,943,595
Emp.: 565
Fiscal Year-end: 12/31/23
Holding Company
N.A.I.C.S.: 551112
Peerawat Pumthong *(Deputy CEO)*

Subsidiaries:

RATCH Cogeneration Co., Ltd. (1)
8/22 Moo 18 Paholyothin Road Klongnueng, Klongluang, Pathumthani, 12120, Thailand
Tel.: (66) 25291711
Electric Power Distribution Services
N.A.I.C.S.: 221122

RATCH-Australia Corporation Pty. Ltd. (1)
Level 7 111 Pacific Highway, North Sydney, 2060, NSW, Australia
Tel.: (61) 1800280013
Web Site: https://ratchaustralia.com
Wind Power Generation Services
N.A.I.C.S.: 221115

RATCH-Lao Services Co., Ltd. (1)
187 Unit 12 Phonsa-art Village, Xaysettha District, Vientiane, Lao People's Democratic Republic
Tel.: (856) 21454074
Power Plant Operation Services
N.A.I.C.S.: 221118

RH International Corporation Ltd. (1)
72 Ngamwongwan Road, Bangkhen Muang, Nonthaburi, 11000, Thailand
Tel.: (66) 27949999
Eletric Power Generation Services
N.A.I.C.S.: 221118

Ratch Udom Power Company Limited (1)
19 SCB Park Plaza, Ratchadapisek Road, Jatujak, Bangkok, 19000, Thailand (99.99%)
Tel.: (66) 29785000
Holding Company
N.A.I.C.S.: 551112

Ratchaburi Alliances Company Limited (1)
72 Ngam Wong Wan Rd, Bangkhen Muang, Nonthaburi, Nonthaburi, 11000, Thailand (99.99%)
Tel.: (66) 27949999
Web Site: https://www.ratch.co.th
Sales Range: $75-99.9 Million
Emp.: 110
Holding Company
N.A.I.C.S.: 551112

Ratchaburi Electricity Generating Co., Ltd. (1)
(99.99%)
Tel.: (66) 29785111
Web Site: https://www.ratch.co.th
Electricity Generation
N.A.I.C.S.: 221112

Ratchaburi Energy Co., Ltd. (1)
72 Ngam Wong Wan Rd, Bangkhen Muang, Nonthaburi Nonthaburi, Bangkok, 11000, Thailand (99.99%)
Tel.: (66) 27949999
Power Generation Related Investments
N.A.I.C.S.: 523999
Prayut Thongsuwan *(Mng Dir)*

Ratchaburi Gas Company Limited (1)
19 SCB Park Plaza Ratchadapisek Road, Chatuchak, Bangkok, 10900, Thailand (99.99%)
Tel.: (66) 29785000
Web Site: http://www.ratch.co.th
Holding Company
N.A.I.C.S.: 551112

Sahacogen (Chonburi) Public Co., Ltd. (1)
636 Moo 11 Sukaphiban 8 Road Nongkharm Sriracha, Chon Buri, 20230, Thailand (51%)
Tel.: (66) 38481555
Web Site: https://www.ratchpathana.com
Rev.: $158,262,518
Assets: $290,191,185
Liabilities: $181,193,786
Net Worth: $108,997,399
Earnings: $2,745,270
Emp.: 191
Fiscal Year-end: 12/31/2023
Eletric Power Generation Services
N.A.I.C.S.: 221118
Viroj Theeravatvatee *(Mng Dir)*

Subsidiary (Domestic):

Sahacogen Green Company Limited (2)
88 Moo 5, Pasak Muang, Lamphun, 51000, Thailand
Tel.: (66) 53537444
Eletric Power Generation Services
N.A.I.C.S.: 221118

Sahagreen Forest Company Limited (2)
88 Village No 6, Khue Ban Ong Subdistrict Phran Kratai District, Kamphaeng Phet, 62110, Thailand
Tel.: (66) 55858033
Eletric Power Generation Services
N.A.I.C.S.: 221118

Smart Infranet Co., Ltd. (1)
72 Ngamwongwan Road, Bangkhen Muang Nonthaburi, Nonthaburi, 11000, Thailand
Tel.: (66) 27949999
Web Site: https://www.smartinfranet.co.th
Wired Telecommunication Services
N.A.I.C.S.: 517111
Nopparat Thuampradit *(Chm)*

RATCHAPHRUEK HOSPITAL PCL
456 Mittraphap road, Mueang, Khon Kaen, 40000, Thailand
Tel.: (66) 43333555
Web Site: https://rph.co.th
Year Founded: 1994
RPH—(THA)
Rev.: $34,374,420
Assets: $56,395,675
Liabilities: $4,902,499
Net Worth: $51,493,175
Earnings: $5,384,459
Fiscal Year-end: 12/31/23
Health Care Srvices
N.A.I.C.S.: 621999
Sudhon Sriyapant *(Chm)*

RATEGAIN TRAVEL TECHNOLOGIES LIMITED
Club 125 Plot No A-3 4 5 Tower A 4th floor Sector-125, Noida, 201301, Uttar Pradesh, India
Tel.: (91) 1205057000 In
Web Site: https://www.rategain.com
Year Founded: 2004
543417—(BOM)
Rev.: $52,294,925
Assets: $106,618,922
Liabilities: $22,104,537
Net Worth: $84,514,385
Earnings: $1,149,194
Emp.: 426
Fiscal Year-end: 03/31/22
Software Development Services
N.A.I.C.S.: 541511
Bhanu Chopra *(Founder & Chm)*

Subsidiaries:

Adara, Inc. (1)
800 W El Camino Real Ste 200, Mountain View, CA 94040
Tel.: (408) 876-6360
Web Site: http://www.adaramedia.com
Advertising Services
N.A.I.C.S.: 541890
Charles Mi *(Founder & CEO)*

Myhotelshop GmbH (1)
Flossplatz 6, 04107, Leipzig, Germany
Tel.: (49) 341392816751
Web Site: https://www.myhotelshop.com
Home Management Services
N.A.I.C.S.: 721110

RATH AG
Walfischgasse 14, 1010, Vienna, Austria
Tel.: (43) 151344270

RATH AG

Rath AG—(Continued)

Web Site: https://www.rath-group.com
Year Founded: 1891
RAT—(VIE)
Rev.: $121,502,414
Assets: $139,718,441
Liabilities: $77,207,166
Net Worth: $62,511,275
Earnings: $5,298,627
Emp.: 571
Fiscal Year-end: 12/31/21
Refractory Materials Mfr & Distr
N.A.I.C.S.: 327120
Andreas Pfneiszl *(CFO, Chief Sls Officer & Member-Mgmt Bd)*

Subsidiaries:

Aug. Rath jun. GmbH (1)
Hafnerstrasse 3, A-3375, Krummnussbaum, Austria
Tel.: (43) 2527 21010
Refractory Products Mfr & Sales
N.A.I.C.S.: 327120

Rath GmbH (1)
Ossietzkystrasse 37/38, D-01662, Meissen, Germany
Tel.: (49) 3521 46450
Web Site: http://www.rath-group.com
Refractory Products Mfr & Sales
N.A.I.C.S.: 327120

Rath Hungaria Kft. (1)
Porcelan utca 1, H-1106, Budapest, Hungary
Tel.: (36) 1 43 30043
Emp.: 125
Refractory Products Mfr
N.A.I.C.S.: 327120
Werner Marcov *(Gen Mgr)*

Rath Inc. (1)
300 Ruthar Dr, Newark, DE 19711
Tel.: (302) 294-4446
Web Site: http://www.rath-usa.com
Sales Range: $1-9.9 Million
Emp.: 15
Refractory Products Mfr & Sales
N.A.I.C.S.: 327120
Frank Rowe *(Mgr)*

Rath Polska Sp. z o.o. (1)
Ul Fabryczna 1, PL-42 530, Dabrowa Gornicza, Poland
Tel.: (48) 322684701
Web Site: http://www.rath.com.pl
Emp.: 2
Refractory Products Mfr & Sales
N.A.I.C.S.: 327120
Zijac Richard *(Gen Mgr)*

Rath Ukrajina TOW (1)
Prospekt Osvoboshdenije Donbassa 8b, Office 206, UA-83048, Donetsk, Ukraine
Tel.: (380) 62 345 3306
Refractory Products Mfr & Sales
N.A.I.C.S.: 327120

Rath zarotechnika spol. s r.o. (1)
Vorlesska 290, CZ-54401, Dvur Kralove nad Labem, Czech Republic
Tel.: (420) 499321577
Refractory Products Mfr & Sales
N.A.I.C.S.: 327120

RATHBONES GROUP PLC

30 Gresham Street, London, EC2V 7QN, United Kingdom
Tel.: (44) 2073990000 UK
Web Site: https://www.rathbones.com
Year Founded: 1742
RAT—(LSE)
Rev.: $575,454,431
Assets: $4,351,426,407
Liabilities: $3,550,070,689
Net Worth: $801,355,718
Earnings: $61,832,870
Emp.: 2,170
Fiscal Year-end: 12/31/22
Investment Management Service
N.A.I.C.S.: 523150
Andrew Morris *(Head-Investment Mgmt-North)*

Subsidiaries:

Castle Investment Solutions Limited (1)
Vision House Unit 6A Falmouth Business Park Bickland Water Road, Falmouth, TR11 4SZ, Cornwall, United Kingdom
Tel.: (44) 1326210904
Web Site: https://www.mydfm.co.uk
Fund Management Services
N.A.I.C.S.: 523940

Investec Wealth & Investment Limited (1)
Quayside House Canal Wharf, Leeds, LS11 5PU, United Kingdom
Tel.: (44) 1132454488
Web Site: http://wealthinvestment.investec.co.uk
Financial Management Services
N.A.I.C.S.: 523940
Jonathan Wragg *(CEO)*

Rathbone Investment Management International Limited (1)
26 Esplanade, Saint Helier, JE1 2RB, Jersey
Tel.: (44) 153 474 0500
Investment Management Service
N.A.I.C.S.: 523940

Rathbone Investment Management Ltd. (1)
8 Finsbury Circus, London, EC2M 7AZ, United Kingdom
Tel.: (44) 207 399 0000
Web Site: https://www.rathbones.com
Sales Range: $125-149.9 Million
Fund & Investment Portfolios Management
N.A.I.C.S.: 523940

Unit (Domestic):

Rathbone Greenbank Investments (2)
10 Cream Square, Bristol, BS1 4NT, United Kingdom
Tel.: (44) 1179303000
Web Site: http://www.rathbonegreenbank.com
Sales Range: $50-74.9 Million
Investment Services
N.A.I.C.S.: 523999
John David *(Dir-Investment)*

Rathbone Pension & Advisory Services Limited (1)
159 New Bond Street, London, W1S 2UD, United Kingdom
Tel.: (44) 2073990000
Web Site: http://www.rathbone.com
Sales Range: $400-449.9 Million
Emp.: 800
Financial Planning & Pension Related Services
N.A.I.C.S.: 523999

Rathbone Trust Company (BVI) Limited (1)
The Geneva Place, PO Box 986, 3rd Floor Road Town, Tortola, Virgin Islands (British)
Tel.: (284) 494 6544
Web Site: http://www.hudsun.vg
Emp.: 6
Trust & Financial Services
N.A.I.C.S.: 523999

Rathbone Trust Company Ltd. (1)
1 Curzon St, London, W1J 5FB, United Kingdom
Tel.: (44) 2073990000
Web Site: http://www.rathbones.com
Sales Range: $200-249.9 Million
Emp.: 400
Personal Taxation & Trust Services
N.A.I.C.S.: 523999
Kevin Custis *(Dir-Trusts)*

Rathbone Unit Trust Management Limited (1)
Tel.: (44) 207 399 0399
Web Site: https://www.rathbonefunds.com
Sales Range: $50-74.9 Million
Emp.: 28
Fund Management Services
N.A.I.C.S.: 523991
Julian Chillingworth *(Chief Investment Officer)*

Saunderson House Limited (1)
1 Long Lane, London, EC1A 9HF, United Kingdom
Tel.: (44) 207 315 6500
Web Site: https://www.saundersonhouse.co.uk
Financial Advisory Services
N.A.I.C.S.: 523999
Tony Overy *(CEO)*

Speirs & Jeffrey Limited (1)
George House 50 George Square, Glasgow, G2 1EH, United Kingdom
Tel.: (44) 1412484311
Investment Management Service
N.A.I.C.S.: 523940

Vision Independent Financial Planning Limited (1)
Vision House Unit 6A Falmouth Business Park Bickland Water Road, Falmouth, TR11 4SZ, Cornwall, United Kingdom
Tel.: (44) 1326210904
Web Site: https://www.visionifp.co.uk
Financial Services
N.A.I.C.S.: 523999
Ian Gagg *(Head)*

RATHDOWNEY RESOURCES LTD.

14th Floor 1040 West Georgia Street, Vancouver, V6E 4H1, BC, Canada
Tel.: (604) 684-6365 BC
Web Site: https://www.rathdowney.com
Year Founded: 2008
RATHF—(OTCIQ)
Assets: $75,655
Liabilities: $11,015,021
Net Worth: ($10,939,365)
Earnings: ($1,534,233)
Fiscal Year-end: 12/31/23
Zinc & Lead Mining
N.A.I.C.S.: 212230
David J. Copeland *(Chm, Pres & CEO)*

RATHI BARS LTD.

A-24/7 Mohan Co-operative Industrial Estate Mathura Road, New Delhi, 110044, India
Tel.: (91) 1143165400
Web Site: https://rathisteels.com
Year Founded: 1993
532918—(BOM)
Rev.: $44,240,214
Assets: $20,794,075
Liabilities: $9,201,604
Net Worth: $11,592,472
Earnings: $315,452
Fiscal Year-end: 03/31/21
Wire Ropes Mfr
N.A.I.C.S.: 331110
Kamlesh Kumar Rathi *(Mng Dir)*

RATHI STEEL & POWER LTD.

Plot No 24/1 Block A Mohan Cooperative Industrial Estate Mathura Road, Pocket D & E Sarita Vihar, New Delhi, 110044, India
Tel.: (91) 1145092400
Web Site: https://www.rathisteelandpower.com
Year Founded: 1971
Rev.: $55,837,107
Assets: $66,242,172
Liabilities: $110,601,523
Net Worth: ($44,359,350)
Earnings: ($18,389,088)
Fiscal Year-end: 03/31/18
Wire Ropes Mfr
N.A.I.C.S.: 331110

RATIO OIL EXPLORATION 1992 LP

85 Yehuda Ha-levi St, Tel Aviv, 6579614, Israel
Tel.: (972) 35661338
Web Site: https://ratioenergies.com

INTERNATIONAL PUBLIC

Year Founded: 1993
RATI.L—(TAE)
Rev.: $379,944,000
Assets: $1,118,530,000
Liabilities: $768,113,000
Net Worth: $350,417,000
Earnings: $149,546,000
Fiscal Year-end: 12/31/22
Oil & Gas Exploration Services
N.A.I.C.S.: 213112

RATIO OIL EXPLORATIONS (FINANCE) LTD.

Ehuda Halevi 85, Tel Aviv, 6579614, Israel
Tel.: (972) 35661338
Web Site: http://www.ratioil.com
Year Founded: 1992
RATF—(TAE)
Rev.: $24,393,000
Assets: $366,506,000
Liabilities: $366,478,000
Net Worth: $28,000
Fiscal Year-end: 09/30/21
Natural Gas Extraction Services
N.A.I.C.S.: 211130
Ligad Rotlevy *(Chm)*

RATIO PETROLEUM ENERGY LP

85 Yehuda Ha-levi St, Tel Aviv, 6579614, Israel
Tel.: (972) 36754356
Web Site: https://www.ratiopetroleum.com
RTPT.L—(TAE)
Assets: $38,327,000
Liabilities: $619,000
Net Worth: $37,708,000
Earnings: ($3,378,000)
Fiscal Year-end: 12/31/22
Oil & Gas Exploration Services
N.A.I.C.S.: 213112
Itay Tabibzada Raphael *(CEO)*

RATIONAL AG

Siegfried Meister Strasse 1, 86899, Landsberg am Lech, Germany
Tel.: (49) 81913270
Web Site: https://www.rational-online.com
Year Founded: 1973
RAA—(DUS)
Rev.: $1,242,781,001
Assets: $1,067,276,709
Liabilities: $251,958,327
Net Worth: $815,318,382
Earnings: $238,170,991
Emp.: 2,554
Fiscal Year-end: 12/31/23
Commercial Kitchen Equipment Mfr & Distr
N.A.I.C.S.: 238290
Walter Kurtz *(Chm-Supervisory Bd)*

Subsidiaries:

RATIONAL Australia Pty Ltd. (1)
156 Swann Drive, Derrimut, 3026, VIC, Australia
Tel.: (61) 383694600
Kitchen Appliance Mfr & Distr
N.A.I.C.S.: 332215

RATIONAL Czech Republic s.r.o. (1)
Evropska 859/115 AFI Building, Vokovice, 160 00, Prague, Czech Republic
Tel.: (420) 226521500
Kitchen Appliance Mfr & Distr
N.A.I.C.S.: 332215

RATIONAL Deutschland GmbH (1)
Siegfried-Meister-Strasse 1, 86899, Landsberg am Lech, Germany
Tel.: (49) 81913270
Web Site: https://www.rational-online.com
Kitchen Appliance Distr
N.A.I.C.S.: 423440

RATIONAL Endustriyel Mutfak Ekipmanlari Ticaret Limited Sirketi
Ahi Evran Cad No 11 Olive Plaza Kat 1, Maslak Sariyer, Istanbul, Turkiye
Tel.: (90) 2126036767
Kitchen Appliance Mfr & Distr
N.A.I.C.S.: 332215

RATIONAL NZ Ltd. (1)
477 Great South Road, Penrose, Auckland, New Zealand
Tel.: (64) 96330900
Kitchen Appliance Mfr & Distr
N.A.I.C.S.: 332215

RATIONAL Slovenija Slorational d.o.o. (1)
Ronkova 4, Slovenj Gradec, Slovenia
Tel.: (386) 28821900
Web Site: https://www.slorational.si
Kitchen Appliance Mfr & Distr
N.A.I.C.S.: 332215

RATIONAL Wittenheim S.A.S. (1)
4 Rue de la Charente, BP 52, 68271, Wittenheim, Cedex, France
Tel.: (33) 389570082
Kitchen Appliance Mfr & Distr
N.A.I.C.S.: 332215

Rational Austria GmbH (1)
Munchner Bundesstrasse 10, 5020, Salzburg, Austria
Tel.: (43) 662832799
Kitchen Appliances Mfr
N.A.I.C.S.: 337110

Rational Canada Inc. (1)
6950 Creditview Rd Unit 1, Mississauga, L5N 0A6, ON, Canada
Kitchen Appliances Mfr
N.A.I.C.S.: 337110

Rational Colombia - America Central SAS (1)
Edificio Ibraco Calle 104 No 15-31-Piso 2, Bogota, Colombia
Tel.: (57) 17433837
Kitchen Appliances Mfr
N.A.I.C.S.: 337110

Rational Cooking Systems, Inc. (1)
25 International Business Park 02-15/17 German Centre, Singapore, 609916, Singapore
Tel.: (65) 68095850
Kitchen Appliances Mfr
N.A.I.C.S.: 337110

Rational Endustriyel Mutfak (1)
Maslak Mahallesi Ahi Evran Cad No 11 Olive Plaza Kat 1 Sariyer, Maslak, 34398, Istanbul, Turkiye
Tel.: (90) 2126036767
Kitchen Appliances Mfr
N.A.I.C.S.: 337110
Tolga Okyalaz (Owner)

Rational France S.A.S. (1)
4 Rue de la Charente, BP 52, 68271, Wittenheim, Cedex, France
Tel.: (33) 389570082
Web Site: https://www.rational-online.com
Emp.: 87
Oven & Cooking Appliance Mfr
N.A.I.C.S.: 333310

Rational Iberica Cooking Systems S.L. (1)
Avenida de la Fama 17-19 Edificio Olmo, Cornella, 08940, Barcelona, Spain
Tel.: (34) 934751750
Kitchen Appliances Mfr
N.A.I.C.S.: 337110

Rational International AG (1)
Heinrich-Wild-Strasse 202, 9435, Heerbrugg, Switzerland
Tel.: (41) 717279090
Kitchen Appliances Mfr
N.A.I.C.S.: 337110

Rational International India Private Ltd. (1)
Unit No 601 6th floor Worldmark 3 Sector 65, DLF Cyber City Phase III, Gurgaon, 122018, Haryana, India
Tel.: (91) 1244839333
Web Site: https://www.rational-online.com
Kitchen Appliances Mfr

N.A.I.C.S.: 337110

Rational Italia S.r.l. (1)
Via Impastato 22, 30174, Mestre, VE, Italy
Tel.: (39) 0418629050
Web Site: https://www.rational-online.com
Emp.: 35
Kitchen Appliances Mfr
N.A.I.C.S.: 337110

Rational Kitchen & Catering Equipment Trading FZCO
Building 2 Office 2218 Gold Diamond Park, PO Box 126076, Dubai, United Arab Emirates
Tel.: (971) 43386615
Kitchen Appliances Mfr
N.A.I.C.S.: 337110
Simon Parke-Davis (Mng Dir)

Rational Mexico, S.A. de C.V. (1)
Miguel de Cervantes Saavedra 169 4 piso Ampliacion Granada, 11520, Mexico, Mexico
Tel.: (52) 5552927538
Web Site: https://www.rational-online.com
Kitchen Appliances Mfr
N.A.I.C.S.: 337110

Rational Scandinavia AB (1)
Kabingatan 11, 212 39, Malmo, Sweden
Tel.: (46) 406808500
Web Site: https://www.rational-online.com
Emp.: 23
Kitchen Appliances Mfr
N.A.I.C.S.: 337110

Rational Schweiz AG (1)
Heinrich-Wild-Strasse 202, 9435, Heerbrugg, Switzerland
Tel.: (41) 717279092
Web Site: https://www.rational-online.com
Emp.: 21
Kitchen Appliances Mfr
N.A.I.C.S.: 337110

Rational Sp.z.o.o. (1)
ul Bokserska 66, 02-690, Warsaw, Poland
Tel.: (48) 228649326
Kitchen Appliances Mfr
N.A.I.C.S.: 337110
Anna Pycinska (Dir-Mktg)

Rational UK Ltd. (1)
Unit 4 Titan Court Laporte Way Portenway Business Park, Luton, LU4 8EF, United Kingdom
Tel.: (44) 1582480388
Web Site: https://www.rational-online.com
Emp.: 82
Oven & Cooking Appliance Mfr
N.A.I.C.S.: 333310
Kenny Bondicz (Mgr-IT & Facilities)

RATKO MITROVIC COMPANY
Yuri Gagarin nr 177, 11070, Belgrade, Serbia
Tel.: (381) 112203200
Web Site:
   https://www.rmkompanija.co.rs
Year Founded: 1948
RMBG—(BEL)
Sales Range: Less than $1 Million
Civil Engineering Services
N.A.I.C.S.: 237990
Dusan Polic (Chm & Chm-Mgmt Bd)

RATNABALI CAPITAL MARKETS LTD.
FMC FORTUNA Block A7 & A8 4 F 234 3A Acharya Jagdish Chandra Bose Road, Kolkata, 700020, West Bengal, India
Tel.: (91) 3340150000
Web Site: http://www.ratnabali.com
Sales Range: $100-124.9 Million
Emp.: 100
Stock Broking Services
N.A.I.C.S.: 523150
Rakesh Pandiya (Pres & CFO)

RATNABHUMI DEVELOPERS LIMITED
207 Turquoise Opp Center Point Panchwati C G Road, Ahmedabad, 380 006, Gujarat, India
Tel.: (91) 7948000493
Web Site:
   https://www.ratnagroup.co.in
Year Founded: 1985
540796—(BOM)
Rev.: $27,408
Assets: $26,368,395
Liabilities: $24,725,808
Net Worth: $1,642,587
Earnings: ($25,262)
Emp.: 18
Fiscal Year-end: 03/31/23
Real Estate Development Services
N.A.I.C.S.: 531210
Kaivan Shah (Chm & Mng Dir)

RATNAMANI METALS & TUBES LTD
17 Rajmugat Society Naranpura Cross Roads, Ahmedabad, 380013, Gujarat, India
Tel.: (91) 7927415501
Web Site: https://www.ratnamani.com
520111—(NSE)
Rev.: $319,620,074
Assets: $357,164,248
Liabilities: $85,862,281
Net Worth: $271,301,967
Earnings: $37,674,491
Emp.: 2,247
Fiscal Year-end: 03/31/21
Stainless Steel Wire Mfr
N.A.I.C.S.: 331210
Vimal Katta (Sr VP-Fin)

Subsidiaries:

Ratnamani Inc. (1)
5326 Heath River Ln, Sugar Land, TX 77479
Tel.: (832) 871-9244
Stainless Steel Pipe Mfr & Distr
N.A.I.C.S.: 331210

Ratnamani Metals & Tubes Ltd - Kutch Division (1)
Survey No 474 Village Bhimasar Ta Nr, Gandhidham Dist Kutch, Anjar, 370 240, Gujarat, India
Tel.: (91) 2836285538
Web Site: http://www.ratnamani.com
Sales Range: $450-499.9 Million
Emp.: 1,600
Pipes Mfr
N.A.I.C.S.: 327332

Ratnamani Metals & Tubes Ltd - SAW Pipes Division (1)
Plot No 3306 to 3309 GIDC Estate Chhatral Phase IV, Ahmedabad Mehsana Highway Ta Kalol, Gandhinagar, 383 729, Gujarat, India
Tel.: (91) 2764232234
Web Site: http://www.ratnamani.com
Sales Range: $50-74.9 Million
Emp.: 250
Pipes Mfr
N.A.I.C.S.: 327332

Ratnamani Metals & Tubes Ltd - Stainless Steel Tube & Pipes (SSTP) Division (1)
Survey No 423 Ahmedabad - Mehsana Highway Village Indrad, Ta Kadi Dist Mehsana, Gandhinagar, 382715, Gujarat, India
Tel.: (91) 2764232254
Web Site: http://www.ratnamani.com
Sales Range: $450-499.9 Million
Pipes Mfr
N.A.I.C.S.: 327332

Ratnamani Techno Casts Ltd (1)
17 Rajmugat Society Naranpura Char Rasta, Ankur Road Naranpura, Ahmedabad, 380 013, Gujarat, India
Tel.: (91) 7927415501
Web Site:
   http://www.ratnamanitechnocasts.com
Stainless Steel Tubes & Pipes Mfr
N.A.I.C.S.: 331210
Prakash M Shangavi (Mng Dir)

Ravi Technoforge Private Limited (1)
Plot No 50/P-1 B/h Toll Plaza Rajkot Gondal NH-27, Village Pipaliya, Rajkot, 360311, Gujarat, India
Tel.: (91) 2827350200
Web Site: https://www.ravitechnoforge.com
Bearing Product Mfr & Distr
N.A.I.C.S.: 332991

RATOS AB
Sturegatan 10, PO Box 1661, SE-111 96, Stockholm, Sweden
Tel.: (46) 87001700   SE
Web Site: https://www.ratos.com
Year Founded: 1866
RATO—(OMX)
Rev.: $2,798,149,241
Assets: $3,481,881,106
Liabilities: $2,190,470,838
Net Worth: $1,291,410,267
Earnings: $82,328,809
Emp.: 15,100
Fiscal Year-end: 12/31/22
Privater Equity Firm
N.A.I.C.S.: 523999
Jan Soderberg (Deputy Chm)

Subsidiaries:

Bisnode AB (1)
Rosenborgsgatan 4-6, 169 93, Solna, Sweden
Tel.: (46) 855805900
Web Site: http://www.bisnode.com
Sales Range: $400-449.9 Million
Business Information Services
N.A.I.C.S.: 561499
Eric Wallin (Country Dir)

Subsidiary (Domestic):

AB Svensk Handelstidning Justitia (2)
Sveavagen 151, 105 99, Stockholm, Sweden
Tel.: (46) 63 670 71 60
Web Site: http://www.shj.se
Sales Range: $25-49.9 Million
Emp.: 60
Business Directory Publisher
N.A.I.C.S.: 513140

Subsidiary (Non-US):

BBMS N.V./SA (2)
Allee De La Recherche 65, Brussels, 1070, Belgium
Tel.: (32) 36103300
Sales Range: $25-49.9 Million
Emp.: 150
Business Management Consulting Services
N.A.I.C.S.: 541618
Martina Bayens (Gen Mgr)

Subsidiary (Domestic):

Baby DM Scandinavia AB (2)
Florettgatan 29C, 254 67, Helsingborg, Sweden
Tel.: (46) 42 165900
Web Site: http://www.bdms.se
Marketing Research & Advertising Services
N.A.I.C.S.: 541910
Fredrik Trulsson (Mng Dir)

Subsidiary (Non-US):

Bisnode Austria GmbH (2)
Jakov-Lind Strasse 4 1, 1020, Vienna, Austria
Tel.: (43) 1588610
Web Site: http://www.bisnode.at
Sales Range: $50-74.9 Million
Investment Management Service
N.A.I.C.S.: 523999

Bisnode Austria Holding GmbH (2)
Jakov-Lind-Strasse 4/1, 1020, Vienna, Austria
Tel.: (43) 1 58861 0
Web Site: http://www.bisnode.at
Sales Range: $25-49.9 Million
Digital Business Information
N.A.I.C.S.: 561499

Bisnode Belgium SA (2)
Researchdreef 65 Allee de la recherche, 1070, Anderlecht, Belgium

RATOS AB

Ratos AB—(Continued)
Tel.: (32) 2 555 97 00
Web Site: http://www.bisnode.be
Emp.: 2,400
Data Processing Services
N.A.I.C.S.: 518210
Daniel Agneessens *(Head-Tech Program Mgmt)*

Bisnode Business & Market Information A/S (2)
Gungemose Parkvej 15 8th fl 2860, 2860, Soborg, Denmark
Tel.: (45) 38169700
Sales Range: $25-49.9 Million
Emp.: 80
Data Processing Services
N.A.I.C.S.: 518210
Pirger Prululd *(Gen Mgr)*

Subsidiary (Domestic):

Bisnode Central Invest AB (2)
S 168, Stockholm, 105 99, Sweden
Tel.: (46) 855805949
Investment Management Service
N.A.I.C.S.: 523940

Subsidiary (Non-US):

Bisnode Ceska Republika, a.s. (2)
Siemensova 2717/4, 155 00, Prague, Czech Republic
Tel.: (420) 274 000 000
Web Site: http://www.bisnode.cz
Emp.: 170
Digital Business Information Services
N.A.I.C.S.: 519290
Petra Stepanova *(Dir-PR)*

Bisnode D&B Magyayorszag Kft. (2)
Riverpark irodahaz Kozraktar u 30-32, 1093, Budapest, Hungary
Tel.: (36) 18158500
Web Site: http://www.bisnode.hu
Business Information Reports, Receivables Management, Marketing Services
N.A.I.C.S.: 519290
Jozsef Keleti *(Head-SME Sls South East Europe)*

Bisnode D&B Schweiz AG (2)
Grossmattstrasse 9, 8902, Urdorf, Switzerland
Tel.: (41) 44 735 61 11
Web Site: http://www.bisnode.ch
Sales Range: $25-49.9 Million
Direct Marketing Services
N.A.I.C.S.: 541860
Macario Juan *(Mng Dir)*

Bisnode Danmark A/S (2)
Gyngemose Parkvej 50, 2860, Soborg, Denmark
Tel.: (45) 70220410
Web Site: http://www.bisnode.dk
Business Directory Publisher
N.A.I.C.S.: 513140
Birger Baylund *(Mng Dir)*

Bisnode Deutschland GmbH (2)
Robert-Bosch-Strasse 11, Darmstadt, 64293, Germany
Tel.: (49) 6151 3800
Sales Range: $150-199.9 Million
Emp.: 500
Investment Management Service
N.A.I.C.S.: 523999
Marcus Hartmann *(Dir-Strategy & Dev)*

Bisnode Finland Oy (2)
Kumpulantie 3, 00520, Helsinki, Finland
Tel.: (358) 9272702333
Web Site: http://www.soliditet.fi
Sales Range: $25-49.9 Million
Emp.: 105
Marketing Consulting Services
N.A.I.C.S.: 541613
Are Kivela *(Dir-Customer Rels)*

Bisnode France, S.A.S. (2)
86 rue Henri Farman, 92120, Issy-les-Moulineaux, France
Tel.: (33) 1 46 12 27 00
Web Site: http://www.bisnode.fr
Emp.: 130
Business Information Services
N.A.I.C.S.: 519290
Isabelle Le Clezio *(Mng Dir)*

Bisnode Grundbesitz Darmstadt GmbH (2)
Havelstr 9, Darmstadt, 64295, Germany
Tel.: (49) 6151 3800
Web Site: http://www.bisnode.com
Emp.: 400
Business Information Services
N.A.I.C.S.: 519290

Bisnode Hungary Ltd. (2)
Kozraktar u 30-32, 1093, Budapest, Hungary
Tel.: (36) 18158500
Web Site: http://www.bisnode.hu
Emp.: 100
Business Information Services
N.A.I.C.S.: 519290
Jozsef Keleti *(Mng Dir & Head-SME Sls-South East Europe)*

Subsidiary (Non-US):

KOMPASS ALGERIE INTERNATIONAL, EURL (3)
Villa n 3 lotissement du 20 Aout Oued Romane, El Achour, 16403, Algiers, Algeria
Tel.: (213) 21 30 23 02
Web Site: http://www.dz.kompass.com
Directory Publishing Services
N.A.I.C.S.: 513140

Kompass Georgia (3)
47/57 M Kostava str, Tbilisi, 0179, Georgia
Tel.: (995) 32 2 19 55 55
Directory Publishing Services
N.A.I.C.S.: 513140

Subsidiary (Domestic):

Bisnode InfoData Holding AB (2)
Sveavagen 168, 105 99, Stockholm, Sweden
Tel.: (46) 8 578 888 00
Investment Management Service
N.A.I.C.S.: 523999

Subsidiary (Non-US):

Bisnode Informatics Austria GmbH (2)
Geiselbergstrasse 17-19, Vienna, 1110, Austria
Tel.: (43) 158 8610
Web Site: http://www.bisnode.at
Emp.: 65
Marketing Consulting Services
N.A.I.C.S.: 541613

Subsidiary (Domestic):

Bisnode Informatics Sweden AB (2)
Rosenborgsgatan 4, Solna, 16974, Sweden
Tel.: (46) 8 5785 48 00
Web Site: http://www.bisnode.com
Information Technology Consulting Services
N.A.I.C.S.: 541512

Subsidiary (Non-US):

Bisnode Informatics, Denmark A/S (2)
Gyngemose Parkvej 50 8th Fl, Soborg, 2860, Denmark
Tel.: (45) 38 16 97 00
Sales Range: $25-49.9 Million
Emp.: 70
Business Directory Publisher
N.A.I.C.S.: 513140
Birger Baylund *(Mng Dir)*

Bisnode Ltd. (2)
Field House 72 Oldfield Road, Hampton, TW12 2HQ, United Kingdom
Tel.: (44) 20 8481 8800
Business Information Services
N.A.I.C.S.: 519290

Bisnode Norge AS (2)
Langkaia 1, 0150, Oslo, Norway
Tel.: (47) 22 45 90 00
Web Site: http://www.bisnode.no
Emp.: 200
Business Information Services
N.A.I.C.S.: 519290

Bisnode Norway AS (2)
Langkaia 1, Oslo, 0250, Norway
Tel.: (47) 22 45 93 34
Web Site: http://www.bisnode.no
Emp.: 150
Financial Advisory Services
N.A.I.C.S.: 523940
Jon Slorer *(Dir-Admin)*

Bisnode Polska Sp.z.o.o. (2)
Kwiatka 12, 09400, Plock, Poland
Tel.: (48) 243642310
Web Site: http://www.bisnode.com
Sales Range: $10-24.9 Million
Emp.: 50
Credit Reporting Services
N.A.I.C.S.: 561450

Bisnode Schweiz AG (2)
Grossmattstrasse 9, 8902, Urdorf, Switzerland
Tel.: (41) 447356111
Sales Range: $75-99.9 Million
Emp.: 130
Investment Management Service
N.A.I.C.S.: 523940
Macario Juan *(CEO)*

Bisnode Slovensko, s.r.o. (2)
M R Stefanika 379/19, 911 60, Trencin, Slovakia
Tel.: (421) 32 746 26 40
Web Site: http://www.bisnode.sk
Emp.: 45
Business Information Services
N.A.I.C.S.: 519290

Subsidiary (Domestic):

Bisnode Sverige AB (2)
Rosenborgsgatan 4-6, 169 93, Solna, Sweden
Tel.: (46) 8 558 059 00
Web Site: http://www.bisnode.com
Investment Management Service
N.A.I.C.S.: 523999

Subsidiary (Non-US):

Bisnode UK Holdings Ltd. (2)
Field House 72 Oldfield Road, Hampton, TW12 2HQ, United Kingdom
Tel.: (44) 20 8481 8800
Investment Management Service
N.A.I.C.S.: 523940

Bisnode d.o.o. (2)
Fallerovo Setaliste 22, 10000, Zagreb, Croatia
Tel.: (385) 13030500
Web Site: http://www.bisnode.hr
Sales Range: $25-49.9 Million
Emp.: 50
Business Directory Publisher
N.A.I.C.S.: 513140

Subsidiary (Domestic):

Compnode Sverige AB (2)
Soeder Maelalarstrand 65, 111 37, Stockholm, Sweden
Tel.: (46) 841200600
Web Site: http://www.compnode.se
Emp.: 4
Business Directory Publisher
N.A.I.C.S.: 513140

DirektMedia Sverige AB (2)
Gotgatan 15, 411 05, Gothenburg, Sweden
Tel.: (46) 31 708 43 00
Web Site: http://www.direktmedia.se
Sales Range: $25-49.9 Million
Emp.: 40
Direct Marketing & Customer Relationship Management Services
N.A.I.C.S.: 541613

Subsidiary (Non-US):

Direktmedia 121 Oy (2)
Kumpulantie 3, 00520, Helsinki, Finland
Tel.: (358) 9 2727 020
Web Site: http://www.bsnode.com
Sales Range: $25-49.9 Million
Emp.: 20
Customer Relationship Management Services
N.A.I.C.S.: 541618
Kristina Lonnqvist *(Deputy Mng Dir)*

Dun & Bradstreet Denmark A/S (2)
Tobaksvejen 21, Soborg, 2860, Denmark
Tel.: (45) 36738000
Web Site: http://www.dbdenmark.dnb.com
Sales Range: $25-49.9 Million
Emp.: 60
Business Information Services
N.A.I.C.S.: 519290
Birger Baylund *(Mng Dir)*

Dun & Bradstreet Deutschland GmbH (2)
Robert-Bosch-Strasse 11 64293, 64295, Darmstadt, Germany
Tel.: (49) 61511375777
Web Site: http://www.bisnode.com
Sales Range: $50-74.9 Million
Emp.: 101
Business Information Services
N.A.I.C.S.: 519290

Dun & Bradstreet Finland Oy (2)
Kuaumdulandie-3, Helsinki, 00520, Finland
Tel.: (358) 925344400
Web Site: http://www.dnb.fi
Sales Range: $1-9.9 Million
Emp.: 20
Business-to-Business Credit & Marketing Information
N.A.I.C.S.: 425120
Vesa Kalapuro *(Dir-Production)*

Dun & Bradstreet Information Services GmbH (2)
Geiselbergstrasse 17-19, A-1110, Vienna, Austria
Tel.: (43) 1588610
Web Site: http://www.dnbaustria.at
Sales Range: $25-49.9 Million
Emp.: 60
Business Information Services
N.A.I.C.S.: 519290
Paulo Silva *(Mgr-Fin)*

Dun & Bradstreet Poland Sp. z o.o. (2)
UL Jana Olbrachta 94, 01 102, Warsaw, Poland
Tel.: (48) 225332400
Web Site: http://www.dnb.com.pl
Sales Range: $1-9.9 Million
Emp.: 40
Business Information Supplier
N.A.I.C.S.: 519290
Andre Osimski *(VP)*

Dun & Bradstreet Schweiz AG (2)
Grossmattstrasse 9, CH 8902, Urdorf, Switzerland
Tel.: (41) 447356111
Web Site: http://www.dnb.ch
Sales Range: $25-49.9 Million
Emp.: 100
Business Information Services
N.A.I.C.S.: 519290
Andreas Hungerbuhler *(Dir-Mktg & Bus Dev)*

Subsidiary (Domestic):

Dun & Bradstreet Sverige AB (2)
Rosenborgsgatan 4-6, PO Box 1529, 169 93, Solna, Sweden
Tel.: (46) 855805900
Web Site: http://www.dnbsweden.com
Sales Range: $25-49.9 Million
Emp.: 15
Business Information Services
N.A.I.C.S.: 561499

Subsidiary (Non-US):

Dun & Bradstreet spol s.r.o. (2)
Siemensova 2717/4, CZ-15500, Prague, 5, Czech Republic
Tel.: (420) 226538600
Web Site: http://www.dnbczech.cz
Sales Range: $25-49.9 Million
Emp.: 25
Business Information Services
N.A.I.C.S.: 519290

Subsidiary (Domestic):

Electronic Data Innovation Group EDIG AB (2)
S16b, Box 1396, 171 27, Solna, Sweden
Tel.: (46) 87650725
Web Site: http://www.edig.se
Software Development Services
N.A.I.C.S.: 541511

Subsidiary (Non-US):

HBI Ceska republika, s.r.o. (2)
Siemensova 2717/4, Prague, 150 00, Czech Republic

HBI Polska SP. z.o.o. (2)
Ul Kwiatka 12, 09-400, Plock, Poland
Tel.: (48) 24 364 23 11
Web Site: http://www.hbi.pl
Sales Range: $25-49.9 Million
Emp.: 27
Online Directory Publisher
N.A.I.C.S.: 513140

Hoppenstedt Kreditinformationen GmbH (2)
Normannenweg 16-20, 20537, Hamburg, Germany
Tel.: (49) 40 734 465 0
Business Directory Publisher
N.A.I.C.S.: 513140

Hoppenstedt360 GmbH (2)
Havelstrasse 9, Darmstadt, 64295, Germany
Tel.: (49) 6151 1375 444
Web Site: http://www.lift360.de
Sales Range: $25-49.9 Million
Emp.: 3
Credit Information Services
N.A.I.C.S.: 519290

InfoDirekt A/S (2)
Soren Frichs Vej 42f, Abyhoj, 8230, Arhus, Denmark
Tel.: (45) 5810 8020
Web Site: http://www.infodirekt.dk
Emp.: 7
Business Information Services
N.A.I.C.S.: 541910
Henrik Kristiansen (Pres)

Subsidiary (Domestic):

InfoTorg AB (2)
Rosenborgsgatan 4-6, 169 74, Solna, Sweden
Tel.: (46) 855805900
Web Site: http://www.infotorg.se
Online Information Services
N.A.I.C.S.: 519290

Infodata AB (2)
Rofenberhsh 426, Solna, 16933, Sweden
Tel.: (46) 8 578 888 00
Web Site: http://www.infodata.se
Sales Range: $75-99.9 Million
Emp.: 200
Online Information & Direct Marketing Services
N.A.I.C.S.: 425120

Subsidiary (Non-US):

KOMPASS IRAN CO. (2)
No 157 3rd Floor Dr Beheshti Ave, 15516, Tehran, Iran
Tel.: (98) 2188755510
Web Site: http://www.kompassiran.com
Directory Publisher
N.A.I.C.S.: 513140

KOMPASS Slovakia a.s. (2)
Frantiskanske namestie 7, 811 01, Bratislava, Slovakia
Tel.: (421) 254435443
Web Site: http://www.kompass.sk
Directory Publisher
N.A.I.C.S.: 513140

Kompass Azerbaijan Co. (2)
178 Suleyman Rahimov Str, AZE1014, Baku, Azerbaijan
Tel.: (994) 12 498 09 41
Web Site: http://az.kompass.com
Emp.: 8
Online Directory Publisher
N.A.I.C.S.: 513140

Kompass B.V. (2)
Paasheuvelweg 40, Zuidoost, Amsterdam, 1105 BJ, Netherlands
Tel.: (31) 20 7154333
Web Site: http://nl.kompass.com
Sales Range: $25-49.9 Million
Emp.: 8
Online Directory Publisher
N.A.I.C.S.: 513140

Kompass Belgium SA-NV (2)
Rue Arenbergstraat 44, Brussels, 1000, Belgium
Tel.: (32) 23459070
Web Site: http://be.kompass.com
Emp.: 12
Online Directory Publisher
N.A.I.C.S.: 513140

Kompass Bilgi Dagitim Hizmetleri A.S. (2)
Eski Buyukdere Cad Park Plaza No 14 Kat 18, Maslak, 34398, Istanbul, Turkiye
Tel.: (90) 2122766635
Web Site: http://www.tr.kompass.com
Sales Range: $25-49.9 Million
Online Directory Publisher
N.A.I.C.S.: 513140

Kompass Czech Republic s.r.o. (2)
Doudova 3, 147 00, Prague, Czech Republic
Tel.: (420) 296 337 333
Web Site: http://www.kompass.cz
Sales Range: $25-49.9 Million
Emp.: 40
Directory Publisher
N.A.I.C.S.: 513140

Kompass Danmark A/S (2)
Laplandsgade 4 St, 2300, Copenhagen, Denmark
Tel.: (45) 45 46 09 10
Web Site: http://www.kompass.dk
Directory Publisher
N.A.I.C.S.: 513140

Kompass Finland Oy (2)
Kumpulantie 3, 00520, Helsinki, Finland
Tel.: (358) 9 5860 260
Web Site: http://fi.kompass.com
Sales Range: $25-49.9 Million
Emp.: 100
Online Directory Publisher
N.A.I.C.S.: 513140

Kompass GmbH (2)
Bismarckallee 2 a, 79098, Freiburg, Germany
Tel.: (49) 761137630
Web Site: https://de.kompass.com
Sales Range: $25-49.9 Million
Emp.: 500
Online Directory Publisher
N.A.I.C.S.: 513140

Kompass India Information Pvt. Ltd. (2)
503 Corporate Avenue Sonawala Road No 1, Goregaon East, 400063, Mumbai, Maharashtra, India
Tel.: (91) 22 40456786
Web Site: http://www.kompass.com
Sales Range: $25-49.9 Million
Emp.: 20
Online Directory Publisher
N.A.I.C.S.: 513140

Kompass Info doo (2)
Trg Josipa Langa 4, 10000, Zagreb, Croatia
Tel.: (385) 1 4893 300
Web Site: http://www.hr.kompass.com
Online Directory Publisher
N.A.I.C.S.: 513140

Kompass International S.A. (2)
66 Quai Marechal Joffre, 92415, Courbevoie, France
Tel.: (33) 1 43 34 34 34
Web Site: http://www.kompass.fr
Sales Range: $50-74.9 Million
Emp.: 250
Directory Publisher
N.A.I.C.S.: 513140

Subsidiary (Non-US):

KOMPASS ROMANIA srl (3)
Str Profesor Ion Bogdan nr 4-6 Sector 1, 010539, Bucharest, Romania
Tel.: (40) 213170390
Web Site: http://www.ro.solutions.kompass.com
Sales Range: $25-49.9 Million
Directory Publisher
N.A.I.C.S.: 513140

Subsidiary (Non-US):

Kompass Japan K.K. (2)
2nd floor Kita Aoyama, Minato-ku, Tokyo, 107-0061, Japan
Tel.: (81) 3 6890 0473
Web Site: http://www.kompass.jp
Online Directory Publisher
N.A.I.C.S.: 513140

Kompass Kazakhstan (2)
97 Al Farabi Av 1A, 050060, Almaty, Kazakhstan
Tel.: (7) 727 3336048
Web Site: http://kz.kompass.com
Online Directory Publisher
N.A.I.C.S.: 513140

Kompass Korea Inc. (2)
904 Seoulsub Digital Kolong 2 Seongsudong 2-ga, Seongdong-gu, 333-140, Seoul, Korea (South)
Tel.: (82) 2 562 5337
Web Site: http://www.kompass.co.kr
Sales Range: $25-49.9 Million
Emp.: 30
Directory Publisher
N.A.I.C.S.: 513140
Seon Mi Baek (Asst Mgr)

Kompass Lanka (PVT) Ltd. (2)
155 Park Road 05, Colombo, 00500, Sri Lanka
Tel.: (94) 11 2817553
Web Site: http://lk.kompass.com
Sales Range: $25-49.9 Million
Emp.: 15
Online Directory Publisher
N.A.I.C.S.: 513140

Kompass Norge AS (2)
Nydalsveien 28, 0484, Oslo, Norway
Tel.: (47) 4 546 0910
Web Site: http://www.no.kompass.com
Online Directory Publisher
N.A.I.C.S.: 513140

Subsidiary (Domestic):

Kompass Sverige AB (2)
Soder Malarstrand 65 C 5tr, 118 25, Stockholm, Sweden
Tel.: (46) 8 41 200 600
Web Site: http://www.se.kompass.com
Online Directory Publisher
N.A.I.C.S.: 513140

Subsidiary (Non-US):

Kompass UK Ltd (2)
St James's House 150 London Road, East Grinstead, RH19 1ES, West Sussex, United Kingdom
Tel.: (44) 1342 778560
Web Site: http://www.kompassinfo.co.uk
Sales Range: $25-49.9 Million
Emp.: 50
Business Directory Publisher
N.A.I.C.S.: 513140

Kompass Ukraine JSC (2)
PO Box 3122, Kharkiv, 61072, Ukraine
Tel.: (380) 675716231
Web Site: http://www.kompass.ua
Sales Range: $25-49.9 Million
Online Directory Publisher
N.A.I.C.S.: 513140

Subsidiary (Domestic):

Lundalogik AB (2)
St Lars vag 46, 222 70, Lund, Sweden
Tel.: (46) 46 270 48 00
Web Site: http://www.lundalogik.se
Sales Range: $25-49.9 Million
Emp.: 60
Customer Relationship Management Services
N.A.I.C.S.: 541618

Subsidiary (Non-US):

Lundalogik AS (2)
Langkaia 1 B 6 etg, Oslo, 0150, Norway
Tel.: (47) 21 61 17 10
Web Site: http://www.lundalogik.no
Emp.: 10
Customer Relationship Management Services
N.A.I.C.S.: 541618

Lundalogik Finland Oy (2)
Nilsiankatu 11-13, 00510, Helsinki, Finland
Tel.: (358) 753 252 960
Web Site: http://www.lundalogik.fi
Sales Range: $25-49.9 Million
Emp.: 7
Customer Relationship Management Services
N.A.I.C.S.: 541618

Subsidiary (Domestic):

Marknadsinformation Analys MIA AB (2)
Rosenborgsgatan 4, 105 99, Solna, Sweden
Tel.: (46) 20 529 292
Web Site: http://www.mia.bisnode.se
Business Information Services
N.A.I.C.S.: 519290

Newsline Group AB (2)
Sveavagen 151, Stockholm, Sweden
Tel.: (46) 8 517 577 34
Web Site: http://www.newsline.se
Business Directory Publisher
N.A.I.C.S.: 513140

PAR AB (2)
Arstaangsvagen 11 7 tr, 117 43, Stockholm, Sweden
Tel.: (46) 8 775 36 00
Web Site: http://www.bisnode.com
Sales Range: $25-49.9 Million
Emp.: 800
Business Directory Publisher
N.A.I.C.S.: 513140

Subsidiary (Non-US):

Razpisi d.o.o. (2)
Stegne 13G, 1000, Ljubljana, Slovenia
Tel.: (386) 1 6202815
Web Site: http://www.javnirazpisi.com
Emp.: 4
Business Directory Publisher
N.A.I.C.S.: 513140

Subsidiary (Domestic):

Relevant Information Sverige AB (2)
Sturegatan 3, Box 1529, 172 29, Sundbyberg, Sweden
Tel.: (46) 8 519 115 00
Web Site: http://www.relevant.se
Business Directory Publisher
N.A.I.C.S.: 513140
Christina Freese Ingesson (CEO)

Subsidiary (Non-US):

Soliditet A/S (2)
Tobaksvejen 21, 2860, Soborg, Denmark
Tel.: (45) 36 73 81 84
Web Site: http://www.soliditet.dk
Sales Range: $25-49.9 Million
Emp.: 80
Online Credit Information Services
N.A.I.C.S.: 513199
Ola A. Johansen (Mgr-Relationship)

Subsidiary (Domestic):

Soliditet AB (2)
PO Box 11124, Solna, 1693, Sweden
Tel.: (46) 8 519 013 50
Web Site: http://www.soliditet.se
Credit & Business Information Services
N.A.I.C.S.: 513140
Helene Bodlander (Head)

Subsidiary (Non-US):

Soliditet Decision AS (2)
Langkaia 1, Oslo, 150, Norway
Tel.: (47) 22 45 93 34
Web Site: http://www.bisnode.no
Sales Range: $50-74.9 Million
Emp.: 150
Online Credit Information Services
N.A.I.C.S.: 513199

Soliditet Finland Oy (2)
Business Area Soliditet Kumpulantie 3, 00520, Helsinki, Finland
Tel.: (358) 975119100
Web Site: http://www.soliditet.fi
Emp.: 70
Business Information Services
N.A.I.C.S.: 519290

Soliditet Polska Sp. z.o.o. (2)
Ul Jana Olbrachta 94, 01-102, Warsaw, Poland
Tel.: (48) 22 533 24 00

Ratos AB—(Continued)

Web Site: http://www.soliditet.com.pl
Business Management Consulting Services
N.A.I.C.S.: 541611
Marzena Zysk (Dir-Sls)

Subsidiary (Domestic):

Svenska Nyhetsbrev AB (2)
Torsgatan 21, Stockholm, 11390, Sweden
Tel.: (46) 8 54 600 500
Web Site: http://www.svenskanyhetsbrev.se
Sales Range: $25-49.9 Million
Emp.: 30
Business Directory Publisher
N.A.I.C.S.: 513140
Johan Petersen (Mgr-Sls)

Vendemore Nordic AB (2)
Rosenborgsgatan 4, 113 46, Solna, Sweden
Tel.: (46) 852504100
Web Site: http://www.vendemore.com
Sales Range: $25-49.9 Million
Emp.: 20
Online Marketing Consulting Services
N.A.I.C.S.: 541613

DIAB International AB (1)
Norra Sofieroleden 8, 31232, Laholm, Sweden
Tel.: (46) 43016300
Web Site: http://www.diabgroup.com
Sales Range: $200-249.9 Million
Emp.: 1,250
Core Material Mfr
N.A.I.C.S.: 332312

Subsidiary (Non-US):

DIAB A/S (2)
Leangbukta 40, Vettre, 1392, Hvalstad, Norway
Tel.: (47) 66 98 19 30
Web Site: http://www.diabgroup.com
Sales Range: $25-49.9 Million
Emp.: 5
Core Material Mfr
N.A.I.C.S.: 326150

DIAB Asia Pacific Pte Ltd (2)
300 Beach Road 29-04 Concourse, Singapore, 199955, Singapore
Tel.: (65) 6396 5109
Web Site: http://www.diabgroup.com
Sales Range: $25-49.9 Million
Emp.: 5
Steel Products Mfr
N.A.I.C.S.: 332999

DIAB Australia Pty. Ltd. (2)
PO Box 496, Oxenford, 4210, QLD, Australia
Tel.: (61) 415 191 766
Polymer Foam Core Material Distr
N.A.I.C.S.: 424610

DIAB Composite Material Technology (Kunshan) Co. Ltd. (2)
Rm 535 Fl 4 Section D Joining International Corporation Garden, Huaqiao Town, 215332, Kunshan, Jiangsu, China
Tel.: (86) 512 5763 0666
Web Site: http://www.diabgroup.com
Steel Products Mfr
N.A.I.C.S.: 332999

DIAB Ecuador S.A. (2)
Casilla Postal 16497, Guayaquil, Ecuador
Tel.: (593) 4 360 788
Polymer Foam Core Material Distr
N.A.I.C.S.: 424610

DIAB GmbH (2)
Max-von-Laue Strasse 7, 30966, Hemmingen, Germany
Tel.: (49) 511 42 03 40
Web Site: http://www.diabgroup.com
Sales Range: $25-49.9 Million
Emp.: 5
Steel Products Mfr
N.A.I.C.S.: 332999

Subsidiary (US):

DIAB Inc. (2)
315 Seahawk Dr, Desoto, TX 75115
Tel.: (972) 228-7600
Web Site: http://www.diabgroup.com
Sales Range: $25-49.9 Million
Emp.: 20
Core Material Mfr
N.A.I.C.S.: 332999

Subsidiary (Non-US):

DIAB Ltd (2)
Unit 1141 Regent Court Gloucester Business Park, Gloucester, GL3 4AD, United Kingdom
Tel.: (44) 1452 614234
Web Site: http://www.diabgroup.com
Sales Range: $50-74.9 Million
Emp.: 5
Rubber & Plastic Material Distr
N.A.I.C.S.: 424690

DIAB Middle East (2)
Concord Tower Media City 26th Floor Office 2607 3rd Floor Office No 11, PO Box 25906, Dubai, United Arab Emirates
Tel.: (971) 4 429 86 04
Web Site: http://www.diabgroup.com
Core Material Mfr
N.A.I.C.S.: 332999

DIAB SA (2)
Parc d'Activites Kennedy 5 Avenue Rudolph Diesel, 33700, Merignac, France
Tel.: (33) 5 56 47 20 43
Web Site: http://www.diabgroup.com
Sales Range: $25-49.9 Million
Emp.: 3
Core Material Mfr
N.A.I.C.S.: 332999

DIAB SPAIN S.L. (2)
C/San Atilano 7 piso 4 oficina 1, 49003, Zamora, Spain
Tel.: (34) 98 016 7982
Web Site: http://www.diabgroup.com
Sales Range: $25-49.9 Million
Core Material Mfr
N.A.I.C.S.: 332999

Subsidiary (Domestic):

DIAB Sales AB (2)
Norra Sofieroleden 8, Box 201, 312 22, Laholm, Sweden
Tel.: (46) 430 163 00
Web Site: http://www.diabgroup.com
Sales Range: $50-74.9 Million
Emp.: 220
Core Material Mfr
N.A.I.C.S.: 326150

Subsidiary (Non-US):

DIAB SpA (2)
Via Alemagna 29, 32013, Longarone, Belluno, Italy
Tel.: (39) 0437776820
Web Site: http://www.diabgroup.com
Plastic & Rubber Product Mfr
N.A.I.C.S.: 325211

DIAB sp. z o.o. (2)
ul Wroclawska 44a, 76-200, Slupsk, Poland
Tel.: (48) 60 244 9660
Web Site: http://www.diabgroup.com
Polystyrene Foam Product Mfr
N.A.I.C.S.: 326140

DURI AB (1)
Kryptongatan 1, 431 53, Molndal, Sweden
Tel.: (46) 31 706 19 10
Web Site: http://www.duri.se
Floor Care Product Distr
N.A.I.C.S.: 424950

Elitfonster AB (1)
Brogardsgatan 1, PO Box 153, 574 22, Vetlanda, Sweden
Tel.: (46)104514000
Web Site: http://www.elitfonster.se
Sales Range: $100-124.9 Million
Window & Patio Door Mfr
N.A.I.C.S.: 332321

Finnkino Oy (1)
Koivuvaarankuja 2, Vantaa, 1640, Finland
Tel.: (358) 9 131 191
Web Site: http://www.finnkino.fi
Sales Range: $125-149.9 Million
Emp.: 600
Movie Theater Operation Services
N.A.I.C.S.: 512131
Veronica Lindholm (CEO)

Subsidiary (Non-US):

AS Forum Cinemas (2)
Hobujaama 5, 10151, Tallinn, Harju, Estonia
Tel.: (372) 6800700
Web Site: http://www.forumcinemas.ee
Sales Range: $50-74.9 Million
Emp.: 140
Movie Theater Operation Services
N.A.I.C.S.: 512131

SIA Forum Cinemas (2)
13 Janvara Str 8, 1050, Riga, Latvia
Tel.: (371) 6 735 7625
Web Site: http://www.forumcinemas.lv
Sales Range: $25-49.9 Million
Emp.: 100
Movie Theater Operation Services
N.A.I.C.S.: 512131

GS Hydro Holding OY (1)
Lautatarhankatu 4, 13110, Hameenlinna, Finland
Tel.: (358) 3 656 41
Web Site: http://www.gshydro.com
Emp.: 80
Investment Management Service
N.A.I.C.S.: 523940

Subsidiary (Domestic):

GS-Hydro Oy (2)
Lautatarhankatu 4, FI 02600, Hameenlinna, Finland
Tel.: (358) 365641
Web Site: http://www.gshydro.com
Piping System Mfr
N.A.I.C.S.: 332996

Subsidiary (Non-US):

GS Hydro do Brasil Sistemas Hidraulicos Ltda (3)
Tel.: (55) 2135534515
Web Site: https://br.gshydro.com
Sales Range: $25-49.9 Million
Emp.: 13
Nonwelded Pipe Mfr
N.A.I.C.S.: 332313

GS-Hydro AB (3)
Tel.: (46) 60156700
Web Site: https://www.gshydro.com
Nonwelded Pipe Mfr
N.A.I.C.S.: 332996

GS-Hydro Austria GmbH (3)
Schardingerstrasse 7, A-4061, Pasching, Austria
Tel.: (43) 7229631620
Web Site: https://de.gshydro.com
Sales Range: $25-49.9 Million
Emp.: 25
Nonwelded Pipe Mfr
N.A.I.C.S.: 332996

GS-Hydro Benelux B.V. (3)
Zweth 24, 2991 LH, Barendrecht, Netherlands
Tel.: (31) 886970000
Web Site: https://nl.gshydro.com
Sales Range: $25-49.9 Million
Piping Equipment Mfr
N.A.I.C.S.: 326122

GS-Hydro Danmark AS (3)
Fabriksvej 12, 6000, Kolding, Denmark
Tel.: (45) 7554 1533
Web Site: http://www.dk.gshydro.com
Sales Range: $25-49.9 Million
Hydraulic Piping Equipment Distr
N.A.I.C.S.: 423830

GS-Hydro France (3)
29 Bis rue de la Prairie, 78120, Rambouillet, France
Tel.: (33) 6 62 19 54 53
Nonwelded Piping Product Distr
N.A.I.C.S.: 423510

GS-Hydro Korea Ltd. (3)
Tel.: (82) 512902000
Web Site: https://kr.gshydro.com
Emp.: 50
Piping Equipment Mfr
N.A.I.C.S.: 326122

GS-Hydro Norge AS (3)
Maltrostveien 3, PO Box 93, Frogner, Oslo, 2716, Norway
Tel.: (47) 63866620
Web Site: http://www.gshydro.com
Sales Range: $25-49.9 Million
Emp.: 100
Steel Pipe & Tube Mfr
N.A.I.C.S.: 331210

GS-Hydro Piping Systems (Shanghai) Co. Ltd. (3)
Plot A No 1 Workshop No 679 Shenfu Road, Xinzhuang Industrial Zone Minhang District, Shanghai, 201108, China
Tel.: (86) 2154424150
Web Site: https://cn.gshydro.com
Sales Range: $25-49.9 Million
Piping Equipment Mfr
N.A.I.C.S.: 326122

GS-Hydro Russia (3)
Mitrofanievskoe Shosse 2 bld 1 Business Centre Admiral office 317, 198095, Saint Petersburg, 198095, Russia
Tel.: (7) 812 441 3781
Web Site: http://www.gshydro.ru
Sales Range: $50-74.9 Million
Emp.: 10
Piping Product Distr
N.A.I.C.S.: 423510
Vladimir Abramenko (Mng Dir)

GS-Hydro S.A.U. (3)
C/ Cabo Rufino Lazaro 5, Las Rozas, E-28230, Madrid, Spain
Tel.: (34) 916409830
Web Site: https://es.gshydro.com
Nonwelded Piping Product Distr
N.A.I.C.S.: 423510

GS-Hydro Singapore Pte. Ltd (3)
No 5 Soon Lee Street 06-39 Pioneer Point, Singapore, 627607, Singapore
Tel.: (65) 62650071
Web Site: https://sg.gshydro.com
Sales Range: $25-49.9 Million
Piping Equipment Mfr
N.A.I.C.S.: 326122

GS-Hydro Sp. z o.o. (3)
Golebia 81, 81-185, Gdynia, Poland
Tel.: (48) 587820220
Web Site: https://pl.gshydro.com
Piping Equipment Mfr
N.A.I.C.S.: 326122

GS-Hydro System GmbH (3)
Tel.: (49) 23028780410
Web Site: https://de.gshydro.com
Emp.: 3
Steel Pole Mfr
N.A.I.C.S.: 331210

GS-Hydro U.S. Inc. (3)
Tel.: (281) 209-1000
Web Site: https://us.gshydro.com
Sales Range: $25-49.9 Million
Fabricated Structural Metal Mfr
N.A.I.C.S.: 332312

GS-Hydro UK Ltd. (3)
Unit A Camberwell Way Doxford International Business Park, Sunderland, SR3 3XN, United Kingdom
Tel.: (44) 1915112000
Web Site: https://uk.gshydro.com
Emp.: 50
Welding Pipe Distr
N.A.I.C.S.: 423830

HL Display Holding AB (1)
Cylindervagen 18, 131 52, Nacka, Sweden
Tel.: (46) 8 6837300
Web Site: http://www.hl-display.com
Sales Range: $50-74.9 Million
Investment Management Service
N.A.I.C.S.: 523999

Subsidiary (Domestic):

HL Display AB (2)
Cylindervagen 18, 131 52, Nacka, Sweden
Tel.: (46) 86837300
Web Site: http://www.hl-display.com
Sales Range: $200-249.9 Million
Retail Industry Supplier, Price Display, Products & Campaign Information In-Store Solutions & Off-Shelf Merchandising
N.A.I.C.S.: 459999
Malin Jonsson (Acct Exec)

Subsidiary (Non-US):

Display Ukraine LLC (3)
street Syretska 5 building 3, 04073, Kiev, Ukraine
Tel.: (380) 443913910
Web Site: http://www.d-u.com.ua

Commercial Equipment Whslr
N.A.I.C.S.: 423440

HL Display (Asia) Pte Ltd. (3)
25 Changi South Avenue 2 04-01, Singapore, 486594, Singapore
Tel.: (65) 6396 00 96
Web Site: http://www.hl-display.sg
Supermarket Operator
N.A.I.C.S.: 445110
Pearlyn Chin (Country Mgr)

HL Display (Shanghai) Co Ltd (3)
26th Floor Triumphal Arch Building, 428 Tianmuzhong Road, 200070, Shanghai, China (50%)
Tel.: (86) 2163546998
Sales Range: $25-49.9 Million
Emp.: 10
Retailers Stores
N.A.I.C.S.: 459999

HL Display (Thailand) Ltd. (3)
1754 Soi Ladprao 101 Ladprao Road, Klongchan Bandkapi, 10240, Bangkok, Thailand
Tel.: (66) 2736 9701
Web Site: http://www.hl-display.co.th
Shopping Center Construction Services
N.A.I.C.S.: 236220

HL Display Australia Pty Ltd. (3)
Ste 432 Level 4 14 Lexington Drive Norwest Business Park, Bella Vista, 2153, NSW, Australia
Tel.: (61) 425 467 774
Web Site: http://www.hl-display.com
Emp.: 3
Retail Management Consulting Services
N.A.I.C.S.: 541618

HL Display Belgium NV (3)
De Regenboog 11 Bus 19, Post Bus 33, 2800, Mechelen, Belgium (100%)
Tel.: (32) 34578877
Web Site: http://www.hl-display.com
Emp.: 20
Carpentry Contractor
N.A.I.C.S.: 238350
Joost Bakx (Country Mgr-Benelux)

HL Display Benelux B.V. (3)
ZandFord 17, 4612, Hoogerheide, Netherlands (100%)
Tel.: (31) 164662660
Emp.: 20
Accounting Services
N.A.I.C.S.: 541219
Jurgen Goens (Mgr-Acct)

HL Display Ceska Republika S.r.o. (3)
Zeleny Pruh 95/97, 140 00, Prague, Czech Republic (100%)
Tel.: (420) 24 144 2591
Web Site: http://www.hl-display.cz
General Merchandise Stores
N.A.I.C.S.: 455219

HL Display Deutschland GmbH (3)
Zeppelinstr 4, 85399, Hallbergmoos, Germany (100%)
Tel.: (49) 8119988390
Emp.: 9
Sign Mfr
N.A.I.C.S.: 339950

HL Display Espana S.L (3)
Avda Diagona 466 1 1, 8006, Barcelona, Spain (100%)
Tel.: (34) 932388716
Web Site: http://www.hl-display.com
Sales Range: $50-74.9 Million
Emp.: 7
Industrial Machinery & Equipment Whslr
N.A.I.C.S.: 423830

HL Display France SAS (3)
Z A des Granges Galand 24, 377553, Saint-Avertin, France (100%)
Tel.: (33) 247488500
Sales Range: $25-49.9 Million
Emp.: 100
Tobacco Stores
N.A.I.C.S.: 459991

HL Display Hong Kong Ltd (3)
Unit 1216 12th Floor New Commerce Centre 19 On Sum Street, Siu Lek Yuen, Sha Tin, China (Hong Kong) (100%)
Tel.: (852) 2 646 8611
Web Site: http://www.hl-display.com
Sales Range: $50-74.9 Million
Electrical Appliance Television & Radio Set Whslr
N.A.I.C.S.: 423620

HL Display India Pvt Ltd. (3)
D-Y 3rd Floor Atur Hous, 87A Dr Annie Besant Road Worli, Mumbai, 400018, India (100%)
Tel.: (91) 2224923700
Web Site: http://www.hl-display.com
Sales Range: $25-49.9 Million
Emp.: 8
Business Service Centers
N.A.I.C.S.: 561439
Maxim Boutry (Mgr-Reg Sls)

HL Display Korea Co Ltd (3)
1304 Taeyoung BLDG 144 Mapo-daero, Mapo-gu, Seoul, 04212, Korea (South) (100%)
Tel.: (82) 226592657
Web Site: http://www.hl-display.com
General Merchandise Stores
N.A.I.C.S.: 455219

HL Display Latvia SIA (3)
Jelgavas cels 20, Tiraine, Marupes, 2167, Latvia (100%)
Tel.: (371) 6 781 9999
Web Site: https://www.displaylatvia.com
Plastics Product Mfr
N.A.I.C.S.: 326199

HL Display Ltd Sti (3)
23 ADA No 13-15 ISTOC Istanbul Toptancilar Carsisi, 34 550 Mahmutb, Istanbul, Turkiye (100%)
Tel.: (90) 2126590192
Web Site: http://www.hl-display.com
Sales Range: $25-49.9 Million
Emp.: 7
Plastics Material & Resin Mfr
N.A.I.C.S.: 325211

HL Display Malaysia Sdn Bhd (3)
Jalan Pju 3-41 Sunway Demansara Technology Park, Taman Megah, 47810, Petaling Jaya, Selangor, Malaysia (100%)
Tel.: (60) 378032690
Sales Range: $25-49.9 Million
Emp.: 10
Software Reproducing
N.A.I.C.S.: 334610
Pearlyn Chin (CTO)

HL Display Middle East JLT (3)
Jumeirah Lake Towers Fortune Tower C1, Box 309143, Dubai, United Arab Emirates
Tel.: (971) 4 424 0110
Web Site: http://www.hl-display.com
Sales Range: $25-49.9 Million
In-Store Communication & Merchandising to the Food & Non-Food Retail Sectors
N.A.I.C.S.: 445110

HL Display Nederland BV (3)
Emmastraat 2C, 4811 AG, Breda, Netherlands (100%)
Tel.: (31) 16 466 2660
Web Site: https://www.hl-display.com
Sales Range: $25-49.9 Million
Paperboard Mills
N.A.I.C.S.: 322130

HL Display Norge A/S (3)
Nesbruveien 75, PO Box 18, 1361, Nesbru, Norway (100%)
Tel.: (47) 66983600
Sales Range: $50-74.9 Million
Emp.: 15
Furniture Whslr
N.A.I.C.S.: 423210

HL Display OOO (3)
Vereyskaya street 17 office 217 Business Center Vereyskaya Plaza II, 121357, Moscow, Russia
Tel.: (7) 4957973087
Web Site: http://www.hl-display.com
Sales Range: $25-49.9 Million
Supermarket Operator
N.A.I.C.S.: 445110

HL Display Osterreich GmbH (3)
Mosetiggasse 1A, 1230, Vienna, Austria
Tel.: (43) 1 667 0290
Web Site: http://www.hl-display.at
Supermarket Operator
N.A.I.C.S.: 445110

Renate Huber (Officer-Customer Svc)

HL Display Polska Sp. z o.o. (3)
ul Nakielska 3, 01-106, Warsaw, Poland (100%)
Tel.: (48) 22 877 6200
Web Site: http://www.hl-display.pl
Wood Preservation
N.A.I.C.S.: 321114
Rafal Lewandowski (Dir-Comml)

HL Display Romania SRL (3)
Tudor Vladimirescu Boulevard number, 22 Green Gate Office Building 5th Floor Office 535 5th District, 050883, Bucharest, Romania (100%)
Tel.: (40) 213194811
Web Site: http://www.hl-display.ro
Sales Range: $50-74.9 Million
Non-Durable Goods Whslr
N.A.I.C.S.: 424090

HL Display Slovensko s.r.o. (3)
Cernysevskeho 10, 851 01, Bratislava, Slovakia
Tel.: (421) 908730555
Web Site: http://www.hl-display.sk
Supermarket Operator
N.A.I.C.S.: 445110

HL Display Suomi OY (3)
Metsanneidonkuja 6, 02130, Espoo, Finland
Tel.: (358) 9 562 9180
Web Site: http://www.hl-display.fi
Sales Range: $25-49.9 Million
General Merchandise Stores
N.A.I.C.S.: 455219
Sivrg Bohling (Mng Dir)

HL Display Suzhou Ltd (3)
Building No 4 Junfeng Industrial Premises, Yangshan Industrial Phase II, Suzhou, China (100%)
Tel.: (86) 51266161904
Web Site: http://www.hl-display.com
Sales Range: $25-49.9 Million
Emp.: 50
General Merchandise Stores
N.A.I.C.S.: 455219

Subsidiary (Domestic):

HL Display Sverige AB (3)
Cylindervagen 18, Box 1118, 131 52, Nacka, Sweden
Tel.: (46) 8 683 7363
Web Site: http://www.hl-display.se
Industrial Supplies Whslr
N.A.I.C.S.: 423840
Anders Lautmann (Country Mgr)

Subsidiary (Domestic):

HL Display Falkenberg AB (4)
Akarevagen 39, 31132, Falkenberg, Sweden (100%)
Tel.: (46) 34648950
Web Site: http://www.ho-display.com
Sales Range: $10-24.9 Million
Emp.: 30
Furniture Retailer
N.A.I.C.S.: 449110
Lars Amtenmer (Mng Dir)

HL Display Karlskoga AB (4)
Bofors industriomrade, PO Box 5016, 69105, Karlskoga, Sweden (100%)
Tel.: (46) 586789630
Web Site: http://www.hl-display.com
Sales Range: $25-49.9 Million
Plastics Product Mfr
N.A.I.C.S.: 326199

HL Display Sundsvall AB (4)
Bultgatan 12, Sundsvall, 853 50, Sweden (100%)
Tel.: (46) 60161200
Web Site: http://www.hl-display.com
Plastics Product Mfr
N.A.I.C.S.: 326199
Lars Lundmark (Mgr-Fin)

Subsidiary (Non-US):

HL Display Swizerland AG (3)
Rohrerstrasse 102, 5000, Aarau, Switzerland (100%)
Tel.: (41) 628345030
Web Site: http://www.hl-display.com
Sales Range: $50-74.9 Million
Emp.: 10

Service Establishment Equipment & Supplies Whslr
N.A.I.C.S.: 423850
Peter Moser (Dir-Comml)

HL Display Taiwan Ltd (3)
4th Floor No 69-11 Sec 2, Jhongjheng E Rd Danshuei Towns, Taipei, 251, Taiwan (100%)
Tel.: (886) 228086839
Sales Range: $25-49.9 Million
Emp.: 5
General Merchandise Stores
N.A.I.C.S.: 455219

HL Display d.o.o. (3)
Letaliska cesta 3C, 1000, Ljubljana, Slovenia (100%)
Tel.: (386) 15422031
Sales Range: $25-49.9 Million
Emp.: 3
General Merchandise Stores
N.A.I.C.S.: 455219

HL Display d.o.o. (3)
Spanskih Boraca 22B, 11070, Belgrade, Serbia
Tel.: (381) 11 3131 281
Web Site: http://www.hl-display.rs
Sales Range: $25-49.9 Million
Emp.: 4
Supermarket Operator
N.A.I.C.S.: 445110

P.T HL Display Indonesia (3)
Jl MT Haryono Kav 62, 12780, Jakarta, Indonesia (100%)
Tel.: (62) 217976248
Web Site: http://www.hl-display.com
Sales Range: $25-49.9 Million
Emp.: 20
Tobacco Stores
N.A.I.C.S.: 459991
Sharania Pangalila (Country Mgr)

Inwido AB (1)
Engelbrektsgatan 15, 211 33, Malmo, Sweden (96%)
Tel.: (46) 104514550
Web Site: https://www.inwido.com
Rev.: $894,171,420
Assets: $916,556,614
Liabilities: $418,368,972
Net Worth: $498,187,642
Earnings: $75,641,350
Emp.: 4,900
Fiscal Year-end: 12/31/2022
Window & Door Mfr
N.A.I.C.S.: 332321
Peter Welin (Deputy CEO & CFO)

Subsidiary (Domestic):

Hemmafonster Sverige AB (2)
Granitvagen 2, Box 2103, 550 02, Jonkoping, Sweden
Tel.: (46) 020 530 530
Web Site: http://www.hemmafonster.se
Window & Door Mfr
N.A.I.C.S.: 321911

Subsidiary (Non-US):

INWIDO DENMARK A/S (2)
Fabriksvej 4, Farso, 9640, Denmark
Tel.: (45) 98 63 24 44
Web Site: http://www.inwido.dk
Wood Window & Door Mfr
N.A.I.C.S.: 321911
Mads Storgaard (Pres)

Subsidiary (Non-US):

CARLSON & CO LTD. (3)
G12 Calmount Park Ballymount, Dublin, D12 F9P1, Ireland
Tel.: (353) 1 462 5777
Web Site: https://www.carlson.ie
Sales Range: $25-49.9 Million
Emp.: 20
Window & Door Distr
N.A.I.C.S.: 423310

Subsidiary (Domestic):

DANSK VINDUES INDUSTRI A/S (3)
Sondergarden 11, 9640, Farso, Denmark
Tel.: (45) 98 63 24 44
Wood Window & Door Mfr
N.A.I.C.S.: 321911

RATOS AB

Ratos AB—(Continued)

FROVIN VINDUER OG DORE A/S (3)
Kristen Bernikows Gade 4, 1105, Copenhagen, Denmark
Tel.: (45) 5950 4141
Web Site: http://www.frovin.dk
Sales Range: $25-49.9 Million
Wood Window & Door Mfr
N.A.I.C.S.: 321911

Subsidiary (Non-US):

INWIDO IRELAND LTD. (3)
G1 Calmount Park Ballymount, Dublin, Ireland
Tel.: (353) 1 489 6000
Web Site: http://www.carlson.ie
Sales Range: $25-49.9 Million
Emp.: 9
Window & Door Mfr
N.A.I.C.S.: 321911

Subsidiary (Domestic):

INWIDO PRODUKTION SYD A/S (3)
Cedervej 9, 7400, Herning, Denmark
Tel.: (45) 96 61 42 00
Wood Window & Door Mfr
N.A.I.C.S.: 321911

KPK DORE OG VINDUER A/S (3)
Rogalandsvej 3, 7900, Nykobing, Denmark
Tel.: (45) 9 670 2400
Web Site: https://www.kpk-vinduer.dk
Emp.: 250
Wood Window & Door Mfr
N.A.I.C.S.: 321911

Outline Vinduer A/S (3)
Fabriksvej 4, 9600, Farso, Denmark
Tel.: (45) 9721 6000
Web Site: http://www.outline.dk
Windows & Doors Mfr
N.A.I.C.S.: 332321
Jens Sorensen (Mng Dir)

PRO TEC VINDUER A/S (3)
Nybovej 34, 7500, Holstebro, Denmark
Tel.: (45) 9741 3077
Web Site: http://www.protecvinduer.dk
Window & Door Mfr
N.A.I.C.S.: 321911
Christian Lausen (Mgr-IT)

Subsidiary (Non-US):

PRO TEC WINDOWS UK LTD (3)
The Plough Barn Feltimores Park Chalk Lane, Harlow, DL5 6DS, United Kingdom
Tel.: (44) 1279 424004
Window & Door Mfr
N.A.I.C.S.: 321911

Subsidiary (Domestic):

STORKE A/S (3)
Fabriksvej 4, PO Box 80, Farso, Denmark
Tel.: (45) 9863 2444
Web Site: http://www.storke.dk
Roof Window Distr
N.A.I.C.S.: 423310

Subsidiary (Non-US):

UAB INWIDO SUPPORT (3)
Zalgirio g 92, 09303, Vilnius, Lithuania
Tel.: (370) 5 2051212
Sales Range: $25-49.9 Million
Emp.: 14
Window & Door Mfr
N.A.I.C.S.: 321911
Julia Adomaviciene (Mng Dir)

Subsidiary (Non-US):

INWIDO FINLAND OY (2)
Kivaaritehtaankatu 8C, Jyvaskyla, 40100, Finland
Tel.: (358) 207665700
Web Site: https://www.inwido.com
Window & Door Mfr
N.A.I.C.S.: 321911

Subsidiary (Domestic):

ESKOPUU OY (3)
Teollisuustie 2, 69150, Eskola, Finland
Tel.: (358) 20 7769 200

Web Site: http://www.eskopuu.fi
Sales Range: $50-74.9 Million
Emp.: 140
Window & Door Mfr
N.A.I.C.S.: 321911

PIHLAVAN IKKUNAT OY (3)
Pihlatie 3, Ruovesi, 34600, Finland
Tel.: (358) 20 7665 700
Web Site: http://www.pihla.fi
Sales Range: $125-149.9 Million
Emp.: 350
Window & Door Distr
N.A.I.C.S.: 423310
Antti Vuonokari (CEO)

TIIVITUOTE OY (3)
Konikuja 7, 85800, Haapajarvi, Finland
Tel.: (358) 20 7690 111
Web Site: http://www.tiivi.fi
Sales Range: $50-74.9 Million
Emp.: 200
Window & Door Mfr
N.A.I.C.S.: 321911
Mika Kanervo (Product Mgr)

Subsidiary (Non-US):

INWIDO NORGE AS (2)
Holen 1, Oslo, 5200, Hordaland, Norway
Tel.: (47) 56303300
Sales Range: $50-74.9 Million
Emp.: 140
Window & Door Mfr
N.A.I.C.S.: 321911
Henry Krohnstad (Mng Dir)

Subsidiary (Domestic):

DIPLOMAT NORGE AS (3)
Ulsmagveien 7, 5224, Nesttun, Norway
Tel.: (47) 33 36 04 40
Web Site: http://www.inwido.com
Emp.: 45
Wood Door Distr
N.A.I.C.S.: 423310

DIPLOMAT PROSJEKT AS (3)
Skolmar 29, 3232, Sandefjord, Norway
Tel.: (47) 33 42 04 20
Wood Door Distr
N.A.I.C.S.: 423310

FREKHAUG VINDUET AS (3)
Frekhaug Window Mjatveitflaten 11, 5918, Frekhaug, Norway
Tel.: (47) 56303300
Web Site: http://www.frekhaug.com
Sales Range: $25-49.9 Million
Wood Window & Door Mfr
N.A.I.C.S.: 321911

LYSSAND TREINDUSTRI AS (3)
Holen 1, 5211, Oslo, Norway
Tel.: (47) 56 30 33 00
Web Site: http://www.lyssand.com
Sales Range: $50-74.9 Million
Emp.: 140
Window & Door Mfr
N.A.I.C.S.: 321911

Subsidiary (Non-US):

INWIDO POLAND SA (2)
ul Lotnikow Lewoniewskich 1, 16-100, Sokolka, Poland
Tel.: (48) 85 722 02 50
Web Site: http://www.inwido.pl
Wood Window & Door Distr
N.A.I.C.S.: 423310

Subsidiary (Domestic):

INWIDO SUPPLY AB (2)
Hjartlandavagen 24, Savsjo, 576 33, Sweden
Tel.: (46) 38267670
Web Site: http://www.alackering.se
Sales Range: $50-74.9 Million
Emp.: 150
Hardware Distr
N.A.I.C.S.: 423710
Stefan Persson (Gen Mgr)

Subsidiary (Domestic):

A-LACKERING AB (3)
Hjartlandavagen 24, 57633, Savsjo, Sweden
Tel.: (46) 38267670
Web Site: http://www.alackering.se

Aluminum Powder Coating Mfr
N.A.I.C.S.: 332812
Stefan Persson (Pres)

ABC SNICKERIER I HINDAS AB (3)
Lunkebacken 9B, 430 63, Hindas, Sweden
Tel.: (46) 301 210 25
Web Site: http://www.abc-snickerier.se
Fitting Product Mfr
N.A.I.C.S.: 332919

Subsidiary (Non-US):

ALAKIERNIA SP.ZO.O (3)
Ul b Krzywoustego 1, 84-300, Lebork, Poland
Tel.: (48) 59 86 37 300
Powder Coating Services
N.A.I.C.S.: 332812

Subsidiary (Domestic):

INWIDO PRODUKTION DORRAR AB (3)
Tallvagen 30 SE Bankeryd, Bankeryd, Jonkoping, 564 35, Sweden
Tel.: (46) 104514600
Wood Window & Door Mfr
N.A.I.C.S.: 321911

STEELFORM AB (3)
Varendsgatan 30, 363 45, Lammhult, Sweden
Tel.: (46) 472 269930
Web Site: http://www.steelform.se
Sales Range: $25-49.9 Million
Emp.: 20
Window Hardware Mfr
N.A.I.C.S.: 332510

Subsidiary (Domestic):

INWIDO SVERIGE AB (2)
Brogardsgatan 1, 574 38, Vetlanda, Sweden
Tel.: (46) 10 4514000
Wood Window & Door Distr
N.A.I.C.S.: 423310

Subsidiary (Domestic):

ERA-FONSTER AB (3)
Akraberg 14, Varobacka, 430 22, Sweden
Tel.: (46) 340 66 99 99
Web Site: http://www.erafonster.se
Wood Window Frame Mfr
N.A.I.C.S.: 321911

HANGERDORREN AB (3)
Furuvagen 1 Varnamo Co, Jonkoping, 331 94, Sweden
Tel.: (46) 370418 80
Web Site: http://www.snickarper.se
Wood Door Distr
N.A.I.C.S.: 423310
Tommy Scrom (Gen Mgr)

INWIDO PRODUKTION AB (3)
Hantverkargatan 19 Edsbyn, Edsbyn, 828 31, Sweden
Tel.: (46) 27129920
Wood Window & Door Mfr
N.A.I.C.S.: 321911

OUTLINE I SVERIGE AB (3)
Hjalmar Petris Vag 32, 352 64, Vaxjo, Sweden
Tel.: (46) 10 451 48 00
Web Site: http://www.outline.se
Wood Window & Door Distr
N.A.I.C.S.: 423310

Subsidiary (Non-US):

INWIDO UK LTD (2)
Ord Road, Berwick-upon-Tweed, TD15 2XU, Northumberland, United Kingdom
Tel.: (44) 1289 334 600
Web Site: http://www.inwido.co.uk
Emp.: 150
Window & Door Mfr
N.A.I.C.S.: 321911

Subsidiary (Domestic):

ALLAN BROTHERS LTD. (3)
Allan House Ord Road, Berwick-upon-Tweed, TD15 2XU, Northumberland, United Kingdom
Tel.: (44) 128 933 4600
Web Site: https://www.allanbrothers.co.uk

INTERNATIONAL PUBLIC

Sales Range: $50-74.9 Million
Window & Door Mfr
N.A.I.C.S.: 321911

Subsidiary (Domestic):

LUNDBERGS PRODUKTER AB (2)
Kryptongatan 1, 431 53, Molndal, Sweden
Tel.: (46) 101787700
Web Site: https://www.lundbergs.com
Sales Range: $25-49.9 Million
Emp.: 40
Interior Design Product Mfr
N.A.I.C.S.: 337212

NORSJOKOMPONENTER AB (2)
Bjurtrask, 935 93, Norsjo, Sweden
Tel.: (46) 918 313 00
Sales Range: $25-49.9 Million
Emp.: 80
Windows & Door Mfr
N.A.I.C.S.: 321911
Peter Persson (Mgr)

SNICKAR-PER AB (2)
Furuvagen, Varnamo, 331 94, Sweden
Tel.: (46) 370 418 80
Web Site: http://www.snickarper.se
Wood Window & Door Mfr
N.A.I.C.S.: 321911

KVD Kvarndammen AB (1)
Ellesbovagen 150, SE 442 90, Kungalv, Sweden   **(100%)**
Tel.: (46) 303373100
Web Site: http://www.kvd.se
Sales Range: $25-49.9 Million
Emp.: 17
Online Vehicle Brokerage Services
N.A.I.C.S.: 311211
Ulrika Drotz Molin (CEO)

Min Upplysning Sverige AB (1)
Sturegatan 3, Sundbyberg, Stockholm, 172 31, Sweden
Tel.: (46) 851901000
Web Site: http://www.minupplysning.se
Business Information Services
N.A.I.C.S.: 519290
Pal Ljungberger (Office Mgr)

One Software Holding AS (1)
Langkaia 1 B, 0150, Oslo, Norway
Tel.: (47) 22130000
Investment Management Service
N.A.I.C.S.: 523940

Ratos Fastighets AB (1)
Drottninggatan 2, 111 51, Stockholm, Sweden
Tel.: (46) 87001700
Web Site: http://www.ratos.se
Emp.: 50
Business Management Consulting Services
N.A.I.C.S.: 541611

SOKOLKA SA (1)
ul Lotnikow Lewoniewskich 1, 16-100, Sokolka, Poland
Tel.: (48) 857336440
Web Site: http://www.sokolka.com.pl
Wood Window & Door Distr
N.A.I.C.S.: 423310

Yritystele Oy (1)
Kumpulantie 3, Helsinki, 520, Finland
Tel.: (358) 9 3158 5138
Web Site: http://www.bisnode.fi
Emp.: 100
Business Information Services
N.A.I.C.S.: 519290
Juhasa Aeraksnen (Mgr)

RATTANINDIA GROUP

1 Indiabulls Center Tower 2A 11Th Fl Senapati Bapat Marg, Mumbai, 400013, India
Tel.: (91) 22 3001 7600
Web Site: http://www.rattanindia.com
Year Founded: 2014
Holding Company
N.A.I.C.S.: 551112
Rajiv Rattan (Founder & Chm)

Subsidiaries:

RattanIndia Enterprises Limited (1)
5th Floor Tower-B Worldmark-1, Aerocity, New Delhi, 110037, India   **(42.03%)**

Tel.: (91) 1146611666
Web Site: https://www.rattanindia.com
Rev.: $248,457
Assets: $92,504,658
Liabilities: $85,613
Net Worth: $92,419,045
Earnings: $1,119
Emp.: 4
Fiscal Year-end: 03/31/2021
Electric Power Generation & Distribution Services
N.A.I.C.S.: 221118
R. K. Agarwal *(Officer-Compliance & Sec)*

RattanIndia Power Limited (1)
A49 Ground Floor Road No 4, Mahipalpur, New Delhi, 110037, India **(57.49%)**
Tel.: (91) 1146611666
Web Site: https://www.rattanindia.com
Rev.: $359,562,335
Assets: $2,541,011,177
Liabilities: $2,626,864,668
Net Worth: ($85,853,490)
Earnings: ($128,564,272)
Emp.: 529
Fiscal Year-end: 03/31/2021
Power Production & Generation Services
N.A.I.C.S.: 221118
Himanshu Mathur *(Exec Dir)*

RATTI S.P.A.
Via Madonna 30, 22070, Guanzate, Italy
Tel.: (39) 03135351
Web Site: https://www.ratti.it
Year Founded: 1945
RAT—(ITA)
Rev.: $130,116,533
Earnings: $14,233,421
Emp.: 966
Fiscal Year-end: 12/31/19
Silk & Other Fabrics
N.A.I.C.S.: 313210

RAUBEX GROUP LIMITED
1 Highgrove Office Park 50 Tegel Avenue Highveld, Centurion, South Africa
Tel.: (27) 126489400 ZA
Web Site: https://www.raubex.com
RBX—(JSE)
Rev.: $808,388,291
Assets: $599,012,875
Liabilities: $292,562,131
Net Worth: $306,450,744
Earnings: $45,344,480
Emp.: 4,404
Fiscal Year-end: 02/28/23
Construction Work, Civil Engineering Services
N.A.I.C.S.: 541330
Louis Johannes Raubenheimer *(Mng Dir-Roads & Earthworks Div)*

Subsidiaries:

B&E International (Pty) Limited (1)
94 Maple Road, Pomona AH, Kempton Park, 1619, Gauteng, South Africa
Tel.: (27) 119664300
Web Site: https://www.beinternational.co.za
Sales Range: $125-149.9 Million
Mining Support Services
N.A.I.C.S.: 212114
Dewald Janse van Rensburg *(Mng Dir)*

Comar Plant Design & Manufacturing (Pty) Ltd. (1)
93 & 94 Maple Street, Pomona, Kempton Park, 1619, Gauteng, South Africa
Tel.: (27) 119664300
Web Site: https://www.comar.co.za
Bituminous Product Mfr & Distr
N.A.I.C.S.: 324121

Empa Structures (Pty) Ltd. (1)
20 Pastorale Street, Durbanville Industrial Park Fisantekraal Durbanville, Cape Town, 7550, South Africa
Tel.: (27) 219791129
Web Site: https://www.empa.co.za
Emp.: 500
Building Contractor Services
N.A.I.C.S.: 236220

Milling Techniks (Pty) Limited (1)
11 7th Ave Ashley, Pinetown, 3603, Gauteng, South Africa
Tel.: (27) 317929580
Web Site: http://www.raubex.com
Sales Range: $25-49.9 Million
Emp.: 8
Highway & Street Construction Services
N.A.I.C.S.: 237310
Wolf Roush *(Mng Dir)*

National Asphalt (Pty) Ltd. (1)
47 Graf Road Bon Accord, Pretoria, 0009, South Africa
Tel.: (27) 125629500
Web Site: https://www.nationalasphalt.co.za
Emp.: 300
Asphalt Mfr
N.A.I.C.S.: 324121
Neels Smith *(Reg Mgr)*

OMV Kimberley (Pty) Ltd. (1)
Kimberley- Hopetown Highway N12, Kimberley, Northern Cape, South Africa
Tel.: (27) 873105499
Construction Material Mfr & Distr
N.A.I.C.S.: 327320

Petra Quarry (Pty) Limited (1)
Eeufees Rd, Bloemfontein, 9302, Free State, South Africa
Tel.: (27) 514332965
Web Site: http://www.raubex.com
Sales Range: $50-74.9 Million
Emp.: 46
Stone Quarrying Services
N.A.I.C.S.: 212311
Hein Coetzee *(Area Mgr)*

Queenstown Quarry (Pty) Limited (1)
Doornhoek Farm, Lesseyton Dist, Queenstown, 5319, Eastern Cape, South Africa
Tel.: (27) 458570092
Stone Quarrying Services
N.A.I.C.S.: 212311

Raubex (Pty) Limited (1)
Kenneth Kaunda Rd Ext Noordstad Cleveley, Bloemfontein, 9301, Free State, South Africa
Tel.: (27) 514062000
Web Site: http://www.raubex.com
Sales Range: $25-49.9 Million
Road & Highway Construction Services
N.A.I.C.S.: 237310

Subsidiary (Domestic):

Bauba Resources Limited (2)
1 Wedgewood Link Bryanston, Johannesburg, 2191, South Africa **(61.68%)**
Tel.: (27) 116995720
Web Site: http://www.baubaresources.co.za
Rev.: $17,766,683
Assets: $31,420,188
Liabilities: $12,426,935
Net Worth: $18,993,253
Earnings: ($3,089,181)
Emp.: 470
Fiscal Year-end: 06/30/2020
Platinum Exploration & Mining Services
N.A.I.C.S.: 212290
Nick W. van der Hoven *(CEO)*

Subsidiary (Domestic):

Diamond Quartzite Processing (Pty) Ltd (3)
Number 3 Anerley Road, Johannesburg, 2193, Gauteng, South Africa
Tel.: (27) 115487240
Mineral Exploration Services
N.A.I.C.S.: 212390

Raubex Construction (Pty) Ltd. (1)
10 Tacoma Circuit, Canning Vale, 6155, WA, Australia
Tel.: (61) 863500600
Web Site: https://www.raubex.com.au
Building Contractor Services
N.A.I.C.S.: 236220
Hans Roux *(Mng Dir)*

Raubex Construction Zambia Ltd. (1)
Plot 7452 Lunzua Road Rhodes Park, Lusaka, 10101, Zambia
Tel.: (260) 211256803
Building Contractor Services

N.A.I.C.S.: 236220

Raubex Infra (Pty) Ltd. (1)
28 Tibbie Visser Street, Estoire, Bloemfontein, South Africa
Tel.: (27) 510111593
Web Site: https://raubexinfra.co.za
Building Contractor Services
N.A.I.C.S.: 236220

Raubex KZN (Pty) Ltd. (1)
12 Sterkspruit Road, Cliffdale, 3700, South Africa
Tel.: (27) 317006411
Building Contractor Services
N.A.I.C.S.: 236220

Raudev (Pty) Ltd. (1)
Block B The Stables Office Park 3 Ateljee St, Randpark Ridge, Randburg, 2169, South Africa
Tel.: (27) 117949390
Web Site: https://www.raudev.co.za
Property Development Services
N.A.I.C.S.: 531390

Raumix (Pty) Limited (1)
50 Tegel Avenue, Highveld, Centurion, 0157, Gauteng, South Africa
Tel.: (27) 126520107
Web Site: https://www.raumix.co.za
Sand & Gravel Crushing & Distr
N.A.I.C.S.: 212321

Raumix Aggregates (Pty) Ltd. (1)
50 Tegel Avenue, Centurion, Highveld, South Africa
Tel.: (27) 126520107
Web Site: https://raumix.co.za
Aggregate Mfr & Distr
N.A.I.C.S.: 333120

Roadmac (Pty) Limited (1)
Rudolph Greyling Ave No 1, Bloemfontein, 9301, Free State, South Africa
Tel.: (27) 514300404
Sales Range: $200-249.9 Million
Emp.: 750
Highway & Street Construction Services
N.A.I.C.S.: 237310

Roadmac Surfacing (Pty) Ltd. (1)
34 Empire Road Bartlett, Boksburg, 1459, South Africa
Tel.: (27) 119664000
Building Contractor Services
N.A.I.C.S.: 236220

Roadmac Surfacing Cape (Pty) Limited (1)
58 Range Rd, Blackheath, Cape Town, 7581, Western Cape, South Africa
Tel.: (27) 219050170
Sales Range: $25-49.9 Million
Emp.: 500
Highway & Street Construction Services
N.A.I.C.S.: 237310
Dieter Rencken *(Mng Dir)*

SPH Kundalila (Pty) Limited (1)
18 Marconi Road, Montague Gardens, Cape Town, 7441, Western Cape, South Africa
Tel.: (27) 215275200
Web Site: https://www.sphkundalila.co.za
Sales Range: $350-399.9 Million
Mining Support Services
N.A.I.C.S.: 541330

Shisalanga Construction (Pty) Ltd. (1)
Falcon View 7 Mountain Ridge Road, New Germany, 3610, KwaZulu-Natal, South Africa
Tel.: (27) 317362146
Web Site: https://www.shisalanga.com
Asphalt Mfr
N.A.I.C.S.: 324121

Space Construction (Pty) Limited (1)
Oaklands Farm, PO Box 8, Kwa-Mbonambi, Kwazulu-Natal, South Africa
Tel.: (27) 355801360
Web Site: http://www.spaceconstruction.co.za
Sales Range: $25-49.9 Million
Emp.: 5
Civil Engineering Services
N.A.I.C.S.: 541330

Tosas (Pty.) Ltd. (1)
12 Commercial Road, Wadeville, Germiston, 1422, Gauteng, South Africa **(70%)**
Tel.: (27) 113232000
Web Site: https://www.tosas.co.za
Transporters & Appliers of Bitumens, Tars, Bitumen Emulsions & Modified Bitumens Mfr
N.A.I.C.S.: 336212

Westforce Construction (Pty.) Ltd. (1)
73 - 75 Dowd Street, Welshpool, WA, Australia
Tel.: (61) 892791900
Web Site: https://www.westforce.com.au
Civil & Structural Construction Services
N.A.I.C.S.: 237990

RAUNAQ EPC INTERNATIONAL LIMITED
20 km Mathura Road, PO Box 353, Amar Nagar, Faridabad, 121003, India
Tel.: (91) 1294288888
Web Site: https://www.raunaqinternational.com
Year Founded: 1965
537840—(BOM)
Rev.: $933,949
Assets: $1,526,911
Liabilities: $619,735
Net Worth: $907,176
Earnings: ($285,355)
Emp.: 17
Fiscal Year-end: 03/31/23
Construction Engineering Services
N.A.I.C.S.: 541330
Surinder P. Kanwar *(Chm & Co-Mng Dir)*

Subsidiaries:

Xlerate Driveline India Limited (1)
Shed No 1 & 3, Gurukul Industrial Estate, Faridabad, 121 003, Haryana, India
Tel.: (91) 129 428 8670
Web Site: https://www.xleratedriveline.com
Motor Vehicle Parts Mfr
N.A.I.C.S.: 336350

RAUTE OYJ
Rautetie 2, PO Box 69, 15551, Nastola, Finland
Tel.: (358) 382911 FI
Web Site: https://www.raute.com
Year Founded: 1994
RAUTE—(HEL)
Rev.: $170,865,530
Assets: $99,344,917
Liabilities: $74,634,146
Net Worth: $24,710,771
Earnings: ($12,424,995)
Emp.: 778
Fiscal Year-end: 12/31/22
Wood Industry Machinery Distr
N.A.I.C.S.: 423830
Mika Mustakallio *(Vice Chm)*

Subsidiaries:

Metriguard, Inc. (1)
2465 NE Hopkins Ct, Pullman, WA 99163 **(100%)**
Tel.: (509) 332-7526
Web Site: http://www.metriguard.com
Instrument Mfr for Measuring & Testing Electricity & Electrical Signals
N.A.I.C.S.: 334515
Jim Logan *(Founder & Pres)*

RAV BARIACH 08 INDUSTRIES LTD.
Southern Industrial Zone, PO Box 3032, Ashkelon, 78780, Israel
Tel.: (972) 86794914
Web Site: https://www.rb-doors.com
Year Founded: 1973
BRIH—(TAE)
Rev.: $193,540,480
Assets: $302,111,599
Liabilities: $234,851,960

RAV BARIACH 08 INDUSTRIES LTD.

Rav Bariach 08 Industries Ltd.—(Continued)

Net Worth: $67,259,639
Earnings: $1,596,985
Emp.: 900
Fiscal Year-end: 09/30/23
Building Materials Mfr
N.A.I.C.S.: 327120
Sam Donnerstein (Chm)

RAVAD LTD.
Platinum Tower 21 Ha'Arbaa st, PO Box 20200, Tel Aviv, 64739, Israel
Tel.: (972) 36236161
Year Founded: 1951
RAVD—(TAE)
Rev.: $2,427,960
Assets: $137,355,157
Liabilities: $65,565,685
Net Worth: $71,789,473
Earnings: $3,963,255
Emp.: 6
Fiscal Year-end: 12/31/23
Miscellaneous Financial Investment Activities
N.A.I.C.S.: 523999
Arnon Shapir (Chm)

RAVAGO HOLDING S.A.
7678 Rue De Merl, Luxembourg, 2240, Luxembourg
Tel.: (352) 26480435   LU
Web Site: http://www.ravago.com
Year Founded: 1961
Emp.: 7,000
Plastic, Rubber & Elastomeric Raw Materials Mfr & Distr
N.A.I.C.S.: 326199

Subsidiaries:

Amco Plastic Materials, Inc. (1)
595 Broadhollow Rd, Farmingdale, NY 11735
Tel.: (631) 293-1600
Web Site: http://amco.ws
Sales Range: $1-9.9 Million
Emp.: 62
Plastics Material & Resin Mfr
N.A.I.C.S.: 325211
Amy S. Metzger (Treas)

Channel Prime Alliance Inc. (1)
1803 Hull Ave, Des Moines, IA 50313
Tel.: (515) 264-4110
Web Site: http://www.channelpa.com
Sales Range: $75-99.9 Million
Emp.: 35
Plastic & Rubber Resin Distr
N.A.I.C.S.: 424610
Joe Muhs (Gen Mgr)

Entec Polymers, LLC (1)
1900 Summit Tower Blvd Ste 900, Orlando, FL 32810
Tel.: (407) 875-9595
Web Site: http://www.entecpolymers.com
Sales Range: $450-499.9 Million
Emp.: 115
Plastic Product Distr
N.A.I.C.S.: 424610
Rodney Garrett (Mgr-Fin)

Industrial Resin Recycling, Inc. (1)
1480 Grand Oaks Dr, Howell, MI 48843
Tel.: (517) 548-4140
Web Site: http://www.industrialresin.com
Sales Range: $1-9.9 Million
Emp.: 20
Plastic Recycling & Plastic Products Supplier
N.A.I.C.S.: 326199
Ricky Cottrill (VP-Sls)

Muehlstein Holding Corporation (1)
800 Connecticut Ave, Norwalk, CT 06854-1631
Tel.: (203) 855-6000
Web Site: http://www.muehlstein.com
Sales Range: $1-4.9 Billion
Emp.: 500
Plastics Product Mfr
N.A.I.C.S.: 424610

Subsidiary (Domestic):

H. Muehlstein and Co. Inc. (2)
800 Connecticut Ave, Norwalk, CT 06854-1631
Tel.: (203) 855-6000
Web Site: http://www.muehlstein.com
Sales Range: $800-899.9 Million
Emp.: 110
Plastic Materials Mfr
N.A.I.C.S.: 424610

Muehlstein International Ltd. (2)
800 Connecticut Ave, Norwalk, CT 06854-1631
Tel.: (203) 855-6000
Web Site: http://www.muehlstein.com
Sales Range: $50-74.9 Million
Emp.: 100
Plastic Materials Mfr
N.A.I.C.S.: 424610

Subsidiary (Non-US):

Pegasus Polymers Marketing GmbH (2)
Winterhuder Weg 27, 22085, Hamburg, Germany
Tel.: (49) 402270290
Chemicals Mfr
N.A.I.C.S.: 325998

Ravago Americas LLC (1)
1900 Summit Tower Blvd Ste 900, Orlando, FL 32810
Tel.: (931) 728-7009
Web Site: http://www.ravagomfg.com
Plastic Resins Compounder & Mfr
N.A.I.C.S.: 325991
Joe Hills (Mgr-Sys)

Division (Domestic):

Bolcof-Port Polymers (2)
930 W 10th St, Azusa, CA 91702
Thermoplastic Resins Distr
N.A.I.C.S.: 424610

TMC Materials Inc. (1)
195 Main St, Shrewsbury, MA 01545
Tel.: (508) 770-0076
Web Site: http://www.tmcmaterials.com
Specialty Chemicals Distr
N.A.I.C.S.: 424690
Kevin A. Mulkern (Reg VP)

RAVAL ACS LTD.
11 Dr Felix Zandman, Beersheba, 8488999, Israel
Tel.: (972) 89521000
Web Site: https://www.raval.co.il
Year Founded: 2000
RVL—(TAE)
Rev.: $264,210,015
Assets: $276,615,584
Liabilities: $165,520,181
Net Worth: $111,095,403
Earnings: $2,625,728
Emp.: 1,000
Fiscal Year-end: 12/31/22
Automobile Parts Mfr
N.A.I.C.S.: 336390

Subsidiaries:

Arkal Automotive Ltd. (1)
Kidmat Galil Industrial Park, PO Box 63, Lower Galilee, 1522800, Tiberias, Israel
Tel.: (972) 46640545
Automotive Thermoplastic Parts Mfr
N.A.I.C.S.: 325211

Plant (US):

Arkal Automotive Ltd. - Auburn Plant (2)
2490 Innovation Dr, Auburn, AL 36832
Tel.: (334) 321-4461
Automotive Thermoplastic Parts Mfr
N.A.I.C.S.: 325211

Plant (Non-US):

Arkal Automotive Ltd. - Auengrund Plant (2)
Standort Crock Klaus-Aepfelbach-Str 3, Auengrund, 98673, Hildburghausen, Germany

Tel.: (49) 368636311
Automotive Thermoplastic Parts Mfr
N.A.I.C.S.: 325211
Joerg Hochscheid (Mgr-Plant)

Arkal Automotive Ltd. - Dongguan Plant (2)
Dongye Rd Houjie Science and Technology Industrial Park, Houjie Town, Dongguan, China
Tel.: (86) 2259009978
Automotive Thermoplastic Parts Mfr
N.A.I.C.S.: 325211

Arkal Automotive Ltd. - Leon Plant (2)
Prolongacion de Independencia 2002 Fracciones de Hacienda la Pompa, 37499, Leon, Guanajuato, Mexico
Tel.: (52) 3423423423
Automotive Thermoplastic Parts Mfr
N.A.I.C.S.: 325211

Arkal Automotive Ltd. - London Plant (2)
1550 Global Drive, London, N6N 1R3, ON, Canada
Tel.: (519) 644-2700
Automotive Thermoplastic Parts Mfr
N.A.I.C.S.: 325211
Rick Morris (Mgr-Plant)

Arkal Automotive Ltd. - Orkoien Plant (2)
Poligono Ipertegui I n 13-15, Navarre, 31160, Orkoien, Spain
Tel.: (34) 948321013
Automotive Thermoplastic Parts Mfr
N.A.I.C.S.: 325211
Alberto Gonzalez (Mgr-Plant)

Raval Automotive Shanghai Ltd. (1)
No 7 Building No 255 North He Rd, Jiading District, Shanghai, 201800, China
Tel.: (86) 2133517988
Automotive Thermoplastic Parts Mfr
N.A.I.C.S.: 325211

Raval Europe S.A. (1)
18 rue Heierchen Zone d'Activites Economiques Robert Steichen, L-4940, Bascharage, Luxembourg
Tel.: (352) 2655511
Automotive Thermoplastic Parts Mfr
N.A.I.C.S.: 325211

Raval USA Inc. (1)
1939 Northfield Dr, Rochester Hills, MI 48309
Tel.: (248) 260-4050
Automotive Thermoplastic Parts Mfr
N.A.I.C.S.: 325211

RAVALGAON SUGAR FARM LTD
52 5th Floor Maker Tower F Cuffe Parade, Mumbai, 400 005, India
Tel.: (91) 2222184291
Web Site: https://www.trsfl.in
Year Founded: 1933
507300—(BOM)
Rev.: $1,181,020
Assets: $2,529,501
Liabilities: $2,213,069
Net Worth: $316,432
Earnings: ($275,631)
Emp.: 112
Fiscal Year-end: 03/31/23
Food processing
N.A.I.C.S.: 236210
Harshavardhan B. Doshi (Chm & Mng Dir)

RAVEN GOLD CORP.
595 Howe Street Suite 902 Box 12, Vancouver, V2A 5C7, BC, Canada
Tel.: (604) 484-3701
Mineral Exploration Services
N.A.I.C.S.: 213114
Mike Wood (Pres & CEO)

RAVEN PROPERTY GROUP LIMITED
Second Floor La Vieille Cour La

INTERNATIONAL PUBLIC

Plaiderie, Saint Peter Port, GY1 6EH, Guernsey
Tel.: (44) 1481712955
Web Site: http://www.theravenproperty.com
RAV—(AIM)
Rev.: $208,822,767
Assets: $1,668,800,806
Liabilities: $1,351,515,220
Net Worth: $317,285,587
Earnings: ($19,221,242)
Emp.: 183
Fiscal Year-end: 12/31/20
Real Estate Investment Services
N.A.I.C.S.: 531390
Colin Andrew Smith (COO)

Subsidiaries:

Raven Mount Group Plc (1)
21 Knightsbridge, SW1X 7LY, London, United Kingdom - England
Tel.: (44) 2072350422
Sales Range: $125-149.9 Million
Emp.: 145
Holding Company; Real Estate Investment Services
N.A.I.C.S.: 551112

RAVEN ROCK STRATEGIC INCOME FUND
36 Toronto Street Suite 750, Toronto, M5C 2C5, ON, Canada
Tel.: (416) 323-0477   ON
Web Site: http://www.arrow-capital.com
Year Founded: 2012
Sales Range: Less than $1 Million
Investment Services
N.A.I.C.S.: 523999
James L. McGovern (Founder, CEO & Mng Dir)

RAVENQUEST BIOMED INC.
837 Hastings St Suite 400, Vancouver, V6C 3N6, BC, Canada
Tel.: (604) 638-3886   BC
Web Site: http://www.rqbglobal.com
Year Founded: 1987
RVVQF—(OTCEM)
Sales Range: Less than $1 Million
Emp.: 12
Cannabis Production Management Services, Consulting & Development
N.A.I.C.S.: 523999
Marla K. Ritchie (Sec)

RAVENSBURGER AG
Robert-Bosch-Str 1, 88214, Ravensburg, Germany
Tel.: (49) 751 86 0
Web Site: http://www.ravensburger.de
Year Founded: 1883
Children's Games Mfr
N.A.I.C.S.: 339930
Clemens Maier (CEO)

Subsidiaries:

ThinkFun, Inc. (1)
1321 Cameron St, Alexandria, VA 22314
Tel.: (703) 549-4999
Web Site: http://www.thinkfun.com
Toys & Games Mfr & Distr
N.A.I.C.S.: 423920
Andrea Barthello (Co-Founder & COO)

RAVENSCROFT LIMITED
20 New Street, PO Box 222, Saint Peter Port, GY1 4JG, Guernsey
Tel.: (44) 1481 729 100   GY
Web Site: http://www.ravenscroftgroup.com
Year Founded: 2005
Rev.: $28,545,336
Assets: $49,819,187
Liabilities: $28,441,276
Net Worth: $21,377,911
Earnings: $2,855,295

Emp.: 95
Fiscal Year-end: 12/31/18
Investment Management Service
N.A.I.C.S.: 523999
Jon R. Ravenscroft *(Founder & CEO-Grp)*

Subsidiaries:

Ravenscroft Jersey Limited (1)
13 Broad Street, PO Box 419, Saint Helier, JE4 5QH, Jersey
Tel.: (44) 153 472 2051
Web Site: http://www.ravenscroft.je
Emp.: 7
Financial Management Services
N.A.I.C.S.: 523999
Haydn Taylor *(CEO)*

Royal London Asset Management Limited (1)
55 Gracechurch Street, London, EC3V 0UF, United Kingdom
Tel.: (44) 8450502020
Web Site: http://www.rlam.co.uk
Fund Management
N.A.I.C.S.: 523999
Hans Georgeson *(CEO)*

RAVENSDOWN LIMITED
292 Main South Road Hornby, Christchurch, 8042, New Zealand
Tel.: (64) 800100123   NZ
Web Site:
    http://www.ravensdown.co.nz
Year Founded: 1977
Rev.: $481,428,880
Assets: $429,372,938
Liabilities: $124,466,040
Net Worth: $304,906,898
Earnings: $4,933,566
Fiscal Year-end: 05/31/18
Fertilizer Mfr & Distr
N.A.I.C.S.: 325311
John Francis Clifford Henderson *(Chm)*

Subsidiaries:

Analytical Research Laboratories Limited (1)
890 Waitangi Rd, PO Box 989, Napier, 4130, New Zealand   (100%)
Tel.: (64) 68359222
Web Site: http://www.arllad.co.nz
Sales Range: $25-49.9 Million
Emp.: 35
Testing Laboratories
N.A.I.C.S.: 541380
William Bodeker *(Gen Mgr)*

Ravensdown Aero Work (1)
292 Main South Road, Hornby, Christchurch, 8042, New Zealand   (100%)
Tel.: (64) 800 100 123
Web Site: http://www.ravensdown.co.nz
Sales Range: $25-49.9 Million
Emp.: 50
Farmer Owned Co-operative Land & Aerial Fertilizer Spraying & Animal Husbandry
N.A.I.C.S.: 325312

Ravensdown Growing Media Limited (1)
Level 1, 32 Oxford Terrace, Christchurch, New Zealand   (100%)
Tel.: (64) 33534625
Media Representatives
N.A.I.C.S.: 541840

RAVIKUMAR DISTILLERIES LTD
C-9 C-10 Industrial Estate 2nd Main Road, Thattanchavady, Pondicherry, 605 009, India
Tel.: (91) 4132244007
Web Site:
    https://www.ravikumardistillery.com
Year Founded: 1993
RKDL—(NSE)
Rev.: $25,227,684
Assets: $19,875,205
Liabilities: $10,840,066
Net Worth: $9,035,140
Earnings: $69,629
Emp.: 78
Fiscal Year-end: 03/31/20
Whisky, Brandy, Vodka & Rum Distiller & Marketer
N.A.I.C.S.: 312140
Ramalingam V. Ravikumar *(Chm & Mng Dir)*

RAVILEELA GRANITES LIMITED
H No 6-3-668/10/35 Durganagar Colony Punjagutta, Hyderabad, 500 082, India
Tel.: (91) 4023413733
Web Site:
    https://www.ravileelagranites.com
Year Founded: 1990
526095—(BOM)
Rev.: $3,733,649
Assets: $8,328,829
Liabilities: $6,414,903
Net Worth: $1,913,926
Earnings: ($197,374)
Emp.: 62
Fiscal Year-end: 03/31/23
Building Material Mfr & Distr
N.A.I.C.S.: 327991
P. Srinivas Reddy *(Mng Dir)*

RAVINDER HEIGHTS LTD.
7th Floor Dcm Building 16 Barakhamba Road, New Delhi, 110001, India
Tel.: (91) 1143639000
Web Site:
    https://www.ravinderheights.com
Year Founded: 2019
RVHL—(BOM)
Rev.: $479,320
Assets: $43,415,217
Liabilities: $6,806,982
Net Worth: $36,608,235
Earnings: ($645,741)
Fiscal Year-end: 03/31/21
Construction Services
N.A.I.C.S.: 236220
Sunanda Jain *(Mng Dir)*

RAVINDRA ENERGY LIMITED
BC 105 Havelock Road Camp, Belgaum, 590001, India
Tel.: (91) 8312406600
Web Site:
    https://www.ravindraenergy.com
Year Founded: 1980
504341—(BOM)
Rev.: $44,155,703
Assets: $54,667,295
Liabilities: $32,174,006
Net Worth: $22,493,289
Earnings: $952,497
Emp.: 150
Fiscal Year-end: 03/31/21
Electric Power Distribution Services
N.A.I.C.S.: 221122
Vidya Madhusudan Murkumbi *(Chm)*

RAVNAJA U RESTRUKTURIRANJU A.D.
Kralja Petra I broj 1, Mali Zvornik, Serbia
Tel.: (381) 15 471 133
Year Founded: 1957
RVNJ—(BEL)
Sales Range: $1-9.9 Million
Emp.: 122
Plaster Product Mfr
N.A.I.C.S.: 327420
Spasenovic Nebojsa *(Exec Dir)*

RAVNICA A.D.
Zubaciste 72/a, Bajmok, Serbia
Tel.: (381) 24 762 002
Web Site: http://www.ravnica.co.rs
Year Founded: 2000
Sales Range: $10-24.9 Million
Cereals, Legumes & Oilseeds Farming
N.A.I.C.S.: 111191

RAVNISTE A.D.
Balkanska 3, Krusevac, Serbia
Tel.: (381) 37 427 848
Web Site: http://www.ravniste.com
Year Founded: 1989
RVNS—(BEL)
Sales Range: Less than $1 Million
Building Construction Services
N.A.I.C.S.: 236220
Vladimir Ajduk *(Exec Dir)*

RAW EDGE INDUSTRIAL SOLUTIONS LIMITED
B1401 B Wing Boomerang, Chandivali Farm Road Andheri East, Mumbai, 400072, Maharashtra, India
Tel.: (91) 9724306856
Web Site: https://www.rawedge.in
Year Founded: 2005
541634—(BOM)
Rev.: $6,335,507
Assets: $6,596,751
Liabilities: $3,903,051
Net Worth: $2,693,699
Earnings: $2,710
Emp.: 57
Fiscal Year-end: 03/31/23
Lime Product Mfr & Distr
N.A.I.C.S.: 327410
Bimal Bansal *(Mng Dir)*

RAWLINSON RENAULT
Moreton Hall, Bury Saint Edmunds, IP32 7DF, Suffolk, United Kingdom
Tel.: (44) 1284752999
Web Site:
    http://www.rawlinsongroup.co.uk
Rev.: $29,539,381
Emp.: 50
New & Used Car Dealers
N.A.I.C.S.: 441110
Chris Cooke *(Mgr-Svc & Customer Svcs)*

RAWLPLUG S.A.
ul Kwidzynska 6, 51-416, Wroclaw, Poland
Tel.: (48) 713260100
Web Site: https://www.rawlplug.com
Year Founded: 1999
RWL—(WAR)
Rev.: $296,209,095
Assets: $358,677,591
Liabilities: $179,267,022
Net Worth: $179,410,569
Earnings: $11,202,744
Emp.: 1,500
Fiscal Year-end: 12/31/23
Fastening Systems, Hardware, Wholesale Trade & Plastics Products Mfr
N.A.I.C.S.: 339993
Krystyna Koelner *(Co-Founder & Chm-Supervisory Bd)*

Subsidiaries:

Rawlplug Ltd. (1)
Skibo Dr Thornliebank Ind Est, Glasgow, G46 8JR, United Kingdom
Tel.: (44) 1416387961
Web Site: https://www.rawlplug.co.uk
Sales Range: $50-74.9 Million
Emp.: 150
Building Fixings & Tools Mfr; Cement & Paints Mfr
N.A.I.C.S.: 332216

Subsidiary (Non-US):

Rawlplug Ireland Ltd. (2)
34 Lavery Avenue, Park West, Dublin, 12, Ireland
Tel.: (353) 16251950
Web Site: http://www.rawlplug.ie
Sales Range: $25-49.9 Million
Emp.: 20
Building Fixings & Tools Mfr; Cement & Paints Mfr
N.A.I.C.S.: 332216
Paul Sweny *(Mgr-Accts)*

RAY CORPORATION
Harks Roppongi Bldg 6-15-21 Roppongi Minato-ku, Tokyo, 106-0032, Japan
Tel.: (81) 354103861
Web Site: http://www.ray.co.jp
Year Founded: 1980
4317—(TKS)
Rev.: $79,563,980
Assets: $66,638,910
Liabilities: $20,192,320
Net Worth: $46,446,590
Earnings: $5,799,620
Emp.: 407
Fiscal Year-end: 02/29/24
Business Communications Services
N.A.I.C.S.: 561499
Shiro Wakebe *(Pres)*

Subsidiaries:

McRAY Corporation (1)
6-15-21 Roppongi Harks Roppongi Building, Minato-ku, Tokyo, 106-0032, Japan
Tel.: (81) 354106162
Web Site: http://www.ray.co.jp
Commercial Film Production Services
N.A.I.C.S.: 512110

RAY TLV GROUP LTD
94 Yigal Alon Tower 2 Floor 19 Suite 69, Tel Aviv, 6789156, Israel
Tel.: (972) 35609030
Web Site: https://en.ray-tlv.com
INTL—(TAE)
Rev.: $825,335
Assets: $892,305
Liabilities: $1,357,031
Net Worth: ($464,725)
Earnings: ($8,221,355)
Fiscal Year-end: 12/31/22
Pharmaceuticals Product Mfr
N.A.I.C.S.: 325412
Ori Weiss *(CEO)*

RAYA HOLDING COMPANY
26th July St Touristic Zone 6th of October, Cairo, 12568, Egypt
Tel.: (20) 238276000
Web Site: http://www.rayacorp.com
Sales Range: $900-999.9 Million
Emp.: 2,500
Holding Company Focusing on Technology
N.A.I.C.S.: 551112
Medhat Khail *(Chm & CEO)*

Subsidiaries:

Bridge Technologies (1)
7 Abd El Hady Salah Abd Allah St, Giza, Egypt
Tel.: (20) 27620037
Web Site:
    http://www.bridgetechnologies.com
Sales Range: $25-49.9 Million
Emp.: 8
Provider of Technology Services
N.A.I.C.S.: 541512

Oratech Company (1)
14 Wady El Nil St, Mohandeseen, Giza, 12411, Egypt   (100%)
Tel.: (20) 23056051
Web Site: http://www.oratech-eg.com
Sales Range: $25-49.9 Million
Emp.: 71
Provider of IT Consulting Services
N.A.I.C.S.: 541512

Ostool for Land Transport Company (1)
Raya Holding Building Behind Dar El Fouad Hospital, 6th of October City, Egypt   (62.3%)
Tel.: (20) 238276070

RAYA HOLDING COMPANY

Raya Holding Company—(Continued)
Web Site: https://ostool-eg.com
Glass Mfr
N.A.I.C.S.: 327215

Raya Academy (1)
Arkadia Mall 6th Fl, Corniche El Nil, 11221, Cairo, Egypt
Tel.: (20) 25742700
Web Site: http://www.rayaacademy.com
Sales Range: $25-49.9 Million
Emp.: 15
IT Educational Services
N.A.I.C.S.: 923110

Raya Contact Center (1)
Raya Corporation Building 26th of July Road Touristic Zone, 12568, Cairo, Egypt (100%)
Tel.: (20) 2 38276000
Web Site: http://www.rayacc.com
Sales Range: $1-9.9 Million
Emp.: 500
Outsourcing Contact Services
N.A.I.C.S.: 541512
Ahmed Imam (CEO)

Raya Gulf FZ-LLC (1)
Bldg 14, PO Box 500324, Dubai, United Arab Emirates
Tel.: (971) 43901150
Web Site: http://www.rayacorp.com
Sales Range: $700-749.9 Million
Emp.: 3,500
Technology Services
N.A.I.C.S.: 541512

Raya Integration (1)
26 July St Touristic Zone, 6th of October, Giza, 12568, Egypt
Tel.: (20) 38276000
Web Site: http://www.rayaintegration.com
IT & Telecommunication Systems Integration Services
N.A.I.C.S.: 541512

Raya Networks Services (1)
26th July St Touristic Zone, 6th October, Cairo, 12568, Egypt
Tel.: (20) 238276000
Web Site: http://www.rayacorp.com
Sales Range: $25-49.9 Million
Emp.: 60
Network & Infrastructure Solutions
N.A.I.C.S.: 541512
Wael Ghanayem (Mng Dir)

Raya Saudi Ltd. (1)
PO Box 62956, Riyadh, 11595, Saudi Arabia
Tel.: (966) 96612886500
Web Site: http://www.rayacorp.com
Provider of Technology Services
N.A.I.C.S.: 541512

Raya for Data Centres Company (1)
26th July St, Touristic Zone 6th of October, Giza, Egypt
Tel.: (20) 238276001
Web Site: https://www.rayadatacenter.com
Information Technology Services
N.A.I.C.S.: 541511

Raya for Information Technology & Management Company (1)
26th July St Touristic zone, 6th of October City, 12568, Egypt
Tel.: (20) 238276000
Web Site: https://raya-it.net
Information Technology Consulting Services
N.A.I.C.S.: 518210
Hisham Abdel Rassoul (CEO)

RAYBURNS MARINE WORLD LTD
2330 Enterprise Way, Kelowna, BC, Canada
Tel.: (250) 860-4232
Web Site: http://www.rayburns.com
Year Founded: 1985
Rev.: $15,925,417
Emp.: 35
Boat Dealers
N.A.I.C.S.: 441222
Adam McNichol (Mgr-Svc)

RAYCAP CORPORATION
Telou & Petroutsou 14, Marousi, 151 24, Athens, Greece
Tel.: (30) 210 61 52000 GR
Web Site: http://www.raycap.com
Year Founded: 1987
Sales Range: $50-74.9 Million
Emp.: 200
Telecommunications & Energy Network Technologies, Electrical Surge Protection & Other Electronic Equipment Designer, Mfr, Distr & Support Services
N.A.I.C.S.: 335999
Kostas Samaras (CEO)

Subsidiaries:

Raycap, Inc. (1)
806 S Clearwater Loop Ste C, Post Falls, ID 83854 (100%)
Tel.: (208) 777-1166
Web Site: http://www.raycapinc.com
Sales Range: $25-49.9 Million
Emp.: 80
Electrical Surge Protection Equipment Designer, Mfr & Distr
N.A.I.C.S.: 335999
Kostas Samaras (Pres)

RAYENCE CO., LTD.
14 Samseong 1-ro 1-gil, Hwaseong, 18449, Gyeonggi-do, Korea (South)
Tel.: (82) 3180156245
Web Site: https://www.rayence.com
Year Founded: 2011
228850—(KRS)
Rev.: $112,872,306
Assets: $200,953,209
Liabilities: $27,995,914
Net Worth: $172,957,295
Earnings: $16,911,503
Emp.: 230
Fiscal Year-end: 12/31/22
X-ray Product Mfr & Distr
N.A.I.C.S.: 334516

Subsidiaries:

OSKO Inc. (1)
8085 NW 90th St, Miami, FL 33166
Tel.: (305) 599-7161
Web Site: http://www.oskomedical.com
X-Ray Detector Mfr & Distr
N.A.I.C.S.: 334517

Rayence Inc. (1)
81 Ruckman Rd, Closter, NJ 07624
Tel.: (201) 585-0290
Web Site: http://www.rayence.us
X-Ray Detector Mfr & Distr
N.A.I.C.S.: 334517

RAYGEN CO., LTD.
18-24 Gongdan-ro 5-gil Waegwan-eup, Chilgok-gun, Waegwan, Korea (South)
Tel.: (82) 549795000
Web Site: http://www.raygen.co.kr
Year Founded: 1994
Rev.: $75,460,869
Assets: $62,805,753
Liabilities: $41,736,282
Net Worth: $21,069,471
Earnings: ($26,027,794)
Emp.: 162
Fiscal Year-end: 12/31/17
Backlight Unit Mfr
N.A.I.C.S.: 334419
Jun-Ki Jung (Pres & CEO)

RAYHOO MOTOR DIES CO., LTD.
22 Yinhu Road North, Pilot Free trade Zone, Wuhu, 241006, Anhui, China
Tel.: (86) 5535623215
Web Site: https://www.rayhoo.net
Year Founded: 2002
002997—(SSE)
Rev.: $160,060,019
Assets: $443,618,023
Liabilities: $256,775,364
Net Worth: $186,842,659
Earnings: $17,654,388
Emp.: 1,400
Fiscal Year-end: 12/31/21
Automotive Stamping Mfr & Distr
N.A.I.C.S.: 336370
Zhen Chai (Chm & Gen Mgr)

RAYMED LABS LIMITED
C-273 Sector-63, Noida, 201301, Uttar Pradesh, India
Tel.: (91) 1202426900
Web Site: https://www.raymedlabs.com
Year Founded: 1994
Rev.: $1,807
Assets: $37,999
Liabilities: $314,529
Net Worth: ($276,529)
Earnings: ($7,677)
Fiscal Year-end: 03/31/19
Pharmaceutical Preparation Mfr
N.A.I.C.S.: 325412
Ajai Goyal (Exec Dir)

RAYMOND INDUSTRIAL LIMITED
1801-1813 18/F Grandtech Centre, 8 On Ping Street, Hong Kong, NT, China (Hong Kong)
Tel.: (852) 27903680 HK
Web Site: https://www.raymondfinance.com
Year Founded: 1964
0229—(HKG)
Rev.: $135,539,895
Assets: $108,902,850
Liabilities: $26,554,935
Net Worth: $82,347,915
Earnings: $3,889,260
Emp.: 2,265
Fiscal Year-end: 12/31/22
Household Electrical Appliance Mfr
N.A.I.C.S.: 335210
Wilson Kin Lae Wong (Chm & Exec Dir)

Subsidiaries:

Raymond (Panyu Nansha) Electrical Appliances Development Company Limited
Industrial Road 2 Nansha Economic Technical Development Zone, Nansha, Panyu, 511458, GuangDong, China
Tel.: (86) 2084981668
Household Electrical Appliance Mfr
N.A.I.C.S.: 335210

RAYMOND LIMITED
New Hind House Narottam Morarjee Marg, Ballard Estate, Mumbai, 400001, India
Tel.: (91) 2352232514
Web Site: https://www.raymond.in
RAYMOND—(NSE)
Rev.: $999,577,867
Assets: $982,451,831
Liabilities: $624,681,985
Net Worth: $357,769,846
Earnings: $64,380,205
Emp.: 6,682
Fiscal Year-end: 03/31/23
Fabrics Mfr
N.A.I.C.S.: 313210
Gautam Hari Singhania (Chm & Mng Dir)

Subsidiaries:

Axis Trustee Services Limited (1)
The Ruby 2nd Floor SW 29 Senapati Bapat Marg, Dadar West, Mumbai, 400 028, India
Tel.: (91) 2262300451
Web Site: https://www.axistrustee.in
Emp.: 100
Financial Services
N.A.I.C.S.: 541611

JK Files & Engineering Limited (1)

INTERNATIONAL PUBLIC

New Hind House Narottam Morarjee Marg, Ballard Estate, Mumbai, 400001, India
Tel.: (91) 2261527000
Web Site: https://jkfilesandengineering.com
Industrial Equipment Mfr
N.A.I.C.S.: 334419

R&A Logistics Inc. (1)
7 Abd Almonem Fawzi st New Nozha, Cairo, Egypt
Tel.: (20) 26236693
Web Site: http://www.randalogistic.com
Freight Transport Services
N.A.I.C.S.: 488510

Ring Plus Aqua Limited (1)
2nd Floor J K Files I Ltd Annex Building Jekegram Pokhran Road No 1, Thane, 400606, Maharashtra, India
Tel.: (91) 2261527998
Web Site: https://www.ringplusaqua.com
Auto Component Mfr
N.A.I.C.S.: 336390
Balasubramanian V. (CEO)

Subsidiary (Domestic):

Maini Precision Products Ltd (2)
B-165, Peenya Industrial Estate, 1st Stage, 3rd Cross, Bangalore, Karnataka, 560058, India (59.25%)
Tel.: (91) 8040704000
Web Site: https://www.mainiprecisionproducts.com
Fabricated Metal Mfr
N.A.I.C.S.: 332999

RAYMOND MOTORS (1989) CO. LTD.
124 Broadway North, Raymond, T0K 2S0, AB, Canada
Tel.: (403) 752-3324
Web Site: http://www.raymondmotors.com
Sales Range: $10-24.9 Million
New & Used Car Dealers
N.A.I.C.S.: 441110
Terrence E. Meeks (Principal)

RAYMOND WEIL S.A.
36-38 Ave Eugène Lance, Geneva, 1212, Switzerland
Tel.: (41) 228840055
Web Site: http://www.raymond-weil.com
Year Founded: 1976
Sales Range: $100-124.9 Million
Emp.: 80
Watch Mfr, Importer & Sales
N.A.I.C.S.: 423940
Olivier Bernheim (Pres & CEO)

Subsidiaries:

RW USA Corp. (1)
635 Madison Ave, New York, NY 10022
Tel.: (212) 355-3450
Web Site: http://www.raymond-weil.us
Emp.: 50
Watch Distr
N.A.I.C.S.: 423940
Caroline Leclercq (CFO & VP)

Raymond Weil Deutschland GmbH (1)
Max-Keith-Str 46, 45136, Essen, Germany
Tel.: (49) 201811970
Watch Retailer
N.A.I.C.S.: 458310

RAYMOR INDUSTRIES INC.
3765 La Verendrye, Boisbriand, J7H 1R8, QC, Canada
Tel.: (450) 434-1004 QC
Web Site: http://www.raymor.com
Sales Range: $1-9.9 Million
Emp.: 6
Technologies Developer & Advanced Materials & Nanomaterials Mfr
N.A.I.C.S.: 332812
Roland Veilleux (Chm)

RAYNIER MARCHETTI S.A.

89 Boulevard Malesherbes, 75008, Paris, France
Tel.: (33) 140080818   FR
Web Site: http://www.rayniermarchetti.fr
Rev.: $20,000,000
Emp.: 102
Restaurant
N.A.I.C.S.: 722511
Severine Darck (Dir-Pur)

RAYONG WIRE INDUSTRIES PUBLIC COMPANY LIMITED
Mabtapud Industrial Estate No 5 I-5 Road Tambon Maptapud, Amphur-Muang, Rayong, 21150, Rayong, Thailand
Tel.: (66) 38684522   TH
Web Site: http://www.rwi.co.th
Year Founded: 1994
RWI—(THA)
Rev.: $21,529,595
Assets: $35,523,845
Liabilities: $6,303,102
Net Worth: $29,220,743
Earnings: ($3,248,284)
Emp.: 98
Fiscal Year-end: 12/31/23
Steel Pole Mfr
N.A.I.C.S.: 331222
Udom Tungdetterachai (Exec Dir)

Subsidiaries:

Rayong Wire Industries Public Company Limited - Muang Factory   (1)
No 5 I-5 Rd, Amphur Muang, 21150, Rayong, Thailand
Tel.: (66) 386845227
Steel Pole Mfr
N.A.I.C.S.: 331222

RAYONT INC.
Level 3 26 Marine Parade, 4215, Southport, Queensland, Australia
Tel.: (61) 432051512   NV
Web Site: http://www.rayont.com
Year Founded: 2011
RAYT—(OTCEM)
Rev.: $2,839,000
Assets: $14,193,000
Liabilities: $9,100,000
Net Worth: $5,093,000
Earnings: $244,000
Fiscal Year-end: 06/30/22
Vegetable Seed Distr
N.A.I.C.S.: 424910
Dhurata Toli (Sec)

RAYS CO., LTD.
2-4-7 Nagatanishi, Higashiosaka, 577-0016, Osaka, Japan
Tel.: (81) 6 6787 1110
Year Founded: 1973
Sales Range: $75-99.9 Million
Emp.: 310
Wheel Mfr
N.A.I.C.S.: 336340
Masumi Shiba (CEO)

Subsidiaries:

RAYBROS Darkside Subaru Sport Service   (1)
1-8-8 Kusune, Higashiosaka, Osaka, Japan
Tel.: (81) 667446922
Web Site: http://www.rayswheels.co.jp
Business Services
N.A.I.C.S.: 561499

RAYBROS S.T.W   (1)
1-8-8 Kusune, Higashiosaka, Osaka, Japan
Tel.: (81) 667473451
Store Retailers
N.A.I.C.S.: 459999

RAYS Creative Co., Ltd.   (1)
2-4-1 Tamagawa Denenchofu, Setagaya-ku, Tokyo, Japan
Tel.: (81) 354831103
Web Site: http://www.rayswheels.co.jp

Sales Range: $75-99.9 Million
Advertising Services
N.A.I.C.S.: 541890

RAYS Engineering Co., Ltd.   (1)
7-11-12 Nagayoshi Deto, Hirano-ku, Osaka, Japan
Tel.: (81) 729941341
Web Site: http://www.rayswheels.co.jp
Metal Stamping
N.A.I.C.S.: 332119

RAYS R & D Co., Ltd.   (1)
7-11-12 Nagayoshi Deto, Hirano-ku, Osaka, Japan
Tel.: (81) 729941341
Sales Range: $25-49.9 Million
Emp.: 3
Metal Stamping
N.A.I.C.S.: 332119

RAYS Takamatsu Co., Ltd.   (1)
2043-21 Tsuruichi-cho, Kagawa, Takamatsu, Japan
Tel.: (81) 878811732
Web Site: http://www.rays-msc.com
Business Services
N.A.I.C.S.: 561499

RAYSEARCH LABORATORIES AB
Sveavagen 44, PO Box 3297, SE-103 65, Stockholm, Sweden
Tel.: (46) 851053000
Web Site: https://www.raysearchlabs.com
Year Founded: 2000
RAY.B—(OMX)
Rev.: $79,548,793
Assets: $156,861,080
Liabilities: $72,094,710
Net Worth: $84,766,370
Earnings: ($1,108,486)
Emp.: 394
Fiscal Year-end: 12/31/20
Application Software Development Services
N.A.I.C.S.: 513210
Bjorn Hardemark (Deputy CEO)

Subsidiaries:

RaySearch (Shanghai) Medical Device Co., Ltd.   (1)
1118 South Pudong Road Room 608, Pudong New District, Shanghai, 200120, China
Tel.: (86) 13701115932
Medical Laboratory Research & Development Services
N.A.I.C.S.: 541714
Fei Deng (Bus Dir)

RaySearch Australia Pyd. Ltd.   (1)
C Lumina Chartered Accountants 420 George street, Sydney, 2000, NSW, Australia
Tel.: (61) 411534316
Medical Technology Services
N.A.I.C.S.: 621999

RaySearch Belgium Sprl   (1)
Interleuvenlaan 62, 3001, Heverlee, Belgium
Tel.: (32) 475368007
Medical Laboratory Research & Development Services
N.A.I.C.S.: 541714

RaySearch France SAS   (1)
59 rue des Petits Champs, 75001, Paris, France
Tel.: (33) 176537202
Medical Laboratory Research & Development Services
N.A.I.C.S.: 541714
Henri Pierre-Justin (Reg Dir-Bus)

RaySearch Germany GmbH   (1)
Friedrichstr 154, 10117, Berlin, Germany
Tel.: (49) 1727660837
Medical Laboratory Research & Development Services
N.A.I.C.S.: 541714
Markus Wenke (Reg Dir-Bus)

RaySearch Japan K.K.   (1)

Saiwai Building 9F 1-3-1 Uchisaiwai-cho, Chiyoda-ku, Tokyo, 100-0011, Japan
Tel.: (81) 344056902
Medical Laboratory Research & Development Services
N.A.I.C.S.: 541714
Takeshi Kosuga (Reg Dir-Bus)

RaySearch Korea LLC   (1)
1005 10F Hybro Building 503 Teheran-ro, PO Box 04537, Gangnam-gu, Seoul, Korea (South)
Tel.: (82) 194926432
Medical Laboratory Research & Development Services
N.A.I.C.S.: 541714
Young Jun Kim (Reg Dir-Bus)

RaySearch Singapore Pte. Ltd.   (1)
260 Orchard Road 07-01/04 The Heeren, Singapore, 238855, Singapore
Tel.: (65) 81816082
Medical Laboratory Research & Development Services
N.A.I.C.S.: 541714

RAYSUT CEMENT COMPANY SAOG
Raysut Industrial Area, PO Box 1020, 211, Salalah, Oman
Tel.: (968) 23220600
Web Site: https://raysutcement.com
Year Founded: 1981
RCCI—(MUS)
Rev.: $242,524,513
Assets: $596,303,100
Liabilities: $300,282,485
Net Worth: $296,020,615
Earnings: ($35,202,556)
Emp.: 242
Fiscal Year-end: 12/31/21
Cement Mfr
N.A.I.C.S.: 327310
Mohammed Ahmed Omar Aideed (Gen Mgr-Acting)

Subsidiaries:

Pioneer Cement Industries LLC   (1)
Al Ghayl Industrial Area, PO Box 4423, Al Ghayl, Ras al Khaimah, United Arab Emirates
Tel.: (971) 72584333
Web Site: https://www.pioneercements.ae
Sales Range: $125-149.9 Million
Cement Mfr
N.A.I.C.S.: 327310
Ashley Bryan (Gen Mgr)

RAYTELLIGENCE AB
Birger Jarlsgatan 57 B 3 tr, SE-11356, Stockholm, Sweden
Tel.: (46) 855116090
Web Site: https://www.raytelligence.com
Year Founded: 2015
RTG—(DEU)
Biotechnology Research & Development Services
N.A.I.C.S.: 541714
Sven Otto Littorin (Chm)

RAZAK LABORATORY CO.
Km 10 Karaj Makhsous Road, PO Box 13185-1671, Tehran, Iran
Tel.: (98) 25552009821
Web Site: https://www.razakpharma.com
Year Founded: 1964
DRZK1—(THE)
Sales Range: Less than $1 Million
Pharmaceuticals Product Mfr
N.A.I.C.S.: 325412
Ali Mortazavi (Deputy Chm & CEO)

RAZI PHARMACEUTICAL GLASS
No 5 Parvin St Fatemi-e-Gharbi Ave, PO Box 14155-3911, 14186, Tehran, Iran
Tel.: (98) 21 66941199

Web Site: http://www.raziglass.com
Year Founded: 1984
TSRZ—(THE)
Sales Range: Less than $1 Million
Emp.: 450
Pharmaceutical Glass Mfr
N.A.I.C.S.: 325412
Babak Abdollahi (CMO-Sls Dept)

RAZI PHARMACUTICAL GLASS
No 5 Parvin St Fatemi-e-Gharbi Ave, PO Box 14155-3911, 14186-35843, Tehran, Iran
Tel.: (98) 2166941199
Web Site: https://www.raziglass.com
Year Founded: 1993
TSRZ1—(THE)
Sales Range: Less than $1 Million
Pharma Glass Product Mfr
N.A.I.C.S.: 327215

RAZIOL ZIBULLA & SOHN GMBH
Hagener Strasse 144 152, 58642, Iserlohn, Germany
Tel.: (49) 237450000
Web Site: http://www.raziol.com
Year Founded: 1941
Rev.: $18,759,840
Emp.: 80
Oil Additives Mfr
N.A.I.C.S.: 424690
Georg Gisbert Zibulla (Mng Dir)

RAZOR ENERGY CORP.
800-500 5th Ave SW, Calgary, T2P 3L5, AB, Canada
Tel.: (403) 262-0242   ON
Web Site: https://www.razor-energy.com
Year Founded: 2010
RZE.H—(TSXV)
Rev.: $111,569,856
Assets: $147,880,553
Liabilities: $186,623,503
Net Worth: ($38,742,950)
Earnings: ($16,661,892)
Fiscal Year-end: 12/31/22
Investment Services
N.A.I.C.S.: 523999

RAZOR LABS LTD.
150 Begin Rd, Tel Aviv, 6492105, Israel
Tel.: (972) 35610901
Web Site: https://www.razor-labs.com
Year Founded: 2016
RZR—(TAE)
Rev.: $1,433,762
Assets: $22,455,941
Liabilities: $15,517,868
Net Worth: $6,938,073
Earnings: $4,990,239)
Fiscal Year-end: 09/30/23
Software Development Services
N.A.I.C.S.: 541511
Raz Roditti (Co-Founder & CEO)

RAZOR RESOURCES INC.
8-5-128 Jichexiaoqu, Changchun, Jilin, China
Tel.: (86) 9494196588   NV
Year Founded: 2001
Metal Exploration & Mining Services
N.A.I.C.S.: 212290
Jerome Talbot (Pres & CEO)

RAZVITAK A.D.
Karadjordjeva 37, Lazarevac, Serbia
Tel.: (381) 11 8123 329
Year Founded: 2003
Sales Range: Less than $1 Million
Restaurant Management Services
N.A.I.C.S.: 722511

RAZVOJNA BANKA VOJVODINE A.D. NOVI SAD

Razvitak a.d.—(Continued)

RAZVOJNA BANKA VOJVO-DINE A.D. NOVI SAD
New Strazilovska 4, 21000, Novi Sad, Serbia
Tel.: (381) 21 4894 551
Web Site: http://www.rbv.rs
Banking Services
N.A.I.C.S.: 522110
Ljiljana Sredojev Radomirovic *(Chm)*

RB CAPITAL COMPANHIA DE SECURITIZACAO S.A.
Av Brigadeiro Faria Lima 4440 11 Andar, Itaim Bibi, 04538-132, Sao Paulo, Brazil
Tel.: (55) 1131272870
Web Site: http://www.rbsec.com
Emp.: 100
Real Estate Manangement Services
N.A.I.C.S.: 531210
Flavia Palacios Mendonca Bailune *(CEO & Dir-IR)*

RB CAPITAL SECURITIZA-DORA S.A.
Rua Amauri 255 5 Andar Jardim Europa, Sao Paulo, 01448-000, Brazil
Tel.: (55) 1131272761
Emp.: 100
Real Estate Manangement Services
N.A.I.C.S.: 531210
Flavia Palacios Mendonca Bailune *(Dir-IR)*

RB GLOBAL, INC.
9500 Glenlyon Pkwy, Burnaby, V5J 0C6, BC, Canada
Tel.: (778) 331-5500
Web Site: http://www.rbauction.com
Year Founded: 1958
RBA—(NYSE)
Rev: $3,679,600,000
Assets: $12,037,400,000
Liabilities: $7,018,400,000
Net Worth: $5,019,000,000
Earnings: $174,900,000
Emp.: 7,900
Fiscal Year-end: 12/31/23
Industrial Equipment Auctioneer
N.A.I.C.S.: 425120
Eric D. Jacobs *(CFO)*

Subsidiaries:

AssetNation, Inc. (1)
1001 McKinney St Ste 1700, Houston, TX 77002 (100%)
Tel.: (713) 286-4600
Web Retailing Services
N.A.I.C.S.: 236210

IAA, Inc. (1)
2 Westbrook Corporate Ctr Ste 500, Westchester, IL 60154
Tel.: (708) 492-7000
Web Site: https://www.iaai.com
Rev: $2,098,900,000
Assets: $3,362,900,000
Liabilities: $2,795,600,000
Net Worth: $567,300,000
Earnings: $292,400,000
Emp.: 4,914
Fiscal Year-end: 01/01/2023
Holding Company; Automotive Salvage & Online Marketplace Operator
N.A.I.C.S.: 551112
Tim O'Day *(Pres-Ops-US)*

Subsidiary (Domestic):

Automotive Recovery Services, Inc. (2)
13085 Hamilton Crossing Blvd, Carmel, IN 46032
Tel.: (317) 815-1100
Automobile Auction Whslr
N.A.I.C.S.: 425120

Subsidiary (Non-US):

IAA UK Holdings Limited (2)
Haven Road, Canvey, SS8 0NR, Essex, United Kingdom
Tel.: (44) 1268694590
Web Site: http://www.hbc.co.uk
Holding Company
N.A.I.C.S.: 551112

Subsidiary (Domestic):

1st Interactive Design Limited (3)
HBC House Charfleets Road, Canvey, SS8 0PQ, Essex, United Kingdom
Tel.: (44) 8712884665
Web Site: http://www.1stinteractive.co.uk
Software Development Services
N.A.I.C.S.: 541511

IAA Vehicle Services Limited (3)
HBC House Charfleets Road, Canvey, SS8 0PQ, Essex, United Kingdom
Tel.: (44) 1268696444
Web Site: http://www.hbc.co.uk
Used Car Whslr
N.A.I.C.S.: 441120

Subsidiary (Non-US):

Impact Auto Auctions Ltd. (2)
1717 Burton Road Vars, Ottawa, K0A 3H0, ON, Canada
Tel.: (613) 443-3171
Web Site: http://www.impactauto.ca
Emp.: 20
Automobile Auction Whslr
N.A.I.C.S.: 425120
Carrie Allinott *(Branch Mgr)*

Subsidiary (Domestic):

Impact Auto Auctions Sudbury Ltd. (3)
90 National Street, Garson, P3L 1M5, ON, Canada
Tel.: (705) 560-2723
Web Site: http://www.impactauto.ca
Used Car Whslr
N.A.I.C.S.: 441120
Carmen Duhaime *(Branch Mgr)*

Sudbury Auto Auction Ltd. (3)
90 National St, Garson, Sudbury, P3L 1M5, ON, Canada
Tel.: (705) 560-7210
Web Site: http://www.sudburyautoauction.com
Automobile Auction Services
N.A.I.C.S.: 423110

Subsidiary (Domestic):

Insurance Auto Auctions, Inc. (2)
2 Westbrook Corporate Ctr 10th Fl, Westchester, IL 60154
Tel.: (708) 492-7000
Web Site: http://www.iaai.com
Salvage Vehicle Auction Services
N.A.I.C.S.: 441120

Subsidiary (Domestic):

Decision Dynamics, LLC (3)
1 Wellness Way, 29063, Irmo, SC
Tel.: (803) 808-0117
Web Site: http://www.dditechnology.com
Custom Computer Programing
N.A.I.C.S.: 513210

Division (Domestic):

Insurance Auto Auctions Specialty Salvage Division (3)
2040 E Algonquin Rd Ste 501, Schaumburg, IL 60173-4187
Tel.: (708) 492-7000
Web Site: http://www.iaai.com
N.A.I.C.S.: 425120

Subsidiary (Domestic):

Marisat Inc. (2)
580 Jernee Mill Rd, Sayreville, NJ 08872
Tel.: (732) 238-4006
Web Site: http://www.autoexchangenj.com
Sales Range: $1-9.9 Million
Emp.: 11
Recyclable Material Merchant Whslr
N.A.I.C.S.: 423930
Donald Carroll *(Pres)*

IronPlanet Limited (1)
Unit A Aerodrome Business Park, Rathcoole, Dublin, Ireland
Tel.: (353) 18605000
Web Site: https://www.eu.ironplanet.com
Construction & Mining Equipment Distr
N.A.I.C.S.: 423810

IronPlanet, Inc. (1)
Tel.: (925) 225-8600
Web Site: http://www.ironplanet.com
Online Heavy Construction Equipment Distr
N.A.I.C.S.: 423810

Subsidiary (Domestic):

Asset Appraisal Services, Inc. (2)
10216 F St, Omaha, NE 68124
Tel.: (402) 390-0505
Web Site: http://www.assetappraisalservices.com
Inspection, Appraisal & Online Auction Services
N.A.I.C.S.: 541990

Kramer Auctions Ltd. (1)
PO Box 1807, North Battleford, S9A 3W8, SK, Canada
Tel.: (306) 445-5000
Web Site: http://www.kramerauction.com
Sales Range: $1-9.9 Million
Emp.: 50
Auction Services
N.A.I.C.S.: 561990
Neil Kramer *(Pres & Gen Mgr)*

Leake Auction Co. (1)
7895 E. Acoma Dr Ste 103, Scottsdale, AZ 85260
Tel.: (602) 442-3380
Web Site: http://www.leakecar.com
Wholesale Trade Agents & Brokers
N.A.I.C.S.: 425120
Gary Bennett *(Gen Mgr)*

Mascus Benelux (1)
Vijzelstraat 68-78, 1017 HL, Amsterdam, Netherlands
Tel.: (31) 207073682
Web Site: http://www.mascus.nl
Construction & Mining Equipment Distr
N.A.I.C.S.: 423810
Heidi van der Heijden *(Sls Mgr)*

Mascus USA Inc. (1)
410 S Ware Blvd, Tampa, FL 33619
Tel.: (813) 635-1300
Web Site: http://www.mascus.com
Construction & Mining Equipment Distr
N.A.I.C.S.: 423810
Kyle Plate *(Acct Mgr)*

Ritchie Bros. Auctioneers (America) Inc. (1)
8801 US-6, Lincoln, NE 68507
Tel.: (531) 248-5091
Auctioneers of Heavy Construction & Industrial Equipment
N.A.I.C.S.: 423810
David Scheer *(Mgr-Admin)*

Subsidiary (Domestic):

Rouse Asset Services, Inc. (2)
361 S Robertson Blvd, Beverly Hills, CA 90211
Tel.: (310) 360-9200
Web Site: http://www.rouseservices.com
Sales Range: $1-9.9 Million
Emp.: 60
Business Support Services
N.A.I.C.S.: 561499
Gary McArdle *(COO & Exec VP)*

Ritchie Bros. Auctioneers (Canada) Ltd. (1)
1500 Sparrow Dr, Nisku, T9E 8H6, AB, Canada
Tel.: (780) 955-2486
Business Support Services
N.A.I.C.S.: 561990

Ritchie Bros. Auctioneers (Japan) K.K. (1)
245-2771 Taragai, Chiba Prefecture, Narita, 287-0242, Japan
Tel.: (81) 476490811
Web Site: https://www.rbauction.com
Auction Services
N.A.I.C.S.: 561990
Satoshi Hara *(Mgr-Reg Sls)*

INTERNATIONAL PUBLIC

Ritchie Bros. Auctioneers (Panama) S.A. (1)
Via Interamericana after Tatare River Bridge, Pacora, Panama, Panama
Tel.: (507) 2038938
Web Site: https://www.rbauction.com
Auction Services
N.A.I.C.S.: 561990

Ritchie Bros. Auctioneers (Poland) Sp.z.o.o. (1)
Kryspinow 399, 31-545, Krakow, Poland
Tel.: (48) 660797300
Auction Services
N.A.I.C.S.: 561990

Ritchie Bros. Auctioneers (Spain) S.L.U. (1)
Autovia A4 Km 64 2 Salida 62, Ocana, 45300, Toledo, Spain
Tel.: (34) 925157580
Web Site: http://www.rbauction.com
Auction Services
N.A.I.C.S.: 561990

Ritchie Bros. Auctioneers (UK) Limited (1)
Castle Donington, Derby, DE74 2RP, Derbyshire, United Kingdom
Tel.: (44) 1332819700
Web Site: https://www.rbauction.com
Auction Services
N.A.I.C.S.: 561990

Ritchie Bros. Auctioneers France SAS (1)
Zac Les Champs Chouette 2, sur Gaillon, Saint Aubin, France
Tel.: (33) 232778610
Web Site: https://www.rbauction.fr
Auction Services
N.A.I.C.S.: 561990

Ritchie Bros. Auctioneers GmbH (1)
Berliner Str 2, 49716, Meppen, Germany
Tel.: (49) 593570550
Auction Services
N.A.I.C.S.: 561990

Ritchie Bros. Auctioneers S.r.l. (1)
Via Canada snc, Caorso, 29012, Piacenza, Italy
Tel.: (39) 0523818801
Web Site: https://www.rbauction.it
Auction Services
N.A.I.C.S.: 561990

Ritchie Bros. B.V. (1)
Mark S Clarkelaan 21 Haven M 530 Port of Moerdijk, 4761 RK, Zevenbergen, Netherlands
Tel.: (31) 168392200
Web Site: https://www.rbauction.com
Building Construction Equipment Distr
N.A.I.C.S.: 423830

Ritchie Bros. Deutschland GmbH (1)
Berliner Str 2, 49716, Meppen, Germany
Tel.: (49) 593570550
Web Site: https://www.rbauction.com
Building Construction Equipment Distr
N.A.I.C.S.: 423830

Ritchie Bros. Holdings B.V. (1)
Bijster 3, 4817 HX, Breda, Netherlands
Tel.: (31) 765242600
Holding Company
N.A.I.C.S.: 551112

Ritchie Bros. Holdings Pty Ltd. (1)
1-57 Burnside Road, Yatala, 4207, QLD, Australia
Tel.: (61) 733824444
Web Site: https://www.rbauction.com
Holding Company
N.A.I.C.S.: 551112

Ritchie Bros. Italia S.r.l. (1)
Via Canada snc, Caorso, 29012, Piacenza, Italy
Tel.: (39) 0523818801
Web Site: https://www.rbauction.it
Building Construction Equipment Distr
N.A.I.C.S.: 423830
Nicola Nicelli *(VP-Sls)*

Ritchie Bros. Properties Ltd. (1)
Glenlyon Pky 9500, Burnaby, V5J 0C6, BC, Canada
Tel.: (604) 273-7564
Real Estate Property Management Services

N.A.I.C.S.: 531312

Xcira, LLC (1)
410 S Ware Blvd Ste 900, Tampa, FL 33619
Tel.: (813) 621-7881
Web Site: http://www.xcira.com
Auction Services
N.A.I.C.S.: 561990

RBA HOLDING EDITORIAL S.A.
Perez Galdos 36, Barcelona, 8018, Spain
Tel.: (34) 932170088
Web Site: http://www.rba.es
Sales Range: $550-599.9 Million
Emp.: 1,000
Book & Magazine Publisher
N.A.I.C.S.: 513120
Ricardo Rodrigo (Chm)

Subsidiaries:

RBA FRANCE (1)
NCI Saint-Honore Cambon, Rue Cambon 20, 75001, Paris, France
Tel.: (33) 1 44 50 78 41
Book Publishers
N.A.I.C.S.: 513130

RBA Italia srl (1)
Centro Direzionale Regus Via Roberto Lepetit 8-10, 20124, Milan, Milano, Italy
Tel.: (39) 02 0069 6352
Web Site: http://www.rbaitalia.it
Book Publishers
N.A.I.C.S.: 513130
Stefano Bisatti (Gen Mgr)

RBA Libros, S.A. (1)
Av Diagonal 189, 08018, Barcelona, Spain
Tel.: (34) 932170088
Web Site: http://www.rbalibros.com
Book Publishers
N.A.I.C.S.: 513130
Enrique Iglesias Montejo (Gen Mgr)

RBA MADRID (1)
C/ Lopez de Hoyos 141, 28002, Madrid, Spain
Tel.: (34) 91 510 66 00
Book Publishers
N.A.I.C.S.: 513130
Ignacio Rodriguez-Borlado (Mgr-Comml)

RBA PORTUGAL (1)
R Filipe Floque 40, 1069-124, Lisbon, Portugal
Tel.: (351) 213 164200
Book Publishers
N.A.I.C.S.: 513130
Neus Font Manent (Gen Mgr)

RBA Poland sp. z oo (1)
Ul Moniuszki 1A, 00-014, Warsaw, Poland
Tel.: (48) 22 449 01 82
Book Publishers
N.A.I.C.S.: 513130
Katarzyna Sobanska - Helman (Gen Mgr)

RBA Publicacoes (1)
Fl 4 Rua Filipe Folque 40-44, 1069-124, Lisbon, Portugal
Tel.: (351) 213164200
Sales Range: $25-49.9 Million
Emp.: 40
Magazine Publisher
N.A.I.C.S.: 513110
Teresa Magalhaes (Gen Mgr)

RBC PJSC
78/1 Profsoyuznaya street, Moscow, 117393, Russia
Tel.: (7) 4953631111
Web Site: https://rbc.group
Year Founded: 1993
RBCM—(MOEX)
Sales Range: Less than $1 Million
Holding Company
N.A.I.C.S.: 551114
Nikolay Molibog (CEO)

RBG HOLDINGS PLC
165 Fleet Street, London, EC4A 2DY, United Kingdom
Tel.: (44) 2079550880
Web Site: https://www.rosenblatt-law.co.uk
Year Founded: 1989
RBGP—(AIM)
Rev.: $49,917,075
Assets: $101,692,832
Liabilities: $65,766,796
Net Worth: $35,926,035
Earnings: ($14,054,693)
Fiscal Year-end: 12/31/23
All Other Legal Services
N.A.I.C.S.: 541199
Ian Rosenblatt (Founder)

Subsidiaries:

Convex Capital Limited (1)
Bass Warehouse 4 Castle Street, Manchester, M3 4LZ, United Kingdom
Tel.: (44) 161 819 2500
Web Site: https://www.convexcap.com
Financial Investment Services
N.A.I.C.S.: 523999
Mike Driver (CEO)

LionFish Litigation Finance Limited (1)
9-13 St Andrew Street, London, EC4A 3AF, United Kingdom
Tel.: (44) 2081489575
Web Site: https://www.lflf.co.uk
Litigation Financial Services
N.A.I.C.S.: 921130

Memery Crystal LLP (1)
44 Southampton Buildings, London, WC2A 1AP, United Kingdom
Tel.: (44) 20 7242 5905
Web Site: http://www.memerycrystal.com
Emp.: 32
Law firm
N.A.I.C.S.: 541110
Lindsey Alexander (Partner)

Rosenblatt Limited (1)
9-13 St Andrew Street, London, EC4A 3AF, United Kingdom
Tel.: (44) 2079550880
Financial Investment Services
N.A.I.C.S.: 523999
Barry Roche (Mng Dir)

RBR GROUP LIMITED
Level 5/191 St Georges Terrace, Perth, 6000, WA, Australia
Tel.: (61) 892999690
Web Site: https://www.rbrgroup.com.au
Year Founded: 2007
RBR—(ASX)
Rev.: $5,083,156
Assets: $2,846,004
Liabilities: $1,757,698
Net Worth: $1,088,306
Earnings: ($585,544)
Fiscal Year-end: 06/30/24
Gold, Copper, Zinc & Other Base Metals Mining & Exploration Services
N.A.I.C.S.: 212220
Ian Keith Macpherson (Chm)

RBW INC.
3F Deokyong B/D Nonhyeon-ro28-gil40, Gwangjin-gu, Seoul, Korea (South)
Tel.: (82) 25175748
Web Site: https://www.rbbridge.com
Year Founded: 2010
361570—(KRS)
Rev.: $48,387,307
Assets: $111,083,083
Liabilities: $43,021,554
Net Worth: $68,061,529
Earnings: $300,493
Emp.: 90
Fiscal Year-end: 12/31/22
Music & Video Production Services
N.A.I.C.S.: 512110
Jin Kang (CEO)

RBZ JEWELLERS LIMITED
Block D Mondeal Retail Park Near Rajpath Club SG Highway, Ahmedabad, 380054, Gujarat, India
Tel.: (91) 7969135740
Web Site: https://www.rbzjewellers.com
Year Founded: 2008
544060—(BOM)
Rev.: $35,102,695
Assets: $25,068,996
Liabilities: $13,861,911
Net Worth: $11,207,085
Earnings: $2,706,772
Emp.: 189
Fiscal Year-end: 03/31/23
Gold Product Mfr & Distr
N.A.I.C.S.: 339910

RC365 HOLDING PLC
Cannon Place 78 Cannon Street, London, EC4N 6AF, United Kingdom
Tel.: (44) 2081235806
Web Site: https://www.rc365plc.com
Year Founded: 2013
RCGH—(LSE)
Rev.: $2,815,399
Assets: $11,076,701
Liabilities: $7,040,656
Net Worth: $4,036,045
Earnings: ($4,713,336)
Emp.: 25
Fiscal Year-end: 03/31/24
Offices of Other Holding Companies
N.A.I.C.S.: 551112
Alan King Lun Leung (VP)

Subsidiaries:

RCPay Ltd. (1)
Unit I 17/F MG Tower 133 Hoi Bun Road, Kwun Tong, Kowloon, China (Hong Kong)
Tel.: (852) 31755407
Web Site: https://www.rcpay365.com
Financial Transaction Services
N.A.I.C.S.: 522320

Regal Crown Technology Limited (1)
Level 19 Two International Finance Centre 8 Finance Street, Central, China (Hong Kong)
Tel.: (852) 31571393
Web Site: https://rctech365.com
Software Development Services
N.A.I.C.S.: 541511

RCAPITAL PARTNERS LLP
5th Floor 24 Old Bond Street Mayfair, London, W1S 4AW, United Kingdom
Tel.: (44) 2074997820
Web Site: http://www.rcapital.co.uk
Year Founded: 2004
Sales Range: Less than $1 Million
Privater Equity Firm
N.A.I.C.S.: 523999
Jamie Constable (CEO)

Subsidiaries:

JFN Holdings Limited (1)
Fisher House, PO Box 4, Barrow-in-Furness, LA14 1HR, United Kingdom
Tel.: (44) 1229615400
Emp.: 240
Investment Management Service
N.A.I.C.S.: 523999

JFN Limited (1)
Ennerdale Mill Business Pk, Egremont, CA22 2PN, Cumbria, United Kingdom
Tel.: (44) 1946823502
Sales Range: $10-24.9 Million
Emp.: 50
Other Marine Fishing
N.A.I.C.S.: 114119

Subsidiary (Domestic):

JF Faber Limited (2)
Golden Hill Centre School Lane, Leyland, Preston, PR25 2TU, Lancashire, United Kingdom
Tel.: (44) 1772 622200
Web Site: http://www.jfuclear.co.uk
Electrical Engineering Services

N.A.I.C.S.: 541330
Steve Ellison (Gen Mgr)

Levolux Limited (1)
White House Works Bold Road, Saint Helens, WA9 4JG, Merseyside, United Kingdom
Tel.: (44) 208 863 9111
Web Site: https://www.levolux.com
Sales Range: $25-49.9 Million
Emp.: 60
Curtain & Drapery Mills
N.A.I.C.S.: 314120

Subsidiary (Domestic):

Levolux A.T. Limited (2)
24 Eastville Close Eastern Avenue, Gloucester, GL4 3SJ, United Kingdom
Tel.: (44) 1452500007
Web Site: http://www.levolux.com
Sales Range: $25-49.9 Million
Emp.: 60
Knit Fabric & Lace Mills
N.A.I.C.S.: 313240

Splash News & Picture Agency, LLC (1)
3705 W Pico Blvd Suite 2544, Los Angeles, CA 90019
Tel.: (310) 525-5808
Web Site: http://www.splashnews.com
Celebrity News Syndicate
N.A.I.C.S.: 516210

Temple Lifts Limited (1)
Regency House 33-49 Farwig Lane, Bromley, BR1 3RE, United Kingdom
Tel.: (44) 2084601332
Web Site: http://www.templelifts.com
Construction & Engineering Services
N.A.I.C.S.: 541330
Nigel Kirkham (Mng Dir)

RCB BANK LTD.
2 Amathuntos Street, PO Box 56868, CY-3310, Limassol, Cyprus
Tel.: (357) 25355722
Web Site: http://www.rcbcy.com
Year Founded: 1995
Commercial Banking Services
N.A.I.C.S.: 522110
Sotirios Zackheos (Exec Dir)

RCC CEMENTS LIMITED
702 Arunachal Building19 Barakhamba Road Connaught Place, New Delhi, 110 001, India
Tel.: (91) 1143571042
Web Site: https://www.rcccements.com
Year Founded: 1991
Assets: $1,128,370
Liabilities: $506,722
Net Worth: $621,648
Earnings: ($58,727)
Emp.: 3
Fiscal Year-end: 03/31/18
Cement Mfr
N.A.I.C.S.: 327310
Sunil Kumar (Chm & Mng Dir)

RCE CAPITAL BERHAD
802 8th Floor Block C Kelana Square 17 Jalan SS7/26, 47301, Petaling Jaya, Malaysia
Tel.: (60) 378031126
Web Site: https://www.rce.com.my
Year Founded: 1953
RCECAP—(KLS)
Rev.: $74,429,171
Assets: $623,667,937
Liabilities: $453,158,059
Net Worth: $170,509,878
Earnings: $29,372,381
Emp.: 201
Fiscal Year-end: 03/31/23
Loan Financing Services
N.A.I.C.S.: 522291
Fei San Seow (Co-Sec)

RCF GROUP SPA

RCF GROUP SPA

RCF Group SpA—(Continued)

Via Raffaello 13, Reggio Emilia,
42100, RE, Italy
Tel.: (39) 0522 27 44 11   IT
Web Site: http://www.rcf-group.it
Year Founded: 1949
Emp.: 330
Audio Equipment Mfr & Whslr
N.A.I.C.S.: 334310
Arturo Vicari *(Vice Chm & CEO)*

Subsidiaries:

DPA Microphones A/S   (1)
Gydevang 42-44, 3450, Allerod, Denmark
Tel.: (45) 48142828
Web Site: http://www.dpamicrophones.com
Emp.: 40
Microphone Mfr
N.A.I.C.S.: 334310
Anne Berggrein *(Mgr-Mktg)*

Subsidiary (Non-US):

DPA Microphones Ltd.   (2)
Unit 801-2 8/F Asia Orient Tower 33 Lockhart Road, Wanchai, China (Hong Kong)
Tel.: (852) 2617 9990
Web Site: http://www.dpamicrophones.com
Emp.: 3
Microphone Whslr
N.A.I.C.S.: 423990
Ken Kimura *(Gen Mgr)*

Subsidiary (US):

DPA Microphones, Inc.   (2)
1500 Kansas Ave Unit 3A, Longmont, CO 80501
Tel.: (303) 485-1025
Microphone Whslr
N.A.I.C.S.: 423990
Paul Andrews *(Mgr-Sls Support & Bus Dev-Global)*

RCI INDUSTRIES & TECHNOLOGIES LTD

421 Pearls Omaxe Tower Netaji Subhash Place, Delhi, 110034, India
Tel.: (91) 1141681828
Web Site: https://www.rciind.com
537254—(BOM)
Rev: $7,182,783
Assets: $14,200,432
Liabilities: $28,772,795
Net Worth: ($14,572,364)
Earnings: ($8,592,195)
Emp.: 119
Fiscal Year-end: 03/31/22
Cooper Wire Importer & Exporter
N.A.I.C.S.: 335929
Inder Prakash Saboo *(CFO)*

RCM BETEILIGUNGS AG

Fronackerstrasse 34, 71063, Sindelfingen, Germany
Tel.: (49) 70314690960
Web Site: https://www.rcm-ag.de
Year Founded: 1999
RCMN—(DEU)
Rev: $2,649,288
Assets: $39,573,740
Liabilities: $18,920,332
Net Worth: $20,653,408
Earnings: ($2,450,591)
Emp.: 28
Fiscal Year-end: 12/31/23
Real Estate Services
N.A.I.C.S.: 531390
Martin Schmitt *(Chm-Mgmt Bd)*

RCR TOMLINSON LTD.

Suite 1 295 Rokeby Road, Subiaco, West Perth, 6008, WA, Australia
Tel.: 865552950
Web Site: http://www.rcrtom.com.au
Year Founded: 1898
RCR—(ASX)
Sales Range: $900-999.9 Million
Engineeering Services
N.A.I.C.S.: 541330

Darryl A. Edwards *(Sec)*

Subsidiaries:

Applied Laser Salisbury   (1)
Unit1 Bldg 5 121 Evans Rd, Salisbury, 4107, QLD, Australia
Tel.: (61) 7 3255 5144
Laser Technology Resources, Information & Services
N.A.I.C.S.: 333248

Applied Laser Tullamarine   (1)
6 Saligna Drive, Tullamarine, 3043, VIC, Australia
Tel.: (61) 393351739
Web Site: http://www.rcrtomlinson.com.au
Sales Range: $25-49.9 Million
Emp.: 20
Laser Technology Resources, Information & Services
N.A.I.C.S.: 333248

Applied Laser Wetherill Park   (1)
19-20 Ormsby Place, PO Box 6941, Wetherill Park, 2164, NSW, Australia
Tel.: (61) 296094811
Web Site: http://www.rcrtom.com.au
Laser Technology Resources, Information & Services
N.A.I.C.S.: 333248
Gerald Cimarelli *(Gen Mgr)*

Positron Group Pty Ltd   (1)
239 Planet St, Welshpool, 6106, WA, Australia
Tel.: (61) 893558100
Engineeering Services
N.A.I.C.S.: 541330

RCR Construction & Maintenance Pty Ltd.   (1)
239 Planet Street, PO Box 141, Welshpool, 6106, WA, Australia   (100%)
Tel.: (61) 893558155
Web Site: http://www.rcrtom.com.au
Sales Range: $25-49.9 Million
Emp.: 100
Employment Placement Agencies
N.A.I.C.S.: 561311

RCR Corporate Pty Ltd   (1)
239 Planet St, Welshpool, 6106, WA, Australia
Tel.: (61) 893558100
Web Site: http://www.rcrtom.com.au
Sales Range: $25-49.9 Million
Emp.: 100
Engineeering Services
N.A.I.C.S.: 541330
Joe Tufilli *(Mng Dir)*

RCR Energy   (1)
11 Abdon Close, Bennetts Green, 2290, NSW, Australia
Tel.: (61) 249148888
Web Site: http://www.rcrtom.com.au
Sales Range: $25-49.9 Million
Emp.: 74
Engineeering Services
N.A.I.C.S.: 541330
Macheal Donighui *(Mng Dir)*

RCR Energy (Stelform VRBT) Pty Ltd   (1)
5 Laurio Pl, Mayfield, 2304, NSW, Australia
Tel.: (61) 249606900
Web Site: http://www.stelform.com.au
Sewer Line Construction Services
N.A.I.C.S.: 237110

RCR Energy (Stelform) Pty Ltd   (1)
11 Abdon Close, Bennetts Green, 2290, NSW, Australia
Tel.: (61) 2 4914 8888
Sales Range: $25-49.9 Million
Emp.: 100
Plate Work Mfr
N.A.I.C.S.: 332313
Mark Benson *(Gen Mgr)*

RCR Energy Pty Ltd   (1)
11 Howleys Rd, Notting Hill, 3168, VIC, Australia
Tel.: (61) 385516500
Web Site: http://www.rcrtom.com.au
Sales Range: $25-49.9 Million
Emp.: 20
Steam Generator Mfr & Whslr
N.A.I.C.S.: 333611

David Henley *(Mgr-State)*

RCR Engineering Pty Ltd.   (1)
73 Industrial Avenue, PO Box 199, Wacol, 4076, QLD, Australia   (100%)
Tel.: (61) 738793344
Web Site: http://www.rcr.com.au
Sales Range: $25-49.9 Million
Emp.: 90
Engineeering Services
N.A.I.C.S.: 541330
Ian Gibbs *(Gen Mgr)*

RCR Infrastructure Group (xNFK) Ltd.   (1)
Level 38 50 Bridge Street, Sydney, 2000, NSW, Australia
Tel.: (61) 2 8413 3000
Web Site: http://www.rcrtom.com.au
Sales Range: $900-999.9 Million
Emp.: 3,289
Integrated Building & Engineering Services
N.A.I.C.S.: 236210
Keith Blind *(CEO-Haden)*

Subsidiary (Domestic):

RCR Building Products (Holdings) Pty Ltd   (2)
Level 5 50 Berry Street, Sydney, 2000, NSW, Australia
Tel.: (61) 2 8413 3000
Building Product Mfr
N.A.I.C.S.: 332311

RCR Haden (Holdings) Pty Ltd   (2)
Units 6 & 10 38-46 South Street, Rydalmere, 2116, NSW, Australia
Tel.: (61) 2 9933 1000
Web Site: http://www.haden.com.au
Sales Range: $100-124.9 Million
Emp.: 300
Heating & Ventilation & Air Conditioning Maintenance Services
N.A.I.C.S.: 238220
Keith Blind *(CEO)*

RCR Haden Pty Ltd   (2)
Units 6 & 10 38-46 South Street, Rydalmere, 2116, NSW, Australia
Tel.: (61) 2 9933 1000
Web Site: http://www.haden.com.au
Sales Range: $350-399.9 Million
Emp.: 1,000
Heating & Ventilation & Air Conditioning Installation Services
N.A.I.C.S.: 238220
George Komorowski *(Reg Mgr)*

Subsidiary (Non-US):

RCR Infrastructure (New Zealand) Limited   (3)
314 Neilson Street, Onehunga, Auckland, 1061, North Island, New Zealand
Tel.: (64) 96349601
Web Site: http://www.haden.com.au
Sales Range: $25-49.9 Million
Emp.: 60
Heating & Air Conditioning Services
N.A.I.C.S.: 333415
Keith Blind *(CEO)*

Subsidiary (Non-US):

RCR Infrastructure (New Zealand) Limited   (2)
Level 2 8 Pacific Rise, Mount Wellington, Auckland, New Zealand
Tel.: (64) 95730050
Web Site: http://www.norfolkholdings.com
Sales Range: $450-499.9 Million
Electrical, Mechanical, Building Products & Facilities Management Services
N.A.I.C.S.: 238210
Emily Guise *(Mgr-Acctg)*

RCR Metalbilt Doors   (2)
26 Timothy Place, Avondale, Auckland, 1026, New Zealand
Tel.: (64) 9828 1167
Web Site: http://www.metalbilt.co.nz
Sales Range: $10-24.9 Million
Commercial & Industrial Doors Mfr & Service; Heating & Ventilation Products Mfr & Supplier
N.A.I.C.S.: 332321

Subsidiary (Domestic):

RCR O'Donnell Griffin (Holdings) Pty Limited   (2)

INTERNATIONAL PUBLIC

Units 6 & 10-12 38-46 South St, Rydalmere, 2116, NSW, Australia
Tel.: (61) 2 9933 1000
Web Site: http://www.odg.com.au
Electrical Engineering Services
N.A.I.C.S.: 238220

RCR O'Donnell Griffin Pty Limited   (2)
Units 6 & 10-12 38-46 South St, Rydalmere, 2116, NSW, Australia
Tel.: (61) 2 9933 1000
Web Site: http://www.odg.com.au
Sales Range: $300-349.9 Million
Emp.: 1,600
Electrical Engineering Services
N.A.I.C.S.: 541330
Simon Pankhurst *(CEO)*

RCR Resolve FM Pty Limited   (2)
Level 38 50 Bridge Street, Sydney, 2000, NSW, Australia
Tel.: (61) 292135500
Web Site: http://www.rcrtom.com.au
Sales Range: $25-49.9 Million
Emp.: 20
Integrated Facilities Management Services
N.A.I.C.S.: 541618
Mark Ghilardi *(Mgr-Bus Support Svcs)*

RCR Laser Pty Ltd   (1)
L 6 251 Saint Georges Tce, Perth, 6000, WA, Australia
Tel.: (61) 893558100
Web Site: http://www.rcrtom.com.au
Engineeering Services
N.A.I.C.S.: 541330
Paul Dalglish *(Gen Mgr)*

RCR Laser Toowoomba   (1)
4 Finn Court, Toowoomba, 4350, QLD, Australia
Tel.: (61) 746349262
Web Site: http://www.rcrtom.com.au
Laser Technology Mfr
N.A.I.C.S.: 333248

RCR Laser Welshpool   (1)
4 Forge Street, Welshpool, Perth, 6106, WA, Australia
Tel.: (61) 893584111
Web Site: http://www.rcrtom.com.au
Sales Range: $25-49.9 Million
Emp.: 30
Laser Technology Resources, Information & Services
N.A.I.C.S.: 333248
Ken Foster *(Gen Mgr)*

RCR Maintenance Newman   (1)
Lot 1658 Laver Street, Newman, 6753, WA, Australia
Tel.: (61) 891752316
Web Site: http://www.rcrtom.com.au
Engineeering Services
N.A.I.C.S.: 541330

RCR Maintenance Tom Price   (1)
Lot 23 LIA Mine Road, Tom Price, 6751, WA, Australia
Tel.: (61) 891881268
Web Site: http://www.rcrtom.com.au
Engineeering Services
N.A.I.C.S.: 541330

RCR Minng OSR   (1)
7-13 Pearson Street, Bayswater, 6053, WA, Australia
Tel.: (61) 892792522
Web Site: http://www.rcrtom.com.au
Sales Range: $25-49.9 Million
Emp.: 60
Engineeering Services
N.A.I.C.S.: 541330

RCR Power Pty Ltd   (1)
173 Davy St, Booragoon, 6954, WA, Australia
Tel.: (61) 863106000
Electrical Engineering Services
N.A.I.C.S.: 541330

RCR Resources (Heat Treatment) Pty Ltd   (1)
73 Industrial Avenue, Wacol, 4076, QLD, Australia
Tel.: (61) 7 3879 3344
Heat Treatment Operating Services
N.A.I.C.S.: 332811

RCR Resources (Tripower) Pty Ltd   (1)

AND PRIVATE COMPANIES

40-42 Enterprise Street Paget, Mackay, 4740, QLD, Australia
Tel.: (61) 7 4952 3977
Mining & Quarrying Equipment Distr
N.A.I.C.S.: 423810

RCR Resources Pty Ltd (1)
Level 5 251 St Georges Terrace, Perth, 6000, WA, Australia
Tel.: (61) 8 9355 8100
Web Site: http://www.rcrtom.com.au
Sales Range: $25-49.9 Million
Emp.: 100
Industrial Engineering Services
N.A.I.C.S.: 541330

RCR Tomlinson (Custodian) Pty Ltd (1)
239 Planet Street, Welshpool, 6106, WA, Australia
Tel.: (61) 892792522
Emp.: 300
Financial Management Services
N.A.I.C.S.: 523999
Paul Dalgleigh *(CEO)*

RCR Tomlinson Bunbury (1)
Glendale Industrial Estate Unit 3 Temple Road Picton East, Bunbury, 6229, WA, Australia
Tel.: (61) 897264555
Web Site: http://www.rcrtom.com.au
Sales Range: $50-74.9 Million
Emp.: 170
Design, Manufacture & Maintenance of Heavy Equipment & Industrial Boiler Systems
N.A.I.C.S.: 332410
Ian Gibbs *(Gen Mgr)*

Stelform Piping Systems Pty Ltd (1)
11 Abdon Cl, Bennetts Green, 2290, NSW, Australia
Tel.: (61) 249489777
Building Pipe Mfr
N.A.I.C.S.: 327332

Tomlinson Boilers Pty Ltd (1)
239 Planet Street, Welshpool, 6106, Australia
Tel.: (61) 893558100
Web Site: http://www.rcrtom.com.au
Sales Range: $50-74.9 Million
Emp.: 250
Design, Manufacture, Sales, Installation & Service of Boilers
N.A.I.C.S.: 332410
Paul Dilglarsh *(CEO & Mng Dir)*

RCS GMBH
Hockendorfer Str 91, Bautzen, 01936, Germany
Tel.: (49) 357953450
Web Site: http://www.railcomsys-gmbh.de
Rev.: $46,598,875
Emp.: 292
Reinforced Plastic Component Mfr
N.A.I.C.S.: 326199
Matthias Wewel *(Mng Dir)*

RCS MEDIAGROUP S.P.A.
Via Angelo Rizzoli 8, 20132, Milan, Italy
Tel.: (39) 0225841
Web Site: https://www.rcsmediagroup.it
Year Founded: 1927
RCS—(ITA)
Rev.: $600,418,859
Assets: $1,267,534,745
Liabilities: $691,690,777
Net Worth: $575,843,968
Earnings: $15,755,565
Emp.: 3,217
Fiscal Year-end: 12/31/20
Newspapers, Magazines & Books Publisher
N.A.I.C.S.: 513130
Andrea Liso *(Dir-Procurement & Ops)*

Subsidiaries:

Blei S.p.A. (1)
Via Dell'unione 5, 20132, Milan, Italy
Tel.: (39) 02722511
Web Site: http://www.bleispa.com
Sales Range: $25-49.9 Million
Emp.: 50
Radio Stations
N.A.I.C.S.: 516110

City Milano S.p.A. (1)
Via Angelo Rizzoli 2, 20138, Milan, Italy **(90%)**
Tel.: (39) 0267377
Newspaper Publishers
N.A.I.C.S.: 513110
Antonio Perricone *(CEO)*

DadaMobile S.p.A. (1)
Piazza Annigoni 9/B, 50122, Florence, Italy **(100%)**
Tel.: (39) 055200211
Web Site: http://www.dada.net
Sales Range: $100-124.9 Million
Emp.: 300
Software Publisher
N.A.I.C.S.: 513210

EL MUNDO TV (1)
Avenida de San Luis 25, 28033, Madrid, Spain **(99.99%)**
Tel.: (34) 91 050 1629
Web Site: https://www.elmundo.es
Motion Picture & Video Production
N.A.I.C.S.: 512110
Jorge de Esteban *(Chm)*

Ediservicios Madrid 2000 S.I.U. (1)
Calle Pradillo 42, Madrid, Spain **(100%)**
Tel.: (34) 915864889
Newspaper Publishers
N.A.I.C.S.: 513110

Editorial Del Pueblo Vasco S.A. (1)
Camino Capuchinos De Basurtu 2, Bilbao, Spain **(100%)**
Tel.: (34) 944739100
Newspaper Publishers
N.A.I.C.S.: 513110

Editoriale Veneto S.r.l. (1)
2/F Via Rismondo Francesco, 35135, Padua, Italy **(51%)**
Tel.: (39) 0498238801
Web Site: http://corrieredelveneto.corriere.it
Sales Range: $25-49.9 Million
Emp.: 30
Newspaper Publishers
N.A.I.C.S.: 513110
Massimo Monzio Compagnoni *(Gen Mgr)*

La Esfera De Los Libros S.L. (1)
Avda San Luis 25, 28033, Madrid, Spain **(100%)**
Tel.: (34) 91 443 5000
Web Site: https://www.esferalibros.com
Sales Range: $25-49.9 Million
Emp.: 11
Book Publishers
N.A.I.C.S.: 513130
Ymelda Navajo *(Gen Dir)*

Subsidiary (Non-US):

A Esfera dos Livros S.L.U. (2)
R Professor Reinaldo dos Santos N 42 R/C, 1500-507, Lisbon, Portugal
Tel.: (351) 21 340 40 60
Web Site: http://www.esferadoslivros.pt
Sales Range: $25-49.9 Million
Emp.: 5
Books Publishing Services
N.A.I.C.S.: 513130

Log 607 S.r.l. (1)
H-Farm Via Sile 41, 31056, Roncade, Treviso, Italy
Tel.: (39) 0422 789 607
Web Site: http://www.log607.com
Books Publishing Services
N.A.I.C.S.: 513130

Mundinteractivos S.A.U. (1)
Calle Pradillo 42, Madrid, Spain **(100%)**
Tel.: (34) 915864889
Data Processing Services
N.A.I.C.S.: 518210

Pubblibaby S.r.l (1)
Via Fermi 18, Cusago, Italy **(100%)**
Tel.: (39) 029033131
Advertising Agencies
N.A.I.C.S.: 541810

RCS MEDIAGROUP S.P.A.

RCS Broadcast S.p.A. (1)
Viale Giulio Richard 1, Milan, Italy **(98.99%)**
Tel.: (39) 02818771
Web Site: http://www.rcs.com
Periodical Publishers
N.A.I.C.S.: 513120

RCS Direct S.r.l. (1)
Via Rizzoli 8, 20132, Milan, Italy **(100%)**
Tel.: (39) 0250951
Data Processing Services
N.A.I.C.S.: 518210

RCS Investimenti S.p.A. (1)
Via Angelo Rizzoli 8, 20132, Milan, Italy **(99.56%)**
Tel.: (39) 0225841
Open-End Investment Funds
N.A.I.C.S.: 525910

RCS Periodici S.p.A. (1)
Via Rizzoli 8, 20138, Milan, Italy **(100%)**
Tel.: (39) 0225841
Web Site: http://www.rcs.it
Emp.: 500
Periodical Publishers
N.A.I.C.S.: 513120

RCS Produzioni S.p.A. (1)
Via Angelo Rizzoli 2, 20132, Milan, Italy **(100%)**
Tel.: (39) 0225841
Newspaper Publishers
N.A.I.C.S.: 513110

RCS Pubblicita S.p.A. (1)
Via San Marco 31, 20138, Milan, Italy **(100%)**
Tel.: (39) 0250951
Web Site: http://www.rcspubblicita.it
Periodical Publishers
N.A.I.C.S.: 513120

RCS Quotidiani S.p.A. (1)
Via Angelo Rizzoli 2, Milan, 20121, Italy **(100%)**
Tel.: (39) 0225841
Web Site: http://www.rcs.it
Emp.: 1,000
Newspaper Publishers
N.A.I.C.S.: 513110

RCS Sport S.p.A. (1)
Via Solferino 28, 20121, Milan, Italy **(100%)**
Tel.: (39) 0262828712
Book Publishers
N.A.I.C.S.: 513130

Recoprint Dos Hermanas S.L.U. (1)
Poligono Industrial La Palmera Avda De La Palmera 41, Autovia Madrid-Cadiz Km 550, 41700, Dos Hermanas, Spain
Tel.: (34) 954692269
Newspaper Publishing Services
N.A.I.C.S.: 513110

Recoprint Rabade S.L.U. (1)
Poligono Industrial Rabade 2 Fase Parcelas 16B y 17 B, San Vicente de Rabade, 23370, Lugo, Spain
Tel.: (34) 982390246
Newspaper Publishing Services
N.A.I.C.S.: 513110

Recoprint Sagunto S.L.U. (1)
Poligono Industrial Sepes Calle Benjamin Franklin Parcela 5, 46520, Sagunto, Spain
Tel.: (34) 962665317
Newspaper Publishing Services
N.A.I.C.S.: 513110

Rizzoli Publishing Italia S.r.l. (1)
Via Mesenate 91, 20138, Milan, Italy **(100%)**
Tel.: (39) 0250951
Periodical Publishers
N.A.I.C.S.: 513120

Subsidiary (Domestic):

Digital Factory S.r.l. (2)
Via Angelo Rizzoli 8, Milan, 20132, Italy **(100%)**
Tel.: (39) 06 7229 331
Web Site: http://www.cinecittastudios.it
Digital Television Broadcasting Services
N.A.I.C.S.: 516120

Seasons S.r.l. (2)

Via Dei Pradei 7, Grandate, 22070, Como, Italy
Tel.: (39) 031494448
Newspaper Publishing Services
N.A.I.C.S.: 513110

SSD RCS Active Team a r.l. (1)
Via Rizzoli 8, 20132, Milan, Italy
Tel.: (39) 0225847562
Web Site: http://www.rcsactiveteam.it
Media Services
N.A.I.C.S.: 541840

Sfera Editore S.p.A. (1)
Via Rizzoli 8, 20138, Milan, Italy **(100%)**
Tel.: (39) 0250361
Web Site: http://www.sferaeditore.it
Book Publishers
N.A.I.C.S.: 513130

Subsidiary (Non-US):

Sfera Editores Mexico S.A. (2)
Leibenitz No 13 Piso 4, Anzures Seccion Miguel Hidalgo, Mexico, 11590, Mexico
Tel.: (52) 5552500056
Web Site: http://www.sfera.com
Newspaper Publishing Services
N.A.I.C.S.: 513110

Sfera Editores Espana S.L. (1)
Parque Mas Blau Edif Muntadas A C/ Bergueda 1 2 A4, El Prat De Llobregat, 08820, Barcelona, Spain **(100%)**
Tel.: (34) 933708585
Web Site: https://www.sfera.es
Sales Range: $25-49.9 Million
Book Publishers
N.A.I.C.S.: 513130

Subsidiary (Domestic):

Feria Bebe S.L. (2)
Pol Ind Mas Blau Edif Muntadas C Solsones 2 B, 08820, El Prat de Llobregat, Barcelona, Spain
Tel.: (34) 933792216
Web Site: http://www.feriabebe.com
Baby Products Exhibition Services
N.A.I.C.S.: 561920

Sfera Service S.r.l. (1)
Via Rizzoli 8, 20138, Milan, Italy **(100%)**
Tel.: (39) 0229523652
Advertising Agencies
N.A.I.C.S.: 541810

Softec S.p.A. (1)
Via Danubio 14, 50019, Sesto Fiorentino, Italy **(50%)**
Tel.: (39) 0553424674
Web Site: http://www.softecspa.et
Sales Range: $25-49.9 Million
Emp.: 100
Software Publisher
N.A.I.C.S.: 513210
Maurizio Bottini *(Gen Mgr)*

Trend Service, S.A. de C.V. (1)
Leibnitz No 13 Piso 4, Mexico, Mexico **(100%)**
Tel.: (52) 5552500056
Web Site: http://www.miveveyyo.com
Sales Range: $25-49.9 Million
Emp.: 40
Other Commercial Printing
N.A.I.C.S.: 323111
Marco Berdolin *(Gen Mgr)*

Unedisa Comunicaciones S.L.U. (1)
Calle Pradillo 42, Madrid, Spain **(100%)**
Tel.: (34) 915864889
Motion Picture & Video Production
N.A.I.C.S.: 512110

Unidad Editorial, S.A. (1)
Av San Luis 25, 28033, Madrid, Spain **(100%)**
Tel.: (34) 91 443 5000
Web Site: https://www.unidadeditorial.es
Newspaper Publishers
N.A.I.C.S.: 513110
Antonio Fernandez-Galiano *(Pres)*

Subsidiary (Domestic):

Canal Mundo Radio Cataluna S.L. (2)
Paseodegracia 11 5th Fl 8, 08007, Barcelona, Spain
Tel.: (34) 934962400

RCS MEDIAGROUP S.P.A.

RCS MediaGroup S.p.A.—(Continued)
Radio Broadcasting Services
N.A.I.C.S.: 516210

Informacion Estadio Deportivo S.A. (2)
Avda San Francisco Javier 9 Edificio Sevilla 2 Planta 8 Modulo 25, 41018, Seville, Spain
Tel.: (34) 95 493 39 40
Sales Range: $25-49.9 Million
Emp.: 4
Sports News Broadcasting Services
N.A.I.C.S.: 516210
Francisco Garcia *(Gen Mgr)*

Last Lap S.L. (2)
Calle la Granja 22, 28108, Alcobendas, Madrid, Spain
Tel.: (34) 91 661 1500
Web Site: https://web.lastlap.com
Emp.: 65
Sports Event Organizing Services
N.A.I.C.S.: 711310
Oscar Villa *(Mng Dir)*

Logintegral 2000 S.A.U. (2)
Avenida San Luis 25, 28033, Madrid, Spain (100%)
Tel.: (34) 914 435 000
Web Site: http://www.logintegral.com
Sales Range: $25-49.9 Million
Emp.: 70
Book Periodical & Newspaper Whslr
N.A.I.C.S.: 424920

Unedisa Telecomunicaciones S.L.U. (2)
Av Constitucion Zade Torrejon 3, 28850, Madrid, Spain
Tel.: (34) 916761152
Wireless Telecommunication Services
N.A.I.C.S.: 517112

Unidad Editorial Informacion Deportiva S.L.U. (2)
Avda San Luis 25, Madrid, Spain
Tel.: (34) 914435000
Newspaper Publishing Services
N.A.I.C.S.: 513110

Unidad Editorial Informacion General S.L.U. (2)
Avenida de San Luis 25, Madrid, 28033, Spain
Tel.: (34) 91 443 50 00
Newspaper Publishing Services
N.A.I.C.S.: 513110

Unidad Editorial Revistas S.L.U. (2)
Avenida de San Luis 25, 28033, Madrid, Spain
Tel.: (34) 914435000
Newspaper Publishing Services
N.A.I.C.S.: 513110

Upoc Networks Inc. (1)
11 W 42nd St, New York, NY 10036 (100%)
Tel.: (646) 291-6144
Sales Range: $25-49.9 Million
Emp.: 40
Telecommunications
N.A.I.C.S.: 517810

RDB RASAYANS LIMITED
Bikaner Building 3rd Floor Room No 9 8/1 Lal Bazar Street, Kolkata, 700 001, West Bengal, India
Tel.: (91) 3344500500
Web Site: https://www.rdbgroup.in
Year Founded: 1995
533608—(BOM)
Rev.: $14,883,376
Assets: $21,147,809
Liabilities: $1,684,707
Net Worth: $19,463,102
Earnings: $2,921,779
Emp.: 94
Fiscal Year-end: 03/31/23
Plastic & Woven Bag Mfr
N.A.I.C.S.: 322220
Shanti Lal Baid *(Mng Dir)*

RDC SEMICONDUCTOR CO., LTD.
6F-1 No 2-1 Lixing Road, East Dist, Hsinchu, 30078, Taiwan
Tel.: (886) 36662866
Web Site: https://www.rdc.com.tw
Year Founded: 1997
3228—(TPE)
Rev.: $13,007,348
Assets: $26,149,142
Liabilities: $3,611,012
Net Worth: $22,538,130
Earnings: $1,121,064
Fiscal Year-end: 12/31/22
Electronic Design & Testing Services
N.A.I.C.S.: 541420
Jana Yi *(Chm)*

RDF GROUP PLC
Blenheim House 56 Old Steine, Brighton, BN1 1NH, United Kingdom
Tel.: (44) 1273200100
Web Site: http://www.rdfgroup.com
Year Founded: 1994
Sales Range: $50-74.9 Million
Emp.: 65
Information Technology Services
N.A.I.C.S.: 541511
David Wood *(CEO)*

Subsidiaries:

RDF Consulting Limited (1)
Blenheim House 56 Old Steine, Brighton, BN1 1NH, East Sussex, United Kingdom
Tel.: (44) 1273200100
Web Site: http://www.rdfgroup.com
Sales Range: $25-49.9 Million
IT Consulting Services
N.A.I.C.S.: 541512
Matt Thompsett *(Dir-Sls)*

RDF Resources Limited (1)
2 Bartholomews, Brighton, BN1 1HG, United Kingdom
Tel.: (44) 1273200100
Sales Range: $25-49.9 Million
Placement Services
N.A.I.C.S.: 561311
David Wood *(CEO)*

RDL CORPORATION LIMITED
3rd Floor 13-15 Moorgate, London, EC2R 6AD, Surrey, United Kingdom
Tel.: (44) 2072556600   UK
Web Site: http://www.rdlcorp.com
Year Founded: 1987
Rev.: $31,800,000
Emp.: 77
Recruitment Services
N.A.I.C.S.: 541612
Stuart Britton *(CEO)*

Subsidiaries:

SEC Recruitment Ltd (1)
Woolverstone House 61-62 Berners Street, London, W1T 3NJ, United Kingdom
Tel.: (44) 2072556600
Web Site: http://www.secrecruitment.com
Human Resource Consulting Services
N.A.I.C.S.: 541612

RE ROYALTIES LTD.
14th Floor 1040 West Georgia St, Vancouver, V6E 4H1, BC, Canada
Tel.: (778) 374-2000
Web Site: https://www.reroyalties.com
Year Founded: 2016
RE—(TSXV)
Rev.: $7,404,393
Assets: $40,759,902
Liabilities: $27,857,330
Net Worth: $12,902,572
Earnings: ($1,367,448)
Emp.: 9
Fiscal Year-end: 12/31/23
Financial Investment Services
N.A.I.C.S.: 523999
Bernard Tan *(CEO)*

RE&S HOLDINGS LIMITED
32 Tai Seng Street 07-01 RE and S Building, Singapore, 533972, Singapore
Tel.: (65) 62520810   SG
Web Site: https://www.res.com.sg
Year Founded: 1988
1G1—(CAT)
Rev.: $128,978,881
Assets: $106,739,533
Liabilities: $76,326,788
Net Worth: $30,412,745
Earnings: $5,665,061
Emp.: 348
Fiscal Year-end: 06/30/23
Food Service
N.A.I.C.S.: 722310
Ben Yeo *(Chm)*

Subsidiaries:

Kabe No Ana Pte. Ltd. (1)
B1-80 23 Within Shokutsu Ten Japanese Food Street Serangoon Central, Singapore, 556083, Singapore
Tel.: (65) 66348024
Web Site: http://www.kabenoana.com.sg
Restaurant Services
N.A.I.C.S.: 722511

R E & S Enterprises (M) Sdn. Bhd. (1)
B2-2-5 Solaris Dutamas No 1 Jalan Dutamas 1, 50480, Kuala Lumpur, Malaysia
Tel.: (60) 362055530
Restaurant Services
N.A.I.C.S.: 722511

RE&S Japan Co., Ltd. (1)
North 16-8 Osaka Central Wholesale Market 1-1-86, Fukushima-ku, Noda, 553-0005, Osaka, Japan
Tel.: (81) 664600689
Web Site: https://www.resj.jp
Emp.: 6
Restaurant Services
N.A.I.C.S.: 722511

REA VIPINGO PLANTATIONS LIMITED
1st Floor Delta Block Wilson Business Park Langata Road, PO Box 17648, Nairobi, 00500, Kenya
Tel.: (254) 20607091
Web Site: http://www.reavipingo.com
REA—(NAI)
Rev.: $33,632,885
Assets: $49,739,786
Liabilities: $12,285,477
Net Worth: $37,454,309
Earnings: $3,837,901
Emp.: 4,695
Fiscal Year-end: 09/30/23
Sisal & Sisal Fiber Mfr
N.A.I.C.S.: 313110
Ian R. Hodson *(Sec)*

Subsidiaries:

Amboni Plantations Limited (1)
Near Municipal Council, Tanga, Tanzania
Tel.: (255) 272646795
Sales Range: $450-499.9 Million
Emp.: 200
Sisal Fiber Mfr
N.A.I.C.S.: 325220
Neil R. Cuthbert *(Mng Dir)*

REABOLD RESOURCES PLC
The Broadgate Tower 8th Floor 20 Primrose Sreet, London, EC2A 2EW, United Kingdom
Tel.: (44) 2037818331   UK
Web Site: https://www.reabold.com
RBD—(LSE)
Rev.: $1,405,240
Assets: $53,872,972
Liabilities: $1,030,509
Net Worth: $52,842,462
Earnings: ($3,622,397)
Fiscal Year-end: 12/31/20
Investment Management Service
N.A.I.C.S.: 523940

INTERNATIONAL PUBLIC

Anthony John Samaha *(Dir-Fin)*

Subsidiaries:

Adventis Health Limited (1)
32 Cornhill, London, EC3V 3BT, United Kingdom
Tel.: (44) 1628894620
Investment Management Service
N.A.I.C.S.: 523999

Second2 Limited (1)
Adventis House Post Office Lane, Beaconsfield, HP9 1FN, United Kingdom
Tel.: (44) 1494 731 700
Marketing Consulting Services
N.A.I.C.S.: 541613

REACAP FINANCIAL INVESTMENTS
Smart Village - Building B16- Phase 1 Km 28, Cairo, Egypt
Tel.: (20) 235316100
Web Site: https://www.reacap-investment.com
Year Founded: 1997
REAC.CA—(EGX)
Sales Range: Less than $1 Million
Financial Investment Services
N.A.I.C.S.: 523999
Youssef El Far *(Chm)*

REACH
111 Chertsey Rd, Woking, GU21 5BW, Surrey, United Kingdom
Tel.: (44) 1483 711 300
Web Site: http://www.reach.co.uk
Sales Range: $50-74.9 Million
Emp.: 500
N.A.I.C.S.: 541810
Charlene Friend *(CFO)*

Subsidiaries:

Reach GmbH (1)
Prinzenallee 7, 40549, Dusseldorf, Germany
Tel.: (49) 211 52391 356
Emp.: 20
Marketing & Sales Consulting Services
N.A.I.C.S.: 541613

REACH ENERGY BERHAD
Tel.: (60) 364123000
Web Site: https://www.reachenergy.com.my
Year Founded: 2013
REACH—(KLS)
Rev.: $19,686,645
Assets: $322,619,715
Liabilities: $201,960,248
Net Worth: $120,659,468
Earnings: ($48,716,910)
Emp.: 217
Fiscal Year-end: 12/31/20
Oil & Gas Fields Operator
N.A.I.C.S.: 213112
Siew Chaing *(CEO-Interim)*

REACH GLOBAL SERVICES S.A.
Rond Point Schuman 6, Box 5, 1040, Brussels, Belgium
Tel.: (32) 22347778
Web Site: http://www.reach-gs.eu
Marketing Consulting Services
N.A.I.C.S.: 541613

REACH NEW HOLDINGS LIMITED
Sun Tin Lun Industrial Centre No 8 Taihao Road, Sandong Digital Industrial Park Sandong Town, Huizhou, Guangdong, China
Tel.: (86) 35251275   Ky
Web Site: http://www.sthl.com.hk
Year Founded: 2001
8471—(HKG)
Rev.: $9,447,040
Assets: $8,973,526

Liabilities: $1,933,870
Net Worth: $7,039,656
Earnings: ($947,700)
Emp.: 216
Fiscal Year-end: 12/31/22
Print Product Mfr & Distr
N.A.I.C.S.: 313310
Kai Yuen Lam (CEO & Compliance Officer)

Subsidiaries:

Sun Tin Lun Garment Accessories (Huizhou) Company Limited (1)
Xintianlun Ind Center No 6 Taihao Road, Sandong Digital Ind Zone, Huizhou, 516025, Guangdong, China
Tel.: (86) 7525702600
Garment Accessory Mfr & Distr
N.A.I.C.S.: 315990

REACH PLC
One Canada Square Canary Wharf, London, E14 5AP, United Kingdom
Tel.: (44) 2072933000 UK
Web Site: https://www.reachplc.com
Year Founded: 1999
RCH—(LSE)
Rev.: $680,905,080
Assets: $1,425,439,800
Liabilities: $703,662,300
Net Worth: $721,777,500
Earnings: $57,628,980
Fiscal Year-end: 12/25/22
Newspaper & Magazine Publisher
N.A.I.C.S.: 513110
Jim Mullen (CEO)

Subsidiaries:

AMRA Ltd (1)
1 Canada Square, London, WC2N 4LP, United Kingdom (100%)
Tel.: (44) 2078450100
Web Site: http://www.amra.co.uk
Sales Range: $25-49.9 Million
Emp.: 50
Advertising Sales Company
N.A.I.C.S.: 541810

Arrow Interactive Ltd (1)
1 Canada Sq, Canary Wharf, London, E14 5AP, United Kingdom (100%)
Tel.: (44) 2072932093
Web Site: http://www.arrowinteractive.co.uk
Integration Systems
N.A.I.C.S.: 541512

BPM Media (Midlands) Ltd. (1)
Floor 6 Fort Dunlop Fort Parkway, Birmingham, B24 9FF, United Kingdom (100%)
Tel.: (44) 121 236 3366
Web Site: http://www.bpm.co.uk
Rev.: $38,966,537
Emp.: 700
Newspaper Publishing
N.A.I.C.S.: 513110
John Griffith (Editor)

Coventry Newspapers Ltd (1)
Fl 6 Fort Dunlop Fort Pkwy, Birmingham, B24 9FF, W Midlands, United Kingdom (100%)
Tel.: (44) 2476633633
Web Site: http://www.iccoventry.co.uk
Sales Range: $50-74.9 Million
Emp.: 250
Publisher of Newspapers
N.A.I.C.S.: 513110
Simon Edgley (Mng Dir)

Gazette Media Co Ltd (1)
Ground Floor East Hudson Quay The Halyard Middlehaven, Middlesbrough, TS3 6RT, United Kingdom (100%)
Tel.: (44) 1642234262
Web Site: http://www.gazettelive.co.uk
Sales Range: $25-49.9 Million
Emp.: 70
Publisher of Newspapers
N.A.I.C.S.: 513110
Bob Cuffe (Mng Dir)

MGN Limited (1)
One Canada Square, Canary Wharf, London, E14 5AP, United Kingdom
Tel.: (44) 2072932411

Web Site: http://www.mirror.co.uk
Newspaper Publishers
N.A.I.C.S.: 513110
Lloyd Embley (Editor-in-Chief)

Media Wales (1)
6 Park Street, Cardiff, CF10 1XR, United Kingdom (100%)
Tel.: (44) 2920222444
Web Site: http://www.walesonline.co.uk
Sales Range: $50-74.9 Million
Emp.: 200
Publisher of Newspapers & Online Publications
N.A.I.C.S.: 513110

Midland Weekly Media Ltd (1)
Weaman St, Birmingham, B4 6AT, United Kingdom (100%)
Tel.: (44) 212345218
Sales Range: $400-449.9 Million
Emp.: 1,500
Publisher of Newspapers
N.A.I.C.S.: 513110

NCJ Media Limited (1)
Groat Market, Newcastle upon Tyne, NE1 1ED, Tyne And Wear, United Kingdom
Tel.: (44) 191 232 7500
Web Site: http://www.trinity-mirror-north-east.co.uk
Sales Range: $75-99.9 Million
Emp.: 300
Media Advertising Services
N.A.I.C.S.: 541850
Stuart Birkett (Mng Dir)

Net Recruit UK Limited (1)
Glossop Gas Works Arundel Street, Glossop, SK13 7AB, Derbyshire, United Kingdom
Tel.: (44) 145 785 6270
Web Site: https://www.net-recruit.co.uk
Recruitment Services
N.A.I.C.S.: 561311
Rachel Lumb (Acct Mgr)

Newcastle Chronicle & Journal Ltd (1)
Groat Market, Newcastle, United Kingdom (100%)
Tel.: (44) 1912327500
Web Site: http://www.chroniclelive.co.uk
Sales Range: $100-124.9 Million
Emp.: 500
Publisher of Newspapers
N.A.I.C.S.: 513110

Northern & Shell Plc
The Northern Shell Building Number 10 Lower Thames Street, No 10 Lower Thames St, London, EC3R 6EN, United Kingdom
Tel.: (44) 207 308 5400
Web Site: https://www.northernandshell.co.uk
Media Holding Company; Newspaper, Magazine & Online Publishing, Television Broadcasting & Commercial Printing Services
N.A.I.C.S.: 551112
Richard C. Desmond (Chm)

Subsidiary (Domestic):

Express Newspapers (2)
One Canada Square, Canary Wharf, London, E14 5AP, United Kingdom
Tel.: (44) 208 612 7139
Web Site: https://www.express.co.uk
Publisher of Daily Newspapers
N.A.I.C.S.: 513110

O.K. Magazines Limited (1)
One Canada Square, Canary Wharf, London, E14 5AB, United Kingdom
Tel.: (44) 208 612 7000
Web Site: https://www.ok.co.uk
Newspaper Publishing Services
N.A.I.C.S.: 513110

Planet Recruitment Limited (1)
Suite 2 Innovation House Parkway Court John Smith Drive, Oxford Business Park, Oxford, OX4 2JY, United Kingdom
Tel.: (44) 186 525 7455
Web Site: https://www.planetrecruitment.co.uk
Recruitment Services
N.A.I.C.S.: 561311

Reach Printing Services (Oldham) Limited (1)
Hollinwood Ave, Chadderton, Oldham, OL9 8EP, United Kingdom
Tel.: (44) 161 683 6323
Newspaper Publishing Services
N.A.I.C.S.: 513110

Reach Printing Services (Teesside) Limited (1)
Barton Road Riverside Park, Middlesbrough, TS2 1UT, United Kingdom
Tel.: (44) 164 223 4501
Newspaper Publishing Services
N.A.I.C.S.: 513110

Reach Printing Services (Watford) Limited (1)
St Albans Road, Watford, WD24 7RG, Hertfordshire, United Kingdom
Tel.: (44) 192 323 0455
Newspaper Publishing Services
N.A.I.C.S.: 513110

Reach Publishing Services Limited (1)
PO Box 2003, Liverpool, L69 3FR, United Kingdom
Tel.: (44) 116 222 4640
Web Site: https://www.reachpublishingservices.co.uk
Newspaper Publishing Services
N.A.I.C.S.: 513110

Scottish & Universal Newspapers Ltd (1)
Press Bldg, Campbell St, Hamilton, ML3 6AX, United Kingdom (100%)
Tel.: (44) 698283200
Publisher of Newspapers
N.A.I.C.S.: 513110

Scottish Daily Record & Sunday Mail Ltd. (1)
One Central Quay, Glasgow, G3 8DA, United Kingdom
Tel.: (44) 41 309 3000
Web Site: https://www.dailyrecord.co.uk
Newspapers Printing & Publisher
N.A.I.C.S.: 513110

Surrey & Berkshire Media Limited (1)
Stoke Mill Woking Rd, Guildford, GU1 1QA, Surrey, United Kingdom
Tel.: (44) 1483508700
Web Site: http://www.getsurrey.co.uk
Sales Range: $50-74.9 Million
Emp.: 150
Newspaper Publishers
N.A.I.C.S.: 513110
Lynne Baker (Office Mgr)

Trinity Mirror Cheshire Limited (1)
1 Canada Sq, London, E14 5AB, United Kingdom
Tel.: (44) 20 7293 3000
Web Site: http://www.trinitymirror.com
Newspaper Publishing Services
N.A.I.C.S.: 513110
Mark Hollinshead (Mng Dir)

Trinity Mirror Digital Recruitment Ltd. (1)
1 Canada Sq, Canary Wharf, London, E14 5AP, United Kingdom
Tel.: (44) 8454680568
Web Site: http://www.tmdr.com
Emp.: 50
Online Job Posting Services
N.A.I.C.S.: 519290
Sarah El-Doori (Dir-Mktg)

Trinity Mirror Huddersfield Ltd. (1)
Queen St S, Huddersfield, HD1 3DU, United Kingdom (100%)
Tel.: (44) 01484430000
Web Site: http://www.ichuddersfield.com
Sales Range: $25-49.9 Million
Emp.: 60
Publisher of Newspapers
N.A.I.C.S.: 513110

Trinity Mirror Merseyside Limited (1)
One Canada Sq, London, E14 5AP, United Kingdom
Tel.: (44) 1512272000
Web Site: http://www.trinitymirror.com
Newspaper Publishing Services

N.A.I.C.S.: 513110

Trinity Mirror Printing (Blantyre) Limited (1)
Daily Record Building 40 Anderston Quay, Glasgow, G3 8DA, United Kingdom
Tel.: (44) 1698 710055
Newspaper Printing Services
N.A.I.C.S.: 323111

Trinity Mirror Printing (Cardiff) Limited (1)
Tidal Sidings Portmanmoor Road Industrial Estate, Cardiff, CF24 5HD, United Kingdom
Tel.: (44) 1446 701827
Web Site: http://www.trinitymirrorprinting.co.uk
Emp.: 40
Newspaper Printing Services
N.A.I.C.S.: 323111
Tuncan Gilchrist (Gen Mgr)

Trinity Mirror Printing (Midlands) Limited (1)
Wood Lane, Erdington, Birmingham, B24 9PW, West Midlands, United Kingdom
Tel.: (44) 121 386 8501
Web Site: http://www.trinitymirror.com
Sales Range: $25-49.9 Million
Emp.: 80
Newspaper Printing Services
N.A.I.C.S.: 323111
Martin Wright (Plant Mgr)

Trinity Mirror Printing (Oldham) Limited (1)
Hollinwood Avenue, Oldham, OL9 8EP, Lancashire, United Kingdom
Tel.: (44) 161 683 4929
Commercial Printing Services
N.A.I.C.S.: 323111

Trinity Mirror Printing (Watford) Limited (1)
Saint Albans Rd, Watford, WD24 7RG, Hertfordshire, United Kingdom
Tel.: (44) 1923 815139
Commercial Printing Services
N.A.I.C.S.: 323111

Trinity Mirror Printing Limited (1)
Saint Albans Road, Watford, WD24 7RG, Hertfordshire, United Kingdom
Tel.: (44) 1923 815666
Web Site: http://www.trinitymirrorprinting.co.uk
Sales Range: $50-74.9 Million
Emp.: 220
Newspaper Printing Services
N.A.I.C.S.: 323111
Michael Brown (Dir-Sls & Publ)

Trinity Mirror Regionals plc (1)
1 Canada Sq, London, E14 5AP, United Kingdom
Tel.: (44) 20 7293 3000
Web Site: http://www.trinitymirror.co.uk
Emp.: 1,000
Investment Management Service
N.A.I.C.S.: 523999
Michael Greenwood (Grp Exec Editor)

Trinity Mirror Southern Ltd (1)
50 56 Portman Rd, Reading, RG30 1BA, Berkshire, United Kingdom (100%)
Tel.: (44) 189503030
Web Site: http://www.trinitymirrorsouthern.co.uk
Sales Range: $400-449.9 Million
Emp.: 1,825
Publisher of Newspapers
N.A.I.C.S.: 513110

Trinity Publications Ltd (1)
1ST Fl Edward House, Edward St, Birmingham, B1 2RA, United Kingdom (100%)
Tel.: (44) 212338712
Web Site: http://www.trinity.com
Sales Range: $50-74.9 Million
Emp.: 150
Publisher of Magazines
N.A.I.C.S.: 513110

fish4 Limited (1)
One Canada Square Canary Wharf, London, E14 5AP, United Kingdom
Tel.: (44) 20 8600 2170
Web Site: http://www.fish4jobs.co.uk
Sales Range: $25-49.9 Million
Emp.: 15
Online Recruitment Advertising Services

REACH PLC

Reach PLC—(Continued)
N.A.I.C.S.: 541890
Paul Halliwell *(Mng Dir)*

REACH4ENTERTAINMENT ENTERPRISES PLC
Wellington House 125 Strand, London, WC2R 0AP, United Kingdom
Tel.: (44) 20 3978 8590 UK
Web Site: http://www.r4e.com
Rev.: $177,586,705
Assets: $80,621,429
Liabilities: $61,372,387
Net Worth: $19,249,042
Earnings: $798,764
Emp.: 262
Fiscal Year-end: 12/31/19
Advertising Services
N.A.I.C.S.: 541810
Linzi Kristina Allen *(Fin Dir-Grp)*

Subsidiaries:

Newman Displays Ltd (1)
23 Packenham Street, London, WC1X 0LB, United Kingdom
Tel.: (44) 20 7278 1400
Web Site: http://www.newman-displays.com
Sign Board Mfr
N.A.I.C.S.: 339950

REACT GROUP PLC
Holly House Shady Lane, Birmingham, B44 9ER, United Kingdom
Tel.: (44) 1283550503 UK
Web Site: https://www.reactsc.co.uk
Year Founded: 2015
REAT—(AIM)
Rev.: $24,926,711
Assets: $20,891,079
Liabilities: $10,069,984
Net Worth: $10,821,095
Earnings: $63,653
Emp.: 1
Fiscal Year-end: 09/30/23
Investment Advisory Services
N.A.I.C.S.: 523940
Mark Braund *(Chm)*

REACTIVE GROUP
The Granary Hose Hill, Sulhamstead, Reading, RG7 4BB, United Kingdom
Tel.: (44) 118 932 3499
Web Site: http://www.reactive-group.com
Year Founded: 1989
Data Storage Systems Mfr
N.A.I.C.S.: 518210

Subsidiaries:

Arraid, LLC (1)
26 W Lone Cactus 500, Phoenix, AZ 85027
Tel.: (480) 699-3047
Web Site: http://www.arraid.com
Data Storage Solutions
N.A.I.C.S.: 518210
Norman Boudreau *(VP-Ops)*

READ JONES CHRISTOFFERSEN LTD.
1285 West Broadway Suite 300, Vancouver, V6H 3X8, BC, Canada
Tel.: (604) 738-0048
Web Site: https://www.rjc.ca
Year Founded: 1948
Rev.: $18,519,274
Emp.: 195
Engineeering Services
N.A.I.C.S.: 541330
Ronald F. Mazza *(Chm)*

READ-GENE SA
Ul Alabastrowa 8, Grzepnica Dobra, 72-003, Szczecinek, Poland
Tel.: (48) 914334256
Web Site: https://www.read-gene.com
Laboratory Testing Services
N.A.I.C.S.: 621511
Jan Lubinski *(CEO)*

READBOY EDUCATION HOLDING COMPANY LIMITED
No 38 Changyi Road, Wuguishan, Zhongshan, Guangdong, China Ky
Web Site: https://www.readboy.com
Year Founded: 1999
2385—(HKG)
Rev.: $92,724,224
Assets: $147,443,482
Liabilities: $40,260,983
Net Worth: $107,182,499
Earnings: $743,988
Emp.: 553
Fiscal Year-end: 12/31/22
Holding Company
N.A.I.C.S.: 551112

READCLOUD LIMITED
Level 1 126 Church St, Brighton, 3186, VIC, Australia
Tel.: (61) 90784833 AU
Web Site: https://www.readcloud.com
Year Founded: 2009
RCL—(ASX)
Rev.: $8,478,739
Assets: $7,832,432
Liabilities: $1,764,400
Net Worth: $6,068,031
Earnings: ($704,145)
Fiscal Year-end: 09/30/24
Digital Education & Learning Services
N.A.I.C.S.: 611710
Lars Lindstrom *(Founder, CEO & Mng Dir)*

READCREST CAPITAL AG
Colorado-Turm Industriestrasse 4, 70565, Stuttgart, Germany
Tel.: (49) 71149047860
Web Site: http://www.enerxy.com
EXJ—(DEU)
Assets: $388,517
Liabilities: $118,714
Net Worth: $269,804
Earnings: ($107,921)
Fiscal Year-end: 12/31/23
Energy Consulting Services
N.A.I.C.S.: 541690

READEN HOLDING CORP.
Kortenhoefsedijk 155, 1241 LZ, Kortenhoef, Netherlands
Tel.: (31) 356299970
Web Site: https://www.readenholdingcorp.com
RHCO—(OTCIQ)
Sales Range: $1-9.9 Million
Holding Company
N.A.I.C.S.: 551112
John D. T. Leenders *(Chm)*

READLY INTERNATIONAL AB
Gjorwellsgatan 30, 112 60, Stockholm, Sweden
Tel.: (46) 8256770
Web Site: https://corporate.readly.com
Year Founded: 2012
READ—(OMX)
Rev.: $63,409,949
Assets: $27,560,201
Liabilities: $24,310,414
Net Worth: $3,249,787
Earnings: ($5,115,719)
Emp.: 139
Fiscal Year-end: 12/31/23
Digital Marketing Services
N.A.I.C.S.: 541810
Johan Adalberth *(CFO)*

READY MADE CLOTHES CO.
Al-Mahmoodiah Near MIB, Baghdad, Iraq
Tel.: (964) 7814101541
Year Founded: 1976
IRMC—(IRAQ)
Sales Range: Less than $1 Million
Apparels Mfr
N.A.I.C.S.: 315990
Adnan Farhan Mohammed *(Mng Dir)*

READY MIX CONCRETE & CONSTRUCTION SUPPLIES P.L.C
Albayader Branch, PO Box 851602, Amman, 11185, Jordan
Tel.: (962) 65858109
Web Site: https://kingdomconcrete.jo
Year Founded: 1995
RMCC—(AMM)
Rev.: $31,558,996
Assets: $76,754,562
Liabilities: $42,343,890
Net Worth: $34,410,673
Earnings: ($6,498,281)
Emp.: 345
Fiscal Year-end: 12/31/20
Readymix Concrete Mfr
N.A.I.C.S.: 327320

READYPLANET PUBLIC COMPANY LIMITED
51 Major Tower Rama 9-Ramkumhang 17th Floor Unit 1701-1706 Rama 9 Road, Huamak Bangkapi, Bangkok, 10240, Thailand
Tel.: (66) 2166789
Web Site: https://www.readyplanet.com
READY—(THA)
Rev.: $5,543,263
Assets: $11,108,420
Liabilities: $4,846,451
Net Worth: $6,261,969
Earnings: $878,386
Emp.: 130
Fiscal Year-end: 12/31/23
Digital Marketing Services
N.A.I.C.S.: 541810
Ananya Sangratanadech *(Sr VP)*

REAGENS S.P.A.
Via Codronchi 4, San Giorgio di Piano, 40016, Bologna, Italy
Tel.: (39) 0516639111 IT
Web Site: http://www.reagens-group.com
Year Founded: 1952
Sales Range: $50-74.9 Million
Emp.: 200
Polyvinyl Chloride Specialty Chemical Additive & Other Thermoplastic Stabilizer Mfr
N.A.I.C.S.: 325180
Ettore Nanni *(CEO)*

Subsidiaries:

REAGENS (UK) LIMITED (1)
Unit 7 St George s Court Hanover Business Park, Dairyhouse Lane, Altrincham, WA14 5UA, Cheshire, United Kingdom
Tel.: (44) 161 9297222
Emp.: 10
Additive & Thermoplastic Mfr
N.A.I.C.S.: 325211
Steve Harrison *(Mgr-Technical Sls)*

REAGENS IBERICA S.L. (1)
C/ Baixada Sant Sever 1 1 4, Sant Cugat del Valles, 08172, Barcelona, Spain
Tel.: (34) 93 5441762
Web Site: http://www.reagens.it
Emp.: 2
Additive & Thermoplastic Mfr
N.A.I.C.S.: 325211
Rafael Erro *(Area Mgr)*

Reagens Deutschland GmbH (1)
Gewerbering 25, Lohne, 49393, Germany
Tel.: (49) 44429430
Web Site: http://www.reagen.it

INTERNATIONAL PUBLIC

Sales Range: $75-99.9 Million
Polyvinyl Chloride Specialty Chemical Additives & Other Thermoplastic Stabilizers Mfr
N.A.I.C.S.: 325180
Ettore Nanni *(CEO)*

Reagens U.S.A. Inc. (1)
9640 Bayport Blvd, Pasadena, TX 77507 (100%)
Tel.: (281) 291-8484
Web Site: http://www.reagensusa.com
Polyvinyl Chloride Specialty Chemical Additives & Other Thermoplastic Stabilizers Mfr
N.A.I.C.S.: 325180
Craig Bastian *(Pres)*

REAL AI PIC SECURITIZADORA DE CREDITOS IMOBILIARIOS S.A.
Rua George Eastman 280-Sala Vila Tramontano, Sao Paulo, 05690-000, Brazil
Tel.: (55) 11 3759 3320
Commercial Property Management Services
N.A.I.C.S.: 531312

REAL BULLAND JSC
19 Georg Vashigtov Str 1 floor, 1301, Sofia, 1301, Bulgaria
Tel.: (359) 24219518
Web Site: https://www.realbulland.eu
RBL—(BUL)
Sales Range: Less than $1 Million
Real Estate Manangement Services
N.A.I.C.S.: 531390
Ivan Yanev *(Exec Dir)*

REAL ESTATE & INVESTMENT PORTFOLIO COMPANY
Issam Ajlouni Street - Mahfaza Building 33, PO Box 926660, Shmeisani, Amman, 11190, Jordan
Tel.: (962) 65609000
Web Site: https://aqariya.jo
Year Founded: 1995
AQAR—(AMM)
Rev.: $149,820
Assets: $10,558,928
Liabilities: $527,062
Net Worth: $10,031,866
Earnings: ($22,645)
Emp.: 2
Fiscal Year-end: 12/31/20
Financial Investment & Real Estate Development Services
N.A.I.C.S.: 523999
Mohammad Belbeisi *(Chm)*

REAL ESTATE 11 JOINT STOCK COMPANY
205 Lac Long Quan Ward 3, District 11, Ho Chi Minh City, Vietnam
Tel.: (84) 839634001
Web Site: https://www.diaoc11.com.vn
D11—(HNX)
Rev.: $13,391,200
Assets: $34,497,300
Liabilities: $16,161,300
Net Worth: $18,336,000
Earnings: $2,181,300
Fiscal Year-end: 12/31/22
Real Estate Manangement Services
N.A.I.C.S.: 531390
Trah Thi Kim Hue *(Chm-Mgmt Bd & Gen Dir)*

REAL ESTATE CREDIT INVESTMENTS LTD.
East Wing Trafalgar Court Les Banques, PO Box 656, Saint Peter Port, GY1 3PP, Guernsey
Tel.: (44) 1481727111 GY
Web Site: https://realestatecreditinvest.com
RECI—(LSE)
Rev.: $39,584,619

Assets: $444,650,261
Liabilities: $32,656,207
Net Worth: $411,994,054
Earnings: $27,588,399
Fiscal Year-end: 03/31/24
Real Estate Investment Services
N.A.I.C.S.: 531390
Bob Cowdell *(Chm)*

REAL ESTATE DEVELOPMENT CO.
Wasfi Al-Tal St Redco Complex, PO Box 962756, Amman, 11196, Jordan
Tel.: (962) 5510352
Web Site: http://www.redv.com.jo
REDV—(AMM)
Assets: $67,437,732
Liabilities: $17,243,063
Net Worth: $50,194,668
Earnings: ($1,888,203)
Emp.: 16
Fiscal Year-end: 12/31/19
Real Estate Development Services
N.A.I.C.S.: 531390
Munther Abu Awad *(Gen Mgr-Acting)*

Subsidiaries:

Daret Amman for Housing Projects LLC (1)
Dabuq Amir Ben Malek ST Alazhar Building First Floor, PO Box 2191, 11941, Amman, Jordan
Tel.: (962) 65155311
Web Site: http://www.daretamman.com
Emp.: 30
Building Construction Services
N.A.I.C.S.: 236220

REAL ESTATE INVESTMENTS ZAMBIA PLC.
Central Park Cairo Road, PO Box 30012, Lusaka, Zambia
Tel.: (260) 211227684   ZM
Web Site:
  https://www.realinvestzambia.com
Year Founded: 1981
REIZ—(LUS)
Rev.: $2,242,487
Assets: $36,541,986
Liabilities: $9,211,354
Net Worth: $27,330,632
Earnings: $2,714,784
Emp.: 18
Fiscal Year-end: 12/31/22
Real Estate Development Services
N.A.I.C.S.: 531390
Kenny H. Makala *(Chm)*

REAL ESTATE INVESTORS PLC
2nd Floor 75/77 Colmore Row, Birmingham, B3 2AP, United Kingdom
Tel.: (44) 1212123446
Web Site: https://www.reiplc.com
Year Founded: 2004
RLE—(AIM)
Rev.: $16,779,854
Assets: $235,316,839
Liabilities: $97,769,503
Net Worth: $137,547,337
Earnings: $13,802,070
Emp.: 7
Fiscal Year-end: 12/31/22
Real Estate Investment Services
N.A.I.C.S.: 531390
Paul P. S. Bassi *(CEO)*

REAL ESTATE SOFIA REIT
ul Georgi Rakovski 132 vh A et 1 ofis 3, Sofia, Bulgaria
Tel.: (359) 29811041
RSSA—(BUL)
Sales Range: Less than $1 Million
Real Estate Investment Services
N.A.I.C.S.: 531210

REAL ESTATE TRADE CEN-

TERS COMPANY (K.S.C.C.)
Salhiya Complex Entrance 2 First Floor, PO Box 26400, Safat, 13124, Kuwait, 13124, Kuwait
Tel.: (965) 22412170
Web Site:
  https://www.marakezkw.com
Year Founded: 1999
MARAKEZ—(KUW)
Rev.: $2,151,633
Assets: $95,860,658
Liabilities: $14,555,842
Net Worth: $81,304,817
Earnings: $1,317,189
Emp.: 14
Fiscal Year-end: 12/31/22
Real Estate Manangement Services
N.A.I.C.S.: 531390
Talal Abdul Hameed Dashti *(Chm)*

REAL ESTATES INVESTMENT FUND
Tel.: (359) 28054850
FINI—(BUL)
Sales Range: Less than $1 Million
Financial Investment Fund Services
N.A.I.C.S.: 523999
Dobrin Stefkin *(Dir-Investor Relations)*

REAL GOLD MINING LIMITED
3/F Building B Wealth Plaza New City District, Chifeng, China
Tel.: (86) 4768823620
Web Site:
  http://www.realgoldmining.com
Sales Range: $200-249.9 Million
Emp.: 534
Gold Mining Services
N.A.I.C.S.: 212220
Feng Li *(CFO)*

REAL GOOD FOOD PLC
61 Stephenson Way Wavertree, Liverpool, L13 1 HN, United Kingdom
Tel.: (44) 1515413790   UK
Web Site:
  http://www.realgoodfoodplc.com
RGD—(AIM)
Rev.: $40,285,234
Assets: $39,485,515
Liabilities: $48,462,487
Net Worth: ($8,976,972)
Earnings: ($11,179,925)
Emp.: 202
Fiscal Year-end: 03/31/23
Bakery Product & Food Ingredient Distr
N.A.I.C.S.: 311812
Mike J. Holt *(Chm)*

Subsidiaries:

Renshawnapier Limited (1)
61 Stephenson Way, Wavertree, Liverpool, L13 1HN, United Kingdom (100%)
Tel.: (44) 1517068200
Web Site: https://www.renshawbaking.com
Sales Range: $50-74.9 Million
Emp.: 200
Food Product Packing & Mfr
N.A.I.C.S.: 311423
John Easton *(Mng Dir-R & W Scott)*

REAL GROWTH COMMERCIAL ENTERPRISES LIMITED
G-01 Ground Floor Plot No SU, LSC B-Block RG City Centre, New Delhi, 110035, India
Tel.: (91) 9871714221   In
Web Site:
  https://www.realgrowth.co.in
Year Founded: 1995
Rev.: $31,172,780
Assets: $15,848,342
Liabilities: $13,459,727
Net Worth: $2,388,616
Earnings: $151,617
Emp.: 5

Fiscal Year-end: 03/31/18
Steel Trading Services
N.A.I.C.S.: 523160
Deepak Gupta *(Exec Dir)*

REAL MATTERS, INC.
50 Minthorn Blvd Ste 401, Markham, L3T 7X8, ON, Canada
Tel.: (905) 739-1212
Web Site:
  https://www.realmatters.com
Sales Range: $100-124.9 Million
Real Estate Information Services
N.A.I.C.S.: 519290
Kim Montgomery *(Exec VP)*

Subsidiaries:

Linear Title & Closing, Ltd. (1)
Ocean Tech Plaza 127 John Clarke Rd, Middletown, RI 02842 (100%)
Tel.: (401) 841-9991
Web Site: http://www.lineartitle.com
Sales Range: $1-9.9 Million
Emp.: 500
Direct Title Insurance Services
N.A.I.C.S.: 524127
Nick Liuzza *(Pres & CEO)*

Solidifi Inc. (1)
701 Seneca St Ste 660, Buffalo, NY 14210
Tel.: (312) 268-5679
Web Site: http://www.solidifi.com
Real Estate Appraisal Solution Service
N.A.I.C.S.: 531320
Jason Smith *(CEO)*

Subsidiary (Domestic):

Kirchmeyer & Associates, Inc. (2)
701 Seneca St Ste 660, Buffalo, NY 14210
Tel.: (716) 558-2800
Web Site: http://www.solidifi.com
Sales Range: $1-9.9 Million
Emp.: 80
Real Estate Appraisal & Consulting Services
N.A.I.C.S.: 531320

Southwest Financial Services, Ltd. (2)
537 E Pete Rose Way Ste 300, Cincinnati, OH 45202
Tel.: (513) 621-6699
Web Site: http://www.sfsltd.com
Sales Range: $1-9.9 Million
Emp.: 160
Loan Settlement Services
N.A.I.C.S.: 522320
Greg Schroeder *(Pres)*

iv3 Solutions Inc. (1)
50 Minthorn Blvd Suite 301, Markham, L3T 7X8, ON, Canada
Web Site: http://www.iv3solutions.com
Real Estate Inspection Services
N.A.I.C.S.: 541350
Brian Lang *(CEO)*

REAL NEWS & VIEWS LIMITED
4th Floor KARM Corporate House Opp Vikramnagar Nr Newyork Timber, Ambli Bopal Road, Ahmedabad, 380059, India
Tel.: (91) 7926936006
Web Site: http://realnewsviews.in
Year Founded: 1993
530053—(BOM)
Rev.: $426,012
Assets: $2,158,402
Liabilities: $997,200
Net Worth: $1,161,202
Earnings: ($217,343)
Fiscal Year-end: 03/31/19
Real Estate Development Services
N.A.I.C.S.: 531390
Dharm Swetank Patel *(Mng Dir & Compliance Officer)*

REAL NUTRICEUTICAL GROUP LIMITED
28th Floor The Hennessy 256 Hen-

nessy Road, Wanchai, China (Hong Kong)
Tel.: (852) 3709 9886   Ky
Web Site: http://www.ruinian.com.hk
Year Founded: 1997
Sales Range: $50-74.9 Million
Nutritional Supplements, Health Drinks & Pharmaceuticals Mfr & Sales
N.A.I.C.S.: 325412
Fucai Wang *(Founder, Chm & CEO)*

REAL STRIPS LTD
Survey No 245-256 Village Sari Ahmedabad - Bavla Highway Taluka Sanand, Ahmedabad, 382220, Gujarat, India
Tel.: (91) 9228002011
Web Site: http://www.realstrips.com
513558—(BOM)
Rev.: $14,943,125
Assets: $13,089,457
Liabilities: $14,607,642
Net Worth: ($1,518,185)
Earnings: $636,995
Fiscal Year-end: 03/31/20
Stainless Steel Products Mfr
N.A.I.C.S.: 334416
Amritlal K. Kataria *(Chm)*

REAL TIME MEASUREMENTS, INC.
125 4615-112th Ave S E, Calgary, T2C 5J3, AB, Canada
Tel.: (403) 720-3444
Web Site: http://www.rty.ca
Year Founded: 1995
Electric Equipment Mfr
N.A.I.C.S.: 334512

REAL TOUCH FINANCE LTD.
Arihant Enclave Ground Floor 493B/57A G T Road South, Shibpur, Howrah, 711102, India
Tel.: (91) 3326402042
Web Site:
  https://www.realtouchfinance.com
Year Founded: 1984
538611—(BOM)
Rev.: $1,232,637
Assets: $15,732,899
Liabilities: $11,033,485
Net Worth: $4,699,414
Earnings: $314,082
Emp.: 38
Fiscal Year-end: 03/31/23
Investment Management Service
N.A.I.C.S.: 525990
Arindam Laha *(CFO)*

REALCAN PHARMACEUTICAL CO.,LTD.
No 326 Jichang Road, Zhifu District, Yantai, 264004, Shandong, China
Tel.: (86) 5356735656
Web Site: http://www.realcan.cn
Year Founded: 2004
002589—(SSE)
Rev.: $3,226,559,701
Assets: $4,044,279,774
Liabilities: $2,559,190,730
Net Worth: $1,485,089,044
Earnings: $20,098,088
Fiscal Year-end: 12/31/21
Pharmaceutical Products Distr
N.A.I.C.S.: 424210

REALCO SA
Avenue Albert Einstein 15, 1348, Louvain-la-Neuve, Belgium
Tel.: (32) 10453000
Web Site: https://www.realco.be
REAL—(EUR)
Sales Range: $10-24.9 Million
Biotechnology Research & Development Services

REALCO SA

Realco SA—(Continued)
N.A.I.C.S.: 541714
George Blackman *(CEO & Mng Dir)*

Subsidiaries:

Realzyme LLC (1)
219 S Pioneer Blvd Ste E, Springboro, OH 45066
Tel.: (937) 350-5660
Web Site: http://www.realzyme.com
Biotechnology Products Mfr
N.A.I.C.S.: 325411

REALFICTION HOLDING AB
Antonigade 11 1st floor DK, 1106, Copenhagen, Denmark
Tel.: (45) 70206490
Web Site: https://www.realfiction.com
Year Founded: 2008
REALFI—(OMX)
Rev.: $2,069,179
Assets: $8,647,616
Liabilities: $1,736,585
Net Worth: $6,911,031
Earnings: ($130,003)
Emp.: 11
Fiscal Year-end: 12/31/22
Electronic Components Mfr
N.A.I.C.S.: 334419
Clas Dyrholm *(Founder & CEO)*

REALIA BUSINESS S.A.
Paseo de la Castellana 216, 28046, Madrid, Spain
Tel.: (34) 913534400
Web Site: https://www.realia.es
RLIA—(MAD)
Rev.: $182,753,861
Assets: $2,331,240,845
Liabilities: $997,599,020
Net Worth: $1,333,641,825
Earnings: $80,666,266
Emp.: 90
Fiscal Year-end: 12/31/21
Residential & Non Residential Properties Business
N.A.I.C.S.: 237210
Jose Maria Richi Alberti *(Asst Sec)*

REALIA PROPERTIES INC.
151 Yonge Street 11th Floor, Toronto, M5C 2W7, ON, Canada
Tel.: (647) 775-8337
Web Site: https://www.realiaproperties.com
Year Founded: 2008
RLP—(TSXV)
Rev.: $3,452,916
Assets: $38,091,546
Liabilities: $34,267,731
Net Worth: $3,823,815
Earnings: ($230,801)
Fiscal Year-end: 12/31/22
Real Estate Services
N.A.I.C.S.: 531190
Kyra Dorn *(CFO)*

REALITES SA
1 Impasse Claude Nougaro, 44800, Saint-Herblain, France
Tel.: (33) 240755091
Web Site: https://www.realites.com
Year Founded: 2003
ALREA—(EUR)
Sales Range: $75-99.9 Million
Real Estate Investment Promotion
N.A.I.C.S.: 531390
Yoann Joubert *(Chm & CEO)*

REALLY USEFUL HOLDINGS LIMITED
6 Catherine Street, London, WC2B 5JY, United Kingdom
Tel.: (44) 2072400880 UK
Web Site: http://www.reallyuseful.com
Year Founded: 1977
Sales Range: $150-199.9 Million
Emp.: 40
Copyrights in Musical & Dramatic Works; Marketing of Rights in Theater Productions, Recordings, Music Publishing, Films, Videos & Television
N.A.I.C.S.: 512230

Subsidiaries:

Really Useful Company Asia Pacific Pty Ltd (1)
L 1 24 Bay St, Double Bay, 2028, NSW, Australia
Tel.: (61) 293632499
Theater Operator
N.A.I.C.S.: 711110

The Really Useful Company (Australia) Pty. Ltd. (1)
24 Bay Street 1st Fl, Double Bay, Sydney, 2028, NSW, Australia (100%)
Tel.: (61) 293632449
Web Site: http://www.reallyuseful.com
Theatrical Producer
N.A.I.C.S.: 561311

The Really Useful Company, Inc. (1)
250 W 57th St Ste 1311, New York, NY 10019-3409 (100%)
Tel.: (212) 486-1150
Web Site: http://www.reallyuseful.com
Theatre Production
N.A.I.C.S.: 711110

The Really Useful Group Limited (1)
22 Tower St, London, WC2H 9TW, United Kingdom (100%)
Tel.: (44) 2072400880
Web Site: http://www.reallyuseful.com
Sales Range: $25-49.9 Million
Record Production Company
N.A.I.C.S.: 512250
Max Alexander *(Mng Dir)*

The Really Useful Picture Company (1)
17 Slingsby Place, London, WC2E 9AB, United Kingdom (100%)
Tel.: (44) 20 7557 7300
Web Site: http://www.reallyuseful.com
Sales Range: $25-49.9 Million
Film Production
N.A.I.C.S.: 512110

The Really Useful Theater Company Limited (1)
22 Tower St, London, WC2H 9TW, United Kingdom (100%)
Tel.: (44) 2072400880
Web Site: http://www.reallyuseful.com
Theatre Production
N.A.I.C.S.: 711130

REALORD GROUP HOLDINGS LIMITED
Suites 2403-2410 24/F Jardine House, 1 Connaught Place, Central, China (Hong Kong)
Tel.: (852) 21486118
Web Site: http://www.realord.com
1196—(HKG)
Rev.: $152,848,275
Assets: $2,533,383,818
Liabilities: $1,874,839,305
Net Worth: $658,544,513
Earnings: $77,158,155
Emp.: 478
Fiscal Year-end: 12/31/22
Paper Cartons, Packaging Boxes & Books Mfr & Sales
N.A.I.C.S.: 322299
Xiaohui Lin *(Chm)*

Subsidiaries:

Optima Capital Limited (1)
Suite 1501 15th Floor Jardine House 1 Connaught Place, Central, China (Hong Kong)
Tel.: (852) 3 523 6288
Web Site: https://www.optima-capital.hk
Financial Advisory Services
N.A.I.C.S.: 523940
Mei Leung *(Chm)*

Qualiti Printing & Sourcing Limited (1)
1 Kwai Ting Rd, Kwai Chung, China (Hong Kong)
Tel.: (852) 24858162
Financial Services
N.A.I.C.S.: 523940

Realord Asia Pacific Securities Limited (1)
Room 2402 24th Floor Jardine House 1 Connaught Place, Central, China (Hong Kong)
Tel.: (852) 3 755 5888
Web Site: https://www.realordapsec.com.hk
Investment Services
N.A.I.C.S.: 523150

Realord Environmental Protection Japan Co., Ltd. (1)
2F Taiga Bld 3-6-2 Bingo-machi, Chuo-ku, Osaka, Japan
Tel.: (81) 64 256 1811
Web Site: https://en.realord.co.jp
Material Recovery Services
N.A.I.C.S.: 562920

Realord Manureen Securities Limited (1)
Suites 2402 24/F Jardine House 1 Connaught Place, Central, China (Hong Kong)
Tel.: (852) 37555888
Web Site: http://www.manureen.com.hk
Financial Services
N.A.I.C.S.: 523940

Realord, Shenzhen Technology Co., Ltd. (1)
Bonded Zone Road Fantasia Fu Plaza building 311 B, Futian, Shenzhen, China
Tel.: (86) 88263888
Real Estate Development Services
N.A.I.C.S.: 531390

Strabens Hall (Hong Kong) Limited (1)
Level 7 Nan Fung Tower 88 Connaught Road Central, Central, China (Hong Kong)
Tel.: (852) 34783600
Web Site: http://strabenshall.co.uk
Financial Services
N.A.I.C.S.: 541611

REALTECH AG
Paul-Ehrlich-Strasse 1, 69181, Leimen, Germany
Tel.: (49) 62249871100 De
Web Site: https://www.realtech.com
Year Founded: 1994
RTC—(DEU)
Rev.: $11,667,906
Assets: $9,393,934
Liabilities: $2,296,050
Net Worth: $7,097,884
Earnings: $264,929
Emp.: 66
Fiscal Year-end: 12/31/23
Information Technology Consulting & Systems Management Software Solutions
N.A.I.C.S.: 513210
Daniele Di Croce *(CEO & Member-Exec Bd)*

Subsidiaries:

Globe Technology GmbH (1)
Industriestr 39C, 69190, Walldorf, Baden-Wurttemberg, Germany
Tel.: (49) 62278370
Sales Range: $75-99.9 Million
Emp.: 300
System Management Software Development Services
N.A.I.C.S.: 541511

REALTECH Consulting GmbH (1)
Industriestr 39C, 69190, Walldorf, Baden-Wurttemberg, Germany
Tel.: (49) 62278370
Web Site: http://www.realtech.com
Sales Range: $75-99.9 Million
Emp.: 300
Software Consulting Services
N.A.I.C.S.: 541618
Chris Kohlsdorf *(Gen Mgr)*

INTERNATIONAL PUBLIC

REALTECH Ltd. (1)
Level 4 90 Symonds Street, Grafton, Auckland, 1010, New Zealand
Tel.: (64) 93080900
Web Site: https://www.realtech.co.nz
Enterprise Resource Planning Software Development Services
N.A.I.C.S.: 541511
Joanne Hand *(Mng Dir)*

REALTECH Portugal System Consulting Sociedade Unipessol Lda. (1)
Avenida Da Lgreja 42-7 Esq, Lisbon, 1700 036, Portugal
Tel.: (351) 217997130
Web Site: http://www.realtech.com
Sales Range: $25-49.9 Million
Emp.: 11
Information Technology Consulting Services
N.A.I.C.S.: 541512
Pedra Bonniz *(Gen Mgr)*

REALTECH Service GmbH (1)
Industriestr 39C, 69190, Walldorf, Baden-Wurttemberg, Germany
Tel.: (49) 62278370
Information Technology Consulting Services
N.A.I.C.S.: 541512

REALTECH Verwaltungs GmbH (1)
Industriestr 39C, 69190, Walldorf, Baden-Wurttemberg, Germany
Tel.: (49) 62278370
Web Site: http://www.realtech.com
Sales Range: $75-99.9 Million
Emp.: 300
Software Consulting Services
N.A.I.C.S.: 541618
Peter Weimsbach *(Gen Mgr)*

REALTECH JAPAN CO., LTD.
Aim Tokyo Kudan Bldg 3 F 1-2-11 Kudan-kita, Chiyoda-ku, Tokyo, 102-0073, Japan
Tel.: (81) 332382066 JP
Web Site: http://www.realtech.com
Sales Range: $25-49.9 Million
Emp.: 30
Information Technology Consulting Services
N.A.I.C.S.: 541512
Kavuya Matsura *(Pres)*

REALTECH SYSTEM CONSULTING SL
Torrelaguna 77-4 Planta, 28043, Madrid, Spain
Tel.: (34) 915560013
Web Site: http://www.realtech.com
Software Consulting Services
N.A.I.C.S.: 541512
Jose Pablo de Pedro *(Gen Mgr)*

REALTEK SEMICONDUCTOR CORP.
No 2 Innovation Road II Hsinchu Science Park, Hsin-chu, 300, Taiwan
Tel.: (886) 35780211
Web Site: https://www.realtek.com
Year Founded: 1987
RTKSM—(LUX)
Rev.: $3,112,569,816
Assets: $3,067,963,846
Liabilities: $1,686,683,870
Net Worth: $1,381,279,977
Earnings: $299,317,756
Emp.: 7,268
Fiscal Year-end: 12/31/23
Integrated Circuits, Electronics & Computer Peripherals Mfr
N.A.I.C.S.: 334413
Nan-Horng Yeh *(Chm)*

Subsidiaries:

Bobitag Inc. (1)
6F NO 250 Sec 1 Neihu Rd, Neihu Dist, Taipei, 11493, Taiwan
Tel.: (886) 97 875 8375
Web Site: https://www.bobitag.org
Internet Services
N.A.I.C.S.: 517121

AND PRIVATE COMPANIES

C-Media Electronics Inc (1)
6th Floor 100 Sec 4 Civil Blvd, 106, Taipei, Taiwan
Tel.: (886) 287731100
Computer & Computer Peripheral Equipment & Software Whslr
N.A.I.C.S.: 423430

Cortina Access Inc. (1)
2130 Gold St Ste 250, San Jose, CA 95002
Tel.: (408) 481-2300
Web Site: https://www.cortina-access.com
Internet Services
N.A.I.C.S.: 517121
Zino Chair (Gen Mgr)

Cortina Network Systems Shanghai Co., Ltd. (1)
Room 901 9F Building 2 No 58 Xiangbei Road, Zhangjiang Pudong, Shanghai, China
Tel.: (86) 212 035 3333
Internet Services
N.A.I.C.S.: 517121

Cortina Systems Taiwan Limited (1)
No 2 Innovation Road II Hsinchu Science Park, Hsinchu, 300, Taiwan
Tel.: (886) 3 527 6999
Internet Services
N.A.I.C.S.: 517121

Realsil Microelectronics (SuZhou) Co., Ltd. (1)
No 128 West Shenhu Road Suzhou Industrial Park, Suzhou, Jiangsu, China
Tel.: (86) 51262588966
Research & Development Services
N.A.I.C.S.: 541713

Realtek Semiconductor (Japan) Corp. (1)
KAKIYA Building 8F 2-7-17 Shin-Yokohama, Kohoku-ku, Yokohama, 222-0033, Kanagawa, Japan
Tel.: (81) 454784649
Web Site: https://www.realtek.co.jp
Semiconductor Mfr & Distr
N.A.I.C.S.: 334413

Realtek Semiconductor Corp. (1)
No 2 Innovation Road II Hsinchu Science Park, Hsin-chu, 300, Taiwan (48.53%)
Tel.: (886) 35780211
Web Site: http://www.realtek.com
Semiconductor Mfr
N.A.I.C.S.: 333242

REAM REAL ESTATE COMPANY KPSC
Khaled Ibn Al Waleed Street Injazat Tower 3rd floor, PO Box 29910, Safat, 13153, Kuwait, Kuwait
Tel.: (965) 222 86900
Web Site: http://www.ream.com.kw
Year Founded: 1993
Rev.: $9,721,699
Assets: $81,253,874
Liabilities: $27,483,896
Net Worth: $53,769,979
Earnings: $2,982,832
Emp.: 133
Fiscal Year-end: 12/31/17
Real Estate Management Services
N.A.I.C.S.: 531390
Shlash Haif Al Hajraf (CEO)

REBOSIS PROPERTY FUND LTD.
2nd Floor Roland Garros Building The CampusCorner Main & Sloane Street, Bryanston, Johannesburg, South Africa
Tel.: (27) 115754835
Web Site: https://www.rebosis.co.za
Year Founded: 2010
REB—(JSE)
Rev.: $116,322,188
Assets: $936,853,917
Liabilities: $699,448,519
Net Worth: $237,405,398
Earnings: $7,435,160
Emp.: 211
Fiscal Year-end: 08/31/20
Investment Management Service
N.A.I.C.S.: 525990
Sisa Ngebulana (CEO)

Subsidiaries:

Ascension Properties Limited (1)
70 Pretoria Road Rynfield, Benoni, South Africa
Tel.: (27) 11 425 1263
Web Site: https://www.ascentionproperties.co.za
Real Estate Services
N.A.I.C.S.: 531390

REBRISA SA
Av Las Condes 7700 Floor 1 Tower A, Santiago, Chile
Tel.: (56) 264692571
Web Site: https://www.rebrisa.cl
REBRISA-B—(SGO)
Sales Range: Less than $1 Million
Asset Management Services
N.A.I.C.S.: 523940
Avram Fricth Vaturi (Chm)

REC NARODA A.D.
Takovska 5, 12000, Pozarevac, Serbia
Tel.: (381) 12532309
Web Site: https://www.recnaroda.co.rs
Year Founded: 2006
RNRD—(BEL)
Rev.: $216,975
Assets: $121,054
Liabilities: $18,058
Net Worth: $102,996
Earnings: 4,997
Emp.: 7
Fiscal Year-end: 12/31/23
Newspaper Publication Services
N.A.I.C.S.: 513110

REC SILICON ASA
Lysaker Torg 5 3rd floor, PO Box 63, 1324, Lysaker, Norway
Tel.: (47) 40724086 NO
Web Site: https://www.recsilicon.com
RNWEF—(OTCIQ)
Rev.: $141,100,000
Assets: $552,900,000
Liabilities: $476,500,000
Net Worth: $76,400,000
Earnings: $133,500,000
Emp.: 495
Fiscal Year-end: 12/31/23
Silicon Materials Mfr
N.A.I.C.S.: 334413
Tore Torvund (Pres & CEO)

Subsidiaries:

REC Silicon Inc. (1)
1616 S Pioneer Way, Moses Lake, WA 98837
Tel.: (509) 793-9000
Web Site: http://www.recsilicon.com
Silicon Wafers Mfr
N.A.I.C.S.: 334413

Subsidiary (Domestic):

REC Advanced Silicon Materials LLC (2)
119140 Rick Jones Way, Butte, MT 59750
Tel.: (406) 496-9898
Emp.: 510
Silicon Materials Mfr
N.A.I.C.S.: 334413
Richard Green (Dir-Ops)

REC Solar Grade Silicon LLC (2)
3322 Rd N NE, Moses Lake, WA 98837
Tel.: (509) 765-2106
Web Site: http://www.recgroup.com
Polycrystalline Silicon Material Mfr
N.A.I.C.S.: 334413

REC Technology US Inc. (2)
1159 Triton Dr, Foster City, CA 94404
Tel.: (650) 212-1244
Web Site: http://www.recgroup.com
Silicon Materials Research & Development Services
N.A.I.C.S.: 541715

RECCE PHARMACEUTICALS LTD
Suite 10 3 Brodie Hall Drive Technology Park, Bentley, 6102, WA, Australia
Tel.: (61) 893629860 AU
Web Site: https://www.recce.com.au
Year Founded: 2008
R9Q—(DEU)
Rev.: $2,433,383
Assets: $9,672,016
Liabilities: $1,963,104
Net Worth: $7,708,912
Earnings: ($8,417,576)
Fiscal Year-end: 06/30/22
Pharmaceutical Preparation Manufacturing
N.A.I.C.S.: 325412
Graham J. H. Melrose (Founder)

RECHARGE METALS LIMITED
Level 2 16 Ord St, West Perth, 6005, WA, Australia
Tel.: (61) 894810389 AU
Web Site: https://www.rechargemetals.com.au
Year Founded: 2021
REC—(ASX)
Rev.: $10,111
Assets: $9,482,376
Liabilities: $604,754
Net Worth: $8,877,622
Earnings: ($1,058,251)
Fiscal Year-end: 06/30/23
Metal Exploration Services
N.A.I.C.S.: 213114

RECHARGE RESOURCES LTD.
Royal Centre Suite 1500 1055 West Georgia Street, PO Box 11117, Vancouver, V6E 4N7, BC, Canada
Tel.: (778) 588-5473 BC
Web Site: https://recharge-resources.com
Year Founded: 2010
RR—(CNSX)
Rev.: $190,304
Assets: $5,710,629
Liabilities: $256,515
Net Worth: $5,454,114
Earnings: ($7,517,992)
Fiscal Year-end: 12/31/23
Metal Mining Services
N.A.I.C.S.: 212290
Natasha Sever (CFO)

RECHI PRECISION CO., LTD.
No 943 Sec 2 Chenggong Rd, Guanyin Dist, Taoyuan, 328, Taiwan
Tel.: (886) 34837201
Web Site: https://www.rechi.com
Year Founded: 1989
4532—(TAI)
Rev.: $551,348,781
Assets: $803,930,641
Liabilities: $450,711,419
Net Worth: $353,219,222
Earnings: $26,195,035
Emp.: 3,071
Fiscal Year-end: 12/31/23
Pump Sets Mfr
N.A.I.C.S.: 333996
Sheng-Tien Chen (Chm)

Subsidiaries:

Dongguan Rechi Compressor Co., Ltd. (1)
No 48 Gaokersan Road Xinlian Administrative Division, Humen Town, Dongguan, Guangdong, China
Tel.: (86) 76985528857
Compressor Mfr & Distr
N.A.I.C.S.: 333912

Rechi Precision (Qingdao) Electric Machinery CO., LTD. (1)
No 500 Fenjin Road, Economic Technological District, Qingdao, Shandong, China
Tel.: (86) 53289603000
Compressor Assembling Services
N.A.I.C.S.: 561910

Rechi Precision Mechanism (Huizhou) Co., Ltd. (1)
No 7 East Road Lejin Sonshan Industrial Zone, Guangdong, China
Tel.: (86) 7532611222
Compressor Mfr & Distr
N.A.I.C.S.: 336390

Rechi Precision(Jiujiang) Electric Machinery Co., Ltd. (1)
No 13 No 15 Riverside Road West of Port Development Zone, Jiujiang, Jiangxi, China
Tel.: (86) 7922131888
Compressor Mfr & Distr
N.A.I.C.S.: 333912

TCL Rechi (Huizhou) Refrigeration Equipment Ltd. (1)
No 7 East Road Lejin, Sonshan Industrial Zone, Huizhou, Guangdong, China
Tel.: (86) 7522611222
Compressor Assembly Mfr
N.A.I.C.S.: 333415

RECIPHARM AB
Drottninggatan 29, PO Box 603, SE-101 32, Stockholm, Sweden
Tel.: (46) 86025200 SE
Web Site: http://www.recipharm.com
Year Founded: 1995
Rev.: $826,205,681
Assets: $1,474,862,823
Liabilities: $865,022,655
Net Worth: $609,840,168
Earnings: $36,759,310
Emp.: 6,873
Fiscal Year-end: 12/31/19
Pharmaceuticals Mfr
N.A.I.C.S.: 325412
Thomas Eldered (CEO)

Subsidiaries:

Arranta Bio Holdings LLC (1)
650 Pleasant St, Watertown, MA 02472
Tel.: (833) 177-1682
Web Site: https://arrantabio.com
Contract Development & Mfr
N.A.I.C.S.: 325412

Biologici Italia Laboratories S.r.l. (1)
Via F Serpero 2, 20060, Masate, Italy
Tel.: (39) 029500461
Pharmaceuticals Product Mfr
N.A.I.C.S.: 325412

Edmond Pharma S.r.l. (1)
Strada Statale de Giovi 131, 20037, Paderno Dugnano, MI, Italy
Tel.: (39) 029100111
Pharmaceuticals Product Mfr
N.A.I.C.S.: 325412

Kaysersberg Pharmaceuticals S.A.S. (1)
23 Avenue Georges Ferrenbach, 68240, Kaysersberg, France
Tel.: (33) 389787600
Pharmaceuticals Product Mfr
N.A.I.C.S.: 325412

LIO Immobiliare S.r.l. (1)
Well Road Area Via Frejus N 127/E, Turin, Italy
Tel.: (39) 0113822728
Web Site: http://www.lioimmobiliare.it
Real Estate Management Services
N.A.I.C.S.: 531210

Liosintex S.r.l. (1)
Via Mantova 8/12, 20020, Lainate, MI, Italy
Tel.: (39) 029372032
Pharmaceuticals Product Mfr
N.A.I.C.S.: 325412

Mitim S.r.l. (1)
Via Cacclamali 34, 25125, Brescia, Italy
Tel.: (39) 030349761
Pharmaceuticals Product Mfr
N.A.I.C.S.: 325412

RECIPHARM AB

Recipharm AB—(Continued)

RPH Pharmaceuticals AB (1)
Lagervagen 7, 136 50, Jordbro, Sweden
Tel.: (46) 86025200
Pharmaceuticals Product Mfr
N.A.I.C.S.: 325412

Recipharm Fontaine S.A.S. (1)
Rue des Pres-Potets, Fontaine-Les-Dijon, 21121, Bourgogne, France
Tel.: (33) 380447800
Pharmaceuticals Product Mfr
N.A.I.C.S.: 325412

Recipharm Holdings Limited (1)
Vale of Bardsley, Ashton-under-Lyne, Manchester, OL7 9RR, Lancs, United Kingdom
Tel.: (44) 161 342 6000
Holding Company; Pharmaceutical Products Mfr
N.A.I.C.S.: 551112

Subsidiary (Domestic):

Consort Medical plc (2)
Suite B Breakspear Park Breakspear Way, Hemel Hempstead, HP2 4TZ, Herts, United Kingdom
Tel.: (44) 1442867920
Web Site: http://www.consortmedical.com
Rev.: $387,178,002
Assets: $590,855,712
Liabilities: $288,575,148
Net Worth: $302,280,564
Earnings: $13,324,710
Emp.: 2,053
Fiscal Year-end: 04/30/2019
Holding Company; Drug Delivery Devices Mfr
N.A.I.C.S.: 551112
Jonathan Glenn (CEO)

Division (Domestic):

Bespak Europe Ltd. (3)
Bergen Way, King's Lynn, Norfolk, PE30 2JJ, United Kingdom (100%)
Tel.: (44) 1553691000
Web Site: http://www.bespak.com
Sales Range: $150-199.9 Million
Emp.: 450
Mfr & Distr of Drug Delivery Devices Including Inhalers & Metered Dose Valves
N.A.I.C.S.: 424210
Keyvan Djamarani (Mng Dir)

Unit (Domestic):

Bespak Europe Ltd. - Injectables (4)
199 Newhall Road, Sheffield, S9 2QJ, South Yorkshire, United Kingdom
Tel.: (44) 1142619011
Web Site: http://www.bespakinjectables.com
Sales Range: $25-49.9 Million
Emp.: 20
Injectors Mfr & Distr
N.A.I.C.S.: 339113

Subsidiary (US):

Consort Medical Inc. (3)
2500 Regency Pkwy, Cary, NC 27511-8549 (100%)
Tel.: (919) 387-0112
Web Site: http://www.bespak.com
Mfr & Distr of Drug Delivery Devices Including Inhalers & Metered Dose Valves
N.A.I.C.S.: 332999

H&M Rubber Inc (3)
4200 Mogadore Rd, Kent, OH 44240-7258
Tel.: (330) 678-3323
Sales Range: $50-74.9 Million
Emp.: 103
Rubber Products Mfr
N.A.I.C.S.: 326299

Recipharm Israel Ltd. (1)
Hamazmera 9, 74140, Ness Ziona, Israel
Tel.: (972) 544785711
Pharmaceuticals Product Mfr
N.A.I.C.S.: 325412

Recipharm Laboratories, Inc. (1)
511 Davis Dr Ste 100, Morrisville, NC 27560
Tel.: (919) 884-2064
Web Site: http://www.recipharm.com
Sales Range: $10-24.9 Million
Contract Pharmaceutical Research, Development & Manufacturing Services

Recipharm Leganes S.L.U. (1)
Calle Severo Ochoa 13, Leganes, 28914, Madrid, Spain
Tel.: (34) 916851060
Pharmaceuticals Product Mfr
N.A.I.C.S.: 325412
Guillaume Hery (Project Mgr)

Recipharm Ltd. (1)
Vale of Bardsley, Ashton under Lyne, OL7 9RR, Lancashire, United Kingdom
Tel.: (44) 1613426000
Pharmaceuticals Product Mfr
N.A.I.C.S.: 325412

Recipharm Pharmaservices Pvt. Ltd. (1)
34th KM Tumkur Road, T-Begur Nelamangala, Bengaluru, 562 123, India
Tel.: (91) 80 3928 5450
Web Site: http://www.recipharm.com
Emp.: 1,200
Contract Pharmaceutical Research, Development & Manufacturing Services
N.A.I.C.S.: 325412
Anurag Bagaria (Mng Dir)

Recipharm Stockholm AB (1)
Branningevagen 12, 120 54, Arsta, Sweden
Tel.: (46) 86025200
Pharmaceuticals Product Mfr
N.A.I.C.S.: 325412

Recipharm Venture Fund AB (1)
Box 603, 101 32, Stockholm, Sweden
Tel.: (46) 86025200
Pharmaceuticals Product Mfr
N.A.I.C.S.: 325412

Wasserburger Arzneimittelwerk GmbH (1)
Herderstrasse 2, 83512, Wasserburg am Inn, Germany
Tel.: (49) 807110080
Pharmaceuticals Product Mfr
N.A.I.C.S.: 325412

RECKITT BENCKISER GROUP PLC

103 - 105 Bath Road, Slough, SL1 3UH, Berkshire, United Kingdom
Tel.: (44) 1753217800 UK
Web Site: https://www.reckitt.com
Year Founded: 1823
RBGLY—(OTCIQ)
Rev.: $17,968,066,480
Assets: $36,585,123,120
Liabilities: $26,466,035,960
Net Worth: $10,119,087,160
Earnings: ($28,512,120)
Emp.: 41,800
Fiscal Year-end: 12/31/21
Healthcare Technology Services
N.A.I.C.S.: 541511
Nicandro Durante (CEO)

Subsidiaries:

Durex Limited (1)
Tel.: (44) 3332005345
Web Site: http://www.durex.co.uk
Condom Mfr
N.A.I.C.S.: 326299

Mead Johnson Nutrition (India) Private Limited (1)
3rd Floor Piramal Towers Peninsula Corporate Park, GK Marg Lower Parel, Mumbai, 400 013, India (100%)
Tel.: (91) 2267854100
Pediatric Nutritional Product Mfr
N.A.I.C.S.: 311514

Mead Johnson Nutrition (Philippines), Inc. (1)
2309 Don Chino Roces Avenue, Makati, 1231, Philippines (99.96%)
Tel.: (63) 8418181
Web Site: http://www.meadjohnson.com
Pediatric Nutritional Products Mfr & Distr
N.A.I.C.S.: 311514

Mead Johnson Nutrition (Vietnam) Company Limited (1)
4th Floor The Metropolitan Building 235 Dong khoi, District 1, 9999, Ho Chi Minh City, Vietnam (100%)
Tel.: (84) 838245058
Baby Formulas Mfr
N.A.I.C.S.: 311514

Optrex Limited (1)
Tel.: (44) 3332005345
Web Site: http://www.optrex.co.uk
Eye Care Service
N.A.I.C.S.: 621320

Oxy Reckitt Benckiser LLC (1)
24th floor Two IFC International Finance Center 10 Gukjegeumyung-ro, Yeongdeungpo-gu, Seoul, 150-945, Korea (South)
Tel.: (82) 800229547
Web Site: https://www.reckitt.com
Polish & Other Sanitation Good Mfr
N.A.I.C.S.: 325612

PT Reckitt Benckiser Indonesia (1)
Level 58 Jl Jend Sudirman Kav 52-53, Treasury Tower - District 8, Jakarta, 12190, Indonesia
Tel.: (62) 2151400178
Hygiene & Home Product Distr
N.A.I.C.S.: 424690
Nirma Hutagalung (Mgr-Sls Fin)

RB NL Brands B.V. (1)
Siriusdreef 14, PO Box 721, 2132 WT, Hoofddorp, Netherlands
Tel.: (31) 235584500
Polish & Other Sanitation Good Mfr
N.A.I.C.S.: 325612

Reckitt Benckiser (Australia) Pty. Ltd. (1)
Level 47 World Square 680 George Street, Sydney, 2000, NSW, Australia (100%)
Tel.: (61) 1800226766
Web Site: http://www.rb.com.au
Sales Range: $200-249.9 Million
Emp.: 600
Household Product Mfr & Distr
N.A.I.C.S.: 325612

Reckitt Benckiser (Belgium) SA/NV (1)
Researchdreef/Allee de la Recherche 20, 1070, Brussels, Belgium
Tel.; (32) 25261811
Polish & Other Sanitation Good Mfr
N.A.I.C.S.: 325612

Reckitt Benckiser (Brazil) Ltda. (1)
8015 Km 18, Sao Paulo, 05577-900, Brazil (100%)
Tel.: (55) 1137837000
Web Site: http://www.rb.com
Mfr & Distr of Household Consumer Products
N.A.I.C.S.: 325612

Reckitt Benckiser (Canada) Inc. (1)
1680 Tech Avenue Unit 2, Mississauga, L4W 5S9, ON, Canada (100%)
Tel.: (905) 283-7000
Web Site: http://www.reckittbenckiser.com
Household Product Mfr & Distr
N.A.I.C.S.: 325612

Reckitt Benckiser (Centroamerica) SA (1)
Oficentro Plaza Roble Edificio Los Balcones 3er Piso Escazu Apartado, 4413 - 1000, San Jose, Costa Rica
Tel.: (506) 22018081
Hygiene & Home Product Distr
N.A.I.C.S.: 424690

Reckitt Benckiser (Czech Republic) Spol s. r. o. (1)
Palac Flora Budova A B Vinohradska 151, 130 00, Prague, 3, Czech Republic
Tel.: (420) 224317996
Hygiene & Home Product Distr
N.A.I.C.S.: 424690

Reckitt Benckiser (Egypt) Limited (1)
22 Polyium Building Section 1 5th Settlement, New Cairo, Egypt
Tel.: (20) 226189720
Hygiene & Home Product Distr
N.A.I.C.S.: 424690

Reckitt Benckiser (Hungary) Kft. (1)
Bocskai ut 134-146, Budapest, 1113, Hungary

INTERNATIONAL PUBLIC

Tel.: (36) 14534600
Web Site: http://www.reckittbenckiser.com
Emp.: 130
Pharmaceutical Preparation Mfr
N.A.I.C.S.: 325412

Reckitt Benckiser (India) Ltd. (1)
6th & 7th Floor Tower C DLF Cyber Park 405 B Udyog Vihar Phase III, Sector 20, Gurgaon, 122016, Haryana, India (100%)
Tel.: (91) 1244028000
Sales Range: $50-74.9 Million
Emp.: 250
Mfr & Distr Household Consumer Products
N.A.I.C.S.: 325611

Reckitt Benckiser (Lanka) Limited (1)
No 25 Shrubbery Gardens, 400, Colombo, Sri Lanka
Tel.: (94) 112550900
Hygiene & Home Product Distr
N.A.I.C.S.: 424690

Reckitt Benckiser (Latvia) SIA (1)
Strelnieku Str 1A-2, Riga, 1010, Latvia
Tel.: (371) 67320956
Polish & Other Sanitation Good Mfr
N.A.I.C.S.: 325612

Reckitt Benckiser (Malaysia) Sdn Bhd (1)
Level 5 Menara UAC No 12 Jalan PJU 7/5, Mutiara Damansara, 47800, Petaling Jaya, Selangor, Malaysia
Tel.: (60) 377191000
Hygiene & Home Product Distr
N.A.I.C.S.: 424690

Reckitt Benckiser (Near East) Limited (1)
6 Hangar Street I Z Neve Neeman B, PO Box 6440, Hod Hasharon, 45250, Israel
Tel.: (972) 99611700
Polish & Other Sanitation Good Mfr
N.A.I.C.S.: 325612

Reckitt Benckiser (New Zealand) Limited (1)
Level 1 2 Fred Thomas Drive, Takapuna, Auckland, 0622, New Zealand
Tel.: (64) 98390202
Hygiene & Home Product Distr
N.A.I.C.S.: 424690

Reckitt Benckiser (Planet d.o.o) (1)
Safeta Zajke 271, 71000, Sarajevo, Bosnia & Herzegovina
Tel.: (387) 33491219
Polish & Other Sanitation Good Mfr
N.A.I.C.S.: 325612
Ermin Tarcin (Mgr-Brand)

Reckitt Benckiser (Portugal) SA (1)
Edificio Restelo Rua D Cristovao da Gama Nr 1 -1 C/D, 1400-103, Lisbon, Portugal
Tel.: (351) 213033003
Hygiene & Home Product Distr
N.A.I.C.S.: 424690

Reckitt Benckiser (Romania) Srl (1)
Blvd Iancu de Hunedoara Nr 48 11th floor Crystal Tower Sector 1, 011745, Bucharest, Romania
Tel.: (40) 215296700
Hygiene & Home Product Distr
N.A.I.C.S.: 424690

Reckitt Benckiser (Singapore) Pte Limited (1)
12 Marina Boulevard 19-01 Marina Bay Financial Centre Tower 3, Singapore, 018982, Singapore
Tel.: (65) 66927800
Hygiene & Home Product Distr
N.A.I.C.S.: 424690

Reckitt Benckiser (Slovak Republic) Spol. s. r. o. (1)
Drienova 3, 821 08, Bratislava, Slovakia
Tel.: (421) 248213000
Hygiene & Home Product Distr
N.A.I.C.S.: 424690

Reckitt Benckiser (Switzerland) AG (1)
Richtistrasse 5, Wallisellen, 8304, Zurich, Switzerland
Tel.: (41) 448084949
Hygiene & Home Product Distr

AND PRIVATE COMPANIES

N.A.I.C.S.: 424690

Reckitt Benckiser (Turkey) A.S. (1)
Hakki Yeten Caddesi Suleyman Seba Kompleksi Selenium Plaza 10C K7, Fulya Besiktas, 34349, Istanbul, Turkiye
Tel.: (90) 2123269600
Polish & Other Sanitation Good Mfr
N.A.I.C.S.: 325612

Reckitt Benckiser (Zambia) Ltd. (1)
Zambia Road Skyways, PO Box 71914, Ndola, Zambia
Tel.: (260) 2651407
Hygiene & Home Product Distr
N.A.I.C.S.: 424690

Reckitt Benckiser (Zimbabwe) Pvt. Ltd. (1)
3 Melbourne Road Southerton, PO Box ST93, Harare, Zimbabwe
Tel.: (263) 4620311
Polish & Other Sanitation Good Mfr
N.A.I.C.S.: 325612

Reckitt Benckiser Arabia FZE (1)
Jafza One Tower B Level 27 Jebel Ali Free Zone, PO Box 61344, Dubai, United Arab Emirates
Tel.: (971) 48027500
Hygiene & Home Product Distr
N.A.I.C.S.: 424690
Abdulahad Maud *(Mgr-Shared Svcs)*

Reckitt Benckiser Argentina SA (1)
Ruta Provincial No 36 y Diagonal Perito, Moreno 8300 1890 Ingeniero Allan, Florencio Varela, Buenos Aires, Argentina
Tel.: (54) 1142294838
Hygiene & Home Product Distr
N.A.I.C.S.: 424690

Reckitt Benckiser Austria GmbH (1)
Guglgasse 15, 1110, Vienna, Austria
Tel.: (43) 800017916
Hygiene & Home Product Distr
N.A.I.C.S.: 424690

Reckitt Benckiser Bulgaria EOOD (1)
22 Zlaten Rog Str, 1407, Sofia, Bulgaria
Tel.: (359) 28689472
Polish & Other Sanitation Good Mfr
N.A.I.C.S.: 325612
Svetoslav Stoyanov *(Mgr-Demand Planning)*

Reckitt Benckiser Chile SA (1)
Avda Kennedy 5454 - of 1602, Vitacura, 13340, Santiago, Chile
Tel.: (56) 24298400
Hygiene & Home Product Distr
N.A.I.C.S.: 424690

Reckitt Benckiser Colombia SA (1)
Calle 46 No 5-76, Cali, Colombia
Tel.: (57) 26836100
Polish & Other Sanitation Good Mfr
N.A.I.C.S.: 325612

Reckitt Benckiser Deutschland GmbH (1)
Darwinstr 2-4, 69115, Heidelberg, Germany **(100%)**
Tel.: (49) 622199820
Web Site: https://www.reckitt.com
Sales Range: $25-49.9 Million
Emp.: 150
Mfr & Distr Household Consumer Products
N.A.I.C.S.: 325611

Reckitt Benckiser Espana SL (1)
Paseo De Gracia 9, 08007, Barcelona, 08007, Spain **(100%)**
Tel.: (34) 934813200
Sales Range: $25-49.9 Million
Emp.: 100
Mfr & Distr Household Consumer Products
N.A.I.C.S.: 325611

Reckitt Benckiser France (1)
38 Rue Victor Basch, CS 11018, 91305, Massy, Cedex, France **(100%)**
Tel.: (33) 801841395
Web Site: https://www.rb.com
Sales Range: $50-74.9 Million
Emp.: 200
Mfr & Distr of Household Consumer Products
N.A.I.C.S.: 325611

Reckitt Benckiser Healthcare (Italia) SpA (1)
Via Spadolini 7, 20141, Milan, Italy
Tel.: (39) 0800939388
Web Site: https://www.nutramigen.it
Polish & Other Sanitation Good Mfr
N.A.I.C.S.: 325612
Gabriela Filippini *(Mgr-Demand Planning Healthcare)*

Reckitt Benckiser Healthcare (UK) Ltd. (1)
103-105 Bath Road, Slough, SL1 3UH, Berkshire, United Kingdom **(100%)**
Tel.: (44) 1482326151
Sales Range: $400-449.9 Million
Emp.: 1,200
Healthcare Product Mfr & Marketer
N.A.I.C.S.: 325412

Reckitt Benckiser Hellas Chemicals SA (1)
7 Taki Kavalieratou Str, 145 64, Kifissia, Greece
Tel.: (30) 2108127100
Polish & Other Sanitation Good Mfr
N.A.I.C.S.: 325612
Anastasios Kriebardis *(Mgr-Medical & Regulatory Affairs)*

Reckitt Benckiser Hong Kong Limited (1)
Rooms 2206-11 22/F Chubb Tower Windsor House 311 Gloucester Road, Causeway Bay, China (Hong Kong)
Tel.: (852) 25980328
Web Site: https://www.corporate.reckitt.com.hk
Hygiene & Home Product Distr
N.A.I.C.S.: 424690

Reckitt Benckiser Household & Healthcare Ukraine LLC (1)
28A Moskovskiy Prospect Bld G Office 80, Kiev, Ukraine
Tel.: (380) 443905041
Polish & Other Sanitation Good Mfr
N.A.I.C.S.: 325612

Reckitt Benckiser Household Products (China) Company Limited (1)
Unit 05-09 6th Floor Tower D Parkview Green Fang Cao Di, No 9 Dongdaqiao Road Chaoyang District, Beijing, 100020, China
Tel.: (86) 1057692888
Polish & Other Sanitation Good Mfr
N.A.I.C.S.: 325612

Reckitt Benckiser Inc. (1)
399 Interpace Pkwy, Parsippany, NJ 07054-0225 **(100%)**
Tel.: (973) 404-2600
Web Site: http://www.rb.com
Sales Range: $125-149.9 Million
Emp.: 400
Mfr & Distr of Food & Household Consumer Products
N.A.I.C.S.: 325612

Reckitt Benckiser Ireland Limited (1)
7 Riverwalk Citywest Business Campus, Dublin, 24, Ireland
Tel.: (353) 14689200
Hygiene & Home Product Distr
N.A.I.C.S.: 424690

Reckitt Benckiser Italia SpA (1)
Via Spadolini 7, 20141, Milan, Italy **(100%)**
Tel.: (39) 02844751
Web Site: http://www.reckittbenckiser.it
Sales Range: $50-74.9 Million
Emp.: 150
Mfr & Distr Household Consumer Products
N.A.I.C.S.: 325611

Reckitt Benckiser Japan Limited (1)
Sumitomo Fudosan Takanawa Park Tower 14F 3-20-14 Higashi-Gotanda, Shinagawa, Shinagawa, Tokyo, 141-0022, Japan
Tel.: (81) 364096600
Hygiene & Home Product Distr
N.A.I.C.S.: 424690

Reckitt Benckiser Mexico, SA de CV (1)
Av Ejercito Nacional 769 - Piso 6 Col Granada Del, Miguel Hidalgo, 11570, Mexico, Mexico

Tel.: (52) 8009764100
Hygiene & Home Product Distr
N.A.I.C.S.: 424690

Reckitt Benckiser Nigeria Limited (1)
11th Floor Heritage Place 21 Lugard Avenue, Ikoyi, Lagos, Nigeria
Tel.: (234) 7058255292
Hygiene & Home Product Distr
N.A.I.C.S.: 424690

Reckitt Benckiser Nordic A/S (1)
Vandtarnsvej 83 A, 2860, Soborg, Denmark
Tel.: (45) 44449700
Hygiene & Home Product Distr
N.A.I.C.S.: 424690

Reckitt Benckiser Pakistan Limited (1)
3rd Floor Tenancy 04-05 Corporate Office Block Dolman City HC-3, Block 4 Scheme-5 Clifton, Karachi, 75800, Pakistan
Tel.: (92) 80082273
Hygiene & Home Product Distr
N.A.I.C.S.: 424690

Reckitt Benckiser Poland SA (1)
Mokotow Nova ul Woloska 22, 02-675, Warsaw, Poland **(100%)**
Tel.: (48) 22333310022
Web Site: http://www.reckittbenckiser.com
Sales Range: $25-49.9 Million
Emp.: 100
Mfr & Distr Household Consumer Products
N.A.I.C.S.: 325611

Reckitt Benckiser Services (Kenya) Limited (1)
14 Riverside Drive Arlington Building 3rd Floor, PO Box 78050, 00507, Nairobi, Kenya
Tel.: (254) 204299000
Polish & Other Sanitation Good Mfr
N.A.I.C.S.: 325612

Reckitt Benckiser South Africa (Pty) Limited (1)
8 Jet Park Road, Elandsfontein, 1406, South Africa
Tel.: (27) 118711831
Hygiene & Home Product Distr
N.A.I.C.S.: 424690

Reckitt Benckiser Taiwan Limited (1)
11F-B No 150 Dunhua North Road, Taipei, Taiwan
Tel.: (886) 227680669
Hygiene & Home Product Distr
N.A.I.C.S.: 424690

Reckitt Benckiser Venezuela SA (1)
Av Mara Con Calle San Jose C C Macaracuay Plaza Nivel C3 Local 5 y 12, Urb Colina De La California, Caracas, Venezuela
Tel.: (58) 2122581133
Hygiene & Home Product Distr
N.A.I.C.S.: 424690

Reckitt Benckiser d.o.o (1)
Ulica Grada Vukovara 269D, 10 000, Zagreb, Croatia
Tel.: (385) 16062555
Polish & Other Sanitation Good Mfr
N.A.I.C.S.: 325612

Reckitt Benckiser plc (1)
103-105 Bath Road, Slough, SL1 3UH, Berkshire, United Kingdom
Tel.: (44) 1753217800
Polish & Other Sanitation Good Mfr
N.A.I.C.S.: 325612

Schiff Nutrition International, Inc. (1)
2002 S 5070 W, Salt Lake City, UT 84104-4726 **(75%)**
Tel.: (801) 975-5000
Web Site: http://www.schiffnutrition.com
Emp.: 393
Health Foods, Nutritional Supplements, Vitamins & Personal Care Products Mfr
N.A.I.C.S.: 325411
David N. Chernoff *(Chief Medical Officer)*

Subsidiary (Non-US):

Atlantic Multipower Germany GmbH & Co. (2)
Holsteinischer Kamp 1, 22081, Hamburg, Germany **(100%)**
Tel.: (49) 402986601

Web Site: http://www.haleko.de
Sales Range: $25-49.9 Million
Emp.: 100
Mfr of Chocolate & Cocoa Products
N.A.I.C.S.: 311352

UpSpring, Ltd. (1)
4209 S Industrial Dr, Austin, TX 78744
Tel.: (512) 828-7988
Web Site: http://www.upspringbaby.com
Baby Textile Product Mfr
N.A.I.C.S.: 314999

RECKON LIMITED

Level 2 100 Pacific Highway, North Sydney, 2060, NSW, Australia
Tel.: (61) 291343300 AU
Web Site: https://www.reckon.com
Year Founded: 1987
RKN—(ASX)
Rev.: $34,199,813
Assets: $26,666,614
Liabilities: $14,705,893
Net Worth: $11,960,722
Earnings: $37,929,026
Emp.: 350
Fiscal Year-end: 12/31/22
Software Development Services
N.A.I.C.S.: 541511
Greg Wilkinson *(Co-Founder)*

Subsidiaries:

Reckon New Zealand Pty Limited (1)
12 Piermark Drive North Harbour North Shore City, Auckland, New Zealand
Tel.: (64) 94143650
Software Development Services
N.A.I.C.S.: 541511

SmartVault Corporation (1)
720 N Post Oak Rd Ste 300, Houston, TX 77024
Tel.: (713) 479-5400
Web Site: http://www.smartvault.com
Software Development Services
N.A.I.C.S.: 541511
Eric Pulaski *(Founder)*

nQueue Billback LLC (1)
7890 S Hardy Dr Ste 105, Tempe, AZ 85284
Tel.: (800) 299-5933
Web Site: http://www.nqueue.com
Software Development Services
N.A.I.C.S.: 541511
Rick Hellers *(Pres & CEO)*

RECLAIMS GLOBAL LIMITED

10 Tuas South Street 7, Singapore, 637114, Singapore
Tel.: (65) 66590516 SG
Web Site: https://www.reclaims-enterprise.com
Year Founded: 2009
NEX—(CAT)
Rev.: $19,830,308
Assets: $26,473,509
Liabilities: $4,569,100
Net Worth: $21,904,409
Earnings: $1,479,066
Emp.: 119
Fiscal Year-end: 01/31/23
Waste Recycling Services
N.A.I.C.S.: 236210
Chew Leh Chan *(Chm)*

RECLAY HOLDING GMBH

Im Zollhafen 2-4, 50678, Cologne, Germany
Tel.: (49) 221 580098 0
Web Site: http://www.reclay-group.com
Environmental & Waste Disposal Management Services
N.A.I.C.S.: 562998
Fritz Flanderka *(Mng Dir)*

Subsidiaries:

Curanus GmbH (1)
In der Schlenk 2, 56479, Elsoff, Germany

RECLAY HOLDING GMBH

Reclay Holding GmbH—(Continued)
Tel.: (49) 221 580098 0
Waste Management Services
N.A.I.C.S.: 562998
Martin Schurmann *(Mng Dir)*

REPLA Cycle GmbH (1)
Austrasse 34, 35745, Herborn, Germany
Tel.: (49) 221 580098 0
Waste Management Services
N.A.I.C.S.: 562998
Martin Schurmann *(Mng Dir)*

Reclay Ceska republika s.r.o. (1)
tr Kpt Jarose 26, 602 00, Brno, Czech Republic
Tel.: (420) 545216344
Business Consulting Services
N.A.I.C.S.: 541611
Lubomir Augustin *(Mng Dir)*

Reclay GmbH (1)
Austrasse 34, 35745, Herborn, Germany
Tel.: (49) 221 580098 0
Waste Management Services
N.A.I.C.S.: 562998
Raffael A. Fruscio *(Mng Dir)*

Reclay Osterreich GmbH (1)
Mariahilfer Strasse 37-39, 1060, Vienna, Austria
Tel.: (43) 1 9949969 0
Web Site: http://www.reclay-group.com
Emp.: 24
Waste Management Services
N.A.I.C.S.: 562998
Christian Abl *(Mng Dir)*

Reclay Slovakia, s.r.o. (1)
Bohrova 1, 85101, Bratislava, Slovakia
Tel.: (421) 243422151
Business Consulting Services
N.A.I.C.S.: 541611
Lubomir Augustin *(Mng Dir)*

Reclay StewardEdge Inc. (1)
130 King Street West Suite 1800, Toronto, M5X 2A2, ON, Canada
Tel.: (647) 777-3364
Web Site:
 http://www.reclaystewardedge.com
Business Consulting Services
N.A.I.C.S.: 541611
Ken Friesen *(Pres)*

Reclay UFH GmbH (1)
Mariahilfer Strasse 37-39, 1060, Vienna, Austria
Tel.: (43) 1 9949969 0
Web Site: http://www.reclay-group.com
Emp.: 26
Waste Management Services
N.A.I.C.S.: 562998
Walter Tanzer *(Mng Dir)*

Reclay Vfw GmbH (1)
Austrasse 34, 35745, Herborn, Germany
Tel.: (49) 2234 9587 0
Collection & Recycling Services
N.A.I.C.S.: 562219
Martin Schurmann *(Mng Dir)*

WEM GmbH (1)
Austrasse 34, 35745, Herborn, Germany
Tel.: (49) 221 580098 0
Waste Management Services
N.A.I.C.S.: 562998
Martin Schurmann *(Mng Dir)*

RECO INTERNATIONAL GROUP INC.

100-2051 Viceroy Place, Richmond, V6V 1Y9, BC, Canada
Tel.: (604) 273-2932
Web Site:
 http://www.recointernational.com
Year Founded: 1999
RGI—(TSXV)
Rev.: $2,302,523
Assets: $784,257
Liabilities: $1,425,593
Net Worth: ($641,337)
Earnings: ($510,589)
Fiscal Year-end: 09/30/23
Commercial Construction Services
N.A.I.C.S.: 236220
Hugh Yu Guang Zhen *(CEO)*

Subsidiaries:

Reco Decoration Group Inc. (1)
100-2051 Viceroy Place, Richmond, V6V 1Y9, BC, Canada
Tel.: (604) 273-2932
Web Site:
 http://www.recointernationalgroup.com
Emp.: 25
Commercial Furniture Mfr
N.A.I.C.S.: 337121
Hubert Lau *(Pres)*

RECOCHEM INC.

850 Montee De Liesse Road, Montreal, H4T 1P4, QC, Canada
Tel.: (514) 341-3550
Web Site: http://www.recochem.com
Year Founded: 1951
Sales Range: $100-124.9 Million
Emp.: 420
Industrial & Consumer Chemical Mfr & Distr
N.A.I.C.S.: 325998
Richard E. Boudreaux *(Pres & CEO)*

Subsidiaries:

Luyten S.A. (1)
Rue Roi Chevalier 1, 5024, Marche-les-Dames, Belgium
Tel.: (32) 81 58 85 87
Chemical Products Mfr
N.A.I.C.S.: 325998

Napierville Refineries Inc. (1)
175 rue de l Eglise, Napierville, J0J 1L0, QC, Canada
Tel.: (450) 245-0040
Chemical Products Mfr
N.A.I.C.S.: 325998

Recochem (B.C.) Inc. (1)
1745 Kingsway Avenue Port, Coquitlam, V3C 4P2, BC, Canada
Tel.: (604) 941-9404
Chemical Mfr & Distr
N.A.I.C.S.: 325998

Recochem (India) Private Limited (1)
5-B 5th Floor Fairy Manor R Sidhwa Marg, Fort, Mumbai, 400 001, India
Tel.: (91) 22 2266 047
Chemical Products Distr
N.A.I.C.S.: 424690

Recochem Central District Consumer Division (1)
8725 Holgate Crescent, Milton, L9T 5G7, ON, Canada
Tel.: (905) 878-5544
Sales Range: $75-99.9 Million
Emp.: 150
Chemicals Whslr
N.A.I.C.S.: 424690

Recochem Engine Coolants (Tianjin) Co., Ltd. (1)
No 5 Factory Building Chuang Ye Road Hai Fang Road Standard Factory, Park Nan Gang Industrial Area, Tianjin, China
Tel.: (86) 22 63117176
Chemical Products Distr
N.A.I.C.S.: 424690
Philip Wu *(Gen Mgr)*

Recochem Western District Consumer Division (1)
1745 Kingsway Avenue, Port Coquitlam, V3C 4P2, BC, Canada
Tel.: (604) 941-9404
Web Site: http://www.rechochem.com
Sales Range: $25-49.9 Million
Emp.: 50
Chemical Preparation Whslr
N.A.I.C.S.: 424690
Daniel Ko *(Gen Mgr)*

Recochem Western District Consumer Division (1)
604 - 22nd Avenue, Nisku, T9E 7X6, AB, Canada
Tel.: (780) 955-2644
Sales Range: $50-74.9 Million
Emp.: 80
Chemical Preparation Whslr
N.A.I.C.S.: 424690

Lawrence Winter *(Branch Mgr)*

RECOMM CO. LTD.

Aioi Nissay Dowa Sonpo Shinjuku Building 12F, 25-3 Yoyogi 3-chome Shibuya-ku, Tokyo, Japan
Tel.: (81) 344054566
Web Site: https://www.recomm.co.jp
Year Founded: 1994
3323—(TKS)
Rev.: $67,425,900
Assets: $76,876,870
Liabilities: $41,760,100
Net Worth: $35,116,770
Earnings: $2,226,260
Emp.: 514
Fiscal Year-end: 09/30/23
Information Communication Equipment Distr
N.A.I.C.S.: 423440
Hidehiro Ito *(Chm, CEO, Head-HR Dept & Gen Mgr)*

RECON TECHNOLOGY, LTD.

6th Floor Zhonghe Guoqing Building 1 Shuian South Street, Chaoyang District, Beijing, 100012, China
Tel.: (86) 1084945799
Web Site: https://www.recon.cn
RCON—(NASDAQ)
Rev.: $9,474,664
Assets: $76,011,327
Liabilities: $8,456,574
Net Worth: $67,554,753
Earnings: ($7,077,806)
Emp.: 184
Fiscal Year-end: 06/30/24
Petroleum Extraction Technology
N.A.I.C.S.: 213112
Guangqiang Chen *(Co-Founder, Chm & CTO)*

Subsidiaries:

Beijing BHD Petroleum Technology Co., Ltd. (1)
C-18 Jinglong International Building Fulin Road, Chaoyang District, Beijing, China
Tel.: (86) 1084945188
Oil & Gas Field Machinery Equipment Mfr
N.A.I.C.S.: 333132

RECONNAISSANCE ENERGY AFRICA LTD.

Suite 1250-635 8th Avenue SW, Calgary, T2P 3N3, AB, Canada
Tel.: (604) 423-5384
Web Site: https://reconafrica.com
Year Founded: 1978
0XD—(DEU)
Rev.: $89,045
Assets: $105,120,649
Liabilities: $4,023,209
Net Worth: $101,097,440
Earnings: ($47,485,289)
Emp.: 27
Fiscal Year-end: 03/31/24
Gold Exploration Services
N.A.I.C.S.: 212220
J. Jay Park *(Chm)*

RECONOMY (UK) LTD

Kelsall House Stafford Court Stafford Park 1, Telford, United Kingdom
Tel.: (44) 01952 292 000
Web Site: http://www.reconomy.com
Remediation Activities & Other Waste Management Services
N.A.I.C.S.: 562998

RECORD PLC

Morgan House Madeira Walk, Windsor, SL4 1EP, Berkshire, United Kingdom
Tel.: (44) 1753852222
Web Site: https://recordfg.com
REC—(LSE)
Rev.: $57,280,990

Assets: $45,525,120
Liabilities: $8,976,269
Net Worth: $36,548,851
Earnings: $11,680,131
Emp.: 97
Fiscal Year-end: 03/31/24
Specialist Currency Management Services
N.A.I.C.S.: 523999
Neil Record *(Chm)*

Subsidiaries:

N P Record Trustees Limited (1)
Morgan House Madeira Walk, Windsor, SL4 1EP, Berks, United Kingdom
Tel.: (44) 1753852222
Sales Range: $50-74.9 Million
Emp.: 70
Investment Management & Currency Hedging Services
N.A.I.C.S.: 523150
Neil Records *(Gen Mgr)*

Record Currency Management Limited (1)
Morgan House Madeira Walk, Windsor, SL4 1EP, Berkshire, United Kingdom
Tel.: (44) 1753852222
Web Site: http://www.recordcm.com
Sales Range: $50-74.9 Million
Emp.: 80
Investment Management & Currency Hedging Services
N.A.I.C.S.: 523150
Neil Record *(Chm)*

Record Group Services Limited (1)
Morgan House Madeira Walk, Windsor, SL4 1EP, Berkshire, United Kingdom
Tel.: (44) 1753852222
Web Site: http://www.ir.recordcm.com
Sales Range: $50-74.9 Million
Emp.: 70
Investment Management & Currency Hedging Services
N.A.I.C.S.: 523150
Neil Record *(Mng Dir)*

RECORD S.A.

Av Los Frutales 298 Ate, 03, Lima, Peru
Tel.: (51) 16184100
Web Site: https://www.record.com.pe
RECORDI1—(LIM)
Sales Range: Less than $1 Million
Home Product Mfr
N.A.I.C.S.: 335220
Karin Haustein Van Ginhoven *(VP)*

RECORDATI S.P.A.

Via Matteo Civitali 1, 20148, Milan, Italy
Tel.: (39) 02487871
Web Site: https://recordati.com
Year Founded: 1926
REC—(ITA)
Rev.: $1,940,710,090
Assets: $3,458,968,260
Liabilities: $1,762,001,170
Net Worth: $1,696,967,090
Earnings: $474,058,880
Emp.: 4,303
Fiscal Year-end: 12/31/21
OTC Pharmaceuticals & Pharmaceutical Chemicals Researcher, Marketer & Mfr
N.A.I.C.S.: 325412
Fritz Squindo *(Gen Mgr-Grp)*

Subsidiaries:

Bonafarma Produtos Farmaceuticos S.A. (1)
Av Jacques Delors Ed Inovacao 1 2 Piso 0 - Taguspark, 2740-122, Porto Salvo, Portugal
Tel.: (351) 214329500
Pharmaceuticals Mfr
N.A.I.C.S.: 325412

Bouchara Recordati S.A.S. (1)
Immeuble Le Wilson70 avenue du General De Gaulle, BP 67, 92800, Puteaux, France

AND PRIVATE COMPANIES   RECORDATI S.P.A.

Tel.: (33) 145191000
Web Site: http://www.grouprecordati.com
Sales Range: $25-49.9 Million
Emp.: 70
Pharmaceuticals Product Mfr
N.A.I.C.S.: 325412

Casen Recordati S.L. (1)
Via de las dos Castillas 33 3 Atica-Edificio 7, 28224, Pozuelo de Alarcon, Madrid, Spain
Tel.: (34) 913518800
Web Site: https://casenrecordati.com
Sales Range: $50-74.9 Million
Emp.: 230
Pharmaceuticals & Personal Care Products Mfr
N.A.I.C.S.: 325412

Ecordati Rare Diseases Germany GmbH (1)
Eberhard-Finckh-Strasse 55, 89075, Ulm, Germany
Tel.: (49) 7311405540
Health Care Srvices
N.A.I.C.S.: 622110

FIC Medical S.a.R.L. (1)
70 Avenue Du General De Gaulle, BP 67, 92800, Puteaux, France
Tel.: (33) 145191100
Pharmaceuticals Product Mfr
N.A.I.C.S.: 327910

Herbacos Recordati s.r.o. (1)
Tel.: (420) 227200722
Web Site: https://www.recordati.cz
Pharmaceuticals Product Mfr
N.A.I.C.S.: 325412

Innova Pharma SpA (1)
Via M Civitali 1, 20148, Milan, MI, Italy **(100%)**
Tel.: (39) 02487871
Web Site: https://www.recordati.com
Sales Range: $200-249.9 Million
Mfr of Pharmaceuticals
N.A.I.C.S.: 325412

Italchimici S.p.A (1)
Tel.: (39) 0308922255
Web Site: https://www.italchimici.it
Pharmaceuticals Product Mfr
N.A.I.C.S.: 325412

Jaba Recordati S.A. (1)
Tel.: (351) 214329500
Web Site: https://www.jaba-recordati.pt
Pharmaceutical Products Distr
N.A.I.C.S.: 424210

Jabafarma Produtos Farmaceuticos S.A. (1)
Tel.: (351) 214329500
Pharmaceuticals Product Mfr
N.A.I.C.S.: 325412

Laboratoires Bouchara Recordati S.A.S. (1)
70 Avenue du General De Gaulle, 92800, Puteaux, France
Tel.: (33) 145191000
Pharmaceutical Product Mfr & Distr
N.A.I.C.S.: 325412

Merckle Recordati GmbH (1)
Eberhard-Finckh-Strasse 55, 89075, Ulm, Baden-Wurttemberg, Germany
Tel.: (49) 73170470
Web Site: http://www.recordati.de
N.A.I.C.S.: 424210

Natural Point S.r.l (1)
Tel.: (39) 0227007247
Web Site: https://www.naturalpoint.it
Natural Healthy Supplement Retailer
N.A.I.C.S.: 456191

OPALIA Pharma S.A. (1)
Z I Kalaat El Andalous, 2022, Ariana, Tunisia
Tel.: (216) 70559070
Web Site: https://www.opaliarecordati.com
Emp.: 350
Pharmaceuticals Product Mfr
N.A.I.C.S.: 325412

Opalia Recordati S.A R.L. (1)
Z I Kalaat Al Andalouss, 2022, Ariana, Tunisia
Tel.: (216) 70559070

Pharmaceutical Product Mfr & Distr
N.A.I.C.S.: 325412

Orphan Europe S.A.R.L. (1)
Immeuble Le Wilson 70 Avenue du General de Gaulle, La Defense, 92058, Paris, Hauts-de-Seine, France
Tel.: (33) 147736458
Sales Range: $25-49.9 Million
Emp.: 60
Pharmaceuticals Product Mfr
N.A.I.C.S.: 325412

Subsidiary (Non-US):

Orphan Europe Benelux BVBA (2)
Koning Albert 1 laan 48 bus 3, 1780, Wemmel, Belgium
Tel.: (32) 24610136
Web Site: http://www.orphan-europe.com
Sales Range: $25-49.9 Million
Emp.: 5
Pharmaceutical Product Whslr
N.A.I.C.S.: 424210

Orphan Europe Germany GmbH (2)
Max-Planck-Str 6, 63128, Dietzenbach, Hesse, Germany
Tel.: (49) 6074914090
Web Site: http://www.orphan-europe.com
Sales Range: $25-49.9 Million
Emp.: 11
Pharmaceutical Products Distr
N.A.I.C.S.: 424210

Orphan Europe Italy S.r.l. (2)
Via Cellini 11, 20090, Segrate, Milan, Italy
Tel.: (39) 0226950139
Sales Range: $25-49.9 Million
Emp.: 9
Pharmaceutical Products Distr
N.A.I.C.S.: 424210

Orphan Europe Middle East FZ LLC (2)
Building A/P25 Unit 102, PO Box 505075, Dubai Healthcare City, Dubai, 505075, United Arab Emirates
Tel.: (971) 43635454
Web Site: http://www.orphan-europe.com
Sales Range: $25-49.9 Million
Emp.: 10
Pharmaceutical Products Distr
N.A.I.C.S.: 424210

Orphan Europe Nordic AB (2)
Banergatan 37, 115 22, Stockholm, Sweden
Tel.: (46) 854580230
Web Site: http://www.orphan-europe.com
Sales Range: $25-49.9 Million
Emp.: 3
Pharmaceutical Products Distr
N.A.I.C.S.: 424210

Orphan Europe Portugal Lda. (2)
Rua SA Miranda 40 - 1 Dt, 2785-728, Cascais, Portugal
Tel.: (351) 214 676 186
Sales Range: $25-49.9 Million
Emp.: 1
Pharmaceuticals Producut Sales
N.A.I.C.S.: 424210

Orphan Europe Spain S.L. (2)
Gran Via de les Corts Catalanes 649 Despacho No 1, 08010, Barcelona, Spain
Tel.: (34) 933425120
Sales Range: $25-49.9 Million
Emp.: 9
Pharmaceutical Products Distr
N.A.I.C.S.: 424210

Orphan Europe UK Ltd. (2)
Isis House 43 Station Road, Henley-on-Thames, RG9 1AT, Oxon, United Kingdom
Tel.: (44) 1491414333
Web Site: http://www.orphan-europe.com
Pharmaceutical Products Distr
N.A.I.C.S.: 424210

Recofarma Ilac Ve Hammaddeleri Sanayi Ve Ticaret L.S. (1)
Sumer Sok No 4/21, Mahallesi, 34485, Maslak, Istanbul, Turkiye
Tel.: (90) 2124019100
Health Care Srvices
N.A.I.C.S.: 622110

Recordati AB (1)
Jan Stenbecks Torg 17, 164 40, Kista, Sweden

Tel.: (46) 854580230
Pharmaceuticals Product Mfr
N.A.I.C.S.: 325412

Recordati AG (1)
Lindenstrasse 8, 6340, Baar, Switzerland
Tel.: (41) 417691000
Web Site: https://recordati.ch
Pharmaceuticals Product Mfr
N.A.I.C.S.: 325412

Recordati B.V. (1)
Burgemeester E Demunterlaan 5, 1090, Jette, Belgium
Tel.: (32) 24610136
Web Site: https://recordati.be
Health Care Srvices
N.A.I.C.S.: 622110

Recordati Bulgaria Ltd. (1)
84 Al Stamboliiski Blvd Floor 8 Office No 44, 1303, Sofia, Bulgaria
Tel.: (359) 28293937
Pharmaceuticals Mfr
N.A.I.C.S.: 325412

Recordati Espana S.L. (1)
Edificio Marina Calle Isla de la Palma 37-2, 28703, San Sebastian de los Reyes, Spain **(100%)**
Tel.: (34) 916591550
Web Site: http://www.recordati.es
Emp.: 100
Mfr of Pharmaceutical Products
N.A.I.C.S.: 325412

Recordati Hellas Pharmaceuticals S.A. (1)
7 Zoodochou Pigis Str, K Chalandri, 15231, Athens, Greece
Tel.: (30) 2106773822
Sales Range: $25-49.9 Million
Emp.: 37
Pharmaceutical Products Distr
N.A.I.C.S.: 424210

Recordati Ilac Sanayi Ve Ticaret A.S. (1)
Maslak Office Building Sumer Sokak No 4, Maslak, 34485, Istanbul, Turkiye
Tel.: (90) 2124019100
Web Site: https://www.recordati.com.tr
Pharmaceutical Product Mfr
N.A.I.C.S.: 325412

Recordati Ireland Ltd. (1)
Raheens East, Ringaskiddy, P43 KD30, Cork, Ireland
Tel.: (353) 214379400
Sales Range: $25-49.9 Million
Emp.: 40
Pharmaceuticals Product Mfr
N.A.I.C.S.: 325412

Recordati Pharma GmbH (1)
Eberhard-Finckh-Strasse 55, 89075, Ulm, Germany
Tel.: (49) 73170470
Web Site: https://recordati.de
Pharmaceuticals Mfr
N.A.I.C.S.: 325412

Recordati Pharmaceutical Chemicals Division (1)
Via M Civitali 1, 20148, Milan, Italy **(100%)**
Tel.: (39) 02487871
Web Site: http://www.recordati.it
Sales Range: $200-249.9 Million
Active Ingredients & Intermediates for Pharmaceuticals Mfr
N.A.I.C.S.: 325412

Plant (Domestic):

Recordati Pharmaceutical Chemicals Productions (2)
Via Mediana Cisterna 4, 04011, Campoverde di Aprilia, LT, Italy
Tel.: (39) 0692900010
Web Site: http://www.recordati.it
Sales Range: $100-124.9 Million
Mfr of Specialty Chemicals for Pharmaceuticals
N.A.I.C.S.: 325412

Recordati Pharmaceuticals Ltd. (1)
Tel.: (44) 1491576336
Web Site: http://www.recordati.it
Emp.: 2
Pharmaceutical Products Distr

N.A.I.C.S.: 325412

Recordati Polska Sp. z o.o. (1)
Al Armii Ludowej 26, 00-609, Warsaw, Poland
Tel.: (48) 222068450
Web Site: https://recordati.pl
Pharmaceuticals Mfr
N.A.I.C.S.: 325412

Recordati Rare Diseases Australia Pty. Ltd. (1)
Suite 1802 Level 18 233 Castlereagh Street, Sydney, 2000, NSW, Australia
Tel.: (61) 408061403
Web Site: https://www.recordatiraredisases.com.au
Health Care Srvices
N.A.I.C.S.: 622110

Recordati Rare Diseases Canada Inc. (1)
3080 Yonge Street Suite 6060, Toronto, M4N 3N1, ON, Canada
Tel.: (647) 255-8831
Rare Disease Treatment Services
N.A.I.C.S.: 622310

Recordati Rare Diseases Colombia S.A.S (1)
Carrera 7 N 127-48 Oficina 901, Bogota, Colombia
Tel.: (57) 16472780
Rare Disease Treatment Services
N.A.I.C.S.: 622310

Recordati Rare Diseases Comercio de Medicamentos Ltda. (1)
Tel.: (55) 1144145851
Rare Disease Treatment Services
N.A.I.C.S.: 622310

Recordati Rare Diseases Fzco (1)
Dubai Airport Free Zone Building 8E Office 402, Dubai, United Arab Emirates
Tel.: (971) 43635454
Health Care Srvices
N.A.I.C.S.: 622110

Recordati Rare Diseases Inc. (1)
Tel.: (908) 236-0888
Web Site: https://www.recordatiraredisases.com
Rare Disease Treatment Services
N.A.I.C.S.: 622310
Mohamed H. Ladha (Pres)

Recordati Rare Diseases Italy S.R.L. (1)
Via Matteo Civitali 1, 20148, Milan, Italy
Tel.: (39) 0248787173
Web Site: https://www.recordatiraredisases.com
Health Care Srvices
N.A.I.C.S.: 622110

Recordati Rare Diseases JAPAN K.K. (1)
Tel.: (81) 345102910
Pharmaceuticals Product Mfr
N.A.I.C.S.: 325412

Recordati Rare Diseases Middle East FZ-LLC (1)
Dubai Airport Free Zone Building 8E Office 402, Dubai, United Arab Emirates
Tel.: (971) 43635454
Health Care Srvices
N.A.I.C.S.: 622110

Recordati Rare Diseases S.A DE C.V. (1)
Av Insurgentes Sur 1647 Piso 4 Oficina 421, Colonia San Jose Insurgentes Benito Juarez Districto Federal, 03900, Mexico, Mexico
Tel.: (52) 5526140975
Rare Disease Treatment Services
N.A.I.C.S.: 622310

Recordati Rare Diseases S.A.R.L. (1)
Immeuble Le Wilson 70 avenue du General de Gaulle, 92800, Puteaux, France
Tel.: (33) 147736458
Health Care Srvices
N.A.I.C.S.: 622110

Recordati Rare Diseases Spain S.L. (1)

RECORDATI S.P.A.

Recordati S.p.A.—(Continued)
Via de las Dos Castillas 33 30 Atica-Edificio 7, 28224, Pozuelo de Alarcon, Madrid, Spain
Tel.: (34) 916592890
Health Care Srvices
N.A.I.C.S.: 622110

Recordati Rare Diseases Uk Limited (1)
Breakspear Park Breakspear Way, Hemel Hempstead, HP2 4TZ, United Kingdom
Tel.: (44) 1491414333
Web Site: https://www.recordatirarediseases.uk
Health Care Srvices
N.A.I.C.S.: 622110

Recordati Romania S.R.L. (1)
Tel.: (40) 216671741
Web Site: http://www.recordati.ro
Emp.: 1,700
Pharmaceuticals Product Mfr
N.A.I.C.S.: 325412

Recordati Ukraine LLC (1)
Tel.: (380) 443511863
Web Site: https://www.recordati.com.ua
Pharmaceuticals Product Mfr
N.A.I.C.S.: 325412

Rusfic LLC (1)
Tel.: (7) 4952258001
Web Site: https://rusfic.ru
Pharmaceuticals Product Mfr
N.A.I.C.S.: 325412

Tonipharm S.A.S (1)
Tel.: (33) 145191000
Web Site: http://www.tonipharm.com
Pharmaceutical Laboratory Services
N.A.I.C.S.: 541380

Yeni Recordatilac ve Hammaddeleri Sanayi ve Ticaret A.S. (1)
219 Dogan Arasli Caddesi, Esenyurt, 34510, Istanbul, Turkiye
Tel.: (90) 2126202850
Web Site: http://www.yeniilac.com.tr
Sales Range: $125-149.9 Million
Emp.: 350
Pharmaceuticals Product Mfr
N.A.I.C.S.: 325412
Ismail Yormaz *(Gen Mgr)*

RECREATE ASA

Dokkvegen 11, 3920, Porsgrunn, Norway
Tel.: (47) 94009888
Web Site: https://www.recreate.no
Year Founded: 2010
RCR—(EUR)
Rev.: $25,170,266
Assets: $340,788,127
Liabilities: $287,076,537
Net Worth: $53,711,590
Earnings: ($40,124,440)
Emp.: 44
Fiscal Year-end: 12/31/22
Real Estate Investment Services
N.A.I.C.S.: 531190
Eirik Engaas *(CFO)*

RECRUIT HOLDINGS CO., LTD.

1-9-2 Marunouchi, Chiyoda-ku, Tokyo, 100-6640, Japan
Tel.: (81) 368351111   JP
Web Site: https://recruit-holdings.com
Year Founded: 1960
6098—(TKS)
Rev.: $22,583,012,120
Assets: $20,786,110,060
Liabilities: $7,507,281,060
Net Worth: $13,278,829,000
Earnings: $2,337,652,940
Emp.: 51,000
Fiscal Year-end: 03/31/24
Holding Company; Human Resource Recruitment, Training & Placement Services
N.A.I.C.S.: 551112
Masumi Minegishi *(Chm)*

Subsidiaries:

Advantage Resourcing America, Inc.
220 Norwood Park S, Norwood, MA 02062
Tel.: (781) 251-8000
Web Site: http://www.advantageresourcing.com
Staffing Services
N.A.I.C.S.: 561311

Chandler Macleod Group Limited (1)
Level 5 345 George St, Sydney, 2000, NSW, Australia
Tel.: (61) 9 2269 8666
Web Site: http://www.chandlermacleod.com
Sales Range: $1-4.9 Billion
Emp.: 1,000
Human Resources Outsourcing & Recruitment Services
N.A.I.C.S.: 541612
Hitoshi Motohara *(Chm)*

Subsidiary (Domestic):

Aurion Corporation Pty Limited (2)
Level 2 555 Coronation Drive, Toowong, 4066, QLD, Australia
Tel.: (61) 1300287466
Web Site: http://www.aurion.com
Sales Range: $25-49.9 Million
Emp.: 60
Payroll & Human Resources Software & IT Services
N.A.I.C.S.: 513210

CMHR Pty Limited (2)
Level 5 345 George Street, Sydney, 2000, NSW, Australia
Tel.: (61) 292698666
Recruitment Services
N.A.I.C.S.: 561311

Branch (Domestic):

Chandler Macleod - Brisbane (2)
Level 7 120 Edward Street, Brisbane, 4000, QLD, Australia
Tel.: (61) 730037755
Web Site: http://www.chandlermacleod.com
Emp.: 50
Recruitment Services
N.A.I.C.S.: 561311

Chandler Macleod - Perth (2)
Level 15 108 St Georges Terrace, Perth, 6000, WA, Australia
Tel.: (61) 892170510
Web Site: http://www.chandlermacleod.com
Sales Range: $25-49.9 Million
Emp.: 10
Human Resources Recruiting & Consulting Services
N.A.I.C.S.: 561311
Tania Sinibaldi *(COO-Staffing Svcs)*

Subsidiary (Non-US):

Chandler Macleod Group Pte. Ltd.
26 China Street Far East Square #02-01, Singapore, 049568, Singapore
Tel.: (65) 6225 5077
Web Site: http://www.chandlermacleod.asia
Sales Range: $10-24.9 Million
Emp.: 15
Employment Agency
N.A.I.C.S.: 561311
May Chan *(Mgr-Fin)*

Subsidiary (Domestic):

Chandler Macleod Medical Pty Limited
Level 5 345 George Street, Sydney, 2000, NSW, Australia
Tel.: (61) 292698666
Employment Services in Medical Industry
N.A.I.C.S.: 561311

Chandler Macleod People Insights Pty Ltd (2)
Level 5 345 George Street, Sydney, 2000, NSW, Australia
Tel.: (61) 289137777
Web Site: http://www.chandlermacleod.com
Emp.: 100
Professional & Management Services
N.A.I.C.S.: 541618
Jessica Yang *(Dir-Comml)*

Chandler Macleod Services Pty Limited (2)
Level 13 345 George St, Sydney, 2000, NSW, Australia
Tel.: (61) 292698666
Web Site: http://www.chandlermacleod.com
Recruitment Services
N.A.I.C.S.: 561311

Subsidiary (Non-US):

OCG Consulting Ltd. (3)
Level 8 AMP Centre 29 Customs Street West, Auckland, 1010, New Zealand
Tel.: (64) 9 377 7575
Web Site: http://www.ocg.co.nz
Sales Range: $25-49.9 Million
Human Resources Recruitment & Consulting
N.A.I.C.S.: 561311
Greg McAllister *(Gen Mgr)*

Subsidiary (Domestic):

Chandler Macleod Technical and Engineering Pty Ltd (2)
Level 5 345 George Street, Sydney, 2000, NSW, Australia
Tel.: (61) 292698666
Emp.: 220
Employment Placement Services in Technical & Engineering Fields
N.A.I.C.S.: 561311

Ready Workforce (A Division of Chandler Macleod) Pty Ltd (2)
Level 5 345 George Street, Sydney, 2000, NSW, Australia
Tel.: (61) 289137777
Recruitment Services
N.A.I.C.S.: 561311

Subsidiary (Domestic):

Ready Workforce Australia Pty Ltd (3)
Level 5 345 George Street, Sydney, 2000, NSW, Australia
Tel.: (61) 292698666
Sales Range: $25-49.9 Million
Emp.: 10
Recruitment Services
N.A.I.C.S.: 561311

Glassdoor, Inc. (1)
100 Shoreline Hwy, Mill Valley, CA 94965
Tel.: (415) 339-9105
Web Site: http://www.glassdoor.com
Employment Information Website
N.A.I.C.S.: 513140
Robert Hohman *(Co-Founder & Chm)*

Indeed, Inc. (1)
6433 Champion Grandview Way Bldg 1, Austin, TX 78750
Web Site: https://in.indeed.com
Emp.: 14,600
Employment Services
N.A.I.C.S.: 561311
Rajatish Mukherjee *(Exec VP & Gen Mgr-Employer)*

Media Factory, Inc. (1)
8-4-17 Ginza, Chuo-ku, Tokyo, Japan (100%)
Tel.: (81) 3 5469 4880
Web Site: http://www.mediafactory.co.jp
Sales Range: $75-99.9 Million
Emp.: 168
Book, Periodical & Other Media Publisher
N.A.I.C.S.: 513130

PeopleBank Australia Ltd. (1)
Level 5 345 George St, Sydney, 2000, NSW, Australia
Tel.: (61) 282674600
Web Site: http://www.peoplebank.com.au
Emp.: 225
Information Technology Recruiting Services
N.A.I.C.S.: 561311
Peter Acheson *(CEO)*

RGF International Recruitment Holdings Limited (1)
Unit 903 9/F Tower 2 Silvercord 30 Canton Road, Tsim Tsa Tsui, Kowloon, China (Hong Kong)
Tel.: (852) 25372557
Web Site: https://www.rgf-hr.com
Emp.: 51,000

INTERNATIONAL PUBLIC

Employment Services
N.A.I.C.S.: 561311

RGF Staffing APEJ Pty. Ltd. (1)
Level 13 345 George Street, Sydney, 2000, NSW, Australia
Tel.: (61) 292698888
Web Site: https://www.rgfstaffing.com.au
Emp.: 1,000
Staffing & Recruitment Services
N.A.I.C.S.: 541612

RGF Staffing B.V. (1)
PJ Oudweg 61, 1314 CK, Almere, Netherlands
Tel.: (31) 365299500
Web Site: https://www.rgfstaffing.com
Holding Company; Staffing & Human Resources Services
N.A.I.C.S.: 551112
Rob Zandbergen *(CEO)*

Subsidiary (Non-US):

Receptel NV (2)
Frankrijklei 101, Antwerp, 2000, Belgium
Tel.: (32) 38004060
Web Site: http://www.receptel.be
Employment Services
N.A.I.C.S.: 561311
An De Bleeckere *(Ops Mgr)*

Subsidiary (Domestic):

Secretary Plus Management Support BV (2)
PJ Ougweg 61, 1314 CK, Almere, Netherlands
Tel.: (31) 365299080
Web Site: http://www.secretary-plus.nl
Employment Services
N.A.I.C.S.: 561311
Marleen Smith *(Mktg Mgr)*

Subsidiary (Non-US):

Secretary Plus Management Support GmbH (2)
Landsberger Strasse 370a, 80687, Munich, Germany
Tel.: (49) 89 56 827 0
Web Site: http://www.secretary-plus.de
Employment Services
N.A.I.C.S.: 561311
Benedicte Autem *(Mng Dir)*

Subsidiary (Domestic):

Start People BV (2)
PJ Oudweg 61, 1314 CK, Almere, Netherlands
Tel.: (31) 365299000
Web Site: https://www.startpeople.nl
Employment Services
N.A.I.C.S.: 561311

Subsidiary (Non-US):

Start People NV (2)
Tel.: (32) 38006400
Web Site: http://www.startpeople.be
Employment Services
N.A.I.C.S.: 561311

Start People SAS (2)
12 Parc de la Tannerie, 57070, Saint-Julien-les-Metz, France
Tel.: (33) 811020000
Web Site: https://www.startpeople.fr
Emp.: 800
Employment Services
N.A.I.C.S.: 561311

Technicum GmbH (2)
Landsberger Strasse 370a, 80687, Munich, Germany
Tel.: (49) 89568270
Web Site: http://www.technicum.de
Employment Agency Services
N.A.I.C.S.: 561311
Benedicte Autem *(Mng Dir)*

Subsidiary (Domestic):

Technicum Nederland (2)
PJ Oudweg 61, 1314 Ck, Almere, Netherlands
Tel.: (31) 365299100
Web Site: http://www.technicum.nl
Employment Services
N.A.I.C.S.: 561311

AND PRIVATE COMPANIES — RECTICEL S.A.

Subsidiary (Non-US):

USG People Belgium SA (2)
Frankrijklei 101, 2000, Antwerp, Belgium
Emp.: 1,000
Employment Services
N.A.I.C.S.: 561311

USG Professionals NV (2)
Berchermstadionstraat 76, 2600, Berchem, Belgium
Tel.: (32) 38004020
Web Site: https://www.usgprofessionals.be
Employment Services
N.A.I.C.S.: 561311

Subsidiary (Domestic):

Unique Nederland BV (2)
PJ Oudweg 61, 1314 Ck, Almere, Netherlands
Web Site: http://www.unique.nl
Employment Services
N.A.I.C.S.: 561311

Subsidiary (Non-US):

Unique Personalservice GmbH (2)
Landsberger Strasse 370A, 80687, Munich, Germany
Tel.: (49) 89568270
Web Site: https://www.unique-personal.de
Employment Services
N.A.I.C.S.: 561311
Benedicte Autem (CEO & Mng Dir)

Subsidiary (Domestic):

Unique Personalservice GmbH (3)
Landsberger Str 370a, 80687, Munich, Germany
Tel.: (49) 89568270
Web Site: https://www.ramsayhealth.co.uk
Employment Agency Services
N.A.I.C.S.: 561311

Subsidiary (Non-US):

Unique Personnel Service GmbH (2)
Bahnhofstrasse 9, 31675, Buckeburg, Germany
Tel.: (49) 5722967777
Employment Services
N.A.I.C.S.: 561311

RGF Staffing Germany GmbH (1)
Landsberger Str 370a, 80687, Munich, Germany
Tel.: (49) 89568270
Web Site: https://rgfstaffing.de
Emp.: 250,000
Staffing Services
N.A.I.C.S.: 561330

RGF Staffing UK Limited (1)
Stamford House Northenden Road, Sale, M33 2DH, United Kingdom
Tel.: (44) 1612821770
Web Site: https://www.rgfstaffing.co.uk
Staffing & Recruitment Services
N.A.I.C.S.: 541612

Recruit Career Co., Ltd. (1)
GranTokyo South Tower 1-9-2 Marunouchi, Chiyoda-ku, Tokyo, 100-6640, Japan
Tel.: (81) 335161234
Web Site: http://www.recruitcareer.co.jp
Recruitment Services
N.A.I.C.S.: 561311

Recruit Communications Co., Ltd. (1)
Inui Building Kachidoki 1-13-1, Chuo-ku, Tokyo, 104-0054, Japan
Tel.: (81) 355605555
Web Site: http://www.rco.recruit.co.jp
Web Marketing Services
N.A.I.C.S.: 541613

Recruit Jobs Co., Ltd. (1)
7-3-5 Hulic Ginza 7-chome Building, Ginza Chuo-ku, Tokyo, 104-8227, Japan
Tel.: (81) 335721191
Web Site: http://www.recruitjobs.co.jp
Recruitment Services
N.A.I.C.S.: 561311

Recruit Lifestyle Co., Ltd. (1)
Gran Tokyo South Tower1-9-2, Chiyoda-ku, Tokyo, 100-6640, Japan
Tel.: (81) 368351000
Web Site: http://www.recruit-lifestyle.co.jp
Business Support Services
N.A.I.C.S.: 561499
Ken Asano (Pres)

Recruit Management Solutions Co., Ltd. (1)
Gate City Osaki West Tower 7F 1-11-1, Osaki Shinagawa-ku, Tokyo, 141-0032, Japan
Tel.: (81) 120878300
Web Site: https://www.recruit-ms.co.jp
Emp.: 585
Consulting & Training Services
N.A.I.C.S.: 611430

Recruit Marketing Partners Co., Ltd. (1)
2-13-30 Kamiosaki oak meguro, Shinagawa-ku, Tokyo, 141-0021, Japan
Tel.: (81) 368352840
Web Site: http://www.recruit-mp.co.jp
Recruitment Services
N.A.I.C.S.: 561311

Recruit Staffing Co., Ltd. (1)
8-4-17 Ginza, Chuo-ku, Tokyo, 104-8001, Japan
Tel.: (81) 362743600
Web Site: https://www.r-staffing.co.jp
Emp.: 1,954
Temporary Staffing Services
N.A.I.C.S.: 561320

Recruit Sumai Company Ltd. (1)
Sumitomofudosantamachi Building 3-12-7 Shibaura, Minato-ku, Tokyo, 108-0023, Japan
Tel.: (81) 368352000
Web Site: http://www.recruit-sumai.co.jp
Housing Related Services
N.A.I.C.S.: 624229
Norio Nagahara (Exec Officer)

Staff Service Holdings Co., Ltd. (1)
JEBL Akihabara Square 85, Kanda Renbeicho Chiyoda-k, Tokyo, Japan
Tel.: (81) 352097100
Web Site: http://www.staffservice.co.jp
Temporary Staffing Services
N.A.I.C.S.: 561320

Staffmark Holdings, Inc. (1)
435 Elm St Ste 300, Cincinnati, OH 45202-2644 (97.6%)
Tel.: (513) 651-1111
Web Site: http://www.staffmark.com
Sales Range: $1-4.9 Billion
Emp.: 1,060
Temporary Staffing Services
N.A.I.C.S.: 561320
Kathryn S. Bernard (Gen Counsel & Exec VP)

Subsidiary (Domestic):

CBS Personnel Services, LLC (2)
435 Elm St Ste 100, Cincinnati, OH 45202-2644
Tel.: (513) 651-3600
Web Site: http://www.staffmark.com
Employment Agency
N.A.I.C.S.: 561311

Staffmark Professional Services, LLC (2)
435 Elm St Ste 300, Cincinnati, OH 45202-2644
Tel.: (501) 225-8080
Web Site: http://www.staffmark.com
Sales Range: $100-124.9 Million
Emp.: 2
Employment Agency
N.A.I.C.S.: 561311

The CSI Companies Inc. (1)
9995 Gate Pkwy N Ste 100, Jacksonville, FL 32246
Tel.: (904) 338-9515
Web Site: http://www.thecsicompanies.com
Sales Range: $125-149.9 Million
Emp.: 150
Staffing Services
N.A.I.C.S.: 561311
Chris Flakus (CEO)

USG People Holdings B.V. (1)
P J Oudweg 61, 1314 CK, Almere, Netherlands
Tel.: (31) 365299200

Web Site: https://rgfstaffing.nl
Human Resouce Services
N.A.I.C.S.: 541612

RECRUSUL S.A.
Av Luiz Pasteur 1020, Tres Portos, Sapucaia do Sul, 93212-360, RS, Brazil
Tel.: (55) 5139860200
Web Site: https://www.recrusul.com.br
Year Founded: 1954
RCSL4—(BRAZ)
Rev.: $11,694,384
Assets: $12,493,766
Liabilities: $12,396,291
Net Worth: $97,476
Earnings: ($1,066,255)
Fiscal Year-end: 12/31/23
Transportation Equipment Mfr
N.A.I.C.S.: 336999
Luiz Alcemar Baumart (Dir-Investor Relations)

RECTICEL S.A.
Bourgetlaan 42 Avenue du Bourget, 1130, Brussels, Belgium
Tel.: (32) 27751811   BE
Web Site: https://www.recticel.com
Year Founded: 1896
RECT—(EUR)
Rev.: $518,054,662
Assets: $992,402,993
Liabilities: $580,058,917
Net Worth: $412,344,076
Earnings: $58,638,611
Emp.: 1,144
Fiscal Year-end: 12/31/22
Bedding, Foam & Automotive Products Mfr
N.A.I.C.S.: 326140
Michel De Smedt (Mgr-Comm & IR)

Subsidiaries:

Ascorium North America, Inc. (1)
1653 Atlantic Blvd, Auburn Hills, MI 48326-1503
Tel.: (248) 241-9100
Polyurethane Foam Product Mfr
N.A.I.C.S.: 326140

Bioflex S.r.l. (1)
Str Stefan Cel Mare Nr 191, 003900, Sibiu, Romania (50%)
Tel.: (40) 269244322
Sales Range: $25-49.9 Million
Emp.: 37
Mattress Mfr
N.A.I.C.S.: 337910

Bofoam S.r.o. (1)
Podnikatelska 5, Kosice-Barca, Kosice, Slovakia
Tel.: (421) 556783118
Furniture Whslr
N.A.I.C.S.: 423210

COFEL (1)
57 Rue Yves Kermen, 92100, Boulogne-Billancourt, Cedex, France
Tel.: (33) 14 190 2828
Web Site: https://www.cofel.fr
Mfr of Mattresses & Bed Bases; Joint Venture of Recticel S.A. (50%) & Pikolin S.A. (50%)
N.A.I.C.S.: 337910

Carobel Foam Limited (1)
Norham Road, North Shields, NE29 7AR, United Kingdom (100%)
Tel.: (44) 1912961010
Sales Range: $25-49.9 Million
Emp.: 40
Plastics Product Mfr
N.A.I.C.S.: 326199

Compagnie Pikolin Recticel de Literie S.A.S. (1)
27 Rue du Colonel Pierre Avia, 75015, Paris, 75015, France (51%)
Tel.: (33) 141902828
Web Site: http://www.cofel.biz
Emp.: 60

Mattress Mfr
N.A.I.C.S.: 337910
Luis Flaquer (Gen Mgr)

Glass Machining Services Limited (1)
Unit 1 Marsh House Old Great North Road, Ferrybridge, Knottingley, WF11 8PH, West Yorkshire, United Kingdom (100%)
Tel.: (44) 1977675451
Web Site: http://www.glassmachineservices.co.uk
Glass Products Mfr
N.A.I.C.S.: 327215

Ingeneria De poliuretano Flexible s.l. (1)
Pol Ugaldeguren III 32-33 2-I, 48170, Zamudio, Bizkaia, Spain
Tel.: (34) 946314002
Web Site: https://www.ipfing.com
Sales Range: $25-49.9 Million
Polyurethane Handling Machinery Mfr
N.A.I.C.S.: 333248

Platte GmbH (1)
Nordstr 26, 26817, Rhauderfehn, Germany
Tel.: (49) 52990117
Employment Placement Agencies
N.A.I.C.S.: 561311

Proseat S.A.S. (1)
117 Avenue Victor Hugo, 92100, Boulogne-Billancourt, France (100%)
Tel.: (33) 173025194
Web Site: http://www.proseat.de
Sales Range: $25-49.9 Million
Polystyrene Foam Product Mfr
N.A.I.C.S.: 326140

RAI Most s.r.o. (1)
Havran 138, 435 01, Havran, Czech Republic
Tel.: (420) 415400102
Web Site: http://www.recticel.cz
Polyurethane Foam Product Mfr
N.A.I.C.S.: 326140

REBfoam S.r.l. (1)
Via A Colombo 60, Gorla Minore, Varese, Italy (100%)
Tel.: (39) 0331609111
Polystyrene Foam Product Mfr
N.A.I.C.S.: 326140
B. Lorenzo (Mng Dir)

RUS Inc. (1)
4833 Frnt St Ste B, Castle Rock, CO 80104-7901 (100%)
Tel.: (303) 419-6166
Excavation Contractor
N.A.I.C.S.: 238910

Recticel (UK) Limited (1)
Bluebell Close Clover Nook Industrial Park, Alfreton, DE55 4RD, Derbyshire, United Kingdom (100%)
Tel.: (44) 1773838800
Web Site: http://www.recticel.co.uk
Sales Range: $25-49.9 Million
Polystyrene Foam Product Mfr
N.A.I.C.S.: 326140
Gary Hotchkies (Mgr-Pur)

Division (Domestic):

Recticel Insulation Products (2)
Enterprise Way White Road, Meir Park, Stoke-on-Trent, ST3 7UN, Staffordshire, United Kingdom (100%)
Tel.: (44) 1782590470
Web Site: https://www.recticelinsulation.com
Sales Range: $25-49.9 Million
Polystyrene Foam Product Mfr
N.A.I.C.S.: 326140

Recticel AB (1)
Sodra Storgatan 50, PO Box 507, 332 28, Gislaved, Sweden (100%)
Tel.: (46) 37184500
Web Site: http://www.recticel.se
Sales Range: $50-74.9 Million
Urethane & Foam Product Mfr
N.A.I.C.S.: 326150

Recticel AS (1)
Oysand, Mehus, 7224, Andalsnes, Norway
Tel.: (47) 71227880
Web Site: https://www.recticel.no
Polyurethane Foam Mfr & Distr
N.A.I.C.S.: 326150

RECTICEL S.A.

Recticel S.A.—(Continued)

Recticel B.V. (1)
Wanraaij 4, 6673 DN, Andelst,
Netherlands (100%)
Tel.: (31) 488470120
Web Site: http://local.recticel.com
Sales Range: $75-99.9 Million
Holding Company
N.A.I.C.S.: 551112

Recticel B.V. (1)
Wanraaij 4, 6673 DN, Andelst,
Netherlands (100%)
Tel.: (31) 488470120
Sales Range: $75-99.9 Million
Emp.: 250
Holding Company
N.A.I.C.S.: 551112
Robert Smeets *(Mng Dir)*

Recticel Bedding (Schweiz) GmbH (1)
Bettenweg 12, Buron, 4112, Lucerne,
Switzerland (100%)
Tel.: (41) 419350111
Web Site: http://www.recticel.com
Household Furniture Mfr
N.A.I.C.S.: 337126

Recticel Bedding Romania s.r.l. (1)
Industrial Park Miercurea Sibiului DN1 FN,
Miercurea, 557150, Sibiu, Romania
Tel.: (40) 26 953 3232
Polyurethane Foam Mfr & Distr
N.A.I.C.S.: 326150

Recticel Corby Ltd (1)
83-84 Manton Road, Corby, NN17 4JL,
Northants, United Kingdom
Tel.: (44) 153 640 2345
Web Site: https://www.recticel.com
Polyurethane Foam Product Mfr
N.A.I.C.S.: 326140

Recticel Czech Automotive S.r.o. (1)
Osada 144, Bilina - Chuderice, 41801,
Prague, Czech Republic (100%)
Tel.: (420) 400102
Automotive Parts & Accessories Stores
N.A.I.C.S.: 441330

Recticel Dammsysteme GmbH (1)
Schlaraffiastr 1-10, 44867, Bochum,
Germany (100%)
Tel.: (49) 61116779540
Web Site: https://www.recticelinsulation.com
Sales Range: $25-49.9 Million
Polystyrene Foam Product Mfr
N.A.I.C.S.: 326140

Recticel Foam Corporation Inc. (1)
1105 N Market St, Wilmington, DE
19801-1216 (100%)
Tel.: (302) 427-0824
Holding Company
N.A.I.C.S.: 551112

Recticel Foams (Shanghai) Co Ltd (1)
Rm 2304-2305 18 Xin Jin Qiao Road Ramada Plaza, Pudong, Shanghai, 201206, China
Tel.: (86) 21 5030 8670
Web Site:
http://www.recticelflexiblefoams.com
Emp.: 50
Polyurethane Foam Product Mfr
N.A.I.C.S.: 326140

Recticel Grundstucksverwaltung GmbH & Co. KG (1)
Hagenauer Strasse 42, Wiesbaden, 65203,
Germany
Tel.: (49) 6119276102
Web Site: http://www.recticel.com
Emp.: 12
Management Consulting Services
N.A.I.C.S.: 541618

Recticel Iberica S.L. (1)
P I Concentracio Ind Vallesanu -Avda Riu
Mogent 6, Santa Perpetua De Mogoda,
08170, Montornes del Valles, Spain
Tel.: (34) 935747377
Web Site: http://www.recticelflexiblefoams.com
Sales Range: $50-74.9 Million
Mattress Mfr
N.A.I.C.S.: 337910

Recticel India Private Limited (1)
Plot No L-66, MIDC Industrial Area Taluka - Panvel District Raigad, Taloja, 410208, Maharashtra, India
Tel.: (91) 222 741 1210
Web Site:
http://www.recticelflexiblefoams.com
Polyurethane Foam Product Mfr
N.A.I.C.S.: 326140

Recticel Insulation B.V. (1)
Zuiestraat 15, 8560, Wevelgem, Belgium
Tel.: (32) 56438943
Web Site: http://www.recticelinsulation.com
Sales Range: $150-199.9 Million
Insulation Products Mfr & Distr
N.A.I.C.S.: 321219

Recticel Insulation Oy (1)
Gneissitie 2, 04600, Mantsala, Finland
Tel.: (358) 201551515
Web Site: https://www.recticelinsulation.com
Polyurethane Foam Mfr & Distr
N.A.I.C.S.: 326150

Recticel Insulation S.A.S. (1)
1 rue Ferdinand de Lesseps, CS 50234,
18023, Bourges, Cedex, France
Tel.: (33) 248238720
Web Site: https://www.recticelinsulation.com
Polyurethane Foam Mfr & Distr
N.A.I.C.S.: 326150

Recticel Interiors CZ S.r.o. (1)
Plazy 115, 293 01, Mlada Boleslav, Czech
Republic (100%)
Tel.: (420) 326377111
Web Site: http://recticel.cz
Sales Range: $125-149.9 Million
Polystyrene Foam Product Mfr
N.A.I.C.S.: 326140

Recticel International B.V. (1)
Spoorstraat 69, 4041 CL, Kesteren,
Netherlands (100%)
Tel.: (31) 488489999
Web Site: http://www.recticel.nl
Sales Range: $100-124.9 Million
Emp.: 300
Mattress Mfr
N.A.I.C.S.: 337910
Peter van Doorn *(Gen Mgr)*

Recticel Limited (1)
Bluebell Close, Clover Nook Industrial Park,
Alfreton, DE55 4RD, Derbyshire, United
Kingdom
Tel.: (44) 177 383 8800
Web Site: http://www.recticel.co.uk
Polyurethane Foam Product Mfr
N.A.I.C.S.: 326140
David Wilkinson *(Mng Dir)*

Recticel N.V. (1)
Damstraat 2, 9230, Wetteren, Belgium
Tel.: (32) 9 368 9211
Web Site: http://www.recticel.be
Polyurethane Foam Product Mfr
N.A.I.C.S.: 326140

Recticel OU (1)
Pune Tee 22, 11415, Tallinn, Estonia
Tel.: (372) 6339720
Polyurethane Product Whslr
N.A.I.C.S.: 424990

Recticel Oy (1)
Nevantie 2, PL64, 45101, Kouvola, Finland
Tel.: (358) 578451
Web Site: http://recticelflexiblefoams.com
Bedding, Foam & Automotive Products Mfr
N.A.I.C.S.: 326140

Recticel S.A.S. (1)
7 Rue Du Fosse Blanc, 92622, Gennevilliers, Cedex, France (100%)
Tel.: (33) 145192220
Sales Range: $200-249.9 Million
Emp.: 618
Plastics Pipe & Pipe Fitting Mfr
N.A.I.C.S.: 326122

Recticel Schlafkomfort GmbH (1)
Schlaraffiastrasse 1-10, 44867, Bochum,
Germany (100%)
Tel.: (49) 8001111009
Web Site: https://www.schlaraffia.de
Mattress Mfr
N.A.I.C.S.: 337910

Recticel Teknik Sunger Izolasyon Sanayi ve Ticaret A.S. (1)
Orta Mahalle 30 Agustos Cad No 5/D,
Orhanli Tuzla, 34956, Istanbul, Turkiye
Tel.: (90) 216 581 6100
Polyurethane Foam Mfr & Distr
N.A.I.C.S.: 326150

Recticel Verwaltung GmbH & Co. KG (1)
Rolandsecker Weg 30, D-53619, Rheinbreitbach, Germany (100%)
Tel.: (49) 22247702190
Web Site: http://www.recticel.com
Holding Company
N.A.I.C.S.: 551112

Subsidiary (Domestic):

Recticel Automobilsysteme GmbH (2)
Im Muhlenbruch 10 - 12, 53639, Konigswinter, Germany (100%)
Tel.: (49) 222375000
Web Site: http://www.recticel-automotive.com
Motor Vehicle Parts Mfr
N.A.I.C.S.: 336390

Recticel Beteiligungsmanagement GmbH (1)
Rolandsecker Weg 30, D-53619, Rheinbreitbach, Germany (100%)
Tel.: (49) 22247702190
Web Site: http://www.recticel.com
Sales Range: $150-199.9 Million
Emp.: 450
Investment Advice
N.A.I.C.S.: 523940

Recticel Handel GmbH (2)
Rolandsecker Weg 30, D-53619, Rheinbreitbach, Germany (100%)
Tel.: (49) 22247702430
Sales Range: $200-249.9 Million
Emp.: 700
Paints & Allied Product
N.A.I.C.S.: 424950

Rectigro BV (1)
Spoorstraat 69, 4041 CL, Kesteren, Netherlands
Tel.: (31) 488 489999
Web Site: http://www.recticelholland.com
Sales Range: $50-74.9 Million
Polyurethane Foam Product Mfr
N.A.I.C.S.: 326140
Ad Franke *(Gen Mgr)*

S.A. Intergroup Coordination Services N.V. (1)
Avenue Des Pleiades 15, 1200, Brussels, Belgium (100%)
Tel.: (32) 27751811
Sales Range: $50-74.9 Million
Emp.: 45
Insurance Agencies & Brokerages
N.A.I.C.S.: 524210

S.A. Kingspan Tarec Industrial Insulation N.V. (1)
Visbeekstraat 24, 2300, Turnhout, Belgium (50%)
Tel.: (32) 14442521
Web Site: http://www.kingspantarec.com
Sales Range: $25-49.9 Million
Emp.: 100
Urethane & Foam Product Mfr
N.A.I.C.S.: 326150

S.A. Proseat N.V. (1)
Ave Des Pleiades 15, 1200, Brussels, Belgium (70%)
Tel.: (32) 27751811
Sales Range: $25-49.9 Million
Emp.: 35
Basic Organic Chemical Mfr
N.A.I.C.S.: 325199

S.A. Recticel International Services N.V. (1)
Bourgetlaan 42 Avenue du Bourget, 1130, Brussels, Belgium (100%)
Tel.: (32) 27751811
Web Site: https://www.recticel.com
Sales Range: $25-49.9 Million
Emp.: 45
Management Consulting Services
N.A.I.C.S.: 541618

Sembella GmbH (1)
Aderstrasse 35, Timelkam, 4850, Vocklabruck, Austria

Tel.: (43) 76727960
Web Site: https://www.sembella.at
Sales Range: $50-74.9 Million
Household Furniture Mfr
N.A.I.C.S.: 337126

Splifar S.A. (1)
Rue Chausteur 144, 6060, Charleroi, Belgium (100%)
Tel.: (32) 71489252
Sheet Metal Work Mfg
N.A.I.C.S.: 332322

Teknofoam Hellas E.p.e. (1)
Kosma Etolou Str 13 Neo Iraklio, 14121, Athens, Greece (50%)
Tel.: (30) 2102778020
Web Site: http://www.teknofoam.gr
Sales Range: $25-49.9 Million
Emp.: 20
Chemical Product Whslr
N.A.I.C.S.: 424690

Teknofoam Izolasyon Sanayi ve Ticaret a.s. (1)
Milangaz Caddesi No 40-B Esentepe Kartal, Istanbul, Turkiye
Tel.: (90) 216 517 09 56
Fabricated Rubber Product Mfr
N.A.I.C.S.: 326299

The Soundcoat Company Inc. (1)
1 Burt Dr, Deer Park, NY 11729-5701 (100%)
Tel.: (631) 242-2200
Web Site: https://www.soundcoat.com
Urethane & Foam Product Mfr
N.A.I.C.S.: 326150

Transfoam S.L. (1)
Pol Ind Catarroja C 31 Parc 10 A 1, 46470, Catarroja, Spain
Tel.: (34) 961267001
Plastics Product Mfr
N.A.I.C.S.: 326199

Turvac d.o.o. (1)
Primorska 6b, 3325, Sostanj, Slovenia
Tel.: (386) 38985611
Web Site: https://www.turvac.eu
Emp.: 170
Household Appliances Mfr
N.A.I.C.S.: 335220

Westnofa Industrier AS (1)
Oran Ost, 6300, Andalsnes, Norway
Tel.: (47) 71 22 78 80
Web Site: http://www.westnofa.no
Sales Range: $25-49.9 Million
Emp.: 35
Polyurethane Foam Product Mfr
N.A.I.C.S.: 326140
Gunnar Nypan *(Mgr-Mktg-Export)*

XL Literie S.A.S. (1)
Zac du Vieux Chene - CD 110, Monestier-Merlines, 19340, Correze, France (51%)
Tel.: (33) 555944220
Mattress Mfr
N.A.I.C.S.: 337910

s.a. Recticel Management Services n.v. (1)
Damstraat 2, Wetteren, 9260, Belgium
Tel.: (32) 93689211
Sales Range: $125-149.9 Million
Emp.: 500
Polyurethane Foam Product Mfr
N.A.I.C.S.: 326140
Olivier Chapelle *(Gen Mgr)*

RECTIFIER TECHNOLOGIES LIMITED

97 Highbury Road, Burwood, 3125, VIC, Australia
Tel.: (61) 398967588
Web Site:
https://www.rectifiertechnologies.com
RFT—(ASX)
Rev.: $11,310,131
Assets: $17,568,394
Liabilities: $10,400,911
Net Worth: $7,167,483
Earnings: $376,931
Emp.: 114
Fiscal Year-end: 06/30/22
Electronic Components Mfr

AND PRIVATE COMPANIES — RED BULL GMBH

N.A.I.C.S.: 334419
Yanbin Wang *(CEO)*
Subsidiaries:

Protran Technologies Pty. Ltd. (1)
24 Harker Street, Burwood, 3125, VIC, Australia
Tel.: (61) 39 896 7555
Web Site: https://www.protran.net
Wire Product Mfr
N.A.I.C.S.: 332618

Rectifier Technologies Singapore Pte. Ltd. (1)
9 Tampines Grande Level 2 Asia Green, Singapore, 528735, Singapore
Tel.: (65) 31591954
Rectifier Mfr
N.A.I.C.S.: 335999

RECTRON LTD.
71 Zhongshan Rd, Tucheng Dist, New Taipei City, 23680, Taiwan
Tel.: (886) 222681314
Web Site: https://www.rectron.com
Year Founded: 1975
2302—(TAI)
Rev.: $23,432,584
Assets: $76,336,764
Liabilities: $18,270,871
Net Worth: $58,065,893
Earnings: $2,840,806
Emp.: 700
Fiscal Year-end: 12/31/23
Semiconductor Equipment Mfr
N.A.I.C.S.: 334413
Lin I-Chin *(Chm & Gen Mgr)*
Subsidiaries:

Rectron Europe Limited (1)
Unit 21 Hopewell Business Centre 105 Hopewell Drive, Chatham, ME5 7DX, Kent, United Kingdom
Tel.: (44) 634300087
Electronic Parts Distr
N.A.I.C.S.: 423690

Rectron Semiconductor Inc. (1)
1400 N Harbor Blvd Ste 520, Fullerton, CA 92835
Tel.: (909) 517-3323
Web Site: http://www.rectron.com
Emp.: 10
Discrete Semiconductor Mfr
N.A.I.C.S.: 333242
Sean Kelly *(Gen Mgr)*

RECUPERO ETICO SOSTENIBILE S.P.A.
Zona Industriale snc, Pettoranello del Molise, 86090, Isernia, IS, Italy
Tel.: (39) 0865290645   IT
Web Site: https://www.recuperosostenibile.it
Year Founded: 1989
RES—(ITA)
Waste Disposal Services
N.A.I.C.S.: 562219
Antonio Valerio *(CEO)*

RECURSOS QUELIZ, INC.
Las Caobas 4th Street No 24, San Felipe de Puerto Plata, Dominican Republic
Tel.: (809) 970 2353   NV
Year Founded: 2012
Gold Mining
N.A.I.C.S.: 212220
Juan Alexi Payamps Dominiguez *(Pres, CEO, CFO, Chief Acctg Officer, Treas & Sec)*

RECYCLICO BATTERY MATERIALS INC.
2 17942 55th Avenue, Surrey, V3S 6C8, BC, Canada
Tel.: (778) 574-4444   BC
Web Site: https://recyclico.com
Year Founded: 1987
AMYZF—(OTCQB)

Metal Exploration Services
N.A.I.C.S.: 213114
Larry W. Reaugh *(Pres & CEO)*
Subsidiaries:

Rocher Manganese Inc. (1)
9120 Double Diamond Pkwy Ste 3913, Reno, NV 89521
Tel.: (775) 841-7120
Mineral Mining Services
N.A.I.C.S.: 213115

RECYLEX S.A.
6 Place de la Madeleine, F-75008, Paris, France
Tel.: (33) 158470470
Web Site: http://www.recylex.fr
Year Founded: 1998
RX—(EUR)
Sales Range: $500-549.9 Million
Emp.: 665
Lead, Zinc & Other Metal Recycling & Processing Services
N.A.I.C.S.: 423930
Sebastian Rudow *(Chm & CEO)*
Subsidiaries:

Recylex S.A. - Administrative Office (1)
79 Rue Jean-jacques Rousseau, Cedex, 92158, Suresnes, France   (100%)
Tel.: (33) 158470470
Web Site: http://wwwrecylex.fr
Sales Range: $75-99.9 Million
Emp.: 150
Corporate Administration Services
N.A.I.C.S.: 921140

RECYTECH S.A.
Route de Noyelles, 62740, Fouquieres-les-Lens, France
Tel.: (33) 321791350
Web Site: http://www.recytech.fr
Sales Range: $10-24.9 Million
Emp.: 43
Zinc Mining
N.A.I.C.S.: 212230
Charles Van Cutsam *(Mng Dir)*

RED 5 LIMITED
Level 2 35 Ventnor Avenue, West Perth, 6005, WA, Australia
Tel.: (61) 893224455   AU
Web Site: https://www.red5limited.com
VAU—(ASX)
Rev.: $413,997,060
Assets: $1,447,351,089
Liabilities: $365,114,181
Net Worth: $1,082,236,908
Earnings: ($3,631,143)
Fiscal Year-end: 06/30/24
Gold Exploration Services
N.A.I.C.S.: 212220
Frank J. Campagna *(Sec)*
Subsidiaries:

Greenstone Resources (WA) Pty Ltd. (1)
Level 2 35 Ventnor Ave, West Perth, 6005, WA, Australia
Tel.: (61) 893224455
Sales Range: $50-74.9 Million
Emp.: 4
Gold Mining Services
N.A.I.C.S.: 212220

Silver Lake Resources Limited (1)
Suite 4 Level 3 South Shore Centre 85 South Perth Esplanade, South Perth, 6151, WA, Australia
Tel.: (61) 863133800
Web Site: http://www.silverlakeresources.com.au
Rev.: $458,406,114
Assets: $835,810,621
Liabilities: $149,474,475
Net Worth: $686,336,146
Earnings: $75,243,689
Emp.: 191

Fiscal Year-end: 06/30/2021
Gold Mining
N.A.I.C.S.: 212220
Luke Tonkin *(Mng Dir)*
Subsidiary (Domestic):

Doray Minerals Limited (2)
Level 1 1292 Hay Street West Perth, West Perth, 6005, WA, Australia   (100%)
Tel.: (61) 892260600
Gold Exploration & Mining
N.A.I.C.S.: 212220
Iain Garrett *(Sec & Controller-Fin)*

Unit (Domestic):

Silver Lake Resources Limited-Lakewood Gold Processing Facility (2)
PO Box 750, Kalgoorlie, 6433, WA, Australia
Tel.: (61) 890933964
Gold Ore Processing Services
N.A.I.C.S.: 331410

RED AVENUE NEW MATERIALS GROUP CO., LTD.
25/F Shanghai Tower No 501 Middle Yincheng Road, Pudong New Area, Shanghai, 200120, China
Tel.: (86) 2162109966
Web Site: https://www.rachem.com
Year Founded: 1999
603650—(SHG)
Rev.: $351,007,273
Assets: $963,301,402
Liabilities: $522,146,336
Net Worth: $441,155,066
Earnings: $41,860,471
Fiscal Year-end: 12/31/22
Chemical Products Mfr
N.A.I.C.S.: 325199
Zhang Ning *(Chm)*

RED BULL GMBH
Am Brunnen 1, 5330, Fuschl am See, Austria
Tel.: (43) 66265820
Web Site: http://www.redbull.com
Year Founded: 1987
Sales Range: $1-4.9 Billion
Emp.: 3,900
Energy Drink Mfr
N.A.I.C.S.: 312111
Dietrich Mateschitz *(Mng Dir)*
Subsidiaries:

Jamnica d.o.o. Beograd - Red Bull (1)
Bulevar kneza Aleksandra Karadordevica 13a, 11000, Belgrade, Serbia
Tel.: (381) 113674692
Soft Drink Distr
N.A.I.C.S.: 424490

Red Bull AG (1)
Poststrasse 3, 6341, Baar, Switzerland
Tel.: (41) 417663636
Web Site: http://www.redbull.ch
Soft Drink Distr
N.A.I.C.S.: 424490
Marcel Bannwart *(Mgr-Sls)*

Red Bull Adria d.o.o. (1)
Radnicka cesta 41, 10000, Zagreb, Croatia
Tel.: (385) 16274300
Soft Drink Distr
N.A.I.C.S.: 424490

Red Bull Australia Pty Ltd. (1)
Locked Bag 3100 Strawberry Hills, Sydney, 2012, NSW, Australia
Tel.: (61) 290232800
Soft Drink Distr
N.A.I.C.S.: 424490
Brydee Dixon *(Mgr-Field Sls)*

Red Bull Company Limited (1)
155-171 Tooley Street, London, SE1 2JP, United Kingdom
Tel.: (44) 2031172000
Soft Drink Distr
N.A.I.C.S.: 424490

Red Bull Denmark ApS (1)
Sankt Petri Passage 5 4, 1165, Copenhagen, Denmark
Tel.: (45) 33152001
Soft Drink Distr
N.A.I.C.S.: 424490

Red Bull Deutschland GmbH (1)
Osterwaldstrasse 10, 80805, Munich, Germany
Tel.: (49) 892060350
Web Site: http://www.redbull.de
Soft Drink Distr
N.A.I.C.S.: 424490
Alexander Lehejcek *(Mgr-Trade Mktg)*

Red Bull FZE (1)
Dubai Airport Free Zone East Wing 3 3rd Floor, Dubai, United Arab Emirates
Tel.: (971) 42995151
Soft Drink Distr
N.A.I.C.S.: 424490
Floyd Almeida *(Dir-HR)*

Red Bull Finland Oy (1)
Ruoholahdenkatu 23, 00180, Helsinki, Finland
Tel.: (358) 103285715
Web Site: http://www.redbull.fi
Soft Drink Distr
N.A.I.C.S.: 424490

Red Bull France SASU (1)
12 rue du mail, 75002, Paris, France
Tel.: (33) 140135700
Soft Drink Distr
N.A.I.C.S.: 424490

Red Bull Hellas (1)
3 Thita st, Elliniko, 16777, Athens, Greece
Tel.: (30) 210985974555
Soft Drink Distr
N.A.I.C.S.: 424490

Red Bull Hungaria Kft. (1)
Szepvolgyi Ut 137, 1037, Budapest, Hungary
Tel.: (36) 1 224 7310
Web Site: http://www.redbull.com
Soft Drink Distr
N.A.I.C.S.: 424490

Red Bull Media House GmbH (1)
Oberst-Lepperdinger-Str 11-15 Wals near, 5071, Salzburg, Austria
Tel.: (43) 66222400
Web Site: http://www.redbullmediahouse.com
Television Broadcasting Services
N.A.I.C.S.: 516120
Andreas Gall *(Chief Innovation Officer)*

Red Bull Nederland B.V. (1)
NDSM-Plein 26 adres voor navigatie TT Neveritaweg 34, 1033 WB, Amsterdam, Netherlands
Tel.: (31) 204936110
Web Site: http://www.redbull.nl
Soft Drink Distr
N.A.I.C.S.: 424490
Guido Koning *(Acct Mgr)*

Red Bull New Zealand Limited (1)
27 Mackelvie Street, Grey Lynn, Auckland, New Zealand
Tel.: (64) 93784581
Web Site: http://www.redbull.co.nz
Soft Drink Distr
N.A.I.C.S.: 424490
Janelle Wright *(Mgr-Natl Field Sls)*

Red Bull North America, Inc. (1)
1740 Stuart St, Santa Monica, CA 90404-3596
Tel.: (310) 393-4647
Web Site: http://www.redbullusa.com
Sales Range: $200-249.9 Million
Emp.: 600
Distr of Beverages
N.A.I.C.S.: 312111
Nate Warner *(Head-Social Media)*

Red Bull Norway AS (1)
Molleparken 4, 0459, Oslo, Norway
Tel.: (47) 22380450
Web Site: http://www.redbull.no
Soft Drink Distr
N.A.I.C.S.: 424490
Maximilian Solheim *(Mgr-sls)*

Red Bull S.r.l. (1)

RED BULL GMBH

Red Bull GmbH—(Continued)
Via Savona 97 Int C11, 20144, Milan, Italy
Tel.: (39) 026781701
Soft Drink Distr
N.A.I.C.S.: 424490

Red Bull Singapore Pte Ltd. (1)
2 Alexandra Road Delta House 06-02C,
Singapore, 159919, Singapore
Tel.: (65) 62207978
Soft Drink Distr
N.A.I.C.S.: 424490
Himanshu Arora *(Gen Mgr)*

Red Bull sp. z o.o. (1)
Al Wyscigowa 8a, 02-681, Warsaw, Poland
Tel.: (48) 223319550
Web Site: http://www.redbull.pl
Soft Drink Distr
N.A.I.C.S.: 424490
Pawel Kotowski *(Brand Mgr)*

S.C. Red Bull Romania S.R.L. (1)
Bectro Center Str Sf Vineri 29 Sector 3, Bucharest, 030203, Romania
Tel.: (40) 213020961
Soft Drink Distr
N.A.I.C.S.: 424490

RED CANYON RESOURCES LTD.
1210-1130 West Pender Street, Vancouver, V6E 4A4, BC, Canada
Tel.: (604) 681-9100 BC
Web Site:
https://www.redcanyon.com
Year Founded: 2020
REDC—(CNSX)
Rev.: $29,510
Assets: $985,702
Liabilities: $171,558
Net Worth: $814,145
Earnings: ($193,124)
Fiscal Year-end: 12/31/22
Mineral Exploration Services
N.A.I.C.S.: 213115

RED CAPITAL PLC
28 Esplanade, Channel Islands, Saint Helier, JE2 3QA, Jersey
Tel.: (44) 1534700000 JE
Web Site:
https://www.redcapitalplc.com
Year Founded: 2021
REDC—(LSE)
Assets: $520,754
Liabilities: $69,054
Net Worth: $451,700
Earnings: ($273,750)
Emp.: 2
Fiscal Year-end: 12/31/23
Asset Management Services
N.A.I.C.S.: 523999
David Williams *(Chm)*

RED CRESCENT RESOURCES LIMITED
2 Bloor Street West Suite 1803, Toronto, M4W 3E2, ON, Canada
Tel.: (416) 637-2080 ON
Web Site:
http://www.rcrholding.com.tr
Year Founded: 2005
Sales Range: Less than $1 Million
Emp.: 18
Zinc, Lead, Copper & Manganese Mining Services
N.A.I.C.S.: 212230
Cem Elmastas *(Pres & CEO)*

RED DIRT METALS LIMITED
1202 Hay St, West Perth, Perth, 6005, WA, Australia
Tel.: (61) 863191900
Web Site:
http://www.tntmines.com.au
DLI—(ASX)
Rev.: $2,801,822
Assets: $166,661,629
Liabilities: $5,443,785
Net Worth: $161,217,844
Earnings: ($8,342,327)
Fiscal Year-end: 06/30/24
Mineral Exploration Services
N.A.I.C.S.: 212290
Brett Mitchell *(Exec Dir)*

RED EAGLE MINING CORPORATION
Suite 2348 666 Burrard Street, Vancouver, V6C 2X8, BC, Canada
Tel.: (604) 638-2545 BC
Web Site:
http://www.redeaglemining.com
Year Founded: 2010
RD—(OTCIQ)
Sales Range: Less than $1 Million
Emp.: 186
Metal Mining Services
N.A.I.C.S.: 212290
Ian P. Slater *(Chm & CEO)*

Subsidiaries:

Red Eagle Exploration Limited (1)
Suite 2348 666 Burrard Street, Vancouver, V6C 2X8, BC, Canada (100%)
Tel.: (604) 638-2545
Web Site: http://www.redeaglex.com
Assets: $16,825,000
Liabilities: $1,272,000
Net Worth: $15,553,000
Earnings: ($3,477,000)
Emp.: 11
Fiscal Year-end: 12/31/2017
Gold & Other Mineral Exploration Services
N.A.I.C.S.: 213114
Ian Slater *(Chm & CEO)*

RED HILL MINERALS LIMITED
Level 2 9 Havelock St, West Perth, 6005, WA, Australia
Tel.: (61) 894818627
Web Site:
https://redhillminerals.com.au
RHI—(ASX)
Rev.: $946,679
Assets: $161,670,682
Liabilities: $31,793,828
Net Worth: $129,876,854
Earnings: $102,538,648
Fiscal Year-end: 06/30/24
Gold Exploration Services
N.A.I.C.S.: 212220
Peter Ruttledge *(Sec)*

RED LAKE GOLD, INC.
810 - 789 West Pender Street, Vancouver, V6C 1H2, BC, Canada
Tel.: (604) 687-2038
Web Site: https://www.redlakegold.ca
RGLD—(CNSX)
Assets: $1,537,354
Liabilities: $9,874
Net Worth: $1,527,480
Earnings: ($213,449)
Fiscal Year-end: 11/30/23
Gold Exploration Services
N.A.I.C.S.: 212220
Ryan Kalt *(Chm & CEO)*

RED LEOPARD HOLDINGS PLC
50 Jermyn Street, London, SW1Y 6LX, United Kingdom
Tel.: (44) 2079176826
Web Site:
http://www.redleopardholdings.com
Leisure & Hospitality Properties Development Services
N.A.I.C.S.: 236116
John Joseph May *(Chm)*

RED LIGHT HOLLAND CORP.
1 Adelaide St E Suite 801, Toronto, M5C 2V9, ON, Canada
Tel.: (647) 204-7129 ON
Web Site: https://redlight.co
Year Founded: 1982
TRUFF—(OTCQB)
Assets: $3,036,089
Liabilities: $3,911,749
Net Worth: ($875,660)
Earnings: ($248,835)
Fiscal Year-end: 03/31/20
Holding Company; Hallucinogenic Mushroom & Truffle Grower & Sales
N.A.I.C.S.: 551112
Hans Derix *(Pres)*

Subsidiaries:

Minichamp B.V. (1)
Ruttenweg 2, 5961 PR, Horst, Netherlands
Tel.: (31) 773987926
Web Site: https://minichamp.nl
Mushroom & Toadstool Distr
N.A.I.C.S.: 424490

SR Wholesale B.V. (1)
Rooiseweg 1, 5481 SJ, Schijndel, Netherlands
Tel.: (31) 651335230
Web Site: https://sr-wholesale.com
Health & Wellness Product Whslr
N.A.I.C.S.: 424990

RED METAL LIMITED
Level 15 323 Castlereagh Street, Sydney, 2000, NSW, Australia
Tel.: (61) 292811805
Web Site:
https://www.redmetal.com.au
RDM—(ASX)
Rev.: $1,219,546
Assets: $9,263,358
Liabilities: $1,424,799
Net Worth: $7,838,559
Earnings: ($5,260,617)
Fiscal Year-end: 06/30/24
Uranium Exploration
N.A.I.C.S.: 212290
Patrick John Flint *(Sec)*

RED METAL RESOURCES LTD.
102-278 Bay St, Thunder Bay, P7B 1R8, ON, Canada
Tel.: (807) 345-7384 NV
Web Site:
https://www.redmetalresources.com
Year Founded: 2005
RMESF—(OTCIQ)
Assets: $1,151,261
Liabilities: $1,653,993
Net Worth: ($502,731)
Earnings: ($1,268,858)
Emp.: 2
Fiscal Year-end: 01/31/22
Copper & Gold Mining Services
N.A.I.C.S.: 212230
Caitlin Jeffs *(Pres, CEO & Sec)*

RED MOUNTAIN MINING LTD.
Suite 11 Level 2 23 Railway Road, Subiaco, West Perth, 6008, WA, Australia
Tel.: (61) 865591792
Web Site: https://www.redmm.com.au
Year Founded: 2006
RMX—(ASX)
Rev.: $66,802
Assets: $1,667,862
Liabilities: $145,683
Net Worth: $1,522,179
Earnings: ($1,840,308)
Emp.: 54
Fiscal Year-end: 06/30/24
Gold Mining
N.A.I.C.S.: 212220
Mauro Piccini *(Chm & Sec)*

RED OAK MINING CORP.
Suite 1400 1111 West Georgia Street, Vancouver, V6E 3M3, BC, Canada
Tel.: (604) 689-1799 Ca
Rev.: $165
Assets: $60,131
Liabilities: $97,329
Net Worth: ($37,198)
Earnings: ($238,489)
Fiscal Year-end: 05/31/18
Oil & Gas Exploration Services
N.A.I.C.S.: 211120
Jay M. Roberge *(CEO)*

RED PHASE INC.
Unit 1002 3 Nantou Road, Siming District, Xiamen, 361008, Fujian, China
Tel.: (86) 5928126108
Web Site:
https://www.redphase.com.cn
Year Founded: 2005
300427—(CHIN)
Rev.: $229,789,872
Assets: $592,992,036
Liabilities: $358,114,068
Net Worth: $234,877,968
Earnings: $9,189,180
Fiscal Year-end: 12/31/22
Electrical Testing & Monitoring Equipment
N.A.I.C.S.: 334515
Yang Li *(Chm)*

RED PINE CAPITAL GROUP, INC.
Floor 7 #30 Dongzhong St, Dongcheng District, Beijing, 100027, China
Tel.: (86) 13701379808 NV
Year Founded: 2009
Sales Range: Less than $1 Million
Emp.: 4
Business Consulting Services
N.A.I.C.S.: 541618
Yao Sun *(Pres, CEO, CFO, Chief Acctg Officer, Treas & Sec)*

RED PINE EXPLORATION INC.
145 Wellington Street West Suite 1001, Toronto, M5J 1H8, ON, Canada
Tel.: (416) 364-7024 ON
Web Site:
https://www.redpineexp.com
Year Founded: 1936
RPX—(OTCIQ)
Assets: $3,345,621
Liabilities: $1,392,873
Net Worth: $1,952,748
Earnings: ($12,886,938)
Fiscal Year-end: 07/31/21
Gold Exploration Services
N.A.I.C.S.: 212220
Quentin Yarie *(CEO)*

Subsidiaries:

Augustine Ventures Inc. (1)
141 Adelaide Street West Suite 520, Toronto, M5H 3L5, ON, Canada (100%)
Tel.: (416) 363-2528
Web Site:
http://www.augustineventures.com
Gold Mining Services
N.A.I.C.S.: 212220
Robert Brian Dodds *(Pres & CEO)*

RED POINT SECURITY SP. Z O.O.
Aleja Rozdzienskiego 91, 40-203, Katowice, Poland
Tel.: (48) 323571583
Web Site: http://www.rps.com.pl
Security Services
N.A.I.C.S.: 561612
Grzegorza Demel *(Co-Owner & CEO)*

RED RIBBON ASSET MANAGEMENT PLC

AND PRIVATE COMPANIES

16 Berkeley Street, Mayfair, London, W1J 8DZ, United Kingdom
Tel.: (44) 20 7183 3710   UK
Web Site: http://www.redribbon.co
Year Founded: 2007
Investment Management Service
N.A.I.C.S.: 523940
Suchit Punnose *(Founder & CEO)*

Subsidiaries:

Eco Hotels UK Plc.   (1)
16 Berkeley Street, Mayfair, W1J 8DZ, London , United Kingdom
Tel.: (44) 20 7183 3710
Web Site: https://www.ecohotelsglobal.com
Eco Hotels Management
N.A.I.C.S.: 721110
Suchit Punnose *(Chm)*

Subsidiary (Non-US):

Sharad Fibres & Yarn Processors Limited   (2)
220 Unique Industrial Estate Off Veer Savarkar Marg, Prabhadevi, Mumbai, 400 025, India   **(66.28%)**
Tel.: (91) 8086021121
Web Site: https://www.ehrlindia.in
Rev.: $2,708,561
Assets: $209,416
Liabilities: $49,216
Net Worth: $160,200
Earnings: $2,044,973
Emp.: 19
Fiscal Year-end: 03/31/2021
Fiber & Yarn Processing Services
N.A.I.C.S.: 313110
Ravi Amarchand Dalmia *(Mng Dir)*

Modulex Construction Technologies Limited   (1)
A 82 MIDC Industrial Estate Indapur, Pune, 413-132, Maharashtra, India
Tel.: (91) 2071833710
Web Site: https://www.modulex.in
Rev.: $35,477
Assets: $36,370,961
Liabilities: $5,237,264
Net Worth: $31,133,697
Earnings: ($1,084,132)
Emp.: 2
Fiscal Year-end: 03/31/2023
Electrical Appliance Mfr & Whslr
N.A.I.C.S.: 335210

Subsidiary (Non-US):

Modulex Modular Buildings PLC   (2)
16 Berkeley Street, Mayfair, London, W1J 8DZ, United Kingdom   **(34.81%)**
Tel.: (44) 20 7183 3710
Web Site: http://www.modulex.in
Investment Holding Company
N.A.I.C.S.: 551112

Red Ribbon Advisory Services Pvt. Ltd.   (1)
1102 B Wing Peninsula Business Park S B Road, Lower Parel, Mumbai, 400013, Maharashtra, India
Tel.: (91) 22 6564 1123
Web Site: http://www.redribbonindia.com
Investment Advisory Services
N.A.I.C.S.: 523940
Suchit Punnose *(Chm)*

Red Ribbon Impact Investments Limited   (1)
1 Berkeley Street, Mayfair, London, W1J 8DJ, United Kingdom
Tel.: (44) 20 7016 9686
Web Site: http://www.redribbon.co
Venture Capital Investment Firm
N.A.I.C.S.: 523999
Suchit Punnose *(CEO)*

RED RIVER CAPITAL CORP.
1900 520-3rd Avenue SW, Calgary, T2P 0R3, AB, Canada
Tel.: (780) 423-7215
XBT.P—(TSXV)
Rev.: $3,169
Assets: $190,461
Liabilities: $12,189
Net Worth: $178,272
Earnings: ($34,023)
Fiscal Year-end: 03/31/20
Asset Management Services
N.A.I.C.S.: 523940
Julian Klymochko *(CEO)*

RED RIVER COOPERATIVE LTD.
10 Prairie Way, Winnipeg, R2J 3J8, MB, Canada
Tel.: (204) 631-4600
Web Site: https://www.redriverco-op.crs
Year Founded: 1937
Sales Range: $250-299.9 Million
Emp.: 595
Gas & Oil Distr
N.A.I.C.S.: 213112

RED ROCK CAPITAL CORP.
Suite 2200 885 West Georgia Street HSBC Building, Vancouver, V6C 3E8, BC, Canada
Tel.: (778) 331-8505   BC
Year Founded: 2012
RES—(TSXV)
Assets: $1,258,584
Liabilities: $47,213
Net Worth: $1,211,371
Earnings: ($186,645)
Fiscal Year-end: 12/31/23
Investment Services
N.A.I.C.S.: 523999
Thomas N. Rollinger *(CEO)*

RED ROCK RESOURCES PLC
71-91 Aldwych House, London, WC2B 4HN, United Kingdom
Tel.: (44) 2077479990   UK
Web Site: https://www.rrrplc.com
Year Founded: 2004
RRR—(AIM)
Assets: $23,403,750
Liabilities: $4,530,966
Net Worth: $18,872,784
Earnings: ($3,494,960)
Fiscal Year-end: 06/30/22
Mineral Exploration Services
N.A.I.C.S.: 212210
Andrew Ronald McMillan Bell *(Founder, Chm & CEO)*

Subsidiaries:

Red Rock Australasia Pty Ltd   (1)
Ballarat Business Centre 706 Sturt Street, Ballarat, 3350, VIC, Australia
Tel.: (61) 353369819
Web Site: http://www.rraustralasia.com.au
Gold Exploration Services
N.A.I.C.S.: 213114
Andrew Bell *(Chm)*

RED SENA BERHAD
D-18-3A Menara Mitraland No 13A Jalan PJU 5/1Kota Damansara, 47810, Petaling Jaya, Selangor, Malaysia
Tel.: (60) 376294239   MY
Web Site:
   http://www.redsena.com.my
Year Founded: 2014
RSENA—(KLS)
Sales Range: $1-9.9 Million
Investment Holding Services
N.A.I.C.S.: 551112
Mu'tamir Mohamed *(Chm)*

RED SKY ENERGY LIMITED
Level 2 480 Collins Street, Melbourne, 3000, VIC, Australia
Tel.: (61) 396140600
Web Site:
   https://www.redskyenergy.com.au
ROG—(ASX)
Rev.: $243,787
Assets: $5,413,140
Liabilities: $1,040,587
Net Worth: $4,372,553
Earnings: ($1,062,471)
Fiscal Year-end: 12/31/23
Crude Petroleum Extraction Services
N.A.I.C.S.: 211120
Adrien Wing *(Co-Sec)*

RED STAR EXPRESS PLC
70 International Airport Road, Lagos, Nigeria
Tel.: (234) 12715670
Web Site: https://www.redstarplc.com
Year Founded: 1992
REDSTAREX—(NIGE)
Rev.: $10,269,953
Assets: $6,408,366
Liabilities: $3,019,921
Net Worth: $3,388,445
Earnings: $232,348
Emp.: 1,900
Fiscal Year-end: 03/31/23
Logistics Consulting Servies
N.A.I.C.S.: 541614
Victor Enobong Ukwat *(Exec Dir-Sls & Mktg)*

RED STAR MACALLINE GROUP CORPORATION LTD.
Suite F801 6/F No 518 Lihyu Road, Pudong New District, Shanghai, China
Tel.: (86) 2122300900   CN
Web Site: http://www.chinaredstar.com
Year Founded: 2007
1528—(HKG)
Rev.: $1,985,020,128
Assets: $18,179,337,244
Liabilities: $10,035,755,917
Net Worth: $8,143,581,326
Earnings: $114,690,514
Emp.: 18,101
Fiscal Year-end: 12/31/22
Home & Shopping Mall Furnishing Services
N.A.I.C.S.: 449129
Jianfang Che *(Deputy Gen Mgr)*

RED WHITE & BLOOM BRANDS INC.
789 West Pender Street Suite 810, Vancouver, V6C 1H2, BC, Canada
Tel.: (604) 687-2038
Web Site:
   https://www.redwhitebloom.com
Year Founded: 1980
RWB—(CNSX)
Rev.: $18,257,264
Assets: $343,525,117
Liabilities: $179,649,364
Net Worth: $163,875,753
Earnings: ($14,532,312)
Emp.: 3
Fiscal Year-end: 12/31/20
Financial Investment Management Services
N.A.I.C.S.: 523940
Brad Rogers *(Chm & CEO)*

REDAN S.A.
10/14 Zniwna Str, 94-250, Lodz, Poland
Tel.: (48) 607196701   PL
Web Site: https://redan-fulfillment.pl
Year Founded: 1995
RDN—(WAR)
Rev.: $17,117,632
Assets: $16,496,189
Liabilities: $15,964,431
Net Worth: $531,758
Earnings: ($591,463)
Fiscal Year-end: 12/31/23
Clothing Whslr
N.A.I.C.S.: 458110
Slawomir Mieczyslaw Lachowski *(Chm-Supervisory Bd)*

REDBANK COPPER LIMITED

REDBUBBLE LIMITED

Level 1 1A Agnew Way, Subiaco, 6008, WA, Australia
Tel.: (61) 893629888   AU
Web Site:
   http://www.redbankcopper.com.au
Year Founded: 1993
NTM—(ASX)
Rev.: $268,680
Assets: $9,032,911
Liabilities: $1,510,710
Net Worth: $7,522,201
Earnings: ($1,085,366)
Fiscal Year-end: 06/30/24
Copper Mining & Exploration
N.A.I.C.S.: 212230
Michael Hannington *(Exec Dir)*

REDBANK ENERGY LIMITED
Suite 2105 Level 21 Westfield Tower 1 520 Oxford Street, Bondi Junction, Sydney, 2022, NSW, Australia
Tel.: (61) 2 9386 4355   AU
Web Site:
   http://www.redbankenergy.com
Sales Range: $900-999.9 Million
Power Generation
N.A.I.C.S.: 221118
Richard Butler *(Sec)*

REDBRICK INVESTMENTS S.A R.L.
33 Boulevard Prince Henri L-1724, Luxembourg, Luxembourg
Tel.: (352) 26008372
Web Site:
   https://redbrickinvestments.lu
Investment Company
N.A.I.C.S.: 523940

REDBRICK TECHNOLOGIES INC.
520-1515 Douglas Street, Victoria, V8W 2G4, BC, Canada
Tel.: (250) 590-1800
Web Site: https://www.rdbrck.com
Year Founded: 2011
Computer Software Services
N.A.I.C.S.: 541512
Tobyn Sowden *(CEO)*

Subsidiaries:

Animoto, Inc.   (1)
214 Sullivan St Ste 2F, New York, NY 10012
Web Site: http://www.animoto.com
Software Publisher
N.A.I.C.S.: 513210
Brad Jefferson *(Co-Founder & CEO)*

Delivra, Inc.   (1)
8415 Allison Pointe Blvd Ste 100, Indianapolis, IN 46250
Tel.: (317) 915-9400
Web Site: http://www.delivra.com
Email Marketing Software
N.A.I.C.S.: 513210
Neil Berman *(Founder & CEO)*

REDBUBBLE LIMITED
Level 3 271 Collins Street, Melbourne, 3000, VIC, Australia
Tel.: (61) 396500138   AU
Web Site: http://www.redbubble.com
Year Founded: 2006
RDBBF—(OTCIQ)
Rev.: $329,705,973
Assets: $87,144,076
Liabilities: $51,719,134
Net Worth: $35,424,942
Earnings: ($5,900,818)
Emp.: 237
Fiscal Year-end: 06/30/24
Online Shopping Services
N.A.I.C.S.: 561422
Martin Hosking *(Founder)*

Subsidiaries:

Redbubble Europe GmbH   (1)

REDBUBBLE LIMITED

Redbubble Limited—(Continued)
Neue Schonhauser Str 3 -5, 10178, Berlin, Germany
Tel.: (49) 3056837185
Logistic Services
N.A.I.C.S.: 541614

REDCAPTOUR CO LTD
18th and 19th floors B-dong 100 Euljiro, Jung-gu, Seoul, 04551, Korea (South)
Tel.: (82) 220014500
Web Site: https://www.redcap.co.kr
Year Founded: 1977
038390—(KRS)
Rev.: $201,003,690
Assets: $476,963,493
Liabilities: $329,142,319
Net Worth: $147,821,174
Earnings: $16,287,456
Emp.: 374
Fiscal Year-end: 12/31/22
Travel & Car Rental Services
N.A.I.C.S.: 561510
Yong Hyeok Joo *(Asst Mng Dir)*

REDCENTRIC PLC
Tel.: (44) 8009832522
Web Site: https://www.redcentricplc.com
Year Founded: 1997
RCN—(AIM)
Rev.: $122,374,296
Assets: $156,635,952
Liabilities: $62,426,232
Net Worth: $94,209,720
Earnings: $9,099,728
Fiscal Year-end: 03/31/22
Computer Related Services & Solutions
N.A.I.C.S.: 541519
Peter Brotherton *(CEO)*

Subsidiaries:

Piksel Industry Solutions Ltd. (1)
1 Innovation Close York Science Park, Heslington, York, YO10 5ZD, North Yorkshire, United Kingdom
Tel.: (44) 1904438000
Emp.: 380
Video Management Software Provider
N.A.I.C.S.: 517111
Kristan Bullett *(Head-Software Architecture)*

Redcentric MS Limited (1)
Newton House Cambridge Business Park, Cowley Road, Cambridge, CB4 0WZ, United Kingdom
Tel.: (44) 8009832522
Sales Range: $25-49.9 Million
Emp.: 50
Specialist Computing Services
N.A.I.C.S.: 541519

REDCO PROPERTIES GROUP LIMITED
Redco Building Tower 5
Qiaochengfang Phase I No 4080
Qiaoxiang Road, Nanshan District, Shenzhen, China
Tel.: (86) 75582221622
Web Site: http://www.redco.cn
1622—(HKG)
Rev.: $2,863,599,523
Assets: $12,538,698,869
Liabilities: $10,255,947,905
Net Worth: $2,282,750,964
Earnings: $353,038,187
Emp.: 3,620
Fiscal Year-end: 12/31/21
Property Developer
N.A.I.C.S.: 237210
Yeuk Hung Wong *(Chm)*

Subsidiaries:

Hong Kong Jiye Holdings Limited (1)
Room 1-2 20th Floor Phase 3 Enterprise Plaza, Kowloon Bay, China (Hong Kong)
Tel.: (852) 23312839
Real Estate Services
N.A.I.C.S.: 531390

REDCO TEXTILES LIMITED
Redco Arcade 78-E Blue Area, Islamabad, 44000, Pakistan
Tel.: (92) 512344257
Web Site: https://www.redcotextiles.com
Year Founded: 1992
REDCO—(KAR)
Rev.: $1,618,803
Assets: $6,857,853
Liabilities: $7,004,233
Net Worth: ($146,380)
Earnings: $6,066
Emp.: 300
Fiscal Year-end: 06/30/19
Timber Product Mfr
N.A.I.C.S.: 313110
Sarah Saif Khan *(CEO)*

REDCOON GMBH
Keltenstrasse 2, 63741, Aschaffenburg, Germany
Tel.: (49) 60214478201
Web Site: http://www.redcoon.com
Sales Range: $200-249.9 Million
Emp.: 650
Electronics, Appliances & Computer Products Online Retailer
N.A.I.C.S.: 423430
Reiner Heckel *(Mng Dir)*

Subsidiaries:

Redcoon Electronic Trade S.L. (1)
Rua do Ouro 40/48 2, 1100-063, Lisbon, Portugal
Tel.: (351) 707785051
Web Site: http://www.redcoon.pt
Online Shopping Services
N.A.I.C.S.: 449210

Redcoon Electronic Trade S.L.U. (1)
Nave 24 1 Calle Cal Fernando 25-35, Zona de actividad logistica ZAL - Prat, 8820, El Prat de Llobregat, Spain
Tel.: (34) 902656400
Web Site: http://www.redcoon.es
Online Shopping Services
N.A.I.C.S.: 449210
Marc Marin *(Head-Showroom)*

redcoon Benelux bv (1)
Havendijk 26, 5017 AM, Tilburg, Netherlands
Tel.: (31) 138200168
Web Site: http://www.redcoon.nl
Online Shopping Services
N.A.I.C.S.: 425120
Erwin Bruggink *(Mng Dir)*

redcoon GmbH (1)
Bosendorferstrasse 9, 1010, Vienna, Austria
Tel.: (43) 720880265
Web Site: http://www.redcoon.at
Online Shopping Services
N.A.I.C.S.: 449210

redcoon Italia S.r.l. (1)
Corso Francia 84, 10143, Turin, Italy
Tel.: (39) 0112173422
Web Site: http://www.redcoon.it
Online Shopping Services
N.A.I.C.S.: 425120
Massa Cristina *(Mng Dir)*

redcoon Polska Sp. z o.o. (1)
Jagiellonska 21, 85-097, Bydgoszcz, Poland
Tel.: (48) 525642323
Web Site: http://www.redcoon.pl
Online Shopping Services
N.A.I.C.S.: 425120

REDE D'OR SAO LUIZ SA
Rua Francisco Marengo No 1312, Tatuape, Sao Paulo, 03313-000, Brazil
Tel.: (55) 1130039285
Web Site: https://www.rededorsaoluiz.com.br
Year Founded: 1977
RDOR3—(BRAZ)
Rev.: $9,464,491,553
Assets: $18,384,669,446
Liabilities: $13,534,115,485
Net Worth: $4,850,553,961
Earnings: $430,138,154
Emp.: 60,000
Fiscal Year-end: 12/31/23
Hospitals & Health Care Services
N.A.I.C.S.: 622110
Paulo Junqueira Moll *(CEO)*

Subsidiaries:

Sul America S.A. (1)
Rua Beatriz Larra Lucas 121 4th Floor, Rio de Janeiro, 20211-903, Brazil
Tel.: (55) 2125069111
Web Site: https://portal.sulamericaseguros.com.br
General Insurance Services
N.A.I.C.S.: 524113

Subsidiary (Domestic):

Saepar Servicos e Participacoes S.A. (2)
Rua Beatriz Larragoiti Lucas 121 6th Fl, Pavimento Ala Sul Cidade Mova, 20211-903, Rio de Janeiro, Brazil
Tel.: (55) 2125068585
General Insurance Services
N.A.I.C.S.: 524114

REDEFINE PROPERTIES LIMITED
4th Floor 155 West Street, Sandown, Sandton, 2196, Johannesburg, South Africa
Tel.: (27) 112830000
Web Site: https://www.redefine.co.za
Year Founded: 1999
RDF—(JSE)
Rev.: $523,290,909
Assets: $5,251,861,289
Liabilities: $2,459,139,144
Net Worth: $2,792,722,145
Earnings: $77,142,608
Emp.: 415
Fiscal Year-end: 08/31/23
Investment Services
N.A.I.C.S.: 523999
David Rice *(COO)*

Subsidiaries:

Redefine Properties International Limited (1)
2nd Floor 30 Charles II Street, London, SW1Y 4AE, United Kingdom (54%)
Tel.: (44) 20 7811 0100
Web Site: http://www.redefineint.com
Sales Range: $100-124.9 Million
Property Investment Trust
N.A.I.C.S.: 525990

Spearhead Property Holdings Ltd. (1)
The Spearhead 42 Hans Strydom Ave, Roggebaai, Cape Town, 8012, Western Cape, South Africa
Tel.: (27) 214251000
Sales Range: $50-74.9 Million
Emp.: 18
Real Estate Development & Leasing Services
N.A.I.C.S.: 531120

REDEIA CORPORATION, S.A.
Paseo del Conde de los Gaitanes 177, Alcobendas, 28109, Madrid, Spain
Tel.: (34) 916508500
Web Site: https://www.ree.es
Year Founded: 1985
RED—(MAD)
Rev.: $2,227,575,005
Assets: $15,632,254,479
Liabilities: $9,665,216,922
Net Worth: $5,967,037,557
Earnings: $776,681,416
Emp.: 2,447

INTERNATIONAL PUBLIC

Fiscal Year-end: 12/31/23
Telecommunication Equipment Mfr & Distr
N.A.I.C.S.: 334290
Roberto Garcia Merino *(CEO)*

Subsidiaries:

Cybercia SRL (1)
Calle Colombia 655 Entre Falsuri Y Costanera, Cochabamba, Bolivia
Tel.: (591) 44580922
Web Site: http://www.cybercia.com
Sales Range: $25-49.9 Million
Emp.: 13
Management Consulting Services
N.A.I.C.S.: 541618

Hispasat, S.A. (1)
Paseo de la Castellana 39, 28046, Madrid, Spain (89.68%)
Tel.: (34) 917 102 540
Web Site: http://www.hispasat.com
Satellite Telecommunications
N.A.I.C.S.: 517410
Miguel Angel Panduro Panadero *(CEO)*

Red Electrica International S.A.U. (1)
Paseo del Conde de Los Gaitanes 177, 28109, Alcobendas, Madrid, Spain
Tel.: (34) 916502012
Web Site: http://www.ree.es
Holding Company
N.A.I.C.S.: 551112

Red Electrica del Sur S.A (1)
Calle Juan De La Fuente 453, Lima, 18, Peru (100%)
Tel.: (51) 12426622
Web Site: http://www.redesur.com.pe
Electric Powertransmision
N.A.I.C.S.: 221122
Luis Belasco *(Gen Mgr)*

Transportadora de Electricidad S.A. (1)
Calle Colombia, Cochabamba, 00655, Bolivia (99.94%)
Tel.: (591) 44259500
Web Site: http://www.tde.com.bo
Sales Range: $125-149.9 Million
Emp.: 130
Electric Power Distribution
N.A.I.C.S.: 221122
Eduardo Pas *(Pres)*

REDELFI S.P.A.
Via A Scarsellini 119-Torre B I Gemelli 11 piano, 16149, Genoa, Italy
Tel.: (39) 0108595690
Web Site: https://www.redelfi.com
Year Founded: 2008
RDF—(ITA)
Information Technology Services
N.A.I.C.S.: 541512
Davide Sommariva *(Pres)*

REDERIAKSJESELSKAPET TORVALD KLAVENESS
Drammensveien 260, 0283, Oslo, Norway
Tel.: (47) 2252 6000   NO
Web Site: http://www.klaveness.com
Year Founded: 1946
Sales Range: $550-599.9 Million
Emp.: 165
Holding Company; Freight Shipping & Ship Management Services
N.A.I.C.S.: 551112
Trond Harald Klaveness *(Chm)*

Subsidiaries:

Klaveness Asia Pte. Ltd. (1)
3 Temasek Avenue 10-02 Centennial Tower, Singapore, 039190, Singapore
Tel.: (65) 630 35560
Freight Shipping Services
N.A.I.C.S.: 488390
Abhishek Karnawat *(Sr Mgr)*

REDFISH LONGTERM CAPITAL S.P.A.

Via del Carmine 11, 20121, Milan, Italy
Tel.: (39) 0298670065
Web Site:
https://longterm.redfish.capital
Year Founded: 2020
RFLTC—(ITA)
Investment Management Service
N.A.I.C.S.: 523999
Andrea Rossotti *(CEO)*

REDFLOW LIMITED
27 Counihan Road Seventeen Mile Rocks, Brisbane, 4073, QLD, Australia
Tel.: (61) 733760008   AU
Web Site: https://www.redflow.com
Year Founded: 2005
RFX—(ASX)
Rev.: $3,766,448
Assets: $11,833,921
Liabilities: $6,872,218
Net Worth: $4,961,703
Earnings: ($7,313,408)
Emp.: 83
Fiscal Year-end: 06/30/21
Energy Storage System Mfr
N.A.I.C.S.: 335910
Tim Mactaggart *(Chief Deployment Officer)*

Subsidiaries:

RedFlow International Pty Ltd (1)
27 Counihan Road, Seventeen Mile Rocks, Brisbane, 4073, QLD, Australia
Tel.: (61) 733760008
Web Site: http://www.redflow.com
Sales Range: $25-49.9 Million
Emp.: 43
Storage Batteries Mfr & Distr
N.A.I.C.S.: 335910

REDGATE MEDIA GROUP
8th Floor CITIC Building Tower B 19 Jianguomenwai St, Chaoyang District, Beijing, 100014, China
Tel.: (86) 1085263128   Ky
Web Site:
http://www.redgatemedia.com
Year Founded: 2003
Sales Range: $10-24.9 Million
Emp.: 143
Television, Radio, Outdoor, Internet & Other Media Advertising Services
N.A.I.C.S.: 541890
Peter B. Brack *(Chm & CEO)*

REDGRAVE PARTNERS LLP
2 Savoy Court, London, WC2R 0EZ, United Kingdom
Tel.: (44) 2078061610
Web Site:
http://www.redgravepartners.com
Year Founded: 2008
Sales Range: $25-49.9 Million
Emp.: 100
Recruitment Services
N.A.I.C.S.: 541612
Brian Hamill *(Chm)*

REDHALL GROUP PLC
Unit 3 Calder Close, Wakefield, WF4 3BA, United Kingdom
Tel.: (44) 1924385386   UK
Web Site:
http://www.redhallgroup.co.uk
Year Founded: 1932
Rev.: $50,944,120
Assets: $53,430,548
Liabilities: $24,968,164
Net Worth: $28,462,385
Earnings: ($5,551,629)
Emp.: 358
Fiscal Year-end: 09/30/18
Heavy Engineering Services
N.A.I.C.S.: 237990
Russell D. Haworth *(CEO-Interim)*

Subsidiaries:

Jordan Manufacturing Limited (1)
Redhall House 14 Millbrook Road, Yate, Bristol, BS37 5JW, United Kingdom
Tel.: (44) 1454328300
Web Site:
http://www.jordanmanufacturing.co.uk
Sales Range: $25-49.9 Million
Emp.: 80
Engineeering Services
N.A.I.C.S.: 541330

R. Blackett Charlton (1)
Chieftain House White Street Walker, Newcastle upon Tyne, NE6 3PJ, United Kingdom
Tel.: (44) 1912635544
Web Site: http://www.redhallgroup.co.uk
Sales Range: $75-99.9 Million
Emp.: 250
Building & Engineering Services
N.A.I.C.S.: 238310

Redhall Engineering (1)
14 Millbrook Road, Stover Trading Estate, Yate, BS37 5JW, Bristol, United Kingdom
Tel.: (44) 1454 328270
Web Site:
http://www.redhallengineering.com
Sales Range: $25-49.9 Million
Emp.: 100
Engineeering Services
N.A.I.C.S.: 541330

Redhall Nuclear Ltd. (1)
9 Belasis Court Belasis Technology Park, Billingham, TS23 4AZ, Teeside, United Kingdom
Tel.: (44) 1642 563700
Web Site: http://www.redhallgroup.co.uk
Sales Range: $25-49.9 Million
Emp.: 100
Engineeering Services
N.A.I.C.S.: 541330

REDHEAD EQUIPMENT LTD
Highway 16 North, Saskatoon, S7K 7E8, SK, Canada
Tel.: (306) 931-4600
Web Site:
http://www.redheadequipment.ca
Sales Range: $100-124.9 Million
Emp.: 255
Heavy Duty Trucks Equipment Whslr
N.A.I.C.S.: 336120
Gary Redhead *(Pres & CEO)*

REDHILL BIOPHARMA LTD.
21 Ha arba a Street, Tel Aviv, 6473921, Israel
Tel.: (972) 35413131   Il
Web Site: https://www.redhillbio.com
Year Founded: 2009
RDHL—(NASDAQ)
Rev.: $61,800,000
Assets: $158,870,000
Liabilities: $207,270,000
Net Worth: ($48,400,000)
Earnings: ($71,669,000)
Emp.: 113
Fiscal Year-end: 12/31/22
Biopharmaceutical Product Mfr
N.A.I.C.S.: 325412
Dror Ben-Asher *(Founder, Chm & CEO)*

REDIFF.COM INDIA LIMITED
Mahalaxmi Engineering Estate LJ Road #1, Mahim (West), Mumbai, 400016, India
Tel.: (91) 2261820000   In
Web Site: http://www.rediff.com
Year Founded: 1996
Holding Company; Online News, Information, Communication, Entertainment & Shopping Services
N.A.I.C.S.: 551112
Ajit Balakrishnan *(CEO)*

Subsidiaries:

India Abroad Publications Inc. (1)
42 Broadway Ste 1836, New York, NY 10004
Tel.: (212) 929-1727
Web Site: http://www.indiaabroad.com
Weekly Newpaper for Indian Community
N.A.I.C.S.: 513110
Rajiv Bhambri *(COO)*

REDIFF.COM INDIA LTD.
Mahalaxmi Engineering Estate L. J. First Cross Road Mahim, Mumbai, 400 016, India
Tel.: (91) 2261820000
Web Site: https://m.rediff.com
Internet & E-commerce Company
N.A.I.C.S.: 518210

REDINGTON (INDIA) LIMITED
DP 30A Thiru Vi Ka Industrial Estate, SIDCO Industrial Estate Guindy, Chennai, 600 032, Tamil Nadu, India
Tel.: (91) 4430682725   In
Web Site:
https://www.redingtongroup.com
Year Founded: 1961
REDINGTON—(NSE)
Rev.: $7,786,177,035
Assets: $1,987,040,055
Liabilities: $1,262,678,235
Net Worth: $724,361,820
Earnings: $107,372,265
Emp.: 1,545
Fiscal Year-end: 03/31/21
Holding Company; Information Technology Products Distr
N.A.I.C.S.: 541614
M. Muthukumarasamy *(Officer-Compliance & Sec)*

Subsidiaries:

Cadensworth (India) Pvt Limited. (1)
J S D Towers 79 J N Road, Vadapalani, Chennai, 600026, Tamil Nadu, India
Tel.: (91) 4430273342
Web Site: http://www.cdwindia.com
Computer Peripheral Equipment Sales & Maintenance Services
N.A.I.C.S.: 423430
Ram Kumar *(Gen Mgr)*

Cadensworth FZE (1)
Shed VC1 8th Roundabout Jebel Ali Free Zone, Dubai, 17441, United Arab Emirates
Tel.: (971) 48835757
Information Technology Management Services
N.A.I.C.S.: 541614
Radha Krishnan *(Gen Mgr)*

Citrus Consulting Services FZ LLC (1)
H-Hotel Office Towers, 1 Sheikh Zayed Road 10th Floor, Dubai, United Arab Emirates
Tel.: (971) 045161500
Web Site: https://www.citrusconsulting.com
IT Services
N.A.I.C.S.: 513210

Ensure IT Services (Pty) Ltd. (1)
International Business Gateway North Wing, Midrand Gate Building Corner New Road 6th Rd, Johannesburg, 1684, South Africa
Tel.: (27) 86 182 6000
Information Technology Services
N.A.I.C.S.: 541512

Ensure Services Arabia LLC (1)
Tel.: (966) 920033446
Web Site: https://www.ensureservices.com
Information Technology Services
N.A.I.C.S.: 541512
Tg Sureshbabu *(Sr VP)*

Ensure Services Bahrain S.P.C. (1)
Building No-44B Shop No-46 and 46A Road No-359 Block No-321, Abdul Rahman Al-Dakhil Avenue, Manama, Bahrain
Tel.: (973) 1 727 1880
Information Technology Services
N.A.I.C.S.: 541512

ProConnect Supply Chain Solutions Limited (1)
Tel.: (91) 4442243211
Web Site: https://www.proconnect.co.in
Logistic Services
N.A.I.C.S.: 541614
Kumar Malay Shankar *(Mng Dir)*

Proconnect Saudi LLC (1)
Block 16 Al Fursan Warehouse complex Plot no 145 to 152, PO Box 66120, Istanbul street Exit-18 Sula, Riyadh, 14328, Saudi Arabia
Tel.: (966) 114625323
Logistic Services
N.A.I.C.S.: 541614

Proconnect Supply Chain Logistics LLC (1)
Plot No S 30902, PO Box 262674, Jebel Ali South, Dubai, United Arab Emirates
Tel.: (971) 48809487
Logistics & Supply Chain Services
N.A.I.C.S.: 541614

RNDC Alliance West Africa Limited (1)
122 - 132 Oshodi/Apapa Expressway Isolo, PO Box 3623, Lagos, Nigeria
Tel.: (234) 14523989
Information Technology Services
N.A.I.C.S.: 541512

Redington (India) Investments Private Limited (1)
Spl Guindy House 95 mount Road Guindy, Chennai, 600032, Tamil Nadu, India
Tel.: (91) 4439181304
Electronic Product Distr
N.A.I.C.S.: 423430

Redington Africa Distribution FZE (1)
Plot No S30902 Next To Thomson Mercantile South Zone 3, Dubai, United Arab Emirates
Tel.: (971) 48809487
Hardware & Software Product Distr
N.A.I.C.S.: 423430

Redington Bahrain SPC (1)
Al hajiyat Shop No 7 Building No 78 Road 3901 Block 939, PO Box 11260, Ar Rifa' al Gharbi, Bahrain
Tel.: (973) 17490330
Computer Peripherals Mfr & Distr
N.A.I.C.S.: 334118

Redington Bangladesh Limited (1)
Tel.: (880) 28854333
Sales Range: $50-74.9 Million
Emp.: 3
Computer Peripheral Equipment Distr
N.A.I.C.S.: 423430

Redington Distribution Company (1)
Tel.: (20) 223520251
Information Technology Services
N.A.I.C.S.: 541512

Redington Distribution Pte Ltd (1)
60 Robinson Road Bea Building Unit 12-01, Singapore, 068892, Singapore
Tel.: (65) 64356626
Emp.: 20
Logistics Management Consulting Services
N.A.I.C.S.: 541614

Redington Gulf & Co. LLC (1)
Tel.: (968) 24791405
Information Technology Services
N.A.I.C.S.: 541512

Redington Gulf FZE (1)
Plot No S30902, PO Box 17266, Jebel Ali Free Zone, 04, Dubai, United Arab Emirates
Tel.: (971) 48809487
Web Site: http://www.redingtongulf.com
Sales Range: $75-99.9 Million
Emp.: 200
Information Technology Products Distr
N.A.I.C.S.: 423430
Raj Shankar *(Chm & Mng Dir)*

Redington International Mauritius Limited (1)
Ifs Court bank Street 28 Cybercity, Ebene, 72201, Mauritius
Tel.: (230) 4673000
Web Site: http://www.ifsmauritius.com
Supply Chain Information Technology Consulting Services
N.A.I.C.S.: 541512

REDINGTON (INDIA) LIMITED

Redington (India) Limited—(Continued)
Sriram Ganeshan *(Mgr)*

Redington Kazakhstan LLP (1)
str Makataeva 117 of 311, 050050, Almaty, Kazakhstan
Tel.: (7) 7273933047
Information Technology Services
N.A.I.C.S.: 541512

Redington Kenya Limited (1)
School Lane, PO Box 383, Westlands, 00606, Nairobi, Kenya
Tel.: (254) 204451792
Information Technology Services
N.A.I.C.S.: 541512

Redington Middle East LLC (1)
Level 16 Burjuman Business Tower - Sheikh Khalifa Bin Zayed St, Al Mankhool, Dubai, United Arab Emirates
Tel.: (971) 45161000
Hardware Maintenance Services
N.A.I.C.S.: 811310

Redington Nigeria Ltd (1)
Oshodi Apapa Expressway No 122 132, Lagos, Nigeria
Tel.: (234) 14523991
Television Broadcasting Services
N.A.I.C.S.: 516120

Redington Qatar Distribution WLL (1)
Hilal West C Ring Road Dawlat Qatar, Doha, 23248, Qatar
Tel.: (974) 44551608
Sales Range: $25-49.9 Million
Emp.: 25
Information Technology Development Services
N.A.I.C.S.: 541512

Redington Qatar WLL (1)
CR No 25255 Zone No 56 Street No 900 Building No 19, PO Box 23248, Barwa Commercial Avenue, Doha, Qatar
Tel.: (974) 40203800
Web Site: http://www.redingtonqatar.com.qa
Information Technology Development Services
N.A.I.C.S.: 541512

Redington SL Private Limited (1)
65C Dharmapala Mawatha, 07, Colombo, Sri Lanka
Tel.: (94) 117440323
Information Technology Services
N.A.I.C.S.: 541512

Redington Saudi Arabia Distribution Company (1)
Al Noor Center Office No 506 Madina Road, Jeddah, Saudi Arabia
Tel.: (966) 114625323
Information Technology Services
N.A.I.C.S.: 541512

Redington Senegal Limited S.A.R.L. (1)
Lot No 24 Pyrotechnique Mermoz VDN In Face Cite Keur Gorgui, Dakar, Senegal
Tel.: (221) 338259113
Information Technology Services
N.A.I.C.S.: 541512

Redington South Africa (Pty.) Ltd. (1)
Unit 6 Mone Je Paul 26 Aloefield Crescent Rochdale Park, Springfield Park, Durban, 4034, KwaZulu Natal, South Africa
Tel.: (27) 861826000
Hardware Maintenance Services
N.A.I.C.S.: 811310

Redington South Africa Distribution (PTY.) Ltd. (1)
20 Hurd Street Newton Park, PO Box No 6045, Port Elizabeth, South Africa
Tel.: (27) 861826000
Hardware Maintenance Services
N.A.I.C.S.: 811310

Redington Uganda Limited (1)
Plot 15 Mulwana Road Industrial Area, PO Box 33009, Kampala, 33009, Uganda
Tel.: (256) 758700333
Web Site: http://www.redingtonea.com
Sales Range: $25-49.9 Million
Emp.: 30
Information Technology Products Distr
N.A.I.C.S.: 423420

REDISHRED CAPITAL CORP.
2233 Argentia Road Suite 202, Mississauga, L5N 2X7, ON, Canada
Tel.: (647) 977-6144 Ca
Web Site: https://www.proshred.com
Year Founded: 2006
KUT—(TSXV)
Rev.: $28,317,754
Assets: $62,061,402
Liabilities: $30,488,581
Net Worth: $31,572,821
Earnings: $1,062,336
Fiscal Year-end: 12/31/21
Investment Services
N.A.I.C.S.: 523999
Jeffrey I. Hasham *(CEO)*

Subsidiaries:

Proshred Franchising Corp. (1)
6790 Century Ave Ste 200, Mississauga, L5N 2V8, ON, Canada
Tel.: (416) 490-8600
Web Site: http://www.proshred.com
Sales Range: $25-49.9 Million
Emp.: 8
Document Shredding Services
N.A.I.C.S.: 561990

Security Shredding Enterprises (1)
200 Speedwell Ave, Morris Plains, NJ 07950
Tel.: (973) 734-1911
Web Site: http://securityshredding.net
Sales Range: $1-9.9 Million
Emp.: 10
Service Establishment Equipment & Supplies Merchant Whslr
N.A.I.C.S.: 423850
John O'Hagan *(Principal)*

REDITUS SGPS S.A.
Estrada do Seminario 2, 2614-522, Alfragide, Portugal
Tel.: (351) 214124100
Web Site: http://www.reditus.pt
Year Founded: 1966
RED—(EUR)
Sales Range: $100-124.9 Million
Outsourcing, Engineering & Mobility Services
N.A.I.C.S.: 561320
Francisco Jose Martins Santana Ramos *(Chm & CEO)*

Subsidiaries:

Caleo, S.A. (1)
421 rue Helene Boucher, PO Box 223, 78532, Buc, France
Tel.: (33) 130972000
Sales Range: $25-49.9 Million
Emp.: 15
Computer System Integration Services
N.A.I.C.S.: 541512

J M Consultores de Informatica e Artes Graficas, S.A. (1)
Avenida Almeida Garrett, 18 2720 030, Lisbon, Portugal
Tel.: (351) 214702160
Sales Range: $25-49.9 Million
Emp.: 15
Information System Management Services
N.A.I.C.S.: 541512

Reditus II Telecomunicacoes, S.A. (1)
Bldg Reditus Estrada Do Seminar, 2 Alfragide, Lisbon, 2614, Portugal
Tel.: (351) 214124100
Web Site: http://www.reditus.pt
Sales Range: $75-99.9 Million
Emp.: 300
Information System Management Services
N.A.I.C.S.: 541512

Redware Sistemas de Informacao, S.A. (1)
Bldg reditus Rd Seminar 2, Alfragide, 2614 522, Amadora, Portugal
Tel.: (351) 214124100
Web Site: http://www.reditus.pt

Emp.: 100
Information System Management Services
N.A.I.C.S.: 541512
Francisco Santana Ramos *(Mng Dir)*

Roff Global (1)
121 Ave des Champs Elysees, 75008, Paris, France
Tel.: (33) 172718550
Web Site: http://www.roffglobal.com
Sales Range: $25-49.9 Million
Emp.: 100
IT Strategic Consultancy Services
N.A.I.C.S.: 541618

Tecnidata BMT Business Management Tecnologies, S.A. (1)
Rua Afonso Praca Emilio, Torre de Monsanto 30 N 6th Fl, Alges, 1495 061, Portugal
Tel.: (351) 218390700
Web Site: http://www.tecnidata.pt
Computer Programming Services
N.A.I.C.S.: 541511
Meeuel Sehhedhr *(Sec)*

Tecnidata IF Investimentos Financeiros SGPS, S.A. (1)
Rua Afonso Emilio Sq Tower Monsanto Nr 30, Miraflores, 1495 061, Lisbon, Portugal
Tel.: (351) 218390700
Web Site: http://www.reditus.pt
Emp.: 1,000
Information System Management Services
N.A.I.C.S.: 541512
Nigel Carrera *(Gen Mgr)*

REDLINE CAPITAL MANAGEMENT SA
26 Avenue Monterey, 2163, Luxembourg, Luxembourg
Tel.: (352) 621284927 LU
Web Site: http://www.redline.lu
Privater Equity Firm
N.A.I.C.S.: 523999
Vladimir Yevtushenkov *(Founder)*

REDLINE PERFORMANCE AUTOMOTIVE LTD
B13 Site 2 RR 1, De Winton, T0L 0X0, AB, Canada
Tel.: (403) 510-0707 NV
Year Founded: 2007
Sales Range: $25-49.9 Million
Emp.: 1
Custom & Stock Replacement Automotive Parts Designer, Mfr & Sales
N.A.I.C.S.: 336390
Lloyd Dixon *(Pres, CEO, CFO, Treas & Sec)*

REDOX PTY. LTD.
2 Swettenham Road, Minto, 2566, NSW, Australia
Tel.: (61) 297333000 AU
Web Site: http://www.redox.com
Year Founded: 1965
Sales Range: $150-199.9 Million
Emp.: 350
Chemical Distr
N.A.I.C.S.: 424690
Renato Coneliano *(Mgr-Mktg)*

Subsidiaries:

Redox Chemicals Sdn Bhd (1)
No 8 Block G Taipan 2 Jalan PJU 1A/3, Ara Damansara, 47301, Petaling Jaya, Selangor, Malaysia
Tel.: (60) 78436833
Chemical Products Distr
N.A.I.C.S.: 424690
Chua Jia Yong *(Bus Mgr)*

REDROVER CO. LTD.
4F 20 Seocho-daero 41-gil Seocho-gu, Seoul, 06595, Korea (South)
Tel.: (82) 221560137
Web Site: http://www.redrover.co.kr
060300—(KRS)
Rev.: $5,513,341
Assets: $14,394,066

INTERNATIONAL PUBLIC

Liabilities: $8,080,592
Net Worth: $6,313,474
Earnings: ($10,059,459)
Emp.: 17
Fiscal Year-end: 12/31/21
Monitors Development & Mfr
N.A.I.C.S.: 339999

REDS S.A.
25 Ermou, 145 64, Athens, Greece
Tel.: (30) 2108184800
Web Site: https://www.reds.gr
KAMP—(ATH)
Rev.: $8,039,078
Assets: $150,143,551
Liabilities: $47,729,264
Net Worth: $102,414,287
Earnings: $1,135,913
Emp.: 26
Fiscal Year-end: 12/31/21
Real Estate & Investment Services
N.A.I.C.S.: 531390
Christos Panagiotopoulos *(Chm)*

REDSENSE MEDICAL AB
Tel.: (46) 35106030
Web Site: https://www.redsensemedical.com
Year Founded: 2006
R0Z—(DEU)
Medical Instrument Mfr
N.A.I.C.S.: 339112
Patrik Byhmer *(CEO)*

REDSTONE RESOURCES LIMITED
60 Havelock Street, West Perth, 6005, WA, Australia
Tel.: (61) 893282552
Web Site: https://www.redstone.com.au
RDS—(ASX)
Rev.: $55,192
Assets: $6,568,305
Liabilities: $262,914
Net Worth: $6,305,391
Earnings: ($774,127)
Fiscal Year-end: 06/30/24
Minerals Exploration
N.A.I.C.S.: 212390
Miranda Conti *(Sec)*

REDSUN PROPERTIES GROUP LTD.
Hongyang Building No 9 Daqiao North Road, Pukou District, Nanjing, 210000, Jiangsu, China
Tel.: (86) 2588019462 Ky
Web Site: http://www.rsunproperty.hk
1996—(HKG)
Rev.: $2,809,885,572
Assets: $14,283,308,146
Liabilities: $10,942,003,379
Net Worth: $3,341,304,767
Earnings: ($552,868,103)
Emp.: 2,136
Fiscal Year-end: 12/31/22
Residential & Commercial Property Development Services
N.A.I.C.S.: 531210
Huansha Zeng *(Founder & Chm)*

REDSUN SERVICES GROUP LIMITED
Rsun building No 9 Daqiao North Road, Pukou, Nanjing, Jiangsu, China
Tel.: (86) 2588019048 Ky
Web Site: http://www.rsunservice.hk
Year Founded: 2003
1971—(HKG)
Property Management Services
N.A.I.C.S.: 531311
Jian Cheng *(VP)*

REDTONE ASIA, INC.

AND PRIVATE COMPANIES

Suite A 15F Sanhe Plaza No 121
Yanping Road, Jingan District,
Shanghai, 200042, China
Tel.: (86) 61032230 NV
Web Site:
  http://www.redtoneasia.com
Year Founded: 2005
RTAS—(OTCIQ)
Sales Range: $1-9.9 Million
Prepaid Mobile Air-Time & Games
Reload; Prepaid Discounted Call Services
N.A.I.C.S.: 517112
Hong Mao *(COO)*

REDWOOD DISTRIBUTION LTD.
1 Paddock Rd, Skelmersdale, WN8 9PL, United Kingdom
Tel.: (44) 1695553830
Web Site: http://www.redwood-ttm.com
Sales Range: $25-49.9 Million
Emp.: 100
Fabric Mfr & Distr
N.A.I.C.S.: 314999
John Atherton *(Dir-Sls)*

Subsidiaries:

Edmund Bell & Co., Limited (1)
Belfry House 1 Roysdale Way Euroway Trade & Estate, Bradford, BD4 6SU, United Kingdom
Tel.: (44) 1274680680
Web Site: http://www.liningsonline.co.uk
Sales Range: $25-49.9 Million
Emp.: 40
Home Furnishing Mfr
N.A.I.C.S.: 449129
Tarren Rose *(Dir-Fin)*

REDWOODS CO., LTD.
4F 7 Hakdong-ro 82-gil, Gangnam-gu, Seoul, Korea (South)
Tel.: (82) 25651676
Entertainment Services
N.A.I.C.S.: 711130

REEBONZ HOLDING LIMITED
5 Tampines North Drive 5 Ste 07-00, Singapore, 528548, Singapore
Tel.: (65) 64999469 Ky
Year Founded: 2009
Rev.: $88,379,000
Assets: $79,139,000
Liabilities: $100,684,000
Net Worth: ($21,545,000)
Earnings: ($35,239,000)
Emp.: 302
Fiscal Year-end: 12/31/18
Holding Company
N.A.I.C.S.: 551112
Samuel Lim *(Founder, Chm & CEO)*

Subsidiaries:

Draper Oakwood Technology Acquisition, Inc. (1)
55 E 3rd Ave, San Mateo, CA 94401
Tel.: (713) 213-7061
Web Site: http://www.draperoakwood.com
Investment Services
N.A.I.C.S.: 523999
Roderick Perry *(Chm)*

REECE GROUP LTD.
Armstrong Works, Newcastle upon Tyne, NE 15 6UX, Tyne & Wear, United Kingdom
Tel.: (44) 191 234 8700
Web Site: http://www.reece-group.com
Year Founded: 1983
Sales Range: $300-349.9 Million
Emp.: 400
Investment Management Service
N.A.I.C.S.: 523940
Phil Kite *(CEO)*

Subsidiaries:

Pipe Coil Technology Ltd. (1)
Armstrong Works Scotswood Road, Newcastle upon Tyne, NE 15 6UX, United Kingdom
Tel.: (44) 1912959910
Coiling Equipment Mfr & Distr
N.A.I.C.S.: 332996

Velocity UK Limited (1)
Woodbine Street Hendon, Sunderland, SR1 2NL, Tyne and Wear, United Kingdom
Tel.: (44) 1915654400
Web Site: http://www.velocitypatching.com
Highway & Street Construction Services
N.A.I.C.S.: 237310
Dominic Gardner *(Mng Dir)*

REECE LIMITED
57 Balmain Street, Cremorne, 3121, VIC, Australia
Tel.: (61) 392740000 AU
Web Site: https://www.reece.com.au
Year Founded: 1919
REH—(ASX)
Rev.: $6,079,575,296
Assets: $4,737,492,636
Liabilities: $2,143,914,254
Net Worth: $2,593,578,381
Earnings: $279,895,164
Emp.: 9,000
Fiscal Year-end: 06/30/24
Plumbing & Bathroom Product Whslr
N.A.I.C.S.: 423720
L. Alan Wilson *(Chm & Exec Dir)*

Subsidiaries:

Actrol Parts Holdings Pty Ltd (1)
19 King Street, Blackburn, 3130, VIC, Australia
Tel.: (61) 398941033
Plumbing Fixture Whslr
N.A.I.C.S.: 423720

Air Plus Pty Ltd (1)
40- 42 Wedgewood Rd, Hallam, 3803, VIC, Australia
Tel.: (61) 397023855
Household Appliance & Utensil Distr
N.A.I.C.S.: 423720

Kirby NZ Limited (1)
12 George Bourke Drive, Mt Wellington, Auckland, 1060, New Zealand
Tel.: (64) 92592279
Web Site: http://www.heatcraft.co.nz
Air-Conditioning & Warm Air Heating Equipment Mfr
N.A.I.C.S.: 333415

MORSCO, Inc. (1)
15850 Dallas Pkwy, Fort Worth, TX 75248
Tel.: (877) 709-2227
Web Site: http://www.morsco.com
Plumbing Fixtures, HVAC & Builder Products Distr
N.A.I.C.S.: 423720
Chip Hornsby *(CEO)*

Subsidiary (Domestic):

Devore & Johnson, Inc. (2)
904 N Chase St, Athens, GA 30601
Tel.: (706) 543-7358
Web Site:
  https://www.devoreandjohnson.com
Plumbing & Heating Equipment & Supplies, Hydronics, Merchant Whslr
N.A.I.C.S.: 423720
Mike Devore *(Co-Owner)*

EP Supply (2)
2321 N Sweet Gum Ave Broken Arrow, Tulsa, OK 74105
Tel.: (918) 587-4431
Plumbing & Hydronic Heating Supplies Whslr
N.A.I.C.S.: 423720
Sam Beakey *(Pres)*

Fortiline, LLC (2)
7025 Northwinds Dr NW, Concord, NC 28027
Tel.: (704) 788-9800
Web Site: https://www.fortiline.com
Underground Utility Supplies Distr
N.A.I.C.S.: 423510

Metalflex (S.A.) Pty Ltd (1)
85 O sullivan Beach Road, Lonsdale, 5160, SA, Australia
Tel.: (61) 881876610
Air Conditioner Distr
N.A.I.C.S.: 423730

Metalflex (W.A.) Pty Ltd (1)
66 Verde Drive, Jandakot, 6164, WA, Australia
Tel.: (61) 894140510
Air Conditioner Distr
N.A.I.C.S.: 423730

Metalflex Pty Ltd (1)
14 Inglewood Drive, Thomastown, 3074, VIC, Australia
Tel.: (61) 384152810
Web Site: http://www.metalflex.com.au
Emp.: 24
Air Conditioner Mfr & Distr
N.A.I.C.S.: 333415

Reece Australia Pty Ltd (1)
62 O Malley Street, Osborne Park, 6017, WA, Australia
Tel.: (61) 894462800
Plumbing Fixture Whslr
N.A.I.C.S.: 423720

Reece New Zealand Limited (1)
134-142 Wellesley Street West Auckland Central, Auckland, 1010, New Zealand
Tel.: (64) 392740000
Plumbing Fixture Whslr
N.A.I.C.S.: 423720

REED LIMITED
No 195 Renmin Road, Xinxiang, 453000, Henan, China
Tel.: (86) 3733337222 Ky
Year Founded: 2016
Emp.: 86
Holding Company
Jiuyi Wang *(Chm, CEO & Acting CFO)*

REEDEREI NORD KLAUS E. OLDENDORFF LIMITED
Libra Tower 23 Olympion Street, PO Box 56345, 3306, Limassol, Cyprus
Tel.: (357) 25841400
Web Site: http://www.reederei-nord.com
Year Founded: 1964
Sales Range: $200-249.9 Million
Emp.: 550
Water Transportation Services
N.A.I.C.S.: 488390
Christiane Scola *(Chm)*

Subsidiaries:

REEDEREI NORD B.V. (1)
Alpha Tower De Entree 53, 1101 BH, Amsterdam, Netherlands
Tel.: (31) 20 76 06 400
Marine Cargo Handling Services
N.A.I.C.S.: 488320

Reederei NORD Klaus E. Oldendorff GmbH (1)
Zirkusweg 2, 20459, Hamburg, Germany
Tel.: (49) 40369020
Web Site: http://www.rnkeo.com
Sales Range: $25-49.9 Million
Emp.: 40
Water Transportation Services
N.A.I.C.S.: 488390
Sergey Simakain *(Mgr-Chartering)*

REEDY LAGOON CORPORATION LTD
Tower 4 Collins Square 727 Collins Street, Melbourne, 3000, VIC, Australia
Tel.: (61) 384206280
Web Site:
  https://www.reedylagoon.com.au
RLC—(ASX)
Rev.: $1,260

REF HOLDINGS LIMITED

Assets: $69,625
Liabilities: $389,366
Net Worth: ($319,742)
Earnings: ($445,978)
Fiscal Year-end: 06/30/24
Mines Exploration
N.A.I.C.S.: 212115
Geoffrey H. Fethers *(Mng Dir & Sec)*

REENOVA INVESTMENT HOLDING LIMITED
60 Paya Lebar Road 10-16 Paya Lebar Square, Singapore, 409051, Singapore
Tel.: (65) 6817 8288 SG
Web Site: http://reenovagroup.com
Year Founded: 2000
Rev.: $51,850
Assets: $28,782,724
Liabilities: $8,726,429
Net Worth: $20,056,294
Earnings: ($5,782,219)
Fiscal Year-end: 12/31/20
Investment Advisory Services
N.A.I.C.S.: 523940
Vincent Chung Ngee Lee *(Sec & Controller-Fin)*

Subsidiaries:

ISR Shanghai Investment Advisory Co., Ltd. (1)
South Road 855 World Plaza 29-I, Pudong, Shanghai, 200120, China
Tel.: (86) 2168886280
Investment Consulting Services
N.A.I.C.S.: 523940

REETECH INTERNATIONAL CARGO & COURIER LIMITED
Sai Kunj Civil Line, Raipur, 492001, India
Tel.: (91) 7714003800
Web Site:
  https://www.reetechinternational.com
Year Founded: 2008
543617—(BOM)
Rev.: $19,957,365
Assets: $2,298,603
Liabilities: $498,975
Net Worth: $1,799,628
Earnings: $91,553
Emp.: 6
Fiscal Year-end: 03/31/23
Coal Product Distr
N.A.I.C.S.: 423520

REEVO S.P.A.
Via Dante 4, 20121, Milan, Italy
Tel.: (39) 0392873925
Web Site: https://www.reevo.it
Year Founded: 2013
REEVO—(EUR)
Information Technology Services
N.A.I.C.S.: 541512
Antonio Giannetto *(CEO)*

REEVOO
Friars Bridge Court 41-45 Friars Bridge Road, London, SE1 8NZ, United Kingdom
Tel.: (44) 20 7654 0350
Web Site: http://www.reevoo.com
Emp.: 60
Internet Consumer Information Management Services
N.A.I.C.S.: 541519
Richard Anson *(Founder)*

REF HOLDINGS LIMITED
6/F & 7/F Nexxus Building 77 Des Voeux Road, Central, China (Hong Kong)
Tel.: (852) 37578877 Ky
Web Site:
  http://www.refholdings.com.hk
Year Founded: 2010

REF HOLDINGS LIMITED

REF Holdings Limited—(Continued)
1631—(HKG)
Rev.: $16,538,025
Assets: $18,844,628
Liabilities: $6,168,195
Net Worth: $12,676,433
Earnings: $1,423,155
Emp.: 109
Fiscal Year-end: 12/31/22
Financial Printing Services
N.A.I.C.S.: 513120
Man Tak Lau *(Founder & Chm)*

REFEX INDUSTRIES LIMITED
2nd Floor No 313 Refex Towers Sterling Road Valluvar Kottam High Road, Valluvar Kottam High Road Nungambakkam, Chennai, 600034, Tamil Nadu, India
Tel.: (91) 4435040050
Web Site: https://www.refex.co.in
532884—(BOM)
Rev.: $196,323,650
Assets: $90,198,549
Liabilities: $52,503,711
Net Worth: $37,694,838
Earnings: $13,915,329
Emp.: 90
Fiscal Year-end: 03/31/23
Refrigerant Gases Distr
N.A.I.C.S.: 221210
T. Anil Jain *(Chm & Mng Dir)*

Subsidiaries:

Refex Green Mobility Limited (1)
3rd Floor Achaiah Chetty Arcade Achaiah Chetty Layout Sadashiva Nagar, Mekhri Circle Junction Armane Nagar, Bengaluru, 560080, India
Tel.: (91) 9019960805
Web Site: https://eveelz.in
Administrative & Transportation Services
N.A.I.C.S.: 926120

REFEX RENEWABLES & INFRASTRUCTURE LIMITED
Second Floor Refex Towers Sterling Road Signal 313, Valluvar Kottam High Road Nungambakkam, Chennai, 600034, Tamil Nadu, India
Tel.: (91) 4443405950
Web Site: https://refexrenewables.com
Year Founded: 1995
531260—(BOM)
Rev.: $11,598,142
Assets: $72,261,195
Liabilities: $67,299,095
Net Worth: $4,962,101
Earnings: ($3,607,158)
Emp.: 109
Fiscal Year-end: 03/31/23
Real Estate Manangement Services
N.A.I.C.S.: 531390
Kalpesh Kumar *(Mng Dir)*

Subsidiaries:

Enrecover Energy Recovery Solutions Private Limited (1)
Plot No-t-57 MIDC Opposite Municipal Rose Garden, Bhosari, Pune, India
Tel.: (91) 9975277357
Web Site: http://www.enrecover.com
Eletric Power Generation Services
N.A.I.C.S.: 221118

Megamic Electronics Private Limited (1)
C11 C-Block 1st Floor Brigade M M K R Road Jayanagar 7th Block, Bengaluru, 560082, India
Tel.: (91) 8041162103
Web Site: http://www.megamic.in
Electronic Equipment Distr
N.A.I.C.S.: 423690

REFINARIA DE PETROLEOS DE MANGUINHOS S.A.
Av Brasil 3141 Manguinhos, 20930041, Rio de Janeiro, Brazil
Tel.: (55) 2136135530
Web Site: http://www.refinariamanguinhos.com
Year Founded: 1954
RPMG3—(BRAZ)
Rev.: $901,187,298
Assets: $1,067,887,746
Liabilities: $2,045,861,121
Net Worth: ($977,973,375)
Earnings: ($175,043,166)
Fiscal Year-end: 12/31/23
Petroleum Refining Services
N.A.I.C.S.: 324191
Jorge Luiz Cruz Monteiro *(Chief Operating & Industrial Officer & Member-Exec Bd)*

REFINE CO., LTD.
4th floor 625 Teheranro, Gangnamgu, Seoul, Korea (South)
Tel.: (82) 221898700
Web Site: https://www.refine.co.kr
Year Founded: 2002
377450—(KRS)
Rev.: $42,244,756
Assets: $116,742,619
Liabilities: $9,813,299
Net Worth: $106,929,321
Earnings: $13,564,141
Emp.: 228
Fiscal Year-end: 12/31/22
Real Estate Investment Services
N.A.I.C.S.: 531390

REFINED ENERGY CORP.
1930 - 1177 West Hastings Street, Vancouver, V6C 1S4, BC, Canada
Tel.: (604) 398-3378
Web Site: https://refinedenergy.com
Year Founded: 2017
RUU—(CNSX)
Assets: $636,858
Liabilities: $544,006
Net Worth: $92,852
Earnings: ($669,070)
Fiscal Year-end: 06/30/23
Cannabis Product Distr
N.A.I.C.S.: 459999
Aman Parmar *(Chm & Interim CEO)*

Subsidiaries:

GSRX Industries Inc. (1)
Building No 3 PR 696 int Jose Efron Ave, Dorado, PR 00646
Tel.: (214) 808-8649
Web Site: http://www.gsrxindustries.com
Rev.: $11,004,406
Assets: $8,046,604
Liabilities: $3,585,303
Net Worth: $4,461,301
Earnings: ($36,257,003)
Emp.: 4
Fiscal Year-end: 12/31/2019
Medicinal Cannabis Products Mfr
N.A.I.C.S.: 325411
Thomas J. Gingerich *(CFO & Sec)*

REFINVERSE, INC.
Kashimichi Ningyocho Building 6th Floor 3-10-1 Nihonbashi Chuo-ku, Tokyo, 103-0013, Japan
Tel.: (81) 356437890
Web Site: http://www.r-inverse.com
6531—(TKS)
Rev.: $22,885,560
Assets: $28,203,780
Liabilities: $22,731,540
Net Worth: $5,472,240
Earnings: ($3,107,580)
Fiscal Year-end: 06/30/19
Wastage Recycled Material Mfr
N.A.I.C.S.: 325211
Akira Ochi *(Pres)*

REFLEX ADVANCED MATERIALS CORP.
915-700 West Pender Street, Vancouver, V6C 1G8, BC, Canada
Tel.: (778) 837-7191 BC
Web Site: https://www.reflexmaterials.com
Year Founded: 2021
RFLX—(CNSX)
Assets: $2,166,404
Liabilities: $258,053
Net Worth: $1,908,352
Earnings: ($4,783,631)
Fiscal Year-end: 01/31/24
Mineral Mining Services
N.A.I.C.S.: 213115
Paul Gorman *(CEO)*

REFNOL RESINS & CHEMICALS LIMITED
Plot No 23 Phase - III GIDC Industrial Estate, Naroda, Ahmedabad, 382 330, India
Tel.: (91) 792 282 0013
Web Site: http://www.refnol.com
Year Founded: 1980
530815—(BOM)
Rev.: $4,357,012
Assets: $4,919,173
Liabilities: $2,155,089
Net Worth: $2,764,084
Earnings: ($109,569)
Emp.: 69
Fiscal Year-end: 03/31/21
Specialty Chemicals Mfr & Distr
N.A.I.C.S.: 325998
Mahendra K. Khatau *(Chm)*

REFORMKONTOR GMBH & CO. KG
Ernst-Litfass-Str 16, 19246, Zarrentin, Germany
Tel.: (49) 38851 51 0 De
Web Site: http://www.reformkontor.de
Year Founded: 1954
Sales Range: $10-24.9 Million
Emp.: 100
Fruit Nut Seed & Grain Distr
N.A.I.C.S.: 424480
Carsten Greve *(Mng Dir)*

REFRIGERATION ELECTRICAL ENGINEERING CORPORATION
364 Cong Hoa Street Ward 13, Tan Binh District, Ho Chi Minh City, Vietnam
Tel.: (84) 2838100017
Web Site: https://www.reecorp.com
Year Founded: 1977
REE—(HOSE)
Rev.: $353,469,131
Assets: $1,438,385,641
Liabilities: $582,657,470
Net Worth: $855,728,171
Earnings: $114,810,312
Emp.: 2,720
Fiscal Year-end: 12/31/23
Electrical Equipment & Component Mfr
N.A.I.C.S.: 335999
Nguyen Thi Mai Thanh *(Chm)*

Subsidiaries:

R.E.E Electric Appliances Joint stock company (1)
364 Cong Hoa-Ward 13, Tan Binh District, Ho Chi Minh City, Vietnam
Tel.: (84) 2838497227
Web Site: http://www.reetech.com.vn
Air Conditioner & Ceiling Mfr
N.A.I.C.S.: 333415

R.E.E Land Corporation (1)
Ground Floor REE Building 364 Cong Hoa Street, Ward 13 Tan Binh District, Ho Chi Minh City, Vietnam
Tel.: (84) 2838130151
Real Estate Services
N.A.I.C.S.: 531390

INTERNATIONAL PUBLIC

R.E.E Mechanical & Electrical Engineering Joint stock company (1)
364 Cong Hoa Street, Ward 13 Tan Binh District, Ho Chi Minh City, Vietnam
Tel.: (84) 2838100017
Web Site: http://www.reeme.com.vn
Mechanical & Electrical Engineering Services
N.A.I.C.S.: 238210
Tran Quang Son *(Deputy Mgr-HR)*

R.E.E Real Estate Company Limited (1)
1 Tower 364 Cong Hoa Street, E town Tan Binh District, Ho Chi Minh City, Vietnam
Tel.: (84) 2838104462
Property Leasing Services
N.A.I.C.S.: 531110

Thac BA Hydropower Joint Stock Company (1)
Residential Group 1, Thac Ba Town Yen Binh District, Yen Bai, Vietnam
Tel.: (84) 2163884116
Web Site: https://www.thacba.vn
Electricity Production Services
N.A.I.C.S.: 221118

REFRIGERATION INDUSTRIES CO. S.A.K.
5th Ring Road Block 1 Sulaibiya Industrial Area, PO Box 22261, Safat, Kuwait, 13083, Kuwait
Tel.: (965) 1833380 KW
Web Site: http://www.ric.com.kw
Year Founded: 1973
Refrigerated Warehousing Services
N.A.I.C.S.: 493120
Saleh Abdullah Salem Al-Mekhlef *(CEO)*

REFUELS N.V.
Evert van de Beekstraat 1-104, The Base B, Amsterdam, Netherlands
Tel.: (31) 852087773
Web Site: https://www.refuels.com
Year Founded: 2017
REFL—(OSL)
Assets: $96,965
Liabilities: $430,352
Net Worth: ($333,387)
Earnings: ($500,080)
Fiscal Year-end: 03/31/23
Renewable Energy Distribution Services
N.A.I.C.S.: 221210
Jasper Nillesen *(Mng Dir)*

REGAL BUILDING MATERIALS LTD.
Bay D 7131 6 Street SE, Calgary, T2H 2M8, AB, Canada
Tel.: (403) 253-2010
Web Site: http://www.regalbuilding.com
Year Founded: 1992
Building Material Supplier
N.A.I.C.S.: 444180
Barry Hanna *(VP)*

REGAL CERAMICS LIMITED
4th Floor Salam Chambers, 22 Link Mcleod Road, Lahore, Pakistan
Tel.: (92) 7243417
Ceramic Products Mfr
N.A.I.C.S.: 327110

REGAL CORPORATION
2-1-8 Hinode, Urayasu, Chiba, 279-8553, Japan
Tel.: (81) 473047050
Web Site: https://www.regal.co.jp
Year Founded: 1902
7938—(TKS)
Rev.: $156,861,910
Assets: $183,731,560
Liabilities: $101,437,060
Net Worth: $82,294,500
Earnings: $2,822,470

AND PRIVATE COMPANIES / REGENCY ALLIANCE INSURANCE PLC.

Emp.: 958
Fiscal Year-end: 03/31/24
Shoe Mfr & Whslr
N.A.I.C.S.: 316210
Kojiro Iwasaki (Pres)

Subsidiaries:

Hong Kong Regal Shoe Co., Ltd. (1)
Rm802 Wing On Plaza 62 Mody Road Tst East Kln, Hong Kong, China (Hong Kong)
Tel.: (852) 221141010
Shoe Mfr & Distr
N.A.I.C.S.: 316210
Lo YinTung Shuta (Mgr-Mktg)

Shanghai Regal Shoes Co., Ltd. (1)
211 Building 1 283 West Jian Guo Road, Shanghai, China
Tel.: (86) 2153825052
Shoe Distr
N.A.I.C.S.: 424340

REGAL ENTERTAINMENT & CONSULTANTS LTD.
5032 Eaze Zone Mall Opp Rustomjee Ozone SBI Bank Near Inorbit Mall, Malad, Mumbai, 400064, India
Tel.: (91) 2222612811   In
Web Site:
    http://www.regalentertainment.in
Year Founded: 1992
531033—(BOM)
Rev.: $11,838
Assets: $253,293
Liabilities: $11,185
Net Worth: $242,108
Earnings: $454
Emp.: 4
Fiscal Year-end: 03/31/21
Financial Investment Services
N.A.I.C.S.: 523999
Shreyash Chaturvedi (Mng Dir & CFO)

REGAL INTERNATIONAL GROUP LTD.
63 Sungei Kadut Loop 02-01, Singapore, 729484, Singapore
Tel.: (65) 65323383
Web Site:
    https://www.regalinternational.com
Rev.: $15,225,257
Assets: $68,988,950
Liabilities: $64,937,328
Net Worth: $4,051,622
Earnings: ($8,973,585)
Fiscal Year-end: 12/31/18
Metallic Precision Designer & Mfr
N.A.I.C.S.: 333519
Pak Kiong Wong (Exec Dir)

Subsidiaries:

Hisaka (Singapore) Pte. Ltd. (1)
No 63 Sungei Kadut Loop, Hisaka Industrial Bldg, Singapore, 729484, Singapore
Tel.: (65) 64551311
Sales Range: $25-49.9 Million
Emp.: 100
Mechanical Motion Products Mfr
N.A.I.C.S.: 811114
Jackie Cheng (Dir)

Hisaka Automation Sdn. Bhd. (1)
5 Jalan Puteri 5 3 Bandar Puteri Puchong, Puchong, Malaysia
Tel.: (60) 8060 3282
Mechanical Motion Products Mfr
N.A.I.C.S.: 334513

Hisaka Shanghai Co., Ltd. (1)
Rm 405 North Fute Rd Waigaoqiao Free Trade Zone, Lian Xi Rd Pu Dong New Area, 201204, Shanghai, China
Tel.: (86) 2150425566
Web Site: http://www.hisaka.com.cn
Sales Range: $25-49.9 Million
Emp.: 100
Mechanical Motion Products Mfr
N.A.I.C.S.: 333914
Eric Lee (Gen Mgr)

REGAL PARTNERS LIMITED
L47 Gateway Building 1 Macquarie Place, Sydney, 2000, NSW, Australia
Tel.: (61) 281974350   AU
Web Site:
    https://www.regalpartners.com
Year Founded: 2004
RPL—(ASX)
Rev.: $68,645,759
Assets: $449,400,143
Liabilities: $72,036,252
Net Worth: $377,363,891
Earnings: $1,603,312
Emp.: 155
Fiscal Year-end: 12/31/23
Asset Management Services
N.A.I.C.S.: 523999
Brendan O'Connor (CEO)

Subsidiaries:

Merricks Capital Pty Ltd. (1)
Level 18 90 Collins Street, Melbourne, 3000, VIC, Australia
Tel.: (61) 3 8319 8111
Web Site: http://www.merrickscapital.com
Sales Range: $25-49.9 Million
Emp.: 18
Financial Investment
N.A.I.C.S.: 523999
Adam Lindell (Co-Founder, Gen Counsel & Head-Structured Credit)

Subsidiary (Domestic):

InvestSMART Financial Services Pty Ltd (2)
36 East Esplanade Suite 8, Manly, 2095, NSW, Australia
Tel.: (61) 289669511
Web Site: http://www.investsmart.com.au
Emp.: 5
Investment Management Service
N.A.I.C.S.: 523999
Laurent Montenay (Mgr)

REGALA INVEST AD
1 Georgi Stamatov St, 9000, Varna, 9000, Bulgaria
Tel.: (359) 52370598
Web Site:
    https://www.regalainvest.bg
RGL—(BUL)
Sales Range: Less than $1 Million
Real Estate Manangement Services
N.A.I.C.S.: 531390

REGALLIA HOLDINGS & INVESTMENTS PUBLIC LTD.
6 Thalasines Esperides Pervolia, Larnaca, Cyprus
Tel.: (357) 22374536
REG—(CYP)
Sales Range: Less than $1 Million
Holding Company
N.A.I.C.S.: 551112
Antonios Andronikou (Chm)

REGATTA LTD.
Risol House Mercury Way, Dumplington, Manchester, M41 7RR, United Kingdom
Tel.: (44) 8448111022
Web Site: http://www.regatta.com
Year Founded: 1981
Sales Range: $150-199.9 Million
Emp.: 534
Outdoor Clothing Distr
N.A.I.C.S.: 458110
Keith Black (Chm & CEO)

Subsidiaries:

REGATTA GMBH (1)
Reichenberger Strasse 1, 84130, Dingolfing, Germany
Tel.: (49) 873131910
Apparel Distr
N.A.I.C.S.: 458110

REGATTA ISRAEL LTD. (1)
10 Plaut St, Rehovot, 76706, Israel

Tel.: (972) 89365444
Apparel Distr
N.A.I.C.S.: 458110

Regatta AS (1)
Greve Landevej 140 New Market, 2670, Greve, Denmark
Tel.: (45) 61338300
Apparel Distr
N.A.I.C.S.: 458110

Regatta Benelux BV (1)
Baalhoek 50, 1853, Strombeek-Bever, Belgium
Tel.: (32) 22670903
Apparel Distr
N.A.I.C.S.: 458110

Regatta Italia S.R.L. (1)
Via Bassanese 61/1, 31044, Montebelluna, Veneto, Italy
Tel.: (39) 0423614140
Apparel Distr
N.A.I.C.S.: 458110

Regatta Nederland (1)
Sportsbusinesscenter C25 Plesmanstraat 1, 3833 LA, Leusden, Netherlands
Tel.: (31) 334669950
Apparel Distr
N.A.I.C.S.: 458110

Regatta Polska Sp. z o.o. (1)
Ul Czestochowska 5, 32-085, Modlnica, Poland
Tel.: (48) 123994071
Apparel Distr
N.A.I.C.S.: 458110

Regatta SAS (1)
32 Rue De Paradis, 75010, Paris, France
Tel.: (33) 140220822
Apparel Distr
N.A.I.C.S.: 458110

Regatta Service Finland Oy (1)
Nuijamiestentie 5C, 00400, Helsinki, Finland
Tel.: (358) 104702630
Apparel Distr
N.A.I.C.S.: 458110

Regatta Sweden AB (1)
Djupdalsvagen 10 2 tr, 192 51, Sollentuna, Sweden
Tel.: (46) 86310070
Apparel Distr
N.A.I.C.S.: 458110
Tommy Osterman (Gen Mgr)

Regatta USA, LLC (1)
55 Main St Ste 219, Newmarket, NH 03857
Tel.: (603) 292-6850
Apparel Distr
N.A.I.C.S.: 458110

Regatta s.r.o. (1)
Sokolovska 1955/278, 190 00, Prague, Czech Republic
Tel.: (420) 737111115
Apparel Distr
N.A.I.C.S.: 458110

REGEN III CORP.
1245 200 Granville Street, Vancouver, V6C 1S4, BC, Canada
Tel.: (604) 806-5275   AB
Web Site: https://www.regeniii.com
Year Founded: 2017
ISRJF—(OTCQX)
Rev.: $58,196
Assets: $8,391,247
Liabilities: $10,009,032
Net Worth: ($1,617,785)
Earnings: ($4,564,714)
Fiscal Year-end: 12/31/19
Mineral Exploration Services
N.A.I.C.S.: 213114
Gregory Clarkes (Chm & CEO)

REGEN THERAPEUTICS LIMITED
Suite 306 73 Watling Street, London, EC4M 9BJ, United Kingdom
Tel.: (44) 2071534920   UK
Web Site:
    http://www.regentherapeutics.com
Year Founded: 1998

Sales Range: Less than $1 Million
Emp.: 6
Healthcare Products Development
N.A.I.C.S.: 325412
Timothy Shilton (CEO)

REGENBOGEN AG
Pahlbloken 3, 24232, Schonkirchen, Germany
Tel.: (49) 4312372370
Web Site: https://www.regenbogen-ag.de
Year Founded: 1991
RGB—(DEU)
Rev.: $25,543,552
Assets: $43,911,949
Liabilities: $29,429,174
Net Worth: $14,482,774
Earnings: $1,181,141
Emp.: 192
Fiscal Year-end: 12/31/23
Camping Resort Operator
N.A.I.C.S.: 721120
Ruediger Vosshall (Member-Mgmt Bd)

REGENCELL BIOSCIENCE HOLDINGS LIMITED
9F Chinachem Leighton Plaza 29 Leighton Road, Causeway Bay, China (Hong Kong)
Tel.: (852) 21550823   Ky
Web Site:
    https://www.regencellbioscience.com
Year Founded: 2014
RGC—(NASDAQ)
Rev.: $34,617
Assets: $340,134
Liabilities: $4,337,771
Net Worth: ($3,997,637)
Earnings: ($1,346,745)
Emp.: 13
Fiscal Year-end: 06/30/21
Holding Company
N.A.I.C.S.: 551112
Yat-Gai Au (Founder & CEO)

REGENCY ALLIANCE INSURANCE PLC.
Regency Place 2 Ebun Street
Gbagada Expressway Phase 1, PO Box 70333, Gbagada, Lagos, Nigeria
Tel.: (234) 8053499074
Web Site:
    https://www.regencyalliance.com
Year Founded: 1994
REGALINS—(NIGE)
Rev.: $4,124,720
Assets: $9,501,304
Liabilities: $4,126,313
Net Worth: $5,374,992
Earnings: $398,148
Emp.: 98
Fiscal Year-end: 12/31/22
Insurance Management Services
N.A.I.C.S.: 524298
Biyi Otegbeye (Mng Dir-Grp)

Subsidiaries:

RIC Microfinance Bank Limited (1)
33 Hawley street, Sangrose Lafiaji Lagos Island, Lagos, Nigeria
Tel.: (234) 7045561845
Micro Financial Services
N.A.I.C.S.: 522291

RIC Properties & Investment Limited (1)
9 Kasumu Ekemode St Off Saka Tinubu St Victoria Island, Lagos, Nigeria
Tel.: (234) 7084077999
Micro Financial Services
N.A.I.C.S.: 522291

Regency NEM Insurance Ghana Limited (1)
65 Patrice Lumumba Road Airport Res Area, Accra, Ghana

REGENCY ALLIANCE INSURANCE PLC.

Regency Alliance Insurance Plc.—(Continued)
Tel.: (233) 302778106
Web Site: http://www.regencynem.com
Micro Financial Services
N.A.I.C.S.: 522291
Musa Badimsugru Adam (Chm)

REGENCY AUTO INVESTMENTS INC
2288 Burrard St, Vancouver, V6J 5A5, BC, Canada
Tel.: (604) 739-1212
Web Site:
  https://www.regencylexus.com
Year Founded: 1983
Rev.: $40,424,024
Emp.: 80
New & Used Car Dealers
N.A.I.C.S.: 441110
Ken Wong (Mgr-Sls)

REGENCY CERAMICS LIMITED
4th Floor Dwaraka Summit Plot No 83 Survey No 43 to 46, 48 Kavuri Hills Guttalabegumpet Serilingampally Mandal, Hyderabad, 500 033, Telangana, India
Tel.: (91) 4023319902
Web Site:
  https://www.regencyceramics.in
Year Founded: 1983
Sales Range: Less than $1 Million
Ceramic Tile Mfr
N.A.I.C.S.: 327120
Gudaru Naraiah Naidu (Chm & Mng Dir)

REGENCY FINCORP.
Unit No 57-58 4th Floor Sushma Infinium, Ambala Highway Zirakpur, Chandigarh, 140603, India
Tel.: (91) 1762435687
Web Site: https://regencyfincorp.com
Year Founded: 1993
540175—(BOM)
Rev.: $1,621,234
Assets: $12,740,939
Liabilities: $11,102,680
Net Worth: $1,638,259
Earnings: $110,917
Fiscal Year-end: 03/31/23
Consumer Lending Services
N.A.I.C.S.: 522291
Gaurav Kumar (Chm & Mng Dir)

REGENCY HOSPITAL LIMITED
A-2 Sarvodaya Nagar, Kanpur, 208005, India
Tel.: (91) 512 3081111
Web Site:
  http://www.regencyhospital.in
Year Founded: 1995
Sales Range: $10-24.9 Million
Emp.: 880
General Medical Services
N.A.I.C.S.: 622110
Rashmi Kapoor (Exec Dir)

REGENCY MEDIA PTY. LTD.
PO Box 210, Braeside, 3195, VIC, Australia
Tel.: (61) 385878900
Web Site: http://www.shock.com.au
Year Founded: 1988
Digital Recording Services
N.A.I.C.S.: 512290
Fiona Horman (Founder & Mng Dir)

REGENCY PLASTICS COMPANY LTD.
50 Brisbane Road, North York, M3J 2K2, ON, Canada
Tel.: (416) 661-3000
Web Site:
  http://www.regencyplastics.com

Year Founded: 1958
Industrial Polyethylene Packaging Mfr
N.A.I.C.S.: 326199
David d'Ancona (Pres)

REGENCY TRUST LIMITED
39 R B C Road Ground Floor, Near DumDum Central Jail, Kolkata, 700028, India
Tel.: (91) 8108892327
Web Site:
  https://www.regencytrust.co.in
Year Founded: 1988
511585—(BOM)
Rev.: $157,083
Assets: $82,224
Liabilities: $106,959
Net Worth: ($24,735)
Earnings: ($55,379)
Fiscal Year-end: 03/31/23
Financial Support Services
N.A.I.C.S.: 523999
Rajesh Kapoor (CFO & Dir-Fin)

REGENER8 RESOURCES NL
Tel.: (61) 892262011 AU
Web Site:
  https://www.regener8resources.com
Year Founded: 2021
R8R—(ASX)
Rev.: $66,768
Assets: $3,134,220
Liabilities: $86,822
Net Worth: $3,047,398
Earnings: ($367,572)
Fiscal Year-end: 06/30/24
Exploration & Mining Services
N.A.I.C.S.: 213115
Robert Boston (Chm)

REGENERYS LTD
The Old Bank 205-207 High Street Cottenham, Cambridge, CB24 8RX, United Kingdom
Tel.: (44) 1143830858
Web Site: http://www.regenerys.com
Year Founded: 2011
Sales Range: $25-49.9 Million
Emp.: 4
Medicinal Product Mfr
N.A.I.C.S.: 325412
David Haddow (Head-Ops & R&D)

Subsidiaries:

Regenerys Ltd (1)
The Innovation Centre 217 Portobello, Sheffield, S1 4DP, South Yorkshire, United Kingdom
Tel.: (44) 1143830858
Web Site: http://www.regenerys.com
Sales Range: $25-49.9 Million
Emp.: 7
Pharmaceuticals Product Mfr
N.A.I.C.S.: 325412
Sue Loizer (Mgr-Bus Dev)

REGENT ENTERPRISES LIMITED
R193 RDC Raj Nagar 2nd floor Adjacent to the Telephone exchange, Ghaziabad, 201001, Uttar Pradesh, India
Tel.: (91) 9999490990
Web Site:
  https://www.regententerprises.in
512624—(BOM)
Rev.: $89,724,801
Assets: $9,543,936
Liabilities: $4,987,087
Net Worth: $4,556,849
Earnings: ($136,095)
Emp.: 43
Fiscal Year-end: 03/31/23
Investment Services
N.A.I.C.S.: 523999
Vikas Kumar (Exec Dir)

REGENT GAS HOLDINGS LIMITED
Regent House Kendal Avenue, London, W3 0XA, United Kingdom
Tel.: (44) 8452412700
Web Site: https://regentgas.co.uk
Year Founded: 2011
Natural Gas Distribution
N.A.I.C.S.: 221210

Subsidiaries:

TClarke PLC (1)
30 St Mary Axe, London, EC3A 8BF, United Kingdom
Tel.: (44) 2079977400
Web Site: https://www.tclarke.co.uk
Rev.: $444,110,212
Assets: $229,726,224
Liabilities: $193,746,644
Net Worth: $35,979,580
Earnings: $8,553,636
Emp.: 1,236
Fiscal Year-end: 12/31/2021
Electrical Engineering & Contractor Services
N.A.I.C.S.: 541330
Mike C. Crowder (Mng Dir)

Subsidiary (Domestic):

J.J. Cross Limited (2)
22 Sceptre Court Bamber Bridge, Preston, PR5 6AW, Lancs, United Kingdom
Tel.: (44) 1772315505
Web Site: http://www.jjcross.co.uk
Sales Range: $25-49.9 Million
Emp.: 10
Electrical Equipment Installation Services
N.A.I.C.S.: 238210
Andy Smith (Mng Dir)

T. Clarke (Bristol) Limited (2)
Unit 1 Montpelier Central Bus Pk, Sta Rd Montpelier, Bristol, BS6 5EE, United Kingdom
Tel.: (44) 1179440550
Web Site: http://www.tclarke-bristol.co.uk
Sales Range: $25-49.9 Million
Emp.: 20
Electrical & Mechanical Equipment Contractors
N.A.I.C.S.: 238210

Division (Domestic):

T. Clarke plc - Falkirk (2)
6 Middlefield Road, Falkirk, FK2 9AG, Scotland, United Kingdom
Tel.: (44) 1324888000
Web Site: http://www.tclarke.co.uk
Sales Range: $25-49.9 Million
Electrical Contractors & Building Services
N.A.I.C.S.: 238210

T. Clarke plc - Huntingdon (2)
Kym Road Kimbolton, Huntingdon, PE28 0LW, Cambs, United Kingdom
Tel.: (44) 1480861544
Web Site: http://www.tclarke.co.uk
Emp.: 100
Construction Services
N.A.I.C.S.: 236117

Subsidiary (Domestic):

T.Clarke (Midlands) Limited (2)
Fengate, Peterborough, PE1 5XB, Cambridgeshire, United Kingdom
Tel.: (44) 1733342624
Sales Range: $25-49.9 Million
Electrical Equipment Installation Services
N.A.I.C.S.: 238210

T.Clarke Midlands Ltd. (2)
Windsor Court Ascot Drive, Derby, DE24 8GZ, Derbyshire, United Kingdom
Tel.: (44) 1332332177
Web Site: http://www.tclarke.co.uk
Sales Range: $25-49.9 Million
Electrical & Mechanical Equipment Contractors
N.A.I.C.S.: 238210

TClarke (2)
Hunter House 17-19 Byron Street, Newcastle upon Tyne, NE21 XH, Tyne and Wear, United Kingdom
Tel.: (44) 1912612727

INTERNATIONAL PUBLIC

Sales Range: $25-49.9 Million
Emp.: 100
Electrical Equipment Installation Services
N.A.I.C.S.: 238210

TClarke Leeds (2)
Low Hall Road, Horsforth, Leeds, LS18 4EF, West Yorkshire, United Kingdom
Tel.: (44) 1132586711
Web Site: http://www.tclarke.co.uk
Sales Range: $25-49.9 Million
Electrical & Mechanical Equipment Contractors
N.A.I.C.S.: 238210

W.E. Manin Limited (2)
Excelsior House, Ufton Ln, Sittingbourne, ME10 1JA, Kent, United Kingdom
Tel.: (44) 1795427181
Sales Range: $25-49.9 Million
Emp.: 70
Electrical & Mechanical Equipment Contractors
N.A.I.C.S.: 238210

Waldon Electrical Contractors Limited (2)
Chapel Hill, Sticker, Saint Austell, PL26 7HG, Cornwall, United Kingdom
Tel.: (44) 172666552
Sales Range: $25-49.9 Million
Emp.: 70
Electrical Equipment Installation Services
N.A.I.C.S.: 238210

REGENT PACIFIC GROUP LIMITED
8th Floor Henley Building 5 Queen's Road Central, Hong Kong, China (Hong Kong)
Tel.: (852) 25146111 Ky
Web Site: http://www.regentpac.com
0575—(DEU)
Rev.: $223,000
Assets: $26,318,000
Liabilities: $23,721,000
Net Worth: $2,597,000
Earnings: ($36,427,000)
Emp.: 15
Fiscal Year-end: 12/31/22
Copper, Zinc, Lead, Gold, Silver & Coal Mining & Exploration Services
N.A.I.C.S.: 212290
Jamie Alexander Gibson (CEO)

Subsidiaries:

Plethora Solutions Holdings plc (1)
Hampden House Monument Business Park Warpsgrove Lane, Chalgrove, OX44 7RW, Oxfordshire, United Kingdom (100%)
Tel.: (44) 2030775400
Web Site: http://www.plethorasolutions.co.uk
Pharmaceuticals Product Mfr
N.A.I.C.S.: 551112
Michael G. Wyllie (Chief Scientific Officer)

Subsidiary (Domestic):

Plethora Solutions Limited (2)
Hampden House Monument Business Park Warpsgrove Lane, Chalgrove, OX44 7RW, Oxfordshire, United Kingdom
Tel.: (44) 2030775400
Web Site: http://www.plethorasolutions.co.uk
Urological Disorder Biopharmaceutical Developer
N.A.I.C.S.: 325412
Michael G. Wyllie (Chief Scientific Officer)

Regent Financial Services Limited (1)
8th Floor Henley Bldg, Central, China (Hong Kong)
Tel.: (852) 25146111
Investment Management Service
N.A.I.C.S.: 541618

REGENT PACIFIC PROPERTIES INC.
2607 Ellwood Drive SW, Edmonton, T6X 0P7, AB, Canada
Tel.: (780) 423-8662
Web Site: http://www.regentpacific.ca

AND PRIVATE COMPANIES

RPP—(TSXV)
Rev.: $1,069,819
Assets: $17,456,366
Liabilities: $14,371,241
Net Worth: $3,085,124
Earnings: $264,995
Fiscal Year-end: 12/31/23
Real Estate Services
N.A.I.C.S.: 531390
Rose Chang *(CFO-Interim)*

REGENT VENTURES LTD.
Penthouse - 1060 Alberni Street, Vancouver, V6E 4K2, BC, Canada
Tel.: (604) 669-7775
Web Site:
http://www.regentventuresltd.com
Year Founded: 1986
Sales Range: Less than $1 Million
Gold Exploration Services
N.A.I.C.S.: 212220
Richard Douglas Wilson *(Pres & CEO)*

REGENT'S UNIVERSITY LONDON
Inner Circle Regent's Park, London, NW1 4NS, United Kingdom
Tel.: (44) 207 487 7700
Web Site: http://www.regents.ac.uk
Sales Range: $50-74.9 Million
Emp.: 440
University
N.A.I.C.S.: 611310
Dan Lanigan *(Chief Comml. Officer)*

Subsidiaries:

Regent's School of Fashion & Design (1)
110 Marylebone High St, London, W1U 4RY, United Kingdom   **(100%)**
Tel.: (44) 2074675600
Sales Range: $50-74.9 Million
Emp.: 200
Vocational Education Services
N.A.I.C.S.: 611310
Gill Stark *(Head)*

REGENX TECH CORP.
Unit 114 8331 Eastlake Drive, Burnaby, V5A 4W2, BC, Canada
Tel.: (250) 751-3661   AB
Web Site: http://www.mineworx.net
MWX—(OTCIQ)
Sales Range: Less than $1 Million
Metal Mining Services
N.A.I.C.S.: 212290
Gregory S. Pendura *(Chm, Pres & CEO)*

REGIE AUTONOME DES TRANSPORTS PARISIENS
54 Quai de la Rapee, 75599, Paris, Cedex 12, France
Tel.: (33) 158782020
Web Site: http://www.ratp.fr
Year Founded: 1949
Sales Range: $1-4.9 Billion
Rail & Bus Services
N.A.I.C.S.: 488210
Alain Le Duc *(CFO)*

Subsidiaries:

Ixxi (1)
Immeuble Maille Nord II 8 avenue Montaigne, 93160, Noisy-le-Grand, France
Tel.: (33) 1 58 78 62 40
Web Site: http://www.ixxi-mobility.com
Transportation Ticketing & Passenger Information Systems
N.A.I.C.S.: 488999

RATP Dev (1)
54 quai de la Rapee, 75012, Paris, France
Tel.: (33) 1 58 78 37 37
Transportation Services
N.A.I.C.S.: 485999
Olivier Badard *(Dir-Asia & Middle East)*

Subsidiary (Non-US):

Autolinee Toscane S.p.A (2)
Viale Del Progresso 6, Borgo San Lorenzo, 50032, Italy
Tel.: (39) 055 8490505
Web Site: http://www.autolineetoscane.it
Sales Range: $25-49.9 Million
Emp.: 36
Rail Transportation Services
N.A.I.C.S.: 485112

Bath Bus Company (2)
6 North Parade, Bath, BA1 1LF, United Kingdom
Tel.: (44) 1225 330444
Web Site: http://www.bathbuscompany.com
Sales Range: $50-74.9 Million
Emp.: 150
Rail Transportation Services
N.A.I.C.S.: 485112
Martin Curtis *(Mng Dir)*

Subsidiary (Domestic):

Ceobus (2)
35 rue des Fossettes, 95 650, Genicourt, France
Tel.: (33) 1 34 42 72 74
Rail Transportation Services
N.A.I.C.S.: 485112

Champagne Mobilites (2)
RueÂ du Docteur Albert Schweitzer Actipole la Neuvillette, 51100, Reims, France
Tel.: (33) 3 26 50 59 40
Web Site: http://www.champagne-mobilites.fr
Sales Range: $25-49.9 Million
Emp.: 65
Rail Transportation Services
N.A.I.C.S.: 485112

Compagnie des Transports de Charleville-Mezieres (2)
11 rue Noel, 08000, Charleville-Mezieres, France
Tel.: (33) 3 24 33 32 32
Web Site: http://www.bustac.fr
Emp.: 96
Rail Transportation Services
N.A.I.C.S.: 485112

FlexCite SA (2)
Lac La 30 54 Quai de la Rapee, 75012, Paris, France
Tel.: (33) 1 82 28 76 02
Web Site: http://www.flexcite.fr
Rail Transportation Services
N.A.I.C.S.: 485112

Subsidiary (US):

Fullington Auto Bus Company (2)
316 E Cherry St, Clearfield, PA 16830
Tel.: (814) 765-7871
Web Site: http://www.fullingtontours.com
Sales Range: $125-149.9 Million
Emp.: 350
Bus Transportation Services
N.A.I.C.S.: 487110
Chris Springer *(Coord)*

Subsidiary (Non-US):

GEST S.p.A. (2)
Via dell'Unita d'Italia 10, 50018, Scandicci, Florence, Italy
Tel.: (39) 055 7352 200
Web Site: http://www.gestramvia.it
Sales Range: $25-49.9 Million
Emp.: 90
Rail Transportation Services
N.A.I.C.S.: 485112

Subsidiary (Domestic):

Impulsyon (2)
173 Boulevard Marechal Leclerc, 85000, La Roche-sur-Yon, France
Tel.: (33) 2 51 44 94 94
Web Site: http://www.impulsyon.fr
Rail Transportation Services
N.A.I.C.S.: 485112

Les Cars Jacquemard (2)
rue Gay Lussac ZI Extension, 27000, Evreux, France
Tel.: (33) 2 32 33 09 66
Web Site: http://www.cars-jacquemard.com
Rail Transportation Services

N.A.I.C.S.: 485112

Subsidiary (US):

McDonald Transit Associates Inc (2)
3800 Sandshell Dr Ste 185, Fort Worth, TX 76137
Tel.: (817) 232-9551
Web Site: http://www.mcdonaldtransit.com
Sales Range: $1-4.9 Billion
Emp.: 3,000
Transportation Management Services
N.A.I.C.S.: 488490
John P. Bartosiewicz *(Exec VP)*

Subsidiary (Non-US):

Metrolink RATP Dev UK (2)
Metrolink House Queens Road, Manchester, M8 ORY, United Kingdom
Tel.: (44) 161 205 2000
Web Site: http://www.metrolink.co.uk
Rail Transportation Services
N.A.I.C.S.: 485112

Subsidiary (Domestic):

RATP DEV Rhone-Alpes (2)
rue Sommelier, 74100, Annemasse, France
Tel.: (33) 4 50 37 41 25
Web Site: http://www.ratpdev-rhonealpes.com
Rail Transportation Services
N.A.I.C.S.: 485112

Subsidiary (US):

RATP Dev America (2)
757 3rd Ave 20th Fl, New York, NY 10017
Tel.: (212) 376-5842
Web Site: http://www.ratpdevamerica.com
Rail Transportation Services
N.A.I.C.S.: 485112
Jeffrey Mong *(VP-Fin)*

Subsidiary (Non-US):

RATP Yellow Buses (2)
Yeomans Way, Bournemouth, BH8 0BQ, United Kingdom
Tel.: (44) 1202636110
Web Site: http://www.bybus.co.uk
Sales Range: $125-149.9 Million
Emp.: 400
Rail Transportation Services
N.A.I.C.S.: 485112
Jenni Wilkinson *(Head-Mktg)*

Subsidiary (Domestic):

STIVO (2)
33 rue des Fossettes, 95650, Genicourt, France
Tel.: (33) 1 34 42 75 15
Web Site: http://www.stivo.com
Sales Range: $125-149.9 Million
Emp.: 330
Rail Transportation Services
N.A.I.C.S.: 485112

Subsidiary (Non-US):

Selwyns Travel Ltd. (2)
Cavendish Farm Road, Weston, Runcorn, WA7 4LT, Cheshire, United Kingdom
Tel.: (44) 1928529036
Web Site: http://www.selwyns.co.uk
Sales Range: $10-24.9 Million
Emp.: 200
Passenger Transportation Services
N.A.I.C.S.: 485510
Selwyn Jones *(Mng Dir)*

Subsidiary (Domestic):

Societe des Transports Departementaux de la Marne (2)
86 Rue De Fagnieres, 51000, Chalons-en-Champagne, France
Tel.: (33) 3 26 65 17 07
Web Site: http://www.stdmarne.fr
Sales Range: $50-74.9 Million
Emp.: 127
Rail Transportation Distr
N.A.I.C.S.: 485112

TIMBUS (2)
ZA de la demi-lune 7 rue des Freres Montgolfier, 95420, Magny-en-Vexin, France
Tel.: (33) 1 34 46 88 00
Web Site: http://www.lesbusduvexin.fr

Rail Transportation Services
N.A.I.C.S.: 485112

SYSTRA (1)
72 rue Henry Farman, 75015, Paris, France
Tel.: (33) 140166100
Web Site: http://www.systra.com
Sales Range: $500-549.9 Million
Emp.: 3,400
Transport Infrastructure Consulting Services
N.A.I.C.S.: 541614
Philippe Naudi *(Exec VP-Bus Dev)*

Telcite (1)
Immeuble Central IV 6 Eme Etage 1 Avenue Montaigne, 93160, Noisy-le-Grand, France
Tel.: (33) 1 58 76 19 84
Web Site: http://www.telcite.fr
Telecommunication Network Services
N.A.I.C.S.: 517810

REGIMEN EQUITY PARTNERS INC.
Suite 570 - 1285 West Pender St, Vancouver, V6E 4B1, BC, Canada
Tel.: (778) 379-1000
Web Site:
https://www.regimenpartners.com
Year Founded: 2014
Holding Company
N.A.I.C.S.: 551112

Subsidiaries:

Plastifab Industries, Inc. (1)
7777 Route Transcanadienne, Saint Laurent, H4S 1L3, Quebec, Canada
Tel.: (514) 325-9840
Web Site: https://www.plastifab.ca
Plastic Mfr
N.A.I.C.S.: 325211

Subsidiary (US):

Marchel Industries, Inc. (2)
100 Southwest Dr, Spartanburg, SC 29303
Tel.: (864) 574-6318
Web Site: http://www.marchelindustries.com
Fasteners, Buttons, Needles, And Pins
N.A.I.C.S.: 339993
Bobby Pitts *(Treas & VP)*

Moldpro, Inc. (2)
36 Denman Thompson Ave, West Swanzey, NH 03469
Tel.: (603) 357-2523
Web Site: http://www.moldproinc.com
Sales Range: $1-9.9 Million
Emp.: 25
Mfg Dies/Tools/Jigs/Fixtures Mfg Plastic Products
N.A.I.C.S.: 333511

REGINA MIRACLE INTERNATIONAL HOLDINGS LTD.
10/F Tower A Regent Centre 63 Wo Yi Hop Road, Kwai Chung, China (Hong Kong)
Tel.: (852) 2 429 4521   Ky
Web Site:
http://reginamiracleholdings.com
Year Founded: 1998
2199—(HKG)
Rev.: $1,076,560,977
Assets: $1,214,962,193
Liabilities: $745,957,765
Net Worth: $469,004,428
Earnings: $67,159,112
Emp.: 45,385
Fiscal Year-end: 03/31/22
Holding Company
N.A.I.C.S.: 551112
Yau Lit Hung *(Founder, Chm & CEO)*

Subsidiaries:

Regina Miracle International (Vietnam) Limited (1)
Units 1001-1010 10/F Tower A Regent Centre 63 Wo Yi Hop Road, Kwai Chung, China (Hong Kong)
Tel.: (852) 24294521
Cut & Sew Apparel Mfr
N.A.I.C.S.: 315250

REGINA MIRACLE INTERNATIONAL HOLDINGS LTD.

Regina Miracle International Holdings Ltd.—(Continued)

Regina Miracle International (Vietnam) Limited Co., Ltd. (1)
No 9 East-West Street VSIP Urban, Industrial and Service Area Duong Quan Commune Thuy Nguyen District, Haiphong, Vietnam
Tel.: (84) 2256263282
Web Site: http://www.reginamiracle.com.vn
Cut & Sew Apparel Mfr
N.A.I.C.S.: 315250

REGION GROUP
Level 6 50 Pitt Street, Sydney, 2000, NSW, Australia
Tel.: (61) 282434900 AU
Web Site: https://regiongroup.au
Year Founded: 2012
RGN—(ASX)
Rev: $254,006,409
Assets: $3,039,463,129
Liabilities: $1,160,122,858
Net Worth: $1,879,340,270
Earnings: $11,551,816
Fiscal Year-end: 06/30/24
Real Estate Investment Services
N.A.I.C.S.: 523999
Anthony Mellowes *(CEO)*

REGIONAL CONTAINER LINES PUBLIC COMPANY LIMITED
30th Floor Panjathani Tower Building 127/35 Ratchadapisek Road, Chongnonsi Yannawa, Bangkok, 10120, Thailand
Tel.: (66) 22961096 TH
Web Site: https://www.rclgroup.com
Year Founded: 1979
RCL—(THA)
Rev.: $792,182,349
Assets: $1,645,911,843
Liabilities: $371,919,286
Net Worth: $1,273,992,557
Earnings: $43,859,734
Emp.: 823
Fiscal Year-end: 12/31/23
Container Liner Services
N.A.I.C.S.: 488510
Hock Eng Kua *(Exec Dir)*

Subsidiaries:

Arrow Shipping Agency Co.,Ltd. (1)
No 33-34 Bayon Market Building 2nd Fl Room 203 St 114, Sangkat Monorom Khan 7 Makara, Phnom Penh, Cambodia
Tel.: (855) 23880241242
Shipping Services
N.A.I.C.S.: 488510

Chun Jee Shipping Co., Ltd. (1)
8th Floor Jeongseok Building 89-14, Jungang-Dong 4-Ga Jung-Gu, Busan, Korea (South)
Tel.: (82) 514682937
Shipping Services
N.A.I.C.S.: 488510

Delmege Forsyth & Co.(Shipping) Ltd. (1)
No 101 Vinayalankara Mawatha, Colombo, Sri Lanka
Tel.: (94) 1126933618
Web Site: https://delmege.com
Freight Forwarding Services
N.A.I.C.S.: 488510

Feeder Shipping Agency Co., Ltd. (1)
Office 460 St 466 Sangkat Tunle Basac, Khan Chamkamorn, Phnom Penh, Cambodia
Tel.: (855) 23 213883
Web Site: http://www.rclgroup.com
Ship Operating Services
N.A.I.C.S.: 488330

Grand Maritime Trasport Ltd. (1)
Room 5-1 5th Floor No 77 Nanking East Road Sec 4, Taipei, Taiwan
Tel.: (886) 225471786
Shipping Services
N.A.I.C.S.: 488510

PT. Bintika Bangunusa (1)
Komplek Griya Riatur Jalan Tengku Amir Hamzah Blok G No 106-108, Medan, Indonesia
Tel.: (62) 618455883
Web Site: https://www.bbngroup.org
Freight Forwarding Services
N.A.I.C.S.: 488510

PT. Jasa Centina Sentosa (1)
Wisma BSG 11th Floor Jl Abdul Muis 40, Jakarta, Indonesia
Tel.: (62) 213516602
Freight Forwarding Services
N.A.I.C.S.: 488510

Pride Shipping Company Ltd. (1)
Unit No 503 Building E9 Emaar Square Jeddah Gate King Abdullah Road, Jeddah, Saudi Arabia
Tel.: (966) 126576657
Shipping Services
N.A.I.C.S.: 488510

RCL (Korea) Ltd. (1)
13f Boryung Bldg B136 Changgyeonggung-ro, Jongno-gu, Seoul, Korea (South)
Tel.: (82) 36710628
Web Site: http://www.rclgroup.com
Sales Range: $25-49.9 Million
Freight Forwarding Services
N.A.I.C.S.: 488510

RCL (Myanmar) Company Limited (1)
422/426 Corner of Strand Road and Botahtaung Pagoda Road 11-01, Botahtaung Township, Yangon, Myanmar
Tel.: (95) 1202065
Shipping Services
N.A.I.C.S.: 488330

RCL (Vietnam) Co., Ltd. (1)
10th Floor SGGP Building 436 - 438 Nguyen Thi Minh Khai St, Ward 5 Dist 3, Ho Chi Minh City, Vietnam
Tel.: (84) 2838181522
Freight Forwarding Services
N.A.I.C.S.: 488510

RCL Agencies (M) Sdn. Bhd. (1)
Suite 6 02 Level 6 IMS 2 88 Jalan Batai Laut 4 Taman Intan, 41300, Port Klang, Selangor, Malaysia (100%)
Tel.: (60) 333422722
Sales Range: $25-49.9 Million
Emp.: 50
Shipping Agents
N.A.I.C.S.: 488510

RCL Australia Pty. Ltd. (1)
1st Flr 60-64 Bay Street, Ultimo, 2007, NSW, Australia (68.75%)
Tel.: (61) 292198700
Web Site: http://www.rclgroup.com
Sales Range: $25-49.9 Million
Shipping Agents
N.A.I.C.S.: 488510

RCL Feeders Phils., Inc. (1)
10th Floor Ayala Life-Fgu Centre Ayala Avenue, Makati, 6811, Philippines (100%)
Tel.: (63) 28153187
Emp.: 36
Shipping Agents
N.A.I.C.S.: 488510

RCL Holdings Ltd. (1)
11 Keppel Road 8th Fl Abi Plaza, Singapore, 89057, Singapore
Tel.: (65) 6220 0388
Web Site: http://www.rclgroup.com
Emp.: 120
Investment Management Service
N.A.I.C.S.: 523999

RCL Investment Pte. Ltd. (1)
11 Keppel Rd 8th Floor ABI Plz, Singapore, 089057, Singapore (100%)
Tel.: (65) 62200388
Web Site: https://www.rclgroup.com
Holding Company
N.A.I.C.S.: 551112

Subsidiary (Domestic):

RCL Feeder Pte. Ltd. (2)
11 Keppel Road 8th Floor ABI Plaza, Singapore, 089057, Singapore (100%)

Tel.: (65) 62200388
Cargo Handling Services
N.A.I.C.S.: 488320

RCL Services S.A. (2)
11 Keppel Road 8th Floor ABI Plaza, Singapore, 089057, Singapore (100%)
Tel.: (65) 62200388
Ship Operations
N.A.I.C.S.: 488390

RCL Shipmanagement Pte. Ltd. (2)
11 Keppel Road 8th Floor ABI Plaza, Singapore, 89057, Singapore (100%)
Tel.: (65) 62200388
Sales Range: $50-74.9 Million
Emp.: 130
Ship Management Services
N.A.I.C.S.: 488390

Regional Container Lines Pte. Ltd. (2)
11 Keppel Road 8th Floor Abi Plaza, Singapore, 089057, Singapore (100%)
Tel.: (65) 62200388
Emp.: 100
Ship Owner & Operator
N.A.I.C.S.: 336611

RCL Logistics Co., Ltd. (2)
14th Fl Panjathani Tower Bldg 127/18 Nonsi Road Ratchadapisek Road, Chongnonsi Yannawa, Bangkok, 10120, Thailand
Tel.: (66) 22961284
Logistics Consulting Servies
N.A.I.C.S.: 541614

Regional Container Line (HK) Co., Ltd. (2)
11th Fl King Kong Commercial Ctr, 9-17 Des Voeux Rd W, Hong Kong, China (Hong Kong) (100%)
Tel.: (852) 25263318
Sales Range: $50-74.9 Million
Emp.: 45
Holding Company; Shipping Agent & Brokerage Services
N.A.I.C.S.: 551112
Kua Hock Eng *(Mng Dir)*

Regional Container Lines Shipping Co., Ltd. (2)
(100%)
Tel.: (86) 2161324500
Sales Range: $50-74.9 Million
Shipping Agent & Brokerage Services
N.A.I.C.S.: 488510

Regional Merchants Maritime Ltd. (2)
11th Floor 9 Des Voeux Road West, Hong Kong, China (Hong Kong) (80%)
Tel.: (852) 25263318
Emp.: 50
Shipping & Logistics Services
N.A.I.C.S.: 488510
Kenneth Chiu *(Mng Dir)*

United Marine Agencies (Pvt) Ltd. (2)
Bahria Complex IV Main Chaudhry Khaliquz-Zaman Road, Girzi Clifton, Karachi, Pakistan
Tel.: (92) 111111862
Web Site: https://umapakistan.com
Shipping Services
N.A.I.C.S.: 488510

REGIONAL DOORS & HARDWARE
44 Scott St W, Saint Catharines, L2R 1C9, ON, Canada
Tel.: (905) 684-8161
Web Site:
http://www.regionaldoors.com
Year Founded: 1983
Rev.: $16,345,651
Emp.: 45
Windows & Doors Mfr
N.A.I.C.S.: 321911
Mike Martineau *(Mgr-Comml Sls Dept)*

REGIONAL EXPRESS HOLDINGS LIMITED
Tel.: (61) 296985414

INTERNATIONAL PUBLIC

Web Site: https://www.rex.com.au
REX—(ASX)
Rev.: $196,261,101
Assets: $317,928,242
Liabilities: $184,298,576
Net Worth: $133,629,666
Earnings: ($2,956,727)
Emp.: 12
Fiscal Year-end: 06/30/20
Air Transport Provision Services
N.A.I.C.S.: 481219
Mayooran Thanabalasingham *(Gen Mgr-IT & Comm)*

Subsidiaries:

Australian Airline Pilot Academy Pty Limited (1)
Don Kendell Drive, PO Box 91, Wagga Wagga Airport, Forest Hill, 2651, NSW, Australia
Tel.: (61) 269267400
Web Site: http://www.aapa.net.au
Emp.: 20
Aviation Training Services
N.A.I.C.S.: 611512
Jacqueline Pak *(Mgr-Corp Svcs)*

Pel-Air Aviation Pty Limited (1)
81-83 Baxter Rd, Mascot, 2020, NSW, Australia
Tel.: (61) 296677700
Web Site: http://www.pelair.com.au
Sales Range: $25-49.9 Million
Emp.: 25
Passenger & Freight Charter Services
N.A.I.C.S.: 481211
Eugene Lee *(COO)*

Regional Express Pty Limited (1)
81-83 Baxter Rd, Mascot, 2020, NSW, Australia
Tel.: (61) 290233555
Web Site: http://www.rex.com.au
Sales Range: $25-49.9 Million
Emp.: 100
Airlines Operation Services
N.A.I.C.S.: 481111
Neville Howell *(CEO)*

Subsidiary (Domestic):

Air Link Pty Limited (2)
Hngr 1 Dubbo Airport, PO Box 223, Dubbo, 2830, NSW, Australia
Tel.: (61) 268842435
Web Site: http://www.airlinkairlines.com.au
Emp.: 17
Aircraft Charter Services
N.A.I.C.S.: 481211
Mark Wardrop *(Co-CEO)*

REGIONAL REIT LIMITED
Mont Crevelt House Bulwer Avenue, Saint Sampson's, GY2 4LH, Guernsey
Tel.: (44) 2078456100 GG
Web Site:
https://www.regionalreit.com
Year Founded: 2015
RGL—(LSE)
Rev.: $115,980,813
Assets: $987,652,108
Liabilities: $601,273,668
Net Worth: $386,378,440
Earnings: ($85,150,215)
Emp.: 70
Fiscal Year-end: 12/31/23
Real Estate Development Services
N.A.I.C.S.: 531190

REGIONAL, S.A.B. DE C.V.
Av Pedro Ramirez Vazquez 200-12 Valle Oriente, 66269, Garza Garcia, Nuevo Leon, Mexico
Tel.: (52) 8183995000
Web Site: http://www.banregio.com
Year Founded: 1994
R—(MEX)
Rev.: $654,978,372
Assets: $13,400,177,177
Liabilities: $11,732,839,010
Net Worth: $1,667,338,167

Earnings: $334,265,701
Emp.: 7,188
Fiscal Year-end: 12/31/23
Financial Management Consulting Services
N.A.I.C.S.: 541611
Manuel Gerardo Rivero Santos *(CEO)*

REGIS GROUP PLC
1 Mount Street Mews, Mayfair, London, W1K 2LF, United Kingdom
Web Site: http://www.regisplc.com
Emp.: 4,500
Private Investment Services
N.A.I.C.S.: 523999
Nick Gould *(Founder & Chm)*

Subsidiaries:

R4 Capital Inc. (1)
780 Third Ave 10th Fl, New York, NY 10017
Tel.: (646) 576-7660
Web Site: http://www.r4cap.com
Asset Management Services
N.A.I.C.S.: 531312
Marc D. Schnitzer *(Founder, Pres & CEO)*

Regis Group France (1)
Les Algorithmes - Le Thales B 2000 route des lucioles, Slophia-Antipolis, 6410, Biot, France
Tel.: (33) 961075357
Web Site: http://www.regisgroupfrance.com
Asset Management Services
N.A.I.C.S.: 531312

REGIS HEALTHCARE LIMITED
607-613 Dandenong Rd, PO Box 8373, Armadale, 3143, VIC, Australia
Tel.: (61) 300998100
Web Site: https://www.regis.com.au
REG—(ASX)
Rev.: $746,734,773
Assets: $1,210,275,102
Liabilities: $1,225,556,218
Net Worth: ($15,281,116)
Earnings: ($14,299,546)
Emp.: 9,000
Fiscal Year-end: 06/30/24
Elderly Care Facilities
N.A.I.C.S.: 623312
Martin Bede *(Gen Counsel & Sec)*

REGIS RESOURCES LIMITED
Level 2 516 Hay Street, Subiaco, 6008, WA, Australia
Tel.: (61) 894422200
Web Site:
https://www.regisresources.com.au
RRL—(OTCIQ)
Rev.: $627,633,733
Assets: $1,772,323,891
Liabilities: $558,445,243
Net Worth: $1,213,878,648
Earnings: $112,015,446
Emp.: 271
Fiscal Year-end: 06/30/21
Copper, Nickel, Lead & Zinc Mining
N.A.I.C.S.: 212230
Tony Hinkley *(Gen Mgr-Duketon Gold Project)*

REGNIS (LANKA) PLC
No 52 Ferry Road Off Borupana Road, Ratmalana, Colombo, Sri Lanka
Tel.: (94) 2635408
Year Founded: 1987
REG.N0000—(COL)
Rev.: $38,687,703
Assets: $26,079,386
Liabilities: $16,241,720
Net Worth: $9,837,666
Earnings: $144,152
Emp.: 517
Fiscal Year-end: 03/31/22
Refrigerator & Washing Machine Equipment Mfr
N.A.I.C.S.: 335220
Pandithage Abeyakumar Mohan *(Chm & CEO)*

REGNON S.A.
Al Walentego Rozdzienskiego 188c, 40-203, Katowice, Poland
Tel.: (48) 323231560
Web Site: http://www.regnon.com
REG—(WAR)
Sales Range: $1-9.9 Million
Emp.: 85
Electronics Mfr
N.A.I.C.S.: 334419
Adam Wysocki *(CEO)*

REGO INTERACTIVE CO., LTD.
2nd Floor Building 8 Yinhu Innovation Center, Fuyang, Hangzhou, 311400, China
Tel.: (86) 57188480000 Ky
Web Site: https://www.regopimc.com
Year Founded: 2009
2422—(HKG)
Rev.: $39,312,307
Assets: $61,238,037
Liabilities: $15,664,037
Net Worth: $45,574,000
Earnings: $10,495,345
Emp.: 181
Fiscal Year-end: 12/31/22
Information Technology Services
N.A.I.C.S.: 541512
Huan Tian *(CEO)*

REGULUS RESOURCES INC.
Suite 1570 200 Burrard Street, Vancouver, V6C 3L6, BC, Canada
Tel.: (604) 685-6800 AB
Web Site:
https://www.regulusresources.com
Year Founded: 2010
RGLSF—(OTCQX)
Rev.: $18,802
Assets: $40,680,988
Liabilities: $1,781,615
Net Worth: $38,899,373
Earnings: ($4,259,592)
Fiscal Year-end: 09/30/21
Metal Ore Exploration & Development
N.A.I.C.S.: 213114
Mark Wayne *(CFO)*

REHABWORKS LTD.
Suffolk House 7 Angel Hill, Bury Saint Edmunds, IP33 1UZ, United Kingdom
Tel.: (44) 333 222 0710 UK
Web Site:
http://www.rehabworks.co.uk
Year Founded: 2003
Emp.: 162
Injury Management & Rehabilitation Services
N.A.I.C.S.: 621999
Greg Kane *(Dir-Ops)*

REHAU VERWALTUNGSZENTRALE AG
Breichtenstrasse 2 4, 3074, Muri, Switzerland
Tel.: (41) 319503111 De
Web Site: http://www.rehau.com
Year Founded: 1948
Polymer-Based Solution
N.A.I.C.S.: 811310
Kurt Plattner *(CFO)*

Subsidiaries:

MB Barter & Trading SA (1)
Erlenweg 8, Zug, 6300, Switzerland
Tel.: (41) 7268383
Web Site: http://www.mbbarter.ch
Polymers & Rubber Mfr
N.A.I.C.S.: 326299
Ronald Huwler *(CFO)*

Subsidiary (Non-US):

Alf Helland Olsen (2)
Baneaasen 2, 3970, Langesund, Norway
Tel.: (47) 90597732
Polymers & Rubber Mfr
N.A.I.C.S.: 326299

Subsidiary (Domestic):

Borotrex SA (2)
Via Cattori 3, Via Cattori 3, CH 6902, Lugano, Paradiso, Switzerland
Tel.: (41) 919857090
Web Site: http://www.mbbarter.ch
Emp.: 3
Polymers & Rubber Mfr
N.A.I.C.S.: 326299

Subsidiary (Non-US):

Chemiplast International (2)
Office 4 Forth Floo, Bank Arcade, 74000, Karachi, Pakistan
Tel.: (92) 21 241 72 058
Polymers & Rubber Mfr
N.A.I.C.S.: 326299

Fountain Trading Company (2)
T-1704 Poonglim Officetel, Seohyun-Dong, Seongnam, Bundang-Gu, Korea (South)
Tel.: (82) 31 702 18 03
Polymers & Rubber Mfr
N.A.I.C.S.: 326299

GDR Comerciall Imprtacao E Exportacao LTDA. (2)
401 Sergipe Street Room 801, 04537-070, Sao Paulo, Brazil
Tel.: (55) 113 1514767
Polymers & Rubber Mfr
N.A.I.C.S.: 326299

ICD / MBT Group (2)
2411 Hopewell Centre, 183 Queen's Road East, Wanchai, China (Hong Kong)
Tel.: (852) 25474500
Polymers & Rubber Mfr
N.A.I.C.S.: 326299

Kuntner & Co., KG (2)
Antonsgasse 16, 2500, Baden, Austria
Tel.: (43) 2252 2246 60
Polymers & Rubber Mfr
N.A.I.C.S.: 326299

M. Sideris & Son Ltd. (2)
Nicosia 45 Dali Industrial Zone, Dhali Industrial Zone, 2540, Nicosia, Cyprus
Tel.: (357) 22610700
Polymers & Rubber Mfr
N.A.I.C.S.: 326299
Constinos Sideis *(Owner)*

MB Barter & Trading (Pty) Ltd. (2)
Unit 16 Eastwood Office Park 11B Riley Road, PO Box 751775, Bedfordview, 2007, South Africa
Tel.: (27) 114552889
Web Site: http://www.mbt.co.za
Polymers & Rubber Mfr
N.A.I.C.S.: 326299

MB Barter & Trading SA (2)
Box 99916, 11625, Riyadh, Saudi Arabia
Tel.: (966) 1488 9707
Polymers & Rubber Mfr
N.A.I.C.S.: 326299

MB Barter & Trading SA Shanghai (2)
Room 2508 No 161, East Lu Jia Zui Road, 200120, Shanghai, China
Tel.: (86) 2158770961
Web Site: http://www.mbbarter.ch
Polymers & Rubber Mfr
N.A.I.C.S.: 326299

MB Barter & Trading Spain, S.L. (2)
Marcus Porcius 1 2nd, Pol Ind Guixeres Edifici BCl, ES-08915, Barcelona, Spain
Tel.: (34) 93 464 80 63
Polymers & Rubber Mfr
N.A.I.C.S.: 326299

MB Barter & Trading d.o.o. (2)
Obrtniska Ulica 39, Trebnje, 8210, Slovenia
Tel.: (386) 73461600
Emp.: 2
Polymers & Rubber Mfr
N.A.I.C.S.: 326299

Franc Ratajc *(Office Mgr)*

Subsidiary (US):

MB Barter (USA) Inc. (2)
402E The Merler 3388 Sage Rd, Houston, TX 77056
Tel.: (713) 505-1101
Rubber Product Distr
N.A.I.C.S.: 424690
Sunjoy Rai *(VP-Ops)*

Subsidiary (Non-US):

MB Barter Singapore Pte Ltd. (2)
1557 Keppel Road 03-10 Inchcape Marketing Build, 089066, Singapore, Singapore
Tel.: (65) 62232025
Polymers & Rubber Mfr
N.A.I.C.S.: 326299

MBT (Far East) Ltd. (2)
3F No 2 Lane 223 Lung Chiang Road, Taipei, Taiwan
Tel.: (886) 225044303
Web Site: http://www.mbbarter.ch
Polymers & Rubber Mfr
N.A.I.C.S.: 326299

MBT East Africa Ltd. (2)
PO Box 781 Village Market Ltd., Nairobi, Kenya
Tel.: (254) 723422043
Polymers & Rubber Mfr
N.A.I.C.S.: 326299

MBT Egypt Ltd. (2)
Salah Hussein, PO Box 21411, EG, Alexandria, Egypt
Tel.: (20) 35858572
Web Site: http://www.mbtegypt.com
Sales Range: $25-49.9 Million
Emp.: 20
Polymers & Rubber Mfr
N.A.I.C.S.: 326299
Sarah Husen *(Mgr)*

MBT Ina Polimer (2)
Kalamis Fener Cad 607, TR-81030, Istanbul, Turkiye
Tel.: (90) 2163471862
Polymers & Rubber Mfr
N.A.I.C.S.: 326299

MBT India (2)
Jeevan Sahakar 5th Floor 5 Homji Street, Mumbai, 400001, India
Tel.: (91) 22 2266 2934
Rubber Product Distr
N.A.I.C.S.: 424690

MBT Kunststoffe GmbH (2)
Falkenstrasse 1, 85521, Ottobrunn, Germany
Tel.: (49) 8966 0558 40
Polymers & Rubber Mfr
N.A.I.C.S.: 326299

MBT Pet Import d.o.o. (2)
Ul Francuska Br 16, 11000, Belgrade, Serbia
Tel.: (381) 11 324 286
Polymers & Rubber Mfr
N.A.I.C.S.: 326299

MBT Polska Sp.z.o.o. (2)
Grazyna Specjalska, Al Niepodleglosci 124 lok 4, 02-570, Warsaw, Poland
Tel.: (48) 228517011
Polymers & Rubber Mfr
N.A.I.C.S.: 326299

MBT PolyTapes GmbH (2)
Erlenbusch 2, Ruhr, 58739, Wickede, Germany
Tel.: (49) 237778720
Web Site: http://www.polytapes.de
Emp.: 50
Polymers & Rubber Mfr
N.A.I.C.S.: 326299
Christian Bunte *(Gen Mgr)*

MBT Polymers (Bulgaria) d.o.o. (2)
Bul Bulgaria 88 office 11, 1680, Sofia, Bulgaria
Tel.: (359) 28548046
Polymers & Rubber Mfr
N.A.I.C.S.: 326299

MBT Polymers Benelux N.V. (2)
Lambrechtshoekenlaan 147, 2170, Antwerp, Merksem, Belgium

REHAU VERWALTUNGSZENTRALE AG

REHAU Verwaltungszentrale AG—(Continued)
Tel.: (32) 36440039
Polymers & Rubber Mfr
N.A.I.C.S.: 326299

MBT Polymers General Trading LLC (2)
116 Hamsah Building A Khalid Bin Waleed Road, Dubai, United Arab Emirates
Tel.: (971) 4 3965 922
Rubber Product Distr
N.A.I.C.S.: 424690

MBT Polymers GmbH (2)
Rotter Viehtrift 2, 53842, Troisdorf, Germany
Tel.: (49) 2241 97395 0
Web Site: http://www.mbt-polymers.com
Polymers & Rubber Mfr
N.A.I.C.S.: 326299
Andreas Kleinmann *(Mng Partner)*

MBT Polymers Hungary Kft. (Ltd.) (2)
Arpard ut 16 1/2, 3580, Tiszaujvaros, Hungary
Tel.: (36) 49 340 380
Polymers & Rubber Mfr
N.A.I.C.S.: 326299

MBT Polymers SRL (2)
5 Piata Alba Iulia, Bl Y4 8th Floor Ap 38, Bucharest, Romania
Tel.: (40) 213173374
Emp.: 2
Polymers & Rubber Mfr
N.A.I.C.S.: 326299
Daniela Andronie *(Gen Mgr)*

MBT UK (2)
Suite 19 The Adur Business Centre, Little High Street, BN43 5EG, Shoreham-by-Sea, United Kingdom - England
Tel.: (44) 1273467596
Sales Range: $25-49.9 Million
Emp.: 100
Polymers & Rubber Mfr
N.A.I.C.S.: 326299

OY Innoteam OY AB (2)
Kari Turpeinen, Pohjantie 3, 2600, Espoo, Finland
Tel.: (358) 400 601 300
Polymers & Rubber Mfr
N.A.I.C.S.: 326299

Subsidiary (Domestic):

Polymag AG (2)
Spinnereistr 12, 8135, Langnau, Switzerland
Tel.: (41) 44 771 77 22
Web Site: http://www.polymag.ch
Polymers & Rubber Mfr
N.A.I.C.S.: 326299

Subsidiary (Non-US):

Sapec-Quimica SA (2)
Carlos Fernandes Lopes, R5 Outobro 4967, 4431-801, Porto, Portugal
Tel.: (351) 227 861 220
Polymers & Rubber Mfr
N.A.I.C.S.: 326299

Teknisk Agentur A/S (2)
Naverland 26 A, 2600, Glostrup, Denmark
Tel.: (45) 43964900
Web Site: http://www.teknisk-agentur.dk
Polymers & Rubber Mfr
N.A.I.C.S.: 326299

UAB Plastima (2)
Rolandas Savickas, Svitrigailos 8/14, Vilnius, 09117, Lithuania
Tel.: (370) 52337485
Web Site: http://www.plastima.lt
Emp.: 9
Polymers & Rubber Mfr
N.A.I.C.S.: 326299

REHM GMBH U. CO. KG SCHWEISSTECHNIK

Ottostrasse 2, 73066, Uihingen, Germany
Tel.: (49) 716130070 De
Web Site: http://www.rehm-online.de
Year Founded: 1974

Sales Range: $25-49.9 Million
Emp.: 140
Welding Equipment Mfr
N.A.I.C.S.: 333992

Subsidiaries:

REHM Hegesztestechnika Kft (1)
Jaszberenyi ut 4, Tapioszele, 2766, Hungary
Tel.: (36) 53380078
Web Site: http://www.rehm.hu
Industrial Machinery Distr
N.A.I.C.S.: 423830

REHM Nederland B.V. (1)
Biezenloop 3, 5032 CD, Tilburg, Netherlands
Tel.: (31) 134684727
Web Site: http://www.rehm.nl
Welding Machinery Mfr
N.A.I.C.S.: 333992

REHM Schweisstechnik GmbH (1)
Neefe Strasse 52 I, 9119, Chemnitz, Germany
Tel.: (49) 371350505
Industrial Machinery Distr
N.A.I.C.S.: 423830

S.C. REHM SUDARE S.R.L (1)
Crizantemelorstr 34, 300142, Timisoara, Romania
Tel.: (40) 256220943
Industrial Machinery Distr
N.A.I.C.S.: 423830

REIBEL N.V.

Grensstraat 7, BE-1831, Brussels, Belgium
Tel.: (32) 24219911
Web Site: http://www.reibel.be
Year Founded: 1923
REI—(EUR)
Sales Range: $1-9.9 Million
Logistic Services
N.A.I.C.S.: 483111

Subsidiaries:

BELPOWER International S.A. (1)
Reibel House Chaussee de Vilvorde 11, 1120, Brussels, Belgium
Tel.: (32) 2 421 99 37
Web Site: http://www.belpower.be
Power Generation Services
N.A.I.C.S.: 221114

Subsidiary (Non-US):

Belpower S.r.l. (2)
Via Accademia Albertina 1, 10123, Turin, Italy
Tel.: (39) 011 7630392
Web Site: http://www.belpower.it
Power Generation Services
N.A.I.C.S.: 221114

REICHL UND PARTNER WERBEAGENTUR GMBH

Harrachstrasse 6, A-4020, Linz, Austria
Tel.: (43) 732 666 222
Web Site: http://www.reichlundpartner.com
Emp.: 120
N.A.I.C.S.: 541810
Rainer Reichl *(CEO)*

REICHLE & DE-MASSARI AG

Binzstrasse 32, 8620, Wetzikon, Switzerland
Tel.: (41) 449319777
Web Site: http://www.rdm.com
Year Founded: 1964
Sales Range: $150-199.9 Million
Emp.: 700
Communication Network Design Services
N.A.I.C.S.: 541512
Michiel Panders *(Gen Mgr-Europe)*

Subsidiaries:

R & M Bulgaria EOOD (1)

Rezbarska 1e, 1510, Sofia, Bulgaria
Tel.: (359) 29021600
Fiber Optic Cable Mfr
N.A.I.C.S.: 335921

R&M Ship Interior AS (1)
Verftsgata 2/4, Molde, 6416, Norway
Tel.: (47) 41649000
Ship Repair & Maintenance Services
N.A.I.C.S.: 532411
Vidar Berg *(Mng Dir)*

Realm Communications Group, Inc. (1)
840 Yosemite Way, Milpitas, CA 95035
Tel.: (408) 945-6626
Web Site: http://www.rcgoptic.com
Sales Range: $1-9.9 Million
Emp.: 48
Mfr & Reseller of Fiber Optic Cables, Fiber Optic Equipment & Communication Products
N.A.I.C.S.: 335921
John Russell *(Pres)*

Reichle & De-Massari - META (1)
Buildings K9 & K10, PO Box 54281, Dubai, United Arab Emirates
Tel.: (971) 42368761
Networking Component Mfr & Distr
N.A.I.C.S.: 334210

Reichle & De-Massari Australia PTY LTD (1)
Level 13 Macquarie House 167 Macquarie Street, Sydney, 2000, NSW, Australia
Tel.: (61) 290436303
Networking Component Mfr & Distr
N.A.I.C.S.: 334210
Emmanuel Beydon *(Mng Dir)*

Reichle & De-Massari Austria GmbH (1)
Eduard-Kittenberger-Gasse 95-97, 1230, Vienna, Austria
Tel.: (43) 186532000
Computer Hardware Distr
N.A.I.C.S.: 423690

Reichle & De-Massari Far East (Pte) Ltd (1)
20 Toh Guan Road #04-00 CJ Logistics Building, 608839, Singapore, Singapore
Tel.: (65) 6506 5600
Web Site: http://www.rdm.com
Network Cable Installation Services
N.A.I.C.S.: 238210
Laurent Amestoy *(Exec VP-Asia Pacific)*

Reichle & De-Massari France (1)
Access 3 - Rue Helene Boucher, 78280, Guyancourt, France
Tel.: (33) 139305990
Mechanical Engineering Services
N.A.I.C.S.: 541330

Reichle & De-Massari GmbH (1)
Hindenburgstrabe 21-25, 51643, Gummersbach, Germany
Tel.: (49) 2261501700
Electrical Component Mfr
N.A.I.C.S.: 334413

Reichle & De-Massari Italia S.r.l. (1)
Via Saronnino 103, 21040, Origgio, Italy
Tel.: (39) 0296952111
Networking Component Mfr & Distr
N.A.I.C.S.: 334210

Reichle & De-Massari KSA (1)
B10 Sulaima Abanami Complex Olaya Musaed Al Angari Street, 11371, Riyadh, Saudi Arabia
Tel.: (966) 114532924
Networking Component Mfr & Distr
N.A.I.C.S.: 334210

Reichle & De-Massari Kft. (1)
1386 Budapest Pf 906/104 Petnehazy u 34-36, 1139, Budapest, Hungary
Tel.: (36) 14122690
Industrial Transmission Supplies Distr
N.A.I.C.S.: 423840

Reichle & De-Massari Netherlands B.V. (1)
Linie 508, 7325 DZ, Apeldoorn, Netherlands
Tel.: (31) 553681800
Fiber Optic Cable Mfr
N.A.I.C.S.: 335921

INTERNATIONAL PUBLIC

Bas Mondria *(Country Mgr)*

Reichle & De-Massari Polska Sp.z o.o. (1)
Farbiarska 49, 02-862, Warsaw, Poland
Tel.: (48) 226444737
Telecommunication Servicesb
N.A.I.C.S.: 517810
Pawe Kripiec *(Brand Mgr)*

Reichle & De-Massari UK Ltd (1)
99 Bishopsgate, London, EC2M 3XD, United Kingdom
Tel.: (44) 2036937595
Telecommunication Servicesb
N.A.I.C.S.: 517810
Pete Gough *(Mng Dir)*

Reichle & de-Massari Iberia S.L.U. (1)
Officina 13 1 Planta, 28230, Las Rozas, Spain
Tel.: (34) 916401333
Telecommunication Servicesb
N.A.I.C.S.: 517810

REICHMANNHAUER CAPITAL PARTNERS INC.

1 First Canadian Place Suite 3300, PO Box 72, Toronto, M5X 1B1, ON, Canada
Tel.: (416) 862-6040 ON
Web Site: http://www.rhcapitalpartners.com
Sales Range: $25-49.9 Million
Emp.: 50
Privater Equity Firm
N.A.I.C.S.: 523999
Philip Reichmann *(Co Founding Partner)*

REID-WORLD WIDE CORPORATION

18140 107 Ave, Edmonton, T5S1K5, AB, Canada
Tel.: (780) 451-7778
Web Site: http://www.rwwc.ca
Year Founded: 1991
Sales Range: $10-24.9 Million
Emp.: 350
Business Management & Investment Services
N.A.I.C.S.: 541611
Greg Hembroff *(VP-Plng & Land Dev)*

Subsidiaries:

THE DESIGN CENTRE (1)
10711-182 Street, Edmonton, T5S 1J5, AB, Canada
Tel.: (780) 444-8426
Building Materials Distr
N.A.I.C.S.: 423390

REIFEN KRUPP GMBH & CO. KG

Ketzerweg 1, 67105, Schifferstadt, Germany
Tel.: (49) 6235490251
Web Site: http://www.reifenkrupp.de
Year Founded: 1951
Rev.: $103,420,059
Emp.: 60
Car & Motor Bike Tires Distr
N.A.I.C.S.: 423130
Herbert Krupp *(Mng Dir)*

REIFENHAUSER GMBH & CO. KG MASCHINENFABRIK

Spicher Strasse 46, 53844, Troisdorf, Germany
Tel.: (49) 2241235100 De
Web Site: http://www.reifenhauser-group.com
Year Founded: 1945
Sales Range: $150-199.9 Million
Emp.: 850
Holding Company; Cast Film Lines, Extrusion Coating Lines, Thermoforming Sheet Lines, Extruders & Die-Heads Mfr

N.A.I.C.S.: 551112
Ulrich Reifenhauser *(Chief Strategy Officer)*

Subsidiaries:

Deutsche Apparate Vertriebsorganisation DAVO GmbH & Co. Polyrema KG (1)
Hertzstrasse 12, Troisdorf, 53844, Bergheim, Germany
Tel.: (49) 228 96 390 0
Web Site: http://www.polyrema.com
Industrial Machinery Mfr
N.A.I.C.S.: 333248
Manfred Kurscheid *(Mng Dir)*

Reifenhauser (India) Marketing Ltd. (1)
229 Udyog Bhavan Sonawala Road, Goregaon, Mumbai, 400 063, India
Tel.: (91) 22 2686 2711
Web Site: http://www.reifenhauserindia.com
Emp.: 250
Industrial Machinery Mfr
N.A.I.C.S.: 333248
Manish Mehta *(Founder)*

Reifenhauser Inc. (1)
12260 W 53rd St, Maize, KS 67101
Tel.: (316) 260-2122
Web Site: http://www.usa.reifenhauser.com
Emp.: 3
Industrial Machinery Mfr
N.A.I.C.S.: 333248
Steve DeSpain *(Dir-Sls & Mktg)*

Reifenhauser Kiefel Extrusion GmbH (1)
Cornelius-Heyl-Str 49, 67547, Worms, Germany
Tel.: (49) 6241 902 0
Web Site: http://www.reifenhauser-kiefel.com
Industrial Machinery Mfr
N.A.I.C.S.: 333248
Bernd Reifenhauser *(Mng Dir)*

Reifenhauser Kiefel S.A. (1)
Miguel Claro 195 Of 207, Providencia, Santiago, Chile
Tel.: (56) 2 25847292
Industrial Machinery Mfr
N.A.I.C.S.: 333248

Reifenhauser Ltd. (1)
Sun Street, Tewkesbury, GL20 5NX, Glos, United Kingdom (100%)
Tel.: (44) 1684299666
Web Site: http://www.reifenhauser.com.de
Sales Range: $1-9.9 Million
Emp.: 100
Marketing & Sales of Plastic Extrusion Machines
N.A.I.C.S.: 423830

Reifenhauser Maskiner A/S (1)
Toldbodgade 16, Kolding, DK 6000, Denmark (100%)
Tel.: (45) 75525733
Web Site: http://www.reifenhauser.com.dk
Sales Range: $50-74.9 Million
Emp.: 3
Marketing & Sales of Plastic Extrusion Machines
N.A.I.C.S.: 423830

Reifenhauser Private Ltd. (1)
25 International Business Park Suite 04-72 German Centre, Singapore, 609916, Singapore
Tel.: (65) 65628740
Industrial Machinery Mfr
N.A.I.C.S.: 333248

Reiloy Westland Corporation (1)
12260 W 53rd St N, Maize, KS 67101
Tel.: (316) 721-1144
Web Site: http://www.reiloyusa.com
Industrial Machinery Mfr
N.A.I.C.S.: 333248
Cindy Hogarth *(Engr-Inside Sls)*

Reimotec Maschinen- und Anlagenbau GmbH (1)
Edisonstrasse 15, 68623, Lampertheim, Germany
Tel.: (49) 6206 9511 0
Web Site: http://www.reimotec.com
Industrial Machinery Mfr

N.A.I.C.S.: 333248
Reimotec Winding Technology srl (1)
Via Pirovano 22 Fraz Albusciago, 21040, Sumirago, Italy
Tel.: (39) 0331 909 536
Web Site: http://www.reimotec-wt.com
Industrial Machinery Mfr
N.A.I.C.S.: 333248

REIG JOFRE GROUP

Gran Capita 10 08970 Sant Joan Despi, Barcelona, 08970, Spain
Tel.: (34) 934806719
Web Site: http://www.reigjofre.com
Year Founded: 1929
Sales Range: $75-99.9 Million
Emp.: 600
Pharmaceuticals Mfr
N.A.I.C.S.: 325412
Ignasi Biosca Reig *(Pres)*

Subsidiaries:

Bioglan AB (1)
Borrgatan 31, Malmo, Sweden
Tel.: (46) 40287500
Web Site: http://www.bioglan.se
Sales Range: $25-49.9 Million
Emp.: 50
Pharmaceutical Development & Mfr
N.A.I.C.S.: 325412
Totte Malmstrom *(CEO & Mgr-IT)*

REIGNWOOD GROUP

Reignwood Centre 8 Yongandongli Jianguomenwai Street, Chaoyang District, Beijing, 100022, China
Tel.: (86) 10 8528 8528
Web Site: http://www.reignwood.com
Year Founded: 1984
Investment Holding Company
N.A.I.C.S.: 551112
Ruayrungruang Chanchai *(Chm)*

REIL ELECTRICALS INDIA LIMITED

No 8-2-409 Road No 6, Banjara Hills, Hyderabad, 500034, India
Tel.: (91) 40 2335 4833
Web Site: http://www.reilindia.com
Year Founded: 1977
Rev.: $2,713,462
Assets: $2,811,583
Liabilities: $2,333,004
Net Worth: $478,579
Earnings: $58,490
Fiscal Year-end: 03/31/18
Electrical Products Mfr
N.A.I.C.S.: 336320
Bhupinder Singh Sahney *(Chm & Mng Dir)*

REILING GLAS RECYCLING GMBH & CO. KG

Bussemasstrasse 49, PO Box 2263, 33428, Marienfeld, Germany
Tel.: (49) 524798030
Web Site: http://www.reiling.eu
Rev.: $29,057,888
Emp.: 135
Glass & Plastic Recycling Service
N.A.I.C.S.: 562920
Bernhard Reiling *(Mng Dir)*

Subsidiaries:

Ruhrglas Recycling GmbH & Co. KG (1)
Frydagstrasse 39, 44536, Lunen, Germany
Tel.: (49) 230620060
Glass Material Mfr
N.A.I.C.S.: 327215

REIMER HARDWOODS LTD.

31135 Peardonville Rd, Abbotsford, V2T 6K6, BC, Canada
Tel.: (604) 850-9281
Web Site: https://www.reimerhardwoods.com
Year Founded: 1977
Rev.: $15,496,163
Emp.: 42
Wood Product Distr
N.A.I.C.S.: 423310
Ron Howard *(Mgr-Ops)*

REINET INVESTMENTS S.C.A.

35 Boulevard Prince Henri, L-1724, Luxembourg, Luxembourg
Tel.: (352) 224210 LU
Web Site: https://www.reinet.com
REINA—(EUR)
Rev.: $563,349,880
Assets: $6,674,940,631
Liabilities: $1,079,214
Net Worth: $6,673,861,417
Earnings: $560,112,237
Emp.: 180
Fiscal Year-end: 03/31/24
Luxury Goods Investment Services
N.A.I.C.S.: 523999
Johann P. Rupert *(Chm)*

Subsidiaries:

Cartier S.A. (1)
13 Rue De La Paix, 75002, Paris, France
Tel.: (33) 158182300
Web Site: http://www.cartier.com
Sales Range: $100-124.9 Million
Fine Jewelry, Watches & Clocks, Stationery, Pens, Leather & Fragrance Mfr & Retailer
N.A.I.C.S.: 458310

Lange Uhren GmbH (1)
Ferdinand-A -Lange-Platz 1, 01768, Glashutte, Germany (90%)
Tel.: (49) 35053440
Web Site: https://www.alange-soehne.com
Sales Range: $100-124.9 Million
Mfr Watches
N.A.I.C.S.: 334519
Wilhelm Schmid *(Exec Mgr)*

Manufacture Jaeger-Le Coultre S.A. (1)
Rue de la Golisse 8, 1347, Le Sentier, Switzerland
Tel.: (41) 216203000
Web Site: https://www.jaeger-lecoultre.com
Sales Range: $200-249.9 Million
Fine Watches Mfr
N.A.I.C.S.: 334519
Nicolas Baretzki *(Dir-Mktg)*

Richemont International Ltd. (1)
15 Hill St, London, W1J 5QT, United Kingdom (67%)
Tel.: (44) 2074992539
Sales Range: $75-99.9 Million
Emp.: 150
Holding Company
N.A.I.C.S.: 551112

Subsidiary (US):

Van Cleef & Arpels, Inc. (2)
744 5th Ave, New York, NY 10022 (80%)
Tel.: (212) 896-9284
Web Site: http://www.vancleefarpels.com
Sales Range: $25-49.9 Million
Emp.: 75
Jewelry Stores
N.A.I.C.S.: 458310
Anejade Vaccarella *(Sls Mgr)*

REINFORCING STEEL CONTRACTORS (PTY) LTD.

30 Industry Road Clayville Ext 4, Olifantsfontein, 1666, South Africa
Tel.: (27) 11 697 0000
Web Site: http://www.rsh.co.za
Steel Product Mfr & Distr
N.A.I.C.S.: 331110
Dean Smith *(Gen Mgr)*

REINHOLD EUROPE AB

Kommendorsgatan 37, 114 58, Stockholm, Sweden
Tel.: (46) 8 5500 5557

Web Site: http://www.reinhold-europe.se
RHD—(WAR)
Sales Range: Less than $1 Million
Real Estate Services
N.A.I.C.S.: 531390
Harry Wiktor Rosenberg *(Chm)*

REINHOLD KELLER GMBH

Gutenberg Str 4, Miltenberg, 63924, Germany
Tel.: (49) 937197900
Web Site: http://www.reinhold-keller.de
Rev.: $46,039,292
Emp.: 133
Carpentry & Interior Services
N.A.I.C.S.: 238350
Reinhold Keller *(Mng Dir)*

REINO CAPITAL SA

Polna Corner Ul Ludwika Warynskiego 3A, 00-645, Warsaw, Poland
Tel.: (48) 222739750
Web Site: https://www.reinocapital.pl
RNC—(WAR)
Rev.: $7,003,303
Assets: $15,401,423
Liabilities: $5,386,941
Net Worth: $10,014,482
Earnings: $75,711
Fiscal Year-end: 12/31/23
Securities Brokerage Services
N.A.I.C.S.: 523999
Dorota Latkowska-Diniejko *(VP)*

REISER SIMULATION & TRAINING GMBH

Oberer Luessbach 29-31, 82335, Berg, Bavaria, Germany
Tel.: (49) 8178 8681 0
Web Site: http://www.reiser-st.com
Year Founded: 1988
Emp.: 200
Aviation Training Products Mfr
N.A.I.C.S.: 423490
Wolfgang Reiser *(Founder & Chm)*

REISSWOLF INTERNATIONAL AG

Wilhelm-Bergner-Strasse 3 C, 21509, Glinde, Germany
Tel.: (49) 8005890329
Web Site: http://www.reisswolf.com
Year Founded: 1985
Sales Range: $200-249.9 Million
Emp.: 2,300
Document Destruction Sevices
N.A.I.C.S.: 561499
Oliver Graumann *(Member-Exec Bd)*

Subsidiaries:

Heikkinen & Puljula Ltd. (1)
Ahjotie 4, 96300, Rovaniemi, Finland
Tel.: (358) 207310494
Data Protection Services
N.A.I.C.S.: 518210
Pretto Heikkinen *(Mng Dir)*

REISSWOLF Albania sh.p.k. (1)
Rr Dhaskal Tod'hri Godina 33 Kashar, 1051, Tirana, Albania
Tel.: (355) 696050650
Web Site: http://www.reisswolf.al
Document Destruction Sevices
N.A.I.C.S.: 561499

REISSWOLF Baleares S.L. (1)
Vial C/ Ollers nave 32 Marratxi, 07141, Marratxi, Spain
Tel.: (34) 971101371
Web Site: http://www.reisswolfbaleares.com
Document Destruction Sevices
N.A.I.C.S.: 561499

REISSWOLF Baltic SIA (1)
Bullu iela 74, Riga, 1067, Latvia
Tel.: (371) 7460295
Document Destruction Sevices

REISSWOLF INTERNATIONAL AG

REISSWOLF International AG—(Continued)
N.A.I.C.S.: 561499

REISSWOLF Budapest Adat- es Dokumentumkezelo Kft (1)
Illatos ut 6, 1097, Budapest, Hungary
Tel.: (36) 12195670
Web Site: http://www.reisswolf.hu
Document Destruction Sevices
N.A.I.C.S.: 561499

REISSWOLF Centre Est Services (SARL) (1)
18 Rue du pre aux moines, 21800, Sennecey-les-Dijon, France
Tel.: (33) 380470586
Web Site: http://www.reisswolf-ces.fr
Document Destruction Sevices
N.A.I.C.S.: 561499

REISSWOLF D.O.O. (1)
Letaliska cesta 29, 1000, Ljubljana, Slovenia
Tel.: (386) 15412266
Web Site: http://www.reisswolf.si
Document Destruction Sevices
N.A.I.C.S.: 561499

REISSWOLF Deutschland GmbH (1)
Normannenweg 28, 20537, Hamburg, Germany
Tel.: (49) 4025304240
Web Site: http://www.reisswolf.de
Document Destruction Sevices
N.A.I.C.S.: 561499

REISSWOLF Macedonia (1)
Ul 5 br 5 Kojlija, 1043, Petrovec, North Macedonia
Tel.: (389) 22780411
Web Site: http://www.reisswolf.mk
Document Destruction Sevices
N.A.I.C.S.: 561499
Filip Jovanovski *(CEO)*

REISSWOLF S.A. (1)
13 rue de l'industrie, Bertrange, 8069, Luxembourg, Luxembourg
Tel.: (352) 313295
Web Site: http://www.reisswolf.lu
Document Destruction Sevices
N.A.I.C.S.: 561499

REISSWOLF SUR, S.L.U. (1)
Poligono Caseria del Rey Calle Residencia, 29532, Mollina, Spain
Tel.: (34) 902103773
Web Site: http://www.reisswolfsur.com
Document Destruction Sevices
N.A.I.C.S.: 561499

REISSWOLF Serbia d.o.o. (1)
Postanski fah 115 Volarsko polje bb, 22300, Stara Pazova, Serbia
Tel.: (381) 22317720
Web Site: http://www.reisswolf.rs
Document Destruction Sevices
N.A.I.C.S.: 561499
Milan Bogovac *(Mng Dir)*

REISSWOLF Slovakia s.r.o. (1)
Drobneho 27, 841 01, Bratislava, Slovakia
Tel.: (421) 263451828
Web Site: http://www.reisswolf.sk
Document Destruction Sevices
N.A.I.C.S.: 561499

REISSWOLF Suroeste S.L.L. (1)
Pol Ind El Carrascal Nave 34-5 Talavera la Real, 06140, Badajoz, Spain
Tel.: (34) 902121302
Web Site: http://www.reisswolf-so.com
Document Destruction Sevices
N.A.I.C.S.: 561499

REISSWOLF Turkey (1)
Merkez Pelitli Ayaz Sok No 27, 41455, Gebze, Kocaeli, Türkiye
Tel.: (90) 4445360
Web Site: http://www.reisswolf.com.tr
Document Destruction Sevices
N.A.I.C.S.: 561499

REISSWOLF d.o.o. (1)
Mosevicka 14, 71387, Podlugovi, Bosnia & Herzegovina
Tel.: (387) 33843400
Web Site: http://www.reisswolf.ba
Document Destruction Sevices

N.A.I.C.S.: 561499

REISSWOLF likvidace dokumentu a dat s.r.o. (1)
U Dyharny 1162, 278 01, Kralupy nad Vltavou, Czech Republic
Tel.: (420) 315722821
Web Site: http://www.reisswolf.cz
Document Destruction Sevices
N.A.I.C.S.: 561499

Reisswolf AG (1)
Kantonsstrasse 5, 6033, Buchrain, Switzerland
Tel.: (41) 4483862
Web Site: http://www.reisswolf.ch
Emp.: 35
Document Destruction Sevices
N.A.I.C.S.: 561499

Reisswolf Akten- u Datenvernichtung GmbH (1)
Reisswolf Strasse 1, 2100, Leobendorf, Austria
Tel.: (43) 2262682000
Web Site: http://www.reisswolf.at
Document Destruction Sevices
N.A.I.C.S.: 561499

Reisswolf Azerbaijan Living Data LLC (1)
Bayil Plaza 4th floor 29 G Abbasov Str, Sabayil Dist, AZ1003, Baku, Azerbaijan
Tel.: (994) 123103282
Data Protection Services
N.A.I.C.S.: 518210
Agateyyub Jafarov *(CEO)*

Reisswolf Bulgaria JSC (1)
10 Europe Blvd Bozhurishte Logistics Park, 2227, Bozhurishte, Bulgaria
Tel.: (359) 24682409
Web Site: http://www.reisswolf.bg
Document Destruction Services
N.A.I.C.S.: 561499
Ivaylo Yordanov *(CEO)*

Reisswolf Cyprus Ltd. (1)
6 Fokionos Industrial Zone, Aradippou, 7101, Larnaca, Cyprus
Tel.: (357) 24533933
Web Site: http://www.reisswolfcy.com
Data Protection Services
N.A.I.C.S.: 518210
Antoun Zoughaib *(Mgr-Bus Dev)*

Reisswolf Dokuman Yonetimi Hiz. A.S. (1)
Koseler Mahallesi 3 Cadde No 22/1, Dilovasi, 41455, Kocaeli, Turkiye
Tel.: (90) 2627281335
Web Site: http://www.reisswolf.com.tr
Data Protection Services
N.A.I.C.S.: 518210
Deniz Eraydin *(Exec Mgr)*

Reisswolf Kazakhstan LLP (1)
St Kazan 34 n p 1, Almaty, Kazakhstan
Tel.: (7) 7272293738
Web Site: http://www.reisswolf.kz
Data Storage & Management Services
N.A.I.C.S.: 518210
Ruslan Kaziyev *(Mgr-Warehouse)*

Reisswolf LLC (1)
Boicovaya Str 22, 107150, Moscow, Russia
Tel.: (7) 4956467051
Data Protection Services
N.A.I.C.S.: 518210

Reisswolf Lda. (1)
Rua dos Jasmins n 396, Batel Industrial Park, 2890-161, Alcochete, Portugal
Tel.: (351) 212348390
Web Site: http://www.reisswolf.pt
Data Management Services
N.A.I.C.S.: 518210
Miguel Santos *(CFO)*

Reisswolf Osterreich GmbH (1)
Reisswolf Strasse 1, 2100, Leobendorf, Austria
Tel.: (43) 2262682000
Web Site: http://www.reisswolf.at
Data Protection Services
N.A.I.C.S.: 518210

Reisswolf Polska Sp. z o.o. (1)
Ul Bardowskiego 4, 03 888, Warsaw, Poland
Tel.: (48) 225119900

Web Site: http://www.reisswolf.net.pl
Document Destruction Services
N.A.I.C.S.: 561499

Reisswolf Randstad I B.V. (1)
Spoorstraat 5, 1687 AE, Wognum, Netherlands
Tel.: (31) 229284577
Data Protection Services
N.A.I.C.S.: 518210
W. A. Horeman *(Mng Dir)*

Reisswolf Ukraine LLC (1)
Street Kruglouniversytetska 2/1b, Kiev, 01024, Ukraine
Tel.: (380) 443345969
Web Site: http://www.reisswolf.ua
Data Protection Services
N.A.I.C.S.: 518210

Reisswolf d.o.o. (1)
Vukomericka bb, 10410, Velika Gorica, Croatia
Tel.: (385) 16222201
Web Site: http://www.reisswolf.hr
Document Destruction Services
N.A.I.C.S.: 561499

SC REISSWOLF Romania SRL (1)
Drum Sabareni No 24-26 District 6, 60647, Bucharest, Romania
Tel.: (40) 214082242
Web Site: http://www.reisswolf.ro
Document Destruction Services
N.A.I.C.S.: 561499

Stena Recycling Sp. Z o.o (1)
Ul Grojecka 208, 02-390, Warsaw, Poland
Tel.: (48) 698000555
Web Site: http://www.stenarecycling.pl
Waste Management Services
N.A.I.C.S.: 562998
Lars Ibsen *(CEO)*

Unistock JSC (1)
Bullu iela 74, LV-1067, Riga, Latvia
Tel.: (371) 67403222
Data Protection Services
N.A.I.C.S.: 518210
Pavel Kurilov *(Mng Dir)*

REIT 1 LTD.

6 HaNechoshet Street, Ramat Hahayal, Tel Aviv, 6971070, Israel
Tel.: (972) 37686700
Web Site: https://www.reit1.co.il
Year Founded: 2006
RIT1—(TAE)
Rev.: $104,993,782
Assets: $2,254,805,601
Liabilities: $1,143,684,193
Net Worth: $1,111,121,408
Earnings: $97,742,781
Fiscal Year-end: 12/31/23
Other Activities Related to Real Estate
N.A.I.C.S.: 531390

REIT AZORIM HF LIVING LTD.

Arnia Street 32, Tel Aviv, Israel
Tel.: (972) 35632695
Web Site: https://www.living-il.co.il
Year Founded: 2019
AZRT—(TAE)
Rev.: $16,051,664
Assets: $895,460,685
Liabilities: $608,931,887
Net Worth: $286,528,798
Earnings: ($20,764,470)
Fiscal Year-end: 12/31/23
Lessors of Other Real Estate Property
N.A.I.C.S.: 531190

REIT-SYD EQUIPMENT LTD.

531 Buchanon Avenue, Dauphin, R7N 2J2, MB, Canada
Tel.: (204) 638-6443
Web Site: http://www.reit-sydequipment.com
Agricultural & Consumer Products Distr
N.A.I.C.S.: 493130
Kevin Bomak *(Mgr-Sls)*

INTERNATIONAL PUBLIC

REITANGRUPPEN AS
Gladengveien 2, Oslo, 661, Norway
Tel.: (47) 73891000 NO
Web Site: http://www.reitangruppen.no
Year Founded: 2001
Sales Range: $1-4.9 Billion
Emp.: 15,000
Holding Company
N.A.I.C.S.: 551112
Odd Reitan *(Chm & CEO)*

Subsidiaries:

REMA 1000 AS (1)
Gladengveien 2, Oslo, 0661, Norway (100%)
Tel.: (47) 24098500
Web Site: http://www.rema.no
Sales Range: $1-4.9 Billion
Emp.: 6,500
Holding Company; Franchise Discount Grocery Stores Operator
N.A.I.C.S.: 551112
Tom Kristeinsen *(Mng Dir)*

Subsidiary (Domestic):

REMA 1000 Norge AS (2)
Gladengvaean 2, 0661, Oslo, Norway (100%)
Tel.: (47) 24098500
Web Site: http://www.rema.no
Sales Range: $25-49.9 Million
Emp.: 50
Franchise Discount Grocery Stores Operator
N.A.I.C.S.: 455211
Ole Robert Reitan *(CEO)*

Reitan Convenience AS (1)
Gladengveien 2, 0603, Oslo, Norway (100%)
Tel.: (47) 95043188
Web Site: http://www.reitangruppen.no
Sales Range: $650-699.9 Million
Emp.: 150
Franchise Convenience Store Operator
N.A.I.C.S.: 551112
Magnus Reitan *(CEO & Head-Reitan Kapital)*

Subsidiary (Non-US):

Narvesen Baltija SIA (2)
Aiviekstes Iela 4, 1003, Riga, Latvia (100%)
Tel.: (371) 67074255
Web Site: http://www.narvesen.lv
Sales Range: $75-99.9 Million
Food & Newsstand Kiosk Operator
N.A.I.C.S.: 445298

R-kioski Oy (2)
Koivuvaarankuja 2, 01640, Helsinki, Finland
Tel.: (358) 9 85 281
Web Site: http://www.r-kioski.fi
Convenience Store Operator
N.A.I.C.S.: 445131

Rautakirja Estonia AS (2)
Poikmae 2, Tanassilma, 76406, Saku, Harju, Estonia
Tel.: (372) 6336080
Web Site: http://www.rautakirja.ee
Convenience Stores Operator; Magazine Distr
N.A.I.C.S.: 445131

Subsidiary (Domestic):

Reitan Convenience Norway AS (2)
Gladengveien 2, 0661, Oslo, Norway
Tel.: (47) 81500909
Web Site: http://www.narvesen.no
Sales Range: $1-4.9 Billion
Franchise Convenience Stores Operator
N.A.I.C.S.: 445131

Subsidiary (Domestic):

YX Energi Norge AS (3)
Lysaker Torg 35, PO Box 202, Skoyen, N-0213, Lysaker, Norway (100%)
Tel.: (47) 22124000
Web Site: http://www.unox.no
Gas Service Stations with Convenience Stores Operator
N.A.I.C.S.: 457110

AND PRIVATE COMPANIES

Subsidiary (Non-US):

Reitan Convenience Sweden AB (2)
Strandbergsgatan 61, PO Box 30185,
S-104 25, Stockholm, Sweden (100%)
Tel.: (46) 858749000
Web Site: http://www.pressbyran.se
Sales Range: $25-49.9 Million
Emp.: 100
Newsstands Operator
N.A.I.C.S.: 459210
Magnus Carlsson (Mng Dir)

Reitan Servicehandel Danmark AS
Buddingevej 195, DK-2860, Soborg, Denmark
Tel.: (45) 39478484
Web Site: http://www.7-eleven.dk
Sales Range: $50-74.9 Million
Franchise Convenience Stores Operator
N.A.I.C.S.: 445131
Jesper Ostergaard (Mng Dir)

Reitan Eiendom AS (1)
Lade Gaard, N-7040, Trondheim,
Norway (67%)
Tel.: (47) 7389 1060
Web Site: http://www.reitangruppen.no
Sales Range: $10-24.9 Million
Real Estate Acquisition & Development
N.A.I.C.S.: 531390

Uno-X Gruppen AS (1)
Lysaker Torg 35, PO Box 127, 1366, Lysaker, Norway
Tel.: (47) 22 12 40 00
Web Site: http://www.unox.no
Petroleum Product Distr
N.A.I.C.S.: 424720

REITEN & CO AS
Haakon VII's gt 1 4th Floor, 0161,
Oslo, Norway
Tel.: (47) 23 11 37 00 NO
Web Site: http://www.reitenco.com
Year Founded: 1992
Privater Equity Firm
N.A.I.C.S.: 523999
Narve Reiten (Founder & Partner)

Subsidiaries:

Competentia Holding AS (1)
Kanalsletta 8, PO Box 67, 4033, Stavanger, Norway (50.6%)
Tel.: (47) 51 53 67 10
Web Site: http://www.competentia.com
Sales Range: $150-199.9 Million
Holding Company
N.A.I.C.S.: 551112

Subsidiary (Domestic):

Competentia AS (2)
Forsuparken 2, 4033, Stavanger, Norway
Tel.: (47) 51 53 67 10
Web Site: http://www.competentia.com
Sales Range: $150-199.9 Million
Emp.: 400
Project Management, Engineering & Supervisory Services to Oil & Gas Industry
N.A.I.C.S.: 213112
John Smith (Chm)

Subsidiary (US):

Argonauta Energy Services LLC (3)
12012 Wickchester Ln Ste 130, Houston, TX 77079
Tel.: (281) 597-9200
Web Site: http://www.argonenergy.com
Sales Range: $1-9.9 Million
Engineering & Technical Consulting Services for Oil & Gas Industry
N.A.I.C.S.: 213112
Neal Jackson (Controller)

Subsidiary (Non-US):

Competentia Japan Corp. (3)
6F Sanno 2-1-2, Ota-ku, Tokyo, 143 0023, Japan
Tel.: (81) 3 6404 8023
Project Management, Engineering & Supervisory Services for Oil & Gas Industry
N.A.I.C.S.: 213112

Competentia Korea Ltd. (3)
2nd Floor 1023-5 Bangeo-Dong, Dong-Gu, Ulsan, Korea (South)
Tel.: (82) 10 2472 3448
Project Management, Engineering & Supervisory Services for Oil & Gas Industry
N.A.I.C.S.: 213112

Competentia Pty Ltd. (3)
Ground Floor 17 Ord Street, West Perth, 6005, WA, Australia
Tel.: (61) 8 9322 2289
Web Site: http://www.competentia.com
Emp.: 10
Project Management, Engineering & Supervisory Services for Oil & Gas Industry
N.A.I.C.S.: 213112

Competentia Singapore Pte Ltd. (3)
78 Shenton Way 19-01, Singapore, 079120, Singapore
Tel.: (65) 6323 2066
Web Site: http://www.competentia.com
Oil & Gas Industry Project Management, Engineering & Supervisory Services
N.A.I.C.S.: 213112

Competentia UK Limited (3)
17 Waterloo Place, St James, London, SW1Y 4AR, United Kingdom
Tel.: (44) 20 7036 8484
Web Site: http://www.competentia.com
Project Management, Engineering & Supervisory Services for Oil & Gas Industry
N.A.I.C.S.: 213112
Graham Robson (Mng Dir)

Webstep ASA (1)
Lilleakerveien 8, 0283, Oslo, Norway
Tel.: (47) 40003325
Web Site: http://www.webstep.com
Project Management Services
N.A.I.C.S.: 561110
Klaus-Anders Nysteen (Chm)

REITIR FASTEIGNAFELAG HF
Kringlunni 4-12, 103, Reykjavik, Iceland
Tel.: (354) 5759000
Web Site: https://www.reitir.is
REITIR—(ICE)
Rev.: $108,480,540
Assets: $1,388,632,773
Liabilities: $955,823,639
Net Worth: $432,809,134
Earnings: $53,884,820
Emp.: 21
Fiscal Year-end: 12/31/23
Real Estate Investment Services
N.A.I.C.S.: 525990
Gudjon Audunsson (CEO)

REITMANS (CANADA) LIMITED
250 Sauve West, Montreal, H3L 1Z2, QC, Canada
Tel.: (514) 384-1140 Ca
Web Site: http://www.reitmanscanadaltd.com
Year Founded: 1926
RET.A—(OTCIQ)
Rev.: $676,544,503
Assets: $361,220,076
Liabilities: $112,305,663
Net Worth: $248,914,413
Earnings: $4,958,542
Emp.: 3,200
Fiscal Year-end: 02/02/19
Women's Specialty Clothing Stores Owner & Operator
N.A.I.C.S.: 458110
Jeremy H. Reitman (Chm & CEO)

Subsidiaries:

Additionelle (1)
250 Sauve St W, H3L 1Z2, Montreal, QC, Canada
Tel.: (514) 384-1140
Web Site: http://www.1-plus.com
Sales Range: $25-49.9 Million
Emp.: 200
Plus-Sized Clothing
N.A.I.C.S.: 315990

Pennington's Additionelle Ltd. (1)
250 Sauve St W, Montreal, H3L 1Z2, QC, Canada
Tel.: (514) 384-1140
Sales Range: $250-299.9 Million
Emp.: 1,000
Provider of Retail & International Licensing Services
N.A.I.C.S.: 926150

RW & Co. (1)
250 Sauve Street West, Montreal, H3L 1Z2, QC, Canada (100%)
Tel.: (250) 381-2214
Web Site: https://www.rw-co.com
Sales Range: $25-49.9 Million
Emp.: 12
Men's Clothing Stores
N.A.I.C.S.: 458110
Sonia Simpson (Mgr)

Thyme Maternity (1)
250 Sauve St W, Montreal, H3L 1Z2, QC, Canada (100%)
Tel.: (514) 385-2694
Web Site: http://www.thymematernity.com
Maternity Clothing Retailer
N.A.I.C.S.: 458110
Gina Thomas (Project Mgr-Store Ops)

REJLERS AB
PO Box 30223, 104 25, Stockholm, Sweden
Tel.: (46) 771780000
Web Site: https://www.rejlers.com
Year Founded: 1942
REJL.B—(OMX)
Rev.: $290,818,976
Assets: $273,324,912
Liabilities: $132,176,016
Net Worth: $141,148,896
Earnings: $34,792,800
Emp.: 2,227
Fiscal Year-end: 12/31/20
Holding Company; Engineering & Technical Consulting Services
N.A.I.C.S.: 551112
Viktor Svensson (Pres & CEO)

Subsidiaries:

Delta-KN OY (1)
Friherrsvagen 2 B, 01650, Vantaa, Finland
Tel.: (358) 20 752 0700
Web Site: https://delta-kn.fi
Engineeering Services
N.A.I.C.S.: 541330

OmegaHoltan AS (1)
Ashaugveien 68, 3170, Sem, Norway
Tel.: (47) 33349999
Web Site: https://www.omegaholtan.no
Emp.: 40
Electrical Engineering Services
N.A.I.C.S.: 541330

Rejlers AS (1)
Kjoita 18, 4630, Kristiansand, Norway
Tel.: (47) 91714600
Web Site: https://www.rejlers.no
Technical Consulting Services
N.A.I.C.S.: 541690

Rejlers Elsikkerhet AS (1)
DEG 16 Dronning Eufemias Gate 16, 0191, Oslo, Norway
Tel.: (47) 95823000
Engineering Consulting Services
N.A.I.C.S.: 541330

Rejlers Embriq AS (1)
DEG 16 Dronning Eufemias gate 16, 0191, Oslo, Norway
Tel.: (47) 2 193 9999
Web Site: https://rejlers.no
Information Technology Services
N.A.I.C.S.: 541512
Thomas Pettersen (Mng Dir)

Rejlers Ingenjoer AB (1)
Agatan 39, 582 22, Linkoping, Sweden
Tel.: (46) 13 25 08 00
Technology Consulting Services
N.A.I.C.S.: 541690
Lars-Ake Akerlund (Area Mgr-Bus-Electricity & Automation)

Rejlers Oy (1)
Graanintie 5, 50190, Mikkeli, Finland
Tel.: (358) 207520700
Web Site: https://www.rejlers.fi
Sales Range: $25-49.9 Million
Technical Consulting Services
N.A.I.C.S.: 541690
Mikko Vaahersalo (CEO)

REKA INDUSTRIAL PLC
Kankurinkatu 4-6, 05800, Hyvinkaa, Finland
Tel.: (358) 207209190
NEO1V—(HEL)
Rev.: $218,929,419
Assets: $93,993,093
Liabilities: $71,059,788
Net Worth: $22,933,305
Earnings: $96,891,863
Emp.: 290
Fiscal Year-end: 12/31/22
Investment Services
N.A.I.C.S.: 523999
Markku E. Rentto (Chm)

Subsidiaries:

Reka Kabel A/S (1)
Skolegade 61, PO Box 8, 7400, Herning, Denmark
Tel.: (45) 20750085
Web Site: https://www.rekakabel.dk
Nordic Cable Mfr
N.A.I.C.S.: 335929

Reka Kabel AB (1)
Jarnvagsgatan 36, 13154, Nacka, Sweden
Tel.: (46) 738414026
Web Site: https://www.rekakabel.se
Nordic Cable Mfr
N.A.I.C.S.: 335929

Reka Kabel AS (1)
Edv Griegs vei 1, 1410, Kolbotn, Norway
Tel.: (47) 66808866
Web Site: https://www.rekakabel.no
Nordic Cable Mfr
N.A.I.C.S.: 335929

REKAB ENTREPRENAD AB
Kardangatan 6, 903 03, Umea, Sweden
Tel.: (46) 90128750
Web Site: http://www.rekab.se
Sales Range: $25-49.9 Million
Emp.: 150
Engineeering Services
N.A.I.C.S.: 541330
Anton Johansson (CEO)

REKAH PHARMACEUTICAL INDUSTRY LTD.
30 Hamelach Street, Holon, 5881904, Israel
Tel.: (972) 35581233
Web Site: https://www.rekah.co.il
Year Founded: 1941
REKA—(TAE)
Rev.: $88,869,456
Assets: $133,919,324
Liabilities: $90,934,106
Net Worth: $42,985,218
Earnings: ($1,909,656)
Emp.: 495
Fiscal Year-end: 12/31/23
Pharmaceutical Preparation Manufacturing
N.A.I.C.S.: 325412

REKATECH CAPITAL BERHAD
D5-U6-3 Publika Jalan Dutamas 1, Solaris Dutamas, 50480, Kuala Lumpur, Malaysia
Tel.: (60) 364119666 MY
Web Site: https://rekatech.com.my
Year Founded: 1994
REKATECH—(KLS)
Rev.: $955,213
Assets: $11,305,535
Liabilities: $200,080
Net Worth: $11,105,454
Earnings: ($3,127,375)

REKATECH CAPITAL BERHAD

Rekatech Capital Berhad—(Continued)
Fiscal Year-end: 06/30/23
Investment Holding Services
N.A.I.C.S.: 551112
Chee Fong Liang *(Chm)*

REKLAIM LTD.
135 Madison Avenue 5th Floor, Toronto, M5R 2S3, ON, Canada
Tel.: (647) 360-3691
Web Site: https://www.killi.io
Year Founded: 2018
MYID—(OTCIQ)
Rev.: $325,763
Assets: $1,678,689
Liabilities: $708,476
Net Worth: $970,213
Earnings: ($3,641,337)
Fiscal Year-end: 12/31/20
Software Development Services
N.A.I.C.S.: 541511
Neil Sweeney *(Chm & CEO)*

REKO INTERNATIONAL GROUP INC.
469 Silver Creek Industrial Drive, Lakeshore, N8N 4W2, ON, Canada
Tel.: (519) 727-3287
Web Site: https://www.rekointl.com
Year Founded: 1976
0VL—(DEU)
Rev.: $32,368,701
Assets: $40,908,096
Liabilities: $10,656,516
Net Worth: $30,251,580
Earnings: ($2,846,709)
Fiscal Year-end: 07/31/24
Plastic Injection Mold & Metal Cutting Product Mfr
N.A.I.C.S.: 333517
Diane Reko *(CEO)*

Subsidiaries:

Concorde Machine Tool (1)
481 Silver Creek Industrial Dr, Tecumseh, NAH4W2, ON, Canada (100%)
Tel.: (519) 727-5100
Web Site: http://www.rekointl.com
Sales Range: $25-49.9 Million
Emp.: 50
Mfr of Machine Tools
N.A.I.C.S.: 333517

Reko Automation Group Inc. (1)
455 Silver Creek Industrial Drive, Windsor, N8N 4W2, ON, Canada
Tel.: (519) 727-2155
Web Site: https://rekoautomation.com
Motor Vehicle Mfr
N.A.I.C.S.: 336991

Reko Machine Builders Inc. (1)
469 Silver Creek Drive, Maidstone, Windsor, N8N 4W2, ON, Canada
Mfr of Metal Machinery
N.A.I.C.S.: 333519

Reko Manufacturing Group Inc. (1)
469 Silver Creek Industrial Drive, Lakeshore, N8N 4W2, ON, Canada (100%)
Tel.: (519) 737-3287
Web Site: http://www.rekointl.com
Sales Range: $50-74.9 Million
Emp.: 150
Industrial Tools Mfr
N.A.I.C.S.: 333517

REKREATURS A.D.
Veljka Mladenovica Bb, 78000, Banja Luka, Bosnia & Herzegovina
Tel.: (387) 51305032
REKT-R-A—(BANJ)
Sales Range: Less than $1 Million
Emp.: 16
Restaurant Management Services
N.A.I.C.S.: 722511
Darko Stamenic *(Chm)*

REKVINA LABORATORIES LIMITED
328 Paradise Complex Sayajigunj, Vadodara, 390 005, Gujarat, India
Tel.: (91) 265 2362966
Web Site: http://www.rekvinalaboratories.com
Rev.: $3,003
Assets: $124,691
Liabilities: $61,564
Net Worth: $63,127
Earnings: ($12,417)
Fiscal Year-end: 03/31/18
Laboratory Testing Services
N.A.I.C.S.: 541380
Mukesh J. Shah *(Chm & Mng Dir)*

RELAIS DE CHAMPAGNE SA
Rue 9 Turgot ZAC Champ du Roy, 02000, Laon, Aisne, France
Tel.: (33) 323271190
Web Site: http://www.relaisdechampagne.fr
Automotive Repair & Distribution
N.A.I.C.S.: 441110

RELAIS GROUP PLC
Mannerheimintie 105, 00280, Helsinki, Finland
Tel.: (358) 105085800
Web Site: https://www.relais.fi
RELAIS—(HEL)
Rev.: $281,332,830
Assets: $333,674,725
Liabilities: $221,454,781
Net Worth: $112,219,944
Earnings: $10,873,084
Emp.: 1,009
Fiscal Year-end: 12/31/22
Vehicle Electrical Equipment Distr
N.A.I.C.S.: 423860

RELAIS VERT
621 Allee Bellecour, 84200, Carpentras, France
Tel.: (33) 490676142
Web Site: http://www.relais-vert.com
Sales Range: $25-49.9 Million
Emp.: 70
Fresh Fruits & Vegetables
N.A.I.C.S.: 424480
Jean-Louis Ginart *(Pres)*

RELAKS AD
Jovana Ducica 22, 78000, Banja Luka, Bosnia & Herzegovina
Tel.: (387) 51213011
Web Site: http://www.relaksad.com
Year Founded: 1947
RLKS-R-A—(BANJ)
Rev.: $157,285
Assets: $1,623,874
Liabilities: $364,269
Net Worth: $1,259,605
Earnings: ($129,242)
Emp.: 42
Fiscal Year-end: 12/31/12
Beauty Treatment & Hairdressing Services
N.A.I.C.S.: 812112
Ljubomir Cubic *(Chm-Mgmt Bd)*

RELATECH S.P.A.
Viale Ercole Marelli 165, Sesto San Giovanni, 20099, Milan, Italy
Tel.: (39) 022404909
Web Site: https://www.iubenda.com
RLT—(ITA)
Rev.: $100,478,897
Assets: $111,950,465
Liabilities: $71,722,631
Net Worth: $40,227,834
Earnings: $3,872,119
Emp.: 542
Fiscal Year-end: 12/31/23
Software Development Services
N.A.I.C.S.: 541511
Pasquale Lambardi *(Founder, Pres & CEO)*

Subsidiaries:

Dialog Sistemi S.R.L. (1)
Via Cosseria 1, 20136, Milan, Italy (100%)
Tel.: (39) 0258310579
Web Site: https://dialog.it
Business Consulting Services
N.A.I.C.S.: 541611

Efa Automazione S.p.A. (1)
Via Isola Guarnieri 13, 20063, Cernusco sul Naviglio, MI, Italy (100%)
Tel.: (39) 0292113180
Web Site: https://www.efa.it
Industrial Equipment Mfr
N.A.I.C.S.: 333415

Venticento S.R.L. (1)
Via L Ariosto 21, 20091, Bresso, MI, Italy
Tel.: (39) 0284980050
Web Site: https://www.venticento.com
Information Technology Consulting Services
N.A.I.C.S.: 541611

RELAXO FOOTWEARS LIMITED
Aggarwal City Square Plot No 10 Manglam Place, District Centre Sector-3, Delhi, 110085, India
Tel.: (91) 1146800600
Web Site: https://www.relaxofootwear.com
530517—(BOM)
Rev.: $335,871,950
Assets: $299,117,559
Liabilities: $76,702,836
Net Worth: $222,414,723
Earnings: $18,520,472
Emp.: 6,736
Fiscal Year-end: 03/31/23
Footwear Mfr
N.A.I.C.S.: 316210
Ramesh Kumar Dua *(Mng Dir)*

RELAYR GMBH
Rotwandstrasse 18, 82049, Pullach, Germany
Tel.: (49) 6197 040020
Web Site: http://www.relayr.io
Custom Computer Programming Services
N.A.I.C.S.: 541511
Josef Brunner *(CEO)*

RELESYS A/S
Orient Plads 1 2nd floor, Nordhavn, 2150, Copenhagen, Denmark
Tel.: (45) 31320942
Web Site: https://www.relesys.net
Year Founded: 2014
NA0—(DEU)
Rev.: $6,334,664
Assets: $7,204,561
Liabilities: $2,727,505
Net Worth: $4,477,057
Earnings: ($3,763,718)
Emp.: 79
Fiscal Year-end: 12/31/22
Software Development Services
N.A.I.C.S.: 541511
Jens Ole Lebeck *(COO)*

RELEVIUM TECHNOLOGIES, INC.
1000 Sherbrooke Street West Suite 2700, Montreal, H3A 3G4, QC, Canada
Tel.: (514) 824-8559
Web Site: https://www.releviumtechnology.com
Year Founded: 2012
RLV—(TSXV)
Rev.: $667,919
Assets: $554,765
Liabilities: $4,139,806
Net Worth: ($3,585,041)
Earnings: ($3,924,522)
Fiscal Year-end: 06/30/24
Ophthalmic Goods Mfr

INTERNATIONAL PUBLIC

N.A.I.C.S.: 339115
Andre Godin *(Chm)*

RELIA, INC.
Odaku Southern Tower 16F 2-2-1 Yoyogi Shibuya-ku, Tokyo, 151-8583, Japan
Tel.: (81) 353517200
Web Site: http://www.relia-group.com
4708—(TKS)
Rev.: $1,167,591,920
Assets: $648,443,840
Liabilities: $173,523,680
Net Worth: $474,920,160
Earnings: $41,633,680
Emp.: 13,859
Fiscal Year-end: 03/31/23
Telemarketing Services
N.A.I.C.S.: 561422
Norihiko Koshida *(Sr Mng Officer)*

Subsidiaries:

Benecom Inc. (1)
2-5-5 Yoyogi, Shibuya-ku, Tokyo, 151-0053, Japan
Tel.: (81) 3 3370 7061
Sales Range: $25-49.9 Million
Emp.: 5
Business Consulting Services
N.A.I.C.S.: 541611

Business Plus Inc. (1)
1-40 Miyamachi KDX Fuchu Building 11F, Fuchu, 183-0023, Tokyo, Japan
Tel.: (81) 42 336 3100
Web Site: https://www.biz-plus.jp
Human Rights Organization Services
N.A.I.C.S.: 813311

IVisit Corp. (1)
14th floor Rise Arena Building 4-5-2 Higashiikebukuro, Toshima-ku, Tokyo, 170-0013, Japan
Tel.: (81) 366279977
Web Site: https://www.ivisit.co.jp
Emp.: 1,516
Human Resource Recruitment Services
N.A.I.C.S.: 541612

Inspiro Relia, Inc. (1)
6th Floor L V Locsin Building Ayala Avenue cor Makati Avenue, Makati, Philippines
Tel.: (63) 2 884 6222
Consulting Services
N.A.I.C.S.: 541612

Maxcom Inc. (1)
2-2-1 Yoyogi Odakyu Southern Tower, Shibuya-ku, Tokyo, 151-8583, Japan
Tel.: (81) 368705800
Web Site: http://www.max-com.co.jp
Emp.: 90
Business Consulting Services
N.A.I.C.S.: 541611

Relia Digital Inc. (1)
Link Square Shinjuku 6F 5-27-5, Sendagaya Shibuya-ku, Tokyo, 151-0051, Japan
Tel.: (81) 36 859 4038
Web Site: https://www.relia-digital.com
Management Consulting Services
N.A.I.C.S.: 541618

Relia Vietnam Joint Stock Company (1)
10F Detech Tower II 107 Nguyen Phong Sac Str, Cau Giay Dist, Hanoi, Vietnam
Tel.: (84) 247 308 6668
Web Site: https://relia-vietnam.com.vn
Data Processing Services
N.A.I.C.S.: 518210

Witellas Inc. (1)
13th Floor Akihabara Center Place Building 1 Kanda Aioicho, Chiyoda-ku, Tokyo, 101-0029, Japan
Tel.: (81) 36 837 1600
Web Site: https://www.witellas.co.jp
Telemarketing Services
N.A.I.C.S.: 561422

RELIABLE DATA SERVICES LTD.
C 69 Sector 2, Noida, 201301, Uttar Pradesh, India

Tel.: (91) 1204089177
Web Site: https://www.rdspl.com
Year Founded: 2001
RELIABLE—(NSE)
Rev.: $8,874,648
Assets: $13,730,640
Liabilities: $7,242,827
Net Worth: $6,487,812
Earnings: $571,512
Fiscal Year-end: 03/31/23
Information Technology Services
N.A.I.C.S.: 541511
Sanjay Pathak *(Chm & Mng Dir)*

Subsidiaries:

Ascent Keyboardlabs Tech Pvt. Ltd. (1)
Block- C Office Building No 69 Gautam-Buddh Nagar, Noida, 201301, Uttar Pradesh, India
Tel.: (91) 1204089104
Web Site:
 https://www.ascentkeyboardlabs.com
Software Development Services
N.A.I.C.S.: 541511

Authentic Healthcare Services Pvt. Ltd. (1)
C-69 Sector-2 Gautam Buddh Nagar, Noida, 201301, Uttar Pradesh, India
Tel.: (91) 1204089104
Web Site: https://www.ahcspl.com
Health Claim Investigation Services
N.A.I.C.S.: 561611

Kandarp Digi Smart BPO Limited (1)
C- 69 C Block Sector 2, Noida, 201301, Uttar Pradesh, India
Tel.: (91) 1204089107
Web Site: https://www.kdsbpo.com
Emp.: 500
Business Process Services
N.A.I.C.S.: 561499

RELIABLE PARTS LTD.
85 North Bend Street, Coquitlam, V3K 6N1, BC, Canada
Tel.: (604) 941-9884
Web Site: http://www.reliableparts.ca
Year Founded: 1933
Rev.: $44,731,305
Emp.: 160
Appliance Parts Distr
N.A.I.C.S.: 449210
Doug Loughran *(Pres)*

RELIABLE VENTURES INDIA LIMITED
A 6 Indore Road Koh-e-Fiza, Bhopal, 462001, Madhya Pradesh, India
Tel.: (91) 7554266601
Year Founded: 1992
532124—(BOM)
Rev.: $2,210,803
Assets: $47,493,855
Liabilities: $43,640,273
Net Worth: $3,853,582
Earnings: $256,076
Emp.: 172
Fiscal Year-end: 03/31/22
Home Management Services
N.A.I.C.S.: 721110
Sikandar Hafiz Khan *(Chm & Mng Dir)*

RELIANCE - ADA GROUP LIMITED
Reliance Centre 19 Walchend Hirachend Marg, Ballard Estate, Mumbai, 400001, India
Tel.: (91) 2230327000
Web Site:
 http://www.relianceadagroup.com
Year Founded: 1999
Sales Range: $25-49.9 Billion
Emp.: 25,000
Holding Company
N.A.I.C.S.: 551112
Amitabh Jhunjhunwala *(Grp Mng Dir)*

Subsidiaries:

Alok Industries Limited (1)
Tower B 2nd & 3rd Floor Peninsula Business Park, Ganpatrao Kadam Marg Lower Parel, Mumbai, 400 013, Maharashtra, India
Tel.: (91) 912261787000
Web Site: https://www.alokind.com
Textile Mfr
N.A.I.C.S.: 314999
Ashok B. Jiwrajka *(Exec Dir)*

Subsidiary (Domestic):

Alok H&A Ltd. (2)
Ashford Center Lower Parel, Mumbai, 400 013, India
Tel.: (91) 22 24997 000
Textile Products Retailer
N.A.I.C.S.: 449129

Subsidiary (Non-US):

Grabal Alok (UK) Ltd. (2)
Unit 1 Plot C1 Central Boulevard, Blythe Valley Business Park, Solihull, B90 8AH, United Kingdom
Tel.: (44) 121 746 7000
Web Site: http://www.storetwentyone.co.uk
Apparel & Accessories Retailer
N.A.I.C.S.: 458110

Subsidiary (Domestic):

Grabal Alok Impex Limited (2)
Peninsula Towers Peninsula Corporate Park Ganpatrao Kadam Marg, Lower Parel, 400013, Mumbai, Maharashtra, India **(100%)**
Tel.: (91) 2224996200
Web Site: http://www.grabalalok.com
Sales Range: $400-449.9 Million
Emp.: 1,107
Embroidery Products Mfr
N.A.I.C.S.: 339930
Surendra B. Jiwrajka *(Mng Dir)*

Subsidiary (Domestic):

Grabal Alok International Limited (3)
Peninsula Corporate Park Ganpatrao Kadam Marg, Lower Parel, Mumbai, 400013, Maharashtra, India
Tel.: (91) 2224996200
Web Site: http://www.alokind.com
Sales Range: $125-149.9 Million
Emp.: 500
Apparel Mfr & Whslr
N.A.I.C.S.: 424350

Subsidiary (Non-US):

Mileta a.s. (2)
Husova 734, 508 01, Horice, Czech Republic
Tel.: (420) 493654400
Web Site: http://www.mileta.cz
Sales Range: $100-124.9 Million
Emp.: 350
Shirt Fabrics Mfr
N.A.I.C.S.: 313210
Otakar Petracek *(Chm)*

IM Global, LLC (1)
8201 Beverly Blvd 5th Fl, Los Angeles, CA 90048
Tel.: (310) 777-3590
Web Site: http://www.imglobalfilm.com
Motion Picture Distribution Services
N.A.I.C.S.: 512120
Stuart Ford *(Founder & CEO)*

Quant Securities Private Limited (1)
Office 612 To 617 6th Floor Maker Chamber 4 Nariman Point, Mumbai, 400021, India
Tel.: (91) 22408801
Securities Brokerage Services
N.A.I.C.S.: 523150

Reliance Capital Limited (1)
Kamala Mills Compound Trade World B Wing 7th Floor, Lower Parel, Mumbai, India **(54.14%)**
Tel.: (91) 2241584000
Web Site: https://www.reliancecapital.co.in
Financial Services
N.A.I.C.S.: 523999
Anil D. Ambani *(Chm)*

Subsidiary (Domestic):

Reliance Capital Trustee Co. Limited (2)
11th Floor & 12th Floor Tower 1 Jupiter Mills Compound 841 Senapati, Bapat Marg Elphinstone Road, Mumbai, 400013, India
Tel.: (91) 22 3099 4600
Financial Investment Services
N.A.I.C.S.: 523999

Reliance Commodities Limited (2)
11th Floor R-Tech Park Nirlon Compound Western Express Highway, Mumbai, 400063, Maharashtra, India
Tel.: (91) 22 33201212
Web Site:
 http://www.reliancecommodities.co.in
Commodity Exchange Services
N.A.I.C.S.: 523210
Ashutosh Mishra *(Head-Bus)*

Reliance Composite Insurance Broking Limited (2)
Rahul Complex Above Axis Bank O P Jindal Road, Jagatpur, Raigarh, 496001, Chhattisgarh, India
Tel.: (91) 9203900801
General Insurance Services
N.A.I.C.S.: 524210

Reliance Equity Advisors (India) Limited (2)
Level 11 Tower I One Indiabulls Center 841 Senapati Bapat Marg, Elphinstone Road, Mumbai, 400013, India
Tel.: (91) 22 3095 7200
Emp.: 12
Financial Investment Services
N.A.I.C.S.: 523999
Ramesh Venkat *(CEO)*

Reliance General Insurance Company Limited (2)
C- 42 Pawane T T C Industrial Area MIDC, Turbhe, Navi Mumbai, Maharashtra, India
Tel.: (91) 22 30284278
Web Site: http://www.reliancegeneral.co.in
Emp.: 12
General Insurance Services
N.A.I.C.S.: 524210
Rajendra P. Chitale *(Chm)*

Reliance Home Finance Limited (2)
3rd Floor 570 Rectifier House Naigaum Cross Road Wadala, Mumbai, 400 031, India
Tel.: (91) 22 0127585
Web Site:
 http://www.reliancehomefinance.com
Home Loan Services
N.A.I.C.S.: 522390
Aakash Mishra *(Mgr-Sls)*

Division (Domestic):

Reliance Home Finance Limited - Reliance Property Division (3)
11th Floor The Ruby Plot no 29 Ruby Mills Compound Senapati Bapat Marg, Dadar W, Mumbai, 400028, India
Tel.: (91) 22 30108200
Web Site:
 http://www.reliancepropertysolutions.co.in
Real Estate Management Services
N.A.I.C.S.: 531390

Subsidiary (Domestic):

Reliance Money Express Limited (2)
Plot No 27 to 30 MCD No 1001 First Floor Faiz Road Karol Bagh, New Delhi, 110005, India
Tel.: (91) 11 2875 8862
Web Site:
 http://www.reliancemoneyexpress.com
Money Transfer Agency
N.A.I.C.S.: 523999

Reliance Money Precious Metals Private Limited (2)
7th Floor B Wing Trade World Kamala Mills Compound S B Marg, Lower Parel, Mumbai, 400 013, Maharashtra, India
Tel.: (91) 22 33201212
Web Site: http://www.reliancemgp.com
Financial Investment Services
N.A.I.C.S.: 523999

Joint Venture (Domestic):

Reliance Nippon Life Insurance Company Limited (2)
H Block 1st Floor Dhirubhai Ambani Knowledge City, Goregaon East, Mumbai, 400710, India
Tel.: (91) 2230007000
Web Site: http://www.reliancenipponlife.com
Life Insurance Products & Services
N.A.I.C.S.: 524113
Srinivasan Iyengar *(COO)*

Subsidiary (Domestic):

Reliance Securities Limited (2)
Lewis Road, Bhubaneswar, 751014, India
Tel.: (91) 674 3200194
Securities Brokerage Services
N.A.I.C.S.: 523150

Reliance Wealth Management Limited (2)
570 Rectifier House Naigaum Cross Road Next to Royal Industrial Estate, Wadala, Mumbai, 400031, India
Tel.: (91) 22 3216 3061
Web Site: http://www.reliancewealth.in
Financial Investment Services
N.A.I.C.S.: 523999
Amrita Farmahan *(Head-Country)*

Reliance Communications Limited (1)
H Block 1st Floor Dhirubhai Ambani Knowledge City, Navi Mumbai, 400 710, India
Tel.: (91) 2230386286
Web Site: https://www.rcom.co.in
Rev.: $106,333,500
Assets: $6,528,249,000
Liabilities: $13,846,287,000
Net Worth: ($7,318,038,000)
Earnings: ($764,536,500)
Emp.: 614
Fiscal Year-end: 03/31/2021
Telecommunication Servicesb
N.A.I.C.S.: 517112
Vishwanath Devaraja Rao *(CFO)*

Subsidiary (Non-US):

Reliance Communications (Australia) Pty Limited (2)
Suite 102 Level 1 201 Elizabeth Street, Sydney, 2000, NSW, Australia
Tel.: (61) 2 8272 5900
Telecommunication Servicesb
N.A.I.C.S.: 517112

Subsidiary (US):

Reliance Communications Inc. (2)
600 3rd Ave Fl 7, New York, NY 10016
Tel.: (212) 319-2997
Telecommunication Servicesb
N.A.I.C.S.: 517112

Reliance Communications International Inc. (2)
570 Lexington Ave 38th Fl, New York, NY 10022
Tel.: (212) 319-3755
Telecommunication Servicesb
N.A.I.C.S.: 517112

Subsidiary (Non-US):

Reliance Globalcom (UK) Limited (2)
Units 5 & 6 Riverbank Wa, Brentford, TW8 9RE, United Kingdom
Tel.: (44) 2082820066
Sales Range: $50-74.9 Million
Emp.: 80
Managed Network & Application Delivery Services
N.A.I.C.S.: 517810
Robert Schellman *(CTO)*

Branch (Non-US):

Reliance Globalcom - Belgium (3)
Pegasuslaan 5, 1831, Dilbeek, Belgium
Tel.: (32) 27092036
Sales Range: $25-49.9 Million
Emp.: 1
Virtual Network Services
N.A.I.C.S.: 517810
Dereil Holphuis *(Mng Dir)*

RELIANCE - ADA GROUP LIMITED

Reliance - ADA Group Limited—(Continued)

Reliance Globalcom - France (3)
8ave de l'Arche Courbevoie, 92088, Paris, Cedex, France
Tel.: (33) 146965400
Web Site: http://www.relianceglobalcom.fr
Sales Range: $25-49.9 Million
Emp.: 65
Virtual Network Services
N.A.I.C.S.: 517810
Eric Havette (Gen Mgr-Southern Europe)

Reliance Globalcom - Italy (3)
Torre Tonda Pzza Don Mapelli 1, Sesto San Giovanni, 20099, Milan, Italy
Tel.: (39) 022412191
Web Site: http://www.relianceglobalcom.it
Sales Range: $25-49.9 Million
Emp.: 10
Virtual Network Services
N.A.I.C.S.: 517810

Reliance Globalcom - Poland (3)
Ul Walicow 11, 00-851, Warsaw, Poland
Tel.: (48) 225839505
Virtual Network Services
N.A.I.C.S.: 517810

Subsidiary (US):

Reliance Globalcom Services, Inc.
114 Sansome St Fl 11, San Francisco, CA 94104
Tel.: (415) 901-2000
Web Site: http://www.relianceglobalcom.com
Sales Range: $75-99.9 Million
Managed Network & Application Delivery Services
N.A.I.C.S.: 517810
Kamran Sistanizadeh (CTO)

Subsidiary (Domestic):

Reliance Vanco Group Limited (3)
Units 1 & 2 Great West Plaza, Riverbank Way, Brentford, TW8 9RE, Mddx, United Kingdom
Tel.: (44) 2086361700
Sales Range: $25-49.9 Million
Managed Network & Application Delivery Services
N.A.I.C.S.: 517810
Jan Huizeling (CIO)

Subsidiary (Non-US):

Reliance Globalcom B.V. (2)
Kruisweg 829 A, 2132 NG, Hoofddorp, Netherlands
Tel.: (31) 20 316 5250
Telecommunication Servicesb
N.A.I.C.S.: 517112

Vanco (Asia Pacific) Pte. Ltd. (2)
SGX Centre 2 4 Shenton Way 07-05/06, 068807, Singapore, Singapore
Tel.: (65) 62811181
Telecommunication Servicesb
N.A.I.C.S.: 517112

Vanco GmbH (2)
Triforum Haus A1 Frankfurter Strasse 233, 63263, Neu-Isenburg, Germany
Tel.: (49) 6102 785555
Telecommunication Servicesb
N.A.I.C.S.: 517112
Anja Ziegler (Mgr-Mktg)

Vanco International Ltd (2)
5-6 Riverbank Way, Brentford, TW8 9RE, Middlesex, United Kingdom
Tel.: (44) 20 8636 1700
Telecommunication Servicesb
N.A.I.C.S.: 517112

Vanco Japan KK (2)
Sawada Kojimachi Bldg 5F 1-10 Kojimachi, Chiyoda-ku, Tokyo, Japan
Tel.: (81) 3 5213 9254
Telecommunication Servicesb
N.A.I.C.S.: 517112

Vanco NV (2)
Weide 2A, 9255, Buggenhout, Belgium
Tel.: (32) 52 336070
Web Site: http://www.vancov.be
Building Renovation Services
N.A.I.C.S.: 236118

Vanco South America Ltda (2)
Avenida Paulista 2300 andar Pilotis, Cerqueira Cesar, 01310-300, Sao Paulo, Brazil
Tel.: (55) 11 6847 4700
Telecommunication Servicesb
N.A.I.C.S.: 517112

Vanco Sweden AB (2)
Tallkrogsplan 93, Enskede, Stockholm, 122 60, Sweden
Tel.: (46) 84480217
Telecommunication Servicesb
N.A.I.C.S.: 517112

Reliance Entertainment Pvt. Ltd. (1)
5th floor 49/50 Maruti Chambers Next to Fun Republic Cinemas, Veera Desai Extn Road Off New Link Road Andheri West, Mumbai, 400053, India
Tel.: (91) 22 3066 4777
Web Site: http://www.relianceentertainment.net
Motion Picture Production Services
N.A.I.C.S.: 512110
Amit Khanduja (CEO-Games)

Reliance Industries Limited (1)
Maker Chambers - IV Nariman Point, Mumbai, 400 021, India
Tel.: (91) 2235555000
Web Site: https://www.ril.com
Rev.: $68,612,134,500
Assets: $180,345,438,000
Liabilities: $71,222,970,000
Net Worth: $109,122,468,000
Earnings: $7,335,373,500
Emp.: 236,334
Fiscal Year-end: 03/31/2021
Oil & Gas Distribution Services
N.A.I.C.S.: 237120
Mukesh D. Ambani (Chm & Mng Dir)

Subsidiary (Non-US):

BP Chemicals Malaysia Sdn. Bhd. (2)
Lot 116 Gebeng Industrial Estate, Balok, Kuantan, 26080, Pahang, Malaysia
Tel.: (60) 95825500
Sales Range: $75-99.9 Million
Emp.: 250
Purified Telepthalic Acid Mfr & Distr
N.A.I.C.S.: 325180
Nemade Baeskar (COO)

Subsidiary (Domestic):

Network 18 Media & Investments Limited (2)
First Floor Empire Complex 414 Senapati Bapat Marg Lower Parel, Mumbai, 400 013, Maharashtra, India (78.06%)
Tel.: (91) 2228069097
Web Site: https://www.nw18.com
Rev.: $866,118,400
Assets: $1,206,221,800
Liabilities: $755,703,200
Net Worth: $450,518,600
Earnings: $7,859,600
Emp.: 699
Fiscal Year-end: 03/31/2020
Media & Entertainment Businesses
N.A.I.C.S.: 516120
Kshipra Jatana (Gen Counsel-Grp)

Subsidiary (Domestic):

Colosceum Media Private Limited (3)
Dhantak Plaza Makhwana Road Marol, Andheri East, Mumbai, 400 059, Maharashtra, India
Tel.: (91) 22 6729 8805
Web Site: http://www.colosceum.com
Television Broadcasting Services
N.A.I.C.S.: 516120
Girish Balan (Asst VP-Production & Ops)

E-18 Limited (3)
Unit No 401-B 4th Floor Turf Estate Shakti Mills Lane Off, Dr E Moses Road Mahalaxmi, Mumbai, 400 011, India
Tel.: (91) 22 6629 1818
Web Site: http://www.e18online.com
Television Broadcasting Services
N.A.I.C.S.: 516120
Navneeth Mohan (COO)

Affiliate (Domestic):

NW18 HSN Holdings Plc (3)
First Floor Empire Complex 414 Senapati Bapat Marg, Lower Parel, Mumbai, 400013, Maharashtra, India
Tel.: (91) 22 4001 9000
Web Site: http://www.nw18.com
Rev.: $303,650,288
Assets: $1,168,412,848
Liabilities: $636,039,896
Net Worth: $532,372,952
Earnings: ($27,149,088)
Emp.: 618
Fiscal Year-end: 03/31/2018
Holding Company; Internet & Television Shopping Services
N.A.I.C.S.: 551112
Adil Zainulbhai (Chm)

Subsidiary (Domestic):

TV18 Broadcast Limited (3)
First Floor Empire Complex 414 Senapati Bapat Marg Lower Parel, Mumbai, 400013, Maharashtra, India (51.17%)
Tel.: (91) 2240019000
Web Site: https://www.nw18.com
Rev.: $622,412,700
Assets: $1,122,323,475
Liabilities: $391,438,320
Net Worth: $730,885,155
Earnings: $101,789,415
Emp.: 3,891
Fiscal Year-end: 03/31/2021
Television Broadcasting Services
N.A.I.C.S.: 516120
Adil Zainulbhai (Chm)

Subsidiary (US):

Radisys Corporation (2)
5435 NE Dawson Creek Dr, Hillsboro, OR 97124
Tel.: (503) 615-1100
Web Site: http://www.radisys.com
Rev.: $133,768,000
Assets: $66,029,000
Liabilities: $59,479,000
Net Worth: $6,550,000
Earnings: ($52,604,000)
Emp.: 647
Fiscal Year-end: 12/31/2017
Embedded Computer Systems Mfr
N.A.I.C.S.: 334118
Brian J. Bronson (Pres & CEO)

Subsidiary (Non-US):

Continuous Computing India Private Limited (3)
6th Floor B-Wing Electra Exora Business Park, Sarjapur-Marathahalli Outer Ring Road, Bengaluru, 560 103, India
Tel.: (91) 8040140000
Web Site: http://www.radisys.com
Emp.: 500
Custom Computer Programming Services
N.A.I.C.S.: 541511

RadiSys Canada ULC (3)
4190 Still Creek Drive Suite 300, Suite 300, Burnaby, V5C 6C6, BC, Canada
Tel.: (604) 918-6300
Web Site: http://www.radisys.com
Open Telecommunication & Wireless Infrastructure Solutions
N.A.I.C.S.: 517111

Radisys India Private Limited (3)
6th Floor B-Wing Electra Exora Business Park, Sarjapur-Marathahalli Outer Ring Road, Bengaluru, 560 103, India
Tel.: (91) 8040140000
Web Site: http://www.radisys.com
Embedded Computer System Mfr
N.A.I.C.S.: 334118

Affiliate (Domestic):

Reliance Industrial Infrastructure Ltd. (2)
NKM International House 5th Floor 178 Backbay Reclamation, Behind LIC Yogakshema Building Babubhai Chinai Road, Mumbai, 400 020, Maharashtra, India
Tel.: (91) 2244779053
Web Site: http://www.riil.in
Rev.: $9,567,340
Assets: $61,234,924
Liabilities: $5,002,902
Net Worth: $56,232,021
Earnings: $1,317,143

INTERNATIONAL PUBLIC

Emp.: 70
Fiscal Year-end: 03/31/2021
Pipeline Transportation of Petroleum Products; Infrastructure Set-up & Operations; Computer Software & Data Processing
N.A.I.C.S.: 486910
Dilip V. Dherai (Exec Dir)

Subsidiary (Domestic):

Reliance Industrial Investments and Holdings Ltd (2)
Makers Chambers IV, Nariman Point, Mumbai, 400 021, India
Tel.: (91) 2222785000
Web Site: http://www.ril.com
Sales Range: $5-14.9 Billion
Emp.: 40,000
Holding Company
N.A.I.C.S.: 551112
Mukesh D. Ambani (Chm & Mng Dir)

Reliance Jio Infocomm Ltd (2)
9th Floor Maker Chambers IV 222, Nariman Point, Mumbai, 400021, Maharashtra, India
Tel.: (91) 2244770000
Telecommunication Servicesb
N.A.I.C.S.: 517810
Mukesh D Ambani (Chm & Mng Dir)

Subsidiary (Domestic):

Reliance Globalcom Limited (3)
BCA 08 1st Floor B-Wing Dhirubhai Ambani Knowledge City, Navi Mumbai, 400710, India
Tel.: (91) 22 3037 3333
Telecommunication Servicesb
N.A.I.C.S.: 517112

Reliance Infratel Ltd (3)
H Block 1st Floor Dhirubhai Ambani Knowledge City, Navi Mumbai, 400710, India
Tel.: (91) 22 3038 6286
Telecommunication Servicesb
N.A.I.C.S.: 517112

Subsidiary (Domestic):

Reliance Retail Ventures Ltd. (2)
4th Floor, Court House Lokmanya Tilak Marg, Dhobi Talao, Mumbai, 400002, India
Tel.: (91) 8008910001
Web Site: https://www.relianceretail.com
Retail & Wholesale - Staples
N.A.I.C.S.: 459999

Subsidiary (Domestic):

Lotus Chocolate Company Limited (3)
Puzzolana Towers IInd Floor Road No 10, Banjara Hills, Hyderabad, 500034, Telangana, India (51%)
Tel.: (91) 9703899918
Web Site: https://www.lotuschocolate.com
Rev.: $24,117,969
Assets: $8,764,234
Liabilities: $3,674,060
Net Worth: $5,090,175
Earnings: $606,118
Emp.: 85
Fiscal Year-end: 03/31/2024
Bakery Products Mfr
N.A.I.C.S.: 311351
Subramanya Ram Ganapath (Exec Dir)

METRO Cash & Carry India Private Limited (3)
Survey No 26/3 A Block, Subramanyanagar Ward No 9 Industrial Suburbs Yeshwanthpur, 560055, Bengaluru, India
Tel.: (91) 9513622737
Web Site: http://www.metro.co.in
Food Product Whslr
N.A.I.C.S.: 424410
Arvind Mediratta (CEO & Mng Dir)

Subsidiary (Domestic):

Reliance Utilities & Power Pvt. Ltd. (2)
Maker Chambers IV 3rd Floor 222 Nariman Point, Mumbai, 400 021, India
Tel.: (91) 2222785500
Power Plant Maintanence Services
N.A.I.C.S.: 561790
Ramesh Dari (Sr Mgr)

Subsidiary (Non-US):

The Hamleys Group Limited (2)

AND PRIVATE COMPANIES

2 Fouberts Place Regent Street, London, W1F 7PA, United Kingdom
Tel.: (44) 3717041977
Web Site: http://www.hamleys.co.uk
Holding Company; Toy Retailer
N.A.I.C.S.: 551112
Alasdair Dunn *(Deputy CEO & CFO)*

Subsidiary (Non-US):

Hamleys Asia Limited (3)
Room 901-2 9/F 9 Chong Yip Street Kwun Tong, Kowloon, China (Hong Kong)
Tel.: (852) 29509808
Footwear Distr
N.A.I.C.S.: 424340
Ethel Chan *(Mgr-Shipping)*

Hamleys Finland Oy (3)
Aleksanterinkatu 52, 100, Helsinki, Finland
Tel.: (358) 91215037
Toy Retailer
N.A.I.C.S.: 423920

Hamleys Norway AS (3)
Steen and Strom Kongensgate 23, 153, Oslo, Norway
Tel.: (47) 22004043
Toy Retailer
N.A.I.C.S.: 423920

Hamleys Swenden AB (3)
Hyllie Stationsvag 10, 215 32, Malmo, Sweden
Tel.: (46) 40136690
Toy Retailer
N.A.I.C.S.: 423920

Hamleys Toys (Ireland) Limited (3)
Dundrum Town Centre, Dublin, Ireland
Tel.: (353) 12924900
Toy Distr
N.A.I.C.S.: 423920

Subsidiary (Domestic):

Hamleys of London Limited (3)
2 Foubert's Place Regent Street, London, W1F 7PA, United Kingdom
Tel.: (44) 371 704 1977
Web Site: http://www.hamleys.com
Sales Range: $50-74.9 Million
Emp.: 252
Toy Retailer
N.A.I.C.S.: 459120

Reliance Infrastructure Limited (1)
Reliance Centre Ground Floor 19 Walchand Hirachand Marg, Ballard Estate, Mumbai, 400 001, India
Tel.: (91) 224 303 1000
Web Site: http://www.rinfra.com
Rev.: $261,159,308
Assets: $855,707,990
Liabilities: $630,604,748
Net Worth: $225,103,242
Earnings: ($12,809,024)
Emp.: 5,157
Fiscal Year-end: 03/31/2022
Power Utility
N.A.I.C.S.: 221121
Anil Dhirubhai Ambani *(Chm)*

Subsidiary (Domestic):

Mumbai Metro One Private Limited (2)
2nd Floor Satellite Silver Building Andheri Kurla Road, Marol Andheri East, Mumbai, 400059, India
Tel.: (91) 22 30310900
Rail Transportation Services
N.A.I.C.S.: 488210

Reliance Energy Trading Limited (2)
2/22A Shanti Niketan, New Delhi, 110 021, India
Tel.: (91) 11 3032 3444
Web Site: http://www.relianceenergytrading.com
Electric Power Distribution Services
N.A.I.C.S.: 221122

Reliance Power Limited (2)
Reliance Centre Ground Floor 19 Walchand Hirachand Marg Ballard Estate, Mumbai, 400 001, India
Tel.: (91) 224 303 1000
Web Site: http://www.reliancepower.co.in
Rev.: $1,049,238,645
Assets: $6,799,291,590
Liabilities: $4,876,811,940
Net Worth: $1,922,479,650
Earnings: $82,706,715
Emp.: 8,093
Fiscal Year-end: 03/31/2022
Power Generation
N.A.I.C.S.: 221118
Anil Dhirubhai Ambani *(Chm)*

Western Region Transmission (Maharashtra) Private Limited (2)
Krishna Chambers 2nd Floor Pune Satara Road Near Laxminarayan Theatre, Mukund Nagar, Pune, 411037, India
Tel.: (91) 9324377415
Emp.: 15
Electric Power Transmission Services
N.A.I.C.S.: 221121
Uday Karandkar *(VP)*

Reliance MediaWorks Limited (1)
Film City Complex Goregaon East, Mumbai, 400065, India **(62.23%)**
Tel.: (91) 2233473600
Web Site: http://www.reliancemediaworks.com
Sales Range: $100-124.9 Million
Emp.: 6,459
Film & Entertainment Services
N.A.I.C.S.: 512110

Subsidiary (Domestic):

Big Synergy Media Ltd. (2)
B/27 Veera Industrial Estate Commerce Centre 4th Floor Off, New Oshiwara Link Road Andheri W, Mumbai, 400053, India
Tel.: (91) 22 30865101
Web Site: http://www.bigsynergy.tv
Television Production & Entertainment Services
N.A.I.C.S.: 512110
Siddartha Basu *(Mng Dir)*

Joint Venture (US):

Instant Karma Films, LLC (2)
212 Marine St, Santa Monica, CA 90405
Tel.: (310) 526-7703
Web Site: http://www.instantkarmafilms.tv
Motion Picture & Video Production Services
N.A.I.C.S.: 512110

Subsidiary (US):

Phoenix BIG Cinemas Management LLC (2)
9111 Cross Park Dr Ste E-275, Knoxville, TN 37923
Tel.: (865) 692-4061
Web Site: http://www.phoenixbigcinemas.com
Motion Picture Theater Operator
N.A.I.C.S.: 512131
Phil Zacheretti *(CEO & Pres)*

Unit (US):

Reliance MediaWorks (USA), Inc. - Burbank (2)
2777 N Ontario St, Burbank, CA 91504
Tel.: (818) 557-7333
Web Site: http://www.rmwusa.com
Sales Range: $10-24.9 Million
Emp.: 70
Digital Image Processing Services
N.A.I.C.S.: 812921
Edward Paulrag *(Dir-HR)*

Viacom 18 Media Pvt. Ltd. (1)
36 B Dr RK Shirodkar Marg Parel East, Mumbai, 400012, India
Tel.: (91) 22 4341 2424
Web Site: http://www.viacom18.com
Media Distr
N.A.I.C.S.: 516120
Ajit Andhare *(COO-Viacom 18 Motion Pictures)*

Subsidiary (Domestic):

Star India Private Limited (2)
Star House Urmi Estate 95 Ganpatrao Kadam Marg Lower Parel West, Mumbai, 400 013, India
Tel.: (91) 2266305555
Web Site: http://www.startv.com
Television Broadcasting Services
N.A.I.C.S.: 516120
K. Madhavan *(Mng Dir)*

Subsidiary (Non-US):

Network Digital Distribution Services FZ-LLC (3)
Boutique Office #9, PO Box 502197, Media City, Dubai, United Arab Emirates
Tel.: (971) 4 391 2333
Web Site: http://www.startv.com
Television Broadcasting Services
N.A.I.C.S.: 516120

Star Middle East FZ-LLC (3)
Boutique Office #9, PO Box 502197, Dubai Media City, Dubai, United Arab Emirates
Tel.: (971) 43912333
Web Site: http://www.startv.com
Television Broadcasting Services
N.A.I.C.S.: 516120

Subsidiary (Domestic):

Star Sports India Private Limited (3)
Star House Urmi Estate 95 Ganpatrao Kadam Marg Lower Parel West, Mumbai, 400 013, India
Tel.: (91) 2266305555
Web Site: http://www.startv.com
Television Broadcasting Services
N.A.I.C.S.: 516120
Gautam Thakar *(CEO)*

Subsidiary (Non-US):

Starvision Hong Kong Limited (3)
Suite 3104 31/f Eight Commercial Tower 8 Sun Yip Street, Chai Wan, China (Hong Kong)
Tel.: (852) 28970975
Web Site: https://www.starvision.com.hk
Media & Entertainment Services
N.A.I.C.S.: 512199

Subsidiary (Domestic):

Vijay Television Private Limited (3)
Star House Urmi Estate 95 Ganpatrao Kadam Marg, Lower Parel West, Mumbai, 400013, India
Tel.: (91) 222 6100084
Web Site: http://www.startv.com
Television Broadcasting Services
N.A.I.C.S.: 516120

RELIANCE BROADCAST NETWORK LIMITED

401 4th Floor Infiniti Mall Link Road Oshiwara Andheri West, Mumbai, 400 053, India
Tel.: (91) 2230689444 In
Web Site: https://reliancebroadcast.in
Rev.: $19,770,701
Assets: $57,414,917
Liabilities: $130,793,931
Net Worth: ($73,379,015)
Earnings: ($16,252,782)
Fiscal Year-end: 03/31/22
Television Broadcasting
N.A.I.C.S.: 516120
Asheesh Chatterjee *(CFO)*

RELIANCE CHEMOTEX INDUSTRIES LTD.

Village Kanpur, Post Box No 73, Udaipur, 313003, Rajasthan, India
Tel.: (91) 2942491489
Web Site: https://www.reliancechemotex.com
503162—(BOM)
Rev.: $35,506,039
Assets: $35,851,493
Liabilities: $21,602,422
Net Worth: $14,249,071
Earnings: $946,122
Emp.: 1,576
Fiscal Year-end: 03/31/21
Synthetic Yarn Mfr
N.A.I.C.S.: 313110
Sanjiv Shroff *(Mng Dir)*

RELIANCE COTTON SPINNING MILLS LTD.

1-Km Warburton Road, Ferozewattoan, Sheikhupura, Pakistan
Tel.: (92) 563731011
Web Site: https://www.reliancespinning.com
Year Founded: 1991
RCML—(PSX)
Rev.: $39,748,245
Assets: $55,096,326
Liabilities: $23,630,285
Net Worth: $31,466,041
Earnings: $4,306,034
Emp.: 1,237
Fiscal Year-end: 06/30/23
Textile Products Mfr
N.A.I.C.S.: 313310
Mian Shayan Abdullah *(CEO)*

RELIANCE DOORS PTY LTD.

8 Oasis Court, Clontarf, 4019, QLD, Australia
Tel.: (61) 13 0028 0620 AU
Web Site: http://www.reliancedoorservice.com
Residential & Industrial Garage Doors Installation & Service
N.A.I.C.S.: 238990
Ray Rankin *(Mgr-Bus Dev)*

Subsidiaries:

Gliderol International Pty Limited (1)
32 Jacobsen Crescent, Holden Hill, 5088, SA, Australia
Tel.: (61) 883600000
Web Site: https://www.gliderol.com.au
Door & Access Systems Mfr
N.A.I.C.S.: 332321
Tom Ainscough *(Natl Sls Mgr)*

RELIANCE GLOBAL HOLDINGS LIMITED

Room 3201 32nd Floor China Resources Building 26 Harbour Road, Wanchai, Hong Kong, China (Hong Kong)
Tel.: (852) 3 618 8383 BM
Web Site: http://www.relianceglobal.com.hk
0723—(HKG)
Rev.: $108,682,546
Assets: $69,186,678
Liabilities: $38,600,747
Net Worth: $30,585,930
Earnings: $4,990,107
Emp.: 51
Fiscal Year-end: 03/31/21
Wood Products Mfr
N.A.I.C.S.: 321999
Jingyu Wang *(Chm)*

RELIANCE HIGH-TECH LTD.

100 Berkshire Place Wharfedale Road, Winnersh, Wokingham, RG41 5RD, Berkshire, United Kingdom
Tel.: (44) 8451210802
Web Site: http://www.rht.co.uk
Sales Range: $25-49.9 Million
Emp.: 70
Security Services
N.A.I.C.S.: 561621
Alistair Enser *(CEO)*

RELIANCE INSURANCE COMPANY LIMITED

181-A Sindhi Muslim Co-operative Housing Society, Karachi, Pakistan
Tel.: (92) 2134539415
Web Site: https://www.relianceins.com
RICL—(PSX)
Rev.: $1,636,178
Assets: $8,213,157
Liabilities: $3,871,594
Net Worth: $4,341,564
Earnings: $610,513
Emp.: 190
Fiscal Year-end: 12/31/23
General Insurance Services
N.A.I.C.S.: 524113

RELIANCE INSURANCE COMPANY LIMITED

Reliance Insurance Company Limited—(Continued)
A. Razak Ahmed (CEO & Mng Dir)

RELIANCE INSURANCE LIMITED
Shanta Western Tower Level-5 Space-503 & 504 186, Tejgaon Industrial Area, Dhaka, 1208, Bangladesh
Tel.: (880) 28878836
Web Site:
https://www.reliance.com.bd
Year Founded: 1988
RELIANCINS—(CHT)
Rev.: $9,686,485
Assets: $114,533,207
Liabilities: $50,258,597
Net Worth: $64,274,610
Earnings: $6,309,907
Emp.: 314
Fiscal Year-end: 12/31/23
General Insurance Services
N.A.I.C.S.: 524210
Shahnaz Rahman (Vice Chm)

Subsidiaries:

Reliance Asset Reconstruction Company Limited (1)
11th Floor North Side R-Tech Park Western Express Highway, Goregoan, Mumbai, India
Tel.: (91) 2241681200
Web Site: https://www.rarcl.com
Securitisation & Reconstruction Services
N.A.I.C.S.: 541618

RELIANCE NAVAL AND ENGINEERING LTD
Reliance Centre 8th Floor South Wing Santa Cruz East, Mumbai, 400055, India
Tel.: (91) 2794305000
Web Site: https://www.rnaval.co.in
RNAVAL—(NSE)
Sales Range: $25-49.9 Million
Ship Building & Repairing; Offshore Construction Services
N.A.I.C.S.: 336611
Debashis Bir (CEO)

RELIANCE WEAVING MILLS LIMITED
E-110 Khyaban-e-Jinah, Lahore, Pakistan
Tel.: (92) 42111328462
Web Site: http://www.fatima-group.com
REWM—(PSX)
Rev.: $117,574,664
Assets: $131,431,959
Liabilities: $95,051,895
Net Worth: $36,380,064
Earnings: $730,698
Emp.: 2,145
Fiscal Year-end: 06/30/23
Yarn & Fabric Mfr
N.A.I.C.S.: 313110
Waheed Ahmed Mushtaq (CFO)

Subsidiaries:

Fatima Holding Limited (1)
2nd Floor Trust Plaza LMQ Road, Multan, Pakistan
Tel.: (92) 6145120312
White Sugar Mfr & Distr
N.A.I.C.S.: 311314

RELIANCE WORLDWIDE CORPORATION LIMITED
Level 26 140 William Street, Melbourne, 3000, VIC, Australia
Tel.: (61) 383521400 AU
Web Site: https://www.rwc.com
Year Founded: 2016
RWC—(ASX)
Rev.: $1,245,754,000
Assets: $2,144,499,000
Liabilities: $880,131,000
Net Worth: $1,264,368,000
Earnings: $110,145,000
Fiscal Year-end: 06/30/24
Holding Company; Plumbing & Heating Products Mfr & Distr
N.A.I.C.S.: 551112
Andrew Johnson (CFO)

Subsidiaries:

EZ-Flo International Inc. (1)
2750 E Mission Blvd, Ontario, CA 91761
Tel.: (909) 947-5256
Web Site: http://www.ez-flo.net
Rev.: $25,345,467
Emp.: 25
Plumbing & Hydronic Heating Supplies
N.A.I.C.S.: 423720
Paul Wilson (Pres)

John Guest Czech S.R.O. (1)
Vrbenska 2290, 370 01, Ceske Budejovice, Czech Republic
Tel.: (420) 38 700 2040
Web Site: https://johnguest.cz
Pipe Fitting Mfr
N.A.I.C.S.: 326122

John Guest GmbH (1)
Ludwig-Erhard-Allee 30, 33719, Bielefeld, Germany
Tel.: (49) 52 197 2560
Web Site: https://speedfit-bielefeld.de
Pipe Fitting Mfr
N.A.I.C.S.: 326122

John Guest Korea Ltd. (1)
A-Dong 212 Ho Togisanup2cha Jisiksanup Center 61 Ganam-Ro, Seo-Gu, Incheon, Korea (South)
Tel.: (82) 32 584 3370
Web Site: https://www.johnguest.co.kr
Pipe Fitting Mfr
N.A.I.C.S.: 326122

Reliance Worldwide Corporation (Aust.) Pty. Ltd. (1)
Ground Floor 555 Bourke Street, Melbourne, 3000, VIC, Australia
Tel.: (61) 390998299
Web Site: http://www.rwc.com
Plumbing & Heating Products Mfr & Distr
N.A.I.C.S.: 332912
Heath Sharp (Grp CEO)

Reliance Worldwide Corporation (UK) Limited (1)
Vale Park Warehouse Units 5 and 6 Grosvenor Business Centre, Enterprise Way, Evesham, WR11 1GS, United Kingdom
Tel.: (44) 138 671 2400
Web Site: https://www.rwc.co.uk
Plumbing Fitting Mfr
N.A.I.C.S.: 332913

Securus Inc. (1)
14284 Danielson St, Poway, CA 92064
Tel.: (760) 744-6944
Web Site: http://www.holdrite.com
Plumbing Fixture Fitting & Trim Mfr
N.A.I.C.S.: 332913
Neil Ross (Product Mgr)

RELIANT SERVICE, INC.
Room 803 No 1188 Qinzhou North Road, Xuhui District, Shanghai, 200235, China
Tel.: (86) 21 17717382386 NV
RLLT—(OTCIQ)
Sales Range: Less than $1 Million
Office Machinery & Equipment Distr
N.A.I.C.S.: 423420
Ming Zhu (Pres, CEO & CFO)

RELIC TECHNOLOGIES LIMITED
J-Block Bhangwadi Shopping Centre Kalbadevi Road, Mumbai, 400 002, Maharashtra, India
Tel.: (91) 2222012231
Web Site: https://relictechnologies.in
Year Founded: 1991
511712—(BOM)
Rev.: $189,109
Assets: $750,837
Liabilities: $31,525
Net Worth: $719,311
Earnings: $52,945
Fiscal Year-end: 03/31/21
Security Brokerage Services
N.A.I.C.S.: 523150
Baijoo Madhusudan Raval (Exec Dir)

RELICAB CABLE MANUFACTURING LIMITED
207 Sahakar Bhavan Kurla ind Estate LBS Marg, Ghatkopar West, Mumbai, 400 086, Maharashtra, India
Tel.: (91) 2225123967
Web Site: https://www.relicab.com
Year Founded: 1992
539760—(BOM)
Rev.: $4,179,989
Assets: $4,219,160
Liabilities: $2,902,836
Net Worth: $1,316,324
Earnings: $180,277
Emp.: 38
Fiscal Year-end: 03/31/23
Cable & Wire Mfr & Distr
N.A.I.C.S.: 335929
Parag Shah (CFO)

RELIEF THERAPEUTICS HOLDING SA
Avenue de Secheron 15, 1202, Geneva, Switzerland
Tel.: (41) 447235959 CH
Web Site:
https://www.relieftherapeutics.com
Year Founded: 2001
RLFFD—(OTCQB)
Rev.: $175,533
Assets: $88,383,621
Liabilities: $12,459,435
Net Worth: $75,924,186
Earnings: ($8,864,975)
Emp.: 250
Fiscal Year-end: 12/31/20
Holding Company; Biopharmaceutical Research & Development
N.A.I.C.S.: 551112
Michelle Lock (Interim CEO)

RELIGARE ENTERPRISES LIMITED
1407 14th Floor Chiranjiv Tower 43 Nehru Place, New Delhi, 110019, India
Tel.: (91) 1144725676
Web Site: https://www.religare.com
RELIGARE—(NSE)
Rev.: $345,409,073
Assets: $1,191,040,510
Liabilities: $1,150,387,861
Net Worth: $40,652,648
Earnings: ($65,222,089)
Emp.: 29
Fiscal Year-end: 03/31/21
Financial Services
N.A.I.C.S.: 523999
Reena Jayara (Officer-Compliance & Sec)

Subsidiaries:

Care Health Insurance Limited (1)
5th Floor 19 Chawla House Nehru Place, New Delhi, 110019, India
Tel.: (91) 8860402452
Web Site: https://careinsurance.com
Insurance Services
N.A.I.C.S.: 524210

Religare Arts Initiative Limited (1)
Ground Floor D3 PB3 District Centre Saket, New Delhi, 110 017, India
Tel.: (91) 11 3912 6922
Web Site: http://www.religareart.com
Emp.: 10
Arts Event & Exhibition Organizer
N.A.I.C.S.: 711310

INTERNATIONAL PUBLIC

Religare Capital Markets Limited (1)
Ground and 1st Floor Sanghvi House Premises No 18 Subhash Road, Vile Parle East, Mumbai, 400057, India
Tel.: (91) 2267288000
Web Site: http://www.religarecm.com
Sales Range: $50-74.9 Million
Emp.: 100
Financial Investment Services
N.A.I.C.S.: 523999

Subsidiary (Non-US):

Religare Capital Markets (Hong Kong) Limited (2)
12/F Henley Building 5 Queen's, Hong Kong, China (Hong Kong)
Tel.: (852) 3923 9388
Emp.: 3
Investment Management Service
N.A.I.C.S.: 523999
Wong Ya Nan (Mng Dir)

Religare Capital Markets (Singapore) Pte Limited (2)
77 Robinson Road 13-00 Robinson 77, Singapore, 068896, Singapore
Tel.: (65) 65006400
Web Site: http://www.religarecm.com
Emp.: 30
Investment Management Service
N.A.I.C.S.: 523999

Subsidiary (Domestic):

Religare Capital Markets Corporate Finance Pte Limited (3)
80 Raffles Place 43rd Floor UOB Plaza 1, Singapore, 48624, Singapore
Tel.: (65) 6671 8000
Financial Investment Services
N.A.I.C.S.: 523999
Jason Barakat-Brown (Head-Advisory)

Religare Global Asset Management Inc. (1)
375 Park Ave Ste 2602, New York, NY 10152
Tel.: (646) 755-9000
Web Site: http://www.religare.com
Asset Management Services
N.A.I.C.S.: 523940
Nalin Nayyar (CEO)

Religare Housing Development Finance Corporation Limited (1)
2nd floor Club 125 Tower B Plot A-3 4 5 Sector 125, Noida, 201301, Uttar Pradesh, India
Tel.: (91) 18602664111
Web Site:
https://www.religarehomeloans.com
Home Finance Services
N.A.I.C.S.: 921130

Religare Securities Limited (1)
D3 P3B District Centre Saket, New Delhi, 110017, India
Tel.: (91) 11 39125000
Web Site: http://www.religaresecurities.com
Securities & Commodities Brokerage Services
N.A.I.C.S.: 523150

RELIQ HEALTH TECHNOLOGIES INC.
Suite 810 - 789 West Pender Street, Vancouver, V6C 1H2, BC, Canada
Tel.: (604) 687-2038
Web Site:
https://www.reliqhealth.com
Year Founded: 2005
RQHTF—(OTCIQ)
Rev.: $133,332
Assets: $2,759,010
Liabilities: $806,723
Net Worth: $1,952,288
Earnings: ($9,531,593)
Fiscal Year-end: 06/30/19
Software Developer
N.A.I.C.S.: 513210
Dave McKay (Chief Tech & Innovation Officer)

RELJIN SLAVKO A.D.
Beogradski put bb, Perlez, Serbia

Tel.: (381) 23 861 039
Year Founded: 1948
Sales Range: Less than $1 Million
Roof Tile & Brick Mfr
N.A.I.C.S.: 327120

RELO GROUP, INC.
23-3-1 Shinjuku, Shinjuku-ku, Tokyo,
160-0022, Japan
Tel.: (81) 353128706
Web Site: https://www.relo.jp
Year Founded: 1967
8876—(TKS)
Rev.: $876,353,800
Assets: $1,917,990,650
Liabilities: $1,651,277,150
Net Worth: $266,713,500
Earnings: ($183,804,270)
Emp.: 3,100
Fiscal Year-end: 03/31/24
Rented Houses & Apartments Management, Administration, Maintenance & Repair Work
N.A.I.C.S.: 531311
Masanori Sasada (Chm)

Subsidiaries:

Associates for International Research, Inc.   (1)
675 Massachusetts Ave, Cambridge, MA 02139
Tel.: (617) 250-6600
Web Site: https://www.air-inc.com
Real Estate Services
N.A.I.C.S.: 531110
Sean Luitjens (VP-Corp Dev)

Chofu Housing Co., Ltd.   (1)
Chofu Station Square Store 1 40 4 Fuda 2F, Chofu, Tokyo, Japan
Tel.: (81) 424438246
Web Site: http://www.choufu.co.jp
Housing Rental Services
N.A.I.C.S.: 531110

Ekimae Real Estate Co., Ltd.   (1)
2851 1 Higashikushihara cho, Kurume, 830-0003, Fukuoka, Japan
Tel.: (81) 942368910
Emp.: 209
Real Estate Services
N.A.I.C.S.: 531110

Fukuri Kousei Club Chubu Co., Ltd.   (1)
Meitetsu Kanayama Daiichi Building 25-1 Hayori-cho, Atsuta-ku, Nagoya, 456-0003, Aichi, Japan
Tel.: (81) 528842297
Welfare Support Services
N.A.I.C.S.: 624120

Fukuri Kousei Club Chugoku Co., Ltd.   (1)
1 3 32 Kokutaijimachi ERE Kokutaiji Building 6F, Naka-ku, Hiroshima, 730-0042, Japan
Tel.: (81) 825435855
Web Site: http://www.fukuri-chugoku.co.jp
Welfare Support Services
N.A.I.C.S.: 624120

Fukurikosei Club Kyushu Co., Ltd.   (1)
Fukuoka Asahi Hall 2-8-41 Tenjin, Chuo-ku, Fukuoka, 810-0001, Japan
Tel.: (81) 927385800
Welfare Support Services
N.A.I.C.S.: 624120

Hot House Co. Ltd.   (1)
Cielo Sendai Building 8F 1-5-31 Honmachi, Aoba-ku, Sendai, 980-0014, Japan
Tel.: (81) 222157787
Emp.: 50
Real Estate Manangement Services
N.A.I.C.S.: 531210

Japanese Assistance Network, Inc.   (1)
3500 W Olive Ave Ste 300, Burbank, CA 91505
Tel.: (818) 505-6080
Sales Range: $1-9.9 Million
Emp.: 22
Customer Management Services
N.A.I.C.S.: 541613

Kent Group Co., Ltd.   (1)
1-3-1 Umeda, Kita-ku, Osaka, Japan
Tel.: (81) 663443000
Logistics Consulting Servies
N.A.I.C.S.: 541614

Live Daikou, Limited   (1)
1-4-2 Sengencho, Omiya Ward, Saitama, 330-0842, Japan
Tel.: (81) 488717788
Housing Rental Services
N.A.I.C.S.: 531110

Nakamichi, Inc.   (1)
Grand Chariot Building-6F 3-10 Futsukamachi, Aoba-ku, Sendai, 980-0802, Miyagi, Japan
Tel.: (81) 223934661
Real Estate Services
N.A.I.C.S.: 531110

Nissho Vecs Co., Ltd.   (1)
Nissho Yoyogi Building 1-45-1 Yoyogi, Shibuya-ku, Tokyo, 151-0053, Japan
Tel.: (81) 333797744
Web Site: https://www.vecs.co.jp
Emp.: 143
Real Estate Non-Life Insurance Agency Services
N.A.I.C.S.: 524210

Pacific Residential Service, Inc.   (1)
Tel.: (81) 364412381
Housing Rental Services
N.A.I.C.S.: 531110
Kenzo Takai (CEO)

Pyramid RELO Pvt. Ltd.   (1)
Enkay Center Lower Ground Floor Block-A Vanijya Nikunj, Udyog Vihar Phase-5, Gurgaon, 122016, Haryana, India
Tel.: (91) 1244370053
Real Estate Services
N.A.I.C.S.: 531110
Prafful Gupta (Mgr-Guest Rels)

Recrea Life Agent Co., Ltd.   (1)
5th floor Osaka Ekimae Daiichi Building 1-3-1 Umeda, Kita-ku, Osaka, 530-0001, Japan
Tel.: (81) 663420333
Real Estate Services
N.A.I.C.S.: 531110

Relo Club, Limited   (1)
4-2-18 Shinjuku, Tokyo, 160-0022, Japan
Tel.: (81) 332260244
Emp.: 400
Welfare Support Services
N.A.I.C.S.: 624120
Shingo Sugiyama (Pres)

Relo Create, Limited   (1)
Shinjuku Kofu Building 4-2-18, Shinjuku-ku, Tokyo, 160-0022, Japan
Tel.: (81) 353128717
Real Estate Services
N.A.I.C.S.: 531110

Relo Estate, Limited   (1)
2nd floor TOKYU REIT Shinjuku Building 4-3-25, Shinjuku-ku, Tokyo, 160-0022, Japan
Tel.: (81) 353128729
Housing Rental Services
N.A.I.C.S.: 531110

Relo Excel International, Inc.   (1)
4-3-25 Shinjuku, Tokyo, 160-0022, Japan
Tel.: (81) 353128956
Web Site: https://www.reloexcel.jp
Welfare Support Services
N.A.I.C.S.: 624120

Relo Financial Solutions, Limited   (1)
TOKYU REIT 2nd Shinjuku Building 4-3-23, Shinjuku-ku, Tokyo, 160-0022, Japan
Tel.: (81) 333546521
Financial Services
N.A.I.C.S.: 523210

Relo Panasonic Excel International Co., Ltd.   (1)
Imabashi Bldg 3-1-7 Imabashi, Chuo-ku, Osaka, 541-0042, Japan
Tel.: (81) 6 6206 1011
Web Site: http://www.rpei.co.jp
Human Resource Consulting Services
N.A.I.C.S.: 541612

Katsushi Numata (Pres)

Relo Partners property, Inc.   (1)
3-1-22 Shinjuku NSO Building 5F, Shinjuku-ku, Tokyo, Japan
Tel.: (81) 364412381
Web Site: https://www.relo-pp.com
Building Managing & Cleaning Services
N.A.I.C.S.: 561720

Relo Partners, Limited   (1)
3-1-22 Shinjuku Tokyo NSO Building 5F, Shinjuku-ku, Tokyo, 160-0022, Japan
Tel.: (81) 332251750
Emp.: 1,497
Housing Rental Services
N.A.I.C.S.: 531110

Relo Redac Strattons Limited   (1)
Charles House 108 110 Finchley Road, London, NW3 5JJ, United Kingdom
Tel.: (44) 2083495010
Real Estate Services
N.A.I.C.S.: 531110
Rebecca Wheatcroft (Mgr-Tenancy & Property)

Relo Redac, Inc.   (1)
1010 Ave of the Americas 4th Fl, New York, NY 10018
Tel.: (212) 379-5041
Web Site: http://reloredac.com
Real Estate Services
N.A.I.C.S.: 531110
Nobue Okahata (Mgr-Real Estate)

Relo TransEuro, Ltd.   (1)
Unit9 Abbey Road Industrial Park Commercial Way, London, NW10 7XF, United Kingdom
Tel.: (44) 2089652441
Web Site: https://sakaieurope.com
International Moving Services
N.A.I.C.S.: 484210

Relo Vacations, Limited   (1)
5-17-9 Shinjuku Nomura Securities Building 6th Floor, Shinjuku Shinjuku-ku, Tokyo, 160-0022, Japan
Tel.: (81) 351555840
Hotel Operator
N.A.I.C.S.: 721110

ReloExcel, Inc.   (1)
Nippon Life Imahashi Building 3-1-7 Imahashi, Chuo-ku, Osaka, 541-0042, Japan
Tel.: (81) 662061011
Web Site: https://www.reloexcel.jp
Human Resource Development Services
N.A.I.C.S.: 541612

Relocation International, Inc.   (1)
4-3-25 Shinjuku, Tokyo, 160-0022, Japan
Tel.: (81) 353128702
Web Site: https://www.relocation-international.co.jp
Housing Rental Services
N.A.I.C.S.: 531110

Relocation Japan, Limited   (1)
7th Floor Shinjuku Kofu Building 4-2-18 Shinjuku, Shinjuku-ku, Tokyo, 160-0022, Japan
Tel.: (81) 353128869
Housing Rental Services
N.A.I.C.S.: 531110

Rex Daikou, Limited   (1)
1-45-2 Daimon-cho, Omiya-ku, Saitama, 330-0846, Japan
Tel.: (81) 486421181
Housing Rental Services
N.A.I.C.S.: 531110

Shinwa Shoji, Limited   (1)
3-40 Showamachi CI Mansion Kita-Sendai 1F, Aoba-ku, Sendai, 981-0913, Miyagi, Japan
Tel.: (81) 227252662
Real Estate Services
N.A.I.C.S.: 531110

Space Management Co., Ltd.   (1)
4F Shinyo Building 2-14 Ageba-cho, Shinjuku-ku, Tokyo, 162-0824, Japan
Tel.: (81) 352278822
Office Space Rental Services
N.A.I.C.S.: 531120

Tohto Co., Ltd.   (1)
Tel.: (81) 334803888

Web Site: http://www.tohto.ne.jp
Housing Rental Services
N.A.I.C.S.: 531110

World Resort Operation, Inc.   (1)
Nomura Securities Building 6th Floor 5 17 9, Shinjuku Shinjuku-ku, Tokyo, 160-0022, Japan
Tel.: (81) 366307970
Web Site: http://www.wro.co.jp
Hotel Operator
N.A.I.C.S.: 721110

Yoshida Fudosan Co., Ltd.   (1)
1-22-29 Minamigyotoku, Ichikawa, 272-0138, Chiba, Japan
Tel.: (81) 473333531
Emp.: 60
Real Estate Services
N.A.I.C.S.: 531110

RELPOL S.A.
St 11 Listopada 37, 68-200, Zary, Lubuskie, Poland
Tel.: (48) 684790800
Web Site: https://www.relpol.pl
Year Founded: 1958
RLP—(WAR)
Rev.: $40,525,915
Assets: $36,669,461
Liabilities: $10,126,524
Net Worth: $26,542,937
Earnings: $2,178,608
Emp.: 700
Fiscal Year-end: 12/31/23
Electromechanical & Electromagnetic Relay Mfr
N.A.I.C.S.: 335314
Piotr Osinski (Vice Chm-Supervisory Bd)

Subsidiaries:

RELPOL BG   (1)
HH Dimitar 26 Vasil Kanchev Str, BC Stefan Karadja ground floor office 14, 1510, Sofia, Bulgaria
Tel.: (359) 24512582
Web Site: http://www.relpol.bg
Sales Range: $25-49.9 Million
Emp.: 5
Industrial Automation Equipments Mfr
N.A.I.C.S.: 335314

Relpol France SARL   (1)
ZA du clos aux Pois, 6 rue des Petits Champs, 91100, Villabe, France
Tel.: (33) 160798500
Web Site: http://www.relpol.fr
Electromechanical & Electromagnetic Relay Distr
N.A.I.C.S.: 423830

Relpol Hungary Kft   (1)
Mogyorodi ut 32, 1149, Budapest, Hungary
Tel.: (36) 12651971
Electromechanical & Electromagnetic Relay Distr
N.A.I.C.S.: 423830

Relpol M Ltd.   (1)
Partizansky pr 23A room 1H room 3, 220033, Minsk, Belarus
Tel.: (375) 173734411
Web Site: http://www.relpol-m.com
Sales Range: $50-74.9 Million
Electromechanical & Electromagnetic Relay Distr
N.A.I.C.S.: 423830

RELSTRUCT BUILDCON LIMITED
201/202 Sunshine Plaza Junction of Kedarmal Road and Subhash lane, Malad, Mumbai, 400 097, India
Tel.: (91) 2228896386
Web Site:
   https://www.relstructbuildcon.com
Year Founded: 2014
Sales Range: Less than $1 Million
Real Estate Development Services
N.A.I.C.S.: 531311
Hemendra Mapara (Mng Dir)

RELX PLC

RELX PLC

RELX plc—(Continued)
1-3 Strand, London, WC2N 5JR, United Kingdom
Tel.: (44) 2071665500 UK
Web Site: https://www.relx.com
Year Founded: 1903
RELX—(NYSE)
Rev.: $11,563,998,990
Assets: $18,829,840,949
Liabilities: $14,488,765,463
Net Worth: $4,341,075,486
Earnings: $2,257,005,807
Emp.: 36,500
Fiscal Year-end: 12/31/23
Holding Company
N.A.I.C.S.: 551112
Henry A. Udow *(Chief Legal Officer & Sec)*

Subsidiaries:

RELX Group plc (1)
1-3 Strand, London, WC2N 5JR, United Kingdom (100%)
Tel.: (44) 2071665500
Web Site: http://www.relx.com
Holding Company; Scientific, Medical, Legal, Business, Risk & Analytics Publisher & Professional Information Services
N.A.I.C.S.: 551112
Henry A. Udow *(Chief Legal Officer & Sec)*

Subsidiary (Domestic):

Cordery Compliance Ltd. (2)
Lexis House 30 Farringdon Street, London, EC4A 4HH, United Kingdom
Tel.: (44) 2071182700
Web Site: https://www.corderycompliance.com
Legal Counsel Services
N.A.I.C.S.: 922130

Crediva Ltd. (2)
Global Reach Dunleavy Drive, Cardiff, CF11 0SN, United Kingdom
Tel.: (44) 8081293210
Web Site: https://crediva.co.uk
Risk Managemeng Srvices
N.A.I.C.S.: 541618

RELX (UK) Limited (2)
1-3 Strand, London, WC2N 5JR, United Kingdom (100%)
Tel.: (44) 2071665500
Web Site: http://www.relx.com
Holding Company; Business Information Services, Trade Journal Publisher & Event Organizer
N.A.I.C.S.: 551112
Henry A. Udow *(Chief Legal Officer & Sec)*

Subsidiary (Non-US):

ICIS Benchmarking Europe B.V. (3)
Radarweg 29, 1043 NX, Amsterdam, Netherlands
Tel.: (31) 205159222
Web Site: https://www.icis.com
Crypto Asset Trading Services
N.A.I.C.S.: 518210

Division (Domestic):

LNRS Data Services Limited (3)
1-3 Strand, London, WC2N 5JR, United Kingdom
Tel.: (44) 2071665500
Trade Journals Publisher, Information & Events Services
N.A.I.C.S.: 513120
Jamie O'Sullivan *(Mng Dir-Proagrica, Nextens, and XpertHR)*

Subsidiary (Non-US):

LNRS Data Services B.V. (4)
Radarweg 29, 1043, Amsterdam, Netherlands
Tel.: (31) 205159222
Trade Journals Publisher & Information Services
N.A.I.C.S.: 513120

Division (US):

LNRS Data Services Inc. (4)
230 Park Ave 7th Fl, New York, NY 10169
Tel.: (212) 309-8100
Trade Journals Publisher & Information Services
N.A.I.C.S.: 513120

Subsidiary (Domestic):

Accuity Inc. (5)
1007 Church St, Evanston, IL 60201
Tel.: (847) 676-9600
Payment Routing Data, Screening Software & Information Services
N.A.I.C.S.: 522320

Subsidiary (Non-US):

FircoSoft SAS (6)
247 rue de Bercy, 75012, Paris, France
Tel.: (33) 153441300
Financial Reporting & Compliance Software Programming Services
N.A.I.C.S.: 541511

Subsidiary (Non-US):

FircoSoft Brasil Consultoria e Servicos de Informatica Ltda (7)
Rua Bela Cintra 200, Consolacao, Sao Paulo, 01415-002, SP, Brazil
Tel.: (55) 1132666868
Software Development Services
N.A.I.C.S.: 513210

FircoSoft India Private Limited (7)
Dr Radhakrishnan Salai Mylapore, Chennai, 600004, Tamil Nadu, India
Tel.: (91) 4442218530
Software Development Services
N.A.I.C.S.: 513210

Unit (Domestic):

Brightmine (5)
300 Connell Dr Ste 1200, Berkeley Heights, NJ 07922
Tel.: (213) 308-3793
Web Site: https://www.brightmine.com
Human Resource Information Publisher & Services
N.A.I.C.S.: 513199

Group (Domestic):

LNRS Data Services Limited - Estates Gazette Group (4)
99 Bishopsgate, London, EC2M 3XD, United Kingdom
Tel.: (44) 2079111802
Web Site: http://www.egi.co.uk
Real Estate Magazine & Website Publisher
N.A.I.C.S.: 513120
David Salisbury *(Dir-Comml)*

LNRS Data Services Limited - Flight Group (4)
99 Bishopsgate 3rd Floor, London, EC2M 3AL, United Kingdom
Tel.: (44) 2079111400
Web Site: https://www.cirium.com
Aviation News & Information Magazine & Internet Publisher
N.A.I.C.S.: 513120
Kevin O'Toole *(Chief Strategy Officer)*

Subsidiary (US):

FlightStats, Inc. (5)
522 SW 5th Ave Ste 200, Portland, OR 97204
Tel.: (503) 274-0938
Web Site: http://www.flightstats.com
Online Flight Information Services
N.A.I.C.S.: 519290

Group (Domestic):

LNRS Data Services Limited - ICIS Group (4)
Quadrant House, The Quadrant, Sutton, SM2 5AS, Surrey, United Kingdom
Tel.: (44) 2086523335
Web Site: http://www.icis.com
Chemical Industry News & Market Information
N.A.I.C.S.: 516210
Dean Curtis *(Pres & CEO)*

Unit (US):

ICIS Chemical Business (5)
230 Park Ave 7th Fl, New York, NY 10169
Tel.: (212) 309-8100
Web Site: https://www.icis.com
Independent Commodity Intelligence Services
N.A.I.C.S.: 561499

Subsidiary (Domestic):

Chemical Data, LLC (6)
2727 Allen Prkwy, Ste 800, Wortham Tower,, Houston, TX 77019
Tel.: (713) 525-2613
Web Site: https://www.icis.com
Petroleum & Petrochemical Industry Information & Business Advisory Services
N.A.I.C.S.: 519290
Debbie Reagan *(Office Mgr)*

Subsidiary (Non-US):

ICIS Italia S.r.l. (5)
Via Sempione 1, Via Marsala, 21013, Gallarate, VA, Italy
Tel.: (39) 03311425311
Web Site: https://www.icis.com
Petroleum & Petrochemical Industry Information & Business Advisory Services
N.A.I.C.S.: 519290

Group (Domestic):

LNRS Data Services Limited - Proagrica Group (4)
Quadrant House, The Quadrant, Sutton, SM2 5AS, Surrey, United Kingdom
Tel.: (44) 2086523500
Web Site: http://www.proagrica.com
Critical Decision-Support Services for Agricultural Industry
N.A.I.C.S.: 561499
Jamie O'Sullivan *(CEO)*

Subsidiary (US):

Crop Data Management Systems, Inc. (5)
376 E Warm Springs Rd Ste 220, Las Vegas, NV 89119
Tel.: (530) 743-7605
Web Site: https://www.cdms.net
Agro-Business & Food Industry Data, Information & Decision Support Services
N.A.I.C.S.: 561499
Liz Magill *(Pres)*

Subsidiary (Non-US):

LNRS Data Services Pte. Ltd. (4)
3 Killiney Road 08-01 Winsland House I, Singapore, 239519, Singapore
Tel.: (65) 67898800
Trade Journals Publisher & Information Services
N.A.I.C.S.: 513120

Subsidiary (Domestic):

REV Venture Partners Limited (3)
1-3 Strand, London, WC2N 5JR, United Kingdom
Tel.: (44) 2071665665
Web Site: http://www.rev.vc
Venture Capital Investment Firm
N.A.I.C.S.: 523999
Tony Askew *(Mng Dir)*

Division (Domestic):

Reed Exhibitions Limited (3)
Gateway House 28 The Quadrant, Richmond, TW9 1DN, Surrey, United Kingdom
Tel.: (44) 2082712134
Web Site: https://rxglobal.com
Business & Consumer Exhibitions Organizer
N.A.I.C.S.: 561920
Hugh M. Jones IV *(CEO)*

Subsidiary (Domestic):

Big Data LDN (4)
Gateway House 28 The Quadrant, Richmond, London, TW9 1DN, Surrey, United Kingdom
Tel.: (44) 2082712151
Web Site: https://www.bigdataldn.com
Data & Analytics Conferences & Exhibitions Hostings Services
N.A.I.C.S.: 518210

Mack-Brooks Exhibitions Limited (4)
Gateway House 28 The Quadrant, Richmond, TW9 1DN, Surrey, United Kingdom
Tel.: (44) 2082712134
Trade Show Organizer
N.A.I.C.S.: 561920

Subsidiary (Non-US):

RELX (SINGAPORE) PTE, LTD (4)
8 Changi Business Park Avenue 1 #07-51 Changi South Tower, Singapore, 486018, Singapore
Tel.: (65) 67898800
Web Site: https://rxglobal.com
Business & Consumer Exhibitions Organizer
N.A.I.C.S.: 561920

RX Japan Co., Ltd. (4)
11th Floor, Yaesu Central Tower Tokyo Midtown Yaesu, 2-2-1 Yaesu, Chuo-ku, Tokyo, 104-0028, Japan
Tel.: (81) 367394101
Web Site: https://www.rxjapan.jp
Emp.: 370
Business & Consumer Exhibitions Organizer
N.A.I.C.S.: 561920
Takeshi Tanaka *(Pres & CEO)*

Reed Exhibitions (China) Co., Ltd. (4)
15/F Tower A Pingan International Finance Center No 1-3, Xinyuan South Road Chaoyang District, Beijing, 100027, China
Tel.: (86) 1059339000
Web Site: https://www.rxglobal.com.cn
Business & Consumer Exhibitions Organizer
N.A.I.C.S.: 561920
Josephine Lee *(COO)*

Joint Venture (Domestic):

Reed Sinopharm Exhibitions Co., Ltd. (5)
15th Floor Tower B Ping An International Finance Center, No 1-3 Xinyuan South Rd, Beijing, 100027, China
Tel.: (86) 1084556677
Web Site: http://www.reed-sinopharm.com
Pharmaceutical Medical & Health Care Exhibition Trade Show Organizer Services
N.A.I.C.S.: 561920

Group (US):

Reed Exhibitions - Americas (4)
201 Merritt 7, Norwalk, CT 06851
Tel.: (203) 840-4800
Web Site: https://rxglobal.com
Business & Consumer Exhibitions Organizer
N.A.I.C.S.: 561920
Gregg Vautrin *(Sr VP-Fin)*

Unit (Domestic):

Jewelers International Showcase (5)
1950 Eisenhower Blvd, Fort Lauderdale, FL 33316
Tel.: (203) 840-5612
Web Site: http://www.jisshow.com
Jewelry Trade Show Organizer
N.A.I.C.S.: 561920
Jordan Tuchband *(Grp VP-USA)*

Subsidiary (Non-US):

Reed Exhibitions Alcantara Machado Ltda. (5)
Rua Bela Cintra No 1200 10th Floor, Sao Paulo, 01415-002, Brazil
Tel.: (55) 1130605000
Web Site: https://rxglobal.com
Business & Consumer Exhibitions Organizer
N.A.I.C.S.: 561920
Caroline Goes *(Dir-Product Management)*

Unit (Domestic):

ReedPOP (5)
201 Merritt 7, Norwalk, CT 06851
Tel.: (203) 840-4800
Web Site: http://www.reedpop.com
Popular Culture Convention & Events Organizer
N.A.I.C.S.: 561920
Michael Kisken *(Sr VP)*

AND PRIVATE COMPANIES — RELX PLC

Subsidiary (Non-US):

Reed Exhibitions Australia Pty. Ltd. (4)
Tower 2 Level 1 475 Victoria Ave, Chatswood, 2067, NSW, Australia
Tel.: (61) 294222500
Web Site: https://www.rxglobal.com
Business & Consumer Exhibitions Organizer
N.A.I.C.S.: 561920
Brad Wheeler *(Sr Mgr-Ops)*

Subsidiary (Non-US):

Standout GmbH (5)
Am Messezentrum 7, 5020, Salzburg, Austria
Tel.: (43) 66293040
Web Site: https://www.standout.eu
Event Management Services
N.A.I.C.S.: 561920

Subsidiary (Non-US):

Reed Expositions France SAS (4)
52-54 quai de Dion Bouton, CS 80001, 92806, Puteaux, Cedex, France
Tel.: (33) 147565000
Web Site: https://www.rxglobal.fr
Business & Consumer Exhibitions Organizer
N.A.I.C.S.: 561920
Delphine Guyon *(Dir-HR)*

Division (Non-US):

Reed MIDEM SAS (4)
52-54 Quai de Dion-Bouton, 92806, Puteaux, Cedex, France
Tel.: (33) 147565000
Web Site: https://rxglobal.fr
Real Estate & Music Industry Trade Show Organizer
N.A.I.C.S.: 561920

Joint Venture (Non-US):

Thebe Reed Exhibitions Pty Limited (4)
Reed Place Bldg 1 Culross on Main Office Park 134 Culross Road, Bryanston, 2191, South Africa
Tel.: (27) 115498300
Convention & Trade Show Planning Services
N.A.I.C.S.: 561920
Carol Weaving *(Mng Dir)*

Subsidiary (US):

RELX Inc. (2)
230 Park Ave, New York, NY 10169
Tel.: (212) 309-8100
Web Site: http://www.lexisnexis.com
Legal, Tax, Regulatory, Risk Management, Information Analytics & Business Information Solutions
N.A.I.C.S.: 513199
Michael F. Walsh *(CEO)*

Subsidiary (Non-US):

LexisNexis (Pty) Limited (3)
Tel.: (27) 112456500
Legal, Tax, Regulatory, Risk Management & Business Information Publisher
N.A.I.C.S.: 513199
Ian Andrews *(CFO)*

Group (Non-US):

LexisNexis Asia Pacific (3)
3 Killiney Road #08-08 Winsland House 1, Singapore, 239519, Singapore
Tel.: (65) 67331380
Web Site: http://www.lexisnexis.com.sg
Holding Company; Legal, Tax, Regulatory, Risk Management & Business Information Publisher
N.A.I.C.S.: 551112
Gaythri Raman *(Mng Dir-Southeast Asia)*

Subsidiary (Domestic):

Lexis-Nexis Philippines Pte Ltd. (4)
3 Killiney Road 08-08 Winsland House 1, Singapore, 239519, Singapore
Tel.: (65) 63490110
Web Site: https://www.lexisnexis.com.sg
Risk Managemeng Srvices

Unit (Non-US):

LexisNexis Australia (4)
Tower 2 475-495 Victoria Avenue, Locked Bag 2222, Chatswood Delivery Centre, Chatswood, 2067, NSW, Australia
Tel.: (61) 1800772772
Web Site: http://www.lexisnexis.com.au
Legal, Tax, Regulatory, Risk Management & Business Information Publisher
N.A.I.C.S.: 513199
Greg Dickason *(Mng Dir)*

Subsidiary (Non-US):

LexisNexis NZ Limited (5)
Level 13, SAP Tower 151 Queen Street, Auckland, 1010, New Zealand
Tel.: (64) 800800986
Web Site: https://store.lexisnexis.co.nz
Legal, Tax, Regulatory, Risk Management & Business Information Publisher
N.A.I.C.S.: 513199
Chris Murray *(Head-Content Mgmt)*

Unit (Non-US):

LexisNexis China - Beijing (4)
Unit 1-6, 7/F Tower W1, Oriental Plaza No. 1, East Chang An Ave,, Dong Cheng District, Beijing, 100738, China
Tel.: (86) 1085185801
Web Site: http://www.lexisnexis.com.cn
Legal, Tax, Regulatory, Risk Management & Business Information Publisher
N.A.I.C.S.: 513199

LexisNexis China - Shanghai (4)
5/F Unit A Shanghai Divine wisdom world No 567, Changning District, Shanghai, 200335, China
Tel.: (86) 2161333000
Web Site: http://www.lexisnexis.com.cn
Legal, Tax, Regulatory, Risk Management & Business Information Publisher
N.A.I.C.S.: 513199
Min Chen *(CTO & VP)*

LexisNexis Hong Kong (4)
3901 Hopewell Centre 183 Queen's Road East, Hong Kong, China (Hong Kong)
Tel.: (852) 29651400
Web Site: http://www.lexisnexis.com.hk
Legal, Tax, Regulatory, Risk Management & Business Information Publisher
N.A.I.C.S.: 513199
Timothy Ho *(Head-Customer Success-Hongkong & Taiwan)*

LexisNexis India (4)
14th Floor Tower B Building No 10 DLF Cyber City Phase-II, Gurgaon, 122002, Haryana, India
Tel.: (91) 1244774477
Web Site: https://www.lexisnexis.in
Legal, Tax, Regulatory, Risk Management & Business Information Publisher
N.A.I.C.S.: 513199
Mahendra Chaturvedi *(Dir-Sls)*

Subsidiary (Non-US):

LexisNexis Japan Co., Ltd. (4)
1-9-15 Higashi Azabu 1-chome Building, Minato-ku, Tokyo, 106-0044, Japan
Tel.: (81) 355613551
Web Site: http://www.lexisnexis.jp
Legal, Tax, Regulatory, Risk Management & Business Information Publisher
N.A.I.C.S.: 513199

LexisNexis Malaysia Sdn. Bhd. (4)
Suite 29-1 Level 29 Vertical Corporate Tower B, Avenue 10 The Vertical, Kuala Lumpur, 59200, Bangsar South City, Malaysia
Tel.: (60) 321087888
Web Site: http://www.lexisnexis.com.my
Legal, Tax, Regulatory, Risk Management & Business Information Publisher
N.A.I.C.S.: 513199
Gaythri Raman *(Mng Dir-Southeast Asia)*

Unit (Domestic):

LexisNexis Singapore (4)
3 Killiney Road #08-08 Winsland House 1, Singapore, 239519, Singapore
Tel.: (65) 67331380

Web Site: http://www.lexisnexis.com.sg
Legal, Tax, Regulatory, Risk Management & Business Information Publisher
N.A.I.C.S.: 513199
Gaythri Raman *(Mng Dir-Southeast Asia)*

Subsidiary (Non-US):

LexisNexis Benelux BV (3)
Radarweg 29, 1043 NX, Amsterdam, Netherlands
Tel.: (31) 204853456
Web Site: http://www.lexisnexis.nl
Legal, Tax, Regulatory, Risk Management & Business Information Publisher
N.A.I.C.S.: 513199
Simon Barker *(VP-Sls-Benelux)*

LexisNexis Canada Inc. (3)
111 Gordon Baker Road Suite 900, Toronto, M2H 3R1, ON, Canada
Tel.: (905) 479-2665
Web Site: http://www.lexisnexis.ca
Legal, Tax, Regulatory, Risk Management & Business Information Publisher
N.A.I.C.S.: 513199
Eric Wright *(CEO)*

LexisNexis GmbH (3)
Heerdter Sandberg 30, 40549, Dusseldorf, Germany
Tel.: (49) 21141743540
Web Site: http://www.lexisnexis.de
Legal & Business Information Distr
N.A.I.C.S.: 519290
Michael Krake *(Mng Dir)*

Division (Domestic):

LexisNexis Legal & Professional (3)
9443 Springboro Pike, Miamisburg, OH 45342
Tel.: (888) 285-3947
Web Site: http://www.lexisnexis.com
Legal, Tax, Regulatory & Business Information Products & Services
N.A.I.C.S.: 519290
Andrew M. Matuch *(Pres-Intellectual Property & Reed Tech)*

Subsidiary (Non-US):

Caselex BV (4)
Wolfhezerweg 5, 6861 AA, Oosterbeek, Netherlands
Tel.: (31) 653897002
Web Site: https://www.caselex.eu
Legal Information Services
N.A.I.C.S.: 519290
Iason Mourellos *(Head)*

Subsidiary (Domestic):

Intelligize, Incorporated (4)
230 Park Ave 7th Fl, New York, NY 10169 (100%)
Web Site: http://www.intelligize.com
Document Analytic Software Platform Developer
N.A.I.C.S.: 541511
Christian Berczely *(CEO & CTO)*

Lex Machina, Inc. (4)
1010 Doyle St Ste 200, Menlo Park, CA 94025
Tel.: (650) 390-9500
Web Site: http://www.lexmachina.com
Legal Data Mining Services & Analytical Platform Developer
N.A.I.C.S.: 518210
Gavin Carothers *(Sr Dir-Software Engrg)*

Matthew Bender & Company, Inc. (4)
230 Park Ave, New York, NY 10169
Tel.: (212) 309-8100
Web Site: http://www.lexisnexis.com
Legal Information Publisher & Distr
N.A.I.C.S.: 513130

Portfolio Media, Inc. (4)
230 Park Ave 7th Fl, New York, NY 10169
Tel.: (646) 783-7100
Web Site: http://www.law360.com
Online Publisher of News, Articles & Newsletters for the Legal Industry
N.A.I.C.S.: 513110

Division (Domestic):

LexisNexis Risk Solutions Inc. (3)
1000 Alderman Dr, Alpharetta, GA 30005
Tel.: (678) 694-3160
Web Site: http://risk.lexisnexis.com
Technology & Information-Based Risk Mitigation Products & Services
N.A.I.C.S.: 518210
William S. Madison *(CEO-Insurance Risk Solutions)*

Subsidiary (Domestic):

Emailage Corp. (4)
25 S Arizona Pl Ste 400, Chandler, AZ 85225
Tel.: (480) 634-8437
Web Site: https://risk.lexisnexis.com
Fraud Prevention & Risk Management Software
N.A.I.C.S.: 541511

Subsidiary (Non-US):

Genilex Information Technology Co., Ltd. (4)
4th Floor South District Digital Technology Plaza No 9, Shangdi 9th Street, Haidian District, Beijing, 100085, China
Tel.: (86) 10 8270 0018
Workflow Efficiency & Business Risk Analytical Software Publisher
N.A.I.C.S.: 541511
Yalei Zhang *(Mktg Mgr)*

Subsidiary (Domestic):

ID Analytics, LLC (4)
15253 Ave of Science, San Diego, CA 92128
Tel.: (858) 312-6200
Web Site: https://risk.lexisnexis.com
Custom Computer Programming Services
N.A.I.C.S.: 541511

Branch (Domestic):

LexisNexis Risk Solutions Inc. - Dayton (4)
9443 Springboro Pike, Dayton, OH 45342
Tel.: (937) 865-6800
Risk Management Products & Services
N.A.I.C.S.: 561499
Scott Sessler *(Sr VP-Strategy & Bus Dev)*

LexisNexis Risk Solutions Inc. - Minneapolis (4)
510 First Ave N Ste 520, Minneapolis, MN 55403
Tel.: (612) 746-5100
Risk Management Software Product Development & Services
N.A.I.C.S.: 513210

LexisNexis Risk Solutions Inc. - Oklahoma City (4)
1900 NW Expy, Oklahoma City, OK 73118
Tel.: (405) 302-6100
Public Record Data Retrieval Services
N.A.I.C.S.: 519290

Subsidiary (Domestic):

LexisNexis Special Services Inc. (4)
1150 18th St NW Ste 250, Washington, DC 20036
Tel.: (202) 378-1002
Web Site: http://lexisnexisspecialservices.com
Government-Specific Information Technology Solutions
N.A.I.C.S.: 541511

LexisNexis VitalChek Network Inc. (4)
One Creekside Crossing 6 Cadillac Dr Ste 400, Brentwood, TN 37027
Tel.: (615) 372-6800
Web Site: http://www.vitalchek.com
Online Government Certificate Preparation Services
N.A.I.C.S.: 518210

ThreatMetrix, Inc. (4)
160 W Santa Clara St Ste 1400, San Jose, CA 95113
Tel.: (408) 200-5755
Web Site: https://risk.lexisnexis.com
Risk-Based Software Developer & Data Services
N.A.I.C.S.: 541511

RELX PLC / INTERNATIONAL PUBLIC

RELX plc—(Continued)

Subsidiary (Non-US):

Tracesmart Ltd. (4)
Global Reach Dunleavy Drive, Cardiff, CF11 0SN, United Kingdom
Tel.: (44) 2920678555
Consumer Data, Identity, Risk & Trace Software Developer & Publisher
N.A.I.C.S.: 513210

Subsidiary (Non-US):

LexisNexis SA (3)
141 rue de Javel, 75747, Paris, Cedex 15, France
Tel.: (33) 171724770
Web Site: http://www.lexisnexis.fr
Legal, Tax, Regulatory, Risk Management & Business Information Publisher
N.A.I.C.S.: 513199
Philippe Carillon (Pres-EMEA)

Subsidiary (Domestic):

LexisNexis Business Information Solutions SA (4)
141 rue de Javel, 75015, Paris, France
Tel.: (33) 171724850
Web Site: http://bis.lexisnexis.fr
Online Legal & Business Information & Analytics Publisher
N.A.I.C.S.: 513199

Division (Non-US):

LexisNexis UK (3)
Halsbury House 35 Chancery Lane, WC2A 1EL, London, United Kingdom - England
Tel.: (44) 2074002984
Web Site: https://www.lexisnexis.co.in
Legal, Tax, Regulatory, Risk Management & Business Information Publisher
N.A.I.C.S.: 513199
Caryn McEwen (Head-Global Licensing & Content Ops-BIS)

Unit (Non-US):

LexisNexis Enterprise Solutions (4)
30 Farringdon Street, London, EC4A 4HH, United Kingdom
Tel.: (44) 3301611234
Web Site: https://www.lexisnexis.co.uk
Legal Information Technologies Services
N.A.I.C.S.: 541513
Andrew Lindsay (Gen Mgr)

Branch (Domestic):

LexisNexis Enterprise Solutions (5)
1 Wellington Pl, Leeds, LS1 4AP, United Kingdom
Tel.: (44) 1132262065
Web Site: http://www.lexisnexis-es.co.uk
Legal File Management Software Developer & Publisher
N.A.I.C.S.: 513210
Andrew Lindsay (Gen Mgr)

Subsidiary (Non-US):

MLex Limited (4)
7th Floor Lexis House 30 Farringdon Street, London, EC4A 4HH, United Kingdom
Tel.: (215) 564-7770
Web Site: https://mlexmarketinsight.com
Regulatory Risk Market Media Publisher & Information Services
N.A.I.C.S.: 519290
Robert McLeod (Co-Founder & Chm)

Subsidiary (Non-US):

LexisNexis Verlag ARD Orac GmbH & Co KG (3)
Trabenstrasse 2A, A-1020, Vienna, Austria
Tel.: (43) 1534520
Web Site: http://www.lexisnexis.at
Legal, Tax, Regulatory, Risk Management & Business Information Publisher
N.A.I.C.S.: 513199
Sonja Spindler (Dir-HR)

Subsidiary (Domestic):

RELX Capital Inc. (3)
1105 N Market St Ste 501, Wilmington, DE 19801-1216
Tel.: (302) 427-9299

Holding Company; Debt Securities Investment Fund
N.A.I.C.S.: 551112
Lynn M. Formica (Treas)

Branch (Domestic):

RELX Inc. - Chicago Office (3)
200 W Madison St Ste 1170, Chicago, IL 60606
Tel.: (312) 236-7903
Legal & Business Information Research Services
N.A.I.C.S.: 541199
Elena Cutri (Dir-Client Education Services)

RELX Inc. - Colorado Springs Office (3)
555 Middlecreek Pkwy, Colorado Springs, CO 80921-3622
Tel.: (719) 488-3000
Legal & Business Information Research Services
N.A.I.C.S.: 513130

RELX Inc. - D.C. Office (3)
1150 18th St NW, Washington, DC 20036
Tel.: (202) 785-3550
Web Site: http://www.lexisnexis.com
Legal & Government Regulatory Information Research Services
N.A.I.C.S.: 519290
Ronald Martin (VP-Federal Govt)

RELX Inc. - Raleigh Office (3)
1801 Varsity Dr, Raleigh, NC 27606
Tel.: (800) 543-6862
Web Site: http://www.lexisnexis.com
Online Legal Information Publisher
N.A.I.C.S.: 519290
Paul Knodel (Sr VP-Client Svcs)

Subsidiary (Non-US):

Reed Elsevier Shared Services (Philippines) Inc. (3)
2nd Floor Bldg H UP-AyalaLand Technohub Commonwealth Avenue, Diliman, Quezon City, 1101, Philippines
Tel.: (63) 22732900
Web Site: http://www.reedelsevier.com.ph
Content Support Services
N.A.I.C.S.: 561499
Roel D. Mapoy (Sr Dir-Editorial Ops)

Branch (Domestic):

Reed Elsevier Shared Services (Philippines) Inc. - Iloilo Office (4)
3rd Floor Richmonde Tower 8 Enterprise Road cor Old Airport Road, Iloilo Business Park Mandurriao, Iloilo, 5000, Philippines
Tel.: (63) 333967333
Web Site: http://www.reedelsevier.com.ph
Call Center, Content Operations & Office Support Services
N.A.I.C.S.: 561499
Timothy J. Vilches (Ops Mgr-EEMG)

Subsidiary (Domestic):

Reed Technology & Information Services Inc. (3)
7 Walnut Grove Dr, Horsham, PA 19044
Tel.: (215) 557-3010
Web Site: https://www.reedtech.com
Electronic Content Management Services
N.A.I.C.S.: 518210
Andrew Matuch (Pres-Intellectual Property)

Unit (Domestic):

Reed Tech IP Services (4)
7 Walnut Grove Dr, Horsham, PA 19044
Tel.: (215) 682-8261
Web Site: http://www.reedtechip.com
Intellectual Property Support Services
N.A.I.C.S.: 561990
Wayne Birch (Dir-IP Product Mgmt & Ops)

Branch (Domestic):

Reed Technology & Information Services Inc. - Virginia (4)
2331 Mill Rd Ste 300, Alexandria, VA 22314
Tel.: (703) 664-6100
Web Site: https://corporate.reedtech.com
Electronic Content Management Services
N.A.I.C.S.: 518210

Subsidiary (Non-US):

RELX Information Analytics (Thailand) Co., Ltd. (2)
2 Ploenchit Centre Ground Floor Sukhumvit Road, Klongteoy, Bangkok, Thailand
Tel.: (66) 23056697
Life Science Research & Development Services
N.A.I.C.S.: 541715

RELX Nederland B.V. (2)
Radarweg 29, 1043 NX, Amsterdam, Netherlands (100%)
Tel.: (31) 204852222
Web Site: http://www.relx.com
Holding Company; Regional Managing Office
N.A.I.C.S.: 551112

Group (Domestic):

Elsevier B.V. (3)
Radarweg 29, Amsterdam, 1043 NX, Netherlands
Tel.: (31) 204853911
Web Site: https://www.elsevier.com
Scientific Medical Books, Journal & Electronic Media Publisher
N.A.I.C.S.: 513130
Anita Chandraprakash (Exec VP-Global Ops)

Subsidiary (Non-US):

Elsevier (Australia) Pty. Limited (4)
Tower 1 Level 12 475 Victoria Avenue, Locked Bag 7500 DC, Chatswood, 2067, NSW, Australia
Tel.: (61) 1800263951
Web Site: http://www.elsevierhealth.com.au
Scientific & Medical Publisher & Book Distr
N.A.I.C.S.: 513130
Ana Mendes (Mgr-Ops & IT)

Elsevier Editora Ltda (4)
City Tower Building 100 Rua de Assembleia St, RJ 20011-904, Rio de Janeiro, Brazil
Tel.: (55) 2139709300
Web Site: http://www.elsevier.com
Educational, Reference & Professional Book Publishing
N.A.I.C.S.: 513130
Ezequiel M. Farre (Reg Dir-Brazil)

Subsidiary (US):

Elsevier Inc. (4)
230 Park Ave, New York, NY 10169
Tel.: (212) 309-8100
Web Site: https://www.elsevier.com
Scientific & Medical Books, Journal & Electronic Media Publisher
N.A.I.C.S.: 513130
Youngsuk Chi (Chm & Dir-Corp Affairs)

Subsidiary (Domestic):

Aries Systems Corporation (5)
50 High St Ste 21, North Andover, MA 01845
Tel.: (978) 975-7570
Web Site: http://www.ariessys.com
Publishing Software Developer & Publisher
N.A.I.C.S.: 513210
Jennifer Fleet (Mng Dir)

Division (Domestic):

Elsevier Health Sciences (5)
230 Park Ave, New York, NY 10169
Tel.: (212) 309-8100
Web Site: http://www.us.elsevierhealth.com
Publishers of Medical Books & Journals
N.A.I.C.S.: 513199

Subsidiary (Domestic):

Elsevier Inc. (6)
230 Park Ave, New York, NY 10169
Tel.: (212) 309-8100
Web Site: http://www.us.elsevierhealth.com
Radiology, Pathology & Anatomy Information Publisher
N.A.I.C.S.: 513130
Joslyn Dumas (Mgr-Inclusion & Diversity Program)

Branch (Domestic):

Elsevier Inc. - Cell Press (5)

50 Hampshire St 5th Fl, Cambridge, MA 02139
Tel.: (617) 397-2800
Web Site: http://www.cell.com
Scientific Publisher
N.A.I.C.S.: 513120
Meredith Adinolfi (VP-Publ Ops)

Subsidiary (Domestic):

Social Science Electronic Publishing, Inc.
100 S Clinton Ave Ste 2407, Rochester, NY 14604
Tel.: (212) 448-2500
Web Site: http://www.ssrn.com
Online Social Sciences & Humanities Paper Database Publisher
N.A.I.C.S.: 513140
Gregory Gordon (Mng Dir-Knowledge Life Cycle Management)

Unit (Domestic):

bepress (5)
2100 Milvia St Ste 300, Berkeley, CA 94704
Tel.: (510) 665-1200
Web Site: http://www.bepress.com
Institutional Publication Repository Services
N.A.I.C.S.: 518210
Eli Windchy (VP-Consulting Svcs)

Subsidiary (Non-US):

Elsevier Information Systems GmbH (4)
2nd Floor St Martin Tower Franklinstrasse 61-63, 60486, Frankfurt, Germany
Tel.: (49) 6950504242
Printed Circuit Assembly Mfr
N.A.I.C.S.: 334418

Elsevier Ireland Limited (4)
Suites 304 305 & 306 Shannon Airport House Shannon Free Zone, Shannon, Ireland
Tel.: (353) 1865843000
Web Site: http://www.elsevier.com
Scientific Publishing
N.A.I.C.S.: 513130
Brendan Curtin (Mng Dir)

Elsevier Japan KK (4)
1-9-15 Higashi-Azabu, Minato-ku, Tokyo, 106 0044, Japan
Tel.: (81) 355615050
Web Site: http://www.elsevierjapan.com
Health Science Publications
N.A.I.C.S.: 513130
Takeshi Shimizu (Mgr-Product Sls)

Elsevier Korea LLC (4)
4Fl Chunwoo Bldg 206 Noksapyeong-daero Itaewon-dong Yongsan-gu, Seoul, 04345, Korea (South)
Tel.: (82) 267143000
Scientific Publishing
N.A.I.C.S.: 513130
Yongsoo Jeun (Reg Dir-Research Solutions-Korea & Taiwan)

Elsevier Limited (4)
125 London Wall, London, EC2Y 5AS, United Kingdom
Tel.: (44) 2074244200
Scientific, Technical & Medical Publishing
N.A.I.C.S.: 513130
Elizabeth Munn (Mng Dir-Education-Euro, Middle East, Africa, Latin America, Asia-Pacific & Mng Dir-Global Medical Education)

Subsidiary (Domestic):

Mendeley Ltd. (5)
AlphaBeta Bldg 14-16 Finsbury Sq, London, EC2A 1BR, United Kingdom
Tel.: (44) 3301613015
Web Site: http://www.mendeley.com
Research Collaboration & Organization Software Developer & Publisher
N.A.I.C.S.: 513210

Unit (Domestic):

The Lancet (5)
125 London Wall, London, EC2Y 5AS, United Kingdom
Tel.: (44) 2074244950
Web Site: http://www.thelancet.com

AND PRIVATE COMPANIES

Weekly General Medical Journal Providing Research, Review Articles, News & Commentary on All Aspects of Medicine
N.A.I.C.S.: 513120
Richard Horton *(Editor-in-Chief)*

Subsidiary (Non-US):

Elsevier Masson SAS (4)
65 rue Camille Desmoulins CS 50083, Issy-les-Moulineaux, Paris, 92442, France
Tel.: (33) 171165500
Web Site: http://www.elsevier-masson.fr
Educational, Scientific & Technical Book Publishing
N.A.I.C.S.: 513130
Frederic Fabre *(Head-Content Project Management)*

Elsevier Services Ireland Ltd. (4)
Suites 304 305 & 306 Shannon Airport House, Shannon Free Zone, Shannon, Ireland
Tel.: (353) 1865843000
Printed Circuit Assembly Mfr
N.A.I.C.S.: 334418

Elsevier Singapore Pte. Ltd. (4)
3 Killiney Road #08-01 Winsland House 1, Singapore, 239519, Singapore
Tel.: (65) 63490200
Scientific Publications
N.A.I.C.S.: 513130
Linda Chan *(Reg Dir-Solution Sales-Asia-Pacific)*

SciBite Ltd. (4)
BioData Innovation Centre Wellcome Genome Campus, Hinxton, Cambridge, CB10 1DR, United Kingdom
Tel.: (44) 1223786120
Web Site: https://www.scibite.com
Software Development Services
N.A.I.C.S.: 541511

Science-Metrix Inc. (4)
500-4428 Boul. Saint Laurent, Montreal, H2W 1Z5, QC, Canada
Tel.: (438) 495-8000
Web Site: http://www.science-metrix.com
Scientific Research & Analytics Services
N.A.I.C.S.: 541990
Isabelle Labrosse *(Administrative Director)*

REM GROUP (HOLDINGS) LTD.
Unit 5 4/F Chai Wan Industrial City Phase II No 70 Wing Tai Road, Hong Kong, China (Hong Kong)
Tel.: (852) 37074197 Ky
Web Site: http://www.rem-group.com.hk
1750—(HKG)
Rev.: $27,959,858
Assets: $30,101,475
Liabilities: $9,363,855
Net Worth: $20,737,620
Earnings: $1,060,290
Emp.: 238
Fiscal Year-end: 12/31/22
Electric Power Distribution Equipment Mfr & Distr
N.A.I.C.S.: 335311
Man Keung Wan *(Chm)*

REMAK ENERGOMONTAZ SA
ul Chlodna 51, 00-867, Warsaw, Poland
Tel.: (48) 774552011
Web Site: https://www.remak.com.pl
Year Founded: 1970
RMK—(WAR)
Rev.: $42,246,857
Assets: $34,038,451
Liabilities: $18,857,027
Net Worth: $15,181,424
Earnings: $549,265
Fiscal Year-end: 12/31/22
Engineeering Services
N.A.I.C.S.: 541330
Jacek Sadowski *(Member-Mgmt Bd & VP)*

REMARO GROUP CORP.
Calle Robles Casa 25, Quito, Ecuador
Tel.: (593) 56 2 2979 1247 NV
Year Founded: 2016
Assets: $3,132
Liabilities: $5,664
Net Worth: ($2,532)
Earnings: ($19,817)
Fiscal Year-end: 07/31/19
Travel Agency
N.A.I.C.S.: 561510
Daniel Capri *(Pres, Sec & Treas)*

REMARUL 16 FEBRUARIE SA
Tudor Vladimirescu str No 2-4, 400225, Cluj-Napoca, Romania
Tel.: (40) 74155555
Web Site: https://www.remarul.eu
Year Founded: 1870
REFE—(BUC)
Rev.: $10,587,551
Assets: $32,572,166
Liabilities: $22,759,882
Net Worth: $9,812,284
Earnings: ($1,683,920)
Emp.: 235
Fiscal Year-end: 12/31/23
Railway Locomotive & Rolling Stock Mfr
N.A.I.C.S.: 336510

REMAT MARAMURES SA
Bd Bucuresti nr 51, 430013, Baia Mare, Maramures, Romania
Tel.: (40) 262222661
Web Site: http://www.remat-mm.ro
Sales Range: $1-9.9 Million
Emp.: 26
Waste Recovery & Sales
N.A.I.C.S.: 562111

REMBRANDTIN LACK GMBH NFG KG
Ignaz-Kock-Strasse 15, 1210, Vienna, Austria
Tel.: (43) 1277020 AT
Web Site: http://www.rembrandtin.com
Sales Range: $50-74.9 Million
Emp.: 100
Specialty Industrial Coating Mfr
N.A.I.C.S.: 325510
Hubert Culik *(Mng Dir)*

REMED CO., LTD.
13647 21-7 Wiryeseoil-ro 1-gil, Bundang-Gu Sampyeong-Dong, Seongnam, Gyeonggi-do, Korea (South)
Tel.: (82) 15887395
Web Site: https://www.remed.kr
Year Founded: 2003
302550—(KRS)
Rev.: $16,385,769
Assets: $59,922,063
Liabilities: $36,910,579
Net Worth: $23,011,483
Earnings: $3,068,100
Emp.: 88
Fiscal Year-end: 12/31/22
Medical Device Mfr & Distr
N.A.I.C.S.: 339112
Eun-Hyun Koh *(CEO)*

REMEDENT, INC.
Zuiderlaan 1-3 box 8, 9000, Gent, Belgium
Tel.: (32) 92415880 NV
Web Site: https://www.remedent.com
Year Founded: 1986
REMI—(OTCIQ)
Rev.: $863,000
Assets: $5,588,000
Liabilities: $2,996,000
Net Worth: $2,592,000
Earnings: ($1,494,000)
Emp.: 3
Fiscal Year-end: 03/31/23
Oral Care & Cosmetic Dentistry Products Mfr
N.A.I.C.S.: 339114

Subsidiaries:

Remedent N.V. (1)
Zuiderlaan 1-3, Box 8, 9000, Gent, Belgium
Tel.: (32) 92415880
Web Site: http://www.remedent.be
Dental Equipment Mfr & Distr
N.A.I.C.S.: 339114
Guy De Vreese *(Chm & CEO)*

REMEDIUM LIFECARE LTD.
Office No 9 K Raheja Prime Marol Industrial Estate, Behind Ravi Vihar Hotel, Mumbai, 400059, Maharashtra, India
Tel.: (91) 8433895251
Web Site: https://www.remlife.com
539561—(BOM)
Rev.: $61,127,822
Assets: $138,387,711
Liabilities: $137,145,063
Net Worth: $1,242,647
Earnings: $650,573
Emp.: 7
Fiscal Year-end: 03/31/23
Pharmaceutical Company
N.A.I.C.S.: 325412
Siddharth Chimmanlal Shah *(Mng Dir)*

REMEDY ENTERTAINMENT PLC
Luomanportti 3, 02200, Espoo, Finland
Tel.: (358) 94355040
Web Site: https://www.remedygames.com
Year Founded: 1995
REMEDY—(HEL)
Emp.: 352
Online Game Development Services
N.A.I.C.S.: 541511
Sami Jarvi *(Creative Dir)*

REMEGEN COMPANY LIMITED
58 Beijing Middle Road, Yantai, Shandong, China
Tel.: (86) 5356113511 CN
Web Site: http://www.remegen.com
Year Founded: 2008
9995—(HKG)
Emp.: 280
Pharmaceutical Product Mfr & Distr
N.A.I.C.S.: 325412
Weidong Wang *(Co-Founder & Chm)*

Subsidiaries:

RemeGen Biosciences, Inc. (1)
650 Gateway Dr Ste 110, South San Francisco, CA 94080
Web Site: http://www.remegenbio.com
Research & Development Services
N.A.I.C.S.: 541714

REMGRO LIMITED
Millennia Park 16 Stellentia Avenue, Stellenbosch, 7600, South Africa
Tel.: (27) 218883000 ZA
Web Site: https://www.remgro.com
Year Founded: 2000
REM—(JSE)
Rev.: $2,542,855,332
Assets: $7,972,464,855
Liabilities: $1,506,353,046
Net Worth: $6,466,111,809
Earnings: $127,113,721
Emp.: 178
Fiscal Year-end: 06/30/23
Investment Holding Company
N.A.I.C.S.: 551112
Jannie Jonathan Durand *(CEO)*

Subsidiaries:

Air Products South Africa (Pty) Ltd. (1)
Silver Stream Business Park Building 3 1st Floor 10 Muswell Drive, Bryanston, 2191, South Africa (50%)
Tel.: (27) 11 570 5000
Web Site: https://www.airproducts.co.za
Sales Range: $50-74.9 Million
Emp.: 350
Industrial Gas Mfr
N.A.I.C.S.: 325120
Robert Richardson *(Mng Dir)*

Energy Exchange of Southern Africa Proprietary Limited (1)
4th Floor Hill House 42 De Smit Street, De Waterkant, Cape Town, South Africa
Tel.: (27) 212865062
Web Site: https://www.energyexchangesa.com
Solar Energy Distr
N.A.I.C.S.: 486210

Enerweb Proprietary Limited (1)
Spaces Waterfall Ground Floor Gateway West 22 Magwa Crescent, Waterfall City, Midrand, South Africa
Tel.: (27) 873795600
Web Site: https://www.enerweb.co.za
Electricity Utility Services
N.A.I.C.S.: 221122

InVenFin (Pty) Limited (1)
16 Stellentia Avenue, Millennia Park, Stellenbosch, 7600, South Africa (100%)
Tel.: (27) 21 888 3355
Web Site: https://www.invenfin.com
Sales Range: $50-74.9 Million
Emp.: 5
Equity Investment Firm
N.A.I.C.S.: 523999
Stuart Gast *(Exec Dir)*

Mediclinic International plc (1)
6th Floor 65 Gresham Street, London, EC2V 7NQ, United Kingdom
Tel.: (44) 2079549548
Web Site: https://www.mediclinic.com
Rev.: $4,423,451,760
Assets: $9,785,088,040
Liabilities: $5,377,928,920
Net Worth: $4,407,159,120
Earnings: $230,812,400
Emp.: 34,964
Fiscal Year-end: 03/31/2022
Healthcare Services
N.A.I.C.S.: 622110
Ronnie Van der merwe *(CEO)*

Subsidiary (Non-US):

Clinique des Grangettes SA (2)
Chemin des Grangettes 7, 1224, Chene-Bougeries, Switzerland
Tel.: (41) 223050111
Hospital & Healthcare Services
N.A.I.C.S.: 622110

Denmar Specialist Psychiatric Hospital (Pty.) Ltd. (2)
507 Lancelot Road x16, Garsfontein, Pretoria, 0081, South Africa
Tel.: (27) 129986062
Web Site: http://www.denmar.co.za
Psychiatric Healthcare Services
N.A.I.C.S.: 622210

Hirslanden AG (2)
Boulevard Lilienthal 2, Glattpark, 8152, Opfikon, Switzerland
Tel.: (41) 443888585
Web Site: http://www.hirslanden.ch
Hospital & Healthcare Services
N.A.I.C.S.: 622110
Marco Fey *(Officer-Data Protection)*

Hirslanden Clinique La Colline S.A. (2)
Avenue Beau-Sejour 6, 1206, Geneva, Switzerland
Tel.: (41) 227022022
Emp.: 300
Hospital & Healthcare Services
N.A.I.C.S.: 622110

Mediclinic Bloemfontein Investments (Pty.) Ltd. (2)
Cnr Kellner and Parfitt Street, Westdene,

REMGRO LIMITED

Remgro Limited—(Continued)

Bloemfontein, 9301, South Africa
Tel.: (27) 514046666
Hospital & Healthcare Services
N.A.I.C.S.: 622110

Mediclinic Brits (Pty.) Ltd. (2)
8 Church Street, Brits, 0250, South Africa
Tel.: (27) 122528000
Hospital & Healthcare Services
N.A.I.C.S.: 622110

Mediclinic Cape Gate Day Clinic Investments (Pty.) Ltd. (2)
Cnr Okavango and Tanner Roads, Brackenfell, Cape Town, 7560, South Africa
Tel.: (27) 219835600
Hospital & Healthcare Services
N.A.I.C.S.: 622110

Mediclinic Durbanville Day Clinic (Pty.) Ltd. (2)
45 Wellington Road, Durbanville, Cape Town, 7550, South Africa
Tel.: (27) 219802135
Hospital & Healthcare Services
N.A.I.C.S.: 622110

Mediclinic Ermelo (Pty.) Ltd. (2)
25 Mel Mentz Street, Ermelo, 2356, South Africa
Tel.: (27) 178012600
Hospital & Healthcare Services
N.A.I.C.S.: 622110

Mediclinic George Investments (Pty.) Ltd. (2)
Cnr Gloucester and York Street, George, 6530, South Africa
Tel.: (27) 448032000
Hospital & Healthcare Services
N.A.I.C.S.: 622110

Mediclinic Hermanus (Pty.) Ltd. (2)
Ravenscroft Road, Hermanus, Cape Town, 7200, South Africa
Tel.: (27) 283130168
Hospital & Healthcare Services
N.A.I.C.S.: 622110

Mediclinic Highveld Investments (Pty.) Ltd. (2)
Barney Molokwane Street, Louis Trichardt, 2300, South Africa
Tel.: (27) 176388000
Hospital & Healthcare Services
N.A.I.C.S.: 622110

Mediclinic Hoogland Investments (Pty.) Ltd. (2)
De Leeuw Street, Bethlehem, 9701, South Africa
Tel.: (27) 583072000
Hospital & Healthcare Services
N.A.I.C.S.: 622110

Mediclinic International Limited (2)
Strand Road, Stellenbosch, 7600, South Africa
Tel.: (27) 218096500
Web Site: http://www.mediclinic.com
Hospital Owner & Operator
N.A.I.C.S.: 622110
Stefan Smuts (Chief Clinical Officer)

Subsidiary (Domestic):

Aukland Medicine Distributors (Proprietary) Limited (3)
Willie Van Skoor Dr, 2nd Fl Tyger Park, Cape Town, 7530, Western Cape, South Africa
Tel.: (27) 219436300
Pharmaceutical Product Whslr
N.A.I.C.S.: 424210

Subsidiary (Non-US):

Clinique Bois-Cerf S.A. (3)
Avenue d'Ouchy 31, 1006, Lausanne, Switzerland
Tel.: (41) 216196969
Web Site: http://www.hirslanden.ch
Medical Devices
N.A.I.C.S.: 622110
Jean Marc Zumwald (Mng Dir)

Clinique Cecil SA (3)
Avenue Ruchonnet 53, 1003, Lausanne, Switzerland

Tel.: (41) 213105000
Web Site: http://www.hirslanden.ch
Emp.: 480
Medical Devices
N.A.I.C.S.: 622110
Igor Schupbach (Mgr-Hospitality & Facility)

Hirslanden Private Hospital Group (3)
Boulevard Lilienthal 2, 8008, Zurich, Switzerland
Tel.: (41) 443888585
Web Site: https://www.hirslanden.ch
Medical Devices
N.A.I.C.S.: 622110
Ole Wiesinger (CEO)

Subsidiary (Domestic):

Hirslanden Klinik Am Rosenberg AG (4)
Hasenbuhlstrasse 11, 9410, Heiden, Switzerland
Tel.: (41) 718985252
Web Site: http://www.hirslanden.ch
Medical Devices
N.A.I.C.S.: 622110
Reiner Backer (Mgr-IT)

Klinik Birshof AG (4)
Reinacherstrasse 28, 4142, Munchenstein, Basel, Switzerland
Tel.: (41) 613352222
Web Site: http://www.hirslanden.ch
Hospital Operations
N.A.I.C.S.: 622110
Beatriz Greuter (Dir)

Klinik Hirslanden AG (4)
Witellikerstrasse 40, 8032, Zurich, Switzerland
Tel.: (41) 443872111
Web Site: http://www.hirslanden.ch
Medical Devices
N.A.I.C.S.: 622110

Klinik am Rosenberg Heiden (4)
Hasenbuhlstrasse 11, 9410, Heiden, Switzerland
Tel.: (41) 718985252
Web Site: http://www.hirslanden.ch
Orthopaedics Related Services
N.A.I.C.S.: 622110

Subsidiary (Domestic):

Medical Human Resources (Proprietary) Limited (3)
Third Floor Tijger Park 1 Willie van Schoor Avenue, Tygervalley, Bellville, 7530, South Africa
Tel.: (27) 219436200
Web Site: http://www.mhr.co.za
Medical Staff Leasing Services
N.A.I.C.S.: 561330

Medical Innovations (Proprietary) Limited (3)
7 Cyclonite St The Interchange, Somerset West, 7130, Western Cape, South Africa
Tel.: (27) 218518484
Web Site: http://www.medicalinnovations.co.za
Hospital Equipments Dealer
N.A.I.C.S.: 423450

Mediclinic Kimberley (3)
177 Du Toitspan Road, Kimberley, 8301, South Africa
Tel.: (27) 538381111
Web Site: http://www.mediclinic.co.za
Multidisciplinary Hospital Services
N.A.I.C.S.: 622110
Denise Coetzee (Mgr-Client Services)

Potchefstroom Medi-Clinic (Proprietary) Limited (3)
66 Meyer Street, Potchefstroom, 2520, South Africa
Tel.: (27) 182937000
Web Site: http://www.mediclinic.co.za
Professional Medical Services
N.A.I.C.S.: 622110

Subsidiary (Non-US):

Salem-Spital AG (3)
Schanzlistrasse 39, 3013, Bern, Switzerland
Tel.: (27) 313376000
Web Site: http://www.hirslanden.ch

Emp.: 680
Hospital & Medical Services
N.A.I.C.S.: 622110

Subsidiary (Non-US):

Mediclinic Klein Karoo Investments (Pty.) Ltd. (2)
185 Church Street, Oudtshoorn, 6625, South Africa
Tel.: (27) 442720111
Hospital & Healthcare Services
N.A.I.C.S.: 622110

Mediclinic Legae Investments (Pty.) Ltd. (2)
8560 Unit M Off Makinta Highway, Mabopane, Pretoria, 0190, South Africa
Tel.: (27) 127978000
Hospital & Healthcare Services
N.A.I.C.S.: 622110

Mediclinic Lephalale (Pty.) Ltd. (2)
Cnr Douwater and Joe Slovo Street, Onverwacht, Lephalale, 0557, South Africa
Tel.: (27) 147620400
Hospital & Healthcare Services
N.A.I.C.S.: 622110

Mediclinic Louis Leipoldt Investments (Pty.) Ltd. (2)
Broadway, Bellville, Cape Town, 7530, South Africa
Tel.: (27) 219576000
Hospital & Healthcare Services
N.A.I.C.S.: 622110

Mediclinic Milnerton Investments (Pty.) Ltd. (2)
Cnr Racecourse and Koeberg Road, Milnerton, Cape Town, 7441, South Africa
Tel.: (27) 215299000
Hospital & Healthcare Services
N.A.I.C.S.: 622110

Mediclinic Morningside Investments (Pty.) Ltd. (2)
Cnr Rivonia and Hill Roads, Morningside, Johannesburg, 2057, South Africa
Tel.: (27) 112825000
Hospital & Healthcare Services
N.A.I.C.S.: 622110

Mediclinic Nelspruit Day Clinic Investments (Pty.) Ltd. (2)
1 Louise Street, Sonheuwel, Nelspruit, 1200, South Africa
Tel.: (27) 137590501
Hospital & Healthcare Services
N.A.I.C.S.: 622110

Mediclinic Otjiwarongo (Pty.) Ltd. (2)
Sonn Street, Otjiwarongo, 9000, Namibia
Tel.: (264) 67303734
Hospital & Healthcare Services
N.A.I.C.S.: 622110

Mediclinic Paarl (Pty.) Ltd. (2)
Berlyn Street, Noorder-Paarl, Paarl, 7646, South Africa
Tel.: (27) 218078000
Hospital & Healthcare Services
N.A.I.C.S.: 622110

Mediclinic Panorama Investments (Pty.) Ltd. (2)
Rothschild Boulevard, Panorama, Cape Town, 7500, South Africa
Tel.: (27) 219382111
Hospital & Healthcare Services
N.A.I.C.S.: 622110

Mediclinic Pietermaritzburg Investments (Pty.) Ltd. (2)
90 Payn Street, Pietermaritzburg, 3201, South Africa
Tel.: (27) 338453700
Hospital & Healthcare Services
N.A.I.C.S.: 622110

Mediclinic Plettenberg Bay Investments (Pty.) Ltd. (2)
Muller Street, Plettenberg Bay, 6600, South Africa
Tel.: (27) 445015100
Hospital & Healthcare Services
N.A.I.C.S.: 622110

Mediclinic Sandton Investments (Pty.) Ltd. (2)

INTERNATIONAL PUBLIC

Cnr Main Road and Peter Place, Bryanston, Johannesburg, 2021, South Africa
Tel.: (27) 117092000
Hospital & Healthcare Services
N.A.I.C.S.: 622110

Mediclinic Stellenbosch (Pty.) Ltd. (2)
1 Elsie Du Toit Drive, Stellenbosch, 7600, South Africa
Tel.: (27) 218612000
Hospital & Healthcare Services
N.A.I.C.S.: 622110

Mediclinic Swakopmund (Pty.) Ltd. (2)
Franziska van Neel Street, Swakopmund, Namibia
Tel.: (264) 64412200
Hospital & Healthcare Services
N.A.I.C.S.: 622110

Mediclinic Thabazimbi (Pty.) Ltd. (2)
173 Van der Bijl Street, Thabazimbi, 0380, South Africa
Tel.: (27) 147772097
Hospital & Healthcare Services
N.A.I.C.S.: 622110

Mediclinic Vereeniging Investments (Pty.) Ltd. (2)
Cnr Joubert Street and Hofmeyer Avenue, Vereeniging, 1939, South Africa
Tel.: (27) 164405000
Hospital & Healthcare Services
N.A.I.C.S.: 622110

Mediclinic Vergelegen Investments (Pty.) Ltd. (2)
Main Road, Somerset West, 7130, South Africa
Tel.: (27) 218509000
Hospital & Healthcare Services
N.A.I.C.S.: 622110

Mediclinic Welkom Investments (Pty.) Ltd. (2)
Meulen Street, Welkom, 9459, South Africa
Tel.: (27) 579165555
Hospital & Healthcare Services
N.A.I.C.S.: 622110

Mediclinic Windhoek (Pty.) Ltd. (2)
Heliodoor Street Eros, Windhoek, 9000, Namibia
Tel.: (264) 614331000
Hospital & Healthcare Services
N.A.I.C.S.: 622110

Mediclinic Worcester Investments (Pty.) Ltd. (2)
67 Fairbairn Street, Worcester, 6850, South Africa
Tel.: (27) 233481500
Hospital & Healthcare Services
N.A.I.C.S.: 622110

RCL Foods Limited (1)
10 The Boulevard Westway Office Park, Durban, 3629, South Africa (73.3%)
Web Site: http://www.rclfoods.com
Rev.: $1,971,892,056
Assets: $1,320,478,031
Liabilities: $708,743,123
Net Worth: $611,734,908
Earnings: $22,786,624
Emp.: 21,829
Fiscal Year-end: 06/30/2023
Holding Company; Chicken Processor & Marketer
N.A.I.C.S.: 551112
Paul D. Cruickshank (COO)

Subsidiary (Domestic):

Foodcorp (Pty.) Ltd. (2)
Parc Nicol Bldg No 1 3001 William Nicol Drive, Bryanston, 2021, South Africa (64.2%)
Tel.: (27) 115491030
Web Site: http://www.foodcorp.co.za
Sales Range: $900-999.9 Million
Emp.: 3,000
Food Products Mfr & Distr
N.A.I.C.S.: 311999
Marlene Edwards (Controller)

Remgro Management Services Limited (1)
Millennia Park 16 Stellentia Ave, Stellenbo-

sch, 7600, Western Cape, South Africa
Tel.: (27) 218883000
Web Site: http://www.remgro.com
Sales Range: $25-49.9 Million
Emp.: 110
Business Management Services
N.A.I.C.S.: 561110
Jannie Durand (CEO)

SEACOM SA SPV Proprietary Limited (1)
Level 1 Block A Anslow Office Park 8 Anslow Crescent Anslow Lane, Bryanston, South Africa
Tel.: (27) 114616355
Web Site: https://www.seacom.co.za
Telecommunication Servicesb
N.A.I.C.S.: 517810

Siqalo Foods Proprietary Limited (1)
6 The Boulevard Westway Office Park, Westville, 3629, South Africa
Tel.: (27) 873628500
Web Site: https://www.siqalofoods.com
Industrial Machinery Mfr
N.A.I.C.S.: 333248
Jan Du Toit (Head)

Stellenbosch Academy Of Sport Proprietary Limited (1)
1 Krige Street, Stellenbosch, 7600, Western Cape, South Africa
Tel.: (27) 21 861 7800
Web Site: https://www.sastraining.co.za
Academy Sports Services
N.A.I.C.S.: 611620
Faffa Knoetze (Chm)

Stellenbosch Football Club Proprietary Limited (1)
1 Krige Street, Stellenbosch, 7600, Western Cape, South Africa
Tel.: (27) 21 861 7812
Web Site: https://www.stellenboschfc.com
Academy Sports Services
N.A.I.C.S.: 611620
Rob Benadie (CEO)

Tsb Sugar Holdings (Pty) Limited (1)
Mhlati Farm, PO Box 47, 1320, Malelane, Mpumalanga, South Africa (100%)
Tel.: (27) 137911000
Web Site: http://www.tsb.co.za
Sales Range: $750-799.9 Million
Emp.: 2,400
Holding Company; Sugarcane Farming & Cane Refining
N.A.I.C.S.: 551112
Peter Holland (Mgr-Mktg)

Subsidiary (Non-US):

Booker Tate Ltd. (2)
Suite 3 Goodson Mews Wellington Street, Thame, OX9 3BX, Oxon, United Kingdom
Tel.: (44) 184 425 1000
Web Site: https://www.booker-tate.co.uk
Sales Range: $25-49.9 Million
Emp.: 25
Sugar Refining
N.A.I.C.S.: 311314
Robert Hodgson (Head-Factory Ops)

Wispeco Holdings Limited (1)
31 Potgieter St, Alberton, Alrode, 1451, South Africa (100%)
Tel.: (27) 113890000
Web Site: https://www.wispeco.co.za
Sales Range: $300-349.9 Million
Emp.: 800
Holding Company; Extruded Aluminum Products Mfr & Distr
N.A.I.C.S.: 551112

REMI GROUP
11 Cama Industrial Estate Walbhat Road, Goregaon East, Mumbai, 400063, India
Tel.: (91) 224058 9888
Web Site: http://www.remigroup.com
Year Founded: 1960
Construaction & Laboratories Equipment Mfr
N.A.I.C.S.: 333120
Rishabh Saraf (Mng Dir)

Subsidiaries:

Bajrang Finance Limited (1)
11 Cama Industrial Estate, Goregaon East, Mumbai, 400063, India
Tel.: (91) 22 26851998
Web Site: http://www.remigroup.com
Rev.: $100,393
Assets: $3,233,794
Liabilities: $6,304
Net Worth: $3,227,490
Earnings: $48,569
Fiscal Year-end: 03/31/2019
Financial Support Services
N.A.I.C.S.: 523999
Mahabir Prasad Sharma (CFO)

K K Fincorp Limited (1)
Plot No 11 Cama Industrial Estate, Goregaon East Walbhat Road, Mumbai, 400063, India
Tel.: (91) 2240589888
Web Site: https://www.remigroup.com
Financial Support Services
N.A.I.C.S.: 523999
Shiv Kumar Sharma (CFO & Officer-Compliance)

Remi Edelstahl Tubulars Limited (1)
Remi House 11 Cama Industrial Estate Goregaon East, Mumbai, 400063, India
Tel.: (91) 2240589888
Web Site: https://www.remigroup.com
Rev.: $16,265,056
Assets: $10,005,168
Liabilities: $4,931,131
Net Worth: $5,074,036
Earnings: $17,709
Emp.: 2,500
Fiscal Year-end: 03/31/2023
Pipes & Tubes Mfr
N.A.I.C.S.: 331210
Vishwambhar C. Saraf (Chm)

Remi Elektrotechnik Limited (1)
Remi House 3rd Floor 11, Cama Industrial Estate Walbhat Road Goregaon East, Mumbai, 400 063, Maharashtra, India
Tel.: (91) 08068092691
Web Site: http://www.remielektrotechnik.com
Rev.: $16,032,789
Assets: $17,436,976
Liabilities: $4,278,592
Net Worth: $13,158,384
Earnings: $1,103,862
Emp.: 200
Fiscal Year-end: 03/31/2019
Analytical Laboratory Instrument Mfr
N.A.I.C.S.: 334516
V. Ramakrishnan (Mgr-Mktg)

Remi Sales & Engineering Limited (1)
3rd Floor 11 Cama Industrial Estate Walbhat Road, Goregaon East, Mumbai, 400063, India
Tel.: (91) 2240589888
Web Site: http://www.remilabworld.com
Rev.: $20,087,316
Assets: $10,677,187
Liabilities: $4,903,041
Net Worth: $5,774,147
Earnings: $776,713
Emp.: 2,500
Fiscal Year-end: 03/31/2019
Electrical Component Distr
N.A.I.C.S.: 423610
Sandeep Kasera (Exec Dir)

Remi Securities Limited (1)
Remi House Plot No 11 Cama Industrial Estate, Goregaon East, Mumbai, 400 063, India
Tel.: (91) 2240589888
Web Site: http://www.remigroup.com
Rev.: $84,114
Assets: $3,442,245
Liabilities: $22,259
Net Worth: $3,419,986
Earnings: $11,845
Fiscal Year-end: 03/31/2021
Investment Management Service
N.A.I.C.S.: 523150
Sanjay Maheshwari (Chm & CFO)

REMI PROCESS PLANT & MACHINERY LIMITED
Remi House 11 Cama Industrial Estate, Walbhat Road Goregaon East, Mumbai, 400063, India
Tel.: (91) 22 26851998
Web Site: http://www.remigroup.com
Year Founded: 1960
Rev.: $2,919,188
Assets: $5,697,500
Liabilities: $2,927,837
Net Worth: $2,769,663
Earnings: $259,860
Emp.: 80
Fiscal Year-end: 03/31/19
Industrial Machinery Mfr
N.A.I.C.S.: 333248
Bhagirath Singh (CFO)

REMICON JOINT STOCK COMPANY
Remicon plant 20th khoroo Songinokhairkhan district, Ulaanbaatar, Mongolia
Tel.: (976) 77777704
Web Site: http://www.remicon.mn
RMC—(MONG)
Sales Range: Less than $1 Million
Cement & Concrete Product Mfr
N.A.I.C.S.: 327310

REMINGTON DEVELOPMENT CORPORATION
Suite 300 200 Quarry Park Blvd SE, Calgary, T2C 5E3, AB, Canada
Tel.: (403) 255-7003
Web Site:
  https://www.remingtoncorp.com
Year Founded: 1994
Rev.: $13,208,800
Emp.: 60
Real Estate Services
N.A.I.C.S.: 531390
Randy Remington (Chm)

REMINGTON RESOURCES INC.
501-837West Hastings Street, Vancouver, V6C 3N6, BC, Canada
Tel.: (604) 685-6851 BC
Year Founded: 2004
Sales Range: Less than $1 Million
Metal Mineral Mining & Exploration Services
N.A.I.C.S.: 212290
Tara Haddad (CEO-Interim & CFO)

REMIXPOINT INC.
Sumitomo Shin-Toranomon Building 4-3-9 Toranomon, Minato-ku, Tokyo, 153-0043, Japan
Tel.: (81) 363030280
Web Site:
  https://www.remixpoint.co.jp
Year Founded: 2004
3825—(TKS)
Rev.: $135,419,070
Assets: $130,309,540
Liabilities: $11,534,450
Net Worth: $118,775,090
Earnings: $7,072,700
Emp.: 125
Fiscal Year-end: 03/31/24
Application Software Development Services
N.A.I.C.S.: 541511
Yoshihiko Takahashi (Pres & CEO)

REMONTMONTAZA D.D. TUZLA
MIJE Kerosevica 24, 75000, Tuzla, Bosnia & Herzegovina
Tel.: (387) 35 320 710
Web Site:
  http://www.remontmontaza.com
Year Founded: 1961
Sales Range: Less than $1 Million
Emp.: 520
Pipelines & Tanks Mfr
N.A.I.C.S.: 332996

REMSDAQ LIMITED
Parkway Deeside Industrial Park, Deeside, CH5 2NL, Flintshire, United Kingdom
Tel.: (44) 1244286495
Web Site: http://www.remsdaq.com
Year Founded: 1974
Rev.: $23,347,412
Emp.: 99
Electronic & Electrical Control Equipment Mfr
N.A.I.C.S.: 335999
Terry Breen (Mng Dir)

REMSENSE TECHNOLOGIES LIMITED
Suite 173 580 Hay Street, Perth, 6000, WA, Australia
Tel.: (61) 861185610 AU
Web Site:
  https://www.remsense.com.au
Year Founded: 2021
REM—(ASX)
Rev.: $1,359,350
Assets: $1,855,034
Liabilities: $923,373
Net Worth: $931,661
Earnings: ($1,978,146)
Fiscal Year-end: 06/30/23
Construction Services
N.A.I.C.S.: 237120
Anthony Roe (Chief Digital Officer)

REMSONS INDUSTRIES LIMITED
401 Gladdiola Near Tilak School Hanuman Road, Vile Parle-East, Mumbai, 400057, India
Tel.: (91) 2235016400
Web Site: https://www.remsons.com
Year Founded: 1959
REMSONSIND—(NSE)
Rev.: $37,695,030
Assets: $22,814,711
Liabilities: $17,747,149
Net Worth: $5,067,562
Earnings: $1,003,549
Emp.: 246
Fiscal Year-end: 03/31/23
Automotive Components Mfr
N.A.I.C.S.: 336330
Krishna Kejriwal (Chm & Mng Dir)

REMSTAR CORPORATION
85 rue St-Paul Ouest, Montreal, H2Y 3V4, QC, Canada
Tel.: (514) 847-1136
Web Site:
  http://www.remstarcorp.com
Emp.: 7
Holding Company; Motion Picture Production & Distribution Services; Television Broadcasting Services
N.A.I.C.S.: 551112
Maxime Remillard (Co-Pres & CEO)

Subsidiaries:

MusiquePlus Inc. (1)
355 rue Sainte-Catherine Ouest, Montreal, H3B 1A5, QC, Canada
Tel.: (514) 284-7587
Web Site: http://www.musiqueplus.com
Sales Range: $50-74.9 Million
Emp.: 200
Music Cable Television Network Operator
N.A.I.C.S.: 516210
Maxime Remillard (Pres & CEO)

Remstar Films (1)
85 rue St-Paul Ouest, Montreal, H2Y 3V4, QC, Canada
Tel.: (514) 847-1136
Web Site: http://www.remstarfilms.com
Motion Picture Production & Distribution
N.A.I.C.S.: 512110
Maxime Remillard (Co-Pres & CEO)

REMUS PHARMACEUTICALS LIMITED

REMUS PHARMACEUTICALS LIMITED

Remus Pharmaceuticals Limited—(Continued)
11th Floor South Tower One42 Near Ashok Vatika Bopal-Ambli Road, Ahmedabad, 380058, Gujarat, India
Tel.: (91) 7929999857
Web Site:
https://www.remuspharma.com
Year Founded: 2015
REMUS—(NSE)
Rev.: $5,648,478
Assets: $4,200,962
Liabilities: $1,881,739
Net Worth: $2,319,223
Earnings: $1,030,539
Emp.: 750
Fiscal Year-end: 03/31/23
Pharmaceutical Product Mfr & Distr
N.A.I.C.S.: 325412
Arpit Shah *(Founder)*

Subsidiaries:

Espee Global Holdings LLC (1)

Relius Pharma S.R.L. (1)
4to Anillo Ed Torre Duo Piso 16 Of B Barrio Equipetrol, Santa Cruz, Bolivia
Tel.: (591) 75444976
Web Site: https://reliuspharma.com
Pharmaceutical Product Distr
N.A.I.C.S.: 424210

Relius Pharmaceuticals Ltda. (1)

REMY COINTREAU S.A.

21 Rue Balzac, 75008, Paris, France
Tel.: (33) 144134413 FR
Web Site: https://www.remy-cointreau.com
Year Founded: 1724
REMYF—(OTCIQ)
Rev.: $1,288,689,831
Assets: $3,637,707,742
Liabilities: $1,645,909,775
Net Worth: $1,991,797,967
Earnings: $199,007,122
Emp.: 1,943
Fiscal Year-end: 03/31/24
Wine, Champagne & Distilled Alcoholic Beverages Mfr & Distr
N.A.I.C.S.: 424820
Marc Heriard Dubreuil *(Chm)*

Subsidiaries:

Denview Limited Moscow (1)
Ulitsa Bolshaya Iakimanka 39, 117049, Moscow, Russia
Tel.: (7) 0952384077
Web Site: http://www.maxxium.ru
Wines & Spirits Distributor
N.A.I.C.S.: 445320

Metaxa Greece (1)
6 A Metaxa St, Kifissia, Athens, 14564, Greece
Tel.: (30) 2106207100
Web Site: http://www.metaxa.com.gr
Sales Range: $25-49.9 Million
Emp.: 8
Markets & Distributes Specialty Spirit Brands Internationally; Imports, Markets & Distributes Spirits in Greece
N.A.I.C.S.: 445320
Spyros Metaxa *(Founder)*

Remy Cointreau USA Inc. (1)
1290 Avenue of the Americas 10th Fl, New York, NY 10104 (99%)
Tel.: (212) 399-4200
Web Site: http://www.remy.com
Sales Range: $75-99.9 Million
Emp.: 150
Importer & Distributor of Wines & Distilled Alcoholic Beverages
N.A.I.C.S.: 424820
Philippe Farnier *(Pres & CEO)*

Westland Distillery (1)
2931 1st Ave S Ste B, Seattle, WA 98134-1821
Tel.: (206) 767-7250
Web Site: https://www.westlanddistillery.com
Breweries
N.A.I.C.S.: 312120

Matt Sossnen *(Pres)*

REN - REDES ENERGETICAS NACIONAIS SGPS, S.A.

United States of America Avenue 55, 1749-061, Lisbon, Portugal
Tel.: (351) 210013500 PT
Web Site: https://www.ren.pt
RENE—(EUR)
Rev.: $890,009,713
Assets: $6,962,654,867
Liabilities: $5,324,910,425
Net Worth: $1,637,744,442
Earnings: $120,624,865
Emp.: 716
Fiscal Year-end: 12/31/22
Electricity Generation & Distribution Services; Natural Gas Transportation Services; Liquified Gas Storage
N.A.I.C.S.: 221122
Joao Caetano Faria Conceicao *(COO)*

Subsidiaries:

EDP Gas - S.G.P.S., S.A. (1)
Praca Marques Pombal 12, 1250-162, Lisbon, Portugal
Tel.: (351) 210 012 500
Web Site: http://www.edp.com
Oil & Gas Exploration Services
N.A.I.C.S.: 213112
Fernando Capitao *(Asst Dir)*

Electrogas, S.A. (1)
Alonso de Cordova N 5900 Of 401, Santiago, Chile
Tel.: (56) 222993400
Web Site: https://www.electrogas.cl
Natural Gas Distr
N.A.I.C.S.: 486210

Gasoduto Campo Maior-Leiria_Braga (1)
Estrada Nacional 116, Vila de Rei, 2674-505, Bucelas, Portugal
Tel.: (351) 21 96 88 200
Sales Range: $25-49.9 Million
Emp.: 100
Gas Transmission Services
N.A.I.C.S.: 486210

OMIP - Operador do Mercado Iberico (Portugal), SGPS, S.A. (1)
Av Casal Ribeiro N 14-8, 1000-092, Lisbon, Portugal
Tel.: (351) 210006000
Web Site: https://www.omip.pt
Electricity Distribution Services
N.A.I.C.S.: 221122

OMIP Operador do Mercado Iberico de Energia S.A. (1)
Av Casal Ribeiro n 14-8, 1000-092, Lisbon, Portugal
Tel.: (351) 210006000
Web Site: http://www.omip.pt
Sales Range: $50-74.9 Million
Emp.: 15
Transactions Management Services
N.A.I.C.S.: 522320

REN Atlantico, Terminal de GNL S.A. (1)
Tel.: (351) 269870000
Sales Range: $50-74.9 Million
Emp.: 40
Natural Gas Extraction Services
N.A.I.C.S.: 211130

REN Gasodutos S.A. (1)
Estrada Nacional 116, PO Box 32 25, Vila de Rei, 2674-505, Bucelas, Portugal
Tel.: (351) 219688200
Sales Range: $125-149.9 Million
Emp.: 300
Gas Transmission Services
N.A.I.C.S.: 486210

REN Trading S.A. (1)
Tel.: (351) 211024500
Sales Range: $50-74.9 Million
Emp.: 250
Electricity & Natural Gas Trading Services
N.A.I.C.S.: 238990

RENAISSANCE ASIA SILK ROAD GROUP LIMITED

Unit 1802 18/F The L Plaza Nos 367-375 Queen's Road Central, Hong Kong, China (Hong Kong)
Tel.: (852) 22014555 Ky
Web Site: http://www.chinabillion.net
0274—(HKG)
Rev.: $26,447,963
Assets: $38,082,975
Liabilities: $54,038,198
Net Worth: ($15,955,223)
Earnings: ($7,891,230)
Emp.: 486
Fiscal Year-end: 12/31/22
Home & Personal Care Products Mfr
N.A.I.C.S.: 325620
Sun Shui *(Sec)*

RENAISSANCE GLOBAL LIMITED

Plot No 36A and 37 Seepz - SEZ, Andheri E, Mumbai, 400 096, India
Tel.: (91) 2240551200
Web Site:
https://www.renaissanceglobal.com
RGL—(NSE)
Rev.: $268,890,402
Assets: $230,160,458
Liabilities: $107,091,038
Net Worth: $123,069,420
Earnings: ($59,888)
Emp.: 542
Fiscal Year-end: 03/31/23
Jewelry Mfr
N.A.I.C.S.: 339910
Niranjan Amratlal Shah *(Chm)*

Subsidiaries:

Renaissance Jewelry New York Inc. (1)
Tel.: (212) 986-7287
Web Site: http://www.verigoldjewelry.com
Emp.: 20
Fashion Jewelry Distr
N.A.I.C.S.: 423940
Suhel Kothari *(Pres)*

Verigold Jewellery (UK) Ltd. (1)
88-90 Hatton Garden, London, EC1N 8PN, United Kingdom
Tel.: (44) 2078314757
Jewellery Distr
N.A.I.C.S.: 423940

RENAISSANCE GROUP

Bolshoy Znamensky 2 Building 3, 199019, Moscow, Russia
Tel.: (7) 4952587777
Web Site:
http://www.renaissancegroup.com
Investment Management, Real Estate & Credit Services
N.A.I.C.S.: 523940
Hans Jochum Horn *(Deputy CEO)*

RENAISSANCE INDUSTRIES SAS

7 Rue Auber, 75009, Paris, France
Tel.: (33) 1 84 17 34 84 FR
Web Site: http://www.renaissance.fr
Investment Holding Services
N.A.I.C.S.: 551112
Eric Lefranc *(Pres)*

Subsidiaries:

GL Altesse SAS (1)
Valamas, 07310, Saint-Martin-de-Valamas, France (100%)
Tel.: (33) 475290211
Web Site: http://www.groupe-gl.com
Jewelry Mfr
N.A.I.C.S.: 339910
Jean-Louis Lecomte *(Gen Mgr)*

Maison Texier SAS (1)
10 rue de la Greurie, 35500, Vitre, France
Tel.: (33) 2 2355 1818
Web Site: http://www.texier.com

INTERNATIONAL PUBLIC

Leather Handbag & Other Accessories Designer, Mfr, Whslr & Online Retailer.
N.A.I.C.S.: 316990
Eric Lefranc *(Pres)*

S.M.V. Thailand Co., Ltd. (1)
80 Moo 4 Northern Region Industrial Estate Highway No 11 Road, T Banlang A Muanglamphun, Lamphun, 51000, Thailand
Tel.: (66) 53581132
Web Site: http://www.smv.co.th
Emp.: 600
Jewelry Mfr
N.A.I.C.S.: 339910
Waranthon Thanachotphokhinan *(Deputy Mng Dir)*

RENAISSANCE MANAGEMENT SA

EPFL Innovation Park Batiment C, 1015, Lausanne, Switzerland
Tel.: (41) 58 201 17 81 CH
Web Site: http://www.renaissance.net
Year Founded: 2003
Capital Development & Buy-Out Services
N.A.I.C.S.: 523999
Christian Waldvogel *(Mng Partner)*

Subsidiaries:

Renaissance Foundation (1)
EPFL Innovation Park Batiment C, 1015, Lausanne, Switzerland
Tel.: (41) 58 201 17 81
Web Site: http://www.renaissance.net
Financial Services
N.A.I.C.S.: 523999
Jean Remy Roulet *(Chm)*

Subsidiary (Domestic):

Maxwell Technologies SA (2)
Route De Montenaz 65, CH 1728, Rossens, Switzerland
Tel.: (41) 264118500
Sales Range: $25-49.9 Million
Emp.: 120
High-Voltage Capacitors Mfr
N.A.I.C.S.: 334416

RENAISSANCE SERVICES SAOG

PO Box 1676, 114, Muttrah, 114, Oman
Tel.: (968) 24765900
Web Site:
https://www.renaissanceservices.com
RNSS—(MUS)
Rev.: $283,568,085
Assets: $588,129,505
Liabilities: $360,016,784
Net Worth: $228,112,721
Earnings: $29,041,385
Emp.: 2,350
Fiscal Year-end: 12/31/21
Holding Company
N.A.I.C.S.: 551112
Samir J. Fancy *(Chm)*

RENAISSANCE UNITED LIMITED

16 Kallang Place 05-10/18 Kallang Basin Industrial Estate, Singapore, 339156, Singapore
Tel.: (65) 62642711 SG
Web Site: https://www.ren-united.com
Year Founded: 1975
I11—(SES)
Rev.: $69,200,445
Assets: $66,741,756
Liabilities: $39,780,659
Net Worth: $26,961,097
Earnings: ($7,314,561)
Emp.: 305
Fiscal Year-end: 04/30/24
Holding Company; Oil, Gas, Power, Transportation, Water, Environment & Industrial Infrastructure Projects Developer, Turnkey Contractor & Investor

AND PRIVATE COMPANIES

N.A.I.C.S.: 551112
James Moffatt Blythman *(CFO & Exec Dir)*
Subsidiaries:

Anlu Jiaxu Natural Gas Company Limited (1)
Block 45 No 102 Qian Kun Street, Qian Kun Yang Guang, Xiaogan, 432100, Hubei, China
Tel.: (86) 7122570037
Natural Gas Distribution Services
N.A.I.C.S.: 221210

ESA Assembly Pte Ltd (1)
16 Kallang Pl 05-10/15 Kallang Basin Industrial Estate, Singapore, 339156, Singapore
Tel.: (65) 62961613
Web Site: http://www.esasing.com
Sales Range: $25-49.9 Million
Electronic Components Mfr
N.A.I.C.S.: 334416
William Koh *(CEO)*

ESA Electronics Pte Ltd (1)
Blk 16 Kallang Place 05-09 to 18, Kallang Basin Industrial Estate, Singapore, 339156, Singapore
Tel.: (65) 63923162
Web Site: https://www.esasing.com
Sales Range: $25-49.9 Million
Emp.: 100
Semiconductor Devices Mfr
N.A.I.C.S.: 334413
Siamraj More *(Mgr-Sls)*

International Project Developers Ltd. (1)
PO Box 1039, Jeddah, 21431, Saudi Arabia
Tel.: (966) 26697220
Web Site: http://www.ipd-intl.com
Turnkey Project Development Services
N.A.I.C.S.: 237990

Ipco Constructors Private Limited (1)
24 Pandan Rd Ipco Bldg, Singapore, 609275, Singapore
Tel.: (65) 62642711
Web Site: http://www.ipco.com.sg
Sales Range: $25-49.9 Million
Emp.: 12
Construction Engineering Services
N.A.I.C.S.: 541330
Goh Hincaln *(Gen Mgr)*

Ipco Constructors Sdn. Bhd. (1)
1E 3A 3rd Floor Jalan SS26/9 Plaza Mayang Taman Mayang Jaya, 47301, Petaling Jaya, Selangor, Malaysia
Tel.: (60) 378036332
Web Site: http://www.ipco.com.sg
Construction Engineering Services
N.A.I.C.S.: 541330

RENAISSANCE URANIUM LIMITED

63 King William Street, Kent Town, 5067, SA, Australia
Tel.: (61) 883631589
Web Site: http://www.renaissanceuranium.com
Uranium Mining Services
N.A.I.C.S.: 212290
David Macfarlane *(Chm)*

RENAISSANCE, INC.

Ryogoku-City-Core 3rd fl 2-10-14 Ryogoku, Sumida-ku, Tokyo, 130-0026, Japan
Tel.: (81) 356005411
Web Site: https://www.s-renaissance.co.jp
Year Founded: 1982
2378—(TKS)
Rev.: $288,374,470
Assets: $351,612,340
Liabilities: $276,093,090
Net Worth: $75,519,250
Earnings: $4,177,520
Emp.: 1,501
Fiscal Year-end: 03/31/24
Sports Club Operator
N.A.I.C.S.: 711211

Naoki Takazaki *(Pres & Corp Officer)*
Subsidiaries:

Beach Town Corporation (1)
34 Nihon Odori, Naka Ward, Yokohama, 231-0021, Kanagawa, Japan
Tel.: (81) 452648991
Web Site: https://www.beachtown.co.jp
Emp.: 20
Sports Parks Management Services
N.A.I.C.S.: 611620

RENAISSANCERE HOLDINGS LTD.

Renaissance House 12 Crow Lane, Pembroke, HM 19, Bermuda
Tel.: (441) 2954513   BM
Web Site: https://www.renre.com
Year Founded: 1993
RNR—(NYSE)
Rev.: $9,134,608,000
Assets: $49,007,105,000
Liabilities: $33,451,316,000
Net Worth: $15,555,789,000
Earnings: $2,525,757,000
Emp.: 925
Fiscal Year-end: 12/31/23
Holding Company; Reinsurance Services
N.A.I.C.S.: 551112
Ross A. Curtis *(Chief Portfolio Officer & Exec VP)*
Subsidiaries:

Glencoe Group Holdings Ltd. (1)
Renaissance House 8 12 East Broadway, Pembroke, HM19, Bermuda
Tel.: (441) 2963235
Sales Range: $100-124.9 Million
Emp.: 120
Reinsurance & Insurance Services
N.A.I.C.S.: 524298

Renaissance Reinsurance Ltd. (1)
Renaissance House 12 Crow Lane, Pembroke, Hamilton, HM 19, Bermuda
Tel.: (441) 2954513
Web Site: http://www.renre.com
Sales Range: $100-124.9 Million
Emp.: 120
Catastrophe Reinsurance
N.A.I.C.S.: 524130

RenaissanceRe Specialty Risks Ltd. (1)
Renaissance House 12 Crow Lane, Pembroke, HM19, Bermuda
Tel.: (441) 4412954513
Reinsurance Services
N.A.I.C.S.: 524130

RenaissanceRe Syndicate 1458 (1)
Lloyd s of London 1 Lime Street, London, EC3M 7HA, United Kingdom
Tel.: (44) 2073275693
Sales Range: $50-74.9 Million
Emp.: 65
Reinsurance & Insurance Products Services
N.A.I.C.S.: 524130
Ross A. Curtis *(Chief Underwriting Officer)*

RenaissanceRe of Europe (1)
Hardwicke House 1st Floor Hatch Street, Dublin, Ireland   **(100%)**
Tel.: (353) 16787388
Web Site: http://www.renreeurope.com
Sales Range: $50-74.9 Million
Emp.: 50
Reinsurance Services
N.A.I.C.S.: 524130

Tokio Millennium Re (UK) Ltd (1)
20 Fenchurch Street, London, EC3M 3BY, United Kingdom
Tel.: (44) 20 7397 4000
Web Site: http://www.tokiomillennium.com
Sales Range: $25-49.9 Million
Emp.: 50
Reinsurance Services
N.A.I.C.S.: 524130
Mark Julian *(Chief Actuary & Chief Risk Officer)*

Top Layer Reinsurance Ltd. (1)
Renaissance House, 12 Crow Lane, Pembroke, HM 19, Bermuda
Tel.: (441) 2954513
Web Site: http://www.renre.com
Sales Range: $75-99.9 Million
Emp.: 130
Reinsurance Services; Joint Venture Renaissance Reinsurance (50%) & State Farm Mutual Automobile Insurance Company (50%)
N.A.I.C.S.: 524130
David A. Eklund *(Pres)*

RENALYTIX PLC

Finsgate 5-7 Cranwood Street, London, EC1V 9EE, United Kingdom
Tel.: (44) 2031392910   UK
Web Site: https://renalytix.com
Year Founded: 2018
RENX—(AIM)
Rev.: $2,289,000
Assets: $7,972,000
Liabilities: $15,826,000
Net Worth: ($7,854,000)
Earnings: ($33,456,000)
Emp.: 48
Fiscal Year-end: 06/30/24
Medical Device Mfr & Distr
N.A.I.C.S.: 339113
Joel R. Jung *(Interim CFO & Principal Acctg Officer)*
Subsidiaries:

Verici Dx Limited (1)
1460 Broadway, New York, NY 10036
Web Site: http://www.vericidx.com
Healthcare Services
N.A.I.C.S.: 621999
Sara Barrington *(CEO)*

RENASANT FINANCIAL PARTNERS LTD.

55 City Centre Drive Suite 800, Mississauga, L5B 1M3, ON, Canada
Tel.: (905) 281-4760   ON
Sales Range: $1-9.9 Million
Emp.: 25
Financial Services
N.A.I.C.S.: 523999
K. Sahi *(Chm)*
Subsidiaries:

MFP Technology Services (UK) Ltd. (1)
Unit 39 Stretford Motorway Estate, Manchester, M32 0ZH, United Kingdom
Tel.: (44) 1618641284
Web Site: http://www.mfetech.com
Computer Mfr
N.A.I.C.S.: 334111

RENASCOR RESOURCES LIMITED

Tel.: (61) 883636989
Web Site: https://www.renascor.com.au
RNU—(ASX)
Rev.: $9,024
Assets: $27,754,739
Liabilities: $798,791
Net Worth: $26,955,947
Earnings: ($672,125)
Fiscal Year-end: 06/30/21
Mineral Exploration Services
N.A.I.C.S.: 213113
David Christensen *(Mng Dir)*

RENATA LIMITED

Plot No 1 Milk Vita Road Section-7, GPO Box No 303, Mirpur, Dhaka, 1216, Bangladesh
Tel.: (880) 800145054
Web Site: https://www.renata-ltd.com
Year Founded: 1972
RENATA—(DHA)
Rev.: $299,778,316
Assets: $444,487,485
Liabilities: $165,963,238
Net Worth: $278,524,247

Earnings: $21,143,465
Emp.: 7,119
Fiscal Year-end: 06/30/23
Human Pharmaceuticals & Animal Therapeutics Mfr
N.A.I.C.S.: 325412
Sarwar Ali *(Chm)*
Subsidiaries:

Purnava Limited (1)
Plot No 1 Milk Vita Road Section-7, Mirpur, Dhaka, 1216, Bangladesh
Tel.: (880) 2800145054
Web Site: http://www.purnava.com
Pharmaceuticals Product Mfr
N.A.I.C.S.: 325412
S. Kaiser Kabir *(Chm)*

RENAUDAT CENTRE CONSTRUCTIONS

Chemin de Soulasse, 36000, Chateauroux, Indre, France
Tel.: (33) 2 54 27 44 80
Web Site: http://www.renaudat.com
Rev.: $14,900,000
Emp.: 41
Building Construction
N.A.I.C.S.: 332312
Philippe Escande *(Pres)*

RENAULT S.A.

122-122 bis avenue du General Leclerc, 92 100, Boulogne-Billancourt, France
Tel.: (33) 176840404   FR
Web Site: https://www.facebook.com
Year Founded: 1898
RNL—(DEU)
Rev.: $56,524,929,851
Assets: $131,570,256,853
Liabilities: $98,509,605,008
Net Worth: $33,060,651,845
Earnings: $2,498,381,179
Emp.: 105,812
Fiscal Year-end: 12/31/23
Automobile Parts Mfr
N.A.I.C.S.: 336330
Laurens van den Acker *(Exec VP-Corp Design)*
Subsidiaries:

Auto Chassis International (ACI) Le Mans (1)
15 Avenue Pierre Piffault, 72086, Le Mans, France
Tel.: (33) 176864343
Sales Range: $400-449.9 Million
Emp.: 2,400
Automobile Parts Mfr
N.A.I.C.S.: 336110
Marcel Brouiller *(Gen Mgr)*

Francaise de Mecanique (1)
Zone Industrielle Douvrin, 62138, Haisnes, France   **(100%)**
Tel.: (33) 321082222
Web Site: http://www.francaisedemecanique.com
Rev.: $1,290,000,000
Emp.: 5,000
Engine Manufacturer
N.A.I.C.S.: 336310
Philip Coene *(Mgr)*

JSC AVTOVAZ (1)
36 Yuzhnoye Shosse, 445024, Togliatti, Samara, Russia
Tel.: (7) 8007005232
Sales Range: $5-14.9 Billion
Emp.: 112,200
Passenger Car Mfr
N.A.I.C.S.: 336110

OAO Remosprom (1)
42 Korp 36 Prospekt Volgogradski, Moscow, 109316, Russia
Tel.: (7) 4957754000
Web Site: http://www.renault.ru
Automobile Parts Mfr
N.A.I.C.S.: 336211
Andrei Pankov *(Pres)*

RENAULT S.A.

INTERNATIONAL PUBLIC

Renault S.A.—(Continued)

Oyak-Renault Otomobil Fabrikalari AS (1)
Kisikli Mahallesi Hanim Seti Sokak No 55, Uskudar, Istanbul, 34692, Turkiye
Tel.: (90) 2165247900
Web Site: http://www.oyak-renault.com.tr
Automobile Parts Mfr
N.A.I.C.S.: 336110

RCI Bank AG (1)
Laaer Berg Strasse 64, Postfach 196, 1100, Vienna, Austria
Tel.: (43) 1680300
Automobile Leasing Services
N.A.I.C.S.: 532112
Frederic Maud (Gen Mgr)

RCI Bank Polska (1)
ul Sailor 13 02 674, Warsaw, 02674, Poland
Tel.: (48) 225411300
Web Site: http://www.renault.pl
Emp.: 70
Automobile Financing Services
N.A.I.C.S.: 525990
Maria Lewandowska (Mng Dir)

RCI Banque (1)
14 Ave Pave Neuf, 93160, Noisy-le-Grand, Cedex, France (100%)
Tel.: (33) 149328000
Web Site: http://www.rcibanque.com
Sales Range: $400-449.9 Million
Emp.: 600
Automotive Financing Services
N.A.I.C.S.: 525990

RCI Finance Maroc (1)
20000 Casablanca place Bandoeng C/o Renault, BP 13700, Casablanca, Morocco
Tel.: (212) 522 349 700
Web Site: http://www.renault.ma
Automobile Financing Services
N.A.I.C.S.: 525990

RCI Finance SA (1)
Bergermoosstrasse 4, 8902, Urdorf, Switzerland
Tel.: (41) 44 871 27 10
Automobile Financing Services
N.A.I.C.S.: 525990

RCI Financial Services BV (1)
Boeingavenue 275, 1119 PD, Schiphol-Rijk, Netherlands
Tel.: (31) 20 354 9666
Web Site: http://www.rcibanque.com
Emp.: 50
Financial Management Consulting Services
N.A.I.C.S.: 541611
Jean-Louis Labauge (CEO-RCI Banque & Mgr-Germany)

RCI Korea (1)
9th floor RSM Tower 327-29, Gasan-dong Geumcheon-gu, Seoul, 153-802, Korea (South)
Tel.: (82) 15886750
Web Site: http://www.renaultcapital.co.kr
Sales Range: $50-74.9 Million
Emp.: 120
Automobile Parts Mfr
N.A.I.C.S.: 336390

RCI Leasing Romania IFN S.A (1)
Bd Aviatorilor No 41 Etaj 3 Cod 011853 Sector 1, Bucharest, Romania
Tel.: (40) 212012000
Automobile Parts Mfr
N.A.I.C.S.: 336390
Florin Chiriac (Mng Dir)

RCI Services Ltd (1)
Gravel Row Reggie Miller St, Gzira, GZR1544, Malta
Tel.: (356) 25 99 3000
Sales Range: $50-74.9 Million
Emp.: 15
General Insurance Services
N.A.I.C.S.: 524210
Michael Aroskin (Gen Mgr)

RCI Versicherungs Service GmbH (1)
Jagenbergstrsse 1, 41468, Neuss, Germany
Tel.: (49) 2131401010
Web Site: http://www.rcibanque.de

Automotive Financing & Services
N.A.I.C.S.: 525990
Jean Louis Laauge (Mng Dir)

Renault Algerie S.p.A. (1)
60A bd Colonel, PO Box 353, Bougara, Tiaret, Algeria
Tel.: (213) 21 92 23 39
Web Site: http://www.renault.dz
Automobile Parts Mfr
N.A.I.C.S.: 336390

Renault Argentina S.A. (1)
Fray Justo Santa Maria de Oro 1744, 1414, Buenos Aires, Argentina (60%)
Tel.: (54) 147782000
Web Site: http://www.renault.com.ar
Sales Range: $100-124.9 Million
Emp.: 400
Vehicle Mfr
N.A.I.C.S.: 336110

Renault Belgique Luxembourg SA (1)
Avenue Mozart 20, 1620, Drogenbos, Belgium
Tel.: (32) 78051115
Web Site: http://fr.renault.be
Sales Range: $50-74.9 Million
Emp.: 50
Automobile Parts Mfr
N.A.I.C.S.: 336110

Renault Credit Polska (1)
ul Marynarskiej 13, 02-674, Warsaw, Poland
Tel.: (48) 228524113
Web Site: http://www.renault.pl
Sales Range: $25-49.9 Million
Emp.: 50
Automobile Parts Mfr
N.A.I.C.S.: 336390

Renault Deutschland GmbH (1)
Renault Nissan Strasse 6 - 10, 50321, Bruhl, Germany
Tel.: (49) 2232 73 0
Web Site: http://www.renault.de
Sales Range: $200-249.9 Million
Emp.: 800
Importer & Distr of Cars & Trucks
N.A.I.C.S.: 441110

Renault Espana SA (1)
Avda De Burgos, Madrid, Spain
Tel.: (34) 913742200
Web Site: http://www.renault.es
Automobile Parts Mfr
N.A.I.C.S.: 336110

Renault Italia SPA (1)
Via Tiburtina n 1159, 00156, Rome, Italy
Tel.: (39) 064156183
Web Site: http://www.renault.it
Automobile Parts Mfr
N.A.I.C.S.: 336390

Subsidiary (Non-US):

Renault Irlande (2)
Hendrick House NVD Complex Browns Barn, Baldonnell, Dublin, D24 KH76, Ireland
Tel.: (353) 16055580
Web Site: http://www.renault.ie
Sales Range: $25-49.9 Million
Emp.: 50
Automobile Parts Mfr
N.A.I.C.S.: 336390

Renault Osterreich (1)
Laaer Berg-Strasse 64, 1100, Vienna, Austria
Tel.: (43) 1680100
Web Site: http://www.renault.at
Emp.: 91
Automobile Parts Mfr
N.A.I.C.S.: 336110

Subsidiary (Non-US):

Renault Nordic (2)
Esbogatan 12, 164 74, Kista, Sweden
Tel.: (46) 771 345 666
Web Site: http://www.renault.se
Sales Range: $25-49.9 Million
Automobile Parts Mfr
N.A.I.C.S.: 336390

Renault Portuguesa (1)
Lagoas Park Building 4, 2740-267, Porto Salvo, Portugal

Tel.: (351) 218502005
Web Site: http://www.renault.pt
Sales Range: $25-49.9 Million
Emp.: 80
Automobile Parts Mfr
N.A.I.C.S.: 336390

Renault Private Ltd (1)
4th Floor Asv Ramana Tower 1-37 & 38 Venkatnarayana Road T Nagar, Chennai, 600017, Tamil Nadu, India
Tel.: (91) 4439104200
Web Site: http://www.renault.co.in
Emp.: 200
Automobile Parts Mfr
N.A.I.C.S.: 336390
Jayakumar David (Dir-HR-Renault Nissan Alliance)

Renault Retail Group SA (1)
2-4-6 Avenue De La Resistance, Laxou, 54520, France
Tel.: (33) 383953333
Web Site: http://www.renault.com
Automobile Parts Mfr
N.A.I.C.S.: 336110

Renault Suisse SA (1)
Bergermoosstrasse 4, 8902, Urdorf, Switzerland
Tel.: (41) 44 777 0200
Web Site: http://www.renault.com
Automobile Parts Mfr
N.A.I.C.S.: 336390

Subsidiary (Non-US):

Renault Polska (1)
ul Marynarskiej 13, 02-674, Warsaw, Poland
Tel.: (48) 228524113
Web Site: http://www.renault.pl
Automotive Part Whslr
N.A.I.C.S.: 423110
Grzigorz Zaliwske (Gen Mgr)

Renault U.K. Ltd. (1)
The Rivers Office Park Denham Way, Maple Cross, WD3 9YS, Rickmansworth, United Kingdom
Tel.: (44) 3443350000
Web Site: http://www.renault.co.uk
Sales Range: $100-124.9 Million
Emp.: 500
New Car Dealers
N.A.I.C.S.: 441110
Vincent Tourette (Mng Dir)

Subsidiary (Domestic):

RCI Financial Services Ltd (2)
Rivers Office Park Denham Way, Rickmansworth, WD3 9YS, United Kingdom
Tel.: (44) 3330090233
Web Site: http://www.rcifinance.com
Sales Range: $75-99.9 Million
Emp.: 250
Automobile Parts Mfr
N.A.I.C.S.: 336390

Renault Retail Group UK Limited (2)
Concord Road Western Avenue, London, W3 0RZ, United Kingdom
Tel.: (44) 2080315162
Web Site: http://www.retailgroup.co.uk
New & Used Car Dealership Operator
N.A.I.C.S.: 561110

Renault USA, Inc. (1)
45 Knollwood Rd Ste 405, Elmsford, NY 10523 (100%)
Tel.: (212) 730-0676
Web Site: http://www.renaultusa.com
Automobile Technical Support Services
N.A.I.C.S.: 423120

Renault Ukraine (1)
street Gaidara 58/10, 01033, Kiev, Ukraine
Tel.: (380) 444906832
Web Site: http://www.renault.ua
Sales Range: $25-49.9 Million
Emp.: 70
New Car Dealers
N.A.I.C.S.: 441110

Renault do Brasil SA (1)
Av Renault 1300 - Borda do Campo, Sao Jose dos Pinhais, 83070-900, Brazil
Tel.: (55) 8000555615
Web Site: http://www.renault.com.br
Automobile Parts Mfr

N.A.I.C.S.: 336390

Renault s.a.s (1)
1 Avenue Du Golf, 78288, Guyancourt, France
Tel.: (33) 1 76 85 49 12
Automobile Parts Mfr
N.A.I.C.S.: 336110

Revoz (1)
Belokranjska cesta 4, 8000, Novo Mesto, Slovenia
Tel.: (386) 73315000
Web Site: http://www.revoz.si
Emp.: 2,500
Automobile Parts Mfr
N.A.I.C.S.: 336110

SNC Renault Douai (1)
1 Avenue Du Golf, 78188, Guyancourt, France
Tel.: (33) 176842994
Sales Range: $800-899.9 Million
Emp.: 4,000
Automobile Parts Mfr
N.A.I.C.S.: 336110

SNR Roulements S.A. (1)
1 rue des Usines, BP 2017, 74010, Annecy, France
Tel.: (33) 450653000
Web Site: http://www.ntn-snr.com
Sales Range: $1-9.9 Million
Emp.: 1,000
Ball & Roller Bearing Mfr
N.A.I.C.S.: 332991

SODICAM 2 (1)
13- 15 quai le Gallo, 92100, Boulogne-Billancourt, France
Tel.: (33) 176834285
Web Site: http://www.sodicam2.fr
Automobile Parts Mfr
N.A.I.C.S.: 336390

Societe de Transmissions Automatiques (1)
ZI De Ruitz, Route D Ouchin, 62620, Barlin, Moulin, France (80%)
Tel.: (33) 321634646
Sales Range: $200-249.9 Million
Emp.: 830
Motor Vehicle Transmissions & Gear Boxes Mfr
N.A.I.C.S.: 336350

RENCO HOLDINGS GROUP LIMITED

Room 6812-13 68F Central Centre, 99 Queen's Road, Central, China (Hong Kong)
Tel.: (852) 27102323 **BM**
Web Site: http://www.hkbridge.com.hk
Year Founded: 1985
2323—(HKG)
Rev: $45,349,455
Assets: $259,793,363
Liabilities: $221,292,060
Net Worth: $38,501,303
Earnings: ($59,432,340)
Emp.: 874
Fiscal Year-end: 12/31/22
Printed Circuit Board Mfr & Distr
N.A.I.C.S.: 334412
Ho Fung Cheok (Founder)

Subsidiaries:

Topsearch Printed Circuits (HK) Limited (1)
Workshops D on the 15th Floor Block 2 of Koon Wah Mirror Factory, 6th Industrial Building Nos 7-9 Ho Tin Street, Tuen Mun, New Territories, China (Hong Kong)
Tel.: (852) 24229228
Investment Holding Services
N.A.I.C.S.: 551112
Eric Liu (Dir-Mktg-Corp)

Topsearch Printed Circuits Macao Commercial Offshore Company Limited (1)
Tel.: (853) 28330811
Printed Circuit Board Distr
N.A.I.C.S.: 423690
Eric Liu (Dir-Mktg-Corp)

RENCOR DEVELOPMENTS INC.
Suite 220 4954 Richard Road SW, Calgary, T3E 6L1, AB, Canada
Tel.: (403) 263-4449
Web Site: http://www.rencor.ca
Year Founded: 1984
Rev.: $12,412,500
Emp.: 3
Real Estate Agency
N.A.I.C.S.: 531210
Ron Renaud (Pres & CEO)

RENDALL & RITTNER LTD.
Portsoken House 155-157, London, EC3N 1LJ, United Kingdom
Tel.: (44) 20 7702 0701
Web Site:
  http://www.rendallandrittner.co.uk
Year Founded: 1990
Real Estate Invetments
N.A.I.C.S.: 531390
Paul Denton (Sr Mgr-Property)

Subsidiaries:

Braemar Estates Limited (1)
Richmond House Heath Road, Hale, WA14 2XP, Cheshire, United Kingdom
Tel.: (44) 1619292300
Web Site: http://www.rendallandrittner.co.uk
Residential Property Management Services
N.A.I.C.S.: 531311

RENDER CUBE SA
Piotrkowska 295 lok 7, 93-004, Lodz, Poland
Web Site: https://www.rendercube.pl
Year Founded: 2012
W63—(DEU)
Emp.: 19
Software Development Services
N.A.I.C.S.: 541511
Michael Nowak (VP)

RENDONG HOLDINGS CO., LTD.
Room 809 West Tower Century Fortune Center, Chaoyang District, Beijing, 311800, China
Tel.: (86) 1057808555
Web Site:
  https://rendongholdings.com
002647—(SSE)
Rev.: $232,625,952
Assets: $675,840,672
Liabilities: $642,130,632
Net Worth: $33,710,040
Earnings: ($19,682,676)
Emp.: 350
Fiscal Year-end: 12/31/22
Copper Product Mfr
N.A.I.C.S.: 331420

RENEGADE EXPLORATION LIMITED
Suite 13 6-10 Douro Street, West Perth, 6005, WA, Australia
Tel.: (61) 409842354   AU
Web Site:
  https://www.renegadeexplore.com
RNX—(ASX)
Rev.: $500,021
Assets: $4,200,487
Liabilities: $636,088
Net Worth: $3,564,399
Earnings: ($750,448)
Emp.: 1
Fiscal Year-end: 06/30/24
Minerals Exploration & Development Services
N.A.I.C.S.: 212323
Ben Vallerine (CEO)

RENEGADE GOLD INC.
1615 - 200 Burrard St, Vancouver, V6C 3L6, BC, Canada
Tel.: (604) 678-5308   Ca
Web Site:
  https://www.renegadegold.com
Year Founded: 2005
TGLDF—(OTCIQ)
Rev.: $4,451
Assets: $1,144,332
Liabilities: $494,546
Net Worth: $649,786
Earnings: ($368,534)
Fiscal Year-end: 06/30/19
Mineral Exploration Services
N.A.I.C.S.: 213114
James Lenec (VP-Bus Dev)

Subsidiaries:

Pacton Gold Inc. (1)
Suite 1680-200 Burrard St, Vancouver, V6C 3L6, BC, Canada
Tel.: (604) 678-5308
Web Site: http://www.pactongold.com
Rev.: $11,452
Assets: $9,565,549
Liabilities: $605,753
Net Worth: $8,959,796
Earnings: ($8,168,502)
Fiscal Year-end: 11/30/2019
Metal Mining Services
N.A.I.C.S.: 212290
P. Joseph Meagher (CFO)

RENEL SAS
19 Route d Amiens, PO Box BP0431, 80004, Amiens, France
Tel.: (33) 322959142   FR
Web Site: http://www.mag-auto-moto.com
Rev.: $25,900,000
Emp.: 55
New & Used Car Dealer
N.A.I.C.S.: 441110
Francis Azema (Pres)

RENERGEN LTD.
First Floor 1 Bompas Road, Dunkeld West, Johannesburg, 2196, South Africa
Tel.: (27) 100456000
Web Site: https://www.renergen.co.za
Year Founded: 2014
RLT—(ASX)
Rev.: $1,576,726
Assets: $147,539,056
Liabilities: $75,591,787
Net Worth: $71,947,269
Earnings: ($5,979,272)
Emp.: 70
Fiscal Year-end: 02/29/24
Eletric Power Generation Services
N.A.I.C.S.: 221118
Fulufhedzani Ravele (CFO)

RENERGETICA S.P.A.
Salita di Santa Caterina 2/1, 16123, Genoa, Italy
Tel.: (39) 0106422384
Web Site: http://www.renergetica.com
Year Founded: 2008
REN—(ITA)
Sales Range: $10-24.9 Million
Energy Consulting Services
N.A.I.C.S.: 541690
Rosa Maria Arnau Noguer (CEO)

RENESAS ELECTRONICS CORPORATION
TOYOSU FORESIA 3-2-24 Toyosu, Koto-ku, Tokyo, 135-0061, Japan
Tel.: (81) 367733000   JP
Web Site: https://www.renesas.com
Year Founded: 2002
RNECF—(OTCIQ)
Rev.: $6,927,714,640
Assets: $15,574,974,800
Liabilities: $9,576,656,320
Net Worth: $5,998,318,480
Earnings: $441,659,680
Emp.: 18,753
Fiscal Year-end: 12/31/20
Semiconductor & Microcontroller Mfr
N.A.I.C.S.: 334413
Tetsuya Tsurumaru (Chm)

Subsidiaries:

Dialog Semiconductor plc (1)
100 Longwater Avenue, Green Park, Reading, RG2 6GP, United Kingdom
Tel.: (44) 1793757700
Web Site:
  http://www.dialog-semiconductor.com
Rev.: $1,566,239,000
Assets: $2,176,984,000
Liabilities: $604,400,000
Net Worth: $1,572,584,000
Earnings: $301,452,000
Emp.: 2,036
Fiscal Year-end: 12/31/2019
Mixed Signal Semiconductors Mfr
N.A.I.C.S.: 334413
Mark Tyndall (Sr VP-Corp Dev & Strategy)

Subsidiary (US):

Adesto Technologies Corporation (2)
3600 Peterson Way, Santa Clara, CA 95054
Tel.: (408) 400-0578
Sales Range: $100-124.9 Million
Semiconductor Device Whslr
N.A.I.C.S.: 423690
Ron Shelton (CFO)

Subsidiary (Domestic):

Echelon Corporation (3)
2901 Patrick Henry Dr, Santa Clara, CA 95054
Tel.: (408) 938-5200
Web Site: http://www.echelon.com
Sales Range: $25-49.9 Million
Hardware & Software Products Distr
N.A.I.C.S.: 238210

Subsidiary (Non-US):

Echelon Asia Pacific Ltd. (4)
Room B 21 F 1 Capital Bay 18 Luard Rd, Wanchai, China (Hong Kong)
Tel.: (852) 28023769
Web Site: http://www.echelon.com
Sales Range: $100-124.9 Million
Emp.: 10
Embedded Control Network & Smart Metering Technology Services
N.A.I.C.S.: 518210

Echelon Europe Ltd. (4)
16 The Courtyards Hatters Ln, Watford, WD18 8YH, Herts, United Kingdom
Tel.: (44) 114419234
Web Site: http://www.echelon.co.uk
Sales Range: $1-9.9 Million
Emp.: 10
Embedded Control Network & Smart Metering Technology Services
N.A.I.C.S.: 518210

Echelon France, S.A.R.L. (4)
Immeuble Le Colombus 1 Rond Point de l'Europe, Colombes, 92250, France
Tel.: (33) 1 47 33 01 48
Web Site: http://www.echelon.com
Sales Range: $100-124.9 Million
Embedded Control Network & Smart Metering Technology Services
N.A.I.C.S.: 518210

Echelon Japan, K.K. (4)
Holland Hills Mori Tower 18F 5 11 2 Toranomon Minato-ku, Tokyo, 105-0001, Japan
Tel.: (81) 357333320
Web Site: http://www.echelon.co.jp
Sales Range: $1-9.9 Million
Emp.: 5
Embedded Control Network & Smart Metering Technology Services
N.A.I.C.S.: 518210

Subsidiary (Non-US):

Dialog Semiconductor (Italy) S.r.l. (2)
Palazzo Orlando Via G D'Alesio 2/Ex Piazza Mazzini 92, 57126, Livorno, Italy
Tel.: (39) 0586 246602
Semiconductor Components Mfr
N.A.I.C.S.: 334413

Dialog Semiconductor (UK) Limited (2) (100%)
Tel.: (44) 1628651700
Web Site: http://www.dialog-semiconductor.com
Sales Range: $25-49.9 Million
Emp.: 82
Semiconductor & Related Device Mfr
N.A.I.C.S.: 334413

Dialog Semiconductor B.V. (2)
Het Zuiderkruis 53, 5215 MV, s-Hertogenbosch, Netherlands
Tel.: (31) 736408822
Semiconductor Mfr
N.A.I.C.S.: 334413
Sean McGrath (Sr VP-Automotive & Industrial)

Dialog Semiconductor GmbH (2) (100%)
Neue Strasse 95, 73230, Kirchheim, Germany
Tel.: (49) 70218050
Web Site: http://www.dialog-semiconductor.com
Sales Range: $25-49.9 Million
Emp.: 100
Other Electronic Component Mfr
N.A.I.C.S.: 334419
Jalal Bagherli (CEO)

Subsidiary (US):

Dialog Semiconductor Inc (2) (100%)
16870 W Bernardo Dr, San Diego, CA 92127-1677
Tel.: (858) 674-6990
Other Electronic Parts & Equipment Whslr
N.A.I.C.S.: 423690

Subsidiary (Non-US):

Dialog Semiconductor KK (2) (100%)
Kamiyacho MT Bldg 16F 4-3-20 Toranomon, Minato-ku, Tokyo, 105 0001, Japan
Tel.: (81) 3 5425 4567
Web Site: http://www.dialog-semiconductor.com
Sales Range: $25-49.9 Million
Emp.: 13
Semiconductor Components Mfr
N.A.I.C.S.: 334413
Christophe Chene (Sr VP-Asia)

Dialog Semiconductor Trading (Shanghai) Limited (2)
Room 703 7F Kehui Building No 1188 North Quinzhou Road, Shanghai, 200233, China
Tel.: (86) 2154249058
Semiconductor Mfr
N.A.I.C.S.: 334413

Subsidiary (US):

Silego Technology, Inc. (2)
1715 Wyatt Dr, Santa Clara, CA 95054
Tel.: (408) 327-8800
Whol Electronic Parts/Equipment
N.A.I.C.S.: 423690

iWatt L.L.C. (2)
625 S Washington St, Greencastle, PA 17225
Tel.: (717) 264-2434
Web Site: http://www.iwatllc.com
Custom Computer Programming Services
N.A.I.C.S.: 541511

iWatt, Inc. (2)
675 Campbell Technology Pkwy Ste 150, Campbell, CA 95008
Tel.: (408) 374-4200
Web Site: http://www.iwatt.com
Sales Range: $50-74.9 Million
Emp.: 180
Digital-Centric Power Management Integrated Circuits Mfr
N.A.I.C.S.: 334413

Subsidiary (Non-US):

iWatt Integrated Circuits (Shenzhen) Limited Company (3)
Rooms 1009-1011 Chang Hong Science & Technology Building, South 12 Road Southern District High Tech Park, Shenzhen, China
Tel.: (86) 755 2981 3669

RENESAS ELECTRONICS CORPORATION — INTERNATIONAL PUBLIC

Renesas Electronics Corporation—(Continued)
Semiconductor Mfr
N.A.I.C.S.: 334413
Marco Cheng (Mgr-Sls)

Integrated Device Technology, Inc. (1)
6024 Silver Creek Valley Rd, San Jose, CA 95138
Tel.: (408) 284-8200
Web Site: http://www.idt.com
Sales Range: $800-899.9 Million
Emp.: 1,821
High-Performance Semiconductors & Modules for Networking & Communications Markets
N.A.I.C.S.: 334413
Mario Montana (Sr VP & Gen Mgr-Automotive & Industrial Grp)

Subsidiary (Domestic):

GigPeak, Inc.
6024 Silver Creek Vly Rd, San Jose, CA 95138
Tel.: (408) 284-8200
Web Site: http://www.idt.com
Semiconductor & High-Speed Circuits Designer & Mfr
N.A.I.C.S.: 334413
Darren Ma (CFO)

Subsidiary (Non-US):

GigOptix-Helix AG (3)
Seefeldstrasse 45, Zurich, 8008, Switzerland
Tel.: (41) 442602434
Semiconductor Mfr
N.A.I.C.S.: 334413

Subsidiary (Non-US):

IDT Canada Inc. (2)
603 March Road, Ottawa, K2K 2M5, ON, Canada
Tel.: (613) 595-6300
Web Site: http://www.idt.com
Sales Range: $50-74.9 Million
Emp.: 80
Semiconductors & Modules for Networking & Communications Markets
N.A.I.C.S.: 334413

IDT Europe GmbH (2)
Grenzstr 28, 1109, Dresden, Germany
Tel.: (49) 35188220
Web Site: http://www.idt.com
Semiconductor Devices Mfr
N.A.I.C.S.: 334413

IDT Singapore Pte. Ltd. (2)
10 Ang Mo Kio St 65 Techpoint 02-10, Singapore, 569059, Singapore
Tel.: (65) 67443356
Web Site: http://www.idt.com
Semiconductors & Related Devices Mfr
N.A.I.C.S.: 334413

Integrated Device Technology (Israel) Ltd. (2)
11 Hamenofim Street, PO Box 2148, Herzliya Pituach, 46120, Israel
Tel.: (972) 99715781
Integrated Circuits & Related Device Mfr
N.A.I.C.S.: 334413

Integrated Device Technology (Malaysia) SDN. BHD (2)
11900 Phase 3 Bayan Lepas Free Industrial Zone, Bayan Lepas, Penang, 11900, Malaysia
Tel.: (60) 46132200
Web Site: http://www.idt.com
Emp.: 500
Semiconductor & Related Device Mfr
N.A.I.C.S.: 334413
Ang Hee Lai (Mng Dir)

Branch (Domestic):

Integrated Device Technology - Longmont (2)
2605 Trade Centre Ave Ste C, Longmont, CO 80503
Tel.: (720) 494-8401
Web Site: http://www.synkera.com
Sales Range: $1-9.9 Million
Emp.: 6
Chemical Sensing & Analysis Services

N.A.I.C.S.: 325180
Debra J. Deininger (Dir-Gas Sensing)

Subsidiary (Non-US):

Integrated Device Technology Europe Limited (2)
Prime House Barnett Wood Lane, Leatherhead, KT22 7DG, Surrey, United Kingdom (100%)
Tel.: (44) 1372363339
Web Site: http://www.idt.com
Sales Range: $1-9.9 Million
Emp.: 6
Production of Integrated Circuits Based on Complementary Enhanced Metal-Oxide Semiconductor (CMOS) & Bipolar CEMOS Technology
N.A.I.C.S.: 334413

Integrated Device Technology UK Limited (2)
Dorset House 297 Kingston Road, Leatherhead, KT22 7PL, Surrey, United Kingdom
Tel.: (44) 1372363339
Semiconductor Product Distr
N.A.I.C.S.: 423690

Subsidiary (Domestic):

Jet City Electronics Inc. (2)
7215 W Greenlake Dr N, Seattle, WA 98103
Tel.: (206) 529-0351
Web Site: http://www.jetcityelectronics.com
Electronic Component Mfr & Distr
N.A.I.C.S.: 334413
John Fallisgaard (Pres)

Subsidiary (Non-US):

Nippon IDT G.K. (2)
Nomura Fudosan Shiba-Daimon Building 6F 1-9-9 Shibadaimon, Minato-ku, Tokyo, 105-0012, Japan
Tel.: (81) 364533010
Web Site: http://www.idt.com
Telecommunications Equipment Mfr
N.A.I.C.S.: 334419

Zentrum Mikroelektronik Dresden AG
Grenzstrasse 28, Dresden, 01109, Germany
Tel.: (49) 35188220
Semiconductor Product Mfr & Distr
N.A.I.C.S.: 334413
Steffi Scharsach (Mgr-Supply Chain Sls & Production)

Intersil Corporation (1)
1001 Murphy Ranch Rd, Milpitas, CA 95035
Tel.: (408) 432-8888
Web Site: http://www.intersil.com
Rev: $542,139,000
Assets: $1,165,341,000
Liabilities: $181,802,000
Net Worth: $983,539,000
Earnings: $48,137,000
Emp.: 970
Fiscal Year-end: 12/30/2016
High Performance Analog Integrated Circuits Designer & Mfr
N.A.I.C.S.: 541410
Richard D. Crowley Jr. (CFO & Sr VP)

Subsidiary (Domestic):

Great Wall Semiconductor Corp. (2)
3800 N Central Ave, Phoenix, AZ 85012
Tel.: (602) 288-5870
Semiconductor & Related Devices Mfr
N.A.I.C.S.: 334413
Andrew Hughes (Sec)

Subsidiary (Non-US):

Intersil (Wuhan) Company Ltd. (2)
Unit 301 Tower A Central Towers 555 Langao Road, Putuo District, Shanghai, 200333, China
Tel.: (86) 2122260888
Analog Integrated Circuits & Semiconductor Device Mfr
N.A.I.C.S.: 334413

Branch (Domestic):

Intersil Corporation - Design Center (2)
440 US Hwy 22 E Ste 100, Bridgewater, NJ 08807

Tel.: (908) 685-6000
Web Site: http://www.intersil.com
Sales Range: $10-24.9 Million
Emp.: 35
Custom & Standard Application Specific ICs Mfr & Distr
N.A.I.C.S.: 334413

Subsidiary (Non-US):

Intersil GmbH (2)
Oskar Messter Strasse 29, 85737, Ismaning, Germany
Tel.: (49) 89462630
Web Site: http://www.intersil.com
Marketing & Sales of Semiconductors
N.A.I.C.S.: 423690

Renesas Design Corp. (1)
4-1-3 Mizuhara, Itami, 664-0005, Hyogo, Japan
Tel.: (81) 72 785 2151
Web Site: http://www.renesas.com
Electronic Components Mfr
N.A.I.C.S.: 334413
Hideharu Takebe (Pres)

Renesas Design France S.A.S (1)
14 A Rue Du Patis Tatelin, 35700, Rennes, France
Tel.: (33) 223212800
Web Site: http://www.rdf.renesasmobile.com
Semiconductor Products Mfr & Sales
N.A.I.C.S.: 334413

Renesas Design Vietnam Co., Ltd. (1)
Lot W 29-30-31a Tan Thuan Road, Tan Thuan Export Processing Zone Tan Thuan, Dong Ward District 7, Ho Chi Minh City, Vietnam
Tel.: (84) 2837700255
Web Site: http://www.vietnam.renesas.com
Semiconductor Devices Mfr
N.A.I.C.S.: 334413

Renesas Eastern Japan Semiconductor, Inc. (1)
2-14-1 Kyobashi, Chuo-ku, Tokyo, 104-0031, Japan
Tel.: (81) 362286477
Sales Range: $550-599.9 Million
Emp.: 1,200
Semiconductor Equipment Mfr & Sales
N.A.I.C.S.: 423690
Hideyuki Todokoro (Pres)

Renesas Electronics (China) Co., Ltd. (1)
Room 101-T01 Floor 1 Building 7 Yard No 7 8th Street Shangdi, Haidian District, Beijing, 100085, China
Tel.: (86) 1082351155
Web Site: https://www.renesas.cn
Semiconductor & Microcontroller Mfr
N.A.I.C.S.: 334413

Renesas Electronics (Penang) Sdn. Bhd. (1)
Phase 3 Bayan Lepas Free Industrial Zone, 11900, Penang, Malaysia
Tel.: (60) 46132200
Electronic Equipment Mfr & Distr
N.A.I.C.S.: 335999

Renesas Electronics (Shanghai) Co., Ltd. (1)
Unit 301 Tower A Central Towers 555 Langao Road, Putuo District, Shanghai, 200333, China
Tel.: (86) 2122260888
Semiconductor Product Mfr & Whslr
N.A.I.C.S.: 334413

Renesas Electronics America Inc. (1)
1001 Murphy Ranch Rd, Milpitas, CA 95035 (100%)
Tel.: (408) 432-8888
Web Site: http://www.am.renesas.com
Sales Range: $150-199.9 Million
Semiconductor & Microcontroller Mfr
N.A.I.C.S.: 334413

Subsidiary (Non-US):

Renesas Electronics Canada Limited (2)
603 March Road, Ottawa, K2K 2M5, ON, Canada

Tel.: (613) 595-6300
Semiconductor & Microcontroller Mfr
N.A.I.C.S.: 334413

Renesas Electronics Brasil-Servicos Ltda. (1)
Avenida Ibirapuera 2907 conjunto 818/819 Indianopolis, 04029-200, Sao Paulo, Brazil
Tel.: (55) 1150418263
Semiconductor Product Mfr & Whslr
N.A.I.C.S.: 334413

Renesas Electronics Corporation - Nishiki Factory (1)
2626 Ichibu Nishikimachi, Kuma-gun, Kumamoto, 868-0394, Japan
Tel.: (81) 966383011
Semiconductor Product Mfr & Whslr
N.A.I.C.S.: 334413

Renesas Electronics Corporation - Oita Factory (1)
4200 Idouda, Nakatsu, 879-0111, Oita, Japan
Tel.: (81) 979327111
Semiconductor Product Mfr & Whslr
N.A.I.C.S.: 334413

Renesas Electronics Corporation - Yonezawa Factory (1)
3-3274 Aza-Yagihashi Higashi Oaza-Hanazawa, Yonezawa, 992-8530, Yamagata, Japan
Tel.: (81) 238225555
Semiconductor Product Mfr & Whslr
N.A.I.C.S.: 334413

Renesas Electronics Europe Limited (1)
Dukes Meadow Millboard Road, Bourne End, SL8 5FH, Buckinghamshire, United Kingdom
Tel.: (44) 162 865 1700
Web Site: http://www.renesas.eu
Semiconductor & Microcontroller Mfr
N.A.I.C.S.: 334413

Subsidiary (Non-US):

Renesas Electronics Europe GmbH (2)
Arcadiastr 10, 40472, Dusseldorf, Germany (100%)
Tel.: (49) 21165030
Web Site: http://www.eu.nec.com
Sales Range: $100-124.9 Million
Semiconductor & Microcontroller Mfr
N.A.I.C.S.: 334413

Renesas Electronics Germany GmbH (1)
Grenzstrasse 28, 01109, Dresden, Germany
Tel.: (49) 3518822306
Semiconductor Product Mfr & Distr
N.A.I.C.S.: 334413

Renesas Electronics Hong Kong Limited (1) (100%)
Tel.: (852) 22656688
Web Site: http://www.hk.renesas.com
Sales Range: $25-49.9 Million
Emp.: 50
Semiconductor & Microcontroller Mfr
N.A.I.C.S.: 334413

Renesas Electronics India Pvt. Ltd. (1)
Tel.: (91) 8067208700
Semiconductor Product Mfr & Whslr
N.A.I.C.S.: 334413

Renesas Electronics Korea Co., Ltd (1)
Tel.: (82) 25583737
Emp.: 50
Electronic Components Mfr
N.A.I.C.S.: 334419

Renesas Electronics Malaysia Sdn. Bhd. (1)
Tel.: (60) 350221288
Web Site: http://www.sg.renesas.com
Sales Range: $25-49.9 Million
Emp.: 8
Semiconductor Devices Mfr
N.A.I.C.S.: 334413

Renesas Electronics Singapore Pte. Ltd. (1)

AND PRIVATE COMPANIES

80 Bendemeer Road Unit 06-02, Hyflux Innovation Centre, Singapore, 339949, Singapore **(100%)**
Tel.: (65) 62130200
Sales Range: $25-49.9 Million
Emp.: 100
Semiconductor & Microcontroller Mfr
N.A.I.C.S.: 334413

Renesas Electronics Taiwan Co., Ltd. (1)
Tel.: (886) 281759600
Sales Range: $25-49.9 Million
Emp.: 40
Semiconductor & Microcontroller Mfr
N.A.I.C.S.: 334413

Renesas Engineering Services Co., Ltd. (1)
5-20-1 Josuihon-cho, Kodaira, 187-8588, Tokyo, Japan
Tel.: (81) 423207328
Engineeering Services
N.A.I.C.S.: 541330

Renesas Kansai Semiconductor Co., Ltd. (1)
Nissay Yodoyabashi East 3-3-13 Imabashi, Chuo-ku, Osaka, 541-0042, Japan
Tel.: (81) 662339500
Web Site: http://www.renesas.com
Semiconductor Devices Mfr
N.A.I.C.S.: 334413

Renesas Micro Systems Co., Ltd. (1)
3-1 Kinkocho, Kanagawa-ku, Yokohama, 221-0056, Kanagawa, Japan
Tel.: (81) 454434800
Sales Range: $350-399.9 Million
Emp.: 1,800
Semiconductor Equipment Mfr
N.A.I.C.S.: 334413
Hiroshi Iguchi (Pres)

Renesas Naka Semiconductor Co., Ltd (1)
730 Horiguchi, Hitachinaka, 312-8504, Ibaraki, Japan
Tel.: (81) 292701950
Semiconductor Devices Mfr
N.A.I.C.S.: 334413

Renesas Northern Japan Semiconductor, Inc. (1)
145-1 Aza Nakajima Nanae-cho, Kamedagun, Hokkaido, 041-1196, Japan
Tel.: (81) 138654111
Sales Range: $75-99.9 Million
Emp.: 275
Semiconductor Equipment Mfr
N.A.I.C.S.: 334413
Kosuke Tanaka (Pres)

Subsidiary (Domestic):

Hokkai Electronics Co., Ltd. (2)
289-12 Higashi-cho Yakumo-cho, Futamigun, Hokkaido, 049-3102, Japan
Tel.: (81) 137.63 2426
Electronic Components Mfr
N.A.I.C.S.: 335999

Renesas Semiconductor (Beijing) Co., Ltd (1)
7 8th Street Shangdi Information Industry Base, Haidian District, Beijing, 100085, China
Tel.: (86) 1057525050
Web Site: https://www.renesas.com
Semiconductor Equipment Mfr
N.A.I.C.S.: 334413

Renesas Semiconductor (Malaysia) Sdn. Bhd. (1)
Bayan Lepas Free Industrial Zone, 11900, Penang, Malaysia
Tel.: (60) 46438121
Web Site: https://www.rsm.renesas.com
Semiconductor Devices Mfr
N.A.I.C.S.: 334413

Subsidiary (Domestic):

Renesas Semiconductor (Kedah) Sdn. Bhd. (2)
Kulim Industrial Estate, 09000, Kulim, Kedah, Malaysia
Tel.: (60) 44892241
Electronic Components Mfr
N.A.I.C.S.: 334419

Renesas Semiconductor (Suzhou) Co., Ltd (1)
No 176 Zhongxin Avenue West, Suzhou Industrial Park, Suzhou, 215021, China
Tel.: (86) 51267626056
Web Site: https://www.renesas.com
Semiconductor Equipment Mfr
N.A.I.C.S.: 334413

Renesas Semiconductor Design (Beijing) Co., Ltd. (1)
Room 101-T02 Floor 1 Building 7 Yard No 7 8th Street Shangdi, Haidian District, Beijing, 100085, China
Tel.: (86) 1056161818
Web Site: https://www.renesas.com
Semiconductor Devices Mfr
N.A.I.C.S.: 334413

Renesas Semiconductor Design (Malaysia) Sdn. Bhd (1)
Bayan Lepas Free Industrial Zone, 11900, Penang, Malaysia
Tel.: (60) 46438121
Semiconductor Devices Mfr
N.A.I.C.S.: 334413

Renesas Semiconductor KL Sdn. Bhd (1)
KM 15 Jalan Banting, 42500, Teluk Panglima Garang, Selangor Darul Ehsan, Malaysia
Tel.: (60) 333268000
Web Site: http://skl.renesas.com
Sales Range: $700-749.9 Million
Emp.: 1,582
Semiconductor Equipment Mfr
N.A.I.C.S.: 334413

Renesas Semiconductor Kyushu Yamaguchi Co., Ltd. (1)
1-1-1 Yahata, Kumamoto, 861-4195, Japan
Tel.: (81) 963572111
Semiconductor Devices Mfr
N.A.I.C.S.: 334413

Renesas Semiconductor Manufacturing Co., Ltd. (1)
751 Horiguchi, Hitachinaka, 312-8511, Ibaraki, Japan
Tel.: (81) 292723111
Semiconductor & Related Device Mfr
N.A.I.C.S.: 334413

Plant (Domestic):

Renesas Semiconductor Manufacturing Co., Ltd. - Kawashiri Factory (2)
1-1-1 Yahata, Minami-ku, Kumamoto, 861-4195, Japan
Tel.: (81) 963572111
Semiconductor Product Mfr & Whslr
N.A.I.C.S.: 334413
Kenji Kanamitsu (VP)

Renesas Semiconductor Manufacturing Co., Ltd. - Saijo Factory (2)
8-6 Hiuchi, Saijo, 793-8501, Ehime, Japan
Tel.: (81) 897551811
Semiconductor Product Mfr & Whslr
N.A.I.C.S.: 334413
Shinji Kimura (VP)

Renesas Semiconductor Manufacturing Co., Ltd. - Shiga Factory (2)
2-9-1 Seiran, Otsu, 520-8555, Shiga, Japan
Tel.: (81) 775372100
Semiconductor Product Mfr & Whslr
N.A.I.C.S.: 334413
Yukio Arai (VP)

Renesas Semiconductor Manufacturing Co., Ltd. - Takasaki Factory (2)
111 Nishiyokotemachi, Takasaki, 370-0021, Gunma, Japan
Tel.: (81) 273522111
Semiconductor Product Mfr & Whslr
N.A.I.C.S.: 334413
Toshiyuki Nakano (VP)

Renesas Semiconductor Manufacturing Co., Ltd. - Yamaguchi Factory (2)
20192-3 Higashimagura Jinga, Ube, 757-0298, Yamaguchi, Japan
Tel.: (81) 836672111
Semiconductor Product Mfr & Whslr
N.A.I.C.S.: 334413
Mikio Okamura (VP)

Renesas Semiconductor Technology (M) Sdn. Bhd. (1)
Bayan Lepas Free Industrial Zone, 11900, Penang, Malaysia
Tel.: (60) 46438121
Sales Range: $350-399.9 Million
Electronic Components Mfr
N.A.I.C.S.: 334419

Renesas Solutions Corp. (1)
Nihon Building 2-6-2 Otemachi, Chiyoda-ku, Tokyo, 100-0004, Japan
Tel.: (81) 352015380
Web Site: http://www.rso.renesas.com
Sales Range: $150-199.9 Million
Emp.: 500
Semiconductor Devices Mfr
N.A.I.C.S.: 334413
Shinji Suda (Pres)

Subsidiary (Non-US):

Renesas System Solutions Korea Co., Ltd. (2)
5F Young Poong Building 33 Seorin-dong, Chongro-Ku, Seoul, 110-752, Korea (South)
Tel.: (82) 2 796 3145
Web Site: http://www.rso.renesas.com
Semiconductor Equipment Mfr
N.A.I.C.S.: 334413

Renesas Yamagata Semiconductor Co., Ltd (1)
1-11-73 Takarada, Tsuruoka, 997-8522, Yamagata, Japan
Tel.: (81) 235 24 1911
Semiconductor Equipment Mfr
N.A.I.C.S.: 334413

Renesas Yanai Semiconductor, Inc. (1)
3 1 1 Minamihama, Yanai, 742-0023, Yamaguchi, Japan
Tel.: (81) 820231121
Semiconductor Equipment Mfr
N.A.I.C.S.: 334413

Transphorm, Inc. (1)
75 Castilian Dr, Goleta, CA 93117
Tel.: (805) 456-1300
Web Site: https://www.transphormusa.com
Rev.: $16,511,000
Assets: $44,452,000
Liabilities: $24,837,000
Net Worth: $19,615,000
Earnings: ($30,598,000)
Emp.: 126
Fiscal Year-end: 03/31/2023
Semiconductor Mfr
N.A.I.C.S.: 334413
Umesh Mishra (Co-Founder, Chm & CTO)

Subsidiary (Non-US):

Transphorm Japan EPI, Inc. (2)
Shin-Yokohama Center Bldg 9F 2-5-15 Shin-Yokohama, Kohoku-ku, Yokohama, 222-0033, Japan
Tel.: (81) 454711370
Semiconductor Device Mfr & Distr
N.A.I.C.S.: 334413

Transphorm Japan, Inc. (2)
Shin-Yokohama Center Bldg 9F 2-5-15, Shin-Yokohama Kohoku-ku, Yokohama, 222-0033, Japan
Tel.: (81) 454711370
Semiconductor Device Distr
N.A.I.C.S.: 423690

Subsidiary (Domestic):

Transphorm Technology, Inc. (2)
75 Castilian Dr, Goleta, CA 93117
Tel.: (805) 456-1300
Web Site: https://www.transphormusa.com
Semiconductor Devices Mfr
N.A.I.C.S.: 334413
Umesh Mishra (CEO & CTO)

RENET JAPAN GROUP, INC.

3-45 Ichiyacho, Obu, 474-0055, Aichi, Japan
Tel.: (81) 562452922
Web Site: https://www.corp.renet.jp
Year Founded: 2000

3556—(TKS)
Rev.: $78,379,950
Assets: $104,825,650
Liabilities: $90,312,420
Net Worth: $14,513,230
Earnings: ($2,495,680)
Emp.: 1,713
Fiscal Year-end: 09/30/23
Internet Recycling Services
N.A.I.C.S.: 561439

RENEUCO BERHAD

D2-3-1 Solaris Dutamas No 1 Jalan Dutamas 1, 50480, Kuala Lumpur, Malaysia
Tel.: (60) 362032929
Web Site: https://reneuco.com
RENEUCO—(KLS)
Rev.: $13,671,111
Assets: $66,156,190
Liabilities: $44,301,164
Net Worth: $21,855,026
Earnings: ($25,181,376)
Emp.: 327
Fiscal Year-end: 09/30/23
Fabrics Mfr
N.A.I.C.S.: 313240
Mohd Abdul Karim Abdullah (Chm)

Subsidiaries:

Granulab (M) Sdn Bhd (1)
14 Jalan Anggerik Mokara 31/47, Kota Kemuning, 40460, Shah Alam, Selangor, Malaysia **(70%)**
Tel.: (60) 351249622
Web Site: https://www.granulab.com
Medical Device Mfr
N.A.I.C.S.: 339112

RENEURON GROUP PLC

Pencoed Business Park, Pencoed, Bridgend, CF35 5HY, United Kingdom
Tel.: (44) 2038198400
Web Site: https://www.reneuron.com
RNUGF—(OTCIQ)
Rev.: $658,154
Assets: $11,977,161
Liabilities: $5,697,378
Net Worth: $6,279,783
Earnings: ($6,715,654)
Emp.: 26
Fiscal Year-end: 03/31/23
Irradiation Apparatus Manufacturing
N.A.I.C.S.: 334517
Michael Hunt (CFO)

RENEW HOLDINGS PLC

3175 Century Way Thorpe Park, Leeds, LS15 8ZB, United Kingdom
Tel.: (44) 1132814200
Web Site: https://www.renewholdings.com
RNWH—(AIM)
Rev.: $1,073,949,731
Assets: $507,946,133
Liabilities: $338,476,881
Net Worth: $169,469,253
Earnings: $41,360,224
Emp.: 3,696
Fiscal Year-end: 09/30/21
Construction Services
N.A.I.C.S.: 236220
David Malcolm Forbes (Chm)

Subsidiaries:

Allenbuild Ltd. (1)
Unit 4 Interchange 25 Bus Pk, Bostocks Ln Sandiacre, Nottingham, NG10 5QG, United Kingdom **(50%)**
Tel.: (44) 1159210150
Web Site: http://www.allenbuild.co.uk
Sales Range: $25-49.9 Million
Emp.: 9
Industrial Building Construction
N.A.I.C.S.: 236210
Ed Carlisle (Dir-Fin)

Amalgamated Construction (Scotland) Ltd. (1)

RENEW HOLDINGS PLC

Renew Holdings plc—(Continued)

Antonine House 5 Carradale Crescent
Broadwood Business Park, Cumbernauld,
G68 9LE, United Kingdom
Tel.: (44) 123 645 7157
Construction Services
N.A.I.C.S.: 236220

Amco Giffen Ltd. (1)
Whaley Road Barugh, Barnsley, S75 1HT,
South Yorkshire, United Kingdom
Tel.: (44) 122 624 3413
Web Site: https://www.amcogiffen.co.uk
Construction Services
N.A.I.C.S.: 236220

Amco Group Ltd. (1)
AMCO Park Acanthus Road North Moons
Moat, Redditch, B98 9EX, Worcestershire,
United Kingdom
Tel.: (44) 190 575 8000
Web Site: https://www.amco-group.co.uk
Logistic Services
N.A.I.C.S.: 541614
Will Allen *(Sr Mgr-Sales)*

Clarke Telecom Ltd. (1)
Unit E Madison Place Northampton Road,
Manchester, M40 5AG, United Kingdom
Tel.: (44) 161 785 4500
Web Site: https://www.clarke-telecom.com
Telecommunication Servicesb
N.A.I.C.S.: 517111
Nigel Newton *(Mng Dir)*

David Lewis Civil Engineering Ltd. (1)
Mwyndy Cross Industries Cardiff Road,
Rhondda Cynon Taff, Pontyclun, CF72 8PN,
United Kingdom
Tel.: (44) 144 344 9200
Web Site: https://www.lewis-ltd.co.uk
Water Construction Services
N.A.I.C.S.: 237110

Envolve Infrastructure Ltd. (1)
Cardiff Road, Mwyndy Cross Industries
Rhondda Cynon Taff, Pontyclun, CF72 8PN,
United Kingdom
Tel.: (44) 1443449200
Web Site: https://envstaging.designdough.co.uk
Construction Engineering Services
N.A.I.C.S.: 541330

Hire One Ltd. (1)
204 Watford Rd, Saint Albans, AL2 3EB,
Hertfordshire, United Kingdom
Tel.: (44) 172 785 7395
Web Site: https://www.hire-one.com
Building Equipment Services
N.A.I.C.S.: 541310

J Browne Construction Ltd. (1)
Unit 1-2 Pavilion Business Centre 6 Kinetic
Crescent, Enfield, EN3 7FJ, United Kingdom
Tel.: (44) 2033000033
Web Site: https://jbconstruction.co.uk
Construction Engineering Services
N.A.I.C.S.: 541330

Knex Pipelines & Cables Ltd. (1)
Mwyndy Cross Industries Cardiff Road,
Rhondda Cynon Taff, Pontyclun, CF72 8PN,
United Kingdom
Tel.: (44) 144 344 9215
Web Site: https://knexpipelines.co.uk
Pipe Bursting Services
N.A.I.C.S.: 237120

P.P.S. Electrical Ltd. (1)
187 Duke Street, Barrow-in-Furness, LA14
1XU, Cumbria, United Kingdom
Tel.: (44) 122 943 3838
Web Site: https://ppselectrical.co.uk
Electrical Engineering Services
N.A.I.C.S.: 541330

Rail Electrification Ltd. (1)
Unit 2 Wellfield Business Park, Preston
Brook, Runcorn, WA7 3AZ, United Kingdom
Tel.: (44) 1270448405
Web Site: https://railelectrification.com
Railway Construction Services
N.A.I.C.S.: 237990

Seymour (Civil Engineering Contractors) Ltd. (1)
Seymour House Harbour Walk, Hartlepool,
TS24 0UX, United Kingdom (100%)
Tel.: (44) 1429233521
Web Site: https://www.seymourcec.co.uk
Sales Range: $25-49.9 Million
Emp.: 150
Engineeering Services
N.A.I.C.S.: 541330

Shepley Engineers Ltd. (1) (100%)
Tel.: (44) 1946599022
Web Site: http://www.shepleyengineers.co.uk
Sales Range: $75-99.9 Million
Emp.: 280
Engineeering Services
N.A.I.C.S.: 541330

VHE Construction Plc (1)
6 Newton Business Centre, Chapeltown,
Sheffield, S35 2PH, United Kingdom (100%)
Tel.: (44) 1226320150
Web Site: https://www.vhe.co.uk
Sales Range: $25-49.9 Million
Emp.: 40
Heavy & Civil Engineering Construction
N.A.I.C.S.: 237990
Gordon Wilson *(Mng Dir)*

West Cumberland Engineering Ltd. (1)
Joseph Noble Road Lillyhall, Workington,
CA14 4JX, Cumbria, United Kingdom
Tel.: (44) 190 087 2787
Web Site: https://westcumberlandengineering.co.uk
Fabricating Pipe Mfr
N.A.I.C.S.: 332996

YJL Infrastructure Ltd. (1)
39 Cornhill, London, EC3V3NU, United Kingdom (100%)
Tel.: (44) 2075223220
Sales Range: $25-49.9 Million
Emp.: 50
New Single-Family Housing Construction
N.A.I.C.S.: 236115

RENEWABLE ENERGY SYSTEMS LTD

Beaufort Court Egg Farm Lane, Kings
Langley, WD4 8LR, Hertfordshire,
United Kingdom
Tel.: (44) 1923 299 200
Web Site: http://www.res-group.com
Year Founded: 1981
Renewable Energy Mfr
N.A.I.C.S.: 541330

Subsidiaries:

System 3 Inc. (1)
5945 Palm Dr, Carmichael, CA 95608-3835
Tel.: (916) 979-0550
Web Site: http://www.system3inc.com
Engineeering Services
N.A.I.C.S.: 541330
Joel Leineke *(Pres)*

RENEWABLE JAPAN CO., LTD.

Toranomon Kotohira Tower 6th Fl
1-2-8 Toranomon, Minato-ku, Tokyo,
105-0001, Japan
Tel.: (81) 355109087
Web Site: https://www.rn-j.com
Year Founded: 2012
9522—(TKS)
Rev.: $238,252,360
Assets: $1,128,054,450
Liabilities: $1,027,879,840
Net Worth: $100,174,610
Earnings: $7,713,920
Emp.: 296
Fiscal Year-end: 12/31/23
Eletric Power Generation Services
N.A.I.C.S.: 221115

Subsidiaries:

RJ Investment Co. (1)
3805 N High St Ste 306, Columbus, OH 43214
Tel.: (614) 268-1777
Web Site: https://www.rjinvestmentsolutions.com
Mutual Funds & Financial Services
N.A.I.C.S.: 525910

RENEWABLE VENTURES NORDIC AB

Humlegardsgatan 4, 11446, Stockholm, Sweden
Tel.: (46) 721827290
Web Site: https://www.reventures.se
Year Founded: 2008
X72—(DEU)
Investment Management Service
N.A.I.C.S.: 523999
Marcus Bonsib *(CEO)*

RENEWI PLC

Enigma Wavendon Business Park
Ortensia Drive Wavendon, Milton
Keynes, MK17 8LX, Buckinghamshire, United Kingdom
Tel.: (44) 1908650650 UK
Web Site: https://www.renewi.com
Year Founded: 1982
RWI—(LSE)
Rev.: $2,061,660,850
Assets: $2,272,152,250
Liabilities: $1,893,768,900
Net Worth: $378,383,350
Earnings: $72,560,700
Fiscal Year-end: 03/31/23
Holding Company; Waste Management & Recycling Services
N.A.I.C.S.: 551112
Philip Griffin-Smith *(Sec)*

Subsidiaries:

ATM Entsorgung Deutschland GmbH (1)
Kaldenkirchener Strasse 25, 41063, Monchengladbach, Germany
Tel.: (49) 2161180337
Waste Management Services
N.A.I.C.S.: 562213

Atm B.V. (1)
Vlasweg 12, 4782 PW, Moerdijk, Netherlands
Tel.: (31) 168389289
Web Site: https://www.atm.nl
Emp.: 220
Waste Processing Services
N.A.I.C.S.: 562211

Coolrec B.V. (1)
Van Hilststraat 7, 5145 RK, Waalwijk, Netherlands
Tel.: (31) 416347373
Web Site: https://www.coolrec.com
Waste Management Services
N.A.I.C.S.: 562213

Coolrec France S.A.S. (1)
Rue d Iena, 59810, Lesquin, France
Tel.: (33) 320971091
Waste Management Services
N.A.I.C.S.: 562213

Coolrec Nederland B.V. (1)
Grevelingenweg 3, 3313 LB, Dordrecht, Netherlands
Tel.: (31) 887003500
Waste Management Services
N.A.I.C.S.: 562213

Coolrec Plastics B.V. (1)
Van Hilststraat 7, 5145 RK, Waalwijk, Netherlands
Tel.: (31) 416347373
Waste Management Services
N.A.I.C.S.: 562213

EcoSmart Nederland B.V. (1)
Spaarpot 6, 5667 KX, Geldrop, Netherlands
Tel.: (31) 88 700 3700
Web Site: https://www.renewi.com
Waste Treatment & Disposal Services
N.A.I.C.S.: 562211

Glasrecycling Noord-Oost Nederland B.V. (1)
Columbusstraat 20, 7825 VR, Emmen, Netherlands
Tel.: (31) 167529529

INTERNATIONAL PUBLIC

Recycler Glass Waste Services
N.A.I.C.S.: 423930

Maltha Glasrecyclage Belgie B.V. (1)
Fabrieksstraat 114, 3920, Lommel, Belgium
Tel.: (32) 11445687
Recycler Glass Waste Services
N.A.I.C.S.: 423930

Maltha Glass Recycling Portugal Lda. (1)
Parque Industrial Da Gala Lote 26/27 R Acacias, 3081-801, Figueira da Foz, Portugal
Tel.: (351) 233402440
Web Site: https://www.maltha.pt
Packaging Glass Waste Mfr
N.A.I.C.S.: 327213

Maltha Groep B.V. (1)
Glasweg 7-9, 4794 TB, Heijningen, Netherlands
Tel.: (31) 167529529
Web Site: https://www.maltha-glassrecycling.nl
Recycler Glass Waste Services
N.A.I.C.S.: 423930

Mineralz B.V. (1)
Van Hilststraat 7, 5145 RK, Waalwijk, Netherlands
Tel.: (31) 407514692
Web Site: https://www.mineralz.com
Semiconductor & Related Device Mfr
N.A.I.C.S.: 334413

Mineralz ES Treatment N.V. (1)
Rue Landuyt 140, 1440, Braine-le-Chateau, Belgium
Tel.: (32) 23672300
Semiconductor & Related Device Mfr
N.A.I.C.S.: 334413

Mineralz Maasvlakte B.V. (1)
Port number 8775 Loswalweg 50, Maasvlakte, 3199 LG, Rotterdam, Netherlands
Tel.: (31) 181363099
Semiconductor & Related Device Mfr
N.A.I.C.S.: 334413

Mineralz Zweekhorst B.V. (1)
Doesburgseweg 16 d, 6902 PN, Zevenaar, Netherlands
Tel.: (31) 316342040
Semiconductor & Related Device Mfr
N.A.I.C.S.: 334413

Ocean Combustion Services N.V. (1)
Terlindenhofstraat 36, 2170, Merksem, Belgium
Tel.: (32) 36462112
Waste Management Services
N.A.I.C.S.: 562213

Orgaworld Nederland B.V. (1)
Lindeboomseweg 15, Postbus 1521, 3800 BM, Amersfoort, Netherlands
Tel.: (31) 889086110
Web Site: https://www.orgaworld.com
Semiconductor & Related Device Mfr
N.A.I.C.S.: 334413

Recydel S.A. (1)
Rue Werihet 72, 4020, Wandre, Belgium
Tel.: (32) 43709460
Waste Management Services
N.A.I.C.S.: 562213

Renewi Commercial B.V. (1)
Lindeboomseweg 15, 3825 AL, Amersfoort, Netherlands
Tel.: (31) 887003800
Waste Collection Services
N.A.I.C.S.: 562119

Renewi Tisselt N.V. (1)
Baeckelmansstraat 125, 2830, Willebroek, Belgium
Tel.: (32) 38860881
Semiconductor & Related Device Mfr
N.A.I.C.S.: 334413

Renewi UK Services Limited (1)
Dunedin House, Auckland Park, Milton Keynes, MK1 1BU, United Kingdom
Tel.: (44) 3458506506
Web Site: https://renewiwakefield.co.uk
Waste Management Services
N.A.I.C.S.: 562211

AND PRIVATE COMPANIES

Renewi Westpoort B.V. (1)
Sicilieweg 38, 1045 AS, Amsterdam, Netherlands
Tel.: (31) 889805000
Waste Processing Services
N.A.I.C.S.: 562211

Semler B.V. (1)
Ockhuizenweg 3, 5691 PJ, Son, Netherlands
Tel.: (31) 499475012
Web Site: https://www.semler.nl
Recyclable Store Services
N.A.I.C.S.: 423930

Shanks Argyll & Bute Limited (1)
Tigh Mhicleoid Locknell Street, Lochgilphead, PA31 8JL, United Kingdom (100%)
Tel.: (44) 1546 603795
Sales Range: $25-49.9 Million
Emp.: 3
Waste Management Services
N.A.I.C.S.: 562998

Shanks B.V. (1)
Stoelmatter 41, 2292 JM, Wateringen, Netherlands
Tel.: (31) 174219900
Holding Company; Regional managing Office; Waste Management Services
N.A.I.C.S.: 551112
Michael van Hulst *(Mng Dir)*

Subsidiary (Domestic):

Shanks Nederland B.V. (2)
Lindeboomseweg 15, 3828 NG, Hoogland, Netherlands (100%)
Tel.: (31) 33 2050 200
Web Site: http://www.shanks.nl
Sales Range: $10-24.9 Million
Emp.: 20
Solid Waste Management Services
N.A.I.C.S.: 562998

Subsidiary (Domestic):

Afvalstoffen Terminal Moerdijk B.V. (3)
Vlasweg 12, Moerdijk, 4782 PW, Netherlands
Tel.: (31) 168389289
Web Site: http://www.atmmoerdijk.nl
Waste Processing Services
N.A.I.C.S.: 562998

BV van Vliet Groep Milieu-dienstverleners (3)
Grote Wade 45, 3439 NZ, Nieuwegein, Netherlands (100%)
Tel.: (31) 302855200
Web Site: http://www.vanvlietgroep.nl
Waste Management Services
N.A.I.C.S.: 562998

Icova B.V. (3)
Kajuitweg 1 Westpoort nr 20-32, 1041 AP, Amsterdam, Netherlands
Tel.: (31) 204476666
Web Site: http://www.icova.nl
Waste Management Services
N.A.I.C.S.: 562998
Maurica Geelen *(Gen Mgr)*

Klok Containers B.V. (3)
Molenvliet 4, 3076 CK, Rotterdam, Netherlands
Tel.: (31) 104929292
Web Site: http://www.klokcontainers.nl
Industrial Waste Collection Services
N.A.I.C.S.: 562998

Orgaworld B.V. (3)
Lindeboomseweg 15, Postbus 1521, 3800 BM, Amersfoort, Netherlands
Tel.: (31) 889086110
Web Site: http://orgaworld.nl
Emp.: 10
Organic Waste Treatment Services
N.A.I.C.S.: 562998

Plant (Domestic):

Orgaworld B.V. - Fermentation Plant (4)
Karperweg 20, PO Box 204, 8221 RB, Lelystad, Netherlands
Tel.: (31) 320245094
Web Site: http://www.orgaworld.nl

Sales Range: $25-49.9 Million
Emp.: 6
Waste Management Services
N.A.I.C.S.: 562998

Orgaworld B.V.- Composting Plant (4)
Stuurboord 11, 9206 BK, Drachten, Netherlands
Tel.: (31) 512544663
Web Site: http://www.orgaworld.nl
Sales Range: $25-49.9 Million
Emp.: 6
Waste Management Services
N.A.I.C.S.: 562998

Subsidiary (Non-US):

Orgaworld Canada Limited (4)
2940 Dingman Drive, PO Box 21070, London, N6K 0C7, ON, Canada
Tel.: (519) 649-4446
Web Site: http://www.orgaworld.nl
Waste Management Services
N.A.I.C.S.: 562998

Subsidiary (Domestic):

Smink Beheer B.V. (3)
Lindeboomseweg 15, 3828 NG, Hoogland, Netherlands (100%)
Tel.: (31) 334558282
Web Site: http://www.smink-groep.nl
Holding Company; Waste Management & Recycling Services
N.A.I.C.S.: 551112

Transportbedrijf van Vliet B.V. (3)
Wateringveldseweg 1, 2291 HE, Wateringen, Netherlands (100%)
Tel.: (31) 174 297 888
Web Site: http://www.vanvlietcontrans.nl
Solid Waste Collection & Management Services
N.A.I.C.S.: 562111
Leo Schipper *(Mgr-Sls)*

Vliko B.V. (3)
Achthovenerweg 17b, Leiderdorp, 2351 AX, Netherlands (100%)
Tel.: (31) 715892901
Web Site: http://www.vliko.nl
Industrial Waste Handling Services
N.A.I.C.S.: 562998
Louie Scierle *(Gen Mgr)*

Subsidiary (Non-US):

Shanks S.A. (2)
Rue des Trois Burettes 65, 1435, Mont-Saint-Guibert, Belgium (100%)
Tel.: (32) 10 65 30 20
Web Site: http://www.shanks.be
Sales Range: $25-49.9 Million
Waste Management Services
N.A.I.C.S.: 562998

Subsidiary (Domestic):

Foronex n.v. (3)
Ooigemstraat 9a, 8710, Wielsbeke, Belgium
Tel.: (32) 56663930
Sales Range: $25-49.9 Million
Emp.: 160
Waste Management Services
N.A.I.C.S.: 562998

Shanks Brussels-Brabant S.A. (3)
Boulevard de l'Humanite 124, 1190, Brussels, Belgium (100%)
Tel.: (32) 25273735
Web Site: http://www.shanks.be
Waste Management Services
N.A.I.C.S.: 562998

Shanks Hainaut S.A. (3)
Rue De LIndustrie 1, B 7321, Bernissart, Belgium (100%)
Tel.: (32) 69560511
Web Site: http://www.shanks.be
Sales Range: $25-49.9 Million
Emp.: 150
Waste Management Services
N.A.I.C.S.: 562998

Shanks Liege-Luxembourg S.A. (3)
Rue de l'Environnement 18, 4100, Seraing, Belgium (100%)
Tel.: (32) 4 338 05 60
Web Site: http://www.shanks.be
Waste Management Services

N.A.I.C.S.: 562998

Shanks Vlaanderen N.V. (3)
Regenbeekstraat 7c, Roeselare, 8800, Belgium (100%)
Tel.: (32) 5123 2011
Web Site: http://www.shanks.be
Sales Range: $10-24.9 Million
Emp.: 50
Waste Management Services
N.A.I.C.S.: 562998
Geert Schoutteten *(Mng Dir)*

Shanks Chemical Services (Scotland) Ltd
W Shore Rd, Edinburgh, EH5 1QD, United Kingdom (100%)
Tel.: (44) 131 552 5621
Web Site: http://www.shanks.co.uk
Waste Management Services
N.A.I.C.S.: 562998

Shanks Cumbria Limited (1)
Hespin Wood MBT Plant Northern Resource Park, Hespin Wood Rockcliffe, Carlisle, CA6 4BJ, United Kingdom (100%)
Tel.: (44) 1228 581 000
Web Site: http://www.shanks.co.uk
Waste Management & Recycling Services
N.A.I.C.S.: 562998

Shanks Waste Management Limited (1)
Dunedin House Auckland Park, Mount Farm, Milton Keynes, MK1 1BU, Bucks, United Kingdom (100%)
Tel.: (44) 1908 650 650
Web Site: http://www.shanks.co.uk
Sales Range: $25-49.9 Million
Emp.: 100
Waste Management Services
John Hodder *(Mgr-Bus Dev-North England & Wales)*

Van Gansewinkel Groep B.V. (1)
Flight Forum 240, 5657 DH, Eindhoven, Netherlands
Tel.: (31) 40 751 4000
Web Site: http://www.vangansewinkelgroep.com
Emp.: 4,350
Holding Company
N.A.I.C.S.: 551112

RENFORTH RESOURCES INC.
269 -1099 Kingston Road, Pickering, L1V 1B5, ON, Canada
Tel.: (416) 818-1393 ON
Web Site:
http://www.renforthresources.com
RFHRF—(OTCQB)
Assets: $1,972,384
Liabilities: $563,912
Net Worth: $1,408,472
Earnings: ($2,705,298)
Fiscal Year-end: 12/31/22
Diamond & Base Metal Exploration & Mining Services
N.A.I.C.S.: 212311
Kyle Appleby *(CFO)*

RENGO CO., LTD.
Nakanoshima Central Tower 2-2-7 Nakanoshima, Kita-ku, Osaka, 530-0005, Japan
Tel.: (81) 662232371
Web Site: https://www.rengo.co.jp
Year Founded: 1909
3941—(TKS)
Rev.: $5,954,228,510
Assets: $7,750,324,150
Liabilities: $4,848,679,570
Net Worth: $2,901,644,580
Earnings: $218,295,250
Emp.: 23,389
Fiscal Year-end: 03/31/24
Paperboard Mfr
N.A.I.C.S.: 322130
Kiyoshi Otsubo *(Chm, Chm & CEO)*

Subsidiaries:

AP Packaging (Hanoi) Co.,Ltd. (1)
Lot 4 Lot 6 Nam Sach Industrial Zone, Ai

Quoc Nam Dong Commune, Hai Duong, Vietnam
Tel.: (84) 2203752862
Corrugated Products Mfr & Sales
N.A.I.C.S.: 322130

Aldez Containers, LLC (1)
42463 Garfield Rd, Clinton, MI 48038
Tel.: (210) 223-8877
Web Site: https://aldez.com
Packaging Services
N.A.I.C.S.: 561910

Asahi Danboru Co., Ltd. (1)
156-2 Kokubunji, Kokubunji-cho, Takamatsu, 769-0102, Kagawa, Japan
Tel.: (81) 878741313
Web Site: http://www.asahidan.co.jp
Emp.: 110
Corrugated Board Mfr
N.A.I.C.S.: 322211

Asahi Shiko Co., Ltd. (1) (100%)
Tel.: (81) 723365360
Web Site: http://www.asahishiko.co.jp
Paper Products Mfr
N.A.I.C.S.: 322130

Daimaru Itagami Kako Co., Ltd. (1)
247 Funami, Yoro-cho Yoro-gun, Gifu, 503-1263, Japan
Tel.: (81) 58 432 3108
Web Site: https://www.daimaruitagami.co.jp
Cardboard Cases Mfr & Distr
N.A.I.C.S.: 322130

Dalian Guoli Packaging Co., Ltd. (1)
Guo Ying Nong Chang Sanshilipu, Puwan District, Dalian, 116103, Liaoning, China
Tel.: (86) 4113 932 3926
Corrugated Cardboard Mfr & Distr
N.A.I.C.S.: 322211

Dalian Marsol Trading Co., Ltd. (1)
International Finance Tower No 15 Renmin Road, Zhongshan District, Dalian, Liaoning, China
Tel.: (86) 4118 250 7201
Flexible Container Distr
N.A.I.C.S.: 424130

Dalian Rengo Packaging Co., Ltd. (1)
No 1 Dianchi Road, Bonded Zone, Dalian, 116600, Liaoning, China
Tel.: (86) 4113 920 6899
Corrugated Cardboard Mfr & Distr
N.A.I.C.S.: 322211

Edogawa Danboru Co., Ltd. (1)
Factory 96 Futatsuka Aza Mozobo, Noda, 278-0016, Chiba, Japan
Tel.: (81) 47 125 5581
Web Site: https://edodan.co.jp
Cardboard Sheet Mfr & Distr
N.A.I.C.S.: 322130

Fuji-Hoso Shiki Co., Ltd. (1)
5-2 Hino No 2 Industrial Complex Kitawaki, Hino-cho Gamo-gun, Shiga, 529-1663, Japan
Tel.: (81) 74 853 1500
Web Site: https://www.fuji-hoso.co.jp
Corrugated Cardboard Mfr & Distr
N.A.I.C.S.: 322211

Hinode Shiki Kogyo Co., Ltd. (1)
2158 Mugiuda Ijuin-cho, Hioki, 899-2513, Kagoshima, Japan
Tel.: (81) 992739111
Web Site: https://www.hinode-shiki.co.jp
Corrugated Boards & Folding Cartons Mfr
N.A.I.C.S.: 322211

Hokkoku Hoso Kizai Co., Ltd. (1)
1-203 Kobu, Kanazawa, 920-0362, Ishikawa, Japan
Tel.: (81) 762141221
Paper Products Mfr
N.A.I.C.S.: 322130

Hokuriku Shiki Co., Ltd. (1)
91 Kojima, Imizu, 939-0274, Toyama, Japan
Tel.: (81) 766523115
Emp.: 85
Paper Products Mfr & Sales
N.A.I.C.S.: 322299

Howa (Shanghai) Co., Ltd. (1)
610 Zhaocheng Building West Tianshan

RENGO CO., LTD.

Rengo Co., Ltd.—(Continued)
Road 120, Changning District, Shanghai, 200335, China
Tel.: (86) 216 225 7006
Packaging Material Mfr & Distr
N.A.I.C.S.: 326112

Howa Matai Packaging (Thailand) Co., Ltd. (1)
200 Moo 4 Jasmine International Tower 6th Floor, Room 607B Chaengwattana Road Pakkred, Nonthaburi, 11120, Thailand
Tel.: (66) 2 584 1814
Web Site: https://hmp.co.th
Packaging Services
N.A.I.C.S.: 561910

Howa Sangyo Co., Ltd. (1)
4-16-12 Narashino, Funabashi, 274-8502, Chiba, Japan
Tel.: (81) 474565011
Web Site: https://www.howa-s.co.jp
Emp.: 1,549
Flexible Packaging Materials Mfr
N.A.I.C.S.: 322220
Yoshitaka Ozawa (Pres & CEO)

Howa Taiwan Co., Ltd. (1)
5th Floor No 473 Section 2 Tiding Avenue, Neihu District, Taipei, 11493, Taiwan
Tel.: (886) 28 752 3211
Web Site: https://www.t-howa.com
Packaging Services
N.A.I.C.S.: 561910

Ihara Shiki Co., Ltd. (1)
310 Nagasaki, Shimizu-ku, Shizuoka, 424-0065, Japan
Tel.: (81) 543451341
Web Site: https://www.ihr-s.co.jp
Paper Products Mfr
N.A.I.C.S.: 322299

Jiangsu Zhongjin Matai Medicinal Packaging Co., Ltd. (1)
Lianyungang Econ and Tech Development Zone, Lianyungang, 222047, Jiangsu, China
Tel.: (86) 5188 234 2729
Web Site: https://www.zhong-jin.com
Medicinal Packaging Services
N.A.I.C.S.: 561910

Kato Danboru Co., Ltd. (1)
5367-1 Kimagase, Noda, 270-0222, Chiba, Japan
Tel.: (81) 47 198 2235
Web Site: https://www.kato-dan.co.jp
Corrugated Board Mfr & Distr
N.A.I.C.S.: 322211

Kofu Daiichi Jitsugyo Co., Ltd. (1)
358 Fuse, Chuo, 409-3841, Yamanashi, Japan
Tel.: (81) 552732222
Web Site: https://www.kofudai1.co.jp
Emp.: 124
Manufacture & Sales of Corrugated Boards & Boxes
N.A.I.C.S.: 322211
Kasai Koichi (Sr Mng Dir)

Kofu Daiichi-Jitugyo Co., Ltd. (1)
358 Fuse, Chuo, 409-3841, Yamanashi, Japan
Tel.: (81) 55 273 2222
Web Site: https://www.kofudai1.co.jp
Corrugated Board Mfr & Distr
N.A.I.C.S.: 322211

Kowa Sangyo Co., Ltd. (1)
Asahi-Kaizuka 31, Kiyosu, 452-0932, Aichi, Japan
Tel.: (81) 524001127
Web Site: https://www.kowa-sangyo.com
Sales Range: $25-49.9 Million
Emp.: 15
Construction Machinery Mfr
N.A.I.C.S.: 333120
Yoshihiro Yasuda (Mng Dir)

Kyoei Danboru Co., Ltd. (1)
9239 Kumashiro Toyookamura, Shimo, Ina, 399-3202, Nagano, Japan
Tel.: (81) 265356288
Emp.: 40
Paper Products Mfr
N.A.I.C.S.: 322220

Kyowa Shigyo Co., Ltd. (1)
3-503-8 Factory Zenibako, Otaru, 047-0261, Hokkaido, Japan **(86.75%)**
Tel.: (81) 134626211
Web Site: https://www.kyowa-shigyo.com
Sales Range: $10-24.9 Million
Emp.: 73
Corrugated Boxes & Folding Cartons Mfr
N.A.I.C.S.: 322211
Yoshimura Shigetoshi (Pres)

Lianyungang Benyi New Material Technology Co., Ltd. (1)
Lianyungang Econ and Tech Development Zone, Jiangsu, 222047, China
Tel.: (86) 5188 234 2748
Packaging Material Mfr & Distr
N.A.I.C.S.: 326112

Marusan Paper Mfg. Co., Ltd. (1)
1-12-1 Aoba-cho, Haramachi-ku, Minamisoma, 975-0039, Fukushima, Japan
Tel.: (81) 244223111
Web Site: http://www.marusan-paper.co.jp
Paper Products Mfr
N.A.I.C.S.: 322130

Matai Resource Co., Ltd. (1)
2-6-7 Moto Asakusa, Taito-ku, Tokyo, 111-0041, Japan
Tel.: (81) 338433411
Web Site: http://www.matai.co.jp
Resin Raw Materials Procurement & Sales
N.A.I.C.S.: 325991

Matai Shiko Co., Ltd. (1)
2-6-7 Motoasakusa, Taito-ku, Tokyo, 111-0041, Japan
Tel.: (81) 338432111
Web Site: http://www.matai.co.jp
Emp.: 800
Paper Products Mfr
N.A.I.C.S.: 322120
Masao Fujita (Pres)

Miyazawa Corporation (1)
2-2-1 Tsujidokandai Eye Cross Shonan 7-A, Fujisawa, 251-0041, Kanagawa, Japan
Tel.: (81) 46 637 3030
Web Site: https://www.miyazawa-inc.com
Corrugated Cardboard Mfr & Distr
N.A.I.C.S.: 322211

Nichidan Co., Ltd. (1)
5-3-5 Hannancho, Abeno-ku, Osaka, 545-0021, Japan
Tel.: (81) 66 623 2551
Web Site: https://nichidan-inc.co.jp
Food Processing Services
N.A.I.C.S.: 236210

Nihon Matai Co., Ltd. (1)
2-6-7 Motoasakusa, Taito-ku, Tokyo, 111-8522, Japan
Tel.: (81) 338432111
Web Site: http://www.matai.co.jp
Sales Range: $150-199.9 Million
Emp.: 391
Packaging Materials Mfr & Distr
N.A.I.C.S.: 322220
Takao Nakanishi (Pres)

Subsidiary (Non-US):

Changshu Matai Packaging Products Co., Ltd. (2)
15-25 Nanxin Road CSDZ, Changshu, 215500, Jiangsu, China
Tel.: (86) 51252577100
Web Site: http://www.matai.co.jp
Container Bags Mfr & Whslr
N.A.I.C.S.: 322220

MATAI (VIETNAM) Co., Ltd. (2)
Tan Thuan Export Processing Zone, Dist 7, Ho Chi Minh City, Vietnam
Tel.: (84) 2837701773
Web Site: http://www.matai.co.jp
Container Bags Mfr
N.A.I.C.S.: 322220

Shanghai Matai Trading Co., Ltd. (2)
Far East International Plaza B-1506 Xianxia Road No 317, Changning Area, Shanghai, 200051, China
Tel.: (86) 2162350099
Web Site: http://www.matai.co.jp
Sales Range: $50-74.9 Million
Emp.: 7
Packaging Machinery & Materials Whslr
N.A.I.C.S.: 423830

Subsidiary (Domestic):

Tohoku Asahi Danboru Co., Ltd. (2)
1-1 Aozuka Hiko Yuza-cho, Akumi-gun, Yamagata, 999-8438, Japan
Tel.: (81) 234753881
Web Site: https://www.tohokuasahi.jp
Emp.: 94
Corrugated Paper Products Mfr & Whslr
N.A.I.C.S.: 322130

Niiyama Kamotsu Co., Ltd. (1)
48-4 Shina, Hamadate, Aomori, 030-0947, Japan
Tel.: (81) 177425421
Paper Products Mfr
N.A.I.C.S.: 322220

Nitto Shiki Kogyo Co., Ltd. (1)
2-9-13 Kozen, Ikaruga-cho, Ikoma, 636-0103, Nara, Japan
Tel.: (81) 745756601
Web Site: http://www.nitto-siki.co.jp
Emp.: 57
Paper Products Mfr
N.A.I.C.S.: 322299
Takeda Kazutomo (Pres)

Osaka Paper Co., Ltd. (1)
7-1-60 Tsukuda, Nishiyodogawa-Ku, Osaka, 555-0001, Japan
Tel.: (81) 664726331
Web Site: https://www.osaka-paper.co.jp
Emp.: 130
Boxboard & Newsprint Paper Mfr
N.A.I.C.S.: 322299

Otsu Seikan Co., Ltd. (1)
5-29 Tamanoura, Otsu, 520-2142, Shiga, Japan
Tel.: (81) 77 545 4350
Web Site: https://otsu-seikan.co.jp
Corrugated Board Mfr
N.A.I.C.S.: 322211

P.T. Surya Rengo Containers (1)
Jl K H Agus Salim No 4 Kotamadya, Tangerang, 15141, Banten, Indonesia
Tel.: (62) 215523542
Web Site: http://www.rengo.co.jp
Sales Range: $150-199.9 Million
Emp.: 300
Corrugated Products Mfr & Sales
N.A.I.C.S.: 322130

PT Marsol Abadi Indonesia (1)
EJIP Industrial Park Plot 9H, Cikarang Selatan, Bekasi, 17550, Indonesia
Tel.: (62) 21 897 0160
Web Site: https://www.marsol.co.id
Container Bag Mfr & Distr
N.A.I.C.S.: 326111

PT Tri-Wall Indonesia (1)
Kawasan Industri Terpadu Indonesia-China KITIC Exit Tol, Jakarta-Cikampek Km 37 Cikarang Pusat Kavling 48 Desa Nagasari, Bekasi, 17330, Indonesia
Tel.: (62) 212 215 7909
Web Site: https://tri-wallindonesia.co.id
Packaging Services
N.A.I.C.S.: 561910

Prepack Thailand Co., Ltd. (1)
30/145 Moo 1 Khok Kham, Muang, Samut Sakhon, 74000, Thailand
Tel.: (66) 34 440 6005
Web Site: https://www.prepack.co.th
Packaging Services
N.A.I.C.S.: 561910

Qingdao Rengo Packaging Co., Ltd. (1)
Qingyin Road South Huaxia Road West, Xiazhuang Town Chengyang District, Qingdao, 266107, Shandong, China
Tel.: (86) 53289653877
Corrugated Paper Products Mfr & Whslr
N.A.I.C.S.: 322211

Rengo Co., Ltd. - Amagasaki Mill (1)
1-4-1 Minamishi-Machi Kuise, Amagasaki, 660-0822, Hyogo, Japan
Tel.: (81) 664882561
Paperboard Mfr
N.A.I.C.S.: 322130

Rengo Co., Ltd. - Aomori Plant (1)
48-1 Shina Hamadate, Aomori, 030-0947, Japan
Tel.: (81) 177422331

Corrugated Paper Product Mfr
N.A.I.C.S.: 322211

Rengo Co., Ltd. - Asahikawa Plant (1)
2-2-31 Kogyo Danchi 2-jo, Asahikawa, 078-8272, Hokkaido, Japan
Tel.: (81) 166363622
Web Site: http://www.rengo.co.jp
Corrugated Paper Product Mfr
N.A.I.C.S.: 322220

Rengo Co., Ltd. - Chiba Plant (1)
1-7-1 Osaku, Sakura, 285-0802, Chiba, Japan
Tel.: (81) 434982331
Folding Cartons Mfr
N.A.I.C.S.: 322212

Rengo Co., Ltd. - Eniwa Plant (1)
193-3 Toiso, Eniwa, 061-1405, Hokkaido, Japan
Tel.: (81) 123393211
Corrugated Paper Product Mfr
N.A.I.C.S.: 322211

Rengo Co., Ltd. - Fukui Plant (1)
18-1 Uryu-cho, Echizen, 915-0096, Fukui, Japan
Tel.: (81) 778241361
Web Site: http://www.rengo.co.jp
Corrugated Paper Product Mfr
N.A.I.C.S.: 322211

Rengo Co., Ltd. - Hiroshima Plant (1)
1-77 Minamimyojin-machi Kaita-cho, Aki-gun, Hiroshima, 736-0055, Japan
Tel.: (81) 828223121
Web Site: http://www.rengo.co.jp
Corrugated Paper Product Mfr
N.A.I.C.S.: 322211

Rengo Co., Ltd. - Hofu Plant (1)
1-1 Yokoirikawa Kohama, Hamakata, Hofu, 747-0833, Yamaguchi, Japan
Tel.: (81) 835380655
Folding Cartons Mfr
N.A.I.C.S.: 322212

Rengo Co., Ltd. - Kanazu Chemicals & Biotechnology Plant (1)
1-8-10 Jiyugaoka, Awara, 919-0698, Fukui, Japan
Tel.: (81) 776731234
Chemicals Mfr
N.A.I.C.S.: 322110

Rengo Co., Ltd. - Katsushika Plant (1)
4-2-15 Kosuge, Katsushika-ku, Tokyo, 124-0001, Japan
Tel.: (81) 336012111
Web Site: http://www.rengo.co.jp
Folding Cartons Mfr
N.A.I.C.S.: 322212

Rengo Co., Ltd. - Maebashi Plant (1)
1144 Amagawaoshima-machi, Maebashi, 379-2154, Gunma, Japan
Tel.: (81) 272631616
Emp.: 100
Corrugated Paper Product Mfr
N.A.I.C.S.: 322211
Minoru Kushida (Pres)

Rengo Co., Ltd. - Matsumoto Sub-Plant (1)
5511-8 Wada, Matsumoto, 390-1242, Nagano, Japan
Tel.: (81) 263481211
Folding Cartons Mfr
N.A.I.C.S.: 322212

Rengo Co., Ltd. - Matsuyama Plant (1)
1861 Minamiyoshida-machi, Matsuyama, 791-8042, Ehime, Japan
Tel.: (81) 899720511
Web Site: http://www.rengo.co.jp
Sales Range: $25-49.9 Million
Emp.: 100
Corrugated Paper Product Mfr
N.A.I.C.S.: 322211

Rengo Co., Ltd. - Nagano Plant (1)
1731 Hizumeoki, Inaba, Nagano, 380-0912, Japan
Tel.: (81) 262212135

Web Site: http://www.rengo.co.jp
Folding Cartons Mfr
N.A.I.C.S.: 322212

Rengo Co., Ltd. - Nagoya Plant (1)
1514-82 Tonmei Akechi-cho, Higashi-ku, Kasugai, 480-0303, Aichi, Japan
Tel.: (81) 568931670
Web Site: http://www.rengo.co.jp
Corrugated Paper Product Mfr
N.A.I.C.S.: 322211

Rengo Co., Ltd. - Niigata Plant (1)
885 Sasaki, Shibata, 957-0082, Niigata, Japan
Tel.: (81) 254273481
Web Site: http://www.rengo.co.jp
Corrugated Paper Product Mfr
N.A.I.C.S.: 322211

Rengo Co., Ltd. - Okayama Plant (1)
900 Kuboki, Soja, 719-1112, Okayama, Japan
Tel.: (81) 866922331
Web Site: http://www.rengo.co.jp
Corrugated Paper Product Mfr
N.A.I.C.S.: 322211

Rengo Co., Ltd. - Oyama Plant (1)
1260 Kayabashi, Oyama, 323-0804, Tochigi, Japan
Tel.: (81) 285492211
Corrugated Paper Product Mfr
N.A.I.C.S.: 322211

Rengo Co., Ltd. - Sanda Plant (1)
19-1 Techno Park, Sanda, 669-1339, Hyogo, Japan
Tel.: (81) 795685111
Folding Cartons Mfr
N.A.I.C.S.: 322212

Rengo Co., Ltd. - Semarang Factory (1)
Jl Raya Semarang-Demak KM 13 5, Semarang, 59563, Central Java, Indonesia
Tel.: (62) 24 658 5000
Web Site: http://www.rengo.co.jp
Sales Range: $75-99.9 Million
Emp.: 170
Corrugated Products Mfr & Sales
N.A.I.C.S.: 322130

Rengo Co., Ltd. - Sendai Plant (1)
4-155-7 Minato, Miyagino-ku, Sendai, 983-0001, Miyagi, Japan
Tel.: (81) 222598911
Web Site: http://www.rengo.co.jp
Corrugated Paper Product Mfr
N.A.I.C.S.: 322211
Horii Toru (Gen Mgr)

Rengo Co., Ltd. - Shiga Plant (1)
565 Tsuji, Ritto, 520-3042, Shiga, Japan
Tel.: (81) 775522331
Web Site: http://www.rengo.co.jp
Sales Range: $50-74.9 Million
Emp.: 70
Corrugated Paper Products & Folding Cartons Mfr
N.A.I.C.S.: 322211

Rengo Co., Ltd. - Shimizu Plant (1)
200 Shibukawa, Shimizu-ku, Shizuoka, 424-0053, Japan
Tel.: (81) 54 348 5100
Web Site: http://www.rengo.co.jp
Corrugated Paper Product Mfr
N.A.I.C.S.: 322211

Rengo Co., Ltd. - Shin-Kyoto Plant (1)
Hattanda Shoryuji, Nagaokakyo, 617-0836, Kyoto, Japan
Tel.: (81) 759542121
Corrugated Paper & Folding Cartons Mfr
N.A.I.C.S.: 322130

Rengo Co., Ltd. - Shonan Plant (1)
3155 Miyayama, Samukawa-machi Koza-gun, Samukawa, 253-0106, Kanagawa, Japan
Tel.: (81) 467745112
Web Site: http://www.rengo.co.jp
Corrugated Paper Product Mfr
N.A.I.C.S.: 322211

Rengo Co., Ltd. - Takefu Plant (1)
39-1-2 Kamimakara-cho, Echizen, 915-0011, Fukui, Japan

Tel.: (81) 778271111
Web Site: http://www.rengo.co.jp
Sales Range: $1-4.9 Billion
Emp.: 3,600
Cellophane Film Mfr
N.A.I.C.S.: 325220

Rengo Co., Ltd. - Tokyo Plant (1)
5-14-8 Ryoke, Kawaguchi, 332-0004, Saitama, Japan
Tel.: (81) 482257111
Corrugated Board Mfr
N.A.I.C.S.: 322211

Rengo Co., Ltd. - Tonegawa Carton Plant (1)
5269 Iwai, Bando, 306-0631, Ibaraki, Japan
Tel.: (81) 297352307
Web Site: http://www.rengo.co.jp
Folding Cartons Mfr
N.A.I.C.S.: 322212

Rengo Co., Ltd. - Tonegawa Converting Plant (1)
5269 Iwai, Bando, 306-0631, Ibaraki, Japan
Tel.: (81) 297352304
Web Site: http://www.rengo.co.jp
Paper Converting & Printing Services
N.A.I.C.S.: 322120

Rengo Co., Ltd. - Tonegawa Division (1)
5269 Iwai, Bando, 306-0631, Ibaraki, Japan
Tel.: (81) 297352301
Web Site: http://www.rengo.co.jp
Emp.: 700
Paperboard & Cartons Mfr
N.A.I.C.S.: 322130

Rengo Co., Ltd. - Tosu Plant (1)
950-1 Todoroki-machi, Tosu, 841-0061, Saga, Japan
Tel.: (81) 942833155
Web Site: http://www.rengo.co.jp
Corrugated Paper Product Mfr
N.A.I.C.S.: 322211

Rengo Co., Ltd. - Toyohashi Plant (1)
1 Oike Nakahara-cho, Toyohashi, 441-3106, Aichi, Japan
Tel.: (81) 532413151
Web Site: http://www.rengo.co.jp
Corrugated Paper Product Mfr
N.A.I.C.S.: 322211

Rengo Co., Ltd. - Wakayama Plant (1)
1758-3 Tsukatsuki Momoyama-cho, Kinokawa, 649-6112, Wakayama, Japan
Tel.: (81) 736662801
Corrugated Paperboard Mfr
N.A.I.C.S.: 322130

Rengo Co., Ltd. - Yashio Mill (1)
330 Nishibukuro, Yashio, 340-0833, Saitama, Japan
Tel.: (81) 489221131
Paperboard Product Mfr
N.A.I.C.S.: 322130

Rengo Logistics Co., Ltd. (1)
Mitejima Green Building 2F 2-15-28 Mitejima, Nishiyodogawa-ku, Osaka, 555-0012, Japan (100%)
Tel.: (81) 5033810150
Web Site: https://www.rengo-logi.co.jp
Emp.: 1,571
General Freight Trucking, Warehousing, Insurance & Real Estate Services
N.A.I.C.S.: 484110

Rengo Nonwoven Products Co., Ltd. (1)
900-5 Kuboki, Soja, 719-1112, Okayama, Japan
Tel.: (81) 866939481
Web Site: http://www.rnp.co.jp
Emp.: 79
Nonwoven Product Mfr
N.A.I.C.S.: 313230

Rengo Packaging Malaysia Sdn. Bhd. (1)
No 11 Jl Trompet 33/8 Sek 33, 40400, Shah Alam, Selangor, Malaysia
Tel.: (60) 35 101 9192
Corrugated Cardboard Mfr & Distr
N.A.I.C.S.: 322211

Rengo Paper Business Co., Ltd. (1)
1-4-1 Kuise Minamishinmachi, Amagasaki, 660-0822, Hyogo, Japan
Tel.: (81) 664882812
Web Site: https://www.rengo-pb.jp
Emp.: 32
Paper Products Mfr
N.A.I.C.S.: 322299

Rengo Toppan Containers Co., Ltd. (1)
2-32-1 Hachimangi, Hatogaya, 334-0012, Saitama, Japan (60%)
Tel.: (81) 482821111
Web Site: http://www.toppan-con.co.jp
Processed Paper Products Mfr & Distr
N.A.I.C.S.: 322299
Taro Shiomi (Pres)

Rosewood Manufacturing Company (Gateshead) Limited (1)
Unit L92 Kingsway Team Valley Trading Estate, Gateshead, NE11 0LB, United Kingdom
Tel.: (44) 191 487 5232
Packaging Material Mfr & Distr
N.A.I.C.S.: 326112

Rosewood Packaging (Manchester) Limited (1)
Unit 3 Shepley Industrial Estate North, Audenshaw, Manchester, M34 5DR, United Kingdom
Tel.: (44) 161 320 1483
Packaging Material Mfr & Distr
N.A.I.C.S.: 326112

Rosewood Packaging (Wolverhampton) Limited (1)
Biddings Lane, Bilston, WV14 9NN, West Midlands, United Kingdom
Tel.: (44) 190 240 3631
Packaging Material Mfr & Distr
N.A.I.C.S.: 326112

S.C. Tri-Wall Romania S.R.L. (1)
Str Canta no 28 Bl 533 Sc Bap2, Iasi, 700529, Romania
Tel.: (40) 74 678 4542
Packaging Services
N.A.I.C.S.: 561910

Saito Shiki Co., Ltd. (1)
107 Kamioshimamachi, Maebashi, 379-2153, Gunma, Japan
Tel.: (81) 272610246
Corrugated Paper Product Mfr
N.A.I.C.S.: 322299

Sakaiminato Gyokan Co., Ltd. (1)
12-5 Showamachi, Sakaiminato, 684-0034, Tottori, Japan
Tel.: (81) 85 944 0825
Web Site: https://www.gyokan.jp
Corrugated Board Mfr & Distr
N.A.I.C.S.: 322211

Sankyo Danboru Co., Ltd. (1)
1-5 Kaori Nishinomachi, Neyagawa, 572-0089, Osaka, Japan
Tel.: (81) 728341021
Web Site: https://www.sankyodanboru.com
Emp.: 46
Packaging Material Mfr & Sales
N.A.I.C.S.: 322211
Seiichi Otsu (Chm)

Settsu Carton Corporation (1)
5-33 Higashiarioka, Itami, 664-0845, Hyogo, Japan
Tel.: (81) 727846001
Web Site: https://www.settsucarton.co.jp
Emp.: 900
Boxboard & Newsprint Paper Mfr
N.A.I.C.S.: 322299

Settsu Carton Vietnam Corporation (1)
Road D4-1 Long Duc Industrial Park, Long Duc Ward, Long Thanh, Dong Nai, Vietnam
Tel.: (84) 251 368 1194
Corrugated Cardboard Mfr & Distr
N.A.I.C.S.: 322211

Shanghai Rengo Packaging Co., Ltd. (1)
No1111 Jinxiang Road China Pilot Free Trade Zone, Shanghai, 201206, China
Tel.: (86) 2158347171
Web Site: http://www.sh-rengo.com.cn

Sales Range: $75-99.9 Million
Emp.: 250
Paper Products Mfr
N.A.I.C.S.: 322299

Shanghai Shengyuan Packaging Co., Ltd. (1)
Building 1 No 188 Lane 5888 Baoqian Road, Jiading District, Shanghai, China
Tel.: (86) 216 993 3228
Packaging Material Mfr & Distr
N.A.I.C.S.: 326112

Shinwa Shiki Co., Ltd. (1)
1-31-29 Sakuragi, Wakaba-ku, Chiba, 264-0022, Japan
Tel.: (81) 43 233 3150
Web Site: https://shinwashikiten.co.jp
Funeral Arrangement Services
N.A.I.C.S.: 812210

Sichuan Zhongjin Medicinal Packaging Co., Ltd. (1)
Jiuding Road Economic Development Zone on the 11th, Dujiangyan, Sichuan, China
Tel.: (86) 288 722 9158
Web Site: https://en.sczhong-jin.com
Medicinal Packaging Services
N.A.I.C.S.: 561910

Sun Tox Co., Ltd. (1)
1-1-10 Ueno ORIX Ueno 1-chome Building 5th Floor, Taito-ku, Tokyo, 110-0005, Japan
Tel.: (81) 35 797 7645
Web Site: https://www.suntox.co.jp
Plastic Film Mfr & Distr
N.A.I.C.S.: 326113

TOM Vietnam Co., Ltd. (1)
No A1 1A Me Linh Square, Ben Nghe Ward District 1, Ho Chi Minh City, Vietnam
Tel.: (84) 283 823 9484
Winding Machinery Distr
N.A.I.C.S.: 423830

TW Mexico Packaging Solutions, S. de R.L de C.V. (1)
Modules 7 and 8 Building E Carretera Federal 45 Libre KM 45 937, Rancho Nuevo, 38160, Apaseo el Grande, Guanajuato, Mexico
Tel.: (52) 1818 254 4188
Packaging Services
N.A.I.C.S.: 561910

TW Mexico Planta Puebla, S. de R.L de C.V. (1)
Calle Rio Atoyac 6-A, Sanctorum, 72730, Puebla, Mexico
Tel.: (52) 1818 254 4188
Packaging Services
N.A.I.C.S.: 561910

TW Michigan Inc. (1)
28501 Goddard Rd Ste 100-103, Romulus, MI 48174
Tel.: (734) 992-6995
Web Site: https://www.twmichigan.com
Packaging Services
N.A.I.C.S.: 561910

TW Packaging Ltd. (1)
99/24 Moo 10 Bypass Chonburi-Pataya Road, Tambol Nongkham Amphur Sriracha, Chon Buri, 20230, Thailand
Tel.: (66) 383 393 9396
Packaging Services
N.A.I.C.S.: 561910

Tachikawa Danboru Kogyo Co., Ltd. (1)
4-8-4 Asumacho, Akishima, 196-0033, Tokyo, Japan
Tel.: (81) 425465511
Packaging Materials Mfr & Distr
N.A.I.C.S.: 322130
Yoshinari Nishimura (Pres)

Taiko Paper Mfg., Ltd. (1)
10 Kamiyokowari, Fuji, 416-0942, Shizuoka, Japan
Tel.: (81) 54 561 2500
Web Site: https://tk-paper.co.jp
Emp.: 191
Kraft Paper Mfr & Distr
N.A.I.C.S.: 322120
Koichi Hirano (Chm)

Taiyo Shigyo Co., Ltd. (1)
6-18-1 Sata Nakamachi, Moriguchi, Osaka, Japan

RENGO CO., LTD.

Rengo Co., Ltd.—(Continued)
Tel.: (81) 66 901 5431
Web Site: https://www.taiyosg.co.jp
Corrugated Cardboard Mfr & Distr
N.A.I.C.S.: 322211

Takedashiki Co., Ltd.
1116-47 Takata, Kashiwa, 277-0861, Chiba, Japan
Tel.: (81) 47 147 2101
Web Site: https://takedashiki.co.jp
Corrugated Cardboard Mfr
N.A.I.C.S.: 322211

Tarutani Industrial Packaging Corporation (1)
2-15-28 Mitejima Mitejima Green Building 1F, Nishiyodogawa-ku, Osaka, 555-0012, Japan
Tel.: (81) 66 478 8700
Web Site: https://tarutani.co.jp
Corrugated Cardboard Mfr & Distr
N.A.I.C.S.: 322211

Tawana Container Co., Ltd. (1)
599 Moo 4 Pattana 1 Rd Praska, Muang, Samut Prakan, 10280, Thailand
Tel.: (66) 2 324 0781
Corrugated Cardboard Mfr & Distr
N.A.I.C.S.: 322211

Thai Containers Group Co., Ltd. (1)
1 Siam Cement Road, Bangsue, Bangkok, 10800, Thailand (30%)
Tel.: (66) 25865555
Web Site: https://www.thaicontainersgroup.com
Sales Range: $100-124.9 Million
Emp.: 500
Corrugated Box Mfr
N.A.I.C.S.: 322211
Poramate Larnroongroj (Mng Dir)

Thai Marsol Co., Ltd.
202 Soi Chalong Krung 31 I-EA-T Lat Krabang Free Zone 3, Chalong Krung Rd Lat Krabang, Bangkok, 10520, Thailand
Tel.: (66) 232 604 7780
Web Site: https://www.thaimarsol.co.th
Packaging Material Mfr & Distr
N.A.I.C.S.: 326112

Tianjin Rengo Packaging Co., Ltd. (1)
No 12 Fengze 4th Road Balitai Industrial Park, Jinnan, Tianjin, 300350, Jinnan, China (100%)
Tel.: (86) 22286695708
Web Site: http://www.rengo.co.jp
Corrugated Board Mfr & Packaging Services
N.A.I.C.S.: 322211

Tin Thanh Packing Joint Stock Company (1)
Lot C20 Duc Hoa Ha Plastic Industrial Zone, Binh Tien Village, 854000, Duc Hoa, Long An, Vietnam
Tel.: (84) 272 377 9747
Web Site: https://www.batico.com
Packaging Services
N.A.I.C.S.: 561910

Tohoku Shiki Co., Ltd. (1)
10-31-1 Nishianiwa, Shizukuishi-cho Iwate-gun, Iwate, 020-0572, Japan
Tel.: (81) 19 692 0333
Web Site: https://tohokushiki.com
Corrugated Cardboard Mfr & Distr
N.A.I.C.S.: 322211

Tokai Shiki Co., Ltd. (1)
5-15-15 Toyota, Minami-ku, Nagoya, 457-0841, Aichi, Japan
Tel.: (81) 526913121
Web Site: https://www.tokaishiki.co.jp
Emp.: 378
Corrugated Packaging Mfr
N.A.I.C.S.: 322211
Kenji Sumita (Pres)

Touhoku Carton Co., Ltd. (1)
20 Takagi, Yamagata, 990-2346, Japan
Tel.: (81) 23 645 3358
Web Site: https://www.tohokucarton.co.jp
Corrugated Cardboard Mfr & Distr
N.A.I.C.S.: 322211

Tri-Wall (Asia) Pte. Ltd. (1)
No 48 Toh Guan Road East 02-101 Enterprise Hub, Singapore, 608586, Singapore
Tel.: (65) 6 225 2223
Web Site: https://www.tri-wall.com.sg
Packaging Services
N.A.I.C.S.: 561910

Tri-Wall (Malaysia) Sdn. Bhd. (1)
Lot 1564 Kampung Jaya Industrial Area Off Jalan Hospital, 47000, Sungai Buloh, Selangor, Malaysia
Tel.: (60) 36 157 0400
Web Site: https://www.tri-wall.com.my
Packaging Services
N.A.I.C.S.: 561910

Tri-Wall (Thailand) Ltd. (1)
33/1 Moo 9 KM 18 Bangna-Trad Road, Tambol Bangchalaong Amphur Bangplee, Samut Sakhon, 10540, Thailand
Tel.: (66) 23 127 2346
Web Site: https://www.tri-wall.co.th
Packaging Services
N.A.I.C.S.: 561910

Tri-Wall Austria Packaging Systems GmbH (1)
Pirching 90, Hofstatten an der Raab, 8200, Weiz, Austria
Tel.: (43) 31 123 8121
Web Site: https://tri-wall-austria.at
Packaging Services
N.A.I.C.S.: 561910

Tri-Wall International Trading Co., Ltd. (1)
Room A5 20F Jiangsu Building No 528 Laoshan East Road, Pudong District, Shanghai, 200122, China
Tel.: (86) 216 867 1747
Packaging Material Mfr & Distr
N.A.I.C.S.: 326112

Tri-Wall Japan Co., Ltd. (1)
Shinagawa Season Terrace 7th Floor 1-2-70 Konan, Minato-ku, Tokyo, 108-0075, Japan
Tel.: (81) 36 433 0755
Web Site: https://www.tri-wall.co.jp
Technical Consulting Services
N.A.I.C.S.: 541690

Tri-Wall Korea Co., Ltd. (1)
No 842 Yuha-ri Janyu-Myeon, Gimhae, 621-842, Gyeongsangnam-do, Korea (South)
Tel.: (82) 55 338 1161
Packaging Material Mfr & Distr
N.A.I.C.S.: 326112

Tri-Wall Limited (1)
19/F Chu Kong Shipping Tower 143 Connaught Road Central, Sheung Wan, China (Hong Kong)
Tel.: (852) 2 866 8803
Web Site: https://tri-wall.com
Packaging Services
N.A.I.C.S.: 561910
Yuji Suzuki (CEO & Chm)

Tri-Wall Packaging (Fuzhou) Co., Ltd. (1)
Fuyao Industrial Zone, Fuqing, Fuzhou, 350301, Fujian, China
Tel.: (86) 5918 536 7057
Packaging Material Mfr & Distr
N.A.I.C.S.: 326112

Tri-Wall Packaging (Jiangsu) Co., Ltd. (1)
No 99 Shuangyuan Road, Gugao Town Jiangyan District, Taizhou, Jiangsu, China
Tel.: (86) 5238 839 8828
Packaging Material Mfr & Distr
N.A.I.C.S.: 326112

Tri-Wall Packaging (Thai) Ltd. (1)
500/23 Moo 3 Hemaraj Eastern Seaboard Industrial Eatate Tambol Tasite, Amphur Pluak Dang, Rayong, 21140, Thailand
Tel.: (66) 38 950 1603
Packaging Services
N.A.I.C.S.: 561910

Tri-Wall Pak Private Limited (1)
Plot No 108 3rd Cross 4th Phase, Bommasandra Industrial Area, Bengaluru, 560099, Karnatka, India
Tel.: (91) 802 783 9969
Packaging Services
N.A.I.C.S.: 561910

Tri-Wall Polska Sp. z o.o. (1)
ul Ofiar Katynia 5, Kopanka, 32-050, Skawina, Poland
Tel.: (48) 12 276 4535
Web Site: https://www.tri-wall.pl
Packaging Material Mfr & Distr
N.A.I.C.S.: 326112

Tri-Wall Slovakia, s.r.o. (1)
J Psotneho 1915 911 05, Trencin, 91101, Slovakia
Tel.: (421) 91 415 5040
Packaging Services
N.A.I.C.S.: 561910

Tri-Wall Swansea Limited (1)
Pleasant Road, Penllergaer, Swansea, SA4 9WH, United Kingdom
Tel.: (44) 179 258 6527
Packaging Material Mfr & Distr
N.A.I.C.S.: 326112

Tri-Wall UK Limited (1)
Wonastow Road, Monmouth, NP25 5TW, United Kingdom
Tel.: (44) 160 077 2222
Web Site: https://tri-wall.co.uk
Packaging Material Mfr & Distr
N.A.I.C.S.: 326112

Tri-Wall Vina Pack Company Limited (1)
Road D1 Yen My 2 Industrial Park, Yen My Town, Hung Yen, Vietnam
Tel.: (84) 221 378 1212
Packaging Services
N.A.I.C.S.: 561910

WiLLiFE K.K. (1)
1-15-2 Hakusan, Midori-ku, Yokohama, 226-0006, Kanagawa, Japan
Tel.: (45) 532 6875
Web Site: https://www.willife.com
Corrugated Coffins Mfr
N.A.I.C.S.: 339995

Wuxi Rengo Packaging Co., Ltd. (1)
21 Huayou Dong Road Huayou Industrial Park, Xinwu District, Wuxi, 214142, Jiangsu, China
Tel.: (86) 51085307707
Web Site: http://www.rengo.co.jp
Corrugated Packaging Products Mfr & Whslr
N.A.I.C.S.: 322130

Yamada Kikai Kogyo Co., Ltd. (1)
3-1 Osaku 2-chome, Sakura, 285-0802, Chiba, Japan
Tel.: (81) 434982711
Web Site: http://www.en.tom-yamada.co.jp
Sales Range: $50-74.9 Million
Emp.: 163
Packaging Machinery Mfr
N.A.I.C.S.: 333993
Hidefumi Niki (Pres)

Division (Domestic):

Yamada Kikai Kogyo Co., Ltd. - Star Maintenance Division (2)
5-1 Techno Park, Sanda, 669-1339, Hyogo, Japan
Tel.: (81) 795600601
Web Site: http://www.kom-yamada.co.jp
Sales Range: $50-74.9 Million
Emp.: 100
Offset Printing Press Maintenance Services & Spare Parts Retailer
N.A.I.C.S.: 423690
Hidefumi Niki (Pres)

Yamato Shiki (Thailand) Co., Ltd. (1)
Ticon-Logistic Park M1 1/9 84/10 Moo9 Tambol Bangwua, Amphur, Bang Pakong, 24180, Chachoengsao, Thailand
Tel.: (66) 3 813 4273
Fiber Drum Mfr & Distr
N.A.I.C.S.: 322219

Yamato Shiki Co., Ltd. (1)
1-5 Nishigawara Kitamachi, Ibaraki, 567-0003, Osaka, Japan
Tel.: (81) 72 624 1101
Web Site: http://www.yamato-shiki.co.jp
Paper Products Mfr
N.A.I.C.S.: 322299

Yamatoya Co., Ltd. (1)
14-8 Takaramachi Higashi, Osaka, 579-8025, Japan
Tel.: (81) 72 985 7201

Web Site: https://yamatoya-int.co.jp
Corrugated Cardboard Mfr & Distr
N.A.I.C.S.: 322211

Yanagisawa Matai Co., Ltd. (1)
Tel.: (81) 485246811
Web Site: http://www.matai.co.jp
Kraft Paper Bags Mfr & Sales
N.A.I.C.S.: 322220

Yantai Marsol Co., Ltd. (1)
No 8 Tonglin Road, South Suburb, Yantai, Shandong, China
Tel.: (86) 535 601 8808
Netting Material Mfr & Distr
N.A.I.C.S.: 314999

INTERNATIONAL PUBLIC

RENHE PHARMACY CO., LTD.
18th Floor Yuanchuang International Zone B Greenland Central Plaza, No 998 Honggu Middle Avenue Honggutan New District, Nanchang, 330038, Jiangxi, China
Tel.: (86) 79183896755
Web Site: https://www.renheyaoye.com
Year Founded: 1996
000650—(SSE)
Rev.: $723,512,088
Assets: $1,071,482,256
Liabilities: $169,862,940
Net Worth: $901,619,316
Earnings: $80,651,376
Fiscal Year-end: 12/31/22
Pharmaceuticals Mfr
N.A.I.C.S.: 325412
Yang Xiao (Chm)

Subsidiaries:

Renhe Zhongfang Pharmaceutical Co., Ltd. (1)
No 158 Yaodu South Avenue, Zhangshu, Jiangxi, China
Tel.: (86) 7957378837
Web Site: http://www.zfrenhe.com
Pharmaceutical Products Distr
N.A.I.C.S.: 424210

RENHENG ENTERPRISE HOLDINGS LIMITED
Room 3805 38/F Far East Finance Centre 16 Harcourt Road, Admiralty, Hong Kong, China (Hong Kong) Ky
Year Founded: 2011
3628—(HKG)
Rev.: $8,910,325
Assets: $33,334,623
Liabilities: $18,976,440
Net Worth: $14,358,183
Earnings: ($304,780)
Emp.: 142
Fiscal Year-end: 12/31/22
Holding Company
N.A.I.C.S.: 551112
Chi Hon Tsang (Sec)

RENISHAW PLC
New Mills, Wotton-under-Edge, GL12 8JR, Gloucestershire, United Kingdom
Tel.: (44) 1453524524 UK
Web Site: https://www.renishaw.com
Year Founded: 1973
RSW—(LSE)
Rev.: $873,737,359
Assets: $1,328,846,054
Liabilities: $187,767,947
Net Worth: $1,141,078,107
Earnings: $122,458,291
Emp.: 5,256
Fiscal Year-end: 06/30/24
Measuring & Calibration Machines & Machine Tool Products Mfr
N.A.I.C.S.: 334519
David McMurtry (Co-Founder & Chm)

Subsidiaries:

Renishaw (Malaysia) Sdn. Bhd. (1)
CT-04-18 Corporate Tower Subang Square

AND PRIVATE COMPANIES

Jalan SS 15/4G, 47500, Subang Jaya, Selangor, Malaysia
Tel.: (60) 35 631 4420
Precision Turned Product Distr
N.A.I.C.S.: 423830

Renishaw Diagnostics Limited (1)
Renishaw Diagnostics Nova Technology Park 5 Robroyston Oval, Glasgow, G33 1AP, United Kingdom
Tel.: (44) 141 5577900
Web Site: http://www.renishawdiagnostics.com
Sales Range: $25-49.9 Million
Emp.: 31
Diagnostic & Clinical Research Products Mfr
N.A.I.C.S.: 334510
Ewen Smith *(Founder & Chief Scientific Officer)*

Renishaw Fixturing Solutions, LLC (1)
5500 Grand Haven Rd, Norton Shores, MI 49441
Tel.: (231) 799-3700
Web Site: https://www.rrfixtures.com
Precision Turned Product Mfr
N.A.I.C.S.: 332721

Renishaw Healthcare, Inc. (1)
1001 Wesemann Dr, West Dundee, IL 60118
Tel.: (847) 286-9953
Neurological Product Distr
N.A.I.C.S.: 423450

Renishaw Hungary Kft (1)
Gyar u 2 Wigner Jeno utca, 2040, Budaors, Hungary
Tel.: (36) 2 350 2183
Precision Turned Product Distr
N.A.I.C.S.: 423830

Renishaw International Ltd (1)
New Mills, Wotton-under-Edge, GL12 8JR, Gloucestershire, United Kingdom **(100%)**
Tel.: (44) 1453524524
Web Site: http://www.renishaw.com
Sales Range: $250-299.9 Million
Emp.: 700
Overseas Holding & Investment Company
N.A.I.C.S.: 551112

Subsidiary (Non-US):

OOO Renishaw (2)
st Kantemirovskaya 58, 115477, Moscow, Russia **(100%)**
Tel.: (7) 4958990202
Web Site: http://www.renishaw.ru
Sales Range: $25-49.9 Million
Emp.: 12
Measuring Machines Mfr
N.A.I.C.S.: 332216
Mikhail Zlotski *(Gen Dir)*

RLS Merilna Tehnika d.o.o. (2)
Poslovna cona Zeje pri Komendi Pod vrbami 2, 1218, Komenda, Dobrunje, Slovenia **(50%)**
Tel.: (386) 15272100
Web Site: http://www.rls.si
Sales Range: $25-49.9 Million
Emp.: 70
Rotary & Linear Encoders Mfr
N.A.I.C.S.: 334514

Renishaw (Austria) GmbH (2)
Industriestrasse 9 Top 4 5, Guntramsdorf, Austria **(100%)**
Tel.: (43) 2236379790
Web Site: http://www.renishaw.at
Sales Range: $25-49.9 Million
Emp.: 2
Measuring Machines Mfr
N.A.I.C.S.: 332216

Renishaw (Canada) Limited (2)
2196 Dunwin Drive, Mississauga, L5L 1C7, ON, Canada **(100%)**
Tel.: (905) 828-0104
Web Site: http://www.renishaw.com
Sales Range: $25-49.9 Million
Emp.: 7
Measuring Machines Mfr
N.A.I.C.S.: 332216

Renishaw (Hong Kong) Ltd. (2)
28F Tower Two Ever Gain Plaza 88 Container Port Road, Hong Kong, China (Hong Kong) **(100%)**
Tel.: (852) 2 753 0638
Web Site: https://www.renishaw.com
Sales Range: $25-49.9 Million
Emp.: 60
Measuring Machines Mfr
N.A.I.C.S.: 332216

Renishaw (Ireland) Limited (2)
Swords Business Pk, Dublin, Ireland **(100%)**
Tel.: (353) 18131111
Web Site: http://www.renishaw.com
Sales Range: $25-49.9 Million
Emp.: 140
Measuring Machines Mfr
N.A.I.C.S.: 332216

Renishaw (Israel) Ltd (2)
HaTnuffa 3 st Kraytek bldg Ground floor, Yokneam, 2069201, Israel **(100%)**
Tel.: (972) 4 953 6595
Web Site: https://www.renishaw.com
Sales Range: $25-49.9 Million
Emp.: 10
Measuring Machines Mfr
N.A.I.C.S.: 332216

Renishaw (Korea) Ltd (2)
RM 1314 Woolim e-Biz Center 28 Digital-ro 33-gil, Guro-gu, Seoul, Korea (South) **(100%)**
Tel.: (82) 22 108 2830
Web Site: https://www.renishaw.co.kr
Sales Range: $25-49.9 Million
Emp.: 12
Measuring Machines Mfr
N.A.I.C.S.: 332216

Renishaw (Shanghai) Trading Company Limited (2)
1F Building 18 No 288 Jiangchang 3rd Road, Jingan District, Shanghai, 200436, China
Tel.: (86) 216 180 6416
Web Site: https://www.renishaw.com.cn
Sales Range: $25-49.9 Million
Emp.: 100
Industrial Machinery Mfr & Whslr
N.A.I.C.S.: 333248

Renishaw (Singapore) Pte Limited (2)
988 Toa Payoh North 06-07/08, Singapore, 319002, Singapore
Tel.: (65) 6 897 5466
Web Site: https://www.renishaw.com
Emp.: 8
Metrology Equipment Mfr
N.A.I.C.S.: 333248
Steve Bell *(Gen Mgr)*

Renishaw (Taiwan) Inc (2)
2 F 2 Jing Seven Road, Nantun District, Taichung, Taiwan
Tel.: (886) 424603799
Web Site: http://www.renishaw.com.tw
Emp.: 20
Machine Tools Mfr
N.A.I.C.S.: 333515

Renishaw A.G. (2)
Stachelhofstrasse 2, 8854, Siebnen, Switzerland **(100%)**
Tel.: (41) 554155060
Web Site: http://www.renishaw.com
Sales Range: $25-49.9 Million
Emp.: 7
Measuring Machines Mfr
N.A.I.C.S.: 332216

Renishaw AB (2)
Biskop Henriks vag 2, 176 76, Jarfalla, Sweden **(100%)**
Tel.: (46) 858490880
Web Site: http://www.renishaw.com
Sales Range: $25-49.9 Million
Emp.: 5
Measuring Machines Mfr
N.A.I.C.S.: 332216

Renishaw Benelux B.V. (2)
Nikkelstraat 3, 4823 AE, Breda, Netherlands **(100%)**
Tel.: (31) 765431100
Web Site: http://www.renishaw.nl
Sales Range: $25-49.9 Million
Emp.: 8
Research & Development, Production, Sales & Service of Metrology & Spectroscopy Equipment
N.A.I.C.S.: 541715

Renishaw GmbH (2)
Karl-Benz Strasse 12, 72124, Pliezhausen, Germany **(100%)**
Tel.: (49) 71279810
Web Site: http://www.renishaw.de
Sales Range: $25-49.9 Million
Emp.: 80
Measuring Machines Mfr
N.A.I.C.S.: 332216
Rainer Lotz *(Mng Dir)*

Subsidiary (Domestic):

itp GmbH (3)
Rathausstr 75 - 79, 66333, Volklingen, Germany
Tel.: (49) 689 885 0910
Web Site: https://www.itp-probes.com
Sales Range: $25-49.9 Million
Emp.: 45
Industrial Styli Mfr
N.A.I.C.S.: 334419

Subsidiary (Non-US):

Renishaw Iberica S.A. (2)
Gava Park C de la Recerca 7, Gava, 08850, Barcelona, Spain **(100%)**
Tel.: (34) 93 663 3420
Web Site: https://www.renishaw.es
Sales Range: $25-49.9 Million
Emp.: 50
Measuring Machines Mfr
N.A.I.C.S.: 332216

Subsidiary (US):

Renishaw Inc. (2)
5277 Trillium Blvd, Hoffman Estates, IL 60192-3602 **(100%)**
Tel.: (847) 286-9953
Web Site: http://www.renishaw.com
Sales Range: $25-49.9 Million
Emp.: 140
Measuring Machines Whslr & Repair
N.A.I.C.S.: 334519
Leo Somerville *(Pres)*

Subsidiary (Non-US):

Renishaw K.K. (2)
29-8 Yotsuya 4-chome, Shinjuku-ku, Tokyo, 160-0004, Japan **(100%)**
Tel.: (81) 35 366 5315
Web Site: https://www.renishaw.jp
Sales Range: $25-49.9 Million
Emp.: 50
Measuring Machines Mfr
N.A.I.C.S.: 332216

Renishaw Latino Americana Ltd. (2)
Calcada dos Cravos 141 C C Alphaville, Barueri, SP, Brazil **(100%)**
Tel.: (55) 112 078 0740
Web Site: https://www.renishaw.com.br
Sales Range: $25-49.9 Million
Emp.: 9
Measuring Machines Mfr
N.A.I.C.S.: 332216

Renishaw Metrology Systems Pvt. Ltd. (2)
No 125 / 1-18 G K Arcade 3rd floor T Mariyappa road, Jayanagar 1st Block, Bengaluru, India **(100%)**
Tel.: (91) 806 623 6000
Web Site: https://www.renishaw.com
Measuring Machines Mfr
N.A.I.C.S.: 332216

Renishaw Oceania Pty Ltd (2)
6 Keysborough Close, Keysborough, 3173, VIC, Australia **(100%)**
Tel.: (61) 395210922
Sales Range: $25-49.9 Million
Emp.: 2
Measuring & Calibration Machines & Machine Tool Products Sales & Support
N.A.I.C.S.: 423830
Mike Brown *(Mng Dir)*

Renishaw S.p.A. (2)
Via dei Prati 5, 10044, Pianezza, Turin, Italy **(100%)**
Tel.: (39) 011 966 6700
Web Site: https://www.renishaw.it
Sales Range: $25-49.9 Million
Emp.: 18
Measuring Machines Mfr
N.A.I.C.S.: 332216

Renishaw SAS (2)
15 rue Albert Einstein, Champs Sur Marne, 77447, Marne-la-Vallee, Cedex 2, France **(100%)**
Tel.: (33) 16 461 8484
Web Site: https://www.renishaw.fr
Emp.: 28
Measuring Machines Mfr
N.A.I.C.S.: 332216

Renishaw s.r.o. (2)
Olomoucka 85, Brno, 627 00, Czech Republic **(100%)**
Tel.: (420) 548216553
Web Site: http://www.renishaw.cz
Sales Range: $25-49.9 Million
Emp.: 20
Measuring Machines Mfr
N.A.I.C.S.: 332216

Renishaw sp. z.o.o. (2)
ul Osmanska 12, 02-823, Warsaw, Poland **(100%)**
Tel.: (48) 22 577 1180
Web Site: https://www.renishaw.pl
Emp.: 10
Measuring Machines Mfr
N.A.I.C.S.: 332216

Renishaw Mayfield SARL (1)
31 Rue Ampere, 69680, Chassieu, France
Tel.: (33) 43 723 8900
Neurological Product Distr
N.A.I.C.S.: 423450

Renishaw Mexico S. de R.L. de C.V. (1)
Iridium 5004 Parque Industrial Milenium, 66626, Apodaca, Nuevo Leon, Mexico
Tel.: (52) 812 282 2900
Precision Turned Product Distr
N.A.I.C.S.: 423830

Renishaw Teknoloji Cozumleri LS (1)
Serifali Mahallesi Turgut Ozal Blv No 193, Umraniye, Istanbul, Turkiye
Tel.: (90) 216 380 9240
Precision Turned Product Distr
N.A.I.C.S.: 423830

Renishaw UK Sales Limited (1)
New Mills, Wotton-under-Edge, GL12 8JR, Gloucestershire, United Kingdom
Tel.: (44) 145 352 4111
Engineeering Services
N.A.I.C.S.: 541330

Renishaw plc - Riccarton (1)
Research Ave N, Riccarton, Edinburgh, EH14 4AP, United Kingdom
Tel.: (44) 1314511616
Web Site: http://www.renishaw.com
Sales Range: $200-249.9 Million
Emp.: 20
Measuring Machines Mfr
N.A.I.C.S.: 332216
David McMurtry *(Chm & CEO)*

Wotton Travel Limited (1)
4 High St, Wotton-under-Edge, GL12 7DB, Gloucestershire, United Kingdom **(100%)**
Tel.: (44) 1453525200
Web Site: https://www.wtlholidays.com
Sales Range: $25-49.9 Million
Emp.: 9
Travel Arrangement Services
N.A.I.C.S.: 561510
Wendy Walker *(Pres)*

RENJIE OLDSICHUAN CATERING MANAGEMENT CONSULT

No 597 Wenxue Rd, Zuoying Dist, Kaohsiung, 813, Taiwan
Tel.: (886) 73416222
2741—(TPE)
Rev.: $31,870,858
Assets: $38,965,596
Liabilities: $29,512,736
Net Worth: $9,452,859
Earnings: $2,757,971
Fiscal Year-end: 12/31/23
Catering Services
N.A.I.C.S.: 722320
Chen Shu Ping *(Chm)*

RENO GOLD CORP.

Reno Gold Corp.—(Continued)

RENO GOLD CORP.
119 Westcreek Drive Unit 3, Woodbridge, L4L 9N6, ON, Canada
Tel.: (905) 893-7188
Web Site:
https://www.renogoldcorp.com
RNGG—(OTCIQ)
Sales Range: Less than $1 Million
Mineral Exploration Services
N.A.I.C.S.: 213114
Patrizio Giampaoli (Pres)

RENOLAB SRL
Via XXV Aprile 19, Poggio Renatico, 40016, San Giorgio di Piano, Italy
Tel.: (39) 0510800110   IT
Web Site: http://www.renolab-glp.com
Sales Range: $10-24.9 Million
Research & Development in the Physical Engineering & Life Sciences
N.A.I.C.S.: 541715
Rita Resca (Mgr-Test Facility & Sls)

RENOLD PLC
Trident 2 Trident Business Park Styal Road, Wythenshawe, Manchester, M22 5XB, United Kingdom
Tel.: (44) 1614984500   UK
Web Site: https://www.renold.com
Year Founded: 1879
RNO—(LSE)
Rev.: $304,721,030
Assets: $300,429,185
Liabilities: $237,061,348
Net Worth: $63,367,836
Earnings: $21,585,458
Emp.: 1,824
Fiscal Year-end: 03/31/24
Mechanical & Hydraulic Products for Power Transmission & Materials Handling Systems
N.A.I.C.S.: 333613
Robert Purcell (CEO)

Subsidiaries:

Brampton Renold SA   (1)
100 rue du Courbillon, 59175, Vendeville, France   (100%)
Tel.: (33) 320162929
Web Site: http://www.renoldfrance.com
Sales Range: $25-49.9 Million
Emp.: 50
Mechanical Power Transmission Equipment Mfr
N.A.I.C.S.: 333613

Jeffrey Chain Corp   (1)
2307 Maden Dr, Morristown, TN 37813   (100%)
Tel.: (423) 586-1951
Web Site: https://www.renoldjeffrey.com
Sales Range: $50-74.9 Million
Emp.: 210
Mfr of Power Transmission Chains
N.A.I.C.S.: 333613
Michael Pelehach (Global Dir-Mktg)

Mac Chain Co. Ltd.   (1)
9445 193A Street, Surrey, V4N 4N5, BC, Canada
Tel.: (604) 888-1229
Web Site: http://www.macchain.com
Rev.: $13,592,882
Emp.: 35
Steel Mfrs
N.A.I.C.S.: 3312211
Andrew McFarland (VP)

Renold (China) Transmission Products Co. Ltd.   (1)
No 489 Fuxing Road, Jintan District, Changzhou, Jiangsu, China
Tel.: (86) 51969690127
Transmission Industrial Chain Product Mfr
N.A.I.C.S.: 333613

Renold (Hangzhou) Co. Limited   (1)
Room A-1403 Asia Sci-Tech Center No 4760 of Jiangnan Road, Binjiang District, Hangzhou, 310053, Zhejiang, China
Tel.: (86) 57182408555

Transmission Industrial Chain Product Mfr
N.A.I.C.S.: 333613

Renold (Malaysia) Sdn Bhd   (1)
No 2 Jalan Anggerik Mokara 31/44, Kota Kemuning Section 31, 40460, Shah Alam, Selangor, Malaysia
Tel.: (60) 355253898
Emp.: 6
Conveyor & Conveying Equipment Mfr
N.A.I.C.S.: 333922
Chanyoke Chan (Mng Dir)

Renold (Switzerland) GmbH   (1)
Ringstrasse 16, 8600, Dubendorf, Switzerland   (100%)
Tel.: (41) 448248484
Web Site: https://www.renold-gmbh.ch
Sales Range: $25-49.9 Million
Emp.: 25
Mechanical Power Transmission Equipment Mfr
N.A.I.C.S.: 333613

Renold (Thailand) Limited   (1)
24F Interchange Building 399 Sukhumvit Road, Bangkok, 10100, Thailand
Tel.: (66) 986565256
Transmission Industrial Chain Product Mfr
N.A.I.C.S.: 333613

Renold A/S   (1)
Kaerup Alle 2 1 Sal, 4100, Ringsted, Denmark
Tel.: (45) 43452611
Web Site: http://www.renold.dk
Sales Range: $50-74.9 Million
Emp.: 10
Industrial Machinery & Equipment Whslr
N.A.I.C.S.: 423830

Renold Australia Proprietary Limited   (1)
508 Wellington Road, Mulgrave, 3170, VIC, Australia
Tel.: (61) 392623355
Web Site: https://www.renold.com.au
Sales Range: $25-49.9 Million
Emp.: 3
Motor Vehicle Parts Mfr
N.A.I.C.S.: 336390

Renold Canada Limited   (1)
622 rue de Hull Ville, La Salle, H8R 1V9, QC, Canada   (100%)
Tel.: (519) 756-6118
Web Site: https://www.renoldcanada.com
Sales Range: $25-49.9 Million
Emp.: 15
Industrial Machinery & Equipment Whslr
N.A.I.C.S.: 423830
Rick Hamilton (Pres)

Renold Continental Limited   (1)
Groendreef 1, 1000, Brussels, Belgium   (100%)
Tel.: (32) 22011262
Sales Range: $25-49.9 Million
Emp.: 20
Industrial Machinery & Equipment Whslr
N.A.I.C.S.: 423830

Renold Crofts (Pty) Limited   (1)
28 Liverpool Road, Nesdadt Industrial Sites, Benoni, 1500, South Africa   (100%)
Tel.: (27) 117479500
Web Site: http://www.renold.co.za
Sales Range: $25-49.9 Million
Emp.: 70
Power Distribution & Specialty Transformer Mfr
N.A.I.C.S.: 335311
Edwin Bauer (Mng Dir)

Renold GmbH   (1)
Franz Fellner Gasse 5, Vienna, 1220, Austria   (100%)
Tel.: (43) 133034840
Web Site: http://www.renold.at
Sales Range: $50-74.9 Million
Emp.: 1
Industrial Machinery & Equipment Whslr
N.A.I.C.S.: 423830

Renold GmbH   (1)
PO Box 1635 1645, Juliusmuhle, 37574, Einbeck, Germany
Tel.: (49) 55 62 81 0
Web Site: http://www.renold.de
Sales Range: $25-49.9 Million
Emp.: 30
Conveyor Chain Mfr & Whslr

Transmission Industrial Chain Product Mfr
N.A.I.C.S.: 333613

Renold Hi-Tec Couplings SA   (1)
Calle d Antoni Gaudi 21, Gava, 08850, Barcelona, Spain
Tel.: (34) 936389641
Transmission Industrial Chain Product Mfr
N.A.I.C.S.: 333613

Renold New Zealand Limited   (1)
594 Rosebank Road, Avondale, Auckland, 1026, New Zealand
Tel.: (64) 98285018
Web Site: https://www.renold.co.nz
Sales Range: $25-49.9 Million
Emp.: 17
Mechanical Power Transmission Equipment Mfr
N.A.I.C.S.: 333613
Allan Grigor (Mgr)

Renold Poland Sp. z o.o.   (1)
Office Center Plac Lotnikow 2, 72-100, Goleniow, Poland
Tel.: (48) 91 836 2155
Transmission Industrial Chain Product Mfr
N.A.I.C.S.: 333613

Renold Polska sp.z o.o.   (1)
Szczecinska 3, 72-100, Goleniow, Poland
Tel.: (48) 913501200
Web Site: https://www.renold.com
Fabricated Metal Products Mfr
N.A.I.C.S.: 332999

Renold Russia OOO   (1)
1st Rizhskij Pereulok No 2 Bld 9 Office 6, 107996, Moscow, Russia
Tel.: (7) 495 645 2250
Web Site: http://www.renold.ru
Industrial Component Mfr
N.A.I.C.S.: 333248
Alexander Zarudin (Gen Mgr)

Renold Technologies (Shanghai) Company Limited   (1)
A02 577 Hua Xu Road Qing Pu, Beicai Town Pudong District, Shanghai, 201204, China
Tel.: (86) 2133785028
Transmission Industrial Chain Product Mfr
N.A.I.C.S.: 333613

Renold Transmission (Shanghai) Company Limited   (1)
3 Ste No 385 Zhen Zhongxin Rd Bei Cai, Pudong District, 201204, Shanghai, China
Tel.: (86) 2133785028
Electrical Apparatus & Equipment Wiring Supplies & Construction Material Whslr
N.A.I.C.S.: 423610

Renold Transmission Limited   (1)
18 Boon Lay Way 09-125 Tradehub 21, Singapore, 609966, Singapore
Tel.: (65) 67602422
Web Site: http://www.renold.sg
Sales Range: $50-74.9 Million
Emp.: 4
Industrial Supplies Whslr
N.A.I.C.S.: 423840

Renold, Inc.   (1)
100 Bourne St, Westfield, NY 14787-9706   (100%)
Tel.: (716) 326-3121
Web Site: https://www.renold.com
Sales Range: $10-24.9 Million
Emp.: 100
Mfr of Flexible Coupling for Director Connected Machines; Vibratory Conveyors & Shaker Drives; Custom Made Gears & Gearboxes; Power Transmission & Mechanical Handling Products
N.A.I.C.S.: 333613
Rob Gizzi (Supvr-Manufacturing)

Transmission Co Limited   (1)
Trident 2 Trident Business Park Styal Road, Wythenshawe, Manchester, United Kingdom
Tel.: (44) 1614984600
Industrial Transmission Supply Services
N.A.I.C.S.: 541420

RENOLIT SE
Horchheimer Str 50, 67547, Worms, Germany

Tel.: (49) 6241 303 0
Web Site: http://www.renolit.com
Year Founded: 1946
Sales Range: $1-4.9 Billion
Emp.: 4,700
Plastic Foam Product Mfr
N.A.I.C.S.: 326199
Michael Kundel (Chm-Exec Bd & CEO)

Subsidiaries:

American RENOLIT Corporation   (1)
6900 Elm St, City of Commerce, CA 90040
Tel.: (323) 725-0050
Web Site: http://www.renolit.com
Sales Range: $50-74.9 Million
Emp.: 150
Plastics Product Mfr
N.A.I.C.S.: 326199

IOOO RENOLIT Trade   (1)
of 200/1 Kulman Street-3, 22013, Minsk, Belarus
Tel.: (375) 17 3870018
Plastic Product Distr
N.A.I.C.S.: 424610

OOO RENOLIT-Rus   (1)
Dom 2 ul Sadovaja village, Rumyantsevo, 142784, Moscow, Russia
Tel.: (7) 495 995 16 15
Web Site: http://www.renolit.ru
Plastic Product Distr
N.A.I.C.S.: 424610
Kjeld Eklund (Gen Mgr-Sls)

RENOLIT Beijing Medical   (1)
18/F Building B Chaoyang MEN office Building No 26 Chaowai Street, Chaoyang District, Beijing, 100020, China
Tel.: (86) 10 8565 3399
Plastic Product Distr
N.A.I.C.S.: 424610

RENOLIT Belgium N.V.   (1)
Industriepark De Bruwaan 43, Oudenaarde, 9700, Belgium   (100%)
Tel.: (32) 55 33 97 11
Web Site: http://www.renolit.com
Sales Range: $50-74.9 Million
Emp.: 200
Thermoplastic Film & Product Mfr
N.A.I.C.S.: 326199
Christian Vergeylen (CEO)

RENOLIT Benelux B.V.   (1)
Alphenseweg 4-j, 5133 NE, Riel, Netherlands
Tel.: (31) 13 5186888
Web Site: http://www.renolit.com
Plastic Product Distr
N.A.I.C.S.: 424610

RENOLIT Cramlington Limited   (1)
Station Road, Cramlington, NE23 8AQ, Northumberland, United Kingdom
Tel.: (44) 1670 718 222
Plastic Product Distr
N.A.I.C.S.: 424610
Simon Wilson (Dir-Fin)

RENOLIT Czech s.r.o.   (1)
Cepirohy 115, 43561, Most, Czech Republic
Tel.: (420) 47 620 6810
Plastic Product Distr
N.A.I.C.S.: 424610

RENOLIT France SASU   (1)
5 rue de la Haye, CS 13943, 95733, Tremblay, Cedex, Roissy, France
Tel.: (33) 1 41 84 30 10
Plastic Product Distr
N.A.I.C.S.: 424610

RENOLIT GOR S.p.A.   (1)
via Pinerolo 7, 10060, Rome, Italy
Tel.: (39) 0121 569 111
Plastic Product Distr
N.A.I.C.S.: 424610
Massimiliano Fogliati (Mgr-R&D)

RENOLIT Guangzhou Ltd.   (1)
2 Hengda Road Yunpu Industrial District, Huangpu, Guangzhou, 510760, China
Tel.: (86) 20 8225 2592
Plastic Product Distr
N.A.I.C.S.: 424610

Yao Dongfeng *(Mgr-HR)*

RENOLIT Hispania, S.A. (1)
Poligono San Miguel Avda de los Castanos s/n, 31132, Villatuerta, Navarra, Spain
Tel.: (34) 948 556315
Plastic Product Distr
N.A.I.C.S.: 424610

RENOLIT Hong Kong Ltd. (1)
Room 1103-05 11/F Tins Enterprise Centre 777 Lai Chi Kok Road, Kowloon, China (Hong Kong)
Tel.: (852) 2192 9088
Plastic Product Distr
N.A.I.C.S.: 424610

RENOLIT Hungary Kft. (1)
Hegyalja ut 7-13, 1016, Budapest, Hungary
Tel.: (36) 1 457 81 64
Plastic Product Distr
N.A.I.C.S.: 424610

RENOLIT ISTANBUL Plastik Sanayi ve Ticaret Limited Sirketi (1)
Barbaros Mah Cigdem Sok No 1 My Office is Merkezi, Atasehir, Istanbul, Türkiye
Tel.: (90) 216 688 42 90
Plastic Product Distr
N.A.I.C.S.: 424610
Ali Kanan *(Mgr-Logistics)*

RENOLIT Iberica, S.A. (1)
Carretera Del Montenegro S N, 08476, Sant Celoni, Barcelona, Spain
Tel.: (34) 938484000
Sales Range: $50-74.9 Million
Emp.: 200
Thermoplastic Film & Product Mfr
N.A.I.C.S.: 326199
Sfrederyc Vimal *(Mgr)*

RENOLIT India Private Limited (1)
Alok Marwaha 9 Vatika Business Centre Vatika Atrium III Floor Block B, Gurgaon, 122002, India
Tel.: (91) 124 4311 267
Plastic Product Distr
N.A.I.C.S.: 424610

RENOLIT Italia srl (1)
Via Uruguay 85, 35127, Padua, Italy
Tel.: (39) 049 0994700
Plastic Product Distr
N.A.I.C.S.: 424610

RENOLIT Mexico S.A. de C.V. (1)
Av Penuelas No 21 int A 10 Fracc Industrial San Pedrito Penuelas, 76148, Queretaro, Mexico
Tel.: (52) 442 220 9000
Web Site: http://www.renolit.com.mx
Plastic Product Distr
N.A.I.C.S.: 424610

RENOLIT Milano S.r.l. (1)
Via G Di Vittorio 2/4, 20068, Peschiera Borromeo, Milan, Italy
Tel.: (39) 02 5165501
Plastic Product Distr
N.A.I.C.S.: 424610
Roberto Rota *(Gen Mgr)*

RENOLIT Nederland B.V. (1)
Flevolann 1, 1601 MA, Enkhuizen, Netherlands (100%)
Tel.: (31) 228355355
Web Site: http://www.renolit.com
Sales Range: $1-9.9 Million
Emp.: 170
Waterproofing Membranes Mfr
N.A.I.C.S.: 326199
Detlef Wolf *(Mgr)*

RENOLIT Nordic K/S (1)
Handelsselskab Naverland 31, 2600, Glostrup, Denmark
Tel.: (45) 43644633
Web Site: http://www.renolit.com
Emp.: 10
Thermoplastic Film & Product Mfr
N.A.I.C.S.: 326199

RENOLIT Ondex S.A.S (1)
Avenue de Tavau, BP 61, Chevigny St Sauveur, 21802, Quetigny, France
Tel.: (33) 3 80 4680 01
Plastic Product Distr
N.A.I.C.S.: 424610

RENOLIT Polska Sp. z o.o. (1)
ul Szeligowska 46, Szeligi, 05-850, Ozarow Mazowiecki, Poland
Tel.: (48) 22 7211 364
Plastic Product Distr
N.A.I.C.S.: 424610

RENOLIT Portugal Lda. (1)
Parque Industrial dos Salgados da Povoa, Apartado 101, 2626-909, Povoa de Santa Iria, Portugal
Tel.: (351) 21 953 40 00
Plastic Product Distr
N.A.I.C.S.: 424610

RENOLIT SE - Frankenthal Plant (1)
Franz-Nissl-Str 2, 67227, Frankenthal, Germany
Tel.: (49) 6233 3210
Plastics Product Mfr
N.A.I.C.S.: 326199

RENOLIT SE - Thansau Plant (1)
Fabrikstrasse 24-28, 83101, Rohrdorf, Germany
Tel.: (49) 8031 722 10
Plastics Product Mfr
N.A.I.C.S.: 326199

RENOLIT SE - Waldkraiburg Plant (1)
Reichenberger Str 6, 84478, Waldkraiburg, Germany
Tel.: (49) 8638 600 30
Plastics Product Mfr
N.A.I.C.S.: 326199

RENOLIT South Africa Pty. Ltd. (1)
Michle St 84, Pomona, Kempton Park, 1619, South Africa
Tel.: (27) 113963532
Web Site: http://www.renolit.com
Emp.: 3
Plastic Product Distr
N.A.I.C.S.: 424610
Richard Watson *(Gen Mgr)*

RENOLIT Tabor s.r.o. (1)
Farskeho 888/15, 390 02, Tabor, Czech Republic
Tel.: (420) 381 213 291
Web Site: http://www.renolit.com
Plastic Product Distr
N.A.I.C.S.: 424610
Chander Ladislaw *(Mng Dir)*

TOO RENOLIT (1)
Prospekt Ryskulova 133 A off 32, 050061, Almaty, Kazakhstan
Tel.: (7) 727 329 44 84
Plastic Product Distr
N.A.I.C.S.: 424610

RENOS HADJIOANNOU FARM PUBLIC COMPANY LTD.
28 Octobriou Avenue 35-37 App 302 Makedonitissa, 2414, Nicosia, Cyprus
Tel.: (357) 22254672
Poultry Farming Services
N.A.I.C.S.: 112390

RENOTEX GROUP LTD.
Pollard Street, Lofthouse Gate, Wakefield, WF3 3HG, United Kingdom
Tel.: (44) 1924 820003
Web Site: http://www.renotex.co.uk
Year Founded: 1993
Property Maintenance & Renovation Products Mfr
N.A.I.C.S.: 811411
David J. Scott *(Mng Dir)*

Subsidiaries:

Eppor-Pack Sdn. Bhd. (1)
2263 Permatang Kling, Seberang Perai Selatan, 14300, Nibong Tebal, Penang, Malaysia
Tel.: (60) 57167697
Web Site: https://www.epporpack.com
Emp.: 300
Packaging Product Distr
N.A.I.C.S.: 423840

RENOVA ENERGIA SA
Av Roque Petroni Junior 999 4 andar, Vila Gertrudes, CEP: 04707910, Sao Paulo, SP, Brazil
Tel.: (55) 1135696746
Web Site: http://www.renovaenergia.com.br
Year Founded: 2001
RNEW11—(BRAZ)
Rev.: $40,728,266
Assets: $549,889,691
Liabilities: $383,103,259
Net Worth: $166,786,431
Earnings: ($1,651,383)
Emp.: 223
Fiscal Year-end: 12/31/23
Eletric Power Generation Services
N.A.I.C.S.: 221111
Ricardo Lopes Delneri *(Chm)*

RENOVA GROUP
Malaya Ordynka Bldg 40, Moscow, 115184, Russia
Tel.: (7) 4957204999
Year Founded: 1991
Privater Equity Firm
N.A.I.C.S.: 523999
Viktor Feliksovich Vekselberg *(Founder & Co-Owner)*

Subsidiaries:

CJSC Integrated Energy Systems (1)
Baltia 26-km business-center VegaLine bldg 3, Moscow, 143421, Russia
Tel.: (7) 495 980 59 00
Eletric Power Generation Services
N.A.I.C.S.: 221118
Boris Vainzikher *(CEO)*

CJSC Orgsyntes Group (1)
Builders Boulevard building 4 housing 1 IX floor, Krasnogorsk, Russia
Tel.: (7) 495 638 55 57
Web Site: http://www.groupsyntez.ru
Chemical Products Mfr
N.A.I.C.S.: 325199
Anna Khudanova *(Dir-Legal Affairs)*

CJSC Rotec (1)
15 Nikoloyamskaya street, 109240, Moscow, Russia
Tel.: (7) 4956443460
Web Site: http://zaorotec.com
Industrial Equipment Repair Services
N.A.I.C.S.: 811310
Mikhail V. Lifshits *(Gen Dir)*

Columbus Nova, LLC (1)
900 3rd Ave 19th Fl, New York, NY 10022
Tel.: (212) 418-9600
Web Site: http://www.columbusnova.com
Rev.: $15,000,000,000
Emp.: 20
Investment Management Firm
N.A.I.C.S.: 523999
Andrew Intrater *(CEO)*

JSC Ekaterinburg Non-Ferrous Metal Processing Plant (1)
131 Uspensky Avenue, Sverdlovsk region, 624097, Verkhnyaya Pyshma, Russia
Tel.: (7) 3433114600
Web Site: http://en.ezocm.ru
Gold Ore Mining Services
N.A.I.C.S.: 212220
Aleksandr Shtyrlov *(Deputy Dir-Production)*

JSC Kamensk-Uralsky Non-Ferrous Metal Working Plant (1)
40 Lermontov Str, Kamensk-Uralsky, 623400, Sverdlovsk, Russia
Tel.: (7) 3439336120
Web Site: https://www.kuzocm.ru
Sales Range: Less than $1 Million
Metal Rolled Product Mfr
N.A.I.C.S.: 339999
Radko Vasily *(Gen Dir)*

KORTROS Group (1)
Shmitovsky Passage 39, 123290, Moscow, Russia
Tel.: (7) 4959339931
Web Site: http://en.kortros.ru
Real Estate Consulting Service
N.A.I.C.S.: 531390
Tatiana Firsova *(Mgr-Intl Tax)*

OJSC Russian Utility Systems (1)
Malaya Polianka 2, 119180, Moscow, Russia
Tel.: (7) 495 783 32 32
Electric Power Distribution Services
N.A.I.C.S.: 221122

Octo Telematics SpA (1)
Via Vincenzo Lamaro 51, 173, Rome, Italy
Tel.: (39) 067265341
Web Site: http://www.octotelematics.com
General Insurance Services
N.A.I.C.S.: 524210
Fabio Sbianchi *(CEO)*

Renova Media (1)
4a Obrazcova St, Moscow, 127055, Russia
Tel.: (7) 4956579671
Web Site: http://www.renova-media.ru
Media & Broadcast Holding Company
N.A.I.C.S.: 551112

Holding (Domestic):

AKADO Co., Ltd. (2)
7a Dmitriya Ulianova Street, 117036, Moscow, Russia
Tel.: (7) 4952313333
Web Site: http://www.akad.ru
Cable Television, Internet Access & Web Hosting
N.A.I.C.S.: 517111

ZAO Urals Turbine Plant (1)
Bld 18 Frontovykh Brigad st, 620091, Ekaterinburg, Russia
Tel.: (7) 3433002109
Web Site: http://en.utz.ru
Measuring Equipment Mfr
N.A.I.C.S.: 334515
Igor P. Sorochan *(Gen Dir)*

Zoloto Kamchatki, JSC (1)
Bol Yakimanka bldg 1, 119180, Moscow, Russia
Tel.: (7) 495 510 52 95
Gold Ore Mining Services
N.A.I.C.S.: 212220
Viktor Radko *(Gen Dir)*

RENOVA, INC.
18F Kyobashi Edogrand 2-2-1 Kyobashi, Chuoku, Tokyo, 104-0031, Japan
Tel.: (81) 335166260
Web Site: https://www.renovainc.com
Year Founded: 2000
9519—(TKS)
Rev.: $295,784,280
Assets: $3,076,287,390
Liabilities: $2,377,623,610
Net Worth: $698,663,780
Earnings: $58,544,770
Emp.: 316
Fiscal Year-end: 03/31/24
Power Plant Development Services
N.A.I.C.S.: 237130
Yosuke Kiminami *(Founder, Pres & CEO)*

RENOVALO S.P.A.
Via Giuseppe Arimondi 3A, 00159, Rome, Italy
Tel.: (39) 0645459176
Web Site: https://www.imprendiroma.it
Year Founded: 2008
RNV—(ITA)
Construction Engineering Services
N.A.I.C.S.: 541330
Guerino Cilli *(CEO)*

RENOWORKS SOFTWARE INC.
2721 Hopewell Place NE, Calgary, T1Y 7J7, AB, Canada
Tel.: (403) 296-3880
Web Site: https://www.renoworks.com
Year Founded: 2000
ROWKF—(OTCIQ)
Rev.: $4,751,669
Assets: $1,263,139

RENOWORKS SOFTWARE INC.

RenoWorks Software Inc.—(Continued)
Liabilities: $1,410,532
Net Worth: ($147,393)
Earnings: ($375,877)
Fiscal Year-end: 12/31/23
Software Development Services
N.A.I.C.S.: 541511
Greg Martineau (Founder & Chm)

RENRENLE COMMERCIAL GROUP CO., LTD.
North side of Zhoushi Road Shiyan Street, Baoan District, Shenzhen, 518053, Guangdong, China
Tel.: (86) 75566633666
Web Site: https://www.renrenle.cn
Year Founded: 1996
002336—(SSE)
Rev.: $557,463,816
Assets: $681,477,732
Liabilities: $665,910,180
Net Worth: $15,567,552
Earnings: ($71,208,072)
Emp.: 17,600
Fiscal Year-end: 12/31/22
Hypermarkets, Supermarkets & Department Store Owner & Operator
N.A.I.C.S.: 445110
Wu Huanxu (CFO & VP)

RENRUI HUMAN RESOURCES TECHNOLOGY HOLDINGS LIMITED
6th Floor A3 Building Dayuan International Center No 688, Middle of Tianfu Avenue High-Tech Zone, Chengdu, Sichuan, China
Tel.: (86) 2865319977   Ky
Web Site: http://www.renruihr.com
Year Founded: 2010
6919—(HKG)
Rev.: $510,803,701
Assets: $298,755,335
Liabilities: $95,232,337
Net Worth: $203,522,998
Earnings: $962,582
Emp.: 1,077
Fiscal Year-end: 12/31/22
Holding Company
N.A.I.C.S.: 551112
Jianguo Zhang (Chm & CEO)

RENS-WERK
Stuttgarter Strasse 83, Waiblingen, 71322, Germany
Tel.: (49) 715117070
Web Site: http://www.rens.de
Year Founded: 1899
Sales Range: $75-99.9 Million
Emp.: 500
Power-Driven Hand Tools Mfr
N.A.I.C.S.: 333991
Rainer Hech (Mng Dir-Albert Roller)

RENTA 4 BANCO, S.A.
Paseo de la Habana 74, 28036, Madrid, Spain
Tel.: (34) 913848500
Web Site: https://www.renta4banco.com
Year Founded: 1985
R4—(MAD)
Rev.: $44,107,517
Assets: $2,417,679,656
Liabilities: $2,261,273,872
Net Worth: $156,405,784
Earnings: $29,322,221
Emp.: 670
Fiscal Year-end: 12/31/23
Investment Management Service
N.A.I.C.S.: 523940
Juan Carlos Ureta Domingo (Chm & CEO)

Subsidiaries:
Renta 4 Burgos, S.A. (1)
C/ Vitoria N 28 Bajo, 09004, Burgos, Spain
Tel.: (34) 947256677
Investment Management Service
N.A.I.C.S.: 523940

Renta 4 Colombia SAS (1)
Calle 93 B 11 A 84 Of 405, Bogota, Colombia
Tel.: (57) 17038904
Web Site: http://www.renta4.com
Investment Management Service
N.A.I.C.S.: 523940
Diana Ortega (Gen Mgr)

Renta 4 Huesca, S.A. (1)
Calle de Cavia 8 Bajo, 22005, Huesca, Spain
Tel.: (34) 974238337
Investment Management Service
N.A.I.C.S.: 523940

RENTA 4 SOCIEDAD DE VALORES, S.A.
Paseo de la Habana 74, 28036, Madrid, Spain
Tel.: (34) 913848500
Web Site: http://www.r4.com
Year Founded: 1986
Sales Range: $75-99.9 Million
Emp.: 294
Financial Services
N.A.I.C.S.: 523940
Carlos Viton (Head-Perimeter Security)

RENTA CORPORACION REAL ESTATE, S.A.
Via Augusta 252-260 5th Floor, 08017, Barcelona, Spain
Tel.: (34) 934949670
Web Site: https://www.rentacorporacion.com
Year Founded: 1991
REN—(BAR)
Rev.: $58,168,573
Assets: $183,700,626
Liabilities: $100,456,508
Net Worth: $83,244,118
Earnings: $3,833,369
Emp.: 44
Fiscal Year-end: 12/31/22
Real Estate Development & Sales
N.A.I.C.S.: 237210
Luis Hernandez De Cabanyes (Founder & Chm)

Subsidiaries:
Renta Corporacion Real Estate ES, S.A. (1)
Velazquez 78 Fl 2, Madrid, 28001, Spain
Tel.: (34) 915750462
Emp.: 25
Real Estate Property Management Services
N.A.I.C.S.: 531390
Luis Hernandez (Gen Mgr)

Renta Properties (UK) Limited (1)
7a Grafton Street, London, W1S 4EH, United Kingdom
Tel.: (44) 7710467078
Real Estate Property Management Services
N.A.I.C.S.: 531390

RENTA GROUP OY
Ayritie 12B, 01510, Vantaa, Finland
Tel.: (358) 20332211   FI
Web Site: https://renta.com
Year Founded: 2016
Emp.: 2,000
Equipment Rental Services
N.A.I.C.S.: 532420
Kari Aulasmaa (CEO)

RENTAL EXPRESS GROUP LTD.
1/288 Newmarket Road, 4051, Brisbane, QLD, Australia
Tel.: (61) 7 3452 9600
Web Site: http://www.rentalexpressproperty.au
Property Management Services
N.A.I.C.S.: 531312
Chris Rolls (Mng Dir)

RENTIAN TECHNOLOGY HOLDINGS LIMITED
Suites 1801-1803 Everbright Centre 108 Gloucester Road, Wanchai, China (Hong Kong)
Tel.: (852) 34228787   Ky
Web Site: http://www.rentiantech.com
Rev.: $22,536,854
Assets: $189,972,194
Liabilities: $271,310,555
Net Worth: ($81,338,361)
Earnings: ($217,669,974)
Emp.: 1,350
Fiscal Year-end: 12/31/19
Holding Company; Investment Management Services
N.A.I.C.S.: 551112
Qian Feng (Exec Dir)

RENTOKIL INITIAL PLC
Compass House Manor Royal, West Sussex, Crawley, RH10 9PY, United Kingdom
Tel.: (44) 1276607444   UK
Web Site: https://www.rentokil-initial.com
Year Founded: 1925
RTO—(NYSE)
Rev.: $6,784,902,802
Assets: $14,045,695,531
Liabilities: $5,160,313,052
Net Worth: $8,885,382,479
Earnings: $480,939,157
Emp.: 62,931
Fiscal Year-end: 12/31/23
Holding Company; Facilities Management, Security, Washroom Hygiene & Pest Control Services
N.A.I.C.S.: 551112
Andy Ransom (CEO)

Subsidiaries:
Agronet SAS (1)
191 rue des Docks, 76120, Le Grand-Quevilly, France
Tel.: (33) 23 276 1407
Web Site: https://www.agronet.fr
Fertilizer Mfr & Distr
N.A.I.C.S.: 325314

Allgood Services, Inc. (1)
2385 Satellite Blvd, Duluth, GA 30096-2358
Tel.: (678) 671-3144
Web Site: http://www.allgoodservices.com
Exterminating & Pest Control Services
N.A.I.C.S.: 561710
Jimmy Allgood (Founder)

Ambius, Inc. (1)
2050 Clearwater Dr, Des Plaines, IL 60018   (100%)
Tel.: (847) 257-4400
Web Site: http://www.ambius.com
Sales Range: $350-399.9 Million
Interior Plants Landscaping Services
N.A.I.C.S.: 561790

Subsidiary (Non-US):
Ambius B.V. (2)
Impact 6, Duiven, NL-6920 AD, Netherlands   (100%)
Tel.: (31) 263195500
Web Site: http://www.ambius-nl.nl
Interior Plants Landscaping Services
N.A.I.C.S.: 561790
Rene Peters (Mgr-Admin)

Ambius Inc (2)
6741 Cariboo Rd Unit 106, Burnaby, V3N 4A3, BC, Canada
Tel.: (604) 430-8330
Interior Landscaping Services
N.A.I.C.S.: 561730

Ambius NV (2)

INTERNATIONAL PUBLIC

Ingbertoeveweg 17, 2630, Aartselaar, Belgium
Tel.: (32) 3 450 65 00
Web Site: http://www.ambius.be
Landscaping Services
N.A.I.C.S.: 561730

Ambius SAS (2)
3 Rue de Rome, BP 19, F-93114, Rosny-sous-Bois, Cedex, France   (100%)
Tel.: (33) 148949293
Web Site: http://www.rentokilinitial.com
Interior Plants Landscaping Services
N.A.I.C.S.: 561790

Cannon Hygiene International Limited (1)
Unit 38 Airways Industrial Estate, Santry, Dublin, Ireland
Tel.: (353) 1 704 7700
Web Site: https://cannonhygieneinternational.com
Hygienic & Washroom Services
N.A.I.C.S.: 561720

Cannon Hygiene Portugal Lda (1)
Parque Industrial JE Pav Cannon, Carrascal de Manique, 2645 423, Alcabideche, Portugal
Tel.: (351) 808 202 114
Web Site: http://www.cannonhygiene.pt
Facilities Support Services
N.A.I.C.S.: 561210

Cannon Hygiene SA (1)
Calle Manzanares 36, Velilla de San Antonio, 28891, Madrid, Spain
Tel.: (34) 916705010
Web Site: http://www.cannonhygiene.es
Facilities Services
N.A.I.C.S.: 561210
Antonio Santos (Mng Dir)

Direct Line Sales Limited (1)
3325 North Service Rd Unit 104, Burlington, L7N 3G2, ON, Canada
Tel.: (905) 631-7887
Web Site: https://directlinesales.com
Pest Control Management Product Distr
N.A.I.C.S.: 424690

Dudley Industries Ltd (1)
Preston Road, Lytham Saint Anne's, FY8 5AT, Lancashire, United Kingdom
Tel.: (44) 1253738311
Web Site: http://www.dudleyindustries.com
Sales Range: $25-49.9 Million
Washroom Products Mfr
N.A.I.C.S.: 325620

Environmental Pest Service, LLC (1)
5670 W Cypress St Ste B, Tampa, FL 33607
Tel.: (941) 735-4344
Web Site: http://www.environmentalpestservice.com
Lawn Care Services
N.A.I.C.S.: 561730
George Pickhardt (Chm)

Subsidiary (Domestic):
PICKHARDT SARASOTA, INC. (2)
6225 Tower Ln, Sarasota, FL 34240
Tel.: (941) 377-0888
Web Site: http://www.arrowservices.com
Sales Range: $1-9.9 Million
Emp.: 110
Exterminating, Pest Control & Lawn Care Services
N.A.I.C.S.: 561710
George D. Pickhardt (Chm)

Subsidiary (Domestic):
Bug Out Service, Inc. (3)
6972 Blanding Blvd, Jacksonville, FL 32244
Tel.: (904) 743-8272
Web Site: https://florida.bugoutservice.com
Exterminating & Pest Control Services
N.A.I.C.S.: 561710
Linda Prentice (Dir-Tech)

Eradico Services, Inc. (1)
41169 Vincenti Ct, Novi, MI 48375
Tel.: (248) 477-4800
Web Site: http://www.eradicopest.com
Sales Range: $1-9.9 Million
Emp.: 100
Pest Control & Lawn Care Services
N.A.I.C.S.: 561710

AND PRIVATE COMPANIES — RENTOKIL INITIAL PLC

Charles Russell *(Pres)*

Branch (Domestic):

Eradico Services, Inc. - Metro North Service Center (2)
6750 Oakhill Dr, Ortonville, MI 48462
Tel.: (248) 625-3903
Web Site: http://www.eradicoservices.com
Emp.: 20
Exterminating & Pest Control Services
N.A.I.C.S.: 561710
Gregory Pickett *(Mgr)*

Eradico Services, Inc. - Northern Michigan Service Center (2)
1426 Trade Center Dr Bldg C #15, Traverse City, MI 49686
Tel.: (231) 929-1155
Web Site: http://www.eradicoservices.com
Sales Range: $1-9.9 Million
Emp.: 100
Exterminating & Pest Control Services
N.A.I.C.S.: 561710
William Russell *(Pres)*

Florida Pest Control & Chemical Co. (1)
116 NW 16th Ave, Gainesville, FL 32601
Tel.: (352) 376-2661
Web Site: http://www.flapest.com
Sales Range: $50-74.9 Million
Emp.: 600
Pest Control Services
N.A.I.C.S.: 561710
Dempsey R. Sapp *(Founder, Pres & CEO)*

Fumigaciones Young S.A.S. (1)
Cra 20 162-11, Bogota, Colombia
Tel.: (57) 3057341925
Web Site: https://www.fumigacionesyoung.com
Pest Control Services
N.A.I.C.S.: 561710

Holland Herstel Groep / Ureco B.V. (1)
Frontstraat 1a, Uden, 5405 AK, Netherlands
Tel.: (31) 413335330
Web Site: http://www.hollandherstelgroep.nl
Emp.: 65
Industrial Cleaning Services
N.A.I.C.S.: 561720
Michel van Drunen *(Gen Mgr)*

Hometrust Limited (1)
61 South Street, Exeter, EX1 1EE, United Kingdom
Tel.: (44) 139 249 3113
Web Site: https://www.hometrust.co.uk
Real Estate Services
N.A.I.C.S.: 531210

Ingeclean S.A. (1)
Av Pedro de Valdivia 291 Piso 4, Providencia, Santiago, Chile
Tel.: (56) 22 280 2515
Web Site: https://www.ingeclean.cl
Pest Control Services
N.A.I.C.S.: 561710

Initial Austria GmbH (1)
Dieselstrasse 12 U 13, Mauer, Amstetten, 3362, Austria (100%)
Tel.: (43) 7472617700
Web Site: http://www.initial.at
Sales Range: $50-74.9 Million
Emp.: 250
Washroom Hygiene & Textiles Supply Services
N.A.I.C.S.: 561720
Holger May *(CEO)*

Initial B.V. (1)
Westeinde 50, NL-2275 AE, Voorburg, Netherlands (100%)
Tel.: (31) 703576357
Web Site: http://www.initial.nl
Sales Range: $150-199.9 Million
Emp.: 950
Washroom Hygiene & Textiles Supply Services
N.A.I.C.S.: 561720

Initial BTB SA (1)
145 rue de Billancourt, 92514, Boulogne-Billancourt, Cedex, France (100%)
Tel.: (33) 147123400
Web Site: http://www.initial-services.fr
Sales Range: $650-699.9 Million
Washroom Hygiene & Cleaning Services
N.A.I.C.S.: 561720

Initial Belux N.V. (1)
Brandekensweg 2, 2627, Schelle, Belgium
Tel.: (32) 33768660
Hygiene & Facilities Management Services
N.A.I.C.S.: 561210

Initial Ecotex s.r.o. (1)
V Zahradkach 25, CZ-130 00, Prague, 3, Czech Republic (100%)
Tel.: (420) 284860753
Web Site: http://www.initial.cz
Washroom Hygiene Services
N.A.I.C.S.: 561720

Initial Hygiene Co Ltd (1)
7F No 56 Lane 258 Rueiguang Rd, Neihu District, Taipei, 114, Taiwan
Tel.: (886) 2 2797 8333
Web Site: http://www.hygiene-initial.com.tw
Sales Range: $10-24.9 Million
Emp.: 55
Industrial Building Cleaning Services
N.A.I.C.S.: 561720
Tesmond Louk *(Chm)*

Initial Italia Srl (1)
Via Galileo Galilei 7, 20068, Peschiera Borromeo, Milan, Italy
Tel.: (39) 02 54776634
Web Site: http://www.initial.it
Industrial Cleaning Services
N.A.I.C.S.: 561720
Elena Ossanna *(Mng Dir)*

Initial Matador Sp.z.o.o. (1)
Ul Matuszewska 14, 03-876, Warsaw, Poland
Tel.: (48) 22 744 21 00
Web Site: http://www.initial.pl
Industrial Cleaning Services
N.A.I.C.S.: 561720

Initial Medical Services (Ireland) Ltd (1)
Hazel House Millennium Park, Kildare, Ireland
Tel.: (353) 59 913 4811
Sales Range: $25-49.9 Million
Emp.: 18
Clinical Waste Treatment Services
N.A.I.C.S.: 562211
Margo Atkins *(CEO)*

Initial Medical Services Ltd (1)
2 City Place Beehive Ring Rd, Gatwick, RH6 0HA, West Sussex, United Kingdom
Tel.: (44) 1293 858000
Clinical Waste Management Services
N.A.I.C.S.: 562998

Initial Portugal - Servicos de Protecao Ambiental Lda (1)
Complexo Industrial De Vialonga Fraccao C-1, Vialonga, 2625-607, Portugal
Tel.: (351) 219738400
Sales Range: $25-49.9 Million
Emp.: 100
Environmental Consulting Services
N.A.I.C.S.: 541620
Angelino Pina *(Mgr-Technical)*

Initial Services Co Ltd (1)
273-273B Duong Vo Van Kiet Phuong Co Giang Quan 1, Ho Chi Minh City, Vietnam
Tel.: (84) 8 39 208 208
Web Site: http://www.hygiene.initial.vn
Sales Range: $25-49.9 Million
Emp.: 90
Industrial Cleaning & Maintenance Services
N.A.I.C.S.: 561720
Cherry Le Claire *(Mng Dir)*

Initial Sverige AB (1)
Avestagatan 61, 163 53, Spanga, Sweden
Tel.: (46) 8 410 47 300
Web Site: http://www.initial.se
Sales Range: $25-49.9 Million
Emp.: 60
Carpet Cleaning Services
N.A.I.C.S.: 561720

Initial Textile Luxembourg Sarl (1)
66 Rue De Koerich, 8437, Steinfort, Luxembourg
Tel.: (352) 26 30 88 20
Web Site: http://www.initial.com
Linen Supply Services
N.A.I.C.S.: 812331
Helson Jean Pol *(Mgr)*

Initial Textile Service Gmbh & Co. KG (1)
Herzforder Strasse 9, D-49808, Lingen, Germany (100%)
Tel.: (49) 591916001
Web Site: http://www.initialservice.de
Textile Supply Services
N.A.I.C.S.: 812331
Holger May *(Chm-Mgmt Bd)*

Initial Textile Services Sro (1)
Centrala Pri Kalvarii 20, 917 01, Trnava, Slovakia
Tel.: (421) 33 533 37 37
Web Site: http://www.initial.sk
Mats Cleaning Services
N.A.I.C.S.: 812332

Initial Textiles e Higiene SLU (1)
Mar Mediterraneo 1, 28830, San Fernando de Henares, Madrid, Spain
Tel.: (34) 916270284
Web Site: http://www.initial.es
Industrial Laundry Services
N.A.I.C.S.: 812332

Initial Textiles nv/sa (1)
Ingbertweg 17, B-2630, Brecht, Belgium (100%)
Tel.: (32) 32171100
Web Site: http://www.initialservices.be
Sales Range: $350-399.9 Million
Emp.: 1,350
Washroom Hygiene & Textiles Supply Services
N.A.I.C.S.: 561720
Alain van Lidth *(CEO)*

Knightsbridge Guarding Ltd (1)
Victoria House Ground Floor 1-3 College Hill, London, EC4R 2RA, United Kingdom
Tel.: (44) 20 7332 2700
Web Site: http://www.knightsbridgeguarding.co.uk
Security Guard Services
N.A.I.C.S.: 561612

Knock Out Pest Control Pty Limited (1)
PO Box 994, Gymea, 2227, NSW, Australia
Tel.: (61) 29 545 4455
Web Site: https://www.knockoutpestcontrol.com.au
Termite Services
N.A.I.C.S.: 561710

MITIE Pest Control Ltd. (1)
1 King Alfred Way, Cheltenham, GL53 6QP, Glos, United Kingdom (100%)
Tel.: (44) 1242696969
Web Site: http://www.mitie.co.uk
Sales Range: $10-24.9 Million
Emp.: 30
Exterminating & Pest Control Services
N.A.I.C.S.: 561710

Medentex GmbH (1)
Piderits Bleiche 11, 33689, Bielefeld, Germany
Tel.: (49) 5205 75 16 0
Web Site: http://www.medentex.eu
Sales Range: $10-24.9 Million
Emp.: 35
Dental Waste Disposal Services
N.A.I.C.S.: 562211

National Pest Control LLC (1)
Office 401 Oud Metha Offices Building Oud Metha, Dubai, United Arab Emirates
Tel.: (971) 4 324 2342
Web Site: https://www.natpest.com
Pest Control Services
N.A.I.C.S.: 561710

Oy Rentokil Initial Ab (1)
Valuraudankuja 3, 01530, Helsinki, Finland
Tel.: (358) 92766310
Web Site: http://www.initial.fi
Emp.: 40
Pest Control Services
N.A.I.C.S.: 561710

PCI Pest Control Private Limited (1)
2 3 4 Floor Narayani Ambabai Temple Compound, Near Bank of Maharashtra Aarey Road Goregaon West, Mumbai, 400 062, Maharashtra, India
Tel.: (91) 226 260 4746
Web Site: https://www.pestcontrolindia.com
Pest Control Services
N.A.I.C.S.: 561710
Anil S. Rao *(CEO & Mng Dir)*

PT Rentokil Indonesia (1)
Wisma Kalimanis 11th Floor Suite 1101 Jl MT Haryono Kav 33, Jakarta, 12770, Indonesia
Tel.: (62) 21 7990033
Web Site: http://www.rentokil.co.id
Pest Control Services
N.A.I.C.S.: 561710

Perception UK LLP (1)
Victoria House Ground Floor 1-3 College Hill, London, EC4R 2RA, United Kingdom
Tel.: (44) 2073322702
Web Site: http://www.theperception.co.uk
Emp.: 60
Building Decorations Services
N.A.I.C.S.: 561790

Po Hong Services Ltd (1)
27/F Two Chinachem Exchange Sq 338 King'S Rd, North Point, China (Hong Kong)
Tel.: (852) 23886010
Industrial Cleaning Services
N.A.I.C.S.: 561720

R-Control Desinfections SA (1)
Rte D'Echternach 43, Luxembourg, 53500, Luxembourg
Tel.: (352) 432771
Pest Control Services
N.A.I.C.S.: 561710

RI Services Co Ltd (1)
446 Vo Van Kiet Street Cogiang Ward District 1, Dist 1, Ho Chi Minh City, Vietnam
Tel.: (84) 839208208
Web Site: http://www.rentokilinitial.com
Emp.: 10
Pest Control Services
N.A.I.C.S.: 561710
Willis Wang *(Mng Dir)*

Rentokil AB (1)
Avestagatan 61, 163 53, Spanga, Sweden
Tel.: (46) 104704950
Web Site: http://www.rentokil.se
Sales Range: $10-24.9 Million
Cleaning Services And Pest Control Services
N.A.I.C.S.: 561710

Rentokil Bahamas Ltd (1)
Rentokil House Dowdeswell Street, Nassau, Bahamas
Tel.: (242) 3252213
Web Site: http://www.initial.bs
Washroom Hygiene Services
N.A.I.C.S.: 561720

Rentokil Ding Sharn Co Ltd (1)
114 7th Floor No 56 Lane 258 Ruiguang Road, Neihu District, Taipei, 11491, Taiwan
Tel.: (886) 2 2658 0581
Web Site: http://www.rentokil.com.tw
Pest Control Services
N.A.I.C.S.: 561710

Rentokil Enguard Ltd (1)
634 -6 Sungsan-Dong, Mapo-Gu, Seoul, 121250, Korea (South)
Tel.: (82) 215771196
Pest Control Services
N.A.I.C.S.: 561710

Rentokil India Pte Ltd (1)
No 105 4th Floor Sreela Terrace 1st Main Road Gandhi Nagar, Adayar, Chennai, 600020, India
Tel.: (91) 4442939006
Web Site: http://www.rentokil.in
Sales Range: $25-49.9 Million
Emp.: 60
Pest Control Services
N.A.I.C.S.: 561499
Sam Easaw *(Mng Dir)*

Rentokil Initial (Austria) GmbH (1)
Boveri-Strasse 8/2/8, 2351, Wiener Neudorf, Austria (100%)
Tel.: (43) 223662828
Web Site: http://www.rentokil.at
Sales Range: $10-24.9 Million
Emp.: 50
Pest Control Services
N.A.I.C.S.: 561710
Holger May *(Gen Mgr)*

RENTOKIL INITIAL PLC

Rentokil Initial plc—(Continued)

Rentokil Initial (Barbados) Ltd. (1)
Rentokil House Chelston Avenue Off Cull-oden Road, Saint Michael, 14018, Barbados **(100%)**
Tel.: (246) 4293546
Web Site: http://www.bb.rentokil.com
Pest Control & Washroom Hygiene Services
N.A.I.C.S.: 561710
Trevor De Silvia *(Gen Mgr)*

Division (Domestic):

Rentokil Initial (Barbados) Ltd. - Washroom Hygiene Services (2)
Rentokil House Chelston Avenue Off Cull-oden Road, Saint Michael, 14018, Barbados
Tel.: (246) 429 3546
Web Site: http://www.initial.bb
Sales Range: $10-24.9 Million
Emp.: 50
Washroom Hygiene Services
N.A.I.C.S.: 561720
Trevor DeSilvia *(Gen Mgr)*

Rentokil Initial (Fiji) Ltd. (1)
Kaua Road Laucala Beach Estate, PO Box 486, Nasinu, Suva, Fiji **(100%)**
Tel.: (679) 3395977
Web Site: http://www.rentokil.com.fj
Sales Range: $25-49.9 Million
Emp.: 100
Pest Control & Washroom Hygiene Services
N.A.I.C.S.: 561710

Rentokil Initial (Jamaica) Ltd. (1)
8 Terrence Avenue, Kingston, Jamaica **(100%)**
Tel.: (876) 9264236
Web Site: http://www.jm.rentokil.com
Sales Range: $25-49.9 Million
Emp.: 35
Pest Control & Washroom Hygiene Services
N.A.I.C.S.: 561710

Rentokil Initial (M) Sdn. Bhd. (1)
15th Floor Menara Yayasan Selangor, 18A Jalan Persiaran Barat, Petaling Jaya, 46000, Selangor, Malaysia **(100%)**
Tel.: (60) 378490200
Web Site: http://www.rentokil-initial.com.my
Sales Range: $100-124.9 Million
Emp.: 500
Pest Control & Washroom Hygiene Services
N.A.I.C.S.: 561710
Carol Lam *(Mng Dir)*

Rentokil Initial (Philippines) Inc. (1)
73 Elisco Road Brgy, Kalawaan, 1600, Pasig, Philippines **(100%)**
Tel.: (63) 283335888
Web Site: http://www.rentokil.com.ph
Sales Range: $25-49.9 Million
Pest Control Services
N.A.I.C.S.: 561710

Rentokil Initial (Thailand) Ltd. (1)
PO Box Tower 6th Floor 1000/9 Sukhumvit 71 Road, Klongton Nua Wattana, Bangkok, 10110, Thailand
Tel.: (66) 27132000
Web Site: http://www.rentokil.co.th
Pest Control & Washroom Hygiene Services
N.A.I.C.S.: 561710

Rentokil Initial (Trinidad) Ltd (1)
Field 82 Kk Ll, Aranguez South, Port of Spain, Trinidad & Tobago
Tel.: (868) 6220047
Web Site: http://www.rentokil.tt
Sales Range: $10-24.9 Million
Pest Control Services
N.A.I.C.S.: 561710

Rentokil Initial A/S (1)
Paul Bergsoes Vej 22, 2600, Glostrup, Denmark
Tel.: (45) 43260505
Web Site: http://www.rentokil-initial.com
Pest Control, Washroom Hygiene & Interior Landscaping Services
N.A.I.C.S.: 561710

Unit (Domestic):

Initial Hygoform (2)
Paul Bergsoes Vej 22, Glostrup, 2600, Denmark
Tel.: (45) 70103310
Web Site: http://www.initial.dk
Washroom Hygiene Services
N.A.I.C.S.: 561720

Rentokil Skadedyrskontrol (2)
Paul Bergsoes Vej 22, 2600, Glostrup, Denmark
Tel.: (45) 70103311
Web Site: http://www.rentokil.dk
Pest Control Services
N.A.I.C.S.: 561710

Rentokil Initial B.V. (1)
Ravenswade 54S, 3439 LD, Nieuwegein, Netherlands **(100%)**
Tel.: (31) 850184369
Web Site: http://www.rentokil.nl
Pest Control Services
N.A.I.C.S.: 561710

Rentokil Initial Espana S.A. (1)
Calle Mar Mediterraneo 1, 28830, San Fernando de Henares, Spain **(100%)**
Tel.: (34) 916573329
Web Site: http://www.rentokil-initial.es
Pest Control, Washroom Hygiene, Textiles Supply, Interior Landscaping & Facilities Support Services
N.A.I.C.S.: 561710

Subsidiary (Domestic):

Initial Facilities Services - Spain (2)
Avd Camino de lo Cortado 15, S S de los Reyes, 28709, Madrid, Spain
Tel.: (34) 916276800
Integrated Facilities Support Services
N.A.I.C.S.: 561210

Rentokil Initial Fire Services Limited (1)
Mountergate, Norwich, NR1 1PY, United Kingdom
Tel.: (44) 1603 727000
Industrial Cleaning Services

Rentokil Initial GmbH (1)
Robert-Perthel-Strasse 81, 50739, Cologne, Germany
Tel.: (49) 2219453430
Web Site: http://www.rentokil-initial.de
Sales Range: $50-74.9 Million
Washroom Hygiene, Pest Control & Interior Landscaping Services
N.A.I.C.S.: 561720

Rentokil Initial Guadeloupe Sarl (1)
7 Allee Des Papillons Dothemare, 97139, Abymes, Guadeloupe
Tel.: (590) 590209594
Web Site: http://www.rentokil.gp
Pest Control Services
N.A.I.C.S.: 561710

Rentokil Initial Guyana Ltd. (1)
Lot 8 Charles & Drysdale Streets, PO Box 10650, Charlestown, Georgetown, Guyana **(100%)**
Tel.: (592) 2269658
Web Site: http://www.rentokil.gy
Sales Range: $25-49.9 Million
Pest Control & Washroom Hygiene Services
N.A.I.C.S.: 561710

Rentokil Initial Hellas EPE (1)
6 Polycratis Street, Rentis, 182 33, Athens, Greece **(100%)**
Tel.: (30) 2104836666
Web Site: http://www.rentokil-initial.gr
Emp.: 19
Pest Control & Washroom Hygiene Services
N.A.I.C.S.: 561710
Stavros Gaganis *(Gen Mgr)*

Rentokil Initial Holdings Ltd (1)
Felcourt Road Felcourt, East Grinstead, RH19 2JY, West Sussex, United Kingdom
Tel.: (44) 1342 833 022
Investment Management Service
N.A.I.C.S.: 523999

Rentokil Initial Hong Kong Ltd. (1)
23 Fl Westin Centre, 26 Hung To Road Kwun Tong, Hong Kong, China (Hong Kong) **(100%)**
Tel.: (852) 29546888
Sales Range: $25-49.9 Million
Emp.: 60
Pest Control Services
N.A.I.C.S.: 561710

Rentokil Initial Italia SpA (1)
Via Galilei 7, 20068, Milan, Peschiera Borromeo, Italy **(100%)**
Tel.: (39) 0254776611
Web Site: http://www.rentokil-initial.it
Pest Control & Washroom Hygiene Services
N.A.I.C.S.: 561710

Rentokil Initial Kenya Ltd. (1)
Witu Road, PO Box 44360, 00100, Nairobi, Kenya **(100%)**
Tel.: (254) 20552300
Sales Range: $100-124.9 Million
Emp.: 309
Pest Control & Washroom Hygiene Services
N.A.I.C.S.: 561710

Rentokil Initial Ltd (1)
Hazel House Millennium Park, Naas, Kildare, Ireland
Tel.: (353) 45850799
Web Site: http://www.rentokil.ie
Emp.: 30
Pest Control Services
N.A.I.C.S.: 561710
Michael O'Mahoney *(Gen Mgr)*

Rentokil Initial Martinique Sarl (1)
Soudon, 97232, Lamentin, Fort-de-France, Martinique **(100%)**
Tel.: (596) 512576
Web Site: http://www.mq.initial.com
Pest Control & Washroom Hygiene Services
N.A.I.C.S.: 561710

Rentokil Initial New Zealand (1)
89 Carbine Road Level 1 Mt Wellington, Auckland, 1060, New Zealand **(100%)**
Tel.: (64) 95805000
Web Site: http://www.rentokil-initial.co.nz
Pest Control Services
N.A.I.C.S.: 561710
Kennedy Short *(Head-Sls Capability & Mktg)*

Rentokil Initial Norge AS (1)
Sanitetsveien 17, PO Box 84, Skjetten, 2026, Norway **(100%)**
Tel.: (47) 23006600
Web Site: http://www.rentokil.no
Pest Control Services
N.A.I.C.S.: 561710

Rentokil Initial Portugal-Servicos de Protecao Ambiental Lda. (1)
Complexo Industrial de Vialonga Fraccao C1, Granja de Alpriate, 2626-501, Vialonga, Portugal **(100%)**
Tel.: (351) 219738400
Web Site: http://www.rentokil.pt
Pest Control & Washroom Hygiene Services
N.A.I.C.S.: 561710

Rentokil Initial Pty. Ltd. (1)
Unit A1 Lidcombe Bus Pk, 3-29 Birnie Ave, Lidcombe, 2141, NSW, Australia **(100%)**
Tel.: (61) 287196100
Web Site: http://www.rentokilinitial.com.au
Emp.: 200
Pest Control, Washroom Hygiene & Cleaning Services
N.A.I.C.S.: 561710
Kate Levy *(Head-Mktg)*

Rentokil Initial SA (1)
13-27 Avenue Jean Moulin, BP 28, 93114, Stains, Cedex, France **(100%)**
Tel.: (33) 148949293
Web Site: http://www.rentokil-initial.fr
Sales Range: $10-24.9 Million
Emp.: 30
Pest Control Services
N.A.I.C.S.: 561710
Thierry Bussod *(Mng Dir)*

Rentokil Initial Singapore Pte. Ltd. (1)
16-18 Jalan Mesin, Singapore, 368815, Singapore **(100%)**
Tel.: (65) 63478138

INTERNATIONAL PUBLIC

Web Site: http://www.rentokil.com.sg
Sales Range: $75-99.9 Million
Emp.: 400
Pest Control Services
N.A.I.C.S.: 561710
Min Hui Lim *(Mgr-Tech)*

Rentokil Initial UK Limited (1)
Compass House Manor Royal, Crawley, RH10 9PY, W Sussex, United Kingdom
Tel.: (44) 8082731010
Web Site: http://www.rentokil.co.uk
Pest Control Products Distr & Property Surveying Services
N.A.I.C.S.: 424698

Rentokil Insurance Ltd (1)
Garland Rd, East Grinstead, RH19 1DY, West Sussex, United Kingdom
Tel.: (44) 1342 332664
Web Site: http://www.rentokil.co.uk
Insurance Management Services
N.A.I.C.S.: 524298

Rentokil Luxembourg Sarl (1)
47 Rue De La Chapelle, 4967, Clemency, Luxembourg
Tel.: (352) 26887575
Web Site: http://www.rentokil.com
Sales Range: $10-24.9 Million
Pest Control Services
N.A.I.C.S.: 561710

Rentokil N.V. (1)
Ingberthoeveweg 17, 2630, Aartselaar, Belgium **(100%)**
Tel.: (32) 34506500
Web Site: http://www.rentokil.be
Pest Control Services
N.A.I.C.S.: 561710

Rentokil North America, Inc. (1)
1125 Berkshire Blvd Ste 150, Reading, PA 19610
Tel.: (610) 372-9700
Web Site: https://www.rentokil.com
Pest Control Services
N.A.I.C.S.: 561710
John Myers *(Pres & CEO-Pest Control-North America)*

Subsidiary (Domestic):

Buffalo Exterminating Co., Inc. (2)
3636 N Buffalo St, Orchard Park, NY 14127
Tel.: (716) 362-9103
Web Site: http://www.buffaloexterminating.com
Emp.: 92
Exterminating & Pest Control Services
N.A.I.C.S.: 561710
Lou Danzi *(Supvr-Svc)*

Garrie Pest Control, LLC (2)
312 Washington St, Peekskill, NY 10566
Tel.: (914) 271-2650
Web Site: http://www.garriepestcontrol.com
Sales Range: $1-9.9 Million
Emp.: 15
Exterminating & Pest Control Services
N.A.I.C.S.: 561710
Fred Gillen *(Pres)*

Insect IQ, Inc. (2)
1604 Ford Ave Ste 11, Modesto, CA 95350-4655
Tel.: (209) 574-0492
Web Site: http://www.insectiq.net
Emp.: 100
Exterminating & Pest Control Services
N.A.I.C.S.: 561710

Subsidiary (Non-US):

Rentokil Pest Control Canada Limited (2)
99 Locke Street Unit 1, Concord, L4k 0J2, ON, Canada
Tel.: (416) 226-5880
Web Site: http://www.rentokil.ca
Pest Control Services
N.A.I.C.S.: 561710

Rentokil Ou (1)
Turi 3, Tallinn, 11313, Estonia
Tel.: (372) 800 2002
Web Site: http://www.rentokileesti.ee
Pest Control Services
N.A.I.C.S.: 561710

Rentokil Schweiz AG (1)

AND PRIVATE COMPANIES

Hauptstrasse 181, 4625, Oberbuchsiten, Switzerland
Tel.: (41) 623898700
Web Site: http://www.ch.rentokil.com
Emp.: 100
Pest Control Services
N.A.I.C.S.: 561710

S & A Service und Anwendungstechnik GmbH (1)
An der Ziegelei 47, Westerholz, 27383, Schleswig, Germany
Tel.: (49) 42 633 0170
Web Site: https://www.s-und-a.de
Emp.: 48
Pest Control Services
N.A.I.C.S.: 561710
Elena Vasileva *(Gen Mgr)*

SR Dental AB (1)
Jarnvagsgatan 19, Hovmantorp, 360 51, Sweden
Tel.: (46) 478 475 00
Dental Reclamation Services
N.A.I.C.S.: 621210

Servicios Depec S.L. (1)
C/ Nena Casas 71, 08017, Barcelona, Spain
Tel.: (34) 934050140
Web Site: https://www.depec.es
Pest Management Services
N.A.I.C.S.: 561710

Sweden Recycling AB (1)
Avestagatan 61, 163 53, Spanga, Sweden
Tel.: (46) 84 108 8525
Web Site: https://www.swedenrecycling.se
Hazardous Waste Water Treatment Services
N.A.I.C.S.: 562211

Technivap SAS (1)
Za Des 4 Chemins, 95540, Mery-sur-Oise, France
Tel.: (33) 130363030
Facilities Management Services
N.A.I.C.S.: 561210

Terminix Global Holdings, Inc. (1)
150 Peabody Pl, Memphis, TN 38103
Tel.: (901) 597-1400
Web Site: http://www.terminix.com
Rev.: $2,045,000,000
Assets: $4,410,000,000
Liabilities: $2,035,000,000
Net Worth: $2,375,000,000
Earnings: $125,000,000
Emp.: 11,700
Fiscal Year-end: 12/31/2021
Holding Company; Residential & Commercial Contract Cleaning, Landscaping, Pest Control, Inspection & Furniture Repair Services
N.A.I.C.S.: 551112
Robert Doty *(CIO)*

Subsidiary (Domestic):

Bruce-Terminix Company, Inc. (2)
4500 Central Ave Pike, Knoxville, TN 37912
Tel.: (865) 248-0410
Web Site: https://www.terminixknoxville.com
Pest Control Services
N.A.I.C.S.: 811420

Burke Pest Control, Inc. (2)
585 Conklin Rd, Binghamton, NY 13903
Tel.: (607) 722-9042
Web Site: https://www.insectcontrolbinghamton.com
Exterminating & Pest Control Services
N.A.I.C.S.: 561710

Gregory Pest Control, LLC (2)
200 Smith Hines Rd, Greenville, SC 29607
Tel.: (864) 675-6226
Web Site: http://smarterpestcontrol.com
Exterminating & Pest Control Services
N.A.I.C.S.: 561710
Ben Walker *(Pres)*

Division (Domestic):

Gregory Pest Control, Inc. (3)
1710 Cumberland Pt Dr SE Ste 10, Marietta, GA 30067-9203
Web Site:
  http://www.gregorypestcontrol.com
Exterminating & Pest Control Services
N.A.I.C.S.: 561710

Michael Jackson *(Mgr)*

Subsidiary (Domestic):

Heritage Termite & Pest Services (3)
320 Troy Cir Ste H, Knoxville, TN 37919-6104
Tel.: (865) 525-8900
Web Site: http://www.heritagetermite.com
Exterminating & Pest Control Services
N.A.I.C.S.: 561710

Subsidiary (Non-US):

Pelias Norsk Skadedyrkontroll AS (2)
Martnsvegen 59, 2409, Elverum, Norway
Tel.: (47) 33330000
Web Site: http://www.pelias.no
Pest Control Services
N.A.I.C.S.: 561710

Pest Pulse Limited (2)
15 Oxford Lane, Ranelagh, Dublin, D06 W5K2, Ireland
Tel.: (353) 1 901 5257
Web Site: https://www.pestpulse.com
Pest Control Services
N.A.I.C.S.: 561710
Brian Monaghan *(CEO)*

Pest Pulse UK Limited (2)
71-75 Shelton Street Covent Garden, London, WC2H 9JQ, United Kingdom
Tel.: (44) 2080899257
Pest Control Services
N.A.I.C.S.: 561710

SVM Services Canada, Ltd. (2)
29 Tandem Road Unit 3, Concord, L4K 3G1, ON, Canada
Tel.: (905) 738-6676
Web Site: https://terminix.ca
Residential & Commercial Cleaning Services
N.A.I.C.S.: 561720

Subsidiary (Domestic):

ServiceMaster Commercial Solutions L.L.C. (2)
330 State Hwy H, Sikeston, MO 63801
Tel.: (573) 472-0441
Residential & Commercial Cleaning Services
N.A.I.C.S.: 561720

Subsidiary (Non-US):

Servicos Depec, S.L. (2)
C/ Nena Casas 71, 08017, Barcelona, Spain
Tel.: (34) 93 405 0140
Web Site: https://www.depec.es
Pest Control Services
N.A.I.C.S.: 561710

Terminix U.K. Limited (2)
Unit 1 Athelney Way, Cheltenham, GL52 6RT, Gloucestershire, United Kingdom
Tel.: (44) 3443350330
Web Site: http://www.terminixuk.com
Pest Control Services
N.A.I.C.S.: 561710
David Wareing *(Mng Dir)*

The Steritech Group, Inc. (1)
6701 Carmel Rd Ste 300, Charlotte, NC 28226
Tel.: (704) 544-1900
Web Site: http://www.steritech.com
Pest Prevention, Brand Auditing & Consulting Services
N.A.I.C.S.: 561710

Tropical Exterminators Limited (1)
5th Terrace Centreville, Nassau, Bahamas
Tel.: (242) 322 2157
Web Site:
  https://www.tropicalexterminators.bs
Pest Control Services
N.A.I.C.S.: 561710
Mark McCluskey *(Gen Mgr)*

Western Exterminator Company (1)
305 N Crescent Way, Anaheim, CA 92801-6709
Tel.: (714) 517-9000
Web Site: http://www.west-ext.com
Sales Range: $150-199.9 Million
Emp.: 800

Provider of Disinfecting & Pest Control Services
N.A.I.C.S.: 561710

Wise Property Care Limited (1)
HO 8 Muriel Street, Barrhead, Glasgow, G78 1QB, United Kingdom
Tel.: (44) 141 530 7704
Web Site:
  https://www.wisepropertycare.com
Damp Proofing Construction Services
N.A.I.C.S.: 238390

RENTRACKS CO., LTD.

5F Nextage 5-2-3 Nishikasai
Edogawa-ku, Tokyo, 134-0088, Japan
Tel.: (81) 338784159
Web Site: http://www.rentracks.co.jp
6045—(TKS)
Rev.: $21,779,950
Assets: $61,320,970
Liabilities: $40,849,800
Net Worth: $20,471,170
Earnings: $2,240,790
Emp.: 20
Fiscal Year-end: 03/31/24
Advertising Services
N.A.I.C.S.: 541890
Eiji Kaneko *(Chm)*

Subsidiaries:

Anything Co., Ltd. (1)
5F Nextage Nishikasai 5-2-3 Nishikasai, Edogawa-ku, Tokyo, 134-0088, Japan
Tel.: (81) 364135156
Digital Advertisement Services
N.A.I.C.S.: 541890

Atena Shanghai Co., Ltd. (1)
10N No 1590 West Yanan Road, Changning District, Shanghai, China
Tel.: (86) 2164388085
Web Site: https://www.atena.com.cn
Emp.: 28
Advertising Services
N.A.I.C.S.: 541890

Bearis One Co., Ltd. (1)
ORO Service Office Room8 246 Times Square Building 10thFl, Soi Sukhumvit 12-14 Sukhumvit Rd Klongtoey, Bangkok, 10110, Thailand
Tel.: (66) 26532236
Digital Advertisement Services
N.A.I.C.S.: 541890

Growth Power Co., Ltd. (1)
No 28 Yamahide Bld 6F 5-6-2 Nishikasai, Edogawa-ku, Tokyo, 134-0088, Japan
Tel.: (81) 368080120
Digital Advertisement Services
N.A.I.C.S.: 541890

P.T. Rentracks Cocreation Indonesia (1)
Jl North Kemang II No 5 RT 6/RW 6 Bangka Kec Mampang Prpt, South Jakarta, 12730, Indonesia
Tel.: (62) 81918686861
Digital Advertisement Services
N.A.I.C.S.: 541890

P.T. Rentracks Creative Works (1)
Thamrin City Floor 7A, South Jakarta, 10230, Indonesia
Tel.: (62) 2122394420
Web Site: https://rentracks.co.id
Advertising Services
N.A.I.C.S.: 541890

Rentracks Lanka (Private) Limited (1)
1st Floor 410/22 Galle Road 03, Colombo, Sri Lanka
Tel.: (94) 117021540
Digital Advertisement Services
N.A.I.C.S.: 541810

Rentracks Malaysia Sdn. Bhd. (1)
Penthouse Level 27 Centrepoint South The Boulevard Mid Valley City, Lingkaran Syed Putra, 59200, Kuala Lumpur, Malaysia
Tel.: (60) 320969634
Digital Advertisement Services
N.A.I.C.S.: 541810

Rentracks Mongol LLC (1)

RENUKA CITY HOTELS PLC

Door 10 Apartment 10, 7th sub-District 11th Micro-District Irkutsk Street Sukhbaatar, Ulaanbaatar, Mongolia
Tel.: (976) 99119804
Digital Advertisement Services
N.A.I.C.S.: 541810

Rentracks Taiwan Co., Limited (1)
2F No 72 Sec 1 Zhongxiao W Rd, Zhongzheng, Taipei, 100, Taiwan
Tel.: (886) 277421868
Digital Advertisement Services
N.A.I.C.S.: 541810

Rentracks Vietnam Co., Ltd. (1)
3rd Floor HBT Building 456-458 Hai Ba Trung, Tan Dinh Ward District 1, Ho Chi Minh City, Vietnam
Tel.: (84) 2862647049
Web Site: https://rentracks.com.vn
Advertising Services
N.A.I.C.S.: 541890

Technopal Co., Ltd. (1)
5F NEXTAGE Nishikasai 5-2-3 Nishikasai, Edogawa-ku, Tokyo, 134-0088, Japan
Tel.: (81) 368081877
Digital Advertisement Services
N.A.I.C.S.: 541890

Universal Media Japan Co., Ltd. (1)
942 Win Aoyama 2-2-15 Minami-Aoyama, Minato-ku, Tokyo, 107-0062, Japan
Tel.: (81) 364030575
Web Site: https://universalmediajapan.co.jp
Advertising Services
N.A.I.C.S.: 541890

RENTUNDER HOLDING AB

Tel.: (46) 706008574
Web Site:
  https://driveinboatwash.com
Year Founded: 2009
Industrial Machinery Maintenance Services
N.A.I.C.S.: 811310
Mikael Alven *(CEO)*

RENU ENERGY LIMITED

Corporate House Kings Row 1 Level 2 52 McDougall Street, PO Box 2046, Milton, 4064, QLD, Australia
Tel.: (61) 721023654
Web Site:
  https://www.renuenergy.com.au
RNE—(ASX)
Rev.: $500,394
Assets: $11,333,343
Liabilities: $859,339
Net Worth: $10,474,004
Earnings: ($3,397,353)
Fiscal Year-end: 06/30/24
Electric Power Generation
N.A.I.C.S.: 221122
Tim Scholefield *(Exec Dir)*

RENUKA AGRI FOODS LIMITED

Renuka House 69 Sri Jinaratana Road, PO Box 961, 2, Colombo, 2, Sri Lanka
Tel.: (94) 112314750
Web Site:
  https://www.renukagroup.com
RAL—(COL)
Rev.: $24,007,199
Assets: $26,358,795
Liabilities: $12,111,115
Net Worth: $14,247,680
Earnings: $1,658,036
Emp.: 762
Fiscal Year-end: 03/31/23
Coconut Products Mfr
N.A.I.C.S.: 311999
Skantha Ranjit Rajiyah *(Chm)*

RENUKA CITY HOTELS PLC

328 Galle Road, 3, Colombo, 3, Sri Lanka
Tel.: (94) 112573598

Renuka City Hotels PLC—(Continued)

Web Site:
https://www.renukacityhotel.com
RENU—(COL)
Rev.: $2,681,876
Assets: $29,051,654
Liabilities: $450,564
Net Worth: $28,601,091
Earnings: $2,379,856
Emp.: 44
Fiscal Year-end: 03/31/21
Home Management Services
N.A.I.C.S.: 721110
M. A. Jayawardena *(Sec)*

RENUKA HOTELS PLC
328 Galle Road 3, Colombo, Sri Lanka
Tel.: (94) 112573598
Web Site:
http://www.renukahotel.com
RCH—(COL)
Rev.: $914,587
Assets: $42,260,489
Liabilities: $537,189
Net Worth: $41,723,300
Earnings: $6,654,943
Fiscal Year-end: 03/31/23
Hotel & Restaurant Operator
N.A.I.C.S.: 721110
R. B. Thambiayah *(Chm & Mng Dir)*

RENWICK JAJNESWAR & CO. (BD)
Chini Shilpa Bhaban Share office 5th floor 3 Dilkusha C/A, Dhaka, 1000, Bangladesh
Tel.: (880) 9565868
Year Founded: 1988
RENWICKJA—(DHA)
Sales Range: Less than $1 Million
Industrial Machinery Mfr
N.A.I.C.S.: 333998
Khadiza Sultana *(Sec)*

RENYCO INC.
425 Galipeau Rang 5, Thurso, J0X 3B0, QC, Canada
Tel.: (819) 985-3773
Web Site:
http://www.silhouetteflooring.com
Rev.: $14,208,200
Emp.: 75
Hardwood Flooring Products Mfr
N.A.I.C.S.: 321918
Earl Laforest *(Pres)*

RENZO PIANO BUILDING WORKSHOP
34 Rue Des Archives, 75004, Paris, France
Tel.: (33) 144614900
Web Site: http://www.rpbw.com
Rev.: $21,600,000
Emp.: 70
Piano Building Services
N.A.I.C.S.: 541310
Philippe Goubet *(Partner)*

REOBIJN B.V.
Industriestraat 28, 7482 EZ, Haaksbergen, Netherlands
Tel.: (31) 535740404
Web Site: http://www.reobijn.nl
Sales Range: $25-49.9 Million
Emp.: 45
Plastic Container Mfr
N.A.I.C.S.: 326199
Jan Bernard Wolters *(Mng Dir)*

REPARE THERAPEUTICS INC.
7210 Frederick-Banting Suite 100, Saint Laurent, H4S 2A1, QC, Canada
Tel.: (857) 412-7018
Web Site: https://www.reparerx.com
Year Founded: 2016
RPTX—(NASDAQ)
Rev.: $131,830,000
Assets: $364,075,000
Liabilities: $84,558,000
Net Worth: $279,517,000
Earnings: ($29,047,000)
Emp.: 180
Fiscal Year-end: 12/31/22
Biotechnology Research & Development Services
N.A.I.C.S.: 541714
Cameron Black *(Exec VP-Discovery)*

REPATRIATES CO-OPERATIVE FINANCE AND DEVELOPMENT BANK LIMITED
Repco Towers 33 North Usman Road, T Nagar, Chennai, 600017, India
Tel.: (91) 44 28340715
Web Site: http://www.repcobank.com
Year Founded: 1969
Banking Services
N.A.I.C.S.: 522110
R. S. Isabella *(Mng Dir)*

Subsidiaries:

Repco Home Finance Limited (1)
Alexander Square Third Floor Old No 34/35, New No 2 Sardar Patel Road Guindy, Chennai, 600032, India
Tel.: (91) 4442106650
Web Site: https://www.repcohome.com
Rev.: $190,039,395
Assets: $1,695,263,115
Liabilities: $1,406,857,725
Net Worth: $288,405,390
Earnings: $39,257,400
Emp.: 977
Fiscal Year-end: 03/31/2021
Housing Finance Services
N.A.I.C.S.: 522310
T. S. Krishna Murthy *(Chm)*

REPECHAGE INVESTMENTS LIMITED
Suite 503 Box 245 5657 Spring Garden Road, Halifax, B3J 3R4, NS, Canada
Tel.: (902) 444-3056
Privater Equity Firm
N.A.I.C.S.: 523999
David Dobbins *(Pres)*

REPLEK AD
Kozle 188, 1000, Skopje, North Macedonia
Tel.: (389) 23081343
Web Site: https://replek.mk
REPL—(MAC)
Rev.: $28,546,867
Assets: $53,973,394
Liabilities: $12,646,112
Net Worth: $41,327,282
Earnings: $5,046,741
Fiscal Year-end: 12/31/23
Pharmaceutical Mfr & Whslr
N.A.I.C.S.: 325412
Liljana Makraduli *(Mgr-R&D)*

REPLENISH NUTRIENTS HOLDING CORP.
111th-5th avenue Sw suite 3100, Calgary, T2P 5L3, AB, Canada
Tel.: (403) 509-7500
Web Site:
https://replenishnutrients.com
ERTH—(CNSX)
Rev.: $396,506
Assets: $4,411,336
Liabilities: $746,773
Net Worth: $3,664,562
Earnings: ($3,033,272)
Emp.: 15
Fiscal Year-end: 12/31/20
Metal Exploration Services
N.A.I.C.S.: 213114
Keith Driver *(CEO)*

REPLICEL LIFE SCIENCES INC.
Suite 900-570 Granville Street, Vancouver, V6C 3P1, BC, Canada
Tel.: (604) 248-8730
Web Site: https://www.replicel.com
REPCF—(OTCIQ)
Rev.: $276,720
Assets: $624,430
Liabilities: $5,251,820
Net Worth: ($4,627,390)
Earnings: ($581,412)
Emp.: 1
Fiscal Year-end: 12/31/22
Hair Cell Replication Technology
N.A.I.C.S.: 541715
David Hall *(Chm)*

REPLY S.P.A.
Corso Francia 110, 10143, Turin, Italy
Tel.: (39) 0117711594
Web Site: https://www.reply.com
Year Founded: 1996
REY—(ITA)
Rev.: $1,535,534,594
Assets: $1,850,427,080
Liabilities: $1,020,189,655
Net Worth: $830,237,426
Earnings: $152,554,777
Emp.: 9,059
Fiscal Year-end: 12/31/20
Consultancy, Marketing, Public Relations & Technology Services for E-Businesses
N.A.I.C.S.: 541613
Mario Rizzante *(Chm & Co-CEO)*

Subsidiaries:

4brands Reply GmbH & Co. KG (1)
Potsdamer Strasse 14, 32423, Minden, Germany
Tel.: (49) 57138540
Web Site: https://www.reply.com
Sales Range: $25-49.9 Million
Emp.: 90
IT Consulting & Support Services
N.A.I.C.S.: 541513

Aim Reply Ltd. (1)
160 Victoria St 2nd Floor Nova South, Westminster, London, SW1E 5LB, United Kingdom
Tel.: (44) 2077306000
Financial Services
N.A.I.C.S.: 921130

Alpha Reply GmbH (1)
Uhlandstrasse 2, 60314, Frankfurt am Main, Germany
Tel.: (49) 6999999370
Systems Integration & Digital Services
N.A.I.C.S.: 541512

Arlanis Reply Ltd. (1)
160 Victoria Street, Westminster, London, SW1E 5LB, United Kingdom
Tel.: (44) 2077306000
Marketing Consulting Services
N.A.I.C.S.: 541613

Atlas Reply S.r.l. (1)
Corso Francia 110, 10047, Turin, 10047, Italy
Tel.: (39) 0117711594
Web Site: http://www.reply.at
Sales Range: $25-49.9 Million
Emp.: 100
Software Publisher
N.A.I.C.S.: 513210
Tattiana Rizzante *(CEO)*

Avantage Reply (Belgium) Sprl (1)
Congresstraat / Rue du Congres 5, 1000, Brussels, Belgium
Tel.: (32) 28800320
Systems Integration & Digital Services
N.A.I.C.S.: 541512

Avantage Reply (Luxembourg) Sarl (1)
21-25 Allee Scheffer, 2570, Luxembourg, Luxembourg
Tel.: (352) 2868431
Systems Integration & Digital Services

N.A.I.C.S.: 541512

Avantage Reply (Netherlands) BV (1)
The Atrium Strawinskylaan 3051, 1077 ZX, Amsterdam, Netherlands
Tel.: (31) 2030121231077
Systems Integration & Digital Services
N.A.I.C.S.: 541512

Avantage Reply GmbH (1)
Luise-Ullrich-Strasse 14, 80636, Munich, Germany
Tel.: (49) 894111420
Web Site: http://www.xuccess.com
Sales Range: $25-49.9 Million
Emp.: 200
Business Consulting & Advisory Services
N.A.I.C.S.: 561499

Avvio Reply Ltd. (1)
160 Victoria St 2nd Floor Nova South Westminster, London, SW1E 5LB, United Kingdom
Tel.: (44) 2077306000
Web Site: https://www.avvioreply.co.uk
Digital Marketing Services
N.A.I.C.S.: 541613

Avvio Reply S.r.l. (1)
Via Robert Koch 1/4, 20152, Milan, Italy
Tel.: (39) 0253 5761
Web Site: https://www.reply.com
Systems Integration & Digital Services
N.A.I.C.S.: 541512

Bitmama S.r.l. (1)
Via Luisa del Carretto 58, 10131, Turin, Italy
Tel.: (39) 0118810711
Web Site: http://www.bitmama.it
Advertising Services
N.A.I.C.S.: 541810
Claudio Papetti *(CEO)*

Blue Reply S.r.l. (1)
Corso Francia 110, 10143, Turin, Italy
Tel.: (39) 0117711594
Web Site: http://www.reply.com
Sales Range: $800-899.9 Million
Emp.: 3,000
Software Publisher
N.A.I.C.S.: 513210

Business Elements Group B.V. (1)
Gulledelle 96, 1200, Brussels, Belgium
Tel.: (32) 27620801
Web Site: https://www.businesselements.eu
Information Technology Services
N.A.I.C.S.: 541511

Cluster Reply Dynamics GmbH (1)
Bartholomausweg 26, 33334, Gutersloh, Germany
Tel.: (49) 524150090
Information Technology Services
N.A.I.C.S.: 541511

Cluster Reply GmbH & Co. KG (1)
Tel.: (49) 894111420
Software Support Services
N.A.I.C.S.: 541519

Cluster Reply Roma S.R.L. (1)
Via Cardinale Massaia 83, 10147, Turin, Italy
Tel.: (39) 01129100
Information Technology Services
N.A.I.C.S.: 541511

Cluster Reply S.r.l. (1)
Corso Francia 110, 10143, Turin, 10143, Italy
Tel.: (39) 0117711594
Web Site: http://www.reply.eu
Software Publisher
N.A.I.C.S.: 513210

Comsysto Reply GmbH (1)
Riesstrasse 22, 80992, Munich, Germany
Tel.: (49) 89411142880
Web Site: https://www.comsystoreply.de
Software Services
N.A.I.C.S.: 541511

Comsysto d.o.o. (1)
Ilirska ul 33, 10000, Zagreb, Croatia
Tel.: (385) 16461195
Web Site: https://croatia.comsysto.com
Software Services
N.A.I.C.S.: 541511

AND PRIVATE COMPANIES / REPOXIT AG

Comwrap Reply GmbH (1)
Hanauer Landstrasse 126-128, 60314, Frankfurt am Main, Germany
Tel.: (49) 69380795200
Web Site: https://www.comwrap.com
Information Technology Services
N.A.I.C.S.: 541511

Concept Reply GmbH (1)
Luise-Ullrich-Strasse 14, 80636, Munich, Germany
Tel.: (49) 894111420
Systems Integration & Digital Services
N.A.I.C.S.: 541512

Concept Reply LLC (1)
691 N Squirrel Rd Ste 202, Auburn Hills, MI 48326
Tel.: (248) 686-2481
Systems Integration & Digital Services
N.A.I.C.S.: 541512

Data Reply S.r.l. (1)
Tel.: (39) 01129100
Systems Integration & Digital Services
N.A.I.C.S.: 541512

E Finance Consulting Reply S.r.l. (1)
Via Castellanza 11, 20151, Milan, Italy
Tel.: (39) 02535761
Financial Management Consulting Services
N.A.I.C.S.: 541611

Elbkind Reply GmbH (1)
Palmaille 33, 22767, Hamburg, Germany
Tel.: (49) 40696323600
Web Site: https://www.elbkind.de
Advertising Services
N.A.I.C.S.: 541890
Thomas Hartmann (Mng Dir)

Fincon Reply GmbH (1)
Admiralitatstrasse 59, 20459, Hamburg, Germany
Tel.: (49) 40237681440
Information Technology Services
N.A.I.C.S.: 541511

Frank Reply GmbH (1)
Uhlandstrasse 2, 60314, Frankfurt am Main, Germany
Tel.: (49) 6999999370
Information Technology Services
N.A.I.C.S.: 541511

Go Reply GmbH (1)
Bartholomausweg 26, 33334, Gutersloh, Germany
Tel.: (49) 524150090
Systems Integration & Digital Services
N.A.I.C.S.: 541512

Go Reply S.r.l. (1)
Via Cardinale Massaia 83, 10147, Turin, Italy
Tel.: (39) 01129100
Systems Integration & Digital Services
N.A.I.C.S.: 541512

Gray Matter Ltd. (1)
The Old Maltings Prigg Meadow, Ashburton, Devon, TQ13 7DF, United Kingdom
Tel.: (44) 1364654100
Web Site: https://greymatter.com
Software Services
N.A.I.C.S.: 541511

Ki Reply GmbH (1)
Bartholomausweg 26, 33334, Gutersloh, Germany
Tel.: (49) 524150090
Software Services
N.A.I.C.S.: 541511

Leadvise Reply GmbH (1)
Uhlandstrasse 2, 60314, Frankfurt am Main, Germany
Tel.: (49) 699999937800
Web Site: https://www.leadvise.de
Pharmaceuticals Mfr
N.A.I.C.S.: 325412
Tobias Layer (Partner)

Like Reply GmbH (1)
Riesstrasse 22, 80992, Munich, Germany
Tel.: (49) 89411142880
Information Technology Services
N.A.I.C.S.: 541511

Like Reply S.r.l. (1)
Via Castellanza 11, 20151, Milan, Italy
Tel.: (39) 02535761

Systems Integration & Digital Services

Live Reply GmbH (1)
Hansaallee 299, 40549, Dusseldorf, Germany
Tel.: (49) 21117609550
Systems Integration & Digital Services
N.A.I.C.S.: 541512

Net Reply S.R.L. (1)
Via Cardinal Massaia 71, 10147, Turin, Italy
Tel.: (39) 01129100
Information Technology Services
N.A.I.C.S.: 541511

Neveling.net GmbH (1)
Alstertwiete 3, 20099, Hamburg, Germany
Tel.: (49) 40 328 0760
Web Site: https://nevelingreply.de
Software Services
N.A.I.C.S.: 541511

Nexi Digital Polska Sp. z o.o. (1)
Wroclawska 54, 40217, Katowice, Poland
Tel.: (48) 322313006
Software Services
N.A.I.C.S.: 541511

Portaltech Reply Ltd. (1)
38 Grosvenor Gardens, London, SW1W 0EB, United Kingdom
Tel.: (44) 2077306000
Systems Integration & Digital Services
N.A.I.C.S.: 541512

Protocube Reply S.r.l. (1)
Via Cardinal Massaia 71, 10147, Turin, Italy
Tel.: (39) 01129100
Web Site: https://protocube.it
Graphic Design Services
N.A.I.C.S.: 541430

Reply (1)
Via Giorgione 59, 00147, Rome, Italy
Tel.: (39) 06844341
Sales Range: $100-124.9 Million
Emp.: 300
Consulting, Systems Integration, Application Management & Business Process Outsourcing Services
N.A.I.C.S.: 334610
Giovanni Vetrella (Mng Dir)

Reply Croatia d.o.o. (1)
Sky Office Tower A 17th floor Ul Roberta Frangesa Mihanovica 9, 10000, Zagreb, Croatia
Tel.: (385) 16461195
Information Technology Services
N.A.I.C.S.: 541511

Reply France Sarl (1)
3 rue du Faubourg Saint Honore, 75008, Paris, France
Tel.: (33) 170230874
Systems Integration & Digital Services
N.A.I.C.S.: 541512

Reply GmbH (1)
Rennweg 28, 8001, Zurich, Switzerland
Tel.: (41) 524150090
Systems Integration & Digital Services
N.A.I.C.S.: 541512

Reply do Brasil Sistemas de Informatica Ltda. (1)
Av Nossa Senhora do Carmo 660 - 1 andar - Sao Pedro, Belo Horizonte, 30330-000, Minas Gerais, Brazil
Tel.: (55) 3125145900
Systems Integration & Digital Services
N.A.I.C.S.: 541512

Riverland Reply GmbH (1)
Luise-Ullrich-Str 14, 80636, Munich, Germany
Tel.: (49) 894111420
Web Site: https://www.reply.com
Software Solutions Services
N.A.I.C.S.: 541511

Sagepath LLC (1)
1 Alliance Ctr 3500 Lenox Rd Ste 1200, Atlanta, GA 30326
Tel.: (404) 926-0078
Web Site: https://sagepath-reply.com
Information Technology Services
N.A.I.C.S.: 541511

Shield Reply Ltd. (1)
Nova South 160 Victoria Street, Westminster, London, SW1E 5LB, United Kingdom
Tel.: (44) 2077306000
Information Technology Services
N.A.I.C.S.: 541511

Solidsoft Reply Ltd. (1)
160 Victoria St 2nd Floor Nova South Westminster, London, SW1E 5LB, United Kingdom
Tel.: (44) 2077306000
Systems Integration & Digital Services
N.A.I.C.S.: 541512

Spike Reply GmbH (1)
Oskar Jager Str 173/K4, 50825, Cologne, Germany
Tel.: (49) 2219544660
Web Site: http://www.reply.com
Computer Distr & IT Services
N.A.I.C.S.: 423430
Frank Puetz (Mng Dir-Security)

Spike Reply Ltd. (1)
38 Grosvenor Gardens, London, SW1W 0EB, United Kingdom
Tel.: (44) 2077306000
Information Technology Services
N.A.I.C.S.: 541511

Storm Reply Inc. (1)
71 S Wacker Dr Ste 3090, Chicago, IL 60606
Tel.: (248) 686-2481
Information Technology Services
N.A.I.C.S.: 541511

Storm Reply Roma S.R.L. (1)
Via Nizza 250, 10126, Turin, Italy
Tel.: (39) 01129100
Information Technology Services
N.A.I.C.S.: 541511

Syskoplan Reply LLC (1)
3 Great Valley Pkwy Ste 190, Malvern, PA 19355
Tel.: (610) 296-3640
Web Site: https://www.syskoplan-reply.com
Information Technology Services
N.A.I.C.S.: 541511

Syskoplan Reply S.r.l. (1)
Corso Francia 110, 10143, Turin, Italy
Tel.: (39) 0117711594
Systems Integration & Digital Services
N.A.I.C.S.: 541512

TD Reply GmbH (1)
Lutzowstrasse 106, 10785, Berlin, Germany
Tel.: (49) 302787600
Web Site: https://www.tdreply.de
Data Processing Services
N.A.I.C.S.: 518210
Holger Nosekabel (CTO)

Technology Reply S.r.l. (1)
Tel.: (39) 02535761
Web Site: http://www.reply.it
Emp.: 500
Software Reproducing
N.A.I.C.S.: 334610

Threepipe Reply Ltd. (1)
28-30 Grosvenor Gardens, London, SW1W 0TT, United Kingdom
Tel.: (44) 2077306000
Web Site: https://threepipereply.com
Digital Marketing Services
N.A.I.C.S.: 541613
Alistair Gammell (Assoc Partner)

Triplesense Reply GmbH (1)
Uhlandstrasse 2, 60314, Frankfurt am Main, Germany
Tel.: (49) 6999999370
Web Site: https://www.triplesensereply.de
Digital Marketing Services
N.A.I.C.S.: 541613
Oliver Bohl (Mng Dir)

Valorem LLC (1)
2101 Broadway Ste 11, Kansas City, MO 64108
Tel.: (816) 398-8949
Web Site: https://valoremreply.com
Specialty Software & Services
N.A.I.C.S.: 541511
Andrew Fletcher (Partner)

WM Reply GmbH (1)
Palmaille 33, 22767, Hamburg, Germany
Tel.: (49) 40696323600

Information Technology Services
N.A.I.C.S.: 541511

WM Reply Inc. (1)
71 S Wacker Dr Ste 3090, Chicago, IL 60606
Tel.: (248) 686-2481
Systems Integration & Digital Services
N.A.I.C.S.: 541512

WM Reply LLC (1)
Office 416 2 Talbuchina Street, Minsk, 220012, Belarus
Tel.: (375) 17 284 6629
Systems Integration & Digital Services
N.A.I.C.S.: 541512

WM Reply Ltd. (1)
28 Customs Street East Auckland CBD, 1010, Auckland, New Zealand
Tel.: (64) 277777307
Systems Integration & Digital Services
N.A.I.C.S.: 541512

WM Reply S.R.L. (1)
C so Francia 110, 10143, Turin, Italy
Tel.: (39) 0117711594
Information Technology Services
N.A.I.C.S.: 541511

Xenia Reply S.R.L. (1)
Via Nizza 250, 10126, Turin, Italy
Tel.: (39) 01129100
Health Care Srvices
N.A.I.C.S.: 621999

Xister Reply S.r.l. (1)
Via Giovanni da Castel Bolognese 18, 00153, Rome, Italy
Tel.: (39) 0658335926
Web Site: https://www.xister.com
Digital Marketing Services
N.A.I.C.S.: 541613

avantage Reply Limited (1)
5th Floor Dukes House 32 38 Dukes Place, London, EC3A 7LP, United Kingdom
Tel.: (44) 2077094000
Web Site: http://www.avantage.eu.com
Sales Range: $25-49.9 Million
Emp.: 6
Consulting Services
N.A.I.C.S.: 541611

macros Reply GmbH (1)
Erika-Mann-Strasse 57, 80636, Munich, Germany
Tel.: (49) 89411142400
Web Site: http://www.macrosreply.de
Sales Range: $25-49.9 Million
Emp.: 150
Document Management Software Solutions
N.A.I.C.S.: 334610

REPOWER ENERGY DEVELOPMENT CORPORATION

3/F JTKC Centre 2155 Don Chino Roces Avenue, Makati, 1231, Philippines
Tel.: (63) 288138892
Web Site: https://www.repowerenergy.com.ph
Year Founded: 2013
REDC—(PHI)
Rev.: $8,446,523
Assets: $97,756,900
Liabilities: $59,523,396
Net Worth: $38,233,504
Earnings: $3,108,880
Emp.: 5
Fiscal Year-end: 12/31/23
Renewable Energy Distribution Services
N.A.I.C.S.: 221210
Eric Peter Y. Roxas (Pres)

REPOXIT AG

Spinnereiweg 9 8307 Illnau, 8404, Effretikon, Switzerland
Tel.: (41) 522440909 CH
Web Site: http://www.repoxit.com
Sales Range: $10-24.9 Million
Emp.: 70
Coatings & Adhesives Mfr & Sales
N.A.I.C.S.: 325520

REPRO INDIA LIMITED

Repoxit AG—(Continued)

REPRO INDIA LIMITED
11th Floor Sun Paradise Business Plaza B Wing Senapati Bapat Marg, Lower Parel, Mumbai, 400013, India
Tel.: (91) 2271914000 In
Web Site:
https://www.reproindialtd.com
Year Founded: 1984
REPRO—(NSE)
Rev.: $39,377,520
Assets: $58,558,500
Liabilities: $21,902,790
Net Worth: $36,655,710
Earnings: ($3,165,435)
Emp.: 426
Fiscal Year-end: 03/31/22
Printing Solution Mfr
N.A.I.C.S.: 561439
Mukesh Dhruve *(CFO & Fin Dir)*

Subsidiaries:

Repro Books Limited (1)
Tel.: (91) 2271914000
Web Site: https://www.reprobooks.in
Books Publishing Services
N.A.I.C.S.: 513130

REPROCELL INC.
MetLife Shin-yokohama 381 Bldg 9F
3-8-11 Shin-yokohama, Kohoku-ku,
Yokohama, 222-0033, Kanagawa,
Japan
Tel.: (81) 454753887
Web Site: https://www.reprocell.com
Year Founded: 2003
4978—(TKS)
Rev.: $16,035,860
Assets: $59,833,720
Liabilities: $4,898,010
Net Worth: $54,935,710
Earnings: ($204,910)
Fiscal Year-end: 03/31/24
Reagent Research Services
N.A.I.C.S.: 541715
Chikafumi Yokoyama *(CEO)*

Subsidiaries:

BioServe Biotechnologies (India) Private Limited (1)
Unit D4-D7 1st Floor Industrial Estate
Moula-Ali, Medchal-Malkagiri Dist, Hyderabad, 500040, Telangana,, India
Tel.: (91) 4029558178
Web Site: http://www.bioserveindia.com
Medical Product Distr
N.A.I.C.S.: 424210

ReproCELL USA, Inc. (1)
9000 Virginia Manor Rd Ste 207, Beltsville, MD 20705
Tel.: (301) 470-3362
Reagent Research Services
N.A.I.C.S.: 541715

REPSOL, S.A.
Repsol Campus C/ Mendez Alvaro
44, 28045, Madrid, Spain
Tel.: (34) 917538100 ES
Web Site: https://www.repsol.com
Year Founded: 1987
REP—(MAD)
Rev.: $63,175,048,565
Assets: $66,515,216,922
Liabilities: $35,142,456,292
Net Worth: $31,372,760,630
Earnings: $3,418,951,004
Emp.: 25,059
Fiscal Year-end: 12/31/23
Oil & Gas Distribution Services
N.A.I.C.S.: 551112
Antonio Brufau Niubo *(Chm)*

Subsidiaries:

Gaviota RE S.A. (1)
74 Rue de Merl, 2146, Luxembourg, Luxembourg
Tel.: (352) 24 69 54 1

Sales Range: $50-74.9 Million
Emp.: 3
General Insurance Services
N.A.I.C.S.: 524210
Bryan Collins *(Gen Mgr)*

Grupo Repsol de Peru, S.A. (1)
Av Victor Andres Belaunde 147, San Isidro, Lima, 27, Peru (90.99%)
Tel.: (51) 1 215 6225
Web Site: https://www.repsol.com
Emp.: 2,991
N.A.I.C.S.: 324110

Noroil, S.A. (1)
Calle Las Delicias 2, Valle de Trapaga, 48510, Spain
Tel.: (34) 944720590
Oil & Gas Exploration Services
N.A.I.C.S.: 213112

Petroleos Transandinos YPF S.A. (1)
Avenida Lerbosque 177 Fl 4, Las Condes, Santiago, Chile (100%)
Tel.: (56) 26557000
Web Site: http://www.repsolypf.com
Sales Range: $100-124.9 Million
Emp.: 200
Exploration, Exploitation, Transport & Industrialization of Oil
N.A.I.C.S.: 213112

Petroleos del Norte, S.A. (1)
Barrio San Martin 5 - Ed Munatones, Muskiz, 48550, Spain
Tel.: (34) 94 635 70 00
Web Site: http://www.repsol.com
Emp.: 900
Petroleum Product Distr
N.A.I.C.S.: 424720

Refineria la Pampilla SA (1)
Carretera a Ventanilla km 25 Callao 6, Lima, 1, Peru (45%)
Tel.: (51) 517 2022
Web Site: https://www.repsol.pe
Sales Range: $125-149.9 Million
Emp.: 300
Oil Refinery
N.A.I.C.S.: 324110

Repso E&P de Bolivia, S.A. (1)
Av Las Ramblas 100 Centro Empresarial Edificio Itc Tower, Santa Cruz, Bolivia
Tel.: (591) 33660000
Oil & Gas Exploration Services
N.A.I.C.S.: 213112

Repsol Butano, S.A. (1)
Paseo de la Castellana 278-280, 28046, Madrid, Spain (100%)
Tel.: (34) 913488100
Web Site: http://www.repsolypf.com
Sales Range: $150-199.9 Million
Emp.: 300
Liquid Petroleum Gas Distr
N.A.I.C.S.: 457210

Subsidiary (Non-US):

Duragas, S.A. (2)
Km 7.5 Via a la Costa Sector Salitralc, Guayas, Ecuador
Tel.: (593) 4 3705300
Liquefied Petroleum Gas Distr
N.A.I.C.S.: 424720

Repsol Comercial, S.C.A. (2)
Av VA Belaunde 147 T Real 5 Sotano Pisos Del 3 Al 8 Y 10, Centro Empresarial San Isidro, Lima, 27, Peru
Tel.: (51) 12156225
Petroleum Product Distr
N.A.I.C.S.: 424720

Repsol France SA (2)
56 Boulevard L'embouchure Immeuble Central Park, 31201, Toulouse, France
Tel.: (33) 534403800
Web Site: http://www.sogasud.fr
Emp.: 2
Liquefied Petroleum Gas Distr
N.A.I.C.S.: 424720
Mark Brauer *(Gen Mgr)*

Repsol Gas Portugal, S.A. (2)
Av Jose Malhoa 16B 8, 1099-091, Lisbon, Portugal
Tel.: (351) 213119000
Web Site: http://www.repsol.com

Oil & Gas Exploration Services
N.A.I.C.S.: 213112

Subsidiary (Domestic):

Solgas Distribuidora de Gas, S.L. (2)
Glorieta Quevedo 9 - Piso 6, Madrid, 28015, Spain
Tel.: (34) 913488672
Sales Range: $25-49.9 Million
Emp.: 92
Liquefied Petroleum Gas Distr
N.A.I.C.S.: 424720
Jose Hernandez *(Gen Mgr)*

Repsol Capital, S.L. (1)
Paseo Castellana 278, Madrid, Spain
Tel.: (34) 913483190
Financial Management Services
N.A.I.C.S.: 523999

Repsol Chemical (U.K.) Ltd. (1)
24 Trosvenor Garden, London, SW1W 0DH, United Kingdom (100%)
Tel.: (44) 2077302044
Web Site: http://www.repsolypf.com
Sales Range: $25-49.9 Million
Emp.: 10
Energy Exploration
N.A.I.C.S.: 324110

Repsol Chemie Deutschland (1)
Colmarer Str 11, 60528, Frankfurt am Main, Germany (100%)
Tel.: (49) 696109320
Web Site: http://www.repsolypf.com
Sales Range: $25-49.9 Million
Emp.: 10
Energy Exploration
N.A.I.C.S.: 324110

Repsol Comercial, S.A.C. (1)
Avenida Victor Andres Belaunde 147, San Isidro, Lima, Peru
Tel.: (51) 1 215 6225
Lubricant & Oil Distr
N.A.I.C.S.: 424720

Repsol Directo, S.A. (1)
Mendez Alvaro 44, 28045, Madrid, Spain
Tel.: (34) 901212021
Web Site: http://www.repsol.com
Oil & Petroleum Products Distr
N.A.I.C.S.: 424720

Repsol Exploracao Brasil, Ltda. (1)
Av Brigadeiro Faria Lima 3729 5th Floor Office 502, Itaim Bibi, Sao Paulo, 04538-905, Brazil
Tel.: (55) 112 505 9349
Petrochemical Mfr
N.A.I.C.S.: 325110

Repsol Exploracion (1)
Ave Esparta Centro Empressarial Bahia Pozulo 2nd Fl, Puerta La Cruz, Barcelona, 6001, Ancoadegue, Venezuela
Tel.: (58) 2812625700
Web Site: http://www.repsol.com
Sales Range: $50-74.9 Million
Emp.: 200
Energy Exploration
N.A.I.C.S.: 324110

Repsol Exploracion Algerie, S.A. (1)
Hotel Sofitel 172 Rue Hassiba, Ben Bouali, Algeria (99.4%)
Tel.: (213) 692022
Oil & Gas Exploration & Production
N.A.I.C.S.: 211120

Repsol Exploracion, S.A. (1)
Paseo de la Castellana 278-280, 28046, Madrid, Spain (100%)
Tel.: (34) 913488119
Web Site: http://www.repsol.com
Sales Range: $200-249.9 Million
Emp.: 736
The Prospection & Production of Hydrocarbons in Spain & Abroad
N.A.I.C.S.: 325110

Subsidiary (Non-US):

Repsol Ecuador, S.A. (2)
Av Isabela La Catolica Lamb Cordero N340, Planta Baja, Quito, Ecuador
Tel.: (593) 2 2976 600
Web Site: http://www.repsol.com.ec
Oil & Gas Exploration Services

INTERNATIONAL PUBLIC

N.A.I.C.S.: 213112

Repsol Exploracion Colombia, S.A. (2)
Calle 77# 7-44 Edificio Torre 7 77 Floor 13, Bogota, Colombia
Tel.: (57) 17051999
Web Site: http://www.repsol.com
Sales Range: $50-74.9 Million
Emp.: 6
Oil & Gas Exploration Services
N.A.I.C.S.: 213112

Repsol Exploracion Kazakhstan, S.A. (2)
Arman Business Centre Sary Arka Av 6 Office 630, Nur-Sultan, 010000, Kazakhstan
Tel.: (7) 317 2990189
Oil & Gas Exploration Services
N.A.I.C.S.: 213112

Repsol Exploracion Peru, S.A. (2)
Avda Camino Real, 159, Oficina 502, San Isidro, Peru (100%)
Tel.: (51) 14419986
Web Site: http://www.repsol.com
Provider of Oil & Gas Exploration & Production Services
N.A.I.C.S.: 211120

Subsidiary (Domestic):

Repsol Exploracion Secure, S.A. (2)
Pso Castellana 280, 28046, Madrid, Spain
Tel.: (34) 913488100
Oil & Gas Exploration Services
N.A.I.C.S.: 213112

Subsidiary (Non-US):

Repsol Exploration Norge AS (2)
Stortingsgata 8, 0161, Oslo, Norway
Tel.: (47) 23 10 36 44
Oil & Gas Exploration Services
N.A.I.C.S.: 213112

Subsidiary (Domestic):

Repsol Oriente Medio, S.A. (2)
Paseo Castellana 280, Madrid, 28046, Spain
Tel.: (34) 917538001
Oil & Gas Exploration Services
N.A.I.C.S.: 213112

Subsidiary (US):

Repsol USA Holdings Corp (2)
2001 Timberloch Pl Ste 3000, The Woodlands, TX 77380-1335
Tel.: (281) 297-1001
Investment Management Service
N.A.I.C.S.: 523999

Subsidiary (Domestic):

Repsol E&P USA, Inc (3)
2001 Timberloch Pl Ste 3000, The Woodlands, TX 77380
Tel.: (281) 297-1000
Oil & Gas Exploration Services
N.A.I.C.S.: 213112

Repsol Energy North America Corp. (3)
2455 Technology Forest Blvd, The Woodlands, TX 77381
Tel.: (832) 442-1000
Web Site: http://www.repsolenergy.com
Natural Gas Distribution Services
N.A.I.C.S.: 221210
Phillip Ribbeck *(Pres-Comml Svcs)*

Repsol Greece Ionian, S.L. (1)
C/ Mendez Alvaro 44, 28045, Madrid, Spain
Tel.: (34) 91 753 8100
Petrochemical Mfr
N.A.I.C.S.: 325110

Repsol Italia S.p.A. (1)
Via Caldera 21, 20153, Milan, Italy
Tel.: (39) 024093391
Web Site: http://www.repsol.com
Sales Range: $50-74.9 Million
Emp.: 24
Representative Office
N.A.I.C.S.: 211120

Repsol Marketing, S.A.C. (1)
Av Victor A Belaunde 147 Piso 3 Torre Real V Of 301, San Isidro, 27, Lima, Peru

AND PRIVATE COMPANIES **REPSOL, S.A.**

Tel.: (51) 1 2156225
Web Site: http://www.repsol.com
Petroleum Product Distr
N.A.I.C.S.: 424720

Repsol Morocco (1)
Castellane 280 4th Floor B, Madrid, 28046, Spain
Tel.: (34) 91 753 0902
Web Site: http://www.repsol.com
Petroleum Refinery & Distr
N.A.I.C.S.: 324110

Repsol Nuevas Energias, S.A. (1)
Paseo Castellana 278, Madrid, 28046, Spain
Tel.: (34) 913488100
Oil & Gas Exploration Services
N.A.I.C.S.: 213112

Repsol Oil & Gas Canada Inc. (1)
2000 888 - 3rd St S W, Calgary, T2P 5C5, AB, Canada
Tel.: (403) 237-1234
Web Site: https://www.repsol.ca
Rev.: $1,831,000,000
Assets: $11,638,000,000
Liabilities: $6,419,000,000
Net Worth: $5,219,000,000
Earnings: ($740,000,000)
Emp.: 1,940
Fiscal Year-end: 12/31/2016
Oil & Gas Producer & Distr
N.A.I.C.S.: 211120
Luis Cabra Duenas *(Vice Chm & CEO)*

Subsidiary (US):

FEI Shale L.P. (2)
50 Pennwood Pl, Warrendale, PA 15086
Tel.: (403) 237-4840
Oil & Gas Exploration Services
N.A.I.C.S.: 213112

FEX L.P. (2)
3601 C St Ste 370, Anchorage, AK 99503
Tel.: (907) 339-5493
Rev.: $170,000
Emp.: 2
Oil & Gas Exploration Services
N.A.I.C.S.: 213112
James W. Buckee *(Principal)*

Subsidiary (Domestic):

Fortuna (US) L.P. (2)
888 Third Street Southwest Suite 2000, Calgary, T2P 5C5, AB, Canada
Oil & Gas Exploration Services
N.A.I.C.S.: 213112

Fortuna Exploration LLC (2)
888 Third Street Sothwest Suite 2000, Calgary, T2P 5C5, AB, Canada
Oil & Gas Exploration Services
N.A.I.C.S.: 213112

Subsidiary (Non-US):

Oleum Insurance Company, Limited (2)
20-22 Bedford Row, London, WC1R 4JS, United Kingdom
Insurance Companies
N.A.I.C.S.: 524210

Subsidiary (Domestic):

Repsol Central Alberta Partnership (2)
888 Third Street Southwest Suite 2000, Calgary, T2P 5C5, AB, Canada
Oil & Gas Exploration Services
N.A.I.C.S.: 213112

Repsol Groundbirch Partnership (2)
888 Third Street Southwest Suite 2000, Calgary, T2P 5C5, AB, Canada
Oil & Gas Exploration Services
N.A.I.C.S.: 213112

Subsidiary (Non-US):

Rift Oil LImited (2)
17 Hanover Square, London, W1S 1HU, United Kingdom
Tel.: (44) 2079178500
Emp.: 14
Oil & Gas Exploration Services
N.A.I.C.S.: 213112
David Smith *(Sec)*

TE Holding SARL (2)
3 Rue Marcel Fischbach, Luxembourg, 1547, Luxembourg
Tel.: (352) 1111111
Holding Company
N.A.I.C.S.: 551112

Subsidiary (Domestic):

TLM Finance Corp. (2)
888 Third Street Southwest Suite 2000, Calgary, T2P 5C5, AB, Canada
Finance Services
N.A.I.C.S.: 522320

Subsidiary (Non-US):

Talisman (Asia) Limited (2)
Indonesian Stock Exchange Building Tower 1 11th Floor, Sudirman Central Business District Jl.Jend Sudirman Kavling 52-53, Jakarta, 12920, Indonesia (100%)
Tel.: (62) 21 515 1601
Web Site: http://www.talismanasia.com
Sales Range: $50-74.9 Million
Emp.: 30
Fuel & Energy Services
N.A.I.C.S.: 211120

Talisman (Colombia) Oil & Gas Ltd. (2)
Carrera 7 North 77-07 Piso 12, Bogota, 110111, Colombia
Tel.: (57) 1 640 5552
Web Site: http://www.talisman-energy.com
Oil & Gas Exploration Services
N.A.I.C.S.: 213112

Talisman (Jambi Merang) Limited (2)
Suite 1 3rd Floor 11-12, St James's Square, London, SW1Y 4LB, United Kingdom
Tel.: (44) 2078232626
Oil & Gas Exploration Services
N.A.I.C.S.: 213112

Talisman (Jambi) Limited (2)
20-22 Bedford Row, London, WC1R 4JS, United Kingdom
Oil & Gas Exploration Services
N.A.I.C.S.: 213112
Luis Antonio Garcia Sanchez *(Dir)*

Talisman (Sageri) Ltd. (2)
Indonesian Stock Exchange Building Tower 1 11th Floor, Sudirman Central Business District Jl.Jend Sudirman Kavling 52-53, Jakarta, 12920, Indonesia
Tel.: (62) 621 515 1601
Fuel & Energy Services
N.A.I.C.S.: 211120

Talisman Energy Norway AS (2)
Verven 4 Sentrum 2000, 4003, Stavanger, Norway
Tel.: (47) 5200 2000
Oil & Gas Production
N.A.I.C.S.: 213111

Talisman Energy Sweden AB (2)
Hovslagargatan 5, Stockholm, 11148, Sweden
Tel.: (46) 84 40 54 50
Oil & Gas Exploration Services
N.A.I.C.S.: 213112

Talisman Holding International SARL (2)
3 Rue Marcel Fishbach, Luxembourg, 1855, Luxembourg
Privater Equity Firm
N.A.I.C.S.: 551112

Talisman Indonesia Ltd. (2)
Indonesian Stock Exchange Building Tower 1 11th Floor, Sudirman Central Business District Jl.Jend Sudirman Kavling 52-53, Jakarta, 12920, Indonesia
Tel.: (62) 621 515 1601
Web Site: http://www.talismanasia.com
Fuel & Energy Services
N.A.I.C.S.: 211120

Talisman UK (South East Sumatra) Limited (2)
20-22 Bedford Row, London, WC1R 4JS, United Kingdom
Oil & Gas Exploration Services
N.A.I.C.S.: 213112
Luis Antonio Garcia Sanchez *(Dir)*

Subsidiary (Domestic):

Talisman Wild River Partnership (2)
888 Third Street Southwest Suite 2000, Calgary, T2P 5C5, AB, Canada
Oil & Gas Exploration Services
N.A.I.C.S.: 213112

Subsidiary (Non-US):

Thang Long Joint Operating Company (2)
6th Floor Riverbank Place Building 3C Ton Duc Thang Street, District 1, Ho Chi Minh City, 700000, Vietnam
Tel.: (84) 283 823 0234
Web Site: https://www.tljoc.com.vn
Oil & Gas Exploration Services
N.A.I.C.S.: 213112

Subsidiary (Domestic):

Triad Oil Manitoba Ltd. (2)
333 Fifth Avenue Southwest, Calgary, T2P 3B6, AB, Canada
Tel.: (403) 237-1234
Oil & Gas Exploration Services
N.A.I.C.S.: 213112

Vietnam American Exploration Company LLC (2)
888 Third Street Southwest Suite 2000, Calgary, T2P 5C5, AB, Canada
Privater Equity Firm
N.A.I.C.S.: 551112

Repsol Petroleo, S.A. (1)
Paseo De La Castellana 278, 28046, Madrid, Spain (99.9%)
Tel.: (34) 913488100
Web Site: http://www.repsol.com
Acquisition & Transport of Crude Oil Sale & Basic Petrochemical Products; Refining
N.A.I.C.S.: 486110

Subsidiary (Domestic):

Repsol Comercial de Productos Petroliferos, S.A. (2)
Glorieta Mar Caribe 1 Edificio Tucuman-3a Planta, Madrid, 28043, Spain
Tel.: (34) 91 753 87 54
Oil & Gas Exploration Services
N.A.I.C.S.: 213112

Repsol Electrica de Distribucion, S.L. (2)
Paseo Castellana 278 - 280, Madrid, Spain
Tel.: (34) 913488100
Electric Power Distribution Services
N.A.I.C.S.: 221122

Repsol Lubricantes y Especialidades, S.A. (2)
Glorieta Mar Caribe 1, Madrid, 28043, Spain
Tel.: (34) 913488100
Sales Range: $100-124.9 Million
Emp.: 400
Petroleum Lubricant Mfr
N.A.I.C.S.: 324191
Patricia Borghini *(Mng Dir)*

Repsol Portuguesa, S.A. (1)
Av Jose Malhoa 16B, 1099-091, Lisbon, Portugal
Tel.: (351) 213119000
Web Site: https://www.repsol.com
Oil & Gas Exploration Services
N.A.I.C.S.: 213112

Subsidiary (Domestic):

Repsol Directo LDA (2)
Avenida Jose Malhoa 16, Lisbon, 1070-159, Portugal
Tel.: (351) 213119374
Web Site: http://www.repsoldirecto.com
Emp.: 6
Petroleum Product Distr
N.A.I.C.S.: 424720
Carlos Sousa *(Mgr)*

Repsol Portugal Petroleo e Denvados Lda. (2)
Rua Mario Dionisio 2 2A 3 Planta, 2795, Linda-a-Velha, Portugal (100%)
Tel.: (351) 214149000
Web Site: http://www.repsolportugal.com

Sales Range: $25-49.9 Million
Emp.: 45
Commercializing of Oil Derivatives
N.A.I.C.S.: 325110

Repsol Quimica S.A. (1)
San Siro Uffici No 5 2 Via Caldera 21, 20153, Milan, Italy (100%)
Tel.: (39) 024093391
Web Site: http://www.repsol.com
Sales Range: $25-49.9 Million
Emp.: 7
Petroleum Products
N.A.I.C.S.: 324110

Repsol Quimica, S.A. (1)
C/ Mendez Alvaro 44, 28045, Madrid, Spain (100%)
Tel.: (34) 91 753 8100
Sales Range: $50-74.9 Million
Emp.: 200
Mfr & Sale of Petrochemical Derivative Products.
N.A.I.C.S.: 325110

Subsidiary (Domestic):

General Quimica, S.A. (2)
Ctra Miranda de Ebro-Puentelarra Km 5, PO Box 13, Miranda de Ebro Zubillaga, 9200, Lantaron, Alava, Spain
Tel.: (34) 945 33 21 45
Web Site: http://www.gequisa.es
Sales Range: $50-74.9 Million
Emp.: 20
Specialty Chemicals Mfr
N.A.I.C.S.: 325998
Fedro Santamaria *(Mng Dir)*

Polidux, S.A. (2)
Carretera Nacional 240 Km 147, 22400, Monzon, Huesca, Spain
Tel.: (34) 97 441 8100
Web Site: http://www.repsol.com
Emp.: 88
Plastics Product Mfr
N.A.I.C.S.: 326199

Subsidiary (Non-US):

Repsol Polimeros LDA (2)
Apartado 41 Monte Feio, Sines, 7520-954, Portugal
Tel.: (351) 269 860 100
Sales Range: $125-149.9 Million
Emp.: 50
Chemical Products Distr
N.A.I.C.S.: 424690
Jockeng Garcea *(Gen Mgr)*

Repsol Sinopec Brasil, S.A. (1)
Praia de Botafogo 300 - 7 andar Botafogo, Rio de Janeiro, 22250-040, Brazil
Tel.: (55) 212 559 7000
Oil & Gas Distr
N.A.I.C.S.: 424720

Repsol Sinopec Resources UK Ltd. (1)
20-22 Bedford Row, London, WC1R 4JS, United Kingdom (51%)
Tel.: (44) 1224352500
Oil & Gas Exploration Services
N.A.I.C.S.: 213112
Adam Sheikh *(VP-Decommissioning & Energy Transition)*

Repsol Trading Peru, S.A.C. (1)
Av Victor Andres Belaunde 147, San Isidro, Lima, Peru
Tel.: (51) 1 215 6225
Oil & Gas Mfr
N.A.I.C.S.: 333132

Repsol Trading Singapore Pte. Ltd. (1)
14 Marina Bay Financial Centre Tower 2, Singapore, 018983, Singapore
Tel.: (65) 6 808 1000
Oil & Gas Mfr
N.A.I.C.S.: 333132

Repsol Trading USA Corporation (1)
337 Daniel Zenker Dr, Horseheads, NY 14845
Tel.: (607) 562-4000
Oil & Gas Mfr
N.A.I.C.S.: 333132

Repsol U.K. Ltd. (1)
5th Floor 40 Princes Street, Edinburgh, EH2

REPSOL, S.A.

Repsol, S.A.—(Continued)
2BY, United Kingdom
Tel.: (44) 131 557 7101
Petrochemical Mfr
N.A.I.C.S.: 325110

Repsol Venezuela, S.A. (1)
Av Principal La Castellana c/ Calle Jose
Angel Lamas Torre La Casellan, Piso 13
Ofc 13-A, Caracas, Venezuela
Tel.: (58) 281 262 5712
Sales Range: $100-124.9 Million
Emp.: 200
Oil & Gas Exploration Services
N.A.I.C.S.: 213112

Subsidiary (Domestic):

Repsol Venezuela Gas, S.A. (2)
Pozuelos Piso 1 Av Nueva Esparta C/C
Cerro Sur, Barcelona, 6001, Venezuela
Tel.: (58) 281 262 5712
Sales Range: $50-74.9 Million
Emp.: 10
Oil & Gas Exploration Services
N.A.I.C.S.: 213112

Saint John LNG Development Company Ltd. (1)
2530 Red Head Road, PO Box 2029, Saint John, NB, Canada
Tel.: (506) 638-1300
Web Site: https://www.saintjohnlng.com
Liquefied Natural Gas Distr
N.A.I.C.S.: 486210

Societat Catalana de Petrolis S.A. (1)
Avenida Diagonal 605 4th Floor 6th St, 08028, Barcelona, Spain
Tel.: (34) 934005070
Web Site: http://www.petrocat.com
Gasoline Service Stations
N.A.I.C.S.: 457120

Tierra Solutions Inc. (1)
2 Tower Ctr Blvd Fl 10, East Brunswick, NJ 08816-1100
Tel.: (732) 247-3400
Sales Range: $50-74.9 Million
Emp.: 20
Oil & Gas Exploration Services
N.A.I.C.S.: 213112
David Rabbe *(Pres)*

YPF Guyana, Ltd. (1)
44 B High Street, Kingston, Georgetown, 97354, Guyana
Tel.: (592) 226 1810
Oil & Gas Exploration Services
N.A.I.C.S.: 213112

REPUBLIC BANK (GHANA) LIMITED
No 35 Sixth Avenue North Ridge, PO Box CT 4603, Cantonments, Accra, Ghana
Tel.: (233) 302429577
Web Site: https://www.republicghana.com
Year Founded: 1990
RBGH—(GHA)
Rev.: $79,603,612
Assets: $623,869,036
Liabilities: $515,706,634
Net Worth: $108,162,402
Earnings: $9,611,515
Emp.: 1,162
Fiscal Year-end: 12/31/20
Banking, Investment & Mortgage Loan Services
N.A.I.C.S.: 522110
Beatrix Ama Amoah *(Sec)*

REPUBLIC FINANCIAL HOLDINGS LIMITED
Republic House 9-17 Park Street, PO Box 1153, Port of Spain, Trinidad & Tobago
Tel.: (868) 625 4411 TT
Web Site: http://www.republictt.com
Rev.: $643,284,082
Assets: $12,706,159,893
Liabilities: $11,074,859,071
Net Worth: $1,631,300,822
Earnings: $249,181,442
Emp.: 5,816
Fiscal Year-end: 09/30/19
Bank Holding Company
N.A.I.C.S.: 551111
Anna-Maria Garcia-Brooks *(Gen Mgr-Grp HR)*

Subsidiaries:

Cayman National Corporation Ltd. (1)
Peter A Tomkins Building 200 Elgin Avenue, PO Box 1097, Georgetown, KY1-1102, Grand Cayman, Cayman Islands **(74.99%)**
Tel.: (345) 949 4655
Web Site: http://www.caymannational.com
Bank Holding Company; Financial Services
N.A.I.C.S.: 551111
Truman Bodden *(Chm)*

Subsidiary (Non-US):

Cayman National (Dubai) Ltd. (2)
Level 4 The Gate Building West Office 401, PO Box 506754, Dubai International Financial Centre, Dubai, United Arab Emirates
Tel.: (971) 43276695
Commercial Banking Services
N.A.I.C.S.: 522110

Cayman National Bank & Trust Company (Isle of Man) Ltd. (2)
Cayman National House 4-8 Hope Street, London, IM1 1AQ, Isle of Man, United Kingdom
Tel.: (44) 1624 646900
Commercial Banking Services
N.A.I.C.S.: 522110
Nigel Gautrey *(Mng Dir)*

Subsidiary (Domestic):

Cayman National Trust Co., Ltd. (2)
Suite 6201 62 Forum Lane, PO Box 30239, Camana Bay, KY1-1201, Grand Cayman, Cayman Islands
Tel.: (345) 6409267
Trust Management Services
N.A.I.C.S.: 523940
Nigel Gautrey *(Mng Dir)*

Republic Bank (BVI) Limited (1)
PO Box 434, Wickham's Cay 1 Road Town, Tortola, VG1110, Virgin Islands (British)
Tel.: (284) 494 2526
Web Site: http://www.republicbankbvi.com
Commercial Banking
N.A.I.C.S.: 522110
Marion Blyden *(Mng Dir)*

Republic Bank (Barbados) Limited (1)
Independence Square, Bridgetown, Barbados **(98.6%)**
Tel.: (246) 2227 2700
Web Site: http://www.republicbarbados.com
Sales Range: $200-249.9 Million
Emp.: 500
Banking Services
N.A.I.C.S.: 522110
Sasha Shillingford *(Gen Counsel & Sec)*

Republic Bank (EC) Limited (1)
6 Wm Peter Boulevard, PO Box 301, Castries, Saint Lucia
Tel.: (758) 456 2100
Web Site: http://republicbankec.com
Commericial Banking
N.A.I.C.S.: 522110
Michelle Palmer-Keizer *(Mng Dir)*

Subsidiary (Non-US):

Republic Bank (Anguilla) Limited (2)
Box 250, The Valley, Anguilla, Anguilla **(100%)**
Tel.: (264) 497 3333
Web Site: http://www.republicbankanguilla.com
Commericial Banking
N.A.I.C.S.: 522110
Darrelle Harrigan *(Country Mgr)*

Representative Office (Non-US):

Republic Bank (EC) Limited - Dominica (2)
28-Hillsborough Street, Roseau, Dominica
Tel.: (767) 4485800
Web Site: http://www.republicbankdominica.com
Commericial Banking
N.A.I.C.S.: 522110
Gina Severin *(Country Mgr)*

Republic Bank (EC) Limited - St. Kitts & Nevis (2)
Box 433, Basseterre, Saint Kitts & Nevis
Tel.: (869) 4654141
Web Site: http://www.republicbankstkitts.com
Commericial Banking
N.A.I.C.S.: 522110
Pamela Herbert-Daniel *(Country Mgr)*

Division (Domestic):

Republic Bank (EC) Limited - St. Lucia (2)
6 William Peter Boulevard, Castries, Saint Lucia
Tel.: (758) 4562100
Web Site: http://www.republicbankstlucia.com
Commericial Banking
N.A.I.C.S.: 522110
Gordon Julien *(Country Mgr)*

Representative Office (Non-US):

Republic Bank (EC) Limited - St. Vincent & Grenadines (2)
Tel.: (784) 4571601
Web Site: http://www.republicbankstvincent.com
Commericial Banking
N.A.I.C.S.: 522110
Gregory Bardouille *(Country Mgr)*

Subsidiary (Non-US):

Republic Bank (St. Maarten) N.V. (2)
Philipsburg Back Street #62, Philipsburg, Saint Martin **(100%)**
Tel.: (721) 542 2262
Web Site: http://www.republicbankstmaarten.com
Commericial Banking
N.A.I.C.S.: 522110
Sterl Lyons *(Gen Mng Dir)*

Republic Bank (Grenada) Limited (1)
Maurice Bishop Highway, Grand Anse, Saint George's, Grenada **(84.9%)**
Tel.: (473) 4442265
Web Site: http://republicgrenada.com
Rev.: $25,171,456
Assets: $663,807,855
Liabilities: $581,911,270
Net Worth: $81,896,585
Earnings: $3,067,404
Emp.: 210
Fiscal Year-end: 09/30/2020
Commericial Banking
N.A.I.C.S.: 522110
Gregory I. Thomson *(Chm)*

Republic Bank (Guyana) Limited (1)
155-156 New Market Street, North Cummingsburg, Georgetown, Guyana **(51%)**
Tel.: (592) 2237938
Web Site: http://www.republicguyana.com
Rev.: $42,783,167
Assets: $848,560,312
Liabilities: $742,002,675
Net Worth: $106,557,636
Earnings: $18,113,629
Emp.: 655
Fiscal Year-end: 09/30/2019
Banking Services
N.A.I.C.S.: 522110
Nigel Baptiste *(Chm)*

Republic Bank (Suriname) N.V. (1)
Kerkplein 1, PO Box 1836, Paramaribo, Suriname
Tel.: (597) 471555
Web Site: http://www.republicbanksr.com
Sales Range: $10-24.9 Million
Emp.: 180
Commericial & Investment Banking
N.A.I.C.S.: 522110

Republic Bank Trinidad & Tobago (Barbados) Limited (1)
59 Independence Square, Port of Spain, Trinidad & Tobago
Tel.: (868) 627 3617
Bank Holding Company; Offshore Banking Services
N.A.I.C.S.: 551111

Subsidiary (Non-US):

Republic Bank (Cayman) Limited (2)
Suite 308 Smith Rd Centre 150 Smith Rd, PO Box 2004, Georgetown, KY1-1104, Cayman Islands **(100%)**
Tel.: (345) 949 7844
Offshore Banking Services
N.A.I.C.S.: 523150
Gary Darwent *(Mng Dir)*

Republic Finance & Merchant Bank Limited (1)
9-17 Park Street, PO Box 1153, Port of Spain, Trinidad & Tobago
Tel.: (868) 6254411
Web Site: http://www.republictt.com
Banking Services
N.A.I.C.S.: 522110

Subsidiary (Domestic):

London Street Project Company Limited (2)
Republic House 9-17 Park Street, Port of Spain, Trinidad & Tobago
Tel.: (868) 623 1056
Web Site: http://www.republictt.com
Specialized Project Financing
N.A.I.C.S.: 525990

Republic Finance & Trust (Barbados) Corporation (1)
Mezzanine Floor, Bridgetown, Saint Michael, Barbados
Tel.: (246) 246 431 1262
Financial Services
N.A.I.C.S.: 523999

Republic Life Insurance Company Limited (1)
2nd Floor Corner Murray Street and Ariapita Avenue, Woodbrook, Port of Spain, Trinidad & Tobago
Tel.: (868) 6253617
Banking Services
N.A.I.C.S.: 522110
Robert Soverall *(Mng Dir)*

Republic Securities Limited (1)
2nd Floor Promenade Centre 72 Independence Square, Port of Spain, Trinidad & Tobago **(100%)**
Tel.: (868) 623 0435
Web Site: http://www.rsltt.com
Sales Range: $50-74.9 Million
Emp.: 12
Stock Broking Firm
N.A.I.C.S.: 523150

REPUBLIC GLASS HOLDINGS CORPORATION
6F Republic Glass Bldg 196 Salcedo St, Legaspi Village, Makati, 1229, Philippines
Tel.: (63) 288175011
Web Site: https://www.rghc.net
REG—(PHI)
Rev.: $1,184,003
Assets: $48,003,231
Liabilities: $4,089,429
Net Worth: $43,913,803
Earnings: $929,367
Emp.: 6
Fiscal Year-end: 12/31/23
Purchase, Lease & Sale Property Services
N.A.I.C.S.: 561612
Florence C. Wong *(CFO, Officer-Information & Data Protection & VP)*

REPUBLIC HEALTHCARE LTD.
1 Scotts Road 16-05 Shaw Centre, Singapore, 228208, Singapore
Tel.: (65) 69261678 Ky
Web Site: http://www.republichealthcare.asia
Year Founded: 2010

8357—(HKG)
Rev.: $7,575,834
Assets: $11,848,015
Liabilities: $2,189,972
Net Worth: $9,658,043
Earnings: ($647,670)
Emp.: 37
Fiscal Year-end: 12/31/23
Healtcare Services
N.A.I.C.S.: 621491
Alan Cher Sen Tan *(Chm & Compliance Officer)*

Subsidiaries:

Dtap @ Duo Pte. Ltd. (1)
7 Fraser St B3-18 DUO Galleria Bugis MRT, Singapore, 189356, Singapore
Tel.: (65) 69765023
Clinical Healthcare Services
N.A.I.C.S.: 621999

Dtap @ Holland V Pte. Ltd. (1)
15B Lorong Liput Next to Holland Piazza, Singapore, 277730, Singapore
Tel.: (65) 62351339
Clinical Healthcare Services
N.A.I.C.S.: 621999

Dtap @ Somerset Pte. Ltd. (1)
1 Grange Road 10-08 Orchard Building Office Tower, Singapore, 239693, Singapore
Tel.: (65) 62620762
Clinical Healthcare Services
N.A.I.C.S.: 621999

S Aesthetics Clinic Pte. Ltd. (1)
1 Scotts Road 03-02 Shaw Centre, Singapore, 228208, Singapore
Tel.: (65) 62350338
Web Site: https://saestheticsclinic.com
Clinical Healthcare Services
N.A.I.C.S.: 621999

REPUBLIC INSURANCE COMPANY LIMITED
HR Bhaban 9th Floor 26/1 Kakrail, Dhaka, 1000, Bangladesh
Tel.: (880) 58313334
Web Site: https://www.riclbd.com
REPUBLIC—(DHA)
Rev.: $1,703,449
Assets: $15,130,404
Liabilities: $6,404,369
Net Worth: $8,726,035
Earnings: $1,101,950
Fiscal Year-end: 12/31/23
Fire, Marine Cargo, Marine Hull, Motor & Engineering Insurance Services
N.A.I.C.S.: 524126
Mohammad Hanif Chowdhury *(Chm)*

REPUBLICA HOLDING AD
16 Srebarna Street Park Lane Office Building, 1000, Sofia, Bulgaria
Tel.: (359) 24521932
Web Site: https://www.republika-ad.com
HREP—(BUL)
Sales Range: Less than $1 Million
Holding Company
N.A.I.C.S.: 551112

REPUESTOS PARA EQUIPO PESADO F.M. S.A.
350 metros norte de la plaza deportes de La Uruca, San Jose, Costa Rica
Tel.: (506) 22577655   CR
Transportation Services
N.A.I.C.S.: 485999

RES GESTAE SOCIMI, S.A.
Marques de Larios 6 3rd left, 29005, Malaga, Spain
Tel.: (34) 952211711
Web Site: https://www.regestae.com
Year Founded: 2020
MLJDL—(EUR)
Rev.: $2,193,386
Assets: $18,874,505
Liabilities: $2,457,664
Net Worth: $16,416,841
Earnings: $1,615,082
Fiscal Year-end: 12/31/21
Real Estate Investment Services
N.A.I.C.S.: 531190

RES PUBLICA CONSULTING GROUP INC.
1155 Metcalfe Street Suite 800, Montreal, H3B 0C1, QC, Canada
Tel.: (514) 843-2343
Web Site: http://www.respublica.ca
Holding Company; Public Relations
N.A.I.C.S.: 551112
Andrew T. Molson *(Chm & Partner)*

Subsidiaries:

Avenir Global, Inc (1)
1155 Metcalfe Street Suite 800, Montreal, H3B 0C1, QC, Canada
Tel.: (514) 843-2343
Web Site: https://avenir.global
Holding Company
N.A.I.C.S.: 551112
Andrew T. Molson *(Chm & Partner)*

Subsidiary (Domestic):

NATIONAL Public Relations Inc. (2)
1155 Metcalfe Street Suite 800, Montreal, H3B 0C1, QC, Canada
Tel.: (514) 843-7171
Web Site: http://www.national.ca
Emp.: 275
Public Relations
N.A.I.C.S.: 541820
Andrew T. Molson *(Chm)*

Branch (Domestic):

NATIONAL Public Relations (3)
220 Laurier Avenue West Suite 610, Ottawa, K1P 5Z9, ON, Canada
Tel.: (613) 233-1699
Web Site: http://www.national.ca
Public Relations
N.A.I.C.S.: 541820

NATIONAL Public Relations (3)
140 Grande Allee East Suite 670, Quebec, G1R 5M8, QC, Canada
Tel.: (418) 648-1233
Web Site: http://www.national.ca
Emp.: 16
Public Relations Services
N.A.I.C.S.: 541820
Julie-Anne Vien *(Mng Partner)*

NATIONAL Public Relations (3)
320 Front Street West Suite 1600, Toronto, M5V 3B6, ON, Canada
Tel.: (416) 586-0180
Web Site: http://www.national.ca
Public Relations
N.A.I.C.S.: 541820
Martin Daraiche *(Mng Partner)*

NATIONAL Public Relations (3)
1600-675 West Hastings Street, Box 34, Vancouver, V6B 1N2, BC, Canada
Tel.: (604) 684-6655
Web Site: http://www.national.ca
Emp.: 20
Public Relations
N.A.I.C.S.: 541820
Mark Seland *(Mng Partner)*

Branch (US):

NATIONAL Public Relations (3)
230 Park Ave S 3rd Fl, New York, NY 10003-1566
Tel.: (212) 614-4124
Web Site: http://www.national.ca
Public Relations
N.A.I.C.S.: 541820
Mark Bonacci *(Mng Partner)*

Branch (Domestic):

NATIONAL Public Relations (3)
330 5th Avenue SW Suite 1920, Calgary, T2P 0L4, AB, Canada
Tel.: (403) 531-0331
Web Site: http://www.national.ca
Public Relations
N.A.I.C.S.: 541820

Mark Seland *(Mng Partner)*
NATIONAL Public Relations (3)
931 Fort St 4th Fl, Victoria, V8W 2C4, BC, Canada
Tel.: (250) 361-1713
Web Site: http://www.national.ca
Public Relations
N.A.I.C.S.: 541820

NATIONAL Public Relations (3)
1625 Grafton Street Suite 1600 South Tower, Halifax, B3J 0E8, NS, Canada
Tel.: (902) 420-1860
Web Site: http://www.mtlpr.ca
Emp.: 28
Public Relations
N.A.I.C.S.: 541820

Subsidiary (Non-US):

NATIONAL Public Relations (3)
Hill House Heron Sq, Richmond, TW9 1EP, Surrey, United Kingdom
Tel.: (44) 208 439 9459
Sales Range: $75-99.9 Million
Public Relations
N.A.I.C.S.: 541820

Subsidiary (Domestic):

National Equicom, Inc. (3)
320 Front St West Suite 1600, Toronto, M5V 3B6, ON, Canada
Tel.: (416) 815-0700
Web Site: http://www.nationalequicom.com
Emp.: 400
Investor Relations Services
N.A.I.C.S.: 541820
Ronald Alepian *(Gen Mgr)*

Subsidiary (US):

SHIFT Communications (3)
275 Washington St, Newton, MA 02458
Tel.: (617) 779-1800
Web Site: http://www.shiftcomm.com
Public Relations Agency
N.A.I.C.S.: 541820
Jim Joyal *(Partner)*

Branch (Domestic):

SHIFT Communications - New York (4)
125 5-Ave, New York, NY 10003
Tel.: (646) 756-3700
Web Site: http://www.shiftcomm.com
Advetising Agency
N.A.I.C.S.: 541810

SHIFT Communications - San Francisco (4)
275 Sacramento St, San Francisco, CA 94111
Tel.: (415) 591-8400
Web Site: http://www.shiftcomm.com
Public Relations Agency
N.A.I.C.S.: 541820
Nathan Beers *(VP)*

RESAAS SERVICES INC.
Suite 1530-401 West Georgia Street, Vancouver, V6B 5A1, BC, Canada
Tel.: (604) 558-2929   BC
Web Site: http://www.resaas.com
Year Founded: 2009
RSS—(OTCIQ)
Rev.: $513,776
Assets: $523,352
Liabilities: $548,573
Net Worth: ($25,221)
Earnings: ($2,174,996)
Fiscal Year-end: 12/31/20
Real Estate Internet Networking Services
N.A.I.C.S.: 531390
Thomas Rossiter *(Pres & CEO)*

RESAPHENE SUISSE AG
Rutistrasse 8b, 9325, Roggwil, Switzerland
Tel.: (41) 714500668
Web Site: http://www.resaphene.ch
Medical Equipment Mfr
N.A.I.C.S.: 339112

Subsidiaries:

Resaphene Deutschland GmbH (1)
Max-Stromeyer-Strasse 116, 78467, Konstanz, Germany
Tel.: (49) 7531716401027
Medical Tehnology Mfr
N.A.I.C.S.: 339112
Johann Keller *(Sls Mgr)*

Resaphene UK Ltd. (1)
20-22 Wenlock Road, London, N1 7GU, United Kingdom
Tel.: (44) 2032396853
Medical Tehnology Mfr
N.A.I.C.S.: 339112
Thomas Rauterkus *(CEO)*

Resaphene US LLC (1)
8 The Green Ste 5494, Dover, DE 19901
Tel.: (786) 600-1462
Medical Tehnology Mfr
N.A.I.C.S.: 339112
Thomas Rauterkus *(CEO)*

RESBUD SE
Jarvevana Tee 9-40, 11314, Tallinn, Estonia
Tel.: (372) 6027780
Web Site: http://www.resbud.pl
RES—(WAR)
Rev.: $11,908,537
Assets: $113,985,772
Liabilities: $43,601,880
Net Worth: $70,383,892
Earnings: $5,861,026
Fiscal Year-end: 12/31/23
Building Construction Services
N.A.I.C.S.: 236210
Krzysztof Dlugosz *(Chm-Mgmt Bd)*

RESERVE BANK OF FIJI
Reserve Bank Bldg Pratt St, Private Mail Bag, Suva, Fiji
Tel.: (679) 3313611
Web Site: http://www.rbf.gov.fj
Sales Range: $25-49.9 Million
Central Bank
N.A.I.C.S.: 521110
Lorraine Seeto *(Chief Mgr)*

RESERVE BANK OF INDIA
4th Floor RBI Byculla Office Building, PO Box 406, Opp Mumbai Central Railway Station Byculla, Mumbai, 400 008, India
Tel.: (91) 23022028
Web Site: http://www.rbi.org.in
Year Founded: 1935
Sales Range: $1-4.9 Billion
Emp.: 22,192
Banking Services
N.A.I.C.S.: 521110
Rakesh Mohan *(Vice Chm)*

Subsidiaries:

Bharatiya Reserve Bank Note Mudran Pvt. Ltd. (1)
No 3 & 4 Ist Phase Ist Stage BTM Layout Bannerghatta Road, Bengaluru, 560 029, Karnataka, India (100%)
Tel.: (91) 80 66602000
Web Site: http://www.brbnmpl.co.in
Banknote Printing Services
N.A.I.C.S.: 323111
Kaza Sudhakar *(Mng Dir)*

Deposit Insurance and Credit Guarantee Corporation (1)
Reserve Bank of India 2nd Floor Opp Mumbai Central Railway Station, Byculla, Mumbai, 400 008, India
Tel.: (91) 22 2308 4121
Web Site: http://www.dicgc.org.in
Credit Insurance Services
N.A.I.C.S.: 524126

National Housing Bank (1)
Core 5-A India Habitat Centre Lode Road, New Delhi, 110003, India
Tel.: (91) 11 2464 9031
Web Site: http://www.nhb.org.in
Emp.: 99

RESERVE BANK OF INDIA

Reserve Bank of India—(Continued)

Housing Financing
N.A.I.C.S.: 522310

RESERVE BANK OF MALAWI
Convention Dr City Centre, PO Box 30063, Lilongwe, 3, Malawi
Tel.: (265) 1770600
Web Site: http://www.rbm.mw
Year Founded: 1965
Sales Range: $200-249.9 Million
Emp.: 600
Central Bank
N.A.I.C.S.: 521110
Mary C. Nkosi *(Deputy Governor)*

RESERVE BANK OF NEW ZEALAND
2 The Terrace, PO Box 2498, Wellington, 6140, New Zealand
Tel.: (64) 44722029
Web Site: http://www.rbnz.govt.nz
Rev.: $410,646,990
Assets: $17,942,786,730
Liabilities: $16,171,157,490
Net Worth: $1,771,629,240
Earnings: $163,317,870
Emp.: 274
Fiscal Year-end: 06/30/19
Central Bank
N.A.I.C.S.: 521110
Mike Wolyncewicz *(CFO-Fin)*

RESERVE BANK OF VANUATU
PMB 9062, Port-Vila, Vanuatu
Tel.: (678) 23333
Web Site: http://www.rbv.gov.vu
Sales Range: $25-49.9 Million
Emp.: 74
Central Bank
N.A.I.C.S.: 521110

RESERVE BANK OF ZIMBABWE
80 Samora Machel Ave, PO Box 1283, Harare, Zimbabwe
Tel.: (263) 4703000
Web Site: http://www.rbz.co.zw
Year Founded: 1956
Sales Range: $450-499.9 Million
Emp.: 2,000
Central Bank
N.A.I.C.S.: 521110
G. Gono *(Chm)*

RESERVOIR LINK ENERGY BERHAD
E-33-01 Menara SUEZCAP 2 KL Gateway No 2 Jalan Kerinchi Gerbang, Kerinchi Lestari, 59200, Kuala Lumpur, Malaysia
Tel.: (60) 327112128   MY
Web Site: https://www.reservoirlink.com
Year Founded: 2008
RL—(KLS)
Rev.: $40,910,899
Assets: $34,143,047
Liabilities: $16,477,975
Net Worth: $17,665,071
Earnings: $379,683
Emp.: 164
Fiscal Year-end: 06/30/23
Oil & Gas Distribution Services
N.A.I.C.S.: 221210
Hassan Mohd Jamil *(CEO & Mng Dir)*

Subsidiaries:

Amsito Oilwell Services (Malaysia) Sdn. Bhd.   (1)
29-5 Menara 1MK No 1, Jalan Kiara, 50480, Kuala Lumpur, Malaysia
Tel.: (60) 362019969
Web Site: http://www.amsito.com
Wire Line Services
N.A.I.C.S.: 213112

Hassan Mohd Jami *(CEO)*

Reservoir Link (Labuan) Ltd.   (1)
Multi Bay No 6 and 7 Asian Supply Base Main Base, Rancha-Rancha Industrial Estate, 87017, Labuan, Malaysia
Tel.: (60) 87411696
Well Leak Repair Services
N.A.I.C.S.: 213112

Reservoir Link Sdn. Bhd.   (1)
D-2-13a Miri Times Square Marina Parkcity, 98000, Miri, Sarawak, Malaysia
Tel.: (60) 85427004
Well Services
N.A.I.C.S.: 213112

RESGEN LIMITED
919 Maker Chambers V, Nariman Point, Mumbai, 400021, India
Tel.: (91) 2222810181   In
Web Site: https://www.resgen.in
Year Founded: 2018
543805—(BOM)
Natural Gas Extraction Services
N.A.I.C.S.: 211130
Karan Bora *(CEO)*

RESHAM TEXTILE INDUSTRIES LIMITED
36 A - Lawrence Road, Lahore, Pakistan
Tel.: (92) 42 111767676
Web Site: http://www.reshamtextile.com
Rev.: $24,574,381
Assets: $15,740,737
Liabilities: $6,495,768
Net Worth: $9,244,969
Earnings: $434,068
Emp.: 907
Fiscal Year-end: 06/30/19
Textile Mfr
N.A.I.C.S.: 314999
Muhammad Ali Chaudhry *(CFO & Sec)*

RESIDENTIAL SECURE INCOME PLC
The Pavilions Bridgwater Road, Bristol, BS13 8FD, United Kingdom
Tel.: (44) 2073820900   UK
Year Founded: 2017
RESI—(LSE)
Rev.: $53,760,281
Assets: $529,122,492
Liabilities: $281,485,226
Net Worth: $247,637,266
Earnings: $15,234,976
Fiscal Year-end: 09/30/21
Real Estate Investment Trust Services
N.A.I.C.S.: 523940
Pete Redman *(Exec Dir)*

RESILIENT ASSET MANAGEMENT BV
de Cuserstraat 91 Amsterdam, Noord-Holland, 1081 CN, Netherlands
Tel.: (31) 901318342
Finance Leasing
N.A.I.C.S.: 532112

RESILIENT REIT LIMITED
4th Floor Rivonia Village Rivonia Boulevard, Rivonia, 2191, South Africa
Tel.: (27) 116126800
Web Site: https://www.resilient.co.za
RES—(JSE)
Rev.: $194,717,210
Assets: $1,944,109,867
Liabilities: $765,835,744
Net Worth: $1,178,274,122
Earnings: $182,680,243
Emp.: 30
Fiscal Year-end: 12/31/23

Investment Services
N.A.I.C.S.: 523999
Desmond de Beer *(CEO)*

Subsidiaries:

Diversified Property Fund Ltd   (1)
4th Fl Rivonia Blvd, Cnr Mutual Rd Rivonia Blvd, 2555, Johannesburg, South Africa
Tel.: (27) 116126800
Sales Range: $50-74.9 Million
Emp.: 60
Property Management Services
N.A.I.C.S.: 531311
David John Lewis *(Mng Dir)*

Subsidiary (Domestic):

Property Index Tracker Managers (Pty) Ltd.   (2)
4th Fl Rivonia Vlg, PO Box 2555, Cnr Mutual Rd Rivonia Blvd, Johannesburg, South Africa
Tel.: (27) 116126800
Web Site: http://www.proptrax.co.za
Property Management Services
N.A.I.C.S.: 531311

RESILUX NV
Damstraat 4, 9230, Wetteren, Belgium
Tel.: (32) 93657474   BE
Web Site: https://www.resilux.com
Year Founded: 1992
RES—(EUR)
Rev.: $460,694,400
Assets: $332,129,607
Liabilities: $136,937,706
Net Worth: $195,191,901
Earnings: $28,003,872
Emp.: 957
Fiscal Year-end: 12/31/20
Plastic Bottle Mfr & Distr
N.A.I.C.S.: 326160
Dirk De Cuyper *(Mng Dir)*

Subsidiaries:

Eastern Holding NV   (1)
Reukenwegel 40, 9070, Destelbergen, Belgium
Tel.: (32) 92300541
Investment Management Service
N.A.I.C.S.: 523940

Resilux America, LLC   (1)
265 John Brooks Rd, Pendergrass, GA 30567
Tel.: (706) 693-7110
Plastics Bottle Mfr
N.A.I.C.S.: 326160

Resilux Central Europe Packaging Kft.   (1)
Ipari Park Lot No 092/14, Tuzser, 4623, Budapest, Hungary
Tel.: (36) 45541050
Web Site: http://www.resilux.hu
Plastics Bottle Mfr
N.A.I.C.S.: 326160

Subsidiary (Non-US):

Resilux South East Europe srl.   (2)
B-dul Stefan Augustin Doinas 47 Bl L4 Sc B Ap 4, 310001, Arad, Romania
Tel.: (40) 25 721 3513
Plastic Bottle Distr
N.A.I.C.S.: 424610

Resilux Distribution LLC   (1)
Zoologicheskaya St 26 Build 2 Room IX, 123056, Moscow, 123056, Russia
Tel.: (7) 4957896397
Packaging Services
N.A.I.C.S.: 561910

Resilux Iberica Packaging S.A.u.   (1)
Ctra Nacional 435 Km 99, 06350, Higuera la Real, Badajoz, Spain
Tel.: (34) 924727000
Plastic Bottle Mfr & Distr
N.A.I.C.S.: 326160

Resilux Packaging South East Europe S.R.L   (1)
Sat Dascalu Comuna Dascalu Calea Bucuresti nr 63, Village Dascalu Commune Das-

INTERNATIONAL PUBLIC

calu Ilfov County, 077075, Judetul Ilfov, Romania
Tel.: (40) 314334527
Packaging Services
N.A.I.C.S.: 561910

Resilux Packaging South Europe A.B.E.E   (1)
Industrial Area of Patra Street B2-A5 building OT 21, 25018, Patras, Greece
Tel.: (30) 2610242030
Plastic Bottle Mfr & Distr
N.A.I.C.S.: 326160
Asimakis Theodoropoulos *(Plant Mgr)*

Resilux Schweiz AG   (1)
Industrie Ost, 8865, Bilten, Switzerland
Tel.: (41) 556196900
Web Site: http://www.resilux.ch
Plastic Bottle Mfr & Distr
N.A.I.C.S.: 326160

Resilux Ukraine LLC   (1)
Vul Zhyljanskaja d 146, 01032, Kiev, Ukraine
Tel.: (380) 445844963
Packaging Services
N.A.I.C.S.: 561910

Resilux-Volga OOO   (1)
Bazovaya Street 12, Kostroma, 156019, Russia
Tel.: (7) 4942427043
Plastic Bottle Mfr & Distr
N.A.I.C.S.: 326160

RESIMAC GROUP LIMITED
PO Box H284, Australia Square, Sydney, 1215, NSW, Australia
Tel.: (61) 292480300   AU
Web Site: https://www.resimac.com.au
Year Founded: 1985
RMC—(ASX)
Rev.: $664,610,040
Assets: $10,079,263,447
Liabilities: $9,801,244,618
Net Worth: $278,018,829
Earnings: $23,231,170
Emp.: 300
Fiscal Year-end: 06/30/24
Non-Bank Mortgage Services
N.A.I.C.S.: 522310
Scott McWilliam *(CEO)*

Subsidiaries:

Resimac Limited   (1)
Level 9 45 Clarence Street, Sydney, 2000, NSW, Australia   (100%)
Tel.: (61) 2 9248 0300
Web Site: http://www.resimac.com.au
Renting Services
N.A.I.C.S.: 522310
Mary Ploughman *(Co-CEO)*

Subsidiary (Non-US):

RHG Mortgage Corporation Limited   (2)
Tel.: (61) 130 065 8489
Web Site: https://www.rhgmortgages.com.au
Sales Range: $150-199.9 Million
Emp.: 12
Holding Company; Residential Mortgage Loan Services
N.A.I.C.S.: 551112

Subsidiary (Domestic):

RHG Home Loans Pty. Ltd.   (3)
Level 6 222 Pitt Street, Sydney, 2000, NSW, Australia
Tel.: (61) 2 8028 2333
Web Site: http://www.rhgl.com.au
Residential Mortgage Loan Services
N.A.I.C.S.: 522292
Hal Benson *(Mgr-Treasury)*

RESINS, INC.
E Rodriguez Jr Ave Bagong Ilog, Pasig, 1600, Philippines
Tel.: (63) 6719842
Web Site: http://www.ri-chem.com
Year Founded: 1958
Emp.: 500

AND PRIVATE COMPANIES / RESONA HOLDINGS, INC.

Holding Company
N.A.I.C.S.: 551112
Subsidiaries:

AVC Chemical Corporation (1)
RI Chemical Compound No 13 Joe Borris Street, E Rodriguez Jr Ave, Bagong Ilog, Pasig, 1600, Manila, Philippines
Tel.: (63) 2 671 91 57
Web Site: http://www.richem.com.ph
Sales Range: $25-49.9 Million
Emp.: 10
Chemicals Mfr
N.A.I.C.S.: 325998
Neil R. Bueno *(Gen Mgr)*

RI Chemical Corp. (1)
E Rodriguez Jr Ave Corner Jose Borres St, Bagong Ilong, Pasig, 1600, Philippines
Tel.: (63) 26719842
Web Site: http://www.richem.com.ph
Sales Range: $50-74.9 Million
Emp.: 80
Supplier of Chemicals
N.A.I.C.S.: 424690
Meneleo J. Carlos *(Pres)*

RESINTECH BERHAD
Lot 3 & 5 Jalan Waja 14 Kawasan Perindustrian Telok Panglima Garang, 42500, Teluk Panglima Garang, Selangor, Malaysia
Tel.: (60) 331222422   MY
Web Site: https://www.resintechmalaysia.my
RESINTC—(KLS)
Rev.: $19,043,386
Assets: $54,187,725
Liabilities: $17,345,608
Net Worth: $36,842,116
Earnings: $211,852
Fiscal Year-end: 03/31/23
Plastic Tank Mfr
N.A.I.C.S.: 325211
Kim Poo Teh *(Founder & Mng Dir)*

Subsidiaries:

Resintech Plastics (M) Sdn. Bhd. (1)
Lot 3 and 5 Jalan Waja 14, Kawasan Perindustrian Telok Panglima Garang, 42500, Kuala Langat, Selangor Darul Ehsan, Malaysia
Tel.: (60) 331222422
Web Site: https://www.fimasfitting.com
Pipe Fitting Mfr
N.A.I.C.S.: 326122
Teh Kim Poo *(Founder & Mng Dir)*

RESISTOTECH INDUSTRIES PVT LTD
C-11, MIDC Sinnar, Nasik, 422113, India
Tel.: (91) 20993054
Web Site: https://www.resistotech.com
Industrial Machinery Mfr
N.A.I.C.S.: 333248
Prashant Patil *(Mng Dir)*

Subsidiaries:

SGL Carbon India Pvt. Ltd. (1)
Plot No 236 237 Next to Tata Ficosa, Taluka Mulshi Hinjewadi, 411 057, Pune, India
Tel.: (91) 2022932932
Industrial Process Furnace & Oven Mfr
N.A.I.C.S.: 333994

RESMI FINANCE & INVESTMENT HOUSE JSC
Al-Farabi Ave 34, Almaty, Kazakhstan
Tel.: (7) 7273553722   KZ
Web Site: https://tenizcap.kz
Year Founded: 1997
TCIB—(KAZ)
Rev.: $1,286,190
Assets: $8,744,157
Liabilities: $4,572,545
Net Worth: $4,171,612
Earnings: $1,261,063
Fiscal Year-end: 12/31/23
Financial Services
N.A.I.C.S.: 523999
Alexandr Manayenko *(Chm-Mgmt Bd)*

RESMI GROUP LTD.
110e Al-Farabi Ave, 050040, Almaty, Kazakhstan
Tel.: (7) 7272667077
Web Site: http://www.resmi.kz
Investment Services
N.A.I.C.S.: 523999
Larissa Borovkova *(Dir-Internal Audit & Compliance Dept)*

Subsidiaries:

JSC RG Brands (1)
212b Raiymbek ave, 050034, Almaty, Kazakhstan (86%)
Tel.: (7) 7272505740
Web Site: http://www.brands.kz
Sales Range: $200-249.9 Million
Emp.: 1,980
Juices, Carbonated Soft Drinks & Milk Mfr & Marketer
N.A.I.C.S.: 311411
Kairat Mazhibayev *(Chm)*

RESOLUTE MINING LIMITED
Level 17 2 The Esplanade, Perth, 6000, WA, Australia
Tel.: (61) 892616100   AU
Web Site: https://www.rml.com.au
Year Founded: 1983
RSG—(OTCIQ)
Rev.: $651,129,000
Assets: $868,793,000
Liabilities: $397,299,000
Net Worth: $471,494,000
Earnings: ($34,665,000)
Emp.: 1,148
Fiscal Year-end: 12/31/22
Gold Ore & Silver Ore Mining
N.A.I.C.S.: 212220
Marthinus Johan Botha *(Chm)*

Subsidiaries:

Carpentaria Gold Pty. Ltd. (1)
Ravenswood Gold Mine, PO Box 5802, Ravenswood, 4810, QLD, Australia
Tel.: (61) 747523100
Web Site: http://www.rml.com.au
Sales Range: $50-74.9 Million
Emp.: 100
Gold Mining Services
N.A.I.C.S.: 212220

Resolute (Tanzania) Limited (1)
Plot 1670 Mwaya Street, Dar es Salaam, Tanzania
Tel.: (255) 222600490
Web Site: http://www.rml.com.au
Sales Range: $200-249.9 Million
Emp.: 300
Gold Ore Mining Services
N.A.I.C.S.: 212220
Gerald Mturi *(Gen Mgr)*

Resolute Resources Pty Ltd (1)
L 4 28 The Esp, Perth, 6000, WA, Australia
Tel.: (61) 892616100
Web Site: http://www.rml.com.au
Sales Range: $50-74.9 Million
Emp.: 30
Gold Mining Services
N.A.I.C.S.: 212220

RESOLUTION CAPITAL LIMITED
2 Queen Annes Gate, London, SW1H 9AA, United Kingdom
Tel.: (44) 20 3372 2900   UK
Web Site: http://www.resolutionlife.com
Investment Holding Company
N.A.I.C.S.: 551112
Clive Cowdery *(Founder & CEO)*

Subsidiaries:

Lincoln Benefit Life Company (1)
1221 N St Ste 200, Lincoln, NE 68508
Tel.: (402) 475-4061
Web Site: http://www.lbl.com
Life Insurance, Annuities, Retirement & Investment Products
N.A.I.C.S.: 524298
W. Weldon Wilson *(CEO)*

Resolution Operations LLP (1)
23 Savile Row, London, W1J 2ET, United Kingdom
Tel.: (44) 2070169266
Investment Management
N.A.I.C.S.: 523999

RESOLUTION LIFE GROUP HOLDINGS LP
Wessex House 2nd Floor 45 Reid Street, Hamilton, HM12, Bermuda
Tel.: (441) 542 4599   BM
Web Site: http://resolutionlife.com
Year Founded: 2003
Fire Insurance Services
N.A.I.C.S.: 524298
John C. R. Hele *(Pres & COO)*

Subsidiaries:

AMP Life Ltd. (1)
2-12 Macquarie St, PO Box 300, Parramatta, 2150, NSW, Australia
Tel.: (61) 1300 157 820
Sales Range: $100-124.9 Million
Emp.: 200
Insurance & Related Personal Financial Services
N.A.I.C.S.: 524128
Megan Beer *(CEO)*

Resolution Life Group Services Limited (1)
The Caxton 1 Brewers Green, London, SW1H 0RH, United Kingdom
Tel.: (44) 2076613600
Insurance Carrier
N.A.I.C.S.: 524130
John Hack *(Mng Partner)*

RESOLUTION MINERALS LTD.
Level 4 29-31 King William Street, Adelaide, 5000, SA, Australia
Tel.: (61) 861187110   AU
Web Site: https://www.resolutionminerals.com
Year Founded: 2017
RML—(ASX)
Rev.: $138,739
Assets: $13,339,405
Liabilities: $377,216
Net Worth: $12,962,189
Earnings: ($1,116,365)
Fiscal Year-end: 06/30/24
Mineral Exploration Services
N.A.I.C.S.: 213114
Paul Kitto *(Board of Directors & Dir)*

RESONA HOLDINGS, INC.
Fukagawa Gatharia W2 Bldg 5-65 Kiba 1-Chome, Koto-ku, Tokyo, 135-0042, Japan
Tel.: (81) 367043111   JP
Web Site: https://www.resona-gr.co.jp
Year Founded: 2001
DW1—(DEU)
Rev.: $6,224,392,430
Assets: $503,357,363,070
Liabilities: $484,993,639,540
Net Worth: $18,363,723,530
Earnings: $72,710
Emp.: 19,721
Fiscal Year-end: 03/31/24
Bank Holding Company
N.A.I.C.S.: 551111
Kazuhiro Higashi *(Pres, Exec Officer & Chm-Resona Bank Limited)*

Subsidiaries:

DFL Lease Co. Ltd. (1)
Meiji Yasuda Life Osaka Midosuji Building 4-1-1 Fushimi-cho, Chuo-ku, Osaka, 541-0044, Japan (100%)
Tel.: (81) 662322737
Web Site: https://www.dfl-lease.co.jp
Lease & Finance Services
N.A.I.C.S.: 525990

Daiwa Bank (Capital Management) Ltd. (1)
6th Floor 4 Broadgate, London, EC2M 2AH, United Kingdom (100%)
Tel.: (44) 1716231494
International Banking
N.A.I.C.S.: 522299

Daiwa Guarantee Co., Ltd. (1)
Risonaginkouosakahonsha Bldg, Osaka, 541-0051, Japan
Tel.: (81) 662311820
Credit Intermediation Services
N.A.I.C.S.: 522299

Kansai Mirai Financial Group, Inc. (1)
2-1 Bingomachi 2 chome, Chuo-ku, Osaka, Japan (60.39%)
Tel.: (81) 677337000
Web Site: http://www.kmfg.co.jp
Rev.: $8,141,639,520
Assets: $554,899,203,180
Liabilities: $533,656,494,700
Net Worth: $21,242,708,480
Earnings: $1,397,746,420
Fiscal Year-end: 03/31/2020
Bank Holding Company
N.A.I.C.S.: 551111
Tetsuya Kan *(Exec VP)*

Subsidiary (Domestic):

Kansai Mirai Bank, Limited (2)
2-1 Bingomachi 2-Chome, Chuo-ku, Osaka, Japan
Tel.: (81) 677337000
Banking Services
N.A.I.C.S.: 522110
Tetsuya Kan *(Pres)*

The Minato Bank, Ltd. (2)
2-1-1 Sannomiya-cho, Chuo-ku, Kobe, 651-0193, Hyogo, Japan
Tel.: (81) 78 331 8141
Web Site: https://www.minatobk.co.jp
Emp.: 1,990
Retail & Commercial Banking Services
N.A.I.C.S.: 522110
Shinya Kimura *(Sr Mng Exec Officer)*

Subsidiary (Domestic):

Minato Capital Co., Ltd. (3)
2-1-2 Tamondori Omori Minato Building 5F, Chuo-ku, Kobe, 650-0015, Hyogo, Japan
Tel.: (81) 78 361 1511
Web Site: http://www.minatocp.co.jp
Investment Business Services
N.A.I.C.S.: 523150
Katsushi Yamashita *(Pres)*

Minato Card Co., Ltd. (3)
35 Nishimachi Chuo-Ku 5th Floor Mitsui Kobe Building, Kobe, 651-0170, Hyogo-ken, Japan
Tel.: (81) 783222222
Web Site: http://www.minatocard.com
Credit Card Issuing Services
N.A.I.C.S.: 522210

Kinki Osaka Shinyo Hosho Co., Ltd. (1)
1-7-6 Bingomachi, Chuo-Ku, Osaka, 541-0051, Japan
Tel.: (81) 662622522
Credit Intermediation Services
N.A.I.C.S.: 522299

P.T. Bank Resona Perdania (1)
Menara Mulia 5th & 6th Floor Suites 501 & 601, Jl Jend Gatot Subroto Kav 9-11 Karet Semanggi Setiabudi, Jakarta, 12930, Indonesia (43.42%)
Tel.: (62) 21 570 1958
Web Site: https://www.perdania.co.id
Sales Range: $100-124.9 Million
Emp.: 250
Banking Services
N.A.I.C.S.: 522110
Ichiro Hiramatsu *(Chm)*

Resona Asset Management Co., Ltd. (1)
1-5-65 Kiba Fukagawa Gatharia W2 Building, Koto-ku, Tokyo, Japan
Tel.: (81) 12 022 3351
Web Site: https://www.resona-am.co.jp

RESONA HOLDINGS, INC.

Resona Holdings, Inc.—(Continued)

Investment Banking Services
N.A.I.C.S.: 523150

Resona Bank (Capital Management) PLC (1)
Level 18 City Tower 40 Basinghall St, London, EC2V 5DE, United Kingdom
Tel.: (44) 2072565661
N.A.I.C.S.: 522299
Research & Business Consulting Services

Resona Bank, Limited (1)
2-2-1 Bingomachi Resona Main Store Building, Sakaisuji Hommachi Station North Subway Sakaisuji Line Chuo-ku, Osaka, 540-8610, Japan **(100%)**
Tel.: (81) 662711221
Web Site: http://www.resonabank.co.jp
International Banking Services
N.A.I.C.S.: 522299
Kazuhiro Higashi *(Chm, Pres & Exec Officer)*

Subsidiary (Domestic):

Asahi Bank Business Service Co., Ltd. (2)
Saitama Shi Urawaku, Takasagu 2 9 15, Saitama, Japan **(100%)**
Tel.: (81) 488342951
Sales Range: $10-24.9 Million
Emp.: 30
Cash Adjustment, Mailing & Printing Services
N.A.I.C.S.: 561431

Asahi Bank Career Service Co., Ltd. (2)
1 9 Kanda Surugadai 2 Chome, Chiyoda-Ku, Tokyo, Japan **(100%)**
Tel.: (81) 332315861
Personnel Agency
N.A.I.C.S.: 525920

Affiliate (Domestic):

Asahi Bank Finance Service Co., Ltd. (2)
10 5 Nihonbashi Kayabacho 1 Chome, Chuo Ku, Tokyo, 113 0025, Japan **(100%)**
Tel.: (81) 356408181
Web Site: http://www.resona-ks.co.jp
Sales Range: $75-99.9 Million
Emp.: 160
Receivables Purchasing
N.A.I.C.S.: 522299
Mitsuo Abe *(Pres)*

Subsidiary (Domestic):

Asahi Bank Property Co., Ltd. (2)
14-6 Shiba Daimon 1-chome, Minato-ku, Tokyo, Japan **(100%)**
Provider of Collateral Evaluation & Administrative Services
N.A.I.C.S.: 541611

Subsidiary (Non-US):

Asahi Finance (Australia) Ltd. (2)
Level 5 Barclays House, 25 Bligh Street, Sydney, 2000, NSW, Australia **(100%)**
Tel.: (61) 2 9221 5511
Branches & Agencies of Foreign Banks
N.A.I.C.S.: 522299

Resona Bank, Ltd. - Singapore Representative Office (2)
20 Cecil street Level 12 Unit 03 Equity Plaza, Singapore, 049705, Singapore
Tel.: (65) 63330378
Web Site: http://www.resonabank.co.jp
Sales Range: $50-74.9 Million
Emp.: 3
Financial Future Business
N.A.I.C.S.: 522299

Subsidiary (Domestic):

Resona Card Co. Ltd. (2)
1-5-25 Kiba, Koto-ku, Tokyo, 135-0042, Japan **(58.2%)**
Tel.: (81) 35 665 0601
Web Site: https://www.resonacard.co.jp
Sales Range: $75-99.9 Million
Emp.: 250
Provider of Credit Card Administration Services
N.A.I.C.S.: 522210

Resona Research Institute Co., Ltd. (2)
1-5-25 Kiba Fukagawa Galleria Tower S Building, Koto-ku, Tokyo, 135-0042, Japan **(92.4%)**
Tel.: (81) 35 653 3701
Web Site: https://www.rri.co.jp
Sales Range: $25-49.9 Million
Emp.: 170
Research & Business Consulting Services
N.A.I.C.S.: 541690

Resona Business Service Co., Ltd. (1)
1-4-27 Shiromi OBP Castle Tower 8th Floor, Chuo-ku, Osaka, 540-0001, Japan
Tel.: (81) 66 945 5093
Web Site: https://www.resona-bs.com
Placement Agency Services
N.A.I.C.S.: 561311

Resona Kessai Service Co., Ltd. (1)
Sf Kayabacho Bldg, Chuo-Ku, Tokyo, 103-0025, Japan
Tel.: (81) 3 5640 8181
Credit Intermediation Services
N.A.I.C.S.: 522299

Saitama Resona Bank, Ltd. (1)
7-4-1 Tokiwa, Urawa-ku, Saitama, 330-9088, Japan **(100%)**
Tel.: (81) 48 824 2411
Web Site: http://www.saitamaresona.co.jp
Commericial Banking
N.A.I.C.S.: 522110
Kazuyoshi Ikeda *(Pres)*

Shutoken Leasing Co., Ltd. (1)
9-1 Kanda-mitoshirocho, Chiyoda-ku, Tokyo, 101-0053, Japan **(90.97%)**
Tel.: (81) 352801657
Web Site: http://www.shutoken-lease.co.jp
Sales Range: $100-124.9 Million
Emp.: 139
Leasing Services
N.A.I.C.S.: 532490

RESONAC HOLDINGS CORPORATION

13-9 Shiba Daimon 1-Chome, Minato-Ku, Tokyo, 105-8518, Japan
Tel.: (81) 354703599 JP
Web Site: https://www.resonac.com
Year Founded: 1939
SHWDF—(OTCIQ)
Rev.: $9,634,152,078
Assets: $14,530,712,478
Liabilities: $11,472,264,678
Net Worth: $3,058,447,800
Earnings: $263,285,244
Emp.: 23,840
Fiscal Year-end: 12/31/22
Bulk & Specialty Chemicals, Plastics, Aluminum Products, Electrodes, Ceramics & Electronics Materials Mfr & Sales
N.A.I.C.S.: 325998
Jiro Ishikawa *(Officer-Electronics Materials Div & Gen Mgr-Device Solutions Div)*

Subsidiaries:

Eternal Showa Highpolymer Co., Ltd. (1)
19th Floor Bangkok City Tower 179/90-92 South Sathorn Rd Tungmahamek, Sathorn, Bangkok, 10120, Thailand
Tel.: (66) 22872000
Web Site: http://www.eshp.co.th
Plastic Bulk Molding Compound Mfr & Distr
N.A.I.C.S.: 325211
Pornchai Uvimolchai *(Chm)*

F2 Chemicals Limited (1)
Lea Lane, Lea Town, Preston, PR4 0RZ, Lancashire, United Kingdom
Tel.: (44) 177 277 5800
Web Site: https://www.f2chemicals.com
Perfluorocarbons Mfr
N.A.I.C.S.: 325120
Andy Penman *(Mng Dir)*

Fuyo Perlite Co., Ltd. (1)
3041-1 Toyohashi Shimosuwa-machi, Suwa-gun, Nagano, 393-0001, Japan

Tel.: (81) 266272018
Web Site: http://www.fuyo-p.co.jp
Sales Range: $25-49.9 Million
Emp.: 34
Perlite Aggregates Mfr
N.A.I.C.S.: 327992

Plant (Domestic):

Fuyo Perlite Co., Ltd. - Suwa Plant (2)
3041-1 Toyohashi Shimosuwa-machi, Suwa-gun, Nagano, 393-0001, Japan
Tel.: (81) 266272018
Web Site: http://www.fuyo-p.co.jp
Soil Conditioners, Heat & Sound Insulation Products, Moisture-Proofing & Oil Absorbing Agents Mfr
N.A.I.C.S.: 325199

Ganzhou Zhaori Rare Earth New Materials Co., Ltd. (1)
No 22 jinlong Road Ganzhou Economic and Technological Development Zone, Ganzhou, Jiangxi, China
Tel.: (86) 7978380900
Web Site: http://www.sdk.co.jp
Rare Earth Magnetic Alloys Mfr
N.A.I.C.S.: 331110

Hanacans Joint Stock Company (1)
Hanaka Industrial Park Dong Nguyen, Tu Son, Bac Ninh, Vietnam
Tel.: (84) 2226260888
Web Site: http://www.hanacans.vn
Emp.: 280
Aluminum Beverage Can Mfr
N.A.I.C.S.: 332431
Hidetaka Makabe *(Gen Mgr)*

Helvetica Capital AG (1)
Nuschelerstrasse 1, 8001, Zurich, Switzerland
Tel.: (41) 55 511 20 20
Web Site: http://www.helvetica-capital.ch
Emp.: 3,000
Private Investment Services
N.A.I.C.S.: 523999
Johannes Suter *(CEO & Mng Partner)*

Holding (Domestic):

Industrielack AG (2)
Hammerli 1, PO Box 139, Wangen, 8855, Switzerland
Tel.: (41) 554512929
Web Site: http://www.ilag.ch
Sales Range: $25-49.9 Million
Emp.: 50
Paints & Coatings Mfr
N.A.I.C.S.: 325510
Hans Georg Geisel *(CEO)*

Hipack Co., Ltd. (1)
1-13-9 Shibadaimon, Minato-ku, Tokyo, 105-0012, Japan
Tel.: (81) 354035750
Web Site: http://www.hi-pack.jp
Zipper Bags & Tapes Mfr
N.A.I.C.S.: 313220

Kitakata Light Metal Co., Ltd. (1)
7840 Nagauchi, Kitakata, 966-0845, Fukushima, Japan
Tel.: (81) 241221084
Web Site: https://www.kitakata-casting.co.jp
Sand Mold Aluminium Casting Mfr
N.A.I.C.S.: 331524

Korea Showa Chemicals Co. (1)
Sunhwa Tower 2F 43 Sejong-daero 7 gil, Gangnam-gu, Seoul, 100130, Korea (South)
Tel.: (82) 2 3454 1831
Sales Range: $50-74.9 Million
Emp.: 10
Industrial Chemical Whslr
N.A.I.C.S.: 424690
Antoag Masami *(Pres)*

Lianyungang Zaoling Abrasives Co., Ltd. (1)
No 1 Changbaishan Road Economic & Technical Development Zone, Lianyungang, Jiangsu, China
Tel.: (86) 5182349200
All Other Miscellaneous Chemical Product & Preparation Mfr
N.A.I.C.S.: 325998

INTERNATIONAL PUBLIC

Niigata Showa K.K. (1)
1265 Mukaikanose Agamachi, Higashikambara-gun, Niigata, 959-4301, Japan
Tel.: (81) 254922210
Cement Mfr
N.A.I.C.S.: 327310

Nippon Polytech Corp. (1)
370-1 Nibukata-machi, Hachioji, 193-0822, Tokyo, Japan
Tel.: (81) 426520216
Web Site: http://www.nptcorp.com
Sales Range: $25-49.9 Million
Emp.: 47
Fluxes Mfr
N.A.I.C.S.: 325998
Kazuo Ito *(Pres)*

P.T. Showa Esterindo Indonesia (1)
Graha Indochem 7th Floor Jl Pantai Indah Kapuk Boulevard Kav SSB/E, Jakarta, 14470, Indonesia
Tel.: (62) 2156948671
Petrochemical Mfr
N.A.I.C.S.: 325110

PT Indonesia Chemical Alumina (1)
Aneka Tambang Building 4th Floor Jl Letjen TB Simatupang No 1, Lingkar Selatan Tanjung Barat, Jakarta, 12530, Indonesia
Tel.: (62) 217803340
Web Site: http://www.pt-ica.com
Aluminium Products Mfr
N.A.I.C.S.: 331524

Resonac Corporation (1)
GranTokyo South Tower 1-9-2 Marunouchi, Chiyoda-ku, Tokyo, 100-6606, Japan
Tel.: (81) 355337000
Emp.: 6,872
Chemicals Mfr
N.A.I.C.S.: 325998
Hisashi Maruyama *(Pres & Rep Dir)*

Subsidiary (Non-US):

Hitachi Chemical (China) Co., Ltd. (2)
Unit 2002B-2004 2101-2103 Park Place No 1601 Nanjing W Road, Jing An District, Shanghai, 200040, China
Tel.: (86) 2162888870
Web Site: http://www.hitachi-chem.co.jp
Electronic & Chemical Product Whslr
N.A.I.C.S.: 423690

Hitachi Chemical (Dongguan) Co. Ltd. (2)
No 2 Yuanzhong 2nd Road, Chashan Town, Dongguan, 523380, Guangdong, China
Tel.: (86) 769 8641 3898
Web Site: http://www.hitachi-chem.co.jp
Photosensitive Dry Film Mfr & Distr
N.A.I.C.S.: 322220
Shigeru Ishikawa *(Chm & Pres)*

Hitachi Chemical (M) Sdn Bhd (2)
Plot 501 Prai Industrial Estate, 13600, Penang, Malaysia
Tel.: (60) 4 390 3977
Emp.: 300
Epoxy Molding Compound Mfr & Distr
N.A.I.C.S.: 325211
Yorihiro Nakano *(Mng Dir)*

Subsidiary (Domestic):

Hitachi Chemical (Johor) Sdn Bhd (3)
PLO 458 Jalan Keluli 10, 81700, Pasir Gudang, Johor Darul Takzim, Malaysia
Tel.: (60) 72514601
Sales Range: $50-74.9 Million
Emp.: 250
Specialty Chemicals Mfr
N.A.I.C.S.: 325998
Razak Haji Idoo *(Mgr-HR)*

Subsidiary (Non-US):

Hitachi Chemical (Shanghai) Co., Ltd. (2)
188 Hedan Road, Shanghai Waigaoqiao Free Trade Pilot Zone, Shanghai, 200131, China
Tel.: (86) 2158660202
Web Site: http://www.hitachi-chem.co.jp
Electronic & Chemical Products Distr
N.A.I.C.S.: 423690

AND PRIVATE COMPANIES — RESONAC HOLDINGS CORPORATION

Hitachi Chemical (Thailand) Co., Ltd. (2)
319 Chamchuri Square Building Room No 1609 16th Floor Phayathai Road, Pathumwan, Bangkok, 10330, Thailand
Tel.: (66) 2 160 5412
Powder Metal & Chemical Products Distr
N.A.I.C.S.: 423510
Toshinori Osumi *(Exec VP)*

Hitachi Chemical (Yantai) Co., Ltd. (2)
No 1 Fuzhou Road, Yantai Eco and Tech Development Area, Shandong, 264006, China
Tel.: (86) 535 6952 777
Web Site: http://www.hitachi-chem.co.jp
Photosensitive Dry Film Distr
N.A.I.C.S.: 423410

Hitachi Chemical Asia-Pacific Pte Ltd. (2)
180 Clemenceau Avenue 02-01 Haw Par Centre, Singapore, 239922, Singapore
Tel.: (65) 6836 6988
Web Site: http://www.hitachi-chemical.com.sg
Chemical Products Mfr
N.A.I.C.S.: 325998

Subsidiary (Domestic):

Hitachi Chemical Singapore Pte Ltd. (3)
32 Loyang Way, Singapore, 508730, Singapore
Tel.: (65) 65428511
Web Site: http://www.hitachihcs.com.sg
Sales Range: $150-199.9 Million
Emp.: 700
Printed Circuit Board Mfr
N.A.I.C.S.: 334412

Subsidiary (Non-US):

Hitachi Chemical Co. (Hong Kong) Ltd. (2)
Unit 702 7/F Building 20E Phase 3 Pak Shek Kok, Hong Kong Science Park Pak Shek Kok, Tai Po, New Territories, China (Hong Kong)
Tel.: (852) 2366 9304
Web Site: http://www.hitachi-chem.co.jp
Electric Component Whslr
N.A.I.C.S.: 423690

Subsidiary (US):

Hitachi Chemical Co. America Ltd. (2)
2150 N 1 St Ste 350, San Jose, CA 95131
Tel.: (408) 873-2200
Web Site: http://www.hitachi-chemical.com
Sales & Purchase of Various Chemical Products
N.A.I.C.S.: 424690
Dennis Parker *(Pres & CEO)*

Subsidiary (Domestic):

Hitachi Chemical Diagnostics, Inc. (3)
630 Clyde Ct, Mountain View, CA 94043
Tel.: (650) 961-5501
Web Site: http://www.hcdiagnostics.com
Sales Range: $10-24.9 Million
Medical Laboratory Operating Services
N.A.I.C.S.: 621511

Hitachi Chemical Research Center, Inc. (3)
1003 Health Sciences Rd, Irvine, CA 92617
Tel.: (949) 725-2721
Web Site: http://www.hitachi-chem.co.jp
Sales Range: $25-49.9 Million
Emp.: 15
Biotechnology Research & Development Services
N.A.I.C.S.: 541714
Bunichiro Nakajima *(Pres & CEO)*

PCT, LLC (3)
4 Pearl Ct Ste C, Allendale, NJ 07401 (100%)
Tel.: (201) 883-5300
Web Site: http://www.pctcelltherapy.com
Cellular Therapy Mfr
N.A.I.C.S.: 339112
Kazuchika Furuishi *(CEO)*

Unit (Domestic):

Hitachi Chemical Co., Ltd. - Goi Works (2)
14 Goiminamikaigan, Ichihara, 290-8567, Chiba, Japan
Tel.: (81) 436 21 6141
Web Site: http://www.hitachi-chem.co.jp
Semiconductor Devices Mfr
N.A.I.C.S.: 334413

Hitachi Chemical Co., Ltd. - Shimodate Works (2)
1500 Ogawa, Chikusei, 308-8521, Ibaraki, Japan
Tel.: (81) 296 28 1111
Printed Wiring Board Mfr
N.A.I.C.S.: 334412

Hitachi Chemical Co., Ltd. - Yamazaki Works (2)
4-13-1 Higashi-cho, Hitachi, 317-8555, Ibaraki, Japan
Tel.: (81) 294 22 5111
Web Site: http://www.hitachi-chem.co.jp
Printed Wiring Board Mfr
N.A.I.C.S.: 334419

Subsidiary (Domestic):

Hitachi Chemical Diagnostics Systems Co., Ltd. (2)
Harumi Triton Square X-4F 1-8-10 Harumi, Chuo-Ku, Tokyo, 104-6004, Japan
Tel.: (81) 3 6219 7605
Web Site: http://www.hitachi-chem-ds.co.jp
Pharmaceuticals Product Mfr
N.A.I.C.S.: 325412
Makoto Yanagida *(Pres & CEO)*

Subsidiary (Non-US):

Hitachi Chemical Diagnostics Systems (Shanghai) Co., Ltd. (3)
Suite 30 E1 Junyao International Plaza 789 Zhaojiabang Road, Shanghai, 200032, China
Tel.: (86) 21 6418 3427
Web Site: http://www.hitachi-chem-ds.co.jp
Pharmaceuticals Product Mfr
N.A.I.C.S.: 325412

Plant (Domestic):

Hitachi Chemical Diagnostics Systems Co., Ltd. - Fuji Plant (3)
600-1 Minami-ishiki Nagaizumi-cho, Sunto-gun, Shizuoka, 411-0932, Shizuoka, Japan
Tel.: (81) 55 988 6000
Web Site: http://www.hitachi-chem-ds.co.jp
Pharmaceuticals Product Mfr
N.A.I.C.S.: 325412

Subsidiary (Non-US):

Hitachi Chemical Electronic Materials (Korea) Co., Ltd. (2)
Neunggil-Ro 106, Danwon-Gu, Ansan, 15421, Gyeonggi-Do, Korea (South)
Tel.: (82) 31 599 5500
Web Site: http://www.hitachi-chem.co.jp
Sales Range: $25-49.9 Million
Emp.: 63
Photosensitive Dry Film Distr
N.A.I.C.S.: 424610

Hitachi Chemical Europe GmbH (2)
Berliner Allee 22, 40212, Dusseldorf, Germany
Tel.: (49) 211 166730
Web Site: http://www.hitachi-chem.co.jp
Sales Range: $25-49.9 Million
Emp.: 21
Electronic Components Distr
N.A.I.C.S.: 423690
Chikara Noguchi *(Mng Dir)*

Hitachi Chemical International Co., (Taiwan) Ltd. (2)
Room No 606 Chia Hsin Building 96 Sec 2 Chung Shan N Road, Taipei, 104, Taiwan
Tel.: (886) 2 2581 3632
Web Site: http://www.hitachi.com.tw
Sales Range: $25-49.9 Million
Emp.: 50
Electronic & Chemical Products Distr
N.A.I.C.S.: 424690

Hitachi Chemical Mexico S.A. de C.V. (2)
Av Encino No 1020, Montemorelos Industrial Park, Montemorelos, 67500, Nuevo Leon, Mexico
Tel.: (52) 826 263 0100
Web Site: http://www.hitachi.com.mx
Sales Range: $75-99.9 Million
Emp.: 200
Automotive Brake Part Mfr & Whslr
N.A.I.C.S.: 423110

Subsidiary (Domestic):

Hitachi Kasei Shoji Co., Ltd. (2)
GranTokyo South Tower 1-9-2 Marunouchi, Chiyoda-ku, Tokyo, 100-6605, Japan (100%)
Tel.: (81) 355337790
Web Site: http://www.hitachi-chem-shoji.co.jp
Emp.: 55
Electronic Equipment, Medical Equipment & Industrial Chemical Whslr
N.A.I.C.S.: 424690
Kastsuhide Kii *(Pres & Dir)*

Hitachi Powdered Metals Co., Ltd. (2)
5 2 1 Minoridai, Matsudo shi, Matsudo, 270 2295, Chiba, Japan (100%)
Tel.: (81) 47 362 1171
Web Site: http://www.hitachi-pm.co.jp
Sales Range: $150-199.9 Million
Emp.: 750
Metallurgy Products & Marketing Parts Mfr
N.A.I.C.S.: 332117

Subsidiary (Non-US):

Hitachi Powdered Metals (S) Pte Ltd. (3)
No 7 Tuas Avenue 5, Singapore, 639333, Singapore
Tel.: (65) 6861 5633
Web Site: http://www.hitachi-pm.com.sg
Sales Range: $25-49.9 Million
Emp.: 100
Powder Metallurgical Parts Mfr
N.A.I.C.S.: 332117

Hitachi Powdered Metals (Thailand) Co., Ltd. (3)
1/1 Moo 22 Suvintawong, Saladang Bangnumprieo, Chachoengsao, 24000, Thailand
Tel.: (66) 38 59 3023
Web Site: http://www.hitachi.co.th
Sintered Metal Parts Mfr
N.A.I.C.S.: 332117

Subsidiary (US):

Hitachi Powdered Metals (USA), Inc. (3)
1024 Barachel Ln, Greensburg, IN 47240
Tel.: (812) 663-5058
Web Site: http://www.hitachi-pm.us
Emp.: 250
Powdered Metal Products Mfr
N.A.I.C.S.: 336390
Gregory Owens *(Pres & CEO)*

Subsidiary (Non-US):

ISOLITE GmbH (2)
Industriestrasse 125, 67063, Ludwigshafen, Germany
Tel.: (49) 621 91109 444
Web Site: http://www.isolite.de
Emp.: 500
High Temperature Insulation Systems & Sealing Systems; Thermal & Acoustic Management Solutions
N.A.I.C.S.: 339999
Matthias Kroll *(Mng Dir)*

Subsidiary (Domestic):

Shin-Kobe Electric Machinery Co., Ltd. (2)
Saint Luke Tower 8-1 Akashi-cho, Chuo-ku, Tokyo, 104-0044, Japan (97.78%)
Tel.: (81) 368112360
Web Site: http://www.shinkobe-denki.co.jp
Sales Range: $450-499.9 Million
Emp.: 1,216
Storage Batteries & Electric-Powered Machinery Mfr
N.A.I.C.S.: 335910
Makoto Konishi *(Pres)*

SHOTIC Europa Industria de Aluminio Lda. (1)
Parque industrial de Vendas Novas Lote 7/8, Vendas Novas, 7080-341, Portugal
Tel.: (351) 265809700
Web Site: http://www.sdk.co.jp
Sales Range: $25-49.9 Million
Emp.: 34
Aluminum Forged Products Mrf
N.A.I.C.S.: 331313

SHOWA DENKO CARBON Austria GmbH (1)
Elektrodenwerkplatz 1, 4822, Bad Goisern am Hallstattersee, Austria
Tel.: (43) 613586410
All Other Miscellaneous Chemical Product & Preparation Mfr
N.A.I.C.S.: 325998

SHOWA DENKO CARBON Holding GmbH (1)
Werner-von-Siemens-Str 18, Meitingen, 86405, Augsburg, Germany
Tel.: (49) 827142432603
Web Site: http://www.showadenkocarbon.com
Graphite Electrode Mfr
N.A.I.C.S.: 335991
Masami Tobito *(Mng Dir)*

SHOWA DENKO CARBON Malaysia Sdn. Bhd. (1)
No 11 Jalan Graphite 1 Kaw Perindustrian Bandar Mahkota Banting, 42700, Kuala Langat, Selangor, Malaysia
Tel.: (60) 331823188
All Other Miscellaneous Chemical Product & Preparation Mfr
N.A.I.C.S.: 325998

SHOWA DENKO CARBON Products Germany GmbH & Co. KG (1)
Abraham-Lincoln-Strasse 44, 65189, Wiesbaden, Germany
Tel.: (49) 8271832319
All Other Miscellaneous Chemical Product & Preparation Mfr
N.A.I.C.S.: 325998

SHOWA DENKO CARBON Spain S.A. (1)
Zona Industrial de la Grela Ctra Banos de Arteixo No 34, 15008, La Coruna, Spain
Tel.: (34) 981173171
All Other Miscellaneous Chemical Product & Preparation Mfr
N.A.I.C.S.: 325998
Carmen Torrado *(Mgr-HR)*

Shanghai Showa Chemicals Co., Ltd. (1)
18F Wangwang Building No 211 Shimen Yi Road, Shanghai, China
Tel.: (86) 2162175111
Web Site: http://www.showachem.com
Sales Range: $25-49.9 Million
Emp.: 30
Petrochemical Mfr
N.A.I.C.S.: 325110

Shanghai Showa Electronics Materials Co., Ltd. (1)
No 28 Beiyinghe Road Shanghai Chemical Industry Park, Fengxian District, Shanghai, China
Tel.: (86) 2137593368
All Other Miscellaneous Chemical Product & Preparation Mfr
N.A.I.C.S.: 325998

Shanghai Showa Highpolymer Co., Ltd. (1)
No 8333 Songze Avenue Qingpu Industrial Park near Xinshui Road, Shanghai, China
Tel.: (86) 2169212122
Web Site: http://www.sshp.com.cn
Synthetic Resin Mfr
N.A.I.C.S.: 325211
Qiu Jia *(Gen Mgr)*

Shanghai Showa Highpolymer Trading Co., Ltd. (1)
18F Wangwang Building No 211 Shimen Yi Road, Shanghai, China
Tel.: (86) 2162175222
All Other Miscellaneous Chemical Product & Preparation Mfr
N.A.I.C.S.: 325998

RESONAC HOLDINGS CORPORATION

Resonac Holdings Corporation—(Continued)

Shanghai Showa Specialty Gases Purification Co., Ltd. (1)
1388 Haitan cun liu dui, Pudong New Area, Shanghai, 210201, China
Tel.: (86) 21 6890 8981
Web Site: http://www.sdk.co.jp
Catalyst Recycling & Waste Gas Management Services
N.A.I.C.S.: 562920

Shodex China Co., Ltd. (1)
18F WangWang Building No 211 Shimen Yi Road, Shanghai, China
Tel.: (86) 2162176111
All Other Miscellaneous Chemical Product & Preparation Mfr
N.A.I.C.S.: 325998
Richie Shi *(Deputy Dir)*

Shotic (Singapore) Pte. Ltd. (1)
84 2nd Lok Yang Rd, Jurong, 628160, Singapore
Tel.: (65) 62619541
Web Site: http://www.sdk.co.jp
Sales Range: $25-49.9 Million
Emp.: 30
Mfr of Chemicals
N.A.I.C.S.: 325998

Shotic Malaysia Sdn. Bhd. (1)
PLO168 Jalan Persiaran Tanjung Langsat Kompleks Perindustrian, Tanjung Langsat, 81700, Pasir Gudang, Johor, Malaysia
Tel.: (60) 72571800
All Other Miscellaneous Chemical Product & Preparation Mfr
N.A.I.C.S.: 325998
Nur Hafiza Yahya *(Officer-ESH)*

Showa Aluminum (Thailand) Co., Ltd. (1)
46 Moo 9 Rojana Industrial Park Tambol Thanu Amphur U-Thai, Ayutthaya, 13210, Thailand
Tel.: (66) 35330750
Sales Range: $250-299.9 Million
Emp.: 570
Chemicals Mfr & Distr
N.A.I.C.S.: 325180
Chinichi Ueda *(Mng Dir)*

Showa Aluminum Can Corp. (1)
Win Gotanda Bldg 7F 1-30-2 Nishigotanda, Shinagawa-ku, Tokyo, 141-0031, Japan
Tel.: (81) 357451051
Web Site: http://www.showacan.co.jp
Sales Range: $100-124.9 Million
Emp.: 460
Aluminium Cans Mfr
N.A.I.C.S.: 331318
Masahiro Endo *(Pres)*

Plant (Domestic):

Showa Aluminum Can Corp. - Hikone Plant (1)
370 Nirecho, Hikone, 529-1151, Shiga, Japan
Tel.: (81) 749251501
Web Site: http://www.sdk.co.jp
Aluminium Cans Mfr
N.A.I.C.S.: 332431

Showa Aluminum Can Corp. - Omuta Plant (2)
1-16 Misakimachi, Omuta, 836-0037, Fukuoka, Japan
Tel.: (81) 944412111
Emp.: 200
Aluminium Cans Mfr
N.A.I.C.S.: 331318
Heiroya Abay *(Plant Mgr)*

Showa Aluminum Can Corp. - Oyama Plant (2)
30-3 Inuzuka 1-chome, Oyama, 323-0811, Tochigi, Japan
Tel.: (81) 285212311
Web Site: http://www.sdk.co.jp
Aluminium Cans Mfr
N.A.I.C.S.: 332431

Showa Aluminum Corp of America (1)
10500 Oday Harrison Rd, Mount Sterling, OH 43143
Tel.: (740) 869-3333
Rev.: $14,907,894
Emp.: 250
Aluminum Forgings
N.A.I.C.S.: 332112
Scott Mortimer *(CFO)*

Showa Aluminum Manufacturing Philippines Corporation (1)
Lot 1 Block 1 Phase 3 FCIE Barangay Langkaan 1, Dasmarinas, 4114, Cavite, Philippines
Tel.: (63) 46 402 0435
Chemicals Mfr & Distr
N.A.I.C.S.: 325180

Showa Chemicals of America, Inc. (1)
9101 Burnet Rd Ste 105, Austin, TX 78758
Tel.: (512) 237-7787
All Other Miscellaneous Chemical Product & Preparation Mfr
N.A.I.C.S.: 325998

Showa Denko (Dalian) Co., Ltd. (1)
No 36 Fu'an Street Economic and Technical Development Zone, Dalian, Liaoning, China
Tel.: (86) 41187334298
Web Site: http://www.sdk.co.jp
Extruded Aluminum Products Mfr
N.A.I.C.S.: 331318

Showa Denko (Shanghai) Co., Ltd. (1)
18F Wangwang Building No 211 Shimen Yi Road, Jingan, Shanghai, China
Tel.: (86) 2162175000
Web Site: http://www.sdsh-showadenko.com
Sales Range: $25-49.9 Million
Petrochemical Mfr
N.A.I.C.S.: 325110

Showa Denko Aluminum Trading K.K. (1)
1-1-1 Nishitanabe-cho, Abeno-ku, Osaka, 545-0014, Japan
Tel.: (81) 666953364
Web Site: http://www.sdat.co.jp
Sales Range: $25-49.9 Million
Emp.: 125
Aluminium Products Mfr
N.A.I.C.S.: 331318

Showa Denko America, Inc. (1)
420 Lexington Ave Ste 2335A, New York, NY 10170   (100%)
Tel.: (212) 370-0033
Web Site: http://showadenko.us
Sales Range: $50-74.9 Million
Emp.: 24
Import & Export of Chemicals, Ceramics & Plastic Products
N.A.I.C.S.: 424690

Showa Denko Carbon Germany GmbH (1)
Daimlerstrasse 19, 86368, Gersthofen, Germany
Tel.: (49) 821207150
Web Site: https://www.showadenkocarbon.com
Electrode Distr
N.A.I.C.S.: 423690

Showa Denko Carbon, Inc. (1)
478 Ridge Rd, Ridgeville, SC 29472
Tel.: (843) 875-3200
All Other Miscellaneous Chemical Product & Preparation Mfr
N.A.I.C.S.: 325998

Showa Denko Ceramics Co., Ltd. (1)
1 Oaza Soga, Shiojiri, 399-6461, Nagano, Japan
Tel.: (81) 263520180
Ceramic & Electronic Material Mfr & Whslr
N.A.I.C.S.: 325998
Takuya Okubo *(Pres)*

Showa Denko Europe GmbH (1)
Konrad-Zuse-Platz 3, 81829, Munich, Germany   (100%)
Tel.: (49) 899399620
Web Site: http://www.showa-denko.com
Sales Range: $150-199.9 Million
Emp.: 35
Mfr of Chemical Products & Automotive Products
N.A.I.C.S.: 325998
Kiyofumi Matsuoka *(Mng Dir)*

Showa Denko Gas Products Co., Ltd. (1)
Nichirei Suidobashi Building 3-3-23 Misaki-cho, Chiyoda-ku, Tokyo, 101-0061, Japan
Tel.: (81) 332372355
Web Site: http://www.showa-tansan.co.jp
Sales Range: $75-99.9 Million
Emp.: 242
Industrial Gases Mfr & Sales
N.A.I.C.S.: 325120

Showa Denko HD (Malaysia) Sdn.Bhd. (1)
Lot 1944 Industrial Zone Phase 2 Kulim Hi Tech Park, 09000, Kulim, Kedah, Malaysia
Tel.: (60) 44031711
Chemicals Mfr & Distr
N.A.I.C.S.: 325180

Showa Denko HD Singapore Pte Ltd. (1)
2 Pioneer Crescent, Singapore, 628553, Singapore
Tel.: (65) 63092000
Web Site: http://www.showadenkohd.com.sg
Sales Range: $400-449.9 Million
Emp.: 800
Storage Devices Mfr & Sales
N.A.I.C.S.: 334112
Jiro Ishikawa *(Mng Dir)*

Showa Denko HD Trace Corp. (1)
8 Technology Fifth Road Science-Based Industrial Park, Hsinchu, Taiwan
Tel.: (886) 35770777
Web Site: http://www.shdt.com.tw
Sales Range: $400-449.9 Million
Emp.: 600
Hard Disks Mfr
N.A.I.C.S.: 334112

Showa Denko HD Yamagata K.K. (1)
5400-2 Higashinekou, Higashine, 999-3701, Yamagata, Japan
Tel.: (81) 237436111
Web Site: http://www.sdk.co.jp
Sales Range: $125-149.9 Million
Emp.: 359
Development, Production & Sales of HD Media
N.A.I.C.S.: 334310

Showa Denko K.K. - Chiba Plant (1)
3 Yawata Kaigan Dori, Ichihara, 290-0067, Chiba, Japan
Tel.: (81) 436415111
Web Site: http://www.sdk.co.jp
Petrochemical Mfr
N.A.I.C.S.: 324110

Showa Denko K.K. - Chichibu Plant (1)
1505 Oaza Shimo Kagemori, Chichibu, 369-1893, Saitama, Japan
Tel.: (81) 494236111
Sales Range: $125-149.9 Million
Emp.: 400
Petrochemical Mfr
N.A.I.C.S.: 325110
Endo Tetsuo *(Plant Mgr)*

Showa Denko K.K. - Chidori Plant (1)
2-3 Chidoricho, Kawasaki-ku, Kawasaki, 210-0865, Kanagawa, Japan
Tel.: (81) 442765803
Petrochemical Mfr
N.A.I.C.S.: 325110

Showa Denko K.K. - Higashinagahara Plant (1)
111 Aza Nagayachi Higashinagahara Kawahigashimachi, Aizuwakamatsu, 969-3431, Fukushima, Japan
Tel.: (81) 242 75 2121
Web Site: http://www.sdk.co.jp
Petrochemical Mfr
N.A.I.C.S.: 324110

Showa Denko K.K. - Hikone Plant (1)
60 Kiyosaki-cho, Hikone, 529-1195, Shiga, Japan
Tel.: (81) 749251511
Web Site: http://www.sdk.co.jp
Beer Cans Mfr
N.A.I.C.S.: 332431

Showa Denko K.K. - Isesaki Plant (1)
1019 Tomizuka-cho, Isesaki, 372-0833, Gunma, Japan
Tel.: (81) 270321151
Petrochemical Mfr
N.A.I.C.S.: 324110

Showa Denko K.K. - Kawasaki Plant (1)
5-1 Ogimachi, Kawasaki-ku, Kawasaki, 210-0867, Kanagawa, Japan
Tel.: (81) 443226813
Web Site: http://www.sdk.co.jp
Organic Chemical Mfr
N.A.I.C.S.: 325180

Showa Denko K.K. - Kitakata Plant (1)
7840 Nagauchi, Kitakata, 966-0846, Fukushima, Japan
Tel.: (81) 241221261
Emp.: 400
Petrochemical Mfr
N.A.I.C.S.: 325110

Showa Denko K.K. - Omachi Plant (1)
6850 Oaza Omachi, Omachi, 398-0002, Nagano, Japan
Tel.: (81) 261220401
Web Site: http://www.sdk.co.jp
Graphite Electrode Mfr
N.A.I.C.S.: 335991

Showa Denko K.K. - Oyama Plant (1)
480 Inuzuka, Oyama, 323-8678, Tochigi, Japan
Tel.: (81) 285301230
Petrochemical Mfr
N.A.I.C.S.: 324110

Showa Denko K.K. - Oyama Plant (Nasu) (1)
1841 Aza Higashiyama Kamiishigami, Otawara, 324-0037, Tochigi, Japan
Tel.: (81) 287 26 1105
Web Site: http://www.sdk.co.jp
Petrochemical Mfr
N.A.I.C.S.: 325110

Showa Denko K.K. - Sakai Plant (1)
224 Kaisancho 6-cho, Sakai-ku, Sakai, 590-8576, Osaka, Japan
Tel.: (81) 72 225 2111
Petrochemical Mfr
N.A.I.C.S.: 324110

Showa Denko K.K. - Shiojiri Plant (1)
1 Oaza Soga, Shiojiri, 399-6461, Nagano, Japan
Tel.: (81) 263520180
Emp.: 200
Petrochemical Mfr
N.A.I.C.S.: 325110

Showa Denko K.K. - Tatsuno Plant (1)
251-1 Ibonaka, Ibo-cho, Tatsuno, 679-4155, Hyogo, Japan
Tel.: (81) 791671111
Web Site: http://www.sdk.co.jp
Petrochemical Mfr
N.A.I.C.S.: 324110

Showa Denko K.K. - Tokuyama Plant (1)
4980 Kaisei-cho, Shunan, 746-0006, Yamaguchi, Japan
Tel.: (81) 834624121
Web Site: http://www.sdk.co.jp
Electrochemicals Mfr
N.A.I.C.S.: 325411

Showa Denko K.K. - Yokohama Plant (1)
8 Ebisu-cho, Kanagawa-ku, Yokohama, 221-8517, Kanagawa, Japan
Tel.: (81) 454535111
Web Site: http://www.sdk.co.jp
Emp.: 100
Aluminum Hydroxide Mfr
N.A.I.C.S.: 325180

Showa Denko Kenso Co., Ltd. (1)
3-1 Nishinomiya-machi, Toyama, 931-8335, Japan
Tel.: (81) 764384083
Web Site: http://www.sdk.co.jp

Sales Range: $25-49.9 Million
Emp.: 29
Elastic Polishing Grindstone Mfr
N.A.I.C.S.: 325612

Showa Denko Kenzai K.K. (1)
8 Ebisu-cho, Kanagawa-ku, Yokohama,
221-8517, Kanagawa, Japan (100%)
Tel.: (81) 454441690
Web Site: http://www.sdk-k.com
Sales Range: $75-99.9 Million
Emp.: 60
Building Materials Mfr
N.A.I.C.S.: 327120
Tooru Terada (Pres)

Plant (Domestic):

Showa Denko Kenzai K.K. - Chiba Plant (2)
857 Onoda, Funabashi, 274-0081, Chiba, Japan
Tel.: (81) 474 57 1272
Web Site: http://www.sdk.co.jp
Construction Materials Mfr
N.A.I.C.S.: 327120

Showa Denko Kenzai K.K. - Higashi Matsuyama Plant (2)
1511 Shimogarako, Higashimatsuyama, 355-0076, Saitama, Japan
Tel.: (81) 493270111
Construction Materials Mfr
N.A.I.C.S.: 327120

Showa Denko Kenzai K.K. - Ishioka Plant (2)
6-2 Oaza Kashiwabara, Ishioka, 315-854, Ibaraki, Japan
Tel.: (81) 299243071
Bricks Mfr
N.A.I.C.S.: 327120

Showa Denko Kenzai K.K. - Osaka Plant (2)
1-2-8 Aoshinke, Minoh, 562-0024, Osaka, Japan
Tel.: (81) 727296365
Construction Materials Mfr
N.A.I.C.S.: 327120

Showa Denko New Material (Zhuhai) Co., Ltd. (1)
No 448 Langwan Road Fine Chemical Zone, Gaolan Port Economic District, Zhuhai, Guangdong, China
Tel.: (86) 7567235805
All Other Miscellaneous Chemical Product & Preparation Mfr
N.A.I.C.S.: 325998

Showa Denko Packaging Co., Ltd. (1)
31 Suzukawa, Isehara, 259-1146, Kanagawa, Japan (100%)
Tel.: (81) 463945225
Web Site: http://www.sdk-pack.co.jp
Sales Range: $100-124.9 Million
Aluminum Foil Mfr
N.A.I.C.S.: 331315
Katsuyuki Tsuji (Chm)

Showa Denko Sichuan Carbon Inc. (1)
Guangyuan Lizhou, Huilong River Industrial Park, Sichuan, China
Tel.: (86) 8393423222
Web Site: http://www.sdksdsc.com
Carbon Product Mfr & Distr
N.A.I.C.S.: 335991
Ihara Eiji (Pres)

Showa Denko Singapore (Pte) Ltd (1)
2 Shenton way 15-03/04 SGX Centre 1, Singapore, 068804, Singapore
Tel.: (65) 62231889
Web Site: http://www.sds.com.sg
Emp.: 20
Chemicals Mfr & Sales
N.A.I.C.S.: 325180

Showa Highpolymer Singapore Pte. Ltd. (1)
2 Shenton Way Sgx Centre 1, Singapore, Singapore
Tel.: (65) 62231889
Web Site: http://www.shps.com.sg
Chemicals Mfr & Distr

N.A.I.C.S.: 325211

Showa Specialty Gas (Taiwan.) Co., Ltd. (1)
14th Fl 125 Nangking East Road Section 2, Taipei, Taiwan
Tel.: (886) 225165267
Web Site: http://www.ssg.com.tw
Emp.: 50
Industrial Gases Mfr & Distr
N.A.I.C.S.: 325120

Showa Titanium Co., Ltd. (1)
3-1 Nishinomiya-cho, Toyama, 931-8577, Japan
Tel.: (81) 764379201
Web Site: http://www.sdk.co.jp
Rev.: $27,087,120
Emp.: 77
Titanium Oxide Mfr
N.A.I.C.S.: 325180

Sun Allomer Ltd. (1)
Tennoz Central Tower 27F 2-24 Higashi-Shinagawa 2-Chome, Shinagawa-ku, Tokyo, 140-0002, Japan
Tel.: (81) 357815608
Web Site: http://www.sunallomer.co.jp
Sales Range: $75-99.9 Million
Emp.: 210
Synthetic Resins Mfr & Distr
N.A.I.C.S.: 325211
Toru Goto (Exec VP)

Plant (Domestic):

Sun Allomer Ltd. - Kawasaki Plant (2)
13-1 Chidori-cho, Kawasaki-ku, Kawasaki, 210-0865, Japan
Tel.: (81) 442763675
Web Site: http://www.sunallomer.co.jp
Sales Range: $50-74.9 Million
Synthetic Resin Mfr
N.A.I.C.S.: 325211

Sun Allomer Ltd. - Oita Plant (2)
2 Nakanosu, Oita, 870-0111, Japan
Tel.: (81) 975215125
Web Site: http://www.sunallomer.co.jp
Sales Range: $50-74.9 Million
Synthetic Resin Mfr
N.A.I.C.S.: 325211

Taiwan Showa Chemicals Manufacturing Co., Ltd. (1)
No 3 Gong Huan Road, Tainan City, Taiwan
Tel.: (886) 63841811
All Other Miscellaneous Chemical Product & Preparation Mfr
N.A.I.C.S.: 325998

Taiwan Showa Denko Electronics Co., Ltd. (1)
No 206 Bade Rd, Hsinchu, 30069, Taiwan
Tel.: (886) 35160189
Web Site: http://www.tsel.com.tw
Electric Equipment Mfr
N.A.I.C.S.: 334419

Tohoku Metal Chemical Co., Ltd. (1)
10 Gechiuchi Nakakabeya Taira, Iwaki, 970-8021, Fukushima, Japan
Tel.: (81) 246342112
Web Site: http://www.sdk.co.jp
Sales Range: $25-49.9 Million
Emp.: 40
Polishing Materials Mfr
N.A.I.C.S.: 325612

Tokyo Aluminum Wire Corporation (1)
33 Hachiman, Ichihara, 290-0067, Chiba, Japan
Tel.: (81) 436413351
Web Site: http://www.taw-co.jp
Sales Range: $25-49.9 Million
Emp.: 28
Aluminum Wire Rods Mfr
N.A.I.C.S.: 331313
Takashi Ando (Pres)

Tokyo Liquefied Oxygen Co., Ltd. (1)
30-1 Shin-Isogocho, Isogo-ku, Yokohama, 235-0017, Kanagawa, Japan
Tel.: (81) 457511841
Web Site: http://www.sdk.co.jp
Sales Range: $25-49.9 Million
Emp.: 22
Liquefied Gases Mfr

N.A.I.C.S.: 325120

Union Showa K.K. (1)
8-40 Konan, Minato-ku, Tokyo, 108-0073, Japan (50%)
Tel.: (81) 354957031
Web Site: http://www.uskk.co.jp
Sales Range: Less than $1 Million
Emp.: 40
Electronics Mfr & Whslr
N.A.I.C.S.: 423690
Shunji Fukuda (Pres & CEO)

Zhejiang Quzhou Juhua Showa Electronic Chemical Materials Co., Ltd. (1)
No 21 Building No 1 Rean Road Juhua, Kecheng District, Quzhou, Zhejiang, China
Tel.: (86) 5703098061
All Other Miscellaneous Chemical Product & Preparation Mfr
N.A.I.C.S.: 325998

RESONANCE HEALTH LIMITED
141 Burswood Road, PO Box 71, Burswood, 6100, WA, Australia
Tel.: (61) 892865300
Web Site:
  https://www.resonancehealth.com
RHT—(ASX)
Rev.: $5,878,528
Assets: $13,543,648
Liabilities: $6,244,213
Net Worth: $7,299,435
Earnings: $113,050
Fiscal Year-end: 06/30/24
Instrument Manufacturing for Measuring & Testing Electricity & Electrical Signals
N.A.I.C.S.: 334515
Martin A. Blake (Chm)

Subsidiaries:

Resonance Health Analysis Services Pty Ltd (1)
141 Burswood Road, PO Box 71, Burswood, 6100, WA, Australia
Tel.: (61) 892865300
Web Site: http://www.resonancehealth.com
Sales Range: $10-24.9 Million
Emp.: 14
Medical Imaging Laboratory Services
N.A.I.C.S.: 621512

RESONANCE SPECIALTIES LTD.
Plot No 54-D Kandivli Industrial Estate, Kandivli West, Mumbai, 400 067, India
Tel.: (91) 2268572800
Web Site:
  https://www.resonancesl.com
Year Founded: 1989
524218—(BOM)
Rev.: $7,245,021
Assets: $7,888,460
Liabilities: $1,211,019
Net Worth: $6,677,441
Earnings: $599,640
Emp.: 67
Fiscal Year-end: 03/31/23
Pharmaceuticals Product Mfr
N.A.I.C.S.: 325412
Dwarika Agrawal (CFO & Fin Dir)

RESORT SAVINGS & LOANS PLC
5th Floor St Nicholas House 6 Catholic Mission Street, Lagos, Nigeria
Tel.: (234) 1 462 2081
Web Site: http://www.resortng.com
Year Founded: 1993
Mortgage Banking Services
N.A.I.C.S.: 522310
Kolawole Adesina (COO & Exec Dir-Ops & Fin)

RESORT TRUST INC.
2-18-31 Higashisakura, Naka-ku, Nagoya, 460-8490, Aichi, Japan
Tel.: (81) 529336000
Web Site:
  https://www.resorttrust.co.jp
Year Founded: 1973
4681—(TKS)
Rev.: $1,333,917,830
Assets: $3,097,214,650
Liabilities: $2,200,852,380
Net Worth: $896,362,270
Earnings: $105,046,120
Emp.: 8,404
Fiscal Year-end: 03/31/24
Construction & Operation Of Membership Resort Hotels
N.A.I.C.S.: 721110
Ariyoshi Fushimi (Pres)

Subsidiaries:

COMPLEX BIZ INTERNATIONAL Co., Ltd. (1)
RT-Shirakawa Building 2-6-1 Sakae, Naka-Ku, Nagoya, 460-0008, Aichi, Japan
Tel.: (81) 523102450
Web Site: https://www.complex-biz.com
Sales Range: $100-124.9 Million
Emp.: 274
Clothing Merchant Whslrs
N.A.I.C.S.: 315210

HIMEDIC Inc. (1)
4-36-19 Yoyogi, Shibuya-Ku, Tokyo, 151-0053, Japan
Tel.: (81) 367310706
Medical Care Services
N.A.I.C.S.: 622110
Katsuyasu Ito (Pres)

R.C.I. Japan Co., Ltd. (1)
4-36-19 Resort Trust Tokyo Bldg 6F Yoyogi, Shibuya-ku, Tokyo, 151-0053, Japan
Tel.: (81) 353513581
Web Site: http://www.aspac.rciaffiliates.com
Brokerage Services
N.A.I.C.S.: 523150

Tokyo Midtown Medicine Co., Ltd. (1)
Midtown Tower 6F Akasaka 9-7-1, Minato-ku, Tokyo, 107-6206, Japan
Tel.: (81) 354130080
Web Site: https://www.tokyomidtown-mc.jp
General Medical & Surgical Hospital Services
N.A.I.C.S.: 622110
Toshiomi Kusano (Pres-Medicine-Intl)

RESORTS OF THE CANADIAN ROCKIES, INC.
1505 17th Avenue SW, Calgary, T2T 0E2, AB, Canada
Tel.: (403) 254-7669
Web Site: https://www.skircr.com
Year Founded: 2001
Sales Range: $100-124.9 Million
Emp.: 1,000
Resort Services
N.A.I.C.S.: 721110
Paul Whitham (Mgr-Sls)

Subsidiaries:

Kicking Horse Mountain Resort (1)
1500 Kicking Horse Trail, PO Box 839, Golden, V0A 1H0, BC, Canada
Tel.: (250) 439-5400
Web Site:
  https://www.kickinghorseresort.com
Sales Range: $100-124.9 Million
Emp.: 250
Recreation Resort
N.A.I.C.S.: 713920

RESOURCE BASE LIMITED
Level 17 500 Collins Street, Melbourne, 3000, VIC, Australia
Tel.: (61) 396140600
Web Site:
  http://www.resourcebase.com.au
Year Founded: 2005
Sales Range: Less than $1 Million
Gold Explorer

RESOURCE BASE LIMITED

Resource Base Limited—(Continued)
N.A.I.C.S.: 212220

RESOURCE CAPITAL GOLD CORP.
1055 W Hastings St Suite 400, Vancouver, V6E 2E9, BC, Canada
Tel.: (604) 685-9316   BC
Web Site: http://www.rcgcorp.ca
RCG.V—(TSXV)
Rev.: $456
Assets: $26,357,780
Liabilities: $15,915,345
Net Worth: $10,442,435
Earnings: ($3,307,487)
Fiscal Year-end: 06/30/18
Gold Exploration Services
N.A.I.C.S.: 212220
Jack R. Cartmel (CFO)

RESOURCE CENTRIX HOLDINGS INC.
409-22 Leader Lane, Toronto, M5E 0B2, ON, Canada
Tel.: (647) 980-7323   BC
Web Site: https://recentrix.com
Year Founded: 2021
RECE—(CNSX)
Rev.: $3,095
Assets: $231,704
Liabilities: $1,865
Net Worth: $229,839
Earnings: ($135,143)
Fiscal Year-end: 01/31/23
Holding Company
N.A.I.C.S.: 551112
Billy Chan (Dir)

RESOURCE DEVELOPMENT GROUP LIMITED
Level 3 14 Walters Drive, Osborne Park, 6017, WA, Australia
Tel.: (61) 894432928
Web Site:
  https://www.resdevgroup.com.au
RDG—(ASX)
Rev.: $90,932,631
Assets: $235,642,391
Liabilities: $146,926,054
Net Worth: $88,716,336
Earnings: $11,614,320
Emp.: 352
Fiscal Year-end: 06/30/24
Mining Contract Management & Engineering Services
N.A.I.C.S.: 213114
Andrew Ellison (Chm & Mng Dir)

Subsidiaries:

Engenium Pty Ltd   (1)
Level 2 88 William Street, Perth, 6000, WA, Australia
Tel.: (61) 8 6460 0300
Web Site: http://www.engenium.com.au
Sales Range: $50-74.9 Million
Emp.: 10
Iron Ore Mining Services
N.A.I.C.S.: 212210
Wayne Peel (Mng Dir)

RESOURCE GENERATION LIMITED
Level 1 17 Station Road, Indooroopilly, Brisbane, 4068, QLD, Australia
Tel.: (61) 27 12 345 1057
Web Site: http://www.resgen.com.au
Rev.: $430,050
Assets: $153,934,482
Liabilities: $58,333,823
Net Worth: $95,600,659
Earnings: ($8,071,828)
Emp.: 43
Fiscal Year-end: 06/30/18
Coal Explorer
N.A.I.C.S.: 213113
Hennie van den Aardweg (Gen Mgr)

RESOURCE HOLDING MANAGEMENT LIMITED
Unit C-2-01 Level 2 Capital 3 Oasis Square, No 2 Jalan PJU 1A/7A Ara Damansara PJU 1A, Petaling Jaya, 47301, Selangor, Malaysia
Tel.: (60) 3 7651 0188   Ky
Web Site: http://www.redhot.asia
Year Founded: 2007
Sales Range: $10-24.9 Million
Emp.: 54
Investment Holding Company
N.A.I.C.S.: 551112
Sean Koh Yung Lee (Exec Dir)

RESOURCE MINING CORPORATION LIMITED
Level 5 191 St Georges Terrace, Perth, 6000, WA, Australia
Tel.: (61) 280721400
Web Site: https://www.resmin.com.au
RMI—(ASX)
Rev.: $5,075
Assets: $5,871,841
Liabilities: $261,104
Net Worth: $5,610,737
Earnings: ($2,087,541)
Fiscal Year-end: 06/30/24
Mineral Explorer
N.A.I.C.S.: 213115
Warwick Jeffrey Davies (Mng Dir)

RESOURCEHOUSE LIMITED
Level 19 Two International Finance Centre, 8 Finance Street, Central, China (Hong Kong)
Tel.: (852) 3101 7055
Web Site:
  http://www.resourcehouseltd.com
Mining Services
N.A.I.C.S.: 212290
Domenic Martino (Chm)

RESOURCES & ENERGY GROUP LIMITED
Level 3 Suite 301 66 Hunter Street, Sydney, 2000, NSW, Australia
Tel.: (61) 292278900   AU
Web Site:
  https://www.rezgroup.com.au
Year Founded: 2005
REZ—(ASX)
Assets: $7,713,808
Liabilities: $661,678
Net Worth: $7,052,130
Earnings: ($1,128,052)
Emp.: 3
Fiscal Year-end: 06/30/21
Mineral Exploration Services
N.A.I.C.S.: 212290
Gavin Rezos (Chm)

RESOURCES ACQUISITION CORP.
Ugland House, PO Box 309, Georgetown, KY1-1104, Grand Cayman, Cayman Islands
Tel.: (345) 203 023 5157   Ky
Web Site:
  https://www.wearabledevices.co.il
Year Founded: 2021
LIBY—(NASDAQ)
Investment Services
N.A.I.C.S.: 523999
Marie Pierre Bertrand Boulle (Chm)

RESOURCES COMPANY FOR DEVELOPMENT & INVESTMENT PLC
Shmeisani - Abd Al-Hamid Sharaf St - Building 84, PO Box 930344, Amman, 11193, Jordan
Tel.: (962) 65691971
Year Founded: 1983

JOMA—(AMM)
Rev.: $96,584
Assets: $6,426,320
Liabilities: $1,475,900
Net Worth: $4,950,420
Earnings: ($49,371)
Emp.: 4
Fiscal Year-end: 12/31/20
Real Estate Investment Services
N.A.I.C.S.: 531390
Muhammad Kubba (Gen Mgr)

RESOURCES GLOBAL DEVELOPMENT LIMITED
144 Robinson Road 11-02 Robinson Square, Singapore, 68908, Singapore
Tel.: (65) 62896588   SG
Web Site: https://www.rgd.sg
Year Founded: 2005
V7R—(CAT)
Rev.: $79,987,263
Assets: $91,521,999
Liabilities: $15,854,494
Net Worth: $75,667,505
Earnings: $20,494,032
Emp.: 40
Fiscal Year-end: 12/31/23
Coal Product Distr
N.A.I.C.S.: 423520
Francis Lee (CEO)

RESOURCES HOLDINGS LIMITED
Level 23 240 Queen Street, Brisbane, 4000, QLD, Australia
Tel.: (61) 735222895   AU
Web Site:
  https://www.revolverresources.com
Year Founded: 2021
RRR—(ASX)
Rev.: $18,989
Assets: $15,587,337
Liabilities: $717,736
Net Worth: $14,869,601
Earnings: ($1,830,770)
Fiscal Year-end: 06/30/23
Holding Company
N.A.I.C.S.: 551112

RESOURCES PRIMA GROUP LIMITED
10 Collyer Quay 10-01 Ocean Financial Centre, Singapore, 049315, Singapore
Tel.: (65) 6 531 2266   SG
Web Site:
  http://www.resourcesprima.com.sg
Assets: $1,603,000
Liabilities: $6,622,000
Net Worth: ($5,019,000)
Earnings: ($1,323,000)
Fiscal Year-end: 12/31/20
Holding Company
N.A.I.C.S.: 551112
Agus Sugiono (Chm & CEO)

RESPIRI LIMITED
Suite 1 Level 9 432 St Kilda Road, Melbourne, 3004, VIC, Australia
Tel.: (61) 396539160
Web Site: https://www.respiri.co
RSHUF—(OTCIQ)
Rev.: $1,101,281
Assets: $6,978,131
Liabilities: $1,177,948
Net Worth: $5,800,182
Earnings: ($8,459,003)
Emp.: 19
Fiscal Year-end: 06/30/21
Surgical & Medical Instrument Manufacturing
N.A.I.C.S.: 339112
Nicholas Smedley (Chm)

Subsidiaries:

iSonea (Israel) Limited   (1)

INTERNATIONAL PUBLIC

16 Palyam Avenue, Haifa, 33095, Israel
Tel.: (972) 48615025
Medical Equipment Mfr
N.A.I.C.S.: 339112

RESPONSE INFORMATICS LIMITED
3rd Floor Raghuma Towers Plot No 3 4 5, Madhapur, Hyderabad, 500 081, Telangana, India
Tel.: (91) 4040037073
Web Site:
  https://www.responseinformatics.com
538273—(BOM)
Rev.: $1,353,024
Assets: $1,316,060
Liabilities: $664,972
Net Worth: $651,088
Earnings: $74,084
Emp.: 92
Fiscal Year-end: 03/31/23
Information Technology Consulting Services
N.A.I.C.S.: 541512
K. Ravi Kumar (Compliance Officer & Sec)

Subsidiaries:

Response Informatics Inc.   (1)
22118 20th Ave SE Ste 122, Bothell, WA 98021
Tel.: (425) 486-7171
Software Solution & Management Consulting Services
N.A.I.C.S.: 541611

Technologia Corporation   (1)
5 Independence Way Ste 300, Princeton, NJ 08540
Tel.: (551) 261-6996
Web Site: https://www.technologiacorp.com
Software Development Services
N.A.I.C.S.: 541511

RESPONSIVE INDUSTRIES LTD
Mahagaon Road Betegaon Village Boisar East, Taluka Palghar Dist, Thane, 401501, Maharashtra, India
Tel.: (91) 2266562727
Web Site:
  https://www.responsiveindustries.com
505509—(BOM)
Rev.: $118,663,389
Assets: $167,932,618
Liabilities: $43,424,975
Net Worth: $124,507,643
Earnings: $2,929,920
Emp.: 54
Fiscal Year-end: 03/31/23
Vinyl Floor Mfr
N.A.I.C.S.: 326199
Ruchi Jaiswal (Compliance Officer & Sec)

Subsidiaries:

Axiom Cordages Limited   (1)
Esperanca Building 7th Floor Shahid Bhagat Singh Road Colaba, Mumbai, India   (89.86%)
Tel.: (91) 2266562724
Web Site: http://www.axiomcordages.com
Rope Mfr
N.A.I.C.S.: 314994

Responsive Industries LLC   (1)
360 Old Laurens Rd Ste 100, Simpsonville, SC 29681
Tel.: (864) 757-8358
Web Site: https://responsiveindustries.us
Flooring Installation Services
N.A.I.C.S.: 238330

RESSOURCES APPALACHES INC.
212 avenue De la Cathedrale, Rimouski, G5L 5J2, QC, Canada
Tel.: (418) 724-0901
Web Site:
  http://www.ressourcesappalaches.com

Year Founded: 1944
Metal Exploration & Development Services
N.A.I.C.S.: 213114
Alain Hupe *(Pres & CEO)*

REST EASY GROUP LTD.
Office 3 03 Cargo Works 1-2, London, SE1 9PG, Hatfields, United Kingdom
Tel.: (44) 2036370812   UK
Web Site:
http://www.resteasygroup.com
Real Estate Properties Management
N.A.I.C.S.: 531390
Joshua James *(COO)*

Subsidiaries:

Late Rooms Limited   (1)
The Peninsula Victoria Place, Manchester, M4 4FB, United Kingdom   **(49%)**
Tel.: (44) 333 014 6269
Web Site: http://www.laterooms.com
Online Accommodation Services
N.A.I.C.S.: 561599
Kat Wirth *(Mgr-PR)*

RESTALLIANCE
213 Rue De Gerland, 69007, Lyon, Rhone, France
Tel.: (33) 472765040
Web Site: http://www.restalliance.fr
Year Founded: 1993
Sales Range: $10-24.9 Million
Emp.: 20
Restaurant & Catering Services
N.A.I.C.S.: 722511
Christophe Dassonville *(Pres)*

RESTAR HOLDINGS CORPORATION
Restar building 2-10-9 Konan, Minato-ku, Tokyo, 108-0075, Japan
Tel.: (81) 357811011   JP
Web Site: https://www.restargp.com
Year Founded: 2009
3156—(TKS)
Rev.: $3,387,519,240
Assets: $1,928,163,440
Liabilities: $1,326,494,800
Net Worth: $601,668,640
Earnings: $46,296,440
Fiscal Year-end: 03/31/24
Holding Company; Electronic Components Mfr
N.A.I.C.S.: 551112
Rintaro Miyoshi *(Sr Mng Exec Officer)*

Subsidiaries:

CU-Tech Corporation   (1)
6 Hyeongoksandan-ro 93beon-gil, Cheongbuk-Eup, Pyeongtaek, 17812, Gyeonggi-do, Korea (South)
Tel.: (82) 316868400
Web Site: https://cutech.co.kr
Semiconductor Components Mfr
N.A.I.C.S.: 334413

Infinitec Co., Ltd   (1)
3rd Floor GotandaNN Building 2-12-19 Nishigotanda, Shinagawa-ku, Tokyo, 141 0031, Japan
Tel.: (81) 357596810
Web Site: http://www.infinitec.co.jp
Sales Range: $25-49.9 Million
Emp.: 30
Audio Visual Software Development Services
N.A.I.C.S.: 541511
Shin Haga *(Pres & CEO)*

Kyoshin Communications Co Ltd.   (1)
Restar building 2-10-9 Konan, Minato-ku, Tokyo, 108-0075, Japan
Tel.: (81) 334452074
Web Site: http://www.kycom.co.jp
Sales Range: $75-99.9 Million
Emp.: 170
Communication Equipment Whslr
N.A.I.C.S.: 423690

Subsidiary (Domestic):

HEISEIDO Co., Ltd.   (2)
61 Jyonanchou, Marugame, 763-0031, Kagawa, Japan
Tel.: (81) 877236355
Web Site: http://www.heiseido.co.jp
Broadcasting Equipment Mfr & Distr
N.A.I.C.S.: 334220

Kyoshin Technosonic (Shenzhen) Ltd.   (1)
Room 1308-09 1st Tower Xinwen Building Shennanzhong Road, Futian District, Shenzhen, 518027, Guangdong, China
Tel.: (86) 75582793120
Web Site: http://www.ukcgroup.com
Electronic Components Distr
N.A.I.C.S.: 423690

Kyoshin Technosonic Co., Ltd.   (1)
Gate City Ohsaki East Tower 1-11-2 Osaki Shinagawa-ku, Shinagawa-ku, Tokyo, 141-0032, Japan
Tel.: (81) 354961051
Web Site: http://www.kytec.co.jp
Sales Range: $1-4.9 Billion
Emp.: 200
Electronic Equipment & Components Mfr
N.A.I.C.S.: 334419

Subsidiary (Non-US):

Kyoshin Technosonic (Asia) Ltd.   (2)
1201B 3 12 F Tower1 Ever Gain Plaza No 88 Container Port Road, Kwai Chung, New Territories, China (Hong Kong)
Tel.: (852) 2850 8231
Web Site: http://www.kyoshin.hk
Electronic Components Mfr & Distr
N.A.I.C.S.: 334419

Kyoshin Technosonic (K) CO.,LTD.   (2)
Tong Yong Securities B D 13F 23-8 Yoidodong, Youngdeungpo-gu, Seoul, 158-820, Korea (South)
Tel.: (82) 2 785 3441
Web Site: http://www.kyotech.co.kr
Sales Range: $25-49.9 Million
Emp.: 45
Electronic Device Distr
N.A.I.C.S.: 423620

Leicester Holdings Co., Ltd.   (1)
3-6-5 Higashishinagawa, Shinagawa-ku, Tokyo, Japan
Tel.: (81) 3 3458 4618
Semiconductor & Electronic Components Mfr & Distr
N.A.I.C.S.: 334413
Kuniaki Konno *(Pres & COO)*

PCI Holdings Inc.   (1)
4F Tokyu Taranomon Bldg 21-19 Taranomon 1 Chome, Minato-ku, Tokyo, Japan   **(50.5%)**
Tel.: (81) 368580530
Web Site: https://www.pci-h.co.jp
Rev.: $202,001,190
Assets: $124,975,430
Liabilities: $60,470,610
Net Worth: $64,504,820
Earnings: $7,146,720
Emp.: 1,660
Fiscal Year-end: 09/30/2023
Software Applications
N.A.I.C.S.: 513210
Toyomi Amano *(Chm)*

Subsidiary (Domestic):

PCI AIOS Co., Ltd.   (2)
Iwanami-Shoten Hitotsubashi Bldg 9th Floor 2-5-5 Hitotsubashi, Chiyoda-Ku, Tokyo, 101-0003, Japan
Tel.: (81) 345778777
Web Site: http://www.pci-aios.jp
Information Technology Services
N.A.I.C.S.: 541512

Shanghai Kyotec Electronic Trading Co., Ltd   (1)
1701 Lippo Plaza 222 Huai Hai Zhong Road, Shanghai, 200021, China
Tel.: (86) 2153965511
Web Site: http://www.kyoshin.cn

Sales Range: $25-49.9 Million
Emp.: 12
Electronic Components Mfr
N.A.I.C.S.: 334419

UKC Electronics (H.K.) Co.,Ltd.   (1)
Unit1118-21 Level11 Tower1 Grand Central Plaza, 138 Shatin Rural Committee Road, Sha Tin, New Territories, China (Hong Kong)
Tel.: (852) 29506851
Web Site: http://www.ukc.com.hk
Sales Range: $25-49.9 Million
Emp.: 12
Semiconductor Components Mfr
N.A.I.C.S.: 333242

Subsidiary (Non-US):

USC Electronics (China) Co., Ltd.   (2)
Room 1311-15 1st Tower Xinwen Building Shennanzhong Road, Futian District, Shenzhen, 518027, Guangdong, China
Tel.: (86) 75582091821
Web Site: http://www.usc.co.jp
Electronic Component Sales & Circuit Boards Installation Services
N.A.I.C.S.: 423690

UKC Electronics (S) PTE,LTD.   (1)
78 Shenton Way 16-01, Singapore, 079120, Singapore
Tel.: (65) 63445188
Web Site: http://www.ukc.com.sg
Sales Range: $25-49.9 Million
Emp.: 17
Electronic Component Sales
N.A.I.C.S.: 423690
Masahiro Shibata *(Mng Dir)*

UKC Electronics (Thailand) Co.,Ltd.   (1)
Zone A 22nd Floor Thaniya Plaza Building No 52 Silom Road Suriyawongse, Bangrak, Bangkok, 10500, Thailand
Tel.: (66) 22382710
Electronic Component Sales
N.A.I.C.S.: 423690
Katadaki Yoshida *(Mng Dir)*

USC Corporation   (1)
1-11-2 Osaki Gate City Ohsaki, Shinagawa-ku, 141-0032, Tokyo, Japan   **(100%)**
Tel.: (81) 334918571
Web Site: http://www.usc.co.jp
Sales Range: $50-74.9 Million
Emp.: 200
Electronic Components Mfr; Semiconductors
N.A.I.C.S.: 334419
Yukio Fukuju *(Pres)*

Subsidiary (Non-US):

USC ELECTRONICS (Korea) CO.,LTD.   (2)
14F Korea Sanhak Foundation Building 1337-31 Seocho Dong, Seocho Gu, Seoul, 137-072, Korea (South)
Tel.: (82) 52243671
Web Site: http://www.usckr.com
Electronic Component Sales
N.A.I.C.S.: 423690

USC Electronics (Shanghai) Co.,Ltd.   (1)
Room A210 Shang Mira Commercial Center No 2633, West Yanan Road, Shanghai, 200336, China
Tel.: (86) 21 62090626
Web Site: http://www.usc.co.jp
Electronic Component Sales
N.A.I.C.S.: 423690

Uni Device Corporation Co., Ltd   (1)
Kongou Building Nishi Gotanda 7-10-4, Shinagawa-ku, Tokyo, 141-0031, Japan
Tel.: (81) 3 3490 2173
Web Site: http://www.unidevice.co.jp
Sales Range: $50-74.9 Million
Emp.: 80
Semiconductor Devices Import & Distr
N.A.I.C.S.: 423690

Subsidiary (Non-US):

Uni Device (S) Pte Ltd   (2)
1 Sims Lane 04-10, Singapore, 387355, Singapore

Tel.: (65) 67783811
Web Site: http://www.ukcgroup.com
Semiconductor Device Distr
N.A.I.C.S.: 423690

Uni Device (Shanghai) Co., Ltd   (2)
7N Hengji Building 99 East Huaihai Road, Shanghai, 2000211, China
Tel.: (86) 2153069922
Web Site: http://www.ukcgroup.com
Electronic Components Mfr & Distr
N.A.I.C.S.: 334419

Vitec Electronics (Singapore) Pte. Ltd.   (1)
100 Tras St No 14-01 Amara Corp Tower, Singapore, Singapore
Tel.: (65) 62220192
Semiconductors & Electronic Components Distr
N.A.I.C.S.: 334413

Vitec Electronics (Taiwan) Co., Ltd.   (1)
Unit D 9 F No 146 Songjiang Rd, Taipei, 10458, Taiwan
Tel.: (886) 225421579
Web Site: http://www.vitec-tw.com.tw
Sales Range: $50-74.9 Million
Emp.: 10
Electronic Devices Whslr
N.A.I.C.S.: 423620

Vitec Electronics Trading (Shanghai) Co., Ltd.   (1)
Rm 2612-2613 Shanghai City Ctr A 100 Zunyi Rd, Shanghai, 200336, China
Tel.: (86) 2162372226
Web Site: http://www.vitec.co.jp
Sales Range: $25-49.9 Million
Emp.: 13
Semiconductor & Electronics Component Distr
N.A.I.C.S.: 333242

Vitec Global Operations - Hong Kong   (1)
Unit 1411 14th Floor Tower 1 Silvercord 30 Canton Road, Tsim Sha Tsui, Kowloon, China (Hong Kong)
Tel.: (852) 23118826
Web Site: http://www.vitec.co.jp
Sales Range: $25-49.9 Million
Emp.: 16
Semiconductors & Electronic Components Mfr
N.A.I.C.S.: 334413

RESTART SIIQ
Via Tortona 37, 20144, Milan, Italy
Tel.: (39) 024220171
Web Site: https://www.restart-group.com
LLB2—(BER)
Sales Range: Less than $1 Million
Real Estate Investment Services
N.A.I.C.S.: 531390
Giacomo Garbuglia *(Pres)*

RESTAURANT BRANDS ASIA LTD.
Office No 1003 To 1007 B Wing 10th Floor, Mittal Commercia Asan Pada Road Chimatpada Marol Andheri East, Mumbai, 400059, India
Tel.: (91) 2271933047
Web Site: http://www.burgerking.in
Year Founded: 1954
543248—(BOM)
Rev.: $206,485,052
Assets: $325,161,291
Liabilities: $179,345,439
Net Worth: $145,815,852
Earnings: $32,098,521
Emp.: 7,784
Fiscal Year-end: 03/31/22
Restaurant Services
N.A.I.C.S.: 722511
Rajeev Varman *(CEO)*

Subsidiaries:

P.T. Sari Chicken Indonesia   (1)

RESTAURANT BRANDS INTERNATIONAL INC.

Restaurant Brands Asia Ltd.—(Continued)

RESTAURANT BRANDS INTERNATIONAL INC.
130 King Street West Ste 300, Toronto, M5X 1E1, ON, Canada
Tel.: (905) 339-6011 Ca
Web Site: https://www.rbi.com
Year Founded: 2014
QSR—(NYSE)
Rev.: $7,022,000,000
Assets: $23,391,000,000
Liabilities: $18,661,000,000
Net Worth: $4,730,000,000
Earnings: $1,190,000,000
Emp.: 9,000
Fiscal Year-end: 12/31/23
Holding Company; Fast Food Restaurants Franchisor & Operator
N.A.I.C.S.: 551112
Jill M. Granat (Gen Counsel & Sec)

Subsidiaries:

Carrols Restaurant Group, Inc. (1)
968 James St, Syracuse, NY 13203
Tel.: (315) 424-0513
Web Site: https://www.carrols.com
Rev.: $1,652,370,000
Assets: $1,687,064,000
Liabilities: $1,472,840,000
Net Worth: $214,224,000
Earnings: ($43,029,000)
Emp.: 25,500
Fiscal Year-end: 01/02/2022
Holding Company; Fast-Food Restaurants Owner, Operator & Franchisor
N.A.I.C.S.: 551112
Anthony E. Hull (Interim Pres, Interim CEO, CFO, Treas & VP)

Subsidiary (Domestic):

Cambridge Real Estate Development, LLC (2)
23400 Michigan Ave Ste 301, Dearborn, MI 48126
Tel.: (313) 277-8500
Web Site: https://www.cambridgecre.com
Real Estate Services
N.A.I.C.S.: 531390

Carrols Corporation (2)
968 James St, Syracuse, NY 13203-2503
Tel.: (315) 424-0513
Web Site: https://www.carrols.com
Quick-Service Franchise Restaurants Operator
N.A.I.C.S.: 722513

Texas Taco Cabana, L.P. (2)
8918 Tesoro Dr Ste 200, San Antonio, TX 78217
Tel.: (210) 283-5500
Web Site: https://www.tacocabana.com
Restaurant Operators
N.A.I.C.S.: 722511

Firehouse Restaurant Group, Inc. (1)
3400-8 Kori Rd, Jacksonville, FL 32257
Tel.: (904) 886-8300
Web Site: http://www.firehousesubs.com
Sales Range: $350-399.9 Million
Emp.: 7,000
Fast Food Restaurant Owner, Operator & Franchiser
N.A.I.C.S.: 722513
Robin Sorensen (Co-Founder)

Restaurant Brands International Limited Partnership (1)
130 King Street West Suite 300, PO Box 339, Toronto, M5X 1E1, ON, Canada
Tel.: (905) 339-6011
Web Site: https://www.rbi.com
Rev.: $6,505,000,000
Assets: $22,746,000,000
Liabilities: $18,478,000,000
Net Worth: $4,268,000,000
Earnings: $1,479,000,000
Emp.: 6,400
Fiscal Year-end: 12/31/2022
Holding Company; Fast Food Restaurants Franchisor & Operator
N.A.I.C.S.: 551112

Subsidiary (US):

Burger King Worldwide, Inc. (2)
5505 Blue Lagoon Dr, Miami, FL 33126
Tel.: (305) 378-3000
Web Site: http://www.burgerking.com
Sales Range: $1-4.9 Billion
Emp.: 2,420
Fast Food Restaurant Franchisor & Operator; Holding Company
N.A.I.C.S.: 551112
Alexandre G. Macedo (Exec VP)

Subsidiary (Domestic):

Burger King Holdings, Inc. (3)
5505 Blue Lagoon Dr, Miami, FL 33126 (100%)
Tel.: (305) 378-3000
Web Site: http://www.bk.com
Holding Company; Fast Food Restaurants Franchisor & Operator
N.A.I.C.S.: 551112

Subsidiary (Non-US):

BK Argentina Servicios, S.A. (4)
Av Leandro N Alem 449, 1003, Buenos Aires, Argentina
Tel.: (54) 11 5199 2500
Fast Food Restaurant Operator
N.A.I.C.S.: 722513

Burger King A.B. (4)
Birger Jarlsg 16, 114 34, Stockholm, Sweden
Tel.: (46) 31 720 57 00
Web Site: http://www.burgerking.se
Fast Food Restaurant Operator
N.A.I.C.S.: 722513

Subsidiary (Domestic):

Burger King Corporation (4)
1309 NW 20th St, Miami, FL 33142
Tel.: (305) 325-0968
Web Site: http://www.bk.com
Sales Range: $10-24.9 Million
Emp.: 50
Fast Food Restaurants Franchisor & Operator
N.A.I.C.S.: 722513
Ivette Diaz (Dir-Corp Social Responsibility)

Subsidiary (Non-US):

Burger King Espana S.L.U. (4)
Avda de Europa 26 Atica Edif 7, Pozuelo de Alarcon, 28224, Madrid, Spain
Tel.: (34) 900 814 511
Web Site: http://www.burgerking.es
Fast Food Restaurant Operator
N.A.I.C.S.: 722513

Burger King Limited (4)
15 Bath Rd, Slough, SL1 3UF, United Kingdom
Tel.: (44) 1753500000
Web Site: http://www.burgerking.co.uk
Sales Range: $25-49.9 Million
Emp.: 80
Holding Company; Fast Food Restaurant Franchisor & Operator
N.A.I.C.S.: 551112
Alasdair Murdoch (CEO)

Subsidiary (Domestic):

Burger King (UK) Limited (5)
15 Bath Road, Slough, SL1 3UF, United Kingdom
Tel.: (44) 1753500000
Web Site: http://www.burgerking.co.uk
Sales Range: $25-49.9 Million
Emp.: 25
Fast Food Restaurant Franchisor & Operator
N.A.I.C.S.: 722513

Mini Meals Limited (5)
Park House, Slough, SL1 3UF, Berkshire, United Kingdom
Tel.: (44) 2086222600
Fast Food Restaurant Operator
N.A.I.C.S.: 722513

Subsidiary (Non-US):

Burger King Nederland Services B.V. (4)
Herikerbergweg 238, Amsterdam-Zuidoost, 1101 CM, Amsterdam, Netherlands
Tel.: (31) 10 2863700
Fast Food Restaurants Franchisor

N.A.I.C.S.: 533110

Subsidiary (Domestic):

Goldco Inc. (3)
1435 Ross Clark Cir Ste 2, Dothan, AL 36301-4746
Tel.: (334) 793-0997
Web Site: http://www.goldcoinc.com
Sales Range: $10-24.9 Million
Emp.: 25
Restaurant Services
N.A.I.C.S.: 722513
Benny Arbour (Pres)

RESTILE CERAMICS LIMITED
204 Sakar Complex Opp ABS Tower Vaccine Crossing Old Padra Road, Vadodara, 390015, Gujarat, India
Tel.: (91) 9989069956
Web Site: https://www.restile.com
Year Founded: 1986
515085—(BOM)
Rev.: $249,754
Assets: $2,406,304
Liabilities: $5,557,748
Net Worth: ($3,151,444)
Earnings: ($914,959)
Fiscal Year-end: 03/31/21
Ceramic Products Mfr
N.A.I.C.S.: 327120
Nalinkant Amratlal Rathod (Chm)

RESTOQUE COMERCIO E CONFECCOES DE ROUPAS S.A.
Rua Oscar Freire nos 1 119 and 1 121/405, 01426-001, Sao Paulo, Brazil
Tel.: (55) 1148608860
Web Site: http://www.restoque.com.br
Year Founded: 1982
LLIS3—(BRAZ)
Rev.: $50,383,081
Assets: $295,467,717
Liabilities: $110,863,764
Net Worth: $184,603,953
Earnings: $1,742,550
Emp.: 1,130
Fiscal Year-end: 12/31/23
Women's Fashion Apparel, Accessories & Home Decor Products Designer & Retailer
N.A.I.C.S.: 458110
Livinston Martins Bauermeister (CEO)

RESTORE PLC
7-10 Chandos Street, London, W1G 9DQ, United Kingdom
Tel.: (44) 2074092420
Web Site: https://www.restoreplc.com
RST—(AIM)
Rev.: $352,183,792
Assets: $776,571,573
Liabilities: $431,709,164
Net Worth: $344,862,408
Earnings: $21,206,766
Emp.: 2,881
Fiscal Year-end: 12/31/22
Data & Document Management Services
N.A.I.C.S.: 518210
Sharon Baylay (Chm)

Subsidiaries:

Alfred Thomas Consultancy Limited (1)
17 Brunel Way Segensworth East, Fareham, PO15 5TX, Hampshire, United Kingdom
Tel.: (44) 1489232262
Web Site: https://alfredthomas.co.uk
Waste Electronic Equipment Recycling Services
N.A.I.C.S.: 562111

Capture All Limited (1)
9 Castings Court, Middlefield Industrial Estate, Falkirk, FK2 9HQ, United Kingdom

Tel.: (44) 1324670353
Web Site: https://www.capture-all.co.uk
Storage Services
N.A.I.C.S.: 493110

Harrow Green Limited (1)
2 Oriental Road, London, E16 2BZ, United Kingdom
Tel.: (44) 3456038774
Web Site: https://www.restore.co.uk
Sales Range: $25-49.9 Million
Business Moving Services
N.A.I.C.S.: 561990
Tim Ryder (Mng Dir)

International Technology Products GmbH (1)
Rontgenstrasse 4, 63512, Hainburg, Germany
Tel.: (49) 6182958880
Web Site: https://www.itp-leergut.com
Toner Cartridge Distr
N.A.I.C.S.: 424120

Office Green Limited (1)
52 Burners Lane, PO Box 8127, Kilnfarm, Milton Keynes, MK11 3HD, United Kingdom
Tel.: (44) 1908635330
Web Site: https://www.officegreen.co.uk
Cartridge Recycling Services
N.A.I.C.S.: 811210

PRM Green Technologies Limited (1)
Telford way, Bedford, MK42 0PQ, Bedfordshire, United Kingdom
Tel.: (44) 1462813132
Web Site: https://www.restore.co.uk
Data Management Services
N.A.I.C.S.: 518210

Restore Datashred Limited (1)
Unit 1 QED Purfleet Bypass, Purfleet, RM19 1NA, Essex, United Kingdom
Tel.: (44) 3332209689
Data Management Services
N.A.I.C.S.: 518210

Restore Digital Limited (1)
Village Way, Bilston, Wolverhampton, WV14 0UJ, United Kingdom
Tel.: (44) 3301624505
Web Site: https://www.restore.co.uk
Storage Services
N.A.I.C.S.: 493110

Restore Ltd (1)
Unit 5 Redhill Distr Ctr Salbrook Rd, Redhill, RH1 5DY, Surrey, United Kingdom
Tel.: (44) 8447255540
Web Site: http://www.restore.co.uk
Sales Range: $75-99.9 Million
Emp.: 300
Document Storage Services
N.A.I.C.S.: 493190

Restore Scan Limited (1)
2 Tally Close Agecroft Commerce Park, Swinton, Manchester, M27 8WJ, United Kingdom
Tel.: (44) 3330435483
Sales Range: $10-24.9 Million
Data Scanning Services
N.A.I.C.S.: 518210
Ian Pattison (Dir-Fin)

Restore Technology Limited (1)
Telford Way, Bedford, MK42 0PQ, Bedfordshire, United Kingdom
Tel.: (44) 1462813132
Web Site: https://www.restore.co.uk
Sales Range: $10-24.9 Million
Information Technology Support Services
N.A.I.C.S.: 518210

Takeback Limited (1)
52 Burners Lane, Kilnfarm, Milton Keynes, MK11 3HD, Norfolk, United Kingdom
Tel.: (44) 1908635330
Web Site: https://www.takeback.ltd.uk
Cartridge Recycling Services
N.A.I.C.S.: 811210

The Bookyard Limited (1)
Davy Road, Runcorn, WA7 1PZ, United Kingdom
Tel.: (44) 1514274803
Web Site: https://www.thebookyard.com
Computer Peripheral Distr
N.A.I.C.S.: 423430

AND PRIVATE COMPANIES

Ultratec Limited (1)
Ultratec House Unit 1 Stevenage Business Park Eastman Way, Stevenage, SG1 4SZ, United Kingdom
Tel.: (44) 1438211200
Web Site: https://www.ultratec.co.uk
Hardware Product Mfr & Distr
N.A.I.C.S.: 332510

Ultratest Solutions Limited (1)
Unit 1 Eastman Way, Stevenage, SG1 4SZ, United Kingdom
Tel.: (44) 1438211200
Web Site: https://www.ultratestsolutions.com
Hardware Product Mfr & Distr
N.A.I.C.S.: 332510

RESTORIA
Boulevard De La Romanerie, BP 701, Parc d'Activite d'Angers, 49124, Saint-Barthelemy-d'Anjou, Cedex, France
Tel.: (33) 8 99 183873
Web Site: http://www.restoria.fr
Rev.: $21,700,000
Emp.: 240
Restaurant
N.A.I.C.S.: 722511
Catherine Giraud Gandon *(Mgr)*

RESUL, EQUIPAMENTOS DE ENERGIA S.A.
Rua Pedro Miranda no 76/78, Luanda, Angola
Tel.: (244) 222325890   AO
Electronic Products Mfr
N.A.I.C.S.: 335999

RESUL, EQUIPAMENTOS DE ENERGIA S.A.
Rua da Franca no 90 -3rd left, Maputo, Mozambique
Tel.: (258) 21418057   MZ
Electronic Products Mfr
N.A.I.C.S.: 335999

RESUL, EQUIPAMENTOS DE ENERGIA SA
Parque oriente Rua D Nuno Alvares Pereira Bloco 1/2, 2695-167, Bobadela, Portugal
Tel.: (351) 218394980   PT
Web Site: http://www.resul.pt
Year Founded: 1982
Electronic Products Mfr
N.A.I.C.S.: 335999
Carlos Cunha Torres *(Pres)*

RESURGERE MINES & MINERALS INDIA LIMITED
15 Morvi House 28 30 Goa Street Ballard Estate, Mumbai, 400 038, India
Tel.: (91) 2266582500   In
Web Site: http://www.resurgere.in
Year Founded: 1987
533017—(BOM)
Iron Ore Mining, Exploration & Sales
N.A.I.C.S.: 212210
Subhash Sharma *(Chm, CEO & Mng Dir)*

RESURS HOLDING AB
Ekslingan 9 Vala Norra, PO Box 22209, 250 24, Helsingborg, Sweden
Tel.: (46) 42382000   SE
Web Site:
https://www.resursholding.com
Year Founded: 1977
RESURS—(OMX)
Rev.: $412,309,654
Assets: $5,099,740,691
Liabilities: $4,342,273,984
Net Worth: $757,466,707
Earnings: $25,598,011
Emp.: 660
Fiscal Year-end: 12/31/23
Finance & Banking Services
N.A.I.C.S.: 522110
Erik Frick *(Deputy CEO-Resurs Bank & COO)*

Subsidiaries:

Solid Forsakring AB (1)
Landskronavagen 23, 252 32, Helsingborg, Sweden
Tel.: (46) 42382100
Loan Services
N.A.I.C.S.: 522390

RESVERLOGIX CORP.
300 4820 Richard Road SW, Calgary, T3E 6L1, AB, Canada
Tel.: (403) 254-9252   AB
Web Site:
https://www.resverlogix.com
Year Founded: 2000
RVX—(TSX)
Assets: $10,706,000
Liabilities: $50,601,000
Net Worth: ($39,895,000)
Earnings: ($1,643,000)
Emp.: 27
Fiscal Year-end: 12/31/20
Pharmaceuticals Product Mfr
N.A.I.C.S.: 325412
Donald J. McCaffrey *(Co-Founder, Chm, Pres & CEO)*

Subsidiaries:

Resverlogix Inc. (1)

RETAIL ENGINEERING LTD.
Tsarigradsko Chaussee 7-th Km Building 3, 1784, Sofia, Bulgaria
Tel.: (359) 2971 8145
Web Site: http://www.r-eng.bg
Year Founded: 2004
Engineering Consulting Services
N.A.I.C.S.: 541330

RETAIL ESTATES N.V.
Industrielaan 6, 1740, Ternat, Vlaams-Brabant, Belgium
Tel.: (32) 25681020
Web Site:
https://www.retailestates.com
RET—(EUR)
Rev.: $135,825,599
Assets: $2,151,268,077
Liabilities: $959,746,385
Net Worth: $1,191,521,692
Earnings: $195,808,332
Emp.: 36
Fiscal Year-end: 03/31/23
Real Estate Investment & Development Services
N.A.I.C.S.: 531390
Paul Borghgraef *(Chm)*

Subsidiaries:

Belgium Retail 1 N.V. (1)
Industrielaan 6, Ternat, 1740, Belgium
Tel.: (32) 25681020
Web Site: http://www.retailestates.com
Sales Range: $50-74.9 Million
Emp.: 16
Real Estate Agencies
N.A.I.C.S.: 531210

Finsbury Properties N.V. (1)
Industrielaan 6, 1740, Ternat, Belgium
Tel.: (32) 25681020
Web Site: http://www.retailestates.com
Real Estate Agencies
N.A.I.C.S.: 531210

Wickes Land Development N.V. (1)
Industrielaan 6, 1740, Ternat, Belgium
Tel.: (32) 25681020
Sales Range: $50-74.9 Million
Emp.: 10
Real Estate Rental Services
N.A.I.C.S.: 531390
Gan Denys *(Gen Mgr)*

RETAIL FOOD GROUP LIMITED
Level 4 35 Robina Town Centre Drive, Robina, 4226, QLD, Australia
Tel.: (61) 755913242   AU
Web Site: http://www.rfg.com.au
RFG—(ASX)
Rev.: $81,618,961
Assets: $240,421,857
Liabilities: $104,797,549
Net Worth: $135,624,308
Earnings: $3,775,836
Emp.: 7,000
Fiscal Year-end: 06/28/24
Bakery Products Mfr
N.A.I.C.S.: 424490
Anthony Mark Connors *(Sec & Dir-Corp Svcs)*

Subsidiaries:

Brumby's Bakeries (NZ) Ltd (1)
Unit B3 48 Oakleigh Avenue, Southgate Takanini, Auckland, 2112, New Zealand
Tel.: (64) 93777615
Web Site: http://www.brumbys.co.nz
Bakery Products Retailer
N.A.I.C.S.: 445291

Di Bella Coffee, LLC (1)
11 Hoyle Ave, Castle Hill, 2154, NSW, Australia
Tel.: (61) 180 033 2163
Web Site: https://shop.dibellacoffee.com
Coffee Product Distr
N.A.I.C.S.: 445298

Donutcino Pty Ltd. (1)
1 olympic circuit, Southport, 4215, QLD, Australia
Tel.: (61) 755913242
Sales Range: $25-49.9 Million
Emp.: 50
Bakery Products Retailer
N.A.I.C.S.: 311811

Gourmet Foods Australia Pty Limited (1)
6 Dollier Street, Jandakot, 6164, WA, Australia
Tel.: (61) 89 414 7444
Web Site:
https://www.gourmetfoodsaustralia.com
Gourmet Food Product Mfr & Distr
N.A.I.C.S.: 311999

Hudson Pacific Group Limited (1)
Level 5 52 Phillip Street, Sydney, 2000, NSW, Australia
Tel.: (61) 292517177
Web Site: https://www.hpgl.com.au
Sales Range: $50-74.9 Million
Emp.: 30
Property Investment & Management Services
N.A.I.C.S.: 522299
Francis Choy *(CFO)*

Michel s Patisserie (SA) Pty Ltd. (1)
Cent Markets Shop 28 Victoria Sq Gouger St, Adelaide, 5000, SA, Australia
Tel.: (61) 884101161
Bakery Products Retailer
N.A.I.C.S.: 424420

The Michel's Group Australia Pty Ltd (1)
9 Ferngrove Pl, Granville, 2142, NSW, Australia
Tel.: (61) 297382400
Bakery Products Retailer
N.A.I.C.S.: 424420

bb's Cafe System Pty Ltd (1)
PO Box 1549, Southport, 4215, QLD, Australia
Tel.: (61) 755913242
Web Site: http://www.bbscafe.com.au
Sales Range: $25-49.9 Million
Emp.: 95
Bakery Products Retailer
N.A.I.C.S.: 311811
Tim Peirce *(Mgr-Mktg)*

bb's New Zealand Ltd (1)
10 F Morningside Drive Kingsland, PO Box 68-324, Newton, Auckland, 1025, New Zealand

RETAIL HOLDINGS N.V.

Tel.: (64) 95257700
Web Site: http://www.bbscafe.com.au
Sales Range: $25-49.9 Million
Emp.: 12
Cafeteria Management Services
N.A.I.C.S.: 561110

RETAIL HOLDINGS N.V.
Kaya W F G Jombi Mensing 36, Willemstad, Curacao
Tel.: (599) 94611299   AN
Web Site:
https://www.retailholdings.com
Year Founded: 1851
RHDGF—(OTCEM)
Assets: $1,350,000
Liabilities: $103,000
Net Worth: $1,247,000
Earnings: ($439,000)
Fiscal Year-end: 12/31/23
Holding Company; Consumer Products Mfr, Retailer & Marketer
N.A.I.C.S.: 551112

Subsidiaries:

SINGER ASIA Sourcing LIMITED (1)
7th Floor Baskerville House 13 Duddell Street, Central, China (Hong Kong)
Tel.: (852) 31562860
Home Appliance Distr
N.A.I.C.S.: 423620

Singer (Malaysia) Sdn Bhd (1)
Lot 6 Jalan 51/217 Section 51, 46050, Petaling Jaya, Selangor Darul Ehsan, Malaysia
Tel.: (60) 379859090
Web Site: http://www.singer.com.my
Sales Range: $100-124.9 Million
Home Appliances Retailer
N.A.I.C.S.: 449210

Singer Americas Trading S.A. (1)
Caixa Postal 776 Bairro Viracopos, 13053-901, Campinas, Brazil
Tel.: (55) 1937254433
Industrial Machinery Mfr
N.A.I.C.S.: 333248

Singer Asia Limited (1)
7th Floor Baskerville House 13 Duddell Street, Central, China (Hong Kong)   (54.1%)
Tel.: (852) 3156 2860
Web Site: http://singerindia.net
Holding Company
N.A.I.C.S.: 551112
Gavin J. Walker *(Pres & CEO)*

Subsidiary (Non-US):

Singer Bangladesh Limited (2)
Gulshan center point house 23-26 21st floor rd 90-91 gulshan-2, Dhaka, 1212, Bangladesh   (75%)
Tel.: (880) 9606600600
Web Site: https://www.singerbd.com
Rev.: $179,164,174
Assets: $119,537,522
Liabilities: $82,605,214
Net Worth: $36,932,309
Earnings: $11,937,921
Emp.: 1,653
Fiscal Year-end: 12/31/2019
Sewing machines Mfr
N.A.I.C.S.: 333248
Abu Zafor Mohammed Kibria *(Head-Consumer Svc)*

Singer India Limited (2)
A 26/4 Mohan Co-operative Industrial Estate, New Delhi, 110044, India   (80.1%)
Tel.: (91) 1140617777
Web Site: http://www.singerindia.net
Emp.: 50
Sewing Machine Cabinet Mfr
N.A.I.C.S.: 321999
Rajeev Bajaj *(Mng Dir)*

Subsidiary (Domestic):

Brand Trading (India) Pvt. Limited (3)
A-26/4 IInd Floor Mohan Co-operative Industrial Area, New Delhi, India
Tel.: (91) 1140617777
Home Appliances Retailer
N.A.I.C.S.: 449210

RETAIL HOLDINGS N.V.

Retail Holdings N.V.—(Continued)

Alpana Sarna *(Mgr-HR)*

Subsidiary (Non-US):

Waves Corporation Limited (2)
9 KM Multan Road, Hanjarwal, Lahore, 74400, Pakistan (70.3%)
Tel.: (92) 4235415421
Web Site: https://www.singer.com.pk
Sales Range: $10-24.9 Million
Emp.: 794
Sewing Machines & Home Appliances Mfr & Retailer
N.A.I.C.S.: 335210
Haroon Ahmad Khan *(CEO)*

Singer Guyana Inc (1)
5 A Water St, Georgetown, Guyana
Tel.: (592) 2278885
Web Site: http://www.singer.com
Household Appliance Stores
N.A.I.C.S.: 449210

Singer Italia S.p.A. (1)
Via Quattro Notenbre 92, 20021, Bollate, Italy
Tel.: (39) 02333391
Web Site: http://www.svpworldwide.com
Sales Range: $25-49.9 Million
Emp.: 20
Electrical Appliance Television & Radio Set Whslr
N.A.I.C.S.: 423620

Singer Nederland BV (1)
Gasthuisstraat 96, Tiel, Netherlands
Tel.: (31) 344670908
Web Site: http://www.singer.nl
Sales Range: $50-74.9 Million
Emp.: 4
Electrical Appliance Television & Radio Set Whslr
N.A.I.C.S.: 423620
Gohan Maas *(Mng Dir)*

Singer Shanghai Sewing Machine Company Ltd (1)
1078 Da Yao Rd, Minhang Dist, 200245, Shanghai, China
Tel.: (86) 2164307778
Web Site: http://www.singersh.com
Emp.: 400
Electrical Equipment & Component Mfr
N.A.I.C.S.: 335999

RETAIL PARTNERS CO., LTD.
1936 Edomari, Hofu, 747-8509, Yamaguchi, Japan
Tel.: (81) 835381511
Web Site: https://www.mrk09.co.jp
Year Founded: 1954
8167—(TKS)
Rev.: $1,787,821,490
Assets: $894,991,970
Liabilities: $320,857,950
Net Worth: $574,134,020
Earnings: $33,443,530
Fiscal Year-end: 02/29/24
Store Operator
N.A.I.C.S.: 445110
Yasuo Tanaka *(Pres)*

RETAIL READY FOODS INC
130 Adelaide St W Suite 3302, Toronto, M5H 3P5, ON, Canada
Tel.: (416) 306-8788
Web Site:
 https://www.retailready.com
Year Founded: 1988
Sales Range: $50-74.9 Million
Emp.: 21
Meat Distr
N.A.I.C.S.: 424470
John Ferraro *(Founder & CEO)*

RETAILORS LTD.
Hermon St, PO Box 76, Airport City, 701990, Israel
Tel.: (972) 39051768
Web Site: https://retailors.com
Year Founded: 2008

RTLS—(TAE)
Rev.: $524,365,544
Assets: $763,173,093
Liabilities: $508,055,149
Net Worth: $255,117,944
Earnings: $35,309,636
Fiscal Year-end: 09/30/23
Foot Retailer
N.A.I.C.S.: 458210
Dov Schneidman *(Co-CEO)*

RETEC DIGITAL PLC
Alma Park Woodway Lane, Claybrooke Parva, Lutterworth, LE17 5FB, Leicester, United Kingdom
Tel.: (44) 1455222260
Year Founded: 1999
Sales Range: $10-24.9 Million
Emp.: 48
Multi-Channel Marketing Services
N.A.I.C.S.: 541613
Brian Ivory *(Chm)*

Subsidiaries:

Liquid Digital Limited (1)
12 Berry St, London, EC1V 0AU, United Kingdom
Tel.: (44) 20 7841 3060
Digital Marketing Services
N.A.I.C.S.: 541613

Media 4 (UK) Limited (1)
2220 Kettering Prkwy Kettering Venture Park, Kettering, NN15 6XR, Northamptonshire, United Kingdom
Tel.: (44) 8452252900
Web Site: http://www.media4uk.com
Network Installation Services
N.A.I.C.S.: 541512

RETECH TECHNOLOGY CO., LIMITED
F 18 Tower 2 Fudan Technology Park 335 Guoding Road Yangpu District, Shanghai, China
Tel.: (86) 4006751989
Web Site: http://www.retech-rte.com
RTE—(ASX)
Rev.: $26,303,193
Assets: $81,834,862
Liabilities: $36,239,189
Net Worth: $45,595,673
Earnings: $(1,986,888)
Fiscal Year-end: 12/31/22
Vocational Education Services
N.A.I.C.S.: 611710
Shungang Ai *(Co-Chm)*

Subsidiaries:

Ai English Pty. Ltd. (1)
Level 5 10 Dorcas St, Southbank, 3006, VIC, Australia
Tel.: (61) 386189800
Web Site: http://www.aienglish.com.au
Education Management Services
N.A.I.C.S.: 611710

Prosage Sustainability Development Limited (1)
Unit 4201 and 4209 42/F AIA Tower 183 Electric Road, North Point, China (Hong Kong)
Tel.: (852) 22091799
Web Site: http://www.pro-sage.com
Education Management Services
N.A.I.C.S.: 611710

RETELIT S.P.A.
Via Pola 9, 20124, Milan, Italy
Tel.: (39) 022020451
Web Site: http://www.retelit.it
LIT—(ITA)
Rev.: $92,937,181
Assets: $302,718,315
Liabilities: $120,424,145
Net Worth: $182,294,170
Earnings: $12,180,717
Emp.: 92
Fiscal Year-end: 12/31/19
Broadband Communication Services

N.A.I.C.S.: 517112
Federico Protto *(CEO & Gen Mgr)*

Subsidiaries:

InAsset S.r.l. (1)
Via Spilimbergo, Pasian di Prato, 66-33037, Udine, Italy
Tel.: (39) 04321698050
Construction Engineering Services
N.A.I.C.S.: 541330

Subsidiary (Domestic):

Telenia s.r.l. (2)
via Venezia 4, 73044, Galatone, Lecce, Italy
Tel.: (39) 08331980378
Web Site: http://www.telenia-srl.com
Electric Equipment Mfr
N.A.I.C.S.: 335311

Up Solutions Srl (1)
Via Cavour 2, 22074, Lomazzo, Italy
Tel.: (39) 0312073472
Web Site: http://www.just-mes.com
Textile Mfr
N.A.I.C.S.: 313310

RETEZAT SA
Str I S Bach 4, Sibiu, Romania
Tel.: (40) 269213230
RETZ—(BUC)
Rev.: $3,422,630
Assets: $8,536,331
Liabilities: $201,377
Net Worth: $8,334,954
Earnings: $1,961,029
Emp.: 7
Fiscal Year-end: 12/31/21
Agricultural Machinery Mfr
N.A.I.C.S.: 333111
Maria Alexandra Neamtiu *(Pres)*

RETHMANN AG & CO. KG
Norbert-Rethmann-Platz 1, 59379, Selm, Germany
Tel.: (49) 25922100
Web Site: http://www.rethmann-gruppe.de
Sales Range: $5-14.9 Billion
Emp.: 40,000
Holding Company
N.A.I.C.S.: 551112
Reinhard Lohmann *(Deputy Chm-Supervisory Bd)*

Subsidiaries:

Berndt GmbH (1)
Hauptstr 2-4, 85445, Berlin, Germany
Tel.: (49) 8122 888 0
Web Site: http://www.berndt-gmbh.de
Waste Recycling Services
N.A.I.C.S.: 562998

Bioceval GmbH & Co. KG (1)
Neufelder Strasse 44, 27472, Cuxhaven, Germany
Tel.: (49) 4721 7073 0
Web Site: http://www.bioceval.de
Fish Oil Mfr
N.A.I.C.S.: 311225

GERLICHER GmbH (1)
Rusternstr 7a, 16321, Berlin, Germany
Tel.: (49) 3338 751 18 40
Web Site: http://www.gerlicher.de
Oil Distr
N.A.I.C.S.: 424990

Gebr. Schnittger GmbH (1)
Industriestrasse 2-3, 94327, Bogen, Germany
Tel.: (49) 422 40 09 0
Web Site: http://www.schnittger.com
Leather Product Distr
N.A.I.C.S.: 424990

Heinrich Nagel GmbH & CO. KG (1)
Monckebergstrasse 17, 20095, Hamburg, Germany
Tel.: (49) 30 95 14 0
Web Site: http://www.nagel-kg.de
Vegetable Oil Distr
N.A.I.C.S.: 424990
Minette V. Riedesel *(Sec)*

INTERNATIONAL PUBLIC

(1)
Brunnenstrasse 138, Lunen, 44536, Germany
Tel.: (49) 23061060
Web Site: http://www.remondis.de
Sales Range: $5-14.9 Billion
Emp.: 20,000
Water, Waste & Environmental Services
N.A.I.C.S.: 562998
Thomas Breitkopf *(Member-Exec Bd)*

Subsidiary (Domestic):

REMEX Mineralstoff GmbH (2)
Am Fallhammer 1, 40221, Dusseldorf, Germany
Tel.: (49) 211171600
Web Site: http://www.remex.de
Sales Range: $75-99.9 Million
Emp.: 70
Mineral Waste Processing & Recycling Services
N.A.I.C.S.: 562211
Hans-Joachim Andres *(Mng Dir)*

REMONDIS Aqua GmbH & Co. KG (2)
Brunnenstrasse 138, 44536, Lunen, Germany (100%)
Tel.: (49) 23061068900
Web Site: http://www.remondis-aqua.com
Emp.: 30
Waste Management Services
N.A.I.C.S.: 221310
Andreas Bankamp *(Mng Dir)*

Subsidiary (Domestic):

Eurawasser Aufbereitungs- und Entsorgungs GmbH (3)
Brunnenstr 138, 44536, Lunen, Germany
Tel.: (49) 2 306 106 692
Web Site: http://www.eurawasser.de
Water Purification & Sanitation Services
N.A.I.C.S.: 221310
Marten Eger *(Mng Dir)*

Subsidiary (Domestic):

Eurawasser Aufbereitungs- und Entsorgungsgesellschaft Leuna mbH (4)
Rudolf Breitscheid Str 18, 6237, Leuna, Germany
Tel.: (49) 3461813710
Water Purification & Sanitation Services
N.A.I.C.S.: 221310

Eurawasser Aufbereitungs- und Entsorgungsgesellschaft Saale-Unstrut mbH (4)
Rudolf-Breitscheid-Str 18, 06237, Leuna, Germany
Tel.: (49) 3461 30570
Web Site: http://www.eurawasser.de
Water Purification & Sanitation Services
N.A.I.C.S.: 221310
Julia Brown *(Mng Dir)*

Eurawasser Betriebsführungsgesellschaft mbH (4)
Odermarkplatz 1, 38640, Goslar, Germany
Tel.: (49) 5321 3376 11
Web Site: http://www.eurawasser.de
Water Purification & Sanitation Services
N.A.I.C.S.: 221310
Holger Fricke *(Mng Dir)*

Eurawasser Nord GmbH (4)
Am Augraben 2, Gustrow, 18273, Rostock, Germany
Tel.: (49) 384377600
Web Site: http://www.eurawasser-nord.de
Water Purification & Sanitation Services
N.A.I.C.S.: 221310
Gesine Strohmeyer *(Mng Dir)*

Subsidiary (Non-US):

REMONDIS Electrorecycling Sp. z o.o. (2)
Grodziska 15, PL 05-870, Blonie, Poland
Tel.: (48) 223130613
Web Site:
 https://www.remondiselectrorecycling.pl
Sales Range: $25-49.9 Million
Emp.: 50
Waste Disposal
N.A.I.C.S.: 924110

AND PRIVATE COMPANIES — RETHMANN AG & CO. KG

Miroclow Baciok *(Gen Mgr)*

REMONDIS Pty. Ltd. (2)
Private Bag 8, Saint Marys, 1790, Sydney, NSW, Australia **(100%)**
Tel.: (61) 296234733
Web Site: http://www.remondis.com.au
Sales Range: $25-49.9 Million
Emp.: 75
Waste Disposal & Recycling Services
N.A.I.C.S.: 325998

Joint Venture (Domestic):

TSR Recycling GmbH & Co. KG (2)
Hafenstr 98, 46242, Bottrop, Germany
Tel.: (49) 204170600
Web Site: http://www.tsr.eu
Steel Scrap & Non-Ferrous Metals Recycling
N.A.I.C.S.: 423930

Subsidiary (Non-US):

HKS Metals B.V. (3)
Graanweg 18, 4782 PP, Moerdijk, Netherlands **(100%)**
Tel.: (31) 886065200
Web Site: http://www.hks.nl
Emp.: 2,600
Holding Company; Scrap Metal Recycling Services
N.A.I.C.S.: 551112

Subsidiary (Domestic):

HKS Scrap Metals B.V. (4)
Graanweg 18, 4782 PP, Moerdijk, Netherlands
Tel.: (31) 886065000
Web Site: http://www.hksmetals.eu
Sales Range: $25-49.9 Million
Emp.: 70
Scrap Metal Recycling
N.A.I.C.S.: 562920
Wouter Kusters *(Mng Dir)*

Subsidiary (Domestic):

XERVON GmbH (2)
Theodorstrasse 180, 40472, Dusseldorf, Germany
Tel.: (49) 21154242600
Web Site: http://www.xervon.de
Sales Range: $900-999.9 Million
Emp.: 8,000
Industrial Facility Maintenance & Support Services
N.A.I.C.S.: 561210
Andreas Rittel *(Member-Mgmt Bd)*

REMONDIS Atik Yonetimleri Ltd. Sti (1)
Kirimli Mah 135 Cad No 454, 68100, Ankara, Turkiye
Tel.: (90) 216 5758882
Waste Management Services
N.A.I.C.S.: 562920

REMONDIS SE & Co. KG (1)
Brunnenstrase 138, 44536, Lunen, Germany
Tel.: (49) 23061060
Web Site: http://www.remondis.com
Waste Management Services
N.A.I.C.S.: 562920

Subsidiary (Non-US):

OOO REMONDIS Saransk (2)
Aleksandrowskoe Shaussee 6, 430000, Saransk, Russia
Tel.: (7) 8342 294967
Waste Management Services
N.A.I.C.S.: 562920

OOO Rhenus Automotive (2)
Promzona Kirpichniy Zavod Technopark Russkiy Diesel, Vsevolozhsk, 188676, Saint Petersburg, Leningradskaya, Russia
Tel.: (7) 812 313 09 82
Web Site: http://www.ru.rhenus.com
Logistics Consulting Servies
N.A.I.C.S.: 541614

Subsidiary (Domestic):

REMONDIS ALVA GmbH (2)
Am alten Bahnhof 12, 51645, Gummersbach, Germany
Tel.: (49) 2261 546060
Waste Management Services
N.A.I.C.S.: 562920

Subsidiary (Non-US):

REMONDIS Aqua (India) Private Ltd. (2)
403 Bremen BC City Survey No 2562 University Road, 411007, Pune, India
Tel.: (91) 20 65602674
Waste Management Services
N.A.I.C.S.: 562920
Chaitanya Shah *(Mgr-Sls)*

REMONDIS Aqua B.V. (2)
De Iepenwei 12a, 4191 PD, Geldermalsen, Netherlands
Tel.: (31) 345 570157
Web Site: http://www.redmondisaqua.com
Emp.: 11
Waste Management Services
N.A.I.C.S.: 562920
J. Vandercen *(Mgr)*

REMONDIS Aqua Trzemeszno Sp. z o.o. (2)
ul 1 Maja 21, 62-420, Trzemeszno, Poland
Tel.: (48) 61 4154308
Waste Management Services
N.A.I.C.S.: 562920

REMONDIS Argentia B.V. (2)
Middenweg 7, 4782 PM, Moerdijk, Netherlands
Tel.: (31) 168 385555
Web Site: http://www.remondis.nl
Waste Management Services
N.A.I.C.S.: 562920

REMONDIS Austria GmbH (2)
Vohburggasse 4, 1210, Vienna, Austria
Tel.: (43) 1 3303900
Web Site: http://www.remondis.at
Waste Management Services
N.A.I.C.S.: 562920

REMONDIS BURCU Atik Yonetimleri Geri Donusum ve Temizlik Hizmetleri Ticaret A.S. (2)
Gursu mahallesi 318 sokak No 6/2 Konyaalti, 07070, Antalya, Turkiye
Tel.: (90) 2422 286222
Waste Management Services
N.A.I.C.S.: 562920

REMONDIS Belgien S.P.R.L. (2)
Chemin des Coeuwins, 6720, Brussels, Belgium
Tel.: (32) 63 578078
Waste Management Services
N.A.I.C.S.: 562920

Subsidiary (Domestic):

REMONDIS Brandenburg GmbH (2)
Pernitzer Strasse 19a, 14797, Berlin, Germany
Tel.: (49) 33835 59451
Waste Management Services
N.A.I.C.S.: 562920

Subsidiary (Non-US):

REMONDIS Bydgoszcz Sp. z o.o. (2)
ul Inwalidow 45, 85-749, Bydgoszcz, Poland
Tel.: (48) 52 342 74 40
Web Site: http://www.remondis-bydgoszcz.pl
Waste Management Services
N.A.I.C.S.: 562920

Subsidiary (Domestic):

REMONDIS Chiemgau GmbH (2)
Sondermoninger Str 5, 83339, Berlin, Germany
Tel.: (49) 8664 98850
Waste Management Services
N.A.I.C.S.: 562920

Subsidiary (Non-US):

REMONDIS China Ltd. (2)
19 Lam Lok Street Room 1516-1520 15th Floor Nan Fung, Kowloon Bay, Hong Kong, China (Hong Kong)
Tel.: (852) 657 46302
Waste Management Services
N.A.I.C.S.: 562920

REMONDIS Drobin Komunalna sp. z o.o. (2)
ul Tupadzka 7, 09-210, Warsaw, Poland
Tel.: (48) 24 2674290
Waste Management Services
N.A.I.C.S.: 562920

Subsidiary (Domestic):

REMONDIS EURAWASSER GmbH (2)
Robert-Koch-Str 8, 53501, Berlin, Germany
Tel.: (49) 2225 83938 0
Web Site: http://www.eurawasser.de
Waste Management Services
N.A.I.C.S.: 562920

REMONDIS Eilenburg GmbH (2)
Wurzener Landstrasse 9, 4838, Eilenburg, Germany
Tel.: (49) 3423 690130
Waste Management Services
N.A.I.C.S.: 562920

REMONDIS Elbe-Roder GmbH (2)
Muhlbacher Weg 3, 01561, Dresden, Germany
Tel.: (49) 35248 8360
Waste Management Services
N.A.I.C.S.: 562920

Subsidiary (Non-US):

REMONDIS Electrorecycling S.A.S. (2)
ZAC des Marots Route de l'Ecluse, BP 03, 10800, Saint-Thibault-des-Vignes, France
Tel.: (33) 325 416262
Waste Management Services
N.A.I.C.S.: 562920

REMONDIS Environmental Services Co., Ltd. (2)
MingWah International Convention Centre C - 1301 Nr 8 Guishan Road, Shekou Industrial Zone Nanshan District, 518067, Shenzhen, China
Tel.: (86) 755 21600939
Waste Management Services
N.A.I.C.S.: 562920

REMONDIS France S.A.S. (2)
ZAC les Vallees - rue de Bruxelles, Paris, France
Tel.: (33) 3 44224335
Waste Management Services
N.A.I.C.S.: 562920

REMONDIS Gliwice Sp. z o.o. (2)
ul Kaszubska 2, 44-100, Gliwice, Poland
Tel.: (48) 32 3313333
Waste Management Services
N.A.I.C.S.: 562920

Subsidiary (Domestic):

REMONDIS GmbH (2)
Graf-Zeppelin-Str 9, 57610, Altenkirchen, Germany
Tel.: (49) 2681 95400
Waste Management Services
N.A.I.C.S.: 562920

REMONDIS GmbH & Co. KG (2)
Saarburger Strasse 33, 67071, Ludwigshafen, Germany
Tel.: (49) 621 5950270
Waste Management Services
N.A.I.C.S.: 562920

REMONDIS Holzaufbereitung GmbH (2)
Uhlenbruch 6, 42279, Wuppertal, Germany
Tel.: (49) 202 747920
Waste Management Services
N.A.I.C.S.: 562920

Subsidiary (Non-US):

REMONDIS Industrial Service S.A./N.V. (2)
Rue des Alouettes 131, 4041, Milmort, Belgium
Tel.: (32) 4 2288560
Web Site: http://www.remondis.be
Waste Management Services
N.A.I.C.S.: 562920
Alain Ferette *(Mgr-Sls)*

Subsidiary (Domestic):

REMONDIS Industrie Service GmbH (2)
Tonstrasse 2, 50374, Berlin, Germany
Tel.: (49) 2235 46940
Waste Management Services
N.A.I.C.S.: 562920

REMONDIS Industrie Service Sud GmbH & Co. KG (2)
Im Steingerust 55, 76437, Rastatt, Germany
Tel.: (49) 7222 95260
Waste Management Services
N.A.I.C.S.: 562920

REMONDIS International GmbH (2)
Lahnstrasse 31, 12055, Berlin, Germany
Tel.: (49) 30 68282612
Waste Management Services
N.A.I.C.S.: 562920

Subsidiary (Non-US):

REMONDIS Italia S.r.l. (2)
Via Austria 15 A, 35172, Padua, Italy
Tel.: (39) 0340 6921014
Waste Management Services
N.A.I.C.S.: 562920

REMONDIS KROeko Sp. z o.o. (2)
ul Fredry 1, 38-400, Krosno, Poland
Tel.: (48) 13 47 48 480
Web Site: http://www.kroeko.pl
Waste Management Services
N.A.I.C.S.: 562920

Subsidiary (Domestic):

REMONDIS Kiel GmbH (2)
Am Ihlberg 10, 24109, Melsdorf, Germany
Tel.: (49) 431 69040
Waste Management Services
N.A.I.C.S.: 562920

REMONDIS Kommunale Dienste Sud GmbH (2)
Pasteurstrasse 22, 80999, Munich, Germany
Tel.: (49) 89 892170
Web Site: http://www.remondis-sued.de
Emp.: 100
Waste Management Services
N.A.I.C.S.: 562920

REMONDIS Kyffhauser GmbH (2)
Schachtstrasse 5, Berlin, Germany
Tel.: (49) 3632 770530
Waste Management Services
N.A.I.C.S.: 562920

Subsidiary (Non-US):

REMONDIS Liquid Waste Pty Ltd (2)
32-36 Christie Street, Saint Marys, 2760, NSW, Australia
Tel.: (61) 2 96234733
Waste Management Services
N.A.I.C.S.: 562920

Subsidiary (Domestic):

REMONDIS Maintenance & Services GmbH (2)
Emdener Strasse 278, 50735, Cologne, Germany
Tel.: (49) 221 7177200
Web Site: http://www.remondis-maintenance.com
Waste Management Services
N.A.I.C.S.: 562920
Joerg Sczyslo *(Head-Corporate Dev & Mktg)*

REMONDIS Mecklenburg GmbH (2)
Niederlassung Ludwigslust Am Schlachthof 2, 19288, Ludwigslust, Germany
Tel.: (49) 3874 42290
Waste Management Services
N.A.I.C.S.: 562920

Subsidiary (Non-US):

REMONDIS Medison Sp. z o.o. (2)
ul Puszkina 41, 42 530, Dabrowa Gornicza, Poland
Tel.: (48) 32 3520313
Web Site: http://www.remondis-medison.pl
Waste Management Services
N.A.I.C.S.: 562920

REMONDIS Medison d.o.o. (2)
Draganic 13a, 47 201, Zagreb, Croatia

RETHMANN AG & CO. KG

RETHMANN AG & Co. KG—(Continued)
Tel.: (385) 47 694 750
Web Site: http://www.remondis.hr
Waste Management Services
N.A.I.C.S.: 562920

Subsidiary (Domestic):

REMONDIS Mittelrhein GmbH (2)
Betriebsstatte Koblenz Daimlerstr 7, 56070, Koblenz, Germany
Tel.: (49) 261 9885710
Waste Management Services
N.A.I.C.S.: 562920

Subsidiary (Non-US):

REMONDIS Mragowo Sp. z o.o. (2)
ul Lubelska 5, 11-700, Mragowo, Poland
Tel.: (48) 89 7412004
Waste Management Services
N.A.I.C.S.: 562920

Subsidiary (Domestic):

REMONDIS Munsterland GmbH & Co. KG (2)
Erlenweg 107, 48653, Coesfeld, Germany
Tel.: (49) 2541 944518
Waste Management Services
N.A.I.C.S.: 562920

Subsidiary (Non-US):

REMONDIS Nederland B.V. (2)
Celsiusstraat 14, 6716 BZ, Ede, Netherlands
Tel.: (31) 318 634 864
Web Site: http://www.remondisnederland.nl
Waste Management Services
N.A.I.C.S.: 562920

REMONDIS OUEST France S.A.S (2)
Niederlassung Juigne Parc d Activites de Lanserre, 49610, Paris, France
Tel.: (33) 2 41438688
Waste Management Services
N.A.I.C.S.: 562920

Subsidiary (Domestic):

REMONDIS Olpe GmbH (2)
Raiffeisenstrasse 39, 57462, Olpe, Germany
Tel.: (49) 2761 9230
Web Site: http://www.remondis-rheinland.de
Waste Management Services
N.A.I.C.S.: 562920

Subsidiary (Non-US):

REMONDIS Olsztyn Spolka ograniczona odpowiedzialnoscia S.K.A (2)
Ul Partyzantow 3, 10-522, Olsztyn, Poland
Tel.: (48) 89 544 98 01
Web Site: http://www.remondis.olsztyn.pl
Waste Management Services
N.A.I.C.S.: 562920

REMONDIS Opole Sp. z o.o. (2)
Oddzial Olesno ul Powstancow Slaskich 14, 46-300, Warsaw, Poland
Tel.: (48) 34 3583090
Waste Management Services
N.A.I.C.S.: 562920

REMONDIS Otwock Sp. z o.o. (2)
ul Johna Lennona 4, 05-400, Otwock, Poland
Tel.: (48) 22 7795001
Waste Management Services
N.A.I.C.S.: 562920

REMONDIS Papier B. V. (2)
Produktiestraat 21, 3133 ES, Vlaardingen, Netherlands
Tel.: (31) 10 2621000
Waste Management Services
N.A.I.C.S.: 562920

Subsidiary (Domestic):

REMONDIS Plettenberg GmbH (2)
Bannewerthstr 26, 58840, Plettenberg, Germany
Tel.: (49) 2391 9178560
Web Site: http://www.tsr.com
Emp.: 20
Waste Management Services
N.A.I.C.S.: 562920

Fleshin Berg *(Gen Mgr)*

Subsidiary (Non-US):

REMONDIS Recycling Taiwan Co. Ltd. (2)
Regionalverwaltung Taipei 6F 111 Keelung Road Sec 1, Taipei, Taiwan
Tel.: (886) 2 878725660
Waste Management Services
N.A.I.C.S.: 562920

Subsidiary (Domestic):

REMONDIS Rhein-Wupper GmbH & Co. KG (2)
Karl-Hohmann-Strasse 15-17, 40599, Dusseldorf, Germany
Tel.: (49) 211 998820
Waste Management Services
N.A.I.C.S.: 562920

Subsidiary (Non-US):

REMONDIS Ros S.L. (2)
Calle Barcas 2, 46002, Valencia, Spain
Tel.: (34) 637 460497
Waste Management Services
N.A.I.C.S.: 562920

REMONDIS SUD France S.A.S (2)
Niederlassung Gigean ZAE L embosque, Paris, France
Tel.: (33) 4 67746880
Waste Management Services
N.A.I.C.S.: 562920

Subsidiary (Domestic):

REMONDIS Saar Entsorgung GmbH (2)
Betriebsstatte Kirkel Im Schussler Wald 2, 66459, Kirkel, Germany
Tel.: (49) 6849 90080
Waste Management Services
N.A.I.C.S.: 562920

REMONDIS Sachsen-Anhalt GmbH (2)
Osterweddinger Chaussee 4, 39116, Magdeburg, Germany
Tel.: (49) 391 635170
Web Site: http://www.wertstoffzentrum-magdeburg.de
Waste Management Services
N.A.I.C.S.: 562920

Subsidiary (Non-US):

REMONDIS Sanitech Poznan Sp. z o.o. (2)
ul Gorecka 104, 61-483, Poznan, Poland
Tel.: (48) 61 664 07 33
Web Site: http://www.remondis-sanitech.pl
Waste Management Services
N.A.I.C.S.: 562920

REMONDIS Schweiz AG (2)
Niederlassung Schaffhausen Muhlentalstrasse 371, 8200, Schaffhausen, Switzerland
Tel.: (41) 52 6740880
Web Site: http://www.remondis.ch
Waste Management Services
N.A.I.C.S.: 562920

REMONDIS Sp. z o.o. (2)
ul Profession 16, 02-981, Warsaw, Poland
Tel.: (48) 22 5930300
Web Site: http://www.remondis.pl
Waste Management Services
N.A.I.C.S.: 562920
Torsten Weber *(Mng Dir)*

REMONDIS Su ve Atiksu Teknolojileri Sanayi ve Ticaret A.S. (2)
Antalya Organize Sanayi Bolgesi Atiksu Aritma Tesisi, Burdur Yolu 26 km Yenikoy, 7230, Antalya, Turkiye
Tel.: (90) 242 2581260
Waste Management Services
N.A.I.C.S.: 562920

Subsidiary (Domestic):

REMONDIS Sud GmbH (2)
Niederlassung Augsburg Peter und Paul Strasse 1, 86551, Aichach, Germany
Tel.: (49) 8251 89790
Waste Management Services
N.A.I.C.S.: 562920

Subsidiary (Non-US):

REMONDIS Swidnik Sp. z o.o. (2)
ul Kruczkowskiego 6a, 21-040, Swidnik, Poland
Tel.: (48) 81 7515516
Waste Management Services
N.A.I.C.S.: 562920

REMONDIS Szczecin Sp. z o.o. (2)
ul Janiny Smolenskiej ps Jachna 35, 71-005, Szczecin, Poland
Tel.: (48) 91 4310801
Web Site: http://www.remondis-szczecin.pl
Waste Management Services
N.A.I.C.S.: 562920

REMONDIS Tarnowskie Gory Sp. z o.o. (2)
ul Nakielska 1-3, 42-600, Tarnowskie Gory, Poland
Tel.: (48) 32 2854618
Waste Management Services
N.A.I.C.S.: 562920

Subsidiary (Domestic):

REMONDIS Thermische Abfallverwertung GmbH (2)
Butterwecker Weg 6, 39418, Stassfurt, Germany
Tel.: (49) 392532090
Web Site: http://www.reta-stassfurt.de
Waste Management Services
N.A.I.C.S.: 562920

REMONDIS Trade and Sales GmbH (2)
Brunnenstrasse 138, 44536, Lunen, Germany
Tel.: (49) 2306 1069800
Web Site: http://www.remondis.de
Waste Management Services
N.A.I.C.S.: 562920

REMONDIS Vorpommern GmbH (2)
Feldstr 7, 17373, Ueckermunde, Germany
Tel.: (49) 39771 510 0
Web Site: http://www.remondis-vorpommern.de
Waste Management Services
N.A.I.C.S.: 562920

Subsidiary (Non-US):

Remondis UK Ltd. (2)
Merseyside, Prescot, L34 1JZ, United Kingdom
Tel.: (44) 151 2308800
Web Site: http://www.remondis.co.uk
Waste Management Services
N.A.I.C.S.: 562920

Reym B.V (2)
Computerweg 12d, Amersfoort, 3821 AB, Netherlands **(100%)**
Tel.: (31) 334558890
Web Site: http://www.reym.nl
Industrial Waste Management Services
N.A.I.C.S.: 562998
Marcel Roodenburg *(Mgr-Commercial)*

Rhenus Contract Logistics AG (2)
Lagerstrasse 28, 9470, Buchs, Switzerland
Tel.: (41) 81 750 75 75
Logistics Consulting Servies
N.A.I.C.S.: 541614

Rhenus Contract Logistics SA (2)
Route des Jeunes 6, 1227, Carouge, Switzerland
Tel.: (41) 22 30 13 712
Logistics Consulting Servies
N.A.I.C.S.: 541614

Rhenus Freight Logistics AG (2)
Bonergasse 10, 4019, Basel, Switzerland
Tel.: (41) 61 639 97 87
Web Site: http://www.ch.rhenus.com
Emp.: 21
Logistics Consulting Servies
N.A.I.C.S.: 541614
Werner Hochstrasser *(Mng Dir)*

Rhenus International Limited (2)
Unit 2 Westpoint Enterprise Park Clarence Avenue Trafford Park, Manchester, M17 1QS, United Kingdom
Tel.: (44) 161 886 4200
Web Site: http://www.uk.rhenus.com
Logistics Consulting Servies

INTERNATIONAL PUBLIC

N.A.I.C.S.: 541614

Rhenus Kft. (2)
Ipari Park-Platanfa u 3, 9027, Gyor, Hungary
Tel.: (36) 96 513 626
Web Site: http://www.hu.rhenus.com
Logistics Consulting Servies
N.A.I.C.S.: 541614

Rhenus Logistic Sdn. Bhd. (2)
No 45 Jalan Permata 2/KS9 Taman Perindustrian Air Hitam, 41200, Klang, Selangor, Malaysia
Tel.: (60) 331231925
Web Site: http://www.rhenus.com
Logistics Consulting Servies
N.A.I.C.S.: 541614
Sten Germundsson *(Mng Dir)*

Rhenus Logistics Asia-Pacific Ltd. (2)
Room 1516-1520 15/F Nan Fung Commercial Centre 19 Lam Lok Street, Kowloon Bay, Hong Kong, China (Hong Kong)
Tel.: (852) 2425 4933
Web Site: http://www.hk.rhenus.com
Logistics Consulting Servies
N.A.I.C.S.: 541614

Rhenus Logistics Bulgaria OOD (2)
1 Brussels Blvd, 1540, Sofia, Bulgaria
Tel.: (359) 2 9421951
Web Site: http://www.bg.rhenus.com
Emp.: 100
Logistics Consulting Servies
N.A.I.C.S.: 541614
Alexander Gechev *(Gen Mgr)*

Rhenus Logistics China Ltd. (2)
8th Floor Zhonghuan Modern Building No 468 Xinhui Road, Putuo District, 200060, Shanghai, China
Tel.: (86) 21 6330 8590
Web Site: http://www.cn.rhenus.com
Logistics Consulting Servies
N.A.I.C.S.: 541614

Rhenus Logistics Co., Ltd. (2)
191/14 CTI Tower 28th Floor Ratchadapisek Rd, Klongtoey, 10110, Bangkok, Thailand
Tel.: (66) 2 261 5380
Web Site: http://www.th.rhenus.com
Emp.: 350
Logistics Consulting Servies
N.A.I.C.S.: 541614

Rhenus Logistics France S.A.S. (2)
Batiment Le Dauphin 80 rue Condorcet, 38090, Vaulx-Milieu, France
Tel.: (33) 474 946 000
Web Site: http://www.fr.rhenus.com
Logistics Consulting Servies
N.A.I.C.S.: 541614

Rhenus Logistics GmbH (2)
Seitenhafenstrasse 15, 1023, Vienna, Austria
Tel.: (43) 1 729 66 00 10
Web Site: http://www.at.rhenus.com
Logistics Consulting Servies
N.A.I.C.S.: 541614

Rhenus Logistics Ltd. (2)
Kore Development Park John F Kennedy Drive Naas Road, Dublin, D 12XVP6, Ireland
Tel.: (353) 1 429 2300
Web Site: http://www.ie.rhenus.com
Logistics Consulting Servies
N.A.I.C.S.: 541614

Rhenus Logistics Ltd. (2)
21 Nguyen Trung Ngan Str Room 1205 Floor 12 Ben Nghe Ward, Dist 1, Ho Chi Minh City, Vietnam
Tel.: (84) 8 3 827 3714
Web Site: http://www.vn.rhenus.com
Logistics Consulting Servies
N.A.I.C.S.: 541614

Rhenus Logistics NV (2)
Noordersingel 21, 2140, Antwerp, Belgium
Tel.: (32) 3 224 56 00
Web Site: http://www.be.rhenus.com
Logistics Consulting Servies
N.A.I.C.S.: 541614

Rhenus Logistics OU (2)
Kuma tee 1 Peetri kula Rae vald, 75312, Harjumaa, Estonia

AND PRIVATE COMPANIES — RETHMANN AG & CO. KG

Tel.: (372) 699 04 80
Web Site: http://www.ee.rhenus.com
Logistics Consulting Servies
N.A.I.C.S.: 541614

Rhenus Logistics Pte. Ltd. (2)
17 Changi Business Park Central 1 05-01
Honeywell Building, Singapore, 486073,
Singapore
Tel.: (65) 6709 0540
Web Site: http://www.rhenus.com
Logistics Consulting Servies
N.A.I.C.S.: 541614

Rhenus Logistics S.A. (2)
Kopytow 44a, 05-870, Blonie, Poland
Tel.: (48) 22 463 9500
Web Site: http://www.pl.rhenus.com
Logistics Consulting Servies
N.A.I.C.S.: 541614

Rhenus Logistics S.p.A. (2)
Via delle Azalee 6, 20090, Buccinasco, Italy
Tel.: (39) 0 2 488 525 1
Web Site: http://www.it.rhenus.com
Logistics Consulting Servies
N.A.I.C.S.: 541614

Rhenus Logistics Srl (2)
Bd Republicii nr 222 etaj 2, 110177, Pitesti,
Arges, Romania
Tel.: (40) 248 21 9991
Web Site: http://www.ro.rhenus.com
Logistics Consulting Servies
N.A.I.C.S.: 541614

Rhenus Logistics Sverige AB (2)
Arendals Skans 20 ARU-S, 41879, Gothenburg, Sweden
Tel.: (46) 31 744 7095
Web Site: http://www.se.rhenus.com
Logistics Consulting Servies
N.A.I.C.S.: 541614

Rhenus Logistics Taiwan Ltd. (2)
3F No 411 Sec 2 Tiding Blvd, Neihu, 114,
Taipei, Taiwan
Tel.: (886) 2 2659 9719
Web Site: http://www.tw.rhenus.com
Logistics Consulting Servies
N.A.I.C.S.: 541614

Rhenus Logistics do Brasil Ltda (2)
Rua Bernardino de Campos 318 Conjunto
12 Campo Belo, 04620-001, Sao Paulo,
Brazil
Tel.: (55) 11 24958211
Logistics Consulting Servies
N.A.I.C.S.: 541614
Fabiola Passos *(Head-Ops)*

Rhenus Logistics s.r.o. (2)
Orechova 2/B, 922 10, Bratislava, Slovakia
Tel.: (421) 33 7760 111
Web Site: http://www.sk.rhenus.com
Logistics Consulting Servies
N.A.I.C.S.: 541614

Rhenus Logistics, Inc. (2)
Building 7A-2 Sunblest Compound Km 23
West Service Road, Bo Cupang, 1771,
Muntinlupa, Philippines
Tel.: (63) 2 8097 129
Web Site: http://www.ph.rhenus.com
Logistics Consulting Servies
N.A.I.C.S.: 541614

Rhenus Logistics, S.A.U (2)
P I Pratense Calle 100 No 20, 08820, Barcelona, Spain
Tel.: (34) 93 479 89 00
Web Site: http://www.spain.rhenus.com
Logistics Consulting Servies
N.A.I.C.S.: 541614

Rhenus Logistics, s.r.o. (2)
Na Trojce 369, 252 16, Prague, Czech Republic
Tel.: (420) 311 716 111
Web Site: http://www.cz.rhenus.com
Emp.: 150
Logistics Consulting Servies
N.A.I.C.S.: 541614
Markus Menzel *(Mng Dir)*

Rhenus Port Logistcs Sp. z o. o. (2)
Ul Bytomska 17, 70-603, Szczecin, Poland
Tel.: (48) 91 462 4632
Logistics Consulting Servies
N.A.I.C.S.: 541614

Rhenus Port Logistics B.V. (2)
Kesterenstraat 21 Port 2160-2165, 3087,
Rotterdam, Netherlands
Tel.: (31) 10 440 04 00
Web Site: http://www.nl.rhenus.com
Emp.: 20
Logistics Consulting Servies
N.A.I.C.S.: 541614
Peter Chandersteen *(Gen Mgr)*

Rhenus Transitarios e Logistica Lda. (2)
E N No 10 Km 127 Edificio Norcentro Bloco
E, 2615-042, Alverca do Ribatejo, Portugal
Tel.: (351) 21 792 52 00
Web Site: http://www.pt.rhenus.com
Emp.: 30
Logistics Consulting Servies
N.A.I.C.S.: 541614

Rhenus logistika d.o.o. (2)
Sermin 70, 6000, Koper, Slovenia
Tel.: (386) 59 098346
Web Site: http://www.si.rhenus.com
Logistics Consulting Servies
N.A.I.C.S.: 541614

SAS Rhenus Svoris (2)
Dominante park Saulgozi Kekavas pagasts,
2123, Riga, Latvia
Tel.: (371) 67 141414
Web Site: http://www.lv.rhenus.com
Logistics Consulting Servies
N.A.I.C.S.: 541614

SOOO REMONDIS Minsk (2)
Vaneeva 46, 220033, Minsk, Belarus
Tel.: (375) 17 2485650
Waste Management Services
N.A.I.C.S.: 562920

TOO Rhenus Logistics (2)
Aelita housing estate 1st porch 2nd floor
101 Al-Farabe Ave, 050057, Almaty, Kazakhstan
Tel.: (7) 727 315 81 74
Web Site: http://www.kz.rhenus.com
Logistics Consulting Servies
N.A.I.C.S.: 541614

TOV REMONDIS Artemiwsk (2)
Radianska, 84500, Kiev, Ukraine
Tel.: (380) 6274 21979
Waste Management Services
N.A.I.C.S.: 562920

TOV Rhenus Revival (2)
Promyslowa Str 18, 08702, Kiev, Ukraine
Tel.: (380) 444 92 74 01
Web Site: http://www.ua.rhenus.com
Logistics Consulting Servies
N.A.I.C.S.: 541614

UAB Rhenus Svoris (2)
Meteliu g 4, 2236, Vilnius, Lithuania
Tel.: (370) 52 39 21 00
Web Site: http://www.lt.rhenus.com
Emp.: 60
Logistics Consulting Servies
N.A.I.C.S.: 541614
Arunas Bertasius *(Mng Dir)*

UP Rhenus Logistics (2)
Gintovta 1/512, 220125, Minsk, Belarus
Tel.: (375) 17 286 37 12
Web Site: http://www.by.rhenus.com
Logistics Consulting Servies
N.A.I.C.S.: 541614
Dmitrij Parchomov *(Mgr-Superior Sls)*

Rhenus SE & Co. KG (2)
Rhenus Platz 1, 59439, Holzwickede, Germany
Tel.: (49) 2301290
Web Site: http://www.rhenus.com
Sales Range: $1-4.9 Billion
Emp.: 17,700
Logistics Solutions
N.A.I.C.S.: 541614
Reinhard Lohmann *(Chm-Supervisory Bd)*

Subsidiary (Domestic):

Contargo GmbH & Co. KG (2)
Rheinkaistrasse 2, 68159, Mannheim, Germany
Tel.: (49) 621 59007 185
Web Site: http://www.contargo.net
Sales Range: $550-599.9 Million
Emp.: 800
Logistic Services

N.A.I.C.S.: 541614
Thomas Loffler *(Mng Dir)*

Subsidiary (Non-US):

Contargo Waterway Logistics BV (3)
Scheepmakerij 110, 3331 MA, Zwijndrecht,
Netherlands
Tel.: (31) 78 6254600
Web Site:
   http://www.contargowaterwaylogistics.com
Sales Range: $25-49.9 Million
Emp.: 30
Logistics Consulting Servies
N.A.I.C.S.: 541614

Subsidiary (Non-US):

Rhenus Alpina AG (2)
Wiesendamm 4, Basel, 4019, Switzerland
Tel.: (41) 616393434
Web Site: http://www.rhenus.com
Sales Range: $300-349.9 Million
Emp.: 1,200
Logistics Solutions
N.A.I.C.S.: 541614
Andreas Stockli *(CEO)*

Subsidiary (Domestic):

Rhenus Automotive Systems GmbH (2)
Theodor-Althoff-Strasse 39, 45133, Essen,
Germany
Tel.: (49) 201 89 07 81 01
Web Site: http://www.rhenus.com
Assembly, Materials Management, Supply
Chain Services & Sequencing Activities for
Automotive Industry
N.A.I.C.S.: 541614
Hinnerk Pfluger *(Mng Dir)*

Subsidiary (Non-US):

Rhenus Logistics Alsace S.A. (2)
9 Rue du Havre, Strasbourg, 67100, France
Tel.: (33) 388349550
Freight Forwarding Services
N.A.I.C.S.: 488510

Subsidiary (Domestic):

Rhenus Midi Data GmbH (2)
Hans Bockler Strasse 11, D 64521, Gross-
Gerau, Germany
Tel.: (49) 6152 808 126
High Tech Logistics Services
N.A.I.C.S.: 541614

Subsidiary (Non-US):

Lupprians Ltd. (3)
Keiler House Challenge Road, Ashford,
TW15 1AX, Mddx, United Kingdom
Tel.: (44) 1784 422900
Web Site: http://www.lupprians.com
Emp.: 220
Freight Transportation & Logistics Services
N.A.I.C.S.: 488510
John Fletcher *(Mng Dir)*

SARIA Bio-Industries AG & Co. KG (1)
Werner Strasse 95, 59379, Selm, Germany
Tel.: (49) 25922100
Web Site: http://www.saria.de
Sales Range: $900-999.9 Million
Emp.: 3,800
Waste Recycling Services
N.A.I.C.S.: 562998
Reinhard Lohmann *(Chm-Supervisory Bd)*

SARIA Bio-Industries Belarus (1)
Korotkevitscha Str 9a-304, 220039, Minsk,
Belarus
Tel.: (375) 17 222 15 91
Waste Recycling Services
N.A.I.C.S.: 562998

SARIA Bio-Industries Volga Ltd. (1)
St S-2 building 4/1, PO Box 58, Special
economic zone Alabuga, 423600, Moscow,
Tatarstan, Russia
Tel.: (7) 85557 5 90 89
Waste Recycling Services
N.A.I.C.S.: 562998

SARIA Hungary Kft. (1)
Platanfa u 3, 9027, Gyor, Hungary
Tel.: (36) 96 51 36 22
Waste Recycling Services

N.A.I.C.S.: 562998

SARIA Industries SAS (1)
24 rue Martre, 92110, Clichy, France
Tel.: (33) 1 41 40 30 39
Web Site: http://www.saria.fr
Chemical Products Mfr
N.A.I.C.S.: 325199

SARIA MALOPOLSKA Sp.z.o.o. (1)
Przewrotne 323, 36-003, Warsaw, Poland
Tel.: (48) 17 851 00 84
Waste Recycling Services
N.A.I.C.S.: 562998

SARIA Polska Sp. z o.o. (1)
ul Zawodzie 16, 02-981, Warsaw, Poland
Tel.: (48) 22 593 04 50
Web Site: http://www.saria.pl
Animal Product Distr
N.A.I.C.S.: 424910
Marek Osiecki *(Pres)*

Saria Bio-Industries Espana, S.L.U. (1)
Camino de Pajares 21, 28500, Arganda del
Rey, Spain
Tel.: (34) 91 871 98 52
Web Site: http://www.saria.es
Animal Feed Mfr
N.A.I.C.S.: 311119

Saria SE & Co KG (1)
Norbert-Rethmann-Platz 1, 59379, Selm,
Germany
Tel.: (49) 25922100
Web Site: https://saria.com
All other Miscellaneous Food Mfr
N.A.I.C.S.: 311999

Subsidiary (Non-US):

Devro plc (2)
Moodiesburn, Chryston, G69 0JE, Scotland,
United Kingdom
Tel.: (44) 1236872261
Web Site: http://www.devro.com
Rev.: $342,688,528
Assets: $457,280,096
Liabilities: $287,293,552
Net Worth: $169,986,544
Earnings: $42,225,092
Emp.: 1,895
Fiscal Year-end: 12/31/2021
Sausage Casing Mfr
N.A.I.C.S.: 311999
Rutger Helbing *(CEO)*

Subsidiary (Non-US):

Cutisin A.S. (3)
Dedanska 29, CZ 162200, Prague, Czech
Republic (100%)
Tel.: (420) 220516767
Web Site: http://www.cutisin.cz
Sales Range: $200-249.9 Million
Emp.: 1,000
Sausage Casing Mfr
N.A.I.C.S.: 311612

Devro (Nantong) Technology Co. Limited (3)
No 329 Xingxing East Road Economic and
Technology Development Area, Nantong,
Jiangsu, China
Tel.: (86) 51368512000
Food Products Mfr
N.A.I.C.S.: 311999

Subsidiary (Domestic):

Devro (Scotland) Ltd. (3)
Moodiesburn, Chryston, G69 0JE, United
Kingdom (100%)
Tel.: (44) 123 687 2261
Web Site: https://www.devro.com
Sales Range: $100-124.9 Million
Emp.: 500
Sausage Casing Mfr
N.A.I.C.S.: 311612

Subsidiary (Non-US):

Devro Asia Ltd. (3)
7/F CKK Commercial Ctr 289 Hennessy Rd,
Wanchai, China (Hong Kong) (100%)
Tel.: (852) 25721998
Sales Range: $25-49.9 Million
Emp.: 35
Sausage Casing Mfr
N.A.I.C.S.: 311612

RETHMANN AG & CO. KG

RETHMANN AG & Co. KG—(Continued)

Devro B.V. (3)
Wilhelm Alexanderstraat 9, Gendt, Amsterdam, 6691 EE, Netherlands
Tel.: (31) 481422568
Food Products Mfr
N.A.I.C.S.: 311999

Subsidiary (US):

Devro Inc. (3)
785 Old Swamp Rd, Swansea, SC 29160
Tel.: (803) 796-9730
Sales Range: $150-199.9 Million
Emp.: 380
Sausage Casing Mfr
N.A.I.C.S.: 325220
Nichole Manning (Coord-Export Bus)

Subsidiary (Non-US):

Devro K.K. (3)
Yasuda Shibaura Bldg No 2, Minato-Ku, Tokyo, 108-0022, Japan (100%)
Tel.: (81) 36 453 9624
Web Site: http://www.devro.plc.uk
Sales Range: $25-49.9 Million
Emp.: 6
Sausage Casing Mfr
N.A.I.C.S.: 311612

Devro Ltd. (3)
Postfach 54 02 44, 22502, Hamburg, Germany (100%)
Tel.: (49) 405400030
Web Site: http://www.devro.com
Sales Range: $25-49.9 Million
Emp.: 45
Sausage Casing Mfr
N.A.I.C.S.: 311612

Subsidiary (Domestic):

Devro New Holdings Limited (3)
Gartferry Rd, Glasgow, G69 0JE, Lanarkshire, United Kingdom
Tel.: (44) 1236872261
Food Products Mfr
N.A.I.C.S.: 311999

Subsidiary (Non-US):

Devro Pty. Ltd. (3)
Sydney Road, PO 659, Kelso, Bathurst, 2795, NSW, Australia (100%)
Tel.: (61) 26 330 8200
Web Site: http://www.devro.plc.uk.com
Sales Range: $50-74.9 Million
Emp.: 170
Sausage Casing Mfr
N.A.I.C.S.: 311612

Devro Pty. Ltd. (3)
Unit 3 17 Joval Pl, 2104, Manukau, Auckland, New Zealand (100%)
Tel.: (64) 92622523
Web Site: http://www.devro.plc.uk
Sales Range: $25-49.9 Million
Emp.: 7
Sausage Casing Mfr
N.A.I.C.S.: 311612

Devro s.r.o. (3)
Vichovska 830, 514 19, Jilemnice, Czech Republic
Tel.: (420) 48 156 3111
Web Site: http://www.cutisin.cz
Sausage Casing Mfr
N.A.I.C.S.: 311612

UAB SARIA
Veiveriu g 134-411, 46352, Kaunas, Lithuania
Tel.: (370) 37 390 465
Waste Recycling Services
N.A.I.C.S.: 562998

UNIMELT GmbH (1)
Resenweg 1, 97084, Wurzburg, Germany
Tel.: (49) 931 61 406 0
Web Site: http://www.unimelt.de
Emp.: 50
Chemical Product Mfr & Distr
N.A.I.C.S.: 325199
Juergen Mueller (Gen Mgr)

RETI S.P.A.
Via Dante 6, 21052, Busto Arsizio, Italy
Tel.: (39) 0331357400
Web Site: https://www.reti.it
Year Founded: 1994
RETI—(EUR)
Emp.: 355
Information Technology Services
N.A.I.C.S.: 541512
Bruno Paneghini (Chm)

RETINA PAINTS LIMITED
2nd 3rd Floor Phase5 Survey No184 185, IDA Cherlapally Cherlapally main road Medchal Malkajgiri, Hyderabad, 500051, Telangana, India
Tel.: (91) 4027205580
Web Site: https://www.retinapaints.com
Year Founded: 2010
RETINA—(NSE)
Rev.: $1,362,892
Assets: $2,432,018
Liabilities: $919,071
Net Worth: $1,512,948
Earnings: $36,446
Fiscal Year-end: 03/31/23
Paint Product Mfr
N.A.I.C.S.: 325510
K. Ramu (Pres)

RETO ECO-SOLUTIONS, INC.
Building X-702 60 Anli Road, Chaoyang District, Beijing, 100101, China
Tel.: (86) 1064827328
Web Site: https://www.retoeco.com
Year Founded: 2015
RETO—(NASDAQ)
Rev.: $3,236,286
Assets: $25,245,248
Liabilities: $20,394,074
Net Worth: $4,851,174
Earnings: ($16,069,070)
Emp.: 103
Fiscal Year-end: 12/31/23
Construction Material Mfr & Distr
N.A.I.C.S.: 333120
Hengfang Li (CEO, Founder & Chm)

RETOTUB S.A.S.
Avenue Du 19 Mars 1962, 18100, Vierzon, Cher, France
Tel.: (33) 248530580
Web Site: http://www.retotub.com
Sales Range: $25-49.9 Million
Emp.: 50
Scaffolding System Mfr
N.A.I.C.S.: 332312
Jean-Francois Chene (Pres)

RETRO GREEN REVOLUTION LIMITED
C/231 Siddharth Excellence 2nd Floor Opp D-Mart Vasana Main Road, Vadodara, 390015, Gujarat, India
Tel.: (91) 2652251221
Web Site: http://www.retrogreen.in
Year Founded: 1990
519191—(BOM)
Rev.: $197,724
Assets: $1,042,079
Liabilities: $44,344
Net Worth: $997,735
Earnings: $50,980
Fiscal Year-end: 03/31/23
Agricultural Services
N.A.I.C.S.: 541715
Nimesh B. Shah (Mng Dir)

RETTIG GROUP LTD.
Bulevardi 46, PO Box 115, FI-00121, Helsinki, Finland
Tel.: (358) 9 618 831
Web Site: http://www.rettig.fi
Year Founded: 1770
Rev.: $1,106,217,865
Assets: $1,420,759,663
Liabilities: $873,598,307
Net Worth: $547,161,356
Earnings: $44,203,114
Emp.: 4,221
Fiscal Year-end: 12/31/19
Holding Company
N.A.I.C.S.: 551112
Tomas von Rettig (Chm, Pres & Co-CEO)

Subsidiaries:

AB Markaryds Metallarmatur (1)
Jarnvagsgatan 19, 285 32, Markaryd, Sweden
Tel.: (46) 433 737 00
Web Site: http://www.mma.se
Emp.: 130
Heating & Cooling Equipment Mfr
N.A.I.C.S.: 333415

Emmeti S.p.A. (1)
Via Brigata Osoppo 166, Vigonovo frazione di, 33074, Fontanafredda, PN, Italy
Tel.: (39) 0434567911
Heating Equipment Mfr & Distr
N.A.I.C.S.: 333414

Emmeti UK Ltd. (1)
Tannery Yd Witney St, Burford, OX18 4DQ, United Kingdom
Tel.: (44) 1993824900
Web Site: https://emmeti.co.uk
Plumbing & Heating Products Mfr & Distr
N.A.I.C.S.: 332919

Finimetal SASU (1)
Rue Pasteur Biache St, Biache-Saint-Vaast, 62118, France
Tel.: (33) 321 504 770
Heating & Cooling Equipment Mfr & Distr
N.A.I.C.S.: 333415

Hewing GmbH (1)
Waldstrasse 3, 48607, Ochtrup, Germany
Tel.: (49) 2553 70 01
Web Site: http://hewing.com
Sales Range: $50-74.9 Million
Emp.: 200
Plastic Pipe Mfr & Distr
N.A.I.C.S.: 326122
Dominik Rossler (Mng Dir & Mgr)

NK-East Oy (1)
Skrabbolentie 18, Parainen, 21600, Pargas, Finland
Tel.: (358) 204556999
Heating & Cooling Equipment Mfr & Distr
N.A.I.C.S.: 333415

Nordeka Maden A.S. (1)
Levent Mahallesi Comert Sokak No 1 Yapikredi Plaza, C Block Flat No 40-41 Floor 17 Besiktas, Istanbul, Turkiye
Tel.: (90) 2123174774
Web Site: https://www.nordeka.com.tr
Pulp & Paper Mfr
N.A.I.C.S.: 322110

Nordkalk GmbH (1)
Konrad Adenauer Strasse 6, 23558, Lubeck, Germany
Tel.: (49) 4513009380
Web Site: http://www.nordkalk.de
Emp.: 5
Limestone Distr
N.A.I.C.S.: 424910
Malte Konig (Gen Mgr)

Nordkalk Ukraine TOV (1)
76018 m vul Halytska 10, Ivano-Frankivs'k, Ukraine
Tel.: (380) 445027351
Web Site: https://www.ua-region.com.ua
Webpage Design Services
N.A.I.C.S.: 541511

Purmo Group Belgium N.V. (1)
Vogelsancklaan 250, 3520, Zonhoven, Belgium
Tel.: (32) 11813141
Heating Equipment Mfr & Distr
N.A.I.C.S.: 333414

Purmo Group Denmark ApS (1)
Rosengade 1, 6600, Vejen, Denmark
Tel.: (45) 75555611
Radiator Mfr & Distr
N.A.I.C.S.: 336390

Purmo Group Finland Oy Ab (1)
Tupankankatu, PO Box 16, 68601, Pietarsaari, Finland
Tel.: (358) 67869111
Web Site: https://www.purmo.com
Radiator Mfr & Distr
N.A.I.C.S.: 336390

Purmo Group France SAS (1)
Immeuble Rimbaud 22 Avenue des Nations, 93240, Villepinte, France
Tel.: (33) 145916200
Radiator Mfr & Distr
N.A.I.C.S.: 336390

Purmo Group Latvia SIA (1)
Krasta iela 68a, Riga, 1019, Latvia
Tel.: (371) 67808110
Web Site: https://www.purmo.com
Radiator Mfr & Distr
N.A.I.C.S.: 336390

Purmo Group Poland Sp.z o.o. (1)
ul Przemyslowa 11, 44-203, Rybnik, Poland
Tel.: (48) 324228815
Web Site: https://www.purmo.com
Radiator Mfr & Distr
N.A.I.C.S.: 336390

Purmo Group Sweden AB (1)
Florettgatan 20, 254 67, Helsingborg, Sweden
Tel.: (46) 42153000
Radiator Mfr & Distr
N.A.I.C.S.: 336390

Rettig (China) Co., Ltd (1)
Room 1908 Tower A Ocean International Center 56 East 4th Ring Road, Beijing, 100025, China
Tel.: (86) 10 8586 8499
Web Site: http://www.purmo.com.cn
Heating & Cooling Equipment Distr
N.A.I.C.S.: 423730

Rettig (UK) Ltd (1)
Eastern Avenue Team Valley, Gateshead, NE11 0PG, United Kingdom
Tel.: (44) 845 4023434
Web Site: http://www.myson.co.uk
Heating & Cooling Equipment Mfr & Distr
N.A.I.C.S.: 333415

Rettig Austria GmbH (1)
Vogel und Noot Strasse 4, 8661, Wartberg, Austria
Tel.: (43) 3858 601 0
Web Site: http://www.vogelundnoot.com
Heating & Cooling Equipment Distr
N.A.I.C.S.: 423730

Rettig Belgium N.V. (1)
Vogelsancklaan 50, 3520, Zonhoven, Belgium
Tel.: (32) 11 813 141
Web Site: http://www.radson.com
Emp.: 250
Heating & Cooling Equipment Distr
N.A.I.C.S.: 423730
Mike Conlon (Gen Mgr)

Rettig Germany GmbH (1)
Werk Lilienthal Scheeren 8, 28865, Lilienthal, Germany
Tel.: (49) 4298 919 0
Heating & Cooling Equipment Mfr & Distr
N.A.I.C.S.: 423730

Rettig Group Ceska s.r.o. (1)
Smilovskeho 1121, 570 01, Litomysl, Czech Republic
Tel.: (420) 725 922 411
Heating & Cooling Equipment Distr
N.A.I.C.S.: 423730
Jan Dvorak (Dir-Sls & Mktg)

Rettig Heating Equipment (Jiangsu) Co., Ltd. (1)
Room 1908 Tower A Ocean International Center No 56 East 4th Ring Road, Chaoyang District, Beijing, China
Tel.: (86) 1085868499
Web Site: https://www.purmo.com.cn
Radiator Mfr & Distr
N.A.I.C.S.: 336390

Rettig Heating Group France SAS (1)
157 Avenue Charles Floquet, 93158, Le Blanc-Mesnil, Cedex, France
Tel.: (33) 1 4591 6200
Web Site: http://www.finimetal.fr

AND PRIVATE COMPANIES — REUNERT LIMITED

Heating & Cooling Equipment Mfr & Distr
N.A.I.C.S.: 333414

Rettig Heating Sp.z o.o. (1)
ul Przemyslowa, 44-203, Rybnik, Poland
Tel.: (48) 32 422 2807
Web Site: http://www.purmo.pl
Heating & Cooling Equipment Distr
N.A.I.C.S.: 423730

Rettig Hrvatska d.o.o. (1)
Fallerovo Setaliste 22, 10000, Zagreb, Croatia
Tel.: (385) 1 65 31 151
Heating & Cooling Equipment Distr
N.A.I.C.S.: 423730

Rettig Hungary Kft (1)
Kuhne Ede ter, 9200, Mosonmagyarovar, Hungary
Tel.: (36) 96 88 6101
Web Site: http://www.vogelundnoot.com
Heating & Cooling Equipment Distr
N.A.I.C.S.: 423730

Rettig ICC B.V. (1)
Australielaan 6, 6199 AA, Maastricht, Netherlands
Tel.: (31) 433585870
Radiators, Underfloor Heating & Valves & Controls for Heating Systems
N.A.I.C.S.: 333415
Stig Bjorkqvist *(Controller)*

Rettig Inc. (1)
45 Krupp Dr, Williston, VT 05495
Web Site: http://www.mysoncomfort.com
Heating & Cooling Equipment Mfr & Distr
N.A.I.C.S.: 333415

Rettig Ireland Limited (1)
Newcastle West, Limerick, Ireland
Tel.: (353) 69 622 77
Heating & Cooling Equipment Distr
N.A.I.C.S.: 423730

Rettig Metal Ticaret ve Sanayi A.S. (1)
Ataturk Mahallesi 27 Sokak No 4, Kemalpasa, Izmir, Turkiye
Tel.: (90) 232 877 1787
Heating & Cooling Equipment Distr
N.A.I.C.S.: 423730

Rettig Slovenija d.o.o. (1)
Terceva ulica 12, 2000, Maribor, Slovenia
Tel.: (386) 2 250 24 80
Heating & Cooling Equipment Distr
N.A.I.C.S.: 423730

Rettig Srl. (1)
Ferma 8 Hala 17-18, 407310, Cluj-Napoca, Romania
Tel.: (40) 264 406 771
Heating & Cooling Equipment Distr
N.A.I.C.S.: 423730
Tunde Sandor *(Mng Dir)*

Rettig Sweden AB (1)
Florettgatan 29 C, 250 22, Helsingborg, Sweden
Tel.: (46) 42 15 30 00
Heating & Cooling Equipment Distr
N.A.I.C.S.: 423730

Rettig Varme Ab (1)
Tobaksgatan, PO Box 16, 68601, Jakobstad, Finland
Tel.: (358) 6 786 9111
Web Site: http://www.purmo.com
Heating & Cooling Equipment Distr
N.A.I.C.S.: 423730
Carl Anders Nygard *(CEO)*

SARL Emmeti - FIV France (1)
Parc des Expositions 22 Avenue des Nation Charles de Gaulle, 95926, Roissy-en-France, France
Tel.: (33) 145916235
Web Site: https://www.emmeti.com
Air Conditioning Mfr & Distr
N.A.I.C.S.: 333415

Sigarth AB (1)
Jarnvagsgatan 33, 335 73, Hillerstorp, Sweden
Tel.: (46) 37025400
Web Site: https://www.sigarth.com
Radiator Mfr & Distr
N.A.I.C.S.: 336190

Sigarth Sp.z o.o. (1)
ul 3 Stycznia 72, 64-300, Nowy Tomysl, Poland
Tel.: (48) 614420000
Radiator Mfr & Distr
N.A.I.C.S.: 336390

VNH Fabryka - Grzejnikow Sp.z o.o. (1)
Budowlanych 10, Walcz, Poland
Tel.: (48) 67 356 51 70
Heating & Cooling Equipment Distr
N.A.I.C.S.: 423730

ZAO Rettig Varme RUS (1)
Business Center Gulliver Torfyanya doroga 7 Liter A, 197374, Saint Petersburg, Russia
Tel.: (7) 8124412461
Radiator Mfr & Distr
N.A.I.C.S.: 333414

RETTY, INC.
Sumitomo Real Estate Shibazono Building 2F 2-10-1 Shibakoen, Minato-ku, Tokyo, 105-0011, Japan
Tel.: (81) 368521287
Web Site: https://retty.me
Year Founded: 2010
7356—(TKS)
Application Development Services
N.A.I.C.S.: 541511
Kazuya Takeda *(Co-Founder)*

RETURN ON INNOVATION ADVISORS LTD.
43 Front Street East Suite 301, Toronto, M5E 1B3, ON, Canada
Tel.: (416) 361-6162
Web Site: http://www.roicapital.ca
Investment Fund Management Services
N.A.I.C.S.: 523940
John Sterling *(Chm & Partner)*

Subsidiaries:

ROI Canadian Real Estate Fund (1)
37 Front Street East 4th Floor, Toronto, M5E 1B3, ON, Canada
Tel.: (416) 361-6162
Sales Range: Less than $1 Million
Closed-End Investment Fund
N.A.I.C.S.: 525990

REUBEN BROTHERS SA
9 Place du Molard, 1204, Geneva, Switzerland
Tel.: (41) 22 787 5020   CH
Web Site:
http://www.reubenbrothers.com
Private Equity, Venture Capital, Real Estate Investment & Development Firm
N.A.I.C.S.: 523999

Subsidiaries:

Arena Racing Corporation Limited (1)
3rd Floor Millbank Tower 21-24 Millbank, London, SW1P 4QP, United Kingdom
Tel.: (44) 207 802 5120
Web Site:
http://www.arenaracingcompany.com
Sales Range: $100-124.9 Million
Emp.: 360
Holding Company; Racetrack Owner, Operator & Venue Catering Services
N.A.I.C.S.: 551112
David Thorpe *(Chm)*

Subsidiary (Domestic):

Arena Leisure Catering Limited (2)
3rd Floor Millbank Tower 21-24 Millbank, London, SW1P 4QP, United Kingdom
Tel.: (44) 207 802 5120
Catering & Venue Hospitality Services
N.A.I.C.S.: 722320
Kevin Stuart Robertson *(Dir)*

Arena Leisure Racing Limited (2)
3rd Floor Millbank Tower 21-24 Millbank, London, SW1P 4QP, United Kingdom
Tel.: (44) 207 802 5120
Web Site:
http://www.arenaracingcompany.co.uk
Emp.: 8
Racetrack Operator
N.A.I.C.S.: 711212
Mark Spincer *(Dir-Ops)*

Subsidiary (Domestic):

Lingfield Park Limited (3)
Racecourse Road, Lingfield, RH7 6PQ, Surrey, United Kingdom
Tel.: (44) 1342 834 800
Web Site: http://www.lingfield-racecourse.co.uk
Racetrack, Hotel, Spa & Golf Course Operator
N.A.I.C.S.: 711212
Shaun Steel *(Dir-Resort Facilities)*

Southwell Racecourse Limited (3)
Rolleston, Near Newark, Southwell, NG25 0TS, Notts, United Kingdom
Tel.: (44) 1636 814 481
Web Site: http://www.southwell-racecourse.co.uk
Emp.: 8
Racetrack Operator
N.A.I.C.S.: 711212
Simon Davis *(Mgr-Estates)*

The Doncaster Racecourse Management Company Limited (3)
Leger Way, Doncaster, DN2 6BB, United Kingdom
Tel.: (44) 1302304200
Web Site: http://www.doncaster-racecourse.co.uk
Racetrack Operator
N.A.I.C.S.: 711212
Nikki Griffiths *(Dir-Sls)*

The Windsor Racecourse Company Limited (3)
Maidenhead Road, Windsor, SL4 5JJ, Berks, United Kingdom
Tel.: (44) 1753 498 400
Web Site: http://www.windsor-racecourse.co.uk
Emp.: 40
Racetrack Operator
N.A.I.C.S.: 711212
Hannah Chree *(Mgr-Recruitment & Trng)*

Wolverhampton Racecourse Limited (3)
Dunstall Park, Wolverhampton, WV6 0PE, United Kingdom
Tel.: (44) 1902 390 000
Web Site: http://www.wolverhampton-racecourse.co.uk
Racetrack & Hotel Operator
N.A.I.C.S.: 711212
David Roberts *(Mng Dir)*

Worcester Racecourse Limited (3)
Grandstand Road Pitchcroft, Worcester, WR1 3EJ, United Kingdom
Tel.: (44) 190525364
Web Site: http://www.worcester-racecourse.co.uk
Racetrack Operator
N.A.I.C.S.: 711212
Genny Cheshire *(Mgr)*

Metro International Trade Services LLC (1)
2500 Enterprise Dr, Allen Park, MI 48101
Tel.: (734) 721-3334
Web Site: http://www.metroftz.com
Warehousing, Distribution & Logistics Services
N.A.I.C.S.: 493190
Curt Felch *(VP-Real Estate)*

Reuben Brothers Limited (1)
4th Floor Millbank Tower 21-24, Millbank, London, SW1P 4QP, United Kingdom
Tel.: (44) 207 802 5010
Real Estate Consulting Service
N.A.I.C.S.: 531210

Wellington Pub Company (1)
4th Floor Millbank Tower 21-24, Millbank, London, SW1P 4QP, United Kingdom
Tel.: (44) 207 802 5240
Web Site:
http://www.wellingtonpubcompany.co.uk
Emp.: 8
Commercial Building Leasing Services

N.A.I.C.S.: 531120
Mark Davis *(Mgr-Property & Estates)*

REUNERT LIMITED
Nashua Building Woodmead North Office Park 54 Maxwell Drive, Woodmead, Sandton, 2191, South Africa
Tel.: (27) 115179000   ZA
Web Site: https://www.reunert.co.za
Year Founded: 1888
RNRTF—(OTCIQ)
Rev.: $727,774,903
Assets: $667,096,188
Liabilities: $264,155,726
Net Worth: $402,940,462
Earnings: $50,275,140
Emp.: 5,507
Fiscal Year-end: 09/30/23
Electronic, Telecommunication, Electrical & Engineering Products Mfr
N.A.I.C.S.: 517112
Trevor S. Munday *(Chm)*

Subsidiaries:

Acuo Technologies (Pty) Limited (1)
35 Electron Avenue Techno Park, Stellenbosch, 7600, South Africa   **(100%)**
Tel.: (27) 218095820
Web Site: http://www.acuo.co.za
Sales Range: $25-49.9 Million
Emp.: 21
Software Reproducing
N.A.I.C.S.: 334610
Andrew Nelson *(Gen Mgr)*

African Cables Ltd. (1)
Steel Road Peacehaven, PO Box 172, Vereeniging, 1930, South Africa
Tel.: (27) 164306000
Sales Range: $200-249.9 Million
Emp.: 800
Telecommunication & Energy Cable Mfr
N.A.I.C.S.: 335929

Algoa Office Automation (Pty) Limited (1)
Nashua House Circular Drive, Lorraine, Port Elizabeth, 6001, Eastern Cape, South Africa
Tel.: (27) 41 398 6000
Web Site: http://www.nashua.co.za
Sales Range: $50-74.9 Million
Emp.: 50
Office Automation Products Distr
N.A.I.C.S.: 423420

Bridoun Trade and Invest 197 (Pty) Limited (1)
Nashua House Omurambu Bosmansdam Rd, Cape Town, 7446, Western Cape, South Africa
Tel.: (27) 215502868
Sales Range: $100-124.9 Million
Emp.: 20
Investment Management Service
N.A.I.C.S.: 523999
Franchys Koekemoer *(Gen Mgr)*

CBI Electric-Industrial Controls (1)
9 Derrick Road, PO Box 100, Spartan, 1620, Kempton Park, South Africa
Tel.: (27) 119770700
Web Site: http://www.cbi-electric.com
Sales Range: $100-124.9 Million
Emp.: 54
Electrical Circuit Breaker, Relay & Control Product Mfr
N.A.I.C.S.: 335999

CBI-Electric Aberdare ATC Telecom Cables (Pty) Limited (1)
3 Marthinus Ras Street Industrial Sites, Brits, North West, South Africa   **(74.9%)**
Tel.: (27) 123811400
Sales Range: $100-124.9 Million
Emp.: 491
Mfr of Telecommunications Cables
N.A.I.C.S.: 335929

Circuit Breaker Industries Inc (1)
35 E Uwchlan Ave Ste 328, Exton, PA 19341
Tel.: (610) 524-9949
Web Site: https://www.cbi-lowvoltage.co.za
Circuit Protection Equipment Whslr
N.A.I.C.S.: 423610
James Seypert *(Mgr)*

REUNERT LIMITED

Reunert Limited—(Continued)

Circuit Breaker Industries Limited (1) (100%)
Tel.: (27) 119282000
Sales Range: $400-449.9 Million
Emp.: 1,999
Mfr of Electrical Distribution & Protection Components
N.A.I.C.S.: 335999

Circuit Breaker Industries Qwa Qwa (Pty) Limited (1)
Private Box 2016, Isando, 1600, Johannesburg, South Africa
Tel.: (27) 11 928 2000
Web Site: http://www.cbi-electric.com
Emp.: 80
Electronic Components Mfr
N.A.I.C.S.: 334419

Classic Number Trading 80 (Pty) Limited (1)
Block D 361 Veale Street, Pretoria, 181, South Africa
Tel.: (27) 124332700
Sales Range: $50-74.9 Million
Emp.: 95
Electronic Components Distr
N.A.I.C.S.: 423690
Tienie Vinrenaburg (Gen Mgr)

Just Jasmine Investments 201 (Pty) Limited (1)
3 Kiepersol Close, Parow, 7500, Western Cape, South Africa
Tel.: (27) 219378219
Sales Range: $50-74.9 Million
Emp.: 100
Investment Management Service
N.A.I.C.S.: 523999

Kopano Copier Company (Pty) Limited (1)
54 Maxwell Drive, Halfway House, Johannesburg, 6190, Gauteng, South Africa
Tel.: (27) 112328600
Sales Range: $25-49.9 Million
Emp.: 29
Commercial Printing Services
N.A.I.C.S.: 323111
Peter Mbolekwa (Mng Dir)

Nanoteq (Pty) Limited (1)
Unit C01 Corporate Park 66 269 Von Willich Avenue, 269 Von Willich Avenue, Centurion, 0157, South Africa
Tel.: (27) 12 672 7000
Web Site: https://www.nanoteq.com
Custom Computer Programming Services
N.A.I.C.S.: 541511

Nashua Ltd (1)
Woodmead North Office Park Maxwell Drive, Woodmead, South Africa (100%)
Tel.: (27) 112328000
Sales Range: $50-74.9 Million
Emp.: 100
Office Equipment Whslr
N.A.I.C.S.: 423420
Barry Venter (CEO)

Subsidiary (Domestic):

Zevoli 151 (Pty) Limited (2)
Rock Cottage Shopping Centre Cnr John Voster & Christiaan De Wet Road, Weltevreden Park, Roodepoort, 1709, South Africa
Tel.: (27) 11 670 3000
Web Site: http://www.nashua.co.za
Emp.: 9
Office Automation Products Distr
N.A.I.C.S.: 423420
Alle Marie Singereton (Gen Mgr)

Nashua Mobile (Pty) Ltd (1)
Woodmead North Office Park 54 Maxwell Drive, Woodmead, Johannesburg, 2191, Gauteng, South Africa (100%)
Tel.: (27) 11 232 8000
Web Site: https://www.nashua.co.za
Telecommunications
N.A.I.C.S.: 517810

PWC Office Automation (Pty) Limited (1)
3 Gimnasuim Street, Paarl, 7646, Western Cape, South Africa
Tel.: (27) 218728252
Web Site: http://www.nasiutapwc.co.za
Emp.: 42

Electronic Parts Distr
N.A.I.C.S.: 423690
Deon Boshoff (CEO)

Pansolutions Holdings Limited (1)
Unit 12Aii Growthpoint Office Park, Halfway House, Johannesburg, 1683, Gauteng, South Africa
Tel.: (27) 113131400
Sales Range: $100-124.9 Million
Emp.: 250
Investment Management Service
N.A.I.C.S.: 523999
Neil Stopforth (Mng Dir)

Quince Capital (Pty) Limited (1)
Nashua Building Woodmead North Office Park 54 Maxwell Drive, PO Box 897, Halfway House, Woodmead, 1685, South Africa
Tel.: (27) 112328000
Web Site: https://quincecapital.co.za
Sales Range: $50-74.9 Million
Emp.: 48
Financial Management Services
N.A.I.C.S.: 523999
Rudi Steenkamp (Dir-Sls)

RC&C Manufacturing Company (Pty) Limited (1)
21 Radnor Road, PO Box 275, Parow, 7500, South Africa (100%)
Tel.: (27) 219318181
Web Site: http://www.rccman.co.za
Emp.: 55
Electrical Contractor
N.A.I.C.S.: 238210

Reunert Management Services Limited (1)
Nashua Building Woodmead North Office Park 54 Maxwell Drive, PO Box 784391, Woodmead, 2191, South Africa (100%)
Tel.: (27) 115179000
Web Site: http://www.reunert.com
Sales Range: $25-49.9 Million
Emp.: 29
Management Consulting Services
N.A.I.C.S.: 541618

Reutech Communications (Pty) Limited (1) (100%)
Tel.: (27) 31 719 5700
Web Site: https://www.reutechcomms.com
Power & Communication Transmission Line Construction
N.A.I.C.S.: 237130
George Hiralal (CEO)

Reutech Ltd (1)
Reunert Nashua Building Woodmead North Office Park 54 Maxwell Drive, PO Box 784391, Woodmead, 2191, South Africa
Tel.: (27) 115179000
Web Site: https://www.reunert.com
Sales Range: $25-49.9 Million
Emp.: 30
Electronic Components Mfr
N.A.I.C.S.: 334419

Subsidiary (Domestic):

Fuchs Electronics (Pty) Ltd (2)
15 Combrinck Street Alrode, Alberton, 1451, Gauteng, South Africa (100%)
Tel.: (27) 113894200
Sales Range: $25-49.9 Million
Emp.: 100
Electronic Components Mfr
N.A.I.C.S.: 334419

Reutech Communications (Pty) Limited (2)
9 Valley View Road, New Germany, 3610, Kwa-Zulu Natal, South Africa
Tel.: (27) 31 719 5700
Web Site: https://www.reutechcomms.com
Emp.: 23
Telecommunication Servicesb
N.A.I.C.S.: 517810

Reutech Radar Systems (Pty) Limited (2)
35 Elektron Avenue Technopark, Stellenbosch, 7600, South Africa (57%)
Tel.: (27) 218801150
Sales Range: $50-74.9 Million
Engineering Services
N.A.I.C.S.: 517810
Carl Kies (CEO)

Reutech Solutions (Pty) Limited (2)
628 James Crescent, Halfway House, Midrand, 1685, South Africa
Tel.: (27) 116525555
Sales Range: $100-124.9 Million
Telecommunication Servicesb
N.A.I.C.S.: 517810

Santogyn (Pty) Limited (1)
154 Industria Road, Johannesburg, 2092, South Africa
Tel.: (27) 112498000
Sales Range: $75-99.9 Million
Emp.: 12
Electronic Parts Distr
N.A.I.C.S.: 423690
Phil Mcdiarmid (Gen Mgr)

REUNION NEUROSCIENCE INC.
30 Duncan Street Suite 400, Toronto, M5V 2C3, ON, Canada
Tel.: (403) 617-8779 Ca
Web Site: http://www.fieldtriphealth.com
REUN—(NASDAQ)
Rev.: $541,173
Assets: $23,265,246
Liabilities: $6,606,270
Net Worth: $16,658,976
Earnings: ($37,935,101)
Emp.: 16
Fiscal Year-end: 03/31/23
Oil & Gas Exploration Services
N.A.I.C.S.: 213112
Greg Mayes (Pres)

REUS S.R.O
Ke Karlovu 1102/7, Skvrnany, 301 00, Plzen, Czech Republic
Tel.: (420) 377679111
Web Site: http://www.reus.cz
Sales Range: $50-74.9 Million
Emp.: 270
Book Printing Services
N.A.I.C.S.: 323117
Jiri Ondrousek (CFO)

REVA SA
Str Atelierelor 32, Simeria, Hunedoara, Romania
Tel.: (40) 254260402 RO
Web Site: https://www.revasimeria.ro
Year Founded: 1869
REVA—(BUC)
Rev.: $25,005,929
Assets: $22,668,863
Liabilities: $10,031,984
Net Worth: $12,636,878
Earnings: $1,002,076
Emp.: 539
Fiscal Year-end: 12/31/23
Railway Locomotive & Rolling Stock Mfr
N.A.I.C.S.: 336510
Alina Veronica Magdau (Gen Mgr)

REVATI ORGANICS LTD.
Ganpati Bhavan Plot No 45 1st Floor M G Road, Goregaon W, Mumbai, 400062, Maharashtra, India
Tel.: (91) 2228748995
Year Founded: 1993
524504—(BOM)
Emp.: 4
Chemical Products Mfr
N.A.I.C.S.: 325199
Girish Shah (Mng Dir)

REVENIO GROUP OYJ
Ayritie 22, 01510, Vantaa, Finland
Tel.: (358) 987751150
Web Site: https://www.reveniogroup.fi
Year Founded: 2001
REG1V—(HEL)
Rev.: $104,657,889
Assets: $146,871,358
Liabilities: $48,753,507

INTERNATIONAL PUBLIC

Net Worth: $98,117,850
Earnings: $23,476,149
Emp.: 207
Fiscal Year-end: 12/31/22
Holding Company
N.A.I.C.S.: 551112
Kyosti Kakkonen (Mng Dir)

Subsidiaries:

Done Information Oy (1)
Tukholmankatu 2, FI-00250, Helsinki, Finland
Tel.: (358) 205253000
Web Site: http://www.doneinformation.com
Sales Range: $1-9.9 Million
Emp.: 71
Technical Communication Services
N.A.I.C.S.: 541930

Done Software Solutions Oy (1)
Huhtalantie 2, 60220, Seinajoki, Finland
Tel.: (358) 20 525 3100
Web Site: http://www.donesoftware.fi
Sales Range: $25-49.9 Million
Emp.: 20
Intralogistics Software Development Services
N.A.I.C.S.: 541511
Ari Suominen (Mng Dir)

Finnish LED-Signs Oy (1)
Voudinkatu 35a, 20360, Raisio, Finland
Tel.: (358) 22721100
Web Site: http://www.flsfinland.com
Sales Range: $25-49.9 Million
Emp.: 14
Light Emitting Diode Displays Mfr
N.A.I.C.S.: 334413
Jussi Tomperi (Gen Mgr)

Icare Finland Oy (1)
Ayritie 22, 01510, Vantaa, Finland
Tel.: (358) 987751150
Web Site: https://www.icare-world.com
Sales Range: $25-49.9 Million
Eyecare Instrument Mfr
N.A.I.C.S.: 334516

Providor Logistics Oy (1)
Tuottajantie 7, FI-60100, Seinajoki, Finland
Tel.: (358) 64211100
Sales Range: $10-24.9 Million
Emp.: 13
Food Logistics Services
N.A.I.C.S.: 722310

Revenio Research Oy (1)
Ayritie 22, 01510, Vantaa, Finland
Tel.: (358) 207305511
Web Site: https://www.ventica.net
Medical Equipment Distr
N.A.I.C.S.: 423450

REVENUE GROUP BHD
Wisma Revenue No 12 Jalan Udang Harimau 2 Kepong Business Park, 51200, Kuala Lumpur, Malaysia
Tel.: (60) 392123388
Web Site: https://www.revenue.com.my
Year Founded: 2003
REVENUE—(KLS)
Rev.: $112,578,524
Assets: $43,926,437
Liabilities: $17,784,477
Net Worth: $26,141,960
Earnings: ($18,900,865)
Fiscal Year-end: 09/30/23
Electronic Finance Services
N.A.I.C.S.: 522320

Subsidiaries:

Buymall Services Sdn. Bhd. (1)
34 Jalan 21 Kawasan 10 Jalan Petai, Pandamaran, 42000, Klang, Selangor, Malaysia
Tel.: (60) 327262430
Web Site: https://buymall.com.my
Accessory Distr
N.A.I.C.S.: 458110

Revenue Harvest Sdn (1)
Wisma Revenue No 12 Jalan Udang Harimau 2, Kepong Business Park, 51200, Kuala Lumpur, Malaysia (100%)
Tel.: (60) 392123388

AND PRIVATE COMPANIES

Web Site: https://www.revenue.com.my
Holding Company; Financial Services
N.A.I.C.S.: 551112

Subsidiary (Domestic):

Anypay Sdn. Bhd. (2)
Unit A 1st Floor Amoda 88 No 88 Jalan Yew, 55200, Kuala Lumpur, Malaysia (70%)
Tel.: (60) 103291888
Web Site: https://www.anypay.my
Information Technology Services
N.A.I.C.S.: 541511

Wannapay Sdn. Bhd. (1)
Wisma Revenue Business Park Kepong 12 Jalan Udang Harimau 2, Federal Territory of Kuala Lumpur, 51200, Kuala Lumpur, Malaysia
Tel.: (60) 392123388
Web Site: https://www.wanna.com.my
Electronic Payment Services
N.A.I.C.S.: 522320

REVER HOLDINGS CORPORATION
1-7-2 Otemachi, Chiyoda-Ku, Tokyo, 100-0004, Japan
Tel.: (81) 352041890
Web Site: http://www.re-ver.co.jp
Year Founded: 2007
5690—(TKS)
Rev.: $274,670,000
Assets: $273,401,920
Liabilities: $116,498,800
Net Worth: $156,903,120
Earnings: $11,780,560
Fiscal Year-end: 06/30/20
Holding Company
N.A.I.C.S.: 551112
Takao Suzuki *(Chm)*

Subsidiaries:

Major Venous Japan Co., Ltd. (1)
1-7-2 Otemachi Tokyo Sankei Building 15F, Chiyoda-ku, Tokyo, 100-0004, Japan
Tel.: (81) 35 569 7726
Web Site: https://www.major-venous.co.jp
Waste Management Services
N.A.I.C.S.: 562998

Nakadaya Corp. (1)
15th Floor of Tokyo Sankei Building 1-7-2 Otemachi, Chiyoda-ku, Tokyo, 100-0004, Japan
Tel.: (81) 352041886
Web Site: http://www.ndy.co.jp
Metal Recyclable Product Distr
N.A.I.C.S.: 423930

Phoenix Metal Corp. (1)
15th Floor Tokyo Sankei Building 1-7-2 Otemachi, Chiyoda-ku, Tokyo, 100-0004, Japan
Tel.: (81) 436431261
Web Site: http://www.phoenixmetal.co.jp
Steel & Aluminum Raw Material Distr
N.A.I.C.S.: 423510

Rever Corporation (1)
1-7-2 Otemachi Tokyo Sankei Building 15th Floor, Chiyoda-ku, Tokyo, Japan
Tel.: (81) 352041888
Web Site: http://www.rever-corp.co.jp
Industrial Waste Disposal Services
N.A.I.C.S.: 562998

Sunny Metal Corp. (1)
1-1-13 Tsuneyoshi, Chiyoda-ku, Osaka, 554-0052, Japan
Tel.: (81) 664612818
Web Site: http://www.sunny-metal.co.jp
Recyclable Material Distr
N.A.I.C.S.: 423930

REVERSE CORP LIMITED
Level 1 30 Little Cribb Street, Milton, 4064, QLD, Australia
Tel.: (61) 732950300
Web Site: http://www.reversecorp.com.au
Rev.: $6,288,679
Assets: $7,260,614
Liabilities: $762,593
Net Worth: $6,498,020
Earnings: ($392,706)
Emp.: 17
Fiscal Year-end: 06/30/18
Reverse Charge Calling Services
N.A.I.C.S.: 517121
Peter David Ritchie *(Chm)*

Subsidiaries:

TriTel Australia Pty Limited (1)
23 McDougall St, Milton, 4064, QLD, Australia
Tel.: (61) 732950314
Web Site: http://www.tritel.com.au
Sales Range: $25-49.9 Million
Emp.: 6
Payphone & Public Internet Services
N.A.I.C.S.: 517121
Charles Slaughter *(CEO)*

REVIMPORT
Z I Nord 6 Rue Alphonse Beau De Rochas, 66000, Perpignan, Pyrenees Orientales, France
Tel.: (33) 468612168
Web Site: http://www.revimport.com
Rev.: $25,900,000
Emp.: 48
Homefurnishings
N.A.I.C.S.: 423220
Josephine Revelles *(Gen Mgr)*

REVIVAL GOLD INC.
145 King St W Suite 2870, Toronto, M5H 1J8, ON, Canada
Tel.: (416) 366-4100 Ca
Web Site: https://www.revival-gold.com
Year Founded: 2008
RVLGF—(OTCQX)
Rev.: $24,449
Assets: $10,403,437
Liabilities: $634,222
Net Worth: $9,769,215
Earnings: ($7,642,713)
Emp.: 6
Fiscal Year-end: 06/30/21
Investment Services
N.A.I.C.S.: 523999
Steve Priesmeyer *(VP-Exploration)*

Subsidiaries:

Strata Minerals Pty Ltd. (1)
308 Fitzgerald Street, Perth, 6006, WA, Australia
Tel.: (61) 8 9284 7171
Web Site: http://www.strataminerals.com
Phosphate Rock Mining & Exploration Services
N.A.I.C.S.: 212390

REVIVE THERAPEUTICS LTD.
82 Richmond Street East, Toronto, M5C 1P1, ON, Canada
Tel.: (647) 985-2336 ON
Web Site: https://www.revivethera.com
Year Founded: 2012
RVV—(CNSX)
Rev.: $33,318
Assets: $7,775,381
Liabilities: $2,488,446
Net Worth: $5,286,935
Earnings: ($4,107,494)
Fiscal Year-end: 06/30/24
Specialty Biopharmaceutical Products Mfr
N.A.I.C.S.: 325412
Carmelo Marrelli *(CFO)*

REVNOST A.D.
Balzakova 3, 0, Novi Sad, Serbia
Tel.: (381) 21466688
Web Site: https://www.revnost.com
Year Founded: 1986
RVST—(BEL)
Rev.: $7,064,992
Assets: $1,346,879
Liabilities: $1,043,173
Net Worth: $303,706
Earnings: $81,697
Emp.: 598
Fiscal Year-end: 12/31/23
Private Security Services
N.A.I.C.S.: 561612
Bozidarka Kozomora *(Exec Dir)*

REVO INSURANCE S.P.A.
Via Monte Rosa 91, 20149, Milan, Italy
Tel.: (39) 0292885700
Web Site: https://www.revoinsurance.com
Year Founded: 2022
REVO—(ITA)
Rev.: $164,421,018
Assets: $469,271,443
Liabilities: $220,209,736
Net Worth: $249,061,707
Earnings: $11,662,435
Emp.: 189
Fiscal Year-end: 12/31/23
Fire Insurance Services
N.A.I.C.S.: 524113
Alberto Minali *(CEO)*

REVOCOM LTD.
34 Oyster Bay Sterte Close, Poole, Dorset, BH15 2FN, United Kingdom
Tel.: (44) 1202612121 UK
Communication Equipment Mfr
N.A.I.C.S.: 334290

REVOIL S.A.
5 Kapodistriou str, 16672, Vari, Greece
Tel.: (30) 2108976000
Web Site: https://www.revoil.gr
Year Founded: 1982
REVOIL—(ATH)
Sales Range: $800-899.9 Million
Emp.: 184
Petroleum Product Whslr
N.A.I.C.S.: 424720
Georgios E. Roussos *(CEO)*

REVOLUGROUP CANADA INC.
Suite 1610 - 777 Dunsmuir Street, Vancouver, V7Y 1K4, BC, Canada
Tel.: (604) 687-3376
Web Site: http://www.cubaventures.com
Year Founded: 2016
MPSFF—(OTCIQ)
Rev.: $322,029
Assets: $1,511,861
Liabilities: $639,907
Net Worth: $871,954
Earnings: ($2,072,320)
Fiscal Year-end: 05/31/23
Investment Services
N.A.I.C.S.: 523999

Subsidiaries:

RevoluPAY EP S.L. (1)
Vallespir 19 1, Sant Cugat del Valles, 08173, Barcelona, Spain
Tel.: (34) 938930586
Web Site: https://www.revolupay.es
Financial Services
N.A.I.C.S.: 523999

REVOLUGROUP CANADA, INC.
997 Seymour Street Suite 230 Unit 9, Vancouver, V6B 3M1, BC, Canada
Tel.: (604) 800-9676
Web Site: https://www.revolugroup.com
Year Founded: 1980
REVO—(TSXV)
Rev.: $324,376
Assets: $1,522,880
Liabilities: $644,571
Net Worth: $878,309

REVOLUTION CO., LTD.

Earnings: ($2,087,424)
Fiscal Year-end: 05/31/23
Information Technology Services
N.A.I.C.S.: 541512
James G. Pettit *(Pres & Chm)*

Subsidiaries:

RevoluFIN Inc. (1)
Plaza 2000 39 Planta Baja Calle 53 Este y Calle 50, Marbella Financial District, Panama, Panama
Tel.: (507) 8339003
Web Site: https://revolufin.com
Financial Management Services
N.A.I.C.S.: 523999

RevoluPAY S.L. (1)
Vallespir 19 1, Sant Cugat del Valles, 08173, Barcelona, Spain
Tel.: (34) 93 893 0586
Web Site: https://www.revolupay.es
Banking Services
N.A.I.C.S.: 522110

RevoluVIP International Inc. (1)
Suite 1610 - 777 Dunsmuir Street, Vancouver, V7Y 1K4, BC, Canada
Tel.: (416) 800-0388
Web Site: https://www.revoluvip.club
Travel Services
N.A.I.C.S.: 561510

REVOLUTION BARS GROUP PLC
21 Old Street, Ashton-under-Lyne, Ashton under Lyne, OL6 6LA, United Kingdom
Tel.: (44) 1613303876 UK
Web Site: https://www.revolutionbarsgroup.com
Year Founded: 1991
RBG—(LSE)
Rev.: $53,517,249
Assets: $160,625,065
Liabilities: $194,880,340
Net Worth: ($34,255,276)
Earnings: ($35,702,605)
Emp.: 2,495
Fiscal Year-end: 07/03/21
Bar Beverage Operator
N.A.I.C.S.: 722410
Rob Pitcher *(CEO)*

REVOLUTION BEAUTY GROUP PLC
Units 2 3 Sheet Glass Road Cullet Drive, Queenborough, ME11 5JS, United Kingdom
Tel.: (44) 330 111 0032 UK
Web Site: https://revolutionbeautyplc.com
REVB—(AIM)
Emp.: 100
Beauty Product Supplier
N.A.I.C.S.: 456120
Tom Allsworth *(Co-Founder & Exec Chm)*

Subsidiaries:

BH Cosmetics, LLC (1)
2801 Burton Ave, Burbank, CA 91504
Tel.: (855) 935-1322
Web Site: http://www.bhcosmetics.com
Cosmetics Website
N.A.I.C.S.: 456120
Fred Sadovskiy *(Co-Founder)*

REVOLUTION CO., LTD.
New Otani Garden Court 12F 4-1 Kioicho, Chiyoda-ku, Tokyo, 102-0094, Japan
Tel.: (81) 366273487 JP
Web Site: https://www.revolution.co.jp
Year Founded: 1986
8894—(TKS)
Rev.: $17,037,270
Assets: $13,839,680
Liabilities: $4,686,490
Net Worth: $9,153,190

6313

REVOLUTION CO., LTD.

Revolution Co., Ltd.—(Continued)
Earnings: ($2,637,480)
Emp.: 36
Fiscal Year-end: 10/31/23
Real Estate Manangement Services
N.A.I.C.S.: 531390
Takafumi Okamoto (Pres & CEO)

REVOLVE RENEWABLE POWER CORP.
Suite 580 625 Howe Street, Vancouver, V6C 2T6, BC, Canada
Tel.: (778) 885-5550 BC
Web Site: https://revolve-renewablepower.com
Year Founded: 1989
REVVF—(OTCQB)
Rev.: $86,059
Assets: $154,056
Liabilities: $92,810
Net Worth: $61,246
Earnings: ($13,853)
Fiscal Year-end: 03/31/21
Copper & Gold Mining Services
N.A.I.C.S.: 212230
Marshall L. Farris (Pres)

Subsidiaries:

Philippine Metals Corp. (1)
706 7 Ave SW Ste 810, Calgary, P2P 0Z1, AB, Canada
Tel.: (403) 236-4520
Sales Range: $75-99.9 Million
Emp.: 3
Precious Metal Mining Services
N.A.I.C.S.: 212220

REVOLVE TECHNOLOGIES LIMITED
Prospect House Prospect Way, Hutton, Brentwood, CM13 1XA, Essex, United Kingdom
Tel.: (44) 1277261400 UK
Web Site: http://www.revolve.co.uk
Year Founded: 1995
Sales Range: $25-49.9 Million
Emp.: 60
Motor Vehicle Design, Engineering & Development Services
N.A.I.C.S.: 541330
John Mitchell (Mng Dir)

REWALK ROBOTICS LTD.
3 Hatnufa St 6th floor, Yokneam, 2069203, Ilit, Israel
Tel.: (972) 49590123 IL
Web Site: https://golifeward.com
LFWD—(NASDAQ)
Rev.: $13,854,000
Assets: $63,292,000
Liabilities: $16,782,000
Net Worth: $46,510,000
Earnings: ($22,133,000)
Emp.: 108
Fiscal Year-end: 12/31/23
Medical Device Mfr
N.A.I.C.S.: 339112
Larry Jasinski (CEO)

Subsidiaries:

ReWalk Robotics (1)
Leipziger Platz 15, 10117, Berlin, Germany
Tel.: (49) 3025895080
Medical Device Mfr
N.A.I.C.S.: 339112

ReWalk Robotics, Inc. (1)
200 Donald Lynch Blvd, Marlborough, MA 01752
Tel.: (508) 251-1154
Web Site: https://www.rewalk.com
Medical Device Mfr
N.A.I.C.S.: 339112

REWARD MINERALS LTD
159 Stirling Highway, Nedlands, 6009, WA, Australia
Tel.: (61) 63891032

Web Site: https://www.rewardminerals.com
RWD—(ASX)
Rev.: $28,479
Assets: $16,659,518
Liabilities: $2,946,558
Net Worth: $13,712,960
Earnings: ($15,443,637)
Fiscal Year-end: 12/31/23
Mineral Explorer
N.A.I.C.S.: 213115
Michael Ruane (Exec Dir)

Subsidiaries:

Jinka Minerals Ltd (1)
159 Stirling Hwy, PO Box 1104, Nedlands, 6009, WA, Australia
Tel.: (61) 89287777
Web Site: http://www.kglresources.com.au
Emp.: 9
Mineral Exploration Services
N.A.I.C.S.: 213115

REWARD WOOL INDUSTRY CORPORATION
12th Floor Kuang Fu Building 310 Sec 4 Chung Hsiao East Road, Taipei, Taiwan
Tel.: (886) 227811161
Web Site: https://www.reward.com.tw
Year Founded: 1964
1423—(TAI)
Rev.: $4,061,120
Assets: $102,843,745
Liabilities: $9,245,528
Net Worth: $93,598,217
Earnings: $2,306,583
Emp.: 47
Fiscal Year-end: 12/31/23
Textile Products Mfr
N.A.I.C.S.: 314999
Yang Zun-Wu (Mgr)

Subsidiaries:

Reward Wool Industry Corporation - Hsin-Wu Mill (1)
309 Sec 2 Chung Shang East Road Tou-Chou Vil Hsin-Wu Dist, Taoyuan, Taiwan
Tel.: (886) 34904311
Wool Tops & Carbonated Wool Mfr
N.A.I.C.S.: 313310

Reward Wool Industry Corporation - Liu-Tu Mill (1)
2 Kung Chien South Road Liu-Tu Industrial District, Keelung, Taiwan
Tel.: (886) 224515116
Wool Tops & Carbonated Wool Mfr
N.A.I.C.S.: 313310

REWARDLE HOLDINGS LIMITED
Suite 70 Level 4 80 Market St, South Melbourne, 3205, VIC, Australia
Tel.: (61) 893888290
Web Site: https://www.rewardleholdings.com
Year Founded: 2014
RXH—(ASX)
Rev.: $268,535
Assets: $3,780,760
Liabilities: $2,791,287
Net Worth: $989,473
Earnings: $2,463,398
Fiscal Year-end: 06/30/23
Commerce Based Social Network
N.A.I.C.S.: 551112
Ruwan Weerasooriya (Founder, Founder, Exec Chm, Chm, Chm, Mng Dir & Mng Dir)

REWAY GROUP S.P.A.
Piazza Velasca 8, Lombardia, 20122, Milan, Italy
Tel.: (39) 01871788751
Web Site: https://www.rewaygroup.com
Year Founded: 2021

RWY—(ITA)
Construction Services
N.A.I.C.S.: 237310
Paul Luccini (Chm)

REWE-ZENTRAL-AKTIENGESELLSCHAFT
Domstrasse 20, 50668, Cologne, Germany
Tel.: (49) 2211490 De
Web Site: http://www.rewe-group.com
Year Founded: 1926
Sales Range: $50-74.9 Billion
Emp.: 360,000
Holding Company; Supermarkets, Travel & Tourism Services
N.A.I.C.S.: 551112
Frank Wiemer (Member-Mgmt Bd)

Subsidiaries:

Billa AG (1)
IZ No Sud Strasse 3 Objekt 16, Wiener Neudorf, Austria
Tel.: (43) 22366000
Web Site: http://www.billa.at
Supermarket
N.A.I.C.S.: 445110

DER Touristik Deutschland GmbH (1)
Emil Von Behring Strasse 6, 60424, Frankfurt am Main, Germany (100%)
Tel.: (49) 69958800
Web Site: http://www.dertour.de
Sales Range: $150-199.9 Million
Emp.: 1,000
Travel Agency
N.A.I.C.S.: 561510
Soeren Hartmann (Gen Mgr)

Subsidiary (Non-US):

DER Touristik Nordic AB (1)
Ynglingagatan 2, Stockholm, 113 47, Sweden
Tel.: (46) 86 73 84 00
Web Site: http://www.apollo.se
Travel & Tour Operating Services
N.A.I.C.S.: 561510
Jens Hansen (Mgr-IT Dev)

Representative Office (Non-US):

DER Touristik Denmark (3)
Amager Strandvej 60 1 Floor, DK 2300, Copenhagen, Denmark
Tel.: (45) 35201000
Web Site: http://www.apollorejser.dk
Travel Agency Services
N.A.I.C.S.: 561510

DER Touristik Norway (3)
PO Box 339, 0101, Oslo, Sentrum, Norway
Tel.: (47) 21017540
Web Site: http://www.apollo.no
Tour & Travel Operating Services
N.A.I.C.S.: 561520
Marcus Grahm (Ops Mgr)

Subsidiary (Domestic):

Nova Airlines AB (3)
Ynglingagatan 2, 104 31, Stockholm, Sweden
Tel.: (46) 86738600
Web Site: http://www.novair.se
Tour Operating Services
N.A.I.C.S.: 561520
Peter Sandgren (Dir-Ground Ops)

Subsidiary (Non-US):

DER Touristik Suisse AG (2)
Herostrasse 12, 8048, Zurich, Switzerland (100%)
Tel.: (41) 44 277 4444
Web Site: http://www.dertouristik.ch
Travel Agency
N.A.I.C.S.: 561510
Dieter Zumpel (CEO)

Unit (Domestic):

DER Touristik Suisse AG, Zweigniederlassung Kontiki Reisen (3)

INTERNATIONAL PUBLIC

Bahnhofstrasse 31, 5400, Baden, Switzerland
Tel.: (41) 56 203 66 66
Web Site: http://www.kontiki.ch
Tour & Travel Operating Services
N.A.I.C.S.: 561520
Bruno Bisig (CEO)

DER Touristik Suisse AG, Zweigniederlassung Kuoni Reisen, Kusnacht (3)
Seestrasse 127, CH 8700, Kusnacht, Switzerland
Tel.: (41) 19142525
Web Site: http://www.dertouristik.ch
Travel Agency
N.A.I.C.S.: 561510

DER Touristik Suisse AG, Zweigniederlassung Private Safaris, Zurich (3)
Herostrasse 12, 8048, Zurich, Switzerland
Tel.: (41) 44 386 4646
Web Site: http://www.privatesafaris.ch
Travel Services
N.A.I.C.S.: 561510
Claudio Nauli (Exec Dir)

Subsidiary (Domestic):

Manta Reisen AG (3)
Herostrasse 12, Zurich, 8048, Switzerland (100%)
Tel.: (41) 442774700
Web Site: http://www.manta.ch
Travel Agency
N.A.I.C.S.: 561510
Thomas Meier (Gen Mgr)

Railtour Suisse SA (3)
Bernstrasse 164 Zollikofen, CH 3052, Bern, Switzerland (100%)
Tel.: (41) 313780101
Web Site: http://www.railtoureurope.com
Travel Services
N.A.I.C.S.: 561510
Colette Richter (Head-Mktg Mgmt)

Subsidiary (Non-US):

DER Touristik UK Ltd (2)
Touristik House Dorking Office Park, Dorking, RH4 1HJ, Surrey, United Kingdom (100%)
Tel.: (44) 306740888
Web Site: http://www.kuoni.co.uk
Travel Services
N.A.I.C.S.: 561510
Derek Jones (Mng Dir)

Subsidiary (Domestic):

Carrier Ltd. (3)
One Didsbury Point 2 The Avenue, Manchester, M20 2EY, Didsbury, United Kingdom
Tel.: (44) 161 491 7650
Web Site: http://www.carrier.co.uk
Travel Agency Services
N.A.I.C.S.: 561510

Jules Verne Ltd (3)
96 Great Suffolk Street, London, SE1 0BE, United Kingdom (100%)
Tel.: (44) 2037335762
Web Site: http://www.vjv.com
Travel Services
N.A.I.C.S.: 561510
Jacqueline Farr (Sec)

Kirker Travel Limited (3)
4 Waterloo Court 10 Theed Street, London, SE1 8ST, United Kingdom
Tel.: (44) 20 75932288
Web Site: http://www.kirkerholidays.com
Travel Services
N.A.I.C.S.: 561599
Ted Wake (Dir-Sls & Mktg)

Delvita A.S. (1)
Za Panskou Zahradou 1018, Rudna, 25219, Czech Republic
Tel.: (420) 311609111
Web Site: http://www.delvita.cz
Sales Range: $25-49.9 Million
Emp.: 100
Food Retail Chain
N.A.I.C.S.: 445110

Subsidiary (Domestic):

Delnemo A/S (2)

AND PRIVATE COMPANIES

11018 Za Panskou Zahradou, 252 19
Rudna U Prahy, 25219, Prague, Czech
Republic
Tel.: (420) 311609111
Web Site: http://www.delnemoc.cz
Sales Range: $100-124.9 Million
Contractor of Supermarket Buildings
N.A.I.C.S.: 236220

Lekkerland AG & Co. KG (1)
Europaallee 57, 50226, Frechen, Germany
Tel.: (49) 223418210
Web Site: http://www.lekkerland.com
Rev.: $14,164,674,772
Assets: $1,844,464,316
Liabilities: $1,645,252,699
Net Worth: $199,211,617
Earnings: $78,970,693
Emp.: 4,893
Fiscal Year-end: 12/31/2018
Holding Company; Food, Beverage & Tobacco Products Distr
N.A.I.C.S.: 551112
Lorenz Bresser *(Chm-Supervisory Bd)*

Subsidiary (Domestic):

CSG Convenience Service
GmbH (2)
Wittener Str 56, Innenstadt, 44789, Bochum, Germany
Tel.: (49) 234 3152576
Gasoline Station Operator
N.A.I.C.S.: 457110

Subsidiary (Non-US):

Convenience Concept SL (2)
Cl Vega Del Henares, 19209, Quer, Spain
Tel.: (34) 94 922 6648
Convenience Retailer
N.A.I.C.S.: 445131

Convivo GmbH (2)
Am Euro Platz 2, 1120, Vienna, Austria
Tel.: (43) 1 71728117
Web Site: http://www.convivo-brands.com
Emp.: 10
Convenience Retailer
N.A.I.C.S.: 445131
Marc Lanneau *(CEO)*

Holding (Non-US):

Conway S.A. (2)
C/Vega del Henares parcela no 6 Poligono, Industrial de Quer no 1, 19209, Guadalajara, Spain (70%)
Tel.: (34) 949208190
Web Site: http://www.conway.es
Sales Range: $250-299.9 Million
Emp.: 200
Food Tobacco & Phone Card Delivery Service
N.A.I.C.S.: 722330

Subsidiary (Non-US):

Conway Belgie N.V. (3)
Laagstraat 63, 9140, Temse,
Belgium (100%)
Tel.: (32) 37100311
Web Site: http://www.conway.be
Sales Range: $1-4.9 Billion
Food, Tobacco & Telecommunication Product Delivery Supplier
N.A.I.C.S.: 722330

Subsidiary (Domestic):

EXPRESS MITTE HOLDING GmbH
& Co. KG (2)
Vor den Eichen 6, 65604, Elz, Germany
Tel.: (49) 6431 98500
Holding Company
N.A.I.C.S.: 551112

EXPRESS NORD-WEST HOLDING
GmbH & Co. KG (2)
Torfkuhlenweg 36, Lotte, 49504, Nordrhein-Westfalen, Germany
Tel.: (49) 54048830
Holding Company
N.A.I.C.S.: 551112
Rolf Boeke *(Gen Mgr)*

EZV Gesellschaft fur Zahlungssysteme mbH (2)
Friedrichstr 171, 10117, Berlin, Germany
Tel.: (49) 3060984410

Web Site: http://www.ezv-gmbh.de
Payment Services
N.A.I.C.S.: 541214
Stephan Heintz *(Gen Mgr)*

Subsidiary (Non-US):

Europrocurement AG (2)
Malzgasse 15, 4052, Basel, Switzerland
Tel.: (41) 61 205 17 88
Convenience Retailer
N.A.I.C.S.: 445131

Lekkerland (Schweiz) AG (2)
Industriestrasse 1, Brunegg, 5505, Aarau,
Switzerland (100%)
Tel.: (41) 628874700
Web Site: http://www.lekkerland.ch
Sales Range: $1-4.9 Billion
Emp.: 125
Food, Beverage & Tobacco Products Distr
N.A.I.C.S.: 424490

Lekkerland Czeska republika
s.r.o (2)
Industrialni park Sever budova B2, Do Certous 2622, CZ-193 00, Prague, 9, Czech
Republic (100%)
Tel.: (420) 225107000
Web Site: http://www.lekkerland.cz
Sales Range: $250-299.9 Million
Emp.: 305
Food, Beverage & Tobacco Products Distr
N.A.I.C.S.: 424490

Subsidiary (Domestic):

Lekkerland Deutschland GmbH & Co.
KG (2)
Europallee 57, D-50226, Frechen,
Germany (100%)
Tel.: (49) 223418210
Web Site: http://www.lekkerland.de
Sales Range: $150-199.9 Million
Emp.: 400
Food, Beverage & Tobacco Products Distr
N.A.I.C.S.: 424490

Subsidiary (Non-US):

Lekkerland Handels- und Dienstleistungs AG (2)
Handelsstrasse 1, 2630, Ternitz,
Austria (99.76%)
Tel.: (43) 2630329700
Web Site: http://www.lekkerland.at
Sales Range: $75-99.9 Million
Emp.: 190
Food, Beverage & Tobacco Products Distr
N.A.I.C.S.: 424490

Lekkerland Nederland B.V. (2)
Ekkersrijt 7601 son, 5692 HR, Eindhoven,
Netherlands (100%)
Tel.: (31) 402644400
Web Site: http://www.lekkerland.nl
Sales Range: $1-4.9 Billion
Emp.: 880
Food, Beverage & Tobacco Products Distr
N.A.I.C.S.: 424490
Freek van Beek *(Mng Dir)*

Subsidiary (Domestic):

Lekkerland Vending Services
B.V. (3)
Ekkersrijt 7601, 5692 HR, Son,
Netherlands (100%)
Tel.: (31) 402644900
Web Site: http://www.lekkerland-vs.nl
Vending Machine Services
N.A.I.C.S.: 445132

Subsidiary (Non-US):

Lekkerland Polska S.A. (2)
Ul Pozarowa 6, 03-308, Warsaw, Poland
Tel.: (48) 225186800
Web Site: http://www.lekkerland.pl
Rev.: $207,769,430
Emp.: 750
Food, Beverage & Tobacco Products Distr
N.A.I.C.S.: 424490

Subsidiary (Domestic):

MEDIAPOINT GmbH (2)
Gschwend 62, 87538, Balderschwang, Germany
Tel.: (49) 6334 98 34 47
Web Site: http://www.mediapoint-gmbh.de

Emp.: 3
Food Products Distr
N.A.I.C.S.: 424490
Rita Bleimhofer *(Co-Founder, Mng Dir-Pur
& Sls & Mgr-Admin & Comml)*

Subsidiary (Non-US):

Sutrans N.V. (2)
Laagstraat 63, 9140, Temse, Belgium
Tel.: (32) 3 710 03 11
Logistics Consulting Servies
N.A.I.C.S.: 541614

Subsidiary (Domestic):

TRIMEX Transit Import Export Carl
Nielsen GmbH & Co. KG (2)
Eckernforder Landstrasse 65, 24941, Flensburg, Germany
Tel.: (49) 461 773660
Web Site: http://www.trimex-trading.de
Logistics Consulting Servies
N.A.I.C.S.: 541614

REWE Markt GmbH (1)
Domstrasse 20, 50668, Cologne, Germany
Tel.: (49) 2211490
Web Site: http://www.rewe.de
Supermarket Operator
N.A.I.C.S.: 445110

REWORLD MEDIA SA

8 rue Barthelemy Danjou, 92100,
Boulogne-Billancourt, France
Tel.: (33) 145195800
Web Site:
https://www.reworldmedia.com
ALREW—(EUR)
Rev.: $539,327,674
Assets: $695,258,358
Liabilities: $492,075,823
Net Worth: $203,182,535
Earnings: $47,615,426
Emp.: 1,260
Fiscal Year-end: 12/31/22
Internet Publisher
N.A.I.C.S.: 513199
Gautier Normand *(CEO)*

Subsidiaries:

Mondadori France S.A.S. (1)
43 rue du Colonel-Pierre-Avia, PO Box
75015, Paris, 75015, France
Tel.: (33) 141335001
Web Site: http://www.mondadori.fr
Sales Range: $150-199.9 Million
Emp.: 1,000
Magazine Publisher
N.A.I.C.S.: 513120
Carmine Perna *(Gen Mgr)*

Subsidiary (Domestic):

Mondadori Auto (2)
8 rue Francois Ory, Montrouge, 75754,
France
Tel.: (33) 141335000
Web Site: http://www.mondadori.fr
Sales Range: $200-249.9 Million
Emp.: 750
Magazine Publisher
N.A.I.C.S.: 513120
Thierry Jadot *(Mng Dir)*

Mondadori Nature (2)
27 rue du Colonel Pierre-Avia, 75754,
Paris, Cedex, France
Tel.: (33) 141332200
Sales Range: $25-49.9 Million
Emp.: 100
Magazine Publisher
N.A.I.C.S.: 513120

Mondadori Star (2)
33 Rue Du Colonel Pierre Avia, 75754,
Paris, France
Tel.: (33) 141335002
Sales Range: $400-449.9 Million
Magazine Publisher
N.A.I.C.S.: 513120

REX GORELL GROUP

20-32 Fyans Street, Geelong, 3220,
VIC, Australia
Tel.: (61) 352223888

Web Site:
http://www.rexgorell.com.au
Year Founded: 1980
Emp.: 350
Automotive Retailer
N.A.I.C.S.: 441110
Rex Gorell *(Chm)*

REX INDUSTRY BERHAD

Plot 125 Jalan Perindustrian Bukit
Minyak 5, Simpang Ampat, 14100,
Seberang Perai Tengah, Penang,
Malaysia
Tel.: (60) 45088288 MY
Web Site: https://rexmalaysia.com
Year Founded: 1965
REX—(KLS)
Rev.: $34,372,083
Assets: $37,778,764
Liabilities: $15,860,828
Net Worth: $21,917,936
Earnings: ($9,396,640)
Fiscal Year-end: 06/30/23
Frozen Food Mfr
N.A.I.C.S.: 311411
Mohd Ibrahim Mohd Zain *(Chm)*

REX INTERNATIONAL HOLDING LTD

1 George Street 1401, Singapore,
049145, Singapore
Tel.: (65) 65572477
Web Site: https://www.rexih.com
5WH—(CAT)
Rev.: $170,259,000
Assets: $668,558,000
Liabilities: $480,075,000
Net Worth: $188,483,000
Earnings: $353,000
Emp.: 46
Fiscal Year-end: 12/31/22
Oil & Gas Production
N.A.I.C.S.: 324199
Dan Brostrom *(Chm)*

Subsidiaries:

Lime Petroleum AS (1)
Drammensveien 145A, 0277, Oslo,
Norway (91.65%)
Tel.: (47) 9 604 0602
Web Site: https://www.limepetroleum.com
Hydrocarbon Mfr
N.A.I.C.S.: 324110
Svein Kjellesvik *(Chm)*

REX MINERALS LIMITED

68 St Vincent Highway, PinePoint,
Adelaide, 5571, SA, Australia
Tel.: (61) 390683077
Web Site:
https://www.rexminerals.com.au
RXM—(ASX)
Rev.: $13,791
Assets: $24,118,129
Liabilities: $1,020,565
Net Worth: $23,097,564
Earnings: ($6,726,382)
Emp.: 30
Fiscal Year-end: 06/30/21
Mineral Explorer
N.A.I.C.S.: 213115
Richard Laufmann *(CEO & Mng Dir)*

Subsidiaries:

Rex Minerals (SA) Pty Ltd (1)
68 St Vincent Highway, Pine Point, Scarborough, 5571, SA, Australia
Tel.: (61) 1300822161
Web Site: https://www.rexminerals.com.au
Sales Range: $50-74.9 Million
Emp.: 20
Mineral Exploration Services
N.A.I.C.S.: 213114
Richard Laussmen *(Mng Dir)*

REX PIPES & CABLES INDUSTRIES LIMITED

REX PIPES & CABLES INDUSTRIES LIMITED

Rex Pipes & Cables Industries Limited—(Continued)

F-69A RIICO Industrial Area, Sikar, 332001, Rajasthan, India
Tel.: (91) 9783211999
Web Site: https://rpcil.com
Year Founded: 2002
REXPIPES—(NSE)
Pipe & Cable Product Mfr
N.A.I.C.S.: 331210

REX POWER MAGNETICS

65 Basaltic Road, Concord, L4K1G4, ON, Canada
Tel.: (905) 695-8844
Web Site:
    http://www.rexmanufacturing.com
Year Founded: 1972
Sales Range: $50-74.9 Million
Emp.: 230
Transformer Mfr
N.A.I.C.S.: 335311
Simon Hasserjian (Gen Mgr)

REX SEALING & PACKING INDUSTRIES PVT. LTD.

A-207 Byculla Service Industries D K Road Byculla East, Mumbai, 400027, Maharashtra, India
Tel.: (91) 9136909253
Web Site: https://www.rexseal.com
Year Founded: 1963
543744—(BOM)
Rev.: $3,052,899
Assets: $2,128,302
Liabilities: $623,716
Net Worth: $1,504,586
Earnings: $37,815
Fiscal Year-end: 03/31/23
Adhesive Mfr
N.A.I.C.S.: 325520

REX TRUEFORM GROUP LIMITED

263 Victoria Road, Salt River, Cape Town, 7925, South Africa
Tel.: (27) 214609400   ZA
Web Site:
    https://www.rextrueform.com
Year Founded: 1937
RTO—(JSE)
Rev.: $47,491,207
Assets: $57,940,884
Liabilities: $34,134,919
Net Worth: $23,805,965
Earnings: $4,532,895
Emp.: 540
Fiscal Year-end: 06/30/23
Apparel Mfr & Distr
N.A.I.C.S.: 315210
Adam T. Snitcher (Sec)

REXEL, S.A.

13 boulevard du fort de Vaux, CS 60002, 75838, Paris, Cedex 17, France
Tel.: (33) 142858500   FR
Web Site: https://www.rexel.com
Year Founded: 1967
RXL—(OTCIQ)
Rev.: $20,670,623,786
Assets: $14,730,843,946
Liabilities: $8,761,601,554
Net Worth: $5,969,242,392
Earnings: $836,067,343
Emp.: 26,693
Fiscal Year-end: 12/31/23
Electrical Equipment Distr
N.A.I.C.S.: 423610
Francois Henrot (Deputy Chm)

Subsidiaries:

ABM Rexel (1)
Avda de la Recomba 7 y 9, Parque Industrial La Laguna, 28914, Leganes, Spain
Tel.: (34) 915894100
Web Site: http://www.abm-rexel.com

Sales Range: $150-199.9 Million
Emp.: 300
Electrical Materials
N.A.I.C.S.: 423610
Patrick Berard (Gen Dir & Sr VP-Southern Europe)

Astrotek Ireland Limited (1)
M50 Business Park Ballymount Road Upper, Dublin, D12 RK76, Ireland
Tel.: (353) 14568009
Web Site: http://www.astrotek.ie
Electrical Equipment Distr
N.A.I.C.S.: 423610

Beijing Zhongheng Hengxin Automation Equipment Co. Ltd. (1)
609 6th Floor Building 6 Hanwei International Plaza District 3, Fengtai District No 186 South Fourth Ring Road West, Beijing, China
Tel.: (86) 1053857188
Web Site: http://www.bjzh.com.cn
Electrical Equipment Distr
N.A.I.C.S.: 423610

Brohl & Appell Inc. (1)
140 Lane St, Sandusky, OH 44870
Tel.: (419) 625-6761
Web Site: http://www.brohlandappell.com
Emp.: 60
Industrial Products Distr & Services
N.A.I.C.S.: 423610
Neal Ebert (Pres & CEO)

Digitalfeld AG (1)
Juchstrasse 9, 8048, Zurich, Switzerland
Tel.: (41) 442441616
Web Site: http://digitalfeld.ch
Electrical Equipment Distr
N.A.I.C.S.: 423610

Dismo France S.A.S. (1)
3 Avenue De La Patelle Za Des Bellevues, Saint-Quen-L'Aumone, 95310, Saint-Quentin, France
Tel.: (33) 134308989
Web Site: http://www.dismofrance.fr
Electrical Equipment Whslr
N.A.I.C.S.: 423610

Elektro-Material AG (1)
Heinrichstrasse 200, 8005, Zurich, Switzerland
Tel.: (41) 442781183
Web Site: http://www.elektro-material.ch
Sales Range: $250-299.9 Million
Emp.: 650
Electrical Supplies Distr
N.A.I.C.S.: 423610
Andreas Stahel (CEO)

Elektronabava d.o.o. (1)
Cesta 24 junija 3, Crnuce, 1231, Ljubljana, Slovenia
Tel.: (386) 15899300
Web Site: http://www.elektronabava.si
Electrical Equipment Distr
N.A.I.C.S.: 423610

Elektroskandia Norge AS (1)
Fugleasen 6, Alnabru, 1405, Langhus, Norway
Tel.: (47) 23143000
Web Site: http://www.elektroskandia.no
Electrical Materials
N.A.I.C.S.: 423610
Jan Wilhelmsen (CEO)

Elektroskandia Suomi Oy (1)
Varastokatu 9, Hyvinkaa, 5800, Finland
Tel.: (358) 10509311
Web Site: http://www.elektroskandia.fi
Sales Range: $150-199.9 Million
Emp.: 300
Electrical Materials
N.A.I.C.S.: 423610
Markku Sako (CEO)

Subsidiary (Non-US):

Elektroskandia Latvia (2)
Maskavas iela 456, LV-1003, Riga, Latvia
Tel.: (371) 67241133
Sales Range: $25-49.9 Million
Emp.: 15
Electrical Materials
N.A.I.C.S.: 423610

Elektroskandia Ltd. (2)

Pr Shaumjana 4, Saint Petersburg, 195027, Russia
Tel.: (7) 8123252040
Web Site: http://www.elektroskandia.ru
Sales Range: $50-74.9 Million
Emp.: 146
Electrical Materials
N.A.I.C.S.: 423610
Stanislav Perseilev (Mng Dir)

OU Elektroskandia Baltics (2)
Valukoja 5, 11415, Tallinn, Estonia
Tel.: (372) 6711900
Web Site: http://www.elektroskandia.ee
Sales Range: $25-49.9 Million
Emp.: 50
Electrical Component Distr
N.A.I.C.S.: 423610
Mari-Liis Kivi (Chief Accountant)

UAB Elektroskandia LT (2)
Linkmenu Gatve 15, 09300, Vilnius, Lithuania
Tel.: (370) 52757040
Web Site: http://www.elektroskandia.lt
Sales Range: $25-49.9 Million
Emp.: 22
Electrical Materials
N.A.I.C.S.: 423610

Espace Elec S.A.S. (1)
Lieu-dit Stiletto Bretelle de Geant Casino, 20090, Ajaccio, France
Tel.: (33) 495103050
Web Site: http://www.espace-elec.net
Electrical Equipment Distr
N.A.I.C.S.: 423610

Francofa Eurodis S.A.S. (1)
13 rue Sir Alexander Fleming, Plaisance, 93360, Neuilly, France
Tel.: (33) 184811111
Web Site: http://www.francofa-eurodis.fr
Electrical Equipment Distr
N.A.I.C.S.: 423610

Moel Ab (1)
Kulltorpsvagen 92 Lanna, Bredaryd, 333 74, Jonkoping, Sweden
Tel.: (46) 37083500
Web Site: http://www.moel.se
Electrical Equipment Distr
N.A.I.C.S.: 423610

OOO Elektroskandia Rus (1)
Shaumyan avenue building 4 building 1 letter A room 25H, 195027, Saint Petersburg, Russia
Tel.: (7) 8123252040
Web Site: http://www.elektroskandia.ru
Electrical Equipment Distr
N.A.I.C.S.: 423610

Rexel Arabia Electrical Supplies LLC (1)
Prince Muhammad Ibn Abdulaziz Road, PO Box 2204, Al Olaya, Riyadh, 12212, Saudi Arabia
Tel.: (966) 114666112
Web Site: http://www.rexel.me
Electrical Equipment Distr
N.A.I.C.S.: 423610

Rexel Australia Limited (1)
First Floor Building B 12 Julius Avenue, North Ryde, 2113, NSW, Australia
Tel.: (61) 298876222
Web Site: http://www.rexel.com.au
Rev.: $238,900,000
Emp.: 600
Electrical Apparatus & Equipment, Wiring Supplies & Related Equipment Merchant Whslr
N.A.I.C.S.: 423610
Robert McLeod (Mng Dir)

Rexel Austria GmbH (1)
Walcherstrasse 1A Objekt 6 Stiege 4, 1020, Vienna, Austria
Tel.: (43) 1688038830000
Web Site: http://www.rexel.at
Electrical Equipment Distr
N.A.I.C.S.: 423610

Rexel Belgium NV/SA (1)
Zuiderlaan 91, 1731, Zellik, Belgium
Tel.: (32) 24824848
Web Site: http://rexel.be
Sales Range: $50-74.9 Million
Electrical Supplies
N.A.I.C.S.: 423610

INTERNATIONAL PUBLIC

Rexel Canada Electrical, Inc. (1)
5600 Keaton Crescent, Mississauga, L5R 3G3, ON, Canada
Tel.: (905) 712-4004
Web Site: http://www.rexel.ca
Sales Range: $150-199.9 Million
Electronics & Electrical Products Distr
N.A.I.C.S.: 423610

Rexel China Management Co. Ltd. (1)
KIC Corporate Avenue Building 5 8-9 Floor No 88 Zhengxue Road, Yangpu District, Shanghai, 200433, China
Tel.: (86) 2135961800
Web Site: http://www.rexel.com.cn
Emp.: 740
Electrical Equipment Distr
N.A.I.C.S.: 423610

Rexel Distribuicao de Material Elecrico S.A. (1)
Avenida D Joao II 9I Piso 14 Edificio Adamastor Parque das Nacoes, 1990-077, Lisbon, Portugal
Tel.: (351) 219382321
Web Site: http://www.rexel.pt
Electrical Equipment Distr
N.A.I.C.S.: 423610

Rexel Finland Oy (1)
Varastokatu 9, PL 360, 05800, Hyvinkaa, Finland
Tel.: (358) 10509311
Web Site: http://www.rexel.fi
Electrical Equipment Distr
N.A.I.C.S.: 423610
Marko Kupias (Mgr-Contact Center)

Rexel GmbH (1)
Ridlerstr 57, 80339, Munich, Germany
Tel.: (49) 89444590
Web Site: http://www.rexel.de
Electrical Equipment Distr.
N.A.I.C.S.: 423610

Rexel Holdings USA Corp. (1)
14951 Dallas Pkwy, Dallas, TX 75254
Tel.: (972) 387-3600
Web Site: http://www.rexelusainc.com
Sales Range: $5-14.9 Billion
Emp.: 7,200
Holding Company
N.A.I.C.S.: 551112
Brian McNally (CEO & Exec VP-North America)

Subsidiary (Domestic):

Rexel, Inc. (2)
14951 Dallas Pkwy, Dallas, TX 75254-6784
Tel.: (972) 387-3600
Web Site: http://www.rexelusa.com
Sales Range: $1-4.9 Billion
Emp.: 400
Electrical Parts & Supplies Distr
N.A.I.C.S.: 423610
Mark Daniel (Sr VP & Gen Mgr)

Subsidiary (Domestic):

Gexpro (3)
1000 Bridgeport Ave 5th Fl, Shelton, CT 06484
Tel.: (203) 925-2400
Web Site: http://www.gexpro.com
Emp.: 2,500
Electrical, Voice & Data Products Distr
N.A.I.C.S.: 423610
James F. Hibberd (Gen Mgr)

Rexel India Private Limited (1)
Office No 101 102 103 Plot No 84 Survey No 40 Dr Ambedkar Road, Sangamwadi Near RTO Office, Pune, 411 001, Maharashtra, India
Tel.: (91) 2066663200
Web Site: http://www.rexel.co.in
Electrical Equipment Distr
N.A.I.C.S.: 423610

Rexel Italia SpA (1)
Via Bilbao 101, Sesto San Giovanni, 20099, Milan, Italy
Tel.: (39) 022511121
Web Site: http://www.rexel.it
Electrical Equipment Distr
N.A.I.C.S.: 423610

Rexel Nederland B.V. (1)

Bleiswijkse weg 35, 2712 PB, Zoetermeer, Netherlands
Tel.: (31) 885007000
Web Site: http://www.over.rexel.nl
Sales Range: $250-299.9 Million
Electrical Equipment Distr
N.A.I.C.S.: 423610

Subsidiary (Domestic):

Haagtechno (2)
Europalaan 28, 5232 BC, 's-Hertogenbosch, Netherlands
Tel.: (31) 736402502
Web Site: http://www.panasonic.nl
Sales Range: $50-74.9 Million
Emp.: 140
Electronics Distribution
N.A.I.C.S.: 423690
Ronald Van Venheusel (Mng Dir)

Rexel NCE B.V. (2)
Polarisavenue 19, Hoofddorp, 2132 JH, Netherlands
Tel.: (31) 235542299
Sales Range: $5-14.9 Billion
Emp.: 3
Electrical Materials & Safety Products Distr
N.A.I.C.S.: 423610

Subsidiary (Non-US):

Elektroskandia Polska S.A. (3)
Ul Dziadoszanska 10, 61 248, Poznan, Poland
Tel.: (48) 616464300
Web Site: http://www.elektroskandia.pl
Sales Range: $125-149.9 Million
Emp.: 280
Electrical Components
N.A.I.C.S.: 423610
Janusz Kogut (Dir-Sls)

Hagemeyer Deutschland Gmbh & Co. KG (3)
Landsberger Strasse 312, 80687, Munich, Germany
Tel.: (49) 89444590
Web Site: http://www.hagemeyerce.com
Emp.: 1,700
Electrical Materials
N.A.I.C.S.: 423610
Carsten Suckrow (CEO)

Subsidiary (Domestic):

Hagemeyer Nederland B.V. (3)
Schinkelsebaan 1, 2908, Capelle aan den IJssel, Netherlands
Tel.: (31) 104597555
Web Site: http://www.baloise.ch
Sales Range: $25-49.9 Million
Electrical Products
N.A.I.C.S.: 423610

Rexel Spain, SL (1)
Avda de la Recomba 7 y 9 Parque Industrial, 28914, Leganes, Madrid, Spain
Tel.: (34) 915894100
Web Site: http://www.rexel.es
Electrical Equipment Distr
N.A.I.C.S.: 423610

Rexel Sverige AB (1)
Prastgardsgrand 4, 125 44, Alvsjo, Sweden
Tel.: (46) 855621400
Web Site: http://www.rexel.se
Electrical Equipment Distr
N.A.I.C.S.: 423610

Rexel UK Limited (1)
Eagle Court 2 Hatchford Brook, Hatchford Way Sheldon, Birmingham, B26 3RZ, United Kingdom
Tel.: (44) 3300450606
Web Site: http://www.rexel.co.uk
Sales Range: $200-249.9 Million
Emp.: 300
Electrical Products Distribution
N.A.I.C.S.: 423620

Subsidiary (Domestic):

Denmans Electrical Wholesalers Ltd (2)
Steeple House Unit 17 City Business Park Easton Road, Bristol, BS5 0SP, United Kingdom
Tel.: (44) 1179548140
Web Site: http://www.denmans.co.uk

Sales Range: $25-49.9 Million
Electrical Products
N.A.I.C.S.: 423620

Newey & Eyre (2)
Yardley Court, 11-12 Frederick Road, Edgbaston, Birmingham, B15 1JD, United Kingdom
Tel.: (44) 1214559727
Web Site: http://www.neweyandeyre.co.uk
Sales Range: $450-499.9 Million
Electrical Products Distribution
N.A.I.C.S.: 423610
Rob Pearse (Head-Contractors & Installers Natl Sls)

Subsidiary (Domestic):

Newey & Eyre Industrial Solutions (3)
Eagle court 2 Hatchford Brook Hatchford Way Sheldon, Edgbaston, Birmingham, B26 3RZ, United Kingdom
Tel.: (44) 1214559727
Web Site: http://www.rexel.co.uk
Sales Range: $25-49.9 Million
Emp.: 50
Supply Chain Solutions
N.A.I.C.S.: 541614
John Hogan (Mng Dir)

Subsidiary (Domestic):

Parker Merchanting (2)
John Ogaunts Industrial Estate, Rothwell, Leeds, LS26 0DU, United Kingdom
Tel.: (44) 1132822933
Web Site: http://www.parker-merchanting.com
Sales Range: Less than $1 Million
Emp.: 65
Construction Consumables Distribution
N.A.I.C.S.: 423390

RexelSenate (2)
Senate House, 6-16 Southgate Road, Potters Bar, EN6 5DS, Herts, United Kingdom
Tel.: (44) 1707640000
Electrical Products & Supplies
N.A.I.C.S.: 423620

WF Electrical Limited (2)
Ground Floor Eagle Court 2 Hatchford Brook Hatchford Way, Sheldon, Birmingham, B26 3RZ, United Kingdom
Tel.: (44) 1214559727
Industrial Electrical Products Whslr
N.A.I.C.S.: 423610

Rexel USA, Inc. (1)
14951 Dallas Pkwy, Dallas, TX 75254
Tel.: (972) 387-3600
Web Site: http://www.rexelusainc.com
Electrical Equipment Distr
N.A.I.C.S.: 423610
Jeff Baker (CEO)

Subsidiary (Domestic):

Buckles-Smith Electric Company (2)
540 Martin Ave, Santa Clara, CA 95050
Tel.: (408) 280-7777
Web Site: https://www.buckles-smith.com
Sales Range: $25-49.9 Million
Emp.: 120
Electrical Supplies
N.A.I.C.S.: 423610
Art Cook (Pres)

Teche Electric Supply Inc. (2)
410 Eraste Landry Rd, Lafayette, LA 70506
Tel.: (337) 234-7521
Web Site: http://www.teche-electric.com
Sales Range: $10-24.9 Million
Emp.: 70
Electrical Apparatus & Equipment
N.A.I.C.S.: 423610
Robert Bruin Hays (Pres)

SPT Holdings Inc. (1)
10510 Northup Way Ste 115, Kirkland, WA 98033
Tel.: (425) 256-2900
Web Site: http://www.sptholdings.com
Emp.: 100
Marine Transportation Services
N.A.I.C.S.: 488390
Matthew Pabon (Founder & CEO)

Senate Group Ltd. (1)
13 Love Lane, Liverpool, L3 7DD, United Kingdom
Tel.: (44) 1512223411
Web Site: http://www.senategroup.co.uk
Construction Management Services
N.A.I.C.S.: 541330
Kiera Vogel (Mng Dir)

Shanghai Suhua Industrial Control Equipment Co. Ltd. (1)
F2 Block25 No 879 Zhongjiang Rd, Shanghai, China
Tel.: (86) 2151621188
Electrical Equipment Distr
N.A.I.C.S.: 423610

Suzhou Xidian Co. Ltd. (1)
301 No 57 Zhongxing Rd, Suzhou, Jiangsu, China
Tel.: (86) 51267273570
Web Site: http://www.sz-xd.net
Electrical Equipment Distr
N.A.I.C.S.: 423610

Zhejiang Huazhang Automation Equipment Co. Ltd. (1)
Room 1103 Building 2 Yunhe Advertising Industry Building, No 99 Xiangyuan Road, Hangzhou, 310012, Zhejiang, China
Tel.: (86) 57188223377
Web Site: http://www.huazhangautomation.com
Electrical Equipment Distr
N.A.I.C.S.: 423610

REXIT BERHAD

42 Jalan BM 1/2 Taman Bukit Mayang Emas, 47301, Petaling Jaya, Selangor Darul Ehsan, Malaysia
Tel.: (60) 378031131 MY
Web Site: https://www.rexit.com
Year Founded: 1998
REXIT—(KLS)
Rev.: $5,776,776
Assets: $11,607,426
Liabilities: $1,113,907
Net Worth: $10,493,519
Earnings: $2,329,820
Fiscal Year-end: 06/30/23
Fire Insurance Services
N.A.I.C.S.: 524210
Hon Cheong Chung (CEO)

REXLOT HOLDINGS LIMITED

Office A 32/F YHC Tower No 1 Sheung Yuet Road, Kowloon Bay, Kowloon, China (Hong Kong)
Tel.: (852) 25320088 BM
Web Site: http://www.rexlot.com.hk
Sales Range: $50-74.9 Million
Emp.: 559
Investment Holding Company
N.A.I.C.S.: 551112
Chun Lon Boo (Exec Dir)

Subsidiaries:

REXCAPITAL Securities Limited (1)
Suite 2601 26F Sino Plaza 255-257 Gloucester Road, Causeway Bay, China (Hong Kong)
Tel.: (852) 2532 0088
Web Site: http://www.rexlot.com.hk
Securities Brokerage Services
N.A.I.C.S.: 523150

Shenzhen Sinodata Technology Co Ltd (1)
17 F Tianli Zhongyang Plz, Nanshan Dist, Shenzhen, 518052, Guangdong, China
Tel.: (86) 75526062079
Lottery Machines Supplier
N.A.I.C.S.: 713120

REXNORD ELECTRONICS & CONTROLS LTD.

92-D Govt Indl Estate Sahyadrinagar Charkop, Kandivli West, Mumbai, 400067, India
Tel.: (91) 2262401800
Web Site: https://www.rexnordindia.com

531888—(BOM)
Rev.: $6,990,206
Assets: $7,530,118
Liabilities: $1,891,549
Net Worth: $5,638,569
Earnings: $370,898
Emp.: 71
Fiscal Year-end: 03/31/21
Cooling Fan Mfr
N.A.I.C.S.: 333413
Kishore Chand Talwar (Chm & Mng Dir)

Subsidiaries:

Rexnord Electronics & Controls Ltd. - Thane Factory (1)
Survey No 62 74 75 20 Village Devdal Sagpada, Opp Sagar Hotel Kaman Bhiwandi, Thane, 401208, Maharashtra, India
Tel.: (91) 2262401845
Web Site: http://www.rexnordindia.com
Emp.: 450
Fan & Motor Mfr
N.A.I.C.S.: 333413
Kundan Talwar (CEO)

REXON INDUSTRIAL CORP., LTD.

No 261 Renhua Road, Taichung, 412, Taiwan
Tel.: (886) 424914141
Web Site: https://www.rexon.net
1515—(TAI)
Rev.: $219,381,299
Assets: $301,281,424
Liabilities: $176,285,810
Net Worth: $124,995,613
Earnings: $10,171,653
Emp.: 1,085
Fiscal Year-end: 12/31/23
Stationary Machine Mfr
N.A.I.C.S.: 332216
Sharon Jeng (VP)

Subsidiaries:

Power Tool Specialists, Inc. (1)
684 Huey Rd, Rock Hill, SC 29730
Tel.: (803) 980-7740
Web Site: http://www.rexon.net
Woodworking Machinery Distr
N.A.I.C.S.: 423830

REXON Europe GmbH (1)
Herderstr 17, 40721, Hilden, Nordrhein-Westfalen, Germany
Tel.: (49) 210333280
Web Site: http://www.rexon-europe.de
Woodworking Machinery Distr
N.A.I.C.S.: 423830

REY RESOURCES LIMITED

Suite 23B Macquarie Street, Sydney, 2000, NSW, Australia
Tel.: (61) 292519088
Web Site: https://www.reyresources.com
REY—(ASX)
Rev.: $51,335
Assets: $29,129,778
Liabilities: $10,579,552
Net Worth: $18,550,226
Earnings: ($1,013,669)
Fiscal Year-end: 06/30/21
Coal & Other Mineral Exploration
N.A.I.C.S.: 212115
Shannon Coates (Co-Sec)

REYAL URBIS S.A.

Ayala 3 2a Planta, 28001, Madrid, Spain
Tel.: (34) 902901400
Web Site: http://www.reyalurbis.com
Year Founded: 1970
Sales Range: $25-49.9 Billion
Emp.: 1,046
Construction & Real Estate Management Services
N.A.I.C.S.: 531390

Royal Urbis S.A.—(Continued)
Rafael Santamaria Trigo *(Chm & Pres)*

REYNA SILVER CORP.
Suite 410 325 Howe Street, Toronto, V6C 1Z7, ON, Canada
Tel.: (778) 504-1344
Web Site:
  https://www.reynasilver.com
4ZC—(DEU)
Assets: $11,972,444
Liabilities: $429,642
Net Worth: $11,542,802
Earnings: ($6,392,583)
Fiscal Year-end: 03/31/22
Metal Exploration Services
N.A.I.C.S.: 213114
Jorge Ramiro Monroy *(CEO)*

REYON PHARMACEUTICAL CO., LTD
KT and G Tower 8F Youngdong Street 416, Gangnam-gu, Seoul, 06176, Korea (South)
Tel.: (82) 234075222
Web Site:
  https://www.reyonpharm.co.kr
Year Founded: 1955
102460—(KRS)
Rev.: $118,147,790
Assets: $371,758,566
Liabilities: $181,722,614
Net Worth: $190,035,951
Earnings: $5,701,634
Emp.: 492
Fiscal Year-end: 12/31/22
Pharmaceutical Products Mfr & Sales
N.A.I.C.S.: 325412

Subsidiaries:

Reyon Pharmaceutical Co., Ltd - Jincheon Factory (1)
27-27 Deoksan-myun, Jincheon-gun, Hancheon, 365-843, Chungbuk, Korea (South)
Tel.: (82) 5 228 1596
Pharmaceuticals Product Mfr
N.A.I.C.S.: 325412

REYSAS TASIMACILIK VE LOJISTIK TICARET A.S.
Kucuk Camlica Neighborhood Erkan Ocakli Street No 13 PK 34696, Uskudar, 34087, Istanbul, Turkiye
Tel.: (90) 2165642000
Web Site: https://www.reysas.com
Year Founded: 1990
RYSAS—(IST)
Rev.: $226,871,397
Assets: $334,950,314
Liabilities: $188,426,638
Net Worth: $146,523,676
Earnings: $38,514,878
Emp.: 270
Fiscal Year-end: 12/31/23
Logistics, Freight Forwarding & Warehousing Services
N.A.I.C.S.: 541614
Durmus Doven *(Chm)*

Subsidiaries:

Reysas Gayrimenkul Yatirim Ortakligi A.S. (1)
Abdurrahman Gazi Mh Guleryuz Cd 23, Samadira - Sancaktepe, Istanbul, Turkiye
Tel.: (90) 2165642000
Web Site: http://www.reysasgyo.com.tr
Real Estate Investment Services
N.A.I.C.S.: 525990
Durmus Doven *(Chm)*

REYUU JAPAN INC.
OAP Tower 9F 1-8-30 Tenmanbashi, Kita-ku, Osaka, Japan
Tel.: (81) 668816611
Web Site: https://www.reyuu-japan.com
Year Founded: 1988
9425—(TKS)
Sales Range: Less than $1 Million
Telecommunication Services
N.A.I.C.S.: 517810
Toshiya Okada *(Pres)*

RF ACQUISITION CORP II
111 Somerset 05-07, Singapore, 238164, Singapore
Tel.: (65) 69040766 Ky
Year Founded: 2024
RFAI—(NASDAQ)
Investment Holding Company
N.A.I.C.S.: 551112
Tse Meng Ng *(Bd of Dirs, Chm & CEO)*

RF ACQUISITION CORP.
111 Somerset 05-06, Singapore, 238164, Singapore
Tel.: (65) 69040766 DE
Year Founded: 2021
RFAC—(NASDAQ)
Rev.: $1,447,094
Assets: $118,089,038
Liabilities: $118,240,968
Net Worth: ($151,930)
Earnings: $284,725
Emp.: 2
Fiscal Year-end: 12/31/22
Investment Holding Company
N.A.I.C.S.: 551112
Tse Meng Ng *(Bd of Dirs, Chm & CEO)*

RF CAPITAL GROUP INC.
100 Queens Quay East Suite 2500, Toronto, M5E 1Y3, ON, Canada
Tel.: (416) 943-6696
Web Site:
  https://richardsonwealth.com
Year Founded: 1995
RCG—(OTCIQ)
Rev.: $28,191,442
Assets: $1,039,090,317
Liabilities: $883,853,730
Net Worth: $155,236,586
Earnings: ($40,678,628)
Emp.: 44
Fiscal Year-end: 12/31/19
Holding Company; Financial & Investment Services
N.A.I.C.S.: 551112
Donald A. Wright *(Chm)*

Subsidiaries:

GMP Securities L.P. (1)
145 King St W Ste 300, Toronto, M5H 1J8, ON, Canada
Tel.: (416) 367-8600
Web Site: http://www.gmpsecurities.com
Sales Range: $200-249.9 Million
Emp.: 400
Financial Investment & Management Services
N.A.I.C.S.: 523999
Deborah Starkman *(CFO & Sec)*

Griffiths McBurney (Europe) S.A. (1)
19A rue de la Croix dOr, 1204, Geneva, Switzerland
Tel.: (41) 223197150
Web Site: http://www.gmpeurope.com
Venture Capital & Investor Services
N.A.I.C.S.: 523999

RF Securities Clearing LP (1)

Richardson Wealth Limited (1)
145 King Street West Suite 500, Toronto, M5H 1J8, ON, Canada
Tel.: (416) 943-6696
Web Site: http://www.richardsonwealth.com
Financial Investment & Management Services
N.A.I.C.S.: 523999

RF CAPITAL PTY LTD.
Level 54 Governor Phillip Tower, 1 Farrer Place, Sydney, 2000, NSW, Australia
Tel.: (61) 2 8277 6000 AU
Web Site: http://www.rfcapital.com
Emp.: 160
Fund Management
N.A.I.C.S.: 523999
Damen Purcell *(Head-Retail Distr)*

Subsidiaries:

Signature Capital Investments Limited (1)
Level 11 20 Hunter Street, Sydney, 2000, NSW, Australia
Tel.: (61) 2 8076 7480
Web Site:
  http://www.signaturecapitalinvest.com
Sales Range: Less than $1 Million
Investment Management Service
N.A.I.C.S.: 523940

RF PLAST GMBH
Weinstrasse 8, 91710, Gunzenhausen, Germany
Tel.: (49) 983161960
Web Site: https://www.rf-plast.de
Precision Injection Molding Mfr
N.A.I.C.S.: 332721

Subsidiaries:

RF Duroplast GmbH (1)
Carl-Benz-Strasse 18, 82205, Gilching, Germany
Tel.: (49) 810527300
Machine Construction & Precision Injection Molding Mfr
N.A.I.C.S.: 332721
Manfred Schmidt *(Mgr-Engrg)*

Subsidiary (Domestic):

Helvoet Rubber & Plastic Technologies GmbH (2)
Carl Benz Strasse 18, 82205, Gilching, Germany
Tel.: (49) 810527300
Precision Component Mfr & Distr
N.A.I.C.S.: 333248

RF RUNDFUNK-FERNSEHEN ANTENNEN, MONTAGE UND HANDELS GMBH
Bickelstrasse 6, 08527, Plauen, Germany
Tel.: (49) 3741 4704 75 De
Web Site: http://www.rf-plauen.de
Year Founded: 1956
Consumer & Commercial Electronics & Appliances Sales, Installation & Services
N.A.I.C.S.: 423620
Reiner Huster *(CEO)*

RF SYSCON UMWELTSYSTEME GMBH
Obere Hommeswiese 33 39, Freudenberg, 57258, Germany
Tel.: (49) 273443810
Web Site: http://www.rf-syscon.de
Rev.: $11,539,834
Emp.: 10
Waste Collection Products Mfr
N.A.I.C.S.: 335220
Lucian Rosler *(Co-Mng Dir)*

RF-MATERIALS CO., LTD.
231 215 Gangchon-ro, Danwon-Gu, Ansan, Gyeonggi-do, Korea (South)
Tel.: (82) 7070965615 KR
Web Site: https://www.rf-materials.com
Year Founded: 2007
327260—(KRS)
Rev.: $38,689,207
Assets: $73,564,834
Liabilities: $33,038,885
Net Worth: $40,525,950
Earnings: $2,732,311
Emp.: 132
Fiscal Year-end: 12/31/22
Electron Tube Mfr
N.A.I.C.S.: 334419
Gi-Woo Han *(CEO)*

RFA CAPITAL HOLDINGS INC.
83 Yonge St, Toronto, M5C 1S8, ON, Canada
Tel.: (416) 362-9997
Web Site: http://www.rfacapital.com
Year Founded: 1996
Real Estate Investment & Asset Management Services
N.A.I.C.S.: 523999
Nicholas Lagopoulos *(Mng Partner)*

Subsidiaries:

Street Capital Group Inc. (1)
1 Yonge Street Suite 2401, Toronto, M5E 1E5, ON, Canada
Tel.: (647) 259-7873
Web Site: http://www.streetcapitalgroup.ca
Rev.: $40,284,764
Assets: $692,044,620
Liabilities: $627,640,012
Net Worth: $64,404,608
Earnings: ($32,828,993)
Emp.: 222
Fiscal Year-end: 12/31/2018
Investment Services
N.A.I.C.S.: 523999
Gary Taylor *(Chief Risk Officer & Exec VP)*

Subsidiary (US):

Heritage Global Inc. (2)
12625 High Bluff Dr Ste 305, San Diego, CA 92130 (73.3%)
Tel.: (858) 847-0659
Web Site: https://www.hginc.com
Rev.: $46,914,000
Assets: $67,560,000
Liabilities: $19,261,000
Net Worth: $48,299,000
Earnings: $15,493,000
Emp.: 75
Fiscal Year-end: 12/31/2022
Asset Liquidation Services; Patent Licensing Services
N.A.I.C.S.: 523999
James Sklar *(Gen Counsel, Sec & Exec VP)*

RFC AMBRIAN GROUP LIMITED
Level 14 19-31 Pitt Street, Sydney, 2000, NSW, Australia
Tel.: (61) 292500000 AU
Web Site: http://www.rfc.com.au
Year Founded: 1985
Financial Investments & Advisory Services
N.A.I.C.S.: 523999

RFHIC CORPORATION
41-14 Burim-ro 170 beon-gil, Dongan-gu, Anyang, 14055, Gyeonggi-do, Korea (South)
Tel.: (82) 3180693000
Web Site: https://rfhic.com
Year Founded: 2015
218410—(KRS)
Rev.: $82,861,233
Assets: $363,050,407
Liabilities: $126,931,664
Net Worth: $236,118,743
Earnings: $3,725,773
Emp.: 295
Fiscal Year-end: 12/31/22
Financial Investment Management Services
N.A.I.C.S.: 523940
David Cho *(Founder & CEO)*

RFI BANK JSC
Perevedenovskiy Lane 13 Building 4, 105082, Moscow, Russia
Tel.: (7) 4952760800
Web Site: http://www.rfibank.ru

Year Founded: 2000
Sales Range: Less than $1 Million
Commercial Banking Services
N.A.I.C.S.: 522110

RFM CORPORATION
RFM Corporate Center Pioneer Street, Mandaluyong, 1550, Metro Manila, Philippines
Tel.: (63) 286318101
Web Site: https://www.rfmfoods.com
Year Founded: 1958
RFM—(PHI)
Rev.: $373,403,842
Assets: $415,419,063
Liabilities: $151,576,888
Net Worth: $263,842,175
Earnings: $22,864,927
Emp.: 532
Fiscal Year-end: 12/31/23
Food & Beverage Mfr
N.A.I.C.S.: 311919
Philip V. Prieto *(Asst Treas)*

Subsidiaries:

Integrated Global Low-Temperature Operations Phils. Inc. (1)
Manggahan Light Industrial Park, A Rodriguez Ave, 1610, Pasig, Philippines
Tel.: (63) 26472794
Sales Range: $25-49.9 Million
Emp.: 100
Warehouse Clubs & Superstores
N.A.I.C.S.: 455211

Philippine Townships Inc (1)
6th Floor RFM Corporate Center, Corner Pioneer And Sheridan St, Mandaluyong, Philippines (100%)
Tel.: (63) 26318101
Real Estate Agents & Brokers Offices
N.A.I.C.S.: 531210

RFSEMI TECHNOLOGIES, INC.
12 6 Wanjusandan st, Bongdong-eup Wanju-gun, Jeonbuk, 55321, Korea (South)
Tel.: (82) 632624747 KR
Web Site: https://www.rfsemi.co.kr
Year Founded: 1999
096610—(KRS)
Rev.: $25,493,852
Assets: $59,336,995
Liabilities: $36,184,541
Net Worth: $23,152,453
Earnings: ($10,510,628)
Emp.: 300
Fiscal Year-end: 12/31/22
Semiconductor Devices Mfr
N.A.I.C.S.: 334413
Jin Hyo Lee *(CEO)*

Subsidiaries:

RFsemi Technologies, Inc. - Shenzhen Factory (1)
Room 504-5 5/F trusrt contre 912-914 Cheung Sha Wan Road, Kowloon, China (Hong Kong)
Tel.: (852) 2375 2007
Semiconductor Devices Mfr
N.A.I.C.S.: 334413

RFsemi Technologies, Inc. - Wanju Factory (1)
948-7 Dunsan-ri, Bongdong-eup, 565-902, Jeonbuk, Korea (South)
Tel.: (82) 63 262 4747
Semiconductor Devices Mfr
N.A.I.C.S.: 334413

RFsemi Technologies, Inc. - Weihai Factory (1)
264-209 5/F C Chuangxinchuangyejidi Torch Road No 213, Torch High-Tech Industry Development Zone, Weihai, Shandong, China
Tel.: (86) 631 566 2100
Semiconductor Devices Mfr
N.A.I.C.S.: 334413

RFTECH CO., LTD.
60 Jugyand-daero 1763beon-Gil Wonsam-myeon, Cheoin-Gu, Yongin, Gyeonggi-Do, Korea (South)
Tel.: (82) 313221114
Web Site: https://www.rftech.co.kr
Year Founded: 1995
061040—(KRS)
Rev.: $276,545,174
Assets: $289,429,956
Liabilities: $108,773,690
Net Worth: $180,656,266
Earnings: $9,210,682
Emp.: 247
Fiscal Year-end: 12/31/22
Electric Equipment Mfr
N.A.I.C.S.: 335999
Jin-hyung Lee *(Pres & CEO)*

RG INMOBILIARIA, S.A.
Punta Pacifica Americas Tower Building Fourth Floor No 401, PO Box 0823-05852, Panama, Panama
Tel.: (507) 204 5757
Year Founded: 2006
RGIN—(PAN)
Sales Range: Less than $1 Million
Real Estate Development Services
N.A.I.C.S.: 531390

RG PROPERTIES LTD.
1177 W Hastings Ste 2088, Vancouver, V6E 2K3, BC, Canada
Tel.: (604) 688-8999
Year Founded: 1962
Sales Range: $50-74.9 Million
Emp.: 10
Real Estate Services
N.A.I.C.S.: 531390
Graham S. Lee *(Pres & CEO)*

RGB INTERNATIONAL BHD.
8 Green Hall, 10200, Penang, Malaysia
Tel.: (60) 42631111
Web Site: https://www.rgbgames.com
Year Founded: 1986
RGB—(KLS)
Rev.: $57,681,090
Assets: $98,461,994
Liabilities: $43,687,783
Net Worth: $54,774,211
Earnings: $808,840
Emp.: 467
Fiscal Year-end: 12/31/22
Electronic Gaming Machines & Equipment Mfr & Sales
N.A.I.C.S.: 339930
Ganaser Kaliappen *(Sr VP-Corp & Regulatory Compliance)*

Subsidiaries:

Dreamgate (Singapore) Pte. Ltd. (1)
65 Sims Avenue 08-04 Yi Xiu Factory Building, Singapore, 387418, Singapore
Tel.: (65) 6 744 0089
Web Site: https://www.rgbgames.com
Sales Range: $50-74.9 Million
Emp.: 4
Video Gaming Device Concession Services
N.A.I.C.S.: 713290

RGB (Macau) Limited (1)
Tel.: (853) 28755533
Web Site: http://www.rgbgames.com
Sales Range: $50-74.9 Million
Gaming Concession Management Services
N.A.I.C.S.: 713290

RGB Ltd. (1)
Lot 9 10 3rd Floor Wisma Wong Wo Lo Jalan Tun Mustapha, 87000, Labuan, Sabah, Malaysia
Tel.: (60) 87425769
Web Site: http://www.rgbgames.com
Sales Range: $25-49.9 Million
Gaming Equipment Distr
N.A.I.C.S.: 423690

RGB Sdn. Bhd. (1)
8 Green Hall, 10200, George Town, Penang, Malaysia
Tel.: (60) 42631111
Sales Range: $50-74.9 Million
Emp.: 100
Gaming Equipment Distr
N.A.I.C.S.: 423690
Datuk Chuah Kim Seah *(Mng Dir)*

RGF CAPITAL MARKETS LTD.
14 N S Road 2 nd Floor, Kolkata, 700 001, West Bengal, India
Tel.: (91) 03340055190
Web Site: https://www.rgfcapitalmarkets.com
Year Founded: 1983
539669—(BOM)
Assets: $1,938,663
Liabilities: $24,598
Net Worth: $1,914,065
Earnings: ($36,519)
Emp.: 10
Fiscal Year-end: 03/31/20
Financial Support Services
N.A.I.C.S.: 523999
Sagar Mal Nahata *(Mng Dir)*

RGP VRDNIK A.D.
Milice Stojadinovic 26, 22408, Vrdnik, Serbia
Tel.: (381) 22 465 207
Year Founded: 2005
RGPV—(BEL)
Sales Range: Less than $1 Million
Emp.: 29
Site Preparation Services
N.A.I.C.S.: 238910
Rajko Bojcic *(Exec Dir)*

RGT BERHAD
1032 Jalan Perindustrian Bukit Minyak, Kawasan Perindustrian Bukit Minyak, 14100, Bukit Mertajam, Pulau Pinang, Malaysia
Tel.: (60) 5013990
Web Site: https://rgtberhad.com
RGTBHD—(KLS)
Rev.: $30,006,178
Assets: $58,434,030
Liabilities: $22,192,432
Net Worth: $36,241,598
Earnings: $2,918,364
Emp.: 134
Fiscal Year-end: 06/30/22
Plain & Laminated Particleboard Mfr
N.A.I.C.S.: 337110
Keng Kok Low *(Chm)*

Subsidiaries:

Keenness Precision Engineering Sdn. Bhd. (1)
9 Lintang Beringin 6 Diamond Valley Industrial Park, 11960, Bayan Lepas, Malaysia
Tel.: (60) 46266198
Web Site: https://www.keenness-precision.com
Industrial Machinery Distr
N.A.I.C.S.: 423830

RGT Industries Sdn. Bhd. (1)
972 Jalan Perindustrian Bukit Minyak 6, Taman Perindustrian Bukit Minyak, 14100, Simpang Empat, Malaysia
Tel.: (60) 45022589
Web Site: https://rgt-industries.com
Precision Spray Painting Services
N.A.I.C.S.: 561730

Rapid Growth Technology Sdn. Bhd. (1)
1032 Jalan Perindustrian Bukit Minyak Taman Perindustrian Bukit Minyak, 14100, Simpang Empat, Pulau Pinang, Malaysia
Tel.: (60) 45013990
Web Site: https://rgt.com.my
Plastic Injection Molding Mfr
N.A.I.C.S.: 325620

T-Venture Industries (M) Sdn. Bhd. (1)
No 9 Jalan Anggerik Mokara 31/48 Kota Kemuning Ind Park Section 31, 40460, Shah Alam, Selangor, Malaysia
Tel.: (60) 351222882
Web Site: https://tventure.com.my
Hygiene Consumer Product Distr
N.A.I.C.S.: 424210

Top Degree (M) Sdn. Bhd. (1)
887 Jalan Perindustrian Bukit Minyak Taman Perindustrian Bukit Minyak, 14100, Simpang Empat, Penang, Malaysia
Tel.: (60) 45041221
Web Site: https://topdegree.com.my
Hygiene Consumer Product Distr
N.A.I.C.S.: 424210

RH PETROGAS LIMITED
20 Harbour Drive 06-03, Singapore, 117612, Singapore
Tel.: (65) 62163988 SG
Web Site: https://www.rhpetrogas.com
Year Founded: 1987
T13—(SES)
Rev.: $94,091,000
Assets: $104,520,000
Liabilities: $55,731,000
Net Worth: $48,789,000
Earnings: $3,153,000
Emp.: 367
Fiscal Year-end: 12/31/23
Oil & Gas Exploration Services
N.A.I.C.S.: 213112
Francis Cheng-Hsing Chang *(CEO-Grp)*

Subsidiaries:

Kingworld Resources Limited (1)
Block 2 No 688 Xiamen Street Jingjikaifaqu Economic Development Zone, Songyuan, Jilin, 138000, China
Tel.: (86) 4382165298
Oil & Gas Exploration Services
N.A.I.C.S.: 211130

Petrogas (Basin) Ltd (1)
53rd Floor Sahid Sudirman Center Jalan Jend Sudirman No 86, Jakarta, 10220, Indonesia
Tel.: (62) 2129880628
Oil & Gas Exploration Services
N.A.I.C.S.: 211120
Raihanah Mohamed *(Mgr-HR)*

RHP (Mukah) Pte. Ltd. (1)
Level 15 Menara Darussalam No 12 Jalan Pinang, 50450, Kuala Lumpur, Malaysia
Tel.: (60) 321786430
Oil & Gas Exploration Services
N.A.I.C.S.: 211120

RHP Salawati Holdings BV (1)
Strawinskylaan 1143 C-11, 1077 XX, Amsterdam, Netherlands
Tel.: (31) 205788388
Financial Holding Services
N.A.I.C.S.: 551112

RH TECHNOLOGIES LTD.
Ha'mayan 2 st Har Yona Industriel Park, Nazareth Illit, 17000, Israel
Tel.: (972) 4 6089000
Web Site: http://www.rh-global.com
Year Founded: 2000
Sales Range: $125-149.9 Million
Electric Equipment Mfr
N.A.I.C.S.: 334419
Yacov Rosenberg *(Chm)*

RHB BANK BERHAD
Level 4 Crystal Plaza No 4 Jalan 51a/223 Seksyen 51a, 46100, Petaling Jaya, Selangor, Malaysia
Tel.: (60) 392068118 MY
Web Site: https://www.rhbgroup.com
Year Founded: 1913
1066—(KLS)
Rev.: $1,566,302,018
Assets: $71,661,510,855
Liabilities: $64,723,959,383
Net Worth: $6,937,551,473
Earnings: $649,225,170
Emp.: 14,042
Fiscal Year-end: 12/31/21

RHB BANK BERHAD

RHB Bank Berhad—(Continued)
Banking & Insurance Services
N.A.I.C.S.: 522110
Norazzah Sulaiman *(Chief Comm Officer)*

Subsidiaries:

Banfora Pte Ltd (1)
90 Cecil Street 01-03 Carlton Building, Singapore, 069531, Singapore
Tel.: (65) 62202349
Property Management Services
N.A.I.C.S.: 531311

PT RHB Asset Management Indonesia (1)
Revenue Tower 11th Floor District 8 SCBD Lot 13, Jl Jend Sudirman Kav 52-53, Jakarta, 12190, Indonesia
Tel.: (62) 215 093 9889
Web Site: https://www.rhb-ami.co.id
Asset Management Services
N.A.I.C.S.: 523940
Yap Chee Meng *(Co-Pres & Commissioner)*

RHB Asset Management Pte. Ltd. (1)
6 Shenton Way 19-09 OUE Downtown 2, Singapore, 068809, Singapore
Tel.: (65) 63296399
Web Site: https://www.rhbgroup.com.sg
Asset Management Services
N.A.I.C.S.: 523940
Yap Chee Meng *(Chm)*

RHB Asset Management Sdn. Bhd. (1)
Level 8 Tower 2 and 3 RHB Centre Jalan Tun Razak, 50400, Kuala Lumpur, Malaysia
Tel.: (60) 392058000
Asset Management Services
N.A.I.C.S.: 523940

RHB Bank (L) Ltd (1)
Level 15 B Main Office Tower Financial Park Labuan Jalan Merdeka, Labuan, 87000, Malaysia
Tel.: (60) 87417480
Sales Range: $50-74.9 Million
Emp.: 20
Commercial Banking Services
N.A.I.C.S.: 522110
Rosalint Liau *(Gen Mgr)*

RHB Bank Lao Limited (1)
No 01 House No 008 Kaysone Phomvihane Road, Phonxay Village Saysettha District, Vientiane, Lao People's Democratic Republic
Tel.: (856) 2145 511 7119
Web Site: https://www.rhbgroup.com
Banking Services
N.A.I.C.S.: 522110
Choong Seang Heng *(CEO & Mng Dir)*

RHB Bank Nominees Pte Ltd (1)
90 Cecil St 03-00, Singapore, 69531, Singapore
Tel.: (65) 62253111
Web Site: http://www.rhbbank.com.sg
Commercial Banking Services
N.A.I.C.S.: 522110

RHB Indochina Bank Limited (1)
263 Ang Duong Street, Phnom Penh, 12202, Cambodia (100%)
Tel.: (855) 23 992 833
Web Site: http://www.rhb.com.my
Commericial Banking
N.A.I.C.S.: 522110

RHB Insurance Berhad (1)
Level 9 Tower One RHB Centre Jalan Tun Razak, 50400, Kuala Lumpur, Malaysia (94.7%)
Tel.: (60) 321803000
Web Site: http://www.rhb.com.my
Rev.: $175,736,459
Assets: $442,836,860
Liabilities: $289,246,317
Net Worth: $153,590,543
Earnings: $26,263,926
Emp.: 300
Fiscal Year-end: 12/31/2019
Insurance Services
N.A.I.C.S.: 524298
Shu Yin Kong *(CEO & Mng Dir)*

RHB Investment Bank Berhad (1)
Level 5 Tower One RHB Centre, Jalan Tun Razak, 50400, Kuala Lumpur, Malaysia (100%)
Tel.: (60) 392873888
Web Site: http://www.rhbinvest.com
Rev.: $55,763,267
Fiscal Year-end: 12/31/2018
Investment & Merchant Banking Services
N.A.I.C.S.: 523150
Lina Then *(Officer-Complaint-Kuching)*

Subsidiary (Domestic):

OSK Trustees Berhad (2)
6th Floor Plaza OSK Jalan Ampang, Kuala Lumpur, 50450, Malaysia
Tel.: (60) 3 9207 7777
Web Site: http://www.osktrustees.com.my
Financial Management Consulting Services
N.A.I.C.S.: 523999
Nur Sabrina Soon Abdullah *(VP-Private Trust)*

Subsidiary (Non-US):

PT RHB OSK Securities Indonesia (2)
Plaza CIMB Niaga Lantai 14 Jl Jend Sudirman Kav 25, Jakarta, 12920, Selatan, Indonesia
Tel.: (62) 21 2598 6888
Securities Broker & Dealer
N.A.I.C.S.: 523150

RHB Holdings Hong Kong Limited (2)
12/F World-Wide House 19 Des Voeux Road, Central, China (Hong Kong)
Tel.: (852) 2525 1118
Web Site: http://www.osk188.com.hk
Sales Range: $100-124.9 Million
Emp.: 200
Holding Company; Securities & Commodities Brokerage, Dealing & Wealth Management Services
N.A.I.C.S.: 551112

Subsidiary (Domestic):

OSK International Investments Hong Kong Limited (3)
12/F World-Wide House 19 Des Voeux Road, Central, China (Hong Kong) (100%)
Tel.: (852) 2525 1118
Web Site: http://www.osk188.com.hk
Emp.: 170
Investment Fund Management Services
N.A.I.C.S.: 523940
William Wu *(CEO)*

RHB OSK Capital Hong Kong Limited (3)
12/F World-Wide House 19 Des Voeux Road, Central, China (Hong Kong) (100%)
Tel.: (852) 2525 1118
Web Site: http://www.osk188.com.hk
Emp.: 170
Equity Investment Services
N.A.I.C.S.: 523999
William Wu *(CEO)*

RHB OSK Futures Hong Kong Limited (3)
12/F World-Wide House 19 Des Voeux Road, Central, China (Hong Kong) (100%)
Tel.: (852) 2525 1118
Web Site: http://www.osk188.com.hk
Commodity Futures Brokerage & Dealing Services
N.A.I.C.S.: 523160

RHB OSK Precious Metals Hong Kong Limited (3)
12 F World Wide House 19 Des Voeux Road Central, Hong Kong, China (Hong Kong) (100%)
Tel.: (852) 2525 1118
Web Site: http://www.osk188.com.hk
Emp.: 200
Precious Metals Trading Services
N.A.I.C.S.: 523160

RHB OSK Securities Hong Kong Limited (3)
12/F World-Wide House 19 Des Voeux Road, Central, China (Hong Kong) (100%)
Tel.: (852) 2525 1118
Web Site: http://www.osk188.com.hk

Securities Broker & Dealer
N.A.I.C.S.: 523150

Subsidiary (Domestic):

RHB Investment Management Sdn. Bhd. (2)
Level 10 Tower One RHB Ctr, Jalan Tun Razak, Kuala Lumpur, 50400, Malaysia (100%)
Tel.: (60) 392862666
Web Site: http://www.rhb.com.my
Sales Range: $75-99.9 Million
Emp.: 200
Investment Management Service
N.A.I.C.S.: 523940

Subsidiary (Non-US):

RHB OSK Securities (Thailand) Public Company Limited (2)
Silom Complex Building Floor 16, 191 Silom Road Silom Bang Rak, Bangkok, Thailand (99.43%)
Tel.: (66) 2200 2736
Web Site: http://www.osk188.co.th
Sales Range: $1-9.9 Million
Financial Brokerage Services
N.A.I.C.S.: 522320

Subsidiary (Domestic):

RHB Research Institute Sdn. Bhd. (2)
Level 11 Tower One RHB Ctr, Jalan Tun Razak, Kuala Lumpur, 50400, Malaysia (100%)
Tel.: (60) 392852233
Web Site: http://www.rhb.com.my
Investment Research Services
N.A.I.C.S.: 525990

Subsidiary (Non-US):

RHB Securities Singapore Pte Ltd (2)
10 Collyer Quay 09-08 Ocean Financial Centre, Singapore, 049315, Singapore
Tel.: (65) 331818
Web Site: http://www.rhbinvest.com.sg
Financial Services
N.A.I.C.S.: 523150

RHB Islamic Bank Berhad (1)
Level 10 Tower One RHB Centre Jalan Tun Razak, 50420, Kuala Lumpur, Malaysia (100%)
Tel.: (60) 392878888
Web Site: http://www.rhbgroup.com
Rev.: $853,021,454
Assets: $18,660,913,144
Liabilities: $17,501,719,316
Net Worth: $1,159,193,829
Earnings: $146,277,634
Fiscal Year-end: 12/31/2019
Retail & Commercial Banking Services
N.A.I.C.S.: 522110
Adissadikin Ali *(CEO & Mng Dir)*

RHB Leasing Sdn Bhd (1)
Level 17 Menara Yayasan Tun Razak 200 Jalan Bukit Bintang, Kuala Lumpur, 55100, Malaysia
Tel.: (60) 321610488
Financial Management Services
N.A.I.C.S.: 523999

RHB Securities (Cambodia) Plc. (1)
Level M OHK Tower Corner Street 110 and Street 93, Phnom Penh, Cambodia
Tel.: (855) 23969161
Web Site: https://www.rhbgroup.com.kh
Securities Brokerage Services
N.A.I.C.S.: 523150
Chin Yoong Kheong *(Chm)*

RHB Securities (Thailand) Public Company Limited (1)
No 98 Sathorn Square Office Tower 8th 10th Floor, North Sathorn Road Silom Subdistrict Bang Rak District, Bangkok, 10500, Thailand
Tel.: (66) 20889999
Web Site: https://www.th.rhbtradesmart.com
Securities Brokerage Services
N.A.I.C.S.: 523150

RHB Securities Hong Kong Limited (1)
12/F Hip Shing Hong Kowloon Centre 192-

INTERNATIONAL PUBLIC

194 Nathan Road, Jordan, Kowloon, China (Hong Kong)
Tel.: (852) 21035657
Web Site: http://www.rhbinvest.com.hk
Investment Services
N.A.I.C.S.: 523999

RHB Securities Vietnam Company Limited (1)
Floor 15 IDMC My Dinh Building No 15 Pham Hung Street, My Dinh 2 ward Nam Tu Liem District, Hanoi, Vietnam
Tel.: (84) 2439446066
Web Site: https://www.rhbsecurities.vn
Emp.: 23
Investment Services
N.A.I.C.S.: 523999

RHC HOLDING PRIVATE LIMITED

54 Janpath, New Delhi, 110017, India
Tel.: (91) 1146014600
Web Site: http://www.rhcholding.com
Holding Company
N.A.I.C.S.: 551112
Gunjan Singh *(Officer-Compliance & Sec)*

RHEA GIRISIM SERMAYESI YATIRIM ORTAKLIGI A.S.

Adalet Mah Anadolu Cad No 41/1 Ic Kapi No 2203, Bayrakli, 34398, Izmir, Turkiye
Tel.: (90) 3124668450
Web Site: https://www.rheagirisim.com.tr
Year Founded: 1996
ICUGS—(IST)
Rev.: $447,538
Assets: $9,381,614
Liabilities: $7,821,894
Net Worth: $1,559,720
Earnings: ($251,194)
Fiscal Year-end: 12/31/23
Financial Investment Services
N.A.I.C.S.: 523910
Onur Takmak *(Chm)*

RHEIN-MAIN-VERKEHRSVERBUND GMBH

Alte Bleiche 5, Hofheim, 56571945, Germany
Tel.: (49) 61922940
Web Site: http://www.rmv.de
Rev.: $68,280,300
Emp.: 127
Transportation Support Services
N.A.I.C.S.: 561599
Knut Ringat *(CEO & Co-Mng Dir)*

RHEINGOLD CAPITAL GMBH

Anna-Schneider-Steig 9, 50678, Cologne, Germany
Tel.: (49) 22139893421
Investment Management Service
N.A.I.C.S.: 523999

RHEINGRUND IMMOBILIEN VERWALTUNGS-GMBH

Martin-Luther-Platz 26, 40212, Dusseldorf, Germany
Tel.: (49) 211864930 De
Web Site: http://www.rheingrund-ivg.de
Shopping Center Property Management Services
N.A.I.C.S.: 531312
Patrick Ludwig *(Mng Dir)*

RHEINISCHE-BERGISCHE VERLAGSGESELLSCHAFT MBH

Zulpicher Strasse 10, 40146, Dusseldorf, Germany
Tel.: (49) 211 505 0 De
Web Site: http://www.rheinischepostmedien.de

AND PRIVATE COMPANIES — RHEINMETALL AG

Holding Company; Newspaper Publisher
N.A.I.C.S.: 551112
Karl Hans Arnold *(Mng Partner)*

Subsidiaries:

AMPLEXOR International S.A. (1)
55 rue de Luxembourg, L-8077, Bertrange, Luxembourg
Tel.: (352) 3144111
Emp.: 1,850
Web Based Management Solutions Services
N.A.I.C.S.: 541611
Mark Evenepoel *(CEO)*

Subsidiary (US):

AMPLEXOR, Inc. (2)
625 Whitetail Blvd, River Falls, WI 54022
Tel.: (715) 426-9505
Digital Solutions Services
N.A.I.C.S.: 513210
Joe Bechtel *(VP-Global Language Svcs)*

Subsidiary (Non-US):

AMPLEXOR Singapore Pte. Ltd. (3)
10 Anson Road Unit 03-27, 079903, Singapore, Singapore
Tel.: (65) 69092455
Web Site: http://www.amplexor.com
Digital Solutions Services
N.A.I.C.S.: 513210

DVV Media Group GmbH (1)
Heidenkampsweg 75, 20097, Hamburg, Germany
Tel.: (49) 40 23714 01
Web Site: http://www.dvvmedia.com
Periodical Publishers
N.A.I.C.S.: 513120
Martin Christoph Weber *(Mng Dir)*

Subsidiary (Non-US):

DVV Media International Ltd. (2)
Chancery House St Nicholas Way, Sutton, SM1 1JB, Surrey, United Kingdom
Tel.: (44) 20 8652 5200
Web Site: http://www.dvvmedia.com
Periodical Publishers
N.A.I.C.S.: 513120
Ian Andrew Salter *(Mng Dir)*

Rheinische Post Verlagsgesellschaft mbH (1)
Zuelpicher Strasse 10, 40196, Dusseldorf, Germany
Tel.: (49) 211 505 0
Emp.: 5,000
Digital & Trade Media & Newspaper Publishing
N.A.I.C.S.: 513110
Karl Hans Arnold *(Chm & Mng Dir)*

Subsidiary (Domestic):

Saarbrucker Zeitung Verlag und Druckerei GmbH (2)
Gutenbergstrasse 11 23, D 66117, Saarbrucken, Germany (56%)
Tel.: (49) 6815020
Web Site: http://www.sol.de
Sales Range: $150-199.9 Million
Emp.: 700
Newspapers-Printing
N.A.I.C.S.: 513110

Subsidiary (US):

ForeignExchange Translations Inc. (3)
530 Compton St Ste A, Broomfield, CO 80020
Tel.: (303) 926-7177
Web Site: http://www.fxtrans.com
Medical Translation Services
N.A.I.C.S.: 541930
Andres Heuberger *(Founder & Pres)*

RHEINMETALL AG

Rheinmetall Platz 1, 40476, Dusseldorf, Germany
Tel.: (49) 21147301
Web Site: http://www.rheinmetall.com
Year Founded: 1889
RHM—(MUN)
Rev.: $7,921,371,120
Assets: $12,923,006,090
Liabilities: $9,262,573,170
Net Worth: $3,660,432,920
Earnings: $590,570,450
Emp.: 28,054
Fiscal Year-end: 12/31/23
Automotive Components & Defence Equipment Mfr
N.A.I.C.S.: 336390
Ulrich Grillo *(Chm-Supervisory Bd)*

Subsidiaries:

ARTEC GmbH (1)
Krauss-Maffei-Strasse 11, 80997, Munich, Germany
Tel.: (49) 898921300
Web Site: https://www.artec-boxer.com
Automotive Equipment Distr
N.A.I.C.S.: 423120
Sebastian Buchberger *(Mng Dir)*

Amprio GmbH (1)
Alfred-Pierburg-Str 1, 41460, Neuss, Germany
Tel.: (49) 21315202688
Web Site: http://www.amprio.com
Motorcycle Dealers
N.A.I.C.S.: 441227

BF Engine Parts LLC (1)
Selvili Sokak No 2 Helis Beyaz Ofis is Merkezi / A Blok - No 311, Yesilbaglar Mahallesi, 34893, Istanbul, Turkiye
Tel.: (90) 2164881870
Web Site: https://www.ms-motorservice.com
Engine Parts Distr
N.A.I.C.S.: 423120

BIL Industriemetalle GmbH & Co. 886 KG (1)
Emil-Riedl-Weg 6, Pullach, 82049, Germany
Tel.: (49) 8951200
Electronic Products Mfr
N.A.I.C.S.: 334419

Benntec Systemtechnik GmbH (1)
Karl-Ferdinand-Braun-Strasse 7, 28359, Bremen, Germany
Tel.: (49) 421 43849 0
Web Site: http://www.benntec.de
Sales Range: $25-49.9 Million
Software Development Services
N.A.I.C.S.: 541511

EMG Euromarine Electronics GmbH (1)
Behringstrasse 120, Hamburg, 22763, Germany
Tel.: (49) 4088252006
Industrial Machinery Mfr
N.A.I.C.S.: 333248

Eurometaal Holding N.V. (1)
Goudvisstraat 10, Hengelo, 7559 MP, Overijssel, Netherlands
Tel.: (31) 628243077
Investment Management Service
N.A.I.C.S.: 523999

Eurometaal N.V. (1)
Goudvisstraat 10, Hengelo, 7559 MP, Overijssel, Netherlands
Tel.: (31) 203457313
Automobile Parts Mfr
N.A.I.C.S.: 336390

I.L.E.E. AG (1)
Schutzenstr 29, 8902, Urdorf, Switzerland
Tel.: (41) 44 736 1111
Web Site: http://www.ilee.ch
Sales Range: $25-49.9 Million
Emp.: 25
Industrial Machinery Mfr
N.A.I.C.S.: 333248
Markus Klinger *(Gen Mgr)*

Intec France S.A.S. (1)
4 Avenue Des Pays Bas, 69330, Meyzieu, France
Tel.: (33) 472475161
Sales Range: $25-49.9 Million
Emp.: 12
Actuator Mfr
N.A.I.C.S.: 333995
Regis Serrano *(Gen Mgr)*

KS Aluminium-Technologie GmbH (1)
Hafenstrasse 25, 74172, Neckarsulm, Germany
Tel.: (49) 7132331
Web Site: http://www.kspg-ag.de
Sales Range: $200-249.9 Million
Emp.: 700
Engine Block Mfr
N.A.I.C.S.: 336390

KS CZ Motorservice s.r.o. (1)
Smetanova 716, Chabarovice, 403 17, Usti nad Labem, Czech Republic
Tel.: (420) 604510490
Emp.: 95
Automotive Equipment Distr
N.A.I.C.S.: 423120
Petra Hvezdova *(Plant Mgr)*

KS Gleitlager USA Inc. (1)
800 Woodside Ave, Fountain Inn, SC 29644-2029
Tel.: (864) 688-1400
Web Site: http://www.kspg-ag.de
Motor Vehicle Parts Mfr
N.A.I.C.S.: 336390

KS Kolbenschmidt Czech Rebublic a.s. (1)
Dulni 362, Trmice, 400 04, Czech Republic
Tel.: (420) 475303111
Web Site: http://www.kolben-ustinl.kspg-ag.com
Sales Range: $200-249.9 Million
Emp.: 700
Diesel Engine Mfr
N.A.I.C.S.: 333618

KS Kolbenschmidt France S.A.S. (1)
Z I de Thionville Nord-Est, BP 60154, Basse Ham, 57974, Yutz, Cedex, France
Tel.: (33) 382559286
Sales Range: $100-124.9 Million
Emp.: 30
Automotive Engine Mfr
N.A.I.C.S.: 336390
Martial Habay *(Gen Mgr)*

KS Large Bore Pistons Inc. (1)
2945 Angwall Dr, Marinette, WI 54143
Tel.: (715) 735-2000
Web Site: http://www.kspg.com
Emp.: 80
Mfr of Automotive Components
N.A.I.C.S.: 336310

KSLP (China) Co. Ltd. (1)
Building E No 299 Yuyang Road, Kunshan, 215300, Jiangsu, China
Tel.: (86) 51286184601
Automotive Equipment Distr
N.A.I.C.S.: 423120
Ernst Rassau *(Gen Mgr)*

KSPG (China) Investment Co. Ltd. (1)
9th Floor Building 1 Lane 988 Shenchang Road, Minhang District, Shanghai, 201106, China
Tel.: (86) 2180363450
Automotive Equipment Distr
N.A.I.C.S.: 423120
Wen Jiang *(CFO & VP)*

KSPG AG (1)
Karl-Schmidt-Strasse, 74172, Neckarsulm, 74172, Germany
Tel.: (49) 7132 33 0
Web Site: http://www.kspg-ag.de
Sales Range: $1-4.9 Billion
Emp.: 1,150
Automotive Component Mfr & Distr
N.A.I.C.S.: 336390
Horst Binnig *(CEO)*

Subsidiary (Domestic):

KS ATAG GmbH (2)
Hafenstr 25, Neckarsulm, 74172, Baden-Wurttemberg, Germany
Tel.: (49) 7132330
Web Site: http://www.kspg.com
Emp.: 50
Aluminium Products Mfr
N.A.I.C.S.: 331524

KS Gleitlager GmbH (2)
Am Bahnhof 14, 68789, Sankt Leon-Rot, Germany
Tel.: (49) 6227560
Emp.: 500
Automobile Parts Mfr
N.A.I.C.S.: 336390

Subsidiary (US):

KS Gleitlager North America LLC (2)
975 S Opdyke Rd Ste 100, Auburn Hills, MI 48326
Tel.: (248) 836-3000
Automobile Parts Mfr
N.A.I.C.S.: 336390

Subsidiary (Non-US):

KS Gleitlager de Mexico S. de R.L. de C.V. (2)
Carretera Panamericana Km 284 2a Fraccion de Crespo, 38110, Celaya, Guanajuato, Mexico
Tel.: (52) 4615987800
Automobile Parts Mfr
N.A.I.C.S.: 336390
Adolfo Mendoza *(Gen Mgr)*

Subsidiary (Domestic):

KS Kolbenschmidt GmbH (2)
Karl-Schmidt-Strasse, Neckarsulm, 74172, Germany
Tel.: (49) 7132330
Web Site: http://www.kspg-ag.de
Emp.: 330
Engine Piston Mfr
N.A.I.C.S.: 336310
Alexander Sagl *(Gen Mgr)*

Subsidiary (US):

KS Kolbenschmidt US, Inc. (2)
1731 Industrial Pkwy, Marinette, WI 54143
Tel.: (715) 732-0181
Web Site: http://www.rheinmetall-automotive.com
Automotive Piston Mfr & Distr
N.A.I.C.S.: 336310

Plant (Domestic):

Karl Schmidt Unisia Inc. - Fort Wayne Plant (3)
2425 Coliseum Blvd S, Fort Wayne, IN 46803
Tel.: (260) 426-8081
Automotive Piston Mfr
N.A.I.C.S.: 336310

Subsidiary (Domestic):

KS Personaldienstleistungsgesellschaft mbH i.L. (2)
Karl-Schmidt-Str, Neckarsulm, 74172, Baden-Wurttemberg, Germany
Tel.: (49) 7132330
Web Site: http://www.kspg.com
Sales Range: $350-399.9 Million
Automobile Parts Mfr
N.A.I.C.S.: 336390

Subsidiary (Non-US):

KSPG Automotive Brazil Ltda. (2)
Rod Arnaldo Julio Mauerberg N 4000 Block 04 - Distrito Industrial N 01, Nova Odessa, CEP 13 388 090, Sao Paulo, Brazil
Tel.: (55) 1934669620
Web Site: https://www.ms-motorservice.com
Automotive Piston Ring Mfr
N.A.I.C.S.: 336310

Division (Domestic):

KSPG Automotive Brazil Ltda. - MS Motor Service Brazil Division (3)
Rod Arnaldo Julio Mauerberg 4000 Distr Industrial I, 134600-000, Nova Odessa, Sao Paulo, Brazil
Tel.: (55) 19 3466 9620
Automobile Parts Mfr
N.A.I.C.S.: 336390

KSPG Automotive Brazil Ltda. - Pierburg Pump Technology Division (3)
Rod Arnaldo Julio Mauerberg 4000 Distr Industrial I, Nova Odessa, 13460 000, Sao Paulo, Brazil
Tel.: (55) 19 3466 9700
Oil & Water Pump Mfr
N.A.I.C.S.: 333914

RHEINMETALL AG

Rheinmetall AG—(Continued)

Subsidiary (Non-US):

KSPG Automotive India Private Ltd. (2)
A - 3 MIDC, Ahmednagar, 414 001, Maharashtra, India
Tel.: (91) 2416613202
Automobile Parts Mfr
N.A.I.C.S.: 336390

Subsidiary (US):

KSUS International LLC (2)
1731 Industrial Pkwy N, Marinette, WI 54143
Tel.: (715) 732-0181
Automobile Parts Mfr
N.A.I.C.S.: 336390

Subsidiary (Non-US):

Karl Schmidt Trading Company S. de R.L. de C.V. (2)
Km 284 Carretera Panamericana 2 Fraccion De Crespo, Celaya, 38110, Guanajuato, Mexico
Tel.: (52) 4615987800
Automobile Parts Distr
N.A.I.C.S.: 423120

Subsidiary (US):

Kolbenschmidt USA Inc. (2)
1731 Industrial Pkwy, Marinette, WI 54143
Tel.: (715) 732-0181
Web Site: http://www.rheinmetall-automotive.com
Automobile Parts Mfr
N.A.I.C.S.: 336390

Subsidiary (Non-US):

Kolbenschmidt de Mexico S. de R.L. de C.V. (2)
Carretera Panamericana Km 284 2da Fraccion de Crespo, 38110, Celaya, Guanajuato, Mexico
Tel.: (52) 4615987800
Automotive Piston Mfr
N.A.I.C.S.: 336310
Francisco Velasco (Gen Mgr)

Plant (Domestic):

Kolbenschmidt de Mexico S. de R.L. de C.V. - Celaya Plant (3)
Carretera Panamericana Km 284 2a Fraccion de Crespo, 38110, Celaya, Guanajuato, Mexico
Tel.: (52) 461 598 7811
Automotive Piston Mfr
N.A.I.C.S.: 336310

Subsidiary (Non-US):

Pierburg Gestion S.L. (2)
Calle San Prudentzio Kalea 12, Abadiano Celayeta, 48220, Biscay, Spain
Tel.: (34) 946205525
Business Management Consulting Services
N.A.I.C.S.: 541611

Pierburg Mikuni Pump Technology Corporation (2)
2480 Kuno, Odawara, 250-0055, Kanagawa, Japan
Tel.: (81) 465 35 0451
Sales Range: $25-49.9 Million
Emp.: 7
Pump Equipment Mfr
N.A.I.C.S.: 333914

Pierburg Pump Technology France S.a r.l. (2)
Z A Kickelsberg 1 - Rue Denis Papin, 57970, Basse-Ham, France
Tel.: (33) 382559393
Sales Range: $75-99.9 Million
Emp.: 35
Mechanical & Electrical Pumping Equipment Mfr
N.A.I.C.S.: 333914

Subsidiary (US):

Pierburg Pump Technology US LLC (2)
1731 Industrial Pkwy N, Marinette, WI 54143-3704

Tel.: (248) 836-2895
Web Site: http://www.kspg.com
Industrial Machinery Mfr
N.A.I.C.S.: 333248
Rene Gansauge (Pres)

Subsidiary (Non-US):

Pierburg S.p.A. (2)
Zona Industriale Contrada Cerratina, 66034, Lanciano, Chieti, Italy
Tel.: (39) 08 72 50 01
Web Site: http://www.kspg-ag.de
Automotive Engine Parts Mfr
N.A.I.C.S.: 336310

Pierburg Systems S.L. (2)
Poligono Industrial Boroa Par 2, Amorebieta-Etxano, 48340, Biscay, Spain
Tel.: (34) 946205432
Engineering Services
N.A.I.C.S.: 541330

KSPG Malta Holding Ltd (1)
Palace Court Church Street, San Giljan, STJ3049, Malta
Tel.: (356) 21370535
Investment Management Service
N.A.I.C.S.: 523999

KSPG Netherlands Holding B.V. (1)
Czaar Peterstraat 229, Amsterdam, 1018 PL, Noord-Holland, Netherlands
Tel.: (31) 205312979
Financial Management Services
N.A.I.C.S.: 523999

Kolbenschmidt K.K. (1)
660-1 Takayachogo, Higashi-hiroshima, 739-2124, Japan
Tel.: (81) 824341101
Web Site: http://www.kolbenschmidt.co.jp
Industrial Piston Mfr
N.A.I.C.S.: 336310

Kolbenschmidt Pierburg AG (1)
Karl Schmidt Strasse, D 74172, Neckarsulm, Germany (73%)
Tel.: (49) 7132330
Web Site: http://www.kspg-ag.de
Sales Range: $1-4.9 Billion
Emp.: 11,700
Mfr of Automotive Parts including Pistons & Friction Components; Consulting & Engineering Services
N.A.I.C.S.: 336390

Subsidiary (US):

Karl Schmidt Unisia - ZOLLNER Division (2)
2425 S Coliseum Blvd, Fort Wayne, IN 46803-2939
Tel.: (260) 426-8081
Sales Range: $25-49.9 Million
Emp.: 75
Supplier of Carburetors, Pistons, Rings & Valves
N.A.I.C.S.: 336310

Subsidiary (Domestic):

Pierburg GmbH (2)
Alfred-Pierburg-Strasse 1, 41460, Neuss, Germany
Tel.: (49) 213152001
Sales of Modules & Systems; Air Supply & Pumps; Pistons; Plain Bearings; Aluminum Technology; Motor Service
N.A.I.C.S.: 333914

Subsidiary (Non-US):

Pierburg China Ltd. (3)
Comprehensive Business Dept Section E Bldg 28 No 500 East Fut, Shanghai, 200131, China
Tel.: (86) 2150460142
Automobile Parts Mfr
N.A.I.C.S.: 336390

Subsidiary (Domestic):

Pierburg Pump Technology GmbH (3)
Alfred-Pierburg-Strasse 1, 41460, Neuss, Germany
Tel.: (49) 213152001
Pumping Equipment Mfr
N.A.I.C.S.: 333914

Subsidiary (Non-US):

Pierburg Pump Technology India Private Limited (3)
Gat No 380 Village Takwe Budruk Taluka Maval, Pune, Maharashtra, India
Tel.: (91) 2114307500
Pumps Mfr
N.A.I.C.S.: 333914

Pierburg Pump Technology Italy S.p.A. (3)
Zona Industriale Contrada Cerratina, 66034, Lanciano, Chieti, Italy
Tel.: (39) 08725001
Web Site: http://www.rheinmetall-automotive.com
Industrial Pump Mfr
N.A.I.C.S.: 333914

Pierburg Pump Technology Mexico S.A. de C.V. (3)
Carretera Panamericana Km 284 2 da Fraccion de Crespo, 38110, Celaya, Guanajuato, Mexico
Tel.: (52) 4615987951
Web Site: https://www.kspg-ag.de
Automotive Repair & Maintenance Services
N.A.I.C.S.: 811198

Pierburg S.A. (3)
San Prudencio N 12, 48220, Abadino, Bizkaia, Spain
Tel.: (34) 946205500
Web Site: https://www.pierburg-sa.es
Automotive Break System Mfr
N.A.I.C.S.: 336390

Pierburg s.r.o. (3)
K Pierburgu 1/455, 40004, Trmice, 40004, Czech Republic
Tel.: (420) 475303813
Web Site: https://www.pierburg.cz
Automobile Parts Mfr
N.A.I.C.S.: 336390
Sascha Guenther (Co-CEO)

Kolbenschmidt Pierburg Innovations GmbH (1)
Karl-schmidt-str 2-8, 74172, Neckarsulm, Germany
Tel.: (49) 7132330
Web Site: http://www.kspg.com
Engine Component Mfr
N.A.I.C.S.: 333618

LIGHTHOUSE Development GmbH (1)
Schadowplatz 12, Dusseldorf, 40212, Nordrhein-Westfale, Germany
Tel.: (49) 2112767900
Emp.: 10
Investment Management Service
N.A.I.C.S.: 523940
Holger Gradhivlsky (Office Mgr)

Logistic Solutions Australasia Pty. Ltd. (1)
Level 4 99 Coventry St, Southbank, 3006, VIC, Australia
Tel.: (61) 396823098
Web Site: https://www.lsaust.com.au
Consulting & Professional Services
N.A.I.C.S.: 541611
Ken Hoppe (Gen Mgr)

MS Motor Service Aftermarket Iberica S.L. (1)
Barrio de Matiena, Abadiano Celayeta, 48220, Vizcaya, Spain
Tel.: (34) 94 620 55 30
Web Site: http://www.ms-motor-service.es
Automotive Bearing Distr
N.A.I.C.S.: 423120

MS Motor Service Deutschland GmbH (1)
Mercedesstrabe 18, 71384, Weinstadt, Germany
Tel.: (49) 7151 96 50 0
Web Site: http://www.ms-motor-service.de
Industrial Motor Mfr & Distr
N.A.I.C.S.: 335314

MS Motor Service France S.A.S. (1)
21 rue Gaston Monmousseau, 95190, Goussainville, France
Tel.: (33) 134 38 76 40
Web Site: http://www.ms-motor-service.fr

INTERNATIONAL PUBLIC

Automotive Repair & Maintenance Services
N.A.I.C.S.: 811198

MS Motor Service International GmbH (1)
Wilhelm-Maybach-Strasse 14-18, 74196, Neuenstadt am Kocher, Germany
Tel.: (49) 7139 9376 33 33
Web Site: http://www.ms-motorservice.com
Sales Range: $75-99.9 Million
Emp.: 200
Engine Component Distr
N.A.I.C.S.: 423830
Tobias Kasperlik (Chm)

Subsidiary (Non-US):

MS Motor Service Asia Pacific Co., Ltd. (2)
Section E Building 28 No 500 East Fu Te 2nd Road, Shanghai, 200131, China
Tel.: (86) 21 5046 1928
Web Site: http://www.ms-motor-service.cn
Motor Engine Parts Repair & Maintenance Services
N.A.I.C.S.: 811310

MS Motor Service Istanbul Dis Ticaret ve Pazarlama A.S. (2)
Noramin Is Merkezi Kat 1 No 111, Maslak, 34398, Istanbul, Turkiye
Tel.: (90) 212 285 42 65
Web Site: http://www.ms-motor-service.com.tr
Sales Range: $10-24.9 Million
Emp.: 26
Motor Supplies Parts Maintenance Services
N.A.I.C.S.: 811310
Rafet Mut (Mng Dir)

MS Motorservice Aftermarket Iberica S.L. (1)
Barrio de Matiena San Prudentzio 12, E 48220, Abadiano, Biscay, Spain
Tel.: (34) 946205530
Web Site: https://www.ms-motorservice.com
Automotive Equipment Distr
N.A.I.C.S.: 423120

MS Motorservice Deutschland GmbH (1)
Rudolf-Diesel-Strasse 9, 71712, Tamm, Germany
Tel.: (49) 714186610
Web Site: https://www.msmotorservice.de
Emp.: 65
Automotive Equipment Distr
N.A.I.C.S.: 423120
Alois Sterr (Product Mgr)

MS Motorservice France SAS (1)
Bat L Etoile - Paris Nord II 50 Allee des Impressionnistes, 93420, Villepinte, France
Tel.: (33) 149897200
Web Site: https://www.ms-motorservice.fr
Automotive Equipment Distr
N.A.I.C.S.: 423120
Yves Mailliere (CEO)

MS Motorservice Trading (Asia) Pte. Ltd. (1)
25 International Business Park 03-51/53A German Centre, Singapore, 609916, Singapore
Tel.: (65) 62503234
Web Site: https://www.ms-motorservice.com
Automotive Equipment Distr
N.A.I.C.S.: 423120

MarineSoft Entwicklungs- und Logistikgesellschaft mbH (1)
Friedrich-Barnewitz-Strasse 2, Rostock, 18119, Germany
Tel.: (49) 381 12835 0
Web Site: http://www.marinesoft.de
Sales Range: $25-49.9 Million
Emp.: 40
Software Development Services
N.A.I.C.S.: 541511
Volker Koehler (Dir-Learning Mgmt & Sys & Trng Tech)

Mechadyne International Ltd. (1)
Park Farm Technology Centre Kirtlington, Kidlington, OX5 3JQ, Oxfordshire, United Kingdom
Tel.: (44) 1869350903
Web Site: http://www.mechadyne-int.com
Automotive Equipment Distr

AND PRIVATE COMPANIES

N.A.I.C.S.: 423120
Tim Lancefield (Mng Dir)

Nitrochemie AG (1)
Papersave Unit Niesenstrasse 44, 3752, Wimmis, Switzerland
Tel.: (41) 332281000
Web Site: http://www.nitrochemie.com
Automotive Components Mfr
N.A.I.C.S.: 336992

Nitrochemie Aschau GmbH (1)
Liebigstrasse 17, Aschau am Inn, 84544, Aschau, Germany
Tel.: (49) 8638680
Web Site: http://www.nitrochemie.com
Nitrocellulose Resin Mfr
N.A.I.C.S.: 325211
Markus Kaiser (Gen Mgr)

Nordic Defence Supply AS (1)
Bygdoy Alle 17, 262, Oslo, Norway
Tel.: (47) 22 54 70 50
Web Site: http://www.nordicds.no
Industrial Equipment Distr
N.A.I.C.S.: 423830
Ketil Vanebo (Mng Dir)

Oerlikon Contraves GmbH (1)
Birchstrasse 155, 8050, Zurich, Switzerland
Tel.: (41) 443162211
Air Defense & Antiaircraft System Mfr
N.A.I.C.S.: 332994
Daniel Sigg (Partner-HR Bus)

Pierburg Inc. (1)
5 Southchase Ct, Fountain Inn, SC 29644-9018
Tel.: (864) 963-3788
Web Site: http://www.kspg-ag.de
Automotive Components Mfr
N.A.I.C.S.: 336390

Pierburg Pump Technologie US LLC (1)
1731 Industrial Pkwy N, Marinette, WI 54143-3704
Tel.: (248) 836-2895
Web Site: http://www.kspg.com
Sales Range: $25-49.9 Million
Emp.: 20
Industrial Pump Mfr
N.A.I.C.S.: 333914
Davide Davi (Dir-Sls)

Provectus Robotics Solutions Inc. (1)
1740 Woodroffe Ave Building 400, Ottawa, K2G 3R8, ON, Canada
Tel.: (613) 898-2390
Web Site: https://www.provectus-robotics.com
Robotic System Design & Integration Services
N.A.I.C.S.: 541512

RF Engines Limited (1)
Innovation Centre Saint Cross Business Park, Newport, PO30 5WB, Isle of Wight, United Kingdom
Tel.: (44) 1983 550330
Web Site: http://www.rfel.com
Sales Range: $25-49.9 Million
Emp.: 21
Digital Signal Processing Equipment Mfr
N.A.I.C.S.: 334419
Alex Kuhrt (Mng Dir)

RFEL Ltd. (1)
Unit B-The Apex St Cross Business Park, Newport, PO30 5XW, Isle of Wight, United Kingdom
Tel.: (44) 1983216600
Web Site: http://www.rfel.com
Signal & Video Processing Services
N.A.I.C.S.: 518210
Richard Streeter (Mng Dir)

RH Mexico Simulation & Training S.A. de C.V. (1)
Business Park Torre 1 Avenida Antea No 1088 Nivel 2 Oficina 2a, Mexico, Mexico
Tel.: (52) 4421031600
Infrastructure & Equipment Distr
N.A.I.C.S.: 423830
Carsten Rohl (CEO)

RM Euro B.V. (1)
Goudvisstraat 10, Hengelo, 7559 MP, Overijssel, Netherlands
Tel.: (31) 628243077
Investment Management Service
N.A.I.C.S.: 523940

RTP-UK Ltd. (1)
2630 The Quadrant Aztec West, Almondsbury, Bristol, BS32 4GQ, United Kingdom
Tel.: (44) 1454643100
Web Site: http://www.rheinmetall-defence.com
Sales Range: $25-49.9 Million
Emp.: 70
Logistics Engineering Services
N.A.I.C.S.: 541330
Robert C. Peters (Mng Dir)

RWM Beteiligungsverwaltung Austria GmbH (1)
Kaufing 31, 4690, Schwanenstadt, Oberosterreich, Austria
Tel.: (43) 7673805100
Web Site: http://www.rheinmetall-defence.com
Automobile Mfr
N.A.I.C.S.: 336110

RWM Schweiz AG (1)
Birchstrasse 155, 8050, Zurich, Switzerland
Tel.: (41) 443164414
Naval Application Ammunition Mfr
N.A.I.C.S.: 332992

RWM Zaugg AG (1)
Wassergasse 12, 4573, Lohn-Ammannsegg, Switzerland
Tel.: (41) 326775060
Sales Range: $25-49.9 Million
Emp.: 30
Electro Mechanical Equipment Mfr
N.A.I.C.S.: 334419
Joerg Bunter (Gen Mgr)

Rheinmetall Australia Pty Ltd. (1)
Level 1 25 Geils Court, Deakin West, Canberra, 2600, ACT, Australia
Tel.: (61) 2 6282 3211
Web Site: http://www.rheinmetall-defence.com
Emp.: 60
Automobile Parts Mfr
N.A.I.C.S.: 336390
Peter Hardisty (Mng Dir)

Rheinmetall Automotive AG (1)
Karl-Schmidt-Strasse 2-8, 74172, Neckarsulm, Germany
Tel.: (49) 7132330
Web Site: http://www.rheinmetall-automotive.com
Automotive Equipment Distr
N.A.I.C.S.: 423120
Peter Hartung (Sr VP)

Rheinmetall Burosysteme GmbH (1)
Rheinmetall-Allee 1, 40476, Dusseldorf, Germany
Tel.: (49) 21147301
Office Furniture Mfr
N.A.I.C.S.: 337214

Rheinmetall Chempro GmbH (1)
Putzchens Chaussee 58a, 53227, Bonn, Germany
Tel.: (49) 228 9750 3
Web Site: http://www.rheinmetall-chempro.de
Automotive Protection System Whslr
N.A.I.C.S.: 423120
Frank Gorissen (Mng Dir)

Rheinmetall Defence (1)
Rheinmetall Allee 1, 40476, Dusseldorf, Germany (100%)
Tel.: (49) 21147301
Web Site: http://www.rheinmetall-defence.com
Sales Range: $1-4.9 Billion
Emp.: 9,304
Defense Technology Mfr
N.A.I.C.S.: 334511

Subsidiary (Domestic):

ADS Gesellschaft fur aktive Schutzsysteme mbH (2)
Im Rohnweiher 39, 53797, Lohmar, Germany
Tel.: (49) 2205 90447 0
Web Site: http://www.ads-protection.org
Sales Range: $25-49.9 Million
Emp.: 6
Automobile Equipment Mfr

N.A.I.C.S.: 334290
Peter Kayser (Co-Mng Dir)

Subsidiary (Non-US):

Contraves Advanced Devices, Sdn. Bhd. (2)
Batu Berendam F T Z, Melaka, 75700, Malaysia (100%)
Tel.: (60) 62331888
Web Site: http://www.contraves.com.my
Sales Range: $25-49.9 Million
Emp.: 180
Mfr of Electronic Navigational Devices & Optical Products & Biomedical Equipment
N.A.I.C.S.: 334511

Division (Non-US):

Nitrochemie Wimmis AG (2)
Niesen Strasse 44, 3752, Wimmis, Switzerland
Tel.: (41) 332281300
Web Site: http://www.nitrochemie.com
Sales Range: $25-49.9 Million
Emp.: 200
Propellant Mfr
N.A.I.C.S.: 336415

Subsidiary (Non-US):

Oerlikon Singapore Pte. Ltd. (2)
1 Science Park Road #03-10 Capricorn Building, Singapore, 117528, Singapore (100%)
Tel.: (65) 67704721
Sales Range: $25-49.9 Million
Emp.: 15
Logistical Activities for Oerlikon Contraves Division; Air Defence
N.A.I.C.S.: 332994

RWM Italia S.p.A. (2)
Via Industriale 8/d, 25016, Ghedi, BS, Italy
Tel.: (39) 03090431
Web Site: http://www.rheinmetall-defence.com
Emp.: 600
Automobile Parts Mfr
N.A.I.C.S.: 336390

Division (Non-US):

Rheinmetall Air Defence AG (2)
Birchstrasse 155, CH 8050, Zurich, Switzerland (100%)
Tel.: (41) 3162211
Sales Range: $150-199.9 Million
Emp.: 1,000
Mfr of Anti-Aircraft Defense Systems, Testing Equipment & Space Vehicle Parts
N.A.I.C.S.: 334519

Subsidiary (Non-US):

Oerlikon Contraves Pte Ltd. (3)
12 Tuas Avenue 7, Singapore, 639267, Singapore
Tel.: (65) 64 1601 70
Sales Range: $25-49.9 Million
Emp.: 10
Service & Repair Services
N.A.I.C.S.: 541618
Kurt Hermann Annaheim (Mng Dir)

Subsidiary (Non-US):

Rheinmetall Canada Inc. (2)
225 Blvd Du Seminaire Sud, Saint-Jean-sur-Richelieu, J3B 8E9, QC, Canada (100%)
Tel.: (450) 358-2000
Web Site: http://www.rheinmetall.ca
Sales Range: $25-49.9 Million
Emp.: 400
Defense Technology Mfr
N.A.I.C.S.: 334511
Alain Tremblay (VP-Bus Dev & Innovation)

Division (Domestic):

Rheinmetall Defence Electronics GmbH (2)
Brueggeweg 54, Bremen, 28309, Germany
Tel.: (49) 42145701
Defense Electronics Mfr
N.A.I.C.S.: 334511

Subsidiary (Domestic):

LDT Laser Display Technology GmbH (3)

RHEINMETALL AG

Goschwitzer Str 25, 7745, Jena, Germany
Tel.: (49) 3641 65 2842
Web Site: http://www.ldt-jena.de
Sales Range: $25-49.9 Million
Emp.: 3
Laser Projector Mfr
N.A.I.C.S.: 333310
Henry Schroeder (Mng Dir)

Rheinmetall Soldier Electronics GmbH (3)
Bodenseeallee 3, 78333, Stockach, Germany
Tel.: (49) 7771810
Sales Range: $25-49.9 Million
Emp.: 160
Combat Technology Developer & Mfr
N.A.I.C.S.: 334511

Subsidiary (Non-US):

Rheinmetall Hellas S.A. (2)
Ploutarchou St 18, 10676, Athens, Greece
Tel.: (30) 2107249555
Defense Technology Mfr
N.A.I.C.S.: 334511
Michael Heinzelmann (Mng Dir)

Rheinmetall Italia S.p.A. (2)
Via Affile 102, 00131, Rome, Italy (100%)
Tel.: (39) 0643611
Sales Range: $75-99.9 Million
Emp.: 389
Defense Technology Mfr
N.A.I.C.S.: 334511

Division (Domestic):

Rheinmetall Landsysteme GmbH (2)
Dr Hell Strasse 6, 24107, Kiel, Germany
Tel.: (49) 431218501
Web Site: http://www.rheinmetall.com
Sales Range: $75-99.9 Million
Armored Vehicle Mfr
N.A.I.C.S.: 336992

Subsidiary (Non-US):

Automecanica SA (3)
Str Aurel Vlaicu 41, Sibiu, Medias, Romania (72.5%)
Tel.: (40) 269 803646
Web Site: http://autm.ro
Sales Range: $1-9.9 Million
Emp.: 10
Trailer Mfr
N.A.I.C.S.: 336212

Subsidiary (Domestic):

Rheinmetall MAN Military Vehicles GmbH (2)
Dachauer Str 655, 80995, Munich, 80995, Germany
Tel.: (49) 892885310
Sales Range: $350-399.9 Million
Emp.: 1,300
Military Truck Mfr
N.A.I.C.S.: 336992
Pearto Borko (Gen Mgr)

Subsidiary (Non-US):

Rheinmetall MAN Military Vehicle Systems Ltd. (3)
Level 1 25 Geils Court, Deakin, 2600, ACT, Australia
Tel.: (61) 2 6282 3211
Emp.: 15
Military Truck Mfr
N.A.I.C.S.: 336992
Peter Hardisty (Gen Mgr)

Subsidiary (Non-US):

Rheinmetall Nederland B.V. (2)
Radonstraat 30, Ede, 6718 WS, Netherlands
Tel.: (31) 88 1302 400
Web Site: http://www.rheinmetall.com
Sales Range: $25-49.9 Million
Emp.: 90
Logistics Consulting Servies
N.A.I.C.S.: 541614

Division (Domestic):

Rheinmetall Waffe Munition GmbH (2)
Heinrich Ehrhardt Strasse 2, 29345, Unterluss, Germany

RHEINMETALL AG

Rheinmetall AG—(Continued)
Tel.: (49) 58278002
Web Site: http://www.rheinmetall.com
Weapons & Munitions Mfr
N.A.I.C.S.: 332993

Subsidiary (US):

American Rheinmetall Munition Inc. (3)
125 Woodstream Blvd Ste 105, Stafford, VA 22556
Tel.: (703) 221-9299
Web Site: http://www.americanrheinmetall.com
Cutting Tool Mfr
N.A.I.C.S.: 333515
Brian T. Sullivan (VP-Ops & Engrg)

Joint Venture (Non-US):

Rheinmetall Denel Munition (Pty.) Ltd. (3)
Reeb Road Firgrove, Somerset West, Cape Town, 7130, South Africa **(51%)**
Tel.: (27) 218502911
Sales Range: $200-249.9 Million
Emp.: 700
Ammunition Mfr
N.A.I.C.S.: 332993
Norbert Shculze (Gen Mgr)

Rheinmetall Defence Australia Pty. Ltd. (1)
111 Robert Smith Street, Redbank, Ipswich, 4301, QLD, Australia
Tel.: (61) 734362700
National Security Services
N.A.I.C.S.: 928110
Gary Stewart (Mng Dir)

Rheinmetall Defence Polska sp. z.o.o. (1)
Al Ujazdowskie 51, 00-536, Warsaw, Poland
Tel.: (48) 225847380
National Security Services
N.A.I.C.S.: 928110

Rheinmetall Dienstleistungszentrum Altmark GmbH (1)
Salchauer Chaussee 1, 39638, Gardelegen, Germany
Tel.: (49) 39088 903506
Electronic Components Mfr
N.A.I.C.S.: 334419

Rheinmetall Eastern Markets GmbH (1)
Osterdeich 108, 28205, Bremen, Germany
Tel.: (49) 4214572654
National Security Services
N.A.I.C.S.: 928110

Rheinmetall Electronics GmbH (1)
Bruggeweg 54, 28309, Bremen, Germany
Tel.: (49) 42110800
National Security Services
N.A.I.C.S.: 928110

Rheinmetall Immobilien GmbH (1)
Rheinmetall-Platz 1, 40476, Dusseldorf, 40476, Germany
Tel.: (49) 21147301
Real Estate Investment Services
N.A.I.C.S.: 525990

Rheinmetall Industrietechnik GmbH (1)
Rheinmetall-Allee 1, Dusseldorf, 40476, Nordrhein-Westfalen, Germany
Tel.: (49) 21147301
Industrial Engineering Services
N.A.I.C.S.: 541330

Rheinmetall Insurance Services GmbH (1)
Rheinmetall Platz 1, 40476, Dusseldorf, Germany
Tel.: (49) 2114734020
Web Site: https://www.rh-insuranceservices.com
Industrial Insurance & Personal Insurance Services
N.A.I.C.S.: 524210

Rheinmetall Laingsdale (Pty) Ltd. (1)
28-30 Product St, Maitland, 7404, South Africa

Tel.: (27) 215089400
Precision Mechanical Product Mfr
N.A.I.C.S.: 332721

Rheinmetall MAN Military Vehicles Australia Pty Ltd. (1)
L 15 575 Burke St, Melbourne, 3000, VIC, Australia
Tel.: (61) 262823211
Web Site: http://www.rheinmetall-defence.com
Emp.: 2
Vehicle Mfr
N.A.I.C.S.: 336110
Naomi Mcgillivray (Office Mgr)

Rheinmetall MAN Military Vehicles Canada Ltd. (1)
150 Metcalfe Street, Suite 2204., Ottawa, K2P 1P1, ON, Canada
Tel.: (613) 321-4404
Web Site: http://www.rheinmetall.com
Emp.: 2
Military Vehicles Distr
N.A.I.C.S.: 423860
John Reade (Dir-Ops)

Rheinmetall MAN Military Vehicles Osterreich GesmbH (1)
Brunner Strasse 44-50, 1230, Vienna, Austria
Tel.: (43) 1866200
Motor Vehicle Distr
N.A.I.C.S.: 423110

Rheinmetall MAN Military Vehicles Osterreich Holding GesmbH (1)
Brunner Strasse 44-50, 1230, Vienna, Austria
Tel.: (43) 1866200
Sales Range: $350-399.9 Million
Emp.: 800
Investment Management Service
N.A.I.C.S.: 523999
Herrn Ortner Franz (Mng Dir)

Rheinmetall Maschinenbau GmbH (1)
Rheinmetall-Allee 1, Dusseldorf, 40476, Nordrhein-Westfalen, Germany
Tel.: (49) 58278001
Web Site: http://www.rheinmetall.com
Electronic Components Mfr
N.A.I.C.S.: 334419

Rheinmetall NIOA Munitions Pty. Ltd. (1)
52 Industrial Avenue, Maryborough, 4650, QLD, Australia
Tel.: (61) 743678500
National Security Services
N.A.I.C.S.: 928110
Jeff Crabtree (Project Mgr)

Rheinmetall Nordic AS (1)
Steinklossveien 14, Duken, 3133, Notteroy, Norway **(100%)**
Tel.: (47) 3338 2350
Web Site: http://www.rheinmetall-defence.com
Electro-Optical Instruments Mfr
N.A.I.C.S.: 333310

Subsidiary (Non-US):

Simrad Optronics SAS-Aubagne (2)
792 av de la Fleuride, BP 11061, 13781, Aubagne, France
Tel.: (33) 442180600
Web Site: http://www.simtronics.eu
Sales Range: $25-49.9 Million
Emp.: 30
Fire & Gas Detection Solutions
N.A.I.C.S.: 334511
Salvator La Piana (Gen Mgr)

Subsidiary (Domestic):

Vinghog AS (2)
Lindholmvn 14, Duken, Notteroy, 31332, Norway
Tel.: (47) 33382350
Web Site: http://www.vinghog.com
Sales Range: $25-49.9 Million
Emp.: 160
Weapons Mfrs
N.A.I.C.S.: 332994
Lars Harald Henriksen (Mgr-R&D)

Subsidiary (US):

Vingtech Corp. (2)

15 Morin St, Biddeford, ME 04005
Tel.: (207) 571-5850
Web Site: http://www.vingtech.com
Emp.: 37
Optical Instrument & Lens Mfr
N.A.I.C.S.: 333310
Brad Hittle (CEO)

Rheinmetall Nordic AS (1)
Steinklossveien 14 Duken, 3133, Notteroy, Norway
Tel.: (47) 33382350
National Security Services
N.A.I.C.S.: 928110
Svein Alsterberg (Engr-Software)

Rheinmetall North America Inc. (1)
1731 Industrial Pkwy N, Marinette, WI 54143-3704
Tel.: (715) 732-0181
Automotive Piston Mfr
N.A.I.C.S.: 336310

Rheinmetall Protection Systems GmbH (1)
Putzchens Chaussee 58 a, 53227, Bonn, Germany
Tel.: (49) 22897503
Vehicle Protection Services
N.A.I.C.S.: 561612

Rheinmetall Schweiz AG (1)
Birchstrasse 155, PO Box 6504, 8050, Zurich, Switzerland
Tel.: (41) 58 206 4600
Electric Equipment Mfr
N.A.I.C.S.: 334419

Rheinmetall Simulation Australia Pty. Ltd. (1)
Level 1 25 Geils Court, Deakin West, Deakin, 2600, ACT, Australia
Tel.: (61) 2 6282 3211
Web Site: http://www.rheinmetall-defence.com
Automobile Parts Mfr
N.A.I.C.S.: 336390

Rheinmetall Singapore Pte. Ltd. (1)
12 Tuas Avenue 7, Singapore, 639267, Singapore
Tel.: (65) 64160170
Aviation Marketing & Production Services
N.A.I.C.S.: 488190
Ingo Cammans (CEO)

Rheinmetall Technical Publications GmbH (1)
Flughafenallee 3, 28199, Bremen, Germany
Tel.: (49) 42184102000
Web Site: http://www.rheinmetall-tp.com
Sales Range: $25-49.9 Million
Emp.: 200
Logistics Engineering Services
N.A.I.C.S.: 541330

Rheinmetall Technical Publications Schweiz AG (1)
Birchstrasse 115, 8050, Zurich, Switzerland
Tel.: (41) 443162211
Technical Logistic Services
N.A.I.C.S.: 541614

Rheinmetall Verseidag Ballistic Protection GmbH (1)
Neuer Weg 24, 47803, Krefeld, Germany
Tel.: (49) 215145420
Sales Range: $25-49.9 Million
Emp.: 60
Automotive Ceramic Products Mfr
N.A.I.C.S.: 336390
Onno't Hart (Mgr)

Rheinmetall Verwaltungsgesellschaft mbH (1)
Rheinmetall-Platz 1, Dusseldorf, 40476, Nordrhein-Westfalen, Germany
Tel.: (49) 58278001
Automobile Parts Mfr
N.A.I.C.S.: 336390

Rheinmetall Waffe Munition ARGES GmbH (1)
Kaufing 31, Rustorf, 4690, Schwanenstadt, Austria
Tel.: (43) 7673805100
Web Site: http://www.rheinmetall-defence.com
Sales Range: $25-49.9 Million
Explosives Mfr
N.A.I.C.S.: 325920

INTERNATIONAL PUBLIC

Swiss SIMTEC AG (1)
Frutigenstrasse 4, 3600, Thun, Bern, Switzerland
Tel.: (41) 335330200
Web Site: http://www.swiss-simtec.ch
Sales Range: $25-49.9 Million
Emp.: 12
Prototype Software Development Services & Distr
N.A.I.C.S.: 541511

Werkzeugbau Walldurn GmbH (1)
Karl-Schmidt Strasse, Neckarsulm, 74172, Germany
Tel.: (49) 7132 33 2964
Web Site: http://www.rheinmetall.com
Automotive Tools Mfr
N.A.I.C.S.: 333517
Eugenia Derzapf (Gen Mgr)

RHEINZINK GMBH & CO. KG

Bahnhofstrasse 90, 45711, Datteln, Germany
Tel.: (49) 23636050 De
Web Site: http://www.rheinzink.de
Year Founded: 1966
Sales Range: $125-149.9 Million
Emp.: 750
Sheet Metal Mfr
N.A.I.C.S.: 332322
Ulrich Grillo (Chm & Mng Dir)

Subsidiaries:

Craftmetals Pty. Ltd. (1)
Unit 6 39 Kings Rd, Hornsby, 2077, Australia **(100%)**
Tel.: (61) 294824166
Web Site: http://www.rheinzink.com.au
Sales Range: $25-49.9 Million
Emp.: 10
Zinc Manufacturing
N.A.I.C.S.: 325180

RHEINZINK (Schweiz) AG (1)
Tafernstrabe 18, Baden-Dattwil, 5405, Switzerland **(100%)**
Tel.: (41) 564841414
Web Site: http://www.rheinzink.ch
Sales Range: $25-49.9 Million
Emp.: 7
Zinc Mfr
N.A.I.C.S.: 325180
Heimz Beerkircher (Gen Mgr)

RHEINZINK Austria GmbH (1)
Industriestrasse 23, 3130, Herzogenburg, Austria **(100%)**
Tel.: (43) 2782852470
Web Site: http://www.rheinzink.at
Sales Range: $25-49.9 Million
Emp.: 13
Zinc Manufacturing
N.A.I.C.S.: 325180
Johann Hauser (Pres)

RHEINZINK Belux S.A./N.V. (1)
Chemin de la Vieille Cour 56 B, 1400, Nivelles, Belgium **(100%)**
Tel.: (32) 67556638
Web Site: http://www.rheinzink.be
Sales Range: $25-49.9 Million
Emp.: 5
Zinc Manufacturing
N.A.I.C.S.: 325180

RHEINZINK CR, s.r.o. (1)
Mayaooh 22, 29001, Podebrady, Czech Republic **(100%)**
Tel.: (420) 325615465
Web Site: http://www.rheinzink.cz
Sales Range: $25-49.9 Million
Emp.: 7
Zinc Manufacturing
N.A.I.C.S.: 325180
Marketa Mirkova (Gen Mgr)

RHEINZINK Canada Ltd (1)
4595 Tillicum Street, Burnaby, V5J 3J9, BC, Canada
Tel.: (604) 291-8171
Web Site: http://www.rheinzink.de
Zinc Manufacturing
N.A.I.C.S.: 325180

RHEINZINK Danmark A/S (1)
Sintrupvej 50, 8220, Brabrand, Denmark **(100%)**

AND PRIVATE COMPANIES — RHI MAGNESITA N.V.

Tel.: (45) 87451545
Web Site: http://www.rheinzink.dk
Sales Range: $25-49.9 Million
Emp.: 11
Zinc Mfr
N.A.I.C.S.: 325180
Alexander Laning *(Mgr)*

RHEINZINK France S.A. (1)
La Plassotte B P 5, F 42590, Neulise, France **(100%)**
Tel.: (33) 477664290
Web Site: http://www.rheinzink.fr
Sales Range: $25-49.9 Million
Emp.: 100
Zinc Mfr
N.A.I.C.S.: 325180

RHEINZINK Hungaria Kft. (1)
Bogancs U 1 3, Budapest, 1151, Hungary **(100%)**
Tel.: (36) 13050022
Web Site: http://www.rheinzink.hu
Sales Range: $25-49.9 Million
Emp.: 3
Zinc Mfr
N.A.I.C.S.: 325180
Peter Birghoffer *(Mng Dir)*

RHEINZINK Zinc Manufacturing (Shanghai) Co., Ltd. (1)
T3 4A No 128 Central Ave Central Shanghai, Jinqiao Export Zone, 201201, Shanghai, China **(100%)**
Tel.: (86) 158585881
Web Site: http://www.rheinzink.cn
Zinc Mfr
N.A.I.C.S.: 325180

RHEON AUTOMATIC MACHINERY CO., LTD.
2-3 Nozawa-machi, Utsunomiya, 320-0071, Japan
Tel.: (81) 286651111
Web Site: https://www.rheon.com
Year Founded: 1963
6272—(TKS)
Rev.: $249,216,830
Assets: $294,634,140
Liabilities: $57,440,900
Net Worth: $237,193,240
Earnings: $24,291,750
Emp.: 753
Fiscal Year-end: 03/31/24
Food Processing Machine Mfr & Whslr
N.A.I.C.S.: 333241
Yasunori Tashiro *(Pres)*

Subsidiaries:

Orange Bakery, Inc. (1)
17751 Cowan Ave, Irvine, CA 92614
Tel.: (949) 863-1377
Web Site: https://orangebakery.com
Bakery Products Mfr
N.A.I.C.S.: 311812

Rheon Automatic Machinery Asia Pacific Co., Ltd. (1)
5F No 118 Xinhu 1st Rd, Neihu District, Taipei, 00114, Taiwan
Tel.: (886) 227923525
Food Processing Machinery Distr
N.A.I.C.S.: 423830

Rheon Automatic Machinery Co., Ltd. - Kami-Kawachi Plant (1)
715-1 Nakazato-cho, Utsunomiya, 321-0414, Japan
Tel.: (81) 286743791
Food Processing Machinery Mfr
N.A.I.C.S.: 333241

Rheon Automatic Machinery GmbH (1)
Tiefenbroicher Weg 30, 40472, Dusseldorf, Germany
Tel.: (49) 211 471950
Web Site: http://www.rheon-europe.com
Food Processing Machinery Distr
N.A.I.C.S.: 423830

Rheon U.S.A. Inc. (1)
2 Doppler, Irvine, CA 92618
Tel.: (949) 768-1900
Web Site: http://www.rheon.com

Emp.: 18
Food Processing Machinery Distr
N.A.I.C.S.: 423830

RHI MAGNESITA N.V.
Kranichberggasse 6, A-1120, Vienna, Austria
Tel.: (43) 502136200   AT
Web Site: https://www.rhimagnesita.com
Year Founded: 1834
RHIM—(LSE)
Rev.: $3,854,737,751
Assets: $5,233,757,824
Liabilities: $3,762,249,083
Net Worth: $1,471,508,742
Earnings: $184,869,415
Emp.: 15,659
Fiscal Year-end: 12/31/23
Refractory Products Mfr
N.A.I.C.S.: 332999
Stefan Borgas *(CEO)*

Subsidiaries:

Betriebs- und Baugesellschaft mbH (1)
Hagenauer Str 53-55a, Wiesbaden, 65203, Germany
Tel.: (49) 61173350
Construction Engineering Services
N.A.I.C.S.: 541330

Didier-Werke AG (1)
Hagenauer Strasse 53-55a, 65203, Wiesbaden, 65203, Germany **(100%)**
Tel.: (49) 61173350
Web Site: http://www.rhi.at
Sales Range: $25-49.9 Million
Emp.: 100
N.A.I.C.S.: 541330

Subsidiary (Non-US):

Didier Belgium N.V. (2)
Varenbergstraat 2, 9940, Evergem, Belgium
Tel.: (32) 9 253 11 16
Emp.: 5
Glass & Construction Material Whslr
N.A.I.C.S.: 423390
Hendrik De Smet *(Pres)*

Dolomite Franchi S.p.A. (1)
Via Zanardelli 13, Marone, 25054, Brescia, Italy
Tel.: (39) 03098851
Web Site: http://www.dolomitefranchi.it
Construction Material Mining Services
N.A.I.C.S.: 212321

Dutch MAS B.V. (1)
Velperweg 81, Arnhem, 6824 HH, Netherlands
Tel.: (31) 263635763
Refractory Materials Distr
N.A.I.C.S.: 423320

FC Technik AG (1)
St Gallerstrasse 340, Winterthur, 8409, Switzerland
Tel.: (41) 52 238 01 75
Web Site: http://www.fc-technik.ch
Industrial Machinery Mfr
N.A.I.C.S.: 333248
Christoph Vetterli *(Mng Dir)*

Full Line Supply Africa (Pty) Limited (1)
13 Commas Crescent East, Johannesburg, 2148, South Africa
Tel.: (27) 114447500
Installing Building Equipment & Maintenance Services
N.A.I.C.S.: 238290

Horn & Co Polska Sp. z o.o. (1)
Ul Stefana Batorego 48, 41-506, Chorzow, Poland
Tel.: (48) 323461485
Refractory Minerals Mining Services
N.A.I.C.S.: 212323

Intermetal Engineers Private Limited (1)
377 Gundecha Industrial Complex Akurli Road, Kandivali East, Mumbai, 4001 01, Maharashtra, India
Tel.: (91) 222 846 3905

Web Site: https://intermetal.co.in
Metallurgical Equipment Mfr
N.A.I.C.S.: 332999

Liaoning RHI Jinding Magnesia Co., Ltd. (1)
Shengshui Village Etdz Nanlou, Yingkou, 115103, China
Tel.: (86) 4175286081
Clay Refractory Mfr
N.A.I.C.S.: 327120

Lokalbahn Mixnitz-St. Erhard AG (1)
Tel.: (43) 6765313725
Construction Materials Distr
N.A.I.C.S.: 423320

MARVO Feuerungs- und Industriebau GmbH (1)
Bodelschwinghstrasse 11-15, 50170, Kerpen, Germany
Tel.: (49) 2273 98 57 0
Web Site: http://www.marvo.de
Sales Range: $25-49.9 Million
Emp.: 90
Ceramic Kilns & Furnace Mfr
N.A.I.C.S.: 333994

Magnesit Anonim Sirketi (1)
PK 66 GAR PTT, Dutluca, 26301, Eskisehir, Turkiye
Tel.: (90) 2222110100
Mining Services
N.A.I.C.S.: 213115

Magnesit Anonim Sirketi (MAS) (1)
PC 66 Gar Ptt, 26301, Eskisehir, Turkiye
Tel.: (90) 2222202083
Sales Range: $25-49.9 Million
Emp.: 110
N.A.I.C.S.: 541330

Magnesita Refratarios S.A. (1)
Louis Ensch Square 240 Cidade Industrial, CEP 32210-902, Contagem, MG, Brazil
Tel.: (55) 3133681971
Web Site: http://ri.magnesita.com
Rev.: $1,110,618,039
Assets: $1,913,919,319
Liabilities: $1,329,747,963
Net Worth: $584,171,356
Earnings: $55,249,197
Fiscal Year-end: 12/31/2017
Refractory Materials Mining & Manufacturing Services
N.A.I.C.S.: 212323
Eduardo Guardiano Leme Gotilla *(Chm)*

Subsidiary (Non-US):

Magnesita Refractories GmbH (2)
Itterpark 1, 40724, Hilden, Germany
Tel.: (49) 21038950
Web Site: http://www.magnesita.com.br
Refractory Products Mfr
N.A.I.C.S.: 327120

Magnifin Magnesiaprodukte GmbH & Co KG (1)
Magnesitstr 40, 8614, Breitenau, Austria **(50%)**
Tel.: (43) 38662002
Web Site: http://www.magnifin.com
Sales Range: $25-49.9 Million
Emp.: 54
Magnesium Oxide, Hydroxide Powders & Special Sodium Silicates
N.A.I.C.S.: 325180
Christian Kienesberger *(Mng Dir-Breitenau)*

Minerals and Metals Recovering - Mireco Aktiebolag (1)
Sorbomsbacke 1, 73792, Fagersta, Sweden
Tel.: (46) 22317190
Web Site: https://mireco.se
Refractory Material Mfr
N.A.I.C.S.: 327120

Premier Periclase Limited (1)
Boyne Road, Drogheda, Co Louth, Ireland **(100%)**
Tel.: (353) 419870700
Web Site: http://www.premierpericlase.ie
Sales Range: $50-74.9 Million
Emp.: 110
Manufactures & Supplies Seawater Magnesia Products
N.A.I.C.S.: 325199

Produccion RHI Mexico, S. de R.L. de C.V. (1)

Fernando Montes De Oca No 95, Tlalnepantla, 54030, Mexico
Tel.: (52) 5553332600
Sales Range: $25-49.9 Million
Emp.: 100
Nonclay Refractory Mfr
N.A.I.C.S.: 327120

RHI Canada Inc. (1)
491 Gladwish Dr, Sarnia, N7T 7H3, ON, Canada
Tel.: (519) 337-3241
Construction Material Mfr & Distr
N.A.I.C.S.: 327331
Phil Poulin *(Treas, Sec & Dir-Fin)*

RHI Chile S.A. (1) **(100%)**
Tel.: (56) 23854200
Web Site: http://www.rhi.ag
Sales Range: $25-49.9 Million
Emp.: 22
N.A.I.C.S.: 541330

RHI Clasil Limited (1)
Plot No 195 Flat No 9 Srinilayam Apartments Kavuri Hills, Madhapur, Hyderabad, 500 081, India
Tel.: (91) 9949994341
Web Site: http://www.clasil.com
Refractory Material Mfr
N.A.I.C.S.: 327120

RHI Dinaris GmbH (1)
Hagenauer Str 53-55a, PO Box 2025, Wiesbaden, 65203, Germany
Tel.: (49) 611236611
Web Site: http://www.rhi-ag.com
Sales Range: $25-49.9 Million
Emp.: 22
Construction Materials Distr
N.A.I.C.S.: 423820
Uwe Pusch *(Mng Dir)*

RHI GLAS GmbH (1)
Hagenauer Str 53-55a, PO Box 2025, 65010, Wiesbaden, Germany
Tel.: (49) 611 7335 0
Construction Glass Materials Mfr & Distr
N.A.I.C.S.: 327215

RHI MARVO S.R.L. (1)
St Paris No 6, Prahova, Ploiesti, 100037, Romania
Tel.: (40) 344080220
Refractory Products Mfr
N.A.I.C.S.: 327120

RHI Magnesita India Limited (1)
301 Tower B Emaar Digital Greens Golf Course Road Extension Sector 61, Gurgaon, 122102, Haryana, India **(69.6%)**
Tel.: (91) 1244062930
Web Site: https://www.rhimagnesitaindia.com
Rev.: $454,668,785
Assets: $613,352,898
Liabilities: $152,250,974
Net Worth: $461,101,924
Earnings: ($12,003,117)
Emp.: 1,595
Fiscal Year-end: 03/31/2024
Refractory Material Mfr & Distr
N.A.I.C.S.: 327120
Sanjay Kumar *(Compliance Officer & Sec)*

RHI Magnesita India Refractories Limited (1)
301 Tower B Emaar Digital Greens Golf Course Road Extension Sector 61, Gurgaon, 122102, Haryana, India
Tel.: (91) 1244062930
Web Site: https://www.rhimagnesitaindia.com
Steel Products Mfr
N.A.I.C.S.: 331110

RHI Magnesita Services Europe GmbH (1)
Bodelschwinghstrasse 11-15, 50170, Kerpen, Germany
Tel.: (49) 22 739 8570
Web Site: https://www.marvo.de
Engineeering Services
N.A.I.C.S.: 541330

RHI Magnesita Turkey Refrakter Ticaret Anonim Sirketi (1)
Dutluca Mahallesi Dutluca Sokak 328, Inonu, 26670, Eskisehir, Turkiye

RHI MAGNESITA N.V.

RHI Magnesita N.V.—(Continued)
Tel.: (90) 2222110100
Refractory Material Mfr
N.A.I.C.S.: 327120

RHI Normag AS (1)
Heroya Industripark, Porsgrunn, 3936, Norway
Tel.: (47) 48099500
Sales Range: $25-49.9 Million
Emp.: 60
Chemical Construction Material Mfr
N.A.I.C.S.: 325998

RHI Refractories
Millerstrasse 10, Radenthein, 9545, Carinthia, Austria (100%)
Tel.: (43) 502134272
Web Site: http://www.rhi-at.com
Sales Range: $150-199.9 Million
Emp.: 370
Construction Products; Insulating Products; Building Board
N.A.I.C.S.: 423390
Heimo Wagner *(Plant Mgr)*

RHI Refractories (Site Services) Ltd. (1)
Unit 2 Northern Road Newark Industrial Estate, Newark, NG24 2EU, Nottinghamshire, United Kingdom
Tel.: (44) 1636704494
Web Site: http://www.rhi-ag.com
Sales Range: $25-49.9 Million
Emp.: 2
Refractory Materials Distr
N.A.I.C.S.: 327110

RHI Refractories Africa (Pty.) Ltd. (1)
17 Commerce Crescent E, Eastgate Extn 13, Sandton, 2144, South Africa (100%)
Tel.: (27) 114447500
Web Site: http://www.rhi.co.za
Sales Range: $75-99.9 Million
Emp.: 280
N.A.I.C.S.: 541330

RHI Refractories Andino C.A. (1)
Zona Industrial Matanzas Entre Transversal C y E, Estado Bolivar UD 321 Centro Industrial y Comercial Rio Arauca Galpon, N4 Gal 4, Puerto Ordaz, 8050, Venezuela (100%)
Tel.: (58) 2869941477
Web Site: http://www.rhi-ag.com
Refractory Products Mfr
N.A.I.C.S.: 212323

RHI Refractories Asia Ltd. (1)
Unit 709-74 New East ocean centre 9 Science Museum Rd, Yu Fung Commercial Centre, Hong Kong, China (Hong Kong)
Tel.: (852) 28276482
Web Site: http://www.rhi-ag.com
Sales Range: $75-99.9 Million
Emp.: 10
Production, Sales & Installation of High-Grade Ceramic Refractory Products
N.A.I.C.S.: 212323
Karen Ng *(Mgr-Ops)*

RHI Refractories Asia Pacific Pte Ltd (1)
(100%)
Tel.: (65) 67356862
Web Site: http://www.rhi.ag.com
Sales Range: $25-49.9 Million
Emp.: 25
N.A.I.C.S.: 541330

RHI Refractories Espana S.A. (1)
Avenida Conde Santa Barbara 12, PO Box 1325, Lugones, 33420, Spain (100%)
Tel.: (34) 985101300
Web Site: http://www.rhi.com
Sales Range: $25-49.9 Million
Emp.: 120
N.A.I.C.S.: 541330
Jochen Stuck *(Gen Mgr)*

RHI Refractories France S.A. (1)
38 Route de Dourdan, 91650, Breuillet, France
Tel.: (33) 169946527
Nonclay Refractory Mfr
N.A.I.C.S.: 327120

RHI Refractories Italiana S.r.l. (1)
Via Corsica 14, I 25125, Brescia, Italy (100%)
Tel.: (39) 0302442311
Web Site: http://www.rhi-ag.com
Provider of Engineering Services
N.A.I.C.S.: 541330

RHI Refractories Nord AB (1)
(100%)
Tel.: (46) 851482240
Web Site: https://www.rhi-ag.com
Sales Range: $50-74.9 Million
Emp.: 3
Glass Sales
N.A.I.C.S.: 423990

RHI Refractories Raw Material GmbH (1)
Wienerbergstrasse 9, Vienna, 1100, Austria
Tel.: (43) 1502130
Construction Raw Material Distr
N.A.I.C.S.: 423390

RHI Refractories Site Services GmbH (1)
Tel.: (49) 61173350
Construction Materials Distr
N.A.I.C.S.: 423390

RHI Refractories UK Limited (1)
Stanford St, PO Box 3, Clydebank, G81 1RW, United Kingdom (100%)
Tel.: (44) 419521990
Web Site: http://www.rhi-ag.com
Sales Range: $25-49.9 Million
Emp.: 200
N.A.I.C.S.: 541330

RHI Trading (Dalian) Co., Ltd. (1)
A No 61 Tieshan Middle Rd Economic Technology Development Zone, Dalian, 116600, China
Tel.: (86) 41187337788
Refractory Construction Material Whslr
N.A.I.C.S.: 423390

RHI US Ltd. (1)
Tel.: (513) 527-6160
Web Site: https://interstop-usa.com
Sales Range: $50-74.9 Million
Emp.: 240
Ceramic Refractory Materials Mfr
N.A.I.C.S.: 327120

Subsidiary (Domestic):

RHI Monofrax, Ltd. (2)
1870 New York Ave, Falconer, NY 14733-1797
Tel.: (716) 483-7200
Web Site: http://www.monofrax.com
Emp.: 200
Fused Cast Glass Refractory Mfr
N.A.I.C.S.: 327212
Daryl Clendenen *(Gen Mgr)*

RHI Refractories Holding Company (2)
1105 N Market St Ste 1300, Wilmington, DE 19801-1241
Tel.: (302) 655-6497
Investment Management Service
N.A.I.C.S.: 523999

Division (Domestic):

Zircoa (2)
31501 Solon Rd, Solon, OH 44139-3526
Tel.: (440) 248-0500
Web Site: http://www.zircoa.com
Sales Range: $125-149.9 Million
Emp.: 300
Mix Cermamic
N.A.I.C.S.: 331410

RHI-Refmex, S.A. de C.V. (1)
Av Circunvalacion Washington No 61 Sector Reforma, 44460, Guadalajara, Jalisco, Mexico
Tel.: (52) 3336192592
Sales Range: $25-49.9 Million
Emp.: 40
Construction Materials Distr
N.A.I.C.S.: 423320

Radex Vertriebsgesellschaft mbH (1)
Tel.: (43) 502130
Nonclay Refractory Mfr
N.A.I.C.S.: 327120

Refel S.p.A. (1)
via Pescopagano 12 Z I P R, 33078, San Vito al Tagliamento, PN, Italy (100%)
Tel.: (39) 0434849111
Web Site: https://refel.com
Emp.: 150
Mfr of Refractory Products for Glass Industry
N.A.I.C.S.: 333248
Marco Mayan *(Plant Mgr)*

Refractory Intellectual Property GmbH & Co KG (1)
Wienerbergstrasse Str 9, Vienna, 1100, Austria
Tel.: (43) 502130
Sales Range: $125-149.9 Million
Emp.: 40
Construction Material Mfr & Distr
N.A.I.C.S.: 333120

SAPREF AG (1)
Picasso platz 4, 4053, Basel, Switzerland
Tel.: (41) 612728477
Web Site: http://www.rhi-ag.com
Sales Range: $50-74.9 Million
Emp.: 6
Construction Materials Whslr
N.A.I.C.S.: 423390
Andreas Bier *(Gen Mgr)*

Seven Lakeway Refractories LLC (1)
730 River Rd, Huron, OH 44839
Tel.: (419) 433-3030
Refractory Material Mfr
N.A.I.C.S.: 327120

Seven Refractories (UK) Ltd. (1)
Moor Park House Bawtry Rd, Rotherham, S66 2BL, United Kingdom
Tel.: (44) 7799660215
Refractory Material Mfr
N.A.I.C.S.: 327120

Seven Refractories Deutschland GmbH (1)
Becherstrasse 20, 40476, Dusseldorf, Germany
Tel.: (49) 21154477025
Refractory Material Mfr
N.A.I.C.S.: 327120

Seven Refractories S.R.L. (1)
Via Carlo Mussa 832, 15073, Castellazzo Bormida, AL, Italy
Tel.: (39) 03404820431
Refractory Material Mfr
N.A.I.C.S.: 327120

Seven Refractories d.o.o. (1)
Poslovna cona Risnik 40, 6215, Divaca, Slovenia
Tel.: (386) 57395760
Refractory Material Mfr
N.A.I.C.S.: 327120

Sormas Sogut Refrakter Malzemeleri Anonim Sirketi (1)
Bozouyuk State Highway 3rd km Sogut, Bilecik, Turkiye
Tel.: (90) 2283614100
Web Site: https://www.sormas.com.tr
Refractory Material Mfr
N.A.I.C.S.: 327120

Stopinc AG (1)
Bosch 83a, PO Box 745, 6331, Hunenberg, Switzerland
Tel.: (41) 41 785 75 00
Web Site: http://www.stopinc.ch
Emp.: 48
Engineeering Services
N.A.I.C.S.: 541330

VERA FE (1)
15 Korolenko str office 1, 49076, Dnepropetrovsk, Ukraine
Tel.: (380) 56 374 60 77
Web Site: http://www.rhi-ag.com
Refractory Goods Distr
N.A.I.C.S.: 423390

Vedag GmbH (1)
Geisfelder Strasse 85-91, 96050, Bamberg, Germany (100%)
Tel.: (49) 95178010
Web Site: http://www.vedag.de
Flat Roofing Membranes & Construction Products
N.A.I.C.S.: 238160

INTERNATIONAL PUBLIC

Veitsch-Radex Didier Refractaires S.A. (1)
38 Rte De Dourdan, F 91650, Breuillet, France (100%)
Tel.: (33) 169946327
Web Site: http://www.vrd-europe.com
Sales Range: $25-49.9 Million
Emp.: 20
N.A.I.C.S.: 541330

Veitsch-Radex GmbH & Co OG (1)
Wienerbergstrasse 9, Vienna, 1100, Austria
Tel.: (43) 502130
Web Site: http://www.rhi-ag.com
Fire Resistant Products Mfr
N.A.I.C.S.: 339999

Zimmermann & Jansen GmbH (1)
Bahnstr 52, Duren, 52355, Germany
Tel.: (49) 24216910
Refractory Material Mfr
N.A.I.C.S.: 327120

RHINO EXPLORATION INC.
200 551 Howe Street, Vancouver, V2C 2C2, BC, Canada
Tel.: (604) 683-8610 BC
Year Founded: 2010
Metal Mining
N.A.I.C.S.: 212290
Jerry A. Minni *(CFO & Sec)*

RHINOMED LIMITED
Level 1 132 Gwynne St, Cremorne, 3121, VIC, Australia
Tel.: (61) 3 8416 0900
Web Site: http://www.rhinomed.global
RNO—(ASX)
Rev.: $3,559,011
Assets: $5,016,736
Liabilities: $1,366,735
Net Worth: $3,650,001
Earnings: ($6,619,059)
Emp.: 3
Fiscal Year-end: 06/30/21
Medical Technology Licensing Services
N.A.I.C.S.: 339113
Michael Johnson *(CEO & Mng Dir)*

RHODES FOOD GROUP (PTY) LTD.
Pniel Road Groot Drakenstein, PO Box 3040, Western Cape, Cape Town, 7680, Western Cape, South Africa
Tel.: (27) 21 870 4000 ZA
Web Site: http://www.rfg.com
Year Founded: 1896
Sales Range: $200-249.9 Million
Canned Fruits & Vegetables, Fresh & Frozen Baked Goods, Dairy Products & Prepared Foods Mfr & Distr
N.A.I.C.S.: 311999
Bruce Henderson *(CEO)*

RHOM BHO PROPERTY PCL
444 - 444/1 Pracha Uthit Road, Huaykwang Huaykwang District, Bangkok, 10310, Thailand
Tel.: (66) 21036444
Web Site: https://www.rhombho.co.th
Year Founded: 2007
TITLE—(THA)
Rev.: $12,773,358
Assets: $101,380,867
Liabilities: $76,937,760
Net Worth: $24,443,107
Earnings: $648,277
Emp.: 100
Fiscal Year-end: 12/31/23
Real Estate Investment Services
N.A.I.C.S.: 531390
Dendanai Hutajuta *(CEO)*

RHOMBERG SERSA RAIL HOLDING GMBH
Mariahilfstrasse 29, 6900, Bregenz, Austria
Tel.: (43) 5574 403 0 AT

Web Site: http://www.rhomberg-sersa.com
Year Founded: 2012
Sales Range: $450-499.9 Million
Emp.: 1,660
Holding Company; Railway Engineering Services
N.A.I.C.S.: 551112
Hubert Rhomberg *(CEO)*

Subsidiaries:

Rhomberg Bahntechnik GmbH (1)
Mariahilfstrasse 29, 6900, Bregenz, Austria
Tel.: (43) 5574 403 0
Web Site: http://www.rhombergrail.com
Railway Engineering Services
N.A.I.C.S.: 541330
Gerfried Thur *(Member-Mgmt Bd)*

Rhomberg Fahrleitungsbau GmbH (1)
IZ-No Sud StraSSe 3 Objekt M1/II, 2351, Wiener Neudorf, Austria
Tel.: (43) 2236904000
Rail Transport Support Services
N.A.I.C.S.: 488210

Rhomberg Rail Australia Pty Ltd. (1)
Y1 / 391 Park Road Regents Park, PO Box 603, Sydney, 2143, NSW, Australia
Tel.: (61) 296446044
Web Site: http://www.rhombergrail.com.au
Railway Track Construction Services
N.A.I.C.S.: 237990
Michael Match *(Gen Mgr-Comml & Sys)*

Rhomberg Rail Consult GmbH (1)
Engelbert Weiss Weg 2 Stiege B Ebene 04, 5020, Salzburg, Austria
Tel.: (43) 6624210060
Rail Transport Support Services
N.A.I.C.S.: 488210

Rhomberg Sersa UK Limited (1)
Unit 2 Sarah Court Yorkshire Way, Doncaster, DN3 3FD, United Kingdom
Tel.: (44) 3003030230
Rail Transport Support Services
N.A.I.C.S.: 488210

SWT Sersa Welding Team GmbH (1)
Gross-Berliner Damm 88, 12487, Berlin, Germany
Tel.: (49) 3056546662
Rail Transport Support Services
N.A.I.C.S.: 488210

Sersa B.V. (1)
Palmpolstraat 94, 1327 CJ, Almere, Netherlands
Tel.: (31) 365353402
Rail Transport Support Services
N.A.I.C.S.: 488210

Sersa GmbH (1)
Bremer Strasse 65, 01067, Dresden, Germany
Tel.: (49) 3512606560
Web Site: http://www.sersa.de
Rail Transport Support Services
N.A.I.C.S.: 488210

Sersa Group AG (1)
Wurzgrabenstrasse 5, 8048, Zurich, Switzerland
Tel.: (41) 43 322 2300
Web Site: http://www.sersa-group.com
Emp.: 1,000
Railway Engineering Services
N.A.I.C.S.: 541330
Rudolf Krauer *(CEO)*

Sersa Technik AG (1)
Nordstrasse 1, 5612, Villmergen, Switzerland
Tel.: (41) 433222323
Rail Transport Support Services
N.A.I.C.S.: 488210

RHONE ALPES CREATION SA
10 rue du Chateau d Eau, Champagne-au-Mont-d'Or, France
Tel.: (33) 4 72 52 39 39
Web Site: http://www.r-a-c.fr
Investment Services
N.A.I.C.S.: 523999

Sebastien Touvron *(Pres)*

RHONE MA HOLDINGS BERHAD
Lot 18A & 18B Jalan 241 Seksyen 51A, 46100, Petaling Jaya, Selangor, Malaysia
Tel.: (60) 378737355   MY
Web Site: https://www.rhonema.com
Year Founded: 2000
5278—(KLS)
Rev.: $44,173,818
Assets: $50,193,871
Liabilities: $12,825,131
Net Worth: $37,368,740
Earnings: $2,848,790
Emp.: 2,025
Fiscal Year-end: 12/31/23
Investment Holding Company
N.A.I.C.S.: 551114
Ban Keong Lim *(Mng Dir)*

Subsidiaries:

APSN Lifescience Sdn. Bhd. (1)
Lot 18A and 18B Jalan 241 Seksyen 51A, 46100, Petaling Jaya, Selangor, Malaysia
Tel.: (60) 378737355
Web Site: https://www.apsn.com.my
Nutritional Feed Ingredient Mfr
N.A.I.C.S.: 311119

Asia-Pacific Special Nutrients Sdn. Bhd. (1)
Lot 18A and 18B Jalan 241 Seksyen 51A, 46100, Petaling Jaya, Selangor, Malaysia
Tel.: (60) 378737355
Web Site: http://www.apsn.com
Nutritional Feed Ingredient Mfr
N.A.I.C.S.: 311119

Nor Livestock Farm Sdn. Bhd. (1)
22 Jalan PJS 5/26 Taman Desaria, 46150, Petaling Jaya, Selangor, Malaysia
Tel.: (60) 377824288
Web Site: https://www.norlivestockfarm.com
Livestock Farming Distr
N.A.I.C.S.: 424520

One Lazuli Sdn. Bhd. (1)
No 22 Jalan PJS 5/26 Taman Desaria, 46150, Petaling Jaya, Selangor, Malaysia
Tel.: (60) 377828688
Web Site: https://www.onelazuli.com
Pharmaceutical & Veterinary Product Mfr
N.A.I.C.S.: 311119

Vet Food Agro Diagnostics (M) Sdn. Bhd. (1)
Lot 18B Jalan 241 Seksyen 51A, 46100, Petaling Jaya, Selangor, Malaysia
Tel.: (60) 378736405
Web Site: http://www.vfad.com
Diagnostic Laboratory Services
N.A.I.C.S.: 621511

RHONG KHEN INTERNATIONAL BERHAD
Lot 3356 Batu 7 3/4 Jalan Kapar, 42200, Kapar, Selangor Darul Ehsan, Malaysia
Tel.: (60) 332915401
Web Site: https://www.rkibhd.com
Year Founded: 1988
RKI—(KLS)
Rev.: $137,444,021
Assets: $172,003,598
Liabilities: $26,878,942
Net Worth: $145,124,656
Earnings: $4,625,397
Emp.: 4,185
Fiscal Year-end: 06/30/23
Investment Holding Company
N.A.I.C.S.: 551112
Jui-Fen Chen Lin *(Deputy Chm)*

Subsidiaries:

Brooke Asia Ltd (1)
Level 18 Tower B Hock Lee Centre Jalan Datuk Abang Abdul Rahim, Kuching, 93350, Malaysia
Tel.: (60) 82 481028

Sales Range: $100-124.9 Million
Indoor Wooden Furniture Mfr & Sales
N.A.I.C.S.: 337122
Siew Liong Yek *(Chm)*

Latitude Tree Furniture Sdn Bhd (1)
Lot 3356 Batu 7 3/4 Jalan Kapar, 42200, Kapar, Selangor, Malaysia
Tel.: (60) 332915401
Web Site: https://www.latitude-tree.com
Sales Range: $550-599.9 Million
Emp.: 2,500
Household Furniture Mfr
N.A.I.C.S.: 321999

Latitude Tree Vietnam JSC (1)
29 DT743 Street Song Than II Industrial Zone, Di An, Binh Duong, Vietnam
Tel.: (84) 2743731386
Web Site: https://www.latitudetree.com.vn
Household Wooden Furniture Mfr & Sales
N.A.I.C.S.: 321999

Rhong Khen Industries Sdn. Bhd. (1)
Lot 518 and 519 Jalan Jati Kiri Batu 8 Off Jalan Kapar, 42200, Kapar, Selangor, Malaysia
Tel.: (60) 332503788
Web Site: https://www.rhongkhen.com
Wood Product Mfr & Distr
N.A.I.C.S.: 321999

RHT HEALTH TRUST
302 Orchard Road No 07-03 Tong Building, Singapore, 238862, Singapore
Tel.: (65) 65213828
Web Site: http://www.rhealthtrust.com
RF1U—(SES)
Assets: $12,420,125
Liabilities: $1,169,346
Net Worth: $11,250,780
Earnings: ($366,301)
Fiscal Year-end: 03/31/23
Real Estate Investment Trust Services
N.A.I.C.S.: 531120
Tan Kang Fun *(CEO & CFO)*

RHT HOLDING LTD.
Hugnin Road, Port Louis, Mauritius
Tel.: (230) 4641221
Web Site: https://www.rht.mu
Year Founded: 1954
RHT—(MAU)
Rev.: $5,766,938
Assets: $27,437,606
Liabilities: $12,050,094
Net Worth: $15,387,512
Earnings: ($180,193)
Emp.: 485
Fiscal Year-end: 06/30/23
Holding Company
N.A.I.C.S.: 551112
Sidharth Sharma *(Grp CEO)*

Subsidiaries:

ICL Zambia Ltd. (1)
Second Floor Shreeji House 2 Plot 1209 Addis Ababa Drive, Lusaka, Zambia
Tel.: (260) 978037363
Web Site: http://www.icl.co.zm
Logistic Services
N.A.I.C.S.: 541614

Island Communications Ltd. (1)
13C Volcy de la Faye Street, Rose Hill, Beau Bassin, Mauritius
Tel.: (230) 4672323
Web Site: https://www.icl.mu
Logistic Services
N.A.I.C.S.: 541614

RHT HOLDINGS PTE. LTD.
9 Raffles Place #29-01 Republic Plaza Tower 1, Singapore, 048619, Singapore
Tel.: (65) 63816888
Web Site: http://www.rhtcap.com
Investment Advice
N.A.I.C.S.: 523940

Khong Choun Mun *(CEO)*

Subsidiaries:

CWG International Ltd. (1)
6 Eu Tong Sen Street 04-08 The Central Singapore, Singapore, 059817, Singapore
Tel.: (65) 62240669
Web Site: http://www.cwginternational.com
Sales Range: $650-699.9 Million
Trust Management Services
N.A.I.C.S.: 523940
Jianrong Qian *(Co-Founder, Chm & CEO)*

Subsidiary (Non-US):
CWG Development Pty. Ltd. (2)
1702 Level 17 25 Bligh StreetSydney, Sydney, 2000, NSW, Australia
Tel.: (61) 2 8076 5156
Investment Holding Services
N.A.I.C.S.: 551112
Ying Rao *(CEO)*

RHT Capital Pte.Ltd. (1)
9 Raffles Place #29-01, Republic Plaza Tower 1, Singapore, 048619, Singapore
Tel.: (65) 63816888
Web Site: http://www.rhtcap.com
Investment Advice
N.A.I.C.S.: 327910
Mah How Soon *(Mng Dir)*

RHYOLITE RESOURCES LTD.
595 Burrard Street Suite 1703 Three Bentall Centre, Vancouver, V7X 1J1, BC, Canada
Tel.: (604) 689-1428
Web Site: https://www.rhyoliteresources.com
Year Founded: 2006
RYE—(TSXV)
Rev.: $214,547
Assets: $4,905,987
Liabilities: $56,515
Net Worth: $4,849,472
Earnings: ($271,859)
Fiscal Year-end: 12/31/23
Mineral Exploration Services
N.A.I.C.S.: 213114
Richard A. Graham *(Pres & CEO)*

RHYTHM BIOSCIENCES LTD.
477 Collins Street, Melbourne, 3000, VIC, Australia
Tel.: (61) 382562880
Web Site: https://www.rhythmbio.com
RHY—(ASX)
Rev.: $1,163,479
Assets: $1,014,095
Liabilities: $435,057
Net Worth: $579,037
Earnings: ($4,578,500)
Fiscal Year-end: 06/30/24
Research & Development in Biotechnology (except Nanobiotechnology)
N.A.I.C.S.: 541714
Otto Buttula *(Chm)*

RHYTHM CO., LTD.
299-12 Kitabukurocho 1-chome, Omiya-ku, Saitama, 330-9551, Japan
Tel.: (81) 486437211   JP
Web Site: https://www.rhythm.co.jp
Year Founded: 1950
7769—(TKS)
Rev.: $215,499,220
Assets: $288,017,530
Liabilities: $82,149,080
Net Worth: $205,868,450
Earnings: $3,152,970
Emp.: 2,486
Fiscal Year-end: 03/31/24
Clocks, Music Boxes & Electronic Parts Mfr
N.A.I.C.S.: 334519
Takeo Yumoto *(Pres)*

Subsidiaries:

I Next GE Inc. (1)
2-24-4 Nishigotanda West Hill 6F,

RHYTHM CO., LTD.

Rhythm Co., Ltd.—(Continued)
Shinagawa-ku, Tokyo, 141-0031, Japan
Tel.: (81) 354964317
Web Site: http://www.inge.co.jp
Emp.: 46
Watch Repair Services
N.A.I.C.S.: 811490

Kyoshin Industry Asia Pte Ltd. (1)
175A Bencoolen Street 07 01 Burlington Square, Singapore, 189650, Singapore
Tel.: (65) 63368272
Terminal & Pressed Parts Whslr
N.A.I.C.S.: 423120

Kyoshin Vietnam Co., Ltd. (1)
Lot AM 34b-36-38a and Lot AN 27b-29-31-33-35a Road 12 Tan Thuan EPZ, Tan Thuan Dong Ward District 7, Ho Chi Minh City, Vietnam
Tel.: (84) 2837701416
Web Site: http://www.kyoshin-k.co.jp
Emp.: 322
Metal Stamping Product Mfr
N.A.I.C.S.: 332119
Tsutomu Hagiwara *(Dir-Sls & Pur)*

PT. Rhythm Kyoshin Indonesia (1)
Blok T 1 MM2100, Industrial Town Cibitung, Bekasi, 17520, Jawa Barat, Indonesia
Tel.: (62) 218980945
Metal Stamping Product Mfr
N.A.I.C.S.: 332119

Pritec Co., Ltd. (1)
372-6 Kondo-cho, Tatebayashi, 374-0042, Gunma, Japan
Tel.: (81) 276768451
Web Site: http://www.pritec.jp
Printing & Coating Mfr
N.A.I.C.S.: 323113

Rhythm Industrial (Dongguan) Ltd. (1)
2th Ning Jiang Road, Daning District Humen Town, Dongguan, China
Tel.: (86) 76986232333
Clock Mfr
N.A.I.C.S.: 339910

Rhythm Industrial (H.K.) Co., Ltd (1)
Unit 301 Yen Sheng Centre, 64 Hoi Yuen Rd Kwun Tong, Kowloon, China (Hong Kong)
Tel.: (852) 29500995
Jewelry Watch Precious Stone & Precious Metal Whslr
N.A.I.C.S.: 423940

Rhythm Kaihatsu Co., Ltd. (1)
1-299-12 Kitabukuro-cho, Omiya-ku, Saitama, 330-9551, Japan
Tel.: (81) 486437781
Web Site: http://www.rhythm.co.jp
Watch Whslr
N.A.I.C.S.: 423940

Rhythm Kyoshin Hanoi Co., Ltd. (1)
Plot 69A1 & 69A2, Noi Bai Industrial Zone Mai Dinh Commune Soc Son District, Hanoi, Vietnam
Tel.: (84) 2435824637
Metal Stamping Product Mfr
N.A.I.C.S.: 332119

Rhythm Precision Vietnam Co., Ltd. (1)
Lot 42 & 87A Noi Bai Industrial Park, Quang Tien Commune Soc Son District, Hanoi, Vietnam
Tel.: (84) 24358216611
Web Site: http://www.rhythm.com.vn
Injection Precision Parts Mfr
N.A.I.C.S.: 332721
Kim Oanh *(Mgr-Pur)*

Rhythm Service Co., Ltd. (1)
1500 Osaki Fujigay, Chikusei, 308-0112, Ibaraki, Japan
Tel.: (81) 296378381
Web Site: http://www.rhythm-service.co.jp
Rhythm Product Repair Services
N.A.I.C.S.: 811490

Rhythm U.S.A. Inc. (1)
8601 Dunwoody Pl- Ste 150, Atlanta, GA 30350
Tel.: (770) 640-6311
Web Site: http://www.rhythm.us.com

Sales Range: $25-49.9 Million
Emp.: 7
Watch Clock & Part Mfr
N.A.I.C.S.: 334519
Yuichi Koizumi *(Mng Dir)*

Rhywaco (H.K.) Co., Ltd (1)
12/F Remington Centre 23 Hung To Road, Kwun Tong, Kowloon, China (Hong Kong)
Tel.: (852) 27903882
Web Site: http://www.rhythm.com.hk
Jewelry Watch Precious Stone & Precious Metal Whslr
N.A.I.C.S.: 423940

RI YING HOLDINGS LIMITED
6/F Kai Tak Commercial Building, Nos 317-319 Des Voeux Road, Central, China (Hong Kong)
Tel.: (852) 28918359   Ky
Web Site: http://www.shingchiholdings.com
Year Founded: 1989
1741—(HKG)
Rev.: $14,227,655
Assets: $19,234,916
Liabilities: $13,852,194
Net Worth: $5,382,722
Earnings: ($17,922,287)
Emp.: 158
Fiscal Year-end: 09/30/22
Engineering Consulting Services
N.A.I.C.S.: 541330
Chi Ming Lau *(Co-Founder & Deputy Chm)*

RIANLON CORPORATION
20F Tower F 20 Kaihua Road Huayuan Industrial Park, Tianjin, 300384, China
Tel.: (86) 2283718817
Web Site: https://www.rianlon.com
Year Founded: 2003
300596—(CHIN)
Rev.: $743,470,542
Assets: $1,156,872,193
Liabilities: $554,048,926
Net Worth: $602,823,267
Earnings: $51,056,224
Fiscal Year-end: 12/31/23
Polymer Material Mfr & Distr
N.A.I.C.S.: 325998
Li Haiping *(Chm & Pres)*

Subsidiaries:

Rianlon Americas, Inc. (1)
2141 Richmond Rd, Staten Island, NY 10306
Tel.: (718) 667-4190
Polymer Material Distr
N.A.I.C.S.: 423690

RIAS A/S
Industrivej 11, DK-4000, Roskilde, Denmark
Tel.: (45) 46770000
Web Site: https://www.riasnordic.com
Year Founded: 1959
RIAS.B—(OMX)
Rev.: $50,918,483
Assets: $40,469,882
Liabilities: $11,194,057
Net Worth: $29,275,825
Earnings: $2,082,028
Emp.: 106
Fiscal Year-end: 09/30/20
Semi-Finished Plastic Product Mfr & Distr
N.A.I.C.S.: 333310
Steen Raagaard Andersen *(Vice Chm)*

RIBA MUNDO TECNOLOGIA SA
Calle en proyecto N7 sector 10-2, Loriguilla, 46393, Valencia, Spain
Tel.: (34) 961676749

Web Site: https://www.ribamundotecnologia.es
Year Founded: 2018
RMT—(ITA)
Rev.: $351,734,598
Assets: $78,722,464
Liabilities: $70,850,752
Net Worth: $7,871,712
Earnings: $5,339,725
Emp.: 66
Fiscal Year-end: 12/31/22
Logistic Services
N.A.I.C.S.: 541614
Alessandro Dezi *(COO)*

RIBA NERETVA D.D. KONJIC
Ljuta do br 3, Konjic, Bosnia & Herzegovina
Tel.: (387) 36726756   BA
RIBNR—(SARE)
Rev.: $1,079,182
Assets: $3,421,647
Liabilities: $2,529,604
Net Worth: $892,043
Earnings: $85,420
Emp.: 18
Fiscal Year-end: 12/31/20
Cultivating Freshwater Services
N.A.I.C.S.: 112519

RIBA TEXTILES LIMITED
DD 14 Nehru Enclave Near Kalkaji Post Office, New Delhi, 110019, India
Tel.: (91) 1126236986
Web Site: https://www.ribatextiles.com
531952—(BOM)
Rev.: $25,999,906
Assets: $21,127,074
Liabilities: $11,683,117
Net Worth: $9,443,957
Earnings: $803,207
Emp.: 266
Fiscal Year-end: 03/31/21
Terry Towel Products Mfr
N.A.I.C.S.: 313210
Amit Garg *(Mng Dir)*

RIBARSKO GAZDINSTVO AD
Patrijarha Joanikija 2a, 11000, Belgrade, Serbia
Tel.: (381) 112321122
Web Site: https://www.ribarstvobeograd.com
Year Founded: 1947
RGBG—(BEL)
Rev.: $140,220
Assets: $2,710,755
Liabilities: $554,710
Net Worth: $2,156,045
Earnings: ($51,594)
Emp.: 3
Fiscal Year-end: 12/31/23
Fish Farming Services
N.A.I.C.S.: 112511
Nebojsa Mandic *(Mng Dir)*

RIBARSTVO A.D.
Sakulski put bb, Opovo, Baranda, Serbia
Tel.: (381) 13 686 100
Year Founded: 1991
Sales Range: Less than $1 Million
Emp.: 7
Fish Farming Services
N.A.I.C.S.: 112511

RIBER S.A.
31 rue Casimir Perier, 95870, Bezons, France
Tel.: (33) 139966503
Web Site: https://www.riber.com
ALRIB—(EUR)
Sales Range: $25-49.9 Million
Semiconductor Equipment Mfr

INTERNATIONAL PUBLIC

Subsidiaries:

MBE Control Solutions (1)
6483 Calle Real Ste F, Goleta, CA 93117-1541
Tel.: (805) 683-3152
Web Site: http://www.mbecontrol.com
Sales Range: $1-9.9 Million
Emp.: 5
Semiconductor Equipment Mfr & Supplier
N.A.I.C.S.: 334413
Gabriel Millos *(Mgr-Engrg)*

RIBNJAK SUTJESKA A.D.
Ribarska bb, Sutjeska, Serbia
Tel.: (381) 23 851 027
Web Site: http://www.ribnjaksutjeska.co.rs
Year Founded: 1984
RIBS—(BEL)
Sales Range: Less than $1 Million
Emp.: 26
Fish Farming Services
N.A.I.C.S.: 112511
Vidak Milosevic *(Exec Dir)*

RIBO FASHION GROUP CO., LTD.
No 98 Rongyang Road, Songjiang District, Shanghai, 201600, China
Tel.: (86) 2180104103
Web Site: http://www.ribo.cn
Year Founded: 2002
603196—(SHG)
Rev.: $133,725,230
Assets: $177,131,588
Liabilities: $64,604,372
Net Worth: $112,527,216
Earnings: $2,326,779
Emp.: 1,700
Fiscal Year-end: 12/31/22
Garment Product Mfr & Distr
N.A.I.C.S.: 315250
Liang Feng *(Chm)*

RIBOMIC, INC.
Shirokanedai Usui Bldg 6F 3-16-13 Shirokanedai, Minato-ku, Tokyo, 108-0071, Japan
Tel.: (81) 334403303
Web Site: https://www.ribomic.com
Year Founded: 2003
4591—(TKS)
Sales Range: $1-9.9 Million
Emp.: 24
Pharmaceuticals Mfr
N.A.I.C.S.: 325412
Yoshikazu Nakamura *(Pres & CEO)*

RICARDO PLC
30 Eastbourne Terrace, London, W2 6LA, West Sussex, United Kingdom
Tel.: (44) 1273455611   UK
Web Site: https://www.ricardo.com
RCDO—(LSE)
Rev.: $599,974,721
Assets: $541,961,576
Liabilities: $333,164,812
Net Worth: $208,796,764
Earnings: $1,011,122
Emp.: 3,000
Fiscal Year-end: 06/30/24
Technology, Engineering & Strategic Consulting Services
N.A.I.C.S.: 541690
David Shemmans *(CEO)*

Subsidiaries:

Ricardo Australia Pty. Ltd. (1)
Suite 2 01 Level 2 Tower B The Zenith 821 Pacific Highway, Chatswood, Sydney, 2067, NSW, Australia
Tel.: (61) 29 258 1160
Scientific & Technical Consulting Services
N.A.I.C.S.: 541690

Ricardo Beijing Company Limited (1)

Room 1301 and 1302 Shun Tak Tower 11
No 1 Xiangheyuan Street, Dongcheng District, Beijing, 100028, China
Tel.: (86) 106 403 0868
Scientific & Technical Consulting Services
N.A.I.C.S.: 541690

Ricardo Certification B.V. (1)
Catharijnesingel 33-J, 3511 GC, Utrecht, Netherlands
Tel.: (31) 30 752 4752
Scientific & Technical Consulting Services
N.A.I.C.S.: 541690

Ricardo Certification Denmark ApS (1)
Hoffdingsvej 34, Valby, 2500, Copenhagen, Denmark
Tel.: (45) 2 566 6500
Scientific & Technical Consulting Services
N.A.I.C.S.: 541690

Ricardo Defense, Inc. (1)
175 Cremona Dr Ste 140, Goleta, CA 93117
Tel.: (805) 882-1884
Scientific & Technical Consulting Services
N.A.I.C.S.: 541690

Ricardo Deutschland GmbH (1)
Guglingstrasse 66, 73529, Schwabisch Gmund, Germany
Tel.: (49) 7171 982 1101
Web Site: https://ricardo.com
Sales Range: $25-49.9 Million
Emp.: 200
Engineeering Services
N.A.I.C.S.: 541330

Ricardo Energy Environment & Planning Pty. Ltd. (1)
Level 4 3 Bowen Crescent, Melbourne, 3004, VIC, Australia
Tel.: (61) 39 978 7823
Scientific & Technical Consulting Services
N.A.I.C.S.: 541690

Ricardo Hong Kong Limited (1)
Unit No 1118 11/F Hong Kong Shui On Centre 6-8 Harbour Road, Hong Kong, China (Hong Kong)
Tel.: (852) 3 974 6840
Scientific & Technical Consulting Services
N.A.I.C.S.: 541690

Ricardo India Private Limited (1)
Plaza M6 Suite 6G District Centre Jasola Mathura Road, New Delhi, 110 076, India
Tel.: (91) 114 014 1400
Web Site: http://www.ricardo.com
Sales Range: $25-49.9 Million
Emp.: 400
Engineeering Services
N.A.I.C.S.: 541330

Ricardo Japan K.K. (1)
Shin Yokohama Square Building 18F 2-3-12, Shin Yokohama Kohoku-ku, Yokohama, 222-0033, Kanagawa, Japan
Tel.: (81) 45 471 7622
Scientific & Technical Consulting Services
N.A.I.C.S.: 541690

Ricardo Motorcycle Italia s.r.l. (1)
Rimini Technical Centre, Coriano, Italy
Tel.: (39) 054 175 5009
Motorcycle Mfr
N.A.I.C.S.: 336991

Ricardo Nederland B.V. (1)
Utrecht Technical Centre Catharijnesingel 33, 3511 GC, Utrecht, Netherlands
Tel.: (31) 30 752 4700
Scientific & Technical Consulting Services
N.A.I.C.S.: 541690

Ricardo Prague s.r.o. (1)
Prague Technical Centre Palac Karlin Thamova 11-13, 186 00, Prague, Czech Republic
Tel.: (420) 22 172 9150
Scientific & Technical Consulting Services
N.A.I.C.S.: 541690

Ricardo Rail (Taiwan) Ltd. (1)
11F-2 Westside No 51 Hengyang Road, Zhongzheng District, Taipei, 10045, Taiwan
Tel.: (886) 28 978 7848
Scientific & Technical Consulting Services
N.A.I.C.S.: 541690

Ricardo Rail Australia Pty. Ltd. (1)
Suite 2 01 Level 2 Tower B The Zenith 821 Pacific Highway, Chatswood, Sydney, 2067, NSW, Australia
Tel.: (61) 40 406 6478
Scientific & Technical Consulting Services
N.A.I.C.S.: 541690

Ricardo Shanghai Company Limited (1)
Floor 17 Phoenix Building No 1515 Gumei Road, Xuhui District, Shanghai, 200233, China
Tel.: (86) 213 367 5858
Scientific & Technical Consulting Services
N.A.I.C.S.: 541690

Ricardo South Africa (Pty) Ltd. (1)
111 Pretoria Road, Rynfield, Benoni, South Africa
Tel.: (27) 11 615 3403
Scientific & Technical Consulting Services
N.A.I.C.S.: 541690

Ricardo Strategic Consulting GmbH (1)
Kreuzstrasse 16, 80331, Munich, Germany
Tel.: (49) 89139285100
Web Site: http://rsc.ricardo.com
Sales Range: $25-49.9 Million
Emp.: 70
Strategic Consulting Services
N.A.I.C.S.: 541611

Ricardo UK Limited (1)
Shoreham Technical Centre, Shoreham-by-Sea, BN43 5FG, West Sussex, United Kingdom
Tel.: (44) 127 345 5611
Web Site: http://www.ricardo.com
Sales Range: $75-99.9 Million
Emp.: 500
Engineering & Technological Services
N.A.I.C.S.: 541330
Dave Smith (Mng Dir)

Subsidiary (Domestic):

Ricardo-AEA Limited (2)
The Gemini Building Fermi Avenue, Harwell, Didcot, OX11 0QR, Oxon, United Kingdom
Tel.: (44) 123 575 3000
Web Site: http://ee.ricardo.com
Sales Range: $50-74.9 Million
Emp.: 400
Energy & Environmental Data, Analysis & Consultancy Services
N.A.I.C.S.: 541690

Ricardo, Inc. (1)
40000 Ricardo Dr, Van Buren Township, MI 48111-1641
Tel.: (734) 397-6666
Web Site: https://ricardo.com
Sales Range: $25-49.9 Million
Emp.: 200
Engineeering Services
N.A.I.C.S.: 541330
David McShane (VP-Bus Dev)

Wamarragu Transport Services Pty. Ltd. (1)
Suite 2 01 Level 2 Tower B The Zenith 821 Pacific Highway, Chatswood, 2067, NSW, Australia
Tel.: (61) 43 314 2466
Web Site: https://wamarragu.com.au
Rail Transportation Services
N.A.I.C.S.: 488210

RICCIARELLI S.P.A.
Via U Mariotti 143 ZIS Agostino, 51100, Pistoia, Italy
Tel.: (39) 057344571
Web Site: http://www.ricciarellispa.it
Year Founded: 1843
Packaging Systems Mfr
N.A.I.C.S.: 333993

RICEGROWERS LIMITED
Tel.: (61) 292682000
Web Site: http://www.sunrice.com.au
Rev.: $918,859,950
Assets: $807,151,538
Liabilities: $468,315,073
Net Worth: $338,836,465
Earnings: $35,216,489
Emp.: 2,185
Fiscal Year-end: 04/30/18
Rice Farming, Processing & Marketing
N.A.I.C.S.: 111160
Dimitri C. Courtelis (CFO)

Subsidiaries:

Aqaba Processing Company Ltd (1)
Aloz Street, PO Box 182418, Al-Mokeblein, Amman, 11118, Jordan
Tel.: (962) 64206829
Emp.: 5
Rice Packaging & Storage Services
N.A.I.C.S.: 311212
Al-Ghzawi Al-Ghzawi (Gen Mgr-Bus)

Rice Research Australia Pty Ltd (1)
Old Coree Conargo Road, Deniliquin, 2710, NSW, Australia
Tel.: (61) 358861391
Sales Range: $25-49.9 Million
Emp.: 6
Agricultural Research Services
N.A.I.C.S.: 541715
Glen Indirizzi (Chm)

Riviana Foods Pty Ltd (1)
8 Lakeview Drive, Scoresby, 3179, VIC, Australia
Tel.: (61) 392126000
Web Site: http://www.rivianafoods.com.au
Sales Range: $25-49.9 Million
Emp.: 40
Canned Foods Mfr & Distr
N.A.I.C.S.: 311710

SunFoods LLC (1)
1620 E Kentucky Ave, Woodland, CA 95776
Tel.: (530) 661-1923
Web Site: http://www.hinode.us
Sales Range: $25-49.9 Million
Emp.: 250
Rice Products Mfr & Distr
N.A.I.C.S.: 311212
Matt Alonso (CEO)

SunRice Trading Pty Ltd (1)
37 Yanco Ave, Leeton, 2705, NSW, Australia
Tel.: (61) 269530411
Web Site: http://www.sunrice.com.au
Rice Distr
N.A.I.C.S.: 424490

Trukai Industries Limited (1)
Mataram Street, PO Box 2129, Lae, 411, Papua New Guinea
Tel.: (675) 4722466
Web Site: http://www.trukai.com.pg
Sales Range: $150-199.9 Million
Emp.: 1,000
Rice Mfr
N.A.I.C.S.: 311212
Greg Worthington-Eyre (CEO)

RICH ASIA CORPORATION PUBLIC COMPANY LIMITED
636 Bangkhuntien-Chaitaley Road, Thakham Bangkhuntien, Bangkok, 10150, Thailand
Tel.: (66) 2453 6277
Web Site: http://www.richasiacorp.com
Year Founded: 1999
Rev.: $15,116,187
Assets: $15,698,575
Liabilities: $81,661,842
Net Worth: ($65,963,267)
Earnings: ($2,192,264)
Emp.: 29
Fiscal Year-end: 12/31/19
Steel Products Mfr
N.A.I.C.S.: 331110
Watanachai Chaimuanwong (Chm)

Subsidiaries:

Thai National Product Co., Ltd (1)
33/3 Moo 4 Bangbuathong - Suphanburi Rd Saiyai, Sainoi, Nonthaburi, 11150, Thailand
Tel.: (66) 2985 5300
Web Site: http://www.tnpspunpile.com
Construction Engineering Services
N.A.I.C.S.: 541330

RICH CAPITAL HOLDINGS LIMITED
140 Paya Lebar 07-09 AZ at Paya Lebar, Singapore, 409015, Singapore
Tel.: (65) 62880080   SG
Web Site: https://www.richcapital.com.sg
5G4—(CAT)
Rev.: $9,402,742
Assets: $7,200,445
Liabilities: $3,404,224
Net Worth: $3,796,221
Earnings: $1,532,419
Fiscal Year-end: 03/31/23
Investment Holding Services
N.A.I.C.S.: 551112
Bee Fong Lee (Sec)

Subsidiaries:

First Capital Pte. Ltd. (1)
304 Orchard Road lucky plaza 04-01A/02, Singapore, 238863, Singapore
Tel.: (65) 67347700
Web Site: https://www.1stcapital.com.sg
Cash Loan Services
N.A.I.C.S.: 522291

Merco Pte. Ltd. (1)
140 Paya Lebar Rd No 10-23, Singapore, 409015, Singapore
Tel.: (65) 62880080
Web Site: https://www.merco.sg
Building Design Services
N.A.I.C.S.: 541310

RICH DEVELOPMENT CO., LTD.
8th Floor No 99 Jilin Road, Zhongshan District, Taipei, 104, Taiwan
Tel.: (886) 221002288
Web Site: https://rhd.com.tw
Year Founded: 1992
5512—(TPE)
Rev.: $197,141,794
Assets: $1,256,699,153
Liabilities: $728,238,783
Net Worth: $528,460,370
Earnings: ($3,999,812)
Fiscal Year-end: 12/31/22
Construction Services
N.A.I.C.S.: 236220
Kuo Chi-Kang (Chm)

RICH GOLDMAN HOLDINGS LIMITED
Room 1807 18/F West Tower Shun Tak Centre, 168-200 Connaught Road Central, Hong Kong, China (Hong Kong)
Tel.: (852) 2 330 0333   HK
Web Site: http://www.richgoldman.com.hk
Year Founded: 1972
00070—(HKG)
Rev.: $6,586,364
Assets: $152,338,278
Liabilities: $1,335,975
Net Worth: $151,002,303
Earnings: ($2,833,949)
Emp.: 43
Fiscal Year-end: 06/30/21
Investment Management Service
N.A.I.C.S.: 523999
Yee Man Lin (Chm & Exec Dir)

RICH SPORT PUBLIC COMPANY LIMITED
1152 Punn Tower 18th Floor Room No 1801-1805 and 1808 Rama 4 Road, Klong Toei Sub-district Klong Toei District, Bangkok, 10110, Thailand
Tel.: (66) 22498709   TH
Web Site: https://www.richsport.co.th
Year Founded: 1908

RICH SPORT PUBLIC COMPANY LIMITED

Rich Sport Public Company Limited—(Continued)
RSP—(THA)
Rev.: $44,414,415
Assets: $67,098,035
Liabilities: $17,878,330
Net Worth: $49,219,705
Earnings: $3,026,915
Fiscal Year-end: 12/31/23
Footwear Product Distr
N.A.I.C.S.: 459110
Papitch Wongpaitoonpiya (CEO)

RICH UNIVERSE NETWORK LIMITED
7/125 C-2 2nd Floor Swaroop Nagar, Kanpur, 208 002, India
Tel.: (91) 7880884461
Web Site: https://www.richuninet.com
530271—(BOM)
Rev.: $2,993,190
Assets: $1,790,007
Liabilities: $785,244
Net Worth: $1,004,763
Earnings: $42,525
Fiscal Year-end: 03/31/21
Financial Services
N.A.I.C.S.: 523999
Shashwat Agarwal (Chm & Mng Dir)

RICHA INDUSTRIES LTD.
Plot No 29 DLF Industrial Area Phase - II, Faridabad, 121003, Haryana, India
Tel.: (91) 1294009262
532766—(BOM)
Rev.: $4,804,969
Assets: $24,099,893
Liabilities: $58,446,698
Net Worth: ($34,346,805)
Earnings: ($6,305,430)
Emp.: 1,000
Fiscal Year-end: 03/31/21
Knitted Fabric Mfr
N.A.I.C.S.: 313210
Sandeep Gupta (Chm, Mng Dir & Exec Dir)

RICHA INFO SYSTEMS LIMITED
Corporate House No 17 Times Corporate Park Opp Copper Stone, Thaltej-Shilaj Road Thaltej, Ahmedabad, 380059, Gujarat, India
Tel.: (91) 9157094380
Web Site: https://www.richainfosys.com
Year Founded: 2010
RICHA—(NSE)
Rev.: $4,109,574
Assets: $3,880,295
Liabilities: $2,280,043
Net Worth: $1,600,252
Earnings: $97,860
Emp.: 20
Fiscal Year-end: 03/31/23
Educational Support Services
N.A.I.C.S.: 611710

RICHARD IRVIN & SONS LIMITED
Hareness Road Altens Industrial Estate, Aberdeen, AB12 3LE, United Kingdom
Tel.: (44) 1224367000
Web Site: http://www.richard-irvin.co.uk
Rev.: $80,983,463
Emp.: 24
Building Engineering Services
N.A.I.C.S.: 561790
William C. MacLean (CEO)

RICHARD PIERIS & CO. LTD.
No 310 High Level Road, Nawinna, Maharagama, Sri Lanka
Tel.: (94) 114310500
LK

Web Site: https://www.arpico.com
Year Founded: 1940
RICH—(COL)
Rev.: $301,778,005
Assets: $384,409,272
Liabilities: $274,251,639
Net Worth: $110,157,633
Earnings: $26,950,918
Emp.: 28,000
Fiscal Year-end: 03/31/21
Rubber & Plastic Products Mfr & Distr
N.A.I.C.S.: 326199
Sena Yaddehige (Chm, CEO & Mng Dir)

Subsidiaries:

Arpico Ataraxia Asset Management (Pvt) Ltd. (1)
Level 4 67 A Gregorys Road, 07, Colombo, Sri Lanka
Tel.: (94) 115882865
Mutual Fund Services
N.A.I.C.S.: 523940
Asanth Sebastian (Head-)

Arpico Flexifoam (Pvt) Ltd. (1)
58 Kudamaduwa Road Mattegoda, Colombo, Polgasowita, Sri Lanka
Tel.: (94) 11 4211878
Sales Range: $50-74.9 Million
Emp.: 130
Mattress Mfr
N.A.I.C.S.: 337910

Arpico Interiors (Pvt) Ltd (1) (100%)
Tel.: (94) 112699625
Web Site: http://www.arpicointeriors.com
Sales Range: $1-4.9 Billion
Emp.: 35
All Other Rubber Product Mfr
N.A.I.C.S.: 326299

Arpidag International (Pvt) Ltd. (1)
310 High Level Road Nawinna, Maharagama, Sri Lanka (51%)
Tel.: (94) 114310710
Web Site: http://www.arpico.com
Sales Range: $350-399.9 Million
Emp.: 2,000
Rubber & Plastics Footwear Mfr
N.A.I.C.S.: 316210
Lakshman Watawala (CEO)

Arpitech (Pvt) Ltd. (1)
No 310 High Level Road, Nawinna, Maharagama, Sri Lanka
Tel.: (94) 764224164
Rubber Products Mfr
N.A.I.C.S.: 326299

BGN Industrial Tyre (Pvt) Ltd. (1)
No 310 High Level Road, Nawinna, Maharagama, Sri Lanka
Tel.: (94) 342253250
Solid Tire Mfr
N.A.I.C.S.: 326211

Maskeliya Tea Gardens (Ceylon) Limited (1)
310 Highlevel road, Nawinna, Maharagama, Sri Lanka
Tel.: (94) 777440011
Coffee & Tea Mfr
N.A.I.C.S.: 311920
Dilshan Abeysekera (Gen Mgr)

Namunukula Plantations Ltd (1)
No 310 High Level Road Nawinna, Maharagama, Sri Lanka (59%)
Tel.: (94) 114310500
Sales Range: $25-49.9 Million
Emp.: 20
Rubber & Plastics Hoses & Belting Mfr
N.A.I.C.S.: 326220

Plastishells Ltd. (1)
310 High Level Rd Nawinna, Maharagama, 00940, Sri Lanka
Tel.: (94) 114310500
Web Site: http://www.arpico.com
Sales Range: $50-74.9 Million
Emp.: 250
Plastics Product Mfr
N.A.I.C.S.: 326199
Derrick Perera (Mgr-Mktg)

RPC Construction (Pvt) Ltd. (1)

310 High Level Road Nawinna, Maharagama, 3010, Sri Lanka
Tel.: (94) 114310310
Web Site: http://www.rpcconstructions.org
Other Construction Material Whslr
N.A.I.C.S.: 423390
Thusitha karunadas (Mgr)

Richard Pieris Distributors Ltd. (1)
310 High Level Road Nawinna, Maharagama, Sri Lanka (74%)
Tel.: (94) 114310310
Web Site: http://www.arpico.com
Distribution of Company Manufactured Products
N.A.I.C.S.: 326199

Richard Pieris Exports Ltd. (1)
310 High Level Road, Nawinna, Sri Lanka
Tel.: (94) 114834150
Web Site: http://www.arpicorubber.com
Sales Range: $200-249.9 Million
Emp.: 595
All Other Rubber Product Mfr
N.A.I.C.S.: 326299

Richard Pieris Finance Ltd. (1)
69 Arpico Complex Hyde Park Corner, Colombo, Sri Lanka
Tel.: (94) 115900600
Mutual Fund Services
N.A.I.C.S.: 523940
Sena Yaddehige (Chm)

Richard Pieris Group Services (Pvt) Ltd. (1)
No 310 High Level Road Nawinna, Maharagama, Sri Lanka
Tel.: (94) 114 310500
Rubber Products Mfr
N.A.I.C.S.: 326299

Richard Pieris Natural Foams Ltd. (1)
310 Phase 1 Export Processing Zone, Nawinna Maharagama Biyagama, Malwana, Sri Lanka
Tel.: (94) 1148190014
Web Site: www.arpicolatexfoam.com
Mattress Mfr
N.A.I.C.S.: 337910
Adrian Bogahawatte (Gen Mgr-Sls & Mktg)

Richard Pieris Rubber Compounds Ltd. (1)
310 High Level Road, Nawinna, Maharagama, Sri Lanka (100%)
Tel.: (94) 114310710
Web Site: http://www.arpicorubber.com
Sales Range: $25-49.9 Million
Emp.: 80
Plastics & Rubber Industry Machinery Mfr
N.A.I.C.S.: 333248
Lakshman Watawala (CEO)

Richard Pieris Rubber Products Ltd (1)
No 310 High Level Road, Nawinna, Maharagama, Sri Lanka
Tel.: (94) 114310574
Web Site: https://www.arpicorubber.lk
Sales Range: $25-49.9 Million
Emp.: 100
Rubber Garden Hoses Mfr
N.A.I.C.S.: 326220

Richard Pieris Securities (Pvt) Ltd (1)
69 Hyde Park Corner, 02000, Colombo, Sri Lanka
Tel.: (94) 112683946
Web Site: http://www.rpsecurities.com
Sales Range: $50-74.9 Million
Emp.: 28
Securities Brokerage Services
N.A.I.C.S.: 523150

Richard Pieris Tyre Co. Ltd. (1)
310 High Level Road, Nawinna, Maharagama, Sri Lanka
Tel.: (94) 114310710
Tire Retreading Services
N.A.I.C.S.: 326212

RICHCO INVESTORS INC.
3882 Lawrence Place, North Vancouver, V7K 2X2, BC, Canada
Tel.: (604) 689-4407
Ca

INTERNATIONAL PUBLIC

Year Founded: 1980
RII.H—(TSX)
Rev.: $10,357
Assets: $332,017
Liabilities: $222,566
Net Worth: $109,451
Earnings: ($23,876)
Fiscal Year-end: 12/31/20
Financial Management Services
N.A.I.C.S.: 523910
Christopher Tsakok (Bd of Dirs & Co/Co-Pres)

RICHE ET SEBASTIEN
157 Rue De La Republique, 60280, Clairoix, Oise, France
Tel.: (33) 344904747
Web Site: http://www.climalife.dehon.com
Rev.: $17,800,000
Emp.: 82
N.A.I.C.S.: 423710
Bernard Sebastien (Pres)

RICHEL SERRES DE FRANCE SA
ZA des Grandes Terres, 13810, Eygalieres, France
Tel.: (33) 4 9095 1468
Web Site: http://www.richel.fr
Year Founded: 1964
Sales Range: $150-199.9 Million
Emp.: 370
Plastic & Glass Greenhouses Mfr
N.A.I.C.S.: 326199
Christian Richel (CEO)

RICHELIEU HARDWARE LTD.
7900 boul Henri-Bourassa ouest Ville, Saint-Laurent, H4S 1V4, QC, Canada
Tel.: (514) 336-4144
Web Site: http://www.richelieu.com
3R2—(DEU)
Rev.: $1,410,284,214
Assets: $1,004,341,912
Liabilities: $363,011,558
Net Worth: $641,330,354
Earnings: $132,947,704
Emp.: 2,800
Fiscal Year-end: 11/30/22
Specialty Hardware Manufacturing Services
N.A.I.C.S.: 332510
Richard Lord (Pres & CEO)

Subsidiaries:

Boiserie Lussier (1)
4500 boul Wilfrid-Hamel, Quebec, G1P 2J9, QC, Canada
Tel.: (418) 877-2020
Web Site: http://www.boiserielussier.qc.ca
Sales Range: $25-49.9 Million
Emp.: 15
Hardware Mfr
N.A.I.C.S.: 332510

Cedan Industries Inc. (1)
785 Guimond street, Longueuil, J4G 1M1, QC, Canada
Tel.: (450) 651-9663
Web Site: https://www.cedan.com
Sales Range: $25-49.9 Million
Emp.: 50
Edgebanding Rolls & Wood Veneer Sheets Mfr
N.A.I.C.S.: 321211

Distribution 20/20 (1)
4500 boulevard Wilfrid-Hamel, Quebec, G1P 2J9, QC, Canada
Tel.: (418) 877-2020
Web Site: http://www.2020richelieu.com
Sales Range: $50-74.9 Million
Emp.: 126
Household Furniture Mfr
N.A.I.C.S.: 337126

Distributions 20-20 Inc (1)
4500 Wilfrid-Hamel Blvd, Quebec, G1P 2J9, QC, Canada
Tel.: (418) 877-2020

AND PRIVATE COMPANIES / RICHFIELD INTERNATIONAL LIMITED

Web Site: http://www.2020richelieu.com
Furniture Whslr
N.A.I.C.S.: 423210

E. Kinast Distributors Inc (1)
6350 Church Rd, Hanover Park, IL 60133-4804
Tel.: (630) 233-5250
Sales Range: $25-49.9 Million
Emp.: 25
Kitchen Cabinet & Hardware Laminates Distr
N.A.I.C.S.: 423710
Rodney Vukson (Gen Mgr)

JFH Corp. (1)
2707 Longate Dr, Memphis, TN 38132
Tel.: (901) 332-7714
Web Site: http://www.richelieu.com
Hardware Stores
N.A.I.C.S.: 444140

Laknord (1)
1265 Tellier Street, Laval, H7C 2H1, QC, Canada
Tel.: (450) 664-0163
Web Site: http://www.laknord.ca
Sales Range: $25-49.9 Million
Emp.: 15
Hardware Whslr
N.A.I.C.S.: 423710
Gerald Defcopeaux (Mgr)

Les Industries Cedan inc. (1)
785 Guimond Boulevard, Longueuil, J4G 1M1, QC, Canada
Tel.: (450) 651-9663
Web Site: http://www.cedan.com
Emp.: 40
Veneer Sheet Mfr
N.A.I.C.S.: 321211

Maverick Hardware, LLC (1)
2610 Roosevelt Blvd, Eugene, OR 97402-2542
Tel.: (541) 688-1878
Web Site: http://www.maverickhardware.com
Wood Kitchen Cabinet & Counter Top Mfr
N.A.I.C.S.: 337110
Randy Meadows (Mgr)

Menuiserie des Pins Ltd. (1)
3150 Chemin Royal, Notre-Dame-des-Pins, G0M 1K0, QC, Canada
Tel.: (418) 774-3324
Web Site: https://www.mdpins.qc.ca
Sales Range: $25-49.9 Million
Emp.: 90
Hardware Mfr
N.A.I.C.S.: 332510

Neos Gordonply (1)
272 King Street Unit 2, Barrie, L4N 6L2, ON, Canada
Tel.: (705) 730-0041
Emp.: 12
Hardware Equipment Distr
N.A.I.C.S.: 423710
Sharon Harris (Mgr-Ops)

Neos Products (1)
1010 Lorne Street Unit 12, Sudbury, P3C 4R9, ON, Canada (100%)
Tel.: (705) 674-6284
Web Site: http://www.richlieu.com
Sales Range: $25-49.9 Million
Emp.: 11
Hardware Whslr
N.A.I.C.S.: 423710

Onward (1)
800 Wilson Avenue Unit 2, Kitchener, N2C 0A2, ON, Canada (100%)
Tel.: (519) 578-3770
Web Site: http://www.onward.com
Sales Range: $25-49.9 Million
Emp.: 50
Hardware Whslr
N.A.I.C.S.: 423710

PJ White Hardwoods Ltd (1)
1200 East Kent Avenue SE, Vancouver, V5X 2X8, BC, Canada
Tel.: (604) 327-0241
Web Site: http://www.pjwhitehardwoods.com
Building Materials Distr
N.A.I.C.S.: 423390

Raybern Company, Inc. (1)
90 New Britain Ave, Rocky Hill, CT 06067

Tel.: (860) 529-7704
Web Site: http://www.richelieu.com
Sales Range: $25-49.9 Million
Emp.: 12
Decorative Architectural Hardware Distr
N.A.I.C.S.: 423710

Reliable Fasteners (1)
800 Beriault Street, Longueuil, J4G 1R8, QC, Canada (100%)
Tel.: (450) 674-0888
Web Site: http://www.reliable.com
Sales Range: $25-49.9 Million
Emp.: 50
Hardware Whslr
N.A.I.C.S.: 423710

Richelieu America Ltd (1)
7021 Sterling Ponds Blvd, Sterling Heights, MI 48312-5809
Tel.: (586) 264-1240
Web Site: http://www.richelieu.com
Sales Range: $25-49.9 Million
Emp.: 25
Kitchen Cabinet & House Hold Equipment Mfr
N.A.I.C.S.: 337110
Jeff Follbaum (Gen Mgr)

Richelieu Hardware Ltd. - Boiseries Lussier (1)
40 rue Soumande, Quebec, G1L 4W5, QC, Canada
Tel.: (418) 647-1704
Web Site: http://www.richelieu.com
Hardware Equipment Distr
N.A.I.C.S.: 423710

Richelieu Hardware Ltd. - Boiseries Lussier, Longueuil (1)
961 boulevard Guimond, Longueuil, J4G 2M7, QC, Canada
Tel.: (450) 677-5211
Web Site: http://www.richelieu.com
Sales Range: $50-74.9 Million
Emp.: 10
Hardware Products Distr
N.A.I.C.S.: 423710

Richelieu Hardware Ltd. - Dayvan, Toronto (1)
33 Dufflaw Road, Toronto, M6A 2W2, ON, Canada
Tel.: (416) 781-9118
Web Site: http://www.richelieu.com
Emp.: 20
Hardware Products Distr
N.A.I.C.S.: 423710

Richelieu Hardware Ltd. - Hialeah (1)
626 28th St W, Hialeah, FL 33010
Tel.: (305) 885-1700
Web Site: http://www.richelieu.com
Sales Range: $50-74.9 Million
Emp.: 5
Hardware Products Distr
N.A.I.C.S.: 423710

Richelieu Hardware Ltd. - High Point (1)
2600 Greengate Dr, Greensboro, NC 27406
Tel.: (336) 841-5100
Web Site: http://www.richelieu.com
Emp.: 20
Hardware Products Distr
N.A.I.C.S.: 423710
Mark Siemons (Mgr-Ops)

Richelieu Hardware Ltd. - Laknord, Drummondville (1)
645 Boulevard Saint-Joseph, Drummondville, J2E 1H4, QC, Canada
Tel.: (819) 475-5995
Sales Range: $50-74.9 Million
Emp.: 2
Hardware Equipment Distr
N.A.I.C.S.: 423710

Richelieu Hardware Ltd. - Laknord, Laval (1)
1265 Tellier St, Laval, H7C 2H1, QC, Canada
Tel.: (450) 664-0163
Hardware Equipment Distr
N.A.I.C.S.: 423710
Luc Tardis (Gen Mgr)

Richelieu Hardware Ltd. - Mississauga (1)

6425 Airport Road, Mississauga, L4V 1E4, ON, Canada
Tel.: (905) 672-1500
Web Site: http://www.richelieu.com
Hardware Products Distr
N.A.I.C.S.: 423710

Richelieu Hardware Ltd. - Neos Products, Sudbury (1)
1010 Lorne St Unit 12, Sudbury, P3C 4R9, ON, Canada
Tel.: (705) 674-6284
Hardware Equipment Distr
N.A.I.C.S.: 423710

Richelieu Hardware Ltd. - Onward, Kitchener (1)
800 Wilson Ave Unit 2, Kitchener, N2C 0A2, ON, Canada
Tel.: (519) 578-3770
Hardware Products Distr
N.A.I.C.S.: 423710
Nick Tassone (Gen Mgr)

Richelieu Hardware Ltd. - Reliable Fasteners, Longueuil (1)
800 Beriault St, Longueuil, J4G 1R8, QC, Canada
Tel.: (450) 674-0888
Sales Range: $50-74.9 Million
Emp.: 7
Hardware Equipment Distr
N.A.I.C.S.: 423710
Rene Labrecque (Gen Mgr)

Richelieu Hardware Ltd. - Riviera Beach (1)
3555 Fiscal Ct, Riviera Beach, FL 33404
Tel.: (561) 863-8111
Web Site: http://www.richelieu.com
Building Hardware Products Mfr
N.A.I.C.S.: 332510

Richelieu Hardware Ltd. - Simtab Neos, Laval (1)
4855 Hwy 440 W, Laval, H7P 5P9, QC, Canada
Tel.: (450) 687-5716
Sales Range: $50-74.9 Million
Emp.: 75
Hardware Equipment Distr
N.A.I.C.S.: 423710
Sylvie Laramee (Gen Mgr)

Richelieu Hardware Ltd. - Specialty Supplies, Pompano Beach (1)
3410 Park Central Blvd N, Pompano Beach, FL 33064
Tel.: (954) 968-2900
Web Site: http://www.richelieu.com
Emp.: 40
Building Hardware Product Distr
N.A.I.C.S.: 423710

Richelieu Ltd-Building Specialties Division-Distribution Center (1)
6900 Graybar Road Unit 3220, Richmond, V6W 0A5, BC, Canada (100%)
Tel.: (604) 273-3108
Emp.: 7
Electrical Contractor
N.A.I.C.S.: 238210
Mario Prionsi (Mng Dir)

Simtab Neos (1)
4855 Highway 440 West, Laval, H7P 5P9, QC, Canada (100%)
Tel.: (450) 687-5716
Web Site: http://www.asdecq.ca
Sales Range: $50-74.9 Million
Emp.: 75
Hardware Whslr
N.A.I.C.S.: 423710
Sylvie Laramee (Mgr)

Weston Premium Woods Inc. (1)
25 Automatic Road, Brampton, L6S 5N8, ON, Canada
Tel.: (905) 792-9797
Web Site: https://www.westonpremiumwoods.com
Hardwood & Softwood Product Distr
N.A.I.C.S.: 423310

RICHELL CORPORATION
136 Mizuhashi Sakuragi, Toyama, 939-0592, Japan
Tel.: (81) 764782155

Web Site: http://www.richell.co.jp
Year Founded: 1960
Sales Range: $25-49.9 Million
Emp.: 377
Houseware, Gardening Products, Pet Products, Babyware, Exterior Products & Health Care Products Mfr
N.A.I.C.S.: 423620
Nobuki Watanabe (Pres)

Subsidiaries:

Richell (Shanghai) Co. (1)
1722 No 66 North Shanxi Rd, Jingan, Shanghai, 200041, China
Tel.: (86) 21 5153 1338
Plastics Product Mfr
N.A.I.C.S.: 326199

Richell Korea Corporation (1)
HanKyungHun D B 203-9 Donggyo-dong 31 World Cup Buk-ro 4gil, Mapo-gu, Seoul, 121-819, Korea (South)
Tel.: (82) 2 701 2091
Plastics Product Mfr
N.A.I.C.S.: 326199

Richell Kun Shan Plastic Science and Technolgy Co., Ltd. (1)
257 Zhen Yi Shuo Shi Ba Cheng, Kunshan, Jiangsu, China
Tel.: (86) 512 8617 8667
Plastics Product Mfr
N.A.I.C.S.: 326199

Richell U.S.A. (1)
2100 N State Hwy 360 Ste 1700, Grand Prairie, TX 75050 (100%)
Tel.: (972) 641-9795
Web Site: http://www.richellusa.com
Sales Range: $50-74.9 Million
Emp.: 8
Rubber Products
N.A.I.C.S.: 314910
Issakau Suzuki (COO)

RICHFIELD FINANCIAL SERVICES LTD.
2B Grant Lane 2nd Floor, Kolkata, 700 001, West Bengal, India
Tel.: (91) 3330230347
Web Site: https://www.rfsl.co.in
539435—(BOM)
Rev: $146,293
Assets: $1,085,183
Liabilities: $11,257
Net Worth: $1,073,925
Earnings: $59,449
Emp.: 5
Fiscal Year-end: 03/31/21
Financial Support Services
N.A.I.C.S.: 523999
Siddharth Banthia (CFO)

RICHFIELD INTERNATIONAL LIMITED
10 Hoe Chiang Road 10-01 Keppel Towers, Singapore, 089315, Singapore
Tel.: (65) 68802900   AU
Web Site: http://www.richfield.com.sg
Year Founded: 1984
Sales Range: $1-9.9 Million
Emp.: 26
Port & Shipping Services
N.A.I.C.S.: 488310
Chew Tan Chak (Mng Dir)

Subsidiaries:

Richfield Marine Agencies (S) Pte Ltd (1)
250 Tanjong Pagar Rd, No 08-00 St Andrew, Singapore, 088541, Singapore
Tel.: (65) 62250133
Shipping Agency Services
N.A.I.C.S.: 488330

Speeda Shipping Company (S) Pte Ltd (1)
10 Hoe Chiang Rd Unit 10-01 Capell tower, No 08 St Andrew Ctr, Singapore, 089315, Singapore
Tel.: (65) 68802900

RICHFIELD INTERNATIONAL LIMITED

Richfield International Limited—(Continued)
Web Site: http://www.speeda.com.sg
Sales Range: $25-49.9 Million
Emp.: 25
Shipping Container Services
N.A.I.C.S.: 488330
Pan Chakchew *(Mng Dir)*

RICHINFO TECHNOLOGY CO., LTD.
31st Floor Caixun Technology Innovation Center, High-tech South District Nanshan District No 3176 Keyuan South Road, Shenzhen, 518063, Guangdong, China
Tel.: (86) 75586022519
Web Site: https://www.richinfo.cn
Year Founded: 2004
300634—(CHIN)
Rev.: $210,769,025
Assets: $454,835,961
Liabilities: $79,272,070
Net Worth: $375,563,891
Earnings: $45,724,178
Fiscal Year-end: 12/31/23
Software Development Services
N.A.I.C.S.: 513210
Yang Liangzhi *(Chm)*

RICHIRICH INVENTURES LIMITED
A-1 Emperor Court Ground Floor Yashwant Nagar Vakola, Mumbai, 400055, Maharashtra, India
Tel.: (91) 2279664656
Web Site: http://www.richirichinventures.com
519230—(BOM)
Rev.: $1,152,934
Assets: $25,506,840
Liabilities: $398,962
Net Worth: $25,107,878
Earnings: ($951,719)
Fiscal Year-end: 03/31/21
Investment Management Service
N.A.I.C.S.: 523999
Abhishek Kumar Mishra *(CEO & CFO)*

RICHLY FIELD CHINA DEVELOPMENT LIMITED
Suite 506 ICBC Tower 3 Garden Road, Central, China (Hong Kong)
Tel.: (852) 36287338 Ky
Web Site: http://www.richlyfieldchinagroup.com
Year Founded: 1990
313—(HKG)
Rev.: $5,309,849
Assets: $681,723,919
Liabilities: $731,376,318
Net Worth: ($49,652,399)
Earnings: ($53,614,664)
Emp.: 233
Fiscal Year-end: 03/31/21
Commercial Properties Operations; Construction Services
N.A.I.C.S.: 236115
Yi Feng Li *(Chm & CEO)*

RICHMOND ACURA
5580 Parkwood Crescent, Richmond, V6V 0B5, BC, Canada
Tel.: (604) 278-8999
Web Site: http://www.acurarichmond.com
Year Founded: 1986
Emp.: 50
New & Used Car Dealers
N.A.I.C.S.: 441110
Lam Nguyen *(Sls Mgr)*

RICHMOND INTERNATIONAL TRAVEL & TOURS CO., LTD.
4F 85 Sec 2 NanChing East Road, Zhongshan Dist, Taipei, 104, Taiwan
Tel.: (886) 225612999
2743—(TPE)
Rev.: $17,491,011
Assets: $39,891,849
Liabilities: $22,959,385
Net Worth: $16,932,464
Earnings: ($2,014,883)
Fiscal Year-end: 12/31/22
Travel Support Services
N.A.I.C.S.: 624190
Chico K. S. Chen *(Chm & CEO)*

RICHMOND MINERALS INC.
120 Adelaide Street West Suite 2500, Toronto, M5H 1T1, ON, Canada
Tel.: (416) 603-2114
Web Site: https://www.richmondminerals.com
R520—(DEU)
Assets: $2,074,944
Liabilities: $476,639
Net Worth: $1,598,305
Earnings: ($561,454)
Fiscal Year-end: 05/31/24
Mineral Exploration Services
N.A.I.C.S.: 213114
Warren Hawkins *(Mgr-Exploration)*

RICHMOND SUBARU
3511 No 3 Road, Richmond, V6X 2B8, BC, Canada
Tel.: (604) 273-0333
Web Site: http://www.richmondsubaru.com
Year Founded: 1993
Rev.: $35,212,705
Emp.: 70
Subaru Automotive Dealer
N.A.I.C.S.: 441110
Dan Duskworth *(Gen Mgr-Sls)*

RICHMOND VANADIUM TECHNOLOGY LIMITED
Level 11251 Adelaide Terrace, Perth, 6000, WA, Australia
Tel.: (61) 861419500 AU
Web Site: https://www.richmondvanadium.com
Year Founded: 2017
RVT—(ASX)
Rev.: $164,349
Assets: $31,911,597
Liabilities: $900,608
Net Worth: $31,010,990
Earnings: ($2,392,594)
Fiscal Year-end: 06/30/23
Mineral Exploration Services
N.A.I.C.S.: 212390
Joanne Day *(Sec)*

RICHOUX GROUP PLC
172 Piccadilly, London, W1J 9EJ, United Kingdom
Tel.: (44) 207 493 2204 UK
Web Site: http://www.richouxgroup.co.uk
Year Founded: 1909
Rev.: $14,837,622
Assets: $8,468,426
Liabilities: $3,618,340
Net Worth: $4,850,086
Earnings: ($6,030,566)
Emp.: 246
Fiscal Year-end: 12/31/17
Restaurant Operators
N.A.I.C.S.: 722511
Jonathan Kaye *(CEO)*

RICHREACH CORPORATION PUBLIC LTD.
Office 402 61A Larnakos Avenue, PO Box 14179, Aglantzia, CY2101, Nicosia, Cyprus
Tel.: (357) 22339999 CY
Web Site: https://www.eumbrellacorp.com
Year Founded: 2016
EUMBR—(CYP)
Rev.: $322,569
Assets: $778,639
Liabilities: $237,353
Net Worth: $541,285
Earnings: ($213,290)
Emp.: 7
Fiscal Year-end: 12/31/19
Software Development Services
N.A.I.C.S.: 541511
George Rousou *(CFO & COO)*

RICHTEK TECHNOLOGY CORPORATION
14F No 8 Tai Yuen 1st Street, Chupei, Hsinchu, Taiwan
Tel.: (886) 3 552 6789
Web Site: http://www.richtek.com
Year Founded: 1998
Sales Range: $350-399.9 Million
Emp.: 950
Analog Integrated Circuits Mfr
N.A.I.C.S.: 334413
York Chang *(VP-Admin)*

Subsidiaries:

Richpower Microelectronics Corporation (1)
Room 2102 1077 Zuchongzhi Road, Pudong, Shanghai, China
Tel.: (86) 21 50277077
Web Site: http://www.richpower-ic.com
Electronic Components Mfr
N.A.I.C.S.: 334419

RICHTREE MARKET RESTAURANTS, INC.
401 Bay Ste 1210, Toronto, M5H 2Y4, ON, Canada
Tel.: (416) 366-8122
Web Site: http://www.richtree.ca
Year Founded: 1996
Sales Range: $25-49.9 Million
Emp.: 15
Restaurant Services
N.A.I.C.S.: 722511
Edgar Wijayaratnam *(Dir-Engrg)*

RICHVALE YORK BLOCK INC.
5 Cardico Drive, Gormley, L0H 1G0, ON, Canada
Tel.: (416) 213-7447
Web Site: http://www.richvaleyork.com
Year Founded: 1952
Rev.: $16,053,530
Emp.: 100
Construction Materials Supplier
N.A.I.C.S.: 423320
Stanley Stankiewicz *(Founder)*

RICHWAVE TECHNOLOGY CORPORATION
6F No 5 Alley 20 Lane 407 Sec 2 Tiding Blvd, Taipei, 114, Taiwan
Tel.: (886) 287511358
Web Site: https://www.richwave.com.tw
4968—(TAI)
Rev.: $97,602,305
Assets: $103,873,046
Liabilities: $31,921,742
Net Worth: $71,951,304
Earnings: ($7,269,335)
Emp.: 306
Fiscal Year-end: 12/31/23
Wireless Communications Technology
N.A.I.C.S.: 334290

Subsidiaries:

Aegis Link Corp. (1)
Metropolitan Ctr 1 Meadowlands Plz, East Rutherford, NJ 07073
Tel.: (201) 508-2600
Web Site: https://www.aegislink.com
Emp.: 200

INTERNATIONAL PUBLIC

Mutual Insurance Services
N.A.I.C.S.: 524210

RICHY PLACE 2002 PUBLIC COMPANY LIMITED
667/15 7th Floor Attaboon Building Jaransanitwong Road, Arun Amarin bankkok Noi, Bangkok, 10700, Thailand
Tel.: (66) 28861817
Web Site: https://www.richy.co.th
RICHY—(THA)
Rev.: $23,358,539
Assets: $201,464,294
Liabilities: $116,484,426
Net Worth: $84,979,868
Earnings: ($1,807,567)
Fiscal Year-end: 12/31/23
Residential Real Estate Development
N.A.I.C.S.: 236115
Apa Ataboonwongse *(Vice Chm, Vice Chm & CEO)*

RICI HEALTHCARE HOLDINGS LIMITED
20/F Building 1 Donghang Binjiang Center No 277 Longlan Road, Xuhui District, Shanghai, China
Tel.: (86) 2168865787 Ky
Web Site: http://www.richhealthcare.com
Year Founded: 2000
1526—(HKG)
Rev.: $333,453,791
Assets: $641,186,863
Liabilities: $514,149,293
Net Worth: $127,037,570
Earnings: $37,513,055
Emp.: 8,737
Fiscal Year-end: 12/31/22
Health Care Srvices
N.A.I.C.S.: 622110
Yixin Fang *(Co-Founder & Chm)*

Subsidiaries:

Nantong Rich Hospital Co., Ltd. (1)
No 2000 Xinghu Avenue, Nantong Economic Technological Development Area, Nantong, Jiangsu, China
Tel.: (86) 51385969666
Web Site: https://www.en.nantong.gov.cn
Healtcare Services
N.A.I.C.S.: 621999

RICKMERS HOLDING AG
Neumuhlen 19, 22763, Hamburg, Germany
Tel.: (49) 403891770 De
Web Site: http://www.rickmers.com
Sales Range: $1-4.9 Billion
Emp.: 3,650
Holding Company; Marine Cargo Vessels Owner & Operator
N.A.I.C.S.: 551112
Lutz R. Ristow *(Chm-Supervisory Bd)*

Subsidiaries:

GLOBAL Management Ltd. (1)
196 Makarios III Avenue Ariel Corner Office 401, 3030, Limassol, Cyprus
Tel.: (357) 25898 000
Marine Cargo Handling Services
N.A.I.C.S.: 488320

Subsidiary (Non-US):

Rickmers Marine Agency Romania S.R.L. (2)
GSS Building 158 Mamaia Avenue 2nd Floor Room 1, 900575, Constanta, Romania
Tel.: (40) 241 545 514
Web Site: http://www.rickmers.com
Marine Cargo Handling Services
N.A.I.C.S.: 488320

Rickmers Shipping (Shanghai) Co. Ltd. (2)
Part B 20 /Flr Yangpu Building No 5 Anshan Road, Yangpu District, Shanghai, China

AND PRIVATE COMPANIES

Tel.: (86) 21 6579 1251
Marine Cargo Handling Services
N.A.I.C.S.: 488320

Polaris Shipmanagement Co. Ltd. (1)
2nd floor Railway Chambers Bank Circus, Douglas, Isle of Man
Tel.: (44) 1624 631 680
Marine Cargo Handling Services
N.A.I.C.S.: 488320
Jean Hui *(Mgr-Fin & Acctg)*

Rickmers Reederei GmbH & Cie. KG (1)
Neumuhlen 19, Hamburg, 22763, Germany
Tel.: (49) 403891770
Web Site: http://www.rickmers.de
Sales Range: $125-149.9 Million
Emp.: 400
Sea Freight Transportation
N.A.I.C.S.: 483211
Bertram R.C. Rickmers *(Chm-Exec Bd)*

Subsidiary (Domestic):

ATLANTIC mbH & Co. KG (2)
Neumuhlen 19, D 22763, Hamburg, Germany (100%)
Tel.: (49) 389177900
Web Site: http://www.rickmers.de
Sales Range: $75-99.9 Million
Emp.: 200
International Investment.
N.A.I.C.S.: 523940

Subsidiary (Non-US):

Rickmers Reederei (Singapore) Pte. Ltd. (2)
8 Shenton Way 42-01, 68811, Singapore, Singapore
Tel.: (65) 6372 6300
Marine Cargo Handling Services
N.A.I.C.S.: 488320

Rickmers Trust Management Pte. Ltd. (1)
8 Shenton Way 42-03, RCL Centre, Singapore, 068811, Singapore
Tel.: (65) 65066960
Web Site: http://www.rickmers-maritime.com
Sales Range: $50-74.9 Million
Emp.: 9
Trust Management Services
N.A.I.C.S.: 523991
Elizabeth Krishnan *(Co-Sec)*

RICKSOFT CO., LTD.
2-1-1 Otemachi, Chiyoda-Ku, Tokyo, 100-0004, Japan
Tel.: (81) 362623947
Web Site: https://www.ricksoft.jp
4429—(TKS)
Rev.: $53,111,190
Assets: $42,291,850
Liabilities: $22,673,820
Net Worth: $19,618,030
Earnings: $1,907,210
Emp.: 20
Fiscal Year-end: 02/29/24
Information Technology Services
N.A.I.C.S.: 541512
Hiroshi Ohnuki *(Founder & CEO)*

RICO AUTO INDUSTRIES LIMITED
38 KM Stone Delhi - Jaipur Highway, Gurgaon, 122001, Haryana, India
Tel.: (91) 124284000
Web Site: https://www.ricoauto.com
RICOAUTO—(NSE)
Rev.: $203,172,060
Assets: $224,352,765
Liabilities: $141,236,550
Net Worth: $83,116,215
Earnings: ($1,920,555)
Emp.: 1,598
Fiscal Year-end: 03/31/21
Aluminum Components Supplier
N.A.I.C.S.: 331523
Arvind Kapur *(Chm, CEO & Co-Mng Dir)*

Subsidiaries:

Rico Auto Industries (UK) Ltd. (1)
Unit 1 Lewis House 99 Victoria Road, London, NW10 6DJ, United Kingdom
Tel.: (44) 2031743007
Aluminum Casting Component Mfr
N.A.I.C.S.: 331524

Rico Auto Industries Inc. (1)
6338 Sashabaw, Clarkston, MI 48346
Tel.: (248) 409-0960
Aluminum Casting Component Mfr
N.A.I.C.S.: 331524

RICO ELASTOMERE PROJECTING GMBH
Am Thalbach 8, 4600, Wels, Thalheim, Austria
Tel.: (43) 7242 76460
Web Site: http://www.rico.at
Year Founded: 1994
Elastomer Molded Parts Mfr
N.A.I.C.S.: 325212
Markus Nuspl *(Mng Dir)*

Subsidiaries:

SIMTEC Silicone Parts, LLC (1)
9658 Premier Pkwy, Miramar, FL 33025
Tel.: (954) 289-6161
Web Site: https://www.simtec-silicone.com
Liquid Silicone Rubber Component Mfr
N.A.I.C.S.: 325998

RICOH COMPANY, LTD.
3-6 Nakamagome 1-chome Ohta-ku, Tokyo, 143-8555, Japan
Tel.: (81) 337778111   JP
Web Site: https://www.ricoh.com
Year Founded: 1936
RICOY—(OTCIQ)
Rev.: $17,023,122,160
Assets: $17,939,498,720
Liabilities: $9,171,112,720
Net Worth: $8,768,386,000
Earnings: $293,991,280
Emp.: 78,360
Fiscal Year-end: 03/31/22
Printing & Imaging Equipment Mfr
N.A.I.C.S.: 325992
Seiji Sakata *(CTO & Exec VP)*

Subsidiaries:

Lanier Australia Pty Ltd (1)
650 Lorimer St, Port Melbourne, Port Melbourne, 3207, VIC, Australia
Tel.: (61) 3 9676 1000
Web Site: http://www.ricoh.com.au
Emp.: 110
Photo Copier & Printer Mfr
N.A.I.C.S.: 322230
John Hall *(Mng Dir)*

PFU Limited (1)
No 98 2 Unoke Kahoku, Kanazawa, 929 1192, Ishikawa, Japan
Tel.: (81) 762831212
Web Site: http://www.pfu.co.jp
Sales Range: $200-249.9 Million
Emp.: 650
Mfr & Sales of Small Computer Systems & Workstations
N.A.I.C.S.: 334118

Subsidiary (Domestic):

PFU Applications Limited (2)
658-1 Tsuruma Kk Pfu Tokyo Kaihatsu Center Nai, Machida, Tokyo, 194-0004, Japan
Tel.: (81) 427887660
Application Software Development Services
N.A.I.C.S.: 541511

PFU Creative Services Limited (2)
98-2 Nu Unoke, Kahoku, 929-1125, Ishikawa, Japan
Tel.: (81) 762838625
Human Resource Consulting Services
N.A.I.C.S.: 541612

PFU East Japan Limited (2)
4-4-13 Tsutsujigaoka Densan 88 Bldg, Miyagino-Ku, Sendai, 983-0852, Miyagi, Japan

Tel.: (81) 222932711
Web Site: http://www.pfu.co.jp
Software Development Services
N.A.I.C.S.: 541511

PFU Hokkaido Limited (2)
29-26 Kita11jo-Higashi6, Higashi-ku, Sapporo, Hokkaido, Japan
Tel.: (81) 11 711 6911
Computer Hardware Distr
N.A.I.C.S.: 423430

PFU Human Design Limited (2)
658-1 Tsuruma, Machida, 194-0004, Tokyo, Japan
Tel.: (81) 427887658
Web Site: http://www.pfu.fujitsu.com
Human Resource Consulting Services
N.A.I.C.S.: 541612

Subsidiary (Non-US):

PFU Imaging Solutions Europe Limited (2)
Hayes Park Central Hayes End Road, Hayes, UB4 8FE, Middlesex, United Kingdom
Tel.: (44) 208 573 4444
Emp.: 80
Computer Scanner Distr
N.A.I.C.S.: 423430
Satoshi Yamada *(Co-Pres)*

Subsidiary (Domestic):

PFU Life Agency Limited (2)
98-2 Nu Unoke, Kahoku, Ishikawa, 929-1125, Japan
Tel.: (81) 762836111
Business Support Services
N.A.I.C.S.: 561110

PFU Quality Service Limited (2)
602-9 Funako Sun Intel Net Bldg 2f, Atsugi, 243-0034, Kanagawa, Japan
Tel.: (81) 462266400
Software Development Services
N.A.I.C.S.: 541511

Subsidiary (Non-US):

PFU Shanghai Co., Ltd. (2)
5F Bldg 46 No 555 Guiping Road, Shanghai, 200233, China
Tel.: (86) 2164850118
Web Site: http://www.psh.com.cn
Rev.: $16,611,943
Emp.: 27
Software Development Services
N.A.I.C.S.: 541511
Amai Yutaka *(Chm)*

Subsidiary (Domestic):

PFU Jiangsu Nantong Information Systems Co., Ltd. (3)
2F Bldg No 488 Gongnong Road, Nantong, 226007, Jiangsu, China
Tel.: (86) 513 85281278
Web Site: http://www.pfu.fujitsu.com
Software Development Services
N.A.I.C.S.: 541511

PFU Shanghai Information Systems Co., Ltd. (3)
Floor 3-5 Building 46 No 555 Guiping Road, Xuhui District, Shanghai, 200233, China
Tel.: (86) 2164850118
Web Site: http://www.psh.com.cn
Sales Range: $25-49.9 Million
Software Development Services
N.A.I.C.S.: 541511
Yunfeng Tu *(Pres)*

Subsidiary (Domestic):

PFU Software Limited (2)
98-2 Nu Unoke, Kahoku, Ishikawa, 929-1192, Japan
Tel.: (81) 762835800
Software Development Services
N.A.I.C.S.: 541511

Subsidiary (US):

PFU Systems, Inc. (2)
1250 E Arques Ave, Sunnyvale, CA 94085
Tel.: (408) 992-2900
Web Site: http://www.pfusystems.com
Computer Peripheral Equipment Mfr
N.A.I.C.S.: 334118

RICOH COMPANY, LTD.

Yasuhiko Nagaoka *(Sr VP-Res & Engrg)*

Subsidiary (Non-US):

PFU TECHNOLOGY SINGAPORE PTE LTD (2)
No 8 Kim Chuan Drive 03-02 SIIX Building, Singapore, 537083, Singapore
Tel.: (65) 6285 0330
Web Site: http://www.pfu.fujitsu.com
Sales Range: $25-49.9 Million
Emp.: 9
Computer Peripheral Equipment Mfr
N.A.I.C.S.: 334118
Hitoshi Terashima *(Mng Dir)*

Subsidiary (Domestic):

PFU TOHTO Limited (2)
1-5-7 Kameido Nittetsu ND Tower 2f, Koto-Ku, Tokyo, 136-0071, Japan
Tel.: (81) 356278411
Software Development Services
N.A.I.C.S.: 541511

PFU Techno Wise Limited (2)
1 Shi Takamatsu Prodes Center Nai Prodes Kojo, Kahoku, 929-1215, Ishikawa, Japan
Tel.: (81) 762813380
Computer Peripheral Equipment Mfr
N.A.I.C.S.: 334118

PFU Technoconsul Limited (2)
98-2 Nu Unoke, Kahoku, Ishikawa, 929-1125, Japan
Tel.: (81) 762838600
Software Consulting Services
N.A.I.C.S.: 541512

Ricoh Argentina, S.A. (1)
Dr Nicolas Repetto 3656 piso 7, B1636BYB, Olivos, Buenos Aires, Argentina
Tel.: (54) 114 711 8000
Web Site: http://www.ricoh.com.ar
Office Machinery Mfr
N.A.I.C.S.: 333310

Ricoh Asia Industry (Shenzhen) Ltd. (1)
Color TV Industrial Zone North Huang Gang Road, Shenzhen, China
Tel.: (86) 75583360885
Copier & Laser Printer Mfr
N.A.I.C.S.: 333310

Ricoh Asia Industry Ltd. (1)
3/F Grandmark 8a-10 Granville Rd, Tsim Tsa Tsui, Kowloon, China (Hong Kong)
Tel.: (852) 23110636
Web Site: http://www.ricoh.com
Sales Range: $50-74.9 Million
Emp.: 2
Fax Machine Distr
N.A.I.C.S.: 423420

Ricoh Asia Pacific Operations Ltd. (1)
21/F One Kowloon 1 Wang Yuen Street, Kowloon Bay, Kowloon, China (Hong Kong)
Tel.: (852) 2862 2888
Emp.: 80
Office Equipment Distr
N.A.I.C.S.: 423420

Ricoh Asia Pacific Pte Ltd. (1)
103 Penang Road 08-01/07 Visoncrest Commercial, Singapore, 238467, Singapore (100%)
Tel.: (65) 68305888
Web Site: http://www.ricoh.com.sg
Sales Range: $25-49.9 Million
Emp.: 100
N.A.I.C.S.: 339940

Subsidiary (Non-US):

Gestetner Bangladesh Ltd. (2)
Alad Chamber Ground FL 68, Chittagong, 88031, Bangladesh (100%)
Tel.: (880) 31724060
Sales Range: Less than $1 Million
Emp.: 14
Office Equipment & Supplies
N.A.I.C.S.: 423420

Minosha India Ltd. (2)
Plot No 25 Okhla Phase- 3, District Centre Jasola, New Delhi, 110020, India (73.6%)
Tel.: (91) 114 226 6250
Web Site: https://www.minosha.in

RICOH COMPANY, LTD.

Ricoh Company, Ltd.—(Continued)
Sales Range: $250-299.9 Million
Emp.: 1,050
Photographic Equipment Whslr
N.A.I.C.S.: 423410
Manish Sehgal *(Sec)*

Ricoh (Malaysia) Sdn. Bhd. (2)
Lock Store Level 1 No 5 Jalan Penyair U1/44, 40150, Shah Alam, Selangor Darul Ehsan, Malaysia
Tel.: (60) 300888228
Web Site: https://www.ricoh.com.my
Sales Range: $125-149.9 Million
Wholesale Distributor of Copiers & Office Equipment
N.A.I.C.S.: 423420

Ricoh Electronic Technology (China) Co., Ltd. (2)
11Floor Meiheng Building No 369 Wuzhong Road, Shanghai, 201103, China (100%)
Tel.: (86) 2164851059
Sales Range: $25-49.9 Million
Emp.: 15
N.A.I.C.S.: 423420
Gao Jian Dong *(Mgr-Sls)*

Ricoh Hong Kong Ltd. (2)
20/F One Kowloon 1 Wang Yuen Street, Kowloon Bay, China (Hong Kong) (100%)
Tel.: (852) 2 893 0022
Web Site: https://www.ricoh.com.hk
N.A.I.C.S.: 339940
Eeron Yim *(Mng Dir)*

Ricoh New Zealand Ltd. (2)
200 Victoria Street West, Auckland Central, Newton, 1010, Auckland, New Zealand (100%)
Tel.: (64) 9 374 0701
Web Site: http://www.ricoh.co.nz
Sales Range: $25-49.9 Million
Emp.: 100
Office Equipment Distribution
N.A.I.C.S.: 423420

Subsidiary (Domestic):

Ricoh Singapore Pte. Ltd. (2)
20W Pasir Panjang Road 04-28 Maplestree Business City, Matle Ple Business Park, Singapore, 117439, Singapore (100%)
Tel.: (65) 6 474 0777
Web Site: https://www.ricoh.sg
Sales Range: $50-74.9 Million
Wholesale Distributor of Copiers & Office Equipment
N.A.I.C.S.: 423420
Vincent Lim *(Mng Dir)*

Ricoh Australia Pty, Ltd. (1)
Level 1 2 Richardson Place, North Ryde, 2113, NSW, Australia
Tel.: (61) 137 4264
Web Site: https://www.ricoh.com.au
Managed Document Services
N.A.I.C.S.: 561499
Nobuaki Majima *(Mng Dir)*

Ricoh Brasil, S.A. (1)
Avenida Ceci 286 Centro Empresarial Tambore, Barra da Tijuca, Barueri, 06460-120, Sao Paulo, Brazil
Tel.: (55) 112 575 4400
Web Site: http://www.ricoh.com.br
Sales Range: $50-74.9 Million
Emp.: 40
Office Equipment Distr
N.A.I.C.S.: 423420
Diego Imperio *(Pres)*

Ricoh Chile, S.A. (1)
Rosario Norte 532 Of 301, Las Condes, Santiago, 7561185, Chile
Tel.: (56) 2 367 7200
Web Site: http://www.ricoh.cl
Sales Range: $75-99.9 Million
Emp.: 240
Office Equipment Distr
N.A.I.C.S.: 423420
Roberto Donoso Rojas *(Gen Mgr)*

Ricoh China Co., Ltd. (1)
24th Fl Lansheng Building No 2-8 Huaihai Zhong Road, Shanghai, 200021, China
Tel.: (86) 215 238 0222
Web Site: http://www.ricoh.com.cn
Photo Copier & Printer Distr
N.A.I.C.S.: 424120

Ricoh Colombia, S.A. (1)
Carrera 85K N 46A - 66 Building 2 Floor 5 Industrial Park, San Cayetano, Bogota, Cundinamarca, Colombia
Tel.: (57) 1 457 8999
Web Site: http://www.ricoh.com.co
Office Equipment Distr
N.A.I.C.S.: 423420

Ricoh Company, Ltd. - Atsugi Plant (1)
1005 Shimo-Ogino, Atsugi, 243-0298, Kanagawa, Japan
Tel.: (81) 46 241 1511
Web Site: https://www.ricoh.com
Office Equipments Mfr
N.A.I.C.S.: 333310

Ricoh Company, Ltd. - Fukui Plant (1)
64-1 Ohmi Sakai-cho, Sakai, 919-0547, Fukui, Japan
Tel.: (81) 776 72 2700
Emp.: 200
Office Equipments Mfr
N.A.I.C.S.: 333310
Kunitoshi Sugiyama *(Gen Mgr)*

Ricoh Company, Ltd. - Gotemba Plant (1)
1-10 Komakado, Gotemba, 412-0038, Shizuoka, Japan
Tel.: (81) 550 87 3210
Web Site: https://www.ricoh.com
Printer & Copier Mfr
N.A.I.C.S.: 334118

Ricoh Company, Ltd. - Ikeda Plant (1)
13-1 Himemuro-cho, Ikeda, 563-8501, Osaka, Japan
Tel.: (81) 72 753 1111
Web Site: http://www.ricoh.co.jp
Office Equipments Mfr
N.A.I.C.S.: 322230

Ricoh Company, Ltd. - Numazu Plant (1)
16-1 Hontamachi, Sakai, Numazu, 410-8505, Shizuoka, Japan
Tel.: (81) 55 920 1000
Web Site: https://www.ricoh.com
Office Equipments Mfr
N.A.I.C.S.: 322230

Ricoh Company, Ltd. - Ohmori Plant (1)
3-6 Nakamagome 1-chome, Ohta-ku, Tokyo, 143-8555, Japan
Tel.: (81) 3 3777 8111
Office Equipments Mfr
N.A.I.C.S.: 322230

Ricoh Company, Ltd. - Yashiro Plant (1)
30-1 Saho, Kato, 673-1447, Hyogo, Japan
Tel.: (81) 795 42 6111
Web Site: http://www.ricoh.com
Printer & Copier Mfr
N.A.I.C.S.: 334118

Ricoh Components & Products (Shenzhen) Co., Ltd. (1)
RICOH industry group HaoYeRoad HePing Community, Fuyong Town Baoan District, Shenzhen, Guangdong, China
Tel.: (86) 755 2753 4938
Web Site: http://www.ricoh.com
Printed Circuit Board & Electronic Component Mfr
N.A.I.C.S.: 334418

Ricoh Components Asia (Hong Kong) Co., Ltd. (1)
3/F Grandmark 8a-10 Granville Rd, Tsim Tsa Tsui, Kowloon, China (Hong Kong)
Tel.: (852) 23110636
Web Site: http://www.ricoh.com.hk
Sales Range: $50-74.9 Million
Emp.: 2
Office Equipment Distr
N.A.I.C.S.: 423420
Kenji Takegami *(Mgr)*

Ricoh Costa Rica, S.A. (1)
Heredia La Valencia Oficentro Technopark Costado Oeste de Auto Xiri, Contiguo a Mc Donald's, San Jose, Heredia, Costa Rica
Tel.: (506) 2 210 9300

Web Site: https://www.ricoh-americalatina.com
Office Equipment Distr
N.A.I.C.S.: 423420
Jose Leonardo Rodriguez *(Gen Mgr)*

Ricoh Del Peru S.A.C. (1)
Av Victor Andres Belaunde 147 Torre Real 6 - Of 402, San Isidro, Lima, 12, Peru
Tel.: (51) 1 716 3600
Web Site: http://www.ricoh.pe
Office Equipment Distr
N.A.I.C.S.: 423420

Ricoh Denmark A/S (1)
Vallensbaekvej 44, 2625, Vallensbaek, Denmark
Tel.: (45) 70 10 67 68
Computer Peripheral Equipment Distr
N.A.I.C.S.: 423430

Ricoh El Salvador, S.A. de C.V. (1)
55 Avenida Sur No 153 Entre Alameda Roosevel ty Avenida Olimpica, San Salvador, El Salvador
Tel.: (503) 2 567 3500
Web Site: http://www.ricoh.com.sv
Office Equipment Distr
N.A.I.C.S.: 423420

Ricoh Electronic Devices Korea Co., Ltd. (1)
3rd Floor Haesung 1 Building 942 Daechi-dong, Gangnamgu, Seoul, 135-845, Korea (South)
Tel.: (82) 2 2135 5700
Electronic Components Distr
N.A.I.C.S.: 423690
Yoshitaka Shibata *(Gen Mgr)*

Ricoh Electronic Devices Shanghai Co., Ltd. (1)
Room 403 No 2 Building 690 Bi Bo Road Zhangjiang Hi-Tech Park, Shanghai, 201203, China
Tel.: (86) 215 027 3200
Web Site: https://www.ricoh.com
Electronic Components Mfr
N.A.I.C.S.: 334419
Masahiro Nakamura *(Chm)*

Ricoh Elemex Corporation (1)
3-69 Ida-cho, Chikusa-ku, Okazaki, 444-8586, Aichi, Japan (100%)
Tel.: (81) 56 423 5111
Web Site: https://www.ricohelemex.co.jp
Emp.: 749
High-Precision Manufacturing Technology
N.A.I.C.S.: 334419

Subsidiary (Non-US):

Dongguan Ricoh Elemex Office Machine Co., Ltd. (2)
Xiao -Bian The Second Industry Zone, Chang-An Town, Dongguan, Guangdong, China
Tel.: (86) 2038182008
High-Precision Manufacturing Technology
N.A.I.C.S.: 334419

Subsidiary (Domestic):

Ricoh Elemex AT Corporation (2)
2-14-29, Uchiyama, Chikusa-ku, Nagoya, 464-0075, Japan
Tel.: (81) 527340301
Web Site: http://www.ricohelemex.co.jp
Sales Range: $200-249.9 Million
Emp.: 1,000
High-Precision Manufacturing Technology
N.A.I.C.S.: 334419

Subsidiary (Non-US):

Ricoh Elemex Hong Kong Limited (2)
room 2302, 23/F, Saxon Tower, 7 Cheung Shun St, Lai Chi Kok, Kowloon, China (Hong Kong)
Tel.: (852) 23144138
Web Site: http://www.ricohelemex.co.jp
High-Precision Manufacturing Technology
N.A.I.C.S.: 334419

Ricoh Europe PLC (1)
20 Triton Street, London, NW1 3BF, United Kingdom
Tel.: (44) 207 465 1000
Web Site: https://www.ricoh-europe.com

INTERNATIONAL PUBLIC

Sales Range: $1-4.9 Billion
Emp.: 7,000
Office Equipment & Photographic Supplies
N.A.I.C.S.: 423420

Subsidiary (Non-US):

Gestetner (Israel) Limited (2)
110 Yigal Allon St, 67891, Tel Aviv, Israel (100%)
Tel.: (972) 35657701
Web Site: http://www.gestetner.co.il
Wholesale Distributor of Copiers & Office Supplies
N.A.I.C.S.: 424120

Gestetner Limited (Malawi) (2)
Masauko Chipembere Hwy, PO Box 343, Blantyre, Malawi (100%)
Tel.: (265) 1671433
Sales Range: $1-9.9 Million
Emp.: 100
Wholesale Distributor of Copiers & Office Equipment
N.A.I.C.S.: 423420

Subsidiary (Domestic):

MTI Technology Limited (2)
Mill Pool House Mill Lane, Godalming, GU7 1EY, United Kingdom
Tel.: (44) 148 352 0200
Web Site: https://www.mti.com
Data Storage & Other Information Management Services
N.A.I.C.S.: 334118
Tony Conway *(VP-Customer Svc)*

Subsidiary (Non-US):

MTI France S.A.S. (3)
Parc Claude Monet 3-5 Allee de Giverny, 78290, Croissy-sur-Seine, France
Tel.: (33) 13 009 5200
Web Site: https://fr.mti.com
Data Storage & Other Information Management Services
N.A.I.C.S.: 334118
Damian Saura *(VP-Sls)*

MTI Technology GmbH (3)
Borsigstrasse 36, 65205, Wiesbaden, Germany
Tel.: (49) 6 122 9950
Web Site: https://www.mti.com
Marketing of Disk Drive Peripherals
N.A.I.C.S.: 449210
Thomas Rettig *(Dir-Customer Svc)*

Subsidiary (Non-US):

Rex-Rotary SAS (2)
3 rue Jesse Owens, 93210, Seine-Saint-Denis, La Plaine, France (100%)
Tel.: (33) 155841901
Web Site: http://www.rexrotary.com
Sales Range: $25-49.9 Million
Emp.: 30
Document Management Solutions, Services, Supplies & Consultancy
N.A.I.C.S.: 541611
David Mills *(Pres)*

Ricoh Austria GmbH (2)
Wiedner Girdle 11, 1100, Vienna, Austria (100%)
Tel.: (43) 574 2640
Web Site: https://www.ricoh.at
Office Equipment Sales & Leasing
N.A.I.C.S.: 532420

Ricoh Belgium NV (2)
Medialaan 28A, 1800, Vilvoorde, Belgium (100%)
Tel.: (32) 2 558 2211
Web Site: http://www.ricoh.be
Sales Range: $250-299.9 Million
Emp.: 700
Office Equipment
N.A.I.C.S.: 532420

Subsidiary (Domestic):

Ricoh Capital Limited (2)
Ricoh House, 15 Ullswater Crescent, Coulsdon, CR5 2HR, Surrey, United Kingdom
Tel.: (44) 2086687474
Web Site: http://www.ricoh.co.uk

AND PRIVATE COMPANIES

RICOH COMPANY, LTD.

Sales Range: $75-99.9 Million
Emp.: 200
Office Equipment Leasing & Sales
N.A.I.C.S.: 532490

Subsidiary (Non-US):

Ricoh Danmark A/S (2)
Delta Park 37, 2625, Vallensbaek, Denmark
Tel.: (45) 43666768
Web Site: https://www.ricoh.dk
Sales Range: $50-74.9 Million
Emp.: 180
Office Equipment & Services
N.A.I.C.S.: 423420
Gert Foshammer *(Dir-Svcs)*

Ricoh Deutschland GmbH (2)
Georg- Kohl-Strasse 42, 30179, Brackenheim, Germany (100%)
Tel.: (49) 5116742310
Web Site: http://www.ricoh.de
Sales Range: $50-74.9 Million
Emp.: 250
Marketer & Sales of Office Equipment
N.A.I.C.S.: 423420

Unit (Domestic):

Ricoh Deutschland GmbH (3)
Dornhofstrasse 44, 63263, Neu-Isenburg, Germany
Tel.: (49) 610220230
Office Equipment
N.A.I.C.S.: 423420

Subsidiary (Non-US):

Ricoh Espana, S.A. (2)
Avda Via Augusta 71, 08174, Sant Cugat del Valles, Spain (100%)
Tel.: (34) 902700000
Web Site: http://www.ricoh.es
Marketing & Sales of Office Equipment, Cameras
N.A.I.C.S.: 423420

Ricoh Europe (Netherlands) B.V. (2)
Prof W H Keesomlaan 1, 1183 DJ, Amstelveen, Netherlands (100%)
Tel.: (31) 205474111
Web Site: http://www.ricoh-europe.com
Sales Range: $125-149.9 Million
Emp.: 300
Office Equipment Marketer & Whslr
N.A.I.C.S.: 423420

Subsidiary (Domestic):

NRG Rex-Rotary B.V. (3)
Edelgasstraat 57, 2718 SX, Zoetermeer, Netherlands (100%)
Tel.: (31) 793467500
Sales Range: $25-49.9 Million
Emp.: 100
Provider of Document Management Solutions, Services, Supplies & Consultancy
N.A.I.C.S.: 339940

Ricoh Europe SCM B.V. (3)
Blankenweg 24, 4612 RC, Bergen-op-Zoom, Netherlands
Tel.: (31) 164280808
Web Site: http://www.ricoh.com
Sales Range: $25-49.9 Million
Emp.: 75
Office Equipment
N.A.I.C.S.: 423420
E. Kersjes *(VP)*

Ricoh International B.V. (3)
Nieuw Kronenburg, Prof WH Keesomlaan 1, 1183 DJ, Amstelveen, Netherlands
Tel.: (31) 205474300
Sales Range: $25-49.9 Million
Emp.: 70
Office Equipments Mfr
N.A.I.C.S.: 423420
Katsumi Kurihara *(Sr VP)*

Ricoh Nederland B.V. (3)
Magistratenlaan 2, 5223 MD, 's-Hertogenbosch, Netherlands
Tel.: (31) 73 645 1111
Web Site: https://www.ricoh.nl
Office Equipment
N.A.I.C.S.: 423420
Carol Dona *(CEO & Gen Mgr)*

Subsidiary (Non-US):

Ricoh Europe Holdings B.V. (2)

Prof WH Keesomlaan 1, PO Box 114, 1183 DJ, Amstelveen, Netherlands
Tel.: (31) 205474111
Web Site: http://www.ricoh-europe.com
Sales Range: $125-149.9 Million
Emp.: 500
Holding Company
N.A.I.C.S.: 551112

Ricoh France S.A.S. (2)
383 Ave De General De Gaulle, 92143, Clamart, Cedex, France (100%)
Tel.: (33) 140943838
Web Site: http://www.ricoh.fr
Sales Range: $200-249.9 Million
Emp.: 600
Office Machines, Cameras & Printers
N.A.I.C.S.: 423420

Ricoh Ireland Ltd. (2)
Dublin Industrial Estate 127 Slaney Rd, Glasnevin, Dublin, 11, Ireland (100%)
Tel.: (353) 18301388
Web Site: http://www.ricoh.ie
Sales Range: $25-49.9 Million
Emp.: 30
Office Equipment Sales & Leasing
N.A.I.C.S.: 532420

Ricoh Italia S.p.A. (2)
Via Della Metallurgia 12, 37139, Verona, Italy (100%)
Tel.: (39) 0458181500
Web Site: http://www.ricoh.it
Sales Range: $50-74.9 Million
Emp.: 150
Marketing & Sales of Office Equipment & Cameras
N.A.I.C.S.: 423420

Subsidiary (Domestic):

NPO Sistemi S.R.L. (3)
Viale Martesana 12, Vimodrone, 20055, Milan, Italy
Tel.: (39) 0292 5961
Web Site: https://www.nposistemi.it
IT Services
N.A.I.C.S.: 541990
Stefano Lombardi *(Mktg Mgr)*

Subsidiary (Non-US):

Ricoh South Africa (Pty) Limited (2)
28 Milkyway Avenue Linbro Business Park, Linbro, Bedfordview, 2090, Gauteng, South Africa (100%)
Tel.: (27) 11 723 5000
Web Site: http://www.ricoh.co.za
Sales Range: $125-149.9 Million
Emp.: 400
Document Management Solutions, Hardware & Software Solutions
N.A.I.C.S.: 423420
Richard Pinker *(Mng Dir)*

Ricoh Sweden AB (2)
Rontgenvagen 2, PO Box 1536, 171 29, Solna, Sweden (100%)
Tel.: (46) 8 734 3300
Web Site: https://www.ricoh.se
Sales Range: $25-49.9 Million
Emp.: 60
Copiers & Office Equipment
N.A.I.C.S.: 423420

Subsidiary (Domestic):

Ricoh UK Ltd. (2)
1 Plane Tree Crescent, Feltham, TW13 7HG, Mddx, United Kingdom (100%)
Tel.: (44) 2082614000
Web Site: http://www.ricoh.co.uk
Sales Range: $200-249.9 Million
Emp.: 500
Office Equipment
N.A.I.C.S.: 423420

Ricoh Finance Nederland B.V. (1)
Prof W H Keesomlaan 1, Amstelveen, 1183 DJ, North Holland, Netherlands
Tel.: (31) 205474111
Web Site: http://www.ricoh-europe.com
Financial Management Services
N.A.I.C.S.: 523999

Ricoh Finland Oy (1)
Piispantilankuja 4, 02240, Espoo, Finland
Tel.: (358) 207 370 300
Office Equipment Distr
N.A.I.C.S.: 423420

Ricoh Gestetner South Africa (Pty) Limited (1)
Eastwood Office Park 11B Riley Road, PO Box 2578, Bedfordview Ext 328, Bedfordview, 2008, Gauteng, South Africa
Tel.: (27) 11 723 5000
Office Equipment Distr
N.A.I.C.S.: 423420

Ricoh Hungary Kft. (1)
Vaci Ut 135-139, 1138, Budapest, Hungary
Tel.: (36) 1 270 9797
Sales Range: $50-74.9 Million
Emp.: 80
Office Equipment Distr
N.A.I.C.S.: 423420

Ricoh IT Solutions Co., Ltd. (1)
1-8-10 Harumi Harumi Island Toriton Square Office Tower X, Chuo-Ku, Tokyo, 104-0053, Japan
Tel.: (81) 355608911
Software Development Services
N.A.I.C.S.: 541511

Ricoh Imaging Co., Ltd. (1)
3F Helios II Bldg 1-12-11 Funado, Itabashi-ku, Tokyo, 174-0041, Japan
Tel.: (81) 3 3960 5140
Web Site: http://www.ricoh-imaging.com
Sales Range: $400-449.9 Million
Emp.: 1,900
Digital Camera & Binocular Mfr
N.A.I.C.S.: 333310
Noboru Akahane *(Pres)*

Subsidiary (US):

Ricoh Imaging Americas Corporation (2)
633 17th St Ste 2600, Denver, CO 80202
Tel.: (800) 877-0155
Web Site: http://www.us.ricoh-imaging.com
Digital Camera Distr
N.A.I.C.S.: 423420
James Malcolm *(Pres)*

Subsidiary (Non-US):

Ricoh Imaging Technology (Shanghai) Co., Ltd. (2)
4th Floor Building 3 No 7 Guiqing Road, Caohejing Development Zone, Shanghai, 200233, China
Tel.: (86) 2164958992
Web Site: https://www.ricoh-rits.com
Working Environment Software Development Services
N.A.I.C.S.: 541511

Ricoh Industrie France S.A.S. (1)
144 Route de Rouffach, 68920, Wettolsheim, France
Tel.: (33) 38 920 4000
Web Site: https://www.ricoh-thermal.com
Emp.: 700
Thermal Product Mfr
N.A.I.C.S.: 325992
Kazuo Nishinomiya *(VP)*

Ricoh International (Shanghai) Co., Ltd. (1)
Room F1 5F Zao-fong Universe Building No 1800 Zhongshan West Road, Shanghai, 201103, China
Tel.: (86) 215 046 0698
Web Site: https://www.ricoh.com
Optical Instrument Mfr
N.A.I.C.S.: 333310
Yasutomo Mori *(Chm)*

Ricoh Japan Corporation (1)
G7 Building 7-16-12 Ginza, Chuo-Ku, Tokyo, 104-8180, Japan
Tel.: (81) 3 6278 6600
Office Automation Equipment Distr
N.A.I.C.S.: 423420

Ricoh Leasing Company, Ltd. (1)
14F New Otani Garden Court 4-1 Kioicho, Chiyoda-ku, Tokyo, 102-8563, Japan (53.7%)
Tel.: (81) 362040603
Web Site: http://www.r-lease.co.jp
Rev.: $2,038,094,350
Assets: $8,244,494,360
Liabilities: $6,777,497,400
Net Worth: $1,466,996,960
Earnings: $74,547,580
Emp.: 1,641

Fiscal Year-end: 03/31/2024
Financial Lending Services
N.A.I.C.S.: 522220
Hirofumi Muto *(Exec Officer)*

Ricoh Luxembourg PSF Sarl (1)
Atrium Business Park Z I Bourmicht 37 Rue Du Puits Romain, 8070, Bertrange, Luxembourg
Tel.: (352) 335888
Office Equipment Distr
N.A.I.C.S.: 423420

Ricoh Manufacturing (Thailand) Ltd. (1)
7/152 Amata City Industrial Estate Moo 4 Tambol Mapyangporn, Amphur Pluakdaeng, Rayong, 21140, Thailand
Tel.: (66) 38 650 839
Printing Machinery Mfr
N.A.I.C.S.: 333248

Ricoh Norge A.S. (1)
Valle Wood Innspurten 13, PO Box 4873, Nydalen, Oslo, 0663, Norway
Tel.: (47) 2 258 7800
Web Site: https://www.ricoh.no
Emp.: 120
Office Machinery & Equipment Mfr
N.A.I.C.S.: 333310
Audun Ganstad *(Gen Mgr)*

Ricoh Optical Industries Co., Ltd. (1)
Ohata 10-109, Hanamaki, Iwate, Japan
Tel.: (81) 198 26 4011
Web Site: http://www.optical.ricoh.co.jp
Sales Range: $200-249.9 Million
Emp.: 577
Optical Instrument Mfr
N.A.I.C.S.: 333310
Hiroshi Takemoto *(Pres)*

Ricoh Panama, S.A. (1)
Boulevard Costa del este Edificio Financial Park Piso 31, Curundu, Panama, Panama
Tel.: (507) 831 6200
Web Site: http://www.ricoh.com.pa
Sales Range: $50-74.9 Million
Emp.: 85
Office Equipment Distr
N.A.I.C.S.: 423420

Ricoh Polska Sp. z.o.o. (1)
ul Zwirki i Wigury 18A, 02-092, Warsaw, Poland
Tel.: (48) 22 256 1555
Web Site: https://www.ricoh.pl
Office Machinery & Equipment Mfr
N.A.I.C.S.: 333310

Ricoh Portugal, Unipessoal, Lda (1)
Tower Plaza Building Via Eng Edgar Cardoso n 23 - 1, 4400-676, Vila Nova de Gaia, Portugal
Tel.: (351) 22 608 3800
Web Site: https://www.ricoh.pt
Managed Document Services
N.A.I.C.S.: 561499

Ricoh Printing Systems, Ltd. (1)
Shingawa Intercity Tower A 21st Floor, 15-1 Konan 2-Chome, Minato-ku, Tokyo, 108-6021, Japan
Tel.: (81) 357830140
Web Site: http://www.rps.ricoh.co.jp
Sales Range: $200-249.9 Million
Emp.: 600
Printing Products & Solutions
N.A.I.C.S.: 323111

Subsidiary (US):

Ricoh Printing Systems America, Inc. (2)
2635-A Park Center Dr, Simi Valley, CA 93065
Tel.: (805) 578-4000
Web Site: http://www.rpsa.ricoh.com
Sales Range: $450-499.9 Million
Computer Printers, Printer Supplies, Digital Communications Equipment Mfr & Sales
N.A.I.C.S.: 334118
Marshall Scherr *(Dir-Fin)*

Subsidiary (Domestic):

Anajet Inc. (3)
1100 Valencia Avenue, Tustin, CA 92780 (100%)
Tel.: (714) 662-3200
Web Site: http://www.anajet.com

RICOH COMPANY, LTD.

Ricoh Company, Ltd.—(Continued)

Printer Mfr
N.A.I.C.S.: 333248
Karl Tipre *(CEO)*

Ricoh Rus, Ltd. (1)
st Kozhevnicheskaya 14 building 5, 115114, Moscow, Russia
Tel.: (7) 4955455859
Web Site: http://www.ricoh.ru
Emp.: 10
Printer & Copier Distr
N.A.I.C.S.: 423430

Ricoh Schweiz AG (1)
Hertistrasse 2, 8304, Wallisellen, Switzerland
Tel.: (41) 84 436 0360
Web Site: https://www.ricoh.ch
Sales Range: $150-199.9 Million
Emp.: 48
Office Equipment Distr
N.A.I.C.S.: 423420
Stefan Ammann *(CEO)*

Ricoh Software Research Center (Beijing) Co., Ltd. (1)
28th Floor Tengda Building No 168 Xiwai Street, Haidian District, Beijing, 100044, China
Tel.: (86) 108 857 7878
Web Site: https://www.srcb-ricoh.com
Software Research & Development Services
N.A.I.C.S.: 541715
Hiroshi Kobayashi *(Chm)*

Ricoh Sverige AB (1)
Rontgenvagen 3, PO Box 1536, 171 28, Solna, Sweden
Tel.: (46) 8 734 33 00
Sales Range: $75-99.9 Million
Emp.: 30
Managed Document Services
N.A.I.C.S.: 561499

Ricoh Taiwan Co., Ltd (1)
5th Fl No 550 Zhongxiao E Road Sec 4, Xinyi District, Taipei, 11071, Taiwan
Tel.: (886) 2 2720 9600
Office Equipment Distr
N.A.I.C.S.: 423420

Ricoh Technosystems Co., Ltd (1)
5-20-8 Asakusabashi Cs Tower 12f, Taito-Ku, Tokyo, 111-0053, Japan
Tel.: (81) 358357777
Office Equipment Repair & Maintenance Services
N.A.I.C.S.: 811210

Ricoh Thermal Media (Beijing) Co., Ltd. (1)
No E1 Middle of Chuangyeyuan Area Badachu Hi-Tech Zone, Shijingshan District, Beijing, 100041, China
Tel.: (86) 10 8879 7580
Web Site: http://www.ricoh.com
Sales Range: $100-124.9 Million
Emp.: 300
Optical Equipment Mfr
N.A.I.C.S.: 333310

Ricoh Thermal Media (Wuxi) Co., Ltd. (1)
No 1 Xinchang South Road Country Hi-Tech Industry Development Zone, Wuxi, 214028, Jiangsu, China
Tel.: (86) 510 8533 0555
Thermal Paper & Thermal Ribbon Mfr
N.A.I.C.S.: 325992

Ricoh USA, Inc. (1)
5 Dedrick Pl, West Caldwell, NJ 07006
Tel.: (973) 882-2000
Web Site: http://www.ricoh-usa.com
Emp.: 300
Holding Company
N.A.I.C.S.: 551112
Dennis Dispenziere *(CFO & Sr VP)*

Subsidiary (Domestic):

Automated Business Products, Inc. (2)
385 W 2880 S, Salt Lake City, UT 84115
Tel.: (801) 488-8000
Web Site: http://www.abpweb.com
Sales Range: $25-49.9 Million
Emp.: 100
Office Equipment

N.A.I.C.S.: 423420
Lee Christensen *(Pres & Partner)*

Cenero LLC (2)
1150 Atwater Dr, Malvern, PA 19355
Tel.: (610) 344-7007
Web Site: http://www.cenero.com
Audio & Video Managed Services
N.A.I.C.S.: 512290
Rob Gilfillan *(Pres)*

IKON Office Solutions, Inc. (2)
70 Valley Stream Pkwy, Malvern, PA 19355-1407
Tel.: (610) 296-8000
Web Site: http://www.ikon.com
Sales Range: $1-4.9 Billion
Emp.: 25,000
Office Products & Computer & Software Retailer & Distr
N.A.I.C.S.: 423430

PTI Marketing Technologies, Inc. (2)
201 Lomas Santa Fe Dr Ste 300, Solana Beach, CA 92075
Tel.: (858) 847-6600
Web Site: http://www.pti.com
Sales Range: $1-9.9 Million
Emp.: 40
Marketing Software Publisher
N.A.I.C.S.: 513210
Coleman Kane *(CEO)*

Ricoh Americas Holdings, Inc. (2)
5 Dedrick Pl, West Caldwell, NJ 07006
Tel.: (973) 882-2000
Web Site: http://www.ricoh-usa.com
Investment Management Service
N.A.I.C.S.: 523940

Subsidiary (Non-US):

Ricoh Canada Inc. (2)
100-5560 Explorer Drive, Mississauga, L4W 5M3, ON, Canada
Tel.: (905) 795-9659
Web Site: https://www.ricoh.ca
Emp.: 2,400
Office Equipment Whslr & Services
N.A.I.C.S.: 423420
Dan Newman *(Mgr-PR)*

Branch (Domestic):

Ricoh Canada Inc. - Toronto Sales Office (3)
600 - 4100 Yonge Street, Toronto, M2P 2B5, ON, Canada
Tel.: (416) 218-8200
Web Site: https://www.ricoh.ca
Sales Range: $25-49.9 Million
Emp.: 74
Commercial Equipment Nec
N.A.I.C.S.: 333415
Hede Nonaka *(Exec VP-America)*

Unit (Domestic):

Ricoh Legal Document Services - Toronto (3)
199 Bay Street Level B2 S230, Toronto, M5L 1A1, ON, Canada
Tel.: (416) 777-9797
Web Site: https://www.ricoh.ca
Sales Range: $25-49.9 Million
Emp.: 40
Legal Document Services
N.A.I.C.S.: 561410

Subsidiary (Domestic):

Ricoh Development of California, Inc. (2)
1 Ricoh Sq 1100 Valencia Ave, Tustin, CA 92780 **(100%)**
Tel.: (714) 566-2526
Web Site: http://www.ricoh.com
Sales Range: $400-449.9 Million
Office Machinery Mfr
N.A.I.C.S.: 333310

Ricoh Electronics, Inc. (2)
1 Ricoh Sq 1100 Valencia Ave, Tustin, CA 92780 **(100%)**
Tel.: (714) 566-2500
Web Site: https://www.rei.ricoh.com
Sales Range: $400-449.9 Million
Copiers, Office Machines, Facsimile Equipment & Related Supplies Mfr
N.A.I.C.S.: 333310

Jeffrey A. Briwick *(Pres)*

Plant (Domestic):

Ricoh Electronics, Inc. - Georgia Plant (3)
1125 Hurricane Shoals Rd, Lawrenceville, GA 30243
Tel.: (770) 338-7200
Office Equipment Distr
N.A.I.C.S.: 423420

Subsidiary (Domestic):

Ricoh Innovations, Inc. (2)
2882 Sand Hill Rd Ste 115, Menlo Park, CA 94025-7057
Tel.: (650) 496-5700
Web Site: http://www.crc.ricoh.com
Managed Document Services
N.A.I.C.S.: 561499

Subsidiary (Domestic):

Eyefi Inc. (3)
967 N Shoreline Blvd, Mountain View, CA 94043
Tel.: (650) 265-4460
Web Site: http://www.eyefi.com
Digital Photography Services
N.A.I.C.S.: 541519
Matt DiMaria *(CEO)*

Subsidiary (Non-US):

Ricoh Innovations Private Limited (3)
Embassy Icon Ground Floor No 3 Infantry Road, Vasanthnagar, Bengaluru, 56001, Karnataka, India
Tel.: (91) 8049360700
Web Site: http://www.rii.ricoh.com
Sales Range: $10-24.9 Million
Emp.: 5
Software Applications Research & Development Services
N.A.I.C.S.: 541512
Kaip Sridhar *(Mng Dir)*

Subsidiary (Domestic):

Ricoh Latin America, Inc. (2)
2700 S Commerce Pkwy Ste 201, Weston, FL 33331
Tel.: (954) 745-3300
Web Site: https://www.ricoh-americalatina.com
Sales Range: $10-24.9 Million
Emp.: 70
Managed Document Services
N.A.I.C.S.: 561499
Peter Stuart *(Pres)*

Subsidiary (Non-US):

Ricoh Mexicana, S.A. de C.V. (2)
Edificio Corporativo Lomas Cantabria Cerrada Palomas No 22 Int 301, Int 301 Col Reforma Social, Colonia Reforma Social, 11650, Mexico, Mexico
Tel.: (52) 5552844600
Web Site: http://www.ricoh.com.mx
Sales Range: $25-49.9 Million
Emp.: 70
Office Equipment Distr
N.A.I.C.S.: 423420

Subsidiary (Domestic):

Ricoh Puerto Rico, Inc. (2)
Ave Ponce de Leon 431 Edif Nacional Plz Piso 17, Hato Rey, PR 00917
Tel.: (787) 641-4690
Web Site: http://www.ricohpr.com
Sales Range: $50-74.9 Million
Emp.: 152
N.A.I.C.S.: 339940
Micky Carrero *(Gen Mgr)*

Savin Corporation (2)
93 Lake Ave, Danbury, CT 06810
Tel.: (203) 448-2960
Web Site: http://www.savin.com
Sales Range: $75-99.9 Million
Emp.: 200
Black & White & Full Color Digital Imaging Systems, Laser Printers, Digital Duplicators & Facsimile Systems Parts, Supplies & Services Marketer & Distr
N.A.I.C.S.: 423420

INTERNATIONAL PUBLIC

mindSHIFT Technologies, Inc. (2)
309 Waverley Oaks Rd Ste 301, Waltham, MA 02452
Tel.: (617) 243-2700
Web Site: http://www.mindshift.com
Sales Range: $100-124.9 Million
Emp.: 650
Computer System Design Services
N.A.I.C.S.: 541512
Lawrence M. Ingeneri *(CFO)*

Branch (Domestic):

mindSHIFT Technologies - Southwest (3)
8341 Cross Park Dr, Austin, TX 78754
Tel.: (512) 491-9700
Web Site: http://www.mindshift.com
Sales Range: $25-49.9 Million
Emp.: 100
Managed Information Technology Services
N.A.I.C.S.: 541519
Eric Alvarado *(Dir-Backup & Recovery Ops)*

Ricoh Unitechno Co., Ltd. (1)
713 Tsurugasone, Yashio, 340-0802, Saitama, Japan
Tel.: (81) 48 995 0121
Office Equipments Mfr
N.A.I.C.S.: 333310

Ricoh Vietnam Company Limited (1)
F 17 E town Central 11 Doan Van Bo, Ward 13 District 4, Ho Chi Minh City, 70000, Vietnam
Tel.: (84) 283 528 5252
Web Site: https://www.ricoh.com.vn
Sales Range: $25-49.9 Million
Emp.: 50
Office Automation Equipment Mfr
N.A.I.C.S.: 333310
Takahisa Nakaji *(Gen Dir)*

Shanghai Ricoh Office Equipment Co., Ltd. (1)
No 166 Meigui Road South Waigaoqiao Freetrade Zone, Pudong, Shanghai, China
Tel.: (86) 21 50480936
Office Equipment Mfr & Distr
N.A.I.C.S.: 333310

Yamanashi Electronics Co., Ltd. (1)
1014 Miyabara-cho, Kofu, 400-0058, Yamanashi, Japan
Tel.: (81) 55 241 2221
Web Site: https://www.yec.ricoh.co.jp
Sales Range: $50-74.9 Million
Emp.: 130
Photoconductive Drums
N.A.I.C.S.: 333242
Yosuke Kawaguchi *(Pres)*

RICOLA AG

Baselstrasse 31, Laufen, 4242, Switzerland
Tel.: (41) 617654121
Web Site: http://www.ricola.com
Year Founded: 1930
Sales Range: $10-24.9 Million
Emp.: 400
Marketer of Natural Herbal Product Mfr
N.A.I.C.S.: 445298
Felix Richterich *(Chm-Exec Bd)*

Subsidiaries:

Ricola (Asia-Pacific) Ltd (1)
unit A 23 F Golden Sun Ctr Bonham Starnt W, Hong Kong, 59267, China (Hong Kong)
Tel.: (852) 23677551
Web Site: http://www.ricola-asia.com
Nonchocolate Confectionery Mfr
N.A.I.C.S.: 311340
Cheung Tim *(Reg Dir)*

Ricola Asia Pacific PTE Ltd. (1)
122 Middle Rd, PO Box 268, Tanglin Post Office, Singapore, 188973, Singapore **(100%)**
Tel.: (65) 65389905
Web Site: http://www.ricola-asia.com
Emp.: 3
N.A.I.C.S.: 445298
Axel Lachhein *(Gen Mgr)*

Ricola USA, Inc. (1)

51 Gibraltar Dr, Morris Plains, NJ 07950-1254
Tel.: (973) 984-6811
Web Site: http://www.ricolausa.com
Natural Herbal Products Mfr & Marketer
N.A.I.C.S.: 424210
Peter Burke *(VP-Mktg)*

Ricola Vertriebs AG (1)
Baselstr 31, 4242, Laufen, Switzerland
Tel.: (41) 61 765 41 21
Herb Product Whslr
N.A.I.C.S.: 424210
Selix Richterich *(CEO)*

RICOM-TRUST INVESTMENT COMPANY LIMITED
6 Protochniy Side-St, 121099, Moscow, Russia
Tel.: (7) 4959211555
Web Site: http://www.ricom.ru
Year Founded: 1994
Sales Range: Less than $1 Million
Investment & Asset Management Services
N.A.I.C.S.: 523940

RIDDHI CORPORATE SERVICES LIMITED
10 Mill Officers Colony B/h Old RBI Opp-Times Of India Ashram Road, Ahmedabad, 380 009, India
Tel.: (91) 7926580767
Web Site:
   https://www.riddhicorporate.co.in
Year Founded: 2009
540590—(BOM)
Rev.: $24,164,678
Assets: $23,737,606
Liabilities: $17,570,961
Net Worth: $6,166,645
Earnings: $1,009,532
Emp.: 4,479
Fiscal Year-end: 03/31/23
Business Process Management Services
N.A.I.C.S.: 518210
Pravinchandra Kodarlal Gor *(Chm & Mng Dir)*

Subsidiaries:

RCSPL Share Broking Private Limited (1)
10 Mill Officers Colony B/h Old RBI Opp-Times Of India Ashram Road, Ahmedabad, 380009, Gujarat, India
Tel.: (91) 7805050505
Web Site: http://www.rcspl.trade
Stock Broking Services
N.A.I.C.S.: 523150

RIDDHI SIDDHI GLUCO BIOLS LTD.
10 Abhishree Corporate Park Nr Swagat Bungalow BRTS Bus Stop, Ambli-Bopal Road, Ahmedabad, 380058, India
Tel.: (91) 2717298600
Web Site:
   https://www.riddhisiddhi.co.in
524480—(BOM)
Rev.: $28,774,630
Assets: $202,877,621
Liabilities: $24,263,246
Net Worth: $178,614,376
Earnings: ($10,180,505)
Emp.: 11
Fiscal Year-end: 03/31/23
Starch Mfr
N.A.I.C.S.: 325612
Ganpatraj L. Chowdhary *(Chm & Mng Dir)*

Subsidiaries:

Riddhi Siddhi Gluco Biols Ltd - Gokak Unit (1)
Gokak Falls Rd, PO Box 9, Belgaum Dist, Gokak, 591307, Karnataka, India
Tel.: (91) 8332229240

Sales Range: $100-124.9 Million
Emp.: 500
Starch Gues Mfr
N.A.I.C.S.: 311423

Riddhi Siddhi Gluco Biols Ltd - Pondicherry Unit (1)
Unit III Vazhudavoor Rd, Iyyahkuttipalayam, Pondicherry, 605 009, India
Tel.: (91) 413 2271135
Web Site: http://www.riddhisiddhi.co.in
Sales Range: $25-49.9 Million
Emp.: 25
Starch Gues Mfr
N.A.I.C.S.: 311423

Shree Rama Newsprint Limited (1)
Village Barbodhan Taluka Olpad, Surat, 395 005, Gujarat, India **(74.71%)**
Tel.: (91) 2621224203
Web Site: https://www.ramanewsprint.com
Rev.: $5,795,864
Assets: $74,906,504
Liabilities: $58,063,497
Net Worth: $16,843,007
Earnings: ($14,170,074)
Emp.: 61
Fiscal Year-end: 03/31/2023
Newsprint & Paper Mfr
N.A.I.C.S.: 322120
Siddharth G. Chowdhary *(Exec Dir)*

RIDDHI STEEL & TUBE LIMITED
83/84 Village - Kamod Piplaj - Pirana Road, Opposite Devraj Industrial Park, Ahmedabad, 382 427, Gujarat, India
Tel.: (91) 9512711555
Web Site:
   https://www.riddhitubes.com
Year Founded: 2002
540082—(BOM)
Rev.: $36,579,977
Assets: $21,955,566
Liabilities: $15,666,855
Net Worth: $6,288,712
Earnings: $407,781
Emp.: 24
Fiscal Year-end: 03/31/23
Steel Product Mfr & Distr
N.A.I.C.S.: 331110
Rajesh Ramkumar Mittal *(Mng Dir)*

RIDDOCK INTERNATIONAL LIMITED
Suite 8 Level 6 55 Miller Street, Pyrmont, 2009, NSW, Australia
Tel.: (61) 295718300
Web Site: http://www.riddockint.com
Financial Investment Services
N.A.I.C.S.: 523999
Rizwan Alikhan *(Chm)*

RIDE ON EXPRESS CO., LTD.
Sumitomo Real Estate Mita Twin Building West Wing 17th Floor, 3-5-27 Mita Minato-ku, Tokyo, 108-6317, Japan
Tel.: (81) 354443611
Web Site:
   https://www.rideonexpresshd.co.jp
Year Founded: 2001
6082—(TKS)
Rev.: $158,606,950
Assets: $85,784,580
Liabilities: $37,776,150
Net Worth: $48,008,430
Earnings: $2,406,040
Emp.: 3,440
Fiscal Year-end: 03/31/24
Food Delivery Services
N.A.I.C.S.: 722330
Akira Emi *(Founder, Pres & CEO)*

RIDEAU INC.
473 Deslauriers, Montreal, H4N 1W2, QC, Canada
Tel.: (514) 336-9200
Web Site: http://www.rideau.com

Year Founded: 1912
Sales Range: $10-24.9 Million
Emp.: 160
Rewards & Recognition Products
N.A.I.C.S.: 541611
Gord Feeney *(Chm)*

RIDER HUNT INTERNATIONAL LIMITED
Compass Point 79-87 Kingston Rd, Staines-upon-Thames, TW18 1DT, United Kingdom
Tel.: (44) 1483 540150
Web Site: http://www.rhi-group.com
Sales Range: $10-24.9 Million
Emp.: 100
Project Control Services
N.A.I.C.S.: 541330
Finlay McLay *(Reg Dir-Americas)*

Subsidiaries:

Rider Hunt International (Alberta) Inc. (1)
900 - 801 6th Ave SW, Calgary, T2P 3W2, AB, Canada
Tel.: (403) 629-4418
Engineeering Services
N.A.I.C.S.: 541330
Finlay McLay *(Reg Dir-Americas)*

Rider Hunt International (Malaysia) Sdn. Bhd. (1)
14th Floor Menara Park Jalan Yap Kwan Seng, 50490, Kuala Lumpur, Malaysia
Tel.: (60) 3 2162 9320
Engineeering Services
N.A.I.C.S.: 541330

Rider Hunt International (Singapore) Pte Ltd. (1)
180 Cecil Street 11-01 Bangkok Bank Building, Singapore, 069546, Singapore
Tel.: (65) 6887 3034
Web Site: http://www.rhi-group.com
Engineeering Services
N.A.I.C.S.: 541330
Mike Moore *(Reg Mgr)*

Rider Hunt International (USA) Inc. (1)
1001 S Dairy Ashford Ste 220, Houston, TX 77077
Tel.: (281) 556-8881
Web Site: http://www.rhi-group.com
Engineeering Services
N.A.I.C.S.: 541330
Finlay McLay *(Reg Dir-Americas)*

Rider Hunt International (WA) Pty Ltd. (1)
Level 14 140 St Georges Terrace, Perth, 6000, WA, Australia
Tel.: (61) 8 9278 1866
Engineeering Services
N.A.I.C.S.: 541330

Rider Hunt International BV (1)
Apartment 38 Al-Konak 5 Shahbazi Street, Baku, Azerbaijan
Tel.: (994) 44 1224 650222
Engineeering Services
N.A.I.C.S.: 541330

RIDGE-I INC.
Otemachi building 438 1-6-1 Otemachi, Chiyoda-ku, Tokyo, 100-0004, Japan
Tel.: (81) 342148558
Web Site: https://www.ridge-i.com
Year Founded: 2016
5572—(TKS)
Emp.: 47
Software Development Services
N.A.I.C.S.: 541511
Takashi Yanagihara *(Founder)*

RIDGEBACK RESOURCES INC.
2800 525 - 8th Avenue SW, Vancouver, T2P 1G1, AB, Canada
Tel.: (403) 268-7800
Web Site: https://www.ridgeback.com

Year Founded: 2016
Oil & Gas Exploration & Production
N.A.I.C.S.: 213112
David J. Broshko *(Pres)*

RIDGECREST PLC
Bourne House 475 Godstone Road, Whyteleafe, CR3 6PB, Surrey, United Kingdom
Tel.: (44) 1883341144
Web Site:
   http://www.ridgecrestplc.com
Year Founded: 1983
RDGC—(AIM)
Rev.: $63,332
Assets: $1,009,583
Liabilities: $69,541
Net Worth: $940,043
Earnings: ($1,028,210)
Emp.: 3
Fiscal Year-end: 03/31/21
Recruitment Services Focused on Information Technology Personnel
N.A.I.C.S.: 561311
Tim Sheffield *(Chm)*

Subsidiaries:

Highams Recruitment Limited (1)
Bourne House 475 Godstone Road, Whyteleafe, CR3 0BL, Surrey, United Kingdom
Tel.: (44) 1883341144
Web Site: http://www.highams.com
Sales Range: $25-49.9 Million
Emp.: 20
Permanent & Contract Recruitment Services for Information Technology Personnel
N.A.I.C.S.: 561311
Mark de Lacy *(Dir-Sls)*

RIDGEHILL FORD
217 Hespeler Rd, Cambridge, N1R 3H8, ON, Canada
Tel.: (519) 621-0720
Web Site:
   http://www.ridgehillford.com
Year Founded: 1980
Sales Range: $1-9.9 Million
Emp.: 130
New & Used Car Dealers
N.A.I.C.S.: 441110

RIDGELINE MINERALS CORP.
Suite 1650-1066 West Hastings Street, Vancouver, V6E 3X1, BC, Canada
Tel.: (775) 304-9773
Web Site:
   https://www.ridgelineminerals.com
Year Founded: 2018
RDGMF—(OTCQB)
Rev.: $10,759
Assets: $6,689,803
Liabilities: $189,056
Net Worth: $6,500,747
Earnings: ($1,274,122)
Fiscal Year-end: 12/31/20
Mineral Exploration Services
N.A.I.C.S.: 213115
Mike Harp *(VP-Exploration)*

RIDGESTONE MINING, INC.
Suite 503 - 905 West Pender Street, Vancouver, V6C 1L6, BC, Canada
Tel.: (416) 732-0604
Web Site:
   https://www.ridgestonemining.com
4U50—(DEU)
Assets: $1,186,653
Liabilities: $326,632
Net Worth: $860,021
Earnings: ($1,303,061)
Fiscal Year-end: 12/31/23
Mineral Exploration Services
N.A.I.C.S.: 213114
Erwin Wong *(CFO)*

RIDGEWAY GROUP

RIDGEWAY GROUP

Ridgeway Group—(Continued)

Newbury Motor Park The Triangle,
Newbury, RG14 7HT, Berkshire,
United Kingdom
Tel.: (44) 163 540678
Web Site: http://www.ridgeway.co.uk
Year Founded: 1997
Sales Range: $500-549.9 Million
Emp.: 823
New & Used Car Dealer
N.A.I.C.S.: 441110
David Newman *(Chm)*

RIDHI SYNTHETICS LIMITED

11-B 1ST Floor Mittal Tower Free
Press Journal Marg, Nariman Point,
Mumbai, 400 021, Maharashtra, India
Tel.: (91) 2261155300
Web Site: https://ridhisynthetics.com
Year Founded: 1981
504365—(BOM)
Rev.: $106,576
Assets: $5,400,815
Liabilities: $271,399
Net Worth: $5,129,417
Earnings: $54,337
Emp.: 3
Fiscal Year-end: 03/31/23
Securities Dealing Services
N.A.I.C.S.: 523150
Sunil Sharma *(CFO)*

RIDI POWER COMPANY LIMITED

5th floor Trade Tower Thapathali,
GPO Box 21839, Kathmandu, Nepal
Tel.: (977) 15111015
Web Site:
http://www.ridihydro.com.np
Year Founded: 2000
RIDI—(NEP)
Sales Range: Less than $1 Million
Hydroelectric Power Generation Services
N.A.I.C.S.: 221111
Guru Prasad Neupane *(Chm)*

Subsidiaries:

Rairang Hydropower Development
Co., Ltd. (1)
5th floor Trade Tower, GPO Box 21839,
Thapathali, Kathmandu, Nepal
Tel.: (977) 15111015
Web Site: https://ridipower.com.np
Sales Range: Less than $1 Million
Hydroelectric Power Generation Services
N.A.I.C.S.: 221111
Shiva Ratan Sharda *(Chm)*

Subsidiary (Domestic):

Arun Kabeli Power Limited (2)
2nd Floor Trade Tower Nepal Thapathali,
Kathmandu, 44600, Nepal
Tel.: (977) 15914176
Web Site: https://www.arunkabeli.com.np
Eletric Power Generation Services
N.A.I.C.S.: 221118

RIDINGS CONSULTING ENGINEERS INDIA LTD.

Premises No 429-430 Block-II 2nd
Floor Ganga Shopping Complex,
Sector-29, Noida, 201303, India
Tel.: (91) 1204694500
Web Site:
http://www.ridingsindia.com
Year Founded: 1995
541151—(BOM)
Rev.: $666,315
Assets: $2,070,823
Liabilities: $1,862,238
Net Worth: $208,585
Earnings: $3,885
Emp.: 60
Fiscal Year-end: 03/31/22
Construction Consulting Services
N.A.I.C.S.: 541330

Sudhir Kumar Baveja *(CFO)*

RIDLEY CORPORATION LIMITED

Level 9 South Tower Rialto 525 Collins Street, Melbourne, 3000, VIC,
Australia
Tel.: (61) 386246500
Web Site: https://www.ridley.com.au
Year Founded: 1987
RIDYF—(OTCIQ)
Rev.: $710,809,021
Assets: $469,721,208
Liabilities: $249,407,104
Net Worth: $220,314,104
Earnings: $19,075,066
Emp.: 612
Fiscal Year-end: 06/30/21
Other Animal Food Manufacturing
N.A.I.C.S.: 311119
Alan Maclean Boyd *(CFO & Sec)*

Subsidiaries:

Barastoc Stockfeeds Pty. Ltd. (1)
1325 Boundary Road, 4076, Wacol, QLD,
Australia (100%)
Tel.: (61) 737181000
Web Site: http://www.agriproducts.com.au
Animal Feed Mfr
N.A.I.C.S.: 311119

Camilleri Stockfeeds Pty Ltd (1)
4777 Old Northern Rd, Maroota, Sydney,
2756, NSW, Australia
Tel.: (61) 245668304
Web Site: http://www.ridley.com
Sales Range: $25-49.9 Million
Emp.: 30
Animal Feed Mfr
N.A.I.C.S.: 311119
Brad Hopkins *(Gen Mgr)*

Ridley AgriProducts Pty. Ltd. (1)
70-80 Bald Hill Rd, PO Box 18, Pakenham,
3810, VIC, Australia (100%)
Tel.: (61) 359411633
Web Site: http://www.agriproducts.com.au
Sales Range: $25-49.9 Million
Emp.: 100
Cattle Feedlots
N.A.I.C.S.: 112112
John Murray *(CEO & Mng Dir)*

RIDLEY TERMINALS INC.

2110 Ridley Road, PO Box 8000,
Prince Rupert, V8J 4H3, BC, Canada
Tel.: (250) 624-9511
Web Site: http://www.rti.ca
Year Founded: 1984
Rev.: $86,338,002
Assets: $340,863,301
Liabilities: $71,642,687
Net Worth: $269,220,614
Earnings: $36,499,707
Fiscal Year-end: 12/31/18
Marine Terminal Services
N.A.I.C.S.: 488320
Marc Dulude *(Pres & COO)*

RIEBER & SON AS

Kalfarveien 57A, PO Box 2319, Mollendal, N-5867, Bergen, Norway
Tel.: (47) 55559100
Web Site: http://www.rieberson.no
Privater Equity Firm
N.A.I.C.S.: 523999
Helge Midttun *(Chm)*

RIEDEL RESOURCES LIMITED

4/6 Richardson St, West Perth, 6005,
WA, Australia
Tel.: (61) 892260866
Web Site:
https://www.riedelresources.com.au
RIE—(ASX)
Rev.: $310
Assets: $4,088,258
Liabilities: $91,685
Net Worth: $3,996,573
Earnings: ($2,654,344)

Fiscal Year-end: 06/30/21
Gold & Base Metal Mining Services
N.A.I.C.S.: 212220
Jeffrey Moore *(Chm)*

RIEDEL TEXTIL GMBH

Talstrasse 6, 09212, Limbach-Oberfrohna, Germany
Tel.: (49) 37226500
Web Site: http://www.riedeltextil.de
Rev.: $44,247,193
Emp.: 263
Jersey Mfr
N.A.I.C.S.: 313310
Ulrich Burger *(Mgr-Sls-Fabrics & Garments)*

RIESE ELECTRONIC GMBH

Junghansstrasse 16, Horb am
Neckar, 72160, Germany
Tel.: (49) 745155010
Web Site: http://www.riese-electronic.com
Year Founded: 1958
Rev.: $13,794,000
Emp.: 90
Electronic Devices & Assemblies
Distr
N.A.I.C.S.: 423690
Oliver Riese *(Gen Mgr)*

RIETER HOLDING LTD.

Klosterstrasse 32, CH-8406, Winterthur, Switzerland
Tel.: (41) 522087171
Web Site: https://www.rieter.com
Year Founded: 1975
RIEN—(SWX)
Rev.: $648,905,310
Assets: $1,091,134,845
Liabilities: $693,751,122
Net Worth: $397,383,723
Earnings: ($101,695,806)
Emp.: 4,416
Fiscal Year-end: 12/31/20
Holding Company
N.A.I.C.S.: 551112
This E. Schneider *(Vice Chm)*

Subsidiaries:

Bracker AG (1)
Obermattstrasse 65, 8330, Pfaffikon, Zurich,
Switzerland
Tel.: (41) 449531414
Web Site: https://www.bracker.ch
Sales Range: $50-74.9 Million
Emp.: 135
Spinning Ring & Tube Mfr
N.A.I.C.S.: 333248

Bracker S.A.S. (1)
132 Rue Clemenceau, Wintzenheim,
68920, Colmars, France
Tel.: (33) 389270007
Key Component Mfr
N.A.I.C.S.: 332119

European Excellent Textile Components Co. Ltd. (1)
No 21 Fukang Road, Xinbei District,
Changzhou, 213022, Jiangsu, China
Tel.: (86) 51985178798
Fiber & Spinning Preparation Mfr
N.A.I.C.S.: 313110

Gomitex S.A. (1)
Z I Haut De Treme, Verviers, 4801 RC,
Stembert, Belgium
Tel.: (32) 87315540
Fiber & Spinning Preparation Mfr
N.A.I.C.S.: 313110

Graf + Cie AG (1)
Bildaustrasse 6, 8640, Rapperswil, Switzerland
Tel.: (41) 552217111
Web Site: https://www.graf-companies.com
Sales Range: $50-74.9 Million
Card Clothing & Service Machine Mfr &
Distr
N.A.I.C.S.: 333310

INTERNATIONAL PUBLIC

Subsidiary (Non-US):

Graf France Sarl (2)
49 Rue De Sausheim, 68110, Illzach,
France
Tel.: (33) 389463698
Textile Machinery Distr
N.A.I.C.S.: 423830

Graf Holland B.V. (2)
Lonnekerbrugstraat 130, Postfach 2201,
7547 AM, Enschede, Netherlands
Tel.: (31) 534889588
Web Site: http://www.graf.nl
Sales Range: $25-49.9 Million
Precision Metal Part Mfr
N.A.I.C.S.: 332999

Graf Maquinas Texteis Ind. e Com.
Ltda. (2)
Alameda Rio Preto No 165 Centro Empresarial Tambore, 06460-050, Barueri, Sao
Paulo, Brazil
Tel.: (55) 11 4166 4977
Sales Range: $25-49.9 Million
Card Clothing & Service Equipment Mfr
N.A.I.C.S.: 333310

Graf-Kratzen GmbH (2)
Senefelderstr 8, 86368, Gersthofen, Germany
Tel.: (49) 821 2 49 670
Sales Range: $25-49.9 Million
Emp.: 2
Carding Machinery Mfr
N.A.I.C.S.: 333248

Graf Cardservices Far East Ltd. (1)
20/Fl Pearl Oriental House 60 Stanley
Street, Central, China (Hong Kong)
Flat Card & Roller Card Mfr
N.A.I.C.S.: 322230

Graf Metallic of America Inc. (1)
104 Belton Dr, Spartanburg, SC 29304
Tel.: (864) 576-7450
Sales Range: $25-49.9 Million
Emp.: 35
All Other Miscellaneous General Purpose
Machinery Mfr
N.A.I.C.S.: 333998

M.C. Sheet Metal Ltd. (1)
Unit 12 Heads of the Valley Industrial Estate, Rhymney, Gwent, NP22 5RL, United
Kingdom (100%)
Tel.: (44) 1685 842444
N.A.I.C.S.: 332322

Maschinenfabrik Rieter AG (1)
Klosterstrasse 20, 8406, Winterthur,
Switzerland (100%)
Tel.: (41) 522087171
Web Site: http://www.rieter.com
Sales Range: $400-449.9 Million
Developer & Producer of Machinery & Integrated Systems
N.A.I.C.S.: 333310

Novibra Boskovice s.r.o. (1)
Tel.: (420) 516528184
Web Site: https://www.novibra.com
Sales Range: $100-124.9 Million
Emp.: 35
Textile Machinery Mfr
N.A.I.C.S.: 333248

Rieter America, LLC (1)
Corner I-85 and SC Hwy 9, Spartanburg,
SC 29305
Tel.: (864) 582-5466
Fiber & Spinning Preparation Mfr
N.A.I.C.S.: 313110

Rieter Asia (Hong Kong) Ltd. (1)
10/F Wing Hing Commercial Building 139
Wing Lok Street Sheung, 145 Hennessy
Road, Wanchai, China (Hong
Kong) (100%)
Tel.: (852) 28652161
Automotive Components & Textiles
N.A.I.C.S.: 336340

Rieter Asia (Taiwan) Ltd. (1)
8F 133 Keelung Rd Sec 2, Taipei, 110,
Taiwan (100%)
Tel.: (886) 223777217
Sales Range: $25-49.9 Million
Emp.: 10
Automotive Components & Textiles
N.A.I.C.S.: 336340

AND PRIVATE COMPANIES

Rieter Automatic Winder GmbH (1)
Karl-Arnold-Str 34, 52525, Heinsberg, Germany
Tel.: (49) 24516144100
Automotive Mfr & Distr
N.A.I.C.S.: 336211

Rieter Automotive Argentina S.A. (1)
Av O Higgins 4085, Cordoba, 5014, Argentina
Tel.: (54) 351 4640094
Automobile Parts Mfr
N.A.I.C.S.: 336390

Rieter Automotive Brasil-Artefatos de Fibras Texteis Ltda. (1)
Av Moinho Fabrini 128, Sao Bernardo do Campo, 09861160, Sao Paulo, Brazil
Tel.: (55) 11 21 39 18 00
Automobile Seating Mfr
N.A.I.C.S.: 336360
Marco Silva (Office Mgr)

Rieter Automotive North America Carpet (1)
38555 Hills Tech Dr, Farmington Hills, MI 48331-3423
Tel.: (248) 848-0100
Carpet & Rug Mfr
N.A.I.C.S.: 314110
Richard Derr (Pres & CEO)

Rieter CZ S.r.o (1)
Moravska 519, CZ - 562 01, Usti nad Orlici, Czech Republic
Tel.: (420) 465557104
Web Site: https://www.rieter.cz
Sales Range: $200-249.9 Million
Emp.: 520
Textile Machinery Mfr
N.A.I.C.S.: 333248

Rieter Changzhou Textile Instruments Co. Ltd. (1)
No 21 Central Huashan Road, New District Changzhou, Changzhou, 213022, Jiangsu, China
Tel.: (86) 519 8511 0675
Web Site: http://www.rieter.com
Textile Machinery Mfr
N.A.I.C.S.: 333248

Rieter China Textile Instruments Co. Ltd. (1)
No 390 West Hehai Road, Xinbei District, Changzhou, 213125, Jiangsu, China
Tel.: (86) 51985110675
Fiber & Spinning Preparation Mfr
N.A.I.C.S.: 313110

Rieter Corp. (1)
735 Landers Rd, Spartanburg, SC 29303
Tel.: (864) 582-5466
Web Site: http://www.rieter.com
Sales Range: $25-49.9 Million
Emp.: 50
Textile Machinery Mfr
N.A.I.C.S.: 333248

Rieter Immobilien AG (1)
Klosterstrasse 19, CH-8406, Winterthur, Switzerland (100%)
Tel.: (41) 522087068
Web Site: http://www.rieter-immobilien.ch
Automotive Components & Textiles
N.A.I.C.S.: 336340

Rieter India Pvt. Ltd. (1)
Gat No 768/2 Village Wing Shindewadi - Bhor Road, Khandala, Satara, 412801, Maharashtra, India (100%)
Tel.: (91) 2169664141
Automotive Components & Textiles
N.A.I.C.S.: 336340

Rieter Ingolstadt GmbH (1)
Tel.: (49) 841953601
Textile Machinery Mfr
N.A.I.C.S.: 333248

Rieter Ingolstadt Spinnerelmaschinenbau AG (1)
Friedrich-Ebert-Strasse 84, 85055, Ingolstadt, Germany (92%)
Tel.: (49) 8419536309
Web Site: http://www.rieter.com
Sales Range: $100-124.9 Million
Emp.: 300
Automotive Components & Textiles
N.A.I.C.S.: 336340

Rieter Management AG (1)
Klosterstrasse 20, 8406, Winterthur, Switzerland (100%)
Tel.: (41) 522087171
Web Site: http://www.rieter.com
Automotive Components & Textiles
N.A.I.C.S.: 336340

Rieter South America Ltda. (1)
Alameda Rio Preto no 131 Centro Empresarial Tambore, Barueri, 06460-050, Sau Paulo, Brazil
Tel.: (55) 1141664977
Web Site: http://www.rieter.com
Textile Machinery Sales & Maintenance Services
N.A.I.C.S.: 423830

Rieter Textile Machinery Trading & Services Ltd. (1)
Tel.: (90) 2124384764
Fiber & Spinning Preparation Mfr
N.A.I.C.S.: 313110

Rieter Textile Systems (Shanghai) Co. Ltd. (1)
12/F New Town Centre No 83 Loushanguan Road, Shanghai, 200336, China
Tel.: (86) 21 6236 8013
Textile Machinery & Spare Parts Distr
N.A.I.C.S.: 423830
Martin Hirzel (Gen Mgr)

Rieter Uzbekistan FE LLC (1)
Shota Rustaveli 53B Str, Yakkasaray District, 100100, Tashkent, Uzbekistan
Tel.: (998) 712806183
Fiber & Spinning Preparation Mfr
N.A.I.C.S.: 313110
Sabir Mirzaahmedov (Head-Logistics)

Rieter Vertriebs GmbH (1)
Friedrich-Ebert-Strasse 84, 85055, Ingolstadt, Germany
Tel.: (49) 841953601
Web Site: http://www.rieter.com
Automotive Components & Textiles
N.A.I.C.S.: 336340

SSM Italy S.R.L. (1)
Via Leonardo da Vinci 21, 23851, Galbiate, Italy
Tel.: (39) 0341242611
Textile Machinery Mfr & Distr
N.A.I.C.S.: 313310

SSM Scharer Schweiter Mettler AG (1)
Tel.: (41) 447183331
Web Site: https://www.ssm.ch
Textile Machinery Mfr
N.A.I.C.S.: 333248

Subsidiary (Non-US):

SSM (Zhongshan) Ltd. (2)
1/F Building 4 19 Torch Road Zhongshan Torch Hi-Tech Industrial, Development Zone, Zhongshan, 528437, Guandong, China
Tel.: (86) 76088280606
Industrial Machinery Mfr & Distr
N.A.I.C.S.: 333310

SSM Giudici S.r.l. (2)
Via Leonardo da Vinci 21, 23851, Galbiate, LC, Italy
Tel.: (39) 0341 242 611
Web Site: http://www.ssm-giudici.it
Textile Machinery Mfr
N.A.I.C.S.: 333310

Subsidiary (US):

SSM Scharer Schweiter Mettler Corporation (2)
I-85 & Bryant Rd, Spartanburg, SC 29304
Tel.: (864) 578-7180
Textile Machinery Sales
N.A.I.C.S.: 423830

Subsidiary (Domestic):

SSM Vertriebs AG (2)
Neuhofstrasse 12, 6340, Baar, Switzerland
Tel.: (41) 447183451
Textile Machinery Mfr
N.A.I.C.S.: 333248

Schaltag AG (1)
Industriestrasse 8, 8307, Effretikon, Switzerland (100%)
Tel.: (41) 523542727
Web Site: http://www.schaltag.com
Sales Range: $50-74.9 Million
Mfr of Industrial Controls
N.A.I.C.S.: 335314
Igor Savicic (Mng Dir)

Spindelfabrik Suessen GmbH (1)
Donzdorfer Strasse 4, PO Box 2072, 73079, Suessen, Germany
Tel.: (49) 7162150
Web Site: https://www.suessen.com
Sales Range: $25-49.9 Million
Emp.: 250
Textile Machinery & Components Mfr
N.A.I.C.S.: 333248

Subsidiary (US):

American Suessen Corporation (2)
11600 Goodrich Dr, Charlotte, NC 28273
Tel.: (704) 588-2365
Web Site: http://www.americansuessen.com
Sales Range: $25-49.9 Million
Textile Machinery Equipment & Parts Distr
N.A.I.C.S.: 423830

Wilhelm Stahlecker GmbH (1)
Donzdorfer Strasse 4, 73079, Suessen, Germany
Tel.: (49) 7162150
Sales Range: $25-49.9 Million
Emp.: 50
Textile Machinery & Components Supplier
N.A.I.C.S.: 313310

Xinjiang Rieter Textile Instruments Co. Ltd. (1)
No 568 West Jinggangshan St Economic & Technological Development Zone, Toutunhe District Xinjiang Uygur Autonomous Region, Urumqi, 830022, China
Tel.: (86) 9913075311
Fiber & Spinning Preparation Mfr
N.A.I.C.S.: 313110

RIFA CO., LTD.
299 Samil-daero, Jung-gu, Seoul, Korea (South)
Tel.: (82) 220075555
Web Site: https://www.rifa.co.kr
Year Founded: 1950
000760—(KRS)
Rev: $44,972,240
Assets: $205,930,540
Liabilities: $26,620,914
Net Worth: $179,309,627
Earnings: $40,588
Emp.: 48
Fiscal Year-end: 12/31/22
Chemical & Dyestuff Whslr
N.A.I.C.S.: 424690
Gyeong-seo Min (Exec Dir)

Subsidiaries:

Rifa Advances Materials Co., Ltd. (1)
205 299 Samil-daero, Jung-gu, Seoul, 04537, Korea (South)
Tel.: (82) 2263293217
Web Site: http://www.rifaamc.co.kr
Rubber Additive Mfr
N.A.I.C.S.: 326299

Rifa Co., Ltd. (1)
299 Samil-daero, Jung-gu, Seoul, 04537, Korea (South)
Tel.: (82) 220075555
Dyestuff Mfr
N.A.I.C.S.: 325130

RIFT VALLEY RESOURCES CORP.
Suite 804 - 750 West Pender Street, Vancouver, V6C 2T7, BC, Canada
Tel.: (604) 682-2928 BC
Web Site: https://www.riftvalleyresources.ca
Year Founded: 2013
RVR—(CNSX)
Rev: $95,451
Assets: $1,535,137
Liabilities: $135,547
Net Worth: $1,399,590
Earnings: $653,221
Fiscal Year-end: 12/31/21
Nonmetallic Mineral Mining Services
N.A.I.C.S.: 213115
Griffin Jones (Pres)

RIGAKU CORPORATION

RIGA SUGAR COMPANY LTD
14 Netaji Subhas Road 2nd Floor, Kolkata, 700001, India
Tel.: (91) 3322313414
Web Site: https://www.rigasugar.com
507508—(BOM)
Rev: $11,545,907
Assets: $24,192,714
Liabilities: $33,628,072
Net Worth: ($9,435,358)
Earnings: ($6,466,142)
Emp.: 499
Fiscal Year-end: 03/31/21
Sugar, Ethyl Alcohol, Ethanol, Organic Manure & Fertilizer Producer
N.A.I.C.S.: 311314
O. P. Dhanuka (Chm & Mng Dir)

RIGAKU CORPORATION
4-14-4 Sendagaya, Shibuya-Ku, Tokyo, 151-0051, Japan
Tel.: (81) 3 3479 0618
Web Site: http://www.rigaku.com
Emp.: 1,100
Analytical Instrument Mfr
N.A.I.C.S.: 334516
Toshiyuki Ikeda (Pres)

Subsidiaries:

Applied Rigaku Technologies, Inc. (1)
9825 Spectrum Dr Bldg 4 Ste 475, Austin, TX 78717
Tel.: (512) 225-1796
Web Site: http://www.rigakuedxrf.com
Analytical Instrument Mfr
N.A.I.C.S.: 334516
Robert Bartek (Pres & CEO)

Rigaku Americas Corp (1)
9009 New Trails Dr, The Woodlands, TX 77381-5209
Tel.: (281) 362-2300
Analytical Instrument Distr
N.A.I.C.S.: 423490

Rigaku Analytical Devices, Inc. (1)
30 Upton Dr Ste 2, Wilmington, MA 01887
Tel.: (781) 328-1024
Web Site: http://www.rigakuraman.com
Analytical Instrument Mfr
N.A.I.C.S.: 423490

Rigaku Beijing Corporation (1)
2601A Tengda Plaza No 168 Xizhimenwai Ave, Haidian District, Beijing, 100044, China
Tel.: (86) 1088575768
Web Site: http://www.rigaku.com.cn
Analytical Instrument Distr
N.A.I.C.S.: 423490
Jim He (Gen Mgr)

Rigaku Corporation - Vacuum Products Division (1)
7a Raymond Ave, Salem, NH 03079
Tel.: (603) 890-6001
Analytical Instrument Mfr
N.A.I.C.S.: 334516

Rigaku Europe SE (1)
Am Hardtwald 11, 76275, Ettlingen, Germany
Tel.: (49) 72439493623
Analytical Instrument Distr
N.A.I.C.S.: 423490
Oleksandr Slipeniuk (Mgr-Sls)

Rigaku Innovative Technologies Europe s.r.o. (1)
Novodvorska 994, 142 21, Prague, Czech Republic
Tel.: (420) 239043333
Analytical Instrument Distr
N.A.I.C.S.: 423490
Ladislav Pina (Mng Dir)

Rigaku Corporation—(Continued)

Rigaku Innovative Technologies, Inc. (1)
1900 Taylor Rd, Auburn Hills, MI 48326
Tel.: (248) 232-6400
Analytical Instrument Distr
N.A.I.C.S.: 423490

Rigaku Latin America Consultoria Ltda. (1)
Rua Harmonia 1232 Vila Madalena Sumarezinho, 05435-001, Sao Paulo, Brazil
Tel.: (55) 1130323752
Analytical Instrument Distr
N.A.I.C.S.: 423490

Rigaku Raman Technologies, Inc. (1)
2700 E Executive Dr Ste 150, Tucson, AZ 85756-7182
Tel.: (408) 705-6560
Web Site: http://www.rigakuraman.com
Analytical Instrument Mfr
N.A.I.C.S.: 334516
Eric Roy (Product Mgr)

RIGAS ELEKTROMASIN-BUVES RUPNICA AS
Ganibu dambis 53, Riga, 1005, Latvia
Tel.: (371) 67381193
Web Site: http://www.rer.lv
Year Founded: 1888
RER1R—(RSE)
Rev.: $71,612,652
Assets: $58,185,091
Liabilities: $16,980,648
Net Worth: $41,204,444
Earnings: $7,470,639
Emp.: 729
Fiscal Year-end: 12/31/19
Electric Motor & Generator Mfr
N.A.I.C.S.: 335312
Maiya Vorobyova (Mgr-HR)

Subsidiaries:

AS Latvo (1)
Ganibu dambis 53, Riga, LV-1005, Latvia
Tel.: (371) 67381009
Web Site: http://www.latvo.lv
Electric Equipment Mfr
N.A.I.C.S.: 335999

RIGAS JUVELIERIZSTRADA-JUMU RUPNICA
Terezes str 1, Riga, 1012, Latvia
Tel.: (371) 67272790
Web Site: http://www.rigagold.lv
Year Founded: 1963
W7E—(STU)
Rev.: $1,116,044
Assets: $1,576,271
Liabilities: $161,002
Net Worth: $1,415,269
Earnings: ($36,238)
Emp.: 18
Fiscal Year-end: 12/31/19
Jewelry Mfr
N.A.I.C.S.: 339910
Vladimirs Cadovics (Chm)

RIGAS KUGU BUVETAVA
2 Gales str, Riga, 1015, Latvia
Tel.: (371) 67353433
Web Site: https://www.riga-shipyard.com
Year Founded: 1913
RKB1R—(RSE)
Rev.: $2,707,622
Assets: $9,838,890
Liabilities: $8,342,881
Net Worth: $1,496,008
Earnings: ($639,265)
Fiscal Year-end: 12/31/23
Ship Mfr
N.A.I.C.S.: 336611
Einars Buks (Member-Mgmt Bd)

RIGBY GROUP (RG) PLC
Bridgeway House Bridgeway, Stratford-upon-Avon, CV37 6YX, Warcs, United Kingdom
Tel.: (44) 1789 610 000 UK
Web Site: http://www.rigbygroupplc.com
Year Founded: 1975
Investment Holding Company
N.A.I.C.S.: 551112
Peter Rigby (Founder & Chm)

Subsidiaries:

Regional & City Airports Limited (1)
Bridgeway House Bridgeway, Stratford-upon-Avon, CV37 6YX, United Kingdom
Tel.: (44) 7989 161326
Web Site: http://www.rca.aero
Airport Management Services
N.A.I.C.S.: 488119
Andrew Bell (CEO)

Subsidiary (Domestic):

Bournemouth International Airport Limited (2)
Bournemouth Airport, Christchurch, BH23 6SE, Dorset, United Kingdom
Tel.: (44) 1202 364 235
Web Site: http://www.bournemouthairport.com
Airport Operator
N.A.I.C.S.: 488119

RIGEL SHIPPING CANADA INC.
PO Box 5151, Shediac Cape, E4P 8T9, NB, Canada
Tel.: (506) 533-9000
Web Site: http://www.rigelcanada.com
Year Founded: 1993
Rev.: $15,996,938
Emp.: 100
Marine Transportation Services
N.A.I.C.S.: 484230
Brian Ritchie (Pres)

RIGHT OF REPLY LTD
30 Percy Street, W1T2DB, London, United Kingdom
Tel.: (44) 20 7467 1700 UK
Web Site: http://www.rightofreply.news
Year Founded: 2016
Application Software Development Services
N.A.I.C.S.: 541511
Thomas Brooks (CEO)

RIGHT ON CO., LTD.
6F Kyocera Harajuku Bldg 6-27-8 Jingumae, Shibuya-ku, Tokyo, 150-0001, Japan
Tel.: (81) 368921110
Web Site: https://www.right-on.co.jp
Year Founded: 1980
7445—(TKS)
Rev.: $480,176,400
Assets: $331,685,200
Liabilities: $187,036,960
Net Worth: $144,648,240
Earnings: ($20,037,600)
Emp.: 737
Fiscal Year-end: 08/31/21
Apparel Distr
N.A.I.C.S.: 424350
Yusuke Fujiwara (Pres)

RIGHT PEOPLE TECHNOLOGIES
3 Tenterden Street 4th Floor, London, W1S 1TD, United Kingdom
Tel.: (44) 2075145821
Sales Range: Less than $1 Million
Internet Technology Services Including Social Networking & Online Advertising
N.A.I.C.S.: 541519

Bertrand Gerard-Boucheny (Co-Founder & COO)

RIGHT TUNNELLING PUBLIC COMPANY LIMITED
292 Moo 4 Bangna-Trad Rd, Bangbor, Samut Prakan, 10560, Thailand
Tel.: (66) 23134848 TH
Web Site: https://www.rtco.co.th
Year Founded: 2000
RT—(THA)
Rev.: $91,982,531
Assets: $167,515,380
Liabilities: $136,266,148
Net Worth: $31,249,232
Earnings: $1,180,364
Emp.: 1,229
Fiscal Year-end: 12/31/23
Construction Services
N.A.I.C.S.: 237990
Chawalit Tanomtin (Founder & CEO)

RIGHT WAY INDUSTRIAL CO., LTD.
No 1015 Zhongzheng W Rd, Rende Dist, T'ainan, 717, Taiwan
Tel.: (886) 62664101
Web Site: https://www.rightway.com.tw
Year Founded: 1964
1506—(TAI)
Rev.: $37,304,031
Assets: $103,924,912
Liabilities: $12,639,066
Net Worth: $91,285,846
Earnings: $2,895,745
Fiscal Year-end: 12/31/23
Piston Mfr
N.A.I.C.S.: 336310

Subsidiaries:

Unimax Precision Metal Forming Co., Ltd. (1)
A Building No 1508 Luoning Road, Baoshan District, Shanghai, 200949, China
Tel.: (86) 2151651700
Web Site: http://www.unimax-metalform.com
Aluminum Gravity Casting Mfr
N.A.I.C.S.: 331523

RIGHTMOVE PLC
4th Floor 33 Soho Square, London, W1D 3QU, United Kingdom
Tel.: (44) 2070870605 UK
Web Site: https://plc.rightmove.co.uk
Year Founded: 2000
RMV—(LSE)
Rev.: $460,460,060
Assets: $132,549,292
Liabilities: $44,890,040
Net Worth: $87,659,252
Earnings: $251,707,532
Emp.: 727
Fiscal Year-end: 12/31/23
Online Residential Property Portal Operator
N.A.I.C.S.: 531390
Sandra Odell (Sec)

Subsidiaries:

Rightmove Group Limited (1)
2 Caldecotte Lake Business Park Caldecotte Lake Drive, Caldecotte, Milton Keynes, MK7 8LE, United Kingdom
Tel.: (44) 8453302310
Web Site: https://www.rightmove.co.uk
Sales Range: $50-74.9 Million
Emp.: 100
Real Estate Property Management Services
N.A.I.C.S.: 531390

RIGHTS & ISSUES INVESTMENT TRUST PLC
Hamilton Centre Rodney Way, Chelmsford, CM1 3BY, Essex, United Kingdom
Tel.: (44) 1245398950 UK

Web Site: http://www.maitlandgroup.com
RIII—(LSE)
Assets: $169,894,725
Liabilities: $325,215
Net Worth: $169,569,510
Earnings: ($65,344,125)
Emp.: 5
Fiscal Year-end: 12/31/22
Investment Management Service
N.A.I.C.S.: 523940

RIGHTWAY HOLDINGS CO., LTD.
No 2 Section 1 Guangdu Avenue, Shuangliu District, Chengdu, Sichuan, China
Tel.: (86) 2885783981
Web Site: https://www.rightwayholdings.com
600321—(SHG)
Sales Range: $75-99.9 Million
Wood Product Mfr & Distr
N.A.I.C.S.: 321219

RIK SILEKS AD
Ul Goce Delcev Br 70, Kratovo, North Macedonia
Tel.: (389) 31481481
Year Founded: 1954
SIL—(MAC)
Rev.: $8,970,565
Assets: $21,028,829
Liabilities: $8,066,011
Net Worth: $12,962,818
Earnings: $47,064
Fiscal Year-end: 12/31/19
Mineral Mining Services
N.A.I.C.S.: 212323

RIKEI CORPORATION
Shinjuku Mitsui Building No 2 3-2-11 Nishi-Shinjuku, Shinjuku-ku, Tokyo, 160-0023, Japan
Tel.: (81) 333452150
Web Site: https://www.rikei.co.jp
Year Founded: 1957
8226—(TKS)
Rev.: $80,185,910
Assets: $68,116,050
Liabilities: $36,328,560
Net Worth: $31,787,490
Earnings: $2,525,020
Emp.: 165
Fiscal Year-end: 03/31/24
Information Technology Services
N.A.I.C.S.: 541512
Satoru Isaka (Pres & CEO)

RIKEN KEIKI CO., LTD.
2-7-6 Azusawa, Itabashi-Ku, Tokyo, 174-8744, Japan
Tel.: (81) 339661121
Web Site: https://www.rikenkeiki.co.jp
Year Founded: 1939
7734—(TKS)
Rev.: $301,290,410
Assets: $585,586,510
Liabilities: $106,672,180
Net Worth: $478,914,330
Earnings: $55,378,580
Emp.: 1,349
Fiscal Year-end: 03/31/24
Security Device Mfr & Distr
N.A.I.C.S.: 334519
Hisayoshi Kobayashi (Pres)

Subsidiaries:

Hideo Nakayama Imp. Exp. Com. E Industria Ltda (1)
Rua Santa Amelia 33 Praca da Bandeira, Rio de Janeiro, 20260-030, Brazil
Tel.: (55) 2125903496
Web Site: http://www.nakayama.com.br
Industrial Machinery & Equipment Distr
N.A.I.C.S.: 423830

RKI Instruments, Inc. (1)

33248 Central Ave, Union City, CA
94587 (75%)
Tel.: (510) 441-5656
Web Site: https://www.rkiinstruments.com
Industrial Machinery & Equipment Merchant
Whslr
N.A.I.C.S.: 423830
Bob Pellissier *(Co-Founder & Pres)*

**Riken Keiki Commercial (Shanghai)
Co., Ltd.** (1)
Room 1803 Building 1 Ruihong Enterprise
World No 118 Feihong Road, Hongkou District, Shanghai, 200086, China
Tel.: (86) 2165756700
Web Site: http://www.rkkc.net
Industrial Machinery & Equipment Distr
N.A.I.C.S.: 423830

Riken Keiki GmbH (1)
Mergenthalerallee 77, 65760, Eschborn,
Germany
Tel.: (49) 61967777680
Web Site: http://en.rikenkeikigmbh.com
Industrial Machinery & Equipment Distr
N.A.I.C.S.: 423830

Riken Keiki Korea Co., Ltd. (1)
23 Hwajeonsandan 2-ro 134 beon-gil,
Gangseo-gu, Busan, 46741, Korea (South)
Tel.: (82) 517129900
Web Site: http://www.rikenkeiki.co.kr
Industrial Machinery & Equipment Distr
N.A.I.C.S.: 423830

Riken Keiki Taiwan Co., Ltd. (1)
No 87 Yangming Road, Shanhua District,
Tainan City, 741, Taiwan
Tel.: (886) 65811224
Industrial Machinery & Equipment Distr
N.A.I.C.S.: 423830

RIKEN TECHNOS CORPORATION
Waterras Tower 11th Floor 2-101
Kanda-Awajicho, Chiyoda-ku, Tokyo,
101-8336, Japan
Tel.: (81) 352971650 JP
Web Site:
https://www.rikentechnos.co.jp
Year Founded: 1951
4220—(TKS)
Rev.: $831,134,790
Assets: $764,446,500
Liabilities: $275,194,130
Net Worth: $489,252,370
Earnings: $45,476,800
Emp.: 1,905
Fiscal Year-end: 03/31/24
Plastics Product Mfr
N.A.I.C.S.: 326199
Takeshi Sugie *(Exec Officer, Sr Gen
Mgr-Procurement Div & Gen Mgr-
Logistics Dept)*

Subsidiaries:

Kanekon Co., Ltd. (1)
Kawamata Bldg 2F 4-2-4 Sinbashi, Minatoku, Tokyo, 105-0004, Japan (100%)
Tel.: (81) 334316522
Web Site: http://www.rikentechnos.co.jp
Sales Range: $25-49.9 Million
Emp.: 10
Sales of Compounds & Films
N.A.I.C.S.: 325992

Kyoei Plastic Mfg. Co., Ltd. (1)
88 Mukaehata Yoshioka-Aza Ooaza
Nakajima-Mura, Nishi Shirakawa-Gun, Fukushima, 101-0063, Japan
Tel.: (81) 248218567
Web Site: http://www.rikentechnos.co.jp
Emp.: 63
Plastics Extrusion Services
N.A.I.C.S.: 326199

P.T. Riken Indonesia (1)
Kawasan Industri MM2100 Jl Java Blok H-9
Gandamekar, Cikarang Barat, Bekasi,
17530, West Java, Indonesia (62%)
Tel.: (62) 218980461
Web Site: https://www.rapindo.com
Sales Range: $50-74.9 Million
Emp.: 124
Polyvinyl Chloride Compounds Mfr
N.A.I.C.S.: 325211

**Riken Chemical Products
Corporation** (1)
2-4 Oike-Cho, Konan, 520-3213, Shiga,
Japan (100%)
Tel.: (81) 748750341
Web Site: http://www.rikentechnos.co.jp
Chemical Products Mfr & Whslr
N.A.I.C.S.: 325998

Riken Elastomers Corporation (1)
340 Riken Ct, Hopkinsville, KY 42240
Tel.: (270) 475-2150
Sales Range: $25-49.9 Million
Emp.: 13
Thermoplastic Elastomer Compounds Mfr
N.A.I.C.S.: 325211

Riken Fabro Corporation (1)
Waterras Tower 2-101 Kandaawaji-cho,
Chiyoda-ku, Tokyo, 101-0063,
Japan (100%)
Tel.: (81) 352971530
Web Site: http://www.fabro.co.jp
Sales Range: $150-199.9 Million
Emp.: 49
Consumer Packaging Synthetic Resin Films
Mfr & Distr
N.A.I.C.S.: 326113
Michiaki Tanaka *(Pres)*

**Riken Technos Corporation - Gunma
Plant** (1)
451-12 kamitajima-cho, Ota, 373-0044,
Gunma, Japan
Tel.: (81) 276327020
Web Site: http://www.rikentechnos.co.jp
Sales Range: $200-249.9 Million
Emp.: 800
Polyvinyl Chloride Compounds Mfr
N.A.I.C.S.: 325991

**Riken Technos Corporation - Mie
Plant** (1)
522 Sugauchi-cho, Kameyama, 519-0132,
Mie, Japan
Tel.: (81) 595824751
Web Site: http://www.rikentechnos.co.jp
Sales Range: $50-74.9 Million
Emp.: 250
Extrusion & Injection Molding Compounds
Mfr
N.A.I.C.S.: 325998
Toshiyuki Sato *(Exec Officer)*

**Riken Technos Corporation - Saitama
Plant** (1)
2058 Oka, Fukaya, 369-0295, Saitama,
Japan
Tel.: (81) 485852531
Web Site: http://www.rikentechnos.co.jp
Emp.: 250
Adhesive Sheets Mfr
N.A.I.C.S.: 325520

Riken U.S.A. Corporation (1)
26200 Town Center Dr Ste 135, Novi, MI
48375 (100%)
Tel.: (248) 513-3511
Web Site: https://www.riken-usa.com
Sales of 3D Laminates & Steel Laminates
N.A.I.C.S.: 423990

**Shanghai Riken Technos
Corporation** (1)
No 3700 Jindu Road, Minhang District,
Shanghai, 201108, China (70%)
Tel.: (86) 2154423792
Web Site: http://www.shanghairiken.com.cn
Emp.: 120
Polyvinyl Chloride Compounds Mfr
N.A.I.C.S.: 325211
Arai Kazunari *(Gen Mgr)*

Shinko Electric Wire Co.,Ltd. (1)
108-11 Sayamagahara, Chuo-Ku, Iruma,
358-0032, Saitama, Japan
Tel.: (81) 429346181
Web Site: http://www.shinko-densen.co.jp
Electrical Wire Mfr
N.A.I.C.S.: 335929
Hayano Masakazu *(Pres)*

RIKEN VITAMIN CO., LTD.
1-6-1 Yotsuya Shinjuku-ku, Tokyo,
160-0004, Japan
Tel.: (81) 353621311
Web Site: http://www.rikenvitamin.jp
Year Founded: 1949
4526—(TKS)
Rev.: $859,100,000
Assets: $1,018,558,640
Liabilities: $327,687,360
Net Worth: $690,871,280
Earnings: $62,087,520
Emp.: 1,848
Fiscal Year-end: 03/31/23
Food Ingredient Mfr
N.A.I.C.S.: 311999
Kazuhiko Yamaki *(Pres)*

Subsidiaries:

EIKEN SHOJI CO., LTD. (1)
1-14 Kandajinbo-cho Chiyoda, Tokyo, 101-0051, Japan
Tel.: (81) 3 52839971
Web Site: http://www.eiken-shoji.co.jp
Food Products Distr
N.A.I.C.S.: 424420
Toshiro Miyoshi *(Pres)*

GUYMON EXTRACTS INC. (1)
3001 N Tumbleweed Dr, Guymon, OK
73942
Tel.: (580) 338-2624
Emp.: 20
Food Ingredient Distr
N.A.I.C.S.: 424490
Atushi Fojimori *(Pres)*

Qingdao Fusheng Food Co., Ltd. (1)
Lanzhou East Road, Taiwan Industrial Park,
Jiaozhou, 266300, China
Tel.: (86) 53288266015
Web Site: http://www.fushengfood.com
Food Ingredient Distr
N.A.I.C.S.: 424490

**RIKEN FOOD (DALIAN) CO.,
LTD.** (1)
No 36 The 2nd DD St DD Port Dalian Development Zone, Tieling, 116620, China
Tel.: (86) 41187406868
Food Ingredient Distr
N.A.I.C.S.: 424490

RIKEN FOOD CO., LTD. (1)
2-5-60 Miyauchi, Tagajo, Miyagi, 985-0844,
Miyagi Prefecture, Japan
Tel.: (81) 223656446
Web Site: https://www.rikenfood.co.jp
Emp.: 254
Food Products Distr
N.A.I.C.S.: 424420

**RIKEN VITAMIN EUROPE
GmbH** (1)
Graf-Adolf-Strasse 12, 40212, Dusseldorf,
Germany
Tel.: (49) 2118632400
Web Site: https://www.riken-vitamin.de
Food Ingredient Distr
N.A.I.C.S.: 424490
Yoshinori Miyata *(Mng Dir)*

RIKEN VITAMIN USA INC. (1)
386 Beech Ave Unit B6, Torrance, CA
90501
Tel.: (310) 294-5290
Web Site: https://www.rikenvitamin.jp
Food Ingredient Distr
N.A.I.C.S.: 424490
Carl Brainerd *(Acct Mgr)*

**RIKEVITA (INDIA) PRIVATE
LIMITED** (1)
Workafella AK Estate Off Veer Savarkar
Flyover Swami Vivekanand Road, Goregaon West, Mumbai, 400062, Maharashtra,
India
Tel.: (91) 9022220579
Web Site: https://www.rikenvitamin.jp
Food Ingredient Distr
N.A.I.C.S.: 424490

**RIKEVITA (MALAYSIA) SDN.
BHD.** (1)
No 11 Jalan Bayu, Taman Perindustrian
Tampoi Jaya, 81200, Johor Bahru, Johor,
Malaysia
Tel.: (60) 72381733
Food Ingredient Distr
N.A.I.C.S.: 424490

**RIKEVITA (SINGAPORE) PTE
LTD** (1)
41 Science Park Road 02-01 The Gemini,
Singapore Science Park II, Singapore,
117610, Singapore
Tel.: (65) 62983505
Food Ingredient Distr
N.A.I.C.S.: 424490

RIKEVITA ASIA CO., LTD. (1)
3F-1 No 188 Sec 5 Nan-jing E Rd, Songshan Dist, Taipei, 10571, Taiwan
Tel.: (886) 237656008
Web Site: https://www.rikenvitamin.jp
Food Ingredient Distr
N.A.I.C.S.: 424490

**RIKEVITA FINE CHEMICAL & FOOD
INDUSTRY (SHANGHAI) CO.,
LTD** (1)
Room 105-109 B Building The Rainbow
Center 3051 Hechuan Road, Min Hang Qu,
Shanghai, 201103, China
Tel.: (86) 2134976617
Web Site: https://www.rikenvitamin.jp
Food Ingredient Distr
N.A.I.C.S.: 424490

**Rikevita Turkey Food Industry Limited
Company** (1)
19 Mayis Mah 19 Mayis Cad Golden Plaza
No 3/16, Sisli, Istanbul, Turkiye
Tel.: (90) 2129340439
Food Improving Agents Distr
N.A.I.C.S.: 424490

**TIANJIN RIKEVITA FOOD CO.,
LTD.** (1)
No 24 Xinghua Road Xiqing Development
Zone, Tianjin, 300385, China
Tel.: (86) 2223972047
Web Site: https://www.tj-rikevita.com
Chemical Additive Distr
N.A.I.C.S.: 424690

RIL PROPERTY PLC
Level 1 Parkland No 33 Park Street,
2, Colombo, Sri Lanka
Tel.: (94) 1123328501
Web Site: https://www.rilproperty.lk
Year Founded: 2009
RIL.N0000—(COL)
Rev.: $76,856,944
Assets: $228,694,548
Liabilities: $85,357,325
Net Worth: $143,337,223
Earnings: $4,236,135
Emp.: 943
Fiscal Year-end: 03/31/22
Real Estate Services
N.A.I.C.S.: 531210
S. G. Wijesinha *(Chm)*

Subsidiaries:

Panasian Power PLC (1)
Level 04 BTL Shipping House No 452 Braybrooke Street, 5, Colombo, Sri
Lanka (61.68%)
Tel.: (94) 114651114
Web Site: https://www.panasianpower.com
Rev.: $3,878,674
Assets: $24,236,568
Liabilities: $11,927,892
Net Worth: $12,308,676
Earnings: $1,427,149
Emp.: 66
Fiscal Year-end: 03/31/2021
Hydro Power Generation Services
N.A.I.C.S.: 221118
Prathap Ramanujam *(Chm & CEO)*

RILEY GOLD CORP.
Suite 2390 1055 West Hastings
Street, Vancouver, V6E 2E9, BC,
Canada
Tel.: (604) 443-3830 BC
Web Site: https://rileyresources.ca
Year Founded: 2011
RLYG—(TSXV)
Assets: $2,321,082
Liabilities: $37,143
Net Worth: $2,283,939
Earnings: ($303,261)
Fiscal Year-end: 12/31/20
Investment Services
N.A.I.C.S.: 523999

Riley Gold Corp.—(Continued)

Todd L. Hilditch (Pres & CEO)

RIMAL ENGINEERING PRODUCTS
Baniyas Najda Street, PO Box 5280, Abu Dhabi, United Arab Emirates
Tel.: (971) 26332267
Web Site: http://www.rimal.ae
Kitchen Furniture
N.A.I.C.S.: 337110
Ghassan Elsolh (Gen Mgr)

RIMBACO GROUP GLOBAL LIMITED
309-E 1st Floor Silver Square Perak Road, Penang, Malaysia
Tel.: (60) 42810242
Web Site:
    http://www.rimbaco.com.my
Year Founded: 1985
Rev.: $111,109,491
Assets: $75,787,985
Liabilities: $42,426,426
Net Worth: $33,361,559
Earnings: $4,355,028
Emp.: 140
Fiscal Year-end: 10/31/23
Construction Management Services
N.A.I.C.S.: 236116
Seah Sun Low (Founder & Chm)

RIMBUNAN SAWIT BERHAD
North Wing Menara Rimbunan Hijau 101, Pusat Suria Permata Jalan Upper Lanang, 96000, Sibu, Sarawak, Malaysia
Tel.: (60) 84218555
Web Site: https://www.rsb.com.my
Year Founded: 1993
RSAWIT—(KLS)
Rev.: $143,051,222
Assets: $180,153,397
Liabilities: $105,344,018
Net Worth: $74,809,380
Earnings: ($1,231,261)
Emp.: 786
Fiscal Year-end: 12/31/22
Palm Oil Mfr
N.A.I.C.S.: 311224
Jan Moi Voon (Co-Sec)

RIMEX A.D.
Savski Trg 7, Savski Venac, Belgrade, Serbia
Tel.: (381) 11 7610 367
Web Site: http://www.rimex.ls.rs
Year Founded: 1992
RMKS—(BEL)
Sales Range: $1-9.9 Million
Emp.: 56
Accommodation Services
N.A.I.C.S.: 721110
Aleksandar Stankovic (CEO)

RIMEX METALS (U.K.) LIMITED
Aden Road, Enfield, EN3 7SU, Middlesex, United Kingdom
Tel.: (44) 20 8804 0633 UK
Web Site:
    http://www.rimexmetals.com
Year Founded: 1959
Sales Range: $25-49.9 Million
Emp.: 70
Metals Mfr
N.A.I.C.S.: 332999
Keith Childs (Chm)

Subsidiaries:

Rimex Espana (1)
Lastaola Industrial Estate 101 Pavilion, Donostia, 20018, Hernani, Spain
Tel.: (34) 9432 19291
Web Site: http://www.rimexmetals.com
Emp.: 1

Metals Mfr
N.A.I.C.S.: 332999
Mikel Smith (CEO)

Rimex Metals (Australia) Pty Ltd (1)
6 Warringah Close, Somersby, 2250, NSW, Australia
Tel.: (61) 2 4340 5599
Web Site: http://www.rimexmetals.com.au
Metals Mfr
N.A.I.C.S.: 332999
Brian Hartwig (Gen Mgr)

Rimex Metals (Deutschland) GmbH (1)
Schiesswiesen 4, 73650, Winterbach, Germany
Tel.: (49) 7181 7096 0
Web Site: http://www.rimexmetals.com
Metals Mfr
N.A.I.C.S.: 332999

Rimex Metals (France) SA (1)
10 Rue d'Alsace, 95110, Sannois, France
Tel.: (33) 1 39 82 38 55
Metals Mfr
N.A.I.C.S.: 332999

Rimex Metals (South Africa) Pty Ltd (1)
372 Kruger Road Strydom Park Ext 20, PO Box 1255, 2125, Randburg, South Africa
Tel.: (27) 11 793 3695
Web Site: http://www.mweb.co.za
Emp.: 12
Metals Mfr
N.A.I.C.S.: 332999
Bharat Shah (Gen Mgr)

Rimex Metals (USA) Inc. (1)
2850 Woodbridge Ave, Edison, NJ 08837
Tel.: (732) 549-3800
Web Site: http://www.rimexmetals.com
Sales Range: $1-9.9 Million
Emp.: 25
Metals Mfr
N.A.I.C.S.: 332999

RIMEX SUPPLY LTD.
9726 186th St, Surrey, V4N 3N7, BC, Canada
Tel.: (604) 888-0025
Web Site: http://www.rimex.com
Year Founded: 1976
Rev.: $22,967,191
Emp.: 135
Wheels & Rims Mfr
N.A.I.C.S.: 327910
Derek Weston (Pres)

Subsidiaries:

PT Rimex International Indonesia (1)
Jl Mulawarman No 128 RT 23 Kelurahan Sepinggan, Balikpapan, 76115, Kalimantan, Indonesia
Tel.: (62) 542770381
Motor Vehicle Parts Distr
N.A.I.C.S.: 423120

RIMEX Inc (1)
5801 W Van Buren St, Phoenix, AZ 85043
Tel.: (602) 272-9393
Motor Vehicle Parts Distr
N.A.I.C.S.: 423120
Brian Oesterreicher (Gen Mgr)

RIMEX Supply Ltd do Brasil (1)
Rua Antonio Jose de Oliveira 76 Parque Sao Pedro, Belo Horizonte, 31610-300, Minas Gerais, Brazil
Tel.: (55) 3134572656
Motor Vehicle Parts Distr
N.A.I.C.S.: 423120

RIMEX Wheel Pty Ltd (1)
27 Crichtons Paget, PO Box 5059, MacKay, 4740, QLD, Australia
Tel.: (61) 749525585
Motor Vehicle Parts Distr
N.A.I.C.S.: 423120
Ben Hussie (Mgr)

S.A. Heavy Rim Importers Pty Ltd. (1)
73 Hoog street, Middelburg, Mpumalanga, 1050, South Africa
Tel.: (27) 132461780

Motor Vehicle Parts Distr
N.A.I.C.S.: 423120

RIMFIRE PACIFIC MINING NL
St Kilda Rd Towers Suite 142 Level 1 1 Queens Road, Melbourne, 3004, VIC, Australia
Tel.: (61) 396205866
Web Site: https://www.rimfire.com.au
RIM—(ASX)
Rev.: $7,320
Assets: $11,791,878
Liabilities: $292,455
Net Worth: $11,499,422
Earnings: ($975,107)
Fiscal Year-end: 06/30/24
Mineral Explorer
N.A.I.C.S.: 213115
Melanie Leydin (Sec)

RIMON GROUP
5 Leshem St Northen Ind Zone, Caesarea, 3079869, Israel
Tel.: (972) 46274589
Web Site: https://www.rimongrp.com
Year Founded: 1997
RMON—(TAE)
Rev.: $203,062,198
Assets: $304,663,250
Liabilities: $167,628,654
Net Worth: $137,034,597
Earnings: $17,709,452
Fiscal Year-end: 06/30/23
Waste Water Treatment Services
N.A.I.C.S.: 562998
Yossef Yossi Elmalem (CEO)

Subsidiaries:

Mer-Terre Contracting Company for Marine and Development Work Ltd. (1)
Ha-Tsoref st 19, Ashkelon, Israel
Tel.: (972) 86719694
Web Site: https://www.merterre.com
Marine Engineering & Logistics Services
N.A.I.C.S.: 541330

RIMONI INDUSTRIES LTD.
27 Tzela Hahar St, Modi'in-Maccabim-Re'ut, 49102, Israel
Tel.: (972) 86605050
Web Site: https://www.rimoni-ind.com
Year Founded: 1966
RIMO—(TAE)
Rev.: $58,879,402
Assets: $61,391,351
Liabilities: $11,473,960
Net Worth: $49,917,391
Earnings: $11,579,223
Emp.: 500
Fiscal Year-end: 12/31/23
Industrial Mold Manufacturing
N.A.I.C.S.: 333511
Yotam Rimoni (Founder)

RINA S.P.A.
Via Corsica 12, Genoa, 16128, Italy
Tel.: (39) 010 53851
Web Site: http://www.rinagroup.org
Year Founded: 1861
Sales Range: $350-399.9 Million
Emp.: 2,000
Holding Company; Engineering, Certification, Testing, Inspection & Training Services
N.A.I.C.S.: 551112
Ugo Salerno (Chm & CEO)

Subsidiaries:

Agroqualita S.p.A. (1)
V le Cesare Pavese 305, 00144, Roma, Italy
Tel.: (39) 0654228675
Web Site: http://www.agroqualita.it
Food Product Mfr & Distr
N.A.I.C.S.: 311423

Centro Sviluppo Materiali S.p.A. (1)
Via di Castel Romano 100, 00128, Rome, Italy
Tel.: (39) 0650551
Web Site: http://www.c-s-m.it
Electronic Design & Testing Services
N.A.I.C.S.: 541420
Dante Pocci (Area Mgr-Bus)

D'Appolonia S.p.A. (1)
Via San Nazaro 19, 16145, Genoa, Italy
Tel.: (39) 010 3628148
Web Site: http://www.dappolonia.it
Engineeering Services
N.A.I.C.S.: 541330
Cristina Migliaro (Mgr-Sector Dev)

Subsidiary (Non-US):

D'Appolonia Belgium NV (2)
Tiensesteenweg 28, Leuven, 3001, Heverlee, Belgium
Tel.: (32) 16226290
Engineeering Services
N.A.I.C.S.: 541330
Lucas Garvia (Project Mgr)

ICIC S.p.A. (1)
Via Cesare Pavese n 305 7 piano, 00144, Roma, Italy
Tel.: (39) 0654228601
Web Site: http://www.icic.it
Industrial Construction Management Services
N.A.I.C.S.: 236210

ITA Istituto Tecnologie Avanzate Srl (1)
Strada Comunale Savonesa 9, Rivalta Scrivia, 15050, Alessandria, Italy
Tel.: (39) 0131860700
Laboratory Testing Services
N.A.I.C.S.: 541380

LAB 21 SA (1)
Rue Ibn Al Haytham a cote de la nouvelle mosquée - Zone industrielle, Megrine, Tunis, Tunisia
Tel.: (216) 71433221
Web Site: http://www.lab21.com.tn
Laboratory Testing Services
N.A.I.C.S.: 541380

Polaris - Anserv S.r.l. (1)
Dacia 65 Ap 2 Sector 1, 010407, Bucharest, Romania
Tel.: (40) 212113991
Engineeering Services
N.A.I.C.S.: 541330
Silvia Dinculescu (Dir-Comml)

QIC Inc. (1)
11601 Spring Cypress Rd Ste A, Tomball, TX 77377
Tel.: (281) 370-2700
Web Site: http://www.qicinc.com
Engineeering Services
N.A.I.C.S.: 541330
Chad Fletcher (COO)

Subsidiary (Non-US):

QIC Asia Pacific PTE. LTD. (2)
8 Shenton Way 05-02 Axa Tower, Singapore, 068811, Singapore
Tel.: (65) 96311804
Engineeering Services
N.A.I.C.S.: 541330

QIC UK Ltd. (2)
Regus House 1 Berry Street, Aberdeen, AB25 1HF, United Kingdom
Tel.: (44) 1224841319
Engineeering Services
N.A.I.C.S.: 541330

RINA Check srl (1)
Via Torri Bianche 3 Palazzo Larice 3, Piano di Sorrento, 20871, Vimercate, Italy
Tel.: (39) 0396290991
Web Site: http://www.rinacheck.it
Building Construction Services
N.A.I.C.S.: 236210

SOA RINA S.p.A. (1)
Via Ilva 2/7, 16128, Genoa, Italy
Tel.: (39) 0105385682
Web Site: http://www.soarina.it
Building Construction Services
N.A.I.C.S.: 236210
Lorenzo Maragliano (Dir-Technical)

SSM S.r.l. (1)
Via degli Artigiani 86, Bolzaneto, 16162, Genoa, Italy
Tel.: (39) 010710259
Web Site: http://www.ssmlab.it
Laboratory Testing Services
N.A.I.C.S.: 541380

Sogea S.C.aR.L. (1)
via Ravasco 10, 16128, Genoa, Italy
Tel.: (39) 0105767811
Web Site: http://www.sogeanet.it
Education Training & Support Services
N.A.I.C.S.: 611710

RINANI GROUP BERHAD
No 8-2 Jalan PJU 5/16, Dataran Sunway Kota Damansara, 47810, Petaling Jaya, Malaysia
Tel.: (60) 361579778
Web Site: https://rinani.com.my
Financial Services
N.A.I.C.S.: 523999

RING INTERNATIONAL HOLDING AG
Palais Liechtenstein Alserbachstrasse 14-16, Vienna, 1090, Austria
Tel.: (43) 1 532 2801 0 AT
Web Site: http://www.ringholding.com
Year Founded: 2001
Sales Range: $500-549.9 Million
Emp.: 1,300
Holding Company
N.A.I.C.S.: 551112
Ralph-Leo Lanckohr *(Member-Exec Bd)*

Subsidiaries:

Bensons International Systems B.V. (1)
Bellstraat 7, 3861 NP, Nijkerk, Netherlands
Tel.: (31) 33 2533 220
Web Site: http://www.bensons.net
Binder & Lever Arch Mechanism Mfr & Distr
N.A.I.C.S.: 339999

Subsidiary (Non-US):

Bensons International Systems (S) Pte. Ltd. (2)
2 Essex Road #10-02, Singapore, 309330, Singapore
Tel.: (65) 6368 1959
Web Site: http://www.bensons.net
Sales Range: $10-24.9 Million
Emp.: 5
Binder & Lever Arch Mechanism Mfr & Distr
N.A.I.C.S.: 339999
Stella Lin *(Gen Mgr)*

Subsidiary (US):

Bensons International Systems, Inc. (2)
300 Lackawanna Ave Ste 6, Woodland Park, NJ 07424-2904
Tel.: (973) 256-2383
Web Site: http://www.bensons.net
Sales Range: $25-49.9 Million
Emp.: 7
Binder & Lever Arch Mechanism Distr
N.A.I.C.S.: 424120
Donna Ratta *(Mgr-Logistics)*

Ecopolifix Srl (1)
Via Strada del Confine 41, Tezze sul Brenta, 36056, Vicenza, Italy
Tel.: (39) 0 424 848555
Web Site: http://www.ecopolifix.it
Coating Material Mfr
N.A.I.C.S.: 325510
Bastian Krauss *(Member-Mgmt Bd)*

HWB Kunststoffwerke AG (1)
Friedberg 234, 9427, Wolfhalden, Switzerland
Tel.: (41) 71 898 37 00
Web Site: http://www.hwb.biz
Stationery Product Mfr
N.A.I.C.S.: 322230
Rolf Muller *(Mng Dir)*

Interkov spol.s r.o. (1)
Decinska 32/33, 407 22, Benesov nad Ploucnici, Czech Republic
Tel.: (420) 412 599 111
Web Site: http://www.interkov.cz
Emp.: 100
Stationery Product Mfr
N.A.I.C.S.: 322230
Ralph Martins *(Mng Dir)*

OOO Aurora (1)
Ul Strojinudstrii 3, 18030, Cherkassy, Ukraine
Tel.: (380) 47 27 12 881
Web Site: http://www.aurora.ck.ua
Emp.: 19
Paints Mfr
N.A.I.C.S.: 325510

Rembrandtin Farbexperte GmbH (1)
Perchtoldsdorferstrasse 21, 1230, Vienna, Austria
Tel.: (43) 1 86 58 000
Web Site: http://www.rembrandtin-farbexperte.at
Paints Mfr
N.A.I.C.S.: 325510

pph Kunststofftechnik GmbH (1)
Liebigstrasse 5, 85757, Karlsfeld, Germany
Tel.: (49) 8131 61 553 0
Web Site: http://www.pph-kunststofftechnik.de
Plastic Product Distr
N.A.I.C.S.: 424610

proOFFICE s.r.o. (1)
Cepirohy c p 115, 43401, Most, Czech Republic
Tel.: (420) 477070645
Web Site: http://www.prooffice.cz
Sales Range: $75-99.9 Million
Emp.: 200
Mfr of Soft Plastic Foil Office Supply Products
N.A.I.C.S.: 322230
Michael Kahl *(Mng Dir)*

RINGER HUT CO., LTD.
14F Osaki TOC Bld 1-6-1 Osaki, Shinagawa, 141-0032, Tokyo, Japan
Tel.: (81) 357458611
Web Site: https://www.ringerhut.co.jp
Year Founded: 1970
8200—(TKS)
Rev.: $285,081,810
Assets: $203,667,340
Liabilities: $112,489,940
Net Worth: $91,177,400
Earnings: $5,331,680
Emp.: 547
Fiscal Year-end: 02/29/24
Restaurant Operators
N.A.I.C.S.: 722511
Yonehama Kazuhide *(Chm)*

Subsidiaries:

Lingering Who's Corporation (1)
4-7-35 Kitashinagawa Shinagawa-ku Gotenyama trust tower 3F, Tokyo, Japan
Tel.: (81) 354887441
Restaurant Operators
N.A.I.C.S.: 722511

Ringer Hut Co., Ltd. - Fuji hill Factory (1)
224-5 Tanagashira Oyama-cho Sunto-gun, Shizuoka, 410-1327, Japan
Tel.: (81) 550781351
Restaurant Operators
N.A.I.C.S.: 722511

Ringer Hut Co., Ltd. - Saga Factory (1)
Yoshinogari-cho Omagari 4550-5, Kanzaki-gun, Saga, 842-0102, Japan
Tel.: (81) 952531145
Emp.: 350
Restaurant Operators
N.A.I.C.S.: 722511

Ringer Hut Development Corporation (1)
1-2-3 Hakataekimae 1st building 4F Hakataekiminami Hakata-ku, Fukuoka, Fukuoka, Japan
Tel.: (81) 924328808
Restaurant Operators
N.A.I.C.S.: 722511

RINGIER HOLDING AG
Dufourstrasse 23, 8008, Zurich, Switzerland
Tel.: (41) 442596111 CH
Web Site: http://www.ringier.com
Sales Range: $1-4.9 Billion
Emp.: 7,474
Holding Company; Books, Magazines, Journals & Newspapers Publisher
N.A.I.C.S.: 551112
Michael Ringier *(Chm)*

Subsidiaries:

Beijing Ringier International Advertising Co. Ltd. (1)
Rm 7001 7005 Hua Li Bldg, No 158 Chin Pao St, Beijing, 100005, Dong Cheng, China
Tel.: (86) 1065281841
Web Site: http://www.ringier.cn
Sales Range: $25-49.9 Million
Emp.: 100
Full Service, Magazines
N.A.I.C.S.: 541810

Good News Productions AG (1)
Thurgauerstrasse 105, Zurich, 8152, Glattpark, Switzerland (50%)
Tel.: (41) 44 809 66 66
Web Site: http://www.goodnews.ch
Sales Range: $25-49.9 Million
Emp.: 25
Magazine & Newspaper Publisher
N.A.I.C.S.: 513120
Gerard Jenni *(Mng Dir)*

Ringier CR A.S. (1)
Upruhonu 13/ komulmardu 42, 17000, Prague, Czech Republic (51%)
Tel.: (420) 225977111
Web Site: http://www.ringier.cz
Sales Range: $100-124.9 Million
Emp.: 441
Newspaper & Magazine Publisher
N.A.I.C.S.: 513110

Ringier Ghana Ltd. (1)
5 Labone Crescent, PO Box CT 9364, Cantonments, Accra, Ghana
Tel.: (233) 302 960 494
Web Site: http://www.ringier.ng
Digital Advertising Services
N.A.I.C.S.: 541850

Ringier Kenya Ltd. (1)
Saachi Plaza block A office suite A8, PO Box 40034, 00100, Nairobi, Kenya
Tel.: (254) 20 8022588
Web Site: http://www.ringier.co.ke
Digital Advertising Services
N.A.I.C.S.: 541810

Ringier Kft. (1)
Szugloi utca 81-85, 1141, Budapest, Hungary (100%)
Tel.: (36) 14602500
Web Site: http://www.ringier.hu
Sales Range: $25-49.9 Million
Emp.: 80
Tabloid Publisher
N.A.I.C.S.: 513130

Ringier Media Nigeria Ltd. (1)
3 Iweanya Ugbogoh Street Lekki Phase 1, Lagos, Nigeria
Tel.: (234) 1 2951053
Web Site: http://www.ringier.com.ng
Digital Advertising Services
N.A.I.C.S.: 541810
Olufemi Oyebanjo *(COO)*

Ringier Print Holding AG (1)
Dufourstrasse 23, 8008, Zurich, Switzerland (100%)
Tel.: (41) 442596111
Web Site: http://www.ringier.com
Holding Company; Digital & Print Publishing
N.A.I.C.S.: 551112

Subsidiary (Domestic):

JRP Editions S.A. (2)
Rue des Bains 39, 1205, Geneva, Switzerland
Tel.: (41) 228080109
Web Site: http://www.jrp-editions.com
Book Publishers
N.A.I.C.S.: 513130
Arnaud Hubert *(CEO)*

Ringier AG (2)
Bruhlstrasse 5, 4800, Zofingen, Switzerland (100%)
Tel.: (41) 627463111
Web Site: http://www.ringier.com
Periodical Publishers
N.A.I.C.S.: 513120

Subsidiary (Domestic):

Betty Bossi Verlag AG (3)
Burglistrass 29, Zurich, 8021, Switzerland (50%)
Tel.: (41) 844466466
Web Site: http://www.bettybossi.ch
Sales Range: $50-74.9 Million
Emp.: 100
Catalog & Online Shopping
N.A.I.C.S.: 513120

Ringier Print Adligenswil AG (3)
Ebikonerstrasse 75, 6043, Adligenswil, Switzerland
Tel.: (41) 41 375 11 11
Web Site: http://www.ringierprint.ch
Newspaper Publishers
N.A.I.C.S.: 513110

Ringier SA (3)
Pont Bessieres 3, Postfach 7289, 1002, Lausanne, Switzerland
Tel.: (41) 21 331 70 00
Web Site: http://www.ringier.ch
Newspaper Publishers
N.A.I.C.S.: 513110

Subsidiary (Domestic):

Ringier Axel Springer Media AG (2)
Kreuzstrasse 26, 8008, Zurich, Switzerland
Tel.: (41) 44 267 29 29
Web Site: http://www.ringieraxelspringer.com
Emp.: 20
Book Publishers
N.A.I.C.S.: 513130
Jovan Protic *(Grp Dir-Publ)*

Subsidiary (Non-US):

Ringier Axel Springer Polska Sp. z oo (3)
ul Domaniewska 52, 02-672, Warsaw, Poland
Tel.: (48) 22 232 00 00
Web Site: http://www.ringieraxelspringer.pl
Newspaper Publishers
N.A.I.C.S.: 513110

Ringier Axel Springer d.o.o. (3)
Zorza Klemansoa 19, 11 000, Belgrade, Serbia
Tel.: (381) 11 333 4 701
Web Site: http://www.ringieraxelspringer.rs
Book Publishers
N.A.I.C.S.: 513130
Sandra Djordjevic *(Asst Gen Mgr)*

Subsidiary (Domestic):

Ringier Digital AG (2)
Industriestrasse 44, 3175, Flamatt, Switzerland
Tel.: (41) 31 744 21 70
Web Site: http://www.ringierdigital.ch
Digital Advertising Services
N.A.I.C.S.: 541850

Affiliate (Non-US):

Nhat Viet Group Co., Ltd. (3)
157 Vo Thi Sau Ward 6, District 3, Ho Chi Minh City, Vietnam (50%)
Tel.: (84) 38202334
Web Site: http://www.nvg.vn
Mobile, Platform & Web Media Developer & Publisher
N.A.I.C.S.: 513199

Subsidiary (Non-US):

Ringier Print Budapest Inc. (2)
Campona u 1 Harbor Park a3a Building, 1225, Budapest, Hungary
Tel.: (36) 1 207 8130
Newspaper Publishers

RINGIER HOLDING AG

Ringier Holding AG—(Continued)
N.A.I.C.S.: 513110

Ringier Print CZ a.s. (2)
Na Rovince 876, 720 00, Ostrava, Hrabova, Czech Republic
Tel.: (420) 596668111
Periodical Publishing
N.A.I.C.S.: 513120

Ringier Publishing GmbH (2)
Lennestrasse 1, D-10785, Berlin, Germany (100%)
Tel.: (49) 309819410
Web Site: http://www.ringier.de
Sales Range: $25-49.9 Million
Emp.: 60
Magazine Publisher
N.A.I.C.S.: 513120

Ringier Vietnam Co., Ltd. (2)
3rd Floor Copac Building 12 Ton Dan Street Ward 13, District 4, Ho Chi Minh City, Vietnam
Tel.: (84) 83 440 5071
Web Site: http://www.ringier.vn
Periodical Publishers
N.A.I.C.S.: 513120
Dale Nottingham (Mng Dir)

Unit (Domestic):

New Fashion (3)
24 Thanh Mien Street, Dong Da District, Hanoi, Vietnam
Tel.: (84) 47761660
Publisher of Fashion Magazines
N.A.I.C.S.: 513120

Vietnam Economic Times (3)
96 Hoang Quoc Viet Rd, Hanoi, Vietnam
Tel.: (84) 47552060
Web Site: http://www.vneconomy.com.vn
Sales Range: $25-49.9 Million
Emp.: 13
Publisher of the English-Language Monthly, Vietnam Economic Times
N.A.I.C.S.: 513120

Ringier Senegal S.A. (1)
Sacre Coeur 3 Villa 9343, 45940, Dakar, Senegal
Tel.: (221) 33 827 83 03
Emp.: 12
Digital Advertising Services
N.A.I.C.S.: 541850

Ringier Slovakia, a.s. (1)
Prievozska 14, 821 09, Bratislava, Slovakia (60%)
Tel.: (421) 258227400
Web Site: http://www.ringier.sk
Sales Range: $100-124.9 Million
Emp.: 300
Magazine Publisher
N.A.I.C.S.: 513120
Milan Dubec (CEO)

Ringier TV (1)
Haganholfstrasse 83 B, 8050, Zurich, Switzerland (100%)
Tel.: (41) 3085454
Web Site: http://www.ringiertv.ch
Sales Range: $25-49.9 Million
Emp.: 100
N.A.I.C.S.: 513120

SC Ringier Romania SRL (1)
Novo Parc 6 Dimitrie Pompeiu Blvd, District 2, 020337, Bucharest, Romania
Tel.: (40) 212030800
Web Site: http://www.ringier.ro
Sales Range: $100-124.9 Million
Emp.: 500
N.A.I.C.S.: 513120

Sat.1 Schweiz AG (1)
Fahnlibrunnenstrasse 5, Kusnacht, 8700, Zurich, Switzerland (40%)
Tel.: (41) 449148400
Web Site: http://www.sat1.ch
Sales Range: $25-49.9 Million
Television Advertising & Program Services
N.A.I.C.S.: 541890

Schule fur Medienintegration (SMI) AG (1)
Untere Grabenstrasse 26, Zofingen, 4800, Switzerland (51%)
Tel.: (41) 12596912

Web Site: http://www.smi.ch
Publishing & Printing
N.A.I.C.S.: 513120

Schweizer Mediendatenbank (SMD) AG (1)
Badenerstrasse 119, 8036, Zurich, Switzerland
Tel.: (41) 443156080
Web Site: http://www.smd.ch
Sales Range: $1-9.9 Million
Emp.: 20
Online Operator & Services
N.A.I.C.S.: 812990
Mumprecht Jurg (Gen Mgr)

Shenzhen Ringier Trade Advertising Ltd. (1)
Room 201-08 2F Wing B Haisong Building Tai Ran 9 Road Fudia Dist, Futian district, Shenzhen, 518040, Guangdong, China
Tel.: (86) 755 8835 0829
Web Site: http://www.industrysourcing.com
Book Publishers
N.A.I.C.S.: 513130

Ticketcorner AG (1)
Riedmatt Center, 8153, Rumlang, Switzerland (50%)
Tel.: (41) 900 800 800
Web Site: http://www.ticketcorner.ch
Sales Range: $25-49.9 Million
Emp.: 130
International & Local Ticket & Event Retailer
N.A.I.C.S.: 711310
Andreas Angehrn (CEO)

RINGIER TRADE MEDIA LTD.
9/F Cheong Sun Tower 118 Winglok Street, Sheung Wan, China (Hong Kong)
Tel.: (852) 23698788   HK
Web Site: http://www.industrysourcing.com
Trade Magazine & Other Media Publisher
N.A.I.C.S.: 513120
Michael R. Hay (Pres)

Subsidiaries:

Apex Print Ltd. (1)
11-13 Dai Kwai Street, Tai Po Industrial Estate, Tai Po, China (Hong Kong)
Tel.: (852) 2660 2666
Web Site: http://www.apexprint.com.hk
Sales Range: $50-74.9 Million
Commercial Printing Services
N.A.I.C.S.: 323111
Michael R. Hay (Pres)

Asia Inflight Ltd. (1)
9/F Cheong Sun Tower 118 Wing Lok Street, Sheung Wan, China (Hong Kong)
Tel.: (852) 2524 1520
Web Site: http://www.asiainflight.com
Contract Magazine Publisher
N.A.I.C.S.: 513120

RINGKJOBING LANDBOBANK A/S
Torvet 1, DK-6950, Ringkobing, Denmark
Tel.: (45) 4597321166
Web Site: https://www.landbobanken.dk
Year Founded: 1886
RILBA—(CSE)
Rev.: $414,102,097
Assets: $9,980,984,358
Liabilities: $8,636,080,942
Net Worth: $1,344,903,416
Earnings: $216,303,772
Emp.: 646
Fiscal Year-end: 12/31/22
Banking Services
N.A.I.C.S.: 522110
Martin Krogh Pedersen (Chm)

Subsidiaries:

Nordjyske Bank A/S (1)
Torvet 4, 9400, Norresundby, Denmark
Tel.: (45) 98703333
Web Site: http://www.nordjyskebank.dk

Banking Services
N.A.I.C.S.: 522320
Mikael Jakobsen (Dir-Bank)

RINGMETALL AG
Innere Wiener Str 9, 81667, Munich, Germany
Tel.: (49) 89 4522098 0
Web Site: http://ringmetall.de
Year Founded: 1997
Private Investment Firm
N.A.I.C.S.: 523999
Klaus F. Jaenecke (Chm-Supervisory Bd)

Subsidiaries:

Protective Lining Corp. (1)
601 39th St, Brooklyn, NY 11232
Tel.: (718) 854-3838
Web Site: http://www.prolining.com
Rev.: $8,800,000
Emp.: 55
Farm Machinery & Equipment Mfr
N.A.I.C.S.: 333111
Steven Howard (Pres)

Self Industries Inc. (1)
3491 Mary Taylor Rd, Birmingham, AL 35235
Tel.: (205) 655-3284
Web Site: http://www.selfindustries.com
Sales Range: $10-24.9 Million
Emp.: 60
Metal Products Mfr
N.A.I.C.S.: 332119
J. Michael McDowell (Pres)

Branch (Domestic):

Self Industries Inc. (2)
5000 Hampton St, Los Angeles, CA 90058
Tel.: (323) 589-6794
Web Site: http://www.selfindustries.com
Sales Range: Less than $1 Million
Emp.: 7
Metal Barrels, Drums & Pails Warehousing
N.A.I.C.S.: 493110

Sorini Ring Manufacturing Inc. (1)
2524 S Blue Is Ave, Chicago, IL 60608-4934
Tel.: (773) 247-5858
Web Site: http://www.soriniring.com
Metal Tank Mfr
N.A.I.C.S.: 332431
Peter M. May (Pres)

RINKO CORPORATION
Bandai 5-11-30, Chuo Ward, Niigata, 950-8540, Japan
Tel.: (81) 252454113
Web Site: https://www.rinko.co.jp
Year Founded: 1905
9355—(TKS)
Rev.: $86,657,100
Assets: $255,073,290
Liabilities: $137,071,570
Net Worth: $118,001,720
Earnings: $2,359,770
Emp.: 349
Fiscal Year-end: 03/31/24
Marine Transportation Services
N.A.I.C.S.: 483111
Harushige Motoki (Exec Officer)

RINNAI CORPORATION
2-26 Fukuzumi-cho, Nakagawa-ku, Nagoya, 454-0802, Japan
Tel.: (81) 523618211
Web Site: https://www.rinnai.co.jp
Year Founded: 1950
5947—(TKS)
Rev.: $2,843,529,460
Assets: $3,814,551,680
Liabilities: $923,086,500
Net Worth: $2,891,465,180
Earnings: $176,268,870
Emp.: 10,837
Fiscal Year-end: 03/31/24
Household Cooking Equipment, Gas Appliances, Water Heaters, Room Heating Equipment Manufacturing & Sales

INTERNATIONAL PUBLIC

N.A.I.C.S.: 335220
Kenji Hayashi (Chm)

Subsidiaries:

Brivis Climate Systems Pty. Ltd. (1)
61 Malcolm Road, Braeside, 3195, VIC, Australia
Tel.: (61) 392649555
Web Site: http://www.brivis.com.au
Refrigeration & Heating Equipment Mfr
N.A.I.C.S.: 333415
Celeste Camillo (Gen Mgr)

Equipamentos NGK-Rinnai, Ltda. (1)
200 Rua Tenente Onofre Rodrigues Aguiar, VI Industrial, Sao Paulo, CEP 08770-041, Mogi das Cruzes, Brazil
Tel.: (55) 1147919696
Web Site: http://www.rinnai.com.br
Sales Range: $50-74.9 Million
Emp.: 200
Appliance Mfr
N.A.I.C.S.: 335220

Gastar Co., Ltd. (1)
3-4 Fukamidai, Yamato, 242-8577, Kanagawa, Japan
Tel.: (81) 46 262 0161
Web Site: https://www.gastar.co.jp
Air Leak Tester Mfr
N.A.I.C.S.: 334519

Guangzhou Rinnai Gas and Electric Appliance Co., Ltd. (1)
Tianshou Road No 31 Building 2804-2805, Tianhe District, Guangzhou, 510000, China
Tel.: (86) 2038217976
Web Site: http://www.gzrinnai.com.cn
Emp.: 63
Gas Appliances Distr
N.A.I.C.S.: 423720
Zhang Huiqiang (Gen Mgr)

Japan Ceramics Co., Ltd. (1)
200 Sakagawa, Kakegawa, 436-0084, Shizuoka, Japan
Tel.: (81) 537270114
Web Site: https://www.rtk.co.jp
Emp.: 584
N.A.I.C.S.: 335220

Kyushu Training Center (1)
2-3 Komondo-cho, Hakata-ku, Fukuoka, 812-0029, Japan
Tel.: (81) 922813234
Web Site: http://www.rinnai.co.jp
Training Center
N.A.I.C.S.: 611513

P.T. Rinnai Indonesia (1)
Jl Raya Pejuangan No 11 - 13 Komp Ruko Sastra Graha No 9, Kebon Jeruk, Jakarta, 11530, Indonesia (100%)
Tel.: (62) 21 533 1638
Web Site: https://www.rinnai.co.id
Sales Range: Less than $1 Million
Emp.: 25
Laundry Dryer Mfr
N.A.I.C.S.: 335220
Mishela Oktora (Gen Mgr)

RB Controls Co., Ltd. (1)
71 Kanondochoro, Kanazawa, 920-0352, Ishikawa, Japan
Tel.: (81) 76 268 0198
Web Site: https://www.rbcontrols.co.jp
Emp.: 557
Household Appliance Repair & Maintenance Services
N.A.I.C.S.: 811412

RB Korea Ltd. (1)
4 Baekbeom-ro 603beon-gil, Seo-gu Gajwadong, 22845, Incheon, Korea (South)
Tel.: (82) 325830451
Web Site: http://www.rbk.co.kr
Electronic Control Unit Mfr
N.A.I.C.S.: 334419

RK Precision Co., Ltd. (1)
NamDong Industrial ZN 91B/L 3L Gojan-Dong, Namdong-Gu, Incheon, Korea (South)
Tel.: (82) 32 811 3651
Web Site: http://www.rkpkorea.co.kr
Sales Range: $25-49.9 Million
Emp.: 80
Precision Equipment Mfr
N.A.I.C.S.: 332721

AND PRIVATE COMPANIES

RS Korea Ltd. (1)
532-1 Gajwa-dong, Seo-gu, Incheon, 404-250, Korea (South)
Tel.: (82) 32 584 3500
Gas Control Valve Mfr
N.A.I.C.S.: 334512
Makino Mitsuhiro *(Pres)*

RT Engineering Co., Ltd. (1)
2-1236 Kamiikecho, Toyota, 471-0804, Aichi, Japan
Tel.: (81) 565 88 3721
Web Site: http://www.rte-c.co.jp
Sales Range: $50-74.9 Million
Emp.: 157
Heating Equipment Mfr & Distr
N.A.I.C.S.: 333414
Takeshi Umemura *(Pres)*

Rinnai America Corp. (1)
103 International Dr, Peachtree City, GA 30269-1911 **(100%)**
Tel.: (678) 829-1700
Web Site: https://www.rinnai.us
Sales Range: $10-24.9 Million
Emp.: 100
Wholesale Gas Appliances
N.A.I.C.S.: 423730
Frank Windsor *(Pres)*

Rinnai Austrailia W.A (1)
100 Atlantic Drive, Keysborough, 3173, VIC, Australia **(100%)**
Tel.: (61) 1300555545
Web Site: http://www.rinnai.com.au
Sales Range: $25-49.9 Million
Emp.: 13
Household Cooking Equipment, Gas Appliances, Water Heaters & Room Heating Equipment Mfr, Developer & Distr
N.A.I.C.S.: 335220

Rinnai Australia Pty. Ltd. (1)
100 Atlantic Drive, Keysborough, 3173, Australia **(100%)**
Web Site: http://www.rinnai.com.au
Sales Range: $125-149.9 Million
Emp.: 170
Appliance & Heating Services
N.A.I.C.S.: 335220
Greg Ellis *(Mng Dir)*

Rinnai Chubu (1)
14-27 Sumiike-cho, Nakagawa-ku, Nagoya, 454-0806, Japan **(100%)**
Tel.: (81) 523638001
Web Site: http://www.rianai.co.jp
Sales Range: $25-49.9 Million
Emp.: 30
Household Cooking Equipment, Gas Appliances, Water Heaters, Room Heating Equipment Mfr, Developer & Distr
N.A.I.C.S.: 335220

Rinnai Corporation (1)
2-26 Fukuzumi-cho, Nakagawa-ku, Nagoya, 454-0802, Japan
Tel.: (81) 523618211
Web Site: https://www.rinnai.co.jp
Emp.: 3,587
Household Appliances Mfr
N.A.I.C.S.: 335220

Rinnai Corporation (1)
2-26 Fukuzumi-cho, Nakagawa-ku, Nagoya, 454-0802, Aichi, Japan
Tel.: (81) 52 361 8211
Web Site: https://www.rinnai.co.jp
Emp.: 3,605
Provider of Household Manufacturing Services
N.A.I.C.S.: 335220
Naito Hiroyasu *(Pres)*

Rinnai Corporation (1)
4-2-1 Shoko Center, Nishi-ku, Hiroshima, 733-0833, Japan
Web Site: http://www.rinnai.co.jp
Emp.: 3,722
Household Cooking Equipment, Gas Appliances, Water Heaters & Room Heating Equipment Mfr, Developer & Distr
N.A.I.C.S.: 335220

Rinnai Enterprise Co., Ltd. (1)
2-26 Fukuzumi-cho, Nakagawa-ku, Nagoya, 454-0802, Aichi, Japan
Tel.: (81) 52 361 8408
Web Site: https://www.rinnai-kigyou.co.jp
Insurance Services
N.A.I.C.S.: 524210

Rinnai Holdings (Pacific) Pte Ltd. (1)
61 Ubi Road 1 02-20 21 Oxley Bizhub, Singapore, 408727, Singapore
Tel.: (65) 67489011
Web Site: https://www.rinnai.sg
Gas Rice Cooker & Ovens Whslr
N.A.I.C.S.: 423440

Rinnai Hong Kong Ltd. (1)
Rm 1205 Technology Plz 651 Kings Rd, North Point, China (Hong Kong)
Tel.: (852) 25777465 **(100%)**
Web Site: http://www.rinnai.com.hk
Sales Range: $25-49.9 Million
Emp.: 2
N.A.I.C.S.: 335220
Shunsuke Tsutsumi *(Mng Dir)*

Rinnai Hyogo (1)
6-1-12 Daikai-dori, Hyogo-ku, Kobe, 652-0803, Hyogo, Japan
Tel.: (81) 785121351
Web Site: http://www.rinnai.co.jp
Household Cooking Equipment, Gas Appliances, Water Heaters, Room Heating Equipment Mfr & Distr
N.A.I.C.S.: 335220

Rinnai Italia s.r.l. (1)
via Liguria 37, 41012, Carpi, MO, Italy
Tel.: (39) 0596229248
Web Site: https://www.rinnai.it
Water Heater Whslr
N.A.I.C.S.: 423720

Rinnai Korea Corporation (1)
48 Baekbeom-ro 577 beon-gil Sipjeong-dong, Bupyeong-gu, Incheon, 21449, Korea (South) **(100%)**
Tel.: (82) 325708300
Web Site: http://www.rinnai.co.kr
Sales Range: $400-449.9 Million
Emp.: 800
Laundry Dryer Mfr
N.A.I.C.S.: 335220

Rinnai Kyushu (1)
2-3 Komondo-cho, Hakata-ku, Fukuoka, 812-0029, Japan **(100%)**
Tel.: (81) 922813234
Web Site: http://www.rinnai.co.jp
Household Cooking Equipment, Gas Appliances, Water Heaters, Room Heating Equipment Mfr & Distr
N.A.I.C.S.: 335220

Rinnai Malaysia Sdn. Bhd. (1)
Web Site: http://www.rinnai.com.my
Sales Range: $25-49.9 Million
Emp.: 39
Kitchen Appliances & Water Heaters Mfr & Retailer
N.A.I.C.S.: 335220

Rinnai Net Co., Ltd. (1)
14-27 Sumiike-cho, Nakagawa-ku, Nagoya, 454-0802, Aichi, Japan
Tel.: (81) 523618481
Web Site: https://www.rinnai-net.co.jp
Industrial Machinery Whslr
N.A.I.C.S.: 423830

Rinnai New Zealand Ltd. (1)
105 Pavilion Drive, Mangere, Auckland, 2150, New Zealand **(100%)**
Tel.: (64) 9 257 3800
Web Site: https://www.rinnai.co.nz
Sales Range: $25-49.9 Million
Emp.: 100
Mfr of Gas & Oil Appliances
N.A.I.C.S.: 335220
Ray Serner *(Gen Mgr)*

Rinnai Osaka Co (1)
(100%)
Web Site: http://www.rinnai.co.jp
Sales Range: $25-49.9 Million
Emp.: 37
Household Cooking Appliance Manufacturing
N.A.I.C.S.: 335220

Rinnai Precision Co., Ltd. (1)
, Komaki, Japan
Mfr of Household Cooking Equipment
N.A.I.C.S.: 335220

Rinnai Taiwan Corporation (1)
577 Section 2 Meishi Road, Yangmei, Taoyuan, 104, Taiwan **(100%)**
Tel.: (886) 34313366
Web Site: http://www.rinnai.com.tw
Sales Range: $50-74.9 Million
Emp.: 200
Household Gas Appliances
N.A.I.C.S.: 335220

Rinnai Takamatsu (1)
2-11-6 Fukuoka-cho, Takamatsu, 760-0066, Kagawa, Japan **(100%)**
Tel.: (81) 878218055
Web Site: http://www.rinnai.co.jp
Sales Range: $25-49.9 Million
Emp.: 30
Household Cooking Equipment, Gas Appliances, Water Heaters & Room Heating Equipment Mfr, Developer & Distr
N.A.I.C.S.: 335220

Rinnai Tech Hiroshima Co., Ltd. (1)
3-4-21 Syokocenter Nishi-ku, Hiroshima, 733-0833, Japan
Sale of Gas Appliances, Equipment & Repair
N.A.I.C.S.: 423720

Rinnai Tech Kinki Co., Ltd. (1)
3-10-21 Kita-horie, Nishi-ku, Osaka, 550 0014, Japan **(100%)**
Tel.: (81) 665323004
Sales of Cooking Appliances
N.A.I.C.S.: 423990

Rinnai Tech Sapporo Co., Ltd. (1)
2 Kita-ichijo Higashi Chuo Ku, Sapporo, 060 0031, Hokkaido, Japan **(100%)**
Tel.: (81) 112812506
Sales Range: $25-49.9 Million
Emp.: 20
Gas Appliance Sales & Repairing
N.A.I.C.S.: 335220

Rinnai Thailand Co., Ltd. (1)
37/6 Moo 3 Soi Kaisakdawat Thepharak Rd, Bangpla Bangplee, Samut Prakan, 10540, Thailand **(39%)**
Tel.: (66) 23121438
Web Site: http://www.rinnaithailand.com
Sales Range: $100-124.9 Million
Emp.: 500
Laundry Dryer Mfr
N.A.I.C.S.: 335220

Rinnai UK Ltd. (1)
9 Christleton Court Manor Park, Runcorn, WA7 1ST, Cheshire, United Kingdom
Tel.: (44) 3003730660
Web Site: https://www.rinnai-uk.co.uk
Gas Water Heater Whslr
N.A.I.C.S.: 423720
Ian Jenkins *(Mgr-Technical)*

Rinnai Vietnam Co., Ltd. (1)
(100%)
Sales Range: $50-74.9 Million
Emp.: 200
N.A.I.C.S.: 335220

Shanghai Rinnai Co., Ltd. (1)
No 4500 Tuanqing Road, Fengcheng Town Fengxian Shanghai, 201411, China
Web Site: http://www.rinnai.com.cn
Emp.: 3,112
Household Cooking Product Mfr
N.A.I.C.S.: 335220

Techno Parts Co., Ltd. (1)
, Nagoya, Japan
N.A.I.C.S.: 335220

Yanagisawa Manufacturing Co., Ltd. (1)
17-1 Yanagimachi, Kadoma, 571-0041, Osaka, Japan
Tel.: (81) 6 6908 2212
Web Site: http://www.yanagisawa-ss.co.jp
Sales Range: $100-124.9 Million
Emp.: 302
Household Appliances Mfr
N.A.I.C.S.: 335210
Keishi Moribe *(Pres)*

RINO MASTROTTO GROUP S.P.A.

Via Dell Artigianato 100, Trissino, 36070, Italy
Tel.: (39) 0445969696
Web Site: http://www.rinomastrottogroup.com
Sales Range: $100-124.9 Million
Emp.: 800
Leather Goods Mfr
N.A.I.C.S.: 316990
Rino Mastrotto *(Pres)*

Subsidiaries:

Bermas L.T.D.A. (1)
Av Do Contorno S/N, 61939-160, Maracanau, Ceara, Brazil
Tel.: (55) 85 40093700
Web Site: http://www.rinomastrottogroup.com
Emp.: 200
Leather Product Mfr
N.A.I.C.S.: 316990
Luis Eduardo Mendes *(Mgr)*

Elmo Leather AB (1)
Kyrkogatan 18, Svenljunga, 512 50, Sweden
Tel.: (46) 325661400
Web Site: http://www.elmoleather.com
Sales Range: $75-99.9 Million
Emp.: 100
Leather Mfr for the Automotive & Furniture Industries
N.A.I.C.S.: 316110
Anders Bengtsson *(VP-Fin)*

RMG AUSTRALIA Pty. Ltd (1)
346 William Street, Perth, 6000, WA, Australia
Tel.: (61) 8 9328 1077
Leather Product Distr
N.A.I.C.S.: 424990

RMG HONG KONG (1)
1903 Lyndhurst Tower 1 Lyndhurst Terrace, Central, China (Hong Kong)
Tel.: (852) 290884336
Leather Product Distr
N.A.I.C.S.: 424990

Rino Mastrotto Group S.p.A. - Area Design Division (1)
Via V Strada 55 Z I, 36071, Arzignano, Vicenza, Italy
Tel.: (39) 0444 475111
Leather Product Mfr
N.A.I.C.S.: 316990

Rino Mastrotto Group S.p.A. - Basmar Division (1)
Via Stazione N 84, 36070, Trissino, Vicenza, Italy
Tel.: (39) 0445 499200
Leather Product Mfr
N.A.I.C.S.: 316990

Rino Mastrotto Group S.p.A. - Pomari Division (1)
Via Casette 3, Almisano di Lonigo, 36045, Vicenza, Italy
Tel.: (39) 0444 831092
Leather Product Mfr
N.A.I.C.S.: 316990

Rino Mastrotto Group S.p.A. - RMG CHINA Division (1)
12 f/l Hao Pan Shoe Materials Square n 53-55 East of Houjie Road, 523960, Dongguan, Guangdong, China
Tel.: (86) 76985059808
Leather Product Mfr
N.A.I.C.S.: 316990

Rino Mastrotto Group S.p.A. - RMG Vietnam Division (1)
Hamlet 05, Thanh Phu, Vinh, Dong Nai, Vietnam
Tel.: (84) 613 966600
Leather Product Mfr
N.A.I.C.S.: 316990

RINSOCO TRADING CO. LIMITED

15 Agiou Pavlou Ledra House Agios Andreas, Lefkosia, 1105, Nicosia, Cyprus
Tel.: (357) 91 6676 5368
Asset Management Services
N.A.I.C.S.: 523999

RINSOCO TRADING CO. LIMITED

Rinsoco Trading Co. Limited—(Continued)

Subsidiaries:

Uralkali PJSC **(1)**
6/2 Presnenskaya Emb 34th floor, 123112,
Berezniki, Russia **(96.73%)**
Tel.: (7) 4957302371
Web Site: http://www.uralkali.com
Rev.: $2,781,854,000
Assets: $9,202,306,000
Liabilities: $7,096,854,000
Net Worth: $2,105,452,000
Earnings: $1,206,511,000
Fiscal Year-end: 12/31/2019
Mineral Fertilizer Mfr
N.A.I.C.S.: 212390
Marina Shvetsova *(Dir-Legal & Corp Affairs)*

Subsidiary (Non-US):

Uralkali Trading S.A. **(2)**
Ave des Morgines 12, Petit-Lancy, 1213,
Switzerland
Tel.: (41) 228791060
Sales Range: $50-74.9 Million
Emp.: 4
Potash Fertilizer Mfr
N.A.I.C.S.: 212390
Alexander Terletsky *(CEO)*

RIO SILVER INC.

1600-595 Burrard St, Vancouver, V7X
1L4, BC, Canada
Tel.: (604) 762-4448
Web Site:
  https://www.riosilverinc.com
RYOOF—(OTCIQ)
Assets: $54,814
Liabilities: $626,077
Net Worth: ($571,263)
Earnings: ($417,574)
Fiscal Year-end: 12/31/23
Mineral Exploration Services
N.A.I.C.S.: 213114
Steve Brunelle *(Chm)*

RIO SUD

4810 Jean Talon Ouest Suite 203,
Montreal, H4P 2N5, QC, Canada
Tel.: (514) 731-3916
Web Site: http://www.riosud.com
Year Founded: 1975
Rev.: $15,897,401
Emp.: 200
Womens Apparel Stores
N.A.I.C.S.: 316210
Silvio Pittarelli *(Pres)*

RIO TINTO PLC

6 St James's Square, London, SW1Y
4AD, United Kingdom
Tel.: (44) 2077812000   UK
Web Site: https://www.riotinto.com
Year Founded: 1873
RIO—(NYSE)
Rev.: $54,041,000,000
Assets: $103,549,000,000
Liabilities: $47,208,000,000
Net Worth: $56,341,000,000
Earnings: $9,953,000,000
Emp.: 57,174
Fiscal Year-end: 12/31/23
Mineral Resources Mining & Processing Services
N.A.I.C.S.: 212210
Simon R. Thompson *(Chm)*

Subsidiaries:

Rio Tinto Limited **(1)**
Level 7 360 Collins Street, Melbourne,
3000, VIC, Australia
Tel.: (61) 392833333
Web Site: http://www.riotinto.com
Rev.: $55,553,999,999
Assets: $96,743,999,999
Liabilities: $44,469,999,999
Net Worth: $52,273,999,999
Earnings: $12,419,999,999
Emp.: 53,725
Fiscal Year-end: 12/31/2022
Mineral Resources Miner & Processor

N.A.I.C.S.: 212210
Simon R. Thompson *(Chm)*

Subsidiary (Non-US):

Agua De La Falda S.A. **(2)**
Barrio Industrial Sitio 58 Alto Penuelas, Coquimbo, Chile
Tel.: (56) 23402000
Metal & Gold Mining
N.A.I.C.S.: 212220

Aluminium & Chemie Rotterdam B.V. **(2)**
Oude Maasweg 80, Botlek, 3197 KJ, Rotterdam, Netherlands
Tel.: (31) 10 472 7911
Web Site: https://www.aluchemie.nl
Emp.: 300
Aluminum Mfr
N.A.I.C.S.: 331313
Geir Arne Nilsen *(Mng Dir)*

Subsidiary (Domestic):

Argyle Diamonds Limited **(2)**
Level 16 Central Park152-158 St Georges
Terrace, Perth, 6000, WA, Australia
Tel.: (61) 89 168 4900
Diamond Mining Services
N.A.I.C.S.: 212390

Subsidiary (Non-US):

Bougainville Copper Limited **(2)**
Level 5 BSP Haus Harbour City, PO Box
1274, Port Moresby, NCD, Papua New
Guinea **(53.58%)**
Tel.: (675) 3092800
Web Site: https://www.bcl.com.pg
Rev.: $904,460
Assets: $27,804,606
Liabilities: $2,818,380
Net Worth: $24,986,225
Earnings: ($2,151,211)
Emp.: 18
Fiscal Year-end: 12/31/2023
Copper Mining Services
N.A.I.C.S.: 212230
Melchior Pesa Togolo *(Chm)*

Subsidiary (Domestic):

Boyne Smelters Limited **(2)**
Handley Drive, PO Box 524, Boyne Island,
4680, QLD, Australia **(71.04%)**
Sales Range: $350-399.9 Million
Emp.: 1,250
Aluminum Producer
N.A.I.C.S.: 331313

Subsidiary (Non-US):

ELYSIS Limited Partnership **(2)**
1 Place Ville Marie Suite 2323, Montreal,
H3B 3M5, QC, Canada
Tel.: (514) 848-8398
Web Site: https://www.elysis.com
Aluminum Mfr
N.A.I.C.S.: 331313
Vincent Christ *(CEO)*

Group (Domestic):

Energy Resources of Australia Ltd. **(2)**
Level 8 Tio Centre 24 Mitchell Street, GPO
Box 2394, Darwin, 0801, NT,
Australia **(86.3%)**
Tel.: (61) 889243500
Web Site: https://www.energyres.com.au
Rev.: $154,009,553
Assets: $655,805,007
Liabilities: $994,784,319
Net Worth: ($338,979,312)
Earnings: ($498,185,932)
Emp.: 204
Fiscal Year-end: 12/31/2021
Uranium Mining
N.A.I.C.S.: 212290
James O'Connell *(Co-Sec)*

Division (Domestic):

Energy Resources Of Australia **(3)**
Locked Bag 1, Jabiru, 0886, NT,
Australia **(100%)**
Tel.: (61) 889381211
Web Site: http://www.energyres.com
Sales Range: $350-399.9 Million
N.A.I.C.S.: 212290

Subsidiary (Domestic):

Hamersley Holdings Limited **(2)**
Level 18 Central Park 152-158 St Georges
Terrace, Perth, 6000, WA, Australia
Tel.: (61) 893272327
Coal Mining Services
N.A.I.C.S.: 213113

Kelian Pty Limited **(2)**
L 33 120 Collins St, Melbourne, 3000, VIC,
Australia
Tel.: (61) 392833333
Investment Management Service
N.A.I.C.S.: 523940

Subsidiary (Non-US):

NZAS Retirement Fund Trustee Limited **(2)**
PO Box 1849, Wellington, 6140, New Zealand
Tel.: (64) 50 826 6787
Web Site:
  https://www.nzasretirementfund.com
Retirement Fund Services
N.A.I.C.S.: 525110

Subsidiary (Domestic):

Nhulunbuy Corporation Limited **(2)**
Shops 2 and 3 Westal Street, Nhulunbuy,
0880, NT, Australia
Tel.: (61) 88 939 2200
Web Site: https://www.ncl.net.au
Emp.: 30
Municipal Services
N.A.I.C.S.: 921190

North IOC Holdings Pty Limited **(2)**
L 33 120 Collins St, Melbourne, 3000, VIC,
Australia
Tel.: (61) 392833333
Investment Management Service
N.A.I.C.S.: 523940

Pacific Aluminium Pty Limited **(2)**
Level 3 500 Queen St, Brisbane, 4000,
QLD, Australia
Tel.: (61) 730282000
Aluminum Mining Services
N.A.I.C.S.: 212290

Subsidiary (Non-US):

New Zealand Aluminium Smelters Ltd. **(3)**
Tiwai Rd, Private Bag 90110, Invercargill,
812, New Zealand **(100%)**
Tel.: (64) 32185999
Sales Range: $250-299.9 Million
Emp.: 800
Aluminum Smelting
N.A.I.C.S.: 331313
Stewart Hamilton *(CEO & Gen Mgr)*

Subsidiary (Non-US):

Palabora Holdings Ltd. **(2)**
1 Copper Road, Phalaborwa, 1390, South
Africa
Tel.: (27) 157802911
Web Site: http://www.palabora.com
Emp.: 3,000
Investment Management Service
N.A.I.C.S.: 523940

QIT Madagascar Minerals SA **(2)**
Lot 35 5e etage Immeuble Ivandry Business Center, BP 4003, 101, Antananarivo,
Madagascar
Tel.: (261) 202242559
Ilmenite Mining Services
N.A.I.C.S.: 212290

QMP Metal Powders (Suzhou) co., Ltd **(2)**
418 Nanshi Street, Suzhou Industrial Park,
Suzhou, 215021, China
Tel.: (86) 51262836100
Metal Mining Services
N.A.I.C.S.: 212290

Quebec Metal Powders Ltd **(2)**
1655 Route Marie-Victorin, Sorel-Tracy, J3R
4R4, QC, Canada
Tel.: (450) 746-5050
Web Site: https://www.qmp-powders.com
Steel & Metal Powder Mfr
N.A.I.C.S.: 331110

INTERNATIONAL PUBLIC

Quebec North Shore & Labrador Railway Company **(2)**
1 Retty street, Sept-Iles, G4R 3C7, QC,
Canada
Tel.: (418) 968-7603
Web Site: https://www.qnsl.ca
Railway Freight Services
N.A.I.C.S.: 482111

Subsidiary (Domestic):

Rio Tinto (Commercial Paper) Limited **(2)**
120 Collins St, Melbourne, 3000, VIC, Australia
Tel.: (61) 3 9283 3333
Web Site: http://www.riotinto.com.au
Financial Management Services
N.A.I.C.S.: 523999

Subsidiary (Non-US):

Rio Tinto (Hong Kong) Limited **(2)**
Unit 33018 33/F AIA Tower 183 Electric
Road, North Point, China (Hong Kong)
Tel.: (852) 2839 9292
Web Site: http://www.riotinto.com
Metal Mining Services
N.A.I.C.S.: 212290

Rio Tinto Brasil Limitada **(2)**
Rua Lauro Muller 116 35 andar, Torre Rio
Sul, Rio de Janeiro, 22290 160,
Brazil **(100%)**
Tel.: (55) 2121974200
Web Site: http://www.riotinto.com.br
Metal Mining
N.A.I.C.S.: 212290

Rio Tinto Canada Inc **(2)**
1188 Sherbrooke Street West, Montreal,
H3A 3G2, QC, Canada
Tel.: (514) 841-2454
Investment Management Service
N.A.I.C.S.: 523999

Subsidiary (Domestic):

Rio Tinto Alcan Inc. **(3)**
1188 Sherbrooke St West, Montreal, H3A
3G2, QC, Canada
Tel.: (514) 848-8000
Holding Company; Aluminum & Bauxite
Processing Services; Aluminum Cable,
Packaging & Aerospace Products Mfr
N.A.I.C.S.: 551112

Group (Non-US):

Rio Tinto Copper **(2)**
No 6 James's Square, London, SW1Y4AD,
United Kingdom
Tel.: (44) 2077812000
Web Site: http://www.riotinto.com
Sales Range: $200-249.9 Million
Emp.: 100
Copper Mining & Production
N.A.I.C.S.: 212230

Subsidiary (US):

Kennecott Utah Copper LLC **(3)**
4700 Daybreak Pkwy, South Jordan, UT
84009 **(100%)**
Tel.: (801) 204-2000
Web Site: http://www.riotintokennecott.com
Copper & Lead Ore Mining
N.A.I.C.S.: 212230

Group (Non-US):

Rio Tinto Diamonds **(2)**
2 Eastbourne Terrace, London, W2 6LG,
United Kingdom
Tel.: (44) 2077812000
Web Site: http://www.riotintodiamonds.com
Sales Range: $50-74.9 Million
Emp.: 50
Diamond Exploration, Mining & Marketing
N.A.I.C.S.: 212390

Subsidiary (Non-US):

Argyle Diamonds Australia **(3)**
Level 16 Central Park 152-158 St Georges
Terrace, PO Box PMB 11, Perth, 6000, WA,
Australia **(100%)**
Tel.: (61) 891684900
Diamond Mining
N.A.I.C.S.: 212390

AND PRIVATE COMPANIES — RIO TINTO PLC

Subsidiary (Non-US):

Argyle Pink Diamonds (4)
Tel.: (61) 894821052
Diamond Jewelry Mfr & Distr
N.A.I.C.S.: 339910

Subsidiary (Non-US):

Rio Tinto Diamonds NV (2)
Diamond Exchange Building Hoveniersstraat 53, 2018, Antwerp, Belgium
Tel.: (32) 3 303 6800
Web Site: http://www.riotintodiamonds.com
Sales Range: $50-74.9 Million
Emp.: 80
Diamond Mining Services
N.A.I.C.S.: 212390

Subsidiary (Non-US):

Rio Tinto Eastern Investments BV (2)
Drentestraat 20, Amsterdam, 1083 HK, Netherlands
Tel.: (31) 442077532116
Investment Management Service
N.A.I.C.S.: 523940

Group (Non-US):

Rio Tinto Energy (2)
6 St James Sq, London, SW1Y 4AD, United Kingdom
Tel.: (44) 2077812000
Coal & Uranium Production
N.A.I.C.S.: 423520

Subsidiary (Non-US):

Rio Tinto Coal Australia Pty Limited (3)
123 Albert Street, Brisbane, 4000, QLD, Australia (100%)
Tel.: (61) 733614200
Web Site: http://www.riotintocoalaustralia.com.au
Sales Range: $50-74.9 Million
Emp.: 100
Holding Company
N.A.I.C.S.: 551112

Subsidiary (Domestic):

Australian Coal Holdings Pty Limited (4)
Level 33 120 Collins Street, Melbourne, 3000, VIC, Australia
Tel.: (61) 392833333
Investment Management Service
N.A.I.C.S.: 523940

Blair Athol Coal Pty Ltd (4)
Level 3 West Tower, PO Box 391, Brisbane, 4001, QLD, Australia
Tel.: (61) 733614200
Coal Mining
N.A.I.C.S.: 213113

Hail Creek Coal Pty Ltd (4)
21 Ecvan Ave, PO Box 3097, Mackay, 4740, QLD, Australia (92%)
Tel.: (61) 749405711
Web Site: http://www.riotintocoalaustralia.com.au
Sales Range: $50-74.9 Million
Emp.: 10
Coal Mining
N.A.I.C.S.: 212114

Kestrel Coal Pty. Ltd. (4)
Lilyvale Road, PO Box 1969, Emerald, 4720, QLD, Australia (80%)
Tel.: (61) 735573000
Web Site: https://kestrelcoal.com
Sales Range: $75-99.9 Million
Coal Mining
N.A.I.C.S.: 212114

Subsidiary (US):

Rio Tinto Energy America Inc. (3)
4700 Daybreak Pkwy, South Jordan, UT 84009
Tel.: (801) 204-2000
Holding Company; Coal Mining
N.A.I.C.S.: 551112

Subsidiary (Non-US):

Rio Tinto European Holdings Limited (2)
2 Eastbourne Terrace, London, W2 6LG, United Kingdom
Tel.: (44) 2077812000
Investment Management Service
N.A.I.C.S.: 523940

Subsidiary (Domestic):

Rio Tinto Finance (USA) Limited (2)
Level 43 120 Collins Street, Melbourne, 3000, VIC, Australia
Tel.: (61) 392833333
Emp.: 37
Financial Management Services
N.A.I.C.S.: 523999

Rio Tinto Finance Limited (2)
Level 33 120 Collins Street, Melbourne, 3000, VIC, Australia
Tel.: (61) 392833333
Financial Management Services
N.A.I.C.S.: 523999
Keith Barry *(Treas)*

Subsidiary (Non-US):

Rio Tinto Finance plc (2)
2 Eastbourne Terrace, London, W2 6LG, United Kingdom
Tel.: (44) 2077812000
Sales Range: $150-199.9 Million
Emp.: 500
Financial Management Services
N.A.I.C.S.: 523999

Rio Tinto Iceland Ltd. (2)
PO Box 244, 222, Hafnarfjordur, Iceland
Tel.: (354) 560 7000
Web Site: https://www.riotinto.is
Emp.: 390
Aluminum Mfr
N.A.I.C.S.: 331313

Rio Tinto India Private Limited (2)
21st Floor DLF Building No 5 Tower A DLF Cyber City Phase-III, Gurgaon, 122 002, Haryana, India
Tel.: (91) 1244407300
Sales Range: $50-74.9 Million
Emp.: 155
Metal Product Distr
N.A.I.C.S.: 423510

Subsidiary (Domestic):

Rio Tinto Investments One Pty Limited (2)
L 33 120 Collins St, Melbourne, 3000, VIC, Australia
Tel.: (61) 392833333
Investment Management Service
N.A.I.C.S.: 523940

Rio Tinto Investments Two Pty Limited (2)
120 Collins St, Melbourne, 3000, VIC, Australia
Tel.: (61) 3 9283 3289
Investment Management Service
N.A.I.C.S.: 523940

Subsidiary (Non-US):

Rio Tinto Iron & Titanium Limited (2)
6 St James s Square, London, SW1 Y4AD, United Kingdom
Tel.: (44) 2077812000
Metal Mining Services
N.A.I.C.S.: 213114

Group (Domestic):

Rio Tinto Iron Ore (2)
152-158 St Georges Terrace, Perth, 6000, WA, Australia
Tel.: (61) 893272000
Iron Ore Mining & Processing
N.A.I.C.S.: 212210

Subsidiary (Domestic):

Hamersley Iron Pty Ltd (3)
152-158 St Georges Ter, Perth, WA, Australia (100%)
Tel.: (61) 893272327
Web Site: http://www.hamersleyiron.com
Sales Range: $1-4.9 Billion
Emp.: 4,500
Iron Mining
N.A.I.C.S.: 212210

Subsidiary (Non-US):

Iron Ore Company of Canada (3)
1190 Ave des Canadiens-de-Montreal Suite 400, Montreal, H3B 0E3, QC, Canada (100%)
Tel.: (514) 285-8413
Web Site: http://www.ironore.ca
Sales Range: $700-749.9 Million
Emp.: 1,800
Open Pit Mines, Concentrators & Pellet Plants
N.A.I.C.S.: 212390
Chantal Lavoie *(COO)*

Richards Bay Minerals Pty Ltd. (3)
PO Box 401, Richards Bay, 3900, Kwazulu Natal, South Africa (74%)
Tel.: (27) 359013111
Web Site: http://www.richardsbayminerals.co.za
Sales Range: $800-899.9 Million
Emp.: 1,800
Metal Ore Mining
N.A.I.C.S.: 212290

Subsidiary (Domestic):

Robe River Mining Co. Pty. Ltd. (3)
Level 18 Central Park 152-158 St Georges Terrace, Perth, 6000, WA, Australia (53%)
Tel.: (61) 892174747
Sales Range: $1-4.9 Billion
Emp.: 13,000
Iron Mining
N.A.I.C.S.: 212210

Subsidiary (Non-US):

Rio Tinto Japan Limited (2)
1 Kojimachi 4, Chiyoda-ku, Tokyo, 102-0083, Japan (100%)
Tel.: (81) 332222411
Web Site: https://riotintojapan.com
Sales Range: $25-49.9 Million
Emp.: 50
Aluminium Whslr
N.A.I.C.S.: 331313

Rio Tinto Korea Ltd (2)
6th Floor Textile Center 944-31 Daechi 3-dong, Gangnam-gu, Seoul, 135-713, Korea (South)
Tel.: (82) 2 561 4560
Metal Mining Services
N.A.I.C.S.: 212290

Rio Tinto Ltd China (2)
1818 China World Tower 2, 1 Jainwai Dajie, Beijing, 100004, China (100%)
Tel.: (86) 10 6505 7293
Web Site: http://www.riotinto.com
Sales Range: $25-49.9 Million
Emp.: 40
Metal Mining
N.A.I.C.S.: 212290

Group (Non-US):

Rio Tinto Minerals (2)
2 Eastbourne Terr, London, W2 6LG, United Kingdom
Tel.: (44) 2077812000
Web Site: http://www.riotintominerals.com
Salt, Talc & Borate Mining & Production
N.A.I.C.S.: 212390

Subsidiary (Non-US):

Dampier Salt Limited (3)
PO Box 7073, Cloisters Sq, Perth, 6850, W Australia, Australia (65%)
Web Site: http://www.dampiersalt.com.au
Sales Range: $25-49.9 Million
Emp.: 20
Producer of Salt
N.A.I.C.S.: 325998

Division (US):

Rio Tinto Borax (3)
8051 E Maplewood Ave, Greenwood Village, CO 80111 (100%)
Tel.: (303) 713-5000
Web Site: http://www.borax.com
Sales Range: $800-899.9 Million
Emp.: 1,500
Mfr of Industrial Chemical Products Including Borax, Boric Acid & Various Inorganic Boron Compounds
N.A.I.C.S.: 212390
Terry Carra *(Global Publications Coord)*

Subsidiary (Domestic):

Rio Tinto Minerals Development Limited (3)
6 St James's Square, London, SW1Y 4AD, United Kingdom
Tel.: (44) 2077812000
Mineral Exploration Services
N.A.I.C.S.: 213115

Subsidiary (Non-US):

Talc de Luzenac S.A. (3)
131 Ave Charles De Gaulle, Neuilly, F 92200, France (99%)
Tel.: (33) 147459040
Web Site: http://www.luzenac.com
Sales Range: $200-249.9 Million
Emp.: 412
Mininig Processing & Sale of Talc & Other Minerals
N.A.I.C.S.: 212390

Subsidiary (Non-US):

Rio Tinto Mongolia LLC (2)
7 Floor Monnis Tower Chinggis Avenue 15, Sukhbaatar, Ulaanbaatar, 14240, Mongolia
Tel.: (976) 11 331880
Web Site: http://www.riotintomongolia.com
Metal Ore Mining Services
N.A.I.C.S.: 212290

Rio Tinto Namibian Holdings Limited (2)
2 Eastbourne Terrace, London, W2 6LG, United Kingdom
Tel.: (44) 2077812000
Investment Management Service
N.A.I.C.S.: 523940

Rio Tinto Overseas Holdings Limited (2)
6 St James's Square, London, SW1Y4AD, United Kingdom
Tel.: (44) 20 7781 2000
Web Site: http://www.riotinto.com
Sales Range: $150-199.9 Million
Emp.: 300
Metal Mining Services
N.A.I.C.S.: 212290

Subsidiary (US):

Rio Tinto Procurement (2)
4700 Daybreak View Pkwy, South Jordan, UT 84095-5120 (100%)
Tel.: (801) 363-4357
Web Site: http://procurement.riotinto.com
Mining Services
N.A.I.C.S.: 213113

Subsidiary (Non-US):

Rio Tinto Shipping (Asia) Pte Ltd (2)
12 Marina Boulevard 20-1 Marina Bay Financial Centre Tower 3, Singapore, 018982, Singapore
Tel.: (65) 66799000
Sales Range: $25-49.9 Million
Emp.: 85
Deep Sea Freight Transportation Services
N.A.I.C.S.: 483111

Subsidiary (Domestic):

Rio Tinto Shipping Pty. Limited. (2)
120 Collins Street, Melbourne, 3000, VIC, Australia
Tel.: (61) 392833333
Deep Sea Freight Transportation Services
N.A.I.C.S.: 483111

Subsidiary (Non-US):

Rio Tinto Singapore Holdings Pte Ltd (2)
12 Marina Boulevard 20-01 Marina Bay Financial Centre Tower 3, Singapore, 018982, Singapore
Tel.: (65) 66799000
Investment Management Service
N.A.I.C.S.: 523940
Simon Trott *(Chief Comml Officer)*

Rio Tinto Uranium Limited (2)
2 Eastbourne Terrace, London, W2 6LG, United Kingdom

RIO TINTO PLC

Rio Tinto plc—(Continued)
Tel.: (44) 207 781 1379
Uranium Ore Mining Services
N.A.I.C.S.: 212290

Rio Tinto Western Holdings Limited (2)
6 St James's Square, London, W2 6LG, United Kingdom
Tel.: (44) 2077812000
Investment Management Service
N.A.I.C.S.: 523940

Rio Tinto, Fer et Titane (2)
1625 Marie-Victorin, Sorel-Tracy, J3R 1M6, QC, Canada
Tel.: (450) 746-3000
Web Site: http://www.riotinto.com
Powder Coating Mfr & Distr
N.A.I.C.S.: 325510

Turquoise Hill Resources Ltd. (2)
Suite 3680-1 Place Ville Marie, Montreal, H3B 3P2, QC, Canada **(100%)**
Tel.: (514) 848-1567
Web Site: http://www.turquoisehill.com
Rev.: $1,971,042,000
Assets: $14,124,689,000
Liabilities: $5,015,731,000
Net Worth: $9,108,958,000
Earnings: $524,890,000
Emp.: 3,478
Fiscal Year-end: 12/31/2021
Copper & Gold Mining Services
N.A.I.C.S.: 212210
Jo-Anne Dudley (COO)

Subsidiary (Non-US):

Ivanhoe Philippines Inc. (3)
7th Fl Builders Ctr Bldg 170 Salcedo St, Lagaspi Vlg, Makati, 1229, Philippines
Tel.: (63) 28189197
Web Site: http://www.pmea.com.ph
Sales Range: $50-74.9 Million
Emp.: 20
Copper & Gold Mining Services
N.A.I.C.S.: 212220

Affiliate (Non-US):

Oyu Tolgoi LLC (3)
Monnis Tower Chinggis Avenue 15, Sukhbaatar District, Ulaanbaatar, 14240, Mongolia
Tel.: (976) 11331880
Web Site: http://www.ot.mn
Copper & Gold Mining; Owned by Ivanhoe Mines Ltd. & the Government of Mongolia
N.A.I.C.S.: 212230
Batsukh Galsan (Chm)

Affiliate (Domestic):

SouthGobi Resources Ltd. (3)
20th Floor 250 Howe Street, Vancouver, V6C 3R8, BC, Canada **(35.36%)**
Tel.: (604) 762-6783
Web Site: http://www.southgobi.com
Rev.: $331,506,000
Assets: $295,738,000
Liabilities: $437,070,000
Net Worth: ($141,332,000)
Earnings: $908,000
Emp.: 554
Fiscal Year-end: 12/31/2023
Coal Mining Services
N.A.I.C.S.: 212115
Allison Snetsinger (Sec)

Subsidiary (Non-US):

SouthGobi Resources (Hong Kong) Ltd (4)
Suite 6503 The Center 99 Queens Road Central, Hong Kong, China (Hong Kong)
Tel.: (852) 21567029
Web Site: http://www.southgobi.com
Coal Mining Services
N.A.I.C.S.: 213113

SouthGobi Sands LLC (4)
8th Floor Monnis Building Orgil Stadium 22, Great Mongolian State Street 15th Khoroo Khan-Uul District, Ulaanbaatar, 17011, Mongolia
Tel.: (976) 70070710
Coal Mining Services
N.A.I.C.S.: 213113

Subsidiary (US):

US Borax Holdings Inc. (2)
8051 E Maplewood Ave, Greenwood Village, CO 80111
Tel.: (303) 713-5000
Investment Management Service
N.A.I.C.S.: 523940

Subsidiary (Non-US):

Borax Espana S.A (3)
Carretera Nacional 340 pg ind la Mina KM 954, 12520, Nules, Castellon, Spain
Tel.: (34) 964659030
Specialty Chemicals Mfr
N.A.I.C.S.: 325998

Borax Francais S.A. (3)
89 Route de Bourbourg, BP 59, Coudekerque-Branche, 59210, France
Tel.: (33) 3 28 29 28 30
Borate Mining Services
N.A.I.C.S.: 212390

Borax South America (3)
Av Das Nacoes Unidas-12551 cj 2208 Brooklin Novo, Sao Paulo, 04578-000, Brazil
Tel.: (55) 11 3043 7230
Borate Mining Services
N.A.I.C.S.: 212390

Plant (Non-US):

US Borax Holdings Inc. - Changshu Operations - Shipping Facility (3)
Xinghua Gangqu, Changshu, 215513, Jiangsu, China
Tel.: (86) 512 5269 5858
Borate Mining Services
N.A.I.C.S.: 212390

US Borax Holdings Inc. - Rotterdam Operations - Shipping Facility (3)
Welplaatweg 104 Botlek, Harbour, 3197 KS, Rotterdam, Netherlands
Tel.: (31) 10 490 9600
Borate Mining Services
N.A.I.C.S.: 212390
Rob Boere (Mgr)

RIO2 LIMITED
701 West Georgia street suite 1500, Vancouver, V7Y 1C6, BC, Canada
Tel.: (604) 762-4720   ON
Web Site: https://www.rio2.com
Year Founded: 1990
RIO—(LIM)
Mineral Exploration Services
N.A.I.C.S.: 213114
Jose Luis Martinez (Chief Strategy Officer & Exec VP)

Subsidiaries:

Fenix Gold Limitada (1)
Camino Internacional Route CH-31 Km 6 Holvoet Industrial Park, Atacama Region, Copiapo, Chile
Tel.: (56) 938623933
Web Site: https://www.fenixgold.cl
Gold Mining Services
N.A.I.C.S.: 212220

RIOCAN REAL ESTATE INVESTMENT TRUST
2300 Yonge Street Suite 500, Box 2386, Toronto, M4P 1E4, ON, Canada
Tel.: (416) 646-8326   ON
Web Site: https://www.riocan.com
Year Founded: 1993
REI—(TSX)
Rev.: $1,014,956,943
Assets: $11,622,714,588
Liabilities: $5,267,234,923
Net Worth: $6,355,479,666
Earnings: $593,699,210
Emp.: 605
Fiscal Year-end: 12/31/19
Real Estate Investment Trust
N.A.I.C.S.: 525990
Paul V. Godfrey (Chm)

RION CO. LTD.
3-20-41 Higashimotomachi Kokubunji, Tokyo, 185-8533, Japan
Tel.: (81) 423597857
Web Site: https://www.rion.co.jp
Year Founded: 1944
6823—(TKS)
Rev.: $170,048,860
Assets: $245,495,400
Liabilities: $52,410,690
Net Worth: $193,084,710
Earnings: $17,529,720
Emp.: 1,026
Fiscal Year-end: 03/31/24
Hearing Instruments & Medical Equipment Mfr & Sales
N.A.I.C.S.: 334510
Kiyokatsu Iwahashi (Pres & CEO)

Subsidiaries:

Kyushu Rion Co., Ltd. (1)
5-18 Reisenmachi, Hakata-Ku, Fukuoka, 812-0039, Japan
Tel.: (81) 922815361
Web Site: http://www.krion.co.jp
Sales Range: $550-599.9 Million
Emp.: 165
Industrial Machinery Equipment Whslr
N.A.I.C.S.: 423830

Rion Service Center Co., Ltd. (1)
2-22-2 Bei, Hachioji, 192-0918, Tokyo, Japan
Tel.: (81) 426321131
Web Site: https://www.rion-service.co.jp
Sales Range: $50-74.9 Million
Emp.: 96
Medical Equipment Maintenance Services
N.A.I.C.S.: 423450

Rion Techno Co., Ltd. (1)
2-22-2 Bei, Hachioji, 192-0918, Tokyo, Japan
Tel.: (81) 426321130
Web Site: https://www.rion-techno.co.jp
Sales Range: $50-74.9 Million
Emp.: 97
Medical Equipment Mfr & Whslr
N.A.I.C.S.: 423450

RIOPAILA AGRICOLA SA
Cra 1 No 24 - 56 Colombina Building - 7th Floor - Of 722, Cali, Colombia
Tel.: (57) 6024855974
Web Site: https://www.riopailaagricola.com.co
Year Founded: 2008
RIOPAILA—(COLO)
Sales Range: Less than $1 Million
Sugar Cane Product Mfr
N.A.I.C.S.: 311314
Gustavo Adolfo Barona Torres (CEO & Principal)

RIOZIM LIMITED
No 1 Kenilworth Road Newlands, Harare, Zimbabwe
Tel.: (263) 8677007168
Web Site: https://www.riozim.co.zw
Year Founded: 1956
RIOZ.ZW—(ZIM)
Rev.: $1,592,884
Assets: $5,065,436
Liabilities: $2,868,923
Net Worth: $2,196,513
Earnings: ($1,604,603)
Fiscal Year-end: 12/31/19
Healtcare Services
N.A.I.C.S.: 621999
Saleem Rashid Beebeejaun (Chm)

RIPERT FRERES S.A.S.
13 Rue des Mejuteaux, 49800, Brain-sur-l'Authion, France
Tel.: (33) 241804467
Web Site: http://www.ripert-freres.com
Sales Range: $10-24.9 Million
Emp.: 14
Grain, Seeds & Animal Feeds Whslr

N.A.I.C.S.: 424510
Joel Ripert (Pres)

RIPLEY CORP S.A.
Avenida Cerro Colorado 5240 Torre del Parque 1 Piso 11, Las Condes, Santiago, Chile
Tel.: (56) 6941042
Web Site: https://simple.ripley.cl
Year Founded: 1956
RIPLEY—(SGO)
Sales Range: Less than $1 Million
Departmental Store Operator
N.A.I.C.S.: 455110
Michel Calderon (Vice Chm)

RIPOCHE INDUSTRIES
6 Tour Du Village, 27800, Chatenay, Eure Et Loir, France
Tel.: (33) 237996634
Web Site: http://groupe-ripoche.fr
Rev.: $10,100,000
Emp.: 98
N.A.I.C.S.: 332119
Herve Ripoche (Pres)

RIPPLE E-BUSINESS INTERNATIONAL, INC.
Unit 2202-C/D E Tower Philippine Stock Exchange Bldg, Exchange Rd Ortigas Ctr, Pasig, 1605, Philippines
Tel.: (63) 26874412
Web Site: http://www.iripple.com
Year Founded: 2000
Sales Range: $10-24.9 Million
Emp.: 40
Software Publisher
N.A.I.C.S.: 513210

RISA INTERNATIONAL LIMITED
7 Plot 27/33 Beaumon Chambers Nagindas Master Lane, Hutatma Chowk Fort, Mumbai, 400001, Maharashtra, India
Tel.: (91) 226668104
Web Site: https://risainternational.in
Year Founded: 1993
530251—(BOM)
Assets: $3,619,423
Liabilities: $1,206,139
Net Worth: $2,413,285
Earnings: ($38,559)
Fiscal Year-end: 03/31/23
Textile Fabric Distr
N.A.I.C.S.: 424310
Abhinandan Jain (CFO)

RISA PARTNERS, INC.
19F Shinagawa Intercity Tower C 2-15-3 Konan, Minato-ku, Tokyo, 108-6219, Japan
Tel.: (81) 3 5796 8500   JP
Web Site: http://www.risa-p.com
Year Founded: 1998
Sales Range: $125-149.9 Million
Emp.: 145
Investment Banking
N.A.I.C.S.: 523150
Yoshio Narukage (Pres)

Subsidiaries:

AdvanIDe Pte. Ltd. (1)
7 Temasek Boulevard # 06-01 Suntec Tower One, 038987, Singapore, Singapore
Tel.: (65) 3157 0271
Web Site: http://www.advanide.de
Sales Range: $25-49.9 Million
Emp.: 15
Semiconductor Distr
N.A.I.C.S.: 423690
Holger Roessner (Mng Dir)

Subsidiary (Non-US):

AdvanIDe GmbH (2)
Am Klingenweg 6a, Wallut, Germany
Tel.: (49) 6123 791 400

INTERNATIONAL PUBLIC

AND PRIVATE COMPANIES — RISHI LASER LTD.

Web Site: http://www.advanide.de
Semiconductor Device Distr
N.A.I.C.S.: 423690

Subsidiary (US):

AdvanIDe Inc. (2)
19 Sylvester Rd, Natick, MA 01760
Tel.: (617) 710-1974
Web Site: http://www.advanide.com
Semiconductor Distr
N.A.I.C.S.: 423690
Ken Hutchins *(Regl Dir-Sls)*

RISCO ENERGY PTE. LTD.
8 Temasak Boulevard #37-02 Suntec Tower 3, Singapore, 038988, Singapore
Tel.: (65) 68365880   SG
Web Site: http://www.risco-energy.com
Energy Investment Holding Company
N.A.I.C.S.: 551112
Tom Soulsby *(CEO)*

RISCO LTD.
14 Hachoma Street, 75655, Rishon le Zion, Israel
Tel.: (972) 3 963 7777   Il
Web Site: http://www.riscogroup.com
Year Founded: 1978
Emp.: 400
Security Systems Software Developer, Publisher & Whslr
N.A.I.C.S.: 513210
Moshe Alkelai *(Founder, Chm & CEO)*

Subsidiaries:

Electronics Line 3000 Ltd. (1)
14 Hachoma Street, 75655, Jerusalem, Israel   (100%)
Tel.: (972) 3 9637777
Web Site: http://www.electronics-line.com
Rev.: $12,200,000
Assets: $7,071,000
Liabilities: $2,622,000
Net Worth: $4,449,000
Earnings: ($2,238,000)
Emp.: 19
Fiscal Year-end: 12/31/2014
Security Solution Services
N.A.I.C.S.: 561621
Tal Rosner *(Dir-Ops)*

RISCO Group Australia Pty. Ltd. (1)
Unit C11 12-14 Solent Circle, Norwest Business Park, Baulkham Hills, 2153, NSW, Australia
Tel.: (61) 1800 991 542
Web Site: http://www.riscogroup.com
Security Software Whslr
N.A.I.C.S.: 423430
Tim Prag *(Dir-Sls & Bus Dev)*

RISCO Group France SAS (1)
Les Villas d'Enterprises 57 Avenue de l'Europe, Emerainville, 77184, Paris, France
Tel.: (33) 1 6473 2850
Web Site: http://www.riscogroup.com
Security Software Whslr
N.A.I.C.S.: 423430
Jean-Baptiste Covarel *(Project Mgr-Technical Support)*

RISCO Group Iberia S.L. (1)
Edificio Europa III Portal 6-2-H Calle San Rafael 1, 28108, Alcobendas, Spain
Tel.: (34) 91 4902 133
Web Site: http://www.riscogroup.com
Security Software Whslr
N.A.I.C.S.: 423430
Jose Manuel Menendez Lorenzo *(Sls Mgr)*

RISCO Group UK Ltd. (1)
Commerce House Whitbrook Way Stakehill Industrial Estate, Middleton, Manchester, M24 2SS, United Kingdom
Tel.: (44) 161 655 5500
Web Site: http://www.riscogroup.com
Security Software Whslr
N.A.I.C.S.: 423430

RISCO Group, Inc. (1)
105 Maxess Rd Ste S-124, Melville, NY 11747

Tel.: (631) 719-4400
Web Site: http://www.riscogroup.com
Security Software Whslr
N.A.I.C.S.: 423430

RISE CONSULTING GROUP, INC.
34th floor Izumi Garden Tower 1-6-1 Roppongi, Minato-ku, Tokyo, 106-6034, Japan
Tel.: (81) 364412915
Web Site: https://www.rise-cg.co.jp
Year Founded: 2012
9168—(TKS)
Rev.: $43,646,040
Assets: $60,420,980
Liabilities: $23,864,940
Net Worth: $36,556,040
Earnings: $9,323,350
Emp.: 306
Fiscal Year-end: 02/29/24
Asset Management Services
N.A.I.C.S.: 523999
Ryudai Matsuoka *(Chief Innovation Officer)*

RISE GOLD CORP.
650-669 Howe Street, Vancouver, V6C 0B4, BC, Canada
Tel.: (604) 260-4577   NV
Web Site: https://www.risegoldcorp.com
Year Founded: 2007
RYES—(OTCQX)
Rev.: $18,365
Assets: $5,155,398
Liabilities: $2,777,728
Net Worth: $2,377,670
Earnings: ($3,565,631)
Emp.: 1
Fiscal Year-end: 07/31/24
Metal Mining Services
N.A.I.C.S.: 212290
Eileen Au *(Sec)*

RISE INC.
3F Atago East Building 16-11 Nishi-Shinbashi 3-chome, Minato-Ku, Tokyo, 105-0003, Japan
Tel.: (81) 366320711
Web Site: https://www.rise-i.co.jp
Year Founded: 1947
8836—(TKS)
Rev.: $3,504,160
Assets: $23,232,000
Liabilities: $3,523,520
Net Worth: $19,708,480
Earnings: ($513,040)
Fiscal Year-end: 03/31/22
Real Estate Development Services
N.A.I.C.S.: 531390

RISECOMM GROUP HOLDINGS LIMITED
Skyworth Building C501 Hi-tech Industrial Park, Shenzhen, 518057, China
Tel.: (86) 75533955360   Ky
Web Site: http://www.risecomm.com.cn
Year Founded: 2006
1679—(HKG)
Rev.: $21,039,080
Assets: $47,924,136
Liabilities: $37,481,044
Net Worth: $10,443,092
Earnings: ($16,720,938)
Emp.: 151
Fiscal Year-end: 12/31/22
Electronic Parts Mfr & Distr
N.A.I.C.S.: 334413
Jingxing Yue *(Founder & CEO)*

Subsidiaries:

Beijing Risecomm Communication Technology Company Limited (1)
E-518-B 4/F No 6 Taiping street, Xicheng District, Beijing, 100050, China
Tel.: (86) 1059361766
Semiconductor & Related Device Mfr
N.A.I.C.S.: 334413

Changsha Risecomm Communication Technology Company Limited (1)
Bldg C4 Jindao Yuan No 179 Mid Huizhi Rd New Hi-Tech Deve Zone, Changsha, 410000, Hunan, China
Tel.: (86) 73188606627
Electronic Parts Mfr
N.A.I.C.S.: 334413

Risecomm Microelectronics (Shenzhen) Co., Ltd. (1)
41/F Block A Building 8 Shenzhen International Innovation Valley, Xili Street Nanshan District, Shenzhen, 518055, China
Tel.: (86) 75533955360
Semiconductor & Related Device Mfr
N.A.I.C.S.: 334413
Ricky Lin *(Mgr-Bus Dev)*

Wuxi Risecomm Communication Technology Company Limited (1)
21-1-802 Changjiang Road, Wuxi New District, Wuxi, 214028, China
Tel.: (86) 51085252425
Semiconductor & Related Device Mfr
N.A.I.C.S.: 334413

RISEN ENERGY CO., LTD.
Tashan Industry Zone Meilin, Sub-district Ninghai County, Ningbo, 315609, Zhejiang, China
Tel.: (86) 57459953588
Web Site: https://www.risenenergy.com
Year Founded: 1906
300118—(CHIN)
Rev.: $4,125,614,688
Assets: $5,371,928,640
Liabilities: $3,911,775,660
Net Worth: $1,460,152,980
Earnings: $132,633,072
Emp.: 10,000
Fiscal Year-end: 12/31/22
Solar Energy Products Mfr
N.A.I.C.S.: 334413
P. Ponsekar *(Gen Mgr-Risen India Company)*

Subsidiaries:

Risen Energy Europe & Latam S.L. (1)
Veganova - Avda De la Vega 1 Edif 2-Planta 1, 28108, Alcobendas, Madrid, Spain
Tel.: (34) 91 020 3614
Cell & Module Mfr
N.A.I.C.S.: 334413

Risen Energy Hong Kong Co., Ltd. (1)
Bishal Nagar Marg, Kathmandu, Nepal
Tel.: (977) 1 444 0620
Cell & Module Mfr
N.A.I.C.S.: 334413

Zhejiang Twinsel Electronic Technology Co., Ltd. (1)
Meilin Street, Tashan Industrial Park Ninghai, Ningbo, Zhejiang, China
Tel.: (86) 5745 995 3561
Web Site: https://www.twinsel.cn
Light Emitting Diode Mfr
N.A.I.C.S.: 335131

RISESUN REAL ESTATE DEVELOPMENT CO., LTD.
No 81 Xiangyun Road, Economic and Technological Development Zone, Langfang, 065001, Hebei, China
Tel.: (86) 3165909688
Web Site: https://www.risesun.cn
Year Founded: 1996
002146—(SSE)
Rev.: $4,463,807,400
Assets: $35,039,083,248
Liabilities: $31,522,418,460
Net Worth: $3,516,664,788
Earnings: ($2,290,119,156)
Fiscal Year-end: 12/31/22

Real Estate Manangement Services
N.A.I.C.S.: 531210
Shan Liu *(Pres)*

RISHAB FINANCIAL SERVICES LIMITED
Hanwat Complex Old No 58 Govindappa Naicken St 1st Floor, Chennai, 600 001, Tamil Nadu, India
Tel.: (91) 44 32966268
Web Site: http://www.rishabfinance.com
Year Founded: 1990
Sales Range: Less than $1 Million
Financial Management Services
N.A.I.C.S.: 523999

RISHAB SPECIAL YARNS LTD.
2070 Rasta Bara Gangore, Jaipur, 302 003, Rajasthan, India
Tel.: (91) 141 2575213
Web Site: http://www.rishabspecial.com
Sales Range: Less than $1 Million
Cotton Yarn Mfr
N.A.I.C.S.: 313110
Amitabh Hirawat *(Mng Dir & Compliance Officer)*

RISHABH DIGHA STEEL & ALLIED PRODUCTS LTD.
514 B Amarkunj Building 2nd Floor RP Masani Road, Matunga, Mumbai, 400 019, India
Tel.: (91) 2224100773
Web Site: https://www.rishabhdighasteel.com
531539—(BOM)
Rev.: $116,449
Assets: $1,037,687
Liabilities: $17,466
Net Worth: $1,020,221
Earnings: ($34,604)
Emp.: 17
Fiscal Year-end: 03/31/21
Steel & Allied Products Processing Services
N.A.I.C.S.: 541330
Ashok Maganlal Mehta *(Chm & Mng Dir)*

Subsidiaries:

Rishabh Digha Steel & Allied Products Ltd. - Industrial Unit 2 (1)
Plot No C-17/3 & 4 MIDC Ind Area, Raigad, Taloja, Maharashtra, India
Tel.: (91) 22 6561 1791
Steel Products Mfr
N.A.I.C.S.: 331110

RISHABH INSTRUMENTS LIMITED
F-31 MIDC Satpur, Nashik, 422007, Maharashtra, India
Tel.: (91) 2532202028
Web Site: https://www.rishabh.co.in
Year Founded: 1982
543977—(BOM)
Rev.: $24,447,923
Assets: $37,083,501
Liabilities: $7,506,246
Net Worth: $29,577,254
Earnings: $2,271,002
Emp.: 500
Fiscal Year-end: 03/31/23
Measuring Product Mfr
N.A.I.C.S.: 334519
Ajinkya Joglekar *(Officer)*

RISHI LASER LTD.
612 Veena Killedar Industrial Estate 10/14 Pais Street Byculla W, Mumbai, 400 011, India
Tel.: (91) 2223075677
Web Site: https://www.rishilaser.com

Rishi Laser Ltd.—(Continued)
526861—(BOM)
Rev.: $16,301,505
Assets: $10,071,471
Liabilities: $4,715,521
Net Worth: $5,355,950
Earnings: $592,590
Emp.: 270
Fiscal Year-end: 03/31/23
Sheet Metal Components Mfr
N.A.I.C.S.: 332999
Harshad B. Patel *(Mng Dir)*

RISHI TECHTEX LIMITED
612 Veena Killedar Industrial Estate
10/14 Pais Street Byculla W, Mumbai, 400 011, India
Tel.: (91) 2223074897
Web Site:
    https://www.rishitechtex.com
523021—(BOM)
Rev.: $12,859,073
Assets: $8,725,376
Liabilities: $5,068,905
Net Worth: $3,656,471
Earnings: $133,397
Emp.: 190
Fiscal Year-end: 03/31/23
Woven Fabrics & Sacks Mfr
N.A.I.C.S.: 313310
Abhishek Patel *(Mng Dir)*

RISHIROOP LTD.
65 Atlanta Nariman Point, Mumbai, 400 021, India
Tel.: (91) 2240952000
Web Site: https://www.rishiroop.in
Year Founded: 1984
526492—(BOM)
Rev.: $9,018,633
Assets: $12,888,288
Liabilities: $1,087,138
Net Worth: $11,801,149
Earnings: $4,094,890
Emp.: 36
Fiscal Year-end: 03/31/21
Plastic Resin & Rubber Products Mfr
N.A.I.C.S.: 325211
Aditya Arvind Kapoor *(Mng Dir)*

RISING JAPAN EQUITY, INC.
1-7-2 Otemachi Tokyo Sankei Building 27F, Chiyoda-ku, Tokyo, Japan
Tel.: (81) 3 4500 9590   JP
Web Site: http://rje.jp
Year Founded: 2010
Investment Services
N.A.I.C.S.: 523999
Tetsuo Maruyama *(Partner)*

Subsidiaries:

SENQCIA MAXCO, Ltd.   (1)
1245 Kennestone Cir, Marietta, GA 30066
Tel.: (770) 424-9350
Web Site: http://www.senqciamaxco.com
Power Transmission Chain, Engineering Chains & Related Parts & Components Mfr, Distr & Sls
N.A.I.C.S.: 332618
David Egbert *(Mng Dir)*

RISION LIMITED
Level 4 100 Albert Road, South Melbourne, 3025, VIC, Australia
Tel.: (61) 39 088 0386   AU
Web Site: http://www.rision.com
Year Founded: 2002
RNL—(ASX)
Sales Range: Less than $1 Million
Human Resource Management Services
N.A.I.C.S.: 541612

Subsidiaries:

Employment Management Systems
Pty Ltd.   (1)
U 10 128 Carrington Road, Randwick,
2031, NSW, Australia
Tel.: (61) 4 1147 5727
Information Technology Consulting Services
N.A.I.C.S.: 541511

RISK CAPITAL PARTNERS LTD.
31 North Row, London, W1K 6DA, United Kingdom
Tel.: (44) 2070160700
Web Site:
    http://www.riskcapitalpartners.co.uk
Year Founded: 2001
Privater Equity Firm
N.A.I.C.S.: 523999
Luke Johnson *(Co-Founder & Partner)*

Subsidiaries:

Neilson Active Holidays Limited   (1)
Locksview, Brighton Marina, Brighton, BN2 5HA, East Sussex, United Kingdom
Tel.: (44) 333 014 3351
Web Site: http://www.neilson.co.uk
Travel & Tour Operator
N.A.I.C.S.: 561520

RISKIFIED LTD.
30 Kalisher Street, Tel Aviv, 6525724, Israel
Web Site: https://www.riskified.com
Year Founded: 2012
RSKD—(NYSE)
Rev.: $261,247,000
Assets: $608,965,000
Liabilities: $112,548,000
Net Worth: $496,417,000
Earnings: ($103,989,000)
Emp.: 781
Fiscal Year-end: 12/31/22
Software Development Services
N.A.I.C.S.: 541511
Eido Gal *(Co-Founder & CEO)*

RISKMONSTER.COM
RMG Bldg 2-16-5 Nihombashi, Chuo-ku, Tokyo, Japan
Tel.: (81) 362140331
Web Site:
    https://www.riskmonster.co.jp
Year Founded: 2000
3768—(TKS)
Rev.: $36,251,600
Assets: $67,179,200
Liabilities: $10,125,280
Net Worth: $57,053,920
Earnings: $4,443,120
Emp.: 156
Fiscal Year-end: 03/31/22
Credit Management Services
N.A.I.C.S.: 561990

Subsidiaries:

Nippon Outsource Incorporation   (1)
7th floor Nishi-Gotanda 102 Building 7-24-5 Nishi-Gotanda, Shinagawa-ku, Tokyo, 141-0031, Japan
Tel.: (81) 357195445
Web Site: http://www.outsource.co.jp
Data Entry Services
N.A.I.C.S.: 518210

Rismon Muscle Data Co., Ltd.   (1)
2-2-1 Otemachi Chiyoda-ku, Tokyo, 100-8105, Japan
Tel.: (81) 362140061
Data Entry Services
N.A.I.C.S.: 518210

RISMA SA
97 Boulevard Massira El Khadra
5eme Etage, Casablanca, Morocco
Tel.: (212) 520401010
Web Site: https://risma.com
Year Founded: 1993
RIS—(CAS)
Sales Range: $125-149.9 Million
Hotel Operator
N.A.I.C.S.: 721110

Amine Echcherki *(Chm-Mgmt Bd)*

RISMA SYSTEMS A/S
Ejby Industrivej 34-38, 2600, Glostrup, Denmark
Tel.: (45) 70254700
Web Site:
    https://www.rismasystems.com
Year Founded: 2014
RISMA—(CSE)
Rev.: $4,443,287
Assets: $4,831,214
Liabilities: $4,223,640
Net Worth: $607,573
Earnings: ($184,631)
Emp.: 34
Fiscal Year-end: 12/31/23
Software Development Services
N.A.I.C.S.: 541511
Lars Nybro Munksgaard *(Founder)*

RISO KAGAKU CORPORATION
5-34-7 Shiba, Minato-ku, Tokyo, 108-8385, Japan
Tel.: (81) 354416611   JP
Web Site: https://www.riso.co.jp
Year Founded: 1946
6413—(TKS)
Rev.: $493,119,220
Assets: $585,831,080
Liabilities: $143,668,350
Net Worth: $442,162,730
Earnings: $31,932,910
Emp.: 2,958
Fiscal Year-end: 03/31/24
Digital Printing Technology Development, Manufacturing & Sales
N.A.I.C.S.: 323111
Yasuo Tazawa *(Auditor)*

Subsidiaries:

RISO (SHANGHAI) INTERNATIONAL TRADING CO., LTD.   (1)
No 125 Fute North Road Waigaoqiao Free Trade Zone, Pudong, Shanghai, 200131, China
Tel.: (86) 21 58669338
Web Site: http://www.riso.co.jp
Printing Machinery Whslr
N.A.I.C.S.: 423690

RISO EURASIA KAZAKHSTAN LLC   (1)
Office 707/1 531 Seyfullin av, Almaty, Kazakhstan
Tel.: (7) 7272725208
Web Site: https://www.riso.kz
Sales Range: $50-74.9 Million
Emp.: 5
Electronic Printing Machinery Distr
N.A.I.C.S.: 423690

RISO INDIA PRIVATE LTD.   (1)
D-7 Ground Floor Sector-3, Noida, 201 301, Uttar Pradesh, India
Tel.: (91) 1204721300
Web Site: https://www.risoindia.com
Emp.: 36
Electronic Products Mfr & Distr
N.A.I.C.S.: 334419
Sanjeev Madan *(Auditor)*

RISO LATIN AMERICA, INC.   (1)
13680 NW 5th St Ste 100, Sunrise, FL 33325
Tel.: (954) 499-7476
Sales Range: $25-49.9 Million
Emp.: 12
Photocopying & Printing Machinery Distr
N.A.I.C.S.: 423690
Noboru Hayama *(Founder)*

RISO OKINAWA CORPORATION   (1)
4-6-3 Omoromachi, Naha, 900-0006, Okinawa, Japan
Tel.: (81) 989512112
Web Site: https://riso-okinawa.com
Emp.: 13
Electrical Apparatus & Equipment Whslr
N.A.I.C.S.: 423610

Riso (Deutschland) GmbH   (1)
Steilshooper Allee 80, 22309, Hamburg, Germany
Tel.: (49) 405328610
Emp.: 34
Digital Printing Technology Development, Manufacturing & Sales
N.A.I.C.S.: 323111

Riso (Thailand) Limited   (1)
825 Phairojkijja Tower 10th Floor Debaratna Road Bangna Nuea, Bang Na, Bangkok, 10260, Thailand
Tel.: (66) 23614643
Digital Printing Technology Development, Manufacturing & Sales
N.A.I.C.S.: 323111

Riso (UK) Limited   (1)
Unit 23 Building 6 Croxley Park Hatters Lane, Watford, WD18 8YH, Hertfordshire, United Kingdom
Tel.: (44) 2082365800
Web Site: https://www.riso.co.uk
Sales Range: $25-49.9 Million
Emp.: 50
Digital Printing Technology Development, Manufacturing & Sales
N.A.I.C.S.: 323111
Tatsuo Murakami *(Mng Dir)*

Riso Africa (Pty) Ltd.   (1)
154 Lechwe Avenue, Corporate Park South, Midrand, 1683, South Africa
Tel.: (27) 113140562
Web Site: https://www.riso.co.za
Sales Range: $25-49.9 Million
Emp.: 39
Digital Printing Technology Development, Manufacturing & Sales
N.A.I.C.S.: 323111

Riso Canada, Inc.   (1)
1 Valleywood Dr Unit 2, Markham, L3R 5L9, ON, Canada
Tel.: (905) 475-7476
Digital Printing Technology Development, Manufacturing & Sales
N.A.I.C.S.: 323111

Riso France S.A.   (1)
49 Rue de la Cite, 69003, Lyon, Cedex 3, France
Tel.: (33) 472113888
Web Site: http://www.risofrance.fr
Sales Range: $50-74.9 Million
Emp.: 260
Digital Printing Technology Development, Manufacturing & Sales
N.A.I.C.S.: 323111
Fabrice Sposito *(CEO)*

Riso Hong Kong Ltd.   (1)
Unit C 1/F Hop Hing Industrial Building 704 Castle Peak Road, Lai Chi Kok, Hong Kong, Kowloon, China (Hong Kong)
Tel.: (852) 27863911
Web Site: http://www.riso.com.hk
Sales Range: $25-49.9 Million
Emp.: 40
Digital Printing Technology Development, Manufacturing & Sales
N.A.I.C.S.: 323111

Riso Iberica S.A.   (1)
Avda les Garrigues 38-40 floor 2, Local B1 08820 El Prat de Llobregat, Barcelona, Spain
Tel.: (34) 934793750
Web Site: https://www.risoiberica.es
Digital Printing Technology Development, Manufacturing & Sales
N.A.I.C.S.: 323111

Riso Industries (H.K.) Ltd.   (1)
Room 1213A Level 12 Landmark North 39 Lung Sum Avenue, 1 Science Museum Road Tsim Sha Tsui East, Sheung Shui, New Territories, China (Hong Kong)
Tel.: (852) 21750261
Web Site: http://www.riso.co.jp
Electronic Equipment Distr
N.A.I.C.S.: 423690

Riso Korea Ltd.   (1)
331 Pangyo-ro, Bundang-gu, Seongnam, 13488, Gyeonggi-do, Korea (South)
Tel.: (82) 3180170318
Sales Range: $25-49.9 Million
Emp.: 25

Digital Printing Technology Development, Manufacturing & Sales
N.A.I.C.S.: 323111

Riso Technology China Co., Ltd. (1)
Tel.: (86) 7563323300
Web Site: http://www.riso.com.cn
Digital Printing Technology Development, Manufacturing & Sales
N.A.I.C.S.: 323111

Riso de Mexico, S.A. de C.V. (1)
Blvd Manuel Avila Camacho 88-104, Lomas de Chapultepec, 11000, Mexico, Mexico
Tel.: (52) 5552027475
Web Site: http://www.risolatin.com
Sales Range: $25-49.9 Million
Emp.: 9
Digital Printing Technology Development, Manufacturing & Sales
N.A.I.C.S.: 323111

Riso, Inc. (1)
10 State St Ste 201, Woburn, MA 01801-2105
Tel.: (978) 777-7377
Web Site: http://www.us.riso.com
Sales Range: $125-149.9 Million
Emp.: 300
Digital Printing Technology Development, Manufacturing & Sales
N.A.I.C.S.: 323111
Kentaro Harada (Pres & CEO)

Risograph Italia (1)
Via Archimede 42, Ingresso 3, 20864, Agrate Brianza, MB, Italy
Tel.: (39) 039656191
Web Site: https://www.risograph.it
Digital Printing Technology Development, Manufacturing & Sales
N.A.I.C.S.: 323111

RISTIA BINTANG MAHKO-TASEJATI TBK
Gedung Ribens Jl RS Fatmawati No 188, Jakarta, 12420, Indonesia
Tel.: (62) 217511441
Web Site: https://www.ristiagroup.com
Year Founded: 1985
RBMS—(INDO)
Rev.: $11,664,958
Assets: $46,242,469
Liabilities: $13,886,744
Net Worth: $32,355,725
Earnings: ($1,344,701)
Emp.: 19
Fiscal Year-end: 12/31/23
Real Estate Development Services
N.A.I.C.S.: 531390
Deddy Indrasetiawan (Chm)

RISUNTEK, INC.
Jiuwei Industrial Zone, Qishi Town, Dongguan, 523000, Guangdong, China
Tel.: (86) 76986768336
Web Site: http://www.risuntek.com
Year Founded: 2005
002981—(SSE)
Rev.: $194,518,584
Assets: $225,813,744
Liabilities: $106,862,652
Net Worth: $118,951,092
Earnings: $8,158,644
Fiscal Year-end: 12/31/22
Electronic Product Mfr & Distr
N.A.I.C.S.: 334419
Guo Liqin (Chm & Gen Mgr)

RIT CAPITAL PARTNERS PLC
27 St James s Place, London, SW1A 1NR, United Kingdom
Tel.: (44) 2076478565 UK
Web Site: https://www.ritcap.com
Year Founded: 1988
RCP—(OTCIQ)
Rev.: $764,260,588
Assets: $5,491,298,540
Liabilities: $616,540,652
Net Worth: $4,874,757,888
Earnings: $684,155,108
Emp.: 52
Fiscal Year-end: 12/31/20
Investment Services
N.A.I.C.S.: 523910
Jacob Rothschild (Chm)

Subsidiaries:

Atlantic and General Investment Trust Limited
27 St James Pl, London, SW1A 1NR, United Kingdom
Tel.: (44) 2075141944
Web Site: http://www.ritcap.com
Emp.: 60
Investment Management Service
N.A.I.C.S.: 523999
Christopher Wise (Sec-RIT)

J. Rothschild Capital Management Limited (1)
27 St James's Place, London, SW1A 1NR, United Kingdom (100%)
Tel.: (44) 207 493 8111
Web Site: https://www.ritcap.com
Sales Range: $50-74.9 Million
Emp.: 50
Investment Management
N.A.I.C.S.: 523940
Ron Tabbouche (Chief Investment Officer)

RIT Capital Partners Associates Limited (1)
27 St James Place, London, SW1 A1NR, United Kingdom
Tel.: (44) 2074938111
Sales Range: $50-74.9 Million
Emp.: 50
Trusts Estates & Agency Accounts
N.A.I.C.S.: 525920
Jacob Rothschild (Chm)

RIT Capital Partners Securities Limited (1)
27 St James Pl, London, SW1A 1NR, United Kingdom
Tel.: (44) 2074938111
Web Site: http://www.ritcap.co.uk
Sales Range: $50-74.9 Million
Emp.: 50
Securities Brokerage
N.A.I.C.S.: 523150
Jacob Rothschild (Chm)

RITA FINANCE & LEASING LTD.
D-328 Basement Floor Defence Colony, Rohini, New Delhi, 110024, India
Tel.: (91) 9810260127
Web Site: https://ritafinance.in
543256—(BOM)
Rev.: $138,984
Assets: $1,880,115
Liabilities: $8,908
Net Worth: $1,871,207
Earnings: $89,851
Emp.: 4
Fiscal Year-end: 03/31/23
Investment Management Service
N.A.I.C.S.: 523940
Priya Gupta (Sec & Compliance Officer)

RITAMIX GLOBAL LIMITED
No 7 Jalan TP7 UEP Industrial Park, 40400, Shah Alam, Selangor, Malaysia Ky
Web Site: https://www.ritamix-global.com
Year Founded: 1982
1936—(HKG)
Rev.: $33,210,045
Assets: $39,388,140
Liabilities: $2,608,898
Net Worth: $36,779,243
Earnings: $2,799,968
Emp.: 52
Fiscal Year-end: 12/31/22
Animal Feed Mfr & Distr
N.A.I.C.S.: 311119
Howard Haw Yih Lee (CEO)

Subsidiaries:

Gladron Chemicals Sdn. Bhd. (1)
No 7 Jalan TP 7 UEP Industrial Park Darul Ehsan, 40400, Shah Alam, Selangor, Malaysia
Tel.: (60) 351918989
Animal Feed Additives Distr
N.A.I.C.S.: 423820

Kevon Sdn. Bhd. (1)
No 7 Jalan TP 7 UEP Industrial Park Darul Ehsan, 40400, Shah Alam, Selangor, Malaysia
Tel.: (60) 351918989
Web Site: https://www.kevonfoods.com
Food Ingredient Distr
N.A.I.C.S.: 424480

Ritamix Sdn. Bhd. (1)
No 1 Jalan Sapir 33/7 Shah Alam Premier Industrial Park, 40400, Shah Alam, Selangor, Malaysia
Tel.: (60) 351918989
Web Site: https://ritamix.com
Emp.: 60
Animal Feed Mfr & Distr
N.A.I.C.S.: 311119

RITCO LOGISTICS LIMITED
Udyog Vihar Phase - II Ritco House 336 Sector 20, Gurgaon, 122006, India
Tel.: (91) 1244702300
Web Site: https://www.ritcologistics.com
542383—(BOM)
Rev.: $90,407,889
Assets: $43,706,636
Liabilities: $25,891,841
Net Worth: $17,814,795
Earnings: $2,915,784
Emp.: 795
Fiscal Year-end: 03/31/24
Freight Forwarding & Logistics Consulting Services
N.A.I.C.S.: 488510
Manmohan P. S. Chadha (Chm & CFO)

RITDISPLAY CORPORATION
No 12 Kuanfu N Road, Hsin Chu Industrial Park, Hsinchu, 30316, Taiwan
Tel.: (886) 35989999
Web Site: https://www.ritdisplay.com
Year Founded: 2000
8104—(TAI)
Rev.: $87,714,343
Assets: $164,333,098
Liabilities: $96,179,858
Net Worth: $68,153,240
Earnings: ($6,691,749)
Emp.: 196
Fiscal Year-end: 12/31/23
Semiconductor Devices Mfr
N.A.I.C.S.: 334413
Jack Chen (Asst VP)

RITE INTERNET VENTURES HOLDING AB
Artillerigatan 6, 114 51, Stockholm, Sweden
Tel.: (46) 76 022 0300
Web Site: http://riteventures.com
Privater Equity Firm
N.A.I.C.S.: 523999
Philip Berglof (CFO)

RITE UGLJEVIK AD
Gradsko naselje BB, 76330, Ugljevik, Bosnia & Herzegovina
Tel.: (387) 55774600
Web Site: https://www.riteugljevik.com
Year Founded: 1899
RTEU-R-A—(BANJ)
Sales Range: Less than $1 Million
Electric Power Distribution Services
N.A.I.C.S.: 221121

RITEK CORPORATION
No 42 Kuangfu N Road Hsin-Chu Industrial Park, Hsin-chu, 30351, Taiwan
Tel.: (886) 35985696
Web Site: https://www.ritek.com
Year Founded: 1988
2349—(TAI)
Rev.: $249,502,917
Assets: $617,084,839
Liabilities: $282,924,055
Net Worth: $334,160,784
Earnings: ($12,381,601)
Emp.: 6,000
Fiscal Year-end: 12/31/23
Optical Storage Media Mfr & Distr
N.A.I.C.S.: 334112

Subsidiaries:

Cashido Corporation (1)
No 5-29 Laoqi, Toufen, 351, Miaoli, Taiwan
Tel.: (886) 37585575
Web Site: http://www.cashido.com.tw
Compact Disk Product Mfr
N.A.I.C.S.: 334112

Finesil Technology Inc. (1)
No 78 Guangfu N Rd, Hukou Township, Hsinchu, 303, Taiwan
Tel.: (886) 35982929
Silicone Chemical Mfr & Distr
N.A.I.C.S.: 334413

Formosa Sun Energy Corp. (1)
No222 Hwa-Ya Road, Kuei-Shan Hsiang, Taoyuan, 33383, Taiwan
Tel.: (886) 33961111
Renewable Energy Generation Services
N.A.I.C.S.: 221118

Kunshan Hutek Corporation (1)
No 88 Second Avenue Kunshan Free Trade Zone, Suzhou, 215301, Jiangsu, China
Tel.: (86) 51257358989
Chemical Product Mfr & Distr
N.A.I.C.S.: 325998

Kunshan Protek Co. Ltd. (1)
No 88 Second Avenue Kunshan Free Trade Zone, Kunshan, 215301, Jiangsu, China
Tel.: (86) 51257358989
Compact Disc Mfr
N.A.I.C.S.: 334610

Kunshan Ritek Trading Company, Ltd. (1)
No 88 Second Avenue Kunshan Free Trade Zone, Kunshan Free Trade Zone, Kunshan, 215301, Jiangsu, China
Tel.: (86) 51236863400
Compact Disc Distr
N.A.I.C.S.: 423690

Lai Gongchang Co., Ltd. (1)
No 222 Hwa-Ya Road, Kuei-Shan Hsiang, Taoyuan, 33383, Taiwan
Tel.: (886) 33280728
Chemical Product Mfr & Distr
N.A.I.C.S.: 325998

Prorit Corporation (1)
No 14 Zhongxing Rd, Tongluo Township, Miao-li, 366, Taiwan
Tel.: (886) 37235658
Plastic Injection Mfr & Distr
N.A.I.C.S.: 333248

RITEK Foundation Co., Ltd. (1)
No 42 Guangfu North Road, Hukou Township, Hsinchu, 30351, Taiwan
Tel.: (886) 35985696
Web Site: https://www.ritekfound.org
Educational & Cultural Services
N.A.I.C.S.: 923110

Ritek Latin America, Inc. (1)
France Field Zona Libre de Colon Rep de, Panama, Panama
Tel.: (507) 62191069
Compact Disc Mfr
N.A.I.C.S.: 334610

Ritek Vietnam Co., Ltd. (1)
Plot 213 Amata Road, Amata Industrial Park Long Binh Ward, 810000, Bien Hoa, Dong Nai, Vietnam
Tel.: (84) 2513936111
Compact Disc Mfr & Distr

RITEK CORPORATION

RITEK CORPORATION—(Continued)
N.A.I.C.S.: 334610

Ritwin Corporation (1)
No 17 Kuangfu N Rd, Hukou Township, Hu-kou, 30351, Hsinchu, Taiwan
Tel.: (886) 35985696
Electronic Parts & Component Mfr
N.A.I.C.S.: 334419

RITES LTD
Shikhar Plot No 01 Sector 29, Gurgaon, 122001, Haryana, India
Tel.: (91) 1242571666
Web Site: https://rites.com
Year Founded: 1974
RITES—(NSE)
Rev.: $327,320,904
Assets: $716,063,785
Liabilities: $390,049,757
Net Worth: $326,014,028
Earnings: $69,134,944
Emp.: 1,710
Fiscal Year-end: 03/31/23
Technical Consulting Services
N.A.I.C.S.: 541690
Rahul Mitha (Chm & Mng Dir)

Subsidiaries:

REMC Limited (1)
Plot No 7 8th Floor PNB Building Bhikaji Cama Place, New Delhi, 110066, India
Tel.: (91) 1169203000
Web Site: https://remcltd.com
Solar Energy Generation Services
N.A.I.C.S.: 221114

RITES (Afrika) (Pty.) Limited (1)
Plot No 1245 Haile Silassie Road, PO Box 403921, Gaborone, Botswana
Tel.: (267) 3914113
Engineeering Services
N.A.I.C.S.: 541330

RITESH INTERNATIONAL LIMITED
Momnabad Road Village Akbarpura Ahmedgarh, Sangrur, 148021, Punjab, India
Tel.: (91) 1615047085
Web Site:
https://www.riteshinternational.com
Year Founded: 1981
519097—(BOM)
Rev.: $15,196,583
Assets: $3,138,829
Liabilities: $815,958
Net Worth: $2,322,870
Earnings: $126,275
Emp.: 215
Fiscal Year-end: 03/31/23
Organic Chemical Mfr
N.A.I.C.S.: 325199
Neha Bedi (Co-Sec)

RITESH PROPERTIES & INDUSTRIES LTD.
Chandigarh Road, Ludhiana, 141011, Punjab, India
Tel.: (91) 1612174104
Web Site:
https://www.riteshindustries.us
Year Founded: 1987
526407—(BOM)
Rev.: $17,209,876
Assets: $14,796,981
Liabilities: $3,567,542
Net Worth: $11,229,439
Earnings: $3,044,449
Emp.: 12
Fiscal Year-end: 03/31/21
Real Estate Services
N.A.I.C.S.: 531390
Sanjeev Arora (Chm & Mng Dir)

RITHWIK FACILITY MANAGEMENT SERVICES LIMITED
RR Tower III Thiru-vi-ka Industrial Estate Guindy, Chennai, 600 032, India
Tel.: (91) 4443534441
Web Site: https://www.rithwik.co.in
Year Founded: 2010
540843—(BOM)
Rev.: $3,835,592
Assets: $2,977,503
Liabilities: $779,474
Net Worth: $2,198,029
Earnings: $302,352
Emp.: 105
Fiscal Year-end: 03/31/23
Building Maintenance Services
N.A.I.C.S.: 561790
Rithwik Rajshekar Raman (Chm & Mng Dir)

RITO GROUP CORP.
Room 6C 4/F Block C Hong Kong Industrial Centre, 489-491 Castle Peak Road Lai Chi Kok, Hong Kong, China (Hong Kong)
Tel.: (852) 23858598
Web Site: http://www.rito.hk
Year Founded: 2015
RTTO—(OTCIQ)
Rev.: $438,845
Assets: $697,015
Liabilities: $604,171
Net Worth: $92,844
Earnings: ($747,721)
Fiscal Year-end: 06/30/20
Online Shopping Services
N.A.I.C.S.: 455219
Addy Tak Yin Choi (Pres & CEO)

RIU HOTELS S.A.
C/ Llaud s/n RIU Centre, 07610, Palma de Mallorca, Spain
Tel.: (34) 871930290
Web Site: http://www.riu.com
Year Founded: 1953
Sales Range: $1-4.9 Billion
Emp.: 28,000
Hotel Owner, Operator & Franchiser
N.A.I.C.S.: 721110
Carmen Riu Guell (Owner)

RIVA FORNI ELETTRICI
V le Certosa 249, 20151, Milan, Italy
Tel.: (39) 0230700
Web Site: http://www.rivagroup.com
Year Founded: 1954
Sales Range: $250-299.9 Million
Emp.: 24,676
Production & Sale of Structural Steel Services
N.A.I.C.S.: 238120

Subsidiaries:

ILVA S.P.A. in AS (1)
viale Certosa 239, 20151, Milan, Italy
Tel.: (39) 02300351
Web Site: http://www.gruppoilva.com
Sales Range: $1-4.9 Billion
Emp.: 14,000
Steel Mfrs
N.A.I.C.S.: 331110
Piero Gnudi (Commissioner-Extraordinary)

Holding (Non-US):

Ilva (UK) Ltd. (2)
Arden House Warwick Rd Acocks Green, Birmingham, B27 6BH, W Midlands, United Kingdom (100%)
Tel.: (44) 217062332
Sales Range: $25-49.9 Million
Emp.: 3
N.A.I.C.S.: 334220

Riva Acciaio (1)
Via le Certosa 249, 20151, Milan, Italy
Tel.: (39) 0230700
Web Site: http://www.rivagroup.com
Sales Range: $25-49.9 Million
Emp.: 9,500
Producer of Welded Wire Mesh & Electrically Welded Steel Lattice Reinforcement; Cold Drawn Wire Plain & Ribbed in Bars & Coils
N.A.I.C.S.: 331222

Riva Acier S.A. (1)
ZI Limay Porcheville, 78440, Gargenville, France (100%)
Tel.: (33) 130982000
Web Site: http://www.rivaacier.com
Sales Range: $25-49.9 Million
Emp.: 50
Concrete Reinforcement Bars, Spacers & Special Sections Mfr
N.A.I.C.S.: 327331

RIVAGES DU MONDE
3 Rue Camille Desmoulins, 94230, Cachan, Val De Marne, France
Tel.: (33) 149491550
Web Site:
http://www.rivagesdumonde.fr
Year Founded: 2001
Sales Range: $25-49.9 Million
Emp.: 22
Cruise Tours Operator
N.A.I.C.S.: 561520
Lydia Kesselmann (Mng Partner)

RIVALRY CORP.
116 Spadina Av Suite 701, Toronto, M5V 2K6, ON, Canada
Tel.: (416) 565-4713
Web Site:
https://www.rivalrycorp.com
Year Founded: 2016
RVLCF—(OTCQX)
Rev.: $19,869,206
Assets: $13,469,933
Liabilities: $2,502,938
Net Worth: $10,966,995
Earnings: ($23,218,714)
Fiscal Year-end: 12/31/22
Media Advertising Services
N.A.I.C.S.: 541840
Kejda Qorri (CFO)

RIVER & MERCANTILE UK MICRO CAP INVESTMENT COMPANY LIMITED
BNP Paribas House St Julians Avenue, Saint Peter Port, GY1 1WA, Guernsey
Tel.: (44) 1481750858
Web Site:
http://www.riverandmercantile.com
Year Founded: 2014
RMMC—(LSE)
Rev.: $4,184,239
Assets: $76,768,171
Liabilities: $326,173
Net Worth: $76,441,998
Earnings: $2,807,700
Fiscal Year-end: 09/30/23
Investment Management Service
N.A.I.C.S.: 523940

RIVER ELETEC CORPORATION
Tel.: (81) 551221211
Web Site: https://www.river-ele.co.jp
Year Founded: 1951
6666—(TKS)
Rev.: $36,050,940
Assets: $67,283,190
Liabilities: $37,881,910
Net Worth: $29,401,280
Earnings: ($879,130)
Emp.: 417
Fiscal Year-end: 03/31/24
Quartz Crystal Mfr
N.A.I.C.S.: 339999
Fujio Wakao (Chm & Pres)

Subsidiaries:

Aomori River Techno Co., Ltd. (1)
245-11 Yamaguchi Nogi, Aomori, 030-0142, Japan
Tel.: (81) 17 739 1177
Electronic Components Mfr
N.A.I.C.S.: 334419

River Electronics (Ipoh) Sdn. Bhd. (1)
Plot 46 Medan Tasek Tasek Industrial Estate, Perak Darul Ridzuan, 31400, Ipoh, Perak, Malaysia
Tel.: (60) 5 546 4562
Web Site: https://www.river-ele.co.jp
Electronic Components Distr
N.A.I.C.S.: 423690
Fujio Wakao (Chm)

River Electronics (Singapore) Pte. Ltd. (1)
49 Jalan Pemimpin, 04-03 Aps Industrial Building, Singapore, 577203, Singapore
Tel.: (65) 6 258 7874
Web Site: https://www.river-ele.co.jp
Electronic Component Mfr & Distr
N.A.I.C.S.: 334419
Susan Lim (Mng Dir)

Taiwan River Co., Ltd. (1)
3F No 14 Lane 128 Sec 1 Jung Shing Rd, Wu-Gu Dist, Taipei, Taiwan
Tel.: (886) 289882811
Electronic Components Distr
N.A.I.C.S.: 423690
Pieng I. Lee (Engr-Sls)

Xi'an River Electronics Corporation (1)
Guanzhong Comprehensive Bonded Zone A Fengcheng 12 Road, No 7 Factory Building 1st Floor, Xi'an, 710018, China
Tel.: (86) 2986658920
Web Site: https://www.river-ele.co.jp
Electronic Components Distr
N.A.I.C.S.: 423690

RIVER ISLAND CLOTHING CO. LTD.
Chelsea House, Westgate, London, W5 1DR, United Kingdom
Tel.: (44) 208 991 4500
Web Site: http://www.riverisland.com
Sales Range: $1-4.9 Billion
Emp.: 11,700
Clothing Retailer
N.A.I.C.S.: 458110
Clive Robert Lewis (Mng Dir)

RIVER TECH P.L.C.
Aragon House Business Center Dragonara Road, Saint Julian's, STJ 3140, Malta
Tel.: (356) 21383993
Web Site: https://www.river.tech
Year Founded: 2017
RIVER—(OSL)
Rev.: $16,974,606
Assets: $18,081,107
Liabilities: $3,009,519
Net Worth: $15,071,588
Earnings: $9,293,974
Fiscal Year-end: 12/31/23
Software Development Services
N.A.I.C.S.: 541511
Daniela Pulis (CFO)

RIVERA (HOLDINGS) LIMITED
Rooms 1507-12 15th Floor Wing On Centre, 111 Connaught Road Central, Central, China (Hong Kong)
Tel.: (852) 28456618
Web Site: http://www.rivera.com.hk
0281—(HKG)
Rev.: $14,283,525
Assets: $332,839,092
Liabilities: $4,588,659
Net Worth: $328,250,433
Earnings: $1,889,076
Emp.: 4
Fiscal Year-end: 12/31/20
Investment Holding Company
N.A.I.C.S.: 523940
Yuen Han Lee (Sec)

RIVERCITY MOTORWAY PTY. LTD.
82 Campbell St, Bowen Hills, 4006, QLD, Australia
Tel.: (61) 738374868   AU
Sales Range: $500-549.9 Million
Emp.: 15
Investment Services
N.A.I.C.S.: 523940
Flan Cleary *(CEO)*

RIVERFORT GLOBAL OPPORTUNITIES PLC
Suite 39 18 High Street, High Wycombe, HP11 2BE, Bucks, United Kingdom
Tel.: (44) 2033688978   UK
Web Site:
https://www.riverfortglobal.com
RGO—(AIM)
Rev.: $1,473,591
Assets: $13,782,754
Liabilities: $417,773
Net Worth: $13,364,981
Earnings: ($1,093,701)
Emp.: 3
Fiscal Year-end: 12/31/22
Investment Services
N.A.I.C.S.: 523999
Nicholas Lee *(Dir-Investments)*

RIVERINA HOTEL PLC
33 St Michaels Rd, 3, Colombo, Sri Lanka
Tel.: (94) 112333320
Web Site:
http://www.confifihotels.com
Sales Range: $1-9.9 Million
Hotel Owner & Operator
N.A.I.C.S.: 721110
Stefan Furkhan *(Mng Dir)*

RIVERINE CHINA HOLDINGS LIMITED
14th Floor Jiushi Tower 28 South Zhongshan Road, Shanghai, 200010, China
Tel.: (86) 2163333599   Ky
Web Site: http://www.riverinepm.com
Year Founded: 2002
1417—(HKG)
Rev.: $128,826,828
Assets: $142,742,574
Liabilities: $90,867,582
Net Worth: $51,874,992
Earnings: $3,476,725
Emp.: 5,143
Fiscal Year-end: 12/31/22
Real Estate Manangement Services
N.A.I.C.S.: 531210
Xingtao Xiao *(Co-Founder & Chm)*

RIVERROCK EUROPEAN CAPITAL PARTNERS LLP
15 Wright Lane, London, W8 5SL, United Kingdom
Tel.: (44) 207 842 7650
Web Site: http://www.riverrock.eu
Privater Equity Firm
N.A.I.C.S.: 523999
Michel Peretie *(Parrtner & CEO)*

Subsidiaries:

Neue Alno GmbH (1)
Heiligenberger Strasse 47, 88630, Pfullendorf, Germany
Tel.: (49) 7552 21 0
Web Site: http://www.alno.de
Kitchen Cabinetry & Related Products Mfr & Distr
N.A.I.C.S.: 337110
Thomas Kresser *(Mng Dir)*

Subsidiary (Non-US):

Lekka Trading Co., Ltd. (2)
Park Grace 1F 4-32-6 Nishi-Shinjuku, Shinjuku- ku, Tokyo, 160-0023, Japan
Tel.: (81) 5350 4471
Web Site: http://www.lekka-tr.co.jp
Kitchen Furniture Mfr
N.A.I.C.S.: 337110

RIVERSGOLD LIMITED
Suite 23 513 Hay Street, Subiaco, 6008, WA, Australia
Tel.: (61) 61436747   AU
Web Site:
https://www.riversgold.com.au
Year Founded: 2017
RGL—(ASX)
Rev.: $43,118
Assets: $5,240,282
Liabilities: $152,359
Net Worth: $5,087,923
Earnings: ($4,630,736)
Fiscal Year-end: 06/30/24
Mineral Exploration Services
N.A.I.C.S.: 213114
Xavier Braud *(Exec Dir)*

RIVERSIDE DODGE CHRYSLER JEEP
160 38th Street East, Prince Albert, S6W 1A6, SK, Canada
Tel.: (306) 764-4217
Web Site:
http://www.riversidedodge.ca
Rev.: $13,650,357
Emp.: 30
New & Used Car Dealers
N.A.I.C.S.: 441110
Trent Hargrave *(Gen Mgr)*

RIVERSIDE FORD SALES LIMITED
25 Eleanor Street, Brockville, K6V 4H9, ON, Canada
Tel.: (613) 342-0234
Web Site: http://www.riversideford.ca
Year Founded: 2006
New & Used Car Dealers
N.A.I.C.S.: 441110
Scot Birnie *(Pres)*

RIVERSIDE MILLWORK GROUP
563 Barton Street, Stoney Creek, L8E 5S1, ON, Canada
Tel.: (226) 241-6864
Web Site:
https://www.riversidemillwork.ca
Year Founded: 2005
Emp.: 100
Wholesale Building Materials
N.A.I.C.S.: 321911

RIVERSIDE RESOURCES INC.
550-800 West Pender Street, Vancouver, V6C 2V6, BC, Canada
Tel.: (778) 327-6671   BC
Web Site: https://www.rivres.com
Year Founded: 2006
RRI—(OTCIQ)
Rev.: $32,592
Assets: $9,444,177
Liabilities: $1,743,883
Net Worth: $7,700,293
Earnings: ($1,003,100)
Emp.: 100
Fiscal Year-end: 09/30/19
Mineral Exploration Services
N.A.I.C.S.: 212390
John-Mark Staude *(Pres & CEO)*

Subsidiaries:

Riverside Resources Mexico, S.A. de C.V. (1)
Gral Bernando Reyes 109, Col San Benito, 83190, Hermosillo, Sonora, Mexico
Tel.: (52) 6672670957
Web Site: https://www.rivres.com
Asset Management Services
N.A.I.C.S.: 523940

RIVERSTONE CREDIT OPPORTUNITIES INCOME PLC
5th Floor 20 Fenchurch Street, London, EC3M 3BY, United Kingdom
Tel.: (44) 2896930221
Web Site:
https://www.riverstonecoi.com
RCOI—(LSE)
Rev.: $15,910,000
Assets: $100,370,000
Liabilities: $1,890,000
Net Worth: $98,480,000
Earnings: $12,850,000
Fiscal Year-end: 12/31/22
Portfolio Management & Investment Advice
N.A.I.C.S.: 523940
Reuben Jeffery III *(Chm)*

RIVERSTONE ENERGY LIMITED
Floor 2 Trafalgar Court Les Banques, PO Box 286, Saint Peter Port, GY1 4HY, Guernsey
Tel.: (44) 1481742742   GY
Web Site:
https://www.riverstonerel.com
Year Founded: 2013
RSE—(LSE)
Assets: $674,081,000
Liabilities: $512,000
Net Worth: $673,569,000
Earnings: ($2,268,000)
Fiscal Year-end: 12/31/23
Investment Management Service
N.A.I.C.S.: 523940
Pierre F. Lapeyre Jr. *(Co-Founder)*

RIVERSTONE HOLDINGS LIMITED
9 Raffles Place 26-01 Republic Plaza, Singapore, 048619, Singapore
Tel.: (65) 62363333
Web Site:
https://www.riverstone.com.my
Year Founded: 1989
AP4—(SES)
Rev.: $199,124,076
Assets: $397,298,218
Liabilities: $31,263,387
Net Worth: $366,034,830
Earnings: $47,970,396
Emp.: 2,743
Fiscal Year-end: 12/31/23
Gloves & Plastic Product Mfr
N.A.I.C.S.: 326199
Teek Son Wong *(Co-Founder, Chm & CEO)*

Subsidiaries:

Eco Medi Glove Sdn Bhd (1)
Lot 32586 No 118 Jalan Logam 7, Kamunting Raya Industrial Estate, 34600, Taiping, Perak, Malaysia
Tel.: (60) 58912777
Web Site:
https://www.ecomediglove.com.my
Glove Mfr
N.A.I.C.S.: 339113

Protective Technology Company Limited (1)
208 Moo 7 Tambol Thatoom, Srimahaphot Amphur, Nonthaburi, 25140, Prachinburi, Thailand
Tel.: (66) 37210997
Web Site: https://www.protectivetech.co.th
Glove Mfr
N.A.I.C.S.: 339113

Riverstone Resources Sdn Bhd (1)
Lot 55 56 No 13 Jalan Jasmin 2, Kawasan Perindustrian Bukit Beruntung, 48300, Kuala Lumpur, Selangor, Malaysia
Tel.: (60) 60283033
Glove Mfr & Distr
N.A.I.C.S.: 339113
K. L. Lee *(Mgr-Bus Dev)*

Subsidiary (Non-US):

Riverstone Resources (Wuxi) Company Limited (2)
Standard Factory 10 Xiangnan Road Shuofang Industrial Park, Wuxi New District, Jiangsu, 214142, China
Tel.: (86) 51085311811
Cleanroom Product Distr
N.A.I.C.S.: 424490

RIVERVIEW RUBBER ESTATES BERHAD
Level 2 Weil Hotel 292 Jalan Sultan Idris Shah, 30000, Ipoh, Perak Darul Ridzuan, Malaysia
Tel.: (60) 52540288   MY
Web Site:
https://www.riverview.com.my
RVIEW—(KLS)
Rev.: $7,493,830
Assets: $86,916,566
Liabilities: $7,203,075
Net Worth: $79,713,491
Earnings: $1,394,494
Emp.: 411
Fiscal Year-end: 12/31/23
Rubber Mfr
N.A.I.C.S.: 326299
Chow Jan Liang Eugene *(Sec)*

Subsidiaries:

The Narborough Plantations, plc (1)
33 1st Floor Jalan Dato Maharajarela, 30000, Ipoh, Perak Darul Ridzuan, Malaysia (100%)
Tel.: (60) 52559015
Web Site:
http://www.narboroughplantations.com
Sales Range: $1-9.9 Million
Emp.: 75
Oil Palm Cultivation Services
N.A.I.C.S.: 115112
Jan Liang Chow *(Sec)*

RIVERY EXPLOITATION
Av De La Defense Passive, 80136, Amiens, France
Tel.: (33) 322702828
Sales Range: $25-49.9 Million
Emp.: 72
Miscellaneous General Merchandise Stores
N.A.I.C.S.: 459999
Stephane Leclair *(Pres)*

RIVET PTY. LTD.
Level 4 697 Burke Road, Camberwell, 3124, VIC, Australia
Tel.: (61) 3 8832 0100   AU
Web Site: http://www.rivet.com.au
Holding Company; Specialized Mining & Transportation Support Services
N.A.I.C.S.: 551112
Mark Rowsthorn *(Chm)*

Subsidiaries:

Rivet Energy Aviation Pty. Limited (1)
Level 4 697 Burke Road, Camberwell, 3124, VIC, Australia
Tel.: (61) 3 8832 0100
Air Transportation Refueling & Support Services
N.A.I.C.S.: 488190
Philip Tonks *(CEO)*

Subsidiary (Domestic):

Sunshine Refuellers Pty. Ltd. (2)
602-606 Somerville Road, Sunshine, 3020, VIC, Australia
Tel.: (61) 3 8311 6600
Web Site: http://www.refuelin.com
Aviation Refuelling & Support Services
N.A.I.C.S.: 488190
Geoffrey Pinner *(Gen Mgr)*

Rivet Energy Pty. Ltd. (1)
Level 4 697 Burke Road, Camberwell, 3124, VIC, Australia
Tel.: (61) 3 8832 0100

RIVET PTY. LTD.

Rivet Pty. Ltd.—(Continued)
Web Site: http://www.rivet.com.au
Liquified Petroleum Gas & Liquid Fuel Logistics & Transportation Services
N.A.I.C.S.: 484230
Philip Tonks *(CEO)*

Rivet Mining Services Pty. Ltd. (1)
Level 4 697 Burke Road, Camberwell, 3124, VIC, Australia
Tel.: (61) 3 8832 0100
Web Site: http://www.rivet.com.au
Mining Freight Transportation & Logistics Support Services
N.A.I.C.S.: 484230
Philip Tonks *(CEO)*

SMS Rental (WA) Pty. Ltd. (1)
96 Ewing Street, Welshpool, 6106, WA, Australia
Tel.: (61) 8 9277 5177
Web Site: http://www.smsmining.com.au
Mining Equipment Rental & Contract Mining Services
N.A.I.C.S.: 532412
Daniel Sweeney *(Founder)*

RIWI CORP.
33 Bloor St E 5th Floor, Toronto, M4W 3H1, ON, Canada
Tel.: (416) 205-9984   Ca
Web Site: https://www.riwi.com
Year Founded: 2009
5RW—(DEU)
Rev.: $4,184,877
Assets: $4,065,634
Liabilities: $1,375,587
Net Worth: $2,690,047
Earnings: ($813,341)
Fiscal Year-end: 12/31/23
Software Publishing Services
N.A.I.C.S.: 513210
Neil Seeman *(Founder, Chm, CEO & Chief Privacy Officer)*

RIX CORPORATION
1-15-15 Sanno, Hakata-ku, Fukuoka, 812-8672, Japan
Tel.: (81) 924727311
Web Site: https://www.rix.co.jp
Year Founded: 1907
7525—(TKS)
Rev.: $328,860,720
Assets: $271,783,370
Liabilities: $112,660,840
Net Worth: $159,122,530
Earnings: $18,369,190
Emp.: 723
Fiscal Year-end: 03/31/24
Machinery Equipment, Industrial Materials, Rotary Joints & High Pressure Cleaning Equipment Mfr, Distr & Sales
N.A.I.C.S.: 333248
Takashi Yasui *(Pres)*

Subsidiaries:

RIX Corporation Co., Ltd. (1)
MinHang District, Shanghai, China
Tel.: (86) 2154681666
Web Site: http://www.rix.co.jp
Machine Tools & Parts Mfr
N.A.I.C.S.: 333517
Hideaki Kakimori *(Mng Dir)*

RIX Technology (Thailand) Co., Ltd. (1)
1588/5 Bangna-Trad Rd, Bangna, Bangkok, 10260, Thailand
Tel.: (66) 21820146
Web Site: http://www.rix.co.jp
Sales Range: $25-49.9 Million
Emp.: 8
Machine Tools Mfr
N.A.I.C.S.: 333517
Akihiro Nakashima *(Pres & Mng Dir)*

RIYAD BANK
PO Box 22622, Riyadh, 11416, Saudi Arabia
Tel.: (966) 114013030
Web Site: https://www.riyadbank.com
Year Founded: 1957
1010—(SAU)
Rev.: $3,310,032,796
Assets: $103,145,961,605
Liabilities: $87,079,284,895
Net Worth: $16,066,676,710
Earnings: $2,145,272,364
Emp.: 7,887
Fiscal Year-end: 12/31/23
Commercial Banking Services
N.A.I.C.S.: 522110
Abdullah Mohammed Al-Issa *(Chm)*

Subsidiaries:

Riyad Capital Company (1)
2414 Unit No 69, Al-Shuhada District, Riyadh, 13241-7279, Saudi Arabia
Tel.: (966) 92 001 2299
Web Site: https://www.riyadcapital.com
Corporate Investment Banking Services
N.A.I.C.S.: 523150
Najeeb Abdullatif Alissa *(Chm)*

RIYAD REIT FUND
2414 - Al Shohda Dist Unit No 69, Riyadh, 13241-7279, Saudi Arabia
Tel.: (966) 920012299
Web Site: http://www.riyadcapital.com
4330—(SAU)
Rev.: $68,793,706
Assets: $810,879,476
Liabilities: $419,660,045
Net Worth: $391,219,431
Earnings: $5,774,030
Fiscal Year-end: 12/31/23
Investment Management Service
N.A.I.C.S.: 525990
Adel Ibrahim Al-Ateeq *(Chm)*

RIYUE HEAVY INDUSTRY CO., LTD.
Dongwu Town, Yinzhou district, Ningbo, Zhejiang, China
Tel.: (86) 57455007007
Web Site: https://www.riyuehi.com
Year Founded: 1984
603218—(SHG)
Rev.: $683,048,597
Assets: $1,778,447,699
Liabilities: $432,193,109
Net Worth: $1,346,254,589
Earnings: $48,343,525
Emp.: 1,500
Fiscal Year-end: 12/31/22
Heavy Industry Equipment Casting Product Mfr & Distr
N.A.I.C.S.: 331511
Mingkang Fu *(Founder, Chm, Pres & Gen Mgr)*

RIZAL RESOURCES CORPORATION
600 666 Burrard Street, Vancouver, V6C 3P6, BC, Canada
Tel.: (778) 370-1372
Web Site: http://www.rizalresources.com
RZL—(TSXV)
Metal Exploration Services
N.A.I.C.S.: 213114
Peter Main *(Interim Pres & CEO)*

Subsidiaries:

Philco Holdings Inc. (1)
7 Hamilton Crt, Cobourg, K9A 1V2, ON, Canada
Tel.: (905) 372-9429
Investment Management Service
N.A.I.C.S.: 523999

Tribal Holdings Inc. (1)
179 Charlotte St, Peterborough, K9J 2T7, ON, Canada
Tel.: (905) 982-1130
Emp.: 2
Investment Management Service
N.A.I.C.S.: 523999

RIZAP GROUP, INC.
Sumitomo Realty & Development Shinjuku Grand Tower 36F, 8-17-1 Nishi-Shinjuku Shinjuku-ku, Tokyo, 160-0023, Japan
Tel.: (81) 353371335   JP
Web Site: https://www.rizapgroup.com
Year Founded: 2003
2928—(SAP)
Rev.: $1,571,635,120
Assets: $1,353,147,840
Liabilities: $1,004,077,360
Net Worth: $349,070,480
Earnings: $20,628,080
Emp.: 1,135
Fiscal Year-end: 03/31/22
Holding Company; Beauty, Health & Food-Related Businesses
N.A.I.C.S.: 551112
Seto Ken *(Pres)*

Subsidiaries:

BRUNO, Inc. (1)
Ichigo Mita Building 3F 13-18 Shiba 5-chome, Minato-ku, Tokyo, 108-0014, Japan   (71.1%)
Tel.: (81) 354469505
Web Site: https://bruno-inc.com
Rev.: $80,486,800
Assets: $64,289,920
Liabilities: $32,642,560
Net Worth: $31,647,360
Earnings: ($2,077,480)
Emp.: 290
Fiscal Year-end: 06/30/2024
Watches, Clocks, Electric Appliances, Small Furniture & Organic Cosmetics Mfr & Whslr
N.A.I.C.S.: 334519

HAPiNS Co., Ltd. (1)
TOC Building 10F 37 7-22-22 Nishigotanda, Shinagawa-ku, Tokyo, 141-0031, Japan
Tel.: (81) 3 34944491
Web Site: http://www.hapins.co.jp
Retail Store Operator
N.A.I.C.S.: 459999
Tsuge Keisuke *(Chm & Pres)*

Jeans Mate Corporation (1)
1-49-4 Tomigaya, Shibuya-ku, Tokyo, 151-0063, Japan   (64%)
Tel.: (81) 03 57385555
Web Site: http://www.jeansmate.jp
Sales Range: $75-99.9 Million
Emp.: 121
Apparel Distr
N.A.I.C.S.: 424350
Shigeru Tomizawa *(Pres)*

MISUZU Co., Ltd. (1)
TOC Building 10F 7-22-17 Nishigotanda, Shinagawa-ku, Tokyo, 141-0031, Japan
Tel.: (81) 354348101
Web Site: http://www.carina-closet.com
Womens Apparel Mfr & Whslr
N.A.I.C.S.: 458110
Masami Onishi *(Pres)*

Pado Corporation (1)
Meguro Tokyu Bldg 2-13-17 Kamiosaki, Shinagawa-ku, Tokyo, 141-0021, Japan   (71.11%)
Tel.: (81) 120090810
Web Site: http://www.success-holders.inc
Rev.: $99,641,220
Assets: $28,766,290
Liabilities: $17,056,200
Net Worth: $11,710,090
Earnings: ($4,328,240)
Emp.: 388
Fiscal Year-end: 03/31/2020
Magazine Publications
N.A.I.C.S.: 322120
Yasuji Ozawa *(Pres)*

Subsidiary (Domestic):

Comiu-style Corp. (2)
2F Kyoto Research Park No 6 93 Chudoji-Awata-cho, Shimogyou-ku, Kyoto, 600-8815, Japan
Tel.: (81) 75 325 0877
Web Site: http://www.comiu.com
Software Development Services
N.A.I.C.S.: 541511

INTERNATIONAL PUBLIC

Kyushu Pado Corp. (2)
7F Fukuoka Asahi Bldg 2-1-1 Hakataekimae, Hakata-ku, Fukuoka, 812-0011, Japan   (100%)
Tel.: (81) 92 686 8100
Web Site: http://www.pado.co.jp
Advetising Agency
N.A.I.C.S.: 541810

Sendai Pado Corp. (2)
5F odakyu sendai higashiguchi Bldg 1-2-26 shintera, Wakabayashi-ku, Sendai, 984-0051, Miyagi, Japan   (100%)
Tel.: (81) 22 792 8101
Web Site: http://www.pado.co.jp
Advetising Agency
N.A.I.C.S.: 541810

SD Entertainment Inc. (1)
Minami 3 Nishi 1 8-banchi, Chuo-ku, Sapporo, Hokkaido, Japan   (73%)
Tel.: (81) 112413951
Web Site: http://www.sugai-dinos.com
Rev.: $24,688,350
Assets: $28,026,400
Liabilities: $18,157,670
Net Worth: $9,868,730
Earnings: $773,370
Emp.: 86
Fiscal Year-end: 03/31/2024
Entertainment Facility Operator
N.A.I.C.S.: 713950
Masaatsu Hirakawa *(Chm & Pres)*

Sankei Living Shimbun Inc. (1)
3-23 Chiyoda-ku, Kioi-cho, Tokyo, 102-8515, Japan   (80%)
Tel.: (81) 3 5216 9211
Web Site: http://www.sankeiliving.co.jp
Emp.: 369
Newspaper Publishing Services
N.A.I.C.S.: 513110
Hosoi Hidehisa *(Pres)*

Wonder Corporation Co., Ltd. (1)
4181 Hasugawa Shinmachi, Tsuchiura, 300-0821, Ibaraki, Japan   (75.1%)
Tel.: (81) 298797030
Web Site: http://www.wonder.co.jp
Rev.: $561,276,553
Assets: $249,865,380
Liabilities: $185,674,738
Net Worth: $64,190,642
Earnings: $9,638,266
Emp.: 775
Fiscal Year-end: 03/31/2020
Music Software & Video Game Distr
N.A.I.C.S.: 513210
Masayoshi Naito *(Pres)*

Holding (Domestic):

SHINSEIDO CO., LTD. (2)
3F Tsukuba Kasumi Center 599-1 Nishi Ohashi, Tsukuba, 305-0831, Ibaraki, Japan   (51.08%)
Tel.: (81) 29 8607070
Web Site: http://www.shinseido.co.jp
Musical Product Whslr
N.A.I.C.S.: 459140
Masamichi Aso *(Pres & Chief Dir-Sls)*

RIZHAO PORT CO., LTD.
No 81 Haibin 2nd Road, Rizhao, 276826, Shandong, China
Tel.: (86) 6338382576
Web Site: https://www.rzpcl.com
Year Founded: 2002
600017—(SHG)
Rev.: $1,052,648,635
Assets: $4,617,412,568
Liabilities: $2,463,128,951
Net Worth: $2,154,283,616
Earnings: $88,570,147
Emp.: 9,000
Fiscal Year-end: 12/31/22
Cost Management Services
N.A.I.C.S.: 488320
Mou Wei *(Chm)*

Subsidiaries:

Rizhao Port Jurong Co., Ltd. (1)
South End Haibin 5th Road, Donggang District, Rizhao, 276826, Shandong, China
Tel.: (86) 6337381569
Web Site: https://www.rzportjurong.com
Rev.: $117,021,996

Assets: $407,756,138
Liabilities: $49,229,716
Net Worth: $358,526,423
Earnings: $28,062,169
Emp.: 335
Fiscal Year-end: 12/31/2022
Warehousing Services
N.A.I.C.S.: 531130
Zhaodi He *(Exec Dir)*

RIZZO GROUP AB
Ringvagen 100 11 tr, Box 4011,
Stockholm, 102 61, Sweden
Tel.: (46) 850899200
Web Site: http://www.venueretail.com
RIZZO.B—(OMX)
Rev.: $52,913,134
Assets: $47,285,246
Liabilities: $59,728,861
Net Worth: ($12,443,614)
Earnings: ($12,439,952)
Emp.: 297
Fiscal Year-end: 08/31/21
Apparel Stores & Services
N.A.I.C.S.: 315990
Ulf Eklof *(Chm)*

RIZZON AUTOMOBILES
Parc d'Activites Europarc rue R
Schuman, BP 324, 22190, Ploeren,
France
Tel.: (33) 296522424
Web Site: http://www.rizzon-automobiles-plerin.fr
Rev.: $21,200,000
Emp.: 27
Automobile Dealership
N.A.I.C.S.: 441110
Jean-Marc Rizzon *(Pres)*

RJK EXPLORATIONS LTD.
PO Box 1053, Kirkland Lake, P2N
3L1, ON, Canada
Tel.: (705) 568-7956
Web Site: https://rjkexplorations.com
Year Founded: 1922
RJKAF—(OTCIQ)
Rev.: $19,881
Assets: $314,432
Liabilities: $411,310
Net Worth: ($96,878)
Earnings: ($478,034)
Fiscal Year-end: 12/31/23
Mineral Exploration Services
N.A.I.C.S.: 213114
Glenn C. Kasner *(Pres & CEO)*

RKB AGRO INDUSTRIES LIMITED
Kushal Chambers 1st Floor M G
Road, Raichur, 584101, Karnataka,
India
Tel.: (91) 8532236814
530891—(BOM)
Rev.: $1,007,882
Assets: $2,967,062
Liabilities: $1,999,754
Net Worth: $967,308
Earnings: $98,159
Fiscal Year-end: 03/31/14
Cotton Farming Services
N.A.I.C.S.: 111920
S. K. Bhandari *(Mng Dir)*

RKB MAINICHI HOLDINGS CORP.
2-3-8 Momochihama, Sawara-Ku,
Fukuoka, 814-8585, Japan
Tel.: (81) 928526666
Web Site: https://rkb.jp
Year Founded: 1951
9407—(FKA)
Rev.: $224,537,280
Assets: $474,871,760
Liabilities: $124,678,400
Net Worth: $350,193,360
Earnings: $9,641,280

Fiscal Year-end: 03/31/22
Television Broadcasting Services
N.A.I.C.S.: 516120
Izumi Sato *(Pres & CEO)*

RKD AGRI & RETAIL LTD.
B-102 Saraswati Apt Radhakrishna
Marg Mogra Village, Andheri East,
Mumbai, 400069, India
Tel.: (91) 2226875180
Web Site: https://www.hfpltd.in
511169—(BOM)
Rev.: $199,529
Assets: $516,620
Liabilities: $433,185
Net Worth: $83,435
Earnings: $4,606
Fiscal Year-end: 03/31/23
Food Products Mfr
N.A.I.C.S.: 311999
Nilesh Malshi Savla *(CFO)*

RKEC PROJECTS LTD.
10-12-1 Rednam Alcazar Rednam
Gardens Old Jail Road, Opp SBI
Main Branch, Visakhapatnam,
530002, Andhra Pradesh, India
Tel.: (91) 8912574517
Web Site: https://www.rkecprojects.com
Year Founded: 1985
RKEC—(NSE)
Rev.: $36,476,508
Assets: $52,794,123
Liabilities: $34,967,572
Net Worth: $17,826,551
Earnings: $1,489,924
Emp.: 516
Fiscal Year-end: 03/31/23
Building Construction Services
N.A.I.C.S.: 236210
Shri Garapati Radhakrishna
(Founder, Chm & Mng Dir)

RKO STEEL LTD
85 MacDonald Avenue, Dartmouth,
B3B 1T8, NS, Canada
Tel.: (902) 468-1322
Web Site: http://www.rkosteel.com
Year Founded: 1983
Rev.: $15,476,201
Emp.: 100
Steel Mfrs
N.A.I.C.S.: 331221
Tom Skinner *(Dir-Fin)*

RKR GEBLASE UND VERDICHTER GMBH
Braasstrasse 16, Rinteln, 31737, Germany
Tel.: (49) 575140040
Web Site: http://www.rkr.de
Year Founded: 1976
Rev.: $21,078,549
Emp.: 65
Industrial Equipments Repair, Maintenance & Installation Services
N.A.I.C.S.: 811310
Lothar Stoll *(Mng Dir)*

RKW SE
Nachtweideweg 1-7, 67227, Frankenthal, Germany
Tel.: (49) 623387090 De
Web Site: http://www.rkw-group.com
Sales Range: $1-4.9 Billion
Emp.: 3,000
Polyethylene & Polypropylene Product Mfr
N.A.I.C.S.: 326199
Harald Biederbick *(CEO)*

Subsidiaries:

RKW Agri GmbH & Co. KG (1)
Rossbacher Weg 5, 64720, Michelstadt,
Germany
Tel.: (49) 6061 77 278

Polyethylene Product Mfr
N.A.I.C.S.: 326199
Marion Link *(Head-Mktg & Comm)*

RKW Castelletta S.A.S (1)
2 allee de la Richelande, BP 3, Chamboeuf,
42330, Saint-Galmier, France
Tel.: (33) 477 540 385
Packaging Product Distr
N.A.I.C.S.: 423840
Jean Pascal Coste *(Mng Dir & Dir-Sls)*

RKW Finland Ltd. (1)
PO Box 22, 28601, Pori, Finland
Tel.: (358) 8 2 517 88 99
Packaging Products Mfr
N.A.I.C.S.: 326112
Pekka Saariluoma *(Mng Dir)*

RKW Guangzhou Company Ltd. (1)
Block 8 No 2 Hengda Road, Yunpu Industrial District Huangpu, Guangzhou, 510760,
China
Tel.: (86) 2022303500
Emp.: 74
Printed Film Sheet Mfr
N.A.I.C.S.: 326113

RKW HydroSpun GmbH (1)
Osttangente 17, 38820, Halberstadt, Germany
Tel.: (49) 3941 5 95 43 10
Polyethylene Product Mfr
N.A.I.C.S.: 326199
Andreas Kirsch *(Mng Dir & Dir-Sls)*

RKW Hyplast NV (1)
Sint-Lenaartseweg 26, 2320, Hoogstraten,
Belgium
Tel.: (32) 3 340 25 50
Emp.: 150
Polyethylene Product Mfr
N.A.I.C.S.: 326199
Paul Leenders *(Gen Mgr)*

RKW Iter S.A.U. (1)
Avenida Cataluna 243, 50014, Zaragoza,
Spain
Tel.: (34) 976 46 58 00
Polyethylene Product Mfr
N.A.I.C.S.: 326199

RKW Lotus Ltd. (1)
D4/14 Tinh lo 10, Tan Tao Binh Tan, Ho Chi
Minh City, Vietnam
Tel.: (84) 838 776 470
Packaging Products Mfr
N.A.I.C.S.: 326112
Oliver Dirmeier *(Mng Dir)*

RKW North America, Inc. (1)
270 Reasoner Dr, Franklin, KY 42134
Tel.: (270) 598-7700
Web Site: http://www.rkw-group.com
Plastics Films Mfr
N.A.I.C.S.: 326112
Erik Powell *(VP & Gen Mgr)*

RKW Remy S.A.S. (1)
63 Avenue Henri Barbusse, 59990, Saultain, France
Tel.: (33) 3 27 14 72 00
Packaging Products Mfr
N.A.I.C.S.: 326112
Arnaud Stibling *(Mng Dir)*

RKW Saint Freres Emballage
S.A.S. (1)
Rue Marius Sire, BP 4, 80420, Ville-le-Marclet, France
Tel.: (33) 3 22 39 49 00
Packaging Product Distr
N.A.I.C.S.: 423840
Andre Wozniak *(Mng Dir & Dir-Sls)*

RKW Sweden AB (1)
Bunkagardsgatan 2, 253 68, Helsingborg,
Sweden
Tel.: (46) 42 29 59 00
Polyethylene Product Mfr
N.A.I.C.S.: 326199

RLE INTERNATIONAL PRODUKTENTWICKLUNGSGESELLSCHAFT MBH
Brodhausen 1, 51491, Overath, Germany
Tel.: (49) 22 04 97 25 0 De
Web Site: http://www.rle.international

Year Founded: 1985
Emp.: 2,300
Development, Technology & Consultation Services to Mobility & Energy
Industries
N.A.I.C.S.: 541690
Ralf Laufenberg *(CEO)*

Subsidiaries:

RLE Global Operations (China)
Inc. (1)
602 B Bldg 391 Guiping Road, Xuhui District, Shanghai, 200233, China
Tel.: (86) 21 6408 6999
Sales Range: $25-49.9 Million
Emp.: 20
Automobile Parts Mfr
N.A.I.C.S.: 336390

RLE India Private Limited (1)
8th Floor Innovator International Tech Park,
Whitefield, 560066, India
Tel.: (91) 8043510100
Consultation Services
N.A.I.C.S.: 541618
Vijay Machigad *(Mng Dir)*

RLE International China Inc. (1)
34 th Floor Bldg A 391 Guiping Road International Business Center, Xuhui District,
Shanghai, 200233, China
Tel.: (86) 2164086999
Consultation Services
N.A.I.C.S.: 541618
Lane Mu *(Mng Dir)*

RLE International North America
Inc. (1)
31701 Research Park Dr, Madison Heights,
MI 48071
Tel.: (248) 498-5200
Web Site: http://www.rleusa.com
Emp.: 100
Engineering, Research & Development Solutions for Transportation Industry
N.A.I.C.S.: 541330
Robert Kokx *(Pres)*

RLF AGTECH LTD.
61 Dowd Street, Welshpool, 6106,
WA, Australia
Tel.: (61) 861870753 AU
Web Site: https://www.rlfagtech.com
Year Founded: 2017
RLF—(ASX)
Rev.: $7,397,144
Assets: $11,501,597
Liabilities: $5,981,613
Net Worth: $5,519,984
Earnings: ($2,283,367)
Fiscal Year-end: 06/30/23
Agricultural Services
N.A.I.C.S.: 212312
Don McLay *(Chm)*

RLF LIMITED
14 Kms Gurgaon-Pataudi Road Village Jhund Sarai Veeran, Gurgaon,
Haryana, India
Tel.: (91) 1141644996
Web Site: https://www.rlfltd.com
Year Founded: 1979
512618—(BOM)
Rev.: $115,845
Assets: $3,928,732
Liabilities: $596,721
Net Worth: $3,332,011
Earnings: ($333,364)
Fiscal Year-end: 03/31/23
Embroidery Mfr
N.A.I.C.S.: 313110
Aditya Khanna *(Mng Dir)*

RLG INTERNATIONAL INC.
2800 4710 Kings Way, Burnaby, V5H
4M2, BC, Canada
Tel.: (604) 669-7178
Web Site: http://www.rlginternational.com
Year Founded: 1983
Rev.: $10,260,000

RLG INTERNATIONAL INC.

RLG International Inc.—(Continued)

Emp.: 240
Professional Services
N.A.I.C.S.: 561110
Jerry Weisenfelder (Pres)

RLH PROPERTIES SAB DE CV
Corporativo Reforma Diana Paseo de la Reforma 412-Floor 21 Col Juarez, Delegacion Cuauhtemoc, 06600, Mexico, Mexico
Tel.: (52) 5563963000
Web Site: https://rlhproperties.com
Year Founded: 2013
RLH—(MEX)
Hotel & Resort Operator
N.A.I.C.S.: 721110
Borja Escalada (CEO)

RLX TECHNOLOGY INC.
35/F Pearl International Financial Center, Bao 'an District, Shenzhen, Guangdong, China
Tel.: (86) 1021737265   Ky
Web Site: https://ir.relxtech.com
Year Founded: 2018
RLX—(NYSE)
Rev.: $748,722,172
Assets: $2,299,586,890
Liabilities: $117,718,520
Net Worth: $2,181,868,369
Earnings: $202,347,148
Emp.: 707
Fiscal Year-end: 12/31/22
Vapor Product Mfr & Distr
N.A.I.C.S.: 325998
Chao Lu (CFO)

RM INDUSTRIAL GROUP A/S
Industriparken 40, 2750, Ballerup, Denmark
Tel.: (45) 44208800
Web Site: http://www.rmig.com
Sales Range: $150-199.9 Million
Emp.: 600
Holding Company; Perforated Metal Mfr
N.A.I.C.S.: 551112
Henriette Kristensen (Mgr-Sls)

Subsidiaries:

RMIG AG   (1)
Industriestrasse 28, Olten, 4601, Switzerland
Tel.: (41) 622878888
Web Site: http://www.rmig.com
Sales Range: $25-49.9 Million
Emp.: 30
Perforated Metal Products Whslr
N.A.I.C.S.: 423510
Hains Mueller (Mgr-HR)

RMIG AS   (1)
Lillevarskogen 14, 3160, Stokke, Norway
Tel.: (47) 33336666
Web Site: http://www.rmig.com
Sales Range: $50-74.9 Million
Emp.: 5
Perforated Metal Products Whslr
N.A.I.C.S.: 423510
Barron Torrent (Gen Mgr)

RMIG GmbH   (1)
Hallesche Strasse 39, 06779, Raguhn, Germany
Tel.: (49) 34906500
Web Site: http://www.rmig.com
Sales Range: $50-74.9 Million
Emp.: 117
Perforated Metal Products Mfr
N.A.I.C.S.: 332999
Torben Svanholm (Gen Mgr)

RMIG Lochbleche GmbH   (1)
Aumuehlweg 21/114 ARED-Park, 2544, Leobersdorf, Austria
Tel.: (43) 225662482
Web Site: http://www.rmig.com
Sales Range: $25-49.9 Million
Emp.: 3
Metal Structures Mfr

N.A.I.C.S.: 332999
Claudia Lendl (Gen Mgr)

RMIG Ltd.   (1)
Adlington Court Risley Road, Birchwood, Warrington, WA3 6PL, Cheshire, United Kingdom
Tel.: (44) 1925839600
Sales Range: $25-49.9 Million
Emp.: 45
Perforated Metal Sales
N.A.I.C.S.: 423510
Clare Gibson (Mgr-Stock Sls)

RMIG Nold GmbH   (1)
Am Katzloch 1, Rhein, 64589, Stockstadt, Germany
Tel.: (49) 61588210
Web Site: http://www.rmig.com
Sales Range: $50-74.9 Million
Emp.: 55
Perforated Metal Mfr & Whslr
N.A.I.C.S.: 423510

RMIG Perforacion, S.A.   (1)
Pl Igeltzera Barrikako Bide Kalea 4, 48610, Urduliz, Vizcaya, Spain
Tel.: (34) 946760061
Web Site: http://www.rmig.com
Sales Range: $25-49.9 Million
Emp.: 22
Perforated Metal Products Whslr
N.A.I.C.S.: 423510

RMIG S.A.S.   (1)
12 rue Andre Citroen, BP 314, ZA des Grandes Terres, Genas, Cedex, France
Tel.: (33) 472474343
Web Site: http://rmig.com
Sales Range: $25-49.9 Million
Emp.: 15
Perforated Metal Products Whslr
N.A.I.C.S.: 423510

RMIG Sp. z o.o.   (1)
Pokrzywno 4A, 61-315, Poznan, Poland
Tel.: (48) 618863270
Web Site: http://www.rmig.com
Sales Range: $50-74.9 Million
Emp.: 6
Perforated Metal Product Distr
N.A.I.C.S.: 423510
Anna Siwek (Mgr-Sls)

RMIG Sweden AB   (1)
Vasterangsvagen 1, 542 22, Mariestad, Sweden
Tel.: (46) 50168200
Sales Range: $25-49.9 Million
Emp.: 50
Perforated Metal Products Whslr
N.A.I.C.S.: 423510

RMIG bv   (1)
Kubus 120, 3364 DG, Sliedrecht, South Holland, Netherlands
Tel.: (31) 184491919
Web Site: http://www.rmperfo.nl
Sales Range: $50-74.9 Million
Emp.: 4
Perforated Metal Products Whslr
N.A.I.C.S.: 423510

RMIG nv/sa   (1)
Victor Bocquestraat 11/1, Industrieterrein Noord IV, 9300, Aalst, Belgium
Tel.: (32) 53767740
Web Site: http://www.rmig.com
Perforated Metal Products Whslr
N.A.I.C.S.: 423510

RM INFRASTRUCTURE INCOME PLC
6th Floor 125 London Wall, London, EC2Y 5AS, United Kingdom
Tel.: (44) 1316037060
RMII—(LSE)
Rev.: $10,479,150
Assets: $154,633,710
Liabilities: $23,572,065
Net Worth: $131,061,645
Earnings: $6,492,255
Fiscal Year-end: 12/31/22
Renting Services
N.A.I.C.S.: 522390

RM PLC
142B Park Drive Milton Park, Milton, Abingdon, OX14 4SE, Oxfordshire, United Kingdom
Tel.: (44) 1235645316   UK
Web Site: https://www.rmplc.com
Year Founded: 1973
RM—(LSE)
Rev.: $248,486,315
Assets: $177,929,982
Liabilities: $155,233,610
Net Worth: $22,696,372
Earnings: ($55,134,310)
Emp.: 1,831
Fiscal Year-end: 11/30/23
Educational Software Designer
N.A.I.C.S.: 334610
David Brooks (CEO)

Subsidiaries:

Lightbox Education   (1)
Sovereign House Stockport Road, Cheadle, SK8 2EA, United Kingdom   (100%)
Tel.: (44) 1614957800
Web Site: http://www.rmlightbox.com
Sales Range: $25-49.9 Million
Emp.: 250
Learning Solutions & Interactive Resources for Classroom & Home
N.A.I.C.S.: 611710

RM Education plc   (1)
142B Park Drive, Milton Park Milton, Abingdon, OX14 4SE, Oxfordshire, United Kingdom
Tel.: (44) 845 070 0300
Web Site: https://www.rm.com
Sales Range: $150-199.9 Million
Educational Support Services
N.A.I.C.S.: 611710
Jeremy Cooper (Mng Dir)

Subsidiary (Non-US):

RM Education Solutions India Pvt Ltd   (2)
Unit No 8A Carnival Techno Park, Technopark Kariyavattom PO, Trivandrum, 695 581, Kerala, India   (100%)
Tel.: (91) 471 233 5577
Web Site: https://www.rmesi.co.in
Emp.: 700
Educational Books & CD-Rom Publisher
N.A.I.C.S.: 513210

SpaceKraft Ltd   (1)
29 Saltaire Road Shipley, Shipley, BD18 3HH, West Yorkshire, United Kingdom
Tel.: (44) 1274581007
Emp.: 40
Sensor Product Mfr
N.A.I.C.S.: 334511

TTS Group Ltd   (1)
Building 1 Heyworth Road Off A611, Hucknall, Nottingham, NG15 6XJ, Nottinghamshire, United Kingdom
Tel.: (44) 8001381370
Sales Range: $25-49.9 Million
Emp.: 250
Educational Support Services
N.A.I.C.S.: 611710
Marie Barr (Head-Bus Dev)

RM2 INTERNATIONAL S.A.
5 rue de la Chapelle, L-1325, Luxembourg, Luxembourg
Tel.: (352) 27 44 96 53
Web Site: http://www.rm2.com
Year Founded: 2007
Rev.: $6,557,044
Assets: $66,779,926
Liabilities: $11,712,160
Net Worth: $55,067,766
Earnings: ($43,857,024)
Emp.: 93
Fiscal Year-end: 12/31/17
Pallet Products Mfr
N.A.I.C.S.: 321920
Jeff Blouvac (CFO)

RMA ENERGY LIMITED
Level 8/16 St Georges Terrace, Perth, 6000, WA, Australia

INTERNATIONAL PUBLIC

Tel.: (61) 862180200
Web Site: http://www.rmaenergy.com.au
Rev.: $5,321
Assets: $21,560
Liabilities: $619,967
Net Worth: ($598,407)
Earnings: ($120,656)
Emp.: 5
Fiscal Year-end: 12/31/18
Uranium & Coal Exploration Services
N.A.I.C.S.: 212115
Qin Weihong (Mng Dir)

RMA GLOBAL LIMITED
Level 1 112-114 Balmain Street, Cremorne, 3121, VIC, Australia
Tel.: (61) 416816758   AU
Web Site: https://www.rma-global.com
RMY—(ASX)
Rev.: $12,536,807
Assets: $3,326,439
Liabilities: $5,616,276
Net Worth: ($2,289,837)
Earnings: ($2,461,339)
Fiscal Year-end: 06/30/24
Digital Marketing Services
N.A.I.C.S.: 541870
Mark Armstrong (Bd of Dirs, Co-Founder & CEO)

RMB GROUP
PO Box 35193, Abu Dhabi, United Arab Emirates
Tel.: (971) 2 666 0109
Web Site: http://www.rmb-group.com
Year Founded: 2007
Holding Company
N.A.I.C.S.: 551112
Rashed Mahran Alblooshi (Chm)

RMB HOLDINGS LIMITED
Zero 01 Solution House 42 Gazelle Avenue Corporate Park South, Midrand, 1685, South Africa
Tel.: (27) 764448960
Web Site: https://www.rmh.co.za
RMH—(JSE)
Rev.: $42,916,670
Assets: $271,487,170
Liabilities: $4,707,870
Net Worth: $266,779,300
Earnings: $41,688,530
Emp.: 44,916
Fiscal Year-end: 03/31/22
Investment Holding Company; Financial Services
N.A.I.C.S.: 551112
Ellen J. Marais (Sec)

RMC SWITCHGEARS LIMITED
7 Km from Chaksu Khotkawda Road Village Badodiya Tehsil Chaksu Tonk Rd, Jaipur, 303901, Rajasthan, India
Tel.: (91) 1414400222
Web Site: https://www.rmcindia.in
Year Founded: 1994
540358—(BOM)
Rev.: $15,075,127
Assets: $13,975,241
Liabilities: $8,494,059
Net Worth: $5,481,182
Earnings: $1,407,673
Emp.: 120
Fiscal Year-end: 03/31/23
Electrical Equipment Mfr & Distr
N.A.I.C.S.: 335932
Ashok Kumar Agarwal (Chm & Mng Dir)

RMD WASSERSTRASSEN GMBH
Blutenburgstrasse 20, 80636, Munich, Germany
Tel.: (49) 8999222190   De

Web Site: http://www.rmd-wasserstrassen.de
Sales Range: $25-49.9 Million
Emp.: 125
Hydraulic Engineering Services
N.A.I.C.S.: 541330
Albrecht Schleich *(Co-Mng Dir)*

RMG LIMITED
Suite 5 Level 1 12-20 Railway Road, Subiaco, 6008, WA, Australia
Tel.: (61) 8 9388 6020 AU
Web Site: http://www.rmgltd.com.au
Rev.: $4,086
Assets: $1,570,750
Liabilities: $469,437
Net Worth: $1,101,313
Earnings: ($939,000)
Emp.: 2
Fiscal Year-end: 06/30/18
Mineral Exploration Services
N.A.I.C.S.: 212290
Ken Poon *(Sec)*

RMH HOLDINGS LIMITED
17-01/02 Paragon Office Tower 290 Orchard Road, Singapore, 238859, Singapore
Tel.: (65) 67332668 Ky
Web Site: https://www.rmhholdings.com.sg
8437—(HKG)
Rev.: $2,408,544
Assets: $3,141,710
Liabilities: $12,623,646
Net Worth: ($9,481,936)
Earnings: ($5,190,487)
Emp.: 30
Fiscal Year-end: 12/31/23
Health Care Srvices
N.A.I.C.S.: 621111
Teck Hiong Loh *(Chm & Compliance Officer)*

Subsidiaries:

Dermatology & Surgery Clinic (Orchard) Pte. Ltd. (1)
15-09 Paragon Office Tower 290 Orchard Road, Singapore, 238859, Singapore
Tel.: (65) 67332668
Dermatology Clinic Services
N.A.I.C.S.: 621111

Dermatology & Surgery Clinic (Shenton) Pte. Ltd. (1)
03-08/09 Ocean Financial Centre No 10 Collyer Quay, Singapore, 049315, Singapore
Tel.: (65) 66725001
Dermatology Clinic Services
N.A.I.C.S.: 621111

RMH LACHISH INDUSTRIES LTD.
Industrial Zone, PO Box 105, Sderot, 80100, Israel
Tel.: (972) 86891121
Web Site: https://www.rmhmixer.com
Year Founded: 1956
LHIS—(TAE)
Rev.: $50,850,117
Assets: $33,279,734
Liabilities: $16,480,177
Net Worth: $16,799,558
Earnings: $4,224,617
Emp.: 93
Fiscal Year-end: 12/31/23
Farm Machinery & Equipment Manufacturing
N.A.I.C.S.: 333111

RMK PROMET D.D. ZENICA
Kucukovici 2, 72000, Zenica, Bosnia & Herzegovina
Tel.: (387) 32243336
Web Site: http://www.rmkpromet.ba
Year Founded: 1977

RPRZRK2—(SARE)
Rev.: $584,181
Assets: $12,976,103
Liabilities: $787,704
Net Worth: $12,188,399
Earnings: $4,554
Emp.: 25
Fiscal Year-end: 12/31/20
Iron & Steel Products Whslr
N.A.I.C.S.: 331110
Mustafa Burek *(CEO)*

RMR SCIENCE TECHNOLOGIES, INC.
3355 Grandview Hwy Unit 2, Vancouver, V5M 1Z5, BC, Canada
Tel.: (604) 398-4314
Web Site: https://turnium.com
RMMRF—(OTCIQ)
Assets: $129,461
Liabilities: $123,292
Net Worth: $6,169
Earnings: ($229,413)
Fiscal Year-end: 09/30/19
Financial Management Services
N.A.I.C.S.: 522320
Rob Hutchison *(Pres & CEO)*

RMS MEZZANINE, A.S.
Templova 654/6, Stare Mesto, 110 00, Prague, Czech Republic
Tel.: (420) 734144504
Web Site: https://rmsmezzanine.cz
Year Founded: 1990
Sales Range: $1-9.9 Million
Financial Services
N.A.I.C.S.: 523999
Martin Bucko *(Chm-Supervisory Bd)*

RMU BANOVICI D.D.
ul Alije Izetbegovica broj 52, 75290, Banovici, Bosnia & Herzegovina
Tel.: (387) 3 587 1087
Web Site: http://www.rmub.ba
RMUBR—(SARE)
Rev.: $91,013,715
Assets: $153,634,824
Liabilities: $81,170,059
Net Worth: $72,464,765
Earnings: $423,586
Emp.: 2,786
Fiscal Year-end: 12/31/20
Coal Mining Services
N.A.I.C.S.: 212115

RMU KAMENGRAD D.D. SANSKI MOST
Gornji Kamengrad bb, 79260, Sanski Most, Bosnia & Herzegovina
Tel.: (387) 37 696 473
RMUKR—(SARE)
Sales Range: Less than $1 Million
Coal Mining Services
N.A.I.C.S.: 212115

RN2 TECHNOLOGIES CO., LTD.
11 Dongtansandan 9-gil, Hwaseong, 18487, Gyeonggi-do, Korea (South)
Tel.: (82) 313765400
Web Site: https://rn2.co.kr
Year Founded: 2002
148250—(KRS)
Rev.: $18,209,743
Assets: $47,148,152
Liabilities: $14,052,755
Net Worth: $33,095,397
Earnings: ($91,517)
Emp.: 179
Fiscal Year-end: 12/31/22
Ceramic Chips Mfr Used for Mobile Communication Equipment, Semiconductors & Medical Equipment
N.A.I.C.S.: 334419
Hyojong Lee *(Pres & CEO)*

RNB INDUSTRIES LIMITED
110 pankaj plaza plot no-10 sector-6, New Delhi, India
Tel.: (91) 9999 779 914
Web Site: http://www.rnbindustries.com
Year Founded: 2017
Sales Range: Less than $1 Million
Information Technology & Software Development Services
N.A.I.C.S.: 541512
Raj Kumar *(CEO)*

RNI NEGOCIOS IMOBILIARIOS S.A.
Tel.: (55) 982068463
Web Site: https://rni.com.br
Year Founded: 1991
RDNI3—(BRAZ)
Rev.: $71,646,554
Assets: $344,055,156
Liabilities: $261,619,557
Net Worth: $82,435,600
Earnings: ($34,856,723)
Emp.: 981
Fiscal Year-end: 12/31/23
Residential Building Construction Services
N.A.I.C.S.: 236117
Milton Jorge de Miranda Hage *(Vice Chm)*

RNK GLOBAL DEVELOPMENT ACQUISITION CORP.
Suite 101 26 Wen Hua East Road, Huilongguan, Changpin District, Beijing, 102208, China
Tel.: (86) 10 8405 3678 VG
Investment Services
N.A.I.C.S.: 523999
Remo Richli *(CFO)*

RO JEWELS LIMITED
810 Eighth Floore Addore Asspire Nr Gulbai tekra BRTS Stop, Panjrapole to University Road, Ahmedabad, 380015, Gujarat, India
Tel.: (91) 79221444429
Web Site: https://rojewels.co.in
Year Founded: 2018
543171—(BOM)
Jewellery Distr
N.A.I.C.S.: 458310
Shubham Bharatbhai Shah *(Mng Dir, CFO & Compliance Officer)*

ROAD ENVIRONMENT TECHNOLOGY CO., LTD.
3F Building 4 Zone E Phase VI Optics Valley Software Park, No 4 Software Park Middle Road East Lake High-tech Zone, Wuhan, 430075, Hubei, China
Tel.: (86) 2787206891
Web Site: https://www.road-group.com
Year Founded: 2006
688156—(SHG)
Rev.: $48,027,990
Assets: $167,992,629
Liabilities: $51,326,997
Net Worth: $116,665,633
Earnings: $3,640,024
Fiscal Year-end: 12/31/22
Application Development Services
N.A.I.C.S.: 541511
Guangming Ji *(Chm & Gen Mgr)*

ROAD KING INFRASTRUCTURE LIMITED
Suite 501 5th Floor Tower 6 The Gateway 9 Canton Road, Tsimshatsui, Kowloon, China (Hong Kong)
Tel.: (852) 29576800
Web Site: http://www.roadking.com.hk

1098—(HKG)
Rev.: $2,167,442,625
Assets: $11,475,302,558
Liabilities: $7,298,340,975
Net Worth: $4,176,961,583
Earnings: $58,473,030
Emp.: 4,374
Fiscal Year-end: 12/31/22
Toll Roads Investment, Development, Operation & Management Services; Infrastructure Projects Services
N.A.I.C.S.: 237310
Yuk Bing Ko *(Deputy Chm, CEO & Mng Dir)*

Subsidiaries:

Shanxi Lutong Yuci Highway Co., Ltd. (1)
269 Pingyang Rd, Taiyuan, Shanxi, China
Tel.: (86) 3517233409
Construction Services
N.A.I.C.S.: 237310

ROAD MARSHALL, INC.
194 Pandan Loop 05-08, Singapore, 128383, Singapore
Tel.: (65) 66848088 DE
Web Site: http://www.roadmarshall.com
Year Founded: 2015
RDMR—(OTCIQ)
Assets: $8,000
Liabilities: $1,076
Net Worth: $6,924
Earnings: ($23,701)
Fiscal Year-end: 09/30/21
Mobile Technology Services
N.A.I.C.S.: 334220
Engchoon Peh *(CEO)*

ROADHOUND ELECTRONICS PTY. LIMITED
14 Pendlebury Road, PO Box 460, Cardiff, 2285, NSW, Australia
Tel.: (61) 249493000
Web Site: http://www.roadhound.com.au
Electronics Product Repair Services
N.A.I.C.S.: 811210
Ben Sharma *(Mng Dir)*

ROADMAINT CO., LTD.
101 -1 -4 F No 9 Yard Dijin Road, Haidian District, Beijing, 100095, China
Tel.: (86) 1082364131
Web Site: http://www.roadmaint.com
Year Founded: 2007
603860—(SHG)
Rev.: $31,555,756
Assets: $121,938,537
Liabilities: $19,395,769
Net Worth: $102,542,769
Earnings: $5,398,043
Fiscal Year-end: 12/31/22
Road Equipment Mfr & Distr
N.A.I.C.S.: 333120
Cheng Ning *(Chm & Gen Mgr)*

ROADMAN INVESTMENTS CORP.
800-1199 West Hastings Street, Vancouver, V6E 3T5, BC, Canada
Tel.: (778) 772-1751
Web Site: https://rightseasoninvestments.com
Year Founded: 2007
LITT—(TSXV)
Rev.: $4,032
Assets: $4,319,212
Liabilities: $577,614
Net Worth: $3,741,598
Earnings: ($1,294,306)
Fiscal Year-end: 06/30/24
Investment Advisory Services
N.A.I.C.S.: 523940

ROADMAN INVESTMENTS CORP.

Roadman Investments Corp.—(Continued)
Luke Montaine *(CEO & Interim CFO)*

ROADPOST INC.
7A Taymall Avenue, Toronto, M8Z 3Y8, ON, Canada
Tel.: (416) 253-4539
Web Site: http://www.roadpost.com
Year Founded: 1991
Communication Service
N.A.I.C.S.: 517410
Morris Shawn *(Pres)*

Subsidiaries:

Fonebill LLC (1)
7251 W Lk Mead Blvd, Las Vegas, NV 89128-8351
Web Site: http://www.satworx.com
Satellite Telecommunications
N.A.I.C.S.: 517410
Sean McCready *(Dir-Mktg)*

Roadpost USA, Inc. (1)
4746 44th Ave SW Ste 201, Seattle, WA 98116-4476
Tel.: (888) 290-1616
Web Site: https://www.roadpost.com
Communication Service
N.A.I.C.S.: 517810
Morris Shawn *(Pres & CEO)*

ROADS NIGERIA PLC.
Bye Pass Road, PO Box 24, Sokoto, Nigeria
Tel.: (234) 60 235 736
ROADS—(NIGE)
Sales Range: $10-24.9 Million
Civil Engineering Services
N.A.I.C.S.: 237990
J. M. Dansu *(CEO & Mng Dir)*

ROADSIDE REAL ESTATE PLC
First Floor 115 Olympic Avenue Milton Park, Saint Mellons, Abingdon, OX14 4SA, Oxfordshire, United Kingdom
Tel.: (44) 2037574980 UK
Web Site: https://www.roadsideplc.com
BARK—(LSE)
Rev.: $13,981,801
Assets: $24,027,571
Liabilities: $34,482,015
Net Worth: ($10,454,444)
Earnings: ($12,917,348)
Emp.: 162
Fiscal Year-end: 07/31/22
Real Estate Manangement Services
N.A.I.C.S.: 531390
Charles Dickson *(Chm)*

ROADZEN TECHNOLOGIES PRIVATE LIMITED
17 Barakhamba Road Office 802-804, New Delhi, 110001, India
Tel.: (91) 11 4150 3530 In
Web Site: http://www.roadzen.io
Insurance Services
N.A.I.C.S.: 524298
Mohit Pasricha *(CFO)*

Subsidiaries:

Roadzen Assistance India Private Limited (1)
A-26 Sector 16, Noida, 201301, Uttar Pradesh, India
Tel.: (91) 120 665 6600
General Assistance Services
N.A.I.C.S.: 524298

ROAN HOLDINGS GROUP CO., LTD.
No 1 Building 5 Bailiantan Road, Yuhang District, Hangzhou, 311100, Zhejiang, China
Tel.: (86) 57186621775 VG
Year Founded: 2014

RAHGF—(OTCIQ)
Rev.: $793,291
Assets: $66,642,978
Liabilities: $11,693,298
Net Worth: $54,949,680
Earnings: $371,091
Emp.: 35
Fiscal Year-end: 12/31/21
Holding Company;Investment Services
N.A.I.C.S.: 551112
Junfeng Wang *(Chm)*

ROBBINS PARKING SERVICE
1102 Fort Street, Victoria, V8V 3K8, BC, Canada
Tel.: (250) 382-4411
Web Site: https://www.robbinsparking.com
Year Founded: 1958
Emp.: 120
Parking Lot Services
N.A.I.C.S.: 812930
Paul T. Clough *(Chm & CEO)*

ROBERT BERNARD PNEUS ET MECANIQUE
765 Rue Principale, Abbotsford, J0E 1A0, QC, Canada
Tel.: (450) 379-5757
Web Site: http://www.robertbernard.com
Year Founded: 1950
Emp.: 700
Holding Company; Tire Retailer
N.A.I.C.S.: 551112

Subsidiaries:

Groupe Robert Inc. (1)
500 Route 112, Rougemont, J0L 1M0, QC, Canada
Tel.: (450) 469-3153
Web Site: http://www.robert.ca
Logistics Services; Owned 37.5% by Gestion Claude Robert Inc., 37.5% by Placements Robert Bernard Ltee. & 25% by Fonds de Solidrite des Travailleurs du Quebec
N.A.I.C.S.: 541614

Subsidiary (Domestic):

Rollex Transportation Inc (2)
910 boul Lionel-Boulet, Varennes, J3X 1P7, QC, Canada
Tel.: (450) 652-4482
Web Site: http://www.rollex.ca
Waste Transportation Services
N.A.I.C.S.: 562211

ROBERT BOSCH GMBH
Robert-Bosch-Platz 1, 70839, Gerlingen, Germany
Tel.: (49) 7118110 De
Web Site: http://www.bosch.com
Year Founded: 1886
Rev.: $87,036,639,060
Assets: $99,701,135,800
Liabilities: $53,698,406,860
Net Worth: $46,002,728,940
Earnings: $2,306,911,600
Emp.: 400,000
Fiscal Year-end: 12/31/19
Automotive Components, Industrial Machinery & Household Appliance Marketer, Mfr & Whslr
N.A.I.C.S.: 336390
Peter Tyroller *(Member-Mgmt Bd)*

Subsidiaries:

AIG Planungs- und Ingenieurgesellschaft mbH (1)
Mittlerer Pfad 2, 70499, Stuttgart, Germany
Tel.: (49) 71199884100
Web Site: http://www.aig-mbh.com
Engineering Services
N.A.I.C.S.: 541330

AJNS New Media GmbH (1)
Storkower Str 115, 10407, Berlin, Germany

Tel.: (49) 3069518291
Web Site: http://www.kitchenstories.com
Restaurant Services
N.A.I.C.S.: 722511

ARESI S.p.A. (1)
Via dei Murari 12, 24041, Brembate di Sopra, Italy
Tel.: (39) 03541972
Automobile Component Distr
N.A.I.C.S.: 423120

Ampack GmbH (1)
Lechfeldgraben 7, 86343, Konigsbrunn, Germany
Tel.: (49) 823160050
Web Site: http://www.boschpackaging.com
Emp.: 350
Industrial Machinery Mfr
N.A.I.C.S.: 333998

Australian Industrial Abrasives Pty. Ltd. (1)
2-4 Union Circuit, Yatala, 4207, QLD, Australia
Tel.: (61) 1300551006
Automobile Component Distr
N.A.I.C.S.: 423120

BSH Drives & Pumps s.r.o. (1)
Tovarenska 2, 07190, Michalovce, Slovakia
Tel.: (421) 566417404
Motor Pump Mfr
N.A.I.C.S.: 333996

BSH Electrocasnice S.R.L. (1)
Sos Bucuresti-Ploiesti no 19-21 Baneasa Center etj 1 sector 1, Bucharest, Romania
Tel.: (40) 212039778
Home Appliance Mfr
N.A.I.C.S.: 335220

BSH Electrodomesticos Espana, S.A. (1)
Ronda del Canal Imperial de Aragon 18-20 Pla-Za Business Park, 50197, Zaragoza, Spain
Tel.: (34) 976578000
Home Appliance Mfr
N.A.I.C.S.: 335220

BSH Electrodomesticos S.A.C. (1)
Av Faucett 3551, Callao, Peru
Tel.: (51) 15941800
Web Site: http://www.bosch-home.pe
Home Appliance Mfr
N.A.I.C.S.: 335220

BSH Ev Aletleri Sanayi ve Ticaret A.S. (1)
Balkan Caddesi No 51 Fatih Sultan Mehmet Mahallesi, Umraniye, Istanbul, Turkiye
Tel.: (90) 2165289000
Home Appliance Mfr
N.A.I.C.S.: 335220

BSH Hausgerate AG (1)
Fahrweldstrasse 80, 8954, Geroldswil, Switzerland
Tel.: (41) 848888200
Web Site: http://www.bosch-home.com
Home Appliance Mfr
N.A.I.C.S.: 335220

BSH Hausgerate Gesellschaft mbH (1)
Quellenstrasse 2 A, 1100, Vienna, Austria
Tel.: (43) 1605750
Home Appliance Mfr
N.A.I.C.S.: 335220

BSH Hausgerate GmbH (1)
Carl-Wery-Strasse 34, 81739, Munich, Germany (100%)
Tel.: (49) 89459001
Web Site: http://www.bsh-group.de
Rev.: $13,195,750,960
Assets: $10,598,080,080
Liabilities: $7,831,247,760
Net Worth: $2,766,832,320
Earnings: $517,912,080
Emp.: 53,211
Fiscal Year-end: 12/31/2014
Electrical Household Appliances & Entertainment Electronics Mfr & Distr
N.A.I.C.S.: 335220
Elmar Freund *(Vice Chm-Supervisory Bd)*

Subsidiary (Non-US):

BSH Continental Eletrodomesticos Ltda. (2)

INTERNATIONAL PUBLIC

Rua Sarapui 164, CEP 03123 900, Mooca, Sao Paulo, Brazil
Tel.: (55) 1121233000
Web Site: http://www.bsh-group.com
Sales Range: $200-249.9 Million
Emp.: 2,700
Gas & Electric Ovens & Stoves, Cooking Hoods, Washing Machines, Dishwashers, Refrigerators, Upright Freezers & Microwaves Mfr
N.A.I.C.S.: 335220

Subsidiary (US):

BSH Home Appliances Corporation (2)
1901 Main St Ste 600, Irvine, CA 92614
Tel.: (949) 440-7100
Web Site: http://www.thermador.com
Sales Range: $500-549.9 Million
Home Appliance Mfr & Distr
N.A.I.C.S.: 335220
Christofer von Nagel *(Pres & CEO)*

Subsidiary (Domestic):

Gaggenau Hausgerate GmbH (2)
Carl-Wery-Str 34, 81739, Munich, Germany
Tel.: (49) 8920355366
Web Site: http://www.gaggenau.com
Mfr of Kitchen Appliances
N.A.I.C.S.: 335220

Subsidiary (Non-US):

Neff UK (2)
Grand Union House Old Wolverton Road, Wolverton, Milton Keynes, MK12 5PT, United Kingdom
Tel.: (44) 3448928989
Web Site: http://www.neff-home.com
Sales Range: $25-49.9 Million
Mfr of Household Appliances
N.A.I.C.S.: 335220

BSH Haztartasi Keszulek Kereskedelmi Kft. (1)
Arpad fejedelem utja 26-28, 1023, Budapest, Hungary
Tel.: (36) 680200201
Home Appliance Mfr
N.A.I.C.S.: 335220

BSH Hisni Aparati d.o.o. (1)
Savinjska cesta 30, Nazarje, 3331, Velenje, Slovenia
Tel.: (386) 38398222
Home Appliance Mfr
N.A.I.C.S.: 335220

BSH Home Appliances (Pty.) Ltd. (1)
15th Road, Midrand, Johannesburg, South Africa
Tel.: (27) 112657800
Home Appliance Mfr
N.A.I.C.S.: 335220

BSH Home Appliances AB (1)
Landsvagen 32, Sundbyberg, 169 29, Solna, Sweden
Tel.: (46) 87341200
Home Appliance Mfr
N.A.I.C.S.: 335220

BSH Home Appliances Co., Ltd. (1)
No 1 Century Avenue, Chuzhou, 239000, Anhui, China
Tel.: (86) 5503899998
Home Appliance Mfr
N.A.I.C.S.: 335220

BSH Home Appliances FZE (1)
PO Box 17312, Jebel Ali, Dubai, United Arab Emirates
Tel.: (971) 48030400
Home Appliance Mfr
N.A.I.C.S.: 335220

BSH Home Appliances Holding (China) Co., Ltd. (1)
21F Zhongnan Mansion No 129 Zhongshan Road, Nanjing, 210005, Jiangsu, China
Tel.: (86) 2584701918
Home Appliance Mfr
N.A.I.C.S.: 335220

BSH Home Appliances Ltd. (1)
Grand Union House Old Wolverton Road, Milton Keynes, MK12 5PT, United Kingdom
Tel.: (44) 1908328500
Home Appliance Mfr

AND PRIVATE COMPANIES — ROBERT BOSCH GMBH

N.A.I.C.S.: 335220

BSH Home Appliances Ltd. (1)
Unit 1 & 2 3/F North Block Skyway House 3 Sham Mong Road Tai Kok Tsui, Kowloon, China (Hong Kong)
Tel.: (852) 25656161
Home Appliance Mfr
N.A.I.C.S.: 335220

BSH Home Appliances Ltd. (1)
Bet Maskit 25 Maskit St, Herzliya Pituach, Israel
Tel.: (972) 99730000
Home Appliance Mfr
N.A.I.C.S.: 335220

BSH Home Appliances Ltd. (1)
Ital Thai Tower 2nd Floor 2034/31-39 New Petchburi Road, Bangkapi Huay Kwang, Bangkok, Thailand
Tel.: (66) 27697900
Home Appliance Mfr
N.A.I.C.S.: 335220

BSH Home Appliances Ltd. (1)
Smales Farm Business Park Air New Zealand Building Level 3 74 Taharoto, Takapuna, Auckland, New Zealand
Tel.: (64) 94770492
Home Appliance Mfr
N.A.I.C.S.: 335220

BSH Home Appliances Pte. Ltd. (1)
38C Jalan Pemimpin 01-01, Singapore, 577180, Singapore
Tel.: (65) 67515000
Web Site: http://www.bosch-home.com.sg
Home Appliance Mfr
N.A.I.C.S.: 335220
Daniel Lum (Mgr-Brand & Product)

BSH Home Appliances Pty. Ltd. (1)
1555 Centre Road, Clayton, 3168, VIC, Australia
Tel.: (61) 385511100
Web Site: http://www.bosch-home.com.au
Home Appliance Mfr
N.A.I.C.S.: 335220

BSH Home Appliances Sdn. Bhd. (1)
Unit No 2-1 Level 2 CP Tower No 11 Jalan 16/11 Pusat Dagang Seksyen 16, 46350, Petaling Jaya, Selangor, Malaysia
Tel.: (60) 379509338
Web Site: http://www.bosch-home.com.my
Home Appliance Mfr
N.A.I.C.S.: 335220
Gary Te (CEO)

BSH Household Appliances Manufacturing Private Limited (1)
Arena House 2nd Floor Main Building Plot No 103 Road No 12 MIDC, Andheri East, Mumbai, 400093, India
Tel.: (91) 2267518000
Home Appliance Mfr
N.A.I.C.S.: 335220

BSH Huishoudapparaten B.V. (1)
Inspiration House 20 20 Taurusavenue 36, 2132 LS, Hoofddorp, Netherlands
Tel.: (31) 884244444
Home Appliance Mfr
N.A.I.C.S.: 335220

BSH Hvidevarer A/S (1)
Telegrafvej 4, 2750, Ballerup, Denmark
Tel.: (45) 44898080
Home Appliance Mfr
N.A.I.C.S.: 335220

BSH Kodinkoneet Oy (1)
PL 123, 00201, Helsinki, Finland
Tel.: (358) 207510700
Home Appliance Mfr
N.A.I.C.S.: 335220

BSH Sprzet Gospodarstwa Domowego Sp. z o.o. (1)
1 Service Salon Al Jerozolimskie 183, 02-222, Warsaw, Poland
Tel.: (48) 422715555
Home Appliance Mfr
N.A.I.C.S.: 335220

Bosch (China) Investment Ltd. (1)
13th Floor Building E2 Area E Tianfu Software Park No 1268, Middle Section of Tianfu Avenue, Chengdu, China
Tel.: (86) 4008310669
Web Site: http://www.bosch.com.cn
Automobile Component Distr
N.A.I.C.S.: 423120

Bosch (Zhuhai) Security Systems Co., Ltd. (1)
20 Jichang North Road Qingwan Ind Zone, Sanzao Town, Zhuhai, 519040, China
Tel.: (86) 7567633888
Automobile Component Distr
N.A.I.C.S.: 423120

Bosch Access Systems GmbH (1)
Charlottenburger Allee 50, Aachen, 52068, Germany
Tel.: (49) 24151542955
Automobile Component Distr
N.A.I.C.S.: 423120

Bosch BKK (1)
Kruppstrasse 19, 70469, Stuttgart, Germany (100%)
Tel.: (49) 711250880
Web Site: http://www.bosch-bkk.de
Sales Range: $200-249.9 Million
Emp.: 350
Health Insurance
N.A.I.C.S.: 524113

Bosch Chassis Systems India Ltd. (1)
Godrej Millennium 3rd Floor 9 Koregaon Park, 411 001, Pune, India
Tel.: (91) 20 3061 6308
Automobile Component Distr
N.A.I.C.S.: 423120
Neha Parekh (Asst Mgr-HR)

Bosch Communication Center Magdeburg GmbH (1)
Otto-von-Guericke-Strasse 13, 39104, Magdeburg, Saxony-Anhalt, Germany
Tel.: (49) 711 400 40990
Automobile Component Distr
N.A.I.C.S.: 423120
Gordon Gissy (Engr-Sys)

Bosch Communication Center S.R.L. (1)
AGN Business Centre Calea Aradului 8, 300088, Timisoara, Romania
Tel.: (40) 256200000
Web Site: http://www.boschcommunicationcenter.ro
Business Process Outsourcing Services
N.A.I.C.S.: 561110
Alina Cotescu (Project Mgr)

Bosch Communications Center B.V. (1)
Mercator 2 Toernooiveld 300, 6525 EC, Nijmegen, Netherlands
Tel.: (31) 243511300
Business Process Outsourcing Services
N.A.I.C.S.: 561110

Bosch Connected Devices and Solutions GmbH (1)
Ludwig-Erhard-Strasse 2, 72760, Reutlingen, Germany
Tel.: (49) 71213539513
Web Site: http://www.bosch-connectivity.com
Semiconductor Devices Mfr
N.A.I.C.S.: 334413
Marco Lammer (Chm-Mgmt Bd)

Bosch Diesel s.r.o. (1)
Pavov 121, 586 06, Jihlava, Czech Republic
Tel.: (420) 567581111
Web Site: http://www.bosch.cz
Valve Mfr
N.A.I.C.S.: 332911

Bosch Electrical Drives Co., Ltd. (1)
115 Geumhosunmal-gil Bugang-myon, Sejong, 339-942, Korea (South)
Tel.: (82) 442796777
Web Site: http://www.bosch-ed.co.kr
Automotive Components Mfr
N.A.I.C.S.: 336390

Bosch Electrical Drives India Private Ltd. (1)
Plot A-20/2 SIPCOT Industrial Growth Centre Sriperumbadur Taluk, Kancheepuram District, Oragadam, 602105, India
Tel.: (91) 4467411000

Consumer Goods Distr
N.A.I.C.S.: 423620

Bosch Electronic Service Kft. (1)
Korhankozi utca 10, Kecskemet, 6000, Hungary
Tel.: (36) 76889703
Web Site: http://www.bosch.hu
Emp.: 50
Automobile Component Distr
N.A.I.C.S.: 423120
Attila Fodor (Gen Mgr)

Bosch Emission Systems GmbH & Co. KG (1)
Heilbronnerstrasse 362, 70469, Stuttgart, Germany
Tel.: (49) 7118110
Web Site: http://www.besg.com
Engineering Services
N.A.I.C.S.: 541330

Bosch Energy and Building Solutions GmbH (1)
Ingersheimer Strasse 16, 70499, Stuttgart, Germany
Tel.: (49) 71136530
Web Site: http://www.boschbuildingsolutions.com
Real Estate Manangement Services
N.A.I.C.S.: 531190

Bosch Energy and Building Solutions Italy S.r.l. (1)
Societa Unipersonale Via Marco Antonio Colonna 35, 20149, Milan, Italy
Tel.: (39) 0236961
Web Site: http://www.boschbuildingsolutions.com
Heating & Cooling Equipment Mfr
N.A.I.C.S.: 333414

Bosch Financial Software GmbH (1)
Ziegelei 5, 88090, Immenstaad, Germany
Tel.: (49) 7545202400
Web Site: http://www.bosch-si.com
Software Development Services
N.A.I.C.S.: 541511
Thomas Cotic (Member-Mgmt Bd)

Bosch Fren Sistemleri Sanayi ve Ticaret A.S. (1)
Sari Cad No 26, Fethiye OSB Mah Nilufer, 16372, Bursa, Turkiye
Tel.: (90) 2242706700
Web Site: https://www.boschfren.com.tr
Automobile Parts Mfr
N.A.I.C.S.: 336390
Daniel Archip Werner Korioth (Chm)

Bosch General Aviation Technology GmbH (1)
Gollnergasse 15-17, 1030, Vienna, Austria
Tel.: (43) 1797224300
Web Site: http://www.bosch-aviation.com
Aircraft Components Mfr
N.A.I.C.S.: 334511
Miorini Hanno (Mng Dir)

Bosch HUAYU Steering Systems (Nanjing) Co., Ltd. (1)
No 1 Lianxi Road Nanjing Economic and Technology Development Zone, Nanjing, 210033, Jiangsu, China
Tel.: (86) 2566815881
Automotive Steering System Mfr
N.A.I.C.S.: 336330

Bosch HUAYU Steering Systems (Wuhan) Co., Ltd. (1)
No 66 General Motors Avenue Jiangxia DVZ, Wuhan, 430208, Hubei, China
Tel.: (86) 2759106600
Automotive Steering System Mfr
N.A.I.C.S.: 336330

Bosch HUAYU Steering Systems (Yantai) Co., Ltd. (1)
No 1000 Yongda Road, Fushan, Yantai, 265500, Shangdong, China
Tel.: (86) 5353803055
Automotive Steering System Mfr
N.A.I.C.S.: 336330

Bosch HUAYU Steering Systems Co., Ltd. (1)
No 2001 Yongsheng Road, Jiading Industrial Development Zone, Shanghai, 201821, China
Tel.: (86) 2167079000

Web Site: http://www.boschhuayu-steering.com
Automotive Steering System Mfr
N.A.I.C.S.: 336330
Angelo Marchio (Mgr-Platform Dev)

Bosch Healthcare Solutions GmbH (1)
Stuttgarter Str 130, 71332, Waiblingen, Germany
Tel.: (49) 71181158277
Heatlcare Services
N.A.I.C.S.: 621610
Martin Schulz (Sr Project Mgr)

Bosch Industriekessel Austria GmbH (1)
Haldenweg 7, 5500, Bischofshofen, Austria
Tel.: (43) 646225270
Web Site: http://www.bosch.at
Emp.: 60
Boiler Mfr
N.A.I.C.S.: 333414
Alexandra Bichlmayer (Plant Mgr)

Bosch Industriekessel GmbH (1)
Nurnberger Strasse 73, 91710, Gunzenhausen, Germany
Tel.: (49) 9831560
Web Site: http://www.bosch-industrial.com
Boiler System Mfr
N.A.I.C.S.: 333414
Thomas Spinner (Chm)

Bosch K.K. (1)
6-7 Shibuya 3-chome, Shibuya-ku, Tokyo, 150-8360, Japan (100%)
Tel.: (81) 334001551
Web Site: http://www.bosch.co.jp
Sales Range: $300-349.9 Million
Emp.: 700
Imports, Sells & Supports Automotive Aftermarket Equipment, Workshop Testing Equipment, Power Tools & Security Systems.
N.A.I.C.S.: 336340
Klaus Meder (Pres & Member-Mgmt Bd)

Plant (Domestic):

Bosch Corporation - Higashimatsuyama Plant (2)
13-26 Yakyu-cho 3-chome, Higashimatsuyama-shi, Saitama, 355-8603, Japan
Tel.: (81) 493221551
Automotive Components Mfr
N.A.I.C.S.: 336390

Bosch Corporation - Musashi Plant (2)
1464-4 Tsukinowa, Namegawa-machi Hikigun, Saitama, 355-0813, Japan
Tel.: (81) 493566200
Automotive Components Mfr
N.A.I.C.S.: 336390

Bosch Corporation - Ota Plant (2)
3000 Serada-cho, Ota, Gunma, 370-0426, Japan
Tel.: (81) 276525361
Automotive Components Mfr
N.A.I.C.S.: 336390

Bosch Corporation - Tochigi Plant (2)
1588-1 Kita-akada, Nasushiobara-shi, Tochigi, 329-2741, Japan
Tel.: (81) 287374601
Automotive Components Mfr
N.A.I.C.S.: 336390

Bosch Corporation - Yorii Plant (2)
1744-1 Oaza-Orihara, Yorii-machi Osatogun, Saitama, 369-1234, Japan
Tel.: (81) 485811231
Automotive Components Mfr
N.A.I.C.S.: 336390

Subsidiary (Domestic):

Bosch Engineering K.K. (2)
2-3-5 Minatomirai Queen's Tower C18 floor, Nishi-ku, Yokohama, 220-6218, Kanagawa, Japan
Tel.: (81) 456505610
Web Site: http://www.bosch-engineering.jp
Automobile Component Distr
N.A.I.C.S.: 423120

Bosch KWK Systeme GmbH (1)

ROBERT BOSCH GMBH

Robert Bosch GmbH—(Continued)
Justus-Kilian-Strasse 29-33, Lollar, 35457,
Hessen, Germany
Tel.: (49) 640691030
Web Site: http://www.bosch-kwk.de
Heating Product Mfr
N.A.I.C.S.: 335220
Ralf Klein *(Chm-Exec Bd)*

Bosch Laser Equipment (Dongguan) Limited
Fuzhu 4th St Zhangyang Village Z, Dongguan, 523636, China
Tel.: (86) 76986907088
Automobile Parts Mfr
N.A.I.C.S.: 336390
Edward Liao *(Sr Project Mgr)*

Bosch Limited (1)
Hosur Rd Adugodi, PO Box 3000, Bengaluru, 560 030, India (51%)
Tel.: (91) 8022220088
Web Site: http://www.boschindia.com
Sales Range: $1-4.9 Billion
Emp.: 19,400
Mfr & Distr of Diesel Engine Equipment, Spark Plugs & Other Automotive Equipment
N.A.I.C.S.: 336340
Soumitra Bhattacharya *(Co-Mng Dir & Member-Mgmt Bd)*

Bosch Management Support GmbH (1)
Daimlerstrasse 6, 71229, Leonberg, Germany
Tel.: (49) 71181137962
Automobile Parts Distr
N.A.I.C.S.: 423120

Bosch Packaging Services AG (1)
Industriestrasse 8, 8222, Beringen, Switzerland
Tel.: (41) 586741000
Automobile Parts Distr
N.A.I.C.S.: 423120

Bosch Packaging Services S.a.r.l. (1)
31 route de la Wantzenau, 67800, Hoenheim, France
Tel.: (33) 388209782
Web Site: http://www.bosch.com
Emp.: 10
Packaging Services
N.A.I.C.S.: 561910
Suhro Patrick *(Gen Mgr)*

Bosch Packaging Systems GmbH (1)
Fohrenbachstr 14, 73630, Remshalden, Germany
Tel.: (49) 715170070
Packaging Products Mfr
N.A.I.C.S.: 326112

Bosch Pensionsfonds AG (1)
Heidehofstr 31, 70184, Stuttgart, Germany
Tel.: (49) 71181146000
Pension Fund Management Services
N.A.I.C.S.: 523940

Bosch Power Tec GmbH (1)
Herrenberger Str 130, Boblingen, 71034, Germany
Tel.: (49) 711 8110
Sales Range: $50-74.9 Million
Emp.: 60
Developer of Power Electronics for Renewable Energy
N.A.I.C.S.: 334419

Subsidiary (Domestic):

voltwerk electronics GmbH (2)
Anckelmannsplatz 1, 20537, Hamburg, Germany
Tel.: (49) 40 27142 2800
Web Site: http://www.voltwerk.com
Sales Range: $75-99.9 Million
Photovoltaic Software Development & Electronic Components Mfr
N.A.I.C.S.: 334513

Bosch Power Tools Engineering Sdn. Bhd.
Bayan Lepas Free Industrial Zone 9Â, Bayan Lepas, Penang, Malaysia
Tel.: (60) 46382888
Mechanical Equipment Mfr
N.A.I.C.S.: 333613

Bosch Rexroth Ghana Ltd. (1)
No 3 Airport Road Airforce, Takoradi, Ghana
Tel.: (233) 540123766
Hydraulic Valve & Pump Mfr
N.A.I.C.S.: 332912

Bosch Rexroth Kenya Ltd. (1)
Unit A4 Kampala Road, Ashray Industrial Park, Nairobi, Kenya
Tel.: (254) 207606700
Hydraulic Valve & Pump Mfr
N.A.I.C.S.: 332912

Bosch Rexroth Morocco S.A.R.L. (1)
Lot n 121 Ouled Salah, CFCIM Ouled Salah Industrial Park, Casablanca, Morocco
Tel.: (212) 522012692
Hydraulic Components Mfr
N.A.I.C.S.: 333996

Bosch Sanayi ve Ticaret A.S. (1)
Organize Sanayi BolgesiÂ Yesil Cad No 27, Bursa, 16066, Turkiye
Tel.: (90) 2242192500
Mechanical Equipment Mfr
N.A.I.C.S.: 333613

Bosch Security Systems, S.A. (1)
Av Infante D Henrique Lote 2E-3E, 1800-220, Lisbon, Portugal
Tel.: (351) 218500000
Electrical & Electronic Product Mfr
N.A.I.C.S.: 335999

Bosch Sensortec GmbH (1)
Gerhard-Kindler-Strasse 9, 72770, Reutlingen, Germany
Tel.: (49) 71213535900
Mobile Sensor Mfr
N.A.I.C.S.: 334413
Stefan Finkbeiner *(Chm)*

Bosch Service Solutions Corporation (1)
Kitano 3-4-1, Niiza, Saitama, Japan
Tel.: (81) 484583500
Electrical & Electronic Equipment Mfr
N.A.I.C.S.: 335999

Bosch Service Solutions GmbH (1)
Lahnstrasse 34-40, 60326, Frankfurt am Main, Germany
Tel.: (49) 39159081988
Web Site: http://www.boschservicesolutions.com
All Telecommunication Services
N.A.I.C.S.: 517810

Bosch Service Solutions Ltd. (1)
The Plaza 100 Old Hall Street, Liverpool, L3 9QJ, United Kingdom
Tel.: (44) 1512373503
Business Outsourcing Services
N.A.I.C.S.: 541611
John Milburn *(Gen Mgr)*

Bosch Service Solutions Magdeburg GmbH (1)
Otto-von-Guericke-Strasse 13, 39104, Magdeburg, Germany
Tel.: (49) 39159081988
All Telecommunication Services
N.A.I.C.S.: 517810

Bosch Service Solutions S.R.L. (1)
Bd Take Lonescu nr 46B ISHO Offices Building A, Timis, 300043, Timisoara, Romania
Tel.: (40) 256200000
Business Outsourcing Services
N.A.I.C.S.: 541611

Bosch Service Solutions, Inc. (1)
29th Floor Fort Legend Tower 3rd Avenue corner 31st Street, Bonifacio GlobalÂ, 1634, Taguig, Philippines
Tel.: (63) 22388400
Internet Communication Services
N.A.I.C.S.: 517810

Bosch Service Solutions, S.A.U. (1)
Avenida de Bruselas 15, 28108, Alcobendas, Madrid, Spain
Tel.: (34) 986900800
Business Outsourcing Services
N.A.I.C.S.: 541611

Bosch Sicherheitssysteme Engineering GmbH (1)
Nordring 69, 90409, Nuremberg, Germany
Tel.: (49) 911934560
Internet Communication Services
N.A.I.C.S.: 517810

Bosch Sicherheitssysteme Montage und Service GmbH (1)
Carl-Miele-Strasse 12, Amt Wachsenburg, 99334, Ichtershausen, Germany
Tel.: (49) 3620277070
Security Device Mfr
N.A.I.C.S.: 334290
Dirk Kutschki *(Gen Mgr)*

Bosch Silicon Trading GmbH (1)
Haarbergstrasse 71Â, 99097, Erfurt, Germany
Tel.: (49) 3616011220
Mechanical Equipment Distr
N.A.I.C.S.: 423840
Matthias Drinkmann *(Gen Mgr)*

Bosch SoftTec GmbH (1)
Phoenixstrasse 3Â, 31137, Hildesheim, Germany
Software Development Services
N.A.I.C.S.: 541511
Torsten Mlasko *(Member-Mgmt Bd)*

Bosch Software Innovations GmbH (1)
Schoneberger Ufer 89-91, 10785, Berlin, Germany
Tel.: (49) 307261120
Software Development Services
N.A.I.C.S.: 541511
Rainer Kallenbach *(Chm-Mgmt Bd)*

Bosch Solar Energy AG (1)
August Broemel Strasse 6, 99310, Arnstadt, Germany
Solar Product Mfr
N.A.I.C.S.: 334413

Subsidiary (Domestic):

Bosch Solarthermie GmbH (2)
Prozessionsweg 10, 48493, Wettringen, Germany
Tel.: (49) 255793990
Heating & Cooling System Mfr
N.A.I.C.S.: 333415
Uwe Glock *(Chm-Mgmt Bd)*

Bosch Solar Services GmbH (1)
August-Broemel-Strasse 6, 99310, Arnstadt, Germany
Tel.: (49) 36286643100
Web Site: http://www.bosch-solarenergy.de
Solar Energy Services
N.A.I.C.S.: 221114

Bosch Technology Licensing Administration GmbH (1)
Robert-Bosch-Platz 1, 70839, Gerlingen, Germany
Tel.: (49) 7118110
Business Management Services
N.A.I.C.S.: 561110

Bosch Trading (Shanghai) Co., Ltd. (1)
333 Fuquan North Road, Changning, Shanghai, 200050, China
Tel.: (86) 21 2218 1111
Web Site: http://www.bosch.com
Mechanical Equipment Distr
N.A.I.C.S.: 423840
Wang Guoying *(Area Mgr)*

Bosch Transmission Technology B.V. (1)
Dr Hub van Doorneweg 120, PO Box 500, 5000 AMÂ, Tilburg, Netherlands
Tel.: (31) 134640333
Emp.: 900
Mechanical Equipment Mfr
N.A.I.C.S.: 333613

Bosch Vietnam Co., Ltd. (1)
14th Floor Duc House 33 Le Duan, Ben Nghe Ward District 1, Ho Chi Minh City, Vietnam
Tel.: (84) 862583690
Web Site: http://www.bosch.com.vn
Emp.: 1,600
Mechanical Equipment Mfr
N.A.I.C.S.: 333613

Bsh Elettrodomestici S.P.A. (1)
Via M Nizzoli 1, 20147, Milan, Italy

Tel.: (39) 02413361
Industrial Automotive Equipment Mfr
N.A.I.C.S.: 335314

Buderus Guss GmbH (1)
Buderusstrasse 26, Breidenbach, 35236, Hessen, Germany
Tel.: (49) 6465620
Web Site: http://www.buderus-guss.de
Mechanical Equipment Mfr
N.A.I.C.S.: 333613
Ute Abel *(Member-Mgmt Bd)*

Buderus Heiztechnik AG (1)
Netzibodenstrasse 36Â, 4133, Pratteln, Switzerland
Heating Equipment Distr
N.A.I.C.S.: 423720

Buderus Immobilien GmbH (1)
Bannstr 34 - 36, 35576, Wetzlar, Germany
Real Estate Development Services
N.A.I.C.S.: 531210

Centro Studi Componenti per Veicoli S.P.A. (1)
Zona Industriale - Via delleÂ Ortensie 19, Modugno, 70026, Bari, Italy
Tel.: (39) 0805873640
Mechanical Equipment Mfr
N.A.I.C.S.: 333613
Manuel Tavani *(Mgr-Section)*

Circular Economy Solutions GmbH (1)
Wilhelm-Lambrecht-Str 6, 37079, Gottingen, Germany
Tel.: (49) 55150080670
Web Site: http://www.c-eco.com
Core Management Services
N.A.I.C.S.: 561210

Constructa-Neff Vertriebs-GmbH (1)
Carl-Wery-Strasse 34, 81739, Munich, Germany
Tel.: (49) 89459004
Web Site: http://www.neff-home.com
Home Appliance Mfr
N.A.I.C.S.: 335220

DAA Deutsche Auftragsagentur GmbH (1)
Holstentwiete 15, 22763, Hamburg, Germany
Tel.: (49) 40209316970
Web Site: http://www.daa.net
Photovoltaic Heating System Services
N.A.I.C.S.: 221114

Digicontrol Benelux B.V. (1)
Watermanstraat 29a, Apeldoorn, Netherlands
Tel.: (31) 553680530
Building Automation Construction Services
N.A.I.C.S.: 238220

Drivelog GmbH (1)
Fritz-Muller-Str 100, 73730, Esslingen am Neckar, Germany
Tel.: (49) 7112195110
Web Site: http://www.drivelog.de
Car Workshop Services
N.A.I.C.S.: 811111

ECP Energiecontracting GmbH (1)
Im Breitspiel 7, 69126, Heidelberg, Germany
Tel.: (49) 62211371130
Electricity Distribution Services
N.A.I.C.S.: 221122

EDiM S.p.A. (1)
Via Giuseppe Saragat 1, 20852, Villasanta, MB, Italy
Tel.: (39) 039305051
Web Site: http://www.edim-it.com
Die Casting & Machinery Tool Mfr
N.A.I.C.S.: 333517

ETAS Embedded Systems Canada Inc. (1)
419 Phillip Street Unit B, Waterloo, N2L 3X2, ON, Canada
Tel.: (519) 749-3378
Electronic Products Mfr
N.A.I.C.S.: 334419

EVI Audio GmbH (1)
Sachsenring 60, 94315, Straubing, Germany
Tel.: (49) 94217060

AND PRIVATE COMPANIES — ROBERT BOSCH GMBH

Electrical Component Mfr
N.A.I.C.S.: 335313

Evroradiators LLC (1)
Promzona 1st building estate, 413105, Engels, Russia
Tel.: (7) 8453514100
Mechanical Equipment Mfr
N.A.I.C.S.: 333613
Kolchina Svetlana *(Mgr-HR)*

F.A. Niigata Co., Ltd. (1)
376-4 Oaza-Daimon, Izumozaki, Niigata, 949-4352, Japan
Tel.: (81) 258784141
Automobile Parts Distr
N.A.I.C.S.: 423120

FA Niigata Co., Ltd. (1)
376-4 Oaza-Daimon Izumozaki-machi, Santo-gun, Niigata, 949-4352, Japan
Tel.: (81) 258784141
Mechanical Equipment Mfr
N.A.I.C.S.: 333613

FMP Group (Thailand) Ltd. (1)
Eastern Seaboard Industrial Estate, Pluakdaeng, Rayong, 21140, Thailand
Brake Components Mfr
N.A.I.C.S.: 336340

Ferroknepper Buderus S.A. (1)
B P 201 L- 4003 Alzette 20 Op den Drieschen, Esch, Luxembourg, Luxembourg
Heating Equipment Distr
N.A.I.C.S.: 423720

Freud International Trading (Shanghai) Co., Ltd. (1)
Rm 3003-3011 No 588 YinDou Rd, Minhang, Shanghai, 201108, China
Tel.: (86) 2154400733
Wooden Furniture & Door Mfr
N.A.I.C.S.: 321911

Freud S.p.A. (1)
Via Padova 3 Zona Industriale di Feletto Umberto, Tavagnacco, 33010, Udine, Italy
Cutting Tool Mfr
N.A.I.C.S.: 332216

Fuji Aitac Co., Ltd. (1)
1573 Oaza-Hiroki Misato-machi, Kodama-gun, Saitama, 367-0118, Japan
Tel.: (81) 495763221
Mechanical Equipment Mfr
N.A.I.C.S.: 333613

GFR-Gesellschaft fur Regelungstechnik und Energieeinsparung mbh (1)
Kapellenweg 42, 33415, Verl, Germany
Tel.: (49) 52469620
Web Site: http://www.gfr.de
Building Automation Construction Services
N.A.I.C.S.: 238220
Volker Westerheide *(Mng Dir)*

Hagglunds Drives South Africa (Pty.) Ltd. (1)
216 Albert Amon Street, Edenvale, 1614, South Africa
Tel.: (27) 114544933
Automobile Parts Distr
N.A.I.C.S.: 423120

Hawera Probst GmbH (1)
Schutzenstrasse 77, 88212, Ravensburg, Germany
Tel.: (49) 33387843716
Web Site: http://www.hawera.com
Mechanical Equipment Mfr
N.A.I.C.S.: 333613

Holger Christiansen A/S (1)
Hedelundvej 13, 6705, Esbjerg, Denmark
Tel.: (45) 76143322
Automotive Parts Mfr & Distr
N.A.I.C.S.: 336320
Dietmar Wunstorf *(Gen Mgr)*

Holger Christiansen Deutschland GmbH (1)
Elkersberg 1, 57234, Wilnsdorf, Germany
Tel.: (49) 2739403040
Automobile Parts Distr
N.A.I.C.S.: 423120
Stefan Behnke *(Gen Mgr)*

Holger Christiansen France SAS (1)
Zac des Aulnaies 550 Rue de la Juine, 45160, Olivet, France
Tel.: (33) 238496666
Automotive Electrical Component Distr
N.A.I.C.S.: 423120
Germain Hersent *(Gen Mgr)*

Holger Christiansen Italia S.r.l. (1)
Via Cicogna 27-29, San Lazzaro di Savena, 40068, Bologna, Italy
Tel.: (39) 0514998989
Automobile Parts Distr
N.A.I.C.S.: 423120
Rosario Giorgio Mangiapia *(Gen Mgr)*

Holger Christiansen Sverige AB (1)
Sodra Vagen 12, 702 27, Orebro, Sweden
Tel.: (46) 19278800
Automotive Electrical Component Distr
N.A.I.C.S.: 423120
Flemming Hansen *(Gen Mgr)*

Holger Christiansen UK Ltd. (1)
Unit 7-8 Glaisdale Business Centre Glaisdale Parkway Bilborough, Nottingham, NG8 4GP, United Kingdom
Tel.: (44) 1159280086
Automotive Electrical Component Distr
N.A.I.C.S.: 423120
Peter Murray *(Gen Mgr)*

Home Connect GmbH (1)
Carl-Wery-Str 34, 81739, Munich, Germany
Tel.: (49) 89459001
Web Site: http://www.home-connect.com
Home Appliance Mfr
N.A.I.C.S.: 335220
Anton Kessler *(Mng Dir)*

Huttlin GmbH (1)
Hohe-Flum-Strasse 31, 79650, Schopfheim, Germany
Tel.: (49) 762268840
Electromedical Equipment Mfr
N.A.I.C.S.: 334510

Hytec Hydraulics Mocambique Lda. (1)
Unit 16, Beluluane Industrial Park Boane District, Matola, Maputo, Mozambique
Tel.: (258) 21731414
Hydraulic Valve & Pump Mfr
N.A.I.C.S.: 332912

Hytec Namibia Pty. Ltd. (1)
198 3rd Street East, Walvis Bay, Namibia
Tel.: (264) 64203457
Hydraulic Valve & Pump Mfr
N.A.I.C.S.: 332912

Hytec Zambia Ltd. (1)
Plot 2810 Vibhav Business Park Chingola Road, Kitwe, Zambia
Tel.: (260) 212270010
Hydraulic Components Mfr
N.A.I.C.S.: 333996

ITK Engineering GmbH (1)
Im Speyerer Tal 6, Ruelzheim, 76761, Germersheim, Germany
Tel.: (49) 727277030
Web Site: http://www.itk-engineering.de
System Engineering Services
N.A.I.C.S.: 541330
Rudolf Maier *(Chm)*

ITK Engineering Japan, Inc. (1)
1-10-13 Shiba, Minato-ku, Tokyo, Japan
Tel.: (81) 364353811
Software Development Services
N.A.I.C.S.: 541511

ITK Engineering, LLC (1)
28700 Cabot Dr Ste 500, Novi, MI 48377
Tel.: (248) 214-2644
Software Development Services
N.A.I.C.S.: 541511

KHS Handel und Service GmbH (1)
Wiescher Weg 92, 45472, Mulheim an der Ruhr, Germany (100%)
Tel.: (49) 2089413590
Web Site: http://www.daf-khs.de
Car, Truck Repair & Maintenance Services
N.A.I.C.S.: 811111

Kanto Seiatsu Kogyo Co., Ltd. (1)
2101 Akiyama Kodama-machi, Saitama, Honjo, 367-0213, Japan
Tel.: (81) 495722951
Mechanical Equipment Mfr
N.A.I.C.S.: 333613

Kanto-Seiatsu Kogyo Co., Ltd. (1)
2101 Akiyama, Kodama-machi Honjo-shi, Saitama, 367-0213, Japan
Tel.: (81) 495722951
Automobile Parts Distr
N.A.I.C.S.: 423120

Koller + Schwemmer GmbH (1)
Rothensteig 21, 90408, Nuremberg, Germany
Tel.: (49) 911361030
Mechanical Equipment Mfr
N.A.I.C.S.: 333613

Landau Electronic GmbH (1)
Opelstrasse 24, 64546, Morfelden-Walldorf, Germany
Tel.: (49) 610592460
Web Site: http://www.landau-electronic.de
Electrical Component Mfr
N.A.I.C.S.: 335313

MIVIN Engineering Technologies Private Ltd. (1)
81 Vstppl Compound Mysore Road, Manchanayakanahalli Ramanagar, Bengaluru, India
Tel.: (91) 9686576846
Automobile Parts Distr
N.A.I.C.S.: 423120
Pavanv Kulkarni *(Engr-Production Planner & Procurement)*

Makat Candy Technology GmbH (1)
Feldstrasse 52, 56269, Dierdorf, Germany
Tel.: (49) 268994340
Web Site: http://www.makat.de
Confectionery Machinery Mfr
N.A.I.C.S.: 333241
Emp.: 100
Uwe Jansen *(CEO)*

Metapar Usinagem Ltda. (1)
Rua Eng Joao Bley Filho 288 Pinheirinho, Curitiba, 81870-370, Parana, Brazil
Tel.: (55) 4121036644
Confectionery Machinery Mfr
N.A.I.C.S.: 333241

Mobility Media GmbH (1)
Bismarckstrasse 71, 10627, Berlin, Germany
Tel.: (49) 3032788530
Web Site: http://www.mobility-media.com
Automobile Parts Distr
N.A.I.C.S.: 423120
Florian Bankoley *(Mng Dir)*

Moehwald GmbH (1)
Michelinstrasse 21, 66424, Homburg, Germany
Tel.: (49) 68417070
Web Site: http://www.moehwald.de
Automobile Parts Distr
N.A.I.C.S.: 423120

Moeller & Devicon A/S (1)
Elmevej 9, 4262, Naestved, Denmark
Tel.: (45) 55462400
Web Site: http://www.boschpackaging.com
Industrial Machinery Mfr
N.A.I.C.S.: 333248
Soeren Braeutigam *(CEO)*

OOO Robert Bosch (1)
Vashutinskoe shosse 24, 141400, Khimki, Russia (100%)
Tel.: (7) 495 560 9560
Web Site: http://www.bosch.ru
Motor Vehicle Parts & Accessory Mfr
N.A.I.C.S.: 336340
Steffen Hoffmann *(Pres)*

Subsidiary (Domestic):

OOO Robert Bosch Saratov (2)
Friedrich Engels Prospect 139, 413105, Engels, Russia
Tel.: (7) 8453514739
Emp.: 1,500
Ceramic Products Mfr
N.A.I.C.S.: 327120
Kolchina Svetlana *(Mgr-HR)*

P.T. Robert Bosch (1)
Palma Tower 10th Floor Jl RA Kartini II-S Kaveling 6 Sek II Pondok, Kebayoran Lama, Jakarta, 12310, Indonesia
Tel.: (62) 217803639
Automobile Parts Distr
N.A.I.C.S.: 423690
Adrian Mulkan *(Mgr-Sls-Natl)*

PT BSH Home Appliances (1)
APL Tower 20th Fl suite 7-9 Jl Letjen S Parman Kav 28, Jakarta, Indonesia
Tel.: (62) 2129346100
Home Appliance Mfr
N.A.I.C.S.: 335220

Pharmatec GmbH (1)
Elisabeth-Boer-Strasse 3, 1099, Dresden, Germany
Tel.: (49) 351282780
Emp.: 200
Pharmaceutical Equipment Distr
N.A.I.C.S.: 423450
Ralf Kretzschmar *(Gen Mgr)*

Prufzentrum Boxberg GmbH (1)
Robert Bosch Strasse 25, 97944, Boxberg-Windischbuch, Germany
Tel.: (49) 7930600210
Automobile Parts Distr
N.A.I.C.S.: 423120

ROBERT BOSCH (MALAYSIA) SDN. BHD. (1)
Industrial Zone Phase 1, Bayan Lepas, 11900, Penang, Malaysia
Tel.: (60) 46382262
Automobile Parts Distr
N.A.I.C.S.: 423120
Andreas Neutel *(Sr Mgr-Engrg-Plant Products)*

ROBERT BOSCH ESPANA FABRICA MADRID S.A. (1)
Calle Hermanos Garcia Noblejas 19, 28037, Madrid, Spain
Tel.: (34) 938916030
Automobile Parts Distr
N.A.I.C.S.: 423120

ROBERT BOSCH ESPANA FABRICA TRETO S.A. (1)
Ctra Santander-Bilbao s/n, Treto, 39760, Cantabria, Spain
Tel.: (34) 942629500
Automobile Parts Distr
N.A.I.C.S.: 423120
Javier Del Campo Alvarez *(Mgr-Facilities Maintenance)*

ROBERT BOSCH POWER TOOLS SDN. BHD. (1)
Bayan Lepas Free Industrial Zone Phase 1, Bayan Lepas, 11900, Penang, Malaysia
Tel.: (60) 46382888
Automobile Parts Distr
N.A.I.C.S.: 423120
Mohsein Wan *(Mgr-Design)*

ROBERT BOSCH S.R.L. (1)
sector 1 str Horia Macelariu nr 30-34 subsol parter et 1 et 2 si et 4, 013937, Bucharest, Romania
Tel.: (40) 212048800
Web Site: http://www.bosch.ro
Automobile Parts Distr
N.A.I.C.S.: 423120
Razvan Birla *(Officer-Data Security)*

ROBERT BOSCH S.p.A. Societa Unipersonale (1)
Via M A Colonna 35, 20149, Milan, Italy
Tel.: (39) 0236961
Web Site: http://www.bosch.it
Automobile Parts Mfr
N.A.I.C.S.: 336390

ROBERT BOSCH Sp. z o.o. (1)
ul Jutrzenki 105, 02-231, Warsaw, Poland
Tel.: (48) 22 715 40 00
Web Site: http://www.bosch.pl
Emp.: 200
Automotive Parts Mfr & Distr
N.A.I.C.S.: 336390
Konrad Pokutycki *(Member-Mgmt Bd)*

Robert Bosch (Australia) Pty Ltd. (1)
1555 Ctr Rd Clayton, Melbourne, 3169, VIC, Australia (100%)
Tel.: (61) 395415555
Web Site: http://www.bosch.com.au
Sales Range: $400-449.9 Million
Emp.: 1,600
Automotive Equipment
N.A.I.C.S.: 336340

Robert Bosch (Cambodia) Co., Ltd. (1)

ROBERT BOSCH GMBH

Robert Bosch GmbH—(Continued)
VTrust Tower 8th Floor St 169 Czechoslovakia Blvd Sangkat Veal Vong, Khan 7 Makara, 12306, Phnom Penh, Cambodia
Tel.: (855) 23880217
Web Site: http://www.bosch.com.kh
Automobile Parts Distr
N.A.I.C.S.: 423120

Robert Bosch (France) SAS (1)
32 Ave Michelet, PO Box 170, 93404, Saint-Ouen, France **(100%)**
Tel.: (33) 40107111
Web Site: http://www.bosch.fr
Sales Range: $25-49.9 Million
Emp.: 1,000
Mfr of Automotive Equipment
N.A.I.C.S.: 336340
Heiko Carrie (Pres & Member-Mgmt Bd)

Robert Bosch (Pty) Ltd. (1)
Peterautenbach Industrial Ests, PO Box 348, 250, Brits, South Africa **(100%)**
Tel.: (27) 0123813300
Sales Range: $150-199.9 Million
Emp.: 1,000
Mfr of Automotive Equipment; Sales & Service of Bosch Products in South Africa
N.A.I.C.S.: 336340

Robert Bosch (South East Asia) Pte. Ltd. (1)
11 Bishan St 21, Singapore, 573943, Singapore
Tel.: (65) 62585511
Web Site: http://www.bosch.com.sg
Emp.: 10,000
Home Appliance Mfr
N.A.I.C.S.: 335220

Robert Bosch A/S (1)
Telegrafvej 1, PO Box 40, Ballerup, 2750, Denmark **(100%)**
Tel.: (45) 44898989
Web Site: http://www.bosch.dk
Sales Range: $100-124.9 Million
Emp.: 180
Marketing & Sales of Automotive Equipment
N.A.I.C.S.: 441330
Thore Pedersen (Mng Dir)

Robert Bosch AB (1)
Isafjordsgatan 15, PO Box 1154, 16426, Kista, Sweden **(100%)**
Tel.: (46) 87501500
Web Site: http://www.bosch.se
Sales Range: $25-49.9 Million
Emp.: 100
Sales & Service of Bosch Products in Sweden
N.A.I.C.S.: 336340

Robert Bosch AG (1)
Geiereckstrasse 6, 1110, Vienna, Austria **(100%)**
Tel.: (43) 01797220
Web Site: http://www.bosch.at
Sales Range: $50-74.9 Million
Emp.: 250
Mfr of Diesel Fuel-Injection Equipment; Sales & Servicer of Bosch Products in Austria
N.A.I.C.S.: 336310
Klaus Peter Fouquet (Member-Mgmt Bd)

Robert Bosch AG (1)
Luterbachstrasse 10, 4528, Zuchwil, Switzerland
Tel.: (41) 326853333
Web Site: http://www.bosch.ch
Emp.: 2,100
Electrical Engineering Product Mfr
N.A.I.C.S.: 336320

Robert Bosch AS (1)
Rosenholmveien 25, 1414, Trollasen, Norway
Tel.: (47) 64878900
Web Site: http://www.bosch.no
Industrial Automotive Equipment Mfr
N.A.I.C.S.: 335314
Thore Pedersen (Mng Dir)

Robert Bosch Argentina Industrial S.A. (1)
Av Cordoba 5160, C1414BAW, Buenos Aires, Argentina
Tel.: (54) 800444426724
Web Site: http://www.argentina.bosch.com.ar

Emp.: 255
Automobile Parts Distr
N.A.I.C.S.: 423120
Fernando Calvo (CFO)

Robert Bosch Automotive Technologies (Thailand) Co., Ltd. (1)
7/102 Moo 4 Amata City Industrial Estate T Mabyangporn, Pluak Daeng, 21140, Rayong, Thailand
Tel.: (66) 38958888
Automobile Parts Distr
N.A.I.C.S.: 423120
Satid Malairodsiri (Mgr-Engrg Sls)

Robert Bosch Automotive Technology Group (1)
Robert Bosch Platz 1, Gerlingen, 70839, Germany
Tel.: (49) 7118110
Web Site: http://www.bosch.com
Rev.: $41,538,726,288
Emp.: 167,709
Automotive Engine, Chassis, Electronic & Interior Parts Mfr
N.A.I.C.S.: 336390

Subsidiary (Non-US):

Bosch Automotive Diesel Systems Co., Ltd. (2)
17 Xinhua Road, New District, Wuxi, 214028, China
Tel.: (86) 51085333888
Automobile Component Distr
N.A.I.C.S.: 423120

Bosch Automotive Electronics India Private Ltd. (2)
Naganathapura plant Electronics City PO, PB No 6887, Naganathapura, Bengaluru, 560 100, Karnataka, India
Tel.: (91) 8067521111
Web Site: http://www.bosch.in
Automobile Component Distr
N.A.I.C.S.: 423120

Bosch Automotive Service Solutions (Suzhou) Co., Ltd. (2)
Fengqiao Industrial Park No158-128 Huashan Road, New District, Suzhou, 215000, Jiangsu, China
Tel.: (86) 51266655556
Automobile Component Distr
N.A.I.C.S.: 423120
Ming Liu (Engr-Sourcing)

Bosch Automotive Service Solutions Ltd. (2)
Bird Hall Ln, Stockport, SK3 0XG, Cheshire, United Kingdom
Tel.: (44) 1614919191
Automobile Component Distr
N.A.I.C.S.: 423120

Bosch Automotive Service Solutions Pty. Ltd. (2)
300 Wellington Road, Mulgrave, 3170, VIC, Australia
Tel.: (61) 395446222
Automobile Component Distr
N.A.I.C.S.: 423120

Bosch Automotive Service Solutions S.A. de C.V. (2)
Mitla No 442, Distrito Federal, Mexico, 03600, Mexico
Tel.: (52) 5544334211
Automobile Component Distr
N.A.I.C.S.: 423120

Bosch Automotive Service Solutions S.R.L. (2)
Via Monte Aquila 2, 43124, Parma, Italy
Tel.: (39) 0521632401
Web Site: http://www.bosch.it
Automotive Component Mfr & Distr
N.A.I.C.S.: 336390

Bosch Automotive Systems Corporation (2)
6-7 Shibuya 3-chome, Shibuya-ku, Tokyo, 150-8360, Japan **(55%)**
Tel.: (81) 334001551
Web Site: http://www.bosch.co.jp
Sales Range: $1-4.9 Billion
Emp.: 6,925
Fuel-Injection Equipment for Diesel Engines & Air Conditioning Systems for Automotive Industry

N.A.I.C.S.: 333618

Bosch Automotive Thailand Co. Ltd. (2)
7/102 M 4 Amata City T Mabyangporn, Pluak Daeng, Rayong, Thailand
Tel.: (66) 3895601923
Automobile Component Distr
N.A.I.C.S.: 423120
Komjak Panadit (Controller-Cost)

Bosch Car Multimedia Portugal, S.A. (2)
Rua Max Grundig 35 Lomar, 4705-820, Braga, Portugal
Tel.: (351) 253306100
Electronic Components Mfr
N.A.I.C.S.: 334419
Luis Miguel Santos (Mgr-Dev Dept)

Subsidiary (Domestic):

ETAS GmbH (2)
Borsigstrasse 14, 70469, Stuttgart, Germany **(90%)**
Tel.: (49) 71134230
Web Site: http://www.etas.com
Sales Range: $150-199.9 Million
Emp.: 800
Provider of Products & Services for Developing, Manufacturing & Servicing Automotive Embedded Systems
N.A.I.C.S.: 541512
Christoph Hartung (Chm-Mgmt Bd)

Subsidiary (Non-US):

ETAS Automotive India Private Ltd. (3)
3rd Floor Godrej Millennium 9 Koregaon park Road, Pune, 411 001, Maharashtra, India
Tel.: (91) 2067254760
Mechanical Engineering Services
N.A.I.C.S.: 541330
Amit Sharma (Acct Mgr)

ETAS Automotive Technology (Shanghai) Co., Ltd. (3)
333 Fuquan Road North IBP, Changning, Shanghai, 200335, China
Tel.: (86) 2122185858
Hardware & Software Product Distr
N.A.I.C.S.: 423430

ETAS K.K. (3)
Queens Tower C-17F 2-3-5, Minatomirai, Yokohama, 220-6217, Japan
Tel.: (81) 452220900
Mechanical Engineering Services
N.A.I.C.S.: 541330

ETAS Korea Co., Ltd. (3)
4F ABN Tower 331 Pangyo-ro, Bundang-gu, Seongnam, 013488, Gyeonggi-do, Korea (South)
Tel.: (82) 313266200
Mechanical Engineering Services
N.A.I.C.S.: 541330

ETAS Ltd. (3)
Bacchus House Osbaldwick Link Road, Osbaldwick, York, YO10 3JB, United Kingdom
Tel.: (44) 1904562626
Mechanical Engineering Services
N.A.I.C.S.: 541330

ETAS S.A.S. (3)
32 avenue Michelet, BP 170, 93404, Saint-Ouen, Cedex, France
Tel.: (33) 175345050
Mechanical Engineering Services
N.A.I.C.S.: 541330

Subsidiary (US):

ETAS, Inc. (3)
15800 N Haggerty Rd, Plymouth, MI 48170
Tel.: (734) 997-9393
Web Site: http://www.etasgroup.com
Sales Range: $25-49.9 Million
Emp.: 90
Automotive Control Systems Tools
N.A.I.C.S.: 336390

Subsidiary (Non-US):

LiveDevices Ltd (3)
Atlas House Link Business Park, Osbaldwick Rd, York, YO10 3JB, United Kingdom **(100%)**

Tel.: (44) 904562580
Web Site: http://www.livedevices.com
Sales Range: $25-49.9 Million
Emp.: 19
Provider of Embedded Software Solutions for the Automotive & Industrial Markets
N.A.I.C.S.: 541512
Jo Pears (Office Mgr)

Subsidiary (US):

Vetronix Corporation (3)
2030 Alameda Padre Serra, Santa Barbara, CA 93103-1716
Tel.: (805) 966-2000
Web Site: http://www.vetronix.com
Diagnostic Service Tools for Vehicle Electronics
N.A.I.C.S.: 334519

Subsidiary (Non-US):

Pacifica Group Limited (2)
264 E Boundary Rd, Melbourne, 3165, VIC, Australia
Tel.: (61) 395752222
Web Site: http://www.pacifica.com.au
Sales Range: $300-349.9 Million
Automotive Brake System Mfr
N.A.I.C.S.: 336340
Russell McCart (Founder & Mng Dir)

Division (Domestic):

Bosch Chassis Systems Australia (3)
246 E Boundary Rd, East Bentleigh, Melbourne, 3165, VIC, Australia
Tel.: (61) 395752200
Web Site: http://www.pbr.com.au
Sales Range: $100-124.9 Million
Emp.: 380
Mfr & Developer of Brake Systems & Clutch Products
N.A.I.C.S.: 336340

F M P Group Australia Pty Ltd (3)
Elizabeth Street, PO Box 631, Ballarat, 3353, VIC, Australia
Tel.: (61) 1800819666
Web Site: http://www.bendix.com.au
Sales Range: $100-124.9 Million
Emp.: 300
Mfr & Marketer of Friction Materials for Automotive Industry
N.A.I.C.S.: 441330
George Kyriakopoulos (Gen Mgr)

Subsidiary (Domestic):

Robert Bosch Automotive Steering GmbH (2)
Richard-Bullinger-Strasse 77, 73527, Schwabisch Gmund, Germany **(100%)**
Tel.: (49) 7171310
Web Site: http://www.bosch-automotive-steering.com
Sales Range: $5-14.9 Billion
Emp.: 13,118
Automotive Steering Systems & Components Developer, Mfr & Whslr
N.A.I.C.S.: 336330
Marcus Parche (Member-Mgmt Bd & Exec VP)

Subsidiary (Non-US):

Robert Bosch Automotive Steering Kft. (3)
Kistalyai ut 2, 3300, Eger, Hungary
Tel.: (36) 36520 810
Web Site: http://www.bosch-automotive-steering.com
Emp.: 600
Automotive Steering Systems & Components Mfr & Whslr
N.A.I.C.S.: 336330

Subsidiary (Domestic):

ZF Lenksysteme Nacam GmbH (3)
Zum Huchtinger Bahnhof 25, 28241, Bremen, Germany
Tel.: (49) 421 8788 0
Web Site: http://www.zf-lenksysteme.com
Emp.: 278
Automotive Steering Column Systems & Related Components Mfr & Whslr
N.A.I.C.S.: 336330

AND PRIVATE COMPANIES — ROBERT BOSCH GMBH

Affiliate (Non-US):

ZF Steering Gear (India) Limited (3)
Gat No 1242/44 Village Vadu Budurk, Taluka Shirur, Pune, 412216, India **(25.79%)**
Tel.: (91) 2137305100
Web Site: http://www.zfindia.com
Rev.: $55,597,386
Assets: $61,356,034
Liabilities: $11,157,604
Net Worth: $50,198,429
Earnings: $2,942,270
Emp.: 341
Fiscal Year-end: 03/31/2023
Automotive Steering Components Mfr
N.A.I.C.S.: 336330
Dinesh Munot *(Chm)*

Division (Domestic):

Robert Bosch GmbH Automotive Aftermarket Division (2)
PO Box 106050, 70049, Stuttgart, Germany **(100%)**
Tel.: (49) 7219422318
Web Site: http://www.bosch.de
Sales Range: $450-499.9 Million
Emp.: 1,300
Distribution of Automotive Aftermarket Equipment & Service
N.A.I.C.S.: 423830

Division (US):

Robert Bosch LLC - Automotive Division (2)
38000 Hills Tech Dr, Farmington Hills, MI 48331
Tel.: (248) 876-1000
Web Site: http://www.bosch.us
Sales Range: $350-399.9 Million
Emp.: 2,000
Auto Parts, Appliances & Power Tools Mfr
N.A.I.C.S.: 336390
Mike Mansuetti *(Pres-North America)*

Subsidiary (Domestic):

Bosch Automotive Service Solutions LLC (3)
28635 Mound Rd, Warren, MI 48092-5509
Tel.: (586) 578-7224
Web Site: http://www.boschcarservice.us
Sales Range: $50-74.9 Million
Emp.: 150
Vehicle Services
N.A.I.C.S.: 811198
Oliver Schlueter *(Dir-Mktg & Product Mgmt)*

Subsidiary (Non-US):

Bosch Automotive Service Solutions Corporation (4)
8th Fl Gotanda Building West Tower, 5-6-2 Osaki, Tokyo, Shinagawa, Japan
Tel.: (81) 454501512
Web Site: http://www.spxservicesolutions.co.jp
Sales Range: $10-24.9 Million
Emp.: 40
Automotive Services
N.A.I.C.S.: 811198

Bosch Automotive Service Solutions GmbH (4)
Am Dorrenhof 1, 85131, Pollenfeld, Germany
Tel.: (49) 84219731
Web Site: http://www.bosch.com
Automotive Services
N.A.I.C.S.: 811198

Subsidiary (Domestic):

Climatec, LLC (3)
2851 W Kathleen Rd, Phoenix, AZ 85053
Tel.: (602) 944-3330
Web Site: http://www.climatec.com
Building Automation Services
N.A.I.C.S.: 541420

Plant (Domestic):

Robert Bosch Fuel Systems (3)
4300 44th St SE, Kentwood, MI 49512-4009 **(49%)**
Tel.: (616) 554-6500
Web Site: http://www.boschusa.com
Diesel Fuel Injector Mfr
N.A.I.C.S.: 336390

Division (Domestic):

Robert Bosch LLC - Automotive Aftermarket Division (3)
2800 S 25th Ave, Broadview, IL 60155-4532
Tel.: (708) 865-5200
Web Site: http://www.boschusa.com
Automotive Aftermarket Products Mfr
N.A.I.C.S.: 336390
Tony Pauly *(Dir-Adv & Brand Mgmt-North America)*

Unit (Domestic):

Robert Bosch LLC Research and Technology Center North America (3)
4009 Miranda Ave, Palo Alto, CA 94304
Tel.: (650) 320-2900
Web Site: http://www.boschresearch.com
Automotive Research Services
N.A.I.C.S.: 541715

Robert Bosch B.V. (1)
Ringwade 31A, 3439 LM, Nieuwegein, Netherlands
Tel.: (31) 332479160
Web Site: http://www.bosch.nl
Emp.: 3,300
Industrial Automotive Equipment Mfr
N.A.I.C.S.: 335314

Robert Bosch Battery Solutions GmbH (1)
Robert-Bosch-Allee 1, 99817, Eisenach, Thuringen, Germany
Tel.: (49) 3691640
Automobile Parts Distr
N.A.I.C.S.: 423120

Robert Bosch Battery Systems GmbH (1)
Kruppstrasse 20, 70469, Stuttgart, Germany
Tel.: (49) 7118110
Automobile Parts Mfr
N.A.I.C.S.: 336390
Joachim Fetzer *(Member-Mgmt Bd)*

Robert Bosch CZ s.r.o. (1)
Radlicka 350/107d, 158 00, Prague, Czech Republic
Tel.: (420) 261300101
Web Site: http://www.bosch.cz
Sales Range: Less than $1 Million
Mfr of Motor Vehicle Parts & Accessories.
N.A.I.C.S.: 336340
Karl Strobel *(CEO-Vienna)*

Robert Bosch Car Multimedia GmbH (1)
Robert-Bosch-Strasse 200, 31139, Hildesheim, Germany
Tel.: (49) 5121490
Automobile Parts Mfr
N.A.I.C.S.: 336390
Dorte Eimers-Klose *(Member-Mgmt Bd)*

Robert Bosch Consumer Goods & Building Technology Group (1)
Robert Bosch Platz 1, 70839, Gerlingen, Germany
Tel.: (49) 89459001
Household Appliance, Power Tool & Security System Mfr
N.A.I.C.S.: 335220

Subsidiary (Domestic):

Bosch Sicherheitssysteme Gmbh (2)
Robert Bosch Ring 5-7, 85630, Grasbrunn, Germany
Tel.: (49) 8962900
Web Site: http://www.boschsecurity.com
Sales Range: $125-149.9 Million
Emp.: 800
Security & Surveillance Systems Mfr
N.A.I.C.S.: 561621
Andreas Bartz *(Member-Mgmt Bd & Exec VP-Fin & Admin)*

Subsidiary (Non-US):

Bosch Security Systems B.V. (3)
Torenallee 49, 5617 BA, Eindhoven, Netherlands
Tel.: (31) 402577200
Security Device Mfr
N.A.I.C.S.: 334290

Bosch Security Systems Ltd. (3)
Broadwater Park North Orbital Road, Denham, UB9 5HJ, United Kingdom
Tel.: (44) 3301239979
Web Site: http://www.uk.boschsecurity.com
Security Device Mfr
N.A.I.C.S.: 334290
Thomas Quante *(Pres & Member-Mgmt Bd)*

Bosch Security Systems Ltd. (3)
Bosch Bldg Akasaka 9F 2 13 Nagata-cho, Chiyoda-ku, Tokyo, 100-0014, Japan
Tel.: (81) 354854427
Security Device Mfr
N.A.I.C.S.: 334290

Bosch Security Systems Ltd. (3)
Room 515-521 5th Floor Topsail Plaza 11 On Sum Street, Shatin, Hong Kong, China (Hong Kong)
Tel.: (852) 26352815
Security Device Mfr
N.A.I.C.S.: 334290

Bosch Security Systems Pty. Ltd. (3)
25 Huntingwood Drive, Huntingwood, 2148, NSW, Australia
Tel.: (61) 296721233
Security Device Mfr
N.A.I.C.S.: 334290

Bosch Security Systems S.A. (3)
Hermanos Garcia Noblejas 19, 28037, Madrid, Spain
Tel.: (34) 914102011
Security Device Mfr
N.A.I.C.S.: 334290

Bosch Security Systems S.p.A. (3)
Via MA Colonna 35, 20149, Milan, Italy
Tel.: (39) 0236961
Web Site: http://www.boschsecurity.it
Security Device Mfr
N.A.I.C.S.: 334290

Subsidiary (US):

Bosch Security Systems, Inc. (3)
130 Perinton Pkwy, Fairport, NY 14450-9107
Tel.: (585) 223-4060
Web Site: http://www.boschsecurity.com
Sales Range: $50-74.9 Million
Emp.: 250
Commercial & Residential Security & Surveillance System Mfr
N.A.I.C.S.: 561621

Division (Domestic):

Bosch Security Systems (4)
1706 Hemstead Rd, Lancaster, PA 17601-5871
Tel.: (717) 735-6300
Web Site: http://www.boschsecurity.com
Sales Range: $75-99.9 Million
Emp.: 100
Security Control Equipment & Systems Mfr
N.A.I.C.S.: 335999
Christopher Gerace *(CFO & Reg Pres)*

Subsidiary (Domestic):

Bosch Systems (4)
12000 Portland Ave, Burnsville, MN 55337-1522
Tel.: (952) 884-4051
Electronic Audio Communication Devices Mfr
N.A.I.C.S.: 334290

Subsidiary (Domestic):

Bosch Thermotechnik GmbH (2)
Sophienstrasse 30-32, 35576, Wetzlar, Germany
Tel.: (49) 64414180
Web Site: http://www.bosch-thermotechnology.com
Sales Range: $1-4.9 Billion
Emp.: 300
Heating & Water Heating Systems Mfr
N.A.I.C.S.: 333415
Thomas Bauer *(Member-Mgmt Bd-Sls & Mktg)*

Subsidiary (US):

BBT North America Corporation (3)
50 Wentworth Ave, Londonderry, NH 03053
Tel.: (603) 552-1100
Web Site: http://www.buderus.us
Heating Products Mfr
N.A.I.C.S.: 333415

Subsidiary (Domestic):

Bosch Water Heating (4)
50 Wentworth Ave, Londonderry, NH 03053-7475
Tel.: (802) 496-4436
Web Site: http://www.boschhotwater.com
Rev.: $34,000,000
Emp.: 30
Water Heater Sales
N.A.I.C.S.: 423720

Division (Domestic):

Buderus Hydronic Systems (4)
50 Wentworth Ave, Londonderry, NH 03053
Tel.: (603) 898-0505
Web Site: http://www.buderus.net
Sales Range: $10-24.9 Million
Emp.: 40
Boilers & Heating Equipment Mfr
N.A.I.C.S.: 333415

Branch (Domestic):

BBT Themotechnik GmbH (3)
Junkerstr 20 24, 73249, Wernau, Germany **(100%)**
Tel.: (49) 71533060
Web Site: http://www.bosch-thermotechnik.de
Sales Range: $150-199.9 Million
Emp.: 300
N.A.I.C.S.: 336330
Uwe Glock *(Chm-Mgmt Bd)*

Subsidiary (Non-US):

Bosch Termotechnologia, S.A. (3)
E N 16 Km 3 7, Cacia, Aveiro, Portugal
Tel.: (351) 234925300
Heating & Cooling System Mfr
N.A.I.C.S.: 333415

Bosch Termotecnologia Ltda. (3)
Rua Sao Paulo 144 Alphaville Empresarial, 06465-130, Barueri, Brazil
Tel.: (55) 1141664600
Heating & Cooling System Mfr
N.A.I.C.S.: 333415
Volker Kallwellis *(Mgr-Product Dev)*

Bosch Termoteknik Sanayi ve Ticaret A.S. (3)
Organize Sanayi Bolgesi No 2, 45030, Manisa, Turkiye
Tel.: (90) 2362261101
Heating & Cooling System Mfr
N.A.I.C.S.: 333415
Fatih Sezen *(Dir-Plant Logistics)*

Bosch Thermotechniek B.V. (3)
Zweedsestraat 1, 7418 BG, Deventer, Netherlands
Boiler Mfr
N.A.I.C.S.: 333414

Subsidiary (US):

Bosch Thermotechnik GmbH FHP Manufacturing Plant (3)
601 N W 65th Center, Fort Lauderdale, FL 33309
Tel.: (954) 776-5471
Air Conditioner Distr
N.A.I.C.S.: 423730

Plant (Domestic):

Bosch Thermotechnik GmbH Lollar Plant (3)
Justus-Kilian-Strasse 1, 35457, Hessen, Germany
Tel.: (49) 64414180
Automobile Parts Distr
N.A.I.C.S.: 423120

Bosch Thermotechnik GmbH Wernau Plant (3)
Junkersstrasse 20 - 24, 73249, Wernau, Germany
Tel.: (49) 71533060
Automobile Parts Distr
N.A.I.C.S.: 423120

Subsidiary (Non-US):

Bosch Thermotechnika s.r.o. (3)

ROBERT BOSCH GMBH

INTERNATIONAL PUBLIC

Robert Bosch GmbH—(Continued)
Ve Vrbine 588/3, 794 01, Krnov, Czech Republic
Tel.: (420) 554694111
Heating & Cooling System Mfr
N.A.I.C.S.: 333415

Bosch Thermotechnology (Beijing) Co., Ltd. (3)
F 6 South Yongchang Road BEDA, Beijing, 100176, China
Tel.: (86) 4008206017
Emp.: 250
Heating & Cooling System Mfr
N.A.I.C.S.: 333415

Bosch Thermotechnology (Shandong) Co., Ltd. (3)
No 77 Dongfeng Road Chenzhuang, Huantai, 256404, Zibo, Shandong, China
Tel.: (86) 5338556777
Emp.: 200
Heating & Cooling System Mfr
N.A.I.C.S.: 333415

Bosch Thermotechnology (Wuhan) Co., Ltd. (3)
JiuFeng WestRoad Canglongdao Technology Park, Jiangxia, Wuhan, 430223, Hubei, China
Tel.: (86) 2781977510
Emp.: 550
Heating & Cooling System Mfr
N.A.I.C.S.: 333415

Bosch Thermotechnology Ltd. (3)
Cotswold Way, Warndon, WR4 9SW, Worcs, United Kingdom
Tel.: (44) 3301239339
Web Site: http://www.worcester-bosch.co.uk
Sales Range: $200-249.9 Million
Emp.: 1,000
Oil & Gas Boiler Mfr
N.A.I.C.S.: 332410

Bosch Thermotechnology N.V. / S.A. (3)
Kontichsesteenweg 60Â, Aartselaar, Belgium
Boiler Mfr
N.A.I.C.S.: 333414

Bosch Thermoteknik AB (3)
Hjalmarydsvagen 8, PO Box 1012, 573 28Â, Tranas, Sweden
Tel.: (46) 140384300
Heating & Cooling Equipment Mfr
N.A.I.C.S.: 333415

OOO Bosch Thermotechnik (3)
Kotlyakovskaya str 3, 115201, Moscow, Russia
Tel.: (7) 4955103310
Water Heater Mfr
N.A.I.C.S.: 335220

Subsidiary (Domestic):

Robert Bosch Hausgerate GmbH (2)
Carl Wery Strasse 34, 81739, Munich, Germany (100%)
Tel.: (49) 89459000
Web Site: http://www.bosch-home.com
Sales Range: $50-74.9 Million
Household refrigerators & freezers
N.A.I.C.S.: 336340

Division (Domestic):

Robert Bosch Power Tools Division (2)
Max Lang Str 40-46, 70771, Echterdingen, Germany
Tel.: (49) 7117580
Web Site: http://www.boschpt.com
Sales Range: $350-399.9 Million
Electrical Household Appliances & Entertainment Electronics Mfr & Distr
N.A.I.C.S.: 335210

Subsidiary (US):

Robert Bosch Tool Corporation (3)
1800 W Central Rd, Mount Prospect, IL 60056 (100%)
Tel.: (224) 232-2000
Web Site: http://www.robertboschtoolcorp.com
Power Tool Mfr
N.A.I.C.S.: 333991

Heiko Fischer *(Pres & CEO)*

Unit (Domestic):

CST/berger (4)
1435 Win Hentschel Blvd Ste 215, West Lafayette, IN 47906
Tel.: (765) 464-0700
Web Site: http://www.cstberger.com
Sales Range: $75-99.9 Million
Surveying Equipment, Measuring Device & Safety Products Mfr
N.A.I.C.S.: 334519

Subsidiary (Domestic):

David White, LLC (4)
255 W Fleming, Watseka, IL 60970
Tel.: (815) 432-5237
Web Site: http://www.davidwhite.com
Sales Range: $75-99.9 Million
Emp.: 300
Optical Instrument Mfr
N.A.I.C.S.: 333310

Unit (Domestic):

Dremel (4)
4915 21st St, Racine, WI 53406-5028
Tel.: (262) 554-1390
Web Site: http://www.dremel.com
Sales Range: $25-49.9 Million
Emp.: 30
Rotary Tools, Multi Purpose Saws & Electric Engraving Tool Mfr
N.A.I.C.S.: 332510
Jennifer Uzumcu *(Engr-Safety)*

Representative Office (Non-US):

Robert Bosch Tool Corporation - Canada Office (4)
6975 Creditview Road Unit 3, Mississauga, L5N 8E9, ON, Canada
Tel.: (905) 567-0044
Power Tools Whslr
N.A.I.C.S.: 423710
Barbara Warnick *(Mktg Mgr)*

Plant (Domestic):

Robert Bosch Tool Corporation-Greenville (4)
310 Staton Rd, Greenville, NC 27834
Tel.: (252) 758-4101
Sales Range: $25-49.9 Million
Emp.: 200
Twist Drills & Special Purpose Cutting Tools Mfr
N.A.I.C.S.: 333515

Robert Bosch Tool Corporation-Lincolnton (4)
124 Legionaire Rd, Lincolnton, NC 28093
Tel.: (704) 735-1405
Web Site: http://www.vermontamerican.com
Sales Range: $25-49.9 Million
Emp.: 225
Steel Circular Saw Blades, Chuck Keys, Threadcutting Taps, Dies & Screw Extractors Mfr
N.A.I.C.S.: 333248

Unit (Domestic):

Vermont American (4)
1800 W Central Rd, Mount Prospect, IL 60056
Tel.: (224) 232-2213
Web Site: http://www.vermontamerican.com
Power Tool Accessories Mfr & Whslr
N.A.I.C.S.: 333515
Kevin Enke *(Mktg Dir)*

Subsidiary (Non-US):

Scintilla AG (3)
Postfach 632, Solothurn, 4500, Switzerland (85%)
Tel.: (41) 32 686 31 11
Web Site: http://www.scintilla.ch
Sales Range: $350-399.9 Million
Power Tools & Saw Blades Mfr
N.A.I.C.S.: 333991
Nicholas Marx *(Mgr-HR)*

sia Abrasives Industries AG (3)
Muhlewiesenstrasse 20, 8501, Frauenfeld, Switzerland (100%)
Tel.: (41) 527244444
Web Site: http://www.siaabrasives.com
Sales Range: $250-299.9 Million
Emp.: 637
Surface Processing & Refinement Solutions
N.A.I.C.S.: 327910

Subsidiary (Non-US):

Guangzhou sia Abrasives Co., Ltd. (4)
Bihua Bldg Bihua Street 3 Jinxiu Road, Guangzhou Economic & Technological Development District, Guangzhou, 510730, China
Tel.: (86) 20 8222 13 28
Surface Processing & Refinement Solutions
N.A.I.C.S.: 327910
Rocky Wang *(Gen Mgr)*

Joint Venture (Non-US):

part GmbH (4)
Stuttgarter Str 139, 72574, Bad Urach, Germany
Tel.: (49) 71259696500
Web Site: http://www.part-info.com
Automotive Abrasive & Surface Treatment Mfr
N.A.I.C.S.: 327910
Jochen Gaukel *(Mng Dir)*

Subsidiary (Non-US):

sia Abrafoam Ltd. (4)
Keys Rd, Nix's Hill Industrial Estate, Alfreton, DE55 7FQ, Derbyshire, United Kingdom
Tel.: (44) 1773832524
Web Site: http://www.sia-abrafoam.com
Sales Range: $25-49.9 Million
Emp.: 100
Surface Processing & Refinement Solutions
N.A.I.C.S.: 327910

sia Abrasives (G.B.) Ltd. (4)
Ellistones Lane, Greetland, Halifax, HX4 8NH, West Yorkshire, United Kingdom
Tel.: (44) 845 556 4259
Sales Range: $25-49.9 Million
Emp.: 50
Surface Processing & Refinement Solutions
N.A.I.C.S.: 327910
Ray Bardsley *(Gen Mgr)*

sia Abrasives Australia Pty. Ltd. (4)
958 Stud Road, PO Box 2070, Rowville, 3178, VIC, Australia (100%)
Tel.: (61) 397534333
Sales Range: $25-49.9 Million
Emp.: 35
Surface Processing & Refinement Solutions
N.A.I.C.S.: 327910
John Bright *(Gen Mgr)*

sia Abrasives Belgium N.V./S.A. (4)
Z 5 Mollem 580, 1730, Asse, Belgium
Tel.: (32) 24540020
Sales Range: $25-49.9 Million
Emp.: 15
Surface Processing & Refinement Solutions
N.A.I.C.S.: 327910
Yannick Dartus *(Gen Mgr)*

sia Abrasives Deutschland GmbH (4)
Lohdorfer Str 51, 42699, Solingen, Germany
Tel.: (49) 212258190
Web Site: http://www.sia-abrasives.de
Sales Range: $25-49.9 Million
Surface Processing & Refinement Solutions
N.A.I.C.S.: 327910

sia Abrasives Espana S.A.U. (4)
Avda Hermanos Garcia Noblejas 19, 28037, Madrid, Spain (100%)
Tel.: (34) 914 104 067
Sales Range: $25-49.9 Million
Emp.: 40
Surface Processing & Refinement Solutions
N.A.I.C.S.: 327910
Francisco Tirado *(Gen Mgr)*

sia Abrasives France sarl (4)
Paris Nord 2 22 Avenue des Nations, BP 60073, Villepinte, 95972, Roissy-en-France, France
Tel.: (33) 14817 80 90
Sales Range: $25-49.9 Million
Emp.: 23
Surface Processing & Refinement Solutions
N.A.I.C.S.: 327910
Yannick Dartus *(Gen Mgr)*

sia Abrasives GmbH (4)
Mindelheimerstrasse 8, Schwaz, 6130, Austria
Tel.: (43) 524273666
Sales Range: $25-49.9 Million
Emp.: 8
Surface Processing & Refinement Solutions
N.A.I.C.S.: 327910
Stefan Hiltpolt *(Gen Mgr)*

sia Abrasives Holding Ltd. (4)
Ellistones Lane, Halifax, HX4 8NH, United Kingdom
Tel.: (44) 1422313319
Web Site: http://siaabrasives.com
Holding Company
N.A.I.C.S.: 551112
Ray Bardsley *(Gen Mgr)*

Subsidiary (US):

sia Abrasives, Inc. USA (4)
1980 Indian Creek Rd, Lincolnton, NC 28092
Tel.: (704) 587-7355
Web Site: http://www.sia-usa.com
Sales Range: $25-49.9 Million
Emp.: 23
Surface Processing & Refinement Solutions
N.A.I.C.S.: 327910

Subsidiary (Non-US):

sia Abrasivos Industriais Ltda. (4)
Rua Teodoro Franco de Oliveira 240, Colonia Afonso Pena, Sao Jose dos Pinhais, 83065-190, Brazil (100%)
Tel.: (55) 4133825333
Sales Range: $25-49.9 Million
Emp.: 26
Surface Processing & Refinement Solutions
N.A.I.C.S.: 327910
Augusto Ferreira *(Mgr-Sls)*

sia Abrasivos Mexico S.A. de C.V. (4)
Circuito G Gonzalez Camarena 333, Col Centro de Ciudad Santa Fe, 01210, Mexico, Mexico (100%)
Tel.: (52) 55 5284 3000
Surface Processing & Refinement Solutions
N.A.I.C.S.: 327910
Daniel Mendoza *(Mgr-Mktg)*

sia Fibral Ltd. (4)
Ellistones Lane, Greetland, Halifax, HX4 8NH, West Yorkshire, United Kingdom
Tel.: (44) 1422313000
Web Site: http://www.sia-fibral.com
Surface Processing & Refinement Solutions
N.A.I.C.S.: 327910

Robert Bosch DOO (1)
Omladinskih Brigada 90E, 11070, Belgrade, Serbia
Tel.: (381) 112052600
Web Site: http://www.bosch.rs
Emp.: 1,500
Home Appliance Mfr
N.A.I.C.S.: 335220
Jovanka Jovanovic *(Gen Mgr)*

Robert Bosch EOOD (1)
51b Cherni vrah blvd, 1407, Sofia, Bulgaria
Tel.: (359) 70010668
Web Site: http://www.bosch.bg
Emp.: 43
Automobile Parts Distr
N.A.I.C.S.: 423120

Robert Bosch East Africa Ltd. (1)
Fedha Plaza - 4th Floor Junction of Mpaka and Parklands Roads, Westlands, 00606, Nairobi, Kenya
Tel.: (254) 203752244
Web Site: http://www.bosch.co.ke
Automobile Parts Distr
N.A.I.C.S.: 423120

Robert Bosch Elektronik GmbH (1)
John F Kennedy Strasse 43, Salzgitter, 38228, Germany (100%)
Tel.: (49) 53412850
Web Site: http://www.bosch.de
Sales Range: $400-449.9 Million
Emp.: 2,000
Mfr of Electronic Control Units
N.A.I.C.S.: 334513

AND PRIVATE COMPANIES — ROBERT BOSCH GMBH

Robert Bosch Elektronik Thuringen GmbH (1)
August-Broemel-Strasse 6, 99310, Arnstadt, Germany
Tel.: (49) 71140040990
Web Site: http://www.bosch.com
Emp.: 130
Automobile Parts Distr
N.A.I.C.S.: 423120

Robert Bosch Elektronika Gyarto Kft. (1)
Robert Bosch ut 1, 3000, Hatvan, Hungary
Tel.: (36) 37549100
Automobile Parts Distr
N.A.I.C.S.: 423120
Gyula Garai (Mgr-Customer Quality)

Robert Bosch Elektrowerkzeuge GmbH (1)
Siedlerstrasse 2, 01855, Sebnitz, Germany
Tel.: (49) 35971810
Automobile Parts Distr
N.A.I.C.S.: 423120

Robert Bosch Energy and Body Systems Kft. (1)
Robert Bosch park 3, Miskolc, 3526, Hungary
Tel.: (36) 46518300
Automobile Parts Distr
N.A.I.C.S.: 423120
Orsolya Eniko Lalik (Coord-Project)

Robert Bosch Engineering and Business Solutions Ltd. (1)
123 Industrial Layout Hosur Road, Koramangala, Bengaluru, 560 095, India
Tel.: (91) 8066575757
Automobile Parts Distr
N.A.I.C.S.: 423120
Jacob Peter (Head-Sls & Mktg)

Robert Bosch Engineering and Business Solutions Vietnam Co. Ltd. (1)
UNIT 11 7 e-Town 2364 Cong Hoa Ward 13, Tan Binh District, Ho Chi Minh City, Vietnam
Tel.: (84) 838128029
Automobile Parts Distr
N.A.I.C.S.: 423120

Robert Bosch Ghana Ltd. (1)
21 Kofi Annan Street Airport Residential Area Airport, Accra, Ghana
Tel.: (233) 302794616
Electrical & Electronic Equipment Mfr
N.A.I.C.S.: 335999

Robert Bosch Immobilienverwaltungs GmbH & Co. KG (1)
Heidehofstrasse 31, 70184, Stuttgart, Germany
Tel.: (49) 711460840
Automobile Parts Distr
N.A.I.C.S.: 423120

Robert Bosch Inc. (1)
28th Floor Fort Legend Towers 3rd Avenue corner 31st Street, Fort Bonifacio Global City, Taguig, 1634, Philippines
Tel.: (63) 8999091
Web Site: http://www.bosch.com.ph
Automobile Parts Mfr
N.A.I.C.S.: 336390
Gemma Stephanie Alviso (Officer-Mktg)

Robert Bosch Inc. (1)
6955 Creditview Rd, Mississauga, L5N 1R1, ON, Canada (100%)
Tel.: (905) 826-6060
Web Site: http://www.bosch.com
Sales Range: $50-74.9 Million
Emp.: 105
Automotive Parts
N.A.I.C.S.: 441330

Robert Bosch Industrial Technology Group (1)
Robert Bosch Platz 1, 70839, Gerlingen, Germany
Tel.: (49) 7118110
Web Site: http://www.bosch.com
Rev.: $8,712,488,304
Emp.: 1,500
Industrial Automation & Packaging Machinery Developer & Mfr
N.A.I.C.S.: 333993

Subsidiary (Domestic):

Bosch Rexroth AG (2)
Zum Eisengiesser 1, 97816, Lohr am Main, Germany (100%)
Tel.: (49) 9352180
Web Site: http://www.boschrexroth.com
Sales Range: $1-4.9 Billion
Hydraulic Component Continuous Casting & Electric Servo-Drive Machine Tool Mechanical Gear Unit Coupling & Sliding Bearing & Axial Ball Bearing Mfr
N.A.I.C.S.: 332912
Rolf Najork (Pres & Member-Exec Bd)

Subsidiary (Non-US):

Bosch Rexroth (Beijing) Hydraulic Co., Ltd. (3)
No 6 South YongChang Road Beijing Economic-Technological Development Â, Beijing, 100176, China
Tel.: (86) 1067827000
Mechanical Equipment Mfr
N.A.I.C.S.: 333613
Zheting Jin (Dir-Fin Controlling)

Bosch Rexroth (Changzhou) Co., Ltd. (3)
No 16 East Renmin Road, Wujin, Changzhou, 213161, China
Tel.: (86) 51988175000
Mechanical Equipment Mfr
N.A.I.C.S.: 333613

Bosch Rexroth (China) Ltd. (3)
1 Fl 19 Cheung Shun Street, Cheung Sha Wan, Kowloon, China (Hong Kong) (100%)
Tel.: (852) 2 262 5110
Web Site: http://www.boschrexroth.com.cn
Sales Range: $25-49.9 Million
Emp.: 100
N.A.I.C.S.: 334220

Bosch Rexroth (India) Ltd. (3)
Near Village Iyava Sanand Viramgam Highway, Sanand, Ahmedabad, 382170, India
Tel.: (91) 2717 678000
Mechanical Equipment Mfr
N.A.I.C.S.: 333613
Johannes Thomas Grobe (Mng Dir)

Bosch Rexroth (Xi'an) Electric Drives and Controls Co., Ltd. (3)
No 3999 Shangji Road Economic and Technological Development Zone, Xi'an, Shaanxi, China
Tel.: (86) 2986555138
Mechanical Equipment Mfr
N.A.I.C.S.: 333613

Bosch Rexroth A/S (3)
Telegrafvej 1, 2750, Ballerup, Denmark (100%)
Tel.: (45) 36774466
Web Site: http://www.boschrexroth.com
Sales Range: $25-49.9 Million
Emp.: 90
Mfr & Distributor of Hydraulics & Pneumatics
N.A.I.C.S.: 333310

Bosch Rexroth AB (3)
Varuvagen 7, 12581, Stockholm, Sweden (100%)
Tel.: (46) 87279300
Web Site: http://www.boschrexroth.com
Sales Range: $50-74.9 Million
Emp.: 200
hydraulics, electric drive & control systems, linear & mounting technology to service & support
N.A.I.C.S.: 334220

Branch (Domestic):

Bosch Rexroth (4)
Drakegatan 6, 41250, Gothenburg, Sweden (100%)
Tel.: (46) 31893460
Web Site: http://www.boschrexroth.se
Sales Range: $10-24.9 Million
Emp.: 35
Hydraulics & Pneumatics Distr
N.A.I.C.S.: 333310

Subsidiary (Domestic):

Bosch Rexroth Technique AB (4)
Varuvagen 7, 12581, Alvsjo, Stockholm, Sweden (100%)
Tel.: (46) 87279200

Web Site: http://www.boschrexroth.se
Sales Range: $150-199.9 Million
Emp.: 650
Mfr & Distributor of Hydraulic Pumps & Pneumatics
N.A.I.C.S.: 333310

Bosch Rexroth Teknik AB (4)
Varuvagen 7, Alvsjo, 125 30Â, Stockholm, Sweden
Tel.: (46) 87279200
Mechanical Equipment Distr
N.A.I.C.S.: 423840
Jens Lindfeldt (Mgr-Sls)

Plant (Domestic):

Bosch Rexroth AG - Elchingen (3)
Glockeraustrasse 2, 89275, Elchingen, Germany
Tel.: (49) 730881701
Web Site: http://www.boschrexroth.com
Sales Range: $350-399.9 Million
Emp.: 2,500
Mfr of Hydraulic Pumps & Motors
N.A.I.C.S.: 333310
Stefan Spindler (Member-Exec Bd)

Unit (Domestic):

Bosch Rexroth AG - Industrial Hydraulics (3)
Beckerstrasse 31, 91200, Chemnitz, Germany (100%)
Tel.: (49) 37135550
Web Site: http://www.boschrexroth.com
Machinery Mfr
N.A.I.C.S.: 333310

Plant (Domestic):

Bosch Rexroth AG - Lohr am Main (3)
Zum Eisengiesser 1, 97816, Lohr am Main, Germany
Tel.: (49) 9352 18 0
Web Site: http://www.boschrexroth.com
Sales Range: $150-199.9 Million
Emp.: 700
Industrial, Engineering & Automobile Manufacturing
N.A.I.C.S.: 336110
Steffen Haack (Member-Exec Bd)

Subsidiary (Non-US):

Bosch Rexroth AS (3)
Berghagen 1, 1405, Langhus, Norway (100%)
Tel.: (47) 64864100
Web Site: http://www.boschrexroth.com
Sales Range: $25-49.9 Million
Emp.: 100
Pneumatic & Hydraulic Equipment Mfr & Distr
N.A.I.C.S.: 333310

Bosch Rexroth BV (3)
Kruisbroeksestraat 1, Noord-Brabant, 5281 RV, Boxtel, Netherlands (100%)
Tel.: (31) 411651951
Web Site: http://www.boschrexroth.com
Sales Range: $150-199.9 Million
Emp.: 700
Distr of Pneumatics
N.A.I.C.S.: 333310

Subsidiary (Domestic):

Bosch Rexroth Services BV (4)
Kruisbroeksestraat 1, 5281 RV, Boxtel, Netherlands (100%)
Tel.: (31) 411651951
Web Site: http://www.boschrexroth.com
Sales Range: $125-149.9 Million
Emp.: 600
Drive & Control Technology
N.A.I.C.S.: 334519
E. de Brouwer (Project Mgr)

Subsidiary (Non-US):

Bosch Rexroth Canada (3)
490 Prince Charles Dr S, Welland, L3B 5X7, ON, Canada
Tel.: (905) 735-0510
Web Site: http://www.boschrexroth.com
Sales Range: $25-49.9 Million
Emp.: 4
Sale & Service of Hydraulic Motor & Drive System Mfr

N.A.I.C.S.: 335312

Bosch Rexroth Co. Ltd. (3)
1F No 1 Tzuchiang Street, Tucheng, Taipei, 23678, Taiwan
Tel.: (886) 222681347
Industrial Equipment Distr
N.A.I.C.S.: 423830

Subsidiary (US):

Bosch Rexroth Corporation (3)
5150 Prairie Stone Pkwy, Hoffman Estates, IL 60192-3707
Tel.: (847) 645-3600
Web Site: http://www.boschrexroth.com
Sales Range: $200-249.9 Million
Emp.: 200
Automobile Parts Mfr
N.A.I.C.S.: 336390
Greg Gumbs (Pres, CEO & Member-Mgmt Bd)

Branch (Domestic):

Bosch Rexroth Corporation (4)
14001 S Lakes Dr, Charlotte, NC 28273
Web Site: http://www.boschrexroth.com
Hydraulic Pump Valve & System Mfr
N.A.I.C.S.: 332912
Christoph Kleu (CFO, Member-Mgmt Bd & Exec VP)

Subsidiary (Non-US):

Bosch Rexroth Corporation (3)
3-6-7 Shibuya, Shibuya-ku, Tokyo, 150-0002Â, Japan
Tel.: (81) 354857146
Mechanical Equipment Mfr
N.A.I.C.S.: 333613

Bosch Rexroth DSI S.A.S. (3)
91 Bld Irene Joliot Curie, 69634, Venissieux, Cedex, France
Tel.: (33) 825721234
Mechanical Equipment Mfr
N.A.I.C.S.: 333613

Bosch Rexroth GmbH (3)
Industriepark 18, 4061, Pasching, Austria (100%)
Tel.: (43) 72216050
Web Site: http://www.boschrexroth.com
Sales Range: $100-124.9 Million
Emp.: 350
Mfr & Distributor of Hydraulic Pumps & Pneumatics
N.A.I.C.S.: 333310

Subsidiary (Domestic):

Bosch Rexroth Interlit GmbH (3)
Stolberger Strasse 374, PO Box 10 05 43, 50933, Cologne, Germany
Industrial Equipment Mfr & Distr
N.A.I.C.S.: 333517

Subsidiary (Non-US):

Bosch Rexroth Kft. (3)
1103 Budapest Gyomroi ut 104, 1103, Budapest, Hungary (80%)
Tel.: (36) 14223200
Web Site: http://www.boschrexroth.com
Sales Range: $25-49.9 Million
Emp.: 80
Electric Drives & Controls, Industrial Hydraulics, Linear Motion Assembly Technologies, Mobile Hydraulics, Pneumatics & Casting
N.A.I.C.S.: 333612
Istvan Acs (Exec Dir)

Bosch Rexroth Korea Ltd. (3)
29 Mieumsandan 1-ro, 618-260, Pusan, Korea (South) (100%)
Tel.: (82) 512600700
Web Site: http://www.boschrexroth.co.kr
Sales Range: $50-74.9 Million
Emp.: 170
Mfr & Distributor of Hydraulics & Pneumatics
N.A.I.C.S.: 333310

Bosch Rexroth Limited (3)
15 Cromwell Road, Saint Neots, PE19 2ES, Cambridgeshire, United Kingdom (100%)
Tel.: (44) 1480223200
Web Site: http://www.boschrexroth.com

ROBERT BOSCH GMBH   INTERNATIONAL PUBLIC

Robert Bosch GmbH—(Continued)

Sales Range: $125-149.9 Million
Emp.: 500
Industrial Hydraulics Assembly Technologies
Mobile Hydraulics
N.A.I.C.S.: 423830
Alastair Johnstone *(Mng Dir)*

Bosch Rexroth Ltd. (3)
15 Cromwell Road, Saint Neots, PE19 2ES,
Cambridgeshire, United Kingdom **(100%)**
Tel.: (44) 1480223200
Web Site: http://www.boschrexroth.com
Sales Range: $50-74.9 Million
Emp.: 170
N.A.I.C.S.: 334220

Bosch Rexroth Ltda (3)
Rue Georg Rexroth 609 Villa Padre Anchieda, BR 09951 270, Diadema,
Brazil **(100%)**
Tel.: (55) 407590000
Web Site: http://www.boschrexroth.com.br
Sales Range: $150-199.9 Million
Emp.: 600
N.A.I.C.S.: 334220

Bosch Rexroth Mellansel AB (3)
Vasterselsvagen 12, 890 42, Mellansel,
Sweden
Tel.: (46) 66087000
Web Site: http://www.boschrexroth.se
Emp.: 400
Mechanical Equipment Distr
N.A.I.C.S.: 423840

Bosch Rexroth Mexico SA de CV (3)
Neptuno 72 Unidad Industrial Vallejo, Deleg
Gustavo A Madero, 77000, Mexico,
Mexico **(100%)**
Tel.: (52) 5557541711
Web Site: http://www.boschrexroth.com.mx
Sales Range: $25-49.9 Million
Emp.: 100
N.A.I.C.S.: 334220

Bosch Rexroth N.V. (3)
Henri-Joseph Genessestraat 1, 1070, Brussels, Belgium
Tel.: (32) 25823180
Mechanical Equipment Mfr
N.A.I.C.S.: 333613

Bosch Rexroth Oil Control S.p.A. (3)
Via Leonardo da Vinci 5, Nonantola, 41015,
Modena, Italy
Tel.: (39) 059887611
Mechanical Equipment Mfr
N.A.I.C.S.: 333613

**Bosch Rexroth Otomasyon San.ve
Tic A.S.** (3)
TOSB Taysad Organize Sanayi Bolgesi 1
Cad 14 Sok No 10, Kocaeli, 41480,
Turkiye **(100%)**
Tel.: (90) 2626760000
Web Site: http://www.boschrexroth.com
Sales Range: $25-49.9 Million
Emp.: 55
Mfr & Distributor of Hydraulics & Pneumatics
N.A.I.C.S.: 333310
Thomas Markus Ilkow *(Chm)*

Bosch Rexroth Oy (3)
Ansatie 6b, 01740, Vantaa, Finland
Tel.: (358) 103441000
Mechanical Equipment Mfr
N.A.I.C.S.: 333613

Bosch Rexroth Pte. Ltd. (3)
16D Tuas Avenue 1 05-60 & 62, Singapore,
639536, Singapore **(100%)**
Tel.: (65) 65084128
Web Site: http://www.boschrexroth.com
Sales Range: $25-49.9 Million
Emp.: 100
Mfr & Distributor of Hydraulics & Pneumatics
N.A.I.C.S.: 333310

Bosch Rexroth Pty. Ltd. (3)
3 Valediction Road, Kings Park, 2148,
NSW, Australia **(100%)**
Tel.: (61) 298317788
Web Site: http://www.boschrexroth.com
Sales Range: $25-49.9 Million
Emp.: 100
Mfr & Distributor of Hydraulics & Pneumatics

N.A.I.C.S.: 333310
Ronald Suurd *(Mng Dir & Member-Mgmt
Bd)*

Subsidiary (Non-US):

Bosch Rexroth Ltd. (4)
6 Echelon Place, East Tamaki, Auckland,
New Zealand **(100%)**
Tel.: (64) 92744172
Web Site: http://www.boschrexroth.com
Sales Range: $10-24.9 Million
Emp.: 14
Hydraulic & Pneumatic Products Distr
N.A.I.C.S.: 423830

Subsidiary (Non-US):

Bosch Rexroth S.A. (3)
Calle B Av Sanatorio Del Avila Ed empresarial Ciudad Center, Caracas, 1010,
Venezuela **(100%)**
Tel.: (58) 2122074571
Web Site: http://www.boschrexroth.com.ve
Sales Range: $25-49.9 Million
Emp.: 25
Mfr & Distributor of Hydraulics & Pneumatics
N.A.I.C.S.: 333310

Bosch Rexroth S.A. (3)
37 Ercheias Str, 19 400, Koropi, Greece
Tel.: (30) 2105701400
Mechanical Equipment Mfr
N.A.I.C.S.: 333613

Bosch Rexroth S.A.I.C. (3)
Neuquen 5801, Carapachay, B1606DLD,
Buenos Aires, Argentina **(100%)**
Tel.: (54) 52899000
Web Site: http://www.boschrexroth.com
Sales Range: $25-49.9 Million
Emp.: 50
Electronic Components, eMobility Solutions,
Household Appliances, Car Parts & Accessories & Automotive Technology Mfr
N.A.I.C.S.: 423620

Bosch Rexroth S.A.S. (3)
91 bd Joliot Curie, BP 101, 69634, Venissieux, Cedex, France **(100%)**
Tel.: (33) 443240000
Web Site: http://www.boschrexroth.com
Sales Range: $25-49.9 Million
Emp.: 50
Mfr & Distribute Pneumatic Components &
Filter Regulator Lubricators
N.A.I.C.S.: 333310

Bosch Rexroth S.A.S. (3)
91 Boulevard Irene Joliot Curie, 69634,
Venissieux, Cedex, France
Tel.: (33) 7 78 78 52 52
Web Site: http://www.boschrexroth.fr
Communication Equipment Mfr
N.A.I.C.S.: 334220

Bosch Rexroth S.R.L. (3)
Aurel Vlaicu Street no 2, Alba, Blaj, Romania
Tel.: (40) 258807134
Mechanical Equipment Mfr
N.A.I.C.S.: 333613

Bosch Rexroth SA (3)
Henri-Joseph Genessestraat 1, 1070, Brussels, Belgium **(100%)**
Tel.: (32) 25823180
Web Site: http://www.boschrexroth.com
Sales Range: $50-74.9 Million
Emp.: 175
Mfr & Distributor of Hydraulics & Pneumatics
N.A.I.C.S.: 333310

Bosch Rexroth SA (3)
Centro Industrial Santiga, E 08130, Santa
Perpetua de Mogoda, Spain **(100%)**
Tel.: (34) 937479400
Web Site: http://www.boschrexroth.es
Sales Range: $50-74.9 Million
Emp.: 250
Mfr & Distributor of Hydraulics & Pneumatics
N.A.I.C.S.: 333310

Bosch Rexroth Schweiz AG (3)
Hemrietstrasse 2, 8863, Buttikon,
Switzerland **(100%)**
Tel.: (41) 554646111
Web Site: http://www.boschrexroth.com

Sales Range: $50-74.9 Million
Emp.: 150
Hydraulic & Pneumatic Components Mfr
N.A.I.C.S.: 333310
Norbert Renz *(Mng Dir)*

Subsidiary (Domestic):

Bosch Rexroth Pneumatic AG (4)
Hemrietstrasse 2, 8863, Buttikon,
Switzerland **(100%)**
Tel.: (41) 554646111
Web Site: http://www.bosch.ch
Mfr & Distr of Hydraulics, Pneumatics, Electrical Drives & Controls & Linear Motion &
Assembly Technology
N.A.I.C.S.: 334418

Subsidiary (Non-US):

Bosch Rexroth Sdn. Bhd. (3)
No 11 Jalan Astaka U8/82, Bukit Jelutong,
40150, Shah Alam, Selangor,
Malaysia **(100%)**
Tel.: (60) 378448000
Web Site: http://www.boschrexroth.com.my
Sales Range: $25-49.9 Million
Emp.: 70
Mfr & Distributor of Hydraulics & Pneumatics
N.A.I.C.S.: 333310

Bosch Rexroth Sp.zoo (3)
Ul Jutrzenki 102/104, 02-230, Warsaw,
Poland **(100%)**
Tel.: (48) 227381800
Web Site: http://www.boschrexroth.com
Sales Range: $25-49.9 Million
Emp.: 60
Mfr & Distributor of Hydraulics & Pneumatics
N.A.I.C.S.: 333310

Bosch Rexroth SpA (3)
Strada Statale Padana Superiore 11 N 41,
Cernusco sul Naviglio, 20063, Milan,
Italy **(100%)**
Tel.: (39) 02923651
Web Site: http://www.boschrexroth.com
Sales Range: $100-124.9 Million
Emp.: 500
Electric Equipment Mfr
N.A.I.C.S.: 335999

Bosch Rexroth, S.A. de C.V. (3)
Neptuno 72 Zona Industrial Vallejo, Mexico,
07000, Mexico
Tel.: (52) 55 5754 1711
Mechanical Equipment Mfr
N.A.I.C.S.: 333613

Bosch Rexroth, S.L. (3)
Francisco Grandmontagne 2 Parque Empresarial Zuatzu, 20018, San Sebastian,
Spain
Tel.: (34) 943318400
Mechanical Equipment Mfr
N.A.I.C.S.: 333613

Bosch Rexroth, spol. s.r.o. (3)
Tezebni 1238/2, 627 00, Brno, Czech
Republic **(100%)**
Tel.: (420) 548126111
Web Site: http://www.boschrexroth.cz
Sales Range: $50-74.9 Million
Emp.: 250
Mfr & Distributor of Hydraulic & Pneumatic
Components
N.A.I.C.S.: 333310

Lidan Marine AB (3)
Fiskaregatan 3, Box 854, 531 18, Lidkoping, Sweden
Tel.: (46) 510545250
Web Site: http://www.lidanmarine.com
Sales Range: $1-9.9 Million
Emp.: 45
Mfr of Hydraulic Motors
N.A.I.C.S.: 335312
Lors Berglund *(Mng Dir)*

OOO Bosch Rexroth (3)
Vashutinskoje Chaussee 24, Khimki,
141400, Moscow, Russia
Tel.: (7) 4955609595
Web Site: http://www.boschrexroth.com
Automobile Parts Distr
N.A.I.C.S.: 423120

P.T. Bosch Rexroth (3)
Building 202 Cilandak Commercial Estate Jl

Cilandak KKO, Jakarta, 12560, Indonesia
Tel.: (62) 217891169
Automobile Parts Distr
N.A.I.C.S.: 423690
Ronald Suurd *(Gen Mgr)*

Subsidiary (Domestic):

Rexroth Indramat GmbH (3)
Buergermeister Dr Nebel Strasse 2, 97816,
Lohra, Germany **(100%)**
Tel.: (49) 9352405060
Web Site: http://www.boschrexroth.com
Sales Range: $350-399.9 Million
Emp.: 1,400
N.A.I.C.S.: 334220

Rexroth Pneumatics AG (3)
Ulmer Strasse 4, 30880, Laatzen,
Germany **(100%)**
Tel.: (49) 51121360
Web Site: http://www.boschrexroth.com
Sales Range: $50-74.9 Million
Emp.: 200
Producer of Pneumatic, Electronic & Electropneumatic Components & Systems for
the Automation of Machines & Production
Equipment
N.A.I.C.S.: 334419

Robert Bosch Internationale Beteiligungen AG (1)
Luterbachstrasse 10, 4528, Zuchwil, Switzerland
Tel.: (41) 32 686 39 90
Web Site: http://www.bosch.com
Emp.: 300
Automobile Parts Distr
N.A.I.C.S.: 423120

Robert Bosch Korea Ltd. (1)
567 Shinsu-ro, Giheung-gu, 16923, Yongin,
Gyeonggi-do, Korea (South)
Tel.: (82) 215993567
Web Site: http://www.bosch.co.kr
Automobile Parts Distr
N.A.I.C.S.: 423120
Alex Drljaca *(Pres)*

Robert Bosch LLC (1)
2800 S 25th Ave, Broadview, IL
60155-4532 **(100%)**
Tel.: (708) 865-5200
Web Site: http://www.boschusa.com
Motor Vehicle Components & Tools Mfr
N.A.I.C.S.: 336390
Mike Mansuetti *(Pres)*

Subsidiary (Domestic):

Akustica Inc. (2)
2835 E Carson St Ste 301, Pittsburgh, PA
15203
Tel.: (412) 390-1730
Web Site: http://www.akustica.com
Semiconductor Mfr & Distr
N.A.I.C.S.: 333242

Joint Venture (Domestic):

**Associated Fuel Pump Systems
Corp.** (2)
110 Scotts Br Rd, Anderson, SC 29622
Tel.: (864) 224-0012
Web Site: http://www.afco.com
Sales Range: $75-99.9 Million
Emp.: 350
Automotive Gasoline Pumps Mfr
N.A.I.C.S.: 333914
Kevin Hardy *(Supvr-Acctg)*

Subsidiary (Domestic):

BSE PV LLC (2)
2988 Campus Dr Ste100, San Mateo, CA
94403
Tel.: (650) 275-3450
Solar Power Structure Installation Services
N.A.I.C.S.: 238220

**Bosch Software Innovations
Corp.** (2)
161 N Clark St Ste 3550, Chicago, IL
60601
Tel.: (312) 368-2500
Software Development Services
N.A.I.C.S.: 541511
Matthew Jennings *(Pres)*

Bosch Thermotechnology Corp. (2)
50 Wentworth Ave, Londonderry, NH 03053

AND PRIVATE COMPANIES

Tel.: (603) 552-1100
Web Site: http://www.bosch-climate.us
Emp.: 12,900
Heating & Cooling System Mfr
N.A.I.C.S.: 333415

Escrypt Inc. (2)
3019 Miller Rd, Ann Arbor, MI 48103
Tel.: (734) 997-7860
Software Development Services
N.A.I.C.S.: 541511
Robert Wesley (Pres)

FHP Manufacturing Company (2)
601 N W 65th Ct, Fort Lauderdale, FL 33309
Tel.: (954) 776-5471
Heating & Cooling Equipment Mfr
N.A.I.C.S.: 333415

Freud America Inc. (2)
218 Feld Ave, High Point, NC 27263
Web Site: http://www.freudtools.com
Wooden Furniture & Door Mfr
N.A.I.C.S.: 321911

Subsidiary (Non-US):

Freud Canada Inc. (3)
7450 Pacific Circle, Mississauga, L5T 2A3, ON, Canada
Tel.: (905) 670-1025
Sawing Machine Tool Mfr
N.A.I.C.S.: 333517

Subsidiary (Domestic):

RBAJ Holding, Inc. (2)
2 Jetview Dr, Rochester, NY 14624
Tel.: (585) 464-5000
Automobile Parts Distr
N.A.I.C.S.: 423120

Robert Bosch Battery Systems LLC (2)
3740 Lapeer Rd S, Orion, MI 48359
Tel.: (248) 620-5700
Web Site: http://www.cobasys.com
Automobile Parts Mfr
N.A.I.C.S.: 336390

Robert Bosch Healthcare, Inc. (2)
2400 Geng Rd Ste 200, Palo Alto, CA 94303
Tel.: (650) 690-9100
Web Site: http://www.bosch-telehealth.com
Sales Range: $25-49.9 Million
Technology Solutions for Remote Health Monitoring & Management
N.A.I.C.S.: 339112

Seeo, Inc. (2)
3906 Trust Way, Hayward, CA 94545
Tel.: (510) 782-7336
Web Site: http://www.seeo.com
Sales Range: $1-9.9 Million
Rechargeable Lithium-Ion Battery Mfr & Whslr
N.A.I.C.S.: 335910
Hany Eitouni (Founder, CTO & VP-Advanced Engrg)

Robert Bosch Lanka (Pvt.) Ltd. (1)
385 The Landmark 4th Floor Galle Road, Colombo, Sri Lanka
Tel.: (94) 113690650
Web Site: http://www.bosch.lk
Automotive Electronic Equipment Mfr
N.A.I.C.S.: 336320

Robert Bosch Limited (1)
52-54 Isaac John Street Landmark House, Ikeja, Lagos, Nigeria
Tel.: (234) 14489092
Automobile Parts Distr
N.A.I.C.S.: 423120
Okenna Igbokwe (Mgr-Bus Dev-Security Sys)

Robert Bosch Lizenzverwaltungsgesellschaft mbH (1)
Gewerbering 15, 83607, Holzkirchen, Germany
Tel.: (49) 7118110
Automobile Parts Distr
N.A.I.C.S.: 423120

Robert Bosch Lollar Guss GmbH (1)
Justus-Kilian-Strasse 1, Lollar, 35457, Giessen, Germany
Tel.: (49) 64414180

Web Site: http://www.bosch-kundenguss.de
Car Brake Disc Mfr
N.A.I.C.S.: 336340

Robert Bosch Ltd. (1)
FYI Center Tower 1 5th Floor 2525 Rama IV Road 1, Khlong Toei, Bangkok, 10110, Thailand
Tel.: (66) 20128888
Web Site: http://www.bosch.co.th
Automobile Parts Mfr
N.A.I.C.S.: 336390

Robert Bosch Ltd. (1)
Pavlo Tychyny Avenue 1B office A701, 02152, Kiev, Ukraine
Tel.: (380) 444902400
Web Site: http://www.bosch.ua
Automobile Parts Distr
N.A.I.C.S.: 423120

Robert Bosch Ltd. (1)
14 Constellation Drive Sunset North, North Shore, Auckland, New Zealand
Tel.: (64) 800426724
Automobile Parts Distr
N.A.I.C.S.: 423120

Robert Bosch Ltda (1)
Via Anhanguera km 98 Villa, Boa Vista, 13065 900, Campinas, Sao Paulo, Brazil (100%)
Tel.: (55) 1921031954
Web Site: http://www.bosch.com.br
Sales Range: $1-9.9 Million
Emp.: 13,000
Mfr of Automotive Equipment, Power Tools, Car Radios, Hydraulic Products & Products in Testing & Measuring Technology
N.A.I.C.S.: 336340

Robert Bosch Ltda. (1)
Autonorte 108A-50, 110111, Bogota, Cundinamarca, Colombia
Tel.: (57) 16585010
Web Site: http://www.bosch.com.co
Emp.: 94
Automobile Parts Distr
N.A.I.C.S.: 423120
Claudia Mejia (Dir-Country Bus)

Robert Bosch Mexico Sistemas Automotrices, S.A. de C.V. (1)
Eje Central Sahop No 245, Sinaloa, Mexico
Tel.: (52) 4448267400
Automobile Parts Distr
N.A.I.C.S.: 423120
Sergio Obregon (Mgr-Ops)

Robert Bosch Middle East FZE (1)
DAFZA West Wing 5A Office 701, PO Box 54307, Dubai, United Arab Emirates
Tel.: (971) 42123710
Web Site: http://www.bosch-middleeast.com
Automobile Parts Distr
N.A.I.C.S.: 423120

Robert Bosch Motorlu Araclar Yan Sanayi ve Ticaret AS (1)
Ahi Evran Caddesi 21, Polaris Plaza Kat 22 24, Sisli, 34398, Istanbul, Turkiye (80%)
Tel.: (90) 2123350600
Sales Range: $10-24.9 Million
Emp.: 6,500
Automotive Equipment
N.A.I.C.S.: 336340

Robert Bosch N.V. (1)
Rue Henri Genesse 1, 1070, Brussels, Belgium (100%)
Tel.: (32) 025255111
Web Site: http://www.bosch.be
Sales Range: $50-74.9 Million
Emp.: 150
Mfr of Automotive Equipment
N.A.I.C.S.: 336320
Patrick Incoletti (Member-Mgmt Bd)

Robert Bosch OU (1)
Kesk tee 10 Juri alevik, 75301, Harjumaa, Estonia
Tel.: (372) 6549561
Web Site: http://www.bosch.ee
Automobile Parts Distr
N.A.I.C.S.: 423120
Kaspars Kalviskis (Member-Mgmt Bd)

Robert Bosch Oy (1)
Ayritie 8 E, 01510, Vantaa, Finland
Tel.: (358) 10 480 80
Web Site: http://www.bosch.fi

Power Tool Distr
N.A.I.C.S.: 423710

Robert Bosch Packaging Technology B.V. (1)
Industriekade 43, Postbus 16, 6001 SE, Weert, Netherlands
Tel.: (31) 495574000
Web Site: http://www.boschpackaging.com
Packaging Services
N.A.I.C.S.: 561910
Rene Peeters (Engr-Turn Key Solutions)

Robert Bosch Panama S.A. (1)
Calle 56 Este Paitilla Mall Office Tower 1403, Panama, Panama
Tel.: (507) 3010960
Web Site: http://www.bosch.com.pa
Emp.: 31
Automobile Parts Distr
N.A.I.C.S.: 423120
Helmuth Obilcnik (Pres)

Robert Bosch Production N.V. (1)
Hamelendreef 80, 3300, Tienen, Belgium
Tel.: (32) 16800711
Automobile Parts Distr
N.A.I.C.S.: 423120
Herve Bratec (Project Mgr-R & D)

Robert Bosch S.A. (1)
Henri Joseph Genessestraat 1, 1070, Brussels, Belgium
Tel.: (32) 25255185
Web Site: http://www.bosch.be
Automobile Parts Distr
N.A.I.C.S.: 423120
Heiko Carrie (Chm-Mgmt Bd)

Robert Bosch S.A. (1)
Hermanos Garcia Noblejas 19, Madrid, 28037, Spain (100%)
Tel.: (34) 914081700
Web Site: http://www.robertboschespana.es
Sales Range: $1-4.9 Billion
Emp.: 5,700
Mfr of Automotive Equipment; Sales & Service of Bosch Products in Spain
N.A.I.C.S.: 336340

Robert Bosch S.A. (1)
San Eugenio 40 - Nunoa, 7500000, Santiago, Chile
Tel.: (56) 224055500
Web Site: http://www.bosch.cl
Emp.: 200
Automobile Parts Distr
N.A.I.C.S.: 423120

Robert Bosch S.A. (1)
Calle B Av Sanatorio del Avila Edif Empresarial, Ciudad Center Torre D piso 2 y 3 Urb Boleita Norte Miranda, 1071, Caracas, Venezuela
Tel.: (58) 2122074511
Web Site: http://www.bosch.com.ve
Emp.: 35
Automobile Parts Distr
N.A.I.C.S.: 423120

Robert Bosch S.A.C. (1)
Avenida Primavera 781 Piso 2 y 3 15037, Lima, Peru
Tel.: (51) 12190332
Web Site: http://www.bosch.com.pe
Emp.: 67
Automobile Parts Distr
N.A.I.C.S.: 423120

Robert Bosch SA (1)
Erxeias 37, PO Box 44073, 19400, Koropi, Athens, Greece
Tel.: (30) 2105701200
Web Site: http://www.bosch.gr
Sales Range: $50-74.9 Million
Sells Automotive Spare Parts, Power Tools, Car Multimedia, Thermotechnology & Security.
N.A.I.C.S.: 441330
Capra Loannis (CEO)

Robert Bosch SIA (1)
Mukusalas iela 101, Riga, 1004, Latvia (100%)
Tel.: (371) 67802080
Web Site: http://www.bosch.lv
Sales Range: $25-49.9 Million
Mfr of Motor Vehicle Parts & Accessories.
N.A.I.C.S.: 336340
Kaspars Kalviskis (Member-Mgmt Bd)

ROBERT BOSCH GMBH

Robert Bosch Sdn. Bhd. (1)
No 8A Jalan 13/6, 46200, Petaling Jaya, Selangor, Malaysia
Tel.: (60) 379663000
Automobile Parts Distr
N.A.I.C.S.: 423120
Woon Janesta (Gen Mgr)

Robert Bosch Semiconductor LLC (1)
7501 Foothills Blvd, Roseville, CA 95747-6504
Tel.: (916) 786-3900
Web Site: http://www.tsisemi.com
Emp.: 250
Semiconductor & Related Device Mfr
N.A.I.C.S.: 334413
Sagar Pushpala (CEO)

Robert Bosch Service Solutions - Costa Rica, S.A. (1)
America Free Zone Building C-12 5th Floor, San Francisco, Heredia, 40103, Costa Rica
Tel.: (506) 40525720
Business Outsourcing Services
N.A.I.C.S.: 541611

Robert Bosch Sistemas Automotrices, S.A. de C.V. (1)
Prolongacion Hermanos Escobar 6965 Parque Industrial Omega, 32320, Ciudad Juarez, Mexico
Tel.: (52) 6566882300
Automobile Parts Distr
N.A.I.C.S.: 423120
R. Daniel (Mgr-Ops)

Robert Bosch Start-Up GmbH (1)
Gronerstrasse 5, 71636, Ludwigsburg, Germany
Tel.: (49) 71181135024
Web Site: http://www.bosch-startup.com
Automobile Parts Mfr
N.A.I.C.S.: 336390
Amos Albert (Member-Mgmt Bd)

Robert Bosch Taiwan Co., Ltd. (1)
6F No 90 Jian Guo N Road Sec 1, Taipei, 10491, Taiwan
Tel.: (886) 277342580
Web Site: http://www.bosch.com.tw
Automobile Parts Mfr
N.A.I.C.S.: 336390
Jan Hollmann (Mng Dir)

Robert Bosch Unipessoal, Lda. (1)
Av Infante D Henrique Lt 2E 3E, 1800-220, Lisbon, Portugal (100%)
Tel.: (351) 808100202
Web Site: http://www.pt.bosch-automotive.com
Sales Range: $25-49.9 Million
Emp.: 100
Household Appliances & Car Services
N.A.I.C.S.: 335210

Robert Bosch Uruguay S.A. (1)
Av Italia 7519 local 004 Corner Barradas-Art Carrasco Business, 11500, Montevideo, Uruguay
Tel.: (598) 26047010
Web Site: http://www.bosch-uruguay.com
Electrical & Electronic Equipment Mfr
N.A.I.C.S.: 335999

Robert Bosch d.o.o. (1)
Kneza Branimira 22 pp 139, Dubrava, 10040, Zagreb, Croatia
Tel.: (385) 12958060
Web Site: http://www.bosch.hr
Home Appliance Mfr
N.A.I.C.S.: 335220
Mirsada Kudric (Mng Dir)

Robert Bosch spol. s.r.o. (1)
Ambrusova 4, 821 04, Bratislava, Slovakia
Tel.: (421) 2 48 703 888
Web Site: http://www.bosch.sk
Automobile Parts Mfr
N.A.I.C.S.: 336390

Robert Bosch, Limitada (1)
Condominio Bengo Tower Belas Business Park IV Piso4-404, Talatona, Luanda, Angola
Tel.: (244) 939106406
Electrical & Electronic Equipment Mfr
N.A.I.C.S.: 335999

Robert Bosch, S. de R.L. de C.V. (1)

ROBERT BOSCH GMBH

Robert Bosch GmbH—(Continued)
G Gonzalez Camarena 333 Colonia Centro de Ciudad Santa Fe, 01210, Mexico, Mexico
Tel.: (52) 9177595
Web Site: http://www.bosch.com.mx
Automobile Parts Mfr
N.A.I.C.S.: 336390

Robert Bosch, S.A. de C.V. (1)
Sierra Gamon 120, Col Lomas de Chapulteped, 11000, Mexico, DF, Mexico (100%)
Tel.: (52) 5552843000
Web Site: http://www.bosch.com.mx
Sales Range: $25-49.9 Million
Emp.: 100
Automobile Parts Distr
N.A.I.C.S.: 441330
Charles Visconti (Pres)

Robert Bosch, spol. s.r.o. (1)
Roberta Bosche 2678, 370 04, Ceske Budejovice, Czech Republic
Tel.: (420) 261300999
Web Site: http://www.bosch.cz
Automobile Parts Mfr
N.A.I.C.S.: 336390

SBM Schoeller-Bleckmann-Medizintechnik GmbH (1)
Pharmastr 1, 2630, Ternitz, Austria
Tel.: (43) 26303120
Automobile Parts Distr
N.A.I.C.S.: 423120
Regine Hrozek (Mgr-Sls)

SEG Hausgerate GmbH (1)
Carl-Wery-Str 34, 81739, Munich, Germany
Tel.: (49) 89459009
Web Site: http://www.siemens-home.bsh-group.com
Home Appliance Mfr
N.A.I.C.S.: 335220

SIA Abrasives Polska Sp. z o.o. (1)
Prosta 21, Lozienica, 72-100, Goleniow, Poland
Tel.: (48) 918883000
Coated Abrasive Product Mfr
N.A.I.C.S.: 327910

Saguaro Electronica, S.A. de C.V. (1)
Periferico poniente 310-C Col Las Quintas, 83240, Hermosillo, Sonora, Mexico
Tel.: (52) 6622607012
Automobile Parts Distr
N.A.I.C.S.: 423120

Security & Safety Things GmbH (1)
Sendlinger Strasse 7, 80331, Munich, Germany
Tel.: (49) 8962902992
Web Site: http://www.securityandsafetythings.com
Emp.: 110
Security App Development Services
N.A.I.C.S.: 541511
Hartmut Schaper (CEO)

Shanghai Bosch Rexroth Hydraulics & Automation Ltd. (1)
4/F China Marine Tower 1 Pu Dong Avenue, Pudong, Shanghai, China
Tel.: (86) 2122181111
Automobile Parts Distr
N.A.I.C.S.: 423120

Sieger Heizsysteme GmbH (1)
Eiserfelder Strasse 98, 57072, Siegen, Germany
Tel.: (49) 27123430
Web Site: http://www.sieger.net
Boiler Mfr
N.A.I.C.S.: 332410

TOO Robert Bosch (1)
st Muratbaeva 180 Business Center Hermes 7th floor, 050012, Almaty, Kazakhstan
Tel.: (7) 7273313100
Web Site: http://www.bosch.kz
Automobile Parts Mfr
N.A.I.C.S.: 336390

Taixiang Vehicle Replace Parts (Shenzhen) Co., Ltd. (1)
8 Fu-Ping Chung Road, Pingdi Town Longgang, Shenzhen, 518117, Guangdong, China
Tel.: (86) 75589941868
Automobile Parts Distr
N.A.I.C.S.: 423120

Technics Plasma GmbH Plasma- und Ionenstrahlsysteme (1)
, Kirchheim, Germany
N.A.I.C.S.: 333310

Tecnologie Diesel S.p.A. (1)
Via degli Oleandri 8/10, Industrial area, 70026, Modugno, BA, Italy
Tel.: (39) 0805875111
Industrial Automotive Equipment Mfr
N.A.I.C.S.: 335314

Tecnologie Diesel e Sistemi Frenanti S.p.A. (1)
Zona Industriale - Via degli Oleandri 8/10, Modugno, 70026, Bari, Italy
Tel.: (39) 0805875111
Pumps Mfr
N.A.I.C.S.: 333914
Francesco Basile (Dir-HR & Comm)

UAB Robert Bosch (1)
Ateities pl 79A, 52104, Kaunas, Lithuania
Tel.: (370) 37713350
Web Site: http://www.bosch.lt
Automobile Parts Distr
N.A.I.C.S.: 423120
Kaspars Kalviskis (Member-Mgmt Bd)

Unipoint Electric MFG Co., Ltd. (1)
No 20 Lane 421 Fude 1st Rd, Xizhi Dist, Taipei, Taiwan
Tel.: (886) 226943300
Web Site: http://www.unipoint.com.tw
Emp.: 500
Automobile Parts Mfr
N.A.I.C.S.: 336320

United Automotive Electronic Systems Co., Ltd. (1)
No 555 Rongqiao Road New Area, Pudong, Shanghai, 201206, China
Tel.: (86) 21 6168 8888
Web Site: http://www.uaes.com
Automobile Parts Distr
N.A.I.C.S.: 423120

VHIT S.p.A. (1)
Strada Vicinale delle Sabbione 5, Offanengo, 26010, Cremona, CR, Italy
Tel.: (39) 03732491
Web Site: https://vhit-weifu.com
Emp.: 550
Hydraulic Pump Mfr & Distr
N.A.I.C.S.: 333996
Davide Fortini (Project Mgr-Customer)

Valicare GmbH (1)
Eschborner Landstrasse 130-132, 60461, Frankfurt, Germany
Tel.: (49) 697909343
Pharmaceutical Equipment Mfr
N.A.I.C.S.: 423450

Valicare s.r.o. (1)
Jesenskeho 34, 911 01, Trencin, Slovakia
Tel.: (421) 326400414
Pharmaceutical Equipment Mfr
N.A.I.C.S.: 334516
Marcin Nowak (Project Mgr & Sr Engr-Validation)

Worcester Group plc (1)
Cotswold Way, Warndon, Worcester, WR4 9SW, United Kingdom
Tel.: (44) 3301239339
Web Site: http://www.worcester-bosch.co.uk
Boiler Mfr
N.A.I.C.S.: 333414

escrypt GmbH Embedded Security (1)
Lise-Meitner-Allee 4Â , 44801, Bochum, Germany
Security System Design Services
N.A.I.C.S.: 541512
Thomas Wollinger (Mng Dir)

for you Insurance Services GmbH (1)
Robert-Bosch-Platz 1, 70839, Gerlingen, Germany
Tel.: (49) 71561751751
Web Site: http://www.for-you-insuranceservices.de
Insurance Services
N.A.I.C.S.: 524210

grow platform GmbH (1)
Gronerstrasse 9, 71636, Ludwigsburg, Germany
Tel.: (49) 7118110
Web Site: http://www.growplatform.com
Entrepreneur Platform Services
N.A.I.C.S.: 513210

ROBERT KENNEDY PUBLISHING
400 Matheson Blvd W, Mississauga, L5R 3M1, ON, Canada
Tel.: (905) 507-3545
Web Site: http://www.rkpubs.com
Year Founded: 1974
Magazine Publisher
N.A.I.C.S.: 513120
Hemant Pradhan (CFO)

Subsidiaries:

Oxygen (1)
400 Matheson Blvd W, Mississauga, L5R 3M1, ON, Canada
Tel.: (905) 507-3545
Web Site: http://www.oxygenmag.com
Sales Range: $25-49.9 Million
Emp.: 50
Magazine
N.A.I.C.S.: 513120
Benny Reuven (VP-Dev)

ROBERT KRAEMER GMBH & CO. KG
Zum Roten Hahn 9, 26180, Rastede, Germany
Tel.: (49) 440297880
Web Site: http://www.rokra.com
Year Founded: 1912
Sales Range: $10-24.9 Million
Printing Ink & Specialty Resin Mfr
N.A.I.C.S.: 325910
Werner Sarfert (Gen Mgr)

ROBERT MOTORS
5450 Dundas Street West, Toronto, M9B 1B4, ON, Canada
Tel.: (416) 231-1984
Web Site: http://www.robertvolvo.com
Year Founded: 1927
Rev: $13,650,357
Emp.: 30
New & Used Car Dealers
N.A.I.C.S.: 441110
Jeremy Hill (Mgr-Parts)

ROBERT SCOTT & SONS LTD.
Oak View Mills Manchester Road, Oldham, OL3 7HG, United Kingdom
Tel.: (44) 1457819400
Web Site: http://www.robert-scott.co.uk
Year Founded: 1925
Sales Range: $25-49.9 Million
Emp.: 230
Cleaning Supplies & Equipment Mfr
N.A.I.C.S.: 333310
Alastair Scott (Dir-Sls)

Subsidiaries:

Contico Manufacturing Limited (1)
Cardrew Way, Redruth, TR15 1ST, United Kingdom
Tel.: (44) 1209312123
Web Site: http://www.conticospraychem.com
Sales Range: $25-49.9 Million
Emp.: 80
Cleaning Supplies & Equipment Mfr
N.A.I.C.S.: 333310
N. Man (Mgr-Quality)

ROBERT WALTERS PLC
11 Slingsby Place St Martin's Courtyard, London, WC2E 9AB, United Kingdom
Tel.: (44) 2073793333 UK
Web Site:
https://www.robertwalters.co.uk

INTERNATIONAL PUBLIC

RWA—(LSE)
Rev: $1,274,084,448
Assets: $560,195,272
Liabilities: $330,333,276
Net Worth: $229,861,996
Earnings: $7,739,004
Emp.: 3,598
Fiscal Year-end: 12/31/20
Permanent, Temporary & Contract Personnel Services
N.A.I.C.S.: 541612
Robert C. Walters (CEO)

Subsidiaries:

Merryck and Co Limited (1)
81 Kings Road, London, SW3 4NX, United Kingdom
Tel.: (44) 207 823 0516
Web Site: https://www.merryck.com
Sales Range: $25-49.9 Million
Emp.: 10
Employment Placement Agencies
N.A.I.C.S.: 561311
Coretha M. Rushing (Mng Dir-ExCo Grp)

PT. Robert Walters Indonesia (1)
World Trade Centre 3 18th Floor Jl Jend Sudirman Kav 29-31, Jakarta, 12920, Indonesia
Tel.: (62) 2129651500
Financial Services
N.A.I.C.S.: 523150

RS Resource Solutions Germany GmbH (1)
Main Tower 33 Stock Neue Mainzer Str 52-58, 60311, Frankfurt am Main, Germany
Tel.: (49) 69920384004
Recruitment Agency Services
N.A.I.C.S.: 561311

Resource Solutions Limited (1)
11 Slingsby Place St Martin's Courtyard, London, WC2E 9AB, United Kingdom
Tel.: (44) 207 071 7000
Web Site:
https://www.resourcesolutions.com
Sales Range: $25-49.9 Million
Human Resource Consulting Services
N.A.I.C.S.: 541612
Faye Walshe (Dir-Innovation)

Robert Walters (Hong Kong) Limited (1)
Unit 2001 20/F Nexxus Building 41 Connaught Road Central, Central, China (Hong Kong) (100%)
Tel.: (852) 2 103 5300
Web Site: https://www.robertwalters.com.hk
Sales Range: $25-49.9 Million
Employment Placement Agencies
N.A.I.C.S.: 561311

Robert Walters (Singapore) Pte Limited (1)
6 Battery Road 09-01 Floor, Singapore, 049909, Singapore (100%)
Tel.: (65) 6 228 0200
Web Site: https://www.robertwalters.com.sg
Sales Range: $25-49.9 Million
Emp.: 80
Employment Placement Agencies
N.A.I.C.S.: 561311

Robert Walters Associates Inc. (1)
7 Times Sq Ste 4301, New York, NY 10036 (100%)
Tel.: (212) 704-9900
Web Site: http://www.robertwalters.us
Sales Range: $10-24.9 Million
Employment Placement Agencies
N.A.I.C.S.: 561311

Robert Walters B.V. (1)
WTC Tower H Zuidplein 28, 1077 XV, Amsterdam, Netherlands (100%)
Tel.: (31) 20 644 4655
Web Site: https://www.robertwalters.nl
Sales Range: $25-49.9 Million
Management Consulting Services
N.A.I.C.S.: 541618
Rob Vermaak (Mng Dir-Benelux)

Robert Walters Brazil Limitada (1)
Rua do Rocio 350 4 andar Vila Olimpia, Sao Paulo, 04552-000, Brazil
Tel.: (55) 112 655 0888
Web Site: https://www.robertwalters.com.br

Human Resource Consulting Services
N.A.I.C.S.: 541612

Robert Walters Business Consulting (Shanghai) Ltd. (1)
2206-2207 22nd Floor Park Place Office Tower No 1601, West Nanjing Road, Shanghai, 200040, China
Tel.: (86) 2151535888
Recruitment Agency Services
N.A.I.C.S.: 561311

Robert Walters Canada Inc. (1)
145 King Street West Suite 720, Toronto, M5H 1J8, ON, Canada
Tel.: (647) 288-2438
Financial Services
N.A.I.C.S.: 523150

Robert Walters Chile SpA (1)
Rosario Norte 555 Office 1802 Floor 18 Las Condes, Santiago, Chile
Tel.: (56) 232513600
Financial Services
N.A.I.C.S.: 523150

Robert Walters Company Limited (1)
Room F 10th Floor No 1 Songzhi Road, Xin-yi District, Taipei, Taiwan
Tel.: (886) 287580700
Financial Services
N.A.I.C.S.: 523150

Robert Walters Eastern Seaboard Ltd. (1)
4/222 Harbor Office Level 12 Room No 1260 Sukhumvit Road Moo 10, Thungsukhla Sriracha, Chon Buri, 20230, Thailand
Tel.: (66) 33030780
Financial Services
N.A.I.C.S.: 523150

Robert Walters Germany GMBH (1)
Furstenwall 172, 40217, Dusseldorf, Germany
Tel.: (49) 2113 018 0050
Web Site: https://www.robertwalters.de
Human Resource Consulting Services
N.A.I.C.S.: 541612
Nick Dunnett *(Mng Dir)*

Robert Walters Holdings Limited (1)
11 Slingsby Place Saint Martin's Courtyard, London, WC2E 9AB, United Kingdom
Tel.: (44) 207 379 3333
Web Site: https://www.robertwalters.co.uk
Sales Range: $200-249.9 Million
Emp.: 350
Investment Management Service
N.A.I.C.S.: 523999
Robert Walters *(CEO)*

Robert Walters Holdings SAS (1)
Paseo De Recoletos N 7-9 6 Planta, 28004, Madrid, Spain
Tel.: (34) 91 309 7988
Web Site: https://www.robertwalters.es
Investment Management Service
N.A.I.C.S.: 523999

Robert Walters Japan KK (1)
3-12-18 Shibuya Shibuya South Tokyu Building 14th floor, Shibuya-ku, Tokyo, 150-0002, Japan (100%)
Tel.: (81) 34 570 1500
Web Site: https://www.robertwalters.co.jp
Sales Range: $25-49.9 Million
Management Consulting Services
N.A.I.C.S.: 541618
David Swan *(Mng Dir)*

Robert Walters Korea Limited (1)
21f East Center Center 1 Building 26 Euljiro 5 gil, Jung-gu, Seoul, 04539, Korea (South)
Tel.: (82) 26 454 7000
Web Site: https://www.robertwalters.co.kr
Human Resource Consulting Services
N.A.I.C.S.: 541612

Robert Walters Limited (1)
Level 3 Custom House Plaza 2 IFSC, 21 - 23 City Quay, Dublin, Ireland (100%)
Tel.: (353) 1 673 0812
Web Site: https://www.robertwalters.ie
Sales Range: $25-49.9 Million
Emp.: 30
Management Consulting Services
N.A.I.C.S.: 541618

Robert Walters Middle East Limited (1)
Al Khatem Tower ADGM Square, Al Maryah Island, Abu Dhabi, United Arab Emirates
Tel.: (971) 48180100
Web Site: https://www.robertwalters.ae
Recruitment Agency Services
N.A.I.C.S.: 561311

Robert Walters New Zealand Limited (1)
Level 9 PwC Tower 15 Customs Street West, Auckland, 1010, New Zealand
Tel.: (64) 9 374 7300
Web Site: https://www.robertwalters.co.nz
Sales Range: $25-49.9 Million
Human Resource Consulting Services
N.A.I.C.S.: 541612

Robert Walters Operations Limited (1)
Level 4 Wakefield House 90 The, Auckland, New Zealand (100%)
Tel.: (64) 44710338
Employment Placement Agencies
N.A.I.C.S.: 561311

Robert Walters Portugal Unipessoal Lda. (1)
Avenida Da Liberdade 110 1st Floor, 1269-046, Lisbon, Portugal
Tel.: (351) 211221863
Financial Services
N.A.I.C.S.: 523150

Robert Walters Pty Limited (1)
L 41 385 Bourke St, Melbourne, 3000, VIC, Australia (100%)
Tel.: (61) 386282100
Sales Range: $25-49.9 Million
Emp.: 120
Employment Placement Agencies
N.A.I.C.S.: 561311
Robert C. Walters *(CEO)*

Robert Walters Recruitment (Thailand) Ltd (1)
Q House Lumpini 12th Floor Unit 1201 1 South Sathorn Road, Thungmahamek, Bangkok, 10120, Thailand
Tel.: (66) 2 344 4800
Web Site: https://www.robertwalters.co.th
Sales Range: $25-49.9 Million
Human Resource Consulting Services
N.A.I.C.S.: 541612

Robert Walters SA (1)
Avenue Louise 326 10th Floor, PO Box 33, 1050, Brussels, Belgium (100%)
Tel.: (32) 2 511 6688
Web Site: https://www.robertwalters.be
Sales Range: $25-49.9 Million
Emp.: 25
Management Consulting Services
N.A.I.C.S.: 541618
Ozlem Simsek *(Mng Dir)*

Robert Walters Sarl (1)
25 Rue Balzac, 75008, Paris, France (100%)
Tel.: (33) 14 067 8800
Web Site: https://www.robertwalters.fr
Sales Range: $25-49.9 Million
Employment Placement Agencies
N.A.I.C.S.: 561311

Robert Walters Sdn Bhd (1)
Unit 35 02 Level 35 Mercu 2 No 3 Jalan Bangsar KL Eco City, 59200, Kuala Lumpur, Malaysia
Tel.: (60) 32 303 7000
Web Site: https://www.robertwalters.com.my
Human Resource Consulting Services
N.A.I.C.S.: 541612

Robert Walters South Africa Proprietary Limited (1)
15th Floor GreenPark Corner Cnr West Road South and Lower Road, Morningside Sandton, Johannesburg, 2196, South Africa
Tel.: (27) 118812400
Financial Services
N.A.I.C.S.: 523150
Samantha-Jane Gravett *(Assoc Dir)*

Robert Walters Switzerland AG (1)
Claridenstrasse 41, 8002, Zurich, Switzerland
Tel.: (41) 44 809 3500
Web Site: https://www.robertwalters.ch
Human Resource Consulting Services
N.A.I.C.S.: 541612

Robert Walters Talent Consulting (Shanghai) Ltd (1)
2206-2207 22nd Floor Park Place Office Tower No 1601 West Nanjing Road, Jing An District, Shanghai, 200040, China
Tel.: (86) 215 153 5888
Web Site: https://www.robertwalters.cn
Emp.: 60
Human Resource Consulting Services
N.A.I.C.S.: 541612

Robert Walters Vietnam Company Limited (1)
Unit 1 Level 9 The Metropolitann 235 Dong Khoi Street, Ho Chi Minh City, Vietnam
Tel.: (84) 2835207900
Financial Services
N.A.I.C.S.: 523150

Walters Interim SA (1)
Avenue Louise 250, PO Box 32, Brussels, 1050, Belgium (100%)
Tel.: (32) 25116688
Web Site: http://www.waltersinterim.com
Sales Range: $25-49.9 Million
Emp.: 15
Management Consulting Services
N.A.I.C.S.: 541618

Walters People (1)
6th floor 251 boulevard Pereire, 75017, Paris, France (100%)
Tel.: (33) 14 076 0505
Web Site: https://www.walterspeople.fr
Sales Range: $25-49.9 Million
Emp.: 100
Employment Placement Agencies
N.A.I.C.S.: 561311
Alain Mlanao *(Mng Dir)*

Walters People BV (1)
WTC Tower H 3rd floor Zuidplein 28, 1077 XV, Amsterdam, Netherlands
Tel.: (31) 20 796 9040
Web Site: https://www.walterspeople.nl
Human Resource Consulting Services
N.A.I.C.S.: 541612

Walters People Chile Empresa de Servicios Transitorios SpA (1)
Avenida Presidente Riesco 5435 Oficina 1303, Las Condes, Santiago, Chile
Tel.: (56) 942979475
Web Site: https://www.walterspeople.cl
Temporary Staffing Services
N.A.I.C.S.: 561320

Walters People SA (1)
Avenue Louise 326, 1050, Brussels, Belgium
Tel.: (32) 2 542 4040
Web Site: https://www.walterspeople.be
Emp.: 30
Temporary Staffing Services
N.A.I.C.S.: 561320

ROBERTET S.A.

ROBERTET S.A.
37 avenue Sidi Brahim, BP 52100, 06130, Grasse, Cedex, France
Tel.: (33) 493403366
Web Site: https://www.robertet.com
Year Founded: 1850
0R7—(DEU)
Rev.: $796,035,986
Assets: $1,023,435,258
Liabilities: $509,572,801
Net Worth: $513,862,457
Earnings: $82,598,521
Emp.: 2,358
Fiscal Year-end: 12/31/23
Flavor, Perfume Additives & Ingredients Mfr & Distr
N.A.I.C.S.: 325199
Philippe Maubert *(Chm & CEO)*

Subsidiaries:

Bionov SA (1)
Site Agroparc Batiment Orion Chemin des Meinajaries, CS 80501, 84908, Avignon, Cedex, France
Tel.: (33) 490843170
Web Site: http://www.bionov.fr
Food Ingredient Distr
N.A.I.C.S.: 424490

Charabot Korea Ltd. (1)
4F Borim Building 86 Gukhoe-daero, Yangcheon-gu, Seoul, Korea (South)
Tel.: (82) 226075678
Fragrance & Perfume Product Mfr
N.A.I.C.S.: 325620

PT Robertet Group Indonesia (1)
Graha Pratama West Tebet, South Jakarta, Jakarta, Indonesia
Tel.: (62) 2183793577
Fragrance & Perfume Product Mfr
N.A.I.C.S.: 325620

Robertet Andina SAS (1)
Calle 21A No 69B-87 Bodega UC 16-1, Zona Industrial Montevideo, Bogota, Colombia
Tel.: (57) 17437783
Fragrance & Perfume Product Mfr
N.A.I.C.S.: 325620

Robertet Argentina S.A. (1)
Santos Dumont 2646, C1426DCH, Buenos Aires, Argentina
Tel.: (54) 1147714105
Web Site: https://www.robertet.com
Perfume Additives Mfr & Distr
N.A.I.C.S.: 325199

Robertet Asia Pte. Ltd. (1)
19 Wan Lee Rd, Singapore, 627948, Singapore
Tel.: (65) 66840551
Fragrance & Perfume Product Mfr
N.A.I.C.S.: 325620

Robertet De Mexico, S.A. De C.V. (1)
Avenida Ano de Juarez 65 Granjas San Antonio Deleg, Iztapalapa, 09070, Mexico, Mexico
Tel.: (52) 5556866164
Emp.: 130
Flavors & Fragrance Extracts Distr
N.A.I.C.S.: 424490

Robertet Espana SA (1)
Calle Muntaner no 479 3-4, 08021, Barcelona, Spain
Tel.: (34) 934177104
Perfume Additives Mfr & Distr
N.A.I.C.S.: 325199

Robertet Flavours & Fragrances India Pvt. Ltd. (1)
Unit A-2 Tower A 10th Floor Urmi Estate Ganpatrao Kadam Marg, Lower Parel, Mumbai, 400 013, Maharastra, India
Tel.: (91) 2262288989
Sales Range: $25-49.9 Million
Emp.: 35
Flavors & Fragrance Extracts Mfr
N.A.I.C.S.: 311930

Robertet Fragrance, Inc. (1)
400 International Dr, Mount Olive, NJ 07828
Tel.: (201) 337-7100
Web Site: http://www.robertet.com
Sales Range: $25-49.9 Million
Perfume Company
N.A.I.C.S.: 325620
Michael Degen *(Dir-Environmental, Health, Safety & Sustainability)*

Robertet Fragrances And Ingredients (1)
400 International Dr, Mount Olive, NJ 07828
Tel.: (201) 337-7100
Natural Raw Material Whslr
N.A.I.C.S.: 424590

Robertet GmbH (1)
Rodenkirchener Strasse 93, 50997, Cologne, Germany
Tel.: (49) 223339440
Sales Range: $50-74.9 Million
Perfume Distr
N.A.I.C.S.: 424210

Robertet Hiyoki Ltd. (1)
2-7-13 Nihonbashi Bakuro-cho, Chuo-ku, Tokyo, 103-0002, Japan
Tel.: (81) 336661241
Fragrance & Perfume Product Mfr
N.A.I.C.S.: 325620

Robertet India Private Limited (1)
10th floor Urmi Estates Opposite Peninsula Business Park 95, Ganapatrao Kadam Marg Lower Parel W, Mumbai, 400 013, India

ROBERTET S.A.

Robertet S.A.—(Continued)
Tel.: (91) 2262288989
Fragrance & Perfume Product Mfr
N.A.I.C.S.: 325620

Robertet Italia Srl (1)
Via Giuseppe FRUA 22 CAP, 20146, Milan, Italy
Tel.: (39) 0248008990
Sales Range: $50-74.9 Million
Flavors & Fragrance Whslr
N.A.I.C.S.: 424210

Robertet S.A. (1)
Geneva business center 12 avenue des Morgines, Petit-Lancy, Lancy, Geneva, Switzerland
Tel.: (41) 22 311 31 55
Sales Range: $25-49.9 Million
Emp.: 2
Perfume Additives Mfr
N.A.I.C.S.: 325199

Robertet South Africa Aromatics Ltd. (1)
Dinie Estates Road Waterkloof Area, PO Box 732, Rustenburg, 0299, North West, South Africa
Tel.: (27) 827491197
Sales Range: $25-49.9 Million
Emp.: 25
Perfume Mfr
N.A.I.C.S.: 325620

Robertet UK Ltd. (1)
Kings Road, Haslemere, GU27 2QU, Surrey, United Kingdom
Tel.: (44) 1428647240
Sales Range: $25-49.9 Million
Perfume Mfr & Distr
N.A.I.C.S.: 325620

Robertet do Brasil Ind. e Com. Ltda. (1)
Alameda Amazonas 628 Alphaville, Barueri, 06454-070, Sao Paulo, Brazil
Tel.: (55) 1141337103
Web Site: http://www.robertet.com
Sales Range: $25-49.9 Million
Flavors & Fragrance Mfr
N.A.I.C.S.: 311930

Robertet et Cie SA (1)
Rue de Lausanne 45/47 A, 1201, Geneva, Switzerland
Tel.: (41) 223113155
Fragrance & Perfume Product Mfr
N.A.I.C.S.: 325620

Robertet, Inc. (1)
100 International Dr, Mount Olive, NJ 07828-3123 (100%)
Tel.: (201) 337-7100
Sales Range: $25-49.9 Million
Emp.: 45
Produces Essential Aromatic & Specialty Oils, Perfume Compounds
N.A.I.C.S.: 424490
Arnaud Adrian *(VP-Raw Matls Div)*

Division (Domestic):

Robertet Flavors (2)
10 Colonial Dr, Piscataway, NJ 08854-6840
Tel.: (732) 981-8300
Web Site: http://www.robertet.com
Sales Range: $25-49.9 Million
Flavorings, Extracts & Syrups
N.A.I.C.S.: 311942

ROBERTO COIN S.P.A.
Viale Trieste 13, 36100, Vicenza, Italy
Tel.: (39) 0444202202
Web Site: http://www.robertocoin.com
Sales Range: $10-24.9 Million
Emp.: 100
Jewelry
N.A.I.C.S.: 339910
Roberto Coin *(Owner)*

ROBEX RESOURCES INC.
Edifice Le Delta 1 2875 boulevard Laurier bureau 1000, Quebec, G1V 2M2, QC, Canada
Tel.: (581) 741-7421
Web Site: https://robexgold.com
RSRBF—(OTCIQ)
Rev.: $94,523,040
Assets: $91,350,119
Liabilities: $19,975,268
Net Worth: $71,374,851
Earnings: $34,896,797
Emp.: 872
Fiscal Year-end: 12/31/20
Gold Exploration Services
N.A.I.C.S.: 212220
Georges Cohen *(Pres)*

ROBIN HOLDINGS PTE LTD
Parkway Parade 80, Singapore, 449269, Singapore
Tel.: (65) 64403456
Year Founded: 1976
Sales Range: $50-74.9 Million
Emp.: 6
Holding Company; Financial Services
N.A.I.C.S.: 551112

Subsidiaries:

Robina Land Corporation Pty Ltd (1)
Level 8 The Rocket 203 Robina Town Centre Drive, Robina, 4226, QLD, Australia
Tel.: (61) 755930888
Web Site: http://www.robina.com.au
Sales Range: $10-24.9 Million
Property Development & Investment Services
N.A.I.C.S.: 237210
Richard Wyatt *(CEO)*

ROBIN MARIETON
2 rue Henri Damet, 69550, Amplepuis, France
Tel.: (33) 474893306
Web Site: http://www.robinmarieton.fr
Year Founded: 1850
Sales Range: $10-24.9 Million
Emp.: 42
Cotton & Wool Household Textiles Mfr
N.A.I.C.S.: 314120
Cyril Robin Marieton *(Gen Mgr)*

ROBINSON & CO. (S) PTE. LTD.
176 Orchard Rd No 05 05 Centrepoint, Singapore, 238843, Singapore
Tel.: (65) 621678401
Web Site: http://www.robinsons.com.sg
Year Founded: 1858
Sales Range: $200-249.9 Million
Emp.: 450
Manages & Operates Department Stores
N.A.I.C.S.: 455110
Christopher James Williams *(Chm)*

Subsidiaries:

John Little Private Ltd. (1)
6 Raffles Boulevard 02238 Marina Square, 039594, Singapore, Singapore
Tel.: (65) 65109030
Web Site: http://www.johnlittle.com.se
Sales Range: $50-74.9 Million
Emp.: 250
Department Stores
N.A.I.C.S.: 455110
Donna Chua *(Mgr-Mktg)*

ROBINSON BUICK GMC
875 Woodlawn Road West, Guelph, N1K 1B7, ON, Canada
Tel.: (519) 821-0520
Web Site: http://www.robinsonbuickgmc.com
New & Used Car Dealers
N.A.I.C.S.: 441110
Sam Hirani *(VP)*

ROBINSON PLC
Field House Wheatbridge, Chesterfield, S40 2AB, United Kingdom
Tel.: (44) 1246389280
Web Site: https://www.robinsonpackaging.com
RBN—(AIM)
Rev.: $63,783,136
Assets: $62,198,940
Liabilities: $31,976,774
Net Worth: $30,222,166
Earnings: $2,958,849
Emp.: 368
Fiscal Year-end: 12/31/22
Paperboard & Plastic Packaging Mfr & Sales
N.A.I.C.S.: 333243
Alan Raleigh *(Chm)*

Subsidiaries:

Robinson Packaging Danmark A/S (1)
Erhvervsvej 2, Lindknud, 6650, Brorup, Denmark
Tel.: (45) 75388200
Web Site: https://www.schela.dk
Plastic Packaging Services
N.A.I.C.S.: 561910

Robinson Packaging Polska sp. Z oo (1)
238 Gen J Dabrowskiego St, 93-231, Lodz, Poland
Tel.: (48) 691500641
Sales Range: $25-49.9 Million
Emp.: 60
Packaging Plastic Products Mfr
N.A.I.C.S.: 326199

Robinson Plastic Packaging Ltd. (1)
Tel.: (44) 1623752869
Sales Range: $50-74.9 Million
Emp.: 115
Plastic Packaging Products Mfr
N.A.I.C.S.: 326199

Subsidiary (Domestic):

Robinson Plastic Packaging (Stanton Hill) Limited (2)
Brierley Park Close, Stanton Hill, Sutton in Ashfield, NG17 3FW, Nottinghamshire, United Kingdom
Tel.: (44) 162 355 0045
Web Site: https://www.robinsonpackaging.com
Sales Range: $25-49.9 Million
Emp.: 60
Injection Molding Plastic Products Mfr
N.A.I.C.S.: 326199

ROBINSON WAY LIMITED
Carolina Way Quays Reach, Salford, Manchester, M50 2ZY, United Kingdom
Tel.: (44) 1617432483 UK
Web Site: http://www.robinson-way.com
Year Founded: 1974
Sales Range: $25-49.9 Million
Emp.: 250
Debt Collection & Purchasing Agency
N.A.I.C.S.: 561440
Louise Schofield *(Dir-Ops)*

ROBINSONS MOTOR GROUP
Heigham Street, Norwich, NR2 4TF, United Kingdom
Tel.: (44) 1603 751000
Web Site: http://www.robinsonsmotor.co.uk
Year Founded: 1927
Sales Range: $250-299.9 Million
Emp.: 450
New & Used Car Dealer
N.A.I.C.S.: 441110
David Consibonfield *(Dir-Fin)*

ROBINSONS RETAIL HOLDINGS, INC.
110 East Rodriguez Jr Avenue, Bagumbayan, Quezon City, 1110, Philippines
Tel.: (63) 86350751 PH

INTERNATIONAL PUBLIC

Web Site: https://www.robinsonsretail.com.ph
Year Founded: 2002
RRETY—(OTCIQ)
Rev.: $3,468,915,045
Assets: $2,799,005,407
Liabilities: $1,365,803,434
Net Worth: $1,433,201,973
Earnings: $83,942,852
Emp.: 23,172
Fiscal Year-end: 12/31/23
Supermarkets, Department Stores, Home Improvement Stores, Convenient Stores, Drugs Stores & Other Specialty Stores
N.A.I.C.S.: 445110
James L. Go *(Vice Chm & Vice Chm)*

Subsidiaries:

Robinsons Appliances Corp. (1)
110 Eulogio Rodriguez Jr Ave, Bagumbayan, Quezon City, 1110, Metro Manila, Philippines
Tel.: (63) 998 846 6415
Web Site: https://www.robinsonsappliances.com.ph
Appliance Distr
N.A.I.C.S.: 423620

Robinsons HandyMan Inc. (1)
110 E Rodriguez Jr Avenue, Libis, Quezon City, Philippines
Tel.: (63) 635 0751
Web Site: https://www.handyman.com.ph
Hardware Distr
N.A.I.C.S.: 444140

Rose Pharmacy, Inc. (1)
3/F FLC Center 888 Hernan Cortes Street, Subangdaku, Mandaue, 6014, Philippines
Tel.: (63) 32 230 5000
Web Site: https://www.rosepharmacy.com
Pharmaceutical Products Distr
N.A.I.C.S.: 456110

Rustan Supercenters, Inc. (1)
Morning Star Center 347 Sen Gil Puyat Ave, Makati, 1200, Philippines
Tel.: (63) 2 909 9000
Web Site: http://www.rustansfresh.com
Supermarket Operator
N.A.I.C.S.: 445110

ROBIT PLC
Vikkiniityntie 9, Lempaala, 33880, Tampere, Finland
Tel.: (358) 331403400
Web Site: https://www.robitgroup.com
ROBIT—(HEL)
Rev.: $120,830,995
Assets: $117,762,789
Liabilities: $62,914,958
Net Worth: $54,847,831
Earnings: $955,105
Emp.: 259
Fiscal Year-end: 12/31/22
Button Bits & Casing Systems for Drilling
N.A.I.C.S.: 332510
Harri Sjoholm *(Chm)*

Subsidiaries:

Drilling Tools Australia Pty. Ltd. (1)
24-26 Gauge Circuit, Canning Vale, 6155, WA, Australia (100%)
Tel.: (61) 86 245 5600
Web Site: http://www.drillingtools.com.au
Drill Consumables & Drill Spares Mfr
N.A.I.C.S.: 333998

Halco USA LLC (1)
20269 Mack St, Hayward, CA 94545
Tel.: (510) 783-1400
Web Site: https://www.halcousa.com
Hook & Loop Fastening Fabric Mfr
N.A.I.C.S.: 313220

Robit Australia Pty Ltd. (1)
24-26 Gauge Circuit, Canning Vale, 6155, WA, Australia
Tel.: (61) 862455600
Drilling Tool Mfr & Distr
N.A.I.C.S.: 333131

ROBLON A/S
Fabriksvej 7, Gaerum, 9900, Frederikshavn, Denmark
Tel.: (45) 96203300
Web Site: https://www.roblon.com
Year Founded: 1954
RBLN.B—(CSE)
Rev.: $51,838,898
Assets: $54,497,964
Liabilities: $23,460,132
Net Worth: $31,037,832
Earnings: ($682,609)
Emp.: 281
Fiscal Year-end: 10/31/23
All Other Industrial Machinery Manufacturing
N.A.I.C.S.: 333248
Jorgen Jacobsen *(Chm)*

Subsidiaries:

Roblon US Inc. (1)
3908 Hickory Blvd, Granite Falls, NC 28630
Tel.: (828) 396-2121
Internet Services
N.A.I.C.S.: 517111

Vamafil, spol. s r.o. (1)
Jamska 2360/49, 591 01, Zdar nad Sazavou, Czech Republic
Tel.: (420) 566620022
Web Site: https://www.vamafil.com
Synthetic Fiber Mfr
N.A.I.C.S.: 325220

ROBNA KUCA TUZLANKA D.D.
ul Univerzitetska 16, 75 000, Tuzla, Bosnia & Herzegovina
Tel.: (387) 35321555
RKTZR—(SARE)
Rev.: $1,582,589
Assets: $18,415,133
Liabilities: $4,483,628
Net Worth: $13,931,505
Earnings: $789,736
Emp.: 28
Fiscal Year-end: 12/31/20
Shopping Mall Operator
N.A.I.C.S.: 531120

ROBNO TRANSPORNI CENTAR A.D. SABAC
Marsala Tita 29a Misar, 15000, Sabac, Serbia
Tel.: (381) 15381348
Web Site: https://www.rtcsabac.rs
Year Founded: 1953
SLBZ—(BEL)
Sales Range: Less than $1 Million
Cargo Warehousing Services
N.A.I.C.S.: 561990
Aljosa Garibovic *(Gen Dir)*

ROBO TECHNIK INTELLIGENT TECHNOLOGY CO., LTD.
No 3 Weiting Ganglang Road Suzhou Industrial Park, Jiangsu, 215122, China
Tel.: (86) 51262535580
Web Site: http://www.robo-technik.com
Year Founded: 2011
300757—(SSE)
Rev.: $126,809,280
Assets: $306,407,556
Liabilities: $184,199,184
Net Worth: $122,208,372
Earnings: $3,671,460
Fiscal Year-end: 12/31/22
Automation Equipment Mfr & Distr
N.A.I.C.S.: 334519
Jun Dai *(Chm, CEO & Interim Sec)*

ROBO3 CO LTD
3 Hakdong-ro 42-gil, Gangnam-gu, Seoul, 06098, Korea (South)
Tel.: (82) 25449145
Web Site: https://www.robo3.com
Year Founded: 2003
Robot Mfr
N.A.I.C.S.: 336110
Kim Jun-Hyung *(CEO)*

ROBOGROUP T.E.K. LTD.
13 Hamelacha St, Afeq Industrial Park, Rosh Ha'Ayin, 48091, Park Afek, Israel
Tel.: (972) 39004111
Web Site: https://www.robo-group.com
Year Founded: 1982
ROBO—(TAE)
Rev.: $13,025,000
Assets: $21,734,000
Liabilities: $12,155,000
Net Worth: $9,579,000
Earnings: ($2,644,000)
Emp.: 130
Fiscal Year-end: 12/31/23
Electrical Apparatus & Equipment, Wiring Supplies & Related Equipment Merchant Wholesalers
N.A.I.C.S.: 423610

Subsidiaries:

Intelitek Inc. (1)
13 Hamelacha St, Afek Industrial Park, Rosh Ha'Ayin, 4809129, Israel **(82%)**
Tel.: (972) 39004111
Web Site: http://www.intelitek.com
Sales Range: $25-49.9 Million
Emp.: 80
Developer, Producer & Supplier of e-Learning Systems & Technology Training Products
N.A.I.C.S.: 541512
Noam Kra-Oz *(Mng Dir)*

Intelitek, Inc. (1)
18 Tsienneto Rd, Derry, NH 03038 **(100%)**
Tel.: (603) 413-2600
Web Site: https://www.intelitek.com
Sales Range: $75-99.9 Million
Developer, Producer & Supplier of Technology Training Products
N.A.I.C.S.: 423990
Linda Osgood *(Controller)*

Yaskawa Eshed Technology Ltd. (1)
13 Hamelacha St, Afeq Industrial Estate, Rosh Ha'Ayin, 48091, Israel **(100%)**
Tel.: (972) 39004114
Web Site: http://www.yetmotion.com
Sales Range: $25-49.9 Million
Emp.: 35
Devloper of Advanced Motion Control Technology
N.A.I.C.S.: 334513

ROBORE HOLDINGS LTD.
Unit 16 Mitcham Industrial Estate, Streatham Road, Mitcham, CR4 2AP, Surrey, United Kingdom
Tel.: (44) 20 8646 4466
Web Site: http://www.robore.com
Year Founded: 1986
Sales Range: $10-24.9 Million
Emp.: 150
Holding Company; Diamond Drilling, Diamond Sawing & Controlled Demolition Contractor
N.A.I.C.S.: 551112
Paul Nattrass *(Fin Dir)*

Subsidiaries:

Kingstar Contracts (1)
Unit 16 Mitcham Industrial Estate, Streatham Road, Mitcham, CR4 2AP, Surrey, United Kingdom
Tel.: (44) 1462 436 006
Web Site: http://www.kingstar.co.uk
Specialty Contractor
N.A.I.C.S.: 238990

London Diamond Drilling Services Ltd. (1)
Newington Industrial Estate Unit 19, London, SE17 3AZ, United Kingdom
Tel.: (44) 20 7277 3877
Web Site: http://www.londondiamonddrilling.co.uk
Emp.: 12
Concrete Drilling & Cutting Contractor
N.A.I.C.S.: 238990
Marc Seagroatt *(Mng Dir)*

Division (Domestic):

LDD Fire Protection (2)
Newington Industrial Estate Unit 19, London, SE17 3AZ, United Kingdom
Tel.: (44) 20 7277 3875
Web Site: http://www.lddfireprotection.co.uk
Fire Protection
N.A.I.C.S.: 922160
Kang Yau *(Mgr-Comml)*

LDD Special Works (2)
7 Eastbury Road, London, E6 6LP, United Kingdom
Tel.: (44) 20 7277 3877
Web Site: http://www.lddspecialworks.co.uk
Emp.: 20
Special Works Contractor
N.A.I.C.S.: 238990

Robore Cuts Limited (1)
Unit 16 Mitcham Industrial Estate, Streatham Road, Mitcham, CR4 2AP, Surrey, United Kingdom
Tel.: (44) 20 8646 4466
Web Site: http://www.robore.com
Emp.: 82
Diamond Drilling, Diamond Sawing & Controlled Demolition Contractor
N.A.I.C.S.: 238990
Colin Hibbert *(Mgr-Ops)*

Robore Special Projects (1)
Unit 16 Mitcham Industrial Estate, Streatham Road, Mitcham, CR4 2AP, Surrey, United Kingdom
Tel.: (44) 20 8646 4466
Web Site: http://www.robore.com
Emp.: 15
Metal Machining Special Projects Contractor
N.A.I.C.S.: 238990
Jeff Lawrence *(Dir-Div)*

ROBOROBO CO., LTD.
Roborobo Bldg 6 Dobong-ro 54-gil, Gangbuk-gu, Seoul, Korea (South)
Tel.: (82) 9095050
Web Site: https://www.eng.roborobo.co.kr
215100—(KRS)
Rev.: $9,098,973
Assets: $24,286,951
Liabilities: $1,628,725
Net Worth: $22,658,226
Earnings: ($269,888)
Emp.: 41
Fiscal Year-end: 12/31/22
Robot Kit Product Mfr & Distr
N.A.I.C.S.: 333998
Hyun-Jin Cho *(Exec Dir)*

ROBOSOFT TECHNOLOGIES PVT. LTD.
217 NH 66 Santhekatte, Udupi, 576 105, Karnataka, India
Tel.: (91) 820 2593930
Web Site: http://www.robosoftin.com
Sales Range: $75-99.9 Million
Emp.: 500
Mobile App & Game Developer
N.A.I.C.S.: 513210
Rohith Bhat *(CEO)*

ROBOSTAR CO., LTD.
700 Suin-ro, Sangrok-gu, Ansan, Gyeonggi-do, Korea (South)
Tel.: (82) 314003600
Web Site: http://www.robostar.com
Year Founded: 1999
090360—(KRS)
Rev.: $109,865,248
Assets: $104,654,928
Liabilities: $35,693,507
Net Worth: $68,961,421
Earnings: $2,517,200
Emp.: 216
Fiscal Year-end: 12/31/22
Industrial Robots Mfr
N.A.I.C.S.: 333248
Chung-ho Kim *(CEO)*

Subsidiaries:

Robostar (Shanghai) Co., Ltd. (1)
Industrial Robots Mfr
N.A.I.C.S.: 333248

Robostar Co., Ltd. - 2nd Plant (1)
945 Gosaek-dong, Gwonseon-gu, Suwon, Gyeonggi-do, Korea (South)
Tel.: (82) 31 80127800
Sales Range: $100-124.9 Million
Emp.: 300
Industrial Robots Mfr
N.A.I.C.S.: 333248

ROBOT HOME, INC.
6-10-1-9F Ginza, Chuo-ku, Tokyo, Japan
Tel.: (81) 358607565
Web Site: https://corp.robothome.jp
Year Founded: 2006
1435—(TKS)
Rev.: $61,151,250
Assets: $85,214,710
Liabilities: $24,283,250
Net Worth: $60,931,460
Earnings: $6,281,740
Emp.: 228
Fiscal Year-end: 12/31/23
Real Estate Support Services
N.A.I.C.S.: 531390
Daisaku Furuki *(CEO)*

Subsidiaries:

Robot Home Co., Ltd. (1)
2F 3-4-14 Ebisuminami, Shibuya-ku, Tokyo, 150-0022, Japan
Tel.: (81) 367210724
Web Site: http://www.robothome.co.jp
Housing Rental Services
N.A.I.C.S.: 531110

Tabict, Inc. (1)
4-36-8 Ryogoku General Reception 2F, Sumida-ku, Tokyo, 130-0026, Japan
Tel.: (81) 367210723
Web Site: http://corp.tabict.jp
Building Development Services
N.A.I.C.S.: 236220

ROBOTIS CO., LTD.
37 Magok Jungang 5-ro 1-gil, Gangseo-gu, Seoul, 07594, Korea (South)
Tel.: (82) 7086712609
Web Site: https://en.robotis.com
Year Founded: 1999
108490—(KRS)
Rev.: $19,831,897
Assets: $94,183,520
Liabilities: $29,250,983
Net Worth: $64,932,537
Earnings: ($199,087)
Emp.: 139
Fiscal Year-end: 12/31/22
Industrial Machinery Maintenance Services
N.A.I.C.S.: 811310
Byung-Soo Kim *(CEO)*

ROBOTNIK.COM INCORPORATED
32 McQuade Lake Crescent, Halifax, B3S 1G8, NS, Canada
Tel.: (902) 425-1599
Web Site: http://www.robotnik.com
Year Founded: 1998
Sales Range: $10-24.9 Million
Computer Products & Software Retailer
N.A.I.C.S.: 449210
Harold Nied *(Pres)*

ROBUS GROUP AS

ROBUS GROUP AS

Robus Group AS—(Continued)
Town Mills North Rue du Pre, Saint Peter Port, GY1 6HS, Guernsey
Tel.: (44) 1481742550
Web Site:
https://www.robusgroup.com
Year Founded: 2011
ROBUS—(OMX)
Emp.: 3
Health Care Srvices
N.A.I.C.S.: 621610
Ronan Ryan (Chief Comml Officer)

ROC PARTNERS PTY LTD
Level 11 2 Blight Street, Sydney, 2000, NSW, Australia
Tel.: (61) 290991900
Web Site: http://www.rocp.com
Privater Equity Firm
N.A.I.C.S.: 523999
Stephen Zhang (Partner)

Subsidiaries:

Capilano Honey Limited (1)
399 Archerfield Road, PO Box 531, Richlands, 4077, QLD, Australia
Tel.: (61) 7 3712 8282
Web Site: http://www.capilanohoney.com
Rev.: $108,111,805
Assets: $81,370,495
Liabilities: $28,049,037
Net Worth: $53,321,458
Earnings: $7,667,381
Fiscal Year-end: 06/30/2018
Honey Producer
N.A.I.C.S.: 311999
Dirk Kemp (Gen Mgr-Fin)

Pace Farm Pty Ltd (1)
1 Kippist Ave, Minchinbury, Sydney, 2770, NSW, Australia
Tel.: (61) 298309800
Web Site: http://www.pacefarm.com
Egg Products Mfr
N.A.I.C.S.: 112310
Frank Pace (Founder & Mng Dir)

ROC SEARCH LTD.
The Blade Abbey Square, Reading, RG1 3BE, Berkshire, United Kingdom
Tel.: (44) 1189 006750
Web Site: http://www.roc-search.com
Year Founded: 2007
Sales Range: $10-24.9 Million
Emp.: 160
Information Technology Recruitment Services
N.A.I.C.S.: 561311
Trevor Doran (Mgr-Bus-Engrg Div)

Subsidiaries:

Roc Search GmbH (1)
Rossmarkt 10 3 OG, 60311, Frankfurt am Main, Germany
Tel.: (49) 69365065055
Web Site: http://www.roc-search.de
Employee Placement Services
N.A.I.C.S.: 561311

ROCA MINES INC.
490-1122 Mainland Street, Vancouver, V6B 5L1, BC, Canada
Tel.: (604) 684-2900   BC
Web Site:
https://www.rocamines.com
Year Founded: 2001
ROCAF—(TSXV)
Sales Range: Less than $1 Million
Mineral Exploration Services
N.A.I.C.S.: 213114
John Kiernan (VP)

ROCA SANITARIO, S.A.
Avenida Diagonal 513, Barcelona, 08029, Spain
Tel.: (34) 933661200
Web Site: http://www.roca.es
Bathroom Space Architecture, Construction & Interior Design
N.A.I.C.S.: 332999
Roger Massana (Sr Fin Controller-Foreign Subsidiaries)

ROCCO FORTE & FAMILY PLC.
70 Jermyn Street, London, SW1Y 6NY, United Kingdom
Tel.: (44) 20 7321 2626
Web Site:
http://www.roccofortecareers.com
Year Founded: 1996
Sales Range: $250-299.9 Million
Emp.: 2,255
Home Management Services
N.A.I.C.S.: 721110
Rocco Forte (Chm)

ROCEDES APPAREL S.A.
Zona Franca Industrial Park, Managua, Nicaragua
Tel.: (505) 2263 2032
Web Site: http://www.rocedes.com.ni
Year Founded: 1993
Sales Range: $50-74.9 Million
Emp.: 2,500
Women's Casual Pants & Jeans Mfr
N.A.I.C.S.: 458110
Joe Stephenson (CEO)

ROCHE BOBOIS SA
18 Rue de Lyon, 75012, Paris, France
Tel.: (33) 153461000
Web Site: https://www.roche-bobois.com
RBO—(EUR)
Sales Range: $300-349.9 Million
Furniture Product Distr
N.A.I.C.S.: 423210
Guillaume Demulier (Chm-Exec Bd & CEO)

ROCHE HOLDING AG
Grenzacherstrasse 124, 4058, Basel, Switzerland
Tel.: (41) 616881111   CH
Web Site: https://www.roche.com
Year Founded: 1896
ROG—(SWX)
Rev.: $74,573,149,500
Assets: $104,546,232,990
Liabilities: $72,446,370,840
Net Worth: $32,099,862,150
Earnings: $16,913,439,450
Emp.: 100,000
Fiscal Year-end: 12/31/21
Holding Company; Pharmaceutical & Diagnostic Products Developer & Mfr
N.A.I.C.S.: 551112
Alan Hippe (Chief Financial & IT Officer)

Subsidiaries:

Chugai Pharmaceutical Co., Ltd. (1)
1-1 Nihonbashi-Muromachi 2-Chome Nihonbashi Mitsui Tower, Chuo-ku, Tokyo, 103-8324, Japan   (62%)
Tel.: (81) 332816611
Web Site: https://www.chugai-pharm.co.jp
Rev.: $7,879,592,030
Assets: $13,701,758,230
Liabilities: $2,176,396,030
Net Worth: $11,525,362,200
Earnings: $2,307,596,480
Emp.: 7,604
Fiscal Year-end: 12/31/2023
Pharmaceuticals Mfr
N.A.I.C.S.: 325412
Motoo Ueno (Deputy Chm)

Affiliate (Non-US):

C&C Research Laboratories (2)
146 141 Annyung Ri Taean Up, Hwasun, Kyunggi Do, Korea (South)   (100%)
Tel.: (82) 3312306503
Sales Range: $25-49.9 Million
Emp.: 60
Provider of Pharmaceutical Research Services
N.A.I.C.S.: 325412

Subsidiary (Domestic):

Chugai Business Support Co., Ltd. (2)
5-5-1 Ukima, Kita-ku, Tokyo, 115-8543, Japan
Tel.: (81) 3 3968 8760
Web Site: http://www.chugai-pharm.co.jp
General Insurance Services
N.A.I.C.S.: 524210

Chugai Clinical Research Center Co., Ltd. (2)
1-1 Nihonbashi-Muromachi 2-Chome, Chuo-ku, Tokyo, 103-8324, Japan
Tel.: (81) 3 3273 1173
Clinical Trial Services
N.A.I.C.S.: 541715

Chugai Distribution Co., Ltd. (2)
1-20 Okuwa, Kazo, 347-0010, Saitama, Japan
Tel.: (81) 480 76 0381
Pharmaceutical Products Distr
N.A.I.C.S.: 424210

Subsidiary (Non-US):

Chugai Pharma (Shanghai) Consulting Co., Ltd. (2)
Unit 2901 Central Plaza No 381 Central Huaihai Road, Shanghai, 200020, China
Tel.: (86) 2163190388
Web Site: http://www.chugai-pharm.co.jp
Pharmaceuticals Product Mfr
N.A.I.C.S.: 325412

Chugai Pharma Europe Ltd. (2)
Mulliner House Flanders Rd, London, W4 1NN, United Kingdom
Tel.: (44) 2089875600
Web Site: http://www.chugai.co.uk
Sales Range: $25-49.9 Million
Emp.: 50
Provider of Pharmaceuticals
N.A.I.C.S.: 325412

Subsidiary (Domestic):

Chugai Pharma U.K. Ltd. (3)
Mulliner House Flanders Road Turnham Green, London, W4 1NN, United Kingdom   (100%)
Tel.: (44) 2089875680
Web Site: http://www.chugai.co.uk
Sales Range: $25-49.9 Million
Emp.: 50
Provider of Pharmaceuticals
N.A.I.C.S.: 325412

Subsidiary (Non-US):

Chugai Pharma France S.A.S. (2)
Tour Franklin Arche Sud 100/101 Quartier Boieldieu, 92042, Paris, France
Tel.: (33) 1 56 37 05 20
Web Site: http://www.chugai.fr
Pharmaceuticals Product Mfr
N.A.I.C.S.: 325412

Chugai Pharma Marketing Ltd. (2)
Mulliner House Flanders Road, Turnham Green, London, W4 1NN, United Kingdom   (100%)
Tel.: (44) 2089875600
Web Site: http://www.chugai.co.uk
Marketer of Pharmaceuticals
N.A.I.C.S.: 424210

Chugai Pharma Science (Beijing) Co., Ltd. (2)
2103 Beijing Fortune Bldg No 5 Dong San Huan Bei Lu, Chao Yang District, Beijing, 100004, China
Tel.: (86) 10 6590 95
Web Site: http://www.chugai-pharm.co.jp
Pharmaceuticals Product Mfr
N.A.I.C.S.: 325412

Chugai Pharma Taiwan Ltd. (2)
3rd Floor No 73 Zhou Zi Street, Neihu District, Taipei, 11493, Taiwan
Tel.: (886) 226588800
Web Site: http://www.chugai-pharm.co.jp
Sales Range: $25-49.9 Million
Emp.: 50
Pharmaceuticals Mfr & Whslr

INTERNATIONAL PUBLIC

N.A.I.C.S.: 325412
Chugai Pharmabody Research Pte. Ltd. (2)
3 Biopolis Drive 04 - 11 to 17 Synapse, Singapore, 138623, Singapore
Tel.: (65) 6933 4888
Web Site: http://www.chugai-pharmabody.com
Emp.: 95
Drug Research & Development Services
N.A.I.C.S.: 541715
David Lane (Chm)

Plant (Domestic):

Chugai Pharmaceutical Co., Ltd. - Fujieda Plant (2)
2500 Takayanagi, Fujieda, 426-0041, Shizuoka, Japan
Tel.: (81) 54 635 2311
Web Site: http://www.chugai-pharm.co.jp
Pharmaceuticals Product Mfr
N.A.I.C.S.: 325412

Chugai Pharmaceutical Co., Ltd. - Ukima Plant (2)
5-5-1 Ukima, Kita-ku, Tokyo, 115-8543, Japan
Tel.: (81) 3 3968 6111
Web Site: http://www.chugai-pharm.co.jp
Pharmaceuticals Product Mfr
N.A.I.C.S.: 325412

Chugai Pharmaceutical Co., Ltd. - Utsunomiya Plant (2)
16-3 Kiyohara-Kogyodanchi, Utsunomiya, 321-3231, Tochigi, Japan
Tel.: (81) 28 667 7611
Pharmaceuticals Product Mfr
N.A.I.C.S.: 325412

Subsidiary (Domestic):

Chugai Research Institute for Medical Science, Inc. (2)
1-135 Komakado, Gotemba, 412-8513, Shizuoka, Japan
Tel.: (81) 550 87 5425
Web Site: http://www.chugai-pharm.co.jp
Drug Research Services
N.A.I.C.S.: 541715

Joint Venture (Non-US):

Chugai Sanofi-Aventis S.N.C. (2)
20 Avenue Raymond Aron, 92165, Antony, Cedex, France
Tel.: (33) 141247552
Web Site: http://www.sanofiaventis.com
Sales Range: $25-49.9 Million
Emp.: 17
Pharmaceuticals Product Mfr
N.A.I.C.S.: 325412

Subsidiary (US):

Chugai USA, Inc. (2)
444 Madison Ave, New York, NY 10022-6903
Tel.: (212) 486-7780
Web Site: http://www.chugai-pharm.co.jp
Sales Range: $25-49.9 Million
Emp.: 2
Mfr of Pharmaceuticals
N.A.I.C.S.: 424210

Subsidiary (Domestic):

Chugai Pharma U.S.A., LLC (3)
300 Connell Dr Ste 3100, Berkeley Heights, NJ 07922
Tel.: (908) 516-1350
Web Site: http://www.chugai-pharm.com
Sales Range: $25-49.9 Million
Pharmaceuticals Product Mfr
N.A.I.C.S.: 325412

Subsidiary (Domestic):

Medical Culture Inc. (2)
Muromachi CS Bldg 4-6-5 Nihonbashi-Muromachi, Chuo-ku, Tokyo, 103-0022, Japan
Tel.: (81) 3 5202 8270
Document Publication Services
N.A.I.C.S.: 561410

Subsidiary (Non-US):

PharmaLogicals Research Pte. Ltd (2)

ROCHE HOLDING AG

No 11 Biopolis Way 05-08/09 Helios, Singapore, 138667, Singapore
Tel.: (65) 6776 6556
Web Site: http://www.chugai-pharm.co.jp
Laboratory Testing Services
N.A.I.C.S.: 541380

Shanghai Chugai Pharma Co., Ltd. (2)
Unit 1209 A Lansheng Building No 2 8 Huaihai Rd Centre, Shanghai, 200021, China
Tel.: (86) 2163191882
Sales Range: $25-49.9 Million
Emp.: 20
Provider of Pharmaceuticals
N.A.I.C.S.: 325412

F. Hoffmann-La Roche AG (1)
Grenzacherstrasse 124, CH-4070, Basel, Switzerland
Tel.: (41) 616881111
Web Site: https://www.roche.ch
Sales Range: $1-4.9 Billion
Emp.: 14,200
Pharmaceutical, Vitamin, Fine Chemical, Diagnostic, Fragrance, Flavor & Liquid Crystal Developer, Researcher & Mfr
N.A.I.C.S.: 325412

Subsidiary (Non-US):

Axolabs GmbH (2)
Fritz-Hornschuch Strasse 9, 95326, Kulmbach, Germany
Tel.: (49) 9221827620
Web Site: http://www.axolabs.com
Research & Development Services
N.A.I.C.S.: 541715
Roland Kreutzer *(Co-Founder & Member-Mgmt Bd)*

DSM (China) Ltd. (2)
No 476 Li Bing Road Zhangjiang High-Tech Park, Pudong Area, 201203, Shanghai, China (100%)
Tel.: (86) 2161418188
Web Site: http://www.dsm.com
Sales Range: $50-74.9 Million
Emp.: 200
Provider of Pharmaceuticals
N.A.I.C.S.: 325412

Grupo Roche Syntex de Mexico S.A. de C.V. (2)
Cerrada de Bezares No 9 Col Lomas de Bezares, 11910, Mexico, DF, Mexico (100%)
Tel.: (52) 55 5258 5000
Web Site: http://www.roche.com
Sales Range: $400-449.9 Million
Emp.: 2,000
Pharmaceutical Mfr & Packager
N.A.I.C.S.: 325412

Hoffmann-La Roche AG (2)
Emil-Barell-Strasse 1, PO Box 1270, 79639, Grenzach-Wyhlen, Germany (100%)
Tel.: (49) 762490880
Web Site: http://www.roche.de
Sales Range: $200-249.9 Million
Emp.: 1,000
Mfr of Vitamins & Diagnostics
N.A.I.C.S.: 325412

Subsidiary (US):

Hoffmann-La Roche Inc. (2)
340 Kingsland St, Nutley, NJ 07110-1199
Tel.: (973) 235-5000
Web Site: http://www.rocheusa.com
Sales Range: $1-4.9 Billion
Emp.: 6,600
Pharmaceuticals, Fine Chemicals, Vitamins & Diagnostics Mfr
N.A.I.C.S.: 325412

Subsidiary (Domestic):

Foundation Medicine, Inc. (3)
150 2nd St, Cambridge, MA 02141
Tel.: (617) 418-2200
Web Site: https://www.foundationmedicine.com
Rev.: $152,903,000
Assets: $169,003,000
Liabilities: $137,335,000
Net Worth: $31,668,000
Earnings: ($161,466,000)
Emp.: 662

Fiscal Year-end: 12/31/2017
Pharmaceuticals Mfr
N.A.I.C.S.: 325412
Priti Hegde *(Chief Scientific Officer)*

Genentech, Inc. (3)
1 DNA Way Mailstop 258A, South San Francisco, CA 94080-4918 (100%)
Tel.: (650) 225-1000
Web Site: https://www.gene.com
Sales Range: $5-14.9 Billion
Researcher of Human Genetic Information to Discover, Develop, Manufacture & Market Human Pharmaceuticals
N.A.I.C.S.: 325411
Steve E. Krognes *(Reg Head-Fin & IT)*

Ignyta, Inc. (3)
1 DNA Way MS 24 S, San Francisco, CA 94080
Tel.: (858) 255-5959
Bio Technology Services
N.A.I.C.S.: 541714

Roche Palo Alto LLC (3)
3431 Hillview Ave, Palo Alto, CA 94304-1320
Tel.: (650) 855-5050
Web Site: http://www.roche.com
Sales Range: $300-349.9 Million
Emp.: 1,300
Discovers, Develops, Manufactures & Markets Human & Veterinary Pharmaceutical & Medical Diagnostic Products
N.A.I.C.S.: 541715

Roche Professional Service Centers, Inc. (3)
685 S Rte 17, Paramus, NJ 07652-3110
Tel.: (201) 652-2040
Web Site: http://www.mauricevillency.com
Sales Range: $10-24.9 Million
Emp.: 13
Retail of Furniture
N.A.I.C.S.: 621610

Ventana Medical Systems, Inc. (3)
1910 E Innovation Park Dr, Tucson, AZ 85755
Tel.: (520) 887-2155
Web Site: http://www.ventana.com
Sales Range: $200-249.9 Million
Emp.: 952
Medical Diagnostic Instruments & Reagent Systems
N.A.I.C.S.: 339112
Mara G. Aspinall *(Executives)*

Subsidiary (Non-US):

Ventana Medical Systems S.A. (4)
Parc d Innovation Rue G de Kaysersberg, F-67404, Illkirch-Graffenstaden, Cedex, France
Tel.: (33) 390405200
Sales Range: $125-149.9 Million
Emp.: 350
Medical Diagnostic Instruments & Reagent Systems
N.A.I.C.S.: 339112

Subsidiary (Non-US):

Hoffmann-La Roche Limited (2)
7070 Mississauga Road, Mississauga, L5N 5M8, ON, Canada (100%)
Tel.: (905) 542-5555
Web Site: http://www.rochecanada.com
Sales Range: $200-249.9 Million
Emp.: 700
Mfr & Sales of Pharmaceuticals
N.A.I.C.S.: 325412
Ronald Miller *(Pres & CEO)*

Karachi (Pharma & Dia) Roche Pakistan Ltd. (2)
37 C Block 6 PECHS, Karachi, 75400, Pakistan (100%)
Tel.: (92) 2134540731
Web Site: http://www.roche.com
Sales Range: $50-74.9 Million
Emp.: 115
Mfr & Sales of Pharmaceuticals
N.A.I.C.S.: 325412

N.V. Roche S.A. (2)
75 Dantestraat, Brussels, 1070, Belgium
Tel.: (32) 2 5258211
Web Site: http://www.roche.com
Drug Product Whslr

N.A.I.C.S.: 424210
Hans Warrinnar *(Dir-Medical)*

P.T. Roche Indonesia (2)
AIA Central 32nd 35th 36th Floor 48A Jl Gen Sudirman Kav, Jakarta, 12930, Indonesia
Tel.: (62) 2130413000
Pharmaceuticals Product Mfr
N.A.I.C.S.: 325412

PT Roche Indonesia Diagnostics (2)
Artha Graha Bldg Fl 22 Demndrral Business District, Lot 25 Jl Jend, Jakarta, 12190, Indonesia
Tel.: (62) 151400091
Web Site: http://www.roche.co.id
Mfr & Sales of Pharmaceuticals
N.A.I.C.S.: 325412

Pharma Research Toronto (2)
201 Armand-Frappier Boulevard, Laval, H7V 4A2, QC, Canada
Tel.: (450) 686-7050
Web Site: http://www.rochecanada.com
Sales Range: $1-9.9 Million
Emp.: 500
Cancer Research & Pharmaceutical Mfr
N.A.I.C.S.: 541715

Productos Roche (El Salvador) S.A. (2)
Complejo Holcim y Calle Holcim Salon Bicentenario local No 3, Av El Espino Urb Madre Selva Antiguo Cuscatlan La Libertad, Santa Elena Colonia San Benito, San Salvador, El Salvador
Tel.: (503) 22433444
Pharmaceuticals Product Mfr
N.A.I.C.S.: 325412

Productos Roche (Guatemala) S.A. (2)
AVIA Building level 6 office 600-601 12 calle 2-25 zona 10, 01901, Guatemala, Guatemala
Tel.: (502) 24241616
Pharmaceutical Supplier
N.A.I.C.S.: 325412

Productos Roche Guatemala, SA (2)
5A Avenida 5-55 Zona 14 Edificio Europlaza Tower 3 Level 15, Torre III Nivel 5, Guatemala, 01014, Guatemala
Tel.: (502) 2424 1616
Web Site: http://www.roche.com
Pharmaceutical Diagnostics
N.A.I.C.S.: 424210

Productos Roche Ltda. (2)
Avenida Quilin 3750, Santiago, 6901094, Chile (100%)
Tel.: (56) 24413200
Web Site: http://www.roche.cl
Sales Range: $25-49.9 Million
Emp.: 10
Mfr of Pharmaceuticals
N.A.I.C.S.: 325412

Productos Roche Panama S.A. (2)
MMG Building 16th Floor Ave Vista del Pacifico and Ave Paseo del Mar, Panama, Panama
Tel.: (507) 3781200
Sales Range: $25-49.9 Million
Emp.: 8
Provider of Pharmaceuticals
N.A.I.C.S.: 325412

Productos Roche Quimica Farmaceutica S.A. (2)
Calle Dionisio Derteano 144 Oficina 1301, San Isidro, Lima, Peru (100%)
Tel.: (51) 16188888
Web Site: http://www.roche.pe
Sales Range: $50-74.9 Million
Emp.: 130
Pharmaceuticals Mfr & Whslr
N.A.I.C.S.: 325412

Productos Roche Quimicos E Farmaceuticos S.A. (2)
Ave Englenheiro Billings 1729, Sao Paulo, 05321-010, SP, Brazil (100%)
Tel.: (55) 1137194566
Web Site: http://www.roche.com.br
Sales Range: $100-124.9 Million
Emp.: 500
Mfr & Sales of Pharmaceuticals
N.A.I.C.S.: 325412

Productos Roche S.A. (2)
Edificio Cortezza 93 Piso 6 7 Carrera 14 93-68, DC 110221, Bogota, Colombia
Tel.: (57) 14178860
Pharmaceuticals Product Mfr
N.A.I.C.S.: 325412

Productos Roche S.A. (2)
Apartado 68 168 Altamira, Caracas, 1062 A, Venezuela (100%)
Tel.: (58) 2122734611
Web Site: http://www.roche.com.ve
Sales Range: $50-74.9 Million
Emp.: 200
Mfr & Sales of Pharmaceuticals
N.A.I.C.S.: 325412

Productos Roche S.A, Quimica E Industrial (2)
Rawson 3150, B1610BAL, Buenos Aires, Ricardo Rojas, Argentina
Tel.: (54) 1151298000
Web Site: http://www.roche.com.ar
Sales Range: $50-74.9 Million
Emp.: 225
Mfr & Sales of Pharmaceuticals
N.A.I.C.S.: 325412

Roche (Hellas) S.A. (2)
Alamanas 4 & Delfon St Maroussi Town, GR 151 25, Athens, Greece (100%)
Tel.: (30) 2106166100
Web Site: http://www.roche.com
Sales Range: $125-149.9 Million
Emp.: 270
Sales of Pharmaceuticals
N.A.I.C.S.: 424210

Roche (Hungary) Ltd. (2)
Edison Utca 1, H 2040, Budaors, Hungary (100%)
Tel.: (36) 23446800
Web Site: http://www.roche.hu
Sales Range: $25-49.9 Million
Emp.: 100
Provider of Pharmaceuticals
N.A.I.C.S.: 325412
Stuart Knight *(Gen Mgr)*

Roche (Philippines), Inc. (2)
2252 Don Chino Rocas Ave, 1200, Makati, Philippines (100%)
Tel.: (63) 28934567
Web Site: http://www.roche.com
Sales Range: $50-74.9 Million
Emp.: 200
Sales of Pharmaceuticals & Contract Manufacturing
N.A.I.C.S.: 325412

Roche AB (2)
Liljeholmsstranden 5, Stockholm, 117 43, Sweden
Tel.: (46) 87 26 12 00
Web Site: http://www.roche.se
Emp.: 100
Pharmaceuticals Product Mfr
N.A.I.C.S.: 325412
Krsten Jung *(Gen Mgr)*

Roche Austria GmbH (2)
Engelhorngasse 3, 1211, Vienna, Austria (100%)
Tel.: (43) 1277390
Web Site: https://www.roche.at
Sales Range: $50-74.9 Million
Emp.: 160
Sales of Pharmaceuticals
N.A.I.C.S.: 424210
Wolfram Schmidt *(Mng Dir)*

Roche Beteiligungs GmbH (2)
Emil-Barell-Strasse 1, 79639, Grenzach-Wyhlen, Germany
Tel.: (49) 762490880
Pharmaceuticals Product Mfr
N.A.I.C.S.: 325412

Roche Bulgaria EOOD (2)
Ul Racho Petkov Kazandzhiyata 2, jk Sofia Park - Vitosha District - Municipality Stolichna, 1766, Sofia, Bulgaria
Tel.: (359) 28184444
Web Site: http://www.roche.bg
Pharmaceuticals Product Mfr
N.A.I.C.S.: 325412

Roche Chile Limitada (2)
Las Artes Floor 12 Av Cerro del Plomo 5630, Las Condes, 7550000, Santiago, Chile

ROCHE HOLDING AG

Roche Holding AG—(Continued)
Tel.: (56) 224413200
Web Site: http://www.roche.cl
Pharmaceuticals Product Mfr
N.A.I.C.S.: 325412

Roche Deutschland Holding GmbH (2)
Emil-Barell-Strasse 1, 79639, Grenzach-Wyhlen, Germany
Tel.: (49) 7624140
Pharmaceuticals Product Mfr
N.A.I.C.S.: 325412

Subsidiary (Domestic):

Roche Diabetes Care AG (2)
Kirchbergstrasse 190, CH-3401, Burgdorf, Switzerland (100%)
Tel.: (41) 34 424 2400
Sales Range: $75-99.9 Million
Emp.: 355
Mfr of Medical & Surgical Apparatus & Equipment
N.A.I.C.S.: 339112
Gaurav Laroia *(Gen Mgr-India)*

Subsidiary (Non-US):

Roche Diagnostics GmbH (2)
Sandhofer Strasse 116, PO Box 310120, 68305, Mannheim, Germany
Tel.: (49) 6217590
Sales Range: $1-4.9 Billion
Emp.: 7,000
Pharmaceuticals, Diagnostic Instruments, Medicinal Chemicals & Consumer Products Mfr
N.A.I.C.S.: 325412
Michael Heuer *(Interim CEO)*

Subsidiary (Domestic):

Consulab Mannheim GmbH (3)
Sandhofer Strasse 116, 68305, Mannheim, Germany (100%)
Tel.: (49) 6217590
Web Site: http://www.roche.com
Sales Range: Less than $1 Million
Emp.: 20
Pharmaceutical Services
N.A.I.C.S.: 325412

Galenus Mannheim GmbH (3)
Sandhofer Strasse 116, 68305, Mannheim, Germany (100%)
Tel.: (49) 6217591067
Web Site: http://www.rochediagonistics.com
Rev.: $30,591,600
Emp.: 111
Sales of Chemicals, Pharmaceutical & Diagnostic Products
N.A.I.C.S.: 424690

Subsidiary (Non-US):

Limited Liability Company Roche Diagnostics Rus (3)
Business center Vivaldi Plaza bldg 2 Letnikovskaya street 2, Moscow, 115114, Russia
Tel.: (7) 4952292999
Web Site: http://www.roche.ru
Cancer Treatment Drug Mfr
N.A.I.C.S.: 325412

Roche Diagnostics (Hellas) S.A. (3)
54 A Akakion Str, 151 25, Athens, Greece
Tel.: (30) 210 8174 000
Laboratory Testing Services
N.A.I.C.S.: 541380

Roche Diagnostics (Hong Kong) Limited (3)
Level 17 Tower 1 Metroplaza 223 Hing Fong Road, Kwai Chung, New Territories, China (Hong Kong)
Tel.: (852) 24813387
Sales Range: $50-74.9 Million
Emp.: 60
Diagnostic Equipment Distr
N.A.I.C.S.: 423450

Roche Diagnostics (India) Pvt. Ltd. (3)
501 601 B Silver Utopia Cardinal Gracious Road, Andheri East, Mumbai, 400 069, Chakala Andheri, India
Tel.: (91) 2266974900
Web Site: http://www.roche-diagnostics.co.in
Laboratory Testing Services
N.A.I.C.S.: 541380

Roche Diagnostics (Shanghai) Limited (3)
8/F Building 2 The Hub 900 Shen Chang Road, Shanghai, 200335, China
Tel.: (86) 2133971000
Web Site: http://www.roche-diagnostics.cn
Cancer Treatment Drug Mfr
N.A.I.C.S.: 325412
Wong Fatt Heng *(Gen Mgr)*

Roche Diagnostics (Thailand) Limited (3)
18th-19th Floor Rasa Tower 1 555 Phaholyothin Road, Chatuchak, Bangkok, 10900, Thailand
Tel.: (66) 27912200
Medical Equipment Whslr
N.A.I.C.S.: 423450

Roche Diagnostics AB (3)
Karlsbodavagen 30, PO Box 147, Bromma, 161 26, Sweden (100%)
Tel.: (46) 84048800
Web Site: http://www.roche.se
Sales Range: $25-49.9 Million
Emp.: 100
Mfr of Medical & Surgical Apparatus & Equipment
N.A.I.C.S.: 339112
Magnus Goransson *(Gen Mgr)*

Roche Diagnostics Asia Pacific Pte. Ltd. (3)
8 Kallang Avenue Unit 10-01/09 Aperia Tower 1, Singapore, 339509, Singapore
Tel.: (65) 62727500
Sales Range: $75-99.9 Million
Emp.: 200
Diagnostic Equipment Whslr
N.A.I.C.S.: 423450

Roche Diagnostics Australia Pty. Limited (3)
2 Julius Avenue, North Ryde, 2113, NSW, Australia
Tel.: (61) 298602222
Sales Range: $25-49.9 Million
Emp.: 150
Diagnostic Equipment Mfr
N.A.I.C.S.: 334510

Roche Diagnostics Belgium S.A. (3)
Schaarbeeklei 198, 1800, Vilvoorde, Belgium
Tel.: (32) 2 247 4747
Web Site: http://www.roche.be
Sales Range: $50-74.9 Million
Emp.: 160
Pharmaceuticals Product Mfr
N.A.I.C.S.: 325412

Subsidiary (US):

Roche Diagnostics Corporation (3)
9115 Hague Rd, Indianapolis, IN 46250-1025 (100%)
Tel.: (317) 521-2000
Web Site: http://www.roche-diagnostics.us
Sales Range: $800-899.9 Million
Emp.: 4,125
Diagnostic Instruments & Reagents, Orthopedic Implants & Biochemicals Distributer & Mfr
N.A.I.C.S.: 334516
Susan Zienowicz *(Sr VP-Applied Science)*

Subsidiary (Domestic):

Ariosa Diagnostics, Inc. (4)
5945 Optical Ct, San Jose, CA 95138
Tel.: (925) 854-6246
Web Site: http://www.ariosadx.com
Emp.: 200
Medical Testing Services
N.A.I.C.S.: 621511
Dave Mullarkey *(CEO)*

Roche Diagnostics Operations, Inc. (4)
9115 Hague Rd, Indianapolis, IN 46256-1025
Tel.: (317) 521-2000
Laboratory Testing Services
N.A.I.C.S.: 541380
Richard Benton *(Mgr-Investigations)*

Division (Domestic):

Roche Applied Science (5)

N.A.I.C.S.: 541380

9115 Hague Rd, Indianapolis, IN 46250
Tel.: (317) 521-2000
Web Site: http://www.roche-applied-science.com
Sales & Marketing Biochemicals
N.A.I.C.S.: 541714

Unit (Domestic):

Roche Diagnostic Systems (5)
1080 US Hwy 202 S, Branchburg, NJ 08876-3733
Tel.: (908) 253-7200
Web Site: http://www.roche.com
Sales Range: $200-249.9 Million
Emp.: 700
N.A.I.C.S.: 325412

Roche Molecular Diagnostics (5)
4300 Hacienda Dr, Pleasanton, CA 94588
Tel.: (925) 730-8200
Web Site: http://www.roche-diagnostics.com
Sales Range: $125-149.9 Million
Emp.: 2,400
Develops & Commercializes Diagnostic & Blood Screening Tests
N.A.I.C.S.: 325412
Stephen Will *(Sr Dir)*

Subsidiary (Domestic):

Roche Health Solutions Inc. (4)
11800 Exit 5 Pkwy Ste 120, Fishers, IN 46037
Tel.: (317) 570-5100
Web Site: http://www.accu-chekinsulinpumps.com
Sales Range: $50-74.9 Million
Emp.: 150
Medical & Surgical Apparatus & Equipment Mfr
N.A.I.C.S.: 339112

Subsidiary (Non-US):

Roche Diagnostics France S.A.S. (3)
2 Avenue du Vercors, BP 59, 38240, Meylan, Cedex, France
Tel.: (33) 476763000
Web Site: http://www.rochediagnostics.fr
Mfr of Medical & Surgical Apparatus & Equipment
N.A.I.C.S.: 339112

Roche Diagnostics GmbH (3)
Engelhorngasse 3, Vienna, 1210, Austria (100%)
Tel.: (43) 1277870
Web Site: http://www.roche.at
Sales Range: $50-74.9 Million
Emp.: 300
Mfr of Medical & Surgical Apparatus & Equipment
N.A.I.C.S.: 339112
Andrijka Kashan *(Gen Mgr)*

Roche Diagnostics Graz GmbH (3)
Kratkystrasse 2, 8020, Graz, Austria
Tel.: (43) 316 277 87 0
Web Site: http://www.roche.com
Sales Range: $50-74.9 Million
Emp.: 130
Diagnostic Equipment Mfr
N.A.I.C.S.: 334510

Roche Diagnostics International Ltd. (3)
Forrenstrasse 2, 6343, Rotkreuz, Switzerland
Tel.: (41) 417992244
Web Site: https://www.roche.ch
Pharmaceuticals Product Mfr
N.A.I.C.S.: 325412

Roche Diagnostics K.K. (3)
6-1 Shiba 2-Chome, Minato-Ku, Tokyo, 105-0014, Japan
Tel.: (81) 3 54437041
Web Site: http://www.roche-diagnostics.jp
Sales Range: $100-124.9 Million
Emp.: 500
Diagnostic Equipment Mfr
N.A.I.C.S.: 334510

Roche Diagnostics Korea Co., Ltd. (3)
4th Floor-Seokyung Building 108-gil 22 Teheranro, Gangnam-gu, Seoul, 06174, Korea (South)

INTERNATIONAL PUBLIC

Tel.: (82) 25503300
Web Site: http://www.roche-diagnostics.co.kr
Emp.: 250
Pharmaceuticals Product Mfr
N.A.I.C.S.: 325412

Roche Diagnostics Ltd. (3)
2 Min Quan East Road Sec 3, Taipei, 10477, Taiwan
Tel.: (886) 221836688
Pharmaceuticals Product Mfr
N.A.I.C.S.: 325412

Roche Diagnostics NZ Limited (3)
ANZ Raranga Building Level 1 286 Mt Wellington Highway, Mount Wellington Sylvia Park, Auckland, 1060, New Zealand
Tel.: (64) 92764157
Sales Range: $25-49.9 Million
Emp.: 50
Diagnostic Equipment Mfr
N.A.I.C.S.: 334510

Roche Diagnostics Nederland B.V. (3)
Transistorstraat 41, 1322 CK, Almere, Netherlands (100%)
Tel.: (31) 365394911
Web Site: http://www.roche-diagnostics.nl
Sales Range: $100-124.9 Million
Emp.: 200
Mfr of Medical & Surgical Apparatus & Equipment
N.A.I.C.S.: 339112

Roche Diagnostics Norge A/S (3)
Brynsengfaret 6B, 0667, Oslo, Norway
Tel.: (47) 23373300
Medical Equipment Whslr
N.A.I.C.S.: 423450

Roche Diagnostics Oy (3)
Revontulenpuisto 2 C, 02101, Espoo, Finland
Tel.: (358) 10554511
Web Site: https://www.roche.fi
Medical Instrument Mfr
N.A.I.C.S.: 339112

Roche Diagnostics Polska Sp. z.o.o. (3)
Domaniewska 28, 02-672, Warsaw, Poland
Tel.: (48) 224815555
Web Site: https://www.roche.pl
Laboratory Testing Services
N.A.I.C.S.: 541380

Subsidiary (US):

Roche Diagnostics Puerto Rico (3)
2875 Ponce By Pass, Ponce, PR 00732-7085
Tel.: (787) 843-6195
Web Site: http://www.rochediagnostics.us
Sales Range: $50-74.9 Million
Emp.: 230
Pharmaceuticals Mfr
N.A.I.C.S.: 325412

Subsidiary (Domestic):

Roche Diagnostics Corange International Limited (4)
2875 Ponce Byp, Ponce, PR 00732-7085
Tel.: (787) 843-6195
Web Site: http://www.rochediagnostics.com
Sales Range: $50-74.9 Million
Emp.: 200
Mfr of Medical & Surgical Apparatus & Equipment
N.A.I.C.S.: 339112
Miguel Santano *(Gen Mgr)*

Subsidiary (Non-US):

Roche Diagnostics S.L. (3)
Avda de la Generalitat 171-173, 08174, Sant Cugat del Valles, Barcelona, Spain
Tel.: (34) 935834000
Web Site: http://www.rochediagnostics.es
Pharmaceuticals Product Mfr
N.A.I.C.S.: 325412

Roche Diagnostics S.p.A. (3)
Piazza F Durante 11, 20131, Milan, Italy
Tel.: (39) 039 28 17 1
Diagnostic Equipment Mfr
N.A.I.C.S.: 334510

AND PRIVATE COMPANIES — ROCHE HOLDING AG

Roche Diagnostics Vietnam Co., Ltd. (3)
Unit 3 3 e-town 2 Building 364 Cong Hoa Street, Tan Binh District, Ho Chi Minh City, 70000, Vietnam
Tel.: (84) 8 3810 1888
Emp.: 100
Health Care Srvices
N.A.I.C.S.: 621999
Rod Ward *(Gen Mgr)*

Roche Diagnostics a/s (3)
Industriholmen 59, Hvidovre, 2650, Denmark
Tel.: (45) 36 39 98 98
Web Site: http://www.roche.dk
Diagnostic Equipment Mfr
N.A.I.C.S.: 334510

Subsidiary (Non-US):

Roche Ecuador S.A. (2)
EKOPARK Corporate Center Tower 5-2nd floor, PO Box 171 106 185, Av Simon Bolivar and via Nayon, Quito, Ecuador **(100%)**
Tel.: (593) 22464934
Web Site: http://www.roche.com.ec
Sales Range: $25-49.9 Million
Emp.: 90
Sales & Marketing of Pharmaceuticals
N.A.I.C.S.: 424210

Roche Eesti OU (2)
Lootsa 2A, 11415, Tallinn, Estonia
Tel.: (372) 6177380
Web Site: https://www.roche.ee
Pharmaceuticals Product Mfr
N.A.I.C.S.: 327910

Roche Farma S.A. (2)
Eucalipto 33, ES 28016, Madrid, Spain **(100%)**
Tel.: (34) 913248100
Web Site: http://www.mad.roche.com
Sales Range: $100-124.9 Million
Emp.: 300
Mfr & Sales of Pharmaceuticals
N.A.I.C.S.: 325412

Roche Farma, S.A. (2)
C/ Ribera del Loira 50, 28042, Madrid, Spain **(100%)**
Tel.: (34) 913248100
Web Site: https://www.roche.es
Sales Range: $100-124.9 Million
Emp.: 300
N.A.I.C.S.: 325412

Roche Farmaceutica Quimica Lda. (2)
Estrada Nacional 249-1, 2720-413, Amadora, Portugal **(100%)**
Tel.: (351) 214257000
Sales Range: $75-99.9 Million
Emp.: 200
Sales of Pharmaceuticals
N.A.I.C.S.: 424210

Subsidiary (Domestic):

Roche Glycart AG (2)
Wagistrasse 10, CH-8952, Schlieren, Switzerland
Tel.: (41) 432151000
Sales Range: $25-49.9 Million
Emp.: 80
Biotechnology Products Mfr
N.A.I.C.S.: 325412

Subsidiary (Non-US):

Roche Holding (UK) Limited (2)
Hexagon Place 6 Falcon Way, Shire Park, Welwyn Garden City, AL7 1TW, Hertfordshire, United Kingdom
Tel.: (44) 1707366000
Web Site: https://www.roche.co.uk
Investment Management Service
N.A.I.C.S.: 523940

Roche Hong Kong Limited (2)
24/F Caroline Centre 2-28 Yun Ping Road, Causeway Bay, China (Hong Kong)
Tel.: (852) 2723 2832
Web Site: http://www.roche.com.hk
Sales Range: $50-74.9 Million
Emp.: 100
Pharmaceutical Product Mfr & Distr
N.A.I.C.S.: 325412

Roche Innovation Center Copenhagen A/S (2)
Fremtidsvej 3, DK 2970, Horsholm, Denmark
Tel.: (45) 4517 9800
Web Site: http://www.santaris.com
Pharmaceuticals Mfr
N.A.I.C.S.: 325412

Roche International Ltd. (2)
26 Reid Street AS Cooper Building 5th Floor, Hamilton, HM 11, Bermuda
Tel.: (441) 2953391
Web Site: http://www.roche.com
Emp.: 10
Pharmaceuticals Product Mfr
N.A.I.C.S.: 325412

Roche International Ltd. (2)
Edificio WTC Montevideo Torre IV Piso 35, Dr Luis Bonavita 1266, 11300, Montevideo, Uruguay **(100%)**
Tel.: (598) 26261400
Sales Range: $50-74.9 Million
Emp.: 107
Mfr & Sales of Pharmaceuticals
N.A.I.C.S.: 325412

Roche Intertrade Limited (2)
Solferino 4096, Montevideo, 11400, Uruguay
Tel.: (598) 26137888
Web Site: http://www.roche.com
Pharmaceutical Products Distr
N.A.I.C.S.: 424210

Roche Ireland Limited (2)
Clarehill, Clarecastle, Clare, Ireland **(100%)**
Tel.: (353) 656867200
Sales Range: $50-74.9 Million
Emp.: 250
Provider of Pharmaceuticals
N.A.I.C.S.: 325412

Roche Korea Company Ltd. (2)
17th Floor GT Tower East 411 Seocho-Daero, Seocho-Gu, Seoul, 06655, Korea (South) **(100%)**
Tel.: (82) 234513600
Web Site: https://www.roche.co.kr
Sales Range: $100-124.9 Million
Emp.: 260
Pharmaceutical Products Mfr & Distr
N.A.I.C.S.: 325412
Svend Petersen *(Gen Mgr)*

Roche Latvija SIA (2)
Miera iela 25, Riga, LV - 1001, Latvia
Tel.: (371) 67039831
Web Site: https://www.roche.lv
Pharmaceuticals Product Mfr
N.A.I.C.S.: 325412

Roche Malaysia Sdn. Bhd. (2)
Level 21 The Pinnacle Persiaran Lagoon, Bandar Sunway, 47500, Kuala Lumpur, Selangor Darul Ehsan, Malaysia
Tel.: (60) 376285600
Web Site: http://www.roche.it
Sales of Pharmaceuticals
N.A.I.C.S.: 325412

Roche Moscow Ltd. (2)
Business Center Neglinnaya Plaza Trubnaya ploshchad 2, 107031, Moscow, Russia **(100%)**
Tel.: (7) 4952292999
Web Site: http://www.roche.ru
Sales Range: $25-49.9 Million
Emp.: 10
Pharmaceuticals Mfr
N.A.I.C.S.: 325412

Roche Mustahzarlari A.S. (2)
Eski Buyukdere Caddesi No 13 Maslak, Istanbul, 34398, Turkiye
Tel.: (90) 2123669000
Web Site: http://www.roche.com.tr
Mfr & Sales of Pharmaceuticals
N.A.I.C.S.: 325412
Mirel Tarablus *(Gen Mgr)*

Roche N.V./S.A. (2)
75 Rue Dante, Brussels, 1070, Belgium **(100%)**
Tel.: (32) 25258211
Web Site: http://www.roche.be
Sales Range: $50-74.9 Million
Emp.: 150
Provider of Pharmaceuticals

N.A.I.C.S.: 325412
Richard Arvin *(Mng Dir)*

Roche Nederland B.V. (2)
Bnelluxlaan No 2, Postbus 44, 3440 AA, Woerden, Netherlands **(100%)**
Tel.: (31) 348438000
Web Site: https://www.roche.nl
Pharmaceuticals Mfr
N.A.I.C.S.: 325412

Roche Norge A/S (2)
Brynsengfaret 6 B, PO Box 41, 0667, Oslo, Norway **(100%)**
Tel.: (47) 22789000
Sales Range: $25-49.9 Million
Emp.: 60
Marketing & Sales of Pharmaceuticals
N.A.I.C.S.: 424210

Roche Oy (2)
Revontulenpuisto 2 C PL 112, PO Box 12, 02100, Espoo, Finland **(100%)**
Tel.: (358) 10554500
Sales Range: $50-74.9 Million
Emp.: 100
Sales & Marketing of Pharmaceuticals
N.A.I.C.S.: 424210

Subsidiary (Domestic):

Roche Pharma (Switzerland) Ltd. (2)
Schonmattstrasse 2, CH 4153, Reinach, Switzerland **(100%)**
Tel.: (41) 617154111
Web Site: http://www.roche-pharma.ch
Sales Range: $50-74.9 Million
Emp.: 160
Provider of Pharmaceuticals
N.A.I.C.S.: 325412
David Louw *(Mng Dir)*

Subsidiary (Non-US):

Roche Pharma AG (2)
Emil-Barell-Strasse 1, 79639, Grenzach-Wyhlen, Germany
Tel.: (49) 7624140
Emp.: 1,000
Diagnostic Equipment Mfr & Distr
N.A.I.C.S.: 334510

Roche Pharmaceuticals (Israel) Ltd. (2)
Kiryat Matalon, PO Box 7543, Petah Tiqwa, 49170, Israel **(100%)**
Tel.: (972) 39203333
Pharmaceuticals Mfr
N.A.I.C.S.: 325412
Avi Danziger *(Gen Mgr)*

Roche Polska Sp. z o.o. (2)
ul Domaniewska 28, 02-672, Warsaw, Poland **(100%)**
Tel.: (48) 223451888
Sales Range: $100-124.9 Million
Emp.: 300
Provider of Pharmaceuticals
N.A.I.C.S.: 325412

Roche Products (India) Pvt. Ltd. (2)
146-B A Unit No 7 8 9 8th Floor R City Office, R City Mall Lal Bahadur Shastri Marg Ghatkopar, Mumbai, 400 086, India
Tel.: (91) 9619213075
Web Site: https://www.rocheindia.com
Sales Range: $25-49.9 Million
Emp.: 60
Pharmaceuticals Product Mfr
N.A.I.C.S.: 325412

Roche Products (Ireland) Limited (2)
3004 Lake Drive, Citywest, Dublin, 24, Ireland
Tel.: (353) 14690700
Provider of Pharmaceuticals
N.A.I.C.S.: 325412

Roche Products (New Zealand) Ltd. (2)
98 Carlton Gore Road Newmarket, PO Box 12492, Auckland, 1023, Penrose, New Zealand **(100%)**
Tel.: (64) 95239400
Sales Range: $25-49.9 Million
Emp.: 85
Sales of Pharmaceuticals
N.A.I.C.S.: 424210

Roche Products (Proprietary) Limited (2)
4 Brewery St, PO Box 129, 1601, Isando, South Africa **(100%)**
Tel.: (27) 119288700
Web Site: http://www.roche.co.za
Sales Range: $100-124.9 Million
Emp.: 450
Provider of Pharmaceuticals
N.A.I.C.S.: 325412

Roche Products (Pty.) Ltd. (2)
4-10 Inman Road, PO Box 255, Dee Why, 2099, NSW, Australia **(100%)**
Tel.: (61) 294549000
Web Site: http://www.roche-australia.com
Sales Range: $350-399.9 Million
Emp.: 400
Mfr & Sales of Pharmaceuticals
N.A.I.C.S.: 325412

Roche Products Ltd. (2)
100 Songren Rd, Xinyi Dist 40F, Taipei, 11073, Taiwan
Tel.: (886) 227153111
Sales Range: $25-49.9 Million
Emp.: 100
Pharmaceuticals Mfr, Marketer & Sales
N.A.I.C.S.: 325412

Roche Products Ltd. (2)
Hexigan Pl 6 Falcon Shera Pk, Welwyn Garden City, AL71TW, United Kingdom **(100%)**
Tel.: (44) 1707366000
Web Site: http://www.rocheuk.com
Sales Range: $200-249.9 Million
Emp.: 1,000
Mfr of Vitamins & Pharmaceuticals
N.A.I.C.S.: 325412

Roche R&D Center (China) Ltd. (2)
Building 5 371 Li Shizhen Road, Shanghai, 201203, Pudong, China
Tel.: (86) 2128922888
Sales Range: $25-49.9 Million
Emp.: 100
Biotechnology Research & Development Services
N.A.I.C.S.: 541714

Roche Registration Limited (2)
Hexagon Place 6 Falcon Way, Shire Park, Welwyn Garden City, AL7 1TW, Hertfordshire, United Kingdom
Tel.: (44) 1707366000
Pharmaceuticals Product Mfr
N.A.I.C.S.: 325412

Roche Romania S.R.L. (2)
Poligrafiei Boulevard no 1A Ana Tower Reception, Floor 15 Sector 1, 013704, Bucharest, Romania
Tel.: (40) 212064701
Web Site: https://www.roche.ro
Sales Range: $125-149.9 Million
Emp.: 400
Pharmaceuticals Product Mfr
N.A.I.C.S.: 325412
Dan Zamonea *(Pres & Gen Mgr)*

Roche S.A. (2)
52 Blvd Du Parc, 92521, Neuilly-sur-Seine, France **(100%)**
Tel.: (33) 146405000
Web Site: http://www.roche.fr
Rev.: $544,687,000
Emp.: 600
Mfr & Sales of Pharmaceuticals & Diagnostic Products
N.A.I.C.S.: 325412

Roche S.A. (2)
225 Boulevard d'Anfa, 20100, Casablanca, Morocco
Tel.: (212) 522959000
Web Site: http://www.roche.com
Sales Range: $50-74.9 Million
Emp.: 150
Medical Equipment Mfr
N.A.I.C.S.: 339112

Roche S.A.S. (2)
4 cours de l'Ile Seguin, 92650, Boulogne-Billancourt, Cedex, France
Tel.: (33) 147614000
Web Site: http://www.roche.fr
Pharmaceuticals Product Mfr
N.A.I.C.S.: 325412

Roche S.p.A. (2)
Via GB Stucchi 110, IT 20900, Monza, MB, Italy

ROCHE HOLDING AG

Roche Holding AG—(Continued)
Tel.: (39) 0392471
Web Site: http://www.roche.com
Emp.: 1,000
Pharmaceuticals Mfr & Whslr
N.A.I.C.S.: 325412

Roche Scientific Company (India) Private Ltd. (2)
The View 2nd Floor 165 Dr Annie Besant Road, Worli, Mumbai, 400 018, India (100%)
Tel.: (91) 2224941414
Web Site: http://www.rocheindia.com
Sales Range: $25-49.9 Million
Emp.: 45
Pharmaceuticals Mfr
N.A.I.C.S.: 325412

Roche Servicios S.A. (2)
Zona Franca Ultrapark Noreste de Real Cariari 1 km, Zona Franca Ultrapark Edificio, Zona Franca Ultrapark - La Aurora, 1000, Heredia, Costa Rica
Tel.: (506) 22981500
Sales Range: $200-249.9 Million
Emp.: 1,000
Pharmaceuticals
N.A.I.C.S.: 325412
Alfaro Soto (Reg Mgr)

Roche Singapore Pte. Ltd. (2)
1 Paya Lebar Link 09-03 PLQ 1 Paya Lebar Quarter, Great World City W Tower, Singapore, 408533, Singapore (100%)
Tel.: (65) 67350550
Web Site: http://www.roche.com.sg
Sales Range: $25-49.9 Million
Emp.: 50
Sales & Marketer of Pharmaceuticals
N.A.I.C.S.: 424210

Roche Singapore Technical Operations, Pte. Ltd. (2)
10 Tuas Bay Link, Singapore, 637394, Singapore
Tel.: (65) 64914000
Pharmaceuticals Product Mfr
N.A.I.C.S.: 325412

Roche Sistemas de Diagnosticos, Lda.
Estrada Nacional 249-1, 2720-413, Amadora, Portugal
Tel.: (351) 21 425 70 00
Web Site: http://www.roche.pt
Sales Range: $25-49.9 Million
Emp.: 100
Pharmaceuticals Product Mfr
N.A.I.C.S.: 325412

Roche Thailand Ltd. (2)
89 AIA Capital Center 26th Floor Ratchadapisek Road, Kwaeng Dindaeng Khet Dindaeng, Bangkok, 10400, Thailand (100%)
Tel.: (66) 20175600
Web Site: http://www.rochethai.com
Sales Range: $50-74.9 Million
Emp.: 180
Pharmaceuticals Whslr
N.A.I.C.S.: 424210

Roche Ukraine LLC (2)
str Velika Vasylkivska 139 5th floor, 03150, Kiev, Ukraine
Tel.: (380) 442988833
Web Site: https://www.roche.ua
Drugs Whslr
N.A.I.C.S.: 424210

Affiliate (Non-US):

Roche Zhongya (Wuxi) Citric Acid Ltd. (2)
West Side of Jincheng Bridge, Wuxi, 214024, Jiangsu, China
Tel.: (86) 86 www.roche.com.cn
Producer of Citric Acid
N.A.I.C.S.: 325199

Subsidiary (Non-US):

Roche a/s (2)
Industriholmen 59, Hvidovre, 2650, Denmark (100%)
Tel.: (45) 36399999
Web Site: http://www.roche.dk

Sales Range: $50-74.9 Million
Emp.: 120
Sales & Marketer of Pharmaceuticals
N.A.I.C.S.: 424210
Ron Park (Mng Dir)

Roche d.o.o. (2)
Milutina Milankovica 11a, 11070, Belgrade, Serbia
Tel.: (381) 112022803
Pharmaceuticals Product Mfr
N.A.I.C.S.: 325412

Roche d.o.o. Pharmaceutical Company (2)
Vodovodna cesta 109, Ljubljana, 1000, Slovenia
Tel.: (386) 1 360 26 00
Sales Range: $25-49.9 Million
Emp.: 75
Pharmaceuticals Product Mfr
N.A.I.C.S.: 325412

Roche mtm laboratories AG (2)
BioPark Im Neuenheimer Feld 583, 69120, Heidelberg, Germany
Tel.: (49) 6221 64966 0
Web Site: http://www.mtmlabs.com
Diagnostic Equipment Mfr
N.A.I.C.S.: 334510

Roche s.r.o. (2)
Sokolovska 685/136f, 186 00, Prague, Czech Republic (100%)
Tel.: (420) 220382111
Web Site: https://www.roche.cz
Sales Range: $50-74.9 Million
Emp.: 200
Sales
N.A.I.C.S.: 424210
Tomas Votruba (Gen Mgr)

Swisslab GmbH (2)
Pascalstr 10, 10587, Berlin, Germany
Tel.: (49) 30 62601 0
Web Site: http://www.swisslab.de
Medical Laboratories Information Services
N.A.I.C.S.: 519290

GenMark Diagnostics, Inc. (1)
5964 La Pl Ct, Carlsbad, CA 92008-8829
Tel.: (760) 448-4300
Web Site: http://www.genmarkdx.com
Rev: $171,554,000
Assets: $223,534,000
Liabilities: $129,336,000
Net Worth: $94,198,000
Earnings: ($18,644,000)
Emp.: 618
Fiscal Year-end: 12/31/2020
Molecular Diagnostic Testing Systems Mfr
N.A.I.C.S.: 339112
Michael Gleeson (Sr VP-Corp Accounts)

Subsidiary (Non-US):

GenMark Diagnostics Europe GmbH (2)
General-Guisan-Strasse 6, 6303, Zug, Switzerland
Tel.: (41) 412294260
Web Site: http://www.genmarkdx.com
Electromedical & Electrotherapeutic Apparatus Mfr
N.A.I.C.S.: 334510

Promedior, Inc. (1)
81 Hartwell Ave Ste 100, Lexington, MA 02421
Tel.: (781) 538-4200
Web Site: http://www.promedior.com
Pharmaceutical Preparation Mfr
N.A.I.C.S.: 325412
William Hodder (VP-Bus Dev)

Spark Therapeutics, Inc. (1)
3737 Market St Ste 1300, Philadelphia, PA 19104
Tel.: (855) 772-7589
Web Site: http://www.sparktx.com
Rev: $20,183,000
Assets: $814,352,000
Liabilities: $317,839,000
Net Worth: $496,513,000
Earnings: ($123,653,000)
Emp.: 368
Fiscal Year-end: 12/31/2018
Pharmaceuticals Mfr
N.A.I.C.S.: 325412
Jeffrey D. Marrazzo (CEO)

ROCHE LTD., CONSULTING GROUP

Centre daffaires Henri-IV 1015 Wilfrid-Pelletier Ave, Quebec, G1W 0C4, QC, Canada
Tel.: (418) 654-9600 Ca
Web Site: http://www.roche.ca
Year Founded: 1963
Sales Range: $200-249.9 Million
Emp.: 1,400
Engineering & Construction Consulting Services
N.A.I.C.S.: 541330
Alex Brisson (Pres & CEO)

Subsidiaries:

A2EP (1)
14 rue Edouard Glasser Motor Pool, BP 8176, 98807, Noumea, Cedex, New Caledonia
Tel.: (687) 27 55 00
Web Site: http://www.a2ep.net
Engineering Consulting Services
N.A.I.C.S.: 541330
Carine Martin (Engr-Project)

Evimbec Ltd. (1)
102-1191 rue de Courchevel, Levis, G6W 0N9, QC, Canada (100%)
Tel.: (418) 834-7000
Web Site: https://www.evimbec.ca
Sales Range: $200-249.9 Million
Emp.: 150
Engineeering Services
N.A.I.C.S.: 541330

Forchemex Ltd. (1)
1389 avenue Galilee bureau 205, Quebec, G1P 4G4, QC, Canada
Tel.: (418) 654-9652
Web Site: http://www.forchemex.ca
Forest Management Services
N.A.I.C.S.: 115310

Geomog Inc. (1)
Centre d'affaires Henri-IV 1015 Wilfrid-Pelletier Ave, Quebec, G1W 0C4, QC, Canada
Tel.: (418) 988-0680
Web Site: http://www.geomog.com
Surveying & Geomatics Services
N.A.I.C.S.: 541360
Alexandre Gagne (Founder & Pres)

Roche Construction Inc. (1)
Centre d'affaires Henri-IV 1015 Wilfrid-Pelletier Ave, Quebec, G1W 0C4, QC, Canada (100%)
Tel.: (418) 654-9600
Web Site: https://norda.com
Sales Range: $150-199.9 Million
Emp.: 1,000
Construction Services
N.A.I.C.S.: 541330

Roche Consulting Group (1)
630 Rene Levesque Blvd W Ste 1500, Montreal, H3B 1S6, QC, Canada (100%)
Tel.: (514) 393-3363
Web Site: http://www.roche.ca
Sales Range: $10-24.9 Million
Emp.: 80
Transport & Traffic Studies for Canada
N.A.I.C.S.: 561499

Roche Engineering, Inc. (1)
9815 S Monroe St Ste 502, Sandy, UT 84070
Tel.: (801) 871-2400
Web Site: http://www.roche-engineering.com
Emp.: 17
Engineering Consulting Services
N.A.I.C.S.: 541330
Eric Larochelle (Pres)

Roche Maghreb (1)
Ilot D 6 Zhun Garidi II, Kouba, 16005, Algiers, Algeria
Tel.: (213) 21 56 37 10
Engineering Consulting Services
N.A.I.C.S.: 541330

ROCHESTER RESOURCES LTD.

1090 West Georgia Street Suite

INTERNATIONAL PUBLIC

1305, Vancouver, V6E 3V7, BC, Canada
Tel.: (604) 685-9316 BC
Web Site:
  https://rochesterresourcesltd.com
Year Founded: 1989
RCT—(OTCIQ)
Rev.: $10,185,722
Assets: $4,285,611
Liabilities: $20,837,180
Net Worth: ($16,551,569)
Earnings: $1,915,241
Fiscal Year-end: 05/31/21
Gold Mining & Exploration Services
N.A.I.C.S.: 212220
Jose Manuel Silva (CFO)

ROCHLING SE & CO. KG

Richard-Wagner-Str 9, 68165, Mannheim, Germany
Tel.: (49) 62144020 De
Web Site: http://www.roechling.com
Year Founded: 1822
Emp.: 100
Automotive Plastic Equipment Distr
N.A.I.C.S.: 423830
Daniel Buhler (Member-Exec Bd)

Subsidiaries:

CircleSmartCard GmbH (1)
Am Urbicher Kreuz 16, 99099, Erfurt, Germany
Tel.: (49) 361 55088 0
Web Site: http://www.circlesmartcard.com
Smart Card Distr
N.A.I.C.S.: 424610
Anett Kulka (Head-Acct Dept)

MAYWO Kunststoff GmbH (1)
Hinter den Garten 20, 87730, Bad Gronenbach, Germany
Tel.: (49) 83 34 98 57 0
Web Site: http://www.maywo.de
Thermoplastic Product Mfr
N.A.I.C.S.: 325211
Andreas Zodel (Mgr-Ops)

Rochling Automotive Araia S.L.U. (1)
Calle Aran n 7, Araia, 01250, Alava, Spain
Tel.: (34) 945314522
Automobile Parts Mfr
N.A.I.C.S.: 336310
Selenia Fornari (Dir-HR)

Rochling Automotive Asan Co., Ltd. (1)
No 77 Asanvalleynam-ro 110-beon-gil, Dunpo-myeon, 31409, Asan, Chungcheongdo, Korea (South)
Tel.: (82) 7042425743
Automobile Parts Mfr
N.A.I.C.S.: 336310
Joungmin Lee (Mgr-Sls & Tech)

Rochling Automotive Asia GmbH (1)
Richard-Wagner Str 9, 68165, Mannheim, Germany
Tel.: (49) 621440550
Automobile Parts Mfr
N.A.I.C.S.: 336310
Rene Benz (Gen Mgr)

Rochling Automotive Filters S.r.l. (1)
Europa Sud/Europe South Via Mendosio 30, 20081, Abbiategrasso, Milan, Italy
Tel.: (39) 02 9462866
Automotive Plastic Product Distr
N.A.I.C.S.: 424610

Rochling Automotive Germany SE & Co. KG (1)
Europa Nord/Europe North Obertsroter Str 2, 76593, Gernsbach, Germany
Tel.: (49) 7224 61 0
Automotive Plastic Product Mfr
N.A.I.C.S.: 326199

Rochling Automotive Gijzegem N.V. (1)
Europa Nord/Europe North Nijverheidslaan 12, 9308, Gijzegem, Belgium
Tel.: (32) 537 67400
Automotive Plastic Product Distr
N.A.I.C.S.: 424610

AND PRIVATE COMPANIES — ROCHLING SE & CO. KG

Rochling Automotive Koprivnice s.r.o (1)
Europa Nord/Europe North Prumysloypark c p 308, 74221, Koprivnice, Czech Republic
Tel.: (420) 556 806 061
Automotive Plastic Product Distr
N.A.I.C.S.: 424610

Rochling Automotive Mexico S. de R.L. de C.V. (1)
Mina de Calderones No 200 Int 1 Puerto Interior, Silao, Guanajuato, Mexico
Tel.: (52) 4721372600
Automobile Parts Mfr
N.A.I.C.S.: 336310
Jorge Navarrete (Mgr)

Rochling Automotive Milzkalne SIA (1)
Europa Nord/Europe North Smardes pag Tukuma raj, 3148, Milzkalne, Latvia
Tel.: (371) 6310 72 91
Automotive Plastic Product Mfr
N.A.I.C.S.: 326199
Miervaldis Zarins (Plant Mgr)

Rochling Automotive Parts Changchun Co., Ltd. (1)
No 222 Gao ErFu Road Changchun Automotive Industrial Development Area, 130013, Changchun, Jilin, China
Tel.: (86) 431 8574 2000
Automotive Plastic Product Distr
N.A.I.C.S.: 424610
Xiugang Wu (Mgr-Quality)

Rochling Automotive Parts Chengdu Co., Ltd. (1)
38 Dalian Road, Longquanyi Industrial Zone, 610100, Chengdu, Sichuan, China
Tel.: (86) 28 848 58441
Automotive Plastic Product Distr
N.A.I.C.S.: 424610

Rochling Automotive Parts Kunshan Co., Ltd. (1)
No 18 ShanSong Road, YuShan Town, 215316, Kunshan, Jiangsu, China
Tel.: (86) 512 36639 669
Automotive Plastic Product Distr
N.A.I.C.S.: 424610

Rochling Automotive Parts Shenyang Co., Ltd. (1)
No 306 Kaifa 22 Road, Economic and Technology Development Park, Shenyang, 110141, China
Tel.: (86) 2431853066
Automobile Parts Mfr
N.A.I.C.S.: 336310
Lin Lin (Mgr-HR)

Rochling Automotive Parts Suzhou Co., Ltd. (1)
68 Yingsheng Road, Suzhou Industrial Park, 215126, Suzhou, Jiangsu, China
Tel.: (86) 512 83639557
Automotive Plastic Product Distr
N.A.I.C.S.: 424610
Jackon Huang (Mgr-Sls)

Rochling Automotive Pitesti srl. (1)
WDP Industrial Park, 117545, Oarja, Arges, Romania
Tel.: (40) 348 730 011
Automotive Plastic Product Distr
N.A.I.C.S.: 424610

Rochling Automotive SE & Co. KG (1)
2 rue Helene Boucher, Parc Ariane Imm Venus, 78280, Guyancourt, France
Tel.: (33) 176783390
Automobile Parts Mfr
N.A.I.C.S.: 336310

Rochling Automotive Slovakia s.r.o (1)
Rakoluby 264, Kocovce, 91631, Trencin, Slovakia
Tel.: (421) 322213610
Automobile Parts Mfr
N.A.I.C.S.: 336310
Lehmbruck Erhard (Mgr)

Rochling Automotive USA L.L.P. (1)
245 Parkway E, Duncan, SC 29334
Tel.: (864) 486-0888
Automotive Plastic Product Distr
N.A.I.C.S.: 424610
Andie Burleson (Mgr-HR)

Rochling Automotive do Brasil Ltda (1)
Av Emilio Chechinatto 4195 c, 13295-000, Itupeva, Sao Paulo, Brazil
Tel.: (55) 11 4593 7999
Automotive Plastic Product Distr
N.A.I.C.S.: 424610

Rochling Engineering Plastics (India) Pvt. Ltd. (1)
201 A Wing Leo Building 24th Road, Khar West, 400 052, Mumbai, India
Tel.: (91) 22 4217 8787
Web Site: http://www.roechling-india.com
Thermoplastic Product Mfr & Distr
N.A.I.C.S.: 326199
Rogers Colaco (Mgr-Production)

Rochling Engineering Plastics (India) Pvt. Ltd. - Vadodara Plant (1)
Plot No 8A Savli GIDC, Alindra, 391755, Vadodara, India
Tel.: (91) 2667 2900 52
Thermoplastic Product Mfr
N.A.I.C.S.: 326199

Rochling Engineering Plastics (Russia) Ltd. (1)
Tambovskaya 12 43, 192007, Saint Petersburg, Russia
Tel.: (7) 8123209280
Industrial Plastic Product Mfr
N.A.I.C.S.: 326199
Jaroslav Bilek (Mng Dir)

Rochling Engineering Plastics (UK) Ltd (1)
Waterwells Business Park Waterwells Drive, Gloucester, GL2 2AA, United Kingdom
Tel.: (44) 1452 727900
Web Site: http://www.roechling-plastics.co.uk
Thermoplastic Product Mfr & Distr
N.A.I.C.S.: 326199
Greg O'Leary (Mgr-Sls)

Rochling Engineering Plastics Italia s.r.l. (1)
Via della Vigne 18, Venegono Inferiore, 21040, Milan, Italy
Tel.: (39) 0331869441
Industrial Plastic Product Mfr
N.A.I.C.S.: 326199
Nicola Strazzeri (Mng Dir)

Rochling Engineering Plastics Japan Co., Ltd. (1)
Shin-Yokohama Daini Center Bldg 8F 3-19-5, Shin-Yokohama Kohoku-ku, Yokohama, Japan
Tel.: (81) 454702351
Industrial Plastic Product Mfr
N.A.I.C.S.: 326199
Maik Hammarin (Gen Mgr)

Rochling Engineering Plastics KG (1)
Rochlingstr 1, 49733, Haren, Germany
Tel.: (49) 59347010
Web Site: http://www.roechling-plastics.com
Sales Range: $150-199.9 Million
Emp.: 500
Plastics Processing & Manufacturing
N.A.I.C.S.: 326199
Ludger Bartels (CEO)

Subsidiary (US):

Glastic Corporation (2)
4321 Glenridge Rd, Cleveland, OH 44121-2805
Tel.: (216) 486-0100
Web Site: http://www.glastic.com
Sales Range: $25-49.9 Million
Emp.: 160
Mfr & Sale of Glass Fiber-Reinforced Plastic Materials
N.A.I.C.S.: 326199
Kerry Mullally (Mgr-Key Acct)

Unit (Non-US):

Glastic Corporation-Birmingham (3)
Unit 5, Block 2, Shenstone Trading Estate, Bromsgrove Road, Halesowen, B63 3XN, W Midlands, United Kingdom
Tel.: (44) 121 585 7908
Mfr & Sales of Glass Fiber-Reinforced Plastic Materials
N.A.I.C.S.: 326199

Subsidiary (US):

Rochling Engineered Plastics (2)
903 Catonia Technology Pkwy, Dallas, NC 28034
Tel.: (704) 922-7814
Web Site: http://www.roechling-plastics.us
Rev: $12,400,000
Emp.: 100
Unsupported Plastics Film & Sheet
N.A.I.C.S.: 326113
Lewis H. Carter (Pres-Bus Ops)

Rochling Engineering Plastics Ltd. (1)
21 Tideman Drive, Orangeville, L9W 3K3, ON, Canada
Tel.: (519) 941-5300
Web Site: http://www.roechling-plastics.us
Emp.: 100
Thermoplastic Product Distr
N.A.I.C.S.: 424610
Tim Brown (CEO)

Rochling Engineering Plastics, s.r.o. (1)
Prumyslova 451 Sezimovo Usti 2, 391 11, Plana nad Luznici, Czech Republic
Tel.: (420) 381 200 271
Web Site: http://www.roechling-plastics.cz
Thermoplastic Product Mfr & Distr
N.A.I.C.S.: 326199

Rochling Engineering Plastiques S.A.S. (1)
2 Rue de Barcelone, 69153, Decines-Charpieu, Cedex, France
Tel.: (33) 472 148960
Thermoplastic Product Mfr & Distr
N.A.I.C.S.: 326199

Rochling Engineering S.A.R.L. (1)
8 Rue Andre Fruchard, BP 12, 54320, Maxeville, Laxou, France
Tel.: (33) 383 342424
Thermoplastic Product Distr
N.A.I.C.S.: 424610

Rochling Fibracon Ltd. (1)
Bowden Hey Road-Chapel-en-le-Frith, High Peak, Buxton, SK23 0QZ, Derbyshire, United Kingdom
Tel.: (44) 1298811800
Thermoplastic Product Mfr & Distr
N.A.I.C.S.: 326199
Gary Willshire (Ops Mgr)

Rochling Formaterm AB (1)
Malillavagen 13, Box 27, 570 80, Virserum, Sweden
Tel.: (46) 495 249090
Web Site: http://www.formaterm.se
Thermoplastic Product Mfr & Distr
N.A.I.C.S.: 326199

Rochling Hydroma GmbH (1)
Lemberger Str 101, 66953, Ruppertsweiler, Germany
Tel.: (49) 6395 9222 0
Web Site: http://www.roechling-hydroma.com
Emp.: 24
Thermoplastic Product Mfr
N.A.I.C.S.: 326199
Matthias Weber (Mgr-Sls)

Rochling Industrial Laupheim GmbH (1)
Berblingerstrasse 18, 88471, Laupheim, Germany
Tel.: (49) 73929780
Automobile Parts Mfr
N.A.I.C.S.: 336310
Sonja Schmidt (Head-Pur)

Rochling Industrial Nove Mesto NM s.r.o. (1)
Petrovicka 312, 59231, Nove Mesto na Morave, Czech Republic
Tel.: (420) 566618205
Industrial Plastic Product Mfr
N.A.I.C.S.: 326199
Vlastimil Pospisil (Mng Dir)

Rochling Industrial Xanten GmbH (1)
Hagdornstrasse 3, 46509, Xanten, Germany
Tel.: (49) 2801760
Web Site: http://www.schwartz-plastic.eu
Engineering Plastic Product Mfr
N.A.I.C.S.: 326199
Heinz Dirksen (Mng Dir)

Rochling Insoll Ltd. (1)
39 Wilbury Way, Hitchin, SG4 0TW, Hertfordshire, United Kingdom
Tel.: (44) 1462450741
Thermoplastic Product Distr
N.A.I.C.S.: 424610
Elizabeth Elliott (Sec & Controller-Fin)

Rochling Leripa Papertech GmbH & Co. KG (1)
Rochlingstrasse 1, 4151, Oepping, Austria
Tel.: (43) 7289 4611
Web Site: http://www.leripa.com
Emp.: 230
Plastics Product Mfr
N.A.I.C.S.: 326199
Dominik Feiken (Product Mgr)

Subsidiary (US):

Rochling LERIPA Papertech LLC (2)
710 Ford St, Kimberly, WI 54136
Tel.: (920) 954-9154
Plastic Product Distr
N.A.I.C.S.: 424610

Subsidiary (Non-US):

Rochling Machined Components (Kunshan) Co., Ltd. (2)
No 238 Chenfeng Road, Kunshan, 215300, Jiangsu, China
Tel.: (86) 512 5513 2188
Web Site: http://www.roechling-rmc.cn
Plastic Product Distr
N.A.I.C.S.: 424610
Bernhard Zdrahal (Gen Mgr)

Rochling Lutzen SE & Co. KG (1)
Planckstrasse 3, 06686, Lutzen, Germany
Tel.: (49) 34444308200
Emp.: 62
Thermoplastic Product Mfr
N.A.I.C.S.: 326199
Joachim Gorzitze (Mng Dir)

Rochling Machined Plastics Italia s.r.l. (1)
Via Morena 66, 28024, Novara, Gozzano, Italy
Tel.: (39) 0322 95 421
Web Site: http://www.roechling.it
Thermoplastic Product Distr
N.A.I.C.S.: 424610
Massimo Terfani (Gen Mgr)

Rochling Medical Neuhaus GmbH & Co. KG (1)
Waldweg 16, 98724, Neuhaus am Rennweg, Germany
Tel.: (49) 3679726060
Industrial Plastic Product Mfr
N.A.I.C.S.: 326199
Jacqueline Hampe (Mgr-Sls & Acct)

Rochling Medical Rochester, L.P. (1)
Holleder Technology Park 999 Ridgeway Ave, Rochester, NY 14615
Tel.: (585) 254-2000
Industrial Plastic Product Mfr
N.A.I.C.S.: 326199
Lewis H. Carter (Pres)

Rochling Medical Waldachtal AG (1)
Herbert Frank Strasse 26, Waldachtal, 72178, Germany
Tel.: (49) 74861810
Web Site: https://www.roechling.com
Emp.: 290
Thermoplastic Mfr
N.A.I.C.S.: 325211
Klaus Kantorczyk (Head-Area Sls & Mktg & Dir)

Rochling Meta-Plast A/S (1)
Tojstrupvej 31, 8961, Allingabro, Denmark
Tel.: (45) 86 48 17 11
Web Site: http://www.meta-plast.dk
Plastic Product Mfr & Distr
N.A.I.C.S.: 326199
Paul Busk Jensen (Co-Founder)

ROCHLING SE & CO. KG

Rochling SE & Co. KG—(Continued)

Subsidiary (Non-US):

SIA LSEZ Meta-Plast (2)
Kapsedes Street 2, Liepaja, 3402, Latvia
Tel.: (371) 63 48 85 39
Thermoplastic Product Distr
N.A.I.C.S.: 326199
Dmitrijs Titovs *(Branch Mgr)*

Rochling Meta-Plast LSEZ SIA (1)
Kapsedes Str 2, LV-3414, Liepaja, Latvia
Tel.: (371) 63488539
Industrial Plastic Product Mfr
N.A.I.C.S.: 326199
Lauris Puteklis *(Sls Mgr)*

Rochling Oertl Kunststofftechnik GmbH (1)
Hochster Str 100, 64395, Brensbach, Germany
Tel.: (49) 6161 9308 0
Thermoplastic Product Mfr
N.A.I.C.S.: 326199

Rochling Permali Composites S.A.S. (1)
8 Rue Andre Fruchard, BP 12, 54520, Maxeville, France
Tel.: (33) 383342424
Industrial Plastic Product Mfr
N.A.I.C.S.: 326199
Jean-Paul Klecha *(Mng Dir & Dir-Composites-Europe)*

Rochling Plasticos Tecnicos S.A.U. (1)
Ctra Villena s/n - Apartado 34, Bocairent, 46880, Valencia, Spain
Tel.: (34) 962 350165
Web Site: http://www.roechling-plastics.es
Thermoplastic Product Mfr & Distr
N.A.I.C.S.: 326199

Rochling Plasticos de Engenharia do Brasil Ltda. (1)
Rua Antonio Christi 453, Parque Industrial Jundiai III, 13213-183, Jundiai, Sao Paulo, Brazil
Tel.: (55) 1131094600
Industrial Plastic Product Mfr
N.A.I.C.S.: 326199
Rodrigo Maldonado *(Gen Mgr)*

Rochling Precision Components (Suzhou) Co., Ltd. (1)
No 68 Yinsheng Road, Suzhou, 215126, China
Tel.: (86) 51265952829
Industrial Plastic Product Mfr
N.A.I.C.S.: 326199
Irene Lu *(Mgr-Fin & HR)*

Rochling Precision Components Kraslice spol. s r.o. (1)
Dukelska 44, 35801, Kraslice, Czech Republic
Tel.: (420) 351120022
Industrial Plastic Product Mfr
N.A.I.C.S.: 326199

Rochling Precision Components Pitesti S.R.L. (1)
Cladirea 1 A1 Bucuresti-Pitesti Km 102, WDP Industrial Park, 117545, Pitesti, Romania
Tel.: (40) 730266938
Industrial Plastic Product Mfr
N.A.I.C.S.: 326199
Valentin-Gabriel Duminica *(Plant Mgr)*

Rochling Rimito Plast Oy (1)
Harjutie 12, 21290, Rusko, Finland
Tel.: (358) 2 436 0100
Web Site: http://www.rimitoplast.fi
Plastic Sheet Mfr
N.A.I.C.S.: 326130
Eija Laakso *(Mgr-Fin)*

Rochling Roding GmbH (1)
Bayerschmidtweg 1, 93426, Roding, Germany
Tel.: (49) 9461 4026 0
Thermoplastic Product Mfr & Distr
N.A.I.C.S.: 326199

Rochling SGT Spritzgiesstechnik GmbH (1)
Winter-Ring 3, 95466, Weidenberg, Germany
Tel.: (49) 92 78 9 93 0
Web Site: http://www.roechling.com
Plastics Product Mfr
N.A.I.C.S.: 326199
Andre Dupont *(Gen Mgr)*

Rochling Sustaplast SE & Co. KG (1)
Sustaplast-Str 1, 56112, Lahnstein, Germany
Tel.: (49) 2621 693 0
Thermoplastic Product Mfr & Distr
N.A.I.C.S.: 326199

Rochling Technische Kunststoffe KG (1)
Planckstrasse 3, 06686, Lutzen, Germany
Tel.: (49) 3 44 44 30 8 200
Web Site: http://www.roechling-luetzen.de
Thermoplastic Product Mfr
N.A.I.C.S.: 326199

Rochling Technische Teile KG (1)
Paul-Munsterer-Str 1, 84048, Mainburg, Germany
Tel.: (49) 8751 8606 0
Plastics Product Mfr
N.A.I.C.S.: 326199

Roechling Automotive Chonburi Co., Ltd. (1)
700/19 WHA Eastern 1 Moo 7, Seaboard Industrial Estate Kaokhansong, 20110, Si Racha, Chonburi, Thailand
Tel.: (66) 924878954
Automobile Parts Mfr
N.A.I.C.S.: 326199
Thanakiat Keawwappee *(Sls Mgr)*

Roechling Engineering Plastics (Suzhou) Co., Ltd (1)
448 Chang Yang Street Suzhou Industrial Park, 215024, Suzhou, Jiangsu, China
Tel.: (86) 512 62652899
Web Site: http://www.roechling.com.sg
Emp.: 36
Thermoplastic Product Distr
N.A.I.C.S.: 424610
Eugen Schmidt *(CEO)*

Roechling Engineering Plastics Pte Ltd (1)
14 Tuas Ave 8, Singapore, 639229, Singapore
Tel.: (65) 6863 1877
Web Site: http://www.roechling.com.sg
Thermoplastic Product Mfr & Distr
N.A.I.C.S.: 326199

Roechling International (Shanghai) Co., Ltd (1)
26/F Shanghai Times Square Office Tower 93 Huai Hai Zhong Road, 200021, Shanghai, China
Tel.: (86) 21 5117 6360
Thermoplastic Product Distr
N.A.I.C.S.: 424610

Roechling Medical Lancaster LLC (1)
44 Denver Rd, Denver, PA 17517
Tel.: (717) 335-3700
Medical Device Mfr
N.A.I.C.S.: 339112
Lewis H. Carter *(Pres)*

Starlite Roechling Automotive Co., Ltd. (1)
Burex Five Hulic & New Shinbashi 4f 2-11-10, Shimbashi Minato-ku, Tokyo, 105-0004, Japan
Tel.: (81) 8034917440
Automotive Vehicle Mfr
N.A.I.C.S.: 336110
Katherine Sun *(Dir-HR-Asia)*

ROCK FIELD CO., LTD.
15-2 Uozakihama-machi, Higashinada-ku, Kobe, 658-0024, Hyogo, Japan
Tel.: (81) 784352800
Web Site: https://www.rockfield.co.jp
2910—(TKS)
Rev.: $339,469,770
Assets: $238,105,420
Liabilities: $45,496,630
Net Worth: $192,608,790
Earnings: $8,275,720
Emp.: 1,635
Fiscal Year-end: 04/30/24
Food Products Production & Sales
N.A.I.C.S.: 311942
Kozo Iwata *(Founder & Chm)*

ROCK PAINT CO., LTD.
3-1-47 Himeshima, Nishiyodogawa-ku, Osaka, 555-0033, Japan
Tel.: (81) 66 473 1551
Web Site: http://www.rockpaint.co.jp
Year Founded: 1927
4621—(TKS)
Rev.: $247,914,480
Assets: $477,611,200
Liabilities: $91,621,200
Net Worth: $385,990,000
Earnings: $11,403,040
Emp.: 499
Fiscal Year-end: 03/31/22
Paint & Coating Mfr & Distr
N.A.I.C.S.: 325510
Togo Utsumi *(Pres)*

Subsidiaries:

PT. Rock Paint Indonesia (1)
Jln Harapan IV Lot KK-9b, Kawasan Industri KIIC, Karawang, 41361, Jawa Barat, Indonesia
Tel.: (62) 2189114321
Web Site: http://www.rockpaint.co.id
Chemical Product Retailer
N.A.I.C.S.: 424690
Yuji Ogino *(Pres)*

ROCK TECH LITHIUM INC.
2400-333 Bay Street, Toronto, M5H 2T6, ON, Canada
Tel.: (778) 358-5200   Ca
Web Site: https://rocktechlithium.com
RCK—(DEU)
Assets: $47,992,170
Liabilities: $6,391,553
Net Worth: $41,600,617
Earnings: ($45,537,666)
Fiscal Year-end: 12/31/22
Lithium Exploration Services
N.A.I.C.S.: 213114
Dirk Harbecke *(Chm & Co-CEO)*

ROCKAWAY CAPITAL SE
Na Hrebenech II 1718/8, 140 00, Prague, 4, Czech Republic
Tel.: (420) 739 917 468   CZ
Web Site: http://www.rockawaycapital.com
Year Founded: 2013
Privater Equity Firm
N.A.I.C.S.: 523999
Jan Jirovec *(Partner-Investment)*

ROCKET ELECTRIC CO., LTD.
758 Ilgok-dong, Buk-gu, Gwangju, Korea (South)
Tel.: (82) 62 570 2500
Web Site: http://www.rocket.co.kr
Year Founded: 1946
Battery Mfr
N.A.I.C.S.: 335910
Jong Sung Kim *(Chm & CEO)*

Subsidiaries:

ROCKET ELECTRIC CO., LTD. (1)
606 Owl Tower 4-21-1 Higashi ikebukuro, Toshima-Ku, Tokyo, Japan
Tel.: (81) 3 5956 1553
Battery Mfr
N.A.I.C.S.: 335999

ROCKET POLAND CO., LTD (1)
ul Kosciuszki 112-114, 83-200, Starogard Gdanski, Poland
Tel.: (48) 58 775 12 21
Web Site: http://www.rocketpoland.com
Battery Mfr
N.A.I.C.S.: 335999

ROCKET THAI CO., LTD (1)
116 Moo3 Takham, Bang Pakong, 24130, Chacheongsao, Thailand
Tel.: (66) 38 573 193
Web Site: http://www.rocket.co.th
Battery Mfr
N.A.I.C.S.: 335999

Rocket Electric Co., Ltd. - Gwangju Factory (1)
758 Ilgok-dong, Buk-gu, Gwangju, 500-866, Korea (South)
Tel.: (82) 62 570 250
Battery Mfr
N.A.I.C.S.: 335999

Rocket Electric Co., Ltd. - Ochang Factory (1)
643-1 Gak-ri Orchang-eup, Cheongwon, 363-885, Chungcheongbuk-do, Korea (South)
Tel.: (82) 43 241 0090
Battery Mfr
N.A.I.C.S.: 335999

Rocket Electric Co., Ltd. - ROCKET SUZHOU FACTORY (1)
No 99 Gangtian Road Industrial park Zone, Suzhou, 215024, Jiangsu, China
Tel.: (86) 512 6507 6210
Battery Mfr
N.A.I.C.S.: 335999

ROCKET INTERNET GROWTH OPPORTUNITIES CORP.
Boundary Hall Cricket Square, Grand Cayman, Georgetown, KY1-1102, Cayman Islands
Tel.: (345) 8155716   Ky
Year Founded: 2021
RKTA—(NYSE)
Rev.: $12,760,474
Assets: $271,019,888
Liabilities: $281,136,170
Net Worth: ($10,116,282)
Earnings: $11,136,196
Emp.: 3
Fiscal Year-end: 12/31/22
Investment Services
N.A.I.C.S.: 523999
Oliver Samwer *(Founder, Chm & Co-CEO)*

ROCKET INTERNET SE
Charlottenstrasse 4, 10969, Berlin, Germany
Tel.: (49) 30300131800
Web Site: https://www.rocket-internet.com
Year Founded: 2007
Rev.: $358,131,228
Assets: $4,649,322,762
Liabilities: $194,295,710
Net Worth: $4,455,027,052
Earnings: $319,608,044
Emp.: 404
Fiscal Year-end: 12/31/19
Online Business Development Services
N.A.I.C.S.: 541512
Marcus Englert *(Chm-Supervisory Bd)*

Subsidiaries:

GFC Global Founders Capital GmbH (1)
Charlottenstrasse 4, 10969, Berlin, Germany
Tel.: (49) 30300131800
Web Site: http://www.globalfounderscapital.com
Capital Firm Services
N.A.I.C.S.: 523940
Arnt Jeschke *(Mng Dir)*

HelloFresh SE (1)
Prinzenstrasse 89, 10969, Berlin, Germany
Tel.: (49) 3056839568
Web Site: https://www.hellofreshgroup.com
Rev.: $8,198,359,594
Assets: $2,785,775,955
Liabilities: $1,686,056,551

Net Worth: $1,099,719,404
Earnings: $19,533,779
Emp.: 19,012
Fiscal Year-end: 12/31/2023
Food Products Distr
N.A.I.C.S.: 424420
Dominik S. Richter *(Co-Founder, Co-CEO & Member-Mgmt Bd)*

Internet Services Polen sp. z o.o. (1)
ul Bialozora 1, 02-817, Warsaw, Poland
Tel.: (48) 226442340
Web Site: http://www.internet-services.com
Ecommerce Services
N.A.I.C.S.: 541219

RCKT GmbH & Co. KG (1)
Lutzowstrasse 106, 10785, Berlin, Germany
Tel.: (49) 3022012249
Web Site: http://www.rckt.com
Digital Consultancy Services
N.A.I.C.S.: 541613
Nils Seger *(Mng Dir)*

ROCKET SHARING COMPANY S.P.A.
Galleria San Babila 4/a, 20122, Milan, Italy
Tel.: (39) 0282955175
Web Site: https://www.rocketcompany.it
Year Founded: 2019
RKT—(EUR)
Online Shopping Services
N.A.I.C.S.: 459999
Luigi Maisto *(Chm)*

ROCKETDNA LTD.
30 Dov Hoz, Kiryat Ono, Tel Aviv, 5555626, Israel
Tel.: (972) 36885252
Web Site: http://www.parazero.com
Year Founded: 2013
RKT—(ASX)
Rev.: $4,180,240
Assets: $4,637,599
Liabilities: $1,485,573
Net Worth: $3,152,026
Earnings: ($1,266,923)
Emp.: 75
Fiscal Year-end: 12/31/23
Safety Device Mfr & Distr
N.A.I.C.S.: 339113
Eden Attias *(Chm & CEO)*

ROCKETT LUMBER & BUILDING SUPPLIES LTD.
3350 Wolfedale Road, Mississauga, L5C 1W4, ON, Canada
Tel.: (905) 275-1800
Web Site: http://www.rockettlumber.com
Year Founded: 1952
Rev.: $85,755,124
Emp.: 225
Lumber & Wood Products Supplier
N.A.I.C.S.: 423310
Stephen Rockett *(Pres)*

ROCKEX MINING CORPORATION
580 New Vickers St, Thunder Bay, P7E 6P1, ON, Canada
Tel.: (807) 623-0661 AB
Web Site: https://www.rockexmining.com
RXM—(CNSX)
Assets: $14,967,502
Liabilities: $2,689,732
Net Worth: $12,277,770
Earnings: ($87,371)
Emp.: 1
Fiscal Year-end: 12/31/19
Metal Mining Services
N.A.I.C.S.: 212290
Pierre Gagne *(CEO)*

ROCKFIRE RESOURCES PLC
201 Temple Chambers 37 Temple Avenue, Temple, London, EC4Y 0DT, United Kingdom
Web Site: https://www.rockfireresources.com
ROCK—(AIM)
Assets: $9,242,488
Liabilities: $280,075
Net Worth: $8,962,413
Earnings: ($2,278,795)
Fiscal Year-end: 12/31/23
Gold & Copper Mining
N.A.I.C.S.: 212220
David Price *(CEO)*

ROCKHAVEN RESOURCES LTD.
510-1100 Melville Street, Vancouver, V6E 4A6, BC, Canada
Tel.: (604) 416-4585
Web Site: https://www.rockhavenresource.com
Year Founded: 1938
8RR—(DEU)
Rev.: $39,056,317
Assets: $37,100,551
Liabilities: $2,882,724
Net Worth: $34,217,827
Earnings: ($343,490,496)
Fiscal Year-end: 12/31/23
Gold & Silver Exploration Services
N.A.I.C.S.: 212220
Matthew A. Turner *(Pres & CEO)*

Subsidiaries:

Mina Real Mexico S.A. de C.V. (1)
Calle Rio Tajo No 6, Lindavista, Tepic, 63110, Nayarit, Mexico
Tel.: (52) 3112187271
Gold & Silver Mining Services
N.A.I.C.S.: 212220

ROCKHOPPER EXPLORATION PLC
Warner House 123 Castle Street, Salisbury, SP1 3TB, Wiltshire, United Kingdom
Tel.: (44) 1722414419 UK
Web Site: https://www.rockhopperexplore.com
Year Founded: 2004
RCKHF—(NASDAQ)
Rev.: $652,000
Assets: $264,461,000
Liabilities: $63,994,000
Net Worth: $200,467,000
Earnings: $35,545,000
Emp.: 11
Fiscal Year-end: 12/31/22
Oil & Gas Exploration Services
N.A.I.C.S.: 213112
Samuel J. Moody *(CEO)*

ROCKINGHAM CARS LTD
Cockerell Road Northants, Corby, NN17 5DU, United Kingdom
Tel.: (44) 1536268991
Web Site: http://www.rockinghamcars.co.uk
Year Founded: 1978
Rev.: $24,834,827
Emp.: 47
New & Used Car Dealers
N.A.I.C.S.: 441110
David Hall *(Co-Founder)*

ROCKLEY PHOTONICS HOLDINGS, LTD.
108 Robinson Road Suite 10-00, Singapore, 068900, Singapore
Tel.: (65) 64381080 Ky
Web Site: http://www.schealthcorp.com
Year Founded: 2018
SCPE.U—(NYSE)
Rev.: $644,101
Assets: $174,788,957
Liabilities: $169,788,955
Net Worth: $5,000,002
Earnings: ($1,091,958)
Emp.: 3
Fiscal Year-end: 12/31/20
Investment Services
N.A.I.C.S.: 523999
David Sin *(Chm)*

ROCKON ENTERPRISES LIMITED
E-109 Crystal Plaza New Link Road, Opp Infinity Mall Andheri West, Mumbai, 400053, India
Tel.: (91) 52096140
Web Site: http://www.rockonfintech.com
531447—(BOM)
Rev.: $270,389
Assets: $2,192,988
Liabilities: $170,669
Net Worth: $2,022,320
Earnings: ($249,828)
Emp.: 7
Fiscal Year-end: 03/31/19
Hardware & Software Product Services
N.A.I.C.S.: 449210
Tanu Giriraj Kishor Agarwal *(Mng Dir)*

ROCKONTROL TECHNOLOGY GROUP CO., LTD.
14F Building T3 Baoli Daduhui Yard No 2 Guanyinan South Street, Tongzhou, Beijing, 100005, China
Tel.: (86) 1057230290
Web Site: http://www.rockontrol.com
Year Founded: 2007
688051—(SHG)
Rev.: $36,686,253
Assets: $207,990,413
Liabilities: $63,614,327
Net Worth: $144,376,086
Earnings: ($40,397,657)
Fiscal Year-end: 12/31/22
Application Development Services
N.A.I.C.S.: 541511
Wei Li *(Chm & Gen Mgr)*

ROCKPOOL ACQUISITIONS PLC
Arthur House 41 Arthur Street, Northern Ireland, Belfast, BT1 4GB, United Kingdom
Tel.: (44) 2890446733 UK
Web Site: https://www.rockpoolacquisitions.uk
Year Founded: 2017
ROC—(LSE)
Assets: $898,702
Liabilities: $138,503
Net Worth: $760,199
Earnings: ($368,925)
Fiscal Year-end: 03/31/23
Vehicle Investment Management Services
N.A.I.C.S.: 525990

ROCKRIDGE RESOURCES LTD.
777 Dunsmuir Street - Suite 1610, Vancouver, V7Y 1K4, BC, Canada
Tel.: (604) 687-3376
Web Site: https://www.rockridgeresources.com
RRRLF—(OTCQB)
Rev.: $61,790
Assets: $4,230,709
Liabilities: $13,043
Net Worth: $4,217,666
Earnings: ($1,346,711)
Fiscal Year-end: 07/31/21
Metal Exploration Services
N.A.I.C.S.: 213114
Jonathan Wiesblatt *(CEO)*

ROCKWELL DIAMONDS INC.
C/O Fasken Martineau DuMoulin LLP Bay Adelaide Centre Ste 2400 333, 333 Bay Street, Toronto, M5H 2T6, ON, Canada
Tel.: (416) 366-8381 BC
Web Site: http://www.rockwelldiamonds.com
Year Founded: 1988
RDI—(JSE)
Sales Range: Less than $1 Million
Diamond Mining & Exploration
N.A.I.C.S.: 212390
Johan Oosthuizen *(CFO-Interim)*

ROCKWELL PETROLEUM INC.
32470 255 5th Ave SW, Calgary, T2P 3G6, AB, Canada
Tel.: (403) 537-7300 Ca
Web Site: http://www.rockwellpetroleum.com
Oil & Gas Exploration & Extraction Services
N.A.I.C.S.: 211120
Peter Hanrahan *(CFO & VP-Fin)*

ROCKWOOL A/S
Hovedgaden 584, DK 2640, Hedehusene, Denmark
Tel.: (45) 46560300
Web Site: https://www.rockwool.com
Year Founded: 1937
ROCK-B—(CSE)
Rev.: $3,800,174,560
Assets: $3,782,979,200
Liabilities: $842,572,640
Net Worth: $2,940,406,560
Earnings: $372,156,720
Emp.: 11,968
Fiscal Year-end: 12/31/21
Stone Wool & Related Products Mfr
N.A.I.C.S.: 327993
Thomas Kahler *(Sr VP & Head-Sys Div)*

Subsidiaries:

A/S Rockwool (1)
Gjerdrums vei 19, Pb 4215, Nydalen, 0401, Oslo, Norway (100%)
Tel.: (47) 2 202 4000
Web Site: http://www.rockwool.no
Emp.: 240
N.A.I.C.S.: 327993

Division (Domestic):

Rockwool Technical Insulation - Norway (2)
Gjerdrums Vei 19, PB 4215, Nydalen, 0401, Oslo, Norway
Tel.: (47) 2202 4000
Web Site: http://www.rockwool-rti.no
Marine Insulation Materials Distr
N.A.I.C.S.: 423330

BuildDesk Polska Sp. z.o.o. (1)
ul Kwiatowa 14, 66-131, Cigacice, Poland
Tel.: (48) 683850022
Sales Range: $25-49.9 Million
Emp.: 5
Energy Building Software Consulting Service
N.A.I.C.S.: 541512
Piotr Pawlak *(Gen Mgr)*

Deutsche ROCKWOOL GmbH & Co. KG (1)
Rockwool Str 37-41, 45966, Gladbeck, Germany
Tel.: (49) 20439888957
Insulation Material Distr
N.A.I.C.S.: 423330

Deutsche Rockwool Mineralwoll GmbH & Co. OHG (1)
Rockwool Str 37-41, 45966, Gladbeck, Germany (100%)
Tel.: (49) 20434080
Web Site: http://www.rockwool.de
Insulation Product Mfr
N.A.I.C.S.: 327993

ROCKWOOL A/S
INTERNATIONAL PUBLIC

ROCKWOOL A/S—(Continued)

Subsidiary (Domestic):

HECK Wall Systems GmbH & Co. KG
Tholauer Strasse 25, 95615, Marktredwitz, Germany
Tel.: (49) 9231 802 0
Web Site: http://www.wall-systems.com
Sales Range: $75-99.9 Million
Mortars, Construction Materials & Heat Insulation Systems Mfr
N.A.I.C.S.: 327320

Subsidiary (Domestic):

HECK Wall Systems Verwaltungs-GmbH (3)
Tholauer Str 25, 95615, Marktredwitz, Germany
Tel.: (49) 92318020
Construction Materials Distr
N.A.I.C.S.: 423390
Volker Christmann *(Mng Dir)*

Subsidiary (Domestic):

Rockwool Beteiligungs GmbH (2)
Rockwool Str 37-41, 45966, Gladbeck, Germany (100%)
Tel.: (49) 20434080
Web Site: http://www.rockwool.de
Emp.: 1,000
Holding Company
N.A.I.C.S.: 551112
Volker Christmann *(Chm-Mgmt Bd)*

Rockwool Mineralwolle GmbH (2)
Rockwool Str 37-41, 45966, Gladbeck, Germany
Tel.: (49) 20434080
Web Site: http://www.rockwool.de
Mineral Wool Mfr
N.A.I.C.S.: 327993

Rockwool.com GmbH (2)
Rockwool Strasse 37-41, 45966, Gladbeck, Germany
Tel.: (49) 20434080
Web Site: http://www.rockwool.com
Insulation Building Materials Distr
N.A.I.C.S.: 423330
Volker Christmann *(Chm-Mgmt Bd)*

Etablissements Charles Wille et cie S.A.
Avenue W A Mozartlaan 46, 7700, Mouscron, Belgium
Tel.: (32) 5 685 9494
Insulation Material Distr
N.A.I.C.S.: 423330

FAST Sp. z.o.o. (1)
Ul Foluszowa 112, 65-751, Zielona Gora, Poland
Tel.: (48) 68 328 62 00
Web Site: http://www.fast.zgora.pl
Sales Range: $10-24.9 Million
Construction Chemicals Mfr
N.A.I.C.S.: 325998

Flumroc AG (1)
Industriestrasse 8, 8890, Flums, Switzerland
Tel.: (41) 817341111
Web Site: https://www.flumroc.ch
Mineral Wool Mfr
N.A.I.C.S.: 327993

Grodan B.V. (1)
Industrieweg 15, PO Box 1160, Roermond, 6045JG, Netherlands (100%)
Tel.: (31) 475353535
Web Site: http://www.rockwool.com
Sales Range: $25-49.9 Million
Emp.: 40
Horticultural Substances
N.A.I.C.S.: 327993

Subsidiary (Non-US):

Grodan Inc. (2)
2800 Highpoint Drive Suite 202, Milton, L9T 6W3, ON, Canada (100%)
Tel.: (905) 636-0611
Web Site: http://www.grodan.com
Sales Range: $25-49.9 Million
Emp.: 9
Agricultural Stone Wool Substrate Products Mfr
N.A.I.C.S.: 327993

Branch (US):

Grodan Inc. (3)
5152 Commerce Ave, Moorpark, CA 93021
Tel.: (805) 746-2662
Web Site: http://www.grodan101.com
Sales Range: $50-74.9 Million
Emp.: 1
Insulation Building Materials Distr
N.A.I.C.S.: 423330

Subsidiary (Non-US):

Grodan MED S.A. (2)
Avda de los Principes de Espana 116, El Ejido, Almeria, Spain
Web Site: http://www.rockwool.de
Horticultural Substances
N.A.I.C.S.: 327993

Grodan S. de R.L de C.V. (2)
Av Camino Real de Carretas 188-A Milenio III, 76060, Queretaro, Mexico
Tel.: (52) 442 198 2198
Web Site: http://www.grodan.com
Emp.: 1
Stone Wool Insulation Mfr
N.A.I.C.S.: 327993

Grodan Sp. z o.o. (2)
Postepu 6, 02-676, Warsaw, Poland (100%)
Tel.: (48) 22 375 0780
Web Site: https://www.grodan.pl
Sales Range: $25-49.9 Million
Emp.: 9
Horticultural Substances
N.A.I.C.S.: 327993

LLC Rockwool (1)
Serebryanicheskaya Embankment 29 BC Silver City, Moscow, 109028, Russia
Tel.: (7) 4957777979
Insulation Material Mfr & Distr
N.A.I.C.S.: 327993

LLC Rockwool North (1)
Pos Lazarevka Industrial Area, Vyborg, 188 800, Leningrad, Russia
Tel.: (7) 8124498249
Web Site: http://www.rockwool.ru
Emp.: 300
Insulation Building Materials Distr
N.A.I.C.S.: 423330
Withuld Bania *(Mgr-Factory)*

LLC Rockwool Ukraine (1)
St Bryullova building 7 office C22, 03049, Kiev, Ukraine
Tel.: (380) 445864978
Insulation Material Mfr
N.A.I.C.S.: 327993

PAMAG Engineering AG (1)
Industriestrasse 1a, 8890, Flums, Switzerland
Tel.: (41) 817341511
Web Site: https://www.pamag.ch
Construction Services
N.A.I.C.S.: 236220

ROCKWOOL Australia Pty. Ltd. (1)
Level 12 90 Arthur Street, North Sydney, 2060, NSW, Australia
Tel.: (61) 428961428
Construction Material Mfr & Distr
N.A.I.C.S.: 327993

ROCKWOOL Belgium B.V. (1)
Oud Sluisstraat 5, 2110, Wijnegem, Belgium
Tel.: (32) 27156805
Web Site: https://www.rockwool.com
Insulation Material Distr
N.A.I.C.S.: 423330

ROCKWOOL Bulgaria EooD (1)
Dragan Tsankov Blvd 23 A, 1113, Sofia, Bulgaria
Tel.: (359) 29439560
Construction Material Mfr & Distr
N.A.I.C.S.: 327993

ROCKWOOL Danmark A/S (1)
Hovedgaden 501, 2640, Hedehusene, Denmark
Tel.: (45) 46561616
Construction Material Mfr & Distr
N.A.I.C.S.: 327993

ROCKWOOL GmbH (1)
Baarersstrasse 21, 6300, Zug, Switzerland
Tel.: (41) 417104148
Web Site: https://www.de.rockfon.ch
Insulation Material Mfr
N.A.I.C.S.: 327993

ROCKWOOL Hungary Kft. (1)
Keszthelyi ut 53, 8300, Tapolca, Hungary
Tel.: (36) 87512100
Construction Material Mfr & Distr
N.A.I.C.S.: 327993

ROCKWOOL Insaat ve Yalitim Sistemleri San. Ve Tic. Ltd. Sti. (1)
Osmaniye Mah Cobancesme Kosuyolu Blv No 3, Garden Office Kat 2 No 6-7-8 Marmara Forum AVM kompleksi Bakirkoy, Istanbul, 34568, Turkiye
Tel.: (90) 2124666536
Web Site: https://rwhr-turkey.inforce.dk
Insulation Material Mfr
N.A.I.C.S.: 327993

ROCKWOOL Romania s.r.l. (1)
S O S Bucharest Ploiesti No 1A Building A Floor 4, Sector 1, 013681, Bucharest, Romania
Tel.: (40) 212334440
Web Site: https://en.rockwool.ro
Cladded Facade Product Distr
N.A.I.C.S.: 423390

ROCKWOOL Technical Insulation India Pvt. Ltd. (1)
Wing B-2 2nd Floor Unit No 206 Boomerang Near Chandivali Film Studio, Chandivali Farm Road Andheri E, Mumbai, 400072, Maharashtra, India
Tel.: (91) 2267157700
Insulation Product Whslr
N.A.I.C.S.: 423330

RockDelta a/s (1)
Hovedgaden 584, 2640, Hedehusene, Denmark (100%)
Tel.: (45) 46565020
Web Site: http://www.rockdelta.com
Sales Range: $25-49.9 Million
Emp.: 9
Noise & Vibration Control, Biofilters
N.A.I.C.S.: 334519

Rockfon A/S (1)
Hovedgaden 501, 2640, Hedehusene, Denmark (100%)
Tel.: (45) 46562122
Web Site: http://www.rockfon.dk
Sales Range: $25-49.9 Million
Emp.: 45
Acoustic Ceilings
N.A.I.C.S.: 238310
Andres Aughomsen *(Gen Mgr)*

Subsidiary (US):

Chicago Metallic Company LLC (2)
4849 S Austin Ave, Chicago, IL 60638
Tel.: (708) 563-4600
Web Site: http://www.chicagometallic.com
Sales Range: $125-149.9 Million
Architectural Metalwork
N.A.I.C.S.: 332323
John Medio *(Pres-North America)*

Branch (Domestic):

Chicago Metallic - Elkridge (3)
6750 Santa Barbara Ct, Elkridge, MD 21075
Tel.: (410) 796-8220
Sales Range: $10-24.9 Million
Emp.: 70
Architectural Metal Work Mfr
N.A.I.C.S.: 332323
Steve Noeth *(Mgr-Sls-Reg)*

Subsidiary (Non-US):

Rockfon AB (1)
Kompanigatan 5, Box 115 05, 550 11, Jonkoping, Sweden
Tel.: (46) 36 570 5200
Web Site: http://www.rockfon.se
Sales Range: $25-49.9 Million
Emp.: 10
Acoustic Ceilings
N.A.I.C.S.: 238310

Rockfon B.V. (2)
Industrieweg 15, 6045 JG, Roermond, Netherlands (100%)

Tel.: (31) 47 535 3035
Web Site: https://www.rockfon.nl
Sales Range: $25-49.9 Million
Acoustic Ceilings
N.A.I.C.S.: 238310

Rockfon Limited (2)
14th Floor Chiswick Tower 389 Chiswick High Road, London, W4 4AL, United Kingdom (100%)
Tel.: (44) 20 8222 7457
Web Site: http://www.rockfon.co.uk
Sales Range: $25-49.9 Million
Acoustic Ceilings
N.A.I.C.S.: 238310

Rockfon Sp. z o.o. (2)
ul Postepu 6, 02-676, Warsaw, Poland (100%)
Tel.: (48) 228433810
Web Site: https://www.rockfon.pl
Sales Range: $25-49.9 Million
Emp.: 8
Wool Insulation Whslr
N.A.I.C.S.: 327993

Rockfon Rockfon GmbH (2)
Rockwool Strasse 37-41, 45966, Gladbeck, Germany (100%)
Tel.: (49) 2043408190
Web Site: https://www.rockfon.de
Sales Range: $25-49.9 Million
Insulation
N.A.I.C.S.: 327993
Volker Christmann *(Pres)*

Rockpanel A/S (1)
Hovedgaden 501, 2640, Hedehusene, Denmark (100%)
Tel.: (45) 46562211
Web Site: http://www.rockpanel.dk
Sales Range: $200-249.9 Million
Emp.: 800
Cladding Boards
N.A.I.C.S.: 238150
Hansove Larsen *(Dir-Bus Unit)*

Rockwool (Thailand) Limited (1)
B Grimm Building 11th Floor No 5 Soi Krungthep Kreetha, Hua Mak Subdistrict Bang Kapi District, Bangkok, 10240, Thailand
Tel.: (66) 2731751114
Web Site: http://www.rockwoolasia.com
Insulation Building Materials Distr
N.A.I.C.S.: 423330

Rockwool A/S (1)
Hovedgaden 584, 2640, Hedehusene, Denmark (100%)
Tel.: (45) 46560300
Web Site: http://www.rockwool.com
Sales Range: $200-249.9 Million
Emp.: 700
Insulation
N.A.I.C.S.: 327993
Henrik Frank Nielsen *(Mng Dir)*

Rockwool AB (1)
Kompanigatan 5, Box 11505, 11505, Jonkoping, Sweden
Tel.: (46) 365705200
Web Site: https://www.rockwool.com
Insulation Building Materials Distr
N.A.I.C.S.: 423330

Rockwool Adriatic d.o.o. (1)
Poduzetnicka zona Pican Jug 130, Zajci, 52333, Potpican, Croatia
Tel.: (385) 16197600
Web Site: https://www.rockwool.com
Fire Insulation Building Materials Distr
N.A.I.C.S.: 423330

Rockwool Benelux B.V. (1)
Industrieweg 15, 6045 JG, Roermond, Netherlands (100%)
Tel.: (31) 475353535
Web Site: http://www.rockwool.nl
Sales Range: $450-499.9 Million
Emp.: 1,200
Engineered Fibres
N.A.I.C.S.: 325220

Subsidiary (Domestic):

Rockwool B.V. (2)
PO Box 1160, 6040 KD, Roermond, Netherlands
Tel.: (31) 47 535 3535
Web Site: https://www.grodan.com

Emp.: 1,100
Agricultural Substrate Mfr
N.A.I.C.S.: 325998

Subsidiary (Domestic):

Rockwool Lapinus Productie B.V. (3)
Industrieweg 15, 6045 JG, Roermond, Netherlands (100%)
Tel.: (31) 475353535
Web Site: https://www.rockwool.com
Sales Range: $500-549.9 Million
Emp.: 1,200
Mineral Fibre Products Mfr
N.A.I.C.S.: 327993
Jos Dumoulin *(Mng Dir)*

Subsidiary (Non-US):

Lapinus Fibres B.V. (4)
(100%)
Tel.: (31) 47 535 3555
Web Site: https://www.lapinus.com
Sales Range: $25-49.9 Million
Emp.: 30
Precision Engineered Mineral Fibres Mfr
N.A.I.C.S.: 327993

Subsidiary (Domestic):

Rockwool Rockpanel B.V. (3)
Konstruktieweg 2, 6045 JD, Roermond, Netherlands (100%)
Tel.: (31) 475353000
Web Site: http://www.rockpanel.nl
Sales Range: $25-49.9 Million
Emp.: 45
Cladding Boards
N.A.I.C.S.: 444110

Substra Nederland B.V. (3)
Terheijdenseweg 441, NL 4825 BK, Breda, Netherlands (100%)
Tel.: (31) 765710089
Web Site: http://www.substra.nl
Sales Range: $25-49.9 Million
Emp.: 20
Horticultural Substances
N.A.I.C.S.: 327993

Subsidiary (Domestic):

Rockwool Benelux Holding B.V. (2)
Industrieweg 15, 6045 JG, Roermond, Netherlands (100%)
Tel.: (31) 475353535
Web Site: http://www.rockwool.nl
Holding Company
N.A.I.C.S.: 551112
Erwin Prince *(Mng Dir)*

Subsidiary (Non-US):

Rockwool N.V. (3)
Lromboutspraat 7, 1932, Zaventem, Belgium (100%)
Tel.: (32) 27156800
Web Site: http://www.rockwool.be
Sales Range: $25-49.9 Million
Emp.: 50
Acoustic Ceilings
N.A.I.C.S.: 238310

Subsidiary (Domestic):

Rockwool Lapinus N.V. (4)
Romboutsstraat 7, Zaventem, 1932, Belgium
Tel.: (32) 27156805
Web Site: http://www.rockwool.be
Sales Range: $25-49.9 Million
Emp.: 50
Insulation
N.A.I.C.S.: 327993
Jean Seghers *(Mgr)*

s.a. Etablissements n.v. Charles Wille & Co (4)
Avenue Mozart 46, 7700, Mouscron, Belgium
Tel.: (32) 2 715 6800
Sales Range: $25-49.9 Million
Emp.: 3
Insulation Building Materials Distr
N.A.I.C.S.: 327993
Zean Seghers *(Gen Mgr)*

Rockwool Building Materials (Singapore) Pte Ltd. (1)
No 7 Tuas Avenue 1, Jurong, 639492, Singapore

Tel.: (65) 68614722
Web Site: https://www.rockwool.com
Insulation Building Materials Distr
N.A.I.C.S.: 423330
Davis Ong *(Dir-Sls)*

Rockwool Building Materials Ltd. (1)
Unit 301-2 3/F Koon Wah Building 2 Yuen Shun Circuit, Yuen Chau Kok, Sha Tin, New Territories, China (Hong Kong)
Tel.: (852) 2754 0877
Steel Wool Mfr
N.A.I.C.S.: 332999

Rockwool Bulgaria Ltd. (1)
83 Tsar Ivan Asen II Str, Sofia, 1124, Bulgaria
Tel.: (359) 2 943 95 60
Insulation Building Materials Distr
N.A.I.C.S.: 423330

Rockwool EE OU (1)
Osmussaare 8, EE-13811, Tallinn, Estonia
Tel.: (372) 6826711
Web Site: https://www.rockwool.com
Insulation Building Materials Distr
N.A.I.C.S.: 423330

Rockwool Finland OY (1)
Silkkitehtantie 5 G 3rd floor, 01300, Vantaa, Finland
Tel.: (358) 985635880
Web Site: https://www.rockwool.com
Insulation Building Materials Distr
N.A.I.C.S.: 423330
Esa Maki *(Mng Dir)*

Rockwool Firesafe Insulation (Guangzhou) Co. Ltd. (1)
A4 1101-1 Zhitai Plaza, Huangpu Dist, Guangzhou, 510530, Guangdong, China
Tel.: (86) 2082038829
Web Site: https://www.rockwool.com
Building Materials Distr
N.A.I.C.S.: 423320

Subsidiary (Non-US):

Rockwool Building Materials (Philippines) Ltd. (2)
Unit 702 7f Page 1 Bldg Acacia Avenue Madrigal Business Park, Ayala Alabang, Muntinlupa, 1215, Philippines
Tel.: (63) 2 7710 650
Web Site: http://rtivia-asia.inforce.dk
Sales Range: $25-49.9 Million
Insulation Material Distr
N.A.I.C.S.: 423330

Rockwool Firesafe Insulation (Shanghai) Co. Ltd. (1)
Room 2605 Summit Centre 1088 Yan'an West Rd, Changning Dist, Shanghai, 200052, China
Tel.: (86) 21 6211 6725
Insulation Building Materials Distr
N.A.I.C.S.: 423330
Terry Mak *(Gen Mgr)*

Rockwool France S.A.S (1)
111 rue du Chateau des Rentiers, 75013, Paris, France
Tel.: (33) 140778282
Web Site: https://www.rockwool.com
Sales Range: $50-74.9 Million
Emp.: 100
Insulation Building Materials Distr
N.A.I.C.S.: 423330
Bernard Plancade *(Gen Dir)*

Subsidiary (Domestic):

Rockwool Isolation S.A. (2)
111 Rue Du Chateau Des Rentiers, 75013, Paris, France (100%)
Tel.: (33) 140778282
Web Site: http://www.rockwool.fr
Sales Range: $50-74.9 Million
Insulation & Acoustic Ceilings
N.A.I.C.S.: 327993

Rockwool Handelsgesellschaft m.b.H (1)
Eichenstrasse 38, 1120, Vienna, Austria (100%)
Tel.: (43) 1797260
Web Site: https://www.rockwool.com
Sales Range: $25-49.9 Million
Emp.: 17
Insulation Mfr

N.A.I.C.S.: 327993
Manfred Wagner *(Mng Dir)*

Rockwool Hungaria Kft. (1)
Alkotas u 39 / c, 1123, Budapest, Hungary
Tel.: (36) 1 225 2400
Web Site: https://www.rockwool.com
Insulation
N.A.I.C.S.: 327993

Rockwool Iberica S.A. (1)
Calle Del Bruc 50, 8010, Barcelona, Spain (100%)
Tel.: (34) 933189028
Web Site: http://www.rockwool.es
Sales Range: $50-74.9 Million
Emp.: 150
Insulation & Acoustic Ceilings
N.A.I.C.S.: 327993

Subsidiary (Domestic):

Rockwool Peninsular S.A. (2)
Bruc 50 3, 08010, Barcelona, Spain
Tel.: (34) 902430430
Sales Range: $50-74.9 Million
Emp.: 20
Insulation Building Materials Distr
N.A.I.C.S.: 423330

Rockwool Italia S.r.l. (1)
Via Canova 12, 20145, Milan, Italy
Tel.: (39) 02346131
Web Site: https://www.rockwool.com
Sales Range: $25-49.9 Million
Emp.: 40
Insulation & Acoustic Ceilings
N.A.I.C.S.: 327993

Rockwool Limited (1)
Pencoed, Bridgend, CF35 6NY, United Kingdom (100%)
Tel.: (44) 165 686 2621
Web Site: https://www.rockwool.com
Sales Range: $125-149.9 Million
Emp.: 500
Insulation
N.A.I.C.S.: 327993

Subsidiary (Domestic):

Rockwool Investments Ltd. (2)
Pencoed, Bridgend, CF35 6NY, United Kingdom
Horticultural Substances
N.A.I.C.S.: 327993

Rockwool Limited (1)
Hemaraj Eastern Industrial Estate, Huaypong Muang, Rayong, 21150, Thailand
Tel.: (66) 3868 5110
Sales Range: $75-99.9 Million
Emp.: 11
Insulation Building Materials Distr
N.A.I.C.S.: 423330
Kukkong Hanpadung-dhamma *(Gen Mgr)*

Rockwool Ltd. (1)
Unit 11 Northwood Court Northwood Business Campus, Santry, Dublin, Ireland
Tel.: (353) 1 891 1055
Web Site: http://www.rockwool.ie
Insulation Building Materials Distr
N.A.I.C.S.: 423330

Rockwool Malaysia Sdn. Bhd. (1)
Lot 4 Solok Waja 1, Bukit Raja Industrial Estate, 41050, Kelang, Selangor, Malaysia
Tel.: (60) 333413444
Web Site: http://www.rockwoolasia.com
Sales Range: $75-99.9 Million
Insulation Building Materials Distr
N.A.I.C.S.: 423330

Rockwool Polska Sp. z.o.o. (1)
ul Kwiatowa 14, 66-131, Cigacice, Poland
Tel.: (48) 683850250
Insulation Building Materials Distr
N.A.I.C.S.: 423330

Rockwool Slovensko s.r.o. (1)
Cesta na Senec 2/A, 821 04, Bratislava, Slovakia
Tel.: (421) 249200915
Sales Range: $50-74.9 Million
Emp.: 1
Insulation Building Materials Distr
N.A.I.C.S.: 423330
Peter Vilina *(Mgr-Sls)*

Rockwool a.s. (1)

Cihelni 769, 735 31, Bohumin, Czech Republic
Tel.: (420) 596094111
Web Site: https://www.rockwool.com
Sound Insulation Building Materials Distr
N.A.I.C.S.: 423330

Rockwool, a.s. (1)
Cihelni 769, 735 31, Bohumin, Czech Republic
Tel.: (420) 596094111
Web Site: http://www.rockwool.cz
Mfr of Stone Mineral Wool Used in Thermal Insulation, Fire Protection & Acoustic Requirements in Building Structures
N.A.I.C.S.: 327993

Roxul Inc. (1)
420 Bronte St 105, Milton, L9T 0H9, ON, Canada (100%)
Tel.: (905) 878-8474
Web Site: http://www.roxul.com
Sales Range: $50-74.9 Million
Emp.: 160
Electrical Insulation Providers
N.A.I.C.S.: 327993

Roxul Rockwool Insulation India Ltd. (1)
Plot-Z/4 Dahej SEZ Dahej, District Bharuch, Bharuch, 392 130, Gujarat, India
Tel.: (91) 2641264400
Web Site: http://www.rockwool.in
Sales Range: $75-99.9 Million
Emp.: 23
Insulation Building Materials Distr
N.A.I.C.S.: 423330

Roxul Rockwool Technical Insulation India Pvt Ltd. (1)
Wing B-2 2nd Floor Unit No 206 Boomerang Near Chandivali Film Studio, Chandivali Farm Road Andheri E, Mumbai, 400072, Maharashtra, India
Tel.: (91) 2267157700
Web Site: https://www.roxulrockwool.in
Sales Range: $50-74.9 Million
Emp.: 20
Insulation Building Materials Mfr
N.A.I.C.S.: 326150

SIA Rockwool (1)
76 Gustava Zemgala gatve, Riga, 1039, Latvia
Tel.: (371) 67032585
Web Site: https://www.rockwool.lv
Sales Range: $50-74.9 Million
Insulation Building Materials Distr
N.A.I.C.S.: 423330

Tripplex ApS (1)
Hovedgaden 501, Flong, 2640, Hedehusene, Denmark
Tel.: (45) 98339591
Web Site: https://www.tripplex.dk
Wooden Furniture Mfr
N.A.I.C.S.: 337212

UAB Rockwool (1)
A Gostauto str 40B, 01112, Vilnius, Lithuania
Tel.: (370) 52126024
Insulation Material Distr
N.A.I.C.S.: 423330

ROCKWORTH PUBLIC COMPANY LIMITED

294-300 Asoke-Dindaeng Rd Huaykwang, Bangkok, 10320, Thailand
Tel.: (66) 22468888
Web Site: https://www.rockworth.com
Year Founded: 1988
ROCK—(THA)
Rev.: $19,019,152
Assets: $26,230,153
Liabilities: $14,913,886
Net Worth: $11,316,267
Earnings: $601,355
Emp.: 700
Fiscal Year-end: 12/31/23
Furniture Mfr & Distr
N.A.I.C.S.: 423210
Surapong Sithanukul *(Co-Founder)*

Subsidiaries:

Rockworth Public Company Limited - Ayudhaya Facility (1)

Rockworth Public Company Limited—(Continued)
Bangpa-In Industrial Estate 681 Moo 2 Tambon Klong Jig, Bangpa-In, Ayutthaya, 13160, Thailand
Tel.: (66) 22468888
Web Site: http://www.rockworth.com
Office Furniture Mfr
N.A.I.C.S.: 337214

Rockworth Systems Furniture India Pvt. Ltd. (1)
No 800 West R1-South Sri City SEZ-Processing Area, Irugulam Post Satyavedu Mandal, Chittoor, 517588, Andhra Pradesh, India
Tel.: (91) 8040985438
Web Site: http://www.rockworthindia.com
Emp.: 250
Office Furniture Mfr & Distr
N.A.I.C.S.: 337214

ROCKY MOUNTAIN EQUIPMENT ALBERTA LTD.
3345 8th Street S E, Calgary, T2G 3A4, AB, Canada
Tel.: (403) 265-7364
Web Site: https://www.rockymtn.com
Rev.: $593,114,567
Assets: $538,618,000
Liabilities: $394,094,774
Net Worth: $144,523,226
Earnings: ($832,581)
Emp.: 755
Fiscal Year-end: 12/31/19
Agricultural & Construction Equipment Dealer
N.A.I.C.S.: 423830
Matthew C. Campbell (Chm)

Subsidiaries:

Rocky Mountain Equipment (1)
3345 8th Street S E, Calgary, T2G 3A4, AB, Canada
Tel.: (403) 265-7364
Web Site: http://www.rockymtn.com
Sales Range: $25-49.9 Million
Emp.: 1,000
Construction Equipment Repair & Maintenance Services
N.A.I.C.S.: 811310

Division (Domestic):

Rocky Mountain Equipment (2)
4722 47th Ave, Vermilion, T9X 1H8, AB, Canada
Tel.: (780) 853-6851
Sales Range: $25-49.9 Million
Emp.: 15
Agriculture Equipment Dealers
N.A.I.C.S.: 423820

ROCKY MOUNTAIN LIQUOR INC.
11478 149 Street, Edmonton, T5M 1W7, AB, Canada
Tel.: (780) 483-8177
Web Site: https://uminvestor.com
Year Founded: 2007
RUM—(TSXV)
Rev.: $31,319,408
Assets: $17,206,368
Liabilities: $10,448,473
Net Worth: $6,757,895
Earnings: $349,667
Fiscal Year-end: 12/31/23
Beverage Store Operator
N.A.I.C.S.: 445320
Peter J. Byrne (Chm)

ROCTOOL SA
Savoie Technolac, BP 80341, 34 Allee du Lac d Aiguebelette, 73370, Le Bourget du Lac, Cedex, France
Tel.: (33) 479262707
Web Site: https://www.roctool.com
Year Founded: 2000
ALROC—(EUR)
Sales Range: $1-9.9 Million

Molding Technologies Including RTM, LFT Processing, Thermo Compression & Thermoplastic Injection
N.A.I.C.S.: 326199
Steve Verschaeve (VP-Bus Dev-North America)

Subsidiaries:

RocTool North America (1)
3495 Piedmont Rd Bldg 11 Ste 710, Atlanta, GA 30305
Tel.: (866) 260-2572
Molding Services
N.A.I.C.S.: 333511

RocTool Taiwan (1)
6 Ln910 Sec2 Dongda Rd Taya, Taichung, 52879, Taiwan
Tel.: (886) 425678659
Plastic Injection Mold Mfr
N.A.I.C.S.: 326199
Michael Yang (Branch Mgr)

Roctool Japan (1)
C O Erai Japan Dai 2 Izumi Shoji Bldg 4 F 2 6, Kojimachi 4 Chome, Tokyo, 102-0083, Chiyoda-Ku, Japan
Tel.: (81) 368210310
Web Site: http://www.roctool.com
Molding Services
N.A.I.C.S.: 333511
Nicolas Renou (Mgr)

RODA VIVATEX TBK
Jl Prof Dr Satrio No 164, Jakarta, 12950, Selatan, Indonesia
Tel.: (62) 2125532222
Web Site: https://www.rodavivatex.co.id
Year Founded: 1980
RDTX—(INDO)
Rev.: $34,632,890
Assets: $223,415,228
Liabilities: $36,050,527
Net Worth: $187,364,700
Earnings: $19,663,978
Emp.: 191
Fiscal Year-end: 12/31/23
Textile Products Mfr
N.A.I.C.S.: 314999
Wiriady Widjaja (Chm)

Subsidiaries:

PT Dwimitra Graha Mandiri (1)
Komplek Graha Kencana Block AA Jl Pejuangan No 88, Jakarta, 11530, Indonesia
Tel.: (62) 215332401
Web Site: http://www.dwimitrasm.com
Electrical Products Mfr
N.A.I.C.S.: 335999

RODAMIENTOS Y ACCESORIOS SA DE CV
Nuestra Oficina Matriz Se Encuentra En Ave, Nogalar sur 107 col Cuauhtemoc San Nicolas de los Garza N L, 66450, Mexico, Nuevo Leon, Mexico
Tel.: (52) 81 8158 9500
Web Site: http://www.ryasa.com.mx
Emp.: 1,500
Power Transmission Products Distr
N.A.I.C.S.: 335311
Iuten Villagomez (CEO)

Subsidiaries:

Delamac de Mexico, S.A. de C.V. (1)
Poniente 128 Num 496, Industrial Vallejo, 02300, Mexico, Mexico
Tel.: (52) 55 67 08 22
Industrial Products Mfr
N.A.I.C.S.: 423840

RODE MICROPHONES
107 Carnarvon Street, Silverwater, 2128, NSW, Australia
Tel.: (61) 2 9648 5855
Web Site: http://www.rode.com
Audio Equipment Mfr

N.A.I.C.S.: 334310

Subsidiaries:

Aphex Systems Ltd. (1)
11068 Randall St, Sun Valley, CA 91352
Tel.: (818) 767-2929
Web Site: http://www.aphex.com
Sales Range: $1-9.9 Million
Emp.: 25
Radio & Television Broadcasting & Wireless Communications Equipment Mfr
N.A.I.C.S.: 334220
Marvin Caesar (Pres)

RODEO CAPITAL II CORP.
1500 850 2nd Street SW, Calgary, T2P 0R8, AB, Canada
Tel.: (604) 484-6628   AB
Year Founded: 2010
Investment Services
N.A.I.C.S.: 523999
Michael Thomson (Pres, CEO & CFO)

RODEX FASTENERS CORP.
No 29 Sung Chiang North Rd, Chung Li Ind Park, Taoyuan, 32062, Taiwan
Tel.: (886) 34511493
Web Site: http://www.rodex.com.tw
Year Founded: 1984
5015—(TPE)
Rev.: $85,402,307
Assets: $77,961,198
Liabilities: $27,460,463
Net Worth: $50,500,735
Earnings: $17,937,498
Emp.: 200
Fiscal Year-end: 12/31/22
Stainless Steel Wire & Screw Mfr
N.A.I.C.S.: 332618

RODINA
Lyubertsy Ulitsa 20, Skopinskiy Rayon, Il'inka Selo, Ryazan, 391822, Russia
Tel.: (7) 8616462635
Grain Farming Services
N.A.I.C.S.: 111199

RODINA-91 AD
Bul 25 ti Septemvri 43, Dobrich, 9300, Bulgaria
Tel.: (359) 58602765
RDNA—(BUL)
Sales Range: Less than $1 Million
Real Estate Agency Services
N.A.I.C.S.: 531210

RODINIA LITHIUM INC.
65 Queen Street West 8th Floor, Toronto, M5H 2M5, ON, Canada
Tel.: (416) 861-1685
Web Site: http://rodinialithium.com
RM—(TSXV)
Sales Range: Less than $1 Million
Lithium Exploration Services
N.A.I.C.S.: 213114
David Stein (Pres & CEO)

RODIUM REALTY LIMITED
401/402/501 XCube Plot 636 Opp to Fun Republic Theater Off Link Road, Andheri West, Mumbai, 400 053, Maharashtra, India
Tel.: (91) 2242310800
Web Site: https://www.rodium.net
531822—(BOM)
Rev.: $5,322,115
Assets: $14,425,250
Liabilities: $12,658,258
Net Worth: $1,766,992
Earnings: $106,648
Emp.: 15
Fiscal Year-end: 03/31/23
Real Estate Services
N.A.I.C.S.: 531390
Deepak Chheda (Chm & Mng Dir)

RODNA ZEMYA HOLDING AD
Sofia p k 1836 Kremikovtsi Blvd, Municipality Stolichna, Sofia, Bulgaria
Tel.: (359) 29812192
Web Site: https://rodnazemya.bg
HRZ—(BUL)
Sales Range: Less than $1 Million
Holding Company
N.A.I.C.S.: 551112

RODOBO INTERNATIONAL, INC.
380 Changjiang Road, Nangang District, Harbin, 150001, China
Tel.: (86) 45182260522   NV
Web Site: http://www.rodobo.com
Sales Range: $50-74.9 Million
Emp.: 2,767
Powdered Milk Products Mfr & Distr
N.A.I.C.S.: 311514
Yanbin Wang (Founder, Chm & CEO)

RODOCANACHI CAPITAL INC.
1002 Sherbrooke 28e etage, Montreal, H3A 3L6, QC, Canada
Tel.: (514) 282-7815   QC
Year Founded: 2008
Investment Services
N.A.I.C.S.: 523999
Jean-Sebastian Besner (Pres, CEO, CFO, Treas & Sec)

RODOPSKA SLAVA AD
Benkovski Obsht Kirkovo Obl, Kardjhali, 6865, Bulgaria
Tel.: (359) 36762209
RDSL—(BUL)
Sales Range: Less than $1 Million
Home Furnishing Cloth Mfr
N.A.I.C.S.: 314999

RODOVIAS DAS COLINAS S.A.
Rod Marechal Rondon Km 112-Marginal Oeste, 13312-000, Itu, SP, Brazil
Tel.: (55) 1135089617
Emp.: 100
Transportation Support Services
N.A.I.C.S.: 488991
Jose Renato Ricciardi (CEO)

RODRIGO TEKSTIL SANAYI VE TICARET AS
M Nesih Ozmen Mahallesi Kasim Sokak no 35-A, 5 Gungoren, Istanbul, Turkiye
Tel.: (90) 2128750741
Web Site: https://www.rodrigo.com
RODRG—(IST)
Rev.: $1,297,877,068
Assets: $2,096,017
Liabilities: $1,241,196
Net Worth: $854,821
Earnings: $34,294
Fiscal Year-end: 12/31/22
Denim & Sportswear Mfr
N.A.I.C.S.: 315250
Bekir Kucukdogan (Chm & Gen-Mgr)

ROEBUCK FOOD GROUP PLC
6th Floor South Bank House Barrow Street, Dublin, 2, Ireland
Tel.: (353) 830257760
Web Site: https://www.roebuckfoodgroup.com
RFG—(AIM)
Rev.: $39,574,602
Assets: $18,194,900
Liabilities: $10,999,748
Net Worth: $7,195,153
Earnings: ($1,575,360)
Emp.: 16
Fiscal Year-end: 12/31/22
Food Warehousing & Logistics Services

AND PRIVATE COMPANIES — ROGERS INSURANCE LTD.

N.A.I.C.S.: 493120
Ted O'Neill *(Chm)*

Subsidiaries:

Norish Limited **(1)**
Northern Way, Northern Industrial Estate, Bury Saint Edmunds, IP32 6NL, Suffolk, United Kingdom
Tel.: (44) 3332021023
Web Site: http://www.norish.com
Sales Range: $50-74.9 Million
Property Management Services
N.A.I.C.S.: 531312
Steve Vincent *(Mgr-Health & Safety)*

ROFF LOGISTICS INC.
7956 Torbram Rd, Brampton, L6T 5A2, ON, Canada
Tel.: (905) 793-7294
Rev.: $24,588,000
Emp.: 200
Truck Services
N.A.I.C.S.: 484110
Ron Schott *(VP-Ops)*

ROGERS & COMPANY LIMITED
5th Floor Rogers House No 5 President John Kennedy Street, PO Box 60, Port Louis, Mauritius
Tel.: (230) 2026666
Web Site: https://www.rogers.mu
Year Founded: 1899
ROGE—(MAU)
Rev.: $256,689,125
Assets: $1,010,283,170
Liabilities: $449,877,361
Net Worth: $560,405,809
Earnings: $55,082,097
Emp.: 4,826
Fiscal Year-end: 06/30/23
Aviation, Hotels, Leisure, Logistics & Shipping
N.A.I.C.S.: 481111
Philippe Espitalier-Noel *(CEO)*

Subsidiaries:

Cerena Management Limited **(1)**
Industrial Zone Trianon, Quatre Bornes, Mauritius **(100%)**
Tel.: (230) 4676520
Web Site: http://www.cerenagroup.com
Rev.: $64,576,264
Investment & Management Services; Agricultural Chemicals, Pharmaceuticals & Industrial Paints; Consumer Goods Wholesale Trade Broker
N.A.I.C.S.: 523999

Division (Domestic):

Cerena Agro Science **(2)**
Industrial Zone Trianon, Quatre Bornes, Mauritius
Tel.: (230) 4676520
Agricultural Chemicals & Pesticides Mfr, Importer & Distr
N.A.I.C.S.: 325320

Cerena Healthcare **(2)**
Industrial Zone Trianon, Quatre Bornes, Mauritius
Tel.: (230) 4676520
Healthcare & Pharmaceutical Distr
N.A.I.C.S.: 424210

Cerena Trade Services **(2)**
Industrial Zone Trianon, Quatre Bornes, Mauritius
Tel.: (230) 4676520
Consumer Goods, Wines, Spirits Wholesale Distr; Alcoholic Drink Bottler & Packager
N.A.I.C.S.: 425120

Plaisance Air Transport Services Limited **(1)**
Freight Forwarding Centre, Plaine Magnien, Mauritius
Tel.: (230) 6379816
Sales Range: $50-74.9 Million
Emp.: 130
Airport Ground Handling
N.A.I.C.S.: 488119

Rogers Asset Management Limited **(1)**
5 John Kennedy Street, Port Louis, Mauritius
Tel.: (230) 2026666
Web Site: http://www.rogers.mu
Sales Range: $50-74.9 Million
Emp.: 6
Asset Management Services
N.A.I.C.S.: 523999
Ziyad Bundhun *(Gen Mgr)*

Veranda Leisure & Hospitality Limited **(1)**
Village Labourdonnais, Mapou, 31803, Mauritius **(68.3%)**
Tel.: (230) 2605101
Web Site: http://www.vlh.mu
Sales Range: $10-24.9 Million
Emp.: 1,450
Hotel Operator
N.A.I.C.S.: 721110

Division (Domestic):

Heritage Awali Golf & Spa Resort **(2)**
Domaine de Bel Ombre, Bel Ombre, Mauritius
Tel.: (230) 2669700
Web Site: http://www.heritageawali.com
Golf & Spa Resort Operations
N.A.I.C.S.: 721110

Paul & Virgine Hotel **(2)**
Royal Rd Grand Gaube, Mapou, 31803, Mauritius
Tel.: (230) 2669700
Web Site: http://www.veranda-resorts.com
Emp.: 150
Hotel Operations
N.A.I.C.S.: 721110
Kaviraj Bhunjun *(Gen Mgr)*

Veranda Hotel **(2)**
Village Labourdonnais, Mapou, Mauritius
Tel.: (230) 2669700
Web Site: http://www.veranda.mu
Hotel Operations
N.A.I.C.S.: 721110
Francois Eynaud *(CEO)*

Veranda Palmar Beach Hotel **(2)**
Village Labourdonnais, Mapou, Mauritius
Tel.: (230) 2605101
Sales Range: $10-24.9 Million
Emp.: 105
Hotel Resort Operations
N.A.I.C.S.: 721110
Jean-Marie Chinnapen *(Gen Mgr)*

Veranda Pointe aux Biches Hotel **(2)**
Village Labourdonnais, Mapou, Mauritius
Tel.: (230) 2605101
Sales Range: $10-24.9 Million
Emp.: 100
Hotel Operations
N.A.I.C.S.: 721110
Clifford Pierre *(Mgr)*

ROGERS COMMUNICATIONS INC.
333 Bloor Street East 10th Floor, Toronto, M4W 1G9, ON, Canada
Tel.: (416) 935-7777 BC
Web Site: https://www.rogers.com
Year Founded: 1960
RCI—(NYSE)
Rev.: $14,263,130,679
Assets: $51,179,729,630
Liabilities: $43,467,533,427
Net Worth: $7,712,196,203
Earnings: $627,169,979
Emp.: 25,200
Fiscal Year-end: 12/31/23
Telecommunication Servicesb
N.A.I.C.S.: 551112
Melinda Mary Rogers-Hixon *(Deputy Chm)*

Subsidiaries:

Canadian Broadcast Sales **(1)**
45 St Clair Avenue West 5th Floor, Toronto, M4V 1K9, ON, Canada
Tel.: (416) 961-4770
Sales Range: $25-49.9 Million
Emp.: 32
National Radio Advertising Sales Representation; Owned 50% by Corus Entertainment Inc. & 50% by Rogers Communications, Inc.
N.A.I.C.S.: 541840
Jamie Barnes *(Grp Dir-Sls-West)*

Maple Leaf Sports & Entertainment Ltd. **(1)**
50 Bay St Suite 400, Toronto, M5J 2L2, ON, Canada **(39.76%)**
Tel.: (416) 815-5400
Web Site: http://www.mlse.com
Sales Range: $550-599.9 Million
Emp.: 900
Holding Company; Professional Sports Teams, Broadcast Media Licensing, Internet Publishing, Sports & Entertainment Venues Owner & Operator
N.A.I.C.S.: 551112
Larry Tanenbaum *(Chm)*

Unit (Domestic):

The Air Canada Centre **(2)**
40 Bay Street, Toronto, M5J 2L2, ON, Canada
Tel.: (416) 815-5982
Web Site: https://www.scotiabankarena.com
Sports & Entertainment Facility Operator
N.A.I.C.S.: 711310

Subsidiary (Domestic):

Toronto Maple Leafs Hockey Club Inc. **(2)**
50 Bay Street Suite 500, Toronto, M5J 2L2, ON, Canada
Tel.: (416) 815-5700
Web Site: http://www.mapleleafs.com
Professional Hockey Club
N.A.I.C.S.: 711211
Brendan Shanahan *(Pres)*

Toronto Raptors Basketball Club Inc. **(2)**
40 Bay Street Suite 400, Toronto, M5J 2X2, ON, Canada
Tel.: (416) 815-5500
Web Site: http://www.raptors.com
Professional Basketball Team
N.A.I.C.S.: 711211
Bobby Webster *(Gen Mgr)*

Rogers Cable Inc. **(1)**
333 Bloor St E, Toronto, M4W 1G9, ON, Canada **(100%)**
Tel.: (416) 935-6666
Web Site: http://www.rogers.com
Sales Range: $1-4.9 Billion
Emp.: 7,990
Digital Cable, Internet & Telecommunications Services
N.A.I.C.S.: 517111

Subsidiary (Domestic):

Rogers Telecommunications Limited **(2)**
1 Blue Jays Way Gate 8, Toronto, M5V 1J1, ON, Canada
Tel.: (416) 341-1800
Web Site: http://www.rogers.com
Telecommunication Servicesb
N.A.I.C.S.: 517111
Alan Douglas Horn *(Pres & CEO)*

Rogers Communications Partnership **(1)**
333 Bloor Street, Toronto, M4W 1G9, ON, Canada
Tel.: (416) 935-7777
Wireless Telecommunication Services
N.A.I.C.S.: 517112

Rogers Media Inc. **(1)**
333 Bloor St E 6th Fl, Toronto, M4Y 3B7, ON, Canada **(100%)**
Tel.: (416) 935-8200
Web Site: http://www.rogers.com
Sales Range: $600-649.9 Million
Emp.: 3,000
Business Publications, Consumer Magazines, Trade & Consumer Shows
N.A.I.C.S.: 513120
Timothy L. Root *(Pres-iMedia & Exec VP-Pub Rels)*

Subsidiary (Domestic):

Toronto Blue Jays Baseball Club **(2)**
1 Blue Jays Way Suite 3200, Toronto, M5V 1J1, ON, Canada **(80%)**
Tel.: (416) 341-1000
Web Site: http://www.bluejays.com
Sales Range: $75-99.9 Million
Emp.: 300
Professional Baseball Club
N.A.I.C.S.: 711211
Honsing Leung *(Mgr-Client Svc)*

Rogers Wireless Communications Inc. **(1)**
One Mount Pleasant Rd, Toronto, M4Y 2Y5, ON, Canada **(100%)**
Tel.: (416) 935-1100
Sales Range: $1-4.9 Billion
Emp.: 5,000
Holding Company
N.A.I.C.S.: 551112

Shaw Communications Inc. **(1)**
Suite 900 630 3rd Avenue SW, Calgary, T2P 4L4, AB, Canada
Tel.: (403) 750-4500
Web Site: http://www.shaw.ca
Rev.: $4,309,580,520
Assets: $12,353,765,760
Liabilities: $7,626,447,720
Net Worth: $4,727,318,040
Earnings: $771,328,080
Emp.: 9,400
Fiscal Year-end: 08/31/2021
Entertainment, Information & Communications Services
N.A.I.C.S.: 516210
Zoran Stakic *(COO & CTO)*

Subsidiary (Domestic):

Freedom Mobile Inc. **(2)**
207 Queen's Quay West Suite 710, PO Box 114, Toronto, M5J 1A7, ON, Canada
Tel.: (647) 700-2435
Web Site: https://www.freedommobile.ca
Wireless Telecommunication Services
N.A.I.C.S.: 517112

Shaw Satellite Services, Inc. **(2)**
2055 Flavelle Blvd, Mississauga, L5K 1Z8, ON, Canada **(94.5%)**
Tel.: (905) 403-2020
Web Site: http://www.cancom.ca
Sales Range: $50-74.9 Million
Emp.: 150
Satellite Communication Services
N.A.I.C.S.: 517410

Affiliate (Domestic):

Shaw Broadcast Services **(3)**
5440 DeCarie Blvd, Montreal, H3X 2J1, QC, Canada **(100%)**
Tel.: (514) 937-7313
Web Site: http://www.shawbroadcast.com
Sales Range: $25-49.9 Million
Emp.: 5
Broadcast Services
N.A.I.C.S.: 516120
Karen Baglole *(Mgr)*

Subsidiary (Domestic):

Shaw Telecom Inc. **(2)**
630 3 Ave SW Suite 900, Calgary, T2P 4L4, AB, Canada
Tel.: (403) 750-4500
Web Site: http://www.shaw.ca
Television Broadcasting Services
N.A.I.C.S.: 516120

ROGERS INSURANCE LTD.
Ste 600 1000 Ctr St N, Calgary, T2E 7W7, AB, Canada
Tel.: (403) 296-2400
Web Site: http://www.rogersinsurance.ca
Year Founded: 1995
Rev.: $48,081,438
Emp.: 120
Insurance Agencies
N.A.I.C.S.: 524210
Peter Rogers *(Chm)*

Subsidiaries:

A-Win Insurance Ltd. **(1)**

6383

ROGERS INSURANCE LTD.

Rogers Insurance Ltd.—(Continued)
1331 Macleod Trail SE #800, Calgary, T2G 0K3, AB, Canada
Tel.: (866) 278-1050
Web Site: https://www.awinins.ca
Emp.: 76
Insurance Brokerage Services
N.A.I.C.S.: 524210

ROGERS SUGAR INC.
123 Rogers St, Vancouver, V6A 3N2, BC, Canada
Tel.: (604) 253-1131
Web Site:
  https://www.lanticrogers.com
Year Founded: 1890
RSI—(TSX)
Sales Range: $500-549.9 Million
Holding Company
N.A.I.C.S.: 551112
Patrick Dionne *(VP-Ops & Supply Chain)*

Subsidiaries:

Lantic, Inc. (1)
4026 Notre Dame Street East, Montreal, H1W 2K3, QC, Canada
Tel.: (514) 527-8686
Web Site: http://www.lanticrogers.com
Sales Range: $125-149.9 Million
Emp.: 450
Sugar & Syrup Refining & Distr; Sugar Beet Farming
N.A.I.C.S.: 311314
John Holliday *(Pres & CEO)*

ROHAS TECNIC BERHAD
15th Floor East Wing Rohas Tecnic No 9 Jalan P Ramlee, 50250, Kuala Lumpur, Malaysia
Tel.: (60) 321633900
Web Site:
  https://www.rohastecnic.com
Year Founded: 1995
ROHAS—(KLS)
Rev: $92,296,534
Assets: $139,839,566
Liabilities: $63,132,957
Net Worth: $76,706,609
Earnings: $4,326,214
Emp.: 858
Fiscal Year-end: 12/31/22
Plastics Product Mfr
N.A.I.C.S.: 326199
Kim Huat Gan *(Chm)*

Subsidiaries:

HG Power Transmission Sdn. Bhd. (1)
15th Floor East Wing Rohas Tecnic 9 Jalan P Ramlee, 50250, Kuala Lumpur, Malaysia
Tel.: (60) 321633900
Web Site: https://www.hgptsb.com
Eletric Power Generation Services
N.A.I.C.S.: 221118

P.T. Century Abadi Perkasa (1)
Plaza Marein Lt 23 Jalan Jenderal Sudirman Kav 76-78, Jakarta, 12910, Indonesia
Tel.: (62) 2180657808
Web Site: https://www.lawesikap.com
Eletric Power Generation Services
N.A.I.C.S.: 221118

ROHDE & SCHWARZ GMBH & CO. KG
Muehldorfstrasse 15, 81671, Munich, Germany
Tel.: (49) 8941290
Web Site: http://www.rohde-schwarz.com
Year Founded: 1933
Sales Range: $1-4.9 Billion
Emp.: 6,400
Holding Company; Radio Communications, Testing, Measurement & Information Technology Equipment Developer & Mfr

N.A.I.C.S.: 551112
Robert Obertreis *(Mgr-Mktg)*

Subsidiaries:

GEDIS GmbH (1)
Sophienblatt 100, 24114, Kiel, Germany
Tel.: (49) 431 600 51 0
Web Site: http://www.gedis-online.de
Electronic Testing Equipment Distr
N.A.I.C.S.: 423690

HAMEG Instruments GmbH (1)
Industriestr 6, 63533, Mainhausen, Germany
Tel.: (49) 6182 800 0
Web Site: http://www.hameg.com
Electronic Testing Equipment Distr
N.A.I.C.S.: 423690
Holger Asmussen *(CEO)*

PT. ROHDE & SCHWARZ INDONESIA (1)
Ratu Prabu 2 5th Floor Jl T B Simatupang Kav 1B, Jakarta, 12560, Indonesia
Tel.: (62) 21 29245400
Electronic Testing Equipment Distr
N.A.I.C.S.: 423690

ROHDE & SCHWARZ RUS OOO (1)
Pavlovskaya Street b7 Str 1 5th Floor Business Center Pavlovskiy, 115093, Moscow, Russia
Tel.: (7) 495 9813560
Web Site: http://www.rohde-schwarz.ru
Electronic Testing Equipment Distr
N.A.I.C.S.: 423690
Alex Krasnojen *(Project Mgr & Mgr-Svc)*

Rhode & Schwarz DVS GmbH (1)
Krepenstr 8, 30165, Hannover, Germany
Tel.: (49) 511 67 80 70
Web Site: http://www.dvs.de
Emp.: 130
Electronic Testing Equipment Distr
N.A.I.C.S.: 423690
Andreas Loges *(CEO)*

Rhode & Schwarz UK Ltd. (1)
Ancells Business Park, Fleet, GU51 2UZ, Hampshire, United Kingdom
Tel.: (44) 1252818888
Web Site: http://www.rohde-schwarz.co.uk
Sales Range: $50-74.9 Million
Emp.: 70
Telecommunications & Testing Equipment Whslr & Technical Support Services
N.A.I.C.S.: 423440
Frank Mackel *(Mng Dir)*

Rohde & Schwarz (Australia) Pty Ltd (1)
Unit 2 75 Epping Road, North Ryde, 2113, NSW, Australia
Tel.: (61) 2 8874 5100
Web Site: http://www.rohde-schwarz.com.au
Emp.: 45
Electronic Testing Equipment Distr
N.A.I.C.S.: 423690
Lyndell James *(Mgr-Marcom)*

Rohde & Schwarz (Philippines), Inc. (1)
Unit 1601 BDO Equitable Bank Tower Condominium 8751, Paseo de Roxas, Makati, 1226, Philippines
Tel.: (63) 2 843 0114
Web Site: http://www.rohde-schwarz.com.ph
Emp.: 11
Electronic Testing Equipment Distr
N.A.I.C.S.: 423690
Wilben Conti *(Mng Dir)*

Rohde & Schwarz (Thailand) Co., Ltd. (1)
89 AIA Capital Center 9th Floor Unit 905 Ratchadaphisek Road, Dindaeng, Bangkok, 10140, Thailand
Tel.: (66) 21191200
Telecommunication Servicesb
N.A.I.C.S.: 517810

Rohde & Schwarz - Praha, s.r.o. (1)
Hadovka Office Park Evropska 33c, 160 00, Prague, Czech Republic
Tel.: (420) 2 2431 1247
Web Site: http://www.rohde-schwarz.cz
Electronic Testing Equipment Distr

Rohde & Schwarz Belgium N.V. (1)
Excelsiorlaan 31, 1930, Zaventem, Belgium
Tel.: (32) 2 721 50 02
Web Site: http://www.rohde-schwarz.be
Electronic Testing Equipment Distr
N.A.I.C.S.: 423690

Rohde & Schwarz Canada Inc. (1)
1 Hines Road Suite 100, Kanata, K2K 3C7, ON, Canada
Tel.: (613) 592-8000
Web Site: https://www.rohde-schwarz.com
Electronic Testing Equipment Distr
N.A.I.C.S.: 423690

Rohde & Schwarz Colombia S.A. (1)
Carrera 17 A No 119 A-80, Bogota, Colombia
Tel.: (57) 1 601 9760
Web Site: http://www.rohde-schwarz.com.co
Emp.: 60
Electronic Testing Equipment Distr
N.A.I.C.S.: 423690
Andres Betancourt *(Mng Dir)*

Rohde & Schwarz Danmark A/S (1)
Lysaer 3D 1, 2730, Herlev, Denmark
Tel.: (45) 4343 6699
Web Site: http://www.rohde-schwarz.dk
Electronic Testing Equipment Distr
N.A.I.C.S.: 423690
Soren Hojer Larsen *(Mgr-Sls)*

Rohde & Schwarz Emirates LLC (1)
HQ Aldar Building 2nd Floor Al Raha Beach, Abu Dhabi, 31156, United Arab Emirates
Tel.: (971) 2 4926 299
Web Site: http://www.rohde-schwarz.com
Emp.: 51
Electronic Testing Equipment Distr
N.A.I.C.S.: 423690
Kim Schneidewind *(Dir-Sls & Ops)*

Rohde & Schwarz Engineering & Sales GmbH (1)
Muehldorfstrasse 15, Munich, 81671, Germany (100%)
Tel.: (49) 8941290
Web Site: http://www.rohde-schwarz.com
Sales Range: $700-749.9 Million
Emp.: 2,000
Engineeering Services
N.A.I.C.S.: 541330
Ulerich Eckenberger *(Mng Dir)*

Rohde & Schwarz Espana, S.A. (1)
C/Salcedo 11, 28034, Madrid, Spain
Tel.: (34) 91 334 1070
Web Site: http://www.rohde-schwarz.es
Electronic Testing Equipment Distr
N.A.I.C.S.: 423690

Rohde & Schwarz Finland Oy (1)
Teknobulevardi 3-5 G, 01530, Vantaa, Finland
Tel.: (358) 207 600 400
Web Site: http://www.rohde-schwarz.com
Emp.: 27
Electronic Testing Equipment Distr
N.A.I.C.S.: 423690
Seppo Suomaa *(Acct Mgr)*

Rohde & Schwarz France SAS (1)
9-11 Rue Jeanne Braconnier, 92366, Meudon, France
Tel.: (33) 1 41 36 10 00
Web Site: http://www.rohde-schwarz.fr
Electronic Testing Equipment Distr
N.A.I.C.S.: 423690

Rohde & Schwarz GmbH Werk Koln (1)
Graf Zeppelin Strasse 18, 51147, Cologne, Germany
Tel.: (49) 2203490
Web Site: http://www.rohde-schwarz.com
Sales Range: $100-124.9 Million
Emp.: 300
Mfr of Test & Measurement, Telecommunications & Broadcasting Equipment
N.A.I.C.S.: 334220

Rohde & Schwarz Hellas SA (1)
2 Astronafton & Pantanassis Str, 15125, Maroussi, Greece
Tel.: (30) 210 74002 00
Web Site: http://www.rohde-schwarz.gr
Electronic Testing Equipment Distr
N.A.I.C.S.: 423690

INTERNATIONAL PUBLIC

Dimitris Kynigopoulos *(Mng Dir)*

Rohde & Schwarz Hong Kong Ltd. (1)
Units 105-107 1/F Wireless Centre Hong Kong Science Park, Shatin New Territories, Hong Kong, China (Hong Kong)
Tel.: (852) 22643788
Web Site: http://www.rohde-schwarz.com.hk
Electronic Testing Equipment Distr
N.A.I.C.S.: 423690
Frank Wong *(Mng Dir)*

Rohde & Schwarz India (Pvt) Limited (1)
A-27 1st Floor Mohan Co-Operative Industrial Estate Mathura Road, New Delhi, 110 044, India
Tel.: (91) 11 42535400
Web Site: http://www.rohde-schwarz.co.in
Emp.: 120
Electronic Testing Equipment Distr
N.A.I.C.S.: 423690
Yatish Mohan *(Mng Dir)*

Rohde & Schwarz International GmbH (1)
Muehldorfstrasse 15, 81671, Munich, Germany
Tel.: (49) 8941290
Telecommunication Servicesb
N.A.I.C.S.: 517810

Rohde & Schwarz Japan K.K. (1)
Sakura Urawa Bldg 4F 4-2-11 Harigaya, Urawa-ku, Saitama, 330-0075, Japan
Tel.: (81) 48 829,8061
Web Site: http://www.rohde-schwarz.co.jp
Electronic Testing Equipment Distr
N.A.I.C.S.: 423690
Masanori Uchida *(Dir-Bus Ops)*

Rohde & Schwarz Korea Limited (1)
26-5 Eoniju-ro 133-gil, Gangnam-gu, Seoul, Korea (South)
Tel.: (82) 2 3485 1900
Electronic Testing Equipment Distr
N.A.I.C.S.: 423690

Rohde & Schwarz Malaysia Sdn Bhd (1)
No 2 Jln Pengaturcara U1/51 Temasya Industrial Park, 40150, Shah Alam, Selangor, Malaysia
Tel.: (60) 3 5569 0011
Web Site: http://www.rohde-schwarz.com.my
Electronic Testing Equipment Distr
N.A.I.C.S.: 423690
Josephine Chin *(Mgr-HR)*

Rohde & Schwarz Messgeraetebau GmbH (1)
Rohde & Schwarz Street 1, Memmingen, 87700, Germany (100%)
Tel.: (49) 83311080
Web Site: http://www.rohde-schwarz.com
Sales Range: $400-449.9 Million
Emp.: 1,500
Mfr of Measurement Instruments
N.A.I.C.S.: 334220
Gorgen Steigmoeller *(Pres)*

Rohde & Schwarz Middle East and Africa FZ-LLC (1)
Office No 210 Building No 01 2nd Floor, PO Box 502075, Dubai, United Arab Emirates
Tel.: (971) 44461900
Web Site: http://www.rohde-schwarz.com
Electronic Testing Equipment Distr
N.A.I.C.S.: 423690
Lutfu Gonultas *(Area Mgr-Sls)*

Rohde & Schwarz Nederland B.V. (1)
Perkinsbaan 1, PO Box 1315, 3430 BH, Nieuwegein, Netherlands (100%)
Tel.: (31) 306001700
Web Site: http://www.rohdeschwarz.com
Sales Range: $25-49.9 Million
Emp.: 35
Developer of Radio Communications, Test & Measurement & Information Technology Equipment
N.A.I.C.S.: 334513
Rob Den Hartog *(Mng Dir)*

Rohde & Schwarz Norge AS
Ostensjoveien 34, 0667, Oslo, Norway
Tel.: (47) 23 3866 00

Web Site: http://www.rohde-schwarz.no
Electronic Testing Equipment Distr
N.A.I.C.S.: 423690
Anja Buchholz (Mgr-Fin)

Rohde & Schwarz Osterreich Ges.m.b.H. (1)
Technologiestrasse 10 Building E, 1120, Vienna, Austria
Tel.: (43) 1 602 61 41 0
Web Site: http://www.rohde-schwarz.at
Emp.: 40
Electronic Testing Equipment Distr
N.A.I.C.S.: 423690

Rohde & Schwarz Osterreich SP z o.o. (1)
Al Jerozolimskie 92 Entrance A, 00-807, Warsaw, Poland
Tel.: (48) 22 337 6490
Web Site: http://www.rohde-schwarz.pl
Electronic Testing Equipment Distr
N.A.I.C.S.: 423690

Rohde & Schwarz Pakistan (Private) LTD (1)
21 West 4th Floor Sardar Plaza Fazal Ul Haq Road, Islamabad, Pakistan
Tel.: (92) 51 2879557
Web Site: http://www.rohde-schwarz.com.pk
Electronic Testing Equipment Distr
N.A.I.C.S.: 423690
Zia Ullah (CTO)

Rohde & Schwarz Portugal, Lda. (1)
Alameda Antonio Sergio n 7 - RC - Sala A, 2795-023, Linda-a-Velha, Portugal
Tel.: (351) 21 4155700
Web Site: http://www.rohde-schwarz.com
Emp.: 6
Electronic Testing Equipment Distr
N.A.I.C.S.: 423690
Jose-Manuel Novoa (Mng Dir)

Rohde & Schwarz Regional Headquarters Singapore Pte. Ltd. (1)
9 Changi Business Park Vista 03-01, Singapore, 486041, Singapore
Tel.: (65) 63070000
Telecommunication Servicesb
N.A.I.C.S.: 517810
Samuel Lur (Gen Mgr)

Rohde & Schwarz SIT GmbH (1)
Am Studio 3, 12489, Berlin, Germany (100%)
Tel.: (49) 3065884231
Web Site: http://www.sit.rohde-schwarz.com
Sales Range: $50-74.9 Million
Emp.: 120
Mfr of Communications Test & Measurement Equipment
N.A.I.C.S.: 334514

Rohde & Schwarz Saudi Arabia Ltd. (1)
King Fahd Road King Faisal Foundation South Tower 5th Flr, Riyadh, 11411, Saudi Arabia
Tel.: (966) 11 293 2035
Web Site: http://www.rohde-schwarz.com
Electronic Testing Equipment Distr
N.A.I.C.S.: 423690
Feras Khasawneh (Head-Programs)

Rohde & Schwarz Sverige AB (1)
Flygfaltsgatan 15, 128 30, Skarpnack, Sweden
Tel.: (46) 8 605 19 00
Web Site: http://www.rohde-schwarz.se
Electronic Testing Equipment Distr
N.A.I.C.S.: 423690
Jan Ploug (Mng Dir)

Rohde & Schwarz Taiwan Ltd. (1)
14F No 13 Sec 2 Pei-Tou Road, Taipei, 11268, Taiwan
Tel.: (886) 2 28931088
Web Site: http://www.rohde-schwarz.com.tw
Electronic Testing Equipment Distr
N.A.I.C.S.: 423690
Min-Hsuan Chen (Sr Engr-Sls)

Rohde & Schwarz Vertriebs GmbH (1)
Muehldorfstrasse 15, Munich, 81671, Germany (100%)
Tel.: (49) 8941290
Web Site: http://www.rohdeschwarz.com

Sales Range: $400-449.9 Million
Emp.: 2,000
Sales of Electronic Test & Measurement Instruments
N.A.I.C.S.: 334220

Rohde & Schwarz Vietnam Co., Ltd. (1)
Suite 706 7/F Indochina Plaza Hanoi IPH Offices 241 Xuan Thuy, Cau Giay, Hanoi, Vietnam
Tel.: (84) 4 38501440
Web Site: http://www.rohde-schwarz.com.vn
Emp.: 30
Electronic Testing Equipment Distr
N.A.I.C.S.: 423690
La Tien Dung (Mgr-Sls-Info & Comm Div)

Rohde & Schwarz de Mexico S de RL de CV (1)
Edificio Park Plaza Torre 1 Javier Barros Sierra No 540, Col Lomas de Santa Fe, 01210, Mexico, Mexico
Tel.: (52) 55 85039913
Web Site: http://www.rohde-schwarz.com.mx
Electronic Testing Equipment Distr
N.A.I.C.S.: 423690

Rohde & Schwarz do Brasil Ltda (1)
Avenida Sargento Lourival Alves de Sousa 161 Campo Grande, 04675-020, Sao Paulo, Brazil
Tel.: (55) 11 2246 0000
Web Site: http://www.rohde-schwarz.com.br
Electronic Testing Equipment Distr
N.A.I.C.S.: 423690
Roberto Monteiro (Acct Mgr)

Rohde & Schwarz, Inc. (1)
8661A Robert Fulton Dr, Columbia, MD 21046-2265
Tel.: (410) 910-7800
Web Site: http://www.rohde-schwarz.com
Emp.: 55
Electronic Test & Measurement, Communications & Direction Finding Equipment Sales & Services
N.A.I.C.S.: 423690

Rohde and Schwarz South Africa (Pty) Ltd. (1)
Building 1 Clearwater Office Park Cnr Christiaan de, Wet & Millenium Boulevard Strubens Valley Ext 12, Roodepoort, 1724, South Africa
Tel.: (27) 11 671 8800
Web Site: http://www.rohde-schwarz.com
Electronic Testing Equipment Distr
N.A.I.C.S.: 423690

Roschi Rohde & Schwarz AG (1)
Muhlestrasse 7, 3063, Ittigen, Switzerland
Tel.: (41) 31 9221522
Web Site: http://www.rohde-schwarz.com
Emp.: 25
Electronic Testing Equipment Distr
N.A.I.C.S.: 423690

Shenzhen Rohde & Schwarz Trading Co., Ltd. (1)
Building 9-5 West Jiangtai Road, Chaoyang, Beijing, China
Tel.: (86) 10 6431 2828
Web Site: http://www.rohde-schwarz.com.cn
Electronic Testing Equipment Distr
N.A.I.C.S.: 423690

ROHM CO., LTD.
21 Saiin Mizosaki-cho, Ukyo-ku, Kyoto, 615 8585, Japan
Tel.: (81) 753112121 JP
Web Site: https://www.rohm.com
Year Founded: 1958
6963—(TKS)
Rev.: $3,092,025,800
Assets: $9,791,221,140
Liabilities: $3,392,066,920
Net Worth: $6,399,154,220
Earnings: $356,708,650
Emp.: 23,319
Fiscal Year-end: 03/31/24
Electronic Components Mfr
N.A.I.C.S.: 334413
Isao Matsumoto (Pres, Pres & CEO)

Subsidiaries:

Kionix, Inc. (1)
36 Thornwood Dr, Ithaca, NY 14850
Tel.: (607) 257-1080
Web Site: http://www.kionix.com
Accelerometer & Gyroscope Mfr
N.A.I.C.S.: 334419
Scott A. Miller (CTO & VP-Engrg)

Narita Giken Co., Ltd. (1)
1 19 28 Minamimukonoso, Amagasaki, 661 0033, Hyogo, Japan
Tel.: (81) 664330410
Web Site: http://www.naritagiken.co.jp
Sales Range: $25-49.9 Million
Emp.: 20
Design & Development of Electronic Circuitry
N.A.I.C.S.: 334416

Oki Semiconductor Co., Ltd. (1)
2-4-8 Shinyokohama, Kouhoku-ku, Yokohama, 222-8575, Hachioji-shi, Japan (95%)
Tel.: (81) 454769212
Web Site: https://www.lapis-semi.com
Sales Range: $1-4.9 Billion
Emp.: 689
Development, Manufacturing & Sales of Semiconductors & Related Products
N.A.I.C.S.: 334413

Subsidiary (Non-US):

Oki (Thailand) Co., Ltd. (2)
1168/63 Lumpini Tower 22nd Floor Rama 4 Road, Thungmahamek Sathorn, Bangkok, 10120, Thailand
Tel.: (66) 26799235
Web Site: http://www.okisemi.com
Sales Range: $150-199.9 Million
Emp.: 993
Semiconductor Mfr
N.A.I.C.S.: 334413

Subsidiary (US):

Oki Semiconductor America, Inc. (2)
2000 Bishops Gate Blvd, Mount Laurel, NJ 08054-4620
Tel.: (856) 235-2600
Web Site: http://www.okidata.com
Sales Range: $200-249.9 Million
Emp.: 10
Printer/Fax Machine Sales & Services
N.A.I.C.S.: 561439

Subsidiary (Domestic):

Oki Semiconductor Miyazaki Co., Ltd. (2)
727 Kihara Kiyotake-cho, Miyazaki-gun, Miyazaki, 889-1695, Japan (100%)
Tel.: (81) 985855111
Web Site: https://www.lapis-semi.com
Sales Range: $150-199.9 Million
Emp.: 979
Semiconductor Integrated Circuits Mfr
N.A.I.C.S.: 334413
Tadashi Mori (Pres)

ROHM Semiconductor (China) Co., Ltd. (1)
No 7 Weisan Road Microelectronics Industrial Zone Jingang Road, Xiqing District, Tianjin, 301900, China
Tel.: (86) 2283989000
Web Site: https://www.rohmtj.com
Emp.: 1,400
Semiconductor Devices Mfr
N.A.I.C.S.: 334413
Zhang Ju (Chm)

ROHM Semiconductor (Shanghai) Co., Ltd. (1)
22F Central Towers 567 Langao Road, Shanghai, 200333, China
Tel.: (86) 2160728612
Web Site: http://www.rohm.com
Sales Range: $75-99.9 Million
Emp.: 200
Semiconductor Device Distr
N.A.I.C.S.: 423690

ROHM Semiconductor (Thailand) Co., Ltd. (1)
11th Floor GPF Witthayu Towers A 93/1 Wireless Road Lumpini, Pathumwan, Bangkok, 10330, Thailand

Tel.: (66) 2 254 4890
Web Site: http://www.rohm.com
Semiconductor Equipment Distr
N.A.I.C.S.: 334413

ROHM Semiconductor Hong Kong Co., Ltd. (1)
Room 1402-06 Tower 1 Silvercord 30 Canton Road, Tsimshatsui, Kowloon, China (Hong Kong)
Tel.: (852) 27406262
Sales Range: $25-49.9 Million
Emp.: 80
Semiconductor Devices Mfr
N.A.I.C.S.: 334413

ROHM Semiconductor India Pvt. Ltd. (1)
Unit 715 7Fl Spencer Pl Anna Salai, Chennai, 600002, Tamil Nadu, India
Tel.: (91) 44 4352 0008
Web Site: http://www.rohm.com
Sales Range: $25-49.9 Million
Emp.: 11
Semiconductor Device Distr
N.A.I.C.S.: 423690
Kenny Lau (Pres)

ROHM Semiconductor Korea Corporation (1)
159-13 Gasan Digital 1-ro, Gumcheon-gu, Seoul, 08506, Korea (South)
Tel.: (82) 28182700
Web Site: http://www.rohm.co.kr
Sales Range: $50-74.9 Million
Emp.: 20
Semiconductor Equipment Mfr
N.A.I.C.S.: 333242
Choang Hoon (Mng Dir)

ROHM Semiconductor Malaysia Sdn. Bhd. (1)
L12-01-02 Level 12 PJX-HM Shah Tower NO16A Persiaran Barat, 46050, Petaling Jaya, Selangor, Malaysia
Tel.: (60) 379318155
Emp.: 19
Semiconductor Device Distr
N.A.I.C.S.: 423690
Adan Zainuddin (Mng Dir)

ROHM Semiconductor Philippines Corporation (1)
Unit 4B Frabelle Alabang Building 1100 Madrigal Business Park, Zapote Road Ayala Alabang, Muntinlupa, 1780, Philippines
Tel.: (63) 28076872
Web Site: http://www.rohm.com
Sales Range: $25-49.9 Million
Emp.: 20
Semiconductor Equipment Distr
N.A.I.C.S.: 423690

ROHM Semiconductor Singapore Pte. Ltd. (1)
83 Clemenceau Avenue 05-01 UE Square, Singapore, 239920, Singapore
Tel.: (65) 64365100
Web Site: http://www.rohm.com
Sales Range: $25-49.9 Million
Emp.: 80
Semiconductor Devices Mfr
N.A.I.C.S.: 334413

ROHM Semiconductor Taiwan Co., Ltd. (1)
11F No 6 Sec 3 Min Chuan E Road, Taipei, 10477, Taiwan
Tel.: (886) 225006956
Web Site: http://www.rohm.com
Sales Range: $50-74.9 Million
Emp.: 100
Semiconductor Equipment Distr
N.A.I.C.S.: 423690

ROHM Semiconductor Trading (Dalian) Co., Ltd. (1)
1201 Swissotel 21 Wuhui Road, Zhong Shan District, Dalian, 116001, China
Tel.: (86) 411 8230 8549
Semiconductor Equipment Mfr & Distr
N.A.I.C.S.: 423690

ROHM Tsukuba Co., Ltd. (1)
10 Kitahara, Tsukuba, 300-3293, Ibaraki, Japan
Tel.: (81) 29 877 1010
Web Site: http://www.rohm.com
Emp.: 100

ROHM CO., LTD.

ROHM Co., Ltd.—(Continued)
Electronic Components Mfr
N.A.I.C.S.: 334419

ROHM USA, Inc. (1)
6815 Flanders Dr Ste 150, San Diego, CA 92121-3925 (100%)
Tel.: (858) 625-3630
Web Site: http://www.rohm.com
Sales Range: $50-74.9 Million
Emp.: 100
Holding Company; Regional Managing Office
N.A.I.C.S.: 551112
Satoshi Sawamura (Pres)

Subsidiary (Domestic):

ROHM Semiconductor U.S.A., LLC (2)
2323 Owen St, Santa Clara, CA 95054 (100%)
Tel.: (408) 720-1900
Web Site: http://www.rohm.com
Sales Range: $50-74.9 Million
Emp.: 22
Provider of Electronic Product Sales
N.A.I.C.S.: 423690
Debra Butala (Mgr-HR)

Unit (Domestic):

ROHM Semiconductor U.S.A., LLC - Alpharetta (3)
11680 Great Oaks Way Ste 140, Alpharetta, GA 30022-2414
Tel.: (770) 754-5972
Web Site: http://www.rohm.com
Sales Range: $50-74.9 Million
Emp.: 7
Semiconductor Products
N.A.I.C.S.: 423690
Scott Dougherty (Mgr-Sls)

ROHM Semiconductor U.S.A., LLC - Dallas (3)
5048 Tennyson Pkwy Ste 218, Plano, TX 75024
Tel.: (972) 473-3748
Web Site: http://www.rohm.com
Sales Range: $25-49.9 Million
Emp.: 11
Electronic Products Sales
N.A.I.C.S.: 423690

Rohm Amagi Co., Ltd. (1)
258-1 Oguma, Amagi, 838 0052, Japan (100%)
Tel.: (81) 946230021
Web Site: http://www.rohmamagi.com
Sales Range: $100-124.9 Million
Emp.: 80
Mfr of Hybrid ICs, LCDs, Thermal Heads, Image Sensor Heads & IC Cards
N.A.I.C.S.: 334413

Rohm Apollo Co. Ltd. (1)
Oji Hiyoshi 1164 2 Hirokawa-cho, Yamegun, Fukuoka, 834-0111, Japan (100%)
Tel.: (81) 943323000
Web Site: http://www.micro.rohm.com
Sales Range: $200-249.9 Million
Emp.: 603
Mfr of Transistors, Diodes & Capacitors, Monolithic ICS
N.A.I.C.S.: 334413

Rohm Apollo Device Co., LTD. (1)
883 Kamikitajima, Chikugo, 833 0033, Japan (75%)
Tel.: (81) 942541832
Sales Range: $50-74.9 Million
Emp.: 114
Wafer Process
N.A.I.C.S.: 334413

Rohm Electronics (Dalian) Co., LTD. (1)
No 20 Four street East North Dalian Economic, Technical Development Zone Zhong Shan District, Dalian, 116600, China (100%)
Tel.: (86) 41182308549
Sales Range: $25-49.9 Million
Emp.: 100
Mfr of LCDs, Capacitors, Thermal Heads, Power Modules & Image Sensorheads
N.A.I.C.S.: 334416

Rohm Electronics (H.K.) Co., Ltd. (1)
Room 1402 8 Tower 1 Silvercord 30 Canton Road Tsimshatsui, Kowloon, China (Hong Kong) (100%)
Tel.: (852) 27406262
Web Site: http://www.rohmelectronics.com.hk
Sales Range: $50-74.9 Million
Emp.: 100
Provider of Electronic Product Sales
N.A.I.C.S.: 449210
Ichikawa Yoshihiro (Pres)

Rohm Electronics (Malaysia) SDN. BHD. (1)
2 2 Lvl 2 Menara Axis 2 Jalan 51A 223 Sec 14 Jalan Semangat, 46100, Petaling Jaya, Selangor, Malaysia (49%)
Tel.: (60) 379588355
Web Site: http://www.rohm.com
Sales Range: $25-49.9 Million
Emp.: 18
Provider of Electronic Product Sales
N.A.I.C.S.: 334417

Rohm Electronics (Philippines) Sales Corporation (1)
Unit 4 B Citibank Frabelle Building Madnrigal Business Park, Alabng-zapote Road, Muntinlupa, 1770, Philippines (99%)
Tel.: (63) 28076872
Sales Range: $25-49.9 Million
Emp.: 20
Provider of Electronic Product Sales
N.A.I.C.S.: 449210
Ken Sato (Pres & CEO)

Rohm Electronics (Philippines), Inc. (1)
Block 3 and Block 5 People's Avenue, People's Technology Complex Special Economic Zone Carmona, Cavite, 4116, Philippines (100%)
Tel.: (63) 28941536
Sales Range: $400-449.9 Million
Emp.: 2,000
Monolithic IC's, Resistors & Capacitors Mfr
N.A.I.C.S.: 334416

Rohm Electronics (Taiwan) Co., Ltd. (1)
11F No 6 Sec 3, Min Chuan E Rd, Taipei, Taiwan (100%)
Tel.: (886) 225006956
Web Site: http://www.rohmelectronics.com
Sales Range: $100-124.9 Million
Emp.: 300
Electronic Product Sales & Distr
N.A.I.C.S.: 449210

Rohm Electronics Asia Pte. Ltd. (1)
9 Temasek Blvd 20-02 Suntec Tower 2nd, Singapore, 038989, Singapore (100%)
Tel.: (65) 63322322
Web Site: http://www.rohm.com
Sales Range: $75-99.9 Million
Emp.: 170
Holding Company for Asian Operations
N.A.I.C.S.: 551112

Rohm Electronics Components (Tianjin) Co., Ltd. (1)
3501 Golden Emperor Building 20 Nanjing Road, Hexi District, Tianjin, 300040, China (100%)
Tel.: (86) 2223029181
Web Site: http://www.rohm.com.cn
Sales Range: $50-74.9 Million
Emp.: 133
Transistor, Diode, LED, Resisitor, Capacitor & LED Display Mfr
N.A.I.C.S.: 334416

Rohm Fukuoka Co., Ltd. (1)
3F Sanix Hakata Building 2-1-23 Hakataekihigashi Hakata-ku, Fukuoka, 812-0013, Japan (100%)
Tel.: (81) 92 483 3496
Web Site: http://www.rohm.com
Sales Range: $100-124.9 Million
Emp.: 300
Mfr, Sales & Distr of Monolithic ICs, Resistors & Capacitors
N.A.I.C.S.: 334416
Yushiyasu Okuda (Pres)

Rohm Hamamatsu Co., Ltd. (1)
10 Sanwa-cho, Minami-ku, Hamamatsu, 435-0038, Japan (100%)
Tel.: (81) 534681000

Web Site: https://micro.rohm.com
Emp.: 205
Water Processing
Hidekazu Eguchi (Pres)

Rohm Integrated Semiconductor (Thailand) Co., LTD. (1)
101 94 Navanakorn Industrial Est, Moo 20 Tambol Khlong Nung Amph, Pathumthani, 12120, Thailand (100%)
Tel.: (66) 29092060
Sales Range: $400-449.9 Million
Emp.: 2,000
Mfr of Monolithic IC's & Other Electronic Products
N.A.I.C.S.: 449210

Rohm Integrated Systems (Thailand) Co., Ltd. (1)
101/94 102 Navanakorn Industrial Zone Moo 20 Phaholyothin Road, Tambol Khlong-Nueng Amphur Khlong-Luong, Pathumthani, 12120, Thailand (100%)
Tel.: (66) 29097100
Web Site: https://www.rohmthai.co.th
Sales Range: $400-449.9 Million
Emp.: 1,050
Transistors, Capacitors, Resistors & Diodes Mfr
N.A.I.C.S.: 334419
Katsunori Matsui (Mgr-Div)

Rohm Korea Corporation (1)
(86.4%)
Tel.: (82) 28182600
Web Site: http://www.rohmkorea.com
Sales Range: $200-249.9 Million
Emp.: 1,000
Monolithic ICs, Transistors, Diodes, LEDs, LED Displays & Resistors Mfr
N.A.I.C.S.: 334419

Rohm Logistec Co., Ltd. (1)
75 Masusaka Kamogata-cho, Asakuchi, Okayama, 719-0234, Japan (100%)
Tel.: (81) 865443181
Web Site: http://www.rohm.com
Sales Range: $75-99.9 Million
Emp.: 170
Distribution of Rohm's Products
N.A.I.C.S.: 423690

Rohm Mechatech (Philippines), Inc. (1)
Block 5 Lots 4 5 Complex Avenue, People's Technology Complex-Special Economic Zone, Cavite, 4116, Philippines (100%)
Tel.: (63) 464302281
Sales Range: $100-124.9 Million
Emp.: 345
Mfr of Lead Frames & Molding Dies
N.A.I.C.S.: 333514

Rohm Mechatech Co., Ltd. (1)
3-6-1 Tsuchida Oimachi, Kameoka, 621-0011, Kyoto, Japan (100%)
Tel.: (81) 771254717
Web Site: https://www.rohm-mechatech.co.jp
Sales Range: $50-74.9 Million
Emp.: 83
Lead Frame Molding Dies Mfr
N.A.I.C.S.: 333514

Rohm Semiconductor (Thailand) Co., Ltd. (1)
11th Floor GPF Witthayu Towers A 93/1 Wireless Road, Lumpini Pathumwan, Bangkok, 10330, Thailand
Tel.: (66) 22544890
Web Site: http://www.rohm.com
Electronic Products Sales
N.A.I.C.S.: 449210

Rohm Semiconductor GmbH (1)
Karl-Arnold-Strasse 15, 47877, Willich, Germany (100%)
Tel.: (49) 21549210
Web Site: http://www.rohm.com
Sales Range: $75-99.9 Million
Emp.: 150
Electronic Products Sales
N.A.I.C.S.: 423690
Toshimitsu Suzuki (Pres)

Rohm Semiconductor GmbH (1)
Sunningdale House 41 Caldecotte Lake Drive, Caldecotte Lake Business Park, Milton Keynes, MK7 8LF, Buckinghamshire, United Kingdom (100%)
Tel.: (44) 1908272400
Web Site: http://www.rohm.com
Sales Range: $50-74.9 Million
Emp.: 7
Electronic Products Sales
N.A.I.C.S.: 423690
Greg Pidgeon (Mgr-Mktg-Europe)

Rohm Wako Co., Ltd. (1)
100 Tomioka, Kasaoka, 714-8585, Okayama, Japan (100%)
Tel.: (81) 865670111
Web Site: https://micro.rohm.com
Sales Range: $100-124.9 Million
Emp.: 325
Diodes, LEDs, Sensors & Laser Diodes Mfr
N.A.I.C.S.: 334413
Hirofumi Yoshioka (Pres)

Rohm Wako Device Co., LTD. (1)
55 Tomioka, Kasaoka, 714 0092, Okayama, Japan (75%)
Tel.: (81) 865670309
Sales Range: $100-124.9 Million
Emp.: 500
Wafer Process
N.A.I.C.S.: 334413

Rohm-Wako Electronics (Malaysia) Sdn. Bhd. (1)
Lot 1320 Kawasan Perindustrian Pengkalan Chepa II, 16100, Kota Baharu, Malaysia (100%)
Tel.: (60) 97741500
Web Site: http://www.rohm.com
Sales Range: $1-4.9 Billion
Emp.: 1,000
Mfr of Diodes, LEDs & Resistors
N.A.I.C.S.: 334416
Yukihiro Takizawa (Mng Dir)

SiCrystal AG (1)
Thurn-und-Taxis-Strasse 20, 90411, Nuremberg, Germany
Tel.: (49) 91181775990
Web Site: https://www.sicrystal.de
Sales Range: $50-74.9 Million
Emp.: 8
Crystalline Silicon Carbide Wafer Distr
N.A.I.C.S.: 424690
Johannes Wolters (Mgr-Sls-Europe)

ROHRDORFER GRUPPE

Sinning 1, 83101, Rohrdorf, Germany
Tel.: (49) 80321820
Web Site: http://www.rohrdorfer.eu
Holding Company; Cement, Ready-Mix Concrete & Precast Concrete Products Mfr
N.A.I.C.S.: 551112
Mike Edelmann (CEO)

Subsidiaries:

SPZ Zementwerk Eiberg GmbH & Co. KG (1)
Eiberger Bundesstrasse, 6330, Kufstein, Austria
Tel.: (43) 8032182120
Web Site: http://www.rohrdorfer.eu
Sales Range: $25-49.9 Million
Emp.: 49
Cement Mfr
N.A.I.C.S.: 327310
Josef Bloessl (Mgr-Ops)

Sudbayerisches Portland-Zementwerk Gebr. Wiesbock & Co. GmbH (1)
Sinning 1, 83101, Rohrdorf, Germany
Tel.: (49) 80321820
Web Site: http://www.rohrdorfer.eu
Sales Range: $25-49.9 Million
Emp.: 100
Cement Mfr
N.A.I.C.S.: 327310

ROHRS AG

Celler Strasse 101-103, 29614, Soltau, Germany
Tel.: (49) 519198410
Web Site: http://www.roehrs-ag.de
Year Founded: 1971
Rev: $39,534,845
Emp.: 250

Plant Constructions, Piping Installations & Industrial Services
N.A.I.C.S.: 541330
Hans-Gert Kalender (Chm)

Subsidiaries:

Roehrs Poland Sp. zo.o. (1)
Ul Staszica 5a, 67-100, Nowa Sol, Poland
Tel.: (48) 68 3871963
Web Site: http://www.roehrs-ag.de
Piping Installations
N.A.I.C.S.: 326122

Rohrs Kraftwerkstechnik GmbH (1)
Vor dem Weiherbusch 8, 29614, Soltau, Germany (100%)
Tel.: (49) 5191 9841 751
Web Site: http://www.roehrs-ag.de
Piping Installations & Power Technology
N.A.I.C.S.: 326122
Michael Rathje (Co-CEO)

Rohrs Kranverleih GmbH (1)
Celler Strasse 101-103, 29614, Soltau, Germany (100%)
Tel.: (49) 5191 9841 728
Web Site: http://www.roehrs-ag.de
Heavy Equipment Crane Rentals
N.A.I.C.S.: 333923
Hans-Hermann Nohr (Co-CEO)

ROHTO PHARMACEUTICAL CO. LTD.
1-8-1 Tatsumi-nishi, Ikuno-ku, Osaka, 544-8666, Japan
Tel.: (81) 667581231
Web Site: https://www.rohto.co.jp
Year Founded: 1899
4527—(TKS)
Rev.: $1,790,252,400
Assets: $2,288,216,750
Liabilities: $655,308,790
Net Worth: $1,632,907,960
Earnings: $204,486,960
Emp.: 7,259
Fiscal Year-end: 03/31/24
Pharmaceuticals Mfr
N.A.I.C.S.: 325412
Kunio Yamada (Chm & CEO)

Subsidiaries:

Ceres Okinawa Co., Ltd. (1)
554-1 Hirae Ishigaki, Okinawa, 907-0003, Japan
Tel.: (81) 980822771
Pharmaceuticals Product Mfr
N.A.I.C.S.: 325412

DAX Cosmetics Sp. z o.o. (1)
Duchnow ul Spacerowa 18, Wiazowna, 05-462, Otwock, Poland
Tel.: (48) 227790500
Web Site: https://www.dax.com.pl
Emp.: 250
Pharmaceuticals Product Mfr
N.A.I.C.S.: 325412

Episteme Trading (Shanghai) Co., LTD (1)
3201 No 1266 Nan Jing Xi Lu, Jing An District, Shanghai, 200040, China
Tel.: (86) 2162886777
Pharmaceuticals Product Mfr
N.A.I.C.S.: 325412

Hokushinfoods Co., Ltd. (1)
3-1-1 Midoricho Nishi, Ebetsu, 067-0002, Hokkaido, Japan
Tel.: (81) 120004227
Web Site: https://www.hokushinfoods.co.jp
Prepared Food Mfr
N.A.I.C.S.: 311991

Interstem Co., Ltd. (1)
3-1-7 Myojincho NTB Hachioji Building 4th floor, Hachioji, 192-0046, Japan
Tel.: (81) 426316240
Web Site: https://www.interstem.co.jp
Emp.: 33
Medical Research & Development Services
N.A.I.C.S.: 541715

MG Pharma Inc. (1)
7-7-25 Saito-Asagi, Ibaraki, 567-0085, Osaka, Japan
Tel.: (81) 72 643 0171
Web Site: https://www.mgpharma.co.jp
Emp.: 15
Pharmaceuticals Product Mfr
N.A.I.C.S.: 325412
Lekh Raj Juneja (Pres)

Mayado Pharmaceutical Co., Ltd. (1)
67-1 Tamatsu-cho, Nishi-ku, Kobe, Japan
Tel.: (81) 789290113
Web Site: https://www.mayado.jp
Emp.: 75
Pharmaceuticals Product Mfr
N.A.I.C.S.: 325412

Mentholatum (AP) Ltd. (1)
337 Eonju-ro Dongyeong Cultural Center 7th floor, Gangnam-gu Yeoksam-dong, Seoul, 135-080, Korea (South)
Tel.: (82) 27171821
Web Site: https://www.mentholatum.co.kr
Pharmaceutical Products Distr
N.A.I.C.S.: 424210

Mentholatum (China) Pharmaceuticals Company Limited (1)
The Second Industrial Estates San Xiang, Zhongshan, Guangdong, China
Tel.: (86) 2038773800
Cosmetics Products Mfr
N.A.I.C.S.: 325620

Mentholatum Taiwan Limited (1)
6F No 57 Lane 10 Jihu Rd, Neihu Dist, Taipei, 114, Taiwan
Tel.: (886) 287518818
Web Site: https://www.mentholatum.com.tw
Pharmaceuticals Product Mfr
N.A.I.C.S.: 325412

Mentholatum de Mexico, Sociedad Annima DE Capital variable (1)
Arquimedes 199-302 Col Chapultepec Morales Miguel Hidalgo, 11560, Mexico, Mexico
Tel.: (52) 5552548311
Web Site: http://www.mentholatum.com.mx
Pharmaceuticals Product Mfr
N.A.I.C.S.: 325412

Mentolatum (Asia-Pacific) Limited (1)
Room 2101 Tower 1 No 138 Rural Affairs Road, New City Central Plaza New Territories, Sha Tin, China (Hong Kong)
Tel.: (852) 26990078
Web Site: https://mentholatum.com.hk
Cosmetics Products Mfr
N.A.I.C.S.: 325620

Nitten Pharmaceutical Co., Ltd. (1)
76 Nishisakura-cho, Minami-ku, Nagoya, 457-0039, Japan
Tel.: (81) 528225512
Web Site: http://www.nitten-eye.co.jp
Pharmaceuticals Product Mfr
N.A.I.C.S.: 325412

Ophthalmos S/A (1)
Avenida Manoel Monteiro de Araujo 1051 Parque Sao Domingos, Sao Paulo, 05113-020, SP, Brazil
Tel.: (55) 8002098080
Web Site: https://www.ophthalmos.com.br
Pharmaceuticals Product Mfr
N.A.I.C.S.: 325412

Qualitech Pharma Co., Ltd. (1)
1-2-20 Kaigan Shiodome Big Dinge 20 floor, Minato-ku, Tokyo, 105-0022, Japan
Tel.: (81) 354012201
Web Site: https://www.qualitech-pharma.co.jp
Pharmaceuticals Product Mfr
N.A.I.C.S.: 325412

ROHTO Medical China Co., Ltd. (1)
2F Carlowitz and Co 168 Jiujiang Road, Huangpu District, Shanghai, China
Tel.: (86) 2163337897
Pharmaceuticals Product Mfr
N.A.I.C.S.: 325412

Rohto Advanced Reserch HK Ltd. (1)
Units 312 to 313 of the 3rd Floor of Building 15W Phase Three, Hong Kong Science Park Pak Shek Kok, Hong Kong, China (Hong Kong)
Tel.: (852) 38453600
Pharmaceuticals Product Mfr
N.A.I.C.S.: 325412

Rohto Mentholatum (Bangladesh) Limited (1)
N B Tower Level-14 40/7 North Avenue Gulshan C/A, Dhaka, 1212, Bangladesh
Tel.: (880) 1755543344
Web Site: http://www.rohto.com.bd
Pharmaceuticals Product Mfr
N.A.I.C.S.: 325412

Rohto Mentholatum Ru LLC (1)
12 6 1 12th Floor No 37 Leningradsky Avenue, 125167, Moscow, Russia
Tel.: (7) 4957348008
Pharmaceuticals Product Mfr
N.A.I.C.S.: 325412

Rohto Nitten Co., Ltd. (1)
40-2 Sakurahoncho, Minami-ku, Nagoya, 457-0038, Japan
Tel.: (81) 528225512
Web Site: https://www.rohto-nitten.co.jp
Emp.: 322
Medical Equipment Mfr & Distr
N.A.I.C.S.: 334510

Rohto Pharma (India) Pvt. Ltd. (1)
Unit Nos DPC 102 103 First Floor Block No 4A Corporate Park M G Road, DLF City Phase-III, Gurgaon, 122002, Haryana, India
Tel.: (91) 1242355315
Web Site: http://www.in.rohto.com
Pharmaceuticals Product Mfr
N.A.I.C.S.: 325412

Rohto-Mentholatum (Cambodia) Co., Ltd. (1)
Phnom Penh Tower 12nd Floor No 445-232/93 Monivong Blvd, Phnom Penh, Cambodia
Tel.: (855) 23964610
Pharmaceuticals Product Mfr
N.A.I.C.S.: 325412

Rohto-Mentholatum (Kenya) Limited (1)
Mmid Studio Westlands Road, PO Box 66835, 00800, Nairobi, Kenya
Tel.: (254) 716280375
Web Site: https://www.rohto.co.ke
Pharmaceuticals Product Mfr
N.A.I.C.S.: 325412

Rohto-Mentholatum (Malaysia) Sdn. Bhd. (1)
Unit 9-1 Level 9 Wisma Averis Avenue 5 Bangsar South City, No 8 Jalan Kerinchi, 59200, Kuala Lumpur, Malaysia
Tel.: (60) 322414889
Web Site: https://www.mentholatum.com.my
Pharmaceuticals Product Mfr
N.A.I.C.S.: 325412

Rohto-Mentholatum (Myanmar) Co., Ltd. (1)
Room 1110 11th Floor Shwegondine, Bahan Township, Yangon, Myanmar
Tel.: (95) 9546304
Pharmaceuticals Product Mfr
N.A.I.C.S.: 325412

Rohto-Mentholatum (Nepal) Co., Ltd. (1)
Durbar Marg, Kathmandu, Nepal
Tel.: (977) 14260031
Pharmaceuticals Product Mfr
N.A.I.C.S.: 325412

Rohto-Mentholatum (Thailand) Limited (1)
317 Kamolsukosol Bldg 9th Floor Unit D-E Silom Road, Silom Bangrak, Bangkok, 10500, Thailand
Tel.: (66) 263102915
Web Site: http://www.rohto.com.th
Cosmetics Products Mfr
N.A.I.C.S.: 325620

Rohto-Mentholatum (Vietnam) Co., Ltd. (1)
18th Floor Room 1808 Saigon Trade Center 37 Ton Duc Thang, Ben Nghe Ward District 1, Ho Chi Minh City, Vietnam
Tel.: (84) 2838229322
Web Site: https://rohto.com.vn
Health Care Products Mfr
N.A.I.C.S.: 325412

Rohto-Mentholatum Do Brasil Comercio De Produtos Para Saude Ltda. (1)
Alameda Santos 1800 sala 406, Sao Paulo, 01418-102, SP, Brazil
Tel.: (55) 1131703297
Pharmaceuticals Product Mfr
N.A.I.C.S.: 325412

The Mentholatum Company (1)
707 Sterling Dr, Orchard Park, NY 14127-1557 (100%)
Tel.: (716) 677-2500
Web Site: http://us.mentholatum.com
Sales Range: $150-199.9 Million
Proprietary Drugs Mfr
N.A.I.C.S.: 325412

Holding (Non-US):

Mentholatum (Asia Pacific) Ltd. (2)
2111-21 Tower 2 Grand Central Plaza 138 Shatin Rural Committee Road, Sha Tin, NT, China (Hong Kong) (100%)
Tel.: (852) 2 699 0078
Web Site: http://www.mentholatum.hk
Sales Range: $25-49.9 Million
Emp.: 50
Mfr & Sales of Pharmaceutical Preparations
N.A.I.C.S.: 325412
Anita Ng (Reg VP-North Asia)

Mentholatum Australasia Pty. Ltd. (2)
12-16 Janine Street, Scoresby, 3179, VIC, Australia (100%)
Tel.: (61) 397630232
Web Site: https://www.mentholatum.com.au
Sales Range: $25-49.9 Million
Mfr & Sales of Pharmaceutical Preparations
N.A.I.C.S.: 325412

Mentholatum South Africa (Pty) Ltd. (2)
1st Floor Silverberg Terrace Steenberg Office Park Silverwood Close, Tokai, Cape Town, 7945, South Africa
Tel.: (27) 21 702 0620
Web Site: https://www.mentholatum.co.za
Sales Range: $25-49.9 Million
Pharmaceuticals Mfr
N.A.I.C.S.: 325412
Andrew Lawlor (Mng Dir)

The Mentholatum (Zhongshan) Pharmaceuticals Co., Ltd. (2)
The Second Industrial Estates Sam Heung, Zhongshan, Guangdong, China (65%)
Tel.: (86) 7606685596
Web Site: http://www.mentholatum.com.cn
Sales Range: $50-74.9 Million
Emp.: 126
Mfr & Sales of Pharmaceuticals
N.A.I.C.S.: 325412

The Mentholatum Company Limited (2)
1 Redwood Avenue Peel Park Campus, East Kilbride, Glasgow, G74 5PE, United Kingdom (100%)
Tel.: (44) 1355848484
Web Site: https://www.mentholatum.co.uk
Sales Range: $25-49.9 Million
Mfr & Sales of Pharmaceutical Preparations
N.A.I.C.S.: 325412

The Mentholatum Company of Canada, Limited (1)
45 Hannover Drive Unit 2, Saint Catharines, L2W 1A3, ON, Canada
Tel.: (905) 688-1665
Web Site: https://www.mentholatum.ca
Pharmaceuticals Product Mfr
N.A.I.C.S.: 325412

Tianjin ROHTO Herbal Medicine Co., Ltd. (1)
No 15 Northern First Road of XEDA, Xiqing Economic Development Area, Tianjin, China
Tel.: (86) 2258062681
Pharmaceuticals Product Mfr
N.A.I.C.S.: 325412

Yaeyama Farm Co., Ltd. (1)
554-1 Halser Building 2F, Hiratoku, Ishigaki, 907-0003, Okinawa, Japan
Tel.: (81) 980838788
Web Site: https://www.yaeyamafarm.net
Emp.: 11

ROHTO PHARMACEUTICAL CO. LTD.

Rohto Pharmaceutical Co. Ltd.—(Continued)
Prepared Food Mfr
N.A.I.C.S.: 311991

ROI LAND INVESTMENTS LTD.
1002 Sherbrooke West Suite 1430,
Montreal, H3A 3L6, QC, Canada
Tel.: (438) 920-2853   NV
Web Site:
    http://roilandinvestments.com
Year Founded: 2007
Real Estate Investment Services
N.A.I.C.S.: 531390
Martin Scholz *(CEO)*

ROISERV LIFESTYLE SERVICES COMPANY LIMITED
Rongsheng Development Building 81
Xiangyun Road, Economic Development Zone, Langfang, 065000, Hebei, China
Tel.: (86) 3165766562   CN
Web Site: https://www.roiserv.com
Year Founded: 2000
2146—(HKG)
Emp.: 8,000
Property Management Services
N.A.I.C.S.: 531311
Geng Jianfu *(Chm)*

ROIVANT SCIENCES LTD.
7th Fl 50 Broadway, London, SW1H
0DB, United Kingdom
Tel.: (44) 2074003347   BM
Web Site: http://www.roivant.com
Year Founded: 2014
ROIV—(NASDAQ)
Rev.: $124,795
Assets: $7,222,482
Liabilities: $773,953
Net Worth: $6,448,529
Earnings: $4,348,926
Emp.: 908
Fiscal Year-end: 03/31/24
Biotechnology & Biopharma
N.A.I.C.S.: 541714
Matthew Gline *(CEO)*

Subsidiaries:

Dermavant Sciences GmbH   (1)
Viaduktstrasse 8, 4051, Basel, Switzerland
Tel.: (41) 9197673277
Skin Healthcare Services
N.A.I.C.S.: 812112

Immunovant, Inc.   (1)
320 W 37th St 6th Fl, New York, NY
10018   **(54.6%)**
Tel.: (917) 580-3099
Web Site: https://www.immunovant.com
Assets: $515,564,000
Liabilities: $45,739,000
Net Worth: $469,825,000
Earnings: ($156,730,000)
Emp.: 124
Fiscal Year-end: 03/31/2022
Holding Company
N.A.I.C.S.: 551112
Peter Salzmann *(CEO)*

ROJANA INDUSTRIAL PARK PUBLIC COMPANY LIMITED
2034/115 Italthai Tower 26th Floor
New Phetchburi Road Bang Kapi,
Huai Khwang, Bangkok, 10310, Thailand
Tel.: (66) 27161750
Web Site: https://www.rojana.com
Year Founded: 1998
ROJNA—(THA)
Rev.: $533,081,655
Assets: $1,392,335,748
Liabilities: $810,424,602
Net Worth: $581,911,146
Earnings: $33,670,949
Fiscal Year-end: 12/31/23
Real Estate Development, Including
Industrial Zones & Industrial Parks

N.A.I.C.S.: 531390
Kitipong Urapeepatanapong *(Chm)*

Subsidiaries:

Operational Energy Group
Limited   (1)
3/7 Moo 2 Ban Khai-Ban Bung Road, Tambol Nongbua, Rayong, Thailand
Tel.: (66) 38961870
Electric Power Distribution
N.A.I.C.S.: 221122

Rojana Industrial Management Co., Ltd.   (1)
1 Moo 5 Rojana Road Tambol Kanharm,
Rojana Industrial Park Amphur U-Thai,
Ayutthaya, 13210, Thailand   **(90%)**
Tel.: (66) 353300008
Web Site: http://www.rojana.com
Sales Range: $50-74.9 Million
Emp.: 50
Water Supply & Irrigation Systems
N.A.I.C.S.: 221310

Rojana Industrial Park (Changzhou)
Co., Ltd.   (1)
Room 2208 Investment Plaza No 59, Yanling West Road, Changzhou, 213003, Jiangsu, China
Tel.: (86) 519 86766666
Web Site: http://www.rojana.com
Real Estate Development
N.A.I.C.S.: 531390

Rojana Power Co., Ltd   (1)
32 32 Sino-Thai Tower 11th Floor
Sukhumvit 21 Rd Soi Asoke, Bangkok,
10110, Wattana, Thailand
Tel.: (66) 22592403
Web Site: http://www.rojana.com
Sales Range: $50-74.9 Million
Emp.: 30
Electric Power Distribution
N.A.I.C.S.: 221122

Rojana Property Co., Ltd.   (1)
32 32 Sino-Thai Tower 11th Fl Sukhumvit
21 Rd, Soi Asoke Klongtoey-Nu, Bangkok,
10110, Wattana, Thailand   **(100%)**
Tel.: (66) 22601248
Web Site: http://www.rojana.com
Residental Development
N.A.I.C.S.: 531311

ROJUKISS INTERNATIONAL PUBLIC COMPANY LIMITED
100/8 100/51-54 Wongwanich Complex B 12th Floor 19 Rama 9 Road,
Huai Khwang District, Bangkok,
10310, Thailand
Tel.: (66) 26451155   TH
Web Site:
    https://www.rojukissnational.com
Year Founded: 2007
KISS—(THA)
Rev.: $28,163,492
Assets: $40,944,740
Liabilities: $9,048,465
Net Worth: $31,896,275
Earnings: $4,464,640
Emp.: 145
Fiscal Year-end: 12/31/23
Personal Care Product Mfr
N.A.I.C.S.: 326299
Worrawan Chaikamnerd *(CEO)*

ROK RESOURCES INC.
Tel.: (306) 522-0011
Web Site:
    https://www.rokresources.ca
8P2N—(DEU)
Rev.: $65,579,691
Assets: $124,645,710
Liabilities: $48,052,527
Net Worth: $76,593,183
Earnings: ($8,296,454)
Fiscal Year-end: 12/31/23
Oil Exploration & Production Services
N.A.I.C.S.: 211120
Lynn Chapman *(CFO)*

Subsidiaries:

PetroSouth Energy Corporation Sucursal Colombia   (1)

CII 113 7 21 T A Of 1018, Bogota, Colombia
Tel.: (57) 1 6292030
Oil & Gas Field Exploration Services
N.A.I.C.S.: 211120

ROK STARS PLC
ROK House Kingswood Business
Park Holyhead Road, Albrighton,
Wolverhampton, WV7 3AU, United
Kingdom
Tel.: (44) 1902374896
Web Site: http://www.rokstars.com
Alcoholic Beverage Product Mfr
N.A.I.C.S.: 312111
Jonathan M. Kendrick *(Co-Founder & Chm)*

Subsidiaries:

ABK Betriebgesellschaft der Akitienbrauerei Kaufbeuren GmbH   (1)
Hohe Buchleuthe 3, 87600, Kaufbeuren, Germany
Tel.: (49) 834143040
Web Site: http://www.aktienbrauerei.de
Soft Drink Mfr & Retailer
N.A.I.C.S.: 312111

ROKANA INDUSTRIES PLC.
Plot 4 Ajayi Street Off 52 Allen Avenue, Ikeja, Lagos, Nigeria
Tel.: (234) 803 318 7785
Web Site: http://www.rokana.com
Year Founded: 1978
Toilet Product & Cosmetic Mfr.
N.A.I.C.S.: 325620

ROKEL COMMERCIAL BANK (SIERRA LEONE) LIMITED
25/27 Siaka Stevens Street, PO Box
12, Freetown, Sierra Leone
Tel.: (232) 22222501   SL
Web Site: http://www.rokelbank.sl
Year Founded: 1917
Sales Range: $1-9.9 Million
Emp.: 265
Banking Services
N.A.I.C.S.: 522110
Victor Keith Cole *(CEO & Mng Dir)*

ROKISKIO SURIS AB
Pramones Str 3, Rokiskis, 42150,
Panevezys, Lithuania
Tel.: (370) 45855200
Web Site: https://www.rokiskio.com
Year Founded: 1964
RSU1L—(VSE)
Rev.: $335,858,263
Assets: $265,222,431
Liabilities: $87,232,586
Net Worth: $177,989,844
Earnings: $16,638,702
Emp.: 1,133
Fiscal Year-end: 12/31/23
Cheese Products Mfr
N.A.I.C.S.: 311513
Antanas Trumpa *(Chm)*

Subsidiaries:

Rokiskio pienas UAB   (1)
Pramones st 8, 28216, Utena, Lithuania
Tel.: (370) 38964402
Milk & Yogurt Mfr
N.A.I.C.S.: 311511

Rokiskio pieno gamyba UAB   (1)
Kauno st 65, 20119, Ukmerge, Lithuania
Tel.: (370) 34060360
Milk & Yogurt Mfr
N.A.I.C.S.: 311511

ROKKEDAHL HOLDING A/S
Nymollevej 126 B, 9240, Nibe, Denmark
Tel.: (45) 22210155   DK
Web Site: https://rokkedahl.dk
Holding Company
N.A.I.C.S.: 551112

INTERNATIONAL PUBLIC

Subsidiaries:

Rokkedahl Food Holding A/S   (1)
Nymollevej 126 B, 9240, Nibe, Denmark
Tel.: (45) 22210155
Food Production Mfr
N.A.I.C.S.: 311999

Subsidiary (Domestic):

Rokkedahl Food ApS   (2)
Nymollevej 126B, 9240, Nibe,
Denmark   **(100%)**
Tel.: (45) 22210155
Web Site: https://www.rokkedahl.dk
Food Production Mfr
N.A.I.C.S.: 311999

ROKKO BUTTER CO., LTD.
1-3-13 Sakaguchi-dori, Chuo-ku,
Kobe, 651-0062, Hyogo, Japan
Tel.: (81) 782314681
Web Site: https://www.qbb.co.jp
Year Founded: 1948
2266—(TKS)
Sales Range: $350-399.9 Million
Confectionery Product Mfr & Distr
N.A.I.C.S.: 311351
Tetsuo Tsukamoto *(Chm)*

ROKKO HOLDINGS LTD.
61 Kaki Bukit Road 2, Singapore,
417869, Singapore
Tel.: (65) 67495885
Web Site: http://www.rokko.com.sg
Year Founded: 1992
Sales Range: $25-49.9 Million
Emp.: 330
Semiconductor Equipment Mfr
N.A.I.C.S.: 333242
Vincent Bock Hui Lim *(Sec)*

Subsidiaries:

Rokko Leadframes Pte Ltd   (1)
27 Tuas Avenue 2, Singapore, 639458,
Singapore
Tel.: (65) 68612955
Web Site: http://www.rokkogroup.com
Precision Engineering Services
N.A.I.C.S.: 332216

Rokko Materials Pte. Ltd.   (1)
61 Kaki Bukit Road 2, Singapore, 417869,
Singapore
Tel.: (65) 6749 5885
Web Site: http://www.rokkogroup.com
Stamping & Leadframes Mfr
N.A.I.C.S.: 332119

Rokko Stamping Pte. Ltd.   (1)
73 Loyang Way, Singapore, 508763, Singapore
Tel.: (65) 6542 6233
Web Site: http://www.rokkostamping.com
Emp.: 40
Connector Stampings Mfr
N.A.I.C.S.: 332119

Rokko Technology Pte. Ltd.   (1)
61 Kaki Bukit Rd 2, Singapore, Singapore
Tel.: (65) 67477677
Web Site: http://www.rokkogroup.com
Precision Tools Mfr & Distr
N.A.I.C.S.: 332216
Gary Lin *(Mng Dir)*

Subsidiary (Non-US):

Rokko Technology Europe Ltd   (2)
92 Sallynoggin Park, Dunlaoire, Dublin,
Leinster, Ireland
Tel.: (353) 12856141
Emp.: 1
Semiconductor Product Distr
N.A.I.C.S.: 423690

Rokko Ventures Pte. Ltd.   (1)
61 Kaki Bukit Road 2, Singapore, 417869,
Singapore
Tel.: (65) 67495885
Industrial Automated Equipment Mfr
N.A.I.C.S.: 334513

Subsidiary (Domestic):

Finix Technology Pte. Ltd.   (2)

73 Loyang Way, Singapore, 508763, Singapore
Tel.: (65) 67477677
Web Site: http://www.rokkogroup.com
Sales Range: $25-49.9 Million
Emp.: 20
Industrial Automated Equipment Mfr
N.A.I.C.S.: 334513
Gary Lim *(Mgr-Sls)*

Rokko Mechatronics Pte. Ltd. (2)
30 Kaki Bukit Industrial Terrace, Singapore, 416110, Singapore
Tel.: (65) 67477661
Web Site: http://www.rokkogroup.com
Industrial Automated Equipment Mfr
N.A.I.C.S.: 334513

Rokko Systems Pte. Ltd. (2)
61 Kaki Bukit Road 2, Singapore, 417869, Singapore
Tel.: (65) 67495885
Web Site: http://www.rokko.com
Sales Range: $25-49.9 Million
Emp.: 25
Industrial Automated Equipment Mfr
N.A.I.C.S.: 334513
James Seung Ho Baek *(Gen Mgr)*

ROKMASTER RESOURCES CORP.
615-625 Howe Street, Vancouver, V6C 2T6, BC, Canada
Tel.: (604) 290-4647 BC
Web Site: https://www.rokmaster.com
Year Founded: 2010
RKR—(OTCIQ)
Assets: $594,856
Liabilities: $814,616
Net Worth: ($219,760)
Earnings: ($326,778)
Fiscal Year-end: 12/31/19
Gold, Silver & Other Metal Mining
N.A.I.C.S.: 212220
John M. Mirko *(Pres & CEO)*

ROLACO TRADING & CONTRACTING CO.
Medina Rd, PO Box 1044, Jeddah, 21411, Saudi Arabia
Tel.: (966) 122523456
Web Site: http://www.rolaco.com.sa
Year Founded: 1968
Sales Range: $150-199.9 Million
Emp.: 350
Building Materials Distr
N.A.I.C.S.: 423390
Abdulaziz A. Al Sulaiman *(Chm)*

Subsidiaries:

Rolaco Trading & Contracting Co. - Building Material Division (1)
Al Haramen Street, PO Box 222, Sulaimaniyah, 21411, Jeddah, Saudi Arabia
Tel.: (966) 2 2523456
Construction Materials Whslr
N.A.I.C.S.: 423390

ROLAND BERGER STRATEGY CONSULTANTS GMBH
Sederanger 1, 80538, Munich, Germany
Tel.: (49) 8992300 De
Web Site: http://www.rolandberger.com
Year Founded: 1967
Sales Range: $700-749.9 Million
Emp.: 2,000
Business Strategy Consulting Services
N.A.I.C.S.: 541611
Tijo J. G. Collot d'Escury *(Member-Exec Bd)*

Subsidiaries:

PT. Roland Berger Strategy Consultants (1)
Level 11 One Pacific Place Jl Jendral Sudirman Kav 52-53, Sudirman Central Business District, Jakarta, 12190, Indonesia
Tel.: (62) 21 298 59800
Business Management & Consulting Services
N.A.I.C.S.: 541611
Rezki Wibowo *(Principal)*

Roland Berger AG Strategy Consultants (1)
Holbeinstrasse 22, 8008, Zurich, Switzerland
Tel.: (41) 43 336 8600
Web Site: http://www.rolandberger.ch
Business Management & Consulting Services
N.A.I.C.S.: 541611
Adrian Weber *(Co-Partner)*

Roland Berger Consultores de Estrategia Lda. (1)
Rua Castilho 165 2nd Floor, 1070-050, Lisbon, Portugal
Tel.: (351) 21 3567 600
Web Site: http://www.roland-berger.com.pt
Business Management & Consulting Services
N.A.I.C.S.: 541611
Antonio Bernardo *(Mng Partner)*

Roland Berger Ltd. (1)
ARK Mori Building 23rd Floor 1-12-32 Akasaka, Minato-ku, Tokyo, 107-6023, Japan
Tel.: (81) 335876660
Web Site: http://www.rolandberger.co.jp
Sales Range: $25-49.9 Million
Emp.: 100
Management Consultants
N.A.I.C.S.: 541611
Isao Endo *(Chm)*

Roland Berger Strategy Consultants (Beijing) Ltd. (1)
Suites D&E 20th Fl Tower A Gateway Plaza, 18 Xiaguangli E 3rd Ring N Rd, 100027, Beijing, PR, China (100%)
Tel.: (86) 1084400088
Web Site: http://www.rolandberger.com.cn
Sales Range: $25-49.9 Million
Emp.: 50
Management Consulting Services
N.A.I.C.S.: 541618
Qi Wu *(Gen Mgr)*

Roland Berger Strategy Consultants (Shanghai) Ltd. (1)
23rd Fl Shanghai Kerry Ctr, 1515 Nanjing W Rd, Shanghai, 200040, China (100%)
Tel.: (86) 2152986677
Web Site: http://www.rolandberger.com.cn
Emp.: 200
Management Consulting Services
N.A.I.C.S.: 541618
Qian Grace *(Mgr-HR)*

Roland Berger Strategy Consultants - Paris (1)
64 Rue de Liseonn, Paris, 75008, France (100%)
Tel.: (33) 153670320
Web Site: http://www.rolandberger.com
Sales Range: $25-49.9 Million
Emp.: 100
Management Consultancy Services
N.A.I.C.S.: 541618

Roland Berger Strategy Consultants AB (1)
Vasagatan 43b, 411 37, Gothenburg, Sweden
Tel.: (46) 31 757 5500
Web Site: http://www.rolandberger.se
Business Management & Consulting Services
N.A.I.C.S.: 541611
Hans Nyctelius *(Co-Partner)*

Roland Berger Strategy Consultants B.V. (1)
World Trade Center Strawinskylaan 581, Amsterdam, 1077 XX, Netherlands
Tel.: (31) 207960600
Web Site: http://www.rolandberger.com
Sales Range: $25-49.9 Million
Emp.: 70
Management Consulting Services
N.A.I.C.S.: 541618
Tijo J. G. Collot d'Escury *(Mng Partner)*

Roland Berger Strategy Consultants Co., Ltd. (1)
37th Floor Sathorn Square 98 North Sathorn Road, Silom Bangrak, Bangkok, 10500, Thailand
Tel.: (66) 21056342
Business Management & Consulting Services
N.A.I.C.S.: 541611

Roland Berger Strategy Consultants GmbH (1)
Freyung 3 2 10, 1010, Vienna, Austria (100%)
Tel.: (43) 15360201
Web Site: http://www.rolandberger.com
Sales Range: $25-49.9 Million
Emp.: 30
Management Consulting Services
N.A.I.C.S.: 541611
Barbara Lischka *(Dir-Recruiting)*

Roland Berger Strategy Consultants Inc. (1)
1501 McGill College Avenue Suite 2220, Montreal, H3A 3M8, QC, Canada
Tel.: (514) 875-2000
Web Site: https://www.rolandberger.com
Business Management & Consulting Services
N.A.I.C.S.: 541611
Alexis Gardy *(Co-Partner)*

Roland Berger Strategy Consultants Kft. (1)
Sas utca 10-12, 1051, Budapest, Hungary
Tel.: (36) 1 301 70 70
Web Site: http://www.rolandberger.hu
Emp.: 15
Business Management & Consulting Services
N.A.I.C.S.: 541611
Frigyes Schannen *(Co-Mng Partner)*

Roland Berger Strategy Consultants LLC (1)
230 Park Ave Ste 1000 Rm 112, New York, NY 10169
Tel.: (212) 651-9660
Web Site: http://www.strategy-consultants.us
Sales Range: $25-49.9 Million
Emp.: 100
Business Strategy Consulting Services
N.A.I.C.S.: 541611

Holding (Domestic):

Roland Berger Strategy Consultants, LLC - Detroit (2)
37000 Woodward Ave Ste 200, Bloomfield Hills, MI 48304
Tel.: (248) 729-5000
Web Site: http://www.rolandberger.com
Sales Range: $1-9.9 Million
Emp.: 24
Business Strategy Consulting Services
N.A.I.C.S.: 541611
Diane Greyerbiehl *(Mgr-HR)*

Roland Berger Strategy Consultants Limited (1)
Mulliner Towers Office 330 3rd floor 39 Alfred Rewane Road, Ikoyi, Lagos, Nigeria
Tel.: (234) 809 436 2998
Web Site: http://www.rolandberger.com.ng
Business Management & Consulting Services
N.A.I.C.S.: 541611

Roland Berger Strategy Consultants Ltd. (1)
6th Floor 55 Baker St, London, W1U 8EW, United Kingdom
Tel.: (44) 20 3075 1100
Web Site: http://www.rolandberger.co.uk
Business Management & Consulting Services
N.A.I.C.S.: 541611
Anand Raghavan *(Co-Partner)*

Roland Berger Strategy Consultants Middle East (1)
Almoayyed Tower 32nd Floor, PO Box 18696, Al Seef District, Manama, Bahrain (100%)
Tel.: (973) 13609900
Web Site: http://www.rolandberger.com
Management Consulting Services
N.A.I.C.S.: 541611

Roland Berger Strategy Consultants Middle East (1)
Al Fardan Office Tower 8th Floor, PO Box 31316, Doha, Qatar
Tel.: (974) 4410 1780
Business Management & Consulting Services
N.A.I.C.S.: 541611

Roland Berger Strategy Consultants Middle East (1)
Al Thuraya Tower No 01 12th Floor Office No 1201, PO Box 502254, Dubai, United Arab Emirates
Tel.: (971) 4 44 64 080
Web Site: http://www.rolandberger.com
Emp.: 55
Business Management & Consulting Services
N.A.I.C.S.: 541611
Dorukhan Acar *(Principal)*

Roland Berger Strategy Consultants Pte Ltd. (1)
50 Collyer Quay 10-02 OUE Bayfront, Singapore, 049321, Singapore
Tel.: (65) 6597 4530
Business Management & Consulting Services
N.A.I.C.S.: 541611
Damien Dujacquier *(Co-Partner)*

Roland Berger Strategy Consultants Pvt. Ltd. (1)
Vibgyor Tower office No 702 7th Floor Plot No C - 62, Bandra Kurla Complex Bandra East, Mumbai, 400 051, India
Tel.: (91) 22 3953 7501
Web Site: http://www.rolandberger.in
Business Management & Consulting Services
N.A.I.C.S.: 541611
Wilfried Aulbur *(Sr Partner-Automotive Practice-US)*

Roland Berger Strategy Consultants S.A. (1)
Calle Genova no 17 7a pl, 28004, Madrid, Spain
Tel.: (34) 91 5903 140
Web Site: http://www.rolandberger.es
Business Management & Consulting Services
N.A.I.C.S.: 541611
Joao Saint-Aubyn *(Principal)*

Roland Berger Strategy Consultants S.A./N.V. (1)
100 Boulevard du Souverain Vorstlaan, Brussels, 1170, Belgium (100%)
Tel.: (32) 26610300
Web Site: http://www.rolandberger.com
Sales Range: $25-49.9 Million
Emp.: 40
Management Consulting Services
N.A.I.C.S.: 541618
Isabel Hanssens *(Gen Mgr)*

Roland Berger Strategy Consultants S.r.l. (1)
Via Melchiorre Gioia 8, 20124, Milan, Italy
Tel.: (39) 02 29501 1
Web Site: http://www.rolandberger.com
Business Management & Consulting Services
N.A.I.C.S.: 541611
Andrea Airoldi *(Co-Partner)*

Roland Berger Strategy Consultants S/C Ltda. (1)
Av Presidente Juscelino Kubitschek 510, 15 Floor, 04543 906, Sao Paulo, Itaim Bibi, Brazil (100%)
Tel.: (55) 1130467111
Web Site: http://www.rolandberger.com
Sales Range: $25-49.9 Million
Emp.: 50
Management Consulting Services
N.A.I.C.S.: 541618

Roland Berger Strategy Consultants SARL (1)
8 boulevard Roudani angle rue Jean Jaures, 20 000, Casablanca, Morocco
Tel.: (212) 5 29 01 13 55
Web Site: http://www.rolandberger.ma
Business Management & Consulting Services
N.A.I.C.S.: 541611

ROLAND BERGER STRATEGY CONSULTANTS GMBH

Roland Berger Strategy Consultants GmbH—(Continued)
Laurent Benarousse *(Mng Partner)*

Roland Berger Strategy Consultants SRL (1)
Popa Savu Street No 79-81, 011432, Bucharest, Romania
Tel.: (40) 21 306 05 00
Web Site: http://www.rolandberger.ro
Business Management & Consulting Services
N.A.I.C.S.: 541611
Codrut Pascu *(Mng Partner)*

Roland Berger Strategy Consultants Sdn Bhd (1)
39th Floor Menara Standard Chartered 30 Jalan Sultan Ismail, 50250, Kuala Lumpur, Malaysia
Tel.: (60) 3 2203 8600
Business Management & Consulting Services
N.A.I.C.S.: 541611
Anthonie Versluis *(Partner)*

Roland Berger Strategy Consultants Sp.z o.o. (1)
Plac Bankowy 1, 00-139, Warsaw, Poland
Tel.: (48) 22 323 74 60
Web Site: http://www.rolandberger.pl
Emp.: 20
Business Management & Consulting Services
N.A.I.C.S.: 541611
Piotr Malik *(Project Mgr)*

Roland Berger Strategy Consultants TOV (1)
vul Shovkovychna 42/44, 01601, Kiev, Ukraine
Tel.: (380) 44 49408 65
Web Site: http://www.rolandberger.ua
Business Management & Consulting Services
N.A.I.C.S.: 541611
Artem Zakomirnyi *(Principal)*

Roland Berger Strategy Consultants d.o.o. (1)
Trg bana Jelacica, 10000, Zagreb, Croatia
Tel.: (385) 1 4804 801
Business Management & Consulting Services
N.A.I.C.S.: 541611

Roland Berger Strategy Consultants, Ltd. (1)
Kyobo Building 22nd Floor 1 Jongno, Jongno-gu, Seoul, 110-714, Korea (South)
Tel.: (82) 2 2288 0004
Web Site: http://www.rolandberger.co.kr
Business Management & Consulting Services
N.A.I.C.S.: 541611
Huntaek Jung *(Principal)*

Roland Berger Strateji Danismanlik Ltd. Sti. (1)
Levent 193 Buyukdere Caddesi No 193 Kat 2, Levent, 34394, Istanbul, Turkiye
Tel.: (90) 212 371 46 40
Business Management & Consulting Services
N.A.I.C.S.: 541611
Dorukhan Acar *(Principal)*

ROLAND BOULANGER & CIE LTEE
235 rue St Louis, Warwick, J0A 1M0, QC, Canada
Tel.: (819) 358-4100
Web Site: http://www.boulanger.qc.ca
Year Founded: 1942
Sales Range: $25-49.9 Million
Emp.: 360
Mouldings & Wood Components Mfr
N.A.I.C.S.: 321999
Guy Boulanger *(Pres & Gen Mgr)*

ROLAND CORPORATION
2036-1 Nakagawa Hosoe-cho, Kita-ku, Hamamatsu, 431-1304, Shizuoka, Japan
Tel.: (81) 53 523 0230
Web Site: http://www.roland.com
Year Founded: 1972
Sales Range: $800-899.9 Million
Emp.: 2,945
Electronic Musical Instruments & Other Audio Products Mfr
N.A.I.C.S.: 339992
Kazuya Yanase *(COO)*

Subsidiaries:

Electronic Musical Instruments Roland Scandinavia A/S
Skagerrakvej 7, 2100, Copenhagen, Denmark
Tel.: (45) 39166200
Sales Range: $25-49.9 Million
Emp.: 4
Musical Instrument Distr
N.A.I.C.S.: 424990
Christian Gramkow *(Mng Dir)*

Rodgers Instruments Corporation (1)
1300 NE 25th Ave, Hillsboro, OR 97124
Tel.: (503) 648-4181
Web Site: http://www.rodgersinstruments.com
Sales Range: $25-49.9 Million
Emp.: 65
Stereo Imaged Church & Pipe Combination Organs Mfr
N.A.I.C.S.: 321999
Dan Miller *(Product Mgr)*

Roland (Switzerland) AG (1)
Landstrasse 5 Postfach, 4452, Itingen, Switzerland (100%)
Tel.: (41) 619759999
Web Site: http://www.rolandmusik.ch
Sales Range: $25-49.9 Million
Emp.: 15
Musical Instrument & Supplies Stores
N.A.I.C.S.: 459140
Michael Heuser *(Pres & CEO)*

Roland (U.K.) Ltd. (1)
Atlantic Close, Swansea, SA7 9FJ, United Kingdom (100%)
Tel.: (44) 1792702701
Web Site: http://www.roland.co.uk
Sales Range: $25-49.9 Million
Emp.: 50
Musical Instrument & Supplies Stores
N.A.I.C.S.: 459140

Roland Asia Pacific Sdn. Bhd. (1)
45-1 Block C2 Jalan PJU 1-39, Dataran Prima, 47301, Petaling Jaya, Selangor, Malaysia (100%)
Tel.: (60) 378053263
Web Site: http://www.rolandap.com
Sales Range: $25-49.9 Million
Emp.: 10
Musical Instrument & Supplies Stores
N.A.I.C.S.: 459140
Dennis Tan *(Mng Dir)*

Roland Brasil Importacao, Exportacao, Comercio, Representacao e Servicos Ltda.
Rua San Jose 211 Parque Industrial San Jose, 06715-862, Cotia, SP, Brazil
Tel.: (55) 11 3087 7700
Web Site: http://www.roland.com.br
Musical Instruments & Electronic Equipment Distr
N.A.I.C.S.: 423990

Roland Canada Music Ltd. (1)
5480 Parkwood Way, V6V 2M4, Richmond, BC, Canada
Tel.: (604) 270-6626
Web Site: http://www.roland.ca
Sales Range: $25-49.9 Million
Emp.: 20
Computer Music Hardware & Instruments Mfr & Distr
N.A.I.C.S.: 339992
Paul McCabe *(Pres)*

Roland Central Europe N.V. (1)
Bell telephone laan 2G, Geel, 2440, Belgium
Tel.: (32) 14575911
Web Site: http://www.rolanddg.com
Sales Range: $50-74.9 Million
Emp.: 52
Musical Instrument Distr
N.A.I.C.S.: 423990

Roland Corporation - Matsumoto Factory (1)
4010-5 Wada, Matsumoto, 390-1242, Nagano, Japan
Tel.: (81) 263 48 0211
Musical Instrument Mfr
N.A.I.C.S.: 339992

Roland Corporation - Miyakoda Factory
1-5-3 Shinmiyakoda, Kita-ku, Hamamatsu, 431-2103, Shizuoka, Japan
Tel.: (81) 53 428 5141
Web Site: http://www.roland.com
Musical Instrument Mfr
N.A.I.C.S.: 339992

Roland Corporation Australia Pty. Ltd. (1)
38 Campbell Ave, Dee Why, 2099, NSW, Australia
Tel.: (61) 299828266
Web Site: http://www.rolandcorp.com.au
Audio & Video Equipment Mfr
N.A.I.C.S.: 334310

Roland Corporation U.S. (1)
5100 S E Ave, Los Angeles, CA 90040-2938
Tel.: (323) 890-3700
Web Site: http://www.rolandus.com
Sales Range: $50-74.9 Million
Emp.: 125
Musical Instrument & Supplies Stores
N.A.I.C.S.: 459140
Richard Katz *(Mgr-Sls-Southeast & Puerto Rico)*

Roland East Europe Ltd. (1)
Torokbalint FSD Park 3, Torokbalint, 2045, Hungary (100%)
Tel.: (36) 23511011
Web Site: http://www.hu.rolandee.com
Sales Range: $25-49.9 Million
Emp.: 21
Audio & Video Equipment Mfr
N.A.I.C.S.: 334310
Csaba Toth *(Mng Dir)*

Roland Elektronische Musikinstrumente Handelsgesellschaft mbH (1)
Oststrasse 96, 22844, Norderstedt, Germany
Tel.: (49) 405260090
Web Site: http://www.rolandmusik.de
Sales Range: $25-49.9 Million
Emp.: 50
Musical Instrument Mfr
N.A.I.C.S.: 339992

Roland Europe S.p.A. (1)
Via Leonardo Da Vinci 11, Acquaviva Picena, 63030, Ascoli Piceno, Italy
Tel.: (39) 07 35 58 35 90
Web Site: http://www.rolandeur.com
Electronic Component Mfr & Distr
N.A.I.C.S.: 334419
Tim Walter *(CEO)*

Roland Iberia S.L. (1)
P-Garcia Faria 33-35 1st Fl, 08005, Barcelona, Spain
Tel.: (34) 933081000
Sales Range: $25-49.9 Million
Emp.: 40
Industrial Supplies Merchant Whslr
N.A.I.C.S.: 423840

Roland Italy S.p.A. (1)
Viale delle industrie 8, 20020, Milan, Italy
Tel.: (39) 02937781
Web Site: http://www.roland.it
Sales Range: $25-49.9 Million
Emp.: 15
Musical Instrument Mfr
N.A.I.C.S.: 339992
Manuele Barbini *(Pres)*

Roland Music LLC
Dorozhnaya St 3 Korp 6, 117545, Moscow, Russia
Tel.: (7) 495 981 49 64
Web Site: http://www.rolandmusic.ru
Emp.: 25
Musical Instrument Distr
N.A.I.C.S.: 423990
Andrey Voronov *(Gen Mgr)*

Roland Polska Sp. z o.o. (1)
Ul Katy Grodziskie 16/b, 03-289, Warsaw, Poland
Tel.: (48) 22 678 95 12
Web Site: http://www.roland.com
Musical Instrument Distr
N.A.I.C.S.: 423990

Roland Scandinavia A/S (1)
Skagerrakvej 7, PO Box 880, 2100, Copenhagen, Denmark (100%)
Tel.: (45) 39166200
Web Site: http://www.roland.dk
Sales Range: $25-49.9 Million
Emp.: 30
Audio & Video Equipment Mfr
N.A.I.C.S.: 334310

Roland Shanghai Electronics Co., Ltd. (1)
5F Xindonggong Plaza No 1500 Pingliang Rd, Yangpu, Shanghai, 200090, China
Tel.: (86) 21 55800800
Web Site: http://www.roland.com
Sales Range: $50-74.9 Million
Emp.: 200
Musical Instrument Mfr
N.A.I.C.S.: 339992

Roland Systems Group EMEA, S.L. (1)
Paseo Garcia Faria 33-35, 08005, Barcelona, Spain
Tel.: (34) 93 493 91 36
Web Site: http://www.rolandsystemsgroup.eu
Emp.: 10
Audio & Video Equipment Distr
N.A.I.C.S.: 423620
Joan Garrobe *(Mng Dir)*

Roland Systems Group France S.A. (1)
11 rue Louis Philippe, 92200, Neuilly-sur-Seine, France
Tel.: (33) 1 41 43 04 30
Audio & Video Equipment Distr
N.A.I.C.S.: 423620

Roland Systems Group Scandinavia (1)
Skagerrakvej 7, Copenhagen, 2150, Denmark
Tel.: (45) 39 16 62 00
Web Site: http://www.rolandsystemsgroup.dk
Emp.: 25
Audio & Video Equipment Distr
N.A.I.C.S.: 423690
Morten Rasmussen *(Mgr-Sls)*

Roland Systems Group U.S. (1)
801 W Orchard Dr Ste 3, Bellingham, WA 98225
Tel.: (360) 594-4282
Web Site: http://www.rolandsystemsgroup.com
Audio & Video Equipment Distr
N.A.I.C.S.: 423690

Roland Taiwan Enterprise Co., Ltd. (1)
Rm 5 9th Floor No 112, Chung Shan N Rd Section 2, Taipei, 104, Taiwan
Tel.: (886) 225613339
Web Site: http://www.rolandtaiwan.com.tw
Sales Range: $25-49.9 Million
Emp.: 30
Electronic Parts & Equipment Merchant Whslr
N.A.I.C.S.: 423690
S. Ho *(Gen Mgr)*

ROLAND DG CORPORATION
1-1-2 Shinmiyakoda, Hamana-ku, Hamamatsu, 431-2103, Shizuoka-ken, Japan
Tel.: (81) 534841200 JP
Web Site: https://www.rolanddg.com
Year Founded: 1981
6789—(TKS)
Rev.: $382,990,612
Assets: $384,871,107
Liabilities: $123,519,286
Net Worth: $261,351,821
Earnings: $30,503,619
Emp.: 1,361
Fiscal Year-end: 12/31/23

AND PRIVATE COMPANIES — ROLLS-ROYCE HOLDINGS PLC

Computer Peripheral Equipment Mfr
N.A.I.C.S.: 334118
Hidenori Fujioka *(Chm)*

Subsidiaries:

DGSHAPE Corporation (1)
Tel.: (81) 534827069
Printing Machinery & Equipment Mfr
N.A.I.C.S.: 333248

Roland DG (China) Corporation (1)
Shanghai Mart 10A85 Room No 2299
Yan'an Road West, Shanghai, 200336,
China
Tel.: (86) 2162360909
Printing Machinery & Equipment Distr
N.A.I.C.S.: 423830

Roland DG (U.K.) Ltd. (1)
Griffin House Windmill Road Clevedon
Business Park, North Somerset, Clevedon,
BS21 6UJ, United Kingdom
Tel.: (44) 1275335540
Printing Machinery & Equipment Distr
N.A.I.C.S.: 423830
Rob Goleniowski *(Head-Sls)*

Roland DG Australia Pty. Ltd. (1)
14/25 Frenchs Forest Rd East Frenchs Forest, Allambie Grove Business Park, Sydney,
2086, NSW, Australia
Tel.: (61) 299750000
Printing Machinery & Equipment Distr
N.A.I.C.S.: 423830
John Wall *(Mng Dir)*

Roland DG Benelux N.V. (1)
Bell-Telephonelaan 2G, Westerlo, 2440,
Geel, Belgium (100%)
Tel.: (32) 1 457 5911
Web Site: https://www.rolanddg.eu
Sales Range: $25-49.9 Million
Emp.: 30
Office Equipment Merchant Whslr
N.A.I.C.S.: 423420

Roland DG Brasil Ltd. (1)
Rua San Jose 780, Parque Industrial San
Jose Cotia, Sao Paulo, 06715-862, Brazil
Tel.: (55) 113 500 2600
Web Site: https://www.rolanddg.com.br
Printing Machinery & Equipment Distr
N.A.I.C.S.: 423830

Roland DG Deutschland GmbH (1)
Halskestrasse 7, 47877, Willich, Germany
Tel.: (49) 215 488 0860
Web Site: https://www.rolanddg.eu
Commercial Printing Machinery Mfr
N.A.I.C.S.: 323111

Roland DG Europe Holdings
B.V. (1)
Professor JH Bavincklaan 2, 1183 AT, Amstelveen, Netherlands
Tel.: (31) 207233670
Printing Machinery & Equipment Distr
N.A.I.C.S.: 423830

Roland DG France SAS (1)
4 Rue Paul Henri Spaak, 77400, Saint-Thibault-des-Vignes, France
Tel.: (33) 160079049
Printing Machinery & Equipment Distr
N.A.I.C.S.: 423830

Roland DG Korea Inc. (1)
1207 Triplex Mullaebuk-ro 116,
Yeongdeungpo-gu, Seoul, 07293, Korea
(South)
Tel.: (82) 7045047100
Printing Machinery & Equipment Distr
N.A.I.C.S.: 423830

Roland DG Mid Europe S.r.l. (1)
via L Da Vinci 1/B - Zona Industriale,
63075, Acquaviva Picena, AP, Italy
Tel.: (39) 073 558 6558
Web Site: https://www.rolanddg.eu
Emp.: 43
Printing Equipment Distr
N.A.I.C.S.: 423420
Steffania Cimino *(Pres)*

Roland DG North Europe A/S (1)
Engholm Parkvej 5, 3450, Allerod, Denmark
Tel.: (45) 88822000
Printing Machinery & Equipment Distr
N.A.I.C.S.: 423830

Roland DG RUS LLC (1)
St Nizhnyaya Syromyatnicheskay 10 building 2 Artplay 2 Design Center, Moscow,
Russia
Tel.: (7) 4959812307
Web Site: http://www.rolanddg.eu
Commercial Printing Machinery Mfr
N.A.I.C.S.: 323111

Roland DGA Corporation (1)
15363 Barranca Pkwy, Irvine, CA 92618
Tel.: (949) 727-2100
Web Site: https://www.rolanddga.com
Printing Machinery & Supplies Distr
N.A.I.C.S.: 423830
Andrew Oransky *(Pres & CEO)*

Roland Digital Group Iberia, S.L. (1)
Parc Tecnologic del Valles Ceramistes 6,
8290, Cerdanyola del Valles, Spain
Tel.: (34) 935918400
Sales Range: $25-49.9 Million
Emp.: 3
Printing Machinery Mfr
N.A.I.C.S.: 333248

ROLCON ENGINEERING COMPANY LIMITED
Vithal Udyognagar, P B NO 20, Sojitra Road, Anand, 388 120, Gujarat,
India
Tel.: (91) 2692230766
Web Site:
  https://www.rolconengineering.com
Year Founded: 1967
505807—(BOM)
Rev.: $3,565,532
Assets: $2,738,797
Liabilities: $1,152,447
Net Worth: $1,586,349
Earnings: $76,240
Fiscal Year-end: 03/31/21
Sprocket Mfr
N.A.I.C.S.: 333613
Suresh H. Amin *(Chm)*

ROLEX RINGS LIMITED
Nr Kotharia Railway Crossing Opp
Hotel Krishna Park Gondal Road,
Kotharia, Rajkot, 360004, Gujarat,
India
Tel.: (91) 2816699677
Web Site: https://www.rolexrings.com
Year Founded: 2003
543325—(BOM)
Rev.: $84,596,831
Assets: $108,780,126
Liabilities: $60,086,072
Net Worth: $48,694,055
Earnings: $11,869,358
Fiscal Year-end: 03/31/21
Industry Machinery Mfr
N.A.I.C.S.: 333248
Bhautik Dayashankar Madeka *(Exec Dir)*

ROLEX S.A.
3-5-7 rue Francois-Dussaud, 1211,
Geneva, Switzerland
Tel.: (41) 22 302 2200   CH
Web Site: http://www.rolex.com
Year Founded: 1905
Sales Range: $550-599.9 Million
Emp.: 3,000
Luxury Watches Mfr
N.A.I.C.S.: 334519
Jean-Frederique Dufour *(CEO)*

Subsidiaries:

Rolex Watch U.S.A., Inc. (1)
665 5th Ave, New York, NY 10022
Tel.: (212) 758-7700
Web Site: http://www.rolex.com
Sales Range: $150-199.9 Million
Emp.: 500
Mfr of Watches
N.A.I.C.S.: 423940
John Flaherty *(Mgr-Natl Adv)*

ROLF C. HAGEN, INC.
20500 Trans Canada Hwy, Baie
d'Urfe, Montreal, H9X 0A2, QC,
Canada
Tel.: (514) 457-0914
Web Site: http://www.ca-en.hagen.com
Year Founded: 1955
Sales Range: $150-199.9 Million
Emp.: 1,000
Pet Cages & Food Mfr & Distr
N.A.I.C.S.: 459910

Subsidiaries:

HAGEN Deutschland GmbH & Co.
KG (1)
Lehmweg 99-105, 25488, Holm, Germany
Tel.: (49) 41039602000
Web Site: http://www.hagen-deutschland.com
Pet Product Distr
N.A.I.C.S.: 459910

Rolf C. Hagen (France) S.A. (1)
Zone Parisud 4 Boulevard Jean Monnet,
77388, Combs-la-Ville, France
Tel.: (33) 1 64 88 14 18
Web Site: http://www.hagen.com
Pet Product Distr
N.A.I.C.S.: 459910

Rolf C. Hagen (Sea) Sdn. Bhd. (1)
Lot 14A Jalan 3A Kawasan Perusahaan
Cheras Jaya, Balakong, 43200, Selangor,
Malaysia
Tel.: (60) 3 9074 2388
Pet Product Distr
N.A.I.C.S.: 459910

Rolf C. Hagen (UK) Ltd. (1)
California Drive Whitwood Industrial Estate,
Castleford, WF10 5QH, West Yorkshire,
United Kingdom
Tel.: (44) 1977 556622
Web Site: http://uk.hagen.com
Pet Product Distr
N.A.I.C.S.: 459910

Rolf C. Hagen (USA) Corp. (1)
305 Forbes Blvd, Mansfield, MA 02048
Tel.: (508) 339-9531
Web Site: http://www.usa.hagen.com
Emp.: 100
Pet Product Distr
N.A.I.C.S.: 459910
Thomas Marshall *(COO)*

ROLKE PHARMA GMBH
Friedrich-Ebert-Damm 112, 22047,
Hamburg, Germany
Tel.: (49) 40 696 5450
Web Site:
  http://www.roelkepharma.de
Pharmaceuticals Product Mfr
N.A.I.C.S.: 325412
Thomas Rolke *(Mng Dir)*

ROLL N OILFIELD INDUSTRIES LTD.
305 5208 53 Avenue, Red Deer, T4N
5K2, AB, Canada
Tel.: (403) 343-1710
Web Site: http://www.rolln.com
Year Founded: 1977
Drilling Services
N.A.I.C.S.: 213111
Brad Rowbotham *(Pres)*

ROLL-UP CAPITAL CORP.
1500 850-2nd Street SW, Calgary,
T2P 0R8, AB, Canada
Tel.: (403) 268-3100
Year Founded: 2015
Investment Services
N.A.I.C.S.: 523999

ROLLATAINERS LIMITED
73-74 Phase III Industrial Area,
Dharuhera, 123106, Haryana, India
Tel.: (91) 1274243326
Web Site: https://www.rollatainers.in
Year Founded: 1968
502448—(BOM)
Rev.: $9,382,519
Assets: $22,346,784
Liabilities: $15,923,735
Net Worth: $6,423,048
Earnings: ($1,282,786)
Emp.: 111
Fiscal Year-end: 03/31/21
Carton Packaging Products Mfr
N.A.I.C.S.: 322220

ROLLMAN GROUP PLC
14 Zaozernaya Street, Saint Petersburg, Russia
Tel.: (7) 812 336 3704
Web Site: http://www.rollman-gk.com
Year Founded: 1993
RLMN—(RUS)
Sales Range: Less than $1 Million
Holding Company
N.A.I.C.S.: 551112

ROLLS-ROYCE HOLDINGS PLC
Kings Place 90 York Way, London,
N1 9FX, United Kingdom
Tel.: (44) 1332242424   UK
Web Site: https://www.rolls-royce.com
Year Founded: 1884
RR—(LSE)
Rev.: $16,053,681,280
Assets: $40,075,821,240
Liabilities: $46,694,706,240
Net Worth: ($6,618,885,000)
Earnings: ($4,302,614,680)
Emp.: 48,200
Fiscal Year-end: 12/31/20
Holding Company
N.A.I.C.S.: 551112
Richard Wray *(Dir-External Comm)*

Subsidiaries:

Bergen Engines India Private
Limited (1)
2nd Floor 52-B Okhla Industrial Estate
Phase III, New Delhi, 110 020, India
Tel.: (91) 1140778700
Investment Holding Company Services
N.A.I.C.S.: 551112

Europea Microfusioni Aerospaziali
S.p.A. (1)
Via Zona Industriale, 83040, Morra De
Sanctis, AV, Italy
Tel.: (39) 082 743 8211
Web Site: https://www.emaht.com
Engine Mfr
N.A.I.C.S.: 336412
Gianpaolo Verde *(Mgr-Comml)*

MTU Africa (Proprietary) Limited (1)
36 Marconi Road Montage Gardens, 7441,
Cape Town, South Africa
Tel.: (27) 215295760
Diesel Engine Distr
N.A.I.C.S.: 424720

MTU Hong Kong Limited (1)
1-3 Wing Yip Street Kwai Chung New Territories, Hong Kong, China (Hong Kong)
Tel.: (852) 24184800
Diesel Engine Distr
N.A.I.C.S.: 424720

MTU Japan Co. Limited (1)
Takanawa-Meiko Building 2-15-19 Takanawa, Minato-ku, Tokyo, 108-0074, Japan
Tel.: (81) 357939080
Diesel Engine Distr
N.A.I.C.S.: 424720

MTU Korea Limited (1)
23rd Floor Pacific Tower 41 Sejongdaero 9
Gil Junggu, 04513, Seoul, Korea (South)
Tel.: (82) 7050552891
Diesel Engine Distr
N.A.I.C.S.: 424720

MTU Polska Sp. z o.o. (1)
Ul Slaska 9, 73-110, Stargard Szczecinski,
Poland
Tel.: (48) 915788710

ROLLS-ROYCE HOLDINGS PLC

Rolls-Royce Holdings plc—(Continued)

Diesel Engine Distr
N.A.I.C.S.: 424720

Metlase Limited (1)
Building 3 AMP Technology Centre Brunel Way, Catcliffe, Sheffield, S60 5WG, United Kingdom
Tel.: (44) 1143830610
Web Site: https://www.metlase.com
Engineering Consultancy Services
N.A.I.C.S.: 541330

PT Rolls-Royce (1)
Secure Building Blok B MTU Indonesia Jl Raya Protokol Halim Perdana, Kusuma, Jakarta, 13610, Indonesia
Tel.: (62) 2122808333
Investment Holding Company Services
N.A.I.C.S.: 551112

R-R (Thailand) Limited (1)
11th Floor Tonson Tower 900 Ploenchit Road, Bangkok, 10330, Thailand
Tel.: (66) 2 263 0500
Web Site: http://www.rolls-royce.com
Aircraft Part Mfr
N.A.I.C.S.: 336413

Rolls-Royce (1)
Ansty, Coventry, CV7 9JR, United Kingdom (100%)
Tel.: (44) 1332241638
Web Site: http://www.rolls-royce.com
Sales Range: $200-249.9 Million
Emp.: 800
Mfr & Maintenance Aero-derived Gas Turbines
N.A.I.C.S.: 336412

Rolls-Royce (Thailand) Limited (1)
4 4/5 Level 12 Unit 1299 1301 Zen World Tower Rajdamri Road Pathumwan, Bangkok, 10330, Thailand
Tel.: (66) 22630500
Investment Holding Company Services
N.A.I.C.S.: 551112

Rolls-Royce Brasil Limitad (1)
Av Almirante Barroso 52- 20th Floor, 20031 000, Rio de Janeiro, Brazil
Tel.: (55) 21 2277 0100
Industrial Machinery Mfr
N.A.I.C.S.: 333248

Rolls-Royce China Holding Limited (1)
305-306 Indigo Building A 20 Jiuxianqiao Road, Chaoyang Dist, Beijing, 100016, China
Tel.: (86) 1085655000
Investment Holding Company Services
N.A.I.C.S.: 551112

Rolls-Royce Civil Nuclear SAS (1)
23 Chemin Du Vieux Chene, 38240, Meylan, Cedex, France
Tel.: (33) 4 76 61 15 00
Web Site: http://www.rolls-royce.com
Sales Range: $200-249.9 Million
Nuclear Component Mfr
N.A.I.C.S.: 334517

Rolls-Royce Fuel Cell Systems Limited (1)
Charnwood Building Holywell Park Ashby Road, Loughborough, LE11 3GR, United Kingdom
Tel.: (44) 1509 225 500
Web Site: http://www.rolls-royce.com
Fuel Cell Mfr
N.A.I.C.S.: 325998

Rolls-Royce India Private Limited (1)
2nd Floor West Tower Birla House 25 Barakhambha Road, New Delhi, 110001, India
Tel.: (91) 1123357118
Investment Holding Company Services
N.A.I.C.S.: 551112

Rolls-Royce International Limited (1)
62 Buckingham Gate, London, SW1E 6AT, United Kingdom (100%)
Tel.: (44) 2072229020
Support & Commercial Information Services
N.A.I.C.S.: 519290
Simon M. Robertson *(Chm)*

Subsidiary (Non-US):

Rolls-Royce AB (2)
Box 1010, 68129, Kristinehamn, Sweden (100%)
Tel.: (46) 55084000
Web Site: http://www.rolls-royce.com
Sales Range: $75-99.9 Million
Emp.: 450
Mfr of Marine Propulsion Systems
N.A.I.C.S.: 336611

Rolls-Royce Australia Services Pty Limited (2)
Suite 102 Level 1 2-4 Lyonpark Road, Macquarie Park, 2113, NSW, Australia (100%)
Tel.: (61) 293251333
Web Site: http://www.rolls-royce.com
Sales Range: $25-49.9 Million
Emp.: 12
Development of Gas Turbine Aero Engines in Civil & Military Aviation
N.A.I.C.S.: 336412

Rolls-Royce Canada Ltd. (2)
9500 Cote De Liesse Road, Lachine, Montreal, H8T 1A2, QC, Canada (100%)
Tel.: (514) 636-0964
Web Site: https://www.rolls-royce.com
Sales Range: $350-399.9 Million
Emp.: 1,400
Mfr & Designer of Industrial Gas Turbines
N.A.I.C.S.: 333132

Division (Domestic):

Rolls-Royce Canada Limited - Naval Marine (3)
461 Windmill Rd, Dartmouth, NS, Canada
Tel.: (902) 468-2928
Sales Range: $25-49.9 Million
Emp.: 40
Marine Oriented Construction Services
N.A.I.C.S.: 237990

Branch (Domestic):

Rolls-Royce Canada Limited - Naval Marine (4)
597 The Queensway, Peterborough, K9J 7J6, ON, Canada
Tel.: (705) 743-9249
Ship Building Services
N.A.I.C.S.: 336611

Subsidiary (Non-US):

Rolls-Royce Deutschland Ltd & Co. KG (2)
Eschenweg 11 OT Dahlewitz, 15827, Blankenfelde-Mahlow, Germany (100%)
Tel.: (49) 337 0860
Web Site: http://www.rolls-royce.com
Emp.: 2,000
Design, Mfr & Maintenance of Aircraft Engines
N.A.I.C.S.: 336412

Rolls-Royce India Limited (2)
2nd Floor Birla Tower West 25 Barakhambha Road, New Delhi, 110 001, India (100%)
Tel.: (91) 1141811000
Web Site: http://www.rolls-royce.com
Sales Range: $25-49.9 Million
Mfr of Aero Engines & Services Integrated Power Systems for use on Land & Sea
N.A.I.C.S.: 336412

Branch (Non-US):

Rolls-Royce International (2)
W Wing Ofc 406, PO Box 54254, Dubai, 5, United Arab Emirates (100%)
Tel.: (971) 42994343
Sales Range: $25-49.9 Million
Emp.: 12
Support & Commercial Information Services
N.A.I.C.S.: 519290

Rolls-Royce International (2)
Av Almirante Barroso 52 20th Fl, 20031 000, Rio de Janeiro, Brazil (50%)
Tel.: (55) 2122770100
Web Site: http://www.rolls-royce.com
Sales Range: $25-49.9 Million
Emp.: 30
Support & Commercial Information Services
N.A.I.C.S.: 519290

Rolls-Royce International (2)
305-306 3rd Floor INDIGO 1 No 20 Jiuxianqiao Road, ChaoyangDistrict, Beijing, 100016, China

Tel.: (86) 108 565 5000
Web Site: https://www.rolls-royce.com
Sales Range: $25-49.9 Million
Emp.: 30
Engine & Integrated Power System Mfr
N.A.I.C.S.: 336412

Rolls-Royce International (2)
Rm 1008 B Shui-on-Centre, 6-8 Harbour Road, Wanchai, China (Hong Kong) (100%)
Tel.: (852) 28024843
Web Site: http://www.rolls-royce.com
Support & Commercial Information Services
N.A.I.C.S.: 519290

Rolls-Royce International (2)
3-2-5 Kasumigaseki 31st Floor Kasumigaseki Building, Chiyoda Ku, Tokyo, 100 6031, Japan
Tel.: (81) 335920966
Web Site: http://www.rolls-royce.com
Support & Commercial Information Services
N.A.I.C.S.: 519290

Rolls-Royce International (2)
Olipe Tower, Seosununtong Joogu, Seoul, 137-840, Korea (South) (100%)
Tel.: (82) 234767750
Sales Range: $25-49.9 Million
Emp.: 6
Support & Commercial Information Services
N.A.I.C.S.: 519290
Junalx Alex *(Reg Dir)*

Rolls-Royce International (2)
1 Seletar Aerospace Crescent, Singapore, 797565, Singapore (100%)
Tel.: (65) 62403333
Web Site: http://www.rolls-royce.com
Sales Range: $25-49.9 Million
Support & Commercial Information Services
N.A.I.C.S.: 519290

Rolls-Royce International (2)
11th Floor Tonson Tower 900 Ploenchit Road, Lumpini pathumwan, Bangkok, 10330, Thailand (100%)
Tel.: (66) 2 263 0500
Web Site: http://www.rolls-royce.com
Sales Range: $25-49.9 Million
Emp.: 2
Support & Commercial Information Services
N.A.I.C.S.: 519290

Rolls-Royce International (2)
Reu Foroissart No 95 to 99, Brussels, BE 1040, Belgium (100%)
Tel.: (32) 22308652
Web Site: http://www.rolls-royce.com
Sales Range: $25-49.9 Million
Emp.: 2
Support & Commercial Information Services
N.A.I.C.S.: 519290

Rolls-Royce International (2)
IBC Bldg Pobrezni 3, 18600, Prague, Czech Republic (100%)
Tel.: (420) 224835069
Web Site: http://www.rolls-royce.com
Sales Range: $350-399.9 Million
Emp.: 12
Support & Commercial Information Services
N.A.I.C.S.: 519290

Rolls-Royce International (2)
122 Avenue Charles de Gaulle, 92522, Neuilly-sur-Seine, Cedex, France (100%)
Tel.: (33) 14 722 1440
Web Site: http://www.rolls-royce.com
Emp.: 100
Support & Commercial Information Services
N.A.I.C.S.: 519290

Subsidiary (Non-US):

Rolls-Royce International LLC (2)
Office 26 B Sadovaya St 10, Moscow, 123001, Russia
Tel.: (7) 495 651 9330
Web Site: http://www.rolls-royce.com
Aircraft & Marine Engine Distr
N.A.I.C.S.: 423860

Branch (Non-US):

Rolls-Royce International Limited (2)
Al Taif Bldg, Malaz, Riyadh, 11494, Saudi Arabia (100%)
Tel.: (966) 112235275
Web Site: http://www.rolls-royce.com

INTERNATIONAL PUBLIC

Engine & Integrated Power System Mfr
N.A.I.C.S.: 336412

Rolls-Royce International Limited (2)
Secure Building Blok B MTU Indonesia Jl Raya Protokol, Halim Perdana Kusuma, Jakarta, 13610, Indonesia (100%)
Tel.: (62) 2122808333
Web Site: http://www.rolls-royce.com
Sales Range: $25-49.9 Million
Provider of Support & Commercial Information Services
N.A.I.C.S.: 519290

Rolls-Royce International Limited (2)
Via IV Novembre 114, 00187, Rome, Italy
Tel.: (39) 06 6976 671
Web Site: http://www.rolls-royce.com
Aircraft & Marine Engine Distr
N.A.I.C.S.: 423860

Rolls-Royce International Limited (2)
Jagerstrabe 59, 10117, Berlin, Germany
Tel.: (49) 30 2094 2501
Industrial Machinery Mfr
N.A.I.C.S.: 333248

Rolls-Royce International Limited (2)
Unit 402 4th floor Asia Tower Building 6 Nha Tho Street, Hoan Kiem District, Hanoi, Vietnam
Tel.: (84) 4 39380 228
Web Site: http://www.rolls-royce.com
Emp.: 10
Industrial Machinery Mfr
N.A.I.C.S.: 333248

Subsidiary (Non-US):

Rolls-Royce Japan Co. Ltd (2)
31st Floor Kasumigaseki Building 3-2-5 Kasumigaseki, Chiyoda-Ku, Tokyo, 100-6031, Japan
Tel.: (81) 3 3592 0966
Web Site: http://www.rolls-royce.com
Aerospace Parts Mfr
N.A.I.C.S.: 336413

Rolls-Royce Malaysia Sdn Bhd (2)
Letterbox No 102 32nd Floor Ubn Tower 10 Jalan P Ramlee, 50250, Kuala Lumpur, Malaysia
Tel.: (60) 3 2026 1990
Web Site: https://www.rolls-royce.com
Engine & Integrated Power System Mfr
N.A.I.C.S.: 336412

Rolls-Royce OY AB (2)
Suojantie 5, Rauma, 26100, Satakunta, Finland
Tel.: (358) 283791
Marine Propulsion System Distr
N.A.I.C.S.: 423860
Olli Rantanen *(Gen Mgr)*

Rolls-Royce Singapore Pte Limited (2)
6 Seletar Aerospace Rise, Singapore, 797575, Singapore
Tel.: (65) 62403333
Industrial Machinery Mfr
N.A.I.C.S.: 333248
Andrew Geow *(Mgr-Comml)*

Rolls-Royce Marine (Shanghai) Limited (1)
Room 1204 1206 Swiss Hotel No 21 Wuhui Road, Zhongshan District, 116001, Dalian, China
Tel.: (86) 41182305198
Sales Range: $25-49.9 Million
Emp.: 16
Marine Engineering Services
N.A.I.C.S.: 541330
Jack Wang *(Gen Mgr)*

Rolls-Royce Marine AS (1)
Sjogata 98, 6065, Ulsteinvik, Norway
Tel.: (47) 81520070
Web Site: http://www.rolls-royce.com
Design, Development, Supply & Support of Products & Systems for Commercial & Naval Customers
N.A.I.C.S.: 333923
Anette Bonnevie Wollebaek *(Sr Mgr-Comm)*

Branch (Domestic):

Rolls-Royce Marine AS (2)
Hjorungavag, PO Box 193, 6069, Hareid, Norway

AND PRIVATE COMPANIES

ROLLS-ROYCE HOLDINGS PLC

Tel.: (47) 70013300
Web Site: http://www.rolls-royce.com
Sales Range: $300-349.9 Million
Emp.: 902
Marine Technology Services, Including Development & Sales of Automated Handling Systems for Seismic & Offshore Vessels
N.A.I.C.S.: 333923

Rolls-Royce Marine AS (2)
Nerbo, 6480, Aukra, Norway
Tel.: (47) 70 31 15 00
Web Site: http://www.odim.com
Deck Cranes Building Services
N.A.I.C.S.: 333120
Einar Ravn Stovreide *(Mgr-Sls)*

Rolls-Royce Marine Electrical Systems Limited (1)
Building 49 Broad Oak Works Airport Service Road, Portsmouth, PO3 5PQ, Hampshire, United Kingdom
Tel.: (44) 23 9231 0000
Emp.: 35
Marine Electrical Equipment Mfr & Distr
N.A.I.C.S.: 335999
Gary Doherty *(Sr Engr-Software)*

Rolls-Royce Marine Power Operations Limited (1)
Naval Support Group, Helensburgh, G84 8TF, United Kingdom
Tel.: (44) 1436 672379
Marine Engineering Services
N.A.I.C.S.: 541330

Rolls-Royce New Zealand Limited (1)
Part Level 11 79 Boulcott Street, Wellington, New Zealand
Tel.: (64) 43850001
Investment Holding Company Services
N.A.I.C.S.: 551112

Rolls-Royce North America Inc. (1)
1875 Explore St Ste 200, Reston, VA 20190 (100%)
Tel.: (703) 834-1700
Web Site: http://www.rolls-royce.com
Sales Range: $1-4.9 Billion
Holding Company; Design, Mfr & Marketing of Jet Engines
N.A.I.C.S.: 423860
Tom Bell *(Chm & CEO)*

Joint Venture (Domestic):

International Aero Engines AG (2)
400 Main St, East Hartford, CT 06118
Tel.: (860) 565-0140
Web Site: http://www.i-a-e.com
Sales Range: $75-99.9 Million
Emp.: 400
Aircraft Engine Mfr
N.A.I.C.S.: 336412
Earl E. Exum *(Executives)*

Subsidiary (Domestic):

Optimized Systems & Solutions, LLC
1875 Explorer St Ste 200, Reston, VA 20190 (100%)
Tel.: (703) 889-1300
Web Site: http://www.o-sys.com
Sales Range: $125-149.9 Million
Emp.: 11
Consulting, Solutions Development & Safety-Critical Systems & Services
N.A.I.C.S.: 541690

Subsidiary (Non-US):

Rolls-Royce Controls and Data Services Limited (3)
Shaftmoor Lane Hall Green, Birmingham, B28 8SW, United Kingdom
Tel.: (44) 1217077111
Web Site: http://www.controlsdata.com
Power System Controls Software Services
N.A.I.C.S.: 541512

Subsidiary (Domestic):

R. Brooks Associates, Inc. (2)
6546 Pound Rd, Williamson, NY 14589
Tel.: (315) 589-4000
Web Site: http://www.rbrooks.com
Sales Range: $25-49.9 Million
Emp.: 85
Inspection Services

N.A.I.C.S.: 541990

Subsidiary (Domestic):

R.O.V. Technologies Inc. (3)
49 Bennett Dr, Brattleboro, VT 05301
Tel.: (802) 254-9353
Web Site: http://www.rovtech.com
Sales Range: $1-9.9 Million
Emp.: 45
Nuclear Reactor Inspection & Cleaning Solutions
N.A.I.C.S.: 811310

Subsidiary (Domestic):

Rolls-Royce Corporation (2)
450 S Meridian St, Indianapolis, IN 46225-1103
Tel.: (317) 230-2000
Web Site: https://www.rolls-royce.com
Sales Range: $700-749.9 Million
Emp.: 4,000
Design & Mfr of Aircraft, Industrial & Marine Gas Turbine Engines
N.A.I.C.S.: 336412

Rolls-Royce Crosspointe LLC (2)
8800 Wells Station Rd, Prince George, VA 23875
Tel.: (804) 518-7000
Aerospace Parts Mfr
N.A.I.C.S.: 336413
Janet Rickman *(Office Mgr)*

Plant (Domestic):

Rolls-Royce Crosspointe LLC - Rolls-Royce Outdoor Jet Engine Test Facility (3)
John C Stennis Space Center H-1 Test Site Building 5002, Stennis Space Center, MS 39529
Tel.: (228) 813-2437
Industrial Technology Development Services
N.A.I.C.S.: 541714

Subsidiary (Domestic):

Rolls-Royce Defense Services Inc. (2)
2001 S Tibbs Ave, Indianapolis, IN 46241
Tel.: (703) 621-2786
Nautical System & Instrument Mfr
N.A.I.C.S.: 334511
Nadine Melind *(Dir-Svcs Strategy)*

Rolls-Royce Engine Services-Oakland Inc. (2)
7200 Earhart Rd, Oakland, CA 94621
Tel.: (510) 613-1000
Web Site: http://www.rollroyce.com
Sales Range: $125-149.9 Million
Aircraft Engine Overhaul
N.A.I.C.S.: 336412
Jay Gross *(CFO)*

Rolls-Royce Naval Marine Inc. (2)
110 Norfolk St, Walpole, MA 02081 (100%)
Tel.: (508) 668-9610
Web Site: http://www.roll-royce.com
Sales Range: $50-74.9 Million
Emp.: 160
Mfr of Marine Propulsion Systems; Mfr of Variable & Fixed Pitch Marine Propeller Systems
N.A.I.C.S.: 333998
Mark Nittel *(Mgr-Bus Dev & Ops)*

Subsidiary (Domestic):

Rolls-Royce Naval Marine Inc. (3)
3719 Industrial Rd, Pascagoula, MS 39568-1528
Tel.: (508) 668-9610
Web Site: http://www.rolls-royce.com
Sales Range: $25-49.9 Million
Emp.: 60
Mfr of Fixed & Variable-Pitch Marine Propellers
N.A.I.C.S.: 333998

Rolls-Royce Oman Limited Liability Company (1)
Bait Al Reem Business Office 131 Building No 81 Way No 3409, PO Box 20, Block No 234 Al Thaqafa Street Al Khuwair, 103, Muscat, Oman
Tel.: (968) 24403747

Investment Holding Company Services
N.A.I.C.S.: 551112

Rolls-Royce Power Development Limited (1)
Allington House 150 Victoria Street, London, SW1E 5LB, United Kingdom
Tel.: (44) 1355277113
Industrial Machinery Mfr
N.A.I.C.S.: 333248

Rolls-Royce Power Engineering Plc (1)
Nucleus London Science and Bus Pk Brunel Way, Dartford, DA1 5GA, Kent, United Kingdom (100%)
Tel.: (44) 1322312028
Web Site: http://www.rolls-royce.com
Sales Range: $25-49.9 Million
Emp.: 3
Service & Repair of Fixed & Variable Pitched Propellers for Commercial & Military Craft; Lateral & Rotatable Thrust Units & Water Jet Propulsion Systems; Water-Tight Doors for Ships
N.A.I.C.S.: 333310

Rolls-Royce Power Systems AG (1)
Maybachplatz 1, 88045, Friedrichshafen, Germany (100%)
Tel.: (49) 75419091
Web Site: http://www.rrpowersystems.com
Sales Range: $5-14.9 Billion
Holding Company; Diesel & Gasoline Engines Mfr
N.A.I.C.S.: 551112
Jasmin Staiblin *(Chm-Supervisory Bd)*

Subsidiary (Domestic):

MTU Friedrichshafen GmbH (2)
Maybachplatz 1, 88045, Friedrichshafen, Germany
Tel.: (49) 7541900
Web Site: http://www.mtu-online.com
Sales Range: $700-749.9 Million
Emp.: 10,000
Mfr of Diesel Engines & Drive Systems
N.A.I.C.S.: 336310

Subsidiary (US):

MTU America Inc. (3)
39525 MacKenzie Dr, Novi, MI 48377
Tel.: (248) 560-8000
Web Site: http://www.mtuamericacareers.com
Sales Range: $75-99.9 Million
Diesel Engine Mfr
N.A.I.C.S.: 333618

Subsidiary (Domestic):

MTU Onsite Energy (4)
100 Power Dr, Mankato, MN 56001
Tel.: (507) 625-7973
Web Site: http://www.mtuonsiteenergy.com
Sales Range: $125-149.9 Million
Mfr of Custom Generators
N.A.I.C.S.: 335312

Subsidiary (Non-US):

MTU do Brasil Ltda. (4)
Rodovia Anhaguera km 29, 05276-000, Sao Paulo, Brazil
Tel.: (55) 139158900
Web Site: http://www.mtu.com.br
Marine Engineering Services
N.A.I.C.S.: 541330

Subsidiary (Non-US):

MTU Asia Pte. Ltd. (3)
10 Tukang Innovation Drive, Singapore, 618302, Singapore
Tel.: (65) 68615922
Web Site: http://www.mtu-online.com
Sales Range: $125-149.9 Million
Diesel Engines & Drive Systems Distr
N.A.I.C.S.: 423860
Chai Chew Phua Chin *(Sr Mgr-Fin)*

Subsidiary (Non-US):

MTU China Co. Ltd. (4)
17/F Kerry Parkside 1155 Fang Dian Road, Pudong District, Shanghai, 201204, China
Tel.: (86) 2120302800
Web Site: http://www.mtuonline.com
Diesel Engines Distr

N.A.I.C.S.: 423860

MTU Engineering (Suzhou) Co. Ltd. (4)
No 9 Long Yun Road Suzhou Industrial Park, Suzhou, 215024, Jiangsu, China
Tel.: (86) 51262850188
Web Site: http://www.mtu-online.com.sg
Sales Range: $25-49.9 Million
Emp.: 200
Diesel Engines Repair & Maintenance Services
N.A.I.C.S.: 811198

MTU India Pvt. Ltd. (4)
159/1 Tathawade, Off Mumbai-Bangalore Highway, Pune, 411 033, Maharashtra, India
Tel.: (91) 2067209200
Web Site: http://www.mtu-online.com
Sales Range: $25-49.9 Million
Diesel Engines Distr
N.A.I.C.S.: 423860

MTU Marubeni Co. Ltd. (4)
Yushi Kogyo-Kaikan Bldg 3-13-11 Nihonbashi, Chuo-ku, Tokyo, 103-0027, Japan
Tel.: (81) 352058300
Web Site: http://www.mtu-online.com.sg
Sales Range: $50-74.9 Million
Emp.: 6
Diesel Engines Distr
N.A.I.C.S.: 423860

MTU Vietnam Co. Ltd. (4)
C/O V-Trac Level 16 106 Hoang Quoc Viet Street, Cau Giay District, Hanoi, Vietnam
Tel.: (84) 4 3755 1100
Web Site: http://www.mtu-online.com
Diesel & Gas Engines Distr
N.A.I.C.S.: 423120

PT MTU Indonesia (4)
Secure Building Blok B Jl Raya Protokol Halim Perdanakusuma, Jl Cilandak KKO, Jakarta, 13610, Indonesia
Tel.: (62) 2180875750
Web Site: http://www.mtu-online.com.sg
Sales Range: $25-49.9 Million
Emp.: 50
Diesel Engines Distr
N.A.I.C.S.: 423860

Subsidiary (Non-US):

MTU Benelux B.V. (3)
Merwedestraat 86, 3313 CS, Dordrecht, Netherlands
Tel.: (31) 786395777
Web Site: http://www.mtu-solutions.com
Diesel Engine Systems Sales
N.A.I.C.S.: 423120

MTU DD Benelux B.V. (3)
Merwedestraat 86, Dordrecht, 3313CS, Netherlands
Tel.: (31) 786395777
Web Site: http://www.mtudd-benelux.com
Sales Range: $25-49.9 Million
Emp.: 60
Engine Equipment Mfr
N.A.I.C.S.: 333618

MTU Detroit Diesel Israel Ltd. (3)
45 Hamelacha Street, Poleg South Industrial Zone, 42505, Netanya, Israel
Tel.: (972) 732866010
Web Site: http://www.mtu-online.com
Sales Range: $50-74.9 Million
Emp.: 6
Diesel Engines Distr
N.A.I.C.S.: 423860

MTU Detroit Diesel UK Ltd (3)
Birches Industrial Estate Unit 29, East Grinstead, RH19 1XZ, West Sussex, United Kingdom
Tel.: (44) 1342335450
Web Site: http://www.mtu-online.com
Sales Range: $10-24.9 Million
Emp.: 50
Engineering Services
N.A.I.C.S.: 541330

MTU France SAS (3)
Immeuble Colorado 8/10 Rue de Rosa Luxembourg Parc des Bellevues, 95610, Eragny-sur-Oise, France
Tel.: (33) 134186060
Web Site: http://www.mtu-online.fr

ROLLS-ROYCE HOLDINGS PLC

Rolls-Royce Holdings plc—(Continued)

Sales Range: $25-49.9 Million
Emp.: 65
Marine Engineering Services
N.A.I.C.S.: 541330

MTU Iberica Propulsion y Energia S.L. (3)
C Copernicico 28, 28823, Coslada, Madrid, Spain
Tel.: (34) 914851900
Web Site: http://www.mtu-solutions.com
Sales Range: $25-49.9 Million
Engines & Turbines Mfr
N.A.I.C.S.: 333611
Schuh Hubert *(Co-CEO)*

MTU Italia S.r.l. (3)
Via Aurelia Nord 328, 19021, Arcola, La Spezia, Italy
Tel.: (39) 0187952601
Sales Range: $25-49.9 Million
Emp.: 80
Marine Engineering Services
N.A.I.C.S.: 541330
Emanuela Pagani *(Dir-Mktg)*

MTU Motor Turbin Sanayi ve Ticaret A.S. (3)
Omerli Mah Hatira Sok No 5 Arnavutkoy, 34555, Istanbul, Turkiye
Tel.: (90) 2128672000
Web Site: http://www.mtu-online.com
Sales Range: $25-49.9 Million
Engineeering Services
N.A.I.C.S.: 541330

Subsidiary (Domestic):

MTU Onsite Energy GmbH (3)
Dasinger Str 11, 86165, Augsburg, Germany
Tel.: (49) 82174800
Web Site: http://www.mtu-solutions.com
Sales Range: $250-299.9 Million
Fossil Fuel Power Generation Services
N.A.I.C.S.: 221112

MTU Reman Technologies GmbH (3)
Friedrich-List-Strasse 8, 39122, Magdeburg, Germany
Tel.: (49) 391 5046 0
Web Site: http://www.mturemantechnologies.mtu-online.com
Sales Range: $25-49.9 Million
Emp.: 196
Engine Systems Mfr
N.A.I.C.S.: 333618

Subsidiary (Non-US):

MTU South Africa Pty. Ltd. (3)
36 Marconi Road Montage Gardens, 7441, Cape Town, Western Cape, South Africa
Tel.: (27) 215295760
Web Site: http://www.mtu-online.co.za
Emp.: 60
Port Facility Construction & Engineering Services
N.A.I.C.S.: 237990

MTU UK Ltd. (3)
Birches Industrial Estate Unit 29, East Grinstead, RH19 1XZ, West Sussex, United Kingdom
Tel.: (44) 1342335450
Web Site: http://www.mtu-online.co.uk
Sales Range: $25-49.9 Million
Emp.: 60
Diesel & Gas Engines Distr
N.A.I.C.S.: 423120
Bruce Phillips *(Mng Dir)*

Rolls-Royce Saudi Arabia Limited (1)
PO Box 88545, Riyadh, 11672, Saudi Arabia
Tel.: (966) 112235280
Investment Holding Company Services
N.A.I.C.S.: 551112

Rolls-Royce Sp z.o.o. (1)
Opolska Street 100 Vinci Office Centre, 31-323, Krakow, Poland
Tel.: (48) 123900040
Human Resource Support Services
N.A.I.C.S.: 541612

Rolls-Royce Technical Support SARL (1)
46 av Jean Monnet, Haute Garonne, Colomiers, 31770, France
Tel.: (33) 561164170
Emp.: 70
Aero Engineering Project Management Services
N.A.I.C.S.: 541618
Christophe Molus *(Gen Mgr)*

Scandinavian Electric Holding AS (1)
Janaflaten 28 Godvik, Bergen, 5882, Norway
Tel.: (47) 55 50 60 70
Electrical Equipment Mfr & Distr
N.A.I.C.S.: 334419

Servowatch Systems Limited (1)
Endeavour House Holloway Road, Heybridge, Maldon, CM9 4ER, Essex, United Kingdom
Tel.: (44) 1621855562
Web Site: https://www.servowatch.com
Marine Engineering Services
N.A.I.C.S.: 541330

Sharing in Growth UK Limited (1)
ML-67, PO Box 31, Derby, DE24 8BJ, United Kingdom
Tel.: (44) 1332269096
Web Site: http://www.sig-uk.org
Aerospace Product & Parts Mfr
N.A.I.C.S.: 336411

Turbine Surface Technologies Limited (1)
Unit 13a Little Oak Drive Sherwood Park, Annesley, NG15 0DR, Nottinghamshire, United Kingdom
Tel.: (44) 1623720040
Web Site: http://www.tst-ltd.com
Aerospace Product & Parts Mfr
N.A.I.C.S.: 336411
Joe Barker *(Head-Ops, Health, Safety & Environment)*

ROLMEX SA
ul Olkuska 7, 02-604, Warsaw, French Polynesia
Tel.: (48) 225428000
Web Site: https://www.rolmexsa.pl
Year Founded: 1987
Emp.: 100
International Goods Trading, Real Estate & Capital Investment Services
N.A.I.C.S.: 425120

ROLTA INDIA LTD.
Rolta Tower A Rolta Technology Park MIDC Andheri East, Mumbai, 400 093, India
Tel.: (91) 2229266666
Web Site: https://www.rolta.com
500366—(BOM)
Rev.: $205,248,225
Assets: $1,102,268,895
Liabilities: $1,460,596,410
Net Worth: ($358,327,515)
Earnings: ($124,885,215)
Emp.: 416
Fiscal Year-end: 03/31/20
Information Technology Services
N.A.I.C.S.: 519290
Kamal K. Singh *(Chm & Mng Dir)*

Subsidiaries:

Orion Technology, Inc. (1)
80 Whitehall Drive Suite 3, Markham, L3R 0P3, ON, Canada
Tel.: (905) 754-8100
Web Site: http://www.oriongis.com
Application Software Development Services
N.A.I.C.S.: 541511

Rolta Defence Technology Systems Pvt. Ltd. (1)
Rolta Tower C Rolta Technology Park, MIDC Andheri East, Mumbai, 400 093, India
Tel.: (91) 2229266666
Information Technology Services
N.A.I.C.S.: 541511

Rolta International Inc (1)
Rolta Ctr 5865 N Point Pkwy, Alpharetta, GA 30022
Tel.: (678) 942-5000
Information Technology Consulting Services
N.A.I.C.S.: 541512

Subsidiary (Non-US):

Rolta Asia Pacific Pty Ltd. (2)
Level 32 101 Miller Street, North Sydney, 2060, NSW, Australia
Tel.: (61) 2 8019 7222
Web Site: http://www.rolta.com
Geophysical Engineering Services
N.A.I.C.S.: 541330

Rolta Middle East FZ – LLC (1)
Office No 209-214 Building No 9, PO Box 500106, Dubai Internet City, Dubai, United Arab Emirates
Tel.: (971) 43915212
Information Technology Services
N.A.I.C.S.: 541511
Kamal K. Singh *(Chm)*

Rolta Middle East FZ LLC UAE (1)
Office No 209-214 Building No 9, PO Box 500106, Dubai, United Arab Emirates
Tel.: (971) 4 391 5212
Emp.: 50
Information Technology Consulting Services
N.A.I.C.S.: 541512
Manish Singh *(Mgr-Mktg)*

Rolta UK Limited (1)
100 Longwater Avenue Green Park, Theale, Reading, RG2 6GP, Berkshire, United Kingdom
Tel.: (44) 1189450450
Web Site: https://www.rolta.com
Sales Range: $25-49.9 Million
Emp.: 15
Information Technology Consulting Services
N.A.I.C.S.: 541512

Subsidiary (Non-US):

Rolta Benelux B.V. (2)
Jupiterstraat 96 Building Pluspoint Nr 2, Hoofddorp, 2132HE, Netherlands
Tel.: (31) 23 557 1916
Emp.: 5
Information Technology Consulting Services
N.A.I.C.S.: 541512

Rolta Deutschland GmbH (2)
Dornhofstrasse 34, 63263, Neu-Isenburg, Germany
Tel.: (49) 61 02 29 99 85
Information Technology Consulting Services
N.A.I.C.S.: 541512

ROMA (META) GROUP LIMITED
22/F China Overseas Building, 139 Hennessy Road, Wanchai, China (Hong Kong)
Tel.: (852) 25296878
Web Site: http://www.romagroup.com
8072—(HKG)
Rev.: $11,781,291
Assets: $62,586,900
Liabilities: $15,425,234
Net Worth: $47,161,666
Earnings: ($4,496,759)
Emp.: 62
Fiscal Year-end: 03/31/22
Investment Advisory Services
N.A.I.C.S.: 523940
Michael Sheung Him Li *(Exec Dir)*

Subsidiaries:

Excellent Success Investment Limited (1)
Rooms 1101-4 11/F Harcourt House 39 Gloucester Road, Wan Chai, Hong Kong, China (Hong Kong)
Tel.: (852) 25296012
Web Site: https://yuenmeta.com
Securities Brokerage Services
N.A.I.C.S.: 523150

ROMAERO S.A.
Bulevardul Ficusului number 44 Sector 1, 13975, Bucharest, Romania

INTERNATIONAL PUBLIC

Tel.: (40) 215994104
Web Site: https://www.romaero.com
RORX—(BUC)
Rev.: $30,805,798
Assets: $227,694,642
Liabilities: $155,826,098
Net Worth: $71,868,544
Earnings: ($14,046,240)
Emp.: 902
Fiscal Year-end: 12/31/20
Civil & Military Transport Aircraft Maintenance Services
N.A.I.C.S.: 488190

ROMANDE ENERGIE HOLDING S.A.
Rue de Lausanne 53, Po Box 950, 1110, Morges, Switzerland
Tel.: (41) 218029111
Web Site: http://www.romande-energie.ch
REHN—(SWX)
Rev.: $1,103,176,853
Assets: $3,130,255,540
Liabilities: $601,812,458
Net Worth: $2,528,443,082
Earnings: $255,412,409
Emp.: 1,338
Fiscal Year-end: 12/31/23
Offices of Other Holding Companies
N.A.I.C.S.: 551112
Mustaki Guy *(Chm)*

Subsidiaries:

Bosson et Pillet S.A. (1)
Small City Chemin Louis-Hubert 2, 1213, Petit-Lancy, Switzerland
Tel.: (41) 228790909
Web Site: https://www.bosson-pillet.ch
Mechanical Equipment Whslr
N.A.I.C.S.: 423830

Effitec SA (1)
Rue des Artisans 10, 1026, Echandens, Switzerland
Tel.: (41) 84 870 1000
Web Site: https://www.effitec.ch
Electric Wire Installation Services
N.A.I.C.S.: 238210

Enerbois SA (1)
Chemin de Forchy 18, 1046, Rueyres, Switzerland
Tel.: (41) 218876692
Web Site: http://www.enerbois.ch
Emp.: 10
Electric Power Generation & Distribution Services
N.A.I.C.S.: 221118
Mattia Pedrini *(Pres)*

J.M. Lambelet S.A. (1)
Vy-d'Etra 33, 2000, Neuchatel, Switzerland
Tel.: (41) 327566010
Web Site: https://www.jmlambelet-sa.ch
Air Conditioning Installation Services
N.A.I.C.S.: 238220

Romande Energie Commerce SA (1)
Rue de Lausanne 63, Morges, 1110, Switzerland
Tel.: (41) 218029111
Web Site: http://www.romande-energie.ch
Sales Range: $500-549.9 Million
Emp.: 700
Electric Power Distribution Services
N.A.I.C.S.: 221122
Pierre-Alain Urech *(CEO)*

Romande Energie Renouvelable SA (1)
Rue De Lausanne 53, Morges, 1110, Switzerland
Tel.: (41) 218029705
Electric Power Distr
N.A.I.C.S.: 221122

Romande Energie S.A. (1)
Tel.: (41) 218029111
Web Site: http://www.romande-energie.ch
Sales Range: $550-599.9 Million
Emp.: 350
Electric Power Generation & Distribution Services

N.A.I.C.S.: 221111
Urech Pierre-alain *(Gen Mgr)*

Romande Energie Services S.A. (1)
Rue de Lausanne 53, 1110, Morges, Switzerland
Tel.: (41) 848802900
Web Site: https://www.romande-energie.ch
Renewable Energy Production Services
N.A.I.C.S.: 221114

ROMANIJAPUTEVI A.D.
Podromanija bb, 71350, Sokolac, Bosnia & Herzegovina
Tel.: (387) 57448508
Web Site:
https://www.romanijaputevi.com
Year Founded: 1992
ROPT—(BANJ)
Sales Range: $10-24.9 Million
Emp.: 289
Civil Engineering Construction Services
N.A.I.C.S.: 237990

ROMANS AUTOMOBILES SA
Quartier Les Chirouzes, Pizancon, Chatuzange-le-Goubet, 26300, Drome, France
Tel.: (33) 475707408
Web Site:
http://www.citroenromans.com
Sales Range: $25-49.9 Million
Emp.: 48
New Car Dealers
N.A.I.C.S.: 441110
Jean-Pierre Kaminski *(Pres)*

ROMANTA ESTIVAL 2002 SA
Hotel Romanta, Neptun, Constanta, Romania
Tel.: (40) 241491073
ANTA—(BUC)
Assets: $2,145,034
Liabilities: $97,566
Net Worth: $2,047,468
Earnings: ($13,087)
Emp.: 1
Fiscal Year-end: 12/31/23
Accommodation Services
N.A.I.C.S.: 721110
Calin-Silviu Vere *(Pres)*

ROMCARBON S.A.
132 Transilvaniei Street, Buzau, Romania
Tel.: (40) 238711155
Web Site:
https://www.romcarbon.com
Year Founded: 1952
ROCE—(BUC)
Rev.: $65,595,382
Assets: $62,987,542
Liabilities: $30,253,833
Net Worth: $32,733,709
Earnings: ($1,105,696)
Emp.: 780
Fiscal Year-end: 12/31/23
Plastic Materials Mfr
N.A.I.C.S.: 326122
Cristinel Dobrota *(Deputy Gen Mgr-Dev)*
Subsidiaries:

Living Jumbo Industry SA (1)
132 Transilvaniei St, 120012, Buzau, Romania
Tel.: (40) 338101120
Web Site: https://www.livingjumbo.ro
Big Bag Mfr
N.A.I.C.S.: 326111
Radu Andrei *(Gen Mgr)*

RC Energo Install SRL (1)
Transilvaniei 132, Buzau, Romania
Tel.: (40) 238713545
Web Site: https://www.energoinstall.ro
Electrical Installation Services
N.A.I.C.S.: 238210
Duca Eugen *(Gen Mgr)*

ROME RESOURCES PLC
35 Berkeley Sq, London, W1J 5BF, United Kingdom
Tel.: (44) 2031436748
Web Site: https://romeresources.com
PFP—(AIM)
Assets: $74,476
Liabilities: $244,888
Net Worth: ($170,412)
Earnings: ($474,628)
Emp.: 5
Fiscal Year-end: 12/31/22
Mineral Mining Services
N.A.I.C.S.: 212390
Peter Taylor *(CEO)*

ROMERIKE SPAREBANK
Tel.: (47) 63804200
Web Site: https://www.rsbank.no
Year Founded: 1887
LSTSB-ME—(OSL)
Sales Range: Less than $1 Million
Commercial Banking Services
N.A.I.C.S.: 522110
Siri Berggreen *(CEO-IR & Mgr-Amin)*

ROMFOR SA
19 Liliacului, Boldesti-Scaeni, Prahova, Romania
Tel.: (40) 244 210 669
Web Site: http://www.romfor.ro
Year Founded: 1983
Drilling Oil & Gas Well
N.A.I.C.S.: 213111
Naita Marcu *(Pres & Gen Mgr)*

ROMIKA SHOES GMBH
Brothers-Seibel-Str 7-9, 76846, Trier, Germany
Tel.: (49) 651204313   De
Web Site: http://www.romika.de
Year Founded: 1936
Sales Range: $25-49.9 Million
Emp.: 110
Shoe Mfr
N.A.I.C.S.: 316210
Andreas Garnier *(Mng Dir)*
Subsidiaries:

Romika AG (1)
Fashion Order Mall C Zuliani Pfadackerstrasse 9, CH-8957, Spreitenbach, Switzerland
Tel.: (41) 4101366
Web Site: http://www.romika.de
Shoe Mfr
N.A.I.C.S.: 316210

Romika USA, Inc. (1)
8730 Northwest 36th Ave, Miami, FL 33147-3934
Tel.: (305) 696-4611
Sales Range: $100-124.9 Million
Mfr of Shoes
N.A.I.C.S.: 316210

ROMIOS GOLD RESOURCES INC.
Suite 500 2 Toronto St, Toronto, M5C 2B6, ON, Canada
Tel.: (416) 221-4124
Web Site: https://www.romios.com
Year Founded: 1995
RG—(OTCIQ)
Rev.: $688
Assets: $3,016,277
Liabilities: $894,863
Net Worth: $2,121,414
Earnings: ($275,639)
Fiscal Year-end: 06/30/21
Mineral Exploration Services
N.A.I.C.S.: 213114
Thomas Skimming *(VP-Exploration)*
Subsidiaries:

McLymont Mines Inc. (1)
2 Toronto Street 5th Floor Suite 500, Toronto, M5C 2B6, ON, Canada
Tel.: (416) 221-4124
Web Site: http://www.romios.com
Sales Range: $50-74.9 Million
Emp.: 2
Gold Mining Services
N.A.I.C.S.: 212220

Romios Gold Nevada Inc. (1)

ROMNAV S.A.
Str Anghel Saligny Nr 4, 810118, Braila, Romania
Tel.: (40) 239612405
Web Site: https://www.romnav.ro
BRNA—(BUC)
Rev.: $18,868,959
Assets: $26,513,166
Liabilities: $4,735,271
Net Worth: $21,777,896
Earnings: $6,232,871
Emp.: 162
Fiscal Year-end: 12/31/23
River Freight Transport & Handling Services
N.A.I.C.S.: 483211

ROMPETROL RAFINARE S.A.
215 Navodari Blvd Administrative Building, Navodari, Constanta, Romania
Tel.: (40) 241506868
Web Site: http://www.rompetrol-rafinare.ro
Year Founded: 1974
RRC—(BUC)
Rev.: $4,111,720,627
Assets: $2,416,994,662
Liabilities: $2,137,391,986
Net Worth: $279,602,675
Earnings: ($234,855,647)
Emp.: 1,176
Fiscal Year-end: 12/31/23
Crude Oil & Gas Refining Services
N.A.I.C.S.: 324110
Yedil Utekov *(Co-Chm)*
Subsidiaries:

Rompetrol Downstream S.R.L. (1)
3-5 Piata Presei Libere City Gate Northern Tower 2nd Floor, 011028, Bucharest, Romania
Tel.: (40) 212067500
Petroleum Product Mfr & Distr
N.A.I.C.S.: 324199

ROMPETROL WELL SERVICES S.A.
Str Clopotei No 2 bis, Ploiesti, Romania
Tel.: (40) 244544321
Web Site:
https://rompetrolwellservices.com
PTR—(BUC)
Rev.: $16,769,610
Assets: $31,788,446
Liabilities: $9,763,604
Net Worth: $22,024,842
Earnings: $2,555,953
Emp.: 135
Fiscal Year-end: 12/31/23
Oil & Natural Gas Field Services
N.A.I.C.S.: 213112
Luiza Roxana Moise *(Dir-Economics)*

ROMPLUMB SA
Str Gutinului 9, Maramures, Baia Mare, Romania
Tel.: (40) 262 210540
Year Founded: 1990
Sales Range: $10-24.9 Million
Emp.: 678
Lead & Zinc Ore Mining Services
N.A.I.C.S.: 212230
Ciprian Gata *(Gen Mgr)*

ROMRADIATOARE SA
Str Zizinului Nr 113A, Brasov, Romania
Tel.: (40) 268313500
Web Site:
https://www.romradiatoare.com
Year Founded: 1926
RRD—(BUC)
Rev.: $6,592,774
Assets: $8,191,312
Liabilities: $2,773,596
Net Worth: $5,417,716
Earnings: $191,319
Emp.: 123
Fiscal Year-end: 12/31/23
Heat Exchange Product Mfr
N.A.I.C.S.: 332410

ROMREAL LTD.
Burnaby Building 16 Burnaby Street, Hamilton, HM11, Bermuda
Tel.: (441) 4006000
Web Site: https://www.romreal.com
Year Founded: 2005
ROM—(OSL)
Rev.: $257,597
Assets: $19,204,710
Liabilities: $514,558
Net Worth: $18,690,152
Earnings: $65,653
Emp.: 12
Fiscal Year-end: 12/31/23
Real Estate Investment Services
N.A.I.C.S.: 531210
Kjetil Gronskag *(Chm & CEO)*

ROMSDAL SPAREBANK
Torget 14, 6440, Elnesvagen, Norway
Tel.: (47) 71268000
Web Site:
https://www.romsdalsbanken.no
Year Founded: 1971
ROMSB—(EUR)
Emp.: 50
Investment Management Service
N.A.I.C.S.: 523999
Christian Sollid *(Head-Corporate Marketing)*

ROMY FOODS CORPORATION LTD.
Junction Business Center 1st Floor Sqaq Lourdes, Saint Julian, SWQ 3334, Malta
Tel.: (356) 21666933   Mt
Web Site:
https://www.romyfoods.com
Year Founded: 2011
Food Service Contractors
N.A.I.C.S.: 722310
Subsidiaries:

Anglia Crown Limited (1)
84 Grosvenor Street, London, W1K 3JZ, United Kingdom
Tel.: (44) 1206854564
Web Site: http://www.angliacrown.co.uk
Food Mfr & Distr
N.A.I.C.S.: 311412
Paul Howell *(Dir)*

RON HODGSON PONTIAC BUICK GMC LTD.
5 Galarneau Pl, Saint Albert, T8N 2Y3, AB, Canada
Tel.: (780) 458-7100
Web Site:
https://www.ronhodgson.com
Year Founded: 1978
Rev.: $46,167,768
Emp.: 90
New & Used Car Dealers
N.A.I.C.S.: 441110

RON MACGILLIVRAY CHEV BUICK GMC LTD.
75 St Andrews Street, Antigonish, B2G 2S3, NS, Canada
Tel.: (902) 863-2803

RON MACGILLIVRAY CHEV BUICK GMC LTD.

Ron MacGillivray Chev Buick Gmc Ltd.—(Continued)
Web Site:
http://www.ronmacgillivraychev.com
Year Founded: 1986
Rev.: $19,119,921
Emp.: 36
New & Used Car Dealers
N.A.I.C.S.: 441110

RON SANTATERESA C.A.
Hacienda Santa Teresa El Consejo, Carretera Panamericana, Hacienda Santa Teresa, Maracay, 2118, Estada Aragua, Venezuela
Tel.: (58) 244 400 2500
Web Site:
http://www.ronsantateresa.com
Year Founded: 1796
RST—(BVC)
Sales Range: Less than $1 Million
Alcoholic Beverage Mfr & Whslr
N.A.I.C.S.: 312140
Alberto C. Vollmer de Marcellus *(Chm & Pres)*

RONAL AG
Lerchenbuhl 3, 4624, Harkingen, Switzerland
Tel.: (41) 62 389 05 10
Web Site: http://www.ronalgroup.com
Emp.: 150
Alloy Wheel & Shower Enclosure Mfr
N.A.I.C.S.: 336390
Yvo Schnarrenberger *(Mng Dir)*
Subsidiaries:

RONAL CR s.r.o. (1)
Jungmannova 1117, 506 01, Jicin, Czech Republic
Tel.: (420) 493587111
Web Site: http://www.ronal-wheels.cz
Alloy Steel Mfr
N.A.I.C.S.: 336390

RONAL France S.A.S (1)
Centre d'affaires 4 Boulevard de treves, 57070, Metz, France
Tel.: (33) 387164242
Web Site: http://www.ronal-wheels.fr
Alloy Wheel Distr
N.A.I.C.S.: 423120
J. F. Grom *(Mgr-Sls)*

RONAL GmbH (1)
Werner von Siemens Strasse 28, 76694, Forst, Germany
Tel.: (49) 72517010
Web Site: http://www.ronal.de
Emp.: 80
Light Alloy Wheel Mfr
N.A.I.C.S.: 336390
Hans Nagel *(Mng Dir)*

RONAL Iberica S.A.U. (1)
Poligono La Paz s/n, 44195, Teruel, Spain
Tel.: (34) 978617130
Web Site: http://www.ronal-wheels.es
Alloy Steel Mfr
N.A.I.C.S.: 336390
Manuel Martin Resa *(Mgr-Quality)*

RONAL Polska Sp.z o.o. (1)
Ul W Orkana 155, 58-307, Walbrzych, Poland
Tel.: (48) 748865105
Web Site: http://www.ronal-wheels.pl
Alloy Steel Mfr
N.A.I.C.S.: 336390
Slawomir Krynda *(Head-Production)*

RONAL Queretaro S.A. de C.V. (1)
Parque Industrial Queretaro Km 28, 5 Carr Qro-S L Potosi San Pedrito 108, 76220, Santiago de Queretaro, Mexico
Tel.: (52) 4422389300
Alloy Wheel Distr
N.A.I.C.S.: 423120
Michael Gassner Sr. *(Mgr-Infrastructure)*

RONESANS HOLDING A.S.
Portakal Cicegi Sokak No 33 Y Ayranci, 06540, Ankara, Turkiye
Tel.: (90) 312 840 10 00   TR
Web Site: http://www.ronesans.com
Year Founded: 1993
Emp.: 60
Holding Company; Construction, Real Estate, Energy Services
N.A.I.C.S.: 551112
Erman Ilicak *(Pres)*
Subsidiaries:

Ballast Nedam N.V. (1)
Ringwade 71, 3439 LM, Nieuwegein, Netherlands (100%)
Tel.: (31) 302853333
Web Site: http://www.ballast-nedam.nl
Rev.: $887,087,202
Assets: $576,418,617
Liabilities: $559,449,732
Net Worth: $16,968,885
Earnings: ($53,243,679)
Emp.: 1,747
Fiscal Year-end: 12/31/2017
Civil Engineering & General Building Contracts; Marine Dredging & Land Reclamation; General & Industrial Building, Housing & Road Construction Services
N.A.I.C.S.: 237990
Olav Padberg *(Member-Mgmt Bd)*

Subsidiary (Domestic):
Ballast Nedam Bouw en Ontwikkeling Holding B.V. (2)
Ringwade 71, 3439 LM, Nieuwegein, Netherlands
Tel.: (31) 30 285 33 33
Web Site: http://www.ballast-nedam.com
Holding Company
N.A.I.C.S.: 551112

Subsidiary (Domestic):
Ballast Nedam Bouw en Ontwikkeling B.V. (3)
Ringwade 71, 3439 LM, Nieuwegein, Netherlands
Tel.: (31) 30 285 33 33
Web Site: http://www.ballast-nedam.com
Civil Engineering Construction Services
N.A.I.C.S.: 237990

Subsidiary (Domestic):
Bouwcombinatie Kohnstammlocatie v.o.f. (4)
Ringwade 71, 3439 LM, Nieuwegein, Netherlands
Tel.: (31) 30 285 33 33
Industrial Building Construction Services
N.A.I.C.S.: 236210

Subsidiary (Domestic):
Ballast Nedam Ontwikkelingsmaatschappij B.V. (3)
Ringwade 71, 3439 LM, Nieuwegein, Netherlands
Tel.: (31) 30 285 33 33
Web Site: http://www.ballast-nedam.com
Real Estate Development Services
N.A.I.C.S.: 531390

Subsidiary (Non-US):
Ballast Nedam IPM (2)
Amsterdamstraat 38, 2321, Meer, Belgium
Tel.: (32) 366 543 41
Web Site: http://www.bnipm.nl
Gas Station Maintenance & Construction Services
N.A.I.C.S.: 237120

Subsidiary (Domestic):
Ballast Nedam Infra B.V. (2)
Ringwade 71, 3439 LM, Nieuwegein, Netherlands (100%)
Tel.: (31) 302853030
Web Site: http://www.ballast-nedam.com
Infrastructure, Civil Engineering, Dry Earth Moving, Roads, Railways, Sand Supply & Environmental Technology Services
N.A.I.C.S.: 237990

Subsidiary (Domestic):
Ballast Nedam Asfalt B.V. (3)
Ringwade 71, 3439 LM, Nieuwegein, Netherlands
Tel.: (31) 30 285 33 33
Web Site: http://www.ballast-nedam.com
Civil Engineering Construction Services
N.A.I.C.S.: 237990

Ballast Nedam Engineering B.V. (3)
Ringwade 71, 3439 LM, Nieuwegein, Netherlands
Tel.: (31) 30 285 33 33
Web Site: http://www.ballast-nedam.com
Civil Engineering Construction Services
N.A.I.C.S.: 237990

Ballast Nedam Funderingstechnieken B.V. (3)
Ringwade 71, 3439 LM, Nieuwegein, Netherlands
Tel.: (31) 30 285 33 33
Web Site: http://www.ballast-nedam.com
Offshore Engineering Services
N.A.I.C.S.: 541330

Ballast Nedam ICT B.V. (3)
Ringwade 71, 3439 LM, Nieuwegein, Netherlands
Tel.: (31) 30 285 33 33
Web Site: http://www.ballast-nedam.com
Construction & Engineering Services
N.A.I.C.S.: 237990

Ballast Nedam Infra Business Development B.V. (3)
Ringwade 71, 3439 LM, Nieuwegein, Netherlands
Tel.: (31) 30 285 33 33
Web Site: http://www.ballast-nedam.com
Commercial Building Construction Services
N.A.I.C.S.: 236220

Ballast Nedam Infra Materieel B.V. (3)
Straatweg 29a, 3603 CV, Maarssen, Netherlands
Tel.: (31) 346 24 91 91
Web Site: http://www.ballast-nedam.com
Civil Engineering Construction Services
N.A.I.C.S.: 237990

Ballast Nedam Infra Specialiteiten B.V. (3)
Nijverheidstraat 12, 4143 HM, Leerdam, Netherlands
Tel.: (31) 345639200
Web Site: http://www.infraspecialiteiten.nl
Infrastructure Consulting & Engineering Services
N.A.I.C.S.: 237310

Subsidiary (Domestic):
Spanstaal B.V. (4)
Nijverheidstraat 12, 4143 HM, Leerdam, Netherlands
Tel.: (31) 345 639 200
Civil Construction & Engineering Services
N.A.I.C.S.: 236220

Subsidiary (Domestic):
Ballast Nedam International Product Management B.V. (3)
Nijverheidstraat 12, 4143 HM, Leerdam, Netherlands
Tel.: (31) 345639250
Web Site: http://www.bnipm.nl
Civil Engineering Construction Services
N.A.I.C.S.: 237990

Ballast Nedam Milieutechniek B.V. (3)
Ringwade 71, 3439 LM, Nieuwegein, Netherlands
Tel.: (31) 30 285 33 33
Web Site: http://www.ballast-nedam.com
Engineering & Construction Services
N.A.I.C.S.: 236220

Ballast Nedam Offshore B.V. (3)
Ringwade 71, 3439 LM, Nieuwegein, Netherlands
Tel.: (31) 30 285 33 33
Web Site: http://www.ballast-nedam.com
Offshore Wind Energy Construction Services
N.A.I.C.S.: 237130

Ballast Nedam Specialistisch Grondverzet B.V. (3)
Straatweg 29A, 3762 EC, Maarssen, Netherlands

Tel.: (31) 346 24 91 91
Web Site: http://www.bnmc.ballast-nedam.nl
Specialized Earthmoving Contractor
N.A.I.C.S.: 238910

Ballast Nedam West (3)
Fascinatio Boulevard 582, 2909 VA, Capelle aan den IJssel, Netherlands
Tel.: (31) 10 235 00 00
Web Site: http://www.bnw.ballast-nedam.nl
Civil Engineering Construction Services
N.A.I.C.S.: 237990
Marcek Pfaff *(Dir)*

Dibec B.V. (3)
Celsiuslaan 4b/c, 3439 NC, Nieuwegein, Netherlands
Tel.: (31) 30 285 37 30
Web Site: http://www.dibec.nl
Environmental Technology Consulting Services
N.A.I.C.S.: 541620

Gebr. Van Leeuwen Harmelen B.V. (3)
Ampereweg 17, 3442 AB, Woerden, Netherlands
Tel.: (31) 348 441499
Web Site: http://gvlboringen.com
Hydraulic Engineering Services
N.A.I.C.S.: 541330

Hoco Beton B.V. (3)
Trancheeweg 16-18, 6002 ST, Weert, Netherlands
Tel.: (31) 495579679
Web Site: http://www.hoco-beton.nl
Prefabricated Concrete Products Distr
N.A.I.C.S.: 238120

Ingenieursbureau voor Systemen en Octrooien Spanstaal B.V. (3)
Nijverheidstraat 12, 4143 HM, Leerdam, Netherlands
Tel.: (31) 345 63 92 00
Web Site: http://www.ballast-nedam.com
Civil Engineering Construction Services
N.A.I.C.S.: 237990

Subsidiary (Domestic):
Ballast Nedam International Projects B.V. (2)
Ringwade 71, 3439 LM, Nieuwegein, Netherlands (100%)
Tel.: (31) 30 285 37 27
Web Site: http://www.ballast-nedam.com
Civil Engineering & General Building Contractor
N.A.I.C.S.: 541330

Subsidiary (Domestic):
Ballast Nedam IPM B.V. (3)
Nijverheidstraat 12, 4143 HM, Leerdam, Netherlands
Tel.: (31) 345 639 200
Web Site: http://www.bnipm.nl
Gas Station Maintenance & Construction Services
N.A.I.C.S.: 237120

Subsidiary (Domestic):
Hollestelle Vastgoed Ontwikkeling B.V. (2)
Keern 31, 1624 NB, Hoorn, Netherlands
Tel.: (31) 229 282 400
Construction Engineering Services
N.A.I.C.S.: 541330

IQ Woning B.V. (2)
Peelterbaan 1, 6002 NK, Weert, Netherlands
Tel.: (31) 495 54 46 81
Web Site: http://www.ballast-nedam.com
Commercial Building Construction Services
N.A.I.C.S.: 236220

Laudy Bouw & Ontwikkeling B.V. (2)
Irenelaan 8, 6133 BG, Sittard, Netherlands (100%)
Tel.: (31) 46 451 69 33
Web Site: http://www.laudybouw.nl
Commercial Building Construction Services
N.A.I.C.S.: 236220

Haitsma Beton B.V. (1)
Pinksterblomstrijtte 2, Kootstertille, 9288 ZG, Amsterdam, Friesland, Netherlands
Tel.: (31) 512335678

AND PRIVATE COMPANIES
ROOTS SUSTAINABLE AGRICULTURAL TECHNOLOGIES LTD.

Web Site: http://www.haitsma.nl
Fabrication, Supply & Installation of Prefabricated Concrete Elements
N.A.I.C.S.: 327390
Hendrik Herder *(Acct Mgr-Bridges & Viaducts, Barriers & Industrial Buildings)*

RONG VIET SECURITIES CORPORATION
Floor 1-2-3-4 Viet Dragon Tower 141 Nguyen Du Ben Thanh Ward, District 1, Ho Chi Minh City, Vietnam
Tel.: (84) 862992006   VN
Web Site: http://www.vdsc.com.vn
Year Founded: 2006
Rev.: $13,275,894
Assets: $91,981,820
Liabilities: $50,164,050
Net Worth: $41,817,770
Earnings: $1,385,811
Emp.: 288
Fiscal Year-end: 12/31/19
Investment Banking & Securities Brokerage Services
N.A.I.C.S.: 523150
Nguyen Mien Tuan *(Chm)*

RONGAN PROPERTY CO., LTD.
Rongan Building No 700 Tiantong South Road, Yinzhou district, Ningbo, 315100, Zhejiang, China
Tel.: (86) 57489136789
Web Site: https://www.rongan.com.cn
Year Founded: 1995
000517—(SSE)
Rev.: $1,712,538,481
Assets: $10,382,730,684
Liabilities: $8,769,135,221
Net Worth: $1,613,595,463
Earnings: $266,971,489
Fiscal Year-end: 12/31/20
Real Estate Property Development Services
N.A.I.C.S.: 531311

RONGFENG HOLDING GROUP CO., LTD.
2F Building No 17 Zone 8 No 305 Guanganmenwai Street, Xicheng District, Beijing, 100055, China
Tel.: (86) 1051757685
Web Site: http://www.rongfengholding.com
Year Founded: 1988
000668—(SSE)
Rev.: $89,663,652
Assets: $326,814,696
Liabilities: $142,462,476
Net Worth: $184,352,220
Earnings: ($5,325,372)
Fiscal Year-end: 12/31/22
Holding Company
N.A.I.C.S.: 551112
Huanxin Wang *(Vice Chm, Pres & Gen Mgr)*

RONGFU AQUACULTURE, INC.
Dongdu Room 321 475 Huanshidong Road, Guangzhou, 510075, China
Tel.: (86) 20 87621778   NV
Year Founded: 2008
Sales Range: $25-49.9 Million
Emp.: 188
Fresh Water Fish Aquaculture & Sales
N.A.I.C.S.: 112511
Zhisheng Chen *(Chm)*

RONGSHENG PETRO CHEMICAL CO., LTD.
No 98 Hongyang Road, Yinong Town Xiaoshan District, Hangzhou, 311247, Zhejiang, China
Tel.: (86) 57183529163   CN
Web Site: https://www.cnrspc.com
Year Founded: 1995
002493—(SSE)
Rev.: $40,588,915,536
Assets: $50,907,273,768
Liabilities: $37,265,198,256
Net Worth: $13,642,075,512
Earnings: $468,958,464
Emp.: 3,500
Fiscal Year-end: 12/31/22
Petrochemical Mfr
N.A.I.C.S.: 325110
Subsidiaries:

Zhejiang Rongxiang Chemical Fibre Co., Ltd. (1)
No 98 Hongyang Road Yinong Town, Xiaoshan District, Hangzhou, 311247, Zhejiang, China
Tel.: (86) 571 82527888
Synthetic Fiber Mfr
N.A.I.C.S.: 325220

Zhejiang Yisheng Petrochemical Co.,Ltd. (1)
8 Gangkou Road Xiaogang, Beilun District, Ningbo, 315803, Zhejiang, China
Tel.: (86) 57486189078
Web Site: http://www.rongshengpetrochemical.com
Phosphotungstic Acid Mfr & Distr
N.A.I.C.S.: 325130

RONI HOUSEHOLDS LTD.
No F-55 Addl MIDC Area Ajanta Road, Jalgaon, 425003, Maharashtra, India
Tel.: (91) 7796542369
Web Site: https://www.ronihouseholds.com
Year Founded: 2017
542145—(BOM)
Rev.: $1,731,083
Assets: $2,750,435
Liabilities: $1,208,717
Net Worth: $1,541,718
Earnings: $16,426
Emp.: 9
Fiscal Year-end: 03/31/23
Plastic Household Product Mfr
N.A.I.C.S.: 326199
Nidhi Sirwani *(Co-Founder & CFO)*

RONIN RESOURCES LIMITED
Level 21 459 Collins Street, Melbourne, 3000, VIC, Australia
Tel.: (61) 386303321   AU
Web Site: https://www.roninresources.com.au
Year Founded: 2017
RON—(ASX)
Rev.: $23,441
Assets: $2,591,175
Liabilities: $53,188
Net Worth: $2,537,987
Earnings: ($405,032)
Fiscal Year-end: 06/30/23
Exploration & Mining Services
N.A.I.C.S.: 213115
Joseph Van Den Elsen *(Chm & Exec Chm)*

RONNER VERWALTUNGSGESELLSCHAFT MBH
Riedemannstr. 3, 27572, Bremerhaven, Germany
Tel.: (49) 47180960900
Web Site: https://www.hr-gruppe.de
Year Founded: 1982
Emp.: 1,200
Maritime & Construction Services
N.A.I.C.S.: 541330
Heinrich Ronner *(Owner)*

RONSHINE CHINA HOLDINGS LTD.
Tower 2 Ronshine Sunkwan Center Lane 77 Shangkun Road, Minhang District, Shanghai, China
Tel.: (86) 591963888   Ky
Web Site: https://www.rongxingroup.com
3301—(HKG)
Rev.: $4,220,324,597
Assets: $26,568,222,221
Liabilities: $22,267,135,753
Net Worth: $4,301,086,468
Earnings: ($1,746,568,980)
Emp.: 1,215
Fiscal Year-end: 12/31/22
Holding Company
N.A.I.C.S.: 551112
Feiyan Zeng *(Exec Dir)*

RONSON DEVELOPMENT SE
al Komisji Edukacji Narodowej 57, 02-797, Warsaw, Poland
Tel.: (48) 22 823 9798   NL
Web Site: http://www.ronson.pl
Year Founded: 2007
RON—(WAR)
Rev.: $129,655,179
Assets: $260,604,217
Liabilities: $147,355,885
Net Worth: $113,248,332
Earnings: $10,877,955
Emp.: 78
Fiscal Year-end: 12/31/21
Real Estate Services
N.A.I.C.S.: 531110
Andrzej Gutowski *(Member-Mgmt Bd & Dir-Sls & Mktg)*

ROO HSING CO., LTD.
13F4 No 57 Fuxing North Road, Taipei, 10595, Taiwan
Tel.: (886) 227513111
Web Site: https://www.roohsing.com.tw
4414—(TAI)
Rev.: $442,048,971
Assets: $388,629,012
Liabilities: $250,232,634
Net Worth: $138,396,378
Earnings: ($18,236,469)
Fiscal Year-end: 12/31/23
Garments Mfr
N.A.I.C.S.: 315250
Shih-Hsiu Chen *(Chm)*
Subsidiaries:

Nanjing USA, Inc. (1)
3925 NW 126th Ave, Coral Springs, FL 33065
Tel.: (954) 341-5663
Web Site: https://www.nanjingusa.com
Fashion Cloth Mfr & Whslr
N.A.I.C.S.: 315250

Paneffort (Cambodia) Garment Co., Ltd. (1)
National Road No 2 Kleang Sambatt, Bati District, Pot Sar, 21309, Takeo, Cambodia
Tel.: (855) 93908830
Web Site: http://www.paneffort.com
Medical Safety Product Mfr
N.A.I.C.S.: 339113

ROOLIFEGROUP LIMITED
Unit B11 431 Roberts Road, Subiaco, 6008, WA, Australia
Tel.: (61) 864441702   AU
Web Site: https://www.roolifegroup.com.au
RLG—(ASX)
Rev.: $6,428,425
Assets: $3,399,310
Liabilities: $1,828,547
Net Worth: $1,570,763
Earnings: $1,406,084)
Fiscal Year-end: 06/30/24
Software Development Services
N.A.I.C.S.: 513210

ROOPA INDUSTRIES LTD.
6-2-1012 3rd Floor TGV Mansion Khairatabad, Hyderabad, 500004, Andhra Pradesh, India
Tel.: (91) 8096330007
Web Site: https://www.roopaindustries.com
530991—(BOM)
Rev.: $9,211,114
Assets: $6,780,025
Liabilities: $5,108,291
Net Worth: $1,671,734
Earnings: $161,789
Emp.: 59
Fiscal Year-end: 03/31/23
Pharmaceutical Drug Mfr
N.A.I.C.S.: 325412
T. G. Raghavendra *(Chm & Mng Dir)*

ROOPSHRI RESORTS LIMITED
No 246 Plot No 99 Matheran Tal, Raigad Karjat, Mumbai, 410102, India
Tel.: (91) 2148230069
Web Site: https://www.roopshriresorts.co.in
Year Founded: 1990
542599—(BOM)
Rev.: $85,055
Assets: $1,223,200
Liabilities: $27,253
Net Worth: $1,195,947
Earnings: $3,933
Emp.: 15
Fiscal Year-end: 03/31/23
Resort Operator
N.A.I.C.S.: 721110
Shreyas Shah *(Exec Dir)*

ROOS SPEDITION GMBH
Malscher Strasse 19, Durmersheim, 76448, Germany
Tel.: (49) 72459130
Web Site: http://www.roos-spedition.com
Rev.: $38,854,077
Emp.: 270
Transport Services
N.A.I.C.S.: 488999
Marcus Simpson *(Chief Admin Officer)*
Subsidiaries:

Roos Spedition S.A. (1)
Avenida Catalunya 40-42, Torredembarra, 43830, Tarragona, Spain
Tel.: (34) 977646006
Logistics Consulting Servies
N.A.I.C.S.: 541614

Roos Spedition Sp.z.o.o. (1)
Ul Bobrecka 27, 43-400, Cieszyn, Poland
Tel.: (48) 338184001
Logistics Consulting Servies
N.A.I.C.S.: 541614

ROOTS CORPORATION
1400 Castlefield Avenue, Toronto, M6B 4C4, ON, Canada
Tel.: (416) 781-3574
Web Site: https://www.roots.com
Year Founded: 1973
ROOT—(TSX)
Rev.: $214,214,862
Assets: $307,987,547
Liabilities: $162,438,877
Net Worth: $145,548,670
Earnings: $17,807,040
Emp.: 2,044
Fiscal Year-end: 01/29/22
Hotel Operator
N.A.I.C.S.: 721110
Michael Budman *(Co-Founder)*

ROOTS SUSTAINABLE AGRICULTURAL TECHNOLOGIES LTD.
Beit Halevy 202, Netanya, 4287000, Israel
Tel.: (972) 97689995
Web Site: https://www.rootssat.com

ROOTS SUSTAINABLE AGRICULTURAL TECHNOLOGIES LTD.

Roots Sustainable Agricultural Technologies Ltd.—(Continued)
Year Founded: 2009
ROO—(ASX)
Rev.: $154,000
Assets: $269,000
Liabilities: $1,169,000
Net Worth: ($900,000)
Earnings: ($2,130,000)
Fiscal Year-end: 12/31/22
Agricultural Technology Product Mfr & Distr
N.A.I.C.S.: 333111
Sharon Devir (Co-Exec Dir-Business Development & Co-Founder)

ROPA SIETE LEGUAS SA DE CV
Blvd. del Tecnologico Placido Domingo, Cd Lerdo Dgo, Durango, DG 35159, Mexico
Tel.: (52) 8 717 481400
Web Site:
   http://www.sieteleguas.com
Year Founded: 1959
Clothing Mfr
N.A.I.C.S.: 424350

Subsidiaries:

Aalf's Manufacturing Inc. (1)
1005 4th St, Sioux City, IA 51101-1806
Tel.: (712) 252-1877
Web Site: http://www.aalfs.com
Mens & Boys Trousers & Slacks Mfr
N.A.I.C.S.: 315250
Doug Boden (Pres)

ROPEOK TECHNOLOGY GROUP CO., LTD.
No 188 Fengqi Road Software Park Phase III Xiamen Torch High-tech Zone, Luopute Technology Park, Xiamen, 361008, Fujian, China
Tel.: (86) 5923662258
Web Site: https://www.ropeok.com
Year Founded: 2006
688619—(SHG)
Rev.: $23,756,438
Assets: $263,775,236
Liabilities: $91,707,441
Net Worth: $172,067,796
Earnings: ($19,629,872)
Fiscal Year-end: 12/31/22
Information Technology Services
N.A.I.C.S.: 541512
Yanxing Chen (Chm & Gen Mgr)

ROQUEFORT THERAPEUTICS PLC
27/28 Endcastle Street, London, W1W 8DH, United Kingdom
Tel.: (44) 2039188633
Web Site:
   https://www.roquefortplc.com
Year Founded: 2020
ROQ—(LSE)
Assets: $9,805,879
Liabilities: $708,888
Net Worth: $9,096,991
Earnings: ($2,039,153)
Emp.: 9
Fiscal Year-end: 12/31/22
Biotechnology Research & Development Services
N.A.I.C.S.: 541714
Ajan Reginald (CEO)

ROQUETTE FRERES SA
1 Rue De La Haute Loge, 62136, Lestrem, France
Tel.: (33) 321633600
Web Site: http://www.roquette.com
Year Founded: 1933
Food Products Mfr
N.A.I.C.S.: 311423
Marc Roquette (Pres)

Subsidiaries:

Crest Cellulose Private Limited (1)
Plot No 12 & 13 APIIC Industrial Park, Menakuru Village Naidupet Mandal SPS Nellore District, Nellore, 524 004, Andhra Pradesh, India
Tel.: (91) 9848745566
Food Products Mfr
N.A.I.C.S.: 311999
Anbazhagan Rajendran (Gen Mgr)

Guangxi Nanning Chemical Pharmaceutical Co., Ltd.
8 Pengzhan Road Nanning Economic and Technological Development Area, Nanning, 530031, Guangxi, China
Tel.: (86) 7718013388
Food Products Mfr
N.A.I.C.S.: 311999

OOO Roquette Rus (1)
Schipok str 11 bld 1 floor 1 premises 1 room 13, 115054, Moscow, Russia
Tel.: (7) 4957757587
Web Site: http://www.roquette.com
Emp.: 21
Dehydrated Food Mfr
N.A.I.C.S.: 311423

Qualicaps Co., Ltd. (1)
321-5 Ikezawacho, Yamato-koriyama, 639-1032, Nara, Japan
Tel.: (81) 743560651
Web Site: http://en.qualicaps.co.jp
Sales Range: $150-199.9 Million
Emp.: 338
Pharmaceutical Capsules Mfr
N.A.I.C.S.: 325412
Michikazu Horie (Exec Officer)

Subsidiary (US):

Qualicaps, Inc. (2)
6505 Franz Warner Pkwy, Whitsett, NC 27377-9215
Tel.: (336) 449-3900
Web Site: http://www.qualicaps.com
Sales Range: $50-74.9 Million
Emp.: 180
Pharmaceutical Capsules Mfr
N.A.I.C.S.: 325412

Roquette America Inc. (1)
1003 S 5th St, Keokuk, IA 52632-3915 (100%)
Tel.: (319) 524-5757
Sales Range: $100-124.9 Million
Emp.: 500
Mfr of Hi-Fructose Corn Syrup, Corn Syrup Solids, Corn Starch; Wet Corn Milling
N.A.I.C.S.: 311221
Tara Gilpin (Mgr-Supply Chain Plng & Svc Grp)

Roquette Amilina, AB (1)
J Janonio str 12, LT-35101, Panevezys, Lithuania
Tel.: (370) 45461133
Web Site: http://www.roquetteamilina.com
Food Products Mfr
N.A.I.C.S.: 311999
Edvinas Bernotas (Plant Mgr)

Roquette ApS (1)
Gydevang 39-41, 3450, Allerod, Denmark
Tel.: (45) 69 663 200
Dehydrated Food Mfr
N.A.I.C.S.: 311423

Roquette Asia Pacific Pte. Ltd. (1)
The Metropolis Tower 1 9 North Buona Vista Drive 11-04/05/06, Singapore, 138588, Singapore
Tel.: (65) 62292777
Food Products Mfr
N.A.I.C.S.: 311999
Dominique Baumann (CEO)

Roquette Belgium S.A. (1)
Excelsiorlaan 7 B2, 1930, Zaventem, Belgium
Tel.: (32) 27141300
Food Products Mfr
N.A.I.C.S.: 311999
Hendrik Bierens (Acct Mgr)

Roquette Biotech Nutritionals (Wuhan) Co., Ltd. (1)
No 2 Zhang Bai Road, Dongxihu District, Wuhan, 430040, Hubei, China
Tel.: (86) 2783896688
Food Products Mfr
N.A.I.C.S.: 311999

Roquette CH SA
Chemin de Blandonnet 10, 1214, Vernier, Switzerland
Tel.: (41) 581000700
Food Products Mfr
N.A.I.C.S.: 311999
Edith Martel (Mgr-Cash)

Roquette Canada Ltd. (1)
40117 Road 65N, Box 187, Portage la Prairie, R1N 3B5, MB, Canada
Tel.: (431) 304-0200
Food Products Mfr
N.A.I.C.S.: 311423

Roquette China Co., Ltd. (1)
No 23 Zhen Xing Road, Song Tiao Industrial Area Economic & Technical Development Zone, Lianyungang, 222 069, Jiangsu, China
Tel.: (86) 51885525588
Food Products Mfr
N.A.I.C.S.: 311999

Roquette Czech Republic s.r.o (1)
Za Trati 752 Klatovy IV, 33901, Klatovy, Czech Republic
Tel.: (420) 376370028
Food Products Mfr
N.A.I.C.S.: 311999
Ivana Kudrnkova (Acct Mgr-Support)

Roquette GmbH (1)
Darmstadter Landstrasse 182, 60598, Frankfurt am Main, Germany
Tel.: (49) 69 60 91 050
Dehydrated Food Mfr
N.A.I.C.S.: 311423

Roquette India Private Limited (1)
Office N 702 7th Floor Powai Plaza Hiranandani Gardens-Powai, Mumbai, 400 076, India
Tel.: (91) 22 2570 6775
Dehydrated Food Mfr
N.A.I.C.S.: 311423

Roquette Italia S.p.A. (1)
Via Serravalle 26, Cassano Spinola, 15063, Alessandria, Italy
Tel.: (39) 0143 7741
Dehydrated Food Mfr
N.A.I.C.S.: 311423

Roquette Japan Inc. (1)
Izumi Garden Tower 10 F, PO Box 1 6 1, Minato-ku, Tokyo, 106 6010, Japan (100%)
Tel.: (81) 335853830
Sales Range: $25-49.9 Million
Emp.: 20
Mfr of Sweeteners
N.A.I.C.S.: 325199

Roquette Japan K.K. (1)
2F Kasuga Business Center Building 1-15-15 Nishikata, Bunkyo, Tokyo, 113-0024, Japan
Tel.: (81) 3 3830 1510
Dehydrated Food Mfr
N.A.I.C.S.: 311423

Roquette Klotze GmbH & Co. KG (1)
Lockstedter Chaussee 1 D, 38486, Klotze, Germany
Tel.: (49) 390947260
Food Products Mfr
N.A.I.C.S.: 311999
Jorg Ullmann (Mng Dir & Mgr-Scientific Project)

Roquette Korea Ltd. (1)
12th Fl Samheung Yeoksam Bldg Teheran-ro 14-gil 5 Gangnam-gu 735-10, Yeoksam Dong Kangnam Ku, Seoul, 135-923, Korea (South)
Tel.: (82) 2 2141 3400
Dehydrated Food Mfr
N.A.I.C.S.: 311423

Roquette Laisa Spain, S.A. (1)
Avenida Jaime I S N, Benifaio, 46450, Valencia, Spain
Tel.: (34) 96 178 98 00
Web Site: http://www.roquette.com

Dehydrated Food Mfr
N.A.I.C.S.: 311423

Roquette Malaysia Sdn. Bhd. (1)
Suite 907 Lot 9 01 Level 9 Menara Summit Persiaran Kewajipan USJ 1, UEP, 47600, Subang Jaya, Selangor, Malaysia
Tel.: (60) 386017212
Food Products Mfr
N.A.I.C.S.: 311999

Roquette Management (Shanghai) Co., Ltd. (1)
Room 501-K Wah Centre 1010 Huai Hai Zhong Road, Shanghai, 200031, China
Tel.: (86) 2124229797
Food Products Mfr
N.A.I.C.S.: 311999

Roquette Mexico S.A. de C.V (1)
Blvd Bernardo Quintana 9750 Of 321 Fracc Centro sur Queretaro Qro, 76090, Mexico, Mexico
Tel.: (52) 44 2229 1270
Dehydrated Food Mfr
N.A.I.C.S.: 311423

Roquette Netherlands B.V. (1)
Saturnusstraat 15, 2132 HB, Hoofddorp, Netherlands
Tel.: (31) 233035100
Food Products Mfr
N.A.I.C.S.: 311999

Roquette Nordica Oy (1)
Ahventie 4A 20, 02170, Espoo, Finland
Tel.: (358) 9 315 85 700
Dehydrated Food Mfr
N.A.I.C.S.: 311423

Roquette Poland Sp. z o.o. (1)
Mszczonowska str 4, 02-337, Warsaw, Poland
Tel.: (48) 225741500
Food Products Mfr
N.A.I.C.S.: 311999
Tomasz Siedlecki (Acct Mgr)

Roquette Romania S.A. (1)
Platforma Industriala Sud-Vest Nr 5, 205200, Calafat, Dolj, Romania
Tel.: (40) 251 333 067
Dehydrated Food Mfr
N.A.I.C.S.: 311423

Roquette Sales (Shanghai) Co., Ltd (1)
Room 505-K Wah Centre 1010 Huai Hai Zhong Road, Shanghai, 200031, China
Tel.: (86) 21 54 03 99 22
Dehydrated Food Mfr
N.A.I.C.S.: 311423

Roquette Singapore Pte. Ltd (1)
298 Tiong Bahru Road Suite 14-02/03 Central Plaza, Singapore, 168730, Singapore
Tel.: (65) 6416 3377
Dehydrated Food Mfr
N.A.I.C.S.: 311423

Roquette Tarim ve Gida San. ve Tic. Ltd. Sti. (1)
Buyukdere Cad Harman Sok Duran I Smerkezi No 4 K 334394 Levent, Istanbul, Turkiye
Tel.: (90) 212 234 83 73
Dehydrated Food Mfr
N.A.I.C.S.: 311423

Roquette UK Ltd (1)
Sallow Road Weldon Industrial Estate, Corby, NN17 5JX, Northamptonshire, United Kingdom
Tel.: (44) 15 36 273000
Dehydrated Food Mfr
N.A.I.C.S.: 311423

Sethness-Roquette (China) Co., Ltd. (1)
23 Zhenxing Road Songtiao Industry Zone, Lianyungang, 222069, Jiangsu, China
Tel.: (86) 51886083333
Food Products Mfr
N.A.I.C.S.: 311999
Andre Kwee (Sls Mgr-Technical)

Sethness-Roquette India Ltd. (1)
17/18/19 Gujarat Vepari Maha Mandal Odhav Road, Ahmedabad, 382410, Gujarat, India
Tel.: (91) 7922901030

Food Products Mfr
N.A.I.C.S.: 311999
Hasmukh Patel *(Plant Mgr)*

Sethness-Roquette SAS (1)
3422 W Touhy Ave, Skokie, IL 60076
Tel.: (847) 329-2080
Web Site: http://www.sethness.com
Caramel Color Producer
N.A.I.C.S.: 311999

Sethness-Roquette SASU (1)
Route D Estaires, 59660, Merville, France
Tel.: (33) 328500050
Food Products Mfr
N.A.I.C.S.: 311999
Pierrick Lenne *(Acct Mgr-Global)*

RORZE CORPORATION
1588-2 Michikami Kannabe-cho, Fukuyama-shi, Hiroshima, 720-2104, Japan
Tel.: (81) 849600001
Web Site: https://www.rorze.com
Year Founded: 1985
6323—(TKS)
Rev.: $661,121,230
Assets: $1,107,004,240
Liabilities: $401,194,740
Net Worth: $705,809,500
Earnings: $138,793,840
Emp.: 4,121
Fiscal Year-end: 02/29/24
Conveying Robots & Transportation Equipment Developer, Mfr & Sales
N.A.I.C.S.: 333922
Yoshiyuki Fujishiro *(Pres & CEO)*

Subsidiaries:

Rorze Automation, Inc. (1)
41215 Albrae St, Fremont, CA 94538
Tel.: (510) 687-1340
Web Site: https://www.rorzeautomation.com
Emp.: 1,988
Mfr Services For Semiconductor
N.A.I.C.S.: 334413

Rorze Createch Co., Ltd. (1)
Room 105 No958 Kangqiao East Road, Pudong New District, Shanghai, 201315, China
Tel.: (86) 215 010 1028
Automation Product Mfr
N.A.I.C.S.: 334512

Rorze Engineering GmbH (1)
Lobtauer Str 67, 01159, Dresden, Germany
Tel.: (49) 3515 019 9050
Equipment Broking Services
N.A.I.C.S.: 425120

Rorze Robotech Co., Ltd. (1)
Land plot No F2-F3-F4 Nomura-Haiphong Industrial Zone, An Duong Dist, Haiphong, Vietnam
Tel.: (84) 2253743030
Web Site: https://www.rorzerobotech.com
Sales Range: $100-124.9 Million
Emp.: 1,783
Online News Publishers
N.A.I.C.S.: 513199

Rorze Technology Singapore Pte. Ltd. (1)
Blk 73 Ubi Road1 09-64 Oxley BizHub, 10 11 Biztech Centre, Singapore, 408733, Singapore
Tel.: (65) 67027993
Web Site: http://www.rorze.com
Sales Range: $25-49.9 Million
Semiconductor Material Mfr
N.A.I.C.S.: 333242

Rorze Technology Trading Co., Ltd. (1)
Rm 1705 No 2277 LongYang Rd, Pudong New District, 201204, Shanghai, China
Tel.: (86) 2150101028
Web Site: http://www.rorze.com
Sales Range: $25-49.9 Million
Emp.: 7
Importing ,Exporting & Marketing Services
N.A.I.C.S.: 541910

Rorze Technology, Inc. (1)
1F No 30 Industry E Rd IX, Science-based Industrial Park, Hsinchu, Taiwan
Tel.: (886) 35776482
Web Site: https://www.rorze.com.tw
Semiconductor Wafers Mfr
N.A.I.C.S.: 334413

RORZE SYSTEMS CORPORATION
448-34 Wanjangcheon-ro, Namsamyeon Cheoin-gu, Yongin, Gyeonggido, Korea (South)
Tel.: (82) 313359100
Web Site: https://www.rorze.co.kr
Year Founded: 1997
071280—(KRS)
Rev.: $110,889,945
Assets: $102,596,323
Liabilities: $22,472,854
Net Worth: $80,123,469
Earnings: $15,532,536
Emp.: 242
Fiscal Year-end: 12/31/22
Robot Mfr
N.A.I.C.S.: 333242
Ki-Hwan Park *(CEO)*

ROS AGRO PLC
25 Aphrodite Street 3rd Floor Office 300, 1060, Nicosia, Cyprus
Tel.: (357) 22460890
Web Site: http://www.rusagrogroup.ru
Agriculture Product Distr
N.A.I.C.S.: 327910
Maxim Basov *(CEO)*

ROSAN RESOURCES HOLDINGS LIMITED
Unit C 11/F China Overseas Building 139 Hennessy Road, Wanchai, China (Hong Kong)
Tel.: (852) 2892 0510   BM
Web Site: http://www.rosanresources.com
Rev.: $64,787,468
Assets: $70,291,634
Liabilities: $81,022,858
Net Worth: ($10,731,224)
Earnings: ($13,797,526)
Emp.: 916
Fiscal Year-end: 12/31/19
Holding Company
N.A.I.C.S.: 551112
Cunling Dong *(Exec Dir)*

ROSAR SA
122 Volovatului Street, Radauti, 725400, Romania
Tel.: (40) 230563805
Web Site: http://www.rosar.ro
ROSV—(BUC)
Rev.: $344,367
Assets: $983,301
Liabilities: $177,746
Net Worth: $805,555
Earnings: $2,566
Emp.: 18
Fiscal Year-end: 12/31/19
Cutting Tool Mfr
N.A.I.C.S.: 333517
Danut Mironiuc *(Gen Mgr)*

ROSCAN GOLD CORP.
1550 Bedford Highway Suite 802-Sun Tower, Bedford, B4A 1E6, NS, Canada
Tel.: (902) 832-5555
Web Site: https://www.roscan.ca
2OJ—(DEU)
Rev.: $3,684,966
Assets: $115,298
Liabilities: $1,932,738
Net Worth: ($1,817,440)
Earnings: $3,679,002)
Fiscal Year-end: 10/31/23
Gold Exploration & Mining Services
N.A.I.C.S.: 212220
Nana Bompeh Sangmuah *(Pres & CEO)*

Subsidiaries:

Komet Mali SARL (1)

ROSDERRA IRISH MEATS GROUP LTD
Carrick Road, Offaly, Edenderry, Ireland
Tel.: (353) 469733600   IE
Web Site: http://www.rosderra.ie
Year Founded: 2008
Sales Range: $100-124.9 Million
Emp.: 800
Pork & Bacon Product Mfr
N.A.I.C.S.: 311611
Jim Hanley *(CEO)*

Subsidiaries:

Rosderra Irish Meats Group Ltd - Edenderry Factory (1)
Carrick Road, Offaly, Edenderry, Ireland
Tel.; (353) 46 9733 600
Processed Pork Mfr
N.A.I.C.S.: 311612
Jim Hanley *(Mng Dir)*

ROSDEV MANAGEMENT INC.
7077 Park Ave Ste 600, Montreal, H3N 1X7, QC, Canada
Tel.: (514) 270-7000
Web Site: http://www.rosdev.com
Real Estate Manangement Services
N.A.I.C.S.: 531390
Sal Fratino *(CFO)*

Subsidiaries:

Rosdev Management Inc. - USA Division (1)
418 Clifton Ave Ste 200, Lakewood, NJ 08701
Tel.: (732) 941-0303
Real Estate Manangement Services
N.A.I.C.S.: 531390

Stamford Plaza & Conference Center (1)
2701 Summer St, Stamford, CT 06905
Tel.: (203) 359-1300
Web Site: http://www.stamfordplazahotel.com
Sales Range: $10-24.9 Million
Emp.: 200
Hotel Operations
N.A.I.C.S.: 721110
Sanj Rai *(Gen Mgr)*

ROSDORBANK OJSC
86 Dubininskaya str, Moscow, 115093, Russia
Tel.: (7) 4952760022
Web Site: https://www.rdb.ru
Year Founded: 1991
RDRB—(MOEX)
Sales Range: $25-49.9 Million
Emp.: 250
Commercial Banking Services
N.A.I.C.S.: 522110
Gurin Gleb Yurievich *(Chm)*

ROSE DRUCK GMBH
In den Waldstucken 2, 76829, Landau, Germany
Tel.: (49) 6341590250
Web Site: http://www.rose-druck.de
Year Founded: 1843
Sales Range: $10-24.9 Million
Emp.: 100
Commercial Printing Services
N.A.I.C.S.: 323111
Bernd Rose *(Owner & CEO)*

ROSE MERC LIMITED
Office No 12 PriyadarshaniRoj Bazar Soc Sector 10 Khanda Colony, New-Panvel West, Mumbai, 410206, Maharashtra, India
Tel.: (91) 2235138397
Web Site: https://www.rosemerc.in
Year Founded: 1985

512115—(BOM)
Rev.: $43,095
Assets: $365,707
Liabilities: $37,932
Net Worth: $327,775
Earnings: ($40,068)
Fiscal Year-end: 03/31/22
Management Consulting Services
N.A.I.C.S.: 541618

ROSEDALE AVIATION HOLDINGS LTD
Jack Walker House, Exeter International Airport, Exeter, EX5 2HL, Devon, United Kingdom
Tel.: (44) 1392366669
Web Site: http://www.flybe.com
Sales Range: $25-49.9 Million
Emp.: 15
Holding Company; Aviation Services
N.A.I.C.S.: 551112

ROSEKAMAL TEXTILES LTD.
Dr Amichand Shah's Wadi, Rampura Tunki, Surat, 395 003, India
Tel.: (91) 0261 2419019   In
Web Site: http://www.rosekamal.com
Sales Range: Less than $1 Million
Commercial Trading Services
N.A.I.C.S.: 523150
Rupesh V. Diwan *(CFO)*

ROSELABS FINANCE LIMITED
412 17G Vardhaman Chamber Cawasji Patel Road Horniman Circle Fort, Mumbai, 400001, India
Tel.: (91) 2261334400
Web Site: https://www.roselabsfinancelimited.in
Year Founded: 1995
531324—(BOM)
Rev.: $18,080
Assets: $13,548
Liabilities: $529,573
Net Worth: ($516,024)
Earnings: $241,700
Fiscal Year-end: 03/31/23
Finance Management Services
N.A.I.C.S.: 522291
Nilesh Rawat *(Mng Dir)*

ROSENBAUER INTERNATIONAL AG
Paschinger Strasse 90, 4060, Leonding, Austria
Tel.: (43) 73267940
Web Site: https://www.rosenbauer.com
ROI—(STU)
Rev.: $1,049,260,738
Assets: $1,050,682,063
Liabilities: $849,757,177
Net Worth: $200,924,887
Earnings: ($24,117,203)
Emp.: 4,078
Fiscal Year-end: 12/31/22
Fire Fighting Vehicles, Aircraft & Related Components Mfr
N.A.I.C.S.: 336110
Christian Reisinger *(Chm-Supervisory Bd)*

Subsidiaries:

Eskay Rosenbauer Sdn. Bhd. (1)
Block C Unit 11 Ground Floor Simpang 145 Jalan Pasir Berakas, BB1314, Bandar Seri Begawan, Brunei Darussalam
Tel.: (673) 2345670
Fire Service Vehicle & Firefighting Equipment Mfr
N.A.I.C.S.: 336211

Metz Aerials GmbH & Co. KG (1)
Carl-Metz-Strasse 9, 76185, Karlsruhe, Germany   (100%)
Tel.: (49) 72159650
Web Site: http://www.metz-online.de

ROSENBAUER INTERNATIONAL AG

Rosenbauer International AG—(Continued)
Sales Range: $50-74.9 Million
Emp.: 250
Motor Vehicle Electrical & Electronic Equipment Mfr
N.A.I.C.S.: 336320

Metz Aerials Management GmbH (1)
Carl-Metz-Strasse 9, Karlsruhe, 76135, Germany
Tel.: (49) 72159650
Web Site: http://www.metz-online.de
Sales Range: $50-74.9 Million
Emp.: 216
Motor Vehicle Electrical & Electronic Equipment Mfr
N.A.I.C.S.: 336320

Rosenbauer America, LLC (1)
5240 257th St, Wyoming, MN 55092
Tel.: (605) 543-5591
Web Site: https://rosenbaueramerica.com
Fire Fighting Vehicle & Equipment Mfr
N.A.I.C.S.: 336120

Rosenbauer Australia Pty. Ltd. (1)
Unit 2 01 1 2-6 Leonardo Drive Airport, Brisbane, 4008, QLD, Australia
Tel.: (61) 738606010
Fire Service Vehicle & Firefighting Equipment Mfr
N.A.I.C.S.: 336211
Arthur Welmer (Mng Dir)

Rosenbauer Brandschutz Deutschland GmbH (1)
Krugbackerstrasse 3, Mogendorf, 56424, Gladbeck, Germany
Tel.: (49) 262396420
Web Site: http://www.gs-brandschutz.de
Fire Service Vehicle & Firefighting Equipment Mfr
N.A.I.C.S.: 336211

Rosenbauer Deutschland GmbH (1)
Bahnhofstrasse 16 B, Passau, 94032, Germany (100%)
Tel.: (49) 8516096
Web Site: http://www.rosenbauer.com
Sales Range: $50-74.9 Million
Emp.: 10
Automobile & Motor Vehicle Whslr
N.A.I.C.S.: 423110

Rosenbauer Deutschland GmbH (1)
Rudolf Breitscheid Strasse 79, 14943, Luckenwalde, Germany
Tel.: (49) 3371 6905 0
Web Site: http://www.rosenbauer.com
Emp.: 270
Fire Fighting Equipment Mfr
N.A.I.C.S.: 336390

Rosenbauer E-Technology Development GmbH (1)
Paschinger Strasse 90, 4060, Leonding, Austria
Tel.: (43) 73267940
Fire Service Vehicle & Firefighting Equipment Mfr
N.A.I.C.S.: 336211

Rosenbauer Espanola SA (1)
Marques de Monteagudo 24 3 B, 28028, Madrid, Spain
Tel.: (34) 915939822
Web Site: http://www.rosenbauer.es
Sales Range: $25-49.9 Million
Emp.: 15
Motor Vehicle Parts Mfr
N.A.I.C.S.: 336390

Rosenbauer Finanzierung GmbH (1)
Bahnhofstr 16B, Passau, Germany (100%)
Tel.: (49) 8516096
Sales Range: $300-349.9 Million
Emp.: 1,800
Business Services
N.A.I.C.S.: 561499

Rosenbauer France S.A.R.L. (1)
1 Bis Boulevard Monge, 69330, Meyzieu, France
Tel.: (33) 479791740
Emp.: 35
Automotive Mfr & Distr
N.A.I.C.S.: 332119

Rosenbauer Holdings Inc. (1)
5181 260th St, Wyoming, MN 55092 (100%)
Tel.: (651) 462-1000
Web Site: http://www.rosenbauer.com
Sales Range: $75-99.9 Million
Emp.: 180
Holding Company
N.A.I.C.S.: 551112

Rosenbauer Italia S.R.L. (1)
Sonnenstrasse 34, 39010, Andria, Italy
Tel.: (39) 0471510316
Emp.: 10
Fire Fighting Vehicle Equipment Mfr & Distr
N.A.I.C.S.: 336120

Rosenbauer Karlsruhe GmbH (1)
Carl-Metz-Strasse 9, 76185, Karlsruhe, Germany
Tel.: (49) 72159650
Automatic Hydraulic Turntable Ladder Mfr & Whslr
N.A.I.C.S.: 336340

Rosenbauer Management Services GmbH (1)
Paschinger Strasse 90, 4060, Leonding, Austria (100%)
Tel.: (43) 73267940
Web Site: http://www.rosenbauer.com
Sales Range: $200-249.9 Million
Emp.: 1,000
Motor Vehicle Electrical & Electronic Equipment Mfr
N.A.I.C.S.: 336320

Rosenbauer Mode Handels GmbH (1)
Landstrasse 12, 4020, Linz, Austria
Tel.: (43) 732777459
Automobile & Motor Vehicle Whslr
N.A.I.C.S.: 423110

Rosenbauer Motors LLC (1)
5181 260th St, Wyoming, MN 55092 (100%)
Tel.: (651) 462-1000
Web Site: http://www.rosenbauer.com
Sales Range: $50-74.9 Million
Emp.: 170
Motor Vehicle Parts Mfr
N.A.I.C.S.: 336390

Rosenbauer Osterreich GmbH (1)
Paschinger Strasse 90, 4060, Leonding, Austria (100%)
Tel.: (43) 73267940
Web Site: http://www.rosenbauer.com
Sales Range: $200-249.9 Million
Emp.: 1,000
Motor Vehicle Electrical & Electronic Equipment Mfr
N.A.I.C.S.: 336320

Rosenbauer Polska Sp.z. o.o. (1)
Ul Konarskiego 50, 05-092, Lomianki, Poland
Tel.: (48) 227516896
Fire Service Vehicle & Firefighting Equipment Mfr
N.A.I.C.S.: 336211

Rosenbauer Rovereto Srl (1)
Viale Caproni 7, 38068, Rovereto, Italy
Tel.: (39) 0464658800
Fire Service Vehicle & Firefighting Equipment Mfr
N.A.I.C.S.: 336211

Rosenbauer Saudi Arabia Ltd. (1)
King Fahad Road 6605 Al Ulaya Unit No 3 12211-3529, PO Box 14175, 11424, Riyadh, Saudi Arabia
Tel.: (966) 112172233
Fire Service Vehicle & Firefighting Equipment Mfr
N.A.I.C.S.: 336211

Rosenbauer Schweiz AG (1)
Eichweg 4, 8154, Oberglatt, Switzerland
Tel.: (41) 434111212
Fire Fighting Vehicle Equipment Mfr & Distr
N.A.I.C.S.: 336120

Rosenbauer South Africa (Pty.) Ltd. (1)
997 Richards Drive Unit 10 Halfway House 1685, Johannesburg, South Africa
Tel.: (27) 118057912
Fire Service Vehicle & Firefighting Equipment Mfr

N.A.I.C.S.: 336211

Rosenbauer South Dakota, LLC (1)
100 3rd St, Lyons, SD 57041
Tel.: (605) 543-5591
Web Site: http://www.rosenbaueramerica.com
Sales Range: $50-74.9 Million
Firefighting Vehicles & Equipment Mfr
N.A.I.C.S.: 336120
Scott Oyen (CEO)

Rosenbauer Switzerland AG (1)
Eichweg 4, 8154, Oberglatt, Switzerland
Tel.: (41) 434111212
Web Site: http://www.rosenbauer.com
Motor Vehicle Electrical & Electronic Equipment Mfr
N.A.I.C.S.: 336320

Rosenbauer UK Plc (1)
Concept House Huddersfield Road, Meltham, Holmfirth, HD9 4AN, West Yorkshire, United Kingdom
Tel.: (44) 1484854134
Web Site: http://www.rosenbauer.co.uk
Fire Protection Equipments Distr
N.A.I.C.S.: 423840

Rosenbauer YongQiang Fire Fighting Vehicles Ltd. (1)
Jinfu Road Tangchun Industrial Estate, Liaobu, Dongguan, 523407, Guangdong, China
Tel.: (86) 76983269793
Web Site: http://www.rosenbauer.com
Motor Vehicle Electrical & Electronic Equipment Mfr
N.A.I.C.S.: 336320

Rosenbauer d.o.o. (1)
Pot K Sejmiscu 28 A, 1231, Ljubljana, Slovenia
Tel.: (386) 15309110
Fire Service Vehicle & Firefighting Equipment Mfr
N.A.I.C.S.: 336211

S.K. Rosenbauer Pte. Ltd. (1)
8 Tuas Drive 2, Singapore, 638643, Singapore (100%)
Tel.: (65) 68623155
Web Site: http://www.rosenbauer.com
Motor Vehicle Electrical & Electronic Equipment Mfr
N.A.I.C.S.: 336320

Service18 S.A.R.L. (1)
12 Rue de la Petite Eau, La Motte-Servolex, 73290, Tours-en-Savoie, France
Tel.: (33) 479791740
Fire Service Vehicle & Firefighting Equipment Mfr
N.A.I.C.S.: 336211

ROSETTA CAPITAL LIMITED
Rectory House Thame Road, Haddenham, Aylesbury, HP17 8DA, Bucks, United Kingdom
Tel.: (44) 1844 291 444 UK
Web Site: http://www.rosettacapital.com
Privater Equity Firm
N.A.I.C.S.: 523999
Jonathan Hepple (Partner)

Subsidiaries:

ClanoTech AB (1)
Fogdevreten 2, 17165, Solna, Sweden
Tel.: (46) 70 3747179
Web Site: http://www.clanotech.se
Pharmaceutical Developer & Mfr
N.A.I.C.S.: 325412
Yihai Cao (Founder)

ROSETTI MARINO S.P.A.
Via Trieste 230, 48122, Ravenna, Italy
Tel.: (39) 0544878111
Web Site: https://www.rosetti.it
Year Founded: 1925
YRM—(ITA)
Sales Range: $350-399.9 Million
Emp.: 792
Engineeering Services
N.A.I.C.S.: 541330

Medardo Ranieri (Chm)

Subsidiaries:

Basis Engineering Srl (1)
Via Corradino d'Ascanio 4, 20142, Milan, Italy
Tel.: (39) 02 8934641
Web Site: http://www.basisengineering.it
Engineeering Services
N.A.I.C.S.: 541330

Fores Engineering Srl (1)
Via Secondo Casadei 12, 47122, Forli, Italy
Tel.: (39) 0543 813811
Web Site: http://www.fores.it
Engineeering Services
N.A.I.C.S.: 541330

Green Methane S.R.L. (1)
Via Trieste 230, 48122, Ravenna, Italy
Tel.: (39) 0544878111
Web Site: https://www.greenmethane.it
Power Generation Services
N.A.I.C.S.: 221118

Rosetti Doo (1)
Verdieva 9, 51000, Rijeka, Croatia
Tel.: (385) 51 312138
Emp.: 1
Engineeering Services
N.A.I.C.S.: 541330
Ognjen Antunac (Mgr)

Rosetti General Contracting Lda (1)
Edificio Cooperativa Agricola do Funchal Bloco D 4 Andar Sala DN, Madeira, 9050-555, Funchal, Portugal
Tel.: (351) 291 745122
Engineeering Services
N.A.I.C.S.: 541330

Rosetti Kazakhstan L.L.P. (1)
Grand Nur Plaza Hotel 29 A Microdistrict, 130000, Aktau, Kazakhstan
Tel.: (7) 7292 201141
Engineeering Services
N.A.I.C.S.: 541330

Rosetti Marino Project OOO (1)

Tecon S.r.l. (1)
Milanofiori - Strada 1 Palazzo WTC, Assago, 20090, Milan, Italy
Tel.: (39) 029 288 2150
Web Site: https://teconsrl.it
Gas Pipeline & Related Structures Construction Services
N.A.I.C.S.: 237120

ROSGOSSTRAKH INSURANCE COMPANY PJSC
Parkovaya street house 3, Lyubertsy, 140002, Russia
Tel.: (7) 8002009977
Web Site: https://www.rgs.ru
Year Founded: 1921
RGSS—(MOEX)
Sales Range: Less than $1 Million
Risk Managemeng Srvices
N.A.I.C.S.: 524113

ROSHAN PACKAGES LIMITED
325 G-III M A, Johar Town, Lahore, Pakistan
Tel.: (92) 42352907348
Web Site: https://www.roshanpackages.com.pk
Year Founded: 2002
RPL—(PSX)
Rev.: $43,398,990
Assets: $45,710,367
Liabilities: $15,667,853
Net Worth: $30,042,514
Earnings: $105,818
Emp.: 516
Fiscal Year-end: 06/30/23
Flexible Packaging Products Mfr
N.A.I.C.S.: 326112
Junaid Iqbal (Asst Mgr-Comml)

ROSHOW TECHNOLOGY CO., LTD.
No 38 Luxiao Road, Diankou Town, Zhuji, 311814, Zhejiang, China

Tel.: (86) 57587061113
Web Site:
http://www.roshowtech.com
Year Founded: 1984
002617—(SSE)
Rev.: $469,194,336
Assets: $1,393,551,432
Liabilities: $536,006,484
Net Worth: $857,544,948
Earnings: ($35,915,724)
Fiscal Year-end: 12/31/22
Electromagnetic Wire Products Mfr
N.A.I.C.S.: 335929
Lu Yong (Chm)

Subsidiaries:

Zhuji Roshow Electromagnetic Wire Co., Ltd. (1)
Roshow Road No 38 Diankou, Zhuji, 311814, Zhejiang, China
Tel.: (86) 575 87613666
Copper Wires Mfr
N.A.I.C.S.: 331420
Xiaojun Lu (Gen Mgr)

ROSMERTA TECHNOLOGIES LIMITED

137 Udyog Vihar Phase-I, Gurgaon, 122016, Haryana, India
Tel.: (91) 1244990800
Web Site:
http://www.rosmertatech.com
Sales Range: $10-24.9 Million
Emp.: 400
Optical Smart Card Technology Researcher & Developer Services
N.A.I.C.S.: 541715
Satjit Singh Dhillon (Mng Dir)

Subsidiaries:

Rosmerta Engineering Pvt. Ltd. (1)
137 Udyog Vihar Phase - I, Gurgaon, 122016, India
Tel.: (91) 124 4990800
Web Site: http://www.rosmertaengg.com
Electric Equipment Mfr
N.A.I.C.S.: 334511
Arun Manchanda (Asst Gen Mgr-Bus Dev)

ROSS GROUP PLC

71 - 75 Shelton Street Convent Garden, London, WC2H 9JQ, United Kingdom
Tel.: (44) 2380675500 UK
Web Site:
https://therossgroupplc.com
RGP—(LSE)
Rev.: $58,382
Assets: $1,968,694
Liabilities: $8,772,229
Net Worth: ($6,803,535)
Earnings: ($1,986,344)
Emp.: 11
Fiscal Year-end: 12/31/20
Consumer Electronic Products Distr
N.A.I.C.S.: 423620
Barry Richard Pettitt (Chm, CEO & Mng Dir)

ROSS RIVER MINERALS INC.

Suite 1050 - 1040 West Georgia St, Vancouver, V6E 4H1, BC, Canada
Tel.: (604) 638-8063 BC
Year Founded: 1996
RRMLF—(OTCEM)
Assets: $10,436
Liabilities: $405,623
Net Worth: ($395,188)
Earnings: ($38,062)
Fiscal Year-end: 12/31/23
Mineral Exploration Services
N.A.I.C.S.: 213114

ROSS VIDEO LIMITED

8 John Street, Iroquois, K0E 1K0, ON, Canada
Tel.: (613) 652-4886

Web Site: http://www.rossvideo.com
Audio & Video Equipment Mfr
N.A.I.C.S.: 334310
Jared Schatz (VP-Sls-US & Canada)

Subsidiaries:

Abekas, Inc. (1)
1233 Midas Way, Sunnyvale, CA 94085
Tel.: (650) 470-0900
Web Site: http://www.abekas.com
Sales Range: $1-9.9 Million
Emp.: 12
Mfg Radio/Tv Communication Equipment
N.A.I.C.S.: 334220
Junaid Sheikh (Pres & CEO)

ROSSANO JOINT STOCK COMPANY

Lot No 12 Road No 2 Tan Tao Industrial Park, Binh Tan District, Ho Chi Minh City, Vietnam
Tel.: (84) 8 7505 684 VN
Web Site:
http://www.rossanoonline.com
Year Founded: 1999
Furniture Mfr
N.A.I.C.S.: 337121
Eric Kah Meng Ong (Founder & Gen Dir)

ROSSARI BIOTECH LIMITED

201-A & B Ackruti Corporate Park Lbs Marg Next To Ge Gardens, Kanjurmarg W, Mumbai, 400078, India
Tel.: (91) 2261233800
Web Site: https://www.rossari.com
Year Founded: 2003
543213—(BOM)
Rev.: $98,080,028
Assets: $76,623,866
Liabilities: $20,826,488
Net Worth: $55,797,378
Earnings: $10,926,279
Emp.: 370
Fiscal Year-end: 03/31/21
Chemicals Mfr
N.A.I.C.S.: 325199
Puneet Arora (CEO)

Subsidiaries:

Buzil Rossari Private Limited (1)
201-A & B Ackruti Corporate Park Next to GE Gardens, Kanjurmarg W, Mumbai, 400078, India
Tel.: (91) 2261233800
Web Site: https://www.buzil-rossari.com
Chemical Products Mfr
N.A.I.C.S.: 325998

ROSSELL INDIA LTD.

Jindal Towers Block B 4th Floor 21/1A/3 Darga Road, Kolkata, 700017, India
Tel.: (91) 3322801120
Web Site: https://www.rosselltea.com
533168—(BOM)
Rev.: $42,871,674
Assets: $61,593,789
Liabilities: $27,175,853
Net Worth: $34,417,937
Earnings: $3,314,969
Emp.: 5,725
Fiscal Year-end: 03/31/23
Tea Mfr
N.A.I.C.S.: 311920
Harsh Mohan Gupta (Chm & Co-CEO)

Subsidiaries:

Rossell Techsys Inc. (1)
2400 W Southern Ave Ste 103, Tempe, AZ 85282
Tel.: (415) 630-3124
Education Training Services
N.A.I.C.S.: 611710

Rossell Techsys Ltd. (1)
No 58 - C Road No 2 Hi-Tech Defence Aerospace Park, Behind KIADB Industrial Area Devanahalli Jala Hobli Budigere Post, Bengaluru, 562165, India
Tel.: (91) 8068434500
Web Site: https://www.rosselltechsys.com
Emp.: 650
Electric Panel & Rack Mfr
N.A.I.C.S.: 335313

ROSSI RESIDENCIAL SA

Henri Dunant 873 6th Floor, Santo Antonio Farm, Sao Paulo, 04709-111, SP, Brazil
Tel.: (55) 1140582502
Web Site:
https://www.rossiresidencial.com.br
Year Founded: 1992
RSID3—(BRAZ)
Rev.: $1,772,761
Assets: $96,973,595
Liabilities: $249,591,527
Net Worth: ($152,617,933)
Earnings: $45,530,647
Fiscal Year-end: 12/31/23
Commercial & Residential Real Estate & Construction Services
N.A.I.C.S.: 236220
Fernando Miziara de Mattos Cunha (CFO & Officer-IR)

ROSSITTIS GMBH

Naturstein-Import Stehfenstr 59-61, Holzwickede, 59439, Germany
Tel.: (49) 2301 91332 0
Web Site: http://www.rossittis.de
Sales Range: $25-49.9 Million
Emp.: 60
Cut Stone Distr
N.A.I.C.S.: 423940
Gerhard Rossittis (Mng Dir)

ROSSIYA BANK JSC

2 Liter A Rastrelli Sq, 191124, Saint Petersburg, Russia
Tel.: (7) 8123358500
Web Site: http://www.abr.ru
Year Founded: 1990
Financial Consulting Services
N.A.I.C.S.: 523940
Boris Aleksandrovich Tikhonenko (Deputy CEO)

ROSSLYN DATA TECHNOLOGIES PLC

60 Gracechurch Street 6th Floor, Hampshire, London, EC3V 0HR, United Kingdom
Tel.: (44) 2032858008
Web Site:
https://www.rosslyndatatech.com
RDT—(AIM)
Rev.: $10,070,209
Assets: $14,209,898
Liabilities: $7,926,369
Net Worth: $6,283,528
Earnings: ($2,677,424)
Emp.: 66
Fiscal Year-end: 04/30/21
Data Analysis
N.A.I.C.S.: 518210
Charles Clark (Pres)

ROSSMANN SAS

La Vancelle Gare, BP 80068, 67602, Selestat, France
Tel.: (33) 388579077
Web Site: http://en.rossmann.com
Year Founded: 1922
Sales Range: $600-649.9 Million
Emp.: 244
Corrugated Cardboard Mfr
N.A.I.C.S.: 322211
Bernard Rossmann (Chm)

ROSSMAX INTERNATIONAL LTD.

12F No 189 Kang Chien Road, Taipei, 114, Taiwan

Tel.: (886) 226597888
Web Site: https://www.rossmax.com
Year Founded: 1988
4121—(TPE)
Rev.: $135,851,796
Assets: $124,902,167
Liabilities: $64,104,399
Net Worth: $60,797,768
Earnings: $6,783,791
Fiscal Year-end: 12/31/22
Blood Pressure Monitor Mfr & Distr
N.A.I.C.S.: 339112
Chih-Ping Liu (Chm & Pres)

Subsidiaries:

Rossmax (Shanghai) Incorporation Ltd. (1)
No 6018 Huyi Rd Waigang, Jiading District, Shanghai, China
Tel.: (86) 2169575888
Healthcare Product Retailer
N.A.I.C.S.: 524114

Rossmax Swiss GmbH (1)
Widnauerstrasse 1 CH, 9435, Heerbrugg, Switzerland
Tel.: (41) 715444325
Healthcare Product Mfr & Distr
N.A.I.C.S.: 334510

ROSSS SPA

Viale Kennedy 97, Scarperia, 50038, Florence, Italy
Tel.: (39) 05584001
ROS—(ITA)
Sales Range: $10-24.9 Million
Emp.: 134
Storage Solutions
N.A.I.C.S.: 493110
Fabio Berti (CFO & Dir-Fin)

ROSTRA HOLDINGS PTE. LTD.

07/12 Manhattan House, 151 Chin Swee Road, Singapore, Singapore
Tel.: (65) 64388039 SG
Web Site:
https://www.rostraholdings.com
Investment Services
N.A.I.C.S.: 523999

Subsidiaries:

Decheng Technology AG (1)
Martin-Luther-Platz 26, Dusseldorf, 40212, Germany (68.37%)
Tel.: (49) 21178179033
Web Site:
http://www.dechengtechnology.com
Sales Range: $10-24.9 Million
Emp.: 119
Polyurethane Resin Mfr
N.A.I.C.S.: 326150
Xiao Fang Zhu (Chief Exec & Fin Officer)

ROSULARIA VERMOGENS-VERWALTUNGSGESELL-SCHAFT MBH

Palmaille 67, Hamburg, 22767, Germany
Tel.: (49) 40380227580
Sales Range: $1-9.9 Million
Asset Management
N.A.I.C.S.: 523999
Jesus Antonio Ramirez Garza (Pres)

ROTAK INSTRUMENTS (PVT) LTD

No 38 Sri Dewananda Mawatha, Piliyandala, 10300, Sri Lanka
Tel.: (94) 112609592 LK
Web Site: http://www.rotak.lk
Year Founded: 2007
Laboratory Equipment Distr
N.A.I.C.S.: 423490

ROTALA GROUP LIMITED

Hallbridge Way Tipton Rd Tividale, Tipton, B69 3HW, W Midlands, United Kingdom
Tel.: (44) 1213222222

ROTALA GROUP LIMITED

Rotala Group Limited—(Continued)

Emp.: 100
Local Bus Transportation Services
N.A.I.C.S.: 485113

Subsidiaries:

Rotala Plc (1)
Hallbridge Way Tipton Rd Tividale, Tipton,
B69 3HW, W Midlands, United Kingdom
Tel.: (44) 1213222222
Web Site: http://www.rotalaplc.com
Rev.: $115,231,054
Assets: $115,312,517
Liabilities: $73,485,237
Net Worth: $41,827,280
Earnings: $1,584,459
Emp.: 1,418
Fiscal Year-end: 11/30/2022
Local Bus Transportation Services
N.A.I.C.S.: 485113
Simon Dunn *(CEO)*

Subsidiary (Domestic):

Flights Hallmark Limited (2)
Beacon House Long Acre, Aston, Birmingham, B7 5JJ, West Midlands, United Kingdom
Tel.: (44) 1213222222
Web Site: http://www.flightshallmark.com
Sales Range: $25-49.9 Million
Emp.: 20
Transportation Services
N.A.I.C.S.: 485991

The Diamond Bus Company Limited (2)
Hallbridge Way Tipton Road, Tividale, Warley, B69 3HW, West Midlands, United Kingdom
Tel.: (44) 1213222222
Web Site: http://www.diamondbuses.com
Sales Range: $125-149.9 Million
Emp.: 300
Bus Shuttle Services
N.A.I.C.S.: 485113

ROTAM GLOBAL AGROSCIENCES LTD.

26/F E-Trade Plaza 24 Lee Chung Street, Chai Wan, China (Hong Kong)
Tel.: (852) 28960662
Web Site: http://www.rotam.com
4141—(TAI)
Rev.: $277,739,012
Assets: $555,194,402
Liabilities: $378,939,976
Net Worth: $176,254,426
Earnings: ($15,041,103)
Emp.: 1,030
Fiscal Year-end: 12/31/19
Herbicides, Insecticides & Fungicides Mfr
N.A.I.C.S.: 325320
William Yuen *(CFO-Rotam Crop-Sciences Limited)*

Subsidiaries:

Jiangsu Rotam Chemistry Co., Ltd. (1)
No 88 Rotam Rd ETDZ, Kunshan, 215301, Jiangsu, China
Tel.: (86) 512 5771 1988
Web Site: http://www.rotamchina.com
Agricultural Chemical Mfr
N.A.I.C.S.: 325320

Rotam Agro Colombia S.A.S. (1)
Calle 90 19C 74 Of 201 Blue Tower, Bogota, Colombia
Tel.: (57) 1 635 6885
Web Site: http://www.rotam.com
Emp.: 23
Agricultural Chemical Distr
N.A.I.C.S.: 424910
Alok Kumar *(Gen Mgr)*

Rotam Agrochemical Co., Ltd. (1)
7/F Cheung Tat Centre No 18 Cheung Lee Street, Chai Wan, China (Hong Kong)
Tel.: (852) 2505 3798
Agricultural Chemical Distr
N.A.I.C.S.: 424690

Rotam Agrochemical Europe Limited (1)
75 cours Albert Thomas 6eme avenue Batiment D, 69003, Lyon, France
Tel.: (33) 427027333
Web Site: http://www.rotam.com
Sales Range: $25-49.9 Million
Emp.: 30
Agricultural Chemical Mfr
N.A.I.C.S.: 325320
Jeanmichel Guhamel *(Mng Dir)*

Rotam Costa Rica CRI S.A. (1)
Costado Norte Walmart Curridabat Carretera Vieja a Tres Rios, Condominio Higueron No 7, San Jose, Costa Rica
Tel.: (506) 2271 6106
Sales Range: $50-74.9 Million
Emp.: 2
Agricultural Chemical Distr
N.A.I.C.S.: 424910

Rotam Europe Ltd. (1)
Hamilton House Mabledon Place, London, WC1H 9BB, United Kingdom
Tel.: (44) 2 079 530447
Web Site: http://www.rotam.co.uk
Agricultural Chemical Distr
N.A.I.C.S.: 424910

Rotam MAGHREB Limited (1)
Cite 1200 logements Coop Granitex Bt 4 No 3, Bab Ezzouar, Algiers, Algeria
Tel.: (213) 661 548 929
Agricultural Chemical Mfr
N.A.I.C.S.: 325320

Rotam Mexico S.A. de C.V. (1)
Av Vallarta No 6503 Local G-12, Col Ciudad Granja, Zapopan, 45010, Jalisco, Mexico
Tel.: (52) 33 3110 0888
Web Site: http://www.rotammexico.com
Agricultural Chemical Mfr
N.A.I.C.S.: 325320

Rotam North America, Inc. (1)
4900 Koger Blvd Ste 140, Greensboro, NC 27407
Tel.: (336) 346-8802
Web Site: http://www.rotamnorthamerica.com
Agricultural Chemical Mfr
N.A.I.C.S.: 325320
Tom Chavez *(Gen Mgr)*

Rotam Taiwan Limited (1)
3F No 81 Sec 2 Chengde Rd, Datong Dist, Taipei, 10352, Taiwan
Tel.: (886) 2 2555 5218
Agricultural Chemical Mfr
N.A.I.C.S.: 325320

Rotam de Argentina Agroquimica SRL (1)
1363 Santa Fe St Floor 12, 2000, Rosario, Santa Fe, Argentina
Tel.: (54) 341 424 0612
Web Site: http://www.rotamargentina.com.ar
Agricultural Chemical Mfr
N.A.I.C.S.: 325320

Rotam de Chile Agroquimica Ltda. (1)
2318 - Oficina 31, Providencia, Santiago, 7510052, Chile
Tel.: (56) 2 233 9152
Web Site: http://www.rotamchile.com
Agricultural Chemical Mfr
N.A.I.C.S.: 325320

ROTANA HOTEL MANAGEMENT CORPORATION LTD

PO Box 95100, Abu Dhabi, United Arab Emirates
Tel.: (971) 26444412
Web Site: http://www.rotana.com
Year Founded: 1992
Hotel Owner & Operator
N.A.I.C.S.: 721110
Hamid Abou Sahyoun *(CFO & Exec VP)*

ROTARY ENGINEERING PTE. LTD.

No 17 Tuas Avenue 20, Singapore, 638828, Singapore
Tel.: (65) 68660800
Web Site: http://www.rotaryeng.com.sg
Year Founded: 1980
R07—(OTCIQ)
Sales Range: $150-199.9 Million
Oil & Gas Infrastructure Services
N.A.I.C.S.: 211120
Roger Chia Kim Piow *(Founder, Chm & Mng Dir)*

Subsidiaries:

PT Eastern Logistics (1)
Gedung Menara Sudirman Lt 18 C Jalan Jendral Sudirman Kav 60, Jakarta, 12190, Indonesia
Tel.: (62) 2152961116
Offshore Exploration Services
N.A.I.C.S.: 213112

Sixty-six Switchgears Co Pte. Ltd. (1)
No 2 Gul St 2 Off Gul Circle, Jurong, Singapore, 629287, Singapore
Tel.: (65) 68615711
Web Site: http://www.sixtysix.com.sg
Electric Equipment Mfr
N.A.I.C.S.: 335999
Kasi Parthipan *(Sr Supvr-Electrical)*

Supermec (M) Sdn. Bhd. (1)
No 16 PJS 7/21 Phase 8D, Bandar Sunway, 46150, Petaling Jaya, Selangor, Malaysia
Tel.: (60) 356315370
Electric Equipment Mfr
N.A.I.C.S.: 335999

Supermec Middle East FZE (1)
2-217-thub2 Dubai Silicon Oasis, Dubai, United Arab Emirates
Tel.: (971) 556294004
Electric Equipment Mfr
N.A.I.C.S.: 335999

Supermec Proizvodnja in Prodaja Elektronike d.o.o (1)
Gojace Industrial Area, Crnice, 5262, Ajdovscina, Slovenia
Tel.: (386) 39335471319
Electric Equipment Mfr
N.A.I.C.S.: 335999

Supermec Pte. Ltd. (1)
17 Tuas Avenue 20, Singapore, 638828, Singapore
Tel.: (65) 68619522
Electric Equipment Mfr
N.A.I.C.S.: 335999
Jonathan Tan *(Sr Engr-Sls)*

Supermec Vietnam Co. Ltd. (1)
42/55 Nguyen Minh Hoang Str, Ward 12 Tan Binh District, Ho Chi Minh City, Vietnam
Tel.: (84) 838110448
Electric Equipment Mfr
N.A.I.C.S.: 335999
Hong An Nguyen *(Sls Mgr)*

Thai Rotary Engineering Public Company Limited (1)
No 168 Moo 5, Sumnaktorn Sub-District Banchang District, Rayong, 21130, Thailand
Tel.: (66) 38923500
Web Site: http://www.rotaryeng.co.th
Emp.: 1,200
Construction Engineering Services
N.A.I.C.S.: 541330
Prapan Piriyasathit *(Mgr-Bus Dev & Proposal Dept)*

ROTAS A.D.

Brace Pisteljica 6, 78000, Banja Luka, Bosnia & Herzegovina
Tel.: (387) 51301770
ROTS-R-A—(BANJ)
Rev.: $595,951
Assets: $1,299,039
Liabilities: $1,060,239
Net Worth: $238,800
Earnings: $549
Emp.: 41
Fiscal Year-end: 12/31/12
Freight Transportation Services
N.A.I.C.S.: 484220

INTERNATIONAL PUBLIC

Ljubomir Cubic *(Chm-Mgmt Bd)*

ROTEM ENERGY MINERAL

94 Yigal Alon St, Tel Aviv, 6789156, Israel
Tel.: (972) 39590077
Web Site: http://www.rem-energy.com
RTEN—(TAE)
Assets: $8,770,000
Liabilities: $1,346,000
Net Worth: $7,424,000
Earnings: ($990,000)
Fiscal Year-end: 12/31/23
Mineral Services
N.A.I.C.S.: 212390
Yaakov Mimran *(Chm)*

ROTEM SHANI LTD.

Kibbutz Galil Yam, Herzliya Pituach, 4690500, Israel
Tel.: (972) 99579577
Web Site: https://www.rotemshani.com
RTSN—(TAE)
Rev.: $76,145,003
Assets: $170,426,495
Liabilities: $115,417,819
Net Worth: $55,008,676
Earnings: $15,912,911
Fiscal Year-end: 09/30/23
Investment Management Service
N.A.I.C.S.: 523940
Avi Turiski *(Chm)*

ROTHSCHILD & CO SCA

23 Bis Avenue de Messine, 75008, Paris, France
Tel.: (33) 140744366 FR
Web Site: http://www.rothschildandco.com
Year Founded: 1838
PIEJF—(OTCEM)
Rev.: $2,798,645,546
Assets: $19,990,072,859
Liabilities: $15,910,917,322
Net Worth: $4,079,155,537
Earnings: $472,446,186
Emp.: 4,200
Fiscal Year-end: 12/31/23
Holding Company; Merchant Banking, Financial Advisory & Asset Management Services
N.A.I.C.S.: 551112
David R. J. Baron de Rothschild *(Chm-Supervisory Bd)*

Subsidiaries:

Arrowpoint Advisory LLP (1)
15 Adam Street, London, WC2N 6RJ, United Kingdom
Tel.: (44) 207 484 4700
Web Site: https://www.arrowpointadvisory.com
Financial Advisory Services
N.A.I.C.S.: 523940
Graham Carberry *(Mng Dir)*

City Business Finance Limited (1)
Chartside House High Street, Brasted, Westerham, TN16 1HU, Kent, United Kingdom
Tel.: (44) 1959 568280
Web Site: http://www.printfinance.com
Financial Advisory Services
N.A.I.C.S.: 523940
Paul Coggins *(Mng Dir)*

Concordia Holding SARL (1)
Apollolaan 133-135, Amsterdam, 1077 AR, Netherlands
Tel.: (31) 20 570 2900
Investment Banking Services
N.A.I.C.S.: 523150

Fineline Media Finance Limited (1)
Heron House 5 Heron Square Richmond upon Thames, London, TW9 1EL, Surrey, United Kingdom
Tel.: (44) 20 8334 2100
Web Site: http://www.fineline.co.uk

AND PRIVATE COMPANIES

Financial Advisory Services
N.A.I.C.S.: 523940
Gareth Wilding (Mng Dir)

Five Arrows Capital Partners (1)
366 Madison Ave 4th Fl, New York, NY 10017
Tel.: (212) 300-1900
Web Site: http://www.rothschildandco.com
Privater Equity Firm
N.A.I.C.S.: 523999
Ari Benacerraf (Partner)

Holding (Domestic):

Stepping Stones Healthcare Services, LLC (2)
184 High St Ste 701, Boston, MA 02110
Web Site: https://thesteppingstonesgroup.com
Holding Company; Pediatric Physical Therapy, Occupational Therapy & Speech Pathology Professional Employment Services
N.A.I.C.S.: 551112
Douglas Moes (Chief Clinical Dev Officer)

Subsidiary (Domestic):

EBS Healthcare, Inc. (3)
200 Skiles Blvd, West Chester, PA 19382
Tel.: (610) 455-4055
Web Site: https://ebshealthcare.com
Offices of Physical, Occupational & Speech Therapists & Audiologists
N.A.I.C.S.: 621340
Jill Parmenter (Reg Dir)

Five Arrows Managers SAS (1)
23Bis Avenue de Messine 51st floor, Paris, 75008, France
Tel.: (33) 1 40 74 40 49
Web Site: http://www.roghschild.com
Financial Advisory Services
N.A.I.C.S.: 523940

Subsidiary (Domestic):

Harvest S.A. (2)
5 rue de La Baume, 75008, Paris, France (93.25%)
Tel.: (33) 153302800
Web Site: http://www.harvest.fr
Financial & Business Software Publisher
N.A.I.C.S.: 513210
Brice Pineau (Co-Founder)

Joint Venture (Non-US):

RLDatix Limited (2)
10 York Road, London, SE1 7ND, United Kingdom
Tel.: (44) 2089711971
Web Site: http://www.rldatix.com
Healtcare Services
N.A.I.C.S.: 621610
Terence Clifton (CTO)

Subsidiary (Domestic):

Allocate Software plc (3)
1 Church Road, Richmond, TW9 2QE, United Kingdom
Tel.: (44) 207 355 5555
Web Site: https://www.allocatesoftware.com
Workforce Optimization Software Developer
N.A.I.C.S.: 513210
Terence Clifton (CTO)

Subsidiary (Non-US):

Allocate Software Pty. Ltd. (4)
Suite 4 Level 4 441 St Kilda Road, Melbourne, 3004, VIC, Australia
Tel.: (61) 39 534 4477
Web Site: https://www.allocatesoftware.com
Workforce Optimization Software Developer
N.A.I.C.S.: 513210
Matt Durston (Mng Dir)

Time Care AB (4)
Tel.: (46) 85 055 1800
Web Site: https://www.allocatesoftware.se
Workforce Management Software Mfr
N.A.I.C.S.: 541511
Marie Munkhammar (Mgr-Mgmt Svcs)

Subsidiary (US):

Ecteon, Inc. (3)
5214 Maryland Way Ste 110, Brentwood, TN 37027
Tel.: (212) 268-9800
Web Site: https://www.ecteon.com
Rev.: $2,100,000
Emp.: 20
Contract Management Solutions Services
N.A.I.C.S.: 561499
Amy G. Harkins (Dir & Sr VP)

Galen Healthcare Solutions (3)
PO Box 36715, Grosse Pointe, MI 48236
Tel.: (888) 425-3644
Web Site: http://www.galenhealthcare.com
Sales Range: $1-9.9 Million
Emp.: 29
Electronic Health Records
N.A.I.C.S.: 541519
Stephen McQueen (Chm)

Verge Solutions, LLC (3)
11 eWall St, Mount Pleasant, SC 29464
Tel.: (843) 628-4168
Web Site: http://www.vergehealth.com
Software Publisher
N.A.I.C.S.: 513210
Jon Piebenga (Partner)

iContracts, Inc. (3)
1011 US Route 22 W Ste 104, Bridgewater, NJ 08807
Tel.: (908) 393-9550
Web Site: http://www.icontracts.com
Contract, Policy & Revenue Management Services
N.A.I.C.S.: 541611
Todd Venetianer (COO)

Subsidiary (Domestic):

PolicyStat, LLC (4)
550 Congressional Blvd Ste 100, Carmel, IN 46032-9439
Tel.: (317) 644-1296
Web Site: http://www.policystat.com
Policy Management Software Publisher
N.A.I.C.S.: 513210
Jill Sawyer (Mgr-Product Mktg)

Subsidiary (US):

n2y LLC (2)
PO Box 550, Huron, OH 44839
Tel.: (419) 433-9800
Web Site: http://www.n2y.com
Special Education Curriculum & Materials Developer
N.A.I.C.S.: 513210
Don Wostmann (COO)

K Developpement SAS (1)
564 montee des vraies richesses, 04100, Manosque, France
Tel.: (33) 9 62 14 87 37
Financial Advice Services
N.A.I.C.S.: 523940

Lanebridge Investment Management Ltd (1)
Fulshaw Hall Alderley Road, Wilmslow, SK9 1RL, Cheshire, United Kingdom
Tel.: (44) 1625 535 366
Financial Advisory Services
N.A.I.C.S.: 523940

Lease Portfolio Management Ltd (1)
30 Windsor Street, Uxbridge, UB8 1AB, Middlesex, United Kingdom
Tel.: (44) 20 8429 2616
Web Site: http://www.faof.co.uk
Emp.: 100
Portfolio Management Services
N.A.I.C.S.: 523940
Madeleine Bowd (Gen Mgr)

N M Rothschild & Sons (Brasil) Limitada (1)
Avenue Brigadeira Faria Lima 2055 18th Floor Jardim Paulistano, Sao Paulo, 01451-000, Brazil
Tel.: (55) 11 3039 5828
Investment Banking Services
N.A.I.C.S.: 523150

PO Participations S.A. (1)
1 Place d Armes, 1136, Luxembourg, Luxembourg
Tel.: (352) 27489685
Web Site: http://www.parisorleans.com
Financial Advisory Services
N.A.I.C.S.: 523940

PT Rothschild Indonesia (1)
Level 15 Tower 1 Jl Jend Sudirman Kav 52-53, Jakarta, 12190, Indonesia
Tel.: (62) 21 515 3588
Financial Advisory Services
N.A.I.C.S.: 523940

PT RothschildCo Advisory Indonesia (1)
Indonesia Stock Exchange Building Tower 1 Level 17, Sudirman Central Business District Jl Jend Sudirman Kav 52-53, Jakarta, 12190, Indonesia
Tel.: (62) 2129220900
Financial Advisory Services
N.A.I.C.S.: 523940

RTS Geneva SA (1)
Rue du Commerce 3, 1204, Geneva, Switzerland
Tel.: (41) 22 818 5965
Trust & Financial Services
N.A.I.C.S.: 523991

Redburn (Europe) Limited (1)
10 Aldermanbury, London, EC2V 7RF, United Kingdom
Tel.: (44) 207 000 2020
Web Site: https://www.redburn.com
Financial Advisory Services
N.A.I.C.S.: 523940
Jeremy Evans (Founder)

Rothschild & Cie Banque SCS (1)
23Bis Avenue de Messine, 75008, Paris, France
Tel.: (33) 140744074
Web Site: http://www.rothschild.com
Financial Advisory Services
N.A.I.C.S.: 523940

Rothschild & Co Advisory (Beijing) Company Limited (1)
Unit 1057 10/F Beijing Kerry Centre South Tower No 1 Guanghua Road, Chaoyang District, Beijing, 100020, China
Tel.: (86) 1056617376
Financial Advisory Services
N.A.I.C.S.: 523940

Rothschild & Co Australia Limited (1)
Level 34 88 Phillip Street, Sydney, 2000, NSW, Australia
Tel.: (61) 293232000
Financial Advisory Services
N.A.I.C.S.: 523940
Marc Rubinstein (Mng Dir)

Rothschild & Co Belgium SA NV (1)
Wetenschapsstraat 14B Rue de la Science, Brussels, 1040, Belgium
Tel.: (32) 22740400
Financial Advisory Services
N.A.I.C.S.: 523940

Rothschild & Co Brasil Ltda (1)
Av Brigadeiro Faria Lima 2055/18th Floor, Sao Paulo, 01451-000, SP, Brazil
Tel.: (55) 1130395828
Financial Advisory Services
N.A.I.C.S.: 523940

Rothschild & Co Deutschland GmbH (1)
Borsenstrasse 2 - 4, Frankfurt am Main, 60313, Germany
Tel.: (49) 692998840
Financial Advisory Services
N.A.I.C.S.: 523940

Rothschild & Co Doha LLC (1)
Office 1417 Al Fardan Office Towers, PO Box 31316, Doha, Qatar
Tel.: (974) 44101680
Financial Advisory Services
N.A.I.C.S.: 523940

Rothschild & Co Espana S.A. (1)
Paseo de la Castellana 35 - 3, Madrid, 28080, Spain
Tel.: (34) 917022600
Financial Advisory Services
N.A.I.C.S.: 523940

Rothschild & Co Greece SMSA (1)
Ploutarchou Street 2, 10676, Athens, Greece
Tel.: (30) 2107209520
Financial Advisory Services

ROTHSCHILD & CO SCA

N.A.I.C.S.: 523940

Rothschild & Co Hong Kong Limited (1)
16/F Alexandra House 18 Chater Road, Central, China (Hong Kong)
Tel.: (852) 21319900
Financial Advisory Services
N.A.I.C.S.: 523940
Finlay Wright (Mng Dir)

Rothschild & Co India Private Limited (1)
103 1st Floor Piramal Towers Peninsula Corp, Park Ganpatrao Kadam Marg Lower Parel, Mumbai, 400 013, India
Tel.: (91) 2240817000
Financial Advisory Services
N.A.I.C.S.: 523940
Ratnakar Dalvi (CFO & Dir-Accts & Compliance)

Rothschild & Co Israel BV (1)
32 Rothschild Blvd, Tel Aviv, 66882, Israel
Tel.: (972) 722204100
Financial Advisory Services
N.A.I.C.S.: 523940

Rothschild & Co Japan Ltd. (1)
Kamiyacho MT Building Level 20 4-3-20, Toranomon Minato-ku, Tokyo, 105-0001, Japan
Tel.: (81) 364501200
Financial Advisory Services
N.A.I.C.S.: 523940

Rothschild & Co Kurumsal Finansman Hizmetleri Limited Sirketi (1)
Akmerkez Rezidans No 14 D 2 Akmerkez Is Merkezi Yani Nispetiye, Caddesi Etiler, Istanbul, 34340, Turkiye
Tel.: (90) 2123710800
Financial Advisory Services
N.A.I.C.S.: 523940

Rothschild & Co Mexico, S.A. de C.V (1)
Campos Eliseos 345 - 8 piso, Mexico, 11550, Mexico
Tel.: (52) 5553271450
Financial Advisory Services
N.A.I.C.S.: 523940
Daniel Nicolaievsky (Mng Dir)

Rothschild & Co Middle East Limited (1)
DIFC Gate District 3 Office 504 Level 5, PO Box 506570, Dubai, United Arab Emirates
Tel.: (971) 44284300
Financial Advisory Services
N.A.I.C.S.: 523940

Rothschild & Co Nordic AB (1)
Hovslagargatan 5B, 111 48, Stockholm, Sweden
Tel.: (46) 858633590
Financial Advisory Services
N.A.I.C.S.: 523940

Rothschild & Co Portugal Limitada (1)
Calcada do Marques de Abrantes 40 - 1 Esq, Lisbon, 1200-719, Portugal
Tel.: (351) 213975378
Financial Advisory Services
N.A.I.C.S.: 523940

Rothschild & Co Singapore Limited (1)
One Raffles Quay North Tower 10-02 1 Raffles Quay 10-02, Singapore, 048583, Singapore
Tel.: (65) 65358311
Financial Advisory Services
N.A.I.C.S.: 523940
K. Chandramouli (Mng Dir & Head-Power-Asia Pacific)

Rothschild & Co Wealth Management Italy SIM SpA (1)
Passaggio Centrale 3, 20123, Milan, Italy
Tel.: (39) 02724431
Wealth Management Services
N.A.I.C.S.: 523940
Alvise Franzolin (VP-Wealth Mgmt)

Rothschild & Co Wealth Management Spain, A.V., S.A. (1)
Paseo de la Castellana 40 Bis, 28046, Madrid, Spain

ROTHSCHILD & CO SCA

Rothschild & Co SCA—(Continued)
Tel.: (34) 911713661
Investment Banking & Financial Services
N.A.I.C.S.: 523150

Rothschild & Co Wealth Management UK Limited (1)
New Court St Swithin's Lane, London, EC4N 8AL, United Kingdom
Tel.: (44) 2072805000
Wealth Management Services
N.A.I.C.S.: 523940

Rothschild (Mexico) SA de CV (1)
Edifico Omega, Polanco, 11550, Mexico
Tel.: (52) 5553271450
Financial Advisory Services
N.A.I.C.S.: 523940

Rothschild (Middle East) Limited (1)
Office 0 Level 7 Precinct Building 6 DIFC, PO Box 506570, Dubai, United Arab Emirates
Tel.: (971) 4 4284300
Financial Advisory Services
N.A.I.C.S.: 523940

Rothschild Bank AG (1)
Zollikerstrasse 181, 8034, Zurich, Switzerland
Tel.: (41) 443847111
Web Site: http://www.rothschildbank.com
Sales Range: $700-749.9 Million
Emp.: 2,000
Financial Services
N.A.I.C.S.: 523940
Eric de Rothschild (Chm)

Rothschild Bank International Limited (1)
St Julian's Court, Saint Peter Port, GY1 3BP, Guernsey
Tel.: (44) 1481713713
Banking Services
N.A.I.C.S.: 523150

Rothschild Inc. (1)
1251 Avenve of the Americas 33rd Fl, New York, NY 10020-1104
Tel.: (212) 403-3500
Web Site: http://www.rothschild.com
Sales Range: $200-249.9 Million
Emp.: 300
Investment Banking & Trust Services
N.A.I.C.S.: 523150
Todd R. Snyder (Mng Dir)

Subsidiary (Non-US):

Rothschild (Canada) Holdings Limited (2)
161 Bay Street Brookfield Place Suite 4230, Toronto, M5J 2S1, ON, Canada
Tel.: (416) 369-9600
Financial Advisory Services
N.A.I.C.S.: 523940

Rothschild (Canada) Inc. (2)
Suite 1910 525 8 Avenue SW, Calgary, T2P 1G1, AB, Canada
Tel.: (403) 537-6300
Financial Advisory Services
N.A.I.C.S.: 523940

Subsidiary (Domestic):

Rothschild Asset Management Inc. (2)
1251 Avenue of the Americas 33rd fl, New York, NY 10020
Tel.: (212) 403-3500
Web Site: https://www.rothschildandco.com
Emp.: 215
Financial Advisory Services
N.A.I.C.S.: 523940
Tom Rawlings (COO)

Subsidiary (Non-US):

Rothschild S.A. de C.V. (2)
Campos Eliseos 345 Piso 8, Polanco, 11550, Mexico, DF, Mexico
Tel.: (52) 55 5327 1450
Web Site: http://www.rothschild.com
Investment Management Service
N.A.I.C.S.: 523999

Rothschild Malaysia Sendirian Berhad (1)
28-12 Level 28 Q Sentral Jalan Stesen Sentral Kuala Lumpur Sentral, Letter Box No 42, 50470, Kuala Lumpur, Malaysia
Tel.: (60) 323033688
Web Site: https://www.rothschildandco.com
Financial Advisory Services
N.A.I.C.S.: 523940

Rothschild Martin Maurel (1)
43 rue Grignan, PO Box 154, 13006, Marseille, Cedex 6, France
Tel.: (33) 49 104 8282
Web Site: http://www.rothschild.com
Investment Banking Services
N.A.I.C.S.: 523150

Rothschild Nordic AB (1)
Strandvagen 7A, 114 56, Stockholm, Sweden
Tel.: (46) 8586 335 90
Financial Advisory Services
N.A.I.C.S.: 523940

Rothschild Polska Sp. z o.o. (1)
Warsaw Financial Centre Emilii Plater 53, 00-113, Warsaw, Poland
Tel.: (48) 225406400
Financial Advisory Services
N.A.I.C.S.: 523940

Rothschild Portugal Limitada (1)
Calcada do Marques de Abrantes 40 1 Esq, 1200-719, Lisbon, Portugal
Tel.: (351) 21 397 5378
Financial Advisory Services
N.A.I.C.S.: 523940

Rothschild S.A. (1)
Paseo de la Castellana 35 Fl 3, 28046, Madrid, Spain
Tel.: (34) 91 702 2600
Financial Advisory Services
N.A.I.C.S.: 523940

Rothschild S.p.a (1)
Passaggio Centrale 3, 20123, Milan, Italy
Tel.: (39) 0272 4431
Web Site: http://www.rothschild.com
Financial Advisory Services
N.A.I.C.S.: 523940

Rothschild Trust (Schweiz) AG (1)
Zollikerstrasse 181, 8034, Zurich, Switzerland
Tel.: (41) 44 384 7111
Web Site: http://www.rothschild.com
Emp.: 400
International Trust & Financial Services
N.A.I.C.S.: 523991

Rothschild Trust (Singapore) Limited (1)
One Raffles Quay North Tower 49-00, Singapore, 048583, Singapore
Tel.: (65) 6531656162
Trust & Financial Services
N.A.I.C.S.: 523991

Rothschild Trust B.V.I. Limited (1)
Palm Grove House, PO Box 438, Road Town, Tortola, Virgin Islands (British)
Tel.: (284) 284 494 7106
Financial Advisory Services
N.A.I.C.S.: 523940

Rothschild Trust Guernsey Limited (1)
St Julian's Court St Julian's Avenue, PO Box 472, Saint Peter Port, GY1 6AX, Guernsey
Tel.: (44) 1481 707860
Web Site: http://www.rothschild.com
Emp.: 35
Trust & Financial Services
N.A.I.C.S.: 523991
David Oxburgh (Mng Dir)

Rothschild Vermogensverwaltungs GmbH (1)
Borsenstrasse 2-4, 60313, Frankfurt am Main, Germany
Tel.: (49) 694080260
Web Site: https://www.rothschildandco.com
Wealth Management Services
N.A.I.C.S.: 523999

Rothschild Wealth Management (Hong Kong) Limited (1)
16th Floor Alexandra House 16-20 Chater Road, Central, China (Hong Kong)
Tel.: (852) 25255333

Financial Advisory Services
N.A.I.C.S.: 523940
Alois Mueller (Mng Dir & Head-North Asia)

Rothschild Wealth Management (Singapore) Limited (1)
One Raffles Quay Unit 10-02 North Tower, Singapore, 48583, Singapore
Tel.: (65) 6532 0866
Wealth Management Services
N.A.I.C.S.: 523999
Mike Hue (Head-Wealth Mgmt)

Rothschild Wealth Management (UK) Limited (1)
New Court Saint Swithins Lane, London, EC4N 8AL, United Kingdom
Tel.: (44) 2072805000
Web Site: http://www.nmrothschild.com
Sales Range: $800-899.9 Million
Emp.: 914
International Investment & Banking Services
N.A.I.C.S.: 522110
Nigel Higgins (Co-Head-Global Investment Banking)

RothschildCo Malaysia Sdn. Bhd. (1)
28-12 Level 28 Q Sentral Jalan Stesen Sentral Kuala Lumpur Sentral, Kuala Lumpur, 50470, Malaysia
Tel.: (60) 323033688
Financial Advisory Services
N.A.I.C.S.: 523940

Sagitas AG Glarus (1)
Spielhof 3, 8750, Glarus, Switzerland
Tel.: (41) 55 6402544
Financial Advisory Services
N.A.I.C.S.: 523940

Specialist Fleet Services Limited (1)
Ross Road Weedon Road Industrial Estate, Northampton, NN5 5AX, United Kingdom
Tel.: (44) 160 423 4601
Web Site: https://www.sfs.co.uk
Fleet Management Services
N.A.I.C.S.: 532112
Bob Sweetland (Mng Dir)

Wargny BBR SA (1)
4 avenue Hoche, 75008, Paris, France
Tel.: (33) 14 225 8585
Web Site: https://www.wargnybbr.com
Wealth Management Services
N.A.I.C.S.: 523940

ROTHWELL INTERNATIONAL CO LTD
Unit 402 4th Floor Fairmont No 8 Cotton Tree Drive Admira, Hong Kong, China (Hong Kong)
Tel.: (852) 163845579 900260—(KRS)
Rev.: $56,632,570
Assets: $196,035,147
Liabilities: $58,019,172
Net Worth: $138,015,976
Earnings: ($10,750,273)
Emp.: 605
Fiscal Year-end: 12/31/22
Automotive Parts Mfr & Distr
N.A.I.C.S.: 336320
Xiangdong Zhou (Chm & CEO)

ROTKAEPPCHEN-MUMM SEKTKELLEREIEN GMBH
Sektkellereistrasse 5, Freyburg, D 06632, Sachsen Anhalt, Germany
Tel.: (49) 34464340
Web Site: http://www.rotkaeppchen.de
Year Founded: 1856
Sales Range: $75-99.9 Million
Emp.: 120
Wines Mfr & Distr
N.A.I.C.S.: 312130
Ulrich Wiegel (Mng Dir)

ROTKÄPPCHEN-MUMM SEKTKELLEREIEN GMBH
Sektkellereistrasse 5, 06632, Freyburg, Germany

Tel.: (49) 34464340
Web Site: http://www.rotkaeppchen.de
Year Founded: 1856
Sales Range: $1-4.9 Billion
Emp.: 544
Wine, Champagne & Distilled Alcoholic Beverages Mfr & Distr
N.A.I.C.S.: 312130
Christof Queisser (Pres)

Subsidiaries:

Chantre & Cie GmbH (1)
Matheus-Muller-Platz 1, 65343, Eltville am Rhein, Germany
Tel.: (49) 61 2360 60
Web Site: http://www.chantre.de
Sales Range: $125-149.9 Million
Emp.: 150
Brandy & Other Distilled Alcoholic Beverage Mfr
N.A.I.C.S.: 312140
Mike Eberle (Mng Dir)

Nordbrand Nordhausen GmbH (1)
Bahnhofstrasse 25 Harz, PO Box 100462, 99734, Nordhausen, Germany
Tel.: (49) 3631 636 0
Web Site: http://www.nordbrand-nordhausen.de
Sales Range: $125-149.9 Million
Emp.: 121
Distilled Alcoholic Beverage Mfr & Distr
N.A.I.C.S.: 312140
Christof Queisser (Mng Dir & Member-Mgmt Bd)

ROTO PUMPS LTD.
Roto House 13 Noida Special Economic Zone, Noida, 201305, India
Tel.: (91) 1202567902
Web Site: https://www.rotopumps.com 517500—(BOM)
Rev.: $17,963,063
Assets: $21,061,348
Liabilities: $6,961,338
Net Worth: $14,100,011
Earnings: $2,502,181
Emp.: 202
Fiscal Year-end: 03/31/21
Pumps Mfr
N.A.I.C.S.: 333996
Ashwani K. Verma (Compliance Officer & Sec)

Subsidiaries:

Roto Pumpen GmbH (1)
Fockestrasse 5/2, 88471, Laupheim, Germany
Tel.: (49) 739295730418
Pump Mfr & Distr
N.A.I.C.S.: 333914

Roto Pumps (Africa) Pty Ltd (1)
3 Sun Rock Close, Germiston, 1401, South Africa
Tel.: (27) 101003774
Web Site: https://www.rotopumps.co.za
Pumps Mfr
N.A.I.C.S.: 333914

Roto Pumps (Malaysia) Sdn. Bhd. (1)
No 27 Jalan PP 16/4, Perdana Industrial Park Taman Putra Perdana, 47130, Puchong, Selangor, Malaysia
Tel.: (60) 383221040
Web Site: https://www.rotopumps.com.my
Pump Mfr & Distr
N.A.I.C.S.: 333914

Roto Pumps GmbH (1)
Fockestrasse 5/2, 88471, Laupheim, Germany
Tel.: (49) 739295730411
Web Site: https://www.rotopump.de
Water Pump Mfr & Distr
N.A.I.C.S.: 333996

Roto Pumps North America, Inc. (1)
5889 S Garnett Rd, Tulsa, OK 74146
Tel.: (918) 280-9144
Web Site: https://rotopumpsna.com

AND PRIVATE COMPANIES — ROTORK PLC

Pumps Mfr
N.A.I.C.S.: 333914
Jim Patterson *(Reg Sls Mgr)*

Roto Pumps North Americas Inc. (1)
300 Springhill Farm Rd - Ste 106, Fort Mill, SC 29715
Tel.: (918) 280-9144
Web Site: https://rotopumpsna.com
Water Pump Mfr & Distr
N.A.I.C.S.: 333996

ROTO-GRO INTERNATIONAL LIMITED
Level 4 96-100 Albert Rd, South Melbourne, 3205, VIC, Australia
Tel.: (61) 39 692 7245 AU
Web Site: http://www.rotogro.com
Year Founded: 2015
RGI—(ASX)
Rev.: $676,082
Assets: $7,396,141
Liabilities: $1,101,090
Net Worth: $6,295,051
Earnings: ($11,103,624)
Fiscal Year-end: 06/30/20
Rotating Hydroponic Gardens Mfr
N.A.I.C.S.: 333111
Melanie Leydin *(CFO & Sec)*

Subsidiaries:

Global Fertigation Solutions, Inc. (1)
4345 Wagon Trail Ave, Las Vegas, NV 89118
Tel.: (702) 796-5558
Web Site: http://www.fertigationsolutions.com
Technological Water Treatment & Automated Fertilization Systems Services
N.A.I.C.S.: 221320
Stephen Everett *(Pres)*

Subsidiary (Domestic):

Hanson's Water Treatment Inc. (2)
3870 W Ali Baba Ln, Las Vegas, NV 89118
Tel.: (702) 364-4550
Web Site: http://www.hansonfertigation.weebly.com
Waste Treatment Services
N.A.I.C.S.: 221320

ROTOGRAPHICS INDIA LTD.
Unit 8 Ground Floor Pocket M Sarita Vihar, New Delhi, 110076, India
Tel.: (91) 1147366600
Web Site: https://www.rotoindia.co.in
Year Founded: 1976
539922—(BOM)
Rev.: $24,697
Assets: $443,261
Liabilities: $10,402
Net Worth: $432,859
Earnings: $1,862
Emp.: 3
Fiscal Year-end: 03/31/23
Paper Products Mfr
N.A.I.C.S.: 322299
Mohd Sagir *(Sec)*

ROTOPRECISION INC.
304 Watline Ave, Mississauga, L4Z 1P4, ON, Canada
Tel.: (905) 712-3330
Web Site: http://www.rotoprecision.ca
Year Founded: 1958
Holding Company; High Precision Industrial Components Designer
N.A.I.C.S.: 551112
Keith A.D. Mayo *(Mng Dir)*

Subsidiaries:

Davley Darmex Precision Lubricants (1)
930 Westport Crescent, Mississauga, L5T 1G1, ON, Canada
Tel.: (905) 795-1150
Web Site: http://www.davley-darmex.com
Lubricant Distr
N.A.I.C.S.: 424720

Strongbar (UK) Limited (1)
Aylsham Industrial Estate, Aylsham, Norwich, NR11 6LP, United Kingdom
Tel.: (44) 1263 734 034
Web Site: http://www.strongbar.co.uk
Bearing Products Mfr
N.A.I.C.S.: 332991

WIB S.A. (1)
Champ Barby 61, 1630, Bulle, Switzerland
Tel.: (41) 269191122
Web Site: http://www.wib-bearings.com
Sales Range: $25-49.9 Million
Emp.: 200
Mfr & Sales of Bearings
N.A.I.C.S.: 332991
Kieth Mayo *(CEO)*

ROTOR A.D.
Aleksandra Dubceka 5-9, Zemun, Serbia
Tel.: (381) 11 2616 126
Web Site: http://www.rotor-zemun.com
Year Founded: 1948
Sales Range: Less than $1 Million
Engineering & Repair Services
N.A.I.C.S.: 811412

ROTORK PLC
Brassmill Lane, Bath, BA1 3JQ, United Kingdom
Tel.: (44) 1225733200 UK
Web Site: http://www.rotork.com
RTOXF—(OTCIQ)
Rev.: $820,801,480
Assets: $1,035,819,523
Liabilities: $244,906,891
Net Worth: $790,912,632
Earnings: $126,713,292
Emp.: 3,507
Fiscal Year-end: 12/31/20
Fluid Power Cylinder & Actuator Manufacturing
N.A.I.C.S.: 333995
Kevin G. Hostetler *(CEO)*

Subsidiaries:

Bifold Fluidpower Limited (1)
Broadgate Broadway Business Park, Chadderton, Oldham, OL9 9XA, Greater Manchester, United Kingdom
Tel.: (44) 1613454777
Web Site: https://www.bifold.co.uk
Industrial Valve Mfr
N.A.I.C.S.: 332911

Centork Valve Control S.L. (1)
Po 110 Ipintza Txatxamendi 24-26, 20100, Lezo, Gipuzkoa, Spain
Tel.: (34) 94 331 6137
Web Site: https://www.centork.com
Electric Actuator Whslr
N.A.I.C.S.: 423830

Costruzioni Meccaniche Legnanesi Srl (1)
Via del Brugo 5, 20025, Legnano, Italy
Tel.: (39) 0331548847
Web Site: http://www.mastergearworldwide.com
Valve & Actuator Mfr
N.A.I.C.S.: 332911

Exeeco LTD (1)
Brown Lane West, Bramley Ring Road, Leeds, LS12 6BH, United Kingdom **(100%)**
Tel.: (44) 1132567922
Web Site: http://www.rotork.com
Sales Range: $50-74.9 Million
Emp.: 200
Electrical Contractor
N.A.I.C.S.: 238210

Flowco Limited (1)
Tel.: (44) 1761411440
Industrial Valve Mfr
N.A.I.C.S.: 332911

M&M International S.r.l. (1)
Via Portico 17, Orio Al Serio, 240 50, Bergamo, Italy **(100%)**
Tel.: (39) 035531298
Web Site: http://www.mminternational.net

Electron Tube Mfr
N.A.I.C.S.: 334419
Maurizio Forno *(Mng Dir)*

Max Process GmbH (1)
Rastenweg 10, 53489, Sinzig, Germany
Tel.: (49) 2642992360
Web Site: http://www.max-process.com
Industrial Valve Distr
N.A.I.C.S.: 423830

Rotork (Actuation) Sdn Bhd (1) **(100%)**
Tel.: (60) 355251665
Web Site: https://www.rotork.com
Sales Range: $25-49.9 Million
Fluid Power Cylinder & Actuator Mfr
N.A.I.C.S.: 333995

Rotork (Malaysia) Sdn Bhd (1) **(100%)**
Tel.: (60) 355253931
Sales Range: $50-74.9 Million
Emp.: 20
Industrial Machinery & Equipment Whslr
N.A.I.C.S.: 423830

Rotork (Thailand) Ltd (1) **(100%)**
Tel.: (66) 25302420
Industrial Valve Mfr
N.A.I.C.S.: 332911

Rotork Africa (Pty) Ltd (1)
136 Kuschke Street Meadowdale, PO Box 178, Edenvale, Johannesburg, 1601, Gauteng, South Africa **(100%)**
Tel.: (27) 114539741
Sales Range: $25-49.9 Million
Emp.: 34
Industrial Valve Mfr
N.A.I.C.S.: 332911

Rotork Australia Pty Ltd (1)
21 Decor Drive, PO Box 265, Hallam, 3803, VIC, Australia **(100%)**
Tel.: (61) 353225000
Sales Range: $25-49.9 Million
Emp.: 20
Electrical Apparatus & Equipment Wiring Supplies & Construction Material Whslr
N.A.I.C.S.: 423610

Rotork BV (1)
Mandenmakerstraat 45, Po Box 255, Hoogvliet, 3194 DA, Rotterdam, Netherlands **(100%)**
Tel.: (31) 10 414 6911
Web Site: http://www.rotork.nl
Sales Range: $25-49.9 Million
Emp.: 25
Industrial Supplies Whslr
N.A.I.C.S.: 423840

Rotork Chile SpA (1)
Av Kennedy Lateral 4700 Oficina 1001 Edificio New Century, Vitacura, Chile
Tel.: (56) 222604184
Industrial Valve Mfr
N.A.I.C.S.: 332911

Rotork Controls (Canada) Ltd (1)
Bay 6 820 28th St NE, Calgary, T2A 6K1, AB, Canada
Tel.: (403) 569-9455
Emp.: 28
Industrial Valve & Actuator Mfr
N.A.I.C.S.: 332911
Darin White *(Gen Mgr)*

Rotork Controls (Deutschland) GmbH (1)
Siemensstr 33, 40721, Melle, Germany **(100%)**
Tel.: (49) 210354098
Sales Range: $25-49.9 Million
Emp.: 10
Measuring & Controlling Device Mfr
N.A.I.C.S.: 334519
Juergen Vogel *(Gen Mgr)*

Subsidiary (Domestic):

Rotork Controls (Deutschland) GmbH - RFS Melle Division (2)
Maschweg 51, Melle, 49324, Germany
Tel.: (49) 5422 94140
Sales Range: $25-49.9 Million
Emp.: 60
Precision Equipment Mfr
N.A.I.C.S.: 333248

Wolfgang Funk *(Gen Mgr)*

Rotork Controls (Espana) SL (1)
Crta B A Sopelana 9, Vizcaya, 48650, Bilbao, Spain **(100%)**
Tel.: (34) 946766011
Holding Company
N.A.I.C.S.: 551112

Rotork Controls (India) PVT Ltd-Chennai (1)
28-b Sidco Industrial Estate-north Phase Ambattur North Phase, Ambattur, Chennai, 600 098, TAN, India **(100%)**
Tel.: (91) 443 955 5600
Web Site: http://www.rotork.com
Valve Control Systems & Industrial Valve Actuators Mfr
N.A.I.C.S.: 333995

Rotork Controls (India) Private Limited
28-B SIDCO Industrial Estate-North Phase Ambattur, North Phase Ambattur, Chennai, India
Tel.: (91) 4461385700
Flow Control Equipment Mfr
N.A.I.C.S.: 334513

Rotork Controls (Italia) Srl (1)
Viale Europa 17, 20090, Cusago, LOM, Italy **(100%)**
Tel.: (39) 02 901 6711
Web Site: http://www.rotork.it
Sales Range: $25-49.9 Million
Emp.: 25
Hardware Whslr
N.A.I.C.S.: 423710

Rotork Controls (Korea) Co. Ltd (1) **(100%)**
Tel.: (82) 317688151
Web Site: http://www.rotork.co.kr
Sales Range: $25-49.9 Million
Emp.: 40
Industrial Supplies Whslr
N.A.I.C.S.: 423840

Rotork Controls (Shanghai) Ltd (1)
No 7001 Zhongchun Rd Minhang Dist, Shanghai, China
Tel.: (86) 2164785015
Professional Equipment & Supplies Whslr
N.A.I.C.S.: 423490

Rotork Controls (Singapore) Pte Ltd (1)
426 Tagore Industrial Avenue, Sindo Industrial Estate, Singapore, 787808, Singapore **(100%)**
Tel.: (65) 64571233
Sales Range: $25-49.9 Million
Emp.: 30
Industrial Machinery & Equipment Whslr
N.A.I.C.S.: 423830
Aaron Ow *(Gen Mgr)*

Rotork Controls Beijing (1)
Room 302 F3 Building 18B No 10 Jiuxianqiao Rd , Chaoyang District, Beijing, 100 026, China **(100%)**
Tel.: (86) 1059756422
Web Site: http://www.rotork.com
Sales Range: $25-49.9 Million
Emp.: 10
Controls, Fluid Systems & Gears Mfr
N.A.I.C.S.: 334519

Rotork Controls Comercio De Atuadores Ltd. (1)
Condominio Industrial Veccon Zeta Estrada Mineko Ito N 4 305, Sumare, 13178-542, SP, Brazil
Tel.: (55) 1931151050
Industrial Valve Mfr
N.A.I.C.S.: 332911

Rotork Controls Ltd (1)
Rotork House Brassmill Lane, Bath, BA1 3JQ, som, United Kingdom **(100%)**
Tel.: (44) 122 573 3200
Web Site: http://www.rotork.com
Sales Range: $100-124.9 Million
Emp.: 400
Motor Vehicle Parts Mfr
N.A.I.C.S.: 336390

Subsidiary (Non-US):

Rotork Trading (Shanghai) Co. Ltd (2)

ROTORK PLC

Rotork Plc—(Continued)
Tel.: (86) 2154452910
Emp.: 30
Industrial Valve Actuator Distr
N.A.I.C.S.: 423830

Rotork Controls de Venezuela SA (1)
Avenida Casanova En Sabana Grande Torre Banco Plaza Piso 3 Ofic 3d, Parroquia El Recreo, Caracas, 1050, Distrito Capital, Venezuela
Tel.: (58) 2127626706
Sales Range: $25-49.9 Million
Emp.: 10
Industrial Valve Actuator Mfr
N.A.I.C.S.: 333995

Rotork Fluid System Srl (1)
Via Padre Jacques Hamel 138B, Porcari, Lucca, 55012, TOS, Italy (100%)
Tel.: (39) 0583 2221
Web Site: http://www.rotork.com
Sales Range: $50-74.9 Million
Emp.: 230
Relay & Industrial Control Mfr
N.A.I.C.S.: 335314

Rotork Gears (Holdings) BV (1)
Nijverheidstraat 25, Losser, 7581 PV, Enschede, Netherlands (100%)
Tel.: (31) 535388677
Sales Range: $25-49.9 Million
Emp.: 45
Religious Organizations
N.A.I.C.S.: 813110

Rotork Gears BV (1)
Nijverheidstraat 25, Losser Overijssel, 7581 PV, Enschede, Netherlands (100%)
Tel.: (31) 535388677
Sales Range: $25-49.9 Million
Industrial Valve Mfr
N.A.I.C.S.: 332911

Rotork Gears Srl (1)
Viale Europa 17 Cusago, Milan, Italy
Tel.: (39) 029016711
Industrial Valve Mfr
N.A.I.C.S.: 332911

Rotork GmbH (1)
Siemensstrasse 33, D-40721, Hilden, Germany
Tel.: (49) 210395876
Industrial Valve Mfr
N.A.I.C.S.: 332911

Rotork Inc. (1)
675 Mile Crossing Blvd, Rochester, NY 14624-6212 (100%)
Tel.: (585) 247-2304
Sales Range: $25-49.9 Million
Emp.: 100
Relay & Industrial Control Mfr
N.A.I.C.S.: 335314

Subsidiary (Domestic):

Fairchild Industrial Products Company (2)
3920 Westpoint Blvd, Winston Salem, NC 27103
Tel.: (336) 659-3400
Web Site: https://www.fairchildproducts.com
Sales Range: $10-24.9 Million
Process Control Instruments Mfr & Distr
N.A.I.C.S.: 334513

Subsidiary (Non-US):

Fairchild India Private Limited (3)
E-199 Sector 63, Distt Gautam Budh Nagar, Noida, 201307, India
Tel.: (91) 120 4237211
Emp.: 9
Process Control Instruments Whslr
N.A.I.C.S.: 423830
Sandeep Sethi (Gen Mgr)

Fairchild Industrial Products (Sichuan) Company Limited (3)
E-15 Block B No 1 Mansion Chengdu Hi-Tech Incubation Park Nan Yan Xian, Tian Fu Avenue, Chengdu, 610042, China
Tel.: (86) 28 660 70300
Web Site: http://www.fairchildproducts.com
Process Control Instruments Distr
N.A.I.C.S.: 423830

Fairchild do Brasil, Ltda. (3)
Av Pereira Barreto 1395 Sala 114, Torre Norte, Santo Andre, 09190 610, SP, Brazil
Tel.: (55) 11 9670 7718
Web Site: http://www.fairchildproducts.com
Industrial Process Controls Distr
N.A.I.C.S.: 423830

Subsidiary (Domestic):

Flow-Quip Inc (2)
7440 E 46th Pl, Tulsa, OK 74145-6306
Tel.: (918) 663-3313
Web Site: http://www.flowquip.com
Sales Range: $25-49.9 Million
Emp.: 23
Industrial Valve Distr
N.A.I.C.S.: 423830

K Tork International Inc. (2)
10410 Vista Park Rd, Dallas, TX 75238
Tel.: (214) 343-9980
Web Site: http://www.ktork.com
Sales Range: $25-49.9 Million
Emp.: 37
Actuator Mfr
N.A.I.C.S.: 333995

Ralph A. Hiller Company Inc (2)
6005 Enterprise Dr, Export, PA 15632
Tel.: (724) 325-1200
Web Site: http://www.rotork.com
Sales Range: $25-49.9 Million
Emp.: 57
Fluid Power Component Distr
N.A.I.C.S.: 423830
Tom Back (Gen Mgr)

Renfro Associates, Inc. (2)
501 S 12th St, Broken Arrow, OK 74012
Tel.: (918) 259-8100
Web Site: http://www.renfroassociates.com
Sales Range: $25-49.9 Million
Emp.: 20
Valve Automation Hardware, Actuators, Gears & Custom Fabricated Components
N.A.I.C.S.: 332510

Roto Hammer Industries, Inc. (2)
2804 W 40th St, Tulsa, OK 74107
Tel.: (918) 446-3500
Web Site: http://www.rotohammerinc.com
Sales Range: $1-9.9 Million
Emp.: 25
Machine Shops
N.A.I.C.S.: 332710

Rotork Controls Inc. (2)
675 Mile Crossing Blvd, Rochester, NY 14624-6212 (100%)
Tel.: (585) 247-2304
Sales Range: $25-49.9 Million
Relay & Industrial Control Mfr
N.A.I.C.S.: 335314

Unit (Domestic):

Rotork Process Controls - USA (3)
5607 W Douglas Ave, Milwaukee, WI 53218 (100%)
Tel.: (414) 461-9200
Web Site: http://www.rotorkprocesscontrols.com
Relay & Industrial Control Mfr
N.A.I.C.S.: 335314

Rotork Instruments Italy Srl (1)
Via Portico 17 Orio al Serio, 24050, Oriolo, BG, Italy
Tel.: (39) 035451161
Industrial Valve Mfr
N.A.I.C.S.: 332911

Rotork Japan Co. Ltd (1)
(100%)
Tel.: (81) 356322941
Sales Range: $25-49.9 Million
Emp.: 33
Electrical Apparatus & Equipment Wiring Supplies & Construction Material Whslr
N.A.I.C.S.: 423610

Rotork Ltd (1)
(100%)
Tel.: (852) 25202390
Sales Range: $50-74.9 Million
Emp.: 4
Industrial Machinery & Equipment Whslr
N.A.I.C.S.: 423830

Rotork Middle East FZE (1)
R8 OA LC07 Jebel Ali Free Zone, PO Box 262903, 262903, Dubai, United Arab Emirates
Tel.: (971) 48876408
Flow Control & Pressure Control Distr
N.A.I.C.S.: 423850

Rotork Middle East FZE Jebel Ali (1)
RA 08 LC07 Jebel Ali Free Zone, PO Box 262903, Dubai, United Arab Emirates
Tel.: (971) 4 887 6408
Emp.: 20
Industrial Valve Actuator Mfr
N.A.I.C.S.: 333995
Stuart Medford (Gen Mgr)

Rotork Midland Limited (1)
(100%)
Tel.: (44) 1902384638
Sales Range: $75-99.9 Million
Emp.: 100
Pumping Equipment Mfr
N.A.I.C.S.: 333914

Plant (Domestic):

Rotork Midland Limited - Wolverhampton Plant (2)
Patrick Gregory Road, Wolverhampton, WV11 3DZ, West Midlands, United Kingdom
Tel.: (44) 190 238 4638
Web Site: http://www.rotork.com
Fluid Valves & Instruments Mfr & Sales
N.A.I.C.S.: 333914

Rotork Motorisation SAS (1)
(100%)
Tel.: (33) 143111550
Web Site: https://www.rotork.com
Sales Range: $25-49.9 Million
Electrical Apparatus & Equipment Wiring Supplies & Construction Material Whslr
N.A.I.C.S.: 423610

Rotork Norge AS (1)
Ormahaugvegen 3, 5347, Agotnes, Norway
Tel.: (47) 56312900
Industrial Valve Mfr
N.A.I.C.S.: 332911

Rotork Norway (1)
Ormahaugveien 3, PO Box 43, 5346, Agotnes, Norway
Tel.: (47) 56 31 29 00
Sales Range: $25-49.9 Million
Emp.: 14
Valve & Actuator Repair & Maintenance Services
N.A.I.C.S.: 811310
Vidar Rossgard (Gen Mgr)

Rotork Polska Sp. z o.o. (1)
Plutonowego Ryszarda Szkubacza 8/C3, 41-800, Zabrze, Poland
Tel.: (48) 517126699
Flow Control Mfr & Distr
N.A.I.C.S.: 334512

Rotork Rus LLC (1)
Office 106 Otradnaya Street 2B Building 6, Moscow, 127273, Russia
Tel.: (7) 4956452147
Web Site: http://www.rotork.com
Sales Range: $25-49.9 Million
Emp.: 20
Industrial Valve Actuator Mfr
N.A.I.C.S.: 333995
Simon Brown (Gen Mgr)

Rotork Saudi Arabia LLC (1)
Building No 7413 Dhahran Industrial Area, Dhahran, 34521-2482, Saudi Arabia
Tel.: (966) 138022343
Flow Control Mfr & Distr
N.A.I.C.S.: 334512

Rotork Servo Controles de Mexico S.A de C.V (1)
Centeotl 223 Col Industrial San Antonio, DF, CP 02760, Mexico, Mexico
Tel.: (52) 5555592959
Industrial Valve Mfr
N.A.I.C.S.: 332911

Rotork Sweden AB (1)
Kontrollvagen 15, Falun, Sweden
Tel.: (46) 2358700
Flow Control Equipment Mfr
N.A.I.C.S.: 332912

INTERNATIONAL PUBLIC

Rotork Tulsa Inc. (1)
Roto Hammer Industries 4433 W 49th St Ste D, Tulsa, OK 74107
Tel.: (918) 446-3500
Industrial Valve Mfr
N.A.I.C.S.: 332911

Rotork Turkey Akis Kontrol Sistemleri Ticaret Limited (1)
Tel.: (90) 2166507800
Industrial Valve Mfr
N.A.I.C.S.: 332911

Rotork YTC Limited (1)
81 Hwanggeum-ro 89 beon-gil, Gimpo, Gyeonggi, Korea (South)
Tel.: (82) 319868545
Web Site: https://www.ytc.co.kr
Flow Control Equipment Mfr
N.A.I.C.S.: 332912

Schischek GmbH (1)
Muhlsteig 45 Gewerbegebiet Sued 5, 90579, Langenzenn, Germany
Tel.: (49) 910190810
Web Site: https://www.schischek.com
Industrial Valve Mfr
N.A.I.C.S.: 332911

Valvekits Ltd (1)
(100%)
Tel.: (44) 1623440211
Web Site: https://www.valve-kits.co.uk
Emp.: 50
Metal Valve & Pipe Fitting Mfr
N.A.I.C.S.: 332919
Craig Mellins (Mng Dir)

ROTOTEC GEOTHERMAL ENERGY PLC

316 King Street, Hammersmith, London, W6 0RR, United Kingdom
Tel.: (44) 208 741 5254
Web Site: http://www.rototecgeoenergy.com
Year Founded: 2007
Geothermal Energy Systems
N.A.I.C.S.: 423730
Timo Ojanne (Chm & CEO)

Subsidiaries:

Rototec Oy (1)
Teollisuustie 12, 33330, Tampere, Finland
Tel.: (358) 10 422 3300
Web Site: http://www.rototec.fi
Geothermal Drilling Services
N.A.I.C.S.: 237110
Jouni Salakari (Gen Mgr)

ROTRADA HOLDING B.V.

Dalkruidbaan 149, Capelle aan den IJssel, 2908, Netherlands
Tel.: (31) 102922222
Web Site: http://www.laagland.nl
Sales Range: $10-24.9 Million
Emp.: 25
Holding Company
N.A.I.C.S.: 551112
Eddo Cammaraat (Chm)

Subsidiaries:

Laagland B.V. (1)
Pieter Zeemanweg 76, 3316 GZ, Dordrecht, Netherlands
Tel.: (31) 102922222
Web Site: http://www.laagland.nl
Machine Tools Mfr
N.A.I.C.S.: 333517

ROTSHTEIN REALESTATE LTD.

49 Hasevim St Yanai Park Building 6, Petach Tikva, Israel
Tel.: (972) 732555444
Web Site: https://www.rotshtein.co.il
Year Founded: 1961
ROTS—(TAE)
Rev.: $194,112,996
Assets: $587,528,655
Liabilities: $441,851,077
Net Worth: $145,677,578
Earnings: $21,168,117

Emp.: 13
Fiscal Year-end: 12/31/23
New Multifamily Housing Construction (except For-Sale Builders)
N.A.I.C.S.: 236116
Avishai Ben Haim *(CEO)*

ROTZINGER AG
Rinaustrasse 30, 4303, Kaiseraugst, Switzerland
Tel.: (41) 61 815 11 11
Web Site: http://www.rotzinger.ch
Year Founded: 1948
Sales Range: $10-24.9 Million
Emp.: 75
Supplier of Conveyor, Discharge & Storage Systems
N.A.I.C.S.: 333310
Markus Kaufmann *(CEO)*

Subsidiaries:

Transver AG (1)
Zurcherstrasse 42, 8852, Altendorf, Switzerland
Tel.: (41) 55 451 88 88
Web Site: http://www.transver.com
Emp.: 40
Packaging Machinery Mfr
N.A.I.C.S.: 333993
Marcel Baenziger *(Mng Dir)*

ROUGHRIDER EXPLORATION LIMITED
904 - 409 Granville Street, Vancouver, V6C 1T2, BC, Canada
Tel.: (604) 697-0028   BC
Web Site:
  https://coastcoppercorp.com
Year Founded: 2011
COCCF—(OTCIQ)
Rev.: $2,076
Assets: $1,877,912
Liabilities: $155,318
Net Worth: $1,722,594
Earnings: ($733,986)
Fiscal Year-end: 12/31/23
Mining Exploration Services
N.A.I.C.S.: 212290
Tim Thiessen *(CFO & Sec)*

ROUGIER S.A.
44 rue de la Bienfaisance, 75008, Paris, France
Tel.: (33) 153772500
Web Site: https://www.rougier.fr
Year Founded: 1923
ALRGR—(EUR)
Sales Range: $150-199.9 Million
Emp.: 3,000
Log, Timber & Panel Producer
N.A.I.C.S.: 321999
Marie-Yvonne Charlemagne *(Deputy Mng Dir)*

Subsidiaries:

Marotte SA (1)
47 Rue Eugene Berthoud, 96402, Saint-Ouen, France   (100%)
Tel.: (33) 149481360
Web Site: http://www.marotte.fr
Sales Range: $25-49.9 Million
Emp.: 70
Wood Products Mfr
N.A.I.C.S.: 321999

Mokabi S.A. (1)
Avenue du marechal Lyautey No 3210, BP 14512, Brazzaville, Congo, Republic of
Tel.: (242) 5563662
Lumber Mfr
N.A.I.C.S.: 321113

Rougier Gabon S.A. (1)
Zone Industrielle D Oloumi, Libreville, Gabon
Tel.: (241) 743150
Veneer & Plywood Mfr
N.A.I.C.S.: 333243

Rougier International SA (1)
155 Avenue de La Rochelle, BP 8826, 79028, Niort, France
Tel.: (33) 549772030
Web Site: http://www.rougier.fr
Sales Range: $25-49.9 Million
Emp.: 50
Wood Products Mfr
N.A.I.C.S.: 321999
Marie-Yvonne Charlemagne *(Mng Dir-Fin)*

Rougier Panneaux S.A.S. (1)
9 Impasse des Petits Marais, 92230, Gennevilliers, Hauts-de-Seine, France
Tel.: (33) 147982626
Emp.: 10
Plywood Whslr
N.A.I.C.S.: 423310
Gehliht Peschargaere *(Mgr)*

ROULARTA MEDIA GROUP NV
Meiboomlaan 33, West-Vlaanderen, BE-8800, Roeselare, Belgium
Tel.: (32) 51266111
Web Site: https://www.roularta.be
ROU—(EUR)
Rev.: $370,321,606
Assets: $411,238,938
Liabilities: $167,560,976
Net Worth: $243,677,962
Earnings: $598,964
Emp.: 1,293
Fiscal Year-end: 12/31/22
Magazine & Newspaper Publisher; Radio & TV Broadcasting Services; Internet Broadcasting
N.A.I.C.S.: 513110
Rik De Nolf *(Chm)*

Subsidiaries:

VNU Business Publications B.V. (1)
Ceylonpoort 5 25, 2037 AA, Haarlem, Netherlands
Tel.: (31) 235463463
Web Site: http://www.vnubp.nl
Sales Range: $125-149.9 Million
Emp.: 400
Business & Technology Magazines Publisher
N.A.I.C.S.: 513120

Subsidiary (Domestic):

Array Publications BV (2)
Lemelerberg 19-23, Alphen aan den Rijn, 2402ZN, South Holland, Netherlands
Tel.: (31) 172469030
Web Site: http://www.array.nl
Sales Range: $25-49.9 Million
Emp.: 20
Publisher of Computer Related Magazines
N.A.I.C.S.: 513120

Vlaamse Media Maatschappij (1)
Medialaan 1, 1800, Vilvoorde, Belgium
Tel.: (32) 2 255 3211
Web Site: http://www.roularta.be
Sales Range: $25-49.9 Million
Emp.: 33
Audio Visual & Media Activities
N.A.I.C.S.: 334310
Dirk Lodewyck *(Mng Dir)*

ROUND ONE CORPORATION
23F NAMBA SkyO 5-1-60 Namba, Chuo-ku, Osaka, 542-0076, Japan
Tel.: (81) 666476600
Web Site: https://www.round1.co.jp
Year Founded: 1980
4680—(TKS)
Rev.: $1,052,186,410
Assets: $1,225,917,040
Liabilities: $759,667,470
Net Worth: $466,249,570
Earnings: $103,552,260
Emp.: 1,367
Fiscal Year-end: 03/31/24
Operation Of Bowling Alleys & Billiard Tables
N.A.I.C.S.: 339920
Masahiko Sugino *(Pres)*

ROUNDTOP MACHINERY INDUSTRIES CO., LTD.
No 1056 Zhongshan Rd, Shengang Dist, Taichung, 42952, Taiwan
Tel.: (886) 425624721
Web Site:
  https://www.johnford.com.tw
1540—(TAI)
Rev.: $18,826,612
Assets: $56,204,027
Liabilities: $9,344,288
Net Worth: $46,859,739
Earnings: $3,632,493
Fiscal Year-end: 12/31/23
Lathes Mfr
N.A.I.C.S.: 333517

Subsidiaries:

Roundtop Machinery Industries Co., Ltd. - Shen Kang Factory (1)
No 1056 Zhongshan Rd, Shengang, Taichung, 42952, Taiwan
Tel.: (886) 425624721
Web Site: http://www.johnford.com.tw
Sales Range: $50-74.9 Million
Emp.: 250
Molding Machine Mfr
N.A.I.C.S.: 333517

ROUSSEAU METAL, INC.
105 W De Gaspe Ave, Saint-Jean-Port-Joli, G0R 3G0, QC, Canada
Tel.: (418) 598-3381
Web Site:
  http://www.rousseaumetal.com
Year Founded: 1950
Sales Range: $50-74.9 Million
Emp.: 350
Storage Systems, Shelving Cabinets & Workstations Mfr
N.A.I.C.S.: 332510
Simon Pierre Pare *(Pres & Gen Mgr)*

ROUSSELET CENTRIFUGATION SA
Avenue Rhin et Danube Zone Industrielle Marenton, 07104, Annonay, France
Tel.: (33) 4 75 69 22 11
Web Site: http://www.rousselet.fr
MLROU—(EUR)
Sales Range: $10-24.9 Million
Industrial Machinery Mfr
N.A.I.C.S.: 333998

Subsidiaries:

ROBATEL UK Ltd. (1)
Parkside House 17 East Parade, Harrogate, HG1 5LF, Yorkshire, United Kingdom
Tel.: (44) 1 423 530 093
Industrial Machinery Distr
N.A.I.C.S.: 423840

ROBATEL, Inc. (1)
703 W Housatonic St, Pittsfield, MA 01201
Tel.: (413) 499-4818
Emp.: 10
Industrial Machinery Distr
N.A.I.C.S.: 423830
Kevin Robbins *(Project Engr)*

Rousselet Centrifugation SA (1)
Bierbacher Str 30, Woerschweiler, 66424, Homburg, Germany
Tel.: (49) 6848730580
Centrifuge & Solvent Extraction Equipment Mfr
N.A.I.C.S.: 333248

ROUTE1 INC.
8 King St East Suite 1801, Toronto, M5C 1B5, ON, Canada   ON
Web Site: https://www.route1.com
Year Founded: 2004
ROIUF—(OTCIQ)
Rev.: $21,333,761
Assets: $11,810,019
Liabilities: $9,675,962
Net Worth: $2,134,057
Earnings: $174,496
Fiscal Year-end: 12/31/21
Digital Security & Identity Management Solutions
N.A.I.C.S.: 561621
Tony P. Busseri *(CEO)*

Subsidiaries:

Group Mobile International, LLC (1)
5590 W Chandler Blvd Ste 3, Chandler, AZ 85226
Tel.: (480) 705-6100
Web Site: http://www.groupmobile.com
Computer Peripheral Equipment & Software Whslr
N.A.I.C.S.: 423430

Portable Computer Systems, Inc. (1)
12851 W 43rd Dr Ste 2, Golden, CO 80403   (100%)
Tel.: (303) 346-2487
Computer System Design Services
N.A.I.C.S.: 541512

ROUTON ELECTRONIC CO., LTD.
No 70 Optics Valley Avenue East lake Development Zone, Wuhan, 430223, Hubei, China
Tel.: (86) 18971172321
Web Site: https://www.routon.com
Year Founded: 1994
600355—(SHG)
Rev.: $25,079,526
Assets: $46,487,577
Liabilities: $16,055,990
Net Worth: $30,431,588
Earnings: ($4,533,839)
Emp.: 700
Fiscal Year-end: 12/31/22
Electronic Product Mfr & Whslr
N.A.I.C.S.: 334220
Xueyang Zhang *(Chm & Gen Mgr)*

Subsidiaries:

Shanghai Powermax Technology, Inc. (1)
5F Building 12A NO 88 Xinjun Ring Rd, Pujiang Town Minhang District, Shanghai, China
Tel.: (86) 2133887999
Web Site: http://www.powermaxtech.com
Sewing Machine Mfr & Distr
N.A.I.C.S.: 333248

ROUXEL SECAMA
Aucfer, Rieux, 56350, Brittany, France
Tel.: (33) 299710571
Web Site: http://www.rouxel.com
Industrial Equipment Whslr
N.A.I.C.S.: 423830
Claude Rouxel *(Owner)*

ROVENSA SA
Edifício Lumnia Rua Antonio Mega Ferreira n 61-5B, 1800-424, Lisbon, Portugal
Tel.: (351) 213222750   PT
Web Site: https://www.rovensa.com
Year Founded: 1965
Agricultural Solutions Services
N.A.I.C.S.: 325320
Javier Calleja *(CEO)*

Subsidiaries:

Agro-K Corp. (1)
8030 Main St NE, Minneapolis, MN 55432
Tel.: (763) 780-4116
Web Site: http://www.agro-k.com
Sales Range: $1-9.9 Million
Emp.: 13
Phosphatic Fertilizer, Prepared Feeds & Agricultural Chemical Mfr
N.A.I.C.S.: 311119

ROVER METALS CORP.
Suite 908 938 Howe Street, Vancouver, V6Z 1N9, BC, Canada
Tel.: (778) 754-2855

Rover Metals Corp.—(Continued)

Web Site:
https://www.rovermetals.com
ROVMF—(OTCQB)
Rev.: $1,181
Assets: $803,797
Liabilities: $190,230
Net Worth: $613,566
Earnings: ($596,010)
Fiscal Year-end: 12/31/19
Metal Exploration Services
N.A.I.C.S.: 213114
Judson Culter (CEO)

ROVERT PTY LTD
4 Bronte Rd, Broadmeadows, 2292,
New South Wales, Australia
Tel.: (61) 249525600
Web Site: http://www.rovert.com.au
Sales Range: $75-99.9 Million
Emp.: 45
Electrical Equipment Whslr
N.A.I.C.S.: 423610
Troy Griggs (Gen Mgr)

ROVITA S.A.
Ul Niedomicka 2, 33-132, Niedomice,
Poland
Tel.: (48) 146457555
Web Site: http://www.rovita.nazwa.pl
Year Founded: 1991
Dairy Products Mfr
N.A.I.C.S.: 311512
Urszula Mroz (Chm)

ROVSING A/S
Ejby Industrivej 34-38, 2600,
Glostrup, Denmark
Tel.: (45) 44200800
Web Site: https://www.rovsing.dk
Year Founded: 1992
ROV—(CSE)
Rev.: $4,099,926
Assets: $4,802,419
Liabilities: $3,844,251
Net Worth: $958,169
Earnings: ($249,888)
Emp.: 25
Fiscal Year-end: 06/30/23
Engineeering Services
N.A.I.C.S.: 541330
Hjalti P. Thorvardarson (CEO)

ROWAD TOURISM COMPANY
4 A Aziz Abaza Str in front of Indian
Embassy, Cairo, Egypt
Tel.: (20) 27355281
Web Site:
https://www.rowadtourism.com
Year Founded: 1994
ROTO.CA—(EGX)
Sales Range: Less than $1 Million
Emp.: 15
Tourism Development Services
N.A.I.C.S.: 561520
Lotfy Mohamed Hassan Shash (Chm)

ROWAN WILLIAMS DAVIES & IRWIN INC.
650 Southgate Drive, Guelph, N1G
4P6, ON, Canada
Tel.: (519) 823-1311
Web Site: http://www.rwdi.com
Year Founded: 1972
Engineeering Services
N.A.I.C.S.: 541330
Michael J. Soligo (Pres & CEO)

ROWLINSON KNITWEAR LIMITED
Woodbank Mills Turncroft Lane,
Stockport, SK1 4AR, United Kingdom
Tel.: (44) 1614777791
Web Site: http://www.rowlinson-knitwear.com
Year Founded: 1935

Sales Range: $10-24.9 Million
Emp.: 63
School Wear Mfr
N.A.I.C.S.: 458110
Jon Lock (Acct Mgr-North)

ROX EQUITY PARTNERS LIMITED
1st Floor 1 Mayfair Place Mayfair,
London, W1J8AJ, United Kingdom
Tel.: (44) 203 205 7179
Web Site:
https://www.roxequitypartners.co.uk
Year Founded: 2017
Privater Equity Firm
N.A.I.C.S.: 523940
Barney Esterhuyzen (Chm)

ROX HAMANN GMBH
Hagenheimer Strasse 20, 86928,
Landsberg am Lech, Germany
Tel.: (49) 8196750
Web Site: http://www.rox-international.com
Year Founded: 1890
Rev.: $22,237,249
Emp.: 70
Leather Goods Mfr
N.A.I.C.S.: 316990
Peter Hamann (Mng Dir)

ROX RESOURCES LIMITED
Level 2 87 Colin Street, West Perth,
6005, WA, Australia
Tel.: (61) 892260044   AU
Web Site:
https://www.roxresources.com.au
RXL—(ASX)
Rev.: $50,080
Assets: $38,122,997
Liabilities: $9,672,142
Net Worth: $28,450,855
Earnings: ($9,147,302)
Emp.: 7
Fiscal Year-end: 06/30/24
Mineral Mining & Exploration
N.A.I.C.S.: 212290
Alex Passmore (Mng Dir)

ROXAS & COMPANY, INC.
7th Floor Cacho Gonzales Building
101 Aguirre Street, Legaspi Village,
Makati, 1229, Philippines
Tel.: (63) 288108901
Web Site:
https://www.roxascompany.com.ph
Year Founded: 1918
RCI—(PHI)
Rev.: $10,403,182
Assets: $259,146,035
Liabilities: $99,140,621
Net Worth: $160,005,414
Earnings: ($23,928,237)
Emp.: 360
Fiscal Year-end: 12/31/20
Real Estate Services
N.A.I.C.S.: 531210
Peter D. A. Barot (Sec)

Subsidiaries:

Roxaco Land Corporation   (1)
7/F Cacho-Gonzales Building 101 Aguirre
Street, 101 Aguirre Street, Legaspi Village,
Makati, 1229, Philippines
Tel.: (63) 288108901
Web Site: https://roxaco.com
Real Estate Development Services
N.A.I.C.S.: 531390

ROXAS HOLDINGS, INC.
14th Floor Net One Center 26th
Street corner 3rd Avenue, Bonifacio
Global City Metro Manila, Taguig,
1634, Philippines
Tel.: (63) 87717800   PH
Web Site:
https://www.roxasholdings.com.ph

Year Founded: 1927
ROX—(PHI)
Rev.: $74,992,491
Assets: $240,098,326
Liabilities: $183,724,347
Net Worth: $56,373,979
Earnings: ($30,154,374)
Fiscal Year-end: 09/30/23
Holding & Investment Company;
Sugar Cane Production & Refining
N.A.I.C.S.: 551112
Pedro E. Roxas (Chm)

ROXBORO EXCAVATION, INC.
1620 Croissant Newman, Dorval,
H9P 2R8, QC, Canada
Tel.: (514) 631-1889
Web Site: http://www.roxboro.biz
Year Founded: 1972
Sales Range: $25-49.9 Million
Emp.: 500
Civil Engineering & Construction Services
N.A.I.C.S.: 237990
Yvon Theoret (Pres & CEO)

ROXCEL HANDELSGES.M.B.H.
Thurngasse 10, 1090, Vienna, Austria
Tel.: (43) 1 401560
Web Site: http://www.roxcel.com
Year Founded: 1993
Sales Range: $900-999.9 Million
Paper Mills; Paper & Board Distr
N.A.I.C.S.: 423840
Christian Priesner (Chief Digital Officer)

Subsidiaries:

Brigl & Bergmeister GmbH   (1)
Proleberstrasse 10, 8712, Niklasdorf, Austria
Tel.: (43) 3842 800 0
Web Site: http://www.brigl-bergmeister.com
Label Paper & Flexible Packaging Paper Mfr
N.A.I.C.S.: 322120
Norbert Peintinger (Dir-Sls-Central Europe)

PT. Roxcel Indonesia   (1)
Karawaci Warehouse Jl Imam Bonjol Baru
km 2,58 no, 3A Tangerang, Banten, 15115,
Indonesia
Tel.: (62) 21 558 8920
Web Site: http://www.roxcel.com
Paper Product Whslr
N.A.I.C.S.: 424130
Hendy Junaidi (Sls Mgr)

Papirnica Vevce d. o. o.   (1)
Papirniska pot 25, Dobrunje, 1261, Ljubljana, Slovenia
Tel.: (386) 15877200
Web Site: http://www.papir-vevce.si
Paper Whslr
N.A.I.C.S.: 424110
David Ravnjak (Head-R&D)

ROXCEL Istanbul - Kagit Pazarlama
ve Ticaret Limited Sirketi   (1)
Gulbahar Mah Salih Tozan Sokak Iyigun Is
Merkezi No 13 Kat 6, Sisli, 34394, Istanbul,
Turkiye
Tel.: (90) 2122742223
Paper Whslr
N.A.I.C.S.: 424110

ROXCEL Moscow Joint Stock
Co.   (1)
4 Maliy Kakovinsky per App 4, Moscow,
Russia
Tel.: (7) 4952586929
Paper Whslr
N.A.I.C.S.: 424110
Sergei Veligorsky (Mgr-Sls)

Roxcal S.a.r.l.   (1)
Logt El Achour Batiment No D49 Logt No 2,
1016, Algiers, Algeria
Tel.: (213) 21 948 080
Paper Mfr
N.A.I.C.S.: 322120
Abdelhakim Ait Tigrine (Mng Dir)

Roxcel Argentina   (1)
Peru 913 Acassuso San Isidro, Buenos Aires, CP 1640, Argentina
Tel.: (54) 11 4798 2558
Web Site: http://www.roxcel.com
Emp.: 2
Paper Whslr
N.A.I.C.S.: 424130
Diego Rodriguez (Mng Dir)

Roxcel Australasia Pty Ltd.   (1)
PO Box 2162, Salisbury, 4107, QLD, Australia
Tel.: (61) 7 3299 5977
Web Site: http://www.roxcel.com
Paper Products Sales
N.A.I.C.S.: 424130
Sallyann Carlile (Mgr-Sls)

Roxcel Corporation   (1)
530 Howell Rd Ste 107, Greenville, SC
29615
Tel.: (864) 241-0180
Web Site: http://www.roxcel.com
Emp.: 6
Paper Whslr
N.A.I.C.S.: 424130
Luis Vazquez (Gen Mgr)

Roxcel Italia S.r.l.   (1)
Via Zago 6, 37069, Villafranca di Verona,
Verona, Italy
Tel.: (39) 045 630 57 96
Web Site: http://www.roxcel.com
Paper Whslr
N.A.I.C.S.: 424130
Enzo Anastasia (Mng Dir & Head-Graphics)

Roxcel South Africa (Pty) Ltd   (1)
732 Taurus Road Sundowner Ext 14 Randburg, Johannesburg, 2193, South Africa
Tel.: (27) 11 794 4618
Web Site: http://www.roxcel.com
Emp.: 2
Paper Whslr
N.A.I.C.S.: 424130
Lin Larsen (Dir-Sls)

Roxcel Thailand Ltd.   (1)
88/1-2 Industrial Ring Road Chongnonsi,
Yannawa, Bangkok, 10120, Thailand
Tel.: (66) 2 294 9570 76 305
Web Site: http://www.roxcel.com
Paper Products Mfr & Distr
N.A.I.C.S.: 424130
Chakhrit Phaewatanaloet (Mng Dir)

Roxcel Trading China Limited   (1)
Unit 815 Kerry Center South of Renmin
Road, Luohu District, Shenzhen, 518001,
China
Tel.: (86) 755 8249 9309
Web Site: http://www.roxcel.com
Emp.: 4
Paper Whslr
N.A.I.C.S.: 424130
Thomas Bauer (Mng Dir)

Roxcel Trading Corporation   (1)
4854A SW Scholls Ferry Rd, Portland, OR
97225
Tel.: (503) 610-0853
Paper Whslr
N.A.I.C.S.: 424130
John Dryden (Sls Mgr-Recycled Fibers)

Roxcel do Brasil   (1)
Rua Dr Renato Paes de Barros 750 cj 75,
Sao Paulo, 04530-001, Brazil
Tel.: (55) 11 3284 7565
Web Site: http://www.roxcel.com
Paper Whslr
N.A.I.C.S.: 424130
Marta Tarcay (Sls Mgr)

ROY ASSET HOLDING SE
Alexander-Wiegand-Str 8, 63911,
Klingenberg, Germany
Tel.: (49) 9372131270
Web Site: https://royasset.de
RY8—(DEU)
Rev.: $8,817,181
Assets: $44,369,739
Liabilities: $8,229,009
Net Worth: $36,140,730
Earnings: ($36,391,107)
Emp.: 90
Fiscal Year-end: 12/31/21
Sanitary Ware Mfr

N.A.I.C.S.: 327110
Suriya Toaramrut (Mng Dir)

ROY FOSS MOTORS LTD.
7200 Yonge Street, Thornhill, L4J
1V8, ON, Canada
Tel.: (905) 886-2000
Web Site: http://www.royfoss.com
Year Founded: 1962
New & Used Car Dealers
N.A.I.C.S.: 441110
James Ricci (Gen Mgr)

ROY HANKINSON (HOLDINGS) LIMITED
Cotton Place 2 Ivy Street, Birkenhead, Wirral, CH41 5EF, United Kingdom
Tel.: (44) 3339966224 UK
Web Site:
  http://www.hankinsongroup.co.uk
Year Founded: 1975
Holding Company; Contract Painting Services
N.A.I.C.S.: 551112
Stephen Roy Hankinson (Founder, Chm & Pres)

Subsidiaries:

Whittle Programmed Maintenance Limited (1)
Cotton Place 2 Ivy Street, Birkenhead, Wirral, CH41 5EF, United Kingdom
Tel.: (44) 3339966223
Web Site: http://www.hankinson.co.uk
Painting & Decoration Services
N.A.I.C.S.: 238320
Neil Hand (Mng Dir)

Subsidiary (Domestic):

Whittle Painting Group Ltd. (2)
Cotton Place 2 Ivy Street, Birkenhead, Wirral, CH41 5EF, United Kingdom
Tel.: (44) 3339966224
Holding Company; Painting Services
N.A.I.C.S.: 551112

Subsidiary (Domestic):

Whittle Painting Nottingham Ltd. (3)
Ryan House, Ryan Business Park, Nottingham, NG7 7EF, Notts, United Kingdom
Tel.: (44) 1159708770
Contract Painting & Wallpapering Services
N.A.I.C.S.: 238320

ROY NICHOLS MOTORS LTD.
2728 Courtice Road, Courtice, L1E 2M7, ON, Canada
Tel.: (289) 274-6898
Web Site:
  http://www.roynicholsmotors.com
Year Founded: 1922
New & Used Car Dealers
N.A.I.C.S.: 441110
Bob Adams (Mgr-Parts)

ROYAL AIR MAROC SA
Aeroport Casa-Anfa, Casablanca, 20200, Morocco
Tel.: (212) 890000800 Ma
Web Site:
  http://www.royalairmaroc.com
Year Founded: 1957
Sales Range: Less than $1 Million
Emp.: 5,283
International & Domestic Airline Cargo Transportation Aircraft Maintenance Pilot Training Airline Catering Hotel Services
N.A.I.C.S.: 481111

Subsidiaries:

SNECMA Morocco Engine Services (1)
Mohammed V International Airport, PO Box 87, 20400, Casablanca, Morocco (100%)
Tel.: (212) 22536900
Web Site: http://www.snecma.ma
Aircraft Engine Overhaul & Maintenance; Joint Venture of Royal Air Maroc (49%) & SNECMA-Societe Nationale d'Etude et de Construction de Moteurs d'Aviation (51%)
N.A.I.C.S.: 336412

Sotoram (1)
16 Blvd Moulay Youssef, Casablanca, 20000, Morocco (98%)
Tel.: (212) 22 88 95 01
Hotels; Airline Catering
N.A.I.C.S.: 722320

ROYAL ARCTIC LINE A/S
Aqqusinersuaq 52, PO Box 1580, 3900, Nuuk, Greenland
Tel.: (299) 349100 GL
Web Site: http://www.ral.gl
Year Founded: 1993
Sales Range: $100-124.9 Million
Emp.: 677
Ocean Cargo Services
N.A.I.C.S.: 488390
Verner Hammeken (CEO)

Subsidiaries:

Aalborg Stevedore Company A/S (1)
Stykgodsvej 3-5, 9000, Aalborg, Denmark
Tel.: (45) 98135301
Ocean Freight Services
N.A.I.C.S.: 488320

Arctic Container Operation A/S (1)
Langerak 17, PO Box 8432, DK-9220, Aalborg, Denmark
Tel.: (45) 99303161
Web Site: http://www.ral.dk
Sales Range: $10-24.9 Million
Emp.: 127
Container Services
N.A.I.C.S.: 488320

Royal Arctic Havneservice (1)
Umiarsualiviup Aqqusinersuaq B-745, 3962, Upernavik, Greenland
Tel.: (299) 962033
Sales Range: $25-49.9 Million
Emp.: 219
Harbor Services
N.A.I.C.S.: 488390

Royal Arctic Logistics A/S (1)
Gronlandshavnen Vejdybet 16, PO Boxo8100, 9220, Aalborg, Denmark
Tel.: (45) 99 30 32 34
Web Site: http://www.ralog.dk
Emp.: 180
Logistics Consulting Servies
N.A.I.C.S.: 541614
Esper Boel (Mgr-Sls)

Royal Arctic Spedition A/S (1)
Gronlandshavnen Langerak 17, PO Box 1800, Aalborg, 9220, Denmark
Tel.: (45) 99303227
Web Site: http://www.ral.gl
Sales Range: $50-74.9 Million
Emp.: 150
Freight Forwarding Services
N.A.I.C.S.: 483111
Lars Oaestergaard (Gen Mgr)

ROYAL AUPING B.V.
Laan van Borgele, 7415 DK, Deventer, Netherlands
Tel.: (31) 570681911
Web Site: http://www.auping.com
Sales Range: $75-99.9 Million
Emp.: 340
Mattress Mfr
N.A.I.C.S.: 337910
Aart Roos (Pres)

ROYAL BAFOKENG HOLDINGS (PTY) LIMITED
37 High Street Block C 2nd Floor, Melrose Arch, 2076, Johannesburg, South Africa
Tel.: (27) 11 530 8000
Web Site:
  http://www.bafokengholdings.com
Rev.: $3,551,440,000
Investment Services
N.A.I.C.S.: 523999

Albertinah Kekana (CEO)

Subsidiaries:

Fraser Alexander (pty) Ltd (1)
1 Marlin Rd Jet Park, Boksburg, 1459, South Africa
Tel.: (27) 119293600
Web Site: http://www.fraseralexander.co.za
Waste Management Services
N.A.I.C.S.: 562219
Velile Nhlapo (CEO)

M-tech Industrial (pty) Ltd (1)
Block E & F 24 Totius Street Totius Park, Potchefstroom, 2531, South Africa
Tel.; (27) 182970326
Web Site: http://www.mtechindustrial.com
Energy Consulting Services
N.A.I.C.S.: 541690
W. A. Landman (CEO)

MOGS (Pty) Ltd (1)
1st Floor 37 High Street Melrose Arch, 2076, Johannesburg, South Africa
Tel.: (27) 115308062
Web Site: http://www.mogs.co.za
Natural Gas Services
N.A.I.C.S.: 211130

ROYAL BANK OF CANADA
200 Bay Street Royal Bank Plaza, PO Box 1, Toronto, M5J 2J5, ON, Canada
Tel.: (416) 569-2431 CA
Web Site: https://www.rbc.com
Year Founded: 1869
RY—(NYSE)
Rev.: $42,395,566,080
Assets: $1,605,494,004,240
Liabilities: $1,511,458,414,800
Net Worth: $94,035,589,440
Earnings: $12,006,556,800
Emp.: 98,000
Fiscal Year-end: 10/31/24
Bank Holding Company
N.A.I.C.S.: 551111
Kathleen P. Taylor (Chm)

Subsidiaries:

City National Bank (1)
555 S Flower St, Los Angeles, CA 90071 (100%)
Tel.: (213) 673-7700
Web Site: http://www.cnb.com
Sales Range: $1-4.9 Billion
Emp.: 3,570
Federal Savings Bank
N.A.I.C.S.: 522180
Michael R. Walker (Exec VP & Head-Comml Banking)

Subsidiary (Domestic):

Convergent Capital Management LLC (2)
500 W Madison Ste 2620, Chicago, IL 60661
Tel.: (312) 444-6000
Web Site: http://www.convergentcapital.com
Rev.: $15,500,000
Emp.: 5
Investment Banking Services
N.A.I.C.S.: 523150

Subsidiary (Domestic):

Clifford Swan Investment Counsel LLC (3)
1778 Coloardo blvd Ste 550, Pasadena, CA 91101
Tel.: (626) 792-2228
Web Site: http://www.cliffordswan.com
Investment Advisory & Portfolio Management Services
N.A.I.C.S.: 523940
James R. Brown (COO & Principal)

Convergent Wealth Advisors (3)
12505 Park Potomac Ave Ste 400, Potomac, MD 20854
Tel.: (301) 770-6300
Web Site: http://www.convergentwealth.com
Sales Range: $125-149.9 Million
Health Management Consulting Services
N.A.I.C.S.: 523999
Douglas Wolford (CEO)

Lee Munder Capital Group, LLC (3)
200 Clarendon St 28th Fl, Boston, MA 02116
Tel.: (617) 380-5600
Web Site: http://www.leemunderpim.com
Investment Services
N.A.I.C.S.: 523940

Mid-Continent Capital LLC (3)
150 S Wacker Dr Ste 400, Chicago, IL 60606
Tel.: (312) 551-8200
Web Site: http://www.mccllc.com
Investment Counselors
N.A.I.C.S.: 523940
John D. Mabie (Founder & Chm)

Subsidiary (Domestic):

First American Commercial Bancorp, Inc. (2)
255 Woodcliff Dr, Fairport, NY 14450
Tel.: (585) 598-0900
Web Site: http://www.faef.com
Sales Range: $10-24.9 Million
Commercial Equipment Financing & Leasing Services
N.A.I.C.S.: 522220
Bruce Masterson (Gen Counsel)

Rochdale Investment Management LLC (2)
570 Lexington Ave, New York, NY 10022-6837
Tel.: (212) 702-3500
Web Site: http://www.rochdale.com
Rev.: $4,800,000,000
Emp.: 100
Investment Management Service
N.A.I.C.S.: 523940
Garrett R. D'Alessandro (CEO)

HSBC Bank Canada (1)
885 West Georgia Street, Vancouver, V6C 3E9, BC, Canada
Tel.: (604) 685-1000
Web Site: https://www.hsbc.ca
Rev.: $1,521,486,900
Assets: $76,774,547,610
Liabilities: $72,226,018,710
Net Worth: $4,548,528,900
Earnings: $532,122,120
Emp.: 5,210
Fiscal Year-end: 12/31/2017
Retail & Commercial Banking Services
N.A.I.C.S.: 522110
Jason Henderson (Mng Dir, Exec VP & Head)

Moneris Solutions Corporation (1)
3300 Bloor Street West, Toronto, M8X 2X2, ON, Canada
Tel.: (416) 734-1000
Web Site: https://www.moneris.com
Sales Range: $700-749.9 Million
Emp.: 1,500
Payment Processing Services; Owned by RBC Financial Group & Bank of Montreal
N.A.I.C.S.: 522320
Malcolm Fowler (Chief Product & Partnership Officer)

Division (Domestic):

Ernex (2)
4259 Canada Way Ste 225, Burnaby, V5G 1H1, BC, Canada
Tel.: (604) 415-1500
Web Site: http://www.ernex.com
Sales Range: $1-9.9 Million
Emp.: 65
Electronic Marketing Services
N.A.I.C.S.: 541512
Grant Finnighan (Gen Mgr)

Subsidiary (Domestic):

MSC Moneris Services Corp. (2)
7350 Rue Transcanadienne, Saint Laurent, H4T 1A3, QC, Canada
Tel.: (514) 733-5403
Web Site: http://www.msposcorp.com
Sales Range: $150-199.9 Million
Emp.: 300
Payment Processing Services
N.A.I.C.S.: 522320
Shalini Desa (Reg Mgr-Ops)

RBC Bank, (Georgia) N.A. (1)

ROYAL BANK OF CANADA

Royal Bank of Canada—(Continued)

3475 Piedmont Rd NE Ste 550, Atlanta, GA 30305
Web Site: http://www.rbcbank.com
Savings Bank
N.A.I.C.S.: 522180
Tracy Stevenson (CEO)

RBC Direct Investing Inc. (1)
Royal Bank Plaza 200 Bay Street North Tower, Toronto, M5J 2J5, ON, Canada (100%)
Tel.: (416) 974-7493
Web Site: http://www.rbcdirectinvesting.com
Sales Range: $75-99.9 Million
Emp.: 3
Online Investment Banking Services
N.A.I.C.S.: 523150

RBC Finance B.V. (1)
Keizergracht 604, 1017 EP, Amsterdam, Netherlands (100%)
Tel.: (31) 205233233
Sales Range: $75-99.9 Million
Emp.: 8
Bank Services
N.A.I.C.S.: 522299

RBC Holdings (Luxembourg) S.A R.L. (1)
16 Rue Notre Dame, 2240, Luxembourg, Luxembourg
Tel.: (352) 26 63 64
Banking Services
N.A.I.C.S.: 522110

Subsidiary (Non-US):

RBC Holdings (Channel Islands) Limited (2)
Canada Court, Upland Road, Saint Peter Port, GY1 3BQ, Guernsey
Tel.: (44) 1481 744103
Banking Services
N.A.I.C.S.: 522110

RBC Insurance Holding Inc. (1)
6880 Financial Dr Tower 1, Mississauga, L5N 7Y5, ON, Canada (100%)
Tel.: (905) 949-3663
Web Site: http://www.rbcinsurance.com
Sales Range: $250-299.9 Million
Emp.: 5,000
Insurance Holding Company
N.A.I.C.S.: 551112

Division (Domestic):

RBC Insurance Company of Canada (2)
6880 Financial Drive, Mississauga, L5N 7Y5, ON, Canada (100%)
Tel.: (905) 791-8700
Web Site: https://www.rbcinsurance.com
Sales Range: $50-74.9 Million
Emp.: 50
Travel Insurance Products & Services
N.A.I.C.S.: 524128
Neil Skelding (Pres)

Subsidiary (Domestic):

Assured Assistance Inc. (3)
6880 Financial Drive Tower 1, Mississauga, L5N 7Y5, ON, Canada (100%)
Tel.: (905) 793-9666
Web Site: http://www.rbctravelprotection.com
Sales Range: $1-9.9 Million
Emergency Medical & Travel Assistance Services
N.A.I.C.S.: 524298

Division (Domestic):

RBC Insurance Services Inc. (2)
6880 Financial Dr Tower 1, Mississauga, L5N 7Y5, ON, Canada
Tel.: (905) 606-1000
Web Site: http://www.rbcinsurance.com
Insurance Services
N.A.I.C.S.: 524298

RBC Life Insurance Company (2)
6880 Financial Drive Tower 1, Mississauga, L58 7Y5, ON, Canada
Tel.: (905) 606-1000
Web Site: http://www.rbcinsurance.com
Emp.: 7,000
Life & Health Insurance Carrier

N.A.I.C.S.: 524113

RBC Investor Services Limited (1)
Riverbank House, 2 Swan Lane, London, EC4R 3AF, United Kingdom (100%)
Tel.: (44) 2073296677
Web Site: http://www.rbccn.com
Sales Range: $800-899.9 Million
Emp.: 1,500
Holding Company; Custody, Fund & Pension Administration, Distribution Support & Other Shareholder Services
N.A.I.C.S.: 551112

Subsidiary (Non-US):

RBC Dexia Investor Services (Malaysia) Sdn. Bhd. (2)
Prima Avenue, Block 3508, Jalan Teknokrat 6, 63000, Cyberjaya, Malaysia
Tel.: (60) 8686 3888
Federal Reserve Bank
N.A.I.C.S.: 521110

RBC Dexia Investor Services Espana, S.A. (2)
Fernando El Santo 20, Madrid, 28010, Spain
Tel.: (34) 913609900
Web Site: http://www.rbc.com
Sales Range: $75-99.9 Million
Emp.: 150
Federal Reserve Bank
N.A.I.C.S.: 521110

RBC Investor & Treasury Services (2)
77 Robinson Road #18-00, Singapore, 068896, Singapore
Tel.: (65) 6230 1999
Web Site: http://www.rbcits.com
Sales Range: $50-74.9 Million
Emp.: 63
Fund Administration & Transfer Agent Services
N.A.I.C.S.: 524292
Ronan Doyle (Head-Product Mgmt-Global)

RBC Investor Services Canada (2)
155 Wellington St W 7th Fl, Toronto, M5V 3L3, ON, Canada
Tel.: (416) 955-6507
Web Site: http://www.rbcis.com
Sales Range: $300-349.9 Million
Emp.: 1,000
Investor Services
N.A.I.C.S.: 523999
Francis Jackson (CEO)

RBC Wealth Management (1)
Royal Bank Plz 200 Bay St, Toronto, M5J 2J5, ON, Canada
Tel.: (416) 974-5151
Web Site: http://www.rbcwealthmanagement.com
Rev: $254,456,800,000
Emp.: 4,500
Wealth Management Services
N.A.I.C.S.: 523940
David Agnew (CEO)

Subsidiary (Non-US):

BlueBay Asset Management LLP (2)
77 Grosvenor Street, London, W1K 3JR, United Kingdom (100%)
Tel.: (44) 20 7389 3700
Web Site: http://www.bluebayinvest.com
Emp.: 200
Holding Company; Fixed Income & Alternative Investment Fund Management Services
N.A.I.C.S.: 551112
Erich Gerth (CEO)

Subsidiary (Domestic):

BlueBay Asset Management (Services) Ltd. (3)
77 Grosvenor Street, London, W1K 3JR, United Kingdom (100%)
Tel.: (44) 2073893700
Web Site: http://www.bluebayinvest.com
Sales Range: $50-74.9 Million
Emp.: 220
Fixed Income & Alternative Investment Fund Management Services
N.A.I.C.S.: 523940

Subsidiary (Non-US):

FT Securities Limited (2)

28/F-29/F Three Exchange Square, 8 Connaught Place, Central, China (Hong Kong) (100%)
Tel.: (852) 39203600
Private Banking & Wealth Management Services
N.A.I.C.S.: 523991

Subsidiary (Domestic):

RBC Dominion Securities Inc. (2)
Royal Bank Plaza 200 Bay Street, Toronto, M5J 2W7, ON, Canada (100%)
Tel.: (416) 842-7575
Web Site: https://www.rbccm.com
Sales Range: $800-899.9 Million
Emp.: 1,500
Investment Banking, Securities Dealing & Brokerage Services
N.A.I.C.S.: 523150

Subsidiary (Domestic):

RBC Capital Markets (Quebec) Inc. (3)
Place Ville Marie 1 Place Ville Marie Suite 300, Montreal, H3B 4R8, QC, Canada (100%)
Tel.: (514) 878-7000
Web Site: http://www.rbccm.com
Sales Range: $75-99.9 Million
Emp.: 150
Investment Services
N.A.I.C.S.: 523940
Derek Neldner (CEO)

Subsidiary (US):

RBC Capital Markets Corporation (3)
3 World Financial Ctr 200 Vesui St, New York, NY 10281
Tel.: (212) 858-7000
Web Site: http://www.rbccm.com
Investment Banking & Securities Brokerage Services
N.A.I.C.S.: 523150
Jim Wolfe (Mng Dir & Co-Head-Investment Banking)

Unit (Domestic):

RBC Capital Markets (4)
2 Embarcadero Ctr Ste 1200, San Francisco, CA 94111
Tel.: (415) 633-8500
Web Site: http://www.rbccm.com
Sales Range: $25-49.9 Million
Emp.: 100
Equity Research Investment
N.A.I.C.S.: 523150
Derek Neldner (CEO)

Subsidiary (Domestic):

RBC Daniels L.P. (4)
3200 Cherry Creek S Dr Ste 500, Denver, CO 80209
Tel.: (303) 778-5555
Web Site: http://www.rbcdaniels.com
Sales Range: $10-24.9 Million
Emp.: 37
Merger & Acquisition, Private Equity & Debt Financing, Corporate Restructuring & Financial Advisory Services
N.A.I.C.S.: 525990

Subsidiary (Domestic):

RBC Capital Markets Real Estate Group Inc. (3)
Royal Bank Plz North Tower 4th Fl, 200 Bay Street, Toronto, M5J 2J5, ON, Canada
Tel.: (416) 842-8900
Web Site: http://www.rbcrealestate.com
Sales Range: $50-74.9 Million
Emp.: 25
Real Estate Investment Bank
N.A.I.C.S.: 525990

Subsidiary (Domestic):

RBC Global Asset Management Inc. (2)
155 Wellington St Ste 2200, Toronto, M5V 3K7, ON, Canada (100%)
Tel.: (416) 974-0616
Web Site: https://www.rbcgam.com
Sales Range: $350-399.9 Million
Emp.: 1,000

INTERNATIONAL PUBLIC

Mutual Funds & Asset Management Services
N.A.I.C.S.: 523940
Daniel Chornous (Chief Investment Officer)

Division (US):

RBC Wealth Management - USA (2)
60 S 6th St, Minneapolis, MN 55402-4422
Tel.: (612) 371-2711
Web Site: http://www.rbcwm-usa.com
Sales Range: $700-749.9 Million
Emp.: 2,000
Portfolio Management Services
N.A.I.C.S.: 523940
Tom Sagissor (Pres)

Subsidiary (Domestic):

RBC Correspondent Services (3)
500 N Broadway, Saint Louis, MO 63310 (100%)
Tel.: (314) 589-5000
Web Site: http://www.rbc.com
Sales Range: $25-49.9 Million
Emp.: 20
Investment Banking & Stockbrokers
N.A.I.C.S.: 561499
Craig Gordon (Mgr-Bus Dev-West Reg)

Branch (Domestic):

RBC Wealth Management - USA (3)
75 State St Ste 1700, Boston, MA 02109
Tel.: (617) 725-2000
Web Site: http://www.rbcwm-usa.com
Emp.: 50
Brokerage Firm; Retail & Institutional Brokerage, Corporate Finance & Underwriting
N.A.I.C.S.: 523940

RBC Wealth Management - USA (3)
4 Gatehall Dr, Parsippany, NJ 07054-4518
Tel.: (973) 829-1000
Sales Range: $50-74.9 Million
Emp.: 330
Security Brokers & Dealers
N.A.I.C.S.: 523150
Ann Marie Vibert (Head-Private Client Wealth Mgmt-Offshores)

RBC Wealth Management - USA (3)
345 California St, San Francisco, CA 94104
Tel.: (415) 445-8500
Web Site: http://www.rbcwm-usa.com
Sales Range: $1-4.9 Billion
Emp.: 1,000
Investment & Trading Services
N.A.I.C.S.: 523150
Michael Armstrong (CEO)

RBC Wealth Management - USA (3)
25 Hanover Rd Ste 2, Florham Park, NJ 07932-1410
Tel.: (973) 822-2500
Web Site: http://www.rbcusa.com
Sales Range: $75-99.9 Million
Emp.: 210
Bank Services
N.A.I.C.S.: 523150

RBTT Financial Holdings Limited (1)
Royal Court 19-21 Park Street, Port of Spain, Trinidad & Tobago
Tel.: (868) 623 1322
Web Site: http://www.rbtt.com
Sales Range: $800-899.9 Million
Emp.: 7,000
Bank Holding Company
N.A.I.C.S.: 551111

Subsidiary (Non-US):

RBC Royal Bank (Aruba) N.V. (2)
Italiestraat 36, Oranjestad, Aruba
Tel.: (297) 5233100
Web Site: http://www.rbcroyalbank.com
Savings, Commercial & Investment Banking Services
N.A.I.C.S.: 522110

RBC Royal Bank (Barbados) Limited (2)
Lower Broad Street, Bridgetown, Barbados
Tel.: (246) 4312500
Web Site: http://www.rbcroyalbank.com
Sales Range: $100-124.9 Million
Emp.: 120
Commercial Banking Services
N.A.I.C.S.: 522110

AND PRIVATE COMPANIES — ROYAL COSUN U.A.

Subsidiary (Domestic):

RBC Royal Bank (Trinidad & Tobago) Limited (2)
Royal Court 19-21 Park Street, Port of Spain, Trinidad & Tobago
Tel.: (868) 625 7288
Web Site: http://www.rbcroyalbank.com
Sales Range: $250-299.9 Million
Commercial Banking Services
N.A.I.C.S.: 522110

Subsidiary (Non-US):

RBC Royal Bank N.V. (2)
Kaya Flamboyan 1, Rooi Catootje, Willemstad, Curacao
Tel.: (599) 97638000
Web Site: http://www.rbcroyalbank.com
Sales Range: $150-199.9 Million
Emp.: 225
Savings, Loans, Commercial & Investment Banking Services
N.A.I.C.S.: 522110

RBTT Bank Caribbean Limited (2) (100%)
Tel.: (784) 456 1501
Web Site: http://www.rbtt.com
Commercial Banking Services
N.A.I.C.S.: 522110

Division (Domestic):

RBTT Bank (SKN) Limited (3)
Chapel Street, PO Box 60, Charlestown, Saint Kitts & Nevis (95.4%)
Tel.: (869) 4695277
Web Site: http://www.rbtt.com
Commercial Banking Services
N.A.I.C.S.: 522110

RBTT Bank Caribbean Ltd.-Antigua (3)
45 High Street, PO Box 1324, Saint John's, Antigua & Barbuda (100%)
Tel.: (268) 4624217
Web Site: http://www.rbtt.com
Sales Range: $50-74.9 Million
Emp.: 45
Commercial Banking Services
N.A.I.C.S.: 522110

RBTT Bank Caribbean Ltd.-Saint Lucia (3)
22 Micoud Street, PO Box 1531, Castries, Saint Lucia (100%)
Tel.: (758) 4522265
Web Site: http://www.rbtt.com
Commercial Banking Services
N.A.I.C.S.: 522110

RBTT Bank Grenada Limited (3)
Corner Cross & Halifax St, PO Box 4, Saint George's, Grenada (62%)
Tel.: (473) 440 3521
Web Site: http://www.rbtt.com
Commercial Banking Services
N.A.I.C.S.: 522110

Subsidiary (Domestic):

RBTT Insurance Agency Limited (2)
55 Independence Sq, Port of Spain, Trinidad & Tobago (100%)
Tel.: (868) 6257271
Web Site: http://www.rbtt.com
Sales Range: $50-74.9 Million
Emp.: 8
Insurance Services
N.A.I.C.S.: 524210

RBTT Merchant Bank Limited (2)
Royal Ct 19-21 Pk St, Port of Spain, Trinidad & Tobago (100%)
Tel.: (868) 625 7288
Web Site: http://www.rbtt.com
Capital Market Financial Services
N.A.I.C.S.: 523150

RBTT Trust Limited (2)
Albion Plaza, Port of Spain, Trinidad & Tobago (100%)
Tel.: (868) 625 7288
Web Site: http://www.rbtt.com
Asset Management Services
N.A.I.C.S.: 523940

West Indies Stockbrokers Limited (2)
Saint Clair Place 8 Sweet Briar Road, Port of Spain, Trinidad & Tobago (100%)
Tel.: (868) 6289473
Web Site: http://www.wisett.com
Sales Range: $50-74.9 Million
Emp.: 25
Securities Broker
N.A.I.C.S.: 523150
Adrian Manmohan *(Head-Ops & Trading)*

Royal Bank Mortgage Corporation (1)
180 Wellington Street West, Toronto, M5J 1J1, ON, Canada
Tel.: (416) 974-5151
Mortgage Banking Services
N.A.I.C.S.: 522292

Royal Bank of Canada (Asia) Limited (1)
3 Church St 27-01-08 Sansung Hub, Singapore, 049483, Singapore (100%)
Tel.: (65) 065369206
Web Site: http://www.rbcnet.fg.rvc.com
Sales Range: $75-99.9 Million
Emp.: 70
Bank Services
N.A.I.C.S.: 522299

Royal Bank of Canada Europe Ltd. (1)
St river bank house, London, EC4V 3BF, United Kingdom
Tel.: (44) 2074891188
Web Site: http://www.rbccm.com
Sales Range: $700-749.9 Million
Emp.: 1,300
International Banking
N.A.I.C.S.: 522299
Wendy Phillis *(Mng Dir-Governance & Regulatory Solutions-Investor & Treasury Svc)*

ROYAL BOSKALIS WESTMINSTER N.V.
Rosmolenweg 20, 3356 LK, Papendrecht, Netherlands
Tel.: (31) 786969000
Web Site: http://www.boskalis.com
Year Founded: 1910
Civil Engineering Services
N.A.I.C.S.: 327910
C. Van Noort *(CFO)*

ROYAL BRUNEI AIRLINES SDN. BHD.
RBA Plaza Jalan Sultan, PO Box 737, Bandar Seri Begawan, BS 8811, Brunei Darussalam
Tel.: (673) 236 7797
Web Site: http://www.flyroyalbrunei.com
Year Founded: 1974
Airline Services
N.A.I.C.S.: 481111
Karam Chand *(CEO)*

Subsidiaries:

Mulaut Abattoir Sdn. Bhd (1)
PO Box 28, BG1121, Sengkurong, Brunei Darussalam (100%)
Tel.: (673) 2670678
Sales Range: $25-49.9 Million
Emp.: 100
Ritual Animal Slaughtering Services
N.A.I.C.S.: 311611
Pengiran Imran *(Gen Mgr)*

RBA Golf Club Sdn. Bhd. (1)
PO Box 998, Bandar Seri Begawan, Brunei Darussalam
Tel.: (673) 2343724
Web Site: http://www.rbagc.com.bn
Golf Course Operator
N.A.I.C.S.: 713910
Asmadi Alimustapha *(Gen Mgr)*

Royal Brunei Catering Sdn Bhd (1)
1-2 F Bangunan Gadong Properties, PO Box 2248, Km 3 jalan Gadong, Bandar Seri Begawan, S674, Brunei Darussalam
Tel.: (673) 2440577
Web Site: http://www.rbcatering.com
Sales Range: $125-149.9 Million
Emp.: 580

Aircraft Catering & Restaurant Operation Services
N.A.I.C.S.: 722511

Subsidiary (Domestic):

Royal Brunei Trading Sdn Bhd (2)
1st Floor Bangunan Gadong Properties, Km 3 Jalan Gadong, Bandar Seri Begawan, Brunei Darussalam
Tel.: (673) 2448123
Sales Range: $25-49.9 Million
Emp.: 41
Consumer Products Distr & Sales
N.A.I.C.S.: 423990

ROYAL CANADIAN MINT
320 Sussex Drive, Ottawa, K1A 0G8, ON, Canada
Tel.: (613) 954-2626   ON
Web Site: https://www.mint.ca
Year Founded: 1908
MNT—(TSX)
Rev.: $1,112,208,234
Assets: $328,980,502
Liabilities: $214,036,863
Net Worth: $114,943,639
Earnings: $26,623,465
Emp.: 1,099
Fiscal Year-end: 12/31/19
Coins & Other Precious Metals Distr
N.A.I.C.S.: 423940
Michel Boucher *(VP-HR)*

ROYAL CENTURY RESOURCES HOLDINGS LIMITED
Suite 2201 22/F China Resources Building, 26 Harbour Road, Wanchai, China (Hong Kong)
Tel.: (852) 2 180 7291   HK
Web Site: http://www.royalcentury.hk
8125—(HKG)
Rev.: $7,436,987
Assets: $13,183,562
Liabilities: $3,844,120
Net Worth: $9,339,442
Earnings: ($2,717,351)
Emp.: 37
Fiscal Year-end: 03/31/22
Holding Company; Furnishings & Materials Production, Project Implementation, Management & Procurement
N.A.I.C.S.: 551112
Chi Yuen Chan *(Chm)*

Subsidiaries:

Oenoluxe Wines Limited (1)
2201 22/F China Resources Building 26 Harbour Road, Wanchai, China (Hong Kong)
Tel.: (852) 21807291
Web Site: http://www.oenoluxe.com
Wine Mfr
N.A.I.C.S.: 312130

ROYAL CERAMICS LANKA PLC
No 20 R A De Mel Mawatha, 3, Colombo, 3, Sri Lanka
Tel.: (94) 114799400
Web Site: https://www.rocell.com
Year Founded: 1990
RCL—(COL)
Rev.: $306,136,826
Assets: $458,803,442
Liabilities: $186,424,102
Net Worth: $272,379,341
Earnings: $72,828,615
Emp.: 8,859
Fiscal Year-end: 03/31/22
Ceramic Tiles & Ceramic Porcelain Tiles Mfr
N.A.I.C.S.: 327120
Tharana G. Thoradeniya *(Dir-Mktg & Bus Dev)*

Subsidiaries:

Lanka Ceramic PLC (1)

No 20 R A de Mel Mawatha, Colombo, 03, Sri Lanka
Tel.: (94) 114336644
Ceramic Wall & Floor Tile Mfr
N.A.I.C.S.: 327120
Jayasekera J. A. P. M. *(Mng Dir)*

Rocell Bathware Ltd. (1)
No 10 R A De Mal Mawatha, Colombo, 00300, Western Province, Sri Lanka
Tel.: (94) 114799400
Sales Range: $50-74.9 Million
Emp.: 190
Sanitary Ware Mfr
N.A.I.C.S.: 332999
Nimal Perara *(Mgr)*

Royal Porcelain (Pvt) Ltd (1)
No 10 R A de Mel Mawatha, Colombo, 00300, Western Province, Sri Lanka
Tel.: (94) 114799400
Web Site: http://www.rocell.com
Ceramic Tile Mfr
N.A.I.C.S.: 327120

ROYAL COAL CORP.
70 York Street Suite 1410, Toronto, M5J 1S6, ON, Canada
Tel.: (416) 861-8775
Web Site: http://www.royalcoal.com
Year Founded: 2007
Sales Range: $10-24.9 Million
Coal Exploration Services
N.A.I.C.S.: 213113
Tom Griffis *(Chm)*

ROYAL COSUN U.A.
Van de Reijtstraat 15, 4814 NE, Breda, Netherlands
Tel.: (31) 765303222
Web Site: http://www.cosun.com
Year Founded: 1899
Rev.: $2,340,651,856
Assets: $2,071,289,311
Liabilities: $646,355,729
Net Worth: $1,424,933,582
Earnings: $2,058,822
Emp.: 3,848
Fiscal Year-end: 12/31/18
Seeds, Sugar, Food Ingredients & Products Producer
N.A.I.C.S.: 111930
M. J. C. W. van den Maagdenberg *(Member-Exec Bd, Sec & Dir-Corp Dev)*

Subsidiaries:

Aviko B.V. (1)
Dr A Ariensstraat 28, 7221 CD, Steenderen, Netherlands (100%)
Tel.: (31) 575458200
Web Site: http://www.corporate.aviko.com
Sales Range: $150-199.9 Million
Emp.: 450
Mfr & Processor of Potatoes & Potato Products
N.A.I.C.S.: 111211
Ton Christiaanse *(Interim CEO)*

Duynie Holding B.V. (1)
Kortsteekterweg 57a, 2407 AJ, Alphen aan den Rijn, Netherlands
Tel.: (31) 172460606
Web Site: http://www.duynie.nl
Holding Company
N.A.I.C.S.: 551112

Subsidiary (Domestic):

Novidon B.V. (2)
Handelsweg 34, 6541 CT, Nijmegen, Netherlands
Tel.: (31) 172 460604
Web Site: http://www.novidon.com
Starch Solution Mfr
N.A.I.C.S.: 311221

Subsidiary (Non-US):

Novidon Ltd. (3)
Coed Aben Road, Wrexham Industrial Estate, Wrexham, LL13 9UH, United Kingdom
Tel.: (44) 1978 664384
Web Site: http://www.novidon-starch.com
Starch Solution Mfr

ROYAL COSUN U.A.

Royal Cosun U.A.—(Continued)
N.A.I.C.S.: 311221

Limako Suiker B.V. (1)
Noordzeedijk 113, 4671 TL, Dinteloord, Netherlands
Tel.: (31) 165525025
Web Site: http://www.limako.com
Sales Range: $25-49.9 Million
Emp.: 6
Sugarcane Farming
N.A.I.C.S.: 111930

Rixona B.V. (1)
Westervalge 82, Warffum, 9989EE, Groningen, Netherlands
Tel.: (31) 0478524747
Web Site: http://www.rixona.nl
Sales Range: $25-49.9 Million
Emp.: 80
Dried & Dehydrated Food Mfr
N.A.I.C.S.: 311423

SVZ International B.V. (1)
Reduitlaan 41, PO Box 27, 4814 DC, Breda, Netherlands (100%)
Tel.: (31) 765049494
Web Site: http://www.svz.com
Sales Range: $75-99.9 Million
Emp.: 225
Fresh Fruit & Vegetable Whslr
N.A.I.C.S.: 424490

Subsidiary (Non-US):

SVZ Espana S.A (2)
Ctra Almonte-El Rocio km 9 5, Poligono Industrial Matalagran, Huelva, 21730, Spain
Tel.: (34) 959450301
Web Site: http://www.svz.com
Sales Range: $25-49.9 Million
Emp.: 13
Fresh Fruit & Vegetable Whslr
N.A.I.C.S.: 424480

SVZ France SA (2)
Site Agroparc, Eden Vlg Bat 15 BP 61508, 84916, Avignon, France (100%)
Tel.: (33) 432707185
Web Site: http://www.svz.com
Sales Range: $25-49.9 Million
Emp.: 2
Fresh Fruit & Vegetable Whslr
N.A.I.C.S.: 424480

SVZ Maroc S.A. (2)
Ctra Moulay Bousselham km 15, Larache, Morocco
Tel.: (212) 539925658
Web Site: http://www.svz.com
Fresh Fruit & Vegetable Whslr
N.A.I.C.S.: 424480

SVZ Poland Sp. z o.o. (2)
Ul Lwowska 128, 22-600, Tomaszow Lubelski, Poland
Tel.: (48) 846644786
Web Site: http://www.svz.com
Sales Range: $50-74.9 Million
Emp.: 200
Fresh Fruit & Vegetable Whslr
N.A.I.C.S.: 424480

SVZ Rijkevorsel NV (2)
Gammel 85, Rijkevorsel, 2310, Belgium
Tel.: (32) 33408400
Web Site: http://www.svz.com
Sales Range: $25-49.9 Million
Emp.: 60
Canned Fruit Mfr
N.A.I.C.S.: 311421
Peter Heijnen (Plant Mgr)

Subsidiary (Non-US):

SVZ Karczmiska Sp. z o.o. (3)
Karczmiska Pierwsze Pogodna 79 Street 24-310, Karczew, 42310, Poland
Tel.: (48) 81 827 6623
Web Site: http://www.svz.com
Sales Range: $25-49.9 Million
Emp.: 200
Canned Fruit Mfr
N.A.I.C.S.: 311421

Subsidiary (Non-US):

SVZ UK Ltd. (2)
Bishops Court, 17A Broadway, Hatfield, AL95HZ, United Kingdom (100%)

Tel.: (44) 1707820020
Web Site: http://www.svz.com
Sales Range: $25-49.9 Million
Emp.: 3
Fresh Fruit & Vegetable Whslr
N.A.I.C.S.: 424480

Subsidiary (US):

SVZ-USA, Inc (2)
1700 N Broadway, Othello, WA 99344
Tel.: (509) 488-6563
Web Site: http://www.svz-usa.com
Sales Range: $25-49.9 Million
Emp.: 100
Fresh Fruit & Vegetable Whslr
N.A.I.C.S.: 424480

Sensus B.V. (1)
Oostelijke Havendijk 15, 4704 RA, Roosendaal, Netherlands
Tel.: (31) 165582500
Web Site: http://www.inspiredbyinulin.com
Sales Range: $25-49.9 Million
Emp.: 89
Perishable Prepared Food Mfr
N.A.I.C.S.: 311991

Subsidiary (US):

Sensus America Inc. (2)
Princeton Pike Corporate Ctr 100 Lenox Dr Ste 104, Lawrenceville, NJ 08648
Tel.: (646) 452-6140
Web Site: http://www.sensus.us
Food Products Distr
N.A.I.C.S.: 424490

Sisterna B.V. (1)
Belder 30A, 4704 RK, Roosendaal, Netherlands
Tel.: (31) 165524730
Web Site: http://www.sisterna.com
Perishable Prepared Food Mfr
N.A.I.C.S.: 311991

Suiker Unie B.V. (1)
Oud-Gastel, PO Box 100, Oud Gastel, 4671 TL, Netherlands
Tel.: (31) 165525252
Web Site: http://www.suikerunie.nl
Sales Range: $25-49.9 Million
Emp.: 100
Sugarcane Farming
N.A.I.C.S.: 111930
Albert Markusse (Gen Mgr)

ROYAL CUSHION VINYL PRODUCTS LIMITED
60CD SHLOK Govt Industrial Estate Charkop, Kandivali West, Mumbai, 400 067, India
Tel.: (91) 2228603514
Web Site: https://www.rcvp.in
Year Founded: 1983
526193—(BOM)
Rev.: $8,482,873
Assets: $3,439,746
Liabilities: $51,828,835
Net Worth: ($48,389,089)
Earnings: $23,308
Emp.: 126
Fiscal Year-end: 03/31/23
Vinyl Product Mfr
N.A.I.C.S.: 326199
Mahesh Kantilal Shah (Chm & Mng Dir)

ROYAL DELUXE HOLDINGS LIMITED
Unit A 22/F T G Place 10 Shing Yip Street Kwun Tong, Kowloon, China (Hong Kong)
Tel.: (852) 2 180 7387   Ky
Web Site: http://www.royal-deluxe.com
Year Founded: 1994
3789—(HKG)
Rev.: $60,674,772
Assets: $53,618,663
Liabilities: $16,801,967
Net Worth: $36,816,696
Earnings: $872,679
Emp.: 100

Fiscal Year-end: 03/31/22
Construction Management Services
N.A.I.C.S.: 238190
Kei Ming Wang (Chm)

Subsidiaries:

Ming Tai Construction Engineering Company Limited (1)
Unit A 22/F TG Place No 10 Shing Yip Street, Kwun Tong, Kowloon, China (Hong Kong)
Tel.: (852) 28664878
Web Site: http://www.ming-tai.com.hk
Construction Engineering Services
N.A.I.C.S.: 541330

ROYAL DISTRICT NURSING SERVICE
31 Alma Rd, Saint Kilda, 3182, VIC, Australia
Tel.: (61) 395365222
Web Site: http://www.rdns.com.au
Year Founded: 1885
Sales Range: $125-149.9 Million
Emp.: 1,528
Home Nursing & Health Care Services
N.A.I.C.S.: 621610
Paul Montgomery (Chm)

Subsidiaries:

RDNS HomeCare Limited (1)
Building A Level 2 20 Lexington Drive Norwest Business Park, Bella Vista, 2153, NSW, Australia
Tel.: (61) 1300 665 444
Web Site: http://www.rdnshomecare.com.au
Women Healthcare Services
N.A.I.C.S.: 621610

Royal District Nursing Service New Zealand Limited (1)
8 Hugo Johnson Dr Penrose Subway, PO Box 17-122, Greenlane, Auckland, 1061, New Zealand
Tel.: (64) 9 589 8900
Web Site: http://www.rdns.org.nz
Women Healthcare Services
N.A.I.C.S.: 621610
Jan Bennett (Area Mgr-Northern)

ROYAL EUROPA LTD.
ul Royal 1, Polkowice, 59101, Poland
Tel.: (48) 76 846 31 00
Web Site: http://www.royaleuropa.com
Year Founded: 1999
Sales Range: $75-99.9 Million
Emp.: 200
PVC Building Components Mfr
N.A.I.C.S.: 326199
Boguslaw Fusiek (Pres)

ROYAL EXCHANGE PLC.
New Africa House 31, Marina, Lagos, Nigeria
Tel.: (234) 14606690
Web Site: https://www.royalexchangeplc.com
Year Founded: 1921
ROYALEX—(NIGE)
Rev.: $194,060
Assets: $5,291,853
Liabilities: $3,733,899
Net Worth: $1,557,955
Earnings: ($213,526)
Emp.: 108
Fiscal Year-end: 12/31/22
Financial Services
N.A.I.C.S.: 523999
Kenneth Ezenwani Odogwu (Chm)

Subsidiaries:

Royal Exchange General Insurance Company Limited (1)
New Africa House 31 Marina, PO Box 112, Lagos, Nigeria
Tel.: (234) 146066909

INTERNATIONAL PUBLIC

Web Site: http://www.royalexchangeinsurance.com
Micro Financial Services
N.A.I.C.S.: 522291
Alhaji R. M. Gwarzo (Chm)

ROYAL GROUP CO., LTD.
No 65 Fengda Road Hi-tech Zone, Guangxi, Nanning, 530009, China
Tel.: (86) 7713211086
Web Site: http://www.gxhsry.com
Year Founded: 2001
002329—(SSE)
Rev.: $381,518,946
Assets: $928,261,088
Liabilities: $572,251,607
Net Worth: $356,009,481
Earnings: ($20,867,202)
Emp.: 630
Fiscal Year-end: 12/31/20
Dairy Products Mfr & Distr
N.A.I.C.S.: 112120

ROYAL GROUP HOLDINGS INTERNATIONAL COMPANY LIMITED
Unit 1201 12/F Great Smart Tower 230 Wan Chai Road, Wanchai, China (Hong Kong)
Tel.: (852) 23889423   Ky
Web Site: http://www.hkrcg.com
Year Founded: 1993
8300—(HKG)
Rev.: $4,669,850
Assets: $9,590,179
Liabilities: $4,037,977
Net Worth: $5,552,202
Earnings: ($1,312,758)
Emp.: 32
Fiscal Year-end: 03/31/22
Restaurant Operators
N.A.I.C.S.: 722511
Man Wai Wong (Chm, Chm, CEO, CEO, Compliance Officer & Compliance Officer)

ROYAL GROUP OF COMPANIES LTD.
246 Monivong Blvd, Phnom Penh, Cambodia
Tel.: (855) 23 426 414
Web Site: http://www.royalgroup.com.kh
Investment & Development Holding Company
N.A.I.C.S.: 551112
Neak Oknha Kith Meng (Chm & CEO)

Subsidiaries:

Cambodia Life Insurance Plc (1)
21st Floor Canadia Tower 315 Ang Doung St Corner Monivong Blvd, Phnom Penh, Cambodia (100%)
Tel.: (855) 23 431 111
Web Site: http://www.camlife.com.kh
Life Insurance
N.A.I.C.S.: 524113
Tondy Suradiredja (Deputy Dir Gen)

Infinity General Insurance PLC (1)
126 Norodom Blvd, Phnom Penh, Cambodia
Tel.: (855) 23 999 888
Web Site: http://www.infinity.com.kh
Emp.: 60
General Insurance Products & Services
N.A.I.C.S.: 524126
David Adair (COO)

J Trust Royal Bank Ltd. (1)
20 Kramuon Sar & Corner of Street 67, PO Box 624, Doun Penh District, Phnom Penh, Cambodia (45%)
Tel.: (855) 23 999 000
Web Site: http://www.jtrustroyal.com
Emp.: 522
Commercial Banking Services
N.A.I.C.S.: 522110
Leonie Lethbridge (CEO)

AND PRIVATE COMPANIES

Kampuchea Food Corporation Co., Ltd. (1)
5th Floor Royal Group Building, 246 Preah Monivong Blvd, Phnom Penh, Cambodia
Tel.: (855) 23 224 593
Web Site: http://www.kfc.com.kh
Fast Food Restaurants
N.A.I.C.S.: 722513
Benjamin Jerome *(CEO & Gen Mgr)*

Royal Railway Co. Ltd (1)
Central Railway Station Russian Federation Boulevard, PO Box 32, Sangkat Sras Chork Daun Penh, Phnom Penh, Cambodia
Tel.: (855) 23 992 379
Web Site: http://www.royal-railway.com
Freight & Passenger Rail Services
N.A.I.C.S.: 482111
John Guiry *(CEO)*

ROYAL HALI IPLIK TEKSTIL MOBILYA SANAYI VE TICARET A.S.
4 Organize Sanayi Bolgesi 83402 No'lu Cadde No 3, Sehitkamil, Gaziantep, Turkiye
Tel.: (90) 3422112626
Web Site: https://www.royalhali.com
ROYAL—(IST)
Rev.: $23,738,075
Assets: $77,789,030
Liabilities: $56,429,228
Net Worth: $21,359,802
Earnings: $6,680,623
Emp.: 783
Fiscal Year-end: 12/31/23
Yarn Carpet Mfr
N.A.I.C.S.: 313110
Nevzat Avunc *(Chm)*

ROYAL HELIUM LTD.
602 224 4th Ave South, Saskatoon, S7K 5M5, SK, Canada ON
Web Site: https://www.royalheliumltd.ca
Year Founded: 2008
RHC—(TSXV)
Rev.: $74,124
Assets: $69,331,190
Liabilities: $31,869,945
Net Worth: $37,461,246
Earnings: ($8,339,261)
Emp.: 4
Fiscal Year-end: 12/31/23
Oil & Gas Exploration & Production
N.A.I.C.S.: 211120
Andrew Davidson *(Chm, Pres & CEO)*

Subsidiaries:

Imperial Helium Corp. (1)

ROYAL HOLDINGS CO., LTD.
1-34-6 Sakurashimmachi, Setagaya-ku, Tokyo, 154-8584, Japan
Tel.: (81) 357078800
Web Site: https://www.royal-holdings.co.jp
Year Founded: 1950
8179—(TKS)
Rev.: $985,084,600
Assets: $892,411,210
Liabilities: $553,360,320
Net Worth: $339,050,890
Earnings: $28,608,150
Emp.: 1,905
Fiscal Year-end: 12/31/23
Holding Company
N.A.I.C.S.: 551112
Tadao Kikuchi *(Chm & Chm)*

Subsidiaries:

Royal Contract Service Corporation (1)
1-34-6 Sakurashinmachi, Setagaya-ku, Tokyo, 154-0015, Japan
Tel.: (81) 357078021
Web Site: https://www.royal-contract-service.co.jp
Restaurant Management Services
N.A.I.C.S.: 722511

ROYAL INDIA CORPORATION LTD.
3501 Floor 35 Vertu Tower Katrak Road, Wadala Market Wadala, Mumbai, 400031, Maharashtra, India
Tel.: (91) 2246001922
Web Site: https://www.ricl.in
Year Founded: 1984
512047—(BOM)
Rev.: $4,652,797
Assets: $19,731,738
Liabilities: $21,361,661
Net Worth: ($1,629,923)
Earnings: ($446,453)
Emp.: 5
Fiscal Year-end: 03/31/23
Financial Services
N.A.I.C.S.: 523999
Nitin Kamalkishore Gujral *(Mng Dir)*

ROYAL INTERNATIONAL CORPORATION
Baichay, Ha Long, Vietnam
Tel.: (84) 2033848999
Web Site: https://royalhalonghotel.com
Year Founded: 1994
RIC—(HNX)
Rev.: $4,976,707
Assets: $39,264,569
Liabilities: $12,080,655
Net Worth: $27,183,914
Earnings: ($2,555,378)
Emp.: 1,171
Fiscal Year-end: 12/31/22
Amusement & Recreation Center Operator
N.A.I.C.S.: 713990
Do Tri Vy *(Exec Dir)*

ROYAL JORDANIAN AIRLINES
Mohammad Ali Janah St Abdoun Near 5th Circle Building No 37, Amman, Jordan
Tel.: (962) 65202000
Web Site: http://www.rj.com
Year Founded: 1963
RJAL—(AMM)
Sales Range: $1-4.9 Billion
Emp.: 4,319
Airline Services
N.A.I.C.S.: 481111
Iman Rihani *(Exec Asst-Corp Social Responsibility)*

ROYAL MONETARY AUTHORITY OF BHUTAN
PO Box No 154, Chhophel Lam, Thimphu, Bhutan
Tel.: (975) 2323111 BT
Web Site: http://www.rma.org.bt
Sales Range: $25-49.9 Million
Banking Services
N.A.I.C.S.: 521110
Julien Gurung *(Dir-AFD)*

ROYAL NATIONAL THEATRE
Upper Ground Southbank, London, SE1 9PX, United Kingdom
Tel.: (44) 2074523333
Web Site: http://www.nationaltheatre.org.uk
Year Founded: 1963
Sales Range: $75-99.9 Million
Emp.: 800
Theatre Production
N.A.I.C.S.: 711110
Damon Buffini *(Chm)*

Subsidiaries:

National Theatre Productions Limited (1)
Upper Ground South Bank, London, SE1 9PX, United Kingdom
Tel.: (44) 2074523333
Stage Play Production Services
N.A.I.C.S.: 711310

ROYAL NIRMAN PVT LTD.
#16/1 1st Floor Anjaneya Temple Street, V V Puram, Bengaluru, 560004, India
Tel.: (91) 9743424454
Web Site: http://www.rjrnirman.com
Investment Services
N.A.I.C.S.: 523940
N. Jayarami Reddy *(Chm & Mng Dir)*

Subsidiaries:

MPF Systems Limited (1)
108 Prime Plaza JV Platel Compound BM Road Elphistone Road, Mumbai, 400 013, Maharashtra, India
Tel.: (91) 2027442100
Web Site: http://www.mpfsl.co.in
Rev.: $10,491
Assets: $4,136
Liabilities: $149,859
Net Worth: ($145,723)
Earnings: ($10,611)
Fiscal Year-end: 03/31/2023
Fire Security System Mfr
N.A.I.C.S.: 334290

ROYAL OLYMPIC CRUISE LINES, INC.
Akti Miaouli 87 Attiki, 185 38, Piraeus, Greece
Tel.: (30) 3014291000
Cruise Ship Services
N.A.I.C.S.: 561599
Leonidas Xanthakos *(CEO)*

ROYAL ORCHID HOTELS LIMITED
No 1 Golf Avenue Adjoining KGA Golf Course Airport Road, Kodihalli, Bengaluru, 560 008, Karnataka, India
Tel.: (91) 8041783000
Web Site: https://www.royalorchidhotels.com
ROHLTD—(NSE)
Rev.: $12,126,537
Assets: $57,183,303
Liabilities: $33,567,357
Net Worth: $23,615,947
Earnings: ($5,461,829)
Emp.: 839
Fiscal Year-end: 03/31/21
Hotel Owner & Operator
N.A.I.C.S.: 721110
Chander Kamal Baljee *(Chm & Mng Dir)*

ROYAL PALMS BEACH HOTELS PLC
Royal Palms Beach Hotel De Abrew Road, PO Box 195, 03, Waskaduwa, Sri Lanka
Tel.: (94) 342228113
Web Site: https://www.tangerinehotels.com
RPBH—(COL)
Rev.: $803,072
Assets: $14,711,370
Liabilities: $2,136,096
Net Worth: $12,575,274
Earnings: ($685,522)
Emp.: 157
Fiscal Year-end: 03/31/21
Home Management Services
N.A.I.C.S.: 721110
Ravi Kurukulasooriya *(Gen Mgr)*

ROYAL PLUS PUBLIC COMPANY LIMITED
No 84/3-7 Rama II Soi 69, Samae Dam Sub-district Bang Khun Thian District, Bangkok, 10150, Thailand
Tel.: (66) 24169209
Web Site: https://www.royalplus.co.th

ROYAL SWAZILAND SUGAR CORPORATION LIMITED

Year Founded: 1998
PLUS—(THA)
Rev.: $41,937,701
Assets: $49,176,602
Liabilities: $9,632,743
Net Worth: $39,543,858
Earnings: $5,489,620
Emp.: 712
Fiscal Year-end: 12/31/23
Beverages Product Mfr & Distr
N.A.I.C.S.: 312111
Phonseang Saebe *(Mng Dir)*

ROYAL ROAD MINERALS LIMITED
32 Hue Street, Saint Helier, JE2 3NR, Jersey
Tel.: (44) 1534887166 JE
Web Site: https://www.royalroadminerals.com
Year Founded: 2010
RLU—(DEU)
Rev.: $431,098
Assets: $10,778,454
Liabilities: $276,640
Net Worth: $10,501,813
Earnings: ($11,678,070)
Fiscal Year-end: 12/31/23
Gold Ore & Silver Ore Mining
N.A.I.C.S.: 212220
Timothy Coughlin *(Pres & CEO)*

ROYAL SHAKESPEARE COMPANY
Waterside, Stratford-upon-Avon, CV37 6BB, Warwickshire, United Kingdom
Tel.: (44) 1789296655 UK
Web Site: http://www.rsc.org.uk
Year Founded: 1879
Sales Range: $50-74.9 Million
Emp.: 600
Theatre Production
N.A.I.C.S.: 711110
Chris O'Brien *(Head-IT)*

Subsidiaries:

Royal Shakespeare Company of America, Inc. (1)
PO Box 1956, New York, NY 10101
Tel.: (212) 247-1705
Sales Range: $25-49.9 Million
Emp.: 10
Charitable Organization
N.A.I.C.S.: 813990
Kim Jackson *(Bus Mgr)*

ROYAL STANDARD MINERALS INC.
82 Richmond Street East Suite 200, Toronto, M5C 1P1, ON, Canada
Tel.: (416) 848-7744 Ca
RYSMF—(OTCIQ)
Assets: $9,693
Liabilities: $295,484
Net Worth: ($285,791)
Earnings: ($28,909)
Fiscal Year-end: 01/31/22
Gold Mining Services
N.A.I.C.S.: 212220
Carmelo Marrelli *(Pres & CEO)*

ROYAL SWAZILAND SUGAR CORPORATION LIMITED
King's Road Off MR3 Road, PO Box 1, Simunye, L301, Eswatini
Tel.: (268) 23134000 SZ
Web Site: https://www.res.co.sz
Year Founded: 1979
RSC—(ESE)
Rev.: $250,842,886
Assets: $278,839,590
Liabilities: $115,099,189
Net Worth: $163,740,402
Earnings: $33,615,545
Fiscal Year-end: 03/31/24

ROYAL SWAZILAND SUGAR CORPORATION LIMITED

Royal Swaziland Sugar Corporation Limited—(Continued)
Sugar Producer
N.A.I.C.S.: 111930
Muhawu I. Maziya *(Gen Mgr-Comml)*

Subsidiaries:

Royal Swazi Distiller (Pty) Ltd. (1)
PO Box 985, Durban, South Africa
Tel.: (27) 2683134000
Wine & Distilled Beverages
N.A.I.C.S.: 312140

ROYAL UNIBREW A/S
Faxe Alle 1, 4640, Fakse, Denmark
Tel.: (45) 56771500 DK
Web Site:
https://www.royalunibrew.com
RBREW—(CSE)
Rev.: $1,662,108,782
Assets: $2,094,312,049
Liabilities: $1,347,976,444
Net Worth: $746,335,605
Earnings: $215,739,897
Emp.: 3,365
Fiscal Year-end: 12/31/22
Brewery Operator
N.A.I.C.S.: 312120
Walther Thygesen *(Chm)*

Subsidiaries:

Albani Bryggerierne A/S (1)
Tvaegade 2, 5100, Odense, Denmark
Tel.: (45) 56771500
Web Site: http://albani.dk
Sales Range: $150-199.9 Million
Alcoholic Beverages Mfr.
N.A.I.C.S.: 312120

Albani Sverige AB (1)
Jons filsgatan 4, 211 33, Malmo, Sweden
Tel.: (46) 40 611 19 51
Alcoholic Beverages Mfr
N.A.I.C.S.: 312120

Bruce Ashley Group Inc. (1)
80 Tiverton Crt Suite 702, Markham, L3R 0G4, ON, Canada
Tel.: (905) 475-0139
Web Site:
https://www.bruceashleygroup.com
Beverage Distr
N.A.I.C.S.: 424490

Centre Nordique d'Alimentation SA (1)
Les Vignes De La Croix, Talloires, 74290, Annecy, France (100%)
Tel.: (33) 450607558
Sales Range: $50-74.9 Million
Emp.: 2
Beer & Ale Whslr
N.A.I.C.S.: 424810
Rask Schmidt *(Mng Dir)*

Ceres S.p.A. (1)
Via Paolo Imperiale 4/13, 16126, Genoa, Italy
Tel.: (39) 010 275 101
Web Site: http://www.ceres.com
Alcoholic Beverages Mfr
N.A.I.C.S.: 312120
Roberto Roccatti *(Gen Mgr)*

Cuveco AS (1)
Vollsveien 13B, 1366, Lysaker, Norway
Tel.: (47) 24112380
Web Site: https://www.cuveco.no
Beverage Distr
N.A.I.C.S.: 424490

Faxe Bryggeri A/S (1)
Faxe Alle 1, 4640, Fakse, Denmark
Tel.: (45) 5677 1500
Emp.: 250
Alcoholic Beverage Distr
N.A.I.C.S.: 424820
Conrad Nielsen *(Founder)*

Impec Martinique S.A. (1)
ZI Lezarde, 97232, Lamentin, Martinique
Tel.: (596) 596 51 81 79
Alcoholic Beverages Mfr.
N.A.I.C.S.: 312120

Import-Export Compagnie S.A. (1)
Zone Industrielle Moudong, PO Box 2218, 97122, La Baie Mahault, Guadeloupe (100%)
Tel.: (590) 5 90 25 03 03
Beverage Product Distr
N.A.I.C.S.: 424820

Oy Hartwall AB (1)
Hiomotie 32, PO Box 200, 00371, Helsinki, Finland
Tel.: (358) 2 071 7111
Web Site: https://www.hartwall.fi
Emp.: 700
Malt Beverage Mfr
N.A.I.C.S.: 312120
Marko Airamaa *(Dir-Sls)*

Royal Unibrew Caribbean Inc. (1)
Citi Twr Ste 501 250 Ponce de Leon Ave, San Juan, PR 00918
Tel.: (787) 200-7480
Web Site: http://www.royalunibrew.com
Alcoholic Beverages Mfr
N.A.I.C.S.: 312120

Royal Unibrew Eesti OU (1)
Raekula Tee 5 Rae kula Rae Vald, Harjumaa, 75310, Estonia
Tel.: (372) 53778270
Web Site: https://royalunibreweesti.ee
Beverage Distr
N.A.I.C.S.: 424490

Solera Norge AS (1)
Karenslyst Alle 10, PO Box 246, Skoyen, 0213, Oslo, Norway
Tel.: (47) 24111730
Web Site: https://www.solera.no
Beverage Distr
N.A.I.C.S.: 424490

Solera Sverige AB (1)
Karlavagen 108, 104 51, Stockholm, Sweden
Tel.: (46) 708128735
Web Site: https://www.solera.se
Beverage Retailer
N.A.I.C.S.: 722515

Solera Uteliv AS (1)
Karenslyst Alle 10, 0278, Oslo, Norway
Tel.: (47) 93030004
Web Site: https://www.solerauteliv.no
Beverage Distr
N.A.I.C.S.: 424490

The Danish Brewery Group Inc. (1)
10773 NW 58 St Ste 322, Miami, FL 33178
Tel.: (305) 436-8788
Web Site: http://www.royalunibrew.com
Beverage Product Distr.
N.A.I.C.S.: 424820

UAB Kalnapilio-Tauro Grupe (1)
Taikos al 1, 34147, Panevezys, Lithuania
Tel.: (370) 45505223
Web Site: https://www.kalnapilis.lt
Sales Range: $100-124.9 Million
Emp.: 30
Alcoholic Beverages Mfr
N.A.I.C.S.: 312120
Marijus Valdas Kirstukas *(Gen Mgr)*

Subsidiary (Domestic):

UAB Vilkmerges alus (2)
Antakalnio III k Pivonijos sen, Ukmerge, 20101, Lithuania
Tel.: (370) 34 063 770
Web Site: http://www.vilkmergesalus.lt
Alcoholic Beverages Mfr
N.A.I.C.S.: 312120

ROYALE HOME HOLDINGS LTD.
Room 607 6/F Tsim Sha Tsui Centre 66 Mody Road, Tsim Sha Tsui East, Kowloon, China (Hong Kong)
Tel.: (852) 26366648 Ky
Web Site: http://royale.todayir.com
1198—(HKG)
Rev.: $196,888,744
Assets: $812,425,802
Liabilities: $460,334,005
Net Worth: $352,091,797
Earnings: $11,388,934
Emp.: 1,328
Fiscal Year-end: 12/31/21

Holding Company
N.A.I.C.S.: 551112

ROYALE MANOR HOTELS AND INDUSTRIES LIMITED
3JMH CX6 Airport Cross Road International Airport Circle, Ahmedabad, 382475, India
Tel.: (91) 7922868641
Web Site: https://www.rmhil.com
526640—(BOM)
Rev.: $2,783,190
Assets: $7,940,363
Liabilities: $1,717,895
Net Worth: $6,222,469
Earnings: $454,613
Emp.: 152
Fiscal Year-end: 03/31/23
Home Management Services
N.A.I.C.S.: 721110
Ummedsingh Padamsingh Champawat *(Chm & Mng Dir)*

ROYALTEK CO., LTD.
8th Floor No 40 Wenhwa 2nd Rd, Guishan, Taoyuan, 333010, Taiwan
Tel.: (886) 33960001
Web Site: https://www.royaltek.com
Year Founded: 1997
3306—(TPE)
Rev.: $38,109,715
Assets: $55,549,417
Liabilities: $9,516,556
Net Worth: $46,032,861
Earnings: $399,869
Fiscal Year-end: 12/31/22
Wireless Communication Product Mfr
N.A.I.C.S.: 334220
Chun-Hao Su *(Chm & CEO)*

ROYCE IMAGING INDUSTRIES (PTY) LIMITED
260 Arbeid Avenue, Randburg, South Africa
Tel.: (27) 11 792 9530
Web Site:
http://www.royceimaging.co.za
Year Founded: 1989
Sales Range: $50-74.9 Million
Emp.: 100
Remanufactures & Supplies Printer Cartridges
N.A.I.C.S.: 333248

ROZACHIM AD
Anton Strashimirov Str 57, 5100, Gorna Oryahovitsa, Bulgaria
Tel.: (359) 895482993
Web Site: http://www.rozachim.com
Year Founded: 1960
ROZH—(BUL)
Sales Range: Less than $1 Million
Paint Product Mfr & Distr
N.A.I.C.S.: 325510
Ivo Kirilov Tsanev *(Chm)*

RP BIO INC.
634 Samseong-ro Samseong-dong, Gangnam-gu, Seoul, Korea (South)
Tel.: (82) 220029715
Web Site: https://rpskorea.com
Year Founded: 1983
314140—(KRS)
Pharmaceutical Product Mfr & Distr
N.A.I.C.S.: 325412
Jae H. Yoon *(Chm & CEO)*

RP MARTIN HOLDINGS LIMITED
Cannon Bridge House 25 Dowgate Hill, London, EC4R 2BB, United Kingdom
Tel.: (44) 2074699000
Web Site: http://www.martin-brokers.com
Sales Range: $50-74.9 Million

INTERNATIONAL PUBLIC

Emp.: 200
Brokerage Firm
N.A.I.C.S.: 523150
David Caplin *(CEO)*

Subsidiaries:

RP Martin Stockholm AB (1)
Riddargatan 30, 114 57, Stockholm, Sweden
Tel.: (46) 866 75200
Emp.: 8
Securities Brokerage Services
N.A.I.C.S.: 523150
Stephen Welch *(Chm)*

Wallich & Matthes BV (1)
Keizersgracht 307, PO Box 3590, 1016 ED, Amsterdam, Netherlands
Tel.: (31) 205357800
Web Site: http://www.wallich.eu
Sales Range: $50-74.9 Million
Emp.: 50
Financial Institution
N.A.I.C.S.: 523940
Michael Zan Seters *(Gen Mgr)*

Wallich & Matthes Dubai Limited (1)
DIFC Currency House Level 3 Office 12, Dubai, United Arab Emirates
Tel.: (971) 4 447 5727
Web Site: http://www.wallich.ae
Financial Brokerage Services
N.A.I.C.S.: 523160

RPC DATA LIMITED
Plot 39 Unit 5 Commerce Park, Private Bag-Br 42, Gaborone, Botswana
Tel.: (267) 3903644 BW
Web Site: http://www.rpcdata.com
Year Founded: 1989
Sales Range: $1-9.9 Million
Computer Integration & Consulting Services; Computer Sales & Distr
N.A.I.C.S.: 541512
John Robert Pool *(Chm)*

Subsidiaries:

RPC Data (Zambia) (1)
Plot No 5309 Dedan Kimathi Rd 2nd Fl Mukuba Pension House, PO Box 31723, Lusaka, Zambia
Tel.: (260) 1237 880
Software Development & Training Services
N.A.I.C.S.: 449210

RPCG PUBLIC COMPANY LIMITED
86/ 2 Sammakorn Place Building Ramkhamhaeng Road, Saphan Sung, Bangkok, 10240, Thailand
Tel.: (66) 23723600
Web Site: https://www.rpcthai.com
Year Founded: 1995
RPC—(THA)
Rev.: $300,103,535
Assets: $263,158,270
Liabilities: $146,492,905
Net Worth: $116,665,365
Earnings: $1,506,924
Emp.: 1,063
Fiscal Year-end: 12/31/23
Petroleum & Petrochemical Services
N.A.I.C.S.: 213112
Satja Janetumnugul *(Chm & Mng Dir-Acting)*

Subsidiaries:

Pure Thai Energy Co., Ltd. (1)
14 Fl Tower 3 SCB Park Plz, 10900, Bangkok, Thailand
Tel.: (66) 25158600
Web Site: http://www.husky.ca
Sales Range: $200-249.9 Million
Emp.: 300
Activities for Oil & Gas Operations
N.A.I.C.S.: 213112
John Galt *(CEO)*

Rayong Purifier Public Company Limited - Rayong Factory. (1)
7/3 Pakorn Songkrohrad Rd, Tambol Mapta-phut Amphur Muang-Rayong, Rayong,

21150, Thailand
Tel.: (66) 38 685 816 9
Petrochemical Mfr
N.A.I.C.S.: 325110

RPDA
Zac Saint Anne Route De Vedene,
84700, Sorgues, Vaucluse, France
Tel.: (33) 490030056
Web Site: http://www.relaysgor.sr
Rev.: $36,800,000
Emp.: 125
N.A.I.C.S.: 424420
Christelle Gauthier *(Mgr-Pur)*

RPG GROUP
RPG House 463 Dr Annie Besant Road, Worli, Mumbai, 400030, Maharashtra, India
Tel.: (91) 2224930621
Web Site: http://www.rpggroup.com
Year Founded: 1979
Mechanical & Industrial Engineering Company
N.A.I.C.S.: 541330
Harsh Goenka *(Chm)*

Subsidiaries:

RPG Life Sciences Limited (1)
RPG House 463 Dr Annie Besant Road, Worli, Mumbai, 400 030, India
Tel.: (91) 2266606375
Web Site: https://www.rpglifesciences.com
Rev.: $53,241,825
Assets: $41,412,735
Liabilities: $11,867,310
Net Worth: $29,545,425
Earnings: $5,460,000
Emp.: 1,107
Fiscal Year-end: 03/31/2021
Pharmaceutical Products Marketing & Mfr
N.A.I.C.S.: 325412
Rajesh Shirambekar *(Compliance Officer, Sec & Head-Legal)*

Zensar Technologies Ltd (1)
Zensar Knowledge Park Kharadi Plot No 4, MIDC Off Nagar Road, Pune, 411 014, Maharashtra, India
Tel.: (91) 2066074444
Web Site: https://www.zensar.com
Rev.: $519,633,660
Assets: $468,655,005
Liabilities: $145,005,315
Net Worth: $323,649,690
Earnings: $41,902,770
Emp.: 6,878
Fiscal Year-end: 03/31/2021
Computer Softwares Mfr
N.A.I.C.S.: 541512
Prameela Kalive *(COO)*

Subsidiary (Domestic):

Zensar OBT Technologies Limited (2)
Ananth Info Park Hi-Tech, Madhapur, Hyderabad, 500 0081, Andhra Pradesh, India
Tel.: (91) 4040230032
Web Site: http://www.zensar.com
Emp.: 300
SAP Services
N.A.I.C.S.: 518210

Subsidiary (US):

Zensar Technologies Inc. (2)
2107 N 1st St Ste 100, San Jose, CA 95131
Tel.: (408) 477-3606
Web Site: http://www.zensar.com
Digital Solutions & Technology Services
N.A.I.C.S.: 513210
Vivek Gupta *(CEO-Global Infrastructure Mgmt Svcs)*

Subsidiary (Domestic):

Aquila Technology Corp. (3)
15 New England Executive Park Ste 2101, Burlington, MA 01803-5202
Tel.: (781) 993-9004
Web Site: http://www.aquilatc.com
Computer System Design Services
N.A.I.C.S.: 541512

Thomas D. Willson *(Treas)*

Indigo Slate, Inc. (3)
14475 NE 24th St Ste 110, Bellevue, WA 98007
Tel.: (425) 739-3200
Web Site: http://www.indigoslate.com
Digital Marketing Services
N.A.I.C.S.: 541613

PSI Holding Group Inc. (3)
4 Technology Dr, Westborough, MA 01581
Tel.: (508) 621-4576
Sales Range: $125-149.9 Million
Emp.: 350
Computer Software Development
N.A.I.C.S.: 541511

Zensar Technologies, Inc. - New Jersey (3)
103 College Rd E, Princeton, NJ 08540
Tel.: (609) 452-1414
Web Site: http://www.zensar.com
Computer Related Consulting Services
N.A.I.C.S.: 541512

RPM AUTOMOTIVE GROUP LIMITED
1-7 Ausco Place, Dandenong South, 3175, VIC, Australia
Tel.: (61) 399982476
Web Site: https://www.rpmgroup.net.au
RPM—(ASX)
Rev.: $78,953,037
Assets: $77,077,430
Liabilities: $40,489,480
Net Worth: $36,587,951
Earnings: $3,011,151
Fiscal Year-end: 06/30/24
Crude Petroleum Extraction Services
N.A.I.C.S.: 211120

RPMGLOBAL HOLDINGS LTD.
Level 14 310 Ann Street, Brisbane, 4000, QLD, Australia
Tel.: (61) 731007200
Web Site: https://www.rpmglobal.com
Year Founded: 1968
RUL—(ASX)
Rev.: $73,173,744
Assets: $75,776,576
Liabilities: $38,485,577
Net Worth: $37,290,999
Earnings: $5,779,915
Fiscal Year-end: 06/30/24
Research & Development in Biotechnology (except Nanobiotechnology)
N.A.I.C.S.: 541714
Richard Mathews *(CEO)*

Subsidiaries:

RPM Global Canada Ltd. (1)
Office 2526 Level 25 639 5 Ave SW, Calgary, T2P 0M9, AB, Canada
Tel.: (403) 217-4981
Metal Mining Services
N.A.I.C.S.: 213114

RPM Global Turkey Danismanlik Hizmetleri ve Ticaret A.S. (1)
Mutlukent Sitesi No 10 Dicle Cd, Ankara, 06800, Turkiye
Tel.: (90) 3122841175
Metal Mining Services
N.A.I.C.S.: 213114

RPM Global USA, Inc. (1)
Ste 210 7921 Southpark Plz, Littleton, CO 80120
Tel.: (303) 986-6950
Metal Mining Services
N.A.I.C.S.: 213114

RPMGlobal Africa (Pty) Ltd (1)
2nd Floor Block A Southdowns Ridge Office Park Corner, John Vorster and Nellmapius Road, Centurion, 0062, South Africa
Tel.: (27) 126482700
Metal Mining Services
N.A.I.C.S.: 213114

RPMGlobal Asia Limited (1)
Suite 2 3/F Sino Plaza 255-257 Gloucester Road, Causeway Bay, 999077, China (Hong Kong)
Tel.: (852) 28016103
Metal Mining Services
N.A.I.C.S.: 213114

RPMGlobal Chile Limitada (1)
Oficina 602 Av Presidente Riesco 5711, Las Condes, 756 1114, Santiago, 756 1114, Chile
Tel.: (56) 227639400
Metal Mining Services
N.A.I.C.S.: 213114

RPMGlobal China Limited (1)
Room 1118 Level 11 China World Office 1 1 Jianguomenwai Avenue, Chaoyang District, Beijing, 100004, China
Tel.: (86) 1053876410
Metal Mining Services
N.A.I.C.S.: 213114

RPMGlobal Kazakhstan LLP (1)
Al Farabi Avenue Building 7 Business Center Nurly Tau Block 4 A, Office 50 Level 11, A25D5M2, Almaty, A25D5M2, Kazakhstan
Tel.: (7) 7273110050
Metal Mining Services
N.A.I.C.S.: 213114

RPMGlobal LLC (1)
13th Floor Central Park Chinggis Avenue, Ulaanbaatar, Mongolia
Tel.: (976) 70100130
Metal Mining Services
N.A.I.C.S.: 213114

RPP INFRA PROJECTS LTD
SF No 454 Raghupathynaiken Palayam Railway Colony Post Poondurai Road, Erode, 638002, Tamil Nadu, India
Tel.: (91) 4242284077
Web Site: https://www.rppipl.com
Year Founded: 1988
533284—(BOM)
Rev.: $71,571,045
Assets: $86,509,605
Liabilities: $47,407,815
Net Worth: $39,101,790
Earnings: $2,115,750
Emp.: 217
Fiscal Year-end: 03/31/21
Civil Engineering & Construction Services
N.A.I.C.S.: 237990
P. Arul Sundaram *(Chm & Mng Dir)*

RPS GROUP PLC
20 Western Avenue Milton Park, Abingdon, OX14 4SH, Oxfordshire, United Kingdom
Tel.: (44) 1235821888 UK
Web Site: http://www.rpsgroup.com
Year Founded: 1970
RPS—(LSE)
Rev.: $736,020,012
Assets: $826,444,164
Liabilities: $352,599,884
Net Worth: $473,844,280
Earnings: $(42,225,092)
Emp.: 5,055
Fiscal Year-end: 12/31/20
N.A.I.C.S.: 541620
Gary Young *(Dir-Fin)*

Subsidiaries:

Applied Science Associates, Inc. (1)
70 Dean Knauss Dr, Narragansett, RI 02882
Tel.: (401) 789-6224
Web Site: http://www.asascience.com
Sales Range: $25-49.9 Million
Emp.: 50
Scientific Consulting Services
N.A.I.C.S.: 541690

Aquaterra Consulting Pty Limited (1)
Suite 4 125 Melville Pde, Como, WA, Australia
Tel.: (61) 8 9368 4044
Environmental Consulting Services
N.A.I.C.S.: 541620

Boyd Exploration Consultants Limited (1)
700-555 4 Ave SW Calgary, Calgary, T2P 3E7, AB, Canada
Tel.: (403) 233-2455
Web Site: http://www.boydpetro.com
Geophysical Consulting Services
N.A.I.C.S.: 541360
Larry Herd *(Pres)*

Cambrian Consultants (CC) America Inc (1)
411 N Sam Houston Pkwy E, Houston, TX 77060
Tel.: (281) 877-9400
Oil & Gas Extraction Services
N.A.I.C.S.: 213112
Ruth Greenwood *(Office Mgr)*

Geoprojects Canada Limited (1)
2nd Floor 1545 Birmingham St, B3J2J6, Halifax, NS, Canada (100%)
Tel.: (902) 425-1622
Geophysical Surveying & Mapping Services
N.A.I.C.S.: 541360

Iris Environmental (1)
1438 Webster St Ste 302, Oakland, CA 94612-3228
Tel.: (510) 834-4747
Web Site: http://www.irisenv.com
Sales Range: $10-24.9 Million
Emp.: 35
Environmental Consulting & Engineering Services
N.A.I.C.S.: 541620
Craig Pelletier *(Principal)*

Klotz Associates, Inc. (1)
1160 Dairy Ashford Ste 500, Houston, TX 77079
Tel.: (281) 589-7257
Web Site: http://www.klotz.com
Sales Range: $25-49.9 Million
Emp.: 116
Engineeering Services
N.A.I.C.S.: 541330
David W. Klotz *(Pres)*

Metier OEC AS (1)
Hovfaret 10, Oslo, Norway
Tel.: (47) 24124500
Web Site: https://www.metieroec.com
Business Management Consulting Services
N.A.I.C.S.: 541611

Point Project Management (PNG) Ltd. (1)
Level 5 Era Rumana Building NCD, Port Moresby, Papua New Guinea
Tel.: (675) 3095238
Environmental Development & Consulting Services
N.A.I.C.S.: 541620

RPS Advies BV (1)
Elektronicaweg 2, PO Box 5094, 2600 GB, Delft, Netherlands (100%)
Tel.: (31) 157501616
Web Site: http://www.rps.nl
Sales Range: $25-49.9 Million
Emp.: 50
Management Consulting Services
N.A.I.C.S.: 541618

RPS Analyse BV (1)
Tolweg 11, Ulvenhout, 4851SJ, Utrecht, Netherlands (100%)
Tel.: (31) 765715880
Sales Range: $25-49.9 Million
Emp.: 80
Physical Engineering & Life Sciences Research & Development
N.A.I.C.S.: 541715

RPS Australia East Pty Ltd (1)
Level 4 Hq South 520 Wickham Street, Fortitude Valley, 4006, QLD, Australia
Tel.: (61) 7 3124 9500
Web Site: http://www.rpsgroup.com.au
Sales Range: $75-99.9 Million
Energy Consulting Services
N.A.I.C.S.: 541690

RPS Consultants NZ Limited (1)
119-123 Featherston Street, Wellington, 6011, New Zealand
Tel.: (64) 43901309
Environmental Development & Consulting Services

RPS GROUP PLC

INTERNATIONAL PUBLIC

RPS Group plc—(Continued)
N.A.I.C.S.: 541620

RPS Consultants Pty Limited (1)
38 Station St, Subiaco, 6008, WA, Australia
Tel.: (61) 892111111
Web Site: http://www.rpsgroup.com.au
Sales Range: $25-49.9 Million
Emp.: 100
Management Consulting Services
N.A.I.C.S.: 541611
John Tompson (CEO)

RPS Consulting Engineers Limited (1)
West Pier Business Campus, Dun Laoghaire, Dublin, Ireland
Tel.: (353) 14882900
Web Site: http://www.rpsgroup.com
Sales Range: $25-49.9 Million
Emp.: 130
Engineeering Services
N.A.I.C.S.: 541330

RPS Energy Canada Limited (1)
555 4th Avenue SW Suite 600, Calgary, T2P 3E7, AB, Canada
Tel.: (403) 265-7226
Web Site: https://www.rpsgroup.com
Sales Range: $25-49.9 Million
Seismic Geophysical Surveying Services
N.A.I.C.S.: 541360

RPS Energy Limited (1)
Goldvale House 27-41 Church Street West, Woking, GU21 6DH, Surrey, United Kingdom (100%)
Tel.: (44) 148 374 6500
Web Site: http://www.rpsgroup.com
Sales Range: $25-49.9 Million
Emp.: 250
Physical Engineering & Life Sciences Research & Development
N.A.I.C.S.: 541715

RPS Energy Pty Limited (1)
L 3 38 Station St, Subiaco, 6008, WA, Australia
Tel.: (61) 892111111
Web Site: http://www.rpsgroup.com.au
Emp.: 20
Energy Consulting Services
N.A.I.C.S.: 541690

RPS Engineering Services Limited (1)
Block C Cookstown court, Tallght, Dublin, 24, Ireland (100%)
Tel.: (358) 14620800
Sales Range: $75-99.9 Million
Emp.: 280
Engineeering Services
N.A.I.C.S.: 541330

RPS Environment Subiaco (1)
L 3 38 Station Street, Subiaco, 6008, WA, Australia (100%)
Tel.: (61) 893824744
Web Site: http://www.rpsgroup.com.au
Sales Range: $25-49.9 Million
Emp.: 250
Physical Engineering & Life Sciences Research & Development
N.A.I.C.S.: 541715

RPS Espey (1)
4801 SW Pkwy Ste 150, Austin, TX 78735
Tel.: (512) 326-5659
Web Site: http://www.espeyconsultants.com
Sales Range: $25-49.9 Million
Emp.: 40
Environmental, Water & Civil Engineering Consultancy Services
N.A.I.C.S.: 541620
Brian Reis (VP)

RPS Evans-Hamilton, Inc. (1)
4608 Union Bay Pl NE, Seattle, WA 98105
Tel.: (206) 526-5622
Web Site: http://www.evanshamilton.com
Sales Range: $1-9.9 Million
Emp.: 20
Oceanographic Consulting Services
N.A.I.C.S.: 541690

Division (Domestic):

RPS Evans-Hamilton, Inc. (2)
3662 Westchase Dr, Houston, TX 77042
Tel.: (281) 495-0883

Web Site: http://www.evanshamilton.com
Emp.: 30
Oceanographic Consulting Services
N.A.I.C.S.: 541690

RPS Groep BV (1)
Elektronicaweg 2, PO Box 5094, 2600GB, Delft, Netherlands (100%)
Tel.: (31) 157501616
Web Site: http://www.rps.nl
Sales Range: $25-49.9 Million
Emp.: 100
Management Consulting Services
N.A.I.C.S.: 541618
Frank Vrolijk (Mng Dir)

RPS Group Limited (1)
Cooks Town Industrial Estate, 24, Dublin, Ireland (100%)
Tel.: (353) 14620800
Web Site: http://www.rpsgroup.com
Engineeering Services
N.A.I.C.S.: 541330

RPS Group PLC (1)
Crake Holme, Muker, Richmond, DL11 6QH, North Yorkshire, United Kingdom (100%)
Tel.: (44) 1748886421
Web Site: http://www.rpsgroup.com
Sales Range: $25-49.9 Million
Emp.: 2
Provider of Ecological Consultancy Services
N.A.I.C.S.: 541611

RPS Health in Business Limited (1)
Suite C Wilson House Crab Lane, Warrington, WA2 0XP, Cheshire, United Kingdom
Tel.: (44) 1925 846 333
Web Site: http://www.healthinbusiness.com
Health Care Srvices
N.A.I.C.S.: 621999
Jon Dance (Mgr-Physiotherapy Ergonomic & Rehabilitation Svcs)

RPS JD Consulting Inc (1)
Cielo Ctr 1250 S Capital Texas Hwy Bldg 3 St 200, Austin, TX 78746
Tel.: (512) 347-7588
Emp.: 141
Environmental Consulting Services
N.A.I.C.S.: 541620
Chisum Cooke (Mgr)

RPS Knowledge Reservoir, LP (1)
1800 West Loop S Ste 1000, Houston, TX 77027 (100%)
Tel.: (713) 586-5950
Web Site: http://www.knowledge-reservoir.com
Sales Range: $1-9.9 Million
Emp.: 15
Oil And Gas Field Services, Nec, Nsk
N.A.I.C.S.: 213112

RPS Kraan Consulting BV (1)
Schorpioenstraat 57, Rotterdam, 3067 GG, Netherlands
Tel.: (31) 10 286 6100
Web Site: http://www.rps.nl
Sales Range: $25-49.9 Million
Emp.: 50
Management Consulting Services
N.A.I.C.S.: 541618

RPS Water Services Limited (1)
Marsh Barton Trading Est, Exeter, EX28PF, United Kingdom (100%)
Tel.: (44) 1392677333
Web Site: http://www.rpsgroup.com
Sales Range: $25-49.9 Million
Emp.: 11
Engineering Services
N.A.I.C.S.: 541330

The Environmental Consultancy Limited (1)
20 Farringdon Street, London, EC4A 4AB, United Kingdom
Tel.: (44) 2036910500
Web Site: http://www.rpsgroup.com
Environmental Consulting Services
N.A.I.C.S.: 541620

RPSG VENTURES LIMITED
Cesc House Chowringhee Square, Kolkata, 700001, India
Tel.: (91) 3366340684

Web Site: https://www.rpsgventuresltd.com
Year Founded: 2017
542333—(BOM)
Rev.: $876,210,059
Assets: $1,577,679,995
Liabilities: $1,097,333,493
Net Worth: $480,346,502
Earnings: ($7,076,314)
Emp.: 96
Fiscal Year-end: 03/31/23
Asset Management Services
N.A.I.C.S.: 523940
Arvind Vats (CEO)

Subsidiaries:

One Advantage LLC (1)
127 E Shore Pkwy Ste A, La Porte, IN 46350
Tel.: (219) 324-6835
Web Site: https://oneadvantagellc.com
Debt Collection Services
N.A.I.C.S.: 561440

RR FINANCIAL CONSULTANTS LTD.
412-422 4thFloor Indraprakash Building 21-Barakhamba Road, New Delhi, 110001, India
Tel.: (91) 1144441111
Web Site: https://www.rrfinance.com
Rev.: $3,222,964
Assets: $8,357,284
Liabilities: $1,584,978
Net Worth: $6,772,306
Earnings: $56,857
Emp.: 1
Fiscal Year-end: 03/31/19
Financial Services
N.A.I.C.S.: 525990
Rajat Prasad (Chm & Mng Dir)

Subsidiaries:

RR Equity Brokers Private Limited (1)
No 224 AJC Bose Road, Kolkata, 700 015, West Bengal, India
Tel.: (91) 33 40174805
Equity Brokerage Services
N.A.I.C.S.: 523150

Subsidiary (Domestic):

RR Information and Investmet Research Private Limited (2)
4th Floor Indraprakash Building Connaught Place, New Delhi, 110 001, India
Tel.: (91) 1123352496
Web Site: http://www.rrfinance.com
Financial Services
N.A.I.C.S.: 523999
J. C. Sharma (Gen Mgr)

RR Investor Retail services Private Limited (2)
47 MM Road Rani Jhanshi Marg Jhandewalan, New Delhi, 110 055, India
Tel.: (91) 11 2363 6363
Emp.: 275
Investor Retail Service Provider
N.A.I.C.S.: 524298
Brajesh Kumar Srivastav (Mgr)

RR Insurance Brokers Private Limited (1)
47 Mm Road Rani Jhansi Marg Jhandewalan, New Delhi, 110 055, India
Tel.: (91) 11 23636362
Web Site: http://www.fcl.com
Emp.: 125
Insurance Brokerage Services
N.A.I.C.S.: 524210
Rajneesh Chauhan (Sr Mgr)

RR METALMAKERS INDIA LIMITED
B-001 & B-002 Ground Floor Antop Hill Warehousing Complex Ltd, Barkat Ali Naka Salt Pan Rd Wadala E, Mumbai, 400037, Maharashtra, India
Tel.: (91) 2224103973

Web Site: https://www.rrmetalmakers.com
Year Founded: 1995
531667—(BOM)
Rev.: $15,143,399
Assets: $7,191,938
Liabilities: $6,246,688
Net Worth: $945,251
Earnings: $245,731
Fiscal Year-end: 03/31/21
Commodities Trading Services
N.A.I.C.S.: 523160
Navin Madhavji Mehta (Exec Dir)

Subsidiaries:

RR Lifecare Pvt. Ltd. (1)
B-001 and B-002 Ground Floor, Barkat Ali Naka Salt Pan Road Wadala E, Mumbai, 400037, MH, India
Tel.: (91) 2261925555
Web Site: http://www.rrlifecare.com
Pharmaceuticals Product Mfr
N.A.I.C.S.: 325412
Virat Sevantial Shah (Chm & Mng Dir)

RREEF CHINA COMMERCIAL TRUST
48/F Cheung Kong Center 2 Queens Rd, Central, China (Hong Kong)
Tel.: (852) 85222037872
Real Estate Investment Trust Services
N.A.I.C.S.: 531190
Wendy Tsz (Sec)

RRIL LIMITED
A-325 Hari Om Plaza MG Road Near Om Kareshwar Temple, Borivali West, Mumbai, 400 066, India
Tel.: (91) 2228959644
Web Site: https://www.rrilimited.com
Year Founded: 1991
531307—(BOM)
Rev.: $18,925,124
Assets: $15,400,468
Liabilities: $4,303,483
Net Worth: $11,096,985
Earnings: $1,649,302
Emp.: 4
Fiscal Year-end: 03/31/23
Textile Fabric Distr
N.A.I.C.S.: 424990
Rakeshchand M. Jain (Chm, Mng Dir & CFO)

RRJ CAPITAL LTD.
1201-02 Man Yee Building 68 Des Voeux Road, Central, China (Hong Kong)
Tel.: (852) 3915 6222
Web Site: http://www.rrjcap.com
Year Founded: 2011
Emp.: 40
Privater Equity Firm
N.A.I.C.S.: 523999
Richard Ong (Co-Chm & Co-CEO)

Subsidiaries:

RRJ Management (HK) Limited (1)
802-804 Man Yee Building 68 Des Voeux Road, Hong kong, China (Hong Kong)
Tel.: (852) 39156222
Privater Equity Firm
N.A.I.C.S.: 523999
Richard Ong (Chm & CEO)

Holding (Non-US):

gategroup Holding AG (2)
Sagereistrasse 20, 8152, Glattbrugg, Switzerland (100%)
Tel.: (41) 445337000
Web Site: http://www.gategroup.com
Rev.: $5,110,492,928
Assets: $3,509,525,056
Liabilities: $3,157,553,088
Net Worth: $351,971,968
Earnings: ($110,596,224)
Emp.: 43,000
Fiscal Year-end: 12/31/2019

AND PRIVATE COMPANIES

Holding Company; Airport & In-Flight Hospitality, Catering & Retail Transaction Services
N.A.I.C.S.: 551112
Herman Anbeek *(Pres-Americas, Europe & Middle East)*

Subsidiary (Domestic):

Gate Gourmet Switzerland GmbH (3)
Sagereistrasse 20, 8152, Glattbrugg, Switzerland
Tel.: (41) 44 533 7000
Web Site: http://www.gategourmet.com
Airline Catering Services
N.A.I.C.S.: 488190

Subsidiary (Non-US):

Gate Gourmet (Holdings) Pty. Ltd. (4)
263-273 King Street, Mascot, 2020, NSW, Australia
Tel.: (61) 283371300
Sales Range: $10-24.9 Million
Emp.: 100
Airline Catering Services
N.A.I.C.S.: 722310

Gate Gourmet Aeroport de Bale-Mulhouse SAS (4)
Aeroport Bale Mulhouse Batiment Catering, 68300, Saint Louis, France
Tel.: (33) 389903901
Web Site: http://www.gategourmet.com
Catering Services
N.A.I.C.S.: 722310

Gate Gourmet Amsterdam B.V. (4)
Cateringweg 3 Schiphol North, PO Box 7528, Schiphol, 1118 AM, Netherlands
Tel.: (31) 206019222
Web Site: http://www.gategourmet.com
Sales Range: $50-74.9 Million
Airline Catering Services
N.A.I.C.S.: 722310
Sim Schneeberger *(Gen Mgr)*

Gate Gourmet Argentina S.r.L. (4)
Avda Teniente General Morillas S/N, Ezeiza International Airport, Buenos Aires, B1802EZE, Argentina
Tel.: (54) 11 5480 9011
Web Site: http://www.gategroup.com
Airline Catering Services
N.A.I.C.S.: 722310
Lorena Garea *(Mgr-Comml)*

Gate Gourmet Canada Inc. (4)
2498 Britannia Road East, Mississauga, L5P 1A2, ON, Canada
Tel.: (905) 405-4100
Web Site: http://www.gategroup.com
Airline Catering Services
N.A.I.C.S.: 722310
Sean McLaughlin *(Gen Mgr)*

Gate Gourmet Colombia Ltda. (4)
Calle 26 No 92 - 32 Lote 1, Bogota, Colombia
Tel.: (57) 1 414 79 79
Web Site: http://www.gategroup.com
Airline Catering Services
N.A.I.C.S.: 722310
Antonio Sanchez *(Gen Mgr)*

Gate Gourmet Denmark ApS (4)
Kystvejen 42, 2770, Kastrup, Denmark
Tel.: (45) 32470888
Web Site: http://www.gategroup.com
Catering Services
N.A.I.C.S.: 722310
Palle Orting *(Mgr-Unit)*

Gate Gourmet GmbH Deutschland (4)
Admiral Rosendahl Str 2 8, 63263, Neu-Isenburg, Germany
Tel.: (49) 69969500
Web Site: http://www.gategroup.com
Airline Catering Services
N.A.I.C.S.: 722310
Udo Fischer *(Gen Mgr)*

Gate Gourmet GmbH West (4)
Frachtstrasse 33, 40474, Dusseldorf, Nordrein-Westfalen, Germany
Tel.: (49) 211 4178 10
Web Site: http://www.gategourmet.com

Airline Catering Services
N.A.I.C.S.: 722310
Stefan Krauthauser *(Gen Mgr)*

Gate Gourmet Holdings UK Ltd. (4)
Heathrow West Building 1071 Southampton Road, Heathrow Airport, Hounslow, TW6 3AQ, Middlesex, United Kingdom
Tel.: (44) 208 757 6400
Web Site: http://www.gategroup.com
Airline Catering Services
N.A.I.C.S.: 722310

Gate Gourmet Ireland Ltd (4)
South Apron Dublin Airport Co, Dublin, Leinster, Ireland
Tel.: (353) 18149100
Web Site: http://www.gategroup.com
Airline Catering Services
N.A.I.C.S.: 722310
Helder Ponte Rodrigues *(Gen Mgr)*

Gate Gourmet London Ltd. (4)
Heathrow West Building 1071 Southampton Road, Heathrow Airport, Hounslow, TW6 3AQ, Middlesex, United Kingdom
Tel.: (44) 2087576400
Web Site: http://www.gategroup.com
Airline Catering Services
N.A.I.C.S.: 722310

Gate Gourmet Northern Europe ApS (4)
Amager Landevej 119, 2770, Kastrup, Denmark
Tel.: (45) 32470800
Web Site: http://www.gategroup.com
Sales Range: $50-74.9 Million
Catering Services
N.A.I.C.S.: 722310

Gate Gourmet Norway AS (4)
Fridtjof Nansens Vei, Gardermoen, 2060, Norway
Tel.: (47) 64810100
Airline Catering Services
N.A.I.C.S.: 722310
Pal Jullumstro *(Mgr-Unit)*

Gate Gourmet Peru S.R.L. (4)
Aeropuerto Internacional Jorge Chavez Zona Norte s/n, PO Box Casilla, Callao, Peru
Tel.: (51) 15751621
Web Site: http://gategroup.com
Airline Catering Services
N.A.I.C.S.: 722310
Claudio Carballo *(Gen Mgr)*

Gate Gourmet Singapore Pte Ltd (4)
460 Alexandra Road 14 05/06 PSA Building, Singapore, Singapore
Tel.: (65) 64960138
Web Site: http://www.gategroup.com
Sales Range: $10-24.9 Million
Emp.: 50
Airline Catering Services
N.A.I.C.S.: 722310
Mei Foong *(CFO)*

Gate Gourmet Sweden AB (4)
Sturup Flygplats Malmo Sturup, Malmo, Scania, Sweden
Tel.: (46) 40556000
Sales Range: $10-24.9 Million
Emp.: 20
Airline Catering Services
N.A.I.C.S.: 722310

Gate Gourmet del Ecuador Cia Ltda. (4)
Av de las Americas s/n Junto American Airlines Cargo Aeropuerto Jose, Joaquin de Olmedo, Guayaquil, Guayas, Ecuador
Tel.: (593) 4 2287 626
Web Site: http://www.gategroup.com
Airline Catering Services
N.A.I.C.S.: 722310
Juan Bernardo Rosero *(Gen Mgr)*

Subsidiary (US):

Gate Gourmet, Inc. (4)
1880 Campus Commons Dr Ste 200, Reston, VA 20191
Tel.: (703) 964-2300
Web Site: http://www.gategourmet.com
Airline Catering Services
N.A.I.C.S.: 488190

Subsidiary (Non-US):

Pourshins Ltd. (3)
Ash House Littleton Road, Ashford, TW15 1TZ, United Kingdom
Tel.: (44) 2089175777
Web Site: http://www.pourshins.com
Sales Range: $75-99.9 Million
Logistics & Supply Chain Management Solutions
N.A.I.C.S.: 541614
Marc Tornatore *(Dir-Supply Chain & Plng-Asia Pacific)*

RS AUTOMATION CO., LTD.
38 Jinwi Industrial Complex Road, Jinwi-Myeon, Pyeongtaek, Gyeonggi-do, Korea (South)
Tel.: (82) 316859300
Web Site:
  https://www.rsautomation.co.kr
Year Founded: 2009
140670—(KRS)
Rev.: $78,578,231
Assets: $68,743,577
Liabilities: $36,671,624
Net Worth: $32,071,953
Earnings: $665,949
Emp.: 200
Fiscal Year-end: 12/31/22
Electronic Components Mfr
N.A.I.C.S.: 334419
Kun-Min Lee *(Sr Mng Dir)*

RS GROUP PLC
Fifth Floor Two Pancras Square, London, N1C 4AG, United Kingdom
Tel.: (44) 2072398400 UK
Web Site: https://www.rsgroup.com
Year Founded: 1937
RS1—(LSE)
Rev.: $3,701,332,530
Assets: $3,157,358,400
Liabilities: $1,488,203,010
Net Worth: $1,669,155,390
Earnings: $352,596,510
Fiscal Year-end: 03/31/23
Distribution of Component Parts & Original Equipment for Electronic, Electrical & Mechanical Devices
N.A.I.C.S.: 423610
David Egan *(CFO)*

Subsidiaries:

Allied Electronics (Canada) Inc. (1)
1900 City Park Dr, Ottawa, K1J1A3, ON, Canada (100%)
Tel.: (613) 228-1964
Web Site: http://www.alliedelec.com
Sales Range: $200-249.9 Million
Emp.: 12
Distr of Electronic Components
N.A.I.C.S.: 334419

Allied Electronics Inc. (1)
7151 Jack Newell Blvd S, Fort Worth, TX 76118 (100%)
Tel.: (817) 595-3500
Web Site: http://www.alliedelec.com
Sales Range: $150-199.9 Million
Emp.: 475
Supplier of Electrical Components
N.A.I.C.S.: 423690
Frank Cantwell *(VP-Product & Supplier Mgmt)*

Amidata S.A. (1)
Avenida de Bruxelles 6, Alcobendas, 28108, Spain
Tel.: (34) 915129699
Web Site: https://es.rs-online.com
Sales Range: $25-49.9 Million
Emp.: 70
Distr of Electronic Components & Providers of Logistics Support
N.A.I.C.S.: 334419

Amidata S.A. (1)
Av de Europa 19, Pozuelo De Alarcon, 28224, Madrid, Spain (100%)
Tel.: (34) 902100711
Web Site: http://www.amidata.es
Sales Range: $25-49.9 Million
Emp.: 50
Distr of Electronic Components & Providers of Logistics Support

RS GROUP PLC

N.A.I.C.S.: 334419
Anna Bella *(Mng Dir)*

Domnick Hunter-RL (Thailand) Co., Ltd. (1)
99/1-3 Narathiwat Ratchanakharin Rd, Chongnonsee Yannawa, Bangkok, 10120, Thailand
Tel.: (66) 26782224
Web Site: https://www.domnickthailand.com
Air Compressor Machine Whslr
N.A.I.C.S.: 423730

Electrocomponents France SARL (1)
Rue Norman King, 60000, Beauvais, France
Tel.: (33) 344101500
Web Site: http://www.rs.ww.fr
Sales Range: $150-199.9 Million
Emp.: 430
Electronic Components Distr
N.A.I.C.S.: 423690
Maffli Stephane *(Mng Dir)*

Electrocomponents UK Limited (1)
International Managment Centre 8050 Oxford Business Park North, Oxford, OX4 2HW, United Kingdom
Tel.: (44) 1865 204000
Web Site:
  http://www.electrocomponents.com
Emp.: 90
Electronic Component Mfr & Distr
N.A.I.C.S.: 334419
Ian Mason *(CEO)*

John Liscombe Limited (1)
Unit 2 Mariner Way, Felnex Trading Estate, Newport, NP19 4PQ, United Kingdom
Tel.: (44) 1633284111
Web Site: http://www.liscombe.co.uk
Leather Glove Mfr & Distr
N.A.I.C.S.: 316990

Needlers Limited (1)
Wyke Way Melton West Business Park, Melton, HU14 3BQ, United Kingdom
Tel.: (44) 1482467500
Web Site: http://www.needlers.co.uk
Hygiene Food Mfr & Distr
N.A.I.C.S.: 311999
Bruce Stroud *(Acct Mgr)*

OKdo Technology Limited (1)
Fifth Floor Two Pancras Square, London, N1C 4AG, United Kingdom
Tel.: (44) 2031090210
Web Site: http://www.okdo.com
Electric Equipment Mfr
N.A.I.C.S.: 334419

RS Americas (Canada), Inc. (1)
1155 Lola St, Ottawa, K1K4C1, ON, Canada
Tel.: (613) 228-1964
Electronic Product Mfr & Distr
N.A.I.C.S.: 334416

RS Americas, Inc. (1)
7151 Jack Newell Blvd S, Fort Worth, TX 76118
Web Site: https://us.rs-online.com
Electronic Product Mfr & Distr
N.A.I.C.S.: 334416

RS Componentes Electronicos Limitada (1)
Av Presidente Eduardo Frei M 6001-71, Conchali, Santiago, Chile (100%)
Tel.: (56) 950121156
Web Site: http://cl.rsdelivers.com
Sales Range: $25-49.9 Million
Emp.: 20
Provider of Electronic Equipment
N.A.I.C.S.: 449210

RS Components (Shanghai) Company Limited (1)
Unit 501 5th Floor Building C Phase 2 Qiantan World Trade Center, No 3 Lane 227 Dongyu Road Pudong New District, Shanghai, 200126, China
Tel.: (86) 4008218857
Web Site: https://www.rsonline.cn
Sales Range: $50-74.9 Million
Emp.: 10
Electronic Components Distr
N.A.I.C.S.: 423690

6417

RS GROUP PLC

RS Group plc—(Continued)

RS Components A/S (1)
Nattergalevej 6, 2400, Copenhagen,
Denmark **(100%)**
Tel.: (45) 38169900
Web Site: https://dk.rs-online.com
Sales Range: $50-74.9 Million
Emp.: 60
Distribution Equipment for Electronic, Electrical & Mechanical Devices
N.A.I.C.S.: 423620

RS Components AB (1)
Fabriksgatan 7 3v, 412 50, Gothenburg,
Sweden **(100%)**
Tel.: (46) 771458900
Web Site: http://se.rs-online.com
Sales Range: $25-49.9 Million
Emp.: 4
Distr of Electronic Components
N.A.I.C.S.: 334419

RS Components AS (1)
Fredrik Selmers vei 6 10th floor, 0663,
Oslo, Norway
Tel.: (47) 64834000
Web Site: https://www.no.rs-online.com
Sales Range: $50-74.9 Million
Emp.: 6
Electronic Components Distr
N.A.I.C.S.: 423690

RS Components B.V. (1)
Bingerweg 19, 2031 AZ, Haarlem,
Netherlands **(100%)**
Tel.: (31) 235166555
Web Site: https://nl.rs-online.com
Sales Range: $25-49.9 Million
Emp.: 70
Distribution Equipment for Electronic, Electrical & Mechanical Devices
N.A.I.C.S.: 423620

RS Components B.V. (1)
Bd Paepsemlaan 22, Anderlecht, 1070,
Belgium **(100%)**
Tel.: (32) 25280788
Web Site: http://www.rsonline.be
Sales Range: $25-49.9 Million
Emp.: 70
Distr of Electronic Components
N.A.I.C.S.: 334419
Hans Devras (Mgr-Sls)

RS Components Co., Ltd. (1)
50 GMM Grammy Place 19th Floor Unit
1901-1904 Sukhumvit 21 Road Asoke,
Klongtoey Nua Wattana, Bangkok, 10110,
Thailand
Tel.: (66) 26486868
Web Site: https://www.th.rs-online.com
Electric Equipment Mfr
N.A.I.C.S.: 334419

RS Components GesmbH (1)
Albrechtser Strasse 11, PO Box 79, 3950,
Gmund, Austria **(100%)**
Tel.: (43) 2852537650
Web Site: http://www.rs-components.at
Sales Range: $25-49.9 Million
Emp.: 80
Distr of Electronic Components
N.A.I.C.S.: 334419

RS Components GmbH (1)
Mainzer Landstrasse 180, 60327, Frankfurt am Main, Germany **(100%)**
Tel.: (49) 69580014234
Web Site: https://de.rs-online.com
Sales Range: $150-199.9 Million
Emp.: 300
Distribution of Electronic Components for Electronic, Electrical & Mechanical Devices
N.A.I.C.S.: 423620

RS Components Handelsges.m.b.H. (1)
Albrechtser Strasse 11, 3950, Gmund, Austria
Tel.: (43) 2852537650
Web Site: https://at.rs-online.com
Electronic Components Distr
N.A.I.C.S.: 423690

RS Components Holdings Limited (1)
International Management Center 8050 Oxford Business North, Oxford, OX4 2HW,
United Kingdom
Tel.: (44) 1865 204000
Investment Management Service
N.A.I.C.S.: 523999
Alexander von Schirmeister (Chief Innovation Officer)

RS Components KK (1)
134 Kobe-cho Yokohama Business Park
West Tower 12th floor, Hodogaya-ku, Yokohama, 240-0005, Kanagawa,
Japan **(100%)**
Tel.: (81) 453358888
Web Site: https://jp.rs-online.com
Sales Range: $50-74.9 Million
Emp.: 140
Distr of Electronic Components
N.A.I.C.S.: 334419
Kapstsukuni Hyodo (Gen Mgr)

RS Components Ltd (1)
8F-2 No 1 Zhongzheng Rd, Tucheng Dist,
New Taipei City, 23670, Taiwan **(100%)**
Tel.: (886) 800088238
Web Site: http://twen.rs-online.com
Sales Range: $25-49.9 Million
Emp.: 19
Distr of Electronic Components & Providers of Logistics Support
N.A.I.C.S.: 334419

RS Components Ltd. (1)
Birchington Road, Corby, NN17 9RS,
Northants, United Kingdom **(100%)**
Tel.: (44) 3457201201
Web Site: https://uk.rs-online.com
Sales Range: $550-599.9 Million
Emp.: 2,250
Supplier of Electronic Components
N.A.I.C.S.: 423690

RS Components Ltd. (1)
Suite 1608 Level 16 Tower 1 Kowloon Commerce Centre, 51 Kwai Cheong Road, Kwai Chung, China (Hong Kong) **(100%)**
Tel.: (852) 24219898
Web Site: http://hken.rs-online.com
Sales Range: $25-49.9 Million
Emp.: 100
Distr of Electronic Components
N.A.I.C.S.: 541614
Kinnie Luk (Gen Mgr)

RS Components Ltd. (1)
Unit 30-31 761 Great South Road, Penrose, 1006, Auckland, New Zealand **(100%)**
Tel.: (64) 95261600
Web Site: http://www.rsnewzealand.com
Sales Range: $25-49.9 Million
Emp.: 15
Distribution of Electronic Components
N.A.I.C.S.: 561499
Murray Lobb (Country Mgr)

RS Components Pte Ltd (1)
Robinson Road, PO Box 1582, Singapore, 903132, Singapore **(100%)**
Tel.: (65) 68653400
Web Site: https://sg.rs-online.com
Sales Range: $25-49.9 Million
Emp.: 90
Distr of Electronic Components
N.A.I.C.S.: 334419

RS Components Pty Ltd (1)
25 Pavesi St, Smithfield, 2164, NSW,
Australia **(100%)**
Tel.: (61) 1300656636
Web Site: https://au.rs-online.com
Sales Range: $50-74.9 Million
Emp.: 150
Distr of Electronic Components
N.A.I.C.S.: 334419

RS Components S.R.L. (1)
Viale T Edison 110 Edificio C, Sesto San Giovanni, 20099, Milan, Italy
Tel.: (39) 02660581
Web Site: https://it.rs-online.com
Electronic Product Mfr & Distr
N.A.I.C.S.: 334416

RS Components SA (1)
20 Indianapolis Street Kyalami Business Park Kyalami, PO Box 12182, Vorna Valley, Midrand, 1686, South Africa **(100%)**
Tel.: (27) 116919300
Web Site: http://za.rs-online.com
Sales Range: $25-49.9 Million
Emp.: 120
Electronic Components Distr
N.A.I.C.S.: 334419
Brian Andrew (Mng Dir)

RS Components SAS (1)
Rue Norman King, CS40453, 60031, Beauvais, Cedex, France
Tel.: (33) 825034034
Web Site: https://fr.rs-online.com
Sales Range: $200-249.9 Million
Electronic Components Distr
N.A.I.C.S.: 423690

RS Components Sdn Bhd (1)
PO Box 10188, 50706, Kuala Lumpur,
Malaysia **(100%)**
Tel.: (60) 350215888
Web Site: http://my.rs-online.com
Sales Range: $25-49.9 Million
Emp.: 35
Distr of Electronic Components
N.A.I.C.S.: 334419

RS Components SpA (1)
Viale T Edison 110 Edificio C, Sesto San Giovanni, 20099, Milan, Italy **(100%)**
Tel.: (39) 02660581
Web Site: http://it.rs-online.com
Sales Range: $50-74.9 Million
Emp.: 250
Distr of Electronic Equipment
N.A.I.C.S.: 335999

RS Integrated Supply UK Limited (1)
RS Works Daten Park, Birchwood, Warrington, WA3 6UT, Cheshire, United Kingdom
Tel.: (44) 1925882500
Web Site: https://rs-integratedsupply.com
Electronic Product Distr
N.A.I.C.S.: 423610

Radionics Ltd. (1)
Glenview Industrial Estate Herberton Road, Rialto, Dublin, 12, Ireland **(100%)**
Tel.: (44)
Web Site: http://ie.rs-online.com
Sales Range: $25-49.9 Million
Emp.: 70
Provider of Electronic Equipment
N.A.I.C.S.: 449210

Risoul Dominicana S.R.L. (1)
Autopista Duarte KM 17 Calle Los Armejo Palma Enana No 13 Nave 1, Palmarejo-Villa Linda Oeste, Santo Domingo, Dominican Republic
Tel.: (809) 9553541
Web Site: https://www.risoul.do
Industrial Automation Machinery Equipment Mfr & Distr
N.A.I.C.S.: 333248

Risoul Iberica S.A. (1)
Carrer Mas Pujol 45 Nave 11, Les Franqueses del Valle, 08520, Barcelona, Spain
Tel.: (34) 930369556
Web Site: https://www.risoul.com.es
Industrial Automation Machinery Equipment Mfr & Distr
N.A.I.C.S.: 333248

Synovos, Inc. (1)
2 Radnor Corporate Ctr Ste 400 100 Matsonford Rd, Radnor, PA 19087
Tel.: (610) 293-5940
Web Site: http://synovos.com
Supply Chain, Asset & Technology Services
N.A.I.C.S.: 541614
Larry Newhart (Chm)

Subsidiary (Domestic):

Storeroom Solutions (2)
16888 State Route 706, Montrose, PA 18801-0319 **(100%)**
Tel.: (570) 278-4040
Web Site: http://www.storeroomsolutions.com
Sales Range: $10-24.9 Million
Emp.: 45
Inventory Management Of Spare & Repair Replacement Parts For Manufacturing & Industrial Facilities
N.A.I.C.S.: 541611
Carlos Tellez (Pres & CEO)

Storeroom Solutions Costa Rica Corp. (2)
2 Radnor Corporate Ctr Ste 400 100 Matsonford Rd, Radnor, PA 19087
Tel.: (610) 293-5940

INTERNATIONAL PUBLIC

Web Site: http://www.storeroomsolutions.com
Sales Range: $10-24.9 Million
Emp.: 50
Supply Chain Management Services
N.A.I.C.S.: 541614
Angelica Nardi (Mgr)

Storeroom Solutions Puerto Rico Corp. (2)
PO Box 2361, Manati, PR 00674
Tel.: (787) 635-7948
Material Management Services
N.A.I.C.S.: 541614

RS PUBLIC COMPANY LIMITED

27 RS Group Bldg Prasert-Manukitch Rd Sena Nikhom, Chatuchak, Bangkok, 10900, Thailand
Tel.: (66) 20378888
Web Site: http://www.rs.co.th
Year Founded: 1976
RS—(THA)
Rev.: $106,564,208
Assets: $234,432,246
Liabilities: $147,289,806
Net Worth: $87,142,440
Earnings: $40,244,956
Emp.: 1,338
Fiscal Year-end: 12/31/23
Television Broadcasting Services
N.A.I.C.S.: 516102
Danasidh Peslapunt (Chief Legal Officer)

Subsidiaries:

Coolism Co., Ltd. (1)
27 RS Group Bldg Tower C 4th Floor Prasert-Manukitch Rd, Sena Nikhom Chatuchak, Bangkok, 10900, Thailand
Tel.: (66) 20378888
Commerce & Entertainment Services
N.A.I.C.S.: 512110

Fourth Apple Co., Ltd. (1)
27 RS Group Bldg Tower C 2nd Floor Prasert-Manukitch Rd, Sena Nikhom Chatuchak, Bangkok, 10900, Thailand
Tel.: (66) 20378888
Commerce & Entertainment Services
N.A.I.C.S.: 512110

Lifestar Co., Ltd. (1)
27 RS Group Tower Building A Floor 5th Prasert-Manukit Road, Senanikhom Chatuchak, Bangkok, 10900, Thailand
Tel.: (66) 20378955
Web Site: http://www.lifestar.co.th
Health & Beauty Product Mfr
N.A.I.C.S.: 325620
Pongnarin Wongrattanakulthon (Sr Product Mgr)

R Alliance Co., Ltd. (1)
27 RS Group Bldg Tower B 3rd Floor Prasert-Manukitch Rd, Sena Nikhom Chatuchak, Bangkok, 10900, Thailand
Tel.: (66) 20378888
Commerce & Entertainment Services
N.A.I.C.S.: 512110

RS Alpha Co., Ltd. (1)
27 RS Group Bldg Tower A Prasert-Manukitch Rd, Sena Nikhom Chatuchak, Bangkok, 10900, Thailand
Tel.: (66) 20378888
Commerce & Entertainment Services
N.A.I.C.S.: 512110

RS Connect Co., Ltd. (1)
27 RS Group Building Tower A Floor 3 & 7 Prasert-Manukitch Road, Sena Nikhom Chatuchak, Bangkok, 10900, Thailand
Tel.: (66) 20378888
Cosmetic Product Distr
N.A.I.C.S.: 424210

RS Livewell Co., Ltd. (1)
27 RS Group Building Tower A Floor 5 Prasert-Manukitch Road, Sena Nikhom Chatuchak, Bangkok, 10900, Thailand
Tel.: (66) 20378888
Commerce & Entertainment Services
N.A.I.C.S.: 512110

AND PRIVATE COMPANIES

RS Mall Co., Ltd. (1)
27 RS Group Tower A Building 5th Floor
Prasert-Manukitch Road, Senanikom Sub-
district Chatuchak District, Bangkok, 10900,
Thailand
Tel.: (66) 20859999
Web Site: https://www.rsmall.com
Shopping Mall Services
N.A.I.C.S.: 531120

RS Multimedia Co., Ltd. (1)
27 RS Group Building Tower B Floor 3
Prasert-Manukitch Road, Sena Nikhom
Chatuchak, Bangkok, 10900, Thailand
Tel.: (66) 20378888
Commerce & Entertainment Services
N.A.I.C.S.: 512110

RS pet all Co., Ltd. (1)
27 RS Group Building Tower A Floor 1
Prasert-Manukitch Road, Sena Nikhom
Chatuchak, Bangkok, 10900, Thailand
Tel.: (66) 20378785
Commerce & Entertainment Services
N.A.I.C.S.: 512110

RS TECHNOLOGIES CO., LTD.
17F NT Building 1-47-1 Oi,
Shinagawa-ku, Tokyo, 140-0014, Japan
Tel.: (81) 357097685
Web Site: https://www.rs-tec.jp
Year Founded: 2010
3445—(TKS)
Rev.: $367,921,370
Assets: $997,314,850
Liabilities: $178,930,330
Net Worth: $818,384,520
Earnings: $54,614,270
Emp.: 1,534
Fiscal Year-end: 12/31/23
Semiconductor Mfr
N.A.I.C.S.: 334413
Nagayoshi Ho (Pres & CEO)

Subsidiaries:

Beijinng GRINM RS Semiconductor
Materials Co., Ltd. (1)
No 2 Xinjiekouwai Street, Beijing, 100088,
China
Tel.: (86) 1082087088
Web Site: http://www.gritek.com
Emp.: 700
Silicon Wafer & Semiconductor Equipment
Mfr
N.A.I.C.S.: 334413

RS Technologies Co., Ltd. - Osaki
Factory (1)
26-2 Yamazaki Sanbongi Otonashi, Osaki,
Miyagi, Japan
Tel.: (81) 229525803
Silicon Wafers Mfr
N.A.I.C.S.: 334413

RSTEC Semiconductor Taiwan Co.,
Ltd. (1)
No 1 Nanke7th RD Southern Taiwan Science Park, Tainan City, 74144, Taiwan
Tel.: (886) 65050977
Web Site: https://www.rs-tec.tw
Silicon Wafer & Semiconductor Equipment
Mfr
N.A.I.C.S.: 334413

RS2 SOFTWARE PLC
RS2 Buildings Fort Road, Mosta,
MST 1859, Malta
Tel.: (356) 21345857
Web Site: https://www.rs2.com
Year Founded: 1988
RS2—(MAL)
Rev.: $40,487,871
Assets: $46,786,370
Liabilities: $20,722,648
Net Worth: $26,063,721
Earnings: ($269,794)
Emp.: 480
Fiscal Year-end: 12/31/22
Software Development Services
N.A.I.C.S.: 541511
Radi Abdul El Haj (CEO)

Subsidiaries:

RS2 Germany GmbH (1)
Martin Behaim Strasse 15 A, 63263, Neu-
Isenburg, Germany
Tel.: (49) 6102730030
Business Support Services
N.A.I.C.S.: 561990

RS2 Smart Processing Ltd. (1)
RS2 Buildings Fort Road, Mosta, MST
1859, Malta
Tel.: (356) 20928700
Transaction Processing Services
N.A.I.C.S.: 522320
Patrick Gauci (Head-Svc Delivery)

RS2 Software APAC Inc. (1)
1501 ACCRALAW Tower 2nd Avenue corner 30th Street, Bonifacio Global City,
Taguig, Philippines
Tel.: (63) 28288700
Business Support Services
N.A.I.C.S.: 561990

RS2 Software Inc. (1)
4643 S Ulster St Ste 1285, Denver, CO
80237
Tel.: (720) 881-8670
Transaction Processing Services
N.A.I.C.S.: 522320

RSC INTERNATIONAL LTD.
Plot No 30 Sangam Colony Opposite
VKI Road No 14 Sikar Road, Jaipur,
302013, India
Tel.: (91) 9324541587
Web Site: https://www.rscltd.in
Year Founded: 1993
530179—(BOM)
Rev.: $6,195
Assets: $8,917
Liabilities: $7,715
Net Worth: $1,202
Earnings: ($9,326)
Fiscal Year-end: 03/31/21
Textile Product Mfr & Distr
N.A.I.C.S.: 314999
Gyan Chand Jain (Mng Dir)

RSD FINANCE LIMITED
224 AJC Bose Road Room No 902
9th Floor Krishna Building, Kolkata,
700017, India
Tel.: (91) 3369000200
Web Site:
https://www.rsdfinancelimited.com
Year Founded: 1963
539875—(BOM)
Rev.: $7,545,895
Assets: $29,242,062
Liabilities: $4,979,098
Net Worth: $24,262,964
Earnings: $1,081,366
Emp.: 9
Fiscal Year-end: 03/31/21
Mortgage Banking Services
N.A.I.C.S.: 521110
Rajeev Singh Dugal (Mng Dir)

RSG GROUP GMBH
Tannenberg 4, 96132, Schlusselfeld,
Germany
Tel.: (49) 9552 93190
Web Site: http://rsggroup.com
Year Founded: 1997
Emp.: 41,000
Fitness & Lifestyle Products
N.A.I.C.S.: 713940
Rainer Schaller (Mng Dir)

RSG KAPITAL D.O.O.
Breg 14, 1000, Ljubljana, Slovenia
Tel.: (386) 82055358   SI
Web Site: http://www.rsg-capital.si
Year Founded: 2006
Sales Range: Less than $1 Million
Emp.: 5
Venture Capital
N.A.I.C.S.: 523999

Tatjana Zabasu (Partner & Dir-Investment)

Subsidiaries:

ShoutEm, Inc. (1)
175 Varick St, New York, NY 10014
Tel.: (914) 330-9950
Web Site: http://www.shoutem.com
Sales Range: $25-49.9 Million
Emp.: 35
Mobile Applications
N.A.I.C.S.: 513210

RSK GROUP PLC
Spring Lodge 172 Chester Road,
Helsby, WA6 0AR, Cheshire, United
Kingdom
Tel.: (44) 01928726006   UK
Web Site: http://www.rsk.co.uk
Year Founded: 1989
Sales Range: $100-124.9 Million
Emp.: 960
Environmental Strategy & Support
Services Training Engineering Consulting & Environmental Management
Services
N.A.I.C.S.: 541620
Alan Ryder (Founder & CEO)

Subsidiaries:

RSK (Ireland) Ltd. (1)
Regus House Block Fl Harcourt Ctr Harcourt Rd, Dublin, 4, Ireland
Tel.: (353) 12952602
Web Site: http://www.rskgroup.ie
Sales Range: $25-49.9 Million
Emp.: 22
Environmental Strategy & Support Services;
Training, Engineering, Consulting & Environmental Management
N.A.I.C.S.: 541620

RSK Aberdeen (1)
5 Golden Sq, Aberdeen, AB10 1RD, United
Kingdom
Tel.: (44) 1224624624
Web Site: http://www.rsk.co.uk
Sales Range: $25-49.9 Million
Emp.: 6
Environmental Strategy & Support Services;
Training, Engineering, Consulting & Environmental Management
N.A.I.C.S.: 541620
Alan Rider (Gen Mgr)

RSK Benelux bvba (1)
Antwerpsesteenweg 45, 2830, Willebroek,
Belgium
Tel.: (32) 3 451 93 00
Web Site: http://www.rskgroup.be
Emp.: 45
Environmental Consulting Services
N.A.I.C.S.: 541620
Dirk Van Look (Sr Project Mgr)

RSK Cevre Hizmetleri AS (1)
Nenehatun Caddesi 69/1, 06700, Cankaya,
Ankara, Turkiye
Tel.: (90) 312 437 70 73
Environmental Consulting Services
N.A.I.C.S.: 541620

RSK EMN bv (1)
Burgemeester de Zeeuwstraat 2, 2985 AB,
Ridderkerk, Netherlands
Tel.: (31) 180 46 33 30
Web Site: http://www.rskgroup.nl
Environmental Consulting Services
N.A.I.C.S.: 541620
Jeroen Meisters (Gen Mgr)

RSK Environment LLC (1)
Office 937 8th & 9th Floors Al Fardan Office
Tower, PO Box 31316, West Bay, Doha,
Qatar
Tel.: (974) 44101 520
Environmental Consulting Services
N.A.I.C.S.: 541620

RSK Environnement SAS (1)
Zone Actimart Batiment Le Vinci 1140 Rue
Ampere, 13 851, Aix-en-Provence, France
Tel.: (33) 4 86 31 80 35
Web Site: http://www.rsk.co.uk
Emp.: 25
Environmental Consulting Services

N.A.I.C.S.: 541620
Stefan Bangels (Mng Dir)

RSK Germany GmbH (1)
Ulmer Strasse 239, 70327, Stuttgart, Germany
Tel.: (49) 711 75 88 40 40
Environmental Consulting Services
N.A.I.C.S.: 541620

RSK Hemel Hempstead (1)
18 Frogmore Road, Hemel Hempstead,
HP3 9RT, Hertfordshire, United Kingdom
Tel.: (44) 1442437500
Web Site: http://www.rsk.co.uk
Sales Range: $25-49.9 Million
Emp.: 80
Environmental Strategy & Support Services;
Training, Engineering, Consulting & Environmental Management
N.A.I.C.S.: 541620
Abrian Marsh (Gen Mgr)

RSK Polska Sp. z o.o. (1)
Ul Bitwy Warszawskiej 1920r 7A, 02-366,
Warsaw, Poland
Tel.: (48) 22 2081380
Environmental Consulting Services
N.A.I.C.S.: 541620
Blazej Samel (Engr-Geo-Environmental)

RSK Romania Srl (1)
Str Sevastopol 13-17 Diplomat Business
Centre 105 Rm, 1st Floor Room 109 Sector
1, Bucharest, 010991, Romania
Tel.: (40) 21 313 05 98
Environmental Consulting Services
N.A.I.C.S.: 541620

RSL ELECTRONICS LTD.
Ramat Gabriel Industrial Zone, PO
Box 21, Migdal Ha'Emeq, 23100,
Israel
Tel.: (972) 46547510
Web Site: https://www.rsl-electronics.com
RSEL—(TAE)
Rev.: $8,596,491
Assets: $10,565,824
Liabilities: $1,942,533
Net Worth: $8,623,290
Earnings: $1,640,834
Fiscal Year-end: 12/31/23
Search, Detection, Navigation, Guidance, Aeronautical & Nautical System
& Instrument Manufacturing
N.A.I.C.S.: 334511
Zeev Degani (CEO)

RSM INTERNATIONAL LIMITED
11 Old Jewry, London, EC2R 8DU,
United Kingdom
Tel.: (44) 20 7601 1080   UK
Web Site: http://www.rsm.global
Accounting, Auditing, Tax & Consulting Services
N.A.I.C.S.: 541211
Jean M. Stephens (CEO)

RSR SINGULAR ASSETS EUROPE SOCIMI, S.A.
C/ Jose Abascal 42 7 Derecha,
28003, Madrid, Spain
Tel.: (34) 915597793
Web Site:
https://www.rsrsingularsocimi.com
Year Founded: 2015
MLRSR—(EUR)
Rev.: $441,140
Assets: $136,499,333
Liabilities: $97,409,987
Net Worth: $39,089,346
Earnings: ($1,697,237)
Emp.: 4
Fiscal Year-end: 12/31/21
Real Estate Investment Services
N.A.I.C.S.: 531190

RSUPPORT CO., LTD.
12 Godeok Biz Valley-ro 2-ga-gil,

RSUPPORT Co., Ltd.—(Continued)
Gangdong-gu, Seoul, 05203, Korea (South)
Tel.: (82) 7070113900
Web Site: https://www.rsupport.com
Year Founded: 2001
131370—(KRS)
Rev.: $37,275,614
Assets: $73,755,376
Liabilities: $7,855,218
Net Worth: $65,900,158
Earnings: $3,233,305
Emp.: 309
Fiscal Year-end: 12/31/22
Remote Support Software Services
N.A.I.C.S.: 513210
Hyungsu Seo *(Pres & CEO)*

RSWM LTD.
Bhilwara Towers A-12 Sector I, Noida, 201301, Delhi, India
Tel.: (91) 1204390300
Web Site: https://www.rswm.in
500350—(BOM)
Rev.: $322,880,676
Assets: $282,367,449
Liabilities: $174,283,214
Net Worth: $108,084,235
Earnings: $2,843,254
Emp.: 15,344
Fiscal Year-end: 03/31/21
Yarn Mfr
N.A.I.C.S.: 313110
Surender Gupta *(Compliance Officer & Sec)*

Subsidiaries:

Chesland Textiles Ltd. (1)
B Muduganapalli Hosur Taluk, Krishnagiri District, Bagalur, 635103, Tamil Nadu, India
Tel.: (91) 4344255500
Web Site: http://www.cheslind.co.in
Sales Range: $25-49.9 Million
Emp.: 1,000
Yarn Mfr
N.A.I.C.S.: 313110
P. V. S. Murthy *(CFO & Gen Mgr-Fin)*

RT MINERALS CORP.
Suite 1210 1130 Pender Street W, Vancouver, V6E 4A4, BC, Canada
Tel.: (604) 681-3170
Web Site: https://www.rtmcorp.com
RTMFF—(OTCIQ)
Assets: $1,299,929
Liabilities: $478,087
Net Worth: $821,841
Earnings: ($1,175,200)
Fiscal Year-end: 11/30/22
Metal Mineral Exploration & Mining Services
N.A.I.C.S.: 212290
Sandra Wong *(CFO & Sec)*

RTA LABORATUVARLARI BIYOLOJIK URUNLER ILAC VE MAKINE SANAYI TICARET A.S.
Gebze Plastikciler Organize Sanayi Bolgesi inonu Mah Balck Koyu; Yolu uzeri Geposb ici Cumhuriyet Cad No 3 Gebze, 41400, Kocaeli, Turkiye
Tel.: (90) 2626485300
Web Site: https://www.rtalabs.com
RTALB—(IST)
Rev.: $4,593,788
Assets: $39,527,384
Liabilities: $5,739,080
Net Worth: $33,788,304
Earnings: $15,375,899
Fiscal Year-end: 12/31/22
In-Vitro Diagnostic Substance Mfr
N.A.I.C.S.: 325413
Resat Ultav *(Chm & Gen Mgr)*

RTC GROUP PLC
The Derby Conference Centre London Road, Derby, DE24 8UX, United Kingdom
Tel.: (44) 3330112044
Web Site: https://www.rtcgroupplc.co.uk
RTC—(AIM)
Rev.: $90,768,745
Assets: $25,593,285
Liabilities: $17,773,290
Net Worth: $7,819,995
Earnings: ($443,070)
Emp.: 186
Fiscal Year-end: 12/31/22
Recruitment, Training & Conferencing Services
N.A.I.C.S.: 561311
William J. C. Douie *(Chm)*

Subsidiaries:

ATA Recruitment Limited (1)
The Derby Conference Centre London Road, Derby, DE24 8UX, United Kingdom
Tel.: (44) 8081642000
Web Site: http://www.ata-recruitment.co.uk
Sales Range: $25-49.9 Million
Recruiting Services
N.A.I.C.S.: 541612

Catalis Limited (1)
London Rd, Derby, DE24 8UX, United Kingdom
Tel.: (44) 8458808108
Web Site: http://www.catalis.com
Training Solutions & Services
N.A.I.C.S.: 611430
William L. Ballhaus *(Exec Chm)*

The Derby Conference Centre Limited (1)
London Rd, Derby, DE24 8UX, United Kingdom
Tel.: (44) 1332861842
Web Site: https://www.thederbyconference.com
Sales Range: $25-49.9 Million
Emp.: 50
Room Services
N.A.I.C.S.: 812990

RTC LUKA LEGET A.D.
Jaracki put 10, 22000, Sremska Mitrovica, Serbia
Tel.: (381) 22 621 977
Web Site: http://www.portleget.com
Year Founded: 1969
LKLG—(BEL)
Sales Range: $1-9.9 Million
Emp.: 99
Food Transportation Services
N.A.I.C.S.: 485999
Zoran Nesic *(Exec Dir)*

RTCL LIMITED
6926Delhi Jaipuria Mills Clock Tower Subzi Mandi, Delhi, 110007, Uttar Pradesh, India
Tel.: (91) 1123852583
Web Site: https://www.rtcllimited.in
Year Founded: 1994
531552—(BOM)
Rev.: $209,316
Assets: $5,918,302
Liabilities: $1,088,172
Net Worth: $4,830,130
Earnings: $50,153
Emp.: 9
Fiscal Year-end: 03/31/23
Real Estate Development Services
N.A.I.C.S.: 531390
Manoj Kumar Pandey *(Chm)*

RTE GROUP
12th Floor Khashoggi Building, PO Box 30530, Al Khobar, 31952, Saudi Arabia
Tel.: (966) 3 8991955
Web Site: http://www.rteksa.com
Year Founded: 1988
Supplier of Drilling Fluids & Services to Oil & Gas Industry
N.A.I.C.S.: 213112
H. H. Al Merry *(Pres & CEO)*

Subsidiaries:

Saudi Emirates Pulverization Industries Company (1)
Ahmed Bin Rashid Free Trade Zone, PO Box 1056, Umm al-Quwain, United Arab Emirates
Tel.: (971) 6 7652889
Web Site: http://www.sepico.com
Mineral Powders, Drilling Fluids & Cementing Products Mfr & Supplier
N.A.I.C.S.: 325998

RTG MINING INC.
Level 1 516 Hay Street, Subiaco, 6008, WA, Australia
Tel.: (61) 864892900
Web Site: https://www.rtgmining.com
RTTGF—(OTCIQ)
Rev.: $351
Assets: $5,634,972
Liabilities: $2,366,466
Net Worth: $3,268,506
Earnings: ($6,322,200)
Emp.: 5
Fiscal Year-end: 12/31/22
Gold Ore Exploration & Mining Services
N.A.I.C.S.: 212220
Michael J. Carrick *(Chm)*

RTI ROHRTECHNIK INTERNATIONAL GMBH
Bruckbachweg 23, Altenberg, 4203, Linz, Austria
Tel.: (43) 7230 8686 0
Web Site: http://www.rti.eu
Year Founded: 1963
Holding Company; Engineering, Construction & Pipe Rehabilitation Services
N.A.I.C.S.: 551112
Wolfgang Steinbichler *(Mng Dir)*

Subsidiaries:

RTi Austria GmbH (1)
Bruckbachweg 23, Altenberg, 4203, Linz, Austria
Tel.: (43) 7230 8686 0
Engineering, Construction & Pipe Rehabilitation Services
N.A.I.C.S.: 237990
M. Griebaum *(Mng Dir)*

RTi Germany GmbH (1)
Muhlenfeld 18, 30853, Langenhagen, Germany
Tel.: (49) 511 725 358 0
Engineering, Construction & Pipe Rehabilitation Services
N.A.I.C.S.: 237990
Frank Rust *(Mng Dir)*

RTO LIMITED
Level 5 59 High Street The Southern Cross Building, PO Box 42-258, Auckland, 1745, New Zealand
Tel.: (64) 98016008
Web Site: https://www.bgholdings.co.nz
RTO—(NZX)
Rev.: $5,510
Assets: $568,616
Liabilities: $322,249
Net Worth: $246,367
Earnings: ($158,324)
Emp.: 5
Fiscal Year-end: 03/31/23
Financial Services
N.A.I.C.S.: 523940
Mark Thornton *(CEO)*

Subsidiaries:

NZF Money Limited (1)
Level 2 88 Broadway, Newmarket, Auckland, 1023, New Zealand
Tel.: (64) 95209350

Sales Range: $25-49.9 Million
Emp.: 10
Financial & Investment Services
N.A.I.C.S.: 541611

New Zealand Mortgage Finance Limited (1)
Level 2 88 Broadway, Newmarket, Auckland, 1023, New Zealand
Tel.: (64) 93738010
Web Site: http://www.nzmf.co.nz
Sales Range: $50-74.9 Million
Emp.: 14
Mortgage Lending & Brokerage Services
N.A.I.C.S.: 522310

Subsidiary (Domestic):

Approved Mortgage Brokers Limited (2)
Level 2 88 Broadway, Newmarket, Auckland, 1023, New Zealand
Tel.: (64) 95235871
Web Site: http://www.approved.co.nz
Sales Range: $50-74.9 Million
Emp.: 6
Mortgage Brokerage Services
N.A.I.C.S.: 522310

RTS POWER CORPORATION LIMITED
56 Netaji Subhas Road, Kolkata, 700001, West Bengal, India
Tel.: (91) 3322426025
Web Site: https://www.rtspower.com
531215—(BOM)
Rev.: $11,449,989
Assets: $24,263,749
Liabilities: $6,950,771
Net Worth: $17,312,978
Earnings: $318,564
Emp.: 58
Fiscal Year-end: 03/31/21
Power Distribution Services
N.A.I.C.S.: 221122
Abhay Bhutoria *(Mng Dir)*

Subsidiaries:

Reengus Wires Private Limited (1)
C-174 Rd Number 9 J Vishwakarma Industrial Area Murlipura, V K I Area, Jaipur, 302013, RAJ, India
Tel.: (91) 9549535121
Web Site: https://www.reenguswires.com
Silo Mfr
N.A.I.C.S.: 335931

RTS RIEGER TEAM WERBEAGENTUR GMBH
Bunsenstrasse 7-9, 70771, Leinfelden-Echterdingen, Germany
Tel.: (49) 7 11 97 52 0
Web Site: http://www.rts-riegerteam.de
Year Founded: 1969
Emp.: 100
Business-To-Business, Communications, Full Service
N.A.I.C.S.: 541810
Jorg Dambacher *(Mng Dir-Stuttgart)*

Subsidiaries:

RTS Rieger Team Werbeagentur GmbH (1)
Hohenzollernstrasse 11-13, 40211, Dusseldorf, Germany
Tel.: (49) 2 11 94 4 87 0
Web Site: http://www.rts-riegerteam.de
Sales Range: $10-24.9 Million
Emp.: 15
N.A.I.C.S.: 541810
Matthihs Zeft *(Mng Dir)*

RTX A/S
Stroemmen 6, 9400, Norresundby, Denmark
Tel.: (45) 96322300
Web Site: https://www.rtx.dk
RTX—(OMX)
Rev.: $75,462,906
Assets: $80,110,122

Liabilities: $32,481,979
Net Worth: $47,628,142
Earnings: $602,175
Emp.: 280
Fiscal Year-end: 09/30/21
Wireless Telecommunications Equipment Mfr
N.A.I.C.S.: 334220
Peter Christensen *(Pres-Bus Comm)*

Subsidiaries:

RTX America, Inc (1)
10620 Treena St Ste 230, San Diego, CA 92131
Tel.: (858) 935-6152
Web Site: http://www.rtx.dk
Wireless Equipments Mfr
N.A.I.C.S.: 334210

RTX Products Hong Kong Ltd. (1)
8/F Corporation Square 8 Lam Lok St, Kowloon Bay, Kowloon, China (Hong Kong)
Tel.: (852) 24873718
Web Site: http://www.rtx.dk
Sales Range: $25-49.9 Million
Emp.: 40
Wireless Telecommunications Equipment Mfr
N.A.I.C.S.: 334220

RUA GOLD INC.
915 700 West Pender Street, Vancouver, V6C 1G8, BC, Canada
Tel.: (604) 646-1553
RUA—(CNSX)
Assets: $5,824,635
Liabilities: $157,137
Net Worth: $5,667,499
Earnings: ($3,317,708)
Emp.: 4
Fiscal Year-end: 06/30/23
Mineral Exploration Services
N.A.I.C.S.: 213115
Robert Dubeau *(Pres & CEO)*

RUA LIFE SCIENCES PLC
163 Bath Street, Ayrshire, Glasgow, G2 4SQ, United Kingdom
Tel.: (44) 1294317073   UK
Web Site: https://www.rualifesciences.com
RUA—(AIM)
Rev.: $2,206,295
Assets: $10,353,973
Liabilities: $1,414,744
Net Worth: $8,939,228
Earnings: ($2,806,207)
Emp.: 38
Fiscal Year-end: 03/31/22
Biomedical Polymer Technology, Components & Medical Devices Developer
N.A.I.C.S.: 339112
William Donald Brown *(Chm)*

Subsidiaries:

RUA Medical Devices Limited (1)
2 Drummond Crescent Riverside Business Park, Irvine, KA11 5AN, Ayrshire, United Kingdom
Tel.: (44) 1294317073
Web Site: https://www.ruamedical.com
Medical Device Mfr
N.A.I.C.S.: 339112
Lachlan Smith *(CFO)*

RUAG HOLDING AG
Stauffacherstrasse 65, 3000, Bern, Switzerland
Tel.: (41) 313766450   CH
Web Site: http://www.ruag.com
Year Founded: 1999
Rev.: $2,062,609,280
Assets: $1,920,502,400
Liabilities: $859,849,600
Net Worth: $1,060,652,800
Earnings: ($25,744,000)
Emp.: 9,091
Fiscal Year-end: 12/31/19

Holding Company
N.A.I.C.S.: 551112
Urs Kiener *(Co-CEO & Co-CFO)*

Subsidiaries:

Clearswift Limited (1)
1310 Waterside Arlington Business Park, Theale, Reading, RG7 4SA, United Kingdom
Tel.: (44) 1189038903
Web Site: http://www.clearswift.com
Computer Security Software
N.A.I.C.S.: 513210
Ciaran Rafferty *(Mng Dir)*

Subsidiary (Non-US):

Clearswift (Asia/Pacific) Pty Ltd (2)
Hub Hyde Park 223 Liverpool Street, Darlinghurst, Sydney, 2010, NSW, Australia
Tel.: (61) 2 9424 1200
Web Site: http://www.clearswift.com
Computer Security Software
N.A.I.C.S.: 513210

Subsidiary (US):

Clearswift Corporation (2)
309 Fellowship Rd Ste 200, Mount Laurel, NJ 08054
Tel.: (856) 359-2360
Web Site: http://www.clearswift.com
Computer Security Software Mfr
N.A.I.C.S.: 513210

Subsidiary (Non-US):

Clearswift GmbH (2)
Hinter Hoben 149, 53129, Bonn, Germany
Tel.: (49) 22892939350
Web Site: http://www.clearswift.com
Computer Security Software Services
N.A.I.C.S.: 513210

Clearswift K.K. (2)
Shinjuku Park Tower N30th Floor 3-7-1 Nishi-Shinjuku, Shinjuku-ku, Tokyo, 163-1030, Japan
Tel.: (81) 35326 3470
Web Site: http://www.clearswift.com
Computer Security Software
N.A.I.C.S.: 513210

GAVAP SAS (1)
Chemin Jean Thomas, BP8, 81150, Terssac, Finland
Tel.: (358) 5 63 48 04 04
Web Site: http://www.gavap.com
Shooting Equipment Mfr
N.A.I.C.S.: 332992

Gluckauf Logistik GmbH & Co. (1)
Landgraf-Karl-Strasse 1, 34131, Kassel, Germany
Tel.: (49) 561 93579 0
Web Site: http://www.glueckauf-logistik.de
Automobile Parts Mfr
N.A.I.C.S.: 336390

RUAG Aerospace Services GmbH (1)
Sonderflughafen Oberpfaffenhofen, Claude-Dornier-Strasse, Wessling, 82230, Germany
Tel.: (49) 8153300
Electronic Product Distr
N.A.I.C.S.: 423690
Stephanie Fehr *(Acct Mgr)*

RUAG Ammotec AG (1)
Uttigenstrasse 67, 3602, Thun, Switzerland   (100%)
Tel.: (41) 338544400
Web Site: http://www.ruag.com
Sales Range: $125-149.9 Million
Ammunition Mfr & Marketer
N.A.I.C.S.: 332992

Subsidiary (Non-US):

Norma Precision AB (2)
Jagargatan, 670 40, Amotfors, Sweden
Tel.: (46) 571 315 00
Web Site: http://www.norma-ammunition.com
Shooting Equipment Mfr
N.A.I.C.S.: 332992
Paul-Erik Toivo *(CEO)*

RUAG Ammotec Austria GmbH (2)
IZ NO-Sud Strasse 7 Obj 58D, 2355, Wiener Neudorf, Austria
Tel.: (43) 2236 677735
Web Site: http://www.ruag-ammotec.at
Electronic Product Distr
N.A.I.C.S.: 423690

RUAG Ammotec Benelux B.V.B.A. (2)
Kapelleveldstraat 18, 2530, Boechout, Belgium
Tel.: (32) 3 455 7508
Web Site: http://www.ruag.be
Electronic Product Distr
N.A.I.C.S.: 423690
Serge Warreyn *(Sr Mgr-Sls & Logistics)*

RUAG Ammotec France S.A.S. (2)
47 Avenue des Genottes, 95803, Cergy, France
Tel.: (33) 134 35 15 90
Web Site: http://ruag-ammotec.fr
Electronic Product Distr
N.A.I.C.S.: 423690

RUAG Ammotec GmbH (2)
Kronacherstrasse 63, 90765, Furth, Germany
Tel.: (49) 911 7930 0
Web Site: http://www.ruag.com
Electronic Product Distr
N.A.I.C.S.: 423690

RUAG Ammotec UK Ltd. (2)
Upton Cross, Cornwall, Liskeard, PL14 5BQ, United Kingdom
Tel.: (44) 1579 362319
Web Site: http://www.ruag.co.uk
Electronic Product Distr
N.A.I.C.S.: 423690
Charlie Lucas *(Mgr-Mktg)*

Subsidiary (US):

RUAG Ammotec USA Inc. (2)
5402 E Diana St, Tampa, FL 33610
Tel.: (813) 626-0077
Web Site: http://www.ruag.com
Emp.: 15
Electronic Product Distr
N.A.I.C.S.: 423690

Subsidiary (Non-US):

RUAG Hungarian Ammotec Inc. (2)
Belso Gyartelep 1002/35 hrsz, PO Box 9, Sirok, 3332, Eger, Hungary
Tel.: (36) 36 561 303
Web Site: http://www.ruag.com
Emp.: 300
Electronic Product Distr
N.A.I.C.S.: 423690

RUAG Aviation AG (1)
Schiltwald, PO Box 301, 6032, Emmen, Switzerland   (100%)
Tel.: (41) 412683801
Web Site: http://www.ruag.com
Aircraft, Spacecraft & Missle System Product Developer, Mfr, Installation & Maintenance Services
N.A.I.C.S.: 336413
Philipp M. Berner *(CEO)*

Subsidiary (Non-US):

RUAG Australia Pty Ltd (2)
836 Mountain Highway, Bayswater, 3153, VIC, Australia
Tel.: (61) 3 9721 1300
Web Site: http://www.ruag.com.au
Emp.: 130
Electronic Product Distr
N.A.I.C.S.: 423690
Paul Pingnam *(Head-Programs)*

Branch (Domestic):

RUAG Australia (3)
836 Mountain Highway, Airport West, Bayswater, 3153, VIC, Australia   (100%)
Tel.: (61) 397211300
Web Site: http://www.ruag.com.au
Emp.: 40
Aircraft Maintenance Repair & Overhaul Services
N.A.I.C.S.: 488190
Aidan Butler-Bonnice *(Mgr)*

RUAG Components AG (1)
Industrial Zone Schachenwald, CH-6460, Altdorf, Switzerland   (100%)

Tel.: (41) 418757218
Web Site: http://www.ruag.com
Sales Range: $150-199.9 Million
Emp.: 400
Industrial & Mechanical Components Mfr
N.A.I.C.S.: 332999

RUAG Defence Deutschland GmbH (1)
Feldstrasse 156, 22880, Wedel, Germany
Tel.: (49) 410393950
Web Site: http://www.ruag.com
Electronic Product Distr
N.A.I.C.S.: 423690

RUAG Electronics AG (1)
Stauffacherstrasse 65, 3000, Bern, 3000, Switzerland   (100%)
Tel.: (41) 313766666
Web Site: http://www.ruag.com
Sales Range: $125-149.9 Million
Emp.: 500
Training, Communications & Integrated Data Technologies Developer & Mfr
N.A.I.C.S.: 334290

RUAG Land Systems AG (1)
Allmendstrasse 86, CH-3602, Thun, Switzerland   (100%)
Tel.: (41) 332282111
Web Site: http://www.ruag.com
Sales Range: $250-299.9 Million
Emp.: 600
Military Weapon Systems, Vehicles & Equipment Developer & Mfr
N.A.I.C.S.: 336992

RUAG Schweiz AG (1)
Seetalstrasse 175, 6032, Emmen, Switzerland
Tel.: (41) 31 376 64 50
Web Site: http://www.ruag.com
Electronic Product Distr
N.A.I.C.S.: 423690

RUAG Space AG (1)
Schaffhauserstrasse 580, 8052, Zurich, Switzerland
Tel.: (41) 44 306 22 11
Electronic Product Distr
N.A.I.C.S.: 423690

Subsidiary (Non-US):

RUAG Space AB (2)
Solhusgatan 11, Gothenburg, 40515, Sweden
Tel.: (46) 317350000
Web Site: http://www.ruag.com
Sales Range: $1-9.9 Million
Emp.: 380
Aerospace Computer System, Antenna & Microwave Electronics Mfr
N.A.I.C.S.: 334511
Mats Warstedt *(Sr VP-Electronics)*

RUAG Space GmbH (2)
Stachegasse 16, 1120, Vienna, Austria
Tel.: (43) 1801990
Web Site: http://www.space.at
Sales Range: $50-74.9 Million
Aerospace Electronic System, Thermal Hardware & Ground Support Equipment Mfr
N.A.I.C.S.: 334511

Subsidiary (US):

RUAG Space USA (2)
6870 W 52nd Ave Ste 110, Denver, CO 80002
Tel.: (720) 318-3949
Electronic Product Distr
N.A.I.C.S.: 423690
Patrick McKenzie *(Exec Dir-Bus Dev)*

RUBBER LEAF INC.
Qixing Road Weng'ao Industrial Zone, Chunhu Subdistrict Fenghua District, Ningbo, Zhejiang, China
Tel.: (86) 57488733850   NV
Year Founded: 2021
Rev.: $10,648,175
Assets: $18,754,876
Liabilities: $17,931,005
Net Worth: $823,871
Earnings: $757,381
Emp.: 53
Fiscal Year-end: 12/31/22

RUBBER LEAF INC.

Rubber Leaf Inc.—(Continued)

Rubber Products Mfr
N.A.I.C.S.: 326299
Hua Wang (CFO)

RUBBER RESOURCES HOLDING N.V.
Agro Business Park 48, NL-6708 PW, Wageningen, Netherlands
Tel.: (31) 534888888 **NI**
Year Founded: 1908
Holding Company
N.A.I.C.S.: 551112
Jaap Van Schaik (Gen Dir)

Subsidiaries:

Rubber Resources B.V. (1)
Tel.: (31) 433290444
Web Site: https://www.rubber-resources.com
Sales Range: $10-24.9 Million
Emp.: 85
Rubber Recycling Services
N.A.I.C.S.: 562920

Subsidiary (Non-US):

Rubber Resources S.A. (Pty) Ltd. (2)
PO Box 17109, Alberton, 1457, Randhart, South Africa
Tel.: (27) 118641720
Rubber Recycling Services
N.A.I.C.S.: 562920

RUBBERLINE PRODUCTS LTD.
81 Bleams Road, Kitchener, N2C 2G2, ON, Canada
Tel.: (519) 894-0400
Web Site: http://www.rubberline.com
Year Founded: 1967
Rev.: $21,040,678
Emp.: 70
Industrial Product Distr
N.A.I.C.S.: 423840
Gary Meyer (Gen Mgr)

RUBEAN AG
Tel.: (49) 89357560
Web Site: https://www.rubean.com
R1B—(EUR)
Emp.: 34
Software Development Services
N.A.I.C.S.: 541511
Hermann Geupel (Chm & CEO)

RUBELLITE ENERGY CORP.
Suite 3200 605 5 Avenue SW, Calgary, T2P 3H5, AB, Canada
Tel.: (403) 269-4400 **AB**
Web Site: https://www.rubelliteenergy.com
Year Founded: 2021
RBY—(TSX)
Rev.: $36,388,388
Assets: $152,206,380
Liabilities: $33,223,110
Net Worth: $118,983,270
Earnings: $18,355,330
Fiscal Year-end: 12/31/22
Oil & Gas Exploration Services
N.A.I.C.S.: 237120
Marcello Rapini (VP)

Subsidiaries:

Perpetual Energy Inc. (1)
Suite 3200 605 5 Avenue SW, Calgary, T2P 3H5, AB, Canada
Tel.: (403) 269-4400
Web Site: https://www.perpetualenergyinc.com
Rev.: $48,287,409
Assets: $184,536,096
Liabilities: $147,790,801
Net Worth: $36,745,294
Earnings: ($71,944,039)
Emp.: 56
Fiscal Year-end: 12/31/2019
Natural Gas Exploration & Production
N.A.I.C.S.: 211130
Susan L. Riddell Rose (Pres & CEO)

Subsidiary (Domestic):

Perpetual Energy Operating Corp. (2)
605 5th Avenue SW Suite 3200, Calgary, T2P 3H5, AB, Canada (100%)
Tel.: (403) 269-4400
Web Site: http://www.perpetualenergyinc.com
Emp.: 150
Natural Gas Exploration, Drilling & Extraction Services
N.A.I.C.S.: 211130
Susan L. Riddell Rose (Pres & CEO)

RUBEX INTERNATIONAL FOR PLASTIC & ACRYLIC MANUFACTURING
87 Abdel Aziz Fahmy St Heliopolis Saint Fatima, Cairo, Egypt
Tel.: (20) 27756480
Web Site: http://www.rubexegypt.eg
Year Founded: 1987
RUBX.CA—(EGX)
Plastic & Acrylic Product Mfr
N.A.I.C.S.: 326199
Mokhtar Abdul Ghani Al Taher (Chm & Mng Dir)

RUBFILA INTERNATIONAL LTD.
New Industrial Development Area Kanjikode, Palakkad, 678621, Kerala, India
Tel.: (91) 4912567261
Web Site: https://www.rubfila.com
500367—(BOM)
Rev.: $55,596,343
Assets: $37,276,194
Liabilities: $7,052,035
Net Worth: $30,224,159
Earnings: $3,111,648
Emp.: 265
Fiscal Year-end: 03/31/23
Coated Rubber Thread Mfr
N.A.I.C.S.: 326299

Subsidiaries:

Premier Tissues India Limited (1)
Tel.: (91) 8043331500
Web Site: https://www.premiertissues.com
Tissue Mfr & Distr
N.A.I.C.S.: 322291

RUBICON ORGANICS, INC.
Suite 505 - 744 W Hastings, Vancouver, V6C 1A5, BC, Canada
Tel.: (604) 288-5566
Web Site: https://www.rubiconorganics.com
Year Founded: 2015
ROMJF—(OTCQX)
Assets: $30,438,202
Liabilities: $16,269,481
Net Worth: $14,168,722
Earnings: ($10,922,878)
Fiscal Year-end: 12/31/19
Pharmaceuticals Product Mfr
N.A.I.C.S.: 325412
Peter Doig (CEO)

RUBICON PARTNERS LIMITED
8-12 York Gate, London, NW1 4QG, United Kingdom
Tel.: (44) 2074990500 **UK**
Web Site: http://www.rubiconpartners.com
Sales Range: $25-49.9 Million
Emp.: 4
Privater Equity Firm
N.A.I.C.S.: 523999
Andrew Fischer (Partner)

Subsidiaries:

ABL-TECHNIC Entlackung GmbH (1)
Beim Hammerschmied 4-6, 88299, Leutkirch, Germany
Tel.: (49) 756182680
Web Site: http://www.abl-technic.de
Sales Range: $10-24.9 Million
Waste Management Services
N.A.I.C.S.: 562998
Stefan Jost (CEO)

Subsidiary (Non-US):

ABL-TECHNIC Bogensberger Ges.m.b.H. (2)
Eisenstrasse 7, 4502, Sankt Marien, Austria
Tel.: (43) 7229785990
Web Site: http://www.abl.at
Paint Stripping Services
N.A.I.C.S.: 238320

CMD, Ltd. (1)
Sycamore Road Eastwood Trading Est., Rotherham, S65 1EN, S Yorkshire, United Kingdom
Tel.: (44) 1709385485
Web Site: https://www.cmd-ltd.com
Commercial Lighting & Office Furniture System Developer & Mfr
N.A.I.C.S.: 337214
Jon Holding (Gen Mgr)

EnServe Group Limited (1)
8-12 York Gate, Wakefield, NW1 4QG, Leeds, United Kingdom
Tel.: (44) 8451642020
Web Site: http://www.enservegroup.com
Commercial, Public & Utilities Support Services
N.A.I.C.S.: 561499
Mark Perkins (CEO)

Subsidiary (Domestic):

Meter-U Limited (2)
159 Huddersfield Road, Oldham, OL1 3PA, United Kingdom
Tel.: (44) 8450505102
Web Site: http://www.meter-u.co.uk
Meter Reading Services
N.A.I.C.S.: 561499
Matthew Hardcastle (Mng Dir)

National Industrial Fuel Efficiency Limited (2)
Hawson Hubilee House 32 Duncan Close Moulton Park, Industrial Estate, Northampton, NN3 6WL, England, United Kingdom
Tel.: (44) 1619694901
Web Site: http://www.nifes.co.uk
Energy Management Services
N.A.I.C.S.: 541690
Douglas McNicol (Mng Dir & Member-Mgmt Bd)

The Freedom Group of Companies Limited (2)
Freedom House 3 Red Hall Avenue, Paragon Business Village, Wakefield, WF1 2UL, United Kingdom
Tel.: (44) 8451642400
Web Site: http://www.freedom-group.co.uk
Emp.: 1,000
Electrical Engineering Services
N.A.I.C.S.: 541330
Mark Perkins (CEO)

Rubicon Partners Industries LLP (1)
8-12 York Gate, London, NW1 4QG, United Kingdom
Tel.: (44) 20 7499 0500
Web Site: http://www.rubiconpartners.com
Investment Holding Company
N.A.I.C.S.: 551112

Holding (Non-US):

Metallwarenfabrik Gemmingen GmbH (2)
Industriestr 1, 75050, Gemmingen, Germany
Tel.: (49) 7267 806 0
Web Site: http://www.metallwarenfabrik.com
Electronic Components Mfr
N.A.I.C.S.: 335312

Holding (Domestic):

Stylex Auto Products Ltd. (2)

INTERNATIONAL PUBLIC

2 Atkinsons Way Foxhills Industrial Estate, Scunthorpe, DN15 8QJ, United Kingdom
Tel.: (44) 1724 272400
Web Site: http://www.stylex.co.uk
Automotive Products Mfr
N.A.I.C.S.: 336360
Ann Elwell (Mgr-Bus & Design)

Volvox Group (Leeds) Ltd. (2)
Gelderd Road, Leeds, LS12 6NA, United Kingdom
Tel.: (44) 113 213 7300
Web Site: http://www.volvox.uk.com
Lighting & Electrical Products for Transportation Industry
N.A.I.C.S.: 336999
Henry Bisson (Mgr-Press & Comm)

RUBICON PARTNERS S.A.
28 Emilii Plater Street 2th Floor, 00-688, Warsaw, Poland
Tel.: (48) 22 209 9800
Web Site: http://www.rubiconpartners.pl
Investment Bank Services
N.A.I.C.S.: 523150
Grzegorz Golec (Partner)

RUBICOR GROUP LIMITED
Level 24 68 Pitt Street, Sydney, 2000, NSW, Australia
Tel.: (61) 280610000
Web Site: http://www.rubicor.com.au
RUB—(ASX)
Rev.: $147,614,854
Assets: $22,062,891
Liabilities: $25,737,438
Net Worth: ($3,674,547)
Earnings: ($10,611,542)
Emp.: 250
Fiscal Year-end: 06/30/18
Recruitment & Temporary Staffing Services
N.A.I.C.S.: 561320
Sharad Loomba (CEO)

Subsidiaries:

Cadden Crowe (Queensland) Pty Limited (1)
Level 3 370 Queen Street, Brisbane, 4000, QLD, Australia
Tel.: (61) 7 3003 0466
Web Site: http://www.caddencrowe.com.au
Emp.: 5
Recruitment Services
N.A.I.C.S.: 561311

Cadden Crowe (Victoria) Pty Limited (1)
L 10 499 St Kilda Rd, Melbourne, 3004, VIC, Australia
Tel.: (61) 3 8506 2888
Emp.: 3
Recruitment Services
N.A.I.C.S.: 561311
Scott Roberts (Gen Mgr)

Care Direct Limited (1)
31J Railway Ave Alicetown, Lower Hutt, 5010, New Zealand
Tel.: (64) 800 424 227
Web Site: http://www.caredirect.co.nz
Emp.: 5
Health Care Srvices
N.A.I.C.S.: 622110
David Fleming (CEO)

Gaulter Russell NZ Limited (1)
Level 1 Gaulter Russell House 347 Parnell Road, PO Box 37 557, Parnell, Auckland, 1052, New Zealand
Tel.: (64) 9 529 2334
Web Site: http://www.gaulterrussel.co.nz
Emp.: 30
Recruitment Services
N.A.I.C.S.: 561311
Bob Walker (Mng Dir)

Gel Group Pty Limited (1)
Level 6 89 St Georges Terrace, Perth, 6000, WA, Australia
Tel.: (61) 8 9324 1411
Web Site: http://www.gelgroup.com.au
Recruitment Services
N.A.I.C.S.: 561311

AND PRIVATE COMPANIES

Juliet Magee *(Gen Mgr)*

James Gall & Associates Pty Limited (1)
80 Richmond Rd, Keswick, 5035, SA, Australia
Tel.: (61) 8 8297 5788
Web Site: http://www.jamesgall.com.au
Recruitment Services
N.A.I.C.S.: 561311
Craig Woodall *(Gen Mgr)*

Numero (NZ) Limited (1)
Level 1 347 Parnell Road, PO Box 137 279, Parnell, Auckland, 1052, New Zealand
Tel.: (64) 9 302 3810
Web Site: http://www.numero.co.nz
Emp.: 15
Recruitment Services
N.A.I.C.S.: 561311
Rachael Lewis-Green *(Dir-Ops)*

Rubicor (T1) Pty Limited (1)
Level 11 1 Alfred Street, Sydney, 2000, NSW, Australia
Tel.: (61) 2 8061 0000
Web Site: http://www.rubicor.com
Recruitment Services
N.A.I.C.S.: 561311

Rubicor SW Personnel Pty Limited (1)
101 Belmont Ave, Belmont, 6104, WA, Australia
Tel.: (61) 8 9479 4455
Web Site: http://www.swpersonnel.com.au
Recruitment Services
N.A.I.C.S.: 561311

Xpand Group Pty Limited (1)
Level 24 68 Pitt Street, Sydney, 2000, NSW, Australia
Tel.: (61) 280474000
Web Site: http://www.xpand.com.au
Recruitment Services
N.A.I.C.S.: 561311
Brenton Phillips *(Office Mgr)*

RUBIN A.D.
Nade Markovic 57, 37000, Krusevac, Serbia
Tel.: (381) 37 412 751
Web Site: http://www.rubin.rs
Year Founded: 1955
RUBN—(BEL)
Sales Range: $25-49.9 Million
Emp.: 340
Alcoholic & Non-Alcoholic Drink Mfr
N.A.I.C.S.: 312130
Zoran Bekric *(Mng Dir)*

RUBIS SCA
46 rue Boissiere, 75116, Paris, France
Tel.: (33) 144179595
Web Site: https://www.rubis.fr
Year Founded: 1990
RUI—(OTCIQ)
Rev.: $4,792,596,165
Assets: $6,053,523,316
Liabilities: $2,835,125,512
Net Worth: $3,218,397,804
Earnings: $364,669,369
Emp.: 4,142
Fiscal Year-end: 12/31/20
Petroleum & Other Liquid Products Storage & Distribution Services
N.A.I.C.S.: 424720
Olivier Heckenroth *(Chm-Supervisory Bd)*

Subsidiaries:

Alpha energies Renouvelables (1)
265 Chemin du derontet - ZA des 2B, 01360, Beligneux, France
Tel.: (33) 478065528
Web Site: https://alphaenergie.eu
Air Conditioning & Installation Services
N.A.I.C.S.: 238220

Easigas (Pty.) Ltd. (1)
Gate 5 Hibiscus Avenue Alrode Industrial, Alberton, Johannesburg, 1451, South Africa
Tel.: (27) 113897700
Web Site: https://easigas.com
Liquefied Petroleum Gas Whslr
N.A.I.C.S.: 424720

Electropalma (1)
R Afonso de Albuquerque 148 A - Deposito de Gas, 8100-234, Loule, Portugal
Tel.: (351) 289416527
Web Site: https://www.electropalma.pt
Gas Bottle Distr
N.A.I.C.S.: 424720

KenolKobil Limited (1)
5th Floor Avenue 5 Building Rose Avenue Off Lenana Road, PO Box 44202, 00100, Nairobi, Kenya
Tel.: (254) 703022000
Web Site: http://www.kenolkobil.com
Sales Range: $1-4.9 Billion
Petroleum Product Mfr.
N.A.I.C.S.: 211120
Martin Kimani *(Gen Mgr-Kenya)*

Subsidiary (Non-US):

Kobil Burundi SA (2)
205 Av Ruvyironza, Bujumbura, Burundi
Tel.: (257) 22244946
Petroleum Product Distr
N.A.I.C.S.: 424720

Kobil Ethiopia Limited (2)
Debre - Zeit Road Kabele 06, PO Box 2868, Kirkos Sub City, Addis Ababa, 1250, Ethiopia
Tel.: (251) 11 4674500
Sales Range: $25-49.9 Million
Emp.: 27
Petroleum Products Retailer
N.A.I.C.S.: 424710

Kobil Petroleum Rwanda SARL (2)
Plot No 5627 Byumba Rd, PO Box 6074, Gatsata, 2992, Kigali, Rwanda
Tel.: (250) 788183241
Web Site: http://www.kobil.com
Sales Range: $50-74.9 Million
Emp.: 54
Petroleum Product Distr
N.A.I.C.S.: 424720

Kobil Tanzania Limited (2)
Mafuta Road, PO Box 2238, Kurasini, Dar es Salaam, Tanzania
Tel.: (255) 222128846
Web Site: http://www.kobil.co.tz
Sales Range: $25-49.9 Million
Emp.: 27
Lubricant Distr
N.A.I.C.S.: 424720
Fabrice Ezavi *(Mng Dir)*

Maido (1)
31 Rue Gioffredo, 06000, Nice, France
Tel.: (33) 983047000
Web Site: https://www.restaurant-maido.fr
Restaurant & Bar Management Services
N.A.I.C.S.: 722515

Phoebus (1)
126 avenue du General Leclerc, 92100, Boulogne-Billancourt, France
Tel.: (33) 173286853
Web Site: https://www.phoebus.fr
House Maintenance Services
N.A.I.C.S.: 811490

Photosol (1)
40 - 42 Rue de la Boetie, 75008, Paris, France
Tel.: (33) 170225097
Web Site: https://www.photosol.fr
Power Generation Services
N.A.I.C.S.: 221118

RUBiS Energy Bermuda Ltd. (1)
2 Ferry Road, Saint Georges, GE 01, Bermuda (100%)
Tel.: (441) 2971577
Web Site: http://www.rubis-bermuda.com
Natural Gas Distribution
N.A.I.C.S.: 221210
Jermaine Simons *(Sls Mgr)*

Renewstable Barbados (1)
Hastings Business Centre 1st Floor Marine Gardens Hastings, Christ Church, BB15154, Barbados
Tel.: (246) 2343288
Web Site: https://www.renewstable-barbados.com
Power Generation Services
N.A.I.C.S.: 221111

Rubis Energy Kenya PLC (1)
Avenue 5 Building Rose Avenue Off Lenana Road, PO Box 44202, Kilimani, 00100, Nairobi, Kenya
Tel.: (254) 703022000
Web Site: https://rubiskenya.com
Petroleum Product Distr
N.A.I.C.S.: 424720

Rubis Energy Rwanda Ltd. (1)
KBC Building 4th Floor KN5 Road, BP 6074, Kimihurura, Kigali, Rwanda
Tel.: (250) 781826017
Web Site: https://rubisrwanda.com
Petroleum Product Distr
N.A.I.C.S.: 424720

Rubis Energy Uganda Ltd. (1)
Plot 4 Wankulukuku Road, PO Box 27478, Nalukolongo Industrial Area, Kampala, Uganda
Tel.: (256) 326211150
Web Site: https://rubisuganda.com
Petroleum Product Distr
N.A.I.C.S.: 424720

Rubis Energy Zambia Ltd. (1)
Plot No 1630 Malambo Road, PO Box 320089, Lusaka, Zambia
Tel.: (260) 630373340
Web Site: https://rubiszambia.com
Petroleum Product Distr
N.A.I.C.S.: 424720

Rubis Terminal SA (1)
33 avenue de Wagram, 75017, Paris, France (55%)
Tel.: (33) 153818620
Web Site: http://www.rubis-terminal.com
Sales Range: $300-349.9 Million
General Warehousing & Storage Facilities
N.A.I.C.S.: 493110

Division (Domestic):

Rubis Terminal (2)
65 Quai Jacoutot, 67000, Strasbourg, France
Tel.: (33) 388459010
Web Site: http://www.rubis-terminal.com
Petroleum & Petroleum Products Distr
N.A.I.C.S.: 424720

Societe Europeenne de Stockage (1)
28 rue de Rouen, Strasbourg, F 67000, France
Tel.: (33) 388618578
Sales Range: $25-49.9 Million
Emp.: 200
General Warehousing & Storage Facilities
N.A.I.C.S.: 493110

Societe Reunionnaise de Produits Petroliers (1)
BP 2015, 97824, Le Port, Reunion
Tel.: (262) 427708
Sales Range: $250-299.9 Million
Petroleum & Liquefied Petroleum Gas Products Distr
N.A.I.C.S.: 424720

Societe du depot de St Priest (1)
113 chemin du Charbonnier, 69800, Saint Priest, France
Tel.: (33) 472900969
Web Site: http://www.rubis-terminal.com
Sales Range: $25-49.9 Million
Non Metal Waste & Scrap Recycling
N.A.I.C.S.: 325612

Sodigas Braga Sociedade de Distribuicao de Gas, S.A. (1)
Rua Rio Mau N 6 Panoias, Panoias, 4700-760, Braga, Portugal
Tel.: (351) 253300270
Gas Bottle Distr
N.A.I.C.S.: 424720

Sodigas Seixal Sociedade de Distribuicao de Gas S.A. (1)
Av 23 de Julho de 1833 Flor da Mata, Fernao Ferro, 2840-263, Seixal, Portugal
Tel.: (351) 212260340
Gas Bottle Distr
N.A.I.C.S.: 424720

Spelta - Produtos Petroliferos S.A. (1)
Rua Achada Diogo Dias N 2 Sitio da Nogueira, Camacha, 9135-401, Madeira, Portugal
Tel.: (351) 291922223
Web Site: https://www.spelta.pt
Gas Exploration Services
N.A.I.C.S.: 213112

Stockbrest S.A. (1)
ZI Portuaire Saint Marc rue Alain Colas, Brest, France
Tel.: (33) 298801611
Sales Range: $25-49.9 Million
Emp.: 10
General Warehousing & Storage Facilities
N.A.I.C.S.: 493110

Territoires Energies Nouvelles (1)
20 boulevard Latour-Maubourg, 75007, Paris, France
Tel.: (33) 140621640
Web Site: http://www.territoire-energie.com
Power Generation Services
N.A.I.C.S.: 221111

Vitogaz (1)
Tour Franklin - 100 Terrasse Boieldieu, 92800, Puteaux, France
Tel.: (33) 149011010
Web Site: http://www.vitogaz.com
Sales Range: $50-74.9 Million
Petroleum & Petroleum Products Merchant Whslr
N.A.I.C.S.: 424720

RUBIX GROUP INTERNATIONAL LIMTIED
St Ann's House 1 Old Market Place, Knutsford, WA16 6PD, United Kingdom
Tel.: (44) 2070097000
Web Site: http://www.rubix-group.com
Year Founded: 1920
Sales Range: $1-4.9 Billion
Industrial Maintenance, Repair & Overhaul Products & Services
N.A.I.C.S.: 811198
Martin Gaarn Thomsen *(CEO)*

Subsidiaries:

Orexad SA (1)
61 Ave Tony Garnier, 69007, Lyon, France
Tel.: (33) 472801140
Web Site: http://www.orexad-groupe.com
Emp.: 2,400
Industrial & Technical Supplies Distr
N.A.I.C.S.: 423840
Franck Voisin *(Mng Dir)*

Subsidiary (Domestic):

Legoueix SAS (2)
185 Avenue Des Gresillons, Gennevilliers, 92635, France
Tel.: (33) 141323342
Web Site: http://www.legoueix.fr
Rev.: $11,800,000
Emp.: 22
N.A.I.C.S.: 423830

Rubix GmbH (1)
Scheiblerstr 3, Plattling, 94447, Bavaria, Germany
Tel.: (49) 99319600
Web Site: http://www.zitec-gruppe.com
Industrial Equipment & Supplies Distr
N.A.I.C.S.: 423830
Reinhard Banasch *(Chm)*

Subsidiary (Domestic):

Lerbs AG (2)
Handelshof 32, 28816, Stuhr, Germany
Tel.: (49) 42189920
Web Site: http://www.lerbs.de
Logistic Services
N.A.I.C.S.: 541614
Kai-Uwe Meyer *(COO)*

RUBIX RESOURCES LIMITED

RUBIX RESOURCES LIMITED
Level 11 216 St Georges Terrace, Perth, 6000, WA, Australia
Tel.: (61) 894810389   AU

RUBIX RESOURCES LIMITED

Rubix Resources Limited—(Continued)

Web Site:
https://www.rubixresources.com.au
Year Founded: 2021
RB6—(ASX)
Assets: $1,624,577
Liabilities: $127,926
Net Worth: $1,496,651
Earnings: ($934,248)
Fiscal Year-end: 06/30/23
Exploration & Mining Services
N.A.I.C.S.: 213115
Ben Smith *(Sec)*

RUBY CABLES LIMITED
15 G I D C Manjusar Taluka-Savli, Vadodara, 391 775, India
Tel.: (91) 2667264554
Web Site: http://www.rubycables.com
539836—(BOM)
Electrical Equipment Mfr & Distr
N.A.I.C.S.: 335929
Chirag Gada *(Chm, Mng Dir & Officer-Compliance)*

RUBY TEXTILE MILLS LIMITED
Room 203-Faiyaz Centre 2nd Floor 3-A SMCHS Shahrah-e-Faisal, Karachi, 74400, Pakistan
Tel.: (92) 2134396600 PK
Web Site:
https://www.rubytextile.com.pk
Year Founded: 1991
RUBY—(PSX)
Rev.: $44,244
Assets: $3,473,101
Liabilities: $905,933
Net Worth: $2,567,168
Earnings: ($216,827)
Emp.: 27
Fiscal Year-end: 06/30/23
Cotton Yarn Mfr
N.A.I.C.S.: 313110
Noor Elahi *(Co-Chm & CEO)*

RUBYCON CORPORATION
1938-1 Nishi-Minowa, Ina, 399-4593, Nagano, Japan
Tel.: (81) 265727111
Web Site: http://www.rubycon.co.jp
Year Founded: 1952
Emp.: 695
Aluminum Electrolytic Capacitors & Switching Power Supply Unit Mfr
N.A.I.C.S.: 334416
Koichi Sato *(Pres & CEO)*

Subsidiaries:

Rubycon America Inc. (1)
4293 Lee Ave, Gurnee, IL 60031-2140
Tel.: (847) 249-3450
Web Site: http://www.rubycon.com
Sales Range: $25-49.9 Million
Emp.: 11
Distr of Electronic Parts & Equipment
N.A.I.C.S.: 423690

Rubycon International (Shanghai) Co., Ltd. (1)
Rm 1307 New Town Center No83 Lou Shan Guan Road, Shanghai, 200336, China
Tel.: (86) 21 6236 9786
Aluminum Electrolytic Capacitor Distr
N.A.I.C.S.: 423690

Rubycon International (Thailand) Co., Ltd. (1)
11th Floor Sitthivorakit Bld 5 Soi Pipat SilomRoad, Bangkok, 10500, Thailand
Tel.: (66) 2 266 8359
Aluminum Electrolytic Capacitor Distr
N.A.I.C.S.: 423690

Rubycon Korea Co., Ltd. (1)
Leaders Tower 301 60-15 Kasan-Dong, Kumcheon-ku, Seoul, Korea (South)
Tel.: (82) 2 855 8127
Aluminum Electrolytic Capacitor Distr
N.A.I.C.S.: 423690

Rubycon Singapore Pte., Ltd. (1)
2 Jurong East Street 21 IMM Building 05-36, Singapore, 609601, Singapore
Tel.: (65) 6472 2466
Aluminum Electrolytic Capacitor Distr
N.A.I.C.S.: 423690

RUBYTECH CORP.
3F No 1 Ln 50 Sec 3 Nangang Rd, Nangang Dist, Taipei, 115, Taiwan
Tel.: (886) 227853961
Web Site:
https://www.rubytech.com.tw
Year Founded: 1981
8048—(TPE)
Rev.: $33,902,354
Assets: $43,719,882
Liabilities: $10,305,850
Net Worth: $33,414,032
Earnings: $4,134,321
Fiscal Year-end: 12/31/22
Networking Equipment Mfr & Distr
N.A.I.C.S.: 334118
Lin Kuan-Ming *(Chm)*

RUCHI INFRASTRUCTURE LTD
101 The Horizon 1st Floor Nath Mandir Road, 11/5 South Tukoganj, Indore, 452 001, Madhya Pradesh, India
Tel.: (91) 7314755209
Web Site:
https://www.ruchiinfrastructure.com
Year Founded: 1984
RUCHINFRA—(NSE)
Rev.: $8,805,943
Assets: $50,480,621
Liabilities: $34,527,498
Net Worth: $15,953,124
Earnings: ($723,737)
Emp.: 134
Fiscal Year-end: 03/31/21
Storage & Transportation of Edible Oils, Petroleum, Liquid Bulk Chemicals & Agricultural Products
N.A.I.C.S.: 493130
Ashish Mehta *(Compliance Officer & Sec)*

RUCHIRA PAPERS LTD.
Trilokpur Road Kala-Amb, Sirmaur, Shimla, 173030, Himachal Pradesh, India
Tel.: (91) 8053800897
Web Site:
https://www.ruchirapapers.com
532785—(BOM)
Rev.: $96,451,568
Assets: $60,948,145
Liabilities: $15,330,196
Net Worth: $45,617,949
Earnings: $8,108,267
Emp.: 1,025
Fiscal Year-end: 03/31/23
Paper Products Mfr
N.A.I.C.S.: 322299
Umesh Chander Garg *(Mng Dir)*

RUCHSER FENSTERBAU-MASCHINEN GMBH
Bahnhofstrasse 49, Brackenheim, 74336, Germany
Tel.: (49) 713598270
Web Site: http://www.ruchser.com
Rev.: $10,361,087
Emp.: 50
Windows Machinery Mfr
N.A.I.C.S.: 333120
Werner Ruchser *(Mgr-Sls)*

RUDEN HOLDINGS CO., LTD.
4F Mitsui Hanagiri Bldg 7-22-36 Nishi-Shinjuku, Shinjuku-Ku, Tokyo, 160-0023, Japan
Tel.: (81) 3 53325377
Web Site: http://www.ruden.jp

Year Founded: 2000
1400—(JAS)
Rev.: $25,419,680
Assets: $30,656,560
Liabilities: $4,326,960
Net Worth: $26,329,600
Earnings: $774,400
Fiscal Year-end: 12/31/20
Holding Company
N.A.I.C.S.: 551112
Nishioka Takashi *(Pres)*

RUDING A.D.
Trg D Mihajlovica 2, 76330, Ugljevik, Bosnia & Herzegovina
Tel.: (387) 55 771 758
Web Site: http://www.ruding.eu.pn
Sales Range: Less than $1 Million
Emp.: 25
Limestone Quarrying Services
N.A.I.C.S.: 212312

RUDISA HOLDING-MAATSCHAPPIJ N.V.
Ds Martin Luther Kingweg 8-9, PO Box 1648, Paramaribo, Suriname
Tel.: (597) 488 081
Web Site: http://www.rudisa.net
Year Founded: 1975
Sales Range: $250-299.9 Million
Emp.: 600
Holding Company Producer/Supplier of Various Consumer Products
N.A.I.C.S.: 551112
Dilip Kumar Sardjoe *(Owner & CEO)*

Subsidiaries:

GUCO N.V. (1)
Anton Dragtenweg 266, Paramaribo, Suriname
Tel.: (597) 458110
Web Site: http://www.rudisa.net
Sales Range: $50-74.9 Million
Emp.: 13
Apartment Rental Services
N.A.I.C.S.: 531110
Jane Mancodh *(Mng Dir)*

Mining Development Corporation N.V. (1)
Ds Martin Luther Kingweg 8-9, Paramaribo, Suriname
Tel.: (597) 488081
Web Site: http://www.rudisa.net
Sales Range: $350-399.9 Million
Emp.: 20
River Sand Mining Services
N.A.I.C.S.: 212321
Warsha Torilal-Sardjoe *(Mng Dir)*

Rudisa Agencies N.V. (1)
Abonestraat 66-68 Geyersvlijt, Paramaribo, Suriname
Tel.: (597) 551560
Sales Range: $75-99.9 Million
Emp.: 140
Grocery Import & Distr
N.A.I.C.S.: 424410
Gregory Kaersenhout *(Mgr-Sls-Personal Care)*

Rudisa Beverages & Juices N.V. (1)
Ds Martin Luther Kingweg 8-9, PO Box 1648, Paramaribo, Suriname
Tel.: (597) 485727
Web Site: http://www.rudisa.net
Sales Range: $25-49.9 Million
Emp.: 191
Beverage & Juice Mfr
N.A.I.C.S.: 312111
Dilip Sardjoe *(Founder & Chm)*

Rudisa Broadcasting, Communications & Publications N.V. (1)
Twee Kinderenweg 52-54, PO Box 1648, Paramaribo, Suriname
Tel.: (597) 551904
Web Site: http://www.surinametimes.com
Sales Range: $50-74.9 Million
Emp.: 120
Newspaper Publishers
N.A.I.C.S.: 513110
Dilip Sardjoe *(Owner)*

INTERNATIONAL PUBLIC

Rudisa Furniture (1)
Gemenelandsweg 98-100, PO Box 1648, Paramaribo, Suriname
Tel.: (597) 424547
Web Site: http://www.rudisa.net
Sales Range: $25-49.9 Million
Emp.: 18
Furniture Whslr
N.A.I.C.S.: 423210
Winston Makhanlal *(Mng Dir)*

Rudisa Jamaica Ltd. (1)
693 Spanish Town Road, Kingston, Jamaica
Tel.: (876) 765 9211
Grocery Import & Distr
N.A.I.C.S.: 424410

Rudisa Motor Company N.V. (1)
Hofstede Crull'laan/Mauriciusstraat 2, PO BOX 1648, Paramaribo, Suriname
Tel.: (597) 422791
Car Dealership & Repair Services
N.A.I.C.S.: 441110

Rudisa Shipping Company N.V. (1)
Ds Martin Luther Kingweg 8-9, Paramaribo, Suriname
Tel.: (597) 484094
Cargo Handling Services
N.A.I.C.S.: 488320

Suriname Cable and Communication Network N.V. (1)
Hofstede Crull'laan 38, Paramaribo, Suriname
Tel.: (597) 478153
Web Site: http://www.sccn.tv
Television Broadcasting Services
N.A.I.C.S.: 516120

Suriname Hout & Houtverwerking Industrie N.V. (1)
Highway Km 17 Perc No 358, PO Box 1648, Wanica, Suriname
Tel.: (597) 372233
Sales Range: $25-49.9 Million
Emp.: 35
Lumber Distr
N.A.I.C.S.: 423310

Waterland Cement Industry N.V. (1)
Dageraadweg 87, Paramaribo, Suriname
Tel.: (597) 484900
Cement Whslr
N.A.I.C.S.: 423320
Perkash Ramdjiawan *(Mgr)*

RUDNICI BANJANI
s Kuceviste, Cucer Sandevo, 1011, Skopje, North Macedonia
Tel.: (389) 22666021
Web Site: http://www.banjani.mk
BANA—(MAC)
Rev.: $1,325,276
Assets: $3,006,684
Liabilities: $99,900
Net Worth: $2,906,784
Earnings: $80,819
Emp.: 50
Fiscal Year-end: 12/31/23
Metal Exploration Services
N.A.I.C.S.: 213114

RUDNIK KAOLINA MOTAJICA A.D.
Kobas, 78420, Srbac, Bosnia & Herzegovina
Tel.: (387) 51 740 136
MTKS—(BANJ)
Sales Range: Less than $1 Million
Emp.: 5
Kaolin & Clay Mining Services
N.A.I.C.S.: 212323
Dragoljub Stankovic *(Chm)*

RUDNIK KOVIN U RESTRUKTURIRANJU A.D.
st Cara Lazar no 85, 26220, Kovin, Serbia
Tel.: (381) 13744014
Web Site: https://www.rudnikkovin.rs
Year Founded: 2005
RDKV—(BEL)
Rev.: $8,858,827

AND PRIVATE COMPANIES

Assets: $12,885,515
Liabilities: $2,599,705
Net Worth: $10,285,811
Earnings: $468,638
Emp.: 92
Fiscal Year-end: 12/31/23
Coal Mining Services
N.A.I.C.S.: 212115
Ivica Zarkov *(Exec Dir)*

RUDNIK MANGANA D.D.

Vrhovska bb, 77245, Buzim, Bosnia & Herzegovina
Tel.: (387) 37410118
RUMBR—(SARE)
Sales Range: Less than $1 Million
Emp.: 5
Manganese Mining Services
N.A.I.C.S.: 212290

RUDNIK SOLI TUZLA D.D.

Tusanj broj 66, 75000, Tuzla, Bosnia & Herzegovina
Tel.: (387) 3 532 1450
Web Site: http://www.rudniksoli.ba
RSTTR—(SARE)
Rev.: $8,375,337
Assets: $96,706,036
Liabilities: $8,564,523
Net Worth: $88,141,513
Earnings: $362,416
Emp.: 133
Fiscal Year-end: 12/31/20
Salt Mfr
N.A.I.C.S.: 325199

RUDNIK ZELJEZNE RUDE D.D. VARES

Rudarska br 1, Vares, Bosnia & Herzegovina
Tel.: (387) 32 843 030
RZRVR—(SARE)
Sales Range: Less than $1 Million
Emp.: 25
Iron Ore Mining Services
N.A.I.C.S.: 212210

RUDO A.D.

Bul Vojvode Putnika 7, 11000, Belgrade, Serbia
Tel.: (381) 112650299
Web Site: https://www.rudo.rs
Year Founded: 1919
RUDO—(BEL)
Rev.: $1,610,643
Assets: $3,306,781
Liabilities: $245,257
Net Worth: $3,061,524
Earnings: $107,096
Emp.: 50
Fiscal Year-end: 12/31/23
Medical Instrument Mfr
N.A.I.C.S.: 339112
Madid Pajic *(Mng Dir)*

RUDOLF ACHENBACH GMBH & CO KG

Hauptstrasse 106, 65843, Sulzbach, Germany
Tel.: (49) 6196600930
Web Site: http://www.achenbach.com
Year Founded: 1954
Rev.: $48,554,880
Emp.: 120
Food Products Mfr
N.A.I.C.S.: 311999
Rudolf Achenbach *(Founder & Pres)*

RUDOLF GROSSFURTNER GES.M.B.H. & CO

Hofmark 1, 4972, Utzenaich, Austria
Tel.: (43) 77517171
Web Site: http://www.grossfurtner.at
Year Founded: 1972
Rev.: $184,700,000
Emp.: 400
Meat Product Distr
N.A.I.C.S.: 424470
Rudolf Grossfurtner *(Gen Mgr)*

RUDOLF HAUFE VERLAG GMBH & CO. KG

Hindenburgstrasse 64, 79102, Freiburg, Germany
Tel.: (49) 796 3683 0
Publishing Services
N.A.I.C.S.: 513199
Isabel Blank *(Exec Dir)*

Subsidiaries:

Schaffer-Poeschel Verlag fur Wirtschaft. Steuern. Recht GmbH (1)
Reinsburgstr 27, 70178, Stuttgart, Germany (100%)
Tel.: (49) 711 2194 0
Web Site: http://www.schaeffer-poeschel.de
Sales Range: $25-49.9 Million
Emp.: 30
Trade & Professional Book Publishing Service
N.A.I.C.S.: 513130
Volker Dabelstein *(Mng Dir)*

RUDOLF ROST SPERRHOLZ GMBH

Lohe 4, 25462, Rellingen, Germany
Tel.: (49) 410159390
Web Site: http://www.rudolf-rost.de
Year Founded: 1969
Rev.: $13,660,854
Emp.: 20
Vehicle, Ship & Railcar Construction Component Mfr
N.A.I.C.S.: 336390
Volker Rost *(Gen Mgr)*

Subsidiaries:

Rudolf Rost Interiors GmbH (1)
Flugstrasse 8, 76532, Baden, Germany
Tel.: (49) 72219711966
Interior Design Services
N.A.I.C.S.: 541410
Volker Rost *(Co-CEO)*

RUDOLF WILD GMBH & CO. KG

Rudolf-Wild-Strasse 107-115, 69214, Eppelheim, Germany
Tel.: (49) 62217990 De
Year Founded: 1931
Sales Range: $150-199.9 Million
Emp.: 1,000
Flavors Or Flavoring Materials, Synthetic
N.A.I.C.S.: 325199
Hans-Peter Wild *(Owner & Chm-Mgmt Bd)*

Subsidiaries:

INDAG GmbH & Co. Betriebs KG (1)
Rudolf-Wild-Strasse 107-115, 69214, Eppelheim, Germany
Tel.: (49) 6221 799 0
Web Site: http://www.wild-indag.de
Food & Beverage Processing Machinery Developer & Mfr
N.A.I.C.S.: 333248
Carsten Kaisig *(Mng Dir)*

Rudolf Wild (Beijing) Food Ingredients Co., Ltd (1)
No 19 Zhonghe Street BDA, Beijing, 100176, China
Tel.: (86) 10 678 744 55
Dairy Products Distr
N.A.I.C.S.: 424430

WILD Amazon Flavors Concentrados e Corantes para bebidas LTDA. (1)
1695 Torquato Tapajos Avenue-Paz Flores, 69048-010, Manaus, Brazil
Tel.: (55) 92 3654 1532
Dairy Products Distr
N.A.I.C.S.: 424430

WILD Aseptics, LLC (1)
2924 Wyetta Dr, Beloit, WI 53511
Tel.: (608) 362-5012
Mint Oil Extraction Services
N.A.I.C.S.: 325998

WILD Dairy Ingredients GmbH (1)
Rudolf-Wild-Strasse 107-115, 69214, Eppelheim, Germany
Tel.: (49) 6221 799 0
Web Site: http://www.wild-fruit.com
Food Industry Fruit Processing & Ingredients Whslr
N.A.I.C.S.: 311411
Hans-Peter Voss *(Mng Dir)*

Subsidiary (Non-US):

WILD Polska Sp. z o.o. (2)
Karas 18C, 14 202, Ilawa, Poland
Tel.: (48) 89 648 6556
Web Site: http://www.wild-fruit.com
Emp.: 25
Flavoring Materials Whslr
N.A.I.C.S.: 424490

Plant (Domestic):

WILD Polska Sp. z o.o. - Mragowo Plant (3)
Zaklad Produkcyjny Mragowo Marcinkowo 127, 11-700, Mragowo, Poland
Tel.: (48) 89 741 95 01
Dairy Products Distr
N.A.I.C.S.: 424430

WILD Dairy Ingredients Nauen GmbH (1)
Berliner Str 119, 14641, Nauen, 14641, Germany
Tel.: (49) 3321 4484 0
Dairy Products Distr
N.A.I.C.S.: 424430

WILD Flavors Middle East FZE (1)
Jebel Ali Free Zone South, PO Box 261060, Dubai, United Arab Emirates
Tel.: (971) 4 8861618
Mint Oil Extraction Services
N.A.I.C.S.: 325998

WILD France S.A.S (1)
10 Rue Richard Dufour, PO Box 16, 76770, Le Houlme, France
Tel.: (33) 232 82 37 50
Dairy Products Distr
N.A.I.C.S.: 424430

WILD KK (1)
1-3 Shinminato, Mihama-ku, Chiba, Japan
Tel.: (81) 43 203 1871
Dairy Products Distr
N.A.I.C.S.: 424430

WILD Szymbark Sp. z o.o (1)
Kamionka, 14-200, Ilawa, Poland
Tel.: (48) 89 648 63 44
Dairy Products Distr
N.A.I.C.S.: 424430

Wild Flavors (Schweiz) AG (1)
Zipriostrabe 1, 4334, Sisseln, Switzerland
Tel.: (41) 62 866 60 60
Mint Oil Extraction Services
N.A.I.C.S.: 325998

RUDOLF-ERICH MULLER GMBH & CO KG

Reichenbacherstr 12, 97702, Bad Kissingen, Germany
Tel.: (49) 9733610
Web Site: http://www.remog.de
Rev.: $28,409,433
Emp.: 220
Engineering Machines Mfr
N.A.I.C.S.: 333517
Wilfried Muller *(Mng Partner)*

RUDRA GLOBAL INFRA PRODUCTS LIMITED

Plot No D-60 Rudra House, 2nd Floor Nr Ram Mantra Mandir, Bhavnagar, 364002, Gujarat, India
Tel.: (91) 8238041111
Web Site: https://www.rudratmx.com
Year Founded: 1991

539226—(BOM)
Rev.: $54,189,737
Assets: $37,433,799
Liabilities: $26,322,463
Net Worth: $11,111,336
Earnings: $1,664,205
Emp.: 129
Fiscal Year-end: 03/31/23
Steel Products Mfr
N.A.I.C.S.: 331110

RUDRABHISHEK ENTERPRISES LIMITED

820 Antriksh Bhawan 22 Kg Marg, New Delhi, 110001, India
Tel.: (91) 1141069500
Web Site: https://www.repl.global
Year Founded: 1992
REPL—(NSE)
Rev.: $10,139,670
Assets: $14,023,450
Liabilities: $3,049,860
Net Worth: $10,973,590
Earnings: $1,880,656
Emp.: 222
Fiscal Year-end: 03/31/21
Engineeering Services
N.A.I.C.S.: 541330
Pradeep Misra *(Chm & Mng Dir)*

Subsidiaries:

Rudrabhishek Infosystem Private Limited (1)
820 Antariksh Bhawan 22 KG Marg, New Delhi, 110001, India
Tel.: (91) 1141069500
Web Site: https://www.replinfosys.com
Software Development Services
N.A.I.C.S.: 541511

RUDSTROJ D.D. KAKANJ

Rudarska br 8, 72240, Kakanj, Bosnia & Herzegovina
Tel.: (387) 32 554 487
Web Site: http://www.rudstroj.ba
RUSTR—(SARE)
Sales Range: Less than $1 Million
Emp.: 147
Coal Mining Services
N.A.I.C.S.: 212115

RUEN HOLDING AD

Tel.: (359) 78550440
Web Site: https://ruen.elcomis.com
Year Founded: 1996
HRU—(BUL)
Sales Range: Less than $1 Million
Holding Company
N.A.I.C.S.: 551112

RUENTEX GROUP

14F 308 Bade Road Sec 2, Taipei, 10492, Taiwan
Tel.: (886) 281619888
Web Site: http://www.ruentex.com.tw
Holding Company
N.A.I.C.S.: 551112
Yen-Liang Yin *(Pres)*

Subsidiaries:

Nan Shan Life Insurance Company, Ltd. (1)
Nan Shan Life Insurance Bldg Sec 28th Fl, 144 Minchuan East Rd, Taipei, 11049, Taiwan
Tel.: (886) 225013333
Web Site: http://www.nanshanlife.com.tw
Sales Range: $1-4.9 Billion
Emp.: 4,100
Fire Insurance Services
N.A.I.C.S.: 524113
Ernest Chan *(Gen Mgr)*

Subsidiary (Domestic):

Nan Shan General Insurance Co., Ltd. (2)
18/F No 6 Section 1 Zhongxiao West Road, Zhongzheng District, Taipei, 10041, Taiwan

RUENTEX GROUP

Ruentex Group—(Continued)
Tel.: (886) 223161188
Web Site:
http://www.nanshangeneral.com.tw
Emp.: 200
Property & Casualty Insurance Products & Services
N.A.I.C.S.: 524126
Kianpiong Lim *(Gen Mgr)*

New Zone Fashion Limited (1)
Rm 322 Office Tower Beijing Hui No 58 East Xing'Long Ave, Beijing, China
Tel.: (86) 10 83914397
Web Site:
http://www.charlesriverfashion.com
Apparel Distr
N.A.I.C.S.: 424350

Ruentex Development Co., Ltd. (1)
11 F No 308 Section 2 Bade Road, Taipei, Taiwan
Tel.: (886) 81619888
Web Site: http://www.rt-develop.com.tw
Rev.: $895,788,476
Assets: $5,784,927,210
Liabilities: $2,455,566,312
Net Worth: $3,329,360,899
Earnings: $295,217,529
Emp.: 2,626
Fiscal Year-end: 12/31/2023
Real Estate Lending Services
N.A.I.C.S.: 531190
Tsang-Jiunn Jean *(Chm)*

Ruentex Engineering & Construction Co., Ltd. (1)
10F No 308 Sec 2 Bade Road, Taipei, 10492, Taiwan
Tel.: (886) 281619999
Web Site: http://www.rtc.com.tw
Rev.: $799,441,339
Assets: $726,441,841
Liabilities: $463,795,817
Net Worth: $262,646,024
Earnings: $6,919,280
Emp.: 486
Fiscal Year-end: 12/31/2022
Construction & Civil Engineering Services
N.A.I.C.S.: 237990
Shih-Syun Lai *(Chm)*

Ruentex Industries Limited (1)
13/F No 308 Section 2 Bade Road, Taipei, Taiwan
Tel.: (886) 81617999
Web Site: http://www.ruentex.com.tw
Sales Range: $250-299.9 Million
Textile Products Mfr
N.A.I.C.S.: 314999
Yee Fan Wong *(Chm)*

Ruentex Materials Co., Ltd. (1)
10/F No 308 Sec 2 Bade Road, Taipei, Taiwan
Tel.: (886) 281619999
Web Site: http://www.rtm.com.tw
Rev.: $138,183,171
Assets: $241,021,492
Liabilities: $159,724,744
Net Worth: $81,296,748
Earnings: $3,349,137
Emp.: 300
Fiscal Year-end: 12/31/2022
Cement & Mortar Mfr
N.A.I.C.S.: 327310

RUF GRUPPE
Rutistrasse 13, 8952, Schlieren, Switzerland
Tel.: (41) 447338111
Web Site: http://www.ruf.ch
Sales Range: $50-74.9 Million
Emp.: 200
Software Mfr
N.A.I.C.S.: 334610

Subsidiaries:

Ruf Deutschland GmbH (1)
Lise-Meitner-Strasse 5-9, 42119, Wuppertal, Germany
Tel.: (49) 202 31 713 128
Information Technology Consulting Services
N.A.I.C.S.: 541512

Ruf Diffusion SA (1)
Rue Des Champs-Lovats 21, Yverdon-les-Bains, 1400, Switzerland
Tel.: (41) 24 423 39 00
Sales Range: $25-49.9 Million
Emp.: 4
Information Technology Consulting Services
N.A.I.C.S.: 541512

RUFFER INVESTMENT CO., LTD.
80 Victoria Street, London, SW1E 5JL, United Kingdom
Tel.: (44) 2079638100
Web Site: https://www.ruffer.co.uk
Open-End Investment Funds
N.A.I.C.S.: 525910
Hamish Baillie *(Dir-Investment)*

RUFUS LEONARD
The Drill Hall 57 A Faringdon Rd, London, EC1M 3JB, United Kingdom
Tel.: (44) 20 740 44490
Web Site:
http://www.rufusleonard.com
Emp.: 130
Advetising Agency
N.A.I.C.S.: 541810
Neil Svensen *(CEO)*

RUGBY MINING LIMITED
Suite 1890 1075 West Georgia Street, Vancouver, V6E 3C9, BC, Canada
Tel.: (604) 688-4941   BC
Web Site:
https://www.rugbyresourcesltd.com
Year Founded: 2007
64O—(DEU)
Rev.: $7,551
Assets: $948,406
Liabilities: $176,424
Net Worth: $771,982
Earnings: ($2,615,271)
Fiscal Year-end: 02/29/24
Gold, Silver & Base Metals Mining & Exploration Services
N.A.I.C.S.: 212290
Bryce Gordon Roxburgh *(Pres & CEO)*

RUGVISTA GROUP AB
Ringugnsgatan 11, 216 16, Limhamn, Sweden
Tel.: (46) 406688104
Web Site:
https://www.rugvistagroup.com
Year Founded: 2005
RUG—(OMX)
Rev.: $58,839,944
Assets: $64,900,305
Liabilities: $18,665,143
Net Worth: $46,235,162
Earnings: $5,404,450
Emp.: 91
Fiscal Year-end: 12/31/22
Online Shopping Services
N.A.I.C.S.: 425120
Anders Matthiesen *(COO)*

Subsidiaries:

RugVista AB (1)
Ringugnsgatan 11, SE-216 16, Malmo, Sweden
Tel.: (46) 40182225
Web Site: https://www.rugvista.com
Emp.: 75
Online Rug Retailer
N.A.I.C.S.: 423220

RUHLE GMBH
Reichenbacherstr 12, Munnerstadt, 97702, Bad Kissingen, Germany
Tel.: (49) 9733610
Web Site: http://www.remog.de
Year Founded: 1966
Rev.: $37,539,941
Emp.: 220
Engineering Machines Mfr
N.A.I.C.S.: 541330

Wilfried Muller *(Mng Dir)*

RUHNN HOLDING LIMITED
11F Building 2 Lvgu Chuangzhi Development Center 788 Hong Pu Road, Jianggan District, Hangzhou, 310016, China
Tel.: (86) 571 2882 5222   Ky
Web Site: http://www.ruhnn.com
Year Founded: 2018
RUHN—(NASDAQ)
Rev.: $185,436,135
Assets: $205,212,698
Liabilities: $36,674,956
Net Worth: $168,537,742
Earnings: ($13,235,462)
Emp.: 779
Fiscal Year-end: 03/31/20
Holding Company
N.A.I.C.S.: 551112
Min Feng *(Co-Founder & Chm)*

RUI FENG GROUP HOLDINGS COMPANY LIMITED
Room 2404 24/F World-Wide House 19 Des Voeux Road, Central, China (Hong Kong)
Tel.: (852) 34231017   Ky
Web Site:
http://www.chinahanya.com.hk
Apparel Distr
N.A.I.C.S.: 424350

Subsidiaries:

Shining Securities Company Limited (1)
Room 9A CKK Commercial Centre 289-295 Hennessy Road, Wanchai, China (Hong Kong)
Tel.: (852) 39773333
Web Site: http://www.shiningsec.com
Securities Brokerage Services
N.A.I.C.S.: 523150

RUIA GROUP
46 Syed Amir Ali Avenue, Kolkata, 700017, West Bengal, India
Tel.: (91) 33 2289 4747
Web Site: http://www.ruiagroup.co.in
Holding Company
N.A.I.C.S.: 551112
Pawan K. Ruia *(Chm)*

Subsidiaries:

Dunlop Auto Tyres Pvt. Limited (1)
Bank of Baroda Building 7th Floor 16 Parliament Street, New Delhi, 110 001, India
Tel.: (91) 1164649950
Tiles Mfr
N.A.I.C.S.: 326199
J. K. Sharma *(VP-Mktg & Admin)*

Dunlop Polymers Pvt. Ltd. (1)
139 A B C - Belagola Industrial Area Metagalli Industrial Estate, Mysore, 570 016, Karnataka, India
Tel.: (91) 8212582449
Tiles Mfr
N.A.I.C.S.: 326199
Richa Bhagat *(Asst Mgr-F&A)*

Fibre Foam (Bombay) Pvt. Limited (1)
F-1 S T I C E Sinnar Nasik, 422 112, Nasik, Maharashtra, India
Tel.: (91) 2551240304
Rubber Mfr
N.A.I.C.S.: 326299

India Tyre & Rubber Co. (India) Ltd. (1)
Berger House 5th Floor 129 Park Street, Kolkata, 700017, West Bengal, India
Tel.: (91) 3322178775
Rubber Mfr
N.A.I.C.S.: 326299

Jessop & Company Ltd. (1)
21 & 22 Jessore Road, Kolkata, 700 028, India
Tel.: (91) 3325290139
Web Site: http://www.jessop.co.in

INTERNATIONAL PUBLIC

Engineering Equipment Mfr
N.A.I.C.S.: 334513
Ashok Agarwal *(VP)*

Monotona Tyres Ltd. (1)
Gut No 279 286 & 287 P Dakivli Village Bhiwandi Wada Road, Near Tansa River Taluka Wada Dist, Thane, 421 312, Maharashtra, India
Tel.: (91) 2526645010
Web Site: http://www.monotona.com
Tiles Mfr
N.A.I.C.S.: 326199
Sakchi Ruia *(Exec Dir)*

Ruia Global Fasteners AG (1)
Augustenthaler Strasse 87, 56567, Neuwied, Germany
Tel.: (49) 26315010
Sales Range: $100-124.9 Million
Emp.: 2,030
Bolts, Nuts, Screws, Rivets & Washers Mfr
N.A.I.C.S.: 332722

RUICHENG CHINA MEDIA GROUP LIMITED
Room 201 2/F Building C1 Phase II Dongyi International Media Industry, Park No 8 Gaojing Cultural Park Road Chaoyang, Beijing, China
Tel.: (86) 1085769398   Ky
Web Site: http://www.reach-ad.com
Year Founded: 2003
1640—(HKG)
Rev.: $57,937,324
Assets: $80,612,766
Liabilities: $51,672,956
Net Worth: $28,939,810
Earnings: ($1,637,345)
Emp.: 25
Fiscal Year-end: 12/31/22
Digital Marketing Services
N.A.I.C.S.: 541840
Zi Lin *(Deputy Gen Mgr)*

RUIDA FUTURES CO., LTD.
26-29F No 18 Taoyuan Road, Siming, Xiamen, 361000, Fujian, China
Tel.: (86) 5922681653
Web Site: http://www.rdqh.com
Year Founded: 1993
002961—(SSE)
Rev.: $295,646,022
Assets: $2,206,964,785
Liabilities: $1,847,932,150
Net Worth: $359,032,635
Earnings: $41,221,454
Fiscal Year-end: 12/31/22
Investment Brokerage Services
N.A.I.C.S.: 524210
Zhibin Lin *(Chm)*

RUIFENG POWER GROUP COMPANY LIMITED
No 69 Taishan East Road, Hengshui, Hebei, China
Tel.: (86) 3183312629   Ky
Web Site: http://www.hbsgt.com
2025—(HKG)
Rev.: $84,308,375
Assets: $225,202,442
Liabilities: $86,974,150
Net Worth: $138,228,293
Earnings: $2,865,845
Emp.: 816
Fiscal Year-end: 12/31/22
Automotive Parts Mfr & Distr
N.A.I.C.S.: 336310
Lianzhou Meng *(Co-Founder, Chm & CEO)*

RUILI GROUP CO., LTD.
No 2666 Development Zone Avenue Ruian Economic Development Zone, Ruian, China
Tel.: (86) 577 65609900
Web Site: http://www.sorl.com.cn
Auto Parts Mfr
N.A.I.C.S.: 336340

Subsidiaries:

SORL Auto Parts, Inc. (1)
No 2666 KaiFaqu Avenue Ruili Industry Area, Ruian, 325200, Zhejiang, China
Tel.: (86) 57765008000
Web Site: http://www.sorl.cn
Rev.: $540,188,479
Assets: $817,721,344
Liabilities: $587,742,345
Net Worth: $229,978,999
Earnings: $25,413,931
Emp.: 6,756
Fiscal Year-end: 12/31/2019
Commercial Vehicle Air Brake Valves & Related Components Mfr & Distr
N.A.I.C.S.: 336390
Xiao Ping Zhang *(Chm & CEO)*

RUITAI MATERIALS TECHNOLOGY CO., LTD.
Bldg 27 Compound 1 Wuliqiao 1st street, Chaoyang District, Beijing, 100024, China
Tel.: (86) 1057987988
Web Site: https://www.bjruitai.com
002066—(SSE)
Rev.: $645,977,791
Assets: $572,821,548
Liabilities: $405,378,339
Net Worth: $167,443,209
Earnings: $4,250,045
Fiscal Year-end: 12/31/20
Refractory Material Mfr
N.A.I.C.S.: 327120

Subsidiaries:

Ningguo Kaiyuan Electrical power wear resistant materials CO., Ltd (1)
HeLi Industrial Zone In NingGuo Economic Technical, Ningguo, 242300, Anhui, China
Tel.: (86) 5634309019
Web Site: http://www.kysteeleaalls.com
Emp.: 300
Corrugated Packaging Material Mfr
N.A.I.C.S.: 322211
Defa Wang *(Gen Mgr)*

RUIXIN INTERNATIONAL HOLDINGS LIMITED
Room A 10th Floor Times Media Centre, 133 Wan Chai Road, Hong Kong, China (Hong Kong)
Tel.: (852) 21103618
0724—(HKG)
Rev.: $24,574,478
Assets: $7,735,425
Liabilities: $21,330,623
Net Worth: ($13,595,198)
Earnings: ($7,417,695)
Emp.: 34
Fiscal Year-end: 12/31/22
Wireless & Networking Services
N.A.I.C.S.: 517112
Yat Keung Lam *(Exec Dir)*

Subsidiaries:

Fast Harvest Limited (1)
Rm 2605-2609 CCT Telecom Bldg 11 Wo Shing St, Fotan, Sha Tin, New Territories, China (Hong Kong)
Tel.: (852) 26888100
Web Site: http://www.sentech.com.hk
Management Services
N.A.I.C.S.: 561110

Semtech Electronics Limited (1)
12-18 Baiye Cheng Rd Shang Tun Indus Zone, Liaobu, Dongguan, 523416, Guangdong, China
Tel.: (86) 76983302928
Semiconductors Mfr & Distr
N.A.I.C.S.: 334413

RULLION LIMITED
Trafalgar House 110 Manchester Road, Altrincham, WA14 1FG, Cheshire, United Kingdom
Tel.: (44) 16 1926 1717
Web Site: http://www.rullion.co.uk
Year Founded: 1978
Sales Range: $400-449.9 Million
Emp.: 1,327
Human Resource Consulting Services
N.A.I.C.S.: 541612
Laura Hyde *(Controller-Credit)*

RULQUIN DISTRIBUTION
Pole Des Sablons Chemin De Custines, Millery, Givors, 54670, Meurthe Et Moselle, France
Tel.: (33) 383848586
Sales Range: $25-49.9 Million
Emp.: 97
Toilet Preparations
N.A.I.C.S.: 325620
Juan Cuellar *(Mgr-DP)*

RUM GROUP FOR TRANSPORTATION & TOURISM INVESTMENT P.L.C.
Airport St - Close to Maa daba Bridge, PO Box 921513, Amman, 11192, Jordan
Tel.: (962) 64290333
Web Site: http://www.rumgroup.com
Year Founded: 2002
RUMM—(AMM)
Rev.: $1,704,295
Assets: $40,636,446
Liabilities: $11,703,103
Net Worth: $28,933,343
Earnings: ($1,821,654)
Emp.: 49
Fiscal Year-end: 12/31/20
Tour Operating Services
N.A.I.C.S.: 561520

RUMAH & CO. PTE. LTD.
1 Lorong 2 Toa Payoh Braddell House, Singapore, 319637, Singapore
Tel.: (65) 6 351 1000
Web Site: https://www.rumahgroup.com
Emp.: 100
Investment Services
N.A.I.C.S.: 523999

Subsidiaries:

GYP Properties Limited (1)
1 Lorong 2 Toa Payoh Braddell House, Singapore, 319637, Singapore (93.11%)
Tel.: (65) 6 351 1000
Web Site: http://www.gypproperties.com
Rev.: $37,935,733
Assets: $136,371,741
Liabilities: $82,291,730
Net Worth: $54,080,011
Earnings: $1,478,231
Fiscal Year-end: 06/30/2021
Telephone Directories Publishing Services
N.A.I.C.S.: 323111
Stanley Poh Ieng Tan *(CEO)*

Subsidiary (Non-US):

Global YP Sdn Bhd (2)
Unit 6.02 Level 6 Menara Mexisegar Jalan Pandan Indah 4/2, 55100, Kuala Lumpur, Malaysia
Tel.: (60) 342512288
Web Site: http://www.yps.com.sg
Sales Range: $25-49.9 Million
Emp.: 10
Business Directory Publisher
N.A.I.C.S.: 513140

Pakuranga Plaza Limited (2)
10 Aylesbury St, Pakuranga, Auckland, 2010, New Zealand
Tel.: (64) 99789100
Web Site: http://www.pakurangaplaza.co.nz
Property Investment Services
N.A.I.C.S.: 531390
Matt Mihalicz *(Mgr-Facilities)*

Subsidiary (Domestic):

SG Innovation Hub Pte. Ltd. (2)
33 Ubi Avenue 3 02-12 Vertex Building, Singapore, 408868, Singapore
Tel.: (65) 62211157
Web Site: http://www.innovativehub.com.sg
Ecommerce Services
N.A.I.C.S.: 541511
Zoe Zuo *(Mng Dir)*

Singapore Information Services Pte Ltd (2)
1 Lorong 2 Toa Payoh Yellow Pages Building, Singapore, 319637, Singapore
Tel.: (65) 63568080
Web Site: http://www.insis.com.sg
Online Directory Publishing Services
N.A.I.C.S.: 513140

RUMATRANS A.D.
Industrijska bb, Ruma, Serbia
Tel.: (381) 22 478 455
Year Founded: 1956
RMTR—(BEL)
Sales Range: $1-9.9 Million
Emp.: 94
Food Transportation Services
N.A.I.C.S.: 484121
Slobodan Borovica *(Gen Mgr)*

RUMBLE RESOURCES INC.
503 905 West Pender Street, Vancouver, V6C 1L6, BC, Canada
Tel.: (604) 377-8758 BC
Year Founded: 2017
RTRFF—(OTCIQ)
Assets: $232,198
Liabilities: $73,055
Net Worth: $159,143
Earnings: ($74,771)
Fiscal Year-end: 07/31/22
Mineral Mining Services
N.A.I.C.S.: 213115
Erwin Wong *(CFO)*

RUMBLE RESOURCES LIMITED
Level 1 16 Ord St, West Perth, 6005, WA, Australia
Tel.: (61) 865553980
Web Site: https://www.rumbleresources.com
RTR—(ASX)
Rev.: $749,080
Assets: $43,587,799
Liabilities: $1,105,686
Net Worth: $42,482,113
Earnings: ($563,365)
Fiscal Year-end: 06/30/21
Metal Mining Services
N.A.I.C.S.: 212290
Shane Sikora *(Mng Dir)*

RUMERE CO., LTD.
Room 2901 Building A Shimao Business Center Plaza, No 11 Minjiang East Road, Changshu, 215500, Jiangsu, China
Tel.: (86) 51253969003
Web Site: https://www.rumere.com
Year Founded: 2012
301088—(CHIN)
Rev.: $133,212,924
Assets: $380,913,624
Liabilities: $20,301,840
Net Worth: $360,611,784
Earnings: $23,452,416
Fiscal Year-end: 12/31/22
Apparel Product Mfr & Distr
N.A.I.C.S.: 315990
Jian Guo *(Chm)*

RUMO MALHA NORTE SA
Av Historiador Rubens Mendonca 2000 Saude, Cuiaba, 78050000, MT, Brazil
Tel.: (55) 4121417369
FRRN5B—(BRAZ)
Rev.: $1,047,283,002
Assets: $1,397,470,512
Liabilities: $870,710,011
Net Worth: $526,760,502
Earnings: $239,120,317
Fiscal Year-end: 12/31/23
Railway Transportation Services
N.A.I.C.S.: 488210
Ricardo Lewin *(CFO & Dir-IR)*

RUN LONG CONSTRUCTION CO., LTD.
8F No 267 Lequn 2nd Road, Zhongshan Dist, Taipei, 104, Taiwan
Tel.: (886) 285015696
Web Site: https://www.runlong.com.tw
1808—(TAI)
Rev.: $1,003,431,762
Assets: $1,391,110,186
Liabilities: $949,283,361
Net Worth: $441,826,825
Earnings: $251,857,344
Emp.: 339
Fiscal Year-end: 12/31/23
Real Estate Development Services
N.A.I.C.S.: 531390
Tsung-Pin Tsai *(Chm & Pres)*

RUNA SMART EQUIPMENT CO., LTD.
No 039 Fengxia Road East Shuangfeng Economic Development Zone, Changfeng County, Hefei, 231131, Anhui, China
Tel.: (86) 55166850062
Web Site: https://www.runachina.com
Year Founded: 2008
301129—(CHIN)
Rev.: $60,785,549
Assets: $286,916,084
Liabilities: $52,889,169
Net Worth: $234,026,915
Earnings: $9,458,634
Emp.: 600
Fiscal Year-end: 12/31/23
Heating Equipment Mfr & Distr
N.A.I.C.S.: 333414
Dayong Yu *(Chm & Gen Mgr)*

RUNGE ICT GROUP PTY LIMITED
Mezzanine Level 110 Eagle Street, Brisbane, 4000, QLD, Australia
Tel.: (61) 7 3218 3300
Web Site: http://www.rungeict.com
Year Founded: 1977
Sales Range: $125-149.9 Million
Emp.: 500
Full-Service Information Technology Solutions
N.A.I.C.S.: 519290
Jonathon Runge *(Mng Dir)*

Subsidiaries:

GeoGAS Pty. Ltd. (1)
103 Kenny St, PO Box 342, Wollongong, 2520, NSW, Australia
Tel.: (61) 242259279
Web Site: http://www.geogas.com.au
Sales Range: $25-49.9 Million
Emp.: 25
Mining Technology Services
N.A.I.C.S.: 541330

MRM Mining Services Pty Ltd. (1)
Whitby Manor, 167 14th Road Extension, 32 Noordwyk, Midrand, 1682, Johannesburg, South Africa
Tel.: (27) 113186800
Web Site: http://www.mrms.co.za
Sales Range: $25-49.9 Million
Emp.: 10
Mining Technology Services
N.A.I.C.S.: 541330

Pincock, Allen & Holt (1)
165 S Union Blvd Ste 950, Lakewood, CO 80228-1813
Tel.: (303) 986-6950
Web Site: http://www.pincock.com
Sales Range: $25-49.9 Million
Emp.: 37
Mining Technology Services

RUNGE ICT GROUP PTY LIMITED

Runge ICT Group Pty Limited—(Continued)
N.A.I.C.S.: 541330

Runge Asia Limited (1)
Level 69 Central Plaza, 19 Harbour Road,
Wanchai, China (Hong Kong)
Tel.: (852) 35582090
Mining Technology Services
N.A.I.C.S.: 541330

Runge Latin America Limitada (1)
San Pio X 2460 Offc 804, Providencia, Santiago, Chile
Tel.: (56) 23330304
Web Site: http://www.runge.com.au
Sales Range: $25-49.9 Million
Emp.: 10
Mining Technology Services
N.A.I.C.S.: 541330

RUNGTA IRRIGATION LIMITED
101 Pragati Towers 26 Rajendra Place, New Delhi, 110 008, India
Tel.: (91) 1140453330
Web Site:
https://www.rungtairrigation.in
Year Founded: 1986
530449—(BOM)
Rev.: $15,817,385
Assets: $12,421,905
Liabilities: $3,209,256
Net Worth: $9,212,649
Earnings: $357,676
Emp.: 159
Fiscal Year-end: 03/31/23
Irrigation Equipment Mfr & Distr
N.A.I.C.S.: 333111
Mahabir Prasad Rungta (Chm & Co-Mng Dir)

Subsidiaries:

Rungta Irrigation Limited - PONDICHERRY UNIT (1)
Plot No F-3-2-1 Adavipolam Village, Yanam, Pondicherry, 533 464, India
Tel.: (91) 884 2321038
Emp.: 100
Irrigation Equipment Mfr
N.A.I.C.S.: 333111
S. N. Sharma (Branch Mgr)

Rungta Irrigation Limited - UTTAR-PRADESH UNIT (1)
C-165 Bulandshahar Road Industrial Area, Ghaziabad, 201 001, India
Tel.: (91) 120 3240778
Irrigation Equipment Mfr
N.A.I.C.S.: 333111

RUNHUA LIVING SERVICE GROUP HOLDINGS LTD.
6th Floor Building 1 Lemeng Center No 28988 Jingshi Road, Huaiyin, Jinan, China
Web Site: https://www.sdrhwy.cn
Year Founded: 1996
2455—(HKG)
Rev.: $106,021,167
Assets: $82,795,756
Liabilities: $52,027,052
Net Worth: $30,768,705
Earnings: $6,186,773
Emp.: 8,755
Fiscal Year-end: 12/31/22
Holding Company
N.A.I.C.S.: 551112
Lili Fu (CFO)

RUNJIAN CO., LTD.
No 16 Huaxia Road Liede Street, Tianhe District, Guangzhou, Guangdong, China
Tel.: (86) 2037392999
Web Site: https://www.runjian.com
Year Founded: 2003
002929—(SSE)
Rev.: $1,145,572,473
Assets: $1,787,145,577
Liabilities: $1,160,889,159
Net Worth: $626,256,418

Earnings: $59,547,908
Fiscal Year-end: 12/31/22
Telecommunication & Network Maintenance Services
N.A.I.C.S.: 517111
Jianguo Li (Chm)

RUNNER XIAMEN CORP.
No 69 Tianfeng Road, Jimei District, Xiamen, 361021, Fujian, China
Tel.: (86) 5926298668
Web Site: http://www.runner-corp.com.cn
Year Founded: 1990
603408—(SHG)
Rev.: $587,749,149
Assets: $617,766,135
Liabilities: $214,433,355
Net Worth: $403,332,780
Earnings: $64,311,498
Fiscal Year-end: 12/31/22
Household Appliance Mfr & Distr
N.A.I.C.S.: 335220
Lizhen Lv (Board of Directors & Chm)

RUNSYSTEM CO., LTD.
5-7-11 Nishi-Iwata, Toshima-Ku, Tokyo, 171-0014, Japan
Tel.: (81) 369078111
Web Site: http://www.runsystem.co.jp
Year Founded: 1991
3326—(TKS)
Rev.: $48,689,260
Assets: $26,069,840
Liabilities: $24,906,480
Net Worth: $1,163,360
Earnings: $654,390
Emp.: 128
Fiscal Year-end: 03/31/24
Complex Store Operator
N.A.I.C.S.: 713120
Mitsuo Nishihara (Chm)

RUNTIME REVOLUTION LTD.
25a Thistle Street Lane South West, Edinburgh, EH2 1EW, Scotland, United Kingdom
Tel.: (44) 8452198923
Web Site: http://www.runrev.com
Year Founded: 1997
Sales Range: $1-9.9 Million
Software Publisher
N.A.I.C.S.: 513210
Kevin Miller (Founder & CEO)

RUPA & CO LIMITED
1 Ho Chi Minh Sarani Metro Tower 8th Floor, Kolkata, 700071, India
Tel.: (91) 3340573100
Web Site: https://www.rupa.co.in
533552—(BOM)
Rev.: $138,991,403
Assets: $166,405,347
Liabilities: $57,087,273
Net Worth: $109,318,074
Earnings: $6,442,276
Emp.: 778
Fiscal Year-end: 03/31/23
Knitted Innerwear Mfr
N.A.I.C.S.: 313240
Prahlad Rai Agarwala (Chm)

Subsidiaries:

Euro Fashion Inners International Private Limited (1)
1 Metro Tower 8th Flr Ho Chi Minh Sarani Midleton Row, Kolkata, 700 071, India
Tel.: (91)-3330572100
Sales Range: $25-49.9 Million
Emp.: 100
Hosiery Mfr
N.A.I.C.S.: 315120

Imoogi Fashions Private Limited (1)
Metro Tower 1 Ho Chi Minh Sarani, Kolkata, 700 071, West Bengal, India
Tel.: (91) 334 057 3100
Web Site: https://www.femmora.com

Hosiery Mfr
N.A.I.C.S.: 315120

RUPALI BANK PLC
34 Dilkusha C/A Rupali Bank PLC, Dhaka, 1000, Bangladesh
Tel.: (880) 29555094
Web Site: https://rupalibank.com.bd
Year Founded: 1986
RUPALIBANK—(DHA)
Rev.: $226,597,011
Assets: $7,323,232,518
Liabilities: $7,111,364,081
Net Worth: $211,868,437
Earnings: $2,354,130
Emp.: 5,935
Fiscal Year-end: 12/31/20
Banking Services
N.A.I.C.S.: 522110
Monzur Hossain (Chm)

Subsidiaries:

Rupali Bank Securities Limited (1)
Ispahani Building 6th Floor 14-15 Motijheel C/A, Dhaka, 1000, Bangladesh
Tel.: (880) 29551680
Web Site: http://www.rbsl.com.bd
Financial Services
N.A.I.C.S.: 522110
Abu Hena Mostafa Kamal (COO)

Rupali Investment Limited (1)
Shadharan Bima Tower 7th Floor 37/A Dilkusha C/A, Dhaka, 1000, Bangladesh
Tel.: (880) 47112923
Web Site: https://www.riltd.org
Emp.: 14
Merchant Banking Services
N.A.I.C.S.: 523150
Mostafa Shazzadul Haque (CFO)

RUPALI INSURANCE COMPANY LIMITED
Rupali Bima Bhaban 7 Rajuk Avenue, Dhaka, 1000, Bangladesh
Tel.: (880) 9565625
Web Site:
https://www.rupaliinsurance.com
Year Founded: 1988
RUPALIINS—(CHT)
Rev.: $820,255
Assets: $23,926,945
Liabilities: $6,113,611
Net Worth: $17,813,334
Earnings: $450,883
Emp.: 208
Fiscal Year-end: 12/31/23
Insurance Services
N.A.I.C.S.: 524298
Mostafa Golam Quddus (Chm)

RUPALI LIFE INSURANCE CO. LTD.
Rupali Life Tower 50, Kakrail, Dhaka, 1000, Bangladesh
Tel.: (880) 28392361
Web Site: https://www.rupalilife.com
Year Founded: 1999
RUPALILIFE—(CHT)
Rev.: $19,920,535
Assets: $57,838,294
Liabilities: $3,246,224
Net Worth: $54,592,070
Earnings: $19,886,214
Emp.: 749
Fiscal Year-end: 12/31/22
Insurance Services
N.A.I.C.S.: 524298
Abdul Matin (Dir-Technical)

RUPALI POLYESTER LIMITED
241-242 Upper Mall Scheme Anand Road, Lahore, 54000, Pakistan
Tel.: (92) 4235713101
Web Site:
https://www.rupaligroup.com
RUPL—(KAR)
Rev.: $65,005,860
Assets: $43,184,792

INTERNATIONAL PUBLIC

Liabilities: $25,814,232
Net Worth: $17,370,560
Earnings: $394,721
Emp.: 1,468
Fiscal Year-end: 06/30/19
Polyester Fiber Mfr
N.A.I.C.S.: 325220
Abdul Hayee (Exec Dir)

Subsidiaries:

Rupali Polyester Limited - Polyester Plant (1)
30.2 Kilometer Lahore Sheikhupura Rd, Sheikhupura, 39350, Punjab, Pakistan
Tel.: (92) 56340624045
Web Site: http://www.rupaligroup.com
Sales Range: $350-399.9 Million
Polyester Fiber & Filament Yarn Mfr
N.A.I.C.S.: 313110
Khalid Daud Raja (Mgr)

RUPERT RESOURCES LTD.
82 Richmond Street East Suite 203, Toronto, M5C 1P1, ON, Canada
Tel.: (416) 304-9004
Web Site:
https://www.rupertresources.com
Year Founded: 1981
RUP—(TSX)
Assets: $130,783,889
Liabilities: $11,691,881
Net Worth: $119,092,009
Earnings: ($9,677,158)
Emp.: 31
Fiscal Year-end: 02/28/23
Gold Exploration Services
N.A.I.C.S.: 212220
James Withall (CEO)

Subsidiaries:

Rupert Finland Oy (1)
Pahtavaarantie 440 Sattasvaara, 99655, Loviisa, Finland
Tel.: (358) 401247338
Gold Exploration Services
N.A.I.C.S.: 212220
Jukka Nieminen (Mng Dir)

RUPF INDUSTRIES GMBH
Altkönigstrasse 41, 61462, Königstein, Germany
Tel.: (49) 222592270
Web Site: http://www.rupf-industries.com
Sales Range: $100-124.9 Million
Emp.: 520
Holding Services
N.A.I.C.S.: 551112
Wolfgang Rupf (Mng Dir)

Subsidiaries:

BHC Gummi-Metall GmbH (1)
Buschstrasse 8, D-53340, Meckenheim, Germany
Tel.: (49) 2225 9227 0
Web Site: http://www.bhcgummi-metall.de
Rubber-Metal Connector & Vibration Control Components Mfr
N.A.I.C.S.: 339999

Integral Hydraulik GmbH & Co. (1)
Hanns Martin Schleyer Str 20, Willich, 47877, Germany
Tel.: (49) 215441310
Web Site: http://www.integral-hydraulik.de
Sales Range: $10-24.9 Million
Emp.: 60
Hydraulic Sets, Hydraulic Components, Hydraulic Accumulators, Electohydraulic Drives
N.A.I.C.S.: 333611
Stephan Muetz (Gen Mgr)

Subsidiary (US):

PTR-Precision Technologies, Inc. (2)
120 Post Rd, Enfield, CT 06082-5690 (100%)
Tel.: (860) 741-2281
Web Site: http://www.ptreb.com
Mfr of Electron Beam Systems, Laser Systems
N.A.I.C.S.: 335999

Deanna Holcomb *(Coord-Customer Support)*

KHT Fahrzeugteile GmbH (1)
Industriestrasse 13, 41515, Grevenbroich, Germany
Tel.: (49) 2182 1701 0
Web Site: http://www.kht-fahrzeugteile.de
Automotive Components Mfr
N.A.I.C.S.: 336390

Ulmer Maschinenteile GmbH (1)
August-Nagel-Str 7, D-89079, Ulm, Germany
Tel.: (49) 7305 171 160
Web Site:
  http://www.ulmermaschinenteile.de
Mechanical Component Mfr
N.A.I.C.S.: 332990

Ulmer Werkzeugschleiftechnik GmbH & Co. KG (1)
August-Nagel-Str 7, D-89079, Ulm, Germany
Tel.: (49) 7305 171 324
Web Site:
  http://www.ulmerwerkzeugschleiftech.de
Industrial Machinery Mfr
N.A.I.C.S.: 333248

RUPP AG
Kruzastrasse 8, 6912, Horbranz, Austria
Tel.: (43) 55738080 **AT**
Web Site: http://www.ruppcheese.at
Year Founded: 1908
Sales Range: $50-74.9 Million
Emp.: 350
Cheese Mfr
N.A.I.C.S.: 311513

Subsidiaries:

Rupp Cheese Innovation GmbH (1)
Kruezastrasse 8, 6912, Horbranz, Austria
Tel.: (43) 55738080
Web Site: http://www.rupp.at
Sales Range: $25-49.9 Million
Emp.: 49
Cheese & Cheese Products Mfg & Sales
N.A.I.C.S.: 311513
Harald Fischli *(Mng Dir)*

Rupp Kaseexport GmbH (1)
Kruezastrasse 8, 6912, Horbranz, Austria
Tel.: (43) 55744973
Dairy Product Whslr
N.A.I.C.S.: 424430

RUPPERTSBERGER WINZERVEREIN HOHEBURG EG
Hauptstrasse 94, 67152, Bad Durkheim, Germany
Tel.: (49) 6326962970
Web Site:
  http://www.ruppertsberger.de
Year Founded: 1968
Rev.: $10,943,056
Emp.: 50
Wine Mfr
N.A.I.C.S.: 312130
Gerhard Brauer *(Mng Dir)*

RURAL FUNDS MANAGEMENT LTD.
Level 2 2 King Street, Deakin, 2600, ACT, Australia
Tel.: (61) 262039700
Web Site:
  https://www.ruralfunds.com.au
RFF—(ASX)
Rev.: $62,724,144
Assets: $1,075,599,742
Liabilities: $372,995,083
Net Worth: $702,604,658
Earnings: $819,823
Fiscal Year-end: 06/30/22
Miscellaneous Financial Investment Activities
N.A.I.C.S.: 523999
Daniel Edwards *(Natl Mgr)*

RURAL PRESS PTY LIMITED
159 Bells Line of Rd, Richmond, 2754, NSW, Australia
Tel.: (61) 245704444
Year Founded: 1911
Sales Range: $250-299.9 Million
Emp.: 300
Agricultural & Regional Publisher, Broadcaster & Printer
N.A.I.C.S.: 513120
J. B. Fairfax *(Chm)*

Subsidiaries:

Border Mail Printing Pty Ltd (1)
1 Mckoy St, Wodonga, 3689, VIC, Australia
Tel.: (61) 260240555
Commercial Printing Services
N.A.I.C.S.: 323111

Illawarra Newspaper Holdings Pty. Limited (1)
AHM Building 77 Market Street, PO Box 1215, Wollongong, 2500, NSW, Australia **(100%)**
Tel.: (61) 242212206
Web Site:
  http://www.illawarramercury.com.au
Sales Range: $50-74.9 Million
Emp.: 200
Newspaper Publishers
N.A.I.C.S.: 513110
Ben Marsh *(Gen Mgr)*

Newcastle Newspapers Pty. Limited (1)
28 Honeycastle Drive, Newcastle, 2300, NSW, Australia **(100%)**
Tel.: (61) 249795000
Web Site: http://www.theherald.com.au
Sales Range: $100-124.9 Million
Emp.: 350
Newspaper Publishers
N.A.I.C.S.: 513110
Jason King *(Gen Mgr)*

The Examiner Newspaper Pty Ltd (1)
113 Cimitiere St, PO Box 99, Launceston, 7250, TAS, Australia
Tel.: (61) 3 6336 7111
Web Site: http://www.examiner.com.au
Newspaper Publishing Services
N.A.I.C.S.: 513110
Kylie Boyle *(Mgr-Media Sls)*

Wimmera Mail Times Pty Ltd (1)
183-185 Baillie Street, PO Box 519, Horsham, 3400, VIC, Australia
Tel.: (61) 353620000
Web Site: http://www.mailtimes.com.au
Sales Range: $25-49.9 Million
Emp.: 24
Newspaper Publishers
N.A.I.C.S.: 513110
Tim Lewis *(Gen Mgr)*

RUSFOREST AB
PO Box 134, 111 73, Stockholm, Sweden
Tel.: (46) 8 771 85 00 **SE**
Web Site: http://www.rusforest.com
Year Founded: 2005
Sales Range: $10-24.9 Million
Wood Products Mfr
N.A.I.C.S.: 321999
Gustav Wetterling *(CFO)*

Subsidiaries:

Boguchansky LPK LLC (1)
8 km vostochnee derevni Yarki urochische Abakan, Boguchanskiy rayon, 663431, Krasnoyarsk, Russia
Tel.: (7) 3916244200
Wood Product Distr
N.A.I.C.S.: 424990

Lesprom LLC (1)
Gorkogo Str 54, Izhevsk, 426008, Udmurt Republic, Russia
Tel.: (7) 341 277 23 27
Wood Product Distr
N.A.I.C.S.: 424990

RusForest LLC (1)
1st Truzhennikov Lane 12 bldg 2 7th floor, 119121, Moscow, Russia
Tel.: (7) 495 980 24 13
Wood Product Distr
N.A.I.C.S.: 424990

Sibartles LLC (1)
rayon p Artyugino ul Lenina d 50, Boguchansky, Krasnoyarsk, 663442, Russia
Tel.: (7) 3916236122
Wood Product Distr
N.A.I.C.S.: 424990

Vanavarales LLC (1)
Tungussko Chunsky rayon s Vanavara ul Mira d 12 kv 4, Evenkysky avtonomny okrug, Krasnoyarsk, 648490, Russia
Tel.: (7) 902 173 30 11
Wood Product Distr
N.A.I.C.S.: 424990

RUSH RARE METALS CORP.
6001090 W Georgia St, Vancouver, V6E 3V7, BC, Canada
Tel.: (778) 999-7030 **BC**
Web Site:
  https://www.rushraremetals.com
Year Founded: 2021
K9A—(DEU)
Mineral Mining Services
N.A.I.C.S.: 213115
Nelson Lamb *(CFO)*

RUSH TRUCK CENTRES OF CANADA
7450 Torbram Rd, Mississauga, ON L4T1G9, ON, Canada
Tel.: (905) 671-7600
Web Site:
  https://www.rushtruckcentres.ca
Year Founded: 1973
Emp.: 133
Truck Transportation
N.A.I.C.S.: 484110
Ray Veeneman *(VP)*

RUSHIL DECOR LIMITED
Rushil House Near Neelkanth Green Bungalow Off Sindhu Bhavan Road, Shilaj, Ahmedabad, 380058, India
Tel.: (91) 7961400400
Web Site: https://www.rushil.com
Year Founded: 1993
533470—(BOM)
Rev.: $46,378,137
Assets: $110,350,421
Liabilities: $74,294,334
Net Worth: $36,056,087
Earnings: $1,872,548
Emp.: 604
Fiscal Year-end: 03/31/21
Decorative Laminate Sheets & Particle Boards Mfr
N.A.I.C.S.: 326130
Ghanshyambhai Ambalal Thakkar *(Chm & Exec Dir)*

RUSNANO JSC
10A Prospekt 60-letiya Oktyabrya, Moscow, 117036, Russia
Tel.: (7) 495 988 5388
Web Site: http://www.rusnano.com
Investment Holding Company
N.A.I.C.S.: 551112
Anatoly Chubais *(Chm-Exec Bd)*

Subsidiaries:

METACLAY CJSC (1)
15 Karl Marx str, Karachev, 242500, Bryansk, Russia
Tel.: (7) 4999698130
Web Site: http://www.metaclay.ru
Chemical Products Mfr
N.A.I.C.S.: 325411
Roman Popov *(Dir-Production)*

RUSNANO Capital LLC (1)
Office 450 10A Prospekt 60 letiya Oktyabrya, Moscow, 117036, Russia
Tel.: (7) 4956633874
Web Site: http://www.rncapital.ru
Financial Investment Management Services
N.A.I.C.S.: 523940

Irina Rapoport *(CEO)*

RUSNANO USA, Inc. (1)
3000 Sand Hill Rd, Menlo Park, CA 94025
Tel.: (650) 681-0747
Portfolio Management Services
N.A.I.C.S.: 523940
Dmitry Sergeevich Akhanov *(Pres & CEO)*

Rosana Ltd. (1)
building No1 5 Viktorenko st, Moscow, 125617, Russia
Tel.: (7) 4999951035
Web Site: http://www.rsna.ru
Chemical Products Mfr
N.A.I.C.S.: 325320
Mikhail Chichulin *(CEO)*

RUSNARBANK JSC
Upper Krasnoselskaya Street D 11a, Moscow, 107140, Russia
Tel.: (7) 4956625021
Web Site: http://www.rusnarbank.com
Sales Range: Less than $1 Million
Commercial Banking Services
N.A.I.C.S.: 522110

RUSORO MINING LTD.
Suite 3123 - 595 Burrard Street, PO Box 49139, Vancouver, V7X 1J1, BC, Canada
Tel.: (604) 609-6110
Web Site: https://www.rusoro.com
RML—(OTCIQ)
Assets: $36,855
Liabilities: $137,515,797
Net Worth: ($137,478,942)
Earnings: ($18,974,835)
Fiscal Year-end: 12/31/20
Gold Mining & Processing
N.A.I.C.S.: 212220
Szascha Lim *(CFO)*

Subsidiaries:

Rusoro Mining Ltd. (1)
Av Francisco de Miranda Urbanizacion El Rozal, Torre Dozsa Piso 6, Caracas, 1060, Venezuela
Tel.: (58) 2129522222
Gold Exploration
N.A.I.C.S.: 212220

Branch (Domestic):

Rusoro Mining Ltd. (2)
Zona Industrial Unare 1 Calle Zuruapy, Manzana 10 No 06, Puerto Ordaz, Bolivar, Venezuela
Tel.: (58) 2869520094
Gold Mining & Exploration
N.A.I.C.S.: 212220

Venezuela Holdings (BVI) Ltd. (1)

RUSPETRO LIMITED
Aerodom Business Center 37 bld Leningradsky prospect, 37A/4 Leningradsky Prospect, 125167, Moscow, Russia
Tel.: (7) 4957455665 **UK**
Web Site: http://www.ruspetro.com
Year Founded: 2011
Sales Range: $25-49.9 Million
Emp.: 205
Oil & Gas Exploration Services
N.A.I.C.S.: 213112
Alexander Chistyakov *(Chm)*

RUSSEL METALS INC.
6600 Financial Drive, Mississauga, L5N 7J6, ON, Canada
Tel.: (905) 819-7777 **Ca**
Web Site:
  https://www.russelmetals.com
Year Founded: 1929
RUS—(TSX)
Rev.: $3,292,225,380
Assets: $1,810,587,060
Liabilities: $834,066,936
Net Worth: $976,520,124
Earnings: $338,101,416

RUSSEL METALS INC.

Russel Metals Inc.—(Continued)
Fiscal Year-end: 12/31/21
Metals Distr & Processing Services
N.A.I.C.S.: 423510
James F. Dinning (Chm)

Subsidiaries:

A.J. Forsyth (1)
830 Carlisle Rd Annacis Business Park,
Delta, V3M 5P4, BC, Canada
Tel.: (604) 525-0544
Emp.: 100
Metal Services & Distr
N.A.I.C.S.: 423510
Allan Willis (Gen Mgr)

Acier Leroux (1)
1331 Rue Graham-Bell, Boucherville, J4B
6A1, QC, Canada
Tel.: (450) 641-2280
Web Site: http://www.acier-leroux.com
Sales Range: $50-74.9 Million
Emp.: 200
Mfr of Steel & Other Industrial Products
N.A.I.C.S.: 331210

Unit (Domestic):

Megantic Metal (2)
1400 Bd Frontenac E, Thetford Mines, G6G
6Z2, QC, Canada
Tel.: (418) 338-3188
Web Site: http://www.russelmetals.com
Sales Range: $25-49.9 Million
Metal Products Mfr
N.A.I.C.S.: 332999

Division (Domestic):

Metaux Russel Produits
Specialises (2)
1300 Rue Graham-Bell, Boucherville, J4B
6H5, QC, Canada
Tel.: (450) 641-1130
Web Site: http://www.acier-leroux.com
Sales Range: $25-49.9 Million
Emp.: 5
Metal Products Maintenance Services
N.A.I.C.S.: 423510

Apex Distribution Inc (1)
407 2 Street SW Suite 550, Calgary, T2P
2Y3, AB, Canada
Tel.: (403) 268-7333
Web Site: http://www.apexdistribution.com
Sales Range: $500-549.9 Million
Emp.: 300
Oilfield Distr, Drilling Equipment Services
N.A.I.C.S.: 213111
Bill Ouwejan (VP-Sls & Mktg)

Comco Pipe and Supply
Company (1)
5910 17th Street Northwest, Edmonton,
T6P 1S5, AB, Canada (100%)
Tel.: (780) 440-2000
Web Site: http://www.comcopipe.com
Sales Range: $25-49.9 Million
Emp.: 90
N.A.I.C.S.: 332996

Dubose Steel Inc. (1)
767 Dr MLK Jr Blvd, Roseboro, NC 28382
Tel.: (910) 525-4161
Web Site: http://www.dubosesteel.com
Provider of Metals Processing Distr
N.A.I.C.S.: 423510

Subsidiary (Domestic):

Mid-Atlantic Transportation Services,
LLC (2)
767 Doctor Martin Luther King Jr Blvd,
Roseboro, NC 28382
Tel.: (910) 525-4161
Local Non Storage Trucking Services
N.A.I.C.S.: 484110

Elite Supply Partners Inc. (1)
2794 S Hwy 385, Odessa, TX 79766
Tel.: (432) 332-1541
Web Site: https://elitesupplypartners.com
Pipe, Valves & Fittings Distr
N.A.I.C.S.: 332919

Fedmet International Corporation (1)
30403 Bruce Industrial Pkwy, Solon, OH
44139-3941
Tel.: (440) 248-9500

Web Site:
http://www.baldwininternational.com
Sales Range: $25-49.9 Million
Emp.: 18
Metals Service Center
N.A.I.C.S.: 423510

Fedmet Tubulars (1)
Ste 1050 635 8th Ave SW, Calgary, T2P
3M3, AB, Canada (100%)
Tel.: (403) 237-0955
Sales Range: $25-49.9 Million
Emp.: 20
N.A.I.C.S.: 331210
Jason Kaiser (Gen Mgr)

Frontier Steel Company (1)
4990 Grand Ave, Neville Island, PA 15225
Tel.: (412) 865-4444
Web Site: http://www.frontiersteel.com
Steel Plate Mfr & Distr
N.A.I.C.S.: 331221
John Matig (Pres)

JMS Russel Metals Corp. (1)
1455 Bloom Ave, Paducah, KY 42001
Tel.: (270) 575-0308
Web Site: http://www.jmsrusselmetals.com
Emp.: 65
Metals Service Center
N.A.I.C.S.: 423510

Metaux Russel Inc. (1)
2149 rue de la Fonderie, Chicoutimi, G7H
8C1, QC, Canada
Tel.: (418) 545-8881
Sales Range: $25-49.9 Million
Emp.: 30
Metals Service Center
N.A.I.C.S.: 423510
Steeves Munger (Gen Mgr)

Milspec Strapping Systems (1)
5155 Harvester Road Unit 2, Burlington,
L7L 6V2, ON, Canada
Tel.: (905) 333-0646
Web Site: http://www.russelmetals.com
Steel Strapping Products Whslr
N.A.I.C.S.: 423510

Pioneer Steel & Tube Corp. (1)
1660 Lincoln St Ste 1950, Denver, CO
80264-2301
Tel.: (303) 289-3201
Web Site: http://www.pioneerpipe.com
Sales Range: $25-49.9 Million
Emp.: 20
Steel Pipe Distr
N.A.I.C.S.: 423510

Russel Metals Williams Bahcall
Inc. (1)
999 W Armour Ave, Milwaukee, WI 53221-2419
Tel.: (414) 481-7100
Web Site: http://www.metalsusa.com
Sales Range: $50-74.9 Million
Metals Service Center
N.A.I.C.S.: 423510

Unit (Domestic):

Russel Metals Williams Bahcall Inc. -
Appleton (2)
975 N Meade St, Appleton, WI 54912-1054
Tel.: (920) 734-9271
Web Site: http://www.williamsbahcall.com
Metals Service Center
N.A.I.C.S.: 423510

Samuel Coil Processing-Calgary (1)
1401 17th Ave SE, Calgary, T2G 1J9, AB,
Canada
Tel.: (403) 531-0600
Web Site: http://www.samuel.com
Sales Range: $25-49.9 Million
Emp.: 22
Metal Service Center & Office
N.A.I.C.S.: 423510
Craig Campbell (Reg Mgr)

Sanborn Tube Sales of Wisconsin
Inc. (1)
N28 W24402 Watertown Road Suite 100,
Pewaukee, WI 53072
Tel.: (262) 797-4000
Web Site: http://www.sanborntube.com
Iron & Steel Pipe & Tube Manufacturing
from Purchased Steel
N.A.I.C.S.: 331110

Linda Martin (Acct Mgr)

Siemens Laserworks Inc. (1)
503 50th St, Saskatoon, S7K 6H3, SK,
Canada
Tel.: (306) 244-7511
Components & Sub Assemblies Mfr
N.A.I.C.S.: 334418

Sunbelt Group L.P. (1)
1990 Post Oak Blvd Ste 2100, Houston, TX
77056-3817
Tel.: (713) 840-0550
Web Site: http://www.russelmetals.com
Sales Range: $25-49.9 Million
Emp.: 40
Steel Distr
N.A.I.C.S.: 423510

Tampa Bay Steel Corporation (1)
6901 E 6th Ave, Tampa, FL 33619-3374
Tel.: (813) 621-4738
Web Site: http://www.tampabaysteel.com
Steel Distributor
N.A.I.C.S.: 423510
Buck McInnis (CEO)

Thunder Bay Terminals Ltd. (1)
375 Carpenter Street McKellar Island, PO
Box 1800, McKellar Island, Thunder Bay,
P7C 5J7, ON, Canada
Tel.: (807) 625-7800
Web Site: https://www.russelmetals.com
Emp.: 25
Coal Mining Transportation Services
N.A.I.C.S.: 488999

Triumph Tubular & Supply Ltd (1)
441 - 5th Ave SW Ste 875, Calgary, T2P
2V1, AB, Canada
Tel.: (403) 262-3777
Emp.: 18
Oil Tabular Goods Distr
N.A.I.C.S.: 423830
Travis Peckham (Pres)

Wirth Steel, a General
Partnership (1)
1 Westmount Square Suite 200, Montreal,
H3Z 2P9, QC, Canada
Tel.: (514) 939-5555
Web Site: https://www.wirthsteel.com
Sales Range: $50-74.9 Million
Emp.: 13
Steel Investments & Distributors
N.A.I.C.S.: 425120

RUSSELL BREWERIES INC.
100 - 13018 80 Ave, Surrey, V3W
3B2, BC, Canada
Tel.: (604) 599-1190 BC
Web Site:
https://www.russellbeer.com
Year Founded: 2000
RB—(TSXV)
Sales Range: Less than $1 Million
Emp.: 40
Beer Brewer & Distr
N.A.I.C.S.: 312120
Jason Hope (Mgr-Territory-Vancouver
Islands)

Subsidiaries:

Russell Brewing Company Ltd. (1)
100 - 13018 80th Ave, Surrey, V3W 3B2,
BC, Canada
Tel.: (604) 599-1190
Web Site: https://www.russellbeer.com
Beer Mfr
N.A.I.C.S.: 312120

RUSSELL CO., LTD.
36, Oksansandan-ro Oksan-myeon
Heungdeok-gu, Cheongju, 28101,
Chungcheongbuk-do, Korea (South)
Tel.: (82) 0435328818
Year Founded: 2015
217500—(KRS)
Rev.: $32,157,349
Assets: $60,156,316
Liabilities: $17,587,665
Net Worth: $42,568,651
Earnings: $2,935,026
Emp.: 59
Fiscal Year-end: 12/31/22

INTERNATIONAL PUBLIC

Financial Investment Management
Services
N.A.I.C.S.: 523940

RUSSIAN AGRICULTURAL BANK JSC
3 Gagarinsky Pereulok, 119034, Moscow, Russia
Tel.: (7) 4957877787
Web Site: http://www.rshb.ru
Year Founded: 2000
Sales Range: $1-4.9 Billion
Financial Support Services
N.A.I.C.S.: 541611

Subsidiaries:

Jointstock company
RSHB-Insurance (1)
Gagarinsky per 3, 119034, Moscow, Russia
Tel.: (7) 84952130915
Web Site: http://www.rshbins.ru
Insurance Services
N.A.I.C.S.: 524210

RSHB Asset Management Limited
Liability Company (1)
Presnenskaya nab Building 10 building 2,
123112, Moscow, Russia
Tel.: (7) 4956604765
Web Site: http://www.rshb-am.ru
Asset Management Services
N.A.I.C.S.: 523940

RUSSIAN NATIONAL REINSURANCE COMPANY JSC
6 Gasheka Street Floor 5 Ducat
Place III Business Centre, 125047,
Moscow, Russia
Tel.: (7) 4957304480
Web Site: http://www.rnrc.ru
Year Founded: 2016
Emp.: 100
Reinsurance Services
N.A.I.C.S.: 524130
Natalya Karpova (Chm & Pres)

RUSSIAN REGIONAL DEVELOPMENT BANK JSC
Suschevsky Val d 65 bldg 1, 129594,
Moscow, Russia
Tel.: (7) 4959330343
Web Site: http://www.vbrr.ru
Year Founded: 1996
Sales Range: Less than $1 Million
Mortgage Banking Services
N.A.I.C.S.: 522292
Dina R. Malikova (Pres & Member-Exec Bd)

RUSSIAN TECHNOLOGIES STATE CORPORATION
24 Usacheva Street, 119048, Moscow, Russia
Tel.: (7) 4952872525 RU
Web Site: http://www.rostec.ru
Year Founded: 2007
Holding Company
N.A.I.C.S.: 551112
Denis Manturov (Chm-Supervisory Bd)

Subsidiaries:

AO OPK Oboronprom (1)
29/141 Vereiskaya Str, 121357, Moscow, Russia (83.95%)
Tel.: (7) 4957975548
Web Site: http://www.oboronprom.ru
Holding Company
N.A.I.C.S.: 551112
Pavel Osin (Co-Deputy Gen Dir)

Subsidiary (Domestic):

Chernyshev Moscow Machine-Building Enterprise, JSC (2)
Vishnevaya st 7, Moscow, 125362, Russia
Tel.: (7) 491 64 65
Web Site: http://www.avia500.ru
Aircraft Engine Mfr
N.A.I.C.S.: 336412

AND PRIVATE COMPANIES — RUSSIAN TECHNOLOGIES STATE CORPORATION

Amir Khakimov (Mng Dir)

JSC Klimov (2)
11 Kantemirovskaya st, 194100, Saint Petersburg, Russia
Tel.: (7) 8124547100
Web Site: http://www.klimov.ru
Aircraft Engine Mfr
N.A.I.C.S.: 336412
Alexander Grachev (Dir-Economic Affairs)

JSC Kuznetsov (2)
29 Zavodskoye shosse, 443009, Samara, Russia
Tel.: (7) 8462273252
Web Site: http://www.kuznetsov-motors.ru
Aircraft Engine Mfr & Repair Services
N.A.I.C.S.: 336412
Igor Volkov (Head-Fin & Banking Dept)

JSC STAR (2)
Kuibyshev str building 140A, 614990, Perm, Russia
Tel.: (7) 3422491984
Web Site: http://www.ao-star.ru
Aircraft Engine Mfr
N.A.I.C.S.: 336412
Sergey Ostapenko (Gen Dir)

JSC Ufa Engine Industrial Association (2)
Ferin Street 2, Ufa, 450039, Russia
Tel.: (7) 3472 38 18 63
Aircraft Engine Mfr & Distr
N.A.I.C.S.: 336412
Aleksandr Artyukhov (Gen Dir)

MMP Vpered JSC (2)
pr Entuziastov d 15, Moscow, 111024, Russia
Tel.: (7) 4956734427
Aircraft Engine Mfr
N.A.I.C.S.: 336412

Russian Helicopters, JSC (2)
29 Bldg 141 Vereyskaya St, 121357, Moscow, Russia (88%)
Tel.: (7) 4956452530
Web Site: http://www.russianhelicopters.aero
Sales Range: $1-4.9 Billion
Helicopter Mfr & Whslr
N.A.I.C.S.: 336411

Subsidiary (Domestic):

AO 12 Aircraft Repair Plant (3)
39 Vostochnoe Shosse, Khabarovsk, 680014, Russia
Tel.: (7) 4212 275 780
Web Site: http://www.russianhelicopters.aero
Helicopter Repair & Maintenance Services
N.A.I.C.S.: 488190
Alexander Shpakov (Mng Dir)

AO 150 Aircraft Repair Plant (3)
4 Garnizonnaya street, Liublino, 238347, Svetly, Kaliningrad, Russia
Tel.: (7) 4015224172
Web Site: http://www.russianhelicopters.aero
Aircraft Repair & Maintenance Services
N.A.I.C.S.: 488190
Yakov Kazhdan (Mng Dir)

AO 356 Aircraft Repair Plant (3)
Ulitsa Engels-1, 41301, Engels, Saratov Region, Russia (69.85%)
Tel.: (7) 8453749602
Web Site: http://www.russianhelicopters.aero
Helicopter Repair & Maintenance Services
N.A.I.C.S.: 488190
Igor Markov (Mng Dir)

AO 419 Aircraft Repair Plant (3)
16 Ulitsa Politruka Pasechnika Building 2, Saint Petersburg, 198326, Russia
Tel.: (7) 812 746 13 77
Web Site: http://www.russianhelicopters.aero
Helicopter Repair & Maintenance Services
N.A.I.C.S.: 488190

AO 810 Aircraft Repair Plant (3)
1 Ulitsa Vertolevnaya, 672045, Chita, Russia
Tel.: (7) 3022283411
Web Site: http://www.russianhelicopters.aero

Helicopter Repair & Maintenance Services
N.A.I.C.S.: 488190
Dneprovsky Eugeny (Mng Dir)

AO Helicopter Service Company (3)
1 Bolshaya Pionerskaya St, 115054, Moscow, Russia (100%)
Tel.: (7) 4956605560
Web Site: http://www.hsc-copter.com
Aircraft Repair & Maintenance Services
N.A.I.C.S.: 488190
Dmitry Borisenko (Mng Dir)

AO Kumertau Aviation Production Enterprise (3)
15A Ulitsa Novozarinskaya, 453300, Kumertau, Bashkortostan, Russia (100%)
Tel.: (7) 3476123346
Helicopter Mfr
N.A.I.C.S.: 336411
Victor Novikov (Mng Dir)

AO MIL Moscow Helicopter Plant (3)
26/1 Ulitsa Garshina Tomilino, Lyuberetsky District, Moscow, 140070, Russia (80.8%)
Tel.: (7) 495 669 70 54
Helicopter Mfr
N.A.I.C.S.: 336411
Mikhail Korotkevich (Mng Dir)

AO Novosibirsk Aircraft Repair Plant (3)
2/4 Ulitsa Aeroport, 630123, Novosibirsk, Russia (95.1%)
Tel.: (7) 3832289650
Web Site: http://www.rushelicopters.com
Helicopter Repair & Maintenance Services
N.A.I.C.S.: 488190
Yury Lipatnikov (Mng Dir)

AO Reductor-PM (3)
93 Komsomolsky Prospekt, 692335, Perm, Russia (100%)
Tel.: (7) 3422408011
Helicopter Mfr & Maintenance Services
N.A.I.C.S.: 336411
Nikolay Semikopenko (Mng Dir)

AO Stupino Machine Production Plant (3)
42 Ulitsa Akademika Belova, Stupino, 142800, Moscow, Russia (69.3%)
Tel.: (7) 4966448021
Aircraft Parts Mfr & Maintenance Services
N.A.I.C.S.: 336413
Anatoly Polyakov (Mng Dir)

AO Ulan-Ude Aviation Plant (3)
1 Ulitsa Khorinskaya, 670009, Ulan-Ude, Russia (98.4%)
Tel.: (7) 3012253386
Helicopter Mfr
N.A.I.C.S.: 336411
Leonid Belykh (Mng Dir)

JSC Aviation gearboxes and transmissions - Perm Motors (3)
Komsomolsky prospect 93, Perm, 614990, Russia
Tel.: (7) 3422408011
Aircraft Equipment Mfr
N.A.I.C.S.: 336412

OAO KAMOV (3)
8a Ulitsa 8 Marta, Lyubertsy, 140007, Moscow, Russia (99.8%)
Tel.: (7) 495 700 34 04
Web Site: http://www.kamov.ru
Helicopter Mfr
N.A.I.C.S.: 336411
Dmitry Tretyakov (Exec Dir)

OOO Purchase and Logistic Center of the Helicopter Industry (3)
1 Elektrichesky Pereulok building 1, Moscow, 123557, Russia
Tel.: (7) 495 980 55 64
Helicopter Parts Distr
N.A.I.C.S.: 423860
Alexander Tikhomirov (Mng Dir)

PAO Arsenyev Aviation Company PROGRESS (3)
5 Ploshchad Lenina, 692335, Arsenyev, Primorsky Krai, Russia (85.1%)
Tel.: (7) 4236145231
Web Site: http://www.progressaviation.ru
Helicopter Mfr
N.A.I.C.S.: 336411
Yuri Denisenko (Mng Dir)

PAO Kazan Helicopter Plant (3)
14 Ulitsa Tetsevskaya, 420085, Kazan, Russia (98.3%)
Tel.: (7) 8435496699
Web Site: http://www.russianhelicopters.aero
Helicopter Mfr
N.A.I.C.S.: 336411
Vadim Ligai (Gen Dir)

PAO Rostvertol (3)
5 Ulitsa Novatorov, 344038, Rostov-na-Donu, Russia (73.9%)
Tel.: (7) 8632977209
Helicopter Mfr
N.A.I.C.S.: 336411
Petr Motrenko (Mng Dir & Gen Dir)

Subsidiary (Domestic):

UEC - Gas Turbines, JSC (2)
16 Tolbukhina Street, Rybinsk, 152914, Yaroslavl, Russia
Tel.: (7) 4855 293 205
Web Site: http://www.saturn-gt.ru
Power Generator Mfr & Distr
N.A.I.C.S.: 333611
Aleksey Ye. Stekolshikov (Deputy Mng Dir-Economics)

Avia Capital Services LLC (1)
18 bld 1 office 303 Malaya Pirogovskaya Street, Moscow, 119435, Russia
Tel.: (7) 4952230304
Web Site: http://www.a-c-s.aero
Aircraft Leasing Services
N.A.I.C.S.: 532411
Roman V. Pakhomov (Gen Dir)

Concern Radioelectronic Technologies (1)
20/1 p 1 Goncharnaya str, Moscow, 109240, Russia
Tel.: (7) 495 587 70 70
Web Site: http://www.kret.com
Holding Company
N.A.I.C.S.: 551112
Nikolay Kolesov (Gen Dir)

Subsidiary (Domestic):

Radium JSC (2)
28 ul Sovetskaya, Kasli, 456830, Russia
Tel.: (7) 3514922270
Web Site: http://www.radiy.ru
Holding Company
N.A.I.C.S.: 551112

Concern Sozvezdie OJSC (1)
14 Plekhanovskaya Street, Voronezh, Russia
Tel.: (7) 4732521259
Web Site: http://www.eng.sozvezdie.su
Communication Equipment Mfr
N.A.I.C.S.: 334220
Bekkiyev Azret Yusupovich (Gen Dir)

Design Bureau of Experimental Works OJSC (1)
No 3 1-st Shchipkovskiy Lane office 412 414 418, Moscow, 115093, Russia
Tel.: (7) 4997645877
Communication Equipment Mfr
N.A.I.C.S.: 334220

Electromashina JSC (1)
21 Mashinostroitelei, Chelyabinsk, 454129, Russia
Tel.: (7) 3512536721
Web Site: http://www.electromasina.md
Electric Motor Mfr
N.A.I.C.S.: 335314

Information and Telecommunication Technologies OJSC (1)
Kantemirovskaya ul 5, Saint Petersburg, 197342, Russia
Tel.: (7) 8122955069
Web Site: http://www.inteltech.ru
Communication Equipment Mfr
N.A.I.C.S.: 334220

J-S.C. AVTODIZEL (1)
75 prospect Oktyabrya, Yaroslavl, 150040, Russia
Tel.: (7) 4852588120
Web Site: http://www.adzl.ru
Diesel Engine Mfr
N.A.I.C.S.: 333618

JSC "KBP" Instrument Design Bureau (1)
59 Shcheglovskaya Zaseka St, 300001, Tula, Russia
Tel.: (7) 4872410068
Web Site: http://www.kbptula.ru
Military Weapon Mfr
N.A.I.C.S.: 336992
Dmitry V. Konoplev (Mng Dir)

JSC AVTOVAZ (1)
36 Yuzhnoye Shosse, 445024, Togliatti, Samara, Russia
Tel.: (7) 8007005232
Sales Range: $5-14.9 Billion
Emp.: 112,200
Passenger Car Mfr
N.A.I.C.S.: 336110

JSC L-ZOS (1)
Parkovaya ulitsa 1, 140080, Lytkarino, Moskovskaya oblast, Russia
Tel.: (7) 4955529955
Aircraft Equipment Mfr
N.A.I.C.S.: 336412

JSC NPO Saturn (1)
163 Lenin Avenue, Rybinsk, 152903, Yaroslavl, Russia
Tel.: (7) 4855296100
Web Site: http://www.npo-saturn.ru
Automobile Equipment Mfr
N.A.I.C.S.: 334519

JSC NPP Motor (1)
ul Selskaya Bogorodskaya 2, Ufa, 450039, Russia
Tel.: (7) 3472381681
Automobile Equipment Mfr
N.A.I.C.S.: 334519

JSC Polyus research institute of M.F.Stelmakh (1)
Building 1 3 Vvedenskogo St, 117342, Moscow, Russia
Tel.: (7) 4953339144
Web Site: http://niipolyus.ru
Aircraft Equipment Mfr
N.A.I.C.S.: 336412

JSC SDB Turbina (1)
2b Linin Avenue, Chelyabinsk, Russia
Tel.: (7) 3512101547
Web Site: http://www.skb-turbina.com
Gas Turbine Engine Mfr
N.A.I.C.S.: 333618

JSC Tulamashzavod (1)
2 Mosin Street, Tula, 300002, Russia
Tel.: (7) 4872321009
Web Site: http://www.tulamash.ru
Military Weapon Mfr
N.A.I.C.S.: 336992
Evgeny A. Dronov (Gen Dir)

JSC ZOMZ (1)
212 V prospekt Krasnoy Armii, Sergiev Posad, 141300, Moscow, Russia
Tel.: (7) 4965460466
Web Site: http://zomz.ru
Aircraft Equipment Mfr
N.A.I.C.S.: 336412

Joint stock company Concern Avtomatika (1)
Botanicheskaya st 25, 127106, Moscow, Russia
Tel.: (7) 4952503333
Web Site: http://www.ao-avtomatika.ru
Communication Equipment Mfr
N.A.I.C.S.: 334220
Bukashkin S. A. (Gen Dir)

Microgen (1)
10 the 2nd Volkonsky lane, 127473, Moscow, Russia
Tel.: (7) 4957907773
Web Site: http://www.microgen.ru
Pharmaceuticals Product Mfr
N.A.I.C.S.: 325412

Nudelman KBTochmash JSC (1)
8 Vvedenskogo Street, Moscow, 117342, Russia
Tel.: (7) 4953335535
Web Site: http://www.kbtochmash.com
Military Weapon Mfr
N.A.I.C.S.: 336992

OJSC RT-Stankoinstrument (1)
bld1 h 65 Guilyarovskogo st, 107996, Mos-

RUSSIAN TECHNOLOGIES STATE CORPORATION

Russian Technologies State Corporation—(Continued)
cow, Russia
Tel.: (7) 495 681 16 18
Web Site: http://www.rt-stanko.ru
Holding Company
N.A.I.C.S.: 551112
Sergey Makarov *(Dir Gen)*

OJSC Rosoboronexport (1)
Str Stromynka 27, 107076, Moscow, Russia
Tel.: (7) 4955346183
Web Site: http://www.roe.ru
Military Equipment Distr
N.A.I.C.S.: 423860
Anatoly P. Isaykin *(Gen Dir)*

RT-Chemcomposite (1)
Bolshoy Savvinsky 11, 119435, Moscow, Russia
Tel.: (7) 4957836444
Web Site: http://www.rt-chemcomposite.ru
Holding Company
N.A.I.C.S.: 551112
Kuzmitskiy Alexey Alexeevich *(Chm)*

Rotor JSC (1)
ul dobrolyubova d 76, 160019, Vologda, Vologda Oblast, Russia
Tel.: (7) 8172241715
Military Weapon Mfr
N.A.I.C.S.: 336992

Ruselectronics JSC (1)
Vereiskaya st 29 p 141, Moscow, Russia
Tel.: (7) 4957774282
Web Site: http://www.ruselectronics.ru
Semiconductor Devices Mfr
N.A.I.C.S.: 334413
Andrey Zverev *(CEO)*

Subsidiary (Domestic):

Ferrite Domen Company (1)
Tsvetochnaya ulitsa 25, 196084, Saint Petersburg, Russia
Tel.: (7) 8125765901
Web Site: http://www.ferrite-domen.com
Semiconductor Devices Mfr
N.A.I.C.S.: 334413

JSC MARS Factory (2)
Lunocharskogo st 121, Torzhok, 172010, Tverskaya, Russia
Tel.: (7) 825155035
Web Site: http://www.z-mars.ru
Semiconductor Devices Mfr
N.A.I.C.S.: 334413

Meteor plant JSC (2)
Gorkogo street 1, 404130, Volzhsky, Russia
Tel.: (7) 8443342694
Web Site: http://www.meteor.su
Semiconductor Devices Mfr
N.A.I.C.S.: 334413

OJSC NRI Electron (2)
Toreza ave 68, 194223, Saint Petersburg, Russia
Tel.: (7) 8122970403
Web Site: http://www.niielectron.ru
Semiconductor Devices Mfr
N.A.I.C.S.: 334413

Pulsar State Plant JSC (2)
Okruzhnoy proezd 27, Moscow, 105187, Russia
Tel.: (7) 4953690475
Web Site: http://www.gz-pulsar.ru
Semiconductor Devices Mfr
N.A.I.C.S.: 334413

Russian Telecom Equipment Company CJSC (2)
3 Kapranov lane business centre Premier Plaza, Moscow, 123242, Russia
Tel.: (7) 4957805060
Web Site: http://www.pkcc.ru
Measuring Equipment Mfr
N.A.I.C.S.: 334519

Scientific-Research Institute of Communication and Management OJSC (1)
Starokaluzhskoye w 58, Moscow, 117630, Russia
Tel.: (7) 4953337503
Web Site: http://www.niissu.ru
Communication Equipment Mfr
N.A.I.C.S.: 334220

Technodinamika (1)
29 Ibragimova street, 105318, Moscow, Russia
Tel.: (7) 495 627 1099
Emp.: 30,000
Automobile Equipment Mfr
N.A.I.C.S.: 334519
Maxim Kuzyuk *(CEO)*

Subsidiary (Domestic):

Agregat JSC (2)
Ul Pushkina 1, Chelyabinsk, 456021, Russia
Tel.: (7) 3515979022
Web Site: http://www.agregat-avia.ru
Automobile Equipment Mfr
N.A.I.C.S.: 334519

Gidroagregat JSC (2)
78 Kommunisticheskaya Street, Pavlovo, 606100, Russia
Tel.: (7) 8432577574
Web Site: http://www.gidroagregat.innov.ru
Automobile Equipment Mfr
N.A.I.C.S.: 334519

Gidroavtomatika JSC (2)
D 53 Zavodskoe Shosse, 443052, Samara, Russia
Tel.: (7) 8469311855
Web Site: http://www.gidroavtomatika.ru
Automobile Equipment Mfr
N.A.I.C.S.: 334519

JSC Concern of Aviation equipment (2)
Ibragimova ulitsa 29, 105058, Moscow, Russia
Tel.: (7) 4959892939
Automobile Equipment Mfr
N.A.I.C.S.: 334519

JSC PCP RESPIRATOR (2)
1 Gagarin st, Orekhovo-Zuevo, Moscow, Russia
Tel.: (7) 4964131669
Web Site: http://www.respiro-oz.ru
Automobile Equipment Mfr
N.A.I.C.S.: 334519

Sarapul Electrogenerator Plant JSC (2)
Ul Elektrozavodskaya 15, 427961, Sarapul, Russia
Tel.: (7) 3414797700
Web Site: http://www.segz.ru
Automobile Equipment Mfr
N.A.I.C.S.: 334519

RUSSKAYA AKVAKULTURA
4-B Belovejskaya St, Moscow, 121353, Russia
Tel.: (7) 4952589928
AQUA—(RUS)
Sales Range: Less than $1 Million
Fish & Seafood Product Merchant Whslr
N.A.I.C.S.: 424460

RUSSKIYE SAMOTSVETY CORPORATION
8 Carl Faberge sq, 195112, Saint Petersburg, Russia
Tel.: (7) 8005550980
Web Site: http://www.russam.ru
Year Founded: 1912
Jewelry Mfr & Sales
N.A.I.C.S.: 339910
Sergey A. Dokuchaev *(Gen Dir)*

RUSSNEFT PJSC
69 Pyatnitskaya st, 115054, Moscow, 115054, Russia
Tel.: (7) 4954116309   RU
Web Site: https://www.russneft.ru
Year Founded: 2002
RNFT—(MOEX)
Rev.: $3,868,743,916
Assets: $4,390,638,729
Liabilities: $2,958,953,367
Net Worth: $1,431,685,362
Earnings: $118,377,952
Emp.: 6,310

Fiscal Year-end: 12/31/22
Oil & Gas Exploration Services
N.A.I.C.S.: 211130
Dmitry Vyacheslavovich Romanov *(VP-Corp Rels)*

Subsidiaries:

LLC Belye Nochi (1)
Bld 13 m/d 1 Khmao, Raduzhny, Khanty-Mansiysk, 628461, Tyumen, Russia
Tel.: (7) 3466841577
Oil & Natural Gas Exploration Services
N.A.I.C.S.: 213112
Alexandr Tropin *(Gen Mgr)*

LLC NK Russneft-Bryansk (1)
Shkolnaya str 1 Ghecha, Starodubsky rayon, Bryansk, 243300, Russia
Tel.: (7) 84835125097
Oil & Natural Gas Exploration Services
N.A.I.C.S.: 213112
Alexander Titov *(Gen Mgr)*

LLC Neftebytservis (1)
Banny Lane Building 2, Moscow, 129110, Russia
Tel.: (7) 4957408259
Web Site: http://www.nefteservis.com
Oil & Gas Exploration Services
N.A.I.C.S.: 213112
Ivanov Vyacheslav Yurievich *(CEO)*

LLC Tomskaya Neft (1)
Petropavlovskaya str 4, Tomsk, 634034, Russia
Tel.: (7) 83822530000
Oil & Natural Gas Exploration Services
N.A.I.C.S.: 213112
Aleksey Tychinsky *(Gen Mgr)*

OJSC NAK Aki-Otyr (1)
1 Mikhalla Znamenscogo str, Khanty-Mansiysk Autonomous District-Yugra, Khanty-Mansiysk, 628010, Tyumen, Russia
Tel.: (7) 3467396382
Oil & Natural Gas Exploration Services
N.A.I.C.S.: 213112
Alexey Shatalov *(Gen Mgr)*

OJSC Saratovneftegaz (1)
Sakko i Vantsetti str 21, Saratov, 410600, Russia
Tel.: (7) 8452393555
Oil & Natural Gas Exploration Services
N.A.I.C.S.: 213112
Mikhail Devyatkin *(Gen Mgr)*

OJSC Ulyanovskneft (1)
Minayeva str 32, Ulyanovsk, 433870, Russia
Tel.: (7) 8422411717
Oil & Natural Gas Exploration Services
N.A.I.C.S.: 213112
Oleg Shulga *(Gen Mgr)*

ST JSC Goloil (1)
26 Chapaeva St Khmao-Yugra, Nizhnevartovsk, 628615, Tyumen, Russia
Tel.: (7) 83466495229
Oil & Natural Gas Exploration Services
N.A.I.C.S.: 213112
Aleksandr Tropin *(Gen Mgr)*

RUTLAND PARTNERS LLP
Cunard House 15 Regent Street, London, SW1Y 4LR, United Kingdom
Tel.: (44) 2074510700
Web Site:
http://www.rutlandpartners.com
Year Founded: 1986
Sales Range: $25-49.9 Million
Emp.: 16
Privater Equity Firm
N.A.I.C.S.: 523999
Nick Morrill *(Mng Partner)*

Subsidiaries:

CeDo Folien und Haushaltsprodukte GmbH (1)
Henn Weisweiler Allee 18, Monchengladbach, 41179, Germany
Tel.: (49) 21615767600
Web Site: http://www.cedo.com
Sales Range: $200-249.9 Million
Household Products Mfr
N.A.I.C.S.: 322220

INTERNATIONAL PUBLIC

Alan Jamieson *(Chm)*

Laidlaw Interiors Group Ltd (1)
Milnhay Road Langley Mill, Nottingham, NG16 4AZ, United Kingdom
Tel.: (44) 1773 530500
Web Site:
http://www.laidlawinteriorsgroup.com
Door Mfr & Distr
N.A.I.C.S.: 332321

Subsidiary (Non-US):

Laidlaw Asia Limited (2)
Room 2/l - 2nd Floor On Hing Mansion 156-164 Queens Road East, Wanchai, China (Hong Kong)
Tel.: (852) 5987 6950
Wood Whslr
N.A.I.C.S.: 423310
Sharon Cheung *(Acct Mgr-Sls)*

Laidlaw Interiors Gulf LLC (2)
, PO Box 185292, Dubai, United Arab Emirates
Tel.: (971) 4885 7404
Wood Whslr
N.A.I.C.S.: 423310
Laster Lloyd Magalued *(Mgr-Technical & Specification)*

Maplin Electronics Ltd (1)
Brookfields Way Manvers Wath Upon Dearne, Rotherham, S63 5DL, United Kingdom
Tel.: (44) 333 400 9500
Web Site: http://www.maplin.co.uk
Online Shopping Retailer
N.A.I.C.S.: 425120
Oliver Meakin *(Dir-Comml)*

Pizza Hut (UK) Limited (1)
Building 1 Imperial Place, Elstree Way, Borehamwood, WD6 1JN, Herts, United Kingdom   (100%)
Tel.: (44) 3301230790
Web Site: http://www.pizzahut.co.uk
Sales Range: $25-49.9 Million
Franchise Restaurant Operator
N.A.I.C.S.: 722511
Jens Hofma *(CEO)*

Rutland Fund Management Ltd. (1)
Rutland House, Rutland Gardens, London, SW7 1BX, United Kingdom   (100%)
Tel.: (44) 2075562600
Web Site: http://www.rutlandpartners.com
Sales Range: $50-74.9 Million
Investment Fund Management
N.A.I.C.S.: 523940

RUTRONIK ELEKTRONISCHE BAUELEMENTE GMBH
Industriestrasse 2, 75228, Ispringen, Germany
Tel.: (49) 72318010
Web Site: http://www.rutronik.com
Year Founded: 1973
Rev.: $549,927,000
Emp.: 1,150
Electronic Components Distr
N.A.I.C.S.: 423690
Thomas Rudel *(CEO)*

Subsidiaries:

BEK Systemtechnik GmbH & Co.KG (1)
Burknersfelder Strasse 5b, 13053, Berlin, Germany
Tel.: (49) 30 98 19 02 22
Web Site: http://www.bek-systemtechnik.de
Emp.: 75
Electronic Component Mfr & Whslr
N.A.I.C.S.: 334419
Uwe Feiler *(Mng Dir)*

RUTRONIK Beteiligungsgesellschaft mbH (1)
Leningradskoye Hwy 57, 125195, Moscow, Russia
Tel.: (7) 4999633184
Electronic Parts Whslr
N.A.I.C.S.: 423690

RUTRONIK Espana S.L. (1)
Ctra Canillas 134 - 1a Planta, 28043, Madrid, Spain
Tel.: (34) 91 300 55 28

AND PRIVATE COMPANIES

Electronic Parts Whslr
N.A.I.C.S.: 423690
Stephan Keune (Country Mgr)

RUTRONIK Italia S.r.l. (1)
21 Via Caldera Centro Direzionale S Siro,
'20153, Milan, Italy
Tel.: (39) 02 40 951 1
Electronic Parts Whslr
N.A.I.C.S.: 423690
Vittorio Terraneo (Mgr-Bus Dev)

RUTRONIK Magyarorszag Kft. (1)
Fehervari ut 89-95, 1119, Budapest, Hungary
Tel.: (36) 1 371 06 66
Electronic Parts Whslr
N.A.I.C.S.: 423690

RUTRONIK Polska Sp. z o.o. (1)
Ul Bojkowska 37, 44-101, Gliwice, Poland
Tel.: (48) 32 461 2000
Electronic Equipment Whslr
N.A.I.C.S.: 423690

Rutronik Electronics Asia HK Ltd (1)
54/F Hopewell Centre 183 Queens Road East, Wanchai, China (Hong Kong)
Tel.: (852) 5337 0119
Electronic Parts Whslr
N.A.I.C.S.: 423690

Rutronik Nordic AB (1)
Kista Science Tower Farogatan 33, 16451, Kista, Sweden
Tel.: (46) 850554900
Web Site: http://www.rutronik.com
Sales Range: $25-49.9 Million
Emp.: 18
Electronic Components Distr
N.A.I.C.S.: 449210
Lars Mistander (VP)

Rutronik S.A.S (1)
6 Mail de I Europe, La Celle, 78170, Saint-Cloud, France
Tel.: (33) 1 30 08 33 00
Electronic Parts Whslr
N.A.I.C.S.: 423690
Pascal Coustau (Country Mgr)

Rutronik UK Limited (1)
Deakins Bus Pk Blackburn Rd, Egerton, Bolton, BL7 9RP, Lancashire, United Kingdom
Tel.: (44) 1204602200
Sales Range: $25-49.9 Million
Emp.: 30
Electronic Components Distr
N.A.I.C.S.: 423690
Gary Anderton (Mgr-Sls)

RUTSCHI FLUID AG
Gewerbepark Bata 8, CH 4313, Mohlin, Switzerland
Tel.: (41) 564605500
Web Site:
https://www.grupperutschi.com
Nuclear Grade Pumps & Related Customisation Services
N.A.I.C.S.: 221118

RUTTER INC.
63 Thorburn Road, Saint John's, A1B 3M2, NL, Canada
Tel.: (709) 576-6666   Ca
Web Site: http://www.rutter.ca
Year Founded: 2003
Sales Range: $10-24.9 Million
Marine Transportation Developer & Marketer
N.A.I.C.S.: 488390
Fraser H. Edison (Owner & Pres)

RUTTONSHA INTERNATIONAL RECTIFIER LTD.
139 / 141 Solaris 1 B Wing 1st Floor Saki Vihar Road Powai, Opp L and T Gate No 6 Andheri East, Mumbai, 400072, Maharashtra, India
Tel.: (91) 2228471956
Web Site: https://www.ruttonsha.com
517035—(BOM)
Rev: $8,236,674
Assets: $13,277,810

Liabilities: $5,743,798
Net Worth: $7,534,012
Earnings: $842,729
Fiscal Year-end: 03/31/24
Power Semiconductor Devices Mfr
N.A.I.C.S.: 334413
Bhavin P. Rambhia (Sec)

Subsidiaries:

Visicon Power Electronics Pvt. Ltd. (1)
139/141 B Wing Ist Floor Solaris 1 Saki Vihar Road, Powai, Mumbai, 400072, India
Tel.: (91) 2228471958
Web Site: https://www.visiconpower.com
Semiconductor Device Mfr & Distr
N.A.I.C.S.: 334413

RV ASSURANCES SA
Boulevard Kleyer 17, 4000, Liege, Belgium
Tel.: (32) 42524042
Emp.: 20
Insurance Brokerage Services
N.A.I.C.S.: 524298
Jean-Francois Desmare (CEO & CFO)

RVH INC.
8-5-28 Akasaka, Minato-ku, Tokyo, 107-0052, Japan
Tel.: (81) 362778084
Web Site: https://rvh.jp
Year Founded: 1996
6786—(TKS)
Rev.: $8,434,360
Assets: $8,559,950
Liabilities: $2,075,540
Net Worth: $6,484,410
Earnings: ($5,373,930)
Fiscal Year-end: 03/31/24
Software Development Services
N.A.I.C.S.: 541511
Yuichi Wada (Pres)

RW PACKAGING LTD.
200 Omand's Creek Blvd, Winnipeg, R2R 1V7, MB, Canada
Tel.: (204) 786-6873   BC
Web Site:
https://www.rwconsumerprod.com
Year Founded: 1919
Sales Range: $10-24.9 Million
Emp.: 53
Consumer Product Packaging Services
N.A.I.C.S.: 561910
Henry A. De Ruiter (Pres & CEO)

RWE AG
RWE Platz 1, 45141, Essen, Germany
Tel.: (49) 20151790   De
Web Site: https://www.rwe.com
Year Founded: 1898
RWE—(DUS)
Rev.: $31,533,150,420
Assets: $117,555,531,780
Liabilities: $82,707,459,750
Net Worth: $34,848,072,030
Earnings: $1,600,611,500
Emp.: 19,749
Fiscal Year-end: 12/31/23
Energy Holding Company
N.A.I.C.S.: 551112
Rolf Martin Schmitz (Chm-Exec Bd, CEO & Dir-Labour)

Subsidiaries:

4Motions GmbH (1)
Rosa-Luxemburg-Str 19/21, 04103, Leipzig, Germany
Tel.: (49) 34121829850
Web Site: http://www.4motionsgmbh.de
Marketing Services
N.A.I.C.S.: 541613

A/V/E GmbH (1)

Magdeburger Strasse 51, 06112, Halle, Germany
Tel.: (49) 34513240
Web Site: http://www.ave-online.de
Administrative Management Services
N.A.I.C.S.: 541611

Agrupacio Energias Renovables, S.A.U (1)
Edificio El Crianjle Catalunaa 1 Fl 3, Barcelona, 8002, Spain
Tel.: (34) 932064810
Web Site: http://www.rwe.com
Sales Range: $50-74.9 Million
Emp.: 50
Eletric Power Generation Services
N.A.I.C.S.: 221118

Awel y Mor Offshore Wind Farm Limited (1)
Windmill Hill Business Park, Whitehill Way, Swindon, SN5 6PB, Wiltshire, United Kingdom
Tel.: (44) 8001978232
Web Site: https://awelymor.cymru
Wind Electric Power Generation Services
N.A.I.C.S.: 221115

BEW Netze GmbH (1)
Sonnenweg 30, 51688, Wipperfurth, Germany
Tel.: (49) 22676860
Web Site: https://www.bew-netze.de
Gas Distribution Services
N.A.I.C.S.: 221210
Jens Langner (Mng Dir)

BTB-Blockheizkraftwerks, Trager- und Betreibergesellschaft mbH (1)
Gaussstrasse 11, 10589, Berlin, Germany
Tel.: (49) 303499070
Web Site: https://www.btb-berlin.de
Administrative Management Services
N.A.I.C.S.: 541611
David Weiblein (Mng Dir)

Belectric Australia Pty. Limited (1)
Suite 329 25 Milton Parade, Malvern, 3144, VIC, Australia
Tel.: (61) 398320773
Web Site: http://www.australia.belectric.com
Emp.: 10
Electric Power Generation Services
N.A.I.C.S.: 221112
Tom Huber (Mgr-HSE)

Belectric France S.a.r.l. (1)
ZAE Via Europa Est Rue de Stockholm, Vendres, 34350, Beziers, France
Tel.: (33) 467628780
Emp.: 19
Eletric Power Generation Services
N.A.I.C.S.: 221112
Jochen Meyer (CEO)

Belectric Inc. (1)
951 Mariners Island Blvd Ste 300, San Mateo, CA 94404
Tel.: (510) 896-3940
Solar Energy Services
N.A.I.C.S.: 221114
Matthew Lusk (Dir-Bus Dev)

Belectric Italia s.r.l. (1)
Strada Pantano d Inferno 5B B Go Faiti, 04010, Latina, Italy
Tel.: (39) 0773320801
Eletric Power Generation Services
N.A.I.C.S.: 221112
Quirino Quaglieri (CEO)

Belectric Solar & Battery GmbH (1)
Wadenbrunner Str 10, Kolitzheim, 97509, Schweinfurt, Germany
Tel.: (49) 93855489000
Web Site: http://belectric.com
Emp.: 621
Solar Energy Services
N.A.I.C.S.: 221114

Subsidiary (Non-US):

Belectric Chile Energia Fotovoltaica Ltda. (2)
Isidora Goyenechea 3356 Oficina 10 Santiago, Las Condes, Chile
Tel.: (56) 223830250
Eletric Power Generation Services
N.A.I.C.S.: 221112
Paloma Mendez Perez (Mng Dir)

Belectric Israel Ltd. (2)
Hakotzer St 20, PO Box 2280, Beersheba, 8480909, Israel
Tel.: (972) 86776060
Emp.: 66
Electric Power Generation Services
N.A.I.C.S.: 221112
Anna Velikansky (CEO)

Subsidiary (Domestic):

Belectric PV Dach GmbH (2)
Am Unterwege 7, 99610, Sommerda, Germany
Tel.: (49) 3634314560
Eletric Power Generation Services
N.A.I.C.S.: 221112

Subsidiary (Non-US):

Belectric Photovoltaic India Private Limited (2)
Unit No 601 & 602 F Wing 6th Floor Lotus Corporate Park, Gram Path Compound Off Western Express Highway Goregaon East, Mumbai, 400063, Maharashtra, India
Tel.: (91) 2268156099
Emp.: 145
Electric Power Generation Services
N.A.I.C.S.: 221112
Jitendra Singh (CEO & Mng Dir)

Belectric Solar Ltd. (2)
The Switch 1-7 The Grove, Slough, SL1 1QP, United Kingdom
Tel.: (44) 2039530000
Emp.: 22
Eletric Power Generation Services
N.A.I.C.S.: 221112
Amit Oza (Mng Dir)

Subsidiary (Domestic):

hoch.rein Beteiligungen GmbH (2)
Steigweg 24, 97318, Kitzingen, Germany
Tel.: (49) 9381710870
Web Site: http://www.hoch-rein.com
Real Estate & IT Services
N.A.I.C.S.: 531390

Budapesti Elektromos Muvek Zrt. (1)
Vaci ut 72-74, Budapest, 1132, Hungary
Tel.: (36) 12381223
Web Site: http://www.elmu.hu
Electric Power Distribution Services
N.A.I.C.S.: 221122

Carl Scholl GmbH (1)
Holz- Impragnierwerk Rosrather Strasse 770, D-51107, Cologne, Germany
Tel.: (49) 22051015
Web Site: https://www.carlscholl.de
Administrative Management Services
N.A.I.C.S.: 541611

Cegecom S.A. (1)
3 rue Jean Piret, BP 2708, L-1027, Luxembourg, Luxembourg
Tel.: (352) 264991
Web Site: https://www.cegecom.lu
Telecommunication Servicesb
N.A.I.C.S.: 517810

Cerberos S.r.o. (1)
Lannova 2061/8, 110 00, Prague, Czech Republic
Tel.: (420) 326100000
Web Site: http://www.cerberos.cz
Telecommunication Servicesb
N.A.I.C.S.: 517121

Comco MCS S.A. (1)
48 route d Arlon, 8310, Capellen, Luxembourg
Tel.: (352) 4097911
Web Site: http://www.comco.lu
Emp.: 400
Facilities Management Services
N.A.I.C.S.: 561210

Con Edison Clean Energy Businesses, Inc. (1)
100 Summit Lake Dr, Valhalla, NY 10595
Tel.: (914) 286-7000
Energy Efficiency Services
N.A.I.C.S.: 541350

Subsidiary (Domestic):

Consolidated Edison Development, Inc. (2)

RWE AG

INTERNATIONAL PUBLIC

RWE AG—(Continued)
100 Summit Lake Dr, Valhalla, NY 10595
Tel.: (914) 993-2166
Develop Renewable & Energy Infrastructure Projects
N.A.I.C.S.: 221118

RWE Clean Energy Solutions, Inc. (2)
100 Summit Lake Dr Ste 210, Valhalla, NY 10595
Tel.: (914) 286-7000
Energy Services
N.A.I.C.S.: 221122
Mark Noyes *(Pres & CEO)*

Subsidiary (Domestic):

Custom Energy Services, LLC (3)
9217 Cody St, Overland Park, KS 66214-1735
Tel.: (913) 888-8050
Energy Services
N.A.I.C.S.: 221122

Subsidiary (Domestic):

RWE Clean Energy Wholesale Services, Inc. (2)
100 Summit Lake Dr, Ste 210,, Valhalla, NY 10595
Tel.: (914) 286-7000
Web Site: https://americas.rwe.com
Renewable Energy
N.A.I.C.S.: 221122

Decadia GmbH (1)
Kokereiallee 9-11, 45141, Essen, Germany
Tel.: (49) 2011220200
Web Site: https://decadia.com
Pension Services
N.A.I.C.S.: 525110
Jorg Passmann *(Mng Dir)*

DigiKoo GmbH (1)
Opernplatz 1, 45128, Essen, Germany
Tel.: (49) 2131712025
Web Site: http://www.digikoo.de
Electric Power Distribution Services
N.A.I.C.S.: 221122
Peter Mathis *(Mng Dir & COO)*

ELE Verteilnetz GmbH (1)
Ebertstrasse 30, 45879, Gelsenkirchen, Germany
Tel.: (49) 20916515
Web Site: https://www.evng.de
Electric Power Distribution Services
N.A.I.C.S.: 221122

EVIP GmbH (1)
Niels-Bohr-Strasse 2, 06749, Bitterfeld-Wolfen, Germany
Tel.: (49) 349351670
Web Site: https://www.evip.de
Electricity & Gas Distribution Services
N.A.I.C.S.: 221210
Thomas Tschakert *(Mng Dir)*

EWV Energie- und Wasser-Versorgung GmbH (1)
Willy-brandt-platz 2, 52222, Stolberg, Germany
Tel.: (49) 8003981000
Web Site: https://www.ewv.de
Electric Power Distribution Services
N.A.I.C.S.: 221122
Mayor Patrick Haas *(Chm-)*

Edgware Energy Limited (1)
Whitehill Way Trigonos, Swindon, SN5 6PB, Wiltshire, United Kingdom
Tel.: (44) 1793475215
Energy Holding Company
N.A.I.C.S.: 551112

El Pimiento (SpA) (1)
Las Condes, Santiago, Chile
Tel.: (56) 999388407
Web Site: http://www.elpimiento.cl
Soup & Pulp Distr
N.A.I.C.S.: 424490

Elektrocieplownia Bedzin S.A. (1)
ul Boleslawa Krzywoustego 7, 61-144, Poznan, Poland
Tel.: (48) 536544512
Web Site: http://www.ecbedzin.pl
Rev: $62,020,833
Assets: $50,764,482

Liabilities: $208,165,396
Net Worth: ($157,400,914)
Earnings: ($50,532,266)
Fiscal Year-end: 12/31/2023
Electric Power Generation & Distribution Services
N.A.I.C.S.: 221118
Bartosz Dryjski *(Member-Mgmt Bd)*

Emscher Lippe Energie GmbH (1)
Ebertstrasse 30, 45879, Gelsenkirchen, Germany
Tel.: (49) 209 165 10
Web Site: http://www.ele.de
Sales Range: $250-299.9 Million
Electric Power Distribution Services
N.A.I.C.S.: 221122

EnergieRevolte GmbH (1)
Arnoldsweilerstr 60, 52351, Duren, Germany
Tel.: (49) 24213059520
Web Site: http://www.energierevolte.de
Electric Power Distribution Services
N.A.I.C.S.: 221122

Energienetze Berlin GmbH (1)
Gaussstrasse 11, 10589, Berlin, Germany
Tel.: (49) 30398409200
Web Site: https://www.energienetze-berlin.de
Electricity Distribution Services
N.A.I.C.S.: 221118
Christian Gunther *(Mng Dir)*

Energies France S.A.S. (1)
198B Rue La Fayette, 75010, Paris, France
Tel.: (33) 182880899
Web Site: http://www.energiesfrance.fr
Electricity Device Mfr
N.A.I.C.S.: 334515

Energiewacht Groep B.V. (1)
Lippestraat 1, 8000 AL, Zwolle, Netherlands
Tel.: (31) 882008555
Web Site: http://www.energiewacht.com
Heat Pump Mfr
N.A.I.C.S.: 333415

Energiewacht West Nederland B.V. (1)
Tel.: (31) 885553000
Web Site: https://www.energiewacht.nl
Emp.: 400
Heating Contractor Services
N.A.I.C.S.: 238220

Energis GmbH (1)
Heinrich-Bocking-Str 10-14, 66121, Saarbrucken, Germany
Tel.: (49) 68190690
Web Site: http://www.energis.de
Electric Power & Gas Distribution Services
N.A.I.C.S.: 221122

Envia Netzservice GmbH (1)
Magdeburger Strasse 36, 06112, Halle, Germany
Tel.: (49) 345 216 0
Web Site: http://www.envia-nsg.de
Electric Power Generation & Distribution Services
N.A.I.C.S.: 221111

EuroSkyPark GmbH (1)
Heinrich-Barth Strasse 30, 66115, Saarbrucken, Germany
Tel.: (49) 6819761720
Web Site: http://euroskypark.com
Information Technology & Services
N.A.I.C.S.: 541511

GWG Grevenbroich GmbH (1)
Nordstrasse 36, 41515, Grevenbroich, Germany
Tel.: (49) 218165050
Web Site: http://www.gwg-grevenbroich.de
Electric Power Generation Services
N.A.I.C.S.: 221118

Geas Energiewacht B.V. (1)
Spoordijkstraat 6, 7521 CA, Enschede, Netherlands
Tel.: (31) 538528500
Web Site: http://www.geas.nl
Emp.: 130
Electric Power Generation Services
N.A.I.C.S.: 221118

Greenswitch Wind, LLC (1)
353 N Clark St Ste 3000, Chicago, IL 60654
Tel.: (312) 307-0981
Web Site: https://greenswitchwind.com
Wind Electric Power Generation Services
N.A.I.C.S.: 221115

HELIOS MB s.r.o. (1)
Lannova 2061/8, 110 00, Prague, Czech Republic
Tel.: (420) 774486726
Web Site: http://www.heliosmb.cz
Telecommunication Servicesb
N.A.I.C.S.: 517810

Heizungs- und Sanitarbau WIJA GmbH (1)
Christine-Demmer-Strasse 34, 53474, Bad Neuenahr-Ahrweiler, Germany
Tel.: (49) 2641918960
Web Site: http://wija.de
Building Services
N.A.I.C.S.: 561790

INDI Energie B.V. (1)
Rotsoord 13a, 3523 CL, Utrecht, Netherlands
Tel.: (31) 732032179
Web Site: https://www.indienergie.nl
Solar Panels Installation Services
N.A.I.C.S.: 238210

Innogy Renewables UK Limited (1)
Windmill Hill Business Park Whitehill Way, Swindon, SN5 6PB, Wiltshire, United Kingdom
Tel.: (44) 1793877777
Elletric Power Generation Services
N.A.I.C.S.: 221118

Isoprofs Belgie BVBA (1)
Maastrichtersteenweg 211/1, 3500, Hasselt, Belgium
Tel.: (32) 11325222
Web Site: http://www.isoprofs.be
Insulation Services
N.A.I.C.S.: 238310

KWS Kommunal-Wasserversorgung Saar GmbH (1)
Heinrich-Bocking-Strasse 10-14, 66121, Saarbrucken, Germany
Tel.: (49) 68190691499
Web Site: http://www.kws-gmbh.com
Business Support Services
N.A.I.C.S.: 561499

Kernkraftwerk Gundremmingen GmbH (1)
Dr -August-Weckesser Strasse 1, 89355, Gundremmingen, Germany
Tel.: (49) 8224 78 1
Web Site: http://www.kkw-gundremmingen.de
Electric Power Distribution Services
N.A.I.C.S.: 221122

Kernkraftwerke Lippe-Ems GmbH (1)
Am Hilgenberg, 49811, Lingen, Germany
Tel.: (49) 5918061611
Emp.: 300
Electric Power Distribution Services
N.A.I.C.S.: 221122

KlickEnergie GmbH & Co. KG (1)
Moselstr 25-27, 41464, Neuss, Germany
Tel.: (49) 21315310123
Web Site: https://www.klickenergie.de
Gas Distribution Services
N.A.I.C.S.: 221210

Koprivnica Opskrba d.o.o. (1)
Mosna ulica 15, 48000, Koprivnica, Croatia
Tel.: (385) 48251833
Web Site: http://koprivnica-opskrba.hr
Gas Distribution Services
N.A.I.C.S.: 221210

Koprivnica Plin d.o.o. (1)
Mosna 15, 48000, Koprivnica, Croatia
Tel.: (385) 48251869
Web Site: http://www.koprivnica-plin.hr
Gas Distribution Services
N.A.I.C.S.: 221210

LEW Service & Consulting GmbH (1)
Schaezlerstrasse 3, 86150, Augsburg, Germany

Tel.: (49) 8213284311
Web Site: https://www.lew-betriebsrestaurant.de
Consultancy Services
N.A.I.C.S.: 541618
Verena Haselbeck *(Mng Dir)*

LEW TelNet GmbH (1)
Oskar-von-Miller-Strasse 1 b, 86356, Neuss, Germany
Tel.: (49) 8213282929
Web Site: https://telnet.lew.de
Emp.: 140
Telecommunication Contractor Services
N.A.I.C.S.: 517810
Jorg Steins *(Mng Dir)*

LEW Verteilnetz GmbH (1)
Schaezlerstrasse 3, 86150, Augsburg, Germany
Tel.: (49) 8213282222
Web Site: https://www.lew-verteilnetz.de
Electric Power Distribution Services
N.A.I.C.S.: 221122
Christian Barr *(Chm-)*

Lechwerke AG (1)
Schaezlerstrasse 3, 86150, Augsburg, Germany
Tel.: (49) 8213280
Web Site: https://www.lew.de
Rev: $1,696,394,300
Assets: $1,960,738,049
Liabilities: $1,373,832,447
Net Worth: $586,905,602
Earnings: $151,263,306
Emp.: 402
Fiscal Year-end: 12/31/2023
Electric Power Distr
N.A.I.C.S.: 221122
Markus Litpher *(Member-Mgmt Bd)*

Leitungspartner GmbH (1)
Arnoldsweilerstrasse 60, 52351, Duren, Germany
Tel.: (49) 242148650
Web Site: https://www.leitungspartner.de
Emp.: 200
Elletric Power Generation Services
N.A.I.C.S.:

Lemonbeat GmbH (1)
Revierstrasse 3, 44379, Dortmund, Germany
Tel.: (49) 2315869370
Web Site: https://www.lemonbeat.com
Emp.: 31
Information Technology Services
N.A.I.C.S.: 541511
Oliver Van Der Mond *(CEO & Member-Exec Bd)*

MITGAS Mitteldeutsche Gasversorgung GmbH (1)
Industriestr 10, 06184, Kabelsketal, Germany
Tel.: (49) 3452160
Web Site: https://www.mitgas.de
Natural Gas Distr
N.A.I.C.S.: 221210
Diddo Diddens *(Chm-)*

Matrai Eromu Zartkoruen Mukodo Reszvenytarsasag (1)
Eromu utca 11, 3271, Visonta, Hungary
Tel.: (36) 637334000
Web Site: http://www.mert.hu
Electric Power Distribution Services
N.A.I.C.S.: 221122

Mitteldeutsche Netzgesellschaft Gas mbH (1)
Industriestrasse 10, 06184, Kabelsketal, Germany
Tel.: (49) 3452160
Web Site: https://www.mitnetz-gas.de
Gas Distribution Services
N.A.I.C.S.: 221210
Dirk Sattur *(Mng Dir)*

MotionWerk GmbH (1)
Opernplatz 1, 45128, Essen, Germany
Tel.: (49) 1739964549
Web Site: http://www.motionwerk.com
Information Technology Services
N.A.I.C.S.: 541511

NEW Re GmbH (1)
Odenkirchener Strasse 201, 41236, Monchengladbach, Germany

AND PRIVATE COMPANIES — RWE AG

Tel.: (49) 21666880
Web Site: http://www.new-re.de
Information Technology Services
N.A.I.C.S.: 541511

Qualitas-AMS GmbH (1)
Eiserfelder Str 316, 57080, Siegen, Germany
Tel.: (49) 27180919949
Web Site: http://www.qualitas-ams.de
Information Technology Services
N.A.I.C.S.: 541511

RV Rheinbraun Handel und Dienstleistungen GmbH (1)
Stuttgenweg 2, 50935, Cologne, Germany
Tel.: (49) 2214800
Mining & Metal Distr
N.A.I.C.S.: 423520

RWE Beteiligungsgesellschaft mbH (1)
Opernplatz 1, 45128, Essen, Germany
Tel.: (49) 2011200
Web Site: http://www.rwe.com
Elictric Power Generation Services
N.A.I.C.S.: 221112

RWE Deutschland Aktiengesellschaft (1)
Kruppstr 5, Essen, 45128, Nordrhein-Westfalen, Germany
Tel.: (49) 2011208
Electric Power Generation & Distribution Services
N.A.I.C.S.: 221111

RWE Effizienz GmbH (1)
Freistuhl 7, Dortmund, 44137, Germany
Tel.: (49) 23143807
Electric Power Distribution Services
N.A.I.C.S.: 221122

RWE Energie, a.s. (1)
Kliskka 940, Usti nad Labem, 407 17, Czech Republic
Tel.: (420) 475325269
Web Site: http://www.rwe.cz
Sales Range: $75-99.9 Million
Emp.: 25
Electric Power Distribution Services
N.A.I.C.S.: 221122

RWE Energy Nederland N.V. (1)
Postbus 90, 2130 AB, Hoofddorp, Netherlands
Tel.: (31) 235691400
Web Site: http://www.rwe.nl
Natural Gas Distr
N.A.I.C.S.: 221210

RWE Gas Storage CZ, s.r.o. (1)
Prosecka 855/68, Prague, 190 00, Czech Republic
Tel.: (420) 267971111
Web Site: http://www.rwe-gasstorage.cz
Natural Gas Storage Services
N.A.I.C.S.: 213112

RWE GasNet, s.r.o. (1)
Kliskka 940/96 Klise, 400 01, Usti nad Labem, Czech Republic
Tel.: (420) 475325306
Web Site: http://www.gasnet.cz
Natural Gas Distr
N.A.I.C.S.: 221210

RWE Generation SE (1)
RWE Platz 3, 45141, Essen, Germany
Tel.: (49) 20151790
Energy Holding Company
N.A.I.C.S.: 551112
Roger Miesen (Chm & CEO)

RWE Hrvatska d.o.o. (1)
Capraska 6, 10000, Zagreb, Croatia
Tel.: (385) 16427100
Web Site: http://www.rwe.hr
Gas Distribution Services
N.A.I.C.S.: 221210
Karl Kraus (CEO)

RWE Innogy GmbH (1)
Gildehofstrasse 1, Essen, 45127, Germany
Tel.: (49) 2011214499
Web Site: http://www.rwe.com
Elictric Power Generation Services
N.A.I.C.S.: 221118

RWE Kundenservice GmbH (1)
Wielandstr 82, Bochum, 44791, Germany

Tel.: (49) 2345150
Electric Power Distribution Services
N.A.I.C.S.: 221122

RWE Ljubljana d.o.o. (1)
Bravnicarjeva ulica 13, 1000, Ljubljana, Slovenia
Tel.: (386) 803636
Web Site: http://www.rwe.si
Renewable Energy Services
N.A.I.C.S.: 213112
Juraj Drahovsky (CFO)

RWE Npower plc
Windmill Hill Business Park Whitehill Way, Swindon, SN5 6PB, Wilts, United Kingdom (100%)
Tel.: (44) 793877777
Sales Range: $1-4.9 Billion
Emp.: 4,000
Supply, Generation & Asset Management.
N.A.I.C.S.: 531390

Division (Domestic):

Generation Aggregates - Ash Products (2)
Windmill Hill Business Park Whitehill Way, Swindon, SN5 6PB, Wilts, United Kingdom
Tel.: (44) 8007312865
Sales Range: $50-74.9 Million
Emp.: 500
Potash Mining
N.A.I.C.S.: 212390
Lisa Crow (Head-Generation Aggregates)

Subsidiary (Domestic):

RWE Npower Holdings plc (2)
Windmill Hill Business Park Whitehill Way, Swindon, SN5 6PB, Wilts, United Kingdom
Tel.: (44) 1793877777
Emp.: 1,000
Holding Company
N.A.I.C.S.: 551112
Paul Massara (CEO)

RWE Npower Renewables Limited (2)
Auckland House Lydiard Fields Great Western Way, Swindon, SN5 8ZT, Wilts, United Kingdom (100%)
Tel.: (44) 845 672 0090
Web Site: http://www.npower-renewables.com
Sales Range: $50-74.9 Million
Emp.: 12
Wind Farm Developer & Operater
N.A.I.C.S.: 221115

Division (Domestic):

npower Cogen (2)
Cranmore Blvd Cogen Ct, Shirley, B90 4LN, Surrey, United Kingdom
Tel.: (44) 215068000
Web Site: http://www.cogen.com
Sales Range: $25-49.9 Million
Emp.: 54
Mfr of Electronic & Gas Products
N.A.I.C.S.: 324199

RWE Nuclear GmbH (1)
RWE Platz 2, 45141, Essen, Germany
Tel.: (49) 20151790
Emp.: 1,200
Energy Holding Company
N.A.I.C.S.: 551112
Nikolaus Valerius (CTO)

RWE Plin d.o.o. (1)
Capraska ulica 6, 10000, Zagreb, Croatia
Tel.: (385) 16427100
Gas Distribution Services
N.A.I.C.S.: 221210

RWE Power Aktiengesellschaft (1)
Stuttgenweg 2, 50935, Cologne, Germany
Tel.: (49) 2214800
Web Site: http://www.rwe.com
Electric Power Distribution Services
N.A.I.C.S.: 221122

RWE Renewables GmbH (1)
RWE Platz 4, 45141, Essen, Germany
Tel.: (49) 20151790
Elictric Power Generation Services
N.A.I.C.S.: 221115

Subsidiary (Non-US):

RWE Energie Odnawialne Sp. z o.o. (2)

Plac Rodla 8 lokal 2003, 70-419, Szczecin, Poland
Tel.: (48) 913594281
Eletric Power Generation Services
N.A.I.C.S.: 221118

RWE Renewables Sweden AB (2)
Pildammsvagen 6B van 2, 211 46, Malmo, Sweden
Tel.: (46) 738401542
Eletric Power Generation Services
N.A.I.C.S.: 221118

RWE Rhein-Ruhr Verteilnetz GmbH (1)
Reeser Landstrabe 41, Wesel, 46483, Germany
Tel.: (49) 2812012441
Electric Power Distribution Services
N.A.I.C.S.: 221122

RWE Service GmbH (1)
Flamingoweg 1, Dortmund, 44139, Nordrhein-Westfalen, Germany
Tel.: (49) 23143800
Eletric Power Generation Services
N.A.I.C.S.: 221111

RWE Stoen Operator Sp. z o.o. (1)
ul Rudzka 18, 22-821, Warsaw, Poland
Tel.: (48) 228213111
Web Site: http://www.rwestoenoperator.pl
Electricity Transmission & Control Services
N.A.I.C.S.: 221121
Klaus Engelbertz (Member-Mgmt Bd)

RWE Supply & Trading (India) Private Limited (1)
Office No 203 Windfall Sahar Plaza Complex J B Nagar, Andheri Kurla Road Andheri, Mumbai, 400 059, India
Tel.: (91) 2242082400
Energy Holding Company
N.A.I.C.S.: 551112

RWE Supply & Trading Asia-Pacific Pte. Ltd. (1)
9 Raffles Place 60-01 Republic Plaza, Singapore, 048619, Singapore
Tel.: (65) 66714200
Energy Holding Company
N.A.I.C.S.: 551112

RWE Supply & Trading CZ GmbH (1)
Altenessener Strasse 27, 45141, Essen, Germany
Tel.: (49) 2011209
Energy Holding Company
N.A.I.C.S.: 551112

RWE Supply & Trading CZ, a.s. (1)
Limuzska 12/3135 Strasnice, 100 98, Prague, Czech Republic
Tel.: (420) 267971111
Energy Holding Company
N.A.I.C.S.: 551112

RWE Supply & Trading GmbH (1)
RWE Platz 6, 45141, Essen, Germany
Tel.: (49) 20151790
Web Site: https://www.rwe.com
Elictric Power Generation Services
N.A.I.C.S.: 221111
Michael Muller (CFO & Member-Exec Bd)

RWE Supply & Trading Japan KK (1)
5F Marunouchi Trust Tower Main 1-8-3 Marunouchi, Chiyoda-ku, Tokyo, 100-0005, Japan
Tel.: (81) 345109800
Wind Power Generation Services
N.A.I.C.S.: 221118

RWE Supply & Trading Switzerland S.A. (1)
1 rue de Jargonnant, 1207, Geneva, Switzerland
Tel.: (41) 229183000
Logistics Management Consulting Services
N.A.I.C.S.: 541614

RWE Technology International GmbH (1)
Ernestinenstrasse 60, 45141, Essen, Germany
Tel.: (49) 2011201
Energy Holding Company
N.A.I.C.S.: 551112

Ingo Brinkraut (CEO & Mng Dir-Sls)

RWE Transgas, a.s. (1)
Limuzska 12/3135, 100 98, Prague, Czech Republic
Tel.: (420) 267971111
Web Site: http://www.rwe-transgas.cz
Sales Range: $1-4.9 Billion
Emp.: 300
Natural Gas Distr
N.A.I.C.S.: 221210

RWE Vertrieb Aktiengesellschaft (1)
Freistuhl 7, Dortmund, 44137, Germany
Tel.: (49) 2314382915
Web Site: http://www.rwe.com
Natural Gas Distr
N.A.I.C.S.: 221210

RWE Westfalen-Weser-Ems Netzservice GmbH (1)
Florian Street, Dortmund, 44139, Germany
Tel.: (49) 23143808
Electric Power Distribution Services
N.A.I.C.S.: 221122

RWE Westfalen-Weser-Ems Verteilnetz GmbH (1)
Bochumer Strsse 2, 45661, Recklinghausen, Germany
Tel.: (49) 2361381222
Web Site: http://www.wwe-verteilnetz.com
Electricity & Gas Network Construction Services
N.A.I.C.S.: 237120

RWW Rheinisch-Westfalische Wasserwerksgesellschaft mbH (1)
Am Schloss Broich 1-3, 45479, Mulheim an der Ruhr, Germany
Tel.: (49) 20844331
Web Site: https://www.rww.de
Sales Range: $250-299.9 Million
Water Supply Services
N.A.I.C.S.: 221310
Stefan Kuppers (Chm-)

Rheinbraun Brennstoff GmbH (1)
Ludwigstrasse, 50226, Frechen, Germany
Tel.: (49) 2234109
Web Site: https://www.rheinbraun-brennstoff.de
Electric Power Distribution Services
N.A.I.C.S.: 221122

SMP Net, s.r.o. (1)
Plynarni 420/2, 702 00, Ostrava, Czech Republic
Tel.: (420) 840 113 355
Natural Gas Distr
N.A.I.C.S.: 221210

SRS EcoTherm GmbH (1)
Neuenkirchener Strasse 8, 48499, Salzbergen, Germany
Tel.: (49) 5976945633
Web Site: https://www.srs-ecotherm.de
Waste Disposal & Reprocessing Services
N.A.I.C.S.: 562219
Heinz-Jurgen Wullenweber (CEO-Technical)

SchlauTherm GmbH (1)
Malstatter Markt 3, 66115, Saarbrucken, Germany
Tel.: (49) 6819590280
Web Site: http://www.schlautherm.de
Office Administrative Services
N.A.I.C.S.: 561110

Stadtwerke Duren GmbH (1)
Arnoldsweilerstr 60, 52351, Duren, Germany
Tel.: (49) 24 21 126 0
Web Site: http://www.stadtwerke-dueren.de
Electric Power Distribution Services
N.A.I.C.S.: 221122

Sudwestsachsische Netz GmbH (1)
Amselstrasse 3, 08451, Crimmitschau, Germany
Tel.: (49) 3762769300
Web Site: http://www.suwesanetz.de
Electricity & Gas Distribution Services
N.A.I.C.S.: 221210

Suwag Energie AG (1)
Schutzenbleiche 9-11, 65929, Frankfurt am Main, Germany
Tel.: (49) 6931070
Web Site: https://www.suewag.com
Emp.: 2,000

RWE AG

RWE AG—(Continued)

Electric Power Distribution Services
N.A.I.C.S.: 221122

Suwag Netz GmbH (1)
Schuetzen Eleiche 9-11, 65929, Frankfurt am Main, Germany
Tel.: (49) 6931071060
Web Site: http://www.suewag-netz.de
Sales Range: $500-549.9 Million
Emp.: 700
Electric Power Distribution Services
N.A.I.C.S.: 221122

Syna GmbH (1)
Ludwigshafener Strasse 4, 65929, Frankfurt am Main, Germany
Tel.: (49) 6931071060
Web Site: https://www.syna.de
Electricity & Gas Distribution Services
N.A.I.C.S.: 221210
Markus Coenen (Chm-)

TWS Technische Werke der Gemeinde Saarwellingen GmbH (1)
Vorstadtstrasse 77, Saarwellingen, 66793, Saarlouis, Germany
Tel.: (49) 683890050
Web Site: https://www.tws-saarwellingen.de
Gas Distribution Services
N.A.I.C.S.: 221210

Uberlandwerk Krumbach GmbH (1)
Bahnhofstrasse 4 Krumbach, 86381, Markt Schwaben, Germany
Tel.: (49) 82829010
Web Site: https://www.uewk.de
Electricity & Gas Distribution Services
N.A.I.C.S.: 221210
Martin Glink (Mng Dir)

VSE Agentur GmbH (1)
Neugrabenweg 4, 66123, Saarbrucken, Germany
Tel.: (49) 68121300
Web Site: http://www.vse-agentur.de
Consulting Services
N.A.I.C.S.: 541618

VSE NET GmbH (1)
Tel.: (49) 6816071111
Web Site: https://vsenet.de
Communication Service
N.A.I.C.S.: 516210
Stephan Tenge (Chm)

VSE Verteilnetz GmbH (1)
Heinrich-Bocking-Str 10-14, 66121, Saarbrucken, Germany
Tel.: (49) 68140301221
Web Site: https://www.vse-verteilnetz.de
Network Operator Services
N.A.I.C.S.: 517121
Roman Fixemer (Mng Dir)

VWS Verbundwerke Sudwestsachsen GmbH (1)
Hartensteiner Strasse 7, 09350, Lichtenstein, Germany
Tel.: (49) 372045850
Web Site: http://www.vws-verbundwerke.de
Emp.: 65
Electricity & Gas Distribution Services
N.A.I.C.S.: 221210

Vliegasunie B.V. (1)
Belle van Zuylenlaan 3, 4105 JX, Culemborg, Netherlands
Tel.: (31) 345509988
Web Site: http://www.vliegasunie.nl
Building Materials Mfr
N.A.I.C.S.: 327120

Volta Limburg B.V. (1)
Breinderveldweg 5, 6365 CM, Schinnen, Netherlands
Tel.: (31) 880278888
Web Site: https://www.voltalimburg.nl
Heating Equipment Whslr
N.A.I.C.S.: 423720

Volta Solar B.V. (1)
Eisterweg 6, 6422 PN, Heerlen, Netherlands
Tel.: (31) 880237480
Web Site: http://voltasolar.nl
Solar Energy Installation Services
N.A.I.C.S.: 238210

Vychodoceska plynarenska, a.s. (1)
Pralska Ulice 702, Hradec Kralove, 50004, Czech Republic
Tel.: (420) 495060111
Web Site: http://www.vcp.cz
Natural Gas Distr
N.A.I.C.S.: 221210

WGK Windenergie Grosskorbetha GmbH & Co.KG (1)
Hallesche Strasse 3, 06679, Lutzen, Germany
Tel.: (49) 3443419206
Web Site: http://www.windenergie-grosskorbetha.de
Solar Energy Services
N.A.I.C.S.: 221114

Walden Green Energy LLC (1)
40 Worth St 10th Fl, New York, NY 10013
Tel.: (646) 527-7288
Web Site: https://www.waldengreenenergy.com
Renewable Energy Firm Services
N.A.I.C.S.: 221118

Walden Renewables Development LLC (1)
5 Columbus Cir 16th Fl, New York, NY 10019
Tel.: (917) 880-0063
Web Site: https://www.waldenrenewables.com
Wind Electric Power Generation Services
N.A.I.C.S.: 221115

Wendelsteinbahn Verteilnetz GmbH (1)
Kerschelweg 30, 83098, Brannenberg, Germany
Tel.: (49) 8034308159
Web Site: http://www.wendelsteinbahn.de
Network Services
N.A.I.C.S.: 517112

Westerwald-Netz GmbH (1)
Geishardtstrasse 44, Betzdorf, 57518, Alsdorf, Germany
Tel.: (49) 274192110
Web Site: https://www.ww-netzgesellschaft.de
Network Services
N.A.I.C.S.: 517112
Andreas Esser (Mng Dir)

Windkraft Hochheim GmbH & Co. KG (1)
Hallesche Strasse 3, 06686, Lutzen, Germany
Tel.: (49) 3443419206
Web Site: http://www.windkraft-hochheim.de
Windmill Mfr
N.A.I.C.S.: 333611

bildungszentrum energie GmbH (1)
Forsterstrasse 53, 06112, Halle, Germany
Tel.: (49) 3452163800
Web Site: http://www.bze-online.de
Electric Power Distribution Services
N.A.I.C.S.: 221122

energis-Netzgesellschaft mbH (1)
Heinrich-Bocking-Strasse 10-14, 66121, Saarbrucken, Germany
Tel.: (49) 68140301566
Web Site: https://www.energis-netzgesellschaft.de
Emp.: 210
Electricity & Gas Distribution Services
N.A.I.C.S.: 221210

enermarket GmbH (1)
Ludwigshafener Str 4, 65929, Frankfurt, Germany
Tel.: (49) 6980880700
Web Site: http://www.enermarket.de
Environmental Engineer Services
N.A.I.C.S.: 541330

enervolution GmbH (1)
Kortumstr 68, 44787, Bochum, Germany
Tel.: (49) 23423979568
Web Site: https://www.enervolution.de
Design Agency Services
N.A.I.C.S.: 541490
Dirk Lang (Mng Dir)

envia Mitteldeutsche Energie AG (1)
Chemnitztalstrasse 13, 09114, Chemnitz, Germany
Tel.: (49) 3714820

Web Site: https://www.enviam.de
Telecommunication Servicesb
N.A.I.C.S.: 517810
Stephan Lowis (Chm)

envia THERM GmbH (1)
Niels-Bohr-Str 2, 06749, Bitterfeld-Wolfen, Germany
Tel.: (49) 349351674499
Web Site: https://www.envia-therm.de
Emp.: 169
Electric Power Generation Services
N.A.I.C.S.: 221118
Holger Linke (Mng Dir)

envia Verteilnetz GmbH (1)
Magdeburger Strasse 36, 06112, Halle, Germany
Tel.: (49) 345 216 0
Web Site: http://www.envia-netz.de
Electric Power Distribution Services
N.A.I.C.S.: 221122

eprimo GmbH (1)
Flughafenstrasse 20, 63263, Neu-Isenburg, Germany
Tel.: (49) 696976700
Web Site: https://www.eprimo.de
Sales Range: $75-99.9 Million
Emp.: 160
Electric Power Distribution Services
N.A.I.C.S.: 221122
Katja Steger (Chm-Mgmt Bd)

innogy Consulting GmbH (1)
Lysegang 11, 45139, Essen, Germany
Tel.: (49) 20181330
Web Site: http://www.innogyconsulting.com
Consulting Management Services
N.A.I.C.S.: 541618

innogy Direkt GmbH (1)
Freistuhl 7, 44137, Dortmund, Germany
Tel.: (49) 2011248470
Web Site: http://www.direkt.innogy.com
Emp.: 200
Electric Power Distribution Services
N.A.I.C.S.: 221122
Klaus Grellmann (Mng Dir)

innogy Gas Storage NWE GmbH (1)
Flamingoweg 1, 44139, Dortmund, Germany
Tel.: (49) 2314382110
Web Site: http://www.innogy-gasstorage-nwe.com
Self Storage Services
N.A.I.C.S.: 531130

innogy Innovation GmbH (1)
Rellinghauser Str 27, 45128, Essen, Germany
Tel.: (49) 2011248332
Web Site: http://www.innovationhub.innogy.com
Venture Capital Services
N.A.I.C.S.: 523910

innogy Metering GmbH (1)
At the Castle Broich 1-3, 45479, Mulheim an der Ruhr, Germany
Tel.: (49) 2084433800
Web Site: http://www.iam.innogy.com
Venture Capital Services
N.A.I.C.S.: 523910

innogy Polska S.A. (1)
Wlodarzewska 68, 02-384, Warsaw, Poland
Tel.: (48) 228214646
Web Site: http://www.innogy.pl
Electric Power Generation Services
N.A.I.C.S.: 221118

innogy Slovensko s.r.o. (1)
Hviezdoslavovo nam 13, 811 02, Bratislava, Slovakia
Tel.: (421) 850123313
Web Site: http://www.innogy.sk
Electric Power Generation Services
N.A.I.C.S.: 221118

innogy Stiftung fur Energie und Gesellschaft gGmbH (1)
Openplatz 1, 45128, Essen, Germany
Tel.: (49) 2011215183
Web Site: http://www.innogy-stiftung.com
Business Management Services
N.A.I.C.S.: 541611

innogy Stoen Operator Sp. z o.o. (1)
ul Niesswieska 52, 03-867, Warsaw, Poland

Tel.: (48) 228213011
Web Site: http://www.innogystoenoperator.pl
Eletric Power Generation Services
N.A.I.C.S.: 221118

innogy Ventures GmbH (1)
Kettwiger Str 62-64, 45127, Essen, Germany
Tel.: (49) 20189078900
Venture Capital Services
N.A.I.C.S.: 523910
Alina Hassenruck (Office Mgr)

rhenag Rheinische Energie Aktiengesellschaft (1)
Bayenthalgurtel 9, 50968, Cologne, Germany
Tel.: (49) 221937310
Web Site: http://www.rhenag.de
Natural Gas Distr
N.A.I.C.S.: 221210

INTERNATIONAL PUBLIC

RWS HOLDINGS PLC
Europa House Chiltern Park Chiltern Hill, Chalfont Saint Peter, SL9 9FG, Buckinghamshire, United Kingdom
Tel.: (44) 1753480200 UK
Web Site: https://www.rws.com
Year Founded: 1958
RWS—(AIM)
Rev.: $934,178,766
Assets: $1,675,105,506
Liabilities: $418,203,495
Net Worth: $1,256,902,011
Earnings: ($35,264,039)
Fiscal Year-end: 09/30/23
Intellectual Property Support Services
N.A.I.C.S.: 523940
Andrew S. Brode (Chm)

Subsidiaries:

Alpha Translations Canada Inc. (1)
Suite 200 86 Boulder Boulevard, Stony Plain, T7Z 1V7, AB, Canada
Tel.: (780) 962-7821
Translation Language Services
N.A.I.C.S.: 541930

Article One Partners, LLC (1)
90 Broad St Ste 402, New York, NY 10004
Tel.: (347) 901-4820
Patent Research Services
N.A.I.C.S.: 541199
Peter Vanderheyden (CEO)

Beijing RWS Science & Technology Information Consultancy Co. Ltd. (1)
A601 Building B-2 Northern Territory Dongsheng Technology Park, Haidian District, Beijing, 100192, China
Tel.: (86) 106 060 0077
Translation Language Services
N.A.I.C.S.: 541930

Corporate Translations UK Limited (1)
Wyndhams Croft Whiteditch Lane, Newport, CB11 3UD, Essex, United Kingdom
Tel.: (44) 179 954 1666
Web Site: https://www.corporatetranslations.co.uk
Translation Language Services
N.A.I.C.S.: 541930

Document Service Center GmbH. (1)
Joachimsthaler Str 15, 10719, Berlin, Germany
Tel.: (49) 3049857200
Web Site: http://www.dsc-translation.de
Sales Range: $25-49.9 Million
Emp.: 100
Technical Translation Services
N.A.I.C.S.: 541930
Andreas Siegmund (Mng Dir)

Eclipse Translations Limited (1)
Birch Close Lionheart Enterprise Park, Alnwick, NE66 2EP, Northumberland, United Kingdom
Tel.: (44) 1665511000
Web Site: http://www.eclipse-translation.co.uk
Sales Range: $25-49.9 Million
Emp.: 30
Technical Translation Services

AND PRIVATE COMPANIES — RWS HOLDINGS PLC

N.A.I.C.S.: 541930

Iconic Translation Machines Ltd. (1)
Invent Building DCU Campus, Glasnevin, Dublin, Ireland
Tel.: (353) 1 443 3168
Web Site: https://www.iconictranslation.com
Translation Language Services
N.A.I.C.S.: 541930
John Tinsley *(Mng Dir)*

KK RWS Group (1)
Kasumigaseki Common Gate West Tower 32nd Floor 3-2-1, Kasumigaseki Chiyoda-ku, Tokyo, 100-0013, Japan
Tel.: (81) 364579680
Web Site: http://www.rws.com
Sales Range: $25-49.9 Million
Emp.: 20
Patent, Technical & Legal Translation Services
N.A.I.C.S.: 541930

Lawyers and Merchants Translation Bureau Inc. (1)
11 Broadway, New York, NY 10004-1387
Tel.: (212) 344-2930
Sales Range: $25-49.9 Million
Emp.: 8
Legal Translation Services
N.A.I.C.S.: 541930

RWS Group Deutschland GmbH (1)
Joachimsthaler Str 15, 10719, Berlin, Germany
Tel.: (49) 304 985 7200
Translation Language Services
N.A.I.C.S.: 541930

RWS Holdings plc - Medical Translation Division (1)
Ad-Ex House 296 Kingston Rd, London, SW20 8LX, United Kingdom
Tel.: (44) 2085452300
Sales Range: $25-49.9 Million
Emp.: 12
Medical Translation Services
N.A.I.C.S.: 541930

RWS Information Limited (1)
Tavistock House Tavistock Square, London, WC1H 9LG, United Kingdom
Tel.: (44) 2075545400
Web Site: http://www.rws.com
Sales Range: $25-49.9 Million
Emp.: 30
Technical Translation Services
N.A.I.C.S.: 541930

RWS Life Sciences, Inc. (1)
101 E River Dr, East Hartford, CT 06108
Tel.: (860) 727-6000
Web Site: https://lifesciences.rws.com
Translation & Linguistic Validation Solutions
N.A.I.C.S.: 541930
Sheena Dempsey *(Mng Dir)*

RWS Translations Limited (1)
Chiltern Park Chiltern Hill Chalfont St Peter, Bucks, SL9 9FG, Buckinghamshire, United Kingdom
Tel.: (44) 1753480200
Web Site: http://www.rws.com
Sales Range: $75-99.9 Million
Emp.: 300
Language Translation Services
N.A.I.C.S.: 541930

SDL Plc (1)
New Globe House Vanwall Business Park Vanwall Road, Berkshire, Maidenhead, United Kingdom
Tel.: (44) 1628410100
Web Site: http://www.sdl.com
Rev: $493,555,080
Assets: $528,968,280
Liabilities: $197,789,280
Net Worth: $331,179,000
Earnings: $25,707,360
Emp.: 4,242
Fiscal Year-end: 12/31/2019
Language Translation Software Developer
N.A.I.C.S.: 561499
Roddy Temperley *(Chief HR Officer)*

Subsidiary (Domestic):

Alterian Limited (2)
The Spectrum Building, Bond Street, Bristol, CS1 3LG, United Kingdom
Tel.: (44) 1179703200
Web Site: http://www.alterian.com
Sales Range: $200-249.9 Million
Emp.: 407
Holding Company; Marketing & Consumer Research Software Services
N.A.I.C.S.: 551112
Chris Nolan *(CTO)*

Subsidiary (US):

Alterian (Stamford) Inc. (3)
1010 Washington Blvd 9th Fl, Stamford, CT 06901
Tel.: (203) 653-9090
Web Site: http://www.alterian.com
Sales Range: $25-49.9 Million
Emp.: 10
Enterprise Content Management Software
N.A.I.C.S.: 513210

Subsidiary (Non-US):

Alterian Deutschland GmbH (3)
Nymphenburgerstr 4, 80335, Munich, Germany
Tel.: (49) 89 288 90 164
Sales Range: $50-74.9 Million
Emp.: 3
Financial Management Services
N.A.I.C.S.: 523999

Alterian Technologies India Pvt. Ltd. (3)
Diamond District No 150, Old Airport Road Kodihalli, Bengaluru, 560 058, India
Tel.: (91) 8025210739
Web Site: http://www.sdl.com
Sales Range: $25-49.9 Million
Emp.: 50
Enterprise Content Management Software
N.A.I.C.S.: 334610

Subsidiary (US):

Alterian, Inc. (3)
25152 Springfield Ct, Valencia, CA 91355 (100%)
Tel.: (312) 704-1700
Web Site: http://www.alterian.com
Sales Range: $25-49.9 Million
Emp.: 9
Marketing & Consumer Research Software Services
N.A.I.C.S.: 541511

Intrepid Consultants Inc (3)
124 NW Canal St, Seattle, WA 98107-4933
Tel.: (206) 547-1588
Web Site: http://www.alterian.com
Sales Range: $25-49.9 Million
Emp.: 15
Market Research Consulting Services
N.A.I.C.S.: 541910

Subsidiary (Domestic):

Intrepid Consultants Limited (3)
68 Rochester Place, London, NW1 9JX, United Kingdom
Tel.: (44) 2074859372
Web Site: http://www.intrepidlondon.com
Sales Range: $25-49.9 Million
Business Development Consulting Services
N.A.I.C.S.: 541611

SDL Alterian (3)
Kings Orchard 5th Floor 1 Queen Street, Bristol, BS2 0HQ, United Kingdom (100%)
Tel.: (44) 1628410100
Web Site: http://www.sdl.com
Sales Range: $25-49.9 Million
Emp.: 70
Brand Management
N.A.I.C.S.: 541910

Subsidiary (Non-US):

SDL Technologies (Australia) Pty. Ltd. (3)
Building 34 Suakin Drive, Sydney, 2088, NSW, Australia
Tel.: (61) 299682449
Sales Range: $25-49.9 Million
Emp.: 11
Enterprise Content Management Software & Related Services
N.A.I.C.S.: 513210

Subsidiary (Domestic):

Computype Ltd. (2)
Connaught Road, Kingston upon Hull, HU7 3AP, United Kingdom
Tel.: (44) 1482835366
Web Site: http://www.computype.com
Label Equipment Whslr
N.A.I.C.S.: 423610

Subsidiary (Non-US):

LLC SDL Rus (2)
Zastavskaya Street No 22 Letter A, 196084, Saint Petersburg, Russia
Tel.: (7) 8126550330
Business Support Services
N.A.I.C.S.: 561499

LLC SDL Ukraine (2)
Stepana Bandery Avenue 28-A letter G 5th Floor, Kiev, Ukraine
Tel.: (380) 442290967
Business Support Services
N.A.I.C.S.: 561499

Subsidiary (US):

Language Weaver Inc. (2)
6060 Center Dr Ste 150, Los Angeles, CA 90045
Tel.: (310) 437-7300
Web Site: http://www.languageweaver.com
Sales Range: $10-24.9 Million
Emp.: 100
Automated Language Translation Technology Developer
N.A.I.C.S.: 513210
Daniel Marcu *(Co-Founder, COO & CTO)*

Subsidiary (Non-US):

Language Weaver SRL (2)
Str Senina 16, Cluj-Napoca, Romania
Tel.: (40) 722364807
Automated Translation Software Development Services
N.A.I.C.S.: 541511

SDL Belgium NV (2)
Vital Decosterstraat 44, 3000, Leuven, Belgium
Tel.: (32) 16790994
Business Support Services
N.A.I.C.S.: 561499

SDL CZ sro (2)
Nerudova 866, Hradec Kralove, 50002, Czech Republic
Tel.: (420) 495531501
Software Development Services
N.A.I.C.S.: 541511

SDL Chile SA (2)
Monsenor Nuncio Sotero Sanz 161 Of 405, Providencia, Santiago, Chile
Tel.: (56) 229557893
Business Support Services
N.A.I.C.S.: 561499

SDL France SARL (2)
Tour Gallieni II 36 avenue du General de Gaulle, 93170, Bagnolet, France
Tel.: (33) 172591110
Business Support Services
N.A.I.C.S.: 561499

SDL Global Solutions (Ireland) Ltd (2)
La Vallee House Upper Dargle Road, Bray, Wicklow, Ireland
Tel.: (353) 12050200
Web Site: http://www.sdl.com
Sales Range: $25-49.9 Million
Emp.: 35
Information Technology Consulting Services
N.A.I.C.S.: 541512

SDL Hellas MEPE (2)
Philippou 6 Metamorfosi, Athens, 144 51, Greece
Tel.: (30) 210 281 95 40
Computer Programming Services
N.A.I.C.S.: 541511

SDL Holdings BV (2)
Hoogoorddreef 60, Amsterdam, 1101 BE, Noord-Holland, Netherlands
Tel.: (31) 202010500
Web Site: http://www.sdl.com
Emp.: 165
Software Development Services
N.A.I.C.S.: 541511

SDL Hong Kong Ltd. (2)
Level 3 Henley Building 5 Queens Road, Central, China (Hong Kong)
Tel.: (852) 25092712
Business Support Services
N.A.I.C.S.: 561499

Subsidiary (US):

SDL Inc. (2)
69 Hickory Dr, Waltham, MA 02451-1011
Tel.: (781) 464-6000
Web Site: http://www.sdl.com
Sales Range: $1-9.9 Million
Emp.: 100
Content Globalization Management Software Developer
N.A.I.C.S.: 513210

SDL Inc. (2)
3401 Quebec St Ste 5070, Denver, CO 80207-2322 (100%)
Tel.: (303) 333-4848
Sales Range: $25-49.9 Million
Emp.: 6
Freight Transportation Arrangement
N.A.I.C.S.: 488510

Subsidiary (Non-US):

SDL International (Canada) Inc. (2)
1555 Peel Street and 1550 Metcalfe Street 8th Floor Suite 800, Montreal, H3A 1X6, QC, Canada (100%)
Tel.: (514) 844-2577
Translation & Interpretation Services
N.A.I.C.S.: 541930

SDL International Belgium NV (2)
Vital Decosterstraat 44, 3001, Leuven, Belgium (100%)
Tel.: (32) 16790994
Web Site: http://www.sdl.com
Sales Range: $25-49.9 Million
Emp.: 50
Computer Related Services
N.A.I.C.S.: 541519

SDL International Nederland B.V. (2)
Industrieplein 3, 7553 LL, Hengelo, Overijssel, Netherlands (100%)
Tel.: (31) 742403740
Web Site: http://www.sdl.com
Sales Range: $25-49.9 Million
Emp.: 60
Libraries & Archives
N.A.I.C.S.: 519210

SDL Italia Srl (2)
Via Antonio Bertoloni 29, Rome, 197, Italy
Tel.: (39) 0650930127
Software Development Services
N.A.I.C.S.: 541511

SDL Japan KK (2)
Level 4 Nakameguro Gt Tower 2-1-1 Kamimeguro, Meguro-ku, Tokyo, 153-0051, Japan (100%)
Tel.: (81) 3 5720 2591
Web Site: http://www.sdl.com
Sales Range: $25-49.9 Million
Software Developer
N.A.I.C.S.: 513210

SDL Luxembourg SAR (2)
26B Boulevard Royal, 2449, Luxembourg, Luxembourg
Tel.: (352) 99995192
Business Support Services
N.A.I.C.S.: 561499

SDL Multi-Lingual Solutions (Singapore) PTE Ltd (2)
138 Cecil St 15-00 Cecil Ct, Singapore, 069538, Singapore
Tel.: (65) 63397282
Web Site: http://www.sdl.com
Sales Range: $25-49.9 Million
Emp.: 30
Translation Software Development Services
N.A.I.C.S.: 541511

SDL Multilingual Services GmbH & Co KG (2)
Waldburgstr 21, Stuttgart, 70563, Baden-Wurttemberg, Germany
Tel.: (49) 711780600
Web Site: http://www.sdl.com
Sales Range: $25-49.9 Million
Emp.: 100

RWS HOLDINGS PLC

RWS Holdings plc—(Continued)
Enterprise Resource Planning Software Development Services
N.A.I.C.S.: 541511

SDL Multilingual Solutions Private Ltd. (2)
Unit Number 1319 13th Floor Building A1 Rupa Solitaire Sector 1, Millennium Business Park Mahape, Navi Mumbai, 400 710, India
Tel.: (91) 2241384500
Business Support Services
N.A.I.C.S.: 561499

SDL Nederland Holding BV (2)
Spoorstraat 102, PO Box 277, 7551 CA, Hengelo, Netherlands
Tel.: (31) 747999800
Web Site: http://www.sdl.com
Sales Range: $25-49.9 Million
Emp.: 60
Enterprise Resource Planning Software Development Services
N.A.I.C.S.: 541511

SDL Passolo GmbH (2)
Waldburgstr 21, Stuttgart, 70563, Baden-Wurttemberg, Germany
Tel.: (49) 711780600
Web Site: http://www.sdl.com
Sales Range: $25-49.9 Million
Emp.: 10
Software Development Services
N.A.I.C.S.: 541511

SDL Poland Sp. z o.o. (2)
Ul Fordonska 246, 85-766, Bydgoszcz, Poland
Tel.: (48) 525824404
Web Site: http://www.sdl.com
Translation Software Developer
N.A.I.C.S.: 561499

SDL Portugal Unipessoal Lda (2)
Rua Santo Antonio de Contumil 130, 4350-289, Porto, Portugal
Tel.: (351) 220046266
Business Support Services
N.A.I.C.S.: 561499

SDL Quatron BV (2)
Hoogoorddreef 60, Amsterdam, 1101 BE, Netherlands
Tel.: (31) 202010500
Web Content Software Development Services
N.A.I.C.S.: 541511
Denis Feeke (Gen Mgr)

Subsidiary (Domestic):

SDL Sheffield Limited (2)
Derwent House 150 Arundel Gate, Pond Hill, Sheffield, S1 2JY, South Yorkshire, United Kingdom (100%)
Tel.: (44) 1142535300
Web Site: http://www.sdl.com
Sales Range: $25-49.9 Million
Emp.: 160
Translation & Interpretation Services
N.A.I.C.S.: 541930

Subsidiary (Non-US):

SDL Spain SL (2)
Calle Andres Segovia 53 Planta 4, 18008, Granada, Spain
Tel.: (34) 958 805401
Web Site: http://www.sdl.com
Enterprise Resource Planning Software Development Services
N.A.I.C.S.: 541511

SDL Sweden AB (2)
Fatbursgatan 1, 118 28, Stockholm, Sweden (100%)
Tel.: (46) 859921900
Web Site: http://www.sdl.com
Sales Range: $25-49.9 Million
Emp.: 50
Computer Programming Services
N.A.I.C.S.: 541511

SDL Technologies (Vietnam) Co. Ltd. (2)
14th Floor Ree Tower No 9 Doan Van Bo Str, Ward 12 District 4, Ho Chi Minh City, Vietnam
Tel.: (84) 839443301

Business Support Services
N.A.I.C.S.: 561499

SDL Traduceri SRL (2)
28-30 Mendeleev Street 3rd Floor, District 1, 010365, Bucharest, Romania
Tel.: (40) 213168066
Business Support Services
N.A.I.C.S.: 561499

SDL Tridion BV (2)
Hoogoorddreef 60, Amsterdam, 1101 BE, Netherlands
Tel.: (31) 20 20 10 500
Web Site: http://www.sdl.com
Web Content Management Solutions
N.A.I.C.S.: 541511

SDL Tridion BVBA (2)
Vital Decosterstraat 44, 3000, Leuven, Belgium
Tel.: (32) 16790994
Web Site: http://www.sdltridion.com
Web Content Management Solutions
N.A.I.C.S.: 541512

SDL Tridion Corporate Services BV (2)
Hoogoorddreef 60, Amsterdam, 1101 BE, Netherlands
Tel.: (31) 20 201 0500
Web Site: http://www.sdl.com
Web Content Management Services
N.A.I.C.S.: 541618

SDL Tridion GmbH (2)
SDL PLC Zweigniederlassung fur Deutschland, 81669, Munich, Germany
Tel.: (49) 8925552970
Business Support Services
N.A.I.C.S.: 561499

SDL Tridion Hispania SL (2)
Lopez de Hoyos 35 1 Planta, Madrid, 28002, Spain
Tel.: (34) 91 745 99 32
Software Development Services
N.A.I.C.S.: 541511

SDL Tridion Holding BV (2)
Hoogoorddreef 60, Amsterdam, 1101 BE, Noord-Holland, Netherlands
Tel.: (31) 202010500
Web Site: http://www.sdl.com
Emp.: 200
Software Development Services
N.A.I.C.S.: 541511

Subsidiary (US):

SDL Tridion Inc (2)
1515 Broadway 11th Fl, New York, NY 10036
Tel.: (212) 704-4135
Web Site: http://www.sdl.com
Software Management Services
N.A.I.C.S.: 541511

Subsidiary (Non-US):

SDL Tridion KK (2)
Nakameguro GT Tower 4F 2-1-1 Kamimeguro, Meguro-Ku, Tokyo, 153-0051, Japan
Tel.: (81) 3 5724 8750
Web Site: http://www.sdl.com
Emp.: 150
Software Development Services
N.A.I.C.S.: 541511

Subsidiary (Domestic):

SDL Tridion Ltd (2)
Globe House Clivemont Road, Maidenhead, SL6 7DY, Berkshire, United Kingdom
Tel.: (44) 1628 760610
Web Site: http://www.sdl.com
Sales Range: $25-49.9 Million
Emp.: 250
Web Content Management Solutions
N.A.I.C.S.: 541512

Subsidiary (Non-US):

SDL Tridion SAS (2)
Tour Gallieni II 36 Ave du General de Gaulle, Bagnolet, 93170, France
Tel.: (33) 172591182
Sales Range: $25-49.9 Million
Emp.: 100
Web Content Management Solutions
N.A.I.C.S.: 541512

SDL Turkey Translation Services & Commerce Ltd. (2)
Kosuyolu Mahallesi Mahmut Yesari Caddesi No 51, Kosuyolu, 34718, Istanbul, Turkiye
Tel.: (90) 2163212349
Business Support Services
N.A.I.C.S.: 561499

SDL Xopus BV (2)
Floor 3 Koninginnegracht 12B, 2514 AA, Hague, Netherlands
Tel.: (31) 88 8873500
Web Site: http://www.xopus.com
Sales Range: $25-49.9 Million
Emp.: 10
Editing Software Development Services
N.A.I.C.S.: 541511

Subsidiary (US):

SDL XyEnterprise LLC (2)
201 Edgewater Dr Ste 225, Wakefield, MA 01880
Tel.: (781) 756-4400
Business Support Services
N.A.I.C.S.: 561499

Subsidiary (Non-US):

SDL Zagreb LLC (2)
Bednjanska 14, Zagreb, 10000, Croatia
Tel.: (385) 1 6156 744
Sales Range: $25-49.9 Million
Emp.: 10
Translation Software Development Services
N.A.I.C.S.: 513210
Bozidar Burazer (Gen Mgr)

SDL do Brasil Servicos de Traducao Ltda. (2)
Barao do Triunfo 73 Conjuntos 63/67, Sao Paulo, 04602-000, Brazil
Tel.: (55) 1150916666
Sales Range: $25-49.9 Million
Emp.: 25
Software Publisher
N.A.I.C.S.: 513210
Simao Cuncha (Gen Mgr)

SDL do Brazil Global Solutions Ltda. (2)
Rua Barao do Triunfo 73-6-8 Andar, Brooklin Paulista, Sao Paulo, 04602-000, Brazil
Tel.: (55) 1150916666
Business Support Services
N.A.I.C.S.: 561499

SDL doo Ljubljana (2)
Ulica Jozeta Jame 14, Ljubljana, 1210, Slovenia
Tel.: (386) 15114380
Web Site: http://www.sdl.com
Sales Range: $25-49.9 Million
Emp.: 12
Software Development Services
N.A.I.C.S.: 541511

Trados GmbH (2)
Waldburgstr 21, 70563, Stuttgart, Germany
Tel.: (49) 71120909600
Web Site: http://www.sdl.com
Translation Software Development Services
N.A.I.C.S.: 541511

RYANAIR HOLDINGS PLC

Ryanair Dublin Office Airside Business Park, Swords, Dublin, Ireland
Tel.: (353) 19451212
Web Site: https://www.ryanair.com
Year Founded: 1985
RYAAY—(NASDAQ)
Rev.: $14,430,871,625
Assets: $18,436,668,105
Liabilities: $10,263,417,780
Net Worth: $8,173,250,325
Earnings: $2,057,857,450
Emp.: 27,076
Fiscal Year-end: 03/31/24
Holding Company; Airline Operator
N.A.I.C.S.: 551112
Juliusz Komorek (Chief Legal Officer & Sec)

Subsidiaries:

Air Malta plc (1)
Level 2 Skyparks Business Centre Malta International Airport, Luqa, LQA 4000, Malta
Tel.: (356) 22999000
Web Site: http://www.airmalta.com
Sales Range: $350-399.9 Million
Emp.: 1,400
Airline Operator
N.A.I.C.S.: 481111
Clifford Chetcuti (CEO)

Subsidiary (Non-US):

Holiday Malta (Hellas) Tourism EPE (2)
91 Alexandras, Athens, Greece
Tel.: (30) 2106411778
Oil Transportation Services
N.A.I.C.S.: 488190

Malta Air Limited (1)
Level 2 Skyparks Business Centre Malta International Airport, Luqa, LQA 4000, Malta
Tel.: (356) 2 299 9000
Web Site: https://www.airmalta.com
Airline Services
N.A.I.C.S.: 481111
David G. Curmi (Chm)

Ryanair Limited (1)
Dublin Airport, Dublin, Ireland
Tel.: (353) 18121212
Web Site: http://www.ryanair.com
Emp.: 300
Airplane Passenger Transportation Services
N.A.I.C.S.: 481111
David Bonderman (Chm)

RYDER CAPITAL LIMITED

Level 28 88 Phillip Street, Sydney, 2000, NSW, Australia
Tel.: (61) 290009020 AU
Web Site:
https://www.rydercapital.com.au
Year Founded: 2015
RYD—(ASX)
Rev.: $2,472,269
Assets: $76,826,836
Liabilities: $512,599
Net Worth: $76,314,236
Earnings: $1,355,730
Fiscal Year-end: 06/30/24
Portfolio Management Services
N.A.I.C.S.: 523940
Peter Charles Constable (Chm & Chief Investment Officer)

RYDON GROUP LTD

Rydon House Station Road, Forest Row, RH18 5DW, East Sussex, United Kingdom
Tel.: (44) 1342825151
Web Site: http://www.rydon.co.uk
Year Founded: 1978
Rev.: $262,200,000
Emp.: 750
Construction Services
N.A.I.C.S.: 236220
Robert Bond (CEO)

Subsidiaries:

Ryhurst Ltd (1)
Rydon House, Forest Row, RH18 5DW, East Sussex, United Kingdom
Tel.: (44) 1342825151
Web Site: http://www.ryhurst.co.uk
Asset Management Services
N.A.I.C.S.: 531390
Stephen Collinson (Mng Dir)

RYKADAN CAPITAL LIMITED

Rooms 2701 & 2801 Rykadan Capital Tower 135 Hoi Bun Road, Kwun Tong, Kowloon, China (Hong Kong)
Tel.: (852) 39501800
Web Site: https://www.rykadan.com
Year Founded: 1986
2288—(HKG)
Rev.: $11,213,779
Assets: $205,216,338
Liabilities: $46,340,450
Net Worth: $158,875,887
Earnings: $(5,028,285)
Emp.: 27

Fiscal Year-end: 03/31/22
Investment Holding Company
N.A.I.C.S.: 551112
William Chan *(Chm, CEO & Exec Dir)*

Subsidiaries:

Sundart Timber Products Company
Limited (1)
7F Millennium City 3, 370 Kwun Tong Rd
Kwun Tong, Kowloon, China (Hong Kong)
Tel.: (852) 24132333
Web Site: http://www.sundart.com.cn
Sales Range: $25-49.9 Million
Emp.: 100
Interior Design Consulting Services
N.A.I.C.S.: 541410

Subsidiary (Non-US):

Sundart Engineering & Contracting-
(Beijing) Limited (2)
Building 5&9 Zhongxin Enterprise Plaza No
88 Wuwei Road, PuTuo District, Shanghai,
200383, China
Tel.: (86) 2132505580
Civil Engineering Services
N.A.I.C.S.: 541330

Sundart Engineering Services(Macau)
Limited (2)
Tel.: (853) 28757851
Interior Design Services
N.A.I.C.S.: 541410

RYM BUSINESS MANAGE-
MENT CORPORATION

0th Floor MGO Building Legaspi
Street corner De la Rosa Street, Le-
gaspi Village, Makati, 1227, Philip-
pines
Tel.: (63) 288899009 PH
Emp.: 100
Holding Company
N.A.I.C.S.: 551112
Remegio C. Dayandayan Jr. *(Pres)*

Subsidiaries:

Prime Media Holdings Inc (1)
16th floor BDO Towers Valero 8741 Paseo
de Roxas, Makati, Philippines
Tel.: (63) 8314479
Web Site: https://primemedia.com.ph
Rev.: $55,436
Assets: $1,141,211
Liabilities: $4,140,393
Net Worth: ($2,999,182)
Earnings: ($61,914)
Fiscal Year-end: 12/31/2020
Financial Investment Services
N.A.I.C.S.: 523999
Bernadeth A. Lim *(VP)*

RYMAN HEALTHCARE LTD.

Airport Business Park 92D Russley
Road, PO Box 771, Christchurch,
8140, New Zealand
Tel.: (64) 33664069
Web Site:
   https://www.rymanhealthcare.co.nz
Year Founded: 1984
RHCGF—(OTCIQ)
Rev.: $599,569,378
Assets: $7,482,430,622
Liabilities: $4,693,018,541
Net Worth: $2,789,412,081
Earnings: $154,208,134
Emp.: 198
Fiscal Year-end: 03/31/23
Elderly Healthcare Facilities Owner &
Manager
N.A.I.C.S.: 623312
David Kerr *(Chm)*

Subsidiaries:

Anthony Wilding Retirement Village
Limited (1)
5 Corbett Cres, Halswell, Christchurch,
8025, New Zealand
Tel.: (64) 33385820
Sales Range: $10-24.9 Million
Emp.: 100
Retirement Living Village Services
N.A.I.C.S.: 623990

Beckenham Courts Retirement Vil-
lage Limited (1)
222 Colombo St, Christchurch, 8004, New
Zealand (100%)
Tel.: (64) 33372702
Web Site: http://www.rymanhealthcare.co.nz
Continuing Care Retirement Communities
N.A.I.C.S.: 623311
Rosemary Deane *(Mgr)*

Bob Owens Retirement Village
Limited (1)
112 Carmichael Road, Bethlehem, Tau-
ranga, 3110, New Zealand
Tel.: (64) 75793041
Health Care Srvices
N.A.I.C.S.: 622110

Bob Scott Retirement Village
Limited (1)
25 Graham St, Petone, Lower Hutt, 5012,
New Zealand
Tel.: (64) 45705800
Health Care Srvices
N.A.I.C.S.: 622110

Bruce McLaren Retirement Village
Limited (1)
795 Chapel Road, Howick, Auckland, 2016,
New Zealand
Tel.: (64) 95350220
Health Care Srvices
N.A.I.C.S.: 622110

Charles Brownlow Retirement Village
Pty. Ltd. (1)
1 Vintner Court, Highton, Geelong, 3216,
VIC, Australia
Tel.: (61) 352608000
Health Care Srvices
N.A.I.C.S.: 622110

Charles Upham Retirement Village
Limited (1)
24 Charles Upham Drive, Rangiora, 7400,
New Zealand
Tel.: (64) 33108600
Health Care Srvices
N.A.I.C.S.: 622110

Diana Isaac Retirement Village
Limited (1)
1 Lady Isaac Way, Mairehau, Christchurch,
8052, New Zealand
Tel.: (64) 33863018
Health Care Srvices
N.A.I.C.S.: 622110

Edmund Hillary Retirement Village
Limited (1)
221 Abbotts Way, Remuera, Auckland,
1050, New Zealand
Tel.: (64) 95700070
Emp.: 250
Retirement Living Village Services
N.A.I.C.S.: 623990

Ernest Rutherford Retirement Village
Limited (1)
49 Covent Drive, Stoke, Nelson, 7011, New
Zealand
Tel.: (64) 35380880
Sales Range: $25-49.9 Million
Emp.: 120
Retirement Living Village Services
N.A.I.C.S.: 623990

Essie Summers Retirement Village
Limited (1)
222 Colombo Street, Beckenham,
Christchurch, 8023, New Zealand
Tel.: (64) 33372702
Health Care Srvices
N.A.I.C.S.: 622110

Evelyn Page Retirement Village
Limited (1)
30 Ambassador Glade, Orewa, Auckland,
0931, New Zealand
Tel.: (64) 94211915
Sales Range: $25-49.9 Million
Emp.: 180
Retirement Living Village Services
N.A.I.C.S.: 623990

Frances Hodgkins Retirement Village
Limited (1)
40 Fenton Crescent, St Clair, Dunedin,
9012, New Zealand (100%)
Tel.: (64) 34550277
Web Site: http://www.ryman.com
Sales Range: $10-24.9 Million
Emp.: 50
Continuing Care Retirement Communities
N.A.I.C.S.: 623311

Grace Joel Retirement Village
Limited (1)
184 St Heliers Bay Rd, St Heliers, Auck-
land, 1071, New Zealand (100%)
Tel.: (64) 95751572
Web Site: http://www.gracejoel.co.nz
Sales Range: $25-49.9 Million
Emp.: 150
Continuing Care Retirement Communities
N.A.I.C.S.: 623311

Hilda Ross Retirement Village
Limited (1)
30 Ruakura Road, Hamilton East, Hamilton,
3216, New Zealand (100%)
Tel.: (64) 78559542
Web Site: http://www.hildaross.co.nz
Sales Range: $25-49.9 Million
Emp.: 186
Continuing Care Retirement Communities
N.A.I.C.S.: 623311

James Wattie Retirement Village
Limited (1)
122 Te Aute Road North, Havelock, 4130,
New Zealand
Tel.: (64) 68770701
Health Care Srvices
N.A.I.C.S.: 622110

Jane Mander Retirement Village
Limited (1)
262 Fairway Dr, Te Kamo, Whangarei,
0112, New Zealand
Tel.: (64) 94353850
Web Site:
   https://www.rymanhealthcare.co.nz
Sales Range: $50-74.9 Million
Emp.: 400
Retirement Living Village Services
N.A.I.C.S.: 623990

Jane Winstone Retirement Village
Limited (1)
49 Oakland Ave, St Johns Hill, Wanganui,
4500, New Zealand (100%)
Tel.: (64) 63456783
Web Site:
   https://www.rymanhealthcare.co.nz
Sales Range: $10-24.9 Million
Emp.: 50
Continuing Care Retirement Communities
N.A.I.C.S.: 623311

Jean Sandel Retirement Village
Limited (1)
Tel.: (64) 67514420
Retirement Living Village Services
N.A.I.C.S.: 623990

John Flynn Retirement Village Pty.
Ltd. (1)
6 Foundation Boulevard, Burwood East,
3151, VIC, Australia
Tel.: (61) 388498700
Health Care Srvices
N.A.I.C.S.: 622110

Julia Wallace Retirement Village
Limited (1)
28 Dogwood Way Clearview Park, Milson,
Palmerston North, 4414, New Zealand
Tel.: (64) 63549262
Emp.: 140
Retirement Living Village Services
N.A.I.C.S.: 623990

Keith Park Retirement Village
Limited (1)
3 Scott Road, Hobsonville, Auckland, 0616,
New Zealand
Tel.: (64) 94160751
Health Care Srvices
N.A.I.C.S.: 622110

Kiri Te Kanawa Retirement Village
Limited (1)
Gwyneth Place 12, Lytton West, Gisborne,
4010, New Zealand
Tel.: (64) 68633636
Sales Range: $10-24.9 Million
Emp.: 2
Retirement Living Village Services
N.A.I.C.S.: 623990

Linda Jones Retirement Village
Limited (1)
1775 River Road, Flagstaff, Hamilton, 3210,
New Zealand
Tel.: (64) 78533381
Health Care Srvices
N.A.I.C.S.: 622110

Logan Campbell Retirement Village
Limited (1)
187 Campbell Road, Greenlane, Auckland,
1061, New Zealand
Tel.: (64) 96363888
Health Care Srvices
N.A.I.C.S.: 622110

Malvina Major Retirement Village
Limited (1)
134 Burma Road, Khandallah, Wellington,
6037, New Zealand (100%)
Tel.: (64) 44783754
Web Site: http://www.malvinamajor.co.nz
Sales Range: $25-49.9 Million
Emp.: 190
Continuing Care Retirement Communities
N.A.I.C.S.: 623311

Margaret Stoddart Retirement Village
Limited (1)
23 Bartlett Street, Riccarton, Christchurch,
8011, New Zealand (100%)
Tel.: (64) 33484955
Web Site:
   http://www.margaretstoddart.co.nz
Sales Range: $10-24.9 Million
Emp.: 50
Continuing Care Retirement Communities
N.A.I.C.S.: 623311

Miriam Corban Retirement Village
Limited (1)
211 Lincoln Road, Henderson, Auckland,
0610, New Zealand
Tel.: (64) 98380888
Health Care Srvices
N.A.I.C.S.: 622110

Murray Halberg Retirement Village
Limited (1)
11 Commodore Drive, Lynfield, Auckland,
1041, New Zealand
Tel.: (64) 96272700
Health Care Srvices
N.A.I.C.S.: 622110

Nellie Melba Retirement Village Pty.
Ltd. (1)
2 Collegium Ave, Wheelers Hill, Melbourne,
3150, VIC, Australia
Tel.: (61) 385131900
Health Care Srvices
N.A.I.C.S.: 622110

Ngaio Marsh Retirement Village
Limited (1)
95 Grants Road, Papanui, Christchurch,
8052, New Zealand (100%)
Tel.: (64) 33525140
Web Site: http://www.ngaiomarsh.co.nz
Sales Range: $25-49.9 Million
Emp.: 120
Continuing Care Retirement Communities
N.A.I.C.S.: 623311

Possum Bourne Retirement Village
Limited (1)
5 Lisle Farm Drive, Pukekohe, Auckland,
2120, New Zealand
Tel.: (64) 92380370
Health Care Srvices
N.A.I.C.S.: 622110

Princess Alexendra Retirement
Village (1)
145 battery road, 4110, Napier, New
Zealand (100%)
Tel.: (64) 68359085
Sales Range: $25-49.9 Million
Emp.: 120
Continuing Care Retirement Communities
N.A.I.C.S.: 623311
Jodie Robb *(Mgr-Village)*

RYMAN HEALTHCARE LTD.

Ryman Healthcare Ltd.—(Continued)

Rita Angus Retirement Village Limited (1)
66 Coutts Street, Kilbirnie, Wellington, 6022, New Zealand (100%)
Tel.: (64) 43877626
Web Site: http://www.ritaangus.co.nz
Sales Range: $10-24.9 Million
Emp.: 100
Continuing Care Retirement Communities
N.A.I.C.S.: 623311

Rowena Jackson Retirement Village Limited (1)
40 O'Byrne Street North, Waikiwi, Invercargill, 9810, New Zealand
Tel.: (64) 32159988
Web Site: https://www.rymanhealthcare.co.nz
Sales Range: $25-49.9 Million
Emp.: 150
Retirement Living Village Services
N.A.I.C.S.: 623990

Ryman Healthcare (Australia) Pty. Ltd. (1)
PO Box 33119, Melbourne, 3004, VIC, Australia
Tel.: (61) 1300363992
Web Site: https://www.rymanhealthcare.com.au
Health Care Srvices
N.A.I.C.S.: 622110

Shona McFarlane Retirement Village Limited (1)
66 Mabey Road Avalon lowerhutt, Wellington, 5011, New Zealand (100%)
Tel.: (64) 45771090
Web Site: http://www.shonamcfarlane.co.nz
Sales Range: $25-49.9 Million
Emp.: 112
Continuing Care Retirement Communities
N.A.I.C.S.: 623311

Weary Dunlop Retirement Village Pty. Ltd. (1)
242 Jells Rd, Wheelers Hill, Melbourne, 3150, VIC, Australia
Tel.: (61) 385451400
Health Care Srvices
N.A.I.C.S.: 622110

William Sanders Retirement Village Limited (1)
7 Ngataringa Road, Devonport, Auckland, 0624, New Zealand
Tel.: (64) 94450900
Health Care Srvices
N.A.I.C.S.: 622110

Woodcote Retirement Village (1)
29 Woodcote Avenue, Hornby, 8042, Christchurch, New Zealand
Tel.: (64) 33498788
Emp.: 40
Retirement Living Village Services
N.A.I.C.S.: 623990
Liz Hampton (Mgr)

Yvette Williams Retirement Village Limited (1)
383 Highgate, Roslyn, Dunedin, 9010, New Zealand
Tel.: (64) 34640390
Retirement Living Village Services
N.A.I.C.S.: 623990

RYOBI KISO HOLDINGS LTD.

58A Sungei Kadut Loop Ryobi Industrial Building, Singapore, 729505, Singapore
Tel.: (65) 65060000
Web Site: http://www.ryobi-kiso.com
BDN—(SES)
Sales Range: $10-24.9 Million
Emp.: 600
Heavy Engineering Services
N.A.I.C.S.: 237990
Tiong Siew Ong (Founder & CEO)

RYOBI LIMITED

762 Mesaki-cho, Fuchu, 726-8628, Hiroshima, Japan
Tel.: (81) 847411111
Web Site: https://www.ryobi-group.co.jp
Year Founded: 1943
5851—(TKS)
Rev.: $2,004,293,370
Assets: $2,260,568,510
Liabilities: $1,121,056,620
Net Worth: $1,139,511,890
Earnings: $71,715,350
Emp.: 7,916
Fiscal Year-end: 12/31/23
Die Casting Mfr
N.A.I.C.S.: 331523
Akira Urakami (Pres & CEO)

Subsidiaries:

ASAHI SANGYO CO. (1)
762 Mesaki-cho, Fuchu, 726-0033, Hiroshima, Japan
Tel.: (81) 847 41 1517
Insurance Agency Services
N.A.I.C.S.: 524210

Hoei Industries Co., Ltd. (1)
2781 Kamikasada Inabe-cho, Inabe, 511-0207, Mie, Japan
Tel.: (81) 594743311
Web Site: https://www.hoei-kk.co.jp
Emp.: 50
Forged Aluminum Product Mfr
N.A.I.C.S.: 332112

Ikuno Co. (1)
580 Mayumi Ikuno-cho, Asago, 679-3311, Hyogo, Japan
Tel.: (81) 796793001
Web Site: http://www.ryobi-group.co.jp
Aluminum Alloy Bullion Mfr
N.A.I.C.S.: 331314

RDCM, S. de R.L. de C.V (1)
Av Rio San Lorenzo No 2152, Parque Industrial Castro Del Rio, 36810, Irapuato, Guanajuato, Mexico
Tel.: (52) 4621660000
Die Casting Mfr
N.A.I.C.S.: 331523

RYOBI DIE CASTING CHANGZHOU CO., LTD. (1)
No 118 Wujin Ave West Rd, Changzhou, 213166, China
Die Casting Mfr & Distr
N.A.I.C.S.: 331523

RYOBI DIE CASTING DALIAN CO., LTD. (1)
No 10 Wanda Road Dalian Economic and Technological Development Zone, Dalian, 116600, China
Tel.: (86) 41187333111
Web Site: https://www.rdd.ryobi-group.cn
Die Casting & Die Manufacturing Mfr & Distr
N.A.I.C.S.: 331523

RYOBI IMAGIX CO. (1)
5-2-8 Toshima, Kita-ku, Tokyo, 114-0003, Japan
Tel.: (81) 3 3927 3300
Printing Equipment Distr
N.A.I.C.S.: 423830

Ryobi (Shanghai) Sales, Ltd. (1)
2004 ShanghaiMart No 2299 Yan'an Road West, Changning District, Shanghai, 200336, China
Tel.: (86) 2162369811
Die Casting Distr
N.A.I.C.S.: 441330

Ryobi Aluminium Casting (UK), Limited (1)
5 Meadowbank Road Trooperslane Industrial Estate, Carrickfergus, BT38 8YF, County Antrim, United Kingdom (100%)
Tel.: (44) 2893351043
Web Site: http://www.ryobi.co.uk
Sales Range: $75-99.9 Million
Emp.: 400
Distr of Power Tools & Lawn & Garden Equipment
N.A.I.C.S.: 423820
David Watson (Mng Dir)

Ryobi Aluminum Casting (UK), Limited (1)
5 Meadowbank Rd Trooperslane Industrial Estate, Carrickfergus, Antrim, BT38 8YF, United Kingdom
Mfr & Distributor of Dye Castings
N.A.I.C.S.: 331523

Ryobi Australia Pty. Ltd. (1)
359 361 Horsley Rd, Milperra, 2214, NSW, Australia (100%)
Tel.: (61) 2 9772 2444
Web Site: http://www.ryobi.com.au
Sales Range: $75-99.9 Million
Emp.: 130
Mfr of Power Tools, Lawn & Garden Equipment & Builders' Hardware
N.A.I.C.S.: 332510

Ryobi Computer Business Co. (1)
762 Mesaki-cho Fuchu, Hiroshima, 726-0033, Japan
Information Management Services
N.A.I.C.S.: 541512

Ryobi Die Casting (Thailand) Co., Ltd. (1)
7/348 Moo 6 Mabyangporn, Pluakdaeng, Rayong, 21140, Thailand
Tel.: (66) 38036450
Web Site: http://www.ryobi-group.co.jp
Die Casting Machinery Mfr
N.A.I.C.S.: 333248

Ryobi Die Casting (USA), Inc. (1)
525 Industrial Dr, Shelbyville, IN 46176 (100%)
Tel.: (317) 398-3398
Web Site: https://www.ryobidiecasting.com
Sales Range: $200-249.9 Million
Emp.: 700
Mfr & Sales of Die Castings
N.A.I.C.S.: 336350
Tom Johnson (Pres)

Ryobi Finance Corporation (1)
120 North La Salle St Ste 1410, Chicago, IL 60602-2458 (100%)
Tel.: (312) 578-1990
Sales Range: $50-74.9 Million
Emp.: 3
Financing Operations
N.A.I.C.S.: 522299

Ryobi Land Development Ltd. (1)
600 Itabashi-cho, Shobara, 727-0014, Hiroshima, Japan
Tel.: (81) 824721122
Web Site: https://www.shobaracc.com
Golf Course Management
N.A.I.C.S.: 713910

Ryobi Life Services Ltd. (1)
625-1 Mesaki-cho, Fuchu, 726-0033, Hiroshima, Japan
Tel.: (81) 847436712
School Management Services
N.A.I.C.S.: 611710

Ryobi Limited - Hiroshima East Plant (1)
800-2 Ukai-cho, Fuchu, 726-0002, Hiroshima-ken, Japan
Tel.: (81) 847 40 1600
Web Site: http://www.ryobi-group.co.jp
Aluminium Die Casting Products Mfr
N.A.I.C.S.: 331523

Ryobi Limited - Hiroshima Plant (1)
762 Mesaki-cho, Fuchu, 726-8628, Hiroshima-ken, Japan
Tel.: (81) 847 41 1111
Web Site: http://www.ryobi-group.co.jp
Aluminium & Magnesium Die Casting Products Mfr
N.A.I.C.S.: 331523

Ryobi Limited - Shizuoka Plant (1)
5215-1 Kanbara, Shimizu-ku, Shizuoka, 421-3292, Japan
Tel.: (81) 54 385 3101
Web Site: http://www.ryobi-group.co.jp
Aluminium Die Casting Products Mfr
N.A.I.C.S.: 331523

Ryobi Ltd. - Tokyo Branch (1)
5 2 8 Toshima Kita Ku, 1148518, Tokyo, Japan (100%)
Tel.: (81) 339275541
Sales Range: $550-599.9 Million
Emp.: 2,000
Printing Equipment & Related Products Whslr
N.A.I.C.S.: 423830

Akira Urakami (Mng Dir)

Ryobi MHI Graphic Technology Ltd. (1)
800-2 Ukai-cho, Fuchu, Hiroshima, Japan
Tel.: (81) 847401600
Printing Equipment Mfr & Distr
N.A.I.C.S.: 333248
Akira Urakami (Chm)

Ryobi Mirasaka Co. (1)
10075-1 Kaize Mirasaka-cho, Miyoshi, 729-4307, Hiroshima, Japan
Mfr of Die Casts
N.A.I.C.S.: 331523

Ryobi Mitsugi Co. (1)
200 Takao Mitsugi-cho, Onomichi, 722-0353, Hiroshima, Japan
Mfr of Die Casts
N.A.I.C.S.: 331523

Ryobi Power Tool Co. (1)
52 Hongo Sera-cho Sera, Hiroshima, 722-1112, Japan
Mfr of Power Tools, Lawn & Garden Equipment
N.A.I.C.S.: 333991

Ryobi-Tech Corporation (1)
No 52 5 Hu Kun Lane Shin Kuang Tsun Min Chen Hsian, Nan Tou, Hsien, Taiwan (100%)
Tel.: (886) 492731101
Sales Range: Less than $1 Million
Emp.: 100
Mfr of Builders' Hardware
N.A.I.C.S.: 332510

Sanyo Optical Instruments Co. (1)
686 Mesaki-cho, Fuchu, Hiroshima, 726-0033, Japan
Provider of Optical Instruments, Office Equipment & Die-Cast Precision Machining
N.A.I.C.S.: 333310

Tokyo Light Alloy Co., Ltd. (1)
1-21-1 Fujimi-cho, Gyoda, 361-8510, Saitama, Japan
Mfr & Sales of Cast Aluminum & Die Castings
N.A.I.C.S.: 331523

RYODEN CORPORATION

3-15-15 Higashi Ikebukuro, Toshima-ku, Tokyo, 170-8448, Japan
Tel.: (81) 353966111
Web Site: https://www.ryoden.co.jp
8084—(TKS)
Rev.: $1,712,042,880
Assets: $1,031,338,470
Liabilities: $455,719,840
Net Worth: $575,618,630
Earnings: $37,914,960
Emp.: 1,360
Fiscal Year-end: 03/31/24
Electronic Components Distr
N.A.I.C.S.: 423690
Hitoshi Chihara (Sr Exec Officer)

Subsidiaries:

Mitsubishi Electric (Shanghai) Co., Ltd. (1)
No 1386 12th Floor Mitsubishi Electric Automation Center Hongqiao Road, Changning District, Shanghai, 200336, China
Tel.: (86) 216 119 9066
Web Site: https://www.ryosho.net
Semiconductor Equipment Mfr
N.A.I.C.S.: 334413

Ryosho (Thailand) Company, Limited (1)
Unit 1507 Empire Tower 15th Floor 1 South Sathorn Road Yannawa, Yannawa Sathorn, Bangkok, 10120, Thailand
Tel.: (66) 26700385
Sales Range: $50-74.9 Million
Emp.: 12
Electric & Electronic Parts Distr
N.A.I.C.S.: 423610
Miya Mota (Mgr)

Ryosho Electronics (Shanghai) Co. LTD. (1)
12th Floor Mitsubishi Electric Automation Center No 1386 Hongqiao Road, Changn-

AND PRIVATE COMPANIES

RYUK-IL C&S., LTD.

ing District, Shanghai, 200336, China
Tel.: (86) 2161199066
Web Site: https://www.ryosho.net
Electronic Product Distr
N.A.I.C.S.: 423690
Hitoshi Chihara *(Pres)*

Ryosho Europe GmbH (1)
Voltastr 1, 60486, Frankfurt am Main, Germany
Tel.: (49) 6979583900
Web Site: https://ryosho-europe.com
Semiconductor Equipment Mfr
N.A.I.C.S.: 334413

Ryosho Hon Kong Co., Ltd. (1)
Unit Nos 01-03 Level 30 Tower1 Millennium City 1 No 388 Kwun Tong Road, Kwun Tong, Kowloon, China (Hong Kong)
Tel.: (852) 28610111
Semiconductor Equipment Mfr
N.A.I.C.S.: 334413

Ryosho Hong Kong Company, Limited (1)
Unit Nos 01-03 Level 30 Tower1 Millennium City 1 No 388 Kwun Tong Road, Kwun Tong, Kowloon, China (Hong Kong)
Tel.: (852) 28610111
Electronic Device Distr
N.A.I.C.S.: 423690

Ryosho Korea Co., Ltd. (1)
C-718 719 161-8 Magokjungang-ro, Gangseo-gu, Seoul, 07788, Korea (South)
Tel.: (82) 226490228
Semiconductor Equipment Mfr
N.A.I.C.S.: 334413

Ryosho Malaysia Sdn. Bhd. (1)
E-Gate 1-05-29 Lebuh Tunku Kudin 2, Gelugor, 11700, Penang, Malaysia
Tel.: (60) 43721988
Electronic Device Distr
N.A.I.C.S.: 423690

Ryosho Mexico, S.A. de C.V (1)
Anillo Vial II Junipero Serra 2601 Interior 602 Residencial Juriquilla, Santa Fe, 76230, Queretaro, Mexico
Tel.: (52) 4423254545
Semiconductor Equipment Mfr
N.A.I.C.S.: 334413

Ryosho Taiwan Company, Limited (1)
13F - 1 No 207 Dunhua N Rd, Songshan Dist, Taipei, 10595, Taiwan
Tel.: (886) 225465006
Sales Range: $50-74.9 Million
Emp.: 10
Electric & Electronic Parts Distr
N.A.I.C.S.: 423610
Akashi Kaiichi *(Pres)*

Ryosho Techno Company, Limited (1)
3-15-15 Higashiikebukuro, Toshima-ku, Tokyo, 170-0013, Japan
Tel.: (81) 3 5396 6315
Web Site: http://www.ryoshotechno.co.jp
Air Conditioning & Refrigeration Device Mfr & Distr
N.A.I.C.S.: 333415

Ryosho Techno Singapore Private Limited (1)
12 Woodlands square 11-74 woods Square, Singapore, 737715, Singapore
Tel.: (65) 64737118
Web Site: https://www.ryoden.co.jp
Sales Range: $25-49.9 Million
Emp.: 24
Electronic Device Distr
N.A.I.C.S.: 423690
Yuji Wakebe *(Mng Dir)*

Ryosho U.S.A. Incorporated (1)
2700 Augustine Dr Ste 140, Santa Clara, CA 95054
Tel.: (408) 496-5777
Web Site: https://www.ryoden.co.jp
Electronic Components Distr
N.A.I.C.S.: 423690

Ryosho Vietnam Co., Ltd. (1)
5 Floor Linco Group Building 61A-63A Vo Van Tan St, Ward Vo Thi Sau District 3, Ho Chi Minh City, Vietnam
Tel.: (84) 2836360430

Elevator Distr
N.A.I.C.S.: 423830

Taiwan Ryosho Co., Ltd. (1)
13F-4 No 207 Dunhua N Rd, Songshan Dist, Taipei, 10595, Taiwan
Tel.: (886) 225465006
Semiconductor Equipment Mfr
N.A.I.C.S.: 334413

RYOHIN KEIKAKU CO., LTD.
Iidabashi First Building 2-5-1 Koraku, Bunkyo-ku, Tokyo, 112-0004, Japan
Tel.: (81) 120146404
Web Site: https://www.ryohin-keikaku.jp
Year Founded: 1989
RYKKF—(OTCIQ)
Rev.: $4,802,935,280
Assets: $3,865,456,320
Liabilities: $1,495,288,960
Net Worth: $2,370,167,360
Earnings: $237,721,440
Emp.: 9,175
Fiscal Year-end: 08/31/22
General Merchandise Retailer, Distr & Mfr
N.A.I.C.S.: 455219
Masaaki Kanai *(Chm)*

Subsidiaries:

Muji (Hong Kong) Co., Ltd. (1)
Unit 1901-05 19/F Mira Place Tower A 132 Nathan Road, Tsim Sha Tsui, Kowloon, China (Hong Kong)
Tel.: (852) 2 208 4748
Web Site: https://www.muji.com.hk
Household Products Mfr
N.A.I.C.S.: 335220

Muji (Singapore) Private Ltd. (1)
OG Albert Complex 60 Albert Street 15-03/04, Singapore, 189969, Singapore
Tel.: (65) 63383113
Web Site: http://www.muji.com.sg
Online Shopping Services
N.A.I.C.S.: 455110
Jasmine Sng *(Gen Mgr)*

Muji Canada Limited (1)
20 Dundas Street West, Toronto, M5G 2C2, ON, Canada
Tel.: (416) 591-2233
Web Site: https://www.muji.ca
Household Product Distr
N.A.I.C.S.: 449210

Muji Deutschland GmbH (1)
Kurfurstendamm 236, 10719, Berlin, Germany
Tel.: (49) 308 871 0543
Household Product Distr
N.A.I.C.S.: 449210

Muji Europe Holdings Limited (1)
Bedford House 21a John Street, London, WC1N 2BF, United Kingdom
Tel.: (44) 2072393500
Web Site: http://www.muji.eu
Online Shopping Services
N.A.I.C.S.: 455110

Muji Finland Oy (1)
Kamppi Shopping Center 4th Floor Urho Kekkosen katu 1, 00100, Helsinki, Finland
Tel.: (358) 10 212 2536
Household Product Distr
N.A.I.C.S.: 449210

Muji House Co., Ltd. (1)
4-26-3 Higashiikebukuro, Toshima-ku, Tokyo, 170-8424, Japan
Tel.: (81) 12 019 6404
Web Site: https://www.muji.net
Household Product Distr
N.A.I.C.S.: 423620

Muji Korea Co., Ltd. (1)
7F Fidelia Building 12 Yonsei-ro, Seodaemun-gu, Seoul, 03779, Korea (South)
Tel.: (82) 1 577 2892
Web Site: https://www.mujikorea.net
Household Product Distr
N.A.I.C.S.: 449210

Muji Portugal, Lda. (1)

Rua Do Carmo 65-73, Chiado, 1200-093, Lisbon, Portugal
Tel.: (351) 21 347 8115
Household Product Distr
N.A.I.C.S.: 449210

Muji Retail (Australia) Pty. Ltd. (1)
Level 5 90 William Street, Melbourne, 3000, VIC, Australia
Tel.: (61) 38 306 2770
Household Product Distr
N.A.I.C.S.: 449210

Muji Spain, S.L. (1)
c / Provenca 292 2-1, 08008, Barcelona, Spain
Tel.: (34) 93 496 1033
Household Product Distr
N.A.I.C.S.: 449210

Muji Switzerland AG (1)
Einkaufszentrum Glatt Neue Winterthurerstrasse 99, 8304, Wallisellen, Switzerland
Tel.: (41) 44 554 9221
Household Product Distr
N.A.I.C.S.: 449210

Ryohin-Keikaku Reliance India Private Limited (1)
Shop No T-1A 3rd Floor Palladium High Street Phoenix Lower Parel, Mumbai, 400013, India
Tel.: (91) 797 794 6492
Household Product Distr
N.A.I.C.S.: 449210

RYOSAN COMPANY, LIMITED
2-3-5 Higashi-Kanda, Chiyoda-ku, Tokyo, 101-0031, Japan
Tel.: (81) 338622591
Web Site: https://www.ryosan.co.jp
Year Founded: 1953
Emp.: 610
Electronic Components Distr
N.A.I.C.S.: 334413

RYOWA CO., LTD.
245 Yonezawa, Chino, 391-0266, Nagano, Japan
Tel.: (81) 266735470
Web Site: http://www.ryowacoltd.co.jp
Year Founded: 1988
Sales Range: $25-49.9 Million
Emp.: 130
Printed Wiring Board Mfr & Sales
N.A.I.C.S.: 334513
Ken Gomi *(Pres)*

RYOYO ELECTRO CORPORATION
Konwa Bldg 1-12-22 Tsukiji, Chuo-ku, Tokyo, 104-8408, Japan
Tel.: (81) 33 543 7711
Web Site: http://www.ryoyo.co.jp
Year Founded: 1961
8068—(TKS)
Semiconductor & Computer Equipment Whslr
N.A.I.C.S.: 423690
Masaaki Tanabe *(Mng Exec Officer)*

Subsidiaries:

Ryoyo Electro (Shanghai) Co., Ltd. (1)
Room 601a Finance Square 333 Jiujiang Road, Shanghai, 200001, China
Tel.: (86) 2162713377
Semiconductor Device Distr
N.A.I.C.S.: 423690

Ryoyo Electro Hong Kong Ltd. (1)
Room 1507-08 15/F The Metropolis Tower No 10 Metropolis Drive Hunghom, Kowloon, China (Hong Kong)
Tel.: (852) 25737418
Web Site: https://www.ryoyo.co.jp
Semiconductor Device Distr
N.A.I.C.S.: 423690

Ryoyo Electro Singapore Pte., Ltd. (1)
180B Bencoolen Street 07-04 The Bencoolen, Singapore, 189648, Singapore
Tel.: (65) 62769636

Web Site: https://www.ryoyo.co.jp
Semiconductor Device Distr
N.A.I.C.S.: 423690

Ryoyo Electro Taiwan Co., Ltd. (1)
Room 707 7th Floor No 96 Chung Shan North Road Section 2, Taipei, Taiwan
Tel.: (886) 225118766
Web Site: https://www.ryoyo.co.jp
Semiconductor Device Distr
N.A.I.C.S.: 423690

Ryoyo Electro Trading (Dalian) Co., Ltd. (1)
9K International Finance Tower No 15 Renmin Road Zhongshan District, Dalian, 116001, China
Tel.: (86) 41182506377
Semiconductor Device Distr
N.A.I.C.S.: 423690

Ryoyo Electro USA, Inc. (1)
5201 Great America Pkwy Ste 320, Santa Clara, CA 95054
Tel.: (408) 524-2951
Semiconductor Device Distr
N.A.I.C.S.: 423690

RYOYU SYSTEMS CO., LTD.
19th floor Seavans S Building 1-2-3 Shibaura, Minato-ku, Tokyo, 105-0023, Japan
Tel.: (81) 368093750
Web Site: https://www.ryoyu.co.jp
Year Founded: 1968
4685—(TKS)
Rev.: $244,979,820
Assets: $177,326,470
Liabilities: $57,288,870
Net Worth: $120,037,600
Earnings: $15,969,760
Emp.: 1,245
Fiscal Year-end: 03/31/24
Information Technology Solutions Services
N.A.I.C.S.: 541511
Haruo Watanabe *(Chm)*

RYU APPAREL INC.
1745 West 4th Avenue, Vancouver, V6J 1M2, BC, Canada
Tel.: (604) 428-6778 BC
Web Site: http://www.ryu.com
Year Founded: 2014
RYPPF—(OTCIQ)
Rev.: $995,803
Assets: $2,354,433
Liabilities: $9,807,893
Net Worth: ($7,453,460)
Earnings: ($7,853,976)
Fiscal Year-end: 12/31/21
Holding Company; Performance Training & Fitness Apparel Designer, Marketer & Online Retailer
N.A.I.C.S.: 551112
Cesare Fazari *(Chm & CEO)*

Subsidiaries:

Respect Your Universe, Inc. (1)
818 N Russell St, Portland, OR 97227
Web Site: http://www.ryu.com
Emp.: 11
Fiscal Year-end: 12/31/2013
Performance Training & Fitness Apparel Designer, Marketer & Online Retailer
N.A.I.C.S.: 315990

RYUK-IL C&S., LTD.
2-2001 AceHightechCity 775 Gyeongin-ro, Yeongdeungpo-gu, Seoul, Korea (South)
Tel.: (82) 226591116
Web Site: https://www.61cns.com
Year Founded: 2007
191410—(KRS)
Rev.: $25,247,653
Assets: $31,586,668
Liabilities: $15,067,124
Net Worth: $16,519,543
Earnings: $515,118
Emp.: 30

RYUK-IL C&S., LTD.

RYUK-IL C&S., Ltd.—(Continued)
Fiscal Year-end: 12/31/22
Mobile Phone Equipment Mfr
N.A.I.C.S.: 334210
Ja-Ok Koo *(Pres & CEO)*

RZ EKONOMIKA AD
16 Makedonska Brigada 18, Skopje,
North Macedonia
Tel.: (389) 70359832
Web Site:
https://www.rzekonomika.com.mk
RZEK—(MAC)
Rev.: $347,152
Assets: $3,059,810
Liabilities: $59,361
Net Worth: $3,000,449
Earnings: $11,227
Fiscal Year-end: 12/31/23
Financial Services
N.A.I.C.S.: 523999

RZ INSTITUT SKOPJE
ul 16 Makedonska brigada br 18,
Skopje, Makedonija, North Macedonia
Tel.: (389) 23288000
Web Site:
http://www.rzinstitut.com.mk
Year Founded: 1967
RZIN—(MAC)
Rev.: $1,874,285
Assets: $4,518,919
Liabilities: $3,749,798
Net Worth: $769,121
Earnings: ($715,989)
Emp.: 56
Fiscal Year-end: 12/31/19
Alloy Mfr
N.A.I.C.S.: 331420

RZ TEHNICKA KONTROLA AD
Ul 16-ta Makedonska Brigada Br 18,
1000, Skopje, North Macedonia
Tel.: (389) 25514336
Web Site: https://www.rztk.mk
Year Founded: 1965
RZTK—(MAC)
Rev.: $2,205,316
Assets: $3,858,224
Liabilities: $330,592
Net Worth: $3,527,632
Earnings: $450,139
Fiscal Year-end: 12/31/23
Chemical Testing Services
N.A.I.C.S.: 541380

S 11 GROUP PUBLIC COMPANY LIMITED
888 Chatuchot Soi 10 Chatuchot
Road, Ao-Ngoen Sub District Saimai
District, Bangkok, 10220, Thailand
Tel.: (66) 20228888
Web Site: https://www.sgroup.co.th
Year Founded: 2011
S11—(THA)
Rev.: $43,664,343
Assets: $209,370,344
Liabilities: $114,147,763
Net Worth: $95,222,582
Earnings: $1,446,785
Emp.: 512
Fiscal Year-end: 12/31/23
Motorcycle Financing Services
N.A.I.C.S.: 522220
Thosaporn Lerdbhan *(Mgr-IT)*

S A DISTRIBUTION AUTOMOBILE COMPIEGNOISE
Zac De Mercieres 16 Rue Du Fonds
Pernant, 60200, Compiegne, Oise,
France
Tel.: (33) 344303636
Rev.: $28,900,000
Emp.: 45
New & Used Car Dealers
N.A.I.C.S.: 441110
Gerard Mariscal *(Pres)*

S A S GAUTHIER
8 Guicherie, 41170, Choue, France
Tel.: (33) 254808606
Rev.: $22,600,000
Emp.: 90
N.A.I.C.S.: 311615

S CHAND & COMPANY LIMITED
A-27 2nd Floor Mohan Co-Operative
Industrial Estate, New Delhi, 110 044,
India
Tel.: (91) 1149731800
Web Site:
https://www.schandgroup.com
Year Founded: 1939
540497—(BOM)
Rev.: $77,121,875
Assets: $146,286,314
Liabilities: $37,903,003
Net Worth: $108,383,310
Earnings: $6,905,102
Emp.: 602
Fiscal Year-end: 03/31/23
Content Development Services
N.A.I.C.S.: 513130
Desh Raj Dogra *(Chm)*

Subsidiaries:

BPI (India) Private Limited (1)
B1/A26, Mohan Cooperative Industrial Estate Near Badarpur, New Delhi, 110044,
India
Tel.: (91) 1143394307
Web Site: http://www.bpiindia.com
Kid Learning Services
N.A.I.C.S.: 611710

Chhaya Prakashani Private
Limited (1)
1 Bidhan Sarani, Kolkata, 700073, India
Tel.: (91) 3322573157
Web Site: https://www.chhaya.co.in
Book Publishers
N.A.I.C.S.: 513130

DS Digital Private Limited (1)
D-92 Sector 2, Noida, 201301, Uttar
Pradesh, India
Tel.: (91) 1204682700
Web Site: https://www.dsdigital.in
Teacher Training Services
N.A.I.C.S.: 611710

Edutor Technologies India Private
Limited (1)
RR Towers Plot No 188 & 189 Block - B
Phase II Kavuri Hills, Madhapur, Hyderabad, 500 081, India
Tel.: (91) 4064502055
Web Site: https://www.ignitorlearning.com
Digital Learning Space Services
N.A.I.C.S.: 611710

New Saraswati House (India) Private
Limited (1)
Second Floor MGM Tower 19 Ansari Road,
Daryaganj, New Delhi, 110002, India
Tel.: (91) 1143556600
Web Site: https://www.saraswatihouse.com
Book Publishers
N.A.I.C.S.: 513130

S. Chand Edutech Private
Limited (1)
A-27, Mohan Co-operative Industrial Area,
New Delhi, 110044, India
Tel.: (91) 1149731800
Web Site: https://www.schandedutech.com
Book Publishers
N.A.I.C.S.: 513130

Vikas Publishing House Private
Limited (1)
E-28 Sector-8, Noida, 201301, India
Tel.: (91) 1204078900
Web Site: https://www.vikaspublishing.com
Book Publishers
N.A.I.C.S.: 513130

S FOODS INC
1-22-13 Naruohama, Nishinomiya,
663-8142, Hyogo, Japan
Tel.: (81) 798431065
Web Site: https://www.sfoods.co.jp
2292—(TKS)
Rev.: $3,013,327,990
Assets: $1,589,861,600
Liabilities: $692,437,760
Net Worth: $897,423,840
Earnings: $64,327,570
Emp.: 2,467
Fiscal Year-end: 02/29/24
Food Product Whslr
N.A.I.C.S.: 424470
Akihiro Tsujita *(Gen Mgr-Imported Meat Div)*

Subsidiaries:

S Foods Inc - Funabashi No 2
Factory (1)
3-2-3 Hamacho, Funabashi, Chiba, 273-0012, Japan
Tel.: (81) 47 435 0041
Web Site: http://www.sfoods.co.jp
Processed Meat Product Mfr
N.A.I.C.S.: 311612

S Foods Inc - Funabashi No.2
Factory (1)
2-3-3 Hama-Cho Funabashi, Funabashi,
Chiba, 273-0012, Japan
Tel.: (81) 474350041
Web Site: http://www.sfoods.co.jp
Sales Range: $25-49.9 Million
Emp.: 100
Processed Meat Product Mfr
N.A.I.C.S.: 311612
Shoji Hikino *(Branch Mgr)*

S Foods Inc - Nishinomiya
Factory (1)
1- 22- 13 Naruohama, Nishinomiya, 663 8142, Hyogo, Japan
Tel.: (81) 798431065
Processed Meat Mfr
N.A.I.C.S.: 311612

S Foods Inc - Nishinomiya No.2
Factory (1)
16-11 Naruohama 1-chome, Nishinomiya,
663 8142, Hyogo, Japan
Tel.: (81) 798431063
Web Site: http://www.sfoods.co.jp
Processed Meat Product Mfr
N.A.I.C.S.: 311612

S Foods Singapore Pte. Ltd. (1)
48 Woodlands Terrace, Singapore, Singapore
Tel.: (65) 67594388
Web Site: https://yakinikuplaza.com.sg
Meat Related Food Product Mfr & Distr
N.A.I.C.S.: 311999

S IMMO AG
Wienerbergstrasse 9/7th floor, 1100,
Vienna, Austria
Tel.: (43) 1227951111
Web Site: https://www.simmoag.at
Year Founded: 1987
SPI—(VIE)
Rev.: $281,127,779
Assets: $4,073,344,485
Liabilities: $2,152,053,745
Net Worth: $1,921,290,740
Earnings: $29,358,947
Emp.: 108
Fiscal Year-end: 12/31/22
Real Estate Investment Management
Services
N.A.I.C.S.: 531390
Martin Hoffmann *(Head-Property Portfolio Mgmt-Austria)*

Subsidiaries:

Maior Domus Hausverwaltungs
GmbH (1)
Landgrafenstrasse 14, 10787, Berlin, Germany
Tel.: (49) 3033007340
Web Site: https://www.maior-domus.de
Real Estate Manangement Services
N.A.I.C.S.: 531390

INTERNATIONAL PUBLIC

S IMMO Germany GmbH (1)
Lutzouwfer 26, 10787, Berlin, Germany
Tel.: (49) 3026395580
Web Site: https://www.simmoag.de
Real Estate Manangement Services
N.A.I.C.S.: 531390
Robert Neumuller *(Mng Dir & Exec Dir)*

S IMMO Hungary Kft. (1)
Bajcsy-Zsilinszky ut 12, 1051, Budapest,
Hungary
Tel.: (36) 1 429 50 50
Web Site: http://www.simmoag.hu
Emp.: 13
Real Estate Manangement Services
N.A.I.C.S.: 531390
Katalin Sermer *(Country Mgr)*

S J LOGISTICS (INDIA) LIMITED
901902903 Centrum Opposite Raila
Devi Lake Wagle Estate, Thane,
400604, Maharashtra, India
Tel.: (91) 2261982800
Web Site: https://www.sjlogistics.co.in
Year Founded: 1999
SJLOGISTIC—(NSE)
Rev.: $18,125,654
Assets: $9,961,343
Liabilities: $6,154,548
Net Worth: $3,806,795
Earnings: $1,001,233
Emp.: 20
Fiscal Year-end: 03/31/23
Logistic Services
N.A.I.C.S.: 541614

S K BAJORIA GROUP
3 Netaji Subhas Road, Kolkata, 700
001, India
Tel.: (91) 3322482411
Web Site: http://www.bajoria.com
Holding Company
N.A.I.C.S.: 551112

Subsidiaries:

Bajoria Estate Pvt. Ltd. (1)
13A Kashinath Mullick Lane, Kolkata,
700073, West Bengal, India
Tel.: (91) 3322139421
Refractory Product Distr
N.A.I.C.S.: 423320

Bajoria Financial Services Private
Limited (1)
3, Netaji Subhas Road, Kolkata, 700001,
India
Tel.: (91) 3322482411
Web Site: http://bajoria.in
Finance
N.A.I.C.S.: 522220

Subsidiary (Domestic):

IFGL Refractories Ltd. (2)
Mcleod House 3 Netaji Subhas Road, Kolkata, 700 001, India **(72.43%)**
Tel.: (91) 3340106100
Web Site: https://ifglgroup.com
Rev.: $14,229,429
Assets: $161,601,804
Liabilities: $40,049,482
Net Worth: $121,552,322
Earnings: $8,953,172
Emp.: 793
Fiscal Year-end: 03/31/2021
Steel Industry Refractories
N.A.I.C.S.: 212323
Shishir Kumar Bajoria *(Chm)*

Subsidiary (US):

EI Ceramics LLC (3)
2600 Commerce Blvd, Cincinnati, OH
45241
Tel.: (513) 772-7001
Refractory Product Mfr & Distr
N.A.I.C.S.: 327120
Jackie Jones *(Mgr-Acctg & Office Mgr)*

Subsidiary (Domestic):

Heritage Health TPA Private
Limited (3)
Nicco House 5th Floor 2 Hare Street, Kol-

kata, 700001, India
Tel.: (91) 33 2248 6430
Web Site: http://www.heritagehealthtpa.com
Healtcare Services
N.A.I.C.S.: 621498
Sunil Parakh *(CEO)*

Subsidiary (Non-US):

Hofmann Ceramic CZ s.r.o. (3)
Smolovska 218, 34526, Bela nad Radbuzou, Czech Republic
Tel.: (420) 602147723
Ceramic Products Mfr
N.A.I.C.S.: 327120

Hofmann Ceramic GmbH (3)
Muhlweg 14, 35767, Breitscheid, Erdbach, Germany
Tel.: (49) 27 77 9 145 0
Web Site: http://www.hofmannceramic.de
Emp.: 150
Ceramic Products Mfr
N.A.I.C.S.: 327120
Thorsten Reuther *(CEO)*

Hofmann Ceramic Limited (3)
291 Thompson Hill High Green, Sheffield, S35 4JT, South Yorkshire, United Kingdom
Tel.: (44) 114 284 8161
Ceramic Product Distr
N.A.I.C.S.: 423320

Subsidiary (US):

Mono Ceramics Inc. (3)
2235 Pipestone Rd, Benton Harbor, MI 49022
Tel.: (269) 925-0212
Emp.: 20
Ceramic Product Distr
N.A.I.C.S.: 423320
Mukesh Rawal *(Pres)*

Subsidiary (Non-US):

Monocon International Refratories Limited (3)
Old Denaby, Doncaster, DN 12 4LQ, South Yorkshire, United Kingdom
Tel.: (44) 1709 864848
Web Site: http://www.monocon.com
Refractory Product Mfr & Distr
N.A.I.C.S.: 327120
Peter Jackson *(Mgr-Pur)*

Monotec Refratarios Ltda (3)
R Caio Prado 225, Parangaba, Fortaleza, 60740-100, Brazil
Tel.: (55) 85 3245 2078
Refractory Product Distr
N.A.I.C.S.: 423320

Tianjin Monocon Aluminous Refratories Company Limited (3)
Jin Bin Warehouse No 14 No 33 Baihe Road, Teda, Tianjin, 300457, China
Tel.: (86) 22 66293 245
Emp.: 30
Refractory Products Mfr
N.A.I.C.S.: 327120
Russel Kingsley *(Gen Mgr)*

S K S TEXTILES LTD.
H No 1246/1K GALA 1-9 1st Floor Blndg B-4 Prithvi Complex, 4th Floor Senapati Bapat Marg, Thane, 421302, India
Tel.: (91) 2261206222
Web Site: http://www.groupsks.com
Year Founded: 1982
SKSTEXTILE—(NSE)
Rev.: $155,816
Assets: $3,935,229
Liabilities: $9,883,238
Net Worth: ($5,948,009)
Earnings: ($1,374,801)
Emp.: 4
Fiscal Year-end: 03/31/22
Textile Mfr
N.A.I.C.S.: 313310
Sukanraj Shah *(Chm)*

S KUMARS ONLINE LIMITED
4-B Industrial Area No 2 A B Road, G K Marg Worli, Dewas, 455001, Madhya Pradesh, India
Tel.: (91) 7272258656
Web Site: https://www.skumarsonline.com
Year Founded: 1999
Rev.: $83
Assets: $217
Liabilities: $1,828
Net Worth: ($1,611)
Earnings: ($35)
Emp.: 6
Fiscal Year-end: 03/31/18
Electronic Commerce Services
N.A.I.C.S.: 513210
Omprakash Prahladrai Pacheria *(Mng Dir)*

S LINE CO., LTD.
68 Heisei 4-chome, Hashima, 501-6013, Gifu, Japan
Tel.: (81) 582453131
Web Site: https://www.sline.co.jp
Year Founded: 1938
9078—(TKS)
Rev.: $467,098,720
Assets: $403,104,240
Liabilities: $154,715,440
Net Worth: $248,388,800
Earnings: $9,350,880
Fiscal Year-end: 03/31/22
Transportation Services
N.A.I.C.S.: 488510
Yoshihiko Yamaguchi *(Chm, Pres & CEO)*

S M A D
46 Avenue Docteur Rene Dieras, 17300, Rochefort, Charente Maritime, France
Tel.: (33) 546874155
Sales Range: $25-49.9 Million
Emp.: 60
New & Used Car Dealers
N.A.I.C.S.: 441110
Audrey Schmidt *(Mgr-Mktg)*

S MACNEILLIE & SON LIMITED
Stockton Close, Walsall, WS2 8LD, West Midlands, United Kingdom
Tel.: (44) 1922725560
Web Site: http://www.macneillie.co.uk
Year Founded: 1912
Rev.: $37,441,591
Emp.: 320
Specialist Vehicle Mfr
N.A.I.C.S.: 336110
Keith Bradley *(Chm)*

S MARK CO., LTD.
21 Gajunonggong 2-gil, Chungju, Korea (South)
Tel.: (82) 2 757 9171   KR
Year Founded: 1986
Rev.: $12,796,058
Assets: $55,493,803
Liabilities: $31,390,425
Net Worth: $24,103,378
Earnings: ($31,046,124)
Emp.: 53
Fiscal Year-end: 12/31/18
Textile Products Mfr
N.A.I.C.S.: 313110
Hui-Ju Sin *(CEO)*

Subsidiaries:

KAHEE Co., LTD. - Gaju Mill (1)
54-1 Gaju-Dong, Chungju, Chungbook, Korea (South)
Tel.: (82) 43 851 9005
Textile Products Mfr
N.A.I.C.S.: 313110

KAHEE Co., LTD. - Sinni Mill (1)
3 Kyunhak-Ri, Sinni-Myun, Chungju, Chungbook, Korea (South)
Tel.: (82) 43 856 9011 Textile Products Mfr
N.A.I.C.S.: 313110

S P SETIA BERHAD
12 Persiaran Setia Dagang Setia Alam Seksyen U13, 40170, Shah Alam, Selangor Darul Ehsan, Malaysia
Tel.: (60) 350212525
Web Site: https://spsetia.com
Year Founded: 1974
SPSETIA—(KLS)
Rev.: $942,740,106
Assets: $6,310,939,048
Liabilities: $3,063,017,354
Net Worth: $3,247,921,693
Earnings: $76,944,762
Emp.: 1,984
Fiscal Year-end: 12/31/22
Property Development Services
N.A.I.C.S.: 531312
Chap Jen Khor *(Pres & CEO)*

Subsidiaries:

Aeropod Sdn Bhd (1)
I-1-1 Block I Level 1 Aeropod Commercial Square Jalan Aeropod, Off Jalan Kepayan, 88200, Kota Kinabalu, Sabah, Malaysia
Tel.: (60) 88218255
Real Estate Services
N.A.I.C.S.: 531390

Biltmore (M) Sdn Bhd (1)
No 6 Jalan Bistari 13, Taman Industri Jaya, 81300, Skudai, Johor Darul Takzim, Malaysia
Tel.: (60) 72412255
Real Estate Services
N.A.I.C.S.: 531390

Bukit Indah (Johor) Sdn Bhd (1)
Wisma S P Setia S3-0111 Laman Indah 3 Jalan Indah 15, Taman Bukit Indah, 79100, Iskandar Puteri, Johor Darul Takzim, Malaysia
Tel.: (60) 72412255
Real Estate Services
N.A.I.C.S.: 531390

Eco Meridian Sdn Bhd (1)
Setia SPICE Convention Centre SPICE 108C Jalan Tun Dr Awang, 11900, Bayan Lepas, Penang, Malaysia
Tel.: (60) 4 643 2525
Real Estate Services
N.A.I.C.S.: 531390

Ganda Anggun Sdn Bhd (1)
15-G Jalan Remia 2/KS6, Bandar Botanic, 41200, Klang, Selangor, Malaysia
Tel.: (60) 331623322
Real Estate Services
N.A.I.C.S.: 531390

Gita Kasturi Sdn Bhd (1)
Setia Sky Seputeh Sales Galleria No1 Jalan Taman Seputeh Satu, Taman Seputeh, 58000, Kuala Lumpur, Malaysia
Tel.: (60) 322765252
Real Estate Services
N.A.I.C.S.: 531390

I & P Kota Bayuemas Sdn Bhd (1)
4 Jalan Bayu Impian 10/KS9, Kota Bayuemas, 41200, Klang, Selangor, Malaysia
Tel.: (60) 33 325 1700
Real Estate Services
N.A.I.C.S.: 531390

I & P Menara Sendirian Berhad (1)
No 1 Persiaran Alam Sari 2, Alam Sari, 43000, Kajang, Selangor, Malaysia
Tel.: (60) 387362255
Real Estate Services
N.A.I.C.S.: 531390

I&P Group Sdn. Berhad (1)
Eight Kinrara Block B Jalan BK5A/1 Bandar Kinrara, 47180, Puchong, Selangor Darul Ehsan, Malaysia (100%)
Tel.: (60) 8082 9600
Web Site: http://www.inp.my
Holding Company; Property Developer
N.A.I.C.S.: 551112

Subsidiary (Domestic):

I & P Setiawangsa Sdn.Bhd. (2)
24-31 Jalan Setiawangsa 8, Taman Setiawangsa, Kuala Lumpur, 54200, Malaysia (100%)
Tel.: (60) 342567100
Web Site: http://www.inp.my
Land Subdivision
N.A.I.C.S.: 237210

Pelangi Sdn. Berhad (2)
03 05 Jalan Sri Pelangi 3, Taman Pelangi, 80400, Johor Bahru, Johor Darul Takzim, Malaysia (100%)
Tel.: (60) 73332255
Holding Company; Real Estate Developer
N.A.I.C.S.: 551112

Perumahan Kinrara Berhad (2)
Bandar Kinrara Welcome CentreEight Kinrara-Block B, Jalan BK5A/1 Bandar Kinrara, 47180, Puchong, Selangor Darul Ehsan, Malaysia (51%)
Tel.: (60) 380829525
Real Estate Agency
N.A.I.C.S.: 531210
Jamaludin Osman *(Mng Dir)*

Subsidiary (Domestic):

Kinrara Golf Club Sdn. Bhd. (3)
Jalan Kinrara 6, Bandar Kinrara, 47180, Puchong, Selangor, Malaysia (51%)
Tel.: (60) 38 076 2100
Web Site: https://www.kinraragolf.com
Golf Courses & Country Clubs
N.A.I.C.S.: 713910

KL Eco City Sdn Bhd (1)
Setia International Centre Lot 215 Pantai Baru Jalan Bangsar, 59200, Kuala Lumpur, Malaysia
Tel.: (60) 322875522
Real Estate Services
N.A.I.C.S.: 531390

Kay Pride Sdn Bhd (1)
Setia Sky Ville Sales Suite Lorong Slim, Bandar Jelutong, 11600, Penang, Malaysia
Tel.: (60) 42828255
Real Estate Services
N.A.I.C.S.: 531390

Kesas Kenangan Sdn Bhd (1)
Pejabat Tapak Lot 2110 KM 5 5 Jalan Gelang Patah-Ulu Choh, 81550, Johor Bahru, Johor Darul Takzim, Malaysia
Tel.: (60) 75552525
Real Estate Services
N.A.I.C.S.: 531390

Petaling Garden Sdn Bhd (1)
41 Jalan Warisan Sentral 1 Seksyen U13, Setia Alam, 43900, Sepang, Selangor, Malaysia
Tel.: (60) 387062552
Property Development Services
N.A.I.C.S.: 531390

S P Setia Eco-Projects Management Sdn Bhd (1)
Setia Eco Park Sales Gallery 5A Jalan Setia Nusantara U13/17, Setia Eco Park Seksyen U13, 40170, Shah Alam, Selangor Darul Ehsan, Malaysia
Tel.: (60) 333432228
Real Estate Services
N.A.I.C.S.: 531390

S P Setia Marketing Sdn Bhd (1)
Lot 5 6 Jalan Indah 1/3, Taman Industri Rawang Indah, 48000, Rawang, Selangor Darul Ehsan, Malaysia
Tel.: (60) 360928022
Real Estate Services
N.A.I.C.S.: 531390

S P Setia Property Services Sdn Bhd (1)
1 3 Jalan Setia Dagang AG U13/AG Setia Alam Seksyen U13, 40170, Shah Alam, Selangor Darul Ehsan, Malaysia
Tel.: (60) 333595252
Real Estate Services
N.A.I.C.S.: 531390

Setia (Bukit Timah) Pte. Ltd. (1)
11A Toh Tuck Road Daintree Residence Sales Gallery, Singapore, 596157, Singapore
Tel.: (65) 83682255
Real Estate Services
N.A.I.C.S.: 531390

S P SETIA BERHAD

S P Setia Berhad—(Continued)

Setia (Melbourne) Development Company Pty. Ltd. (1)
Level 1 155 Franklin Street, Melbourne, 3000, VIC, Australia
Tel.: (61) 396162525
Real Estate Services
N.A.I.C.S.: 531390

Setia A Beckett (Melbourne) Pty. Ltd. (1)
119 A'Beckett Street, Melbourne, 3000, VIC, Australia
Tel.: (61) 396162525
Real Estate Services
N.A.I.C.S.: 531390

Setia Alam Recreation Sdn Bhd (1)
Lot No 2 Jalan Setia Prima K U13/K Sek U13, Setia Alam, 40170, Shah Alam, Selangor Darul Ehsan, Malaysia
Tel.: (60) 333449255
Recreation Club Services
N.A.I.C.S.: 713940

Setia Alamsari Sdn Bhd (1)
Setia Alamsari Welcome Centre 1 Persiaran Alam Sari 2 Alam Sari, 43000, Kajang, Selangor Darul Ehsan, Malaysia
Tel.: (60) 387362255
Real Estate Services
N.A.I.C.S.: 531390

Setia City Development Sdn Bhd (1)
03 05 Jalan Sri Pelangi 3 Taman Pelangi, 80400, Johor Bahru, JOHOR DARUL TAKZIM, Malaysia
Tel.: (60) 73332255
Real Estate Services
N.A.I.C.S.: 531390

Setia Eco Glades Sdn Bhd (1)
1 Persiaran Setia Eco Glades Setia Eco Glades Cyber 1, 63000, Cyberjaya, Selangor Darul Ehsan, Malaysia
Tel.: (60) 380082228
Real Estate Services
N.A.I.C.S.: 531390

Setia Eco Templer Recreation Sdn Bhd (1)
No 1 Jalan Ipoh - Rawang KM-20 Taman Rekreasi Templer, 48000, Rawang, Selangor Darul Ehsan, Malaysia
Tel.: (60) 360921555
Food & Beverage Distr
N.A.I.C.S.: 445298

Setia Eco Templer Sdn Bhd (1)
No 1 Jalan Ipoh-Rawang KM-20 Taman Rekreasi Templer, 48000, Rawang, Selangor, Malaysia
Tel.: (60) 360922288
Property Development Services
N.A.I.C.S.: 531390

Setia Ecohill 2 Sdn Bhd (1)
Kelab 360 No 1 Persiaran Ecohill Barat Setia Ecohill, 43500, Semenyih, Selangor Darul Ehsan, Malaysia
Tel.: (60) 387242255
Real Estate Services
N.A.I.C.S.: 531390

Setia Ecohill Recreation Sdn Bhd (1)
Club 360 No 1 Persiaran Ecohill Barat Setia Ecohill, 43500, Semenyih, Selangor Darul Ehsan, Malaysia
Tel.: (60) 387235525
Real Estate Services
N.A.I.C.S.: 531390

Setia Ecohill Sdn Bhd (1)
Kelab 360 No 1 Persiaran Ecohill Barat, Setia Ecohill, 43500, Semenyih, Selangor, Malaysia
Tel.: (60) 387242255
Property Development Services
N.A.I.C.S.: 531390

Setia Fontaines Sdn Bhd (1)
Setia Experience Centre 2296 Lingkaran Setia Bandar Setia Fontaines, Kepala Batas, 13200, Penang, Malaysia
Tel.: (60) 45762255
Real Estate Services
N.A.I.C.S.: 531390

Setia Indah Sdn Bhd (1)
Wisma S P Setia 1 Jalan Setia 3/6 Taman Setia Indah, 81100, Johor Bahru, Johor, Malaysia
Tel.: (60) 73512255
Real Estate Services
N.A.I.C.S.: 531390

Setia Mayuri Sdn Bhd (1)
Setia Mayuri Welcome Centre 6 Jalan 3/1A Setia Mayuri, 43500, Semenyih, Selangor Darul Ehsan, Malaysia
Tel.: (60) 389252255
Real Estate Services
N.A.I.C.S.: 531390

Setia Precast Sdn Bhd (1)
12 Persiaran Setia Dagang Setia Alam Seksyen U13, 40170, Shah Alam, Selangor Darul Ehsan, Malaysia
Tel.: (60) 333482255
Real Estate Services
N.A.I.C.S.: 531390

Setia Promenade Sdn Bhd (1)
Setia Experience Centre 2296 Lingkaran Setia Bandar Setia Fontaines, Kepala Batas, 13200, Penang, Malaysia
Tel.: (60) 45762255
Real Estate Services
N.A.I.C.S.: 531390

Setia Putrajaya Development Sdn Bhd (1)
Setia Putrajaya Galleria No 5 Jalan P15H Presint 15, Wilayah Persekutuan, 62050, Putrajaya, Putrajaya, Malaysia
Tel.: (60) 388616500
Real Estate Services
N.A.I.C.S.: 531390

Setia Putrajaya Sdn Bhd (1)
No 5 Jalan P15H Presint 15, 62050, Putrajaya, Wilayah Persekutuan, Malaysia
Tel.: (60) 388616500
Property Development Services
N.A.I.C.S.: 531390

Setia Safiro Sdn Bhd (1)
Setia Eco Glades Lifestyle Gallery 1 Persiaran Setia Eco Glades, Setia Eco Glades Cyber 1, 63000, Cyberjaya, Selangor Darul Ehsan, Malaysia
Tel.: (60) 380082228
Real Estate Services
N.A.I.C.S.: 531390

Setia-Wood Industries Sdn Bhd (1)
Lot 5 and 6 Jalan Indah 1/3, Taman Industries Rawang Indah, 48000, Rawang, Selangor, Malaysia
Tel.: (60) 360928022
Wood Product Mfr & Distr
N.A.I.C.S.: 321999

SetiaBecamex Joint Stock Company (1)
R11-1 Street EcoLakes My Phuoc Block 6, Thoi Hoa ward, Ben Cat, Binh Duong, Vietnam
Tel.: (84) 2743577255
Real Estate Services
N.A.I.C.S.: 531390

Taman Gunong Hijau Sdn Bhd (1)
PTD 46378 Jalan Balau, Taman Rinting, 81750, Masai, Johor Darul Takzim, Malaysia
Tel.: (60) 73829188
Real Estate Services
N.A.I.C.S.: 531390

Temasya Development Co. Sdn. Bhd. (1)
TemasyaGlenmarie Welcome Centre 6 8 Jalan Kurator U1/61, Temasya Glenmarie Seksyen U1, 40150, Shah Alam, Selangor Darul Ehsan, Malaysia
Tel.: (60) 355696100
Real Estate Services
N.A.I.C.S.: 531390

S P V I PUBLIC COMPANY LIMITED

1213/58-59 Soi Ladprao 94 Sriwara Road, Phlabphla Wang Thong Lang, Bangkok, 10310, Thailand
Tel.: (66) 25592901
Web Site: https://www.spvi.co.th
Year Founded: 1989
SPVI—(THA)
Rev.: $197,631,103
Assets: $35,954,482
Liabilities: $19,021,968
Net Worth: $16,932,514
Earnings: $2,924,814
Emp.: 559
Fiscal Year-end: 12/31/23
Apple Products & Other Computer Related Products Reseller
N.A.I.C.S.: 423430
Teera Aphaiwongse (Chm)

S R G SECURITIES FINANCE LIMITED

322 SM Lodha Complex Near Shastri Circle, Udaipur, 313001, Rajasthan, India
Tel.: (91) 2942412609
Web Site: https://www.srgfin.com
536710—(BOM)
Rev.: $255,404
Assets: $1,741,358
Liabilities: $69,204
Net Worth: $1,672,154
Earnings: $62,238
Emp.: 5
Fiscal Year-end: 03/31/23
Asset Financing Services
N.A.I.C.S.: 522220
Vinod K. Jain (Mng Dir)

S T SERVICES LTD.

92b Chittaranjan Avenue 2nd Floor, Kolkata, 700 012, West Bengal, India
Tel.: (91) 3322366439
Web Site: http://www.stservices.org.in
Rev.: $33,847
Assets: $812,714
Liabilities: $2,724
Net Worth: $809,989
Earnings: $1,492
Fiscal Year-end: 03/31/18
Financial Support Services
N.A.I.C.S.: 523999
Goutam Kumar Mondal (Mng Dir)

S V GLOBAL MILL LIMITED

No 3/1 New No 5/1 6th Cross Street CIT Colony, Mylapore, Chennai, 600004, Tamil Nadu, India
Tel.: (91) 4424997751
Web Site: https://www.svgml.com
Year Founded: 2007
535621—(BOM)
Rev.: $999,527
Assets: $9,005,242
Liabilities: $184,668
Net Worth: $8,820,574
Earnings: $93,636
Emp.: 16
Fiscal Year-end: 03/31/22
Property Development Services
N.A.I.C.S.: 531390
M. Ethiraj (Chm)

S V J ENTERPRISES LIMITED

02/A Sonam Palace CHS Old Golden Nest-1 Mira Bhaindar Road, Mira Road East, Thane, 401107, India
Tel.: (91) 3328121275
Web Site: https://www.svjenterprises.co.in
Year Founded: 2009
543799—(BOM)
Agricultural Product Mfr & Distr
N.A.I.C.S.: 325320
Veena Suresh Jha (CFO)

S&B FOODS INC.

18-6 Nihonbashi Kabuto-cho, Chuo-ku, Tokyo, 103-0026, Japan
Tel.: (81) 336680551
Web Site: https://www.sbfoods-worldwide.com
Year Founded: 1923
2805—(TKS)
Rev.: $835,788,230
Assets: $926,926,910
Liabilities: $446,432,790
Net Worth: $480,494,120
Earnings: $44,399,370
Fiscal Year-end: 03/31/24
Spice Mfr & Whslr
N.A.I.C.S.: 311942
Kazuya Ikemura (Pres, CEO, Exec Mng Dir & Exec Mng Dir)

Subsidiaries:

S&B International Corporation (1)
21241 S Western Ave Ste 110, Torrance, CA 90501
Tel.: (310) 327-7000
Rice Distr
N.A.I.C.S.: 424490

S&C ENGINE GROUP LIMITED

Room 1613 16/F Tai Yau Building 181 Johnston Road, Wanchai, China (Hong Kong)
Tel.: (852) 29407730
Web Site: http://www.scengine.co.kr
Year Founded: 1987
900080—(KRS)
Rev.: $91,348,291
Assets: $393,897,756
Liabilities: $14,158,627
Net Worth: $379,739,129
Earnings: $4,685,261
Emp.: 1,223
Fiscal Year-end: 12/31/19
Automobile Parts Mfr
N.A.I.C.S.: 336110

Subsidiaries:

Jinjiang Chengda Gear Co., Ltd. (1)
Economic Development Zone Wuli Park Ling Cheung Road 7, Jinjiang, China
Tel.: (86) 59585668929
Web Site: http://www.chengda-gear.com.cn
Automobile Gearbox & Engine Gears Mfr
N.A.I.C.S.: 336350

S&D CO.,LTD.

163 Oson Eup 4th Osong Life insurance Bldg, Heungduk-gu, Cheongju, Korea (South)
Tel.: (82) 437108000
Web Site: https://www.isnd.co.kr
Year Founded: 1998
Food Additive Mfr & Distr
N.A.I.C.S.: 325998
Yeo Gyeong-Mok (CEO)

S&J CORPORATION

8F Nishi-Shinbashi PR-EX 2-4-12 Nishi-Shinbashi, Minato-ku, Tokyo, 105-0003, Japan
Tel.: (81) 362058500
Web Site: https://www.sandj.co.jp
Year Founded: 2008
5599—(TKS)
Emp.: 103
Information Technology Services
N.A.I.C.S.: 541512

S&J INTERNATIONAL ENTERPRISES PUBLIC COMPANY LIMITED

2 Naradhiwas Rajanagarindra Road, Tungwatdon Sathon, Bangkok, 10120, Thailand
Tel.: (66) 26762727
Web Site: https://www.snjinter.com
Year Founded: 1980
S.&.J—(THA)
Rev.: $203,321,139
Assets: $199,094,939
Liabilities: $44,689,724
Net Worth: $154,405,214
Earnings: $22,281,348
Emp.: 1,818

AND PRIVATE COMPANIES

Fiscal Year-end: 12/31/23
Contract Mfr of High Quality Cosmetics & Personal Care Products
N.A.I.C.S.: 812199
Boonkiet Chokwatana *(Chm)*

Subsidiaries:

S&J International (UK) Ltd (1)
9 Lydden Road, London, SW18 4LT, United Kingdom
Tel.: (44) 203 167 0095
Marketing Consulting Services
N.A.I.C.S.: 541613
Simon Knight *(Mng Dir)*

S&K POLYTEC CO., LTD.
515 Sihwa Venture-ro, Danwon-Gu, Ansan, 15617, Gyeonggi-do, Korea (South)
Tel.: (82) 314328061
Web Site: http://www.snkpolytec.com
Year Founded: 1999
091340—(KRS)
Rev.: $257,779,077
Assets: $204,249,372
Liabilities: $110,621,778
Net Worth: $93,627,594
Earnings: ($930,162)
Emp.: 92
Fiscal Year-end: 12/31/22
Foam Sheet Mfr
N.A.I.C.S.: 326140
Wonhyung Kang *(CEO & Mng Dir)*

Subsidiaries:

NPD Co., Ltd. (1)
112 Seonggeo-gil Seounggeo-eu, Seobuk-gu, Cheonan, 31044, Chungcheongnam, Korea (South)
Tel.: (82) 314978112
Web Site: http://www.eng.newportdisplay.co.kr
Emp.: 26
Management Consulting Services
N.A.I.C.S.: 541618
Kang Won Hyung *(CEO)*

S&O AGRAR AG
Ziegelhauser Landstrasse 1, Heidelberg, 69120, Germany
Tel.: (49) 6221649240
Web Site: http://www.soagrar.de
BUF—(DEU)
Biofuel Product Distr
N.A.I.C.S.: 424690
Karim Serrar *(Member-Mgmt Bd)*

S&P INTERNATIONAL HOLDING LIMITED
No 27-3 Jalan PJU 5/13 Dataran Sunway Kota Damansara, 47810, Petaling Jaya, Selangor, Malaysia
Tel.: (60) 361572226
Web Site: http://www.spfood.com
Year Founded: 1983
1695—(HKG)
Rev.: $12,002,484
Assets: $22,994,726
Liabilities: $6,251,698
Net Worth: $16,743,028
Earnings: ($253,285)
Emp.: 337
Fiscal Year-end: 12/31/23
Food Product Mfr & Distr
N.A.I.C.S.: 311999
Koon Fook Tang *(Chm)*

Subsidiaries:

S & P Industries Sdn. Bhd. (1)
No 27-3 Jalan PJU 5/13, Kota Damansara, 47810, Petaling Jaya, Selangor Darul Ehsan, Malaysia
Tel.: (60) 361572226
Web Site: https://spfood.com
Coconut Cream Powder Mfr
N.A.I.C.S.: 311999

Stancodex Sdn. Bhd. (1)
16 Jalan Teknology 3/1, Kota Damansara, 47810, Petaling Jaya, Selangor, Malaysia
Tel.: (60) 361561391
Web Site: https://www.stancodex.com
Coconut Cream Powder Mfr
N.A.I.C.S.: 311999

S&P SISTEMAS DE VENTILACIÓN, S.L.U.
Llevant, 4 Polígono Industrial Llevant, Parets del Vallès, 08150, Barcelona, Spain
Tel.: (34) 935719300
Web Site: https://www.solerpalau.com
Appliances, Electrical & Electronics Mfg
N.A.I.C.S.: 335220

Subsidiaries:

S&P USA Ventilation Systems, LLC (1)
6393 Powers Ave, Jacksonville, FL 32217
Tel.: (904) 731-4711
Web Site: https://www.solerpalau-usa.com
Blowers And Fans
N.A.I.C.S.: 333413
Deborah Forsberg *(Controller)*

Subsidiary (Domestic):

United Enertech Corp. (2)
3005 S Hickory St, Chattanooga, TN 37407
Tel.: (423) 643-2520
Web Site: http://www.unitedenertech.com
Mechanical Air Movement & Control Products Mfr
N.A.I.C.S.: 333415
Ken Trent *(Chm & Pres)*

Subsidiary (Domestic):

Metal Form Manufacturing, Inc. (3)
5960 W Washington St, Phoenix, AZ 85043-3523
Tel.: (602) 233-1211
Web Site: http://www.mfmca.com
Sales Range: $1-9.9 Million
Emp.: 60
Air Purification Equipment Mfr
N.A.I.C.S.: 333413

S&P SYNDICATE PUBLIC COMPANY LIMITED
2034/100-103 Italthai Tower 23rd Floor New Petchburi Rd, Bangkapi Huaykwang, Bangkok, 10310, Thailand
Tel.: (66) 27854000
Web Site: https://www.snpfood.com
Year Founded: 1973
SNP—(THA)
Rev.: $181,694,722
Assets: $147,266,507
Liabilities: $66,691,993
Net Worth: $80,574,515
Earnings: $14,222,871
Emp.: 4,456
Fiscal Year-end: 12/31/23
Restaurant & Bakery Chain Owner & Operator
N.A.I.C.S.: 722511
Sathimon Tawantiang *(Dir-Supply Chain)*

Subsidiaries:

MSP Property Limited (1)
Sutherland House 1795 London Road, Leigh-on-Sea, SS9 2RZ, Essex, United Kingdom
Tel.: (44) 2088746503
Real Estate Services
N.A.I.C.S.: 531390

Patara (Geneva) SA (1)
No 94 rue des Eaux-Vives, CH-1207, Geneva, Switzerland (62%)
Tel.: (41) 22 735 0517
Restaurant Operators
N.A.I.C.S.: 722511

Patara International Restaurant Management (Beijing) Co., Ltd. (1)
6th Fl Jinbao Place 88 Jinbao Street, Dongcheng, Beijing, 100005, China (91.86%)
Tel.: (86) 10 8522 1678
Web Site: http://www.patarachina.com
Restaurant Operators
N.A.I.C.S.: 722511

Patara Restaurant, Vienna GmbH
Petersplatz 1 Goldschmiedgasse 9 Graben 27-28 Top 7, Vienna, Austria (93.05%)
Tel.: (43) 19971938
Web Site: https://www.patara-vienna.at
Restaurant Operators
N.A.I.C.S.: 722511

Patio International Company Limited (1)
7F-3 No 28 Jen Ai Road Sec 3, Taipei, Taiwan (60%)
Tel.: (886) 2 2721 5998
Restaurant Operators
N.A.I.C.S.: 722511

S&P Asset Company Limited (1)
1/2 Soi Attakravil Sukhumvit 26 Road, Klongtan Klongtoei, Bangkok, Thailand (99.93%)
Tel.: (66) 2185 1313
Real Estate Manangement Services
N.A.I.C.S.: 531390

S&P Food Solution Company Limited (1)
457-457/6 Sukhumvit 55 Klongtannua, Vadhana, Bangkok, Thailand (99.99%)
Tel.: (66) 2185 1313
Restaurant Operators
N.A.I.C.S.: 722511

S&P Global Company Limited (1)
457 Sukhumbit 55 Klongrannua Vadhana, Bangkok, Thailand (80%)
Tel.: (66) 2185 1313
Restaurant Operators
N.A.I.C.S.: 722511

S&P International Foods (Cambodia) Company Limited (1)
Villa No 21 Street 214, Village 2 Sangkat Beoung Raing Khan Daun Penh, Phnom Penh, Cambodia
Tel.: (855) 639988
Restaurant Operators
N.A.I.C.S.: 722511

S&P International Foods Company Limited (1)
1/2 Soi Attakravil Sukhumvit 26 Rd, Klongtan Klongtoei, Bangkok, Thailand (99.99%)
Tel.: (66) 21851313
Restaurant Operators
N.A.I.C.S.: 722511

S&P Restaurant Company Limited (1)
Suite 416 130 Shaftesbury Avenue, London, W1D 5BU, United Kingdom (96%)
Tel.: (44) 20 7031 1168
Restaurant Operators
N.A.I.C.S.: 722511

S&P Training Co., Ltd. (1)
1/2 Soi Attakravi1 Sukhumvit 26 Rd Klongtan, Khlong Toei, Bangkok, Thailand
Tel.: (66) 26646260
Skill Development Training Services
N.A.I.C.S.: 611519

Shanghai Yueshi Restaurant Management Limited (1)
Sky Mall No 5001 Dushi Road Room 07/08/09 4th Floor, Xinzhuang Minhang District, Shanghai, China
Tel.: (86) 1002134687591
Restaurant Operators
N.A.I.C.S.: 722511

Umenohana S&P Co., Ltd. (1)
No 2034/100 New Petchburi Road, Bangkapi Huay Kwang, Bangkok, Thailand (60%)
Tel.: (66) 2785 4000
Restaurant Operators
N.A.I.C.S.: 722511

S&S HEALTHCARE HOLDING LTD
11494 7F No 85 Xinhu 1st Rd, Neihu Dist, Taipei, 114, Taiwan
Tel.: (886) 287922699
Web Site: http://www.swissray.com
Year Founded: 1988
4198—(TPE)
Rev.: $7,955,383
Assets: $16,604,384
Liabilities: $9,868,930
Net Worth: $6,735,453
Earnings: ($2,162,368)
Fiscal Year-end: 12/31/22
Medical Imaging Device Mfr
N.A.I.C.S.: 334510

Subsidiaries:

Swissray International, Inc. (1)
1 International Blvd Ste 400, Mahwah, NJ 07495
Medical Device Mfr & Distr
N.A.I.C.S.: 339113

Swissray Medical AG (1)
Turbistrasse 25 - 27, 6280, Hochdorf, Switzerland
Tel.: (41) 419141212
Medical Imaging Equipment Mfr
N.A.I.C.S.: 334510

S&S TECH CO., LTD.
42 Hosandong-ro, Dalseo-Gu, Daegu, Korea (South)
Tel.: (82) 535891600
Web Site: https://www.snstech.co.kr
Year Founded: 2001
101490—(KRS)
Rev.: $94,729,635
Assets: $173,917,477
Liabilities: $27,887,221
Net Worth: $146,030,257
Earnings: $13,395,046
Emp.: 257
Fiscal Year-end: 12/31/22
Electronic Components Mfr
N.A.I.C.S.: 334419
Soo Hong Jeong *(Founder & CEO)*

S&T CORPORATION LIMITED
195 Walkeshwar Road Teen Batti Near Bank of India, Mumbai, 400 006, India
Tel.: (91) 2223635386
Web Site: https://www.stcl.co.in
514197—(BOM)
Rev.: $135,023
Assets: $1,798,100
Liabilities: $25,551
Net Worth: $1,772,548
Earnings: $92,836
Emp.: 6
Fiscal Year-end: 03/31/22
Construction Engineering & Travel Arrangement Services
N.A.I.C.S.: 541330
Surendra Tulsidas Savai *(Co-Founder, Chm & Co-Mng Dir)*

S&U PLC
Tel.: (44) 1217057777
Web Site: https://www.suplc.co.uk
Year Founded: 1938
SUS—(LSE)
Rev.: $119,328,653
Assets: $444,285,358
Liabilities: $163,580,821
Net Worth: $280,704,537
Earnings: $51,568,921
Emp.: 200
Fiscal Year-end: 01/31/22
Consumer Credit & Automobile Loans
N.A.I.C.S.: 522310
Anthony Coombs *(Chm)*

Subsidiaries:

Advantage Finance Ltd. (1)
Unit 7 Acorn Business Park Moss Road, Grimsby, DN32 0LW, United Kingdom
Tel.: (44) 1472233200

S&U PLC

S&U PLC—(Continued)
Web Site: https://www.advantage-finance.co.uk
Sales Range: $50-74.9 Million
Emp.: 70
Vehicle Finance Services
N.A.I.C.S.: 522310

Wilson Tupholme Ltd. (1)
290 Pitsmoor Road, Sheffield, S3 (AX,
United Kingdom
Tel.: (44) 1142728176
Loan Services
N.A.I.C.S.: 522310

S&W CORPORATION
29 Dadae-ro 170beon-gil, Saha-gu,
Busan, 49444, Korea (South)
Tel.: (82) 512057411
Web Site: https://www.snwcorp.com
Year Founded: 1967
103230—(KRS)
Rev.: $27,624,174
Assets: $47,580,814
Liabilities: $14,962,395
Net Worth: $32,618,419
Earnings: $1,783,383
Emp.: 109
Fiscal Year-end: 12/31/22
Engine Parts Mfr
N.A.I.C.S.: 336310
Woo Jin Jung (CEO)

Subsidiaries:

S&W Corporation - Second
Factory (1)
Sinpyung 532, Saha, Busan, Korea (South)
Tel.: (82) 51 209 2327
Machine Tools Mfr
N.A.I.C.S.: 333517
Jung Hwa-Sup (CEO)

S'PORTER LTD
GD International Centre, Draycott Industrial Estate, Moreton-in-Marsh,
GL56 9JY, Glos, United Kingdom
Tel.: (44) 1386 702700
Web Site: http://www.sporter.co.uk
Year Founded: 1995
Sales Range: $25-49.9 Million
Emp.: 80
Sports Apparel Mfr & Retailer
N.A.I.C.S.: 315990
George Davies (Mng Dir)

S-CONNECT CO., LTD.
30 Marudeul-gil 172beon-gil Opo-eup,
Gwangju, Gyeonggi-do, Korea
(South)
Tel.: (82) 317990700
Web Site: http://www.s-connect.co.kr
Year Founded: 1998
096630—(KRS)
Rev.: $153,674,478
Assets: $127,373,926
Liabilities: $91,157,047
Net Worth: $36,216,879
Earnings: $2,080,227
Emp.: 71
Fiscal Year-end: 12/31/22
Mobile Metal Parts Mfr
N.A.I.C.S.: 332999
Soon Kwan Park (CEO)

S-ENERGY CO., LTD.
20 Pangyoyeok-ro 241beon-gil,
Bundang-gu, Seongnam, Gyeonggi-do, Korea (South)
Tel.: (82) 7043397100
Web Site: https://www.s-energy.com
Year Founded: 2001
095910—(KRS)
Rev.: $160,107,334
Assets: $268,115,350
Liabilities: $180,486,473
Net Worth: $87,628,877
Earnings: ($17,003,529)
Emp.: 138

Fiscal Year-end: 12/31/22
Solar Cell Mfr
N.A.I.C.S.: 334413

Subsidiaries:

S-Energy Co., Ltd. - Factory 1 (1)
328 Techno 2-ro, Yuseong-gu, Daejeon,
Korea (South)
Tel.: (82) 42 933 7715
Solar Cell Mfr
N.A.I.C.S.: 334413

S-Energy Co., Ltd. - Factory 2 (1)
260 Gapcheon-ro, Yuseong-gu, Daejeon,
Korea (South)
Tel.: (82) 42 717 7100
Solar Cell Mfr
N.A.I.C.S.: 334413

S-Energy Japan Co., Ltd. (1)
6F Nishikicho BLDG 1-8-11 Kandanishiki-cho, Chiyoda-ku, Tokyo, 102-0092, Japan
Tel.: (81) 362613759
Emp.: 5
Solar Cell Distr
N.A.I.C.S.: 423690

SEAI America, Inc. (1)
20 Corporate Park Ste 190, Irvine, CA
92606
Tel.: (949) 281-7897
Solar Cell Distr
N.A.I.C.S.: 423690

S-ENJOY SERVICE GROUP CO., LIMITED
12th Floor Seazen Holdngs Tower B
No 5 Lane 388 Zhongjiang Rd, Putuo, Shanghai, China
Tel.: (86) 2122835888 Ky
Web Site: http://www.xinchengyue.com
Year Founded: 2018
1755—(HKG)
Rev.: $727,209,241
Assets: $863,550,839
Liabilities: $455,194,210
Net Worth: $408,356,629
Earnings: $66,654,479
Emp.: 26,681
Fiscal Year-end: 12/31/22
Property Management Services
N.A.I.C.S.: 531311
Xiaoming Qi (Chm & CEO)

S-FUELCELL CO., LTD.
20 Pangyoyeok-ro 241beon-gil,
Bundang-gu, Seongnam, 13230,
Gyeonggi-do, Korea (South)
Tel.: (82) 7046134900
Web Site: https://s-fuelcell.com
Year Founded: 2014
288620—(KRS)
Rev.: $35,877,421
Assets: $117,434,452
Liabilities: $63,433,061
Net Worth: $54,001,391
Earnings: $575,871
Emp.: 54
Fiscal Year-end: 12/31/22
Phosphoric Acid Product Mfr
N.A.I.C.S.: 325199
Seongmin Hong (CEO)

S-POOL, INC.
6F Akihabara Daibiru 1-18-13 Sotokanda, Chiyoda-ku, Tokyo, 101-0021,
Japan
Tel.: (81) 368595599
Web Site: https://www.spool.co.jp
Year Founded: 1999
2471—(TKS)
Rev.: $182,808,560
Assets: $236,657,110
Liabilities: $176,434,650
Net Worth: $60,222,460
Earnings: $12,265,700
Emp.: 1,178
Fiscal Year-end: 11/30/23

Human Resource Outsourcing Services
N.A.I.C.S.: 561320
Sohei Urakami (Chm & Pres)

Subsidiaries:

S-Pool Human Solutions, Inc. (1)
1 Chome-25-1 Nishishinjuku Shinjuku-Ku,
Tokyo, 160-0023, Japan
Tel.: (81) 368948811
Web Site: http://www.spool-hs.co.jp
Human Resource Consulting Services
N.A.I.C.S.: 541612

S-SCIENCE CO., LTD.
7F K-18 Bldg 8-9-13 Ginza, Chuo-ku,
Tokyo, 104-0061, Japan
Tel.: (81) 335733721 JP
Web Site: http://www.s-science.jp
Year Founded: 1946
5721—(TKS)
Rev.: $10,205,840
Assets: $21,641,140
Liabilities: $1,745,040
Net Worth: $19,896,100
Earnings: $2,815,860
Fiscal Year-end: 03/31/24
Non-Ferrous Metal Fabricated Products Mfr
N.A.I.C.S.: 332999
Moritoshi Shinada (Chm)

S. ALAM COLD ROLLED STEELS LIMITED
2119 Asadgonj, Chittagong, 4100,
Bangladesh
Tel.: (880) 31636997
Web Site: https://www.s.alamgroupbd.com
Year Founded: 1995
SALAMCRST—(CHT)
Rev.: $54,951,074
Assets: $185,666,503
Liabilities: $167,745,014
Net Worth: $17,921,488
Earnings: $404,096
Emp.: 388
Fiscal Year-end: 06/30/23
Cold Rolled Strip Coil & Sheets Mfr
N.A.I.C.S.: 331110
Abdus Samad (Chm)

S. B. & T. INTERNATIONAL LIMITED
Yusuf Building 1st Floor Room No 15
Abdul Rehman Street, Mumbai, 400
003, India
Tel.: (91) 22 23636804
Web Site: http://www.sbtindia.com
Year Founded: 1986
Rev.: $1,936,953
Assets: $21,256,393
Liabilities: $15,669,567
Net Worth: $5,586,826
Earnings: $174,980
Fiscal Year-end: 03/31/16
Jewelry Mfr
N.A.I.C.S.: 339910

S. BURDE & CO.
Davey Street, Germiston, Gauteng,
South Africa
Tel.: (27) 11 873 3949 ZA
Web Site: http://www.sburde.co.za
Year Founded: 1983
Emp.: 100
Gutters & Down Pipes Mfr & Distr
N.A.I.C.S.: 332322
Gareth Rees (Owner)

S. ISHIMITSU & CO., LTD.
4-40 Iwaya Minamicho Nada Ward,
Kobe, 657-0856, Japan
Tel.: (81) 788617791
Web Site: https://www.ishimitsu.co.jp
Year Founded: 1906

INTERNATIONAL PUBLIC

2750—(TKS)
Rev.: $409,985,250
Assets: $242,468,020
Liabilities: $154,958,230
Net Worth: $87,509,790
Earnings: $6,933,890
Fiscal Year-end: 03/31/24
Coffee Product Mfr
N.A.I.C.S.: 311920
Tomohiro Ishiwaki (Pres)

Subsidiaries:

Kansai Allied Coffee Roasters Co.,
Ltd. (1)
12-3 Fukaehamacho, Higashinada-ku,
Kobe, 658-0023, Hyogo, Japan
Tel.: (81) 784525741
Web Site: https://kacr.co.jp
Emp.: 123
Coffee Bean Mfr & Distr
N.A.I.C.S.: 311920

Premio Coffee Co., Ltd. (1)
4-4-19 Kashiwagi-cho, Sakai-ku, Osaka,
590-0837, Japan
Tel.: (81) 72 280 3839
Web Site: http://www.premiocoffee.com
Coffee Bean Distr
N.A.I.C.S.: 424490

Si-Cafe Co., Ltd. (1)
2-1-6 Kyabiku Buld 1F & BF1 Sanno, Otai-ku, Tokyo, 143-0023, Japan
Tel.: (81) 337767216
Web Site: https://si-cafe.jp
Restaurant Operators
N.A.I.C.S.: 722511

Tokyo Allied Coffee Roasters Co.,
Ltd. (1)
2-23-21 Nakaikekami, Ota-ku, Tokyo, 146-0081, Japan
Tel.: (81) 337546411
Web Site: https://www.tacr.co.jp
Coffee Bean Mfr & Distr
N.A.I.C.S.: 311920

US Foods Co., Ltd. (1)
6-8-25 Ayase, Adachi-ku, Tokyo, 120-0005,
Japan
Tel.: (81) 356977390
Web Site: https://usfoods.co.jp
Sales Range: Less than $1 Million
Coffee Bean Distr
N.A.I.C.S.: 424490

S. JENNINGS LTD.
Parsons Road, Washington, NE37
1EZ, United Kingdom
Tel.: (44) 3334149750
Web Site: http://www.jenningsmotorgroup.com
Sales Range: $75-99.9 Million
Emp.: 500
Car Dealership Owner & Operator
N.A.I.C.S.: 441110
Nas Khan (Mng Dir)

S. KARGER AG
Allschwilerstrasse 10, Basel, CH
4009, Switzerland
Tel.: (41) 613061111
Web Site: http://www.karger.com
Year Founded: 1890
Sales Range: $25-49.9 Million
Emp.: 215
Medical Book Publisher
N.A.I.C.S.: 513130
Gabriella Karger (Chm, Member-Mgmt Bd & Publr)

Subsidiaries:

Karger China (1)
51F Raffles City Centre 268 Xi Zang Middle
Road, Huang Pu District, Shanghai,
200001, China
Tel.: (86) 21 2312 7673
Web Site: http://www.karger.cn
Scientific & Medical Journal Publisher
N.A.I.C.S.: 513199
Veronica Zhang-Fan (Mgr-Editorial)

Karger Japan, Inc. (1)

AND PRIVATE COMPANIES

Shiba Daimon Asahi Bldg 2F 1-2-23 Shiba Daimon, Minato-ku, Tokyo, 105-0012, Japan
Tel.: (81) 3 6435 6242
Scientific & Medical Journal Publisher
N.A.I.C.S.: 513199
Kogi Furukawa *(Gen Mgr)*

S. Karger / Karger Libri (1)
152 Soi Sutjarit 2 Rama 5 Road Suanjit-lada, Dusit, Bangkok, 10300, Thailand
Tel.: (66) 2 668 55 40
Web Site: http://www.libri.ch
Scientific & Medical Journal Publisher
N.A.I.C.S.: 513199

S. Karger GmbH (1)
Wilhelmstrasse 20A, Freiburg, 79098, Germany
Tel.: (49) 761 45 20 70
Sales Range: $25-49.9 Million
Emp.: 17
Scientific & Medical Journal Publisher
N.A.I.C.S.: 513199
Joachim Flickinger *(Mng Dir)*

S. Karger Publishers, Inc. (1)
26 W Avon Rd, Unionville, CT 06085
Tel.: (860) 675-7834
Scientific & Medical Journal Publisher
N.A.I.C.S.: 513199
Amy Gibson *(Mgr-Mktg)*

S. KHON KAEN FOODS PUBLIC COMPANY LIMITED
259/13 Soi Pridi Banomyong 13 Sukhumvit 71 Road, Watthana, Bangkok, 10110, Thailand
Tel.: (66) 23911010
Web Site: http://www.sorkon.co.th
Year Founded: 1984
SORKON—(THA)
Rev.: $92,338,804
Assets: $86,931,024
Liabilities: $48,690,016
Net Worth: $38,241,008
Earnings: $1,468,171
Emp.: 1,192
Fiscal Year-end: 12/31/23
Food Mfr
N.A.I.C.S.: 311999
Charoen Rujirasopon *(Bd of Dirs, Chm-Exec Bd & CEO)*

Subsidiaries:

S. Khon Kaen Foods Public Company Limited - Bangplee Factory (1)
44/4 Moo 13 Pracharaj-Utit Rd Rachatheva, Bang Phli, 10540, SamutPrakan, Thailand
Tel.: (66) 2738 9350 5
Food Product Mfr & Distr
N.A.I.C.S.: 311710

S. KUMARS NATIONWIDE LIMITED
B2 5th Floor Marathon NextGen Off G K Marg Lower Parel, Mumbai, 400 013, India
Tel.: (91) 2224824500   In
Web Site: http://www.sknl.co.in
Sales Range: $900-999.9 Million
Garment & Home Textiles Mfr & Distr
N.A.I.C.S.: 313310

Subsidiaries:

Leggiuno S.p.A. (1)
Via Dante 1, Alighieri, 21038, Varese, Leggiuno, Italy (100%)
Tel.: (39) 0332646811
Web Site: http://www.leggiunospa.it
Sales Range: $25-49.9 Million
Emp.: 220
Cotton Fabrics Weaving
N.A.I.C.S.: 313240

Reid & Taylor (India) Limited (1)
Thandya Industrial Area Thandavapura, Nanjangud Taluka, Mysore, 571 302, Karnataka, India (76.97%)
Tel.: (91) 8221228713
Web Site: http://www.bondwiththebest.com
Sales Range: $125-149.9 Million
Worsted & Natural Fiber Suits Mfr
N.A.I.C.S.: 315150

S. NORMAN SANCTON
85 McIlveen Drive, Saint John, E2J 4Y6, NB, Canada
Tel.: (506) 635-8500
Web Site: http://www.sancton.com
Year Founded: 1900
Rev.: $7,651,156
Emp.: 26
Industrial Equipment Whsr
N.A.I.C.S.: 811310
Zig Rans *(Dir-Fin)*

S. P. APPARELS LIMITED
39 - A Extention Street Kaikattipudur Avinashi, Tirupur, 641 654, Tamilnadu, India
Tel.: (91) 4296714000
Web Site: https://www.s-p-apparels.com
Year Founded: 1989
540048—(BOM)
Rev.: $13,199,341
Assets: $13,153,360
Liabilities: $5,076,974
Net Worth: $8,076,386
Earnings: $989,293
Emp.: 7,460
Fiscal Year-end: 03/31/23
Apparel Mfr & Distr
N.A.I.C.S.: 315250
P. V. Jeeva *(CEO)*

Subsidiaries:

Young Brand Apparel Private Limited (1)
Kattuputhur Village Ozhaiyur Post, Uthiramerur Taluk, Kanchipuram, 603107, Tamilnadu, India
Tel.: (91) 4427283000
Web Site: https://www.youngbrand.in
Apparel Product Mfr
N.A.I.C.S.: 315990

S. SHLOMO HOLDINGS LTD.
Kryat S;hlomo Zrifin, Nir Tzvi, 72905, Israel
Tel.: (972) 8 9191111
Web Site: http://www.shlomogroup.co.il
Sales Range: $1-4.9 Billion
Holding Company; Vehicle Leasing & Rental Services
N.A.I.C.S.: 551112
Atalia Shmeltzer *(Pres)*

S. SMITH & SON PTY. LTD.
40 Eden Valley Road, PO Box 10, Angaston, 5353, SA, Australia
Tel.: (61) 885613200
Web Site: http://www.yalumba.com
Year Founded: 1849
Sales Range: $50-74.9 Million
Emp.: 400
Wine Distr
N.A.I.C.S.: 312130

Subsidiaries:

Negociants International P/L (1)
Eden Vly Rd, PO Box 10, Angaston, 5353, SA, Australia
Tel.: (61) 885613200
Web Site: http://www.negociants.com
Sales Range: $100-124.9 Million
Emp.: 350
Distr of Wine & Brandy
N.A.I.C.S.: 312130
Brenton Fry *(Dir-Negociants Intl)*

S.A INDUSTRIAS CELULOSA ARAGONESA CIF
Calle San Juan de la Pena 144, 50015, Zaragoza, Spain
Tel.: (34) 97 610 31 00   ES
Web Site: http://www.saica.com
Year Founded: 1943
Paper & Packaging Products Mfr & Recycling Services
N.A.I.C.S.: 322120

Subsidiaries:

Lemapack B.V. (1)
Nesland 5 F, 1382 MZ, Weesp, Netherlands
Tel.: (31) 294 43 00 36
Web Site: http://www.lemapack.nl
Packaging Services
N.A.I.C.S.: 561910

S.A. AGRIVOLT
45 impasse des Trembles, ZA Les Bougeries, 74550, Perrignier, France
Tel.: (33) 4 5072 5193
Web Site: http://www.granulatex.com
Emp.: 19
Recycling Services
N.A.I.C.S.: 562998
Gilberte Morand *(Chm, CEO & Dir-Admin & fin)*

S.A. ARMSTRONG LIMITED
23 Bertrand Ave, Scarborough, M1L 2P3, ON, Canada
Tel.: (416) 755-2291   Ca
Web Site: http://www.armstrongpumps.com
Year Founded: 1934
Sales Range: $50-74.9 Million
Emp.: 350
Pumps, Valves, Heat Exchangers Mfr for Industrial & Commerical Building Applications
N.A.I.C.S.: 333914

Subsidiaries:

Armstrong Holden Brooke Pullen Limited (1)
1 Wolverton Street, Manchester, M11 2ET, United Kingdom (100%)
Tel.: (44) 1612232223
Web Site: http://www.armstrongintegrated.com
Sales Range: $25-49.9 Million
Emp.: 40
Pumps Service, Repair & Mfr
N.A.I.C.S.: 333914
Andrew Kilmister *(Dir-Fin)*

Armstrong Integrated Systems Limited (1)
Heyward Wharf Mucklow Hill, Halesowen, B62 8DJ, West Midlands, United Kingdom
Tel.: (44) 1215505333
Web Site: http://www.armlink.com
Sales Range: $25-49.9 Million
Emp.: 60
Pumps Mfr
N.A.I.C.S.: 333914

Armstrong Pumps Inc. (1)
93 E Ave, North Tonawanda, NY 14120-6594
Tel.: (716) 693-8813
Web Site: http://www.armstrongfluidtechnology.com
Sales Range: $25-49.9 Million
Emp.: 120
Pumps Mfr
N.A.I.C.S.: 333914
Terry McCraith *(Mgr-IT)*

S.A. D'IETEREN N.V.
rue du Mail 50, 1050, Brussels, Belgium
Tel.: (32) 25365439   BE
Web Site: https://www.dieterengroup.com
Year Founded: 1805
DJDA—(DEU)
Rev.: $8,532,871,680
Assets: $7,704,124,160
Liabilities: $3,992,288,640
Net Worth: $3,711,835,520
Earnings: $545,408,640
Emp.: 29,840
Fiscal Year-end: 12/31/23
Vehicle Distribution, Windshield Repair & Automobile Rental Services
N.A.I.C.S.: 532111
Nicolas D'Ieteren *(Chm)*

Subsidiaries:

AD Bosch Recanvis S.L. (1)
N-IIa Km 711, Fornells de la Selva, 17458, Girona, Spain
Tel.: (34) 972181800
Web Site: https://adbosch.com
Automotive Spare Parts Distr
N.A.I.C.S.: 486210

AD Marche S.r.l. (1)
Via Ferruccio Fioretti 18, 60131, Ancona, Italy
Tel.: (39) 0712906002
Web Site: https://www.admarche.it
Automotive Spare Parts Distr
N.A.I.C.S.: 486210

Attrezzauto.Com S.R.L. (1)
Via Chieri 109, Andezeno, 10020, Turin, Italy
Tel.: (39) 0119415777
Web Site: https://www.attrezzauto.it
Automotive Spare Parts Distr
N.A.I.C.S.: 486210

Auto Natie Wommelgem N.V. (1)
Herentalsebaan 495b, 2160, Wommelgem, Belgium
Tel.: (32) 33533939
Car Repair & Maintenance Services
N.A.I.C.S.: 811198

Auto Recambios Vilber, S.L. (1)
Horno de Alcedo on Avda Carlos Marx 73, Valencia, Spain
Tel.: (34) 961522933
Web Site: https://www.advilber.com
Automotive Component Mfr & Distr
N.A.I.C.S.: 336390

Autodis Italia S.R.L. (1)
Via Newton n 12, 20016, Pero, Italy
Tel.: (39) 0233931
Web Site: https://autodisitalia.it
Motor Vehicle Parts Distr
N.A.I.C.S.: 423120

Belron S.A. (1)
The Kings Observatory Old Deer Park, Richmond, TW9 2AZ, United Kingdom (77.4%)
Tel.: (44) 2083320099
Web Site: http://www.belron.com
Sales Range: $1-4.9 Billion
Emp.: 12,000
Vehicle Glass Repair & Replacement Services
N.A.I.C.S.: 811122
Thomas M. Feeney *(Chm-North America)*

Subsidiary (Non-US):

Belron Canada Inc. (2)
8288 Pie IX Boulevard, Montreal, H1Z 3T6, QC, Canada
Tel.: (514) 593-7000
Web Site: http://www.belroncanada.com
Sales Range: $150-199.9 Million
Emp.: 1,200
Automotive Glass Repair, Replacement & Vehicle Glass Distribution
N.A.I.C.S.: 811122
Bruno Carignan *(VP-Digital & IT)*

Subsidiary (Domestic):

Apple Auto Glass, Ltd. (3)
7111 Kennedy Road Unit 4, Mississauga, L5S 0A4, ON, Canada (100%)
Tel.: (905) 669-7800
Web Site: http://www.appleautoglass.com
Sales Range: $25-49.9 Million
Emp.: 10
Automotive Glass Repair & Replacement
N.A.I.C.S.: 811122

Subsidiary (US):

Safelite Group, Inc. (2)
7400 Safelite Way, Columbus, OH 43235
Tel.: (877) 664-8931
Web Site: http://www.safelite.com
Auto Glass Repair Services
N.A.I.C.S.: 811122
Jason Nathaniel Judd *(CFO & Exec VP)*

Subsidiary (Domestic):

Auto Glass Specialists, Inc. (3)

S.A. D'IETEREN N.V.

s.a. D'Ieteren n.v.—(Continued)

2400 Farmers Dr, Columbus, OH 43235-2762
Tel.: (608) 827-0101
Web Site: http://www.littleredtruck.com
Sales Range: $75-99.9 Million
Emp.: 500
Vehicle Glass Repair & Replacement Services
N.A.I.C.S.: 811122

Breaker Glass Co Inc. (3)
131 Placerville Dr, Placerville, CA 95667
Tel.: (530) 626-3795
Web Site: http://www.breakerglass.com
Other Building Material Dealers
N.A.I.C.S.: 444180

Elite Safelite Auto Glass (3)
5433 Quebec St, Commerce City, CO 80022
Tel.: (303) 853-9564
Web Site: http://www.eliteautoglass.com
Sales Range: $50-74.9 Million
Emp.: 16
Vehicle Glass Repair & Replacement Services
N.A.I.C.S.: 811122

Intermountain Auto Glass (3)
Sun Vly Rd N Ste 24, Ketchum, ID 83340
Tel.: (208) 725-5885
Web Site: http://www.intermountainautoglass.com
Other Building Material Dealers
N.A.I.C.S.: 444180

Premium Auto Glass Inc. (3)
5358 Montebello Ln, Colorado Springs, CO 80918-1956
Tel.: (303) 423-3500
Web Site: http://www.premiumautoglass.com
Other Building Material Dealers
N.A.I.C.S.: 444180
Doug Johnson (Mgr)

Safelite Solutions LLC (3)
7400 Safelite Way, Columbus, OH 43230
Tel.: (614) 210-9000
Web Site: http://www.safelite.com
Sales Range: $50-74.9 Million
Emp.: 100
Auto Glass Repair Claims Management Services
N.A.I.C.S.: 524298
Brenda Schuler (Dir-First Impressions)

Subsidiary (Domestic):

Glasspro, Inc. (4)
1407 Stuart Engals Blvd, Mount Pleasant, SC 29464
Tel.: (843) 856-9777
Web Site: http://www.glasspro.net
Glass & Other Building Material Dealers
N.A.I.C.S.: 444180
Paul Heinauer (Owner & Pres)

Safelite Glass Corp. (4)
18388 US Hwy 301, Enfield, NC 27823
Tel.: (252) 445-1122
Web Site: http://www.safelite.com
Windshield Mfr & Distr
N.A.I.C.S.: 336390

Brussels Auto Group Groot-Bijgaarden n.v. (1)
R Dansaertlaan 102, 1702, Groot-Bijgaarden, Belgium
Tel.: (32) 24667666
New & Used Car Distr
N.A.I.C.S.: 441120

Brussels Auto Group Ternat b.v. (1)
Assesteenweg 101-103, 1740, Ternat, Belgium
Tel.: (32) 25821312
New & Used Car Distr
N.A.I.C.S.: 441120

CarASAP S.A. (1)
Place Eugene Flagey 18, 1050, Brussels, Belgium
Tel.: (32) 28800390
Web Site: https://www.justhusk.be
Taxi Limousine Services
N.A.I.C.S.: 541850

D'Ieteren Automotive S.A. (1)
Rue du Mail 50, 1050, Brussels, Belgium
Tel.: (32) 25365111
Web Site: https://www.dieteren.be
Automobile Vehicle Services
N.A.I.C.S.: 811111
Denis Gorteman (CEO)

Don Bosco b.v.b.a. (1)
Francois Gaystraat 129, Sint-Pieters-Woluwe, 1150, Brussels, Belgium
Tel.: (32) 27712100
Web Site: https://donbosco.be
Residential Building Construction Services
N.A.I.C.S.: 236210

Geevers Auto Parts B.V. (1)
De Run 5141, 5503 LV, Veldhoven, Netherlands
Tel.: (31) 402558311
Web Site: https://www.geevers.eu
Motor Vehicle Parts Distr
N.A.I.C.S.: 423120

General Auto Electric Corporation (1)
Via M Cervantes de Saavedra 55/27, 80133, Naples, Italy
Tel.: (39) 0815228490
Web Site: https://ggroup.eu
Automotive Component Mfr & Distr
N.A.I.C.S.: 423120

Kronos Automobiles s.a. (1)
Chaussee De Tirlemont 91/1, Gembloux, 5030, Belgium
Tel.: (32) 81626911
Emp.: 16
Automotive Distr
N.A.I.C.S.: 423110
Marco Stacchiotti (Gen Mgr)

Moleskine America Inc. (1)
210 11th Ave Ste 1004, New York, NY 10001-1210
Notebook & Diary Mfr & Distr
N.A.I.C.S.: 322230

Moleskine Germany GmbH (1)
Im Zollhafen 2-4, 50678, Cologne, Germany
Tel.: (49) 22151091780
Converted Paper Product Mfr
N.A.I.C.S.: 322299

Moleskine SpA (1)
viale Stelvio 66, Milan, 20159, Italy (100%)
Tel.: (39) 02 4344981
Web Site: http://it.moleskine.com
Stationery Product Mfr
N.A.I.C.S.: 322230
Arrigo Berni (CEO)

Overijse Automotive n.v. (1)
Brusselsesteenweg 303, 3090, Overijse, Belgium
Tel.: (32) 26868686
Automobile Vehicle Distr
N.A.I.C.S.: 423110

Poppy Mobility NV (1)
Sanderusstraat 25, 2018, Antwerp, Belgium
Tel.: (32) 32836262
Web Site: https://poppy.be
Shared Mobility Apps & Services
N.A.I.C.S.: 513210
Alexander van Laer (Founder & CEO)

Power To Wheels s.a. (1)
Parc Industriel de la Vallee du Hain 37, 1440, Wauthier Brain, Belgium
Tel.: (32) 2 367 14 80
Web Site: http://www.powertowheels.com
Electric Vehicle Mfr
N.A.I.C.S.: 336320
Bernard de Longueville (Gen Mgr)

Ricauto S.p.A. (1)
Prima Strada 41, 35129, Padova, Italy
Tel.: (39) 0490997799
Motor Vehicle Parts Distr
N.A.I.C.S.: 423120

Taxi Radio Bruxellois S.A. (1)
Rue des Carburants 54, 1190, Brussels, Belgium
Tel.: (32) 23494949
Web Site: https://en.taxisverts.be
Taxi Transportation Services
N.A.I.C.S.: 485310

s.a. D'Ieteren Services n.v. (1)
Maliestraat 50, 1050, Brussels, Belgium
Tel.: (32) 25365140
Web Site: http://www.dieteren.be
Emp.: 150
Automotive Parts Repair & Maintenance Services
N.A.I.C.S.: 811121

s.a. D'Ieteren Sport n.v. (1)
Rue De La Telrier, Tubize, 1480, Belgium
Tel.: (32) 2 367 14 11
Web Site: http://www.yamaha-motor.eu
Emp.: 25
Motor Vehicle Parts Distr
N.A.I.C.S.: 423120

s.a. D'Ieteren Treasury n.v. (1)
Rue Du Mail 50, 1050, Brussels, Belgium
Tel.: (32) 25365140
Web Site: http://www.dIeteren.be
Emp.: 150
Automotive Parts Repair & Maintenance Services
N.A.I.C.S.: 811121
Paul Clinch (Gen Mgr-Head)

S.A. FERIA DE LOS AGRICULTORES

Camino A San Clemente Cruce Las Rastras, PO Box 466, Talca, Chile
Tel.: (56) 242655
Web Site: http://www.agricultorestalca.cl
Veterinary Services
N.A.I.C.S.: 115210
Juan Carlos Alvarez Valderrama (CEO)

S.A. INMOBILIARIA SPORT FRANCAIS

Lo Beltran 2500 Vitacura, Santiago, Chile
Tel.: (56) 7685700
SPORTFRAN—(SGO)
Sales Range: Less than $1 Million
Real Estate Development Services
N.A.I.C.S.: 531390
Gabriel Berczely Apor (Pres)

S.A. LA NACION

Calle Hipolito Bouchard 557 Piso 4-6, C1106 ABG, Buenos Aires, Argentina
Tel.: (54) 143191600
Web Site: http://www.lanacion.com.ar
Year Founded: 1870
Sales Range: $125-149.9 Million
Emp.: 800
Newspaper Publishers
N.A.I.C.S.: 513110
Lorena Artal (CTO)

Subsidiaries:

ImpreMedia LLC (1)
1 Metrotech Ctr 18th Fl, Brooklyn, NY 11201
Tel.: (212) 807-4785
Web Site: http://www.impremedia.com
Spanish-Language Newspaper, Magazine & Website Publisher
N.A.I.C.S.: 513110
Damian Mazzotta (Gen Mgr-West)

Subsidiary (Domestic):

El Diario La Prensa (2)
1 Metrotech Ctr 11th Fl, New York, NY 11201
Tel.: (212) 807-4600
Web Site: http://www.eldiariony.com
Sales Range: $10-24.9 Million
Emp.: 122
Spanish-language Newspaper Publisher
N.A.I.C.S.: 513110

S.A. POWER SERVICES (PTY) LTD.

Unit 14 Meadowbrook Business Estates, Jacaranda Ave Olivedale Randburg, 2158, Johannesburg, South Africa
Tel.: (27) 114628810
Web Site: http://www.sapower.co.za
Year Founded: 1969

Sales Range: $25-49.9 Million
Emp.: 20
Industrial Equipment Distr
N.A.I.C.S.: 423830
Anton Van Zyl (Mgr)

S.A. SAN MIGUEL A.G.I.C.I. Y F.

Cazadores de Coquimbo 2860 Edificio 2 Piso 1, 1605, Vicente Lopez, Buenos Aires, Argentina
Tel.: (54) 1147218300
Web Site:
  https://www.sanmiguelglobal.com
Agricultural Services
N.A.I.C.S.: 115116
Martin Otero Monsegur (Vice Chm)

S.A. SPADEL N.V.

Avenue des Communautes 110, B-1200, Brussels, Belgium
Tel.: (32) 27023811   BE
Web Site: https://www.spadel.com
Year Founded: 1980
SPA—(EUR)
Rev.: $304,510,037
Assets: $430,225,556
Liabilities: $158,763,220
Net Worth: $271,462,335
Earnings: $28,759,983
Emp.: 1,265
Fiscal Year-end: 12/31/21
Bottled Water, Lemonades & Syrups Producer & Distr
N.A.I.C.S.: 424490

Subsidiaries:

Bru-Chevron NV (1)
La Bruyere 151, Stoumont, 4987, Liege, Belgium (99.99%)
Tel.: (32) 86433337
Web Site: http://www.bru.be
Sales Range: $25-49.9 Million
Emp.: 31
Soft Drinks Mfr
N.A.I.C.S.: 312111
Nazi Vencent (Mng Dir)

Eaux Minerales de Ribeauville SA
48 Rte Bergheim, Ribeauville, 68150, France
Tel.: (33) 3 89 73 24 24
Sales Range: $10-24.9 Million
Emp.: 50
Mineral Water Mfr
N.A.I.C.S.: 312112

Spa Monopole SA (1)
Rue Auguste Laporte 34, 4900, Liege, Belgium
Tel.: (32) 87794111
Web Site: http://www.spa.be
Sales Range: $100-124.9 Million
Emp.: 500
Soft Drinks Mfr
N.A.I.C.S.: 312111
Vincent Mazy (Gen Mgr)

Spadel Nederland B.V. (1)
Brieltjenspolder 28 D, 4921 PJ, Made, Netherlands (100%)
Tel.: (31) 162690760
Web Site: http://www.spa.nl
Sales Range: $25-49.9 Million
Emp.: 60
Bottled Water
N.A.I.C.S.: 312112
Stefan De Clercq (Mng Dir)

Spadel UK Ltd (1)
Llwyndewi Isaf Trap, Llandeilo, Newport, FA196TT, United Kingdom
Tel.: (44) 1269850175
Web Site: http://www.breconwater.co.uk
Sales Range: $25-49.9 Million
Emp.: 29
Soft Drinks Mfr
N.A.I.C.S.: 312111
Jeff Phills (Mgr-Production)

S.A.F. SPECIAL STEEL PUBLIC COMPANY LIMITED

110 Thientalay 24 Bangkhunthien-Chytalay Road, Ta-kam Sub-district Bangkhunthien District, Bangkok, 10150, Thailand
Tel.: (66) 289748003
Web Site: https://www.saf.co.th
Year Founded: 1992
SAF—(THA)
Rev.: $4,981,610
Assets: $11,797,935
Liabilities: $3,675,269
Net Worth: $8,122,666
Earnings: $37,074
Fiscal Year-end: 12/31/23
Steel Products Mfr
N.A.I.C.S.: 331210
Mongkol Preukwatana *(Chm)*

S.A.I. LEISURE GROUP COMPANY LIMITED
5th Floor Nanyang Plaza 57 Hung To Road, Kwun Tong, Kowloon, China (Hong Kong) Ky
Web Site: https://www.saileisuregroup.com
Year Founded: 1997
1832—(HKG)
Rev.: $15,751,000
Assets: $158,508,000
Liabilities: $84,331,000
Net Worth: $74,177,000
Earnings: ($11,494,000)
Emp.: 372
Fiscal Year-end: 12/31/22
Hotel Operator
N.A.I.C.S.: 721110
Henry Tan *(Vice Chm)*

Subsidiaries:
Hawes Group, LLC (1)
222 NE Park Plz Dr Ste 125, Vancouver, WA 98684
Tel.: (541) 912-8915
Web Site: https://www.hawesgroup.net
Business Consulting Services
N.A.I.C.S.: 541611

S.A.L. STEEL LTD.
5/1 Shreeji House B/h M J Library Ashram Road, Ahmedabad, 380006, Gujarat, India
Tel.: (91) 2764661100
Web Site: https://www.salsteel.co.in
Year Founded: 2003
532604—(BOM)
Rev.: $61,162,496
Assets: $33,182,015
Liabilities: $28,202,578
Net Worth: $4,979,438
Earnings: $425,178
Emp.: 420
Fiscal Year-end: 03/31/23
Ferro Alloy Products Mfr
N.A.I.C.S.: 331110
Sujalkumar Ashokkumar Shah *(Exec Dir)*

S.A.S. DORIA AUTOMOBILES
La Boisnarderie Avenue Sainton 1 Rue De Voiville, 17100, Saintes, France
Tel.: (33) 495301300
Web Site: http://www.doria-auto.fr
Sales Range: $25-49.9 Million
Emp.: 48
Automobile Sales
N.A.I.C.S.: 441110
Franck Galligani *(VP)*

S.A.S. DRAGON HOLDINGS LIMITED
SAS Tower 55 Lei Muk Road, Kwai Chung, China (Hong Kong)
Tel.: (852) 38922888
Web Site: http://www.sasdragon.com.hk

1184—(HKG)
Rev.: $3,183,503,130
Assets: $1,037,705,670
Liabilities: $653,873,805
Net Worth: $383,831,865
Earnings: $71,898,143
Emp.: 450
Fiscal Year-end: 12/31/22
Distribution Of Electronic Components
N.A.I.C.S.: 327110
Peter Wai Tai Wong *(CFO & Sec)*

Subsidiaries:
HAS Electronic Company Limited (1)
SAS Tower 55 Lei Muk Road, Kwai Chung, China (Hong Kong)
Tel.: (852) 38922888
Electronic Component & Semiconductor Product Distr
N.A.I.C.S.: 423690

Hi-Level Technology Limited (1)
Room 614 6/F Tower B Hunghom Commercial Centre 37 Ma Tau Wai Road, Hung-Hom, Kowloon, China (Hong Kong)
Tel.: (852) 38921838
Web Site: https://www.hi-levelhk.com
Rev.: $128,790,000
Emp.: 110
Semiconductor Component Distr
N.A.I.C.S.: 423690

RSL Microelectronics Company Limited (1)
SAS Tower 55 Lei Muk Road, Hung Hom, Kwai Chung, China (Hong Kong)
Tel.: (852) 38922818
Web Site: http://www.rslgroup.com.hk
Sales Range: $25-49.9 Million
Emp.: 30
Electronic Product Distr
N.A.I.C.S.: 334220

S.A.S. Electronic Company Limited (1)
Rm 601-604 6 F Tower B Hunghom Comml Ctr 37 Ma Tau Wai Rd, Hunghom, Kowloon, China (Hong Kong)
Tel.: (852) 23620271
Web Site: http://www.sasdragon.com.hk
Sales Range: $25-49.9 Million
Emp.: 40
Semiconductor Distr
N.A.I.C.S.: 423690

S.A.S. Enterprises Company Lim (1)
6 F Tower B Hunghom Comml Ctr 37 Ma Tau Wai Rd, Hunghom, Kowloon, China (Hong Kong)
Tel.: (852) 23620271
Web Site: http://www.sasdragon.com.hk
Sales Range: $50-74.9 Million
Emp.: 100
Electronic Product Distr
N.A.I.C.S.: 423690

S.A.S. Enterprises Company Limited (1)
Room 912 No 2 Building No 16 Guangshun South Street, Chaoyang District, Beijing, China
Tel.: (86) 84763925
Electronic Component Mfr & Distr
N.A.I.C.S.: 334419

S.A.S. Lighting Company Limited (1)
SAS Tower 55 Lei Muk Road, New Territories, Kwai Chung, China (Hong Kong)
Tel.: (852) 38921888
Electronic Component & Semiconductor Product Distr
N.A.I.C.S.: 423690
Wilson Wong *(Dir-Project)*

S.A.S. JAMBON ET FILS
6 Rue du Stade, 15300, Murat, France
Tel.: (33) 471203121 FR
Web Site: http://www.jambon-fils.fr
Rev.: $18,500,000
Emp.: 65
Flour Mfr
N.A.I.C.S.: 311211
Pierre Barthelemy *(Chm)*

S.A.S. JSC
1/8 Kabdolov st, 050062, Almaty, Kazakhstan
Tel.: (7) 7272601819
SAS—(KAZ)
Rev.: $5,401,111
Assets: $7,069,271
Liabilities: $18,735,451
Net Worth: ($11,666,180)
Earnings: $150,373
Fiscal Year-end: 12/31/23
Real Estate Development Services
N.A.I.C.S.: 531390
Beisenbaev Gabit *(Pres & CEO)*

S.BIOMEDICS CO., LTD.
4th floor Wooil Venture Town 28 Seongsu-iro 26-gil, Seongdong-gu, Seoul, 04797, Korea (South)
Tel.: (82) 222050023
Web Site: https://www.sbiomedics.com
Year Founded: 2005
304360—(KRS)
Biotechnology Research & Development Services
N.A.I.C.S.: 541714
Tony Kang *(Pres)*

S.C CONPET S.A.
No 1-3 Anul 1848 Street, 100559, Ploiesti, Prahova, Romania
Tel.: (40) 244401360
Web Site: https://www.conpet.ro
Year Founded: 1901
COTE—(BUC)
Rev.: $113,390,131
Assets: $175,397,784
Liabilities: $26,813,684
Net Worth: $148,584,099
Earnings: $13,393,196
Emp.: 1,463
Fiscal Year-end: 12/31/22
Crude Oil Pipeline Transportation Services
N.A.I.C.S.: 486110
Anamaria Mihaela Dumitrache *(Deputy Dir Gen)*

S.C FORCONCID S.A.
Str Remus Bellu nr 1, Valcea, Ramnicu Valcea, Romania
Tel.: (40) 250 734820
Web Site: http://www.forconcid.ro
Year Founded: 1963
Sales Range: $1-9.9 Million
Emp.: 104
Industrial & Commercial Construction Services
N.A.I.C.S.: 236210

S.C NEW ENERGY TECHNOLOGY CORPORATION
No 62 Jinniu EastRoad Zhukeng Community Longtian Street, Pingshan District, Shenzhen, Guangdong, China
Tel.: (86) 75581449696
Web Site: https://www.chinasc.com.cn
Year Founded: 2003
300724—(CHIN)
Rev.: $1,230,103,221
Assets: $5,511,973,884
Liabilities: $4,279,326,504
Net Worth: $1,232,647,381
Earnings: $230,087,306
Fiscal Year-end: 12/31/23
Photovoltaic Equipment Mfr
N.A.I.C.S.: 335999
Zuo Guojun *(Chm)*

Subsidiaries:
Zuvay Technologies Pvt. Ltd. (1)
H-316FF Sushant Shopping Arcade Sushant Lok Phase, Gurgaon, Haryana, India
Tel.: (91) 1244011400

Web Site: https://zuvay.in
Solar Product Mfr
N.A.I.C.S.: 334413

S.C SERVICIILE COMERCIALE ROMANE S.R.L.
12 Muncii Blvd, Cluj-Napoca, Romania
Tel.: (40) 264 415086
Web Site: http://www.scrgrup.ro
Year Founded: 1993
Sales Range: $100-124.9 Million
Emp.: 2,400
Industrial Holding Company
N.A.I.C.S.: 551112
Stefan Vuza *(Chm)*

Subsidiaries:
S.C. IASITEX S.A. (1)
B-dul Ficusului nr 44 Corp A Etaj 2 Camera 17 Sector 1 Bucuresti, 013975, Bucharest, Romania
Tel.: (40) 212327667
Web Site: http://www.iasitex.ro
Rev.: $2,760,998
Assets: $32,512,935
Liabilities: $433,419
Net Worth: $32,079,517
Earnings: $396,762
Emp.: 4
Fiscal Year-end: 12/31/2022
Textile Industry
N.A.I.C.S.: 314999

S.C. SOMES S.A. (1)
63 Bistritei Street, 405200, Dej, Romania
Tel.: (40) 264 223417
Web Site: http://www.somes.ro
Paper & Pupl Product Mfr
N.A.I.C.S.: 322299
Adrian Itu *(Chm & Dir Gen)*

SC Caromet SA (1)
DN 68 Km 3, 325400, Caransebes, Romania
Tel.: (40) 255512583
Web Site: https://www.caromet.ro
Rev.: $3,201,742
Assets: $11,741,475
Liabilities: $2,398,501
Net Worth: $9,342,973
Earnings: $257,688
Emp.: 83
Fiscal Year-end: 12/31/2021
Locomotive & Parts Mfr
N.A.I.C.S.: 336510

SC Chimcomplex SA (1)
3 Industriilor St, Onesti, 601124, Bacau, Romania
Tel.: (40) 234302400
Web Site: http://www.chimcomplex.ro
Chemical Products Mfr
N.A.I.C.S.: 325180
Anisoara Alexa *(Mgr-Fin)*

SC Inav SA (1)
44A Ficusului Blvd Sector 1, 013975, Bucharest, Romania
Tel.: (40) 212323724
Web Site: https://www.inav.ro
Aircraft Engineering Services
N.A.I.C.S.: 488190
Sanziana Kalamar *(Member-Mgmt Bd)*

SC Nova Textile Bumbac SRL (1)
Str George Cosbuc nr 70, 110103, Pitesti, Arges, Romania
Tel.: (40) 248282883
Web Site: http://www.nova-textile.ro
Cotton Apparel Mfr
N.A.I.C.S.: 314999

SC Uzuc SA (1)
11 Marin Brutaru str, 100305, Ploiesti, Romania
Tel.: (40) 244401119
Web Site: http://www.uzuc.ro
Chemical Industry Machine Distr
N.A.I.C.S.: 423830
Marian Guta *(Dir-Technical)*

S.C SIGSTRAT S.A
Str Unirii nr 40, 435500, Sighetu Marmatiei, Maramures, Romania
Tel.: (40) 262317575

S.C SIGSTRAT S.A

S.C Sigstrat S.A—(Continued)
Web Site: https://www.sigstrat.ro
Year Founded: 1993
SIGS—(BUC)
Rev.: $7,752,958
Assets: $6,429,248
Liabilities: $768,189
Net Worth: $5,661,060
Earnings: $499,010
Emp.: 226
Fiscal Year-end: 12/31/22
Wood Products Mfr
N.A.I.C.S.: 321999

S.C TMD S.A FILIASI

Str Uzinei 2, Filiasi, Dolj, Romania
Tel.: (40) 251441101
Web Site: http://www.tmdsa.ro
Year Founded: 1972
Sales Range: Less than $1 Million
Transformer & Induction Motors Mfr
N.A.I.C.S.: 334416

S.C. ALIMENTARA S.A.

Str Arinului Nr 1, Olt, Slatina, Romania
Tel.: (40) 249422092
Web Site: https://www.alimentara-slatina.ro
ALRV—(BUC)
Rev.: $1,323,642
Assets: $4,608,198
Liabilities: $97,176
Net Worth: $4,511,023
Earnings: $204,317
Emp.: 2
Fiscal Year-end: 12/31/23
Grocery Store Operator
N.A.I.C.S.: 445110

S.C. AMCO OTOPENI S.A.

Sos Bucuresti-Ploiesti Km 13 200, Otopeni, 075100, Ilfov, Romania
Tel.: (40) 21 3519379
Web Site: http://www.amco-otopeni.ro
Measuring Instruments Mfr
N.A.I.C.S.: 334519
Mihai Staicu (Pres & Gen Mgr)

S.C. ARCOM S.A.

81 Virgiliu Street, Section 1, 010882, Bucharest, Romania
Tel.: (40) 216370311
Web Site: http://www.arcom.ro
Sales Range: $75-99.9 Million
Emp.: 500
Industrial Building Construction Services
N.A.I.C.S.: 236220
Juambzi Vesile (Mng Dir)

S.C. ARMATURA S.A.

Garii Street No 19, Cluj-Napoca, 400267, Romania
Tel.: (40) 264 435 367
Web Site: http://www.armatura.ro
Year Founded: 1884
Sales Range: $1-9.9 Million
Emp.: 212
Taps & Valves Mfr
N.A.I.C.S.: 332919
Gerhard Glinzerer (Pres)

S.C. ARMAX GAZ S.A.

Strada Aurel Vlaicu nr 35A Medias, 551041, Sibiu, Romania
Tel.: (40) 269 845 864
Web Site: http://www.armaxgaz.ro
Emp.: 200
Gas & Oil Equipment Mfr
N.A.I.C.S.: 333132
Mircea Simion Vescan (CEO)

S.C. AROMET S.A.

Sos Brailei Nr 15, 120118, Buzau, Romania
Tel.: (40) 238 710 301
Web Site: http://www.aromet.eu
Year Founded: 1928
Emp.: 200
Iron Casting
N.A.I.C.S.: 331511
Simona Savulescu (Gen Mgr)

S.C. ARTEGO S.A.

Strada Ciocarlau 38, Targu Jiu, Romania
Tel.: (40) 253226370
Web Site: https://www.artego.ro
Year Founded: 1973
ARTE—(BUC)
Rev.: $49,418,555
Assets: $36,386,453
Liabilities: $16,071,806
Net Worth: $20,314,647
Earnings: $2,674,996
Emp.: 692
Fiscal Year-end: 12/31/22
Rubber Products Mfr
N.A.I.C.S.: 326299
David Viorel (Chm & Gen Mgr)

S.C. ASIGURARE REASIGURARE ASTRA S.A.

STR Nerva Traian nr 3 Bloc M101, Sector 3, 031041, Bucharest, Romania
Tel.: (40) 21 318 80 80
Web Site: http://www.astrasig.ro
Year Founded: 1991
Emp.: 1,823
Insurance Services
N.A.I.C.S.: 524298
Dan Grigore Adamescu (Chm-Supervisory Bd)

S.C. ATC-AGROTOTALCONSTRUCT S.A.

Strada Fagarasului No 26, Brasov, Ghimbav, Romania
Tel.: (40) 268258435
Web Site: https://agrototalconstruct.ro
Year Founded: 1989
GHIM—(BUC)
Rev.: $515,595
Assets: $645,256
Liabilities: $294,903
Net Worth: $350,352
Earnings: $11,859
Emp.: 6
Fiscal Year-end: 12/31/23
Crop Farming Services
N.A.I.C.S.: 111998

S.C. ATELIERELE CFR GRIVITA S.A

Sectorul 1 Calea Grivitei nr 359, 010 718, Bucharest, Romania
Tel.: (40) 212240908
Web Site: https://www.grivita.ro
Year Founded: 1897
ATRD—(BUC)
Rev.: $16,679,991
Assets: $25,699,720
Liabilities: $3,060,024
Net Worth: $22,639,696
Earnings: $2,169,187
Emp.: 309
Fiscal Year-end: 12/31/23
Railway Locomotives & Rolling Stock Mfr
N.A.I.C.S.: 336510
Alexandru Claudiu (Dir Gen)

S.C. AUTONOVA S.A.

Str Fagului nr 35, 440186, Satu-Mare, Romania
Tel.: (40) 261769564
Web Site: http://www.autonova.ro
AUTQ—(BUC)
Rev.: $7,347,987
Assets: $7,280,155
Liabilities: $2,505,876
Net Worth: $4,774,279
Earnings: $651,696
Emp.: 162
Fiscal Year-end: 12/31/20
Motor Vehicle Parts Mfr
N.A.I.C.S.: 336390
Ciprian Dan Costea (VP)

S.C. BEGA TEHNOMET S.A. TIMISOARA

Calea Stan Vidrighin ex Buziasului no 5A, 300571, Timisoara, Romania
Tel.: (40) 256 22 27 46
Web Site: http://www.tehnomet.ro
Sales Range: $1-9.9 Million
Fabricated Processing
N.A.I.C.S.: 332999

S.C. BIRZAVA S.A.

Str Carpati Nr 5, Caras-Severin, Bocsa, 325300, Romania
Tel.: (40) 255 525410
Web Site: http://www.birzava.cabanova.ro
Year Founded: 1991
Sales Range: Less than $1 Million
Food Transportation Services
N.A.I.C.S.: 484121

S.C. BRAICONF S.A.

Str Scolilor nr 53, 810517, Braila, Romania
Tel.: (40) 239692200
Web Site: https://www.braiconf.ro
Year Founded: 1950
BRCR—(BUC)
Rev.: $5,693,424
Assets: $7,440,365
Liabilities: $2,010,406
Net Worth: $5,429,959
Earnings: $117,454
Emp.: 229
Fiscal Year-end: 12/31/22
Textile Products Mfr
N.A.I.C.S.: 314999

S.C. BUCUR OBOR S.A.

Sos Colentina nr 2 sector 2, Bucharest, Romania
Tel.: (40) 21 2526384
Web Site: http://www.bucurobor.ro
Sales Range: $1-9.9 Million
Emp.: 151
Supermarket Operator
N.A.I.C.S.: 455219
Gelu Manea (Pres & Gen Mgr)

S.C. BUCUR S.A.

Str Visinilor Nr 25, Bucharest, Romania
Tel.: (40) 213236730
Web Site: https://www.bucurcom.ro
Year Founded: 1946
BUCV—(BUC)
Rev.: $2,447,836
Assets: $25,441,437
Liabilities: $2,131,857
Net Worth: $23,309,580
Earnings: ($11,904)
Emp.: 26
Fiscal Year-end: 12/31/23
Food Product Whslr
N.A.I.C.S.: 424420
Bogdan Iustin Hrisca (Pres)

S.C. BUCURESTI TURISM S.A.

Calea Victoriei 63-81 Sector 1, Bucharest, Romania
Tel.: (40) 213124088
Web Site: http://www.hbu.ro
Sales Range: $25-49.9 Million

INTERNATIONAL PUBLIC

Hotel Operator & Other Accommodation Services
N.A.I.C.S.: 721110
Luc Frans Marie Ronsmans (Pres & Gen Mgr)

S.C. CAPITOL SA

Str Academiei nr 17 Sector 1, Bucharest, Romania
Tel.: (40) 21 3136957
Web Site: http://www.capitolsa.ro
Hotel & Restaurant Management Services
N.A.I.C.S.: 541611
Pupaza Niculae (Pres)

S.C. CARBOCHIM S.A.

Bulevardul Muncii nr 18, 4000641, Cluj-Napoca, Romania
Tel.: (40) 264437005
Web Site: https://www.carbochim.ro
Year Founded: 1949
CBC—(BUC)
Rev.: $7,864,800
Assets: $25,338,160
Liabilities: $7,825,493
Net Worth: $17,512,667
Earnings: $5,662
Emp.: 164
Fiscal Year-end: 12/31/22
Abrasive Product Mfr
N.A.I.C.S.: 327910
Viorel Dorin Popoviciu (Pres, CEO & Gen Mgr)

S.C. CARS S.A.

Str Avram Iancu Nr 270 Judetul Mures, 545600, Tarnaveni, Romania
Tel.: (40) 265 442035
Web Site: http://www.sccarssa.ro
Sales Range: $1-9.9 Million
Emp.: 131
Brick Product Mfr
N.A.I.C.S.: 327331
Daniela Andreescu (Dir-Comml)

S.C. CASA DE BUCOVINA - CLUB DE MUNTE S.A.

Piata Republicii nr 18, 725300, Gura Humorului, Suceava, Romania
Tel.: (40) 230207000
Web Site: https://www.bestwesternbucovina.ro
Year Founded: 1998
BCM—(BUC)
Rev.: $2,028,387
Assets: $8,716,092
Liabilities: $818,707
Net Worth: $7,897,384
Earnings: ($171,022)
Emp.: 66
Fiscal Year-end: 12/31/23
Hotel & Motel Services
N.A.I.C.S.: 721110
Ion Romica Tamas (CEO)

S.C. CHIMICA S.A.

str Codrului nr 24, Orastie, Hunedoara, 335700, Romania
Tel.: (40) 254 241250
Web Site: http://www.chimica.ro
Year Founded: 1937
Sales Range: $10-24.9 Million
Emp.: 421
Plastics Product Mfr
N.A.I.C.S.: 326199
Alexandru Farcas (Chm-Supervisory Bd)

S.C. COMALIM S.A.

Str Field of Tranquility, Arad, Romania
Tel.: (40) 741164496
Web Site: https://www.comalim.ro
Year Founded: 1991

AND PRIVATE COMPANIES — S.C. ICSIM- S.A.

MALI—(BUC)
Rev.: $4,000,299
Assets: $7,568,014
Liabilities: $640,417
Net Worth: $6,927,597
Earnings: ($132,728)
Emp.: 5
Fiscal Year-end: 12/31/22
Meat Product Whslr
N.A.I.C.S.: 424470

S.C. COMNORD S.A.
Calea Grivitei 136 Sector 1, 010741, Bucharest, Romania
Tel.: (40) 212066800
Web Site: http://www.comnord.ro
Rev.: $16,654,639
Assets: $32,882,752
Liabilities: $11,176,155
Net Worth: $21,706,597
Earnings: ($92,344)
Emp.: 64
Fiscal Year-end: 12/31/16
Civil & Industrial Construction Services
N.A.I.C.S.: 236220

S.C. COMPANIA DE INFORMATICA APLICATA S.A. CLUJ-NAPOCA
Gheorghe Bilascu Republicii street no 107, Cluj-Napoca, 400489, Romania
Tel.: (40) 264 595477
Web Site: http://www.cianet.ro
Data Processing Services
N.A.I.C.S.: 518210

S.C. COMTRAM S.A.
str Henri Coanda nr 75, Sibiu, Romania
Tel.: (40) 269236767
Web Site: http://www.comtram.ro
Sales Range: $1-9.9 Million
Emp.: 112
Highway Construction Services
N.A.I.C.S.: 237990

S.C. COMTURIST S.A.
Bd I C Bratianu nr 29-33 Camera 1 Etaj 2 Sect 3, Bucharest, Romania
Tel.: (40) 213150597
Web Site: https://www.comturist.ro
COUT—(BUC)
Rev.: $1,118,850
Assets: $2,542,394
Liabilities: $109,348
Net Worth: $2,433,046
Earnings: $163,369
Emp.: 4
Fiscal Year-end: 12/31/22
Grocery Store Operator
N.A.I.C.S.: 445110

S.C. CONTACTOARE S.A.
Str Mesteacsnului Nr 10, 120031, Buzau, Romania
Tel.: (40) 238710933
Web Site: https://www.contactoare.ro
CONQ—(BUC)
Rev.: $1,014,605
Assets: $9,517,524
Liabilities: $520,707
Net Worth: $8,996,817
Earnings: $20,794
Emp.: 23
Fiscal Year-end: 12/31/20
Electric Power Distribution Services
N.A.I.C.S.: 221122
Adrian Tuca (Gen Dir)

S.C. CONTED S.A DOROHOI
Str December 1 no 8, Dorohoi, Botosani, Romania
Tel.: (40) 231610064
Web Site: https://conted.ro
Year Founded: 1963

CNTE—(BUC)
Rev.: $6,743,885
Assets: $3,615,271
Liabilities: $1,612,933
Net Worth: $2,002,337
Earnings: $246,899
Emp.: 500
Fiscal Year-end: 12/31/22
Outerwear Mfr
N.A.I.C.S.: 315120

S.C. EL-CO S.A.
Str Fabricii Nr 9, 525400, Targu Secuiesc, Covasna, Romania
Tel.: (40) 267 362520
Web Site: http://www.el-co.ro
Sales Range: $10-24.9 Million
Emp.: 402
Ceramic Fuses Mfr
N.A.I.C.S.: 335999
Viorica Nanca (Mgr-Economic)

Subsidiaries:

EL-CO CERAM Inc. (1)
804 Boul Guimond, Longueuil, J4G 1T5, QC, Canada
Tel.: (450) 677-9595
Web Site: http://www.el-co.ca
Ceramic Product Distr
N.A.I.C.S.: 423320
Christiane Pelletier (Mgr-Sls)

EL-CO d.o.o. (1)
Trg Oslobodenja 8, 21700, Backa Palanka, Serbia
Tel.: (381) 21 751174
Web Site: http://www.el-co.co.rs
Electronic Components Mfr
N.A.I.C.S.: 334419

S.C. ELECTROMONTAJ CARPATI S.A.
Str Lector Nr 12, 550245, Sibiu, Romania
Tel.: (40) 269215106
Web Site: https://www.elmontaj.ro
Year Founded: 1949
ELJA—(BUC)
Rev.: $10,210,074
Assets: $7,305,577
Liabilities: $1,575,029
Net Worth: $5,730,548
Earnings: ($1,987,514)
Emp.: 250
Fiscal Year-end: 12/31/22
Power & Communication Line Construction Services
N.A.I.C.S.: 237130
Popescu Adrian (Gen Mgr)

S.C. ELECTROUTILAJ S.A.
Str Bobalna Nr 44, Campina, Prahova, Romania
Tel.: (40) 244 335 751
Web Site: http://www.electroutilaj.ro
Year Founded: 1951
Sales Range: $1-9.9 Million
Electric Equipment Mfr
N.A.I.C.S.: 335999

S.C. FAM S.A.
jud Galati str Calea Prutului nr 50A, 800219, Galati, 800219, Romania
Tel.: (40) 236448621
Web Site: https://www.fam-galati.ro
FAMZ—(BUC)
Rev.: $1,018,957
Assets: $1,709,015
Liabilities: $103,221
Net Worth: $1,605,795
Earnings: ($94,123)
Emp.: 36
Fiscal Year-end: 12/31/23
Metal Products Mfr
N.A.I.C.S.: 332999

S.C. FAUR S.A.

256 Basarabia Bvd, 030352, Bucharest, Romania
Tel.: (40) 21 255 65 59
Web Site: http://www.faur.ro
Year Founded: 1921
Emp.: 512
Construction Machinery Mfr
N.A.I.C.S.: 333120
Mariana Hristea (Gen Dir)

S.C. FAVIL S.A.
Str Depozitelor nr 10, Ramnicu Valcea, 240050, Romania
Tel.: (40) 250 730330
Web Site: http://www.favil.ro
Year Founded: 1982
Sales Range: $1-9.9 Million
Cotton Yarn Mfr & Whslr
N.A.I.C.S.: 313110

S.C. FEPA S.A.
Republicii 316 Street, Barlad, 731120, Romania
Tel.: (40) 235 411812
Web Site: http://www.fepa.ro
Sales Range: $1-9.9 Million
Emp.: 480
Industrial Machinery & Equipment Mfr
N.A.I.C.S.: 333998

S.C. FIMARO SA
167 Corneliu Coposu Street, 400282, Cluj-Napoca, Romania
Tel.: (40) 264502701
Web Site: http://www.fimaro.ro
Year Founded: 1924
FIMA—(BUC)
Rev.: $2,476,058
Assets: $2,690,000
Liabilities: $827,208
Net Worth: $1,862,792
Earnings: $26,952
Emp.: 50
Fiscal Year-end: 12/31/23
Machinery Mfr
N.A.I.C.S.: 333248

S.C. FORADEX S.A.
No 14 Cap Av Gheorghe Demetriade Street District 1, 011849, Bucharest, Romania
Tel.: (40) 212000830
Web Site: http://www.foradex.ro
Year Founded: 1939
Drilling Contractor
N.A.I.C.S.: 213111
Razvan-Florin Calangiu (Pres & Gen Mgr)

Subsidiaries:

Foradex SUD SRL (1)
Milcov Nr 5 Sector 1, Bucharest, Romania
Tel.: (40) 722305789
Geothermal Drilling Services
N.A.I.C.S.: 237110

S.C. FORAJ SONDE S.A.
Str Petrolului 16, 145300, Videle, 145300, Teleorman, Romania
Tel.: (40) 247453833
Web Site: https://www.fsv.ro
FOJE—(BUC)
Rev.: $30,898,555
Assets: $30,935,298
Liabilities: $16,105,132
Net Worth: $14,830,166
Earnings: $4,170,302
Emp.: 240
Fiscal Year-end: 12/31/23
Drilling Oil & Gas Wells
N.A.I.C.S.: 213111

S.C. FORESTIND S.A.
com Sucevita 622a, Suceava, Romania
Tel.: (40) 230 560 563
Web Site: http://www.forestindsa.ro

Year Founded: 1998
Sales Range: $1-9.9 Million
Emp.: 35
Wood Production & Sawmilling Services
N.A.I.C.S.: 321113

S.C. GALFINBAND S.A.
Str Smardan no 2A Mittal Steel Platform, 800701, Galati, Romania
Tel.: (40) 236833101
Web Site: https://www.galfinband.ro
Year Founded: 1984
GALF—(BUC)
Rev.: $5,040,420
Assets: $3,590,009
Liabilities: $1,056,105
Net Worth: $2,533,904
Earnings: $288,020
Emp.: 38
Fiscal Year-end: 12/31/22
Steel Sheet Mfr
N.A.I.C.S.: 331110

S.C. GRUPUL INDUSTRIAL ELECTROCONTACT S.A.
Horse Nationala 6, 710010, Botosani, Romania
Tel.: (40) 231517172
Web Site: http://www.electrocontact.ro
ECT—(BUC)
Rev.: $152,007
Assets: $3,364,672
Liabilities: $114,747
Net Worth: $3,249,924
Earnings: $12,051
Emp.: 1
Fiscal Year-end: 12/31/22
Electricity Distribution & Equipments Mfr
N.A.I.C.S.: 335999

Subsidiaries:

Fabrica DE Matrite SRL (1)
B-Dul Bucuresti Noi Nr 192-204 BL C9 Sect 1, Bucharest, 012369, Romania
Tel.: (40) 74 133 2345
Emp.: 20
Industrial Mold Mfr
N.A.I.C.S.: 333511
Alexandra Alecu (Gen Mgr)

S.C. HERCULES S.A.
str Incinta Docuri no 1, Braila, Romania
Tel.: (40) 239613514
Web Site: https://www.hercules-braila.ro
HLEB—(BUC)
Rev.: $28,839,969
Assets: $14,667,360
Liabilities: $7,270,772
Net Worth: $7,396,588
Earnings: ($2,714,624)
Emp.: 152
Fiscal Year-end: 12/31/23
Water Transportation Services
N.A.I.C.S.: 488390

S.C. ICSIM- S.A.
str Valsanesti Nr 1 Cladire Administrativa Parter S 3, Bucharest, Romania
Tel.: (40) 2560428
Web Site: http://www.icsim.ro
Year Founded: 1950
ICSI—(BUC)
Rev.: $475,924
Assets: $5,028,520
Liabilities: $39,782
Net Worth: $4,988,738
Earnings: $1,854
Emp.: 6
Fiscal Year-end: 12/31/20
Building Construction Services
N.A.I.C.S.: 236116

S.C. Icsim- S.A.—(Continued)

S.C. INAR S.A.
Strada Poienelor Nr 5, 2200, Brasov, Romania
Tel.: (40) 368 413506   RO
Web Site:
http://www.inarbrasov.rdsweb.ro
Year Founded: 1966
Rev.: $244,623
Assets: $740,978
Liabilities: $34,736
Net Worth: $706,243
Earnings: $12,487
Emp.: 5
Fiscal Year-end: 12/31/17
Automotive Engineering Research & Development Services
N.A.I.C.S.: 541715

S.C. INDUSTRIE MICA PRAHOVA S.A.
Street Gageni nr 107, 100137, Ploiesti, Prahova, Romania
Tel.: (40) 244543515
Web Site:
https://www.industriemica.ro
Year Founded: 1980
INMA—(BUC)
Rev.: $848,982
Assets: $489,783
Liabilities: $109,241
Net Worth: $380,542
Earnings: $4,004
Emp.: 24
Fiscal Year-end: 12/31/23
Traffic Signal Equipment Production
N.A.I.C.S.: 334515
Ioan Matres (Chm & Gen Mgr)

S.C. INTERAGRO S.A.
1-3 Verii Street, Bucharest, 20723, Romania
Tel.: (40) 212103700
Web Site: http://www.interagro.ro
Year Founded: 1994
Sales Range: $650-699.9 Million
Emp.: 230
Chemical Fertilizer Mfr & Distr
N.A.I.C.S.: 325320
Ioan Niculae (Pres)

Subsidiaries:

S.C. Cerealcom S.A.   (1)
Str Sos Turnu Magurele NR 1, Alexandria, Teleorman, Romania
Tel.: (40) 247313440
Web Site: http://www.cerealcomteleorman.ro
Vegetable Oil Production Services
N.A.I.C.S.: 311224

S.C. Cicalex S.A.   (1)
Poraskia, Teleorman, 147280, Bucharest, Romania
Tel.: (40) 247319010
Web Site: http://www.cicalex.ro
Sales Range: $25-49.9 Million
Emp.: 200
Meat Processed from Carcasses
N.A.I.C.S.: 311612

S.C. Club A.RO Srl   (1)
31-33 Carol I Blvd Sector 2, 20912, Bucharest, Romania
Tel.: (40) 212507110
Restaurant & Club
N.A.I.C.S.: 722511

S.C. InterAgro Srl   (1)
38 Portului St Zimnicea, Bucharest, 147400, Romania
Tel.: (40) 247367100
Web Site: http://www.interagro.ro
Breakfast Cereal Mfr
N.A.I.C.S.: 311230
Ioan Niculae (Pres)

Subsidiary (Domestic):

SC InterGaz SRL   (2)
Str Portului nr 38, Zimnicea, 145400, Teleorman, Romania
Tel.: (40) 247 368 638
Web Site: http://www.intergaz.ro
Natural Gas Distr
N.A.I.C.S.: 221210

SC ZimTub SA   (2)
11 Portului Street, 145400, Zimnicea, Teleorman, Romania
Tel.: (40) 247 890 268
Web Site: http://www.zimtub.ro
Steel Pole Mfr
N.A.I.C.S.: 331210
Constantin Tecuceanu (CEO)

S.C. Rom - Ital Srl   (1)
3 Plopilor St Zimnicea, Bucharest, 145400, Romania
Tel.: (40) 247366688
Web Site: http://www.interagro.ro
Farm Supplies Merchant Whslr
N.A.I.C.S.: 424910

S.C. Sofert S.A.   (1)
1 Chimiei St, 600289, Bacau, Romania
Tel.: (40) 234575440
Web Site: http://www.interagro.ro
Sales Range: $200-249.9 Million
Pesticide & Agricultural Chemical Mfr
N.A.I.C.S.: 325320

S.C. Viromet S.A.   (1)
Aleea Uzinei Nr 8 Victoria, 505700, Brasov, Romania
Tel.: (40) 268 241120
Web Site: http://www.viromet.ro
Sales Range: $200-249.9 Million
Pesticide & Agricultural Chemical Mfr
N.A.I.C.S.: 325320
Hanes Dorina (Dir-Sls)

Subsidiary (Domestic):

SC Donau Chem SRL   (2)
Turnu Magurele Str Portului Nr 1, Bucharest, 145200, Teleorman, Romania
Tel.: (40) 247 416438
Web Site: http://www.donauchem.ro
Fertilizer Mfr
N.A.I.C.S.: 325311

SC Galaxy Tobacco SA   (1)
Boulevard Regie No 2 Sector 6, Bucharest, Romania
Tel.: (40) 213174400
Web Site: http://www.galaxy-tobacco.ro
Tobacco Product Mfr
N.A.I.C.S.: 312230

SC Nitroporos SRL   (1)
situata in Fagaras Sos Combinatului nr 14, Brasov, Romania
Tel.: (40) 268206500
Web Site: http://www.nitroporos.ro
Agrochemical Product Mfr
N.A.I.C.S.: 325311

Sc Hidro Olt Srl   (1)
Str Dunarii Bloc L 28 A Parter, Teleorman, Alexandria, 140010, Romania
Tel.: (40) 247311023
Web Site: http://www.hidroolt.ro
Civil Engineering Services
N.A.I.C.S.: 541330

S.C. INTFOR S.A.
Strada Portului 157, 800211, Galati, Romania
Tel.: (40) 236 460 361
Web Site: http://www.intfor.ro
Year Founded: 1921
Sales Range: $10-24.9 Million
Emp.: 198
Steel Pipe & Tube Mfr
N.A.I.C.S.: 331210
Andrei Lisinschi (Gen Mgr)

S.C. IOR S.A.
Str Bucovina nr 4 Sector 3, 30393, Bucharest, Romania
Tel.: (40) 213244210
Web Site: https://www.ior.ro
Year Founded: 1936
IORB—(BUC)
Rev.: $7,492,980
Assets: $41,183,594
Liabilities: $11,149,653
Net Worth: $30,033,941
Earnings: $141,934
Emp.: 279
Fiscal Year-end: 12/31/23
Optical Instrument Mfr
N.A.I.C.S.: 333310

S.C. IPROCHIM S.A. BUCURESTI
Str Mihai Eminescu No 19-21 Sector 1, 010512, Bucharest, Romania
Tel.: (40) 212117654
Web Site: https://www.iprochim.ro
IPHI—(BUC)
Rev.: $2,261,860
Assets: $32,478,249
Liabilities: $1,150,926
Net Worth: $31,327,323
Earnings: $669,941
Emp.: 40
Fiscal Year-end: 12/31/23
Engineeering Services
N.A.I.C.S.: 541330

S.C. IPROEB S.A.
Str Drumul Cetatii nr 19, Bistrita, Romania
Tel.: (40) 263238150
Web Site: https://www.iproeb.ro
Year Founded: 1977
IPRU—(BUC)
Rev.: $41,998,749
Assets: $35,302,349
Liabilities: $3,279,631
Net Worth: $32,022,717
Earnings: $3,654,867
Emp.: 254
Fiscal Year-end: 12/31/23
Electrical Wire & Cable Mfr
N.A.I.C.S.: 335999

S.C. IPROMET S.A.
20A Constructorilor Blvd 6, Bucharest, 060512, Romania
Tel.: (40) 21 220 32 40
Web Site: http://www.ipromet-sa.ro
Sales Range: Less than $1 Million
Engineeering Services
N.A.I.C.S.: 541330

S.C. LACTA S.A.
Strada Gloriei nr 2, Giurgiu, Romania
Tel.: (40) 246 210225
Web Site: http://www.lactagiurgiu.ro
INEM—(BUC)
Sales Range: $1-9.9 Million
Emp.: 94
Dairy & Cheese Mfr
N.A.I.C.S.: 112120
Antonel-Cristi Bunu (Pres)

S.C. LEGUME FRUCTE BUZAU S.A.
Sos Spatarului 7, Buzau, Romania
Tel.: (40) 238 710001
Web Site: http://www.legumefructe-buzau.ro
Year Founded: 1970
Sales Range: $1-9.9 Million
Emp.: 41
Fruit & Vegetable Processing & Preserving Services
N.A.I.C.S.: 311421

S.C. LIDO S.A
Poligrafiei Nr 75 Etaj 1 Camera 14 Sector 1, Bucharest, Romania
Tel.: (40) 213121621
Web Site: http://www.lidosa.ro
LIDO—(BUC)
Rev.: $813,475
Assets: $4,846,503
Liabilities: $10,354
Net Worth: $4,836,149
Earnings: $256,341
Emp.: 4
Fiscal Year-end: 12/31/19

Travel Agency Services
N.A.I.C.S.: 561510

S.C. LUCEAFARUL S.A.
Tel.: (40) 234511923
Web Site: https://www.luceafarul.ro
MEBY—(BUC)
Rev.: $252,032
Assets: $664,173
Liabilities: $147,699
Net Worth: $516,474
Earnings: $38,521
Emp.: 11
Fiscal Year-end: 12/31/23
Shopping Center Operator
N.A.I.C.S.: 531120

S.C. MACOFIL S.A.
Str Barsesti Nr 217, Gorj, Targu Jiu, Romania
Tel.: (40) 253212690
Web Site: https://www.macofilsa.ro
Year Founded: 1979
MACO—(BUC)
Rev.: $19,163,986
Assets: $23,645,420
Liabilities: $3,753,653
Net Worth: $19,891,767
Earnings: $5,115,307
Emp.: 179
Fiscal Year-end: 12/31/22
Construction Materials Mfr
N.A.I.C.S.: 327331

S.C. MAGAZIN UNIVERSAL MARAMURES S.A.
Bd Unirii nr 10, 430272, Baia Mare, Maramures, Romania
Tel.: (40) 262225285
Web Site:
https://www.maramuresul.ro
MAMA—(BUC)
Rev.: $3,361,534
Assets: $9,507,494
Liabilities: $262,652
Net Worth: $9,244,842
Earnings: $836,135
Emp.: 3
Fiscal Year-end: 12/31/23
Shopping Mall Operator
N.A.I.C.S.: 531120

S.C. MARA COM MIXT S.A.
B-dul Revolutiei nr 55 ap 4, Arad, Romania
Tel.: (40) 357 100 900
Web Site: http://www.maracom.ro
Sales Range: $1-9.9 Million
Emp.: 4
Industrial Building Construction Services
N.A.I.C.S.: 236210

S.C. MARTENS S.A.
Str Grigore Ventura nr 1, Galati, Romania
Tel.: (40) 236472380
Web Site: http://www.martens.ro
Year Founded: 1990
MABE—(BUC)
Rev.: $8,810,324
Assets: $12,397,103
Liabilities: $17,124,785
Net Worth: $(4,727,682)
Earnings: $(1,337,883)
Emp.: 121
Fiscal Year-end: 12/31/20
Beer Mfr
N.A.I.C.S.: 312120

S.C. MECANICA CODLEA S.A.
Str Rampei nr 1, 505100, Bucharest, 505100, Brasov, Romania
Tel.: (40) 268254200
Web Site: https://www.mecod.ro
Year Founded: 1991

MEOY—(BUC)
Rev.: $654,891
Assets: $4,733,822
Liabilities: $265,331
Net Worth: $4,468,491
Earnings: $214,025
Emp.: 4
Fiscal Year-end: 12/31/23
Welded Steel Construction Services
N.A.I.C.S.: 331513

S.C. MECANICA ROTES S.A.
Soseaua Gaesti 6, Targoviste, Dambovita, Romania
Tel.: (40) 245632792
Web Site: https://www.rotes.ro
METY—(BUC)
Rev.: $125,179
Assets: $2,480,048
Liabilities: $812,755
Net Worth: $1,667,293
Earnings: $558,441
Emp.: 8
Fiscal Year-end: 12/31/23
Industrial Machinery Mfr
N.A.I.C.S.: 333998

S.C. MECANICA S.A.
Str Uzinei Nr 1, Marsa, 555250, Sibiu, Romania
Tel.: (40) 269 526266   RO
Web Site: http://www.mecmirsa.ro
Year Founded: 1939
Sales Range: $1-9.9 Million
Emp.: 107
Truck & Trailer Mfr
N.A.I.C.S.: 333924
Constantin Cotora *(Chm & CEO)*

S.C. MECANICA SIGHETU S.A.
Unirii 44, Maramures, Sighetu Marmatiei, Romania
Tel.: (40) 262 312121
Web Site: http://www.mecanica-sighet.ro
Year Founded: 1975
Sales Range: $10-24.9 Million
Emp.: 123
Fastener Product Mfr
N.A.I.C.S.: 339993
Vasile Prodan *(Gen Mgr)*

S.C. MECON S.A.
Sos Cristianului nr 6, Brasov, Romania
Tel.: (40) 268549124
Web Site: http://www.mecon.ro
Year Founded: 1949
MECP—(BUC)
Rev.: $427,179
Assets: $5,120,790
Liabilities: $44,476
Net Worth: $5,076,314
Earnings: $59,838
Emp.: 6
Fiscal Year-end: 12/31/23
Industrial Construction Services
N.A.I.C.S.: 236210

S.C. MEDIMFARM S.A.
Targovistei 11, Ploiesti, 100299, Romania
Tel.: (40) 244 55 66 16
Web Site: http://www.medimfarm.ro
Year Founded: 1991
Sales Range: $10-24.9 Million
Emp.: 196
Pharmaceutical Product Whslr
N.A.I.C.S.: 424210

S.C. MEDUMAN S.A.
Str Eroilor 28, Maramures, 435700, Viseu de Sus, Romania
Tel.: (40) 262 354 430
Web Site: http://www.meduman.ro
Year Founded: 1923
Sales Range: $1-9.9 Million
Emp.: 83
Pharmaceuticals Product Mfr
N.A.I.C.S.: 325412

S.C. METALICA S.A.
Petre Ispirescu Street No 75 Sector 5, Bucharest, Bihor, Romania
Tel.: (40) 214205150
Web Site: https://www.metalicagrup.ro
Year Founded: 1994
MEOR—(BUC)
Rev.: $2,118,839
Assets: $3,148,298
Liabilities: $1,448,042
Net Worth: $1,700,256
Earnings: $173,836
Emp.: 18
Fiscal Year-end: 12/31/23
Appliance Mfr
N.A.I.C.S.: 335220

S.C. METAV S.A.
67-77 Biharia Street District 1, Bucharest, Romania
Tel.: (40) 21 599 77 65
Web Site: http://www.metav.ro
Year Founded: 1991
Sales Range: $1-9.9 Million
Emp.: 54
Real Estate Property Management Services
N.A.I.C.S.: 531190

S.C. MINDO S.A.
str Herta nr 45, Botosani, Dorohoi, Romania
Tel.: (40) 231610210
Web Site: https://www.mindo.ro
Year Founded: 1967
MINO—(BUC)
Rev.: $6,663,409
Assets: $2,914,968
Liabilities: $1,553,643
Net Worth: $1,361,325
Earnings: $201,520
Emp.: 49
Fiscal Year-end: 12/31/23
Drilling Services
N.A.I.C.S.: 238910

S.C. MOBAM S.A.
Strada Transilvaniei no 6A block TJ2/65 Ap 24, Baia Mare, Romania
Tel.: (40) 725516856
Web Site: http://www.mobam.ro
Year Founded: 1959
MOBD—(BUC)
Rev.: $4,521,472
Assets: $3,457,122
Liabilities: $360,682
Net Worth: $3,096,440
Earnings: $2,483,108
Emp.: 6
Fiscal Year-end: 12/31/20
Wooden Furniture Mfr
N.A.I.C.S.: 337211
Petrica Vasvari *(Pres & Gen Dir)*

S.C. MOBEX S.A.
2 Caprioarei Street, 540314, Tirgu Mures, Romania
Tel.: (40) 265210652
Web Site: http://www.mobex.ro
Year Founded: 1948
MOBG—(BUC)
Rev.: $2,728,481
Assets: $9,228,489
Liabilities: $702,979
Net Worth: $8,525,509
Earnings: ($680,941)
Emp.: 124
Fiscal Year-end: 12/31/23
Wooden Furniture Mfr
N.A.I.C.S.: 337122

S.C. MOBICRASNA S.A.
Calea Armatei Romane Nr 39, Satu-Mare, 445100, Carei, Romania
Tel.: (40) 261 865153
Web Site: http://www.mobicrasna.ro
Year Founded: 1948
Sales Range: Less than $1 Million
Furniture Mfr
N.A.I.C.S.: 337214

S.C. MOBILA RADAUTI S.A.
82 Municipiul Strada Volovatului, Suceava, 725400, Radauti, Romania
Tel.: (40) 230561539
Web Site: https://mobilaradauti.ro
Year Founded: 1960
MOBT—(BUC)
Rev.: $203,936
Assets: $1,516,660
Liabilities: $101,078
Net Worth: $1,415,582
Earnings: ($819,760)
Emp.: 4
Fiscal Year-end: 12/31/23
Furniture Mfr
N.A.I.C.S.: 337126
Radu Ott *(Pres & Gen Mgr)*

S.C. MOBILEXTRA S.A.
Str Calea Transilvaniei 180 A, Jud Suceava, 725100, Campulung, Moldovenesc, Romania
Tel.: (40) 230 314833
Web Site: http://www.mobilextra.ro
Year Founded: 1968
Sales Range: Less than $1 Million
Wooden Furniture Mfr
N.A.I.C.S.: 337126

S.C. MOLDOVA S.A.
str Stefan cel Mare nr 70, 730167, Vaslui, 730167, Romania
Tel.: (40) 235311353
Web Site: https://www.moldovasa.ro
MODY—(BUC)
Rev.: $359,204
Assets: $1,065,455
Liabilities: $56,229
Net Worth: $1,009,226
Earnings: $78,304
Fiscal Year-end: 12/31/23
Grocery Store Operator
N.A.I.C.S.: 445110

S.C. NATURA QUATTUOR ENERGIA HOLDINGS S.A.
str 5-7 Dimitrie Pompeiu Bvd Body A 5th Floor, District 2, 020335, Bucharest, Romania
Tel.: (40) 768 560 813
Web Site: http://nqeholdings.com
Year Founded: 2012
Sales Range: Less than $1 Million
Emp.: 6
Holding Company
N.A.I.C.S.: 551112

S.C. NEPTUN S.A.
57-63 Bobalna Street, Campina, 105600, Prahova, Romania
Tel.: (40) 244 33 56 51
Web Site: http://www.neptun-gears.ro
Sales Range: $25-49.9 Million
Emp.: 322
Industrial Equipment Mfr
N.A.I.C.S.: 333248
Roxana Elena Gheorghe *(Chm)*

S.C. NIMB CONSMETAL S.R.L.
Platforma CNE, Constanta, 905200, Cernavoda, Romania
Tel.: (40) 241238488   RO
Web Site: http://www.nimbconsmetal.ro
Year Founded: 1999
Sales Range: $25-49.9 Million
Emp.: 100
Steel Structure Erection Contracting & Industrial Equipment Maintenance & Installation Services
N.A.I.C.S.: 238120
Bucur Vasile *(Gen Mgr)*

S.C. NUTRICOM S.A.
Strada Portului nr 52, Oltenita, Calarasi, Romania
Tel.: (40) 242 515 430
Web Site: http://www.nutricom.ro
Sales Range: $100-124.9 Million
Emp.: 442
Swine & Pig Processing
N.A.I.C.S.: 112210

S.C. NUTRIENTUL S.A.
Str Campului Nr 1, 417516, Santandrei, Bihor, Romania
Tel.: (40) 259 471811
Web Site: http://www.nutrientul.ro
Year Founded: 1972
Sales Range: $50-74.9 Million
Emp.: 157
Animal Feed Mfr
N.A.I.C.S.: 311119

S.C. PERLA COVASNEI S.A.
Bdul Pipera Nr 1/I Cladirea Admin Etaj 5, 077190, Voluntari, Romania
Tel.: (40) 213167774
Web Site: http://www.perlacovasnei.ro
Sales Range: $10-24.9 Million
Emp.: 51
Bottled Water Mfr
N.A.I.C.S.: 312112

S.C. PETRODESIGN S.A.
Str Caderea Bastiliei 56-58, 10616, Bucharest, Romania
Tel.: (40) 21 317 3004
Web Site: http://www.petrodesign.ro
Year Founded: 1948
Sales Range: $1-9.9 Million
Emp.: 40
Engineeering Services
N.A.I.C.S.: 541330
Ioan Botgros *(Pres)*

S.C. PETROUTILAJ S.A.
1 Principala Street, 107425, Poiana Campina, Prahova, Romania
Tel.: (40) 723 80 14 46
Web Site: http://www.petroutilaj.ro
Year Founded: 1899
Sales Range: $1-9.9 Million
Emp.: 440
Mining Machinery Mfr
N.A.I.C.S.: 333131
Andrei Hortopan *(Gen Mgr)*

S.C. PLASTIDRUM S.R.L.
Soseaua Alexandria Nr 156 Sector 5, Bucharest, Romania
Tel.: (40) 214202480   RO
Web Site: http://www.plastidrum.ro
Year Founded: 1996
Highway & Street Construction Services
N.A.I.C.S.: 237310

S.C. PREFAB S.A.
Str Bucuresti Nr 396, Bucharest, Calarasi, Romania
Tel.: (40) 213315116
Web Site: http://www.prefab.ro
Year Founded: 1967
PREH—(BUC)
Rev.: $21,413,226
Assets: $55,304,032
Liabilities: $8,100,200
Net Worth: $47,203,832
Earnings: $1,684,722
Emp.: 313
Fiscal Year-end: 12/31/22

S.C. PREFAB S.A.

S.C. Prefab S.A.—(Continued)
Concrete Products Mfr
N.A.I.C.S.: 327390
Milut Petre Marian (CEO)

S.C. PRIMCOM S.A.
B-dul Aerogarii 33 Parter Sector 1, Bucharest, Romania
Tel.: (40) 212556424
Web Site: https://www.primcom.ro
PRIB—(BUC)
Rev.: $292,594
Assets: $1,717,124
Liabilities: $340,622
Net Worth: $1,376,502
Earnings: $73,688
Emp.: 5
Fiscal Year-end: 12/31/23
Real Estate Prorperty Leasing Services
N.A.I.C.S.: 531190

S.C. PRODLACTA S.A.
Str Ecaterina Teodoroiu 5, Brasov, Romania
Tel.: (40) 268441400
Web Site: https://www.prodlacta.ro
PRAE—(BUC)
Rev.: $31,549,672
Assets: $17,503,756
Liabilities: $8,661,286
Net Worth: $8,842,470
Earnings: $462,056
Emp.: 298
Fiscal Year-end: 12/31/22
Dairy Products Mfr
N.A.I.C.S.: 311513

S.C. RAFINARIA STEAUA ROMANA S.A. CAMPINA
Calea Doftanei Nr 15, 105600, Campina, Prahova, Romania
Tel.: (40) 244 336 151
Web Site:
 http://www.steauaromana.ro
Refined Petroleum Mfr
N.A.I.C.S.: 213112
Elena Manoiu (Pres)

S.C. RELEE S.A.
Str Gloria nr 5, 551061, Medias, Romania
Tel.: (40) 269845902
Web Site: https://www.relee.ro
Year Founded: 1954
RELE—(BUC)
Rev.: $5,219,439
Assets: $3,042,016
Liabilities: $1,656,593
Net Worth: $1,385,423
Earnings: ($187,842)
Emp.: 206
Fiscal Year-end: 12/31/23
Electrical Control Apparatus Mfr
N.A.I.C.S.: 335999

S.C. ROFEP S.A.
Sos Bucuresti - Buzau km 57 5, 925300, Urziceni, Ialomita, Romania
Tel.: (40) 243255959
Web Site: http://www.rofep.ro
Year Founded: 1968
Sales Range: Less than $1 Million
Soft & Hard Ferrite Mfr.
N.A.I.C.S.: 339999
Dumitru Stoian (Pres)

S.C. ROMAN S.A.
Str Poienelor nr 5, Brasov, 500419, Romania
Tel.: (40) 268 312850
Web Site: http://www.roman.ro
Sales Range: $25-49.9 Million
Emp.: 559
Trucks Mfr
N.A.I.C.S.: 336120

Carol Ludovic Rugacs (Gen Mgr)

S.C. ROMCAB S.A.
Str Voinicenilor Nr 35, Targu Mures, 540252, Romania
Tel.: (40) 265312541
Web Site: http://www.romcab.ro
Year Founded: 1950
Sales Range: $50-74.9 Million
Emp.: 171
Copper Cable & Electrical Wire Mfr
N.A.I.C.S.: 331420
Zoltan Prosszer (CEO)

S.C. ROPHARMA S.A.
Nr 55 Iuliu Maniu Str Etaj 1, Brasov, Romania
Tel.: (40) 731505273
Web Site: https://www.ropharma.ro
Year Founded: 1952
RPH—(BUC)
Rev.: $122,465,036
Assets: $106,088,625
Liabilities: $63,358,318
Net Worth: $42,730,307
Earnings: $1,674,451
Emp.: 747
Fiscal Year-end: 12/31/22
Pharmaceuticals Product Mfr
N.A.I.C.S.: 325412
Mihai Miron (Chm & CEO)

S.C. RULMENTI S.A.
Pictor Ion Negulici Street No 2 Sector 1, PO Box 011941, Bucharest, Romania
Tel.: (40) 212300180
Web Site: http://www.urb.ro
Year Founded: 1953
Machinery Mfr
N.A.I.C.S.: 333248

S.C. SANTIERUL NAVAL ORSOVA S.A.
Strada Tufari nr 4, 225200, Orsova, 225200, Mehedinti, Romania
Tel.: (40) 252362399
Web Site: https://www.snorsova.ro
Year Founded: 1890
SNO—(BUC)
Rev.: $21,494,558
Assets: $21,487,248
Liabilities: $3,956,365
Net Worth: $17,530,883
Earnings: $743,544
Emp.: 344
Fiscal Year-end: 12/31/23
Ship Building Services
N.A.I.C.S.: 336611
Fercala Mihai (Pres)

S.C. SATURN S.A.
Str Cabanei Nr 57, Alba Iulia, Romania
Tel.: (40) 258812764
Web Site: https://www.saturn-alba.ro
Year Founded: 1972
SATU—(BUC)
Rev.: $22,314,170
Assets: $12,903,434
Liabilities: $2,379,445
Net Worth: $10,523,989
Earnings: $733,291
Emp.: 364
Fiscal Year-end: 12/31/23
Iron Casting
N.A.I.C.S.: 331511

S.C. SEMBRAZ S.A.
Str Henri Coanda Nr 12, 550234, Sibiu, Romania
Tel.: (40) 369409924
Web Site: https://www.sembraz.ro
Year Founded: 1935
SEBZ—(BUC)
Rev.: $287,000

Assets: $800,754
Liabilities: $32,193
Net Worth: $768,561
Earnings: ($36,398)
Emp.: 11
Fiscal Year-end: 12/31/23
Agricultural Machinery Mfr
N.A.I.C.S.: 333111

S.C. SERICO S.A.
Sos Pipera Nr 46 S2, Bucharest, Romania
Tel.: (40) 212305955
Web Site: https://www.serico.ro
Year Founded: 1973
SERC—(BUC)
Rev.: $871,278
Assets: $11,603,484
Liabilities: $222,576
Net Worth: $11,380,909
Earnings: $142,420
Emp.: 16
Fiscal Year-end: 12/31/23
Furniture Product Whslr
N.A.I.C.S.: 423210

S.C. SEVERNAV S.A.
Calea Timisoarei No 204, 220242, Drobeta-Turnu Severin, Mehedinti, Romania
Tel.: (40) 252308000
Web Site: https://www.severnav.ro
SEVE—(BUC)
Rev.: $22,073,950
Assets: $52,937,906
Liabilities: $26,223,678
Net Worth: $26,714,228
Earnings: $36,398
Emp.: 425
Fiscal Year-end: 12/31/23
Ship Building Services
N.A.I.C.S.: 336611
Borintis Grigore (Dir-Economic)

S.C. SIBAREX S.A.
Str Prundului nr 1, Campina, Vrancea, Romania
Tel.: (40) 237 221 361
Year Founded: 1987
Construction Services
N.A.I.C.S.: 236210
Ioan Manea (Pres)

S.C. SILCOM S.A.
Str Timisorii Nr 143-147, Lugoj, 305500, Romania
Tel.: (40) 256 307 300
Web Site: http://www.silcomlugoj.ro
Year Founded: 1974
Sales Range: $1-9.9 Million
Emp.: 62
Industrial Machinery Mfr
N.A.I.C.S.: 333998

S.C. SIMEROM S.A.
Str Lector Nr 3, Sibiu, Sibiu, Romania
Tel.: (40) 269 431659
Web Site: http://www.simerom.ro
Year Founded: 1921
Sales Range: Less than $1 Million
Emp.: 2
Machine Tools Mfr
N.A.I.C.S.: 333517

S.C. SINTOFARM S.A.
Str Ziduri intre Vii nr 22 Sector 2, 23324, Bucharest, Romania
Tel.: (40) 212521715
Web Site: https://www.sintofarm.ro
Year Founded: 1973
SINT—(BUC)
Rev.: $2,524,595
Assets: $2,820,777
Liabilities: $504,140
Net Worth: $2,316,636
Earnings: $105,828
Emp.: 49

INTERNATIONAL PUBLIC

Fiscal Year-end: 12/31/23
Pharmaceuticals Product Mfr
N.A.I.C.S.: 325412
Georgescu Mariana (Gen Mgr)

S.C. SOMETA S.A.
Str Nicolae Balcescu no 29, Tasnad, 445300, Satu-Mare, Romania
Tel.: (40) 744564148
Web Site: https://www.someta.ro
Year Founded: 1952
SOTA—(BUC)
Rev.: $2,842,651
Assets: $1,571,144
Liabilities: $763,352
Net Worth: $807,792
Earnings: $122,295
Emp.: 53
Fiscal Year-end: 12/31/22
Metal Tank Mfr
N.A.I.C.S.: 332420

S.C. STICLOVAL S.A.
Str Franghesti ne 17 19, 106400, Valenii de Munte, Romania
Tel.: (40) 44280928
Web Site: https://www.sticloval.ro
STOZ—(BUC)
Rev.: $1,139,003
Assets: $2,254,766
Liabilities: $822,360
Net Worth: $1,432,407
Earnings: ($173,289)
Fiscal Year-end: 12/31/23
Quartz Sand Mining
N.A.I.C.S.: 212322

S.C. STOFE BUHUSI S.A.
Strada Libertatii 36, Buhusi, Bacau, Romania
Tel.: (40) 234261001
Web Site: https://www.stofebuhusi.ro
Year Founded: 1885
STOF—(BUC)
Rev.: $2,323,888
Assets: $5,098,298
Liabilities: $118,409
Net Worth: $4,979,889
Earnings: $120,246
Emp.: 56
Fiscal Year-end: 12/31/23
Wool Product Mfr
N.A.I.C.S.: 313110

S.C. SUBANSAMBLE AUTO S.A.
Str Lt Paius David Nr 9, Sfantu Gheorghe, 520077, Romania
Tel.: (40) 267310790
Web Site:
 http://www.subansambleauto.ro
Motor Vehicle Parts Mfr
N.A.I.C.S.: 333612

S.C. TALC DOLOMITA S.A.
Zlasti Street nr 121, Hunedoara, Romania
Tel.: (40) 726742810
Web Site: http://www.talcdolomita.ro
Talcum Quarry
N.A.I.C.S.: 212319
Irina Nicoleta Leu (Gen Mgr)

S.C. TARNAVA S.A.
Strada Mihai Eminescu 69 Sighisoara, 545400, Sighisoara, Mures, Romania
Tel.: (40) 265771950
Web Site: https://www.tarnava.ro
Year Founded: 1949
TIGH—(BUC)
Rev.: $1,086,717
Assets: $1,309,454
Liabilities: $1,069,011
Net Worth: $240,442
Earnings: ($136,781)
Emp.: 92

Fiscal Year-end: 12/31/23
Outerwear Mfr
N.A.I.C.S.: 315120

Subsidiaries:

Tarnava UG (1)
Bachstrasse 43, 48527, Nordhorn, Germany
Tel.: (49) 59218504455
Web Site: http://www.tarnava.de
Apparel Retailer
N.A.I.C.S.: 458110

S.C. TCI CONTRACTOR GENERAL S.A.
Alexandru Vaida Voivod Street No 2, 400592, Cluj-Napoca, Romania
Tel.: (40) 264 419313
Web Site: http://www.tcicgcluj.ro
Year Founded: 1992
Emp.: 174
Construction Services
N.A.I.C.S.: 236210
Enesel Horea Vasile *(Pres & Gen Mgr)*

S.C. TELEROM PROIECT INSTITUTUL NATIONAL DE PROIECTARI TELECOMUNICATII S.A.
Str Mendeleev nr 21-25 sector 1, Bucharest, 010362, Romania
Tel.: (40) 21 307 47 00
Web Site: http://www.telerom.ro
Year Founded: 1952
Sales Range: Less than $1 Million
Engineeering Services
N.A.I.C.S.: 541330

S.C. TESATORIILE REUNITE S.A.
Str Spataru Preda nr 5 sector 5, 50185, Bucharest, Romania
Tel.: (40) 21 324 6060
Web Site: http://www.tesatoriilereunite.ro
Year Founded: 1933
Sales Range: Less than $1 Million
Textile Products Mfr
N.A.I.C.S.: 313210
Daniel Florian Miron *(Pres & Gen Mgr)*

S.C. TEXTILA OLTUL S.A.
Str Kos Karoly Nr 19, Sfantu Gheorghe, Covasna, Romania
Tel.: (40) 267 352284
Web Site: http://www.textila-oltul.ro
Year Founded: 1879
Textile Products Mfr
N.A.I.C.S.: 314999
Doina Buturuga *(Pres)*

S.C. TRANSCOM S.A.
str Frigoriferului nr 1, 550047, Sibiu, Romania
Tel.: (40) 269 228040
Web Site: http://www.transcomsibiu.ro
Sales Range: $1-9.9 Million
Emp.: 40
Truck Transportation Services
N.A.I.C.S.: 484121
Marius Mutiu *(Pres)*

S.C. TRANSCOM S.A.
Str Spataru Preda Nr 7B Birou - C2 - Et 1 Camera 4 Sector 5, 50185, Bucharest, Romania
Tel.: (40) 213177148
Web Site: http://www.transcom.ro
Year Founded: 1991
TRVM—(BUC)
Rev.: $303,874
Assets: $11,948,959
Liabilities: $4,058,315
Net Worth: $7,890,644
Earnings: ($85,885)
Emp.: 13
Fiscal Year-end: 12/31/22
Food Transportation Services
N.A.I.C.S.: 484121

S.C. TRANSILANA S.A.
44 Fabricilor Street, 507075, Ghimbav, Brasov, Romania
Tel.: (40) 268475448
Web Site: https://www.transilana.ro
Year Founded: 1936
TRSK—(BUC)
Rev.: $7,484,529
Assets: $5,261,412
Liabilities: $3,505,708
Net Worth: $1,755,704
Earnings: $26,256
Emp.: 137
Fiscal Year-end: 12/31/23
Yarn Spinning Mills
N.A.I.C.S.: 313110

S.C. TURISM COVASNA S.A.
Str 1 Decembrie 1918 Nr 1-2, Covasna, 525200, Sfantu Gheorghe, 525200, Romania
Tel.: (40) 267340401
Web Site: https://www.turismcovasna.ro
TUAA—(BUC)
Rev.: $6,293,428
Assets: $19,531,038
Liabilities: $1,031,386
Net Worth: $18,499,652
Earnings: $1,023,640
Emp.: 142
Fiscal Year-end: 12/31/23
Accommodation Services
N.A.I.C.S.: 721110

S.C. TURISM, HOTELURI, RESTAURANTE MAREA NEAGRA S.A.
Mangalia Str Lavrion nr 29 Jud, Mangalia, Constanta, Romania
Tel.: (40) 241752452
Web Site: http://www.thrmareaneagra.ro
EFO—(BUC)
Rev.: $14,979,145
Assets: $104,114,038
Liabilities: $56,921,196
Net Worth: $47,192,842
Earnings: $7,504,108
Emp.: 33
Fiscal Year-end: 12/31/22
Hotel Services
N.A.I.C.S.: 721110

Subsidiaries:

Balneoterapia Saturn SRL (1)
Saturn-Hora/Balada/Sirena Str Greenport, Mangalia, Romania
Tel.: (40) 241755990
Web Site: http://www.balneoterapiasaturn.ro
Hotel Services
N.A.I.C.S.: 721110

S.C. TURNATORIA CENTRALA ORION S.A.
29 Ecaterina Teodoroiu Street, 2150, Campina, Romania
Tel.: (40) 244 334661
Web Site: http://www.tco.ro
Year Founded: 1971
Sales Range: $1-9.9 Million
Emp.: 218
Iron Casting Services
N.A.I.C.S.: 331511

S.C. TUSNAD S.A.
Str Oltului 87, Harghita, 535100, Baile Tusnad, Romania
Tel.: (40) 266335204
Web Site: https://www.tusnad.ro
TSND—(BUC)
Rev.: $4,004,919
Assets: $6,733,844
Liabilities: $608,057
Net Worth: $6,125,787
Earnings: $143,529
Emp.: 98
Fiscal Year-end: 12/31/22
Hotel Services
N.A.I.C.S.: 721110

S.C. UNIREA SHOPPING CENTER S.A.
Sector 3 P-ta Unirii nr 1, Bucharest, Romania
Tel.: (40) 213030208
Web Site: https://www.unireashop.ro
SCDM—(BUC)
Rev.: $14,562,639
Assets: $67,084,638
Liabilities: $13,915,907
Net Worth: $53,168,732
Earnings: ($218,853)
Emp.: 19
Fiscal Year-end: 12/31/23
Shopping Center Operator
N.A.I.C.S.: 531120
Carmen Adamescu *(Pres & Gen Mgr)*

S.C. UNITEH S.A.
Serghei Vasilievichi Rachmaninov Street No 46 - 48 Basement room U3, Sector 2, Bucharest, Romania
Tel.: (40) 212330773
Web Site: http://www.uniteh-timisoara.ro
Year Founded: 1966
Sales Range: Less than $1 Million
Emp.: 3
Building Leasing Services
N.A.I.C.S.: 531120

S.C. UNIVERS S.A.
Str Regina Maria Nr 4, Valcea, Ramnicu Valcea, Romania
Tel.: (40) 250731895
Web Site: https://www.univers-valcea.ro
UNVR—(BUC)
Rev.: $2,010,175
Assets: $11,355,608
Liabilities: $424,700
Net Worth: $10,930,909
Earnings: $407,317
Emp.: 5
Fiscal Year-end: 12/31/22
Grocery Product Whslr
N.A.I.C.S.: 424490

S.C. URB RULMENTI SUCEAVA S.A.
Industrial Area Scheia, Suceava, 727525, Suceava, Romania
Tel.: (40) 330101605
Web Site: http://www.urb-s.ro
Year Founded: 1989
URUL—(BUC)
Rev.: $2,041,681
Assets: $6,688,515
Liabilities: $3,023,191
Net Worth: $3,665,324
Earnings: ($325,304)
Emp.: 7
Fiscal Year-end: 12/31/19
Bearing Component Mfr
N.A.I.C.S.: 332991

S.C. UTILAJ GREU S.A.
Str Ciocirliei Nr 1, Murfatlar, Constanta, Romania
Tel.: (40) 241234395
Web Site: https://www.utilaj-greu.ro
Year Founded: 1991
UTGR—(BUC)
Rev.: $299,237
Assets: $829,153
Liabilities: $46,934
Net Worth: $782,219
Earnings: ($46,400)
Emp.: 7
Fiscal Year-end: 12/31/22
Construction Equipment Rental Services
N.A.I.C.S.: 532412

S.C. UZUC S.A.
16 Depoului str, 100335, Ploiesti, Romania
Tel.: (40) 752008802
Web Site: https://www.uzuc.ro
Year Founded: 1904
UZC—(BUC)
Rev.: $2,195,335
Assets: $26,370,803
Liabilities: $3,894,372
Net Worth: $22,476,431
Earnings: $50,891
Emp.: 55
Fiscal Year-end: 12/31/23
Pressure Equipment Mfr
N.A.I.C.S.: 339999

S.C. VEST ENERGO S.A.
str Preciziei nr 12A sector 6, Bucharest, Romania
Tel.: (40) 21 317 89 35
Web Site: http://www.vestenergo.ro
Sales Range: $25-49.9 Million
Emp.: 68
Eletric Power Generation Services
N.A.I.C.S.: 221118

S.C. VICTORIA S.A.
Str Marasesti Nr 44-46, Arad, 310032, Romania
Tel.: (40) 257 270367
Web Site: http://www.victoria-arad.ro
Year Founded: 1951
Sales Range: Less than $1 Million
Emp.: 14
Watches & Clock Mfr
N.A.I.C.S.: 334519

S.C. VICTORIA S.A.
B-dul Iuliu Maniu nr 309-317 sector 6, 061101, Bucharest, Romania
Tel.: (40) 21 318 15 00   RO
Web Site: http://www.victoriagroup.ro
Year Founded: 2002
Sales Range: $1-9.9 Million
Emp.: 12
Mattress Mfr
N.A.I.C.S.: 337910
Imad Mahmoud Jaffal *(Pres)*

S.C. VINALCOOL ARGES S.A.
B-dul Nicolae Balcescu nr 156, Arges, Pitesti, Romania
Tel.: (40) 348730787
Web Site: https://www.vinalcoolarges.ro
Year Founded: 1954
VIAG—(BUC)
Rev.: $2,197,622
Assets: $4,352,114
Liabilities: $759,603
Net Worth: $3,592,511
Earnings: $753,996
Emp.: 10
Fiscal Year-end: 12/31/20
Agricultural Production Services
N.A.I.C.S.: 111998
Mircea-Marian Dragusin *(Pres)*

S.C. VITIMAS S.A. TECUCI
Str Gh Petrascu Nr 20 Tecuci, 805300, Galati, Romania
Tel.: (40) 236820391
Web Site: https://www.vitimas.ro
Year Founded: 1951
VITK—(BUC)
Rev.: $160,993
Assets: $2,264,071

S.C. VITIMAS S.A. TECUCI

S.C. Vitimas S.A. Tecuci—(Continued)
Liabilities: $180,887
Net Worth: $2,083,185
Earnings: ($66,855)
Emp.: 4
Fiscal Year-end: 12/31/23
Industrial Machinery Parts Mfr
N.A.I.C.S.: 333248

S.C. ZAREA S.A.
176 Bucurestii Noi Ave sect 1, Bucharest, Romania
Tel.: (40) 216670020
Web Site: http://www.zarea.ro
Year Founded: 1912
Sales Range: $10-24.9 Million
Wine Mfr & Whslr
N.A.I.C.S.: 424820

S.C. ZECASIN S.A.
Splaiul Independentei Nr 202 Sectorul 6, Bucharest, Romania
Tel.: (40) 728 16 53 84
Web Site: http://www.zecasin.ro
Natural Science Research & Development Services
N.A.I.C.S.: 541715

S.C.T. PTY LTD
824 Bourke St, Waterloo, 2017, NSW, Australia
Tel.: (61) 296909999
Web Site: http://www.sydneycitytoyota.com.au
Sales Range: $100-124.9 Million
Emp.: 230
Automobile Dealers
N.A.I.C.S.: 441110
Robert Kirwan (Mgr-Sls-Retail)

S.E. JOHNSON MANAGEMENT LTD.
4330 - 122 Ave SE, Calgary, T2Z 0A6, AB, Canada
Tel.: (403) 291-9600
Web Site: https://www.sej.ca
Year Founded: 1929
Rev.: $14,000,000
Emp.: 35
Mechanical Contracting Service
N.A.I.C.S.: 238190
Bruce A. Thorlakson (Pres & Principal)

S.E.C. AUTO SALES & SERVICES PCL
107 109 111 113 115 117 119 Rama 9 Road, Huaikhwang, Bangkok, 10310, Thailand
Tel.: (66) 26430003
Sales Range: $25-49.9 Million
Automobile Whslr
N.A.I.C.S.: 423110
Sapphaphon Ratanarungrot (Chm & CEO)

S.F. HOLDING CO., LTD.
Wanji Business Building Xinzhou Shiyi Street, Futian District, Shenzhen, 518048, Guandong, China
Tel.: (86) 7559533883
Web Site: http://www.sf-express.com
Year Founded: 1993
002352—(SSE)
Rev.: $31,743,066,647
Assets: $32,158,775,936
Liabilities: $17,157,180,483
Net Worth: $15,001,595,453
Earnings: $654,068,811
Fiscal Year-end: 12/31/21
Holding Company
N.A.I.C.S.: 551112

Subsidiaries:

Kerry Express (Thailand) Public Company Limited (1)
No 89 Chao Phraya Tower Building 9th Floor Room 906 Soi Wat Suan Phlu, Charoen Krung Road Bang Rak Subdistrict Bang Rak District, Bangkok, 10500, Thailand (62.66%)
Tel.: (66) 22385558
Web Site: https://th.kerryexpress.com
Rev.: $334,841,734
Assets: $264,353,869
Liabilities: $187,202,440
Net Worth: $77,151,428
Earnings: ($113,873,350)
Emp.: 12,840
Fiscal Year-end: 12/31/2023
Logistic Services
N.A.I.C.S.: 541614

S.H. DAYTON LTD.
144 Industrial Road, PO Box 277, Shoal Lake, R0J 1Z0, MB, Canada
Tel.: (204) 759-2065
Web Site: https://www.shdayton.ca
Year Founded: 1979
Rev.: $10,647,285
Emp.: 20
Agricultural Equipment Mfr
N.A.I.C.S.: 333112
Kim Kimpinski (Sec)

S.I.F. ITALIA S.P.A.
Via Lovanio 6, 20121, Milan, Italy
Tel.: (39) 0229000707
Web Site: https://www.sifitalia.it
Year Founded: 1980
SIF—(EUR)
Real Estate Investment Services
N.A.I.C.S.: 531190
Luca Giuseppe Reale Ruffino (Chm)

S.KIJCHAI ENTERPRISE PUBLIC COMPANY LIMITED
99/9 Moo 7 Huaiyang, Klaeng, Rayong, 21110, Thailand
Tel.: (66) 38928188 TH
Web Site: https://www.skn.co.th
Year Founded: 2010
SKN—(THA)
Rev.: $95,418,428
Assets: $141,334,661
Liabilities: $31,688,467
Net Worth: $109,646,194
Earnings: $12,399,342
Emp.: 335
Fiscal Year-end: 12/31/23
Wood Products Mfr
N.A.I.C.S.: 321999
Harnsiri Sangwongkit (Sr VP)

Subsidiaries:

SKN Kraft and Paper Co., Ltd. (1)
99/9 M 7, Huay Yang Sub-district Kleang District, Rayong, 21110, Thailand
Tel.: (66) 38928188
Recycled Pulp & Paper Mfr
N.A.I.C.S.: 325991

S.L. HORSFORD & COMPANY LIMITED
Marshall House Independence Square West, PO Box 45, Basseterre, Saint Kitts & Nevis
Tel.: (869) 4652616 KN
Web Site: http://www.horsfords.com
Year Founded: 1875
SLH—(ECA)
Rev.: $60,277,413
Assets: $70,799,095
Liabilities: $10,952,692
Net Worth: $59,846,403
Earnings: $4,184,694
Fiscal Year-end: 09/30/23
Diversified Wholesale Trading Services
N.A.I.C.S.: 425120
W. Anthony Kelsick (Chm & Mng Dir)

Subsidiaries:

Marshall Plantations Limited (1)
Marshall House, Independence Square West, Basseterre, Saint Kitts & Nevis
Tel.: (869) 465 2616
Web Site: http://www.horsfords.com
Investments; Masonry Products
N.A.I.C.S.: 523999

Ocean Cold Storage (St. Kitts) Ltd. (1)
C A Paul Southwell Industrial Park, Basseterre, Saint Kitts & Nevis
Tel.: (869) 465 5024
Web Site: http://www.horsfords.com
Emp.: 26
Meats, Chicken & Dry Goods Whslr
N.A.I.C.S.: 424470

S.L. Horsford Finance Company Limited (1)
Marshall House 1 Independence Square West, Basseterre, Saint Kitts & Nevis
Tel.: (869) 465 6507
Web Site: http://www.horsfords.com
Car Rental
N.A.I.C.S.: 532111

S.M. ENTERTAINMENT CO., LTD.
83-21 Wangsimni-ro, Seongdong-gu, Seoul, Korea (South)
Tel.: (82) 262409800
Web Site: https://www.smentertainment.com
041510—(KRS)
Rev.: $652,540,060
Assets: $1,122,139,019
Liabilities: $442,475,730
Net Worth: $679,663,288
Earnings: $62,915,899
Emp.: 581
Fiscal Year-end: 12/31/22
Audio Publishing Services
N.A.I.C.S.: 516210

Subsidiaries:

SM Culture & Contents Co., Ltd. (1)
648 Samseong-ro, Gangnam-gu, Seoul, Korea (South)
Tel.: (82) 237880000
Web Site: https://www.smcultureandcontents.com
Rev.: $121,119,461
Assets: $255,672,167
Liabilities: $173,933,728
Net Worth: $81,738,440
Earnings: $4,086,667
Emp.: 449
Fiscal Year-end: 12/31/2022
Travel Management Services
N.A.I.C.S.: 561510
Namgung Cheol (CEO)

S.M. GOLD LIMITED
Shop No 1 To 3 2Nd Floor 24 Caret Building Law Garden C G Road, Ahmedabad, 380009, Gujarat, India
Tel.: (91) 9428138019
Web Site: https://www.smgoldltd.com
Year Founded: 2017
542034—(BOM)
Rev.: $6,252,482
Assets: $3,787,691
Liabilities: $1,851,461
Net Worth: $1,936,230
Earnings: $127,805
Emp.: 25
Fiscal Year-end: 03/31/23
Jewellery Mfr & Distr
N.A.I.C.S.: 339910
Pulkitkumar Sureshbhai Shah (Mng Dir)

S.M. JALEEL & CO. LTD.
Otaheite Industrial Estate, Fyzabad, South Oropouche, Trinidad & Tobago
Tel.: (868) 677 7520
Web Site: http://www.chubbysd.com
Year Founded: 1924
Sales Range: $100-124.9 Million
Emp.: 700
Mfr of Soft Drinks
N.A.I.C.S.: 312111

INTERNATIONAL PUBLIC

Anna Mohammed (VP-Mktg)

Subsidiaries:

Jamaica Beverages Ltd. (1)
5 Henderson Avenue Naggo Head Industrial Complex, Saint Catherine, Portmore, Jamaica
Tel.: (876) 704 6003
Sales Range: $25-49.9 Million
Emp.: 100
Non Alcoholic Drink Mfr
N.A.I.C.S.: 312111
Michael Lee (Mgr-Natl Sls)

S.M.J Beverages (Barbados) Inc. (1)
Lodge Hill, Saint Michael, Barbados
Tel.: (246) 424 0361
Non Alcoholic Drink Mfr
N.A.I.C.S.: 312111
Barrow McArthur (Gen Mgr)

S.M.J Beverages (St. Lucia) Ltd (1)
St Judes Highway Vieux Fort Industrial Highway, Vieux Fort, Saint Lucia
Tel.: (758) 454 7777
Sales Range: $25-49.9 Million
Emp.: 100
Non Alcoholic Drink Mfr
N.A.I.C.S.: 312111

SMJ Beverages ASIA (1)
56-A Kiadb Industrial Area Opp Ttk, Philgumbe Village Hoskote, Bengaluru, 562114, India
Tel.: (91) 8027971219
Sales Range: $25-49.9 Million
Emp.: 7
Non Alcoholic Drink Mfr
N.A.I.C.S.: 312111

SMJ Beverages SA (PTY) Ltd. (1)
22 Otto Otto Volek Rd, PO Box 1000, New Germany, 3610, Durban, Kwa-Zulu Natal, South Africa
Tel.: (27) 31 705 7860
Non Alcoholic Drink Mfr
N.A.I.C.S.: 312111

S.M.A.I.O SA
2 Place Berthe Morisot Parc Technologique, Saint-Priest, 69800, Lyon, France
Tel.: (33) 469842302
Web Site: https://www.smaio.com
Year Founded: 2010
ALSMA—(EUR)
Medical Device Mfr
N.A.I.C.S.: 339112
Philippe Roussouly (CEO)

S.N. NUCLEARELECTRICA S.A.
65 Polona Street, District 1, 10494, Bucharest, Romania
Tel.: (40) 212038200 RO
Web Site: https://www.nuclearelectrica.ro
Year Founded: 1998
SNN—(BUC)
Rev.: $1,620,605,262
Assets: $2,856,038,229
Liabilities: $307,854,353
Net Worth: $2,548,183,877
Earnings: $540,058,513
Emp.: 2,348
Fiscal Year-end: 12/31/23
Nuclear Electric Power Generation
N.A.I.C.S.: 221113
Valentina Dinu (Mgr-Comm & IR)

Subsidiaries:

Cernavoda NPP (1)
Str Medgidiei no 2 CP 42, Cernavoda, 905200, Constanta, Romania
Tel.: (40) 241239340
Web Site: http://www.cne.ro
Eletric Power Generation Services
N.A.I.C.S.: 221113

FCN Pitesti (1)
Str Campului nr 1 OPMioveni CPNR 1, Arges, 115400, Mioveni, Romania
Tel.: (40) 248207700
Web Site: http://www.nuclearelectrica.ro

AND PRIVATE COMPANIES

Fossil Fuel Power Generation Services
N.A.I.C.S.: 221112

S.N.G.N. ROMGAZ S.A.
P-ta CI Motas Nr 4, 551130, Medias, Romania
Tel.: (40) 374401020
Web Site: https://www.romgaz.ro
Year Founded: 1909
SNG—(BUC)
Rev.: $1,955,187,333
Assets: $3,576,297,213
Liabilities: $1,065,206,229
Net Worth: $2,511,090,984
Earnings: $610,783,649
Emp.: 5,980
Fiscal Year-end: 12/31/23
Natural Gas Extraction
N.A.I.C.S.: 211130
Dumitru Gheorghe Rotar *(Deputy CEO)*

Subsidiaries:

Filiala de Inmagazinare Gaze Naturale DEPOGAZ Ploiesti S.R.L. (1)
184 Ghe Grigore Cantacuzino, Prahova, 100492, Ploiesti, Romania
Tel.: (40) 374403800
Web Site: https://www.depogazploiesti.ro
Natural Gas Distr
N.A.I.C.S.: 221210

S.N.P. SOUTHEAST NETWORK PUBLIC LTD.
Anexartisias & Athenon Nora Court 2nd Flooor Office 203, 3040, Limassol, Cyprus
Tel.: (357) 2581757
Investment Services
N.A.I.C.S.: 523940

S.NORTON & CO. LTD.
Bankfield House Bankfield Mill Regent Road, Liverpool, L20 8RQ, United Kingdom
Tel.: (44) 151 955 3300
Web Site: http://www.s-norton.com
Year Founded: 1960
Sales Range: $550-599.9 Million
Emp.: 122
Recyclable Metals Whslr
N.A.I.C.S.: 423930
Matt Norton *(Dir-Technical)*

S.OLIVER BERND FREIER GMBH & CO. KG
s Oliver Strasse 1, 97228, Wurzburg, Germany
Tel.: (49) 93023090
Web Site: http://www.soliver.com
Year Founded: 1969
Rev.: $824,639,805
Emp.: 1,000
Apparel Distr
N.A.I.C.S.: 315210
Bernd Freier *(CEO)*

S.P. CAPITAL FINANCING LIMITED
The Ruby 5SC 5th Floor South Wing Level 8th JK Sawant Marg, Dadar wes, Mumbai, 400 028, Maharashtra, India
Tel.: (91) 2240372424
Web Site: http://www.spcapital.in
Year Founded: 1983
530289—(BOM)
Rev.: $798,619
Assets: $3,011,659
Liabilities: $41,827
Net Worth: $2,969,832
Earnings: $742,412
Emp.: 6
Fiscal Year-end: 03/31/21
Financial Services
N.A.I.C.S.: 523999
S. P. Jain *(Founder, Chm & Mng Dir)*

S.R. INDUSTRIES LIMITED
E-217 Industrial Area Phase 8B, Mohali, 160071, Punjab, India
Tel.: (91) 1724602888
Web Site: https://www.srfootwears.com
Year Founded: 1989
513515—(BOM)
Rev.: $1,712,829
Assets: $3,140,441
Liabilities: $6,363,622
Net Worth: ($3,223,181)
Earnings: ($313,260)
Emp.: 91
Fiscal Year-end: 03/31/22
Sport Shoe Mfr
N.A.I.C.S.: 316210
Amit Mahajan *(CFO)*

S.S. INFRASTRUCTURE DEVELOPMENT CONSULTANTS LIMITED
No 15 Jabbar Buildings Begumpet, Hyderabad, 500016, India
Tel.: (91) 4027766312
Web Site: https://www.ssidcon.org
Year Founded: 1987
SSINFRA—(NSE)
Emp.: 80
Structural Engineering Consultancy Services
N.A.I.C.S.: 541330
Satyanarayana Sundara *(Chm & Mng Dir)*

S.S. LAZIO SPA
Via di Santa Cornelia 1000, Formello, 00060, Rome, Italy
Tel.: (39) 0697607111
Web Site: https://www.sslazio.it
Year Founded: 1900
SSL—(ITA)
Sales Range: $250-299.9 Million
Emp.: 140
Soccer Team
N.A.I.C.S.: 711211
Claudio Lotito *(Pres)*

S.S. ORGANICS LIMITED
Plot no 43 Sy no 55 to 58 The Park View 1st Fl Beside Sky View Suites, Saketa Nilayam Behind Preston Prime Mall Lumbini Avenue, Hyderabad, 500032, Telangana, India
Tel.: (91) 4023353690
Web Site: https://oxygentapharma.com
Year Founded: 1990
Rev.: $2,214,255
Assets: $2,639,660
Liabilities: $7,604,302
Net Worth: ($4,964,642)
Earnings: ($704,570)
Emp.: 65
Fiscal Year-end: 03/31/18
Pharmaceuticals Product Mfr
N.A.I.C.S.: 325412
Muralidhar Rambathri *(Dir-Technical)*

S.S.OIL MILLS LIMITED
2-Tipu Block Garden Town, Lahore, Pakistan
Tel.: (92) 35831981
Web Site: https://www.ssgroup.pk
Year Founded: 1990
SSOM—(PSX)
Rev.: $22,415,305
Assets: $9,849,781
Liabilities: $3,327,988
Net Worth: $6,521,793
Earnings: $483,278
Emp.: 123
Fiscal Year-end: 06/30/23
Refined Oil Mfr
N.A.I.C.S.: 311225

S.T. CORPORATION
1-4-10 Shimo-ochiai, Shinjuku-ku, Tokyo, 161-8540, Tokyo, Japan
Tel.: (81) 333676111
Web Site: https://www.st-c.co.jp
4951—(TKS)
Rev.: $293,959,920
Assets: $295,863,600
Liabilities: $72,445,600
Net Worth: $223,418,000
Earnings: $8,421,140
Emp.: 827
Fiscal Year-end: 03/31/24
Repellent & Sanitary Products Mfr & Sales
N.A.I.C.S.: 424130
Takashi Suzuki *(Chm, CEO & Exec Officer)*

Subsidiaries:

Family Glove (Taiwan) Co., Ltd. (1)
No 33 Ta-liao Tsun Ta-liao Hsiang, Kaohsiung, 83162, Taiwan
Tel.: (886) 77872799
Sales Range: $25-49.9 Million
Emp.: 50
Hand Gloves Mfr & Whslr
N.A.I.C.S.: 315990

Family Glove (Thailand) Co., Ltd. (1)
624/1-4 MOO 11 Sukhapiban 8 Rd, Nongkham, Si Racha, 20230, Chon Buri, Thailand
Tel.: (66) 38480042
Web Site: http://www.fg.co.th
Sales Range: $25-49.9 Million
Emp.: 150
Hand Gloves Mfr & Whslr
N.A.I.C.S.: 315990

Family Glove (Vietnam) Co., Ltd. (1)
Tan Thuan Rd Tan Thuan EPZ Dist 7, Ho Chi Minh City, Vietnam
Tel.: (84) 837700347
Web Site: http://www.familyglove.com
Sales Range: $100-124.9 Million
Emp.: 500
Glove Mfr
N.A.I.C.S.: 315990

S.T. Business Support Co., Ltd. (1)
1-4-10 Shimoai, Shinjuku-ku, Tokyo, 161-8540, Japan
Tel.: (81) 333676501
Web Site: https://www.st-c.co.jp
Sales Range: $25-49.9 Million
Emp.: 22
Temporary Staffing & Contract Services
N.A.I.C.S.: 561320

Shaldan (Philippines) Inc. (1)
Pamutongan Jubay Liloan, Cebu, 6002, Philippines
Tel.: (63) 324246358
Web Site: http://www.shaldan.com.ph
Sales Range: $25-49.9 Million
Emp.: 35
Airfreshners Mfr
N.A.I.C.S.: 333413
Darwin Dabia *(Mgr)*

S.V.A. JEAN ROZE
Rue Victor Baltard, BP 90237, 35500, Vitre, France
Tel.: (33) 2 99 74 65 94
Web Site: http://www.sva-jeanroze.com
Year Founded: 1955
Sales Range: $1-4.9 Billion
Emp.: 3,650
Meat Processing
N.A.I.C.S.: 311612
Dominique Langlois *(Dir-Publ)*

Subsidiaries:

Cornille (1)
Lieu Dit Les Guichardieres, Cornille, 35500, Angers, France
Tel.: (33) 299496420
Web Site: http://www.sas-cornille.com
Rev.: $20,700,000
Emp.: 32
Meat Processing Plants
N.A.I.C.S.: 311613

Societe Armoricaine de Valorisation Energetique (1)
ZA Bois de Cornille Route Dep 104, Cornille, 35500, Dordogne, France
Tel.: (33) 299496375
Web Site: http://www.save-valorisation.fr
Waste Water Treatment Services
N.A.I.C.S.: 221320

S.W.I.F.T. SCRL
Avenue Adele 1, B-1310, La Hulpe, Belgium
Tel.: (32) 26553111   BE
Web Site: http://www.swift.com
Year Founded: 1973
Rev.: $981,654,718
Assets: $1,125,878,128
Liabilities: $629,836,141
Net Worth: $496,041,987
Earnings: $44,604,024
Emp.: 3,145
Fiscal Year-end: 12/31/19
Financial Communications Processing Services
N.A.I.C.S.: 518210
Yawar Shah *(Chm)*

Subsidiaries:

S.W.I.F.T. Germany GmbH (1)
Floor 13 Kastor Tower Platz der Einheit 1, 60327, Frankfurt, Germany (100%)
Tel.: (49) 6975412200
Financial Communications Processing Services
N.A.I.C.S.: 518210

S.W.I.F.T. Nordic AB (1)
Oxtorgsgatan 4 7th Floor, PO Box 7638, 103 94, Stockholm, Sweden (100%)
Tel.: (46) 850895300
Financial Communications Processing Services
N.A.I.C.S.: 518210
Eric Ahman *(Gen Mgr)*

S.W.I.F.T. Pan-Americas, Inc. (1)
7 Times Sq 45th Fl, New York, NY 10036-6524 (100%)
Tel.: (212) 455-1800
Web Site: http://www.swift.com
Sales Range: $75-99.9 Million
Financial Communications Processing Services
N.A.I.C.S.: 518210

S.W.I.F.T. Securenet Ltd. (1)
6th floor Tha Corn Exchange, 55 Mark Lane, EC3R7NE, London, United Kingdom
Tel.: (44) 2077622000
Sales Range: $25-49.9 Million
Emp.: 120
Financial Communications Processing Services
N.A.I.C.S.: 518210

S.W.I.F.T. Services Australia Pty. Ltd. (1)
Suite 1 Level 23 259 George Street, Sydney, 2000, NSW, Australia (100%)
Tel.: (61) 292258100
Web Site: http://www.swift.com
Sales Range: $50-74.9 Million
Financial Communications Processing Services
N.A.I.C.S.: 518210

S.W.I.F.T. Terminal Services (Pte) Ltd. (1)
8 Marina View Asia Square Tower 1 28-04, Singapore, 018960, Singapore (100%)
Tel.: (65) 6347 8000
Web Site: http://www.swift.com
Financial Communications Processing Services
N.A.I.C.S.: 518210

SWIFT Japan Ltd. (1)
20th Floor Nippon Life Marunouchi Building 1-6-6 Marunouchi, Chiyoda-ku, Tokyo, 100-0005, Japan
Tel.: (81) 3 5223 7400
Banking Services
N.A.I.C.S.: 522110

S2 RESOURCES LTD.

S2 RESOURCES LTD.

S2 Resources Ltd.—(Continued)
Level 14 333 Collins Street, Perth, 3000, VIC, Australia
Tel.: (61) 861660240 AU
Web Site: https://www.s2resources.com.au
S2R—(ASX)
Rev.: $313,192
Assets: $6,001,004
Liabilities: $599,665
Net Worth: $5,401,339
Earnings: ($5,155,017)
Fiscal Year-end: 06/30/24
Mineral Exploration Services
N.A.I.C.S.: 213115
Mark Bennett (Exec Chm & Chm)

S2MEDICAL AB
Sunnorpsgatan 5, 582 73, Linkoping, Sweden
Tel.: (46) 87000050
Web Site: https://www.s2m.se
Year Founded: 2013
S2M—(OMX)
Rev.: $188,098
Assets: $2,321,989
Liabilities: $1,673,055
Net Worth: $648,934
Earnings: ($671,976)
Fiscal Year-end: 12/31/22
Medical Equipment Mfr & Distr
N.A.I.C.S.: 339112
Marten Skog (COO)

S4 CAPITAL PLC
12 St Jamess Place, London, SW1A 1NX, United Kingdom
Tel.: (44) 2037930003 UK
Web Site: https://www.s4capital.com
Year Founded: 2016
SFOR—(LSE)
Rev.: $1,288,200,705
Assets: $2,341,957,530
Liabilities: $1,318,602,285
Net Worth: $1,023,355,245
Earnings: ($192,274,335)
Fiscal Year-end: 12/31/22
Media Representatives
N.A.I.C.S.: 541840
Martin Sorrell (Chm)

Subsidiaries:

Made.for.Digital B.V. (1)
Amsteldijk 216, 1079 LK, Amsterdam, Netherlands
Tel.: (31) 208202425
Film Production Services
N.A.I.C.S.: 512110
Jelle Kolleman (Mng Partner-Creative)

MediaMonks B.V. (1)
Oude Amersfoortseweg 125, 1212 AA, Hilversum, Netherlands
Tel.: (31) 356212150
Marketing & Advertising Services
N.A.I.C.S.: 541810
Petra Van Veldhooven (Bus Dir)

Subsidiary (US):

Zemoga, Inc. (2)
120 Old Ridgefield Rd, Wilton, CT 06897
Tel.: (203) 663-6214
Web Site: http://www.zemoga.com
Rev.: $4,900,000
Emp.: 70
Data Processing Hosting Related Services
N.A.I.C.S.: 518210
D. J. Edgerton (Co-Founder & CEO)

MediaMonks Buenos Aires SRL (1)
Concepcion Arenal 2931, Colegiales Ciudad Autonoma de, C1426DGG, Buenos Aires, Argentina
Tel.: (54) 1153682189
Marketing & Advertising Services
N.A.I.C.S.: 541810

MediaMonks FZ-LLC (1)
Dubai Media City Building 9 Office 318, PO Box 502921, Dubai, United Arab Emirates
Tel.: (971) 45149510

Marketing & Advertising Services
N.A.I.C.S.: 541810

MediaMonks Information Technology (Shanghai) Co. Ltd. (1)
No 5 Lane 18 Yanqing Road, Xuhui District, Shanghai, China
Tel.: (86) 15601945025
Marketing & Advertising Services
N.A.I.C.S.: 541810

MediaMonks London Ltd. (1)
42 St John St Clerkenwell, London, EC1M 4DL, United Kingdom
Tel.: (44) 2074403580
Marketing & Advertising Services
N.A.I.C.S.: 541810

MediaMonks Mexico City S. de R.L. de C.V.
Amsterdam 271 Hipodromo, 06100, Cuauhtemoc, Mexico
Tel.: (52) 15575839511
Marketing & Advertising Services
N.A.I.C.S.: 541810

MediaMonks Sao Paolo Serv. De Internet Para Publicidade Ltda. (1)
R Fidalga 162 Vila Madalena, 05432-000, Sao Paulo, Brazil
Tel.: (55) 1130970508
Marketing & Advertising Services
N.A.I.C.S.: 541810

MediaMonks Singapore Pte. Ltd. (1)
69 Neil Road, Singapore, 088899, Singapore
Tel.: (65) 31292969
Marketing & Advertising Services
N.A.I.C.S.: 541810
Jason Choi (Sr Project Mgr)

MediaMonks Stockholm AB (1)
Norrlandsgatan 18, 111 43, Stockholm, Sweden
Tel.: (46) 850703500
Marketing & Advertising Services
N.A.I.C.S.: 541810

MightyHive Inc. (1)
394 Pacific Ave Fl B100, San Francisco, CA 94111
Web Site: https://www.mightyhive.com
Media Marketing Services
N.A.I.C.S.: 541810
Christopher S. Martin (Founder)

Superhero Cheesecake B.V. (1)
Oostelijke Handelskade 637, 1019 BW, Amsterdam, Netherlands
Tel.: (31) 207630020
Web Site: https://www.superherocheesecake.com
Digital Studio Services
N.A.I.C.S.: 541810
Lot Van de Weerdt (Office Mgr)

S4E S.A.
ul Inflancka 4B, 00-189, Warsaw, Poland
Tel.: (48) 122964545
Web Site: https://www.s4e.pl
Year Founded: 2000
Information Technology Services
N.A.I.C.S.: 541511
Pawel Pietka (Chm)

S5 NORTH EUROPE BV
Dockworks IV Waalhaven O Z 77, 3087 BM, Rotterdam, Netherlands
Tel.: (31) 10 506 20 00
Web Site: http://www.s5eurasia.com
Emp.: 96
Port Agency Services
N.A.I.C.S.: 488510

Subsidiaries:

S5 Asia Limited (1)
Unit 1811-1812 18F Tower Two Ever Gain Plaza 88 Container Port Road, Kwai Chung, New Territories, China (Hong Kong)
Tel.: (852) 24183398
Web Site: http://www.s5eurasia.com
Emp.: 58
Shipping Agents
N.A.I.C.S.: 488510
Raymond Cheng (Country Mgr)

SA AGRILOIRE
10 Boulevard De La Republique, 49380, Angers, France
Tel.: (33) 241540751
Sales Range: $25-49.9 Million
Emp.: 60
Hardware Stores
N.A.I.C.S.: 444140
Jean Mignot (Gen Mgr)

SA BOUTES
9 Rue Ernest Cognacq, 11100, Narbonne, Aude, France
Tel.: (33) 468323637
Web Site: http://www.boutes.com
Rev.: $20,500,000
Emp.: 42
Wood Barrel Producer
N.A.I.C.S.: 321920
Eric Barthe (Co-Pres)

SA CHAUMONTAISE DES AUTOMOBILES MAUBREY
Route De Neuilly, 52000, Chaumont, Haute Marne, France
Tel.: (33) 899 235037
Rev.: $27,800,000
Emp.: 48
New & Used Car Dealers
N.A.I.C.S.: 441110
Christophe Maubrey (Dir)

SA CORPORATE REAL ESTATE LIMITED
GreenPark Corner 16th Floor Corner Lower Road and West Road South, Morningside, Johannesburg, 2196, South Africa
Tel.: (27) 100202530
Web Site: https://www.sacorporatefund.co.za
SAC—(JSE)
Rev.: $135,085,743
Assets: $1,085,563,379
Liabilities: $484,602,725
Net Worth: $600,960,654
Earnings: $65,840,016
Emp.: 499
Fiscal Year-end: 12/31/23
Real Estate Investment Services
N.A.I.C.S.: 531190
Terence Rory Mackey (CEO)

SA DESIGNER PARFUMS LTD.
Amertrans Park Bushey Mill Lane, Watford, WD24 7JG, United Kingdom
Tel.: (44) 1923 208111
Web Site: http://www.designerparfums.com
Year Founded: 2002
Emp.: 100
Perfume Mfr
N.A.I.C.S.: 456120

Subsidiaries:

Fekkai Brands, LLC (1)
712 5th Ave Henri Bendel 4 Fl, New York, NY 10019
Tel.: (212) 753-9500
Web Site: http://www.fekkai.com
Beauty Salons Owner & Operator
N.A.I.C.S.: 812112
Frederic Fekkai (Founder)

Subsidiary (Domestic):

Frederic Fekkai (Mark NY), LLC (2)
25 E 77th St, New York, NY 10075
Tel.: (212) 396-4600
Web Site: http://www.fekkai.com
Beauty Salons
N.A.I.C.S.: 812112
Tammy Sherman (Creative Dir)

Frederic Fekkai Dallas, LLC (2)
30-B Highland Park Vlg, Dallas, TX 75205
Tel.: (214) 219-3600
Web Site: http://www.fekkai.com
Emp.: 17
Beauty Salons

INTERNATIONAL PUBLIC

N.A.I.C.S.: 812112
Jamie Moreland (Gen Mgr)

Frederic Fekkai Greenwich, LLC (2)
2 Lewis Ct, Greenwich, CT 06830
Tel.: (203) 861-6700
Web Site: http://www.fekkai.com
Beauty Salons
N.A.I.C.S.: 812112
Alexandre Chouery (Creative Dir)

Frederic Fekkai New York, LLC (2)
712 5th Ave 4th Fl, New York, NY 10019
Tel.: (212) 753-9500
Web Site: http://www.fekkai.com
Beauty & Hairstyling Salons
N.A.I.C.S.: 812112
Stephane Andre (Creative Dir)

SA DUFRA
Avenue De La 2e Db, 61200, Argenteuil, Orne, France
Tel.: (33) 233358066
Rev.: $26,900,000
Emp.: 35
Miscellaneous General Merchandise Stores,
N.A.I.C.S.: 444180
Sylvain Montfort (Dir)

SA EQUUS
2 T Chemin De La Dime, 95700, Roissy-en-France, Val D Oise, France
Tel.: (33) 134385050
Rev.: $27,700,000
Emp.: 15
Meats & Meat Products
N.A.I.C.S.: 424470
Claude Bouvry (Gen Mgr)

SA GARAGE NELLO CHELI
5 Rue Du Clos Mutaut, 21300, Chenove, Cote D Or, France
Tel.: (33) 380525007
Rev.: $29,700,000
Emp.: 48
New & Used Car Dealers
N.A.I.C.S.: 441110
Josiane July (Dir-Pur)

SA GUIET
49 Avenue Georges Pompidou, Aurillac, 1500, Cantal, France
Tel.: (33) 471630510
Rev.: $24,200,000
Emp.: 45
Automobile Dealership
N.A.I.C.S.: 441110
Michel Besse (Mgr-Fin)

SA H L M PIERRES ET LUMIERES
29 Avenue Henri Barbusse, 92700, Colombes, Hauts de Seine, France
Tel.: (33) 146687650
Web Site: http://www.pierres-et-lumieres.com
Rev.: $28,200,000
Emp.: 103
Apartment Building Operator
N.A.I.C.S.: 531110
Serge Bantos (Gen Mgr)

SA HLM LE NOUVEAU LOGIS CENTRE- LIMOUSIN
12 Rue Du Docteur Herpin, 37000, Tours, Indre Et Loire, France
Tel.: (33) 247608787
Rev.: $28,200,000
Emp.: 64
Apartment Building Operator
N.A.I.C.S.: 531110
Michele Dejonghe (DP Mgr)

SA HYDRAULIQUE PB
Le Void d' Escles, 88260, Escles, France
Tel.: (33) 329075496

AND PRIVATE COMPANIES — SAAB AB

Web Site: https://www.hydraulique-pb.fr
Year Founded: 1976
MLHYD—(EUR)
Sales Range: $10-24.9 Million
Hydraulic Cylinder Mfr
N.A.I.C.S.: 333995

SA ITAM DISTRIBUTION
ZAC du Roubian Lieu-dit Roubian, 13150, Tarascon, France
Tel.: (33) 490914133
Rev.: $22,400,000
Emp.: 36
Grocery Stores
N.A.I.C.S.: 445110
Georges Colom *(Mgr)*

SA LES HOTELS DE PARIS
256 Rue Saint-Honore, 75001, Paris, France
Tel.: (33) 155737575
Web Site: http://www.leshotelsdeparis.biz
Year Founded: 1994
HDP—(EUR)
Sales Range: $10-24.9 Million
Casino Hotel Operator
N.A.I.C.S.: 721120

SA SA INTERNATIONAL HOLDINGS LIMITED
8/F Block B MP Industrial Centre 18 Ka Yip Street, Chai Wan, China (Hong Kong)
Tel.: (852) 2 889 2331   Ky
Web Site: http://corp.sasa.com
Year Founded: 1978
0178—(HKG)
Rev.: $440,173,528
Assets: $269,158,431
Liabilities: $142,382,957
Net Worth: $126,775,474
Earnings: $(44,334,553)
Emp.: 3,100
Fiscal Year-end: 03/31/22
Perfume & Cosmetics Retailer
N.A.I.C.S.: 456120
Simon Siu Ming Kwok *(Co-Founder, Chm & CEO)*

Subsidiaries:

Natio Pty Ltd (1)
110 Dougharty Rd, Heidelberg, 3081, VIC, Australia
Tel.: (61) 394159911
Web Site: http://www.natio.com.au
Cosmetics Product Mfr & Distr
N.A.I.C.S.: 325620

SA TRANSPORTS AUTOMOBILES DE SOLOGNE
Route De Dhuizon, 41250, Paris, France
Tel.: (33) 254464959
Sales Range: $25-49.9 Million
Emp.: 173
Trucking Except Local
N.A.I.C.S.: 484121
Andree Warsemann *(Gen Mgr)*

SA ZUB
22 Rue De Reims, Couloisy, 60350, Compiegne, France
Tel.: (33) 344857086
Web Site: http://www.zub.fr
Rev.: $28,000,000
Emp.: 140
Nonresidential Construction
N.A.I.C.S.: 236220
Patrick Neuillet *(Dir)*

SAAB AB
Olof Palmes gata 17, 111 22, Stockholm, Sweden
Tel.: (46) 13180000   SE
Web Site: https://www.saabgroup.com
Year Founded: 1937
SAAB.B—(OMX)
Rev.: $4,325,416,480
Assets: $7,394,141,440
Liabilities: $4,773,572,160
Net Worth: $2,620,569,280
Earnings: $130,991,840
Emp.: 18,037
Fiscal Year-end: 12/31/20
Producer of Aircraft, Missiles, Space Equipment, Electronics, Industrial Automation Equipment & Military Training Equipment
N.A.I.C.S.: 336992
Marcus Wallenberg *(Chm)*

Subsidiaries:

Alpha Thames Subsea Ltd. (1)
Fyfield Business & Research Park Fyfield Road, Ongar, CM5 0GN, Essex, United Kingdom   **(100%)**
Tel.: (44) 1277 365890
Web Site: http://www.alpha-thames.co.uk
Sales Range: $25-49.9 Million
Emp.: 10
Subsea Hydrocarbon Recovery Services
N.A.I.C.S.: 562910

Celsius Invest AB (1)
Svista, Eskilstuna, 635 02, Sweden
Tel.: (46) 16169000
Investment Management Service
N.A.I.C.S.: 523999

Combitech AB (1)
Universitetsvagen 14, PO Box 15042, SE-580 15, Linkoping, Sweden
Tel.: (46) 102169000
Web Site: https://www.combitech.se
Rev.: $135,538,950
Emp.: 120
Information Technology Consulting Services
N.A.I.C.S.: 541512
Fredrik Tengel *(Mgr-Sls-East)*

Combitech OY (1)
Metsanneidonkuja 8, Espoo, FI-02130, Finland
Tel.: (358) 2079 60600
Web Site: http://www.combitech.fi
Sales Range: $50-74.9 Million
Emp.: 70
Defense & Security Systems Distr
N.A.I.C.S.: 423610

EMC Services Elmiljoteknik AB (1)
Sallarangsgatan 3, 431 37, Molndal, Sweden
Tel.: (46) 313375900
Web Site: https://www.emcservices.se
Problem Solving & Testing Services
N.A.I.C.S.: 541511

FFV Ordnance AB (1)
Bruksen 4, 691 50, Karlskoga, Sweden
Tel.: (46) 58682992
Industrial Machinery Distr
N.A.I.C.S.: 423830
Bo Thorn *(Mng Dir)*

Fastighets AB (1)
Tel.: (46) 705475045
Real Estate Lending Services
N.A.I.C.S.: 531190

Goteborg Electronic Defence Systems (1)
Solhusgatan 10 Kallebacks Teknikpark, Gothenburg, SE 412 89, Sweden
Tel.: (46) 3 17 94 90 00
Web Site: http://www.saabgroup.com
Aircraft Equipment Distr
N.A.I.C.S.: 423860

Linkoping City Airport AB (1)
Akerbogatan 20, 582 54, Linkoping, Sweden
Tel.: (46) 1 326 2800
Web Site: https://www.linkopingcityairport.se
Sales Range: $25-49.9 Million
Oil Transportation Services
N.A.I.C.S.: 481219
Charlotta Bjorklund *(Deputy Mgr-Station)*

Muskovarvet AB (1)
Musko naval port, Musko, 148 95, Stockholm, Sweden
Tel.: (46) 768305400
Web Site: https://www.muskovarvet.se
Marine & Ship Maintenance Services
N.A.I.C.S.: 488390
Krister Andersson *(CEO)*

N. Sundin Dockstavarvet AB (1)
Varvsvagen 1, Docksta, SE-870 33, Kramfors, Sweden
Tel.: (46) 613711600
Web Site: https://www.dockstavarvet.se
Aluminum Boats Mfr
N.A.I.C.S.: 336612

Saab (1)
PO Box 70363, Stockholm, 10724, Sweden   **(100%)**
Tel.: (46) 84630000
Web Site: http://www.saab.group.com
Sales Range: $350-399.9 Million
Emp.: 2,000
N.A.I.C.S.: 562910
Hakam Buskhe *(Mng Dir)*

Saab Aircraft Leasing Holdings AB (1)
Broderna Ugglas Gata, 581 88, Linkoping, Sweden
Tel.: (46) 13187411
Web Site: http://www.saabaircraftleasing.com
Investment Management Service
N.A.I.C.S.: 523999

Saab Asia Pacific Co. Ltd. (1)
Two Pacific Place Building, Khlong Toei, Bangkok, 10110, Thailand
Tel.: (66) 265326502
Aircraft Mfr
N.A.I.C.S.: 336411

Saab Australia Pty. Ltd. (1)
C1/192 Burwood Road, Hawthorn, 3122, VIC, Australia
Tel.: (61) 396973700
Emp.: 800
Aerospace Fastening Product Distr
N.A.I.C.S.: 423860

Saab Barracuda AB (1)
Hammarsvagen 1, SE-594 32, Gamleby, Sweden
Tel.: (46) 49314800
Sales Range: $25-49.9 Million
Emp.: 10
Plastics Product Mfr
N.A.I.C.S.: 326199
Anders Wiman *(Mgr-Mktg)*

Saab Canada, Inc. (1)
340 Albert St Suite 1320, Ottawa, K1R 7Y6, ON, Canada
Tel.: (613) 238-8784
Aerospace Fastening Product Distr
N.A.I.C.S.: 423860

Saab Czech s.r.o (1)
Sokolovska 79 cp 192, 18600, Prague, Czech Republic
Tel.: (420) 234703811
Security System Software Development Services
N.A.I.C.S.: 541511

Saab Danmark A/S (1)
Porten 6, DK-6400, Sonderborg, Denmark
Tel.: (45) 36383000
Sales Range: $25-49.9 Million
Information Technology Consulting Services
N.A.I.C.S.: 541512

Saab Dynamics AB (1)
Broderna Ugglas gata, SE 581 88, Linkoping, Sweden   **(100%)**
Tel.: (46) 13180000
Rev.: $636,959,000
Emp.: 1,475
Defense Systems, Training Equipment, Space Products, Level-Gauging, Products for Industrial Applications, Automotive Electronics
N.A.I.C.S.: 334511

Subsidiary (Domestic):

AB Werba (2)
PO Box 280, 15123, Sodertalje, Sweden   **(100%)**
Tel.: (46) 855039970
Web Site: http://www.werba.se
Sales Range: $10-24.9 Million
Emp.: 35
Electrical Power, Software Development & System Architecture for Transport & Defence Industries
N.A.I.C.S.: 513210

Saab Bofors Dynamics AB (2)
Svista industriomrade, 63187, Eskilstuna, Sweden   **(100%)**
Tel.: (46) 16169000
Sales Range: $10-24.9 Million
Emp.: 50
Aerodynamics & Defence Systems
N.A.I.C.S.: 334511

Subsidiary (Domestic):

Bofors Missiles AB (3)
Chalmer Technikpark, SE-691 80, Karlskoga, Sweden   **(100%)**
Tel.: (46) 58681000
Web Site: http://www.saab.se
Sales Range: Less than $1 Million
N.A.I.C.S.: 562910

Subsidiary (Domestic):

Saab Training Systems AB (2)
Stensholmsvagen 20, Huskvarna, 561 39, Sweden   **(100%)**
Tel.: (46) 36388000
Web Site: http://www.saabgroup.com
Sales Range: $25-49.9 Million
Emp.: 400
Laser Simulators, CGI-Simulators, Artillery Simulators & Target Equipment
N.A.I.C.S.: 336413

Affiliate (Non-US):

TAURUS Systems GmbH (2)
PO Box 1340, D-86523, Schrobenhausen, Germany
Tel.: (49) 8252996766
Web Site: http://www.taurus-systems.de
Weapon Systems Design & Mfr
N.A.I.C.S.: 336419
Helmut Hederer *(Mng Dir)*

Saab Electronic Defence Systems (1)
Nettovagen 6, 175 88, Jarfalla, Sweden   **(100%)**
Tel.: (46) 858084000
Web Site: http://www.saabgroup.com
Sales Range: $350-399.9 Million
Emp.: 1,500
Electronic Defense Systems
N.A.I.C.S.: 334419

Saab Grintek Defence (Pty.) Ltd. (1)
185 Witch-Hazel Avenue Highveld Technopark, Centurion, 0157, South Africa
Tel.: (27) 124924400
Aerospace Fastening Product Distr
N.A.I.C.S.: 423860

Saab India Technologies Private Limited (1)
7th Floor DLF Centre Sansad Marg, New Delhi, 110001, India
Tel.: (91) 1146102222
Aircraft Mfr
N.A.I.C.S.: 336411
Harjeet Singh Saini *(Dir-Mktg)*

Saab International Canada Ltd (1)
340 Albert St Suite 1320, Ottawa, K1P 7Y6, ON, Canada   **(100%)**
Tel.: (613) 238-8784
Web Site: http://www.saab.com
Sales Range: $25-49.9 Million
Marketing Division for Head Office Located In Sweden
N.A.I.C.S.: 562910

Saab International Deutschland GmbH (1)
Hohchtreuzallee 1, Bonn, 53175, Germany   **(100%)**
Tel.: (49) 228367560
Sales Range: $25-49.9 Million
Emp.: 1
Aerodynamics & Defence Systems
N.A.I.C.S.: 334511

Saab International Finland Oy (1)
Sinikalliontie 3C, PO Box 96, FIN 02631, Espoo, Finland   **(100%)**
Tel.: (358) 94391210

SAAB AB

Saab AB—(Continued)
Sales Range: $25-49.9 Million
Emp.: 2
Aerodynamics & Defence Systems
N.A.I.C.S.: 334511

Saab Nordic Defence Industries A/S (1)
Stenholm 11, DK-9400, Norresundby, Denmark
Tel.: (45) 98171818
Aerospace Fastening Product Distr
N.A.I.C.S.: 423860

Saab North America, Inc. (1)
99 M St SE Ste 1050, Washington, DC 20003
Tel.: (703) 406-7900
Web Site: http://www2.saabgroup.com
Sales Range: $25-49.9 Million
Emp.: 100
Aircraft Mfr
N.A.I.C.S.: 336411
Wes Walters *(Exec VP-Bus Dev-Land Domain)*

Subsidiary (Domestic):

Saab Aerotech of America LLC (2)
21300 Ridgetop Cir, Sterling, VA 20166-6520 **(100%)**
Tel.: (703) 406-7200
Web Site: http://www2.saabgroup.com
Sales Range: $25-49.9 Million
Emp.: 40
Military & Commercial Aircraft
N.A.I.C.S.: 423860
John Belanger *(Sr VP-Comm-North America)*

Saab Barracuda LLC (2)
608 E McNeill St, Lillington, NC 27546
Tel.: (910) 893-2094
Web Site: http://www.saabgroup.com
Sales Range: $25-49.9 Million
Camouflage Mfr
N.A.I.C.S.: 314999

Saab PerformIT AB (1)
Bryggaregatan 11, 653 40, Karlstad, Sweden
Tel.: (46) 10 216 6403
Web Site: http://www.saabperformit.com
Emergency Software Development Services
N.A.I.C.S.: 541511
Ingeborg Palmgren *(Office Mgr)*

Saab South Africa (Pty) Ltd (1)
44 Oak Avenue Highveld Technopark, PO Box 8792, Centurion, 157, South Africa
Tel.: (27) 126728300
Sales Range: $50-74.9 Million
Emp.: 24
Telecommunication Servicesb
N.A.I.C.S.: 517810
Adel Demian *(Gen Mgr)*

Subsidiary (Domestic):

Saab Grintek Technologies (Pty) Ltd (2)
50 Oak Avenue Highveld Technopark, PO Box 11212, Centurion, 11212, South Africa
Tel.: (27) 126728000
Sales Range: $100-124.9 Million
Emp.: 30
Telecommunication Servicesb
N.A.I.C.S.: 517810
Vincent Scholtz *(Pres)*

Saab Support & Services (1)
Broderna Ugglas gata, 581 88, Linkoping, Sweden **(100%)**
Tel.: (46) 13180000
Web Site: http://www.saab.com
Sales Range: $400-449.9 Million
Commercial Aircraft Mfr
N.A.I.C.S.: 336411

Subsidiary (Domestic):

Saab AB (2)
Nobymalmsvagen 1, SE 571 82, Linkoping, Sweden **(100%)**
Tel.: (46) 13 23 10 00
Web Site: http://www.saabgroup.com
Sales Range: $300-349.9 Million
Emp.: 1,200
Aerotech Communications & Support Services

N.A.I.C.S.: 517810

Subsidiary (Domestic):

AerotechTelub Test Systems AB (3)
Dalvagen 2, PO Box 1381, S 100 74, Stockholm, Sweden **(100%)**
Tel.: (46) 87755400
Web Site: http://www.saab-systems.com
Sales Range: $50-74.9 Million
Emp.: 140
Provider of Computerized Test Systems for Large-Scale Electronics Manufacturing & Military
N.A.I.C.S.: 334514

Subsidiary (Domestic):

Saab AVtronics AB (2)
Nettovagen 6 Jakobsberg, 17588, Jarfalla, Sweden **(100%)**
Tel.: (46) 858084000
Web Site: http://www.saabgroup.com
Sales Range: $350-399.9 Million
Emp.: 1,700
Electronic Systems
N.A.I.C.S.: 335999

Unit (Domestic):

Saab AB - Electronic Defense Systems (3)
Slottsgatan 40, PO Box 1017, SE 55111, Jonkoping, Sweden
Tel.: (46) 36194000
Rev.: $57,458,700
Emp.: 500
Electronic Defense Systems Mfr
N.A.I.C.S.: 334419
Ronny Nykeist *(Mgr)*

Saab Systems Pty. Ltd. (1)
21 3rd Avenue Technology Park, Mawson Lakes, Canberra, 5095, SA, Australia **(100%)**
Tel.: (61) 883433800
Web Site: http://www.saabsystems.com.au
Sales Range: $100-124.9 Million
Emp.: 400
Producer of Aircraft, Missiles, Space Equipment, Electronics, Industrial Automation Equipment & Military Training Equipment
N.A.I.C.S.: 336992

Subsidiary (Domestic):

Saab Technologies Australia Pty Ltd (2)
Unit 2 71 Leichardt Street, Campbell, Kingston, 2604, ACT, Australia
Tel.: (61) 262670200
Web Site: http://www.saabsystem.com.au
Technology & Automation Services
N.A.I.C.S.: 513210

Saab Technologies B.V. (1)
Laan Van Malkenschoten 40, 7333 NP, Apeldoorn, Netherlands
Tel.: (31) 555432500
Aircraft Mfr
N.A.I.C.S.: 336411

Saab Technologies Ltd. (1)
300-3500 Gilmore Way, Burnaby, V5G 0B8, BC, Canada
Tel.: (604) 689-7117
Aircraft Mfr
N.A.I.C.S.: 336411

Saab Technologies Norway AS (1)
Isebakkeveien 49, 1788, Halden, Norway
Tel.: (47) 95709000
Aircraft Mfr
N.A.I.C.S.: 336411

Saab Technologies s.r.o. (1)
Sokolovska 79/192, 186 00, Prague, Czech Republic
Tel.: (420) 234703811
Aircraft Mfr
N.A.I.C.S.: 336411

Saab Training Systems B.V. (1)
Prins Bernhardplein 200, Amsterdam, 1097 JB, Netherlands
Tel.: (31) 205214777
Professional Training Services
N.A.I.C.S.: 611430

Saab TransponderTech AB (1)
Vreten Vagen 12, PO Box 4113, Solna, SE

171, Sweden **(100%)**
Tel.: (46) 13188000
Web Site: http://www.transpondertech.se
Sales Range: $10-24.9 Million
Emp.: 40
N.A.I.C.S.: 562910

Saab Underwater Systems AB (1)
Agneshogsdatan 273, PO Box 910, S 591 29, Motala, Sweden **(100%)**
Tel.: (46) 141224500
Sales Range: $50-74.9 Million
Emp.: 250
Aerodynamics & Defence Systems
N.A.I.C.S.: 334511

SaabTech AB (1)
Hus 209-7, Linkoping, 581 88, Sweden
Tel.: (46) 8 580 840 00
Web Site: http://www.saabgroup.com
Information Technology Consulting Services
N.A.I.C.S.: 541512

Wikers AB (1)
Boforsvagen, S 691 84, Karlskoga, Sweden
Tel.: (46) 58681577
Remediation Services
N.A.I.C.S.: 562910

SAAB OF KW PREMIUM FINE CARS
663 Victoria St N, Kitchener, N2H 5G3, ON, Canada
Tel.: (519) 744-5811
Web Site: http://www.saabofkw.com
Year Founded: 1980
Sales Range: $1-9.9 Million
Emp.: 43
New Car Dealers
N.A.I.C.S.: 441110
Ron Kraishnik *(Co-Owner)*

SAAD GROUP
PO Box 3250, Al Khobar, 31952, Saudi Arabia
Tel.: (966) 38822220
Web Site: http://www.saadgroup.com
Year Founded: 1980
Sales Range: $750-799.9 Million
Emp.: 6,000
Diversified Holding Company
N.A.I.C.S.: 551112
Maan A. Al-Sanea *(Chm & Controller)*

Subsidiaries:

MAAN Al Sanea Furniture (1)
PO Box 3250, Al Khobar, 31952, Saudi Arabia
Tel.: (966) 38822220
Web Site: http://www.maan.net
Sales Range: $25-49.9 Million
Emp.: 50
Furniture & Furnishings Designer & Mfr
N.A.I.C.S.: 337121

Oasis Residential Resorts (1)
Golden Belt Rd, PO Box 3250, Al Khobar, 31952, Saudi Arabia
Tel.: (966) 38871777
Web Site: http://www.oasisresorts.net
Residential Property Manager & Owner
N.A.I.C.S.: 531311

SAAD Agriculture (1)
PO Box 3250, Al Khobar, 31952, Saudi Arabia
Tel.: (966) 38822220
Web Site: http://www.saadtrading.com
Sales Range: $25-49.9 Million
Emp.: 30
Landscaping Services
N.A.I.C.S.: 561730

SAAD Al Sanea Centre For Children With Communication Disorders (1)
PO Box 30535, Al Khobar, 31952, Saudi Arabia
Tel.: (966) 38821188
Diagnosis, Therapy & Educational Services for Children with Communications, Mental & Physical Disorders
N.A.I.C.S.: 621498

SAAD Design and Engineering (1)
PO Box 3250, Al Khobar, 31952, Saudi Arabia

INTERNATIONAL PUBLIC

Tel.: (966) 38822220
Designing & Engineering Services
N.A.I.C.S.: 541310

SAAD Financial Services S.A. (1)
PO Box 76, 1216, Geneva, Switzerland
Tel.: (41) 227150303
Web Site: http://www.saadinvestments.com
Sales Range: $75-99.9 Million
Emp.: 10
Investment & Financial Services
N.A.I.C.S.: 523999

SAAD Information Technology (1)
PO Box 30531, Al Khobar, 31952, Saudi Arabia
Tel.: (966) 3 801 7192
Web Site: http://www.saadit.com
Computer Services
N.A.I.C.S.: 541519

SAAD Investments Company Limited (1)
PO Box 76, Pointirin, 1216, Geneva, Switzerland
Tel.: (41) 227150303
Web Site: http://www.saadinvestments.com
Sales Range: $75-99.9 Million
Emp.: 10
Investment Services
N.A.I.C.S.: 523999

SAAD Medical Centre (1)
PO Box 30353, Al Khobar, 31952, Saudi Arabia
Tel.: (966) 38826666
Web Site: http://www.saad.net.com
Medical Devices
N.A.I.C.S.: 622110
Maan A. Al-Sunea *(Chm)*

SAAD National Schools (1)
PO Box 30531, Al Khobar, 31952, Saudi Arabia
Tel.: (966) 38 584120
Web Site: http://www.saadschools.com
Educational Services for Boys & Girls
N.A.I.C.S.: 923110

SAAD Trading and Contracting Co. (1)
PO Box 3250, Al Khobar, 31952, Saudi Arabia
Tel.: (966) 38822220
Web Site: http://www.saad.com.sa
Carpentry, Masonry, Plumbing & Electrical Contractor
N.A.I.C.S.: 238990

SAAD Transport (1)
PO Box 3250, Al Khobar, 31952, Saudi Arabia
Tel.: (966) 38822220
Web Site: http://www.saadtransport.com
Regional Transportation Services
N.A.I.C.S.: 485999

SAAD Travel & Tourism (1)
PO Box 2288, Al Khobar, 31952, Saudi Arabia
Tel.: (966) 38949977
Web Site: http://www.saadtravel.com
Sales Range: $10-24.9 Million
Emp.: 50
Travel Arrangement Services
N.A.I.C.S.: 561599

SAAG CONSOLIDATED (M) BHD.
No 25M Jalan Maharajalela, 50150, Kuala Lumpur, Selangor Darul Ehsan, Malaysia
Tel.: (60) 3 2145 4490
Sales Range: $10-24.9 Million
Petrochemical & Power Machinery Mfr
N.A.I.C.S.: 333998
Anand Subramanian *(CEO)*

Subsidiaries:

SAAG RR Infra Limited (1)
No 51 R K Mutt Road, Mylapore, Chennai, 600 004, India
Tel.: (44) 24614942
Web Site: http://www.saagrr.co.in
Sales Range: $1-9.9 Million
Emp.: 18
Property Development Services

N.A.I.C.S.: 531390
Raju Sriram *(Mng Dir)*

SAAKSHI MEDTECH & PANELS LIMITED
Plot No EL-23 J Block MIDC Bhosari, Pune, 411026, Maharashtra, India
Tel.: (91) 7709151631
Web Site: https://www.smtpl.co
Year Founded: 2001
SAAKSHI—(NSE)
Electric Equipment Mfr
N.A.I.C.S.: 333414

SAAM DEVELOPMENT PUBLIC COMPANY LIMITED
Major Tower ThongloR Room No 2 2 10th Floor 141, Soi Sukhumvit 63 Ekamai Sukhumvit Road Klongton Nua Wattana, Bangkok, 10110, Thailand
Tel.: (66) 209619367
Web Site: https://www.saam.co.th
Year Founded: 2007
SAAM—(THA)
Rev.: $3,455,028
Assets: $14,749,410
Liabilities: $2,710,684
Net Worth: $12,038,726
Earnings: $1,796,944
Fiscal Year-end: 12/31/23
Asset Management Services
N.A.I.C.S.: 523940
Songsri Nitayasuth *(Chm)*

SAAND INC.
250 Brockport Drive, Etobicoke, M9W 5S1, ON, Canada
Tel.: (416) 798-2345
Web Site: http://saand.ca
Glass Products Mfr
N.A.I.C.S.: 327211

Subsidiaries:

Saand Inc. - Rexdale (1)
355 Attwell Drive, Etobicoke, M9W 5C2, ON, Canada
Tel.: (416) 674-6945
Web Site: http://saand.ca
Glass Mfr
N.A.I.C.S.: 327211

SAARSTAHL AG
Bismarckstrasse 57-59, 66333, Volklingen, Germany
Tel.: (49) 68 98 10 0
Web Site: http://www.saarstahl.de
Year Founded: 1881
Sales Range: $1-4.9 Billion
Emp.: 7,200
Steel Products Mfr
N.A.I.C.S.: 332111
Tim Hartmann *(Chm-Mgmt Bd)*

Subsidiaries:

Acciai della Saar SpA. (1)
Via Aristotele 42, 20128, Milan, Italy
Tel.: (39) 0227001073
Web Site: http://www.acciaidellasaar.it
Steel Products Mfr
N.A.I.C.S.: 332111

Conflandey Industries SAS (1)
Le Technipole 722 231 rue La Fontaine, 94132, Fontenay-sous-Bois, France
Tel.: (33) 141797700
Web Site: http://www.conflandey-industries.com
Sales Range: $75-99.9 Million
Emp.: 300
Steel Pole Mfr
N.A.I.C.S.: 332618
Patrick Claus *(Mng Dir)*

DWK Drahtwerk Koln GmbH (1)
Schanzenstr 40, PO Box 80 50 03, 51063, Cologne, Germany
Tel.: (49) 22196720
Web Site: http://www.en.dwk-koeln.de
Emp.: 250

Steel Products Mfr
N.A.I.C.S.: 332111
Alex Wower *(Chm)*

Drahtwerk Luisenthal GmbH (1)
Strasse des 13 Januar 286, Luisenthal, 66333, Volklingen, Germany
Tel.: (49) 68988790
Steel Products Mfr
N.A.I.C.S.: 332111

Drahtwerk St. Ingbert GmbH (1)
Alleestrasse 11, 66386, Saint Ingbert, Germany
Tel.: (49) 68941040
Web Site: http://www.draht-dwi.de
Silo Mfr
N.A.I.C.S.: 331222
Peter Holz *(Mng Dir)*

Eurofil Polska Sp. z o. o. (1)
Al Kasztanowa 90, 05-831, Mlochow, Poland
Tel.: (48) 223931064
Web Site: http://www.eurofil.pl
Steel Products Mfr
N.A.I.C.S.: 332111
Marek Husak *(Mgr-Bus & Member-Mgmt Bd)*

Les Aciers Fins de la Sarre S.A. (1)
40 Rue de Droixhe, 4020, Liege, Belgium
Tel.: (32) 43456750
Web Site: http://www.lafs.be
Steel Products Mfr
N.A.I.C.S.: 332111

Metalfil S.A. (1)
Salvador Llobet 16 Pol Indl El Ramassar, 08400, Granollers, Spain
Tel.: (34) 938409282
Steel Products Mfr
N.A.I.C.S.: 332111

Metallurgische Gesellschaft Saar GmbH (1)
Im Alten Bruhl, PO Box 10 1870, 66333, Volklingen, Germany
Tel.: (49) 6898104933
Steel Products Mfr
N.A.I.C.S.: 332111

ROGESA Roheisengesellschaft Saar mbH (1)
Werkstrasse 1, 66763, Dillingen, Germany
Tel.: (49) 6831472320
Web Site: http://www.rogesa.de
Hot Metal & Iron Ore Mfr
N.A.I.C.S.: 331110
Margit Meyer *(Co-Sec)*

SHS - Stahl-Holding-Saar GmbH & Co. KGaA (1)
Werkstrasse 1, 66763, Dillingen, Germany
Tel.: (49) 6831471470
Web Site: http://www.stahl-holding-saar.de
Emp.: 13,700
Iron & Steel Mfr
N.A.I.C.S.: 327910
Tim Hartmann *(Chm)*

Subsidiary (Domestic):

SHS Logistics GmbH (2)
Werkstrasse 1, 66763, Dillingen, Germany
Tel.: (49) 6831472709
Web Site: http://www.shs-logistics.de
Rail Logistic & Transportation Services
N.A.I.C.S.: 488210

SHS Services GmbH (2)
Bismarkstrasse 145, 66333, Volklingen, Germany
Tel.: (49) 6898104866
Web Site: http://www.shsservices.de
Commodity Trading Services
N.A.I.C.S.: 523160
Tanja Waigel *(Mgr-Pur)*

Saar Stahlbau GmbH (1)
Huttenstrasse 2, 66115, Saarbrucken, Germany
Tel.: (49) 6898108110
Web Site: http://www.saarstahlbau.de
Steel Products Mfr
N.A.I.C.S.: 332111

Saarstahl (S.E.A.) (1)
Suite 807 8th Floor Block A Dama nsara Intan No 1 Jalan SS20/27, 47400, Petaling Jaya, Selangor, Malaysia

Tel.: (60) 377280311
Steel Product Distr
N.A.I.C.S.: 423390

Saarstahl AG (1)
Vulkanstrasse 126, 8048, Zurich, Switzerland
Tel.: (41) 444346868
Steel Product Distr
N.A.I.C.S.: 423390

Saarstahl Export India Pvt Ltd (1)
Office 606 Maithili Signet Plot No 39/4 Sector 30A, Vashi, Mumbai, 400705, India
Tel.: (91) 2241223520
Steel Product Distr
N.A.I.C.S.: 423390
Sulina Mishra *(Mgr-Sls)*

Saarstahl Shanghai Limited (1)
The Place Unit 2611 Tower A 100 Zunyi Road, Changning, 200051, Shanghai, China
Tel.: (86) 2162415306
Steel Product Distr
N.A.I.C.S.: 423390

Saarstahl s.r.o. (1)
Jureckova 1812/16, 702 00, Ostrava, Czech Republic
Tel.: (420) 558842507
Steel Product Distr
N.A.I.C.S.: 423390

Saarstahl-Export GmbH (1)
Kasernenstrasse 1, 40213, Dusseldorf, Germany
Tel.: (49) 21187770
Steel Product Distr
N.A.I.C.S.: 423390

Saarsteel Inc. (1)
445 S Livernois Rd Ste 222, Rochester Hills, MI 48307
Tel.: (248) 608-0849
Steel Product Distr
N.A.I.C.S.: 423390

Secosar Etirage S.A.S. (1)
Z I 7 rue Eugene Henaff, 69638, Venissieux, Cedex, France
Tel.: (33) 472900072
Steel Pole Mfr
N.A.I.C.S.: 332618

Secosar S.A.S. (1)
2 Boulevard de, Bussy Saint Georges, 77600, Strasbourg, France
Tel.: (33) 164768890
Steel Product Distr
N.A.I.C.S.: 423390

Stahlguss Saar GmbH (1)
Kahlenbergstrasse 5, Rohrbach, 66386, Saint Ingbert, Germany
Tel.: (49) 68945980
Web Site: http://www.stahlguss-saar.de
Steel Pole Mfr
N.A.I.C.S.: 332618

Versicherungskontor Saarstahl GmbH (1)
Hofstattstrasse 106, 66333, Volklingen, Germany
Tel.: (49) 689810494045
Steel Products Mfr
N.A.I.C.S.: 332111

Zentralkokerei Saar GmbH (1)
Werkstrasse 1, 66763, Dillingen, Germany
Tel.: (49) 6831472320
Web Site: http://www.zentralkokerei.de
Blast Furnace Coke Mfr
N.A.I.C.S.: 331110

SAB EVENTS & GOVERNANCE NOW MEDIA LIMITED
7th Floor Adhikari Chambers, New Link Road Andheri West, Mumbai, 400053, India
Tel.: (91) 2240230711
Web Site: https://www.governancenow.com
Year Founded: 2014
SABEVENTS—(NSE)
Rev.: $196,132
Assets: $709,656
Liabilities: $442,434
Net Worth: $267,222

Earnings: ($207,859)
Emp.: 11
Fiscal Year-end: 03/31/21
Magazine Publisher
N.A.I.C.S.: 513120
Markand Adhikari *(Founder & Chm)*

SAB INDUSTRIES LIMITED
Sco 49-50 Sector 26, Madhya Marg, Chandigarh, 160019, India
Tel.: (91) 1722792385
Web Site: https://www.sabindustries.in
Year Founded: 1978
539112—(BOM)
Rev.: $579,671
Assets: $28,578,543
Liabilities: $9,029,545
Net Worth: $19,548,999
Earnings: ($410,828)
Emp.: 21
Fiscal Year-end: 03/31/21
Civil Engineering Services
N.A.I.C.S.: 541330
Bhagwan Singh Negi *(CFO)*

SAB INGENIERIE INFORMATIQUE
36 boulevard de Vincennes, 94120, Fontenay-sous-Bois, France
Tel.: (33) 1 43 94 94 01
Web Site: http://www.sab-tm.com
Year Founded: 1989
Sales Range: $50-74.9 Million
Emp.: 500
Banking & Financial Software Developer
N.A.I.C.S.: 513210
Olivier Peccoux *(Pres)*

SAB INTERNATIONAL SARL
Zac De Tournezy 137 Rue Maurice Le Boucher, 34070, Montpellier, Herault, France
Tel.: (33) 4 67 65 5646
Web Site: http://www.sabcomputer.com
Year Founded: 1994
Sales Range: $10-24.9 Million
Emp.: 50
Computer Software & Services
N.A.I.C.S.: 423430
Annie Amphonesinh *(Dir-Personnel)*

SABAA INTERNATIONAL COMPANY FOR PHARMACEUTICAL & CHEMICAL INDUSTRY
6 Ahmed Shaker Street, Heliopolis, Egypt
Tel.: (20) 24148529
Web Site: https://www.sabaapharmagroup.com
Year Founded: 1999
SIPC.CA—(EGX)
Sales Range: Less than $1 Million
Pharmaceuticals Product Mfr
N.A.I.C.S.: 325412
Al Sayed Abdulnabi Mohammed Al Bialy *(Chm)*

SABABA SECURITY S.P.A.
Via Isaac Newton 15, 20016, Pero, MI, Italy
Tel.: (39) 0250301681
Web Site: https://www.sababasecurity.com
Year Founded: 2019
SBB—(EUR)
Information Technology Services
N.A.I.C.S.: 541512
Stefano Odaglia *(COO)*

SABAF S.P.A.
Via Dei Carpini 1, Ospitaletto, 25035, Brescia, Italy

SABAF S.P.A.

Sabaf S.p.A.—(Continued)
Tel.: (39) 0306843001
Web Site: http://www.sabaf.it
Year Founded: 1949
Sales Range: $100-124.9 Million
Emp.: 520
Mfr & Producer of Components for Domestic Gas Cooking Appliances, Valves, Thermostats, Burners & Accessories
N.A.I.C.S.: 332919
Ettore Saleri *(Deputy Chm)*

Subsidiaries:

Faringosi Hinges s.r.l. (1)
Via A De Gasperi 92, 20010, Bareggio, Milan, Italy (100%)
Tel.: (39) 0290279411
Web Site: http://www.faringosi-hinges.com
Sales Range: $25-49.9 Million
Emp.: 18
Provider of Business Services
N.A.I.C.S.: 561499

Sabaf Appliance Components (Kunshan) Co. Ltd. (1)
Building 7 No 278 Jujin Road, 215300, Kunshan, Jiangsu, China
Tel.: (86) 51257293600
Household Cooking Appliance Distr
N.A.I.C.S.: 423620
Nicloa Belpietro *(Gen Mgr)*

Sabaf Appliance Components (Kunshan) Co., Ltd. (1)
Building 7 No 278 Jujin Road, Zhangpu Town, 215300, Kunshan, Jiansu, China (100%)
Tel.: (86) 512 57293600
Web Site: http://www.sabaf.it
Household Cooking Appliance Mfr
N.A.I.C.S.: 335220
Nicola Belpietro *(Gen Mgr)*

Sabaf Beyaz Esya Parcalari Sanayi Ve Ticaret Limited Sirteki (1)
Hasan Turek Bulvari No 12, Organize Sanayi Bolgesi, 45030, Manisa, Turkiye (100%)
Tel.: (90) 236 214 0620
Web Site: http://www.sabaf.it
Household Cooking Appliance Mfr
N.A.I.C.S.: 335220
Onur Yilmaz *(Gen Mgr)*

Sabaf Immobiliare s.r.l. (1)
Via Dei Carpini 1, 25035, Brescia, Italy (100%)
Tel.: (39) 0306843001
Web Site: http://www.sabaf.it
Real Estate Services
N.A.I.C.S.: 531210

Sabaf do Brasil Ltda (1)
Rua Gustavo Henrique Meerson n355 Condominio Fazgran, Parque Industrial III Jundiai, Sao Paulo, 13213-186, Brazil (100%)
Tel.: (55) 11 45255402
Web Site: http://www.sabaf.it
Household Cooking Appliance Mfr
N.A.I.C.S.: 335220
Paulo Cezar de Medeiros *(Mgr-Admin)*

Sabaf do Brasil Ltada. (1)
Rua Gustavo Henrique Meerson n 355 Condominio Fazgran Parque, Jundiai, Sao Paulo, 13213-186, Brazil
Tel.: (55) 1145255402
Household Cooking Appliance Distr
N.A.I.C.S.: 423620
Marcelo Astrini *(Mgr-Indus)*

SABANA SHARI'AH COMPLIANT INDUSTRIAL REAL ESTATE INVESTMENT TRUST

151 Lorong Chuan 02-03 New Tech Park, Singapore, 556741, Singapore
Tel.: (65) 65807750 SG
Web Site: https://www.sabana-reit.com.sg
SBBSF—(OTCIQ)
Rev.: $84,734,530
Assets: $762,016,965
Liabilities: $325,344,997
Net Worth: $436,671,968
Earnings: $21,142,165
Emp.: 28
Fiscal Year-end: 12/31/23
Real Estate Investment Trust
N.A.I.C.S.: 525990
Tan Cheong Hin *(Chm)*

SABET KHORASAN-FARIMAN SUGAR FACTORY COMPANY

Dr Shariati St North corner of Kolahdoz Dolat St, Negin Qalhak Commercial Tower Fifth Floor Unit 51, 1939616883, Tehran, Iran
Tel.: (98) 22623077
Web Site: https://farimansugar.ir
Year Founded: 1957
Sugar Products Mfr
N.A.I.C.S.: 311314
Massoud Ahanforush *(Chm)*

SABIC AGRI-NUTRIENTS CO.

PO Box 11044, Jubail Industrial City, Jubail, 31961, Saudi Arabia
Tel.: (966) 133422841 SA
Web Site: https://www.sabic-agrinutrients.com
Year Founded: 1965
2020—(SAU)
Rev.: $5,060,879,883
Assets: $7,214,154,113
Liabilities: $1,622,905,746
Net Worth: $5,591,248,367
Earnings: $2,789,266,764
Emp.: 1,266
Fiscal Year-end: 12/31/22
Chemicals Mfr
N.A.I.C.S.: 325998
Ahmed Mohammed Al-Jabr *(CEO)*

SABIEN TECHNOLOGY GROUP PLC

71-75 Shelton Street, London, WC2H 9JQ, United Kingdom
Tel.: (44) 2079933700
Web Site: https://sabien.com
SNT—(AIM)
Rev.: $897,369
Assets: $1,086,954
Liabilities: $872,091
Net Worth: $214,863
Earnings: ($695,145)
Emp.: 11
Fiscal Year-end: 06/30/24
Manufacture & Sale Of M2G Design
N.A.I.C.S.: 624229
Tony Willis *(Dir-Technical)*

Subsidiaries:

Sabien Technology Limited (1)
Burlington House 1-13 York Road, Maidenhead, SL6 1SQ, Berkshire, United Kingdom
Tel.: (44) 2079933700
Web Site: http://www.sabien-tech.co.uk
Sales Range: $25-49.9 Million
Emp.: 20
Electronic Boiler Controls Mfr
N.A.I.C.S.: 334513
Alan O'Brian *(CEO & Mng Dir)*

SABINA CORPORATION LIMITED

34 Hinchcliffe Drive, Beaudesert, 4285, QLD, Australia
Tel.: (61) 755446698
Web Site: http://www.sabina.com.au
Year Founded: 1987
Investment Services
N.A.I.C.S.: 523999
Peter B. Chen *(Chm & CEO)*

Subsidiaries:

G8 Consultants Pty. Ltd. (1)
PO Box 655, Launceston, 7250, Tasmania, Australia
Tel.: (61) 3 63269088
Web Site: http://www.g8consultants.com.au
Real Estate Development & Consulting Services
N.A.I.C.S.: 531390

SABINA PUBLIC COMPANY LIMITED

12 Arun-amarin Rd Arun-amarin Bangkoknoi, Bangkok, 10700, Thailand
Tel.: (66) 24229400
Web Site: http://www.sabina.co.th
Year Founded: 1995
SABINA—(THA)
Rev.: $100,723,263
Assets: $84,087,282
Liabilities: $29,342,943
Net Worth: $54,744,339
Earnings: $13,532,786
Emp.: 1,536
Fiscal Year-end: 12/31/23
Women's Apparel & Clothes Mfr
N.A.I.C.S.: 315250
Viroj Thanalongkorn *(Chm)*

Subsidiaries:

Sabina Fareast Co., Ltd (1)
305 Moo 12 Phutthamonthon V, Rai King, Sam Phran, 10600, Nakhonpathom, Thailand
Tel.: (66) 2811822031
Web Site: http://www.sabina.co.th
Women's Clothing Mfr
N.A.I.C.S.: 315250

Sabina Public Company Limited - Chainat Factory (1)
177 Moo 8 Wang Kai Tuen, Hankha, 17130, Chainat, Thailand
Tel.: (66) 24229400
Web Site: http://www.sabina.co.th
Women's Clothing Mfr
N.A.I.C.S.: 315250

Sabina Public Company Limited - Phuttamonthon Sai 5 Factory (1)
30/5 Moo 12 Phuttamonthon Sai 5 Rd Raiking, Sam Phran, Nakhon Pathom, 73210, Thailand
Tel.: (66) 2 811 8220
Women's Clothing Mfr
N.A.I.C.S.: 315250

Sabina Public Company Limited - Yasothorn Factory (1)
236 Moo 10 Dootung Muangyasothorn, Yasothon, 35000, Thailand
Tel.: (66) 4 5 582 565
Women's Clothing Mfr
N.A.I.C.S.: 315250

SABIO HOLDINGS INC.

Brookfield Place 181 Bay St Suite 4400, Toronto, M5J 2T3, ON, Canada
Tel.: (604) 889-4790
Year Founded: 2017
SABOF—(OTCQX)
Rev.: $42,305,732
Assets: $21,790,734
Liabilities: $19,442,680
Net Worth: $2,348,054
Earnings: ($846,765)
Emp.: 110
Fiscal Year-end: 12/31/22
Asset Management Services
N.A.I.C.S.: 523940
Aziz Rahimtoola *(CEO)*

Subsidiaries:

AppScience, Inc. (1)
16350 Ventura Blvd Ste D827, Encino, CA 91436
Web Site: https://www.appscience.inc
Advertising Services
N.A.I.C.S.: 541810

Vidillion Corp. (1)
16350 Ventura Blvd Ste D827, Encino, CA 91436
Web Site: https://www.vidillion.com
Information Technology Services
N.A.I.C.S.: 541519

INTERNATIONAL PUBLIC

SABIO HOLDINGS INC.

90 Adelaide Street West Suite 400, Toronto, M5H 4A6, ON, Canada
Tel.: (647) 998-4149
SBCC.P—(TSXV)
Rev.: $13,161
Assets: $813,684
Liabilities: $65,260
Net Worth: $748,423
Earnings: ($158,295)
Fiscal Year-end: 12/31/19
Asset Management Services
N.A.I.C.S.: 523940
Aneel Waraich *(Pres & CEO)*

SABLE HOLDINGS LIMITED

Sable Place Fairway Office Park 52 Grosvenor Road, Bryanston, 2021, South Africa
Tel.: (27) 112675700
Web Site: http://www.sableholdings.co.za
Sales Range: $1-9.9 Million
Emp.: 45
Property Investment Services
N.A.I.C.S.: 523999
Gavin B.J. Bowes *(Mng Dir)*

Subsidiaries:

Sable Group Holdings (Pty) Limited (1)
Grosvenor Road 52, Bryanston, 2191, Sandton, Gauteng, South Africa
Tel.: (27) 112675700
Commercial Banking Services
N.A.I.C.S.: 522110
Paul Nash *(CEO)*

SABLE RESOURCES LTD.

900-999 West Hastings Street, Vancouver, V6C 2W2, BC, Canada
Tel.: (236) 317-2090 Ca
Web Site: https://www.sableresources.com
Year Founded: 1962
SBLRF—(OTCQB)
Rev.: $39,020
Assets: $22,271,154
Liabilities: $2,432,148
Net Worth: $19,839,006
Earnings: ($7,931,995)
Emp.: 3
Fiscal Year-end: 12/31/21
Mineral Exploration Services
N.A.I.C.S.: 213114
Tom Obradovich *(Chm)*

SABO-MASCHINENFABRIK GMBH

Auf Dem Hochsten 22, D 51645, Gummersbach, Germany
Tel.: (49) 22617040 De
Web Site: http://www.sabo-online.com
Year Founded: 1932
Sales Range: $50-74.9 Million
Emp.: 1,500
Walk-Behind Mowers
N.A.I.C.S.: 423820
Lars Daniel *(Mng Partner)*

SABOO BROTHERS LIMITED

332 B block Anand Plaza University Road, Udaipur, 313001, Rajasthan, India
Tel.: (91) 8107237775
Web Site: http://www.saboobrothers.com
530267—(BOM)
Rev.: $67,394
Assets: $1,265,224
Liabilities: $26,221
Net Worth: $1,239,002
Earnings: $5,455
Emp.: 3
Fiscal Year-end: 03/31/23
Industrial Machinery Mfr

N.A.I.C.S.: 333248
Neha Jian *(Compliance Officer)*

SABOO SODIUM CHLORO LTD.
Surya House L-5 B II Krishna Marg C-Scheme, Jaipur, 302 001, Rajasthan, India
Tel.: (91) 1412379483
Web Site: https://www.suryasalt.com
Year Founded: 1993
530461—(BOM)
Rev.: $5,991,200
Assets: $8,253,954
Liabilities: $2,699,670
Net Worth: $5,554,283
Earnings: $10,371
Fiscal Year-end: 03/31/23
Refined Salt Mfr & Distr
N.A.I.C.S.: 325199
Girdhar Gopal Saboo *(Mng Dir)*

SABRE GOLD MINES CORP.
18 King Street East Suite 902, Toronto, M5C 1C4, ON, Canada
Tel.: (416) 855-9305   Ca
Web Site: http://www.arizona-gold.com
Year Founded: 1984
SGLDF—(OTCQB)
Assets: $24,742,883
Liabilities: $24,552,830
Net Worth: $190,053
Earnings: ($3,816,748)
Emp.: 6
Fiscal Year-end: 06/30/21
Gold Ore Exploration, Development & Mining
N.A.I.C.S.: 212220
Martin Kostuik *(Pres)*

SABRE INSURANCE GROUP PLC
Sabre House 150 South Street, Dorking, RH4 2YY, Surrey, United Kingdom
Tel.: (44) 3300244696   UK
Web Site: https://www.sabreplc.co.uk
Year Founded: 1982
SBRE—(LSE)
Rev.: $237,624,337
Assets: $795,427,922
Liabilities: $489,429,437
Net Worth: $305,998,485
Earnings: $22,803,585
Emp.: 161
Fiscal Year-end: 12/31/23
Insurance Brokerage Services
N.A.I.C.S.: 524210
Geoff Carter *(CEO)*

SABRE RESOURCES LIMITED
Level 1 8 Parliament Place, West Perth, 6005, WA, Australia
Tel.: (61) 894817833
Web Site: https://sabresources.com
SBR—(ASX)
Rev.: $155,106
Assets: $8,885,351
Liabilities: $116,705
Net Worth: $8,768,645
Earnings: ($1,100,360)
Fiscal Year-end: 06/30/24
Metal-Based Exploration & Mining Services
N.A.I.C.S.: 212290
Martin Stein *(CFO & Sec)*

SABRIMALA INDUSTRIES INDIA LIMITED
906 9th Floor D-Mall Netaji Subhash Place, New Delhi, 110 034, India
Tel.: (91) 1141514958   In
Web Site: https://sabrimala.co.in
Year Founded: 1984
540132—(BOM)
Rev.: $171,381
Assets: $805,491
Liabilities: $67,802
Net Worth: $737,690
Earnings: ($32,000)
Fiscal Year-end: 03/31/23
Consumer Goods Distr
N.A.I.C.S.: 423620
Sanjay Garg *(Mng Dir)*

SABUY TECHNOLOGY PUBLIC COMPANY LIMITED
230 Bang Khun Thian-Chai Talay Road, Samaedam Bang Khun Thian, Bangkok, 10150, Thailand
Tel.: (66) 20090500   TH
Web Site: https://www.sabuytech.com
Year Founded: 2014
SABUY—(THA)
Rev.: $281,113,334
Assets: $608,610,158
Liabilities: $288,559,581
Net Worth: $320,050,578
Earnings: ($9,261,435)
Emp.: 2,141
Fiscal Year-end: 12/31/23
Electrical Equipment Mfr & Distr
N.A.I.C.S.: 335210
Chakkrit Parapuntakul *(Chm)*

SABVEST LIMITED
Ground Floor Commerce Square Building 4 39 Rivonia Road, Sandhurst, Sandton, 2196, South Africa
Tel.: (27) 11 268 2400   ZA
Web Site: http://www.sabvest.com
SBV—(JSE)
Sales Range: $25-49.9 Million
Emp.: 13
Investment Management Service
N.A.I.C.S.: 523999
Christopher Stefan Seabrooke *(CEO)*

SAC'S BAR HOLDINGS INC.
The third Derica Bldg 1-48-14 Shinkoiwa, Katsushika-ku, Tokyo, 124-8558, Japan
Tel.: (81) 336545315
Web Site: https://www.sacs-bar.co.jp
Year Founded: 1974
9990—(TKS)
Rev.: $344,334,730
Assets: $260,334,850
Liabilities: $76,404,990
Net Worth: $183,929,860
Earnings: $16,439,070
Emp.: 572
Fiscal Year-end: 03/31/24
Holding Company
N.A.I.C.S.: 551112
Shigetoshi Kiyama *(Chm)*

Subsidiaries:

Aishin Tsusho Co., Ltd.   (1)
6-7-5 Soto-kanda, Chiyoda-ku, Tokyo, 101-0021, Japan
Tel.: (81) 358123133
Bag Mfr
N.A.I.C.S.: 316990

Carnival Company, Ltd.   (1)
Satou Bld 4F A 2-1-12 Ebisuminami Shibuya-ku, Tokyo, 150-0022, Japan
Tel.: (81) 357253061
Sales Range: Less than $1 Million
Accessory Distr
N.A.I.C.S.: 458110

SACCHERIA F.LLI FRANCESCHETTI S.P.A
Via Stazione Vecchia 80, Provaglio d'Iseo, 25050, Brescia, Italy
Tel.: (39) 0309823841
Web Site: https://www.saccheriafrances.com
Year Founded: 1970
SAC—(ITA)
Textile Packaging Product Mfr
N.A.I.C.S.: 314910

SACEN A.D.
Nardnog fronta 53, 21000, Novi Sad, Serbia
Tel.: (381) 0658238005
Web Site: http://www.sacenad.com
Year Founded: 1969
Sales Range: Less than $1 Million
Emp.: 3
Market Research & Consulting Services
N.A.I.C.S.: 541910

SACGASCO LIMITED
Level 1 31 Cliff Street, Fremantle, 6160, WA, Australia
Tel.: (61) 894353200
Web Site: https://www.sacgasco.com
AOK—(ASX)
Rev.: $6,037,133
Assets: $15,928,256
Liabilities: $21,141,919
Net Worth: ($5,213,663)
Earnings: $427,732
Fiscal Year-end: 12/31/23
Oil & Gas Exploration
N.A.I.C.S.: 213112
Andrew Childs *(Chm)*

SACHETA METALS LIMITED
Sej Plaza Bldg 502/5th Floor Marve Road Near Nutan School, Malad West, Mumbai, 400064, Maharashtra, India
Tel.: (91) 2228725948
Web Site: https://sacheta.com
Year Founded: 1990
531869—(BOM)
Rev.: $11,904,586
Assets: $8,404,065
Liabilities: $3,938,265
Net Worth: $4,465,799
Earnings: $247,095
Emp.: 178
Fiscal Year-end: 03/31/23
Aluminium Utensils Mfr & Distr
N.A.I.C.S.: 332215
Pranavkumar S. Shah *(Exec Dir)*

Subsidiaries:

Parishram Trading Co.   (1)
134 Kathlal Road Near Bank of India, Kapadvanj, 387630, India
Tel.: (91) 2691 243430
Utensil Mfr & Distr
N.A.I.C.S.: 332215

SACHTLEBEN MINERALS GMBH & CO. KG
Meistergasse 14, 77756, Hausach, Germany
Tel.: (49) 7831 96922 0
Web Site: http://www.sachtleben-minerals.com
Barite Mining & Processing
N.A.I.C.S.: 212390
Moritz Ostenrieder *(Mng Dir)*

Subsidiaries:

Deutsche Baryt-Industrie Dr. Rudolf Alberti GmbH und Co. KG   (1)
Bahnhofstrasse 21-39, 37431, Bad Lauterberg im Harz, Germany
Tel.: (49) 552485010
Web Site: http://www.baryt.com
Sales Range: $25-49.9 Million
Emp.: 60
Processing & Refining Rock Containing Barytes
N.A.I.C.S.: 212390
Georg Kuehler *(Mng Dir)*

SACMI IMOLA S.C.A.R.L.
Via Selice Provinciale 17/A, Imola, 40026, Bologna, Italy
Tel.: (39) 0542607111
Web Site: http://www.sacmi.com
Sales Range: $1-4.9 Billion
Emp.: 1,000
Machines & Systems Designer, Producer & Marketer for the Ceramics, Plastics, Beverage, Packaging & Food Processing Industries
N.A.I.C.S.: 333414
Giuliano Airoli *(VP)*

Subsidiaries:

Alpha Ceramics GmbH   (1)
Julicher Str 334, Aachen, 52070, Germany
Tel.: (49) 241160030
Web Site: http://www.alpha-ceramics.de
Sales Range: $25-49.9 Million
Emp.: 10
Social Sciences & Humanities Research & Development
N.A.I.C.S.: 541720
Robert Guntiln *(Gen Mgr)*

Carle & Montanari USA Inc.   (1)
625-107 Hutton St, Raleigh, NC 27606
Tel.: (919) 664-7401
Confectionery Merchant Whslr
N.A.I.C.S.: 424450

Carle & Montanari/C&G S.p.A.   (1)
Via Trebbia 22, Loc Quinto de Stampl, 20089, Milan, Italy
Tel.: (39) 02824521
Sales Range: $25-49.9 Million
Emp.: 11
Confectionery Merchant Whslr
N.A.I.C.S.: 424450

Gaiotto Automation S.p.A.   (1)
Strada Statale 415 Km 27, Vaiano Cremasco, Cremona, 26010, Italy
Tel.: (39) 0373279111
Web Site: http://www.gaiotto.it
Sales Range: $25-49.9 Million
Emp.: 80
Industrial Machinery Mfr
N.A.I.C.S.: 333248
Battista Gaiotto *(Gen Mgr)*

H.P.S. S.p.A.   (1)
Via Selice Provinciale 17/a Imola, Imola, Bologna, 40026, Italy
Tel.: (39) 0542642607
Web Site: http://www.hps-sacmi.com
Holding Company
N.A.I.C.S.: 551112
Augusto Machirelli *(Pres)*

Hayes Machine Company Inc.   (1)
3434 106th Cir, Des Moines, IA 50322
Tel.: (515) 252-1216
Web Site: http://www.hayesmachine.com
Sales Range: $10-24.9 Million
Emp.: 30
Packaging & Labeling Services
N.A.I.C.S.: 561910
Luca Cerrone *(CEO)*

IN.TE.SA S.p.A.   (1)
Via dell Artigianato 10, Salvaterra di, 42013, Casalgrande, Italy
Tel.: (39) 05221885188
Web Site: http://www.intesa.sacmi.it
Ceramic Tile Mfr & Distr
N.A.I.C.S.: 327120
Stefano Felicani *(Area Mgr-Export)*

Iprel Progetti S.r.l.   (1)
Via Nicoli 1, Imola, Bologna, 40026, Italy
Tel.: (39) 0542645921
Web Site: http://www.iprel.it
Emp.: 100
Electrical Equipment & Component Mfr
N.A.I.C.S.: 335999
Davive Liverani *(Gen Mgr)*

Italiansped S.p.A.   (1)
Via Togliatti 19/A, Imola, 40026, Bologna, Italy
Tel.: (39) 0542645711
Web Site: http://www.italiansped.com
Sales Range: $25-49.9 Million
Emp.: 7
Freight Transportation Arrangement
N.A.I.C.S.: 488510
Mauro Geminiani *(Gen Mgr)*

SACMI IMOLA S.C.A.R.L.

INTERNATIONAL PUBLIC

Sacmi Imola S.C.A.R.L.—(Continued)

Italmex S.A. (1)
Lic DM Trevino 1413-A, Col Santa Maria,
64650, Monterrey, NL, Mexico
Tel.: (52) 8183355042
Web Site: http://www.sacmi.it
Sales Range: $25-49.9 Million
Emp.: 50
Chemical Product & Preparation Mfr
N.A.I.C.S.: 325998
Lazaro Garcia (Gen Mgr)

Laeis GmbH (1)
Am Scheerleck 7, L 6868, Wecker, Luxembourg
Tel.: (352) 276120
Web Site: http://www.laeis-gmbh.com
Sales Range: $25-49.9 Million
Emp.: 70
Mfr of HPF Hydraulic Presses
N.A.I.C.S.: 333912
Ralph Lutz (Gen Mgr)

Subsidiary (Non-US):

LAEIS (Dalian) Trading Co. Ltd. (2)
Room 512 Market Building Xiguanmen -
Dalian Free Trade Zone, 116600, Dalian,
China
Tel.: (86) 411 87313962
Industrial Equipment Whsr
N.A.I.C.S.: 423830

Moldes Ceramicos S.A. (1)
Lic DM Trevino 1413-A, Col Santa Maria,
64650, Monterrey, NL, Mexico
Tel.: (52) 8183354931
Web Site: http://www.molcer.com
Sales Range: $25-49.9 Million
Emp.: 25
Ornamental & Architectural Metal Work Mfr
N.A.I.C.S.: 332323
Sergio Gutierrez (Gen Mgr)

Negri Bossi S.p.A. (1)
Viale Europa 64, Cologno Monzese, 20093,
Milan, Italy
Tel.: (39) 02273481
Web Site: http://www.negribossi.com
Industrial Machinery Mfr
N.A.I.C.S.: 333248
Craig Ward (CEO)

Subsidiary (Non-US):

Negri Bossi Brasil Ltda (2)
Rua Manoel Garcia 187-Casa Verde,
02523-040, Sao Paulo, Brazil
Tel.: (55) 1138584646
Web Site: http://www.negribossi.com.br
Commercial & Service Industry Machinery
Mfr
N.A.I.C.S.: 333310

Negri Bossi France S.A.S. (2)
8 Rue Fulgencio Gimenez, 69120, Vaulx-en-Velin, France
Tel.: (33) 472018090
Web Site: http://www.negri-bossi.fr
Industrial Machinery & Equipment Whslr
N.A.I.C.S.: 423830

Negri Bossi USA Inc. (1)
210 Exe Dr Ste 3, Newark, DE 19702
Tel.: (302) 737-8001
Web Site: http://www.negribossiusa.com
Sales Range: $25-49.9 Million
Emp.: 5
Commercial & Service Industry Machinery
Mfr
N.A.I.C.S.: 333310

Niv Verona S.p.A. (1)
Viale Dell industria 2, Mozzecane, 37060,
Verona, Italy
Tel.: (39) 0456347411
Web Site: http://www.nivcasting.it
Enameled Iron & Metal Sanitary Ware Mfr
N.A.I.C.S.: 332999
Pietro Cassani (Pres)

OOO Sacmi Mosca Ltd. (1)
Efremova Street 14, 119048, Moscow, Russia
Tel.: (7) 4997534810
Web Site: http://sacmi-ru.sacmi.com
Sales Range: $25-49.9 Million
Emp.: 20
Industrial Machinery Mfr
N.A.I.C.S.: 333248

Michele Pulpito (Gen Mgr)

Oima S.p.A. (1)
Via Galileo Galilei 3/b, Casella D Asolo,
31011, Casella, Italy
Tel.: (39) 04239535
Web Site: http://www.oima.it
Emp.: 14
Industrial Mold Mfr
N.A.I.C.S.: 333511

PT. Indosped Maju Sejahtera (1)
Jl AM Sangaji No 11, 10130, Jakarta, Indonesia
Tel.: (62) 216302466
Sales Range: $25-49.9 Million
Emp.: 25
Industrial Machinery Mfr
N.A.I.C.S.: 333248

PT. Molds & Dies Indonesia (1)
Kota Industri Suryacipta Jl Surya Madya
Kav A-6, Desa Kutamekar Kec Ciampel,
Karawang, 41361, Jawa Barat, Indonesia
Tel.: (62) 267440272
Web Site: http://www.sacmi.com
Sales Range: $25-49.9 Million
Emp.: 45
Special Die & Tool Die Set Jig & Fixture Mfr
N.A.I.C.S.: 333514
Marcello Bertolani (Mgr)

PT. Sacmi Indonesia (1)
Kota Industri Suryacipta Jl Surya Madya
Kav A-6, Desa Kutamekar Kec Ciampel,
Karawang, Jawa Barat, Indonesia
Tel.: (62) 267440272
Sales Range: $25-49.9 Million
Emp.: 50
Industrial Machinery Mfr
N.A.I.C.S.: 333248
Luca Ferraris (Pres)

Protesa S.p.A. (1)
Via La Malfa 24, Imola, 40026, Bologna,
Italy
Tel.: (39) 0542 644069
Web Site: http://www.protesa.net
Sales Range: $25-49.9 Million
Technological & Organizational Services
N.A.I.C.S.: 541611
Francesco Carati (CEO)

Riedhammer GmbH (1)
Klingenhofstr 72, 90411, Nuremberg, Germany
Tel.: (49) 91152180
Web Site: http://www.riedhammer.de
Sales Range: $75-99.9 Million
Emp.: 120
Professional Equipment & Supplies Whslr
N.A.I.C.S.: 423490

Riedhammer Japan Co Ltd. (1)
Toranomon Garden 806 Minato-Ku, Tokyo,
Japan
Tel.: (81) 354731680
Sales Range: $25-49.9 Million
Emp.: 4
Air-Conditioning & Warm Air Heating Equipment & Commercial & Industrial Refrigeration Equipment Mfr
N.A.I.C.S.: 333415
Hiroshi Abe (Pres)

SACMI (THAILAND) Co. Ltd. (1)
1 MD Tower 13th Floor Unit B Soi Bangna-Trad 25 - Bangna-Trad Rd, Bangna Subdistrict, 10260, Bangkok, Thailand
Tel.: (66) 2 3992686
Web Site: http://www.sacmithailand.com
Emp.: 11
Industrial Machinery Distr
N.A.I.C.S.: 423830
Rachanee Udomsaree (Office Mgr)

SACMI BEVERAGE VENEZUELA, C.A. (1)
Avenida La Estancia Torre Las Mercedes
Piso 5 Oficina 502-A1 Urb, Chuao, 1060,
Caracas, Venezuela
Tel.: (58) 212 9594007
Industrial Machinery Whslr
N.A.I.C.S.: 423840

SACMI CARPMEC S.p.A. (1)
Via G Ansaldo 16, 47122, Forli, Italy
Tel.: (39) 0543 782515
Web Site: http://www.sacmicarpmec.it
Industrial Machinery Mfr

N.A.I.C.S.: 333248
Walter Tontini (Gen Mgr)

SACMI IRAN - SAZEH CERAMIC & MATERIAL IRANIAN CO. (1)
No 1102 11th floor - Elahiyeh trading complex Africa Blvd, Tehran, Iran
Tel.: (98) 21 26212850
Web Site: http://www.sacmiiran.com
Industrial Machinery Mfr
N.A.I.C.S.: 333248
Behzad Nasiri (Mng Dir)

SACMI MOLDS & DIES PARS CO. (1)
No 4 First St 63rd Ave - 18th km of Karaj
Makhsoos Rd, Tehran, Iran
Tel.: (98) 21 44988990
Industrial Supplies Whslr
N.A.I.C.S.: 423840
Payam Pedram (Gen Mgr)

SURFACE INSPECTION Grade Two Limited (1)
Unit 8 City Business Park Easton Road,
Bristol, BS5 0SP, United Kingdom
Tel.: (44) 117 2140808
Web Site: http://www.surface-inspection.com
Industrial Machinery Mfr
N.A.I.C.S.: 333248

Sacmi (Changshu) Machinery Equipment Co., Ltd (1)
No 11 Workshop Maqiao Industrial Square -
Yanjiang, Economic Development Zone,
Changshu, 215513, Jiangsu, China
Tel.: (86) 512 52267620
Web Site: http://www.sacmichangshu.com
Industrial Machinery Distr
N.A.I.C.S.: 423830
Claudio Facchini (Pres & Gen Mgr)

Sacmi (Shanghai) Machinery Equipment Co. Ltd. (1)
Huai Hai Zhong rd Times Square Office Twr
93, 2506-2508 Luwan Dist, 200021, Shanghai, China
Tel.: (86) 53062455
Web Site: http://www.sacmishanghai.com
Sales Range: $25-49.9 Million
Emp.: 50
Industrial Machinery & Equipment Distr
N.A.I.C.S.: 423830
Armando Pratella (Chm)

Sacmi Automation (1)
Via Dell Artigianato 10, Salvaterra di Casalgrande, 42013, Modena, Italy
Tel.: (39) 0522997011
Web Site: http://www.sacmiautomation.com
Industrial Process Furnace & Oven Mfr
N.A.I.C.S.: 333994

Sacmi Beverage de Mexico S.A. de C.V. (1)
Calle Joaquin Argaez No 9 Col San Miguel
Chapultepec, Delegacion Miguel Hidalgo,
11850, Mexico, Mexico
Tel.: (52) 55 52575987
Industrial Supplies Whslr
N.A.I.C.S.: 423840

Sacmi De Mexico S.A. De C.V. (1)
Av Santa Fe 505 - 702, Col Cruz Manca
Santa Fe, 5349, Mexico, Mexico
Tel.: (52) 5552575987
Web Site: http://www.negribossi.com
Sales Range: $25-49.9 Million
Emp.: 11
Retailers Stores
N.A.I.C.S.: 459999
Dedro Lopet (Mng Dir)

Sacmi Deutschland GmbH (1)
St Jobser Str 56, 52146, Aachen, Germany
Tel.: (49) 240544810
Web Site: http://www.sacmideutschland.com
Hydronics Plumbing & Heating Equipment & Supplies Whslr
N.A.I.C.S.: 423720

Sacmi Do Brasil Industria e Comercio Ltda (1)
Rua Imola 133, Mogi Mirim, 13800-970,
Sao Paulo, SP, Brazil
Tel.: (55) 1938057300
Web Site: http://www.sacmidobrasil.com
Sales Range: $25-49.9 Million
Emp.: 30

Mfr of Multi-Channel Horizontal Dryers &
Roller Kilns for the Ceramic Industry
N.A.I.C.S.: 327110
Ermes Gaddoni (Pres)

Sacmi Filling S.p.A. (1)
Via E Ferrari N 1, Ramoscello di Sorbolo,
Parma, 43058, Italy
Tel.: (39) 0521695411
Web Site: http://www.sacmifilling.it
Sales Range: $50-74.9 Million
Emp.: 200
Industrial Machinery Mfr
N.A.I.C.S.: 333248
Matteo Quaimi (Mgr-Sls)

Sacmi Forni S.p.A. (1)
Via Dell Artigianato 10, Salvaterra di Casalgrande, 42013, Modena, Regione Emilia,
Italy
Tel.: (39) 0522997011
Web Site: http://www.sacmiforni.com
Sales Range: $50-74.9 Million
Emp.: 200
Industrial Process Furnace & Oven Mfr
N.A.I.C.S.: 333994

Sacmi Hong Kong Ltd. (1)
Rm A-B 16th Fl Neich Twr, 128 Gloucester
Rd, Wanchai, China (Hong Kong)
Tel.: (852) 25988373
Sales Range: $50-74.9 Million
Emp.: 7
Industrial Machinery & Equipment Whslr
N.A.I.C.S.: 423830
Mauro Masini (Gen Mgr)

Sacmi Iberica S.A. (1)
Zona Industrial Oia Fraccao A Lote A-20
Apartado 129, Oia, 3770-908, Oliveira do
Bairro, Portugal
Tel.: (351) 234 724961
Web Site: http://www.sacmiportugal.com
Industrial Supplies Whslr
N.A.I.C.S.: 423840
Adelino Gonzalez (Mgr-Sls)

Sacmi Iberica S.A. (1)
Gran Via 263, Castellon de la plana, 12006,
Valencia, Spain
Tel.: (34) 964344700
Web Site: http://www.sacmiiberica.com
Sales Range: $25-49.9 Million
Emp.: 50
Vitreous China Fine Earthenware & Pottery
Product Mfr
N.A.I.C.S.: 327110
David Galvez (Gen Mgr)

Sacmi Imola S.C. (1)
Via Provinciale Selice 17 a, 40026, Imola,
Italy
Tel.: (39) 0523578047
Web Site: http://www.sacmi.com
Sales Range: $25-49.9 Million
Emp.: 23
Industrial Machinery Mfr
N.A.I.C.S.: 333248

Sacmi Impianti India Limited (1)
3 Ratnam Sq 3rd Fl Plot No 38 & 39-Sec
19/A, Vashi, 400 705, Mumbai, India
Tel.: (91) 2267901533
Web Site: http://www.sacmiindia.com
Sales Range: $25-49.9 Million
Emp.: 100
Coated & Laminated Packaging Paper &
Plastics Film Mfr
N.A.I.C.S.: 322220
Anand Pande (Mng Dir)

Sacmi Impianti S.A. (1)
San Martin 793 1 Piso B, Buenos Aires,
1004, Argentina
Tel.: (54) 1143121583
Sales Range: $50-74.9 Million
Emp.: 2
Construction Materials Whslr
N.A.I.C.S.: 423390

Sacmi Impianti S.p.A. (1)
Via Emilia Romagna 41, 41049, Sassuolo,
MO, Italy
Tel.: (39) 0536839111
Web Site: http://www.sacmiimpianti.com
Emp.: 80
Construction Material Merchant Whslr
N.A.I.C.S.: 423390
Damiano Noto (Gen Mgr)

Sacmi Istanbul Sanayi Ve Tic. Ltd Sti. (1)

Levent Mahallesi Siklamen Sok No 4, 34330, Istanbul, Besiktas, Turkiye
Tel.: (90) 2122813018
Web Site: http://www.sacmiistanbul.com
Sales Range: $25-49.9 Million
Emp.: 20
Industrial Machinery Mfr
N.A.I.C.S.: 333248
Filippo Ferrari *(Gen Mgr)*

Sacmi Korea Company (1)
Room 802 Wooju Building 416-6 Gil-Tong Gangtong-gu, Officetel 175-12 Jamsil-Dong S, Seoul, 134-814, Korea (South)
Tel.: (82) 234313503
Web Site: http://www.sacmi.com
Sales Range: $25-49.9 Million
Emp.: 4
Industrial Machinery Mfr
N.A.I.C.S.: 333248

Sacmi Labelling S.p.A. (1)
Via Dell Industria 2/A, Veneto Region Mozzecane, Verona, 37060, Italy
Tel.: (39) 0456347511
Web Site: http://www.sacmi.com
Emp.: 250
Industrial Machinery & Equipment Whslr
N.A.I.C.S.: 423830
Ermes Belicchi *(Gen Mgr)*

Sacmi Labelling SCM S.p.A. (1)
Via Achille Grandi 6, Marmirolo, 46045, Mantua, Italy
Tel.: (39) 0376298611
Web Site: http://www.sacmilabellingscm.it
Sales Range: $75-99.9 Million
Emp.: 150
Industrial Machinery & Equipment Whslr
N.A.I.C.S.: 423830

Sacmi Machinery (Foshan Nanhay) Co. Ltd. (1)
Nanhai Science & Technology Ind Pk, Xingye N Rd, 528222, Foshan, Guangdong, China
Tel.: (86) 75781206111
Web Site: http://www.sacminanhai.com
Sales Range: $150-199.9 Million
Emp.: 400
Industrial Machinery & Equipment Whslr
N.A.I.C.S.: 423830

Sacmi Middle East (1)
Dubai Airport Free Zone, PO Box 54665, Dubai, Dalza, United Arab Emirates
Tel.: (971) 42045745
Web Site: http://www.sacmi.com
Industrial Machinery Mfr
N.A.I.C.S.: 333248

Sacmi Molds & Dies Egypt (1)
24 Shoubra St Abu Rawash - Industrial Zone, Cairo, Egypt
Tel.: (20) 2 25790586
Industrial Supplies Whslr
N.A.I.C.S.: 423840
Gamal Bashir *(Gen Mgr)*

Sacmi Molds & Dies S.p.A. (1)
Via Emilia Romagna 41, CP 157, 41049, Sassuolo, Italy
Tel.: (39) 0536998311
Web Site: http://www.sacmimoldsanddies.com
Sales Range: $25-49.9 Million
Emp.: 50
Special Die & Tool Die Set Jig & Fixture Mfr
N.A.I.C.S.: 333514

Sacmi Molds & Dies USA Ltd. (1)
4451 121 St, Des Moines, IA 50323
Tel.: (515) 254-1960
Web Site: http://www.sacmiusa.com
Sales Range: $25-49.9 Million
Emp.: 40
Special Die & Tool Die Set Jig & Fixture Mfr
N.A.I.C.S.: 333514

Sacmi Packaging S.p.A. (1)
Via Brodolini 10/A, Imola, 40026, Bologna, Italy
Tel.: (39) 0542649811
Sales Range: $50-74.9 Million
Emp.: 100
Industrial Machinery & Equipment Whslr
N.A.I.C.S.: 423830

Sacmi Pakim S.r.l. (1)
Via Iginio Giordani 42/44, Goito, 46040, Mantua, Italy
Tel.: (39) 0376 604955
Web Site: http://www.pakim.it
Sales Range: $25-49.9 Million
Emp.: 25
Industrial Packaging Machinery & Equipment Designer & Mfr
N.A.I.C.S.: 423830
Matteo Modenese *(Mgr-Tech)*

Sacmi Polska Sp z o.o. (1)
Ul Warszawska 155, 97-200, Tomaszow Mazowiecki, Lodskie, Poland
Tel.: (48) 447235541
Web Site: http://www.sacmipolska.com
Sales Range: $25-49.9 Million
Emp.: 15
Industrial Machinery Mfr
N.A.I.C.S.: 333248
Barbara Przetakiewicz *(Gen Mgr)*

Sacmi Portugal Lda (1)
Zona Ind Oia Fraccsao A Lote A-20 Apartado 129, Oliveira do Bairro, 3770-908, Aveiro, Portugal
Tel.: (351) 234724961
Sales Range: $25-49.9 Million,
Emp.: 7
Commercial & Service Industry Machinery Mfr
N.A.I.C.S.: 333310
Adelino Gonzalez *(Gen Mgr)*

Sacmi Singapore PTE Ltd. (1)
No 11 Kaki Bukit Place Eunos TechPark, Singapore, 416189, Singapore
Tel.: (65) 62745359
Web Site: http://www.sacmisin.com
Sales Range: $25-49.9 Million
Emp.: 20
Non-Durable Goods Whslr
N.A.I.C.S.: 424990
Massimo Nanni *(Gen Mgr)*

Sacmi USA Ltd. (1)
3434 106th Cir, Des Moines, IA 50322
Tel.: (515) 276-2052
Web Site: http://www.sacmiusa.com
Sales Range: $25-49.9 Million
Emp.: 20
Industrial Machinery & Equipment Merchant Whslr
N.A.I.C.S.: 423830
Luca Berrone *(Gen Mgr)*

Sacmi West Europe Beverage Technology SA (1)
Centre Hermes Ilot n 2, Ave Kastler Valgora, Toulon, 83160, France
Tel.: (33) 494570808
Web Site: http://www.sacmi.com
Sales Range: $25-49.9 Million
Emp.: 3
Commercial & Service Industry Machinery Mfr
N.A.I.C.S.: 333310
Stephane Merle *(Gen Mgr)*

Sama Maschinenbau GmbH (1)
Schillerstrasse 21, Weissenstadt, 95163, Erlangen, Germany
Tel.: (49) 92538890
Web Site: http://www.sama-online.com
Sales Range: $50-74.9 Million
Emp.: 110
Industrial Machinery Mfr
N.A.I.C.S.: 333248

SACOMBANK SECURITIES JOINT STOCK COMPANY
278 Nam Ky Khoi Nghia St Ward 8 Dist 3, Ho Chi Minh City, Vietnam
Tel.: (84) 8 6268 6868
Web Site: http://www.sbsc.com.vn
Year Founded: 2006
Sales Range: $50-74.9 Million
Investment Management Service
N.A.I.C.S.: 523999
Duong Cong Minh *(Chm)*

SACOVEN PLC
No 2 The Forum Grenville Street, Saint Helier, JE1 4HH, Jersey
Tel.: (44) 1534 823000   JE
Year Founded: 2012
Sales Range: Less than $1 Million

Holding Company
N.A.I.C.S.: 551112
Mark Haynes Daniell *(Chm)*

SACRIA INDUSTRIES
4 Rue De La Taye, 28110, Luce, Eure Et Loir, France
Tel.: (33) 237881919
Web Site: http://www.sacria.fr
Rev.: $13,800,000
Emp.: 44
Designs, Manufactures & Markets Vertical Balers & Horizontal or Semi-automatic Machines, Conveyor Systems, Compactors, Sorting Centers & Different Collection Equipment
N.A.I.C.S.: 333243
Jean-Francois Bedos *(Pres)*

SACYR, S.A.
C/ Condesa De Venadito 7, 28027, Madrid, Spain
Tel.: (34) 915455000   ES
Web Site: http://www.sacyr.com
SCYR—(BIL)
Rev.: $6,096,342,219
Assets: $18,395,914,242
Liabilities: $17,893,105,949
Net Worth: $502,808,294
Earnings: ($232,360,900)
Emp.: 42,471
Fiscal Year-end: 12/31/21
Holding Company; Construction, Infrastructure & Real Estate Services
N.A.I.C.S.: 551112
Manuel Manrique Cecilia *(Chm, Pres & CEO)*

Subsidiaries:

Aguas del Valle del Guadiaro, S.L. (1)
Paseo de Levante s/n Edificio E Local 7 A Puerto Deportivo, Sotogrande, 11310, Cadiz, Spain
Tel.: (34) 85 656 0924
Web Site: https://www.aguasvg.com
Purify Water Distribution Services
N.A.I.C.S.: 221310

Alazor Inversiones, S.A. (1)
Carretera Circunvalacion M 50, Villaviciosa de Odon, 28670, Madrid, Spain   (25.16%)
Tel.: (34) 917628700
Sales Range: $50-74.9 Million
Emp.: 250
Electronic Tolling Systems Installation Services
N.A.I.C.S.: 238210

Autoestradas de Galicia, S.A. (1)
Alfredo Vicenti 13 - 2, 15004, La Coruna, Spain
Tel.: (34) 981148918
Web Site: http://www.autoestradas.com
Emp.: 55
Highway Construction Services
N.A.I.C.S.: 237310

Autopista Concesionaria Astur-Leonesa, S.A. (1)
Parque Empresarial de ASIPO Plaza de Santa Barbara 4 - 2 4B, Cayes, 33428, Llanera, Asturias, Spain
Tel.: (34) 985240016
Web Site: http://www.aucalsa.com
Sales Range: $25-49.9 Million
Emp.: 18
Highway Construction & Maintenance Services
N.A.I.C.S.: 237310

Autopista de Navarra, S.A. (1)
Autopista AP-15 Km 83 sur, Tajonar, 31192, Navarra, Pamplona, Spain
Tel.: (34) 948243200
Web Site: http://www.audenasa.es
Toll Motorway Construction & Management Services
N.A.I.C.S.: 237310

Autopistas de Bizkaia, S.A. (1)
Camino Capuchinos de Basurtu 6 - 4 Planta, 48013, Bilbao, Biscay, Spain
Tel.: (34) 944396300

Highway Construction & Maintenance Services
N.A.I.C.S.: 237310

Autopistas del Atlantico, C.E.S.A. (1)
Alfredo Vicenti 15, 15004, La Coruna, Spain
Tel.: (34) 981148914
Web Site: http://www.audasa.es
Toll Highway Construction & Management Services
N.A.I.C.S.: 237310

Autovia del Eresma Conc. de la Junta de Castilla y Leon, S.A. (1)
Autovia A-601 Exit 85, Carbonero el Mayor, 40270, Segovia, Spain
Tel.: (34) 92 156 1976
Web Site: https://www.autoviadeleresma.com
Road Construction Services
N.A.I.C.S.: 237310

Cafestore, S.A. (1)
Av del Partenon 16-18/ 1a planta Campo de las Naciones, 28042, Madrid, Spain
Tel.: (34) 91 545 5000
Infrastructure Development Operator
N.A.I.C.S.: 236220

Empresa Mixta de Aguas de Santa Cruz de Tenerife, S.A. (1)
Comodoro Rolin 4-A, 38007, Santa Cruz de Tenerife, Spain
Tel.: (34) 92 223 0124
Web Site: https://www.emmasa.es
Drinking Water Distr
N.A.I.C.S.: 423990

Erantos, S.A.U. (1)
Paseo Castellana 83 - 85, 28046, Madrid, Spain
Tel.: (34) 916686278
Housing Building Construction Services
N.A.I.C.S.: 236116

Gestion Vial, S.A. (1)
Av Andres Bello 2711 Of 1003, Las Condes, Santiago, Chile
Tel.: (56) 6 538 5184
Web Site: http://www.gesvial.cl
Highway Construction & Maintenance Services
N.A.I.C.S.: 237310

Habitat Network, S.A. (1)
Calle Gran Via 15, 28013, Madrid, Spain   (9.09%)
Tel.: (34) 915241310
Web Site: http://www.habitania.com
Sales Range: $25-49.9 Million
Emp.: 20
Real Estate Management Software Development Services
N.A.I.C.S.: 541511

Subsidiary (Domestic):

Habitat Baix, S.L. (2)
Avenida Diagonal 490, 08006, Barcelona, Spain
Tel.: (34) 934161961
Real Estate Property Development
N.A.I.C.S.: 531210

Intercambiador de Transportes de Moncloa, S.A. (1)
C/ Princesa 98, 28008, Madrid, Spain
Tel.: (34) 914694571
Interchange Station Operation Services
N.A.I.C.S.: 488210

Inversora de Autopistas del Sur, S.L. (1)
Plaza Manuel Gomez-Moreno 2 - Ed Alfredo Mahou Planta 7, 28020, Madrid, Spain   (35%)
Tel.: (34) 911463004
Highway Construction & Maintenance Services
N.A.I.C.S.: 237310

Iparan Promociones Inmobiliarias, S.L. (1)
Calle Elcano 9 - U 1 1 F, 48008, Bilbao, Vizcaya, Spain
Tel.: (34) 944790449
Real Estate Property Development Services
N.A.I.C.S.: 531390

Medgulf Construction Company W.L.L. (1)

SACYR, S.A.

Sacyr, S.A.—(Continued)

Al Manara Building-First Floor Building No 128 B, PO Box 3603, Ring Road Street No 220 Zone 15, Doha, Qatar
Tel.: (974) 4 446 3000
Web Site:
https://www.medgulfconstruction.com
Emp.: 1,000
Building Construction Services
N.A.I.C.S.: 236220
Chakib Nayfe *(Gen Mgr)*

N6 Concession Ltd. (1)
Toll Plaza Building, Cappataggle, Ballinasloe, H53 N672, Galway, Ireland
Tel.: (353) 91843500
Web Site: http://www.n6concession.com
Toll Highway Operation Services
N.A.I.C.S.: 561990

Sacorec, S.L. (1)
Avenida de Kansas City 3-16 Edificio
Realia, 41018, Seville, Spain **(50%)**
Tel.: (34) 954 989 272
Solid Waste Collection Services
N.A.I.C.S.: 562111

Sacyr Agua Chacabuco, S.A. (1)
Joaquin Montero 3000 piso 4th Floor, Vitacura, Santiago, Chile
Tel.: (56) 600 300 2600
Web Site:
https://www.sacyraguachacabuco.cl
Water Treatment Distribution Services
N.A.I.C.S.: 221310

Sacyr Concesiones Chile, S.A. (1)
Edificio Titanium Avda Isidora Goyenechea 2800 Oficina 1101 piso 11, Las Condes, Santiago, Chile
Tel.: (56) 22 975 3333
Infrastructure Development Services
N.A.I.C.S.: 236220

Sacyr Concesiones Mexico, S.A. de C.V. (1)
Calz General Mariano Escobedo 595 Piso 6 Colonia Bosque de Chapultepec, 11589, Mexico, Mexico
Tel.: (52) 775 742 4035
Infrastructure Development Services
N.A.I.C.S.: 236220

Sacyr Concesiones Peru, S.A.C. (1)
Edificio Platinium Plaza-Torre 1 Calle Dean Valdivia N 148-158-Oficina, 1301 Urb Jardin San Isidro, Lima, Peru
Tel.: (51) 1 416 4949
Infrastructure Development Services
N.A.I.C.S.: 236220

Sacyr Concesiones Uruguay, S.A. (1)
Piedras 497 Oficina 202, Montevideo, Uruguay
Tel.: (598) 82 916 2445
Infrastructure Development Services
N.A.I.C.S.: 236220

Sacyr Construccion, S.A.U. (1)
C/ Condesa de Venadito 7, 28027, Madrid, Spain **(100%)**
Tel.: (34) 91 545 5000
Web Site: http://www.sacyr.com
Holding Company
N.A.I.C.S.: 551112

Subsidiary (Domestic):

Prinur, S.A.U. (2)
C/ Puerto 14 1, 29016, Malaga, Spain
Tel.: (34) 95 221 64 07
Web Site: http://www.sacyr.com
Sales Range: $25-49.9 Million
Emp.: 15
Residential Property Development Services
N.A.I.C.S.: 236116

Subsidiary (Domestic):

Ideyco, S.A.U. (3)
Calle Rio Jarama S/n, Toledo, 45007, Spain
Tel.: (34) 925240201
Quality Control & Certification Services
N.A.I.C.S.: 561990

Affiliate (Non-US):

SIS, S.C.P.A. (2)
Via Invorio 24/A, 10146, Rivalta di Torino, Italy
Tel.: (39) 0117172701
Web Site: http://www.sisscpa.it
Residential Property Development Services
N.A.I.C.S.: 531210

Subsidiary (Domestic):

Nodo Di Palermo, S.p.A. (3)
Via Invorio 24a, Turin, 10146, Italy
Tel.: (39) 0117176222
Web Site: http://www.fining.com
Emp.: 30
Commercial Building Construction Services
N.A.I.C.S.: 236220
Giraud Muela *(Gen Mgr)*

Subsidiary (Non-US):

SV-LIDCO Construcciones Generales S.A. (2)
Al Seyahiya Madneen Street, 5948, Tripoli, Libya
Tel.: (218) 214843255
Sales Range: $25-49.9 Million
Emp.: 22
Housing Building Construction Services
N.A.I.C.S.: 236115
Eduardo Cambos *(CEO)*

Sacyr Ireland Limited (2)
Unit 11 Harmony Court Harmony Row, Dublin, 2, Ireland
Tel.: (353) 16618833
Web Site: http://www.sacyr.com
Sales Range: $50-74.9 Million
Emp.: 4
Investment Management Service
N.A.I.C.S.: 523940
Callis Gallagher *(Gen Mgr)*

Subsidiary (Domestic):

Scrinser, S.A. (2)
Avda Corts Catalanes 2 2 Local 3, 8173, Sant Cugat del Valles, Barcelona, Spain
Tel.: (34) 93 589 67 80
Residential Property Development Services
N.A.I.C.S.: 531390

Sacyr Social, S.L. (1)
Av del Partenon 16-18/ 1a planta Campo de Las Naciones, 28042, Madrid, Spain
Tel.: (34) 91 545 5300
Infrastructure Development Services
N.A.I.C.S.: 236220

Sociedad Concesionaria Valles del Bio Bio, S.A. (1)
Peaje Huinanco Ruta 146 Km 33 9, Concepcion, Chile
Tel.: (56) 41 332 0001
Web Site: https://www.vallesdelbiobio.cl
Road Construction Services
N.A.I.C.S.: 237310

Sohar Operation Services LLC (1)
PO Box 9, 327, Sohar, Oman
Tel.: (968) 2 685 2700
Web Site:
https://www.soharportandfreezone.com
Port Services
N.A.I.C.S.: 488310
Mark Geilenkirchen *(CEO)*

VSM Colombia, S.A.S. (1)
Venida Calle 127 60-75 Area Limpia D C S A S E S P, Bogota, Colombia
Tel.: (57) 1 624 1243
Infrastructure Development Services
N.A.I.C.S.: 236220

Vallehermoso Division de Promocion, S.A.U. (1)
Paseo de la Castellana 83-85, 28046, Madrid, Spain **(100%)**
Tel.: (34) 902 24 26 24
Web Site: http://www.vallehermoso.es
Residential & Commercial Real Estate Development & Brokerage Services
N.A.I.C.S.: 531390

Affiliate (Domestic):

M.Capital, S.A. (2)
C/ Puerta del Mar 20, 29005, Malaga, Spain **(4.97%)**
Tel.: (34) 952222704
Web Site: http://www.mcapital.es
Investment Management Service
N.A.I.C.S.: 523940

Valoriza Facilities Chile, SpA (1)
Avda Isidora Goyenechea 2800 Piso 11, Las Condes, Santiago, Chile
Tel.: (56) 95 333 1727
Infrastructure Development Services
N.A.I.C.S.: 236220

Valoriza Gestion, S.A.U. (1)
Paseo de la Castellana 83-85, 28046, Madrid, Spain
Tel.: (34) 915455000
Web Site: http://www.sacyr.com
Sales Range: $75-99.9 Million
Emp.: 400
Management Services
N.A.I.C.S.: 541618
Fernando Lozano Sainz *(Mng Dir)*

Subsidiary (Domestic):

Sacyr Industrial, S.L.U. (2)
Paseo de la Castellana 83-85, 28046, Madrid, Spain **(100%)**
Tel.: (34) 91 545 5000
Power Plant, Waste Treatment Facility, Petroleum Pipeline & Power Line Engineering, Construction & Support Services
N.A.I.C.S.: 237990
Fernando Lozano Sainz *(Mng Dir)*

Valdemingomez 2000, S.A. (2)
Calle Albarracin 44, 28037, Madrid, Spain
Tel.: (34) 913851027
Sales Range: $25-49.9 Million
Emp.: 36
Residential Property Development Services
N.A.I.C.S.: 531210

SADAJUP SA
Clos Folard, CD 28, 84310, Avignon, France
Tel.: (33) 490335555
Rev.: $27,800,000
Emp.: 48
Grocery Stores
N.A.I.C.S.: 445110
Georges Pujadas *(Pres)*

SADBHAV ENGINEERING LTD
Sudbhav House Opp Law Garden Police Chowki Ellisbridge, Ahmedabad, 380006, Gujarat, India
Tel.: (91) 7926463384
Web Site:
https://www.sadbhaveng.com
SADBHAV—(NSE)
Rev.: $354,528,761
Assets: $1,704,106,991
Liabilities: $1,460,533,497
Net Worth: $243,573,494
Earnings: ($32,411,693)
Emp.: 2,691
Fiscal Year-end: 03/31/21
Road Construction Management
N.A.I.C.S.: 237310
Nitin R. Patel *(CFO)*

SADBHAV INFRASTRUCTURE PROJECTS LTD.
Sadbhav House Opp Law Garden Police Chowki Ellisbridge, Ahmedabad, 380 006, India
Tel.: (91) 26463384
Web Site:
https://www.sadbhavinfra.co.in
Year Founded: 2007
539346—(BOM)
Rev.: $219,689,652
Assets: $1,329,939,702
Liabilities: $1,304,421,164
Net Worth: $25,518,539
Earnings: ($37,987,404)
Fiscal Year-end: 03/31/21
Construction Consulting Services
N.A.I.C.S.: 541330
Vasisthra C. Patel *(Mng Dir)*

Subsidiaries:

Maharashtra Border Check Post Network Limited (1)

INTERNATIONAL PUBLIC

Godrej Coliseum 702 C Wing Behind Everard Nagar, Sion East, Mumbai, 400022, India **(86.9%)**
Tel.: (91) 2224095887
Web Site: http://www.mbcpnl.co.in
Border Check Post Services
N.A.I.C.S.: 518210

SADHANA NITRO CHEM LIMITED
Hira Baug 1 Floor Kasturba Chowk C P Tank, Mumbai, 400 004, India
Tel.: (91) 2268663300
Web Site: https://www.sncl.com
Year Founded: 1973
506642—(BOM)
Rev.: $14,736,869
Assets: $37,175,856
Liabilities: $19,456,383
Net Worth: $17,719,473
Earnings: $2,173,757
Emp.: 242
Fiscal Year-end: 03/31/21
Specialty Chemicals Mfr
N.A.I.C.S.: 325998
Asit D. Javeri *(Chm & Mng Dir)*

SADHNA BROADCAST LTD.
37 Rani Jhansi Road Jhandewalan, New Delhi, 110055, India
Tel.: (91) 1123552627
Web Site: https://www.sadhna.com
Year Founded: 1997
540821—(BOM)
Rev.: $2,427,265
Assets: $3,219,855
Liabilities: $1,520,676
Net Worth: $1,699,179
Earnings: ($14,196)
Fiscal Year-end: 03/31/23
Television Broadcasting Services
N.A.I.C.S.: 516120
Tajinder Kaur *(Mng Dir)*

SADIBO
119 Rue Pierre Revelli, 83130, La Garde, France
Tel.: (33) 494086688
Rev.: $28,800,000
Emp.: 104
Grocery Stores
N.A.I.C.S.: 445110
Patricia Lejay *(Gen Mgr)*

SADICO CANTHO JOINT STOCK CORPORATION
366E Cach mang thang 8 Street Bui Huu Nghia Ward, Binh Thuy District, Can Tho, Vietnam
Tel.: (84) 2923884919
Web Site: https://www.sadico.com.vn
SDG—(HNX)
Rev.: $54,140,309
Assets: $36,324,519
Liabilities: $17,449,311
Net Worth: $18,875,207
Earnings: $1,110,614
Fiscal Year-end: 12/31/21
Cement & Cement Cover Mfr
N.A.I.C.S.: 327310

SADO STEAM SHIP CO., LTD.
353 Ryotsuminato, Sado, 952-0014, Niigata, Japan
Tel.: (81) 25 9275174
Web Site: http://www.sadokisen.co.jp
Year Founded: 1913
9176—(JAS)
Rev.: $74,439,200
Assets: $145,596,880
Liabilities: $154,076,560
Net Worth: ($8,479,680)
Earnings: ($24,654,960)
Emp.: 177
Fiscal Year-end: 12/31/20
Marine Cargo Transportation Services
N.A.I.C.S.: 488320

SADOVAYA GROUP S.A.
6 Moskovska Street, Luhansk Oblast, 94204, Alchevsk, Ukraine
Tel.: (380) 644252552 LU
Web Site: https://www.sadovayagroup.com
SGR—(WAR)
Sales Range: $25-49.9 Million
Emp.: 1,619
Coal Mining Services
N.A.I.C.S.: 212115

SADTEM
148 Rue Martin Du Nord, 59500, Douai, Nord, France
Tel.: (33) 327713240
Web Site: http://www.sadtem.com
Rev.: $11,700,000
Emp.: 124
Current & Voltage Instrument Transformers Mfr
N.A.I.C.S.: 335312
Jean-Paul Avocat (Mng Dir, Mng Dir & Chm)

SAEDONG CO., LTD.
8 Jangansandan 8-ro Jangan-eup, Gijang-Gun, Busan, Korea (South)
Tel.: (82) 517967161
Web Site: https://www.saedong.co.kr
053060—(KRS)
Rev.: $119,691,369
Assets: $84,090,185
Liabilities: $62,246,374
Net Worth: $21,843,811
Earnings: $9,487,472
Emp.: 205
Fiscal Year-end: 12/31/22
Automotive Components Mfr
N.A.I.C.S.: 336390
Jung-Sang Yoon (CEO)

SAERTEX GMBH & CO. KG
Brochterbecker Damm 52, 48369, Saerbeck, Germany
Tel.: (49) 2574 902 0 De
Web Site: http://www.saertex.com
Year Founded: 1982
Emp.: 1,400
Industrial Non-Crimp Fabrics & Plastic-Reinforced Components Mfr & Whslr
N.A.I.C.S.: 313220
Bruno Heinrich Lammers (Exec Dir)

Subsidiaries:

Devold AMT AS (1)
Devold Facility, 6030, Langevag, Norway
Tel.: (47) 7019 8500
Web Site: http://www.amt.no
Sales Range: $25-49.9 Million
Fiberglass, Carbon Fiber & Hybrid Reinforcement Fabrics Mfr & Whslr
N.A.I.C.S.: 313220
Kare Dybvik (Mng Dir)

SAERTEX France SAS (1)
2 lot Parc d activites d Arandon, 38510, Arandon, France
Tel.: (33) 474804492
Fabrics Mfr
N.A.I.C.S.: 313210

SAERTEX India Private Limited (1)
Saertex Excellence Centre S No 282 Mann, Mulshi, Pune, 411 057, India
Tel.: (91) 2066537600
Automotive Components Mfr
N.A.I.C.S.: 333618
Meghna Pandya (Deputy Mgr-Supply Chain Mgmt)

SAERTEX Portugal, Unipessoal Lda. (1)
Parque Empresarial de Lanheses Fraccao 5B Estrada do Engenho 320, 4925-432, Paco de Lanhese, Portugal
Tel.: (351) 258840050
Fabrics Mfr
N.A.I.C.S.: 313210

SAERTEX Reinforcements Dongying Co., Ltd. (1)
No 102 Yihe Road, 257091, Dongying, Shandong, China
Tel.: (86) 5467796001
Glass Material Mfr
N.A.I.C.S.: 327215

SAERTEX South Africa (PTY) LTD. (1)
25 Boland Street Daljosafat, 7624, Paarl, South Africa
Tel.: (27) 218627790
Fabrics Mfr
N.A.I.C.S.: 313210

SAERTEX Stade GmbH & Co. KG (1)
Sophie-Scholl-Weg 24, 21684, Stade, Germany
Tel.: (49) 4141 4110 0
Web Site: http://www.saertex.com
Aerospace Plastic Composite Products Mfr
N.A.I.C.S.: 326199
Jens Kuhl (Mng Dir)

SAERTEX Tecidos Brasil Ltda. (1)
Condominio Industrial Caldeira Et General Motors 852 Halls 19 and 20, Indaiatuba, 13347-500, Sao Paulo, Brazil
Tel.: (55) 1931159900
Fabrics Mfr
N.A.I.C.S.: 313210
Christian Kissinger (CEO & Mng Dir)

SAERTEX USA, LLC (1)
12200 Mt Holly-Huntersville Rd Ste A, Huntersville, NC 28078
Tel.: (704) 464-5998
Web Site: http://www.saertex.com
Emp.: 300
Industrial Non-Crimp Fabrics Mfr & Whslr
N.A.I.C.S.: 313220
Randy Orchard (Mgr-Ops)

SAERTEX multiCom GmbH (1)
Brochterbecker Damm 52, 48369, Berlin, Germany
Tel.: (49) 2574 902 400
Web Site: http://www.saertex-multicom.com
Trenchless Sewer Pipe Rehabilitation Glass Fiber Fabric Products Mfr
N.A.I.C.S.: 313220
Bruno Lammers (Founder & Mng Partner)

SAES GETTERS S.P.A.
Viale Italia 77, 20045, Lainate, Italy
Tel.: (39) 0293178001 IT
Web Site: https://www.saesgetters.com
Year Founded: 1940
SG—(ITA)
Rev.: $270,089,575
Assets: $486,987,913
Liabilities: $202,018,131
Net Worth: $284,969,782
Earnings: $13,328,297
Emp.: 1,226
Fiscal Year-end: 12/31/22
Functional Chemicals & Metal Alloy Products Mfr
N.A.I.C.S.: 331492
Giulio Canale (Mng Dir & VP)

Subsidiaries:

Memry Corporation (1)
3 Berkshire Blvd, Bethel, CT 06801
Tel.: (203) 739-1100
Web Site: https://www.memry.com
Emp.: 400
Shape Memory Alloy & Specialty Polymer-Extrusion Products Designer, Engineer & Developer
N.A.I.C.S.: 339112

Subsidiary (Non-US):

Memry GmbH (2)
Am Kesselhaus 5, 79576, Weil am Rhein, Germany (100%)
Tel.: (49) 7621799121
Web Site: http://www.saesgetters.com
Sales Range: $25-49.9 Million
N.A.I.C.S.: 541330

Nanjing SAES Huadong Getters Co., Ltd. (1)
56 Xinangdaogo Xinshengwei Nanjing Economic & Technical, Development Zone, Nanjing, Jiangsu, China (65%)
Tel.: (86) 585802335
Web Site: http://www.saesgetters.com
Engineeering Services
N.A.I.C.S.: 541330

SAES Coated Films S.p.A. (1)
Via Leonardo Da Vinci 3, 20877, Roncello, Italy
Tel.: (39) 0396278321
Web Site: https://www.saescoatedfilms.com
Emp.: 150
Coated Film Mfr
N.A.I.C.S.: 326112

SAES Getters (Nanjing) Co., Ltd. (1)
Room 401 Building A of Maqun Science Entrepreneurship Center, No 18 Xianlin Avenue Qixia District, Nanjing, 210049, China
Tel.: (86) 2585802335
Raw Materials Mfr
N.A.I.C.S.: 325180

SAES Getters Japan Co., Ltd. (1)
2nd Gotanda Fujikoshi Bldg, 23 1 Higashi Gotand 5 Chome, Tokyo, 141-0022, Japan (100%)
Tel.: (81) 354200431
Web Site: http://www.saesgetters.jp
Sales Range: $25-49.9 Million
Mfr Plant
N.A.I.C.S.: 541330

SAES Getters Korea (1)
7th Fl gong won Bldg 143-28 Samsung Dong, Kangnam Ku, Seoul, 135 877, Korea (South) (100%)
Tel.: (82) 234042400
Web Site: http://www.seasgroup.com
Sales Range: $25-49.9 Million
Engineeering Services
N.A.I.C.S.: 541330

SAES Getters Singapore PTE, Ltd. (1)
6 Temasek Boulevard Suntec Tower 4 #41-06, Singapore, 038986, Singapore (100%)
Tel.: (65) 68873343
Web Site: http://www.saespuregas.com
Sales Range: $25-49.9 Million
Emp.: 4
N.A.I.C.S.: 541330

SAES Getters/U.S.A., Inc. (1)
1122 E Cheyenne Mountain Blvd, Colorado Springs, CO 80906
Tel.: (719) 576-3200
Web Site: http://www.saesgetters.com
Industrial Materials Developer & Mfr
N.A.I.C.S.: 339999

SAES RIAL Vacuum S.r.l. (1)
Strada Argini 97/A, 43123, Parma, Italy
Tel.: (39) 0521949311
Raw Materials Mfr
N.A.I.C.S.: 325180

Strumenti Scientifici Cinel S.r.l. (1)
Via dell'Artigianato 14-14/A, 35010, Vigonza, Padova, Italy
Tel.: (39) 049725022
Web Site: https://www.cinel.com
Electric Equipment Mfr
N.A.I.C.S.: 335999

SAETA YIELD SA
Cardenal Marcelo Spinola Number 10, Madrid, 28016, Spain
Tel.: (34) 918228745
Web Site: http://www.saetayield.com
Year Founded: 2009
Eletric Power Generation Services
N.A.I.C.S.: 221118
Jose Luis Martinez Dalmau (Chm & CEO)

SAF MAGELLAN AD
123 Prof Tsvetan Lazarov blvd, 1582, Sofia, Bulgaria
Tel.: (359) 2 810 62 22
Web Site: http://www.saf-bg.com
Meat Product Distr
N.A.I.C.S.: 332999

Georgi Yordanov Ivanov (Exec Dir)

SAF-HOLLAND S.A.
Hauptstrasse 26, D-63856, Bessenbach, Germany
Tel.: (49) 60953010
Web Site: https://safholland.com
Year Founded: 2005
SFQ—(DEU)
Rev.: $1,689,066,480
Assets: $1,617,119,577
Liabilities: $1,140,804,015
Net Worth: $476,315,562
Earnings: $66,077,056
Emp.: 3,366
Fiscal Year-end: 12/31/22
Holding Company; Truck, Trailer & Recreational Vehicle Component Mfr
N.A.I.C.S.: 551112
Martina Merz (Vice Chm-Supervisory Bd)

Subsidiaries:

Axscend Ltd. (1)
Unit B Hampton Court Tudor Road, Runcorn, WA7 1TT, Cheshire, United Kingdom
Tel.: (44) 1303842100
Web Site: https://axscend.com
Truck Transportation Services
N.A.I.C.S.: 484110

KLL Equipamentos Para Transporte Ltda. (1)
Av Presidente Getulio Vargas 9994, Alvorada, 94836-000, Rio Grande do Sul, Brazil
Tel.: (55) 5134839393
Web Site: https://www.kll.com.br
Truck & Trailer Mfr
N.A.I.C.S.: 336212

L.V.Technik Kft. (1)
Kullai Koz 52, Kecskemet, 6050, Hungary
Tel.: (36) 76493507
Emp.: 8
Truck, Trailer & Recreational Vehicle Component Mfr
N.A.I.C.S.: 336390
George Leitem (Gen Mgr)

SAF-HOLLAND GmbH (1)
Hauptstrasse 26, D-63856, Bessenbach, Germany
Tel.: (49) 60953010
Web Site: https://safholland.com
Commercial Vehicle Component Mfr
N.A.I.C.S.: 336390

SAF-HOLLAND Hong Kong Ltd. (1)
Room 2201-03 22/F World Wide House 19 Des Voeux Road, Central, China (Hong Kong)
Tel.: (852) 5926288891
Truck & Trailer Mfr
N.A.I.C.S.: 336212

SAF-Holland (Aust.) Pty. Ltd. (1)
115 High Street, PO Box 63, Melton, Melbourne, 3337, VIC, Australia
Tel.: (61) 399717900
Web Site: https://www.safholland.com.au
Sales Range: $25-49.9 Million
Truck, Trailer & Recreational Vehicle Component Mfr
N.A.I.C.S.: 336390

SAF-Holland (Malaysia) SDN. BHD. (1)
Block A Ascendas Logistics Hub 16 Jalan TP6, Subang Jaya Industrial Park, Petaling Jaya, 47620, Malaysia
Tel.: (60) 60380243433
Truck, Trailer & Recreational Vehicle Component Mfr
N.A.I.C.S.: 336390

SAF-Holland (Thailand) Co., Ltd. (1)
444 Olympia Thai Tower 15th Fl Ratchadaphisek Road, Samsennok Huay Kwang, Bangkok, 10320, Thailand
Tel.: (66) 251387589
Truck, Trailer & Recreational Vehicle Component Mfr
N.A.I.C.S.: 336390

SAF-Holland (Xiamen) Co., Ltd. (1)
1599 DongFu Road, DongFu industrial

SAF-HOLLAND S.A.

SAF-Holland S.A.—(Continued)
zone, 381027, Xiamen, Fujian, China
Tel.: (86) 5926288891
Sales Range: $100-124.9 Million
Emp.: 260
Truck, Trailer & Recreational Vehicle Component Mfr
N.A.I.C.S.: 336390
Thomas Peisker *(Gen Mgr)*

SAF-Holland Austria GmbH (1)
Aura Business Center, Triesterstrasse 10-4-1-5, 2351, Wiener Neudorf, Austria
Tel.: (43) 2236646500
Truck, Trailer & Recreational Vehicle Component Mfr
N.A.I.C.S.: 336390

SAF-Holland Bulgaria EOOD (1)
Bul Akad Ivan Geshov 2E Business Center Serdika, Sofia, 1330, Bulgaria
Tel.: (359) 2 833 4100
Web Site: http://www.safholland.bg
Truck, Trailer & Recreational Vehicle Component Mfr
N.A.I.C.S.: 336390

SAF-Holland Canada, Ltd (1)
595 Athlone Avenue, Woodstock, N4S 7V8, ON, Canada
Tel.: (519) 537-2366
Web Site: https://www.safholland.ca
Sales Range: $50-74.9 Million
Truck, Trailer & Recreational Vehicle Component Mfr
N.A.I.C.S.: 336390
Kim Baechler *(Pres)*

SAF-Holland Czechia spol. s r.o. (1)
Kvitkovicka 1527, 763 61, Napajedla, Czech Republic
Tel.: (420) 572540903
Web Site: https://safholland.com
Truck, Trailer & Recreational Vehicle Component Mfr
N.A.I.C.S.: 336390

SAF-Holland Denmark ApS (1)
Fabriksvej 18, DK-6000, Kolding, Denmark
Tel.: (45) 75504142
Truck, Trailer & Recreational Vehicle Component Mfr
N.A.I.C.S.: 336390

SAF-Holland Equipment, Ltd. (1)
20 Phoebe St, Otterville, N0J 1P0, ON, Canada
Tel.: (519) 863-3414
Truck, Trailer & Recreational Vehicle Component Mfr
N.A.I.C.S.: 336390

SAF-Holland Espana S.L. (1)
Pl Congost Cami Ral 1, Montornes del Valles, E-08170, Barcelona, Spain
Tel.: (34) 938468111
Truck, Trailer & Recreational Vehicle Component Mfr
N.A.I.C.S.: 336390

SAF-Holland GmbH (1)
Hauptstrasse 26, Bessebach, 63856, Aschaffenburg, Germany
Tel.: (49) 60953010
Web Site: http://www.safholland.com
Sales Range: $200-249.9 Million
Truck, Trailer & Recreational Vehicle Component Mfr
N.A.I.C.S.: 336390

Subsidiary (Non-US):

SAF-Holland France SAS (2)
Zone Artisanale Ablis Nord, BP 48, Ablis, 78660, Yvelines, France
Tel.: (33) 130880900
Web Site: https://www.safholland.com
Rev.: $28,700,000
Emp.: 18
Motor Vehicle Supplies & New Parts
N.A.I.C.S.: 423120

YORK Transport Equipment (Asia) Pte. Ltd. (2)
122 Pioneer Rd, Singapore, 639583, Singapore (100%)
Tel.: (65) 68978525
Web Site: http://www.yorktransport.com
Trailer Axles Mfr
N.A.I.C.S.: 336212

SAF-Holland Inc. (1)
1950 Industrial Blvd, Muskegon, MI 49442
Tel.: (231) 773-3271
Web Site: http://www.safholland.us
Sales Range: $100-124.9 Million
Truck, Trailer & Recreational Vehicle Component Mfr
N.A.I.C.S.: 336390

Subsidiary (Domestic):

SAF-Holland International, Inc. (2)
1950 Industrial Blvd, Muskegon, MI 49442-6114
Tel.: (231) 773-3271
Web Site: http://www.safholland.ca
Sales Range: $50-74.9 Million
Emp.: 115
Truck, Trailer & Recreational Vehicle Component Mfr
N.A.I.C.S.: 336390

Plant (Domestic):

SAF-Holland USA, Inc. (2)
430 W 18th St, Holland, MI 49422
Tel.: (616) 396-6501
Sales Range: $25-49.9 Million
Emp.: 50
Truck, Trailer & Recreational Vehicle Component Mfr
N.A.I.C.S.: 336390
David Farragh *(Mgr-Sls & Accts-OE & Trailer)*

SAF-Holland USA, Inc.-Dumas (2)
1103 S Main, Dumas, AR 71639-0825
Tel.: (870) 382-2299
Web Site: http://www.safholland.com
Sales Range: $25-49.9 Million
Emp.: 100
Truck, Trailer & Recreational Vehicle Component Mfr
N.A.I.C.S.: 336390

SAF-Holland USA, Inc.-Warrenton (2)
308 W Walton St, Warrenton, MO 63383-1922
Tel.: (636) 456-3455
Web Site: http://www.safholland.com
Sales Range: $75-99.9 Million
Emp.: 300
Truck, Trailer & Recreational Vehicle Components Mfr
N.A.I.C.S.: 336390

SAF-Holland India Private Ltd. (1)
S No 93/1 Goparasanallur Village Poonamallee High Road, Thiruvallur District, Chennai, India
Tel.: (91) 9843077351
Truck, Trailer & Recreational Vehicle Component Mfr
N.A.I.C.S.: 336390

SAF-Holland International Services Mexico S. de R.L. de C.V. (1)
Recursos Hidraulicos 10 Tlalnepantla de Baz, Mexico, 54060, Mexico
Tel.: (52) 5553628743
Web Site: https://www.safholland.com.mx
Emp.: 9
Industrial Machinery Mfr
N.A.I.C.S.: 333248

SAF-Holland International de Mexico S. de R.L. de C.V. (1)
Av Paseo de las Palmas 405-301, Torre Optima Nivel 3, Col Lomas de Chapultepec, CP 11000', Mexico, Mexico
Tel.: (52) 5554568641
Truck, Trailer & Recreational Vehicle Component Mfr
N.A.I.C.S.: 336390

SAF-Holland Italia S.R.L unipersonale (1)
Via Monte Fiorino 23, 37057, San Giovanni Lupatoto, Italy
Tel.: (39) 0458250560
Web Site: http://www.safholland.it
Sales Range: $25-49.9 Million
Truck, Trailer & Recreational Vehicle Component Mfr
N.A.I.C.S.: 336390

SAF-Holland Middle East FZE (1)
Plot No S20105 Free Zone - South, PO Box 261743, Jebel Ali, Dubai, United Arab Emirates
Tel.: (971) 48157222
Emp.: 14
Industrial Equipment Mfr
N.A.I.C.S.: 333248

SAF-Holland Nippon, Ltd. (1)
Asahi Seimei Miyamasuzaka Building 8F 1-9-8 Shibuya, Shibuya-Ku, Tokyo, 150-0002, Japan
Tel.: (81) 334985777
Web Site: http://www.nippon-safholland.jp
Truck, Trailer & Recreational Vehicle Component Mfr
N.A.I.C.S.: 336390

SAF-Holland Otomotiv Sanayi ve Ticaret Limited Sirketi (1)
Dorus Sanayi Sitesi Islahiye Koyu Dorus Sk No 10, Umraniye, Istanbul, Duzce, Turkiye
Tel.: (90) 3805290100
Web Site: https://safholland.com
Automobile Parts Mfr
N.A.I.C.S.: 336390

SAF-Holland Polska Sp.z o.o. (1)
Wawelska 131, 64-920, Warsaw, Poland
Tel.: (48) 672166570
Truck, Trailer & Recreational Vehicle Component Mfr
N.A.I.C.S.: 336390

SAF-Holland Romania SRL (1)
Strada Stefan cel Mare 369, Ghimbav, 507075, Brasov, Romania
Tel.: (40) 268258830
Web Site: http://ww1.safholland.ro
Sales Range: $25-49.9 Million
Truck, Trailer & Recreational Vehicle Component Mfr
N.A.I.C.S.: 336390

SAF-Holland Rus OOO (1)
Prospect Mira 68 Stroenie 1a Office 21, 129110, Moscow, Russia
Tel.: (7) 496095301247
Web Site: http://www.safholland.ru
Truck, Trailer & Recreational Vehicle Component Mfr
N.A.I.C.S.: 336390

SAF-Holland South Africa (Proprietary) Ltd (1)
Reco Building Cnr Crownwood Modulus Roads, Ormonde, Johannesburg, 2091, South Africa
Tel.: (27) 114963196
Truck, Trailer & Recreational Vehicle Component Mfr
N.A.I.C.S.: 336390

SAF-Holland Verkehrstechnik GmbH (1)
Julius-Buhrer-Strasse 12, 78224, Singen, Germany
Tel.: (49) 773114430
Web Site: https://safholland.com
Sales Range: $75-99.9 Million
Emp.: 60
Commercial Transport Vehicle Fifth Wheel Couplings Mfr
N.A.I.C.S.: 336390

SAF-Holland do Brasil Ltda. (1)
Avenida Presidente Getulio Vargas 9994, Alvorada, 94836-000, Brazil
Tel.: (55) 5134839393
Web Site: http://ww1.safholland.com.br
Sales Range: $25-49.9 Million
Truck, Trailer & Recreational Vehicle Component Mfr
N.A.I.C.S.: 336390

V.Orlandi Australia Pty Ltd. (1)
PO Box 478, South Yarra, Melbourne, 3141, VIC, Australia
Tel.: (61) 390434332
Web Site: http://www.orlandi.com.au
Motor Vehicles Mfr
N.A.I.C.S.: 336211

V.Orlandi S.p.A. (1)
Via Quinzano 3, Flero, 25020, Brescia, Italy
Tel.: (39) 0303582722
Web Site: https://www.orlandi.it
Motor Vehicles Mfr
N.A.I.C.S.: 336211

YTE Transport Equipment (SA) (Pty) Ltd. (1)

INTERNATIONAL PUBLIC

115 Bellefield Ave Mondeor, Johannesburg, 2091, South Africa
Tel.: (27) 823764552
Motor Vehicles Mfr
N.A.I.C.S.: 336211

York Sales (Thailand) Co. Ltd. (1)
2101 M 1 Old Railway Road Samrong Nua, Muang Rayong, 10270, Samutprakarn, Thailand
Tel.: (66) 27435091
Motor Vehicles Mfr
N.A.I.C.S.: 336211

York Transport Equipment (India) Pvt. Ltd. (1)
Gat No 468-472 563-565 Village Badhalwadi, Talegaon MIDC Mawal, Pune, 410507, India
Tel.: (91) 2114645022
Motor Vehicles Mfr
N.A.I.C.S.: 336211

York Transport Equipment (Shanghai) Co. Ltd. (1)
No 228 Nanhui Industrial Park Zone Yuan Xi Road, Pu Dong New District, Shanghai, 201300, China
Tel.: (86) 2129468532
Motor Vehicles Mfr
N.A.I.C.S.: 336211

SAFA SYSTEMS & TECHNOLOGIES LIMITED

Behind Holiday Inn Safa Arcade Door No 46/2361 B Kaniyapilly Road, Chakkaraparambu Vennala PO Ernakulam, Kochi, 682028, India
Tel.: (91) 7593001140
Web Site: https://www.sssinfo.in
Year Founded: 2012
543461—(NSE)
Mobile Product Mfr
N.A.I.C.S.: 334210
Faizal Bavaraparambil Abdul Khader *(Mng Dir)*

Subsidiaries:

Effective Lifestyle Private Limited (1)

SAFA TEXTILES LTD.

20 Sasi Town House Civil Lines, Abdullah Haroon Road, Karachi, Pakistan
Tel.: (92) 21 5653261
Web Site: http://www.safatextile.com
SFAT—(KAR)
Sales Range: $1-9.9 Million
Woven Garments Mfr
N.A.I.C.S.: 315210

SAFAL HERBS LIMITED

305 3rd Floor Neelkanth Chamberse Plot No 14 LSC Saini Enclave, Opp Bus Stand Station Road, Delhi, 110092, Delhi, India
Tel.: (91) 9687009012
Web Site: http://www.safalherbs.com
Rev.: $56,063
Assets: $1,425,511
Liabilities: $28,469
Net Worth: $1,397,042
Earnings: ($2,147)
Fiscal Year-end: 03/31/18
Pharmaceuticals Product Mfr
N.A.I.C.S.: 325412
Amit Kumar Sodhani *(Compliance Officer & Sec)*

SAFAL SECURITIES LIMITED

9 Ankur Complex B/h Town Hall, Opp X- ray House Ellisbridge, Ahmedabad, 380 006, India
Tel.: (91) 7930071299
Web Site: http://www.safalsecurities.co.in
Year Founded: 1995
Rev.: $5,882
Assets: $281
Liabilities: $30,451

AND PRIVATE COMPANIES

Net Worth: ($30,170)
Earnings: ($5,459)
Fiscal Year-end: 03/31/18
Security Brokerage Services
N.A.I.C.S.: 523150

SAFANAD LIMITED
Level 4 The Gate East Dubai International Financial Centre, Dubai, United Arab Emirates
Tel.: (971) 4 312 9700   AE
Web Site: http://www.safanad.com
Emp.: 100
Investment Management Service
N.A.I.C.S.: 523940
Kamal Bahamdan *(Founder & CEO)*

Subsidiaries:

Safanad (UK) Limited   (1)
21/22 Grosvenor Street, London, W1K 4QJ, United Kingdom
Tel.: (44) 207 429 7770
Web Site: http://www.safanad.com
Real Estate & Private Equity Investment Firm
N.A.I.C.S.: 523999
Iain McKillop *(Dir-Investment)*

Safanad Inc.   (1)
500 5th Ave 50th Fl, New York, NY 10110-5099
Tel.: (212) 863-9434
Web Site: http://www.safanad.com
Real Estate & Private Equity Investment Firm
N.A.I.C.S.: 523999
Craig Kahler *(Dir-Private Equity)*

Safanad S.A.   (1)
13 rue du Rhone, 1204, Geneva, Switzerland
Tel.: (41) 22 707 0630
Web Site: http://www.safanad.com
Real Estate & Private Equity Investment Firm
N.A.I.C.S.: 523999
Mark Benn *(Mng Dir & Grp CFO)*

SAFARI INDUSTRIES (INDIA) LTD.
302-303 A Wing The Qube CTS No 1498 A/2, Sir Mathuradas Vasanji Rd Marol Andheri East, Mumbai, 400 059, Maharashtra, India
Tel.: (91) 2240381888
Web Site: https://safaribags.com
SAFARI—(NSE)
Rev.: $146,446,916
Assets: $89,689,827
Liabilities: $38,646,940
Net Worth: $51,042,887
Earnings: $14,997,890
Emp.: 901
Fiscal Year-end: 03/31/23
Plastic Molded Suitcase Mfr
N.A.I.C.S.: 326199
Sudhir M. Jatia *(Chm & Mng Dir)*

SAFARI INVESTMENTS RSA LTD.
410 Lynnwood Road, Lynnwood, Pretoria, 0081, South Africa
Tel.: (27) 123651889   ZA
Web Site: https://www.safari-investments.com
Year Founded: 2000
SAR—(JSE)
Rev.: $24,128,846
Assets: $201,058,207
Liabilities: $72,779,022
Net Worth: $128,279,185
Earnings: $17,052,990
Emp.: 30
Fiscal Year-end: 03/31/23
Investment Management Service
N.A.I.C.S.: 523940
Francois Jakobus Joubert Marais *(Mgr-Asset)*

SAFARI MINERALS INC.
1920 Yonge Street Suite 200, Toronto, M4S 3E2, ON, Canada
Tel.: (416) 572-7545
Web Site: http://www.safariminerals.com
Diamonds & Precious Metals Mining & Production Services
N.A.I.C.S.: 212311
Andrew Lovett *(Pres & CEO)*

SAFARI WORLD PUBLIC COMPANY LIMITED
No 99 Panyaintra Road Kwaeng Samwatawantok, Khet Klongsamwa, Bangkok, 10510, Thailand
Tel.: (66) 25181000
Web Site: https://ticket.safariworld.com
Year Founded: 1985
Sales Range: $50-74.9 Million
Amusement Park Operator
N.A.I.C.S.: 712190
Narong Chulajata *(Chm)*

SAFARICOM PLC
Safaricom House Waiyaki Way, PO Box 66827, 00800, Nairobi, Kenya
Tel.: (254) 722004524
Web Site: https://www.safaricom.co.ke
Year Founded: 1997
SCOM—(NAI)
Rev.: $2,234,161,893
Assets: $3,659,161,502
Liabilities: $1,766,614,145
Net Worth: $1,892,547,357
Earnings: $377,141,401
Emp.: 5,362
Fiscal Year-end: 03/31/23
Telecommunication Servicesb
N.A.I.C.S.: 517112
Sylvia Mulinge *(Chief Customer Bus Officer)*

Subsidiaries:

Comtec Training and Management Services Limited   (1)
United Nations Cre, Nairobi, 0621, Kenya
Tel.: (254) 207120724
Sales Range: $10-24.9 Million
Emp.: 70
Training & Management Services
N.A.I.C.S.: 611430

SAFBON WATER SERVICE (HOLDING) INC., SHANGHAI
No 666 Zhangliatang Rd Qingpu District, Shanghai, 201715, China
Tel.: (86) 2162569366
Web Site: http://www.safbon.com
Year Founded: 1995
300262—(CHIN)
Rev.: $37,015,056
Assets: $502,295,040
Liabilities: $489,070,764
Net Worth: $13,224,276
Earnings: ($54,214,056)
Emp.: 1,000
Fiscal Year-end: 12/31/22
Holding Company; Wastewater, Municipal Sewage & Solid Waste Treatment, Seawater Desalination & Innovation
N.A.I.C.S.: 551112
Hilling Zhang *(Founder & Chm)*

Subsidiaries:

Itn Nanovation AG   (1)
Peter-Zimmer-Strasse 11, 66123, Saarbrucken, Germany   (68%)
Tel.: (49) 6815001460
Web Site: https://company.aquatechtrade.com
Sales Range: Less than $1 Million
Emp.: 23
Ceramic Products Mfr
N.A.I.C.S.: 327110

Ulrich-Peter Kinzl *(Vice Chm-Supervisory Bd)*

SAFE AT SEA AB
Importgatan 15F, 422 46, Hisings Backa, Sweden
Tel.: (46) 303230700
Web Site: https://www.safeatsea.se
Year Founded: 2006
Sea Rescue Services
N.A.I.C.S.: 624230
Henrik Hartman *(CEO)*

SAFE BAG S.P.A.
Via Marsala 34/A, 21013, Gallarate, Italy
Tel.: (39) 0331777154
Web Site: http://www.safe-bag.com
Year Founded: 1997
Emp.: 200
Luggage Security Services
N.A.I.C.S.: 561621

Subsidiaries:

Global Baggage Protection Systems, Inc.   (1)
4050 NW 29th St, Miami, FL 33142   (74.5%)
Tel.: (305) 870-9720
Web Site: http://www.securewrap.com
Sales Range: $1-9.9 Million
Emp.: 100
Airport Baggage Protection
N.A.I.C.S.: 488119
Enrique Ramos *(Chm)*

SAFE BULKERS, INC.
Apt D11 Les Acanthes 6 Avenue Des Citronniers, MC98000, Monaco, Monaco
Tel.: (377) 97988181   MH
Web Site: https://www.safebulkers.com
Year Founded: 2007
SB—(NYSE)
Rev.: $349,718,000
Assets: $1,245,918,000
Liabilities: $474,002,000
Net Worth: $771,916,000
Earnings: $172,554,000
Emp.: 914
Fiscal Year-end: 12/31/22
Bulk Shipping & Transportation Services
N.A.I.C.S.: 483111
Loukas Barmparis *(Pres & Sec)*

SAFE MIX CONCRETE LIMITED
Plot 1 Global Industry Nusrat Bhutto Colony Opposite Jamia Usmania, North Nazimabad, Karachi, Pakistan
Tel.: (92) 34520224734
Web Site: https://www.safemixlimited.com
SMCPL—(PSX)
Rev.: $5,151,751
Assets: $2,680,080
Liabilities: $1,693,303
Net Worth: $986,776
Earnings: $479,801
Emp.: 130
Fiscal Year-end: 06/30/23
Readymix Concrete Mfr
N.A.I.C.S.: 327320
Kashif A. Habib *(CEO)*

SAFE SA
80 rue Montepy, ZA de Montepy, 69210, Fleurieux-sur-L'Arbresle, France
Tel.: (33) 427447380   FR
Web Site: https://safegrp.com
Year Founded: 2010
ALSAF—(EUR)
Sales Range: $1-9.9 Million
Medical Device Mfr

SAFECORP GROUP LTD.

N.A.I.C.S.: 339112
Thomas Droulout *(Co-Founder & Chief Technical Officer)*

Subsidiaries:

Safe Orthopaedics SAS   (1)
80 rue Montepy, ZA de Montepy, ZA de Montepy, 69210, Fleurieux-sur-L'Arbresle, France
Tel.: (33) 481098701
Web Site: https://www.safeorthopaedics.com
Medical Device Mfr & Distr
N.A.I.C.S.: 339112

Subsidiary (Non-US):

Safe Orthopaedics GmbH   (2)
Lebacher Strasse 4, 66113, Saarbrucken, Germany
Tel.: (49) 6819963275
Orthopedic Care Services
N.A.I.C.S.: 621111

Safe Orthopaedics Ltd.   (2)
International House Holborn Viaduct, London, EC1A 2BN, United Kingdom
Tel.: (44) 2035144070
Orthopedic Care Services
N.A.I.C.S.: 621111

Subsidiary (US):

Safe Orthopaedics, LLC   (2)
3175 Lenox Park Blvd Ste 108, Memphis, TN 38115-4256
Tel.: (901) 259-4161
Web Site: http://www.safeortho.com
Medical Device Mfr
N.A.I.C.S.: 339112
Steve Foster *(Pres)*

SAFE SUPPLY STREAMING CO., LTD.
666 Burrard Street 25th Floor, Vancouver, V6C 2X8, BC, Canada
Tel.: (416) 566-3872   BC
Web Site: https://www.safesupply.com
Year Founded: 2023
SSPLF—(OTCIQ)
Rev.: $18,657
Assets: $4,168,693
Liabilities: $118,856
Net Worth: $4,049,837
Earnings: ($1,081,575)
Emp.: 1
Fiscal Year-end: 09/30/22
Pharmaceutical Product Mfr & Distr
N.A.I.C.S.: 325412

SAFECODE DRUG TECHNOLOGIES CORP.
6 Meever HaMiltah Street, Jerusalem, 97761, Israel
Tel.: (972) 25021322   DE
Year Founded: 2010
Emp.: 2
Medical Device Mfr
N.A.I.C.S.: 339112
Itamar Zer *(Sec)*

SAFECORP GROUP LTD.
25-27 Park Way, Braeside, 3195, VIC, Australia
Tel.: (61) 3 9587 9500   AU
Web Site: http://www.safecorp.com.au
Year Founded: 1884
Emp.: 750
Holding Company; Security Locks Mfr & Laundry Services
N.A.I.C.S.: 551112
Jeff Peterson *(Chm)*

Subsidiaries:

Lock Focus Pty. Ltd.   (1)
15-17 Futura Road, Keysborough, 3173, VIC, Australia
Tel.: (61) 397981322
Web Site: http://www.lockfocus.com.au

SAFECORP GROUP LTD.

Safecorp Group Ltd.—(Continued)
Emp.: 100
Electronic Access & Locking Solutions
N.A.I.C.S.: 336320

SAFEGUARD WORLD INTERNATIONAL LTD.
Edwin Foden Business Centre Ste 24/25 Moss Lane, Sandbach, CW11 3AE, Cheshire, United Kingdom
Tel.: (44) 1270 758020
Web Site: http://www.safeguardworld.com
Year Founded: 1969
Payroll Processing Services
N.A.I.C.S.: 541214
John Giles *(COO)*

SAFELAND PLC
1A Kingsley Way, London, N2 0FW, United Kingdom
Tel.: (44) 2088151600   UK
Web Site: http://www.safeland.co.uk
Rev.: $3,912,448
Assets: $44,113,526
Liabilities: $15,027,848
Net Worth: $29,085,678
Earnings: $2,895,212
Emp.: 8
Fiscal Year-end: 03/31/18
Property Trading & Investment Services
N.A.I.C.S.: 531390
Larry Glenn Lipman *(Co-Founder & Mng Dir)*

Subsidiaries:

Safeland Active Management Limited (1)
1A Kingsley Way, London, N2 0FW, United Kingdom
Tel.: (44) 2088151600
Web Site: http://www.safeland.co.uk
Emp.: 15
Investment Management Service
N.A.I.C.S.: 541618
Larry Lipman *(Gen Mgr)*

Safeland Investments Limited (1)
1 A Kingsley Way, London, N2 0FW, United Kingdom
Tel.: (44) 2088151600
Web Site: http://www.safeland.co.uk
Property Development Services
N.A.I.C.S.: 531190
Larry Lipman *(Mng Dir)*

SAFELLO GROUP AB
Malmskillnadsgatan 32, 111 51, Stockholm, Sweden
Tel.: (46) 103440050
Web Site: https://www.safello.com
Year Founded: 2013
SFL—(OMX)
Rev.: $52,637,332
Assets: $3,845,758
Liabilities: $625,381
Net Worth: $3,220,377
Earnings: ($41,867)
Emp.: 24
Fiscal Year-end: 12/31/23
Investment Management Service
N.A.I.C.S.: 523999
Emelie Moritz *(CEO)*

SAFER ALSACE
18 rue des Orphelins, 68067, Mulhouse, Cedex, Haut Rhin, France
Tel.: (33) 389432467
Web Site: http://www.safer.fr
Sales Range: $10-24.9 Million
Emp.: 12
Real Estate Agency
N.A.I.C.S.: 531210
Marc Moser *(Pres)*

SAFER DE HAUTE-NORMANDIE
43rue Join-Lambert, CS 50585, Bois-Guillaume, Cedex, France
Tel.: (33) 235596695
Web Site: http://www.safer.fr
Rev.: $24,800,000
Emp.: 28
Real Estate Services
N.A.I.C.S.: 531210
Pascal Benard *(Deputy CEO)*

SAFEROADS HOLDINGS LIMITED
22 Commercial Dr, PO Box 2030, Pakenham, 3810, VIC, Australia
Tel.: (61) 359456600
Web Site: https://www.saferoads.com.au
Year Founded: 1992
SRH—(ASX)
Rev.: $8,500,259
Assets: $7,846,271
Liabilities: $4,680,308
Net Worth: $3,165,964
Earnings: ($2,549,123)
Fiscal Year-end: 06/30/24
Road Safety Products Mfr & Distr
N.A.I.C.S.: 326199
Darren J. Hotchkin *(CEO)*

Subsidiaries:

Saferoads Pty Ltd (1)
22 Commercial Dr, Pakenham, 3810, VIC, Australia
Tel.: (61) 359456600
Road Safety Product Mfr
N.A.I.C.S.: 334310

SAFESTAY PLC
John Smith House Walworth Rd, Walworth, London, SE17 1JL, United Kingdom
Tel.: (44) 2077038000
Web Site: https://www.safestay.com
Year Founded: 2014
SSTY—(AIM)
Rev.: $24,168,139
Assets: $116,750,820
Liabilities: $79,187,074
Net Worth: $37,563,747
Earnings: ($355,971)
Emp.: 11
Fiscal Year-end: 12/31/22
Hotel Owner & Operator
N.A.I.C.S.: 721110
Larry Glenn Lipman *(Chm)*

Subsidiaries:

Arcadie SA (1)
Rue Gretry 53, 1000, Brussels, Belgium
Tel.: (32) 22194343
Hotel Services
N.A.I.C.S.: 721110

Dream Hostel SK sro (1)
Leskova 4932/9A, Bratislava, Slovakia
Tel.: (421) 233000237
Accommodation Services
N.A.I.C.S.: 721199

Dream Hostel Sp. z o.o. (1)
Krakowskie Przedmiescie 55, 00-071, Warsaw, Poland
Tel.: (48) 224194848
Accommodation Services
N.A.I.C.S.: 721199

Equity Point Lisboa Unipessoal Lda. (1)
Tel.: (351) 218018211
Hotel & Motel Operator
N.A.I.C.S.: 721110

Equity Point Prague s.r.o. (1)
Ostrovni 131/15, Nove Mesto, 110 00, Prague, Czech Republic
Tel.: (420) 222540012
Hotel & Motel Operator
N.A.I.C.S.: 721110

Safestay (Edinburgh) Hostel Limited (1)
Tel.: (44) 1315241989

Hotel Services
N.A.I.C.S.: 721110

Safestay (Elephant & Castle) Limited (1)
144-152 Walworth Road Elephant & Castle, London, SE17 1JL, United Kingdom
Tel.: (44) 2077038000
Hotel Services
N.A.I.C.S.: 721110

Safestay (York) Limited (1)
Micklegate House 88-90 Micklegate, York, YO1 6JX, United Kingdom
Tel.: (44) 1904627720
Hotel Services
N.A.I.C.S.: 721110

Safestay Athens Hostel S.A. (1)
Agias Theklas No 10 Monastiraki, 10554, Athens, Greece
Tel.: (30) 2103225010
Hostel Management Services
N.A.I.C.S.: 721199

Safestay Espana S.L (1)
Passeig de Gracia 33, 08007, Barcelona, Spain
Tel.: (34) 932156538
Hotel & Motel Operator
N.A.I.C.S.: 721110

Safestay Hostel GmbH (1)
Schonbrunner Strasse 41, 1050, Vienna, Austria
Tel.: (43) 18906589
Hotel & Motel Operator
N.A.I.C.S.: 721110

Safestay Hostels Madrid SL (1)
Calle de Sagasta 22, 28004, Madrid, Spain
Tel.: (34) 914450300
Hotel Booking Services
N.A.I.C.S.: 561599

Safestay Italia Srl (1)
Via Filippo Corridoni 29, 56121, Pisa, PI, Italy
Tel.: (39) 03920794111
Accommodation Services
N.A.I.C.S.: 721199

SAFESTORE HOLDINGS PLC
Brittanic House Stirling Way, Borehamwood, WD6 2BT, Hertfordshire, United Kingdom
Tel.: (44) 2087321500
Web Site: https://www.safestore.co.uk
SAFE—(LSE)
Rev.: $240,592,500
Assets: $3,065,431,500
Liabilities: $1,034,944,020
Net Worth: $2,030,487,480
Earnings: $524,435,040
Fiscal Year-end: 10/31/22
Self-Storage Facilities Operator
N.A.I.C.S.: 531130
Frederic Vecchioli *(CEO)*

Subsidiaries:

Safestore Acquisition Limited (1)
Brittanic House Stirling Way, Borehamwood, WD6 2BT, Hertfordshire, United Kingdom
Tel.: (44) 2087321500
Web Site: http://www.safestore.co.uk
Investment Management Service
N.A.I.C.S.: 523940

Une Piece en Plus SAS (1)
159 rue Blomet, 75015, Paris, France
Tel.: (33) 1 56 08 32 32
Web Site: http://www.unepieceenplus.com
Self Storage Facility Operator
N.A.I.C.S.: 531130

SAFESTYLE UK PLC
Style House Eldon Place, Bradford, BD1 3AZ, West Yorkshire, United Kingdom
Tel.: (44) 808 278 3741
Web Site: http://www.safestyle-windows.co.uk
Year Founded: 1992

SFE—(AIM)
Rev.: $194,494,748
Assets: $98,438,773
Liabilities: $50,583,216
Net Worth: $47,855,557
Earnings: $6,483,113
Emp.: 700
Fiscal Year-end: 12/31/21
Double-Glazed Windows & Doors Mfr & Retailer
N.A.I.C.S.: 332321

SAFETIC S.A.
130 rue Archimede, BP 60 454, 13592, Aix-en-Provence, Cedex 3, France
Tel.: (33) 442908560
Web Site: http://www.safetic.eu
Year Founded: 2004
Sales Range: $100-124.9 Million
Emp.: 852
Electronic Security Products Mfr
N.A.I.C.S.: 561621
Marc Ligonesche *(Sec)*

Subsidiaries:

Easydentic (France) (1)
Parc de la Duranne, 730 rue Rene, Descartes, 60454, France
Tel.: (33) 442908560
Digital Electronic Products Installation
N.A.I.C.S.: 811210

Eden (France) (1)
994 Rue de la Gare, 13770, Venelles, France
Tel.: (33) 442545850
Web Site: http://www.tech-eden.com
Sales Range: $25-49.9 Million
Emp.: 20
Security Device Mfr
N.A.I.C.S.: 561621

Innovatys (France) (1)
29 Blvd des Alpes, Meylan, 38240, France
Tel.: (33) 811092121
Information Technology Consulting Services
N.A.I.C.S.: 541618

SafeTIC AG (1)
Flossworthstrasse 57, 68199, Mannheim, Germany
Tel.: (49) 621 842 528 0
Web Site: http://www.safe-tic.de
Digital Electronic Products Installation
N.A.I.C.S.: 811210
Walter Butler *(Chm-Supervisory Bd)*

SAFETONET LIMITED
40 Caversham Road, Reading, RG1 7BT, United Kingdom
Tel.: (44) 203 950 30 47
Web Site: http://safetonet.com
Security System Services
N.A.I.C.S.: 561621
Richard Pursey *(CEO)*

Subsidiaries:

ContentWatch, Inc. (1)
2369 West Orton Cir, Salt Lake City, UT 84119
Tel.: (801) 977-7777
Web Site: http://www.contentwatch.com
Sales Range: $1-9.9 Million
Emp.: 50
Internet Protection Services & Software Mfr
N.A.I.C.S.: 513210
Brent L. Bishop *(Chm)*

Subsidiary (Domestic):

Net Nanny Software International Inc. (2)
625 2nd St 4th Fl, San Francisco, CA 91407
Tel.: (415) 348-7142
Web Site: http://www.netnanny.com
Internet Filtering Software Mfr
N.A.I.C.S.: 541512

SAFETURE AB
Kung Oskars vag 11C, 222 35, Lund, Sweden

Tel.: (46) 46386750
Web Site: https://www.safeture.com
SFTR—(OMX)
Rev.: $2,629,603
Assets: $3,487,826
Liabilities: $2,419,626
Net Worth: $1,068,200
Earnings: ($3,109,378)
Emp.: 44
Fiscal Year-end: 12/31/20
Mobile-Based Personal Security Services
N.A.I.C.S.: 561621
Lars Lidgren (Co-Founder)

SAFETY GODOWN COMPANY LIMITED
Unit 1801 18/F Lu Plaza 2 Wing Yip Street, Kwun Tong, Kowloon, China (Hong Kong)
Tel.: (852) 2 622 1100
Web Site:
http://www.safetygodown.com
0237—(HKG)
Rev.: $15,845,193
Assets: $538,615,321
Liabilities: $19,066,340
Net Worth: $519,548,981
Earnings: ($10,903,711)
Emp.: 36
Fiscal Year-end: 03/31/22
Investment Holding Services
N.A.I.C.S.: 523940
Wayne Wing Yee Lu (Exec Dir)

SAFEX CHEMICALS (INDIA) LIMITED
4th & 5th Floor Block A, NDM-1 Netaji Subhash Place, New Delhi, 110034, India
Tel.: (91) 11 6610 5000
Web Site: https://safexchemicals.com
Year Founded: 1991
Crop Protection Product Mfr
N.A.I.C.S.: 325180
S.K. Chaudhary (Founder)

Subsidiaries:

Briar Chemicals Ltd. (1)
Sweet Briar Road, Norwich, NR6 5AP, Norfolk, United Kingdom
Tel.: (44) 1603242424
Web Site: http://www.briarchemicals.com
Agrochemical Product Mfr
N.A.I.C.S.: 325320
Nigel Beard (Mgr-Engrg)

SAFFRON INDUSTRIES LIMITED
Navabharat Bhawan Chhatrapati Square Wardha Road, Nagpur, 440 015, Maharashtra, India
Tel.: (91) 7122284013
Web Site:
https://www.saffronindustries.in
Year Founded: 1993
Paper Products Mfr
N.A.I.C.S.: 322120
Vinod Maheshwari (Chm)

SAFIC-ALCAN SAS
3 rue Bellini, 92800, Puteaux, France
Tel.: (33) 1 46 92 64 64
Web Site: http://www.safic-alcan.com
Year Founded: 1847
Sales Range: $450-499.9 Million
Emp.: 592
Specialty Chemicals Distr
N.A.I.C.S.: 424690
Liliane Perez (Mgr-Comm)

Subsidiaries:

ChemSpec Ltd. (1)
3570 Executive Dr Ste 211, Uniontown, OH 44685 (75%)
Tel.: (330) 896-0355
Web Site: http://www.chemspecltd.com

Emp.: 5
Rubber & Adhesives Distr
N.A.I.C.S.: 424690
Dave Moreland (Pres)

Safic-Alcan Adriatic d.o.o. (1)
Njegoseva 48, 11000, Belgrade, Serbia
Tel.: (381) 642 429 789
Specialty Chemicals Distr
N.A.I.C.S.: 424690
Dejan Djordjevic (Mng Dir)

Safic-Alcan Benelux S.A./N.V. (1)
Neringstraat 11, 1840, Londerzeel, Belgium
Tel.: (32) 52 30 36 42
Web Site: http://www.safic-alcan.co.fr
Emp.: 9
Specialty Chemicals Distr
N.A.I.C.S.: 424690
Patrick Oerter (Mng Dir)

Safic-Alcan Necarbo B.V. (1)
Noorderkade 28, Beverwijk, 1948 NR, Netherlands
Tel.: (31) 251 278 300
Web Site: http://www.safic-alcan.nl
Industrial Products Mfr & Whslr
N.A.I.C.S.: 423840

Safic-Alcan UK Ltd (1)
812 Fountain Court Birchwood Boulevard, Birchwood, Warrington, WA3 7QZ, United Kingdom
Tel.: (44) 1925 848 135
Web Site: http://www.safic-alcan.co.uk
Specialty Chemicals Distr
N.A.I.C.S.: 424690
Phil Griffin (Bus Mgr-South)

SAFICHEM GROUP AG
Toedistrasse 16, 8002, Zurich, Switzerland
Web Site:
http://www.safichemgroup.com
Emp.: 1,300
Holding Company; Metal Manufacturing & Engineering in Chemical & Petrochemical Industries
N.A.I.C.S.: 551112
Tomas Plachy (CEO)

Subsidiaries:

AQUATIS a.s. (1)
Botanicka 834/56 okres Brno-mesto, 602 00, Brno, Czech Republic
Tel.: (420) 541554111
Web Site: http://www.poyry.cz
Emp.: 140
Water Treatment & Water Pipeline Construction Services
N.A.I.C.S.: 237110
Pavel Kutalek (Mng Dir)

Chemoprojekt, a. s. (1)
Trebohosticka 14, 100 31, Prague, Czech Republic
Tel.: (420) 261305111
Web Site: http://www.chemoprojekt.cz
Construction Engineering Services
N.A.I.C.S.: 541330
Tomas Plachy (CEO & Gen Dir)

DUKLA STROJIRNY, s.r.o. (1)
Ovcarecka 575, Sendrazice, 280 02, Kolin, Czech Republic
Tel.: (420) 321740411
Web Site: http://www.duklastrojirny.cz
Boiler Mfr
N.A.I.C.S.: 332410
Pavel Matousek (Gen Mgr)

ENERGOCHEM a.s. (1)
Karasek 1767/1, Brno, 621 00, Czech Republic
Tel.: (420) 544520004
Web Site: http://www.energochem.cz
Construction Engineering Services
N.A.I.C.S.: 541330
Martin Luke (Head-Quality Mgmt Dept)

IDO HUTNY PROJEKT a.s. (1)
Tomasikova 64, 83104, Bratislava, Slovakia
Tel.: (421) 232177304
Web Site: http://www.hupro.sk
Construction Engineering Services
N.A.I.C.S.: 541330
Martin Hrusc (Mgr-Engrg)

PACOVSKE STROJIRNY, a.s. (1)
Nadrazni 697, 395 01, Pacov, Czech Republic
Tel.: (420) 565410111
Web Site: http://www.pacovske.cz
Steel Products Mfr
N.A.I.C.S.: 332312
Ludvik Jesatko (Dir Gen)

SAFICHEM ASSETS, a.s. (1)
Videnska 104, 252 42, Vestec, Czech Republic
Tel.: (420) 313033450
Web Site: http://www.safichemassets.com
Asset Management Services
N.A.I.C.S.: 531390

VUAB Pharma a. s. (1)
Vltavska 53, 252 63, Roztoky, Czech Republic
Tel.: (420) 220394504
Web Site: http://www.vuab.cz
Pharmaceuticals Product Mfr
N.A.I.C.S.: 325412
Jan Mengler (Chm & Gen Dir)

ZVU STROJIRNY, a.s. (1)
Kampelikova 758/4 Kukleny, 500 04, Hradec Kralove, Czech Republic
Tel.: (420) 497771270
Web Site: http://www.zvustrojirny.cz
Industrial Machinery & Equipment Mfr
N.A.I.C.S.: 333998
David Duka (Dir-Pur)

SAFIE INC.
Sumitomo Fudosan Osaki Garden Tower 1-1-1 Nishi-Shinagawa, Shinagawa-ku, Tokyo, 141-0033, Japan
Web Site: https://www.safie.co.jp
Year Founded: 2014
4375—(TKS)
Rev.: $83,782,530
Assets: $82,960,090
Liabilities: $11,946,650
Net Worth: $71,013,440
Earnings: ($10,195,420)
Emp.: 468
Fiscal Year-end: 12/31/23
Software Development Services
N.A.I.C.S.: 541511

SAFIG MOYENS DE PAIEMENT
4 Rue Gambetta, 93400, Saint-Ouen, Seine Saint Denis, France
Tel.: (33) 149219500
Web Site: http://www.safig.fr
Rev.: $20,500,000
Emp.: 350
Customer Relationship Management
N.A.I.C.S.: 518210
Isabelle Durou (Dir)

SAFIG STREAMWAY
4 Rue Gambetta, 93400, Saint-Ouen, France
Tel.: (33) 149219500
Web Site: http://www.safig.fr
Rev.: $27,200,000
Emp.: 503
Data Processing & Preparation
N.A.I.C.S.: 518210
Daniel Marechal (Dir)

SAFILO GROUP S.P.A.
Settima Strada 15, 35129, Padua, Italy
Tel.: (39) 0496985111
Web Site:
https://www.safilogroup.com
Year Founded: 1934
SFL—(ITA)
Rev.: $1,162,038,636
Assets: $1,036,334,988
Liabilities: $562,646,234
Net Worth: $473,688,755
Earnings: $56,495,791
Emp.: 4,442
Fiscal Year-end: 12/31/22

Mfr & Distr of Ophthalmic Frames, Sport Goggles & Sunglasses
N.A.I.C.S.: 339115
Barbara Ferrante (Dir-IR)

Subsidiaries:

Safilo America Inc. (1)
801 Jefferson Rd, Parsippany, NJ 07054-3710
Tel.: (973) 952-2800
Web Site: http://www.safilo.com
Eyewear Products Distr
N.A.I.C.S.: 423460

Subsidiary (Domestic):

Safilo Services LLC (2)
801 Jefferson Rd, Parsippany, NJ 07054-3710
Tel.: (973) 952-2800
Web Site: http://www.mysafilo.com
Sales Range: $75-99.9 Million
Emp.: 350
Optical Goods Mfr
N.A.I.C.S.: 333310
Carmine Somma (Gen Mgr)

Safilo Australia Pty Ltd. (1)
Unit 11 120 Taren Point Rd, Taren Point, Sydney, 2229, NSW, Australia
Tel.: (61) 295400500
Sales Range: $25-49.9 Million
Emp.: 40
Ophthalmic Goods Whslr
N.A.I.C.S.: 423460
David Peirson (Gen Mgr)

Safilo Austria GmbH (1)
Johann-Roithner-Str 131, 4050, Traun, Austria
Tel.: (43) 72297733591
Ophthalmic Goods Whslr
N.A.I.C.S.: 423460

Safilo Benelux S.A. (1)
Ikaros Business Park, Ikaroslaan 33 A Gebouw 4, 1930, Zaventem, Belgium
Tel.: (32) 27253242
Web Site: http://www.safilo.com
Sales Range: $25-49.9 Million
Emp.: 25
Photographic Equipment & Supplies Whslr
N.A.I.C.S.: 423410

Safilo Do Brasil Ltda (1)
Tel.: (55) 1121739900
Ophthalmic Goods Whslr
N.A.I.C.S.: 423460

Safilo Espana SA (1)
CL Xaudaro 24, 28037, Madrid, Spain (100%)
Tel.: (34) 913044340
Sales Range: $50-74.9 Million
Emp.: 60
Ophthalmic Goods Whslr
N.A.I.C.S.: 423460
Filippo Pustetto (Gen Mgr)

Safilo Far East Ltd. (1)
1501-07 Tower 6 The Gateway Harbour City 9 Canton Road, Kowloon, China (Hong Kong) (100%)
Tel.: (852) 28892230
Web Site: http://www.safilo.com
Ophthalmic Goods Whslr
N.A.I.C.S.: 423460

Subsidiary (Domestic):

Safilo Hong-Kong Ltd (2)
Rm 1501-07 15/F The Gateway Twr 6 9 Canton Rd Harbour City, Tsim Sha Tsui, Kowloon, China (Hong Kong)
Tel.: (852) 23126138
Web Site: http://www.safilo.com
Emp.: 3
Optical Goods Mfr
N.A.I.C.S.: 333310

Safilo France SARL (1)
20-24 Rue Jacques Ibert, CS 30062, Allee des Erables Villepinte, 92300, Levallois-Perret, Cedex, France
Tel.: (33) 820888081
Ophthalmic Goods Whslr
N.A.I.C.S.: 423460

Safilo GmbH (1)
Tel.: (49) 6996759903

SAFILO GROUP S.P.A.

Safilo Group S.p.A.—(Continued)
Web Site: http://www.safilo.de
Sales Range: $25-49.9 Million
Emp.: 25
Ophthalmic Goods Whslr
N.A.I.C.S.: 423460

Safilo Hellas S.A. (1)
Alimountos 1 St, Ilioupoli, 16341, Athens, Greece
Tel.: (30) 2105322566
Ophthalmic Goods Whslr
N.A.I.C.S.: 423460

Safilo India Private Limited (1)
RPT House Plot No 6, Sec 24 Turbhe Navi Mumbai, 400705, Mumbai, MH, India **(100%)**
Tel.: (91) 2227834949
Web Site: http://www.safiloindia.com
Sales Range: $50-74.9 Million
Emp.: 55
Ophthalmic Goods Whslr
N.A.I.C.S.: 423460

Safilo International B.V. (1)
Naritaweg 165 Telestone 8, 1043, Amsterdam, Netherlands
Tel.: (31) 206712751
Sales Range: $50-74.9 Million
Emp.: 2
Ophthalmic Goods Whslr
N.A.I.C.S.: 423460

Subsidiary (Non-US):

Safilo Hellas Ottica S.a. (2)
1 Alimountos Str & 563 Vouliagmenis Ave Ilioupoli, Haidari, Athens, 16341, Greece
Tel.: (30) 2105322566
Web Site: http://www.safilo.com
Sales Range: $25-49.9 Million
Optical Lens Mfr
N.A.I.C.S.: 333310
George Itsios *(Country Mgr & Gen Mgr)*

Safint Australia Pty Ltd. (2)
U 11 120 Taren Point Rd, Taren Point, Sydney, 2229, NSW, Australia
Tel.: (61) 295400500
Ophthalmic Goods Distr
N.A.I.C.S.: 423460
David Pearson *(Gen Mgr)*

Safilo Japan Co. Ltd. (1)
Jiji Press Bldg Level 9, 5-15-8 Ginza Chouku, Tokyo, 104-0061, Japan **(100%)**
Tel.: (81) 351487741
Web Site: http://www.safilo.com
Sales Range: $25-49.9 Million
Emp.: 30
Ophthalmic Goods Whslr
N.A.I.C.S.: 423460

Safilo Latin America (1)
703 Waterford Ste 100, Miami, FL 33126 **(100%)**
Tel.: (305) 262-5727
Sales Range: $25-49.9 Million
Emp.: 3
Ophthalmic Goods Mfr
N.A.I.C.S.: 339115
Ana Crolla *(Sr Acct Mgr)*

Safilo Netherland BV (1)
PO Box 124, 3720, Bilthoven, Netherlands
Tel.: (31) 302253341
Ophthalmic Goods Whslr
N.A.I.C.S.: 423460

Safilo Nordic AB (1)
Svardvagen 19, PO Box 611, 18233, Danderyd, Sweden **(100%)**
Tel.: (46) 86303820
Sales Range: $25-49.9 Million
Emp.: 40
Ophthalmic Goods Whslr
N.A.I.C.S.: 423460
Viktor Gullbrand *(VP)*

Safilo Optical Sdn. Bhd. (1)
CP 36 Ste 17-03 Central Plz 34, Jalan Sultan Ismail, Kuala Lumpur, 54250, Malaysia **(100%)**
Tel.: (60) 321451988
Sales Range: $25-49.9 Million
Emp.: 16
Ophthalmic Goods Whslr
N.A.I.C.S.: 423460

Safilo Portugal LDA (1)
Rua Poeta Bocage 11 D, 1600-581, Lisbon, Portugal **(100%)**
Tel.: (351) 217121420
Sales Range: $50-74.9 Million
Emp.: 60
Ophthalmic Goods Whslr
N.A.I.C.S.: 423460

Safilo Singapore Pte Ltd. (1)
Biztech Ctr, 627A Aljunied Rd 07-03, 389842, Singapore, 389842, Singapore **(100%)**
Tel.: (65) 67427703
Web Site: http://www.safilo.com
Emp.: 20
Ophthalmic Goods Whslr
N.A.I.C.S.: 423460

Safilo SpA (1)
Via Settima Strada, 35129, Padua, Italy
Tel.: (39) 0496985111
Ophthalmic Goods Mfr
N.A.I.C.S.: 339115
Angelo Trocchia *(CEO)*

Subsidiary (Non-US):

Carrera Optyl D.o.o. (2)
38 A Ljutomerska Cesta, Ormoz, 2270, Slovenia
Tel.: (386) 27410120
Optical Goods Distr
N.A.I.C.S.: 423460

Subsidiary (Domestic):

Lenti S.r.l. (2)
Via B Locatelli 59, Brembate di Sopra, BG, Italy **(100%)**
Tel.: (39) 035553029
Web Site: https://www.lentisrl.com
Optical Instrument Mfr
N.A.I.C.S.: 333310

Safilo Switzerland AG (1)
Oristalstrasse 87, 04410, Liestal, Switzerland **(100%)**
Tel.: (41) 619268500
Web Site: http://www.safilo.ch
Sales Range: $25-49.9 Million
Emp.: 20
Ophthalmic Goods Whslr
N.A.I.C.S.: 423460

Safilo Trading Shenzhen Co. Ltd. (1)
Unit 201-202 Blk 4 A Honghua Rd Fuitan Free Trade Zone, Shenzhen, China
Tel.: (86) 75583593987
Ophthalmic Goods Whslr
N.A.I.C.S.: 423460

Safilo UK Ltd. (1)
(100%)
Tel.: (44) 2078415990
Sales Range: $25-49.9 Million
Ophthalmic Goods Mfr
N.A.I.C.S.: 339115

Safilo USA Inc. (1)
Tel.: (973) 952-2800
Web Site: https://www.mysafilo.com
Sales Range: $50-74.9 Million
Emp.: 120
Mfr of Ski Glasses & Sunglasses
N.A.I.C.S.: 339115

SAFKAR EGE SOGUTMACILIK KLIMA SOGUK HAVA TES-.IHR.ITH. A.S.

Ulukent Sanayi Bolgesi 29 Ekim Mah 10001 Sk No 56 Ulukent, Menemen, Izmir, Turkiye
Tel.: (90) 2328333764
Web Site: https://www.safkar.com
Year Founded: 1988
SAFKR—(IST)
Rev.: $9,798,958
Assets: $10,589,149
Liabilities: $4,188,613
Net Worth: $6,400,536
Earnings: $2,180,259
Fiscal Year-end: 12/31/22
Air Conditioning System Mfr
N.A.I.C.S.: 333415
Abdi Mertturk *(Chm)*

SAFKO SPINNING MILLS LTD.

House 10 6th Floor Block-B Road 1 Niketan Gulshan, Dhaka, 1212, Bangladesh
Tel.: (880) 29841092
Web Site: https://saiham-safko.com
Year Founded: 1997
SAFKOSPINN—(CHT)
Rev.: $3,754,716
Assets: $18,128,017
Liabilities: $13,767,619
Net Worth: $4,360,398
Earnings: ($1,508,444)
Emp.: 449
Fiscal Year-end: 06/30/23
Cotton Yarn & Polyester Mfr
N.A.I.C.S.: 313110
Syed A. B. M. Humayun *(Mng Dir)*

SAFMAR INDUSTRIAL & FINANCIAL GROUP

22 Tverskaya Street, Moscow, 125009, Russia
Tel.: (7) 495 909 89 69   RU
Web Site: http://www.safmargroup.ru
Year Founded: 1992
Holding Company
N.A.I.C.S.: 551112
Mikhail Gutseriev *(Founder & Chm)*

Subsidiaries:

PJSC SAFMAR Financial Investments (1)
Bolshoy Ovchinnikovsky Lane, Moscow, 119049, Russia
Tel.: (7) 4959010361
Web Site: https://safmarinvest.ru
Rev.: $349,789,034
Assets: $6,188,790,595
Liabilities: $4,842,489,871
Net Worth: $1,346,300,725
Earnings: $144,062,450
Emp.: 7,100
Fiscal Year-end: 12/31/2019
Investment Holding Company
N.A.I.C.S.: 551112

Subsidiary (Domestic):

JSC LC Europlan (2)
Koroviy Val str 5, 119049, Moscow, Russia **(100%)**
Tel.: (7) 4952508080
Web Site: http://www.europlan.ru
Emp.: 1,957
Commercial & Industrial Machinery Equipment Mfr
N.A.I.C.S.: 532112
Alexander Mikhaylov *(CEO)*

PJSC M.video (2)
Nizhnyaya Krasnoselskaya St 40/12 building 20 floor 5 premises II, Room 3, Moscow, 105066, Russia
Tel.: (7) 8006007775
Web Site: https://www.mvideo.ru
Sales Range: Less than $1 Million
Consumer Electronic Products Distr
N.A.I.C.S.: 423620
Alexander Tynkovan *(Founder & Pres)*

Subsidiary (Domestic):

LLC ELDORADO (3)
ul Lower Krasnoselskaya d 40/12 Building 20, 105066, Moscow, Russia **(100%)**
Tel.: (7) 8002502525
Web Site: http://www.eldorado.ru
Consumer Electronics & Domestic Appliance Retailer
N.A.I.C.S.: 423620
Sergey Lee *(Mng Dir)*

Subsidiary (Domestic):

OOO Media-Markt-Saturn (4)
Novodmitrovskaya Str 5a Bld 8, 127015, Moscow, Russia
Tel.: (7) 4956609304
Consumer Electronics Retail Store Operating Services
N.A.I.C.S.: 449210

OOO Media-Saturn-Russland (4)
Str 8 5a Novodmitrovskaya Ul, Moscow, 127015, Russia
Tel.: (7) 4956444299
Consumer Electronics Retail Store Operating Services
N.A.I.C.S.: 449210

SAFOCO FOODSTUFF JOINT STOCK COMPANY

1079 Pham Van Dong St Linh Tay Ward, Thu Duc District, Ho Chi Minh City, Vietnam
Tel.: (84) 837245275
Web Site: https://www.safocofood.com
Year Founded: 1975
SAF—(HNX)
Rev.: $79,280,400
Assets: $25,795,600
Liabilities: $8,100,600
Net Worth: $17,695,000
Earnings: $5,120,900
Fiscal Year-end: 12/31/23
Food Products Mfr
N.A.I.C.S.: 311999
Nga Tjhi Nguyen *(Chief Acctg Officer)*

SAFRAN SA

2 boulevard du General Martial Valin, 75015, Paris, France
Tel.: (33) 140608080   FR
Web Site: https://www.safran-group.com
SEJ1—(DEU)
Rev.: $25,524,498,165
Assets: $54,465,788,906
Liabilities: $41,971,724,585
Net Worth: $12,494,064,321
Earnings: $3,716,814,159
Emp.: 87,055
Fiscal Year-end: 12/31/23
Aerospace Products Mfr
N.A.I.C.S.: 551112
Stephane Dubois *(Exec VP-Corp Human & Social Responsibility)*

Subsidiaries:

Airbus Safran Launchers SAS (1)
51-61 Route de Verneuil, 78130, Les Mureaux, Cedex, France
Tel.: (33) 139061234
Web Site: https://www.ariane.group
Emp.: 450
Space Launcher Research & Development Services
N.A.I.C.S.: 336415
Alain Charmeau *(CEO)*

Subsidiary (Domestic):

Arianespace SAS (2)
Boulevard de l'Europe, BP 177, Courcouronnes, 91006, Evry, Cedex, France
Tel.: (33) 16 087 6000
Web Site: https://www.arianespace.com
Emp.: 300
Commercial Space Transportation Services
N.A.I.C.S.: 481212
Louis Laurent *(Sr VP)*

Subsidiary (Non-US):

Arianespace Singapore Pte. Ltd. (3)
No 3 Shenton Way No 18-09A Shenton House, Singapore, 068805, Singapore
Tel.: (65) 62236426
Web Site: http://www.arianespace.com
Commercial Space Transportation Services
N.A.I.C.S.: 481212
Vivian Quenet *(Mng Dir & Head-Sls-Asia Pacific)*

Subsidiary (US):

Arianespace, Inc. (3)
5335 Wisconsin Ave NW Ste 520, Washington, DC 20015
Tel.: (202) 628-3936
Web Site: http://www.arianespace.com
Emp.: 5
Commercial Space Transportation Services
N.A.I.C.S.: 481212
Wiener Kernisan *(Pres)*

AND PRIVATE COMPANIES — SAFRAN SA

Aircelle (1)
Rte Du Pont VIII, PO Box 91, 76700, Le Havre, France **(99.98%)**
Tel.: (33) 235554700
Web Site: http://www.aircelle.com
Sales Range: $800-899.9 Million
Emp.: 3,000
Nacelle, Thrust Reverser & Aerostructure Mfr
N.A.I.C.S.: 336412
Martin Sion (Chm & CEO)

Subsidiary (Domestic):

Aircelle Europe Services SAS (2)
Zone Industrielle de Saint Ulfrant, 27500, Pont Audemer, 27500, France
Tel.: (33) 2 32 20 40 00
Web Site: http://www.aircelle.com
Aeronautical Engineering Services
N.A.I.C.S.: 541330
Pichon Jean-Francois (Gen Mgr)

Subsidiary (Non-US):

Safran Nacelles Limited (2)
Bancroft Road, Burnley, BB10 2TQ, Lancashire, United Kingdom
Tel.: (44) 1282419300
Web Site: http://www.aircelle.com
Emp.: 800
Nacelle, Thrust Reverser & Aerostructure Mfr
N.A.I.C.S.: 336412

CFM International Inc. (1)
1 Neumann Way, Cincinnati, OH 45215-0514
Tel.: (513) 552-3272
Web Site: https://www.cfmaeroengines.com
Sales Range: $150-199.9 Million
Jet Engine Mfr; Owned by SAFRAN & General Electric Company
N.A.I.C.S.: 423860

Corse Composites Aeronautiques (1)
Zone Industrielle Du Vazzio, PO Box 902, 20700, Ajaccio, Cedex, France **(33%)**
Tel.: (33) 49 529 0400
Web Site: https://corse-composites-aeronautiques.com
Sales Range: $50-74.9 Million
Emp.: 190
High Performance Composite Parts for Planes, Helicopters & Engines Mfr
N.A.I.C.S.: 336412

Efficience - MGI (1)
Zone Artisanale Des Mazures, BP 13, 35680, Louvigne-De-Bais, France
Tel.: (33) 299490655
Web Site: http://www.efficience.fr
Commercial Printing Services
N.A.I.C.S.: 323111

Etablissements Vallaroche SA (1)
Rond Point Rene Ravaud Reau, Moissy-Cramayel, 77550, France
Tel.: (33) 1 40 60 80 80
Aircraft Part Mfr
N.A.I.C.S.: 336413
Dominique-Jean Chertier (Chm & CEO)

Europropulsion SA (1)
11 Rue Salomon De Rothschild, F 92150, Suresnes, France **(50%)**
Tel.: (33) 146978383
Sales Range: $25-49.9 Million
Emp.: 27
Solid Rocket Motor Contractor
N.A.I.C.S.: 332994

Evac GmbH (1)
Feldstrasse 124, 22880, Wedel, Germany
Tel.: (49) 41 03 91 68 0
Web Site: http://www.evac-train.com
Sanitary Systems Mfr
N.A.I.C.S.: 332999
Tom Hiett (Sr Sls Mgr-APAC)

Fabrications Mecaniques de l'Atlantique SA (1)
Zone Industrielle De Brais Rue Edison, PO Box 218, 44614, Saint Nazaire, France **(100%)**
Tel.: (33) 240172323
Web Site: http://www.famat.fr
Sales Range: $150-199.9 Million
Emp.: 470

Welded Castings & Other Components for Aircraft Engines Mfr; Owned 50% by Societe Nationale d'Etude et de Construction de Moteurs d'Aviation & 50% by General Electric
N.A.I.C.S.: 336412

Fan Blade Associates, Inc. (1)
1209 Orange St, Wilmington, DE 19801
Tel.: (302) 658-7581
Aircraft Parts & Equipment Mfr
N.A.I.C.S.: 336413

Herakles S.A. (1)
rue de Touban, Les Cinq Chemins, 33185, Le Haillan, France
Tel.: (33) 5 57 20 86 25
Web Site: http://www.herakles.com
Emp.: 3,300
Designer, Developer & Mfr of Solid Rocket Motors for Missiles & Space Launchers
N.A.I.C.S.: 336415
Herve Austruy (Exec VP)

Subsidiary (Domestic):

PyroAlliance (2)
139 Route de Verneuil, BP2052, 78132, Les Mureaux, Cedex, France **(85%)**
Tel.: (33) 13 492 4444
Web Site: http://www.pyroalliance.fr
Emp.: 120
Pyrotechnic Equipment Designer & Mfr
N.A.I.C.S.: 336415
Gilles Fonblanc (CEO)

Joint Venture (Domestic):

ROXEL S.A.S. (2)
La Boursidi Immeuble Jura, 92357, Le Plessis-Robinson, France **(50%)**
Tel.: (33) 141 07 82 95
Web Site: http://www.roxelgroup.com
Propulsion System Mfr
N.A.I.C.S.: 336415

Subsidiary (Domestic):

ROXEL France (3)
Route D Ardon, 45240, La Ferte-Saint-Aubin, France
Tel.: (33) 238516666
Sales Range: $100-124.9 Million
Emp.: 300
Rocket Propulsion Systems Mfr
N.A.I.C.S.: 335312

Hispano Suiza (S.A.) (1)
18 Blvd Louis Seguin, 92707, Colombes, France **(100%)**
Tel.: (33) 0141305010
Web Site: http://www.safran.fr
Sales Range: $200-249.9 Million
Emp.: 990
Power Transmission Systems, Control Equipment
N.A.I.C.S.: 486210

Integrated Biometric Technology Services LLC (1)
1650 Wabash Ave, Springfield, IL 62704
Tel.: (217) 547-2100
Biometric Device Mfr
N.A.I.C.S.: 334118

Orolia Government Systems Inc. (1)
320 N Goodman St Ste 101, Rochester, NY 14607-1185
Tel.: (585) 250-1545
Positioning Navigation & Timing Services
N.A.I.C.S.: 541715

Orolia Spain S.L. (1)
Calle Periodista Rafael Gomez Montero 2 Cetic-Ugr 13, 18014, Granada, Spain
Tel.: (34) 958285024
Aircraft Equipment Mfr & Distr
N.A.I.C.S.: 336413

Parachutes Industries Southern Africa Pty Ltd. (1)
29 Duiker Rd, Verulam, 4340, South Africa
Tel.: (27) 32 533 0333
Parachute Mfr & Distr
N.A.I.C.S.: 314999

SLCA (1)
6 Rue Des Artisans, 57190, Florange, France
Tel.: (33) 382598300
Aircraft Mfr

N.A.I.C.S.: 336411

SOCIETE DE MOTORISATIONS AERONAUTIQUES S.A. (1)
12 Rue Didier Daurat, Bourges, 18000, Cher, France
Tel.: (33) 248675600
Aircraft Mfr
N.A.I.C.S.: 336411

Subsidiary (US):

SMA Engines, Inc. (2)
2802 Safran Dr, Grand Prairie, TX 75052
Tel.: (972) 408-3691
Web Site: http://www.smaengines.com
Aircraft Engine Mfr
N.A.I.C.S.: 336412
Thierry Saint Loup (VP)

Safran Aero Boosters (1)
Route de Liers 121 B, 4041, Milmort, Belgium **(67%)**
Tel.: (32) 42788111
Web Site: http://www.techspace-aero.be
Sales Range: $450-499.9 Million
Emp.: 1,200
Design & Production of Components for Aircraft & Space Propulsion Systems; Engine Assembly Testing & Maintenance
N.A.I.C.S.: 336412

Safran Aerosystems - Chateaudun (1)
Route de Jallans, 28200, Chateaudun, France
Tel.: (33) 237976030
Web Site: http://www.safran-group.com
Aircraft Equipment Design & Mfr
N.A.I.C.S.: 336411

Safran Aerosystems - Compiegne (1)
5 Rue Des Ateliers, 60 200, Compiegne, Hauts De Seine, France
Tel.: (33) 34438 6666
Web Site: http://www.safran-group.com
Aircraft Equipment Design & Mfr
N.A.I.C.S.: 336412

Safran Aerosystems Services UK Limited (1)
610 Avenue West Skyline 120, Braintree, CM77 7AA, Essex, United Kingdom
Tel.: (44) 1376 329194
Web Site: http://www.safran-group.com
Aviation Engineering Services
N.A.I.C.S.: 541330

Safran Aircraft Engines (Guiyang) Co., Ltd (1)
Kechan Road 168, Shawen Baiyun, Guiyang, 550016, Guizhou, China
Tel.: (86) 85187992901
Emp.: 140
Aircraft Parts & Equipment Mfr
N.A.I.C.S.: 336413

Safran Aircraft Engines Suzhou Co., Ltd. (1)
n 70 Qi Ming Road, District B Export and Processing Zone Suzhou Industrial Park, Suzhou, 215126, China
Tel.: (86) 51262601860
Engine Mfr
N.A.I.C.S.: 336412

Safran Cabin Bangkok Ltd. (1)
Bangplee Industrial Estate 139/2-3 Moo 17, Bangsaothong - Sub-District, Bang Sao Thong, 10540, Samutprakarn, Thailand
Tel.: (66) 23303002
Aircraft Interior Cabin Mfr
N.A.I.C.S.: 336413
Tawatchai U-Tis (Mgr-Facility & Maintenance)

Safran Cabin Brazil Ltda. (1)
Av Getulio Vargas-3000, Jacarei, 12305-010, SP, Brazil
Tel.: (55) 1239540700
Emp.: 402
Aircraft Interior Cabin Mfr
N.A.I.C.S.: 336413
Fernanda Barboni (Program Mgr)

Safran Cabin CZ s.r.o. (1)
Univerzitni 34, 301 00, Plzen, Czech Republic
Tel.: (420) 377664111

Emp.: 1,044
Aircraft Interior Cabin Mfr
N.A.I.C.S.: 336413
Rene Ansink (Head-Pur, Strategic Procurement, and SG)

Safran Cabin Canada Co. (1)
18107 Trans-Canada Hwy, Kirkland, H9J 3K1, QC, Canada
Tel.: (514) 697-5555
Emp.: 769
Aircraft Interior Cabin Mfr
N.A.I.C.S.: 336413
Sami Chouchene (Mgr-Supply Chain)

Safran Cabin Lamphun Ltd. (1)
68/2-3 Moo 4 Tumbol Ban Klang, Northern Region Industrial Estate Amphur Muang, 51000, Lamphun, Thailand
Tel.: (66) 53569300
Emp.: 1,800
Aircraft Interior Cabin Mfr
N.A.I.C.S.: 336413
Thomas Deschenes (Dir-Sourcing & Supply Chain)

Safran Cabin Netherlands N.V. (1)
Toermalijnstraat 16, 1812 RL, Alkmaar, Netherlands
Tel.: (31) 883743800
Emp.: 120
Aircraft Interior Cabin Mfr
N.A.I.C.S.: 336413
Ton De Vries (Dir-Engrg)

Safran Cabin Sterling, Inc. (1)
44931 Falcon Pl, Sterling, VA 20166
Tel.: (571) 789-1900
Emp.: 150
Aircraft Interior Cabin Mfr
N.A.I.C.S.: 336413

Safran Colibrys SA (1)
Avenue des Sciences 13, 1400, Yverdon-les-Bains, Switzerland
Tel.: (41) 58 100 5000
Web Site: https://www.colibrys.com
Emp.: 60
Aircraft Equipment Mfr
N.A.I.C.S.: 336413
Marie-Agnes Contal (Mgr-HR)

Safran Data Systems Inc. (1)
3005 Business Pk Dr, Norcross, GA 30071
Tel.: (770) 753-4017
Web Site: http://www.safran-group.com
Aircraft Data Control System Whslr
N.A.I.C.S.: 423610

Safran Electrical & Power Chihuahua SA de CV (1)
Calle Washington 3701 Interior Circuito Industrial Automotriz Edificio, n38 Parque Industrial Las Americas, 31136, Chihuahua, Mexico
Tel.: (52) 6144392000
Aeronautical Electrical System Mfr
N.A.I.C.S.: 336413
Laura Herrera (Plant Mgr)

Safran Electrical & Power Morocco SA (1)
Route de Rhoubula Centre Ain Atiq, BP 5110, Temara, Morocco
Tel.: (212) 37615800
Aeronautical Electrical System Mfr
N.A.I.C.S.: 336413

Safran Electrical & Power SAS (1)
1 rue Louis Bleriot, Parc d activite d Andromede, 31702, Blagnac, Cedex, France
Tel.: (33) 53 428 2000
Web Site: http://www.safran-electrical-power.com
Sales Range: $450-499.9 Million
Emp.: 9,000
Electronic Components Holding Company
N.A.I.C.S.: 551112
Jorge Ortega (VP & Gen Mgr-North America Wiring Div)

Subsidiary (US):

Greenpoint Technologies, Inc. (2)
11724 NE 195th St Ste 200, Bothell, WA 98011
Tel.: (425) 828-2777
Web Site: https://www.greenpoint.com
Aircraft Interior Design Services
N.A.I.C.S.: 541410

SAFRAN SA

Safran SA—(Continued)
John Broback (Mgr)

Subsidiary (Domestic):

Labinal Services (2)
36 Rue Raymond Grimaud, BP 10016,
31007, Blagnac, France
Tel.: (33) 5 34 60 00 00
Emp.: 10
Aircraft Wiring System Mfr
N.A.I.C.S.: 334511

Labinal Vichy (2)
1 rue de lAeroport, 03110, Charmeil, Cedex 449, France
Tel.: (33) 470584500
Web Site: http://www.labinal.com
Sales Range: $25-49.9 Million
Emp.: 117
Electrical Wiring Systems for Aircraft
N.A.I.C.S.: 336413

Labinal Villemur (2)
Zone Industrielle de Pechnauquie Sud 2530 Route de Castres, Villemur-sur-Tarn, 31340, France
Tel.: (33) 5 62 87 05 00
Sales Range: $150-199.9 Million
Emp.: 500
Aircraft Equipment Mfr
N.A.I.C.S.: 334511
Laurent Remuzon (Gen Mgr)

Subsidiary (Non-US):

Labinal de Mexico, SA de CV (2)
Calle Washington 3701 Interior Circuito Industria, Parque Industrial Las Americas, Chihuahua, CP 31200, Mexico (100%)
Tel.: (52) 6144392000
Sales Range: $150-199.9 Million
Aircraft Parts & Auxiliary Equipment
N.A.I.C.S.: 336413

Subsidiary (Domestic):

Labinal de Chihuahua, SA de CV (3)
North America wiring Av Homero y Nicolas Gogol 11322, Complejo Industrial Chihuahua, Chihuahua, 31109, Mexico
Tel.: (52) 614 442 59 00
Sales Range: $400-449.9 Million
Emp.: 200
Electrical Wiring Services
N.A.I.C.S.: 238210
Jorge Ortega (Pres)

Subsidiary (Domestic):

Safran Electrical & Power - Chatou (2)
41 Blvd De La Republique, 78400, Chatou, Cedex, France
Tel.: (33) 134807300
Web Site: https://www.safran-group.com
Aircraft Electrical Systems Mfr
N.A.I.C.S.: 335999

Subsidiary (Domestic):

Thales Avionics Electrical Motors SA (3)
5 Rue Du Closden Haut, PO Box 115, 78702, Conflans-Sainte-Honorine, France (100%)
Tel.: (33) 139196060
Web Site: http://www.thalesgroup.com
Sales Range: $10-24.9 Million
Emp.: 200
Mfr of Electrical Aircraft Motors
N.A.I.C.S.: 336413
Christian Queval (Gen Mgr)

Thales Avionics LCD SA (3)
Zone Industrielle Ctr Alp 760 Rue De Pommarin, 38430, Moirans, France (100%)
Tel.: (33) 476861000
Web Site: http://www.thalesgroup.com
Sales Range: $25-49.9 Million
Emp.: 90
Mfr of Active Matrix Liquid Crystal Displays
N.A.I.C.S.: 334419
Lienard Bruno (Mng Dir)

Subsidiary (US):

Safran Electrical & Power USA, LLC (2)

3790 Russell Newman Blvd, Denton, TX 76208-2936
Tel.: (940) 272-5700
Web Site: http://www.safran-electrical-power.com
Navigation, Guidance & Electrical Wiring Solutions for Aircraft
N.A.I.C.S.: 336413
Karen Bomba (Pres)

Subsidiary (Domestic):

Labinal Salisbury, Inc. (3)
600 Glen Ave, Salisbury, MD 21804-5250
Tel.: (410) 548-7800
Web Site: http://www.labinal.com
Sales Range: $150-199.9 Million
Contract Manufacturing & Electronic Assembly Services
N.A.I.C.S.: 334419
Gregory P. Moffitt (CEO)

Plant (Domestic):

Safran Electrical & Power USA, LLC - Everett (3)
2300 Merrill Creek Pkwy, Everett, WA 98203
Tel.: (425) 407-6700
Web Site: http://www.safran-electrical-power.com
Sales Range: $25-49.9 Million
Emp.: 200
Automotive Engineering Services
N.A.I.C.S.: 541330
Ricardo Varela (Gen Mgr)

Subsidiary (Domestic):

Safran Engineering Services (2)
10 rue Velasquez, Blagnac, 31700, France (100%)
Tel.: (33) 534600200
Web Site: http://www.safran-engineering.com
Sales Range: $450-499.9 Million
Emp.: 3,200
Engineering & Technical Design Services
N.A.I.C.S.: 541330
Bruno Bernard (Pres)

Division (Domestic):

Safran Engineering Services (3)
10 rue du Fort de Saint Cyr, 78280, Montigny-le-Bretonneux, France (100%)
Tel.: (33) 130683800
Web Site: http://www.safran-engineering.com
Sales Range: $25-49.9 Million
Emp.: 100
Aeronautical Equipment & Ground Transportation Services
N.A.I.C.S.: 334511

Subsidiary (Non-US):

Safran Engineering Services (3)
Calle de la Victoria 1 Planta n 3, 47001, Valladolid, Spain
Tel.: (34) 983 36 35 35
Sales Range: $25-49.9 Million
Emp.: 10
Aeronautical Engineering Services
N.A.I.C.S.: 541330
Mercedes Garcia (Mgr)

Safran Engineering Services India Pvt Ltd (3)
The HUB Sy No: 8/2 & 9 Ambalipura Village Varthur Hobli, Bangalore East Taluk Sarjapur, Bengaluru, 560102, Karnataka, India
Tel.: (91) 80 66 77 99 99
Sales Range: $150-199.9 Million
Emp.: 550
Aeronautical Engineering Services
N.A.I.C.S.: 541330
Damodaran Subramaniam (Mng Dir)

Safran Engineering Services UK Ltd (3)
3 West Point Row Great Park Road, Almondsbury, Bristol, BS32 4QG, United Kingdom
Tel.: (44) 1 454 621 140
Web Site: http://www.safran-engineering.com
Emp.: 2
Automotive Engineering Services

N.A.I.C.S.: 541330
Mitchelle Cushion (Gen Mgr)

Subsidiary (Non-US):

Safran Engineering Services GmbH (2)
Hein Sass Weg 36, 21129, Hamburg, Germany (100%)
Tel.: (49) 4074376717
Sales Range: $25-49.9 Million
Emp.: 145
Engineering & Technical Design Services
N.A.I.C.S.: 541330

Safran Electrical & Power UK Ltd (1)
Westfield Road, Pitstone Green, Pitstone, LU7 9GT, Bucks, United Kingdom
Tel.: (44) 1296663000
Sales Range: $125-149.9 Million
Emp.: 500
Aircraft Electrical Equipment Mfr
N.A.I.C.S.: 336413

Subsidiary (US):

Safran Power USA LLC (2)
8380 Darrow Rd, Twinsburg, OH 44087
Tel.: (330) 487-2000
Sales Range: $25-49.9 Million
Emp.: 100
Aircraft Electrical Equipment Mfr
N.A.I.C.S.: 336413
John Poulos (Mgr-Customer Support-USA)

Safran Electrical Components Canada - London Facility (1)
10 Artisans Crescent, London, N5V 4N6, ON, Canada
Tel.: (519) 659-1107
Electrical Products Mfr
N.A.I.C.S.: 335999

Safran Electronics & Defense Canada Inc. (1)
2000 Fisher Drive, Box 4525, Peterborough, ON, Canada
Tel.: (705) 743-6903
Aircraft Equipment Mfr
N.A.I.C.S.: 336413

Safran Electronics & Defense Germany GmbH (1)
Gottlieb-Daimler-Str 60, 71711, Murr, Germany
Tel.: (49) 7144811410
Aircraft Equipment Mfr
N.A.I.C.S.: 336413
Erik Rosen (Project Mgr & Engr-Optics)

Safran Electronics & Defense Services Asia Pte Ltd (1)
26 Changi North Rise, Singapore, 498756, Singapore
Tel.: (65) 65452885
Aircraft Equipment Mfr
N.A.I.C.S.: 336413
Matthieu Pere (CEO)

Safran Helicopter Engines Asia Pte. Ltd (1)
11 Seletar Aerospace Link, Singapore, 797554, Singapore
Tel.: (65) 65486500
Transportation Equipment Whslr
N.A.I.C.S.: 423860
Herve Pasbecq (Mng Dir)

Safran Helicopter Engines Australia Pty Ltd (1)
115 Wackett Street, Bankstown Airport, Bankstown, 2200, NSW, Australia
Tel.: (61) 297966600
Transportation Equipment Maintenance Services
N.A.I.C.S.: 811310
Cecile Chastenet (CFO)

Safran Helicopter Engines Brasil Industria e Comercio do Brasil Ltda (1)
Rua Capitao Guynemer 1626 Cep, Xerem, Duque de Caxias, 25250-615, Rio de Janeiro, Brazil
Tel.: (55) 2136517200
Emp.: 174
Transportation Equipment Mfr
N.A.I.C.S.: 336999

INTERNATIONAL PUBLIC

Francois Haas (CEO)

Safran Helicopter Engines Germany GmbH (1)
Borsteler Chaussee 43, 22453, Hamburg, Germany
Tel.: (49) 405002160
Emp.: 70
Transportation Equipment Maintenance Services
N.A.I.C.S.: 811310
Francis Larribau (CEO)

Safran Helicopter Engines Tianjin Co. Ltd. (1)
6E Tower A Gateway Plaza N 18 Xiaguangli North Road Dongsanhuan, Chaoyang, Beijing, 100027, China
Tel.: (86) 1084400608
Emp.: 29
Transportation Equipment Whslr
N.A.I.C.S.: 423860
Bernard Plaza (CEO)

Safran Helicopter Engines UK Limited (1)
Concorde Way Segensworth North Fareham, Portsmouth, PO15 5RL, Hampshire, United Kingdom
Tel.: (44) 1489564848
Transportation Equipment Mfr
N.A.I.C.S.: 336999
Ken Doig (Mgr-Bus Dev)

Safran Helicopter Engines USA, Inc. (1)
2709 N Forum Dr, Grand Prairie, TX 75052-7027
Tel.: (972) 606-7600
Emp.: 340
Transportation Equipment Maintenance Services
N.A.I.C.S.: 811310
Norma Lantz (Exec VP-Airframer Sls & Mktg)

Safran Landing Systems (1)
Inovel Parc Sud 7 rue du General Valerie Andre, 78140, Velizy-Villacoublay, France
Tel.: (33) 14 629 8100
Web Site: http://www.safran-landing-systems.com
Sales Range: $1-4.9 Billion
Emp.: 6,250
Braking Systems & Hydraulic Equipment, Wheels & Brakes; Repair Services; Equipment & Landing Gear for All Types of Aircraft
N.A.I.C.S.: 336413
Vincent Caro (Exec VP-Programs-Landing Gear & Sys Integration)

Subsidiary (Non-US):

Messier Dowty International Ltd. (2)
Cheltenham Rd E, Gloucester, GL2 9QH, United Kingdom (100%)
Tel.: (44) 1452712424
Web Site: http://www.messier-dowty.com
Rev.: $1,325,520,000
Emp.: 1,000
Design, Development, Manufacturing & Support of Landing Gear
N.A.I.C.S.: 334511
Chris Wilson (VP)

Messier Dowty Mexico SA de CV (2)
Carretera Estatal 200 m 22 N 547 B Parque Aerospatial de Queretaro, Colon, 76278, Queretaro, Mexico
Tel.: (52) 4421533900
Web Site: http://www.safranmbd.com
Aircraft Landing Gear Mfr
N.A.I.C.S.: 336413

Messier Services Ltd. (2)
Meteor Business Park Cheltenham Road East, Gloucester, GL2 9QL, United Kingdom
Tel.: (44) 1 452 713 111
Sales Range: $50-74.9 Million
Emp.: 24
Aircraft Repair & Maintenance Services
N.A.I.C.S.: 488190
Nigel Woodford (Mng Dir)

Messier Services Mexico S.A. de C.V. (2)
Av de la Noria 131 SLP Parque Industrial

AND PRIVATE COMPANIES — SAFRAN SA

Queretaro, Queretaro, 76220, Mexico, Mexico
Tel.: (52) 4421925800
Web Site: http://www.safranmbd.com
Emp.: 250
Aircraft Part Mfr
N.A.I.C.S.: 336413
Claude Gobenceaux (Gen Mgr)

Messier-Dowty (Singapore) Pte Ltd (2)
21 Loyang Crescent, Singapore, 508985, Singapore
Tel.: (65) 6545 9455
Web Site: http://www.safran-group.com
Aircraft Part Mfr
N.A.I.C.S.: 336413

Messier-Dowty (Suzhou) Co., Ltd (2)
No 70 Qi Ming Road Export & Processing Zone Suzhou Industrial Park, District B, 215121, Suzhou, Jiangsu, China
Tel.: (86) 512 62601333
Sales Range: $100-124.9 Million
Emp.: 300
Aircraft Part Mfr
N.A.I.C.S.: 336413

Messier-Dowty Inc. (2)
574 Monarch Avenue, Ajax, L1S 2G8, ON, Canada
Tel.: (905) 683-3100
Sales Range: $75-99.9 Million
Emp.: 50
Aircraft Parts & Equipment Mfr
N.A.I.C.S.: 336413
Bryan Teed (Pres)

Messier-Dowty Ltd. (2)
Cheltenham Road East, Gloucester, GL2 9QL, United Kingdom
Tel.: (44) 1 452 712 424
Web Site: http://www.safran-group.com
Sales Range: $350-399.9 Million
Emp.: 1,200
Aircraft Parts & Equipment Mfr
N.A.I.C.S.: 336413
Peter Hall (Mgr-Mktg)

Safran Landing Systems - Queretaro Facility (2)
Avenida de la Noria 131 Parque Industrial, 76220, Queretaro, Mexico
Tel.: (52) 442 192 5800
Web Site: http://www.safran-landing-systems.com
Aircraft Maintenance Services
N.A.I.C.S.: 811198
Bruno Chiarelli (Exec VP-MRO Div)

Subsidiary (US):

Safran Landing Systems Everett, LLC (2)
7501 Hardeson Rd, Everett, WA 98203-6285
Tel.: (425) 438-1378
Web Site: http://www.safran-landing-systems.com
Aircraft Landing Gear Mfr
N.A.I.C.S.: 336413

Subsidiary (Non-US):

Safran Landing Systems Holdings Singapore Pte. Ltd. (2)
21 Loyang Crescent, Singapore, 508985, Singapore
Tel.: (65) 65459455
Aeronautical Engineering Services
N.A.I.C.S.: 541330

Subsidiary (US):

Safran Landing Systems Kentucky, LLC (2)
1 Carbon Way, Walton, KY 41094
Tel.: (859) 525-8583
Web Site: http://www.safran-landing-systems.com
Emp.: 200
Aircraft Part Mfr
N.A.I.C.S.: 336413

Safran Landing Systems Canada Inc. (1)
574 Monarch Avenue, Ajax, L1S 2G8, ON, Canada
Tel.: (905) 683-3100
Emp.: 700
Aircraft Landing & Braking Product Mfr
N.A.I.C.S.: 334511
Olya Boyko (Comm Mgr)

Safran Landing Systems Malaysia Sdn. Bhd. (1)
Jalan Techvalley 7/2 Sendayan Techvalley, 71950, Bandar Sri Sendayan, Negeri Sembilan, Malaysia
Tel.: (60) 67816666
Aircraft Landing & Braking Product Mfr
N.A.I.C.S.: 334511
Laurent Figari (COO & Ops Mgr)

Safran Landing Systems Mexico S.A. de C.V. (1)
Carretera Estatal 200 km 22 5 No 547-B Parque Aeroespacial, Colon, 76278, Queretaro, Mexico
Tel.: (52) 4421533900
Emp.: 337
Aircraft Landing & Braking Product Mfr
N.A.I.C.S.: 334511
Julio Flores (Mgr-Site)

Safran Landing Systems Services Americas S.A. de C.V. (1)
Av De la Noria 131 Parque Industrial, Queretaro, Mexico
Tel.: (52) 4421925800
Emp.: 260
Aircraft Landing & Braking Product Mfr
N.A.I.C.S.: 334511

Safran Landing Systems Services Miami, Inc. (1)
10255 NW 116th Way Ste 7, Miami, FL 33178
Tel.: (305) 624-4700
Aircraft Landing & Braking Product Mfr
N.A.I.C.S.: 334511
Luc Philippe (Dir-Sls & Mktg)

Safran Landing Systems Services Singapore Pte. Ltd (1)
21 Loyang Crescent, Singapore, 508985, Singapore
Tel.: (65) 65459455
Emp.: 340
Aircraft Landing & Braking Product Mfr
N.A.I.C.S.: 334511
Cheow Beng Shang (Mgr-Site)

Safran Landing Systems Services UK Ltd. (1)
Meteor Business Park Cheltenham Road East, Gloucester, GL2 9QL, United Kingdom
Tel.: (44) 1452713111
Aircraft Landing & Braking Product Mfr
N.A.I.C.S.: 334511
Christina Blake (Dir-HR)

Safran Landing Systems Suzhou Co., Ltd. (1)
No 70 Qi Ming Road Export Processing Zone B, Suzhou Industrial Park, Suzhou, 215121, Jiangsu, China
Tel.: (86) 51262601333
Emp.: 470
Aircraft Landing & Braking Product Mfr
N.A.I.C.S.: 334511
Jessie Wu (Comm Mgr)

Safran Landing Systems UK Ltd. (1)
Cheltenham Road East, Gloucester, GL2 9QH, United Kingdom
Tel.: (44) 1452712424
Emp.: 945
Aircraft Landing & Braking Product Mfr
N.A.I.C.S.: 334511
Chris Wilson (Mgr-Site)

Safran Moteurs d'Helicopteres Canada Inc. (1)
11 800 Helen-Bristol, Mirabel, J7N 3G8, QC, Canada
Tel.: (450) 476-2550
Emp.: 53
Transportation Equipment Support Services
N.A.I.C.S.: 811310
Cedric Jochum (Gen Mgr)

Safran Nacelles Limited (1)
Bancroft Road, Burnley, BB10 2TQ, Lancashire, United Kingdom
Tel.: (44) 1282419300
Emp.: 720
Transportation Equipment Whslr
N.A.I.C.S.: 423860
Robert Payne (Engr-SQA)

Safran Passenger Innovations - Germany (1)
Argelsrieder Feld 22, 82234, Wessling, Germany
Tel.: (49) 8153886780
Web Site: http://www.triagnosys.com
Satellite Telecommunication Services
N.A.I.C.S.: 517410
Nuria Riera Diaz (Mng Dir)

Safran Power Units San Diego, LLC (1)
4255 Ruffin Rd Ste 100, San Diego, CA 92123
Tel.: (858) 223-2210
Aerospace Product & Parts Mfr
N.A.I.C.S.: 336415
Allan Nelson (Engr-Logistics)

Safran Seats France S.A. (1)
Rue Robert Marechal, 36100, Issoudun, France
Tel.: (33) 254033939
Web Site: http://www.safran-group.com
Aircraft Seats Mfr
N.A.I.C.S.: 314999

Safran Seats GB Limited (1)
Kestral House, Llantarnam Industrial Park, Cwmbran, NP44 3HQ, Wales, United Kingdom
Tel.: (44) 1633 793500
Aircraft Interior Parts Mfr
N.A.I.C.S.: 336413

Safran Seats GB Limited (1)
Kestrel House, Cwmbran, NP44 3HQ, United Kingdom
Tel.: (44) 1633793500
Aircraft Seat Mfr
N.A.I.C.S.: 336360
Sian Williams (VP-HR)

Safran Seats Santa Maria LLC (1)
2641 Airpark Dr, Santa Maria, CA 93455
Tel.: (805) 922-5995
Aircraft Seat Mfr
N.A.I.C.S.: 336360

Safran Seats USA LLC (1)
2000 Zodiac Dr, Gainesville, TX 76240
Tel.: (940) 668-4100
Aircraft Seat Mfr
N.A.I.C.S.: 336360
Kevin Reeves (Sr Dir-Certification & Testing)

Safran Test Cells, Inc. (1)
651 Campus Dr Ste 100, New Brighton, MN 55112
Tel.: (651) 203-6100
Web Site: http://www.safran-test-cells.com
Measuring & Controlling Device Mfr
N.A.I.C.S.: 334519
Jerome Morhet (Sr VP)

Safran USA Inc. (1)
2300 Clarendon Blvd Ste 607, Arlington, VA 22201
Tel.: (703) 351-9898
Web Site: http://www.safran-usa.com
Emp.: 10
Investment Management Service
N.A.I.C.S.: 523940
Peter Lengyel (CEO)

Safran Vectronix AG (1)
Max-Schmidheiny-Strasse 202, CH-9435, Heerbrugg, Switzerland
Tel.: (41) 717267200
Web Site: https://www.safran-vectronix.com
Emp.: 240
Opsonic Equipment Mfr & Distr
N.A.I.C.S.: 334511

Safran Ventilation Systems USA, LLC (1)
7501 Hardeson Rd, Everett, WA 98203
Tel.: (425) 438-1378
Aircraft Seat Mfr
N.A.I.C.S.: 336360
Heather Roush (Fin Dir)

Sagem Defense Securite SA (1)
Le Ponant de Paris 27 rue Leblanc, 75512, Paris, Cedex 15, France
Tel.: (33) 158117800
Web Site: http://www.sagem-ds.com
Sales Range: $1-4.9 Billion
Emp.: 6,900
Inertial Navigation & Guidance Stabilization Integrated Systems, Data Processing & Data Storage Electro-Optics Equipment & Systems Mfr
N.A.I.C.S.: 334511
Philippe Petitcolin (Chm & CEO)

Subsidiary (Non-US):

Colibrys SA (2)
Maladiere 83, CH-2000, Neuchatel, Switzerland
Tel.: (41) 32 720 5811
Web Site: http://www.colibrys.com
Sales Range: $10-24.9 Million
Emp.: 70
Micro-Sensors Mfr
N.A.I.C.S.: 334419
Jean-Michel Stauffer (VP-Sls & Mktg)

Subsidiary (US):

Optics1 Inc. (2)
2 Cooper Ln, Bedford, NH 03110
Tel.: (603) 296-0469
Web Site: https://www.optics1.com
Optical Engineering Services
N.A.I.C.S.: 541330
Robert E. Fischer (CEO)

Subsidiary (Non-US):

Safran Electronics & Defense Germany GmbH (2)
Gottlieb-Daimler-Str 60, 71711, Murr, Germany
Tel.: (49) 7144811410
Web Site: http://www.sagem-ds.com
Emp.: 9
Monitoring & Control Equipment Mfr
N.A.I.C.S.: 334519
Wilfried Auch (Mng Dir)

Safran Electronics Canada Inc (2)
2000 Fisher Drive, Box 4525, Peterborough, K9J 7B1, ON, Canada
Tel.: (705) 743-6903
Web Site: http://www.safran-electronics.ca
Sales Range: $25-49.9 Million
Emp.: 130
Software Development Services
N.A.I.C.S.: 541511
Linda Rene (Pres)

Vectronix AG (2)
Max-Schmidheiny-Strasse 202, 9435, Heerbrugg, Switzerland
Tel.: (41) 717267200
Web Site: http://www.vectronix.ch
Sales Range: $25-49.9 Million
Emp.: 250
Optical Equipment for Military Observation, Orientation & Range-finding Mfr
N.A.I.C.S.: 333310

Subsidiary (US):

Vectronix Inc. (3)
801 Sycolin Rd SE Ste 206, Leesburg, VA 20175
Tel.: (703) 777-3900
Web Site: http://www.vectronix.com
Sales Range: $25-49.9 Million
Emp.: 22
Mfr of Optical Equipment for Military Observation, Orientation & Rangefinding
N.A.I.C.S.: 333310
James Lane (Dir-Contracts)

Sagem Security International Trading Co., Ltd. (1)
Dong Gu Yin Zuo 1505 Luo Yu Lu 727 East Lake Development Zone, 430074, Wuhan, Hubei, China
Tel.: (86) 27 5972 2326
Web Site: http://www.morpho.com
Biometric Device Mfr
N.A.I.C.S.: 334118

Sagem Security Ireland Ltd (1)
BIM House Crofton Road, Dun Laoghaire, Dublin, Ireland
Tel.: (353) 1 284 32 33
Web Site: http://www.morpho.com
Sales Range: $25-49.9 Million
Emp.: 20
Software Development Services
N.A.I.C.S.: 541511

SAFRAN SA

INTERNATIONAL PUBLIC

Safran SA—(Continued)
Pierre Heuze *(Gen Mgr)*

Snecma S.A. (1)
10 Allee du Brevent CE1420
Courcouronnes, 91019, Evry, France
Tel.: (33) 1 69 87 09 00
Web Site: http://www.snecma.com
Aircraft Engine Mfr
N.A.I.C.S.: 336412
Philippe Petitcolin *(Chm)*

Joint Venture (Non-US):

SNECMA Morocco Engine Services (2)
Mohammed V International Airport, PO Box 87, 20400, Casablanca, Morocco
Tel.: (212) 22536900
Web Site: http://www.snecma.ma
Aircraft Engine Overhaul & Maintenance; Joint Venture of Royal Air Maroc (49%) & SNECMA-Societe Nationale d'Etude et de Construction de Moteurs d'Aviation (51%)
N.A.I.C.S.: 336412

Subsidiary (Non-US):

Snecma America Engine Services S.A. de C.V. (2)
Carr Estatal 200 Queretaro - Tequisquiapan Km 22 547 Int B1, Parque Aeroespacial Queretaro, 76278, Queretaro, Mexico
Tel.: (52) 442 2965600
Sales Range: $25-49.9 Million
Emp.: 250
Aircraft Repair & Maintenance Services
N.A.I.C.S.: 811198

Snecma Mexico S.A. De C V (2)
Carretera Estatal 200 Queretaro Tequisquiapan - Km 22 5 Int D, Parque Aeroespacial Queretaro, Queretaro, 76120, Mexico
Tel.: (52) 442 153 39 15
Aircraft Part Mfr
N.A.I.C.S.: 336413

Subsidiary (Domestic):

Snecma Moteurs S.A. (2)
10 Allee Du Brevent, CE1420, Courcouronnes, France (100%)
Tel.: (33) 0169870900
Web Site: http://www.snecma-moteurs.com
Sales Range: $25-49.9 Million
Emp.: 60
Aircraft Engine Mfr
N.A.I.C.S.: 336412

Joint Venture (US):

CFAN Inc (3)
1000 Technology Way, San Marcos, TX 78666-8500
Tel.: (512) 353-2832
Web Site: https://c-fan.com
Composite Fan Blades for Aircarft Engines. Joint Venture of General Electric Company (50%) & Societe Nationale d'Etude et de Construction de Moteurs d'Aviation (50%)
N.A.I.C.S.: 336412
Benoit Graby *(VP)*

Subsidiary (Domestic):

Snecma Services (3)
2 Chemin de Viercy Aerodrome de Villaroche, BP 1936, 77019, Melun, France (100%)
Tel.: (33) 164148800
Web Site: http://www.snecma-services.com
Sales Range: $125-149.9 Million
Aero-Engine Support Services
N.A.I.C.S.: 488119

Subsidiary (Non-US):

Snecma Services Brussels NV (2)
Batiment 24 B/101 - Brussels Airport, 1930, Zaventem, Belgium
Tel.: (32) 2 790 45 00
Web Site: http://www.snecma.com
Sales Range: $25-49.9 Million
Emp.: 150
Aircraft Engine Repair & Maintenance Services
N.A.I.C.S.: 811198
Bruno Michel *(CEO)*

Subsidiary (Domestic):

Turbomeca SA (2)
Avenue Joseph Szydlowski, 64510, Bordes, France (100%)
Tel.: (33) 559125000.
Web Site: http://www.turbomeca.fr
Sales Range: $1-4.9 Billion
Emp.: 6,336
Gas Turbine Mfr
N.A.I.C.S.: 333611
Philippe Drouin *(VP-Mfr Ops)*

Joint Venture (Non-US):

MTU Turbomeca Rolls-Royce GmbH (3)
Am Soldnermoos 17, 85399, Hallbergmoos, Germany
Tel.: (49) 81 160 0900
Web Site: https://www.mtr390.com
Sales Range: $25-49.9 Million
Emp.: 15
Mfr of Turboshaft Engines; Owned 33% by MTU Engines Holding AG, 33% by Rolls-Royce Group plc & 33% by Turbomeca
N.A.I.C.S.: 333618
Ralf Breiling *(Mng Dir)*

Subsidiary (Domestic):

Microturbo SA (3)
8 Chemin Du Pont De Rupe, PO Box 62089, Toulouse, F 31019, France (100%)
Tel.: (33) 561375500
Web Site: http://www.microturbo.com
Sales Range: $100-124.9 Million
Emp.: 500
Aircraft Engines & Turbine Mfr
N.A.I.C.S.: 336412

Division (US):

Microturbo, Inc. (3)
2707 Forum Dr, Grand Prairie, TX 75052-7027
Tel.: (972) 606-7600
Sales Range: $75-99.9 Million
Emp.: 400
Small Turbo Jet Engines Mfr
N.A.I.C.S.: 333611
Russ Spray *(Pres)*

Affiliate (Non-US):

Rolls-Royce Turbomeca Limited (3)
4-5 Grosvenor Place, SW1X7HJ, London, United Kingdom (50%)
Tel.: (44) 2072594090
Sales Range: $50-74.9 Million
Engine Parts Mfr
N.A.I.C.S.: 336310

Subsidiary (Non-US):

Safran Helicopter Engines (3)
Rua Capitao Guynemer 1626 Cep, Xerem, Rio de Janeiro, Brazil (100%)
Tel.: (55) 2136517200
Web Site: http://www.turbomeca.com.br
Sales Range: $50-74.9 Million
Emp.: 200
Aircraft Turbine Mfr
N.A.I.C.S.: 336412

Safran Helicopter Engines Asia Pte. Ltd. (3)
11 Seletar Aerospace Link, Singapore, 797554, Singapore (100%)
Tel.: (65) 65486530
Sales Range: $25-49.9 Million
Emp.: 18
Helicopter Gas Turbine Mfr
N.A.I.C.S.: 336412
Aurelien Blanc *(Mng Dir)*

Safran Helicopter Engines UK Limited (3)
Concorde Way Segensworth North, Fareham, PO15 5RL, Hampshire, United Kingdom (100%)
Tel.: (44) 1489564848
Web Site: http://www.turbomeca.co.uk
Emp.: 210
Electronic Connector Mfr
N.A.I.C.S.: 334417

Subsidiary (US):

Safran Helicopter Engines USA (3)
2709 N Forum Dr, Grand Prairie, TX 75052-7027 (100%)
Tel.: (972) 606-7600
Sales Range: $100-124.9 Million
Emp.: 400
Helicopter Maintenance & Repair Services
N.A.I.C.S.: 811210
Russ Spray *(Pres & CEO)*

Subsidiary (Non-US):

Turbomeca (3)
501 Tower B Jiaming Center No 27 Dongsanhuan North Road, Chaoyang District, Beijing, 100020, China
Tel.: (86) 1065815880
Emp.: 29
Aircraft Turbine Mfr
N.A.I.C.S.: 336412

Turbomeca America Latina S.A. (3)
Ruta 8 Km 17 500 Edificio Beta 3 Local 008 of 103 y 104, Zonamerica, 11000, Montevideo, Uruguay
Tel.: (598) 2 518 28 10
Sales Range: $25-49.9 Million
Emp.: 4
Aircraft Engine & Parts Mfr
N.A.I.C.S.: 336412

Turbomeca Australasia Pty. Ltd. (3)
115 Wackett St Bankstown Airport, Condell Park, 2200, NSW, Australia (100%)
Tel.: (61) 297916700
Sales Range: $50-74.9 Million
Emp.: 130
Aircraft Turbine Mfr
N.A.I.C.S.: 336412
Stewart Noel *(Mng Dir)*

Turbomeca Canada Inc. (3)
11800 Helen-Bristol, Mirabel, J7N 3G8, QC, Canada
Tel.: (450) 476-2550
Web Site: http://www.turbomeca.com
Emp.: 55
Aircraft Engine & Parts Mfr
N.A.I.C.S.: 336413

Turbomeca GmbH (3)
Borsteler Chaussee 43, 22453, Hamburg, 22453, Germany
Tel.: (49) 405002160
Sales Range: $25-49.9 Million
Emp.: 14
Aircraft Turbine Mfr
N.A.I.C.S.: 336412
Richard Musil *(Gen Mgr)*

Turbomeca India Engines Pvt Ltd (3)
N 2727 1st Floor 80 Ft Road HAL 3rd Stage, Indiranagar, Bengaluru, 560 075, India
Tel.: (91) 80 4334 7878
Sales Range: $25-49.9 Million
Emp.: 13
Aircraft Part Mfr
N.A.I.C.S.: 336413
Satish Kirtikar *(Mng Dir)*

Turbomeca Japan K.K (3)
Toranomon 40 MT Bldg 9F Toranomon 5-13-1, Minato-ku, Tokyo, 105-0001, Japan
Tel.: (81) 3 5408 1083
Sales Range: $25-49.9 Million
Emp.: 10
Aircraft Engine & Parts Mfr
N.A.I.C.S.: 336412
Guy Bonaud *(Mgr)*

Turbomeca Mexico S.a De C.v (3)
Montes Urales 505 Floor 3 Colonia, Colonia Polanco, 11560, Lomas de Chapultepec, Mexico
Tel.: (52) 55 52 81 28 47
Emp.: 11
Aircraft Engine & Parts Mfr
N.A.I.C.S.: 336412
Bernard Chesson *(Gen Mgr)*

Turbomeca Sud Americana (3)
Rincon 487 Office 808, 11000, Montevideo, Uruguay
Tel.: (598) 29165444
Sales Range: $25-49.9 Million
Emp.: 9
Aircraft Turbine Mfr
N.A.I.C.S.: 336412
Cyrille Poetsch *(VP-Programmes)*

Snecma Suzhou Co. Ltd. (1)
N 70 Qi Ming Road District B Export & Processing Zone, Suzhou Industrial Park, 215126, Suzhou, Jiangsu, China
Tel.: (86) 512 62601860
Aircraft Engine Mfr
N.A.I.C.S.: 336412

Societe d'Exploitation des Materiels Martin Baker SEM MB (SA) (1)
98 ter boulevard Heloise, 95815, Argenteuil, Cedex, France (49.95%)
Tel.: (33) 134345900
Web Site: http://www.martin-baker.fr
Sales Range: $25-49.9 Million
Emp.: 43
Sales & Product Support of Ejection & Crashworthy Seats & Spares
N.A.I.C.S.: 332994

Sofradir SAS (1)
43 47 Rue Camille Pelletan, 92290, Chatenay-Malabry, France (50%)
Tel.: (33) 0141134530
Web Site: http://www.sofradir.com
Sales Range: $150-199.9 Million
Emp.: 550
Infrared Detection Equipment Mfr; Owned 50% by Thales S.A. & 50% by Safran S.A.
N.A.I.C.S.: 334511
Philippe Bensussan *(CEO)*

Sofrance (1)
ZI Des Gannes 6 et 8 Rue Maryse Bastie, PO Box 3, 87800, Nexon, France (100%)
Tel.: (33) 555585000
Web Site: http://www.sofrance.com
Sales Range: $50-74.9 Million
Emp.: 180
Filtration Systems & Components Mfr
N.A.I.C.S.: 336411
Jacky Goualard *(Dir-Fin)*

Soreval S.A. (1)
Route de Traves 6B, Senningerberg, 2633, Luxembourg
Tel.: (352) 34 68 66 1
Investment Management Service
N.A.I.C.S.: 523940

Technofan Inc. (1)
7501 Hardeson Rd, Everett, WA 98203
Tel.: (425) 438-1378
Web Site: http://www.technofan.fr
Avionic Ventilation System Mfr
N.A.I.C.S.: 336413

Technofan SA (1)
ZAC Du Grand Noble 10 Pl Marcel Dassault, 31702, Blagnac, France (100%)
Tel.: (33) 561309200
Web Site: http://www.technofan.com
Sales Range: $50-74.9 Million
Emp.: 300
Aircraft Ventilation Systems
N.A.I.C.S.: 336413
Bruno Bergoend *(CEO)*

Turbomeca Beijing Helicopter Engines Trading Cie Ltd. (1)
Unit A 6/F Suite A Jiacheng Plaza No 18 Xiaguangli Dongsan, Beijing, 100027, China
Tel.: (86) 1084400608
Aircraft Engine Mfr
N.A.I.C.S.: 336412

Turbomeca Helicopter Engines Trading Ltd (1)
6A Building Gateway Plaza 18 Xiaguangli North Road Dongsanhuan, Chaoyang, Beijing, 100027, China
Tel.: (86) 10 84 40 0608
Aircraft Engine Mfr
N.A.I.C.S.: 336412

Turbomeca Tianjing Helicopter Engines Trading Cie Ltd. (1)
Room 314-315 Aviation Industry Support Center Airport Industrial Park, Tianjin Port Free Trade Zone, Tianjin, 300308, China
Tel.: (86) 22 58775800
Web Site: http://www.turmeca.fr
Emp.: 3
Aircraft Engine Mfr
N.A.I.C.S.: 336412
Herve Pasbecq *(Gen Mgr)*

Xi'an Cea Safran Landing Systems Co., Ltd. (1)
No 11 baoshui 1 Road Airport New City Xix-

AND PRIVATE COMPANIES

ian New Area, Shaanxi, 712035, China
Tel.: (86) 2933636468
Aircraft Landing & Braking Product Mfr
N.A.I.C.S.: 334511
Goon Guan Yap *(Dir-Ops)*

Zodiac Aerospace S.A. (1)
61 rue Pierre Curie, 78373, Plaisir, Cedex, France
Tel.: (33) 1 61 34 23 23
Web Site: http://www.zodiacaerospace.com
Rev.: $5,484,708,883
Assets: $6,616,850,026
Liabilities: $3,209,164,374
Net Worth: $3,407,685,653
Earnings: $78,537,102
Emp.: 32,568
Fiscal Year-end: 08/31/2017
Holding Company; Aerospace Technological Components, Safety Systems & Interior Components Mfr
N.A.I.C.S.: 551112
Maurice Pinault *(Deputy CEO-Strategy & Bus Dev & Member-Exec Bd)*

Subsidiary (Domestic):

Aerazur (2)
61 Rue Pierre Curie, 78373, Plaisir, Cedex, France **(100%)**
Tel.: (33) 1 6134 2323
Web Site: http://www.aerazur.com
Emp.: 100
Mfr & Designer of Aeronautical Equipment
N.A.I.C.S.: 334511

Zodiac Automotive Tunisie SRL (1)
Route De Korbous, Soliman, 8020, Tunisia
Tel.: (216) 72 39 22 70
Web Site: http://www.zodiacautomotive.com
Motor Vehicle Parts Mfr
N.A.I.C.S.: 336390

Zodiac Cabin Controls GmbH (1)
Fangdieckstrasse 64, 22547, Hamburg, Germany
Tel.: (49) 405480160
Aircraft Cabin Electronic Mfr
N.A.I.C.S.: 336413

Zodiac US Corporation (1)
1747 State Rte 34, Wall, NJ 07727-3935
Tel.: (732) 681-3527
Web Site: http://www.safran-group.com
Holding Company; Regional Managing Office
N.A.I.C.S.: 551112

Subsidiary (Domestic):

Air Cruisers Company, LLC (2)
1747 State Rte 34, Wall, NJ 07727-3935
Tel.: (732) 681-3527
Web Site: http://www.safran-group.com
Emergency Escape Slides, Inflatable Products, Life Rafts, Life Vests, Shelters & Helicopter Floats Mfr
N.A.I.C.S.: 336360
John Abbate *(Sls Mgr)*

American Fuel Cells & Coated Fabrics Co (2)
601 Firestone Dr, Magnolia, AR 71754-0887
Tel.: (870) 235-7203
Web Site: http://www.amfuel.com
Fuel Tanks & Pneumatic De-Icing Systems Mfr
N.A.I.C.S.: 336413

Avox Systems Inc. (2)
225 Erie St, Lancaster, NY 14086-9501
Tel.: (716) 683-5100
Web Site: http://www.safran-group.com
Respiratory Protective Equipment for the Civil & Military Aerospace Markets Designer & Mfr
N.A.I.C.S.: 339113

Branch (Domestic):

Avox Systems, Inc. - Van Nuys (3)
6734 Valjean Ave, Van Nuys, CA 91406-5818
Tel.: (818) 435-0900
Web Site: http://www.safran-group.com
Industrial Equipment Services
N.A.I.C.S.: 811210

Subsidiary (Domestic):

Safran Cabin, Inc. (2)
5701 Bolsa Ave, Huntington Beach, CA 92647
Tel.: (714) 934-0000
Web Site: http://www.safran-group.com
Aircraft Cabin Systems Mfr
N.A.I.C.S.: 336413

Plant (Domestic):

Safran Cabin, Inc. - Carson (3)
1500 Glenn Curtis St, Carson, CA 90746-4012
Tel.: (310) 884-7000
Web Site: http://www.safran-group.com
Commercial Aircraft Interior Equipment Mfr, Including Passenger Seats, Lavatories, Toilets, On-Board Airstairs & Military Aircraft Escape Systems
N.A.I.C.S.: 336413

Safran Cabin, Inc. - Garden Grove (3)
7330 Lincoln Way, Garden Grove, CA 92841
Tel.: (714) 891-0683
Web Site: http://www.safran-group.com
Aircraft Cabin Systems Mfr
N.A.I.C.S.: 336413

Safran Cabin, Inc. - Marysville (3)
12806 State Ave, Marysville, WA 98271
Tel.: (360) 653-2600
Web Site: http://www.safran-group.com
Aircraft Parts & Equipment Mfr & Sales
N.A.I.C.S.: 336413

Subsidiary (Domestic):

Safran Electrical Components USA, Inc. (2)
3780 Flightline Dr, Santa Rosa, CA 95403-8227
Tel.: (707) 535-2700
Electrical Interconnect Components Designer & Mfr
N.A.I.C.S.: 335999

Subsidiary (Non-US):

Safran Electrical Components UK Limited (3)
220 Bedford Avenue, Slough, SL1 4RY, Berks, United Kingdom
Tel.: (44) 1753 89 66 00
Web Site: http://www.safran-group.com
Electrical Interconnect Components Designer & Mfr
N.A.I.C.S.: 335999

Subsidiary (Domestic):

Safran Ventilation Systems Oklahoma, Inc. (2)
12037 N Hwy 99, Seminole, OK 74868
Tel.: (405) 382-0731
Web Site: http://www.safran-group.com
Aircraft Environmental Control Systems Mfr
N.A.I.C.S.: 334512

SAFTEC CO., LTD.
Hongo TH Building 52514 Hongo, Bunkyo-Ku, Tokyo, 113-0033, Japan
Tel.: (81) 338113188
Web Site: https://www.saftec.co.jp
Year Founded: 1957
7464—(TKS)
Rev.: $66,913,030
Assets: $82,069,760
Liabilities: $34,947,070
Net Worth: $47,122,690
Earnings: $2,287,060
Emp.: 373
Fiscal Year-end: 03/31/24
Safety Guard Equipment Rental & Distr
N.A.I.C.S.: 238990
Isamu Okazaki *(Chm)*

SAFTI GROUPE SA
118 route d'Espagne, 311000, Toulouse, France
Tel.: (33) 810 45 45 40 FR
Web Site: http://www.safti.fr
Year Founded: 2010
Sales Range: $10-24.9 Million
Real Estate Services

N.A.I.C.S.: 531210
Sandra Franconnet *(Head-HR)*

SAFWAN TRADING & CONTRACTING COMPANY K.S.C.C.
Ali Abdulwahab Building 6 St, Shukwaikh Industrial, Kuwait, 13068, Kuwait
Tel.: (965) 22276888
Web Site: http://www.safwantrading.com
Year Founded: 2005
Sales Range: $125-149.9 Million
Emp.: 516
Pharmaceuticals, Cosmetics, Medical Equipment & Foodstuff Importer & Distr
N.A.I.C.S.: 425120
Dina Younan *(COO)*

SAFWOOD S.P.A.
Via Giulio Milani 1, Emilia-Romagna, IT 29121, Piacenza, Italy
Tel.: (39) 0523334680
Web Site: http://www.safwood.com
Sales Range: $150-199.9 Million
Emp.: 1,871
Timber Producer, Importer & Distr
N.A.I.C.S.: 113110
Markus Alois Odermatt *(Chm)*

Subsidiaries:

EFI LTD (1)
Unit 1f Block 17 Nangor Rd, The Plz Park W Bus Park, Dublin, 11, Ireland
Tel.: (353) 16250020
Wooden Panels Mfr
N.A.I.C.S.: 321219

LESKOM DSP (1)
58 4 Promyshlennaya St, Syktyvkar, Komi Republic, Russia
Tel.: (7) 4957290851
Web Site: http://www.leskom-dsp.ru
Laminated Chipboards & Foam Production Services
N.A.I.C.S.: 334419

M.D. Sp. z o.o. (1)
Gracuch 1C, 26 200, Konskie, Poland
Tel.: (48) 413727666
Web Site: http://www.mdspzoo.pl
Sales Range: $50-74.9 Million
Emp.: 150
Wooden Furniture Mfr
N.A.I.C.S.: 337122

SAG GEST - SOLUCOES AUTOMOVEL GLOBAIS, SGPS, S.A.
AlfraPark Estrada de Alfragide N 67 Edificio SGC 2 Piso, 2614-519, Amadora, Portugal
Tel.: (351) 21 359 66 64
Web Site: http://www.sag.pt
Rev.: $742,322,826
Assets: $658,976,925
Liabilities: $650,052,868
Net Worth: $8,924,057
Earnings: ($16,335,696)
Emp.: 677
Fiscal Year-end: 12/31/17
Automobile Whslr
N.A.I.C.S.: 423110
Joao Manuel de Quevedo Pereira Coutinho *(Chm)*

SAGA FALABELLA SA
Paseo de la Republica No 3220, San Isidro, Lima, Peru
Tel.: (51) 6161000
Web Site: http://www.falabella.com.pe
Year Founded: 1953
SAGAC1—(LIM)
Rev.: $991,020,430
Assets: $619,759,803
Liabilities: $422,920,411
Net Worth: $196,839,392

Earnings: $14,088,738
Fiscal Year-end: 12/31/23
Supermarket & Department Store Operator
N.A.I.C.S.: 459999
Alex Zimmermann Franco *(CEO & Gen Mgr)*

SAGA FURS OYJ
Martinkylantie 48, Vantaa, Finland
Tel.: (358) 984981
Web Site: https://www.sagafurs.com
SAGCV—(HEL)
Rev.: $51,440,556
Assets: $131,857,821
Liabilities: $33,778,563
Net Worth: $98,079,258
Earnings: $5,442,102
Emp.: 311
Fiscal Year-end: 10/31/23
All Other Miscellaneous Retailers
N.A.I.C.S.: 459999
Mikko Hoven *(Dir-Sls)*

SAGA PLC
3 Pancras Square, London, N1C 4AG, Kent, United Kingdom
Tel.: (44) 1303771111 UK
Web Site: https://www.saga.co.uk
SAGA—(LSE)
Rev.: $699,934,950
Assets: $2,382,139,650
Liabilities: $1,937,076,900
Net Worth: $445,062,750
Earnings: ($312,206,400)
Fiscal Year-end: 01/31/23
Travel Agency Services
N.A.I.C.S.: 561510
James Quin *(CFO-Grp)*

Subsidiaries:

Destinology Limited (1)
Hercules Business Park Hall Lane, Lostock, Bolton, BL6 4BL, Lancashire, United Kingdom
Tel.: (44) 1204474400
Web Site: https://www.destinology.co.uk
Luxury Hotel Services
N.A.I.C.S.: 721120
Deborah Windle *(Mng Dir)*

MetroMail Limited (1)
MetroMail Unit 6 Fox Cover Enterprise Park Admiralty Way, Seaham, SR7 7DN, United Kingdom
Tel.: (44) 1913011685
Web Site: https://www.metromail.co.uk
Direct Mail Advertising Services
N.A.I.C.S.: 541860
Chris Pygall *(Mng Dir)*

SAGA PURE ASA
Sjolystplass 2, 0278, Oslo, Norway
Tel.: (47) 23014914 NO
Web Site: https://www.sagapure.com
Year Founded: 2010
SAGA—(OSL)
Rev.: $10,420
Assets: $85,662,579
Liabilities: $559,160
Net Worth: $85,103,419
Earnings: ($13,459,951)
Emp.: 7
Fiscal Year-end: 12/31/23
Investment & Management Services
N.A.I.C.S.: 523999
Martin Nes *(Chm)*

Subsidiaries:

S.D. Standard ETC Plc (1)
Chrysanthou Mylona 1 Panayides Building 2nd Floor Flat/Office 3, 3030, Limassol, Cyprus **(46.02%)**
Tel.: (357) 25875474
Web Site: https://www.standard-etc.com
Rev.: $41,934,000
Assets: $139,836,000
Liabilities: $234,000
Net Worth: $139,602,000
Earnings: $39,772,000

SAGA PURE ASA

Saga Pure ASA—(Continued)
Emp.: 3
Fiscal Year-end: 12/31/2022
Offshore Drilling Services
N.A.I.C.S.: 213111
Martin Nes (Chm)

SAGALIO ENERGY LIMITED
62/F The Center 99 Queens Road, Central, Hong Kong, China (Hong Kong)
Tel.: (852) 39606518
Web Site: https://www.feore.com
Year Founded: 2011
SAN—(ASX)
Rev.: $637,000
Assets: $490,000
Liabilities: $8,823,000
Net Worth: ($8,333,000)
Earnings: ($216,000)
Fiscal Year-end: 06/30/22
Iron Ore Mining
N.A.I.C.S.: 212210
Harry King (Chm)

SAGAMI HOLDINGS CORPORATION
2-118 Yatsurugi, Moriyama-ku, Nagoya, 463-8535, Aichi, Japan
Tel.: (81) 527376000
Web Site: https://www.sagami-holdings.co.jp
Year Founded: 1970
9900—(NGO)
Rev.: $204,864,244
Assets: $164,804,262
Liabilities: $53,697,620
Net Worth: $111,106,642
Earnings: $6,009,856
Emp.: 8,422
Fiscal Year-end: 03/31/24
Holding Company; Restaurant Chain Operator; Catering Services
N.A.I.C.S.: 551112
Shuji Ito (Pres & COO)

Subsidiaries:

Sagami Service Co Ltd (1)
6-2-11Shimonagaya, Kounan-ku, 233-0016, Yokohama, Japan
Tel.: (81) 458206000
Drugs & Druggists Whslr
N.A.I.C.S.: 424210

SAGAMI RUBBER INDUSTRIES CO., LTD.
2-1 Moto-cho, Atsugi, 243-0002, Kanagawa, Japan
Tel.: (81) 462212311
Web Site: https://www.sagami-gomu.co.jp
Year Founded: 1934
5194—(TKS)
Rev.: $40,400,320
Assets: $117,102,760
Liabilities: $50,321,930
Net Worth: $66,780,830
Earnings: $264,400
Fiscal Year-end: 03/31/24
Condom Mfr
N.A.I.C.S.: 326299
Ichiro Oato (Pres)

Subsidiaries:

Laboratoires Radiatex S.A. (1)
71 Rue Desnouettes, 75015, Paris, France
Tel.: (33) 182837457
Web Site: https://www.protex.fr
Pretext Condoms Mfr
N.A.I.C.S.: 326299

SAGAR CEMENTS LIMITED
Plot No 111 Road No 10 Jubilee Hills, Hyderabad, 500 033, India
Tel.: (91) 4023351571
Web Site: https://www.sagarcements.in
Year Founded: 1985
SAGCEM—(BOM)
Rev.: $219,804,585
Assets: $459,231,045
Liabilities: $280,492,485
Net Worth: $178,738,560
Earnings: $8,073,975
Emp.: 751
Fiscal Year-end: 03/31/22
Cement Mfr
N.A.I.C.S.: 327310
O. Swaminatha Reddy (Chm)

Subsidiaries:

Sagar Cements Limited - Pedaveedu Village Plant (1)
Via Huzurnagar Pedaveedu Village, Nalgonda, 508 204, Andhra Pradesh, India
Tel.: (91) 8683 216533
Cement Mfr
N.A.I.C.S.: 327310

SAGAR DIAMONDS LIMITED
Plot No 266B Sez Diamond Park Sachin, Surat, 394 230, India
Tel.: (91) 2612397866
Web Site: https://www.sagardiamonds.com
540715—(BOM)
Rev.: $671,190,684
Assets: $1,659,282,405
Liabilities: $1,646,084,204
Net Worth: $13,198,202
Earnings: $2,405,827
Emp.: 113
Fiscal Year-end: 03/31/23
Jewelry Product Mfr & Distr
N.A.I.C.S.: 339910
Vaibhav Dipak Shah (Mng Dir)

SAGAR SOYA PRODUCTS LTD.
CJ Complex Mahatama Gandhi Road, Sagar, 470002, Madhya Pradesh, India
Tel.: (91) 7582222147
Web Site: https://www.sagarsoyaproducts.com
507663—(BOM)
Rev.: $81,333
Assets: $406,886
Liabilities: $257,938
Net Worth: $148,948
Earnings: $29,170
Fiscal Year-end: 03/31/21
Soybean Mfr
N.A.I.C.S.: 111110
Arvindbhai Chhotabhai Patel (Chm & CFO)

SAGAR SYSTECH LIMITED
12A/1 New Sion CHS Ltd Sion-West, Mumbai, 400022, India
Tel.: (91) 2224018218
Web Site: https://www.sagarsystech.com
Year Founded: 1984
511254—(BOM)
Rev.: $78,113
Assets: $657,455
Liabilities: $53,942
Net Worth: $603,513
Earnings: $55,308
Fiscal Year-end: 03/31/23
Software Development Services
N.A.I.C.S.: 541511
Mukesh Babu (Chm)

SAGAR TOURIST RESORTS LIMITED
Anand Vihar Gr Floor Bajaj Road, Vile Parle West, Mumbai, 400056, India
Tel.: (91) 22 26256815
Web Site: http://www.sagarresort.com
Rev.: $181,348
Assets: $346,572
Liabilities: $838,906
Net Worth: ($492,334)
Earnings: ($23,592)
Fiscal Year-end: 03/31/17
Home Management Services
N.A.I.C.S.: 721110
Kuldeep Kumar (CFO)

SAGARDEEP ALLOYS LTD.
Plot No 2070 Rajnagar Patiya Santej Khatraj Road Santej Kalol, Gandhinagar, 382721, India
Tel.: (91) 2764291196
Web Site: https://www.sdalloys.com
Year Founded: 1972
SAGARDEEP—(NSE)
Rev.: $8,990,265
Assets: $5,307,997
Liabilities: $1,789,590
Net Worth: $3,518,407
Earnings: $19,637
Emp.: 15
Fiscal Year-end: 03/12/21
Copper Wires Mfr
N.A.I.C.S.: 331420
Satishkumar Asamal Mehta (Chm & Mng Dir)

SAGARMATHA LUMBINI INSURANCE COMPANY LIMITED
Bhagawati Marg Naxal, PO Box 12211, Kathmandu, Nepal
Tel.: (977) 14512367
Web Site: https://salico.com
Year Founded: 1996
SALICO—(NEP)
Rev.: $15,382,191
Assets: $54,238,966
Liabilities: $32,169,927
Net Worth: $22,069,039
Earnings: $3,762,850
Fiscal Year-end: 07/15/21
Insurance Services
N.A.I.C.S.: 524298
Chunky Chhetry (CEO)

SAGARSOFT (INDIA) LIMITED
Plot 111 1St Floor Road 10 Jubilee Hills, Hyderabad, 500033, Telangana, India
Tel.: (91) 4067191000
Web Site: https://www.sagarsoft.in
Year Founded: 1995
540143—(BOM)
Rev.: $5,715,244
Assets: $4,668,592
Liabilities: $986,397
Net Worth: $3,682,196
Earnings: $730,301
Emp.: 175
Fiscal Year-end: 03/31/21
Software Development Services
N.A.I.C.S.: 541511
Jagadeesh Manupati (Mng Dir)

SAGITTARIUS LIFE SCIENCE CORP.
10F-6 No 3 Yuanyuan Street, Nangang District, Taipei, Taiwan
Tel.: (886) 226557166
Web Site: https://naturalbiokey.com
Year Founded: 1998
3205—(TPE)
Rev.: $16,542,069
Assets: $18,107,119
Liabilities: $3,867,836
Net Worth: $14,239,283
Earnings: ($2,391,489)
Fiscal Year-end: 12/31/22
Medicinal Product Mfr
N.A.I.C.S.: 325412
Le-Wei Chen (Chm)

SAHA PATHANA INTER-

INTERNATIONAL PUBLIC

HOLDING PUBLIC COMPANY LIMITED
530 Sathupradith Bangpongpang, Yannawa, Bangkok, 10120, Thailand
Tel.: (66) 22930030
Web Site: https://www.spi.co.th
Year Founded: 1972
SPI—(THA)
Rev.: $131,815,654
Assets: $1,904,903,977
Liabilities: $548,413,365
Net Worth: $1,356,490,612
Earnings: $90,342,589
Emp.: 168
Fiscal Year-end: 12/31/23
Investment Holding Company; Industrial Parks
N.A.I.C.S.: 551112
Boonsithi Chokwatana (Chm)

Subsidiaries:

I.C.C. International Public Company, Limited (1)
530 Soi 58 Sathupradit Road, Bangpongpang Yannawa, Bangkok, 10120, Thailand
Tel.: (66) 2 293 9000
Web Site: https://www.icc.co.th
Sales Range: $200-249.9 Million
Emp.: 7,000
Cosmetics, Toiletries & Perfumery; Men's, Women's & Children's Apparel; Household Products, Sporting Goods & Toys Retailer
N.A.I.C.S.: 458110
Boonkiet Chokwatana (Chm)

SAHA PATHANAPIBUL PUBLIC COMPANY LIMITED
2156 New Petchburi Road, Bangkapi, Bangkok, 10310, HuayKwang, Thailand
Tel.: (66) 23180062
Web Site: https://www.sahapat.co.th
Year Founded: 1942
SPC—(THA)
Rev.: $1,116,551,362
Assets: $1,104,491,128
Liabilities: $327,154,799
Net Worth: $777,336,329
Earnings: $66,691,603
Emp.: 1,540
Fiscal Year-end: 12/31/23
Consumer Goods Distr
N.A.I.C.S.: 455110
Boonchai Chokwatana (Chm)

Subsidiaries:

BANGKOK RUBBER SAHARATTANA CO., LTD. (1)
225 Moo 3 Tambon Kungsampao, Manorom, 17110, Chainat, Thailand
Tel.: (66) 56 491 577
Footwear Mfr
N.A.I.C.S.: 316210

BANGKOK TOKYO SOCKS CO., LTD. (1)
673 Moo 11 Sukhapibarn 8 Rd Nongkharm, Si Racha, 20230, Chonburi, Thailand
Tel.: (66) 3 848 0355
Socks Mfr
N.A.I.C.S.: 315120
Takeda Shizuo (Gen Mgr)

Bangkok Tower (1999) Co., Ltd. (1)
No 2170 New Petchburi Road, Bangkapi Subdistrict Huai Khwang District, Bangkok, 10310, Thailand
Tel.: (66) 23081000
Web Site: https://www.bangkok-tower.com
Residential Building Services
N.A.I.C.S.: 531110

CHAMP ACE CO., LTD. (1)
58 Soi Charoenraj 7 Bangklo, Bangkholaem, Bangkok, Thailand
Tel.: (66) 2 6898420
Web Site: http://www.champace.co.th
Sporting Goods Whslr
N.A.I.C.S.: 423910
Boonkiet Chokwatana (Pres)

AND PRIVATE COMPANIES / SAHA-UNION PUBLIC COMPANY LIMITED

Subsidiary (Domestic):

Champ Kabin Co., Ltd. (2)
117 Moo 5 Suwankiree Rd, Kabinburi, Prachin Buri, 25110, Thailand
Tel.: (66) 37 281953
Sporting Goods Whslr
N.A.I.C.S.: 423910
Boonkiet Chokwatana (Pres)

ERAWAN TEXTILE CO., LTD. (1)
49 Moo 3 Soi Erawan Poochaosamingprai Rd Samrongtai, Phra Pradaeng, Samut Prakan, 10130, Thailand
Tel.: (66) 2 183 3898
Web Site: http://www.erawantex.co.th
Textile Products Mfr
N.A.I.C.S.: 313310

Subsidiary (Domestic):

Grand Star Industry Co., Ltd. (2)
66 68 70 Soi Rama 3 Soi 29 Sathupradit Road, Bangpongpang Yannawa, Bangkok, 10120, Thailand
Tel.: (66) 2683 8291
Web Site: http://www.grandstar.co.th
Textile Products Mfr
N.A.I.C.S.: 313310

GENERAL GLASS CO., LTD. (1)
549/2 Soi Seangsuk Sadhupradits Rd, Yannawa, Bangkok, 10120, Thailand
Tel.: (66) 2 2940091
Web Site: http://www.generalglass.net
Glass Container Mfr
N.A.I.C.S.: 327213

H & B INTERTEX CO., LTD. (1)
522/215 Soi Sadhupradit 34 Sadhupradit Road Bangpongpang, Yannawa, Bangkok, 10120, Thailand
Tel.: (66) 2 294 8870
Web Site: http://www.hnbinter.com
Soft Toys & Accessory Mfr
N.A.I.C.S.: 339930

INTERNATIONAL LABORATORIES CORP., LTD. (1)
62 Moo 8 Bangna-Trad Road Bangchalong, Bang Phli, 10540, Samutprakarn, Thailand
Tel.: (66) 234682224
Web Site: http://www.ilc-cosmetic.com
Cosmetics Products Mfr
N.A.I.C.S.: 325620
Watanakiat Jirasithithamrong (Pres)

MAKE UP TECHNIQUE INTERNATIONAL CO., LTD. (1)
382 NICE 2 Building 3rd floor Room 3A-3B Ratchadaphisek Road Samsennok, Huaykwang, Bangkok, 10310, Thailand
Tel.: (66) 2 693 2480
Web Site: http://www.mti.co.th
Cosmetic Product Distr
N.A.I.C.S.: 424210

MIT PATHANA HOMESHOPPING CO., LTD. (1)
747/14 -0-141 Soi Wat Chan Nai Sathu Pradit Rd, Yan Nawa, Bangkok, 10120, Thailand
Tel.: (66) 2 683 5981
Home Shopping Services
N.A.I.C.S.: 425120

NUBOON CO., LTD. (1)
984/79 Sukhumvit 71 Road North Klongton, Wattana, Bangkok, 10110, Thailand
Tel.: (66) 2 390 2165
Web Site: https://www.nuboon.com
Beverage Mfr & Distr
N.A.I.C.S.: 312111

NUTRITION HOUSE CO., LTD. (1)
611/277- 279 Soi Watchannai Rajuthit Bangklo, Bangkholaem, Bangkok, 10120, Thailand
Tel.: (66) 2 689 9612
Web Site: http://www.nutritionhouse.co.th
Food Product Mfr & Whslr
N.A.I.C.S.: 311412
Teeranard Chokwatana (Founder)

OSOTH INTER LABORATORIES CO., LTD. (1)
600/9 Moo 11 Sukhaphiban 8 Road Nongkham, Si Racha, 20230, Chonburi, Thailand
Tel.: (66) 3848 0766 7
Web Site: http://www.osi-bkc.in.th
Pharmaceutical Product Mfr & Distr
N.A.I.C.S.: 325412

PEK INDUSTRY CO., LTD. (1)
626/1 Moo 11 Sukhapiban 8 Rd Nongkham, Si Racha, 20230, Chonburi, Thailand
Tel.: (66) 38 480 109
Web Site: http://www.pekindustry.com
Rubber Band & Eyelet Mfr
N.A.I.C.S.: 339993
Chernchai Pinijsutapoj (Pres)

PLANET T&S CO., LTD. (1)
42/1 Rama 9 Soi 43 Seree 4 Road, Suanluang, Bangkok, 10250, Thailand
Tel.: (66) 2 718 9935
Electrical Equipment Distr
N.A.I.C.S.: 423440

PONTEX (THAILAND) CO., LTD. (1)
Aojai Issarindr Bangpakong Industrial Estate 71/21 Bangna-Trad Rd, Bangpakong, Chachoengsao, 24130, Thailand
Tel.: (66) 38 573 053
Footwear Mfr
N.A.I.C.S.: 316210

RAJA UCHINO CO., LTD. (1)
529/1-4 Rama III Road, Bang Phong Phang Yan Nawa, Bangkok, 10120, Thailand
Tel.: (66) 2 294 0130
Web Site: https://www.raja-uchino.co.th
Emp.: 1,000
Towels Mfr
N.A.I.C.S.: 314120

Plant (Domestic):

RAJA UCHINO CO., LTD. - SRIRACHA FACTORY (2)
630 Moo 11 Sukhapiban 8 Road Nongkham, Si Racha, 20230, Chonburi, Thailand
Tel.: (66) 38 480 094
Towels Mfr
N.A.I.C.S.: 314120

RAJA UCHINO CO., LTD. - SUKSAWAD FACTORY (2)
234/51 56 Moo 6 Soi 78/19 Suksawad Road Phrasamuthjedee, Samut Prakan, 10290, Thailand
Tel.: (66) 2 817 5152
Towels Mfr
N.A.I.C.S.: 314120

SAHACHOL FOOD SUPPLIES CO., LTD. (1)
955/559 Moo 11 Sukhapibarn 8 Road, Nong Kham, Si Racha, 20230, Chon Buri, Thailand
Tel.: (66) 384800113
Web Site: http://www.sahachol.com
Food Products Distr
N.A.I.C.S.: 424490

SIAM SAMSUNG LIFE INSURANCE CO., LTD. (1)
2922/222-227 Charnissara Tower II 15th FL New Petchburi Rd, Bangkapi Huaeykwang, Bangkok, 10310, Thailand
Tel.: (66) 2 308 2245
Fire Insurance Services
N.A.I.C.S.: 524113

SRIRACHA TRANSPORT CO., LTD. (1)
661/11 Sriracha Industrial Park Moo 11 Sukhapibal 8 Road Nongkham, Chon Buri, 20280, Thailand
Tel.: (66) 38 480 837
Logistics Consulting Servies
N.A.I.C.S.: 541614

SRP ADVERTISING CO., LTD. (1)
729-729/1 Floor 4-5th Sariraporn Bldg Rachadapisek Rd Bangpongpang, Yannawa, Bangkok, Thailand
Tel.: (66) 2 2954502 5
Web Site: http://www.srp.co.th
Advetising Agency
N.A.I.C.S.: 541810

SSDC (TIGERTEX) CO., LTD. (1)
111 Moo 5 Suwannasorn Rd Nontri, Kabin Buri, Prachin Buri, 25110, Thailand
Tel.: (66) 37 20523
Web Site: http://www.ssdc-tigertex.com
Emp.: 420
Textile Product Mfr & Distr
N.A.I.C.S.: 333248
Suchon Nisamaneepong (Mgr-Sls)

SUKHATASANA CO., LTD. (1)
729/18-20 Ratchadaphisek Rd, Yan Nawa, Bangkok, 10120, Thailand
Tel.: (66) 2295 4264
Emp.: 80
Advetising Agency
N.A.I.C.S.: 541810
Kraite Jaroeng (Gen Mgr)

SUN 108 CO., LTD. (1)
414/25 Soi Phatthanakan 1, Bang Phongphang Subdistrict YanNawa, Bangkok, 10120, Thailand
Tel.: (66) 2295 4255
Web Site: http://www.sun108.co.th
Emp.: 700
Office Supplies Whslr
N.A.I.C.S.: 424120

THAI BUNKA FASHION CO., LTD. (1)
323 United Center Silom Khwang Silom Khet, Bang Rak, Bangkok, 10500, Thailand
Tel.: (66) 22358240
Educational Support Services
N.A.I.C.S.: 611710

THAI GUNZE CO., LTD. (1)
99 Moo 5 Nonsikabin Buri, Prachin Buri, Thailand
Tel.: (66) 37205266
Apparel Retailer
N.A.I.C.S.: 458110

THAI MONSTER CO., LTD. (1)
129/1 Chongnonthri Road, Yan Nawa, Bangkok, 10120, Thailand
Tel.: (66) 2 294 2676
Web Site: http://www.thaimonster.co.th
Apparel Mfr & Distr
N.A.I.C.S.: 315990

THANAKOM INJECTION CO., LTD. (1)
103/11 Chonlaprathan Road Tambon Bang Phra Khru, Amphoe Nakhon Luang, Ayutthaya, 13260, Thailand
Tel.: (66) 35 364 081
Footwear Mfr
N.A.I.C.S.: 316210

TOP TREND MANUFACTURING CO., LTD. (1)
334 M 1 Sriracha Industrial park Sukhapiban 8 RD Bung Sriracha, Chon Buri, 20230, Thailand
Tel.: (66) 3848084851
Web Site: http://www.toptrendmfg.co.th
Cosmetics Products Mfr
N.A.I.C.S.: 325620

Thai Hoover Industry Co., Ltd. (1)
55 Mu 3 Khingkaew Rd Rachateva, Bangplee, Samut Prakan, 10540, Thailand
Tel.: (66) 2 3124660
Web Site: http://www.thaihoover.com
Cosmetics Products Mfr
N.A.I.C.S.: 325620
Voravit Damronguatanapokin (Mng Dir)

Thai Itokin Co., Ltd. (1)
11 Sathupradit Road, Yannawa, Bangkok, 10120, Thailand
Tel.: (66) 2 212 0025
Web Site: http://www.itokin.co.th
Emp.: 658
Apparels Mfr
N.A.I.C.S.: 315990

Thai Staflex Co., Ltd. (1)
12/1 Soi Chan 16 Yak 2 Thungwatdon, Sathon, Bangkok, 10120, Thailand
Tel.: (66) 2 285 6493
Web Site: http://www.thaistaflex.co.th
Apparel Mfr & Distr
N.A.I.C.S.: 315990

Tiger Distribution & Logistics CO., LTD. (1)
530/1-2 Soi Sathupradit 58 Bangpongpang, Yannawa, Bangkok, 10120, Thailand
Tel.: (66) 2 293 9000
Web Site: http://www.tdl.co.th
Logistics Consulting Servies
N.A.I.C.S.: 541614

U.B. CHEMICAL INDUSTRIES CO., LTD. (1)
1095/1101 Charoenkrung 41 Rd Si Phraya, Bangrak, Bangkok, 10500, Thailand
Tel.: (66) 2 266 2993
Cosmetic Product Distr
N.A.I.C.S.: 424210

UNIFAB EXPORT CO., LTD. (1)
33/1 Moo 3 Kingkaew Road Rachatewa, Bangplee, Samut Prakan, 10540, Thailand
Tel.: (66) 2 312 4500
Web Site: http://www.uni-aire.com
Electrical Equipment Distr
N.A.I.C.S.: 423620

UNIQUE FASHION CO., LTD. (1)
128/12 128/13 4th Floor Soi Tantawan Silom Rd Suriyawongse, Bangrak, Bangkok, 10500, Thailand
Tel.: (66) 2 634 0050
Web Site: http://www.camella-cosmetic.com
Cosmetic Product Distr
N.A.I.C.S.: 424210
Pawinee P. U. (Deputy Mng Dir)

Universe Beauty Co., Ltd. (1)
1095-1101 Charoenkrung Road, Si Phraya Subdistrict Bangrak District, Bangkok, 10500, Thailand
Tel.: (66) 2 639 4567
Web Site: https://www.universe-bty.co.th
Cosmetic Product Distr
N.A.I.C.S.: 424210

WASEDA EDUCATION (THAILAND) CO., LTD. (1)
1 Empire Tower 5th floor Unit 501 South Sathorn Rd, Yannawa, Bangkok, 10120, Thailand
Tel.: (66) 2670 3456
Web Site: http://www.waseda.ac.th
Educational Support Services
N.A.I.C.S.: 611710

WIEN CO., LTD. (1)
4236/218-222 Soi Pradu 1 Sathu Pradit Road Bang Khlo, Bangkholaem, Bangkok, 10120, Thailand
Tel.: (66) 2 689 8520
Logistics Consulting Servies
N.A.I.C.S.: 541614

WILD LIVES (THAILAND) CO., LTD. (1)
2 Naradhiwas Rajanagarindra Road Tungwatdon, Sathon, Bangkok, 10120, Thailand
Tel.: (66) 26762727
Web Site: http://www.wildlivesthailand.com
Cosmetic Product Distr
N.A.I.C.S.: 424210

SAHA-UNION PUBLIC COMPANY LIMITED
1828 Sukhumvit Road Phra Khanong Tai Subdistrict, Phrakanong, Bangkok, 10260, Thailand
Tel.: (66) 23115111
Web Site: https://www.sahaunion.com
Year Founded: 1972
SUC—(THA)
Rev.: $267,105,496
Assets: $783,233,179
Liabilities: $66,334,470
Net Worth: $716,898,709
Earnings: $38,908,399
Emp.: 4,970
Fiscal Year-end: 12/31/23
N.A.I.C.S.: 313310
Chantorntree Darakananda (Pres)

Subsidiaries:

Computer Union Co., Ltd. (1)
Saha Union Building 1828 Sukhumvit Rd Phrakanongtai, Phra Khanong, Bangkok, Thailand
Tel.: (66) 23116881
Web Site: http://www.cu.co.th
Sales Range: $100-124.9 Million
Emp.: 400
Computer Hardware Parts Mfr
N.A.I.C.S.: 332510

Jakkarat Unio Footwear Co., Ltd. (1)
146 Moo 14 Petchmatukla Rd, Bangkok, Thailand
Tel.: (66) 44399452

SAHA-UNION PUBLIC COMPANY LIMITED

Saha-Union Public Company Limited—(Continued)
Footwear Mfr
N.A.I.C.S.: 316210

Saha-Union Holding Co., Ltd. (1)
1828 Sukhumvit Road Bangjak Prakhanong, Bangkok, 10260, Thailand
Tel.: (66) 2 311 5111
Web Site: http://www.sahaunion.co.th
Computer Hardware Mfr
N.A.I.C.S.: 332510
Sriwarin Jirapakkana (Chm)

Saha-Union International Ltd. (1)
12th Floor Bangkok Bank Building No 28 Des Voeux Road, Fook Shing Bldg Tokwawan, Central, China (Hong Kong)
Tel.: (852) 25212260
Web Site: http://www.saha.com
Sewing Needlework & Piece Goods Stores
N.A.I.C.S.: 459130

Saha-Union Investment (China) Co., Ltd. (1)
31A-C No 18 Cao Xi Road North, Shanghai, 200030, China
Tel.: (86) 2154590378
Textile & Fabric Finishing Mill Mfr
N.A.I.C.S.: 313310

Soldev Co., Ltd. (1)
39 Soi Vipawadee 62 4-1 Vipawadee - Rangsit Rd, Talad Bangkhen Laksi, Bangkok, 10210, Thailand
Tel.: (66) 29 005 1923
Web Site: https://www.soldev.co.th
Application Development Services
N.A.I.C.S.: 541511

Thai Rubber Enterprise Co., Ltd. (1)
11/1 Moo 14 Serithai Road Minburi, Bangkok, 10510, Thailand
Tel.: (66) 29199930
Rubber Products Mfr
N.A.I.C.S.: 326299

Uni-Fibre Co., Ltd. (1)
1828 Sukhumvit Road Bangjak Prakhanong, Bangkok, 10260, Thailand
Tel.: (66) 2 311 5111
Cotton & Synthetic Textile Distr
N.A.I.C.S.: 424990

Union Button Corp., Ltd. (1)
142 Soi Latphrao 80 Section 22 142 Soi Latphrao 80 Section 22, Wangthonglang, 10310, Bangkok, Thailand
Tel.: (66) 2530704054
Web Site: http://www.union-button.com
Sales Range: $200-249.9 Million
Emp.: 1,000
Fastener Button Needle & Pin Mfr
N.A.I.C.S.: 339993

Union Construction Corp., Ltd. (1)
1828 Sukhumvit Road Bangchak, Phra Khanong, Bangkok, 10250, Thailand
Tel.: (66) 2 311 5111
Web Site: http://www.sahaunion.co.th
Construction Engineering Services
N.A.I.C.S.: 237990

Union Garment Co., Ltd. (1)
1828 Sukhumvit Rd, Bangchak, Bangkok, Thailand
Tel.: (66) 231151119
Womens & Girls Cut & Sew Blouse & Shirt Mfr
N.A.I.C.S.: 315250

Union Microclean Co., Ltd. (1)
205 Moo 4 Sukhumvit Road k m 39 5, Bangpoo Mai Muang District, Bangkok, 10280, Samut Prakan, Thailand
Tel.: (66) 27107693
Web Site: https://unionmicronclean.com
Sales Range: $25-49.9 Million
Carpet & Upholstery Cleaning Services
N.A.I.C.S.: 561740

Union Plastic Public Co., Ltd. (1)
11/1 Soi Serithai 62, Minburi, Bangkok, 10510, Thailand
Tel.: (66) 25170109
Web Site: https://www.unionplastic.co.th
Sales Range: $200-249.9 Million
Emp.: 800
Plastics Product Mfr
N.A.I.C.S.: 326199

Pricha Leelanukrom (Chm)

Union Rubber Products Corp. Ltd. (1)
99 Moo 5 Bangna-Trat Road Km 38, Bang Samak, Bang Pakong, 24180, Chachoengsao, Thailand
Tel.: (66) 895003516
Textile & Fabric Finishing Mill Mfr
N.A.I.C.S.: 313310

Union Spinning Mills Co., Ltd. (1)
142 Soi Latphrao 80 Chantima Latphrao rd, Khwang Wangthonglang Khet Wangthonglang, Bangkok, 10310, Thailand
Tel.: (66) 2 539 6133
Web Site: https://www.saha.com
Sales Range: $100-124.9 Million
Emp.: 400
Textile Spinning Mills
N.A.I.C.S.: 314999

Union Stainless Steel Products Co., Ltd. (1)
11/2 Soi Serithai 62, Minburi, 10510, Bangkok, Thailand (98%)
Tel.: (66) 2 9198996
Web Site: http://www.usp.co.th
Sales Range: $25-49.9 Million
Emp.: 300
Mfr of Stainless Steel Pipe & Tube, Household Products & Press Parts
N.A.I.C.S.: 238120
Thanya Thongnopakao (Mgr-Factory)

Union Textile Industries Plc (1)
205 Moo 4 Sukhumvit Rd km 39 5, Bangpoo Mai, Bangkok, 10280, Muang Samut Prakan, Thailand
Tel.: (66) 23231085
Web Site: http://www.ut.co.th
Sales Range: $150-199.9 Million
Textile Product Mills
N.A.I.C.S.: 314999

Union Thai-Nichiban Co., Ltd. (1)
Bangchan Industrial Estate Minburi, 10510, Bangkok, Thailand
Tel.: (66) 251701004
Packaging & Labeling Services
N.A.I.C.S.: 561910

Union Zojirushi Co., Ltd. (1)
11-3 Mu 4 Bangchan Ind Est, Serithai Rd, 10510, Bangkok, Thailand
Tel.: (66) 29198893
Web Site: http://www.unionzojirushi.com
Sales Range: $200-249.9 Million
Emp.: 821
Structural Steel & Precast Concrete Contractors
N.A.I.C.S.: 238120

Venus Thread, Inc. (1)
3530 Piedmont Rd NE Ste 15-L, Atlanta, GA 30305
Tel.: (404) 365-0678
Web Site: http://vti.saha.com
Sales Range: $25-49.9 Million
Emp.: 20
Thread Mills
N.A.I.C.S.: 313110

SAHAKOL EQUIPMENT PUBLIC COMPANY LIMITED
47/10 Vibhavadeerangsit Road, Ladyao Chatuchak, Bangkok, 10900, Thailand
Tel.: (66) 29410888
Web Site: https://www.sahakol.com
Year Founded: 2001
SQ—(THA)
Rev.: $180,017,538
Assets: $278,954,378
Liabilities: $194,367,726
Net Worth: $84,586,652
Earnings: $3,810,428
Fiscal Year-end: 12/31/23
Mining Services
N.A.I.C.S.: 236210
Sasavat Sirison (CEO)

SAHAM GROUP SA
216 Bd Mohamed Zerktouni, Casablanca, 20040, Morocco
Tel.: (212) 22 435942

Web Site: http://www.sahamgroup.com
Sales Range: $10-24.9 Million
Brokerage, Investment & Management Services
N.A.I.C.S.: 524210
Moulay Hafid Elalamy (Founder)

Subsidiaries:

LIA Insurance sal (1)
Dora Highway Cite Dora 1, PO Box 11-1439, Beirut, Lebanon (91.42%)
Tel.: (961) 1255640
Web Site: http://www.lialebanon.com
Rev.: $115,257,604
Assets: $371,491,852
Liabilities: $371,491,851
Net Worth: $1
Earnings: $10,480,999
Emp.: 100
Fiscal Year-end: 12/31/2017
Life & General Insurance Products & Services
N.A.I.C.S.: 524113
Salam N. Hanna (Gen Mgr)

SAHAMIT MACHINERY PUBLIC COMPANY LIMITED
42 48 Rama 3 Road Soi 53, Yannawa, Bangkok, 10120, Thailand
Tel.: (66) 22951000
Web Site: https://www.sahamit.co.th
Year Founded: 1973
SMIT—(THA)
Rev.: $47,609,890
Assets: $81,904,805
Liabilities: $8,002,024
Net Worth: $73,902,781
Earnings: $3,843,620
Emp.: 461
Fiscal Year-end: 12/31/23
Industrial Products Mfr
N.A.I.C.S.: 333248
Chaisilp Tamesirichai (Chm)

SAHAMITR PRESSURE CONTAINER PUBLIC COMPANY LIMITED
92 Soi Thientalay7 4th Intersection Bangkhunthien Chaitalay Road, Samaedam, Bangkok, 10150, Thailand
Tel.: (66) 28954139
Web Site: https://www.smpcplc.com
Year Founded: 1981
SMPC—(THA)
Rev.: $111,246,715
Assets: $112,961,510
Liabilities: $32,240,196
Net Worth: $80,721,314
Earnings: $10,837,052
Emp.: 481
Fiscal Year-end: 12/31/23
Steel Cylinders Mfr
N.A.I.C.S.: 331221
Thamik Ekahitanond (Asst Mng Dir-Factory)

SAHANA SYSTEM LIMITED
1301 Maple Trade Center Nr Surdhara Circle, Thaltej, Ahmedabad, 380052, Gujarat, India
Tel.: (91) 9664848978
Web Site: https://www.sahanasystem.com
Year Founded: 2009
SAHANA—(NSE)
Rev.: $2,894,587
Assets: $2,892,644
Liabilities: $1,624,603
Net Worth: $1,268,041
Earnings: $744,080
Emp.: 34
Fiscal Year-end: 03/31/23
Software Development Services
N.A.I.C.S.: 541511
Dhaval Joshi (COO)

SAHAND FORKLIFT MFG. CO.

INTERNATIONAL PUBLIC

Gharamalek Industrial Town, 5193653434, Tabriz, Iran
Tel.: (98) 411 2898688
Web Site: http://www.sahand-forklift.com
Year Founded: 1971
Forklift Mfr
N.A.I.C.S.: 339999
Akbar Pouvali (CEO & Mng Dir)

SAHARA ENERGY LTD.
Suite 400 444- 7th Ave, Calgary, T2P 0X8, AB, Canada
Tel.: (403) 232-1359
Web Site: https://www.saharaenergy.ca
Rev.: $156,192
Assets: $3,820,082
Liabilities: $1,582,892
Net Worth: $2,237,190
Earnings: ($2,577,203)
Fiscal Year-end: 12/31/20
Oil & Gas Exploration Services
N.A.I.C.S.: 213112
Yachao Peng (Chm)

SAHARA HOSPITALITY COMPANY S.A.O.G.
Burj Al Sinaw Building Bldg No 1813 Plot No 84 Way No 2728 MBD, PO Box 311, 100, Muscat, 100, Oman
Tel.: (968) 24769800
Web Site: https://www.sahara.com.om
SAHS—(MUS)
Rev.: $30,686,576
Assets: $80,770,293
Liabilities: $8,735,731
Net Worth: $72,034,562
Earnings: $6,655,931
Fiscal Year-end: 12/31/23
Management Consulting Services
N.A.I.C.S.: 541618
Talal Qais Al Zawawi (Chm)

SAHARA HOUSINGFINA CORPORATION LIMITED
46 Dr Sundari Mohan Avenue, Kolkata, 700014, India
Tel.: (91) 3322890148
Web Site: https://www.saharahousingfina.com
Year Founded: 1991
511533—(BOM)
Rev.: $1,343,157
Assets: $12,086,697
Liabilities: $6,057,790
Net Worth: $6,028,907
Earnings: $169,774
Emp.: 32
Fiscal Year-end: 03/31/23
Housing Loan Financial Services
N.A.I.C.S.: 522291
D. J. Bagchi (CEO & Sec)

SAHARA INDIA PARIWAR
Gomti Nagar, PO Box 2, Lucknow, 10, India
Tel.: (91) 9839 125222
Web Site: http://www.saharaindiapariwar.org
Diversified Holding Company: Finance, Infrastructure & Housing, Media & Entertainment
N.A.I.C.S.: 551112
Subrata Roy Sahara (Chm & Mng Dir)

Subsidiaries:

Sahara Asset Management Company Pvt. Ltd. (1)
2nd Floor Parinee Crescenzo Bandra-Kurla Complex, Bandra East, Mumbai, 400051, India
Tel.: (91) 22 39664100
Asset Management Services
N.A.I.C.S.: 531390

Sahara India Commercial Corporation Limited (1)
Sahara India Point S V Road, Goregaon West, Mumbai, 400104, India
Tel.: (91) 22 66688080
Web Site: http://www.ambyvalley.com
Asset Management Services
N.A.I.C.S.: 531390

Sahara India T.V. Network Pvt. Ltd. (1)
Sahara India Complex C-2 3 & 4 Sector XI, Gautambudhanagar, Noida, 201 301, Uttar Pradesh, India
Tel.: (91) 120 2444755
Television Broadcasting Services
N.A.I.C.S.: 516120

Sahara Life Insurance Company Ltd (1)
Sahara India Centre 2 Kapoorthala Complex, Lucknow, 226 024, India
Tel.: (91) 522 2337777
Fire Insurance Services
N.A.I.C.S.: 524113

SAHARA INTERNATIONAL PETROCHEMICAL COMPANY
Sipchem Building King Saud Road District, PO Box 130, Al Khobar, 31952, Saudi Arabia
Tel.: (966) 138019392   SA
Web Site: https://www.sipchem.com
Year Founded: 1999
2310—(SAU)
Rev.: $2,031,396,795
Assets: $5,872,883,217
Liabilities: $1,493,712,991
Net Worth: $4,379,170,225
Earnings: $361,682,094
Emp.: 1,636
Fiscal Year-end: 12/31/23
Petrochemical & Chemical Products Mfr
N.A.I.C.S.: 325110
Fahad S. Al-Rajhi (Vice Chm)

Subsidiaries:

International Methanol Company (1)
PO Box 12021, Jubail Industrial City, Al Jubayl, 31961, Eastern Province, Saudi Arabia
Tel.: (966) 33599999
Methanol Mfr
N.A.I.C.S.: 325199

Sipchem Asia Pte. Ltd. (1)
152 Beach Rd 25-05 Gateway East, Singapore, 189721, Singapore
Tel.: (65) 68846958
Administrative Support Services
N.A.I.C.S.: 488999

SAHARA ONE MEDIA AND ENTERTAINMENT LIMITED.
25-28 Floor-2 Plot No 209 Atlanta Building Jamanlal Bajaj Marg, Nariman Point,, Mumbai, 400021, Maharashtra, India
Tel.: (91) 2242931818
Web Site: https://www.sahara-one.com
503691—(BOM)
Rev.: $8,805
Assets: $39,922,194
Liabilities: $8,421,048
Net Worth: $31,501,146
Earnings: ($1,258,209)
Fiscal Year-end: 03/31/21
Media & Entertainment
N.A.I.C.S.: 541840
Prakash Chandra Tripathy (CFO)

SAHATHAI TERMINAL PCL
51/1 Moo 3, Poochaosamingprai Road Tumbon Bangyaprak, Phra Pradaeng, 10130, Samut Prakan, Thailand
Tel.: (66) 23868000
Web Site: https://www.sahathaiterminal.com
Year Founded: 2007
PORT—(THA)
Rev.: $45,049,048
Assets: $98,042,399
Liabilities: $60,356,149
Net Worth: $37,686,249
Earnings: ($336,875)
Fiscal Year-end: 12/31/23
Transportation Services
N.A.I.C.S.: 485999
Yuth Worachatthan (Chm)

SAHAVIRIYA STEEL INDUSTRIES PUBLIC COMPANY LIMITED
2nd-3rd Floor Prapawit Building 28/1 Surasak Road Silom, Bangrak, Bangkok, 10500, Thailand
Tel.: (66) 22383063
Web Site: http://www.ssi-steel.com
Rev.: $973,031,114
Assets: $792,552,326
Liabilities: $1,964,111,291
Net Worth: ($1,171,558,965)
Earnings: $6,954,315
Fiscal Year-end: 12/31/18
Hot-Rolled Steel Sheet Mfr
N.A.I.C.S.: 331221
Win Viriyaprapaikit (Pres & CEO)

Subsidiaries:

Prachuap Port Co. Ltd. (1)
6th floor Prapawit Bldg 28/1 Surasak Rd, Silom Bangrak, Bangkok, Thailand
Tel.: (66) 2630032332
Web Site: http://www.ppc.co.th
Sales Range: $25-49.9 Million
Emp.: 25
Petroleum Bulk Stations & Terminals
N.A.I.C.S.: 424710

West Coast Engineering Company Limited (1)
28/1 Prapawit Building 3rd Floor Surasak Road Silom, Bangrak, 10500, Bangkok, Thailand
Tel.: (66) 22383063
Web Site: http://www.wce.co.th
Sales Range: $150-199.9 Million
Emp.: 555
Civil Engineering Services
N.A.I.C.S.: 541330
Pongrapree Sapankaew (Deputy Mng Dir-Maintenance & Mgmt Bus Div)

SAHYADRI INDUSTRIES LTD
Swastik House 39 D Gultekdi Jawaharlal Nehru Marg, Pune, 411 037, Maharashtra, India
Tel.: (91) 2026444625
Web Site: https://www.silworld.in
SAHYADRI—(NSE)
Rev.: $71,604,820
Assets: $66,738,205
Liabilities: $26,533,181
Net Worth: $40,205,024
Earnings: $4,449,374
Emp.: 711
Fiscal Year-end: 03/31/23
Cement Mfr
N.A.I.C.S.: 325520
Jayesh Purushottam Patel (Chm)

SAI BABA INVESTMENT & COMMERCIAL ENTERPRISE LIMITED
33/36 Basement West Patel Nagar, New Delhi, 110008, India
Tel.: (91) 7303988341
Web Site: http://www.saibabainvest.co.in
Year Founded: 1981
Rev.: $188,551
Assets: $2,081,946
Liabilities: $201,743
Net Worth: $1,880,203
Earnings: $78,807
Fiscal Year-end: 03/31/19
Real Estate Development Services
N.A.I.C.S.: 531390

Manoj Kumar Gunvantrai Somani (CFO)

SAI GON - HA NOI SECURITIES JOINT STOCK COMPANY
1st 5th Floor Unimex Hanoi building No 41 Ngo Quyen, Hoan Kiem District, Hanoi, Vietnam
Tel.: (84) 438181888
Web Site: https://www.shs.com.vn
SHS—(HNX)
Rev.: $42,695,401
Assets: $242,907,102
Liabilities: $135,213,672
Net Worth: $107,693,430
Earnings: $10,185,531
Fiscal Year-end: 12/31/19
Brokerage Services
N.A.I.C.S.: 523150
Do Quang Hien (Chm)

SAI GON FUEL JOINT STOCK COMPANY
146E Nguyen Dinh Chinh Ward 8, Phu Nhuan District, Ho Chi Minh City, Vietnam
Tel.: (84) 839979292
Web Site: https://www.sfc.com.vn
Year Founded: 1976
SFC—(HOSE)
Rev.: $163,037,700
Assets: $29,226,200
Liabilities: $10,662,300
Net Worth: $18,563,900
Earnings: $2,830,900
Emp.: 177
Fiscal Year-end: 09/30/23
Fuel Supply Services
N.A.I.C.S.: 457210

SAI GON GROUND SERVICES JSC
Tan Son Nhat Intl Airport Office Building 2nd Floor Ward 2, Tan Binh District, Ho Chi Minh City, Vietnam
Tel.: (84) 2835474999
Web Site: https://www.sags.vn
Year Founded: 2004
SGN—(HNX)
Passenger Air Transportation Services
N.A.I.C.S.: 481111
Hua Kien Trung (VP)

SAI GON PLASTICS PACKAGING JOINT STOCK COMPANY
Lot II - 2B Area V Industrial group II, No 10 St Tan Binh Industrial Park Tay Thanh Ward Tan Phu District, Ho Chi Minh City, Vietnam
Tel.: (84) 8 8162765
Web Site: http://www.saplastic.com.vn
SPP—(HNX)
Sales Range: $25-49.9 Million
Paper Bags & Plastic Bags Mfr
N.A.I.C.S.: 322220
Truong Ngoc Khanh (Gen Dir)

SAI GON TELECOMMUNICATIONS TECHNOLOGY JOINT STOCK COMPANY
Saigon ICT Tower Lot 46 Quang Trung Software Park Tan Chanh Hiep Ward, District 12, Ho Chi Minh City, Vietnam
Tel.: (84) 837159909
Web Site: https://www.saigontel.vn
Year Founded: 2002
SGT—(HOSE)
Rev.: $53,962,071
Assets: $294,484,498
Liabilities: $213,571,077
Net Worth: $80,913,422
Earnings: $1,763,772
Fiscal Year-end: 12/31/23

Construction Services
N.A.I.C.S.: 236210
Dang Thanh Tam (Chm)

SAI GON THUONG TIN REAL ESTATE JOINT STOCK COMPANY
253 Hoang Van Thu Ward 2, Tan Binh District, Ho Chi Minh City, Vietnam
Tel.: (84) 838249988
Web Site: http://www.sacomreal.com
Sales Range: $10-24.9 Million
Emp.: 360
Real Estate Services Including Brokerage, Construction & Management Services
N.A.I.C.S.: 531390
Dang Hong Anh (Co-Chm)

SAI GON VIEN DONG E-COMMERCE SERVICES JSC
102A Pho Co Dieu, Ward 4 District 11, Ho Chi Minh City, Vietnam
Tel.: (84) 2839560169
Web Site: https://savitechco.vn
Year Founded: 2003
SVT—(HOSE)
Rev.: $2,926,106
Assets: $9,688,468
Liabilities: $54,054
Net Worth: $9,634,414
Earnings: $1,052,619
Fiscal Year-end: 12/31/23
Software Development Services
N.A.I.C.S.: 541511
Nguyen Thi Thu (Chm-Mgmt Bd)

SAI GON WATER INFRASTRUCTURE CORPORATION
477-479 An Duong Vuong Ward 11, District 6, Ho Chi Minh City, Vietnam
Tel.: (84) 862918483
Web Site: https://www.sii.vn
SII—(HOSE)
Rev.: $10,027,421
Assets: $89,416,484
Liabilities: $50,810,930
Net Worth: $38,605,554
Earnings: ($1,590,361)
Fiscal Year-end: 12/31/23
Structural Engineering Services
N.A.I.C.S.: 541330

SAI INDUSTRIES LIMITED
302 3rd Floor C-2/4 Community Centre Ashok Vihar, Phase-2, New Delhi, 110052, India
Tel.: (91) 01146051307   In
Web Site: http://www.shrisaiindustries.com
Year Founded: 1991
530905—(BOM)
Assets: $37,603
Liabilities: $234,140
Net Worth: ($196,537)
Earnings: ($6,303)
Emp.: 2
Fiscal Year-end: 03/31/23
Financial Investment Services
N.A.I.C.S.: 523999
Niraj Kumar Singh (Mng Dir & CFO)

SAI MICROELECTRONICS INC.
North Ring Center Yard 21 Kechuang 8th Street BDA, Xicheng District, Beijing, 100029, China
Tel.: (86) 1059702088
Web Site: https://www.smeiic.com
Year Founded: 2008
300456—(CHIN)
Rev.: $110,329,128
Assets: $979,538,508
Liabilities: $206,795,160
Net Worth: $772,743,348
Earnings: ($10,299,744)

SAI MICROELECTRONICS INC.

Sai MicroElectronics Inc.—(Continued)
Emp.: 130
Fiscal Year-end: 12/31/22
GPS Receivers, Enclosures & Antennas Mfr
N.A.I.C.S.: 334511
Hanyang Zhao (Supvr)

SAI SILKS (KALAMANDIR) LTD
6-3-790/8 Flat 1 Bathina Apartments Ameerpet, Hyderabad, 500016, India
Tel.: (91) 40 66566555
Web Site: http://www.kalamandir.com
Year Founded: 2005
Sales Range: $25-49.9 Million
Emp.: 270
Sarees, Women's Dresses, Men's Wear & Children's Wear Mfr; Jewelry Mfr & Sales
N.A.I.C.S.: 315250

SAI SON CEMENT JSC
Nam Phuong Tien, Chuong My district, Hanoi, Vietnam
Tel.: (84) 344132183
Web Site: https://www.ximangsaison.com
Year Founded: 1958
SCJ—(HNX)
Rev.: $119,965,000
Assets: $197,957,500
Liabilities: $150,616,300
Net Worth: $47,341,200
Earnings: $464,600
Fiscal Year-end: 12/31/22
Cement Mfr
N.A.I.C.S.: 327310

SAI.TECH GLOBAL CORPORATION
01-05 195 Pearl's Hill Terrace, Singapore, 168976, Singapore
Tel.: (65) 96565641   Ky
Web Site: https://sai.tech
SAI—(NASDAQ)
Rev.: $10,638,000
Assets: $21,100,000
Liabilities: $786,000
Net Worth: $20,314,000
Earnings: ($8,845,000)
Emp.: 28
Fiscal Year-end: 12/31/22
Investment Services
N.A.I.C.S.: 523999
Risheng Li (CEO)

Subsidiaries:
SAI US Inc.   (1)
100 Ryan St Ste 30, South Plainfield, NJ 07080
Tel.: (732) 609-0124
Web Site: https://saiusainc.com
Software Development Services
N.A.I.C.S.: 541511

SAIBO CO., LTD.
1-1-70 Maekawa, Kawaguchi, 333-0842, Saitama, Japan
Tel.: (81) 482675151
Web Site: https://www.saibo.co.jp
Year Founded: 1948
3123—(TKS)
Rev.: $75,499,420
Assets: $287,753,130
Liabilities: $158,454,920
Net Worth: $129,298,210
Earnings: $6,246,450
Emp.: 115
Fiscal Year-end: 03/31/24
Textile Product Mfr & Distr
N.A.I.C.S.: 313220
Eiichi Iizuka (Pres & CEO)

SAIBU GAS HOLDINGS CO., LTD.
1-17-1 Chiyo, Hakata-ku, Fukuoka, Japan
Tel.: (81) 926332440
Web Site: https://www.saibugas.co.jp
Year Founded: 1930
9536—(TKS)
Rev.: $1,694,328,080
Assets: $2,854,098,850
Liabilities: $2,156,254,710
Net Worth: $697,844,140
Earnings: $40,684,550
Emp.: 156
Fiscal Year-end: 03/31/24
Natural Gas Mfr & Distr
N.A.I.C.S.: 211130
Toshio Sakemi (Chm)

Subsidiaries:
Saibu Gas Kumamoto Co., Ltd.   (1)
14-10 Hagiwara-cho, Chuo-ku, Kumamoto, Japan
Tel.: (81) 963700919
Emp.: 114
Gas Appliance Mfr & Distr
N.A.I.C.S.: 333414

Saibu Gas Nagasaki Co., Ltd.   (1)
1-1 Mifunekura-cho, Nagasaki, Japan
Tel.: (81) 958240919
Emp.: 131
Gas Appliance Mfr & Distr
N.A.I.C.S.: 333414

Saibu Gas Sasebo Co., Ltd.   (1)
7-36 Manzu-cho, Sasebo, Japan
Tel.: (81) 956250919
Emp.: 83
Gas Appliance Mfr & Distr
N.A.I.C.S.: 333414

SAIETTA GROUP PLC
Building 210 Heyford Park Camp Road, Bicester, OX25 5HE, Oxfordshire, United Kingdom
Tel.: (44) 1869233121   UK
Web Site: https://www.saietta.com
Year Founded: 2008
SED—(AIM)
Rev.: $2,654,581
Assets: $50,091,741
Liabilities: $13,246,004
Net Worth: $36,845,737
Earnings: ($35,099,910)
Emp.: 189
Fiscal Year-end: 03/31/23
Engineeering Services
N.A.I.C.S.: 541330

SAIF HOLDINGS LIMITED
3rd and 4th Floor Kashmir Commercial Complex Fazal-ul-Haq Road, Blue Area, Islamabad, 44000, Pakistan
Tel.: (92) 512271378
Web Site: http://www.saifgroup.com
Sales Range: $250-299.9 Million
Holding Services
N.A.I.C.S.: 551112
Javed Saifullah Khan (Co-Chm)

Subsidiaries:
Kohat Textile Mills Limited   (1)
3rd Floor City Centre Plot No 40 Main Bank Road Saddar Cantt, Rawalpindi, Pakistan   (47%)
Tel.: (92) 515700824
Web Site: http://www.kohattextile.com
Rev.: $30,620,386
Assets: $45,288,456
Liabilities: $22,777,938
Net Worth: $22,510,517
Earnings: $1,814,978
Emp.: 1,104
Fiscal Year-end: 06/30/2022
Textile Products Mfr
N.A.I.C.S.: 313210
Assad Saifullah Khan (CEO)

Lahore Compost (Pvt) Ltd.   (1)
Mahmood Booti, Bund Road (Ring Road), Lahore, Pakistan   (88%)
Tel.: (92) 42 36885438

Web Site: http://www.lahorecompost.com
Composting of Solid Waste
N.A.I.C.S.: 562998

Mediterranean Textile Company   (1)
4 Omarat Al Yamany Street, Zamalek, Cairo, Egypt
Tel.: (20) 3 9573575
Web Site: http://www.saifgroup.com
Yarn Production
N.A.I.C.S.: 313110
Shiraz William (Exec Dir-Mktg)

Saif Healthcare Limited   (1)
Kulsum Plaza 2020 Blue Are, Jinnah Avenue, Islamabad, Pakistan   (84%)
Tel.: (92) 51 2271154
Web Site: http://www.saifgroup.com
Cardiac Care Hospital
N.A.I.C.S.: 622310
Hoor Yousafzai (CEO)

Saif Power Limited   (1)
1st Floor Kashmir Commercial Complex FazalHaq Road, Block E Blue Area, Islamabad, Pakistan
Tel.: (92) 512271378
Web Site: https://saifpower.com
Rev.: $82,273,658
Assets: $116,414,541
Liabilities: $65,681,542
Net Worth: $50,732,999
Earnings: $7,798,376
Emp.: 42
Fiscal Year-end: 12/31/2022
Eletric Power Generation Services
N.A.I.C.S.: 221116
Hoor Yousafzai (Chm)

Saif Textile Mills Ltd.   (1)
3rd Floor City Centre Plot No-40 Main Bank Road Saddar, Rawalpindi, Pakistan   (49%)
Tel.: (92) 515700824
Web Site: http://www.saiftextile.com
Rev.: $78,649,768
Assets: $86,141,077
Liabilities: $61,724,866
Net Worth: $24,416,211
Earnings: $1,751,698
Emp.: 2,549
Fiscal Year-end: 06/30/2022
Textile Products Mfr
N.A.I.C.S.: 314999
Zaheen-ud-Din Qurashi (CEO)

Softech Systems (Pvt) Limited   (1)
955-L Phase-2 Johar Town, Lahore, Pakistan   (51%)
Tel.: (92) 42 3529 0561
Web Site: http://www.softech.com.pk
Software Development & Technology Services
N.A.I.C.S.: 513210
M. Salman Iqbal (CEO)

SAIF PARTNERS
Suites 2516-2520 Two Pacific Place Queensway, Hong Kong, China (Hong Kong)
Tel.: (852) 29182200
Web Site: http://www.sbaif.com
Year Founded: 2001
Sales Range: $1-4.9 Billion
Privater Equity Firm
N.A.I.C.S.: 523999
Andrew Y. Yan (Mng Partner)

SAIF POWERTEC LIMITED
72 Mohakhali C/A 8th Floor Rupayan Center, Dhaka, 1212, Bangladesh
Tel.: (880) 9856358
Web Site: https://www.saifpowertecltd.com
Year Founded: 2003
SAIFPOWER—(CHT)
Rev.: $526,253
Assets: $2,067,788
Liabilities: $455,544
Net Worth: $1,612,244
Earnings: $75,291
Emp.: 1,842
Fiscal Year-end: 06/30/22
Building Construction Services
N.A.I.C.S.: 236220

INTERNATIONAL PUBLIC

Tarafder Nigar Sultana (Chm)

SAIGON - HANOI COMMERCIAL JOINT STOCK BANK
77 Tran Hung Dao, Hoan Kiem, Hanoi, Vietnam
Tel.: (84) 439423388
Web Site: https://www.shb.com.vn
Year Founded: 1993
SHB—(HOSE)
Rev.: $1,972,912,700
Assets: $63,042,475,100
Liabilities: $58,054,488,500
Net Worth: $4,987,986,600
Earnings: $747,041,000
Emp.: 10,269
Fiscal Year-end: 12/31/23
Banking Services
N.A.I.C.S.: 522110
Nguyen Van Le (CEO & Member-Mgmt Bd)

Subsidiaries:
SHB Cambodia Limited Liability Bank   (1)
Building No 107 Norodom Avenue, Boeing Rang Ward Daun Penh District, Phnom Penh, Cambodia
Tel.: (855) 23221900
Finance Investment Services
N.A.I.C.S.: 523999

SHB Laos single member Limited Liability Bank   (1)
Lanexang Road, HatsadyTai Village Chanthabouly District, Vientiane, Laos
Tel.: (856) 21968888
Finance Investment Services
N.A.I.C.S.: 523999

SHB Securities Company Limited   (1)
2C Van Phuc Street, Ba Dinh District, Hanoi, Vietnam   (98.47%)
Tel.: (84) 4 3726 2275
Web Site: www.shbs.com.vn
Securities Brokerage
N.A.I.C.S.: 523150
The Minh Nguyen (CEO)

Sai Gon - Hanoi Bank Laos Limited   (1)
Unit 1 LaneXang Street, Chanthabul Hatsady Dist, Vientiane, Lao People's Democratic Republic
Tel.: (856) 2 196 8888
Web Site: https://www.shb.la
Commercial Banking Services
N.A.I.C.S.: 522110

SAIGON BEER ALCOHOL BEVERAGE CORP.
187 Nguyen Chi Thanh, Ward 12 District 5, Ho Chi Minh City, Vietnam
Tel.: (84) 2838294081
Web Site: https://sabeco.com.vn
Year Founded: 1875
SAB—(HOSE)
Rev.: $3,497,908,400
Assets: $3,446,507,600
Liabilities: $987,423,000
Net Worth: $2,459,084,600
Earnings: $522,385,100
Emp.: 8,550
Fiscal Year-end: 12/31/22
Alcoholic Beverage Distr
N.A.I.C.S.: 424820
Koh Poh Tiong (Chm)

Subsidiaries:
Sai Gon - Dong Xuan Beer Alcohol Joint Stock Company   (1)
Zone 6, Thanh Ba Town Thanh Ba District, Ho Chi Minh City, Phu Tho, Vietnam
Tel.: (84) 210885604
Web Site: https://www.saigondongxuan.com.vn
Beer Mfr
N.A.I.C.S.: 312120

Saigon Beer Nam Trung Bo Trading Joint Stock Company (1)
National Highway 1, Dien Phu commune Dien Khanh District, Nha Trang, Khanh Hoa, Vietnam
Tel.: (84) 2583771279
Web Site:
https://www.biasaigonnamtrungbo.vn
Beer Mfr
N.A.I.C.S.: 312120

Song Tien Saigon Beer Trading Joint Stock Company (1)
Ap Tan Vinh Thuan Xa, Xa Tan Ngai, Vinh Long, Vietnam
Tel.: (84) 901288525
Alcoholic Beverage Mfr & Distr
N.A.I.C.S.: 312140

SAIGON BEER TRANSPORTATION JOINT STOCK COMPANY
78 Ton That Thuyet phuong 16, quan 4, Ho Chi Minh City, Vietnam
Tel.: (84) 8 3948 5278
Web Site:
http://www.sabetranjsc.com
Food Transportation Services
N.A.I.C.S.: 484121
Dam Phan Liem *(Exec Dir)*

SAIGON FISHING NET JOINT STOCK COMPANY
89 Nguyen Khoai Street, District 4, Ho Chi Minh City, Vietnam
Tel.: (84) 839400534
Web Site: https://www.sfn.vn
Year Founded: 1969
SFN—(HNX)
Rev.: $14,566,400
Assets: $8,102,600
Liabilities: $661,000
Net Worth: $7,441,600
Earnings: $928,300
Fiscal Year-end: 12/31/23
Net Mfr & Supplier
N.A.I.C.S.: 339999

SAIGON GENERAL SERVICE CORPORATION
68 Nam Ky Khoi Nghia, District 1, Ho Chi Minh City, Vietnam
Tel.: (84) 2838213913
Web Site: https://www.savico.com.vn
Year Founded: 2004
SVC—(HOSE)
Rev.: $858,480,733
Assets: $295,563,156
Liabilities: $195,037,998
Net Worth: $100,525,157
Earnings: $1,830,598
Emp.: 925
Fiscal Year-end: 12/31/23
Financial Services
N.A.I.C.S.: 523999

Subsidiaries:

Ben Thanh Automobile Jsc (1)
831 Truong Chinh, Tay Thanh Ward Tan Phu District, Ho Chi Minh City, 700000, Vietnam
Tel.: (84) 287 101 6888
Web Site: https://www.benthanhford.com.vn
New Car Dealers
N.A.I.C.S.: 441110

Hanoi Savico JSC (1)
Long Bien District, Long Bien District, Hanoi, Vietnam
Tel.: (84) 4 6288 8555
Web Site: http://www.savicomegamall.com
Shopping Mall Operator
N.A.I.C.S.: 531120

Long Bien Toyota Co., Ltd (1)
7-9 Nguyen Van Linh, Long Bien District, Hanoi, Vietnam
Tel.: (84) 4 6277 7999
New Car Dealers
N.A.I.C.S.: 441110

Sai Gon Automobile Co., Ltd (1)
61A Cao Thang District 3, Ho Chi Minh City, Vietnam
Tel.: (84) 8 3818 1458
Web Site: http://www.saigonford.com.vn
New Car Dealers
N.A.I.C.S.: 441110

Sai Gon Star JSC (1)
510 Quoc Lo 13 P, Thu Duc, Ho Chi Minh City, Vietnam
Tel.: (84) 8 3726 3023
Web Site: http://www.saigonngoisao.com.vn
Motorcycle & Car Dealer
N.A.I.C.S.: 441227

SAIGON HOTEL CORP.
41-47 Dong Du District 1, Ho Chi Minh City, Vietnam
Tel.: (84) 838299734
Web Site:
https://www.saigonhotel.com.vn
SGH—(HNX)
Rev.: $717,327
Assets: $7,392,085
Liabilities: $581,666
Net Worth: $6,810,419
Earnings: $177,030
Fiscal Year-end: 12/31/21
Hotel & Motel Operator
N.A.I.C.S.: 721110

SAIGON MARITIME JOINT STOCK CO., LTD.
422 Nguyen Tat Thanh Street, Dist 4, Ho Chi Minh City, Vietnam
Tel.: (84) 8 3826 1627
Web Site:
http://www.saigonmaritime.vn
Year Founded: 2002
Forwarders & Multi-Modal Transportation Services
N.A.I.C.S.: 488390
Bach Thai Dung *(Deputy Gen Dir)*

SAIGON PETROLEUM SERVICE COMPANY
16 Phung Khac Khoan Street, District 1, Ho Chi Minh City, Vietnam
Tel.: (84) 838230958
Web Site: http://www.spsc.com.vn
Year Founded: 1993
Sales Range: $10-24.9 Million
Emp.: 205
Petroleum, Gas & Coal Products Exploration & Production
N.A.I.C.S.: 324199

Subsidiaries:

Castrol Vietnam Ltd. (1)
4th Floor Sun Wah Tower, 115 Nguyen Hue Street District, Ho Chi Minh City, Vietnam (40%)
Tel.: (84) 88219153
Oil & Lubricants Mfr & Distr
N.A.I.C.S.: 324191

Joint Venture (Non-US):

Castrol BP Petco Co., Ltd. (2)
Sales Range: $125-149.9 Million
Emp.: 190
Petroleum & Gas Exploration, Production & Sales
N.A.I.C.S.: 211120

SAIGON THUONG TIN COMMERCIAL JOINT STOCK BANK
266-268 Nam Ky Khoi Nghia Street Vo Thi Sau Ward District 3, Ho Chi Minh City, Vietnam
Tel.: (84) 2838469516
Web Site:
https://www.sacombank.com
Year Founded: 1991
STB—(HOSE)
Rev.: $909,380,120
Assets: $27,784,853,992
Liabilities: $25,900,618,795
Net Worth: $1,884,235,197
Earnings: $318,066,979
Emp.: 18,514

Fiscal Year-end: 12/31/23
Banking Services
N.A.I.C.S.: 522110
Tan Thanh Nguyen *(Chm-Supervisory Bd)*

Subsidiaries:

Sacombank Leasing Co., Ltd. (1)
230 Nam Ky Khoi Nghia Street, Vo Thi Sau Ward District 3, Ho Chi Minh City, Vietnam
Tel.: (84) 283 932 6820
Web Site: https://sacombankleasing.com
Leasing Services
N.A.I.C.S.: 532111

SAIGONTOURIST TRANSPORT CORPORATION
25 Pasteur Nguyen Thai Binh District 1, Ho Chi Minh City, Vietnam
Web Site: http://www.saigontourist-stt.com
Year Founded: 1986
Tourism & Transport Services
N.A.I.C.S.: 561520
Shogo Kakazu *(Gen Dir)*

SAIHAM COTTON MILLS LTD.
Saiham Tower House 34 Road 11th floor 136, Gulshan, Dhaka, 1212, Bangladesh
Tel.: (880) 2222262284
Web Site:
https://www.saihamcotton.com
Year Founded: 2002
SAIHAMCOT—(CHT)
Rev.: $50,283,049
Assets: $99,825,007
Liabilities: $51,009,429
Net Worth: $48,815,578
Earnings: $410,619
Emp.: 1,520
Fiscal Year-end: 06/30/23
Cotton Product Mfr
N.A.I.C.S.: 313210
Syed Sayeed Uddin Ahmed *(Chm)*

SAIHAM TEXTILE MILLS LIMITED
Saiham Tower House 34 11th Floor 136 Gulshan 1, Dhaka, 1212, Bangladesh
Tel.: (880) 222262284
Web Site: https://www.saiham.com
SAIHAMTEX—(CHT)
Rev.: $28,206,126
Assets: $58,006,031
Liabilities: $22,926,280
Net Worth: $35,079,751
Earnings: ($408,039)
Emp.: 1,337
Fiscal Year-end: 06/30/23
Fabric Product Mfr
N.A.I.C.S.: 313240
S. F. A. M. Shahjahan *(Chm)*

SAIKAYA DEPARTMENT STORE CO., LTD.
1 Nisshin-cho, Kawasaki-ku, Kawasaki, 210-0024, Kanagawa, Japan
Tel.: (81) 468456803 JP
Web Site: https://www.saikaya.co.jp
Year Founded: 1950
8254—(TKS)
Rev.: $30,789,000
Assets: $73,433,320
Liabilities: $69,595,580
Net Worth: $3,837,740
Earnings: $447,840
Emp.: 141
Fiscal Year-end: 08/31/24
Departmental Store Operator
N.A.I.C.S.: 455110

SAILANI TOURS N TRAVELS LIMITED
AD62 Sec 1, Saltlake, Kolkata, 700064, West Bengal, India
Tel.: (91) 18003136838
Web Site:
https://www.sailanitours.com
Year Founded: 2019
543541—(BOM)
Rev.: $1,378,245
Assets: $911,969
Liabilities: $673,546
Net Worth: $238,423
Earnings: $21,184
Fiscal Year-end: 03/31/22
Booking Agency Services
N.A.I.C.S.: 561599

SAILFISH ROYALTY CORP.
Sea Meadow House, PO Box 116, Road Town, Tortola, VG1110, Virgin Islands (British)
Tel.: (284) 4946401
Web Site:
http://www.sailfishroyalty.com
Metal Royalty & Streaming
N.A.I.C.S.: 212390
Akiba Leisman *(CEO)*

Subsidiaries:

Terraco Gold Corp. (1)
Suite 2390 1055 West Hastings Street, Vancouver, V6E 2E9, BC, Canada
Tel.: (604) 443-3830
Web Site: http://www.terracogold.com
Metal Mining Exploration Service
N.A.I.C.S.: 213114
Todd L. Hilditch *(Pres & CEO)*

Subsidiary (US):

Western Standard Metals USA, Inc. (2)
141 E 2nd St, Weiser, ID 83672
Tel.: (208) 549-4305
Gold Mining Services
N.A.I.C.S.: 212220

SAILING CAPITAL ADVISORS (HONG KONG) LTD.
Unit 2006-08 20/F Harbour Centre 25 Harbour Road, Wanchai, China (Hong Kong)
Tel.: (852) 2630 2000 HK
Web Site: http://www.sailing-capital.com.hk
Year Founded: 2012
Privater Equity Firm
N.A.I.C.S.: 523999
James Xiaodong Liu *(Chm)*

SAILOGY S.A.
Corso San Gottardo 14, 6830, Chiasso, Switzerland
Tel.: (41) 41 5880 515 CH
Web Site: http://www.sailogy.com
Year Founded: 2012
Recreational Boat Charter Services
N.A.I.C.S.: 483212
Manlio Accardo *(Founder & CEO)*

Subsidiaries:

Master Yachting GmbH (1)
VirchowstraSSe 1a, 97072, Wurzburg, Germany
Tel.: (49) 931 46599999
Web Site: http://www.master-yachting.de
Yacht Chartering Services
N.A.I.C.S.: 483212
Larin Heero *(Mng Dir)*

SAILRAIL AUTOMATED SYSTEMS INC.
3200 14th Ave, Markham, L3R 0H8, ON, Canada
Tel.: (905) 948-1500
Web Site: https://www.sailrail.com
Year Founded: 1972
Automated Material Handling Systems Mfr & Distr
N.A.I.C.S.: 334512

SailRail Automated Systems Inc.—(Continued)

Ian Scarth (Owner, Pres & CEO)

SAILUN CO. LTD.
Rubber Valley 43 Zhengzhou Road, Shibei District, Qingdao, 266045, Shandong, China
Tel.: (86) 4006608329 CN
Web Site: https://www.sailungroup.com
Year Founded: 2002
601058—(SHG)
Rev.: $2,757,539,460
Assets: $4,009,956,137
Liabilities: $2,303,582,827
Net Worth: $1,706,373,311
Earnings: $201,160,134
Emp.: 13,723
Fiscal Year-end: 12/31/21
Tiles Mfr
N.A.I.C.S.: 326211
Liu Yanhua (Chm)

Subsidiaries:

MAXAM Tire North America Inc. (1)
300 Rosewood Dr Ste 102, Danvers, MA 01923
Web Site: https://maxamtirena.com
Trucking Tire Mfr & Distr
N.A.I.C.S.: 326211

SAIMO TECHNOLOGY CO., LTD.
No 2 Luoshan Road Development Zone, Xuzhou, 221000, Jiangsu, China
Tel.: (86) 51687885619
Web Site: https://en.saimo.cn
Year Founded: 1996
300466—(CHIN)
Rev.: $112,672,404
Assets: $206,434,332
Liabilities: $87,807,564
Net Worth: $118,626,768
Earnings: $2,976,480
Emp.: 630
Fiscal Year-end: 12/31/22
Coal Energy Measurement & Inspection Equipment Mfr
N.A.I.C.S.: 334513
Huang Xiaoning (Chm)

Subsidiaries:

Hefei Eagle Automation Engineering Technology Co., Ltd. (1)
No 10 Xiangpu Road Baiyan Technopark High-tech Zone, Hefei, Anhui, China
Tel.: (86) 55165309956
Web Site: http://www.hfxykj.com
Emp.: 220
Packaging Machinery Mfr
N.A.I.C.S.: 333993
Lu Yong Jun (Gen Mgr)

Nanjing Sanai Industrial Automation Co., Ltd. (1)
12 Shengli Road, Jiangning District, Nanjing, Jiangsu, China
Tel.: (86) 2552121028
Web Site: https://www.nanjingsanai.com
Weighing Control Equipment Mfr
N.A.I.C.S.: 334513

SAINIK FINANCE & INDUSTRIES LIMITED
129 Transport Centre Rohtak Road, Punjabi Bagh, New Delhi, 110035, India
Tel.: (91) 1128315036
Web Site: https://www.sainikfinance.com
Year Founded: 1991
530265—(BOM)
Rev.: $3,388,640
Assets: $31,953,681
Liabilities: $26,051,844
Net Worth: $5,901,837
Earnings: ($130,385)

Emp.: 6
Fiscal Year-end: 03/31/21
Financial Management Services & Cement Mfr
N.A.I.C.S.: 523999
Jagdish Chandra (CFO)

SAINT CROIX HOLDING IMMOBILIER SOCIMI SA
Glorieta de Cuatro Caminos n 6 y 7, 28020, Madrid, Spain
Tel.: (34) 915140300
Web Site: https://www.saintcroixhi.com
Year Founded: 2011
STCXH—(LUX)
Rev.: $38,580,246
Assets: $590,052,490
Liabilities: $237,571,305
Net Worth: $352,481,186
Earnings: $22,147,631
Emp.: 6
Fiscal Year-end: 12/31/23
Holding Company
N.A.I.C.S.: 551112
Marco Colomer Barrigon (Chm & Mng Dir)

SAINT JEAN GROUPE SA
59 chemin du Moulin Carrron, BP 101, 69573, Dardilly, Cedex, France
Tel.: (33) 472522200
Web Site: https://www.saint-jean-groupe.fr
SABE—(EUR)
Sales Range: $75-99.9 Million
Food Product Mfr & Distr
N.A.I.C.S.: 311824
Marie-Christine Gros-Favrot (Chm)

SAINT JEAN INDUSTRIES SAS
180 Rue des Frere Lumiere St Jean d Ardieres Beaujolais, Belleville, 69220, Villefranche-sur-Saone, France
Tel.: (33) 474 66 68 00
Web Site: http://www.st-ji.com
Year Founded: 1962
Emp.: 1,850
Automotive Components Mfr
N.A.I.C.S.: 336330
Emile Di Serio (Pres)

Subsidiaries:

SJI Inc. (1)
424 Industrial Park Dr, Heber Springs, AR 72543
Tel.: (501) 362-9500
Automobile Component Distr
N.A.I.C.S.: 423120

SJI d.o.o. (1)
Mile Budaka 1, 35000, Slavonski Brod, Croatia
Tel.: (385) 98420077
Automotive Components Mfr
N.A.I.C.S.: 336110

SJI k.k. (1)
301 Playa Kugenuma 5-10-30 Honkugenuma, Kanagawa, Fujisawa, 251-0028, Japan
Tel.: (81) 466219020
Automobile Component Distr
N.A.I.C.S.: 423120

Saint Jean Industries GmbH (1)
Giessereistrasse 2, 04519, Rackwitz, Germany
Tel.: (49) 34294706010
Emp.: 95
Automotive Components Mfr
N.A.I.C.S.: 336110

Saint Jean Industries SAS Saint Jean Aero Plant (1)
ch du Champ-des-Filles, 1228, Plan-les-Ouates, Switzerland
Tel.: (41) 228841950
Automotive Components Mfr
N.A.I.C.S.: 336110

Saint Jean Industries SAS Saint Jean Industries Laval Plant (1)
Route de Fougeres ZA des Dahinieres, 53810, Change, France
Tel.: (33) 243641515
Automotive Components Mfr
N.A.I.C.S.: 336110

Saint Jean Industries SAS Saint Jean Industries Lorraine Plant (1)
430 Route de Mirecourt, 88270, Harol, France
Tel.: (33) 329668408
Automotive Components Mfr
N.A.I.C.S.: 336110

Saint Jean Industries SAS Saint Jean Industries Poitou Plant (1)
ZI de Saint-Ustre, Vienne, 86220, Ingrandes, France
Tel.: (33) 549937700
Automotive Components Mfr
N.A.I.C.S.: 336110

Saint Jean Industries SAS Saint Jean Tooling Plant (1)
300 rue du Sou, 69220, Saint-Jean-d'Ardieres, France
Tel.: (33) 474662152
Automotive Components Mfr
N.A.I.C.S.: 336110

Saint Jean Industries SAS Saint Jean Wheels Plant (1)
Delevegen 2, 6993, Hoyanger, Norway
Tel.: (47) 99206432
Automotive Components Mfr
N.A.I.C.S.: 336110

SAINT JOHN PORT AUTHORITY
111 Water St, Saint John, E2L 0B1, NB, Canada
Tel.: (506) 636-4869
Web Site: http://www.sjport.com
Sales Range: $1-9.9 Million
Emp.: 25
Port Operations
N.A.I.C.S.: 488310
Peter Gaulton (Chm)

SAINT MARC HOLDINGS CO., LTD.
173-104 Hirata, Kita-ku, Okayama, 700-0952, Japan
Tel.: (81) 862460309
Web Site: https://www.saint-marc-hd.com
Year Founded: 1991
3395—(TKS)
Rev.: $426,715,160
Assets: $323,995,760
Liabilities: $124,710,870
Net Worth: $199,284,890
Earnings: $6,405,090
Emp.: 1,262
Fiscal Year-end: 03/31/24
Holding Company
N.A.I.C.S.: 551112
Yuki Fujikawa (Pres & CEO)

SAINT MERRI CHANTILLY
Allee du Coq Chantant, 60500, Chantilly, France
Tel.: (33) 344671900
Web Site: http://www.saintmerri.fr
Automotive Service Center for BMW & Mini
N.A.I.C.S.: 811111

SAINT PETERSBURG CITY BANK JSC
Ul Italian 15, 191186, Saint Petersburg, Russia
Tel.: 8124499559
Web Site: http://www.gorbank.spb.ru
Year Founded: 1994
Sales Range: Less than $1 Million
Commercial Banking Services
N.A.I.C.S.: 522110

SAINT-CARE HOLDING CORPORATION
5F Yomiuri Yaesu Building 2-8-7 Kyobashi, Chuo-Ku, Tokyo, 104-0031, Japan
Tel.: (81) 335382943
Web Site: https://www.saint-care.com
Year Founded: 1983
2374—(TKS)
Rev.: $357,316,770
Assets: $204,824,070
Liabilities: $98,614,590
Net Worth: $106,209,480
Earnings: $13,253,050
Emp.: 5,007
Fiscal Year-end: 03/31/24
Holding Company
N.A.I.C.S.: 551111
Yoshiharu Murakami (Chm)

Subsidiaries:

Care Bot Corporation (1)
2-19-6 Hatchobori Tokyo Yasaka Hatchobori Building 1F, Chuo-ku, Tokyo, 104-0032, Japan
Tel.: (81) 362221062
Web Site: https://www.saintcare-carebot.com
Care Robot Distr
N.A.I.C.S.: 423830

SAINT-GEORGES DOORS
2 rue des Cerisier, Sainte-Aurelie, G0M 1M0, QC, Canada
Tel.: (418) 593-3784
Web Site: http://www.portessaint-georges.com
Year Founded: 1976
Rev.: $10,607,284
Emp.: 75
Door Mfr
N.A.I.C.S.: 321911
Gilles Gaudet (Pres & CEO)

SAIPA AZIN COMPANY
Karaj Special Road Kilometer 14 Golestanak Street No 12, Tehran, Iran
Tel.: (98) 2144922203
Web Site: https://www.saipa-azin.com
Year Founded: 1991
AZIN1—(THE)
Sales Range: Less than $1 Million
Automobile Seats Mfr
N.A.I.C.S.: 336360
Amin Hassanzadeh (Vice Chm & CEO)

SAIPA COMPANY
KM 15 - Karaj Special Road, PO Box 13445 - 554, Tehran, 14584, Iran
Tel.: (98) 21 44196550
Web Site: http://www.saipacorp.com
Year Founded: 1966
Motor Vehicles Mfr
N.A.I.C.S.: 336110

SAIPA DIESEL COMPANY
No 289 14th km of Shahid Lashgari Blvd Makhsoos Karaj Road, PO Box 13895-141, 13961 88783, Tehran, Iran
Tel.: (98) 214419651315
Web Site: http://www.saipadiesel.ir
Year Founded: 1963
Truck & Trailer Mfr
N.A.I.C.S.: 336212

Subsidiaries:

Rena Technical Services Co. (1)
Km19 Road Makhsos Karaj, PO Box 13895-313, Tehran, 1389816431, Iran
Tel.: (98) 2144987510
Web Site: http://www.rena.ir
Automobile Parts Distr
N.A.I.C.S.: 423120

SAIPA GLASS COMPANY
Karaj Makhsoos Ave-Iran Khodrou Crossroad Southwest Side, Tehran, Iran
Tel.: (98) 21 44195280
Web Site: http://www.saipaglass.com
Year Founded: 1998
Emp.: 323
Glass Products Mfr
N.A.I.C.S.: 327212

SAIPA INVESTMENT GROUP COMPANY
Mirdamad Blvd Naft Nourth Street Building 15, Tehran, Iran
Tel.: (98) 2122250198
Year Founded: 1965
SSAP—(THE)
Sales Range: Less than $1 Million
Financial Services
N.A.I.C.S.: 525990

SAIRP COMPOSITES
11 Avenue Ampere Z I 26 Rue Des Freres Lumiere, 45800, Saint Jean de Braye, Loiret, France
Tel.: (33) 238843421
Web Site: http://www.sairp.fr
Rev.: $22,100,000
Emp.: 61
Fiberglass Composites Mfr
N.A.I.C.S.: 326220
Jean Martin *(Chm)*

SAISAN CO., LTD.
1-11-5 Sakuragi-cho Omiya Ward, Saitama, 330-0854, Japan
Tel.: (81) 48 641 8211
Web Site: http://www.saisangas.com
Year Founded: 1945
Sales Range: $550-599.9 Million
Emp.: 1,038
Gas & Water Distr
N.A.I.C.S.: 221210

SAITA CORP.
472 Shimobuchi, Asakura, 838-0016, Fukuoka, Japan
Tel.: (81) 946223875
Web Site: https://saita-hd.co.jp
Year Founded: 1955
1999—(FKA)
Rev.: $62,261,760
Assets: $68,544,080
Liabilities: $30,976,000
Net Worth: $37,568,080
Earnings: $5,285,280
Fiscal Year-end: 06/30/21
Civil Engineering Services
N.A.I.C.S.: 541330
Yoshiyuki Saita *(Pres & CEO)*

SAIZERIYA CO., LTD.
2-5 Asahi, Yoshikawa, 342-0008, Saitama, Japan
Tel.: (81) 489919611
Web Site: https://www.saizeriya.co.jp
Year Founded: 1973
7581—(TKS)
Rev.: $1,396,651,240
Assets: $1,045,805,920
Liabilities: $356,611,260
Net Worth: $689,194,660
Earnings: $50,686,780
Emp.: 2,110
Fiscal Year-end: 08/31/24
Restaurant Operators
N.A.I.C.S.: 722511
Issei Horino *(Pres)*

Subsidiaries:
Saizeriya Australia Pty. Ltd. (1)
2-82 Shogaki Dr, Melton South, Melbourne, 3338, VIC, Australia
Tel.: (61) 399710500

Sales Range: $50-74.9 Million
Emp.: 100
Speciality Foods Whslr
N.A.I.C.S.: 424420
Keizo Inoue *(Mgr)*

SAJJAD TEXTILE MILLS LIMITED
19-B Off Zafar Ali Road Gulberg-V, Lahore, Pakistan
Tel.: (92) 425775501   PK
Web Site: http://www.sajjadtextile.com
Year Founded: 1988
SJTM—(KAR)
Rev.: $51,303
Assets: $1,547,420
Liabilities: $3,616,388
Net Worth: ($2,068,967)
Earnings: ($372,252)
Emp.: 30
Fiscal Year-end: 06/30/19
Yarn Mfr
N.A.I.C.S.: 313110
Safder Hussain Tariq *(CFO)*

SAJKASKA FABRIKA SECERA A.D.
Industrijska zona Curuski put br 3, 21230, Zabalj, Serbia
Tel.: (381) 21831462
Web Site: http://www.secerana-zabalj.co.rs
Year Founded: 1976
SJKS—(BEL)
Sales Range: $25-49.9 Million
Emp.: 189
Beet Sugar Mfr
N.A.I.C.S.: 311313
Petros Gemintzis *(Mng Dir)*

SAJO DAERIM CORP
2159 Nambusnhwan-Ro, Seocho-gu, Seoul, Korea (South)
Tel.: (82) 234706000
Web Site: https://dr.sajo.co.kr
Year Founded: 1964
003960—(KRS)
Rev.: $1,548,383,320
Assets: $896,049,796
Liabilities: $432,910,277
Net Worth: $463,139,519
Earnings: $56,612,627
Emp.: 856
Fiscal Year-end: 12/31/22
Sea Food Processing Services
N.A.I.C.S.: 114111
In-Woo Lee *(CEO)*

Subsidiaries:
Sajo Daerim Co., Ltd. - Ansan Plant (1)
178-116 Gajwa 1-Dong, Seo-gu, Incheon, Korea (South)
Tel.: (82) 32 5700 3000
Seafood Mfr
N.A.I.C.S.: 311710

Sajo Daerim Co., Ltd. - Busan Plant (1)
692-13 Nambumin-dong, Seo-gu, Busan, Korea (South)
Tel.: (82) 51 250 2000
Seafood Mfr
N.A.I.C.S.: 311710

Sajo Industry Co., Ltd. - Cheonan Plant (1)
137-9 Panjeong-ri jiksan-eup, Seobuk-gu, Cheonan, Chungcheongnam-do, Korea (South)
Tel.: (82) 41 581 0011
Seafood Mfr
N.A.I.C.S.: 311710

Sajo Industry Co., Ltd. - Goseong Plant (1)
166-1 Yulde-ri, Goseong, Gyeongsang, Korea (South)
Tel.: (82) 55 673 8700

Seafood Mfr
N.A.I.C.S.: 311710

Sajo Industry Co., Ltd. - Sunchang Plant (1)
732 Nodong-ri, Ingye, Jeollabuk-do, Korea (South)
Tel.: (82) 63 653 4207
Seafood Mfr
N.A.I.C.S.: 311710

Sajo Oyang Corporation (1)
2159 Nambusunhwan-ro, Seocho-gu, Seoul, 137-821, Korea (South) (60.53%)
Tel.: (82) 234706030
Web Site: https://oy.sajo.co.kr
Rev.: $283,119,034
Assets: $263,240,502
Liabilities: $105,279,603
Net Worth: $157,960,899
Earnings: $6,540,051
Emp.: 853
Fiscal Year-end: 12/31/2022
Seafood Product Mfr
N.A.I.C.S.: 311710
Ii-Sik Kim *(CEO)*

SAJO HAEPYO
482-2 Bangbae 3-dong, Seocho-gu, Seoul, Korea (South)
Tel.: (82) 2 2007 3112
Web Site: http://hp.sajo.co.kr
Year Founded: 1966
Rev.: $614,183,231
Assets: $357,467,719
Liabilities: $217,567,769
Net Worth: $139,899,950
Earnings: $13,241,591
Emp.: 361
Fiscal Year-end: 12/31/17
Soybean Oil Processing Services
N.A.I.C.S.: 311224
In-Woo Lee *(CEO)*

Subsidiaries:
Sajo Haepyo - Chilseo Plant (1)
291-1 Daechi Chilseo Industrial Complex, Daechi-ri, Chilseo, Gyeongsangnam-Do, Korea (South)
Tel.: (82) 55 589 2300
Soybean Oil Processing Services
N.A.I.C.S.: 311224

Sajo Haepyo - Incheon Plant (1)
178-116 Gajwa 1-dong, Seo-Gu, Incheon, Korea (South)
Tel.: (82) 32 5700 3000
Soybean Oil Processing Services
N.A.I.C.S.: 311224

Sajo Haepyo - Yeongcheon Plant (1)
200-3 Yuseong-ri Hwasan Agriculture/Industry Complex, Hwasan-myeon, Yeongcheon, Gyeongsangbuk-do, Korea (South)
Tel.: (82) 54 335 8881
Soybean Oil Processing Services
N.A.I.C.S.: 311224

SAJO INDUSTRY CO., LTD.
5F Sajo Industry Bldg 107-39 Tongil-ro, Seodaemun-gu, Seoul, Korea (South)
Tel.: (82) 232771600   KR
Web Site: http://ind.sajo.co.kr
Year Founded: 1971
007160—(KRS)
Rev.: $506,976,506
Assets: $894,791,387
Liabilities: $401,429,376
Net Worth: $493,362,011
Earnings: $61,461,140
Emp.: 565
Fiscal Year-end: 12/31/22
Fishery Business Services & Sea Food Mfr
N.A.I.C.S.: 114119
Ju Lee-Chang *(CEO)*

Subsidiaries:
Ingredion Korea Incorporated (1)
14 Fl Bojeon Building 725 Eonju-ro, Gangnam-gu, Seoul, 135-530, Korea (South)
Tel.: (82) 234851300
Web Site: http://www.ingredion.co.kr
Corn Products & Adhesive Mfr
N.A.I.C.S.: 325520

SAJO SEAFOOD CO., LTD.
502 107-39 Tongil-ro, Seodaemun-gu, Seoul, Korea (South)
Tel.: (82) 27216555
Web Site: http://sf.sajo.co.kr
Year Founded: 1980
014710—(KRS)
Rev.: $154,256,102
Assets: $268,987,249
Liabilities: $85,554,454
Net Worth: $183,432,794
Earnings: $6,362,444
Emp.: 233
Fiscal Year-end: 12/31/22
Seafood Distr
N.A.I.C.S.: 424460
Sehwan Choi *(CEO)*

Subsidiaries:
Sajo Seafood Co., Ltd. - Iksan Plant (1)
604 Yongje-dong Iksan-si, Iksan, Jeollabuk-do, Korea (South)
Tel.: (82) 63 833 3063
Seafood Mfr
N.A.I.C.S.: 311710

SAJODONGAONE CO., LTD.
Sajo Building 12 Bangbaecheon-ro 2-gil, Seocho-gu, Seoul, 06693, Korea (South)
Tel.: (82) 27899556
Web Site: https://do.sajo.co.kr
Year Founded: 2002
008040—(KRS)
Rev.: $484,412,068
Assets: $369,443,746
Liabilities: $192,288,952
Net Worth: $177,154,794
Earnings: $794,148
Emp.: 349
Fiscal Year-end: 12/31/22
Food Products Mfr
N.A.I.C.S.: 311999
In-Woo Lee *(CEO)*

Subsidiaries:
Daesan & Co. Ltd (1)
Woonsan Bldg 18-4 Nonhyeon-dong, Gangnam-gu, 135-010, Seoul, Korea (South)
Tel.: (82) 2 548 8186
Sales Range: $25-49.9 Million
Emp.: 10
Pet Food Mfr
N.A.I.C.S.: 311111

Dana Cellars Corporation (1)
7th floor Building A H Business Park 25 Beopwon-ro 11-gil, Songpa-gu 645 Munjeong-dong, Seoul, Korea (South)
Tel.: (82) 24054300
Wine Import & Distr
N.A.I.C.S.: 424820

DongA Food Co., Ltd. (1)
Woonsan Bldg 18-4 Nonhyun-dong, Gangnam-gu, Seoul, 135-010, Korea (South)
Tel.: (82) 2 514 3176
Web Site: http://www.dongahfood.com
Sales Range: $25-49.9 Million
Emp.: 2
Meat Import & Whslr
N.A.I.C.S.: 424470
Young Kim *(Gen Mgr)*

DongA One Corporation - Busan Factory (1)
601-837 1165-1 Jwacheon-dong, Dong-gu, Busan, Korea (South)
Tel.: (82) 51 630 3100
Web Site: http://www.dongaone.com
Flour Mfr
N.A.I.C.S.: 311211

SAJODONGAONE CO., LTD.

Sajodongaone Co., Ltd.—(Continued)

DongA One Corporation - Incheon Factory (1)
32 Manseok-dong, Dong-gu, Incheon, 401-010, Korea (South)
Tel.: (82) 32 763 6331 3
Web Site: http://www.dongaone.com
Flour Mfr
N.A.I.C.S.: 311211

DongA One Corporation - Wonju Factory (1)
333-3 Usan-dong, Wonju, 220-955, Gangwon, Korea (South)
Tel.: (82) 33 742 8941
Sales Range: $25-49.9 Million
Emp.: 26
Animal Feed Mfr
N.A.I.C.S.: 311119
Joseph L. Herring (CEO)

Korea Industry (1)
631-3 Wanjeon-ri Gwangseok-myeon, Nonsan, Chungnam, Korea (South)
Tel.: (82) 41 732 8200
Rice & Wheat Grain Milling Services
N.A.I.C.S.: 311212

PDP Wine Corporation (1)
Podoplaza 634-1 Sinsa-dong, Gangnam-gu, Seoul, 135895, Korea (South)
Tel.: (82) 2 548 3720
Web Site: http://www.naracellar.com
Wine Retailer
N.A.I.C.S.: 445320

SAJON
186 Rue De Saintes, 16000, Angouleme, Charente, France
Tel.: (33) 545951920
Sales Range: $25-49.9 Million
Emp.: 63
Grocery Stores
N.A.I.C.S.: 445110

SAK INDUSTRIES PVT LTD
SP Infocity 40 MGR Salai Perungudi, Kandanchavadi, Chennai, 600 096, India
Tel.: (91) 4424543500
Web Site:
http://www.sakabrasives.com
Abrasive Products Provider & Mfr
N.A.I.C.S.: 327910
Aditya Krishna (CEO)

Subsidiaries:

Sak Abrasives Ltd (1)
SP Infocity 40 MGR Salai Perungudi, Kandanchavadi, Chennai, 600 096, India
Tel.: (91) 4424543500
Web Site: http://www.sakabrasives.com
Bonded Abrasives for Automotive, DIY, Precision Grinding, Bearing, Food Processing, Welding & Construction, foundry & metal fabrication & aerospace & Turbine Markets Stores & Mfr
N.A.I.C.S.: 327910

Subsidiary (US):

Buffalo Abrasives (2)
960 Erie Ave, North Tonawanda, NY 14120
Tel.: (888) 311-3856
Web Site: http://www.buffaloabrasives.com
Sales Range: $1-9.9 Million
Emp.: 45
Abrasive Products, Nsk
N.A.I.C.S.: 327910
Arthur Russ (Pres)

Jowitt & Rodgers Co. (2)
9400 State Road, Philadelphia, PA 19114
Tel.: (215) 824-0400
Web Site: http://www.jowittandrodgers.com
Rev.: $6,666,666
Emp.: 51
Abrasive Product Mfr
N.A.I.C.S.: 327910
Fred Rodgers (Pres)

SAKAE ELECTRONICS CORPORATION
2-9-10 Soto-Kanda, Chiyoda-Ku, Tokyo, 101-0021, Japan
Tel.: (81) 363857240
Web Site: https://www.sakae-denshi.com
Year Founded: 1971
7567—(TKS)
Rev.: $55,275,835
Assets: $49,877,753
Liabilities: $19,742,314
Net Worth: $30,135,439
Earnings: $1,519,656
Fiscal Year-end: 03/31/24
Electric Component Whslr
N.A.I.C.S.: 423690
Hideo Sometani (Founder & Chm)

SAKAE HOLDINGS LTD.
28 Tai Seng Street Sakae Building Level 7, Singapore, 534106, Singapore
Tel.: (65) 64386629
Web Site:
https://www.sakaeholdings.com
Year Founded: 1996
5DO—(SES)
Rev.: $12,640,237
Assets: $84,935,902
Liabilities: $39,184,883
Net Worth: $45,751,019
Earnings: $955,910
Emp.: 1,000
Fiscal Year-end: 06/30/23
Restaurant & Food Kiosk Owner & Operator
N.A.I.C.S.: 722511
Douglas Peow Yong Foo (Founder & Chm)

Subsidiaries:

Anschluss Pte Ltd (1)
30 Raffles Ave 01-02, Singapore, 039803, Singapore
Tel.: (65) 63382454
Sales Range: $25-49.9 Million
Emp.: 4
Food Store
N.A.I.C.S.: 445298

Nouvelle Events Holdings Pte. Ltd. (1)
28 Tai Seng Street 01-01 Sakae Building, Singapore, 534106, Singapore
Tel.: (65) 62878768
Web Site: https://www.nouvellevents.com
Food & Beverage Consulting Services
N.A.I.C.S.: 541618

SAKAI CHEMICAL INDUSTRY CO., LTD.
5-2 Ebisujima-cho, Sakai-ku, Sakai, 590-8502, Osaka, Japan
Tel.: (81) 722234111
Web Site: https://www.sakai-chem.co.jp
Year Founded: 1918
4078—(TKS)
Rev.: $542,714,050
Assets: $829,191,450
Liabilities: $330,361,190
Net Worth: $498,830,260
Earnings: $46,878,120
Fiscal Year-end: 03/31/24
Chemical Product Mfr & Whslr
N.A.I.C.S.: 325998
Toshiyuki Yagura (Pres)

Subsidiaries:

KATAYAMA SEIYAKUSYO Co., Ltd. (1)
1-12-3 Syodaitajika, Hirakata, 573-1132, Osaka, Japan
Tel.: (81) 72 856 5631
Web Site: http://www.katayama-finechem.co.jp
Emp.: 116
Pharmaceuticals Product Mfr
N.A.I.C.S.: 325412
Shinji Nakahara (Pres)

Plant (Domestic):

KATAYAMA SEIYAKUSYO CO., LTD. - Toyama Plant (2)
1-3 Yasuuchi, Yatsuo Machi, Toyama, 939-2366, Japan
Tel.: (81) 764551500
Pharmaceuticals Product Mfr
N.A.I.C.S.: 325412

Kaigen Pharma Co., Ltd. (1)
2-5-14 Doshomachi, Chuo-ku, Osaka, 541-0045, Japan
Tel.: (81) 662028971
Web Site: https://www.kaigen-pharma.co.jp
Pharmaceutical Product Mfr & Distr
N.A.I.C.S.: 325412

Kyodo Chemical CO., LTD. (1)
3rd floor Taiwa Building 1-3-3 Kanda Izumimachi, Chiyoda-ku, Tokyo, 101-0024, Japan
Tel.: (81) 358350524
Web Site: http://www.kyodo-chem.co.jp
Emp.: 60
Chemical Products Mfr
N.A.I.C.S.: 325199

OSAKI INDUSTRY CO., LTD. (1)
89 Kami, Nishi-ku, Sakai, 593-8311, Osaka, Japan
Tel.: (81) 722731261
Chemical Products Mfr
N.A.I.C.S.: 325998

RESINO COLOR INDUSTRY CO., LTD. (1)
3-1-102 Jusomoto Imazato, Yodogawa-ku, Osaka, 532-0028, Japan
Tel.: (81) 663010636
Web Site: https://www.resinocolor.co.jp
Emp.: 126
Chemical Products Mfr
N.A.I.C.S.: 325998

SC Organic Chemical Co., Ltd. (1)
3-10-24 Tadaoka Kita Tadaoka-cho, Senboku-gun, Osaka, 595-0811, Japan
Tel.: (81) 725 33 0478
Web Site: http://www.sco-sakai-chem.com
Chemical Products Mfr
N.A.I.C.S.: 325998

Plant (Domestic):

SC Organic Chemical Co., Ltd. - Ishizu Factory (2)
3-27-16 Chikko Shinmachi, Nishi-ku, Sakai, 595-0811, Osaka, Japan
Tel.: (81) 722445721
Chemical Products Mfr
N.A.I.C.S.: 325998

Sakai Australia Pty Ltd (1)
Unit 12 14-18 Preston Street, Penrith, 2750, NSW, Australia
Tel.: (61) 247218011
Web Site: https://www.sakai.com.au
Chemical Products Distr
N.A.I.C.S.: 424690

Sakai Chemical (Vietnam) Co., Ltd. (1)
Lot B-1A-CN My Phuoc Industrial Park 3, Ben Cat Town, Ho Chi Minh City, Binh Duong, Vietnam
Tel.: (84) 2743577452
Web Site: https://sakaivn.com
Emp.: 73
Chemical Products Distr
N.A.I.C.S.: 424690
Nguyen Thuyen (Mgr-Pur)

Sakai Chemical Industry Co., Ltd. - Onahama Division (1)
110 Aza Tajuku, Izumi-machi Shimogawa, Iwaki, 971-8183, Fukushima, Japan
Tel.: (81) 246565111
Chemical Products Mfr
N.A.I.C.S.: 325998

Sakai Chemical Industry Co., Ltd. - Otsurugi Works (1)
382 Aza Otsurugi, Izumi-machi Shimogawa, Iwaki, 971-8183, Fukushima, Japan
Tel.: (81) 246566610
Chemical Products Mfr
N.A.I.C.S.: 325998

Sakai Chemical Industry Co., Ltd. - Sakai Division (1)
5-1 Ebisujima-cho, Sakai, 590-0985, Osaka, Japan
Tel.: (81) 722234115
Chemical Products Mfr
N.A.I.C.S.: 325998

Sakai Chemical Industry Co., Ltd. - Semboku Works (1)
1-18 Rinkai-cho, Izumiotsu, 595-0075, Osaka, Japan
Tel.: (81) 725333881
Chemical Products Mfr
N.A.I.C.S.: 325998

Sakai Chemical Industry Co., Ltd. - Yumoto Works (1)
1-1 Sawame Joban Iwagaoka-cho, Iwaki, 972-8313, Fukushima, Japan
Tel.: (81) 246434301
Chemical Products Mfr.
N.A.I.C.S.: 325998

Sakai Taiwan Co., Ltd. (1)
6F-2 Capital Commercial Center Building 81 Sec 2 Cheng Teh Road, Taipei, 10353, Taiwan
Tel.: (886) 225561691
Chemical Products Distr
N.A.I.C.S.: 424690

Sakai Trading (Shanghai) Co., Ltd. (1)
Unit A2 12F Hua Xin Hai Xin Building NO 666 Fuzhou Road, Shanghai, 200001, China
Tel.: (86) 2160910501
Web Site: https://www.sakaitrading.cn
Chemical Products Distr
N.A.I.C.S.: 424690

Sakai Trading (Thailand) Co., Ltd. (1)
5th floor Unit 3 Zuellig House No 1-7 Silom Road, Kwaeng Silom Khet Bangrak, Bangkok, 10500, Thailand
Tel.: (66) 22376841
Web Site: http://www.sakaitrading.co.jp
Emp.: 3
Chemical Products Distr
N.A.I.C.S.: 424690

Sakai Trading Co., Ltd. (1)
Kurabo Annex-Bldg 4-11 Kyutaromachi 2-Chome, Chuo, 541-0056, Osaka, Japan
Tel.: (81) 6 6271 9700
Web Site: http://www.sakaitrading.co.jp
Emp.: 128
Chemical Product Mfr & Distr
N.A.I.C.S.: 325998
Koji Akamizu (Pres & Gen Dir)

Subsidiary (Non-US):

Sakai Trading Europe GmbH (2)
Theodorstr 297, 40472, Dusseldorf, Germany
Tel.: (49) 211 5504280
Web Site: http://www.sakai-trading.eu
Chemical Products Distr
N.A.I.C.S.: 424690

Sakai Trading Korea Co., Ltd. (2)
A/1618 Samho Mulsan Building 275-1 Yangjae-Dong, Seocho-Ku, Seoul, 06775, Korea (South)
Tel.: (82) 25891956
Emp.: 2
Chemical Products Distr
N.A.I.C.S.: 424690
Funyung Yi (Mgr)

Subsidiary (US):

Sakai Trading New York Inc. (2)
370 Lexington Ave Ste 1904, New York, NY 10017
Tel.: (212) 599-1333
Emp.: 3
Chemical Products Distr
N.A.I.C.S.: 424690

SAKAI HEAVY INDUSTRIES LTD
Nomura Shibadaimon Bld 5F 1-9-9 Shibadaimon, Minato-ku, Tokyo, 105-0012, Japan
Tel.: (81) 334343401
Web Site: https://www.sakainet.co.jp
Year Founded: 1918

AND PRIVATE COMPANIES — SAKATA INX CORPORATION

6358—(TKS)
Rev.: $218,262,200
Assets: $292,406,570
Liabilities: $99,625,920
Net Worth: $192,780,650
Earnings: $16,128,400
Emp.: 618
Fiscal Year-end: 03/31/24
Construction Machinery Mfr & Whslr
N.A.I.C.S.: 333120
Ichiro Sakai (Pres)

Subsidiaries:

Comodo Co., Ltd. (1)
2626 Takayanagi, Kuki, 349-1125, Saitama, Japan
Tel.: (81) 480526612
Construction Machinery Mfr & Leasing Services
N.A.I.C.S.: 333120

P.T. SAKAI INDONESIA (1)
EJIP Industrial Park Plot 6G, Cikarang Selatan, Bekasi, 17530, Indonesia
Tel.: (62) 218970374
Web Site: https://sakai.co.id
Construction Equipment Mfr & Distr
N.A.I.C.S.: 333120

SAKAI ENGINEERING Co., Ltd. (1)
849 Nakafuku, Kawagoe, 350-1156, Saitama, Japan
Tel.: (81) 492694025
Web Site: https://www.sakainet.co.jp
Construction Equipment Mfr & Distr
N.A.I.C.S.: 333120

Sakai America, Inc. (1)
90 International Pkwy, Adairsville, GA 30103
Tel.: (770) 877-9433
Web Site: http://www.sakaiamerica.com
Locomotive Engine Equipment Mfr
N.A.I.C.S.: 333618
Gerry Petty (Mgr-Svc & Warranty)

Sakai Heavy Industries (Shanghai) Ltd. (1)
No 999 Xing Qing Road, Jianding, Shanghai, 201815, China
Tel.: (86) 2169169808
Web Site: https://www.sakai.com.cn
Construction Equipment Mfr & Distr
N.A.I.C.S.: 333120

Sakai kikoh Corporation (1)
2626 Takayanagi, Kuki, 349-1125, Saitama, Japan
Tel.: (81) 480531301
Web Site: https://sakai-kikoh.com
Transportation Equipment Mfr & Distr
N.A.I.C.S.: 336999
Mitsuaki Hirabayashi (Pres)

TOKYO FUJI CO., LTD. (1)
3349-1 Mida, Konosu, 365-0062, Saitama, Japan
Tel.: (81) 485963311
Industrial Machinery Mfr & Distr
N.A.I.C.S.: 333248

SAKAI HOLDINGS CO., LTD.
21-20 Chiyoda 5-chome, Naka-ku, Nagoya, 460-0012, Aichi, Japan
Tel.: (81) 120166599
Web Site: https://www.sakai-holdings.co.jp
Year Founded: 1991
9446—(TKS)
Rev.: $105,272,320
Assets: $158,879,810
Liabilities: $128,577,150
Net Worth: $30,302,660
Earnings: $5,778,350
Emp.: 520
Fiscal Year-end: 09/30/23
Communication Equipment Distr
N.A.I.C.S.: 423690

SAKAI MOVING SERVICE CO., LTD.
56 Ishizu Kitamachi, Sakai-ku, Sakai, 590-0823, Osaka, Japan
Tel.: (81) 120001141

Web Site: https://www.hikkoshi-sakai.co.jp
Year Founded: 1956
9039—(TKS)
Rev.: $772,451,210
Assets: $798,560,710
Liabilities: $208,208,390
Net Worth: $590,352,320
Earnings: $55,252,990
Emp.: 5,997
Fiscal Year-end: 03/31/24
Automobile Transportation Services
N.A.I.C.S.: 484110
Yoshifumi Ikura (Exec VP)

SAKAI OVEX CO., LTD.
2-15-1 Hanandoh Naka, Fukui, 918-8530, Japan
Tel.: (81) 776365800
Web Site: http://www.sakaiovex.co.jp
Year Founded: 1891
3408—(TKS)
Rev.: $211,962,960
Assets: $302,722,640
Liabilities: $75,871,840
Net Worth: $226,850,800
Earnings: $13,629,440
Emp.: 507
Fiscal Year-end: 03/31/21
Textile Products Mfr
N.A.I.C.S.: 313310
Shintaro Matsuki (Pres)

Subsidiaries:

SAKAI OVEX Co., Ltd. - Fishery Material Division (1)
201 Ezaki 13 Omachi, Fukui, 918-8116, Japan
Tel.: (81) 776 35 8216
Fishery Material Mfr
N.A.I.C.S.: 339920

SAKAI OVEX Co., Ltd. - Gosen Factory (1)
1-16-45 Hanandoh Naka, Fukui, 918-8014, Japan
Tel.: (81) 776 36 3040
Textile Products Mfr
N.A.I.C.S.: 313310

SAKAI OVEX Co., Ltd. - Hanandoh Factory (1)
2-25-35 Hanandoh Kita, Fukui, 918-8012, Japan
Tel.: (81) 776 36 5802
Textile Products Mfr
N.A.I.C.S.: 313310

Sakai Nagoya Co., Ltd. (1)
1 Okudasakaicho, Inazawa, 492-8621, Aichi, Japan
Tel.: (81) 58 721 2121
Web Site: https://www.sakai-nagoya.co.jp
Textile Products Mfr
N.A.I.C.S.: 313310

SAKAR HEALTHCARE LTD.
Block No 10-13, Changodar Sarkhej-Bavla Highway Sanand, Ahmedabad, 382 213, Gujarat, India
Tel.: (91) 2717250477
Web Site: https://www.sakarhealthcare.com
Year Founded: 2004
SAKAR—(NSE)
Rev.: $13,092,343
Assets: $24,268,661
Liabilities: $10,829,937
Net Worth: $13,438,724
Earnings: $1,458,159
Emp.: 247
Fiscal Year-end: 03/31/21
Pharmaceuticals Product Mfr
N.A.I.C.S.: 325412
Sanjay Shah (Chm & Mng Dir)

SAKATA INX CORPORATION
1-23-37 Edobori, Nishi-ku, Osaka, Japan
Tel.: (81) 664475847   JP

Web Site: https://www.inx.co.jp
Year Founded: 1896
4633—(TKS)
Rev.: $1,618,724,990
Assets: $1,376,076,830
Liabilities: $627,011,240
Net Worth: $749,065,590
Earnings: $52,933,940
Emp.: 5,035
Fiscal Year-end: 12/31/23
Printing Ink Mfr
N.A.I.C.S.: 325910
Kotaro Morita (Pres & CEO)

Subsidiaries:

A.M. Ramp & Co. Gmbh (1)
Lorsbacher Strasse 28, 65817, Eppstein, Germany
Tel.: (49) 6 198 3040
Web Site: https://www.ruco-druckfarben.de
Printing Equipment Mfr & Distr
N.A.I.C.S.: 333248

CDI Sakata Inx Corp. (1)
Don Jesus Boulevard Alabang Hills Village, Alabang, Muntinlupa, 1700, Manila, Philippines
Tel.: (63) 28422070
Web Site: http://www.cdisakatainxcorp.com
Sales Range: $25-49.9 Million
Emp.: 86
Printing Ink Mfr & Distr
N.A.I.C.S.: 325910

Creative Industria e Comercio Ltda. (1)
R Joao Antonio de Souza 131, Sao Bernardo do Campo, Sao Paulo, Brazil
Tel.: (55) 1141274599
Web Site: http://www.creativetintas.com.br
Printing Ink Mfr
N.A.I.C.S.: 325910

Eternal Sakata INX Co. Ltd. (1)
16 Soi Leab Klong Fang 1 Petchkasem Road, Nongkhaem Sub-district Nong Khaem District, Bangkok, 10160, Thailand
Tel.: (66) 2 8064341
Web Site: http://www.esiinx.com
Sales Range: $50-74.9 Million
Print Ink Mfr & Distr
N.A.I.C.S.: 325910

INX Corporation (1)
Ste 700 150 N Martingale Rd, Schaumburg, IL 60173-2009 (100%)
Tel.: (847) 969-9722
Holding Company
N.A.I.C.S.: 325910

INX Digital Italy S.r.l. (1)
Via C Colombo, Fagnano Olona, 21054, Varese, Italy
Tel.: (39) 033161321
Sales Range: $25-49.9 Million
Emp.: 20
Digital Printing Ink Mfr & Distr
N.A.I.C.S.: 325910

INX Europe Ltd. (1)
Hilltop Road Hareshill Distribution Park Off Hareshill Road, Heywood, OL10 2TW, Lancashire, United Kingdom
Tel.: (44) 1706695150
Printing Ink Distr
N.A.I.C.S.: 423840
Peter Lockley (Pres)

INX GRAVURE CO., LTD. (1)
4001-69 Utazucho, Ayauta-gun, Kagawa, 769-0200, Japan
Tel.: (81) 877451119
Printing Ink Mfr
N.A.I.C.S.: 325910

INX International France SAS (1)
44 Av De La Commune De Paris, 91220, Bretigny-sur-Orge, France
Tel.: (33) 160842727
Web Site: http://www.inxinternational.com.fr
Sales Range: $25-49.9 Million
Emp.: 30
Print Ink Mfr & Distr
N.A.I.C.S.: 325910
Delbeau Antoine (Gen Mgr)

INX International Ink Co. (1)

150 N Martingale Rd Ste 700, Schaumburg, IL 60173 (100%)
Tel.: (630) 382-1800
Web Site: https://www.inxinternational.com
Sales Range: $400-449.9 Million
Emp.: 1,350
Printing Ink Mfr
N.A.I.C.S.: 325910
Rick Clendenning (Co-CEO)

INX International UK Ltd. (1)
Hilltop Road Hareshill Distribution Park Off Hareshill Road, Heywood, OL10 2TW, Lancashire, United Kingdom
Tel.: (44) 170 669 5150
Web Site: http://www.inxinternational.com
Sales Range: $25-49.9 Million
Printing Ink Mfr & Distr
N.A.I.C.S.: 325910

INX TECHNO SERVICE CO., LTD. (1)
1-23-37 Edobori, Nishi-ku, Osaka, 550-0002, Japan
Tel.: (81) 664475933
Printing Ink Distr
N.A.I.C.S.: 423840

Inx Digital Czech, A.S. (1)
Do Certous 2621/13 Hall I2, Horni Pocernice, 193 00, Prague, Czech Republic
Tel.: (420) 326374900
Web Site: http://www.inx.co.jp
Sales Range: $25-49.9 Million
Emp.: 20
Digital Printing Ink Mfr & Distr
N.A.I.C.S.: 325910

Inx International Ink Corp. (1)
1247 National Street, Terrebonne, J6W 6H8, QC, Canada
Tel.: (450) 477-9145
Printing Ink Mfr & Distr
N.A.I.C.S.: 336390

MAOMING SAKATA INX CO., LTD. (1)
12th Sub-District Nanhai Eastern Area, Maogang District, Maoming, Guangdong, China
Tel.: (86) 6682089388
Printing Ink Mfr
N.A.I.C.S.: 325910

NANSHA SAKATA INK CORP. (1)
Industrial Road 5 Dayong Special Economic Zone, Nansha, Panyu, 511458, Guangdong, China
Tel.: (86) 2084980097
Printing Ink Mfr
N.A.I.C.S.: 325910
Thomas Yeung (Gen Mgr)

PT. Sakata INX Indonesia (1)
Graha Indochem 7th Floor, Jl Pantai Indah Kapuk Boulevard Kav SSB/E, Jakarta, 14470, Indonesia
Tel.: (62) 2156948580
Printing Ink Distr
N.A.I.C.S.: 423840

SAKATA INX ENG. CO., LTD. (1)
Shimura 2-19-17 Sakata Shimura Building third Floor Yubinbango, Itabashi-ku, Tokyo, 174-0056, Japan
Tel.: (81) 359163947
Web Site: http://www.inx-eng.co.jp
Sales Range: $25-49.9 Million
Printing Machinery Distr
N.A.I.C.S.: 423830

Sakata INX (zhongshan) Corp. (1)
No 9 Jiehong Road Shazai Chemical Industry Park, Minzhong Town, Zhongshan, 528441, Guangdong, China
Tel.: (86) 76085551692
Printing Ink Distr
N.A.I.C.S.: 423840

Sakata INX Corporation - Hanyu Plant (1)
1-603-33 Komatsudai, Hanyu, 348-0038, Saitama, Japan
Tel.: (81) 485633811
Printing Ink Mfr
N.A.I.C.S.: 325910

Sakata INX Corporation - Osaka Plant (1)
4-1-12 Kitagawara, Itami, 664-8507, Hyogo, Japan

SAKATA INX CORPORATION

Sakata INX Corporation—(Continued)
Tel.: (81) 727857701
Sales Range: $50-74.9 Million
Emp.: 200
Printing Ink Mfr
N.A.I.C.S.: 325910

Sakata INX Corporation - Shiga Plant (1)
2060 Umegahara, Maibara, 521-0013, Shiga, Japan
Tel.: (81) 749529261
Printing Ink Mfr
N.A.I.C.S.: 325910

Sakata INX Corporation - Tokyo Plant (1)
2291 Makinouchi, Ozaki-aza, Noda, 270-0235, Chiba, Japan
Tel.: (81) 56896600
Web Site: http://www.inx.co.jp
Ink Printer Mfr
N.A.I.C.S.: 325910

Sakata INX Shanghai Co. Ltd. (1)
2001 Hui Bin Road Qing Pu Industrial Zone, Shanghai, 201707, China
Tel.: (86) 2159868088
Web Site: http://www.inx-sh.com
Emp.: 100
Gravure Inks Mfr
N.A.I.C.S.: 325910

Sakata Inx (India) Private Limited (1)
D-17 Infocity II Sector-33, Gurgaon, 122001, Haryana, India
Tel.: (91) 1244803300
Web Site: https://www.sakataindia.com
Sales Range: $25-49.9 Million
Emp.: 50
Printing Ink Mfr & Distr
N.A.I.C.S.: 325910

Sakata Inx (Malaysia) Sdn. Bhd. (1)
Lot 65 Jalan Teluk Gadung 27/93 Seksyen 27, 40000, Shah Alam, Selangor, Malaysia
Tel.: (60) 35 191 8878
Web Site: https://www.sakatainx.com.my
Printing Ink Distr
N.A.I.C.S.: 423840

Sakata Inx Espana S.A., (1)
Poligono Industrial Riera de Caldes C/ Mercaders 24-26, Palau-Solita I Plegamans, 08184, Barcelona, Spain
Tel.: (34) 93 864 8122
Web Site: https://www.sakatainx.es
Sales Range: $25-49.9 Million
Print Ink Mfr & Distr
N.A.I.C.S.: 325910
Javier Bou Sepulveda (Gen Mgr)

Sakata Inx Minami Osaka Co. Ltd. (1)
4-1-12 Kitagawara, Itami, 412, Hyogo, Japan
Tel.: (81) 727857834
Printing Ink Mfr
N.A.I.C.S.: 325910

Sakata Inx Viet Nam Co., Ltd. (1)
33 Tu Do Boulevard Viet Nam - Singapore Industrial Park, Thuan An, Binh Duong, Vietnam
Tel.: (84) 2743767811
Web Site: http://www.inx.com.vn
Printing Ink Mfr
N.A.I.C.S.: 325910

Plant (Domestic):

Sakata Inx Viet Nam Co., Ltd. - Plant 2 (2)
No 11 Street 10 Viet Nam - Singapore Industrial Park, Thuan An, Binh Duong, Vietnam
Tel.: (84) 2743787118
Printing Ink Distr
N.A.I.C.S.: 423840

Sakata Sangyo, Ltd. (1)
1-23-37 Edobori, Nishi-Ku, Osaka, 550-0002, Japan
Tel.: (81) 66 443 8820
Web Site: https://www.sakata-s.jp
Printing Ink Mfr & Distr
N.A.I.C.S.: 325910

Shenzhen Sakata Inx Co., Ltd. (1)
501 No 8 Fukang Road Pinghu Street, Longgang District, Shenzhen, 518111, Guangdong, China
Tel.: (86) 75589633089
Printing Ink Distr
N.A.I.C.S.: 423840

Taiwan Sakata INX Corp. (1)
21-1 Lane 45 Sec 2 Chung Shan North Road, Taipei, Taiwan
Tel.: (886) 225365087
Emp.: 40
Printing Ink Mfr & Distr
N.A.I.C.S.: 325910

The INX Group Ltd. (1)
150 N Martingale Rd Ste 700, Schaumburg, IL 60173
Tel.: (630) 382-1800
Web Site: http://www.inxinternational.com
Sales Range: $50-74.9 Million
Printing Ink Mfr & Distr
N.A.I.C.S.: 325910

Triangle (Guangzhou) Digital Materials Co., Ltd. (1)
No 18 Dalai South Road Taihe Town, Baiyun, Guangzhou, Guangdong, China
Tel.: (86) 2087427688
Web Site: http://www.inxdigital.com.cn
Digital Printing Ink Mfr
N.A.I.C.S.: 325910

SAKATA SEED CORPORATION

2-7-1 Nakamachidai, Tsuzuki-ku, Yokohama, 224 0041, Kanagawa, Japan
Tel.: (81) 459458800 JP
Web Site:
  https://www.sakataseed.co.jp
Year Founded: 1913
1377—(TKS)
Rev.: $586,154,970
Assets: $1,273,859,370
Liabilities: $212,736,240
Net Worth: $1,061,123,130
Earnings: $106,830,820
Emp.: 2,948
Fiscal Year-end: 05/31/24
Horticultural Engineering, Seed Production & Sales
N.A.I.C.S.: 444240
Hiroshi Sakata (Pres)

Subsidiaries:

Grupo Sakata Seed de Mexico, S.A. de C.V. (1)
Av Vallarta 6503 Local B-10, Colonia Ciudad Granja, 45010, Zapopan, Jalisco, Mexico
Tel.: (52) 3338970776
Web Site: https://www.sakata.com.mx
Agriculture Seed Mfr
N.A.I.C.S.: 325320

Sakata Holland b.v. (1)
Saturnusstraat 1, 2132, Hoofddorp, Netherlands (100%)
Tel.: (31) 235543200
Web Site: http://www.sakataornamentals.eu
Sales Range: $25-49.9 Million
Emp.: 11
Seed Nursery Research; Wholesale of Flower & Vegetable Seeds
N.A.I.C.S.: 424930

Sakata Korea Co., Ltd. (1)
611 Songnam B/D 273 Gangnam-daero, Seocho-gu, Seoul, 06730, Korea (South)
Tel.: (82) 234746671
Web Site: https://www.sakatakorea.co.kr
Agriculture Seed Mfr
N.A.I.C.S.: 325320

Sakata Seed America, Inc. (1)
18095 Serene Dr, Morgan Hill, CA 95037-2833 (90%)
Tel.: (408) 778-7758
Web Site: https://www.sakata.com
Sales Range: $50-74.9 Million
Emp.: 90
Seed Nursery Research; Wholesale of Flower & Vegetable Seeds
N.A.I.C.S.: 424910

Sakata Seed Iberica S.L.U. (1)
Paseo de Aragon 82-84-Bajo, 46021, Valencia, Spain
Tel.: (34) 963563427
Web Site: https://www.sakataiberica.com
Agriculture Seed Mfr
N.A.I.C.S.: 325320

Sakata Seed India Pvt. Ltd. (1)
Office No-105-109 Eros Corporate Park Tower- K Sec-2 IMT, Manesar, Gurgaon, 122052, Haryana, India
Tel.: (91) 124 437 6941
Web Site: https://www.sakata.co.in
Agriculture Seed Mfr
N.A.I.C.S.: 325320

Sakata Seed Southern Africa (Pty) Ltd. (1)
PO Box 160, Lanseria, 1748, South Africa
Tel.: (27) 115482800
Web Site: https://sakata.co.za
Agriculture Seed Mfr
N.A.I.C.S.: 325320
Jan-Louis Bezuidenhout (Mgr-Commercial)

Sakata Seed Sudamerica Ltda. (1)
Av Dr Plinio Salgado 4320-C, 12906-840, Braganca, SP, Brazil (90%)
Tel.: (55) 140348800
Web Site: http://www.sakata.com.br
Ornamental Floriculture & Nursery Products Production
N.A.I.C.S.: 111422

Sakata Seed de Guatemala, S.A. (1)
Calzada Roosevelt 22-43 Z 11 CC Tikal Futura Torre Sol 5to Level Of 5C, Guatemala, Guatemala
Tel.: (502) 24908200
Web Site: https://sakatacentroamerica.com
Agriculture Seed Mfr
N.A.I.C.S.: 325320

Sakata Seed de Mexico, S.A. de C.V. (1)
Av Vallarta 6503 Local B-10, Colonia Ciudad Granja, 45010, Zapopan, Mexico (100%)
Tel.: (52) 333 897 0776
Web Site: https://www.sakata.com.mx
Sales Range: $25-49.9 Million
Emp.: 29
Agricultural Seed & Nursery Production
N.A.I.C.S.: 444240

Sakata Siam Seed Co., Ltd. (1)
260 M 13 T Nonton A, Muang, Khon Kaen, 40000, Thailand
Tel.: (66) 43001314
Web Site: https://www.sakatasiam.co.th
Agriculture Seed Mfr
N.A.I.C.S.: 325320

Sakata Tarim Urunleri ve Tohumculuk San. ve Tic. Ltd. Sti. (1)
Ege Perla B Kule Cinarli Mah Ozan Abay Caddesi No 10 Kat13 D133, Konak, Izmir, Turkiye
Tel.: (90) 232 855 7007
Agriculture Seed Mfr
N.A.I.C.S.: 325320
Ahmet Erbudak (Sls Mgr)

SAKHA DIAMOND CORP.

Sakha Diamond Bldg 3-12-7 Chitose, Sumida-ku, Tokyo, 130-0025, Japan
Tel.: (81) 3 3846 2061
Web Site: http://www.sakha.co.jp
Year Founded: 1965
Bridal Jewelry Mfr
N.A.I.C.S.: 339910
Jie Jiang (Pres)

SAKHA ENTERPRISES CORP.

1 First Canadian Place Suite 350, Toronto, M5X 1C1, ON, Canada
Tel.: (416) 830-0905
Web Site:
  http://www.sakhaenterprises.com
Year Founded: 2000
SAKH—(OTCIQ)
Sales Range: Less than $1 Million
Gold & Metal Mining Services
N.A.I.C.S.: 212290

INTERNATIONAL PUBLIC

SAKOL ENERGY PUBLIC COMPANY LIMITED

15 Village No 1 Chiang Rak Noi Sub-district, Samkhok, Bangkok, 12160, Thailand
Tel.: (66) 25937217
Web Site:
  https://www.sakolenergy.com
Year Founded: 2009
SKE—(THA)
Rev.: $15,980,559
Assets: $55,285,108
Liabilities: $26,672,932
Net Worth: $28,612,175
Earnings: ($3,784,234)
Emp.: 159
Fiscal Year-end: 12/31/23
Natural Gas Pipeline Distr
N.A.I.C.S.: 486210
Direk Lavansiri (Chm)

SAKRAND SUGAR MILLS LTD

41K Block6 PECHS, Karachi, 75400, Pakistan
Tel.: (92) 21111484848
Web Site:
  https://www.sakrandsugar.com
Year Founded: 1989
SKRS—(LAH)
Rev.: $24,322,494
Assets: $30,869,189
Liabilities: $17,082,039
Net Worth: $13,787,151
Earnings: $1,124,740
Emp.: 198
Fiscal Year-end: 09/30/19
Sugar Processor & Mfr
N.A.I.C.S.: 311314
Dinshaw H. Anklesaria (CEO)

SAKSIAM LEASING PUBLIC COMPANY LIMITED

49/47 Chetsada Bodin Road, Tha It Sub-district Muang Uttaradit District, Amphur Muang, 53000, Uttaradit, Thailand
Tel.: (66) 55444495 TH
Web Site: https://www.saksiam.com
Year Founded: 1993
SAK—(THA)
Rev.: $79,980,557
Assets: $384,876,724
Liabilities: $214,623,000
Net Worth: $170,253,724
Earnings: $21,874,169
Emp.: 2,535
Fiscal Year-end: 12/31/23
Financial Investment Services
N.A.I.C.S.: 523999
Suphot Singhasaneh (Chm)

SAKSOFT LTD

Global Infocity Block A 2nd Floor 40 Dr MGR Salai, Kandanchavadi Perungudi, Chennai, 600096, India
Tel.: (91) 4424543500
Web Site: https://www.saksoft.com
Year Founded: 1999
590051—(BOM)
Rev.: $80,934,476
Assets: $68,108,866
Liabilities: $19,606,498
Net Worth: $48,502,368
Earnings: $9,828,787
Emp.: 1,275
Fiscal Year-end: 03/31/23
IT services & Consultancy Company
N.A.I.C.S.: 541512
Aditya Krishna (Chm & Mng Dir)

Subsidiaries:

MC Consulting Pte. Ltd. (1)
2 Kallang Avenue 07-20 CT Hub, Singapore, 339407, Singapore
Tel.: (65) 65354007
Web Site: https://mcconsulting.com.sg

Software Development & Consulting Services
N.A.I.C.S.: 541511

Saksoft GmbH (1)
Lyonerstr 14, 60528, Frankfurt, Germany
Tel.: (49) 6966554218
Web Site: http://www.saksoft.com
Software Consulting Services
N.A.I.C.S.: 541690

Saksoft Pte. Ltd. (1)
100A Eu Tong Sen St call ctr, 3 Shenton Way, Singapore, 059816, Singapore
Tel.: (65) 62242550
Sales Range: $25-49.9 Million
Emp.: 40
Software Consulting Services
N.A.I.C.S.: 541690
Vinay Advani *(Mgr-Reg)*

Saksoft, Inc. (1)
Ste 1240 30 Montgomery St, Jersey City, NJ 07302
Tel.: (201) 451-4609
Web Site: https://www.saksoft.com
Sales Range: $25-49.9 Million
Emp.: 25
IT Consulting Services
N.A.I.C.S.: 519290

SAKTHI FINANCE LIMITED
62 Dr Nanjappa Road, Coimbatore, 641 018, Tamilnadu, India
Tel.: (91) 4222231471
Web Site:
  https://www.sakthifinance.com
Year Founded: 1955
511066—(BOM)
Rev.: $23,012,973
Assets: $155,935,483
Liabilities: $131,132,090
Net Worth: $24,803,393
Earnings: $1,497,956
Emp.: 521
Fiscal Year-end: 03/31/23
Commercial Vehicle Financing Services
N.A.I.C.S.: 525990
S. Venkatesh *(Officer-Compliance & Sec)*

SAKTHI SUGARS LIMITED
180 Race Course Road, Coimbatore, 641 018, India
Tel.: (91) 4222221551
Web Site: https://sakthisugars.com
507315—(BOM)
Rev.: $109,927,736
Assets: $247,402,865
Liabilities: $305,842,064
Net Worth: ($58,439,199)
Earnings: ($20,497,509)
Emp.: 1,288
Fiscal Year-end: 03/31/22
Sugar Marketing & Mfr
N.A.I.C.S.: 311313
S. Baskar *(Officer-Compliance, Sec & Sr VP-Fin)*

Subsidiaries:

Sakthi Portugal SA (1)
Rua Jorge Ferreirinha 679, Vermoim, 4470-314, Maia, Portugal
Tel.: (351) 229430200
Web Site: http://www.sakthiportugal.pt
Sales Range: $100-124.9 Million
Emp.: 40
Iron Casting Mfr
N.A.I.C.S.: 331511
Jose Rego *(Project Mgr)*

Sakthi Sugars Limited - Sakthi Nagar Unit (1)
Sakthi Nagar, Erode Dist, Bhavani, 638 315, India
Tel.: (91) 4256 246341
Sales Range: $750-799.9 Million
Sugar Mfr
N.A.I.C.S.: 311313
M. Manickam *(Mng Dir)*

Sakthi Sugars Limited - Sivaganga Unit (1)
Padamathur B O, Sivaganga, 630 561, India
Tel.: (91) 457 523 6204
Web Site: http://www.sakthisugars.com
Sugar Mfr
N.A.I.C.S.: 311313

Sakthi Sugars Limited - Soya Unit (1)
Marchinaikenpalayam Anbarampalayam, Pollachi, 642 103, India
Tel.: (91) 425 925 3256
Web Site: https://www.sakthisugars.com
Soya Mfr
N.A.I.C.S.: 111110

SAKUMA EXPORTS LIMITED
A-301 Aurus Chambers S S Amrutwar Lane, Worli, Mumbai, 400 013, India
Tel.: (91) 2224999021
Web Site:
  https://www.sakumaexportsltd.com
Year Founded: 1998
SAKUMA—(NSE)
Rev.: $182,020,020
Assets: $58,692,993
Liabilities: $11,034,551
Net Worth: $47,658,443
Earnings: $1,505,718
Emp.: 46
Fiscal Year-end: 03/31/21
Agricultural Commodities Exporter
N.A.I.C.S.: 926140
Saurabh Malhotra *(Chm & Mng Dir)*

SAKURA DEVELOPMENT CO., LTD.
4th Floor No 239 Section 2 Taiwan Avenue, West District, Taichung, 403, Taiwan
Tel.: (886) 436005800
Web Site:
  https://www.sakurad.com.tw
Year Founded: 1976
2539—(TAI)
Rev.: $230,975,301
Assets: $826,704,308
Liabilities: $440,982,717
Net Worth: $385,721,592
Earnings: $62,620,391
Fiscal Year-end: 12/31/23
Real Estate Development Services
N.A.I.C.S.: 531390
Cheng-Hung Chen *(Chm)*

SAKURA FINETEK JAPAN CO., LTD.
31-1 Nihonbashi-Hamacho 2-chome, Chuo-ku, Tokyo, 103 0007, Japan
Tel.: (81) 356432630   JP
Web Site: http://www.sakura-finetek.com
Year Founded: 2001
Emp.: 163
Medical Instruments Mfr & Sales
N.A.I.C.S.: 339112
Satoru Ishizuka *(Pres & CEO)*

Subsidiaries:

Sakura Finetek USA, Inc. (1)
1750 W 214th St, Torrance, CA 90501
Tel.: (310) 972-7800
Web Site: http://www.sakura-americas.com
Medical Instrument Services
N.A.I.C.S.: 541715
George R. Kennedy *(Sr VP-Sls & Mktg)*

Subsidiary (Domestic):

Genemed Biotechnologies, Inc. (2)
458 Carlton Ct, South San Francisco, CA 94080
Tel.: (650) 952-0110
Web Site: http://www.genemed.com
Sales Range: $1-9.9 Million
Emp.: 24
Medical Instruments Mfr & Distr
N.A.I.C.S.: 339112
Dean Tsao *(Founder)*

Subsidiary (Non-US):

Sakura Finetek Europe B.V. (2)
Flemingweg 10A, 2408 AV, Alphen aan den Rijn, Netherlands
Tel.: (31) 88 592 00 00
Web Site: http://www.sakura.eu
Medical Instrument Distr
N.A.I.C.S.: 423450
Irment Werkhoven *(Mgr-Distr & Country Mgr-Holland)*

SAKURA INTERNET INC.
GRAND GREEN OSAKA North JAM BASE 3F 6-38 Ofukacho, Kita-ku, Osaka, 530-0011, Japan
Tel.: (81) 664768790
Web Site: https://www.sakura.ad.jp
Year Founded: 1999
3778—(TKS)
Rev.: $144,269,860
Assets: $199,780,640
Liabilities: $138,168,830
Net Worth: $61,611,810
Earnings: $4,303,110
Emp.: 839
Fiscal Year-end: 03/31/24
Internet Services
N.A.I.C.S.: 518210
Kunihiro Nozaki *(Auditor)*

SAKURA RUBBER COMPANY LIMITED
Sasazuka Taiyo BLDG F5 1-48-3 Sasazuka, Shibuya-ku, Tokyo, 151-8587, Japan
Tel.: (81) 334662171
Web Site: https://www.sakura-rubber.co.jp
Year Founded: 1918
5189—(TKS)
Rev.: $88,263,330
Assets: $116,124,480
Liabilities: $58,472,060
Net Worth: $57,652,420
Earnings: $4,845,130
Emp.: 334
Fiscal Year-end: 03/31/24
Specialty Rubber Product Mfr
N.A.I.C.S.: 326220
Hiroshi Nakamura *(Pres)*

Subsidiaries:

SAKURA Rubber Company Limited - Kanagawa Plant (1)
4-2-26 Yoshioka-higashi, Ayase, 252-1125, Kanagawa, Japan
Tel.: (81) 467793356
Rubber Products Mfr
N.A.I.C.S.: 326299

SAKURA Rubber Company Limited - Ohtawara Plant (1)
799 Midori, Otawara, 324-0045, Tochigi, Japan
Tel.: (81) 287281121
Rubber Products Mfr
N.A.I.C.S.: 326299

SAKURAI LTD.
720 Handa-cho, Chuo-ku, Hamamatsu, 431-3124, Shizuoka, Japan
Tel.: (81) 534321711
Web Site: https://www.sakurai-net.co.jp
Year Founded: 1950
7255—(TKS)
Rev.: $36,612,790
Assets: $47,076,420
Liabilities: $15,619,430
Net Worth: $31,456,990
Earnings: $2,121,810
Emp.: 373
Fiscal Year-end: 03/31/24
Machine Tools Mfr
N.A.I.C.S.: 333517
Seiji Sakurai *(Pres)*

Subsidiaries:

SAKURAI LTD. - Hosoe Plant (1)
7000-18 Nakagawa Hosoe-cho, Kita-ku, Hamamatsu, 431-1304, Shizuoka, Japan
Tel.: (81) 535232411
Web Site: https://www.sakurai-net.co.jp
Emp.: 159
Automobile Parts Mfr
N.A.I.C.S.: 336390

SAKURAI U.S.A., CO. (1)
5650 Blazer Pkwy Ste 151, Dublin, OH 43017
Tel.: (614) 563-3643
Machine Tool Sales & Maintenance Services
N.A.I.C.S.: 423840

SAKURAI VIETNAM CO., LTD. (1)
Lot F2 - Area F - Le Mon Industrial Park, Quang Hung Ward, Thanh Hoa, Vietnam
Tel.: (84) 2373914490
Web Site: https://sakuraivietnam.com
Emp.: 140
Machine Tools Mfr
N.A.I.C.S.: 333517

SAKURAJIMA FUTO KAISHA LTD.
1-1-11 Ume-machi, Konohana-ku, Osaka, 554-0032, Japan
Tel.: (81) 664615331
Web Site: https://www.sakurajima-futo.co.jp
Year Founded: 1948
9353—(TKS)
Rev.: $27,180,320
Assets: $66,602,360
Liabilities: $25,190,710
Net Worth: $41,411,650
Earnings: $1,394,710
Emp.: 74
Fiscal Year-end: 03/31/24
Transportation & Warehousing Services
N.A.I.C.S.: 488320

SAKURASAKU PLUS CO., LTD.
Toho Hibiya Building 1-2-2 Yurakucho, Chiyoda-Ku, Tokyo, 100-0006, Japan
Tel.: (81) 358609539
Web Site:
  https://www.sakurasakuplus.jp
Year Founded: 2017
7097—(TKS)
Rev.: $107,058,640
Assets: $84,828,360
Liabilities: $51,937,000
Net Worth: $32,891,360
Earnings: $3,775,540
Fiscal Year-end: 07/31/24
Real Estate Development Services
N.A.I.C.S.: 531311
Yoshitaka Nisho *(Founder, Pres & CEO)*

SAL SAUDI LOGISTICS SERVICES COMPANY
Prince Sultan Street, PO Box 55078, Jeddah, 23525, Saudi Arabia
Tel.: (966) 920011725
Web Site: https://www.sal.sa
Year Founded: 2019
4263—(SAU)
Rev.: $325,958,490
Assets: $875,387,232
Liabilities: $589,291,574
Net Worth: $286,095,658
Earnings: $96,619,039
Emp.: 930
Fiscal Year-end: 12/31/22
Logistics Consulting Servies
N.A.I.C.S.: 541614

SALA CORPORATION
Sala Tower 1-55 Ekimae-odori, Toyohashi, 440-8533, Aichi, Japan

SALA CORPORATION

Sala Corporation—(Continued)
Tel.: (81) 532511155
Web Site: https://www.sala.jp
Year Founded: 2002
2734—(NGO)
Rev.: $1,716,244,301
Assets: $1,341,938,991
Liabilities: $784,330,998
Net Worth: $557,607,993
Earnings: $44,313,688
Fiscal Year-end: 11/30/23
Investment Management Service
N.A.I.C.S.: 523940
Shoji Nakamura (Chm)

Subsidiaries:

ASCO Co., Ltd. (1)
100 Shirakawa-Cho, Toyohashi, 441-8021, Aichi, Japan
Tel.: (81) 532343821
Animal Pharmaceutical & Feed Distr
N.A.I.C.S.: 424910

Asco Corp. (1)
100 Shirakawa-cho, Toyohashi, 441-8021, Aichi, Japan
Tel.: (81) 532343821
Veterinary Drugs Whslr
N.A.I.C.S.: 812910
Kiyotaka Ozaki (Gen Mgr)

Chubu Building Service Co., Ltd. (1)
28 Tonowari Jinnoshinden-cho, Toyohashi, 441-8077, Aichi, Japan
Tel.: (81) 532329730
General Building Maintenance Services
N.A.I.C.S.: 561790

Chubu Engineering Corporation (1)
28 Tonowari Jinnoshinden-cho, Toyohashi, 441-8588, Aichi, Japan
Tel.: (81) 532311111
Web Site: https://www.chubu.sala.jp
Emp.: 238
Engineeering Services
N.A.I.C.S.: 541330

Chubu Engineering Service Co., Ltd. (1)
28 Tonowari Jinnoshinden-cho, Toyohashi, 441-8077, Aichi, Japan
Tel.: (81) 532329991
Web Site: https://www.ces.sala.jp
General Building Maintenance Services
N.A.I.C.S.: 561790

Chubu Gas Co., Ltd. (1)
Sala Tower 1-55 Ekimae-odori, Toyohashi, 440-8531, Aichi, Japan
Tel.: (81) 532511212
Industrial Gas Distr
N.A.I.C.S.: 457210

Chubu Gas Realtors Co., Ltd. (1)
Sala Hirokoji Bldg 3-91 Hirokoji, Toyohashi, 440-0881, Aichi, Japan
Tel.: (81) 532515800
Real Estate Brokerage Services
N.A.I.C.S.: 531210

Chubu Home Service Co., Ltd. (1)
5-3 Tonya-cho, Toyohashi, 441-8086, Aichi, Japan
Tel.: (81) 532326201
Construction Services
N.A.I.C.S.: 236220

Chubu Propane Stand Ltd. (1)
41-1 Araki Hanada-cho, Toyohashi, 441-8019, Aichi, Japan
Tel.: (81) 532333541
Industrial Gas Distr
N.A.I.C.S.: 457210

Daiwa Pharmaceutical Co,, Ltd. (1)
1-16-19 Sangenjaya, Setagaya-ku, Tokyo, 154-0024, Japan
Tel.: (81) 354304070
Web Site: https://www.daiwa-pharm.com
Emp.: 30
Pharmaceutical Products Distr
N.A.I.C.S.: 424210
Yasuo Ninomiya (Pres)

Eco-Home Panel Co., Ltd. (1)
50 Nishinoyama Minamiyama Fuso-cho, Niwa, 480-0105, Aichi, Japan
Tel.: (81) 587912150

Construction Machinery Mfr & Distr
N.A.I.C.S.: 333120

Gas Living Chubu Co., Ltd. (1)
2-2-1 Sato, Toyohashi, 440-0853, Aichi, Japan
Tel.: (81) 532664111
Industrial Gas Distr
N.A.I.C.S.: 457210

Gas Living Hamamatsu Hokubu Co., Ltd. (1)
1-3-10 Saiwai, Naka-ku, Hamamatsu, 433-8123, Shizuoka, Japan
Tel.: (81) 534723237
Industrial Gas Distr
N.A.I.C.S.: 457210

Gas Living Hamamatsu Seibu Co., Ltd. (1)
1-2-17 Sanarudai, Naka-ku, Hamamatsu, 432-8021, Shizuoka, Japan
Tel.: (81) 534550563
Industrial Gas Distr
N.A.I.C.S.: 457210

Gastec Service Inc. (1)
Sala Tower 1-55 Ekimae-odori, Toyohashi, 440-8532, Aichi, Japan
Tel.: (81) 532511177
Electric Power Distribution Services
N.A.I.C.S.: 221122

Good Life SALA Kanto Co., Ltd. (1)
1 Kozakucho, Totsuka-ku, Yokohama, 244-0004, Kanagawa, Japan
Tel.: (81) 458542801
Web Site: https://gl.sala.jp
Emp.: 115
Petroleum Product Distr
N.A.I.C.S.: 424720

Hamamatsu Propane Stand Ltd. (1)
2-15-14 Sato, Naka-ku, Hamamatsu, 430-0807, Shizuoka, Japan
Tel.: (81) 534643722
Automobile Gas Distr
N.A.I.C.S.: 457210

Hokuyaku Co., Ltd. (1)
Kita 6-jo Nishi 16-1-5, Chuo-ku, Sapporo, 060-0006, Hokkaido, Japan
Tel.: (81) 116110989
Web Site: https://www.hokuyaku.co.jp
Veterinary Pharmaceutical Whslr
N.A.I.C.S.: 424210

Jinno Construction Co., Ltd. (1)
9-1 Konowari Jinnoshinden-cho, Toyohashi, 441-8077, Aichi, Japan
Tel.: (81) 532321021
Engineeering Services
N.A.I.C.S.: 541330

Jinno Oil Center Co., Ltd. (1)
20-1 Honowari Jinnoshinden-cho, Toyohashi, 441-8077, Aichi, Japan
Tel.: (81) 532320869
Oil Storage Services
N.A.I.C.S.: 213112

Kantoh Co., Ltd. (1)
8-3 Kotesashidai, Tokorozawa, 359-1148, Saitama, Japan
Tel.: (81) 429252861
Gas Filling Services
N.A.I.C.S.: 457120

Living SALA Co., Ltd. (1)
100 Shirakawa-cho, Toyohashi, 441 8021, Aichi, Japan
Tel.: (81) 532321441
Web Site: https://www.living-sala.co.jp
Home Renovation Services
N.A.I.C.S.: 236118

Mikawawan Gas Terminal Co., Ltd. (1)
1-11-1 Midorigahama, Tahara, 441-3401, Aichi, Japan
Tel.: (81) 531234800
Gas Filling Services
N.A.I.C.S.: 457120

Miyashita Koumuten Co., Ltd. (1)
964-2 Hatsuoicho, Kita Ward, Hamamatsu, 433-8112, Shizuoka, Japan
Tel.: (81) 534372695
Web Site: https://www.miyashita-koumuten.co.jp
Construction Machinery Distr

N.A.I.C.S.: 423810

SALA Financial Service Co., Ltd. (1)
57 Tachibana-cho, Toyohashi, 441-8028, Aichi, Japan
Tel.: (81) 532332241
Web Site: http://www.shinkyo.sala.jp
Financial Investment Services
N.A.I.C.S.: 523940

SALA Logistics Inc. (1)
Tel.: (81) 533732991
Web Site: http://www.logi.sala.jp
Logistics Consulting Servies
N.A.I.C.S.: 541614

Sala Business Solutions Inc. (1)
100 Shirakawa-cho, Toyohashi, 441-8021, Aichi, Japan
Tel.: (81) 532325151
Information System Services
N.A.I.C.S.: 541512

Sala Cars Japan Co., Ltd. (1)
Sala Tower 1-55 Odori Ekimae Odori, Toyohashi, 440-0888, Aichi, Japan
Tel.: (81) 532511260
Web Site: https://www.salacarsjapan.co.jp
Emp.: 289
Car Distr
N.A.I.C.S.: 441110

Sala E Energy Co., Ltd. (1)
Sala Tower 1-55 Ekimae-odori, Toyohashi, 440-8531, Aichi, Japan
Tel.: (81) 532577250
Electric Power Distribution Services
N.A.I.C.S.: 221122

Sala E Power Co., Ltd. (1)
Sala Tower 1-55 Ekimae-odori, Toyohashi, 440-8531, Aichi, Japan
Tel.: (81) 532577715
Electric Power Distribution Services
N.A.I.C.S.: 221122

Sala Energy Co., Ltd. (1)
Sala Tower 1-55 Ekimae-Odori, Toyohashi, 440-8531, Aichi, Japan
Tel.: (81) 532511212
Civil Engineering Services
N.A.I.C.S.: 541330

Sala Financial Services Co., Ltd. (1)
57 Tachibana-Cho, Toyohashi, 441-8028, Aichi, Japan
Tel.: (81) 532332241
Life & Non Life Insurance Services
N.A.I.C.S.: 524113

Sala Gas Iwata Co., Ltd. (1)
4-6-1 Imanoura, Iwata, 438-0071, Shizuoka, Japan
Tel.: (81) 120105317
Industrial Gas Distr
N.A.I.C.S.: 457210

Sala Hotels & Restaurants Co., Ltd. (1)
SALA Tower 1-55 Ekimae-odori, Toyohashi, 440-8533, Aichi, Japan
Tel.: (81) 532511101
Web Site: http://www.hpdsp.jp
Hotel Operator
N.A.I.C.S.: 721110

Sala House Co., Ltd. (1)
100 Shirakawa-Cho, Toyohashi, 441-8021, Japan
Tel.: (81) 532327272
Web Site: http://www.sala-house.co.jp
Construction Related Services
N.A.I.C.S.: 237990
Yasuhiro Suzuki (Sr Mng Dir)

Sala House Support Co. Ltd. (1)
6-1 Hashira Yonbancho, Toyohashi, 441-8051, Aichi, Japan
Tel.: (81) 532381521
Web Site: https://www.sala-shs.co.jp
Renovation Contracting Services
N.A.I.C.S.: 236118

Sala Lifestyle Innovation Co., Ltd. (1)
100 Shirakawa-cho, Toyohashi, 441-8021, Aichi, Japan
Tel.: (81) 532342522
Marketing Consulting Services
N.A.I.C.S.: 541613

INTERNATIONAL PUBLIC

Sala Sports Co., Ltd. (1)
1107 Sunayama-cho, Naka-ku, Hamamatsu, 430-0926, Shizuoka, Japan
Tel.: (81) 534554141
Web Site: https://www.salasports.co.jp
Sport Fitness Club Services
N.A.I.C.S.: 713940

Sala Water Co., Ltd. (1)
SALA Tower 1-55 Ekimae-odori, Toyohashi, 440-8531, Aichi, Japan
Tel.: (81) 532331051
Electric Power Distribution Services
N.A.I.C.S.: 221122

Seien Concrete Industries Co., Ltd. (1)
4048 Kuramatsu-cho, Minami-ku, Hamamatsu, 432-8064, Shizuoka, Japan
Tel.: (81) 534471489
Asphalt Product Mfr & Distr
N.A.I.C.S.: 324121

Seiwa Security Service Co., Ltd. (1)
1-14-7 Higashi Odakano-cho, Toyohashi, 440-0012, Aichi, Japan
Tel.: (81) 532636740
Traffic Guard Contract Services
N.A.I.C.S.: 561612

Shinkyo Giken Co., Ltd. (1)
1-27-28 Zoshi, Toyokawa, 442-0842, Aichi, Japan
Tel.: (81) 533891516
Web Site: http://www.shinkyo.sala.jp
Emp.: 98
Machine Tools Mfr
N.A.I.C.S.: 333517
Yoshiaki Yamashina (Pres)

Showa Cleaner Co., Ltd. (1)
115 Ihara-cho, Toyohashi, 440-0025, Aichi, Japan
Tel.: (81) 532623124
General Building Maintenance Services
N.A.I.C.S.: 561790

Suzukigumi Co., Ltd. (1)
1522 Kanda-cho, Naka-ku, Hamamatsu, 432-8047, Japan
Tel.: (81) 534422111
Web Site: https://www.suzukigumi.co.jp
Emp.: 83
Construction Services
N.A.I.C.S.: 236220

Taiyo-Co. Inc. (1)
3-3-12 Torii, Chiryu, 472-0055, Aichi, Japan
Tel.: (81) 566835000
Real Estate Brokerage Services
N.A.I.C.S.: 531210

Techno Systems Inc. (1)
28 Tonowari Jinnoshinden-cho, Toyohashi, 441-8077, Aichi, Japan
Tel.: (81) 532311110
Application Development Services
N.A.I.C.S.: 541511

Tokiwa Doro Co., Ltd. (1)
1527 Kanda-cho, Naka-ku, Hamamatsu, 432-8047, Shizuoka, Japan
Tel.: (81) 534446151
Engineeering Services
N.A.I.C.S.: 541330

Yasue Corporation (1)
Arc Shirakawa Park Building 2-2-23 Sakae, Naka-ku, Nagoya, 460-0008, Japan
Tel.: (81) 522231100
Web Site: https://www.yasue.jp
Rev.: $52,458,910
Assets: $30,884,040
Liabilities: $17,909,340
Net Worth: $12,974,700
Earnings: $1,446,360
Emp.: 274
Fiscal Year-end: 12/31/2023
Building Construction Services
N.A.I.C.S.: 236220
Kenji Yamamoto (Pres, CEO, COO & Exec Officer)

emCAMPUS Co., Ltd. (1)
emCampus East 5F 2-81 Ekimae-Odori, Toyohashi, 440-0888, Aichi, Japan
Tel.: (81) 532575016
Civil Engineering Services
N.A.I.C.S.: 541330

SALADA FOODS JAMAICA LIMITED

20 Bell Road, PO Box 71, Kingston, 11, Jamaica
Tel.: (876) 9237114   JM
Web Site:
   https://www.saladafoodsja.com
Year Founded: 1958
SALF—(JAM)
Rev.: $8,256,796
Assets: $8,805,354
Liabilities: $1,833,902
Net Worth: $6,971,452
Earnings: $1,088,372
Fiscal Year-end: 09/30/21
Coffee Mfr & Distr
N.A.I.C.S.: 311920
Dave Lemard *(Mgr-Grp Engrg & Svcs)*

SALAISONS DE L'ADOUR
Zone Pyrene Aeropole Route de Lourdes, Louey, 65290, Tarbes, Hautes Pyrenees, France
Tel.: (33) 5 62 45 60 33
Web Site:
   http://www.salaisonsdeladour.com
Sales Range: $10-24.9 Million
Emp.: 20
Ham Processing
N.A.I.C.S.: 311611
Jean-Marie Phalip *(Mng Dir & Chm)*

SALAISONS PYRENEENNES
2 Rue Anatole France, Borderes Sur L Echez, 65320, Tarbes, Hautes Pyrenees, France
Tel.: (33) 562370001
Web Site: http://www.salaisons-pyreneennes.com
Rev.: $28,700,000
Emp.: 79
Sausages & Other Prepared Meats
N.A.I.C.S.: 311612
Frederic Bonomelli *(Pres)*

SALALAH BEACH RESORT SAOG
Tel.: (968) 23236170
Web Site:
   https://beachresortsalalah.com
Year Founded: 1998
SHCS—(MUS)
Rev.: $3,692,704
Assets: $20,317,658
Liabilities: $5,217,598
Net Worth: $15,100,060
Earnings: ($2,048,570)
Emp.: 170
Fiscal Year-end: 12/31/23
Hotel Operator
N.A.I.C.S.: 721110

SALALAH MILLS COMPANY SAOG
PO Box 67, 217, Salalah, Oman
Tel.: (968) 23219193
Web Site: https://www.salalah-mills.com
Year Founded: 1995
SFMI—(MUS)
Rev.: $168,506,790
Assets: $208,401,002
Liabilities: $124,107,135
Net Worth: $84,293,867
Earnings: $62,911
Fiscal Year-end: 12/31/23
Flour Mill & Grain Production Services
N.A.I.C.S.: 311211
Ahmed Abdullah Al Rawas *(Chm)*

SALALAH PORT SERVICES CO. SAOG
Beach one Building Shatti Al Qurum, PO Box 105, 118, Muscat, Oman
Tel.: (968) 24601003
Web Site: https://salalahport.com.om

Year Founded: 1997
SPSI—(MUS)
Rev.: $178,129,302
Assets: $319,678,433
Liabilities: $123,964,259
Net Worth: $195,714,174
Earnings: $7,283,306
Emp.: 2,238
Fiscal Year-end: 12/31/23
Port Operator
N.A.I.C.S.: 488310

SALAM INTERNATIONAL INVESTMENT LIMITED
The Gate Mall Salam Plaza Tower 1 Omar Al Mukhtar St, 15224, Doha, Qatar
Tel.: (974) 44838733
Web Site:
   https://www.salaminternational.com
SIIS—(QE)
Rev.: $391,438,838
Assets: $1,350,347,782
Liabilities: $866,963,283
Net Worth: $483,384,499
Earnings: $16,100,752
Fiscal Year-end: 12/31/21
Investment Services
N.A.I.C.S.: 523999
Issa Abdul Salam Abu Issa *(Chm & CEO)*

Subsidiaries:

Alu-Nasa Aluminum Industry LLC   (1)
Unit No FG6 Dubai Investment Park, PO Box 5560, Jebel Ali, Dubai, United Arab Emirates
Tel.: (971) 4 8804500
Web Site: http://www.alu-nasa.com
Industrial Building Construction Services
N.A.I.C.S.: 236210

Gulf Industries For Refrigeration and Catering Company O.P.C   (1)
Gate 53 St 15 Doha Industrial Area, PO Box 22028, Doha, Qatar
Tel.: (974) 44600955
Commercial Equipment Whslr
N.A.I.C.S.: 423440

Salam Enterprise Company   (1)
Shop No 189 Building No 191 Road No 328 Block 358 Sh Salman Highway, PO Box 3143, Zinj, Manama, Bahrain
Tel.: (973) 17230950
Web Site: https://salamenterprises.com
Furniture Distr
N.A.I.C.S.: 423210

Salam Enterprises L.L.C.   (1)
Ras Al Khor Complex Showroom No 3, PO Box 28326, Dubai, United Arab Emirates
Tel.: (971) 42896289
Web Site:
   http://www.salamenterprisesllc.com
Emp.: 35
Water Treatment Equipment Distr
N.A.I.C.S.: 423830

Salam Studio & Stores L.L.C.   (1)
Oud Metha Road Wafi Mall, PO Box 4199, Dubai, 0199, United Arab Emirates
Tel.: (971) 47048484
Web Site: http://www.salams.com
Emp.: 500
Beauty Supplies Store Operator
N.A.I.C.S.: 456120
Janet Geronimo *(Mgr)*

Salam Studio & Stores O.P.C.   (1)
63 Maysaloun Street No 860, PO Box 121, Doha, Qatar
Tel.: (974) 8000889
Web Site: http://www.salams.com
Beauty Supplies Store Operator
N.A.I.C.S.: 456120

SALAM INTERNATIONAL TRANSPORT & TRADING CO. PLC
240 Wadi Saqra Arar St, PO Box 212955, Amman, 11121, Jordan
Tel.: (962) 65654510   JO

Web Site:
   https://www.sittcogroup.com
Year Founded: 1977
SITT—(AMM)
Rev.: $6,333,850
Assets: $45,467,141
Liabilities: $14,265,245
Net Worth: $31,201,896
Earnings: $1,410,204
Emp.: 7
Fiscal Year-end: 12/31/20
Marine Shipping & Real Estate Development Services
N.A.I.C.S.: 483111
Ahmad Armoush *(Founder)*

SALAMA COOPERATIVE INSURANCE COMPANY
Salama Tower 12th floor Al Madina Road, PO Box 4020, Jeddah, 7864, Saudi Arabia
Tel.: (966) 920023355
Web Site:
   https://www.salama.com.sa
Year Founded: 1979
8050—(SAU)
Rev.: $145,198,507
Assets: $204,231,436
Liabilities: $194,161,312
Net Worth: $10,070,124
Earnings: ($15,551,793)
Emp.: 267
Fiscal Year-end: 12/31/22
Insurance Services
N.A.I.C.S.: 524126
Ammar Ghurab *(COO)*

SALAMIS TOURS PUBLIC LTD
Tel.: (357) 77778500
Web Site:
   https://www.salamistours.com
Year Founded: 1959
SAL—(CYP)
Sales Range: Less than $1 Million
Travel & Tour Management Services
N.A.I.C.S.: 561599

Subsidiaries:

SALAMIS SHIPPING S.A.   (1)
5-7 Filellinon Str, 18536, Piraeus, Greece
Tel.: (30) 2104529555
Web Site: http://www.salamisshipping.com
Sales Range: $25-49.9 Million
Emp.: 7
Marine Shipping Services
N.A.I.C.S.: 483111
Christos Petoumenos *(Mgr)*

SALAMIS SHIPPING SERVICES LTD   (1)
124 Franklin Roosevelt Ave, PO Box 55609, 3781, Lemesos, Cyprus
Tel.: (357) 25899999
Marine Shipping Services
N.A.I.C.S.: 483111

Salamis Cruise Lines   (1)
Salamis House 1 G Katsounotos Str, PO Box 50531, 3607, Lemesos, Cyprus
Tel.: (357) 25860000
Web Site:
   http://www.salamiscruiselines.com
Cruise Line Operator
N.A.I.C.S.: 483114

SALASAR EXTERIORS & CONTOUR LIMITED
922/923 Corporate Avenue Sonawala Road Near Udyog Bhavan, Goregaon East, Mumbai, 400063, India
Tel.: (91) 2267083366
Web Site:
   http://www.salasarexterior.com
Year Founded: 2018
SECL—(NSE)
Rev.: $205,827
Assets: $4,403,537
Liabilities: $2,969,690
Net Worth: $1,433,847

Earnings: $97,548
Emp.: 15
Fiscal Year-end: 03/31/23
Interior Design Services
N.A.I.C.S.: 541410
Shreekishan Joshi *(Mng Dir)*

SALASAR TECHNO ENGINEERING LIMITED
E-20 South Extension I, New Delhi, 110 049, India
Tel.: (91) 1206546670   In
Web Site:
   https://www.salasartechno.com
Year Founded: 2001
540642—(BOM)
Rev.: $120,771,465
Assets: $109,603,177
Liabilities: $61,534,680
Net Worth: $48,068,497
Earnings: $4,826,377
Emp.: 1,417
Fiscal Year-end: 03/31/23
Steel Product Mfr & Distr
N.A.I.C.S.: 331110
Alok Kumar *(Chm & Co-Mng Dir)*

SALAZAR RESOURCES LIMITED
Suite 1305 - 1090 West Georgia St, Vancouver, V6E 3V7, BC, Canada
Tel.: (604) 685-9316   BC
Web Site:
   https://www.salazarresources.com
Year Founded: 1987
CCG—(DEU)
Rev.: $635,919
Assets: $17,996,222
Liabilities: $346,792
Net Worth: $17,649,430
Earnings: ($4,285,526)
Emp.: 55
Fiscal Year-end: 12/31/23
Mineral Exploration Services
N.A.I.C.S.: 213114
Fredy Salazar *(Pres & CEO)*

SALCEF COSTRUZIONI EDILI E FERROVIARIE SPA
Via di Pietralata 140, 00158, Rome, Italy
Tel.: (39) 06 416281
Web Site: http://www.salcef.com
Year Founded: 1949
Railway Construction, Engineering & Technology Services
N.A.I.C.S.: 488210
Valeriano Salciccia *(Mng Dir)*

Subsidiaries:

Vianini S.p.A.   (1)
Via Barberini 47, 187, Rome, Italy
Tel.: (39) 0642010599
Web Site: https://www.vianinispa.com
Sales Range: Less than $1 Million
Concrete Products Mfr
N.A.I.C.S.: 327390
Elena De Simone *(Chm & CEO)*

SALCO FOOTWEAR IND. LTD.
907 Oxford St, Etobicoke, M8Z 5T1, ON, Canada
Tel.: (416) 674-5171
Web Site:
   http://www.salcofootwear.com
Year Founded: 1974
Rev.: $14,384,045
Emp.: 15
Footwear Distr
N.A.I.C.S.: 424340
M. P. Biyani *(Pres)*

SALCON BERHAD
15th Floor Menara Summit Persiaran Kewajipan USJ 1, 47600, Subang Jaya, Selangor Darul Ehsan, Malaysia

SALCON BERHAD

Salcon Berhad—(Continued)
Tel.: (60) 380248822
Web Site: https://www.salcon.com.my
SALCON—(KLS)
Rev.: $43,197,672
Assets: $125,753,228
Liabilities: $31,016,720
Net Worth: $94,736,508
Earnings: ($8,746,243)
Emp.: 438
Fiscal Year-end: 12/31/22
Waste Management Services
N.A.I.C.S.: 237110
Woo Hock Law (CFO)

Subsidiaries:

BMS Corporate Services Limited (1)
20/F Fung House 19-20 Connaught Road, Central, China (Hong Kong)
Tel.: (852) 28106818
Water & Wastewater Construction Services
N.A.I.C.S.: 237110

Eco Tours Asia Sdn. Bhd. (1)
18-28-1A Gurney Drive Persiaran Gurney, 10250, George Town, Penang, Malaysia
Tel.: (60) 42278668
Web Site: https://www.ecotours.asia
Tourism Services
N.A.I.C.S.: 561520
Vergis Mathews (Mng Dir)

Envitech Sdn. Bhd. (1)
No 67 Jalan SS15/5A, 47500, Subang Jaya, Selangor Darul Ehsan, Malaysia
Tel.: (60) 356318388
Web Site: https://www.envitech.com.my
Environmental Technological Services
N.A.I.C.S.: 541620
Lee Thim Loy (Mng Dir)

Logit Sdn. Bhd. (1)
Suite 13C 13th Floor The Intermark-Vista Tower 348 Jalan Tun Razak, 50400, Kuala Lumpur, Malaysia
Tel.: (60) 327145001
Web Site: https://www.logit.global
Software Development Services
N.A.I.C.S.: 541511

Salcon Investment Consultation (Shanghai) Company Limited (1)
Room 1314 West Wing of Modern Communication Plaza, No 218 Hengfeng Road, Shanghai, 200070, China
Tel.: (86) 2160298092
Water & Wastewater Construction Services
N.A.I.C.S.: 237110

Salcon Petroleum Services (Asia Pacific) Sdn. Bhd. (1)
Spaces Level 30 Menara Prestige No 1 Jalan Pinang, 50450, Kuala Lumpur, Malaysia
Tel.: (60) 12 342 4350
Web Site: https://www.salconpetroleum.com
Petroleum Services
N.A.I.C.S.: 213112
Thomas A. Sjoberg (CEO & Co-Founder)

SALECYCLE LTD.

Ground Floor Alexander House 1 Mandarin Road, Rainton Bridge, Durham, DH4 5RA, United Kingdom
Tel.: (44) 1915007400
Web Site: http://www.salecycle.com
Year Founded: 2010
Sales Range: $1-9.9 Million
Emp.: 78
Software Publishing Services
N.A.I.C.S.: 513210
Graham Charlton (Editor-in-Chief)

Subsidiaries:

SaleCycle Ltd. (1)
Portland House 27th Bressenden Place, London, SW1E 5RS, United Kingdom
Tel.: (44) 208 433 6989
Software Publisher
N.A.I.C.S.: 513210

SALEE COLOUR PUBLIC COMPANY LIMITED

858 Moo 2 Soi 1C/1 Bangpu Industrial Estate Bangpumai, Muang Samutprakarn, Samut Prakan, 10280, Thailand
Tel.: (66) 23232601
Web Site: https://www.saleecolour.com
Year Founded: 2003
COLOR—(THA)
Rev.: $34,401,415
Assets: $41,516,068
Liabilities: $17,650,169
Net Worth: $23,865,899
Earnings: $905,469
Emp.: 300
Fiscal Year-end: 12/31/23
Colors & Additives Mfr
N.A.I.C.S.: 325130
Kwanchai Nuttased (Member-Mgmt Bd)

SALEE INDUSTRY PUBLIC COMPANY LIMITED

18 Moo 10 Tumbol Klong Si Amphur Klong Luang, Pathumthani, 12120, Thailand
Tel.: (66) 25295999
Web Site: https://www.saleeind.com
Year Founded: 1976
SALEE—(THA)
Rev.: $38,022,833
Assets: $52,064,462
Liabilities: $16,644,969
Net Worth: $35,419,493
Earnings: $486,046
Fiscal Year-end: 12/31/23
Plastic Parts Mfr
N.A.I.C.S.: 326199
Sathit Tatawatorn (Vice Chm & Mng Dir-Acting)

Subsidiaries:

Petchsiam (Thailand) Company Limited (1)
4 Soi Phraya Monthat Yaek 9 Khwaeng Khlong Bangbon Khet, Bangbon, Bangkok, 10150, Thailand
Tel.: (66) 24158987
Web Site: http://www.petchsiamthai.com
Plastic Houseware Product Distr
N.A.I.C.S.: 423220
SiraPhat Tatawatron (Mgr-Sls)

SALEE PRINTING PUBLIC COMPANY LIMITED

19 Moo 10 T Klong 4 A Klong Luang, Pathumthani, 12120, Thailand
Tel.: (66) 25296000
Web Site: https://www.saleeprinting.com
SLP—(THA)
Rev.: $15,440,217
Assets: $25,777,677
Liabilities: $2,683,034
Net Worth: $23,094,643
Earnings: ($482,835)
Emp.: 160
Fiscal Year-end: 12/31/23
Adhesive Printing Products Mfr
N.A.I.C.S.: 325520
Suchart Chivapornthip (Chm)

SALEEM DENIM INDUSTRIES LIMITED

33-KM Sheikhupura Road, Faisalabad, Pakistan
Tel.: (92) 41 4689310
Web Site: http://www.saleemdenimindltd.com
Year Founded: 1984
Textile Products Mfr
N.A.I.C.S.: 313210

SALES FORCE NATIONAL PTY. LTD.

20 Southern Court, Keysborough, 3173, VIC, Australia
Tel.: (61) 397068849 AU
Web Site: http://www.zenexus.com.au
Year Founded: 2011
Molded Plastic Product Mfr
N.A.I.C.S.: 326199
Rod Sutton (Mng Dir)

SALES SERVICES INTERNATIONAL

Wilgenweg 22D, Amsterdam, 1031, Netherlands
Tel.: (31) 887701001
Web Site: http://www.ssinetwork.com
Marketing Consulting Services
N.A.I.C.S.: 541613
Dieter Stempel (Founder)

SALFACORP S.A.

Avda Presidente Riesco 5335 Piso 11, Las Condes, Santiago, Chile
Tel.: (56) 229020000
Web Site: https://www.salfacorp.com
SALFACORP—(SGO)
Rev.: $1,180,891,616
Assets: $1,619,802,469
Liabilities: $1,072,522,302
Net Worth: $547,280,166
Earnings: $48,658,832
Fiscal Year-end: 12/31/23
Engineering & Construction Services
N.A.I.C.S.: 541330
Andres Navarro Haeussler (Chm)

SALGUTI INDUSTRIES LIMITED

1-2-288 / 6 / 4 Domalguda, Hyderabad, 500 029, India
Tel.: (91) 4023545939
Web Site: https://www.salguti.com
Year Founded: 1984
526554—(BOM)
Rev.: $12,179,318
Assets: $6,854,973
Liabilities: $5,774,090
Net Worth: $1,080,882
Earnings: $1,043
Fiscal Year-end: 03/31/23
Textile Products Mfr
N.A.I.C.S.: 314999
S. Vishnu Vardhan Reddy (Mng Dir)

SALHIA REAL ESTATE COMPANY K.S.C.

Mohammed Thunayan Al-Ghanim Street, PO Box 23413, Safat, 13095, Kuwait, 13095, Kuwait
Tel.: (965) 22996000
Web Site: https://www.salhia.com
Year Founded: 1974
SRE—(KUW)
Rev.: $116,800,829
Assets: $1,361,242,709
Liabilities: $815,025,285
Net Worth: $546,217,423
Earnings: $47,361,702
Emp.: 263
Fiscal Year-end: 12/31/22
Commercial Properties & Hotels Owner & Manager
N.A.I.C.S.: 531312
Ghazi Fahad AlNafisi (Chm)

SALINI COSTRUTTORI S.P.A.

Via Del Lauro 3, 20121, Milan, Italy
Tel.: (39) 02726260200 IT
Web Site: http://www.salinicostruttori.com
Sales Range: $5-14.9 Billion
Emp.: 34,000
Holding Company Services
N.A.I.C.S.: 551112
Simonpietro Salini (Chm)

Subsidiaries:

Consorzio Cociv (1)

INTERNATIONAL PUBLIC

Via Renata Bianchi 40, 16152, Genoa, Italy
Tel.: (39) 0104218711
Web Site: http://www.cociv.terzovalico.it
Engineering Services
N.A.I.C.S.: 541330

Salini Nigeria Ltd. (1)
Plot 16 Blantyre Street Off Ademola Adetokunbo Crescent Wuse II, Abuja, Nigeria
Tel.: (234) 8034505951
Engineeering Services
N.A.I.C.S.: 541330

Webuild S.p.A (1)
Via dei Missaglia 97, 20142, Milan, Italy (89.95%)
Tel.: (39) 024 442 2111
Web Site: http://www.salini-impregilo.com
Rev.: $7,885,711,032
Assets: $15,144,513,629
Liabilities: $12,860,479,754
Net Worth: $2,284,033,876
Earnings: ($342,391,552)
Emp.: 30,798
Fiscal Year-end: 12/31/2021
Holding Company; Civil & Industrial Construction Services
N.A.I.C.S.: 551112
Pietro Salini (CEO)

Subsidiary (Domestic):

Astaldi S.p.A. (2)
Via Giulio Vincenzo Bona 65, 00156, Rome, Italy
Tel.: (39) 06417661
Web Site: http://www.astaldi.com
Rev.: $1,289,137,024
Assets: $3,510,655,372
Liabilities: $2,255,309,749
Net Worth: $1,255,345,623
Earnings: $2,217,456,845
Emp.: 14,266
Fiscal Year-end: 12/31/2020
Construction, Infrastructure & Engineering Services
N.A.I.C.S.: 237110
Paolo Astaldi (Chm)

Subsidiary (Non-US):

Astaldi Arabia Ltd. (3)
Al Baaz Street, Sulaimaniyah District, Riyadh, 11625, Saudi Arabia
Tel.: (966) 14631199
Sales Range: $25-49.9 Million
Emp.: 50
Construction Engineering Services
N.A.I.C.S.: 237990

Subsidiary (US):

Astaldi Construction Corporation (3)
8220 W State Rd 84 Ste 300, Davie, FL 33324 (66%)
Tel.: (954) 423-8766
Web Site: http://www.astaldiconstruction.com
Sales Range: $50-74.9 Million
Emp.: 200
Highway Street & Bridge Construction
N.A.I.C.S.: 237910
Paolo Astaldi (Pres)

Subsidiary (Domestic):

Co Meri S.p.A (3)
Via Giulio Vincenzo Bona 65, Rome, 00156, Italy (99.99%)
Tel.: (39) 06417661
Heavy & Civil Engineering Construction
N.A.I.C.S.: 237990
Stefano Cerri (Mng Dir)

Subsidiary (Non-US):

Consorcio Rio Pallca (3)
Cal Chinchon Nro 1018 Int 2, San Isidro, Lima, Peru
Tel.: (51) 1 206 4300
Construction Engineering Services
N.A.I.C.S.: 237990

Constructora Astaldi Fe Grande Cachapoal Limitada (3)
Avenida Apoquindo 3846 piso 11, Santiago, Chile
Tel.: (56) 29236000
Hydroelectric Plant Construction Services
N.A.I.C.S.: 237990

AND PRIVATE COMPANIES

Subsidiary (Domestic):

Cospe Srl (3)
Via Madonnina 7, 43044, Collecchio, Italy **(100%)**
Tel.: (39) 0521302730
Excavation Contractor
N.A.I.C.S.: 238910

Garbi Linea 5 S.c.a.r.l. (3)
Via Racconigi Snc, Milan, 20162, Italy
Tel.: (39) 0291431100
Underground Station Monitoring Services
N.A.I.C.S.: 561621

Infraflegrea Progetto S.p.A. (3)
Via Domenico Giustino 3/c, Naples, 80125, Italy
Tel.: (39) 0815709222
Construction Engineering Services
N.A.I.C.S.: 541330

Ospedale Del Mare Societa Consortile A.R.L. (3)
Via Giulio Vincenzo Bona 65, Rome, 00156, Italy **(60%)**
Tel.: (39) 06417661
Nonresidential Property Managers
N.A.I.C.S.: 531312
Stefano Cerri (CEO)

Partenopea Finanza Di Progetto Spa (3)
Via Galileo Ferraris 113B, 80142, Naples, Italy **(59.99%)**
Tel.: (39) 0816585106
Sales Range: $25-49.9 Million
Emp.: 100
Engineering Services
N.A.I.C.S.: 541330

Subsidiary (Non-US):

Portovesme S.r.l. (3)
(80%)
Tel.: (39) 078151131
Web Site: https://www.portovesme.it
Primary Smelting & Refining Nonferrous Metal
N.A.I.C.S.: 331410

Romstrade S.r.l. (3)
Str Buzesti Nr 71 Sector 1, Bucharest, Romania
Tel.: (40) 21 317 58 27
Web Site: http://www.romstrade.ro
Construction Engineering Services
N.A.I.C.S.: 237990
Bogdan Trasculescu (Gen Mgr)

S.C. ASTALROM S.A. (3)
Str Varianta Nord Nr 1 judetul Calarasi, 910053, Calarasi, Romania
Tel.: (40) 242332471
Web Site: http://www.astalrom.eu
Sales Range: $75-99.9 Million
Emp.: 500
Construction Machinery Repair & Maintenance Services
N.A.I.C.S.: 811310

Subsidiary (Domestic):

S.P.T. - Societa Passante Torino S.c.r.l. (3)
Via Giulio Vincenzo Bona 65, Rome, 00156, Italy **(74%)**
Tel.: (39) 06417661
Web Site: http://www.astaldi.et
Heavy & Civil Engineering Construction
N.A.I.C.S.: 237990
Stefano Cerri (CEO)

Subsidiary (Non-US):

SCAR S.c.r.l. (3)
rue des Martyrs 23, Herve, 4650, Liege, Belgium **(60%)**
Tel.: (32) 87692040
Web Site: http://www.scar.be
Heavy & Civil Engineering Construction
N.A.I.C.S.: 237990

Subsidiary (Domestic):

Sartori Sud S.r.l. (3)
7 Via Artom Alessandro, 72100, Brindisi, Italy
Tel.: (39) 0831546104
Construction Engineering Services
N.A.I.C.S.: 237990

Scuola Carabinieri S.C.r.l. (3)
Viale Agosto Localita Pavana, Florence, 50127, Italy
Tel.: (39) 06 41 7661
Construction Engineering Services
N.A.I.C.S.: 237990
Luciano de Crecchio (Gen Mgr)

Subsidiary (Non-US):

CSC Impresa Costruzioni S.A. (2)
Via Pioda 5, PO Box 5400, 6901, Lugano, Switzerland
Tel.: (41) 919109090
Web Site: http://www.csc-sa.ch
Infrastructure Engineering & Construction Services
N.A.I.C.S.: 541330
Gian-Luca Lardi (CEO)

Clough Limited (2)
34 Parliament Place, West Perth, Perth, 6000, WA, Australia
Tel.: (61) 892819281
Engineering & Project Delivery Services
N.A.I.C.S.: 541330
Rajiv Ratneser (Exec VP-Bus Dev & Strategy)

Unit (Domestic):

Clough Engineering Limited (3)
Level 12 58 Mounts Bay Road, Perth, 6000, WA, Australia
Tel.: (61) 61892819281
Sales Range: $500-549.9 Million
Emp.: 4,000
Engineeering Services
N.A.I.C.S.: 541330

Subsidiary (Non-US):

Clough Karachi (3)
C145 Block 2 Clifton, 75600, Karachi, Pakistan
Tel.: (92) 215869991
Sales Range: $25-49.9 Million
Emp.: 20
Provider of Engineering Services
N.A.I.C.S.: 541330

Unit (Domestic):

Clough Lucas (3)
Level 6 301 Coronation Dr, Milton, 4064, QLD, Australia
Tel.: (61) 738587544
Sales Range: $25-49.9 Million
Emp.: 10
Provider of Engineering Services
N.A.I.C.S.: 541330

Clough Melbourne (3)
Level 1 83 113 Batman St West, Melbourne, 3003, VIC, Australia
Tel.: (61) 383270500
Sales Range: $25-49.9 Million
Emp.: 10
Provider of Engineering Services
N.A.I.C.S.: 541330

Subsidiary (US):

Clough North America Holding, Inc. (3)
9800 Richmond Ave Ste 600, Houston, TX 77042
Tel.: (713) 267-5500
Construction & Engineering Services
N.A.I.C.S.: 236210
Martin Siddle (Exec VP)

Subsidiary (Domestic):

J. J. White, Inc. (4)
5500 Bingham St, Philadelphia, PA 19120
Tel.: (215) 722-1000
Web Site: https://www.jjwhiteinc.com
Sales Range: $125-149.9 Million
Emp.: 1,500
Plumbing, Heating & Air-Conditioning Contracting Services
N.A.I.C.S.: 238220
Torino Victor (Project Mgr)

Unit (Domestic):

Clough Offshore (3)
Level 12 Aulliuvion Bld 58 Mount Bay Rd, Perth, 6000, WA, Australia
Tel.: (61) 892819481

Sales Range: $75-99.9 Million
Emp.: 500
Provider of Engineering Services
N.A.I.C.S.: 541330

Subsidiary (Non-US):

Clough Tanjung Batu (3)
Jalan Jend Sudirman 561, Balikpapan, 76114, Indonesia
Tel.: (62) 5427020384
Provider of Engineering Services
N.A.I.C.S.: 541330

Cuel Ltd. (3)
18 SCB Park Plaza Tower II West 9th Floor Ratchadapisek Road, Chatuchak, Bangkok, 10900, Chonburi, Thailand
Tel.: (66) 2 500 1200
Web Site: https://www.cuel.co.th
Sales Range: $75-99.9 Million
Emp.: 400
Provider of Engineering Services
N.A.I.C.S.: 541330
Pairat Tivakornpannarai (Mng Dir-Acting)

Unit (Domestic):

Landrow Limited (3)
Level 5 220 St Georges Ter, Perth, 6000, WA, Australia
Tel.: (61) 893223687
Sales Range: $25-49.9 Million
Emp.: 14
Provider of Engineering Services
N.A.I.C.S.: 541330

Subsidiary (Non-US):

Construtora Impregilo y Associados S.A.-CIGLA S.A. (2)
Gabriel Monteiro Da Silva 2143, 01441, Sao Paulo, Brazil **(100%)**
Tel.: (55) 1130662907
Sales Range: $25-49.9 Million
Infrastructure Engineering & Construction Services
N.A.I.C.S.: 541330

Subsidiary (Domestic):

Fisia Italimpianti S.p.A. (2)
Via De Marini 1, 16149, Genoa, Italy **(100%)**
Tel.: (39) 0106096000
Web Site: http://www.fisiait.com
Sales Range: $100-124.9 Million
Emp.: 135
Water Treatment Plant Engineering & Construction Services
N.A.I.C.S.: 237990
Silvio Oliva (CEO)

Subsidiary (Non-US):

Grupo ICT II S.a.s. (2)
Km 6 7 Via Bucaramanga-Barrancabermeja Campamento De Isagen, Barrancabermeja, Santander, Colombia **(100%)**
Tel.: (57) 76548260
Infrastructure Engineering & Construction Services
N.A.I.C.S.: 541330

Impregilo Colombia SAS (2)
Carrera 45 122 56 Of 701, Bogota, 001012, Colombia
Tel.: (57) 16202626
Engineeering Services
N.A.I.C.S.: 541330

Impregilo International Infrastructures N.V. (2)
World Trade Center Tower A 12th Floor Strawinskylaan 1205, Amsterdam, 1077 XX, Netherlands **(100%)**
Tel.: (31) 205753410
Web Site: http://www.impregilo.nl
Sales Range: $25-49.9 Million
Emp.: 2
Infrastructure Engineering & Construction Services
N.A.I.C.S.: 541330
Saurabh Adavatkar (Controller-Fin)

Subsidiary (Non-US):

Impregilo New Cross Ltd. (3)
85e Centurion Court Milton Park, Abingdon, OX14 4RY, Oxon, United Kingdom **(100%)**
Tel.: (44) 1235831861

Sales Range: $25-49.9 Million
Infrastructure Engineering & Construction Services
N.A.I.C.S.: 541330
Ian Mullins (Mng Dir)

Subsidiary (US):

Lane Industries Incorporated (2)
90 Fieldstone Ct, Cheshire, CT 06410
Tel.: (203) 235-3351
Web Site: http://www.laneconstruct.com
Sales Range: $1-4.9 Billion
Emp.: 4,600
Holding Company; Heavy Construction Services
N.A.I.C.S.: 551112
Robert E. Alger (Pres & CEO)

Subsidiary (Domestic):

The Lane Construction Corporation (3)
90 Fieldstone Ct, Cheshire, CT 06410
Tel.: (203) 235-3351
Web Site: http://www.laneconstruct.com
Sales Range: $1-4.9 Billion
Emp.: 4,600
Highway & Other Heavy Construction Services Contractor & Asphalt Mfr
N.A.I.C.S.: 237310
Robert E. Alger (Pres & CEO)

Subsidiary (US):

P.G.H., Ltd. (2)
47 Pleasant St, Woodstock, VT 50911
Tel.: (802) 457-1210
Infrastructure Engineering Services
N.A.I.C.S.: 541330
Peter G. Hall (Pres)

S.A. Healy Company (2)
901 N Green Vly Pkwy 3260, Henderson, NV 89074 **(100%)**
Tel.: (702) 754-6400
Web Site: http://www.sahealy.com
Sales Range: $25-49.9 Million
Tunnel & Other Heavy Civil Engineering Construction Services
N.A.I.C.S.: 237990
Fulvio Castaldi (Pres)

Subsidiary (Domestic):

S.G.F.-I.N.C. S.p.A. (2)
Via dei Missaglia 97, 20142, Milan, Italy **(100%)**
Tel.: (39) 02 444 23095
Web Site: http://www.sgf-inc.it
Civil Engineering Construction Services
N.A.I.C.S.: 237990

SALISBURY RESOURCES LIMITED

262-266 Pirie Street, Adelaide, 5000, SA, Australia
Tel.: (61) 8 7324 1193
Web Site: http://www.salisburyresources.com
Copper & Gold Exploration Services
N.A.I.C.S.: 212230
Pierre Andre Van Der Merwe (Sec)

SALIX YATIRIM HOLDING AS

Barbaros Mah Ak Zambak Suk Uphill Court Sit 1A Apt No 3, Istanbul, Turkiye
Tel.: (90) 2166881776
Web Site: http://www.salixinvest.com
SALIX—(IST)
Rev: $885
Assets: $706,015
Liabilities: $163,759
Net Worth: $542,256
Earnings: -$122,119
Fiscal Year-end: 12/31/19
Financial Investment Services
N.A.I.C.S.: 523999
Ismet Yazici (Chm)

SALLING BANK A/S

Frederiksgade 6, Skive, 7800, Denmark
Tel.: (45) 97523366

SALLING BANK A/S

Salling Bank A/S—(Continued)
Web Site: http://www.sallingbank.dk
SALB—(OMX)
Rev.: $28,566,850
Assets: $637,324,376
Liabilities: $556,506,396
Net Worth: $80,817,980
Earnings: $4,779,131
Emp.: 108
Fiscal Year-end: 12/31/19
Banking Services
N.A.I.C.S.: 522110

SALLY TEXTILE MILLS LTD.
2-S Gulberg II, Lahore, Pakistan
Tel.: (92) 4235759002
Web Site: http://sallytextile.com
Year Founded: 1969
SLYT—(LAH)
Rev.: $802,327
Assets: $12,321,237
Liabilities: $13,212,581
Net Worth: ($891,344)
Earnings: ($2,267,280)
Emp.: 8
Fiscal Year-end: 06/30/19
Cotton & Yarn Mfr
N.A.I.C.S.: 313110
Iqbal Salah-ud-Din *(CEO)*

SALMAN NOMAN ENTERPRISES LIMITED
41-L Gulberg III, Lahore, Pakistan
Tel.: (92) 425837280   PK
Web Site: https://www.sntextile.com
Year Founded: 1989
SANE—(KAR)
Assets: $6,256,255
Liabilities: $8,551,724
Net Worth: ($2,295,469)
Earnings: ($231,223)
Emp.: 371
Fiscal Year-end: 06/30/19
Textile Mill Operator
N.A.I.C.S.: 314999
Noman Almas *(CEO)*

SALMAR ASA
Industriveien 51 Kverva, 7266, Froya, Norway
Tel.: (47) 72447900
Web Site: https://www.salmar.no
SALRF—(OTCIQ)
Rev.: $1,862,024,663
Assets: $5,773,227,693
Liabilities: $3,542,046,924
Net Worth: $2,231,180,769
Earnings: $343,193,054
Emp.: 2,266
Fiscal Year-end: 12/31/22
Farmed Salmon Producing Services
N.A.I.C.S.: 112511
Ulrik Steinvik *(CFO)*

Subsidiaries:

Arnarlax Ehf   (1)
Strandgata 1, Bildudalur, 465, Hafnarfjordur, Iceland
Tel.: (354) 4560100
Web Site: https://www.arnarlax.is
Seafood Whslr
N.A.I.C.S.: 424460

NTS ASA   (1)
Fjordgata 8, 7900, Rorvik, Norway   **(92.93%)**
Tel.: (47) 74216300
Web Site: http://www.ntsasa.no
Sales Range: Less than $1 Million
Holding Company
N.A.I.C.S.: 551112
Arne Kiil *(CFO)*

Norway Royal Salmon ASA   (1)
Ferjemannsveien 10, 7014, Trondheim, Norway
Tel.: (47) 73924300
Web Site: http://www.norwayroyalsalmon.com
Rev.: $597,320,590
Assets: $678,518,510
Liabilities: $313,198,060
Net Worth: $365,320,449
Earnings: $8,715,226
Emp.: 217
Fiscal Year-end: 12/31/2020
Salmon Production & Marketing Services
N.A.I.C.S.: 112511
Ola Loe *(CFO)*

Subsidiary (Domestic):

Arctic Offshore Farming AS   (2)
Ferjemannsveien 10, 7042, Trondheim, Norway
Tel.: (47) 73924300
Salmon Production & Marketing Services
N.A.I.C.S.: 112511

NRS Farming AS   (2)
Markveien 38 B, Box 1154, 9504, Alta, Norway
Tel.: (47) 73924300
Salmon Production & Marketing Services
N.A.I.C.S.: 112511

Nor Seafood AS   (2)
PO Box 23, Sentrum, 6001, Alesund, Norway
Tel.: (47) 70104343
Web Site: http://www.nor-seafoods.com
Fish Product Distr
N.A.I.C.S.: 424460
Inge K. R. Hansen *(Mng Dir)*

SalMar Japan KK   (1)
Tel.: (81) 356430016
Web Site: https://www.salmar.jp
Emp.: 6
Seafood Whslr
N.A.I.C.S.: 424460
Shigenori Aoyagi *(CEO)*

SalmoSea AS   (1)
Nordvegen 255, 7900, Rorvik, Norway
Tel.: (47) 74360900
Web Site: https://www.salmosea.no
Emp.: 120
Seafood Mfr
N.A.I.C.S.: 311710

Vikenco AS   (1)
Rindaroyvegen 383, 6480, Aukra, Norway
Tel.: (47) 71171000
Web Site: https://www.vikenco.no
Seafood Whslr
N.A.I.C.S.: 424460
Kristen Heggem *(Sls Mgr-Domestic Market)*

SALMON EVOLUTION ASA
Torget 5, 6440, Elnesvagen, Norway
Tel.: (47) 46860000
Web Site: https://www.salmonevolution.no
Year Founded: 2017
SALME—(OSL)
Rev.: $15,557,362
Assets: $250,284,962
Liabilities: $72,870,127
Net Worth: $177,414,835
Earnings: ($13,465,084)
Emp.: 69
Fiscal Year-end: 12/31/23
Salmon Farming Services
N.A.I.C.S.: 114111

Subsidiaries:

Salmon Evolution Sales AS   (1)
Keiser Wilhelmsgate 22, NO-6003, Alesund, Norway
Tel.: (47) 46860000
Salmon Farming Services
N.A.I.C.S.: 112511

SALOMON A. ANGEL LTD.
KANFEYI NESHARIM 1 KIKAR ENZHELI TD 34243, Jerusalem, 9134102, Israel
Tel.: (972) 26580555
Web Site: http://www.angel.co.il
Year Founded: 1957
ANGL—(TAE)
Rev.: $149,457,934
Assets: $145,210,662
Liabilities: $75,853,570
Net Worth: $69,357,092
Earnings: $821,937
Emp.: 1,720
Fiscal Year-end: 12/31/23
Commercial Bakeries
N.A.I.C.S.: 311812

SALONA COTSPIN LTD.
No 9 Ramalinga Nagar IV Cross Saibaba Colony, Coimbatore, 641011, Tamil Nadu, India
Tel.: (91) 4222454415
Web Site: https://www.salonagroup.com
590056—(BOM)
Rev.: $16,642,585
Assets: $11,371,983
Liabilities: $6,991,921
Net Worth: $4,380,062
Earnings: $160,182
Emp.: 237
Fiscal Year-end: 03/31/20
Yarn Mfr
N.A.I.C.S.: 313110
Shyamlal Agarwala *(Co-Mng Dir)*

SALORA COMPONENTS LIMITED
E-7 Sector-26, Gandhinagar, 382044, Gujarat, India
Tel.: (91) 79 23287098
Sales Range: $25-49.9 Million
Emp.: 4
Consumer Electronics Distr
N.A.I.C.S.: 423620
Niranjan Trivedi *(Gen Mgr)*

SALORA INTERNATIONAL LIMITED
D-13/4 Okhla Industrial Area Phase II, New Delhi, 110 020, India
Tel.: (91) 1204030494
Web Site: https://www.salora.com
500370—(BOM)
Rev.: $13,942,497
Assets: $9,889,503
Liabilities: $2,877,010
Net Worth: $7,012,493
Earnings: ($1,075,403)
Emp.: 39
Fiscal Year-end: 03/31/23
Consumer Electronics Product Mfr
N.A.I.C.S.: 334419
Gopal Sitaram Jiwarajka *(Chm & Mng Dir)*

SALT LAKE POTASH LIMITED
Ground Floor 239 Adelaide Terrace, Perth, 6000, WA, Australia
Tel.: (61) 865595800   AU
Web Site: http://www.so4.com.au
SO4—(AIM)
Rev.: $123,825
Assets: $123,974,390
Liabilities: $78,368,962
Net Worth: $45,605,429
Earnings: ($11,960,227)
Fiscal Year-end: 06/30/20
Potash Mining Services
N.A.I.C.S.: 212390
Ian Middlemas *(Chm)*

SALT MOBILE SA
Rue du Caudray 4, 1020, Renens, Switzerland
Tel.: (41) 21 216 10 10   CH
Web Site: http://www.salt.ch
Year Founded: 1998
Wireless Telecommunication Services
N.A.I.C.S.: 517112
Eric Wolff *(CTO)*

SALT TRADING CORPORATION LIMITED

INTERNATIONAL PUBLIC

PO Box 483, Kathmandu, Nepal
Tel.: (977) 5371014
Web Site: https://www.stcnepal.com
Year Founded: 1963
STC—(NEP)
Rev.: $66,597,381
Assets: $67,430,115
Liabilities: $55,427,465
Net Worth: $12,002,650
Earnings: $407,335
Fiscal Year-end: 06/16/23
Salt Production & Distribution
N.A.I.C.S.: 212390
Laxmi Das Manandhar *(Chm)*

SALTANGEN PROPERTY INVEST AB
c/o Hestia Fastighetsforvaltning AB, Box 239, 721 06, Vasteras, Sweden
Tel.: (46) 8 120 322 00
Web Site: http://www.saltangenpropertyinvest.se
Year Founded: 2014
Rev.: $14,635,343
Assets: $155,792,465
Liabilities: $83,385,738
Net Worth: $72,406,727
Earnings: $11,528,685
Fiscal Year-end: 12/31/18
Real Estate Investment
N.A.I.C.S.: 531390
Mikael Igelstrom *(Chm)*

SALTER BROTHERS EMERGING COMPANIES LIMITED
Level 9 477 Collins Street, Melbourne, 3000, VIC, Australia
Tel.: (61) 392582100   AU
Web Site: https://salterbrothers.com.au
Year Founded: 2020
SB2—(ASX)
Rev.: $1,487,253
Assets: $56,321,966
Liabilities: $176,045
Net Worth: $56,145,922
Earnings: ($1,189,933)
Emp.: 80
Fiscal Year-end: 06/30/23
Asset Management Services
N.A.I.C.S.: 523999
John Vatovec *(Chm)*

Subsidiaries:

Prospa Group Limited   (1)
Level 1 4-16 Yurong Street, Sydney, 2000, NSW, Australia
Tel.: (61) 1300882867
Web Site: https://www.prospa.com
Rev.: $176,162,874
Assets: $586,140,053
Liabilities: $525,528,461
Net Worth: $60,611,593
Earnings: ($29,251,483)
Emp.: 240
Fiscal Year-end: 06/30/2023
Financial Investment Services
N.A.I.C.S.: 523999
Ross Aucutt *(CFO)*

Subsidiary (Non-US):

Prospa NZ Limited   (2)
The Mezzanine Floor 19-21 Como Street Takapuna, Auckland, 0622, New Zealand
Tel.: (64) 800005797
Web Site: https://www.prospa.co.nz
Fund Management Services
N.A.I.C.S.: 525910

SALTIM HERMES SA
str Aristide Demetriade Nr 1, Timis, Timisoara, Romania
Tel.: (40) 256 401 638
Sales Range: Less than $1 Million
Building Construction Services
N.A.I.C.S.: 236220
Alupei Petru *(Pres)*

SALTIRE CAPITAL LTD.

510 West Georgia Street Suite 1800, Vancouver, V6B 0M3, BC, Canada
Tel.: (630) 824-8199 BC
Web Site: https://saltirecapitalltd.com
Year Founded: 2021
FGAA.V—(TSX)
Investment Services
N.A.I.C.S.: 523999
Hassan R. Baqar *(CFO)*

Subsidiaries:

Strong/MDI Screen Systems, Inc. (1)
1440 Raoul-Charrette, Joliette, J6E 8S7, QC, Canada
Tel.: (450) 755-3795
Web Site: http://www.strongmdi.com
Emp.: 100
Projection Screen Mfr
N.A.I.C.S.: 326199
Ray F. Boegner *(Pres)*

SALTLUX INC.
9F Hyanggun Tower 123 Olympic-ro 35-gil, Songpa-gu, Seoul, 05510, Korea (South)
Tel.: (82) 221931600
Web Site: https://www.saltlux.com
Year Founded: 1979
304100—(KRS)
Rev.: $23,250,502
Assets: $60,366,371
Liabilities: $25,906,537
Net Worth: $34,459,834
Earnings: ($7,181,984)
Emp.: 165
Fiscal Year-end: 12/31/22
Software Development Services
N.A.I.C.S.: 541511
Tony Lee *(CEO)*

SALTS HEALTHCARE LTD.
Richard Street Aston, Birmingham, B7 4AA, United Kingdom
Tel.: (44) 121 333 2000
Web Site: http://www.salts.co.uk
Year Founded: 1700
Sales Range: $75-99.9 Million
Emp.: 416
Pharmaceuticals Product Mfr
N.A.I.C.S.: 325412

SALTUS PARTNERS LLP
Solent Business Park 4500 Pkwy, Whiteley, PO15 7AZ, Fareham, United Kingdom - England
Tel.: (44) 02074087778
Web Site: https://www.saltus.co.uk
Investment Management Service
N.A.I.C.S.: 551112

Subsidiaries:

Tavistock Partners Limited (1)
Market Place 1 The Cornerstone, Kegworth, Derby, DE74 2EE, United Kingdom
Tel.: (44) 1509674335
Web Site: https://www.tavistockpartners.com
Financial Planning Services
N.A.I.C.S.: 523940

SALTX TECHNOLOGY HOLDING AB
Vastertorpsvagen 135, 129 44, Hagersten, Sweden
Tel.: (46) 87940370
Web Site: https://saltxtechnology.com
Year Founded: 2001
SALT.B—(OMX)
Rev.: $10,987
Assets: $16,556,490
Liabilities: $4,906,395
Net Worth: $11,650,094
Earnings: ($4,416,854)
Emp.: 13
Fiscal Year-end: 12/31/20
Solar-Driven Heating & Cooling Technology
N.A.I.C.S.: 221114

Goran Bolin *(Founder)*

SALUNGANO GROUP
First Floor Building 10 Woodmead Business Park, 142 Western Service Road Sandton, Woodmead, 2191, South Africa
Tel.: (27) 110498611 ZA
Web Site: http://www.wescoal.com
Year Founded: 1996
WSL—(JSE)
Rev.: $350,625,919
Assets: $302,328,153
Liabilities: $246,906,835
Net Worth: $55,421,319
Earnings: ($2,536,177)
Emp.: 263
Fiscal Year-end: 03/31/22
Coal Mining Services
N.A.I.C.S.: 212114
Izak Van Der Walt *(CFO)*

Subsidiaries:

Chandler Coal (Pty) Ltd (1)
228 Voortrekker Road, Noordheuwel, Krugersdorp, 1740, South Africa
Tel.: (27) 11 954 2721
Coal Mining & Distr
N.A.I.C.S.: 213113

Keaton Energy Holdings Limited (1)
Ground Floor Eland House The Braes 3 Eaton Road, Bryanston, 2191, South Africa **(100%)**
Tel.: (27) 113171700
Web Site: http://www.wescoal.com
Holding Company; Coal Exploration & Mining
N.A.I.C.S.: 551112

Wescoal Mining (Pty) Ltd (1)
228 Voortrekker Road, Krugersdorp, 1739, Gauteng, South Africa
Tel.: (27) 119542721
Coal Mining Services
N.A.I.C.S.: 213113

SALUS LJUBLJANA D.D.
Litostrojska cesta 46 A, 1000, Ljubljana, Slovenia
Tel.: (386) 15899100
Web Site: https://www.salus.eu
Year Founded: 1969
SALR—(LJU)
Rev.: $661,703,279
Assets: $238,103,543
Liabilities: $150,694,337
Net Worth: $87,409,206
Earnings: $11,480,296
Emp.: 440
Fiscal Year-end: 12/31/23
Pharmaceuticals Distr
N.A.I.C.S.: 424210
Ziga Hieng *(Pres & Member-Mgmt Bd)*

Subsidiaries:

CARSO pharm d.o.o. (1)
Litostrojska Cesta 46a, 1000, Ljubljana, Slovenia
Tel.: (386) 15899184
Web Site: http://www.carsopharm.com
Medicinal Product Mfr
N.A.I.C.S.: 339112
Gregor Zgur *(Gen Mgr)*

SALUTICA ALLIED SOLUTIONS SDN. BHD.
3 Jalan Zarib 6 Kawasan Perindustrian Zarib, Lahat Ipoh, 31500, Perak, Malaysia
Tel.: (60) 5 320 6800 MY
Web Site: http://www.salutica.com
Sales Range: $200-249.9 Million
Emp.: 800
Electronics Mfr
N.A.I.C.S.: 334419
Chan Wai Khien *(Engr-R&D)*

SALVARX GROUP PLC
Commerce House 1 Bowring Road, Ramsey, IM8 2LQ, Isle of Man
Tel.: (44) 1624811611
Web Site: http://www.salvarx.io
Year Founded: 2007
Assets: $17,083,547
Liabilities: $18,899,515
Net Worth: ($1,815,968)
Earnings: ($4,271,521)
Emp.: 6
Fiscal Year-end: 12/31/18
Investment Services
N.A.I.C.S.: 523999
Gregory H. Bailey *(Executives, Bd of Dirs)*

Subsidiaries:

Lane Energy Poland Sp. z.o.o (1)
Chmielna 13/A, Warsaw, 00-021, Poland
Tel.: (48) 225059177
Oil & Gas Exploration Services
N.A.I.C.S.: 213112

SALVATORE FERRAGAMO SPA
Palazzo Spini Feroni Via dei Tornabuoni 2, 50123, Florence, Italy
Tel.: (39) 0553561
Web Site: https://group.ferragamo.com
Year Founded: 1927
SFER—(ITA)
Rev.: $1,124,852,898
Assets: $2,105,150,546
Liabilities: $1,233,473,531
Net Worth: $871,677,015
Earnings: ($88,059,895)
Emp.: 3,527
Fiscal Year-end: 12/31/20
Footwear, Perfume, Watches, Bags, Eyewear, Clothing & Related Apparel & Accessories
N.A.I.C.S.: 315990
Michele Norsa *(Vice Chm)*

Subsidiaries:

Ferragamo Mexico S. de R.L. de C.V. (1)
Edgar Allan Poe No 119, Colonia Polanco Delegacion Miguel Hidalgo, 11560, Mexico, Mexico
Tel.: (52) 8000622112
Web Site: https://www.ferragamo.com
Luxury Goods Distr
N.A.I.C.S.: 423990

Ferragamo USA Inc. (1)
663 5th Ave, New York, NY 10022
Tel.: (212) 759-3822
Web Site: http://www.ferragamo.com
Emp.: 200
Distr of Footwear, Perfume & Eyewear
N.A.I.C.S.: 424340

Subsidiary (Domestic):

Ferragamo Inc. (2)
663 5th Ave, New York, NY 10022-5309
Tel.: (212) 838-9470
Web Site: http://www.ferragamo.com
Sales Range: $1-9.9 Million
Emp.: 150
Designer Shoes, Handbags & Other Small Leather Products
N.A.I.C.S.: 424340

S-Fer International Inc. (2)
655 5th Ave & 52nd St, New York, NY 10022-5309
Tel.: (212) 759-3822
Web Site: http://www.ferragamo.com
Sales Range: $25-49.9 Million
Emp.: 35
Retailer of Shoes
N.A.I.C.S.: 458210

SALVO CHEMICAL INDUSTRY LIMITED
Suite No 401 3rd Floor 210-211, Nawabpur Road, Dhaka, 1100, Bangladesh
Tel.: (880) 257163548
Web Site: https://www.salvochemical.com
Year Founded: 2003
SALVOCHEM—(CHT)
Rev.: $14,410,397
Assets: $25,283,901
Liabilities: $14,648,126
Net Worth: $10,635,775
Earnings: $1,447,708
Emp.: 242
Fiscal Year-end: 06/30/22
Chemical Products Mfr
N.A.I.C.S.: 325998
Khondoker Afia Sultana *(Mng Dir)*

SALZBURG SCHOKOLADE- UND SUSSWARENFABRIK GES.M.B.H. & CO. KG
Haupstrasse 14, Grodig, 5082, Austria
Tel.: (43) 624689110
Web Site: http://www.schoko.at
Sales Range: $25-49.9 Million
Emp.: 2,000
Candy Mfr & Distr
N.A.I.C.S.: 311352
Ricardo Cisneros *(Mgr)*

SALZER ELECTRONICS LIMITED
Samichettipalayam, Coimbatore, 641 047, Tamil Nadu, India
Tel.: (91) 4224233600
Web Site: https://www.salzergroup.net
Year Founded: 1985
SALZERELEC—(NSE)
Rev.: $85,713,059
Assets: $93,490,297
Liabilities: $47,561,214
Net Worth: $45,929,083
Earnings: $2,918,234
Emp.: 568
Fiscal Year-end: 03/31/21
Electronic Switches & Connector Mfr
N.A.I.C.S.: 334419
Doraiswamy Rangaswamy *(Co-Mng Dir)*

Subsidiaries:

Kaycee Industries Limited (1)
Old Kamani Chambers 32 Ramjibhai Kamani Marg, Ballard Estate, Mumbai, 400 001, India **(76.92%)**
Tel.: (91) 2222613521
Web Site: https://www.kayceeindustries.com
Rev.: $3,148,464
Assets: $2,824,476
Liabilities: $797,665
Net Worth: $2,026,811
Earnings: $115,760
Emp.: 74
Fiscal Year-end: 03/31/2021
Electrical Component Mfr
N.A.I.C.S.: 335999
Raju R. Grover *(Co-Founder)*

SALZGITTER AG
Eisenhuttenstrasse 99, 38239, Salzgitter, Germany
Tel.: (49) 53412101
Web Site: http://www.salzgitter-ag.de
Year Founded: 1858
SZG—(MUN)
Rev.: $11,911,309,235
Assets: $11,592,842,740
Liabilities: $6,264,572,637
Net Worth: $5,328,270,103
Earnings: $220,884,387
Emp.: 22,977
Fiscal Year-end: 12/31/23
Steel & Steel Products Mfr
N.A.I.C.S.: 331513
Hans-Jurgen Urban *(Vice Chm-Supervisory Bd)*

SALZGITTER AG

Salzgitter AG—(Continued)

Subsidiaries:

BSH Braunschweiger Schrotthandel GmbH (1)
Hafenstrasse 35, 38112, Braunschweig, Germany
Tel.: (49) 531313001
Web Site: https://www.braunschweiger-schrotthandel.de
Sales Range: $50-74.9 Million
Emp.: 7
Seal Products Distr
N.A.I.C.S.: 423510

Beck & Co. Industriebedarf GmbH & Co. KG (1)
Friedrich-Ebert-Str 9 - 11, 41352, Korschenbroich, Germany
Tel.: (49) 2166 9860 0
Web Site: http://shop.beckco-werkzeuge.de
Hardware Tool Distr
N.A.I.C.S.: 423710
Gunter Thot (Mng Dir)

Berg Steel Pipe Corporation (1)
5315 W 19th St, Panama City, FL 32401
Tel.: (850) 769-2273
Web Site: https://www.bergpipe.com
Sales Range: $50-74.9 Million
Emp.: 175
Industrial Pipe Mfr
N.A.I.C.S.: 332996

Borusan Mannesmann Boru Yatirim Holding A.S. (1)
Meclis-i Mebusan Caddesi 35, 34427, Istanbul, Turkiye
Tel.: (90) 2123935800
Steel Mfrs
N.A.I.C.S.: 331513

Corpoplast Beverage Equipment (Suzhou) Co., Ltd. (1)
Factory 2B No 28 Heshun Road Industrial Park, Suzhou, 215000, Jiangsu, China
Tel.: (86) 51269170900
Web Site: http://www.cbechina.cn
Beverage Equipment Mfr
N.A.I.C.S.: 333241

DESMA Rubber Injection Machinery (Wuxi) Co. Ltd. (1)
Xihong Rd 15, Wuxi, 214028, China
Tel.: (86) 51085361118
Steel Mfrs
N.A.I.C.S.: 331513
Rock Li (Mgr-Ops)

DESMA Schuhmaschinen GmbH (1)
Desmastrasse 1, 28832, Achim, Germany
Tel.: (49) 42029900
Web Site: https://www.desma.de
Automotive Mfr & Distr
N.A.I.C.S.: 336211

DESMA USA, Inc. (1)
2195 Arbor Tech Dr, Hebron, KY 41048
Tel.: (859) 525-6610
Web Site: https://www.desma-usa.com
Sales Range: $25-49.9 Million
Emp.: 30
Rubber Injection Molding Machinery Mfr
N.A.I.C.S.: 333248
L. Scott Early (Pres & CEO)

DEUMU Deutsche Erz und Metall Union GmbH (1)
Gerhard Lucas Meyer Strase 3 5, 31226, Peine, Germany (99.8%)
Tel.: (49) 51719107
Web Site: https://www.deumu.de
Emp.: 300
Mfr of Scrap & Non-Ferrous Metals
N.A.I.C.S.: 331529
Sandrina Sieverdingbeck (Mng Dir)

EUROPIPE 1. Verwaltungsgesellschaft mbH (1)
Pilgerstr 2, Mulheim an der Ruhr, 45473, Germany
Tel.: (49) 2089760
Sales Range: $200-249.9 Million
Emp.: 700
Steel Pole Mfr
N.A.I.C.S.: 331210
Michael Draef (Gen Mgr)

Europipe France S.A. (1)
Route de Comte Jean, 59760, Grande-Synthe, France
Tel.: (33) 328226000
Steel Mfrs
N.A.I.C.S.: 331513

Exabyters Betriebsges mbH (1)
Ringstrasse 13, 29525, Uelzen, Germany
Tel.: (49) 581973950
Web Site: http://www.exabyters.de
Networking & IT System Services
N.A.I.C.S.: 541511

GESIS Gesellschaft fur Informationssysteme mbH (1)
Eisenhuttenstrasse 99, 38239, Salzgitter, Germany
Tel.: (49) 5341212371
Web Site: http://www.gesis.de
Information Technology Consulting Services
N.A.I.C.S.: 541512

Gewerbepark Am Borsigturm GmbH (1)
Am Borsigturm 40, 13507, Berlin, Germany
Tel.: (49) 3043033519
Web Site: http://www.phoenix-gruenderzentrum.de
Emp.: 1
Real Estate Manangment Services
N.A.I.C.S.: 531390

Gluckauf Immobilien GmbH (GIG) (1)
Am Sackpfeifenberg 22, 31226, Peine, Germany
Tel.: (49) 5171919342
Web Site: https://www.gig-peine.de
Real Estate Manangment Services
N.A.I.C.S.: 531390
Christian Heinrich (Mng Dir)

HSP Hoesch Spundwand und Profil GmbH (1)
Alte Radstrasse 27, 44147, Dortmund, Germany
Tel.: (49) 231 185 60
Web Site: http://www.spundwand.de
Emp.: 45
Steel Products Mfr
N.A.I.C.S.: 331110
Mike J. Schrader (Mgr-Sls)

Hansaport Hafenbetriebsgesellschaft mbH (1)
Am Sandauhafen 20, 21129, Hamburg, Germany
Tel.: (49) 40740030
Web Site: https://www.hansaport.de
Sales Range: $25-49.9 Million
Emp.: 100
Marine Freight Forwarding Services
N.A.I.C.S.: 483111

Hildesheimer Stahlhandel GmbH & Co. KG (1)
Daimlerring 7, Hausanschrift, 31135, Hildesheim, Germany
Tel.: (49) 53412101
Web Site: http://www.hildesheimer-stahlhandel.de
Emp.: 35
Steel Service Centers & Distr
N.A.I.C.S.: 423510
Aidan Candon (Gen Mgr)

Hovelmann & Lueg GmbH (1)
Emil-Rohrmann-Str 22, 58239, Schwerte, Germany
Tel.: (49) 23049440
Web Site: http://www.hl-stahlservice.de
Sales Range: $50-74.9 Million
Emp.: 200
Steel Products Mfr
N.A.I.C.S.: 331110
Gerhard Erdmann (Mng Dir)

KHS AG (Thailand) Ltd. (1)
Sukhumvit 33 Road Klongton-Nua Wattana No 591, 10110, Bangkok, Thailand
Tel.: (66) 65609313
Steel Mfrs
N.A.I.C.S.: 331513
P. Taweesak (Mgr-Sls)

KHS Andes S.A.S. (1)
Calle 93 No 16-46 Oficina 301, 110111, Bogota, Colombia
Tel.: (57) 17423272
Steel Mfrs

N.A.I.C.S.: 331513
Ralf Schaefer (Gen Mgr)

KHS Corpoplast North America Inc. (1)
27 Minneakoning Rd 102, Flemington, NJ 08822-5761
Tel.: (908) 253-9600
Stretch Blow Molding Machinery Mfr
N.A.I.C.S.: 333248

KHS Corpoplast Trading (Shanghai) Co., Ltd. (1)
Rm 1608 Changchun Yuntong Building No 818 Nanjing W Rd, Shanghai, 200040, China
Tel.: (86) 2152286609
Sales Range: $25-49.9 Million
Emp.: 35
Industrial Machinery Distr
N.A.I.C.S.: 423830
Geoffrey Chan (Gen Mgr)

KHS Corpoplast Verwaltungsgesellschaft mbH (1)
Meiendorfer Str 203, Hamburg, 22145, Germany
Tel.: (49) 40679070
Sales Range: $150-199.9 Million
Emp.: 40
Seal Products Distr
N.A.I.C.S.: 423510

KHS East Africa Ltd. (1)
Off Ngong Road, PO Box 1850-00502, Karen, 00100, Nairobi, Kenya
Tel.: (254) 733611253
Steel Mfrs
N.A.I.C.S.: 331513

KHS France S.a.r.l. (1)
Boulevard du Mont d Est 19, 93160, Noisy-le-Grand, France
Tel.: (33) 4953412101
Steel Mfrs
N.A.I.C.S.: 331513

KHS Korea Co. Ltd. (1)
Dongcheon Bldg 2F 267-2 Nonhyun-Dong, Gangnam-Ku, 135-833, Seoul, Korea (South)
Tel.: (82) 7082770101
Steel Mfrs
N.A.I.C.S.: 331513

KHS Machine & Equipment (Qinhuangdao) Co., Ltd. (1)
No 20 Liupanshan Rd Economic Technology Development Zone, Qinhuangdao, 066004, China
Tel.: (86) 3358561918
Web Site: http://www.khs.com
Emp.: 30
Industrial Machinery Mfr
N.A.I.C.S.: 333248

KHS Machinery Pvt. Ltd. (1)
Hirapur Cross Road, Hirapur, 382435, Ahmedabad, India
Tel.: (91) 7966100000
Steel Mfrs
N.A.I.C.S.: 331513
Pramod Kasarekar (Mgr-IT & Sys)

KHS Machines Nigeria Limited (1)
50 Oduduwa Crescent, Lagos, Nigeria
Tel.: (234) 16312463
Steel Mfrs
N.A.I.C.S.: 331513

KHS Makine Sanayi Ve Ticaret Limited Sirketi (1)
Barbaros Bulvari Guzel Konutlar 58, 34349, Istanbul, Turkiye
Tel.: (90) 2123472460
Steel Mfrs
N.A.I.C.S.: 331513

KHS Manufacturing (South Africa) (Pty.) Ltd. (1)
Archimedes Street 6, 2148, Kramerville, South Africa
Tel.: (27) 713814225
Web Site: http://www.khs.com
Emp.: 36
Industrial Machinery Mfr
N.A.I.C.S.: 333248

KHS Myanmar Company Limited (1)
No 17 Kabar Aye Pagoda Road, Yankin

INTERNATIONAL PUBLIC

Township, 11181, Yangon, Myanmar
Tel.: (95) 65609313
Steel Mfrs
N.A.I.C.S.: 331513

KHS Nordic ApS (1)
Egeparken Herstedostervej 27-29 D2, 2620, Albertslund, Denmark
Tel.: (45) 43459477
Steel Mfrs
N.A.I.C.S.: 331513

KHS Panamericana SpA (1)
Panamericana Norte 6199 Oficina 5021, Conchali, 8550001, Santiago, Chile
Tel.: (56) 974987907
Steel Mfrs
N.A.I.C.S.: 331513

KHS Plasmax GmbH (1)
Meiendorfer Str 203, Hamburg, 22145, Germany
Tel.: (49) 40 67 907 0
Web Site: http://www.khsplasmax.com
Sales Range: $125-149.9 Million
Emp.: 400
Plastic Bottle Barrier Coating Mfr
N.A.I.C.S.: 325510
Bernd-Thomas Kempa (Co-Mng Dir)

KHS Polska Sp. z o.o. (1)
ul Wisniowa 40 M 1, 02-520, Warsaw, Poland
Tel.: (48) 74957838100
Steel Mfrs
N.A.I.C.S.: 331513

KHS Rus OOO (1)
Ulitsa Ivana Franko 8, 121108, Moscow, Russia
Tel.: (7) 4957838100
Steel Mfrs
N.A.I.C.S.: 331513

KHS Schweiz GmbH (1)
Vordere Gasse 54, Wolfwil, 4628, Solothurn, Switzerland
Tel.: (41) 629262313
Steel Mfrs
N.A.I.C.S.: 331513

KHS Ukraine OOO (1)
Kurenivska Lane 12, 4073, Kiev, Ukraine
Tel.: (380) 445938616
Steel Mfrs
N.A.I.C.S.: 331513

Kisters Limited (1)
Unit 6 Highlands Road Monkspath Business Park, Solihull, B90 4NY, West Midlands, United Kingdom
Tel.: (44) 121 7136900
Web Site: http://www.khs.com
Sales Range: $25-49.9 Million
Emp.: 4
Industrial Machinery Mfr
N.A.I.C.S.: 333248

Klockner Holstein Seitz S.A. (1)
Carretera Rubi 88 - Plt 1, Sant Cugat del Valles, 08174, Spain
Tel.: (34) 935908170
Web Site: http://www.khs.com
Sales Range: $25-49.9 Million
Emp.: 21
Beverage Bottling Machinery Mfr
N.A.I.C.S.: 333993

Klockner PET-Technologie GmbH (1)
Eisenhuttenstr 99, 38239, Salzgitter, Germany
Tel.: (49) 5341 2101
Steel Products Mfr
N.A.I.C.S.: 331110

Subsidiary (Domestic):

KHS Corpoplast GmbH (2)
Meiendorfer Str 203, 22145, Hamburg, Germany
Tel.: (49) 40 67 907 0
Web Site: http://www.khscorpoplast.com
Stretch Blow Molding Machinery Mfr
N.A.I.C.S.: 333248

KHS GmbH (2)
Juchostrasse 20, 44143, Dortmund, Germany
Tel.: (49) 2315690
Web Site: https://www.khs.com

AND PRIVATE COMPANIES — SALZGITTER AG

Planning, Construction & Installation of Filtration & Filling Systems for Beverage Industry
N.A.I.C.S.: 333993
Kai Acker (CEO)

Branch (Domestic):

KHS AG (3)
Meiendorfer Strasse 203, 22145, Hamburg, Germany
Tel.: (49) 40679070
Web Site: http://www.khs.com
Sales Range: $125-149.9 Million
Emp.: 500
Plastics Bottle Mfr
N.A.I.C.S.: 326160

KHS AG (3)
Boschstrasse 1-3, 47533, Kleve, Germany
Tel.: (49) 2821503705
Web Site: http://www.khs.com
Sales Range: $100-124.9 Million
Emp.: 325
Packaging Machinery Mfr
N.A.I.C.S.: 333993

KHS AG (3)
Planiger Strasse 139-147, 55543, Bad Kreuznach, Germany
Tel.: (49) 6718520
Emp.: 1,000
Industrial Machinery Mfr
N.A.I.C.S.: 333248

KHS AG (3)
Industriegebiet Scheid 16, 56651, Niederzissen, Germany
Tel.: (49) 263697460
Packaging Equipment Mfr
N.A.I.C.S.: 333993

KHS AG (3)
Kapellenstrasse 47-49, 65830, Kriftel, Germany
Tel.: (49) 61924910
Sales Range: $50-74.9 Million
Emp.: 150
Industrial Machinery & Equipment Mfr
N.A.I.C.S.: 333248

Subsidiary (Non-US):

KHS Argentina S.A. (3)
Piedras 383 Fl 5, 1070, Buenos Aires, Argentina
Tel.: (54) 1141163428
Web Site: http://www.khs.com
Sales Range: $25-49.9 Million
Emp.: 11
Industrial Machinery Whslr
N.A.I.C.S.: 423830

KHS Asia Pte Ltd (3)
371 Beach Rd 25-08 Keypoint, 199597, Singapore
Tel.: (65) 609313
Web Site: http://www.khs.com
Sales Range: $25-49.9 Million
Emp.: 25
Industrial Machinery Mfr
N.A.I.C.S.: 333993

KHS Austria GmbH (3)
Iz-No-Sud Strasse 3 Objeckt 64, 2355, Wiener Neudorf, Austria
Tel.: (43) 223662510
Web Site: http://www.khs.com
Sales Range: $50-74.9 Million
Emp.: 7
Industrial Machinery Whslr
N.A.I.C.S.: 423830

KHS BTC Nigeria Ltd. (3)
50 Oduduwa Cresent GRA, Lagos, Nigeria
Tel.: (234) 14529022
Sales Range: $25-49.9 Million
Emp.: 30
Industrial Machinery Mfr
N.A.I.C.S.: 333248

KHS Benelux B.V. (3)
Cosunpark 23, 4814 ND, Breda, Netherlands
Tel.: (31) 765723230
Web Site: http://www.khs.com
Sales Range: $25-49.9 Million
Emp.: 8
Industrial Machinery Mfr
N.A.I.C.S.: 333993
Hendrik van der Graaf (CEO)

KHS Industria de Maquinas Ltda. (3)
Av Franz Liszt 80, Pq Novo Mundo, 02151-100, Sao Paulo, Brazil
Tel.: (55) 1129518100
Web Site: http://khs.com
Sales Range: $50-74.9 Million
Emp.: 192
Industrial Machinery Mfr
N.A.I.C.S.: 333248

KHS Italia S.r.l. (3)
Via Degli Orti 24/B, Pero, 20016, Milan, Italy
Tel.: (39) 0233911890
Web Site: http://www.edpmail.it
Sales Range: $50-74.9 Million
Emp.: 2
Industrial Machinery Mfr & Whslr
N.A.I.C.S.: 423830

KHS Japan Corp. (3)
3-9-35 Juhachijo, Yodogawaku, Osaka, 532-0001, Japan
Tel.: (81) 661501001
Web Site: http://www.khsjapan.com
Sales Range: $25-49.9 Million
Emp.: 17
Industrial Machinery Mfr
N.A.I.C.S.: 333248

KHS Mexico S.A. de C.V. (3)
Independencia 511 Barrio el Calvario, Zinacantepec, 51350, Mexico, Mexico
Tel.: (52) 7222762252
Web Site: http://www.khs.com
Sales Range: $75-99.9 Million
Emp.: 170
Industrial Machinery Mfr & Whslr
N.A.I.C.S.: 423830

KHS Pacific Pty. Ltd. (3)
44-46 Catalina Drive, PO Box 378, Tullamarine, 3043, VIC, Australia
Tel.: (61) 393351211
Web Site: http://www.khs.com
Sales Range: $25-49.9 Million
Emp.: 17
Industrial Machinery Whslr
N.A.I.C.S.: 423830

KHS Skandinavien ApS (3)
Naverland 15, 2600, Glostrup, Denmark
Tel.: (45) 43459477
Web Site: http://www.khs.com
Sales Range: $50-74.9 Million
Emp.: 10
Industrial Machinery Whslr
N.A.I.C.S.: 423830

KHS UK Ltd. (3)
Unit 6 Highlands Road, Monkspath Business Park, Shirley, Solihull, B90 4NY, West Midlands, United Kingdom
Tel.: (44) 01217136900
Web Site: http://www.khs.com
Sales Range: $25-49.9 Million
Emp.: 39
Industrial Machinery Mfr & Whslr
N.A.I.C.S.: 423830

Subsidiary (US):

KHS USA, Inc. (3)
5501 N Washington Blvd, Sarasota, FL 34243
Tel.: (941) 359-4000
Web Site: http://www.khs.com
Sales Range: $25-49.9 Million
Emp.: 85
Packaging Machinery Mfr
N.A.I.C.S.: 333993
Michael Sammons (Mgr-Mechanical Engrg)

KHS USA, Inc. (3)
880 Bahcall Ct, Waukesha, WI 53186-1801
Tel.: (262) 797-7200
Web Site: http://www.khs.com
Sales Range: $100-124.9 Million
Emp.: 220
Packaging Machinery Mfr
N.A.I.C.S.: 333993

Subsidiary (Non-US):

KHS s.r.o. (3)
Husova 636/33A, Ceske Budejovice, 370 01, Czech Republic
Tel.: (420) 385515101
Web Site: http://www.khs.com

Sales Range: $25-49.9 Million
Emp.: 10
Industrial Machinery Mfr
N.A.I.C.S.: 333248

Subsidiary (Domestic):

Kloeckner Desma Elastomertechnik GmbH (2)
An der Bara, 78567, Fridingen an der Donau, Germany
Tel.: (49) 7463 834 0
Web Site: http://www.desma.de
Rubber Injection Moulding Machinery Mfr
N.A.I.C.S.: 326299

Subsidiary (Non-US):

DESMA (Guangzhou) Machinery & Engineering Co., Ltd. (3)
311 Tian'an Technology Entrepreneurship Center, Panyu Energy-Saving Technology Park 555 North Panyu Avenue Panyu Dt, Guangzhou, 511400, Guangdong, China
Tel.: (86) 2039906168
Web Site: http://www.desma-china.com
Injection Mold Machinery Mfr
N.A.I.C.S.: 333248

DESMA Slovakia s.r.o. (3)
Sebesanova 262, 017 04, Povazska, Bystrica, Slovakia
Tel.: (421) 915936920
Web Site: http://www.desmaslovakia.sk
Sales Range: $25-49.9 Million
Emp.: 70
Rubber Injection Moulding Machinery
N.A.I.C.S.: 333248

Subsidiary (US):

DESMA-KDE Sales & Service, Inc. (3)
2195 Arbor Tech Dr, Hebron, KY 41048
Tel.: (859) 525-6610
Web Site: https://www.desma.biz
Sales Range: $25-49.9 Million
Emp.: 30
Injection Molding Machine Mfr
N.A.I.C.S.: 333248
Walter Frick (Mgr-Sls)

Subsidiary (Non-US):

Kloeckner Desma Machinery Pvt. Ltd. (3)
Plot No 10 Road No 1 Nr Torrent Power, Sub Station G.I.D.C., 382 430, Ahmedabad, Kathwada, India
Tel.: (91) 7922901782
Web Site: http://www.desmaindia.com
Sales Range: $25-49.9 Million
Emp.: 90
Injection Molding Machine Mfr
N.A.I.C.S.: 333511

Subsidiary (Domestic):

Kloeckner Desma Schuhmaschinen GmbH (2)
Desmastr 1, 28832, Achim, Germany
Tel.: (49) 42029900
Web Site: http://www.desma.de
Shoe Production Machinery Mfr
N.A.I.C.S.: 326299

Kloeckner Hansel Processing GmbH (2)
Lister Damm 19, 30103, Hannover, Germany
Tel.: (49) 5116267212
Web Site: http://www.kloeckner-haensel.com
Processing, Wrapping & Packaging Systems for the Confectionery Industry
N.A.I.C.S.: 333993

Mannesmann Grossrohr GmbH (1)
Gottfried-Linke-Strasse 200, 38239, Salzgitter, Germany
Tel.: (49) 5341216539
Web Site: https://www.mannesmann-grossrohr.com
Steel Tube Mfr
N.A.I.C.S.: 331210

Mannesmann Line Pipe GmbH (1)
In der Steinwiese 31, 57074, Siegen, Germany
Tel.: (49) 2716910

Web Site: https://www.mannesmann-linepipe.com
Steel Tube Mfr
N.A.I.C.S.: 331210

Mannesmann Precision Tubes France SAS (1)
Z I La Sauniere, 89600, Saint Florentin, France
Tel.: (33) 386435050
Welded Precision Steel Tube Mfr
N.A.I.C.S.: 331210

Mannesmann Precision Tubes GmbH (1)
Wiesenstrasse 36, 45473, Mulheim an der Ruhr, Germany
Tel.: (49) 23814200
Web Site: https://www.mannesmann-precision-tubes.com
Welded Precision Steel Tube Mfr
N.A.I.C.S.: 331210
Burkhard Becker (Chm)

Mannesmann Precision Tubes Mexico S.A. de C.V. (1)
Calle A No 239, Parque Industrial El Salto, El Salto, 45680, Jalisco, Mexico
Tel.: (52) 3336881107
Welded Precision Steel Tube Mfr
N.A.I.C.S.: 331210

Mannesmann Precision Tubes Netherlands B.V. (1)
PO Box 27, 5700 AA, Helmond, Netherlands
Tel.: (31) 492596596
Welded Precision Steel Tube Mfr
N.A.I.C.S.: 331210

Mannesmann SOTEP Stainless Tubes SAS (1)
Les Midors, Chouday, 36100, Issoudun, France
Tel.: (33) 254252139
Web Site: http://www.mannesmann-sotep-stainless-tubes.com
Stainless Steel Precision Tube Mfr
N.A.I.C.S.: 331210
Cyril Olivier (Mng Dir)

Mannesmann Stainless Tubes GmbH (1)
Wiesenstrasse 36, 45473, Mulheim an der Ruhr, Germany
Tel.: (49) 20845801
Web Site: https://www.mannesmann-stainless-tubes.com
Steel Tube Mfr
N.A.I.C.S.: 331210

Mannesmannrohren-Werke GmbH (1)
Mannesmannstrasse 11, 01619, Zeithain, Germany
Tel.: (49) 3525790
Web Site: https://www.mrw.de
Welded Precision Steel Tube Mfr
N.A.I.C.S.: 331210

Mulheim Pipecoatings GmbH (1)
Pilgerstr 2, 45473, Mulheim an der Ruhr, Germany
Tel.: (49) 2089762000
Web Site: http://www.muelheim-pipecoatings.com
Industrial Pipe Mfr
N.A.I.C.S.: 332996

NMP Systems GmbH (1)
Boschstrasse 1-3, 47533, Kleve, Germany
Tel.: (49) 2821503705
Steel Mfrs
N.A.I.C.S.: 331513
Kristina Yabar Jilka (Office Mgr)

NorthStar Telecom GmbH (1)
Sudetenstr 10, 38239, Salzgitter, Germany
Tel.: (49) 53 41 21 88 88
Web Site: http://www.northstartelecom.de
Telephone Apparatus Mfr
N.A.I.C.S.: 334210

PT KHS Packaging Machinery Indonesia (1)
The Prime Office Suites 3rd Floor Zone E Jl Yos Sudarso Kav 30, 14360, Jakarta Utara, Indonesia
Tel.: (62) 65609313
Steel Mfrs

SALZGITTER AG

Salzgitter AG—(Continued)
N.A.I.C.S.: 331513

Peiner Trager GmbH (1)
Gerhard-Lucas-Meyer-Str 10, 31226, Peine, Germany
Tel.: (49) 51719101
Web Site: https://www.peiner-traeger.de
Steel Material Mfr
N.A.I.C.S.: 332312
Jan Schmidt (CEO)

RSE Grundbesitz und Beteiligungs-Aktiengesellschaft (1)
Opernplatz 2, 60313, Frankfurt am Main, Germany
Tel.: (49) 69 90026 200
Web Site: http://www.rse-ag.de
Real Estate Manangement Services
N.A.I.C.S.: 531390

RSE Phoenix Holding GmbH (1)
Opernplatz 2, 60313, Frankfurt am Main, Germany
Tel.: (49) 69 90026410
Sales Range: $50-74.9 Million
Emp.: 4
Investment Management Service
N.A.I.C.S.: 523999

RSE Projektentwicklungs-GmbH (1)
Wiesenstrasse 36, 45473, Mulheim an der Ruhr, Germany
Tel.: (49) 69 90026200
Steel Products Mfr
N.A.I.C.S.: 331110

RSE Projektmanagement GmbH (1)
Opernplatz 2, 60313, Frankfurt am Main, Germany
Tel.: (49) 6990026200
Real Estate Manangement Services
N.A.I.C.S.: 531390

RSE Projektmanagement Holding-Verwaltungs- GmbH (1)
Opernplatz 2, Frankfurt am Main, 60313, Germany
Tel.: (49) 69 900260
Investment Management Service
N.A.I.C.S.: 523999

SESTA Stahl GmbH (1)
Schwannstr 12, Dusseldorf, 40476, Germany
Tel.: (49) 2114300255
Steel Product Distr
N.A.I.C.S.: 423510

SIT Salzgitter Information und Telekommunikation GmbH (1)
Sudetenstr 10, Salzgitter, 38239, Germany
Tel.: (49) 5341218455
Sales Range: $25-49.9 Million
Emp.: 8
Information Technology Consulting Services
N.A.I.C.S.: 541512

Salzgitter Automotive Engineering GmbH & Co.KG (1)
Malberger Str 20, 49124, Georgsmarienhutte, Germany
Tel.: (49) 541599050
Web Site: https://www.szae.de
Sales Range: $150-199.9 Million
Emp.: 222
Automobile Parts Distr
N.A.I.C.S.: 423120
Knut Westpfahl (Mng Dir)

Salzgitter Automotive Engineering Immobilien GmbH & Co. KG (1)
Tel.: (49) 541599050
Sales Range: $50-74.9 Million
Emp.: 220
Automobile Parts Mfr
N.A.I.C.S.: 336390

Salzgitter Automotive Engineering Immobilien Verwaltungsgesellschaft mbH (1)
Industriestrasse 28, 49082, Osnabruck, Germany
Tel.: (49) 541 59905 0
Automotive Engineering Services
N.A.I.C.S.: 541330

Salzgitter Automotive Engineering Verwaltungsgesellschaft mbH (1)
Malberger Str 20, 49124, Osnabruck, Germany
Tel.: (49) 541 599050
Web Site: http://www.szae.de
Emp.: 215
Automotive Engineering Services
N.A.I.C.S.: 541330

Salzgitter Business Service GmbH (1)
Eisenhuttenstrasse 99, 38239, Salzgitter, Germany
Tel.: (49) 5341215052
Web Site: https://www.szbs.eu
Personnel & Accounting Services
N.A.I.C.S.: 541219

Salzgitter Digital Solutions GmbH (1)
Eisenhuttenstrasse 99, 38239, Salzgitter, Germany
Tel.: (49) 5341212371
Web Site: https://www.salzgitter-digital-solutions.de
Information Technology Services
N.A.I.C.S.: 541519

Salzgitter Europlatinen Gesellschaft mit beschrankter Haftung (1)
Eisenhuttenstrasse 99, D-38239, Salzgitter, Germany
Tel.: (49) 5341212694
Web Site: https://www.salzgitter-europlatinen.de
Metal Sheet Mfr
N.A.I.C.S.: 332322
Andre Kroff (Mng Dir)

Salzgitter Hydroforming GmbH & Co. KG (1)
Gewerbering 26 a, 08451, Crimmitschau, Germany
Tel.: (49) 376295970
Web Site: https://www.salzgitter-hydroforming.de
Hydraulic Component Distr
N.A.I.C.S.: 423830

Salzgitter Hydroforming Verwaltungs GmbH (1)
Tel.: (49) 376295970
Web Site: http://www.szhs.de
Sales Range: $75-99.9 Million
Emp.: 20
Seal Products Distr
N.A.I.C.S.: 423510

Salzgitter Hydroforming s.r.o. (1)
Prazska 585, 430 01, Chomutov, Czech Republic
Tel.: (420) 474 336367
Web Site: http://www.szhf.cz
Emp.: 7
Hydroformed Component Distr
N.A.I.C.S.: 423120

Salzgitter Magnesium-Technologie GmbH (1)
Eisenhuttenstr 99, Salzgitter, 38239, Germany
Tel.: (49) 5341 2101
Magnesium Products Mfr
N.A.I.C.S.: 331529

Salzgitter Mannesmann (Espana) S.A. (1)
Avd Alberto Alcocer 46-B, 28016, Madrid, Spain
Tel.: (34) 913440469
Steel Product Distr
N.A.I.C.S.: 423510

Salzgitter Mannesmann (France) S.A.R.L. (1)
5-7 Avenue Du General De Gaulle, Saint-Mande, 94160, France
Tel.: (33) 1 48084345
Emp.: 5
Steel Pipe Distr
N.A.I.C.S.: 423510

Salzgitter Mannesmann (Italia) S.R.L. (1)
Via G B Pirelli 11, 20124, Milan, Italy
Tel.: (39) 02 89075212
Emp.: 7
Steel Pipe Distr
N.A.I.C.S.: 423510
Alessandro Moruzzi (Mng Dir)

Salzgitter Mannesmann (Scandinavia) AB (1)
Holmgatan 4, Box 17055, 200 10, Malmo, Sweden
Tel.: (46) 706833657
Web Site: https://www.salzgitter.se
Steel Pipe Mfr & Distr
N.A.I.C.S.: 331210
Roland Tomicic (Mng Dir)

Salzgitter Mannesmann Acelkereskedelmi Kft (1)
Horvat u 14-24, 1027, Budapest, Hungary
Tel.: (36) 13935220
Web Site: https://www.salzgitter.hu
Sales Range: $25-49.9 Million
Emp.: 18
Steel Product Distr
N.A.I.C.S.: 423510
Kovalik Deak Tamas (Mng Dir)

Salzgitter Mannesmann Distributie S.R.L. (1)
Bulevardul Basarabia 256, 30352, Bucharest, Romania
Tel.: (40) 21 255 56 70
Web Site: http://www.salzgitter.ro
Steel Product Distr
N.A.I.C.S.: 423510

Salzgitter Mannesmann Forschung GmbH (1)
Eisenhuttenstrasse 99, 38239, Salzgitter, Germany
Tel.: (49) 5341212222
Web Site: https://www.salzgitter-mannesmann-forschung.de
Steel Mfrs
N.A.I.C.S.: 331513

Salzgitter Mannesmann GmbH (1)
Eisenhuttenstrasse 99, 38239, Salzgitter, Germany
Tel.: (49) 53412101
Web Site: http://www.salzgitter-ag.de
Investment Management Service
N.A.I.C.S.: 523999

Salzgitter Mannesmann Grobblech GmbH (1)
Sandstrasse 140, 45473, Mulheim an der Ruhr, Germany
Tel.: (49) 2084580
Web Site: https://www.smgb.de
Pipe Bend Mfr
N.A.I.C.S.: 332996
Sebastian Bross (Chm)

Salzgitter Mannesmann Grossrohr GmbH (1)
Gottfried-Linke-Strasse 200, 38239, Salzgitter, Germany
Tel.: (49) 5341 21 6539
Web Site: http://www.smgr.com
Emp.: 14
Spiral Welded Pipe Mfr
N.A.I.C.S.: 331221

Salzgitter Mannesmann Handel GmbH (1)
Tel.: (49) 208207720
Web Site: https://www.salzgitter-mannesmann-handel.com
Emp.: 300
Steel Product Distr
N.A.I.C.S.: 423510
Gunnar Groebler (Chm-)

Subsidiary (Non-US):

Salzgitter Mannesmann Stahlhandel GmbH (2)
Tel.: (49) 208207720
Web Site: https://www.salzgitter-mannesmann-stahlhandel.com
Emp.: 853
Steel Product Distr
N.A.I.C.S.: 423510
Jan Nowak (Mng Dir)

Salzgitter Mannesmann International (Asia) Pte.Ltd. (1)
137 Telok Ayer Street 07-06, Singapore, 68602, Singapore
Tel.: (65) 6327 5372
Sales Range: $50-74.9 Million
Emp.: 5
Steel Pipe Distr
N.A.I.C.S.: 423510

Thomas Karras (Mng Dir)

Salzgitter Mannesmann International (HK) Ltd. (1)
Unit 2801 Fook Lee Commercial Centre Town-Place 33 Lockhart Road, Wanchai, China (Hong Kong)
Tel.: (852) 2736 9796
Web Site: http://www.salzgitter-hk.com
Sales Range: $50-74.9 Million
Emp.: 5
Steel Product Distr
N.A.I.C.S.: 423510

Salzgitter Mannesmann International (Mexico) S.A. de C.V. (1)
Santa Margarita No 508 Colonia Insurgentes San Borja, Mexico, 3100, Mexico
Tel.: (52) 55 55598233
Web Site: http://www.salzgitter-mannesmann-international.com
Sales Range: $25-49.9 Million
Emp.: 8
Steel Products Whslr
N.A.I.C.S.: 331110

Salzgitter Mannesmann International GmbH (1)
Tel.: (49) 208207720
Web Site: https://www.salzgitter-mannesmann-international.com
Steel Product Distr
N.A.I.C.S.: 423510
Alexander Soboll (Mng Dir)

Subsidiary (Non-US):

Salzgitter Mannesmann International (Canada) Inc. (2)
1333 West Broadway, Vancouver, V6H 4C1, BC, Canada
Tel.: (604) 736-3713
Web Site: http://www.salzgittertrade.com
Steel Products Import & Distr
N.A.I.C.S.: 423510
Dave Zaruba (Controller)

Subsidiary (US):

Salzgitter Mannesmann International (USA) Inc. (2)
1770 Saint James Pl Ste 500, Houston, TX 77056-3499
Tel.: (713) 386-7900
Web Site: http://www.salzgitter-usa.com
Sales Range: $25-49.9 Million
Emp.: 30
Steel Product Distr
N.A.I.C.S.: 423510

Salzgitter Mannesmann International do Brasil Ltda. (1)
Alameda Grajau 129-Sala 1702 Alphaville Industrial, Barueri, Sao Paulo, 06454-050, Brazil
Tel.: (55) 1123211320
Web Site: http://www.salzgitter-mannesmann.com.br
Steel Distr
N.A.I.C.S.: 423510

Salzgitter Mannesmann Line Pipe GmbH (1)
In Der Steinwiese 31, 57074, Siegen, Germany
Tel.: (49) 271 691 0
Web Site: http://www.smlp.eu
Sales Range: $200-249.9 Million
Emp.: 60
Steel Pole Mfr
N.A.I.C.S.: 331210

Salzgitter Mannesmann Pentasteel International (India) Pvt. Ltd. (1)
205/206 Maker Chamber V 221 Nariman Point, Mumbai, 400021, India
Tel.: (91) 22 6111 9999
Sales Range: $25-49.9 Million
Emp.: 12
Steel Product Distr
N.A.I.C.S.: 423510

Salzgitter Mannesmann Personalservice GmbH (1)
Wiesenstrasse 36, 45473, Mulheim an der Ruhr, Germany
Tel.: (49) 208 458 0
Temporary Staffing Services
N.A.I.C.S.: 561320

AND PRIVATE COMPANIES

Heinz Jorg Fuhrmann *(Gen Mgr)*

Salzgitter Mannesmann Prazisrohr GmbH
Kissinger Weg, Hamm, 59067, Germany
Tel.: (49) 2381 420 0
Web Site: http://www.smp-tubes.com
Sales Range: $200-249.9 Million
Emp.: 850
Precision Steel Tube Mfr
N.A.I.C.S.: 331210

Salzgitter Mannesmann Precision Etirage SAS (1)
Z I La Sauniere, 89600, Saint Florentin, France
Tel.: (33) 3 86 43 50 50
Web Site: http://www.smp-tubes.fr
Rev.: $210,893,844
Emp.: 300
Steel Tube Mfr & Distr
N.A.I.C.S.: 331210

Salzgitter Mannesmann Precision GmbH (1)
Wiesenstrasse 36, Mulheim an der Ruhr, 45473, Germany
Tel.: (49) 208 458 1507
Web Site: http://www.smp-tubes.com
Rev.: $594,625,500
Emp.: 2,500
Precision Steel Tube Mfr
N.A.I.C.S.: 331210
Clemens Stewing *(Chm-Exec Bd)*

Salzgitter Mannesmann Precision S.A. de C.V. (1)
Calle A No 239 Parque Industrial El Salto, El Salto, 45680, Jalisco, Mexico
Tel.: (52) 33 3688 1107
Web Site: http://www.smp-tubes.com.mx
Emp.: 300
Steel Tube Mfr
N.A.I.C.S.: 331210

Salzgitter Mannesmann Rohr Sachsen GmbH (1)
Mannesmannstrasse 11, 1619, Zeithain, Germany
Tel.: (49) 3525792202
Emp.: 45
Steel Tube Mfr
N.A.I.C.S.: 331210
Frank Lippert *(Gen Mgr)*

Salzgitter Mannesmann Seamless Tubes B.V. (1)
Engelseweg 173, 5705 AD, Helmond, Netherlands
Tel.: (31) 492596596
Web Site: http://www.smp-tubes.com
Sales Range: $25-49.9 Million
Emp.: 80
Precision Steel Pipe Mfr
N.A.I.C.S.: 331210
Heinrich Cloeren *(Member-Exec Bd)*

Salzgitter Mannesmann Staalhandel B.V. (1)
Koopmansweg 11, 4906 CP, Oosterhout, Netherlands
Tel.: (31) 162 480500
Emp.: 90
Steel Product Distr
N.A.I.C.S.: 423510
Patrick Guertner *(Gen Mgr)*

Salzgitter Mannesmann Stahlhandel Austria GmbH (1)
Harter Strasse 1a, 8101, Gratkorn, Austria
Tel.: (43) 31660940
Web Site: http://www.salzgitter-mannesmann-austria.at
Steel Products Mfr
N.A.I.C.S.: 332312

Salzgitter Mannesmann Stahlhandel s.r.o. (1)
Na Bojisti 1470/24, 12000, Prague, Czech Republic
Tel.: (420) 224 900 8 25
Steel Products Mfr & Distr
N.A.I.C.S.: 331110

Salzgitter Mannesmann Stahlhandel sp. z.o.o. (1)
Ul Poznanska 41, 62-400, Slupca, Poland
Tel.: (48) 632743826
Web Site: http://www.salzgitter-mannesmann.pl
Steel Product Distr
N.A.I.C.S.: 423510
Cichon Janusz *(Chm)*

Salzgitter Mannesmann Stahlservice GmbH (1)
Werftstrasse 13, 76189, Karlsruhe, Germany
Tel.: (49) 721955780
Web Site: https://www.salzgitter-ssc.de
Emp.: 310
Steel Mfrs
N.A.I.C.S.: 331513
Michael Schafer *(Mng Dir)*

Salzgitter Mannesmann Stainless Tubes Deutschland GmbH (1)
Bahnstrasse 61, 42859, Remscheid, Germany
Tel.: (49) 21918950
Web Site: http://www.salzgitter-ag.de
Emp.: 30
Stainless Steel Tube Mfr
N.A.I.C.S.: 331210

Salzgitter Mannesmann Stainless Tubes France SAS (1)
Route de Semur, 21500, Montbard, France
Tel.: (33) 3 80 89 52 00
Web Site: http://www.smst-tubes.com
Steel Tube Mfr
N.A.I.C.S.: 331210

Salzgitter Mannesmann Stainless Tubes GmbH (1)
Wiesenstrasse 36, 45473, Mulheim an der Ruhr, Germany
Tel.: (49) 208 458 01
Web Site: http://www.smst-tubes.com
Stainless Steel Tube Mfr
N.A.I.C.S.: 331210
Christophe Le Rigoleur *(Mng Dir)*

Subsidiary (US):

Salzgitter Mannesmann Stainless Tubes USA, Inc. (2)
12050 W Little York, Houston, TX 77041
Tel.: (713) 466-7278
Web Site: http://www.smst-tubes.com
Emp.: 120
Seamless Stainless Steel Mfr
N.A.I.C.S.: 331210

Salzgitter Mannesmann Stainless Tubes Italia S.r.l (1)
Via Pio 30, 24062, Costa Volpino, Bergamo, Italy
Tel.: (39) 035 975 744
Stainless Steel Tube Mfr
N.A.I.C.S.: 331210
Gian-Carlo Rizzi *(Gen Mgr)*

Salzgitter Mannesmann Trade (Beijing) Co. Ltd. (1)
Unit No 880A Beijing Sunflower Tower No 37, Chaoyang District, Beijing, 100125, China
Tel.: (86) 10 85275533
Web Site: http://www.salzgitter-mannesmann-international.com
Steel Product Distr
N.A.I.C.S.: 423510

Salzgitter Mannesmann UK Ltd. (1)
Simpson House Windsor Court Clarence Drive, Harrogate, HG1 2PE, North Yorkshire, United Kingdom
Tel.: (44) 1423566660
Web Site: https://www.salzgitter-mannesmann-uk.com
Sales Range: $25-49.9 Million
Emp.: 12
Steel Product Distr
N.A.I.C.S.: 423510
Julian Thompson *(Mng Dir)*

Salzgitter Maschinenbau AG (1)
Windmuhlenbergstrasse 20-22, 38259, Salzgitter, Germany
Tel.: (49) 53213020
Web Site: http://www.smag.de
Holding Company; Mechanical Engineering Services
N.A.I.C.S.: 237990

Subsidiary (Domestic):

Nordmeyer SMAG Drilling Technologies GmbH (2)
Werner Nordmeyer Strasse 3, D 31226, Peine, Germany
Tel.: (49) 51715420
Web Site: http://www.nordmeyer-smag.com
Earth-Digging Equipment, Tools & Accessories Designer & Mfr
N.A.I.C.S.: 333132

Salzgitter Stahl GmbH (1)
Eisenhuttenstr 99, Salzgitter, 38239, Germany
Tel.: (49) 53412101
Rolled Steel Tube Mfr & Distr
N.A.I.C.S.: 331210

Subsidiary (Domestic):

Ilsenburger Grobblech GmbH (2)
Veckenstedter Weg 10, 38871, Ilsenburg, Germany
Tel.: (49) 39452850
Web Site: https://www.ilsenburger-grobblech.de
Emp.: 800
Steel Products Mfr
N.A.I.C.S.: 331110
Robert Kuhn *(Chm)*

Somlo - Metall Kft. (1)
New Atlantis Industrial Park HRSZ 5715/8 Eastern Sector, Ajka, Hungary
Tel.: (36) 6307487944
Web Site: http://www.web.somlometall.hu
Steel Distr
N.A.I.C.S.: 423510

Stahl-Center Baunatal GmbH (1)
Salzgitterstrasse 32, 34225, Baunatal, Germany
Tel.: (49) 5614912041
Steel Service Center & Distr
N.A.I.C.S.: 423510

TELCAT KOMMUNIKATIONSTECHNIK GmbH (1)
Sudetenstrasse 10, 38239, Salzgitter, Germany
Tel.: (49) 5341 21 191 88
Web Site: http://www.telcat.de
Telecommunication Servicesb
N.A.I.C.S.: 517810

TELCAT MULTICOM GmbH (1)
Sudetenstrasse 10, 38239, Salzgitter, Germany
Tel.: (49) 53412119188
Web Site: https://www.telcat.de
Telecommunication Servicesb
N.A.I.C.S.: 517810

TELEFONBAU MARIENFELD GmbH & Co. KG (1)
Im Teelbruch 104, Essen-Kettwig, 45219, Essen, Kettwig, Germany
Tel.: (49) 2054 1216 0
Telephone Apparatus Mfr
N.A.I.C.S.: 334210

UNIVERSAL Aciers Sarl (1)
5-11 Rue Gabriel Peri, 69270, Couzon-au-Mont-d'Or, France
Tel.: (33) 4 78 01 44 73
Web Site: http://www.universal-aciers.fr
Sales Range: $50-74.9 Million
Emp.: 9
Steel Sheet Distr
N.A.I.C.S.: 423510

UNIVERSAL OCEL spol. s.r.o. (1)
Holeckova 3149/25a, Smichov, Prague, 5, Czech Republic
Tel.: (420) 251 001 811
Web Site: http://www.uniocel.cz
Sales Range: $50-74.9 Million
Emp.: 10
Steel Product Distr
N.A.I.C.S.: 423510
Michael Anus *(Gen Mgr)*

UNIVERSAL STEEL AMERICA CHICAGO, Inc. (1)
225 W Burville Rd, Crete, IL 60417
Tel.: (708) 672-9600
Web Site: http://www.universalsteelamerica.com
Sales Range: $25-49.9 Million
Emp.: 50
Steel Products Mfr
N.A.I.C.S.: 331110

UNIVERSAL STEEL AMERICA, Inc. (1)
1230 E Richey Rd, Houston, TX 77073
Tel.: (281) 821-7400
Web Site: https://www.universalsteelamerica.com
Emp.: 120
Steel Processing Services
N.A.I.C.S.: 423510

UNIVERSAL STEEL HOLLAND B.V. (1)
De Wederik 5b, 3355 SK, Papendrecht, Netherlands
Tel.: (31) 786991516
Web Site: http://www.universalsteel.nl
Emp.: 6
Steel Product Distr
N.A.I.C.S.: 423510

UNIVERSAL Stal sp. z.o.o. (1)
Ul Portowa 24-26, 44-102, Gliwice, Poland
Tel.: (48) 323449700
Web Site: https://www.universal-stal.pl
Sales Range: $25-49.9 Million
Emp.: 20
Plate Steel Storage Services
N.A.I.C.S.: 493110
Piotr Zimny *(Gen Mgr)*

Universal Eisen und Stahl GmbH (1)
Duisburger Str 26, 41460, Neuss, Germany
Tel.: (49) 21311850
Web Site: https://www.universal-stahl.com
Steel Plate Mfr
N.A.I.C.S.: 331221
Goetz Richter *(Mng Dir)*

VPS Infrastruktur GmbH (1)
Am Hillenholz 28, 38229, Salzgitter, Germany
Tel.: (49) 5341217231
Web Site: http://www.vps-infrastruktur.de
Railway Infrastructure Management & Construction Services
N.A.I.C.S.: 488210

Verkehrsbetriebe Peine-Salzgitter Gesellschaft mit beschrankter Haftung (1)
Am Hillenholz 28, 38229, Salzgitter, Germany
Tel.: (49) 53412105
Web Site: https://www.vps-bahn.de
Emp.: 680
Railway Logistics & Transportation Services
N.A.I.C.S.: 488210
Michael Kieckbusch *(Chm-)*

WBV Wohnbau Betreuungs & Verwaltungs GmbH (1)
Windmuhlenbergstrasse 9-11, Salzgitter, Germany
Tel.: (49) 5341 3006 0
Emp.: 50
Property Management Services
N.A.I.C.S.: 531311

Winza Pte. Ltd. (1)
5006 Ang Mo Kio Avenue 5 05-01/12 Techplace 2, Singapore, 569873, Singapore
Tel.: (65) 64821755
Biotechnology Research Services
N.A.I.C.S.: 541714

Wohnungsbaugesellschaft mit beschrankter Haftung (1)
Windmuhlenbergstrasse 9-11, 38259, Salzgitter, Germany
Tel.: (49) 534130060
Steel Mfrs
N.A.I.C.S.: 331513

SALZMANN AG

SALZMANN AG
Rorschacherstrasse 304, 9016, Saint Gallen, Switzerland
Tel.: (41) 71 282 11 10
Web Site: http://www.salzmann-group.ch
Holding Company
N.A.I.C.S.: 551112
Daniel Kunzli *(Pres)*

Subsidiaries:

SWISSLASTIC AG (1)
Rorschacher Strasse 304, 9016, Saint Gallen, Switzerland

SALZMANN AG

Salzmann AG—(Continued)
Tel.: (41) 58 258 42 00
Web Site: http://www.swisslastic.ch
Covered Yarn, Compression Hosiery & Pressure Measuring Device Mfr
N.A.I.C.S.: 315120
Danilo Pieri (Mng Dir)

Salzmann MEDICO (1)
Rorschacher Strasse 304, 9016, Saint Gallen, Switzerland
Tel.: (41) 71 282 12 12
Medical Supplies Distr
N.A.I.C.S.: 423450
Markus Zund (Mng Dir)

SAM CHUN DANG PHARM. CO., LTD.
351 Hyoryeong-ro, Seocho-gu, Seoul, 06643, Korea (South)
Tel.: (82) 220461100
Web Site: https://www.scd.co.kr
Year Founded: 1943
000250—(KRS)
Rev.: $136,016,259
Assets: $286,302,635
Liabilities: $97,895,479
Net Worth: $188,407,156
Earnings: $6,774,006
Emp.: 394
Fiscal Year-end: 12/31/22
Pharmaceuticals Product Mfr
N.A.I.C.S.: 325412
In Seok Chun (Pres)

Subsidiaries:

OPTUS Pharmaceutical Co., Ltd. (1)
108 36th floor Yeoui-daero, Yeongdeungpo-gu, Seoul, Korea (South)
Tel.: (82) 221180030
Web Site: https://optuspharm.com
Rev.: $44,990,332
Assets: $104,496,312
Liabilities: $9,029,742
Net Worth: $95,466,570
Earnings: $3,844,196
Emp.: 173
Fiscal Year-end: 12/31/2022
Pharmaceuticals Mfr
N.A.I.C.S.: 325412
Dea-Hoon Yeou (CEO)

SAM ENGINEERING & EQUIPMENT (M) BERHAD
Plot 17 Hilir Sungai Keluang Tiga Bayan Lepas, Free Industrial Zone Phase IV, 11900, Penang, Malaysia
Tel.: (60) 46436789   MY
Web Site: https://www.sam-malaysia.com
Year Founded: 1994
SAM—(KLS)
Rev.: $305,895,873
Assets: $340,240,635
Liabilities: $167,782,646
Net Worth: $172,457,989
Earnings: $18,804,021
Emp.: 1,972
Fiscal Year-end: 03/31/23
Industrial Equipment Mfr & Distr
N.A.I.C.S.: 334511
Jeffrey Wee Keng Goh (CEO)

Subsidiaries:

Avitron Private Limited (1)
51 Corporation Road, Singapore, 649806, Singapore
Tel.: (65) 62682663
Aerospace Equipment Mfr
N.A.I.C.S.: 336413

Meerkat Precision Sdn. Bhd. (1)
Plot 17 Hilir Sungai Keluang Tiga Phase IV, Bayan Lepas Free Industrial Zone, 11900, Penang, Malaysia
Tel.: (60) 46436789
Aerospace Equipment Mfr
N.A.I.C.S.: 336413

SAM Meerkat (M) Sdn. Bhd. (1)
Plot 103 104 Hilir Sungai Keluang Lima, Taman Perindustrian Bayan Lepas 4, 11900, Penang, Malaysia
Tel.: (60) 46429992
Aerospace Equipment Mfr
N.A.I.C.S.: 336413

SAM Tooling Technology Sdn. Bhd. (1)
Plot 77 Lintang Bayan Lepas Phase 4, Bayan Lepas Non-Free Industrial Zone, 11900, Penang, Malaysia
Tel.: (60) 46465654
Aerospace Equipment Mfr
N.A.I.C.S.: 336413

Subsidiary (Non-US):

SAM Precision (Thailand) Limited (2)
40/34 M 5 U Thai U Thai, Rojana Industrial Park, Ayutthaya, 13210, Thailand
Tel.: (66) 35750161
Aerospace Equipment Mfr
N.A.I.C.S.: 336413

SAM HOLDINGS CORPORATION
127 Ung Van Khiem Street Ward 25, Binh Thanh District, Ho Chi Minh City, Vietnam
Tel.: (84) 2835122919
Web Site: https://www.samholdings.com.vn
Year Founded: 1998
SAM—(HOSE)
Rev.: $90,644,779
Assets: $271,585,950
Liabilities: $81,815,949
Net Worth: $189,770,002
Earnings: $1,369,488
Emp.: 668
Fiscal Year-end: 12/31/23
Cable Mfr
N.A.I.C.S.: 335921

Subsidiaries:

SACOM REAL ESTATE CORPORATION (1)
178/6 Nguyen Van Thuong Street, Ward 25 Binh Thanh District, Ho Chi Minh City, Vietnam
Tel.: (84) 2835120002
Web Site: http://www.samland.com.vn
Real Estate Manangement Services
N.A.I.C.S.: 531390

SAM HWA ELECTRIC CO., LTD.
3 Bongmyeong-ro, Heungdeok-gu, Cheongju, 28589, Chungcheongbuk, Korea (South)
Tel.: (82) 432610200
Web Site: https://www.samwha.co.kr
Year Founded: 1973
009470—(KRS)
Rev.: $183,399,467
Assets: $106,701,412
Liabilities: $38,398,256
Net Worth: $68,303,156
Earnings: $8,172,384
Emp.: 512
Fiscal Year-end: 12/31/22
Electronic Components Mfr
N.A.I.C.S.: 334419
Park Jong On (CEO)

SAM HWA ELECTRONICS CO., LTD.
215 Namsa-myeon Gyeonggidong-r, Cheoin-gu, Yongin, Korea (South)
Tel.: (82) 313745501
011230—(KRS)
Rev.: $37,066,210
Assets: $52,725,339
Liabilities: $39,122,735
Net Worth: $13,602,603
Earnings: ($4,649,847)
Emp.: 109
Fiscal Year-end: 12/31/22

Electric Equipment Mfr
N.A.I.C.S.: 334419
Young-Joo Oh (Chm)

SAM INDUSTRIES LIMITED
12/215B, Calicut, Kerala, 453771, Madhya Pradesh, India
Tel.: (91) 4952282323
Web Site: https://samindus.com
Year Founded: 1994
532005—(BOM)
Rev.: $1,424,431
Assets: $6,913,531
Liabilities: $671,768
Net Worth: $6,241,763
Earnings: $680,314
Emp.: 10
Fiscal Year-end: 03/31/21
Food Crops
N.A.I.C.S.: 111419
Ashutosh Ashokkumar Maheshwari (Chm)

SAM JUNG PLUP CO., LTD.
85 Godeok-ro, Godeok-myeon, Pyeongtaek, Gyeonggi-do, Korea (South)
Tel.: (82) 27437071
Web Site: http://www.sjpulp.com
Year Founded: 1974
009770—(KRS)
Rev.: $133,813,958
Assets: $178,453,149
Liabilities: $15,077,332
Net Worth: $163,375,817
Earnings: ($734,080)
Emp.: 229
Fiscal Year-end: 12/31/22
Paper Products Mfr
N.A.I.C.S.: 322120
Seong Oh Jeon (Pres & CEO)

SAM VERTRIEBS GMBH + CO. KG
Horlecke 110, 58706, Menden, Germany
Tel.: (49) 2373909000   De
Web Site: http://www.sam.de
Sales Range: $10-24.9 Million
Bathroom Accessories Mfr
N.A.I.C.S.: 332999
Simone Schulte (Mng Dir)

Subsidiaries:

Loba Trading (Shanghai) Company Limited (1)
Unit A 10th Floor Jiu Shi Fu Xing Mansion No 918 Huai Hai Middle Road, Shanghai, 200020, China
Tel.: (86) 2164382668
Web Site: http://www.loba.de
Floor Finishing Product Mfr
N.A.I.C.S.: 325612

Loba-Wakol Polska Sp. z o.o. (1)
ul Slawecinska 16, Macierzysz, 05-580, Ozarow Mazowiecki, Poland
Tel.: (48) 224362420
Web Site: http://www.loba-wakol.pl
Floor Finishing Product Mfr
N.A.I.C.S.: 325612

sam Schulte GmbH (1)
Postfach 11, 5015, Salzburg, Austria
Tel.: (43) 14024951
Bathroom Accessory Distr
N.A.I.C.S.: 423220

sam Schulte SA (1)
Aeschstrasse 1, 8127, Forch, Switzerland
Tel.: (41) 433661050
Bathroom Accessory Distr
N.A.I.C.S.: 423220

SAM WOO CONSTRUCTION GROUP LIMITED
10/F Energy Plaza 92 Granville Road, Tsim Sha Tsui East, Kowloon, China (Hong Kong)
Tel.: (852) 2 332 0783

Web Site: http://www.samwoo-group.com
3822—(HKG)
Rev.: $46,757,056
Assets: $103,726,490
Liabilities: $35,096,361
Net Worth: $68,630,129
Earnings: ($12,987,899)
Emp.: 246
Fiscal Year-end: 03/31/22
Foundation Construction Services
N.A.I.C.S.: 238110
Chun Ming Lau (Founder & Chm)

SAM WOOD LTD.
No A979/15 1st Adoley Link, PO Box AN 12719, Sahara-Dansoman, Accra, Ghana
Tel.: (233) 30 2305287
Web Site: http://www.samwoode.com
Year Founded: 1984
SWL—(GHA)
Sales Range: Less than $1 Million
Books Publishing Services
N.A.I.C.S.: 513130
Kwesi Sam-Woode (Chm & Mng Dir)

SAM-A ALUMINUM CO., LTD.
92 Pyeongtaekhang-ro, Poseung-eup, Pyeongtaek, Gyeonggi-do, Korea (South)
Tel.: (82) 314676800
Web Site: http://www.sama-al.com
Year Founded: 1969
006110—(KRS)
Rev.: $239,346,863
Assets: $221,013,573
Liabilities: $115,214,410
Net Worth: $105,799,163
Earnings: $13,197,505
Emp.: 348
Fiscal Year-end: 12/31/22
Aluminium Products Mfr
N.A.I.C.S.: 331315
Sang Yong Ha (CEO)

SAM-A PHARM. CO., LTD.
SAMA Building 440 Apgujeong-ro, Gangnam-gu, Seoul, Korea (South)
Tel.: (82) 220567283
Web Site: https://www.samapharm.co.kr
Year Founded: 1945
009300—(KRS)
Rev.: $62,663,547
Assets: $155,852,823
Liabilities: $17,318,867
Net Worth: $138,533,956
Earnings: $9,136,207
Emp.: 295
Fiscal Year-end: 12/31/22
Pharmaceutical Mfr & Whslr
N.A.I.C.S.: 325412
Jong-Sook Hwang (Dir)

SAMA RESOURCES INC.
1320 Graham suite 132, Mount-Royal, H3P 3C8, QC, Canada
Tel.: (514) 747-4653
Web Site: https://www.samaresources.com
Year Founded: 2006
SME—(TSXV)
Rev.: $129,729
Assets: $11,382,884
Liabilities: $548,671
Net Worth: $10,834,213
Earnings: ($4,568,221)
Fiscal Year-end: 12/31/23
Mineral Exploration Services
N.A.I.C.S.: 213114
Marc-Antoine Audet (CEO)

SAMAD MISR
32 El Nour Street from Mossadak Street, Dokki, Giza, Egypt
Tel.: (20) 237491360

Web Site: https://www.egyfert.com
Year Founded: 1997
SMFR.CA—(EGX)
Sales Range: Less than $1 Million
Fertilizer Mfr
N.A.I.C.S.: 325314
Sherif Mamdouh Abdel Baqi *(Chm)*

SAMAGE
Route Nationale 7 Chemin De La Plaine, 83480, Nice, France
Tel.: (33) 562683636
Sales Range: $25-49.9 Million
Emp.: 80
Grocery Stores
N.A.I.C.S.: 445110
Jean-Pierre Baudouin *(Pres)*

SAMAIDEN GROUP BERHAD
No 7 Lorong Teknologi 3/4A Nouvelle Industrial Park 2, Taman Sains Selangor 1 Kota Damansara, 47810, Petaling Jaya, Malaysia
Tel.: (60) 361507941   MY
Web Site:
  https://www.samaiden.com.my
SAMAIDEN—(KLS)
Rev.: $37,097,108
Assets: $42,246,665
Liabilities: $20,975,673
Net Worth: $21,270,992
Earnings: $2,183,140
Emp.: 88
Fiscal Year-end: 06/30/23
Construction Services
N.A.I.C.S.: 236220
Mohd Makhzumi Ghazali *(Project Mgr)*

SAMAMA HOLDING GROUP
PO Box 2781, Riyadh, 11461, Saudi Arabia
Tel.: (966) 014602545
Web Site: http://www.samama.com
Year Founded: 1979
Sales Range: $800-899.9 Million
Emp.: 16,000
Holding Company
N.A.I.C.S.: 551112
Nasser M. Almutawa Alotaibi *(Founder & Chm)*

Subsidiaries:

Samama Contracting Company   (1)
Al Oruba Street, PO Box 286985, Riyadh, 11232, Saudi Arabia
Tel.: (966) 14641626
Web Site: http://www.samama.com
General Contracting Services
N.A.I.C.S.: 238990

Samama Technical Services (Jeddah)   (1)
Baladiya Str, Aziziah District, Jeddah, 21531, Saudi Arabia
Tel.: (966) 26690471
Web Site: http://www.samama.com
Emp.: 50
HVAC & Building Services
N.A.I.C.S.: 561790
Mohammed Sabir *(Mgr-Svcs)*

SAMARA ASSET GROUP PLC
Beatrice 66 & 67 Amery Street, Sliema, SLM 1707, Malta
Tel.: (356) 79985851   Mt
Web Site: https://www.samara-ag.com
Year Founded: 2018
SRAG—(DEU)
Rev.: $95,885
Assets: $190,202,323
Liabilities: $5,580,146
Net Worth: $184,622,177
Earnings: $6,969,303
Fiscal Year-end: 12/31/22
Asset Management Services
N.A.I.C.S.: 523999
Jefim Gewiet *(COO)*

SAMARA CAPITAL MANAGEMENT LTD.
135 13th Floor Free Press House, 215 Nariman Point, Mumbai, 400 021, India
Tel.: (91) 22 2288 6661   In
Web Site:
  http://www.samaracapital.com
Year Founded: 2006
Privater Equity Firm
N.A.I.C.S.: 523999
Sumeet Narang *(Co-Founder & Mng Dir)*

Subsidiaries:

Adcock Ingram Healthcare (Pty) Limited   (1)
1 New Rd Corner and 7th Rd, Halfway House, Midrand, 1685, Gauteng, South Africa
Tel.: (27) 116350000
Pharmaceutical Products Distr
N.A.I.C.S.: 424210

Cogencis Information Services Ltd.   (1)
Ashok Silk Mills Compound 202 LBS Marg Ghatkopar, opp Damodar Park, Mumbai, 400086, India   (77.5%)
Tel.: (91) 22 6619 0000
Web Site: http://www.cogencis.com
Sales Range: $50-74.9 Million
Emp.: 500
Online Financial News Services
N.A.I.C.S.: 513199
Pankaj Aher *(CEO)*

Samara India Advisors Pvt. Ltd.   (1)
131-133 13th Floor Free Press House 215 Nariman Point, Mumbai, 400 021, India
Tel.: (91) 22 61696600
Web Site: http://www.samaracapital.com
Emp.: 20
Financial Investment Services
N.A.I.C.S.: 523940
Vikram Agarwal *(CEO)*

SAMARANG LLP
78 Pall Mall, London, SW1Y 5ES, United Kingdom
Tel.: (44) 20 7129 1248
Web Site:
  http://www.samarangcapital.com
Miscellaneous Financial Investment Activities & Investment Advice
N.A.I.C.S.: 523999
Greg Fisher *(Portfolio Mgr)*

SAMARIUM GROUP CORPORATION
999 Canada Place Suite 536, Vancouver, V6E 3C2, BC, Canada
Tel.: (604) 357-5270   Ca
Web Site:
  http://www.samariumgroup.com
Year Founded: 2011
Energy & Resource Investment Holding Company
N.A.I.C.S.: 551112
Volkmar Guido Hable *(CEO)*

Subsidiaries:

Samarium Group Pte. Ltd.   (1)
One Raffles Quay Level 25 North Tower, Singapore, 048583, Singapore
Tel.: (65) 6622 5657
Web Site: http://www.samariumgroup.com
Energy & Resource Investment Holding Company
N.A.I.C.S.: 551112

SAMARKAND GROUP PLC
Unit 13 Tonbridge Trade Park Ingot Way, Merton, Tonbridge, TN9 1GN, Kent, United Kingdom
Tel.: (44) 2037403933   UK
Web Site:
  https://www.samarkand.global
Year Founded: 2016
SMK—(AQSE)
Rev.: $22,061,127
Assets: $18,831,941
Liabilities: $8,287,031
Net Worth: $10,544,910
Earnings: ($5,832,953)
Emp.: 109
Fiscal Year-end: 03/31/23
Online Shopping Services
N.A.I.C.S.: 425120
David Hampstead *(CEO)*

Subsidiaries:

Babawest Ltd.   (1)
Unit 3 The Sidings Top Station Road, Brackley, NN13 7U, Northamptonshire, United Kingdom
Tel.: (44) 1280707400
Web Site: https://www.babawest.co.uk
Fertility & Antenatal Clinic Services
N.A.I.C.S.: 621410

Samarkand Global (Japan) KK   (1)
S505 2-4-15 Minami-Aoyama, Minato-Ku, Tokyo, 107-0062, Japan
Tel.: (81) 369105116
Web Site:
  https://www.samarkandglobal.co.jp
Logistics & Freight Forwarding Services
N.A.I.C.S.: 541614

Zita West Products Limited   (1)
Unit 13 & 14 Nelson Trading Estate The Path Merton, London, SW19 3BL, United Kingdom
Tel.: (44) 1280707400
Web Site: https://www.zitawest.com
Fertility & Antenatal Clinic Services
N.A.I.C.S.: 621410

SAMART CORPORATION PUBLIC COMPANY LIMITED
99/1 Moo 4 Software Park Building Mezzanine Floor Chaengwattana Rd, Klong Gluar Pak-kred, Nonthaburi, 11120, Thailand
Tel.: (66) 25026000   TH
Web Site:
  https://www.samartcorp.com
Year Founded: 1989
SAMART—(THA)
Rev.: $300,591,537
Assets: $557,825,217
Liabilities: $373,287,494
Net Worth: $184,537,723
Earnings: $18,804,657)
Emp.: 1,969
Fiscal Year-end: 12/31/23
Telecommunication Servicesb
N.A.I.C.S.: 517810
Charoenrath Vilailuck *(Chm-Exec Bd & CEO)*

Subsidiaries:

Cambodia Air Traffic Services Co., Ltd.   (1)
CATS Building opposite Phnom Penh International Airport, Russian Federation Blvd Phum Kbal Domrey Sankat Kakab Khan Posenchey, Phnom Penh, 120912, Cambodia
Tel.: (855) 23866294
Web Site: https://www.cats.com.kh
Air Traffic Control Services
N.A.I.C.S.: 488111

I-Mobile International Co., Ltd.   (1)
99 3 Moo 4 Software Park Building, 33rd Rd Chaengwattana Rd, 11120, Pak Kret, Klong Gluar, Thailand
Tel.: (66) 25026983
Web Site: http://www.i-mobilephone.com
Sales Range: $200-249.9 Million
Emp.: 1,000
Mobile Communications & Interactive Multimedia Services
N.A.I.C.S.: 517112

Inno Hub Co., Ltd.   (1)
99/10 Moo 4 Software Park Building 10th Floor Chaeng Watthana Road, Khlong Kluea Subdistrict, Pak Kret, 11120, Nonthaburi, Thailand
Tel.: (66) 2 685 0000
Web Site: https://www.innohub.me
Software Research & Development Services
N.A.I.C.S.: 541713

One To One Contacts Public Co., Ltd.   (1)
99/19 Moo 4 Software Park 17 Fl Chaengwattana Rd Klong Gluar, Pak-Kred, Nonthaburi, 11120, Thailand   (68.43%)
Tel.: (66) 26850000
Web Site: http://www.onetoonecontacts.com
Rev.: $17,150,428
Assets: $33,470,725
Liabilities: $2,950,841
Net Worth: $30,519,884
Earnings: ($13,058,181)
Emp.: 1,588
Fiscal Year-end: 12/31/2023
Business Management & Telemarketing Solutions
N.A.I.C.S.: 561499
Vichai Srikwan *(Chm)*

One to One (Cambodia) Co., Ltd.   (1)
18-E4 4TH Floor The Icon Professional Building 216 Norodom Blvd Tonle, Bassac Chamkarmorn, Phnom Penh, Cambodia
Tel.: (855) 23932222
Web Site: http://www.otoc.com.kh
Integrated Management Services
N.A.I.C.S.: 541519

Portalnet Co., Ltd.   (1)
99/7 Moo 4 Software Park 29th Floor Chaeng Watthana Road, Klong Kluea Subdistrict Pakkred District, Nonthaburi, 11120, Thailand
Tel.: (66) 25909850
Web Site: https://www.portalnet.co.th
ICT Outsourcing Services
N.A.I.C.S.: 541611

Samart Digital Public Co., Ltd.   (1)
99/2 Moo 4 Software Park 34 Fl Chaengwattana Rd, Klong Gluar Pak-kred, Nonthaburi, 11120, Thailand
Tel.: (66) 25026000
Web Site: https://www.samartdigital.com
Mobile Phone & Accessory Distr
N.A.I.C.S.: 449210

Samart Engineering Co., Ltd.   (1)
59 Moo 2 Phahonyothin Road, Klong Nuang, Khlong Luang, 12120, Pathumthanee, Thailand
Tel.: (66) 25161188
Web Site: http://www.samart-eng.com
Television & Radio Antennas Mfr & Distr
N.A.I.C.S.: 334220

Samart I-Mobile (Malaysia) Sdn Bhd   (1)
Ste 3B-5-5 Plz Sentral Jalan Stesen Sentral 5 Kuala Lumpur Sentral, 50470, Kuala Lumpur, Malaysia
Tel.: (60) 321789888
Web Site: http://www.i-mobilephone.com.my
Sales Range: $25-49.9 Million
Emp.: 22
Mobile Communications & Interactive Multimedia Services
N.A.I.C.S.: 517112

Samart I-Mobile plc   (1)
99/3 Moo 4 Software Park, Chaengwattana Road, Pak Kret, Thailand   (70.2%)
Tel.: (66) 25026000
Web Site: http://www.samart-i-mobilephone.com
Mobile Communications & Interactive Multimedia Services
N.A.I.C.S.: 517112

Subsidiary (Domestic):

Brain Source Co., Ltd.   (2)
99/12 Moo 4 Software Park 24th Floor Chaengwattana Road, Klong Gluar, Pak Kret, 11120, Nonthaburi, Thailand
Tel.: (66) 2502 6000
Telecommunication System Design
N.A.I.C.S.: 541490

Samart Multimedia Co., Ltd.   (2)
99/12 Moo 4 Software Park 24th Fl Chaengwattana Rd, Klong Gluar, Pak Kret, 11120, Nonthaburi, Thailand

SAMART CORPORATION PUBLIC COMPANY LIMITED

Samart Corporation Public Company Limited—(Continued)
Tel.: (66) 2 502 6000
Web Site: http://www.samartmultimedia.com
Sales Range: $50-74.9 Million
Emp.: 200
Mobile Multimedia Services
N.A.I.C.S.: 517112

Subsidiary (Domestic):

I-Sport Co., Ltd. (3)
99/12 Moo 4 Software Park 24th Fl Chaengwattana Rd, Klong Gluar, Pak Kret, 11120, Nonthaburi, Thailand
Tel.: (66) 2 502 6000
Web Site: https://www.isport.co.th
Telecommunication System Designing Services
N.A.I.C.S.: 517810

Samart Infonet Co., Ltd. (1)
99/7 Village No 4 Software Park Building 29th Floor, Chaeng Watthana Road Klong Kluea Subdistrict Pakkred District, Nonthaburi, 11120, Thailand
Tel.: (66) 25026383
Web Site: https://www.samartinfonet.co.th
Internet Providing Services
N.A.I.C.S.: 517121

Samart Raditech Co., Ltd. (1)
99/2 Moo 4 Software Park 34th Fl Chaengwattana, Klong Gluar, Pak Kret, 11120, Nonthaburi, Thailand
Tel.: (66) 25026278
Web Site: http://www.samartraditech.com
Sales Range: $25-49.9 Million
Emp.: 4
Radiation Technology Services
N.A.I.C.S.: 541380

Samart Research & Development Co., Ltd. (1)
99/5 Moo 4 Software Park 31st Floor Chaengwattana Road, Klong Gluar, Pak Kret, 11120, Bangkok, Thailand
Tel.: (66) 29530101
Web Site:
Telecommunication System Design & Installation Services
N.A.I.C.S.: 517810

Samart Telcoms Public Co., Ltd. (1)
99/7 Software Park 29th Fl Moo 4, Pak Kret, 11120, Nonthaburi, Thailand
Tel.: (66) 25026610
Web Site: https://www.samtel.com
Sales Range: $25-49.9 Million
Communication Networks Services
N.A.I.C.S.: 517112
Sumpun Boonyanun (Co-Chm)

Subsidiary (Domestic):

Oasis Consulting Co., Ltd. (2)
Unit 2202 22nd Fl Liberty Square Bldg 287, Silom Rd, Bangrak, 10500, Bangkok, Thailand
Tel.: (66) 2 631 1999
Web Site: https://www.oasis.co.th
Sales Range: $10-24.9 Million
Emp.: 40
Software Development Services
N.A.I.C.S.: 541511

Samart Communication Services Co., Ltd. (2)
36/28-35 Ngamwongwan Road, Ladyao Chutuchak, Bangkok, 10900, Thailand
Tel.: (66) 25891047
Telecommunication Systems Design & Installation Services
N.A.I.C.S.: 561990

Samart Comtech Co., Ltd. (2)
99/2 Moo 4 Software Park 34th Fl Chaengwattana, Klong Gluar, Pak Kret, 11120, Nonthaburi, Thailand
Tel.: (66) 25026000
Telecommunication System Design & Installation Services
N.A.I.C.S.: 561990

Samart Ed Tech Co., Ltd. (2)
99/29 Moo 4 Software Park 6th Fl Chaengwattana Rd, Klong Gluar, Pak Kret, 11120, Nonthaburi, Thailand
Tel.: (66) 2 502 6000
Web Site: http://www.samartsre.com

Sales Range: $10-24.9 Million
Emp.: 40
Software Consulting Services
N.A.I.C.S.: 541519

Smarterware Co., Ltd. (2)
99/25 Moo 4 Software Park 10th Fl Chaengwattana Rd, Klong Gluar, Pak Kret, 11120, Nonthaburi, Thailand
Tel.: (66) 2 502 6296
Web Site: http://www.samartcorp.com
Sales Range: $10-24.9 Million
Software Development Services
N.A.I.C.S.: 541511

Thai Trade Net Co., Ltd. (2)
99/7 Software Park Building 29th Floor Village No 4, Chaeng Watthana Road Khlong Kluea Subdistrict, Pak Kret, 11120, Nonthaburi, Thailand
Tel.: (66) 25026820
Web Site: https://www.ttn.co.th
Networking & Communication Services
N.A.I.C.S.: 517111

Secure Info Co., Ltd. (1)
99/17 Moo 4 Software Park 19th Floor Chaengwatthana Road Klong Gluar, Pak Kret, Pak Kret, 11120, Nonthaburi, Thailand
Tel.: (66) 2 502 6900
Web Site: https://www.secureinfo.co.th
Software Development Services
N.A.I.C.S.: 541511

Suvarnabhumi Environment Care Co., Ltd. (1)
99/2 Moo 4 Software Park 35 Fl Chaengwattana Rd Klong Gluar, Pak-Kred, Nonthaburi, 11120, Thailand
Tel.: (66) 25026626
Telecommunication System Services
N.A.I.C.S.: 517810

Teda Co., Ltd. (1)
99/2 Village No 4 Software Park Building 34th Floor, Chaeng Watthana Road Khlong Kluea Subdistrict Pak Kret District, Nonthaburi, 11120, Thailand
Tel.: (66) 25026000
Web Site: https://www.teda.co.th
Power & Communication Line Services
N.A.I.C.S.: 237130
Thongchai Petchyim (Mng Dir)

Subsidiary (Domestic):

Transec Power Services Co., Ltd. (2)
99/2 Moo 4 Software Park Building 34th Floor Chaengwattana Road, Klong Gleua, Pak Kret, 11120, Nonthaburi, Thailand
Tel.: (66) 25026000
Web Site: https://transec.co.th
Electrical Engineering Services
N.A.I.C.S.: 541330

Vision & Security System Co., Ltd. (1)
99/2 Moo 4 Software Park 34th Fl Chaengwattana Rd, Klong Gleua Pakkred, Nonthaburi, 11120, Thailand
Tel.: (66) 25026999
Web Site: http://www.vision.co.th
Emp.: 50
Telecommunication System Services
N.A.I.C.S.: 517810

SAMATA GHARELU LAGHUBITTA BITTIYA SANSTHA LTD
Near Banepa Glass House, Kavrepalanchowk district, Banepa, Nepal
Tel.: (977) 11597000 NP
Web Site: https://www.samata.org.np
SMATA—(NEP)
Rev.: $1,726,277
Assets: $23,245,021
Liabilities: $19,013,638
Net Worth: $4,231,383
Earnings: $630,010
Fiscal Year-end: 07/16/23
Commercial Banking Services
N.A.I.C.S.: 522110
D. M. Thebe Limbu (Chm)

SAMATA LEATHER COMPLEX LIMITED
120 Sher-E-Bangla Road, Hazaribagh, Dhaka, 1209, Bangladesh
Tel.: (880) 29662731
Web Site: https://samataleather.com
Year Founded: 1990
SAMATALETH—(DHA)
Rev.: $677,577
Assets: $2,237,241
Liabilities: $515,085
Net Worth: $1,722,156
Earnings: $12,539
Fiscal Year-end: 06/30/21
Leather Finishing Services
N.A.I.C.S.: 316110
Mohammed Munsur Ahmed (Chm)

SAMBANDAM SPINNING MILLS LIMITED
Kamaraj Nagar Colony, PO Box No 1, Salem, 636 014, Tamil Nadu, India
Tel.: (91) 4272240790
Web Site: https://www.sambandam.com
Year Founded: 1973
521240—(BOM)
Rev.: $31,584,762
Assets: $36,787,746
Liabilities: $23,022,022
Net Worth: $13,765,725
Earnings: $1,108,093
Emp.: 1,208
Fiscal Year-end: 03/31/21
Cotton Yarn Mfr & Sales
N.A.I.C.S.: 313110
S. Devarajan (Chm & Co-Mng Dir)

SAMBHAAV MEDIA LIMITED
Sambhaav House Opp Judges Bungalows Premchandnagar Road, Satellite, Ahmedabad, 380015, India
Tel.: (91) 7926873914 In
Web Site: https://www.sambhaav.com
Year Founded: 1990
511630—(BOM)
Rev.: $6,108,484
Assets: $15,351,131
Liabilities: $3,723,679
Net Worth: $11,627,452
Earnings: ($226,235)
Emp.: 8
Fiscal Year-end: 03/31/21
Newspaper Publishers
N.A.I.C.S.: 513110
Kiran B. Vadodaria (Chm & Mng Dir)

SAMBO CORRUGATED BOARD CO., LTD.
120 Gongdan 1daero 28beongi, Wonmi-gu, Bucheon, Gyeonggi-do, Korea (South)
Tel.: (82) 313196523
Web Site: https://www.isambo.com
Year Founded: 1973
023600—(KRS)
Rev.: $446,402,391
Assets: $544,114,694
Liabilities: $117,736,716
Net Worth: $426,377,978
Earnings: $43,137,755
Emp.: 295
Fiscal Year-end: 12/31/22
Corrugated Cardboard Box Mfr
N.A.I.C.S.: 322211
Jin-Ho Ryu (Pres & CEO)

SAMBO INDUSTRIAL CO., LTD.
36 Namuiro 21 Beon-Gil, Jinhae-gu, Changwon, Gyeongsangnam-do, Korea (South)
Tel.: (82) 555527130
Web Site: http://www.samboind.kr
Year Founded: 1974
009620—(KRS)
Rev.: $348,997,542

INTERNATIONAL PUBLIC

Assets: $259,585,529
Liabilities: $221,591,285
Net Worth: $37,994,245
Earnings: ($9,884,447)
Emp.: 134
Fiscal Year-end: 12/31/22
Aluminum Alloy Material Mfr
N.A.I.C.S.: 331314
Ra Sang Moo (Pres & CEO)

SAMBO MOTORS CO., LTD.
142 Seongseodong-ro, Dalseo-gu, Daegu, Korea (South)
Tel.: (82) 535829230 KR
Web Site: https://www.sambomotors.co.kr
Year Founded: 1977
053700—(KRS)
Rev.: $920,287,240
Assets: $663,086,586
Liabilities: $460,756,432
Net Worth: $202,330,154
Earnings: $16,379,215
Emp.: 485
Fiscal Year-end: 12/31/22
Automobile Engine Components & Fuel System Products Mfr & Distr
N.A.I.C.S.: 336310
Jae-Ha Lee (CEO)

Subsidiaries:

Plakor Co., Ltd. (1)
679-24 Hyundai Kia-ro, Namyang-eup, Hwaseong, 445 040, Gyeonggi-do, Korea (South)
Tel.: (82) 313698400
Web Site: https://www.plakor.co.kr
Plastic Component Mfr
N.A.I.C.S.: 326199

SAMBONET PADERNO INDUSTRIE S.P.A.
SR 11 Km 84, 28060, Novara, Italy
Tel.: (39) 0321879711 IT
Web Site: http://www.paderno.it
Year Founded: 1932
Sales Range: $75-99.9 Million
Emp.: 1,400
Cookware & Kitchen Utensil Mfr
N.A.I.C.S.: 332215
Roberto Bagnaschino (Dir Production)

Subsidiaries:

Rosenthal GmbH (1)
Philip Rosenthal Platz 1, D-95199, Selb, Germany
Tel.: (49) 40 226307360
Web Site: www.rosenthal.de
Porcelain, Ceramics, Glass & Cutlery Products Mfr
N.A.I.C.S.: 327110
Pierluigi Coppo (Mng Dir)

Subsidiary (US):

Rosenthal U.S.A. Limited (2)
355 Michelle Pl, Carlstadt, NJ 07072-2304
Tel.: (201) 804-8000
Web Site: http://www.rosenthalchina.com
Sales Range: $25-49.9 Million
Emp.: 25
Marketer of Fine China, Stemware, Crystal & Porcelain & Stainless Flatware
N.A.I.C.S.: 423220

Rosenthal Lifestyle Trading Shanghai Co., Ltd. (1)
Unit 221 Tower 1 German Centre No 88 Keyuan Road, 201203, Shanghai, China
Tel.: (86) 21 2898 6419
Web Site: http://www.rosenthal.cn
Luxury Product Distr
N.A.I.C.S.: 424990

SAMBU CONSTRUCTION CO., LTD.
9-1 Namchang-dong, Jung-gu, Seoul, 100-804, Korea (South)
Tel.: (82) 220368000

Web Site: http://www.sambu.co.kr
Year Founded: 1948
001470—(KRS)
Rev.: $355,241,932
Assets: $392,574,442
Liabilities: $252,838,943
Net Worth: $139,735,499
Earnings: ($56,326,918)
Emp.: 493
Fiscal Year-end: 12/31/22
Civil Engineering Construction Services
N.A.I.C.S.: 237990
Shin Gyu Cheol *(Mng Dir)*

SAMCHAI STEEL INDUSTRIES PUBLIC COMPANY LIMITED
75/14 75/17 85 Village No 5 Soi Wat Sophonaram Ekachai Road, Khok Kham Subdistrict Mueang District, Samut Sakhon, 74000, Thailand
Tel.: (66) 23840099
Web Site:
https://www.samchaisteel.com
Year Founded: 1997
Sales Range: $100-124.9 Million
Hot-Rolled Steel Tubes & Steel Sheets Mfr
N.A.I.C.S.: 331221

SAMCHEM HOLDINGS BERHAD
Lot 6 Jalan Sungai Kayu Ara 32/39 Seksyen 32, Darul Ehsan, 40460, Shah Alam, Selangor, Malaysia
Tel.: (60) 357402000
Web Site:
https://www.samchem.com.my
SAMCHEM—(KLS)
Rev.: $279,748,783
Assets: $111,423,492
Liabilities: $50,022,434
Net Worth: $61,401,058
Earnings: $9,611,217
Fiscal Year-end: 12/31/22
Polyurethane Mfr
N.A.I.C.S.: 326150
Chok Khooi Chooi *(Exec Dir)*

Subsidiaries:

PT Samchem Prasandha (1)
The Blugreen-Boutique Office Tower A-Blue 2nd Floor, Unit AB-02 Jl Lingkar Luar Barat Kavling 88 Kembangan, Jakarta, 11610, Indonesia
Tel.: (62) 2129527291
Web Site:
https://www.samchemprasandha.com
Polyurethane Mfr
N.A.I.C.S.: 326150

Samchem Enviro Cycle Sdn. Bhd. (1)
Lot 6 Jalan Sungai Kayu Ara 32/39, Seksyen 32, Shah Alam, 40460, Malaysia
Tel.: (60) 3 5740 2121
Polyurethane Mfr
N.A.I.C.S.: 326150

Samchem Logistic Services Sdn. Bhd. (1)
Lot 6 Jalan Sungai Kayu Ara 32/39, Seksyen 32, Shah Alam, 40460, Selangor, Malaysia
Tel.: (60) 3 5740 2029
Polyurethane Sales
N.A.I.C.S.: 326150

Samchem Sdn. Bhd. (1)
Lot 6 Jalan Sungai Kayu Ara 32/39, Seksyen 32, 40460, Shah Alam, Selangor Darul Ehsan, Malaysia
Tel.: (60) 357402000
Web Site: https://www.samchem.com.my
Sales Range: $50-74.9 Million
Emp.: 25
Industrial Chemical Distr
N.A.I.C.S.: 424690
Hong Carmen *(Mgr-Admin)*

Samchem TN Pte Ltd (1)
No 29 Kaki Bukit Crescent 05-00 Kaki Bukit Techpark 1, Singapore, 416260, Singapore
Tel.: (65) 8128 6966
Chemical Products Distr
N.A.I.C.S.: 424690

Samchemsphere Export Sdn. Bhd. (1)
Lot 6 Jalan Sungai Kayu Ara 32/39, Seksyen 32, Shah Alam, 40640, Selangor, Malaysia
Tel.: (60) 122043622
Polyurethane Sales
N.A.I.C.S.: 424690

TN Chemie Sdn. Bhd. (1)
PTD 152691 Mukim Pulai Kawasan Perindustrian SiLC Bandar, Gelang Patah, 79200, Johor, Malaysia
Tel.: (60) 7 531 9999
Web Site: http://www.tnchemie.com.my
Chemical Products Distr
N.A.I.C.S.: 424690

SAMCHULLY CO., LTD.
42 Gukjegeumyung-ro 6-gil, Yeongdeungpo-gu, Seoul, 07328, Korea (South)
Tel.: (82) 23683300
Web Site:
https://www.samchully.co.kr
Year Founded: 1955
004690—(KRS)
Rev.: $4,440,243,437
Assets: $3,851,837,542
Liabilities: $2,671,210,669
Net Worth: $1,180,626,872
Earnings: $51,181,067
Emp.: 846
Fiscal Year-end: 12/31/22
Natural Gas Mfr & Distr
N.A.I.C.S.: 211130
Chan-Eui Lee *(Chm, Vice Chm & Co-CEO)*

Subsidiaries:

Samchully Asset Management Co., Ltd. (1)
42 Gukjegeumyung-ro 6-gil, Yeongdeungpo-gu, Seoul, 07328, Korea (South)
Tel.: (82) 27868313
Web Site: https://www.sig-fund.com
Investment Fund Management Services
N.A.I.C.S.: 523940

Samchully Co., Ltd. - Gwangmyeong Combined Heat & Power Plant (1)
17 Jagyeong-Ro, Gwangmyeong, Gyeonggi-do, Korea (South)
Tel.: (82) 28973002
Power Generation Services
N.A.I.C.S.: 221118

Samchully ENG Co., Ltd. (1)
42 Gukjegeumyung-ro 6-gil, Yeongdeungpo-gu, Seoul, Korea (South)
Tel.: (82) 23683500
Web Site: https://www.samchullyeng.co.kr
Facility Management Services
N.A.I.C.S.: 561210

Samchully ES Co., Ltd. (1)
42 Gukjegeumyung-ro 6-gil, Yeongdeungpo-gu, Seoul, Korea (South)
Tel.: (82) 23683368
Web Site: https://www.samchullyes.co.kr
Energy Development Services
N.A.I.C.S.: 926110

Samtan Co., Ltd. (1)
Tel.: (82) 25276100
Coal Mining & Distribution Services
N.A.I.C.S.: 213113
Lee Jang-Gyoon *(Co-Chm)*

Subsidiary (Non-US):

PT. Cirebon Electric Power (2)
Pondok Indah Office Tower 3 23rd Floor Suite 2301, Jl Sultan Iskandar Muda Kav V/TA Pondok Indah, Jakarta, 12310, Indonesia
Tel.: (62) 2129327990
Web Site: http://www.cirebonpower.co.id
Power Generation Services
N.A.I.C.S.: 221118

PT. Perta-Samtan Gas (2)
Jalan Nomor 8 Komperta Sungai Gerong Kec, Banyuasin I Kab Banyuasin Sumatera, Jakarta Selatan, 30962, Indonesia
Tel.: (62) 7115740701
Web Site: http://www.psgas.co.id
Natural Gas Mfr
N.A.I.C.S.: 211130
Baek Weon Son *(Chm)*

PT. Sea Bridge Shipping (2)
Mulia Tower Suite 1605 16th Floor Jl Jend Gatot Subroto Kav 9-11, Jakarta, 12930, Indonesia
Tel.: (62) 2152903135
Transshipment Services
N.A.I.C.S.: 541614

PT. Tata Hamparan Eka Persad (2)
Jl Lembaway 1/37, Pangkal Pinang, 33110, Bangka Belitung, Indonesia
Tel.: (62) 7174298058
Coal Distribution Services
N.A.I.C.S.: 423520

Subsidiary (US):

SAMTAN USA, Inc. (2)
910 Roosevelt Ste 250, Irvine, CA 92620
Tel.: (949) 851-5300
Web Site: https://www.samtanusa.com
Heavy Equipment Distr
N.A.I.C.S.: 423830
Young Chan Kim *(CEO)*

Subsidiary (Non-US):

STI Pacific Pte. Ltd. (2)
8 Eu Tong Sen Street 16-99 The Central, Singapore, 059818, Singapore
Tel.: (65) 62245142
Coal Distribution Services
N.A.I.C.S.: 423520

SAMCHULY BICYCLE CO., LTD.
445 Teheran-ro, Gangnam-gu, Seoul, 06158, Korea (South)
Tel.: (82) 221943021
Web Site: https://www.samchuly.co.kr
Year Founded: 1944
024950—(KRS)
Rev.: $89,152,407
Assets: $109,425,564
Liabilities: $37,771,571
Net Worth: $71,653,993
Earnings: ($3,866,008)
Emp.: 128
Fiscal Year-end: 12/31/22
Bicycle Mfr & Whslr
N.A.I.C.S.: 336991
Hwan Wook Kim *(Dir)*

SAMCO GOLD LIMITED
13 Hanover Square 5th Floor, London, W1S 1HN, United Kingdom
Tel.: (44) 2076472533
Web Site: http://www.samcogold.com
Year Founded: 2009
SGA.H—(TSXV)
Assets: $22,802
Liabilities: $1,613,059
Net Worth: ($1,590,257)
Earnings: ($232,041)
Fiscal Year-end: 12/31/21
Gold & Other Precious Metals Mining Services
N.A.I.C.S.: 212220
Charles Koppel *(Chm & CEO)*

SAMCO INC.
36 Waraya-cho Takeda, Fushimi-ku, Kyoto, 612-8443, Japan
Tel.: (81) 756217841
Web Site: https://www.samcointl.com
Year Founded: 1979
6387—(TKS)
Emp.: 170
Semiconductor Equipment Mfr
N.A.I.C.S.: 333242
Osamu Tsuji *(Chm, Pres & CEO)*

Subsidiaries:

SIMCO Global Technology & Systems Ltd. (1)
4 Bhawani Kunj Behind Sector D-2, vasant kunj, New Delhi, 110070, India
Tel.: (91) 1126899867
LED Chip Mfr
N.A.I.C.S.: 334413

Samco-ucp ltd. (1)
Industriering 10, 9491, Ruggell, Liechtenstein
Tel.: (423) 3775959
Web Site: http://www.samco-ucp.com
LED Chip Mfr
N.A.I.C.S.: 334413

SAMCO MACHINERY, LTD.
351 Passmore Avenue 31, Toronto, M1V 3N8, ON, Canada
Tel.: (416) 285-0619
Web Site: http://www.samco-machinery.com
Year Founded: 1972
Rev.: $12,800,000
Emp.: 80
Rollforming Equipment & Tools Mfr
N.A.I.C.S.: 331221
Gerry Birmingham *(VP)*

SAMCON INC
815 Rene Levesque Est, Montreal, H2L 4V5, QC, Canada
Tel.: (514) 844-7300
Web Site: http://www.samcon.ca
Year Founded: 1991
Rev.: $13,559,000
Emp.: 22
Condominiums Builder
N.A.I.C.S.: 236117

SAMEBEST CO., LTD.
5th Floor No2 Lane 609 Section 5 Zhongzhong Road, Chongqin, New Taipei City, 24159, Taiwan
Tel.: (886) 266355288
Web Site:
https://www.samebest.com.tw
Year Founded: 2006
8489—(TPE)
Rev.: $38,971,454
Assets: $57,777,913
Liabilities: $30,598,318
Net Worth: $27,179,595
Earnings: ($220,367)
Fiscal Year-end: 12/31/22
Educational Support Services
N.A.I.C.S.: 611710
Yung-Hsin Shih *(Chm & CEO)*

SAMEER AFRICA LTD.
Mombasa Enterprise Road Junction, PO Box 30429, 00100, Nairobi, Kenya
Tel.: (254) 203962000
Web Site:
https://www.sameerafrica.com
Year Founded: 1969
SMER—(NAI)
Emp.: 30,000
Financial Investment Services
N.A.I.C.S.: 523999
Peter M. Gitonga *(Mng Dir)*

SAMEERA AGRO & INFRA LIMITED
Plot No 610 Eden Amsri Square St Johns Road, Adjacent to Appollo Hospital, Telangana, 500003, India
Tel.: (91) 4040123364
Web Site:
https://www.sameeraagroinfra.com
Year Founded: 2002
SAIFL—(NSE)
Rev.: $16,824,775
Assets: $7,040,436
Liabilities: $4,764,943

SAMEERA AGRO & INFRA LIMITED

Sameera Agro & Infra Limited—(Continued)
Net Worth: $2,275,493
Earnings: $1,216,521
Emp.: 18
Fiscal Year-end: 03/31/23
Construction Services
N.A.I.C.S.: 236220

SAMEERA HOMES PRIVATE LIMITED
Plot No 54 & 55 AG Arcade Balaji Co-Operative Housing Society, Secunderabad, India
Tel.: (91) 98490 545 66
Web Site:
 http://www.sameerahomes.com
Residential Building Construction Services
N.A.I.C.S.: 236115
SS Murthy *(CEO)*

SAMENA CAPITAL MANAGEMENT LLP
2122 Grosvenor Street, London, W1K 4QJ, United Kingdom
Tel.: (44) 207 319 7600
Web Site:
 http://www.samenacapital.com
Year Founded: 2008
Privater Equity Firm
N.A.I.C.S.: 523999
Shirish Saraf *(Founder & Vice Chm)*

Subsidiaries:

Samena Capital Hong Kong Ltd (1)
8 Queen's Road Central 7th Floor, Hong Kong, China (Hong Kong)
Tel.: (852) 35836000
Investment Management Service
N.A.I.C.S.: 523940
Kenyon Lee *(Mng Dir)*

Samena Capital Investments Ltd (1)
14th Floor South Tower Emirates Financial Towers DIFC, Dubai, United Arab Emirates
Tel.: (971) 44364900
Investment Management Service
N.A.I.C.S.: 523940
Chetan Gupta *(Sr VP)*

SAMETEL CORPORATION
Long Thanh Industrial Park Road No 1 Tam An Commune, Long Thanh, Dong Nai, Vietnam
Tel.: (84) 2513514277
Web Site: https://sametel.com.vn
Year Founded: 2006
SMT—(HNX)
Rev.: $34,010,600
Assets: $18,319,400
Liabilities: $11,172,700
Net Worth: $7,146,700
Earnings: $56,000
Emp.: 80
Fiscal Year-end: 12/31/22
Communications & Electrical Equipment & Materials Mfr & Distr
N.A.I.C.S.: 334220
Nguyen Thien Canh *(Gen Dir)*

SAMETO TECHNIFIL
6 Rue Bertrand Robidou, 22103, Dinan, Cotes D Armor, France
Tel.: (33) 296871380
Web Site: http://www.sameto.com
Sales Range: $10-24.9 Million
Emp.: 21
Industrial Machinery Mfr
N.A.I.C.S.: 423710
Reven Philippe *(Dir-Fin)*

SAMG ENTERTAINMENT CO., LTD.
8th floor Urban Bench Building 325 Teheran-ro, Gangnam-gu, Seoul, 06151, Korea (South)
Tel.: (82) 25356773
Web Site: https://www.samg.net
Year Founded: 2000
419530—(KRS)
Animation Production Services
N.A.I.C.S.: 512191
Kim Soo-Hoon *(CEO)*

SAMHALLSBYGGNADSBOLAGET I NORDEN AB
Strandvagen 1, 114 51, Stockholm, Sweden
Tel.: (46) 20244200   SE
Web Site: https://sbbnorden.se
Year Founded: 2016
SBB—(OMX)
Rev.: $429,065,161
Assets: $10,017,795,761
Liabilities: $6,647,746,963
Net Worth: $3,370,048,798
Earnings: ($2,129,871,590)
Emp.: 35
Fiscal Year-end: 12/31/23
Real Estate Manangement Services
N.A.I.C.S.: 551112
Lennart Schuss *(Chm)*

Subsidiaries:

Bergsundet Herresatet AB (1)
Riddargatan 23, 114 57, Stockholm, Sweden
Tel.: (46) 84425760
Web Site: https://bergsundet.se
Real Estate Services
N.A.I.C.S.: 531390

Hemfosa Fastigheter AB (1)
Strandvagen 3, 114 51, Stockholm, Sweden
Tel.: (46) 54183594
Web Site: http://www.sbbnorden.se
Real Estate Management & Development
N.A.I.C.S.: 531312

North Bridge Property AS (1)
Karenslyst allE 4, 0278, Oslo, Norway
Tel.: (47) 22540380
Web Site: https://northbridge.no
Property Management Services
N.A.I.C.S.: 531311

OH Nynas AB (1)
Lindetorpsvagen 7, PO Box 10700, 12129, Stockholm, Sweden
Tel.: (46) 86021200
Web Site: https://www.nynas.com
Oil & Gas Production Services
N.A.I.C.S.: 213112

SBB Eldsboda AB (1)
Eldsbodavagen 23, 73430, Hallstahammar, Sweden
Tel.: (46) 21188580
Property Management Services
N.A.I.C.S.: 531311

SBB Flugsvampen 7 Fastighets AB (1)
Horsbyvagen 16a, 52432, Herrljunga, Sweden
Tel.: (46) 31220554
Property Management Services
N.A.I.C.S.: 531311

SBB Gorvaln 1 Fastighets AB (1)
Branningevagen 2, Stockholm, Sweden
Tel.: (46) 771404660
Property Management Services
N.A.I.C.S.: 531311

SBB Grottan 7 Fastighets AB (1)
Kullgatan 5, 82430, Hudiksvall, Sweden
Tel.: (46) 60538337
Property Management Services
N.A.I.C.S.: 531311

SBB Guldfisken i Hoganas AB (1)
Jarnvagsgatan 5 7, 26338, Hoganas, Sweden
Tel.: (46) 46166140
Property Management Services
N.A.I.C.S.: 531311

SBB Gullbernahult 23 AB (1)
Backsippevagen 8, 37154, Karlskrona, Sweden
Tel.: (46) 455300030
Property Management Services
N.A.I.C.S.: 531311

SBB Gullbernahult 82 AB (1)
Gullberna Park Flaggskar 1, Karlskrona, Sweden
Tel.: (46) 455300030
Property Management Services
N.A.I.C.S.: 531311

SBB Hallonet 1 Fastighets AB (1)
Mullevagen 3, 19143, Sollentuna, Sweden
Tel.: (46) 86760606
Property Management Services
N.A.I.C.S.: 531311

SBB Hultet 5 Fastighets AB (1)
Lenalundsvagen 20, 19140, Sollentuna, Sweden
Tel.: (46) 86760606
Property Management Services
N.A.I.C.S.: 531311

SBB Kontorsskylten 7 Fastighets AB (1)
Frostviksgatan 1, Stockholm, Sweden
Tel.: (46) 86760606
Property Management Services
N.A.I.C.S.: 531311

SBB Lakaren 5 Fastighets AB (1)
Sankt Olofsgatan 8, 521 43, Falkoping, Sweden
Tel.: (46) 500444600
Property Management Services
N.A.I.C.S.: 531311

SBB Landsdomaren KB (1)
Margaretavagen 1, Lund, Sweden
Tel.: (46) 46166140
Property Management Services
N.A.I.C.S.: 531311

SBB Lejonet 9 Fastighets AB (1)
Enoch Thulins Vag 1, 261 41, Landskrona, Sweden
Tel.: (46) 770775870
Property Management Services
N.A.I.C.S.: 531311

SBB Marieberg 5 KB (1)
Skonsbergsvagen 3, 856 41, Sundsvall, Sweden
Tel.: (46) 60538337
Property Management Services
N.A.I.C.S.: 531311

SBB Marschen 1 Fastighets AB (1)
Radanvagen 27, 191 40, Sollentuna, Sweden
Tel.: (46) 86760606
Property Management Services
N.A.I.C.S.: 531311

SBB Mistein 13 Fastighets AB (1)
Angsgatan 3, 465 31, Nossebro, Sweden
Tel.: (46) 107081240
Property Management Services
N.A.I.C.S.: 531311

SBB Mjolkerskan 1 AB (1)
Hejderidaregatan 2, 271 57, Ystad, Sweden
Tel.: (46) 411557674
Property Management Services
N.A.I.C.S.: 531311

SBB Morteln 1 Fastighets AB (1)
Silverbacksvagen 1, 191 38, Sollentuna, Sweden
Tel.: (46) 86760606
Property Management Services
N.A.I.C.S.: 531311

SBB Niklasberg 13 Fastighets AB (1)
Regementsgatan 11, 462 32, Vanersborg, Sweden
Tel.: (46) 107081240
Property Management Services
N.A.I.C.S.: 531311

SBB Njord 32 Fastighets AB (1)
Parkgatan 49, 521 43, Falkoping, Sweden
Tel.: (46) 500444600
Property Management Services
N.A.I.C.S.: 531311

SBB Noshorningen 15 Fastighets AB (1)
Nysattravagen 21, 152 49, Sodertalje, Sweden
Tel.: (46) 107081200
Property Management Services
N.A.I.C.S.: 531311

INTERNATIONAL PUBLIC

SBB Rosenfinken 2 Fastighets AB (1)
Lovhagsgatan 2, 724 71, Vasteras, Sweden
Tel.: (46) 21188580
Property Management Services
N.A.I.C.S.: 531311

SBB Samfunnsbygg AS (1)
Tordenskioldsgate 8-10, 0160, Oslo, Norway
Tel.: (47) 99099084
Web Site: https://sbbnorden.no
Property Management Services
N.A.I.C.S.: 531311

SBB Solrosen 17 Fastighets AB (1)
Trandogatan 3, 504 33, Boras, Sweden
Tel.: (46) 31220554
Property Management Services
N.A.I.C.S.: 531311

SBB Sporren 9 Fastighets AB (1)
Axvallagatan 14, 532 37, Skara, Sweden
Tel.: (46) 500444600
Property Management Services
N.A.I.C.S.: 531311

SBB Stjarnebo 1 Fastighets AB (1)
Danboms Vag 2a, 590 36, Kisa, Sweden
Tel.: (46) 771908000
Property Management Services
N.A.I.C.S.: 531311

SBB Stockholm AB (1)
Strandvagen 1, 11451, Stockholm, Sweden
Tel.: (46) 200227200
Web Site: https://sbbnorden.se
Property Management Services
N.A.I.C.S.: 531311

SBB Tordyveln 1 Fastighets AB (1)
Bratenvagen 4, 542 42, Mariestad, Sweden
Tel.: (46) 500444600
Property Management Services
N.A.I.C.S.: 531311

SBB Vasthagen 1 Fastighets AB (1)
Universitetsallen 26, 852 34, Sundsvall, Sweden
Tel.: (46) 60525000
Property Management Services
N.A.I.C.S.: 531311

SBB Vinbaret 1 Fastighets AB (1)
Ravgardsvagen 15, 19273, Sollentuna, Sweden
Tel.: (46) 86760606
Property Management Services
N.A.I.C.S.: 531311

SBB Vinguden 1 Fastighets AB (1)
Kornettvagen 44, 19273, Sollentuna, Sweden
Tel.: (46) 86760606
Property Management Services
N.A.I.C.S.: 531311

Sveafastigheter Bostad Vaxholm AB (1)
Hamngatan 38, 185 32, Vaxholm, Sweden
Tel.: (46) 761394850
Rental Apartment Services
N.A.I.C.S.: 531110

Vibogard AB (1)
Ragnar Thorngrens Gata 8, 43145, Molndal, Sweden
Tel.: (46) 702526851
Web Site: https://www.vibogard.se
Property Management Services
N.A.I.C.S.: 531311

SAMHERJI HF
Glerargotu 30, 600, Akureyri, Iceland
Tel.: (354) 5609000
Web Site: http://www.samherji.is
Year Founded: 1983
Sales Range: $250-299.9 Million
Emp.: 751
Frozen Fish & Seafood Product Mfr
N.A.I.C.S.: 311710
Gustaf Baldvinsson *(Mng Dir)*

Subsidiaries:

DSFU GmbH (1)
Bei der Alten Liebe 5, 27472, Cuxhaven, Germany

Tel.: (49) 4721707900
Seafood Mfr
N.A.I.C.S.: 311710
Haraldur Gretarsson *(Mgr)*

Deutsche Fishfang Union GmbH (1)
Bei der Alten Liebe 5, 27472, Cuxhaven, Germany
Tel.: (49) 4721707900
Web Site: http://www.samherji.is
Sales Range: $25-49.9 Million
Emp.: 20
Seafood Mfr
N.A.I.C.S.: 311710

Framherji aps (1)
Tosta Gjogve 6, Toftir, Faroe Islands
Tel.: (298) 447617
Sales Range: $25-49.9 Million
Emp.: 3
Seafood Product Mfr
N.A.I.C.S.: 311710

Ice Fresh Seafood UK Ltd (1)
40 Estate Rd No 5, Grimsby N E Lincs, DN31 2TG, Grimsby, United Kingdom - England
Tel.: (44) 1472241934
Seafood Packaging Services
N.A.I.C.S.: 311710
Lee Chambers *(Mgr-Ops)*

Icefresh GmbH (1)
Union Brauerei-Str 4d, 64521, Gross-Gerau, Germany
Tel.: (49) 6152807990
Web Site: http://www.icefresh.de
Sales Range: $25-49.9 Million
Emp.: 15
Seafood Mfr
N.A.I.C.S.: 311710
Sigmundur Andresson *(Mng Dir)*

Seagold Ltd (1)
The Orangery Hesslewood Country Ofc Park Ferriby Rd, Hessle, HU13 0L, East Yorkshire, United Kingdom
Tel.: (44) 1482645500
Web Site: http://www.samherji.com
Sales Range: $25-49.9 Million
Emp.: 6
Seafood Mfr
N.A.I.C.S.: 311710
Gustaf Baldvinsson *(Mng Dir)*

SAMHO DEVELOPMENT CO., LTD
96 Hyoryeong-ro, Seocho-gu, Seoul, Korea (South)
Tel.: (82) 220467700
Web Site: https://www.samhodev.co.kr
Year Founded: 1976
010960—(KRS)
Rev.: $235,869,462
Assets: $216,595,325
Liabilities: $48,732,951
Net Worth: $167,862,375
Earnings: $4,545,225
Emp.: 350
Fiscal Year-end: 12/31/22
Civil Engineering Services
N.A.I.C.S.: 237990
Jai-Beom Shim *(CEO)*

Subsidiaries:

SAMHO Enviro-Tech Inc
Tel.: (82) 313223507
Web Site: http://www.samhoenv.co.kr
Fuel Mfr
N.A.I.C.S.: 325199

SAMHO Green Investment Inc. (1)
3F Hyoryeong-ro, Secho-gu, Seoul, Korea (South)
Tel.: (82) 234535500
Web Site: http://www.sgivc.com
Investment Management Service
N.A.I.C.S.: 523940
Soobong Cho *(CEO)*

Samho Development Co., Ltd - Dangjin Factory (1)
183 Myeoncheon-ro Myeoncheon-myeon, Dangjin, Chungcheongnam-do, Korea (South)
Tel.: (82) 313331392
Construction Engineering Services
N.A.I.C.S.: 541330

SAMHWA NETWORKS CO., LTD.
5F New Art Space Bldg 8 Seolleung-ro 91-gil, Gangnam-gu, Seoul, 135-080, Korea (South)
Tel.: (82) 234541500
Web Site: http://www.shnetworks.co.kr
Year Founded: 1991
046390—(KRS)
Rev.: $63,132,863
Assets: $63,867,470
Liabilities: $19,476,965
Net Worth: $44,390,505
Earnings: $10,621,633
Emp.: 39
Fiscal Year-end: 12/31/22
Broadcast Program Production Services
N.A.I.C.S.: 512110
Je-hyun Ahn *(CEO)*

SAMHWA PAINTS INDUSTRIAL CO., LTD.
178 Byeolmang-ro, Danwon-gu, Ansan, Gyeonggi, Korea (South)
Tel.: (82) 314990394
Web Site: https://www.samhwa.com
Year Founded: 1946
000390—(KRS)
Rev.: $495,512,321
Assets: $450,371,872
Liabilities: $220,482,830
Net Worth: $229,889,043
Earnings: $4,296,209
Emp.: 861
Fiscal Year-end: 12/31/22
Paint Product Mfr
N.A.I.C.S.: 325510
Jang Yeon Kim *(Chm & Co-CEO)*

Subsidiaries:

Corenet Co., Ltd. (1)
605 Seoul Forest IT Valley 77 Seongsuil-ro, Seongdong-gu, Seoul, Korea (South)
Tel.: (82) 7075804280
Measuring & Controlling Device Mfr
N.A.I.C.S.: 334519

SM2 Newtworks Co., Ltd. (1)
123 Beolmal-ro 12th floor, Dongan-gu, Anyang, 14056, Gyeonggi-do, Korea (South)
Tel.: (82) 314781500
Web Site: https://www.sm2net.co.kr
Information Technology Services
N.A.I.C.S.: 541511

Samhwa Logitech Co., Ltd. (1)
201-2 Administration Building 107 Jiwon-ro, Sihwa Knowledge Center Danwon-gu, Ansan, Gyeonggi, Korea (South)
Tel.: (82) 314348950
Logistic Services
N.A.I.C.S.: 541614

Samhwa Paints (M) Sdn. Bhd. (1)
21B Persiaran Desa Ampang 1 Taman Sri Ampang, 68000, Ampang, Selangor, Malaysia
Tel.: (60) 342924684
Paint & Coating Mfr
N.A.I.C.S.: 325510

Samhwa Paints Industrial Co., Ltd. - Ansan Plant (1)
5-301 677 Seonggok-dong, Sihwa Industrial Complex Danwon-gu, Ansan, 425-110, Gyeonggi, Korea (South)
Tel.: (82) 314990394
Paint & Coating Mfr
N.A.I.C.S.: 325510

Samhwa Paints Industrial Co., Ltd. - Zhangjiagang Factory (1)
No 1 South Road Dongqudadao, Tangshi Yangshe Town, Zhangjiagang, Jiangsu, China
Tel.: (86) 51258162990
Paint & Coating Mfr
N.A.I.C.S.: 325510

Samhwa Paints Vina Co., Ltd. (1)
Lot 6, Tan Hong-Hoan Son Industrial Zone Tan Hong Tu Son, Bac Ninh, Vietnam
Tel.: (84) 2413764590
Paint & Coating Mfr
N.A.I.C.S.: 325510

Sm2 Networks Co., Ltd. (1)
12F 123 Beolmal-ro, Dongan-gu, Anyang, Gyeonggi-do, Korea (South)
Tel.: (82) 314781500
Paint & Coating Mfr
N.A.I.C.S.: 325510

Weihai Samhwa Paints Co., Ltd. (1)
No 287 Changhua Road, Zhangcun Town Industrial Park Huancui Dist, Weihai, Shandong, China
Tel.: (86) 6315750777
Paint & Coating Mfr
N.A.I.C.S.: 325510

SAMHYUN STEEL CO., LTD.
36 Pyeongsan-ro 70beon-gil, Uichang-gu, Changwon, Gyeongsangnam-do, Korea (South)
Tel.: (82) 552526060
Web Site: http://www.samsteel.co.kr
Year Founded: 1984
017480—(KRS)
Rev.: $261,214,744
Assets: $172,030,387
Liabilities: $26,766,226
Net Worth: $145,264,161
Earnings: $12,280,307
Emp.: 96
Fiscal Year-end: 12/31/22
Steel Products Mfr
N.A.I.C.S.: 331221
Yun Seon Cho *(CEO)*

SAMIBOIS-SAMIPLAST
Route Gaizenay, 85220, Coax, France
Tel.: (33) 251552533
Web Site: http://www.samibois.com
Rev.: $24,000,000
Emp.: 127
N.A.I.C.S.: 326199
Francois Tessier *(Dir-Mktg)*

SAMICK MUSICAL INSTRUMENT CO., LTD.
313 Soi-ro Soi-myeon, Eumseong, 403-030, Chungbuk, Korea (South)
Tel.: (82) 4316883151
Web Site: https://www.samick.co.kr
Year Founded: 1958
002450—(KRS)
Rev.: $249,811,584
Assets: $400,035,625
Liabilities: $200,115,004
Net Worth: $199,920,621
Earnings: $11,583,215
Emp.: 66
Fiscal Year-end: 12/31/22
Musical Instrument Mfr
N.A.I.C.S.: 339992
Hyung Gook Lee *(CEO)*

Subsidiaries:

Berlin-Bechstein Shanghai Co., Ltd. (1)
No 753 Huancheng-North road Comprehensive Industrial Development Zone, Fengxian, Shanghai, 201400, China
Tel.: (86) 2157434705
Musical Instrument Parts Mfr
N.A.I.C.S.: 339992

Harbin Samick Corp. (1)
Li-Min Economic & Technical Development Zone, Hulan Xian, Harbin, Heilongjiang, China
Tel.: (86) 45157351164
Web Site: http://www.samick.co.kr
Wood Processing; Piano Parts & Guitar Parts Processing
N.A.I.C.S.: 321999

P.T. Samick Indonesia (1)
JL Perkebunam Desa Kidul Kec Cileungsi, Bogor, 16824, Jawa Barat, Indonesia
Tel.: (62) 218230538
Web Site: http://www.samick.co.id
Musical Instrument Mfr; Wood Processing
N.A.I.C.S.: 339992
Jong-Sup Kim *(Chm)*

Samick Bechstein Trading (Shanghai) Co., Ltd. (1)
Rm 4408 Maxdo Centre 8 XingYi Road, ChangNing District, Shanghai, 200336, China
Tel.: (86) 2152080830
Musical Instrument Parts Mfr
N.A.I.C.S.: 339992

Samick Music Corp. (1)
1329 Gateway Dr, Gallatin, TN 37066
Tel.: (615) 206-0077
Web Site: http://www.smcmusic.com
Sales Range: $25-49.9 Million
Emp.: 40
Musical Instrument Whslr
N.A.I.C.S.: 339992
Simon Jung *(CFO)*

SAMICK THK CO., LTD.
163 Seongseo-dong-ro, Dalseo-gu, Daegu, Korea (South)
Tel.: (82) 536657000   KR
Web Site: https://www.samickthk.co.kr
Year Founded: 1960
004380—(KRS)
Rev.: $260,115,725
Assets: $340,569,157
Liabilities: $178,955,430
Net Worth: $161,613,727
Earnings: $12,769,611
Emp.: 724
Fiscal Year-end: 12/31/22
Industrial Automation Equipments Mfr
N.A.I.C.S.: 333248

SAMIL C&S CO., LTD.
121 Dongtan-daero 23-gil, Jung-gu, Hwaseong, Gyeonggi-do, Korea (South)
Tel.: (82) 3180806724
Web Site: http://www.daelimcns.co.kr
Year Founded: 1962
004440—(KRS)
Rev.: $185,031,994
Assets: $315,574,884
Liabilities: $107,838,113
Net Worth: $207,736,771
Earnings: ($4,510,424)
Emp.: 277
Fiscal Year-end: 12/31/22
Concrete Pile Mfr
N.A.I.C.S.: 327390
Kim Mi-Yeon *(Mng Dir)*

Subsidiaries:

Daelim C&S Co., Ltd. - Bu-yeo Plant (1)
1007 Hapgok-ri Jangam-myun, Buyeo, Chungcheong Nam-do, Korea (South)
Tel.: (82) 02 53 88 99
Concrete Pile Mfr
N.A.I.C.S.: 327390

Daelim C&S Co., Ltd. - Chil-seo Plant (1)
Gyeonae-ri Chilseo-myun, Haman-gun, Gyeongnam, Korea (South)
Tel.: (82) 55 587 4890
Concrete Pile Mfr
N.A.I.C.S.: 327390

Daelim C&S Co., Ltd. - Yong-in Plant (1)
553-3 Wonyang-ro Wonsam-myeon Cheoin-gu, Yongin, Gyeonggi-do, Korea (South)
Tel.: (82) 31 333 3744
Web Site: http://www.daelimcns.co.kr
Functional Pile Mfr
N.A.I.C.S.: 331221

SAMIL CO., LTD.

SAMIL CO., LTD.

Samil Co., Ltd.—(Continued)
125-15 Songdeok-ro Daesong-myeon, Nam-gu, Pohang, 790-240, Gyeongsangbuk-do, Korea (South)
Tel.: (82) 542891051
Web Site: https://www.samil31.co.kr
Year Founded: 1965
032280—(KRS)
Rev.: $70,548,135
Assets: $77,894,225
Liabilities: $31,801,930
Net Worth: $46,092,296
Earnings: $945,027
Emp.: 64
Fiscal Year-end: 12/31/22
Cargo Transportation Services
N.A.I.C.S.: 488490
In-Su An (CEO)

SAMIL ENTERPRISE CO., LTD.
329 Eonju-ro, Gangnam-gu, Seoul, Korea (South)
Tel.: (82) 25643131
Web Site:
https://www.samilenter.com
Year Founded: 1958
002290—(KRS)
Rev.: $48,797,902
Assets: $56,698,666
Liabilities: $8,409,034
Net Worth: $48,289,632
Earnings: $1,913,377
Emp.: 57
Fiscal Year-end: 12/31/22
Construction Engineering Services
N.A.I.C.S.: 236220
Chong-Woong Park (CEO)

SAMIL PHARMACEUTICAL CO., LTD.
155 Hyoryeong-ro, Seocho-Gu, Seoul, 137-061, Korea (South)
Tel.: (82) 25200300   KR
Web Site: http://www.samil-pharm.co.kr
Year Founded: 1947
000520—(KRS)
Rev.: $145,737,676
Assets: $275,137,302
Liabilities: $180,257,435
Net Worth: $94,879,867
Earnings: $1,234,762
Emp.: 518
Fiscal Year-end: 12/31/23
Pharmaceutical Preparation Mfr
N.A.I.C.S.: 325412
Kang Huh (CEO)

SAMJI ELECTRONICS CO,. LTD.
63-27 Geumgok-ro, Geumchun-Gu, Hwaseong, 18511, Gyeonggi-do, Korea (South)
Tel.: (82) 3151878000
Web Site: https://www.samji.com
Year Founded: 1981
037460—(KRS)
Rev.: $2,241,185,508
Assets: $761,814,107
Liabilities: $379,822,353
Net Worth: $381,991,754
Earnings: $59,824,853
Emp.: 146
Fiscal Year-end: 12/31/22
Electric Equipment Mfr
N.A.I.C.S.: 334419
Taehoon Lee (Co-CEO)

Subsidiaries:

SAMT Co., Ltd. (1)
315 Yeongdong-daero, Gangnam-gu, Seoul, Korea (South)
Tel.: (82) 234589000
Web Site: https://www.isamt.com
Rev.: $1,951,543,883
Assets: $539,650,479
Liabilities: $262,700,517
Net Worth: $276,949,962
Earnings: $44,325,088
Emp.: 126
Fiscal Year-end: 12/31/2022
Semiconductor Whslr
N.A.I.C.S.: 423690
Dujin Park (CEO)

SAMJIN CO., LTD.
81 Anyangcheonseo-ro, Manan-gu, Anyang, Gyeonggi-do, Korea (South)
Tel.: (82) 314675800
Web Site: https://www.samjin.com
Year Founded: 1975
032750—(KRS)
Rev.: $118,991,254
Assets: $88,355,388
Liabilities: $17,296,073
Net Worth: $71,059,314
Earnings: $1,454,636
Emp.: 99
Fiscal Year-end: 12/31/22
Remote Controller Mfr
N.A.I.C.S.: 334290

SAMJIN LND CO., LTD.
64-17 Dongtangiheung-ro, Dongtan-myeon, Hwaseong, Gyeonggi-do, Korea (South)
Tel.: (82) 313792000
Web Site: https://www.samjin.co.kr
Year Founded: 1987
054090—(KRS)
Rev.: $196,721,905
Assets: $156,165,863
Liabilities: $84,880,385
Net Worth: $71,285,478
Earnings: ($1,236,930)
Emp.: 117
Fiscal Year-end: 12/31/22
Electronic Components Mfr
N.A.I.C.S.: 334419
Jong Myung Lee (CEO)

Subsidiaries:

Komi Electronics Co., Ltd. (1)
Inside Of Xincheng Science And Technology Industrial Park Liaobu, 523400, Dongguan, Guangdong, China
Tel.: (86) 76983300880
Electronic Components Mfr
N.A.I.C.S.: 334419
Sam Jun Ren Guang (Mgr)

SAMJIN PHARMACEUTICAL CO., LTD.
121 Wausan Ro, Mapo-gu, Seoul, 04054, Korea (South)
Tel.: (82) 231400700
Web Site:
https://www.samjinpharm.co.kr
Year Founded: 1968
005500—(KRS)
Rev.: $210,182,397
Assets: $311,829,176
Liabilities: $100,241,371
Net Worth: $211,587,805
Earnings: $16,792,572
Emp.: 724
Fiscal Year-end: 12/31/22
Pharmaceutical Product Mfr & Distr
N.A.I.C.S.: 325412
Jang Hong Soon (Co-CEO)

Subsidiaries:

Samjin Pharmaceutical Co., Ltd. - Hyangnam plant (1)
1 Gil 52 Pharmaceutical complex Hyangnam Eup, Hwaseong, Gyeonggi, Korea (South)
Tel.: (82) 31 353 1712
Pharmaceuticals Product Mfr
N.A.I.C.S.: 325412

Samjin Pharmaceutical Co., Ltd. - Osong Plant (1)
156 Osongsaengmyeong 6 ro Osong Eup, Cheongwon, Chungcheong, Korea (South)
Tel.: (82) 43 710 3000
Pharmaceuticals Product Mfr
N.A.I.C.S.: 325412

SAMKEE CORP.
147 Pyeongtaekhang-ro 268 Beon-gil, Poseung-eup, Pyeongtaek, 17953, Gyeonggi-do, Korea (South)
Tel.: (82) 314910341
Web Site: https://www.samkee.com
Year Founded: 1978
122350—(KRS)
Rev.: $402,019,401
Assets: $367,378,456
Liabilities: $274,866,059
Net Worth: $92,512,397
Earnings: ($21,175,081)
Emp.: 561
Fiscal Year-end: 12/31/22
Motor Vehicle Parts Mfr
N.A.I.C.S.: 336390
Dongwon Lee (Co-CEO)

Subsidiaries:

Samkee Automotive Co., Ltd. - Seosan Factory (1)
San 210-1 Mujang-ri Jigok, Seosan, Chungnam, Korea (South)
Tel.: (82) 41 661 0800
Automobile Parts Mfr
N.A.I.C.S.: 336390

SAMKO TIMBER LIMITED
7500A Beach Road 8-305/307 The Plaza, Singapore, 199591, Singapore
Tel.: (65) 62982189
Web Site:
https://www.sampoernakayoe.co.id
Year Founded: 1978
E6R—(SES)
Rev.: $146,814,534
Assets: $276,521,988
Liabilities: $316,204,354
Net Worth: ($39,682,366)
Earnings: ($45,558,527)
Emp.: 10,245
Fiscal Year-end: 12/31/23
Timber Products Mfr & Distr
N.A.I.C.S.: 321999
Boon Hong Koh (Founder)

Subsidiaries:

Bioforest Pte Ltd (1)
1 Research Link National University Of Singapore, Singapore, 117604, Singapore
Tel.: (65) 68727099
Web Site: http://www.bio-forest.com
Research & Development Services
N.A.I.C.S.: 541715

Subsidiary (Non-US):

PT Bioforest Indonesia (2)
Wisma Bisnis Indonesia 1st Floor Zone A JL KH Mas Mansyur No 12A, Jakarta, 10220, Indonesia
Tel.: (62) 21 5790 1176
Web Site: http://www.bio-forest.com
Research & Development Services
N.A.I.C.S.: 541715

P.T. Sumber Graha Maluku (1)
Sampoerna Strategic Square North Tower 20th Floor, JI Jend Sudirman Kav 45-46, Jakarta, 12930, Indonesia
Tel.: (62) 215761138
Web Site: https://sgmaluku.co.id
Forest Management Services
N.A.I.C.S.: 541715

PT Sejahtera Usaha Bersama (1)
JL Mayjend Sungkono No 75, Surabaya, 60189, Indonesia
Tel.: (62) 31 5618614
Timber Product Mfr
N.A.I.C.S.: 321999

PT Sumber Graha Sejahtera (1)
Sampoerna Strategic Square North Tower 21st Floor JI Jend Sudirman, Kav 45-46, Jakarta, 12930, Indonesia
Tel.: (62) 215761138
Laminated Veneer & Plywood Mfr
N.A.I.C.S.: 321212

SAMKRG PISTONS & RINGS LIMITED
1-201 Divya Shakti Complex 7-1-58, Ameerpet, Hyderabad, 500 016, Telangana, India
Tel.: (91) 4023735578
Web Site:
https://www.samkrgpistonsrings.com
Year Founded: 1985
520075—(BOM)
Rev.: $28,228,883
Assets: $28,192,327
Liabilities: $6,628,356
Net Worth: $21,563,971
Earnings: $1,760,554
Emp.: 746
Fiscal Year-end: 03/31/23
Automobile Parts Mfr
N.A.I.C.S.: 336310
S. D. M. Rao (Chm & Mng Dir)

SAMLING STRATEGIC CORPORATION SDN. BHD.
Lot 296 Jalan Temenggong Datuk Oyong Lawai Jau, Miri, 98000, Sarawak, Malaysia
Tel.: (60) 85413099
Web Site: http://www.samling.com
Year Founded: 1963
Sales Range: $25-49.9 Million
Emp.: 300
Wood-Based Products Supplier, Contractor, Mfr & Exporter
N.A.I.C.S.: 337126
Chan Hua Eng (Chm)

Subsidiaries:

SAMLING FLOORING PRODUCTS SDN BHD (1)
Lot 191 Block 1 Kuala Baram Industrial Estate CDT 148, 98009, Miri, Sarawak, Malaysia
Tel.: (60) 85 604339
Wood Products Mfr
N.A.I.C.S.: 321215

SAMLING JAPAN CORPORATION (1)
7th Floor Samling Bldg 3-2-7 Akasaka, Minatoku, Tokyo, 107-0052, Japan
Tel.: (81) 3 51143940
Wood Product Distr
N.A.I.C.S.: 423310

SAMLING PLANTATION SDN BHD (1)
No 169 Bintulu Parkcity Commercial Square, 97000, Bintulu, Sarawak, Malaysia
Tel.: (60) 86 311863
Palm Oil Processing Services
N.A.I.C.S.: 311224

SAMLING PLYWOOD (BARAMAS) SDN BHD (1)
Lot 533 Block 1 Kuala Baram Industrial Estate CDT 47, 98009, Miri, Sarawak, Malaysia
Tel.: (60) 85 604209
Wood Product Distr
N.A.I.C.S.: 423310

SAMLING PLYWOOD (BINTULU) SDN BHD (1)
Lot 367 Block 38 Kemena Industrial Estate, PO Box 91, 97007, Bintulu, Sarawak, Malaysia
Tel.: (60) 86 336685
Wood Product Distr
N.A.I.C.S.: 423310

SAMLING PLYWOOD (LAWAS) SDN BHD (1)
Wisma Samling Lot 296 Jalan Temenggong Datuk Oyong Lawai Jau, PO Box 368, 98007, Miri, Sarawak, Malaysia
Tel.: (60) 85 413099
Web Site: http://www.samling.com.my
Wood Product Distr
N.A.I.C.S.: 423310

SAMLING PLYWOOD (MIRI) SDN BHD (1)
Lot 818 Block 1 Kuala Baram Industrial Es-

tate CDT 83, 98009, Miri, Sarawak, Malaysia
Tel.: (60) 85 604311
Wood Product Distr
N.A.I.C.S.: 423310

SAMLING RIVERSIDE CO, LTD (1)
No 38 Guangzhou Road Nantong Economic & Technological Development Zone, Nantong, 226009, Jiangsu, China
Tel.: (86) 513 85960188
Wood Product Distr
N.A.I.C.S.: 423310

SAMLING SINGAPORE PTE LTD (1)
9 Temasek Blvd 33-01 Suntec Tower Two, 038989, Singapore, Singapore
Tel.: (65) 63363030
Wood Product Distr
N.A.I.C.S.: 423310

Samling Global Limited (1)
Wisma Samling Lot 296 Jalan Temenggong Datuk Oyong Lawal Jau, Miri, 98000, Sarawak, Malaysia
Tel.: (60) 85413099
Web Site: http://www.samling.com
Sales Range: $700-749.9 Million
Investment Holding Company
N.A.I.C.S.: 551112

Subsidiary (Non-US):

Barama Company Limited (2)
Land of Canaan, East Bank Demerara, Georgetown, Guyana
Tel.: (592) 2 254 555
Web Site: http://www.baramaguyana.com
Lumber & Plywood Mfr & Distr
N.A.I.C.S.: 423310

Subsidiary (Domestic):

Lingui Development Sdn Berhad (2)
C-3A-1 Plaza Arkadia No 3 Jalan Inti Sari Perdana, Desa Park City, 52200, Kuala Lumpur, Malaysia
Tel.: (60) 364123999
Web Site: http://www.lingui.com.my
Investment & Property Holding Company
N.A.I.C.S.: 551112
Chee Ming Yaw *(Mng Dir)*

Subsidiary (Domestic):

Glenealy Plantations (Malaya) Berhad (3)
Level 42 Menara Maxis Kuala Lumpur City Centre, Kuala Lumpur, 50088, Malaysia
Tel.: (60) 3 2382 3999
Web Site: http://www.glenealy.com.my
Emp.: 50
Investment Holding Company; Oil Palm Plantations, Palm Oil Mills & Forest Plantations
N.A.I.C.S.: 551112
Chee Ming Yaw *(Mng Dir)*

SAMMAKORN PUBLIC COMPANY LIMITED
188 Spring Tower Building 21st floor Thung Phaya Thai Ratchathewi, Sapan Sung, Bangkok, 10400, Thailand
Tel.: (66) 21068300
Web Site: https://www.sammakorn.co.th
Year Founded: 1970
SAMCO—(THA)
Rev.: $58,467,041
Assets: $185,598,955
Liabilities: $108,607,488
Net Worth: $76,991,467
Earnings: $1,720,732
Emp.: 290
Fiscal Year-end: 12/31/23
Real Estate Development Services
N.A.I.C.S.: 531390
Bibit Bijaisoradat *(Chm & Exec Dir)*

SAMMOK S-FORM CO., LTD.
474-40 Anseongmatchum-daero, Miyang-myeon, Anseong, 17604, Gyeonggi-do, Korea (South)
Tel.: (82) 25610941
Web Site: http://www.sammok.co.kr

Year Founded: 1985
018310—(KRS)
Rev.: $193,133,480
Assets: $504,505,489
Liabilities: $145,328,435
Net Worth: $359,177,054
Earnings: $27,856,401
Emp.: 329
Fiscal Year-end: 12/31/21
Metal Products Mfr
N.A.I.C.S.: 332999
Seok Ho Uhm *(CEO)*

SAMOA BREWERIES LIMITED
PO Box 3015, Apia, Samoa (Western)
Tel.: (685) 20200
Year Founded: 1978
Sales Range: $25-49.9 Million
Emp.: 140
Brewery; Soft Drink Bottler
N.A.I.C.S.: 312120
Fomai Lei Sam *(Gen Mgr)*

SAMOR REALITY LIMITED
401 Samor Realty Venus Atlantis Near Shell Petrol Pump, Anand Nagar Road Prahladnagar, Ahmedabad, India
Tel.: (91) 9824645768
Web Site: https://www.samor.in
Year Founded: 1997
543376—(BOM)
Rev.: $1,316,470
Assets: $1,483,806
Liabilities: $1,060,036
Net Worth: $423,771
Earnings: $14,271
Fiscal Year-end: 03/31/21
Real Estate Services
N.A.I.C.S.: 531210
Birjukumar Ajitbhai Shah *(Chm, Mng Dir & CFO)*

SAMOYED HOLDING LIMITED
902/903 B4 Kexing Science Park, No 15 Keyuan Road Science and Technology Park Nanshan District, Shenzhen, China
Tel.: (86) 755 8695 7589   Ky
Year Founded: 2015
Sales Range: $25-49.9 Million
Emp.: 269
Holding Company
N.A.I.C.S.: 551112
Jianming Lin *(Co-Founder & Chm)*

SAMPANN UTPADAN INDIA LTD.
Survey No 54/B Pratapnagar, Savli-Jarod Road Samlaya, Vadodara, 391520, Gujarat, India
Tel.: (91) 8238084487
Web Site: https://suil.in
SEPOWER—(NSE)
Rev.: $3,290,877
Assets: $11,987,038
Liabilities: $10,529,317
Net Worth: $1,457,721
Earnings: $(1,000,315)
Emp.: 84
Fiscal Year-end: 03/31/21
Wind & Bio Gas Electric Power Generation Services
N.A.I.C.S.: 221115
Lipika Garg *(Compliance Officer & Sec)*

SAMPATH BANK PLC
No 110 Sir James Peiris Mawatha, 2, Colombo, 02, Sri Lanka
Tel.: (94) 112303050   LK
Web Site: https://www.sampath.lk
Year Founded: 1986
SAMP—(COL)
Rev.: $580,986,368

Assets: $6,116,326,477
Liabilities: $5,507,640,518
Net Worth: $608,685,959
Earnings: $44,914,185
Emp.: 4,048
Fiscal Year-end: 12/31/20
Banking Services
N.A.I.C.S.: 522110
Dulsiri Jayasinghe *(Asst Gen Mgr-FCBU & Corp Fin)*

Subsidiaries:

SC Securities (Pvt) Ltd. (1) (51%)
Tel.: (94) 114711000
Web Site: https://www.sampathsecurities.lk
Sales Range: $50-74.9 Million
Emp.: 25
Securities Brokerage
N.A.I.C.S.: 523150
Sunil G. Wijesinha *(Chm)*

Sampath Center Limited (1)
110 Sir James Peiris Mawatha, Colombo, 00200, Sri Lanka
Tel.: (94) 112300260
Web Site: http://www.sampathbank.com
Sales Range: $300-349.9 Million
Emp.: 1,000
Property Development
N.A.I.C.S.: 531312

Sampath Information Technology Solutions Limited (1)
Tel.: (94) 117619619
Web Site: https://sits.lk
Software Technology Solutions
N.A.I.C.S.: 334610
R. Samaranayake *(Chm)*

Sampath Leasing & Factoring Ltd. (1)
110 Sir James Peiris Mawatha, Colombo, 2, Sri Lanka   (100%)
Tel.: (94) 112303050
Web Site: http://www.sampath.lk
Emp.: 1,000
Commercial Banking & Leasing Solutions
N.A.I.C.S.: 522110

Sampath Surakam Limited (1)
110 Sir James Peiris Mawatha, Colombo, 02, Sri Lanka
Tel.: (94) 112300260
Web Site: http://www.sampath.lk
Securities Dealer
N.A.I.C.S.: 523150

Siyapatha Finance Plc (1)
Tel.: (94) 117605605
Web Site: https://www.siyapatha.lk
Emp.: 800
Financial Transaction Processing Services
N.A.I.C.S.: 522320
Ananda Seneviratne *(Mng Dir)*

SAMPENSION KP LIVSFORSIKRING A/S
Tuborg Havnevej 14, 2900, Hellerup, Denmark
Tel.: (45) 7733 1877   DK
Web Site: http://www.sampension.dk
Life Insurance & Pension Management Services
N.A.I.C.S.: 524292
Anker Boye *(Chm)*

SAMPO CORPORATION
No 19 Dinghu Rd, Guishan Dist, Taoyuan, 33378, Taiwan
Tel.: (886) 33975151
Web Site: https://www.sampo.com.tw
1604—(TAI)
Rev.: $250,131,257
Assets: $509,783,460
Liabilities: $231,097,149
Net Worth: $278,686,310
Earnings: $25,360,181
Emp.: 1,055
Fiscal Year-end: 12/31/23
Electronic Products Mfr
N.A.I.C.S.: 334419
Ching-Chao Hsu *(Gen Mgr)*

SAMPO PLC
Fabianinkatu 27, 00100, Helsinki, Finland
Tel.: (358) 105160100   FI
Web Site: https://www.sampo.com
Year Founded: 1909
SAMPO—(HEL)
Rev.: $9,083,747,032
Assets: $26,143,967,192
Liabilities: $17,848,046,622
Net Worth: $8,295,920,570
Earnings: $1,503,345,564
Emp.: 13,272
Fiscal Year-end: 12/31/23
Financial Investment Services
N.A.I.C.S.: 551112
Bjorn Wahlroos *(Chm)*

Subsidiaries:

3C Asset Management Ltd. (1)
Boulevardi 10 A, PO Box 152, FIN-00121, Helsinki, Finland   (56%)
Tel.: (358) 934815100
Web Site: http://www.3cfund.com
Investment Banking & Risk Management Funds
N.A.I.C.S.: 525910

AS If Kinnisvarahaldus (1)
Pronksi 19, Tallinn, 10124, Estonia
Tel.: (372) 6671100
Insurance Management Services
N.A.I.C.S.: 524298

Hastings Group Holdings Limited (1)
Conquest House Collington Avenue, Bexhill-on-Sea, TN39 3LW, East Sussex, United Kingdom
Tel.: (44) 1424788225
Web Site: https://www.hastingsgroup.uk
General Insurance Providing Services
N.A.I.C.S.: 524210

If IT Services A/S (1)
Stamholmen 159, Hvidovre, 2650, Denmark
Tel.: (45) 70121212
Information Technology Consulting Services
N.A.I.C.S.: 541512

If P&C Insurance Holding Ltd. (1)
Barks Vag 15, 106 80, Stockholm, Sweden   (100%)
Tel.: (46) 771430000
Web Site: http://wwwif.se
Direct Property & Casualty Insurance Carriers
N.A.I.C.S.: 524126
Torbjorn Magnusson *(Pres & CEO)*

Subsidiary (Domestic):

If Livforsakring Ab (2)
Barks Vag 15, Solna, 106 80, Sweden
Tel.: (46) 771430000
Fire Insurance Services
N.A.I.C.S.: 524113

Holding (Domestic):

If P&C Insurance AB (2)
B15 C62 Barks Vag, 106 80, Stockholm, Sweden
Tel.: (46) 771430000
Web Site: http://www.if.se
Rev.: $4,851,003,904
Emp.: 800
Insurance Services
N.A.I.C.S.: 524113
Torbjorn Magnusson *(CEO)*

Branch (Non-US):

IF P&C (3)
Boompjes 413, NL 3011 XZ, Rotterdam, Netherlands
Tel.: (31) 104110255
Web Site: http://www.if-insurance.com
Property & Casualty Insurance
N.A.I.C.S.: 524126

Subsidiary (Non-US):

If P & C Insurance Company Ltd. (3)
Niittyportti 4, Espoo, 2200, Finland
Tel.: (358) 1051510
Web Site: http://www.if.fi

SAMPO PLC

Sampo plc—(Continued)
Sales Range: $350-899.9 Million
Direct Property & Casualty Insurance Carriers
N.A.I.C.S.: 524126
Torbjorn Magnusson *(CEO-Sweden)*

Subsidiary (Non-US):

If P&C Insurance AS (2)
Lojtsa 8a, 11415, Tallinn, Estonia
Tel.: (372) 7771211
Web Site: https://www.if.ee
Sales Range: $150-199.9 Million
Emp.: 50
Insurance Management Services
N.A.I.C.S.: 524298
Andris Morozovs *(CEO, Member-Mgmt Bd & Head-BA Baltic)*

Kiinteistomaailma Ltd. (1)
Lonnrotinkatu 5, FIN-00120, Helsinki, Finland
Tel.: (358) 106223000
Web Site: http://www.kiinteistomaailma.fi
Sales Range: $50-74.9 Million
Emp.: 15
Real Estate Agents & Brokers
N.A.I.C.S.: 531210

Mandatum Asset Management Ltd. (1)
Bulevardi 56, 00120, Helsinki, Finland
Tel.: (358) 10515225
Web Site: https://www.mandatumam.com
Investment Services
N.A.I.C.S.: 523999

Mandatum Life Insurance Company Limited
Bulevardi 56, 00120, Helsinki, Finland (100%)
Tel.: (358) 10515225
Web Site: https://www.mandatumlife.fi
Sales Range: $200-249.9 Million
Emp.: 500
Insurance Services
N.A.I.C.S.: 524128

Subsidiary (Non-US):

Mandatum Life Insurance Baltic SE (2)
Viru Valjak 2 - Metro Plaza, Tallinn, 10111, Estonia
Tel.: (372) 681 2300
Web Site: http://www.mandatumlife.ee
Sales Range: $75-99.9 Million
Emp.: 45
Insurance Management Services
N.A.I.C.S.: 524298
Erkki Sadam *(Member-Mgmt Bd)*

Branch (Non-US):

Mandatum Life Insurance Baltic SE Lithuanian Branch (3)
Salteonesnese Vilko 2 3rd Fl, Vilnius, LT-08126, Lithuania (100%)
Tel.: (370) 852109390
Web Site: http://www.mandatumlife.lt
Sales Range: $50-74.9 Million
Emp.: 37
Insurance Services
N.A.I.C.S.: 524113

Markesforsakring (1)
Barksvag 15, 10680, Stockholm, Sweden
Tel.: (46) 854170500
Web Site: http://www.if.se
Sales Range: $350-399.9 Million
Emp.: 700
Life Insurance
N.A.I.C.S.: 524114
Torbgorn Magnusson *(Pres & CEO)*

Subsidiary (Non-US):

DIAL Forsikring A/S (2)
PO Box 240, N-1326, Lysaker, Norway
Tel.: (47) 98002400
Web Site: http://www.if.no
Sales Range: $350-399.9 Million
Emp.: 700
N.A.I.C.S.: 524128

DIAL Forsikring A/S (2)
Stamholmen 159, DK-2650, Hvidovre, Denmark
Tel.: (45) 3687 4747

N.A.I.C.S.: 524128

SE Sampo Life Insurance Baltic, Latvian Branch (1)
Kronvalda bulvaris 3, LV-1010, Riga, Latvia
Tel.: (371) 7503333
Web Site: http://www.sampo.lv
Insurance Services
N.A.I.C.S.: 524113

Sampo Fund Management Ltd. (1)
Bulevardi 10 A, PO Box 1396, FIN-00075, Helsinki, Finland
Tel.: (358) 1023610
Web Site: http://www.rahastot.fi
Investment Banking & Securities Dealing
N.A.I.C.S.: 523150

Vertikal Helseassistanse AS (1)
Drammensveien 264, 0283, Oslo, Norway
Tel.: (47) 2 301 4800
Web Site: https://www.vertikalhelse.no
Insurance Services
N.A.I.C.S.: 524210

SAMPRE NUTRITIONS LIMITED

133 Inddustrial Estate, Medchal, Hyderabad, 501 401, Andhra Pradesh, India
Tel.: (91) 8418222428
Web Site: https://www.sampreltd.com
530617—(BOM)
Rev.: $4,457,646
Assets: $5,226,066
Liabilities: $2,689,347
Net Worth: $2,536,718
Earnings: $41,604
Emp.: 128
Fiscal Year-end: 03/31/23
Candy Mfr
N.A.I.C.S.: 311351
Brahma Kishanchand Gurbani *(Chm & Mng Dir)*

SAMPYO CORPORATION

15th Fl E-ma Bldg 42 Jong-ro 1 gil Susong-dong, Jongno-gu, Seoul, Korea (South)
Tel.: (82) 2 460 7111   KR
Web Site: http://www.sampyo.co.kr
Year Founded: 1966
Sales Range: $1-4.9 Billion
Emp.: 1,800
Construction Industry Material Distr
N.A.I.C.S.: 423390
Do-Won Chung *(Chm & CEO)*

Subsidiaries:

Sampyo Cement Co., Ltd. (1)
Dongyang Cement 20 Dongyang-gil, Samcheok, 245-150, Gangwon-do, Korea (South)
Tel.: (82) 237703000
Web Site: http://www.sampyocement.co.kr
Rev.: $553,095,656
Assets: $1,114,290,983
Liabilities: $586,979,320
Net Worth: $527,311,662
Earnings: $23,150,198
Emp.: 601
Fiscal Year-end: 12/31/2022
Cement Mfr
N.A.I.C.S.: 327310

SAMRA MIDAS CO., LTD.

8th Floor 22 Seonyudong 1-ro, Yeongdeungpo-gu, Seoul, 07263, Korea (South)
Tel.: (82) 2 2093 4524
Residential Construction
N.A.I.C.S.: 236116
Oh-Hyeon Woo *(Chm)*

SAMRAT FORGINGS LIMITED

Village PO Ghollu Majra Tehsil Derabassi Distt, Mohali, 140506, Punjab, India
Tel.: (91) 9257240444
Web Site:
https://www.samratforgings.com

Year Founded: 1981
543229—(BOM)
Rev.: $21,782,051
Assets: $15,267,958
Liabilities: $11,851,340
Net Worth: $3,416,618
Earnings: $585,840
Fiscal Year-end: 03/31/23
Automobile Product Distr
N.A.I.C.S.: 441330
Rakesh M. Kumar *(Mng Dir)*

SAMRAT PHARMACHEM LIMITED

701/702 Business Square M A Road, Andheri West, Mumbai, 400 058, India
Tel.: (91) 2226701050   In
Web Site:
https://www.samratpharma.com
Year Founded: 1992
530125—(BOM)
Rev.: $24,499,101
Assets: $7,834,618
Liabilities: $3,789,187
Net Worth: $4,045,430
Earnings: $727,979
Emp.: 27
Fiscal Year-end: 03/31/21
Iodine & Bromine Salt Mfr & Distr
N.A.I.C.S.: 325998
Lalit Damodar Mehta *(Founder, Chm & Mng Dir)*

SAMRUK-ENERGY JSC

15A Kabanbay batyr Business Center Q Block B, Nur-Sultan, 010000, Kazakhstan
Tel.: (7) 172553062
Web Site: http://www.samruk-energy.kz
Year Founded: 2007
SNRG—(KAZ)
Rev.: $852,969,438
Assets: $2,159,666,442
Liabilities: $967,605,217
Net Worth: $1,192,061,225
Earnings: $67,765,907
Fiscal Year-end: 12/31/22
Holding Company
N.A.I.C.S.: 551112
Karymsakov Beibit Yerkinbayevich *(Chm)*

Subsidiaries:

Almaty Power Stations JSC (1)
Dostyk Avenue 7, Almaty, 050002, Kazakhstan
Tel.: (7) 7272540331
Web Site: http://www.ales.kz
Eletric Power Generation Services
N.A.I.C.S.: 221118
Tutebayev Serik Suinbekovich *(Chm)*

AlmatyEnergoSbyt LLP (1)
Markov Str 61/1 corner of Popov Str, Almaty, Kazakhstan
Tel.: (7) 3561527
Web Site: https://www.esalmaty.kz
Electric Power Distribution Services
N.A.I.C.S.: 221122

Energy Solutions Centre LLP (1)
15a Kanbanbai Batyr Avenue 2nd Floor Block B, Nur-Sultan, 010000, Kazakhstan
Tel.: (7) 7172916195
Web Site: http://www.e-s-center.kz
Transportation Services
N.A.I.C.S.: 488510

Samruk Green Energy LLP (1)
100 Shevchenko Street Seifullin's ug 5th Floor 501 Office, 050022, Almaty, Kazakhstan
Tel.: (7) 7273449219
Web Site: http://www.samruk-green.kz
Solar Power Plant Operator
N.A.I.C.S.: 221114
Bukenov Talgat Shakarimovich *(Gen Dir)*

SAMRUK-KAZYNA CON-

INTERNATIONAL PUBLIC

STRUCTION JSC
17/10 E10 Avenue, Nur-Sultan, 010000, Kazakhstan
Tel.: (7) 172575544
Web Site: http://www.fnsk.kz
SKCN—(KAZ)
Rev.: $24,589,577
Assets: $433,425,712
Liabilities: $315,822,429
Net Worth: $117,603,283
Earnings: $17,723,437
Fiscal Year-end: 12/31/19
Building Construction Services
N.A.I.C.S.: 236220
Sandykbayev Bolatkan Aitkozhanovich *(Chm-Mgmt Bd)*

SAMRYOONG CO LTD.

508 SAMRYOONG Induspark 205 Wonmi-ro, Bucheon, Gyeonggi-Do, Korea (South)
Tel.: (82) 24990091
Web Site: https://www.srpack.com
Year Founded: 1980
014970—(KRS)
Rev.: $69,244,975
Assets: $86,265,327
Liabilities: $40,541,310
Net Worth: $45,724,017
Earnings: ($2,010,948)
Emp.: 67
Fiscal Year-end: 12/31/22
Packaging Container Mfr
N.A.I.C.S.: 322219
Hongro Cho *(Pres & CEO)*

Subsidiaries:

SRTECHNOPACK CO., LTD. (1)
293 Bongju-ro Jiksan-eup, Seobuk-gu, Cheonan, 331-812, Chungcheongnam-do, Korea (South)
Tel.: (82) 416298300
Web Site: https://www.srtechno.co.kr
Emp.: 160
Packaging Container Mfr
N.A.I.C.S.: 322219

Plant (Domestic):

SRTECHNOPACK CO., LTD. - Kunsan Plant (2)
264 Oehang 1-gil, Gunsan, 573-400, Jeonbuk, Korea (South)
Tel.: (82) 63 467 9780
Packaging Container Mfr
N.A.I.C.S.: 322219

Samryoong Co Ltd. - Sihwa Factory (1)
192 Beonyeongro, Danwon-Gu, Ansan, 14623, Gyeonggi-Do, Korea (South)
Tel.: (82) 31 498 0091
Web Site: http://www.srpack.com
Emp.: 90
Packaging Container Mfr
N.A.I.C.S.: 322219

SAMSE SA

2 rue Raymond Pitet, 38030, Grenoble, Cedex 2, France
Tel.: (33) 476857800   FR
Web Site: https://www.groupe-samse.fr
Year Founded: 1973
SAMS—(EUR)
Sales Range: $1-4.9 Billion
Earnings: $42,900,000
Building Materials & Hardware Wholesale Distr
N.A.I.C.S.: 444180
Olivier Malfait *(Pres & CEO)*

Subsidiaries:

Doras S.A. (1)
6 rue Antoine Becquerel, 21300, Chenove, France (100%)
Tel.: (33) 380587000
Web Site: http://www.doras.fr
Sales Range: $200-249.9 Million
Emp.: 716

AND PRIVATE COMPANIES

Construction Materials Whslr & Home Centers Operator
N.A.I.C.S.: 423390
Francois Noel *(Chm & Dir Gen)*

SAMSIC
Lotissement Forum De La Rocade 40 Rue Du Bignon, 35510, Cesson Sevigne, Ille Et Vilaine, France
Tel.: (33) 299869290
Web Site: http://www.samsic.fr
Rev.: $26,600,000
Emp.: 11
Real Property Lessor
N.A.I.C.S.: 531190
Christian Roulleau *(Chm)*

SAMSKIP HOLDING B.V.
Waalhaven Oostzijde 81, 3087, Rotterdam, Netherlands
Tel.: (31) 88 400 1000
Web Site: http://www.samskip.com
Emp.: 1,400
Freight Transportation Services
N.A.I.C.S.: 488510
Kari-Pekka Laaksonen *(CEO)*

SAMSON INTERNATIONAL PLC
Akuressa Road, Bogahagoda Galle, Colombo, Sri Lanka
Tel.: (94) 913094469
Web Site:
    https://www.samsonint.com
SIL—(COL)
Rev.: $9,636,363
Assets: $7,109,128
Liabilities: $4,108,632
Net Worth: $3,000,496
Earnings: $309,240
Emp.: 507
Fiscal Year-end: 03/31/23
Vulcanized Rubber Products Mfr
N.A.I.C.S.: 315250
D. Kulatunga Rajapaksa *(Chm & Co-Mng Dir)*

SAMSON OIL & GAS LIMITED
Level 8 99 St Georges Terrace, Perth, 6000, WA, Australia
Tel.: (61) 894864036   AU
Web Site:
    http://www.samsonoilandgas.com
SSNYY—(OTCBB)
Rev.: $12,662,865
Assets: $36,851,634
Liabilities: $46,682,885
Net Worth: ($9,831,251)
Earnings: ($7,148,031)
Emp.: 5
Fiscal Year-end: 06/30/19
Oil & Gas Exploration Services
N.A.I.C.S.: 211120
Terence Maxwell Barr *(Pres, CEO & Mng Dir)*

Subsidiaries:

Samson Oil & Gas USA Montana, Inc. (1)
1331 17th St Ste 710, Denver, CO 80202
Tel.: (303) 296-3994
Oil & Gas Exploration Services
N.A.I.C.S.: 211120

Samson Oil & Gas USA, Inc. (1)
1726 Cole Blvd Ste 210, Lakewood, CO 80401
Tel.: (303) 295-0344
Oil & Gas Exploration Services
N.A.I.C.S.: 211120
Terence Maxwell Barr *(CEO)*

SAMSON PAPER HOLDINGS LIMITED
3/F Seapower Industrial Centre 177 Hoi Bun Road Kwun Tong, Kowloon, China (Hong Kong)
Tel.: (852) 2 342 7181   BM

Web Site:
    http://www.samsonpaper.com
Year Founded: 1965
Rev.: $754,369,663
Assets: $832,901,950
Liabilities: $553,730,366
Net Worth: $279,171,584
Earnings: $15,281,556
Emp.: 1,863
Fiscal Year-end: 03/31/19
Paper Products Mfr
N.A.I.C.S.: 322299
Albert Yue Kong Lee *(CFO & Sec)*

Subsidiaries:

Burotech Limited (1)
3 / F Hoi Yu Industrial Centre 177 Hoi Bun Road, Kwun Tong, Kowloon, China (Hong Kong)
Tel.: (852) 27631383
Web Site: http://www.burotech.com
Commercial Paper & Office Supplies Whslr
N.A.I.C.S.: 424120

High Flyer International Limited (1)
3/F Seapower Industrial Centre 177 Hoi Bun Road, Kwun Tong, Kowloon, China (Hong Kong)
Tel.: (852) 2197 4700
Web Site: http://www.highflyerintl.com
Food Products Distr
N.A.I.C.S.: 424490

Subsidiary (Non-US):

Shenzhen High Flyer International Transportation Company Limited (2)
Room 711 Harbour Building Shenyan Road, Yantian District, Shenzhen, 518081, China
Tel.: (86) 75525290802
Paper Product Distr
N.A.I.C.S.: 424120

Prospec Pte Ltd (1)
132 Gul Circle, Singapore, 629597, Singapore
Tel.: (65) 68977781
Web Site: http://www.prospecpl.com.sg
Hardware Product Mfr
N.A.I.C.S.: 332510

Samson Paper (Beijing) Company Limited (1)
Room 1103 Block B No 3 Building Ping Guo Community 32 Bai Zi Wan Road, Chaoyang District, Beijing, 100022, China
Tel.: (86) 1052097800
Paper Product Distr
N.A.I.C.S.: 424120

Samson Paper (Shanghai) Company Limited (1)
Unit 1 Block 135 ShangZhong Road W, Shanghai, 200237, China
Tel.: (86) 2154298511
Paper Product Distr
N.A.I.C.S.: 424120

Samson Paper (Shenzhen) Company Limited (1)
Room D 37/F Block C Electronic Science & Technology Building, No 2070 Shennan Road Central Futian District, Shenzhen, 518031, China
Tel.: (86) 75583287821
Paper Product Distr
N.A.I.C.S.: 424120

Samson Paper Company Limited (1)
3/F Seapower Industrial Centre No 177 Hoi Bun Road, Kwun Tong, Kowloon, China (Hong Kong)
Tel.: (852) 23427181
Paper Products Mfr
N.A.I.C.S.: 322299

Shun Hing Paper Company Limited (1)
3/F Seapower Industrial Centre No 177 Hoi Bun Road, Kwun Tong, Kowloon, China (Hong Kong)
Tel.: (852) 23462898
Paper Products Mfr
N.A.I.C.S.: 322299

Sino Development (Tianjin) International Trading Co., Ltd. (1)
Room 701 4th Unit No 23 Xiang Yang Avenue Shanghai Road, Tanggu District, Tianjin, 300450, China
Tel.: (86) 2225853002
Paper Product Distr
N.A.I.C.S.: 424120

United Aviation (Singapore) Pte. Ltd. (1)
132 Gul Circle, Singapore, 629597, Singapore
Tel.: (65) 67762356
Paper Product Distr
N.A.I.C.S.: 424120

Universal Pulp & Paper (Shandong) Company Limited (1)
No 3388 Zaocao Road, Xuecheng District, Zaozhuang, 277014, Shandong, China
Tel.: (86) 6324401860
Paper Product Distr
N.A.I.C.S.: 424120

SAMSONITE INTERNATIONAL S.A.

25/F Tower 2 The Gateway Harbour City 25 Canton Road, Tsimshatsui, Kowloon, China (Hong Kong)
Tel.: (852) 24222611   CO
Web Site: http://www.samsonite.com
Year Founded: 1910
1910—(HKG)
Rev.: $2,879,600,000
Assets: $4,721,100,000
Liabilities: $3,641,500,000
Net Worth: $1,079,600,000
Earnings: $338,300,000
Emp.: 10,100
Fiscal Year-end: 12/31/22
Luggage Mfr
N.A.I.C.S.: 314910
Timothy Charles Parker *(Chm)*

Subsidiaries:

AboutBags NV (1)
Westerring 17, 9700, Oudenaarde, Belgium
Tel.: (32) 51280840
Traveling Bag Retailer
N.A.I.C.S.: 458320

PT Samsonite Indonesia (1)
Sahid Sudirman Center Lt 27 Jl Jend Sudirman Kav 86 Karet Tengsin, Tanah Abang, Jakarta Pusat, 10220, Indonesia
Tel.: (62) 80648080
Web Site: http://www.samsonite.co.id
Travel Bag & Accessory Retailer
N.A.I.C.S.: 458320
Magnolia Ranti Manullang *(Mgr-Sls)*

Samsonite (Thailand) Co., Ltd. (1)
98 Sathorn Square Office Tower Building 37th Floor, Room No 3705 - 3706 North Sathorn Road Silom Subdistrict Bang Rak, Bangkok, 10500, Thailand
Tel.: (66) 27619936
Web Site: https://www.samsonite.co.th
Luggage Product Retailer
N.A.I.C.S.: 458320

Samsonite A/S (1)
Ny Ostergade 2, 1100, Copenhagen, Denmark
Tel.: (45) 33111201
Web Site: https://www.samsonite.dk
Luggage Product Whslr
N.A.I.C.S.: 327910

Samsonite AB (1)
Sodra Vagen 6, 412 54, Gothenburg, Sweden
Tel.: (46) 730796031
Web Site: https://www.samsonite.se
Emp.: 13,600
Luggage Product Retailer
N.A.I.C.S.: 458320

Samsonite AG (1)
Riedstrasse 8, 8953, Dietikon, Switzerland
Tel.: (41) 105824517
Luggage Product Retailer
N.A.I.C.S.: 458320

Samsonite Asia Limited (1)
25/F Tower 2 The Gateway Harbour City 25 Canton Rd, Tsim Sha Tsui, Kowloon, China (Hong Kong)
Tel.: (852) 36659377
Web Site: http://www.samsonite.com.hk
Luggage Product Whslr
N.A.I.C.S.: 423990

Samsonite Australia Pty Limited (1)
5 Anzed Court, Mulgrave, 3170, VIC, Australia
Tel.: (61) 1800331690
Web Site: https://www.samsonite.com.au
Luggage Product Retailer
N.A.I.C.S.: 458320

Samsonite B.V. (1)
Koningin Wilhelminaplein 13, 1062 HH, Amsterdam, Netherlands
Tel.: (31) 206712290
Web Site: https://www.samsonite.nl
Emp.: 10
Luggage Product Retailer
N.A.I.C.S.: 458320

Samsonite Brasil Ltda. (1)
Avenida Roque Petroni Junior 850-20th Floor-Torre Jaceru, Itaqui, Sao Paulo, 04707-000, Brazil
Tel.: (55) 44108900
Web Site: https://www.samsonite.com.br
Travel Bag & Accessory Retailer
N.A.I.C.S.: 458320

Samsonite Canada (1)
305 C H Meier Blvd, Stratford, N5A 0H4, ON, Canada
Tel.: (519) 271-5040
Web Site: https://www.samsonite.ca
Sales Range: $25-49.9 Million
Emp.: 60
Luggage & Business Cases Distr
N.A.I.C.S.: 316990

Samsonite Chile S.A. (1)
Av Manquehue North 160 Floor 12, Las Condes, Santiago, Chile
Tel.: (56) 26178883
Web Site: https://www.samsonite.cl
Travel Bag & Accessory Retailer
N.A.I.C.S.: 458320

Samsonite Colombia S.A.S. (1)
Transversal 23 No 97-73, Bogota, Colombia
Tel.: (57) 708709710
Web Site: https://www.samsonite.com.co
Travel Bag & Accessory Retailer
N.A.I.C.S.: 458320

Samsonite Espana S.A. (1)
Maria Tubau 3 4th floor, 28050, Madrid, Spain
Tel.: (34) 910822167
Web Site: https://www.samsonite.es
Luggage Product Retailer
N.A.I.C.S.: 458320

Samsonite Europe N.V (1)
Westerring 17, 9700, Oudenaarde, Belgium
Tel.: (32) 28962872
Web Site: https://www.samsonite.be
Luggage Product Mfr & Distr
N.A.I.C.S.: 316990

Samsonite Finland Oy (1)
Etelaesplanadi 14, 00130, Helsinki, Finland
Tel.: (358) 107597220
Web Site: http://www.samsonite.fi
Luggage Product Retailer
N.A.I.C.S.: 458320

Samsonite GmbH (1)
Colonius Carre Subbelrather Strasse 15a, 50823, Cologne, Germany
Tel.: (49) 2219216410
Web Site: http://www.samsonite.de
Luggage Product Whslr
N.A.I.C.S.: 423990

Samsonite Hungaria Borond KFT (1)
Keselyusi Ut 5, 7100, Szekszard, Budapest, Hungary
Tel.: (36) 74412033
Luggage Product Retailer
N.A.I.C.S.: 458320

Samsonite Japan Co., Ltd. (1)
5F F Nissay Ebisu Building 16-3 Higashi 3-chome, Shibuya-ku, Tokyo, 150-0011, Japan
Tel.: (81) 338321111
Web Site: https://www.samsonite.co.jp
Emp.: 370
Luggage Product Retailer

SAMSONITE INTERNATIONAL S.A.

Samsonite International S.A.—(Continued)

Samsonite Korea Limited (1)
12th floor Hongwoo Building 945-1 Daechi-dong, Gangnam-gu, Seoul, Korea (South)
Tel.: (82) 25672486
Web Site: https://www.samsonite.co.kr
Luggage Product Retailer
N.A.I.C.S.: 458320

Samsonite LLC (1)
575 W St Ste 110, Mansfield, MA 02048
Tel.: (508) 851-1400
Web Site: https://shop.samsonite.com
Sales Range: $1-4.9 Billion
Emp.: 250
Luggage, Business Case & Other Bag Mfr
N.A.I.C.S.: 316990

Subsidiary (Domestic):

Gregory Mountain Products, LLC (2)
2088 E 3900 S, Salt Lake City, UT 84124
Tel.: (801) 993-6633
Web Site: http://www.gregorypacks.com
Backpacks & Outdoor Performance Equipment & Apparel Mfr
N.A.I.C.S.: 339920

HL Operating LLC (2)
575 West St Ste 110, Mansfield, MA 02048
Tel.: (508) 851-1400
Web Site: http://www.hartmann.com
Sales Range: $25-49.9 Million
Emp.: 250
Luggage & Leather Accessories Mfr
N.A.I.C.S.: 316990

High Sierra Sport Company (2)
705 Tri-State Pkwy, Gurnee, IL 60031
Tel.: (847) 913-1100
Web Site: http://www.highsierra.com
Sales Range: $10-24.9 Million
Emp.: 35
Knapsack & Luggage Mfr
N.A.I.C.S.: 314999

eBags, LLC (2)
5500 Greenwood Plz Blvd Ste 160, Greenwood Village, CO 80111
Tel.: (773) 661-4317
Web Site: http://www.ebags.com
Bags, Luggage, Clothing & Accessories Retailer
N.A.I.C.S.: 458320
Mike Frazzini *(CTO & Sr VP-Ops)*

Samsonite Ltd. (1)
5 The Square Stockley Park, Uxbridge, UB11 1ET, Middlesex, United Kingdom
Tel.: (44) 2037476769
Web Site: https://www.samsonite.co.uk
Sales Range: $25-49.9 Million
Emp.: 20
Luggage Mfr & Retailer
N.A.I.C.S.: 316990

Samsonite Mexico, S.A. de C.V (1)
Boulevard Manuel Avila Camacho No 5 Tower B Floor 24 Office B-2402, Colonia Lomas de Sotelo Naucalpan de Juarez, 53390, Mexico, Mexico
Tel.: (52) 5541640513
Web Site: https://www.samsonite.com.mx
Luggage Product Mfr & Whslr
N.A.I.C.S.: 316990

Samsonite Panama S.A. (1)
PH Blue Business Center Piso 5 Ofic 5-2 Calle 67, San Francisco, Panama
Tel.: (507) 3222729
Travel Bag & Accessory Retailer
N.A.I.C.S.: 458320

Samsonite Peru S.A.C. (1)
Av Primavera 1796 Oficina 201 Santiago de Surco Tienda Jockey Plaza, B3-03 boulevard 3 av Javier prado, 4200, Lima, Peru
Tel.: (51) 14378909
Travel Bag & Accessory Retailer
N.A.I.C.S.: 458320

Samsonite Philippines, Inc. (1)
2/F Enzo Building 399 Senator Gil Puyat Avenue, Makati, 1200, Philippines
Tel.: (63) 282421794
Web Site: https://www.samsonite.com.ph
Emp.: 16
Luggage Product Retailer

N.A.I.C.S.: 458320
Cielito Buenviaje *(Gen Mgr)*

Samsonite S.A.S. (1)
7-11 Boulevard Haussmann, 75009, Paris, France
Tel.: (33) 173443233
Web Site: https://www.samsonite.fr
Luggage Product Whslr
N.A.I.C.S.: 423990

Samsonite S.p.A. (1)
Viale Thomas Alva Edison 110, 20099, Sesto San Giovanni, Italy
Tel.: (39) 0230578193
Web Site: https://www.samsonite.it
Luggage Product Whslr
N.A.I.C.S.: 423990

Samsonite Seyahat Urunleri Sanayi ve Ticaret Anonim Sirketi (1)
Yesilkoy IDTM Bloks A2 Block Floor 5 No 209, Bakirkoy, 34149, Istanbul, Türkiye
Tel.: (90) 2126922300
Web Site: https://www.samsonite.com.tr
Travel Bag & Accessory Retailer
N.A.I.C.S.: 458320

Samsonite South Asia Private Limited (1)
402 Ackruti Star Central Road MIDC Opp Centre Point Bldg, Andheri E, Mumbai, 400093, Maharashtra, India
Tel.: (91) 2233212601
Web Site: https://www.samsonite.in
Emp.: 200
Luggage Product Mfr & Distr
N.A.I.C.S.: 316990

Samsonite Southern Africa Ltd. (1)
68 On Main 68 Old Main Road, Westville, Kloof, 3610, KwaZulu-Natal, South Africa
Tel.: (27) 312660620
Web Site: https://www.samsonite.co.za
Luggage Product Retailer
N.A.I.C.S.: 458320

Tumi (UK) Limited (1)
Palmerston House 814 Brighton Road, Purley, CR8 2BR, Surrey, United Kingdom
Tel.: (44) 2039667966
Web Site: https://uk.tumi.com
Clothing Accessory Retailer
N.A.I.C.S.: 458110

Tumi Canada ULC (1)
PO Box 2380, Halifax, B3J 3E5, NS, Canada
Tel.: (908) 156-4400
Travel Bag & Accessory Retailer
N.A.I.C.S.: 458320

Tumi Charlotte Airport LLC (1)
5501 Josh Birmingham Pkwy Space 21A D2011, Charlotte, NC 28208
Tel.: (704) 359-8771
Travel Bag & Accessory Retailer
N.A.I.C.S.: 458320

Tumi Holdings, Inc. (1)
1001 Durham Ave, South Plainfield, NJ 07080
Tel.: (908) 756-4400
Web Site: http://www.tumi.com
Sales Range: $500-549.9 Million
Holding Company; Luggage, Handbags, Wallets & Accessories Designer & Mfr
N.A.I.C.S.: 551112
Peter L. Gray *(Gen Counsel & Exec VP)*

Subsidiary (Domestic):

Tumi, Inc. (2)
1001 Durham Ave, South Plainfield, NJ 07080 (100%)
Tel.: (908) 756-4400
Web Site: http://www.tumi.com
Sales Range: $200-249.9 Million
Luggage, Handbags & Wallets Mfr
N.A.I.C.S.: 316990

Subsidiary (Non-US):

Tumi D2C GmbH (3)
Hans-Bockler-Str 6, 59423, Unna, Germany
Tel.: (49) 23035523015
Web Site: https://eu.tumi.com
Online Luggage Retailer
N.A.I.C.S.: 458320

Tumi Houston Airport LLC (1)

3701 S Terminal Rd Terminal D, Houston, TX 77032
Tel.: (281) 443-0390
Travel Bag & Accessory Retailer
N.A.I.C.S.: 458320

SAMSUNG BIOLOGICS CO., LTD.

300 Songdo bio-daero, Yeonsu-gu, Incheon, 21987, Korea (South)
Tel.: (82) 324553114
Web Site: https://www.samsungbiologics.com
Year Founded: 2011
207940—(KRS)
Rev.: $2,301,993,417
Assets: $12,718,432,548
Liabilities: $5,827,340,687
Net Worth: $6,891,091,861
Earnings: $612,109,113
Emp.: 4,001
Fiscal Year-end: 12/31/22
Biological Product Mfr & Distr
N.A.I.C.S.: 325414
Dongjoong Kim *(CFO & Sr VP)*

Subsidiaries:

AdGear Technologies Inc. (1)
800 Rene-Levesque Blvd W Suite 1000, Montreal, H3B 1X9, QC, Canada
Tel.: (514) 394-7951
Web Site: https://samsungads.ca
Advertising Technology Services
N.A.I.C.S.: 541810

Centrade Cheil Adriatic D.O.O. (1)
Bulevar Oslobodjenja 79, 11000, Belgrade, Serbia
Tel.: (381) 993755000
Advertising Services
N.A.I.C.S.: 541810

Centrade Cheil HU Kft. (1)
Gateway Office Park I Tower 1138 Dunavirag Str 2, Budapest, Hungary
Tel.: (36) 304441034
Advertising Services
N.A.I.C.S.: 541810

Centrade Integrated S.R.L. (1)
Central Business Park Calea Serban Voda 133, Bucharest, Romania
Tel.: (40) 317300600
Web Site: https://centrade-cheil.com
Advertising Services
N.A.I.C.S.: 541810

Corephotonics Ltd. (1)
Menachem Begin 146 21st Floor, Tel Aviv, 6492103, Israel
Tel.: (972) 36419888
Web Site: https://corephotonics.com
Photography Technologies Services
N.A.I.C.S.: 541921

Equipment Trading Solutions Group, LLC (1)
5601 E Slauson Ave Ste 101E, Commerce, CA 90040
Web Site: https://etsgusa.com
Semiconductor Equipment Mfr
N.A.I.C.S.: 334515

Harman Deutschland GmbH (1)
Parkring 3, 85748, Garching, Germany
Tel.: (49) 3022957806
Web Site: https://www.harmankardon.de
Electrical Appliance Whslr
N.A.I.C.S.: 423620

Harman Professional Denmark ApS (1)
Olof Palmes Alle 44, DK-8200, Arhus, Denmark
Tel.: (45) 441707668110
Web Site: https://www.martin.com
Automated Light Mfr
N.A.I.C.S.: 339999

Iris (USA) Inc. (1)
11111 80th Ave, Pleasant Prairie, WI 53158
Web Site: https://www.irisusainc.com
Household Appliances Mfr
N.A.I.C.S.: 335220

Iris Digital Limited (1)
4 & 5th Floor Plot No 47 48 49 Street No 1

INTERNATIONAL PUBLIC

Street 2 Patrika Nagar, Madhapur, Telangana, 500081, India
Tel.: (91) 4067337036
Web Site: https://irisdigitaltech.com
Emp.: 150
Software Development Services
N.A.I.C.S.: 541511

Iris Korea Limited (1)
29 Cheomdan-daero 60beon-gil, Yeonsu-gu, Incheon, Korea (South)
Tel.: (82) 28033
Web Site: https://www.iriskorea.co.kr
Emp.: 120
Digital Advertising Services
N.A.I.C.S.: 541810

Iris London Limited (1)
3rd Floor 10 Queen Street Place, London, EC4R 1BE, United Kingdom
Tel.: (44) 2076547900
Provides Advertising Services
N.A.I.C.S.: 541810

Iris Worldwide (Thailand) Limited (1)
Iris Bangkok 21 Apai Loft Building G Floor Unit 14 Soi Ekkamai, 22 Nuan Noi Kwang Klongton nur Khet Wattana, Bangkok, 10110, Thailand
Tel.: (66) 23922257
Advertising Services
N.A.I.C.S.: 541890

Iris Worldwide Integrated Marketing Private Limited (1)
VR 1 Centre 202 on Level 2 Plot No 83 City Centre Sector 29, Gurgaon, 122001, India
Tel.: (91) 1244264194
Advertising Services
N.A.I.C.S.: 541890

McKinney Ventures LLC (1)
318 Blackwell St, Durham, NC 27701
Tel.: (919) 313-0802
Web Site: https://mckinney.com
Digital Advertising Services
N.A.I.C.S.: 541810

Medialytics Inc. (1)
Building No 28 Electronic Cooperative Estate Ltd Pune-Satara Road, Parvati, Pune, 411009, Maharashtra, India
Tel.: (91) 7756899117
Web Site: https://www.themedialytics.com
Information Technology Managed Services
N.A.I.C.S.: 541512

Pricing Solutions Ltd. (1)
106 Front Street East, Toronto, M5A 1E1, ON, Canada
Tel.: (416) 943-0505
Business Consulting & Services
N.A.I.C.S.: 541618

S.C. Otelinox S.A (1)
16 Gaesti Street, Dambovita, 130087, Targoviste, Romania
Tel.: (40) 245209100
Web Site: https://www.otelinox.com
Cold-Rolled Stainless Steel Mfr
N.A.I.C.S.: 331110

SAMSUNG Zhilabs, S.L. (1)
Av Josep Tarradellas 123 3 C, 08029, Barcelona, Spain
Tel.: (34) 934109010
Web Site: https://www.zhilabs.com
Mobile Telecommunications Services
N.A.I.C.S.: 541618

Samsung C&T Thailand Co., Ltd. (1)
21St Fl Lake Rajada Office Complex 193/90 Rachadapisek Rd Khet, Klongtoey, Bangkok, 10110, Thailand
Tel.: (66) 22640527
Chemical & Energy Mfr
N.A.I.C.S.: 331110

Samsung Electronica Colombia S.A. (1)
Carrera 7 113-43 Of 607, Bogota, Colombia
Tel.: (57) 6001272
Digital Media Research Services
N.A.I.C.S.: 541519

Samsung Electronics Baltics Sia (1)
6 Duntes Street, Riga, LV-1013, Latvia
Tel.: (371) 80057267864
Web Site: https://www.samsung.com
Advertising Technology Services
N.A.I.C.S.: 541810

AND PRIVATE COMPANIES

SAMSUNG GROUP

Samsung Electronics Saudi Arabia Ltd. (1)
9th Floor Hamad Tower, PO Box 3143, Riyadh, 12212, Saudi Arabia
Tel.: (966) 8002474357
Digital Media Research Services
N.A.I.C.S.: 541519

Samsung HVAC America, LLC (1)
776 Henrietta Creek Rd Ste 100, Roanoke, TX 76262
Tel.: (817) 838-6066
Web Site: https www.samsunghvac.com
Heating & Cooling Product Whslr
N.A.I.C.S.: 423730

Samsung Research America, Inc. (1)
665 Clyde Ave, Mountain View, CA 94043
Tel.: (650) 210-1001
Web Site: https://sra.samsung.com
Digital Media Research Services
N.A.I.C.S.: 541519

WDMP Limited (1)
3rd Floor 10 Queen Street Place, London, EC4R 1BE, United Kingdom
Tel.: (44) 7976127761
Advertising Services
N.A.I.C.S.: 541890

SAMSUNG CLIMATE CONTROL CO., LTD.
176 Yeondeok-ro, Seongsan-gu, Changwon, Gyeongsangnam-do, Korea (South)
Tel.: (82) 552802737
Web Site: http://www.samsungcc.co.kr
Year Founded: 1970
006660—(KRS)
Rev.: $73,436,686
Assets: $236,738,225
Liabilities: $38,184,236
Net Worth: $198,553,988
Earnings: $31,417,700
Emp.: 156
Fiscal Year-end: 12/31/22
Automotive Components Mfr
N.A.I.C.S.: 336390
Ho-Kon Ko *(Chm & CEO)*

SAMSUNG GROUP
129 Samseong ro Yeongtong gu, Suwon, 137-857, Gyeonggi-do, Korea (South)
Tel.: (82) 222550114
Web Site: http://www.samsung.com
Year Founded: 1938
Sales Range: Less than $1 Million
Holding Company; Commodities Trading & Construction, Electronics & Semiconductors, Food & Chemicals, Textiles, Paper, Petrochemicals & Ship Building
N.A.I.C.S.: 551112
Ki Nam Kim *(Vice Chm/Co-CEO-Samsung Electronics)*

Subsidiaries:

Cheil Worldwide Inc. (1)
222 Itaewon-ro Yongsan-gu, 04404, Seoul, Korea (South) **(25.2%)**
Tel.: (82) 237802114
Web Site: http://www.cheil.com
Rev.: $3,262,332,688
Assets: $2,110,358,413
Liabilities: $1,173,521,936
Net Worth: $936,836,477
Earnings: $148,592,179
Emp.: 1,410
Fiscal Year-end: 12/31/2022
Advetising Agency
N.A.I.C.S.: 541810
Sunwoo Jung *(Head-Brand Experience Bus)*

Subsidiary (Non-US):

Atom42 Limited (2)
10 Queen Street Place, London, EC4R 1BE, United Kingdom
Tel.: (44) 20 38139578
Web Site: http://www.atom42.co.uk
Advertising Services
N.A.I.C.S.: 541810
Andrew Atalla *(Founder)*

Division (US):

Cheil Americas (2)
112 W 20th St 7th Fl, New York, NY 10011
Tel.: (929) 310-7027
Web Site: http://www.cheil.com
Sales Range: $25-49.9 Million
Emp.: 250
Advetising Agency
N.A.I.C.S.: 541810

Subsidiary (Domestic):

Cheil USA Inc. (3)
112 W 20th St 7th Fl, New York, NY 10011
Tel.: (929) 310-7027
Web Site: http://www.cheil.com
Rev.: $70,000,000
Emp.: 8
Communications, Consumer Marketing, Information Technology
N.A.I.C.S.: 541810
Aaron Lou *(Pres & CEO)*

Subsidiary (Domestic):

McKinney & Silver LLC (4)
318 Blackwell St, Durham, NC 27701
Tel.: (919) 313-0802
Web Site: http://www.mckinney.com
Sales Range: $75-99.9 Million
Advertising Agency Services
N.A.I.C.S.: 541810
Janet Northen *(Dir-Agency Comm)*

The Barbarian Group, LLC (4)
129 S St 2nd Fl, Boston, MA 02111
Tel.: (617) 424-8887
Web Site: http://www.barbariangroup.com
Digital Advertising Agency
N.A.I.C.S.: 541810
Steven Moy *(CEO)*

Branch (Domestic):

The Barbarian Group (5)
11 Beach St 10th Fl, New York, NY 10013
Tel.: (212) 343-4215
Web Site: http://www.barbariangroup.com
Sales Range: $10-24.9 Million
N.A.I.C.S.: 541810

Samsung Asia Pte., Ltd (1)
30 Pasir Panjang Road No 17-31/32 Mapletree Business City, Singapore, 117440, Singapore
Tel.: (65) 6833 3106
Web Site: http://www.samsung.com
Electric Device Mfr
N.A.I.C.S.: 334419
Steve SangChul Lee *(Pres/CEO-Southeast Asia)*

Samsung C&T Corporation (1)
199 Everland-ro Pogok-eup, Cheoin-gu, Yongin, Gyeonggi-do, Korea (South)
Tel.: (82) 313205000
Web Site: https://rnc.samsungcnt.com
Rev.: $31,096,953,235
Assets: $49,082,604,110
Liabilities: $19,469,085,203
Net Worth: $29,613,518,906
Earnings: $2,018,248,977
Emp.: 9,492
Fiscal Year-end: 12/31/2023
Construction & Real Estate Services
N.A.I.C.S.: 236220
Chi Hun Choi *(Chm)*

Joint Venture (Domestic):

Hakuhodo-Cheil, Inc. (2)
8th floor Dabo Building 20 Mapo-daero, Mapo-gu, Seoul, 04175, Korea (South)
Tel.: (82) 22 021 3600
Web Site: https://www.hakuhodocheil.co.kr
Advertising Agency
N.A.I.C.S.: 541810
Chun Hwan Kim *(Pres & CEO)*

Subsidiary (Non-US):

Novaled AG (2)
Elisabeth-Boer-Strasse 9, 01099, Dresden, Germany **(50.1%)**
Tel.: (49) 351 79890 100
Web Site: http://www.novaled.com
Sales Range: $25-49.9 Million
Emp.: 129
Light Emitting Diode & Other Electronic Component Mfr
N.A.I.C.S.: 334419
Jinwook Lee *(Chm-Supervisory Bd)*

Subsidiary (US):

Samsung C&T America, Inc. (2)
105 Challenger Rd 3rd Fl, Ridgefield Park, NJ 07660-2119 **(100%)**
Tel.: (201) 229-5000
Web Site: http://www.samsungamerica.com
Commodities Trading & Marketing Services
N.A.I.C.S.: 523160

Subsidiary (Domestic):

Parallel Petroleum LLC (3)
1004 N Big Spring Street Suite 400, Midland, TX 79701 **(100%)**
Tel.: (432) 684-3727
Web Site: http://www.parallel-petro.com
Sales Range: $150-199.9 Million
Emp.: 46
Oil & Gas Exploration & Production
N.A.I.C.S.: 211120
Cindy Thomason *(Dir-PR)*

Division (Domestic):

Samsung America - Fashion & Entertainment Division (3)
1430 Broadway, New York, NY 10018-7701
Tel.: (212) 997-9600
Web Site: http://www.samsungamerica.com
Sales Range: $25-49.9 Million
Emp.: 42
Showroom
N.A.I.C.S.: 458110

Joint Venture (Domestic):

Samsung Total Petrochemicals Co., Ltd. (2)
103 Dokgot2-Ro Daesan-Eup, Seosan, 356-711, ChungNam, Korea (South) **(38.68%)**
Tel.: (82) 41 660 6114
Web Site: http://www.samsungchem.com
Olefin, Polyolefin & Aromatic Chemical Products Mfr & Distr
N.A.I.C.S.: 325110
Seog-Weon Son *(Pres & CEO)*

Samsung Card Co., Ltd. (1)
Samsung Main Bldg 67 Sejongdaero, Junggu, Seoul, 04514, Korea (South)
Tel.: (82) 0221727988
Web Site: http://www.samsungcard.co.kr
Rev.: $2,997,711,771
Assets: $23,402,322,370
Liabilities: $17,169,596,360
Net Worth: $6,232,726,010
Earnings: $491,580,718
Emp.: 1,981
Fiscal Year-end: 12/31/2022
Credit Card Services
N.A.I.C.S.: 522210
O. Kyu Kwon *(Chm)*

Samsung Denmark Research Center ApS (1)
Niels Jernes Vej 10, 9220, Aalborg, Denmark
Tel.: (45) 9932 4100
Web Site: http://www.samsung.com
Emp.: 40
Software Development Services
N.A.I.C.S.: 541511

Samsung Display Slovakia s.r.o. (1)
Voderady 401, 919 42, Voderady, Slovakia
Tel.: (421) 914324892
Web Site: http://www.samsung.com
Emp.: 1,000
Electric Device Mfr
N.A.I.C.S.: 334419

Samsung Display TianJin Co., Ltd. (1)
No 25 MipFouch Road, Xiqing District, Tianjin, China
Tel.: (86) 22 2380 8100
Electric Device Mfr
N.A.I.C.S.: 334419

Samsung Economic Research Institute (1)
28-31Fls Samsung Life Seocho Tower, Seocho-daero 74-gil 4 Seocho-gu, Seoul, Korea (South)
Tel.: (82) 237808000
Web Site: http://www.seriworld.org
Sales Range: $25-49.9 Million
Emp.: 195
Economic, Management & Policy Research Services
N.A.I.C.S.: 541715
Chung Ki Young *(CEO)*

Samsung Electro-Mechanics Co., Ltd. (1)
150 Maeyeong-ro, Yeongtong-gu, Suwon, Gyeonggi-do, Korea (South)
Tel.: (82) 312105114
Web Site: https://www.samsungsem.com
Rev.: $6,613,013,438
Assets: $8,653,022,877
Liabilities: $2,692,536,427
Net Worth: $5,960,486,451
Earnings: $334,369,109
Emp.: 11,973
Fiscal Year-end: 12/31/2023
Electronic Components Mfr
N.A.I.C.S.: 333248
Kye Hyun Kyung *(CEO)*

Subsidiary (US):

Samsung Electro-Mechanics America, Inc. (2)
3345 Michelson Dr Ste 350, Irvine, CA 92612
Tel.: (949) 797-8000
Web Site: http://www.sem.samsung.com
Sales Range: $25-49.9 Million
Emp.: 4
High-Tech Electronic Components Distr
N.A.I.C.S.: 423690

Samsung Electronics Co., Ltd. (1)
129 Samsung-Ro Maetan-3Dong, Yeongtong-Gu, Suwon, 16677, Gyeonggi-do, Korea (South)
Tel.: (82) 312001114
Web Site: http://www.samsung.com
Rev.: $217,862,428,960
Assets: $347,976,860,560
Liabilities: $94,104,685,840
Net Worth: $253,872,174,720
Earnings: $24,295,205,440
Emp.: 109,495
Fiscal Year-end: 12/31/2020
Electric Appliances Mfr
N.A.I.C.S.: 334419
Jong Hee Han *(Vice Chm & CEO)*

Subsidiary (Domestic):

SEMES Co., Ltd. (2)
77 4Sandan 5-Gil Jiksan-Eup Seobuk-Gu, Cheonan, Chungcheongnam-do, Korea (South)
Tel.: (82) 41 620 8000
Web Site: http://www.semes.com
Semiconductor Equipment Mfr
N.A.I.C.S.: 334413
Chang Jin Kang *(CEO)*

Subsidiary (Non-US):

Samsung (CHINA) Investment Electronics Co., Ltd. (2)
20/F Merchants Mansion No 118 Jianguo Rd, Chaoyang Dist, Beijing, 100022, China
Tel.: (86) 1065689988
Financial Management Services
N.A.I.C.S.: 523940

Subsidiary (Domestic):

Samsung Display Co., Ltd. (2)
1 Samsung-ro, Giheung-gu, Yongin, Gyeonggi-do, Korea (South)
Tel.: (82) 3151811114
Web Site: https://www.samsungdisplay.com
OLED & LCD Display Products Solutions
N.A.I.C.S.: 334413
Joo Sun Choi *(Pres & CEO)*

Subsidiary (US):

eMagin Corporation (3)
700 S Dr Ste 201, Hopewell Junction, NY 12533
Tel.: (845) 838-7900
Web Site: https://www.emagin.com
Rev.: $30,531,000

SAMSUNG GROUP

Samsung Group—(Continued)
Assets: $73,107,000
Liabilities: $49,312,000
Net Worth: $23,795,000
Earnings: ($1,103,000)
Emp.: 107
Fiscal Year-end: 12/31/2022
Circuit & Interface Products Mfr
N.A.I.C.S.: 334413
Olivier Prache *(Sr VP-Product Dev)*

Subsidiary (Non-US):

Samsung Electronica Da Amazonia LTDA. (2)
R Henri Dunant 1383 - Morumbi, 04709-110, Sao Paulo, Brazil
Tel.: (55) 11 4004 0000
Electric Device Mfr
N.A.I.C.S.: 334419

Samsung Electronics (Suzhou) Computer Co., Ltd. (2)
Fengli Street Suzhou Industrial Park, Suzhou, Jiangsu, China
Tel.: (86) 512 6253 8988
Electric Device Mfr
N.A.I.C.S.: 334419

Samsung Electronics (Suzhou) Semiconductor Co., Ltd. (2)
No 15 Jin Ji Hu Road Suzhou Industrial Park, Suzhou, 215021, China
Tel.: (86) 512 6761 7391
Web Site: http://www.samsung.com
Electric Device Mfr
N.A.I.C.S.: 334419

Samsung Electronics (UK) Limited (2)
Samsung House 1000 Hillswood Drive, Chertsey, KT16 0PS, Surrey, United Kingdom
Tel.: (44) 1932455000
Web Site: http://www.samsung.com
Sales Range: $1-4.9 Billion
Emp.: 600
Consumer Electronics Sales
N.A.I.C.S.: 449210
Francis B. J. Chun *(Pres & CEO)*

Subsidiary (US):

Samsung Electronics America, Inc. (2)
85 Challenger Rd, Ridgefield Park, NJ 07660 (100%)
Tel.: (201) 229-4000
Web Site: http://www.samsung.com
Electronic Product Distr
N.A.I.C.S.: 423620
Hoon Eom Young *(Pres/CEO-North America)*

Subsidiary (Domestic):

Dacor, Inc. (3)
14425 Clark Avenue, City of Industry, CA 91745-1235
Tel.: (626) 799-1000
Web Site: http://www.dacor.com
Sales Range: $25-49.9 Million
Household Cooking Equipment Mfr & Distr
N.A.I.C.S.: 335220

Grandis, Inc. (3)
1123 Cadillac Ct, Milpitas, CA 95035
Tel.: (408) 945-2160
Web Site: http://www.grandisinc.com
Sales Range: $25-49.9 Million
Emp.: 15
Computer Storage Device Mfr
N.A.I.C.S.: 334112

Harman International Industries, Incorporated (3)
400 Atlantic St 15th Fl, Stamford, CT 06901
Tel.: (203) 328-3500
Web Site: http://www.harman.com
Video & Audio Systems Mfr
N.A.I.C.S.: 334310
Ralph E. Santana *(CMO & Exec VP)*

Subsidiary (Domestic):

AMX LLC (4)
3000 Research Dr, Richardson, TX 75082-3546
Tel.: (512) 786-0107
Web Site: http://www.amx.com
Audio & Visual Control Devices Mfr
N.A.I.C.S.: 334310

Subsidiary (Non-US):

Aditi Technologies Private Ltd. (4)
C4 Block Wing A Manyata SEZ Park Rachenahalli, Nagawara Villages Outer Ring R, Bengaluru, 560 045, India
Tel.: (91) 8066107000
Web Site: http://www.aditi.com
Custom Computer Programming Services
N.A.I.C.S.: 541511

Subsidiary (Domestic):

Crown Audio, Inc. (4)
8500 Balboa Blvd, Northridge, CA 91329 (100%)
Tel.: (844) 776-4899
Web Site: http://www.crownaudio.com
Power Amplifiers; Pressure Zone & Hand-Held Microphones Mfr
N.A.I.C.S.: 334310

Subsidiary (Non-US):

Harman Becker Automotive Systems GmbH (4)
Becker-Goring-Strasse 16, 76307, Karlsbad, Germany (100%)
Tel.: (49) 7248 715191
Web Site: http://www.beckermappilot.com
Home Audio & Video Equipment Mfr
N.A.I.C.S.: 334310
Frank Groth *(Chm-Supervisory Bd)*

Subsidiary (Domestic):

Harman Becker Autologic Systems GmbH (5)
Raiffeisen Str 34, 70794, Filderstadt, Germany (100%)
Tel.: (49) 711907700
Web Site: http://www.mybecker.com
Sales Range: $50-74.9 Million
Emp.: 200
Provider of Computer Programming Services
N.A.I.C.S.: 541511

Subsidiary (Non-US):

Harman Becker Automotive Systems GmbH (5)
Tillgangligheten 1, Gothenburg, 417 10, Sweden (100%)
Tel.: (46) 728852925
Web Site: http://www.harmanbecker.com
Engine Electrical Equipment Mfr
N.A.I.C.S.: 336320

Harman Becker Automotive Systems S.A. de C.V. (5)
Avenida de las Torres 2290, Ciudad Juarez, Mexico
Tel.: (52) 9152985000
Web Site: http://www.harman.com
Mfr of Automotive Amplifiers & Speakers
N.A.I.C.S.: 334310

Subsidiary (Non-US):

Harman Becker Automotive Systems Italy S.r.l. (4)
Corso Unione Sovietica 612/15 A, Lainate, 20020, Milan, Italy
Tel.: (39) 0522307200
Web Site: http://www.harman.com
Audio Product & Electronic System Design & Mfr
N.A.I.C.S.: 334310

Harman Belgium NV (4)
Drukpersstraat 4, Post Box 1000, Brussels, Belgium
Tel.: (32) 27853232
Web Site: http://www.harmangarden.com
Audio Equipment Mfr
N.A.I.C.S.: 334310

Subsidiary (Domestic):

Harman Embedded Audio, LLC (4)
6602 E 75th St Ste 520, Indianapolis, IN 46250
Tel.: (317) 849-8175
Web Site: http://embedded.harman.com
Audio Product & Electronic Systems Design & Mfr

N.A.I.C.S.: 334310
Bill Esrey *(Sr Dir-Global Sls)*

Subsidiary (Non-US):

Harman Holding GmbH & Co. KG (4)
Im Stoeckmaedle Flst Nr 5708 Front Building Underground Ground, 2nd and 3rd Floor Karlsbad, Karlsruhe, 76307, Baden-Wurttemberg DE, Germany
Tel.: (49) 7248710
Web Site: http://www.harman.com
Investment Management Service
N.A.I.C.S.: 551112

Harman International Industries Ltd. (4)
Ground Floor Westside Two London Road Apsley, Hemel Hempstead, HP3 9TD, Herts, United Kingdom
Tel.: (44) 1244891140
Web Site: http://www.harman.com
Video & Audio Systems Mfr
N.A.I.C.S.: 334310

Subsidiary (Domestic):

BSS Audio (5)
Cranborne House Cranborne Rd, Potters Bar, EN6 3JN, Hertfordshire, United Kingdom (100%)
Tel.: (44) 1707660667
Web Site: http://www.bssaudio.com
Professional Loudspeaker Management Systems Designer
N.A.I.C.S.: 334310

Soundcraft (5)
Cranborne House Cranborne Rd, Potters Bar, EN6 3JN, Hertfordshire, United Kingdom (100%)
Tel.: (44) 1 707 665000
Web Site: http://www.soundcraft.com
Professional Sound Mixing Consoles & Photographic Equipment & Supplies Mfr & Distr
N.A.I.C.S.: 334310

Subsidiary (Non-US):

Harman International Japan Co. Ltd. (4)
Kotokudo Bldg 5-7-7 Ueno, Taito Ku, Tokyo, 110 0005, Japan (100%)
Tel.: (81) 338365641
Web Site: http://www.harman-japan.co.jp
Whslr of Home Audio & Video Equipment
N.A.I.C.S.: 334310

Harman International Singapore Pte. Ltd. (4)
108 Pasir Panjang Road 02-08, Singapore, Singapore
Tel.: (65) 62662527
Web Site: http://www.harman.com
Audio Product & Electronic System Design & Mfr
N.A.I.C.S.: 334310

Subsidiary (Domestic):

Harman Professional, Inc. (4)
1718 W Mishawaka Rd, Elkhart, IN 46517-9439
Tel.: (574) 294-8000
Web Site: http://pro.harman.com
Audio Product & Electronic System Design & Mfr
N.A.I.C.S.: 334310

Subsidiary (Non-US):

ISGPAS General Purpose Applications Systems GmbH (4)
Behringstr 28 A, 22765, Hamburg, Germany
Tel.: (49) 403339550
Audio Product & Electronic System Design & Mfr
N.A.I.C.S.: 334310

Subsidiary (Domestic):

Infinity Systems, Inc. (4)
250 Crossways Park Dr, Woodbury, NY 11797 (100%)
Tel.: (800) 553-3332
Web Site: http://www.infinitysystems.com
Stereo Loud Speakers (for Car & Home) Mfr

INTERNATIONAL PUBLIC

N.A.I.C.S.: 423620

Subsidiary (Non-US):

Martin Professional A/S (4)
Olof Palmes Alle 44, Arhus, DK-8200, Denmark
Tel.: (45) 1707 668110
Web Site: http://www.martin.com
Lighting Equipment Design & Installation Services
N.A.I.C.S.: 335132

Subsidiary (Non-US):

Martin Professional Pte. Ltd. (5)
108 Pasir Panjang Road No 02-08 Golden Agri Plaza, Singapore, 118535, Singapore
Tel.: (65) 6870 5000
Web Site: http://www.martin.com
Lighting Equipment Mfr
N.A.I.C.S.: 335132

Martin Trading Zhuhai Ltd. (5)
3004 Chong Hing Finance Center, Shanghai, 200003, China
Tel.: (86) 21 2306 0000
Web Site: http://www.martin.com
Lighting Equipment Mfr
N.A.I.C.S.: 335132

Subsidiary (Domestic):

Savari, Inc. (4)
2005 De La Cruz Blvd Ste 131, Santa Clara, CA 95050
Tel.: (408) 833-6369
Web Site: http://www.savarinetworks.com
Engineeering Services
N.A.I.C.S.: 541330
Ravi Puvvala *(Founder & CEO)*

Subsidiary (Domestic):

Joyent, Inc. (3)
655 Montgomery St Ste 1600, San Francisco, CA 94111
Tel.: (415) 400-0600
Web Site: http://www.joyent.com
Sales Range: $25-49.9 Million
Emp.: 100
Cloud Software & Solutions
N.A.I.C.S.: 513210
Bryan Cantrill *(CTO)*

NVELO, Inc. (3)
2900 Lakeside Dr Ste 150, Santa Clara, CA 95054
Tel.: (408) 365-4170
Web Site: http://www.nvelo.com
Software Development Services
N.A.I.C.S.: 541511

NeuroLogica Corp. (3)
14 Electronics Ave, Danvers, MA 01923
Tel.: (978) 564-8500
Web Site: http://www.neurologica.com
Sales Range: $25-49.9 Million
Emp.: 65
Surgical & Medical Instrument Mfr
N.A.I.C.S.: 339112
David R. Webster *(COO)*

Nexus Dx, Inc. (3)
6759 Mesa Rdg Pl, San Diego, CA 92121
Tel.: (858) 410-4600
Web Site: http://www.nexus-dx.com
Sales Range: $25-49.9 Million
Emp.: 35
Near Patient Testing Systems & Diagnostic Kits Developer, Mfr & Distr
N.A.I.C.S.: 334510
Nam Shin *(CEO)*

Prismview, LLC (3)
1651 N 1000 W, Logan, UT 84321
Tel.: (435) 774-8800
Web Site: http://www.prismview.com
Electronic Display Mfr
N.A.I.C.S.: 339950

Subsidiary (Non-US):

Samsung Electronics Canada Inc. (3)
2050 Derry Road West, Mississauga, L5N 0B9, ON, Canada (100%)
Tel.: (905) 542-3535
Web Site: http://www.samsung.com

AND PRIVATE COMPANIES — SAMSUNG GROUP

Sales Range: $50-74.9 Million
Electronic Product Distr
N.A.I.C.S.: 423620
Tim Baxter *(Pres/CEO-North America)*

Subsidiary (Domestic):

Samsung Electronics Latinoamerica Miami, Inc. (3)
33166 8240 NW 52 Ter Ste 102, Miami, FL 33166
Tel.: (305) 594-1090
Electronic Device Whslr
N.A.I.C.S.: 423690

Samsung Semiconductor, Inc. (3)
3655 N First St, San Jose, CA 95134-1713
Tel.: (408) 544-4000
Web Site: http://www.samsung.com
Electronic Product Distr
N.A.I.C.S.: 423690
Ilbok Lee *(Co-Founder)*

Subsidiary (Domestic):

Samsung Austin Semiconductor, LLC (4)
12100 Samsung Blvd, Austin, TX 78754-1903
Tel.: (512) 672-1000
Web Site: http://www.samsung.com
Sales Range: $200-249.9 Million
Emp.: 1,000
Semiconductor Mfr
N.A.I.C.S.: 423620
Gil Heyun Choi *(Pres)*

Subsidiary (Domestic):

Samsung Telecommunications America, LLC (3)
1301 Lookout Dr, Richardson, TX 75082 (100%)
Tel.: (972) 761-7000
Web Site: http://www.samsungusa.com
Sales Range: $125-149.9 Million
Telephone Equipment Mfr & Servicer
N.A.I.C.S.: 423690

TeleWorld Solutions, Inc. (3)
43130 Amberwood Plz, Chantilly, VA 20152
Tel.: (703) 760-9507
Web Site: http://www.teleworldsolutions.com
Engineeering Services
N.A.I.C.S.: 541330
Baryalai Azmi *(Pres)*

mSpot, Inc. (3)
435 Portage Ave Ste A, Palo Alto, CA 94306-2213 (100%)
Tel.: (650) 321-7000
Web Site: http://www.mSpot.com
Sales Range: $10-24.9 Million
Emp.: 57
Mobile Phone Music & Ringtone Retail
N.A.I.C.S.: 517112

Subsidiary (Non-US):

Samsung Electronics Argentina S.A. (2)
710 7 TH FL Hipolito Bouchard 547 3 Piso, Buenos Aires, Argentina
Tel.: (54) 11 4109 4000
Electric Device Mfr
N.A.I.C.S.: 334419

Samsung Electronics Australia Pty Ltd (2)
3 Murray Rose Avenue, Sydney, 2127, NSW, Australia
Tel.: (61) 2 9763 9700
Electric Device Mfr
N.A.I.C.S.: 334419
Steve SangChul Lee *(Pres & CEO)*

Samsung Electronics Benelux B.V. (2)
Olof Palmestraat 10, Delft, 2600, Netherlands
Tel.: (31) 15 219 6100
Electric Device Mfr
N.A.I.C.S.: 334419

Samsung Electronics Chile Limitada. (2)
Avda Americo Vespucio Sur 100 Oficina 102, Las Condes, Santiago, Chile
Tel.: (56) 2 24828200
Electronic Device Whslr
N.A.I.C.S.: 423690

Samsung Electronics Czech and Slovak. s.r.o. (2)
The Park V Parku 2323/14, 148 00, Prague, Czech Republic
Tel.: (420) 225 020 777
Web Site: http://www.samsung.cz
Electronic Device Whslr
N.A.I.C.S.: 423690

Samsung Electronics Display(M) SDN. BHD. (2)
HSD 69244 PT 12692 Mukim Ampangan Kawasan Perindustrian Tuanku Jaafar, 71450, Seremban, Malaysia
Tel.: (60) 6 678 7914
Web Site: http://www.samsung.com.my
Emp.: 600
Electronic Device Mfr & Whslr
N.A.I.C.S.: 334419

Samsung Electronics East Africa Ltd. (2)
3rd Floor Westend towers Waiyaki way, Nairobi, Kenya
Tel.: (254) 800 545 545
Electronic Device Whslr
N.A.I.C.S.: 423690

Samsung Electronics Europe Holding (2)
Olof Palmestraat 10, Delft, 2616 LR, Netherlands
Tel.: (31) 152196100
Web Site: http://www.samsung.nl
Holding Company
N.A.I.C.S.: 551112

Samsung Electronics GmbH (2)
Am Kronberger Hang 6, 65824, Schwalbach, Taunus, Germany
Tel.: (49) 180 6 7267864
Electronic Device Whslr
N.A.I.C.S.: 423690

Samsung Electronics Holding GmbH (2)
Am Kronberger Hang 6, Schwalbach Am Taunus, Hessen, 65824, Germany
Tel.: (49) 6196661130
Holding Company
N.A.I.C.S.: 551112
Peter Eckert *(Head-Health Medical Equipment Div)*

Samsung Electronics Hong Kong Co., Ltd. (2)
33/F Central Plz, Wanchai, China (Hong Kong)
Tel.: (852) 28626900
Electronic Device Whslr
N.A.I.C.S.: 423690

Samsung Electronics Huizhou Co., Ltd. (2)
256 Zhong Kai Six-Way Chenjiang Street Zhongkai High-Tech Indus, Huizhou, 516029, Guangdong, China
Tel.: (86) 7523166163
Electric Device Mfr
N.A.I.C.S.: 334419

Samsung Electronics Hungarian Co., Ltd. (2)
SEH-S, Budapest, 1138, Hungary
Tel.: (36) 1 453 1180
Web Site: http://www.samsung.com
Electronic Device Mfr & Whslr
N.A.I.C.S.: 334419

Samsung Electronics Italia S.P.A. (2)
Via Mike Bongiorno 9, 20124, Milan, Italy
Tel.: (39) 02921891
Web Site: http://www.samsung.com
Emp.: 800
Electronic Device Whslr
N.A.I.C.S.: 423690

Samsung Electronics Japan Co., Ltd. (2)
Ichigaya Tokyu Bldg 4-2-1 Kudankita, Chiyoda-ku, Tokyo, 102-0073, Japan
Tel.: (81) 3 6238 4102
Electronic Device Whslr
N.A.I.C.S.: 423690

Samsung Electronics Latinoamerica (2)
Edificio PH Plaza Credicorp Panama Calle 50 No 120 Piso 15 y 16 Apolo, El Dorado, Panama, Panama
Tel.: (507) 210 1122
Electronic Device Whslr
N.A.I.C.S.: 423690

Samsung Electronics New Zealand Ltd. (2)
24 The Warehouse Way Northcote, Auckland, 0627, New Zealand
Tel.: (64) 9 477 7000
Web Site: http://www.samsung.com
Electric Device Mfr
N.A.I.C.S.: 334419
Edward Han *(Mng Dir)*

Samsung Electronics Nordic AB (2)
Torshamnsgatan 27, PO Box 1235, Kista, 164 28, Sweden
Tel.: (46) 8 55505700
Web Site: http://www.samsung.com
Electronic Device Mfr
N.A.I.C.S.: 334419

Samsung Electronics Overseas B.V. (2)
Strawinskylaan 1111, Amsterdam, 1077 XX, Netherlands
Tel.: (31) 20 575 3012
Electronic Device Whslr
N.A.I.C.S.: 423690

Samsung Electronics Peru S.A.C. (2)
Av Ricardo Rivera Navarrete Nro 501, Lima, Peru
Tel.: (51) 1 7114801
Electronic Device Whslr
N.A.I.C.S.: 423690

Samsung Electronics Philippines, Co. (2)
9/F Science Hub Tower 4 McKinley Hill Cyberpark Fort Bonifacio, Taguig, 1634, Philippines
Tel.: (63) 2 241 7777
Electronic Device Whslr
N.A.I.C.S.: 423690

Samsung Electronics Polska, SP.Zo.o. (2)
Ochota Office Park Al Jerozolimskie 181, 02-222, Warsaw, Poland
Tel.: (48) 22 608 4400
Electronic Device Whslr
N.A.I.C.S.: 423690
Marcin Garbarczyk *(Head-IT & Mobile)*

Samsung Electronics Portuguesa S.A. (2)
Rua Mario Dionisio N 2-1, 2795, Linda-a-Velha, Portugal
Tel.: (351) 1 414 8100
Electronic Device Whslr
N.A.I.C.S.: 423690

Samsung Electronics Rus Company LLC. (2)
10 Vozdvizhenka Street, Moscow, 125009, Russia
Tel.: (7) 495 797 24 00
Electronic Device Whslr
N.A.I.C.S.: 423690
Steve SangChul Lee *(Pres/CEO-Southeast Asia)*

Samsung Electronics Rus Kaluga LLC. (2)
1 Proezd Pervy Severny, Koryakovo, 249041, Russia
Tel.: (7) 4843867000
Electronic Device Whslr
N.A.I.C.S.: 423690

Samsung Electronics South Africa Pty. Ltd. (2)
2929 William Nicol Drive, Bryanston, 2021, Gauteng, South Africa
Tel.: (27) 11 254 3600
Electronic Device Whslr
N.A.I.C.S.: 423690
Sung Yoon *(Pres & CEO)*

Samsung Electronics Switzerland GmbH (2)
Giesshubelstrasse 30, Zurich, 8045, Switzerland
Tel.: (41) 44 455 67 00

Samsung Electronics Turkey Ltd. (2)
Flatofis Istanbul Is Merkezi Otakcilar Cad No 78 Kat 3 No B3 34050, Eyup, Istanbul, Turkiye
Tel.: (90) 444 77 11
Electronic Device Whslr
N.A.I.C.S.: 423690

Samsung Electronics Ukraine Company LLC (2)
L va Tolstogo st 57, Kiev, 01032, Ukraine
Tel.: (380) 44 490 6424
Electronic Device Whslr
N.A.I.C.S.: 423690

Samsung Electronics Venezuela, C.A. (2)
Av Blandin con Santa Teresa de Jesus Centro Comercial San Ignacio, Torre Kepler Piso 1 Oficina, 1060, Caracas, Venezuela
Tel.: (58) 800 100 5303
Electronic Device Whslr
N.A.I.C.S.: 423690

Samsung Gulf Electronics (2)
309 Al Dana Centre Al Maktoum Road, Deira, Dubai, United Arab Emirates
Tel.: (971) 4 2225747
Electronic Device Whslr
N.A.I.C.S.: 423690
Chung Lyong Lee *(Pres)*

Samsung India Electronics Ltd (2)
20th to 24th Floor Two Horizon Centre Golf Course Road Sector-43, DLF PH-V, Gurgaon, 122202, Haryana, India
Tel.: (91) 124 488 1234
Electric Device Mfr
N.A.I.C.S.: 334419
Gauri Taneja *(Officer-Grievance)*

Samsung Malaysia Electronics (Sme) Sdn. Bhd (2)
Suite E-09-01 Level 9 East Wing ICON Jalan Tun Razak No 1 Jalan 1/68F, 50400, Kuala Lumpur, Malaysia
Tel.: (60) 3 21650000
Electric Device Mfr
N.A.I.C.S.: 334419
Steve SangChul Lee *(Pres/CEO-Southeast Asia)*

Subsidiary (Domestic):

Samsung Medison Co., Ltd. (2)
2-dong Alpharium Tower 145 Pangyoyeok-ro Bundang-gu, Seongnam, Gyeonggi-do, Korea (South) (65.8%)
Tel.: (82) 2 2194 1000
Web Site: http://www.samsungmedison.com
Ultrasound Imaging Equipment Mfr
N.A.I.C.S.: 334510

Subsidiary (Non-US):

SONOACE Deutschland GmbH (3)
Elbestrasse 10, 45768, Marl, Germany
Tel.: (49) 2365 924 3811
Ultrasound Imaging Equipment Mfr
N.A.I.C.S.: 334510

Subsidiary (US):

Samsung Medison America, Inc. (3)
11075 Knott Ave, Cypress, CA 90630
Tel.: (714) 889-3000
Web Site: http://www.samsungmedisonusa.com
Sales Range: $25-49.9 Million
Emp.: 20
Ultrasound Imaging Equipment Mfr
N.A.I.C.S.: 334510

Subsidiary (Non-US):

Samsung Medison Brasil Ltda. (3)
Centro Empresarial de Sao Paulo Rua Maria Coelho Aguiar No 215 Bloco C, 4o Andar Jd Sao Luis, Sao Paulo, Brazil
Tel.: (55) 11 3747 7102
Web Site: http://www.samsungmedison.com.br
Ultrasound Imaging Equipment Mfr
N.A.I.C.S.: 334510

Samsung Medison France S.A.S. (3)
30 rue Mozart, 92110, Clichy, France

SAMSUNG GROUP

Samsung Group—(Continued)
Tel.: (33) 1 4756 1291
Web Site: http://www.samsungmedison.fr
Ultrasound Imaging Equipment Mfr
N.A.I.C.S.: 334510

Samsung Medison India Private Ltd. (3)
303 Ring Road Mall Mangalam PLACE Rohini Sector 3, Delhi, 110085, India
Tel.: (91) 11 2794 1286
Ultrasound Imaging Equipment Mfr
N.A.I.C.S.: 334510

Samsung Medison Japan Co., Ltd. (3)
Kashiwa bldg 6F 3 40 11 Hongo Bunkyo ku, Tokyo, 113 0033, Japan
Tel.: (81) 3 5805 7631
Web Site: http://www.samsungmedison.co.jp
Ultrasound Imaging Equipment Mfr
N.A.I.C.S.: 334510

Samsung Medison Shanghai Medical Instrument Co., Ltd. (3)
No 7 Lane 720 Cailun Road Zhangjiang Hi-tech Area, Pudong, Shanghai, 201203, China
Tel.: (86) 21 5031 7887
Ultrasound Imaging Equipment Mfr
N.A.I.C.S.: 334510

Subsidiary (Non-US):

Samsung Semiconductor Europe GmbH (2)
Koelner Strasse 12, 65760, Eschborn, Germany
Tel.: (49) 6196 66 3300
Web Site: http://www.samsungsemi.com
Semiconductor Components Mfr
N.A.I.C.S.: 334413

Samsung Semiconductor Israel R&D Center Ltd. (2)
2 Shoham Street, Ramat Gan, 5251003, Israel
Tel.: (972) 3 753 6300
Software Development Services
N.A.I.C.S.: 513210

Shanghai Samsung Semiconductor Co., LTD (2)
15 Floor Cloud Nine Plaza No 1118 Yan An W Road, Shanghai, 200052, China
Tel.: (86) 21 5258 2211
Semiconductor Components Mfr
N.A.I.C.S.: 334413

Thai Samsung Electronics Co., ltd. (2)
195 South Sathorn Road Yanawa, Bangkok, 10120, Thailand
Tel.: (66) 2 695 9000
Electronic Components Mfr
N.A.I.C.S.: 334419

Samsung Engineering Co., Ltd. (1)
Samsung GEC 26 Sangil-ro 6-gil, Gangdong-gu, Seoul, Korea (South)
Tel.: (82) 220533000
Web Site: http://www.samsungengineering.co.kr
Rev.: $7,711,682,328
Assets: $6,019,970,712
Liabilities: $4,043,380,720
Net Worth: $1,976,589,992
Earnings: $510,000,626
Emp.: 6,077
Fiscal Year-end: 12/31/2022
Construction Engineering Services
N.A.I.C.S.: 237990

Samsung Everland Inc. (1)
310 Jeondae-ri Pogok-eup Cheoin-gu Yongin Gyeonggi-do, Seoul, 100-716, Korea (South) (42.3%)
Tel.: (82) 313205000
Web Site: http://www.samsungeverland.com
Holding Company; Business Infrastructure, Food Culture & Resort Infrastructure Services
N.A.I.C.S.: 551212
Bong Yung Kim *(Pres)*

Samsung Fire & Marine Insurance Co., Ltd. (1)
14 Seocho-daero 74-gil, Seocho-gu, Seoul, 06620, Korea (South)
Tel.: (82) 15885114
Web Site: https://www.samsungfire.com
Rev.: $12,633,087,847
Assets: $63,105,139,312
Liabilities: $51,122,004,445
Net Worth: $11,983,134,867
Earnings: $1,352,088,196
Emp.: 5,610
Fiscal Year-end: 12/31/2023
Investment Management Service
N.A.I.C.S.: 523999

Samsung Heavy Industries Co., Ltd. (1)
23 Pangyo-ro 227 Beon-gil, Bundang-gu, Seongnam, 13486, Gyeonggi-do, Korea (South)
Tel.: (82) 3151717000
Web Site: http://www.shi.samsung.co.kr
Rev.: $4,559,559,936
Assets: $11,115,132,354
Liabilities: $8,375,456,371
Net Worth: $2,739,675,983
Earnings: ($475,109,181)
Emp.: 8,775
Fiscal Year-end: 12/31/2022
Commercial & Industrial Ships & Offshore Platforms for Oil Drilling Mfr
N.A.I.C.S.: 336611
Jin-Taek Jung *(CEO)*

Samsung Information Systems America, Inc. (1)
75 W Plumeria Dr, San Jose, CA 95134
Tel.: (408) 544-5700
Electronic Device Whslr
N.A.I.C.S.: 423690

Samsung Life Insurance Co., Ltd. (1)
11 Seocho-daero 74-gil, Seocho-gu, Seoul, 06620, Korea (South)
Tel.: (82) 15883114
Web Site: https://www.samsunglife.com
Rev.: $6,436,845,152
Assets: $233,551,838,546
Liabilities: $200,642,495,881
Net Worth: $32,909,342,666
Earnings: $1,509,514,867
Emp.: 5,148
Fiscal Year-end: 12/31/2023
Investment Management Service
N.A.I.C.S.: 523999
Seong Cheol Hyun *(Pres & CEO)*

Samsung Petrochemical Co., Ltd. (1)
20th Fl Samsung Electronics Bldg 1320-10 Seocho 2-dong, Seocho-gu, Seoul, 100 716, Korea (South)
Tel.: (82) 2 2255 0326
Web Site: http://www.samsungspc.com
Sales Range: $1-4.9 Billion
Emp.: 350
Petrochemical Products Mfr
N.A.I.C.S.: 325110

Samsung R&D Institute Japan Co. Ltd. (1)
2-7 Sugasawa-cho, Tsurumu-ku, Yokohama, 230-0027, Kanagawa, Japan
Tel.: (81) 45 510 3331
Software Development Services
N.A.I.C.S.: 541511
Minoru Kubo *(CEO)*

Samsung SDI Co., Ltd. (1)
150-20 Gongse-ro, Giheung-gu, Yongin, Gyeonggi-do, Korea (South)
Tel.: (82) 3180063100
Web Site: https://www.samsungsdi.com
Rev.: $16,855,173,091
Assets: $25,265,249,613
Liabilities: $10,489,148,505
Net Worth: $14,776,101,107
Earnings: $1,533,517,333
Emp.: 12,452
Fiscal Year-end: 12/31/2023
Digital Display Interface Product Designer & Mfr
N.A.I.C.S.: 335910
Young Hyun Jun *(CEO)*

Subsidiary (Non-US):

Dongguan Samsung SDI Co., Ltd. (2)
Jiang Jun Ling Industrial Zone, Houjie, Dongguan, 511771, Guangdong, China
Tel.: (86) 769 558 2000
Sales Range: $700-749.9 Million
Emp.: 3,910
Mobile LCD & Lithium Battery Mfr
N.A.I.C.S.: 334513

Samsung SDI (HK) Ltd. (2)
Suite 4511 45/F Two Intl Finance Centre, 8 Finance Street, Central, China (Hong Kong)
Tel.: (852) 2 28662 6300
Digital Display Interface Product Designer & Mfr
N.A.I.C.S.: 334513

Samsung SDI (Malaysia) Sdn. Bhd. (2)
Lot 635 & 660 Kawasan Perindustrian Tuanku Jaafar, Sungai Gadut, Negeri Sembilan, 71450, Darul Khusus, Malaysia
Tel.: (60) 66776160
Web Site: http://www.sdimalaysia.com
Sales Range: $700-749.9 Million
Emp.: 3,276
Digital Display Interface Product Designer & Mfr
N.A.I.C.S.: 334513

Subsidiary (US):

Samsung SDI America, Inc. (2)
3655 N 1st St, San Jose, CA 95134
Tel.: (408) 544-4509
Web Site: http://www.samsungsdi.com
Digital Display Interface Product Designer & Mfr
N.A.I.C.S.: 334513

Subsidiary (Non-US):

Samsung Displays Mexicana SA de CV (3)
Blvd Los Olivos No 21014, Parque Industrial El Florido, Tijuana, BC, Mexico
Tel.: (52) 6646276220
Digital Display Interface Product Designer & Mfr
N.A.I.C.S.: 334513

Subsidiary (Non-US):

Samsung SDI Brasil Ltda. (2)
Av Eixo Norte Sul, SN Distrito Industrial, 69088-480, Manaus, Brazil
Tel.: (55) 92 2121 6010
Sales Range: $350-399.9 Million
Emp.: 1,611
Digital Display Interface Product Designer & Mfr
N.A.I.C.S.: 334513

Samsung SDI Hungary Ltd. (2)
Ipartelep Hrsz 6980 God, H-2132, Budapest, Hungary
Tel.: (36) 2 788 7020
Web Site: http://www.samsungsdi.com
Sales Range: $150-199.9 Million
Emp.: 1,000
Digital Display Interface Product Designer & Mfr
N.A.I.C.S.: 334513

Samsung SDI Mexico SA de CV (2)
Blvd Los Olivos No 21014, Parque Industrial El Florido, Tijuana, 22244, Mexico
Tel.: (52) 6646276220
Sales Range: $150-199.9 Million
Emp.: 850
Digital Display Interface Product Designer & Mfr
N.A.I.C.S.: 334513

Shanghai Samsung Vacuum Electron Devices Co., Ltd. (2)
389 RongLedong Rd, Songjiang, Shanghai, 201613, China
Tel.: (86) 2157746000
Sales Range: $150-199.9 Million
Emp.: 657
Digital Display Interface Product Designer & Mfr
N.A.I.C.S.: 334513

Tianjin Samsung SDI Co., Ltd. (2)
Yat-Sen Scientific&Industrial Park, Wuqing, Tianjin, 301726, China
Tel.: (86) 2282129971
Web Site: http://www.samsung.com.cn
Digital Display Interface Product Designer & Mfr
N.A.I.C.S.: 334513

INTERNATIONAL PUBLIC

Subsidiary (Domestic):

Tianjin Samsung LED Co., Ltd. (3)
6 Weisi Road Micro-Electronics Industry Park, Xiqing, Tianjin, 300385, China
Tel.: (86) 2223885588
Electronic Components Mfr
N.A.I.C.S.: 334419

Tianjin Samsung Opto-electronics Co., Ltd. (3)
No 9 Zhangheng Avenue Micro-Electric Industrial Jingang Road, Tianjin, 300385, China
Tel.: (86) 22 2388 7788
Electronic Components Mfr
N.A.I.C.S.: 334419

Samsung SDS Co., Ltd. (1)
Samsung SDS 123 Olympic-ro 35-gil, Songpa-gu, Seoul, 5510, Korea (South) (100%)
Tel.: (82) 261553114
Web Site: https://www.samsungsds.com
Rev.: $9,854,700,804
Assets: $9,145,246,323
Liabilities: $2,483,153,526
Net Worth: $6,662,092,797
Earnings: $514,690,566
Emp.: 25,619
Fiscal Year-end: 12/31/2023
Information Technology Consulting & Support Services
N.A.I.C.S.: 541512

Samsung Securities Co., Ltd. (1)
Sanmsung Electronics Bldg 11 Seocho-daero 74 gil, Seocho-gu, Seoul, 06620, Korea (South)
Tel.: (82) 220208000
Web Site: https://www.samsungsecurities.com
Rev.: $1,195,582,995
Assets: $41,942,839,176
Liabilities: $37,027,151,488
Net Worth: $4,915,687,688
Earnings: $406,310,369
Emp.: 2,586
Fiscal Year-end: 12/31/2023
Investment Banking, Securities Brokerage & Asset Management Services
N.A.I.C.S.: 523999
Seok-Hoon Chang *(Pres, CEO & Head-Mgmt Support Div)*

Subsidiary (Domestic):

Samsung Asset Management Co., Ltd. (2)
25th Floor Samsung Life Insurance Bldg 150 2ga Taepyeongno, Jung-gu, Seoul, 100-716, Korea (South) (65.4%)
Tel.: (82) 237747883
Web Site: http://www.samsungfund.com
Sales Range: $75-99.9 Billion
Emp.: 239
Investment & Asset Management Services
N.A.I.C.S.: 523940
Jeon Youngmuk *(CEO)*

Subsidiary (US):

Samsung Securities (America), Inc. (2)
1330 Avenue of the Americas 26th Fl, New York, NY 10019
Tel.: (212) 972-2454
Web Site: http://www.samsungsecurities.com
Investment Banking & Securities Brokerage Services
N.A.I.C.S.: 523150

Samsung Suzhou Module Co., Ltd (1)
318 FangZhou Road Suzhou Industrial Park, Suzhou, Jiangsu, China
Tel.: (86) 512 62530 188
Web Site: http://www.samsung.com
Electric Device Mfr
N.A.I.C.S.: 334419

SAMSUNG MUST SPECIAL PURPOSE ACQUISITION 3 CO., LTD.
11 Seocho-daero 74-gil, Seocho-gu, Seoul, 06620, Korea (South)
Tel.: (82) 220207637

309930—(KRS)
Rev.: $25,604,132
Assets: $33,166,315
Liabilities: $10,992,951
Net Worth: $22,173,364
Earnings: $1,186,831
Emp.: 112
Fiscal Year-end: 12/31/22
Asset Management Services
N.A.I.C.S.: 523940
Lee Il-Geun (CEO)

SAMSUNG PHARMACEUTI-CAL CO., LTD.
35 Jeyakgongdan 2-gil, Hyangnam-eup, Hwaseong, 445-746, Gyeonggi-do, Korea (South)
Tel.: (82) 313536681   KR
Web Site: https://www.sspharm.co.kr
Year Founded: 1929
001360—(KRS)
Rev.: $39,755,323
Assets: $90,440,658
Liabilities: $11,754,192
Net Worth: $78,686,466
Earnings: ($19,246,355)
Emp.: 83
Fiscal Year-end: 12/31/22
Pharmaceuticals Product Mfr
N.A.I.C.S.: 325412
Sang-Jae Kim (CEO)

SAMSUNG PUBLISHING CO., LTD.
94 Myeongdal-ro, Seocho-gu, Seoul, Korea (South)
Tel.: (82) 234706800
Web Site: http://www.ssbooks.com
Year Founded: 2002
068290—(KRS)
Rev.: $39,627,590
Assets: $162,211,018
Liabilities: $27,532,399
Net Worth: $134,678,619
Earnings: $12,611,009
Emp.: 271
Fiscal Year-end: 12/31/22
Book & Magazine Publishing Services
N.A.I.C.S.: 513120
Jin-Yong Kim (CEO)

SAMSUNGFN REIT CO., LTD.
16th floor Samsung Life Seocho Tower 4 Seocho-daero 74-gil, Seocho-gu, Seoul, 06620, Korea (South)
Tel.: (82) 7044920769
Web Site:
   https://www.samsungfnreit.com
Year Founded: 2022
448730—(KRS)
Real Estate Investment Services
N.A.I.C.S.: 531190
Suk Beom Choi (Gen Mgr)

SAMTEL INDIA LTD
501 Copia Corporate Suites District Centre, Jasola, New Delhi, 110025, India
Tel.: (91) 1142424000
Web Site:
   http://www.samtelgroup.com
Rev.: $328,098
Assets: $1,124,568
Liabilities: $842,792
Net Worth: $281,776
Earnings: $190,019
Fiscal Year-end: 03/31/18
Colour TV Tubes Mfr
N.A.I.C.S.: 334419
Satish K. Kaura (Chm & Mng Dir)

SAMTEX FASHIONS LIMITED
Plot No 163 Udyog Vihar, Noida, 201308, Uttar Pradesh, India
Tel.: (91) 1204209800
Web Site:
   https://www.samtexfashions.com
Year Founded: 1993
521206—(BOM)
Rev.: $3,153
Assets: $43,567,688
Liabilities: $71,703,939
Net Worth: ($28,136,251)
Earnings: ($668,941)
Emp.: 1
Fiscal Year-end: 03/31/23
Apparels Mfr
N.A.I.C.S.: 315250
Atul Mittal (Chm, Mng Dir & CFO)

SAMTRYGG GROUP AB
Olof Palmes gata 20 B, 111 37, Stockholm, Sweden
Tel.: (46) 108848000
Web Site: https://samtrygg.com
Year Founded: 2013
ATP30—(THA)
Rev.: $49,179,384
Assets: $80,954,989
Liabilities: $37,487,770
Net Worth: $43,467,219
Earnings: $5,017,794
Emp.: 374
Fiscal Year-end: 12/31/19
Real Estate Management Services
N.A.I.C.S.: 531390
Jesper Magnusson (CFO)

SAMTY CO., LTD.
4-3-24 Nishinakajima, Yodogawa-ku, Osaka, 532-0011, Japan
Tel.: (81) 668383616
Web Site: http://www.samty.co.jp
Year Founded: 1982
3244—(TKS)
Rev.: $1,243,589,600
Assets: $4,003,589,920
Liabilities: $2,934,966,320
Net Worth: $1,068,623,600
Earnings: $105,182,880
Emp.: 793
Fiscal Year-end: 11/30/22
Real Estate Services
N.A.I.C.S.: 531390
Shigeru Moriyama (Chm)

Subsidiaries:

Samty Asset Management Co., Ltd.   (1)
Marunouchi Trust Tower Main Building 20th Floor 1-8-3 Marunouchi, Chiyoda-ku, Tokyo, 100-0005, Japan
Tel.: (81) 35 220 3841
Web Site: https://www.samtyasset.co.jp
Investment Management Service
N.A.I.C.S.: 523940
Yousuke Masuda (Pres)

Samty Property Management Co., Ltd.   (1)
Samty Shin-Osaka Center Building 7F 4-3-24 Nishinakajima, Yodogawa-ku, Osaka, 532-0011, Japan
Tel.: (81) 668863626
Web Site: http://www.samty-pm.co.jp
Real Estate Rental & Brokerage Services
N.A.I.C.S.: 531210
Shuzo Endo (Pres)

SAMTY RESIDENTIAL INVEST-MENT CORPORATION
1-8-3 Marunouchi, Chiyoda-ku, Tokyo, Japan
Tel.: (81) 352203841
Web Site: https://www.samty-residential.com
34590—(TKS)
Sales Range: Less than $1 Million
Real Estate Related Services
N.A.I.C.S.: 531390
Masafumi Takahashi (Exec Dir)

SAMUEL HEATH & SONS PLC
Leopold Street, Birmingham, B12 0UJ, United Kingdom
Tel.: (44) 1217664200
Web Site: https://www.samuel-heath.com
HSM—(AIM)
Rev.: $18,275,571
Assets: $17,652,187
Liabilities: $3,752,720
Net Worth: $13,899,467
Earnings: $1,156,116
Emp.: 141
Fiscal Year-end: 03/31/23
Builders Hardware Mfr
N.A.I.C.S.: 332510
David J. Pick (Mng Dir)

SAMUEL TAYLOR LIMITED
Arthur Street Central, Redditch, B98 8JY, United Kingdom
Tel.: (44) 1527 504 910
Web Site:
   http://www.samueltaylor.co.uk
Year Founded: 1899
Sales Range: $25-49.9 Million
Emp.: 77
Precision Component Mfr
N.A.I.C.S.: 332721
Alastair Gordon (Mng Dir)

SAMUEL TERRY ASSET MAN-AGEMENT PTY LTD.
120B Underwood St, Paddington, 2021, NSW, Australia
Tel.: (61) 290669240
Web Site:
   https://www.samuelterry.com.au
Emp.: 100
Investment Management Service
N.A.I.C.S.: 523999
Fred Woollard (Founder & Mng Dir)

SAMUEL, SON & CO., LIMITED
1900 Ironoak Way, Oakville, L6H 0N1, ON, Canada
Tel.: (905) 279-5460
Web Site: http://www.samuel.com
Year Founded: 1855
Metals Processor & Distr
N.A.I.C.S.: 423510
Colin Osborne (Pres & CEO)

Subsidiaries:

Associated Tube Industries   (1)
7455 Woodbine Avenue, Markham, L3R 1A7, ON, Canada
Tel.: (905) 475-6464
Web Site: http://www.associatedtube.com
Sales Range: $50-74.9 Million
Emp.: 250
Provider of Metal Tubing
N.A.I.C.S.: 332999
Paul Evers (Grp Dir-Tech)

Subsidiary (US):

Associated Tube USA, Inc.   (2)
333 Peterson Dr, Elizabethtown, KY 42701   (100%)
Tel.: (270) 234-2000
Web Site: http://www.associatedtube.com
Sales Range: $25-49.9 Million
Emp.: 60
Stainless Steel Tubing Products Mfr
N.A.I.C.S.: 331210

Gerrard-Ovalstrapping   (1)
735 Oval Ct, Burlington, L7L6A9, ON, Canada
Tel.: (905) 632-3662
Web Site: http://www.goval.com
Sales Range: $75-99.9 Million
Emp.: 100
Retailer of Packaging Systems & Products for General Industrial Applications & Machinery Systems for the Pulp & Paper Industry
N.A.I.C.S.: 333993
Dan Crespi (Mgr-Sls)

Nelson Steel   (1)
400 Glover Rd, Stoney Creek, L8E 5X1, ON, Canada
Tel.: (905) 662-1404
Web Site: http://www.nelsonsteel.com
Sales Range: $25-49.9 Million
Emp.: 100
Produces & Distributes Steel Products & Related Services
N.A.I.C.S.: 331513
Gillian White (Controller)

Unit (Domestic):

Nelson Steel Consulting & Technology Group   (2)
400 Glover Rd, Stoney Creek, L8E 5X1, ON, Canada
Tel.: (905) 662-1404
Web Site: http://www.nelsonsteel.com
Sales Range: $25-49.9 Million
Emp.: 50
Complete Pickling Lines Planning & Contruction Services
N.A.I.C.S.: 238210
Graham Oakley (Gen Mgr)

Renown Steel   (1)
351 Passmore Ave, Scarborough, M1V 3N8, ON, Canada
Tel.: (416) 291-4272
Web Site: http://www.renownsteel.com
Sales Range: $75-99.9 Million
Emp.: 3
Steel Sheets, Blanks, Slit Coils & Tin Plate Mfr
N.A.I.C.S.: 331315

Samuel Steel Pickling Company   (1)
1400 Enterprise Pkwy, Twinsburg, OH 44087-2242
Tel.: (330) 963-3777
Web Site: http://www.samuelsteel.com
Sales Range: $25-49.9 Million
Emp.: 50
toll Processor
N.A.I.C.S.: 561990

Samuel Strapping Systems Inc   (1)
2370 Dixie Rd, Mississauga, L4Y 1Z4, ON, Canada   (100%)
Tel.: (905) 279-9580
Web Site: http://www.samuelstrapping.com
Sales Range: $25-49.9 Million
Emp.: 25
Steel & Plastic Strapping & Tools Mfr
N.A.I.C.S.: 331221
Keith A. Preston (Pres)

Subsidiary (Non-US):

Samuel Strapping (Australia) Pty Ltd   (2)
10/242 Caroline Springs Boulevard, Caroline Springs, 3023, VIC, Australia
Tel.: (61) 8358 4307
Aluminum & Steel Distr
N.A.I.C.S.: 423510

Plant (Domestic):

Samuel Strapping Systems Inc   (2)
185 The West Mall Suite 1510, Etobicoke, M9C 5L5, ON, Canada
Tel.: (416) 626-2273
Web Site: http://www.samuelstrapping.com
Steel Product Mfr & Distr
N.A.I.C.S.: 331110

Plant (US):

Samuel Strapping Systems-U.S.   (2)
1455 James Pkwy, Heath, OH 43056-4137
Tel.: (740) 522-2500
Web Site: http://www.samuelstrapping.com
Sales Range: $25-49.9 Million
N.A.I.C.S.: 331513
Jay K. Matthews (Mgr-Sls)

Samuel Strapping Systems-U.S.   (2)
2000 K Boyer Rd, Fort Mill, SC 29708-7874
Tel.: (803) 802-3203
Web Site: http://www.samuelstrapping.com
Sales Range: $25-49.9 Million
Emp.: 100
Produce Strappings
N.A.I.C.S.: 332999
Rick Dean (Plant Mgr)

Samuel et Fils et Cie Ltee.   (1)
2225 Francis-Hughes, Laval, H7S 1N5, QC, Canada
Tel.: (514) 384-5220

SAMUEL, SON & CO., LIMITED

Samuel, Son & Co., Limited—(Continued)
Aluminum & Steel Distr
N.A.I.C.S.: 423510

Samuel, Son & Co., Inc. (1)
1401 Davey Rd, Woodridge, IL 60517
Tel.: (630) 257-7700
Web Site: http://www.samuel.com
Holding Company; Regional Managing Office; Metal Products Mfr & Distr
N.A.I.C.S.: 551112

Subsidiary (Domestic):

Basic Stainless, Inc. (2)
2007 S Nikolai Ave, Marshfield, WI 54449
Tel.: (715) 384-9898
Web Site: http://www.samuel.com
Sales Range: $25-49.9 Million
Emp.: 16
Metal Service Centers & Other Metal Merchant Whslr
N.A.I.C.S.: 423510
James M. Young *(Gen Mgr)*

CAID Industries, Inc. (2)
2275 E Ganley Rd, Tucson, AZ 85706
Tel.: (520) 294-3126
Web Site: http://www.caid.com
Fabricated Metal Products Design & Mfr
N.A.I.C.S.: 332999

Main Steel, LLC (2)
2200 Pratt Blvd, Elk Grove Village, IL 60007
Tel.: (847) 916-1220
Web Site: http://www.mainsteel.com
Steel Polishing Services
N.A.I.C.S.: 332813

Group (Domestic):

Samuel Pressure Vessel Group (2)
2121 Cleveland Ave, Marinette, WI 54143
Tel.: (715) 735-9311
Web Site: http://www.samuelpvg.com
Sales Range: $25-49.9 Million
Emp.: 400
Industrial Metal Pressure Vessel Mfr
N.A.I.C.S.: 332420

Plant (Domestic):

Samuel Pressure Vessel Group - Tomahawk Plant (3)
1119A Bridge St, Tomahawk, WI 54487
Tel.: (715) 453-5326
Web Site: http://www.samuelpvg.com
Emp.: 100
Steel Pressure Vessel Mfr
N.A.I.C.S.: 332420
William Wenzel *(Gen Mgr)*

Subsidiary (Domestic):

Samuel Stamping Technologies LLC (2)
1760 Broadway Rd, Hermitage, PA 16148
Tel.: (724) 981-5042
Web Site: http://www.samuel-stamping.com
Metal Door Mfr
N.A.I.C.S.: 332321
Daniel Turner Sr. *(Pres)*

Sierra Aluminum Company (2)
2345 Fleetwood Dr, Riverside, CA 92509
Tel.: (951) 781-7800
Web Site: https://www.samuel.com
Fabricated Metal Products Mfr
N.A.I.C.S.: 332999
Bill Hunter *(Co-Founder)*

Stanrail Corporation (2)
1225 Martin Luther King Dr, Gary, IN 46402
Tel.: (219) 932-5200
Emp.: 90
Railway Equipment Distr
N.A.I.C.S.: 423860
Nancy Backley *(Gen Mgr)*

Steel Fab., Inc. (2)
17403 Lee Hwy, Abingdon, VA 24210-7833 (100%)
Tel.: (276) 628-3843
Web Site: http://www.steelfabtanks.com
Sales Range: $50-74.9 Million
Emp.: 200
N.A.I.C.S.: 331513
David Monk *(Mgr-Ops)*

Tubular Products Company (2)
1400 Red Hollow Rd, Birmingham, AL 35215
Tel.: (205) 856-1300
Web Site: http://www.tubularproducts.com
Emp.: 160
Fabricated Structural Metal Mfr
N.A.I.C.S.: 332312
Charlie Brown *(Pres)*

WorldClass Processing Corp. (2)
21 Century Dr, Ambridge, PA 15003
Tel.: (724) 251-9000
Aluminum & Steel Distr
N.A.I.C.S.: 423510

Samuel, Son & Co., Limited - Custom Plate & Profiles (1)
1223 Derwent Way, Delta, V3M 5V9, BC, Canada
Tel.: (604) 524-8000
Web Site: http://www.customplate.net
Steel Plate Distr
N.A.I.C.S.: 423510
Bob Thornton *(Pres)*

Samuel, Son & Co., Limited - Nash Metal Trading (1)
410 Nash Rd, Hamilton, L8H 7R9, ON, Canada
Emp.: 300
Aluminum & Steel Trade Distr
N.A.I.C.S.: 425120
Mike Holt *(Gen Mgr)*

Tubos Samuel de Mexico, S.A. de C.V.
Calle 17 No 3698 Parque Industrial Amistad, Col Ampliacion Morelos, Saltillo, 25017, Coahuila, Mexico
Tel.: (52) 844 438 6400
Aluminum & Steel Distr
N.A.I.C.S.: 423510
Jesus Alfredo Morales Rodriguez *(Engr-Process)*

Unalloy-IWRC (1)
520 Windmill Road, Dartmouth, B3B 1B3, NS, Canada
Tel.: (902) 482-3125
Web Site: https://herculesslr.com
Sales Range: $50-74.9 Million
Emp.: 4
Distr of Wire Rope & Related Products
N.A.I.C.S.: 423510

Wilkinson Steel & Metals, Inc. (1)
888 Southeast Marine Drive, Vancouver, V5X 2V3, BC, Canada
Tel.: (604) 324-6611
Web Site: http://www.wilkinsonsteel.com
Metal Service Centers & Metal Merchant Whslr
N.A.I.C.S.: 423510
William Hughes *(Pres)*

SAMURAI 2K AEROSOL LIMITED

133 North Bridge Road 08-03 Chinatown Point, Singapore, 059413, Singapore
Tel.: (65) 62732711 SG
Web Site:
https://www.samurai2kaerosol.com
Year Founded: 1997
Y8E—(CAT)
Rev.: $14,871,534
Assets: $27,161,905
Liabilities: $11,257,989
Net Worth: $15,903,915
Earnings: $(2,422,222)
Fiscal Year-end: 03/31/23
Automotive Coating Services
N.A.I.C.S.: 238160
Yoke En Ong *(CEO)*

Subsidiaries:

PT Samurai Paint (1)
Jl Sunter Mas Utara Block H1 no 17j, Jakarta Utara, 14350, Indonesia
Tel.: (62) 2165300624
Paint Product Distr
N.A.I.C.S.: 424950

SAMURAI CAPITAL CORP.

1470 701 West Georgia Street, PO Box 1010112 Pacific Ctr, Vancouver, V7Y 1C6, BC, Canada
Tel.: (604) 646-6906 BC
Year Founded: 2008
Investment Services
N.A.I.C.S.: 523999

SAMVARDHANA MOTHERSON INTERNATIONAL LIMITED

Motherson Plot No 1 Sector-127 Noida-Greater Noida Expressway, Noida, 201301, Uttar Pradesh, India
Tel.: (91) 1206679500 In
Web Site:
https://www.motherson.com
Year Founded: 1986
MOTHERSON—(NSE)
Rev.: $11,883,274,722
Assets: $10,217,873,897
Liabilities: $6,826,946,394
Net Worth: $3,390,927,504
Earnings: $362,894,320
Emp.: 190,000
Fiscal Year-end: 03/31/24
Motor Vehicle Parts Mfr
N.A.I.C.S.: 336320
Pankaj Mital *(COO)*

Subsidiaries:

A Basic Concepts and Designs Pty. Ltd. (1)
18-22 Lexia Place, Mulgrave, 3170, VIC, Australia
Tel.: (61) 385617900
Automotive Industrial Design Services
N.A.I.C.S.: 541420

CTM India Ltd (1)
Survey No 425pt 439pt A-4 SIPCOT Industrial Growth Center, 425pt 439pt A-4 Chengalpattu Sriperumbudur Rd Oragadam, Kanchipuram, 602105, Tamilnadu, India
Tel.: (91) 9840978077
Automobile Mold Mfr
N.A.I.C.S.: 333511

Foshan Peguform Automotive Plastics Technology Co., Ltd. (1)
No 17 Qianjin Road East Guanyao, Shishan Town Nanhai Zone, Foshan, 528237, China
Tel.: (86) 75785862266
Emp.: 50
Automobile Parts Mfr
N.A.I.C.S.: 336390

Kabel-Technik-Polska Sp. z o.o. (1)
5 Plawienska Street, 78 - 550, Czaplinek, Poland
Tel.: (48) 943755300
Automotive Electric Distribution System Mfr
N.A.I.C.S.: 336320

MSSL Mideast FZE (1)
H-3 1 - 6 SAIF Zone, Sharjah, United Arab Emirates
Tel.: (971) 65571661
Web Site: https://msslme.ae
Wiring Harness Mfr
N.A.I.C.S.: 335931

MSSL Wiring System INC. (1)
Tel.: (330) 856-3344
Electric Equipment Mfr
N.A.I.C.S.: 336320

Plant (Non-US):

MSSL - Monclova (2)
Av Adolfo Lopez Mateos No 2101, Monclova, 25770, Mexico
Tel.: (52) 8666325860
Automotive Electrical & Electronic Equipment Mfr
N.A.I.C.S.: 336320

Plant (Domestic):

MSSL - Portland (2)
700 Industrial Dr, Portland, IN 47371-1156
Tel.: (260) 726-6501
Sales Range: $100-124.9 Million
Emp.: 500
Wiring Harness Mfr
N.A.I.C.S.: 326199
James Kennedy *(Mgr)*

Plant (Non-US):

MSSL - Saltillo (2)
Prolongacion Isidro Lopez Zertuche No 950 Capellana, Ramos Arizpe, 25900, Coahuila De Zaragoza, Mexico
Tel.: (52) 8441801578
Sales Range: $100-124.9 Million
Emp.: 500
Automotive Electronic Equipment Mfr
N.A.I.C.S.: 336320

Motherson Advanced Tooling Solutions Limited (1)
A-3 MIDC Industrial Area, Chikalthana, Aurangabad, 431 210, Maharashtra, India
Tel.: (91) 2402485217
Web Site: https://www.matsltd.com
Industrial Cutting Tool Mfr
N.A.I.C.S.: 333515

Motherson Air Travel Agencies Limited (1)
8th Floor Plot No 1 Sector 127, Noida, 201301, Uttar Pradesh, India
Tel.: (91) 1206693623
Web Site: https://holidays.matatravel.com
Travel Agency Operator
N.A.I.C.S.: 561510

Motherson Elastomers Pty. Limited (1)
48-86 Powell Street White Hills, Bendigo, 3550, VIC, Australia
Tel.: (61) 354402069
Automotive Electrical Parts Mfr
N.A.I.C.S.: 336320

Motherson Innovations Deutschland GmbH (1)
Hedelfinger Strasse 60, 70327, Stuttgart, Germany
Tel.: (49) 711185610
Web Site: https://www.motherson-innovations.com
Research & Development Services
N.A.I.C.S.: 541715

Motherson Innovations Lights GmbH & Co. KG (1)
Theodor-Korner-Strasse 14 a, 83301, Traunreut, Germany
Tel.: (49) 866978980
Web Site: https://mi-lights.com
Screen Printing Product Mfr
N.A.I.C.S.: 323113

Motherson Invenzen XLab Private Limited (1)
A-76 Sector-83, Noida, 201301, Uttar Pradesh, India
Tel.: (91) 1204365375
Web Site: https://mi-xlab.com
Software Provider
N.A.I.C.S.: 423430

Motherson Machinery and Automations Limited (1)
D-59 & 60 Sector - 6, Distt Gautam Budh Nagar, Noida, 201301, Uttar Pradesh, India
Tel.: (91) 1204100789
Industrial Machine Tool Distr
N.A.I.C.S.: 423830

Motherson Molds and Die Casting Limited (1)
195 Ground Floor Sector-4 IMT Manesar, Gurgaon, 122050, Haryana, India
Tel.: (91) 1244365966
Industrial Mold Mfr
N.A.I.C.S.: 333511

Motherson PKC Harness Systems FZ-LLC (1)
Plot No 57D Al Hamra Industrial Zone-FZ, Ras al Khaimah, United Arab Emirates
Tel.: (971) 72044333
Automotive Electric Distribution System Mfr
N.A.I.C.S.: 336320

Motherson Sintermetal Products S.A. (1)
Sarria de Ter 20-52, 08291, Ripollet, Spain
Tel.: (34) 935947310
Automobile Spare Parts Mfr
N.A.I.C.S.: 336330

Motherson Techno Tools Limited (1)
A-2 Sector-84, Noida, 201305, Uttar

AND PRIVATE COMPANIES — SAMVARDHANA MOTHERSON INTERNATIONAL LIMITED

Pradesh, India
Tel.: (91) 7303281836
Cutting Equipment Mfr
N.A.I.C.S.: 333515

Motherson Technology Services GmbH (1)
Schlossmattenstrasse 7a, D-79268, Botzingen, Germany
Tel.: (49) 7663612530
Software Development Services
N.A.I.C.S.: 541511

Motherson Technology Services Kabushiki Gaisha (1)
4F Seiki 2nd Building 2-11 Sotokanda 5-chome, Chiyoda-ku, Tokyo, 101-0021, Japan
Tel.: (81) 368060050
Software Provider
N.A.I.C.S.: 423430

Motherson Technology Services Limited (1)
C- 26 Sector 62, Noida, 201309, Uttar Pradesh, India
Tel.: (91) 1204365555
Web Site: https://www.mothersontechnology.com
Software Provider
N.A.I.C.S.: 423430

Motherson Technology Services SG Pte. Limited (1)
178 Paya Lebar Road 04-08/09, Singapore, 409030, Singapore
Tel.: (65) 92386447
Software Provider
N.A.I.C.S.: 423430

Motherson Technology Services USA Limited (1)
1101 Perimeter Dr Ste 650, Schaumburg, IL 60173
Tel.: (312) 967-7088
Software Provider
N.A.I.C.S.: 423430

Motherson Technology Services United Kingdom Limited (1)
100 Berkshire Place, Winnersh, RG41 5RD, Berkshire, United Kingdom
Tel.: (44) 7415567340
Software Provider
N.A.I.C.S.: 423430

PK Cables do Brasil Ltda. (1)
Rua Nicaragua 847 Bacacheri Edificio Brooklyn 4 andar CEP, Curitiba, 82510-170, PR, Brazil
Tel.: (55) 4121099717
Electronic Equipment Mfr & Distr
N.A.I.C.S.: 334419

PKC Group Lithuania UAB (1)
J Janonio g 4, LT-35101, Panevezys, Lithuania
Tel.: (370) 45444780
Electronic Equipment Mfr & Distr
N.A.I.C.S.: 334419

PKC Group Ltd. (1)
Vihikari 10, FI-90440, Kempele, Finland
Tel.: (358) 201752111
Web Site: http://www.pkcgroup.com
Electronic Components Mfr & Distr
N.A.I.C.S.: 334419
Robert Joseph Remenar *(Executives, Bd of Dirs)*

Subsidiary (Non-US):

AEES Manufacturera, S. De R.L de C.V (2)
Carretera a Matamoros Entronque con Mieleres SN, Parque Industrial las Americas, 27278, Torreon, Mexico
Tel.: (52) 8717290009
Web Site: https://www.pkcgroup.com
Electronic Cable & Wire Mfr
N.A.I.C.S.: 335929

AEES, Inc. (2)
Tel.: (248) 489-4700
Web Site: http://www.pkcgroup.com
Automotive Electronic Systems Mfr
N.A.I.C.S.: 336320

Subsidiary (Domestic):

AEES Power Systems Limited Partnership (3)
1677 Park Dr, Traverse City, MI 49686
Tel.: (231) 929-4215
Web Site: http://www.pkcgroup.com
Electronic Cable & Wire Mfr
N.A.I.C.S.: 335929

Subsidiary (Non-US):

Asesoria Mexicana Empresarial, S. de R.L de C.V (2)
Carretera Miguel Aleman 248 Interior Suite 2 Nivel 3, Torre Aeropuerto, 66600, Apodaca, Mexico
Tel.: (52) 8188656500
Web Site: http://www.pkcgroup.com
Motor Vehicle Electronic Equipment Mfr
N.A.I.C.S.: 336320

OOO AEK (2)
Shosse Gornjakov 34, 186930, Kostomuksha, Karelia, Russia
Tel.: (7) 8145972354
Web Site: http://www.pkcgroup.com
Electronic Cable & Wire Mfr
N.A.I.C.S.: 335929

PKC Cables do Brasil Industria e Comercio Ltda (2)
Rua Nicaragua, 847 Bacacheri, CEP 82510-170, Curitiba, Brazil
Tel.: (55) 4121099717
Web Site: https://www.pkcgroup.com
Electronic Cable & Wire Mfr
N.A.I.C.S.: 335929

PKC Eesti AS (2)
Lootsa 8, 11415, Tallinn, Estonia
Tel.: (372) 6390100
Web Site: http://www.pkcgroup.com
Emp.: 80
Electronic Cable & Wire Mfr
N.A.I.C.S.: 335929

PKC Group Mexico S.A. de C.V. (2)
Avenida Fresnel 7650 Col Parque Industrial AJ Bermudez, Juarez, 32470, Chihuahua, Mexico
Tel.: (52) 6566250824
Web Site: https://www.pkcgroup.com
Electronic Cable & Wire Mfr
N.A.I.C.S.: 335929

PKC Group Poland Sp. z.o.o (2)
ul Radomska 86, 27-200, Starachowice, Poland
Tel.: (48) 412608800
Web Site: https://www.pkcgroup.com
Electronic Cable & Wire Mfr
N.A.I.C.S.: 335929

Subsidiary (US):

PKC Group USA Inc. (2)
101 S La Canada Dr Ste 38, Green Valley, AZ 85614
Tel.: (520) 393-8290
Electronic Cable & Wire Mfr
N.A.I.C.S.: 335929

Subsidiary (Non-US):

PKC SEGU Systemelektrik GmbH (2)
Am Eisberg 14, 36456, Barchfeld, Germany
Tel.: (49) 369614890
Web Site: http://www.pkcgroup.com
Electronic Cable & Wire Mfr
N.A.I.C.S.: 335929

PKC Vehicle Technology (Suzhou) Co. Ltd (2)
Block 1 Unit 502-503 Ascendas Xin Su Industry Square I, NO 5 Xinghan Street, Suzhou, 215021, China
Tel.: (86) 51262962671
Web Site: https://www.pkcgroup.com
Motor Vehicle Electronic Equipment Mfr
N.A.I.C.S.: 336320

PKC Wiring Systems d.o.o. (2)
Salinacka 82, 11300, Smederevo, Serbia
Tel.: (381) 26621866
Web Site: https://www.pkcgroup.com
Electronic Cable & Wire Mfr
N.A.I.C.S.: 335929

PKC Group de Piedras Negras, S. de R.L. de C.V. (2)
Libramiento G Manuel Perez Trevino Col Parque Industrial Amistad, 26080, Piedras Negras, Chihuahua, Mexico
Tel.: (52) 6566250824
Automotive Electric Distribution System Mfr
N.A.I.C.S.: 336320

PKC Wiring Systems Oy (1)
Vihikari 10, FI-90440, Kempele, Finland
Tel.: (358) 201752111
Electronic Equipment Distr
N.A.I.C.S.: 423610

SMP Automotive Exterior GmbH (1)
Ludwig-Erhard-Strasse 1, 84069, Schierling, Germany
Tel.: (49) 945177590
Emp.: 530
Automotive Plastic Parts Mfr
N.A.I.C.S.: 336390

SMP Automotive Produtos Automotivos do Brasil Ltda. (1)
Av Leste Km 4 Rua 1 - no 525 Quadra C Bairro Campo Largo de Roseira, Sao Jose dos Pinhais, Curitiba, 83183000, Brazil
Tel.: (55) 4121044936
Emp.: 900
Automotive Plastic Parts Mfr
N.A.I.C.S.: 336390

SMP Automotive Systems Alabama Inc. (1)
10799 Ed Stephens Rd, Cottondale, AL 35453
Tel.: (205) 723-4990
Automotive Plastic Parts Mfr
N.A.I.C.S.: 336390

SMP Automotive Technologies Teruel Sociedad Limitada (1)
Pol Azalenguas, Fuentes Claras, 44340, Teruel, Spain
Tel.: (34) 978731880
Emp.: 60
Automotive Plastic Parts Mfr
N.A.I.C.S.: 336390

SMP Deutschland GmbH (1)
Schlossmattenstrasse 18, 79268, Botzingen, Germany
Tel.: (49) 7663610
Web Site: http://www.smp-automotive.com
Sales Range: $1-4.9 Billion
Emp.: 7,000
Interior & Exterior Molded Plastic Automobile Components Mfr
N.A.I.C.S.: 336390

Subsidiary (Non-US):

SMP Automotive Solutions Slovakia s.r.o. (2)
Matuskovo 1586, 92501, Matuskovo, Slovakia
Tel.: (421) 313213200
Web Site: http://www.smp-automotive.com
Emp.: 240
Automobile Body Parts Mfr
N.A.I.C.S.: 336211

SMP Automotive Systems Mexico SA de CV (2)
Av Tlaxcala 480, Cuautlancingo, 72700, Puebla, Mexico
Tel.: (52) 2222739300
Emp.: 570
Automobile Body Parts Mfr
N.A.I.C.S.: 336211

SMP Automotive Technology Barcelona S.L. (2)
PMDI Cockpit Ctra N II Km 585 Anexo taller 8, 08760, Martorell, Spain
Tel.: (34) 9377550157
Automobile Body Parts Mfr
N.A.I.C.S.: 336211

Samvardhana Motherson Peguform Automotive Technology Portugal S.A. (2)
Parque Industrial Autoeuropa Quinta da Marquesa CCI 102162950-678, Palmela, Portugal
Tel.: (351) 212135650
Emp.: 210
Automobile Body Parts Mfr
N.A.I.C.S.: 336211

SMR Automotive (Langfang) Co. Ltd. (1)
No 4 Baohai Road Xianghe Modern Industrial Park, Langfang, 065400, China
Tel.: (86) 3168872020
Automobile Motorized Mirror Mfr
N.A.I.C.S.: 336390

SMR Automotive Australia Pty. Ltd. (1)
18 Sherriffs Rd, PO Box 37, Lonsdale, 5160, SA, Australia
Tel.: (61) 883017777
Emp.: 400
Motor Vehicle Mirror Mfr
N.A.I.C.S.: 336390

SMR Automotive Brasil Ltda. (1)
Av Pacifico Moneda 3360 Bairro Capotuna, Jaguariuna, 13820000, Brazil
Tel.: (55) 1938379000
Emp.: 220
Automotive Components Mfr
N.A.I.C.S.: 336390

SMR Automotive Mirrors Stuttgart GmbH (1)
Hedelfinger Strasse 60, 70327, Stuttgart, Germany
Tel.: (49) 711185610
Web Site: https://www.smr-automotive.com
Motor Vehicle Mirror Mfr & Whslr
N.A.I.C.S.: 336390
Laksh Vaaman Sehgal *(Member-Mgmt Bd)*

SMR Automotive Mirrors UK Ltd. (1)
Castle Trading Estate East St, Portchester, PO16 9SD, Hampshire, United Kingdom
Tel.: (44) 2392210022
Sales Range: $150-199.9 Million
Motor Vehicle Mirror Mfr
N.A.I.C.S.: 336390

Subsidiary (US):

SMR Automotive Systems USA Inc. (2)
1855 Busha Hwy, Marysville, MI 48040
Tel.: (810) 364-4141
Web Site: https://www.smr-automotive.com
Sales Range: $125-149.9 Million
Motor Vehicle Mirror Mfr
N.A.I.C.S.: 336390
Sally Young *(Coord-Ops)*

SMR Automotive Modules Korea Ltd. (1)
12th Floor C-Dong Bucheon Technopark 187-7 Dodang-dong, Wonmi-gu, Bucheon, 420-806, Gyeonggi-do, Korea (South)
Tel.: (82) 326650511
Automblie Motorized Mirror Mfr
N.A.I.C.S.: 336390

SMR Automotive Operations Japan K.K. (1)
BPR Place Nagoya Marunouchi 4F 1-16-4 Marunouchi, Naka-ku, Nagoya, 4600002, Aichi, Japan
Tel.: (81) 522181038
Automotive Components Mfr
N.A.I.C.S.: 336390

SMR Automotive System (Thailand) Limited (1)
500/49 Moo3 WHA Eastern Seaboard Industrial Estate 1 Tasith, A Pluakdaeng, Rayong, 21140, Thailand
Tel.: (66) 65509477880
Automotive Components Mfr
N.A.I.C.S.: 336390

SMR Automotive Systems France S.A. (1)
Tel.: (33) 164792200
Sales Range: $100-124.9 Million
Motor Vehicle Mirror Mfr
N.A.I.C.S.: 336390

SMR Automotive Systems Spain S.A.U. (1)
Poligono Industrial Valdemuel S/n, 50290, Epila, Spain
Tel.: (34) 976819100
Sales Range: $50-74.9 Million
Motor Vehicle Mirror Mfr
N.A.I.C.S.: 336390

SMR Automotive Vision Systems Mexico S.A de C.V. (1)
Circuito Mexico 260 Parque Industrial Tres Naciones, 78395, San Luis Potosi, Mexico
Tel.: (52) 4448041300

SAMVARDHANA MOTHERSON INTERNATIONAL LIMITED

Samvardhana Motherson International Limited—(Continued)
Automotive Components Mfr
N.A.I.C.S.: 336390

SMR Automotive Yancheng Co., Limited (1)
No7 Jinshajiang Road Economic Development Zone, Yancheng, 224007, China
Tel.: (86) 51588286838
Emp.: 120
Salt Product Mfr
N.A.I.C.S.: 311999

SMRC Automotive Interior Modules Croatia d.o.o. (1)
Jankomir 25, 10090, Zagreb, Croatia
Tel.: (385) 13473592
Automotive Interiors Mfr
N.A.I.C.S.: 336360

SMRC Automotive Smart Interior Tech (Thailand) Ltd. (1)
Eastern Seaboard Industrial Estate 62 Moo 4, Pluakdaeng, Rayong, 21140, Thailand
Tel.: (66) 38954400
Automotive Interiors Mfr
N.A.I.C.S.: 336360

SMRC Automotive Solutions Slovakia s.r.o. (1)
Dolne Hony 2, 949 01, Nitra, Slovakia
Tel.: (421) 376909212
Automotive Interiors Mfr
N.A.I.C.S.: 336360

SMRC Automotive Tech Argentina S.A. (1)
Sullivan 3131 Esq Otto Krause B1667 ACI Tortuguitas Malvinas, Buenos Aires, Argentina
Tel.: (54) 3327416601
Automotive Interiors Mfr
N.A.I.C.S.: 336360

SMRC Fabricacao e Comercio de Produtos Automotivos do Brasil Ltda. (1)
Rod BR290 - KM 67- lot 15, Cruzeiro, 94065-140, Gravatai, Brazil
Tel.: (55) 5134897300
Automotive Interiors Mfr
N.A.I.C.S.: 336360

Samvardhana Motherson Auto System Private Limited (1)
2nd Floor F-7 Block B-1 Mohan Co-Operative Industrial Estate, Mathura Road, New Delhi, 110044, India
Tel.: (91) 1140050950
Web Site: https://www.mothersonautoparts.com
Automobile Parts Distr
N.A.I.C.S.: 423120

Samvardhana Motherson Automotive Systems Group B.V. (1)
Hoogoorddreef 15, 1101 BA, Amsterdam, Netherlands
Tel.: (31) 207944580
Web Site: http://www.smrpbv.com
Automotive Products Mfr
N.A.I.C.S.: 336390

Subsidiary (Non-US):

SAS Autosystemtechnik Verwaltungs GmbH (2)
Siemensallee 84, 76187, Karlsruhe, Germany
Tel.: (49) 721350550
Web Site: http://www.sas-automotive.com
Sales Range: $25-49.9 Million
Emp.: 80
Automotive Safety Component Mfr
N.A.I.C.S.: 336390
Ekkehard Klautke *(CFO & Exec VP)*

SMRC Automotive Modules France SAS (2)
87 rue Leon Duhamel, 62440, Harnes, France
Tel.: (33) 321139000
Web Site: https://www.smrc-automotive.com
Automotive Components Services
N.A.I.C.S.: 423120

Samvardhana Motherson Health Solutions Limited (1)
C-1 A & B Sector-1, Noida, 201301, Uttar Pradesh, India
Tel.: (91) 1204365226
Web Site: https://www.smhs.motherson.com
Software Provider
N.A.I.C.S.: 423430

Samvardhana Motherson Peguform Barcelona S.L.U. (1)
Ctra N II Km 585 Anexo taller 8 SEAT, 08760, Martorell, Spain
Tel.: (34) 937745170
Emp.: 350
Automobile Parts Mfr
N.A.I.C.S.: 336390

Samvardhana Motherson Peguform GmbH (1)
Schlossmattenstrasse 18, 79268, Botzingen, Germany
Tel.: (49) 7663610
Emp.: 1,430
Automotive Plastic Parts Mfr
N.A.I.C.S.: 336390

Samvardhana Motherson Reydel Autotecc Morocco S.A.S. (1)
TAC 2-22 Jouamaa Douar Joumaa, Commune rurale, 94032, Tangiers, Morocco
Tel.: (212) 531066030
Automotive Interiors Mfr
N.A.I.C.S.: 336360

Shanghai SMRC Automotive Interiors Tech Consulting Co., Ltd. (1)
Unit D 8th Floor Building D No 207 Songhong Road, Changning District, Shanghai, 200335, China
Tel.: (86) 2123561640
Automobile Parts Mfr
N.A.I.C.S.: 336390

Vacuform 2000 (Proprietary) Limited (1)
155 Van Eden Crescent Rosslyn East, Pretoria, South Africa
Tel.: (27) 125411575
Web Site: https://www.vacuform.co.za
Vacuum Formed Product Mfr & Distr
N.A.I.C.S.: 326140

Wisetime Oy (1)
Saaristonkatu 23, 90100, Oulu, Finland
Tel.: (358) 207661401
Web Site: https://wisetime.motherson.com
Software Provider
N.A.I.C.S.: 423430

Yujin SMRC Automotive Techno Corp. (1)
927-14 Osin-ro Sinam-myeon, Yesan, Chungnam, Korea (South)
Tel.: (82) 415392800
Web Site: https://www.ysat.kr
Automobile Parts Mfr
N.A.I.C.S.: 336390

SAMWHA CAPACITOR GROUP
Samyoung Bldg 587-8 Sinsa-dong, Kangnam-gu, Seoul, Korea (South)
Tel.: (82) 205455600
Web Site: http://www.samwha.com
Year Founded: 1956
Sales Range: $75-99.9 Million
Emp.: 360
Capacitor Mfr
N.A.I.C.S.: 334416
Young Joo Oh *(Chm & CEO)*

Subsidiaries:

PT. SAMCON (1)
JL Raya Subang Cikumpay Campaka, Purwakarta, Jawa-Barat, Indonesia
Tel.: (62) 264 216 882 7
Capacitor Mfr
N.A.I.C.S.: 334416
Lee Kun-hwa *(CEO)*

Qingdao Samwha Electronics Co., Ltd. (1)
Malan, Pingdu, Qingdao, China
Tel.: (86) 532 8335 1333
Electric Equipment Mfr
N.A.I.C.S.: 334419
Lee baek bum *(CEO)*

Samwha Capacitor Co., Ltd. (1)
124 Buk-Ri Namsa-Myeun, Cheoin-Gu, Yongin, Gyeonggi-do, Korea (South)
Tel.: (82) 313326441
Web Site: http://www.samwha.com
Rev.: $202,080,823
Assets: $220,477,090
Liabilities: $47,570,346
Net Worth: $172,906,743
Earnings: $22,501,574
Emp.: 601
Fiscal Year-end: 12/31/2022
Cheol-Su Kim *(Dir-Mgmt Support)*

Samwha Electric Co., Ltd. (1)
3 Bongmyeong-ro, Heungdeok-gu, Cheongju, Chungbuk, Korea (South)
Tel.: (82) 43 261 0200
Capacitor Mfr
N.A.I.C.S.: 334416
Shin Beck-sik *(CEO)*

Plant (Domestic):

Samwha Electric Co., Ltd. - Chungju Plant (2)
524 Gugwon-daero, Chungju, Chungbuk, Korea (South)
Tel.: (82) 43 853 2404
Capacitor Mfr
N.A.I.C.S.: 334416

Samwha Electronics Co., Ltd. (1)
215 Gyeonggidong-ro Namsa-myeon, Cheoin-gu, Yongin, 17118, Gyeonggi-do, Korea (South)
Tel.: (82) 313745501
Web Site: http://www.samwha.com
Rev.: $37,066,210
Assets: $52,725,339
Liabilities: $39,122,735
Net Worth: $13,602,603
Earnings: ($4,649,847)
Emp.: 109
Fiscal Year-end: 12/31/2022
Mfr of Electronic Equipment
N.A.I.C.S.: 335999
Kun Hwa Lee *(CEO)*

Plant (Domestic):

Samwha Electronics Co., Ltd. - Jochiwon Plant (2)
660 Unjusan-ro, Jeondong-myeon, Sejong, Cheongsong, Korea (South)
Tel.: (82) 868 5501
Electric Equipment Mfr
N.A.I.C.S.: 334419

Samwha Europe GmbH (1)
Lyoner st 44-48, 60528, Frankfurt, Germany
Tel.: (49) 69 9637 650
Emp.: 6
Capacitors Distr
N.A.I.C.S.: 423690
Park Kwang-hyun *(CEO)*

Samwha Hi-Tech Intl, Trading Co., Ltd. (1)
No 12 Shiji Street Saida Industrial Park Xiqing, Economic Development Zone, Tianjin, 300385, China
Tel.: (86) 22 2388 8500
Emp.: 27
Electronic Equipment & Component Distr
N.A.I.C.S.: 423690
Jung Jae-Kyong *(CEO)*

Samwha Hongkong Co., Ltd. (1)
Unit 3 to 9 5th Floor Hi-Tech Center 9choi Yuen Road, Sheung Shui, New Territories, China (Hong Kong)
Tel.: (852) 2668 2460
Emp.: 27
Electronic Equipment & Component Distr
N.A.I.C.S.: 423690
Seo Jung-taek *(CEO)*

Samwha Hungary Kft. (1)
Keleti Marton utca 12, Fot, 2151, Hungary
Tel.: (36) 27 539 581
Emp.: 5
Electronic Equipment & Component Distr
N.A.I.C.S.: 423690
Kim Jun-ku *(CEO)*

Samwha India Energy Savings PVT.Ltd. (1)
A-100 Ground Floor Sector 65, Gautam Budh Nagar, Noida, 201301, Uttar Pradesh, India
Tel.: (91) 120 4523800
Emp.: 2
Electronic Equipment & Component Distr
N.A.I.C.S.: 423690
Lee Chang-yong *(CEO)*

Samwha Poland Sp.Z.o.o. (1)
ul Finska 2, Biskupice Podgorne, Kobierzyce, 55-040, Poland
Tel.: (48) 71 733 7295 6
Emp.: 88
Electronic Equipment & Component Distr
N.A.I.C.S.: 423690
Park Cha-byung *(CEO)*

Samwha Tecom Co., Ltd. (1)
854-5 Sambaek-ro, Baegam-myeon Cheoingu, Yongin, Gyeonggi-do, Korea (South)
Tel.: (82) 31 334 9631
Emp.: 18
Electric Equipment Mfr
N.A.I.C.S.: 334419
Son Young-tae *(CEO)*

Samwha Thailand Co., Ltd. (1)
66 MOO 4 T Takai A Mung, Chachoengsao, 24000, Thailand
Tel.: (66) 38 847571 3
Emp.: 84
Capacitor Mfr
N.A.I.C.S.: 334416
Kim Seung-nam *(CEO)*

Samwha USA Inc. (1)
2555 Melksee, San Diego, CA 92154
Tel.: (619) 671-0870
Sales Range: $10-24.9 Million
Emp.: 20
Sales of Electronic Parts
N.A.I.C.S.: 423690
David B. Yoo *(Mgr-Admin)*

Tianjin Samwha Electric Co., Ltd. (1)
Room 1909 Business Center The Center Point No 2 Dongzong Road, Dongguan, 523400, Guangdong, China
Tel.: (86) 769 2233 3517
Capacitor Mfr
N.A.I.C.S.: 334416

Plant (Domestic):

Tianjin Samwha Electric Co., Ltd. - Tianjin Plant 1 (2)
No 22 XingHua Road Xiqing Economic Development Zone, Tianjin, China
Tel.: (86) 22 2397 3333
Capacitor Mfr
N.A.I.C.S.: 334416

Tianjin Samwha Electric Co., Ltd. - Tianjin Plant 2 (2)
No 12 Saida Shiji Highway Xiqing Economic, Technological Development Area, Tianjin, 300385, China
Tel.: (86) 22 2388 3333
Capacitor Mfr
N.A.I.C.S.: 334416

SAMWHAN CORPORATION
Kpop Building 12th 13th Floor 547 Eonju-ro Yeoksam-dong, Gangnam-gu, Seoul, Korea (South)
Tel.: (82) 2 740 2114
Web Site: http://www.samwhan.co.kr
Year Founded: 1946
Construction Engineering Services
N.A.I.C.S.: 237990
Lee Kye-Yon *(Pres & CEO)*

Subsidiaries:

Samwhan Camus Co., Ltd. (1)
Rm 206 New Airport Plaza 2796-6 Unseodong Jung-gu Incheon 2796-6, Unseodong, 400-833, Seoul, Korea (South)
Tel.: (82) 32 746 6114
Web Site: http://www.swcamus.co.kr
Construction Engineering Services
N.A.I.C.S.: 237990

Samwhan Machinery Co., Ltd. (1)
45 Woongnam-dong, Changwon, 641-290, Korea (South)
Tel.: (82) 5 5282 0335
Web Site: http://www.samwhanmi.co.kr

Emp.: 160
Industrial Machinery Mfr
N.A.I.C.S.: 333248

SAMWONSTEEL CO., LTD.
40 Cheolgangsandan-ro 66 beon-gil
Daesong-myeon Nam-gu, Pohang,
Gyeongsangbuk-do, Korea (South)
Tel.: (82) 542781983
Web Site: http://www.samwon-
 steel.co.kr
023000—(KRS)
Rev.: $279,273,203
Assets: $225,260,309
Liabilities: $48,251,410
Net Worth: $177,008,899
Earnings: $9,981,215
Emp.: 280
Fiscal Year-end: 12/31/22
Automobile Steel Springs Mfr
N.A.I.C.S.: 336390
Jeong Woong Jin *(Co-CEO)*

Subsidiaries:

D&D Springs Poland Co., Ltd (1)
ul Melgiewska 7-9, 20-952, Lublin, Poland
Tel.: (48) 81 749 1900
Web Site: http://www.resor.pl
Sales Range: $50-74.9 Million
Emp.: 20
Automotive Spring Mfr
N.A.I.C.S.: 332613

Daewon America, Inc. (1)
4600 Northpark Dr, Opelika, AL 36801
Tel.: (334) 364-1600
Web Site: http://www.samwon-steel.co.kr
Automobile Parts Mfr
N.A.I.C.S.: 336390

Daewon Chong Up Corp. (1)
5-35 Sejong-daero, Jung-gu, Seoul, 100-800, Korea (South)
Tel.: (82) 2 318 6387
Web Site: http://www.daewoncorp.com
Sales Range: $200-249.9 Million
Automobile Parts Mfr
N.A.I.C.S.: 336390
Jae Moo Hur *(Chm)*

Daewon Precision Industrial Co., Ltd. (1)
100 Beomjigi-ro 141beon-gil, Danwon-gu, Ansan, 15434, Gyeonggi-do, Korea (South)
Tel.: (82) 314950701
Web Site: https://www.dwjm.co.kr
Sales Range: $250-299.9 Billion
Emp.: 674
Steel Products Mfr
N.A.I.C.S.: 331110
Kim Jae Seok *(Vice Chm)*

SAMWORTH BROTHERS LTD.
Chetwode House 1 Samworth Way
Leicester Road, Melton Mowbray,
LE13 1GA, Leicestershire, United
Kingdom
Tel.: (44) 7802946220   UK
Web Site:
 http://www.samworthbrothers.co.uk
Year Founded: 1896
Sales Range: $700-749.9 Million
Emp.: 8,000
Food Mfr
N.A.I.C.S.: 551112

Subsidiaries:

Bradgate Bakery (1)
Madeline Road, Beaumont Leys, Leicester,
LE4 1WX, United Kingdom
Tel.: (44) 1162361100
Web Site: http://www.samworthbrothers.com
Sales Range: $200-249.9 Million
Emp.: 1,000
Sandwich Mfr
N.A.I.C.S.: 311812
Paul Davis *(Dir-Sls)*

Dickinson & Morris Limited (1)
10 Nottingham Street, Melton Mowbray,
LE13 1NW, Leicestershire, United Kingdom
Tel.: (44) 1664482068
Web Site: http://www.porkpie.co.uk
Sales Range: $1-9.9 Million
Emp.: 29
Pork Pie Mfr
N.A.I.C.S.: 311813

Ginsters Limited (1)
Tavistock Road, Callington, PL17 7XG,
Cornwall, United Kingdom
Tel.: (44) 01579386200
Web Site: http://www.ginsters.co.uk
Sales Range: $125-149.9 Million
Emp.: 700
Pasta Mfr
N.A.I.C.S.: 311813
Kieran Hemsworth *(Mng Dir)*

Kensey Foods Limited (1)
Pennygillam Way, Launceston, PL157AS,
Cornwall, United Kingdom
Tel.: (44) 01566778300
Web Site: http://www.samworthbrothers.com
Sales Range: $100-124.9 Million
Emp.: 500
Bread, Cake & Pastry Mfr
N.A.I.C.S.: 311813

Kettleby Foods Limited (1)
2 Samworth Way, Melton Mowbray, LE13
1GA, Leicestershire, United Kingdom
Tel.: (44) 1664502000
Sales Range: $1-9.9 Million
Emp.: 83
Food Mfr
N.A.I.C.S.: 311999
Mujib Nathalia *(Dir-Fin)*

Melton Foods Limited (1)
3 Samworth Way Leicester Rd, Melton
Mowbray, LE13 1GA, Leicestershire, United
Kingdom
Tel.: (44) 01664484400
Web Site: http://www.meltonfoods.co.uk
Sales Range: $1-9.9 Million
Emp.: 480
Food Mfr
N.A.I.C.S.: 311999

Samworth Brothers Distribution
Limited (1)
Woodside Centurian Way Meridian Bus Pk,
Leicester, LE19 1QA, United Kingdom
Tel.: (44) 1162814800
Web Site: http://www.samworth-
 distribution.co.uk
Sales Range: $10-24.9 Million
Emp.: 250
Distribution Services
N.A.I.C.S.: 311999

Tamar Foods Limited (1)
83 Tavistock Road, Callington, PL17 7TA,
Cornwall, United Kingdom
Tel.: (44) 01579386300
Web Site: http://www.tamarfoods.co.uk
Sales Range: $150-199.9 Million
Emp.: 600
Food Mfr
N.A.I.C.S.: 311999

Walkers Charnwood Bakery (1)
200 Madeline Road, Beaumont Leys, Leicester,
LE4 1EX, United Kingdom
Tel.: (44) 1162340033
Sales Range: $150-199.9 Million
Emp.: 643
Food Mfr
N.A.I.C.S.: 311999

Walkers Midshire Foods Limited (1)
78-88 Cobden St Industrial Estate, Leicester,
LE1 2LB, United Kingdom
Tel.: (44) 1162515533
Sales Range: $300-349.9 Million
Emp.: 800
Food Mfr
N.A.I.C.S.: 424470
Tracy Billingham *(Mgr-Personnel)*

Westward Laboratories (1)
Granite Way, Callington, PL17 7SB, Cornwall,
United Kingdom
Tel.: (44) 1579386219
Sales Range: $25-49.9 Million
Emp.: 28
Food Testing Laboratory
N.A.I.C.S.: 541380
Shaun Galloway *(Dir-Fin)*

SAMYAK INTERNATIONAL LIMITED
N-38 Saket Nagar, 2nd Floor, Indore,
452018, Madhya Pradesh, India
Tel.: (91) 8889123123   In
Web Site:
 https://samyakinternational.in
Year Founded: 1995
530025—(BOM)
Rev.: $5,391,607
Assets: $9,331,982
Liabilities: $1,266,027
Net Worth: $8,065,955
Earnings: $362,736
Emp.: 11
Fiscal Year-end: 03/31/23
Petroleum Product Whslr
N.A.I.C.S.: 424720
Shantilal Jain *(Exec Dir)*

SAMYANG FOODS CO., LTD.
104 Opaesan-ro 3-gil, Seongbuk-gu,
Seoul, Korea (South)
Tel.: (82) 29403000
Web Site:
 https://www.samyangfoods.com
Year Founded: 1961
003230—(KRS)
Rev.: $697,231,050
Assets: $709,420,920
Liabilities: $360,617,130
Net Worth: $348,803,790
Earnings: $61,567,904
Emp.: 1,926
Fiscal Year-end: 12/31/22
Food Products Mfr
N.A.I.C.S.: 311999
Kim Jeong-Su *(CEO)*

SAMYANG HOLDINGS CORPORATION
31 Jongro 33-gil, Jongro-gu, Seoul,
Korea (South)
Tel.: (82) 27407271   KR
Web Site: https://www.samyang.com
Year Founded: 2011
000070—(KRS)
Rev.: $2,140,164,180
Assets: $3,086,982,040
Liabilities: $1,341,606,020
Net Worth: $1,745,376,020
Earnings: $53,357,840
Emp.: 166
Fiscal Year-end: 12/31/19
Holding Company
N.A.I.C.S.: 551112
Yoon Kim *(Chm)*

Subsidiaries:

Samyang Biopharm USA, Inc. (1)
200 1 Kendall Sq Ste 402, Cambridge, MA
02139
Tel.: (617) 812-6960
Biological Research & Development Services
N.A.I.C.S.: 541715
Hyun Jung Helen Lee *(Pres & CEO)*

Samyang Corporation (1)
31 Jongno 33-gil, Jongno-gu, Seoul, 03129,
Korea (South)
Tel.: (82) 27407114
Web Site: https://www.samyangcorp.com
Rev.: $2,034,420,713
Assets: $2,262,380,783
Liabilities: $1,088,111,453
Net Worth: $1,174,269,330
Earnings: $63,083,449
Emp.: 1,320
Fiscal Year-end: 12/31/2022
Holding Company; Chemical & Food Products Mfr & Distr
N.A.I.C.S.: 551112
Soon-Cheol Park *(Pres-Chemical Div)*

Subsidiary (Domestic):

Samyang EMS Co., Ltd. (2)
471 Waryong-Ro Yeonseo-Myeon, Sejong,
Korea (South)
Tel.: (82) 44 589 5999
Web Site: http://www.samyang.com
Emp.: 50

Electronic Products Mfr
N.A.I.C.S.: 334419

Subsidiary (Non-US):

Samyang Engineering Plastics (Hungary) Co., Ltd. (2)
Emp.: 85
Plastic Product Mfr & Distr
N.A.I.C.S.: 326199

Samyang Engineering Plastics
(Shanghai) Co., Ltd. (2)
131 Shuangying Road, Qingpu Industrial
Area Qingpu, Shanghai, Qingpu, China
Tel.: (86) 2169222270
Plastic Product Distr
N.A.I.C.S.: 424610
Shin Do-hyun *(CEO)*

Samyang F&D, Inc. (1)
5F Samyang Seven Springs Building 3
Yanghwaro 18-gil, Mapo-gu, Seoul, Korea
(South)
Tel.: (82) 24254081
Food Products Distr
N.A.I.C.S.: 424490
Kim June-young *(CEO)*

Samyang Kasei Co., Ltd. (1)
376 Ongoeulro Palbokno 3-ga, Deokjin-gu,
Jeonju, Jeollabuk-do, Korea (South)
Tel.: (82) 53 210 1114
Web Site: http://www.samyangkasei
Chemical Product Mfr & Distr
N.A.I.C.S.: 325199
Kim Kwangyeol *(Pres)*

Samyang Milmax Corporation (1)
710-46 Asanhoro Yeongin-myeon, Asan,
Chungcheongnam-do, Korea (South)
Tel.: (82) 2 740 7020
Web Site: http://www.samyangmilmax.com
Food Product Mfr & Distr
N.A.I.C.S.: 311821
Kim Myeong-ki *(CEO)*

Samyang Research Corporation (1)
405 Lexington Ave 35th Fl, New York, NY
10174
Tel.: (212) 972-0011
Emp.: 4
Pharmaceutical Products Research Services
N.A.I.C.S.: 541715
Haejeong An *(Branch Mgr)*

Sevensprings Co., Ltd. (1)
4th Fl 18 Bukchon-ro, Jongno-gu, Seoul,
Korea (South)
Tel.: (82) 16705270
Web Site: http://www.sevensprings.co.kr
Food Products Distr
N.A.I.C.S.: 424490

SAMYANG PACKAGING CORP.
31 Jongro 33-gil, Jongro-gu, Seoul,
Korea (South)
Tel.: (82) 27407861
Web Site:
 https://www.samyangpackaging.com
Year Founded: 2014
272550—(KRS)
Rev,: $322,880,120
Assets: $484,917,880
Liabilities: $238,768,680
Net Worth: $246,149,200
Earnings: $24,411,960
Emp.: 476
Fiscal Year-end: 12/31/19
Pet Bottle Mfr
N.A.I.C.S.: 326160
Jo Dokhee *(CEO)*

SAMYANG TONGSANG CO., LTD.
301 Teheran-ro, Gangnam-Gu, Seoul,
Korea (South)
Tel.: (82) 234533073
Web Site:
 https://www.samyangts.com
Year Founded: 1957
002170—(KRS)
Rev.: $137,140,240
Assets: $350,930,707

SAMYANG TONGSANG CO., LTD.

SAMYANG TONGSANG Co., Ltd.—(Continued)
Liabilities: $31,005,301
Net Worth: $319,925,406
Earnings: $11,582,149
Emp.: 271
Fiscal Year-end: 12/31/22
Leather Product Mfr
N.A.I.C.S.: 316110
Park Heejung *(CFO)*

Subsidiaries:

SAMYANG TONGSANG Co., Ltd. - Gunpo Factory (1)
488 Dangjeong-Dong, Gunpo, 15848, Gyeonggi-Do, Korea (South)
Tel.: (82) 31 452 8106
Leather Product Mfr
N.A.I.C.S.: 316990

SAMYOUNG CO., LTD.
13th floor gwanjeong 35 Cheonggyecheon-ro, Jongno-gu, Seoul, 03188, Korea (South)
Tel.: (82) 27572291
Web Site: https://www.sycc.co.kr
Year Founded: 1959
003720—(KRS)
Rev.: $113,322,726
Assets: $104,184,153
Liabilities: $64,224,843
Net Worth: $39,959,310
Earnings: $833,550
Emp.: 192
Fiscal Year-end: 12/31/22
Electronic & Packing Film Mfr
N.A.I.C.S.: 326112
Lee Seok-Jun *(CEO)*

Subsidiaries:

SamYoung Chemical - Cheongju Factory (1)
13F Kwanjeong Bldg 35 Cheonggyecheon-ro, Jongro-gu, Seoul, 03188, Korea (South)
Tel.: (82) 27572295
Plastics Product Mfr
N.A.I.C.S.: 326199

SamYoung Chemical - Dalian Factory (1)
No 73 Zhenpeng Industry Area Development Area, Dalian, China
Tel.: (86) 41137511321
Plastics Product Mfr
N.A.I.C.S.: 326199

SamYoung Chemical - Gumi Factory (1)
77 1Gongdan-ro 7-gil Gongdan-dong, Gumi, 39367, Gyeongsangbuk-do, Korea (South)
Tel.: (82) 544635496
Plastics Product Mfr
N.A.I.C.S.: 326199

SAMYOUNG ELECTRONICS CO., LTD.
47 Sagimakgol-ro Jungwon-gu, Seongnam, 13209, Gyeonggi-do, Korea (South)
Web Site: http://www.samyoung.co.kr
Year Founded: 1968
005680—(KRS)
Rev.: $174,527,593
Assets: $413,671,709
Liabilities: $13,483,560
Net Worth: $400,188,149
Earnings: $13,943,643
Emp.: 495
Fiscal Year-end: 12/31/22
Electronic Components Mfr
N.A.I.C.S.: 334419
Kim Junhwa *(Gen Mgr)*

Subsidiaries:

Samyoung Electronics Co., Ltd. - POSEUNG PLANT 1 (1)
61 Pyeongtaekhang-ro 156beon-gil, Poseung-eup, Pyeongtaek, 451-821, Gyeonggi-do, Korea (South)
Tel.: (82) 31 683 3034
Electronic Components Mfr
N.A.I.C.S.: 334419

Samyoung Electronics Co., Ltd. - QINGDAO FACTORY (1)
No 5 Chang Jiang Road, Pingdu, Shan Dong, China
Tel.: (86) 532 8838 2040
Electronic Components Mfr
N.A.I.C.S.: 334419

Samyoung S&C Co., Ltd. (1)
446 Dunchon-daero, Jungwon-gu, Seongnam, 13229, Gyeonggi-do, Korea (South)
Tel.: (82) 317411830
Web Site: https://www.samyoungsnc.com
Electronic Components Mfr
N.A.I.C.S.: 334419

SAMYOUNG M-TEK CO., LTD.
631-35 Samchil-ro Chilseo-myeon, Haman, 52009, Gyeongsangnam-do, Korea (South)
Tel.: (82) 555897120
Web Site: https://www.symtek.co.kr
Year Founded: 1997
054540—(KRS)
Rev.: $69,549,219
Assets: $77,698,342
Liabilities: $29,048,732
Net Worth: $48,649,609
Earnings: ($6,690,672)
Emp.: 141
Fiscal Year-end: 12/31/22
Steel Products Mfr
N.A.I.C.S.: 339999
Chang-ok Jeon *(CEO)*

Subsidiaries:

Dalian Samyoung Doosan Metal Product Co., Ltd. (1)
Haiqing Road 26 Dagushan Development Zone, Dalian, China
Tel.: (86) 41139223000
Web Site: https://dsdmp.com
Steel Casting Materials Mfr
N.A.I.C.S.: 331511

Samyoung M-TEK Co., Ltd. - First Factory (1)
631-35 Samchil-ro, Haman-gun, 631-35, Gyeongnam, Korea (South)
Tel.: (82) 555897120
Web Site: http://www.symtek.co.kr
Sales Range: $100-124.9 Million
Steel Products Mfr
N.A.I.C.S.: 331110

Samyoung M-TEK Co., Ltd. - Second Factory (1)
59 Gongdanseo-gil, Haman-gun, 52001, Chilseo, Gyeongsangnam-do, Korea (South)
Tel.: (82) 555897770
Web Site: http://www.symtek.co.kr
Sales Range: $25-49.9 Million
Structured Steel Products Mfr
N.A.I.C.S.: 331110

SAMYUNG ENC CO., LTD.
69 Sangni-ro, Yeongdo-gu, Busan, Korea (South)
Tel.: (82) 516016666
Web Site: https://www.samyungenc.com
Year Founded: 1978
065570—(KRS)
Rev.: $24,468,349
Assets: $61,523,894
Liabilities: $33,104,093
Net Worth: $28,419,800
Earnings: ($32,036,774)
Emp.: 277
Fiscal Year-end: 12/31/22
Marine Communication Equipment Mfr
N.A.I.C.S.: 334290
Won Hwang *(Chm)*

SAMYUNG TRADING CO., LTD.
111 Yanghwa-ro Mapo-gu, Seoul, Korea (South)
Web Site: http://www.samyung.co.kr
Year Founded: 1959
002810—(KRS)
Rev.: $377,757,303
Assets: $478,767,584
Liabilities: $86,038,085
Net Worth: $392,729,499
Earnings: $44,255,949
Emp.: 60
Fiscal Year-end: 12/31/22
Chemical & Related Products Distr; Ophthalmic Lens Sales
N.A.I.C.S.: 424690
Seung Yong Lee *(Pres & CEO)*

Subsidiaries:

Sammyung Precision (Jiaxing) Co., Ltd. (1)
No 111 Changsheng East Road, Economic Development Zone, Jiaxing, 314003, Zhejiang, China
Tel.: (86) 57382213101
Web Site: https://www.sammyung.com.cn
Hermetic Sealing Mfr
N.A.I.C.S.: 339991

SAN CHIH SEMICONDUCTOR COMPANY
No 22 Chungshan N Rd 3rd Sec, Taipei, 104, Taiwan
Tel.: (886) 225925252
Web Site: http://www.sanchih.com.tw
Rev.: $212,326,089
Assets: $323,703,907
Liabilities: $378,314,203
Net Worth: ($54,610,296)
Earnings: ($245,019,370)
Emp.: 187
Fiscal Year-end: 12/31/18
Semiconductor Product Mfr
N.A.I.C.S.: 334413
Lung-Ta Lee *(Chm & Pres)*

Subsidiaries:

SAN CHIH Semiconductor Company - Tayuan Plant (1)
No 160-3 Minsheng Road Neihili Dayuan, Taoyuan, Taiwan
Tel.: (886) 3852130
Semiconductor Product Mfr
N.A.I.C.S.: 333242

SAN CRISTOBAL MINING INC.
890 Pender Street West Suite 330, Vancouver, V6C 1J9, BC, Canada
Tel.: (604) 305-3708   Ca
Web Site: https://sancristobalmining.com
Year Founded: 2022
Exploration & Mining Operations Services
N.A.I.C.S.: 212220
Quinton Hennigh *(Pres)*

Subsidiaries:

Minera San Cristobal S.A. (1)
Calacoto calle 15 Torre Ketal piso 5, PO Box 13790, La Paz, Bolivia
Tel.: (591) 22623400
Web Site: https://www.minerasancristobal.com
Metal Mining Services
N.A.I.C.S.: 212290
Kenichiro Tsubaki *(VP)*

SAN FANG CHEMICAL INDUSTRIAL CO., LTD.
402 Fengren Rd, Renwu Dist, Kaohsiung, Taiwan
Tel.: (886) 73712111   TW
Web Site: https://www.sanfang.com
Year Founded: 1973
1307—(TAI)
Rev.: $329,858,256
Assets: $511,166,827
Liabilities: $218,711,264
Net Worth: $292,455,563
Earnings: $24,862,617
Emp.: 2,306
Fiscal Year-end: 12/31/23
Polyurethane Mfr
N.A.I.C.S.: 325211
Lin Meng-Chin *(Chm)*

Subsidiaries:

Bestac Advanced Material Co., Ltd. (1)
No 68 Ln 180 Xinhe Rd, Sanhe Vil Longtan Dist, Taoyuan, 325003, Taiwan
Tel.: (886) 34071960
Web Site: https://www.bestac.com
Emp.: 50
Polishing Pad Mfr
N.A.I.C.S.: 339999

SAN FAR PROPERTY LIMITED
12th Floor No 30 Section 3 Bade Road, Songshan District, Taipei, 10559, Taiwan
Tel.: (886) 225709988
Web Site: https://www.sanfar.com.tw
9946—(TAI)
Rev.: $31,496,156
Assets: $514,755,499
Liabilities: $302,882,326
Net Worth: $211,873,173
Earnings: $2,905,785
Emp.: 61
Fiscal Year-end: 12/31/23
Property Developer
N.A.I.C.S.: 236115

Subsidiaries:

Jingo International Records Co., Ltd. (1)
12th Floor No 30 Section 3 Bade Road, Songshan District, Taipei, 105, Taiwan
Tel.: (886) 225795885
Web Site: https://www.jingo.com.tw
Emp.: 30
Digital Versatile Disc Mfr & Distr
N.A.I.C.S.: 334112

SAN FU CHEMICAL CO., LTD.
7F 21 Chung Shan N Rd Sec 2, Zhongshan Dist, Taipei, 104, Taiwan
Tel.: (886) 225426789
Web Site: https://www.sfchem.com.tw
Year Founded: 1952
4755—(TAI)
Rev.: $163,215,305
Assets: $254,737,555
Liabilities: $109,350,302
Net Worth: $145,387,254
Earnings: $14,518,591
Emp.: 367
Fiscal Year-end: 12/31/23
Chemicals Mfr
N.A.I.C.S.: 325998
Mingzhi Xie *(Head-Fin & Acctg)*

Subsidiaries:

Air Products San Fu Gas Co., Ltd. (1)
5th Fl Shankong Bldg 21 Sec 2, Chung Shan N Rd, Taipei, 10419, Taiwan
Tel.: (886) 225214161
Industrial Gas Mfr
N.A.I.C.S.: 325120

SAN HOLDINGS, INC.
4-6-39 Tenzinbashi, Kita-ku, Osaka, Japan
Tel.: (81) 662083331
Web Site: https://www.san-hd.co.jp
Year Founded: 1944
9628—(TKS)
Rev.: $148,308,570
Assets: $248,436,850
Liabilities: $31,119,880
Net Worth: $217,316,970
Earnings: $15,619,430
Emp.: 709
Fiscal Year-end: 03/31/24

AND PRIVATE COMPANIES

Holding Company
N.A.I.C.S.: 551112
Yuichi Noro *(Chm)*

Subsidiaries:

Life Forward Co., Ltd. (1)
1-1-1 Minami-Aoyama Tokyo Shin-Aoyama Building West Building 14F, Minato-ku, Tokyo, Japan
Tel.: (81) 354132500
Web Site: https://www.life-forward.co.jp
Funeral Support Services
N.A.I.C.S.: 812210

Tarui Co., Ltd. (1)
2-3-2 Hayashizakicho, Akashi, Hyogo, Japan
Tel.: (81) 789221000
Web Site: https://www.tarui365.co.jp
Emp.: 90
Funeral Consulting Services
N.A.I.C.S.: 812210

SAN JU SAN FINANCIAL GROUP, INC.
510 Kyomachi, Matsusaka, 515-8530, Mie, Japan
Tel.: (81) 598213303   JP
Web Site: https://www.33fg.co.jp
Year Founded: 2018
7322—(NGO)
Rev.: $448,285,306
Assets: $29,302,601,640
Liabilities: $27,894,309,996
Net Worth: $1,408,291,644
Earnings: $45,781,289
Fiscal Year-end: 03/31/24
Bank Holding Company
N.A.I.C.S.: 551111
Mitsunori Watanabe *(Chm & Pres)*

Subsidiaries:

The Daisan Bank, Ltd. (1)
510 Kyo-machi, Matsusaka, 515-8530, Mie, Japan
Tel.: (81) 598231111
Web Site: http://www.daisanbank.co.jp
Rev.: $328,300,620
Assets: $17,672,428,580
Liabilities: $16,689,641,800
Net Worth: $982,786,780
Earnings: $28,780,820
Emp.: 1,600
Fiscal Year-end: 03/31/2017
Banking Services
N.A.I.C.S.: 522110
Kenzo Tanikawa *(Chm)*

The Mie Bank, Ltd (1)
7-8 Nishishinchi, Yokkaichi, 510-0087, Mie, Japan
Tel.: (81) 593533111
Web Site: http://www.miebank.co.jp
Rev.: $324,547,320
Assets: $18,412,819,200
Liabilities: $17,203,725,960
Net Worth: $1,209,093,240
Earnings: $32,199,240
Emp.: 1,246
Fiscal Year-end: 03/31/2019
Banking Services
N.A.I.C.S.: 522110
Mitsunori Watanabe *(Pres)*

Subsidiary (Domestic):

Sanju San Institute of Research, Ltd. (2)
7-8 Nishishinchi, Yokkaichi, 510-0087, Mie, Japan
Tel.: (81) 593547102
Web Site: http://www.miebank.co.jp
Research & Consulting Services
N.A.I.C.S.: 523940
Ito Koaki *(Sr Mng Dir)*

The Miegin Card Co., Ltd. (2)
2-4 Sachimachi, Yokkaichi, 510-0069, Mie, Japan
Tel.: (81) 593543344
Web Site: http://www.miegincard.jp
Credit Card Services
N.A.I.C.S.: 522210

The Miegin Computer Service Co., Ltd. (2)
15-1 Jushichikencho, Yokkaichi, 510-0063, Mie, Japan
Tel.: (81) 593514227
Web Site: http://www.m-mcs.co.jp
Custom Computer Programming Services
N.A.I.C.S.: 541511

The Miegin Shinyo-Hosho Co., Ltd. (2)
2-4 Saiwaicho, Yokkaichi, 510-0069, Mie, Japan
Tel.: (81) 593519433
Credit Services
N.A.I.C.S.: 522180

The Miegin Sogo Lease Co., Ltd. (2)
K Bldg Yokkaichi, Yokkaichi, Mie, Japan
Tel.: (81) 593512165
Machinery & Equipment Rental & Leasing
N.A.I.C.S.: 532420

SAN LEON ENERGY PLC
3300 Lake Drive Citywest Business Campus, Dublin, 24, Ireland
Tel.: (353) 12916292   IE
Web Site: https://www.sanleonenergy.com
Rev.: $266,000
Assets: $211,007,000
Liabilities: $8,091,000
Net Worth: $202,916,000
Earnings: ($38,612,000)
Emp.: 24
Fiscal Year-end: 12/31/19
Oil & Gas Exploration Services
N.A.I.C.S.: 211120
Oisin Fanning *(CEO)*

Subsidiaries:

Aurelian Oil & Gas Limited (1)
43 Grosvenor Street, Mayfair, London, W1K 3HL, United Kingdom
Tel.: (44) 20 3617 3913
Sales Range: $50-74.9 Million
Emp.: 49
Oil & Gas Exploration Services
N.A.I.C.S.: 211120
Oliver Horne *(Controller-Fin)*

Subsidiary (Non-US):

Aurelian Oil & Gas Poland Sp. z o.o. (2)
ul Sniadeckich 17, 00-654, Warsaw, Poland
Tel.: (48) 226299037
Sales Range: $50-74.9 Million
Emp.: 15
Oil & Gas Exploration Services
N.A.I.C.S.: 213112

Energia Zachod Sp. z o.o (2)
ul Sniadeckich 17, 00-654, Warsaw, Poland
Tel.: (48) 226299037
Web Site: http://www.aurelianoil.com
Sales Range: $50-74.9 Million
Oil & Gas Exploration Services
N.A.I.C.S.: 213112

Frontera Energy Corporation S.L. (1)
Paseo de la Castellanna 95, 28046, Madrid, Spain
Tel.: (34) 914563400
Oil & Gas Exploration Services
N.A.I.C.S.: 213112

Gold Point Energy Corp. (1)
Suite 700 625 Howe Street, Vancouver, V6C 2T6, BC, Canada
Tel.: (604) 685-2286
Oil & Gas Exploration Services
N.A.I.C.S.: 213112

NovaSeis Sp. z o.o. (1)
Moniuszki 1a, 00-640, Warsaw, Poland
Tel.: (48) 223789712
Web Site: http://www.novaseis.eu
Emp.: 25
Seismic Geophysical Surveying Services
N.A.I.C.S.: 541360
Timothy Branch *(Mng Dir)*

Realm Energy Operations Corporation (1)
601 Cordova St W Suite 310, Vancouver, V6B 1G1, BC, Canada
Tel.: (604) 637-4974

Oil & Gas Exploration Services
N.A.I.C.S.: 213112

SAN NENG GROUP HOLDINGS CO., LTD.
The Grand Pavilion Commercial Centre Oleander Way, PO Box 32052, 802 West Bay Road Grand Cayman, Georgetown, KY1-1208, Cayman Islands
Tel.: (345) 424925850
Web Site: https://www.sannenggroup.com
Year Founded: 2015
6671—(TAI)
Rev.: $62,325,090
Assets: $72,034,825
Liabilities: $15,989,698
Net Worth: $56,045,127
Earnings: $5,836,587
Emp.: 727
Fiscal Year-end: 12/31/23
Food Product Machinery Manufacturing
N.A.I.C.S.: 333241
Xiao Kaifeng *(CFO)*

Subsidiaries:

PT. Sanneng Bakeware Indonesia (1)
Komplek Rukan Puri Mutiara Blok BC No10-11 Jl Griya Utama, Sunter Agung, Jakarta, 14350, Indonesia
Tel.: (62) 2122651332
Baking Equipment Mfr
N.A.I.C.S.: 333241

Sanneng Appliance (Wuxi) Co., Ltd. (1)
No 316 Youyi North Road Xishan Economic Development Zone, Wuxi, Jiangsu, China
Tel.: (86) 51083777515
Baking Equipment Mfr
N.A.I.C.S.: 333241

Sanneng Bakeware (Wuxi) Co., Ltd. (1)
No 316 Youyi North Road Xishan Economic Development Zone, Wuxi, Jiangsu, China
Tel.: (86) 51083777515
Baking Equipment Mfr & Distr
N.A.I.C.S.: 332215

Sanneng Bakeware Corporation (1)
No 58 Gongye 8th Road Dali Industrial Zone, Dali District, Taichung, Taiwan
Tel.: (886) 424925850
Baking Equipment Mfr & Distr
N.A.I.C.S.: 332215

Sanneng Food Appliance Co., Ltd. (1)
No 58 Industry 8 Road, Dali Industrial Zone Dali District, Taichung, Taiwan
Tel.: (886) 424925850
Baking Equipment Mfr
N.A.I.C.S.: 333241

Sanneng Japan Bakeware Co., Ltd. (1)
3-5-2 Burex Kojimachi 301, Kojimachi Chiyoda District, Tokyo, Japan
Tel.: (81) 362724777
Baking Equipment Mfr & Distr
N.A.I.C.S.: 332215

Sanneng Japan Food Equipment Co., Ltd. (1)
211-2 Burex 3-5-2 Chiyoda-Cho, Chiyoda-Ku, Tokyo, Japan
Tel.: (81) 362724777
Baking Equipment Mfr
N.A.I.C.S.: 333241

Squires Kitchen Sugarcraft (Wuxi) Co., Ltd. (1)
No 316 Youyi North Road Xishan Economic Development Zone, Wuxi, Jiangsu, China
Tel.: (86) 51083777515
Baking Equipment Mfr & Distr
N.A.I.C.S.: 332215

SAN SHING FASTECH CORP.
1F No 355 Chung Shan Rd Section 3, Guiren Dist, T'ainan, 711, Taiwan
Tel.: (886) 62391211
Web Site: https://www.sanshing.com.tw
Year Founded: 1965
5007—(TAI)
Rev.: $217,303,566
Assets: $287,222,887
Liabilities: $48,140,454
Net Worth: $239,082,433
Earnings: $33,195,165
Emp.: 1,784
Fiscal Year-end: 12/31/23
Iron & Steel Products Mfr
N.A.I.C.S.: 331110
Chen Hsin Chih *(Pres)*

Subsidiaries:

Acku Metal Industries (M) Sdn. Bhd. (1)
Lot 2937 Mukim 16 Jalan Bagan Lallang Satu Acku Industrial Estate, 13400, Butterworth, Penang, Malaysia
Tel.: (60) 43230888
Web Site: http://www.ackumetal.com
Drywall Screw Mfr & Distr
N.A.I.C.S.: 332722

Hexico Enterprise Co., Ltd. (1)
No 355-3 Sec 3 Zhongshan Rd, Guiren Dist, Tainan City, 711401, Taiwan
Tel.: (886) 62390616
Web Site: https://en.hexico.com.tw
Steel Wire Mfr & Distr
N.A.I.C.S.: 331222

SAN SWISS ARMS AG
Industrieplatz 1, PO Box 1071, Neuhausen, 8212, Switzerland
Tel.: (41) 525512000   CH
Web Site: http://www.swissarms.ch
Year Founded: 2000
Sales Range: $1-9.9 Million
Small Arms Mfr
N.A.I.C.S.: 332994

Subsidiaries:

Blaser Jagdwaffen GmbH (1)
Ziegelstadel 1, D-88316, Isny im Allgau, Germany
Tel.: (49) 75627020
Web Site: http://www.blaser.de
Firearms Mfr
N.A.I.C.S.: 332994
Bernhard Knobel *(CEO)*

Subsidiary (US):

Blaser USA, Inc. (2)
403 E Ramsey Rd Ste 301, San Antonio, TX 78216
Tel.: (210) 377-2527
Web Site: http://www.blaser-usa.com
Firearms Whslr
N.A.I.C.S.: 423990
Christian Socher *(Head-Sls)*

J.P. Sauer & Sohn GmbH (1)
Ziegelstadel 20, Isny, 88316, Germany
Tel.: (49) 7562975540
Web Site: http://www.sauer.de
Firearms Mfr
N.A.I.C.S.: 332994

SAN TEH LTD.
701 Sims Drive No 06-01 LHK Building, Singapore, 387383, Singapore
Tel.: (65) 6749 6386
Year Founded: 1979
Rev.: $12,273,348
Assets: $140,069,162
Liabilities: $9,392,600
Net Worth: $130,676,563
Earnings: ($6,723,209)
Fiscal Year-end: 12/31/18
PVC Pipe & Fitting Mfr
N.A.I.C.S.: 326122
Wee Tziang Lim *(CFO & Sec)*

SAN YANG MA (CHONGQING) LOGISTICS CO., LTD.
No 199-1-80 Tuzhu Middle Road, Tu-

SAN YANG MA (CHONGQING) LOGISTICS CO., LTD.

San Yang Ma (Chongqing) Logistics Co., Ltd.—(Continued)
zhu Town & Shapingba District, Chongqing, 401333, China
Tel.: (86) 2363055149
Web Site: https://www.sanyangma.com
Year Founded: 2005
001317—(SSE)
Rev.: $29,679,436,800
Assets: $1,200,075,037,200
Liabilities: $1,103,784,505,200
Net Worth: $96,290,532,000
Earnings: $8,719,261,200
Fiscal Year-end: 12/31/22
Logistic Services
N.A.I.C.S.: 541614
Hongyang Qiu (Chm)

SAN'AN OPTOELECTRONICS CO., LTD.
No 1721-1725 Lvling Road, Siming District, Xiamen, China
Tel.: (86) 5925937001
Web Site: https://www.sanan-e.com
Year Founded: 2000
600703—(SHG)
Rev.: $1,856,413,180
Assets: $8,197,856,007
Liabilities: $2,870,159,713
Net Worth: $5,327,696,294
Earnings: $96,181,989
Emp.: 7,000
Fiscal Year-end: 12/31/22
LED Product Mfr & Solar Electricity Generation Services
N.A.I.C.S.: 334413

Subsidiaries:

Anhui San'an Optoelectronics Co., Ltd.
No 8 Dongliang Road Economic and Technological Development Zone, Wuhu, China
Tel.: (86) 5535229999
Light Emitting Diode & Optical Chip Mfr
N.A.I.C.S.: 334413

Anhui San'an Technology Co., Ltd. (1)
1733-1751 Lvling Road, Siming District, Xiamen, China
Tel.: (86) 5927705136
Web Site: http://www.lighteraasia.com
Light Emitting Diode & Optical Chip Mfr
N.A.I.C.S.: 334413

Fujian Jing'an Optoelectronics Co., Ltd. (1)
Optoelectronics Industry Park, Hutou Town Anxi County, Quanzhou, 362411, Fujian, China
Tel.: (86) 59526098777
Web Site: http://www.jingan-op.com
Light Emitting Diode Product Mfr & Distr
N.A.I.C.S.: 334413

Fujian Jing'an San'an Optoelectronics Co., Ltd. (1)
Photoelectric Industrial Park, Hutou Town Anxi County, Quanzhou, Fujian, China
Tel.: (86) 59526098777
Light Emitting Diode & Optical Chip Mfr
N.A.I.C.S.: 334413

Tianjin San'an Optoelectronics Co., Ltd. (1)
20th Haitai South Road, Xiqing District, Tianjin, China
Tel.: (86) 2258282999
Light Emitting Diode & Optical Chip Mfr
N.A.I.C.S.: 334413

Wuhu Anrui Optoelectronics Co., Ltd. (1)
No 11 Fengming Hubei Road Economic and Technological Development Zone, Wuhu, 241009, China
Tel.: (86) 5535203088
Web Site: https://www.myanrui.com
Light Emitting Diode Product Mfr & Distr
N.A.I.C.S.: 334413

Xiamen San'an Integrated Circuit Co., Ltd. (1)
753-799 Minan Avenue, Hongtang Town Tongan District, Xiamen, China
Tel.: (86) 5926300505
Web Site: http://www.sanan-ic.com
Semiconductor Components Mfr
N.A.I.C.S.: 334413

Xiamen San'an Optoelectronics Co., Ltd. (1)
No 841-855 Min an Road, Hong Tang Town Tongan Disctrict, Xiamen, China
Tel.: (86) 5923207696
Light Emitting Diode & Optical Chip Mfr
N.A.I.C.S.: 334413

SAN-A CO., LTD.
2-10-7 Oyama, Ginowan, Okinawa, 901-2733, Japan
Tel.: (81) 988982230
Web Site: https://www.san-a.co.jp
Year Founded: 1970
2659—(TKS)
Rev.: $1,613,549,290
Assets: $1,323,724,270
Liabilities: $287,513,680
Net Worth: $1,036,210,590
Earnings: $75,742,470
Emp.: 1,706
Fiscal Year-end: 02/29/24
Apparel Store Operator
N.A.I.C.S.: 458110

SAN-AI OBBLI CO., LTD.
10F Otemachiplace Easttower 2-3-2 Otemachi, Chiyoda-ku, Tokyo, 100-8154, Japan
Tel.: (81) 368803100
Web Site: https://www.san-ai-obbli.com
Year Founded: 1952
8097—(TKS)
Rev.: $4,359,876,680
Assets: $1,444,992,270
Liabilities: $626,482,580
Net Worth: $818,509,690
Earnings: $74,144,370
Emp.: 501
Fiscal Year-end: 03/31/24
Petroleum & Chemical Products Mfr & Sales
N.A.I.C.S.: 324199
Jun Kaneda (Chm)

SAN-EL MUHENDISLIK ELEKTRIK TAAHHUT SANAYI VE TICARET AS
Salacak Iskele Street No 22, Salacak Neighborhood Uskudar, 34668, Istanbul, Turkiye
Tel.: (90) 2164152245
Web Site: https://www.san-el.com
Year Founded: 2005
SANEL—(IST)
Rev.: $3,280,475
Assets: $3,998,062
Liabilities: $3,651,424
Net Worth: $346,639
Earnings: $(729,706)
Fiscal Year-end: 12/31/23
Electrical Control Panels & Related Products Mfr
N.A.I.C.S.: 334513
Fatih Karacanik (Mgr-Investor Relations)

SAN-ES TRADING CO., LTD.
6-15 Sangenjaya 1-chome, Setagaya-ku, Tokyo, 154-0024, Japan
Tel.: (81) 337958121   JP
Web Site: http://www.sanes.co.jp
Year Founded: 1988
Electronic Components, High-Purity Chemicals & Materials Distr
N.A.I.C.S.: 423690
Yoshiyuki Sakano (Pres)

SAN-JIRUSHI CORP.
1 572 1 Akimasa, Kuwana, 511-0823, Mie, Japan
Tel.: (81) 594223333
Web Site: http://www.san-j.co.jp
Year Founded: 1804
Soy Sauce & Soybean Paste Mfr
N.A.I.C.S.: 311224

Subsidiaries:

San-J International, Inc. (1)
2880 Sprouse Dr, Henrico, VA 23231-6039 (100%)
Tel.: (804) 226-8333
Web Site: http://www.san-j.com
Sales Range: $25-49.9 Million
Emp.: 50
Fermented Soy-Based Sauces Mfr
N.A.I.C.S.: 311941
Takashi Sato (Pres)

SANA INDUSTRIES LIMITED
33 D 2 Block 6 P E C H S, Karachi, 75400, Pakistan
Tel.: (92) 2132561728
Web Site: https://www.sana-industries.com
SNAI—(PSX)
Rev.: $18,285,576
Assets: $9,537,144
Liabilities: $7,840,483
Net Worth: $1,696,661
Earnings: $(603,332)
Emp.: 250
Fiscal Year-end: 06/30/23
Artificial Blended Yarn Mfr
N.A.I.C.S.: 313110
Hafiz Mohammed Irfan Nawab (CEO)

SANA KISAN BIKAS LAGHUBITTA BITTIYA SANSTHA LIMITED
Opposite kwality restaurant, arch bridge baramahal,, Kathmandu, 44600, Nepal
Tel.: (977) 15320913
Web Site: https://skbbl.com.np
SKBBL—(NEP)
Financial Services
N.A.I.C.S.: 523999
Annapurna Shrestha (Sr Mgr-Institutional Capacity Dev & Plng Dept)

SANA LINEA A.D.
Ustanicka br 6, 79224, Kostajnica, Bosnia & Herzegovina
Tel.: (387) 52663112
Web Site: https://www.sanalinea.net
Year Founded: 2001
SLIN—(BANJ)
Sales Range: $1-9.9 Million
Emp.: 104
Apparels & Accessories Mfr & Marketer
N.A.I.C.S.: 315990

SANA-ELVIS A.D.
Svodna bb, 79229, Novi Grad, Bosnia & Herzegovina
Tel.: (387) 52 776 226
Web Site: http://www.sana-elvis.com
Year Founded: 2001
SNEL—(BANJ)
Sales Range: Less than $1 Million
Emp.: 108
Textile Products Mfr
N.A.I.C.S.: 313240
Borislav Babic (Chm-Mgmt Bd)

SANAI HEALTH INDUSTRY GROUP COMPANY LIMITED
Unit 1309 13/F West Tower, Shun Tak Centre, Sheung Wan, China (Hong Kong)
Tel.: (852) 28276100

INTERNATIONAL PUBLIC

Web Site: http://www.wuyi-pharma.com
Rev.: $9,322,843
Assets: $53,173,485
Liabilities: $42,774,174
Net Worth: $10,399,311
Earnings: ($33,404,079)
Emp.: 230
Fiscal Year-end: 12/31/18
Pharmaceuticals Product Mfr
N.A.I.C.S.: 325412
Chengqing Chen (Chm)

SANAM REAL ESTATE CO. (K.S.C.C.)
Salhia Muhammad Al Thannayan Al Ghanem Street Salhiya Complex, Gate 1, PO Box 491, Floor 5, Kuwait, 15254, Kuwait
Tel.: (965) 22396666
Web Site: https://www.sanam.com
Year Founded: 1982
SANAM—(KUW)
Rev.: $1,028,802
Assets: $26,061,078
Liabilities: $596,828
Net Worth: $25,464,250
Earnings: ($4,321,193)
Emp.: 5
Fiscal Year-end: 12/31/22
Real Estate Manangement Services
N.A.I.C.S.: 531390
Tarek Hassan Ragab (Dir-Fin & Admin)

SANASA DEVELOPMENT BANK PLC
No 12 Edmonton Road, Kirulapone, 6, Colombo, 06, Sri Lanka
Tel.: (94) 115411411
Web Site: https://www.sdb.lk
Year Founded: 1997
SDB.N0000—(COL)
Rev.: $80,004,448
Assets: $531,011,058
Liabilities: $485,542,482
Net Worth: $45,468,576
Earnings: $203,610
Emp.: 1,381
Fiscal Year-end: 12/31/22
Commercial Banking Services
N.A.I.C.S.: 522110
Champa J. Dasanayake (Head-Small & Medium Enterprises & Asst Gen Mgr)

SANASA TECH FEB LTD.
Tardeo Air Conditioned Market 1st Floor Room No 40 Tardeo Road, Mumbai, 400 034, Maharashtra, India
Tel.: (91) 2264646061
Textile Product Mfr & Distr
N.A.I.C.S.: 314999
Adhi Savinder Singh (Mng Dir)

SANATANA RESOURCES INC.
1910-925 West Georgia Street, Vancouver, V6C 3L2, BC, Canada
Tel.: (604) 408-6680
Web Site: https://www.sanatanaresources.com
Year Founded: 2004
S3D1—(DEU)
Rev.: $42,639
Assets: $3,485,438
Liabilities: $304,901
Net Worth: $3,180,537
Earnings: ($2,677,157)
Fiscal Year-end: 03/31/23
Mineral Exploration Services
N.A.I.C.S.: 213114
Peter L. Miles (CEO)

SANATHNAGAR ENTERPRISES LTD.

412 Floor - 4 17G Vardhaman Chamber Cawasji Patel Road Horniman Circle, Fort, Mumbai, 400001, Maharashtra, India
Tel.: (91) 2261959662
Web Site: https://www.sanathnagar.in
Year Founded: 1947
509423—(BOM)
Rev.: $110,497
Assets: $970,092
Liabilities: $2,518,507
Net Worth: ($1,548,415)
Earnings: $24,584
Fiscal Year-end: 03/31/21
Real Estate Manangement Services
N.A.I.C.S.: 531390
Hitesh Marthak *(Compliance Officer & Sec)*

SANBASE CORPORATION LIMITED
16th Floor Loon Kee Building 267-275 Des Voeux Road, Central, China (Hong Kong)
Tel.: (852) 2 870 0883   Ky
Web Site: http://www.sanbase.com.hk
Year Founded: 2009
8501—(HKG)
Rev.: $62,076,268
Assets: $34,232,453
Liabilities: $14,987,992
Net Worth: $19,244,461
Earnings: $56,751
Emp.: 87
Fiscal Year-end: 03/31/21
Interior Design Services
N.A.I.C.S.: 541410

SANBIAN SCI-TECH CO., LTD.
No 369 Western Boulevard, Haiyou Town Sanmen County, Taizhou, 317100, Zhejiang, China
Tel.: (86) 57689319967
Web Site: https://www.sanbian.cn
Year Founded: 1968
002112—(SSE)
Rev.: $37,954,191,389
Assets: $42,968,597,186
Liabilities: $25,495,052,638
Net Worth: $17,473,544,548
Earnings: $2,813,903,258
Emp.: 1,000
Fiscal Year-end: 12/31/22
Power Transformer Mfr
N.A.I.C.S.: 335311
Xie Weishi *(Chm)*

SANBIO COMPANY LIMITED
St Luke Tower 13F 8-1 Akashi-cho, Chuo-ku, Tokyo, 104-0044, Japan
Tel.: (81) 362643481   JP
Web Site: https://www.sanbio.com
Year Founded: 2001
4592—(TKS)
Assets: $35,783,230
Liabilities: $15,987,950
Net Worth: $19,795,280
Earnings: ($18,745,960)
Emp.: 29
Fiscal Year-end: 01/31/24
Pharmaceuticals Mfr
N.A.I.C.S.: 325412
Michael P. McGrogan *(Sr VP-Production Dev)*

Subsidiaries:
SanBio, Inc (1)
231 S Whisman Rd, Mountain View, CA 94041-1522
Tel.: (650) 625-8965
Web Site: http://www.san-bio.com
Fiscal Year-end: 12/31/2006
Regenerative Medicine Development Services
N.A.I.C.S.: 541714
Keita Mori *(Chm)*

SANBLUE CORPORATION LTD.
22/A Governement Servant Society Near Muncipal Market CG Road, Ahmedabad, 380006, India
Tel.: (91) 7926562055
Web Site: https://www.sanbluecorporation.com
Year Founded: 1993
521222—(BOM)
Rev.: $569,690
Assets: $5,506,780
Liabilities: $616,630
Net Worth: $4,890,150
Earnings: $82,741
Emp.: 4
Fiscal Year-end: 03/31/21
Investment Consulting Services
N.A.I.C.S.: 523940
Jekil Pancholi *(Compliance Officer & Sec)*

SANCAI HOLDING GROUP LTD.
No 6 Fengcheng Second Road Room 401, Xi'an Economic and Technological Development Zone, Xi'an, 710000, Shaanxi, China
Tel.: (86) 2152212192   Ky
Year Founded: 2019
Rev.: $18,440,399
Assets: $25,584,072
Liabilities: $20,923,451
Net Worth: $4,660,621
Earnings: $6,457,658
Emp.: 231
Fiscal Year-end: 09/30/19
Holding Company
N.A.I.C.S.: 551112
Ning Wen *(Founder, Chm & CEO)*

SANCHAY FINVEST LIMITED
209 Rajani Bhawan 569 MG Road, Indore, 452001, Madhya Pradesh, India
Tel.: (91) 2266360891
Web Site: https://www.sanchayfinvest.in
Year Founded: 1991
511563—(BOM)
Sales Range: Less than $1 Million
Financial Investment Services
N.A.I.C.S.: 523999
Vijay Sharma *(Compliance Officer)*

SANCHUAN WISDOM TECHNOLOGY CO., LTD.
Sanchuan Hydraulic Industry Park High-tech Zone, Longgang District, Yingtan, 335000, Jiangxi, China
Tel.: (86) 7016318019
Web Site: https://www.ytsanchuan.com
Year Founded: 2004
300066—(CHIN)
Rev.: $321,803,404
Assets: $458,003,297
Liabilities: $86,120,324
Net Worth: $371,882,973
Earnings: $33,801,930
Fiscal Year-end: 12/31/23
Water Meter Products Mfr
N.A.I.C.S.: 334514
Li Jianlin *(Chm)*

SANCIA GLOBAL INFRAPROJECTS LTD.
Todi Mension 32 Ezra Street 10th Floor Room No. 1060 8th Floor, Kolkata, 700001, India
Tel.: (91) 33 40676220
Web Site: http://www.gremach.com
Rev.: $426,927
Assets: $6,040,162
Liabilities: $36,506,271
Net Worth: ($30,466,109)
Earnings: ($462,271)
Fiscal Year-end: 03/31/16
Commercial & Industrial Machinery & Equipment Rental & Leasing
N.A.I.C.S.: 423830
Sonia Kundu *(Chm)*

SANCO INDUSTRIES LIMITED
D-161 Surajmal Vihar, New Delhi, 110092, India
Tel.: (91) 1147315500   In
Web Site: https://www.sancopipes.com
Year Founded: 1986
SANCO—(NSE)
Rev.: $5,330,530
Assets: $16,930,982
Liabilities: $11,975,814
Net Worth: $4,955,168
Earnings: $39,803
Emp.: 103
Fiscal Year-end: 03/31/20
PVC Pipe, PVC Wires & Cables & LED Lights & Panels Mfr
N.A.I.C.S.: 326122
Sanjay Gupta *(Chm & Mng Dir)*

SANCO TRANS LTD.
S T Tower New No 24 & 25 Second Line Beach Road, Chennai, 600 001, Tamil Nadu, India
Tel.: (91) 4466449000
Web Site: https://www.sancotrans.com
Year Founded: 1979
523116—(BOM)
Rev.: $14,141,400
Assets: $19,334,283
Liabilities: $6,253,365
Net Worth: $13,080,918
Earnings: $397,515
Emp.: 178
Fiscal Year-end: 03/31/21
Logistics Management Services
N.A.I.C.S.: 541614
V. Upendran *(Chm & Co-Mng Dir)*

SANCODE TECHNOLOGIES LTD.
107 Prime Plaza J V Patel Compound B M Road Opp Elphinstone Stn, Mumbai, 400013, Maharashtra, India
Tel.: (91) 2249622853
Web Site: https://www.sancodetech.com
Year Founded: 2016
543897—(BOM)
Software Development Services
N.A.I.C.S.: 541511
Amit Jain *(Chm)*

SANCOR COOPERATIVAS UNIDAS LIMITADA
Tte Gral Richieri 15, Sunchales, Santa Fe, S2322FYA, Argentina
Tel.: (54) 3493428000
Web Site: http://www.sancor.com
Year Founded: 1938
Sales Range: $400-449.9 Million
Emp.: 3,900
Dairy Products Mfr
N.A.I.C.S.: 311512
Jorge Arnaudo *(CEO)*

Subsidiaries:
SanCor Dairy Corporation (1)
80 SW 8th St Ste 2000, Miami, FL 33130-3003
Tel.: (305) 624-8595
Web Site: http://www.sancor.com
Sales Range: $25-49.9 Million
Emp.: 100
Dairy Mfr
N.A.I.C.S.: 112120

SANCTUARY ASIA
602 Maker Chambers V Nariman Point, 400 021, Mumbai, India
Tel.: (91) 2222044217
Web Site: http://www.sanctuaryasia.com
Year Founded: 1981
Emp.: 1,000
Wildlife Conservation & Environmental Protection Organization & Publisher
N.A.I.C.S.: 813312
Bittu Sahgal *(Founder & Mng Dir)*

SANCTUARY HOUSING ASSOCIATION
Chamber Court Castle Street, Worcester, WR1 3ZQ, United Kingdom
Tel.: (44) 1905338600   UK
Web Site: http://www.sanctuary-housing.co.uk
Year Founded: 1969
Sales Range: $650-699.9 Million
Emp.: 5,731
Low-Income Housing Construction & Management Services
N.A.I.C.S.: 531390
David Bennett *(CEO)*

Subsidiaries:
Cumbernauld Housing Partnership Limited (1)
Floor 8 Fleming House 2 Tryst Road, Cumbernauld, G67 1JW, United Kingdom
Tel.: (44) 1236 456 456
Web Site: http://www.sanctuary-cumbernauld.co.uk
Affordable Housing Services
N.A.I.C.S.: 624229
John Campbell *(Officer-Svc Improvement & Policy)*

Glasgow Student Villages Limited (1)
30 George Square, Glasgow, G2 1EG, United Kingdom
Tel.: (44) 8707 125003
Affordable Housing Services
N.A.I.C.S.: 624229

Heart of England Housing and Care Limited (1)
10 Greenhill Street, Stratford-upon-Avon, CV37 6LG, Warwickshire, United Kingdom
Tel.: (44) 345 8 500 500
Web Site: http://www.hoe-consultancy.co.uk
Sales Range: $50-74.9 Million
Emp.: 500
Nursing & Residential Care Services
N.A.I.C.S.: 623110

Property Partners Housing Management (UK) Limited (1)
23 Albert Street, Aberdeen, AB25 1XX, United Kingdom
Tel.: (44) 1224 628 400
Affordable Housing Services
N.A.I.C.S.: 624229

Sanctuary Care Limited (1)
33 Montserrat Road, Lee-on-Solent, PO13 9LT, Hampshire, United Kingdom
Tel.: (44) 23 9255 0793
Nursing & Residential Care Services
N.A.I.C.S.: 623110

Sanctuary Land Company Limited (1)
Chamber Court Castle Street, Worcester, WR1 3ZQ, United Kingdom
Tel.: (44) 1905338600
Sales Range: $150-199.9 Million
Emp.: 808
Property Maintenance & Facility Management Services
N.A.I.C.S.: 561210

Sanctuary Maintenance Contractors Limited (1)
Chamber Court Castle Street, Worcester, WR1 3ZQ, United Kingdom
Tel.: (44) 1905 334596
Web Site: http://www.sanctuary-maintenance.co.uk

SANCTUARY HOUSING ASSOCIATION

Sanctuary Housing Association—(Continued)
Sales Range: $150-199.9 Million
Emp.: 1,000
Property Maintenance & Facility Management Services
N.A.I.C.S.: 561210

Sanctuary Management Services Limited (1)
Central Services Building 13 Caithness Street, Glasgow, G20 7SB, United Kingdom
Tel.: (44) 1905 335861
Web Site: http://www.sanctuary-managementservices.co.uk
Facility Management & Accommodation Services
N.A.I.C.S.: 561210

Sanctuary Scotland Housing Association Limited (1)
7 Freeland Drive, Anderston, Glasgow, G53 6PG, Glasgow, United Kingdom
Tel.: (44) 1224 628 400
Web Site: http://www.sanctuary-scotland.co.uk
Emp.: 125
Affordable Housing Services
N.A.I.C.S.: 624229
Robert Campbell (Gen Mgr)

Tenants First Housing Co-operative Limited (1)
27 Slains Court, Peterhead, AB42 2YF, United Kingdom
Tel.: (44) 1779 474282
Web Site: http://www.tenantsfirst.com
Emp.: 5
Property Rental Services
N.A.I.C.S.: 531110
Pat Cahill (Dir-Housing)

SANCUS LENDING (GIBRALTAR) LIMITED
Third Floor Heritage House 233/3 Main Street, Gibraltar, GX11 1AA, Gibraltar
Tel.: (350) 20013700   GI
Emp.: 100
Financial Banking Services
N.A.I.C.S.: 522110
Stevs O'Brien (Mng Dir)

SANCUS LENDING GROUP LIMITED
St Martins House Le Bordage, Saint Peter Port, GY1 1BR, Guernsey
Tel.: (44) 1481742074   GY
Web Site: https://www.sancus.com
Year Founded: 2005
LEND—(AIM)
Rev.: $15,671,547
Assets: $135,470,402
Liabilities: $137,985,997
Net Worth: ($2,515,595)
Earnings: $11,628,262)
Emp.: 30
Fiscal Year-end: 12/31/23
Business Loan Services
N.A.I.C.S.: 522291
Andrew Noel Whelan (CEO)

Subsidiaries:

BMS Finance AB Limited (1)
58 Wood Lane Shepherds Bush, London, W12 7RZ, United Kingdom
Tel.: (44) 2070926700
Web Site: http://www.bms-finance.com
Financial Banking Services
N.A.I.C.S.: 522110
Jakob Nilsson (Mgr-Investment)

Sancus (Guernsey) Limited (1)
Block C Hirzel Court Hirzel Street, Saint Peter Port, GY1 2NL, Guernsey
Tel.: (44) 708288
Financial Banking Services
N.A.I.C.S.: 522110
Matt Watson (Mng Dir)

Sancus BMS (Ireland) Limited (1)
Harcourt Centre Harcourt Road, Dublin, Ireland
Tel.: (353) 14773611
Financial Banking Services
N.A.I.C.S.: 522110
Michael Mooney (Mng Dir)

Sancus Lending (Ireland) Limited (1)
Harcourt Centre Harcourt Road, Dublin, 2, Ireland
Tel.: (353) 14773611
Financial Lending Services
N.A.I.C.S.: 522390

Sancus Lending (Jersey) Limited (1)
Windward House La Route de la Liberation, Saint Helier, JE2 3BQ, Jersey
Tel.: (44) 1534708900
Financial Banking Services
N.A.I.C.S.: 522110

Sancus Lending (UK) Limited (1)
7th Floor St Albans House 57-59 Haymarket, London, SW1Y 4QX, United Kingdom
Tel.: (44) 2070226528
Financial Banking Services
N.A.I.C.S.: 522110
Gary Mealing (Dir-Credit)

SANDBACKEN DEVELOPMENT AB
Sunnorpsgatan 6, 582 73, Linkoping, Sweden
Tel.: (46) 105572030
Web Site: https://www.sandbackens.se
Year Founded: 1993
Plumbing, Heating & Air-Conditioning Contractors
N.A.I.C.S.: 238220
Mikael Matts (CEO)

SANDBERG CAPITAL SPRAV. SPOL., A.S.
Dvorakovo nabrezie 8, 811 02, Bratislava, Slovakia
Tel.: (421) 2 59 418 111
Web Site: http://www.sandberg.capital.com
Investment Management
N.A.I.C.S.: 523999
Martin Fedor (Chm & CEO)

Subsidiaries:

BENESTRA, s. r. o. (1)
Aupark Tower Einsteinova 24, 851 01, Bratislava, Slovakia   (100%)
Tel.: (421) 2 32 487 111
Web Site: http://www.benestra.sk
Telecommunication Servicesb
N.A.I.C.S.: 517810
Michal Kemenik (Dir-IT/IS)

SANDEN CORPORATION
20 Kotobuki-cho, Isesaki, 372-8502, Gunma, Japan
Tel.: (81) 270241211
Web Site: https://www.sanden.co.jp
Year Founded: 1943
6444—(TKS)
Rev.: $1,271,088,110
Assets: $1,152,401,510
Liabilities: $1,004,674,270
Net Worth: $147,727,240
Earnings: ($23,815,310)
Emp.: 5,587
Fiscal Year-end: 12/31/23
Automobile Air-Conditioners, Vending Machines, Freezers, Heating Systems & Ventilation Systems Mfr
N.A.I.C.S.: 336390
Katsuya Nishi (Pres)

Subsidiaries:

P.T. Sanden Indonesia (1)
Kawasan Industri Deltamas - KITIC Kav No 7A 8 Desa Nagasari, Serang Baru, Bekasi, 17330, Jawa Barat, Indonesia
Tel.: (62) 2150555651
Web Site: https://www.sanden.co.id
Automobile Air-Conditioning Product Mfr
N.A.I.C.S.: 333415
Takeshi Yaginuma (Pres)

Pranav Vikas (India) Ltd (1)
Plot No 45-46 Industrial Area NIT, Industrial area, Faridabad, 121001, Haryana, India
Tel.: (91) 1293093000
Web Site: http://www.pranavvikas.com
Aluminium Products Mfr
N.A.I.C.S.: 331524

Sanden (Suzhou) Precision Parts Co., Ltd. (1)
No 509 Jinzi Road Near Linhu Avenue, Fen Lake High-tech Industrial Development Zone, Wujiang, Jiangsu, China
Tel.: (86) 51282079990
Automobile Parts Mfr
N.A.I.C.S.: 336390

Sanden (Thailand) Co., Ltd. (1)
1/11-12 Moo 5, Rojana Road Tambol Karnharm Amphur Uthai, Ayutthaya, 13210, Thailand
Tel.: (66) 35330030
Web Site: http://www.sanden.co.th
Automobile Air-Conditioning Product Mfr
N.A.I.C.S.: 333415
Manabu Hosono (Mng Dir)

Sanden Advanced Technology Corporation (1)
SGCT Center 20 Kotobuki-cho, Isesaki, 372-8502, Gunma, Japan
Tel.: (81) 270241212
Automobile Air-Conditioning Product Mfr
N.A.I.C.S.: 333415
Toshiyuki Kikuchi (Pres)

Sanden Airconditioning (Malaysia) Sdn. Bhd. (1)
No 16 Jalan Pemaju U1/15 Seksyen U1, HICOM-Glenmarie Industrial Park, 40150, Shah Alam, Selangor, Malaysia
Tel.: (60) 378047777
Web Site: http://www.sanden.com.my
Automobile Air-Conditioning Product Mfr
N.A.I.C.S.: 333415
Kazuhiro Iwata (Mng Dir)

Sanden Automotive Climate Systems Corporation (1)
Akihabara Daibiru Building 1-18-13 Soto Kanda, Chiyoda-ku, Tokyo, 101-8583, Japan
Tel.: (81) 352093232
Automobile Air-Conditioning Product Mfr
N.A.I.C.S.: 333415
Tadashi Kondo (Pres)

Sanden Automotive Components Corporation (1)
Akihabara Daibiru Building 1-18-13 Soto Kanda, Chiyoda-ku, Tokyo, 101-8583, Japan
Tel.: (81) 352093233
Automobile Air-Conditioning Product Mfr
N.A.I.C.S.: 333415
Tsuguo Ito (Pres)

Sanden Automotive Technology (Shanghai) Co., Ltd. (1)
Unit 1012 No 515 Yinxiang Rd, Jiading District, Shanghai, 201802, China
Tel.: (86) 2159117335
Automobile Air-Conditioning Product Mfr
N.A.I.C.S.: 333415

Sanden Bright Partner Corporation (1)
20 Kotobuki-cho, Isesaki, 372-8502, Gunma, Japan
Tel.: (81) 270246486
Automobile Air-Conditioning Product Mfr
N.A.I.C.S.: 333415

Sanden Business Associate Corporation (1)
Akihabara Daibiru Building 1-18-13 Soto Kanda, Chiyoda-ku, Tokyo, 101-8583, Japan
Tel.: (81) 352093268
Automotive & Electrical Equipment Services
N.A.I.C.S.: 811310
Shigenori Sasaki (Pres)

Sanden Chongqing Automotive Air Conditioning Co., Ltd. (1)
No 4 2 Road Export Processing Zone North New Zone, Chongqing, 401122, China
Tel.: (86) 2386961228
Automobile Air-Conditioning Product Mfr
N.A.I.C.S.: 333415

INTERNATIONAL PUBLIC

Sanden Environmental Products Corporation (1)
Akihabara Daibiru Building 1-18-13 Soto Kanda, Chiyoda-ku, Tokyo, 101-8583, Japan
Tel.: (81) 352093236
Natural Refrigerant Product Distr
N.A.I.C.S.: 423740
Tatsuro Hirose (Pres)

Sanden Holdings Corporation (1)
Unit E Floor 2nd Zhao-Feng World Trade Building No 369 Jiang Su Road, Chang Ning District, Shanghai, 200050, China
Tel.: (86) 2152382030
Automobile Air-Conditioning Product Mfr
N.A.I.C.S.: 333415

Sanden Huayu Automotive Air-Conditioning Co., Ltd. (1)
1117 Shengli Road, Pudong District, Shanghai, 201201, China
Tel.: (86) 2163869900
Automobile Parts Mfr
N.A.I.C.S.: 336390

Sanden International (Europe) GmbH (1)
Am Taubenbaum 35-37, 61231, Bad Nauheim, Germany
Tel.: (49) 603280300
Automobile Air-Conditioning Product Mfr
N.A.I.C.S.: 333415

Sanden International (Europe) GmbH (1)
Parc des Barbanniers 3-5 place, du Village des Barbanniers, 92230, Gennevilliers, France
Tel.: (33) 179620235
Automobile Air-Conditioning Product Mfr
N.A.I.C.S.: 333415

Sanden International (Europe) GmbH (1)
Ostra Vagen 1, 462 32, Vanersborg, Sweden
Tel.: (46) 521272764
Automobile Air-Conditioning Product Mfr
N.A.I.C.S.: 333415

Sanden International (Europe) GmbH (1)
Via Villafranca 30, 10024, Moncalieri, TO, Italy
Tel.: (39) 0116672148
Automobile Air-Conditioning Product Mfr
N.A.I.C.S.: 333415

Sanden International (Europe) GmbH (1)
Calle Lopez de Aranda 35 local, 28027, Madrid, Spain
Tel.: (34) 6775293
Automobile Air-Conditioning Product Mfr
N.A.I.C.S.: 333415

Sanden International (Europe) Ltd. (1)
Rosewood Crockford Lane, Chineham Park, Basingstoke, RG24 8UT, Hampshire, United Kingdom   (100%)
Tel.: (44) 1256708888
Sales Range: $25-49.9 Million
Emp.: 60
Motor Vehicle Parts & Accessories
N.A.I.C.S.: 336340

Sanden International (Singapore) Pte. Ltd. (1)
Sanden House 25 Ang Mo Kio Streets 65, Singapore, 569062, Singapore   (100%)
Tel.: (65) 63113113
Web Site: https://www.sanden.com.sg
Sales Range: $75-99.9 Million
Emp.: 262
Motor Vehicle Parts & Accessories
N.A.I.C.S.: 423120
Shigeharu Nakamura (Mng Dir)

Sanden International (USA), Inc. (1)
601 S Sanden Blvd, Wylie, TX 75098-4999   (100%)
Tel.: (972) 442-8400
Web Site: http://www.sanden.com
Sales Range: $125-149.9 Million
Emp.: 500
Mfr of Compressors for Automotive Air Conditioning

AND PRIVATE COMPANIES

N.A.I.C.S.: 336390
Mitsuya Yamamoto (Pres)

Sanden International Australia Pty. Ltd. (1)
6/17 Willfox St, Condell Park, 2200, NSW, Australia **(100%)**
Tel.: (61) 297910999
Web Site: https://www.sanden-hot-water.com.au
Sales Range: $25-49.9 Million
Emp.: 14
Motor Vehicle Parts & Accessories
N.A.I.C.S.: 423120

Sanden International Latin America Eireli (1)
Rua Alcides Ricardini Neves 12 Cj 705/706 Cidade Moncoes, Sao Paulo, 04575-050, SP, Brazil
Tel.: (55) 1137910268
Automobile Air-Conditioning Product Mfr
N.A.I.C.S.: 333415

Sanden International Philippines, Inc. (1)
102 Industry Drive Corner Progress Avenue Canlubang, Carmelray Industrial Park 1, Calamba, Laguna, Philippines
Tel.: (63) 495497957
Web Site: http://www.sanden.com.ph
Automobile Air-Conditioning Product Mfr
N.A.I.C.S.: 333415
Tomohiko Sando (Pres)

Sanden International Taiwan Corporation (1)
No 57 Zhongxing 1st St, Luzhu Dist, Taoyuan, 33857, Taiwan **(100%)**
Tel.: (886) 33135043
Sales Range: $25-49.9 Million
Emp.: 15
Motor Vehicle Parts & Accessories
N.A.I.C.S.: 423120

Sanden Living & Environmental Systems Corporation (1)
SGCT Center 20 Kotobuki-cho, Isesaki, 372-8502, Gunma, Japan
Tel.: (81) 270241243
Environmental Services
N.A.I.C.S.: 541620
Hideyasu Kamioka (Pres)

Sanden Manufacturing Europe S.A. (1)
Le Quilliou, PO Box 30, 35190, Tinteniac, France **(100%)**
Tel.: (33) 299455858
Sales Range: $200-249.9 Million
Emp.: 1,000
Motor Vehicle Parts & Accessories
N.A.I.C.S.: 336340

Sanden Manufacturing Mexico SA de CV (1)
Ave Logistica 1000 Parque Industrial Ramos Arizpe, Carr Saltillo Monclova KM 11 2, 25900, Ramos Arizpe, Mexico
Tel.: (52) 8444504800
Automobile Air-Conditioning Product Mfr
N.A.I.C.S.: 333415

Sanden Manufacturing Poland sp. z o.o. (1)
Fabryczna 11 str, 59-101, Polkowice, Lower Silesian, Poland
Tel.: (48) 767249114
Web Site: https://www.sandensmp.pl
Emp.: 1,100
Automobile Air-Conditioning Product Mfr
N.A.I.C.S.: 333415
Tetsuya Noda (Chm)

Sanden System Engineering Corporation (1)
3450-8 Miyako-machi, Isesaki, 372-0801, Gunma, Japan
Tel.: (81) 270219641
Computer Programming Services
N.A.I.C.S.: 541511

Sanden Technical Center of Vietnam Co., Ltd. (1)
No 14-16th Floor Vincom Center 72 Le Thanh Ton, Ben Nghe Ward Dist1, Ho Chi Minh City, Vietnam
Tel.: (84) 2838223320
Automobile Air-Conditioning Product Mfr

N.A.I.C.S.: 333415

Sanden Vikas (India) Ltd. (1)
Plot No 65 Sector 27-A, Faridabad, 121 003, Haryana, India
Tel.: (91) 1294196000
Web Site: http://www.sandenvikas.com
Automobile Air-Conditioning Product Mfr
N.A.I.C.S.: 333415
Praveen Agarwal (Chm)

Sanden Vikas Precision Parts Pvt. Ltd. (1)
SP2-7 Japanese Zone New Industrial Complex Majrakath, Distt Alwar, Neemrana, 301705, Rajasthan, India
Tel.: (91) 1494246670
Web Site: http://www.sandenvikasprecision.com
Automobile Air-Conditioning Product Mfr
N.A.I.C.S.: 333415
Parveen Yadav (Asst Mgr)

SandenVendo America (1)
10710 Sanden Dr, Dallas, TX 75238
Tel.: (214) 765-9066
Web Site: https://www.vendoco.com
Sales Range: $25-49.9 Million
Emp.: 195
Mfr of Vending Machines
N.A.I.C.S.: 811310
Anthony Harris (Dir-Foodservice Sls & Installations)

Subsidiary (Non-US):

SandenVendo Benelux N.V. (2)
Avenue A Van Oss 1 B21, 1120, Brussels, Belgium **(100%)**
Tel.: (32) 22682595
Sales Range: $1-9.9 Million
Emp.: 15
Vending Machines & Accessories
N.A.I.C.S.: 333310
Steven Van Holsbeek (Mgr-Sls-Natl)

SandenVendo Europe S.p.A. (2)
Regione Cavallino 2, Coniolo, 15030, Alessandria, AL, Italy **(100%)**
Tel.: (39) 0142335111
Web Site: http://www.sandenvendo.it
Sales Range: $1-9.9 Million
Emp.: 120
Vending Machines Sales & Mfr
N.A.I.C.S.: 333310
Danilo Spagna (Mgr-R&D & Tech)

SandenVendo GMBH (2)
Kolberger Strasse 7, 40599, Dusseldorf, Germany **(100%)**
Tel.: (49) 211740390
Sales Range: $1-9.9 Million
Emp.: 35
Vending Machine Sales
N.A.I.C.S.: 423440

Vendo Iberia, S.A. (2)
C Sant Ferran 92 Poligono Industrial La Almeda Sector P 1, Cornella, E 08940, Barcelona, Spain **(100%)**
Tel.: (34) 934741555
Web Site: http://www.sandenvendo.it
Rev.: $750,000
Emp.: 12
Vending Machine Sales
N.A.I.C.S.: 423440

Sanpak Engineering Industries (Pvt.) Ltd. (1)
24-Bank Square Market, Model Town, Lahore, Pakistan
Tel.: (92) 42335830939
Web Site: http://www.sanpak.biz
Automobile Parts Mfr
N.A.I.C.S.: 336390

Sanwa Coatex Corporation (1)
4138-1 Hashie-machi, Isesaki, 372-0001, Gunma, Japan
Tel.: (81) 270244438
Automobile Air-Conditioning Product Mfr
N.A.I.C.S.: 333415

Shenyang Sanden Automotive Air-Conditioning Co. Ltd. (1)
No 16-1 Zhengxin Road, Dadong District, Shenyang, 110045, China
Tel.: (86) 2488261611
Automobile Air-Conditioning Product Mfr
N.A.I.C.S.: 333415

Tianjin Sanden Automotive Air-Conditioning Co., Ltd. (1)
No 8 XEDA NO2 Avenue Xiqing Economic Development Area, Tianjin, 300385, China
Tel.: (86) 2223889988
Web Site: http://www.en.china-tsac.com
Automobile Air-Conditioning Product Mfr
N.A.I.C.S.: 333415

SANDERSON DESIGN GROUP PLC
Voysey House Sandersons Lane, London, W4 4DS, United Kingdom
Tel.: (44) 2034575862
Web Site:
https://www.sandersondesign.group
SDG—(LSE)
Rev.: $152,034,770
Assets: $145,721,372
Liabilities: $35,317,013
Net Worth: $110,404,360
Earnings: $11,981,879
Emp.: 630
Fiscal Year-end: 01/31/23
Wallcovering & Furnishing Fabric Designer & Mfr
N.A.I.C.S.: 313210
Caroline Geary (Sec)

Subsidiaries:

Abaris Holdings Limited (1)
Chalfont House Oxford Road, Denham, UB9 4DX, Buckinghamshire, United Kingdom
Tel.: (44) 7452249288
Web Site: http://abarisholdingltd.co.uk
Furnishing Fabrics Mfr & Distr
N.A.I.C.S.: 314999
James D. Michael (CEO)

Arthur Sanderson & Sons Ltd. (1)
Chalfont House Oxford Road, Denham, UB9 4DX, Bucks, United Kingdom
Tel.: (44) 1895830044
Web Site: http://www.sanderson-uk.com
Sales Range: $50-74.9 Million
Emp.: 100
Decorative Furnishing Fabrics, Wall Coverings, Specialty Carpets & Bed Linens Mfr
N.A.I.C.S.: 541410

Arthur Sanderson & Sons SARL (1)
19 Rue Du Mail, Paris, 75002, France
Tel.: (33) 140411776
Web Site: http://www.saunderssons-uk.com
Sales Range: $25-49.9 Million
Emp.: 12
Furnishing Fabrics Mfr & Distr
N.A.I.C.S.: 332999
John Sachs (Co-Mng Dir)

SANDFIRE RESOURCES LIMITED
Level 2 10 Kings Park Road, West Perth, 6005, WA, Australia
Tel.: (61) 864303800 AU
Web Site:
https://www.sandfire.com.au
SFR—(ASX)
Rev.: $624,457,797
Assets: $2,001,067,032
Liabilities: $887,351,091
Net Worth: $1,113,715,941
Earnings: ($12,734,375)
Emp.: 1,236
Fiscal Year-end: 06/30/24
Gold & Metal Ore Mining Services
N.A.I.C.S.: 212220
Bruce Hooper (Chief Exploration Officer & Chief Bus Dev Officer)

Subsidiaries:

MOD Resources Limited (1)
First Floor 1304 Hay Street, West Perth, 6005, WA, Australia
Tel.: (61) 893228233
Web Site: http://www.modresources.com.au
Gold & Copper Mining
N.A.I.C.S.: 212220

Subsidiary (Non-US):

Australia China Investments Corporation Pty Ltd (2)
Suite 1101 No 15 Xinxi Road Shangdi Haidian District, Beijing, 100085, China
Tel.: (86) 162965805
Web Site: http://www.acinvests.com
Educational Support Services
N.A.I.C.S.: 611710

Sandfire Resources America Inc. (1)
1111 W Hastings St 15th Floor, Vancouver, V6E 2J3, BC, Canada **(78.1%)**
Tel.: (604) 628-1162
Web Site: https://www.sandfireamerica.com
Assets: $16,120,967
Liabilities: $14,273,687
Net Worth: $1,847,279
Earnings: ($14,839,918)
Emp.: 24
Fiscal Year-end: 06/30/2022
Precious & Base Metal Mining
N.A.I.C.S.: 212220
Matthew Leslie Fitzgerald (Chm)

SANDHANI LIFE INSURANCE CO. LTD.
Sandhani Life Tower Rajuk Plot No 34 Bangla Motor, Dhaka, 1000, Bangladesh
Tel.: (880) 29611197
Web Site:
https://www.sandhanilife.com
Year Founded: 1990
SANDHANINS—(CHT)
Rev.: $21,970,605
Assets: $90,041,241
Liabilities: $8,362,169
Net Worth: $81,679,072
Earnings: $64,871,504
Fiscal Year-end: 12/31/23
Insurance Services
N.A.I.C.S.: 524298
Alhaj Mohammad Mockbul Hossain (Chm)

SANDHAR TECHNOLOGIES LTD.
Plot no 13 Sector 44, Gurgaon, 122002, Haryana, India
Tel.: (91) 1244518900
Web Site:
https://www.sandhargroup.com
Year Founded: 1987
SANDHAR—(NSE)
Rev.: $350,266,795
Assets: $258,422,960
Liabilities: $147,528,517
Net Worth: $110,894,443
Earnings: $8,819,207
Emp.: 1,721
Fiscal Year-end: 03/31/23
Motor Vehicle Part & Accessory Mfr
N.A.I.C.S.: 336390
Jayant Davar (Chm & Mng Dir)

SANDHURST AUTOPRINT LTD
1 Vulcan Way, Aldershot, GU47 9DB, Hertfordshire, United Kingdom
Tel.: (44) 1252749808
Web Site:
http://www.sandhurstautoprint.co.uk
Year Founded: 1997
Rev.: $11,841,053
Emp.: 13
Number Plate Components Supplier
N.A.I.C.S.: 336390
Tim Sanders (Mng Dir)

SANDI PROPERTIES CO., LTD.
16F-3 No 175 Zhongzheng 2nd Road, Lingya District, Kaohsiung, 802, Taiwan
Tel.: (886) 072259599
Web Site:
https://www.sandirealestate.com.tw
Year Founded: 1955

SANDI PROPERTIES CO., LTD.

SanDi Properties Co., Ltd.—(Continued)
1438—(TAI)
Rev.: $10,337,388
Assets: $355,420,046
Liabilities: $294,666,786
Net Worth: $60,753,260
Earnings: ($2,124,137)
Fiscal Year-end: 12/31/23
Construction Engineering Services
N.A.I.C.S.: 236220
Yulin Zhong *(Chm & Gen Mgr)*

SANDLEWOOD DEVELOPMENTS LTD.
24 Hemlock Crescent Southwest
Suite 3115, Calgary, T3C 2Zi, AB, Canada
Tel.: (403) 258-3111
Web Site: http://www.sandlewood.com
Year Founded: 1977
Sales Range: $10-24.9 Million
Emp.: 35
Building Construction Services
N.A.I.C.S.: 236115
Jamie Strain *(CEO)*

SANDMARTIN INTERNATIONAL HOLDINGS LIMITED
Unit 04-05 16/F Nam Wo Hong Bldg
No 148 Wing Lok St, Sheung Wan, China (Hong Kong)
Tel.: (852) 25877798
Web Site: http://www.sandmartin.com.hk
0482—(HKG)
Rev.: $95,109,135
Assets: $110,525,288
Liabilities: $108,886,785
Net Worth: $1,638,503
Earnings: ($10,265,663)
Emp.: 669
Fiscal Year-end: 12/31/22
Digital Television Reception Products Mfr & Trade
N.A.I.C.S.: 326199
Wei Chun Chen *(CFO)*

Subsidiaries:

BCN Distribuciones, S.A. (1)
Mila i Fontanals 118-120, 08205, Sabadell, Barcelona, Spain
Tel.: (34) 937292700
Web Site: https://www.ftemaximal.com
Sales Range: $25-49.9 Million
Emp.: 40
Frequency Equipments Mfr
N.A.I.C.S.: 334220

Intelligent Digital Services GmbH (1)
Maria-Goeppert-Str 5, 23562, Lubeck, Germany
Tel.: (49) 45148978323
Web Site: https://www.ids-digital.de
TV Electronic Product & Set Top Box Mfr
N.A.I.C.S.: 334419

My HD Media FZ LLC (1)
Boutique Villa 6 Behind Knowledge Village Media City, PO Box 503050, Dubai, United Arab Emirates
Tel.: (971) 44354888
Web Site: http://www.my-hd.tv
HD Channel Television Services
N.A.I.C.S.: 516120

Pro Brand International, Inc. (1)
1900 W Oak Cir, Marietta, GA 30062
Tel.: (770) 423-7072
Web Site: http://www.probrandintl.com
Sales Range: $75-99.9 Million
Emp.: 31
Antenna & RF Systems Mfr
N.A.I.C.S.: 517410
Jim Crownover *(CEO)*

Pro Brand Technology, Inc. (1)
14F-6 No 1071 Zhongzheng Road, Taoyuan, Taiwan
Tel.: (886) 36687085
Web Site: https://www.pbt.com.tw

RF Electronic & Antenna System Mfr
N.A.I.C.S.: 334419

SMT Electronic Technology Limited (1)
No 52 Zhuhai Free Trade Zone, Hongwan, Zhuhai, 519030, Guangdong, China
Tel.: (86) 7568687998
Sales Range: $800-899.9 Million
Frequency Equipments Mfr
N.A.I.C.S.: 334220

SMT Hong Kong Limited (1)
Rm 1901 19 F China Merchant Tower Shun Tak Ctr 168-200 Connaught Rd, Central Dist, Sheung Wan, China (Hong Kong)
Tel.: (852) 25877798
Web Site: http://www.sandmartin.com.hk
Sales Range: $25-49.9 Million
Emp.: 11
Telecommunications Equipment Mfr
N.A.I.C.S.: 334210

Sandmartin (Zhong Shan) Electronic Co., Ltd. (1)
Industrial Zone No 3 No 16 Qianjin Erlu Xin Qian Jin Village, Tanzhou, Zhongshan, Guangdong, China
Tel.: (86) 76086211777
Precision Product & Accessory Mfr
N.A.I.C.S.: 332721
Chery Wu *(Deputy Mgr-Pur)*

SANDNES SPAREBANK
Tel.: (47) 51676700
Web Site: https://www.rogalandsparebank.no
SADG—(OSL)
Rev.: $91,401,732
Assets: $3,197,370,309
Liabilities: $2,854,513,579
Net Worth: $342,856,731
Earnings: $29,894,536
Emp.: 115
Fiscal Year-end: 12/31/19
Commercial Banking Services
N.A.I.C.S.: 522110
Trine Karin Stangeland *(CEO & Mng Dir)*

Subsidiaries:

Aktiv Eiendomsmegling Jaeren AS (1)
Jernbanegata 5, Bryne, Norway
Tel.: (47) 51778000
Web Site: https://aktiv.no
Real Estate Agent & Broker Services
N.A.I.C.S.: 531210

SANDOLL, INC.
6th Floor 49 Achasan-ro 17-gil, Seongdong-gu, Seoul, Korea (South)
Tel.: (82) 16884001
Web Site: https://www.sandoll.co.kr
Year Founded: 1984
419120—(KRS)
Software Development Services
N.A.I.C.S.: 541511
Donggeun Shin *(Dir)*

SANDON CAPITAL INVESTMENTS LIMITED
Level 5 139 Macquarie Street, Sydney, 2000, NSW, Australia
Tel.: (61) 280141188
Web Site: http://www.sandoncapital.com.au
Year Founded: 2008
SNC—(ASX)
Rev.: $25,626,183
Assets: $97,721,303
Liabilities: $20,819,157
Net Worth: $76,902,146
Earnings: $9,587,852
Fiscal Year-end: 06/30/24
Investment Services
N.A.I.C.S.: 523910
Gabriel F. Radzyminski *(Mng Dir & Portfolio Mgr)*

Subsidiaries:

Mercantile Investment Company Ltd. (1)
Level 5 139 Macquarie Street, Sydney, 2000, NSW, Australia (18.87%)
Tel.: (61) 280141188
Web Site: http://www.mercantileinvestment.com.au
Rev.: $3,145,198
Assets: $67,918,774
Liabilities: $23,881,471
Net Worth: $44,037,303
Earnings: ($4,093,867)
Emp.: 5
Fiscal Year-end: 06/30/2022
Investment Holding Company
N.A.I.C.S.: 551112
Gabriel F. Radzyminski *(Chm)*

Subsidiary (Domestic):

Australian Silica Quartz Group Ltd. (2)
Suite 10 / 295 Rokeby Road, Subiaco, 6008, WA, Australia
Tel.: (61) 892008200
Web Site: https://www.asqg.com.au
Rev.: $168,291
Assets: $4,051,755
Liabilities: $169,974
Net Worth: $3,881,782
Earnings: ($554,591)
Fiscal Year-end: 06/30/2024
Mineral Exploration Services
N.A.I.C.S.: 213115
Robert John Nash *(Chm)*

Subsidiary (Domestic):

BRL Landholdings Pty Ltd. (3)
Suite 10 295 Rokeby Road, Subiaco, 6008, WA, Australia
Tel.: (61) 895762360
Bauxite Ore Mine Site Development Services
N.A.I.C.S.: 212290

SANDOWN & BOURNE
Crownest Mill Skipton Rd, Barnoldswick, BB18 5RH, Lancashire, United Kingdom
Tel.: (44) 1282666000
Web Site: http://www.r-soper.co.uk
Sales Range: $50-74.9 Million
Emp.: 300
Printed Fabric Mfr
N.A.I.C.S.: 313310
Ben Soper *(Mgr)*

Subsidiaries:

Stead McAlpin & Company Limited (1)
Cummersdale Print Works, PO Box 1, Carlisle, CA2 6BT, Cumbria, United Kingdom
Tel.: (44) 1228525224
Web Site: http://www.steadmcalpin.co.uk
Sales Range: $10-24.9 Million
Emp.: 110
Textile Printer, Designer & Finisher
N.A.I.C.S.: 313310
Ben Soper *(Mng Dir)*

SANDOZ GROUP AG
Forum 1 Novartis Campus, 4056, Basel, Switzerland
Tel.: (41) 613241111 CH
Web Site: https://www.sandoz.com
SDZ—(SWX)
Rev.: $375,000,000
Assets: $19,430,000,000
Liabilities: $10,776,000,000
Net Worth: $8,654,000,000
Earnings: $80,000,000
Emp.: 23,848
Fiscal Year-end: 12/31/23
Pharmaceutical Products Distr
N.A.I.C.S.: 456109
Remco Steenbergen *(CFO)*

Subsidiaries:

Sandoz International GmbH (1)
Industriestrasse 25, Holzkirchen, 83607, Germany

INTERNATIONAL PUBLIC

Tel.: (49) 80244760
Web Site: http://www.sandoz.com
Sales Range: $5-14.9 Billion
Emp.: 1,300
Holding Company; Pharmaceuticals Mfr
N.A.I.C.S.: 551112

Subsidiary (Non-US):

EBEWE Pharma Ges.mbH Nfg. KG (2)
Mondseestrasse 11, A-4866, Unterach, Austria
Tel.: (43) 766581230
Web Site: http://www.sandoz.com
Pharmaceuticals Mfr
N.A.I.C.S.: 325412

Subsidiary (Domestic):

HEXAL AG (2)
Industriestrasse 25, 83607, Holzkirchen, Germany (100%)
Tel.: (49) 80249080
Web Site: http://www.hexal.de
Sales Range: $1-4.9 Billion
Emp.: 3,500
Generic Pharmaceuticals Mfr, Marketer & Sales
N.A.I.C.S.: 325412
Jeffrey George *(Pres)*

Subsidiary (Non-US):

Lek Pharmaceuticals d.d. (2)
Verovskova 57, 1526, Ljubljana, Slovenia (100%)
Tel.: (386) 1 580 21 11
Web Site: http://www.lek.si
Sales Range: $400-449.9 Million
Pharmaceuticals Mfr
N.A.I.C.S.: 325412
Andreja Bucik Primozic *(Member-Exec Bd)*

Branch (Non-US):

Lek Pharmaceuticals d.d. (3)
Antuna Hangija bb Poslovni Center, 71000, Sarajevo, Bosnia & Herzegovina (100%)
Tel.: (387) 33563271
Sales Range: $25-49.9 Million
Emp.: 20
Pharmaceuticals Sales & Marketing
N.A.I.C.S.: 424210

Subsidiary (Non-US):

Lek Skopje D.O.O. (3)
Ulica Pero Nakov bb, MK 1000, Skopje, North Macedonia (100%)
Tel.: (389) 22550800
Web Site: http://www.sandoz.com
Sales Range: $25-49.9 Million
Emp.: 40
Pharmaceuticals Sales & Marketing
N.A.I.C.S.: 424210

Sandoz Polska Sp.z o.o. (3)
ul Domaniewska 50C, PL 02672, Warsaw, Poland (100%)
Tel.: (48) 225490700
Web Site: http://www.sandoz.pl
Sales Range: $125-149.9 Million
Emp.: 400
Pharmaceuticals Sales & Marketing
N.A.I.C.S.: 424210

Sandoz S.R.L. (3)
Str Livezeni 7A, Tirgu Mures, 540472, Romania (100%)
Tel.: (40) 265 20 8123
Web Site: http://www.sandoz.com
Emp.: 200
Pharmaceuticals Mfr, Marketing & Sales
N.A.I.C.S.: 325412

Branch (Non-US):

Sandoz d.d. (3)
Galvaniho 15/C, 821 04, Bratislava, Slovakia (100%)
Tel.: (421) 248200600
Web Site: http://www.sandoz.sk
Sales Range: $25-49.9 Million
Emp.: 60
Pharmaceuticals Sales & Marketing
N.A.I.C.S.: 424210

Sandoz d.d. (3)
12 Amosova Street 2nd Building 11th Floor,

Horizon Park Business Center, 03680, Kiev, Ukraine **(100%)**
Tel.: (380) 444952866
Web Site: http://www.sandoz.com
Sales Range: $25-49.9 Million
Emp.: 80
Pharmaceuticals Sales & Marketing
N.A.I.C.S.: 424210

Subsidiary (Non-US):

Sandoz d.o.o. **(3)**
Maksimirska 120, 10000, Zagreb, Croatia **(100%)**
Tel.: (385) 12353111
Web Site: http://www.sandoz.hr
Sales Range: $25-49.9 Million
Emp.: 50
Mfr of Pharmaceutical Products
N.A.I.C.S.: 325412
Igor Haralovic *(Dir)*

Sandoz s. r. o. **(3)**
U Nakladoveho Nadrazi 10, Prague, 130 00, Czech Republic **(100%)**
Tel.: (420) 221 421 611
Web Site: http://www.sandoz.cz
Emp.: 100
Pharmaceuticals Sales & Marketing
N.A.I.C.S.: 424210

Taylek Drugs Company Limited **(3)**
Plot 8 Block M Abimbola Street, Isolo, Lagos, Nigeria
Tel.: (234) 14526037
Pharmaceuticals Mfr
N.A.I.C.S.: 325412

ZAO Sandoz **(3)**
Building 1 8-9 Floors Presnenskaya naberezhnaya 8, 123317, Moscow, Russia
Tel.: (7) 495 660 7509
Web Site: http://www.sandoz.ru
Pharmaceuticals Sales & Marketing
N.A.I.C.S.: 424210

Subsidiary (Non-US):

N.V. Sandoz S.A. **(2)**
Medialaan 40, Vilvoorde, 1800, Belgium
Tel.: (32) 2 722 97 97
Web Site: http://www.sandoz.be
Pharmaceuticals Product Mfr
N.A.I.C.S.: 325412

Sandoz (China) Pharmaceutical Co., Ltd. **(2)**
Room 205 Tower W1 Oriental Plaza No1 East Chang An Avenue, Dong Cheng, Beijing, 100738, China
Tel.: (86) 10 8515 6698
Web Site: http://www.sandoz.com.cn
Pharmaceuticals Product Mfr
N.A.I.C.S.: 325412

Sandoz A/S **(2)**
Edvard Thomsens Vej 14, 2300, Copenhagen, Denmark
Tel.: (45) 63 95 10 00
Web Site: http://www.sandoz.dk
Emp.: 30
Pharmaceuticals Product Mfr
N.A.I.C.S.: 325412
Carsten Gleerup *(Mgr-Nordic)*

Sandoz B.V. **(2)**
Veluwezoom 22, NL-1327 AH, Almere, Netherlands **(100%)**
Tel.: (31) 365241600
Web Site: http://www.sandoz.nl
Sales Range: $25-49.9 Million
Emp.: 70
Pharmaceutical Mfr, Marketing & Sales
N.A.I.C.S.: 325412

Sandoz Egypt Pharma S.A.E. **(2)**
5th Assembly Building 289 Second center, New Cairo, Egypt
Tel.: (20) 222861679
Pharmaceuticals Mfr
N.A.I.C.S.: 325412

Sandoz Farmaceutica Lda. **(2)**
Alameda da Beloura Edificio 1 2 andar Quinta da Beloura, 2765-693, Sintra, Portugal
Tel.: (351) 21 924 19 11
Web Site: http://www.sandoz.pt
Pharmaceuticals Product Mfr
N.A.I.C.S.: 325412

Sandoz Farmaceutica S.A. **(2)**
Parque Norte Business Center Roble Building, 56 Serrano Galvache Street, 28033, Madrid, Spain
Tel.: (34) 91 548 8404
Web Site: https://www.sandozfarma.es
Pharmaceutical Product Mfr & Distr
N.A.I.C.S.: 325412

Sandoz GmbH **(2)**
Biochemiestrasse 10, Kundl, 6250, Austria
Tel.: (43) 53382000
Web Site: http://www.sandoz.at
Sales Range: $800-899.9 Million
Pharmaceuticals Mfr
N.A.I.C.S.: 325412

Branch (Domestic):

Sandoz GmbH **(3)**
Stella-Klein-Loew-Weg 17, 1020, Vienna, Austria **(100%)**
Tel.: (43) 1866590
Web Site: http://www.sandoz.com
Sales Range: $50-74.9 Million
Emp.: 110
Pharmaceuticals Sales & Marketing
N.A.I.C.S.: 424210

Subsidiary (Non-US):

Sandoz Grup Saglik Urunleri Ilaclari Sanayi ve Ticaret A.S. **(2)**
GOSB Ihsan Dede Cad 900 sok, Gebze, 41480, Kocaeli, Turkiye
Tel.: (90) 262 677 8600
Pharmaceuticals Product Mfr
N.A.I.C.S.: 325412

Sandoz Hungaria Kft. **(2)**
Bartok Bela Ut 43-47, Budapest, 1114, Hungary
Tel.: (36) 1 430 2890
Web Site: http://www.sandoz.hu
Pharmaceuticals Product Mfr
N.A.I.C.S.: 325412

Sandoz Hungary Limited Liability Company **(2)**
Bartk Hz Bartk Blat 43-47, 1114, Budapest, Hungary
Tel.: (36) 1 430 2890
Pharmaceuticals Product Mfr
N.A.I.C.S.: 325412

Sandoz Ilac Sanayi ve Ticaret A.S. **(2)**
GEPOSB Ataturk Bulvari 9 Cadde No 1, Gebze, 41400, Kocaeli, Turkiye
Tel.: (90) 216 458 33 00
Web Site: http://www.sandoz.com.tr
Pharmaceuticals Product Mfr
N.A.I.C.S.: 325412

Subsidiary (US):

Sandoz Inc. **(2)**
100 College Rd W, Princeton, NJ 08540 **(100%)**
Tel.: (609) 627-8500
Web Site: https://www.us.sandoz.com
Pharmaceuticals Mfr, Sales & Marketing
N.A.I.C.S.: 325412
Keren Haruvi *(Pres)*

Subsidiary (Domestic):

Fougera Pharmaceuticals Inc. **(3)**
60 Baylis Rd, Melville, NY 11747
Tel.: (631) 454-7677
Web Site: http://www.fougera.com
Sales Range: $400-449.9 Million
Emp.: 700
Pharmaceuticals Mfr
N.A.I.C.S.: 325412

Division (Domestic):

PharmaDerm **(4)**
210 Park Ave, Florham Park, NJ 07932
Tel.: (973) 514-4240
Web Site: http://www.pharmaderm.com
Pharmaceuticals Mfr
N.A.I.C.S.: 325412

Subsidiary (Non-US):

Sandoz Industrial Products S.A. **(2)**
Ctra Granollers Cardedeu, Les Franqueses del Valles, E 08520, Barcelona, Spain **(100%)**
Tel.: (34) 938404400
Web Site: http://www.es.sandoz.com
Sales Range: $50-74.9 Million
Emp.: 200
Pharmaceuticals Research, Mfr, Marketing & Sales
N.A.I.C.S.: 325412

Sandoz Pharmaceuticals AG **(2)**
Hinterbergstrasse 24, Cham, 6330, Switzerland
Tel.: (41) 41 748 85 85
Web Site: http://www.generika.ch
Drug Mfr & Whslr
N.A.I.C.S.: 325412

Subsidiary (Domestic):

Sandoz Pharmaceuticals GmbH **(2)**
Raiffeisenstrasse 11, D 83607, Holzkirchen, Germany
Tel.: (49) 802490240
Web Site: http://www.sandoz.de
Pharmaceuticals Sales & Marketing
N.A.I.C.S.: 424210
Isabell Remus *(CEO)*

Subsidiary (Non-US):

Sandoz Pharmaceuticals d.d. **(2)**
Verovskova 57, Ljubljana, 1000, Slovenia
Tel.: (386) 15 802 111
Pharmaceutical Products Distr
N.A.I.C.S.: 424210

Sandoz Pty Ltd. **(2)**
Level 2 Suite 201 19 Harris Street, Pyrmont, 2009, NSW, Australia
Tel.: (61) 295661500
Web Site: http://www.sandoz.com.au
Pharmaceutical Product Mfr & Distr
N.A.I.C.S.: 325412

Sandoz S.A. **(2)**
Domingo De Acassuso 3780 1st Floor Olivos, Buenos Aires, 1636, Argentina
Tel.: (54) 11 4704 2400
Web Site: http://www.sandoz.com.ar
Pharmaceutical Products Distr
N.A.I.C.S.: 424210

Sandoz S.A. de C.V. **(2)**
Calle Candelaria No 186 Colonia Atlantida Delegacion Coyoacan, Mexico, 04370, Mexico
Tel.: (52) 55 5549 3740
Web Site: http://www.novartis.com.mx
Pharmaceuticals Product Mfr
N.A.I.C.S.: 325412

Sandoz S.A.S. **(2)**
49 Avenue Georges Pompidou, Levallois-Perret, Paris, 92593, France
Tel.: (33) 1 49 64 48 00
Web Site: http://www.sandoz.fr
Emp.: 50
Pharmaceutical Product Mfr & Whslr
N.A.I.C.S.: 325412

Sandoz South Africa (Pty) Ltd. **(2)**
72 Steel Road Spartan, PO Box 154, Isando, Kempton Park, 1600, South Africa
Tel.: (27) 119299000
Web Site: http://www.sandoz.co.za
Emp.: 100
Pharmaceuticals Product Mfr
N.A.I.C.S.: 325412

Sandoz do Brasil Industria Farmaceutica Ltda. **(2)**
Rodovia Celso Garcia Cid KM 87 Parque Industrial, Cambe, 86183-600, Parana, Brazil
Tel.: (55) 43 3174 8000
Web Site: http://www.sandoz.com.br
Pharmaceutical Products Distr
N.A.I.C.S.: 424210

SANDSTORM GOLD LTD.
Suite 3200 733 Seymour Street, Vancouver, V6B 0S6, BC, Canada
Tel.: (604) 689-0234
Web Site: https://www.sandstormgold.com
Year Founded: 2007
SAND—(NYSE)
Rev.: $148,732,000
Assets: $1,974,777,000
Liabilities: $533,372,000
Net Worth: $1,441,405,000
Earnings: $78,450,000
Emp.: 27
Fiscal Year-end: 12/31/22
Gold Ore Streaming Investment Services
N.A.I.C.S.: 522299
David I. Awram *(Co-Founder & Sr Exec VP)*

Subsidiaries:

Nomad Royalty Company Ltd. **(1)**
1275 Avenue des Canadiens-de-Montreal Ste 500, Montreal, H3B 0G4, QC, Canada
Tel.: (438) 538-7555
Web Site: http://www.nomadroyalty.com
Rev.: $27,152,000
Assets: $376,013,000
Liabilities: $86,107,000
Net Worth: $289,906,000
Earnings: $(1,459,000)
Emp.: 6
Fiscal Year-end: 12/31/2021
Mineral Exploration Services
N.A.I.C.S.: 213114
Vincent Metcalfe *(CEO)*

Subsidiary (Domestic):

Coral Gold Resources Ltd. **(2)**
570 Granville Street Suite 900, Vancouver, V6C 3P1, BC, Canada
Tel.: (604) 682-3701
Web Site: http://www.coralgold.com
Rev.: $352,879
Assets: $13,963,467
Liabilities: $88,422
Net Worth: $13,875,045
Earnings: $(407,066)
Fiscal Year-end: 01/31/2020
Gold Mining Services
N.A.I.C.S.: 212220
Nathan Harte *(CFO)*

SANDU PHARMACEUTICALS LTD.
Sandu Nagar DK Sandu Marg, Chembur, Mumbai, 400 071, Maharashtra, India
Tel.: (91) 2225284402
Web Site: https://www.sandu.in
Year Founded: 1899
524703—(BOM)
Rev.: $7,874,372
Assets: $6,494,371
Liabilities: $1,789,497
Net Worth: $4,704,874
Earnings: $182,303
Emp.: 323
Fiscal Year-end: 03/31/23
Ayurvedic Medicines Mfr
N.A.I.C.S.: 325411
Umesh Bhaskar Sandu *(Mng Dir)*

Subsidiaries:

Sandu Brothers Pvt. Ltd. **(1)**
Sandu Nagar D K Sandu Marg Chembur East, Mumbai, 400 071, India
Tel.: (91) 22 25284402
Web Site: http://www.sandu.in
Emp.: 90
Pharmaceuticals Product Mfr
N.A.I.C.S.: 325412
Sashank Sandu *(Mng Dir)*

Sandu Phytoceuticals Private Limited **(1)**
Plot No 25 26 29 & 30 Pilerne Industrial Estate, Marra Bardez Pilerne North Goa Ga, Goa, 403511, India
Tel.: (91) 8326715006
Pharmaceuticals Mfr & Distr
N.A.I.C.S.: 325412

Sandu Research Foundation Pvt. Ltd. **(1)**
Plot No 25 26 29 & 30 Pilerne Industrial Estate Marra Bardez, Goa, 403511, India
Tel.: (91) 832 2407473
Sales Range: $50-74.9 Million
Emp.: 200
Pharmaceuticals Product Mfr
N.A.I.C.S.: 325412
Prasad Naik *(Production Mgr)*

Sandu Pharmaceuticals Ltd.—(Continued)

SANDUR MANGANESE & IRON ORES LIMITED
SATYALAYA No 266 Ward No 1 Palace Road, Sandur, Bellary, 583 119, Karnataka, India
Tel.: (91) 8395260301
Web Site: https://www.sandurgroup.com
Year Founded: 1954
504918—(BOM)
Rev.: $104,334,758
Assets: $235,313,333
Liabilities: $99,753,995
Net Worth: $135,559,338
Earnings: $21,011,117
Emp.: 2,324
Fiscal Year-end: 03/31/21
Manganese & Iron Ore Mining Services
N.A.I.C.S.: 212290
T. R. Raghunandan *(Chm)*

SANDVIK AB
Kungsbron 1 Sektion D plan 5, 111 22, Stockholm, Sweden
Tel.: (46) 84561100 **SE**
Web Site: https://www.home.sandvik
Year Founded: 1862
SAND—(OMX)
Rev.: $12,098,738,400
Assets: $18,985,515,360
Liabilities: $9,544,824,800
Net Worth: $9,440,690,560
Earnings: $1,768,206,720
Emp.: 44,133
Fiscal Year-end: 12/31/21
Holding Company; Mining & Construction Equipment, Metal-Cutting Tools, Steel & Other Metal Material Products Mfr & Distr
N.A.I.C.S.: 551112
Asa Thunman *(Gen Counsel & Exec VP)*

Subsidiaries:

AB Sandvik Materials Technology **(1)**
Storgatan 2, 811 81, Sandviken, Sweden **(100%)**
Tel.: (46) 26263000
Web Site: http://www.materials.sandvik
Sales Range: $1-4.9 Billion
Emp.: 8,246
Holding Company; Stainless Steel, Alloy Steel, Special Metal & Resistance Material Products Mfr
N.A.I.C.S.: 551112
Goran Bjorkman *(Pres)*

Subsidiary (Non-US):

Sandvik Chomutov Precision Tubes s.r.o. **(2)**
V Nezvala 5502, 430 01, Chomutov, Czech Republic **(100%)**
Tel.: (420) 474615342
Web Site: http://www.smt.sandvik.com
Sales Range: $150-199.9 Million
Stainless Steel & Specialty Alloy Tube Mfr
N.A.I.C.S.: 331210

Subsidiary (Domestic):

Sandvik Heating Technology AB **(2)**
Sorkvarnsvagen, Hallstahammar, 73431, Sweden **(100%)**
Tel.: (46) 22021000
Web Site: http://www.home.kanthal.sandvik.com
Sales Range: $200-249.9 Million
Emp.: 400
Furnace & Heating Components Mfr
N.A.I.C.S.: 333414
Nieklas Nilsson *(Pres-Heating Tech)*

Subsidiary (Non-US):

Sandvik Materials Technology do Brasil S.A. Ind. Com. **(3)**
Av das Nacoes Unidas 21732, Santo Amaro, 04795-914, Sao Paulo, SP, Brazil **(100%)**
Tel.: (55) 1156965400
Web Site: http://www.sandvik.com
Sales Range: $100-124.9 Million
Emp.: 50
Furnace, Heating Materials & Other Metal Products Distr
N.A.I.C.S.: 423730

Subsidiary (US):

Sandvik Wire & Heating Technology Corporation **(3)**
119 Wooster St, Bethel, CT 06801 **(100%)**
Tel.: (203) 744-1440
Web Site: http://www.kanthal.com
Sales Range: $25-49.9 Million
Emp.: 100
Resistance Heating Wire, Ribbon & Strip Mfr
N.A.I.C.S.: 332618
Edward Faustino *(Controller)*

Subsidiary (Non-US):

ZN der Sandvik Materials Technology Deutschland GmbH **(3)**
Aschaffenburger Strasse 7a, 64546, Morfelden-Walldorf, Germany **(100%)**
Tel.: (49) 610540010
Web Site: http://www.kanthal.com
Sales Range: $25-49.9 Million
Emp.: 72
Furnace & Heating Components Distr
N.A.I.C.S.: 423730

Unit (Non-US):

Sandvik Materials Technology - Canada **(2)**
425 McCartney Street, Arnprior, K7S 3P3, ON, Canada
Tel.: (613) 623-6501
Web Site: http://www.smt.sandvik.com
Sales Range: $25-49.9 Million
Emp.: 200
Stainless Steel & High Nickel Alloy Tubing Mfr & Distr
N.A.I.C.S.: 331210
Micheal Hall *(Gen Mgr)*

Sandvik Materials Technology - Hungary **(2)**
Gyomroi ut 31 Pf 226, HU-1103, Budapest, Hungary
Tel.: (36) 14312721
Web Site: http://www.sandvik.com
Sales Range: $10-24.9 Million
Emp.: 30
Stainless Steel, Specialty Alloy & Resistance Heating Materials Distr
N.A.I.C.S.: 423510
Phil Belejchak *(VP & Gen Mgr)*

Sandvik Materials Technology - India **(2)**
Mumbai Pune Road Dapodi, Dapodi, Pune, 411012, India
Tel.: (91) 2027104800
Web Site: http://www.sandvik.com
Sales Range: $200-249.9 Million
Emp.: 800
Stainless Steel, Specialty Alloy & Resistance Heating Materials Distr
N.A.I.C.S.: 423510
Parag Satpute *(Mng Dir)*

Unit (US):

Sandvik Materials Technology - USA **(2)**
982 Griffin Pond Rd, Clarks Summit, PA 18411-1220
Tel.: (570) 585-7641
Web Site: http://www.smt.sandvik.com
Sales Range: $125-149.9 Million
Steel & Steel Alloy Tubes, Wire & Other Products Mfr & Distr
N.A.I.C.S.: 331210

Subsidiary (Domestic):

Sandvik Special Metals LLC **(3)**
235407 E State Route 397, Kennewick, WA 99337-7745 **(100%)**
Tel.: (509) 586-4131
Sales Range: $25-49.9 Million
Emp.: 100
Stainless Steel & High Alloy Materials Mfr
N.A.I.C.S.: 331512
Orjan Blom *(Pres)*

Subsidiary (Non-US):

Sandvik Materials Technology Deutschland GmbH **(2)**
Heerdter Landstr 243, 40549, Dusseldorf, Germany **(100%)**
Tel.: (49) 21150270
Web Site: http://www.smt.sandvik.com
Wire & Welding Products Mfr
N.A.I.C.S.: 332618

Subsidiary (Domestic):

Sandvik Materials Technology EMEA AB **(2)**
Storgatan2, 164 93, Sandviken, Sweden
Tel.: (46) 87930500
Steel & Metal Product Distr
N.A.I.C.S.: 423510

Subsidiary (Non-US):

Sandvik Materials Technology France S.A.S. **(2)**
4 Ave Buffon, 45062, Orleans, France **(100%)**
Tel.: (33) 238414141
Web Site: http://www.smt.sandvik.com
Sales Range: $150-199.9 Million
Steel Belts, Press Plates, Conveyor & Processing Systems Distr & Installation Services
N.A.I.C.S.: 423830

Sandvik Materials Technology UK Limited **(2)**
Inveralmond, Perth, PH1 3ED, Scotland, United Kingdom **(100%)**
Tel.: (44) 738493300
Web Site: http://www.kanthal.com
Sales Range: $25-49.9 Million
Emp.: 80
Resistance Heating Materials Mfr & Distr
N.A.I.C.S.: 332618

Subsidiary (Domestic):

Sandvik Materials Technology UK **(3)**
Manor Way, Halesowen, B62 8QZ, West Midlands, United Kingdom **(100%)**
Tel.: (44) 1215045125
Web Site: http://www.smt.sandvik.com
Sales Range: $10-24.9 Million
Emp.: 40
Steel Tube & Conveyor Components Mfr & Distr
N.A.I.C.S.: 331210

Sandvik Osprey Ltd. **(2)**
Red Jacket Works Milland Rd, Neath, SA11 1NJ, United Kingdom **(100%)**
Tel.: (44) 1639634121
Sales Range: $25-49.9 Million
Gas Atomized Metal Powders & Spray-Formed Materials Mfr
N.A.I.C.S.: 332117

Subsidiary (Domestic):

Sandvik Stal Forsaljnings AB **(2)**
Jan Stenbecks Torg 17, PO Box 12, 164 93, Kista, Sweden **(100%)**
Tel.: (46) 87930590
Web Site: http://www.smt.sandvik.com
Sales Range: $25-49.9 Million
Stainless Steel & Steel Alloy Products Whslr
N.A.I.C.S.: 423510

AB Sandvik Service **(1)**
Storgatan 2, Sandviken, 811 81, Sweden **(100%)**
Tel.: (46) 26260000
Web Site: http://www.sandvik.com
Sales Range: $1-4.9 Billion
Emp.: 6,000
Customer Service Center
N.A.I.C.S.: 561421

AB Sandvik Vastberga Service **(1)**
Vastberga Vegan 36, Hagersten, 12680, Sweden
Tel.: (46) 8 726 63 00
Web Site: http://www.sandvik.com
Legal Management Services
N.A.I.C.S.: 541199

Buffalo Tungsten, Inc. **(1)**
2 Main St, Depew, NY 14043
Tel.: (716) 683-9170
Web Site: http://www.buffalotungsten.com
Sales Range: $1-9.9 Million
Emp.: 79
Tungsten Powder Products Mfr
N.A.I.C.S.: 331492
Roger Showalter *(VP-Matls)*

CGTech **(1)**
9000 Research Dr, Irvine, CA 92618
Tel.: (949) 753-1050
Web Site: http://www.cgtech.com
Rev.: $5,816,000
Emp.: 65
Software Publisher
N.A.I.C.S.: 513210
Bill Hasenjaeger *(Mgr-Product Mktg)*

CGTech Co., Ltd. **(1)**
505 Daerung Techno Town 15-Cha 401 Simin-daero, Dongan-gu, Anyang, Gyeonggi-do, Korea (South)
Tel.: (82) 313896070
Vericut Tool Mfr
N.A.I.C.S.: 333517

CGTech Deutschland GmbH **(1)**
Neusser Landstr 386, 50769, Cologne, Germany
Tel.: (49) 221979960
Vericut Tool Mfr
N.A.I.C.S.: 333517

CGTech India Software Solutions Private Limited **(1)**
No 9/36 Vaishnavi Sapphire Centre 2nd Floor Tumkur Road Yeshawanthpur, Bengaluru, 560022, Karnataka, India
Tel.: (91) 8404780
Vericut Tool Mfr
N.A.I.C.S.: 333517

CGTech Limited **(1)**
Curtis House 34 Third Avenue, East Sussex, Hove, BN3 2PD, United Kingdom
Tel.: (44) 1273773538
Web Site: https://www.cgtech.co.uk
Software Development Services
N.A.I.C.S.: 541512

CGTech S.A.R.L. **(1)**
Les Passerelles 104 Avenue Albert 1Er, 92500, Rueil-Malmaison, France
Tel.: (33) 141968850
Web Site: https://cgtech.com
Vericut Tool Mfr
N.A.I.C.S.: 333517

CGTech S.R.L. **(1)**
Via Castaldi 1, 31100, Treviso, Italy
Tel.: (39) 0422583915
Vericut Tool Mfr
N.A.I.C.S.: 333517

CNC Software Inc. **(1)**
671 Old Post Rd, Tolland, CT 06084
Tel.: (860) 875-5006
Web Site: http://www.mastercam.com
Provider of Computer Software Development Services
N.A.I.C.S.: 541511
Mark Summers *(Chm)*

Cambrio Acquisition, LLC **(1)**
1445 Kemper Meadow Dr, Cincinnati, OH 45240-1637
Tel.: (513) 674-0000
Web Site: https://www.cambrio.com
Computer System Design Services
N.A.I.C.S.: 541512

Cimquest Inc. **(1)**
1545 Route 206, Bedminster, NJ 07921
Tel.: (732) 699-0400
Web Site: http://www.cimquest-inc.com
Rev.: $4,000,000
Emp.: 25
Computer System Design Services
N.A.I.C.S.: 541512
Rick Bair *(Dir-Sls)*

Comara GmbH **(1)**
Industriestr 21, 78112, Saint Georgen, Germany
Tel.: (49) 772491580
Web Site: https://www.comara.de
Software Development Services
N.A.I.C.S.: 541511

AND PRIVATE COMPANIES

SANDVIK AB

DSI Schaum Chemie Sp. z o.o. (1)
Ul Podleska 76, 43-190, Mikolow, Poland
Tel.: (48) 323559081
Web Site: https://www.dsi-schaumchemie.pl
Adhesive Mfr
N.A.I.C.S.: 325520

DSI Underground Argentina S.A. (1)
Canning Industrial Park STAGE 2 Perito Moreno 845 Warehouse 57, Buenos Aires, Argentina
Tel.: (54) 1139866915
Mining & Tunnelling Services
N.A.I.C.S.: 541330

DSI Underground Australia Pty. Limited (1)
341 Masonite Road, Heatherton, 2324, NSW, Australia
Tel.: (61) 249489099
Web Site: https://www.dsiunderground.com.au
Mining & Tunnelling Services
N.A.I.C.S.: 541330

DSI Underground Austria GmbH (1)
Alfred-Wagner-Strasse 1, Pasching, 4061, Linz, Austria
Tel.: (43) 7229610490
Web Site: https://www.dsiunderground.at
Mining & Tunnelling Services
N.A.I.C.S.: 541330

DSI Underground Canada Ltd. (1)
3919 Millar Avenue, Saskatoon, S7P 0C1, SK, Canada
Tel.: (306) 244-6244
Web Site: https://www.dsiunderground.ca
Mining & Tunnelling Services
N.A.I.C.S.: 541330

DSI Underground Chemicals Sp. z o.o. (1)
Ul Podleska 76, 43-190, Mikolow, Poland
Tel.: (48) 324387460
Adhesive Mfr
N.A.I.C.S.: 325520

DSI Underground Chile SpA (1)
Avda Cordillera 482, Quilicura, Santiago, Chile
Tel.: (56) 226805300
Mining & Tunnelling Services
N.A.I.C.S.: 541330

DSI Underground Colombia S.A.S. (1)
Carrera 42 54 a 71 South Space Interior 133 Antioqua, Itagui, Colombia
Tel.: (57) 44310390
Mining & Tunnelling Services
N.A.I.C.S.: 541330

DSI Underground GmbH (1)
Destouchesstr 68, 80796, Munich, Germany
Tel.: (49) 89309050200
Mining & Tunnelling Services
N.A.I.C.S.: 532412

DSI Underground Merol Sp. z o.o. (1)
Ul Przemystowa 30, 37-450, Stalowa Wola, Poland
Tel.: (48) 158425008
Adhesive Mfr
N.A.I.C.S.: 325520

DSI Underground Mexico S.A. de C.V. (1)
Av Aviation No 1002 Bod 15 Ferran I Industrial Park, San Juan de Ocotan, 45019, Zapopan, Jalisco, Mexico
Tel.: (52) 3333665794
Mining & Tunnelling Services
N.A.I.C.S.: 532412

DSI Underground Peru S.A.C. (1)
Av Nestor Gambeta 458, Callao, Lima, Peru
Tel.: (51) 17167500
Mining Equipment Mfr & Distr
N.A.I.C.S.: 333131

DSI Underground Poland Sp. z o.o. (1)
Lindego 1c, 30-148, Krakow, Poland
Tel.: (48) 123454961
Web Site: https://www.dsiunderground.pl
Adhesive Mfr
N.A.I.C.S.: 325520

DSI Underground Spain S.A.U. (1)
La Rozona 38 Corvera De, Los Campos, 33416, Asturias, Spain
Tel.: (34) 984114973
Web Site: https://www.dsiunderground.com
Mining Equipment Mfr & Distr
N.A.I.C.S.: 333131

DSI Underground System Brasil Industria e Comercio Ltda. (1)
Rua 1 No 276 - Dist Ind Bela Fama, Nova Lima, Brazil
Tel.: (55) 3135420200
Mining & Tunnelling Services
N.A.I.C.S.: 532412

DSI Underground UK Holdings Ltd. (1)
Systems House Ireland Close Off Fan Road, Chesterfield, S43 3PT, Staveley Derbyshire, United Kingdom
Tel.: (44) 1246477722
Mining Equipment Mfr & Distr
N.A.I.C.S.: 333131

DSI Underground UK Ltd. (1)
Systems House Ireland Close Off Fan Road Staveley, Chesterfield, S43 3PT, Derbyshire, United Kingdom
Tel.: (44) 1246477722
Mining Equipment Mfr & Distr
N.A.I.C.S.: 333131

DSI Underground Ventilation Systems SpA (1)
Calle Villarrica 391 Parque Industrial Vespucio Oriente, Quilicura, Santiago, Chile
Tel.: (56) 225831170
Mining & Tunnelling Services
N.A.I.C.S.: 541330

DWFritz International, Inc. (1)
9600 SW Boeckman Rd, Wilsonville, OR 97070
Tel.: (503) 598-9393
Web Site: https://dwfritz.com
Precision Metrology Product Distr
N.A.I.C.S.: 423830

Deswik Canada Inc. (1)
Suite 600 407-2nd Street SW, Calgary, T2P 2Y3, AB, Canada
Tel.: (587) 430-0911
Mining & Tunnelling Services
N.A.I.C.S.: 541330

Deswik Colombia S.A.S. (1)
Carrera 43A 1-50 Torre Proteccion Torre 1 Piso 6, San Fernando Plaza, 50021, Medellin, Colombia
Tel.: (57) 3106422477
Mining & Tunnelling Services
N.A.I.C.S.: 541330

Deswik Group Pty. Ltd. (1)
Level 9 348 Edward St, Brisbane, 4000, QLD, Australia
Tel.: (61) 732922700
Mining & Tunnelling Services
N.A.I.C.S.: 541330

Deswik Kazakhstan LLP (1)
Ul Tole Bi 101 Block B, 50012, Almaty, Kazakhstan
Tel.: (7) 1494216321
Mining Technology Services
N.A.I.C.S.: 518210

Deswik Mining Consultants (Pty.) Ltd. (1)
Parkview House 2nd Floor Constantia Park, Weltevredenpark, Roodepoort, 1709, Gauteng, South Africa
Tel.: (27) 119580273
Mining Equipment Mfr & Distr
N.A.I.C.S.: 333131

Deswik Peru S.A.C. (1)
Oficina 401b Calle Amador Merino Reyna 465, San Isidro, Lima, Peru
Tel.: (51) 16584517
Mining Equipment Mfr & Distr
N.A.I.C.S.: 333131

Deswik USA Inc. (1)
1660 Lincoln St Ste 2610, Denver, CO 80264
Tel.: (303) 500-6807
Mining Equipment Mfr & Distr
N.A.I.C.S.: 333131

Diamond Tool Coating, LLC (1)
661 Erie Ave, North Tonawanda, NY 14120
Tel.: (716) 693-5050
Web Site: https://www.diamondtc.com
Machine Tools Mfr
N.A.I.C.S.: 332216

Edvirt AB (1)
Foreningsgatan 6, 411 27, Gothenburg, Sweden
Tel.: (46) 31477747
Web Site: https://www.edvirt.com
Mining & Tunnelling Services
N.A.I.C.S.: 541330

FHP - Frezite High Performance, Unipessoal, Lda. (1)
Rua Eng Ferreira Dias N 401-405, 4100-246, Porto, Portugal
Tel.: (351) 220045400
Web Site: https://www.frezitehp.com
Cutting Tool Mfr
N.A.I.C.S.: 333515

FMT Frezite Metal Tooling GmbH (1)
Lange Strabe 66, 72336, Balingen, Germany
Tel.: (49) 7433997410
Brazed PCD Tool Mfr
N.A.I.C.S.: 333517

FMT Tooling Systems Limited (1)
Repton House Bretby Business Park Ashby Road, Burton-on-Trent, DE15 0YZ, United Kingdom
Tel.: (44) 1143520298
Web Site: https://www.fmttooling.co.uk
Cutting Tool Mfr
N.A.I.C.S.: 333515

FMT Tooling Systems S. de R.L. de C.V. (1)
Avenida Industrias N 4700 Int 2 Zona Industrial C P, 78395, San Luis Potosi, SLP, Mexico
Tel.: (52) 4447997453
Brazed PCD Tool Mfr
N.A.I.C.S.: 333517

FREZITE s.r.o. (1)
Textilni 1278, 506 01, Jicin, Czech Republic
Tel.: (420) 491513971
Web Site: https://www.fmttooling.cz
Cutlery & Machine Tools Mfr
N.A.I.C.S.: 333517

Fero Strata Systems Pty. Ltd. (1)
44 Chisholm Crescent, Kewdale, 6105, WA, Australia
Tel.: (61) 894530000
Web Site: https://www.fero.com.au
Mining Equipment Mfr & Distr
N.A.I.C.S.: 333131

Frezigest, SGPS S.A. (1)
Rua Do Vau No 323, Apartado 134, 4786-909, Trofa, Portugal
Tel.: (351) 252400758
Energy Field Equipment Mfr & Distr
N.A.I.C.S.: 333611

Frezite - Ferramentas de Corte S.A. (1)
Rua Do Vau No 173, Apartado 134, 4786-909, Trofa, Portugal
Tel.: (351) 252400360
Web Site: https://www.frezite.pt
Cutting Tool Mfr
N.A.I.C.S.: 333515

Frezite Ferramentas de Corte Ltda. (1)
No 85 Bairro Boehmerwald, Sao Bento do Sul, SC, Brazil
Tel.: (55) 4736352065
Web Site: https://loja.frezite.com.br
Cutting Tool Mfr
N.A.I.C.S.: 333515

Frezite Herramientas de Corte S.L. (1)
11 local No 5 Parque Tecnologico, 46980, Paterna, Spain
Tel.: (34) 963135131
Cutting Tool Mfr
N.A.I.C.S.: 333515

GWS Tool LLC (1)
595 County Rd 448, Tavares, FL 32778
Web Site: https://www.gwstoolgroup.com
Cutting Tool Mfr
N.A.I.C.S.: 333515

Gimo Utbildningsaktiebolag (1)
Gymnasievagen 2, 747 40, Gimo, Sweden
Tel.: (46) 17385050
Sales Range: $25-49.9 Million
Emp.: 18
Engineeering Services
N.A.I.C.S.: 541330

Heintzmann Australia Pty. Ltd. (1)
17 Lucca Road, Wyong, 2259, NSW, Australia
Tel.: (61) 243554545
Web Site: https://www.heintzmann.eu
Mining Engineering Services
N.A.I.C.S.: 541330

Herramientas Preziss, S.L. (1)
vial De Les Pedreres Nave A108390 Montgat, Barcelona, Spain
Tel.: (34) 934690351
Web Site: https://www.preziss.com
Cutting Tool Mfr
N.A.I.C.S.: 333515

ICAM Technologies Corp. (1)
21500 Nassr Street, Sainte-Anne-de-Bellevue, H9X 4C1, QC, Canada
Tel.: (514) 697-8033
Web Site: https://www.icam.com
Software & Hardware Services
N.A.I.C.S.: 541512

INROCK Drilling Systems, Inc. (1)
6000 Brittmoore Rd, Houston, TX 77041
Tel.: (713) 690-5600
Web Site: https://www.inrock.com
Drilling Tools & Equipment Mfr & Distr
N.A.I.C.S.: 333515

Indexable Cutting Tools of Canada Limited (1)
66 Clark St, Welland, L3B 5W6, ON, Canada
Tel.: (905) 735-8665
Web Site: https://www.indexable.com
Cutting Tool Mfr
N.A.I.C.S.: 333515

Kwatani (Pty.) Ltd. (1)
18 Belgrade Avenue Aeroport Spartan Ext 2, Johannesburg, Kempton Park, 1619, South Africa
Tel.: (27) 119239000
Web Site: https://kwatani.com
Mining Equipment Mfr & Distr
N.A.I.C.S.: 333131

Kwatani Global (Pty.) Ltd. (1)
18 Belgrade Avenue Aeroport Spartan Ext 2, Johannesburg, Kempton Park, 1619, South Africa
Tel.: (27) 119239000
Web Site: https://kwatani.com
Mining Equipment Mfr & Distr
N.A.I.C.S.: 333131

LLC Sandvik (1)
Polkovaya Ulitsa 1, 127018, Moscow, Russia (100%)
Tel.: (7) 4959167191
Web Site: http://www.home.sandvik
Sales Range: $200-249.9 Million
Emp.: 300
Mining & Construction Equipment, Metal-Cutting Tools & Heating Materials Distr
N.A.I.C.S.: 423710

Division (Domestic):

LLC Sandvik - Sandvik Coromant Division (2)
1 Polkovaya Sandvik LLC, Moscow, 127018, Russia
Tel.: (7) 495 916 7191
Web Site: http://www.sandvikcoromant.com
Metal Cutting Tool & Equipment Mfr
N.A.I.C.S.: 333515

Metrologic Group GmbH (1)
German Innovation Center Siemensstr 22, D-73066, Uhingen, Germany
Tel.: (49) 71619658766
Software Development Services
N.A.I.C.S.: 541511

Metrologic Group Italia S.R.L. (1)
Italian Innovation Center Corso Unione So-

SANDVIK AB

INTERNATIONAL PUBLIC

Sandvik AB—(Continued)
vietica 612 / 3, D 10035, Rivalta di Torino, Italy
Tel.: (39) 0113989740
Software Development Services
N.A.I.C.S.: 541511

Metrologic Group Spain S.L. (1)
Spanish Innovation Center C/ Zuazobidea 34, Poligono Industrial Jundiz, 01015, Vitoria, Spain
Tel.: (34) 945291089
Software Development Services
N.A.I.C.S.: 541511

Mine & Quarry Supplies (Pty.) Ltd. (1)
Po Box 1374, Kempton Park, 1620, South Africa
Tel.: (27) 118231295
Web Site: https://www.mqs.co.za
Emp.: 30
Industrial Machinery & Equipment Distr
N.A.I.C.S.: 423830

Newtrax Holdings Inc. (1)
360 rue St Jacques Floor 8, Montreal, H2Y 1P5, QC, Canada
Tel.: (514) 288-6398
Web Site: https://newtrax.com
Mining Equipment Mfr & Distr
N.A.I.C.S.: 333131

Newtrax Pty. Ltd. (1)
Equites Park Riverfields 2 Riverfields Boulevard Ground Floor, Kempton Park, 1619, South Africa
Tel.: (27) 827200553
Mining Equipment Mfr & Distr
N.A.I.C.S.: 333131

Oerlikon Balzers Sandvik Coating AB (1)
Arstaangsvagen 31 D-E, 117 43, Stockholm, Sweden
Tel.: (46) 86814140
Web Site: http://www.oerlikon.com
Rev.: $53,743,200
Emp.: 25
PVD Coatings Whslr; Owned 51% by OC Oerlikon Corporation AG & 49% by Sandvik AB
N.A.I.C.S.: 424950
Sara Deering *(CFO)*

Subsidiary (Non-US):

Oerlikon Balzers Sandvik Coating Oy (2)
Vaittintie 10, 33960, Pirkkala, Finland
Tel.: (358) 102398080
Industrial Coating Machinery Distr
N.A.I.C.S.: 423830

P.T. DSI Indonesia (1)
Jl Cendrawasih Raya No 26B Sawah Lama, Ciputat, Tangerang, 15413, Banten, Indonesia
Tel.: (62) 2174706930
Web Site: https://delta-systech.co.id
Mining & Tunnelling Services
N.A.I.C.S.: 532412

P.T. DSI Underground (1)
Jl West Gresik Industrial Estate VI Kav, Gresik, Q16-17, East Java, Indonesia
Tel.: (62) 3151163912
Mining & Tunnelling Services
N.A.I.C.S.: 532412

PT Sandvik SMC (1)
Lot 1 Kuala Kencana Industrial Park, Kuala Kencana, 98663, West Papua, Indonesia
Tel.: (62) 901394399
Mining & Construction Equipment Installation Services
N.A.I.C.S.: 238290

Preziss Diamant S.L. (1)
Pol Ind Les Pedreres Vial de les Pedreres Nave A-1, Montgat, 08390, Barcelona, Spain
Tel.: (34) 934690351
Web Site: https://preziss.com
Cutting Tool Mfr
N.A.I.C.S.: 333515

Pro-micron GmbH (1)
Gottlieb-Daimler-Strasse 6, 87600, Kaufbeuren, Germany
Tel.: (49) 8341956050
Web Site: https://www.pro-micron.de
Wireless Telecommunication Services
N.A.I.C.S.: 541618

Prototyp-Werke GmbH (1)
Franz-Disch-Str 10, 77736, Zell, Germany
Tel.: (49) 7835770
Emp.: 500
Cutting Tool Mfr
N.A.I.C.S.: 333515
Karl F. Lehmann *(Mgr)*

Rocbolt Technologies Africa Pty Ltd. (1)
30 North Reef Road, Germiston, 1429, South Africa
Tel.: (27) 118786800
Web Site: https://www.rocbolt.com
Mining Equipment Mfr & Distr
N.A.I.C.S.: 333131

Rocbolt Technologies Pty. Ltd. (1)
30 North Reef Road, Germiston, 1429, South Africa
Tel.: (27) 118786800
Web Site: https://www.rocbolt.com
Mining Equipment Mfr & Distr
N.A.I.C.S.: 333131

S-Process Equipment Australia Pty. Limited (1)
PO Box 7084, Ferntree Gully, 3156, VIC, Australia
Tel.: (61) 397200357
Web Site: https://www.processequipment.com.au
Hygienic Valve Distr
N.A.I.C.S.: 423840

Safety Production S.A.S. (1)
51 Rue De La Garenne Sevres, Hauts-de-Seine, 92310, France
Tel.: (33) 146105400
Lathes Boring & Drilling Machine Mfr
N.A.I.C.S.: 333515

Safety S.A.S. (1)
51 rue de la Garenne, 92319, Sevres, France
Tel.: (33) 1 46 10 54 00
Metal Cutting Tool & Equipment Mfr
N.A.I.C.S.: 333515

Sandvik (Pty) Ltd. (1)
64 Jet Park Road, Jet Park Boksburg, Johannesburg, 1462, South Africa (100%)
Tel.: (27) 119295300
Web Site: http://www.sandvik.com
Sales Range: $700-749.9 Million
Emp.: 1,200
Mining & Construction Equipment, Metal-Cutting Tools & Heating Materials Distr
N.A.I.C.S.: 423710
George Silen *(Mng Dir)*

Sandvik (Qingdao) Ltd. (1)
Export Processing Zone, Chengyang District, Qingdao, 266113, China
Tel.: (86) 532 870 239 88
Metal Cutting Tool & Equipment Mfr
N.A.I.C.S.: 333515

Sandvik A.E. (1)
294 Kifissias Avenue, Chalandri, 15232, Athens, Chalandri, Greece (100%)
Tel.: (30) 2106823604
Web Site: http://www.sandvik.com
Sales Range: $50-74.9 Million
Emp.: 6
Metal-Cutting Tools & Heating Materials Distr
N.A.I.C.S.: 423710

Sandvik A/S (1)
Herstedvang 14, 2620, Albertslund, Denmark
Tel.: (45) 43465100
Mining & Construction Equipment, Metal-Cutting Tools & Heating Materials Distr
N.A.I.C.S.: 423710

Sandvik AG (1)
Alpenquai 14, Postfach 3869, 6002, Lucerne, Switzerland (100%)
Tel.: (41) 415880692
Sales Range: $75-99.9 Million
Holding Company; Mining & Construction Equipment, Metal-Cutting Tools & Heating Materials Distr
N.A.I.C.S.: 423810

Subsidiary (Domestic):

Santrade Ltd. (2)
Alpenquai 14, 6005, Lucerne, Switzerland (100%)
Tel.: (41) 413683107
Sales Range: $50-74.9 Million
Metal-Cutting Tools & Heating Materials Distr
N.A.I.C.S.: 423710

Sandvik Argentina S.A. (1)
Rincon 3198, San Justo, B1754, Buenos Aires, Argentina
Tel.: (54) 1167776777
Web Site: http://www.coromant.sandvik.com
Metal Cutting Tool & Equipment Mfr
N.A.I.C.S.: 333515

Sandvik Asia Ltd. (1)
Mumbai Pune Road, Dapodi, Pune, 411012, India (97%)
Tel.: (91) 2027104800
Web Site: http://www.rocktechnology.sandvik.com
Sales Range: $350-399.9 Million
Emp.: 700
Mining & Construction Equipment, Metal-Cutting Tools & Heating Materials Distr
N.A.I.C.S.: 423710

Sandvik Australia Pty. Ltd. (1)
Level 5 135 Coronation Drive, Milton, Brisbane, 4064, QLD, Australia (100%)
Tel.: (61) 736377400
Web Site: http://www.sandvik.com
Sales Range: $50-74.9 Million
Emp.: 250
Mining & Construction Equipment, Metal-Cutting Tools, Steel & Other Metal Material Products Distr
N.A.I.C.S.: 423710
Steve Bracks *(Mng Dir)*

Sandvik Benelux (1)
Fountain Plaza Belgicastraat 5 Bus 5/6, 1930, Zaventem, Belgium (100%)
Tel.: (32) 27029802
Web Site: http://www.sandvik.com.be
Sales Range: $25-49.9 Million
Emp.: 30
Sale of Cemented Carbide Products, Special Steels, Saws & Hand Tools
N.A.I.C.S.: 423710

Sandvik Benelux B.V. (1)
Fgiagelends Ewege 401, Schiedam, NL 3125 DG, Netherlands (100%)
Tel.: (31) 0102080208
Web Site: http://www.sandvik.nl
Sales Range: $50-74.9 Million
Emp.: 50
Mining & Construction Equipment, Metal-Cutting Tools & Heating Materials Distr
N.A.I.C.S.: 423710

Sandvik Besoksservice AB (1)
Storgatan 2, 811 81, Sandviken, Sweden
Tel.: (46) 26260000
Real Estate Manangement Services
N.A.I.C.S.: 531390
Bertil Rahm *(Mgr)*

Sandvik Bulgaria Ltd. (1)
PO Box 122, 1404, Sofia, Bulgaria (100%)
Tel.: (359) 29581231
Web Site: http://www.sandvik.bg
Sales Range: $1-9.9 Million
Emp.: 12
N.A.I.C.S.: 332618

Sandvik CZ s.r.o. (1)
Na Pankraci 30, 140 00, Prague, Czech Republic (100%)
Tel.: (420) 228880910
Web Site: http://www.coromant.sandvik.com
Sales Range: $50-74.9 Million
Emp.: 30
Mining & Construction Equipment, Metal-Cutting Tools & Heating Materials Distr
N.A.I.C.S.: 423710

Sandvik Canada, Inc. (1)
Meadowvale Boulevard 2550, Mississauga, L5N 8C2, ON, Canada (100%)
Tel.: (905) 826-8900
Web Site: http://www.coromant.sandvik.com
Sales Range: $50-74.9 Million
Sales of Cemented Carbide Products, Special Steels, Saws & Hand Tools
N.A.I.C.S.: 423710

Sandvik Chile S.A. (1)
Av Presidente Eduardo Frei Montalva, Quilicura, 9990, Santiago, Chile (100%)
Tel.: (56) 26760200
Web Site: www.smt.sandvik.com
Rev.: $100,000,000
Emp.: 400
Construction Materials
N.A.I.C.S.: 423710

Sandvik China Holding Co., Ltd. (1)
1-3 Xin Yuan Nan lu, Beijing, 100027, China
Tel.: (86) 1065399888
Web Site: http://www.sandvik.com
Investment Management Service
N.A.I.C.S.: 523999
Zhiqiang Zhang *(Mng Dir)*

Sandvik China Ltd. (1)
B2 No 10 Jiuxianqiao Road, Chaoyong District, Beijing, 100015, China (100%)
Tel.: (86) 1065399888
Web Site: http://www.sandvik.com
Wire & Welding Products Mfr
N.A.I.C.S.: 332618

Sandvik Colombia S.A.S. (1)
Cre Port M No 1 98-51 4th Floor, Bogota, Colombia
Tel.: (57) 17455858
Mining & Construction Equipment Distr
N.A.I.C.S.: 423810

Sandvik Coromant (1)
Yakacik E-5 Yan Yolu Mermer Sokak, No 18 Kartal, 34876, Istanbul, Türkiye
Tel.: (90) 216 453 0700
Web Site: http://www.coromant.sandvik.com
Metal Cutting Tool & Equipment Mfr
N.A.I.C.S.: 333515

Sandvik Coromant GmbH (1)
Scheydgasse 44, Vienna, 1210, Austria
Tel.: (43) 1 27737 0
Web Site: http://www.coromant.sandvik.com
Metal Cutting Tool & Equipment Mfr
N.A.I.C.S.: 333515

Sandvik Credit AB (1)
Storgatan 4, 811 34, Sandviken, Sweden
Tel.: (46) 26 26 00 00
Web Site: http://www.sandvik.com
Financial Management Services
N.A.I.C.S.: 523999

Sandvik E.M.S. Ticaret A.S. (1)
Yakacik E5 Yanyolu Mermer Sk No 18, Kartal, 34876, Istanbul, Türkiye
Tel.: (90) 216 453 07 00
Web Site: http://www.sandvik.com
Sales Range: $25-49.9 Million
Metal Valve & Pipe Fitting Distr
N.A.I.C.S.: 423830

Sandvik Endustriyel Mamuller Sanayi ve Ticaret A.S. (1)
Ivedik Organize Sanayii Bolgesi 1354 Cad 1371 Sk No 2, Yenimahalle, Ankara, 34876, Turkiye (100%)
Tel.: (90) 3125878000
Web Site: http://www.sandvik.com
Sales Range: $50-74.9 Million
Emp.: 100
Metal-Cutting Tools & Tooling Systems Distr
N.A.I.C.S.: 423710

Sandvik Espanola S.A. (1)
Poligono Industrial Can Volart C/ Garbi 13 nave 10, Parets'del Valles, 08150, Barcelona, Spain (100%)
Tel.: (34) 935717527
Web Site: www.smt.sandvik.com
Emp.: 300
Mining & Construction Equipment, Metal-Cutting Tools & Heating Materials Distr
N.A.I.C.S.: 423710

Sandvik Finance B.V. (1)
's-Gravelandseweg 401, Schiedam, 3125 BJ, Netherlands
Tel.: (31) 102080208
Web Site: http://www.sandvik.com
Sales Range: $50-74.9 Million
Emp.: 70
Financial Services
N.A.I.C.S.: 523999

Sandvik Holding France SAS (1)

AND PRIVATE COMPANIES — SANDVIK AB

4 Ave Buffon, 45100, Orleans,
France **(100%)**
Tel.: (33) 246840057
Web Site:
  https://www.sandvik.coromant.com
Sales Range: $200-249.9 Million
Holding Company; Mining & Construction Equipment, Metal-Cutting Tools & Heating Materials Distr
N.A.I.C.S.: 551112

Sandvik Holding GmbH (1)
Heerdter Landstrasse 243, 40549, Dusseldorf, Germany
Tel.: (49) 21150270
Web Site: http://www.sandvik.de
Emp.: 300
Holding Company; Mining & Construction Equipment, Metal-Cutting Tools & Heating Materials Distr
N.A.I.C.S.: 551112

Sandvik Holdings Ltd. (1)
Manor Way, Halesowen, B62 8QZ, United Kingdom
Tel.: (44) 1215045000
Investment Management Service
N.A.I.C.S.: 523999

Sandvik Hong Kong Ltd. (1)
Suite 2303 23rd Tower 2 Nina Tower N8 Yeung UK Road, Tsuen Wan, China (Hong Kong) **(100%)**
Tel.: (852) 228112689
Web Site: http://www.sandvik.com
Emp.: 50
Mining & Construction Equipment, Metal-Cutting Tools, Steel & Other Metal Material Products Distr
N.A.I.C.S.: 423710

Sandvik Information Technology AB (1)
Sandbacka Park Spangvagen 10, SE-811 81, Sandviken, Sweden **(100%)**
Tel.: (46) 26260000
Web Site: http://www.sandvik.com
Internal Information Technology Services
N.A.I.C.S.: 541513

Sandvik Intellectual Property AB (1)
Storgatan 2, 811 81, Sandviken, Sweden **(100%)**
Tel.: (46) 26260000
Web Site: http://www.sandvif.com
Intellectual Property Management & Leasing Services
N.A.I.C.S.: 533110
Olof Faxander *(VP)*

Sandvik International Trading (Shanghai) Co., Ltd. (1)
No 4599 Yin Du Road Xin Zhuang Industry Park, Shanghai, 201108, China
Tel.: (86) 4008 200 237
Welding & Furnace Product Distr
N.A.I.C.S.: 423840

Sandvik Italia S.p.A. (1)
Via Antonio Raimondi 13, 20156, Milan, Italy **(100%)**
Tel.: (39) 0294752020
Mining & Construction Equipment, Metal-Cutting Tools, Steel & Other Metal Material Products Distr
N.A.I.C.S.: 423710

Sandvik K.K. (1)
2-2-21 Isogami-dori, Chuo-ku, Kobe, 651-0086, Hyogo, Japan **(100%)**
Tel.: (81) 782655370
Web Site: http://www.sandvik.com
Mining & Construction Equipment, Metal-Cutting Tools & Heating Materials Distr
N.A.I.C.S.: 423710

Sandvik Korea Ltd. (1)
18th Floor HANJIN Shipping Bldg 25 Gukjegeumyung-Ro 2-Gil, Yeongdeungpo-gu, Seoul, 150-949, Korea (South) **(49%)**
Tel.: (82) 23690877
Web Site: http://www.sandvik.com
Sales Range: $10-24.9 Million
Emp.: 9
Mining & Construction Equipment, Metal-Cutting Tools & Heating Materials Distr
N.A.I.C.S.: 423710

Sandvik Ltd. (1)
Manor Way, Halesowen, B62 8QZ, United Kingdom **(100%)**
Tel.: (44) 1215045000
Rev.: $242,500,000
Emp.: 2,000
Holding Company; Mining & Construction Equipment, Metal-Cutting Tools, Steel & Other Metal Material Products Mfr & Distr
N.A.I.C.S.: 551112
Dale Lockley *(Mng Dir)*

Sandvik MGS S.A. (1)
Av Paulista 1000 - Bela Vista, 01310-100, Sao Paulo, Brazil
Tel.: (55) 1136131400
Web Site: http://www.sandvik.com
Sales Range: $50-74.9 Million
Emp.: 100
Mining & Construction Equipment Distr
N.A.I.C.S.: 423810

Sandvik Machining Solutions AB (1)
Asgatan 1, 811 81, Sandviken, Sweden **(100%)**
Tel.: (46) 26260000
Web Site: http://www.sandvik.com
Metal Cutting Tools & Tooling Systems Mfr
N.A.I.C.S.: 333515

Subsidiary (Non-US):

Metrologic Group S.A.S. (2)
6 Chemin du Vieux Chene, Inovallee, 38240, Meylan, France
Tel.: (33) 476043030
3D Inspection Software & Dimension Control Systems Mfr & Distr
N.A.I.C.S.: 513210
Bertrand Gili *(Pres)*

Subsidiary (US):

Metrologic Group Services, Inc. (3)
North American Innovation Ctr 28064 Ctr Oaks Ct, Wixom, MI 48393
Tel.: (248) 504-6200
3D Inspection Software & Dimension Control Systems Developer & Distr
N.A.I.C.S.: 513210

Sandvik Magyarorzagon Kft. (1)
Gyoemroei ut 31, Pf 226, 1475, Budapest, Hungary **(100%)**
Tel.: (36) 014312716
Web Site: http://www.coromant.sadvik.com
Mining & Construction Equipment, Metal-Cutting Tools & Heating Materials Distr
N.A.I.C.S.: 423710

Sandvik Malaysia Sdn. Bhd. (1)
5 Jalan 13 6, Petaling Jaya, 46200, Malaysia **(100%)**
Tel.: (60) 379562136
Sales Range: $50-74.9 Million
Emp.: 30
Mining & Construction Equipment, Metal-Cutting Tools & Heating Materials Distr
N.A.I.C.S.: 423710

Sandvik Maroc SARL (1)
Park Plaza 1 Immobile F-2 Office No 4, 28806, Mohammedia, Morocco **(94%)**
Tel.: (212) 523325358
Web Site: http://www.smt.sandvik.com
Sales Range: $50-74.9 Million
Emp.: 4
Mining & Construction Equipment, Metal-Cutting Tools & Heating Materials Distr
N.A.I.C.S.: 423710

Sandvik Mexicana S.A. de C.V. (1)
Gustavo Baz No 352 La Loma, Tlalnepantla, 54060, Mexico
Tel.: (52) 5557293900
Sales Range: $400-449.9 Million
Emp.: 2,000
Steel Products Mfr
N.A.I.C.S.: 331110

Sandvik Middle East FZE (1)
Office 2702 One Lake Plaza Bldg Cluster T Jumeirah Lake Tower, PO Box 261216, Dubai, United Arab Emirates
Tel.: (971) 43647215
Billet Distr
N.A.I.C.S.: 423510

Sandvik Mining & Construction AB (1)
Hamngatan 12, SE-811 81, Sandviken, Sweden **(100%)**
Tel.: (46) 26262000
Sales Range: $1-4.9 Billion
Emp.: 14,429
Holding Company; Mining & Heavy Construction Equipment Mfr
N.A.I.C.S.: 551112

Subsidiary (US):

Allied Construction Products, LLC (2)
3900 Kelley Ave, Cleveland, OH 44114-4536
Tel.: (216) 431-2600
Web Site: http://www.alliedcp.com
Sales Range: $10-24.9 Million
Emp.: 50
Construction Machinery & Equipment Mfr
N.A.I.C.S.: 333120
Kathy Toth *(CFO)*

Subsidiary (Non-US):

LLC Sandvik Mining and Construction Region CIS (2)
Zavodskaya str 1B, Stari Oskol, 309508, Belgorod, Russia
Tel.: (7) 4725233010
Web Site: http://www.sandvik.com
Mining & Construction Machinery Mfr & Distr
N.A.I.C.S.: 333131

P.T. Sandvik Mining and Construction Indonesia (2)
Jalan Proklamasi RT 32 No 38, Manggar, Balikpapan, 76117, Kalimantan Timur, Indonesia
Tel.: (62) 542763066
Web Site: http://www.sandvik.com
Construction & Mining Equipment Distr
N.A.I.C.S.: 423810

Branch (Non-US):

Sandvik Espanola S.A., Mining & Construction (2)
Calle Tapiceros 9, San Fernando de Henares, 28830, Madrid, Spain
Tel.: (34) 916605232
Web Site:
  http://www.miningandconstruction.com
Emp.: 50
Mining & Construction Equipment Distr
N.A.I.C.S.: 423810
Juan Sanz *(Mng Dir)*

Subsidiary (Non-US):

Sandvik Mining & Construction (China) Co., Ltd. (2)
B2 No 10 Jiuxianqiao Road, Chaoyang District, Beijing, 100015, China **(100%)**
Tel.: (86) 1065399888
Web Site:
  http://www.miningandconstruction.com
Mining & Construction Equipment Mfr & Distr
N.A.I.C.S.: 423810

Branch (Non-US):

Sandvik Mining & Construction Hong Kong (3)
Suite 2303 23/F Tower 2 Nina Tower, No 8 Yeung Uk Road, Tsuen Wan, China (Hong Kong)
Tel.: (852) 28112689
Sales Range: $1-9.9 Million
Emp.: 40
Mining & Construction Equipment Distr
N.A.I.C.S.: 423810
Chan Hon To *(Mng Dir)*

Subsidiary (Domestic):

Sandvik Mining & Construction Trading (Shanghai) Co., Ltd. (3)
3F Tower-A Oriento Guoxin Plaza No 388 North Fuquan Road, Changning District, Shanghai, 200072, China **(100%)**
Tel.: (86) 2139960500
Sales Range: $75-99.9 Million
Emp.: 200
Mining & Construction Equipment International Trade Distr
N.A.I.C.S.: 425120

Subsidiary (Non-US):

Sandvik Mining & Construction Australia Pty. Ltd. (2)
60-62 Qantas Drive, Brisbane Airport, Brisbane, 4007, QLD, Australia **(100%)**
Tel.: (61) 736377400
Web Site:
  http://www.sandvikminingconstruction.com
Sales Range: $200-249.9 Million
Emp.: 60
Holding Company; Mining & Construction Equipment Distr
N.A.I.C.S.: 551112
Stewart Evans *(CEO)*

Subsidiary (Domestic):

Sandvik Mining & Construction Perth Pty. Ltd. (3)
285 Collier Road, Bayswater, 6053, WA, Australia **(100%)**
Tel.: (61) 893478500
Web Site: http://www.sandvik.com
Sales Range: $50-74.9 Million
Emp.: 200
Mining & Construction Equipment Distr
N.A.I.C.S.: 423810
Chris Mitchell *(Mgr-Product Line)*

Sandvik Mining and Construction Adelaide Pty. Ltd. (3)
136 Daws Road, Melrose Park, Adelaide, 5039, SA, Australia
Tel.: (61) 8 8276 7655
Web Site:
  http://www.miningandconstruction.com
Emp.: 34
Mining & Construction Machinery Installation Services & Mfr
N.A.I.C.S.: 238290
Rowan Melrose *(Gen Mgr)*

Sandvik Mining and Construction Tomago Pty. Ltd. (3)
13 Old Punt Rd, Tomago, 2322, NSW, Australia
Tel.: (61) 2 4985 2625
Mining & Construction Machinery Installation Services & Mfr
N.A.I.C.S.: 238290

Subsidiary (Non-US):

Sandvik Mining & Construction CIS LLC (2)
4-th Dobrininsky pereulok 8 office D08, 119049, Moscow, Russia **(100%)**
Tel.: (7) 4959807556
Web Site:
  http://www.miningandconstruction.com
Sales Range: $25-49.9 Million
Emp.: 80
Mining & Construction Equipment Distr
N.A.I.C.S.: 423810
Andrey Shemyakin *(Dir Gen)*

Subsidiary (Non-US):

Sandvik Mining & Construction Kazakhstan Ltd. (3)
Timiryazeva Str 42 Business Center block C 7 floor, 50057, Almaty, Kazakhstan **(100%)**
Tel.: (7) 7272744439
Web Site:
  http://www.miningandconstruction.com
Sales Range: $25-49.9 Million
Emp.: 42
Mining & Construction Equipment Distr
N.A.I.C.S.: 423810

Subsidiary (Non-US):

Sandvik Mining & Construction Central Europe GmbH (2)
Gladbecker Strasse 427, 45329, Essen, Germany
Tel.: (49) 2011785300
Web Site:
  http://www.miningandconstruction.com
Sales Range: $150-199.9 Million
Emp.: 350
Mining & Construction Equipment Mfr & Distr
N.A.I.C.S.: 423810

Subsidiary (Domestic):

Sandvik Mining & Construction Supply GmbH (3)
Gurtecstrasse 3, Schoppenstedt, 38170, Germany **(100%)**

SANDVIK AB

Sandvik AB—(Continued)
Tel.: (49) 533293090
Sales Range: $50-74.9 Million
Emp.: 135
Mining & Construction Conveyor Equipment Mfr
N.A.I.C.S.: 333922
Marcus Badent (Mng Dir)

Subsidiary (Non-US):

Sandvik Mining & Construction Chile S.A. (2)
Av Presidente Eduardo Frei Montalva 9990, Quilicura, Santiago, Chile **(100%)**
Tel.: (56) 26760200
Web Site: http://www.miningandconstruction.com
Sales Range: $300-349.9 Million
Emp.: 600
Mining & Construction Equipment Mfr & Distr
N.A.I.C.S.: 423810

Subsidiary (Non-US):

Sandvik Mining & Construction Argentina S.A. (3)
Rincon 3198, 1754, San Justo, Buenos Aires, Argentina **(100%)**
Tel.: (54) 1167776777
Sales Range: $50-74.9 Million
Emp.: 180
Mining & Construction Equipment Distr
N.A.I.C.S.: 423810

Subsidiary (Non-US):

Sandvik Mining & Construction France S.A.S. (2)
19 Avenue de Lattre-de-Tassigny, BP 46, Meyzieu, Cedex, France **(100%)**
Tel.: (33) 472452217
Web Site: https://www.miningandconstruction.com
Sales Range: $75-99.9 Million
Emp.: 200
Mining & Construction Equipment Mfr & Distr
N.A.I.C.S.: 423810
Farid Hadjali (Mgr-Fin)

Subsidiary (Domestic):

Sandvik Mining & Construction Lyon S.A.S. (3)
19 Avenue de Lattre-de-Tassigny, 69881, Meyzieu, France **(100%)**
Tel.: (33) 472452200
Mining & Construction Equipment Mfr
N.A.I.C.S.: 333120

Sandvik Mining and Construction Chauny S.A.S. (3)
20 Rue Louis Blanc, Chauny, 02300, France
Tel.: (33) 323521461
Web Site: http://www.sandvik.com
Emp.: 15
Mining & Construction Equipment Installation Services
N.A.I.C.S.: 238290
Sarah Bauguin (Mgr-Factory)

Subsidiary (Non-US):

Sandvik Mining & Construction Limited (2)
Hearthcote Road, Swadlincote, DE11 9DU, Derbyshire, United Kingdom **(100%)**
Tel.: (44) 1283212121
Web Site: http://www.miningandconstruction.com
Sales Range: $25-49.9 Million
Emp.: 500
Assembler of Underground Mining Machinery
N.A.I.C.S.: 333131

Subsidiary (Domestic):

Sandvik Mining & Construction Mobile Crushers & Screens Limited (3)
Hearthcote Rd, Swadlincote, DE11 9DU, Derbyshire, United Kingdom **(100%)**
Tel.: (44) 1283212121
Web Site: http://www.miningandconstruction.com
Sales Range: $100-124.9 Million
Emp.: 400
Mining Machinery & Equipment Mfr
N.A.I.C.S.: 333131

Branch (Non-US):

Sandvik Mining & Construction Middle East (2)
1 Lake Plaza Tower Cluster T, 261216, Dubai, United Arab Emirates
Tel.: (971) 43647200
Sales Range: $25-49.9 Million
Emp.: 10
Mining & Construction Equipment Distr
N.A.I.C.S.: 423810

Subsidiary (Non-US):

Sandvik Mining & Construction Oy (2)
Pihtisulunkatu 9, Tampere, 33310, Finland **(100%)**
Tel.: (358) 20544121
Sales Range: $700-749.9 Million
Emp.: 1,500
Engineeering Services
N.A.I.C.S.: 333120

Subsidiary (Domestic):

Sandvik Mining & Construction Finland Oy (3)
Ayritie 8B, PO Box 52, Vantaa, 1510, Finland **(100%)**
Tel.: (358) 20544121
Mining & Construction Equipment Distr
N.A.I.C.S.: 423810

Sandvik Mining & Construction Hollola Oy (3)
Keskikankaantie 19, FI-15860, Hollola, Finland **(100%)**
Tel.: (358) 20544181
Web Site: http://www.sandvik.com
Sales Range: $25-49.9 Million
Emp.: 80
Mining & Construction Equipment Distr
N.A.I.C.S.: 423810
Kari Turkia (Mgr-Sls)

Plant (Domestic):

Sandvik Mining & Construction Oy - Tampere Plant (3)
Pihtisulunkatu 9, 33310, Tampere, Finland
Tel.: (358) 205 44 121
Sales Range: $25-49.9 Million
Emp.: 40
Mining & Construction Equipment Mfr
N.A.I.C.S.: 333131

Unit (Domestic):

Sandvik Mining & Construction Oy - Turku (3)
Vahdontie 19, PO Box 434, Turku, 20360, Finland
Tel.: (358) 20544131
Sales Range: $150-199.9 Million
Emp.: 300
Mining & Construction Equipment Mfr & Distr
N.A.I.C.S.: 428810

Subsidiary (Non-US):

Sandvik Mining & Construction R.S.A. (Pty) Ltd. (2)
64 Jet Park Road, Jet Industrial Sites, Boksburg, 1460, South Africa **(100%)**
Tel.: (27) 0115709602
Web Site: http://www.sandvik.com
Sales Range: $200-249.9 Million
Emp.: 2,300
Mining & Construction Equipment Mfr & Distr
N.A.I.C.S.: 423810
Charles Deacon (VP-Mktg-Africa)

Subsidiary (Non-US):

Sandvik Mining & Construction Zambia Ltd. (3)
Plot 5030 Mutentemuko Road, PO Box 20314, Industrial Area, Kitwe, 21149, Zambia **(100%)**
Tel.: (260) 212241000
Web Site: http://www.miningandconstruction.com
Sales Range: $125-149.9 Million
Emp.: 450
Mining & Construction Equipment Distr
N.A.I.C.S.: 423810

Sandvik Mining & Construction Zimbabwe (Pty) Ltd. (3)
Cnr Harare Drive & Bignell Road, PO Box 5096, New Ardbennie, Harare, 21149, Zimbabwe **(100%)**
Tel.: (263) 4661943
Web Site: http://www.miningandconstruction.com
Sales Range: $10-24.9 Million
Emp.: 142
Mining & Construction Equipment Distr
N.A.I.C.S.: 423810

Sandvik Mining and Construction Algerie SpA (3)
74 Lotissement CITMIL, Algiers, 16320, Algeria
Tel.: (213) 20 34 80 19
Mining & Construction Equipment Installation Services
N.A.I.C.S.: 238290

Sandvik Mining and Construction DRC S.P.R.L. (3)
3108 Av Polytechnique Q/Craa, Lubumbashi, Congo, Democratic Republic of
Tel.: (243) 991004042
Web Site: http://www.sandvik.com
Emp.: 21
Construction Engineering Services
N.A.I.C.S.: 541330
Pierre Voue (Gen Mgr)

Sandvik Mining and Construction Mali SARL (3)
Villa No D36 Cite du Niger 2, BPE 3898, 20 21 12 92, Bamako, Mali
Tel.: (223) 20211292
Engineeering Services
N.A.I.C.S.: 423810

Sandvik Mining and Construction Nigeria Ltd. (3)
The Golden Gate Plot 1994 Mobassa Street Wuse Zone 5, Abuja, Nigeria
Tel.: (234) 7098203779
Sales Range: $25-49.9 Million
Emp.: 4
Mining & Construction Equipment Distr
N.A.I.C.S.: 423810

Subsidiary (Domestic):

Sandvik Mining & Construction Sverige AB (2)
Hamngatan 12, SE-811 81, Sandviken, Sweden **(100%)**
Tel.: (46) 26262000
Web Site: http://www.sandvik.com
Sales Range: $300-349.9 Million
Emp.: 550
Mining & Construction Equipment Mfr & Distr
N.A.I.C.S.: 423810

Unit (Domestic):

AB Sandvik Construction Segment (3)
Gyllerogatan 1, Svedala, 233 81, Sweden
Tel.: (46) 40 409000
Mining & Construction Equipment Services
N.A.I.C.S.: 532412

Subsidiary (Domestic):

Sandvik Mining & Construction Haparanda AB (3)
Tjadervagen 2, PO Box 812, SE-953 28, Haparanda, Sweden **(100%)**
Tel.: (46) 92229800
Web Site: http://www.miningandconstruction.com
Sales Range: $25-49.9 Million
Emp.: 50
Mining & Construction Materials Handling Equipment Mfr & Distr
N.A.I.C.S.: 333922

Sandvik Mining and Construction Koping AB (3)
Hantverkaregatan 14, Koping, 731 29, Sweden
Tel.: (46) 221 275 00

Web Site: http://www.sandvik.com
Metal Cutting Tool & Equipment Mfr & Distr
N.A.I.C.S.: 333515

Subsidiary (Domestic):

Sandvik Mining & Construction Tools AB (2)
Hamngatan 12, Sandviken, 811 81, Sweden
Tel.: (46) 26262000
Emp.: 8,000
Mining & Construction Machinery Installation Services & Mfr
N.A.I.C.S.: 238290
Ann-Sofie Gustavsson (Dir-Talent & Dev)

Subsidiary (Non-US):

Sandvik Mining & Construction de Mexico S.A. de C.V. (2)
Benjamin Franklin Lote 8 Manzana 1 Parque Industrial Aeropuerto, Col Santa Maria Tequepexpan, Tlajomulco de Zuniga, 45640, Jalisco, Mexico **(100%)**
Tel.: (52) 3336010362
Web Site: http://www.miningandconstruction.com
Sales Range: Less than $1 Million
Emp.: 62
Wire & Welding Products Mfr
N.A.I.C.S.: 332618

Sandvik Mining and Construction (2)
Ivedik Organize Sanayii Bolgesi, Ankara, 06370, Yeni Mahalle, Turkiye
Tel.: (90) 312 587 8000
Sales Range: $25-49.9 Million
Emp.: 40
Mining & Construction Machinery Mfr & Distr
N.A.I.C.S.: 333131

Sandvik Mining and Construction (Malaysia) Sdn. Bhd (2)
No 5 Jalan Utarid U5/13 Seksyen U5 Mah Sing Integrated Park, Shah Alam, 40150, Malaysia
Tel.: (60) 378423700
Mining & Construction Equipment Mfr & Whslr
N.A.I.C.S.: 333131
Cameron Westwood (VP)

Sandvik Mining and Construction Central Europe GmbH (2)
Vordernbergerstrasse 12, 8740, Leoben, Austria
Tel.: (43) 3577755799
Web Site: http://www.sandvik.com
Construction & Mining Equipment Distr
N.A.I.C.S.: 423810
Klaus Sapetschnig (Mng Dir)

Sandvik Mining and Construction Crushing Technology GmbH (2)
Kolner Str 94, Bergneustadt, 51702, Germany
Tel.: (49) 22 61 40 94 0
Construction & Mining Equipment Whslr
N.A.I.C.S.: 423810

Sandvik Mining and Construction GmbH (2)
Alpinestrasse 1, Zeltweg, 8740, Austria
Tel.: (43) 35777550
Web Site: http://www.sandvikmining.com
Emp.: 400
Mining & Construction Equipment Mfr
N.A.I.C.S.: 333131
Gerhard Hubmann (Gen Mgr)

Subsidiary (Domestic):

Sandvik Mining and Construction Materials Handling GmbH & Co. KG (3)
Vordernbergerstrasse 12, Leoben, 8700, Austria
Tel.: (43) 384220770
Mining & Construction Equipment Installation Services
N.A.I.C.S.: 238290

Subsidiary (Non-US):

Sandvik Mining and Construction Japan K.K. (2)
2-15-16 Shinyokohama, Kohoku, Yokohama, 222-0033, Japan
Tel.: (81) 45 4780660

Web Site:
http://www.miningandconstruction.com
Construction & Mining Equipment Mfr & Whslr
N.A.I.C.S.: 333131

Sandvik Mining and Construction Logistics Ltd. (2)
Johnstown Road, Rathdowney, Ireland
Tel.: (353) 50546613
Logistics Consulting Servies
N.A.I.C.S.: 541614

Sandvik Mining and Construction S.E. Asia Pte. Ltd. (2)
50 ALPS Avenue 04-00 Sandvik Building, Singapore, 498782, Singapore
Tel.: (65) 64773788
Mining & Construction Equipment Installation Services
N.A.I.C.S.: 238290

Sandvik Mining and Construction do Brasil S.A. (2)
Rodovia Anel Rodoviario 1000 - Km 01, 30390-085, Belo Horizonte, Minas Gerais, Brazil
Tel.: (55) 31 3045 3045
Sales Range: $50-74.9 Million
Emp.: 250
Mining & Construction Equipment Distr
N.A.I.C.S.: 423810

Sandvik Tamrock A/S (2)
Sanitetsveien 1, Skjetten, 2026, Norway (100%)
Tel.: (47) 63848100
Sales Range: $25-49.9 Million
Emp.: 50
Mining & Construction Equipment Distr
N.A.I.C.S.: 423810
Knut Pedersen *(Product Mgr-Drills)*

Sandvik Mining and Construction (Luoyang) Co., Ltd. (1)
No 3 Jinxin Road, Luoyang High Tech Industry Development Zone, Luoyang, 471000, Henan, China
Tel.: (86) 37960633200
Component Replace & Repair Services
N.A.I.C.S.: 811210

Sandvik Mining and Construction B.V. (1)
Barbara Strozzilaan 382, 1083 HN, Amsterdam, Netherlands
Tel.: (31) 207091400
Mining Equipment Mfr & Distr
N.A.I.C.S.: 333131

Sandvik Mining and Rock Technology India Private Limited (1)
No 10 Unit No 202 2nd Floor Brigade South Parade M G Road, Bengaluru, 560 001, Karnataka, India
Tel.: (91) 8046245800
Underground Drill Rig Mfr
N.A.I.C.S.: 333120

Sandvik Mining and Rock Technology India Private Ltd. (1)
No 10 Unit No 202 2nd Floor Brigade South Parade M G Road, Bengaluru, 560 001, Karnataka, India
Tel.: (91) 8046245800
Component Replace & Repair Services
N.A.I.C.S.: 811210

Sandvik Mining and Rock Technology do Brasil Ltda. (1)
Avenida Do Contorno 5919 8th Floor, Belo Horizonte, 30110-927, Brazil
Tel.: (55) 3135557300
Component Replace & Repair Services
N.A.I.C.S.: 811210

Sandvik Mongolia LLC. (1)
Monfresh Building Chinggis Avenue 3rd Khoroo Khan-Uul District, Ulaanbaatar, 14201, Mongolia
Tel.: (976) 70121930
Metal Cutting Tool & Equipment Mfr
N.A.I.C.S.: 333515

Sandvik New Zealand Ltd. (1)
52 Preston Road, PO Box 51-154, South Island, 7805, Greymouth, New Zealand (100%)
Tel.: (64) 37680088
Web Site: http://www.sandvik.com

Sales Range: $50-74.9 Million
Emp.: 100
Mining & Construction Equipment, Metal-Cutting Tools & Heating Materials Distr
N.A.I.C.S.: 423710

Sandvik Nora AB (1)
Industrivagen 1, 713 91, Nora, Sweden
Tel.: (46) 587 845 00
Web Site: http://www.hagby.se
Diamond Tool & Core Drill Accessory Mfr
N.A.I.C.S.: 333515
Inga Holmstroem *(Mng Dir)*

Sandvik Norge A/S (1)
Olav Brunborgsvei 6, Billingstad, N 1377, Oslo, Norway (100%)
Tel.: (47) 67175600
Web Site: http://www.coromant.sandvik.com
Sales Range: $10-24.9 Million
Emp.: 100
Mining & Construction Equipment, Metal-Cutting Tools & Heating Materials Distr
N.A.I.C.S.: 423710

Sandvik P&P GmbH (1)
Dammstr 27-29, 33824, Werther, Germany
Tel.: (49) 5203 91 09 0
Web Site: http://www.sandvik.com
Precision Tube Distr
N.A.I.C.S.: 423130

Sandvik Philippines, Inc. (1)
Km 20 East Service Road South Super Highway, Muntinlupa, 1770, Philippines (100%)
Tel.: (63) 28076372
Web Site:
http://www.sandvikcoromant.com.ph
Sales Range: $1-9.9 Million
Emp.: 8
Mining & Construction Equipment, Metal-Cutting Tools & Heating Materials Distr
N.A.I.C.S.: 423710

Sandvik Polska Sp. z o.o. (1)
Ul Pukowca 7, 40-847, Katowice, Poland (100%)
Tel.: (48) 222922347
Web Site: https://www.sandvik.com
Sales Range: $50-74.9 Million
Mining & Construction Equipment, Metal-Cutting Tools & Heating Materials Distr
N.A.I.C.S.: 423710

Plant (Domestic):

Sandvik Polska Sp. z o.o. - Katowice Production Plant (2)
Al Wilanowska 372, 02-655, Warsaw, Poland
Tel.: (48) 605550197
Web Site: http://www.sandvik.com
Sales Range: $25-49.9 Million
Indexable Inserts & Cutting Tools Mfr
N.A.I.C.S.: 333515

Sandvik Powder Solutions AB (1)
Box 54, 735 21, Surahammar, Sweden
Tel.: (46) 22022100
Construction Equipment Distr
N.A.I.C.S.: 423610

Sandvik Powdermet AB (1)
Kontorsvagen 1, 735 21, Surahammar, Sweden
Tel.: (46) 22022100
Web Site: http://www.sandvik.com
Emp.: 60
Cutting Tool Distr
N.A.I.C.S.: 423830
Magnus Nystron *(Gen Mgr)*

Sandvik RC Tools Australia Pty. Ltd. (1)
47-51 Vulcan Rd, Canning Vale, 6155, WA, Australia
Tel.: (61) 8 9455 4433
Web Site: http://www.sandvik.com
Sales Range: $25-49.9 Million
Emp.: 100
Industrial Tools Mfr
N.A.I.C.S.: 333517
Martin Jansson *(Mgr-Production Unit)*

Sandvik SMC Breakers Lahti (1)
Taivalkatu 8, Lahti, 15101, Finland
Tel.: (358) 205 44 161
Web Site: http://www.sandvik.com
Sales Range: $75-99.9 Million
Emp.: 160
Mining & Construction Equipment Distr

N.A.I.C.S.: 423810
Kaj Kouskela *(VP)*

Sandvik SRP AB (1)
Gyllerogatan 1, Svedala, 233 81, Sweden
Tel.: (46) 40409000
Construction & Mining Equipment Distr
N.A.I.C.S.: 423810

Sandvik Saxon Ltd. (1)
Great Central Way, CV21 3XH, Rugby, Warwickshire, United Kingdom - England
Tel.: (44) 1788 55 71 00
Die Cutting Tool Mfr
N.A.I.C.S.: 333514

Sandvik Slovakia s.r.o. (1)
Karadzicova 8, 811 08, Bratislava, Slovakia (100%)
Tel.: (421) 233006510
Sales Range: $50-74.9 Million
Mining & Construction Equipment, Metal-Cutting Tools & Heating Materials Distr
N.A.I.C.S.: 423710

Sandvik South East Asia Pte. Ltd. (1)
50 ALPS Avenue 04-00 Sandvik Building, Singapore, 498782, Singapore (100%)
Tel.: (65) 64773786
Sales Range: $100-124.9 Million
Holding Company; Mining & Construction Equipment, Metal-Cutting Tools & Heating Materials Distr
N.A.I.C.S.: 551112

Sandvik Srbija d.o.o. (1)
Bulevar Mihaila Pupina 10B/II Novi Beograd, Belgrade, 11070, Serbia
Tel.: (381) 11.311 0713
Web Site: http://www.sandvik.com
Mining & Construction Equipment Mfr & Distr
N.A.I.C.S.: 333131

Sandvik Srl (1)
Bulevardul Aviatorilor nr 52 et 1 apt 5 sector 1, 11864, Bucharest, Romania
Tel.: (40) 316309679
Web Site: http://www.smt.sandvik.com
Mining & Construction Equipment, Metal-Cutting Tools & Heating Materials Distr
N.A.I.C.S.: 423710

Sandvik SuhJun Ltd. (1)
Rm 505 Dookkeobi Building 310 Teheran-ro, Gangnam-gu, Seoul, 06211, Korea (South)
Tel.: (82) 25576030
Web Site: http://www.sandvik.com
Machine Tools Mfr
N.A.I.C.S.: 333517

Sandvik Systems Development AB (1)
Spangvagen 10, 811 32, Sandviken, Sweden
Tel.: (46) 2626 00 00
Web Site: http://www.sandvik.com
Software Development Services
N.A.I.C.S.: 541511
Joha Malmgren *(Gen Mgr)*

Sandvik Taiwan Ltd. (1)
Room # 502 #6 Lane 7 Wucyuan Road, Taipei, 248, Taiwan (100%)
Tel.: (886) 222993427
Web Site: http://www.sandvik.com
Sales Range: $50-74.9 Million
Emp.: 35
Mining & Construction Equipment, Metal-Cutting Tools & Heating Materials Distr
N.A.I.C.S.: 423710

Sandvik Thailand Ltd. (1)
4th Floor Chamnan Phenjati Business Center Bldg 65/48, Huay-Kwang, 10310, Bangkok, Thailand (100%)
Tel.: (66) 26143155
Web Site: http://www.coromant.sandvik.com
Sales Range: $50-74.9 Million
Mining & Construction Equipment, Metal-Cutting Tools & Heating Materials Distr
N.A.I.C.S.: 423710

Sandvik Tooling AB (1)
Mossvagen 10, SE-811 81, Sandviken, Sweden (100%)
Tel.: (46) 26266000
Web Site: http://www.sandvik.com

Sales Range: $1-4.9 Billion
Emp.: 15,296
Holding Company; Metal-Cutting Tools & Tooling Accessories Mfr
N.A.I.C.S.: 551112
Anders Thelin *(Pres)*

Subsidiary (Domestic):

AB Sandvik Coromant (2)
Mossvagen 10, 811 81, Sandviken, Sweden
Tel.: (46) 26266000
Web Site: http://www.coromant.sandvik.com
Sales Range: $1-4.9 Billion
Holding Company; Turning, Milling & Drilling Tool Accessories Mfr & Distr
N.A.I.C.S.: 551112

Unit (Non-US):

Sandvik Coromant (3)
Dolgobrodskaya 24 of 42, Minsk, Belarus
Tel.: (375) 17 230 67 09
Web Site: http://www.sandvik.coromant.com
Industrial Cutting Tool Mfr
N.A.I.C.S.: 333515

Sandvik Coromant (3)
Ayritie 8b Vantaa, Helsinki, 01510, Finland
Tel.: (358) 205 44 5900
Web Site: http://www.coromant.sandvik.com
Sales Range: $25-49.9 Million
Emp.: 20
Industrial Cutting Tool Mfr
N.A.I.C.S.: 333515
Satto Salokanto *(Gen Mgr)*

Sandvik Coromant (3)
Polkovaya Street 1, Moscow, 127018, Russia
Tel.: (7) 495 916 71 91
Web Site: http://www.sandvik.coromant.com
Sales Range: $25-49.9 Million
Emp.: 100
Metalworking Machines Mfr
N.A.I.C.S.: 333515
Michel Obolensky *(Gen Mgr)*

Sandvik Coromant (3)
Av Presidente Eduardo Frei Montalva N 9990, Panamericana Norte KM 15 1/2 Quilicura, Santiago, 14510, Chile
Tel.: (56) 26760200
Web Site: http://www.sandvik.com
Sales Range: $100-124.9 Million
Emp.: 300
Machine Tools Mfr
N.A.I.C.S.: 333517

Sandvik Coromant (3)
50 ALPS Ave 04-00 Sandvik Building, Singapore, 498782, Singapore
Tel.: (65) 6477 3786
Web Site: http://www.sandvik.coromant.com
Sales Range: $25-49.9 Million
Metal Cutting Tool Maintenance Services
N.A.I.C.S.: 811310

Sandvik Coromant (3)
Domaniewska 39A, Warsaw, 02-672, Poland
Tel.: (48) 22 647 38 80
Web Site: http://www.coromant.sandvik.com
Sales Range: $25-49.9 Million
Emp.: 30
Cutting Tool Distr
N.A.I.C.S.: 423830

Sandvik Coromant - Brazil (3)
Av das Nacoes Unidas 21 732, Sao Paulo, CEP 04795 914, SP, Brazil
Tel.: (55) 1156965425
Web Site: http://www.sandvik.coromant.com
Sales Range: $250-299.9 Million
Emp.: 600
Turning, Milling & Drilling Tool Accessories Distr
N.A.I.C.S.: 423710

Sandvik Coromant - France (3)
4 Ave Buffon, 45100, Orleans, France
Tel.: (33) 246840057
Web Site: http://www.coromant.sandvik.com
Sales Range: $50-74.9 Million
Emp.: 200
Turning, Milling & Drilling Tool Accessories Mfr & Distr
N.A.I.C.S.: 333515
Josse Coudre *(Mng Dir)*

Sandvik Coromant - Germany (3)

SANDVIK AB

INTERNATIONAL PUBLIC

Sandvik AB—(Continued)
Heerdter Landstrasse 243, 40549, Dusseldorf, Germany
Tel.: (49) 21150270
Web Site: http://www.sandvik.coromant.com
Sales Range: $25-49.9 Million
Emp.: 80
Turning, Milling & Drilling Tool Accessories Distr
N.A.I.C.S.: 423710

Sandvik Coromant - Italy (3)
Via Veresina 184, 20156, Milan, Italy
Tel.: (39) 02307051
Web Site: http://www.coromant.sandvik.com
Sales Range: $50-74.9 Million
Emp.: 150
Turning, Milling & Drilling Tool Accessories Mfr & Distr
N.A.I.C.S.: 333515
Josse Coudre *(Gen Mgr-Sls-Central Europe)*

Sandvik Coromant - UK (3)
Manor Way, Halesowen, B62 8QZ, W Midlands, United Kingdom
Tel.: (44) 1213680305
Web Site: http://www.coromant.sandvik.com
Turning, Milling & Drilling Tool Accessories Mfr & Distr
N.A.I.C.S.: 333515

Unit (US):

Sandvik Coromant - US (3)
1702 Nevins Rd, Fair Lawn, NJ 07410-2803
Tel.: (201) 794-5000
Web Site: http://www.coromant.sandvik.com
Turning, Milling & Drilling Tool Accessories Distr
N.A.I.C.S.: 423710

Unit (Non-US):

Sandvik Coromant A/S
Abildager 26, 2605, Brondby, Denmark
Tel.: (45) 43 46 51 51
Web Site: http://www.coromant.sandvik.com
Cutting Tool Mfr
N.A.I.C.S.: 333515

Sandvik Coromant Benelux BV (3)
Fountain Plaza Belgicastraat 5 Bus 5/6, 1930, Zaventem, Belgium
Tel.: (32) 27029800
Web Site: http://www.coromant.sandvik.com
Cutting Tool Mfr
N.A.I.C.S.: 333515

Sandvik Coromant Pty Ltd (3)
5 Fowler Road, Dandenong, 3175, VIC, Australia
Tel.: (61) 3 9238 7100
Web Site: http://www.sandvik.coromant.com
Sales Range: $25-49.9 Million
Emp.: 30
Metal Cutting Tool Mfr
N.A.I.C.S.: 333517
Patrick Ryan *(Gen Mgr)*

Subsidiary (Domestic):

Sandvik Coromant Sverige AB (3)
Torsnastorget 17, Kista, 164 40, Sweden
Tel.: (46) 87930500
Web Site: http://www.sandvik.coromant.com
Turning, Milling & Drilling Tool Accessories Mfr & Distr
N.A.I.C.S.: 333515

Subsidiary (US):

Dura-Mill Inc. (4)
16 Old Stonebreak Rd, Malta, NY 12020
Tel.: (518) 899-2255
Tool Mfr
N.A.I.C.S.: 333515

Subsidiary (Non-US):

Dormer Tools Ltd. (2)
4 Lindrick Way, Waverley, Chesterfield, S43 4XE, United Kingdom (100%)
Tel.: (44) 1142933800
Web Site: http://www.dormertools.com
Sales Range: $25-49.9 Million
Emp.: 60
Solid Carbide & High-Speed Steel Drill Bits & Other Metal-Cutting Tools Mfr & Distr
N.A.I.C.S.: 333515

John O'Donoghue *(Mng Dir)*

Unit (Non-US):

Dormer Tools - France (3)
4 Avenue Buffon, BP 6209, Orleans, 45100, France
Tel.: (33) 238414015
Web Site: http://www.dormertools.com
Sales Range: $25-49.9 Million
Emp.: 9
Metal-Cutting Drill Bits Whslr
N.A.I.C.S.: 423710
Benoit Thouret *(Gen Mgr)*

Dormer Tools - Italy (3)
via Varesina 184, IT-20156, Milan, Italy
Tel.: (39) 02380451
Web Site: http://www.dormertools.com
Solid Carbide & High-Speed Steel Drill Bits & Other Metal-Cutting Tools Mfr & Distr
N.A.I.C.S.: 333515
Dafne Parigi *(Product Mgr)*

Subsidiary (Non-US):

Dormer Tools AB (3)
Linjegatan 11, Halmstad, 302 50, Sweden (100%)
Tel.: (46) 35165200
Web Site: http://www.dormer.com
Sales Range: $25-49.9 Million
Solid Carbide & High-Speed Steel Drill Bits & Other Metal-Cutting Tools Mfr & Distr
N.A.I.C.S.: 333515
Erling Gunnesson *(Mng Dir)*

Subsidiary (Non-US):

Miranda Tools Pvt. Ltd. (4)
903 / 904 GIDC Industrial Estate, Ankleshwar, 393 002, Gujarat, India
Tel.: (91) 264 625 2368
Web Site: https://www.mirandatools.in
Machine Tools Mfr
N.A.I.C.S.: 333517
Nandan Piramal *(Vice Chm)*

Subsidiary (Non-US):

Dormer Tools S.A. (3)
Av Joao Paulo Da Silva 258, Sao Paulo, 04777-020, SP, Brazil (100%)
Tel.: (55) 1156603000
Web Site: http://www.sandvik.com
Sales Range: $125-149.9 Million
N.A.I.C.S.: 332618
Luiz Manetti *(Mng Dir)*

Precision Dormer Canada (3)
2550 Meadowvale Blvd Unit 3, Mississauga, L5N 8C2, ON, Canada
Tel.: (905) 542-3000
Web Site: http://www.dormerpramet.com
Sales Range: $25-49.9 Million
Emp.: 50
Cutting Tool Distr
N.A.I.C.S.: 423710

Sandvik Tooling Deutschland GmbH (3)
Heerdter Landstrasse 243, 40549, Dusseldorf, Germany (100%)
Tel.: (49) 21150270
Web Site: http://www.dormertools.com
Sales Range: $125-149.9 Million
Cutting Tool Distr
N.A.I.C.S.: 423710

Subsidiary (Non-US):

Sandvik Tooling France S.A.S. (2)
315 Route Thuet, 74130, Bonneville, France
Tel.: (33) 450974798
Steel Product Distr
N.A.I.C.S.: 423510

Walter AG (2)
Derendinger Strasse 53, 72072, Tubingen, Germany (100%)
Tel.: (49) 7 071 7010
Web Site: https://www.walter-tools.com
Emp.: 3,500
Holding Company; Machining Metal Tools Developer, Mfr & Distr
N.A.I.C.S.: 551112
Rudiger Mannherz *(VP-Fin & IT)*

Subsidiary (US):

Balax, Inc. (3)
W305N7697 County Rd E, 53029, Hartland, WI
Tel.: (262) 966-2355
Web Site: http://www.balax.com
Machine Tool Accessories
N.A.I.C.S.: 333515
James Hall *(VP Manufacturing)*

Melin Tool Company, Inc. (3)
5565 Venture Dr, Cleveland, OH 44130
Tel.: (216) 362-4200
Web Site: https://www.melintool.com
Cutting Tool & Machine Tool Accessory Mfr
N.A.I.C.S.: 333515
Mike Wochna *(Pres)*

Subsidiary (Non-US):

OOO Walter (3)
Sinopskaya Nab 50A, 191124, Saint Petersburg, Russia
Tel.: (7) 812 334 54 56
Web Site: http://www.walter-tools.com
Sales Range: $25-49.9 Million
Cutting Tool Distr
N.A.I.C.S.: 423830

Walter (Schweiz) AG (3)
Hunnenweg 2, Postfach 846, 4502, Solothurn, Switzerland
Tel.: (41) 326174072
Metal Cutting Tool Mfr
N.A.I.C.S.: 333517

Walter (Thailand) Co., Ltd. (3)
No 989 AIA East Gateway Building 12th Fl Unit 1204 Debaratana Rd, Bang Na Nuea, Bangkok, 10260, Thailand
Tel.: (66) 26870388
Metal Cutting Tool Maintenance Services
N.A.I.C.S.: 811310

Walter AG Singapore Pte. Ltd. (3)
Block 988 Toa Payoh North 04-05/06, Singapore, 319002, Singapore
Tel.: (65) 67736180
Sales Range: $25-49.9 Million
Emp.: 13
Metal Cutting Tool Mfr
N.A.I.C.S.: 333515

Walter Argentina S.A. (3)
Rincon 3198, San Justo, B1754BIL, Buenos Aires, Argentina
Tel.: (54) 11 4654 2357
Metal Cutting Tool & Equipment Mfr
N.A.I.C.S.: 333515

Walter Australia Pty. Ltd. (3)
47-57 Wedgewood Road, Hallam, VIC, Australia
Tel.: (61) 3 8793 1000
Metal Cutting Tool Mfr
N.A.I.C.S.: 333517

Walter Austria GmbH (3)
Johannesgasse 14, 1010, Vienna, Austria (100%)
Tel.: (43) 151273000
Emp.: 30
Machining Metal Tools Distr
N.A.I.C.S.: 423710

Walter Benelux N.V. / S.A. (3)
Rombouststraat 3, 1932, Zaventem, Belgium
Tel.: (32) 27258500
Sales Range: $25-49.9 Million
Emp.: 20
Metal Cutting Tool Mfr
N.A.I.C.S.: 333515

Walter CZ s.r.o. (3)
Blanenska 1769, 66434, Kurim, Czech Republic
Tel.: (420) 541423352
Metal Cutting Tool & Equipment Mfr
N.A.I.C.S.: 333515

Walter Cutting Tools Industry and Trade LLC (3)
Serifali Mh Barbaros Cad 63, Umraniye, 34775, Istanbul, Turkiye
Tel.: (90) 2165281900
Web Site: http://www.walter-tools.com
Sales Range: $25-49.9 Million
Metal Cutting Tool Distr
N.A.I.C.S.: 423830

Subsidiary (Domestic):

Walter Deutschland GmbH (3)
Eschborner Landstr 112, 60489, Frankfurt am Main, Germany (100%)
Tel.: (49) 6978902100
Web Site: http://www.walter-tools.com
Sales Range: $125-149.9 Million
Emp.: 350
Machining Metal Tools Developer, Mfr & Distr
N.A.I.C.S.: 333515

Subsidiary (Non-US):

Walter France S.A.S. (3)
2 Rue Max Christen, CS 60013, F-67250, Soultz-sous-Forets, France (100%)
Tel.: (33) 388802000
Sales Range: $200-249.9 Million
Emp.: 310
Holding Company; Machining Metal Tools Mfr & Distr
N.A.I.C.S.: 551112

Subsidiary (Domestic):

Gunther Tools S.A.S. (4)
Rue Max Christen, F-67250, Soultz-sous-Forets, France (100%)
Tel.: (33) 388802005
Web Site: http://www.titex.fr
Sales Range: $75-99.9 Million
Machining Metal Tools Mfr & Distr
N.A.I.C.S.: 333515

Subsidiary (Non-US):

Walter GB Ltd. (3)
Buntsford Gate, Bromsgrove, B60 3DJ, Worcs, United Kingdom (100%)
Tel.: (44) 1527839450
Sales Range: $25-49.9 Million
Emp.: 40
Solid Carbide Drilling & Boring Tool Distr
N.A.I.C.S.: 423710
Gerry O'Hagan *(Mng Dir)*

Walter Italia S.R.L. (3)
Via Volta s n c, I-22071, Cadorago, Italy
Tel.: (39) 031926111
Metal Cutting Tool Mfr
N.A.I.C.S.: 333515

Walter Korea Ltd. (3)
Room Nr 106 Keumkang Penterium IT Tower 810 Gwanyang-dong, Dongan-gu, Anyang, 431-060, Gyeonggi-do, Korea (South)
Tel.: (82) 313376100
Sales Range: $25-49.9 Million
Metal Cutting Tool Mfr
N.A.I.C.S.: 333515

Walter Malaysia Sdn. Bhd. (3)
Unit W102-1 West Wing Level 1 Wisma Consplant 1 No 2 Jalan SS16/4, Bandar Sunway Taman Perindustrian Subang USJ 1, 47500, Subang Jaya, Selangor D E, Malaysia
Tel.: (60) 356244265
Metal Cutting Tool Mfr
N.A.I.C.S.: 333517

Walter Norden AB (3)
Norra Station, 302 96, Halmstad, Sweden
Tel.: (46) 35165300
Metal Cutting Tool Mfr
N.A.I.C.S.: 333515

Walter Tooling Japan K.K. (3)
Emura Building West Bldg 1-7-18 Kayaba Chikusa-ku, Nagoya, 464-0086, Aichi, Japan
Tel.: (81) 52 7235800
Metal Cutting Tool Mfr
N.A.I.C.S.: 333515

Walter Tools Iberica S.A.U. (3)
La Selva 18, 08820, El Prat de Llobregat, Spain
Tel.: (34) 934796760
Metal Cutting Tool & Equipment Mfr
N.A.I.C.S.: 333515

Walter Tools India Pvt. Ltd. (3)
India Land Industrial Park Phase I, Village Hinjewadi, Pune, 411 057, India
Tel.: (91) 2067737300
Metal Cutting Tool Mfr
N.A.I.C.S.: 333517

Walter Tools S.A. de C.V. (3)
Blvd Luis Donaldo Colosio 2255 2do Piso

AND PRIVATE COMPANIES

Colonia San Patricio, 25204, Saltillo, Coahuila de Zaragoza, Mexico
Tel.: (52) 844 450 3500
Metal Cutting Tool Mfr
N.A.I.C.S.: 333517

Subsidiary (US):

Walter USA, LLC (3)
N22 W23977 Ridgeview Pkwy W, Waukesha, WI 53188
Tel.: (262) 347-2400
Web Site: http://www.walter-tools.com
Machining Metal Tools Developer, Mfr & Distr
N.A.I.C.S.: 333515

Subsidiary (Non-US):

Walter Wuxi Co. Ltd. (3)
No 3 South Xinchang Road, New District, Wuxi, 214028, Jiangsu, China
Tel.: (86) 51085372199
Metal Cutting Tool Mfr
N.A.I.C.S.: 333515

Walter do Brasil Ltda. (3)
Rua Dionisio Reis dos Santos 186 Jardim do Sol, 18017-034, Sorocaba, Sao Paulob, Brazil
Tel.: (55) 15 32 24 57 00
Metal Cutting Tool Mfr
N.A.I.C.S.: 333517

Sandvik Utbildnings AB (1)
Hamngatan 12, 811 61, Sandviken, Sweden
Tel.: (46) 26265000
Web Site: http://www.goranssonska.com
Education Services
N.A.I.C.S.: 611110

Sandvik Venture AB (1)
kungsbron 1, 11122, Stockholm, Sweden
Tel.: (46) 26200000
Web Site: http://www.sandvik.com
Rev.: $1,199,853,000
Emp.: 4,100
Industrial Machinery Mfr & Distr
N.A.I.C.S.: 333248
Jim Nixon (Pres)

Sandvik d.o.o. (1)
Suceva ulica 25, 4000, Kranj, Slovenia (100%)
Tel.: (386) 16008630
Web Site: http://www.coromant.sandvik.com
Sales Range: $25-49.9 Million
Emp.: 9
Steel Producer
N.A.I.C.S.: 332618
Erwin Speinhaucer (Mng Dir)

Sandvik de Mexico S.A. de C.V. (1)
Benjamin Franklin Lote 8 Manzana 1 Parque Industrial Aeropuerto, Tlajomulco de Zuniga, 45640, Jalisco, Mexico (100%)
Tel.: (52) 3336010362
Web Site: http://www.sandvik.com
Sales Range: $100-124.9 Million
Emp.: 275
Cemented Carbide Products & Components Mfr
N.A.I.C.S.: 332999

Sandvik del Peru S.A. (1)
Av Defensores del Morro 1632, Chorrillos, Lima, 9, Peru (100%)
Tel.: (51) 12133300
Sales Range: $150-199.9 Million
Emp.: 500
Sales of Sandvik Range of Products
N.A.I.C.S.: 423710
Gary Hughes (Pres)

Sandvik do Brasil S.A. (1)
Av Nacoes Unidas 21 732, Sao Paulo, 04602-970, Brazil
Tel.: (55) 11 5696 5400
Industrial Machinery Mfr & Distr
N.A.I.C.S.: 333248

Sandvik in Austria Ges.m.b.H. (1)
Petritschgasse 12, PO Box 90, 1210, Vienna, Austria (100%)
Tel.: (43) 14170147
Web Site: http://www.coromant.sandvik.com
Sales Range: $1-9.9 Million
Emp.: 70
Mining & Construction Equipment, Metal-Cutting Tools & Heating Materials Distr
N.A.I.C.S.: 423710

Sandvik, Inc. (1)
1702 Nevins Rd, Fair Lawn, NJ 07410 (100%)
Tel.: (201) 794-5000
Web Site: http://www.sandvik.com
Sales Range: $100-124.9 Million
Emp.: 250
Holding Company; Regional Managing Office; Mining & Construction Equipment, Metal-Cutting Tools & Heating Materials Distr
N.A.I.C.S.: 551112

Subsidiary (Domestic):

Pennsylvania Extruded Tube Co. (2)
982 Griffin Pond Rd S, Abington, PA 18411-9214
Tel.: (570) 585-7777
Steel Pipe & Tube Mfr
N.A.I.C.S.: 331210
Gerald Bagdonas (Coord-Maintenance Support)

Sandvik Thermal Process, Inc. (2)
19500 Nugget Blvd, Sonora, CA 95370-9248 (100%)
Tel.: (209) 533-1990
Web Site: http://www.mrlind.com
Sales Range: $25-49.9 Million
Emp.: 185
Semiconductor & Solar Cell Machinery Mfr
N.A.I.C.S.: 333242
Tyke Johnson (Dir-Sls & Mktg)

Sandvik, za trgovinu d.o.o. (1)
Josipa Loncara 3, Zagreb, 10000, Croatia
Tel.: (385) 1 6536907
Sales Range: $50-74.9 Million
Emp.: 5
Metal Ore Mining Services
N.A.I.C.S.: 212290
Vladimir Karnincic (Mgr-Engrg)

Schenck Process Austral S.A. (1)
Avenida Vitacura 2736 Of 603, Las Condes, Santiago, Chile
Tel.: (56) 229989900
Industrial Machinery Mfr
N.A.I.C.S.: 333120

Schenck Process Australia Pty. Limited (1)
Ground Floor 65 Epping Road, North Ryde, 2113, NSW, Australia
Tel.: (61) 298866800
Web Site: https://www.schenckprocess.com.au
Mining Equipment Mfr & Distr
N.A.I.C.S.: 333131

Schenck Process Equipamentos Industriais Ltda. (1)
Rua Guglielmo Marconi 240, Taubate, Sao Paulo, 12032-160, Brazil
Tel.: (55) 1131525450
Web Site: https://www.schenckprocess.com.br
Industrial Machinery Mfr
N.A.I.C.S.: 333120

Seco Tools LLC (1)
2805 Bellingham Dr, Troy, MI 48083
Tel.: (248) 528-5200
Web Site: https://www.secotools.com
Tool Mfr
N.A.I.C.S.: 333515
David Ladzick (Mgr-Central Zone)

Shanghai Jianshe Luqiao Machinery Co., Ltd. (1)
188 Gongye Road Jinhui Town, Fengxian District, Shanghai, 201404, China
Tel.: (86) 2151393838
Web Site: http://www.shanbaochina.com
Mining & Construction Machinery Mfr
N.A.I.C.S.: 333131

SigmaNEST GmbH (1)
Uberseeallee 10, 20457, Hamburg, Germany
Tel.: (49) 4030090110
Mining Technology Services
N.A.I.C.S.: 518210

SigmaTEK Australia Pty. Ltd. (1)
1048 Beaudesert Road, Coopers Plains, 4108, QLD, Australia
Tel.: (61) 732465213
Web Site: https://www.sigmanest.com

Software Development Services
N.A.I.C.S.: 541511

SigmaTEK Canada, LLC (1)
2425 Matheson Blvd East Suite 800, Mississauga, L4W 5K4, ON, Canada
Tel.: (519) 400-8676
Software Development Services
N.A.I.C.S.: 541511

SigmaTEK Japan Ltd. (1)
2-4-1 Horai-cho, Naka-ku, Yokohama, 231-0048, Kanagawa, Japan
Tel.: (81) 453156913
Mining Technology Services
N.A.I.C.S.: 518210

SigmaTEK S.R.L. (1)
Corso Canale 10, Alba, 12051, Cuneo, Italy
Tel.: (39) 0173466689
Mining Technology Services
N.A.I.C.S.: 518210

SigmaTEK Systems Brasil Ltda. (1)
Rua Comendador Toriogo Dauntre 74 Sala 209, Campinas, Sao Paulo, 13025-270, Brazil
Tel.: (55) 1933814000
Software Development Services
N.A.I.C.S.: 541511

SigmaTEK Systems China, LLC (1)
Room 805 Building A No 555 Jingjia Road, Ningbo, 315040, China
Tel.: (86) 57487753085
Mining Technology Services
N.A.I.C.S.: 518210

SigmaTEK Systems India Private Limited (1)
2nd Floor A Building Friends Park Lohia Jain Business Centre, Senapati Bapat Road Near Chatushringi Temple, Pune, 411016, Maharashtra, India
Tel.: (91) 7768075606
Mining Technology Services
N.A.I.C.S.: 518210

SigmaTEK Systems, LLC (1)
1445 Kemper Meadow Dr, Cincinnati, OH 45240-1637
Tel.: (513) 674-0005
Web Site: https://www.sigmanest.com
Software Solutions Services
N.A.I.C.S.: 541511

Summerill Tube Corp. (1)
220 Franklin St, Scottdale, PA 15683
Tel.: (724) 887-9700
Web Site: http://www.summerilltube.com
Iron & Steel Pipe & Tube Manufacturing from Purchased Steel
N.A.I.C.S.: 331210

TDM Systems GmbH (1)
Derendinger Strasse 53, 72072, Tubingen, Germany
Tel.: (49) 707194920
Web Site: https://www.tdmsystems.com
Data Management Software Development Services
N.A.I.C.S.: 541511
Dietmar Bohn (Mng Dir)

Subsidiary (US):

TDM Systems, Inc. (2)
1901 N Roselle Rd Ste 800, Schaumburg, IL 60195
Tel.: (847) 605-1269
Web Site: http://www.tdmsystems.com
Software Development Services
N.A.I.C.S.: 541511

Teeness ASA (1)
Ranheimsveien 127 Ranheim, Trondheim, 7053, Norway
Tel.: (47) 73 53 96 00
Sales Range: $50-74.9 Million
Emp.: 115
Cutting Tool Mfr
N.A.I.C.S.: 333515

Thermaltek, Inc. (1)
2800 Armentrout Dr, Concord, NC 28025
Tel.: (704) 784-3001
Web Site: https://www.thermaltek.com
Industrial Process Furnace & Oven Mfr
N.A.I.C.S.: 333994
Vic Neill (VP)

SANDVIKS AS

Tricon Drilling Solutions Pty. Ltd. (1)
85 Belgravia Street, Belmont, Perth, 6104, WA, Australia
Tel.: (67) 894772666
Web Site: https://www.triconds.com.au
Rock Drilling Services
N.A.I.C.S.: 532412

Vaal Triangle Systems Private Limited (1)
2nd Floor A Building Friends Park Lohia Jain Business Centre, Senapati Bapat Road Near Chatushringi Temple, Pune, 411016, Maharashtra, India
Tel.: (91) 2025636323
Web Site: https://www.vaal-triangle.com
Computer Aided Design Services
N.A.I.C.S.: 334118

Velroq Oy (1)
Pihtisulunkatu 9, 33330, Tampere, Finland
Tel.: (358) 31625526906
Web Site: https://www.velroq.com
Automotive Machinery Mfr
N.A.I.C.S.: 336340

Walter Hungaria Kft. (1)
Budafoki ut 209, 1117, Budapest, Hungary
Tel.: (36) 14647160
Tool Mfr
N.A.I.C.S.: 333515

Walter Polska Sp. z o.o. (1)
ul Wyczolki 40, 02-820, Warsaw, Poland
Tel.: (48) 228520495
Tool Mfr
N.A.I.C.S.: 333515

Walter Slovakia s.r.o. (1)
Novozamocka 67, 94 905, Nitra, Slovakia
Tel.: (421) 373260910
Tool Mfr
N.A.I.C.S.: 333515

Walter Tools SRL (1)
Str Mihai Viteazu No 30, 300222, Timisoara, Romania
Tel.: (40) 256406218
Tool Mfr
N.A.I.C.S.: 333515
Sorin Cirlea (Mng Dir)

Walter Tools d.o.o. (1)
Ulica Heroja Nandeta 33, 2000, Maribor, Slovenia
Tel.: (386) 26290130
Tool Mfr
N.A.I.C.S.: 333515

Walter do Brazil Ltda. (1)
Av Gisele Constantino 1850 - Sala 903 Parque Bela Vista, Votorantim, 18110-650, SP, Brazil
Tel.: (55) 1532245700
Cutting Tool Mfr
N.A.I.C.S.: 333515

Werner Schmitt PKD-Werkzeug GmbH (1)
Birkenstrasse 8, D-75223, Niefern-Oschelbronn, Germany
Tel.: (49) 723395300
Web Site: http://www.waltertools.com
Metal Cutting Tool & Equipment Mfr
N.A.I.C.S.: 333515

Wire Sandviken AB (1)
Storgatan 2, Sandviken, 81134, Sweden
Tel.: (46) 26 26 00 00
Web Site: http://www.sandvik.com
Steel Product Mfr & Distr
N.A.I.C.S.: 332999

Wolfram Bergbau und Hutten AG (1)
Bergla 33, A-8543, Sankt Martin im Sulmtal, Austria
Tel.: (43) 34657077
Web Site: https://www.wolfram.at
Metal Mining Services
N.A.I.C.S.: 212290
Andreas Bock (Dir-Technical)

SANDVIKS AS
Strandsvingen 14, 4032, Stavanger, Norway
Tel.: (47) 51440051 NO
Web Site: http://www.sandviks.com
Year Founded: 1965

SANDVIKS AS

Sandviks AS—(Continued)
Children's Early Development & Educational Book, Website & Other Materials Publisher
N.A.I.C.S.: 513130
Marius Sandvik *(Pres & CEO)*

Subsidiaries:

Sandviks, Inc. (1)
83 Wooster Heights Rd, Danbury, CT 06810
Tel.: (203) 205-0188
Web Site: http://www.sandviks.com
Emp.: 14
Children's Early Development & Educational Book, Website & Other Materials Publisher
N.A.I.C.S.: 513130
Robert Israel *(Pres)*

Subsidiary (Domestic):

Sandviks HOP, Inc. (2)
83 Wooster Heights Rd, Danbury, CT 06810
Tel.: (203) 205-0188
Web Site: http://www.hookedonphonics.com
Children's Reading Educational Materials Publisher
N.A.I.C.S.: 513199
Robert Israel *(Pres)*

SANDZAKTRANS - PUTNICKI SAOBRACAJ A.D.
Ul Stevana Nemanje 236, 36300, Novi Pazar, Serbia
Tel.: (381) 20 311 920
Web Site: http://www.sandzaktrans.rs
Year Founded: 1945
Food Transportation Services
N.A.I.C.S.: 488490
Zeev Horen *(Chm-Supervisory Bd)*

SANERGY GROUP LIMITED
2602 26/F China Resources Building 26 Harbour Road, Wan Chai, Hong Kong, China (Hong Kong)
Tel.: (852) 29513500   Ky
Web Site:
https://www.sanergygroup.com
Year Founded: 2018
2459—(HKG)
Rev.: $115,521,000
Assets: $205,851,000
Liabilities: $72,934,000
Net Worth: $132,917,000
Earnings: $7,496,000
Emp.: 210
Fiscal Year-end: 12/31/22
Graphite Product Mfr
N.A.I.C.S.: 335991

Subsidiaries:

Sangraf Italy S.r.l. (1)
Via del Lavoro 8, 05035, Narni, Italy
Tel.: (39) 0744668701
Web Site: https://www.sangrafitaly.com
Graphite Electrodes Mfr & Distr
N.A.I.C.S.: 335991

SANESALTO SANEAMENTO S.A.
Rua 9 de Julho 849, 13320005, Salto, Sao Paulo, Brazil
Tel.: (55) 11 4029 3700
Web Site:
http://www.sanesalto.com.br
SANESALTO—(BRAZ)
Sales Range: Less than $1 Million
Sewage Treatment Services
N.A.I.C.S.: 221320

SANFENG INTELLIGENT EQUIPMENT GROUP CO., LTD.
No 98 Pengcheng Avenue Huangjinshan Industrial New District, Huangshi Economic and Technology Development Zone, Huangshi, 435000, Hubei, China

Tel.: (86) 7146359152
Web Site: https://www.cnsanf.com
Year Founded: 1999
300276—(CHIN)
Rev.: $187,247,268
Assets: $562,360,968
Liabilities: $293,040,072
Net Worth: $269,320,896
Earnings: ($71,432,712)
Emp.: 700
Fiscal Year-end: 12/31/22
Conveying Equipment Mfr
N.A.I.C.S.: 333922

Subsidiaries:

HuBei Sanyang Petrochemical Co., Ltd. (1)
No 86 Zhongshan Avenue, intersection of Zhongshan Avenue and Shengshui Road, Huangshi, 435000, China
Tel.: (86) 7146376416
Web Site: https://www.cn-sany.com
Refined Oil Distr
N.A.I.C.S.: 424720

HuBei Zhongda Intelligent Parking Equipment Co., Ltd. (1)
No 98 Pengcheng Avenue, Economic and Technological Development Zone, Huangshi, 435000, Hubei, China
Tel.: (86) 37165829599
Web Site: https://www.hbzdparking.com
Cutting Machine Mfr
N.A.I.C.S.: 333515

Huangshi Jiufeng Intelligent Mechanical & Electrical Co., Ltd. (1)
Huangshi City magnetic Lake Road No 162, Huangshi, 435003, China
Tel.: (86) 7146356413
Web Site: https://www.cnjiuf.com
Welding Equipment Mfr
N.A.I.C.S.: 333992

SANFORD LIMITED
22 Jellicoe Street Freemans Bay, Auckland, 1010, New Zealand
Tel.: (64) 93794720
Web Site: https://www.sanford.co.nz
Year Founded: 1881
SARDF—(OTCIQ)
Rev.: $330,979,067
Assets: $641,335,526
Liabilities: $231,675,837
Net Worth: $409,659,689
Earnings: $5,987,440
Emp.: 1,485
Fiscal Year-end: 09/30/23
Sea Food Products
N.A.I.C.S.: 311710
Volker Kuntzsch *(CEO)*

Subsidiaries:

Auckland Fish Market Limited (1)
22 Jellicoe St Wynyard Quarter, PO Box 443, Auckland, 1010, New Zealand
Tel.: (64) 93791490
Web Site: https://www.afm.co.nz
Sales Range: $25-49.9 Million
Emp.: 16
Finfish Fishing
N.A.I.C.S.: 114111
Margaret Hall *(Gen Mgr)*

Sanford Investments Limited (1)
Gilbred St, Wanganui, New Zealand
Tel.: (64) 63445039
Finfish Fishing
N.A.I.C.S.: 114111

SANG BO CO., LTD.
50 Daeseomyeong-ro Tongjin-Eup, Gimpo, Gyeonggi-Do, Korea (South)
Tel.: (82) 319879900
Web Site:
https://www.sangbogroup.com
Year Founded: 1989
027580—(KRS)
Rev.: $51,705,375
Assets: $86,113,474
Liabilities: $35,737,573
Net Worth: $50,375,901

Earnings: $6,739,358
Emp.: 167
Fiscal Year-end: 12/31/22
Optical Film Mfr
N.A.I.C.S.: 325992

Subsidiaries:

Sang Bo Co., Ltd. - Gimpo Plant (1)
57-6 Weonsan-ri, Haseong-myeon, Gimpo, Gyeonggi-do, Korea (South)
Tel.: (82) 319994500
Optical Film Mfr
N.A.I.C.S.: 325992

SANG FROID LABS INDIA LTD.
Fourth Floor Plot No 158 Phase-II Shazada Bagh, New Delhi, 110035, India
Tel.: (91) 7926446671
Web Site:
http://www.sangfroidlabs.com
Rev.: $17,411
Assets: $507,830
Liabilities: $55,971
Net Worth: $451,860
Earnings: ($23,248)
Fiscal Year-end: 03/31/18
Pharmaceutical Product Trading Services
N.A.I.C.S.: 523160
Chandubhai Nanubhai Dobariya *(Compliance Officer)*

SANG HING HOLDINGS (INTERNATIONAL) LIMITED
215A-B Central Services Building Nan Fung Industrial City 18, Tin Hau Road, Tuen Mun, New Territories, China (Hong Kong)
Tel.: (852) 2 403 1118   Ky
Web Site: http://www.sang-hing.com.hk
Year Founded: 1990
1472—(HKG)
Rev.: $50,331,736
Assets: $46,901,126
Liabilities: $7,458,269
Net Worth: $39,442,858
Earnings: $3,408,168
Emp.: 230
Fiscal Year-end: 03/31/21
Holding Company
N.A.I.C.S.: 551112
Wai Lai *(Chm)*

SANG-A FRONTEC CO., LTD.
369 Route 18 Namdong-ro, Namdong-gu, Incheon, Korea (South)
Tel.: (82) 324517756
Web Site: https://www.sftc.co.kr
Year Founded: 1974
089980—(KRS)
Rev.: $143,112,848
Assets: $265,407,705
Liabilities: $119,268,907
Net Worth: $146,138,797
Earnings: $5,866,344
Emp.: 491
Fiscal Year-end: 12/31/22
Electronic & Semiconductor Components Mfr
N.A.I.C.S.: 334419
Jung-soon Park *(Mng Dir)*

Subsidiaries:

SANG-A Flontec Co., Ltd. - 3rd Plant (1)
8B-2L 619-5 Namchon-dong, Namdong-Gu, Incheon, Korea (South)
Tel.: (82) 32 722 7660
Web Site: http://www.sftc.co.kr
Sales Range: $125-149.9 Million
Emp.: 500
Disc Packaging Product Mfr
N.A.I.C.S.: 322220
John Kong *(Gen Mgr)*

INTERNATIONAL PUBLIC

SANGAL PAPERS LIMITED
22 Km Stone Meerut Mawana Road, Mawana, Meerut, 250401, Uttar Pradesh, India
Tel.: (91) 1233274324
Web Site:
https://www.sangalpapers.com
Year Founded: 1980
516096—(BOM)
Rev.: $27,351,322
Assets: $10,806,666
Liabilities: $6,114,813
Net Worth: $4,691,853
Earnings: $405,959
Emp.: 252
Fiscal Year-end: 03/31/23
Paper Mfr
N.A.I.C.S.: 322120
Himanshu Sangal *(Mng Dir)*

SANGAM FINSERV LIMITED
B/306-309 Dynasty Business Park Opp Sangam Cinema J B Nagar Andheri E, Mumbai, 400 059, India
Tel.: (91) 2261115222
Web Site: https://www.sftc.co.in
Year Founded: 1981
029400—(KOL)
Rev.: $1,978,754
Assets: $18,478,461
Liabilities: $4,179,030
Net Worth: $14,299,430
Earnings: $772,448
Emp.: 13
Fiscal Year-end: 03/31/23
Electronic Finance Services
N.A.I.C.S.: 522320
V. K. Sodani *(Chm)*

SANGAM HEALTH CARE PRODUCTS LIMITED
Sy No 182 Yellampet Village Medchal Mandal, Medchal-Malkajgiri, Secunderabad, 501401, Telangana, India
Tel.: (91) 4027719551
Year Founded: 1993
531625—(BOM)
Sales Range: $1-9.9 Million
Medical Equipment Mfr
N.A.I.C.S.: 339112
H. C. Pareek *(VP)*

SANGAM INDIA LTD
Sangam House Chittorgarh Road Atun, Bhilwara, 311001, Rajasthan, India
Tel.: (91) 1482245400
Web Site:
https://www.sangamgroup.com
SANGAMIND—(NSE)
Rev.: $186,838,470
Assets: $192,277,995
Liabilities: $116,883,585
Net Worth: $75,394,410
Earnings: $574,665
Emp.: 9,055
Fiscal Year-end: 03/31/21
Fabrics Mfr
N.A.I.C.S.: 313210
Vinod Kumar Sodani *(Exec Dir)*

SANGANI HOSPITALS LIMITED
Sainath Society Opp ST Bus Stand, Keshod, Junagadh, 362220, Gujarat, India
Tel.: (91) 2871235900
Web Site:
https://www.sanganihospitals.com
Year Founded: 2021
SANGANI—(NSE)
Rev.: $1,428,764
Assets: $2,336,945
Liabilities: $149,118
Net Worth: $2,187,827
Earnings: $186,230

Emp.: 371
Fiscal Year-end: 03/31/23
Healthcare Technology Services
N.A.I.C.S.: 541511
Rajeshkumar Sangani *(Chm)*

Subsidiaries:

Ankur Distributors Pvt. Ltd. (1)

SANGETSU CO., LTD.
1-4-1 Habashita, Nishi-ku, Nagoya, 451-8575, Aichi, Japan
Tel.: (81) 525643250
Web Site: https://www.sangetsu.co.jp
Year Founded: 1953
8130—(NGO)
Rev.: $1,254,436,385
Assets: $1,128,179,400
Liabilities: $423,131,695
Net Worth: $705,047,705
Earnings: $94,423,495
Emp.: 2,645
Fiscal Year-end: 03/31/24
Interior Decorating Product Mfr & Distr
N.A.I.C.S.: 332323
Yasumasa Kondo *(Pres & CEO)*

Subsidiaries:

Creanate Inc. (1)
3-20-17 Higashi-Shinagawa, Shinagawa-ku, Tokyo, 140-8611, Japan
Tel.: (81) 334741580
Web Site: https://www.creanate.co.jp
Household Appliances Mfr
N.A.I.C.S.: 335220

Goodrich Global Holdings Pte., Ltd. (1)
Goodrich Building 8 Changi South Lane 05-01, Singapore, 486113,
Singapore (100%)
Tel.: (65) 6 787 8787
Web Site: https://www.goodrichglobal.com
Interior Furnishing Product Distr
N.A.I.C.S.: 423220
Yasushi Furukawa *(CEO)*

Goodrich Global Limited (1)
Units 902-904 9/F Tower 1 Cheung Sha Wan Plaza 833 Cheung Sha Wan Road, Kowloon, China (Hong Kong)
Tel.: (852) 26685757
Building Construction & Supervision Services
N.A.I.C.S.: 541310

Goodrich Global Sdn. Bhd. (1)
Unit M-2-2 Block M Plaza Damas Phase II Jalan Sri Hartamas 1/70A, 50480, Kuala Lumpur, Malaysia
Tel.: (60) 362015757
Building Construction & Supervision Services
N.A.I.C.S.: 541310

Koroseal Interior Products LLC (1)
3875 Embassy Pkwy Ste 110, Fairlawn, OH 44333 (100%)
Web Site: https://koroseal.com
Interior Design Services
N.A.I.C.S.: 541410
John Farrell *(Pres-Operations)*

Metro Acquisition 2004, Inc. (1)
2600B Steeles Avenue West, Concord, L4K 3C8, ON, Canada
Tel.: (905) 738-5177
Building Construction & Supervision Services
N.A.I.C.S.: 541310

Sangetsu (Shanghai) Corporation (1)
25F 137Lane XianXiaRoad ShengGaoInternational Tower ChangNing Area, Shanghai, 200051, China
Tel.: (86) 2164288876
Interior Design Services
N.A.I.C.S.: 541410

Sangetsu Goodrich (Thailand) Co., Ltd. (1)
23/77 Sorachai Building 20Fl Soi Sukhumvit 63 Sukhumvit Rd, Klongton Nua Wattana,
Bangkok, 10110, Thailand
Tel.: (66) 21151838
Building Construction & Supervision Services
N.A.I.C.S.: 541310

Sangetsu Goodrich China Co.,Ltd. (1)
25F Shenggao International Tower No 137 Xianxia Road, Changning District, Shanghai, 200051, China
Tel.: (86) 2164288876
Building Construction & Supervision Services
N.A.I.C.S.: 541310

Sangetsu Goodrich Vietnam Co., Ltd. (1)
2nd Floor Lant Building No 56-58-60 Hai Ba Trung Street, Ben Nghe Ward District 1, Ho Chi Minh City, Vietnam
Tel.: (84) 2835202300
Interior Design Services
N.A.I.C.S.: 541410

Sangetsu Vosne Corporation (1)
3-20-17 Higashi-Shinagawa, Shinagawa-ku, Tokyo, 140-8611, Japan
Tel.: (81) 33 474 2362
Web Site: https://www.sangetsu-vosne.co.jp
Interior Fabric Product Distr
N.A.I.C.S.: 459130

SANGFOR TECHNOLOGIES, INC.
Block A1 Nanshan iPark No 1001 Xueyuan Road, Nanshan District, Shenzhen, Guangdong, China
Tel.: (86) 75586627888
Web Site: https://www.sangfor.com
Year Founded: 2000
300454—(CHIN)
Rev.: $1,079,216,137
Assets: $2,116,821,734
Liabilities: $876,273,373
Net Worth: $1,240,548,361
Earnings: $27,864,384
Emp.: 9,500
Fiscal Year-end: 12/31/23
Information Technology Support Services
N.A.I.C.S.: 518210
He Chaoxi *(Chm & Gen Mgr)*

Subsidiaries:

Sangfor Technologies, Inc. - Fremont Branch (1)
46721 Fremont Blvd, Fremont, CA 94538
Tel.: (510) 573-0715
Information Technology Services
N.A.I.C.S.: 541512

SANGHAR SUGAR MILLS LIMITED
Office 204 2nd Floor Clifton Centre Block 5 Clifton, Karachi, Pakistan
Tel.: (92) 2135371441
Web Site: https://www.sangharsugarmills.com
Year Founded: 1984
SANSM—(PSX)
Rev.: $13,929,968
Assets: $17,834,740
Liabilities: $10,527,494
Net Worth: $7,307,246
Earnings: $372,504
Emp.: 319
Fiscal Year-end: 09/30/23
Sugar Mfr
N.A.I.C.S.: 311314
Khuda Bux Rajar *(Exec Dir)*

Subsidiaries:

Sanghar Sugar Mills Limited - Sanghar Mill (1)
13th Km Sanghar - Sindhri Road, Deh Kehore, Sanghar, Sindh, Pakistan
Tel.: (92) 3453737001
Sugar Mfr
N.A.I.C.S.: 311314

SANGHI CORPORATE SERVICES LIMITED
Bal Moral Apartments Ground Floor Plot No 12 Amrtivan Yashodham, Goregaon E, Mumbai, 400 063, Maharashtra, India
Tel.: (91) 22 28422703
Web Site: http://www.sanghicorp.com
Year Founded: 1989
Rev.: $2,365
Assets: $128,699
Liabilities: $325,865
Net Worth: ($197,166)
Earnings: ($20,619)
Fiscal Year-end: 03/31/18
Securities Dealing Services
N.A.I.C.S.: 523150
Ashok Kumar Vishambardayal Sanghi *(Chm)*

SANGHVI BRANDS LIMITED
105/2 Sanghvi House Shivajinagar, Pune, 411 005, Maharashtra, India
Tel.: (91) 2030533084 In
Web Site: https://www.sanghvibrands.com
Year Founded: 2010
540782—(BOM)
Rev.: $510,630
Assets: $1,299,597
Liabilities: $432,848
Net Worth: $866,749
Earnings: ($784,981)
Fiscal Year-end: 03/31/21
Personal Care Services
N.A.I.C.S.: 812199
Kruti Haresh Shah *(Compliance Officer & Sec)*

SANGHVI FORGING AND ENGINEERING LIMITED
A/8 Parvati Chamber Opp Apsara Cinema, Pratapnagar Road, Vadodara, 390 004, Gujarat, India
Tel.: (91) 265 2580644
Web Site: http://www.sanghviforge.com
Rev.: $9,169,581
Assets: $25,877,979
Liabilities: $29,101,623
Net Worth: ($3,223,644)
Earnings: ($2,876,854)
Emp.: 225
Fiscal Year-end: 03/31/19
Forgings & Machined Components Mfr
N.A.I.C.S.: 332111
Jayantilal Babulal Sanghvi *(Chm & Mng Dir)*

Subsidiaries:

Sanghvi Forging and Engineering Limited - INDIA WORKS (1)
244/6 7 GIDC Industrial Estate, Waghodia, Vadodara, 391 760, Gujarat, India
Tel.: (91) 2668 263020
Steel Forging Mfr
N.A.I.C.S.: 332111

SANGHVI MOVERS LIMITED
Survey No 92 Tathawade, Mulshi, Pune, 411 033, India
Tel.: (91) 2066744700
Web Site: https://www.sanghvicranes.com
Year Founded: 1989
530073—(BOM)
Rev.: $34,538,513
Assets: $130,715,048
Liabilities: $33,936,562
Net Worth: $96,778,486
Earnings: ($3,060,726)
Emp.: 245
Fiscal Year-end: 03/31/21
Crane Operating Services
N.A.I.C.S.: 333923
Sham D. Kajale *(Co-Mng Dir & CFO)*

SANGINITA CHEMICALS LIMITED
301 3rd Floor Shalin Complex, Sector-11, Gandhinagar, 382011, Gujarat, India
Tel.: (91) 7923240270
Web Site: https://www.sanginitachemicals.co.in
Year Founded: 2005
SANGINITA—(NSE)
Rev.: $22,525,271
Assets: $9,571,653
Liabilities: $4,197,252
Net Worth: $5,374,401
Earnings: $104,095
Emp.: 29
Fiscal Year-end: 03/12/21
Chemicals Mfr
N.A.I.C.S.: 325199
Dineshsinh Chavada *(Chm & Mng Dir)*

SANGJI CONSTRUCTION, INC.
5F 12 hakdong-ro 31-gil, Gangnam-gu, Seoul, 06071, Korea (South)
Tel.: (82) 25175174
Web Site: https://www.sangji.co.kr
Year Founded: 1979
042940—(KRS)
Rev.: $38,618,610
Assets: $171,221,533
Liabilities: $126,950,316
Net Worth: $44,271,218
Earnings: ($8,277,230)
Emp.: 67
Fiscal Year-end: 12/31/22
Construction Engineering Services
N.A.I.C.S.: 237990
Yeongshin Kim *(CEO)*

SANGO CO., LTD.
1-1 Miyashita Fukuta-cho, Miyoshi, 470-0294, Aichi, Japan
Tel.: (81) 561 34 8399
Web Site: http://www.sango.jp
Year Founded: 1928
Sales Range: $1-4.9 Billion
Emp.: 8,223
Automotive Products Mfr
N.A.I.C.S.: 336390
Takashi Tsunekawa *(Pres)*

Subsidiaries:

Arvin Sango, Inc. (1)
2905 Wilson Ave, Madison, IN 47250
Tel.: (812) 265-2888
Web Site: http://www.arvinsango.com
Emp.: 835
Automotive Exhaust System Mfr
N.A.I.C.S.: 336310
David Jorgensen *(Controller)*

Arvin Sango, Inc. (1)
2330 Discovery Drive, London, N6M 0C6, ON, Canada
Tel.: (519) 455-5858
Emp.: 16
Exhaust Systems Mfr
N.A.I.C.S.: 336310

Guangzhou Sango Automotive Parts Co., Ltd. (1)
No 11 Shinan Road Huangge Town, Nansha District, Guangzhou, 511455, China
Tel.: (86) 2034973535
Emp.: 576
Motor Vehicle Parts Distr
N.A.I.C.S.: 423120

PT. Sango Indonesia (1)
Kawasan Industri Mitrakarawang Mitra Selatan IV BLOK M1-2 Desa, Kacamatan Ciampel, Karawang, 41361, Jawa Barat, Indonesia
Tel.: (62) 2678638035
Emp.: 17
Motor Vehicle Parts Distr
N.A.I.C.S.: 423120

SANGO FAMILY SERVICE CO., LTD. (1)

SANGO CO., LTD.

Sango Co., Ltd.—(Continued)
3 Fukuta Miyoshi-cho, Miyoshi, Aichi, Japan
Tel.: (81) 561348301
Insurance Services
N.A.I.C.S.: 524210

SANGO Thai Automotive Parts Co., Ltd. (1)
80/1 Moo 1 Tambol Klongprawet, Amphur Banpho, Chachoengsao, 24140, Thailand
Tel.: (66) 38130020
Emp.: 250
Motor Vehicle Parts Distr
N.A.I.C.S.: 423120

Sango Co., Ltd. - Miyoshi Plant (1)
47 Inoguchi Miyoshi-cho, Miyoshi, Aichi, Japan
Tel.: (81) 561323511
Steel Products Mfr
N.A.I.C.S.: 332312

Sango Co., Ltd. - No.3 Miyoshi Plant (1)
63 Ikemorida Miyoshi-cho, Miyoshi, Aichi, Japan
Tel.: (81) 561333595
Steel Products Mfr
N.A.I.C.S.: 332312

Sango Co., Ltd. - Takaoka Plant (1)
14 Miyashita Fukuta-cho, Miyoshi, Aichi, Japan
Tel.: (81) 561323500
Motor Vehicle Parts Mfr
N.A.I.C.S.: 336390

Sango Co., Ltd. - Toyohashi Plant (1)
3-33 Akemi-cho, Toyohashi, Aichi, Japan
Tel.: (81) 532233515
Motor Vehicle Parts Mfr
N.A.I.C.S.: 336390

Sango Co., Ltd. - Toyota Plant (1)
3-1-chome Konosu-cho, Toyota, Aichi, Japan
Tel.: (81) 565283535
Motor Vehicle Parts Mfr
N.A.I.C.S.: 336390

Sango Co., Ltd. - Yawatayama Plant (1)
5-35 Yawatayama, Miyoshi-cho, Miyoshi, Aichi, Japan
Tel.: (81) 561323501
Motor Vehicle Parts Mfr
N.A.I.C.S.: 336390

Sango Hokkaido Co., Ltd. (1)
41-2 Masago-cho, Tomakomai, Hokkaido, Japan
Tel.: (81) 144515135
Emp.: 70
Motor Vehicle Parts Mfr
N.A.I.C.S.: 336390

Sango India Automotive Parts Pvt. Ltd. (1)
Site No 6A SIPCOT Phase 1, Krishnagiri District, Hosur, 635126, Tamil Nadu, India
Tel.: (91) 4344277744
Emp.: 14
Motor Vehicle Parts Distr
N.A.I.C.S.: 423120
Ramalingam Srinivasan *(Mgr-HR & IR)*

Sango Mie Co., Ltd. (1)
2438-1 Kamiaiba Fujiwara-cho, Inabe, Mie, Japan
Tel.: (81) 594 46 8635
Emp.: 339
Motor Vehicle Parts Mfr
N.A.I.C.S.: 336390

Plant (Domestic):

Sango Mie Co., Ltd. - Mie Plant (2)
1 Fujigaoka Fujiwara-cho, Inabe, Mie, Japan
Tel.: (81) 594465135
Motor Vehicle Parts Mfr
N.A.I.C.S.: 336390

Sango Otomotiv Urunleri Sanayi ve Ticaret A.S. (1)
TOSB Organize Sanayi Bolgesi 4 Cad NO 2 PK, Sekerpinar, 41420, Cayirova, Kocaeli, Turkiye
Tel.: (90) 2626796100

Web Site: http://www.sango.com.tr
Emp.: 224
Motor Vehicle Parts Distr
N.A.I.C.S.: 423120
Toru Irie *(Pres)*

Tianjin Sango Automotive Parts Co., Ltd. (1)
5-Wei Road Dongli Economic Development, Tianjin, 300300, China
Tel.: (86) 2258893535
Motor Vehicle Parts Distr
N.A.I.C.S.: 423120

Xiangyang Sango Automotive Parts Co., Ltd. (1)
No 28 Dongfengqiche Aveue North High-tech Zone, Xiangyang, 441004, Hubei, China
Tel.: (86) 7103273535
Emp.: 63
Motor Vehicle Parts Distr
N.A.I.C.S.: 423120

SANGOMA TECHNOLOGIES CORPORATION

100 Renfrew Dr, Markham, L3R 9R6, ON, Canada
Tel.: (905) 474-1990
Web Site: https://www.sangoma.com
Year Founded: 1984
SANG—(NASDAQ)
Rev.: $247,284,000
Assets: $400,645,000
Liabilities: $140,915,000
Net Worth: $259,730,000
Earnings: ($8,659,000)
Emp.: 671
Fiscal Year-end: 06/30/24
Hardware & Software Components for IP Communications Systems
N.A.I.C.S.: 513210
Norman Worthington *(Interim Exec Chm)*

Subsidiaries:

Digium, Inc. (1)
445 Jan Davis Dr NW, Huntsville, AL 35806-4540
Tel.: (256) 428-6262
Web Site: http://www.digium.com
Telecommunications Company
N.A.I.C.S.: 517410
Matt Jordan *(CTO)*

Rockbochs, Inc. (1)
231 E 1st St, Duluth, MN 55802
Tel.: (218) 727-4332
Web Site: http://www.rockbochs.com
Computer System Design Services
N.A.I.C.S.: 541512
Chad Behling *(CEO)*

Sangoma Technologies Inc. (1)
100 Renfrew Dr Suite 100, Markham, L3R 9R6, ON, Canada
Tel.: (905) 474-1990
Communication System Software Development Services
N.A.I.C.S.: 541511

VoIP Innovations LLC (1)
8 Penn Ctr W Ste 101, Pittsburgh, PA 15276
Tel.: (412) 440-6025
Web Site: http://www.voipinnovations.com
Sales Range: $1-9.9 Million
Emp.: 21
VoIP Services
N.A.I.C.S.: 517810
Tim Linn *(Product Mgr)*

VoIP Supply LLC (1)
80 Pineview Dr, Buffalo, NY 14228-2120
Tel.: (716) 630-1555
Web Site: http://www.voipsupply.com
Voice Over Internet Protocol Equipment & Services Sales
N.A.I.C.S.: 517121
Paula Griffo *(Pres & CEO)*

SANGSANGIN CO., LTD.

358 Hwangsaewul-Ro, Bundang-Gu, Seongnam, 153-759, Gyeonggi-Do, Korea (South)
Tel.: (82) 221678500
Web Site: https://www.sangsanginworld.co.kr
Year Founded: 1989
038540—(KRS)
Sales Range: $200-249.9 Million
Information Technology Development Services
N.A.I.C.S.: 541611
Jin-Su Kim *(Pres, CEO & Dir)*

SANGSANGIN INDUSTRY CO., LTD.

1102-171 Gimhae-daero Hallimmyeon, Gimhae, Gyeongnam, Korea (South)
Tel.: (82) 557203000
Web Site: http://www.dongnamcrane.co.kr
Year Founded: 1988
101000—(KRS)
Rev.: $57,087,346
Assets: $41,552,931
Liabilities: $33,105,583
Net Worth: $8,447,348
Earnings: ($10,638,302)
Emp.: 89
Fiscal Year-end: 12/31/22
Marine Crane Mfr
N.A.I.C.S.: 333923

Subsidiaries:

SMT Bio Co., Ltd. (1)
Gasan W-Center 181 Gasan Digital 1-RO, Geumcheon-gu, Seoul, Korea (South)
Tel.: (82) 234610515
Immune Cell Research Services
N.A.I.C.S.: 541714

Sangsangin Heavy Industries Co., Ltd. (1)
116 Yulchonsandan 3-ro, Gwangyang, Jeollanam-do, Korea (South)
Tel.: (82) 618155263
Crane Mfr & Distr
N.A.I.C.S.: 333924

Sangsangin Investment & Securities Co., Ltd. (1)
424 Teheran-Ro, Gangnam-Gu, Seoul, Korea (South)
Tel.: (82) 237793000
Financial Banking Services
N.A.I.C.S.: 522110

Sangsangin Plus Co., Ltd. (1)
Seolleung-ro 94-gil, Gangnam-Gu, Seoul, Korea (South)
Tel.: (82) 24867810
Management Consulting Services
N.A.I.C.S.: 541611

Sangsangin Plus Savings Bank Co., Ltd. (1)
2nd Floor 67-12 Buldang 21-ro, Seobuk-gu, Cheonan, Chungcheongnam-do, Korea (South)
Tel.: (82) 16002100
Financial Banking Services
N.A.I.C.S.: 522110

Sangsangin Savings Bank Co., Ltd. (1)
358 Hwangsaeul-ro, Bundang-gu, Seongnam, Gyeonggi-do, Korea (South)
Tel.: (82) 215771771
Financial Banking Services
N.A.I.C.S.: 522110

SANGSANGIN INVESTMENT & SECURITIES CO. LTD.

358 Hwangsaewul-Ro, Bundang-Gu, Seoul, Gyeonggi-Do, Korea (South)
Tel.: (82) 215660900
Web Site: https://www.sangsanginworld.co.kr
Year Founded: 1954
001290—(KRS)
Rev.: $40,367,355

Assets: $472,465,604
Liabilities: $295,894,411
Net Worth: $176,571,194
Earnings: $2,907,912
Emp.: 260
Fiscal Year-end: 12/31/22
Securities Brokerage Services
N.A.I.C.S.: 523150
Sang-Jun Lee *(Chm)*

SANGSHIN ELECTRONICS CO., LTD.

16-34 269 Bonsan-Ro Jinyeong-Eup, Gimhae, Gyeongsangnam-do, Korea (South)
Tel.: (82) 553433826
Web Site: http://www.sangshin-e.com
Year Founded: 1988
263810—(KRS)
Rev.: $85,401,308
Assets: $58,001,761
Liabilities: $26,427,542
Net Worth: $31,574,219
Earnings: $862,646
Emp.: 121
Fiscal Year-end: 12/31/22
Electronic Components Mfr
N.A.I.C.S.: 334419
Min-Joon Kim *(Asst Mgr)*

SANGSIN BRAKE CO., LTD.

90 Techno Chungangdae-ro, Yugaeup Dalsung-gun, Daegu, Korea (South)
Tel.: (82) 536150101
Web Site: https://www.sangsin.com
Year Founded: 1953
041650—(KRS)
Rev.: $375,074,369
Assets: $416,938,337
Liabilities: $265,387,552
Net Worth: $151,550,785
Earnings: $663,044
Emp.: 628
Fiscal Year-end: 12/31/22
Motor Vehicle Brake System Mfr & Distr
N.A.I.C.S.: 336340
Hyoil Kim *(Co-CEO)*

Subsidiaries:

SANDO BRAKE CO., LTD. (1)
438 Nongong-ro Nongong-eup, Dalsunggun, Daegu, Korea (South)
Tel.: (82) 536169811
Motor Vehicle Brake System Mfr & Distr
N.A.I.C.S.: 336340
Hyun-Chang Kim *(Pres)*

SANDO TECH, Inc. (1)
7 Dasansandan 1-gil, Kyungbuk, Dasan, Goryung-gun, Korea (South)
Tel.: (82) 549560642
N.A.I.C.S.: 336340
Yong-Seong Min *(Pres)*

SANGSIN BRAKE (WUXI) CO., LTD (1)
No 18 Xijin Road, National High Tech Industrial Development Zone, Wuxi, Jiangsu, China
Tel.: (86) 5105322089
Motor Vehicle Brake System Mfr & Distr
N.A.I.C.S.: 336340
Hyo-il Kim *(CEO)*

SANGSIN BRAKE AMERICA, INC (1)
2901 W Macarthur Blvd Ste 208, Santa Ana, CA 92704
Tel.: (714) 708-3456
Motor Vehicle Brake System Mfr & Distr
N.A.I.C.S.: 336340
Hye Jung Song *(Pres)*

SANGSIN BRAKE INDIA PRIVATE LIMITED (1)
Plot No 126 Samthuvapuram Mappedu Ulundai, Tiruvallur, 602 105, Tamilnadu, India
Tel.: (91) 44 276 00063

Motor Vehicle Brake System Mfr & Distr
N.A.I.C.S.: 336340
Seong-ik Jang (Pres)

SANGSING ENG (1)
Tel.: (82) 533557465
Industrial Machinery Mfr
N.A.I.C.S.: 333998
Wan-Kyu Kim (Pres)

Sichuan Sangsin Brake Co., Ltd. (1)
Centralize Industrial Development Zone,
Lezhi Ziyang, Sichuan, China
Tel.: (86) 2827130901
Motor Vehicle Parts Mfr
N.A.I.C.S.: 336390

SANGSIN ENERGY DISPLAY PRECISION CO., LTD.
57 4sandan 6-gil Jiksan-eup, Seobuk-gu, Cheonan, Chungnam, Korea (South)
Tel.: (82) 415835027
Web Site: https://www.ssedp.co.kr
Year Founded: 1985
091580—(KRS)
Rev.: $215,853,753
Assets: $181,472,492
Liabilities: $90,594,396
Net Worth: $90,878,096
Earnings: $18,183,262
Emp.: 259
Fiscal Year-end: 12/31/22
Storage Battery Mfr
N.A.I.C.S.: 335910
Kim Il-Boo (CEO)

SANGSINEDP
32-2 Mangpo-dong, Yeoungtong-gu, Suwon, 443-400, Gyeonggi-do, Korea (South)
Tel.: (82) 312059242
Web Site: http://www.ssedp.co.kr
Year Founded: 1985
091580—(KRS)
Rev.: $223,052,134
Assets: $187,524,312
Liabilities: $93,615,576
Net Worth: $93,908,737
Earnings: $18,789,645
Emp.: 259
Fiscal Year-end: 12/31/22
Storage Battery Mfr
N.A.I.C.S.: 335910
Il Boo Kim (CEO)

Subsidiaries:

SANGSIN ENERTECH SDN BHD (1)
PT 17552 Sri Senawang Light Industrial Area, Jalan Tampin, 71450, Seremban, Negeri Sembilan, Malaysia
Tel.: (60) 66784912
Storage Battery Distr
N.A.I.C.S.: 423610

TIANJIN DAXIN ELECTRONICS Co., Ltd (1)
No 4 Saidahuiya Industrial Park Xiqing, Economic Development Zone, Tianjin, China
Tel.: (86) 2223889121
Storage Battery Distr
N.A.I.C.S.: 423610

SANGSTER'S HEALTH CENTRES
2218 Hanselman Avenue, Saskatoon, S7L 6A4, SK, Canada
Tel.: (306) 653-4481
Web Site: http://www.sangsters.com
Sales Range: $10-24.9 Million
Emp.: 15
Health & Personal Care Stores
N.A.I.C.S.: 456199
Darryl Sangster (Pres & CEO)

SANGUI BIOTECH INTERNATIONAL, INC.
Bleichenbrucke 9, 20354, Hamburg, Germany
Tel.: (49) 406093120 De
Web Site: https://www.sanguibiotech.com
Year Founded: 1996
SGBI—(OTCEM)
Rev.: $93,039
Assets: $90,937
Liabilities: $1,128,813
Net Worth: ($1,037,876)
Earnings: ($147,713)
Emp.: 1
Fiscal Year-end: 06/30/23
Pharmaceutical & Cosmetic Product Mfr
N.A.I.C.S.: 325412
Thomas Striepe (Pres, CEO & CFO)

Subsidiaries:

SanguiBioTech GmbH (1)
c/o HRH GmbH Bleichenbrucke 9, D-20354, Hamburg, Germany
Tel.: (49) 4046093120
Web Site: https://www.sangui.de
Biotechnology Research & Development Services
N.A.I.C.S.: 541714

SANGUINE MEDIA LIMITED
Plaza Center 4th Floor Suit No 349 No 129 G N Chetty Road, Chennai, 600006, Tamil Nadu, India
Tel.: (91) 4428231258
Web Site: https://www.sanguinemedialtd.com
Year Founded: 1995
Rev.: $4,882,563
Assets: $27,357,186
Liabilities: $8,841,322
Net Worth: $18,515,864
Earnings: $33,528
Fiscal Year-end: 03/31/16
Event Management Services
N.A.I.C.S.: 711310
Sanjay Sunderlal Meena (Mng Dir)

SANHE TONGFEI REFRIGERATION CO., LTD.
No 30 ChongyiRoad, Sanhe, 065200, Hebei, China
Tel.: (86) 3163215151
Web Site: https://www.tfzl.com
Year Founded: 2001
300990—(SSE)
Rev.: $141,462,547
Assets: $261,008,893
Liabilities: $31,923,450
Net Worth: $229,085,443
Earnings: $17,945,268
Emp.: 360
Fiscal Year-end: 12/31/22
Refrigeration Equipment Mfr & Distr
N.A.I.C.S.: 333415
Guoshan Zhang (Chm)

SANI-MARC INC.
42 Rue De Lartisan, Victoriaville, G6P 7E3, QC, Canada
Tel.: (819) 758-1541
Web Site: http://www.sanimarc.com
Sales Range: $50-74.9 Million
Emp.: 150
Cleaning Compound Chemicals Mfr
Pierre Goudreault (Pres)

Subsidiaries:

Wood Wyant, Inc. (1)
9585 Rue Ignace, Brossard, J4Y 2P3, QC, Canada
Tel.: (450) 659-7777
Web Site: http://www.woodwyant.com
Sales Range: $25-49.9 Million
Emp.: 60
Janitorial Chemicals, Disinfectants, Floor-care Products, Soaps & Deodorizers
N.A.I.C.S.: 325611

Serge Leroux (VP)

Subsidiary (Domestic):

Chatterson Janitorial Supplies Ltd.
2810 Dewdney Avenue, Regina, S4T 0X7, SK, Canada
Tel.: (306) 525-3568
Web Site: http://www.chatterson.com
Janitorial Equipment Distr
N.A.I.C.S.: 459999

SANIBEL VENTURES CORP.
67 East 5th Av, Vancouver, V5T 1G7, BC, Canada
Tel.: (604) 448-2297 Ca
Year Founded: 2018
SBEL.P—(TSXV)
Assets: $5,280
Liabilities: $22,505
Net Worth: ($17,225)
Earnings: ($36,472)
Fiscal Year-end: 03/31/23
Business Consulting Services
N.A.I.C.S.: 522299
Richard Silas (CEO & CFO)

SANICANI A.D.
Sanicani Bb, 79101, Prijedor, Bosnia & Herzegovina
Tel.: (387) 52325636
SNCN—(BANJ)
Sales Range: $1-9.9 Million
Emp.: 41
Fish Farming Services
N.A.I.C.S.: 112511

SANICHI TECHNOLOGY BERHAD
Unit 27.2 Menara 1MK Kompleks 1 Mont Kiara, No 1 Jalan Kiara Mont Kiara, 50480, Kuala Lumpur, Malaysia
Tel.: (60) 362035828 MY
Web Site: http://www.sanichimould.com
SANICHI—(KLS)
Rev.: $4,435,367
Assets: $64,760,334
Liabilities: $9,872,773
Net Worth: $54,887,561
Earnings: ($4,190,762)
Fiscal Year-end: 03/31/24
Investment Holding Services
N.A.I.C.S.: 551112
Chow Huat Pang (Founder & Mng Dir)

Subsidiaries:

Sanichi Mould (Thailand) Co., Ltd. (1)
888/111 Soi Yingcharoen Moo 19 Bangplee-Damru Rd Bangpleeyai, Bang Phli, 10540, Samutprakarn, Thailand
Tel.: (66) 21747205
Precision Moulding Mfr
N.A.I.C.S.: 333511

Sanichi Property Sdn. Bhd. (1)
Lot 129 Jalan Batang Tiga Klebang Besar, 75260, Malacca, Malaysia
Tel.: (60) 63152888
Web Site: http://www.marinapoint.com.my
Property Development Services
N.A.I.C.S.: 236115

SANIFOAM SUNGER SANAYI VE TICARET A.S.
Gunesli Evren Mah.Bahar Cad Polatsm.B Blok Kat2 D22, Esenler, Istanbul, 34212, Turkiye
Tel.: (90) 2124385300
Web Site: https://www.sanifoam.com.tr
Year Founded: 1990
SANFM—(IST)
Rev.: $23,918,569
Assets: $24,414,797

Liabilities: $14,580,555
Net Worth: $9,834,243
Earnings: $1,503,679
Fiscal Year-end: 12/31/23
Foam Products Mfr
N.A.I.C.S.: 326140
Yildirim Ulkat (Chm)

SANIMA BANK LIMITED
Alakapuri Naxal, GPO Box 20394, Kathmandu, Nepal
Tel.: (977) 15970033
Web Site: https://www.sanimabank.com
Year Founded: 2004
SANIMA—(NEP)
Rev.: $162,034,651
Assets: $1,615,071,887
Liabilities: $1,468,977,495
Net Worth: $146,094,392
Earnings: $19,663,351
Emp.: 1,301
Fiscal Year-end: 07/16/23
Banking Services
N.A.I.C.S.: 522110
Tej Bahadur Chand (Deputy CEO)

Subsidiaries:

Sanima Capital Limited (1)
Sama Marga, Naxal, Kathmandu, 44600, Nepal
Tel.: (977) 14540508
Web Site: https://www.sanima.capital
Emp.: 100
Investment Banking Services
N.A.I.C.S.: 523999
Bhism Raj Chalise (CEO)

SANIMA HYDROPOWER PRIVATE LIMITED
Shankha Park Dhumbarahi, PO Box 19737, Kathmandu, Nepal
Tel.: (977) 14372828
Web Site: https://www.sanimahydro.com.np
Year Founded: 1999
Eletric Power Generation Services
N.A.I.C.S.: 221111
Arun Kumar Ojha (Chm)

SANIMAX INDUSTRIES INC.
9900 Maurice-Duplessis Boulevard, Montreal, H1C 1G1, QC, Canada
Tel.: (514) 648-6001
Web Site: http://www.sanimax.com
Meat Byproduct Processing Services
N.A.I.C.S.: 311613
Martin Couture (CEO)

Subsidiaries:

Kendallville Fertilizer Co., Inc. (1)
7616 N 600 E, Kendallville, IN 46755-9301
Tel.: (260) 347-1250
Sales Range: $1-9.9 Million
Emp.: 15
Animal Food Distr
N.A.I.C.S.: 424910

Sanimax Marketing Limited (1)
5068 Whitelaw Rd, Guelph, N1H 6J3, ON, Canada
Tel.: (519) 824-2381
Web Site: http://www.saminex.com
Sales Range: $150-199.9 Million
Emp.: 13
Commodity Trading Company
N.A.I.C.S.: 523160
M. Couture (Mng Dir)

Sanimax USA LLC (1)
2099 Badgerland Dr, Green Bay, WI 54303
Tel.: (920) 494-5233
Web Site: http://www.sanimax.com
Sales Range: $75-99.9 Million
Emp.: 350
Rendering & Hide Processing Mfr
N.A.I.C.S.: 311613
Brandon Foley (VP-Procurement-US)

SANIONA AB

SANIONA AB

Saniona AB—(Continued)
Smedeland 26B, 2600, Glostrup, Denmark
Tel.: (45) 70705225
Web Site: https://www.saniona.com
Year Founded: 2011
SANION—(OMX)
Rev.: $1,431,435
Assets: $14,395,459
Liabilities: $9,458,728
Net Worth: $4,936,731
Earnings: ($22,980,603)
Emp.: 23
Fiscal Year-end: 12/31/22
Biotechnology Research & Development Services
N.A.I.C.S.: 541714
Jorgen Drejer *(Founder & Chief Scientific Officer)*

SANISITT-COMUTHERM
4 Avenue Joseph Rey, 68000, Colmar, Haut Rhin, France
Tel.: (33) 389210380
Web Site: http://www.sanisitt-comutherm.fr
Year Founded: 1999
Plumbing Fixtures Equipment Mfr
N.A.I.C.S.: 423720

SANITAR COMPANY LTD.
7F No 111-8 Xingde Road, Sanchong District, New Taipei City, 241, Taiwan
Tel.: (886) 285123712
Web Site: https://www.caesar.com.tw
Year Founded: 1988
1817—(TAI)
Rev.: $82,520,321
Assets: $88,407,172
Liabilities: $21,454,494
Net Worth: $66,952,677
Earnings: $7,765,394
Emp.: 1,140
Fiscal Year-end: 12/31/23
Ceramic & Glass Bathroom Products Mfr
N.A.I.C.S.: 327110
Yung Nan Chang *(Dir)*

SANITARIUM HEALTH FOOD COMPANY
1 Sanitarium Drive, Berkeley Vale, 2261, NSW, Australia
Tel.: (61) 243487777
Web Site: http://www.sanitarium.com.au
Year Founded: 1898
Emp.: 800
Health Food Product Mfr & Distr
N.A.I.C.S.: 311999
Kevin Jackson *(CEO)*

SANITAS KRANKENVERSICHERUNG
Jagergasse 3, PO Box 2010, 8021, Zurich, Switzerland
Tel.: (41) 0442986300
Web Site: http://www.sanitas.com
Year Founded: 1958
Sales Range: $1-4.9 Billion
Emp.: 300
Health Insurance
N.A.I.C.S.: 524114
Otto Bitterli *(Interim CEO)*

Subsidiaries:

Wincare Versicherungen
Konradstrasse 14, 8401, Winterthur, Switzerland
Tel.: (41) 52 266 74 74
Emp.: 500
Insurance & Investment Services
N.A.I.C.S.: 524210
Otto Bitterli *(CEO)*

SANITEKS D.D.

Tone Hrovata br 2, 77230, Velika Kladusa, Bosnia & Herzegovina
Tel.: (387) 37 770 433
Web Site: http://www.saniteks.ba
Year Founded: 1962
STVKRK4—(SARE)
Rev.: $2,251,678
Assets: $13,281,841
Liabilities: $6,049,909
Net Worth: $7,231,932
Earnings: ($993,096)
Emp.: 122
Fiscal Year-end: 12/31/20
Medical Device Mfr
N.A.I.C.S.: 339112

SANITIZED AG
Lyssachstrasse 95, Burgdorf, 3400, Switzerland
Tel.: (41) 344271616
Web Site: http://www.sanitized.com
Year Founded: 1935
Sales Range: $10-24.9 Million
Emp.: 50
Hygiene Protection Products
N.A.I.C.S.: 325414
Niklaus J. Luthi *(Owner & Chm)*

Subsidiaries:

Sanitized, Inc. (1)
57 New Milford Tpk, New Preston Marble Dale, CT 06777
Tel.: (860) 868-9491
Bacteriostats, Fungistats & Mildewstats
N.A.I.C.S.: 325414

SANIX INCORPORATED
2-1-23 Hakataekihigashi, Hataka-ku, Fukuoka, 812-0013, Japan
Tel.: (81) 924368870
Web Site: https://www.sanix.jp
Year Founded: 1975
4651—(TKS)
Rev.: $311,773,870
Assets: $244,338,650
Liabilities: $185,430,330
Net Worth: $58,908,320
Earnings: $17,827,170
Emp.: 2,049
Fiscal Year-end: 03/31/24
Environmental Resources Development, Corporate Facilities Sanitation & Home Sanitation Products & Services
N.A.I.C.S.: 561720
Hiroshi Munemasa *(CEO)*

Subsidiaries:

SE Wings Incorporated (1)
504-4 Benten, Tomakomai, 059-1371, Hokkaido, Japan
Tel.: (81) 145268989
Electric Power Distribution Services
N.A.I.C.S.: 221122

Sanix Energy Incorporated K.K (1)
504-4 Benten, Tomakomai, 059-1371, Hokkaido, Japan
Tel.: (81) 145268811
Web Site: http://www.sanix-energy.com
Sales Range: $25-49.9 Million
Emp.: 50
Power Generation & Recycling Services
N.A.I.C.S.: 221122
Shin-ichi Munemasa *(Pres & CEO)*

Sanix Software Design Incorporated K.K
2nd floor 1-3-33 Higashihie, Fukuoka, 812-0007, Hakata-Ku, Japan
Tel.: (81) 924330610
Web Site: https://www.software.sanix.jp
Sales Range: $25-49.9 Million
Emp.: 65
Computer Programming Services
N.A.I.C.S.: 541511

Shanri (Shanghai) Energy Science & Technology Co., Ltd. (1)
No 535 Shennan Road, Minhang District, Shanghai, 201108, China

Tel.: (86) 2138780001
Web Site: https://sanix.jp
Emp.: 20
Solar Modules & Related Parts Mfr & Distr
N.A.I.C.S.: 335999

Sunaim Incorporated (1)
4F Watanabe Dori South Building 1-9-19 Kiyokawa, Chuo-ku, Fukuoka, 810-0005, Japan
Tel.: (81) 925345650
Web Site: http://www.sunaim.co.jp
Emp.: 16
Automobile Leasing & Pharmaceutical Products Distr
N.A.I.C.S.: 424210

SANJIANG SHOPPING CLUB CO., LTD.
No 197 Huancheng West Road North Section, Haishu District, Ningbo, 315010, Zhejiang, China
Tel.: (86) 57483886893
Web Site: http://www.sanjiang.com
Year Founded: 1995
601116—(SHG)
Rev.: $564,959,983
Assets: $709,595,991
Liabilities: $268,075,632
Net Worth: $441,520,359
Earnings: $21,562,772
Fiscal Year-end: 12/31/22
Supermarket Store Operator
N.A.I.C.S.: 445110
Nianci Chen *(Chm)*

SANJIVANI PARANTERAL LIMITED
1202 B Wing O2 Commercial Park Asha Nagar Park Road, Asha Nagar Mulund W, Mumbai, 400080, India
Tel.: (91) 2220812600
Web Site: https://www.sanjivani.co.in
Year Founded: 1994
531569—(BOM)
Rev.: $3,461,300
Assets: $2,631,215
Liabilities: $1,471,197
Net Worth: $1,160,018
Earnings: $193,735
Fiscal Year-end: 03/31/21
Pharmaceuticals Product Mfr
N.A.I.C.S.: 325412
Ashwani Khemka *(Chm & Mng Dir)*

Subsidiaries:

Sanjivani Paranteral Limited - Dehradun Plant (1)
Plot No 323/1 Near Central Hope Town Camp Road Selaqui, Dehradun, 248 197, India
Tel.: (91) 135 2698691
Pharmaceuticals Product Mfr
N.A.I.C.S.: 325412
Sunil Bhatt *(Gen Mgr)*

Sanjivani Paranteral Limited - Mumbai Plant (1)
Plot No R-40 TTC Industrial Area Rabale Thane Belapur Road, Rabale, Mumbai, 400 701, Maharashtra, India
Tel.: (91) 22 66888700
Web Site: http://www.sanjivani.co.in
Emp.: 200
Pharmaceuticals Product Mfr
N.A.I.C.S.: 325412

SANKEI REAL ESTATE, INC.
S-GATE Otemachi-Kita 4F 2-3-4 Uchikanda, Chiyoda-ku, Tokyo, 100-0004, Japan
Tel.: (81) 355421316
Web Site: https://www.s-reit.co.jp
Year Founded: 2018
2972—(TKS)
Real Estate Investment Services
N.A.I.C.S.: 531190
Yuichi Ota *(Exec Dir)*

SANKEN ELECTRIC CO., LTD.

INTERNATIONAL PUBLIC

3-6-3 Kitano, Niiza, 352-8666, Saitama, Japan
Tel.: (81) 484721111
Web Site: https://www.sanken-ele.co.jp
Year Founded: 1946
6707—(TKS)
Rev.: $1,554,810,810
Assets: $2,535,536,510
Liabilities: $1,222,664,920
Net Worth: $1,312,871,590
Earnings: ($53,620,320)
Fiscal Year-end: 03/31/24
Semiconductor Devices, Electronic Equipment & Power Sources Mfr
N.A.I.C.S.: 334413
Takashi Wada *(Chm)*

Subsidiaries:

Allegro MicroSystems, LLC (1)
955 Perimeter Rd, Manchester, NH 03103
Tel.: (603) 626-2300
Web Site: http://www.allegromicro.com
Sales Range: $250-299.9 Million
Emp.: 600
Semiconductor Mfr
N.A.I.C.S.: 334413
Steven Miles *(VP-Tech Dev)*

Subsidiary (Non-US):

Allegro MicroSystems Europe Limited (2)
Melita House 124 Bridge Road, Chertsey, KT16 8LA, Surrey, United Kingdom (100%)
Tel.: (44) 1932566000
Web Site: http://www.allegromicro.com
Sales Range: $25-49.9 Million
Emp.: 15
Mfr of High-performance Power & Hall-effect Sensor Integrated Circuits
N.A.I.C.S.: 334413

Allegro MicroSystems Philippines, Inc. (2)
4756 Sampaguita St Barangay Sun Valley, Marimar Village, Paranaque, 1700, Philippines (100%)
Tel.: (63) 28235000
Web Site: http://www.allegromicro.com
Sales Range: $400-449.9 Million
Semiconductor & Non-Semiconductor Products
N.A.I.C.S.: 334413
James Beuerle *(Gen Mgr)*

Subsidiary (Domestic):

Voxtel, Inc. (2)
15985 NW Schendel Ave #200, Beaverton, OR 97006
Tel.: (971) 223-5646
Web Site: http://www.voxtel-inc.com
Electrical Equipment & Component Mfr
N.A.I.C.S.: 335999
George Williams *(Pres & CEO)*

Dalian Sanken Electric Co., Ltd. (1)
No 7 Zhenpeng South Road, Dalian Economic and Technical Development Zone, Dalian, 116000, Liaoning, China (100%)
Tel.: (86) 41187511417
Web Site: http://www.sanken-ele.co.jp
Sales Range: $100-124.9 Million
Emp.: 400
Mfr of Semiconductor Devices, Electronic Equipment & Power Sources
N.A.I.C.S.: 334413
G. JiguangYu *(Gen Mgr)*

Fukushima Sanken Co., Ltd. (1)
15 Miyado, Nihonmatsu, 964-0811, Fukushima-ken, Japan
Tel.: (81) 243224300
Web Site: http://www.sanken-ele.co.jp
Sales Range: $100-124.9 Million
Emp.: 300
Electronic & Semiconductor Mfr
N.A.I.C.S.: 334413

Ishikawa Sanken Co., Ltd. (1)
Ha-5 Nashitanikoyama, Shikamachi, Hakui, 925-0151, Ishikawa-ken, Japan (100%)
Tel.: (81) 767328111
Web Site: http://www.sanken-ele.co.jp

AND PRIVATE COMPANIES

Semiconductor & Non-Semiconductor Products
N.A.I.C.S.: 334413

Kashima Sanken Co., Ltd. (1)
8073 Yatabe, Hasakimachi, Kashima, 314-0341, Ibaraki, Japan
Tel.: (81) 479481211
Web Site: http://www.sanken-ele.co.jp
Sales Range: $100-124.9 Million
Emp.: 400
Semiconductor & Non-Semiconductor Products
N.A.I.C.S.: 334413

Korea Sanken Co., Ltd. (1)
8 Jayumuyeok 2-gil, Masanhoewon-gu, Changwon, 51339, Gyeongsangnam-do, Korea (South)
Tel.: (82) 552907000
Web Site: http://www.sanken-ele.co.jp
Semiconductor & Non-Semiconductor Products
N.A.I.C.S.: 334413

P.T. Sanken Indonesia (1)
MM2100 Industrial Town Block GG-8, Cikarang Barat, Bekasi, 17520, West Java, Indonesia (99%)
Tel.: (62) 218981252
Sales Range: $250-299.9 Million
Emp.: 900
N.A.I.C.S.: 325412

P.T. Sanken Transformer Indonesia (1)
MM2100 Industrial Town Block GG-8, Cikarang Barat, Bekasi, 17520, West Java, Indonesia (100%)
Tel.: (62) 218981252
Web Site: http://www.sanken-ele.co.jp
Sales Range: $400-449.9 Million
Emp.: 1,603
Mfr & Sales of Switching Power Supplies
N.A.I.C.S.: 335313
Sone Yoshiyuki (Pres & Dir)

Polar Semiconductor, LLC (1)
2800 E Old Shakopee Rd, Bloomington, MN 55425 (100%)
Tel.: (952) 876-3000
Web Site: https://polarsemi.com
Emp.: 500
Semiconductor Mfr
N.A.I.C.S.: 334413
Rajesh Appat (Dir-Quality)

Sanken Business Service Co., Ltd. (1)
3-6-3 Kitano, Niiza, 352-8666, Saitama, Japan
Tel.: (81) 484721111
Semiconductor Product Mfr
N.A.I.C.S.: 334413

Sanken Densetsu Co., Ltd. (1)
677 Shimoakasaka-Ohnohara, Kawagoe, 350-1155, Saitama, Japan
Tel.: (81) 492668095
Semiconductor & Non-Semiconductor Products
N.A.I.C.S.: 334413

Sanken Electric (Shanghai) Co., Ltd. (1)
Room3202 Maxdo Centre Xingyi Road 8, Changning district, Shanghai, China
Tel.: (86) 2152081177
Semiconductor Product Mfr
N.A.I.C.S.: 334413

Sanken Electric (Thailand) Co., Ltd. (1)
1 Empire Tower 26th Floor Unit 2606 South Sathorn Road, Yannawa Sathorn, Bangkok, 10120, Thailand
Tel.: (66) 20597170
Semiconductor Product Mfr
N.A.I.C.S.: 334413

Sanken Electric Hong Kong Co., Ltd. (1)
Suite 1026 Ocean Centre Canton Road, Tsimshatsui, Kowloon, China (Hong Kong) (100%)
Tel.: (852) 27355262
Sales Range: $25-49.9 Million
Emp.: 15
Semiconductor & Non-Semiconductor Products

N.A.I.C.S.: 334413
Kazunobu Ihara (Mng Dir)

Sanken Electric Korea Co., Ltd. (1)
4F Geonwa Bldg 56 Magokdong-ro, Gangseo-gu, Seoul, 07803, Korea (South) (100%)
Tel.: (82) 27143700
Web Site: https://www.sanken.co.kr
Semiconductor Devices, Electronic Equipment & Power Sources Mfr
N.A.I.C.S.: 334413

Sanken Electric Singapore Pte. Ltd. (1)
152 Beach Rd Unit 10- 06, The Gtwy E, Singapore, 189721, Singapore (100%)
Tel.: (65) 62914755
Web Site: http://www.sankenelectric.com
Sales Range: $25-49.9 Million
Emp.: 5
Semiconductor & Non-Semiconductor Products
N.A.I.C.S.: 334413
Makoto Koga (Mng Dir)

Sanken L.D. Electric (Jiangyin) Co., Ltd. (1)
Yungu Road North Side Luqiaoduan, Huashizhen, Jiangyin, Jiangsu, China
Tel.: (86) 51086377888
Semiconductor Product Mfr
N.A.I.C.S.: 334413

Sanken LD Co., Ltd. (1)
Rm703-704 No1 Science Museum Road Concordia Plaza, Hong Kong, 999077, China (Hong Kong) (100%)
Tel.: (852) 27213611
Web Site: http://www.sankenld.com
Sales Range: $25-49.9 Million
Emp.: 6
Rolled Steel Products Mfr
N.A.I.C.S.: 334413

Sanken Logistics Co., Ltd. (1)
1-13-7 Nakano, Niiza, 352-0005, Saitama-ken, Japan (100%)
Tel.: (81) 484801015
Web Site: http://www.sanken-ele.co.jp
Sales Range: $25-49.9 Million
Emp.: 55
Rolled Steel Products Mfr
N.A.I.C.S.: 334413

Sanken Optoproducts Co., Ltd. (1)
Ha-5-4 Nashitani-Koyama Shika-machi, Shika-machi Hakui-gun, Ishikawa, 925-0151, Japan
Tel.: (81) 767328111
Semiconductor Product Mfr
N.A.I.C.S.: 334413

Taiwan Sanken Electric Co., Ltd. (1)
Room 1801 18th Floor 88 Jhung Shiau East Road, Sec 2, Taipei, 100, Taiwan (100%)
Tel.: (886) 223568161
Sales Range: $25-49.9 Million
Emp.: 15
Electronic Services
N.A.I.C.S.: 238210
Terry Lee (Mgr-Sls)

Yamagata Sanken Co., Ltd. (1)
5600-2 Oaza-Higashine-Ko, Higashine, 999-3701, Yamagata, Japan
Tel.: (81) 237435511
Web Site: http://www.sanken-ele.co.jp
Sales Range: $100-124.9 Million
Emp.: 500
Manufacture, Sale & Purchase of Electric Equipment & Apparatus
N.A.I.C.S.: 335999

SANKHYA INFOTECH LTD
House No-1-112/63 2nd Floor V Satyanarayana House WS Colony, Near KIMS Hospital Kondapur, Hyderabad, 500 049, India
Tel.: (91) 9908124562
Web Site: http://www.sankhya.net
532972—(BOM)
Assets: $11,588,632
Liabilities: $7,117,438
Net Worth: $4,471,194
Earnings: ($1,024,610)
Fiscal Year-end: 03/31/21

IT Services
N.A.I.C.S.: 541512
Sridhar Krishna (Chm & Mng Dir)

SANKI SERVICE CORPORATION
576-1 Abo-ko, Himeji, 670-0944, Hyogo, Japan
Tel.: (81) 792894411
Web Site: https://www.sanki-s.co.jp
Year Founded: 1977
6044—(TKS)
Rev.: $128,432,300
Assets: $56,925,320
Liabilities: $29,070,780
Net Worth: $27,854,540
Earnings: $3,086,870
Emp.: 200
Fiscal Year-end: 05/31/24
Facilities Maintenance Services
N.A.I.C.S.: 561210
Yoshikane Nakashima (Founder & Chm)

SANKO CO., LTD.
959 Hirooka Nomura, Shiojiri, 399-0782, Nagano, Japan
Tel.: (81) 263522918
Web Site: https://www.sko.co.jp
Year Founded: 1945
6964—(TKS)
Rev.: $111,946,960
Assets: $143,165,990
Liabilities: $42,284,170
Net Worth: $100,881,820
Earnings: $4,653,440
Emp.: 554
Fiscal Year-end: 03/31/24
Precision Component Mfr
N.A.I.C.S.: 335999
Yoshiyuki Takaki (Pres & CEO)

Subsidiaries:

THAI SANKO Co., Ltd. (1)
Rojana Industrial Park Zone 2 488 Moo 4, Tambol U-Thai Amphur U-Thai, Phra Nakhon Si Ayutthaya, 13210, Thailand
Tel.: (66) 35746488
Web Site: https://www.sko.co.jp
Emp.: 182
Automobile Parts Distr
N.A.I.C.S.: 423120

SANKO DIECASTING (THAILAND) PUBLIC COMPANY LIMITED
Rojana Industrial Park Rayong 3/14 Moo 2 T Nongbua, A Bankhai, Rayong, 21120, Thailand
Tel.: (66) 33010701   TH
Web Site: http://www.sankothai.net
Year Founded: 1996
SANKO—(THA)
Rev.: $22,213,691
Assets: $15,821,784
Liabilities: $8,337,403
Net Worth: $7,484,381
Earnings: $1,594,336
Emp.: 397
Fiscal Year-end: 12/31/23
Aluminum Alloy & Zinc Alloy Die-Casting
N.A.I.C.S.: 331523
Adul Chotinisakorn (Chm)

SANKO GOSEI LTD.
1200 Habushin, Nanto, 939-1698, Toyama-ken, Japan
Tel.: (81) 763521000
Web Site:
  https://www.sankogosei.co.jp
Year Founded: 1940
78880—(TKS)
Rev.: $535,929,964
Assets: $433,300,297
Liabilities: $261,843,409
Net Worth: $171,456,888

Earnings: $13,848,695
Emp.: 2,785
Fiscal Year-end: 05/31/23
Molded Plastic Die Mfr & Distr
N.A.I.C.S.: 333514
Kenso Kuroda (Pres)

Subsidiaries:

PERMINTEX SANKO TECHNOLOGIES SDN BHD. (1)
Lot 9414 9415 9416 Jalan Jasmine 1 Seksyen BB10, Bukit Beruntung, 48300, Rawang, Selangor, Malaysia
Tel.: (60) 360284421
Web Site: http://www.permintex.com.my
Industrial Mold Distr
N.A.I.C.S.: 423840
Khairudin Yusoff (CEO)

PT. Sanko Gosei Technology Indonesia (1)
Kawasan Industri Jababeka Jl Jababeka XII B Blok W 17-20, Bekasi, 17550, Jakarta, Indonesia
Tel.: (62) 2189833239
Industrial Mold Distr
N.A.I.C.S.: 423840
Beng Cheng Chua (Gen Mgr)

S-VANCE LTD. (1)
62-1 Nomuranaka-machi, Hirakata, 573-0144, Osaka, Japan
Tel.: (81) 728581121
Web Site: https://www.s-vance.co.jp
Emp.: 170
Industrial Mold Mfr & Distr
N.A.I.C.S.: 333511
Toshio Mitsushima (Chm)

SANKO GOSEI (THAILAND) LTD. (1)
21/14 Moo 9 T Kanham A U-Thai, Rojana Industrial Park, Phra Nakhon Si Ayutthaya, 13210, Thailand
Tel.: (66) 35950790
Industrial Mold Distr
N.A.I.C.S.: 423840
Kanwara Puangcham (Mgr-Quality Control Dept)

SANKO GOSEI MEXICO, S.A.DE C.V. (1)
Ferropuerto 205 Rincon de Tamayo, 38150, Celaya, Guanajuato, Mexico
Tel.: (52) 4614716100
Web Site: https://www.sankogoseimexico.com
Industrial Mold Distr
N.A.I.C.S.: 423840

SANKO GOSEI PHILIPPINES, INC. (1)
Lot 11-B Phase-1B, First Philippine Industrial Park Brgy Ulango, Tanauan, 4232, Batangas, Philippines
Tel.: (63) 434301081
Industrial Mold Distr
N.A.I.C.S.: 423840
Rhea Clar (Deputy Gen Mgr)

SANKO GOSEI TECHNOLOGY (THAILAND) LTD. (1)
Rayong Factory 64/20 Moo 4, Eastern Seaboard Industrial Estate Tambon Pluakdaeng Amphur, Pluak Daeng, 21140, Rayong, Thailand
Tel.: (66) 38955229
Industrial Mold Distr
N.A.I.C.S.: 423840
Yoshiaki Shibata (Pres)

SANKO GOSEI TECHNOLOGY INDIA PRIVATE LTD. (1)
469-471 Sector-8 IMT Manesar, Gurgaon, Haryana, India
Tel.: (91) 1242291017
Industrial Mold Distr
N.A.I.C.S.: 423840

SANKO SVANCE JRG TOOLING INDIA PRIVATE LTD. (1)
Gate No 3 Plot No 16 Sector -5, Industrial Estate Growth Center HSIIDC Bawal, Rewari, 123501, Haryana, India
Tel.: (91) 1284264218
Web Site: https://sankosvance.com
Industrial Mold Distr
N.A.I.C.S.: 423840

SANKO GOSEI LTD.

Sanko Gosei Ltd.—(Continued)

Bharatdev J. Sandimani *(Head-Mould Design Dept)*

SHANGHAI SANKO GOSEI TECHNOLOGY LTD. (1)
Shanghai International Trade Center 12F Suite 1210 2201 Yan An West Rd, Shanghai, 200336, China
Tel.: (86) 2162196133
Industrial Mold Distr
N.A.I.C.S.: 423840

Sanko Gosei Crech, s.r.o. (1)
Rohacova 188/37, Zizkov, 13000, Prague, Czech Republic
Tel.: (420) 32 176 1151
Synthetic Resin Mfr & Distr
N.A.I.C.S.: 325211

Sanko Gosei Ltd. - Gunma Factory (1)
385 Mizunuma Kurabuchi-machi, Takasaki, Gunma, Japan
Tel.: (81) 273787019
Industrial Mold Mfr
N.A.I.C.S.: 333511

Sanko Gosei Ltd. - Kumagaya Factory (1)
2961-3 Kamino, Kumagaya, 360-0012, Saitama, Japan
Tel.: (81) 48 580 6005
Web Site: https://www.sankogosei.co.jp
Industrial Mold Mfr
N.A.I.C.S.: 333511

Sanko Gosei Ltd. - Shiga Factory (1)
1554 Hebimizo-cho, Higashi-omi, Shiga, Japan
Tel.: (81) 748226100
Industrial Mold Mfr
N.A.I.C.S.: 333511

Sanko Gosei Ltd. - Shizuoka Factory (1)
3560 Simohijikata, Kakegawa, Shizuoka, Japan
Tel.: (81) 537742512
Industrial Mold Mfr
N.A.I.C.S.: 333511

Sanko Gosei Ltd. - Tool & Engineering Business Unit (1)
4185 Koreyasu, Nanto, Toyama, Japan
Tel.: (81) 763623660
Industrial Mold Mfr
N.A.I.C.S.: 333511

Sanko Gosei Technologies USA Inc (1)
6509 Moeller Rd, Fort Wayne, IN 46806
Tel.: (260) 749-5168
Industrial Mold Distr
N.A.I.C.S.: 423840
Laurence Tabner *(CEO)*

Sanko Gosei Technology (Singapore) Pte. Ltd. (1)
2 Jurong East Street 21 02-188 IMM Building, Singapore, 609601, Singapore
Tel.: (65) 68725161
Industrial Mold Distr
N.A.I.C.S.: 423840
Yeah Jie Ling *(Asst Mgr-Accts & Admin)*

Sanko Gosei Technology Technology India Private Ltd. (1)
Plot No 16 Sector-5 HSIDC Growth Bawari, Bawal, 123501, Haryana, India
Tel.: (91) 991 032 0057
Synthetic Resin Mfr & Distr
N.A.I.C.S.: 325211

Sanko Gosei UK Ltd. (1)
15-17 Seddon Place, Stanley Industrial Estate, Skelmersdale, WN8 8EB, Lancashire, United Kingdom
Tel.: (44) 1695455400
Web Site: https://sanko-gosei.co.uk
Industrial Mold Distr
N.A.I.C.S.: 423840
Wayne Ash *(Mng Dir)*

Set Europe Ltd. (1)
15/17 Seddon Place, Stanley Industrial Estate, Skelmersdale, WN8 8EB, Lancashire, United Kingdom
Tel.: (44) 1695455400
Synthetic Resin Mfr & Distr
N.A.I.C.S.: 325211

TIANJIN SANKO GOSEI CO., LTD. (1)
No 156 Nanhai Road Factory No 26 TEDA, Tianjin, 300457, China
Tel.: (86) 2266299281
Industrial Mold Distr
N.A.I.C.S.: 423840

Wuhan Sanko Gosei Co., Ltd. (1)
No 11 Daishan Road, Xiaotian Office Development Zone, Xiaogan, Hubei, China
Tel.: (86) 7122119500
Synthetic Resin Mfr & Distr
N.A.I.C.S.: 325211

SANKO MARKETING FOODS CO., LTD.
Shinnkawa1-10-14, Cyuoku, Tokyo, 171-0022, Japan
Tel.: (81) 335379711
Web Site: https://www.sankofoods.com
Year Founded: 1977
2762—(TKS)
Rev.: $58,020,160
Assets: $14,822,260
Liabilities: $12,788,320
Net Worth: $2,033,940
Earnings: ($4,422,420)
Emp.: 179
Fiscal Year-end: 06/30/24
Restaurant Services
N.A.I.C.S.: 722511

SANKO METAL INDUSTRIAL CO., LTD.
MS Shibaura Bldg 4-13-23 Shibaura, Minato-ku, Tokyo, 108-0023, Japan
Tel.: (81) 3 5446 5600 JP
Web Site: http://www.sankometal.co.jp
Year Founded: 1949
Sales Range: $250-299.9 Million
Emp.: 400
Steel Roofing & Siding Products Mfr & Whslr
N.A.I.C.S.: 332322
Hiroyuki Migita *(Pres)*

SANKO PAZARLAMA ITHALAT IHRACAT AS
Sanko Tekstil Isl San ve Tic A S 3 Organize Sanayi Bolgesi, Baspinar, Gaziantep, Turkiye
Tel.: (90) 3422116341
Web Site: https://www.sankopazarlama.com
SANKO—(IST)
Sales Range: Less than $1 Million
Textile Products Mfr
N.A.I.C.S.: 313210
Gurkan Tural *(Chm)*

SANKO SANGYO CO., LTD.
3-42-6 Jingumae, Shibuya-Ku, Tokyo, 150-8403, Japan
Tel.: (81) 334038134
Web Site: https://www.sankosangyo.co.jp
7922—(TKS)
Rev.: $68,453,160
Assets: $77,925,290
Liabilities: $21,383,350
Net Worth: $56,541,940
Earnings: ($621,340)
Emp.: 250
Fiscal Year-end: 03/31/24
Adhesive Label, Stickers & Panel Mfr & Distr
N.A.I.C.S.: 325520

Subsidiaries:

Sanko Sangyo (Shen Zhen) Ltd. (1)
610B Building C Qianhai Excellence Times Square Xinan Street, Baoan District, Shenzhen, China
Tel.: (86) 75529893488
Printed Product Mfr
N.A.I.C.S.: 325910

Sanko Sangyo (Bangkok) Co.,Ltd. (1)
140/39 ITF Tower-II 18th Fl Silom Rd Suriyawong, Bangrak, Bangkok, 10500, Thailand
Tel.: (66) 26340700
Printed Product Mfr
N.A.I.C.S.: 325910

Sanko Sangyo (Malaysia) Sdn.Bhd. (1)
Lot 78 Jalan Hulu Tinggi 26/6 Hicom industrial Estate, Selangor Darul Ehsan, 40000, Shah Alam, Malaysia
Tel.: (60) 351911351
Web Site: https://www.sankosangyo.com.my
Emp.: 155
Printed Product Mfr
N.A.I.C.S.: 325910

Toms Creative Co., Ltd. (1)
B1 3-42-6 Jingumae, Shibuya-ku, Tokyo, 150-0001, Japan
Tel.: (81) 367210275
Web Site: https://www.toms-creative.com
Emp.: 7
Toy Mfr & Distr
N.A.I.C.S.: 339930

SANKO TECHNO CO., LTD.
3-10-16 Minami Nagareyama, Nagareyama, Chiba, Japan
Tel.: (81) 471573535
Web Site: https://www.sanko-techno.co.jp
Year Founded: 1964
3435—(TKS)
Rev.: $139,748,620
Assets: $162,797,690
Liabilities: $46,699,650
Net Worth: $116,098,040
Earnings: $11,501,400
Emp.: 356
Fiscal Year-end: 03/31/24
Construction Material Mfr & Distr
N.A.I.C.S.: 339999
Hideto Horage *(Pres)*

Subsidiaries:

IKK CO., LTD. (1)
396-59 Ashitaka, Numazu, 410-0001, Shizuoka, Japan
Tel.: (81) 559228811
Hydraulic Power Tool Mfr
N.A.I.C.S.: 333991

Sanko Fastem (Thailand) Ltd. (1)
2 Soi Phaholyothin 96 Prachatipat, Thanyaburi, Pathumthani, 12130, Thailand
Tel.: (66) 251698235
Bolt Mfr & Distr
N.A.I.C.S.: 332722

Subsidiary (Non-US):

Sanko Fastem (Vietnam) Ltd. (2)
Lot No 36 An Sinh Quarter O16-CT2 Tay Ho Tay New Urban Area, Co Nhue 1 Ward Bac Tu Liem District, Hanoi, Vietnam
Tel.: (84) 24395902624
Bolt Distr
N.A.I.C.S.: 423710
Pen Pipi *(Mng Dir)*

SANKOSHA CO., LTD.
Naka-ku 3-20-9, Naka-Ku, Nagoya, 460-0003, Japan
Tel.: (81) 52 961 2211 JP
Web Site: http://www.sanko-sha.co.jp
Year Founded: 1944
Emp.: 200
Adhesive Label, Stickers & Panel Mfr & Distr
N.A.I.C.S.: 541810
Teiji Kawamura *(Chm & CEO)*

Subsidiaries:

Sankosha Co., Ltd. (1)
2-1-13 Dojimahama, Kita-ku, Osaka, 530-0004, Japan
Tel.: (81) 6 345 3471
Web Site: http://www.sanko-sha.co.jp
Yoriaki Matsunami *(Pres & COO)*

Sankosha Co., Ltd. (1)
12 Kohya-machi, Shizuoka, 420-0852, Japan
Tel.: (81) 54 254 7321
Web Site: http://www.sanko-sha.co.jp
N.A.I.C.S.: 541810
Yoriaki Matsunami *(Pres & COO)*

Sankosha Co., Ltd. (1)
13-7 Moto-machi, Naka-ku, Hiroshima, 730-0011, Japan
Tel.: (81) 82 221 5531
Web Site: http://www.sanko-sha.co.jp
Emp.: 10
N.A.I.C.S.: 541810
Yoriaki Matsunami *(Pres & COO)*

Sankosha Co., Ltd. (1)
16-3 1-Chome, Nishi-sinbashi, Minato-ku, Tokyo, 105-0003, Japan
Tel.: (81) 3 5501 7071
Web Site: http://www.sanko-sha.co.jp
N.A.I.C.S.: 541810
Yoriaki Matsunami *(Pres & COO)*

SANKOSHA CORPORATION
3-8 Osaki 4 Chome, Tokyo, 141-0032, Japan
Tel.: (81) 334917181
Web Site: http://www.sankosha.co.jp
Year Founded: 1930
Sales Range: $75-99.9 Million
Emp.: 300
Mfr of Various Protective Devices & Related Equipment for Power Lines, Communication Lines, Signal Lines & Data Transmission Lines
N.A.I.C.S.: 335311
Masayoshi Ito *(Co-Pres)*

Subsidiaries:

P.T. Sankosha Indonesia (1)
Interchange Toll Karawang Timur Desa Anggadita, Karawang, 41371, Jawa Barat, Indonesia
Tel.: (62) 267 433 888
Lighting Device Mfr
N.A.I.C.S.: 335139

Sankosha Co., Ltd. (1)
988 Kanoya Hachioji, Tokyo, 193-0815, Japan
Tel.: (81) 42 621 1181
Web Site: http://www.sankosha-jp.com
Emp.: 101
Packaging Machinery Mfr
N.A.I.C.S.: 333993
Mitsuyuki Uchikoshi *(Chm)*

Subsidiary (Non-US):

Sankosha Thailand Co.,Ltd. (2)
700/720 Moo 3 Tambol Bankao, Amphur Phanthong, Chon Buri, 20160, Thailand
Tel.: (66) 38 447605
Packaging Machinery Mfr
N.A.I.C.S.: 333993

Sankosha Engineering Singapore Pte. Ltd. (1)
102 E Pasir Panjang Rd, 06 05 Citilink Warehouse Comp, Singapore, 118529, Singapore (100%)
Tel.: (65) 62744820
Sales Range: $25-49.9 Million
Emp.: 3
N.A.I.C.S.: 517111

Sankosha Guangzhou Inc. (1)
3rd Fl A2 Plant WanAn Industrial Park No 110 Lanbei Road LanHe Town, PanYu, Guangzhou, Guangdong, China
Tel.: (86) 20 34969113
Lighting Device Mfr
N.A.I.C.S.: 335139

Sankosha Korea Corporation (1)
1609 STX-W Tower Guro-dong 90 Gyeoninnno-53, Guro-gu, Seoul, 152865, Korea (South)
Tel.: (82) 2 6124 3777

AND PRIVATE COMPANIES — SANKYU, INC.

Web Site: http://www.sankosha.kr
Emp.: 5
Lighting Device Mfr
N.A.I.C.S.: 335139
Rhee Keun Young (CEO)

Sankosha U.S.A., Inc. (1)
406 Amapola Ave Ste 135, Torrance, CA 90501-7237
Tel.: (310) 320-1661
Web Site: http://www.sankosha-usa.com
Sales Range: $50-74.9 Million
Emp.: 4
Mfr of Electronic Components
N.A.I.C.S.: 423620

Sankosha Vietnam LLC (1)
6th Floor Thang Long Tower 98A Nguy Nhu Kontum Str, Thanh Xuan, Hanoi, 00084, Vietnam
Tel.: (84) 4 3208 0004
Web Site: http://www.sankosha.vn
Emp.: 20
Lighting Device Mfr
N.A.I.C.S.: 335139
Dang Van Sy (Chm)

Sankosha Yangjiang Inc. (1)
No 3 GongYe First Rd Zhangang Technology Park, PingGang, Yangjiang, GuangDong, China
Tel.: (86) 662 3832338
Lighting Device Mfr
N.A.I.C.S.: 335139

SANKYO FRONTIER. CO., LTD.
5 Shintoyofuta, Kashiwa, 277-8539, Chiba, Japan
Tel.: (81) 471336666
Web Site: https://www.sankyofrontier-global.com
Year Founded: 1969
9639—(TKS)
Rev.: $346,159,090
Assets: $453,353,460
Liabilities: $156,762,760
Net Worth: $296,590,700
Earnings: $34,947,070
Emp.: 1,548
Fiscal Year-end: 03/31/24
Construction Services
N.A.I.C.S.: 236220
Takatsugu Nagatsuma (Pres)

Subsidiaries:

Guangzhou Panyu Sankyo House Co., Ltd. (1)
No 315 Guangzhu Road, Dagang Town Nansha District, Guangzhou, Guangdong, China
Tel.: (86) 2034990501
Mobile Space Construction Services
N.A.I.C.S.: 236220

Sankyo Frontier Malaysia Sdn, Bhd. (1)
Unit 30-01 Level 30 Q Sentral 2A Jalan Stesen Sentral 2, Sentral, 50470, Kuala Lumpur, Malaysia
Tel.: (60) 327805831
Mobile Space Construction Services
N.A.I.C.S.: 236220

Sankyo Frontier Myanmar Co., Ltd. (1)
95-A Level 6 Room No-601 Unit D Kyaik Wine Pagoda Road 8th Mile, Mayangone Township, 11061, Yangon, Myanmar
Tel.: (95) 1664117
Mobile Space Construction Services
N.A.I.C.S.: 236220

Sankyo Frontier Technologies Myanmar Co., Ltd. (1)
Lot D-5 Zone A Thilawa Special Economics Zone, Thanlyin Township, 11301, Yangon, Myanmar
Tel.: (95) 9445393939
Mobile Space Construction Services
N.A.I.C.S.: 236220

SANKYO KASEI CORPORATION
1-9-8 Kitakyuhojimachi, Chuo-ku, Osaka, 541-0057, Japan
Tel.: (81) 662622881
Web Site: https://www.sankyokasei-corp.co.jp
Year Founded: 1947
8138—(TKS)
Rev.: $173,360,470
Assets: $118,087,650
Liabilities: $50,936,660
Net Worth: $67,150,990
Earnings: $2,287,060
Fiscal Year-end: 03/31/24
Chemical Product Mfr & Distr
N.A.I.C.S.: 325998
Kazuo Ogawa (Pres)

Subsidiaries:

Daido Industry Co., Ltd. (1)
3197-52 Aza-Yamanashi Hatta, Iga, 518-1155, Mie, Japan
Tel.: (81) 595201881
Chemical Products Mfr
N.A.I.C.S.: 325998

Kyowa Co., Ltd. (1)
588 Ohyagicho, Takatsuki, 370-0072, Gunma, Japan
Tel.: (81) 273616434
Web Site: https://www.kyj.co.jp
Emp.: 203
Mold Mfr
N.A.I.C.S.: 333511
Shigeharu Nozawa (Pres & CEO)

Sankyo Kasei (Shanghai) Co., Ltd. (1)
B712-713 Far East International Plaza No 317 Xianxia Road, Shanghai, China
Tel.: (86) 2162351383
Chemical Products Mfr
N.A.I.C.S.: 325998

Sankyo Kasei (Thailand) Co., Ltd. (1)
622 Emporium Tower Floor 14/5 Sukhumvit Road, Klongton Sub-district Klongtoey District, Bangkok, 10110, Thailand
Tel.: (66) 22584924
Chemical Products Mfr
N.A.I.C.S.: 325998

Sankyo Kasei Singapore Pte. Ltd. (1)
60 Paya Lebar Road 08-03 Paya Lebar Square, Singapore, 409051, Singapore
Tel.: (65) 62140658
Chemical Products Mfr
N.A.I.C.S.: 325998

Sy Rubber (Thailand) Co., Ltd. (1)
888/30 Moo9, Bangpla Bangphli, Samut Prakan, 10540, Thailand
Tel.: (66) 21800210
Chemical Products Mfr
N.A.I.C.S.: 325998

SANKYO SEIKO CO., LTD.
2-5-6 Azuchi-machi, Chuo Ward, Osaka, 541-0052, Japan
Tel.: (81) 662685000
Web Site: https://www.sankyoseiko.co.jp
Year Founded: 1938
8018—(TKS)
Rev.: $140,601,310
Assets: $440,305,320
Liabilities: $124,829,850
Net Worth: $315,475,470
Earnings: $14,720,470
Emp.: 235
Fiscal Year-end: 03/31/24
Textile Product Mfr & Distr
N.A.I.C.S.: 315990
Kenzo Kawasaki (Chm & CEO)

Subsidiaries:

DAKS Simpson Limited (1)
20 Baltic Street, London, EC1Y 0UL, United Kingdom
Tel.: (44) 2074094000
Web Site: https://www.daks.com
Clothing Product Whslr
N.A.I.C.S.: 458110

Hokuriku Sankyo Seiko Co., Ltd. (1)
1-6-40 Asahimachi, Katsuyama, 911-0803, Japan
Tel.: (81) 779870345
Emp.: 36
Fashion Product Mfr & Whslr
N.A.I.C.S.: 315990

Leonard Fashion S.A.S. (1)
31 rue Jean Giraudoux, 75116, Paris, France
Tel.: (33) 153678787
Emp.: 40
Fashion Product Mfr & Whslr
N.A.I.C.S.: 315990

San Lets Co., Ltd. (1)
2-5-6 Azuchimachi, Chuo, Osaka, 541-0052, Japan
Tel.: (81) 662685950
Emp.: 16
Fashion Product Mfr & Whslr
N.A.I.C.S.: 315990

Sankyo Seiko Apparel Fashion Co., Ltd. (1)
4F Sunrise Building 11-12 Nihonbashi Tomizawa-cho, Chuo, Tokyo, 103-0006, Japan
Tel.: (81) 362311791
Emp.: 42
Fashion Product Mfr & Whslr
N.A.I.C.S.: 315990

Sankyo Seiko Fashion Service Co., Ltd. (1)
9F Sunrise Building 11-12 Nihonbashi Tomizawa-cho, Chuo, Tokyo, 103-0006, Japan
Tel.: (81) 356517890
Emp.: 273
Fashion Product Mfr & Whslr
N.A.I.C.S.: 315990

Yokohama Textile Club Co., Ltd. (1)
205 Yamashita-cho, Naka Ward, Yokohama, 231-0023, Kanagawa, Japan
Tel.: (81) 662685220
Fashion Product Mfr & Whslr
N.A.I.C.S.: 315990

SANKYO TATEYAMA INC.
70 Hayakawa, Takaoka, 933-8610, Toyama, Japan
Tel.: (81) 766202555
Web Site: https://www.st-grp.co.jp
5932—(TKS)
Rev.: $2,333,508,470
Assets: $1,916,734,750
Liabilities: $1,259,152,120
Net Worth: $657,582,630
Earnings: $(6,735,590)
Emp.: 10,289
Fiscal Year-end: 05/31/24
Aluminum Construction Materials Mfr
N.A.I.C.S.: 331313
Makoto Okamoto (Mng Exec Officer)

Subsidiaries:

Aleris Aluminum Duffel BVBA (1)
A Stoctelaan 87, Duffel, 2570, Belgium
Tel.: (32) 15302111
Emp.: 1,000
Aluminum Rolling
N.A.I.C.S.: 331318
Geert Vannuffelen (Mng Dir)

Sansei Industry Co., Ltd. (1)
11-11 Sugahara-Cho, Kita-Ku, Osaka, 530-0046, Japan
Tel.: (81) 6 6365 6760
Aluminum Construction Material Mfr
N.A.I.C.S.: 331313

Shanghai Tateyama Commercial Facilities Co., Ltd. (1)
No 1111 Xingrong Road, Jiading District, Shanghai, China
Tel.: (86) 2131151600
Web Site: https://www.tateyama.com.cn
Emp.: 130
Construction Material Mfr & Distr
N.A.I.C.S.: 327120
Yutaka Kondo (Chm)

Shanghai Tateyama Trading Co., Ltd. (1)
Room 2001 Shenggao International Building No137 XianXia Road, Changning Dist, Shanghai, China
Tel.: (86) 21 6259 0369
Emp.: 40
Construction Material Mfr & Distr
N.A.I.C.S.: 327120
Kokichi Takagi (Chm)

TateyamaAdvance-Company (1)
2-9-5 Nihonbashi-Hamacho, Chuo-ku, Tokyo, 103-0007, Japan
Tel.: (81) 3 3667 7551
Emp.: 442
Sign Mfr & Distr
N.A.I.C.S.: 339950
Takashi Nakano (Pres)

SANKYU, INC.
5-23 Kachidoki 6-chome, Chuo-ku, Tokyo, 104-0054, Japan
Tel.: (81) 335363939   JP
Web Site: https://www.sankyu.co.jp
Year Founded: 1917
9065—(FKA)
Rev.: $5,361,084,080
Assets: $4,476,680,560
Liabilities: $2,069,022,560
Net Worth: $2,407,658,000
Earnings: $219,116,480
Emp.: 31,054
Fiscal Year-end: 03/31/22
Transportation, Construction, Trucking, Warehousing, Machinery Mfr & Real Estate Services
N.A.I.C.S.: 488210
Hideki Miyoshi (Sr Exec Dir)

Subsidiaries:

BEIJING SANKYU LOGISTICS CO., LTD (1)
2003 Beijing Fortune Bldg No5 Dong San Huan Bei Lu, Chaoyang District, Beijing, 100004, China
Tel.: (86) 1065923039
Web Site: http://www.sankyu.co.jp
Freight Forwarding Services
N.A.I.C.S.: 488510

Chubu Kaiun Kaisha, Ltd. (1)
8 Chitose-Cho, Yokkaichi, 510-0051, Japan
Tel.: (81) 593526174
Cargo Handling Services
N.A.I.C.S.: 488320

Chugoku Business Service Co., Ltd. (1)
3-10-35 Ujina-kaigan, Minami-ku, 8800806, Hiroshima, Japan
Tel.: (81) 833410558
Business Process Outsourcing Services
N.A.I.C.S.: 561499

Daiei Shipping Co., Ltd. (1)
5th floor Fujiwa Hatchobori Building 2-20-1 Hatchobori, Chuo-ku, Tokyo, 104-0032, Japan
Tel.: (81) 355666961
Web Site: https://www.daieiship.co.jp
Sales Range: $25-49.9 Million
Emp.: 23
Shipping Agency Services
N.A.I.C.S.: 488330

Dalian Sankyu International Logistics Co., Ltd. (1)
No 102 Huanghai West 2nd Road, Dalian Free Trade Zone, Dalian, China
Tel.: (86) 41187315649
Web Site: https://www.dalian-sankyu.cn
Logistic Services
N.A.I.C.S.: 541614
Noguchi Noguchi (Chm)

Ehime Kaiun Co., Ltd. (1)
1-2 Katahara-cho, Imabari, 794-0013, Japan
Tel.: (81) 899510176
Cargo Handling Services
N.A.I.C.S.: 488320

Heiwa Technos Corporation (1)
1-1 Oazaichinosu, Oita, 870-0112, Japan
Tel.: (81) 975234718
Bridge Construction Engineering Services
N.A.I.C.S.: 237310

SANKYU, INC.

Sankyu, Inc.—(Continued)

Hirobishi Sokounyu Co., Ltd. (1)
3-10-23 Ujinakaigan, Minami-Ku, Hiroshima, 734-0011, Japan
Tel.: (81) 822514311
General Warehousing & Storage Services
N.A.I.C.S.: 493110

Hofu Portbuilding Co., Ltd. (1)
415-15 Ohama Ichinomasu, Hamakata, Hofu, 747-0833, Yamaguchi, Japan
Tel.: (81) 835384954
Cargo Handling Services
N.A.I.C.S.: 488320

Japan Industrial Testing Co., Ltd. (1)
1-5-16 Honmachi, Kawasaki-ku, Kawasaki, 210-0001, Kanagawa, Japan
Tel.: (81) 443666000
Emp.: 531
Non-Destructive Testing Services
N.A.I.C.S.: 541380

Japan Post Sankyu Global Logistics Co., Ltd. (1)
Hokusui BLDG No 2 5-11-11 Kachidoki, Chuo-ku, Tokyo, 104-0054, Japan
Tel.: (81) 3 3536 3417
Logistics Consulting Servies
N.A.I.C.S.: 541614

Kyowa Shipping Co., Ltd. (1)
Hibiya Building 4th Floor 1-1 Shimbashi 1-Chome, Minato-Ku, Tokyo, 105-0004, Japan
Tel.: (81) 355101991
Web Site: https://www.kyowa-line.co.jp
Shipping Agency Services
N.A.I.C.S.: 488330
Hiromitsu Takamatsu *(Pres & CEO)*

Oita Business Service Co., Ltd. (1)
1-1-11 Mukaibaruoki, Oita, 870-0903, Japan
Tel.: (81) 975531757
Construction Equipment Installtion Services
N.A.I.C.S.: 238290

P.T. SANKYU INDONESIA INTERNATIONAL (1)
Summitmas I 5th Floor Jalan Sudirman Kaveling 61-62, Jakarta, 12190, Indonesia
Tel.: (62) 215201255
Sales Range: $450-499.9 Million
Emp.: 154
Cargo Handling Services
N.A.I.C.S.: 488320

Qingdao JSD Logistics Co., Ltd. (1)
Longshan Industrial Park No1 Jifa Road, Jimo, Qingdao, Shandong, China
Tel.: (86) 53286659227
Web Site: https://www.qingdao-jsd.com
Logistic Services
N.A.I.C.S.: 541614

Qingdao Sankyu Asia-Pacific Logistics Co., Ltd. (1)
2004 Galaxy Building 29 Shandong Road, Shinan, Qingdao, 266071, China
Tel.: (86) 53285801839
Logistic Services
N.A.I.C.S.: 541614

SANKYU AIR (HONG KONG) LTD. (1)
Unit 1101 11Fl Commercial Building 2 Chun Wan Road, Chek Lap Kok, Hong Kong, China (Hong Kong)
Tel.: (852) 27548228
Web Site: http://webciss.sankyu.co.jp
Sales Range: $25-49.9 Million
Emp.: 23
Freight Transportation Services
N.A.I.C.S.: 488510

SANKYU ASIA-PACIFIC QINGDAO LOGISTICS CO., LTD (1)
Sales Range: $25-49.9 Million
Emp.: 75
Freight Transportation Services
N.A.I.C.S.: 488510

SANKYU INDIA LOGISTICS & ENGINEERING PRIVATE LIMITED (1)
4th Floor Office Number 409 Sewa Corporate Park MG Road, Gurgaon, 122 015, Haryana, India
Tel.: (91) 1244026600
Web Site: http://www.webciss.sankyu.co.jp

Sales Range: $25-49.9 Million
Emp.: 20
Logistics Consulting Servies
N.A.I.C.S.: 541614

SANKYU LOGISTICS (VIETNAM) CO., LTD. (1)
Sales Range: $25-49.9 Million
Emp.: 86
Logistics Consulting Servies
N.A.I.C.S.: 541614

SANKYU S.A. (1)
Av Do Contorno, Belo Horizonte, 6283-10, Brazil
Tel.: (55) 3130739550
Sales Range: $1-4.9 Billion
Emp.: 5,556
Marine Cargo Handling Services
N.A.I.C.S.: 488320

SANKYU SOUTHEAST ASIA HOLDINGS PTE. LTD. (1)
Tel.: (65) 66310850
Sales Range: $50-74.9 Million
Emp.: 12
Investment Management Service
N.A.I.C.S.: 523999

Sankyo Koun Co., Ltd. (1)
64-96 Anze, Wakamatsu-Ku, Kitakyushu, 808-0022, Fukuoka, Japan
Tel.: (81) 937712751
Cargo Handling Services
N.A.I.C.S.: 488320

Sankyu (Malaysia) Sdn Bhd (1)
Lot 4 Jalan 215, 46050, Petaling Jaya, Selangor, Malaysia
Tel.: (60) 377813911
Web Site: http://www.sankyu.com.my
Sales Range: $50-74.9 Million
Emp.: 553
Freight Transportation Arrangement
N.A.I.C.S.: 488510
Toshiro Ushirosako *(Mng Dir)*

Sankyu (Singapore) Pte. Ltd. (1)
11 Clementi Loop, PO Box 575, Singapore, 129813, Singapore
Tel.: (65) 64693911
Web Site: http://www.sankyu.com.sg
Emp.: 1,089
Freight Transportation Arrangement
N.A.I.C.S.: 488510

Sankyu (Vietnam) Co., Ltd. (1)
Emp.: 40
Freight Transportation Arrangement
N.A.I.C.S.: 488510
Yamashita Shoichi *(Gen Dir)*

Sankyu Arcc Saudi Co. (1)
Al-Mohamadia Tower 6th Floor 3240 King Abdullah Road, Al Khobar, 31952, Saudi Arabia
Tel.: (966) 13 865 5782
Logistic Services
N.A.I.C.S.: 541614

Sankyu Business Service Co., Ltd. (1)
Kachidoki 6-5-3, Chuo-Ku, Tokyo, 104-0054, Japan
Tel.: (81) 335363982
Business Support Services
N.A.I.C.S.: 561499

Sankyu Chubu Service Co., Ltd. (1)
1-3 Misonocho, Yokkaichi, 510-0862, Japan
Tel.: (81) 593487739
Logistics Consulting Servies
N.A.I.C.S.: 541614

Sankyu Clearing Co., Ltd. (1)
Tel.: (81) 335363980
Credit Intermediation Services
N.A.I.C.S.: 522299

Sankyu Delivery & Service Co., Ltd. (1)
6-5-3 Kachidoki Sankyudai 2 Bldg 1 Floor, Chuo-Ku, Tokyo, 104-0054, Japan
Tel.: (81) 335363092
Logistics Consulting Servies
N.A.I.C.S.: 541614

Sankyu Design & Engineering Service Co., Ltd. (1)
16-1 Tsukijicho, Yahatanishi-Ku, Kitakyushu, 806-0001, Fukuoka, Japan

Tel.: (81) 936457270
Engineeering Services
N.A.I.C.S.: 541330

Sankyu Eastern International (HK) Company Limited (1)
38 Kwai Hei Street Room 2206B - 2215 22nd Floor Metropolis Square, Kwai Chung, New Territories, China (Hong Kong)
Tel.: (852) 28381639
Sales Range: $25-49.9 Million
Emp.: 100
Freight Transportation Arrangement
N.A.I.C.S.: 327910

Sankyu Europe BV (1)
Tel.: (31) 104130023
Sales Range: $25-49.9 Million
Emp.: 5
Local Freight Trucking
N.A.I.C.S.: 484110
I. Murakam *(Mgr)*

Sankyu Guangzhou Logistics Co., Ltd. (1)
Room No 1012 times square west wing D No 30 Tianxe Road Ext, Guangzhou, 510610, Panyu, China
Tel.: (86) 2038772239
Sales Range: $125-149.9 Million
Emp.: 500
Local Freight Trucking
N.A.I.C.S.: 484110
Seishichiro Nakamura *(Pres)*

Sankyu Higashi Nihon Service Co., Ltd. (1)
3-1 Nakasode, Sodegaura, Chiba, Japan
Tel.: (81) 438609639
Temporary Staffing Services
N.A.I.C.S.: 561320

Sankyu Insurance Service Corporation (1)
Kachidoki 6-5-3, Chuo-Ku, Tokyo, 104-0054, Japan (100%)
Tel.: (81) 335363429
Insurance Agency Services
N.A.I.C.S.: 524210

Sankyu Jiangsu Logistics Co., Ltd. (1)
21F-D Golden-eagle Hanzhong New City-Build Hanzhongmen-da jie No 1, Jianye-District, Nanjing, 210029, Jiangsu, China
Tel.: (86) 2586651139
Logistic Services
N.A.I.C.S.: 541614

Sankyu Jukiko Co., Ltd. (1)
4-13-1 Shiohama, Kawasaki-Ku, Kawasaki, 210-0826, Kanagawa, Japan (33%)
Tel.: (81) 442801039
Web Site: https://www.sankyujk.co.jp
Emp.: 110
Construction Equipment Installtion Services
N.A.I.C.S.: 238290

Sankyu Kairiku Co., Ltd (1)
3rd floor Yokohama Heiwa Building 3-30-7 Honmachi, Yokohama, 2310005, Kanagawa, Japan
Tel.: (81) 452019991
Web Site: https://www.sankyu.co.jp
Emp.: 470
Cargo Handling Services
N.A.I.C.S.: 488320

Sankyu Kinki Service Co., Ltd. (1)
Tel.: (81) 722237850
Human Resource Consulting Services
N.A.I.C.S.: 541612

Sankyu L&T (ZFTZ) Co., Ltd. (1)
Sales Range: $25-49.9 Million
Emp.: 19
Freight Transportation Services
N.A.I.C.S.: 488510

Sankyu Laem Chabang (Thailand) Company Limited (1)
79/25 Moo 10 Tambol Thungsukla, Sriracha, Chon Buri, 20230, Thailand
Tel.: (66) 38480208
Web Site: http://www.sankyu.co.jp
Freight Transportation Arrangement
N.A.I.C.S.: 488510

Sankyu Logistics Brazil: A.V. (1)
Av Fagundes Filho 141 12 Andar, Sao

Paulo, 04304-010, Brazil
Tel.: (55) 1128896355
Logistic Services
N.A.I.C.S.: 541614

Sankyu Mexico S.A. de C.V. (1)
Centro De Negocios Santa Fe 4 Avenida Mineral De Valenciana No 645, Modulo C5-C6 Parque Industrial Puerto Interior Silao De La Victoria, 36275, Guanajuato, Mexico
Tel.: (52) 4721351900
Logistic Services
N.A.I.C.S.: 541614

Sankyu Oita Business Inc. (1)
1-1-11 Oki Mukaihara, Oita, Oita Prefecture, Japan
Tel.: (81) 975531757
Emp.: 184
Industrial Equipment Installation Services
N.A.I.C.S.: 811310
Tamatoku Sato *(Pres)*

Sankyu Plant Engineering Shanghai Co., Ltd. (1)
Shanghai Bund International Tower 11F No 99 Huang Pu Road, Shanghai, 200080, China
Tel.: (86) 2163933919
Web Site: http://www.sankyu.co.jp
Engineeering Services
N.A.I.C.S.: 541330

Sankyu Plant Techno Co., Ltd. (1)
4-14-1 Minamifujima, Wakamatsu-ku, Kitakyushu, 808-0109, Fukuoka, Japan
Tel.: (81) 335363411
Power Plant Construction Engineering Services
N.A.I.C.S.: 237130

Sankyu Research & Create Co., Ltd. (1)
Kachidoki 6-5-3, Chuo-Ku, Tokyo, 104-0054, Japan
Tel.: (81) 335363970
Professional Training Services
N.A.I.C.S.: 611430
Kengi Hosoi *(Pres)*

Sankyu Road Engineering Co., Ltd. (1)
10 Tsukiji - cho, Yahatanishi-Ku, Kitakyushu, 806-0001, Fukuoka, Japan
Tel.: (81) 936317339
Web Site: https://sankyu-road.co.jp
Emp.: 68
Highway Construction Engineering Services
N.A.I.C.S.: 237310
Takashi Maeda *(CEO)*

Sankyu Saudi Arabia Co., Ltd. (1)
Al Murjanah Tower Floor 8 8 Office 804 Prince Sultan Road, PO Box 40645, Al Rawdhah district, Jeddah, 21511, Saudi Arabia
Tel.: (966) 126833939
Logistic Services
N.A.I.C.S.: 541614

Sankyu Shipping Inc. (1)
4th floor Sankyu Building 6-5-23 Kachidoki, Chuo-Ku, Tokyo, 104-0054, Japan
Tel.: (81) 335363978
Web Site: https://www.ssi-sankyu.co.jp
Sales Range: $25-49.9 Million
Emp.: 7
Marine Cargo Handling Services
N.A.I.C.S.: 488320

Sankyu Transport Chubu Co., Ltd. (1)
Logistics Consulting Servies
N.A.I.C.S.: 541614

Sankyu Transport Chugoku Co., Ltd. (1)
2-904-65 Hayama, Kudamatsu, 744-0000, Yamaguchi, Japan
Tel.: (81) 833472239
Logistics Consulting Servies
N.A.I.C.S.: 541614

Sankyu Transport Higashinihon Co., Ltd. (1)
3-4-24 Tamaskinishi, Ichihara, 290-0044, Chiba, Japan
Tel.: (81) 436222541
Logistics Consulting Servies

N.A.I.C.S.: 541614

Sankyu Transport Kansai Co., Ltd. (1)
2-35-4 Nishinomiyahama, Nishinomiya, 662-0934, Hyogo, Japan
Tel.: (81) 798390391
Logistics Consulting Servies
N.A.I.C.S.: 541614

Sankyu Transport Kyushu Co., Ltd. (1)
120-2 Nishiminatomachi, Kokurakita-Ku, Kitakyushu, 803-0801, Fukuoka, Japan
Tel.: (81) 935813341
Emp.: 148
Logistics Consulting Servies
N.A.I.C.S.: 541614

Sankyu Transport Tokyo Co., Ltd. (1)
Tel.: (81) 335363424
Logistics Consulting Servies
N.A.I.C.S.: 541614

Sankyu USA Incorporated (1)
555 Pierce Rd Ste 125, Itasca, IL 60143
Tel.: (630) 595-3009
Web Site: http://sankyu-usa.com
Sales Range: $25-49.9 Million
Emp.: 25
Freight Transportation Arrangement
N.A.I.C.S.: 488510

Sankyu-Jvan An International Logistics Co., Ltd. (1)
No 2 Lane 43 ShingBang Rd, Taoyuan, 330, Taiwan
Tel.: (886) 286772222
Web Site: https://www.sankyuja.com.tw
Logistic Services
N.A.I.C.S.: 541614

Sankyu-Thai Company Limited (1)
1st 3rd Floor CCT Buld 109 Surawong Road, Bangkok, 10500, Thailand
Tel.: (66) 22663939
Web Site: http://www.sankyu.co.jp
Sales Range: $200-249.9 Million
Emp.: 557
Freight Transportation Arrangement
N.A.I.C.S.: 488510
Takashi Kageyama *(Gen Mgr)*

Shanghai E&T Sankyu Distribution Co., Ltd. (1)
2th Bldg 58 No 180 Riying North Road, Waigaoqiao Free Trade Zone, Shanghai, 200131, China
Tel.: (86) 2150481332
Logistic Services
N.A.I.C.S.: 541614

Shanghai Sankyu Trading Co., Ltd. (1)
Shanghai Bund International Tower 11F No 99 Huang Pu Road, Shanghai, 200080, China
Tel.: (86) 2163933919
Logistic Services
N.A.I.C.S.: 541614

TAIYOUNG SANKYU INTERNATIONAL LOGISTICS CO., LTD (1)
Emp.: 30
Logistics Consulting Servies
N.A.I.C.S.: 541614
Shibata Toshiharu *(Gen Mgr)*

Telstar Co., Ltd. (1)
2-11-11 Tsukiji Moroi Bldg 6f, Chuo-Ku, Tokyo, 104-0045, Japan
Tel.: (81) 335363914
Temporary Staffing Services
N.A.I.C.S.: 561320

Tho-cello Logitech Corporation (1)
142-1 Nogimachi, Shimotsuga-Gun, Tochigi, 329-0114, Japan
Tel.: (81) 280579100
General Warehousing & Storage Services
N.A.I.C.S.: 493110

Tokuyama Kouun Co., Ltd. (1)
2-118-51 Kokai, 745-0814, Shunan, Japan
Tel.: (81) 834260460
Marine Cargo Handling Services
N.A.I.C.S.: 488320

SANLAM KENYA PLC

Sanlam Tower 14th floor Off Waiyaki Way Westlands, PO Box 44041, 00100, Nairobi, Kenya
Tel.: (254) 202781000   KE
Web Site: https://www.sanlam.co.za
Year Founded: 1946
SLAM—(NAI)
Rev.: $113,011,590
Assets: $315,623,827
Liabilities: $310,202,411
Net Worth: $5,421,416
Earnings: ($4,935,467)
Emp.: 177
Fiscal Year-end: 12/31/21
Insurance Services
N.A.I.C.S.: 524126
Emma Wachira *(Chief Legal Officer & Sec)*

Subsidiaries:

Sanlam General Insurance Limited (1)
Sanlam Tower 12th floor Off Waiyaki Way Westlands, PO Box 10493-00100, Nairobi, Kenya
Tel.: (254) 20278100
General Insurance Individual Services
N.A.I.C.S.: 524298

SANLAM LIMITED

2 Strand Road, Bellville, 7530, Western Cape, South Africa
Tel.: (27) 219479111
Web Site: https://www.sanlam.com
Year Founded: 1918
SLM—(NAM)
Sales Range: $5-14.9 Billion
Fire Insurance Services
N.A.I.C.S.: 524126
Johan van Zyl *(Chm)*

Subsidiaries:

Absa Asset Management (Proprietary) Limited (1)
Block A First Floor 65 Empire Road, Parktown, 2193, South Africa
Tel.: (27) 114805146
Web Site: http://www.abam.co.za
Sales Range: $50-74.9 Million
Asset Management Services
N.A.I.C.S.: 523999

Absa Fund Managers Limited (1)
65 Empire Road, Parktown, Johannesburg, 2000, Gauteng, South Africa
Tel.: (27) 114805000
Web Site: http://www.absainvestments.co.za
Fund Management Services
N.A.I.C.S.: 523940

Botswana Insurance Holdings Limited (1)
Plot 66458 Block A 3rd Floor Fairgrounds Office Park, PO Box 336, Gaborone, Botswana (54%)
Tel.: (267) 3707400
Web Site: https://www.bihl.co.bw
Rev.: $283,936,914
Assets: $1,350,537,634
Liabilities: $1,091,642,593
Net Worth: $258,895,041
Earnings: $44,828,497
Emp.: 397
Fiscal Year-end: 12/31/2022
Holding Company; Insurance Services
N.A.I.C.S.: 551112
Batsho Pamela Dambe-Groth *(Chm)*

Glacier Financial Holdings (Pty) Ltd (1)
Tuscan Park Block A cnr Old Oak Road & Twist St, Durbanville, Cape Town, 7550, South Africa
Tel.: (27) 219179002
Web Site: http://www.glacier.co.za
Sales Range: $10-24.9 Million
Emp.: 200
Holding Company
N.A.I.C.S.: 551112
Werner Lotriet *(Member-Exec Bd)*

Subsidiary (Domestic):

Glacier Financial Solutions (Pty) Ltd (2)
No 1 Spotica Creasent Tiger Valley, cnr Old Oak Road & Twist St Durbanville, Cape Town, 7536, South Africa
Tel.: (27) 219179002
Web Site: http://wwwglacier.co.za
Financial Investment & Management Services
N.A.I.C.S.: 523999

Glacier Management Company Ltd. (2)
No 1 Sportica Crescent Tygervalley, Tyger Valley, Cape Town, 7530, South Africa
Tel.: (27) 219179002
Web Site: http://www.glacier.co.za
Financial Management Services
N.A.I.C.S.: 523999

MCIS Insurance Bhd. (1)
Wisma MCIS Jalan Barat, 46200, Petaling Jaya, Selangor Darul Ehsan, Malaysia
Tel.: (60) 3 76523388
Web Site: http://www.mcis.my
Emp.: 30
Investment Advice for Insurance
N.A.I.C.S.: 523940
Wan Mohd Fakruddin Razi *(Chief Investment Officer)*

Pacific & Orient Insurance Co. Berhad (1)
11th Floor Wisma Bumi Raya, No 10 Jalan Raja Laut, 50350, Kuala Lumpur, Malaysia (49%)
Tel.: (60) 326985033
Web Site: https://www.poi2u.com
Direct Life Insurance Carriers
N.A.I.C.S.: 524113
Thye Seng Chan *(CEO & Mng Dir)*

Sanlam Asset Management (Ireland) Limited (1)
Beach House Beech Hill Office Campus Beech Hill Rd, 4, Dublin, Ireland
Tel.: (353) 12053510
Web Site: http://www.sanlam.com
Sales Range: $50-74.9 Million
Emp.: 16
Financial Advisory Services
N.A.I.C.S.: 523940
Richard Aslett *(CEO)*

Sanlam Investment Holdings Limited (1)
2 strand Rd, Bellville, 7532, South Africa
Tel.: (27) 219479111
Web Site: http://www.sanlam.co.za
Emp.: 4,000
Financial Investment Services
N.A.I.C.S.: 523999

Sanlam Investment Management (Pty) Limited (1)
55 Willie van Schoor Avenue, Bellville, South Africa
Tel.: (27) 860100266
Web Site: http://www.sanlam.co.za
Financial Management Services
N.A.I.C.S.: 523999
Phillip Mjoli *(Head-Institutional Clients)*

Sanlam Maroc S.A. (1)
216 Boulevard Zerktouni, 20 000, Casablanca, Morocco (61.7%)
Tel.: (212) 522474040
Web Site: https://sanlam.ma
Sales Range: Less than $1 Million
Financial Insurance Services
N.A.I.C.S.: 524210
Saad Bendidi *(Chm & Mng Dir)*

Sanlam Netherlands Holding BV (1)
Nieuwe Schoolstraat 4, Hague, 2514 HX, Zuid-Holland, Netherlands
Tel.: (31) 703648984
General Insurance Services
N.A.I.C.S.: 524298

Sanlam Private Wealth (UK) (1)
11 West Road, Ponteland, Newcastle upon Tyne, NE20 9SU, United Kingdom
Tel.: (44) 1913 009 242
Web Site: http://www.privatewealth.sanlam.co.uk
Sales Range: $50-74.9 Million
Emp.: 2
Wealth Management Services
N.A.I.C.S.: 523999

Holding (Non-US):

Isle of Man Enterprises plc (2)
Centre House Little Switzerland, Douglas, IM2 4RE, Isle of Man
Tel.: (44) 1624683333
Web Site: http://www.manxshoprite.com
Sales Range: $125-149.9 Million
Emp.: 3,000
Supermarket Operator
N.A.I.C.S.: 445110
Deryck Nicholson *(Chm)*

Sanlam Spec (Pty) Limited (1)
2 Strand Street, Cape Town, 7530, Western Cape, South Africa
Tel.: (27) 219479111
Web Site: http://www.sanlam.co.za
General Insurance Services
N.A.I.C.S.: 524210

Sanlam UK Ltd (1)
St Bartholomew's House, Lewins Mead, Bristol, BS1 2NH, United Kingdom
Tel.: (44) 117 926 6366
Web Site: http://www.sanlam.co.uk
Emp.: 100
Financial Investment Services
N.A.I.C.S.: 523999

Sanman Capital Markets (1)
3A Summit Rd, Dunkeld West, Johannesburg, 2196, South Africa (100%)
Tel.: (27) 117786000
Web Site: http://www.scm.sanlam.co.za
Sales Range: $100-124.9 Million
Emp.: 130
Provides Investment Banking, Asset Management, Equity-Related Activities & Property Services
N.A.I.C.S.: 523150

Santam Limited (1)
1 Sportica Crescent Tyger Valley, Bellville, 7530, South Africa (61.5%)
Tel.: (27) 219157000
Web Site: http://www.santam.co.za
Sales Range: $1-4.9 Billion
Emp.: 2,440
Short Term Insurance Services
N.A.I.C.S.: 524298
Edward Gibbens *(Head-Commercial-Personal)*

Subsidiary (Non-US):

Santam Insurance Ltd. (2)
Tenbergen Village c/o Robert Mugabe & Julius Nyerere Street, Windhoek, Namibia (100%)
Tel.: (264) 612928000
Web Site: http://www.santam.co.za
Sales Range: $50-74.9 Million
Emp.: 40
Insurance Provider
N.A.I.C.S.: 524113

Subsidiary (Domestic):

Santam Structured Insurance (Pty) Ltd. (2)
7th Floor Alice Lane Building 3 Corner Alice Lane and 5th Street, Sandton, 2196, South Africa
Tel.: (27) 11 685 7600
Web Site: http://www.santam.co.za
Credit Insurance Products & Services
N.A.I.C.S.: 524128

Zimnat Lion Insurance Company Ltd. (1)
Cnr 3rd St Nelson Mandela, PO Box 2417, Harare, 2417, Zimbabwe
Tel.: (263) 242701179
Web Site: https://www.zimnat.co.zw
Insurance Services
N.A.I.C.S.: 524298
E. K. Moyo *(Mng Dir)*

SANLI ENVIRONMENTAL LIMITED

28 Kian Teck Drive, Singapore, 628845, Singapore
Tel.: (65) 65789269
Web Site: https://www.sanli.com.sg
Year Founded: 2006
1E3—(CAT)
Rev.: $78,864,765
Assets: $70,365,320
Liabilities: $47,299,741
Net Worth: $23,065,580

SANLI ENVIRONMENTAL LIMITED

Sanli Environmental Limited—(Continued)
Earnings: $3,094,479
Emp.: 540
Fiscal Year-end: 03/31/23
Waste Water Treatment Services
N.A.I.C.S.: 221320
Hock Heng Sim (Co-Founder)

Subsidiaries:

Enviro Plant & Engineering Pte. Ltd. (1)
22 Chin Bee Drive, Singapore, 619870, Singapore
Tel.: (65) 62520780
Web Site: https://www.enviroplant.com.sg
Environmental Engineering Services
N.A.I.C.S.: 541330

Mag Chemical Pte. Ltd. (1)
22 Chin Bee Drive, Singapore, 619870, Singapore
Tel.: (65) 62520780
Web Site: https://www.magchem.com.sg
Environmental Engineering Services
N.A.I.C.S.: 541330

Sanli E&C Pte. Ltd. (1)
22 Chin Bee Drive, Singapore, 619870, Singapore
Tel.: (65) 62520780
Sewage Treatment Facility Services
N.A.I.C.S.: 221320

Sanli Environmental (Myanmar) Co. Ltd. (1)
Room 001-A Block-B Corner of Yuzana Street First Street, Highway Complex Housing Kamaryut Township, Yangon, Myanmar
Tel.: (95) 95011025
Waste Water Management Services
N.A.I.C.S.: 221320
Thein Tun Zaw (Project Mgr-M&E)

Sanli M&E Engineering Pte. Ltd. (1)
22 Chin Bee Drive, Singapore, 619870, Singapore
Tel.: (65) 62520780
Sewage Treatment Facility Services
N.A.I.C.S.: 221320
Joseph Kyaw (Project Mgr)

Sanli M&E Engineering Sdn. Bhd. (1)
28 Jalan Kemajuan Taman Perindustrian Kota Tinggi, 81900, Kota Tinggi, Johor, Malaysia
Tel.: (60) 78828528
Waste Water Management Services
N.A.I.C.S.: 221320
Joseph Kyaw (Sr Project Mgr)

SANLIEN TECHNOLOGY CORP.
5F-3 No 390 Section 1 Fuxing South Road, Da an District, Taipei, 106, Taiwan
Tel.: (886) 227081730
Web Site: https://www.sanlien.com
Year Founded: 1967
5493—(TPE)
Rev.: $121,065,792
Assets: $167,371,556
Liabilities: $77,622,418
Net Worth: $89,749,138
Earnings: $13,817,063
Fiscal Year-end: 12/31/23
Industrial Automation Services
N.A.I.C.S.: 333998
Lin Da Jun (Chm)

SANLORENZO S.P.A.
Via Armezzone 3, Ameglia, 19031, La Spezia, Italy
Tel.: (39) 01876181
Web Site: http://www.sanlorenzoyacht.com
Rev.: $581,197,261
Assets: $485,315,968
Liabilities: $316,406,364
Net Worth: $168,909,604
Earnings: $30,032,405
Emp.: 456
Fiscal Year-end: 12/31/19
Leisure Product Mfr
N.A.I.C.S.: 336612
Massimo Perotti (Chm)

Subsidiaries:

Bluegame S.r.l. (1)
Via Marina di Levante 12, 55049, Viareggio, LU, Italy
Tel.; (39) 0584395334
Web Site: http://www.bluegame.it
Boat Mfr
N.A.I.C.S.: 336612
Luca Santella (Founder)

Sanlorenzo of the Americas LLC (1)
1515 S E 17th St Ste 125, Fort Lauderdale, FL 33316
Tel.: (954) 376-4794
Shipyard Services
N.A.I.C.S.: 336611
Nicola Rossi (Mgr-Svc)

SANLUX CO., LTD.
Yuzhu Village Keyan Street, Shaoxing, 312031, Zhejiang, China
Tel.: (86) 57584365688
Web Site: http://www.v-belt.com
Year Founded: 1984
002224—(SSE)
Rev.: $121,384,224
Assets: $423,785,368
Liabilities: $71,272,094
Net Worth: $352,513,273
Earnings: $9,384,771
Fiscal Year-end: 12/31/22
Rubber Products Mfr
N.A.I.C.S.: 326220
Wu Qiongying (Chm & Gen Mgr)

SANMAR HOLDINGS LTD.
9 Cathedral Road, Chennai, 600 086, Tamil Nadu, India
Tel.: (91) 4428128500
Web Site: http://www.sanmargroup.com
Year Founded: 1962
Sales Range: $75-99.9 Million
Emp.: 2,000
Holding Company; Chemicals & PVC Products Mfr; Shipping Services; Industrial Valve Mfr & Steel Casting Foundries
N.A.I.C.S.: 551112
N. Sankar (Chm)

Subsidiaries:

Cabot Sanmar Ltd. (1)
9 Cathedral Road, Chennai, 600 086, India
Tel.: (91) 4428128500
Web Site: http://www.sanmargroups.com
Emp.: 50
Fumed Silica Mfr; Owned By Sanmar Holdings Ltd. & by Cabot Corporation
N.A.I.C.S.: 325998

Chemplast Sanmar Ltd. (1)
9 Cathedral Road, Chennai, 600 086, Tamil Nadu, India (74.85%)
Tel.: (91) 4428128500
Web Site: http://www.sanmargroup.com
Sales Range: $150-199.9 Million
Chlorochemicals, Polyvinyl Chloride Material & PVC Piping Systems Mfr
N.A.I.C.S.: 325180
P. S. Jayaraman (Chm-Chemical Grp)

Plant (Domestic):

Chemplast Sanmar Limited - Cuddalore Plant (2)
SIPCOT Industrial Complex Phase II, Semmankuppam, Cuddalore, 607 005, Tamil Nadu, India
Tel.: (91) 4142 239 280
Salt Mfr
N.A.I.C.S.: 325180

Chemplast Sanmar Limited - Industrial Alcohol Plant II (2)
Kadampuliyur PO, Panruti Taluk, Cuddalore, 607 103, Tamil Nadu, India
Tel.: (91) 4142 249101

4142 249102
N.A.I.C.S.: 325180

Chemplast Sanmar Limited - Karaikal Plant (2)
Melavanjore Village T R Pattinam Panchayat, Nagore, 611 002, Tamil Nadu, India
Tel.: (91) 4365 256 475
Salt Mfr
N.A.I.C.S.: 325180

Chemplast Sanmar Limited - Mettur Plant I (2)
Mettur Dam RS, Salem, 636 402, Tamil Nadu, India
Tel.: (91) 4298 222 304
Salt Mfr
N.A.I.C.S.: 325180

Chemplast Sanmar Limited - Mettur Plant IV (2)
Raman Nagar PO Mettur Dam, Salem, 636 403, Tamil Nadu, India
Tel.: (91) 4298 230 258
Salt Mfr
N.A.I.C.S.: 325180

Chemplast Sanmar Limited - Vedaranyam Salt Works (2)
Sethu Rastha, Vedaranyam, 614 810, Tamil Nadu, India
Tel.: (91) 4369 250228
Salt Mfr
N.A.I.C.S.: 325180

Subsidiary (Non-US):

TCI Sanmar Chemicals LLC (2)
Flat No 601 5th Floor 111 El Thawra Street, Heliopolis, Cairo, Egypt
Tel.: (20) 212 690 4801
Web Site: http://www.sanmargroup.com
Alkalies & Chlorine Mfr
N.A.I.C.S.: 325180

Plant (Domestic):

TCI Sanmar Chemicals S.A.E. - Port Said Plant (3)
Industrial Area C9 South Port Said, Port-Said, Egypt
Tel.: (20) 66 379 3799
Caustic Soda Mfr
N.A.I.C.S.: 325180

Sanmar Engineering Corp. (1)
147 Karapakkam Village, Chennai, 600 096, India
Tel.: (91) 4428118500
Web Site: http://www.sanmargroup.com
Sales Range: $25-49.9 Million
Emp.: 125
Provider of Engineering Services
N.A.I.C.S.: 541330

Sanmar Engineering Corporation Ltd. (1)
9 Cathedral Road, Chennai, 600 086, India
Tel.: (91) 4428128400
Web Site: http://www.sanmargroup.com
Industrial Valve & Sealing Device Mfr; Steel Investment Foundries
N.A.I.C.S.: 332911

Joint Venture (Domestic):

BS&B Safety Systems (India) Ltd. (2)
9 Cathedral Road, Chennai, 600 686, India
Tel.: (91) 4424504000
Web Site: http://www.sanmargroup.com
Sales Range: $25-49.9 Million
Emp.: 60
Industrial Valve Mfr; Owned by Sanmar Holdings Ltd. & by BS&B Safety Systems, LLC
N.A.I.C.S.: 332911
David Roy (Acct Mgr)

Flowserve Sanmar Ltd. (2)
147 Karapakkam Village, Chennai, 600 097, Tamil Nadu, India
Tel.: (91) 4424504100
Web Site: http://www.sanmar.com
Emp.: 900
Mechanical Sealing Device Mfr; Owned by Sanmar Holdings Ltd. & by Flowserve Corporation
N.A.I.C.S.: 339991

INTERNATIONAL PUBLIC

Subsidiary (US):

Matrix Metals LLC (2)
3972 Main St, Keokuk, IA 52632
Tel.: (319) 524-2661
Web Site: http://www.matrixmetalsllc.com
Steel Investment Castings Foundry
N.A.I.C.S.: 331512

Subsidiary (Domestic):

National Engineering Products Company, Inc. (3)
126 Collins Rd, Richmond, TX 77469-3021
Tel.: (281) 342-5511
Web Site: http://www.matrixmetalsllc.com
Sales Range: $100-124.9 Million
Emp.: 350
Steel Investment Castings Foundry
N.A.I.C.S.: 331512

Subsidiary (Domestic):

Sanmar Engineering Services-Chennai (2)
9 Cathedral Road, Tamil Nadu, Chennai, 600 086, India
Tel.: (91) 44 2812 8500
Web Site: http://www.sanmargroup.com
Industrial Plant Maintenance & Business Support Services
N.A.I.C.S.: 811310

Sanmar Foundries Ltd. (2)
9 Cathedral Road, Chennai, 600086, India
Tel.: (91) 4428128400
Web Site: http://www.sanmarfoundries.com
Steel Investment Foundry
N.A.I.C.S.: 331512

Affiliate (Domestic):

Tyco Sanmar Ltd. (2)
No 147 Old Mahabalipuram Rd Nedunchezian Salai, Karappakam, Chennai, 600097, India
Tel.: (91) 4424504000
Web Site: http://www.sanmargroup.com
Industrial Valve Mfr; Owned by Sanmar Holdings Ltd. & by Tyco International Ltd.
N.A.I.C.S.: 332911

Joint Venture (Domestic):

Vishay Sanmar Ltd. (2)
9 Cathedral Road, Chennai, 600 086, Tamil Nadu, India
Tel.: (91) 44 2812 8500
Web Site: http://www.sanmargroup.com
Sales Range: $100-124.9 Million
Steel Casting Mfr
N.A.I.C.S.: 331513

Xomox Sanmar Ltd. (2)
9 Cathedral Road, Chennai, 600 086, India
Tel.: (91) 4428128400
Web Site: http://www.sunmargroup.com
Emp.: 240
Industrial Valve Mfr; Owned by Sanmar Holdings Ltd. & Xomox Corporation
N.A.I.C.S.: 332911
M. N. Radhakrishnan (Mng Dir)

Sanmar Shipping Ltd. (1)
9 Cathedral Road, Chennai, 600086, TN, India
Tel.: (91) 4428128600
Web Site: http://www.sanmargroup.com
Deep Sea Bulk Freight Transportation Services
N.A.I.C.S.: 483111
P. S. Jayaraman (Chm)

Sanmar Speciality Chemicals Ltd. (1)
9 Cathedral Road, Chennai, 600 086, India
Tel.: (91) 4428128200
Inorganic Chemical Mfr
N.A.I.C.S.: 325180

Unit (Domestic):

ProCitius Research (2)
38 Old Mahabalipuram Road, Perungudi, Chennai, 600 096, Tamil Nadu, India
Tel.: (91) 4442253000
Web Site: http://www.procitius.com
Specialty Chemical Research & Development Services
N.A.I.C.S.: 541715

AND PRIVATE COMPANIES — SANOFI

Plant (Domestic):

Sanmar Speciality Chemicals Limited - Berigai Plant (2)
No 44 Suligunta Village Theertham Road, Berigai Post Hosur Taluk, 635 105, Dharmapuri, Tamil Nadu, India
Tel.: (91) 4344 253 509
Chemical Products Mfr
N.A.I.C.S.: 325199

SANMIT INFRA LIMITED
601 Makhija Royale Plot-753 S V Road Khar W, Mumbai, 400 052, India
Tel.: (91) 2267429100
Web Site: https://www.sanmitinfraltd.com
532435—(BOM)
Rev.: $17,206,031
Assets: $6,002,038
Liabilities: $2,194,185
Net Worth: $3,807,853
Earnings: $619,615
Fiscal Year-end: 03/31/23
Real Estate Development Services
N.A.I.C.S.: 531390
Sanjay K. Makhija (Mng Dir)

SANMITRA COMMERCIAL LIMITED
13 Prem Niwas 652 Dr Ambedkar Road Khar West, Mumbai, 400 052, India
Tel.: (91) 2222821087
Web Site: http://www.sanmitracommercial.com
Year Founded: 1985
Rev.: $667,000
Assets: $325,668
Liabilities: $119,159
Net Worth: $206,509
Earnings: $40,204
Fiscal Year-end: 03/31/19
Commodity Trading Services
N.A.I.C.S.: 523160
Suman Shah (CEO)

SANNO CO., LTD.
Tsunashima-Higashi, Kouhoku-ku, Yokohama, 223-0052, Kanagawa, Japan
Tel.: (81) 455318241
Web Site: https://www.sanno.co.jp
Year Founded: 1958
3441—(TKS)
Rev.: $54,748,440
Assets: $74,975,880
Liabilities: $35,049,700
Net Worth: $39,926,180
Earnings: $1,940,640
Fiscal Year-end: 07/31/24
Metal Products Mfr
N.A.I.C.S.: 332999
Fuminari Koyama (Chm)

SANO BRUNO'S ENTERPRISES LTD.
Haharash Street 11 Neve Ne eman, Hod Hasharon, Israel
Tel.: (972) 97473222
Web Site: https://www.sano.co.il
Year Founded: 1965
SANO1—(TAE)
Rev.: $588,329,318
Assets: $654,280,415
Liabilities: $125,246,026
Net Worth: $529,034,389
Earnings: $66,259,427
Emp.: 1,600
Fiscal Year-end: 12/31/23
All Other Miscellaneous Chemical Product & Preparation Manufacturing
N.A.I.C.S.: 325998
Yuval Landsberg (CEO)

SANOCHEMIA PHARMAZEUTIKA AG
Boltzmanngasse 11, 1090, Vienna, Austria
Tel.: (43) 13191456324
Web Site: http://www.sanochemia.at
Year Founded: 1990
Sales Range: $25-49.9 Million
Emp.: 190
Pharmaceuticals Mfr
N.A.I.C.S.: 325412
Timo Bender (Mng Dir-Production, Tech, Regulatory & Quality)

SANOCKIE ZAKLADY PRZEMYSLU GUMOWEGO STOMIL SANOK S.A.
ul Przemyska 24, 38-500, Sanok, Poland
Tel.: (48) 134654444
Web Site: https://www.sanokrubber.com
SNK—(WAR)
Rev.: $348,847,159
Assets: $255,375,320
Liabilities: $117,857,107
Net Worth: $137,518,213
Earnings: $14,298,598
Fiscal Year-end: 12/31/22
Rubber Products Mfr
N.A.I.C.S.: 326220
Marcin Saramak (Member-Mgmt Bd, VP & Dir-Bus Dev & IT Sys)

Subsidiaries:

PST Stomil Sp z o.o. w Rymanowie Zdroju (1)
ul Swierkowa 1, 38-481, Rymanow-Zdroj, Poland
Tel.: (48) 134357427
Web Site: http://www.rymanow.swierkowyzdroj.pl
Rehabilitation & Medical Services
N.A.I.C.S.: 622310

STOMIL SANOK RUS Sp. z o.o. (1)
ul Amurskaja 2 office 27, building 31 building 50, Moscow, 107553, Russia
Tel.: (7) 4957818495
Web Site: http://www.stomilsanok.ru
Lumber Product Whslr
N.A.I.C.S.: 423990

Stomet Sp. z.o.o. (1)
ul Reymonta 19a, 38-500, Sanok, Poland
Tel.: (48) 134654722
Web Site: https://www.stometsanok.com
Rubber Products Mfr
N.A.I.C.S.: 333248

Stomil EAST Sp. z o.o. (1)
ul Reymonta 19, 38-500, Sanok, Poland
Tel.: (48) 134654795
Web Site: http://www.stomileast.pl
Lumber Product Whslr
N.A.I.C.S.: 424990

Stomil Sanok Ukraina Sp. z o.o. (1)
Kniasia Wolodymyra 75 office 37, 33013, Rivne, Ukraine
Tel.: (380) 362261402
Sales Range: $1-9.9 Million
Rubber Product Distr
N.A.I.C.S.: 423840

Stomil Sanok-Dystrybucja Sp. z o.o. (1)
ul Gnieznienska 99, Bogucin, 62-006, Swarzedz, Poland
Tel.: (48) 61875979394
Web Site: http://www.stomildystrybucja.pl
Sales Range: $75-99.9 Million
Emp.: 150
Lumber Product Whslr
N.A.I.C.S.: 423990

SANOFI
46 avenue de la Grande Armee, 75017, Paris, France
Tel.: (33) 153774000   FR
Web Site: https://www.sanofi.com
Year Founded: 1973
SNY—(NASDAQ)
Rev.: $46,481,761,278
Assets: $136,481,761,278
Liabilities: $56,238,938,053
Net Worth: $80,242,823,225
Earnings: $5,827,757,393
Emp.: 86,088
Fiscal Year-end: 12/31/23
Pharmaceuticals Product Mfr
N.A.I.C.S.: 325412
Olivier Charmeil (Exec VP-Gen Medicines)

Subsidiaries:

A. Nattermann & Cie. GmbH (1)
Nattermannallee 1, 50829, Cologne, Germany
Tel.: (49) 22150901
Pharmaceuticals Product Mfr
N.A.I.C.S.: 325412

Ablynx N.V. (1)
Technologiepark 21 Zwijnaarde, 9052, Gent, Belgium
Tel.: (32) 92620000
Web Site: http://www.ablynx.com
Biopharmaceutical Researcher & Developer
N.A.I.C.S.: 541714

Beijing Med-Pharm Co., Ltd. (1)
5F Min Sheng Life Plaza No 2 Office Building E Third Ring Rd N, Chaoyang District, Beijing, 100026, China
Tel.: (86) 1085879191
Sales Range: $150-199.9 Million
Pharmaceutical Marketer & Distr
N.A.I.C.S.: 424210

Bullivants Natural Health Products (International) Pty Ltd (1)
PO Box 403, Virginia, Brisbane, 4014, QLD, Australia
Tel.: (61) 732128628
Pharmaceutical Product Mfr & Whslr
N.A.I.C.S.: 325412

Canderm General Partnership (1)
5353 Thimens Blvd, Saint Laurent, H4R 2H4, QC, Canada
Tel.: (514) 334-3835
Sales Range: $25-49.9 Million
Emp.: 50
Cosmetic Products Mfr & Whslr
N.A.I.C.S.: 325620

Chattem, Inc. (1)
3708 St Elmo Ave, Chattanooga, TN 37409-1248
Tel.: (423) 822-5000
Sales Range: $450-499.9 Million
Emp.: 547
Over-the-Counter Healthcare Products, Toiletries & Dietary Supplements Marketer & Mfr
N.A.I.C.S.: 325412

Chinoin Private Co. Ltd (1)
To Utca 1-5, Budapest, 1045, Hungary
Tel.: (36) 15050000
Pesticide Mfr
N.A.I.C.S.: 325320

Francopia S.A.R.L. (1)
54 rue La Boetie, 75008, Paris, France
Tel.: (33) 153774033
Pharmaceutical Products Distr
N.A.I.C.S.: 424210

Fujisawa Synthelabo Pharmaceuticals Co., Ltd. (1)
2nd Fl No 325 Sec 1 Tun Hwa South Rd, Taipei, 106, Taiwan
Tel.: (886) 227091980
Provider of Pharmaceuticals; Joint Venture of Fujisawa Pharmaceutical Co., Ltd. (49%) & Sanofi-Synthelabo S.A. (51%)
N.A.I.C.S.: 325412

Genfar S.A. (1)
Transversal 23 97-73 Piso 9, Bogota, Colombia
Web Site: http://www.genfar.com.co
Pharmaceuticals Product Mfr
N.A.I.C.S.: 325412

Genzyme Corporation (1)
500 Kendall St, Cambridge, MA 02142
Tel.: (617) 252-7500
Web Site: http://www.genzyme.com
Sales Range: $1-4.9 Billion
Emp.: 10,100
Pharmaceutical Developer
N.A.I.C.S.: 325414
Brendan O'Callaghan (Partner & Sr VP-Industrial Affairs)

Subsidiary (Non-US):

Genzyme Australia Pty. Ltd (2)
Talavera Corporate Centre Building D 12-24, Talavera Road, Building D 12-24 Talavera Roa, Macquarie, 2113, NSW, Australia
Tel.: (61) 2 9978 3900
Pharmaceuticals Mfr
N.A.I.C.S.: 325412
Carn Hodd (Country Mgr)

Genzyme Austria GmbH (2)
Franz-Klein-Gasse 5, Osterreich, 1190, Vienna, Austria
Tel.: (43) 1 774 65 38
Pharmaceuticals Mfr
N.A.I.C.S.: 325412

Genzyme Belgium NV/SA (2)
Ikaroslaan 53, B 1930, Zaventem, Belgium
Tel.: (32) 2714 1711
Pharmaceuticals Mfr
N.A.I.C.S.: 325412

Genzyme Biopharmaceuticals South Africa (Pty) Ltd (2)
Bryanston Corner, 18 Ealing Crescent, Johannesburg, 2191, Bryanston, South Africa
Tel.: (27) 11 996 3860
Pharmaceuticals Mfr
N.A.I.C.S.: 325412

Division (Domestic):

Genzyme Biosurgery (2)
500 Kendall St, Cambridge, MA 02142   (100%)
Tel.: (617) 252-7500
Devices for Cardiothoracic, Orthopaedic & General Surgery Developer
N.A.I.C.S.: 325412

Subsidiary (Non-US):

Genzyme Chile Ltda. (2)
18th, Las Condes, Santiago, Chile
Tel.: (56) 2 23667000
Web Site: http://www.sanofi.cl
Pharmaceuticals Mfr
N.A.I.C.S.: 325412

Genzyme Colombia S. A. (2)
C Calle 93 B 1725/49 Piso 5, Bogota, Colombia
Tel.: (57) 1 621 6600
Web Site: http://www.genzyme.com.co
Pharmaceuticals Mfr
N.A.I.C.S.: 325412

Genzyme Czech s. r. o. (2)
Amazon Court, Karolinska 661/4, 186 00, Prague, Czech Republic
Tel.: (420) 221 722 511
Web Site: http://www.genzyme.cz
Pharmaceuticals Mfr
N.A.I.C.S.: 325412

Genzyme Denmark A/S (2)
Islands Brygge 57, 2300, Copenhagen, Denmark
Tel.: (45) 32712600
Web Site: http://www.genzyme.nu
Pharmaceuticals Mfr
N.A.I.C.S.: 325412

Genzyme Europe B.V. (2)
Gooimeer 10, 1411 DD, Naarden, Netherlands   (100%)
Tel.: (31) 356991200
Sales Range: $10-24.9 Million
Emp.: 250
Biotechnology Products Mfr
N.A.I.C.S.: 325412

Genzyme France S.A.S. (2)
33/35 Boulevard de la Paix, Zone d Activite du Bel Air, 78105, Paris, Saint Germain, France
Tel.: (33) 130872525
Web Site: http://www.genzyme.fr
Pharmaceuticals Mfr
N.A.I.C.S.: 325412

SANOFI

Sanofi—(Continued)

Genzyme Hellas LLC (2)
599 Vouliagmenis Ave, Argyroupoli, 164 52,
Athens, Greece
Tel.: (30) 210 994 9270
Pharmaceuticals Mfr
N.A.I.C.S.: 325412

Genzyme India Pvt. Ltd (2)
1st Fl Technopolis Golf Course Road Sector
54, Gurgaon, 122001, Haryana, India
Tel.: (91) 124 452 8300
Web Site: http://www.genzyme.com
Pharmaceuticals Mfr
N.A.I.C.S.: 325412

Genzyme Ireland Ltd. (2)
IDA Industrial Park, Old Kilmeaden Road,
Waterford, Ireland
Tel.: (353) 51 594100
Web Site: http://www.genzyme.ie
Pharmaceuticals Mfr
N.A.I.C.S.: 325412

Genzyme Israel Ltd. (2)
Beit-Hapaamon Hataas St 20, Industrial
Zone Kfar Saba, Kefar Sava, Israel
Tel.: (972) 9 7 666640
Web Site: http://www.genzyme.co.il
Pharmaceuticals Mfr
N.A.I.C.S.: 325412

Genzyme Italy S.A.S. (2)
Via Scaglia Est 136, 41126, Modena, Italy
Tel.: (39) 059 349811
Pharmaceuticals Mfr
N.A.I.C.S.: 325412

Genzyme Japan K.K. (2)
37F Akasaka Biz Tower, 5-3-1 Akasaka, Tokyo, 107 0052, Japan (100%)
Tel.: (81) 3 3560 4600
Web Site: http://www.genzyme.co.jp
Sales Range: $25-49.9 Million
Emp.: 70
Pharmaceuticals Product Mfr
N.A.I.C.S.: 325412

Genzyme Korea Co., Ltd (2)
5FL GanNam Finance Center 737, Yeok
Sam-Dong, Seoul, 135925, KangNam-Ku,
Korea (South)
Tel.: (82) 55459400
Web Site: http://www.genzyme.co.kr
Pharmaceuticals Mfr
N.A.I.C.S.: 325412

Genzyme Malaysia Sdn Bhd (2)
11-1-11th Fl Menara Surian, No 1 Jalan
PJU 7/3, 47810, Petaling Jaya, Selangor
Darul Ehsan, Malaysia
Tel.: (60) 3 7711 5511
Pharmaceuticals Mfr
N.A.I.C.S.: 325412

Genzyme Mexico S de RL de CV (2)
Paseo de la Reforma 505 Piso 49, Delacion
Cuauhtemoc, CP 06500, Mexico, Mexico
Tel.: (52) 506 272 5392
Web Site: http://www.genzyme.com.mx
Pharmaceuticals Mfr
N.A.I.C.S.: 325412

Genzyme Middle East FZ LLC (2)
International Media Production Zone, Circular Building D 2nd Fl, Dubai, United Arab
Emirates
Tel.: (971) 4 3692876
Pharmaceuticals Mfr
N.A.I.C.S.: 325412

Subsidiary (Domestic):

Genzyme Oncology, Inc. (2)
4545 Horizon Hill Blvd, San Antonio, TX
78229
Tel.: (210) 949-8200
Web Site: http://www.genzymeoncology.com
Sales Range: $25-49.9 Million
Emp.: 225
Cancer Drug Research, Development & Mfr
N.A.I.C.S.: 325412

Subsidiary (Non-US):

Genzyme Portugal S.A. (2)
Tagus Park Edificio Ciencia II 2 Piso 2 D,
Porto Salvo, 2740 120, Portugal
Tel.: (351) 21 422 0100

Web Site: http://www.genzyme.com.pt
Pharmaceuticals Mfr
N.A.I.C.S.: 325412

Genzyme S.L.U. (2)
Martinez Villergas 52, 28027, Madrid, Spain
Tel.: (34) 91 659 1670
Web Site: http://www.genzyme.es
Pharmaceuticals Mfr
N.A.I.C.S.: 325412

Genzyme Taiwan Ltd. (2)
A101 10th Fl, No 51 Hengyang Rd, Taipei,
10045, Taiwan
Tel.: (886) 2 2313 1889
Pharmaceuticals Mfr
N.A.I.C.S.: 325412

Genzyme Therapeutics Ltd (2)
4620 Kingsgate Cascade Way, Oxford Bus
Pk S, Oxford, OX4 2SU, United
Kingdom (100%)
Tel.: (44) 1865405200
Web Site: http://www.genzyme.co.uk
Sales Range: $50-74.9 Million
Emp.: 50
Biochemicals Mfr
N.A.I.C.S.: 424210

Genzyme Turkey Ltd (2)
Muhittin Ustundag Caddesi No 31, Kosuyolu, Istanbul, Turkiye
Tel.: (90) 216 547 4700
Pharmaceuticals Mfr
N.A.I.C.S.: 325412

Genzyme de Argentina S.A. (2)
Fondo de la Legua 161, B1609JEB, Boulogne Sur Mer, Argentina
Tel.: (54) 11 4708 6900
Web Site: http://www.genzyme.com.ar
Pharmaceuticals Mfr
N.A.I.C.S.: 325412

Genzyme de Peru S.AC (2)
Calle Victor Andres Belaunde, No147 Edif
Real 6 Piso 6 S, Lima, Peru
Tel.: (51) 1 2112576
Pharmaceuticals Mfr
N.A.I.C.S.: 325412

Genzyme do Brasil Ltda. (2)
Av Francisco Matarazzo 1400 10 Andar
Conj 101 Edific, 05001 903, Sao Paulo,
Brazil
Tel.: (55) 11 3874 9950
Web Site: http://www.genzyme.com.br
Pharmaceuticals Mfr
N.A.I.C.S.: 325412

Genzyme in Geel B.V.B.A./S.P.R.L. (2)
Cipalstraat 8, 2440, Geel, Belgium
Tel.: (32) 14 564 911
Pharmaceuticals Mfr
N.A.I.C.S.: 325412

Genzyme Polyclonals SAS (1)
23 Boulevard Chambaud-de-la-Bruyere,
69007, Lyon, France
Tel.: (33) 437281600
Web Site: https://www.sanofi.fr
Pharmaceuticals Product Mfr
N.A.I.C.S.: 325412
Sylvain Soler (Mgr-QC Labs)

Kadmon Holdings, Inc. (1)
450 E 29th St, New York, NY 10016
Tel.: (833) 900-5366
Web Site: http://www.kadmon.com
Rev: $8,288,000
Assets: $162,710,000
Liabilities: $46,687,000
Net Worth: $116,023,000
Earnings: ($111,035,000)
Emp.: 127
Fiscal Year-end: 12/31/2020
Biopharmaceutical Product Research & Development Services
N.A.I.C.S.: 325412
John Ryan (Exec Dir-Medical, Clinical & Regulatory Dev)

Kiadis Pharma N.V. (1)
Entrada 231-234, 1096 EG, Amsterdam,
Netherlands (95.03%)
Tel.: (31) 3140250
Web Site: http://www.kiadispharma.com
Developer of Oncology Products
N.A.I.C.S.: 325412
Andrew S. Sandler (Chief Medical Officer)

Division (Non-US):

Kiadis Pharma Canada (2)
2525 Marie Curie Avenue, Saint Laurent,
H4S 2E1, QC, Canada
Tel.: (514) 336-4886
Sales Range: $25-49.9 Million
Emp.: 20
Biopharmaceutical Mfr
N.A.I.C.S.: 325412

Laboratoire Oenobiol S.A.S. (1)
59 Boulevard Exelmans, 75016, Paris,
France
Tel.: (33) 1 40 71 80 00
Web Site: http://www.oenobiol.fr
Sales Range: $25-49.9 Million
Emp.: 30
Cosmetic Products Mfr & Distr
N.A.I.C.S.: 325620
Marie Bejot (Founder)

Medley S.A. Industria Farmaceutica Ltda (1)
Rua Macedo Costa n 55, Campinas, 13080-180, Sao Paulo, Brazil
Tel.: (55) 19 2117 8222
Web Site: http://www.medley.com.br
Sales Range: $550-599.9 Million
Emp.: 1,500
Pharmaceutical Products Mfr & Whslr
N.A.I.C.S.: 325412

Principia Biopharma Inc. (1)
220 E Grand Ave, South San Francisco, CA
94080
Tel.: (650) 416-7700
Web Site: http://www.principiabio.com
Rev: $35,160,000
Assets: $382,736,000
Liabilities: $23,758,000
Net Worth: $358,978,000
Earnings: ($53,792,000)
Emp.: 103
Fiscal Year-end: 12/31/2019
Pharmaceuticals Product Mfr
N.A.I.C.S.: 325412
Betsy Santos (Sr VP-People)

Protein Sciences Corp. (1)
1000 Research Pkwy, Meriden, CT 06450
Tel.: (203) 686-0800
Web Site: http://www.proteinsciences.com
Pharmaceutical Preparation Mfr
N.A.I.C.S.: 325412

Provention Bio, Inc. (1)
55 Broad St 2nd Fl, Red Bank, NJ 07701
Tel.: (908) 336-0360
Web Site: https://www.proventionbio.com
Rev: $12,895,000
Assets: $236,856,000
Liabilities: $115,007,000
Net Worth: $121,849,000
Earnings: ($113,565,000)
Emp.: 174
Fiscal Year-end: 12/31/2022
Biopharmaceutical Product Research & Development Services
N.A.I.C.S.: 541714
Francisco J. Leon (Co-Founder & Chief Scientific Officer)

Sanofi (China) Investment Co., Ltd. (1)
7/F No 112 Jianguo Rd, Chaoyang Dist,
Beijing, 100022, China
Tel.: (86) 1065685588
Emp.: 45
Medicinal Product Mfr
N.A.I.C.S.: 325411
Yanping Li (Mgr-Assoc Regulatory Affairs)

Sanofi A/S (1)
Lyngbyvej 2, 2100, Copenhagen, Denmark
Tel.: (45) 45167000
Web Site: http://www.sanofi.dk
Pharmaceuticals Product Mfr
N.A.I.C.S.: 325412

Sanofi AB (1)
Tel.: (46) 86345000
Web Site: http://www.sanofi.se
Pharmaceuticals Product Mfr
N.A.I.C.S.: 325412

Sanofi Arabia Trading Company Limited (1)
Tahlia Street Nojoud Center Gate B 2nd
Floor, PO Box 9874, Jeddah, 21423, Saudi
Arabia

INTERNATIONAL PUBLIC

Tel.: (966) 126693318
Web Site: https://www.sanofi.com.sa
Pharmaceuticals Product Mfr
N.A.I.C.S.: 325412

Sanofi Australia Pty Limited (1)
12-24 Talavera Corporate Centre Building D,
12-24 Talavera Road, Sydney, 2113, NSW,
Australia (100%)
Tel.: (61) 286662000
Web Site: http://www.sanofi.com.au
Sales Range: $200-249.9 Million
Emp.: 1,000
Pharmaceutical Preparation Mfr
N.A.I.C.S.: 325412

Sanofi Chimie S.A. (1)
9 R Du Pdt Salvador Allende, Gentilly,
94250, Val-de-Marne, France
Tel.: (33) 141246000
Pharmaceuticals Product Mfr
N.A.I.C.S.: 325412

Sanofi China (1)
Room 3108 Plaza 66 Office Building No
1266 Nanjing West Road, Shanghai,
200040, China
Tel.: (86) 21 6288 1616
Web Site: http://en.sanofi.com
Pharmaceuticals Product Mfr
N.A.I.C.S.: 325412

Sanofi Egypt S.A.E. (1)
3 EL Massaneh St, PO Box 1486, Zeitoun,
Cairo, Egypt
Tel.: (20) 222860000
Web Site: http://www.sanofi.com.eg
Emp.: 1,200
Pharmaceuticals Product Mfr
N.A.I.C.S.: 325412

Sanofi India Limited (1)
Sanofi House CTS No 117-B Saki Vihar
Road, L T Business Park Powai, Mumbai,
400 072, India
Tel.: (91) 2228032000
Web Site: https://www.sanofi.in
Pharmaceutical Preparation Mfr
N.A.I.C.S.: 325412
Rajaram Narayanan (Mng Dir)

Sanofi K.K. (1)
Tokyo Opera City Tower 20-2 Nishishinjuku
3-chome, Shinjuku-ku, Tokyo, 163-1488,
Japan
Tel.: (81) 363013000
Web Site: http://www.sanofi.co.jp
Pharmaceuticals Product Mfr
N.A.I.C.S.: 325412

Sanofi Oy (1)
Revontulenkuja 1, PO Box 505, 02100, Espoo, Finland
Tel.: (358) 201200300
Web Site: https://www.sanofi.fi
Pharmaceuticals Product Mfr
N.A.I.C.S.: 325412

Sanofi Pasteur SA (1)
2 Avenue Pont Pasteur, 69367, Lyon,
France (100%)
Tel.: (33) 437370100
Web Site: http://www.sanofipasteur.com
Sales Range: $1-4.9 Billion
Emp.: 11,000
Vaccines & Immunology Products Mfr
N.A.I.C.S.: 325414

Subsidiary (Non-US):

Acambis Research Ltd. (2)
Peterhouse Technology Park, Cambridge,
CB1 9PT, United Kingdom
Tel.: (44) 1223275300
Sales Range: $10-24.9 Million
Emp.: 206
Vaccine Research & Development Services
N.A.I.C.S.: 325412

Sanofi Pasteur (2)
Level 18-1 Tower B Plaza 33 No 1 Jalan
Kemajuan Seksyen 13, Damansara
Heights, 50490, Petaling Jaya, Malaysia
Tel.: (60) 320893218
Web Site: http://www.sanofipasteur.com
Mfr of Vaccines & Immunology Products
N.A.I.C.S.: 325414

Sanofi Pasteur (2)
Tekfen Tower Buyukdere, Caddesi No 209 4
Levent, 34394, Istanbul, Turkiye

AND PRIVATE COMPANIES — SANOFI

Tel.: (90) 2123391011
Web Site: http://www.sanofipasteur.com.tr
Sales Range: $25-49.9 Million
Emp.: 35
Mfr of Vaccines & Immunology Products
N.A.I.C.S.: 325414

Sanofi Pasteur (2)
Oulansky Pereoulok 5, 4th Fl, 10100, Moscow, Russia
Tel.: (7) 5022225828
Web Site: http://www.aventispasteur.com
Mfr of Vaccines & Immunology Products
N.A.I.C.S.: 325414

Sanofi Pasteur (2)
5th Fl Gammon House 110 Rada St, PO Box 471, 1229, Makati, Manila, Philippines
Tel.: (63) 28161714
Web Site: http://www.aventispasteur.com
Sales Range: $25-49.9 Million
Emp.: 70
Mfr of Vaccines & Immunology Products
N.A.I.C.S.: 325414

Sanofi Pasteur (2)
7F No 112 Jian Guo Lu, Chaoyang District, Beijing, 100 022, China
Tel.: (86) 10 6568 5588
Web Site: http://www.sanofipasteur.cn
Vaccines Mfr
N.A.I.C.S.: 325414

Sanofi Pasteur (2)
Calle Los Sauces N 374 Torre Roja C-2 Oficina 303, San Isidro, Lima, Peru
Tel.: (51) 1 411 4747
Web Site: http://en.sanofi.com
Sales Range: $25-49.9 Million
Emp.: 20
Vaccines Mfr
N.A.I.C.S.: 325414

Sanofi Pasteur (2)
7F No 3 Songren Road, Taipei, 11010, Taiwan
Tel.: (886) 22176558
Web Site: https://www.sanofi.com.tw
Bacterial Vaccine Mfr
N.A.I.C.S.: 325414

Sanofi Pasteur (2)
Private Bag X207, Midrand, 1683, Johannesburg, South Africa
Tel.: (27) 11 256 3700
Web Site: http://www.sanofipasteur.co.za
Vaccine Distr
N.A.I.C.S.: 424210

Sanofi Pasteur (2)
Kr Valdemara 33-17 a, 1010, Riga, Latvia
Tel.: (371) 671 149 78
Web Site: http://en.sanofi.com
Sales Range: $25-49.9 Million
Emp.: 12
Vaccines Mfr
N.A.I.C.S.: 325414

Sanofi Pasteur (2)
Str Herastrau railway station no 4 floors 8-9, Sector 2, 020334, Bucharest, Romania
Tel.: (40) 213173136
Sales Range: $50-74.9 Million
Emp.: 200
Vaccines Mfr
N.A.I.C.S.: 325414

Sanofi Pasteur (2)
Building 119 To u 1-5, 1045, Budapest, Hungary
Tel.: (36) 1 505 2734
Web Site: http://www.sanofipasteur.hu
Sales Range: $25-49.9 Million
Emp.: 6
Pharmaceutical Products Distr
N.A.I.C.S.: 424210

Sanofi Pasteur (2)
Aupark Tower Einsteinova 24, 851 01, Bratislava, Slovakia
Tel.: (421) 2 33100 750
Web Site: http://en.sanofi.com
Vaccines Mfr
N.A.I.C.S.: 325414

Sanofi Pasteur (2)
Micro Zone d Activites Batiment B Hydra, 16035, Algiers, Algeria
Tel.: (213) 20 28 26 46
Vaccines Mfr
N.A.I.C.S.: 325414

Sanofi Pasteur (2)
PH Ocean Business Plaza Calle 47 y Ave, Postal 0819-07069, Apartado, Panama, Panama
Tel.: (507) 305 1416
Web Site: http://www.sanofipasteur.com
Emp.: 200
Vaccines Mfr
N.A.I.C.S.: 325414

Sanofi Pasteur (2)
103 Alexander Stamboliiski Blvd Office Building Sofia Tower Floor 8, Sofia, 1303, Bulgaria
Tel.: (359) 2 980 08 33
Vaccines Mfr
N.A.I.C.S.: 325414

Sanofi Pasteur (2)
Generala Piky 430/26, Dejvice, 160 00, Prague, Czech Republic
Tel.: (420) 233086111
Vaccines Mfr
N.A.I.C.S.: 325414

Subsidiary (US):

Sanofi Pasteur Inc. (2)
1 Discovery Dr, Swiftwater, PA 18370-0187
Tel.: (570) 839-7187
Sales Range: $800-899.9 Million
Emp.: 3,000
Vaccines & Immunology Products Mfr
N.A.I.C.S.: 325412
David Loew (Sr VP-Global Comml Ops)

Branch (Domestic):

Sanofi Pasteur (3)
38 Sidney St, Cambridge, MA 02139
Tel.: (617) 761-4200
Web Site: http://www.sanofipasteur.com
Sales Range: $50-74.9 Million
Emp.: 160
Research & Development of Vaccines
N.A.I.C.S.: 325412

Subsidiary (Non-US):

Sanofi Pasteur K.K (2)
Tokyo Opera City Tower 3-20-2 Nishi Shinjuku, Shinjuku-ku, Tokyo, 163-1488, Japan
Tel.: (81) 3 6301 3070
Web Site: http://www.sanofipasteur.jp
Vaccines & Immunology Products Mfr
N.A.I.C.S.: 325414

Sanofi Pasteur Limited (2)
1755 Steeles Ave West, Toronto, M2R 3T4, ON, Canada
Tel.: (416) 667-2701
Web Site: http://www.sanofipasteur.ca
Sales Range: $400-449.9 Million
Emp.: 1,100
Mfr of Vaccines & Immunology Products
N.A.I.C.S.: 325414

Sanofi Pasteur Ltd (2)
8th Fl Handok Bldg, 735 Yoksam 1-Dong, Kangnam-Ku, Seoul, 135-081, Korea (South)
Tel.: (82) 25546544
Web Site: http://en.sanofi.com
Mfr of Vaccines & Immunology Products
N.A.I.C.S.: 325414
Baptiste de Clarens (Gen Mgr)

Sanofi Pasteur Ltda. (2)
City Park Complex Torre Sucupira, Avenida das Nacoes Unidas 14 401, Sao Paulo, 04794-000, Jardim Morumbi, Brazil
Tel.: (55) 28892000
Sales Range: $25-49.9 Million
Emp.: 200
Mfr of Vaccines & Immunology Products
N.A.I.C.S.: 325414

Joint Venture (Domestic):

Sanofi Pasteur MSD, SNC (2)
8 rue Jonas Salk, 69367, Lyon, France
Tel.: (33) 437284000
Web Site: http://www.sanofi.com
Vaccine Mfr & Distr; Joint Venture of Sanofi-Aventis (50%) & Merck & Co. Inc. (50%)
N.A.I.C.S.: 325414

Subsidiary (Non-US):

Sanofi Pasteur MSD
Hemvarnsgatan 15, 171 54, Solna, Sweden
Tel.: (46) 856488860
Web Site: http://www.spmsd.se
Sales Range: $25-49.9 Million
Emp.: 21
Vaccine Mfr & Distr; Joint Venture of Sanofi-Aventis (50%) & Merck & Co. Inc. (50%)
N.A.I.C.S.: 325412

Sanofi Pasteur MSD AG (3)
Gulmmatt, Baar, 6340, Switzerland
Tel.: (41) 417615665
Sales Range: $25-49.9 Million
Emp.: 10
Mfr of Vaccines & Immunology Products; Joint Venture of Sanofi-Aventis (50%) & Merck & Co. Inc. (50%)
N.A.I.C.S.: 325414
Monthtny Andree (Mgr)

Sanofi Pasteur MSD GmbH (3)
Alexanderufer Str 3, 69181, Berlin, Germany
Tel.: (49) 62245940
Web Site: http://www.spmsd.de
Sales Range: $50-74.9 Million
Emp.: 230
Mfr of Vaccines & Immunology Products; Joint Venture of Sanofi-Aventis (50%) & Merck & Co. Inc. (50%)
N.A.I.C.S.: 325414

Sanofi Pasteur MSD GmbH (3)
Campus 21 Europaring F11/402, Brunn am Gebirge, A 2345, Vienna, Austria
Tel.: (43) 18667022200
Web Site: http://www.spmsd.at
Mfr of Vaccines & Immunology Products; Joint Venture of Sanofi-Aventis (50%) & Merck & Co. Inc. (50%)
N.A.I.C.S.: 325414

Sanofi Pasteur MSD N.V. (3)
Taurusavenue 31a, 2132 LS, Hoofddorp, Netherlands
Tel.: (31) 235679600
Mfr of Vaccines & Immunology Products; Joint Venture of Sanofi-Aventis (50%) & Merck & Co. Inc. (50%)
N.A.I.C.S.: 325414

Sanofi Pasteur MSD Oy (3)
Keilaranda 3, 00810, Espoo, Finland
Tel.: (358) 95658830
Web Site: http://www.spmsd.fi
Mfr of Vaccines & Immunology Products; Joint Venture of Sanofi-Aventis (50%) & Merck & Co. Inc. (50%)
N.A.I.C.S.: 325414

Sanofi Pasteur MSD SpA (3)
Via degli Aldobrandeschi 15, 00163, Rome, Italy
Tel.: (39) 0666409211
Mfr of Vaccines & Immunology Products; Joint Venture of Sanofi-Aventis (50%) & Merck & Co. Inc. (50%)
N.A.I.C.S.: 325414

Sanofi Pasteur MSD, SA (3)
Avenida el Partenon 4-6 2nd Floor, Paseo de la Castellana 141- 2, 28046, Madrid, Spain
Tel.: (34) 913717800
Web Site: http://www.spmsd.com
Sales Range: $50-74.9 Million
Emp.: 100
Mfr of Vaccines & Immunology Products; Joint Venture of Sanofi-Aventis (50%) & Merck & Co. Inc. (50%)
N.A.I.C.S.: 325414

Subsidiary (Non-US):

Sanofi Pasteur S.A. (2)
Av Int Tomkinson 2054, B1642EMU, San Isidro, Buenos Aires, Argentina
Tel.: (54) 1147325900
Web Site: http://www.sanofispasteur.com.ar
Sales Range: $50-74.9 Million
Emp.: 130
Mfr of Vaccines & Immunology Products
N.A.I.C.S.: 325414

Sanofi Pasteur S.A. (2)
Avda Presidente Riesco 5435, Las Condes, Santiago, Chile
Tel.: (56) 233408400
Web Site: https://www.sanofi.cl
Sales Range: $25-49.9 Million
Emp.: 45
Vaccines & Immunology Products Mfr
N.A.I.C.S.: 325414

Plant (Domestic):

Sanofi Pasteur SA (2)
Parc Industriel Incarville Val de Reuil, 16427, Rouen, France
Tel.: (33) 232096700
Web Site: http://www.sanofipasteur.com
Sales Range: $300-349.9 Million
Emp.: 1,500
Pharmaceuticals Res, Devel & Production Facility
N.A.I.C.S.: 541715

Subsidiary (Non-US):

Sanofi Pasteur SA (2)
Carrera 12 No 89 28 Piso 3, Santafe de Bogota, Bogota, DC, Colombia
Tel.: (57) 016422555
Web Site: http://www.sanofipasteur.com.com
Sales Range: $25-49.9 Million
Emp.: 35
Mfr of Vaccines & Immunology Products
N.A.I.C.S.: 325414

Sanofi Pasteur SA (2)
Avenida Universidad No 1738, Mexico, 04000, Mexico (100%)
Tel.: (52) 5554844800
Web Site: http://www.sanofipasteur.com.mx
Sales Range: $25-49.9 Million
Emp.: 65
Mfr of Vaccines & Immunology Products
N.A.I.C.S.: 325414

Sanofi Pasteur VaxDesign Corporation (2)
Web Site: http://www.vaxdesign.com
Sales Range: $25-49.9 Million
Emp.: 70
Biotechnology Research & Development Services
N.A.I.C.S.: 541714
Marva Sanders (CEO)

Subsidiary (US):

Vaxserve Inc. (2)
54 Glenmaura National Blvd Ste 301, Moosic, PA 18507-2101
Web Site: https://www.vaxserve.com
Surgical Product Distr
N.A.I.C.S.: 423450

Sanofi Romania SRL (1)
Strada Gara Herastrau no 4 building B floors 8-9 sector 2, Bucharest, Romania
Tel.: (40) 213173136
Web Site: https://www.sanofi.ro
Pharmaceuticals Product Mfr
N.A.I.C.S.: 325412
Nae Adrian (Mgr-ITS Ops)

Sanofi Saglik Urunleri Limited Sirketi (1)
No 193, Sisli, Istanbul, Turkiye
Tel.: (90) 2123391000
Healtcare Services
N.A.I.C.S.: 621999

Sanofi Sante Grand Public Inc. (1)
2905 Place Louis-R -Renaud, Laval, H7V 0A3, QC, Canada
Tel.: (514) 334-3835
Web Site: https://www.sanofi.ca
Sales Range: $25-49.9 Million
Emp.: 50
Pharmaceuticals Product Mfr
N.A.I.C.S.: 325412

Sanofi Synthelabo H.K. Ltd (1)
Room 2504-2511 Windsor House 311 Gloucester Road, Causeway Bay, Hong Kong, China (Hong Kong)
Tel.: (852) 2506 8333
Pharmaceutical Product Mfr & Distr
N.A.I.C.S.: 325412

Sanofi Winthrop Industrie S.A. (1)
1 rue de la Vierge, BP 599, Ambares, 33440, France
Tel.: (33) 557303000
Pharmaceutical Product Mfr & Whslr
N.A.I.C.S.: 325412

Subsidiary (Non-US):

Winthrop Arzneimittel GmbH (2)

SANOFI

Sanofi—(Continued)
Potsdamerstr 8, Berlin, 10785, Germany
Tel.: (49) 180 20 200 10
Web Site: http://www.winthrop.de
Pharmaceuticals Product Mfr
N.A.I.C.S.: 325412

Subsidiary (Domestic):

Winthrop Medicaments S.A. (2)
1 Blvd Romain Rolland 1 13, 75014, Paris, France
Tel.: (33) 1 57 63 33 33
Pharmaceutical Product Research & Development Services
N.A.I.C.S.: 541715

Subsidiary (Non-US):

Winthrop Pharma Saidal S.P.A. (2)
Lieu Dit Parc Poirson Lotissement, Algiers, Algeria
Tel.: (213) 21793500
Pharmaceuticals Product Mfr
N.A.I.C.S.: 325412

Winthrop Pharmaceuticals (Malaysia) SDN. BHD. (2)
8th Floor No 19 PNB Damansara Lorong Dungun Damansara Heights, Kuala Lumpur, 50490, Malaysia
Tel.: (60) 3 20893333
Pharmaceutical Product Whslr
N.A.I.C.S.: 424210

Winthrop Pharmaceuticals (Proprietary) Limited (2)
Sanofi-Aventis House 2 Bond Street Grand Central Ext 1, Midrand, 1685, South Africa
Tel.: (27) 11 256 3700
Web Site: http://www.pharmachoice.co.za
Pharmaceutical Products Mfr & Whslr
N.A.I.C.S.: 325412

Sanofi de Guatemala S.A. (1)
Kilometro 15 5 Carretera Roosevelt Zona 7, Apartado Postal 3038, Mixco, Guatemala
Tel.: (502) 2429 1000
Web Site: http://www.sanofi.com.gt
Pharmaceuticals Product Mfr
N.A.I.C.S.: 325412

Sanofi-Aventis Algerie Spa. (1)
29 30 31 Micro Activity Zone Batiment B Hydra, 16035, Algiers, Algeria
Tel.: (213) 982300220
Web Site: https://www.sanofi.dz
Healthcare Services
N.A.I.C.S.: 621999
Abdelhamid Bahmed (Mgr-Tax)

Sanofi-Aventis Groupe S.A. (1)
54 rue La Boetie, 75013, Paris, France (100%)
Tel.: (33) 153774000
Web Site: http://www.sanofi-aventis.com
Sales Range: $450-499.9 Million
Emp.: 1,000
Holding Company; Pharmaceutical Research & Development, Mfr & Marketer
N.A.I.C.S.: 551112

Subsidiary (US):

Aventis Holdings Inc. (2)
3711 Kennett Pike Ste 200, Wilmington, DE 19807-2161
Tel.: (302) 777-7222
Investment Management Service
N.A.I.C.S.: 523999

Subsidiary (Non-US):

Aventis Pharma (2)
San Jose Curridabat 25 Mts Este Heladeria Pops Edificio Galerias, San Jose, Costa Rica
Tel.: (506) 225 4630
Pharmaceuticals Product Mfr
N.A.I.C.S.: 325412

Subsidiary (Domestic):

Aventis Pharma SA (2)
20 Ave Raymond Aron, 92165, Antony, France (100%)
Tel.: (33) 155717171
Sales Range: $550-599.9 Million
Pharmaceutical Holding Company
N.A.I.C.S.: 551112

Subsidiary (Non-US):

Aventis Pharma, Lda. (2)
Empreendimento Lagoas Park Edificio 7 2/3 andar / Apartado 78, 2740-244, Oeiras, Porto Salvo, Portugal
Tel.: (351) 21 358 94 00
Web Site: http://sanofi.com
Pharmaceuticals Product Mfr
N.A.I.C.S.: 325412

Joint Venture (Domestic):

Chugai Sanofi-Aventis S.N.C. (2)
20 Avenue Raymond Aron, 92165, Antony, Cedex, France
Tel.: (33) 141247552
Web Site: http://www.sanofiaventis.com
Sales Range: $25-49.9 Million
Emp.: 17
Pharmaceuticals Product Mfr
N.A.I.C.S.: 325412

Subsidiary (Non-US):

Limited Liability Company Sanofi-Aventis Ukraine (2)
Tel.: (380) 443542000
Web Site: http://www.sanofi.ua
Sales Range: $50-74.9 Million
Emp.: 150
Pharmaceuticals Product Mfr
N.A.I.C.S.: 325412

PT Aventis Pharma (2)
Kel Kayu Putih Kec Pulo Gadung Jend Ahmad Yani 2 Pulomat Timur, Pulomas, Jakarta, 13210, Indonesia
Tel.: (62) 214895608
Pharmaceuticals Product Mfr
N.A.I.C.S.: 325412

SIA sanofi aventis Latvia (2)
K Valdemara iela 33-8, 1010, Riga, Latvia
Tel.: (371) 67 332 451
Web Site: http://www.sanofi.lv
Sales Range: $25-49.9 Million
Emp.: 25
Pharmaceutical Products Mfr & Whslr
N.A.I.C.S.: 325412

Sanofi Aventis UK Holdings Limited (2)
1 Onslow Street, Guildford, GU1 4SY, Surrey, United Kingdom
Tel.: (44) 1483505515
Web Site: http://www.sanofi.com
Investment Management Service
N.A.I.C.S.: 523999

Subsidiary (Domestic):

Aventis Pharma Limited (3)
One Onslow Street, Guildford, GU1 4YS, Surrey, United Kingdom
Tel.: (44) 1483505515
Web Site: http://www.sanofi-aventis.co.uk
Sales Range: $100-124.9 Million
Emp.: 500
Sls & Mktg of Pharmaceutical Products
N.A.I.C.S.: 325412

Subsidiary (Non-US):

Sanofi Belgium (2)
Airport Plaza Montreal Building, Leonardo Da Vinci Laan 19, 1831, Diegem, Belgium
Tel.: (32) 27105400
Web Site: https://www.sanofi.be
Emp.: 1,500
Pharmaceuticals Product Mfr
N.A.I.C.S.: 325412

Subsidiary (Domestic):

Sanofi France (2)
82 avenue Raspail, 94255, Gentilly, Cedex, France
Tel.: (33) 141247000
Web Site: https://www.sanofi.fr
Pharmaceutical Products Distr
N.A.I.C.S.: 424210

Subsidiary (Non-US):

Sanofi Produtos Farmaceuticos, Lda (2)
Empreendimento Lagoas Park Edificio 7 3 Piso, 2740-244, Porto Salvo, Portugal
Tel.: (351) 213589400
Web Site: http://www.sanofi.pt
Pharmaceuticals Product Mfr
N.A.I.C.S.: 325412

Sanofi-Aventis (2)
7th Fl No 112 Jian Guo Lu, Chaoyang District, Beijing, 100022, China
Tel.: (86) 1065685588
Web Site: http://www.sanofipasteur.cn
Sales Range: $200-249.9 Million
Emp.: 800
Mfr of Vaccines & Immunology Products
N.A.I.C.S.: 325414

Sanofi-Aventis (Malaysia) SDN. BHD. (2)
8th Floor PNB Damansara No 19 Lorong Dungun Damansara Heights, 50490, Kuala Lumpur, Malaysia
Tel.: (60) 3 2089 3333
Web Site: http://www.sanofi-aventis.com.my
Sales Range: $50-74.9 Million
Emp.: 250
Pharmaceuticals Product Mfr
N.A.I.C.S.: 325412

Sanofi-Aventis (Suisse) SA (2)
3 route de Montfleury, CP 777, 1214, Vernier, Switzerland
Tel.: (41) 584402100
Web Site: https://www.sanofi.ch
Sales Range: $25-49.9 Million
Emp.: 85
Pharmaceuticals Product Mfr
N.A.I.C.S.: 325412

Sanofi-Aventis A.E.B.E. (2)
348A Syggrou St, 17674, Kallithea, Athens, Greece
Tel.: (30) 2109001600
Web Site: https://www.sanofi.gr
Pharmaceuticals Product Mfr
N.A.I.C.S.: 325412

Sanofi-Aventis AB (2)
Guscavlundsvagen 139, 167 51, Bromma, Sweden
Tel.: (46) 87757000
Web Site: http://www.sanofi-aventis.se
Sales Range: $50-74.9 Million
Emp.: 200
Pharmaceuticals Product Mfr
N.A.I.C.S.: 325412

Subsidiary (Domestic):

Sanofi-Aventis Amerique du Nord S.A.S. (2)
54 Rue De La Boetie, 75008, Paris, France
Tel.: (33) 153774000
Pharmaceuticals Product Mfr
N.A.I.C.S.: 325412

Subsidiary (Non-US):

Sanofi-Aventis Argentina S.A. (2)
Av Tomkinson 2054, 1642, San Isidro, Buenos Aires, Argentina
Tel.: (54) 11 4732 5000
Web Site: http://www.sanofi.com.ar
Sales Range: $125-149.9 Million
Emp.: 300
Pharmaceuticals Product Mfr
N.A.I.C.S.: 325412

Sanofi-Aventis Denmark A/S (2)
Slotsmarken 13, Horsholm, 2970, Denmark
Tel.: (45) 45 16 7000
Web Site: http://www.sanofi-aventis.dk
Sales Range: $25-49.9 Million
Emp.: 100
Pharmaceuticals Product Mfr
N.A.I.C.S.: 325412

Sanofi-Aventis Deutschland GmbH (2)
Industriepark Hoechst K703, 65926, Frankfurt am Main, Germany
Tel.: (49) 69 305 80710
Web Site: http://www.sanofi.de
Sales Range: $100-124.9 Million
Emp.: 8,000
Pharmaceuticals Product Mfr
N.A.I.C.S.: 325412
Matthias Braun (Mng Dir-Pharmaceutical Production & Mfg)

Subsidiary (Domestic):

Hoechst GmbH (3)
Industrial Park Hoechst Building K703, 65926, Frankfurt am Main, Germany

Tel.: (49) 6930580710
Web Site: https://www.sanofi.de
Holding Company
N.A.I.C.S.: 551112
Philippe Luscan (Chm-Supervisory Bd)

Subsidiary (Non-US):

Sanofi-Aventis Farmaceutica Ltda (2)
Avenida Major Sylvio de Magalhaes Padilha 5 200, Condominium Parque da Cidade Torre Sucupira-Av das Nacoes Unidas 14401, Sao Paulo, 04794-000, Brazil
Tel.: (55) 1137596000
Web Site: https://www.sanofi.com.br
Sales Range: $100-124.9 Million
Emp.: 400
Pharmaceuticals Product Mfr
N.A.I.C.S.: 325412

Subsidiary (Domestic):

Sanofi-Aventis France S.A. (2)
9 Bld Romain Rolland Cedex 14, Paris, 75159, France
Tel.: (33) 1 57 63 33 33
Pharmaceuticals Product Mfr
N.A.I.C.S.: 325412

Subsidiary (Non-US):

Sanofi-Aventis GmbH (2)
Tower A 29th floor Wienerbergstrasse 11, 1100, Vienna, Austria
Tel.: (43) 1801850
Web Site: https://www.sanofi.at
Sales Range: $50-74.9 Million
Emp.: 220
Pharmaceuticals Product Mfr
N.A.I.C.S.: 325412

Sanofi-Aventis Hong Kong Limited (2)
Unit 702 - 710 Cyberport 3 100 Cyberport Rd, 311 Gloucester Road, Hong Kong, Causeway Bay, China (Hong Kong)
Tel.: (852) 2506 8333
Web Site: http://www.sanofi.hk
Pharmaceuticals Mfr
N.A.I.C.S.: 325412

Sanofi-Aventis Ilaclari Limited Sirketi (2)
Tekfen Tower Buyukdere Caddesi No 209 4, Levent, Istanbul, 34394, Turkiye
Tel.: (90) 212 339 10 00
Web Site: http://www.sanofi.com
Pharmaceuticals Product Mfr
N.A.I.C.S.: 325412

Sanofi-Aventis Ireland Ltd. (2)
18 Riverwalk, Citywest Business Campus, Dublin, 24, Ireland
Tel.: (353) 14035600
Web Site: http://www.sanofi.ie
Sales Range: $50-74.9 Million
Emp.: 83
Sls & Mktg of Pharmaceutical Products
N.A.I.C.S.: 325412

Sanofi-Aventis Israel (2)
10 Beni Gaon St, POB 8090, Netanya, 42504, Israel
Tel.: (972) 9 8633700
Pharmaceuticals Product Mfr
N.A.I.C.S.: 325412

Sanofi-Aventis Korea Co. Ltd (2)
235 Banpo-daero, Seocho-Gu, Seoul, 06578, Korea (South)
Tel.: (82) 21369000
Specialized Drugs & Vaccines Mfr
N.A.I.C.S.: 325411

Sanofi-Aventis Netherlands B.V. (2)
Kempenrengweg 45 E, 2803 PE, Gouda, Netherlands
Tel.: (31) 182557755
Web Site: http://www.sanfoi.nl
Sales Range: $50-74.9 Million
Emp.: 160
Pharmaceutical Products
N.A.I.C.S.: 325412

Sanofi-Aventis Norge AS (2)
Strandveien 15, PO Box 133, NO 1325, Lysaker, Norway
Tel.: (47) 67107100
Web Site: http://www.sanofi.no

AND PRIVATE COMPANIES — SANOFI

Sales Range: $25-49.9 Million
Emp.: 90
Sls & Mktg of Pharmaceutical Products
N.A.I.C.S.: 325412
Aksel Tunold *(Mng Dir)*

Sanofi-Aventis OY (2)
Huopalahdentie 24, PO Box 22, Helsinki, 350, Finland
Tel.: (358) 201200300
Web Site: http://www.sanofi.fi
Sales Range: $50-74.9 Million
Emp.: 85
Pharmaceutical Drug Whslr
N.A.I.C.S.: 424210

Sanofi-Aventis Pharma Slovakia s.r.o. (2)
Aupark Tower Einsteinova 24, 851 01, Bratislava, Slovakia
Tel.: (421) 2 33 100 100
Web Site: http://www.sanofi.sk
Pharmaceuticals Product Mfr
N.A.I.C.S.: 325412

Sanofi-Aventis Pharma Tunisie Sa (2)
34 Avenue de Paris, 2033, Megrine, Tunisia
Tel.: (216) 21631388200
Web Site: https://tn.sanofi.com
Pharmaceutical Products Distr
N.A.I.C.S.: 424210

Sanofi-Aventis Philippines Inc. (2)
3F Feliza Building 108 V A Rufino St, Legaspi Village, 1229, Makati, Philippines
Tel.: (63) 2 859 5555
Web Site: http://www.sanofi-aventis.ph
Emp.: 150
Pharmaceutical Products Research & Development Services
N.A.I.C.S.: 541715

Sanofi-Aventis Private Co., Ltd. (2)
To utca 1-5, Budapest, 1045, Hungary
Tel.: (36) 15050000
Web Site: http://www.sanofi.hu
Pharmaceuticals Product Mfr
N.A.I.C.S.: 325412

Subsidiary (Domestic):

Sanofi-Aventis Research & Development (2)
1 Ave Pierre Brossolette, 91385, Chilly-Mazarin, France
Tel.: (33) 1 60 49 77 77
Web Site: http://www.sanofi-aventis.com
Pharmaceutical Research
N.A.I.C.S.: 541715

Subsidiary (Non-US):

Sanofi-Aventis S.A. (2)
Costanera y Calle 3 Parque Ind Barrail, Casilla de Correo 777, Asuncion, Paraguay
Tel.: (595) 21 492 171
Web Site: http://en.sanofi.com
Pharmaceuticals Product Mfr
N.A.I.C.S.: 325412

Sanofi-Aventis S.A. de C.V. (2)
Ave Universidad 1738 Esq Miguel Angel De Quevedo, Mexico, 04000, Mexico **(100%)**
Tel.: (52) 5554844400
Web Site: http://www.en.sanofi-aventis.com
Pharmaceuticals Product Mfr
N.A.I.C.S.: 325412

Sanofi-Aventis S.A.U (2)
Josep Pla 2 4 Fl, 080 19, Barcelona, Spain **(100%)**
Tel.: (34) 934859400
Web Site: http://www.sanofiaventis.com
Sales Range: $100-124.9 Million
Emp.: 500
Pharmaceutial Res & Mfg
N.A.I.C.S.: 325412

Sanofi-Aventis Singapore Pte. Ltd (2)
38 Beach Road 18-11 South Beach Tower, Singapore, 189767, Singapore
Tel.: (65) 62263836
Web Site: https://www.sanofi.com.sg
Emp.: 500
Therapeutic Drugs Mfr
N.A.I.C.S.: 325411

Subsidiary (Domestic):

Aventis Pharma (Manufacturing) Pte. Ltd (3)
61 Gul Circle, Singapore, 629585, Singapore
Tel.: (65) 68623868
Emp.: 177
Pharmaceuticals Product Mfr
N.A.I.C.S.: 325412

Subsidiary (Non-US):

Sanofi-Aventis South Africa (Proprietary) Ltd (2)
Floor 5 Building I 90 Bekker Road, Hertford Office Park, Midrand, 2196, South Africa
Tel.: (27) 112563700
Web Site: https://www.sanofi.co.za
Pharmaceutical Products Distr
N.A.I.C.S.: 424210

Sanofi-Aventis Sp z.o.o. (2)
ul Bonifraterska 17, 00-203, Warsaw, Poland
Tel.: (48) 222800000
Web Site: https://www.sanofi.pl
Sales Range: $250-299.9 Million
Emp.: 650
Pharmaceutical Products Distr
N.A.I.C.S.: 424210

Sanofi-Aventis SpA (2)
Tel.: (39) 0239391
Web Site: http://www.sanofi.it
Pharmaceutical Products Mfr & Distr
N.A.I.C.S.: 325412

Sanofi-Aventis Taiwan Co. Ltd (2)
12F No 337 Fu Hsing N Rd, Taipei, 10544, Taiwan
Tel.: (886) 227172168
Web Site: http://www.sanofi.com.tw
Health Care Products Mfr
N.A.I.C.S.: 325412

Sanofi-Aventis Thailand Ltd. (2)
87/2 CRC Tower 24th Floor All Seasons Place, Wireless Rd Lumpini Pathumwan, Bangkok, 10330, Thailand
Tel.: (66) 22649999
Web Site: https://www.sanofi.co.th
Sales Range: $100-124.9 Million
Emp.: 400
Pharmaceuticals Product Mfr
N.A.I.C.S.: 325412

Sanofi-Aventis Vostok ZAO (2)
Livenskaya street 1, Orlovsky district Bolshekulikovskoe settlement, 302516, Oryol, Russia
Tel.: (7) 4862440055
Pharmaceuticals Product Mfr
N.A.I.C.S.: 325412

Sanofi-Aventis de Chile SA (2)
Avda Presidente Riesco 5435 piso 18, Las Condes, Santiago, Chile
Tel.: (56) 233408400
Pharmaceuticals Product Mfr
N.A.I.C.S.: 325412

Sanofi-Aventis de Panama S.A. (2)
Pharmaceuticals Product Mfr
N.A.I.C.S.: 325412

Sanofi-Aventis del Peru S.A. (2) **(100%)**
Tel.: (51) 14114710
Web Site: http://www.sanofi.com.pe
Pharmaceuticals Product Mfr
N.A.I.C.S.: 325412

Sanofi-Aventis s.r.o. (2)
Generala Plky 430/26, Dejvice, 160 00, Prague, 6, Czech Republic
Tel.: (420) 233086111
Web Site: https://www.sanofi.cz
Sales Range: $50-74.9 Million
Emp.: 200
Pharmaceuticals Product Mfr
N.A.I.C.S.: 325412

Representative Office (Non-US):

Sanofi-aventis (2)
Mecca Street Al Hijaz Towers for Investment 8th Floor, PO BOX 922464, Amman, 11192, Jordan
Tel.: (962) 65563660
Web Site: http://www.sanofi.com.jo
Pharmaceuticals Product Mfr
N.A.I.C.S.: 325412

Sanofi-aventis (2)
Georges Picot Street Starco Building Bloc C 1st Floor, PO Box 110697, Bloc A 6th Floor, Beirut, 10110697, Lebanon
Tel.: (961) 1 374 555
Web Site: http://www.sanofi.com
Sales Range: $75-99.9 Million
Emp.: 147
Pharmaceutical Products Distr
N.A.I.C.S.: 424210

Sanofi-aventis (2)
Jeddah Nojoud Center Tahlia Street Entrance C, PO Box 9874, Jeddah, 21423, Saudi Arabia
Tel.: (966) 2 6693318
Web Site: http://sa.sanofi.com
Pharmaceuticals Product Mfr
N.A.I.C.S.: 325412

Sanofi-aventis (2)
Mezzeh - Opposite Jalaa Gymnasium, PO Box 2861, Damascus, Syria
Tel.: (963) 11 612 0766
Web Site: http://sy.sanofi-aventis.com
Sales Range: $25-49.9 Million
Emp.: 25
Pharmaceuticals Product Mfr
N.A.I.C.S.: 325412

Sanofi-aventis (2)
Point E Rue de Ziguinchor X Rue de Diourbel PE - 43, BP 3529, Dakar, Senegal
Tel.: (221) 865 02 02
Web Site: http://www.sanofi.sn
Pharmaceuticals Product Mfr
N.A.I.C.S.: 325412

Sanofi-aventis (2)
22 Metekhi Str, 0103, Tbilisi, Georgia
Tel.: (995) 322 27 33 25
Web Site: http://en.sanofi.com
Pharmaceutical Product Mfr
N.A.I.C.S.: 325412

Sanofi-aventis (2)
Immeuble Thanry 1 Boulevard de l'Indenie, BP 4034, Abidjan, Cote d'Ivoire
Tel.: (225) 20 31 60 00
Web Site: http://en.sanofi.com
Pharmaceutical Product Mfr
N.A.I.C.S.: 325412

Subsidiary (Non-US):

Sanofi-aventis Bangladesh Ltd (2)
6/2/A Segun Bagicha, Dhaka, 1000, Bangladesh
Tel.: (880) 2 956 2893
Web Site: http://www.sanofi-aventis.com.bd
Sales Range: $550-599.9 Million
Pharmaceutical Products Distr
N.A.I.C.S.: 424210

Sanofi-aventis Croatia d.o.o. (2)
Hanzalaova 70, Zagreb, 10000, Croatia
Tel.: (385) 1 6003 400
Web Site: http://en.sanofi.com
Sales Range: $25-49.9 Million
Emp.: 35
Pharmaceutical Product Mfr
N.A.I.C.S.: 325412

Sanofi-aventis Cyprus Ltd. (2)
Charalambou Mouskou 14 Artemisia Business Center, 2015, Strovolos, 2015, Nicosia, Cyprus
Tel.: (357) 22 871 600
Web Site: http://en.sanofi.com
Sales Range: $25-49.9 Million
Emp.: 9
Pharmaceutical Product Mfr
N.A.I.C.S.: 325412

Sanofi-aventis Ecuador (2)
Av Simon Bolivar and Calle Nayon Ekopark Corporate Center, Tower 2 Floor 7, Quito, Ecuador
Tel.: (593) 25003020
Sales Range: $25-49.9 Million
Emp.: 70
Pharmaceuticals Mfr
N.A.I.C.S.: 325412

Sanofi-aventis Estonia OU (2)
Parnu Mnt 139E/2, 11317, Tallinn, Estonia
Tel.: (372) 627 3488
Web Site: http://www.sanofi.ee
Pharmaceuticals Product Mfr
N.A.I.C.S.: 325412

Sanofi-aventis Gulf (2)
Block 13 Street 12 Villa 16, Bayan, Kuwait, Kuwait
Tel.: (965) 5385302
Web Site: http://kw.sanofi-aventis.com
Sales Range: $25-49.9 Million
Emp.: 15
Pharmaceuticals Product Mfr
N.A.I.C.S.: 325412

Sanofi-aventis Kazakhstan LLP (2)
21 b Kunayev Str, 050016, Almaty, Kazakhstan
Tel.: (7) 727 244 50 96
Web Site: http://en.sanofi.com
Pharmaceuticals Product Mfr
N.A.I.C.S.: 325412

Sanofi-aventis Nigeria Ltd. (2)
JAPAUL House Plot 8 Dr Nurudeen Olowopopo Avenue, Ikeja Central Business District Agidingbi, Lagos, Nigeria
Tel.: (234) 12710135
Web Site: https://www.sanofi.com.ng
Sales Range: $25-49.9 Million
Emp.: 40
Pharmaceutical Product Whslr
N.A.I.C.S.: 424210

Sanofi-aventis Tunisie (2)
34 avenue de Paris, 2033, Megrine, Tunisia
Tel.: (216) 31388200
Web Site: https://tn.sanofi.com
Emp.: 600
Pharmaceuticals Product Mfr
N.A.I.C.S.: 325412

Sanofi-aventis Uruguay S.A. (2)
Pharmaceutical Products Mfr & Distr
N.A.I.C.S.: 325412

Sanofi-aventis Zrt. (2)
Vaci ut 133 E building 3rd floor, 1138, Budapest, Hungary
Tel.: (36) 15050050
Pharmaceuticals Product Mfr
N.A.I.C.S.: 325412

Sanofi-aventis d.o.o (2)
Dunajska 119, Ljubljana, 1000, Slovenia
Tel.: (386) 1 5604 800
Web Site: http://en.sanofi.com
Pharmaceuticals Product Mfr
N.A.I.C.S.: 325412

UAB "sanofi-aventis Lietuva" (2)
A Juozapaviciaus g 6/2, 09310, Vilnius, Lithuania
Tel.: (370) 52755224
Web Site: http://www.sanofi.lt
Sales Range: $75-99.9 Million
Emp.: 100
Vaccine Mfr & Whslr
N.A.I.C.S.: 325414

ZAO Aventis Pharma (2)
22 Tverskaya Street Business Center Summit, Moscow, 125009, Russia
Tel.: (7) 4957211400
Web Site: http://www.sanofi.ru
Pharmaceuticals Product Mfr
N.A.I.C.S.: 325412

Sanofi-Aventis Liban s.a.l. (1)
Pierre Gemayel Street HOLCOM building 2nd Floor Bloc A, PO Box 110697, Beirut, Lebanon
Tel.: (961) 1440220
Web Site: https://lb.sanofi.com
Emp.: 144
Pharmaceuticals Product Mfr
N.A.I.C.S.: 325412

Sanofi-Aventis Vietnam Company Limited (1)
No 10 Ham Nghi, District 1, Ho Chi Minh City, Vietnam
Tel.: (84) 2838298526
Web Site: https://www.sanofi.com.vn
Pharmaceuticals Product Mfr
N.A.I.C.S.: 325412

Sanofi-Aventis de Mexico S.A. de C.V. (1)
Av Real de Mayorazgo Torre M Piso 25, Col Xoco Benito Juarez, 03330, Mexico, Mexico
Tel.: (52) 5525864400
Web Site: https://www.sanofi.com.mx
Pharmaceuticals Product Mfr
N.A.I.C.S.: 325412
Dulce Toledo *(Mgr-Logistics Ops)*

SANOFI

Sanofi—(Continued)

Sanofi-Aventis de Venezuela S.A. (1)
Extension of Calle Vargas with 2nd Transversal Urb Boleita Norte, Edif Sanofi Sucre Municipality, Caracas, Venezuela
Tel.: (58) 2127189000
Web Site: http://www.sanofi.com.ve
Healthcare Services
N.A.I.C.S.: 621999

Sanofi-Synthelabo (India) Limited (1)
Aventis House 54-A Sir Mathuradas Vasanji Road, Andheri East, Mumbai, 400 093, India
Tel.: (91) 2228278000
Sales Range: $50-74.9 Million
Emp.: 70
Pharmaceutical Products Mfr & Distr
N.A.I.C.S.: 325412

Sanofi-Synthelabo De Honduras S.A. (1)
Edificio San Antonioial - Apartado 271 Contiguo a Farmacia Elite 1er N, Barrio San Rafael, Tegucigalpa, Honduras
Tel.: (504) 239 56 38
Pharmaceuticals Product Mfr
N.A.I.C.S.: 325412

Sanofi-Synthelabo Limited (1)
1 Onslow Street, Guildford, GU1 4YS, Surrey, United Kingdom (100%)
Tel.: (44) 1483505515
Web Site: http://www.sanofi.co.uk
Sales Range: $125-149.9 Million
Emp.: 500
Pharmaceuticals Mfr
N.A.I.C.S.: 325412

Sanofi-Synthelabo UK Ltd (1)
1 Onslow Street, Guildford, GU1 4SY, Surrey, United Kingdom
Tel.: (44) 7725765377
Pharmaceuticals Product Mfr
N.A.I.C.S.: 325412

Sanofi-Synthelabo, Inc. (1)
55 Corporate Dr, Bridgewater, NJ 08807
Tel.: (908) 981-5000
Web Site: http://www.sanofi.us
Sales Range: $5-14.9 Billion
Emp.: 11,400
Holding Company; Pharmaceuticals Research & Development, Mfr & Marketer
N.A.I.C.S.: 551112

Subsidiary (Domestic):

BiPar Sciences, Inc. (2)
400 Oyster Point Blvd Ste 200, South San Francisco, CA 94080
Tel.: (650) 615-7000
Biopharmaceutical Research & Development Services
N.A.I.C.S.: 541714
Barry M. Sherman (Exec VP-Dev)

Sanofi-Aventis US LLC (2)
55 Corporate Dr, Bridgewater, NJ 08807-2854
Tel.: (908) 981-5000
Web Site: https://www.sanofi.us
Sales Range: $1-4.9 Billion
Emp.: 13,000
Sls & Mktg of Pharmaceutical Products
N.A.I.C.S.: 325412

Sanofi-Synthelabo-Taisho Pharmaceuticals Co., Ltd. (1)
3 23 Kioicho, Chiyoda Ku, Tokyo, 102 0094, Japan
Tel.: (81) 352757139
Pharmaceuticals Mfr; Owned 49% by Taisho Pharmaceutical Co., Ltd. & 51% by Sanofi-Aventis
N.A.I.C.S.: 325412

Sanofi-Topaz, Inc. (1)
100 Witmer Rd Ste 280, Horsham, PA 19044
Tel.: (267) 960-3330
Sales Range: $25-49.9 Million
Emp.: 4
Pharmaceuticals Product Mfr
N.A.I.C.S.: 325412

Shenzhen Sanofi Pasteur Biological Products Co. Ltd (1)
7/F HP Tower 112 Jianguo Road, Chaoyang, Beijing, 100022, China
Tel.: (86) 1065685588
Vaccines Mfr & Whslr
N.A.I.C.S.: 325414

Sunstone (TangShan) Pharmaceutical Co., Ltd. (1)
Hi-tech Development Zone, Tangshan, 063020, China
Tel.: (86) 31 5317 7876
Pharmaceutical Product Mfr & Distr
N.A.I.C.S.: 325412

Synthorx, Inc. (1)
11099 N Torrey Pines Rd Ste 290, La Jolla, CA 92037
Tel.: (858) 750-4789
Web Site: http://www.synthorx.com
Rev.: $292,000
Assets: $191,506,000
Liabilities: $260,984,000
Net Worth: ($69,478,000)
Earnings: ($56,609,000)
Emp.: 38
Fiscal Year-end: 12/31/2018
Biotechnology Research & Development Services
N.A.I.C.S.: 541714
Pratik Shah (Chm)

Translate Bio, Inc. (1)
29 Hartwell Ave, Lexington, MA 02421
Tel.: (617) 945-7361
Web Site: http://www.translate.bio
Rev.: $138,811,000
Assets: $889,936,000
Liabilities: $533,179,000
Net Worth: $356,757,000
Earnings: ($53,787,000)
Emp.: 122
Fiscal Year-end: 12/31/2020
Biotechnology Research & Development Services
N.A.I.C.S.: 541714
Ann Barbier (Chief Medical Officer)

SANOH INDUSTRIAL CO., LTD.

3-6-6 Shibuya Shibuya Park Bldg, Shibuya-ku, Tokyo, 150-0002, Japan
Tel.: (81) 368792622
Web Site: https://www.sanoh.com
Year Founded: 1939
6584—(TKS)
Rev.: $1,332,858,560
Assets: $941,670,400
Liabilities: $555,331,920
Net Worth: $386,338,480
Earnings: ($8,779,760)
Emp.: 8,000
Fiscal Year-end: 03/31/23
Motor Vehicle Metal Tubing Products Mfr
N.A.I.C.S.: 331210
Yozo Takeda (CEO)

Subsidiaries:

Able Sanoh Industries (1996) Co., Ltd. (1)
99 Moo 1, Hitech Industrial Estate Tambol Banlane Amphur Bangpain, Phra Nakhon Si Ayutthaya, 13160, Thailand
Tel.: (66) 35350880
Sales Range: $100-124.9 Million
Emp.: 276
Motor Vehicle Brake & Fuel Tubes & Refrigerator Compressor Tubular Products Mfr
N.A.I.C.S.: 331210

Fulton Products Industrial Co., Ltd. (1)
14 Okazato, Koga, 306-0206, Ibaraki, Japan
Tel.: (81) 28 098 3268
Web Site: https://www.fulton.jp
Automobile Parts Mfr & Distr
N.A.I.C.S.: 336110

Geiger Automotive de Mexico S. de R.L. de C.V. (1)
Carretera Estatal 431 Km 2 2 Lote 62 Modulo 5 y 6, Parque Tecnologico Innovacion Queretaro El Marques, 76246, Queretaro, Mexico
Tel.: (52) 442 153 5990
Automobile Parts Mfr & Distr
N.A.I.C.S.: 336110

P.T. Sanoh Indonesia (1)
Jl Inti II Blok C-4 No 10 Kawasan Industri Hyundai, Cikarang Sel, Bekasi, 17530, Jawa Barat, Indonesia
Tel.: (62) 21 89907965
Web Site: http://www.sanohindonesia.co.id
Sales Range: $100-124.9 Million
Emp.: 391
Automobile Parts Mfr
N.A.I.C.S.: 336110

STI Sanoh India Ltd. (1)
Steel Tubes Bewas, Indore, India (100%)
Tel.: (91) 731223244
Web Site: http://www.sanoh.com
Motor Vehicle Metal Tubular Products Mfr & Whslr
N.A.I.C.S.: 336390

Plant (Domestic):

STI Sanoh India Ltd. - Bangalore Plant (2)
471-D1 13th Cross 3rd Main road Peenya Industrial area 4 phase, Kumbalgodu, Bengaluru, 560 058, Karnataka, India
Tel.: (91) 80 32967820
Web Site: http://www.stisanoh.com
Sales Range: $25-49.9 Million
Emp.: 48
Automobile Parts Mfr
N.A.I.C.S.: 336390
Rajesh Maheshwari (Gen Mgr)

Sanoh America, Inc. - Findlay Plant (1)
1849 Industrial Dr, Findlay, OH 45840
Tel.: (419) 425-2600
Web Site: http://www.sanoh-america.com
Sales Range: $200-249.9 Million
Emp.: 733
Motor Vehicle Tubular & Brazed Products Mfr
N.A.I.C.S.: 332996

Sanoh Canada, Ltd. (1)
300 C Line, Orangeville, L9W 3Z8, ON, Canada
Tel.: (519) 941-2229
Sales Range: $25-49.9 Million
Emp.: 80
Motor Vehicle Brake & Cluster Tubes Mfr
N.A.I.C.S.: 332996
Ben Smith (Plant Mgr)

Sanoh Communications Corp. (1)
Tel.: (81) 280301201
Web Site: http://www.sanoh-c.com
Radio & Television Broadcasting & Wireless Communications Equipment Mfr
N.A.I.C.S.: 334220

Sanoh Europe (France) EURL (1)
Zone industrial Ienle Poryur, 59309, Lille, France
Tel.: (33) 327090209
Sales Range: $25-49.9 Million
Emp.: 20
Motor Vehicle Brake & Cluster Tube Mfr
N.A.I.C.S.: 331210

Sanoh Europe GmbH (1)
Leopoldstrasse 244, 80807, Munich, Germany
Tel.: (49) 89208039255
Web Site: http://www.sanoh.com
Automobile Parts Mfr
N.A.I.C.S.: 811121

Subsidiary (Domestic):

Geiger Automotive GmbH (2)
Neu-Egling 11, 82418, Murnau am Staffelsee, Germany
Tel.: (49) 88414070
Web Site: https://www.geigerautomotive.com
Emp.: 900
Mfr & Marketer of Plastic Components for Conveyance & Storage of Fluids & Gases in Drive, Chassis & Brake Systems for Power Train Markets in Automotive Industry
N.A.I.C.S.: 336390
Sven Riehm (CEO)

Subsidiary (Non-US):

Geiger Automotive Polska Sp. z o.o. (3)

INTERNATIONAL PUBLIC

ul Jednosci 10, 41-208, Sosnowiec, Poland
Tel.: (48) 32 3608000
Mfr & Marketer of Plastic Components for Power Train Markets in Automotive Industry
N.A.I.C.S.: 336390

Sanoh Fulton (Philippines) Inc. (1)
No 11 eo Bldg Corner United and 2 Street Barrio Katitolayo No 62, 1603, Manila, Philippines
Tel.: (63) 28863752
Sales Range: $25-49.9 Million
Emp.: 90
Motor Vehicle Brake & Fuel Tubes Mfr
N.A.I.C.S.: 331210

Sanoh Industrial (Wuhan) Co., Ltd. (1)
No 1 Special Jianhua Village, Wuhan, China
Tel.: (86) 2784231003
Web Site: http://www.sanoh.com
Sales Range: $25-49.9 Million
Emp.: 11
Motor Vehicle Brake & Fuel Tubes Whslr
N.A.I.C.S.: 423120

Sanoh Industrial (Wuxi) Co., Ltd. (1)
No 104-B Plot, State High-Tech Industry Dev, Wuxi, China
Tel.: (86) 51085322771
Web Site: http://www.sanoh.com
Sales Range: $50-74.9 Million
Emp.: 75
Automotive Brake Tubes, Various Surface Treatments & Brazing Products Mfr
N.A.I.C.S.: 423120

Sanoh Industrial Co., Ltd. - Koga Factory (1)
2-27 Hon-cho 4-chome, Koga, Japan
Tel.: (81) 280331111
Aircraft Part Mfr
N.A.I.C.S.: 336413

Sanoh Industrial de Mexico S.A. de C.V. (1)
Circuito Aguascalientes Oriente No 130, Parque Industrial Del Valle, Aguascalientes, Mexico
Tel.: (52) 4499730101
Web Site: http://www.sanoh.com
Motor Vehicle Brake & Cluster Tubes & Brazed Pipe Products Mfr
N.A.I.C.S.: 331210

Subsidiary (Domestic):

Sanoh Manufacturing de Mexico S.A. de C.V. (2)
Exportadores 115, Seccion Dorada, Tijuana, Mexico
Tel.: (52) 6646821717
Web Site: http://www.sanoh.com.mx
Refrigerator Air Pipe & Water Tube Mfr
N.A.I.C.S.: 333415

Sanoh Magyar Kft (1)
Ipari park hrsz 20353/10, 2500, Esztergom, Hungary
Tel.: (36) 33505475
Web Site: https://sanoh-magyar.hu
Sales Range: $25-49.9 Million
Emp.: 5
Motor Vehicle Parts Mfr
N.A.I.C.S.: 336390
Voelgyi Tamas (Gen Mgr)

Sanoh UK Manufacturing Ltd. (1)
Fourth Way, Bristol, BS11 8DL, United Kingdom
Tel.: (44) 1179828260
Web Site: https://www.sanoh.co.uk
Sales Range: $50-74.9 Million
Emp.: 300
Motor Vehicle Metal & Plastic Tube & Connector Mfr
N.A.I.C.S.: 332996

Shanghai Sanoh Automotive Tube Fabrication Co., Ltd. (1)
No 1155 Hongde Rd, Jiading Industrial Park, Shanghai, China
Tel.: (86) 2169169370
Web Site: http://www.sanoh.com
Sales Range: $25-49.9 Million
Emp.: 42
Motor Vehicle Brake & Fuel Tube Mfr
N.A.I.C.S.: 332996

AND PRIVATE COMPANIES

SANOMA OYJ

Shanghai Sanoh Mechanical Manufacture Co., Ltd.
1201 Xinqin Rd, Jiaving, Shanghai, China
Tel.: (86) 2139538925
Web Site: http://www.s-sanoh.com
Sales Range: $25-49.9 Million
Emp.: 72
Motor Vehicle Parts & Plastic Tubular Products Mfr
N.A.I.C.S.: 336390

Taiwan Sanoh Electric Co., Ltd. (1)
No 26 Kuang Ya East Rd Ping Cheng City,
Hsien, Taoyuan, Taiwan
Tel.: (886) 34585188
Web Site: https://www.taiwansanoh.com.tw
Sales Range: $50-74.9 Million
Emp.: 130
Motor Vehicle Tubular Products, Refrigerator Wire Condensers & Washing Machine Timer Devices Mfr
N.A.I.C.S.: 332996

United Sanoh Industries Sdn.
Bhd. (1)
Bangunan United Industries, Kelang, Malaysia
Tel.: (60) 333927726
Web Site: http://www.sanoh.com
Sales Range: $125-149.9 Million
Emp.: 280
Motor Vehicle Tubular Products Mfr
N.A.I.C.S.: 331210

SANOLABOR D.D.
Leskoskova 4, 1000, Ljubljana, Slovenia
Tel.: (386) 15854211 SI
Web Site: http://www.sanolabor.si
Medical Device Whslr
N.A.I.C.S.: 423450

SANOMA OYJ
Toolonlahdenkatu 2, 00100, Helsinki,
Finland
Tel.: (358) 1051999 FI
Web Site: https://www.sanoma.com
SAA1V—(HEL)
Rev.: $1,401,143,967
Assets: $2,270,235,269
Liabilities: $1,512,518,886
Net Worth: $757,716,382
Earnings: $83,099,504
Emp.: 4,588
Fiscal Year-end: 12/31/22
Holding Company; Multi-Media Publisher, Broadcasting, News & Information Services
N.A.I.C.S.: 551112
Antti Herlin (Vice Chm)

Subsidiaries:

Alma Manu Oy (1)
Itainenkatu 11, Tampere, 33210, Finland
Tel.: (358) 1066 5112
Web Site: http://www.almamanu.fi
Newspaper Printing & Publishing Services
N.A.I.C.S.: 323111

Bertmark Media AB (1)
Lundavaegen 78, 202 12, Malmo, Sweden
Tel.: (46) 406805600
Web Site: http://www.bertmark.se
Sales Range: $25-49.9 Million
Emp.: 56
Book Publishers
N.A.I.C.S.: 513130

Bertmarks Forlag AB (1)
Florettgatan 16 B, 254 67, Helsingborg,
Sweden
Tel.: (46) 40 680 5600
Web Site: http://www.bertmark.se
Books Publishing Services
N.A.I.C.S.: 513120

Bookwell Oy (1)
Teollisuustie 4, 06100, Porvoo, Finland
Tel.: (358) 1921941
Web Site: http://www.bookwell.fi
Sales Range: $50-74.9 Million
Emp.: 200
Book Printing Services
N.A.I.C.S.: 323117

Clickart, Taller De Comunicacio,
S.L. (1)
Llacuna 161 2nd floor local 7, 08018, Barcelona, Spain
Tel.: (34) 932788204
Web Site: https://clickartedu.com
Web Design & Development Services
N.A.I.C.S.: 541511

Gelukskoffer Scholen B.V. (1)
Magistratenlaan 138, 5223 MB, 's-Hertogenbosch, Netherlands
Tel.: (31) 858771659
Web Site: https://www.gelukskoffer.nl
Educational Institution Services
N.A.I.C.S.: 611310

Hansaprint AB (1)
Kommendorsgatan 8L, PO Box 5106, 102 43, Stockholm, Sweden
Tel.: (46) 86635585
Books & Magazines Printing Services
N.A.I.C.S.: 323111

Iddink Spain S.L.U. (1)
Avda de la Ribera 11, Palleja, 08780, Barcelona, Spain
Tel.: (34) 932388833
Web Site: https://spain.iddink.es
Educational Institution Services
N.A.I.C.S.: 611310

Itslearning A/S (1)
Ryesgade 3A, 2200, Copenhagen, Denmark
Tel.: (45) 82304050
Educational Institution Services
N.A.I.C.S.: 611310

Itslearning AB (1)
Djaknegatan 4, 211 35, Malmo, Sweden
Tel.: (46) 406270490
Web Site: https://itslearning.com
Educational Institution Services
N.A.I.C.S.: 611310

Itslearning France S.A. (1)
32 rue de Paradis, 75010, Paris, France
Tel.: (33) 183648211
Educational Institution Services
N.A.I.C.S.: 611310

Itslearning GmbH (1)
Erich SteinfurthStr 6, 10243, Berlin, Germany
Tel.: (49) 3061674847
Educational Institution Services
N.A.I.C.S.: 611310

Itslearning Nederland B.V. (1)
Boreelplein 40, 7411 EH, Deventer, Netherlands
Tel.: (31) 850067840
Educational Institution Services
N.A.I.C.S.: 611310

Itslearning UK Ltd. (1)
The Leeming Building Ludgate Hill, Leeds,
LS7 7HZ, United Kingdom
Tel.: (44) 1908470126
Multimedia Learning Services
N.A.I.C.S.: 611691

L.C.G. Malmberg B.V. (1)
Magistrates Avenue 138, 5223 MB, 's-Hertogenbosch, Netherlands
Tel.: (31) 736288722
Web Site: https://www.malmberg.nl
Educational Institution Services
N.A.I.C.S.: 611310

Lehtikanta Oy (1)
Lehtikaari 1, 45130, Kouvola, Finland
Tel.: (358) 5280016
Web Site: http://kuvakauppa.lehtikuva.fi
Online Pictures & Videos Retailer
N.A.I.C.S.: 449210

Postituspojat Oy (1)
Koivuvaarankuja 2, 1640, Vantaa, Finland
Tel.: (358) 207642010
Web Site: http://www.postituspojat.fi
Rev.: $3,366,225
Emp.: 30
Marketing Logistics Services
N.A.I.C.S.: 541860

Printcenter Oy (1)
Koivuvaarankuja 2, 01640, Vantaa, Finland
Tel.: (358) 9 836 6380
Web Site: http://www.printcenter.fi

Stationery Product Whslr
N.A.I.C.S.: 424120

Sanoma Digital Oy (1)
Toolonlahdenkatu 2, PL 21, Sanoma, 89,
Helsinki, Finland
Tel.: (358) 91221
Desktop Publishing Services
N.A.I.C.S.: 518210
Jarkko Karhu (Gen Mgr)

Subsidiary (Domestic):

Netwheels Oy (2)
Martinkylantie 9 A, 01770, Vantaa, Finland
Tel.: (358) 942451694
Web Site: https://www.netwheels.fi
Sales Range: $25-49.9 Million
Emp.: 25
Automotive Repair & Maintenance Services
N.A.I.C.S.: 811111

Sanoma Educacion, S.L. (1)
Ronda de Europa 5, Tres Cantos, 28760,
Madrid, Spain
Tel.: (34) 917449060
Web Site: https://santillana.es
Educational Institution Services
N.A.I.C.S.: 611310

Sanoma Italia S.p.A. (1)
Corso Trapani 16, 10139, Turin, Italy
Tel.: (39) 02748231
Web Site: https://sanomaitalia.it
Educational Institution Services
N.A.I.C.S.: 611310

Sanoma Learning B.V. (1)
Magistratenlaan 138, 5223 MB, 's-Hertogenbosch, Netherlands
Tel.: (31) 736287528
Web Site: https://www.sanomalearning.com
Educational & Learning Materials Publishing
Services
N.A.I.C.S.: 513130

Subsidiary (Domestic):

Malmberg B.V. (2)
Magistratenlaan 138, 5223 MB, 's-Hertogenbosch, Netherlands
Tel.: (31) 736288811
Web Site: http://www.malmberg.nl
Educational Book Publisher
N.A.I.C.S.: 513130

Subsidiary (Non-US):

Nowa Era Sp. z o.o. (2)
Aleje Jerozolimskie 146D, 02-305, Warsaw,
Poland
Tel.: (48) 225702580
Web Site: https://www.nowaera.pl
Educational Book Publisher
N.A.I.C.S.: 513130

Young Digital Planet S.A. (2)
Ul Slowackiego 175, 80-298, Gdansk, Pomeranian, Poland
Tel.: (48) 587682220
Web Site: http://www.ydp.eu
Sales Range: $100-124.9 Million
Emp.: 28
Online Educational Book Publishing &
Training Services
N.A.I.C.S.: 513130

Sanoma Manu Oy (1)
Patamaenkatu 9, PO Box 1010, Sarankulma, 33201, Tampere, Finland
Tel.: (358) 107004969
Newspaper & Magazine Distr
N.A.I.C.S.: 424920

Sanoma Media Netherlands B.V. (1)
Capellalaan 65, 2132 JL, Hoofddorp, Netherlands
Tel.: (31) 885565948
Web Site: http://www.sanoma.nl
Magazine Advertising Services
N.A.I.C.S.: 541810
Trix Bunck (Mgr-Compensation & Benefits)

Sanoma News Ltd. (1)
Toolonlahdenkatu 2, PO Box 107, Sanoma,
Helsinki, 89, Finland
Tel.: (358) 91221
Web Site: http://www.sanomanews.com
Rev.: $577,644,210
Emp.: 2,400
Newspaper Publishers

N.A.I.C.S.: 513110
Marja-Leena Tuomola (Sr VP-Bus & Digital Ops Dev)

Subsidiary (Domestic):

Sanoma Data Oy (2)
Toolonlahdenkatu 2, PL 60, Sanoma, Helsinki, 89, Finland
Tel.: (358) 91221
Web Site: http://www.sanomadata.fi
Rev.: $35,008,740
Emp.: 150
Desktop Publishing Services
N.A.I.C.S.: 518210

Skillnet Oy (2)
Ylistoenmaeentie 26, 40500, Jyvaskyla,
Finland
Tel.: (358) 14 445 1525
Web Site: http://www.skillnet.fi
Sales Range: $25-49.9 Million
Emp.: 17
Recruitment Software Development Services
N.A.I.C.S.: 541511

Sanoma Pro Ltd. (1)
Porkkalankatu 20 A, 00180, Helsinki, Finland
Tel.: (358) 20391000
Web Site: https://www.sanomapro.fi
Educational Institution Services
N.A.I.C.S.: 611310

Sanomala Oy (1)
Martinkylantie 9 A, 01770, Vantaa, Finland
Tel.: (358) 91221
Web Site: http://www.sanopaino.fi
Newspaper Printing Services
N.A.I.C.S.: 323111

Sanomapaino Oy (1)
Martinkylantie 9 A, 01770, Vantaa, Finland
Tel.: (358) 91221
Web Site: https://www.sanomapaino.fi
Sales Range: $25-49.9 Million
Emp.: 80
Newspaper Printing Services
N.A.I.C.S.: 323111
Markku Hernberg (Mgr-Production)

Subsidiary (Domestic):

Saimaan Lehtipaino Oy (2)
Lauritsalantie 1, PO Box 3, Lappeenranta,
53100, Finland
Tel.: (358) 5538818
Web Site: http://www.sanomapaino.fi
Sales Range: $25-49.9 Million
Emp.: 30
Newspaper Printing Services
N.A.I.C.S.: 323111
Arto Tiikasalo (Pres & CEO)

Taloussanomat Oy (1)
Toolonlahdenkatu 2, 00100, Helsinki, Finland
Tel.: (358) 91221
Web Site: http://www.taloussanomat.fi
Online Financial Magazine Publishers
N.A.I.C.S.: 513120
Ari Harju (CEO)

UAB Forum Cinemas (1)
Savanoriu ave 7, 03116, Vilnius, Lithuania
Tel.: (370) 52644764
Web Site: http://www.forumcinemas.lt
Sales Range: $25-49.9 Million
Movie Theater Operation Services
N.A.I.C.S.: 512131

UAB Lietuvos spaudos Vilniaus
agentura (1)
Laisves ave 58, 05120, Vilnius, Lithuania
Tel.: (370) 52401477
Web Site: http://www.lspauda.lt
Sales Range: $25-49.9 Million
Emp.: 42
Book Retailer
N.A.I.C.S.: 459210

Uitgeverij Essener B.V. (1)
Zaanweg 67B 1521 DM, Wormerveer, Netherlands
Tel.: (31) 756217291
Web Site: https://www.essener.nl
Educational Institution Services
N.A.I.C.S.: 611310

Veronica Uitgeverij B.V. (1)

SANOMA OYJ

Sanoma Oyj—(Continued)
Olympia 2a, 1213 NT, Hilversum, Netherlands **(100%)**
Tel.: (31) 356463333
Web Site: http://www.veronicauitgeverij.nl
Sales Range: $50-74.9 Million
Emp.: 125
Television Programming Guide & Magazine Publisher
N.A.I.C.S.: 513120

Videolle Productions Oy (1)
Kaikukatu 4 C 5 krs, 00530, Helsinki, Finland
Tel.: (358) 405709690
Web Site: https://www.videolle.fi
Advertising Services
N.A.I.C.S.: 541810

SANOOK ENTERPRISES, INC.
28 14 Moo 3 Bophut, Koh Samui, Surat Thani, 84320, Thailand   NV
Year Founded: 2006
Emp.: 1
Golf Related Travel Services
N.A.I.C.S.: 713990
Robin Mulholland *(Pres, CEO, CFO & Sec)*

SANOTACT GMBH
Hessenweg 10, 48157, Munster, Germany
Tel.: (49) 251 1421 0
Web Site: http://www.sanotact.de
Emp.: 200
Food Products Mfr
N.A.I.C.S.: 311999
Christoph Wenisch *(Mng Dir)*

Subsidiaries:

sanotact (HK) Limited (1)
Suite 505 5/F Laford Centre 838 Lai Chi Kok Road, Cheung Sha Wan, Kowloon, China (Hong Kong)
Tel.: (852) 35260826
Food Products Mfr
N.A.I.C.S.: 311999
Carol Wu *(Dir-Ops)*

SANOVAL
Avenue Des Mourets, 82000, Montauban, Tarn Et Garonne, France
Tel.: (33) 563665533
Rev.: $16,600,000
Emp.: 48
N.A.I.C.S.: 445110
Jean-Marc Aleas *(Mgr)*

SANOYAS HOLDINGS CORPORATION
3-3-23 Nakanoshima, Kita-ku, Osaka, 530-6109, Japan
Tel.: (81) 648036161
Web Site: https://www.sanoyas.co.jp
Year Founded: 2011
7022—(TKS)
Rev.: $154,356,720
Assets: $180,115,890
Liabilities: $119,720,320
Net Worth: $60,395,570
Earnings: $3,033,990
Emp.: 949
Fiscal Year-end: 03/31/24
Holding Company; Ship Building & Repairing; Industrial Machinery Mfr; Engineering Services
N.A.I.C.S.: 551112
Isao Kitatsuji *(Pres)*

Subsidiaries:

DAICHU Co., Ltd. (1)
2-1-5 Sangamaki, Takatsuki, Osaka, Japan
Tel.: (81) 726775332
Web Site: http://www.daichu-net.co.jp
Shot Blasting Machine Mfr & Distr
N.A.I.C.S.: 333517

K.S. SANOYAS Co., Ltd. (1)
501-3 Aza-Miyanomae Fukushima, Sanda, 669-1313, Hyogo, Japan
Tel.: (81) 79 562 6451
Web Site: http://www.ksanoyas.co.jp
Industrial Machinery Parts Mfr & Distr
N.A.I.C.S.: 333998

Katoh Precision Machinery Co., Ltd. (1)
3-14-21 Uenonishi, Toyonaka, Japan
Tel.: (81) 668580501
Web Site: http://www.katohseiki.co.jp
Industrial Machinery Parts Mfr
N.A.I.C.S.: 333998

Mizuho Industrial Co., Ltd. (1)
6-1-109 MinamiTsumori, Nishinari-ku, Osaka, 557-0063, Japan
Tel.: (81) 666584001
Industrial Machinery Parts Mfr & Distr
N.A.I.C.S.: 333998
Hiroshi Tanaka *(Pres)*

Subsidiary (Non-US):

Mizuho Machinery (Wuxi) Co., Ltd. (2)
Tel.: (86) 51083775121
Web Site: https://www.mizuho-ind.com
Industrial Machinery Parts Mfr & Distr
N.A.I.C.S.: 333998

Sanoyas Business Partner Corporation (1)
5-2-7 Kita-Kagaya Suminoe-Ku, Osaka, Japan
Tel.: (81) 666841020
Nonferrous Metal Distr
N.A.I.C.S.: 423510

Sanoyas Construction Machinery Corporation - Hiroshima Factory (1)
2-5-30 Takayadai, Higashi-hiroshima, Hiroshima, Japan
Tel.: (81) 824910037
Construction Machinery Mfr
N.A.I.C.S.: 333120

Sanoyas Engineering Corporation (1)
5-2-7 Kita-Kagaya, Suminoe-Ku, Osaka, 559-0011, Japan
Tel.: (81) 666841027
Parking Equipment Mfr & Distr
N.A.I.C.S.: 334514

Sanoyas Rides Corporation - Kyushu Factory (1)
277-1 Oaza-Yotsuhara Nankan-Machi, Tamano-gun, Kumamoto, 861-0823, Japan
Tel.: (81) 968539211
Amusement Park Equipment Mfr
N.A.I.C.S.: 339999

Sanoyas Rides Corporation - Osaka Factory (1)
2-2-11 Nishi-Kagaya, Suminoe-ku, Osaka, 559-0016, Japan
Tel.: (81) 666841010
Amusement Park Equipment Mfr
N.A.I.C.S.: 339999

Sanoyas Rides Service Corporation (1)
1-3-10 Aomi, Koto-ku, Tokyo, 135-0064, Japan
Tel.: (81) 35 500 2655
Web Site: https://www.daikanransha.com
Amusement Park Operator
N.A.I.C.S.: 713990

Sanoyas Sangyo Co., Ltd. (1)
5-13-37 Minami-Tsumori Nishinari-Ku, Osaka, Japan
Tel.: (81) 666583430
Soft Drink Mfr & Distr
N.A.I.C.S.: 312111

Sanoyas Shipbuilding Corporation - Technical & Design Division (1)
2767-21 Kojima Shionasu, Kurashiki, Okayama, Japan
Tel.: (81) 864751553
Ship Building Services
N.A.I.C.S.: 336611

Yamada Industries Co., Ltd. (1)
1-17-17 Nipponbashi, Chuo-Ku, Osaka, 542-0073, Japan
Tel.: (81) 666328161
Air Conditioner Mfr & Distr
N.A.I.C.S.: 333415

SANPOWER GROUP CO., LTD.
No 68 Software Ave, Yuhuatai Dist, Nanjing, 210012, Jiangsu, China
Tel.: (86) 25 83274891   CN
Web Site: http://www.en.sanpowergroup.com
Year Founded: 1993
Emp.: 60,000
Holding Company
N.A.I.C.S.: 551112
Yafei Yuan *(Chm)*

Subsidiaries:

Guangzhou Jinpeng Group Co., Ltd. (1)
the 9th Guangzhou Science City Shenzhou Road, Guangzhou, 510663, China
Tel.: (86) 2085571601
Web Site: http://www.gzjpg.com
Communication Devices Mfr
N.A.I.C.S.: 334210

Nanjing Xinjiekou Department Store Co., Ltd. (1)
No 1 Zhongshan South Road, Qinhuai District, Nanjing, 210005, Jiangsu, China
Tel.: (86) 2583274900
Web Site: https://www.cenbest.com
Rev.: $902,867,037
Assets: $3,540,236,488
Liabilities: $988,801,833
Net Worth: $2,551,434,655
Earnings: $101,579,386
Emp.: 25,000
Fiscal Year-end: 12/31/2022
Departmental Store Operator
N.A.I.C.S.: 455110
Xuan Zhang *(Pres & Gen Mgr)*

Subsidiary (Non-US):

Highland Group Holdings Limited (2)
27 Baker Street, London, W1U 8AH, United Kingdom **(89%)**
Tel.: (44) 345 602 1073
Web Site: http://www.houseoffraser.co.uk
Sales Range: $1-4.9 Billion
Holding Company; Department Store Operator
N.A.I.C.S.: 551112
Frank Slevin *(Chm-Exec Bd)*

SANQUAN FOOD CO., LTD.
Middle Section Changxing Road, Comprehensive Investment District, Zhengzhou, 450044, Henan, China
Tel.: (86) 37163987832
Web Site: http://www.sanquan.com
Year Founded: 2001
002216—(SSE)
Rev.: $1,043,775,397
Assets: $1,057,336,549
Liabilities: $512,510,095
Net Worth: $544,826,454
Earnings: $112,447,174
Fiscal Year-end: 12/31/22
Frozen Food Product Mfr
N.A.I.C.S.: 311813
Nan Chen *(Chm)*

SANRIN CO., LTD.
40823 Shimohongo Yamagatamura, Higashichikuma-Gun, Nagano, 390-1393, Japan
Tel.: (81) 263973030
Web Site: https://www.sanrinkk.co.jp
Year Founded: 1934
7486—(TKS)
Rev.—$211,797,620
Assets: $183,559,700
Liabilities: $53,983,870
Net Worth: $129,575,830
Earnings: $4,627,000
Emp.: 423
Fiscal Year-end: 03/31/24
Petroleum Product Mfr & Distr
N.A.I.C.S.: 324199

SANRIO COMPANY, LTD.
1-11-1 Osaki Shinagawa-Ku, Tokyo, 141-8603, Japan
Tel.: (81) 337798111   JP
Web Site: http://www.sanrio.co.jp
Year Founded: 1960
SJ8—(DEU)
Rev.: $660,874,410
Assets: $1,031,569,820
Liabilities: $602,600,650
Net Worth: $428,969,170
Earnings: $116,230,240
Emp.: 692
Fiscal Year-end: 03/31/24
Novelties, Toys, School Supplies, Gifts, Greeting Cards & Other Items Mfr; Operator of Restaurants & Theme Parks; Movies & Television Programs Producer; Magazines & Books Publisher
N.A.I.C.S.: 339930
Shintaro Tsuji *(Founder & Chm)*

Subsidiaries:

Kokoro Company Ltd (1)
4-9-1 Shinmeidai, Hamura, 205-8556, Tokyo, Japan
Tel.: (81) 425303911
Web Site: http://www.kokoro-dreams.co.jp
Sales Range: $25-49.9 Million
Emp.: 50
Theater Companies & Dinner Theaters711110
N.A.I.C.S.: 711110
Atsushi Ueda *(Pres)*

San-Byte Taiwan Co., Ltd. (1)
10F-2 No 230 Sec 3 Bade Rd, Taipei, 10555, Taiwan
Tel.: (886) 2 2577 6626
Web Site: http://www.san-byte.com
Sales Range: $25-49.9 Million
Emp.: 20
Toy Character Designing Services
N.A.I.C.S.: 541490

Sanrio (Hong Kong) Company Limited (1)
Rm 02-05 22nd Floor Miramar Twr, Kowloon, China (Hong Kong)
Tel.: (852) 23756682
Sales Range: $25-49.9 Million
Emp.: 30
Gift Novelty & Souvenir Stores
N.A.I.C.S.: 459420

Sanrio Asia Merchandise Co., Ltd. (1)
Rm 902 Fourseas Bldg, Aberdeen, China (Hong Kong)
Tel.: (852) 23756682
Emp.: 30
Toy & Hobby Goods & Supplies Whslr
N.A.I.C.S.: 423920
Chang Charlie *(Country Mgr)*

Sanrio Car Lease Co., Ltd. (1)
1-10-12 Hamamatsu-cho, Minato-ku, Tokyo, Japan
Tel.: (81) 334362338
Automobile Leasing Services
N.A.I.C.S.: 532112

Sanrio Do Brasil Comercio E Representacoes Ltda (1)
Rua Alvars GuimarAes 462, Sao Paulo, Brazil
Tel.: (55) 1130688571
Web Site: http://www.sanrio.br
Sales Range: $25-49.9 Million
Emp.: 45
Stationery & Supplies Whslr
N.A.I.C.S.: 424120

Sanrio Entertainment Co., Ltd. (1)
1-31 Ochiai, Tama, 206-8588, Tokyo, Japan
Tel.: (81) 423726500
Web Site: http://www.sanrio-entertainment.co.jp
Emp.: 350
Theme Park Management Services
N.A.I.C.S.: 541611

Sanrio Far East Co., Ltd. (1)
1-6-1 Osaki, Shinagawa-Ku, Tokyo, 141-0032, Japan
Tel.: (81) 337798082
Web Site: http://www.sanrio.co.jp
Sales Range: $10-24.9 Million
Emp.: 30
Business Services

AND PRIVATE COMPANIES

N.A.I.C.S.: 561499
Andy Y. Toyama *(Pres & CEO)*

Sanrio GmbH (1)
Zwischen den Toren 9, Wentorf bei, 21465, Hamburg, Germany
Tel.: (49) 405477960
Web Site: http://privacycenter.sanrio.eu
Sales Range: $25-49.9 Million
Emp.: 30
Stationery & Supplies Whslr
N.A.I.C.S.: 424120

Sanrio License GmbH (1)
Zwischen Den Toren 9, Wentorf bei Hamburg, 21465, Schleswig-Holstein, Germany
Tel.: (49) 405477960
Sales Range: $25-49.9 Million
Emp.: 50
Gift Product Distr
N.A.I.C.S.: 459420
Ronald Denecke *(Gen Mgr)*

Sanrio Music Publications Co., Ltd. (1)
1-11-1 Osaki Toc Osaki Bldg Sanrio, Shinagawa-ku, Tokyo, 141-0032, Japan
Tel.: (81) 337798071
Music Publishers
N.A.I.C.S.: 512230

Sanrio Puroland, K.K. (1)
1-31 Ochiai Tama, Tokyo, 206-8588, Japan
Tel.: (81) 423391111
Web Site: http://en.puroland.jp
Sales Range: $150-199.9 Million
Emp.: 300
Amusement & Theme Parks
N.A.I.C.S.: 713110
Shintaro Tsuji *(CEO)*

Sanrio Taiwan Co , Ltd (1)
10th Floor No 45 Section 4 Zhongxiao East Road, DA-An District, Taipei, 10682, Taiwan
Tel.: (886) 227524394
Web Site: http://www.sanrio.com.tw
Emp.: 30
Non-Durable Goods Whslr
N.A.I.C.S.: 424990

Sanrio Wave Co., Ltd. (1)
1-6-1 Osaki, Shinagawa-Ku, Tokyo, 141 8603, Japan
Tel.: (81) 337798111
Web Site: http://www.sanrio.co.jp
Sales Range: $10-24.9 Million
Emp.: 10
Restaurant
N.A.I.C.S.: 722511
Amori Susumu *(Gen Mgr)*

Sanrio Wave Hong Kong Co., Ltd. (1)
Rm 2202-05 22nd Fl Miramar Tower, Tsim Sha Tsui, Kowloon, China (Hong Kong)
Tel.: (852) 23756682
Web Site: http://www.sanrio.com
Sales Range: $25-49.9 Million
Emp.: 40
Computer & Computer Peripheral Equipment & Software Whslr
N.A.I.C.S.: 423430
Caroline Tsang *(Mgr-Mktg)*

Sanrio, Inc. (1)
570 Eccles Ave, San Francisco, CA 94080-1949
Tel.: (650) 616-3200
Web Site: http://www.sanrio.com
Sales Range: $25-49.9 Million
Emp.: 100
Gift Novelty & Souvenir Stores
N.A.I.C.S.: 459420
Craig Takiguchi *(COO)*

SANRITSU CORPORATION
12th floor South Port Shinagawa 2-12-32 Konan, Minato-ku, Tokyo, 108-0075, Japan
Tel.: (81) 334710011
Web Site: https://www.srt.co.jp
Year Founded: 1948
9366—(TKS)
Rev.: $128,220,780
Assets: $141,163,160
Liabilities: $69,927,190
Net Worth: $71,235,970
Earnings: $3,780,920
Emp.: 449
Fiscal Year-end: 03/31/24
Packing & Transportation Services
N.A.I.C.S.: 488991
Yasuhide Miura *(Chm, Pres & CEO)*

SANSAN, INC.
Aoyama Oval Building 13F 5-52-2 Jingumae, Shibuya-ku, Tokyo, 150-0001, Japan
Tel.: (81) 367580033   JP
Web Site: https://www.corp-sansan.com
Year Founded: 2007
4443—(TKS)
Rev.: $223,838,722
Assets: $248,377,862
Liabilities: $150,776,304
Net Worth: $97,601,558
Earnings: $6,058,802
Emp.: 1,399
Fiscal Year-end: 05/31/24
Application Development Services
N.A.I.C.S.: 541511
Chika Terada *(CEO)*

Subsidiaries:

Logmi, Inc. (1)
13F Aoyama Garden 5-52-2 Jingu-mae, Shibuya-ku, Tokyo, 150-0001, Japan
Tel.: (81) 362775188
Web Site: https://www.logmi.co.jp
Information Technology Services
N.A.I.C.S.: 541511

SANSEI CO., LTD.
Sansei building 2-24-13 Yushima, Bunkyo-ku, Tokyo, 113-0034, Japan
Tel.: (81) 338343171
Web Site: https://www.san-sei.co.jp
Year Founded: 1963
6307—(TKS)
Rev.: $37,260,570
Assets: $45,219,010
Liabilities: $15,652,480
Net Worth: $29,566,530
Earnings: $2,154,860
Fiscal Year-end: 03/31/24
Ship Repair & Maintenance Services
N.A.I.C.S.: 811310
Atsushi Kojima *(Pres & Chm)*

Subsidiaries:

Sankyo Electronics, Co., Ltd. (1)
138 Higashiyama Akaike, Inazawa, 492-8021, Aichi, Japan
Tel.: (81) 587245050
Web Site: https://3kyodenki.com
Emp.: 50
Concrete Products Mfr
N.A.I.C.S.: 327390

Sansei Vietnam Trading Co., Ltd. (1)
1636 16th Floor Icon4 Tower 243A De La Thanh, Lang Thuong Ward Dong Da, Hanoi, Vietnam
Tel.: (84) 2437606624
Household Appliances Mfr
N.A.I.C.S.: 335220

Shanghai Sansei Co., Ltd. (1)
Rm907 Shengtiandi Mansion 1165 Jiangning Road, Putuo District, Shanghai, China
Tel.: (86) 2152342953
Household Appliances Mfr
N.A.I.C.S.: 335220

Three Minds Ltd. (1)
Room 2101 21/F Kodak House II 39 Healthy St East, Quarry Bay, China (Hong Kong)
Tel.: (852) 25655110
Household Appliances Mfr
N.A.I.C.S.: 335220

SANSEI LANDIC CO., LTD.
Marunouchi Park Building 21F 2-6-1 Marunouchi, Chiyoda-ku, Japan
Tel.: (81) 352527511
Web Site: https://www.sansei-l.co.jp
Year Founded: 1976
3277—(TKS)
Rev.: $102,629,666
Assets: $191,450,281
Liabilities: $118,401,057
Net Worth: $73,049,224
Earnings: $7,003,634
Emp.: 179
Fiscal Year-end: 12/31/22
Real Estate Brokerage Services
N.A.I.C.S.: 531210
Takashi Matsuzaki *(Pres)*

Subsidiaries:

One's Life Home, Inc (1)
3-21-8 Seijo, Setagaya-ku, Tokyo, 157-0066, Japan
Tel.: (81) 363243783
Web Site: http://www.oneslife-home.com
Commercial Building Construction Services
N.A.I.C.S.: 236220

SANSEI TECHNOLOGIES INC.
3-29 4-Chome Miyahara, Yodogawa-ku, Osaka, 532-0003, Japan
Tel.: (81) 663935621
Web Site: https://www.sansei-technologies.com
Year Founded: 1951
6357—(TKS)
Rev.: $345,749,270
Assets: $535,614,910
Liabilities: $258,655,910
Net Worth: $276,959,000
Earnings: $13,695,920
Emp.: 1,364
Fiscal Year-end: 03/31/24
Amusement Rides, Stage Equipment, Elevators & Specifically Designed Equipment Mfr, Install, Repair & Maintenance
N.A.I.C.S.: 333248
Noboru Rachi *(Pres & CEO)*

Subsidiaries:

S&S Worldwide, Inc. (1)
2935 N 400 W, Logan, UT 84341
Tel.: (435) 752-1987
Sales Range: $1-9.9 Million
Amusement Park Ride Mfr & Distr
N.A.I.C.S.: 333310
Scott Holliday *(Mgr-Major Rides)*

Sansei Maintenance Co., Ltd. (1)
3-17 4-Chome Shinjuku, Shinjuku-Ku, Tokyo, 160-0022, Japan
Tel.: (81) 333565651
Amusement Ride Repair & Maintenance Services
N.A.I.C.S.: 713990

Sansei Technologies Inc - KOBE Plant (1)
3-1 2-Chome Akamatsudai, Kita-Ku, Kobe, 651-1516, Hyogo, Japan
Tel.: (81) 789834800
Amusement Park Rides Mfr
N.A.I.C.S.: 333310

TELMIC Corp. (1)
Akiba East Building 1-28-5 Taito, Taito-ku, Tokyo, 110-0016, Japan
Tel.: (81) 358121611
Web Site: https://telmic.co.jp
Emp.: 267
Led Display Screen Mfr & Distr
N.A.I.C.S.: 334413

Plant (Domestic):

TELMIC Corp. - Yoshikawa Factory (2)
531-1 Komatsugawa, Yoshikawa, Saitama, Japan
Tel.: (81) 489816398
Led Display Screen Mfr
N.A.I.C.S.: 334413

SANSERA ENGINEERING LIMITED
Plant 7 No 143/A Jigani Link Road, Bommasandra Industrial Area, Bengaluru, 560105, Karnataka, India
Tel.: (91) 8027839081
Web Site: https://www.sansera.in
Year Founded: 1981
543358—(BOM)
Vehicle Components Mfr
N.A.I.C.S.: 336390
B. R. Preetham *(CEO)*

Subsidiaries:

Fitwel Tools & Forgings Private Limited (1)
Unit No 5 KHT Complex Antharasanahalli, Tumkur, 572106, Karnataka, India
Tel.: (91) 816 221 2600
Web Site: https://www.fitwelforge.com
Precision Forged Machine Component Mfr
N.A.I.C.S.: 333517

SANSHA ELECTRIC MANUFACTURING CO., LTD.
3-1-56 Nishiawaji, Higashiyodogawa-ku, Osaka, 533-0031, Japan
Tel.: (81) 663210321
Web Site: https://www.sansha.co.jp
Year Founded: 1933
6882—(TKS)
Rev.: $204,943,050
Assets: $233,557,740
Liabilities: $72,062,220
Net Worth: $161,495,520
Earnings: $19,532,550
Emp.: 1,418
Fiscal Year-end: 03/31/24
Electric Equipment Mfr & Distr
N.A.I.C.S.: 335999
Hajimu Yoshimura *(Pres)*

Subsidiaries:

SANREX LIMITED (1)
9A Tin On Industrial Building 777-779 Cheung Sha Wan Road, Kowloon, China (Hong Kong)
Tel.: (852) 27441310
Electrical Equipment Distr
N.A.I.C.S.: 423690

SANSHA ELECTRIC MFG. (GUANGDONG) CO., LTD. (1)
Room 903 Jiefang Daily Building No 300 Hankou Road, Huangpu District, Shanghai, 528308, Guangdong, China
Tel.: (86) 63339297
Electrical Equipment Distr
N.A.I.C.S.: 423690

SANSHA ELECTRIC MFG. (SHANGHAI) CO., LTD. (1)
Unit C 13th Floor Huaxin Haixin Building No 666 Fuzhou Road, Huangpu District, Shanghai, 200001, China
Tel.: (86) 2158681058
Electrical Equipment Distr
N.A.I.C.S.: 423690

Sanrex Corporation (1)
50 Seaview Blvd, Port Washington, NY 11050-4618
Tel.: (516) 625-1313
Web Site: http://www.sanrex.com
Electrical Equipment Mfr & Distr
N.A.I.C.S.: 335999

Sansha Electric Manufacturing Co., Ltd. - Okayama Plant (1)
1741 Kaki Nagi-cho, Katsuta-gun, Okayama, 708-1312, Japan
Tel.: (81) 868363111
Semiconductor Equipment Mfr
N.A.I.C.S.: 334413

Sansha Electric Manufacturing Co., Ltd. - Shiga Plant (1)
452-1 Katsube-cho, Moriyama, 524-0041, Shiga, Japan
Tel.: (81) 775838632
Power Supply Equipment Mfr
N.A.I.C.S.: 335999

Sansha Solution Service Co., Ltd. (1)
2-14-3 Awaji, Higashiyodogawa-ku, Osaka, 533-0032, Japan

SANSHA ELECTRIC MANUFACTURING CO., LTD.

Sansha Electric Manufacturing Co., Ltd.—(Continued)
Tel.: (81) 663210616
Electric Equipment Mfr
N.A.I.C.S.: 335999

SANSHENG HOLDINGS (GROUP) CO., LTD.
Room 3207 The Gateway Tower 6
Tsim Sha Tsui, Kowloon, China (Hong Kong)
Tel.: (852) 35806000
Web Site: http://www.sansheng.hk
2183—(HKG)
Rev.: $1,344,969,306
Assets: $8,668,067,486
Liabilities: $7,724,002,174
Net Worth: $944,065,312
Earnings: $130,370,679
Emp.: 1,288
Fiscal Year-end: 12/31/20
Property Development & Investment
N.A.I.C.S.: 237210
Lin Rongbin (Chm)

SANSHENG INTELLECTUAL EDUCATION TECHNOLOGY CO., LTD.
5/F No 21 IRTOUCH Building No 10 Dongbeiwang West Road, Haidian District, Beijing, 100094, China
Tel.: (86) 1084573471
Web Site: http://www.irtouch.com
Year Founded: 2003
300282—(CHIN)
Rev.: $32,091,228
Assets: $374,684,076
Liabilities: $173,370,132
Net Worth: $201,313,944
Earnings: ($33,250,932)
Emp.: 320
Fiscal Year-end: 12/31/22
Touchscreen Mfr
N.A.I.C.S.: 334413

Subsidiaries:

Beijing Irtouchsystems Co., Ltd. (1)
Hospital Xibeiwang Road 10 Building 21 West Building 5th Floor, Sanshenggong Haidian District, Beijing, 100193, China
Tel.: (86) 1084573465
Touch Screen Mfr
N.A.I.C.S.: 334419

Koga Touch Co., Ltd. (1)
5F Sansheng Building No 10 Xibeiwang East Rd, Haidian District, Beijing, 100193, China
Tel.: (86) 15901039998
Web Site: https://kogatouch.com
Information Technology Services
N.A.I.C.S.: 541511
Daniel Yang (Sls Dir-Overseas)

SANSHIN ELECTRIC CO., LTD.
4-1-5 Mokuyama, Nerima Ward, Tokyo, 176-0022, Japan
Tel.: (81) 359875511 JP
Web Site: http://www.sanshin-ele.com
Year Founded: 1978
Sales Range: $10-24.9 Million
Emp.: 50
Semiconductors & Other Electronic Components Mfr & Distr
N.A.I.C.S.: 334413
Toshiaki Imai (Mng Dir)

SANSHIN ELECTRIC CORPORATION
1-16-8 Uchikanda, Chiyoda-ku, Tokyo, 101-0047, Japan
Tel.: (81) 3 3295 1831 JP
Web Site: http://www.sanshin-electric.co.jp
Year Founded: 1949
Electric Marine Equipment Mfr & Distr
N.A.I.C.S.: 335999

Shinichiro Yamada (Pres)
Subsidiaries:

Sanshin Electric Corporation - Adachi Factory (1)
1-13-11 Aoi, Adachi-ku, Tokyo, 120-0012, Japan
Tel.: (81) 3 3848 2111
N.A.I.C.S.: 335999

Sanshin Electric Corporation - Ise Factory (1)
1750 Yamaoyodo Meiwacho, Taki-gun, Mie, 515-0303, Japan
Tel.: (81) 596 55 4095
Electric Equipment Mfr
N.A.I.C.S.: 335999

SANSHIN ELECTRONICS CO., LTD.
4-4-12 Shiba, Minato-ku, Tokyo, 108-0014, Japan
Tel.: (81) 334535111
Web Site: https://www.sanshin.co.jp
8150—(TKS)
Rev.: $926,702,170
Assets: $521,423,240
Liabilities: $267,777,710
Net Worth: $253,645,530
Earnings: $18,111,400
Emp.: 584
Fiscal Year-end: 03/31/24
Electronic Equipment Sales
N.A.I.C.S.: 423620
Toshiro Suzuki (COO & COO)

Subsidiaries:

AXIS DEVICE TECHNOLOGY CO., LTD. (1)
4-3-6 Shiba, Minato-ku, Tokyo, 108-0014, Japan
Tel.: (81) 354847340
Web Site: http://www.sanshin.co.jp
Emp.: 500
Electric Device Mfr
N.A.I.C.S.: 334419

San Shin Electronics (Malaysia) Sdn. Bhd. (1)
Suite 26 03 Level 26 Menara AIA Sentral No 30 Jalan Sultan Ismail, 50250, Kuala Lumpur, Malaysia
Tel.: (60) 321443468
Web Site: http://www.sanshin.co.jp
Sales Range: $25-49.9 Million
Emp.: 11
Electric Device Mfr
N.A.I.C.S.: 334413

Sanshin Electronics (Hong Kong) Co., Ltd. (1)
5F Chuan Hing Ind Bldg 14 Wang Tai Road Kowloon Bay, Kowloon, China (Hong Kong)
Tel.: (852) 27999862
Web Site: http://www.sanshinusa.com
Sales Range: $25-49.9 Million
Emp.: 30
Electric Device Mfr
N.A.I.C.S.: 334419

Sanshin Electronics (Shanghai) Co., Ltd. (1)
916 No 6 JI Rong Road, Wai Gao Qiao Free Duty Zone, Shanghai, 200336, China
Tel.: (86) 2162750222
Web Site: http://www.sanshinusa.com
Electric Device Mfr
N.A.I.C.S.: 334419

Sanshin Electronics (Shenzhen) Co., Ltd. (1)
Unit 07-08A 13F Avic center Building Huafu Road No 1018, Futian District, Shenzhen, 518031, China
Tel.: (86) 75582560432
Web Site: http://www.sanshin.com
Sales Range: $25-49.9 Million
Emp.: 21
Electric Device Mfr
N.A.I.C.S.: 334419
Maeekawa HiroHiko (Mgr)

Sanshin Electronics (Thailand) Co., Ltd. (1)
898 Ploenchit Tower 13F B2 Ploenchit Road Lumpini, Pathumwan, Bangkok, 10330, Thailand
Tel.: (66) 26585870
Web Site: http://www.sanshin.co.jp
Sales Range: $25-49.9 Million
Emp.: 15
Electric Device Mfr
N.A.I.C.S.: 334419

Sanshin Electronics (U.S.A.) Corporation (1)
2855 Coolidge Hwy Ste 109, Troy, MI 48084
Tel.: (248) 781-0299
Web Site: https://www.sanshinusa.com
Electric Device Mfr
N.A.I.C.S.: 334413

Sanshin Electronics Corporation (1)
2855 Coolidge Hwy Ste 109, Troy, MI 48084
Tel.: (248) 781-0299
Electrical & Electronic Mfr
N.A.I.C.S.: 335999

Sanshin Electronics Korea Co., Ltd. (1)
202 2F Hanjin Bldg 6 Teheran-Ro 103-Gil, Gangnam-gu, Seoul, 06173, Korea (South)
Tel.: (82) 25280345
Electric Device Mfr
N.A.I.C.S.: 334419

Sanshin Electronics Singapore (Pte.) Ltd. (1)
28 Genting Lane 05-02 Platinum 28, Singapore, 349585, Singapore
Tel.: (65) 67464266
Web Site: http://www.sanshin.co.jp
Emp.: 18
Electric Device Mfr
N.A.I.C.S.: 334413

Sanshin Media Solutions Co., Ltd. (1)
4-4-12 Shiba, Minato-ku, Tokyo, 108-0014, Japan
Tel.: (81) 354847270
Web Site: http://www.sanshinusa.com
Electric Device Mfr
N.A.I.C.S.: 334416

Sanshin Network Service Co., Ltd. (1)
4-4-12 Shiba Sanshin Electric Building, Minato-ku, Tokyo, 108-8404, Japan
Tel.: (81) 354847280
Web Site: https://www.sanshin-ns.jp
Sales Range: $25-49.9 Million
Emp.: 55
Electric Device Mfr
N.A.I.C.S.: 334416

Sanshin System Design Co., Ltd. (1)
4-4-12 Shiba, Minato-ku, Tokyo, 108-0014, Japan
Tel.: (81) 354847475
Electrical & Electronic Mfr
N.A.I.C.S.: 335999

Taiwan Sanshin Electronics Co., Ltd. (1)
12F No 77 Sec 3 Nanjing E Rd, Zhongshan Dist, Taipei, 10487, Taiwan
Tel.: (886) 225428945
Electrical & Electronic Mfr
N.A.I.C.S.: 335999

Takumi Corporation (1)
4-3-6 Shiba, Minato-ku, Tokyo, 108-0014, Japan
Tel.: (81) 354198690
Electrical & Electronic Mfr
N.A.I.C.S.: 335999

SANSIRI PCL
59 Soi Rim Khlong Phra Khanong, Phra Khanong Nuea Sub-district Vadhana District, Bangkok, 10110, Thailand
Tel.: (66) 20277888
Web Site: https://www.sansiri.com
Year Founded: 1984
SIRI—(THA)
Rev.: $1,140,884,034
Assets: $4,300,075,031
Liabilities: $2,916,128,004
Net Worth: $1,383,947,027
Earnings: $170,644,515
Emp.: 2,044
Fiscal Year-end: 12/31/23
Real Estate Manangement Services
N.A.I.C.S.: 531390
Apichart Chutrakul (Chm)

Subsidiaries:

Arnawat Limited (1)
59 Soi Rim Khlong Phra Khanong, Phra Khanong Nuea Sub-district Vadhana District, Bangkok, 10110, Thailand
Tel.: (66) 20277888
Property Development Services
N.A.I.C.S.: 531311

Chanachai Limited (1)
59 Soi Rim Khlong Phra Khanong, Phra Khanong Nuea Sub-district Vadhana District, Bangkok, 10110, Thailand
Tel.: (66) 20277888
Web Site: https://www.sansiri.com
Sales Range: $150-199.9 Million
Emp.: 475
Property Development Services
N.A.I.C.S.: 531311

Clubhouse Property Limited (1)
475 Siripinyo Building Sri Ayutthaya Road, Phayathai Rajthevi, Bangkok, 10400, Thailand
Tel.: (66) 22013905
Sales Range: $300-349.9 Million
Emp.: 1,000
Real Estate Venture
N.A.I.C.S.: 531311

One Night, LLC (1)
15225 SW 80th Ave, Miami, FL 33157
Web Site: https://www.onenight.com
Hotel & Motel Operator
N.A.I.C.S.: 721110

Piwattana Company Limited (1)
59 Soi Rim Khlong Phra Khanong, Phra Khanong Nuea Sub-district Vadhana District, Bangkok, 10110, Thailand
Tel.: (66) 20277888
Web Site: http://www.piwattana.com
Real Estate Development
N.A.I.C.S.: 531390

Plus Property Company Limited (1)
No 59 Rim Khlong Phra Khanong, Alley Phra Khanong Nuea Subdistrict, Bangkok, 10110, Thailand
Tel.: (66) 26887555
Web Site: https://www.plus.co.th
Property Management Agency Services
N.A.I.C.S.: 531311

Plus Property Partners Co., Ltd. (1)
163 Rajchapark Bldg 10F Sukhumvit 21, Klongtoey Nua Wattana, Bangkok, Thailand
Tel.: (66) 26617555
Web Site: http://www.plus.co.th
Property Management
N.A.I.C.S.: 531390

Plus Property Space Co., Ltd (1)
59 Soi Rim Khlong Phra Khanong, Phra Khanong Nuea Sub-district Vadhana District, Bangkok, 10110, Thailand
Tel.: (66) 20277888
Web Site: https://www.sansiri.com
Property Development Services
N.A.I.C.S.: 531311

Plus Property Venture Company Limited (1)
163 Rajchapark Sukhumvit 21, Klongtoey Nua Wattana, 101110, Bangkok, Thailand
Tel.: (66) 26617555
Web Site: http://www.worldwideweb.plus.co.th
Sales Range: $75-99.9 Million
Emp.: 120
Property Development
N.A.I.C.S.: 531390

Red Lotus Properties Limited (1)
59 Soi Rim Khlong Phra Khanong, Phra Khanong Nuea Sub-district Vadhana District, Bangkok, 10110, Thailand
Tel.: (66) 20277888
Web Site: http://www.red-lotus-properties.com

Sales Range: $25-49.9 Million
Emp.: 35
Real Estate Investment
N.A.I.C.S.: 531390
Metha Angwatamapanich *(Mgr)*

Rojnaruemit Limited (1)
16th Floor Siripinyo Bldg 475 Sri Ayutthaya Road, Ratchathewi, Bangkok, 10400, Thailand
Tel.: (66) 22013999
Web Site: http://www.sansiri.com
Real Estate Venture
N.A.I.C.S.: 531390

S.U.N. Management Co., Ltd (1)
16th Floor 475 Si Ayutthaya Road Thanon Phayathai, Rajthevi District, Bangkok, 10400, Thailand
Tel.: (66) 2 201 3905
Property Development Services
N.A.I.C.S.: 531311

Sansiri Land Limited (1)
59 Soi Rim Khlong Phra Khanong, Phra Khanong Nuea Sub-district Vadhana District, Bangkok, 10110, Thailand
Tel.: (66) 20277888
Web Site: http://www.quintessengially.com
Sales Range: $50-74.9 Million
Emp.: 20
Real Estate Venture
N.A.I.C.S.: 531390
Sroisuwan Montien *(Mng Dir)*

Sansiri Ram-indra Limited (1)
475 Siripinyo Sri Ayutthaya Road, Phayathai, Rajthevi, Bangkok, 10400, Thailand
Tel.: (66) 22013906
Sales Range: $300-349.9 Million
Emp.: 1,000
Real Estate Venture
N.A.I.C.S.: 531390

Sansiri Venture Co., Ltd. (1)
475 Siripinyo Bldg Sri Ayutthaya Rd, Phayathai Rajthevi, Bangkok, 10400, Thailand **(51%)**
Tel.: (66) 22013905
Web Site: http://www.sansiri.com
Property Development
N.A.I.C.S.: 531390

Siri Phuket Limited (1)
Siripinyo Bldg 475 Sri Ayutthaya Road, Phayathai, Ratchathewi, Bangkok, 10400, Thailand **(51%)**
Tel.: (66) 22013905
Web Site: http://www.sansiri.com
Property Development
N.A.I.C.S.: 531390

Touch Property Co., Ltd (1)
No 59 Soi Rim Klong Phra Khanong, Alley Phra Khanong Nuea Subdistrict Watthana District, Bangkok, 10110, Thailand
Tel.: (66) 26887555
Web Site: https://www.touch.co.th
Emp.: 200
Property Management Services
N.A.I.C.S.: 531311

SANSO ELECTRIC CO., LTD.
1-1-1 Aoyamakita, Himeji, 671-2288, Hyogo, Japan
Tel.: (81) 792661200
Web Site: https://www.sanso-elec.co.jp
Year Founded: 1957
6518—(TKS)
Rev.: $116,772,260
Assets: $129,113,130
Liabilities: $51,676,980
Net Worth: $77,436,150
Earnings: $3,258,730
Emp.: 360
Fiscal Year-end: 03/31/24
Motor & Pump Mfr
N.A.I.C.S.: 335312
Subsidiaries:

Harima Sanso Electric Co., Ltd. (1)
336-1 Nakano Yamasaki-cho Shiso, Hyogo, 671-2502, Japan
Tel.: (81) 790650411
Motor & Pump Mfr
N.A.I.C.S.: 333996

Okayama Sanso Electric Co., Ltd. (1)
1714-1 Kamagami, Akaiwa, 709-0733, Okayama, Japan
Tel.: (81) 869951225
Web Site: https://okayama.sanso-elec.co.jp
Emp.: 70
Motor & Pump Mfr
N.A.I.C.S.: 333996

Sanso Seiko Electric Co., Ltd. (1)
13-27 Aoyama-Kita 1chome, Himeji, 671-2221, Hyogo, Japan
Tel.: (81) 792682540
Motor & Pump Mfr
N.A.I.C.S.: 333996

Shingu Sanso Electric Co., Ltd. (1)
538-2 Shingu Shingu-cho, Tatsuno, 679-4313, Hyogo, Japan
Tel.: (81) 791750071
Motor & Pump Mfr
N.A.I.C.S.: 333996

SANSTEEL MINGUANG CO., LTD.
No 3 Gongye Middle Road Qungong 3rd Road, Meilie District, Sanming, 365000, Fujian, China
Tel.: (86) 5988205070
Web Site: http://www.sgmg.com.cn
Year Founded: 2001
002110—(SSE)
Rev.: $6,637,796,868
Assets: $6,672,998,712
Liabilities: $3,830,051,368
Net Worth: $2,842,947,344
Earnings: ($92,441,017)
Fiscal Year-end: 12/31/23
Iron & Steel Product Mfr
N.A.I.C.S.: 331110
Lizhang Li *(Chm)*

SANSURE BIOTECH, INC.
No 680 Lusong Road, Hi-Tech Development Zone Yuelu, Changsha, 410205, Hunan, China
Tel.: (86) 73188883176
Web Site:
https://www.sansure.com.cn
Year Founded: 2008
688289—(SHG)
Rev.: $905,630,067
Assets: $1,287,996,199
Liabilities: $233,202,926
Net Worth: $1,054,793,273
Earnings: $271,926,790
Fiscal Year-end: 12/31/22
Medical Product Mfr & Distr
N.A.I.C.S.: 339112
Lizhong Dai *(Chm & Gen Mgr)*

SANSUY S.A.
Rodovia Regis Bittencourt Km 280, Sao Paulo, 06830-900, Embu, Brazil
Tel.: (55) 1121392600
Web Site: http://www.sansuy.com.br
Year Founded: 1979
Sales Range: $50-74.9 Million
Emp.: 1,350
Plastic Mfr
N.A.I.C.S.: 325211
Subsidiaries:

Kanaflex S.A. Industria de Plasticos (1)
Rua Jose Semiao Rodrigues Agostinho 282, Bairro Quinhau Embu, Sao Paulo, CEP 06833 905, SP, Brazil **(51%)**
Tel.: (55) 1147852100
Web Site: http://www.kanaflex.com.br
Sales Range: $10-24.9 Million
Emp.: 160
Plastic Hoses & Cables Mfr
N.A.I.C.S.: 326199

Sansuy S.A. - EMBU INDUSTRIAL UNIT (1)
Rodovia Regis Bittencourt s/no-km 280 Tingidor, Embu das Artes, Sao Paulo, 06830-900, Brazil
Tel.: (55) 1121392888
Plastics Product Mfr
N.A.I.C.S.: 326199

SANTA FE MINERALS LTD.
Suite 1/9 Hampden Road, Nedlands, 6009, WA, Australia
Tel.: (61) 893868382   AU
Web Site:
https://www.santafeminerals.com.au
Year Founded: 2000
SFM—(ASX)
Rev.: $49,884
Assets: $1,418,478
Liabilities: $98,788
Net Worth: $1,319,689
Earnings: ($571,761)
Fiscal Year-end: 06/30/24
Australian Gold & Base Metals Exploration
N.A.I.C.S.: 212220
Douglas Rose *(Mng Dir)*

SANTACRUZ SILVER MINING LTD.
Suite 480-1140 West Pender St, Vancouver, V6E 4G1, BC, Canada
Tel.: (818) 378-5707
Web Site:
https://www.santacruzsilver.com
Year Founded: 2011
SCZMF—(OTCIQ)
Rev.: $33,097,000
Assets: $32,832,000
Liabilities: $42,251,000
Net Worth: ($9,419,000)
Earnings: ($1,493,000)
Fiscal Year-end: 12/31/20
Silver Exploration Services
N.A.I.C.S.: 212220
Arturo Prestamo Elizondo *(Chm & CFO-Interim)*

SANTANA MINERALS LIMITED
Level 1 371 Queen Street, Brisbane, 4000, QLD, Australia
Tel.: (61) 732217501
Web Site:
https://www.santanaminerals.com
SMI—(ASX)
Rev.: $303,885
Assets: $46,594,452
Liabilities: $1,288,906
Net Worth: $45,305,547
Earnings: ($1,727,042)
Fiscal Year-end: 06/30/24
Gold & Silver Mining
N.A.I.C.S.: 212220
Norman A. Seckold *(Chm)*

SANTEN PHARMACEUTICAL CO., LTD.
Grand Front Osaka Tower A 4-20 Ofuka-cho, Kita-ku, Osaka, 530-8552, Japan
Tel.: (81) 676648621
Web Site: https://santen.com
SZD—(DEU)
Rev.: $1,995,988,650
Assets: $2,879,970,390
Liabilities: $861,481,300
Net Worth: $2,018,489,090
Earnings: $176,103,620
Emp.: 3,744
Fiscal Year-end: 03/31/24
Eye Drops & Medical Devices Whslr
N.A.I.C.S.: 325412
Akira Kurokawa *(Chm & CEO)*
Subsidiaries:

Advanced Vision Science Inc. (1)
5743 Thornwood Dr, Goleta, CA 93117 **(100%)**
Tel.: (805) 683-3851
Web Site:
https://www.advancedvisionscience.com
Emp.: 100
Ophthalmic Goods Mfr
N.A.I.C.S.: 339115

Chongqing Santen Kerui Pharmaceutical Co., Ltd. (1)
Room 2-1 No 57 Baihe Rd, Nan'an District, Chongqing, 400060, China
Tel.: (86) 2362819826
Ophthalmology Services
N.A.I.C.S.: 621320

Claire Co., Ltd. (1)
348-3 Aza-suwa Oaza-shide Taga-cho, Inukami District, Shiga, 522-0314, Japan
Tel.: (81) 749 48 2234
Pharmaceuticals Product Mfr
N.A.I.C.S.: 325412
Kizo Tadashi *(Gen Mgr)*

Innfocus, Inc. (1)
12415 S W 136 Ave Unit 3, Miami, FL 33186
Tel.: (305) 378-2651
Web Site: https://www.innfocusinc.com
Pharmaceuticals Product Mfr
N.A.I.C.S.: 325412

Santen (Thailand) Co., Ltd. (1)
689 Bhiraj Tower 22nd Floor Unit No 2207-2209 Sukhumvit Road, Klongton-Nua Wattana, Bangkok, 10110, Thailand
Tel.: (66) 20605561
Ophthalmology Services
N.A.I.C.S.: 621320

Santen Business Services Co., Ltd. (1)
9-31 Shimoshinjo 3-chome, Higashiyodogawa-ku, Osaka, 533-8651, Japan
Tel.: (81) 663217755
Pharmaceuticals Product Mfr
N.A.I.C.S.: 325412

Santen Canada Inc. (1)
37 Bay Street Suite 400, Toronto, M5J 3B2, ON, Canada
Web Site: https://www.santencanada.ca
Eye Care Service
N.A.I.C.S.: 621320

Santen GmbH (1)
Erika-Mann-Str 21, 80636, Munich, Germany
Tel.: (49) 89 848 0780
Web Site: https://www.santen.de
Sales Range: $25-49.9 Million
Emp.: 50
Pharmaceuticals Product Mfr
N.A.I.C.S.: 325412

Santen Holdings U.S. Inc (1)
555 Gateway Dr, Napa, CA 94558 **(100%)**
Tel.: (707) 254-1750
Web Site: http://www.santen.com
Sales Range: $25-49.9 Million
Emp.: 50
Pharmaceutical Preparation Mfr
N.A.I.C.S.: 325412
Akira Kurokawa *(Pres & CEO)*

Santen Inc. (1)
555 Gateway Dr, Napa, CA 94558 **(100%)**
Tel.: (707) 254-1750
Pharmaceutical Preparation Mfr
N.A.I.C.S.: 325412

Santen India Private Limited (1)
Unit No 201 A Wing Sagar Tech Plaza, Sakinaka, Mumbai, 400072, Maharashtra, India
Tel.: (91) 2249740247
Ophthalmology Services
N.A.I.C.S.: 621320

Santen Italy S.R.L. (1)
Piazza Sigmund Freud 1, 20154, Milan, Italy
Tel.: (39) 026200191
Ophthalmology Services
N.A.I.C.S.: 621320

Santen Limited Liability Company (1)
Nizhniy Susalniy Pereulok 5 Building 19 Office 402, 105064, Moscow, Russia
Tel.: (7) 4959808079
Web Site: http://www.santen.ru

SANTEN PHARMACEUTICAL CO., LTD.

Santen Pharmaceutical Co., Ltd.—(Continued)
Ophthalmology Services
N.A.I.C.S.: 621320

Santen Oy (1)
Niittyhaankatu 20, Tampere, 33720,
Finland (100%)
Tel.: (358) 32848111
Web Site: http://ww2.santen.eu
Sales Range: $125-149.9 Million
Emp.: 500
Pharmaceutical Preparation Mfr
N.A.I.C.S.: 325412

Santen Pharma Malaysia Sdn. Bhd. (1)
Unit 23A-10 Q Sentral No 2A Jalan Stesen Sentral 2, 50470, Kuala Lumpur, Malaysia
Tel.: (60) 322763333
Ophthalmology Services
N.A.I.C.S.: 621320

Santen Pharmaceutical (China) Co., Ltd. (1)
No 169 Tinglan Road, Suzhou Industrial Park, Suzhou, 215026, Jiangsu, China
Tel.: (86) 51262957500
Ophthalmology Services
N.A.I.C.S.: 621320

Santen Pharmaceutical (Hong Kong) Limited (1)
Unit 1607 16/F Concordia Plaza 1 Science Museum Road, Tsim Sha Tsui East, Kowloon, China (Hong Kong)
Tel.: (852) 25656660
Ophthalmology Services
N.A.I.C.S.: 621320

Santen Pharmaceutical Asia Pte. Ltd. (1)
6 Temasek Boulevar 37-01 Suntec Tower Four, Singapore, 038986, Singapore
Tel.: (65) 6 715 7800
Web Site: https://www.santen.com
Pharmaceuticals Product Mfr
N.A.I.C.S.: 325412
Shigeo Taniuchi *(Pres, CEO & Head-HR Div)*

Santen Pharmaceutical Co., Ltd. - Noto Plant (1)
2-14 Shikinami Hodatsushimizu-cho, Hakui, 929-1494, Ishikawa, Japan
Tel.: (81) 76 729 2666
Web Site: https://www.santen.co.jp
Pharmaceuticals Product Mfr
N.A.I.C.S.: 325412

Santen Pharmaceutical Co., Ltd. - Osaka Plant (1)
9-19 Shimoshinjo 3-chome, Higashiyodogawa-ku, Osaka, 533-8651, Japan
Tel.: (81) 663219976
Pharmaceuticals Product Mfr
N.A.I.C.S.: 325412

Santen Pharmaceutical Co., Ltd. - Shiga Plant (1)
348-3 Shide Taga-cho, Inukami-gun, Shiga, 522-0314, Japan
Tel.: (81) 74 948 2900
Web Site: https://www.santen.co.jp
Pharmaceuticals Product Mfr
N.A.I.C.S.: 325412

Santen Pharmaceutical Korea, Co., Ltd (1)
14F SI Tower 203 Teheran-ro Gangnam-gu, Seocho-gu, Seoul, 06141, Korea (South)
Tel.: (82) 27541434
Emp.: 31
Pharmaceuticals Product Mfr
N.A.I.C.S.: 325412
Takahashi Isao *(Pres)*

Santen Pharmaceutical Spain, S.L. (1)
Edificio Prisma Portal 2 3a Pta, 28230, Las Rozas, Madrid, Spain
Tel.: (34) 916407580
Ophthalmology Services
N.A.I.C.S.: 621320

Santen Philippines Inc. (1)
Units 2801 to 2802 28th Floor SM Aura Tower, 26th Street Corner McKinley Parkway The Fort, Taguig, 1630, Philippines
Tel.: (63) 288332570
Ophthalmology Services
N.A.I.C.S.: 621320

Santen S.A.S. (1)
1 Rue Pierre Fontaine Genavenir IV, 91058, Evry, Cedex, France (100%)
Tel.: (33) 1 69 87 40 20
Web Site: http://ww2.santen.eu
Optical Pharmaceutical Products Mfr
N.A.I.C.S.: 325412

Santen Uk Limited (1)
Salisbury Hall, Saint Albans, AL2 1BU, United Kingdom
Tel.: (44) 172 761 5110
Web Site: https://www.santen.uk
Ophthalmology Services
N.A.I.C.S.: 621320

SantenPharma AB (1)
Evenemangsgatan 31 A, 169 79, Solna, Sweden (100%)
Tel.: (46) 8 444 7560
Web Site: https://www.santen.se
Sales Range: $25-49.9 Million
Emp.: 3
Pharmaceutical Preparation Mfr
N.A.I.C.S.: 325412

Taiwan Santen Pharmaceutical Co. Ltd. (1)
9th Floor-1 No 126 Songjiang Road, Zhongshan District, Taipei, 10457, Taiwan (100%)
Tel.: (886) 22 567 8603
Web Site: https://www.santen.com.tw
Sales Range: $50-74.9 Million
Emp.: 3
Drugs & Druggists Sundries Whslr
N.A.I.C.S.: 424210

SANTEX S.P.A.
Via Massina 10 Sarego, 36040, Vicenza, Italy
Tel.: (39) 0444726311
Web Site: http://www.santex.it
Year Founded: 1961
Health Care Products Mfr
N.A.I.C.S.: 339113
Alessandra Castiglioni *(Pres)*

Subsidiaries:

Parentgiving, Inc. (1)
105 Grove St Ste 5, Montclair, NJ 07042
Tel.: (973) 746-2582
Web Site: http://www.parentgiving.com
Software Publisher
N.A.I.C.S.: 513210
David Spain *(CEO)*

SANTHER FABRICA DE PAPEL SANTA THEREZINHA S.A.
Rua Aracati 275, Pehha, Sao Paulo, 03630-900, Brazil
Tel.: (55) 1121427800
Web Site: http://www.santher.com.br
Emp.:100
Paper Products Mfr
N.A.I.C.S.: 322120
Jose Rubens De La Rosa *(CEO)*

SANTHERA PHARMACEUTICALS HOLDING AG
Hohenrainstrasse 24, 4133, Pratteln, Switzerland
Tel.: (41) 619068950
Web Site: https://www.santhera.com
SPHDF—(OTCIQ)
Rev.: $942,477
Assets: $203,046,114
Liabilities: $33,622,534
Net Worth: $169,423,580
Earnings: ($10,831,947)
Emp.: 56
Fiscal Year-end: 12/31/23
Pharmaceutical Development Services
N.A.I.C.S.: 541715
Elmar J. Schnee *(Chm)*

Subsidiaries:

Santhera Pharmaceuticals (Germany) GmbH (1)
Arnulfstrasse 199, 80634, Munich, Germany
Tel.: (49) 8918985100
Web Site: http://www.santhera.com
Pharmaceutical Products Mfr & Sales
N.A.I.C.S.: 424210

Santhera Pharmaceuticals (Switzerland) Ltd (1)
Hammerstrasse 49, 4410, Liestal, Switzerland
Tel.: (41) 619068950
Pharmaceutical Products Mfr & Sales
N.A.I.C.S.: 424210
Thomas Mayo *(CEO)*

Santhera Pharmaceuticals (USA), Inc. (1)
25 Corporate Dr Ste 250, Burlington, MA 01803
Tel.: (781) 365-0301
Web Site: http://www.santhera.com
Sales Range: $50-74.9 Million
Pharmaceutical Products Mfr & Sales
N.A.I.C.S.: 424210

SANTIERUL NAVAL 2 MAI S.A.
Tel.: (40) 241753347
Web Site: https://www.sn2mai.ro
Year Founded: 1974
STNM—(BUC)
Rev.: $944,729
Assets: $5,367,634
Liabilities: $27,486
Net Worth: $5,340,148
Earnings: $152
Emp.: 8
Fiscal Year-end: 12/31/23
Ship Mfr
N.A.I.C.S.: 336611
Ionut-Cosmin Constantinescu *(Pres)*

SANTIERUL NAVAL CONSTANTA S.A.
No 1 Incinta Port, 900 900, Constanta, Romania
Tel.: (40) 241505500
Web Site: https://www.snc.ro
Year Founded: 1892
SNC—(BUC)
Rev.: $56,487,329
Assets: $71,761,600
Liabilities: $42,573,887
Net Worth: $29,187,713
Earnings: $1,652,357
Emp.: 901
Fiscal Year-end: 12/31/23
Ship Repairing Services
N.A.I.C.S.: 336611
Radu Rusen *(Gen Mgr)*

Subsidiaries:

SNC Ship Design S.R.L. (1)
Incinta Port No 1 Santierul Naval Constanta SA 1st Floor, 900900, Constanta, Romania
Tel.: (40) 241505500
Web Site: http://www.shipdesign.snc.ro
Marine Engineering Services
N.A.I.C.S.: 541330

SANTO ANTONIO ENERGIA S.A.
Av Doutora Ruth Cardoso 4777 Andar 6 Sala 1, Sao Paulo, 05477-000, Brazil
Tel.: (55) 1137022270
Web Site: http://www.santoantonioenergia.com
Emp.: 100
Hydroelectric Power Generation Services
N.A.I.C.S.: 221111
Roberto Junqueira Filho *(CEO)*

SANTO CO., LTD.
480 Kami-Kag, Ritto, Shiga, Japan
Tel.: (81) 775531111

Web Site: https://www.santo.co.jp
Year Founded: 1954
1788—(TKS)
Sales Range: Less than $1 Million
Construction Engineering Services
N.A.I.C.S.: 541330
Katsumi Okuda *(Pres & CEO)*

SANTOS BRASIL PARTICIPACOES SA
Joaquim Floriano Joaquim Floriano Street 413 10th floor, Itaim Bibi, Sao Paulo, 04534-011, Brazil
Tel.: (55) 1132793279
Web Site: https://www.santosbrasil.com.br
STBP3—(BRAZ)
Rev.: $240,794,823
Assets: $791,295,885
Liabilities: $456,472,654
Net Worth: $334,823,231
Earnings: $3,806,543
Emp.: 3,026
Fiscal Year-end: 12/31/19
Holding Company & Logistic Services
N.A.I.C.S.: 488320
Maria Amalia Delfim de Melo Coutrim *(Vice Chm)*

Subsidiaries:

Santos Brasil Participacoes SA - Logistics - Distribution Center (1)
Estrada Sadae Takagi 2600 Sada 04 - Cooperativa, Sao Bernardo do Campo, 09852-070, Sao Paulo, Brazil
Tel.: (55) 1143934900
Sales Range: $25-49.9 Million
Emp.: 142
Logistics Distribution Services
N.A.I.C.S.: 541614

Santos Brasil Participacoes SA - Logistics - Foreign Trade - Clia Guaruja (1)
Via Conego Domenico Rangoni 3105, Vila Aurea - Vicente de Carvalho, Guaruja, 11454-630, Sao Paulo, Brazil
Tel.: (55) 1321271199
Web Site: http://www.santobrasil.com.br
Warehousing & Logistics Services
N.A.I.C.S.: 493110

Santos Brasil Participacoes SA - Logistics - Foreign Trade - Clia Santos (1)
Av Marginal Via Anchieta 820 - Alemoa, Santos, 11095-000, Sao Paulo, Brazil
Tel.: (55) 13 3209 6000
Warehousing & Logistics Services
N.A.I.C.S.: 493110

Santos Brasil Participacoes SA - Logistics - Foreign Trade - IPA XXXII (1)
Av Eng Ismael Coelho de Souza S N - Em frente ao Arm 32 - CODESP, Estuario, Santos, 11020-300, Sao Paulo, Brazil
Tel.: (55) 13 3236 2944
Warehousing & Logistics Services
N.A.I.C.S.: 493110

Santos Brasil Participacoes SA - Tecon Imbituba (1)
Av Getulio Vargas S/N - Area Portuaria, Centro, Imbituba, 88780-000, Santa Catarina, Brazil
Tel.: (55) 4832550644
Web Site: http://www.santosbrasil.com.br
Sales Range: $25-49.9 Million
Container Terminal Operation Services
N.A.I.C.S.: 488310
Bruno Sigurele *(Mgr)*

Santos Brasil Participacoes SA-Tecon Vila do Conde (1)
Port Complex of Vila Do Conde, Belem, 68445-000, Para, Brazil
Tel.: (55) 91 3322 7575
Web Site: http://www.santosbrasil.com.br
Sales Range: $50-74.9 Million
Container Terminal Operation & Logistics Services
N.A.I.C.S.: 488310

AND PRIVATE COMPANIES

Union Armazenagem e Operacoes Portuaria S.A. (1)
Nereu Ramos 592, Imbituba, 88780-000, Santa Catarina, Brazil
Tel.: (55) 48 3255 2038
Warehousing & Port Operation Services
N.A.I.C.S.: 493110

SANTOS LIMITED
Ground Floor Santos Centre, 60 Flinders Street, Adelaide, 5000, SA, Australia
Tel.: (61) 881165000 AU
Web Site: https://www.santos.com
Year Founded: 1954
STO—(ASX)
Rev.: $5,889,000,000
Assets: $29,756,000,000
Liabilities: $14,481,000,000
Net Worth: $15,275,000,000
Earnings: $1,416,000,000
Emp.: 3,864
Fiscal Year-end: 12/31/23
Holding Company; Oil & Gas Exploration & Production Services
N.A.I.C.S.: 551112
Bill Ovenden (Exec VP)

Subsidiaries:

Barracuda Limited (1)
Tel.: (675) 3212633
Web Site: http://www.santos.com
Sales Range: $50-74.9 Million
Provider of Oil & Gas Exploration & Production Services
N.A.I.C.S.: 211120

Bridgefield Pty. Ltd. (1)
Cnr Leakes Road and Meadowbank Grove, Rockbank, Melbourne, 3335, VIC, Australia
Tel.: (61) 39 684 8135
Web Site: https://www.bridgefieldliving.com.au
Real Estate Services
N.A.I.C.S.: 531390

Eastern Star Gas Limited (1)
Level 7 51 Pitt Street, Sydney, 2000, NSW, Australia
Tel.: (61) 292515599
Web Site: http://www.easternstar.com.au
Sales Range: $50-74.9 Million
Emp.: 79
Oil & Gas Exploration
N.A.I.C.S.: 213112

Subsidiary (Domestic):

Eastern Energy Australia Pty Limited (2)
Level 7 51 Pitt Street, Sydney, 2000, NSW, Australia
Tel.: (61) 292515599
Sales Range: $50-74.9 Million
Emp.: 15
Oil & Gas Exploration Services
N.A.I.C.S.: 211120

Oil Search Limited (1)
Ground Floor Harbourside East Building Stanley Esplanade, PO Box 842, Port Moresby, NCD 121, Papua New Guinea
Tel.: (675) 3225599
Rev.: $1,584,808,000
Assets: $11,572,853,000
Liabilities: $6,314,442,000
Net Worth: $5,258,411,000
Earnings: $312,420,000
Emp.: 1,607
Fiscal Year-end: 12/31/2019
Oil & Gas Exploration & Development Services
N.A.I.C.S.: 211120

Subsidiary (US):

Oil Search (Alaska) LLC (2)
900 E Benson Blvd, Anchorage, AK 99508
Tel.: (907) 375-4600
Oil & Gas Exploration Services
N.A.I.C.S.: 213112

Subsidiary (Non-US):

Oil Search (Eastern Desert) SAE (2)
2 El-Hegaz St, 6th Floor Roxy Heliopolis, 11341, Cairo, Egypt (100%)
Tel.: (20) 2 454 8310
Crude Petroleum & Natural Gas Extraction
N.A.I.C.S.: 211120

Oil Search (Middle Eastern) Limited (2)
Level 9 Office 904 Tower 3 Etihad Towers Corniche Road, Abu Dhabi, United Arab Emirates (100%)
Tel.: (971) 26736882
Web Site: http://www.oilsearch.com
Sales Range: $50-74.9 Million
Crude Petroleum & Natural Gas Extraction
N.A.I.C.S.: 211120

Subsidiary (Non-US):

Oil Search (Tunisia) Limited (3)
Bureau B1 Entree B bis Immeuble Kenzet Rue du lac Tchad, Les Berges du Lac, 1053, Tunis, Tunisia
Tel.: (216) 71860532
Web Site: http://www.oilsearch.com
Sales Range: $50-74.9 Million
Emp.: 3
Oil & Gas Exploration Services
N.A.I.C.S.: 211120

Subsidiary (Domestic):

Oil Search (PNG) Limited (2)
7th Fl Credit House Cuthbertson St, PO Box 842, Port Moresby, Papua New Guinea
Tel.: (675) 3225599
Web Site: http://www.oilsearch.com
Sales Range: $350-399.9 Million
Emp.: 700
Oil & Gas Exploration Services
N.A.I.C.S.: 213112

Subsidiary (Non-US):

Oil Search (ROY) Limited (2)
Haddah Street Haddah Residential Complex B6 Penthouse, PO Box 16380, Sana'a, Yemen
Tel.: (967) 1423440
Web Site: http://www.oilsearch.com
Oil & Gas Exploration Services
N.A.I.C.S.: 213112

Oil Search (Yemen) Limited (2)
PO Box 16380, Sana'a, Yemen
Tel.: (967) 1423440
Web Site: http://www.oilsearch.com
Crude Petroleum & Natural Gas Extraction
N.A.I.C.S.: 211120

Papuan Oil Search Limited (2)
1 Bligh Street, Sydney, 2000, NSW, Australia
Tel.: (61) 282078400
Sales Range: $25-49.9 Million
Emp.: 200
Management Consulting Services
N.A.I.C.S.: 541618
Peter R. Botten (Gen Mgr)

Santos Asia Pacific Pty Ltd. (1)
Level 4 Ratu Plaza Office Tower, Jalan Jendral Sudirman Kav 9, Jakarta, 10270, Indonesia
Tel.: (62) 2127502750
Web Site: http://www.santos.com.au
Oil & Gas Exploration & Production
N.A.I.C.S.: 211120

Santos International Operations Pty Ltd. (1)
1401 & 1402 Level 14 Narain Manzil 23 Barakhamba Rd, Connaught Pl, New Delhi, 110 001, India
Tel.: (91) 1143512000
Web Site: http://www.santos.com
Sales Range: $50-74.9 Million
Emp.: 3
Oil & Gas Exploration Services
N.A.I.C.S.: 211120

Santos Petroleum Pty. Ltd. (1)
Santos Building 60 Flinders St, Adelaide, 5000, SA, Australia
Tel.: (61) 881165000
Sales Range: $750-799.9 Million
Emp.: 1,500
Petroleum Extraction Services
N.A.I.C.S.: 211120

Santos Resources Pty. Ltd. (1)
Thallon Road, Saint George, QLD, Australia
Tel.: (61) 746253000
Oil & Gas Exploration Services
N.A.I.C.S.: 211120

Santos USA Corporation (1)
600 Las Colinas Blvd E Ste 800, Irving, TX 75039-5632 (100%)
Tel.: (713) 986-1700
Web Site: http://www.santos.com
Sales Range: $50-74.9 Million
Emp.: 55
Provider of Oil & Gas Exploration & Production Services
N.A.I.C.S.: 213112

Santos Vietnam Pty Ltd. (1)
Suite 701 Level 7 39 A Ngo Quyen, Hanoi, Vietnam
Tel.: (84) 422206000
Web Site: http://www.santos.com
Oil & Gas Exploration Services
N.A.I.C.S.: 213112

Santos WA Energy Holdings Pty. Ltd. (1)
Level 7 100 St Georges Terrace, Perth, 6000, WA, Australia
Tel.: (61) 8 6218 7100
Web Site: http://www.quadrantenergy.com.au
Holding Company; Oil & Gas Exploration & Production
N.A.I.C.S.: 551112
Brett Darley (CEO)

Subsidiary (Domestic):

Santos WA Energy Limited (2)
Level 9 100 St Georges Terrace, Perth, 6000, WA, Australia
Tel.: (61) 862187100
Web Site: http://www.quadrantenergy.com.au
Oil & Gas Exploration & Production
N.A.I.C.S.: 211120
Brett Darley (CEO)

Subsidiary (Domestic):

Santos WA Asset Holdings Pty. Ltd. (3)
Level 9 100 St Georges Terrace, Perth, 6000, WA, Australia
Tel.: (61) 862187100
Holding Company; Crude Petroleum & Natural Gas Extraction
N.A.I.C.S.: 551112

Santos WA Northwest Pty. Ltd. (3)
Level 3 256 St George's Terrace, Perth, 6000, WA, Australia
Tel.: (61) 86218 7100
Oil & Gas Exploration Services
N.A.I.C.S.: 213112

Santos WA PVG Holdings Pty. Ltd. (3)
Level 9 100 St Georges Terrace, Perth, 6000, WA, Australia
Tel.: (61) 862187100
Web Site: http://www.quadrantenergy.com.au
Holding Company; Offshore Crude Petroleum & Natural Gas Extraction
N.A.I.C.S.: 551112

SANTOSH FINE-FAB LIMITED
113 Sanjay Building No 6 Mittal Estate, Andheri East, Mumbai, 400059, Maharashtra, India
Tel.: (91) 2228504758
Web Site: https://www.santoshgroup.in
530035—(BOM)
Rev.: $1,015,088
Assets: $1,856,463
Liabilities: $933,836
Net Worth: $922,627
Earnings: $(153,349)
Fiscal Year-end: 03/31/21
Textile Products Mfr
N.A.I.C.S.: 314999
Santosh R. Tulsiyan (Chm & Mng Dir)

SANTOSH INDUSTRIES LIMITED
Suite No 3A 3rd Floor 3A Auckland Place, Kolkata, 700 017, India
Tel.: (91) 3322902277 In
Web Site: http://www.santoshindustrieslimited.in
Year Founded: 1960
Sales Range: $1-9.9 Million
Investment Banking Services
N.A.I.C.S.: 523150
Surendra Kumar Dugar (Mng Dir)

SANTOVA LTD.
Santova House 88 Mahatma Gandhi Road, Durban, 4000, South Africa
Tel.: (27) 313747000 ZA
Web Site: http://www.santova.com
SNV—(JSE)
Rev.: $34,733,717
Assets: $97,331,457
Liabilities: $34,080,523
Net Worth: $63,250,933
Earnings: $8,024,463
Emp.: 252
Fiscal Year-end: 02/29/24
Investment Management Service
N.A.I.C.S.: 523940
Glen H. Gerber (CEO)

Subsidiaries:

Asm Logistics (S) Pte Limited (1)
No 6 Changi South St 2 07-01 Xilin Districentre Building D, Singapore, 486349, Singapore
Tel.: (65) 6 542 6008
Web Site: https://www.asmlogistics.com.sg
Logistic Services
N.A.I.C.S.: 488510
Darem Lim (Mng Dir)

Santova Financial Services (Pty) Limited (1)
Santova House 88 Mahatma Gandhi Road, Durban, 4001, South Africa
Tel.: (27) 31 493 1200
Web Site: https://www.santovafinancialservices.co.za
Financial Services
N.A.I.C.S.: 523210

Santova International Trade Solutions (Pty) Limited (1)
Trading Services
N.A.I.C.S.: 488510

Santova Logistics (Pty) Limited (1)
B6 15-21 Doody Street, Alexandria, 2015, NSW, Australia
Tel.: (61) 286678777
Freight Forwarding Services
N.A.I.C.S.: 488510
Leon Notelovitz (Mng Dir)

Santova Logistics B.V. (1)
Nieuwland Parc 430, 2952 DE, Alblasserdam, Netherlands
Tel.: (31) 108200313
Trading Services
N.A.I.C.S.: 488510

Santova Logistics GmbH (1)
Werrastrasse 6, 65479, Raunheim, Germany
Tel.: (49) 61428738100
Trading Services
N.A.I.C.S.: 488510

Santova Logistics Limted (1)
Centurion House London Road, Staines-upon-Thames, TW18 4AX, United Kingdom
Tel.: (44) 2088970570
Trading Services
N.A.I.C.S.: 488510
Simon Shea (Ops Mgr)

Santova Logistics Limted (1)
Rm01 - 02 15/F Bonham Trade Centre 50 Bonham Strand East, Sheung Wan, China (Hong Kong)
Tel.: (852) 36222106
Trading Services
N.A.I.C.S.: 488510
Wesley Hannam (Reg Mgr)

Tradeway (Shipping) Limited (1)
146 Lowtown Pudsey, Leeds, LS28 9AY, West Yorkshire, United Kingdom

SANTOVA LTD.

Santova Ltd.—(Continued)
Tel.: (44) 113 236 3989
Web Site:
https://www.tradewayshipping.co.uk
Freight Forwarding Services
N.A.I.C.S.: 488510
John Heald *(Sls Dir)*

Subsidiary (Domestic):

Sai Logistics Limited (2)
Unit D Libra Maidstone Road, Kingston, Milton Keynes, MK10 0BD, United Kingdom
Tel.: (44) 190 822 8800
Web Site: https://www.sailogistics.com
Freight Forwarding Services
N.A.I.C.S.: 488510
Simon Phillips *(Mng Dir)*

W.M. Shipping Limited (1)
Ashbrook Office Park Longstone Road, Heald Green, Manchester, M22 5LB, United Kingdom
Tel.: (44) 1614990111
Trading Services
N.A.I.C.S.: 488510
Paul Slade *(Mng Dir)*

SANTUMAS SHAREHOLDINGS PLC
Flat 1 Britannia House 9 Old Bakery Street, Valletta, VLT 1450, Malta
Tel.: (356) 21250345   Mt
Web Site:
https://www.santumasmalta.com
Year Founded: 1963
STS—(MAL)
Rev.: $1,068,612
Assets: $13,430,301
Liabilities: $902,940
Net Worth: $12,527,361
Earnings: $794,175
Emp.: 2
Fiscal Year-end: 04/30/23
Financial Investment Services
N.A.I.C.S.: 523999
Michael Formosa Gauci *(Sec)*

SANU GOLD CORP.
918-1030 West Georgia Street, Vancouver, V6E 2Y3, BC, Canada
Tel.: (647) 473-7268   BC
Web Site:
https://www.sanugoldcorp.com
Year Founded: 2018
SNGCF—(OTCQB)
Assets: $6,508,350
Liabilities: $115,872
Net Worth: $6,392,478
Earnings: $668,031
Fiscal Year-end: 06/30/22
Gold Exploration Services
N.A.I.C.S.: 212220
Martin Pawlitschek *(CEO)*

SANWA COMPANY LTD.
19-19-21F Chayamachi, Kita-ku, Osaka, 530-0013, Yubinbango, Japan
Tel.: (81) 663596660
Web Site:
https://info.sanwacompany.co.jp
Year Founded: 1979
3187—(TKS)
Rev.: $109,859,550
Assets: $64,533,180
Liabilities: $42,887,410
Net Worth: $21,645,770
Earnings: $3,722,250
Emp.: 40
Fiscal Year-end: 09/30/23
Building Materials Online Retailer
N.A.I.C.S.: 444180
Taro Yamane *(Pres)*

Subsidiaries:

SANWA COMPANY RS TAIWAN LTD. (1)
No 127 Minshan St Neihu Dist, Taipei, 11494, Taiwan
Tel.: (886) 287924188

Web Site:
http://www.sanwacompany.com.tw
Housing Equipment Distr
N.A.I.C.S.: 423220

SANWA HOLDINGS CORPORATION
52nd floor Shinjuku Mitsui Building 2-1-1 Nishi-Shinjuku, Shinjuku-ku, Tokyo, 163-0478, Japan
Tel.: (81) 333463019
Web Site: https://www.sanwa-hldgs.co.jp
Year Founded: 1956
5929—(TKS)
Rev.: $4,039,417,270
Assets: $3,250,143,610
Liabilities: $1,362,982,000
Net Worth: $1,887,161,610
Earnings: $285,737,080
Emp.: 12,930
Fiscal Year-end: 03/31/24
Holding Company
N.A.I.C.S.: 551112
Toshitaka Takayama *(Chm)*

Subsidiaries:

Alpha Deuren International B.V. (1)
Pittelderstraat 10, 6942 GJ, Didam, Netherlands
Tel.: (31) 31 622 8066
Web Site: https://www.alpha-deuren.nl
Door Mfr
N.A.I.C.S.: 321911

An-Ho Metal Industrial Co., Ltd. (1)
7th Floor No 27 Section 1 Zhongshan North Road, Zhongshan District, Taipei, 10441, Taiwan
Tel.: (886) 225210013
Web Site: https://www.anho-metal.com
Door Mfr
N.A.I.C.S.: 331221

Bolton Gate Services Ltd. (1)
Units 5-9 Sedgewick Road, North Luton Industrial Estate, Luton, LU4 9DT, Beds, United Kingdom
Tel.: (44) 808 501 5480
Web Site: https://boltongateservices.com
Door Maintenance Services
N.A.I.C.S.: 811490

Docking Solution & Service GmbH (1)
Springrad 4, 30419, Hannover, Germany
Tel.: (49) 511 763 6790
Web Site: https://www.mydocking.com
Industrial Equipment Distr
N.A.I.C.S.: 423830
Michael Menzel *(Mng Dir)*

Dong Bang Novoferm Inc (1)
15 Seoulsiripdae-ro, Dongdaemun-gu, Seoul, 130-804, Korea (South)
Tel.: (82) 222126442
Web Site: https://www.steeldoor.com
Sales Range: $50-74.9 Million
Emp.: 140
Steel Fabricated Door Mfr
N.A.I.C.S.: 332321

Hayashi Kogyo Co., Ltd. (1)
Kitsukogyodanchi 1-20, Konan-ku, Niigata, 950-0213, Japan
Tel.: (81) 253852153
Steel Door Mfr
N.A.I.C.S.: 332321
Kei Saimei *(Pres)*

LIXIL Suzuki Shutter Corporation (1)
1-1-4 Minami-Otsuka, Toshima-ku, Tokyo, 170 0005, Japan
Tel.: (81) 3 3944 1111   (100%)
Web Site: http://www.lixil-suzuki.co.jp
Shutters & Related Parts Mfr & Distr
N.A.I.C.S.: 332321
Makoto Okamoto *(Pres)*

NF Tormatic GmbH (1)
Eisenhuttenweg 6, 44145, Dortmund, Germany
Tel.: (49) 231566020
Web Site: http://www.tormatic.de
Industrial Gate Mfr
N.A.I.C.S.: 332312

Norbert Dyx *(Mng Dir)*

Novoferm (Shanghai) Co., Ltd. (1)
No 118 Mingye Road, Sheshan Industrial Zone Songjiang District, Shanghai, China
Tel.: (86) 215 779 3335
Web Site: https://www.novoferm.com.cn
Door Mfr
N.A.I.C.S.: 321911

Novoferm Door Sp. z.o.o (1)
ul Obornicka Srt 338, 60-689, Poznan, Poland
Tel.: (48) 618279565
Fabricated Metal Door Mfr
N.A.I.C.S.: 332321

Novoferm GmbH (1)
Isselburger Strasse 31, 46459, Rees, Germany
Tel.: (49) 28509100
Web Site: https://www.novoferm.com
Emp.: 3,000
Doors, Garage Doors & Frames Mfr & Supplier
N.A.I.C.S.: 332321
Rainer Schackmann *(CEO)*

Holding (Non-US):

Novoferm Alsal S.A. (2)
Guarnizo Industrial Estate Plots 81 - 82, 39611, Guarnizo, Cantabria, Spain
Tel.: (34) 942544040
Web Site: https://www.novofermalsal.com
Sales Range: $25-49.9 Million
Steel Door Mfr
N.A.I.C.S.: 331513

Novoferm B.V. (2)
Industrieweg 8, 4181 CA, Waardenburg, Netherlands   (100%)
Tel.: (31) 888888400
Web Site: http://www.novoferm.nl
Sales Range: $25-49.9 Million
Steel Door Mfr
N.A.I.C.S.: 331513
Franz-Wilhelm Rieder *(Gen Mgr)*

Novoferm Europe Ltd., UK (2)
Unit 5-9 Luton North Industrial Estate Sedgwick Road, Luton, LU4 9DT, United Kingdom
Tel.: (44) 1582563777
Web Site: https://www.novoferm.co.uk
Sales Range: $25-49.9 Million
Emp.: 35
Steel Door Mfr
N.A.I.C.S.: 331513

Novoferm France S.A. (2)
ZI Les Redoux, 44270, Machecoul, France
Tel.: (33) 240786900
Web Site: https://www.novoferm.fr
Sales Range: $50-74.9 Million
Garage Doors, Doors & Frames Mfr
N.A.I.C.S.: 332321

Subsidiary (Domestic):

Novoferm GmbH (2)
Isselburger Strasse 31, 46459, Rees, Germany   (100%)
Tel.: (49) 28509100
Web Site: https://www.novoferm.com
Sales Range: $25-49.9 Million
Emp.: 20
Steel Mfrs
N.A.I.C.S.: 331513

Holding (Non-US):

Novoferm Hellas E.M.E. (2)
Asklipou 19, Kryoneri, 145 68, Athens, Greece
Tel.: (30) 2106047508
Web Site: https://www.novoferm.gr
Sales Range: $25-49.9 Million
Emp.: 5
Steel Door Mfr
N.A.I.C.S.: 331513

Novoferm Lutermax S.A. (2)
530 Avenue Georges Clemenceau, 77000, Vaux-le-Penil, France
Tel.: (33) 164143800
Web Site: http://www.lutermax.com
Sales Range: $25-49.9 Million
Emp.: 100
Steel Mfrs
N.A.I.C.S.: 331513

INTERNATIONAL PUBLIC

Novoferm Schievano S.r.l. (2)
Via A Volta 1, 35012, Camposampiero, Padova, Italy
Tel.: (39) 0499315111
Web Site: https://www.novoferm.it
Steel Mfrs
N.A.I.C.S.: 331513

Novoferm Schweiz AG (1)
Hochmatt 3, Kappel, 4616, Solothurn, Switzerland
Tel.: (41) 62 209 6677
Web Site: https://www.novoferm.ch
Door Mfr
N.A.I.C.S.: 321911

Novoferm Tormatic GmbH (1)
Eisenhuttenweg 6, 44145, Dortmund, Germany
Tel.: (49) 23 156 6020
Web Site: https://www.tormatic.de
Furniture Product Mfr
N.A.I.C.S.: 337127
Norbert Dyx *(Mng Dir)*

Novoferm UK Limited (1)
Unit 5-9 Luton North Industrial Estate Sedgwick Road, Luton, LU4 9DT, United Kingdom
Tel.: (44) 158 237 7067
Web Site: https://www.novoferm.co.uk
Door Mfr
N.A.I.C.S.: 321911

Okinawa Sanwa Shutter Corporation (1)
84-1 Hirara, Tomigusuku, 901-0212, Okinawa, Japan
Tel.: (81) 988405538
Web Site: https://www.okinawa-sanwa.co.jp
Emp.: 94
Steel Building Materials Mfr & Distr
N.A.I.C.S.: 331221
Hiroaki Onoue *(Pres)*

Overhead Door Corporation (1)
2501 S State Hwy 121 Business Ste 200, Lewisville, TX 75067
Tel.: (469) 549-7110
Web Site: http://www.overheaddoor.com
Sales Range: $50-74.9 Million
Emp.: 150
Sectional Doors for Residential, Commercial & Industrial Installation
N.A.I.C.S.: 332321
Kelly D. Terry *(Pres & CEO)*

Subsidiary (Non-US):

Creative Door Services Ltd. (2)
14904 135 Avenue NW, Edmonton, T5V 1R9, AB, Canada
Tel.: (780) 900-5331
Web Site: http://www.creativedoor.com
Sales Range: $75-99.9 Million
Metal Doors Supplies & Installation Services
N.A.I.C.S.: 332321

Subsidiary (Domestic):

Door Control, Inc. (2)
8 Delta Dr D, Londonderry, NH 03053
Tel.: (603) 216-9222
Web Site: http://www.doorcontrolne.com
Lumber, Plywood, Millwork & Wood Panel Merchant Whslr
N.A.I.C.S.: 423310
Scott Morin *(Mgr-Project)*

Unit (Domestic):

Horton Automatics (2)
4242 Baldwin Blvd, Corpus Christi, TX 78405-3325
Tel.: (361) 888-5591
Web Site: https://www.hortondoors.com
Sales Range: $100-124.9 Million
Emp.: 100
Auto. Doors
N.A.I.C.S.: 332321

Subsidiary (Non-US):

Horton Automatics, Ltd. (3)
Unit A Hortonwood 31, Telford, TF1-7YZ, Shropshire, United Kingdom   (100%)
Tel.: (44) 1952670169
Web Site: https://www.hortondoors.com
Sales Range: $25-49.9 Million
Emp.: 59

AND PRIVATE COMPANIES — SANXIANG IMPRESSION CO., LTD.

Mfr of Automatic Sliding, Swinging & Revolving Doors
N.A.I.C.S.: 332321
Tony O'Keeffe *(Mng Dir)*

Unit (Domestic):

Overhead Door Co of Southwest Louisiana Inc (2)
2707 E Napoleon, Sulphur, LA 70663
Tel.: (337) 625-4117
Web Site: http://www.overheaddoor.com
Lumber, Plywood, Millwork & Wood Panel Merchant Whslr
N.A.I.C.S.: 423310

Overhead Door Corp. - Thermacore Products (2)
3200 Reach Rd, Williamsport, PA 17701-4154
Tel.: (570) 326-7325
Web Site: http://www.overheaddoor.com
Sales Range: $50-74.9 Million
Emp.: 130
Mfr of Insulated Garage Doors
N.A.I.C.S.: 332321

Overhead Door of Casper, Inc. (2)
2760 Fleetwood Pl, Casper, WY 82601
Tel.: (307) 266-1440
Web Site: http://www.overheaddoor.com
Other Building Material Dealers
N.A.I.C.S.: 444180

Division (Domestic):

TODCO, Inc. (2)
1332 Fairground Rd E, Marion, OH 43302
Tel.: (740) 383-6376
Web Site: http://www.todco.com
Sales Range: $25-49.9 Million
Emp.: 100
Truck Doors Mfr
N.A.I.C.S.: 441330
James Dimmick *(Dir-Engrg & OEM Sls)*

Wayne-Dalton Corp. (2)
2501 S State Hwy 121 Business Ste 200, Lewisville, TX 75067
Tel.: (330) 674-7015
Web Site: http://www.wayne-dalton.com
Mfr of Wood, Aluminum, Fiberglass & Steel Overhead Garage Doors & Garage Door Openers
N.A.I.C.S.: 332321
Emmanuel Mullet *(Founder)*

PT. Sanwamas Metal Industry (1)
Jl Raya Bekasi KM 27, Harapan Jaya, Bekasi, Indonesia
Tel.: (62) 218880338
Web Site: http://sanwamas.com
Sales Range: $25-49.9 Million
Emp.: 100
Shutter & Door Mfr & Sales
N.A.I.C.S.: 331221

Robust AB (1)
Kungsvagen 60, Nykroppa, 682 90, Filipstad, Sweden
Tel.: (46) 5 901 8700
Web Site: https://robust.se
Building Door Mfr
N.A.I.C.S.: 332321

Robust UK Limited (1)
Sutherland Road, Longton, Stoke-on-Trent, ST3 1HZ, Staffordshire, United Kingdom
Tel.: (44) 178 259 2900
Web Site: https://www.robust-uk.com
Door Mfr
N.A.I.C.S.: 321911

Sanwa Electronics Engineering Co., Ltd. (1)
Takakuracho 3-10-27, Miyakojimaku, Osaka, 534-0011, Japan
Tel.: (81) 66 922 3816
Door Mfr
N.A.I.C.S.: 321911
Wataru Nakatsuka *(Pres)*

Sanwa Exterior Niigata Plant Co., Ltd. (1)
Oigashima 1397-1, Tsubameshi, Niigata, 959-0113, Tsubame, Japan
Tel.: (81) 256985551
Sales Range: $25-49.9 Million
Emp.: 40
Exterior Building Product Mfr

N.A.I.C.S.: 331221
Yoshinobu Iijima *(Pres)*

Sanwa Mitaka K.K. (1)
Kitakashiwagi-cho 3-48, Eniwa, 061-1496, Hokkaido, Japan
Furniture Product Mfr
N.A.I.C.S.: 337127
Koji Motegi *(Pres)*

Sanwa Shutter Corporation (1)
2-3-5 Shinkawa, Itabashi-ku, Tokyo, 175-0081, Japan
Tel.: (81) 359989111
Web Site: https://www.sanwa-ss.co.jp
Emp.: 3,057
Rolling Steel Shutter, Overhead Doors, Steel Hinge Doors Mfr
N.A.I.C.S.: 331221
Toshifumi Nagano *(Chm)*

Subsidiary (Non-US):

Sanwa Shutter (H.K.) Ltd. (2)
Rm 1211-1213A 12/F Trade Square No 681 Cheung Sha Wan Road, Hennessy Road, Cheung Sha Wan, Kowloon, China (Hong Kong)
Tel.: (852) 28336619
Emp.: 24
Shutter & Door Mfr
N.A.I.C.S.: 331221

Sanwa System Wall Co., Ltd. (1)
6-10-1 Tano, Amagasaki, 661-0951, Hyogo, Japan
Tel.: (81) 66 499 1751
Web Site: https://www.sanwa-s-wall.co.jp
Wooden Partition Mfr
N.A.I.C.S.: 337215

Sanwa Tajima Corporation (1)
Forum Building Ikebukuro 2-77-5, Toshima-ku, Tokyo, 171-0014, Japan
Tel.: (81) 359545880
Web Site: http://www.tajima-st.co.jp
Sales Range: $100-124.9 Million
Emp.: 300
Stainless Steel Building Product Mfr
N.A.I.C.S.: 331221

Shanghai Baosteel-Sanwa Door Co., Ltd. (1)
988 Yueluo Road, Shanghai, 200941, Baoshan, China
Tel.: (86) 2156925550
Web Site: http://www.baosteel-sanwa.com
Sales Range: $50-74.9 Million
Emp.: 150
Shutters & Overhead Doors Mfr & Sales
N.A.I.C.S.: 331221

Showa Front Co., Ltd. (1)
1-13-7 Uchikanda Shikoku Building 3F / 4F TEL, Chiyoda-ku, Tokyo, 101-0047, Japan
Tel.: (81) 332936737
Web Site: https://www.sfn.co.jp
Emp.: 214
Facade & Other Building Materials Mfr
N.A.I.C.S.: 327390
Hideo Sasazawa *(Pres)*

Showa Kensan Co., Ltd. (1)
1453 Nakano Oura-cho, Oura-gun, Gunma, 370-0603, Japan
Tel.: (81) 276882121
Web Site: https://www.s-kensan.co.jp
Sales Range: $25-49.9 Million
Emp.: 60
Automatic Doors for Store Fronts Mfr & Sales
N.A.I.C.S.: 331221

Sun Metal Co., Ltd. (1)
180-184 Sri Krung Wattana Building 4th Floor Ratchawong Road, Samphanthawong, Bangkok, 10100, Thailand
Tel.: (66) 22225190
Web Site: http://www.sun-metal.com
Shutter & Door Mfr & Sales
N.A.I.C.S.: 331221

Suzuka Engineering Co., Ltd. (1)
1-65 Ogoso Higashi 2 chome, Yokkaichi, 510-0951, Mie, Japan
Tel.: (81) 593 46 4774
Web Site: http://www.suzuka.co.jp
Rubber Processing Equipment Mfr
N.A.I.C.S.: 333248
Tatsuo Yada *(Pres)*

Suzuki Shutter Corporation (1)
1-1-4 Minami Otsuka, Toshima-ku, Tokyo, 170-0005, Japan
Tel.: (81) 33 944 1111
Building Material Product Mfr
N.A.I.C.S.: 327120
Keiichi Yamamoto *(Pres)*

Tajima Metalwork Co., Ltd. (1)
Web Site: http://www.metalwork.co.jp
Post Box Designer & Marketer
N.A.I.C.S.: 331221

Tajima Metalwork Kansai Co., Ltd. (1)
Fukanoshiro 221-2 Nosaka Sannan-cho, Hyogo, Tambashi, Japan
Tel.: (81) 795 77 2870
Web Site: http://www.sanwa-hldgs.co.jp
Stainless Steel Doors Mfr
N.A.I.C.S.: 332321
Takayuki Kojima *(Pres)*

Tor System Technik GmbH (1)
Willi-Bleicher-Strasse 7 Gewerbegebiet - Im Grossen Tal, 52353, Duren, Germany
Tel.: (49) 24 219 1580
Web Site: https://www.tst-deutschland.de
Door Mfr
N.A.I.C.S.: 321911

Venix Co., Ltd. (1)
Kamagata 3128 Ranzan-machi, Hiki-gun, Saitama, 355-0225, Japan
Tel.: (81) 493626671
Sales Range: $25-49.9 Million
Emp.: 35
Building Partition Mfr
N.A.I.C.S.: 337215
Koji Kitamura *(Pres)*

Vina-Sanwa Company Liability Ltd. (1)
Hi-Tech Industrial Zone II Hoa Lac Hi-Tech Park, Thach That, Hanoi, Vietnam
Tel.: (84) 2433947922
Web Site: https://www.vina-sanwa.com.vn
Sales Range: $25-49.9 Million
Emp.: 80
Shutter & Door Mfr
N.A.I.C.S.: 331221

Yoshida Seisakusho Co., Ltd. (1)
Nagatoro 168-1, Saku, 385-0021, Nagano, Japan
Tel.: (81) 267684860
Web Site: http://www.sanwa-hldgs.co.jp
Stainless Steel Mfr
N.A.I.C.S.: 331513

SANWARIA CONSUMER LIMITED

E-1/1 Arera Colony, Bhopal, 462016, Madhya Pradesh, India
Tel.: (91) 7554294878
Web Site: https://www.sanwariaconsumer.com
Year Founded: 1991
SANWARIA—(NSE)
Rev.: $417,254,194
Assets: $52,079,538
Liabilities: $131,351,668
Net Worth: ($79,272,130)
Earnings: ($170,747,360)
Fiscal Year-end: 03/31/20
Soya Oil Mfr
N.A.I.C.S.: 311224

SANWEI HOLDING GROUP CO., LTD.

Xiakeng Haiyou Sanmen County, Taizhou, 317100, Zhejiang, China
Tel.: (86) 57683518366
Web Site: https://www.three-v.com
Year Founded: 1990
603033—(SHG)
Rev.: $543,759,077
Assets: $1,049,139,997
Liabilities: $573,962,459
Net Worth: $475,177,538
Earnings: $32,625,562
Fiscal Year-end: 12/31/22
Conveyor Belt Mfr & Distr
N.A.I.C.S.: 326220

Ji Yue Ye *(Chm)*

SANWIL HOLDING S.A.

Ul Cisowa 11, 20-703, Lublin, Poland
Tel.: (48) 814446480
Web Site: http://www.sanwil.com
Year Founded: 1998
SNW—(WAR)
Rev.: $7,981,453
Assets: $18,980,691
Liabilities: $3,877,287
Net Worth: $15,103,404
Earnings: $1,447,917
Fiscal Year-end: 12/31/23
Textile & Leather Product Mfr
N.A.I.C.S.: 314999
Adam Buchajski *(Chm-Mgmt Bd & CEO)*

SANXIANG ADVANCED MATERIALS CO., LTD.

No 292 Jiefang Street Shouning County, Shouning County, Ningde, 355500, Fujian, China
Tel.: (86) 5935518572
Web Site: http://www.fjsx.com
Year Founded: 1991
603663—(SHG)
Rev.: $136,511,664
Assets: $253,617,858
Liabilities: $71,275,197
Net Worth: $182,342,661
Earnings: $21,182,359
Fiscal Year-end: 12/31/22
Fused Zirconia Mfr & Distr
N.A.I.C.S.: 331410
Peng Xia *(Chm & Pres)*

Subsidiaries:

Fujian Sanxiang Advanced Materials Institute Co., Ltd. (1)
2nd Floor Building 14 No 470 Guiping Road Xuhui District, Shanghai, 201101, China
Tel.: (86) 2134663002
Fused Zirconia Mfr & Distr
N.A.I.C.S.: 331410

SANXIANG IMPRESSION CO., LTD.

333 Yixian Road, Shanghai, China
Tel.: (86) 2165361223
Web Site: https://www.sxgf.com
Year Founded: 1996
000863—(SSE)
Rev.: $189,332,994
Assets: $971,481,893
Liabilities: $393,198,933
Net Worth: $578,282,960
Earnings: $4,205,485
Fiscal Year-end: 12/31/22
Real Estate Development Services
N.A.I.C.S.: 531110
Wenzhi Xu *(Chm)*

Subsidiaries:

Hangzhou Sanxiang Impression Real Estate Co., Ltd. (1)
Room 2201 Block A Xizi International Center, Jianggan District, Hangzhou, China
Tel.: (86) 88899265
Real Estate Agency Services
N.A.I.C.S.: 531210

Sanhe Xiangde Real Estate Development Co., Ltd. (1)
7th Floor Dingsheng Real Estate Building No 83 Yifeng Street, Yanjiao Development Zone, Sanhe, Hebei, China
Tel.: (86) 1058412555
Real Estate Agency Services
N.A.I.C.S.: 531210

Shanghai Chengguang Real Estate Co., Ltd. (1)
7th Floor No 333 Yixian Road, Yangpu District, Shanghai, China
Tel.: (86) 2165361223
Real Estate Agency Services
N.A.I.C.S.: 531210

SANXIANG IMPRESSION CO., LTD.

Sanxiang Impression Co., Ltd.—(Continued)

Shanghai Sanxiang Decoration & Design Co., Ltd. (1)
3F No 333 Yixian Road, Yangpu District, Shanghai, China
Tel.: (86) 2165361223
Construction Services
N.A.I.C.S.: 236220

Shanghai Sanxiang Property Service Co., Ltd. (1)
3F No 59 Yujiangxiang Road, Baoshan District, Shanghai, China
Tel.: (86) 2136501278
Construction Services
N.A.I.C.S.: 236220

Shanghai Xiangding Real Estate Co., Ltd. (1)
No 2500 Lanhai Road, Chenjia Town Chongming District, Shanghai, China
Tel.: (86) 2131030880
Real Estate Agency Services
N.A.I.C.S.: 531210

Shanghai Xiangjun Property Development Co., Ltd. (1)
Room 302 No 2 Building Lane 666 Zhangheng Road, Pudong New Area, Shanghai, China
Tel.: (86) 2150939185
Real Estate Agency Services
N.A.I.C.S.: 531210

Shanghai Xiangsheng Property Development Co., Ltd. (1)
Room 302 No 2 Building Lane 666 Zhangheng Road, Pudong New Area, Shanghai, China
Tel.: (86) 2150939200
Real Estate Agency Services
N.A.I.C.S.: 531210

SANXUN HOLDINGS GROUP LIMITED

Room 1702 Bldg A NE of the intersection of Yanzihe Rd & Innovation Ave, High tech Zone, Hefei, Anhui, China
Web Site: https://www.sanxungroup.com
Year Founded: 2004
6611—(HKG)
Rev.: $363,235,767
Assets: $1,544,965,801
Liabilities: $1,255,817,734
Net Worth: $289,148,067
Earnings: ($53,281,319)
Emp.: 223
Fiscal Year-end: 12/31/23
Holding Company
N.A.I.C.S.: 551112
Juan An (Pres)

SANY GROUP CO., LTD.

SANY Industrial Park Economic & Technological Development Zone, Changsha, Hunan, China
Tel.: (86) 73184031888
Web Site: http://www.sanygroup.com
Year Founded: 1989
Sales Range: $5-14.9 Billion
Emp.: 70,000
Holding Company; Industrial & Construction Machinery Mfr
N.A.I.C.S.: 551112
Wengen Liang (Founder & Chm)

Subsidiaries:

PT. SANY Indonesia Machinery (1)
UOB Plaza Unit 1 42th Floor Jl M H Thamrin Kav 8-9, Jakarta, 10230, Indonesia
Tel.: (62) 2129290878
Construction & Mining Machinery Distr
N.A.I.C.S.: 423810

SANY (Nig.) LTD (1)
No 10 Gimbiya Street Area 11, Garki, Abuja, Nigeria
Tel.: (234) 8135037617
Construction & Mining Machinery Distr
N.A.I.C.S.: 423810

SANY (Vietnam) Machinery Co., Ltd (1)
9th floor Viglacera Building, Me Tri Nam Tu Liem, Hanoi, Vietnam
Tel.: (84) 435539631
Construction & Mining Machinery Distr
N.A.I.C.S.: 423810

SANY Algeria Co, Ltd (1)
3eme etage centre d'affaire d'Alger, EL-Mohammadia, Algiers, Algeria
Tel.: (213) 560053188
Construction & Mining Machinery Distr
N.A.I.C.S.: 423810

SANY Angola (1)
Projecto nova vida rua 41 casa 394, Luanda, Angola
Tel.: (244) 922351633
Construction & Mining Machinery Distr
N.A.I.C.S.: 423810

SANY Argentina (1)
Ecuador 1460 P 5 E, Buenos Aires, Argentina
Tel.: (54) 11 6902 2976
Construction & Mining Machinery Distr
N.A.I.C.S.: 423810

SANY Asia Pacific (Philippines) Co. ltd (1)
Jose Abad santos st, Bay view village tambo, Paranaque, Philippines
Tel.: (63) 9272782626
Construction & Mining Machinery Distr
N.A.I.C.S.: 423810

SANY Asia-Pacific Hong Kong Co. Ltd. (1)
Room 1001 Landmark North No 39 Of Lung Sum AV, Sheung Shui, Hong Kong, New Territories, China (Hong Kong)
Tel.: (852) 6038 8785
Construction & Mining Machinery Distr
N.A.I.C.S.: 423810

SANY Cambodia (1)
No 52B National Road No 4, Sangkat Chom Chao Khan Po Senchey, Phnom Penh, Cambodia
Tel.: (855) 97 3383 278
Construction & Mining Machinery Distr
N.A.I.C.S.: 423810

SANY Chile (1)
Flor de azucenas 135 depto 1402 las condes, Santiago, Chile
Tel.: (56) 2 9858753
Construction & Mining Machinery Distr
N.A.I.C.S.: 423810

SANY Costa Rica (1)
Avalon Country Club LA1-102, Rio Oro de Santa Ana, San Jose, Costa Rica
Tel.: (506) 83683865
Construction & Mining Machinery Distr
N.A.I.C.S.: 423810

SANY Ecuador (1)
Decima Etapa MZ 302 Villa 02 y 03, Alborada, Guayaquil, Ecuador
Tel.: (593) 969762752
Construction & Mining Machinery Distr
N.A.I.C.S.: 423810

SANY Ethiopia (1)
Churchill Road, PO Box 702, Addis Ababa, Ethiopia
Tel.: (251) 912649956
Construction & Mining Machinery Distr
N.A.I.C.S.: 423810

SANY Ghana Co., Ltd (1)
Caitec Tower Opp Mallam Junction Kaneshie-Winneba Road, Accra, Ghana
Tel.: (233) 268133331
Construction & Mining Machinery Distr
N.A.I.C.S.: 423810

SANY Guinea (1)
BP 3320, Conakry, Guinea
Tel.: (224) 0067146622
Construction & Mining Machinery Distr
N.A.I.C.S.: 423810

SANY Heavy Industry (Kenya) Co., Ltd (1)
Plot B5 Next to Steel Makers Mombasa Road, PO 39746-00623, Nairobi, Kenya
Tel.: (254) 714212199
Construction & Mining Machinery Distr

N.A.I.C.S.: 423810

SANY Heavy Industry (Thailand) Co., Ltd (1)
252/21 A 17th Floor Muang Thai-Phatra Office Building Ratchadaphisek, Huaykwang, Bangkok, 10310, Thailand
Tel.: (66) 2 693 3108
Web Site: http://www.sanyhi.com
Emp.: 50
Construction & Mining Machinery Distr
N.A.I.C.S.: 423810
Paul Da (Gen Mgr)

SANY Heavy Industry Saudi Arabia Co., Ltd (1)
8 floor Adex Tower, Jeddah, Saudi Arabia
Tel.: (966) 502176891
Construction & Mining Machinery Distr
N.A.I.C.S.: 423810

SANY Japan Co., Ltd (1)
3-2-5-2620B Kasumigaseki, Chiyoda-ku, Tokyo, 100-6026, Japan
Tel.: (81) 3 3503 5318
Construction & Mining Machinery Distr
N.A.I.C.S.: 423810

SANY Kuwait (1)
PO Box 24081, Safat, Kuwait, 13101, Kuwait
Tel.: (965) 90978108
Construction & Mining Machinery Distr
N.A.I.C.S.: 423810

SANY LLP (1)
Taylesyzdyk Street 12/1, Office 220, Nur-Sultan, 010000, Kazakhstan
Tel.: (7) 717 250 0631
Industrial Machinery Mfr
N.A.I.C.S.: 333248

SANY Malaysia (1)
No 33-7 Level 33 UOA II Jalan Pinang, 50450, Kuala Lumpur, Malaysia
Tel.: (60) 142356386
Construction & Mining Machinery Distr
N.A.I.C.S.: 423810

SANY Pakistan (1)
House No 6 Safari villas 2, Bahria Town, Islamabad, Pakistan
Tel.: (92) 3115145389
Construction & Mining Machinery Distr
N.A.I.C.S.: 423810

SANY Panama (1)
Oficina 3005 Edificio BICSA Financial Center, Av Balboa, Panama, Panama
Tel.: (507) 6085 2311
Construction & Mining Machinery Distr
N.A.I.C.S.: 423810

SANY Peru S.A.C (1)
Las Garzas 316, San Isidro, Lima, Peru
Tel.: (51) 1 4403208
Construction & Mining Machinery Distr
N.A.I.C.S.: 423810

SANY Qatar (1)
PO Box 24593, Doha, Qatar
Tel.: (974) 55156782
Construction & Mining Machinery Distr
N.A.I.C.S.: 423810

SANY Russia (1)
Office 12 17-1 Ramenki Street, Moscow, Russia
Tel.: (7) 495 7806213
Web Site: http://www.sany-russia.ru
Construction & Mining Machinery Distr
N.A.I.C.S.: 423810

SANY South Korea (1)
465-97 Dapsimni-dong, Dongdaemun-gu, Seoul, Korea (South)
Tel.: (82) 10 5596 3188
Construction & Mining Machinery Distr
N.A.I.C.S.: 423810

SANY Taiwan (1)
No 1 No 11 building 316 Xinsheng Road, Zhongli, Taoyuan, Taiwan
Tel.: (886) 976611131
Construction & Mining Machinery Distr
N.A.I.C.S.: 423810

SANY Turkey (1)
Barbaros Mah Halk Cad Palladium Residence No 8/A 34746, Atasehir, Istanbul, Turkiye

INTERNATIONAL PUBLIC

Tel.: (90) 5333219948
Construction & Mining Machinery Distr
N.A.I.C.S.: 423810

SANY U.A.E (1)
FZS1AE05 Jebel Ali Free Zone, Dubai, United Arab Emirates
Tel.: (971) 509036040
Construction & Mining Machinery Distr
N.A.I.C.S.: 423810

SANY Venezuel (1)
Piso 9-A Edif Don Manuel Transversal Dos Entre Av Andres Bello y 2, Av Los Palos Grandes, Caracas, Venezuela
Tel.: (58) 212 285 29 48
Construction & Mining Machinery Distr
N.A.I.C.S.: 423810

SANY Zambia (1)
Plot 11721 Thabo Mbeki Road, Lusaka, Zambia
Tel.: (260) 950333111
Construction & Mining Machinery Distr
N.A.I.C.S.: 423810

Sany Australia Pty. Ltd. (1)
C4/15 Forrester Street, Kingsgrove, 2208, NSW, Australia
Tel.: (61) 295 545 318
Web Site: http://www.sanygroup.com
Emp.: 10
Industrial Machinery Mfr
N.A.I.C.S.: 333248
Daisy Peng (Mgr-HR)

Sany Colombia SAS (1)
CRA 7 NO 91-86, Bogota, Colombia
Tel.: (57) 318 3055 113
Construction & Mining Machinery Distr
N.A.I.C.S.: 423810

Sany East Asia Co., Ltd. (1)
1403 Seoul Center Building 14 Floor, 911 Sogong-dong, Seoul, Korea (South)
Tel.: (82) 2 778 3188
Industrial Machinery Mfr
N.A.I.C.S.: 333248

Sany Heavy Equipment International Holdings Co., Ltd. (1)
No 25 16 Kaifa Road Shenyang Economic and Technological Development, Shenyang, 110008, Liaoning, China
Tel.: (86) 2489318111
Web Site: http://www.sanyhe.com
Rev.: $2,181,354,926
Assets: $3,503,438,968
Liabilities: $2,084,869,098
Net Worth: $1,418,569,870
Earnings: $234,337,990
Emp.: 6,441
Fiscal Year-end: 12/31/2022
Coal Machinery Mfr
N.A.I.C.S.: 333132
Jian Qi (Vice Chm & CEO)

Sany Heavy Industry Co., Ltd. (1)
Sany Industrial Park Economic and Technological Development Zone, Changsha Hunan, Beijing, 410100, China (50.3%)
Tel.: (86) 73185835199
Web Site: https://www.sanyglobal.com
Rev.: $11,190,481,419
Assets: $21,980,865,225
Liabilities: $12,841,422,796
Net Worth: $9,139,442,429
Earnings: $591,604,176
Fiscal Year-end: 12/31/2022
Industrial Machinery Mfr
N.A.I.C.S.: 551112
Wengen Liang (Chm)

Subsidiary (Domestic):

Beijing Sany Heavy Machinery Co., Ltd. (2)
Sany Industrial Park Beiqing Road, HuiLongGuan Changping District, Beijing, 102206, China
Tel.: (86) 10 8893 1888
Foundation Construction Machinery Designer, Mfr & Distr
N.A.I.C.S.: 333120

Subsidiary (Non-US):

Putzmeister Holding GmbH (2)
Max Eyth Str 10, 72631, Aichtal, Germany
Tel.: (49) 7127 599 0
Web Site: http://www.putzmeister.de

AND PRIVATE COMPANIES

Sales Range: $750-799.9 Million
Emp.: 3,000
Holding Company; Concrete Pumps, Industrial Pumps & Other Construction Machinery Mfr & Distr
N.A.I.C.S.: 551112
Christian Danninger *(CFO)*

Subsidiary (US):

Putzmeister America, Inc. (3)
1733 90th St, Sturtevant, WI 53177-1805
Tel.: (262) 886-3200
Web Site: http://www.putzmeisteramerica.com
Sales Range: $125-149.9 Million
Emp.: 200
Concrete Pumps, Industrial Pumps & Other Construction Machinery Mfr & Distr
N.A.I.C.S.: 333120
Bill Dwyer *(VP-Sls & Mktg)*

Subsidiary (Domestic):

Putzmeister Shotcrete Technology, Inc. (4)
1733 90th St, Sturtevant, WI 53177
Tel.: (262) 886-3200
Web Site: http://www.putzmeistershotcrete.com
Sales Range: $10-24.9 Million
Shotcrete Equipment Designer, Mfr & Distr
N.A.I.C.S.: 333131
Dave Adam *(Pres)*

Subsidiary (Domestic):

Putzmeister Concrete Pumps GmbH (3)
Max-Eyth-Strasse 10, Aichtal, 72631, Germany
Tel.: (49) 7127 599 0
Web Site: http://www.pmw.de
Concrete Pumps Mfr
N.A.I.C.S.: 333120
Robert Abel *(Member-Exec Bd)*

Subsidiary (Non-US):

Putzmeister France Sarl (3)
3 rue Paul Henri Spaak, ZAE Jean Monnet, Vert-Saint-Denis, 77240, France
Tel.: (33) 1 6464 3939
Web Site: http://www.putzmeister.fr
Concrete Pumps, Industrial Pumps & Other Construction & Mining Machinery Mfr & Distr
N.A.I.C.S.: 333120

Subsidiary (Domestic):

Lancy Mixjet (4)
Parc d"Activites 26 avenue des Mondaults, 33270, Floirac, France
Tel.: (33) 5 5754 2727
Web Site: http://www.lancy.com
Sales Range: $10-24.9 Million
Emp.: 50
Mortar & Other Construction Equipment Mfr
N.A.I.C.S.: 333120
Olivier Saint Paul *(CEO)*

Subsidiary (Non-US):

Putzmeister Iberica S.A. (3)
Camino de Hormigueras 173, 28031, Madrid, Spain
Tel.: (34) 91 428 8100
Web Site: http://www.putzmeister.es
Emp.: 120
Concrete Pumps, Industrial Pumps & Other Construction & Mining Machinery Mfr & Distr
N.A.I.C.S.: 333120
Jose Antonio Nieto *(Dir Gen)*

Putzmeister Italia S.r.l. (3)
Via Marconi 2, 47832, San Clemente, Italy
Tel.: (39) 0541 851511
Web Site: http://www.putzmeister.it
Concrete Pumps, Industrial Pumps & Other Construction & Mining Machinery Mfr & Distr
N.A.I.C.S.: 333120

Putzmeister Japan Ltd. (3)
Chiba East Techno Green Park (CETEC) 1-3 Okayamadai, Togane, 283 2826, Chiba, Japan
Tel.: (81) 47 553 4140
Web Site: http://www.pm-j.co.jp

Construction & Industrial Machinery Distr

Putzmeister Korea Co., Ltd. (3)
1287-1 Chungwang-Dong, Shihwa Ind 3da-502ho, Siheung, 429850, Kyunggi-do, Korea (South)
Tel.: (82) 31 433 4541
Web Site: http://www.putzmeister.co.kr
Emp.: 11
Construction & Industrial Machinery Distr
N.A.I.C.S.: 423810
K. S. Uhm *(CEO)*

Putzmeister Ltd. (3)
Carrwood Road, Chesterfield Trading Estate, Chesterfield, S41 9QB, Derbyshire, United Kingdom
Tel.: (44) 1246 264 200
Web Site: http://www.putzmeister.co.uk
Emp.: 25
Concrete Pumps, Industrial Pumps & Other Construction Machinery Mfr & Distr
N.A.I.C.S.: 333120
Paul Kimberlin *(Mng Dir)*

Putzmeister Machinery (Shanghai) Co., Ltd. (3)
39 Dongjing Road, Songjiang Industrial Zone, Shanghai, 201613, China
Tel.: (86) 21 5774 1000
Web Site: http://www.putzmeister.com.cn
Concrete Pumps, Industrial Pumps & Other Construction Machinery Mfr & Distr
N.A.I.C.S.: 333120

Subsidiary (Domestic):

Putzmeister Mortelmaschinen GmbH (3)
Max-Eyth-Strasse 10, 72631, Aichtal, Germany
Tel.: (49) 7127 599 0
Web Site: http://www.moertelmaschinen.de
Emp.: 1,500
Mortar Machinery Mfr & Distr
N.A.I.C.S.: 333120
Matthias Ruppel *(Mng Dir & Member-Exec Bd)*

Putzmeister Solid Pumps GmbH (3)
Max-Eyth-Strasse 10, Aichtal, 72631, Germany
Tel.: (49) 7127 599 500
Web Site: http://www.pmsolid.com
Industrial Pumps & Augers Mfr
N.A.I.C.S.: 333914
Axel Schulz *(CEO)*

Subsidiary (Non-US):

Putzmeister South Africa (Pty) Ltd. (3)
Corner Braam & Citrus Street Honeydew Ext 21, PO Box 5146, Cresta, Johannesburg, 2118, South Africa
Tel.: (27) 11 794 3790
Web Site: http://www.putzmeister.co.za
Emp.: 25
Construction & Mining Machinery Distr
N.A.I.C.S.: 423810
Ludwig Geyser *(CEO)*

Subsidiary (US):

Sany America, Inc. (2)
100 World Dr Ste 218, Peachtree City, GA 30269
Tel.: (770) 631-8131
Web Site: http://www.sanyamerica.com
Sales Range: $25-49.9 Million
Emp.: 100
Construction Machinery Mfr
N.A.I.C.S.: 333120

Subsidiary (Non-US):

Sany Germany GmbH (2)
Im Mediapark 8, 50670, Cologne, Germany
Tel.: (49) 221 5005 1300
Industrial Machinery Mfr
N.A.I.C.S.: 333248

Sany Heavy Industry India Pvt. Ltd. (2)
Plot No 31 Bhawkar Bhavan 1st FL, Shivaji Nagar, 411005, Mumbai, Maharashtra, India
Tel.: (91) 206 643 4888
Industrial Machinery Mfr
N.A.I.C.S.: 333248

Sany Importacao e Exportacao da America do Sul Ltda. (2)
Av Eng Luiz Carlos Berrini, 1511-12 Andar, Sao Paulo, Brazil
Tel.: (55) 115 103 0631
Industrial Machinery Mfr
N.A.I.C.S.: 333248

Sany Middle & West Africa Company Ltd. (1)
No 759 Central Business District, Abuja FCT, Abuja, Nigeria
Tel.: (234) 803 208 1818
Industrial Machinery Mfr
N.A.I.C.S.: 333248

Sany Southeast Asia Pte. Ltd. (1)
80 Raffles Pl UOB Plz 1 37-02, UIC Building, Singapore, 48624, Singapore
Tel.: (65) 6227 6416
Emp.: 10
Industrial Machinery Mfr
N.A.I.C.S.: 333248
Shally Qian *(Gen Mgr)*

Sany do Brasil Ltda. (1)
Estrada Velha Rio Sao Paulo No 5000 - KM 125 5, Eugenio de Melo, Sao Jose dos Campos, 12247-001, Brazil
Tel.: (55) 12 3908 6150
Construction & Mining Machinery Distr
N.A.I.C.S.: 423810

SANYEI CORPORATION

1-2 Kotobuki 4-chome, Taito-Ku, Tokyo, 111-8682, Japan
Tel.: (81) 338473500
Web Site: https://www.sanyeicorp.com
Year Founded: 1950
8119—(TKS)
Rev.: $242,507,680
Assets: $140,310,470
Liabilities: $64,328,520
Net Worth: $75,981,950
Earnings: $3,556,180
Emp.: 883
Fiscal Year-end: 03/31/24
Furniture Distr
N.A.I.C.S.: 449110
Noriyuki Kobayashi *(Pres & CEO)*

Subsidiaries:

BENEXY CORPORATION (1)
4/F Tokyo Tatemono Aoyama Building 3-Chome-3-5 Kitaaoyama Minato-Ku, Tokyo, Japan
Tel.: (81) 357855680
Web Site: http://www.birkenstockjpn.co.jp
Footwear Mfr
N.A.I.C.S.: 424340
Wataru Shibata *(Pres & CEO)*

Pepica Inc. (1)
3 Chome-1-6 Higashisugano, Ichikawa, 272-0823, Chiba, Japan
Tel.: (81) 473126111
Web Site: https://www.pepica.co.jp
Pet Care Services
N.A.I.C.S.: 812910

S.C. Techno Co., Ltd. (1)
4 1-2 Kotobuki, Taito-ku, Tokyo, 111-8682, Japan
Tel.: (81) 338448181
Web Site: http://www.multichef.co.jp
Professional Equipment Distr
N.A.I.C.S.: 423490

SANFAT ELECTRIC MANUFACTURING (DONGGUAN) CO., LTD. (1)
38 Shapu Ind Zone, Qiaolong Village Tangxia, Dongguan, 523710, China
Tel.: (86) 76986252838
Home Appliance Mfr & Distr
N.A.I.C.S.: 335210

Sanfat Electric Manufacturing Co., Ltd. (1)
Suite 1109 11/F/ Tower 1 China Hong Kong City 33 Canton Road, Tsim Sha Tsui, Kowloon, 999077, China (Hong Kong)
Tel.: (852) 26902976
Web Site: https://www.sanfat.com
Home Appliance Distr
N.A.I.C.S.: 423620

WMF Japan Consumer Goods Co., Ltd. (1)
5/F Sanyei Kotobuki Building 4 Chome-1-2 Kotobuki Taito-Ku, Tokyo, Japan
Tel.: (81) 338476860
Web Site: http://www.wmf.co.jp
Household Utensil Distr
N.A.I.C.S.: 423220

SANYO CHEMICAL INDUSTRIES, LTD.

11-1 Ikkyo Nomoto-cho, Higashiyama-ku, Kyoto, 605-0995, Japan
Tel.: (81) 755414311   JP
Web Site: https://www.sanyo-chemical.co.jp
Year Founded: 1949
4471—(TKS)
Rev.: $1,054,361,100
Assets: $1,360,456,980
Liabilities: $424,633,010
Net Worth: $935,823,970
Earnings: ($56,191,610)
Emp.: 2,042
Fiscal Year-end: 03/31/24
Chemical Products Mfr
N.A.I.C.S.: 325998
Kohei Maeda *(Exec VP)*

Subsidiaries:

DaXiang International Trading (Shanghai) Co., Ltd. (1)
Room 505 No 680 Zhao Jia Bang Rd, Shanghai, 200031, China
Tel.: (86) 2164456920
Chemical Products Distr
N.A.I.C.S.: 424690

Dah Shyang Chemical Co., Ltd. (1)
No 33-6 Sec 2 Jianguo N Rd, Zhongshan Dist, Taipei, 104, Taiwan
Tel.: (886) 22501277
Web Site: https://www.coreunion.com.tw
Water Soluble Polymers Mfr & Distr
N.A.I.C.S.: 325998

SAN NOPCO LIMITED (1)
Web Site: http://www.sannopco.co.jp
Sales Range: $50-74.9 Million
Emp.: 20
Defoaming Agents Mfr
N.A.I.C.S.: 325998

SDP Global (Malaysia) Sdn. Bhd. (1)
PLO 179 Jalan Rumbia 1, Tanjung Langsat Industrial Complex, 81700, Pasir Gudang, Johor, Malaysia
Tel.: (60) 72536200
Superabsorbent Polymer Mfr & Distr
N.A.I.C.S.: 325211

SDP Global Co., Ltd. (1)
4th Fl Hibiya Fort Tower 1-1-1, Minato-ku, Tokyo, 103-0003, Japan
Tel.: (81) 335003495
Superabsorbent Polymer Mfr & Distr
N.A.I.C.S.: 325211

San Chemical Co., Ltd. (1)
13-2 Chidori-cho, Kawasaki, 210-0865, Kanagawa, Japan (50%)
Tel.: (81) 442761811
Chemicals Mfr
N.A.I.C.S.: 325199

San Nopco (Shanghai) Trading Co., Ltd (1)
Web Site: http://www.sannopco-sh.com
Technical Consulting Services
N.A.I.C.S.: 541690

San Nopco Korea Ltd. (1)
(50%)
Tel.: (82) 25713691
Web Site: http://www.sannopco.co.jp
Emp.: 100
Production of Specialty Chemicals
N.A.I.C.S.: 325998

San-Dia Polymers (Nantong) Co., Ltd. (1)
5 Xinkai South Road Nantong Economic Technological Development Area, Nantong Jingji Jishu Kaifaqu, Nantong, 226009, Ji-

SANYO CHEMICAL INDUSTRIES, LTD.

Sanyo Chemical Industries, Ltd.—(Continued)
angsu, China **(60%)**
Tel.: (86) 51385981251
Sales Range: $25-49.9 Million
Emp.: 80
Plastics Material & Resin Mfr
N.A.I.C.S.: 325211

San-Dia Polymers, Ltd. (1)
24th Fl Hibiya Fort Tower 1-1-1 Nishi-shimbashi, Minato-ku, Tokyo, 103-0023, Japan **(60%)**
Tel.: (81) 352001212
Web Site: https://www.sanyo-chemical.co.jp
Sales Range: $25-49.9 Million
Emp.: 65
Plastics Material & Resin Mfr
N.A.I.C.S.: 325211
Kota Kawaguchi *(Mgr-Sls)*

Sanam Corporation (1)
17 Arentzen Blvd Ste 206, Charleroi, PA 15022 **(100%)**
Tel.: (412) 384-5700
Web Site: https://sanyochemicalamerica.com
Sales Range: $25-49.9 Million
Emp.: 11
Chemical & Products Whslr
N.A.I.C.S.: 424690

Sanyo Chemical (Shanghai) Trading Co., Ltd. (1)
Room 1611 Ruijin Building No 205 Maoming South Road, Shanghai, 200020, China
Tel.: (86) 2154667676
Web Site: http://www.sanyo-chemical.co.jp
Chemical Products Distr
N.A.I.C.S.: 424690

Sanyo Chemical (Shanghail) Trading Co., Ltd. (1)
Rm 1611 Ruijin Bldg 205 Maoming Road S, Shanghai, 200020, China
Tel.: (86) 2154667676
Chemical Products Distr
N.A.I.C.S.: 424690

Sanyo Chemical America Incorporated (1)
17 Arentzen Blvd Ste 206, Charleroi, PA 15022
Tel.: (412) 384-5700
Web Site: https://sanyochemicalamerica.com
Agriculture Chemical Mfr & Distr
N.A.I.C.S.: 325320

Sanyo Chemical Texas Industries, LLC (1)
10536 Bay Area Blvd, Pasadena, TX 77507-1722 **(100%)**
Tel.: (281) 474-2617
Sales Range: $25-49.9 Million
Emp.: 12
Manufacture of Thermoplastic Polyurethane Beads for Slush Molding
N.A.I.C.S.: 325998

Sanyo Kasei (Nantong) Co., Ltd. (1)
No 7 Xinkai Road South, Nantong Economic and Technological Development Area, Jiangsu, 226009, China **(100%)**
Tel.: (86) 51385960205
Web Site: http://www.sanyo-chemical.co.jp
Chemicals Mfr
N.A.I.C.S.: 325199

Sanyo Kasei (Taiwan) Ltd. (1)
8FL -2 NO 129 SEC 2 Chung Shan N Road, Taipei, 104, Taiwan
Tel.: (886) 225631620
Web Site: http://www.sanyo-chemical.co.jp
Emp.: 5
Import & Export of Chemicals, Market Surveys & Sales Related Activities
N.A.I.C.S.: 424690

Sanyo Kasei (Thailand) Ltd. (1)
Rojana Industrial Park-Rayong 5/5 Moo 11, Tambol Nongbua, Aumphur Bankhai, Rayong, 21120, Thailand **(89%)**
Tel.: (66) 3862705059
Sales Range: $25-49.9 Million
Emp.: 56
Chemicals Mfr
N.A.I.C.S.: 325199

Sanyo Kasei Korea, Ltd (1)
8th Fl Dong Kyung Bldg 116 Teheran-ro Yeoksam-dong, Gangnam-gu, Seoul, 06233, Korea (South) **(100%)**
Tel.: (82) 25610904
Web Site: http://www.sanyo-chemical.co.jp
Chemical Products Distr
N.A.I.C.S.: 424690

SANYO DENKI CO., LTD.
3-33-1 MinamiOtsuka, Toshima-ku, Tokyo, 170-8451, Japan
Tel.: (81) 359271020
Web Site: https://www.sanyodenki.co.jp
6516—(TKS)
Rev.: $746,295,440
Assets: $996,047,680
Liabilities: $266,482,150
Net Worth: $729,565,530
Earnings: $69,252,970
Emp.: 3,705
Fiscal Year-end: 03/31/24
Electrical Equipments Mfr & Sales
N.A.I.C.S.: 335312
Shigeo Yamamoto *(Chm, CEO & Exec Officer)*

Subsidiaries:

SANYO DENKI (H.K.) CO., LIMITED (1)
Room 1603 16/F South Tower Concordia Plaza 1 Science Museum Road, TST East, Kowloon, China (Hong Kong)
Tel.: (852) 23126250
Web Site: https://www.sanyodenki.com
Emp.: 8
Blowers & Computer Cooling Fans Mfr
N.A.I.C.S.: 334118

SANYO DENKI (Shenzhen) CO., LTD. (1)
Unit 04B-07 11th Floor AVIC Center Office Building No 1018 Huafu Road, Futian District, Shenzhen, 518031, Guangdong, China
Tel.: (86) 75533373868
Web Site: https://www.sanyodenki.com
Emp.: 50
Blowers & Computer Cooling Fans Mfr
N.A.I.C.S.: 333413

SANYO DENKI EUROPE S.A. (1)
11 rue Ferdinand de Lesseps, BP 57286, Roissy CDG, 95190, Goussainville, Cedex, France
Tel.: (33) 148632661
Web Site: https://www.sanyodenki.com
Sales Range: $25-49.9 Million
Emp.: 26
Computer Cooling Fan Mfr
N.A.I.C.S.: 423430

SANYO DENKI GERMANY GmbH (1)
Frankfurter Strasse 80-82, 65760, Eschborn, Germany
Tel.: (49) 6196761130
Web Site: https://www.sanyodenki.com
Sales Range: $50-74.9 Million
Emp.: 19
Computer Cooling Fan Mfr
N.A.I.C.S.: 423430

SANYO DENKI KOREA CO., LTD. (1)
Tel.: (82) 27735623
Web Site: http://www.sanyodenki.com
Sales Range: $25-49.9 Million
Emp.: 9
Computer Cooling Fans Mfr
N.A.I.C.S.: 334118

SANYO DENKI SINGAPORE PTE. LTD. (1)
988 Toa Payoh North 04-08, Singapore, 319002, Singapore
Tel.: (65) 62231071
Web Site: https://www.sanyodenki.com
Sales Range: $25-49.9 Million
Emp.: 20
Blowers & Computer Cooling Fans Mfr
N.A.I.C.S.: 333413
Makoto Hoshi *(Mng Dir)*

SANYO DENKI TAIWAN CO., LTD. (1)
Room N-711 7th Floor Jiaxin Building 2 No 96 Section 2, Zhongshan North Road, Taipei, 10449, Taiwan
Tel.: (886) 225113938
Web Site: https://www.sanyodenki.com
Sales Range: $25-49.9 Million
Emp.: 22
Blowers & Computer Cooling Fans Mfr
N.A.I.C.S.: 333413

SANYO DENKI Techno Service CO., LTD. (1)
5-4 Tonojo, Ueda, 386-8634, Nagano, Japan
Tel.: (81) 268718577
Web Site: https://www.sanyodenki-technoservice.co.jp
Sales Range: $50-74.9 Million
Emp.: 625
Electrical Component Mfr & Sales
N.A.I.C.S.: 335999

SANYODENKI Co. Ltd. - Fujiyama Unit (1)
4016 Fujiyama, Ueda, 386-1212, Nagano, Japan
Tel.: (81) 268388111
Web Site: http://www.sanyodenki.co.jp
Emp.: 527
Power Supplies & Components Mfr
N.A.I.C.S.: 335999

SANYODENKI Co. Ltd. - Kangawa Works (1)
5-4 Tonoshiro, Ueda, 386-8634, Nagano, Japan
Tel.: (81) 268228585
Web Site: http://www.sanyodenki.com
Emp.: 656
Servo, Stepping & Linear Motor Mfr
N.A.I.C.S.: 335312
Shigeo Yamamoto *(Pres, CEO & COO)*

SANYODENKI Co. Ltd. - Shioda Unit (1)
517 Goka, Ueda, 386-1324, Nagano, Japan
Tel.: (81) 268386611
Web Site: http://www.sanyodenki.co.jp
Sales Range: $50-74.9 Million
Emp.: 125
System Controllers Mfr
N.A.I.C.S.: 334513
Shigeru Yamamoto *(Pres)*

Sanyo Denki (Thailand) Co., Ltd. (1)
388 Exchange Tower 25th Floor Unit 2501-1 Sukhumvit Road, Klongtoey, Bangkok, 10110, Thailand
Tel.: (66) 2 261 8670
Web Site: https://www.sanyodenki.com
Electronic Device Mfr & Distr
N.A.I.C.S.: 334111

Sanyo Denki (Tianjin) Co., Ltd. (1)
Block AB 16th Floor TEDA Building No 256 Jiefang South Road, Hexi District, Tianjin, 300042, China
Tel.: (86) 222 320 1186
Web Site: https://www.sanyodenki.com
Electric Equipment Mfr
N.A.I.C.S.: 335999

Sanyo Denki Engineering (Shanghai) Co., Ltd. (1)
Area B 1F Building 8 No 1199 Ji Di Road, Minhang District, Shanghai, China
Tel.: (86) 216 221 7069
Electronic Device Mfr & Distr
N.A.I.C.S.: 334111

Sanyo Denki Engineering (Shenzhen) Co., Ltd. (1)
3rd Floor 11th Building Niucheng 2nd Industrial Area, Niucheng Village Nanshan, Shanghai, 518055, China
Tel.: (86) 7558 342 5095
Electronic Device Mfr & Distr
N.A.I.C.S.: 334111

Sanyo Denki IT Solution Co., Ltd. (1)
5-4 Tonoshiro, Ueda, 386-8634, Nagano, Japan
Tel.: (81) 26 871 8521
Web Site: https://www.sanyodenki.com
Information Technology Consulting Services
N.A.I.C.S.: 541511

Sanyo Denki India Private Limited (1)
14 Old No 6/3 Avenue Road, Nungambakkam, Chennai, 600034, Tamil Nadu, India
Tel.: (91) 444 203 8472
Electronic Device Mfr & Distr
N.A.I.C.S.: 334111

Sanyo Denki Shanghai Co., Ltd. (1)
Room 2106-2110 Building A Far East International Plaza No 319, Xianxia Road, Shanghai, 200051, China
Tel.: (86) 216 235 1107
Web Site: https://www.sanyodenki.com
Electric Equipment Mfr
N.A.I.C.S.: 335999

SANYO ELECTRIC (TAIWAN) CO., LTD.
266 Sung Chiang Road, Taipei, 104, Taiwan
Tel.: (886) 225234476 **TW**
Web Site: http://www.sanyo.com.tw
Home Appliances Production
N.A.I.C.S.: 334310
Wenlin Lee *(Gen Mgr)*

SANYO ELECTRIC RAILWAY CO., LTD.
3-1-1 Miyashiki-dori, Nagata-ku, Kobe, 653-0843, Hyogo, Japan
Tel.: (81) 786122032
Web Site: https://www.sanyo-railway.co.jp
Year Founded: 1933
9052—(TKS)
Rev.: $259,244,200
Assets: $757,063,130
Liabilities: $397,631,160
Net Worth: $359,431,970
Earnings: $20,557,100
Emp.: 763
Fiscal Year-end: 03/31/24
Railway Transportation Services
N.A.I.C.S.: 488210
Kazuhiro Kamikado *(Pres)*

Subsidiaries:

Sanyo Department Store Co., Ltd. (1)
1 Minami-machi, Himeji, 670-0912, Hyogo, Japan **(100%)**
Tel.: (81) 792231231
Web Site: http://www.sanyo-dp.co.jp
Rev.: $186,361,910
Assets: $117,972,050
Liabilities: $96,285,000
Net Worth: $21,687,050
Earnings: $2,402,540
Emp.: 436
Fiscal Year-end: 02/29/2020
Supermarket Operating Services
N.A.I.C.S.: 445110
Masaru Takano *(Pres)*

SANYO ENGINEERING & CONSTRUCTION INC.
3-13 Nibancho, Chiyoda-ku, Tokyo, 102-8440, Japan
Tel.: (81) 332656181
Web Site: http://www.suntec-sec.jp
Year Founded: 1937
1960—(TKS)
Rev.: $336,686,960
Assets: $323,678,480
Liabilities: $131,340,700
Net Worth: $192,337,780
Earnings: ($4,679,880)
Emp.: 1,442
Fiscal Year-end: 03/31/24
Electric Facility Construction Services
N.A.I.C.S.: 237130
Nobutaka Yahata *(Pres & CEO)*

Subsidiaries:

SEC Mashibah Sdn. Bhd. (1)
Lot P66 Salambigar Industrial Park Jalan Utama, Tanah Jambu, BC1515, Bandar Seri Begawan, Brunei Darussalam
Tel.: (673) 2231654
Emp.: 200
Electric Facility Construction Services

N.A.I.C.S.: 237130
Tantau Minn *(Gen Mgr)*

SECM Sdn. Bhd. (1)
Setia Business Park 2 16 Jalan Perniagaan Setia 6, Taman Perniagaan Setia, 81100, Johor Bahru, Johor, Malaysia
Tel.: (60) 75952649
Web Site: https://secm.com.my
Construction Engineering Services
N.A.I.C.S.: 541330

SANYO HOMES CORPORATION
8F Orix Hommachi Bldg 4-1 Nishi-Hommachi 1-Chome, Nishi-ku, Osaka, 550-0005, Japan
Tel.: (81) 665783403
Web Site: https://www.sanyohomes.co.jp
Year Founded: 1969
1420—(TKS)
Rev.: $303,134,600
Assets: $306,743,660
Liabilities: $208,221,610
Net Worth: $98,522,050
Earnings: $4,283,280
Emp.: 884
Fiscal Year-end: 03/31/24
Residential Construction
N.A.I.C.S.: 236117
Fumio Matsumoto *(Pres)*

Subsidiaries:

Sanyo Reform Corporation (1)
Orix Honmachi Building 1-4-1 Nishihommachi, Nishi-ku, Osaka, 550-0005, Japan
Tel.: (81) 120702621
Web Site: https://www.sanyoreform.co.jp
Rental Housing Welfare & Housing Reform Services
N.A.I.C.S.: 624229

SANYO INDUSTRIES, LTD.
2-9-4 Taihei, Sumida-ku, Tokyo, Japan
Tel.: (81) 336853451
Web Site: https://www.sanyo-industries.co.jp
Year Founded: 1948
5958—(TKS)
Rev.: $201,499,240
Assets: $204,394,420
Liabilities: $70,951,740
Net Worth: $133,442,680
Earnings: $12,268,160
Emp.: 390
Fiscal Year-end: 03/31/24
Construction Materials Mfr
N.A.I.C.S.: 332999
Shigeru Yamagishi *(Pres)*

SANYO SHOKAI LTD.
614 Yotsuya Honshiocho, Shinjuku-ku, Tokyo, 160-0003, Japan
Tel.: (81) 333574111
Web Site: https://www.sanyo-shokai.co.jp
Year Founded: 1943
8011—(TKS)
Rev.: $434,992,770
Assets: $416,594,220
Liabilities: $124,075,000
Net Worth: $292,519,220
Earnings: $19,759,830
Emp.: 1,150
Fiscal Year-end: 02/29/24
Textile Product Mfr & Distr
N.A.I.C.S.: 315990
Ikuro Kato *(Mng Officer & Gen Mgr-Bus Headquarters)*

Subsidiaries:

Sanyo Shokai New York, Inc. (1)
434 Greenwich St, New York, NY 10013
Web Site: http://www.sanyonewyork.com
Sales Range: $1-9.9 Million
Apparel Mfr & Distr
N.A.I.C.S.: 315250

Yasutomo Yamane *(Chm)*

SANYO TRADING CO., LTD.
2-11 Kanda Nishiki-cho, Chiyoda-ku, Tokyo, 101-0054, Japan
Tel.: (81) 335181111
Web Site: https://www.sanyo-trading.co.jp
Year Founded: 1947
3176—(TKS)
Rev.: $869,205,640
Assets: $485,927,330
Liabilities: $174,747,230
Net Worth: $311,180,100
Earnings: $34,244,700
Emp.: 687
Fiscal Year-end: 09/30/23
General Trading
N.A.I.C.S.: 425120
Masaaki Masumoto *(Chm)*

Subsidiaries:

Chem-Inter Corporation (1)
Sanyo-Yasuda Bldg 7F 2-11 Kanda Nishiki-Cho, Chiyoda-Ku, Tokyo, 101-0054, Japan (76.85%)
Tel.: (81) 335181051
Chemical Products Distr
N.A.I.C.S.: 424690
Y. Iwata *(Pres)*

Cosmos Shoji Co., Ltd. (1)
2-11 Kanda Nishikicho, Chiyoda-Ku, Tokyo, 101-0054, Japan
Tel.: (81) 335186911
Emp.: 9
Oil & Gas Field Equipment Distr
N.A.I.C.S.: 423830

PT. Sanyo Trading Indonesia (1)
Midplaza 2 16th Floor Jalan Jend Sudirman Kav10-11, Jakarta, 10220, Indonesia
Tel.: (62) 215707560
Chemical Products Distr
N.A.I.C.S.: 424690

San-Thap International Co., Ltd. (1)
11th Floor Ramaland Building 952 Rama 4 Road Suriyawongse, Bangrak, Bangkok, 10500, Thailand
Tel.: (66) 26525100
Web Site: https://www.sanyo-trading.co.th
Emp.: 38
Synthetic Rubber & Chemical Product Distr
N.A.I.C.S.: 424690
Tomoyuki Shiraishi *(Mng Dir)*

Sanyo Corporation (1)
500 5th Ave Ste 3620, New York, NY 10110
Tel.: (212) 221-7890
Web Site: https://www.sanyocorp.com
Emp.: 18
Chemical & Allied Products Merchant Whslr
N.A.I.C.S.: 424690

Sanyo Machinery Co., Ltd. (1)
58-2 Suzukawa, Isehara, 259-1146, Kanagawa, Japan
Tel.: (81) 463759800
Industrial Machinery Mfr
N.A.I.C.S.: 333248

Sanyo Technos Co., Ltd. (1)
Web Site: http://www.sanyo-technos.com
Scientific Equipment Repair & Maintenance Services
N.A.I.C.S.: 811210

Sanyo Trading (Shanghai) Co., Ltd. (1)
Unit 3001 30th Floor Jiahua Center No 1010 Huaihai Middle Road, Xuhui District, Shanghai, 200031, China
Tel.: (86) 2164721620
Web Site: https://www.sanyo-trading-china.com
Emp.: 20
Chemical Products Distr
N.A.I.C.S.: 424690
Masanobu Shintani *(Chm)*

Sanyo Trading (Vietnam) Co., Ltd. (1)
Saigon Riverside Office Center Room 405-406 2A-4A Ton Duc Thang Street, Ben Nghe Ward District 1, Ho Chi Minh City, Vietnam

Tel.: (84) 838244285
Rubber Product Distr
N.A.I.C.S.: 424690

Sanyo Trading India Private Ltd. (1)
Office No 514 5th Floor Golf Course Road Sector 54 Suncity, Business Tower, Gurgaon, 122 002, Haryana, India
Tel.: (91) 1244071950
Rubber Product Distr
N.A.I.C.S.: 424690

Sanyo Trading International (Hong Kong) Co., Ltd. (1)
Units 01-02 8F Ever Gain Plaza Tower 188 Container Port Road, Kwai Chung, New Territories, China (Hong Kong)
Tel.: (852) 29434460
Chemical Products Distr
N.A.I.C.S.: 424690

Sanyo-Touchi (Shanghai) Rubber Co., Ltd. (1)
No 6858 Daye Road, Jinhui Town Fengxian District, Shanghai, 201405, China
Tel.: (86) 2157581127
Rubber Product Distr
N.A.I.C.S.: 424690

Singapore Sanyo Trading Pte. Ltd. (1)
10 Ubi Crescent 06-45 Ubi Techpark, Singapore, 408564, Singapore
Tel.: (65) 67422647
Web Site: http://www.sanyo-trading.co.jp
Emp.: 7
Chemical Products Distr
N.A.I.C.S.: 424690
Yew Sandy *(Dir-Sls)*

Sort Co., Ltd. (1)
1-31-42 Tsukushino, Machida, 194-0001, Tokyo, Japan
Tel.: (81) 428505751
Web Site: http://www.kksort.sakura.ne.jp
Chemical Products Distr
N.A.I.C.S.: 424690

Sun Phoenix Mexico S.A. De C.V. (1)
Paseo De La Altiplanicie No 11 Torre Wolken Int, Ph Col Villas de Irapuato, 36670, Irapuato, Guanajuato, Mexico
Tel.: (52) 4621049193
Web Site: http://www.sunphoenix.mx
Emp.: 9
Chemical Products Distr
N.A.I.C.S.: 424690
Kashiki Uyu *(Pres)*

SANYODO HOLDINGS INC.
18-22 Shinkaicho, Mizuho-ku, Nagoya, 467-0856, Aichi, Japan
Tel.: (81) 528713434
Web Site: https://ir.sanyodo.co.jp
Year Founded: 1978
3058—(TKS)
Rev.: $114,333,170
Assets: $82,525,850
Liabilities: $65,214,260
Net Worth: $17,311,590
Earnings: ($304,060)
Emp.: 178
Fiscal Year-end: 03/31/24
Book Stores
N.A.I.C.S.: 459210
Taku Kamewari *(Sr Exec Officer & VP)*

SANYOU CORPORATION LIMITED
No 27 Center 2nd Road, Putin Lake Tangxia Town, Dongguan, 523719, Guangdong, China
Tel.: (86) 76982618888
Web Site: https://www.sanyourelay.com
Year Founded: 2008
300932—(SSE)
Rev.: $260,065,939
Assets: $388,096,067
Liabilities: $144,839,574
Net Worth: $243,256,492
Earnings: $10,650,576

Emp.: 3,000
Fiscal Year-end: 12/31/22
Electrical Equipment Mfr & Distr
N.A.I.C.S.: 335999
Chaoyang Song *(Chm & Gen Mgr)*

Subsidiaries:

Europe Sanyou Electric Appliance Co., Ltd. (1)
No 5 Gutenberg Street, 65830, Kriftel, Germany
Tel.: (49) 17623510831
Web Site: http://www.sanyourelay.eu
Relay Product Distr
N.A.I.C.S.: 423610

Korea Sanyou Co., Ltd. (1)
1110 STX W-Tower 615-3 Guro-dong, Gurogu, Seoul, Korea (South)
Tel.: (82) 261243939
Web Site: https://www.sanyoukorea.co.kr
Electrical Component Mfr & Distr
N.A.I.C.S.: 335999

Sanyou Electrical Appliances GmbH (1)
Gutenbergstrasse 5, 65830, Kriftel, Germany
Tel.: (49) 61923076025
Electrical Component Mfr & Distr
N.A.I.C.S.: 335999

SANYU CO., LTD.
457 Baba-cho, Hitachiota, 313-0004, Ibaraki, Japan
Tel.: (81) 294722245
Web Site: http://www.sanyu-cfs.co.jp
Year Founded: 1957
5697—(TKS)
Rev.: $158,719,320
Assets: $129,099,910
Liabilities: $61,638,250
Net Worth: $67,461,660
Earnings: $2,551,460
Emp.: 503
Fiscal Year-end: 03/31/24
Steel Product Mfr & Distr
N.A.I.C.S.: 331110
Katogi Katsuya *(Pres & CEO)*

SANYUANDA HOLDINGS CO., LTD.
Building 7 Block Tongpan Road Software Park Gulou Distric, Fuzhou City, Shenzhen, 518048, China
Tel.: (86) 59187883788
Web Site: http://www.sunnada.com
Year Founded: 1998
002417—(SSE)
Sales Range: $25-49.9 Million
Communication Equipment & Software
N.A.I.C.S.: 334220

SAO CARLOS EMPREENDIMENTOS E PARTICIPACOES S.A.
Rua Dr Eduardo de Souza Aranha 153 - 12 Andar Vila Nova Conceicao, 04543-904, Sao Paulo, 04543-904, SP, Brazil
Tel.: (55) 1130485419
Web Site: https://www.scsa.com.br
Year Founded: 1985
SCAR3—(BRAZ)
Rev.: $250,264,737
Assets: $637,195,064
Liabilities: $327,588,165
Net Worth: $309,606,899
Earnings: $54,286,658
Emp.: 64
Fiscal Year-end: 12/31/23
Real Estate Investment & Management Services
N.A.I.C.S.: 531390
Rolando Mifano *(Chm)*

SAO MAI GROUP CORPORATION

Sao Mai Group Corporation—(Continued)

326 Hung Vuong, Phuong My Long, Long Xuyen, An Giang, Vietnam
Tel.: (84) 2963840138
Web Site: https://saomaigroup.com
Year Founded: 1988
ASM—(HOSE)
Rev.: $493,293,945
Assets: $836,667,064
Liabilities: $514,224,245
Net Worth: $322,442,818
Earnings: $10,369,999
Emp.: 10,173
Fiscal Year-end: 12/31/23
Real Estate Development Services
N.A.I.C.S.: 531390

SAO MARTINHO S.A.
Faz Sao Martinho, 14850-000, Pradopolis, SP, Brazil
Tel.: (55) 1639819000
Web Site:
http://www.saomartinho.com.br
Year Founded: 1914
SMTO3—(BRAZ)
Rev.: $1,321,680,327
Assets: $3,753,870,775
Liabilities: $2,574,817,429
Net Worth: $1,179,053,345
Earnings: $202,561,372
Emp.: 12,600
Fiscal Year-end: 03/31/23
Sugar Product Mfr & Whslr
N.A.I.C.S.: 311314
Joao Guilherme Sabino Ometto (Vice Chm)

Subsidiaries:

Sao Martinho S.A. - Boa Vista Mill (1)
Fazenda Boa Vista - s/n, 75860-000, Quirinopolis, Goias, Brazil
Tel.: (55) 64 3615 9700
Sugar Mfr
N.A.I.C.S.: 311314

Sao Martinho S.A. - Iracema Mill (1)
Usina Iracema s/n, 13495-000, 13495-000, Iracemapolis, Sao Paulo, Brazil
Tel.: (55) 19 3456 7700
Sugar Mfr
N.A.I.C.S.: 311314

SAO MIGUEL HOLDING E INVESTIMENTOS S.A.
Avenida Angelica 2250 12 Andar, Consolacao, Sao Paulo, 01228-200, Brazil
Tel.: (55) 11 5505 5550
Web Site:
http://www.saomiguelpar.com.br
Year Founded: 2006
Holding Company
N.A.I.C.S.: 551112
Daniela Manas (Pres)

SAO PAULO TURISMO S/A
R Boa Vista 280 - Historic Center of Sao Paulo, Anhembi, Sao Paulo, 01014-908, Brazil
Tel.: (55) 1122260400
Web Site: https://www.spturis.com
Year Founded: 1970
AHEB5—(BRAZ)
Sales Range: $75-99.9 Million
Emp.: 572
Tourism Management Services
N.A.I.C.S.: 711310
Rodrigo Kluska Rosa (Dir-Investor Relations)

SAO TA FOODS JOINT STOCK COMPANY
Km 2132 National Road 1A, Soc Trang, Vietnam
Tel.: (84) 793822203
Web Site: https://www.fimexvn.com

Year Founded: 1995
FMC—(HOSE)
Rev.: $209,600,592
Assets: $138,274,781
Liabilities: $46,228,172
Net Worth: $92,046,609
Earnings: $12,456,243
Fiscal Year-end: 12/31/23
Seafood Processor & Distr
N.A.I.C.S.: 311710
Quoc Luc Ho (Gen Dir)

SAO THANG LONG INVESTMENT JOINT STOCK COMPANY
13 Minh Khai Street, Nam Dinh, Nam Dinh, Vietnam
Tel.: (84) 3503849498
Web Site: https://saothanglong.vn
Year Founded: 2005
DST—(HNX)
Rev.: $4,983,900
Assets: $41,300,800
Liabilities: $1,734,900
Net Worth: $39,565,900
Earnings: $3,193,900
Fiscal Year-end: 12/31/22
Books Publishing Services
N.A.I.C.S.: 513130
Tran Quoc Hung (Mgr)

SAO VANG RUBBER JOINT STOCK COMPANY
231 Nguyen Trai, Thuong Dinh Ward Thanh Xuan District, Hanoi, Vietnam
Tel.: (84) 2438583656
Web Site: https://www.src.com.vn
Year Founded: 1960
SRC—(HOSE)
Rev.: $49,347,300
Assets: $55,489,808
Liabilities: $37,223,788
Net Worth: $18,266,020
Earnings: $1,211,321
Fiscal Year-end: 12/31/23
Tiles Mfr
N.A.I.C.S.: 326211

SAO VIET SECURITIES CORPORATION
2nd Floor HH3 Building My Dinh Urban Me Tri, Tu Liem District, Hanoi, Vietnam
Tel.: (84) 4 37878086
Web Site: http://www.vssc.com.vn
Sales Range: $25-49.9 Million
Emp.: 70
Investment Banking & Securities Brokerage Services
N.A.I.C.S.: 523150
Su Hong Vu (Chm-Mgmt Bd)

SAOBRACAJ A.D.
Somborska 2, 25250, Odzaci, Serbia
Tel.: (381) 255743441
Web Site: http://www.saobracajodz.rs
Year Founded: 1982
SAOD—(BEL)
Sales Range: $1-9.9 Million
Passenger Transportation Services
N.A.I.C.S.: 485999
Zoran Tojagic (Exec Dir & Dir)

SAOBRACAJ I TRANSPORT A.D.
Petra Drapsina 1, 23000, Zrenjanin, Serbia
Tel.: (381) 2 354 3049
Web Site:
http://www.saobracajitransport.co.rs
Year Founded: 1959
Sales Range: Less than $1 Million
Emp.: 18
Driving School Operator
N.A.I.C.S.: 611692

SAP SE
Dietmar-Hopp-Allee 16, 69190, Walldorf, Germany
Tel.: (49) 6508494000
Web Site: https://www.sap.com
Year Founded: 1972
SAP—(NYSE)
Rev.: $33,679,041,658
Assets: $73,748,111,375
Liabilities: $26,903,734,082
Net Worth: $46,844,377,293
Earnings: $6,625,296,784
Emp.: 107,602
Fiscal Year-end: 12/31/23
Holding Company; Software Development Services
N.A.I.C.S.: 551112
Scott Russell (Member-Exec Bd & Head-Customer Success)

Subsidiaries:

Apex Expert Solutions LLC (1)
15040 Conference Center Dr Ste 300, Chantilly, VA 20151
Web Site: http://www.apexxs.com
Application Software Development Services
N.A.I.C.S.: 541511

Ariba Czech s.r.o. (1)
Bucharova 2817/11, 158 00, Prague, Czech Republic
Tel.: (420) 257118100
Information Technology Services
N.A.I.C.S.: 541519

Ariba Slovak Republic, s.r.o. (1)
Tower C 5th Floor Sturova 27/A, Kosice, 040 01, Slovakia
Tel.: (421) 553102001
Information Technology Services
N.A.I.C.S.: 541519

Ariba Technologies India Private Limited (1)
56/14 3rd Floor Sharada Towers Nandidurga Road, Bengaluru, 560046, India
Tel.: (91) 8046782000
Information Technology Services
N.A.I.C.S.: 541519
Shashidhar Tuppad (Mgr-Bid & Proposal)

Business Objects S.A. (1)
157-159 Rue Anatole France, F-92309, Levallois-Perret, Cedex, France
Tel.: (33) 141252121
Web Site: http://www.sap.com
Business Intelligence Software Developer & Support Services
N.A.I.C.S.: 513210

Subsidiary (Non-US):

Business Objects Software (Shanghai) Co., Ltd. (2)
31/F Ciro's Plaza 388 Nanjing West Road, Shanghai, 200003, China
Tel.: (86) 2133024898
Web Site: http://www.sap.com
Sales Range: $10-24.9 Million
Emp.: 197
Business Intelligence Software Whslr & Support Services
N.A.I.C.S.: 423430

Business Objects Software Limited (2)
Waterside 3 Citywest Business Campus, D24 WA02, Dublin, 24, Ireland
Tel.: (353) 14718001
Sales Range: $800-899.9 Million
Emp.: 165
Parent Company Website
N.A.I.C.S.: 541511

ConTgo Pty. Ltd. (1)
Level 4 123 Epping Road, Macquarie Park, 2113, NSW, Australia
Tel.: (61) 291137358
Management Consulting Services
N.A.I.C.S.: 541618

Crossgate UK Ltd. (1)
Keypoint 17-23 High Street, Slough, SL1 1DY, United Kingdom
Tel.: (44) 1628764764
Software Development Services
N.A.I.C.S.: 541511

Emarsys Beijing Limited (1)
Blue Castle International Xi Da Wang Road, ChaoYang District, Beijing, China
Tel.: (86) 1085999878
Email Marketing Consulting Services
N.A.I.C.S.: 541613

Emarsys Interactive Services GmbH (1)
Willi-Schwabe-Strasse 1, 12489, Berlin, Germany
Tel.: (49) 8954046470
Marketing Services
N.A.I.C.S.: 541613

Emarsys North America, Inc. (1)
10 W Market St Ste 1350, Indianapolis, IN 46204
Marketing Services
N.A.I.C.S.: 541613

Emarsys S.A.S. (1)
35 Rue d Alsace, Levallois-Perret, 92300, Paris, France
Tel.: (33) 177680222
Marketing Services
N.A.I.C.S.: 541613

Emarsys eMarketing Systems GmbH (1)
Lassallestrasse 7b, 1021, Vienna, Austria
Tel.: (43) 147820800
Automatic Data Processing Services
N.A.I.C.S.: 518210

LLC SAP Labs (1)
Kosmodamianskaya nab 52/4, 115054, Moscow, Russia
Tel.: (7) 4957559800
Software Development Services
N.A.I.C.S.: 541511

Limited Liability Company SAP CIS (1)
Kosmodamianskaya nab 52/4, 115054, Moscow, Russia (100%)
Tel.: (7) 4957559800
Web Site: http://www.sap.com
Sales Range: $250-299.9 Million
Emp.: 467
Business Software Whslr & Services
N.A.I.C.S.: 423430

Subsidiary (Non-US):

Limited Liability Company SAP Kazakhstan (2)
Furmanova 240g, 480099, Almaty, Kazakhstan (100%)
Tel.: (7) 7273561093
Sales Range: $1-9.9 Million
Emp.: 9
Business Software Whslr & Services
N.A.I.C.S.: 423430

Limited Liability Company SAP Ukraine (2)
5 Dilova, 3150, Kiev, Ukraine (100%)
Tel.: (380) 444903391
Sales Range: $10-24.9 Million
Emp.: 120
Business Software Whslr & Services
N.A.I.C.S.: 423430

Noteshark, LLC (1)
15040 Conference Ctr Dr Ste 300, Chantilly, VA 20151
Tel.: (703) 721-7600
Web Site: http://www.noteshark.com
Software Development Services
N.A.I.C.S.: 541511

PT Sybase 365 Indonesia (1)
Sampoerna Strategic Square - South Tower Level 18 No - Rt, Setiabudi, Jakarta, 12930, Indonesia
Tel.: (62) 21 575080
Software Development Services
N.A.I.C.S.: 541511

Qualtrics Japan LLC (1)
1-5-1 Marunouchi Shin- Marunouchi Building 37F, Chiyoda-ku, Tokyo, 100-6537, Japan
Tel.: (81) 368453590
Emp.: 6,169
Software Development Services
N.A.I.C.S.: 541511
Satoru Kumashiro (Head-Japan)

AND PRIVATE COMPANIES — SAP SE

SAP (Schweiz) AG (1)
Leugenestrasse 6, Postfach 6130, CH 2500, Biel/Bienne, Switzerland **(100%)**
Tel.: (41) 588716111
Web Site: http://www.sap.ch
Sales Range: $350-399.9 Million
Emp.: 546
Software Reproducing
N.A.I.C.S.: 334610

SAP (UK) Limited (1)
Clockhouse Place Bedfont Road, Feltham, TW14 8HD, Middlesec, United Kingdom
Tel.: (44) 8706084000
Sales Range: $750-799.9 Million
Software Reproducing
N.A.I.C.S.: 334610

Subsidiary (Domestic):

Business Objects (UK) Limited (2)
Objects House Vanwall Business Park Vanwall Road, Maidenhead, SL6 4UB, Berks, United Kingdom **(100%)**
Tel.: (44) 1628764600
Web Site: http://www.sap.com
Sales Range: $50-74.9 Million
Business Intelligence Software Whslr
N.A.I.C.S.: 423430

Division (Domestic):

SAP (UK) Limited (2)
The Scalpel 52 Lime Street, London, EC3M 7AF, United Kingdom
Tel.: (44) 2032074500
Web Site: https://www.sap.com
Sales Range: $25-49.9 Million
Emp.: 1,000
Mobile Messaging Services
N.A.I.C.S.: 517112

Subsidiary (Non-US):

SAP Ireland Limited (2)
1012-1014 Kingswood Avenue, Citywest Business Campus, Dublin, 24, Ireland **(100%)**
Tel.: (353) 14674000
Sales Range: $1-9.9 Million
Emp.: 750
Software Services
N.A.I.C.S.: 513210

Subsidiary (Non-US):

SAP Service & Support (Ireland) Ltd. (3)
Web Site: http://www.sap.com
Software Reproducer & Whslr
N.A.I.C.S.: 334610

SAP AZ LLC (1)
90A Nizami str Landmark Plaza III 2nd Floor, Baku, Azerbaijan
Tel.: (994) 123100012
Software Development Services
N.A.I.C.S.: 541511

SAP America, Inc. (1)
3999 W Chester Pike, Newtown Square, PA 19073 **(100%)**
Tel.: (610) 661-1000
Web Site: http://www.sap.com
Business Software Developer, Publisher & Whslr
N.A.I.C.S.: 513210
Amy Spruill (Sr VP & Mng Dir-Regulated Industries)

Subsidiary (Domestic):

Ariba, Inc. (2)
910 Hermosa Ct, Sunnyvale, CA 94085
Tel.: (650) 390-1000
Web Site: http://www.ariba.com
Sales Range: $400-449.9 Million
Emp.: 2,432
Procurement Solutions Computer Software Developer
N.A.I.C.S.: 513210

Subsidiary (Non-US):

Ariba Belgium (3)
Technologielaan 11B, 3001, Leuven, Belgium **(100%)**
Tel.: (32) 016387570
Web Site: http://www.ariva.com
Sales Range: $1-9.9 Million
Emp.: 8

Internet-Based Business-to-Business Electronic Commerce Solutions
N.A.I.C.S.: 334610

Ariba Deutschland GmbH (3)
An De Welle 4, 60422, Frankfurt, Germany
Tel.: (49) 975938422
Web Site: http://www.ariba.com
Sales Range: $100-124.9 Million
Internet-Based Business-to-Business Electronic Commerce Solutions
N.A.I.C.S.: 334610

Ariba France Sarl (3)
153 Rue Saint Honore, 75116, Paris, France
Tel.: (33) 170373500
Web Site: http://www.ariba.com
Sales Range: $10-24.9 Million
Emp.: 50
Internet-Based Business-to-Business Electronic Commerce Solutions
N.A.I.C.S.: 334610

Ariba Iberia, S.L. (3)
Viriato 71 c/ Orense 85, Edificio Lexington, 28020, Madrid, Spain **(100%)**
Tel.: (34) 917882626
Sales Range: $100-124.9 Million
Internet-Based Business-to-Business Electronic Commerce Solutions
N.A.I.C.S.: 334610

Ariba Iberia, S.L. (3)
Balmes Business Center, Calle Diputacion 260 Planta 1a, 08007, Barcelona, Spain
Tel.: (34) 675906818
Web Site: http://www.ariba.com
Sales Range: $100-124.9 Million
Internet-Based Business-to-Business Electronic Commerce Solutions
N.A.I.C.S.: 334610

Ariba Sweden AB (3)
Frosundaviks Alle 15, 169 70, Stockholm, Sweden
Tel.: (46) 8 655 3642
Sales Range: $100-124.9 Million
Internet-Based Business-to-Business Electronic Commerce Solutions
N.A.I.C.S.: 334610

Ariba Switzerland GmbH SarL LLC (3)
World Trade Center, Leutschenbachstrasse 95, CH-8050, Zurich, Switzerland
Tel.: (41) 13083613
Web Site: http://www.ariba.com
Sales Range: $100-124.9 Million
Internet-Based Business-to-Business Electronic Commerce Solutions
N.A.I.C.S.: 334610

Ariba Technologies Netherlands B.V. (3)
Boeing Ave 5, 1119 PC, Schiphol-Rijk, Netherlands **(100%)**
Tel.: (31) 207979050
Sales Range: $25-49.9 Million
Emp.: 100
Internet-Based Business-to-Business Electronic Commerce Solutions
N.A.I.C.S.: 334610

Ariba Technologies Pvt Ltd. (3)
RMZ ICON No 51 Palace Rd, Bengaluru, 560052, India **(100%)**
Tel.: (91) 8041914300
Sales Range: $100-124.9 Million
Internet-Based Business-to-Business Electronic Commerce Solutions
N.A.I.C.S.: 334610

Ariba U.K. Limited (3)
Baronmede 20 The Ave, Egham, TW20 9AB, Surrey, United Kingdom **(100%)**
Tel.: (44) 1784487100
Sales Range: $10-24.9 Million
Emp.: 50
Internet-Based Business-to-Business Electronic Commerce Solutions
N.A.I.C.S.: 334610

Subsidiary (Domestic):

Ariba, Inc. (3)
Freemarkets Ctr 210 6th Ave, Pittsburgh, PA 15222
Tel.: (412) 434-0500
Web Site: http://www.ariba.com

Sales Range: $250-299.9 Million
Emp.: 967
Computer Software Developer
N.A.I.C.S.: 541511

Ariba, Inc. (3)
8000 Avalon Blvd Ste 500, Alpharetta, GA 30009-1573
Tel.: (678) 585-7300
Sales Range: $10-24.9 Million
Emp.: 200
Computer Software Developer for Supply Chain Management
N.A.I.C.S.: 513210
Tim Minahan (CMO)

Subsidiary (Non-US):

Nihon Ariba, K.K. (3)
1-6-4 Kojimachi SAP Japan Building, Chiyoda-ku, Tokyo, 102-8022, Japan
Tel.: (81) 3 6737 3390
Web Site: http://www.ariba.com
Internet-Based Business-to-Business Electronic Commerce Solutions
N.A.I.C.S.: 334610

Subsidiary (Domestic):

Callidus Software Inc. (2)
4140 Dublin Blvd Ste 400, Dublin, CA 94568 **(100%)**
Tel.: (925) 251-2200
Web Site: http://www.calliduscloud.com
Sales Range: $250-299.9 Million
Software Developer
N.A.I.C.S.: 541511
Brad Compton (Sr VP-Global Pro Svcs)

Subsidiary (Non-US):

Callidus Software Ltd. (3)
14 Grays Inn Rd Holborn, London, WC1X 8HN, United Kingdom **(100%)**
Tel.: (44) 2078496870
Software Developer
N.A.I.C.S.: 513210

Clicktools Ltd. (3)
Bransksome Business Park Suite 7, Poole, BH12 1ED, United Kingdom **(100%)**
Tel.: (44) 8007744065
Cloud-Based Survey Software Developer
N.A.I.C.S.: 513210

Subsidiary (Domestic):

LeadFormix Inc. (3)
4140 Dublin Blvd Ste 400, Dublin, CA 94568 **(100%)**
Tel.: (925) 251-2200
Marketing Software Developer
N.A.I.C.S.: 513210

Subsidiary (Domestic):

Concur Technologies, Inc. (2)
601 108th Ave NE Ste 1000, Bellevue, WA 98014
Tel.: (425) 590-5000
Web Site: https://www.concur.com
Sales Range: $700-749.9 Million
Emp.: 4,900
Cloud-Based Workplace Travel, Expense & Invoicing Platform Developer & Data Services
N.A.I.C.S.: 518210

Subsidiary (Non-US):

Concur (France) SAS (3)
36-38 rue de Saint-Petersbourg, 75008, Paris, France
Tel.: (33) 170 911 000
Web Site: http://www.concur.fr
Software Development Services
N.A.I.C.S.: 513210

Concur Technologies (Hong Kong) Ltd. (3)
Room 1001 10/F Miramar Tower 132 Nathan Road, Tsim Sha Tsui, Kowloon, China (Hong Kong)
Tel.: (852) 39758610
Web Site: https://www.concur.com.hk
Software Development Services
N.A.I.C.S.: 513210

Concur Technologies (Singapore) Pte. Ltd. (3)
30 Pasir Panjang Road 03-32 Mapletree

Business City, Singapore, 117440, Singapore
Tel.: (65) 66644800
Software Development Services
N.A.I.C.S.: 513210

Concur Technologies (UK) Ltd. (3)
7 Bath Road, Slough, SL1 3UE, Berks, United Kingdom
Tel.: (44) 1628 645 100
Web Site: http://www.concur.co.uk
Emp.: 50
Software Development & Solutions
N.A.I.C.S.: 513210

GlobalExpense (Consulting) Limited (3)
Sittingbourne Audit Centre Kent Science Park, 202 Winch Road, Sittingbourne, ME9 8EF, Kent, United Kingdom
Tel.: (44) 2072985757
Web Site: http://www.concur.co.uk
Emp.: 15
Accounting & Auditing Software
N.A.I.C.S.: 513210

Subsidiary (Domestic):

TripIt LLC (3)
888 Brannan St Ste 100, San Francisco, CA 94103
Tel.: (415) 734-4635
Web Site: http://www.tripit.com
Online Travel Management Services
N.A.I.C.S.: 513210

Subsidiary (Domestic):

Fieldglass, Inc. (2)
111 N Canal Ste 600, Chicago, IL 60606
Tel.: (312) 763-4800
Web Site: http://www.fieldglass.com
Emp.: 350
Human Capital Management Software & Services
N.A.I.C.S.: 513210
Jai Shekhawat (Co-Founder)

Outlooksoft Corporation (2)
383 Main Ave Fl 5, Norwalk, CT 06851-1586 **(100%)**
Tel.: (203) 964-3100
Sales Range: $25-49.9 Million
Emp.: 32
Business Performance Management Software Publisher
N.A.I.C.S.: 513210

Subsidiary (Non-US):

SAP Business Services Center Nederland B.V. (2)
Zonnebaan 17, 3542 EA, Utrecht, Netherlands
Tel.: (31) 302478000
Web Site: http://go.sap.com
Enterprise Software Development, Marketing & Support
N.A.I.C.S.: 541511

SAP Canada Inc. (2)
222 Bay St Suite 1800 1900 2000, PO Box 41, Toronto, M5K 1B7, ON, Canada **(100%)**
Tel.: (416) 229-0574
Web Site: http://www.sap.com
Sales Range: $650-699.9 Million
Emp.: 500
Business Software Designer & Distr
N.A.I.C.S.: 513210
Sam Masri (COO)

Unit (Domestic):

SAP Labs Canada - Montreal (3)
111 Duke Street Suite 9000, Montreal, H3C 2M1, QC, Canada
Tel.: (514) 879-7200
Web Site: http://www.sap.com
Sales Range: $100-124.9 Million
Emp.: 500
Business Software Research & Development Services
N.A.I.C.S.: 541715

SAP Labs Canada - Toronto (3)
100 Consilium Place Ste 400, Scarborough, M1H 3E3, ON, Canada
Tel.: (416) 791-7100
Web Site: http://www.sap.com

SAP SE

SAP SE—(Continued)
Sales Range: $50-74.9 Million
Emp.: 200
Business Software Research & Development Services
N.A.I.C.S.: 541715

Subsidiary (Domestic):

SAP Global Marketing Inc. (2)
95 Morton St Ste 200, New York, NY 10014 **(100%)**
Tel.: (212) 653-9600
Web Site: http://www.sap.com
Sales Range: $200-249.9 Million
Emp.: 429
Marketing Support Services
N.A.I.C.S.: 561499

SAP Governance Risk & Compliance, Inc. (2)
3410 Hillview Ave, Palo Alto, CA 94304
Tel.: (650) 849-4000
Web Site: http://www.sap.com
Sales Range: $50-74.9 Million
Emp.: 95
Governance, Risk Management, Transperency & Compliance Software Publisher
N.A.I.C.S.: 513210
Narina Sippy *(Sr VP & Gen Mgr)*

SAP Government Support & Services, Inc. (2)
3999 W Chester Pike, Newtown Square, PA 19073-2305 **(100%)**
Tel.: (610) 661-9473
Sales Range: $10-24.9 Million
Emp.: 31
Government Support Software & Consulting Services
N.A.I.C.S.: 423430

SAP Industries, Inc. (2)
4343 N Scottsdale Rd Ste 260, Scottsdale, AZ 85251 **(100%)**
Tel.: (480) 308-2500
Web Site: http://www.sap.com
Sales Range: $150-199.9 Million
Emp.: 251
Point-of-Sale & Retail Software & Solutions
N.A.I.C.S.: 513210

SAP International, Inc. (2)
5301 Blue Lagoon Dr Ste 790, Miami, FL 33126
Tel.: (305) 476-4400
Sales Range: $25-49.9 Million
Emp.: 42
Holding Company; Regional Managing Office
N.A.I.C.S.: 551112

Subsidiary (Non-US):

SAP Agencia en Chile (3)
Rosario Norte North 100 Piso 13, Edificio Consorcio Las Condes, Santiago, 8320000, Chile
Tel.: (56) 24403500
Web Site: http://www.sap.com
Emp.: 114
Business Software Whslr & Services
N.A.I.C.S.: 423430

SAP Andina y del Caribe, C.A. (3)
Av Principal de la Castellana, Centro Letonia Piso 13 La Castellana, Caracas, 1060, Venezuela
Tel.: (58) 2122765400
Business Software Whslr & Services
N.A.I.C.S.: 423430

Subsidiary (Non-US):

SAP Colombia S.A.S. (3)
Tierra Firme Building Carrera 9na 115-06 24th floor office 2404, Teleport Business Park, Bogota, Colombia **(100%)**
Tel.: (57) 16003000
Sales Range: $50-74.9 Million
Business Software Whslr & Services
N.A.I.C.S.: 423430

SAP Peru S.A.C., Inc. (4)
Av Circunvalacion del Club Golf Los Incas No 154 Piso 16, Oficina No 1601 Santiago de Surco, Lima, Peru **(100%)**
Tel.: (51) 16156900

Sales Range: $10-24.9 Million
Software Whslr
N.A.I.C.S.: 423430

Subsidiary (Non-US):

SAP Argentina S.A. (3)
Panamerican Bureau Sargento Cabral 3770-Piso 2, Munro, B1605EFJ, Buenos Aires, Argentina **(100%)**
Tel.: (54) 1155443600
Business Software Whslr & Services
N.A.I.C.S.: 423430
Lautaro Spotorno *(Mgr-Corp Comm)*

SAP Brasil Ltda. (3)
Av das Nacoes Unidas n 14 171 - Marble Tower - 7th floor, Vila Almeida, Sao Paulo, 04794-000, Brazil **(100%)**
Tel.: (55) 1155032400
Web Site: https://www.sap.com
Business Software Publisher, Whslr & Services
N.A.I.C.S.: 513210

SAP Mexico S.A. de C.V. (3)
Paseo de la Reforma 509 - Piso 20 Col Cuauhtemo, Alcaldia Cuauhtemoc, 06500, Mexico, Mexico **(100%)**
Tel.: (52) 5552577500
Business Software Whslr & Services
N.A.I.C.S.: 423430

Branch (Domestic):

SAP Mexico S.A. de C.V. - Monterrey (4)
Ricardo Margain 444 N Tower 5th Fl, San Pedro, 66260, Garza Garcia, NL, Mexico
Tel.: (52) 8181521700
Web Site: http://www.sap.com
Business Software Whslr & Services
N.A.I.C.S.: 423430

Subsidiary (Domestic):

SAP Labs, LLC (2)
3410 Hillview Ave, Palo Alto, CA 94304 **(100%)**
Tel.: (650) 849-4000
Sales Range: $350-399.9 Million
Emp.: 1,742
Business Software Research & Development Services
N.A.I.C.S.: 541715
Doug Merritt *(Pres)*

Branch (Domestic):

SAP Labs U.S. - Alpharetta (3)
2500 Northwinds Pkwy Ste 500, Alpharetta, GA 30009
Tel.: (770) 619-4200
Web Site: http://www.sap.com
Sales Range: $25-49.9 Million
Emp.: 45
Business Software Research & Development Services
N.A.I.C.S.: 541715

SAP Labs U.S. - Boston (3)
245 1st St, Cambridge, MA 02142
Tel.: (617) 495-0180
Web Site: http://www.sap.com
Sales Range: $25-49.9 Million
Emp.: 100
Business Software Research & Development Services
N.A.I.C.S.: 541715

SAP Labs U.S. - Los Angeles (3)
1925 Century Park E Ste 1600, Los Angeles, CA 90067
Tel.: (310) 286-2220
Web Site: http://www.sap.com
Sales Range: $25-49.9 Million
Emp.: 40
Business Software Research & Development Services
N.A.I.C.S.: 541715

Subsidiary (Domestic):

SAP Public Services, Inc. (2)
1399 New York Ave NW Ste 800, Washington, DC 20005 **(100%)**
Tel.: (202) 312-3500
Sales Range: $350-399.9 Million
Emp.: 218
Public Service Organization Management Software Publisher

N.A.I.C.S.: 513210

SuccessFactors, Inc. (2)
1500 Fashion Island Blvd Ste 300, San Mateo, CA 94404
Tel.: (650) 645-2000
Web Site: http://www.successfactors.com
Emp.: 1,047
Performance & Talent Management Software Solutions
N.A.I.C.S.: 513210
Lars Dalgaard *(Founder)*

Subsidiary (Domestic):

Jobs2Web Inc. (3)
10901 Red Circle Dr Ste 200, Minnetonka, MN 55343
Tel.: (952) 697-2900
Web Site: http://www.jobs2web.com
Sales Range: $1-9.9 Million
Emp.: 68
Online Employee Recruitment Software Mfr
N.A.I.C.S.: 513210

Subsidiary (Non-US):

Plateau Systems, Ltd. (3)
Tel.: (703) 292-0200
Learning & Performance Management Software
N.A.I.C.S.: 611430

Subsidiary (Non-US):

Plateau Systems UK Ltd (4)
Tel.: (44) 01753705006
Sales Range: $25-49.9 Million
Emp.: 15
Computer Software Distr
N.A.I.C.S.: 423430

Subsidiary (Domestic):

TomorrowNow, Inc. (2)
1716 Briarcrest Dr 400, Bryan, TX 77802
Tel.: (979) 691-4100
Web Site: http://www.tomorrownow.com
Software Development Services
N.A.I.C.S.: 541511

SAP Asia Pte. Ltd. (1)
30 Pasir Panjang Road 03-32 Mapletree Business City, Singapore, 117440, Singapore **(100%)**
Tel.: (65) 66646868
Sales Range: $200-249.9 Million
Emp.: 607
Business Software Publisher, Whslr & Support Services
N.A.I.C.S.: 513210

Subsidiary (Non-US):

PT SAP Indonesia (2)
WTC II 9th Floor Metropolitan Complex, Jl Jend Sudirman Kav 29-31, Jakarta, 12920, Indonesia **(100%)**
Tel.: (62) 2130032800
Sales Range: $10-24.9 Million
Emp.: 45
Business Software Whslr
N.A.I.C.S.: 423430

SAP (Beijing) Software System Co., Ltd. (2)
12th Floor Tower 2 China Central Place No 79 Jianguo Road, Chaoyang District, Beijing, 100025, China **(100%)**
Tel.: (86) 1065898888
Web Site: http://www.sap.com
Sales Range: $250-299.9 Million
Business Software Publisher, Whslr & Services
N.A.I.C.S.: 513210

SAP Australia Pty. Ltd. (2)
Level 13 1 Denison Street, North Sydney, Sydney, 2060, NSW, Australia **(100%)**
Tel.: (61) 299354500
Sales Range: $450-499.9 Million
Emp.: 524
Business Software Publisher & Whslr
N.A.I.C.S.: 513210

Subsidiary (Non-US):

SAP New Zealand Limited (3)
Level 15 151 Queen Street, PO Box 108-150, Auckland, 1010, New Zealand
Tel.: (64) 93555800

Sales Range: $25-49.9 Million
Emp.: 36
Business Software Distr
N.A.I.C.S.: 423430

Subsidiary (Non-US):

SAP Hong Kong Co. Ltd. (2)
Suite 1111-1114 11/F Cityplaza 4, 12 Taikoo Wan Road, Taikoo Shing, Taikoo Shing, China (Hong Kong) **(100%)**
Tel.: (852) 25391800
Web Site: http://www.sap.com
Sales Range: $25-49.9 Million
Emp.: 62
Software Reproducer & Whslr
N.A.I.C.S.: 423430

SAP Korea Ltd. (2)
28 Fl MMAA Bldg 2806 Nambusunhwan-ro, Gangnam-gu, Seoul, 06292, Kangnam-Ku, Korea (South)
Tel.: (82) 221942400
Web Site: https://www.sap.com
Sales Range: $100-124.9 Million
Emp.: 181
Software Reproducer & Whslr
N.A.I.C.S.: 423430

Subsidiary (Domestic):

SAP R&D Center Korea, Inc. (3)
28 Fl MMAA Bldg, 467-12 Dogok-Dong, Seoul, 135-270, Kangnam-Ku, Korea (South)
Tel.: (82) 5 228 1709
Sales Range: $1-9.9 Million
Emp.: 55
Software Reproducer & Whslr
N.A.I.C.S.: 423430

Subsidiary (Non-US):

SAP Labs China (2)
Web Site: http://www.sap.com
Business Software Research & Development Services
N.A.I.C.S.: 541715

SAP Malaysia Sdn. Bhd. (2)
Level 29 Menara Southpoint, Mid Valley City Medan Syed Putra Selatan, 59200, Kuala Lumpur, Malaysia
Tel.: (60) 322026000
Sales Range: $50-74.9 Million
Emp.: 129
Software Reproducer & Whslr
N.A.I.C.S.: 423430

SAP Philippines Inc. (2)
32nd Floor Citibank Tower, 8741 Paseo de Roxas, 1200, Makati, Manila, Philippines
Tel.: (63) 28480181
Web Site: http://www.sap.com
Sales Range: $10-24.9 Million
Emp.: 33
Software Reproducer & Whslr
N.A.I.C.S.: 423430

Affiliate (Non-US):

SAP Systems, Applications & Products in Data Processing (Thailand) Ltd. (2)
Units 1401-1402 14th Floor Park Silom Tower, 1 Convent Road Silom Bangrak, Bangkok, 10500, Thailand **(49%)**
Tel.: (66) 28216170
Sales Range: $10-24.9 Million
Emp.: 39
Business Software Whslr & Services
N.A.I.C.S.: 423430

Subsidiary (Non-US):

SAP Taiwan Co., Ltd. (2)
10F Hua Nan Bank Headquarter Office Building No 123 Songren Rd, Taipei, 11073, Taiwan
Tel.: (886) 287800188
Sales Range: $25-49.9 Million
Emp.: 67
Software Reproducer & Whslr
N.A.I.C.S.: 423430

SAP Belgium - Systems Applications & Products NV/SA (1)
Chaussee de la Hulpe 166, Ave Des Olympiard 2, 1140, Brussels, Belgium **(100%)**
Tel.: (32) 26746511
Web Site: http://www.sap.com

AND PRIVATE COMPANIES — SAP SE

Sales Range: $200-249.9 Million
Emp.: 260
Business Software Whslr & Services
N.A.I.C.S.: 423430
Renaud Heyd *(CFO-UK)*

SAP Beteiligungs GmbH (1)
Hasso-Plattner-Ring 7, 69190, Walldorf, Germany
Tel.: (49) 6227747474
Administrative Management Services
N.A.I.C.S.: 561110

SAP Bulgaria EOOD (1)
Srebarna 16, 1407, Sofia, Bulgaria **(100%)**
Tel.: (359) 29157699
Web Site: https://www.sap.com
Sales Range: $1-9.9 Million
Emp.: 12
Business Software Whslr & Services
N.A.I.C.S.: 423430

Subsidiary (Domestic):

SAP Labs Bulgaria EOOD (2)
Srebarna 16, 1407, Sofia, Bulgaria **(100%)**
Tel.: (359) 29950534
Business Software Research & Development Services
N.A.I.C.S.: 541715

SAP CR, spol. s.r.o. (1)
Bucharova 2817/11, 155 00, Prague, 5, Czech Republic **(100%)**
Tel.: (420) 257118111
Sales Range: $125-149.9 Million
Emp.: 221
Software Reproducer & Whslr
N.A.I.C.S.: 334610

Subsidiary (Domestic):

SAP Business Services Center Europe, s.r.o. (2)
Avenir Business Park Radlicka 714, 158 00, Prague, Czech Republic **(100%)**
Tel.: (420) 257118111
Sales Range: $10-24.9 Million
Business Support Services
N.A.I.C.S.: 561499
Andrea Hepnerova *(Mgr)*

SAP Costa Rica, S.A. (1)
Plaza Tempo Piso 4, Escazu, San Jose, Costa Rica
Tel.: (506) 22082600
Software Development Services
N.A.I.C.S.: 541511
Jose Casas *(Sr Project Mgr)*

SAP Cyprus Ltd. (1)
92 Ifigenias Str Athena Building Office 101, 2003, Nicosia, Cyprus **(100%)**
Tel.: (357) 22378777
Sales Range: $1-9.9 Million
Emp.: 3
Software Services
N.A.I.C.S.: 513210
Alex Mouradian *(Country Mgr-SIs)*

SAP Danmark A/S (1)
Marmorvej 4, 2100, Copenhagen, Denmark
Tel.: (45) 39133000
Software Reproducer & Whslr
N.A.I.C.S.: 334610

SAP Deutschland SE & Co. KG (1)
Hasso-Plattner-Ring 7, 69190, Walldorf, Germany
Tel.: (49) 6227747474
Sales Range: $1-4.9 Billion
Emp.: 4,628
Business Software Mangement Services
N.A.I.C.S.: 561499

Joint Venture (Domestic):

Original1 GmbH (2)
Mainzer Landstrasse 205, 60326, Frankfurt, Germany
Tel.: (49) 6917536620
Web Site: http://www.original1.net
Sales Range: $25-49.9 Million
Emp.: 12
Supply Chain Integrity & Security Services; Joint Venture of SAP AG, Nokia Corporation & Giesecke & Devrient GmbH
N.A.I.C.S.: 513210

SAP Dritte Beteiligungs- und Vermogensverwaltung GmbH (1)
Dietmar-Hopp-Allee 16, 69190, Walldorf, Germany
Tel.: (49) 6227747474
Investment Management Service
N.A.I.C.S.: 523940
Bill McDermott *(Gen Mgr)*

SAP EMEA Inside Sales S.L. (1)
C/ Josep Pla 2 planta 1 Torre Diagonal Mar - B1, 08019, Barcelona, Spain
Tel.: (34) 934833500
Sales Range: $10-24.9 Million
Emp.: 100
Resource Planning, Supply Chain, Customer Relationship, Product Life-Cycle & Supplier Relationship Management Software Sales
N.A.I.C.S.: 513210

SAP East Africa Limited (1)
Cavendish Building 4th Floor 14 Riverside Park Riverside Drive, Nairobi, Kenya
Tel.: (254) 703039000
Software Development Services
N.A.I.C.S.: 541511
Jackie Kanja *(Head-Mktg)*

SAP Egypt LLC (1)
Building 14B02 - FLRG Business Park Cairo Festival City, PO Box 145, 11835, Cairo, Egypt
Tel.: (20) 1067773889
Software Development Services
N.A.I.C.S.: 541511

SAP Erste Beteiligungs- und Vermogensverwaltung GmbH (1)
Dietmar-Hopp-Allee 16, 69190, Walldorf, Germany
Tel.: (49) 6227747474
Emp.: 50,000
Investment Management Service
N.A.I.C.S.: 523940

SAP Espana, S.A. (1)
Torrelaguna 77 Bloque SAP, 28043, Madrid, Spain **(100%)**
Tel.: (34) 914567200
Sales Range: $300-349.9 Million
Emp.: 362
Software Reproduction & Services
N.A.I.C.S.: 334610
Belen Martinez Millan *(Mgr-PR)*

SAP Estonia OU (1)
Parnu mnt 15, 10141, Tallinn, Estonia **(100%)**
Tel.: (372) 5087172
Software Whslr
N.A.I.C.S.: 423430

SAP Finland Oy (1)
Keilasatama 5, 02150, Espoo, Finland **(100%)**
Tel.: (358) 104304400
Web Site: https://www.sap.com
Sales Range: $100-124.9 Million
Emp.: 104
Software Reproducer & Whslr
N.A.I.C.S.: 334610

Subsidiary (Domestic):

SAP Labs Finland Oy (2)
Keilasatama 5, 2150, Espoo, Finland **(100%)**
Web Site: http://www.sap.com
Business Software Research & Development Services
N.A.I.C.S.: 541715

SAP Foreign Holdings GmbH (1)
Dietmar-Hopp-Allee 16, 69190, Walldorf, Germany
Tel.: (49) 6227747474
Investment Management Service
N.A.I.C.S.: 523940

SAP France Holding S.A. (1)
Immeuble Defense Plaza 23/25 rue Delariviere, Lefoullon La Defense 9, 92064, Paris, France
Tel.: (33) 144452000
Web Site: http://www.sap.com
Sales Range: $550-599.9 Million
Emp.: 300
Holding Company; Software Reproduction
N.A.I.C.S.: 551112

Subsidiary (Domestic):

SAP France S.A. (2)
Immeuble Defense Plaza 23/25 Rue Delariviere, Lefoullon La Defense 9, Paris, 92064, France **(100%)**
Tel.: (33) 144452000
Web Site: http://www.sap.com
Sales Range: $300-349.9 Million
Software Publisher
N.A.I.C.S.: 513210

SAP Labs France S.A.S (2)
805 avenue Maurice Donat, 6250, Mougins, France **(100%)**
Tel.: (33) 492286200
Sales Range: $25-49.9 Million
Emp.: 200
Business Software Research & Development Services
N.A.I.C.S.: 541715
William R. McDermott *(CEO)*

SAP Hellas Systems Applications & Data Processing S.A. (1)
20 Ellinidon str, P Faliro, 17564, Athens, Greece
Tel.: (30) 2109473800
Web Site: http://www.sap.com
Sales Range: $25-49.9 Million
Emp.: 56
Software Reproducing
N.A.I.C.S.: 513210
Emmanuel Raptopoulos *(Mng Dir)*

SAP Hosting Beteiligungs GmbH (1)
Raiffeisenring 15, Sankt Leon-Rot, 68789, Baden-Wurttemberg, Germany
Tel.: (49) 6227747474
Investment Management Service
N.A.I.C.S.: 523940

SAP Hungary Rendszerek, Alkalmazasok es Termekek az Adatfeldolgozasban Informatikai Kft. (1)
Zahony u 7, H-1031, Budapest, Hungary **(100%)**
Tel.: (36) 14578333
Web Site: http://www.sap.com
Sales Range: $50-74.9 Million
Emp.: 361
Software Reproducer & Whslr
N.A.I.C.S.: 334610

Subsidiary (Domestic):

SAP Labs Hungary (2)
Graphisoft Park, 1031, Budapest, Hungary
Tel.: (36) 18857265
Sales Range: $25-49.9 Million
Emp.: 200
Business Software Research & Development Services
N.A.I.C.S.: 541715

SAP Public Serv. Hungary (2)
Zahony u 7 Graphisoft Park 1, 1031, Budapest, Hungary **(100%)**
Tel.: (36) 14578333
Web Site: http://www.sap.hu
Sales Range: Less than $1 Million
Emp.: 1
Software Services
N.A.I.C.S.: 513210

SAP India Pvt. Ltd. (1)
6th Floor RMZ Ecoworld 8A Campus Sarjapur-Marathahalli Outer Ring Road, Devarabeesanahalli, Bengaluru, 560103, India **(100%)**
Tel.: (91) 8066655555
Sales Range: $200-249.9 Million
Emp.: 4,300
Software Reproducer & Whslr
N.A.I.C.S.: 423430

Subsidiary (Domestic):

SAP Labs India Pvt. Ltd. (2)
138 EPIP Zone, Whitefield, Bengaluru, 560066, India
Tel.: (91) 8041395139
Sales Range: $150-199.9 Million
Business Software Research & Development Services
N.A.I.C.S.: 541715
Dilipkumar Khandelwal *(Mng Dir, VP & Head-Suite Engrg)*

SAP International Panama, S.A. (1)
Costa del Este Torre Financial Park piso 35, Panama, Panama
Tel.: (507) 2322718

Software Development Services
N.A.I.C.S.: 541511

SAP Israel Ltd. (1)
14 Eli Hurvitz Street, Ra'anana, Israel **(100%)**
Tel.: (972) 97780004
Web Site: https://www.sap.com
Sales Range: $10-24.9 Million
Emp.: 71
Technology Infrastructure & Software Solutions
N.A.I.C.S.: 513210

Subsidiary (Non-US):

SAP Labs Israel Ltd. (2)
Web Site: http://www.sap.com
Emp.: 700
Business Software Research & Development Services
N.A.I.C.S.: 541715

Subsidiary (Domestic):

SAP Portals Israel Ltd. (2)
14 Eli Hurvitz Street, Ra'anana, Israel
Tel.: (972) 97780004
Emp.: 288
Business Portal Software Developer, Publisher & Whslr
N.A.I.C.S.: 513210

SAP Italia Sistemi Applicazioni Prodotti in Data Processing S.p.A. (1)
Campus Tecnologico Energy Park Edificio 03, Via Monza 7/a, 20871, Vimercate, MB, Italy **(100%)**
Tel.: (39) 03968791
Web Site: http://www.sap.com
Sales Range: $400-449.9 Million
Emp.: 514
Software Reproducer & Whslr
N.A.I.C.S.: 334610

SAP Labs Korea, Inc. (1)
20 21 Fl 235 Banpo-daero, Seocho-gu, Seoul, 06578, Korea (South)
Tel.: (82) 221435000
Emp.: 250
Software Development Services
N.A.I.C.S.: 541511

SAP Latvia SIA (1)
Ranka dambis 30 - 110, Riga, LV-1048, Latvia **(100%)**
Tel.: (371) 67035227
Sales Range: $1-9.9 Million
Emp.: 1
Software Services
N.A.I.C.S.: 513210
Lubova Vorobjova *(Mng Dir)*

SAP Luxembourg (1)
Avenue de la Liberte 34, L-1930, Luxembourg, Luxembourg
Tel.: (352) 26193601
Web Site: http://www.sap.com
Sales Range: $50-74.9 Million
Emp.: 250
Software Reproduction
N.A.I.C.S.: 334610

SAP Middle East & North Africa LLC (1)
Tel.: (971) 44407222
Web Site: http://www.sap.com
Sales Range: $50-74.9 Million
Emp.: 102
Software Reproducer & Whslr
N.A.I.C.S.: 334610

Subsidiary (Non-US):

SAP Saudi Arabia Software Services Co. Ltd. (2)
4th Floor Centria Centre Olaya Main Road, PO Box 19319, 11435, Riyadh, Saudi Arabia **(51%)**
Tel.: (966) 1 2938200
Web Site: http://www.sap.com
Sales Range: $10-24.9 Million
Emp.: 11
Enterprise Software & Software-Related Services
N.A.I.C.S.: 513210

SAP National Security Services, Inc. (1)

SAP SE

SAP SE—(Continued)

3809 West Chester Pike Ste 210, Newtown Square, PA 19073
Tel.: (610) 492-3023
Web Site: http://www.sapns2.com
Software Development Services
N.A.I.C.S.: 541511
Mark A. Testoni (CEO)

SAP Nederland B.V. (1)
Amerikastraat 10, 5232 BE, 's-Hertogenbosch, Netherlands (100%)
Tel.: (31) 736457500
Sales Range: $400-449.9 Million
Emp.: 407
Software Reproducing
N.A.I.C.S.: 334610

SAP Nederland Holding B.V. (1)
Amerikastraat 10, 5232 BE, 's-Hertogenbosch, Netherlands
Tel.: (31) 736457500
Investment Management Service
N.A.I.C.S.: 523940

SAP Norge AS (1)
(100%)
Tel.: (47) 67529400
Web Site: http://www.sap.com
Sales Range: $75-99.9 Million
Emp.: 93
Software Reproducer & Whslr
N.A.I.C.S.: 334610

SAP North West Africa Ltd (1)
Casenearshore - Shore 10 1100 Boulevard AL QODS, Sidi Maarouf, 20270, Casablanca, Morocco
Tel.: (212) 529311630
Software Development Services
N.A.I.C.S.: 541511
Ali El Alami (CEO)

SAP Osterreich GmbH (1)
Lassallestrasse 7b, A 1021, Vienna, Austria (100%)
Web Site: http://www.sap.com
Sales Range: $200-249.9 Million
Emp.: 369
Software Reproducing
N.A.I.C.S.: 334610

SAP Polska Sp. z o.o. (1)
ul Chmielna 69 Varso Tower, Taurus Building, 00-801, Warsaw, Poland (100%)
Tel.: (48) 225416606
Sales Range: $50-74.9 Million
Emp.: 130
Software Reproducer & Whslr
N.A.I.C.S.: 334610
Kinga Piecuch (Gen Mgr)

SAP Portals Europe GmbH (1)
Dietmar-Hopp-Allee 16, 69190, Walldorf, Germany
Tel.: (49) 6227747474
Software Development Services
N.A.I.C.S.: 541511

SAP Portugal - Sistemas, Aplicacoes e Produtos Informaticos, Sociedade Unipessoal, Lda. (1)
(100%)
Tel.: (351) 214465500
Web Site: http://www.sap.com
Sales Range: $50-74.9 Million
Emp.: 95
Software Reproducer & Whslr
N.A.I.C.S.: 334610
Carlos Lacerda (Mng Dir)

SAP Portugal - Sistemas, Aplicacoes e Produtos Informaticos Sociedade Unipessoal Lda. (1)
Lagoas Park Edificio 14 Piso, 2740-262, Porto Salvo, Portugal
Tel.: (351) 214465500
Software Development Services
N.A.I.C.S.: 541511

SAP Projektverwaltungs- und Beteiligungs GmbH (1)
Dietmar-Hopp-Allee 16, 69190, Walldorf, Germany
Tel.: (49) 6227747474
Investment Management Service
N.A.I.C.S.: 523940

SAP Retail Solutions Beteiligungsgesellschaft mbH (1)
Dietmar-Hopp-Allee 16, 69190, Walldorf, Germany
Tel.: (49) 6227747474
Software Development Services
N.A.I.C.S.: 541511

SAP Romania SRL (1)
Calea Tipografilor 11-15, Cladirea A1 / LA Etaju 2, 013714, Bucharest, Romania (100%)
Tel.: (40) 312252800
Sales Range: $10-24.9 Million
Emp.: 77
Professional Services Software
N.A.I.C.S.: 513210
Cristian Popescu (Mng Dir)

SAP SE - Service Center Rot (1)
SAP-Allee 29, St Leon-Rot, 68789, Rot am See, Germany
Tel.: (49) 6227747474
Sales Range: $1-4.9 Billion
Emp.: 12,000
Business Software Whslr & Support Services
N.A.I.C.S.: 423430

SAP Saudi Arabia Software Trading Ltd. (1)
Nakheel Pr Turki AlAwwal Road ITCC IT-01 Building Ground Floor, PO Box 19319, Riyadh, 11435, Saudi Arabia
Tel.: (966) 112027000
Software Development Services
N.A.I.C.S.: 541511

SAP Sechste Beteiligungs- und Vermogensverwaltungs GmbH (1)
Dietmar-Hopp-Allee 16, 69190, Walldorf, Germany
Tel.: (49) 6227741440
Investment Management Service
N.A.I.C.S.: 523940

SAP Services s.r.o. (1)
Bucharova 2817/11, 158 00, Prague, 5, Czech Republic
Tel.: (420) 257118111
Software Development Services
N.A.I.C.S.: 541511
Denisa Cechova (Mgr-Fin & Ops)

SAP Slovensko s.r.o. (1)
(100%)
Tel.: (421) 258256111
Sales Range: $25-49.9 Million
Emp.: 133
Software Reproducer & Whslr
N.A.I.C.S.: 334610

SAP Svenska AB (1)
Sveavagen 44, 10227, Stockholm, Sweden (100%)
Tel.: (46) 858770000
Sales Range: $100-124.9 Million
Emp.: 160
Software Reproducer & Whslr
N.A.I.C.S.: 334610
Anders Heimer (Mgr-Solutions)

SAP Turkiye Yazilim Uretim ve Ticaret A.S. (1)
Emaar Square Ofis Kulesi Libadiye Cd No 82-F D Kat 17-18, Unalan Uskudar, 34700, Istanbul, Turkiye (100%)
Tel.: (90) 2163300300
Sales Range: $25-49.9 Million
Emp.: 150
Software Whslr
N.A.I.C.S.: 423430

SAP UAB (Lithuania) (1)
Gyneju 16, 01109, Vilnius, Lithuania (100%)
Tel.: (370) 52047230
Web Site: https://www.sap.com
Sales Range: $1-9.9 Million
Emp.: 3
Software Services
N.A.I.C.S.: 513210

SAP Vierte Beteiligungs- und Vermogensverwaltung GmbH (1)
Dietmar-Hopp-Allee 16, 69190, Walldorf, Germany
Tel.: (49) 6227747474
Investment Management Service
N.A.I.C.S.: 523940

SAP Vietnam Company Limited (1)

Level 21 CEO Suite 22 Vietcombank Tower No 5 Me Linh Square, Ben Nghe Ward District 1, Ho Chi Minh City, Vietnam
Tel.: (84) 800588840
Software Development Services
N.A.I.C.S.: 541511

SAP West Balkans d.o.o. (1)
mladinskih Brigada 90e Airport City Belgrade zgrada 2300, 11070, Novi Beograd, Serbia (100%)
Tel.: (381) 113536900
Sales Range: $1-9.9 Million
Emp.: 30
Software Services
N.A.I.C.S.: 513210

SAP Zweite Beteiligungs- und Vermogensverwaltung GmbH (1)
Dietmar-Hopp-Allee, 69190, Walldorf, Baden-Wurttemberg, Germany
Tel.: (49) 6227743708
Investment Management Service
N.A.I.C.S.: 523940

SAP d.o.o. (1)
Hektoroviceva 2, 10000, Zagreb, Croatia (100%)
Tel.: (385) 14820400
Web Site: https://www.sap.com
Sales Range: $10-24.9 Million
Emp.: 14
Resource Planning, Supply Chain, Customer Relationship, Product Life-cycle & Supplier Relationship Management Software
N.A.I.C.S.: 513210
Pekka Ala-Pietila (Chm-Supervisory Bd)

SAP sistemi, aplikacije in produkti za obdelavo podatkov d.o.o. (1)
Dunajska Cesta 165 4th Floor B of the Rotonda Building, Ljubljana, 1000, Slovenia
Tel.: (386) 13072002
Software Development Services
N.A.I.C.S.: 541511

SAP sistemi, aplikacije in produkti za obdelavo podatkov d.o.o. (1)
World Trade Center, Dunajska Cesta 156, 1000, Ljubljana, Slovenia (100%)
Tel.: (386) 15881255
Sales Range: $10-24.9 Million
Emp.: 19
Software Reproducing
N.A.I.C.S.: 334610

SAPV (Mauritius) (1)
2nd Floor Stitch Building Royal Road, Bell Village, Port Louis, Mauritius
Tel.: (230) 2029170
Software Development Services
N.A.I.C.S.: 541511

SmartOps Corp. (1)
1251 Waterfront Pl, Pittsburgh, PA 15222
Tel.: (412) 231-0115
Web Site: http://www.smartops.com
Sales Range: $1-9.9 Million
Emp.: 65
Software Publisher
N.A.I.C.S.: 513210

Sybase Luxembourg S.a.r.l. (1)
Val Saint Andre 37, Luxembourg, 1128, Luxembourg
Tel.: (352) 250 750 352
Software Development Services
N.A.I.C.S.: 541511

Sybase do Brasil Software Ltda. (1)
Av Juscelino Kubitscheck 510 - 1 andar, Itaim Bibi, 04543-906, Sao Paulo, Brazil
Tel.: (55) 11 2588 8000
Web Site: http://www.sybase.com.br
Software Development Services
N.A.I.C.S.: 541511

Systems Applications Products Africa (Pty.) Ltd. (1)
SAP Business Park 1 Woodmead Drive, Woodmead, 2148, South Africa (100%)
Tel.: (27) 112356000
Web Site: http://www.sap.com
Emp.: 400
Holding Company
N.A.I.C.S.: 551112
Johannes Dressler (CFO)

Subsidiary (Domestic):

Systems Applications Products Africa Region (Pty.) Ltd. (2)

INTERNATIONAL PUBLIC

SAP Business Park 1 Woodmead Drive, Woodmead, 2148, South Africa (100%)
Tel.: (27) 112356000
Sales Range: $25-49.9 Million
Emp.: 215
Holding Company
N.A.I.C.S.: 551112

Branch (Non-US):

SAP Africa (Pty.) Ltd. - Kenya (3)
Rahimtulla Trust Towers 4th Floor Upper Hill Road, PO Box 10700 - 00100, Nairobi, Kenya
Tel.: (254) 20 2723477
Business Software Whslr & Services
N.A.I.C.S.: 423430

SAP Africa (Pty.) Ltd. - Namibia (3)
SAP Building 47 Schlettwein Street, Pioneerspark, Windhoek, Namibia
Tel.: (264) 61 253951
Business Software Whslr & Services
N.A.I.C.S.: 423430

Subsidiary (Non-US):

Systems Applications Products Nigeria Limited (3)
Third Floor Oakland Centre Plot 2940 Aguiyi Ironsi Street Maitama, Abuja, Nigeria (100%)
Tel.: (234) 9 4611480 5
Web Site: http://www.sap.com
Sales Range: $1-9.9 Million
Emp.: 10
Business Software Whslr & Services
N.A.I.C.S.: 423430

Subsidiary (Domestic):

Systems Applications Products South Africa (Proprietary) Limited (2)
SAP Business Park 1 Woodmead Drive, Block 3, Woodmead, 2148, South Africa (89.5%)
Tel.: (27) 112356000
Web Site: http://www.sap.com
Sales Range: $150-199.9 Million
Emp.: 318
Software Reproducing
N.A.I.C.S.: 334610

Unit (Domestic):

SAP Research Group - South Africa (3)
SAP Business Park, 1 Woodmead Drive, Woodmead, 2148, South Africa
Tel.: (27) 112356000
Web Site: http://www.sap.com
Sales Range: $25-49.9 Million
Emp.: 32
Business Software Research & Development
N.A.I.C.S.: 541715

Taulia Inc. (1)
250 Montgomery St 4th Fl, San Francisco, CA 94104
Tel.: (415) 376-8280
Web Site: http://www.taulia.com
Emp.: 200
Cloud-Based Invoice Management Solutions
N.A.I.C.S.: 513210
Cedric Bru (CEO)

Subsidiary (Non-US):

Taulia GmbH (1)
Gladbacher Strasse 74, 40219, Dusseldorf, Germany
Tel.: (49) 21163552650
Cloud-Based Invoice Management Solutions
N.A.I.C.S.: 513210
Martin Quensel (Mng Dir)

Taulia UK Ltd. (2)
20 Fortzroy Sq, London, W1T 6EJ, United Kingdom
Tel.: (44) 2037003525
Web Site: http://www.taulia.com
Emp.: 15
Cloud-Based Invoice Management Solutions
N.A.I.C.S.: 513210
Jon Keating (Mng Dir)

TechniData BCS GmbH (1)

AND PRIVATE COMPANIES / SAPPHIRE CORPORATION LIMITED

Bergheimer Str 3, 88677, Markdorf, Germany
Tel.: (49) 32212249164
Software Development Services
N.A.I.C.S.: 541511

TechniData IT-Service GmbH (1)
Planckstrasse 1, 88677, Markdorf, Germany
Tel.: (49) 754496880
Web Site: https://www.technidata-its.de
Emp.: 250
Environmental, Health & Safety Solutions
N.A.I.C.S.: 513210
Peter Jung *(CEO)*

Technology Management Associates Inc. (1)
15040 Conference Center Dr Ste 300, Chantilly, VA 20151
Tel.: (703) 964-5801
Web Site: http://www.tmamission.com
Application Software Development Services
N.A.I.C.S.: 541511
Matt Jones *(Pres)*

WalkMe Ltd. (1)
1 Walter Moses St 1, Tel Aviv, 6789903, Israel
Tel.: (972) 37630333
Web Site: https://www.walkme.com
Rev.: $266,954,000
Assets: $454,057,000
Liabilities: $193,910,000
Net Worth: $260,147,000
Earnings: ($59,136,000)
Emp.: 1,000
Fiscal Year-end: 12/31/2023
Software Development Services
N.A.I.C.S.: 541511

iAnywhere Solutions Canada Ltd. (1)
415 Phillip St, Waterloo, N2L 3X2, ON, Canada
Tel.: (519) 883-6488
Software Development Services
N.A.I.C.S.: 541511

iAnywhere Solutions K. K. (1)
4-15-1 Akasaka Garden City 5f, Minato-Ku, Tokyo, 107-0052, Japan
Tel.: (81) 3 5544 6400
Web Site: http://www.ianywhere.jp
Telecommunication Software Development Services
N.A.I.C.S.: 541511

SAPAN CHEMICALS LIMITED
B 206 Shivam Flats Nr Ayappa Temple Gotri Road, Vadodara, 390021, India
Tel.: (91) 2652226095   In
Web Site:
http://www.sapanchem.com
Rev.: $96,716
Assets: $529,333
Liabilities: $316,449
Net Worth: $212,884
Earnings: ($207)
Fiscal Year-end: 03/31/18
Software Development Services
N.A.I.C.S.: 541511
Mahesh R. Shah *(Mng Dir)*

SAPCOTE GROUP PLC
First Floor 26-30 High Street, Sutton Coldfield, B72 1UP, United Kingdom
Tel.: (44) 1212148900
Web Site: http://www.sapcotes.co.uk
Year Founded: 1853
Real Estate & Property Development
N.A.I.C.S.: 531210
Stuart Sapcote *(Chm)*

SAPEC S.A.
500 Avenue Louise b 6, 1050, Brussels, Belgium
Tel.: (32) 2 513 92 58   BE
Web Site: http://www.sapec.be
Year Founded: 1926
Sales Range: $150-199.9 Million
Emp.: 949
Chemical Product Mfr & Whslr
N.A.I.C.S.: 325998

Antoine Velge *(CEO)*
Subsidiaries:

Interpec Iberica S.A. (1)
Ochandiano 12, Madrid, 28023, Spain
Tel.: (34) 917 10 22 22
Animal Food Distr
N.A.I.C.S.: 424910

Navipor - Operadora Portuaria Geral, Lda. (1)
Av Luisa Todi N 11, 2900-461, Setubal, Portugal
Tel.: (351) 265 547 050
Web Site: http://www.navipor.pt
Marine Cargo Handling Services
N.A.I.C.S.: 488320
Carlos Perpetuo Joaquim Franco *(CEO)*

Trade Corporation International S.A. (1)
C/ Alcala 498 2nd Floor, 28027, Madrid, Spain
Tel.: (34) 91 3273200
Web Site: http://www.tradecorp.com.es
Farm Supplies Distr
N.A.I.C.S.: 424910

Subsidiary (Non-US):

Tradecorp France (2)
Arnaud Malerbe 7 Av de la Reine Astrid, 13090, Aix-en-Provence, France
Tel.: (33) 6 68 72 73 87
Farm Supplies Distr
N.A.I.C.S.: 424910

Subsidiary (Non-US):

Nevada Chemicals SA De CV (3)
Lazaro Cardenas No 2305, Guadalajara, 44920, Jalisco, Mexico
Tel.: (52) 3336714565
Chemical Product Whslr
N.A.I.C.S.: 424690

Subsidiary (Non-US):

Tradecorp do Brasil LTDA. (2)
Rua Oriente 55, Chacara da Barra, Campinas, 13090-740, Brazil
Tel.: (55) 1937093400
Web Site: http://www.tradecorp.com.br
Farm Supplies Distr
N.A.I.C.S.: 424910
Luiz Fernando Schmitt *(Dir-Comml)*

SAPHORE EQUIPEMENTS
D932 Route De Pau, 33213, Mazeres, Langon, France
Tel.: (33) 557980131
Web Site: http://www.saphore.fr
Year Founded: 1925
Sales Range: $10-24.9 Million
Emp.: 35
Tire Mfr & Whslr
N.A.I.C.S.: 423130

SAPIENS INTERNATIONAL CORPORATION N.V.
Azrieli Center 26 Harukmin Street, Holon, 5885800, Israel
Tel.: (972) 37902000   AN
Web Site: https://www.sapiens.com
Year Founded: 1982
SPNS—(NASDAQ)
Rev.: $474,736,000
Assets: $668,344,000
Liabilities: $265,490,000
Net Worth: $402,854,000
Earnings: $52,595,000
Emp.: 4,754
Fiscal Year-end: 12/31/22
Insurance Software Products & Services
N.A.I.C.S.: 513210
Gary J. Sherne *(Chief Revenue Officer-North America & Exec VP-North America)*
Subsidiaries:

Adaptik Corporation (1)
1495 Vly Ctr Pkwy Ste 350, Bethlehem, PA 18017

Tel.: (800) 306-1062
Policy Administration Software Developer
N.A.I.C.S.: 513210
John Pettit *(Pres & CEO)*

Delphi Technology Inc. (1)
470 Atlantic Ave Ste 702, Boston, MA 02210
Tel.: (617) 259-1200
Web Site: http://www.delphi-tech.com
Rev.: $15,200,000
Emp.: 100
System Software Development Services
N.A.I.C.S.: 541512
Sam Fang *(Founder & CEO)*

Knowledge Partners International, LLC (1)
227 Us Highway 206 2-12, Flanders, NJ 07836
Tel.: (973) 543-1339
Web Site: http://www.kpiusa.com
Emp.: 20
Business Rules Training & Services
N.A.I.C.S.: 541511
Barbara von Halle *(Founder & Mng Partner)*

Sapiens (UK) Limited (1)
Suites 338a 338b and 339 Belmont Road, 1 George Street, Uxbridge, UB8 1HE, Mddx, United Kingdom
Tel.: (44) 1895464000
Web Site: https://www.sapiens.com
Insurance Software Products & Services
N.A.I.C.S.: 513210
Raj Ghuman *(Sr VP-Bus Dev-EMEA & APAC)*

Sapiens Americas Corporation (1)
4000 Centre Green Way Ste 150, Cary, NC 27513
Tel.: (919) 405-1500
Insurance Software Products & Services
N.A.I.C.S.: 513210
Roni Al-Dor *(Pres & CEO)*

Sapiens Denmark A/S (1)
Lyngbyvej 2 3rd Floor 2100, Copenhagen, Denmark
Tel.: (45) 70227620
Property & Life Insurance Services
N.A.I.C.S.: 524113

Sapiens Israel Software Systems Ltd. (1)
Weisgal 1 Rabin Science Park, Nes Ziyyona, 74140, Israel
Tel.: (972) 89382888
Insurance Software Products & Services
N.A.I.C.S.: 513210
Roni Al-Dor *(Pres & CEO)*

Sapiens Software Solutions (Poland) Sp. z o.o. (1)
Silesia Business Park building D 146 Chorzowska Street, 40-101, Katowice, Poland
Tel.: (48) 513794458
Property & Life Insurance Services
N.A.I.C.S.: 524113

Sapiens Technologies Ltd. (1)
Park Amhamada Industrial Ctr Rabin, PO Box 4011, Rehovot, 76120, Israel
Tel.: (972) 89382777
Insurance Software Products & Services
N.A.I.C.S.: 513210

Sapiens Technology Japan Co., LTD. (1)
Queens Tower C 17F 2-3-5 Minatomirai, Nishi-ku, Yokohama, Kanagawa, Japan
Tel.: (81) 456824777
Web Site: https://www.sapiens.co.jp
Education & Environment Consulting Services
N.A.I.C.S.: 541620

Sapiens Information Technology (Shanghai) Co., Ltd. (1)
Room 350 Y1 No 112 Liang Xiu Road Pudong New Area, Shanghai, China
Tel.: (86) 2150273370
Property & Life Insurance Services
N.A.I.C.S.: 524113

StoneRiver, Inc. (1)
4601 DTC Blvd Ste 200, Denver, CO 80237   (100%)
Tel.: (800) 943-2851
Web Site: http://www.stoneriver.com

Insurance Technology & Administrative Support Services
N.A.I.C.S.: 513210
Branch (Domestic):

StoneRiver Inc. (2)
4665 Cornell Rd Ste 245, Cincinnati, OH 45241
Tel.: (513) 771-2070
Computer Software Developer for Reinsurance Companies
N.A.I.C.S.: 334610
Lori Zank *(Mgr-QA)*

SAPMER S.A.
Fishing dock, BP 2012, 97823, Le Port, Reunion
Tel.: (262) 262420272
Web Site: https://sapmer.fr
ALMER—(EUR)
Sales Range: $200-249.9 Million
Emp.: 1,029
Fish Farming & Seafood Processing Services
N.A.I.C.S.: 311710
Yannick Lauri *(Chm)*
Subsidiaries:

Soparma S.A.S. (1)
24 Bis Pl Croix de Pierre, PO Box 171, 36100, Issoudun, France
Tel.: (33) 254212521
Seafood Exposition Services
N.A.I.C.S.: 311710

SAPONIA D.D.
Matije Gupca 2, 31000, Osijek, Croatia
Tel.: (385) 31513513
Web Site: http://www.saponia.hr
Year Founded: 1894
Sales Range: $50-74.9 Million
Emp.: 800
Detergents & Personal Hygiene Products
N.A.I.C.S.: 325611
Damir Skender *(Pres)*
Subsidiaries:

Maraska d.d (1)
Biogradska cesta 64a, 23000, Zadar, Croatia
Tel.: (385) 23208800
Web Site: https://www.maraska.hr
Sales Range: Less than $1 Million
Alcoholic Drink Product Distr
N.A.I.C.S.: 424820
Zdravko Pavic *(Chm-Supervisory Bd)*

SAPPE PUBLIC COMPANY LIMITED
9/3 Bang Chan Industrial Estate Soi Seri Thai 56 Seri Thai Road, Khanna Yao Sub-district & district, Bangkok, 10230, Thailand
Tel.: (66) 23194949
Web Site: http://www.sappe.com
SAPPE—(THA)
Rev.: $181,215,287
Assets: $165,817,435
Liabilities: $52,089,452
Net Worth: $113,727,983
Earnings: $30,666,654
Emp.: 701
Fiscal Year-end: 12/31/23
Juice & Other Beverages Mfr
N.A.I.C.S.: 311411
Natee Onin *(Chm)*

SAPPHIRE CORPORATION LIMITED
3 Shenton Way 25-05 Shenton House, Singapore, 068805, Singapore
Tel.: (65) 65351944   SG
Web Site:
https://www.sapphirecorp.com.sg
Year Founded: 1976

SAPPHIRE CORPORATION LIMITED

Sapphire Corporation Limited—(Continued)
BRD—(SES)
Rev.: $13,702,057
Assets: $108,118,390
Liabilities: $12,393,529
Net Worth: $95,724,860
Earnings: $4,412,351
Emp.: 55
Fiscal Year-end: 12/31/22
Investment Holding Company; Property Construction, Mining Resource, Infrastructure & Building Resource Products & Services
N.A.I.C.S.: 551112
Kit Hoi-Gee Ng (CFO)

Subsidiaries:

Hainan I.R.E. Letian Construction & Decoration Engineering Co., Ltd. (1)
6/F CMEC Building, No 22 Guomao Road, Haikou, 570125, Hainan, China (49%)
Tel.: (86) 898 6858 4741
Construction & Engineering Services
N.A.I.C.S.: 541330

Sapphire Construction & Development Pte. Ltd. (1)
3 Shenton Way 25-01 Shenton House, 07-02 Yenom Industrial Bldg, Singapore, 349574, Singapore (100%)
Tel.: (65) 62503838
Sales Range: $25-49.9 Million
Emp.: 20
Construction & Development Services
N.A.I.C.S.: 237990

Sapphire Mineral Resources Pte. Ltd. (1)
3 Shenton Way 25-01 Shenton House, 07-02 Yenom Industrial Bldg, Singapore, 349574, Singapore (100%)
Tel.: (65) 62503838
Web Site: http://www.sapphirecorp.com.sg
Sales Range: $50-74.9 Million
Emp.: 7
Mining Operation Investment & Mineral Trading Services
N.A.I.C.S.: 423520

SAPPHIRE FIBRES LIMITED
316 Cotton Exchange Building II Chundrigar Road, Karachi, Pakistan
Tel.: (92) 21111000100
Web Site: http://www.sapphire.com.pk
SFL—(KAR)
Rev.: $262,954,103
Assets: $409,417,355
Liabilities: $217,422,434
Net Worth: $191,994,921
Earnings: $29,203,938
Emp.: 4,144
Fiscal Year-end: 06/30/19
Textile Products
N.A.I.C.S.: 313110
Shahid Abdullah (CEO)

SAPPHIRE FOODS INDIA LTD.
702 Prism Tower A Wing Mindspace Link Road West, Goregaon, Mumbai, 400062, India
Tel.: (91) 2249186200
Web Site: https://www.sapphirefoods.in
Year Founded: 2015
543397—(BOM)
Restaurant Services
N.A.I.C.S.: 722511
Vijay Jain (CFO)

Subsidiaries:

French Restaurants Private Limited (1)

SAPPHIRE TEXTILE MILLS LTD.
4th Floor Tricon Corporate Center 73-E Jail Road, Gulberg II, Lahore, Pakistan
Tel.: (92) 42111000100
Web Site: https://sapphiretextiles.com.pk
SAPT—(KAR)
Rev.: $245,934,760
Assets: $317,440,661
Liabilities: $199,817,324
Net Worth: $117,623,337
Earnings: $18,376,779
Emp.: 9,120
Fiscal Year-end: 06/30/19
Textile Mill
N.A.I.C.S.: 313210
Nadeem Abdullah (CEO)

Subsidiaries:

Sapphire Retail Limited (1)
7A-K Main Boulevard Gulberg II, Lahore, Pakistan
Tel.: (92) 42111000100
Web Site: https://srl.com.pk
Cloth Distr
N.A.I.C.S.: 458110
Nadeem Abdullah (Chm)

Sapphire Wind Power Company Limited (1)
313 Cotton Exchange I I Chundrigar Rd, Karachi, Sindh, Pakistan
Tel.: (92) 21111000100
Energy & Lighting Products Mfr & Distr
N.A.I.C.S.: 333248

SAPPI LIMITED
108 Oxford Road, Rosebank, Johannesburg, 2196, South Africa
Tel.: (27) 114078111
Web Site: https://www.sappi.com
Year Founded: 1936
SPPJY—(OTCIQ)
Rev.: $5,809,000,000
Assets: $5,796,000,000
Liabilities: $3,351,000,000
Net Worth: $2,445,000,000
Earnings: $259,000,000
Emp.: 13,000
Fiscal Year-end: 09/30/23
Pulp & Paper Products Mfr
N.A.I.C.S.: 322120
Glen Thomas Pearce (CFO)

Subsidiaries:

Sappi Deutschland GmbH (1)
Tel.: (49) 51112333700
Sales Range: $50-74.9 Million
Emp.: 65
Coated Woodfree Paper Products Distr
N.A.I.C.S.: 423840
Peter Goer (Mng Dir)

Subsidiary (Domestic):

Sappi Alfeld GmbH (2)
Muhlenmasch 1, 31061, Alfeld, Germany
Tel.: (49) 5181770
Web Site: https://www.sappi.com
Emp.: 750
Paper Mills
N.A.I.C.S.: 322120

Sappi Ehingen GmbH (2)
Biberacher Strasse 73, 89584, Ehingen, Germany
Tel.: (49) 73915010
Web Site: https://www.sappi.com
Sales Range: $125-149.9 Million
Emp.: 500
Paper Mills
N.A.I.C.S.: 322120

Sappi Europe S.A. (1)
Glaverbel Building 166 Chaussee De La Hulpe, 1170, Brussels, Belgium (100%)
Tel.: (32) 26769700
Sales Range: $50-74.9 Million
Emp.: 125
N.A.I.C.S.: 322120

Sappi Fine Paper North America (1)
225 Franklin St 28th Fl, Boston, MA 02110-2804 (100%)
Tel.: (617) 423-7300
Web Site: http://www.na.sappi.com
Sales Range: $1-4.9 Billion
Emp.: 3,300
Warrens Standard Printing Papers, Scott Printing Papers, Publishing Papers, Release Papers, Converting
N.A.I.C.S.: 322299
Anne Ayer (VP-Corp Dev & Dissolving Wood Pulp)

Subsidiary (Domestic):

Sappi Cloquet LLC (2)
2201 Ave B, Cloquet, MN 55720
Tel.: (218) 879-2300
Sales Range: $200-249.9 Million
Emp.: 720
Paper Mills
N.A.I.C.S.: 322120

US Paper Corporation (2)
2700 Westchester Ave Ste 300, Purchase, NY 10577-2554
Tel.: (914) 253-8660
Sales Range: $50-74.9 Million
Emp.: 9
N.A.I.C.S.: 322120
Laura Hiller (Controller)

Sappi Fine Paper South Africa (1)
48 Ameshoff Street, Braamfontein, 2017, Johannesburg, South Africa (100%)
Tel.: (27) 11 407 8111
Web Site: http://www.sappi.com
Sales Range: $150-199.9 Million
Emp.: 500
Paper & Packaging Mfr
N.A.I.C.S.: 322120

Sappi Forests (Pty) Ltd (1)
108 Oxford Road, Rosebank, Johannesburg, 2196, South Africa (100%)
Tel.: (27) 114078445
Web Site: http://www.sappi.com
Sales Range: $50-74.9 Million
Emp.: 80
Pulpwood, Woodchips, Sawlogs, Mining Timber Logs
N.A.I.C.S.: 423990

Sappi Holding GmbH (1)
Brucker Strasse 21, Gratkorn, 8101, Austria
Tel.: (43) 31242010
Emp.: 140
Investment Management Service
N.A.I.C.S.: 523999

Sappi Lanaken N.V. (1)
Tel.: (32) 89719719
Sales Range: $200-249.9 Million
Emp.: 500
Publication Paper
N.A.I.C.S.: 322120

Sappi Lanaken Press Paper NV (1)
Montaigneweg 2 Ind Zone 2 020, 3620, Lanaken, Belgium
Tel.: (32) 89719719
Web Site: http://www.sappi.com
Sales Range: $250-299.9 Million
Emp.: 500
Pulp & Paper Mfr
N.A.I.C.S.: 322110
Peter Loubele (Dir-Mill)

Sappi Maastricht B.V. (1)
Biesenweg 16, 6211 AA, Maastricht, Netherlands
Tel.: (31) 433822222
Sales Range: $200-249.9 Million
Emp.: 420
Paper Mills
N.A.I.C.S.: 322120
Peter Loubele (Mng Dir)

Sappi Manufacturing (Pty) Limited (1)
48 Ameshoff Street, Braamfontein, 2001, Johannesburg, South Africa
Tel.: (27) 114078467
Web Site: http://www.sappi.com
Sales Range: $200-249.9 Million
Emp.: 700
Paper Products Mfr
N.A.I.C.S.: 322299
Tony Pires (Gen Mgr)

Sappi North America Inc. (1)
255 State St, Boston, MA 02109
Tel.: (617) 423-7300
Paper Products Mfr
N.A.I.C.S.: 325992

INTERNATIONAL PUBLIC

Mike Haws (Pres & CEO)

Sappi Papier Holding GmbH (1)
Alserstrasse 21, 1080, Vienna, Austria
Tel.: (43) 1526912238
Web Site: http://www.sappi.com
Sales Range: $550-599.9 Million
Emp.: 1,000
Holding Company
N.A.I.C.S.: 551112

Subsidiary (Domestic):

Sappi Austria Produktions GmbH & Co. KG (2)
Brucker Strasse 21, 8101, Gratkorn, Austria
Tel.: (43) 31242010
Web Site: https://www.sappi.com
Sales Range: $400-449.9 Million
Paper Mills
N.A.I.C.S.: 322120

Sappi Southern Africa (1)
108 Oxford Road, Rosebank, Johannesburg, 2196, Braamfontein, South Africa (100%)
Tel.: (27) 114078111
Web Site: https://www.sappi.com
Sales Range: $300-349.9 Million
Emp.: 600
Paper Mills
N.A.I.C.S.: 322120

Sappi Stockstadt GmbH (1)
Aschaffenburger Strasse Tor 3, 63811, Stockstadt, Germany
Tel.: (49) 60274200
Web Site: https://www.sappi.com
Sales Range: $75-99.9 Million
Emp.: 150
Paper & Pulp Mfr
N.A.I.C.S.: 322299

Sappi Timber Industries New Business Development (1)
48 Ameshoff St Sappi House, Braamfontein, 2017, Johannesburg, South Africa (100%)
Tel.: (27) 114078111
Web Site: http://www.sappi.com
Sales Range: $250-299.9 Million
Emp.: 600
Particleboard; Medium-Density Fibreboard; Sawn Timber; Mine Support Systems
N.A.I.C.S.: 423310

Sappi Timber Industries Pty Ltd (1)
Sappi House 48 Ameshoff St, 38 Ameshoff St, 2017, Braamfontein, South Africa (100%)
Tel.: (27) 114078111
Web Site: http://www.sappi.com
Sales Range: $300-349.9 Million
Emp.: 1,000
Paper Mills
N.A.I.C.S.: 322120

Sappi Trading Ltd. (1)
28/F One Pacific Centre 414 Kwun Tong Road, Kwun Tong, Kowloon, China (Hong Kong) (100%)
Tel.: (852) 28773473
Sales Range: $25-49.9 Million
Emp.: 50
Printing & Publishing Papers, Chemical Cellulose, Unbleached Kraft Pulp, Release Paper, Flexpack & Technical Papers, Label Paper & Self-Adhesive Paper
N.A.I.C.S.: 322120

Subsidiary (Non-US):

Sappi Trading Africa Pty Ltd (2)
108 Oxford Road, Rosebank, 2198, South Africa (100%)
Tel.: (27) 114078111
Web Site: http://www.zappi.com
Sales Range: $25-49.9 Million
Emp.: 15
N.A.I.C.S.: 322120
Tony Pires (Gen Mgr)

Sappi Trading Australia Pty Ltd (2)
Suite 402 Level 410 Help Street, Chatswood, 2067, NSW, Australia (100%)
Tel.: (61) 294102911
Web Site: https://www.sappi.com
Sales Range: $50-74.9 Million
Emp.: 8
N.A.I.C.S.: 322120

Sappi Trading do Brasil Ltda (2)

AND PRIVATE COMPANIES

SAPPORO HOLDINGS LIMITED

Rua Joaquim Floriano 466 CJ 502 Ed Corporate Itaim Bibi, Sao Paulo, 04534-002, Brazil **(100%)**
Tel.: (55) 1121658250
Web Site: http://www.sappi.com.br
Sales Range: $50-74.9 Million
Emp.: 9
N.A.I.C.S.: 322120
Flavio Ignacio *(Mng Dir)*

Sappi Trenfor Trading Ltd (2)
17 Wiesenstrasse, CH 8008, Zurich, Switzerland **(100%)**
Tel.: (41) 14213355
Sales Range: $25-49.9 Million
Emp.: 50
N.A.I.C.S.: 322120

Tembec Inc. - Matane High-Yield Pulp Mill
400 Rue Du Port, CP 640, Matane, G4W 3P6, QC, Canada
Tel.: (418) 562-7272
Sales Range: $50-74.9 Million
Emp.: 140
High Yield Pulp Mill
N.A.I.C.S.: 322110

SAPPORO CLINICAL LABORATORY INC.
Kita 3jo Nishi 18chome 22, Chuo-ku, Sapporo, 060-0005, Hokkaido, Japan
Tel.: (81) 116416311
Web Site: https://www.saturin.co.jp
Year Founded: 1965
9776—(TKS)
Rev.: $130,098,020
Assets: $110,254,800
Liabilities: $36,335,170
Net Worth: $73,919,630
Earnings: $2,511,800
Emp.: 871
Fiscal Year-end: 03/31/24
Laboratory Testing Services
N.A.I.C.S.: 541380
Chuichi Date *(Founder & Chm)*

SAPPORO DRUG STORE CO., LTD.
1-2-18 Taihei-Sanjo, Kita-ku, Sapporo, 002-8003, Hokkaido, Japan
Tel.: (81) 11 7718100
Web Site: http://satudora.jp
Year Founded: 1972
Drug Store Retailer
N.A.I.C.S.: 456110
Mutsuhiro Tomiyama *(Chm)*

SAPPORO HOLDINGS LIMITED
20-1 Ebisu 4-chome, Shibuya-ku, Tokyo, 150-8522, Japan
Tel.: (81) 354237407   JP
Web Site:
    https://www.sapporoholdings.jp
Year Founded: 1949
2501—(SAP)
Rev.: $3,426,706,310
Assets: $4,384,360,753
Liabilities: $3,173,604,229
Net Worth: $1,210,756,525
Earnings: $57,641,229
Emp.: 7,592
Fiscal Year-end: 12/31/23
Holding Company; Beer, Wines, Soft Drinks & Real Estate Services
N.A.I.C.S.: 551112

Subsidiaries:

Foremost Blue Seal, Ltd. (1)
5-5-6 Makiminato, Urasoe, 901-2610, Okinawa, Japan
Tel.: (81) 988775103
Web Site: https://www.blueseal.co.jp
Emp.: 282
Ice Cream Mfr & Distr
N.A.I.C.S.: 311520

Hanei.Limited (1)
5-2-1 Imazukita, Tsurumi-ku, Osaka, 538-0041, Japan

Tel.: (81) 675036674
Web Site: https://osakaou.net
Food Mfr & Distr
N.A.I.C.S.: 311412

Hokkaido Sapporo Lion Limited (1)
Tanukikoji Lion Building Minami 2-jo Nishi 2-7-1, Chuo-ku, Sapporo, 060-0062, Hokkaido, Japan
Tel.: (81) 112057811
Web Site: https://hokkaido-sapporolion.jp
Restaurant Services
N.A.I.C.S.: 722511

Keiyo Utility Co., Ltd. (1)
11th Takase-cho, Funabashi, 273-0014, Chiba, Japan
Tel.: (81) 474352261
Web Site: https://www.kyu.co.jp
Emp.: 30
Comprehensive Management Services
N.A.I.C.S.: 561110
Kazutoshi Yamazaki *(Pres)*

NEW SANKO INC. (1)
1st Street Mall San 1-3-6 Inaho, Otaru, 047-0032, Japan
Tel.: (81) 134 33 3500
Restaurant Management Services
N.A.I.C.S.: 722511
Noboru Yamada *(Gen Mgr)*

New Sanko Limited (1)
Sun Mall 1st Avenue 1-3-6 Inaho, Otaru, Hokkaido, 047-0032, Japan **(64.4%)**
Tel.: (81) 134333500
Web Site: http://www.newsanko.co.jp
Sales Range: $10-24.9 Million
Emp.: 35
Restaurant Services
N.A.I.C.S.: 722511

Okinawa Pokka Corporation Co., Ltd. (1)
7th floor Daido Life Naha Building 3-1-15 Maejima, Naha, Okinawa, Japan
Tel.: (81) 988637099
Web Site: https://www.pokkasapporo-fb.jp
Beverage & Food Distr
N.A.I.C.S.: 424490

POKKA CORPORATION (1)
Nagoya Hirokoji Place 4-2-29 Sakae, Naka-ku, Nagoya, 460-8415, Japan
Tel.: (81) 522495583
Web Site: http://www.pokka.co.jp
Rev.: $838,858,370
Emp.: 751
Food & Beverage Mfr & Distr
N.A.I.C.S.: 311999

POKKA CREATE CO., LTD. (1)
2-14 Kagurazaka Nobie Bldg 3f, Shinjuku-Ku, Tokyo, 162-0825, Japan
Tel.: (81) 332678010
Coffee Mfr
N.A.I.C.S.: 311920

Pokka Corporation (Singapore) Pte. Ltd. (1)
39 Quality Road, Singapore, 618810, Singapore
Tel.: (65) 6395 9229
Web Site: http://www.pokka.com.sg
Sales Range: $50-74.9 Million
Emp.: 150
Beverage Mfr & Distr
N.A.I.C.S.: 312120

Pokka Pte. Ltd. (1)
39 Quality Road, Singapore, 618810, Singapore
Tel.: (65) 63959229
Web Site: https://www.pokka.co
Beer Beverage Mfr & Distr
N.A.I.C.S.: 312111

Pokka Sapporo Office Support Ltd. (1)
10th floor Fukagawa Gathalia Tower S Building 1-5-25 Kiba, Koto-ku, Tokyo, 135-0042, Japan
Tel.: (81) 356336543
Web Site: https://www.ps-officesupport.jp
Beverage & Food Distr
N.A.I.C.S.: 424490

Ps Beverage Ltd. (1)
10th Floor Fukagawa Gathalia Tower S Building 1-5-25 Kiba, Koto-ku, Tokyo, 135-0042, Japan

Tel.: (81) 356336541
Web Site: https://www.ps-beverage.jp
Beer Beverage Mfr & Distr
N.A.I.C.S.: 312111

SAPPORO CANADA INC. (1)
551 Clair Rd W, Guelph, N1L 0H7, ON, Canada
Tel.: (519) 822-1834
Web Site: http://www.sleeman.ca
Emp.: 400
Beverages Mfr
N.A.I.C.S.: 312120

SAPPORO ENGINEERING LIMITED (1)
20-1 Kamitoda, Toda, 335-0022, Saitama, Japan
Tel.: (81) 48 447 7221
Engineering Services
N.A.I.C.S.: 541330

SAPPORO FINE FOODS CO., LTD (1)
4-20-1 Ebisu Sapporo Beer Honsha Bldg Nai, Shibuya-Ku, Tokyo, 150-0013, Japan
Tel.: (81) 354237098
Food Products Mfr & Distr
N.A.I.C.S.: 311999

SAPPORO FOODS NET CO., LTD (1)
4-20-1 Ebisu Sapporo Beer Honsha Bldg Nai, Shibuya-Ku, Tokyo, 150-0013, Japan
Tel.: (81) 366803022
Food Products Mfr
N.A.I.C.S.: 311999

SAPPORO GROUP MANAGEMENT CO., LTD. (1)
No 1 No 20 four-chome Ebisu, Shibuya-Ku, Tokyo, 150-6037, Japan
Tel.: (81) 354237247
Web Site: http://www.sapporoholdings.co.jp
Investment Management Service
N.A.I.C.S.: 523999

SAPPORO INTERNATIONAL INC. (1)
4-20-1 Ebisu, Shibuya-ku, Tokyo, 150-8522, Japan
Tel.: (81) 354237224
Web Site: http://www.sapporoholdings.co.jp
Sales Range: $350-399.9 Million
Emp.: 200
Alcoholic Beverages Mfr
N.A.I.C.S.: 312120
Yoshiyuki Mochida *(Pres)*

SAPPORO LOGISTICS SYSTEMS CO., LTD. (1)
4-20-1 Ebisu Sapporo Beer Honsha Bldg, Shibuya-Ku, Tokyo, 150-0013, Japan **(100%)**
Tel.: (81) 334448680
Logistics Consulting Servies
N.A.I.C.S.: 541614
Matsuzaki Eiji *(Pres)*

SAPPORO VIETNAM LIMITED (1)
Tel.: (84) 2822217666
Web Site:
    https://www.sapporovietnam.com.vn
Alcoholic Beverages Mfr
N.A.I.C.S.: 312120

STARNET CO., LTD. (1)
4-20-1 Ebisu, Shibuya-Ku, Tokyo, 150-0013, Japan
Tel.: (81) 354237223
Sales Range: $25-49.9 Million
Emp.: 100
Soft Drinks Mfr
N.A.I.C.S.: 312111
Hiroaki Inamoto *(Mgr)*

Sapporo Agency Limited (1)
7 1 10 Ebisu Chome, Shibuya-ku, Tokyo, 150 8405, Japan **(100%)**
Tel.: (81) 354481521
Sales Range: $50-74.9 Million
Emp.: 22
Provider of Non-Life Insurance
N.A.I.C.S.: 524128

Sapporo Beer's Beverage Co., Ltd. (1)
12-14 Ebisu-nishi 1-chome, Shibuya-ku, Tokyo, 150-0021, Japan **(100%)**
Web Site: http://www.sapporobeer.jp

Sales of Solf Drinks
N.A.I.C.S.: 312111

Sapporo Beverage Co., Ltd (1)
4-20-1 Ebisu, Shibuya-ku, 150-8522, Tokyo, Japan
Tel.: (81) 354237224
Web Site: http://www.sapporoholdings.jp
Sales Range: $100-124.9 Million
Emp.: 400
Soft Drink Sls & Mfr
N.A.I.C.S.: 312111

Sapporo Breweries Limited (1)
Yebisu Garden Place 4-20-1 Ebisu, Shibuya-ku, Tokyo, 150-8522, Japan
Tel.: (81) 120207800
Web Site: https://www.sapporobeer.jp
Sales Range: $75-99.9 Million
Emp.: 800
Beer, Wine & Other Spirits Importer & Mfr
N.A.I.C.S.: 424820
Hideya Takashima *(Pres)*

Sapporo Group Logistics Company Limited (1)
4-20-1 Ebisu, Shibuya-ku, Tokyo, Japan
Tel.: (81) 334448680
Web Site: http://www.sapporo-gl.jp
Freight Services
N.A.I.C.S.: 488510
Mashiro Oga *(Pres)*

Sapporo Hotel Enterprise Limited (1)
4-1 Mita 1-chome, Meguro-ku, Tokyo, 153-8580, Japan **(100%)**
Provider of Hotel Services
N.A.I.C.S.: 561599

Sapporo Lion Limited (1)
(57.1%)
Tel.: (81) 120848136
Web Site: https://www.ginzalion.jp
Emp.: 446
Provider of Restaurant Services
N.A.I.C.S.: 722511
Yuichiro Miyake *(Pres)*

Sapporo Logistics System Co., Ltd. (1)
20 1 Ebisu 4 Chome, Shibuya Ku, Tokyo, 150-8686, Japan **(55%)**
Tel.: (81) 354232111
Provider of Transportation Services
N.A.I.C.S.: 541614

Sapporo Real Estate Co.,Ltd. (1)
4-20-3 Ebisu, Shibuya-ku, 150-0013, Japan
Tel.: (81) 354237104
Web Site: https://www.sapporo-re.jp
Real Estate Services
N.A.I.C.S.: 531210

Sapporo U.S.A., Inc. (1)
(100%)
Tel.: (212) 922-9165
Web Site: https://www.sapporobeer.com
Sales Range: $25-49.9 Million
Import & Marketing of Beer in the U.S. & Product Wine Marketing
N.A.I.C.S.: 424690

Branch (Domestic):

Sapporo U.S.A., Inc. (2)
1821250 Hawthorne Blvd, Torrance, CA 90503
Tel.: (310) 792-7458
Web Site: http://www.sapporobeer.com
Sales Range: $25-49.9 Million
Emp.: 5
Import & Marketing of Beer in the U.S. & Producer of Wine
N.A.I.C.S.: 424810

Joint Venture (Domestic):

Silver Springs Citrus Inc. (2)
25411 Mare Ave, Howey in the Hills, FL 34737 **(51%)**
Tel.: (352) 324-2101
Web Site: http://www.silverspringscitrus.com
Sales Range: $100-124.9 Million
Emp.: 227
Grower, Harvester & Processor of Citrus Fruits
N.A.I.C.S.: 311411

Sapporo Wines Limited (1)
20-1 Ebisu 4-chome, Shibuya-ku, Tokyo,

6573

SAPPORO HOLDINGS LIMITED

Sapporo Holdings Limited—(Continued)

150-8686, Japan (100%)
Mfr of Wines
N.A.I.C.S.: 312130

Shimano Europe Fishing Holding BV (1)
High Tech Campus 92, 5656 AG, Eindhoven, Netherlands (100%)
Tel.: (31) 341272233
Sales Range: $25-49.9 Million
Emp.: 280
Sales of Fishing Tackle
N.A.I.C.S.: 339920

Shinsyu-Ichi Miso Co., Ltd. (1)
Yebisu Garden Place 4-20-1 Ebisu, Shibuya-ku, Tokyo, 150-0013, Japan
Tel.: (81) 357951176
Web Site: https://www.shinsyuichi.jp
Emp.: 252
Food Product Mfr & Distr
N.A.I.C.S.: 311999

Sleeman Breweries, Ltd. (1)
551 Clair Road West, Guelph, N1L 1E9, ON, Canada
Tel.: (519) 822-1834
Web Site: http://sleeman.ca
Sales Range: $150-199.9 Million
Emp.: 1,000
Developer, Producer, Importer, Marketer & Distr of Beer
N.A.I.C.S.: 312120

Subsidiary (Domestic):

Sleeman Unibroue Quebec (2)
80 Rue Des Carrieres, Chambly, J3L 2H6, QC, Canada
Tel.: (450) 658-7658
Web Site: http://www.unibroue.com
Brewery
N.A.I.C.S.: 445320

Tokyo Energy Service Co., Ltd. (1)
3rd Floor Ebisu Garden Place Tower, Shibuya-ku, Tokyo, 150-0013, Japan
Tel.: (81) 332808810
Sales Range: $75-99.9 Million
Emp.: 18
Heating & Cooling Energy Supplying Services
N.A.I.C.S.: 221330
Kosuke Sawada (Mgr)

YGP REAL ESTATE CO., LTD. (1)
4-20-3 Ebisu, Shibuya-Ku, Tokyo, 150-0013, Japan
Tel.: (81) 354237101
Web Site: http://www.sapporoholdings.jp
Sales Range: $50-74.9 Million
Emp.: 70
Real Estate Manangement Services
N.A.I.C.S.: 531390

YOKOHAMA KEIWA BUILDING CO., LTD. (1)
4-20-1 Ebisu, Shibuya-Ku, Tokyo, 150-0013, Japan
Tel.: (81) 354237114
Real Estate Manangement Services
N.A.I.C.S.: 531390

Yasuma Co., Ltd. (1)
5-23-2 Nishigotanda, Shinagawa-ku, Tokyo, 141-8559, Japan
Tel.: (81) 334906955
Web Site: https://www.yasuma.co.jp
Emp.: 200
Spice Mfr & Distr
N.A.I.C.S.: 311942

Yebisu Garden Place Co., Ltd. (1)
4-20 Ebisu, Shibuya Ku, Tokyo, 150-0013, Japan (100%)
Tel.: (81) 354237111
Web Site: http://gardenplace.jp
Sales Range: $25-49.9 Million
Provider of Real Estate Management Services
N.A.I.C.S.: 531210

Yebisu Winemart Co., Ltd. (1)
Yebisu Garden Place B1F 20-7 Ebisu 4-Chome, Shibuya-Ku, Tokyo, 150-0013, Japan (100%)
Tel.: (81) 354242580
Web Site: http://www.partywine.com

Sales Range: $25-49.9 Million
Emp.: 30
Sales of Wine
N.A.I.C.S.: 445320

SAPTAK CHEM AND BUSINESS LIMITED
201 Chiranjiv Complex Mahalaxmi Five Road Paldi, Ahmedabad, 380007, Gujarat, India
Tel.: (91) 7976835065 In
Web Site: https://www.saptakchem.com
Year Founded: 1980
Chemical Derivatives Mfr & Distr
N.A.I.C.S.: 325180

SAPURA ENERGY BERHAD
No 7 Jalan Tasik Mines Resort City, 43300, Seri Kembangan, Selangor, Malaysia
Tel.: (60) 386598800 MY
Web Site: https://sapuraenergy.com
Year Founded: 2011
SAPNRG—(KLS)
Rev: $1,014,806,678
Assets: $3,977,015,625
Liabilities: $3,957,714,090
Net Worth: $19,301,535
Earnings: ($2,242,562,603)
Emp.: 4,194
Fiscal Year-end: 01/31/22
Holding Company; Oil & Gas Support Services
N.A.I.C.S.: 551112
Shahril Shamsuddin (Pres & CEO)

Subsidiaries:

Babalon Pty Ltd (1)
1 Ambitious Link, Bibra Lake, 6163, WA, Australia
Tel.: (61) 894116500
Web Site: http://www.tmt.com.au
Emp.: 150
Oil & Gas Support Services
N.A.I.C.S.: 213112
Paul Colley (Pres)

Kencana HL Sdn. Bhd. (1)
Plot D1 Lumut Port Industrial Park Kampung Acheh Mukim Lumut, Daerah Manjung, 32000, Sitiawan, Perak Darul Ridzuan, Malaysia (100%)
Tel.: (60) 5 692 3071
Offshore Oil Rig Engineering, Procurement & Construction Services
N.A.I.C.S.: 237990

Subsidiary (Domestic):

Kencana Marine Sdn, Bhd. (2)
Plot D1 Lumut Port Industrial Park Kampung Acheh, 32000, Sitiawan, Perak Darul Manjung, Malaysia
Tel.: (60) 56923071
Marine Structural Metal Component Fabrication & Engineering Services
N.A.I.C.S.: 332312

Kencana Petroleum Ventures Sdn. Bhd. (1)
Level 6 Menara Kencana Petroleum Solaris Dutamas 1 Jalan Dutamas 1, 50480, Kuala Lumpur, Malaysia
Tel.: (60) 362098000
Web Site: http://www.kencanapetroleum.com.my
Offshore Drilling Services
N.A.I.C.S.: 213111

Kencana Torsco Sdn. Bhd. (1)
Lot 538 & 595 Lumut Port Industrial Park Kampung Acheh Mukim Lumut, Daerah Manjung, 32000, Sitiawan, Perak Darul Ridzuan, Malaysia
Tel.: (60) 5 692 1034
Web Site: http://www.torsco.com
Sales Range: $25-49.9 Million
Emp.: 75
Onshore Steel Fabrication & Construction Services
N.A.I.C.S.: 332312
Ceow Yiusee (Mng Dir)

Ocean Flow International LLC (1)
12120 Wickchester Ln Ste 200, Houston, TX 77079
Tel.: (713) 328-6700
Web Site: https://www.ocean-flow.com
Marine Engineering Services
N.A.I.C.S.: 541330

Peritus International Sdn. Bhd. (1)
Level 8 Sapura Mines No 7 Jalan Tasik The Mines Resort City, Seri Kembangan, 43300, Kuala Lumpur, Selangor, Malaysia
Tel.: (60) 386598800
Offshore Pipeline Engineering Services
N.A.I.C.S.: 541330
Ir Siti Haryana A. Ghani (Mgr-Engineering-Asia Pacific)

Sapura Baker Hughes TPS Sdn. Bhd. (1)
No 24 Jalan Sepadu 25/123 Taman Perindustrian Axis Seksyen 25, 40400, Shah Alam, Selangor, Malaysia
Tel.: (60) 358704575
Web Site: https://www.sapurabakerhughes.com
Gas Turbine Maintenance Services
N.A.I.C.S.: 811310
K. Karunakaran (Co-CEO)

Sapura Energy Sdn. Bhd. (1)
No 7 Jalan Tasik Mines, Resort City, 43300, Seri Kembangan, Selangor, Malaysia
Tel.: (60) 386598800
Web Site: https://www.sapuraenergy.com
Holding Company
N.A.I.C.S.: 551112

Subsidiary (Domestic):

Sapura Power Services Sdn Bhd (2)
No 24 Jalan Sepadu 25/123, Shah Alam, 40400, Selangor, Malaysia
Tel.: (60) 351240644
Marine Engineering Services
N.A.I.C.S.: 327910

Sapura Retail Solutions Sdn Bhd (2)
Lot G3 Incubator 2 Technology Park, Lebuhraya Puchong, 57100, Kuala Lumpur, Malaysia
Tel.: (60) 389919119
Web Site: http://www.srs.my
Emp.: 50
Industrial Automation Control System Mfr
N.A.I.C.S.: 334513
Rose Mat (VP)

Sapura Petroleum (Australia) Pty Ltd (1)
Level 14 Alluvion 58 Mounts Bay Road, Perth, 6000, WA, Australia
Tel.: (61) 894801000
Web Site: http://www.sapurakencana.com.au
Holding Company
N.A.I.C.S.: 551112

SapuraKencana Allied Marine Sdn Bhd (1)
No 2 Jalan SBC 10 Taman Perindustrian, 68100, Batu Caves, Selangor, Malaysia (100%)
Tel.: (60) 3 6196 6800
Web Site: http://www.sapurakencana.com
Underwater Engineering Services
N.A.I.C.S.: 541330

Subsidiary (Domestic):

AME Marine Services Sdn Bhd (2)
No 23 Jalan Industri Batu Caves 1/6 Taman Perindustrian, 68100, Batu Caves, Selangor, Malaysia
Tel.: (60) 361850844
Marine Engineering Services
N.A.I.C.S.: 541330

AME Robotics Corporation (2)
Level 1 Lot 7 Block F Saguking Commercial Building Jalan, Patau-Patau, 87000, Labuan, Malaysia
Tel.: (60) 87 410 745
Industrial Equipment Rental Services
N.A.I.C.S.: 532490

SapuraKencana Energy Malaysia Inc. (1)
Level 53 Tower 2 Petronas Twin Towers Kuala Lumpur City Centre, Kuala Lumpur,

50088, Malaysia (100%)
Tel.: (60) 320901888
Sales Range: $150-199.9 Million
Emp.: 200
Gas Exploration
N.A.I.C.S.: 213111
Kevin Robinson (VP)

Tioman Drilling Company Sdn Bhd (1)
C 6 2 Block C Megan Avenue 1 No 18 Jalan Tun Razak, 51400, Kuala Lumpur, Malaysia
Tel.: (60) 3 2716 0000
Oil & Gas Drilling Services
N.A.I.C.S.: 213111

Total Marine Technology (Malaysia) Sdn. Bhd. (1)
19 Jalan TPP3 Taman Perindustrian Putra, 47130, Puchong, Selangor, Malaysia
Tel.: (60) 380699000
Remotely Operated Vehicle Mfr
N.A.I.C.S.: 336612

Total Marine Technology Pty. Ltd. (1)
1 Ambitious Link, Bibra Lake, 6163, WA, Australia
Tel.: (61) 894116500
Web Site: https://www.tmtrov.com
Emp.: 120
Remotely Operated Vehicle Mfr
N.A.I.C.S.: 336612
Paul Colley (CEO & Founder)

SAPURA HOLDINGS SDN. BHD.
7 Jalan Tasik The Mines Resort City, 43300, Seri Kembangan, Selangor Darul Ehsan, Malaysia
Tel.: (60) 389497000 MY
Web Site: http://www.sapura.com.my
Year Founded: 1975
Sales Range: $800-899.9 Million
Emp.: 5,000
Holding Company
N.A.I.C.S.: 551112
Shahril Shamsuddin (Pres & CEO)

Subsidiaries:

Sapura Industrial Berhad (1)
Lot 2 and 4 Jalan P/11 Seksyen 10 Kawasan Perindustrian Bangi, 43650, Bandar Baru Bangi, Selangor Darul Ehsan, Malaysia
Tel.: (60) 389256011
Web Site: http://www.sapuraindustrial.com.my
Rev.: $63,071,328
Assets: $52,703,513
Liabilities: $26,026,361
Net Worth: $26,677,152
Earnings: $2,226,810
Emp.: 700
Fiscal Year-end: 01/31/2023
Brake, Engine Components & Shock Absorber Mfr
N.A.I.C.S.: 336330
Shahriman Shamsuddin (Exec Dir)

Sapura Resources Berhad (1)
Sapura at Mines 7 Jalan Tasik Mines Resort City, 43300, Seri Kembangan, Selangor Darul Ehsan, Malaysia
Tel.: (60) 389497000
Web Site: http://www.sapura.com.my
Rev.: $13,188,533
Assets: $211,392,968
Liabilities: $157,433,265
Net Worth: $53,959,703
Earnings: $19,728,720
Emp.: 6,000
Fiscal Year-end: 01/31/2023
Petroleum Mfr
N.A.I.C.S.: 211120
Shahriman Shamsuddin (Mng Dir)

Subsidiary (Domestic):

Sapura Aero Sdn. Bhd. (2)
Mezzanine Floor Hangar 3 Old Cargo Complex Sultan Abdul Aziz Shah, International Airport, 47200, Subang Jaya, Malaysia
Tel.: (60) 3 7846 2304
Web Site: http://www.sapura-aero.com
Oil Transportation Services
N.A.I.C.S.: 481219

AND PRIVATE COMPANIES

SARAJEVO PUBLISHING D.D.

SAPUTO INC.
Suite 2900 1000 de la Gauchetiere St W, Montreal, H3B 4W5, QC, Canada
Tel.: (514) 328-6662 QC
Web Site: https://www.saputo.com
Year Founded: 1954
SAP—(TSX)
Rev.: $11,761,579,800
Assets: $10,703,937,240
Liabilities: $5,615,205,840
Net Worth: $5,088,731,400
Earnings: $214,344,720
Emp.: 18,600
Fiscal Year-end: 03/31/22
Food Products Mfr
N.A.I.C.S.: 311514
Gaetane Wagner *(Chief HR Officer)*

Subsidiaries:

Dairy Crest Group plc (1)
5 The Heights Brooklands, Weybridge, KT13 0NY, Surrey, United Kingdom
Tel.: (44) 1372472200
Web Site: https://www.uk.saputo.com
Rev.: $616,278,016
Assets: $847,517,184
Liabilities: $518,736,640
Net Worth: $328,780,544
Earnings: $201,693,440
Emp.: 1,097
Fiscal Year-end: 03/31/2018
Milk & Other Dairy Products Mfr
N.A.I.C.S.: 311511
Mark Allen *(CEO)*

Subsidiary (Domestic):

Dairy Crest Limited (2)
5 The Heights Brooklands, Weybridge, KT13 0NY, Surrey, United Kingdom (100%)
Tel.: (44) 1372472200
Web Site: https://www.uk.saputo.com
Sales Range: $100-124.9 Million
Emp.: 300
Fluid Milk Mfr
N.A.I.C.S.: 311511
Tom Atherton *(Pres & COO)*

Subsidiary (Domestic):

Philpot Dairy Products Limited (3)
Philpot House, Rayleigh, SS6 7HH, Essex, United Kingdom (100%)
Tel.: (44) 1268775522
Web Site: http://www.philpots.co.uk
Sales Range: $25-49.9 Million
Emp.: 5
Dairy Product Whslr
N.A.I.C.S.: 424430
Claud Bilbao *(Mng Dir)*

F&A Dairy Products Inc. (1)
212 Hwy 35 S, Dresser, WI 54009
Tel.: (715) 755-3485
Web Site: http://www.fadairy.com
Sales Range: $150-199.9 Million
Emp.: 170
Natural & Processed Cheese Mfr
N.A.I.C.S.: 311513
Bob Snyder *(VP-New Mexico Ops)*

Neilson Dairy Limited (1)
861 Clyde Ave, Ottawa, K1Z 5A4, ON, Canada
Tel.: (613) 728-1751
Web Site: http://www.neilsondairy.com
Sales Range: $50-74.9 Million
Emp.: 100
Dairy Products
N.A.I.C.S.: 424430

Saputo Cheese USA Inc. (1)
1 Overlook Pt Ste 300, Lincolnshire, IL 60069 (100%)
Tel.: (847) 267-1100
Web Site: https://www.saputospecialty.com
Matured & Processed Cheese
N.A.I.C.S.: 311513
Dominique Delugeau *(Sr VP-Specialty Cheese & Intl Trade)*

Subsidiary (Domestic):

Montchevre-Betin, Inc. (2)
4030 Palos Verdes Dr N Ste 201, Rolling Hills Estates, CA 90274
Tel.: (310) 541-3520
Web Site: http://www.montchevre.com
Cheese Mfr
N.A.I.C.S.: 311513

Plant (Domestic):

Saputo Dairy Products (2)
691 Inyo St, Newman, CA 95360
Tel.: (209) 862-1732
Sales Range: $125-149.9 Million
Cheese Products Mfr
N.A.I.C.S.: 311513

Saputo Dairy Foods USA, LLC (1)
2711 N Haskell Ave Ste 3400, Dallas, TX 75204-2928
Tel.: (800) 236-1014
Web Site: http://www.unordinarydairy.com
Sales Range: $1-4.9 Billion
Emp.: 2,000
Dairy, Non-Dairy Extended Shelf Life Products & Cultured Products Mfr
N.A.I.C.S.: 311514
Paul Corney *(Pres & COO)*

Subsidiary (Domestic):

Friendship Dairies, LLC (2)
6701 County Rd 20, Friendship, NY 14739
Tel.: (585) 973-3031
Web Site: http://www.friendshipdairies.com
Sales Range: $75-99.9 Million
Emp.: 250
Cultured Dairy Products Mfr & Marketer
N.A.I.C.S.: 424430
Paige Pistone *(Dir-Mktg)*

Plant (Domestic):

Saputo Dairy Foods USA (2)
4041 Hwy 61, White Bear Lake, MN 55110
Tel.: (651) 426-1633
Sales Range: $75-99.9 Million
Emp.: 140
Specialty Dairy Products Mfr
N.A.I.C.S.: 311514
Matt Mensink *(Gen Mgr)*

Saputo Dairy Foods USA (2)
100 Milk Lane, Newington, CT 06111-2242
Tel.: (860) 666-1511
Dairy Products Mfr
N.A.I.C.S.: 311514
Mohammad Akbar *(Mgr-Production)*

Saputo Dairy Products Canada G.P. (1)
2365 Chemin de la Cote-de-Liesse, Saint-Laurent, Montreal, H4N 2M7, QC, Canada
Web Site: https://www.saputo.ca
Dairy Product Mfr & Distr
N.A.I.C.S.: 311511

Warrnambool Cheese & Butter Factory Company Holdings Ltd. (1)
5331 Great Ocean Road, Allansford, 3277, VIC, Australia (100%)
Tel.: (61) 355653100
Web Site: http://www.wcbf.com.au
Cheese, Milk Powders, Whey Protein Concentrate, Butter, Cream & Packaged Milk Mfr
N.A.I.C.S.: 311513

Subsidiary (Domestic):

Protein Technology Victoria Pty Ltd (2)
5331 Great Ocean Rd, Allansford, 3277, VIC, Australia
Tel.: (61) 355602200
Sales Range: $150-199.9 Million
Emp.: 700
Dairy Products Mfr & Whslr
N.A.I.C.S.: 424430
Richard Wallace *(Gen Mgr)*

The Warrnambool Cheese And Butter Factory Company Limited (2)
5331 Great Ocean Road, Allansford, 3277, VIC, Australia
Tel.: (61) 355632100
Web Site: http://www.wcbf.com
Sales Range: $100-124.9 Million
Emp.: 300
Dairy Products Mfr
N.A.I.C.S.: 311513
David J. Lord *(CEO & Mng Dir)*

Warrnambool Milk Products Pty Limited (2)
5331 Ocean Rd, Allansford, 3277, Victoria, Australia
Tel.: (61) 3 5563 2160
Web Site: http://www.wcbf.com.au
Sales Range: $75-99.9 Million
Emp.: 200
Dairy Products Mfr & Whslr
N.A.I.C.S.: 424430

SAR AUTO PRODUCTS LIMITED
50/E Bhaktinagar Industrial Estate, Rajkot, 360002, Gujarat, India
Tel.: (91) 2812374726
Web Site: https://www.sarautoproductsltd.com
Year Founded: 1987
538992—(BOM)
Rev.: $1,431,605
Assets: $2,938,193
Liabilities: $1,050,537
Net Worth: $1,887,657
Earnings: $74,072
Emp.: 5
Fiscal Year-end: 03/31/23
Auto Parts Mfr
N.A.I.C.S.: 336390
Rameshkumar D. Virani *(Chm & Mng Dir)*

SARA JSC
Km 2 Avenue VI Lenin, Vinh, Nghe An, Vietnam
Tel.: (84) 383594176
Web Site: https://www.srb.vn
Sales Range: Less than $1 Million
Information Technology Consulting Services
N.A.I.C.S.: 541512

SARA SAE PVT. LTD.
7 1 Pritam Road, Dehradun, 248 001, India
Tel.: (91) 135 267 2395 In
Web Site: http://www.sarasae.com
Year Founded: 1978
Oil & Gas Field Equipment Mfr & Distr
N.A.I.C.S.: 333132

Subsidiaries:

Consolidated Pressure Control, LLC (1)
27260 Oak Ridge Park Dr, Oak Ridge North, TX 77385
Tel.: (281) 893-5900
Web Site: http://www.cpcmfg.com
Oil & Gas Pressure Control Systems & Components Mfr
N.A.I.C.S.: 333132
Jeramiah Niewiadomski *(Mgr-Technical Svc & Electrical)*

STS Products Inc. (1)
27260 Oak Rdg Park, Conroe, TX 77385
Tel.: (832) 575-1444
Web Site: http://www.stsproductsinc.com
Oil & Gas Field Equipment Mfr & Distr
N.A.I.C.S.: 333132
V. K. Dhawan *(Chm, Pres & CEO)*

Subsidiary (Non-US):

STS PRODUCTS FZE (2)
Office/Warehouse No RA08SB05, PO Box 16780, Jebel Ali, Dubai, United Arab Emirates
Tel.: (971) 4 8808871
Oil Field Equipment Distr
N.A.I.C.S.: 423830

STS Products (S) Pte. Ltd. (2)
21 Tuas Avenue 11, Singapore, 639085, Singapore
Tel.: (65) 65 6863 2897
Oil Field Equipment Distr
N.A.I.C.S.: 423830

SARA VIETNAM JSC
Villa No 35 BT5 Phap Van Tu Hiepurban area Hoang Liet Ward, Hoang Mai district, Hanoi, Vietnam
Tel.: (84) 2466863602
Web Site: http://www.sara.com.vn
Year Founded: 2003
SRA—(HNX)
Rev.: $7,748,847
Assets: $17,740,103
Liabilities: $3,662,936
Net Worth: $14,077,167
Earnings: $1,053,284
Fiscal Year-end: 12/31/20
Information Technology Consulting Services
N.A.I.C.S.: 541512
Dang Quang Nam *(Member-Mgmt Bd)*

SARAFIN S.P.A.
Via Melchiorre Gioia 121, 20124, Milano, Italy
Tel.: (39) 03792168380 IT
Web Site: http://www.sarafin.it
Investment Management Service
N.A.I.C.S.: 523999

SARAIVA S.A. LIVREIROS EDITORES
Rua Henrique Schaumann 270, Sao Paulo, Brazil
Tel.: (55) 1146379660 BR
Web Site: http://www.saraivari.com.br
Year Founded: 1914
SLED4—(BRAZ)
Rev.: $165,793,928
Assets: $210,984,953
Liabilities: $253,739,295
Net Worth: ($42,754,343)
Earnings: ($78,748,513)
Emp.: 1,832
Fiscal Year-end: 12/31/19
Book Publisher, Distr & Retailer
N.A.I.C.S.: 513130
Jorge Eduardo Saraiva *(Chm)*

SARAJEVO GAS A.D.
Nikola Tesla 55, 71123, Istocno Sarajevo, Bosnia & Herzegovina
Tel.: (387) 57340113
Web Site: https://sarajevogas.com
Year Founded: 1994
SGAS—(BANJ)
Sales Range: $1-9.9 Million
Emp.: 27
Gas Distribution Services
N.A.I.C.S.: 221210
Nedeljko Elek *(Gen Dir)*

SARAJEVO OSIGURANJE D.D.
Marsala Tita 29, Sarajevo, Bosnia & Herzegovina
Tel.: (387) 33 569 600
Web Site: http://www.sarajevoosiguranje.ba
Insurance Services
N.A.I.C.S.: 524298

SARAJEVO PUBLISHING D.D.
Obala Kulina bana br 4, 71 000, Sarajevo, Bosnia & Herzegovina
Tel.: (387) 33220809 BA
Web Site: http://www.sarajevopublishing.ba
SAPBR—(SARE)
Rev.: $981,368
Assets: $4,298,267
Liabilities: $2,339,434
Net Worth: $1,958,833
Earnings: $28,204
Emp.: 30
Fiscal Year-end: 12/31/20
Books Publishing Services
N.A.I.C.S.: 513130

SARAJEVOPUTEVI D.D. SARAJEVO

Sarajevoputevi d.d. Sarajevo—(Continued)

SARAJEVOPUTEVI D.D. SARAJEVO
Mustajbega Fadilpasica 17, Sarajevo, Bosnia & Herzegovina
Tel.: (387) 3 366 7499
Web Site: http://www.saputevi.ba
SPUSR—(SARE)
Rev.: $5,700,108
Assets: $5,967,456
Liabilities: $1,925,566
Net Worth: $4,041,890
Earnings: $20,697
Emp.: 118
Fiscal Year-end: 12/31/20
Road & Motorways Construction Services
N.A.I.C.S.: 237310

SARAJEVSKA PIVARA D.D.
Franjevacka 15, 71000, Sarajevo, Bosnia & Herzegovina
Tel.: (387) 33491100
Web Site: http://www.sarajevska-pivara.com
Year Founded: 1864
SRPVRK1—(SARE)
Rev.: $14,430,457
Assets: $78,317,168
Liabilities: $20,599,525
Net Worth: $57,717,643
Earnings: $30,917
Emp.: 242
Fiscal Year-end: 12/31/20
Beverages Mfr & Distr
N.A.I.C.S.: 424820

SARAJISHVILI JOINT STOCK COMPANY
4 Sarajishvili Avenue, Tbilisi, 388053, Georgia
Tel.: (995) 322 554444
Web Site: http://www.sarajishvili.ge
Year Founded: 1884
Wine Mfr & Distr
N.A.I.C.S.: 312130

SARAMA RESOURCES LTD.
Suite 8 245 Churchill Avenue, Subiaco, 6008, WA, Australia
Tel.: (61) 893637600 BC
Year Founded: 2010
SRR—(ASX)
Rev.: $336,879
Assets: $2,461,543
Liabilities: $1,128,375
Net Worth: $1,333,168
Earnings: ($2,478,787)
Emp.: 3
Fiscal Year-end: 12/31/23
Gold Exploration
N.A.I.C.S.: 212220
Andrew Dinning *(Co-Founder, CEO & Mng Dir)*

Subsidiaries:

SWA SARL (1)
16 Rue Lena Bernstein, 51100, Reims, France
Tel.: (33) 619671664
Gold Ore Mining Services
N.A.I.C.S.: 212220

SARAMANIS LIMITED
2 Setia Raja Road, 98000, Miri, Sarawak, Malaysia
Tel.: (60) 85322672
Web Site: http://www.saramanis.com
Year Founded: 1996
TG8—(NSXA)
Rev.: $271,521
Assets: $543,865
Liabilities: $1,001,419
Net Worth: ($457,554)
Earnings: ($646,348)
Fiscal Year-end: 12/31/20

Rubber & Palm Oil Seeding
N.A.I.C.S.: 326299
Jason Jong Tze Yun *(CEO)*

SARAMIN CO., LTD.
14th floor 43 Digital-ro 34-gil Gurodong Kolon Science Valley 1, Gurogu, Seoul, 08378, Korea (South)
Tel.: (82) 220254733
Web Site: https://www.saramincorp.co.kr
Year Founded: 2005
143240—(KRS)
Rev.: $908,169
Assets: $161,201,775
Liabilities: $28,812,848
Net Worth: $132,388,927
Earnings: $22,447,782
Emp.: 412
Fiscal Year-end: 12/31/22
Human Resouce Services
N.A.I.C.S.: 541612
Hwang Hyeon-Sun *(CEO)*

Subsidiaries:

Imazins Co., Ltd. (1)
12th floor Jaehwa Square 311 Dokmak-ro, Mapo-gu, Seoul, Korea (South)
Tel.: (82) 262208800
Web Site: http://www.imazins.com
Investment Management Service
N.A.I.C.S.: 523940

Kiwoom Asset Management Co., Ltd. (1)
18 Yeouinaru-ro 4-gil, Yeongdeungpo-gu, Seoul, 07331, Korea (South)
Tel.: (82) 27890300
Web Site: http://www.kiwoomam.com
Rev.: $36,900,000,000
Emp.: 235
Investment Management Service
N.A.I.C.S.: 523940
Seong Hoon Kim *(CEO)*

Kiwoom Asset Planner Inc. (1)
9th floor Sajo Building 424 Yeongdongdaero, Gangnam-gu, 135-502, Seoul, Korea (South)
Tel.: (82) 220365300
Web Site: http://kiwoomap.com
Investment Management Service
N.A.I.C.S.: 523940

SARASWATI COMMERCIAL (INDIA) LIMITED
209-210 Arcadia Building 2nd Floor, 195 Nariman Point, Mumbai, 400 021, India
Tel.: (91) 2240198500
Web Site: https://www.saraswaticomm.com
Year Founded: 1983
512020—(BOM)
Rev.: $3,825,699
Assets: $40,811,521
Liabilities: $2,406,331
Net Worth: $38,405,190
Earnings: $2,910,439
Emp.: 8
Fiscal Year-end: 03/31/21
Investment Banking Services
N.A.I.C.S.: 523150
Vaishali R. Dhuri *(CFO)*

SARATOVENERGO AO
St Them Rakhova VG House 181 Vld, Saratov, 410012, Russia
Tel.: (7) 8452573573
Web Site: http://www.sarenergo.ru
SARE—(MOEX)
Sales Range: Less than $1 Million
Electric Power Distribution Services
N.A.I.C.S.: 221122

SARATOVSKIY NPZ AO
1 Bryanskaya Street, Saratov, 410022, Russia
Tel.: (7) 8452473060
Web Site: http://www.saratov-npz.ru

KRKN—(MOEX)
Sales Range: Less than $1 Million
Petroleum Product Mfr
N.A.I.C.S.: 324199

SARAWAK CABLE BERHAD
Lot 767 Block 8 Muara Tebas Land District Demak Laut, Industrial Estate Phase III Jalan Bako, 93050, Kuching, Sarawak, Malaysia
Tel.: (60) 82434311 MY
Web Site: https://www.sarawakcable.com
SCABLE—(KLS)
Rev.: $115,956,614
Assets: $110,518,095
Liabilities: $124,042,116
Net Worth: ($13,524,021)
Earnings: ($20,884,021)
Fiscal Year-end: 05/31/23
Holding Company; Power Cables & Wires Mfr
N.A.I.C.S.: 551112
Mahmud Abu Bekir Taib *(Chm)*

Subsidiaries:

Aerial Power Lines Sdn. Bhd. (1)
Malaysia International Aerospace Centre Sultan Abdul Aziz Shah Airport, Jalan Riyal U3/36 Bukit Jelutong Industrial Park, 47200, Subang Jaya, Selangor, Malaysia
Tel.: (60) 378400995
Web Site: http://www.apl.com.my
Aircraft Charter Services
N.A.I.C.S.: 481211

Leader Cable Industry Berhad (1)
Lot 1385 Tikam Batu Industrial Estate, Tikam Batu, 08600, Sungai Petani, Kedah, Malaysia
Tel.: (60) 44389988
Web Site: https://www.leadercable.com.my
Power & Telecommunication Cable Distr
N.A.I.C.S.: 423510
Azhar Ariffin *(Mng Dir)*

SCB Power Transmission Sdn. Bhd. (1)
Lot 6072 & 6073 Jalan Haji Abdul Manan Off Jalan Meru Mukim Kapar, 41050, Klang, Selangor, Malaysia
Tel.: (60) 333934825
Power Cable & Wire Mfr
N.A.I.C.S.: 335929

Sarwaja Timur Sdn. Bhd. (1)
Lot 342 Block 8 MTLD Jalan Kampung Sejingkat Off Jalan Bako, 93050, Kuching, Sarawak, Malaysia
Tel.: (60) 82439688
Web Site: https://www.sarwaja.com
Stainless Steel Mfr
N.A.I.C.S.: 331210
Teoh Wen Jinq *(Sec)*

Universal Cable (M) Berhad (1)
No 33 Jalan Tiran, Kangkar Tebrau, 81100, Johor Bahru, Johor, Malaysia
Tel.: (60) 73553333
Web Site: https://www.ucable.com.my
Power Cables & Wires Mfr
N.A.I.C.S.: 335929
Peter Foo *(Mgr-Hedging)*

Plant (Domestic):

Universal Cable (M) Berhad - Plentong Manufacturing Plant (2)
Lot 7650 Muklim Plentong, 81750, Masai, Johor, Malaysia
Tel.: (60) 73877377
Fiber Optic Cable Mfr
N.A.I.C.S.: 335929

Universal Cable (Sarawak) Sdn. Bhd. (1)
Lot 767 Block 8 Jalan Bako, Muara Tebas Land District Demak Laut Industrial Estate Phase III, 93050, Kuching, Sarawak, Malaysia
Tel.: (60) 82433111
Web Site: https://www.ucssb.com.my
Sales Range: $50-74.9 Million
Emp.: 200
Power Cables & Wires Mfr & Whslr
N.A.I.C.S.: 335929

INTERNATIONAL PUBLIC

SARAWAK CONSOLIDATED INDUSTRIES BERHAD
Lot 1258 Jalan Utama Pending Industrial Estate, 93450, Kuching, Sarawak, Malaysia
Tel.: (60) 82334485
Web Site: https://www.scib.com.my
Rev.: $20,925,105
Assets: $28,235,393
Liabilities: $15,589,859
Net Worth: $12,645,535
Earnings: $765,978
Emp.: 281
Fiscal Year-end: 12/31/19
Pipes Mfr
N.A.I.C.S.: 327332
Jan Moi Voon *(Sec)*

SARAWAK OIL PALMS BERHAD
No 124-126 Jalan Bendahara, PO Box 547, 98007, Miri, Sarawak, Malaysia
Tel.: (60) 85436969
Web Site: https://www.sop.com.my
SOP—(KLS)
Rev.: $1,123,446,561
Assets: $1,035,762,116
Liabilities: $306,171,852
Net Worth: $729,590,265
Earnings: $106,719,577
Emp.: 7,290
Fiscal Year-end: 12/31/22
Palm Oil Mfr
N.A.I.C.S.: 311225
Paul Hee Kwong Wong *(CEO-Grp)*

SARAWAK PLANTATION BERHAD
8th Floor Wisma Naim 21/2 Milke Rock Road, 93200, Kuching, Sarawak, Malaysia
Tel.: (60) 233550 MY
Web Site: https://spb.listedcompany.com
Year Founded: 1997
SWKPLNT—(KLS)
Rev.: $150,457,598
Assets: $201,201,458
Liabilities: $51,792,833
Net Worth: $149,408,624
Earnings: $20,601,277
Emp.: 2,873
Fiscal Year-end: 12/31/22
Oil Palm Processing & Farming Services
N.A.I.C.S.: 311224
Amar Abdul Hamed Sepawi *(Chm)*

SARAY MATBAACILIK KAGITCILIK KIRTASIYECILIK TICARET VE SANAYI AS
Yildirim Beyazit Cad No 60, Balikhisar Mah, Ankara, Akyurt, Türkiye
Tel.: (90) 3125272890
Web Site: https://www.saraymatbaa.com.tr
Year Founded: 1982
SAMAT—(IST)
Sales Range: Less than $1 Million
Sanitary Paper Product Mfr
N.A.I.C.S.: 322291
Ali Keles *(Chm & Deputy Chm)*

SARAY MATBAACILIK KAGTCILIK KIRTASIYECILIK TICARET VE SANAYI A.S.
Merkez Mah Parker Street 2 Pursaklar, Ankara, Turkiye
Tel.: (90) 3125272890
Web Site: http://www.saraypaper.com
Year Founded: 1982
Sales Range: $10-24.9 Million
Printing Paper & Stationery Products
N.A.I.C.S.: 323111
Ali Keles *(CEO)*

SARDA ENERGY & MINERALS LTD
Industrial Growth Center Siltara, Raipur, 493 111, Chhattisgarh, India
Tel.: (91) 7712216000
Web Site: https://www.seml.co.in
Year Founded: 1973
SARDAEN—(NSE)
Rev.: $319,856,355
Assets: $617,173,830
Liabilities: $300,208,545
Net Worth: $316,965,285
Earnings: $51,381,330
Emp.: 1,210
Fiscal Year-end: 03/31/21
Steel Producer
N.A.I.C.S.: 331110
Pankaj Sarda *(Co-Mng Dir)*

Subsidiaries:

Madhya Bharat Power Corporation Limited (1)
Vanijya Bhawan 3rd floor Near Devendra Nagar Square, Raipur, 492001, Chhattisgarh, India
Tel.: (91) 7712214200
Web Site: https://www.mbpcl.co.in
Civil Engineering Services
N.A.I.C.S.: 541330

Sarda Energy & Minerals Hongkong Limited (1)
5th Floor Dah Sing Life Building 99-105 Des Voeus Road, Central, China (Hong Kong)
Tel.: (852) 28454112
Steel Mfr & Retailer
N.A.I.C.S.: 331110

Sarda Metals & Alloys Limited (1)
125 B-Wing Mittal Court, Nariman Point, Mumbai, 400 021, Maharashtra, India
Tel.: (91) 2222826680
Steel Mfr & Retailer
N.A.I.C.S.: 331110

SARDA PROTEINS LIMITED
B-536-537 Matsya Industrial Area, Alwar, 301030, Rajasthan, India
Tel.: (91) 7737822222
Web Site: https://www.sardaproteins.com
519242—(BOM)
Rev.: $713,981
Assets: $288,293
Liabilities: $6,117
Net Worth: $282,176
Earnings: ($3,960)
Emp.: 3
Fiscal Year-end: 03/31/23
Edible Oil Whslr
N.A.I.C.S.: 424990
Deepak Data *(Mng Dir)*

Subsidiaries:

Inside Data Ingenious Global Limited (1)
Station Road Durgapura, Jaipur, 302018, India
Tel.: (91) 7737822222
Mustard Oil Mfr
N.A.I.C.S.: 311225

SARE HOLDING, S.A.B. DE C.V.
Bosque de Radiatas No 18 despacho 402 Bosques de las Lomas, 05120, Mexico, CDMX, Mexico
Tel.: (52) 5553267026
Year Founded: 1997
SARE—(MEX)
Sales Range: Less than $1 Million
Holding Company
N.A.I.C.S.: 551112
Guillermo Guzman Cuevas *(Chm, CEO & Mng Dir)*

SAREGAMA INDIA LIMITED
33 Jessore Road, Kolkata, 700028, India
Tel.: (91) 3325512984
Web Site: https://www.saregama.com
Year Founded: 1946
532163—(BOM)
Rev.: $84,020,896
Assets: $230,394,842
Liabilities: $41,897,720
Net Worth: $188,497,122
Earnings: $20,836,124
Emp.: 282
Fiscal Year-end: 03/31/22
Audio & Video Distribution Services
N.A.I.C.S.: 512120
Vikram Mehra *(Mng Dir)*

Subsidiaries:

Pocket Aces Pictures Private Limited (1)
11th Floor Lotus Business Park Off New Link Road Andheri West, Andheri, Mumbai, 400053, Maharashtra, India
Tel.: (91) 2245428436
Web Site: https://pocketaces.in
Media Entertainment Services
N.A.I.C.S.: 541840

Saregama Limited (1)
79 College Road, Harrow, HA1 1BD, Middlesex, United Kingdom
Tel.: (44) 2039485483
Media Entertainment Services
N.A.I.C.S.: 541840

Saregama Plc. (1)
Unit 14 Europa Studios Victoria Road, London, NW10 6ND, United Kingdom
Tel.: (44) 2 8961 3344
Web Site: http://www.saregamaevents.com
Emp.: 2
Musical Event Organizer
N.A.I.C.S.: 711310
Amarpal S. Gaind *(Head-Ops-Europe)*

SARENET S.A.U
Parque Tecnologico 103, 48170, Zamudio, Bizkaia, Spain
Tel.: (34) 94 420 94 70
Web Site: http://www.sarenet.es
Year Founded: 1995
Sales Range: $25-49.9 Million
Emp.: 70
Telecommunication Servicesb
N.A.I.C.S.: 517111
Roberto Beitia *(Gen Mgr)*

SAREUM HOLDINGS PLC
Unit 2A Langford Arch London Road, Pampisford, Cambridge, CB22 3FX, United Kingdom
Tel.: (44) 1223497700
Web Site: https://www.sareum.com
SAR—(AIM)
Rev.: $50,914
Assets: $2,508,436
Liabilities: $1,076,641
Net Worth: $1,431,795
Earnings: ($3,963,826)
Emp.: 5
Fiscal Year-end: 06/30/23
Development Of New Therapeutic Drugs
N.A.I.C.S.: 424210
John Reader *(Co-Founder & Chief Scientific Officer)*

Subsidiaries:

Sareum Limited (1)
Unit 2A Langford Arch London Road, Pampisford, Cambridge, CB22 3FX, Cambridgeshire, United Kingdom
Tel.: (44) 1223497700
Web Site: https://www.sareum.com
Cancer Drug Mfr & Whslr
N.A.I.C.S.: 424210

SARGENT S.A.
Tecnica Thomas C Sargent, Sacel Casilla 166-D, Santiago, Chile
Tel.: (56) 25103000
Web Site: http://www.sargent.biz
Sales Range: $50-74.9 Million
Emp.: 140
Industrial Equipment Distr
N.A.I.C.S.: 423830
Bernandel Moltiva *(Pres)*

SARGODHA SPINNING MILLS LIMITED
Office No A-601/B City Towers 6-K Main Boulevard, Gulberg II, Lahore, Pakistan
Tel.: (92) 42 35788758
Web Site: http://www.sargodhaspinning.com
Rev.: $409,334
Assets: $13,349,545
Liabilities: $3,781,853
Net Worth: $9,567,693
Earnings: ($725,582)
Emp.: 38
Fiscal Year-end: 06/30/17
Yarn, Textile & Piece Goods Mfr & Exporter
N.A.I.C.S.: 313110

SARGON CAPITAL PTY LTD.
Level 9 287 Collins St, Melbourne, VIC, Australia
Tel.: (61) 390972800
Web Site: http://www.sargon.com.au
Software Developer
N.A.I.C.S.: 513210
Philip Kingston *(Co-Founder & CEO)*

Subsidiaries:

Decimal Software Limited (1)
Level 12 680 George Street, Sydney, 2000, NSW, Australia
Tel.: (61) 1 300 220 799
Web Site: http://www.decimal.com.au
Rev.: $1,442,616
Assets: $803,101
Liabilities: $406,899
Net Worth: $396,202
Earnings: ($1,786,581)
Fiscal Year-end: 06/30/2018
Software Developer
N.A.I.C.S.: 513210
Damon Watkins *(CEO)*

Subsidiary (Non-US):

DTD Ltd (2)
Rm 1505 08 & 1515 22 Asia Trade Ctr, 79 Lei Muk Rd, Kwai Chung, New Territories, China (Hong Kong)
Tel.: (852) 24181881
Apparels Mfr
N.A.I.C.S.: 315250
Dora Tong *(Mgr)*

Diversa Pty Ltd (1)
Level 20 357 Collins Street, Melbourne, 3000, VIC, Australia
Tel.: (61) 3 9097 2800
Web Site: http://www.diversa.com.au
Investment Management Service
N.A.I.C.S.: 523940

Subsidiary (Domestic):

Diversa Funds Management Pty Ltd (2)
Level 11 Waterfront Place 1 Eagle Street, Brisbane, 4000, QLD, Australia
Tel.: (61) 732 129250
Investment Management Service
N.A.I.C.S.: 523940

SARHAD TEXTILE MILLS LIMITED
125 Muree Road, Rawalpindi, Pakistan
Tel.: (92) 51 5568051
Yarn Spinning Mill Operator
N.A.I.C.S.: 313110

SARIN GROUP PTY LTD
150 St Andrews Dr, Port Lincoln, 5606, SA, Australia
Tel.: (61) 886214400
Web Site: http://www.saringroup.com.au
Sales Range: $10-24.9 Million
Emp.: 115
Fishing & Property Development Services
N.A.I.C.S.: 114119
Sime Sarin *(Founder)*

Subsidiaries:

Australian Fishing Enterprises Pty Ltd (1)
Billy Lights Point, Port Lincoln, 5606, SA, Australia
Tel.: (61) 8 86214 400
Web Site: http://www.afe.net.au
Emp.: 300
Fish Farming Services
N.A.I.C.S.: 112511
Sam Sarin *(Founder)*

SAMS Sea Farm Pty. Ltd. (1)
17 Pine Freezers Rd, Port Lincoln, 5606, SA, Australia
Tel.: (61) 886214600
Web Site: http://www.samstuna.com.au
Rev.: $11,000,000
Emp.: 20
Fish Farming
N.A.I.C.S.: 112512
Shane Phillips *(Mgr-Processing)*

SARINE TECHNOLOGIES LTD.
4 Haharash St, Hod Hasharon, 4524075, Israel
Tel.: (972) 97903500
Web Site: https://sarine.listedcompany.com
U77—(SES)
Rev.: $42,944,000
Assets: $76,602,000
Liabilities: $16,282,000
Net Worth: $60,320,000
Earnings: ($2,802,000)
Fiscal Year-end: 12/31/23
Diamond Mfr
N.A.I.C.S.: 333514
William L. Kessler *(Grp CFO)*

Subsidiaries:

Galatea Ltd (1)
Fastovska 25, Bila Tserkva, 09100, Kiev, Ukraine
Tel.: (380) 456363713
Proprietary Software Development Services
N.A.I.C.S.: 541511
Uzi Levami *(Exec Dir)*

SARISSA RESOURCES, INC.
99 Bronte Road Suite 708, Oakville, L6L3B7, ON, Canada NV
SRSR—(OTCIQ)
Sales Range: Less than $1 Million
Mineral Exploration Services
N.A.I.C.S.: 213114

SARITOW SPINNING MILLS LIMITED
17-Aziz Avenue Canal Bank Gulberg-V, Lahore, Pakistan
Tel.: (92) 4235715029
Web Site: https://saritowspinningmillsltd.com
SSML—(PSX)
Rev.: $25,092,700
Assets: $16,351,512
Liabilities: $11,888,199
Net Worth: $4,463,313
Earnings: $376,954
Emp.: 1,200
Fiscal Year-end: 06/30/19
Textile Spinning Mill
N.A.I.C.S.: 313110
M. Azam Saigol *(CEO)*

SARKIS GROUP INTERNATIONAL SAL
Sarkis Group Center Dbayeh High-

SARKIS GROUP INTERNATIONAL SAL

Sarkis Group International SAL—(Continued)
way, Beirut, 70033, Lebanon
Tel.: (961) 4544944
Web Site:
http://www.sarkisgroup.com
Year Founded: 1989
Emp.: 6,000
Holding Company Services
N.A.I.C.S.: 551112
Elie R. Sarkis (CEO & VP)

Subsidiaries:

Europharm Holdings S.A. (1)
Strada Ionescu Crum Nr 1, Ionefcu Crum
first brussel, Brasov, 500446, Romania
Tel.: (40) 268307500
Sales Range: $100-124.9 Million
Emp.: 300
Pharmaceuticals Distr
N.A.I.C.S.: 325412
Margareta Mares (Gen Mgr)

SARKUYSAN ELEKTROLITIK BAKIR SANAYI VE TICARET A.S.
Emek Mahallesi Asiroglu Caddesi Cd No 147, Darica, 41700, Kocaeli, Turkiye
Tel.: (90) 2626766600
Web Site:
https://www.sarkuysan.com
Year Founded: 1972
SARKY—(IST)
Rev.: $846,516,262
Assets: $268,713,984
Liabilities: $190,380,909
Net Worth: $78,333,075
Earnings: $34,863,453
Emp.: 1,095
Fiscal Year-end: 12/31/22
Copper Product Mfr
N.A.I.C.S.: 331420
Hayrettin Cayci (Chm)

Subsidiaries:

Bemka Emaye Bobin Teli ve Kablo
San. Tic. A.S. (1)
Birlik Organize Sanayi Bolgesi Bati Cad No 4, Tuzla, 34953, Istanbul, Turkiye
Tel.: (90) 216 593 27 27
Web Site: http://www.bemkawire.com.tr
Copper Wires Mfr
N.A.I.C.S.: 331420

Sarda Dagitim ve Ticaret A.S. (1)
Emek Asiroglu Cd No 147, Darica, 41700, Kocaeli, Turkiye
Tel.: (90) 262 654 0121
Web Site: https://www.sarda.com.tr
Steel Fabricator Mfr
N.A.I.C.S.: 332312

Sarkuysan S.p.a. (1)
Via Caracciolo 30, 20155, Milan, Italy
Tel.: (39) 023 459 2237
Copper Product Mfr
N.A.I.C.S.: 331420

Sarmakina Sanayi ve Ticaret A.S. (1)
Osmangazi Mahallesi Kanuni Sokak No 12, Darica, 41400, Kocaeli, Turkiye
Tel.: (90) 2626539082
Web Site: https://www.sarmakina.com.tr
Machinery Equipment Mfr & Distr
N.A.I.C.S.: 333248
Hayrettin Cayci (Chm & Gen Mgr)

SARL JEAN-MARC BROCARD
3 Route de Thablis Prehy, 89800, Auxerre, France
Tel.: (33) 386414900
Web Site: http://www.brocard.fr
Rev.: $25,600,000
Emp.: 28
Wine & Distilled Beverages
N.A.I.C.S.: 424820
Beno T. Grizard (Mgr-Fin)

SARLA PERFORMANCE FIBERS LIMITED
304 Arcadia 195 Nariman Point, Mumbai, 400 021, India
Tel.: (91) 2222834116
Web Site:
https://www.sarlafibers.com
Year Founded: 1993
SARLAPOLY—(NSE)
Rev.: $37,420,110
Assets: $79,855,230
Liabilities: $32,800,950
Net Worth: $47,054,280
Earnings: $3,624,075
Emp.: 289
Fiscal Year-end: 03/31/21
Yarn Sales & Mfr
N.A.I.C.S.: 313110
Madhusudhan Jhunjhunwala (Chm)

Subsidiaries:

Sarla Europe Lda (1)
Apartado 37, 4786-909, Trofa, Portugal
Tel.: (351) 252312093
Web Site: http://www.sarlaeurope.com
Polyester Distr
N.A.I.C.S.: 424690

Sarlaflex Inc. (1)
1497 Industrial Rd, Walterboro, SC 29488
Tel.: (843) 538-1940
Web Site: https://www.sarlaflex.com
Polyester Fibre Mfr & Distr
N.A.I.C.S.: 313110

SARMA AFARIN COMPANY
194 West Khoramshahr street, Tehran, Iran
Tel.: (98) 2188762301
Web Site:
https://www.sarmaafarin.com
Year Founded: 1968
SRMA—(THE)
Sales Range: Less than $1 Million
Air Conditioning Equipment Mfr
N.A.I.C.S.: 333415

SAROJA PHARMA INDUSTRIES INDIA LIMITED
209 2nd Floor Ecstasy Buisness Park City of Joy Complex Jsd Road, Mulund West, Mumbai, 400080, India
Tel.: (91) 2220810011
Web Site:
https://www.sarojapharma.com
Year Founded: 2019
SAROJA—(NSE)
Rev.: $6,122,665
Assets: $2,594,927
Liabilities: $1,976,398
Net Worth: $618,529
Earnings: $128,971
Emp.: 13
Fiscal Year-end: 03/31/23
Pharmaceutical Product Mfr & Distr
N.A.I.C.S.: 325412
Biju Gopinathan Nair (Founder)

SAROVA HOTEL GROUP LTD.
Valley Rd Of Kenyatta Ave, Nairobi, 72493, Kenya
Tel.: (254) 202713333
Web Site:
http://www.sarovahotels.com
Sales Range: $150-199.9 Million
Emp.: 1,200
Hotel
N.A.I.C.S.: 721110
Jimi Kariuki (Mng Dir)

SARSYS-ASFT AB
Piledalsvagen 51, Kopingebro, 271 73, Ystad, Sweden
Tel.: (46) 41165100
Web Site: https://www.sarsys-asft.com
Year Founded: 1991
Measurement Equipment Mfr
N.A.I.C.S.: 334519
Fredrik Graflind (Pres)

SARTEN AMBALAJ SANAYI VE TICARET A.S.
Ferko Signature Buyukdere Cad No 175/100, Sisli, Istanbul, Turkiye
Tel.: (90) 8507557786
Web Site: http://www.sarten.com.tr
SARTN—(IST)
Rev.: $336,905,564
Assets: $386,055,427
Liabilities: $276,514,489
Net Worth: $109,540,938
Earnings: $41,576,523
Emp.: 3,000
Fiscal Year-end: 12/31/22
Packaging Products Mfr
N.A.I.C.S.: 326199
Mustafa Zeki Saribekir (Chm)

Subsidiaries:

OOO Sarpak (1)
Kombinatskaya 3-A, 357100, Nevinnomyssk, Russia
Tel.: (7) 8655465171
Web Site: http://www.sarpak.ru
Light Metal Packaging Product Mfr
N.A.I.C.S.: 332439

Sarten Ambalaj SRL (1)
Soseaua de Centura Nr 10 Loc Jud, Ilfov, Voluntari, 077190, Romania
Tel.: (40) 213510858
Web Site: http://www.sarten.ro
Metal Packaging Product Mfr
N.A.I.C.S.: 332439

Sarten Ambalaza DOO (1)
Glavica BB, Paracin, Serbia
Tel.: (381) 78612746252
Metal Packaging Product Mfr
N.A.I.C.S.: 332439

Sarten Bulgaria Ltd. (1)
Botevgradsko Shose No 415, Sofia, 1839, Bulgaria
Tel.: (359) 24270610
Web Site: http://www.sarten.bg
Light Metal Packaging Product Mfr
N.A.I.C.S.: 332439
Branimir Mladenov (Exec Dir)

Sarten Packaging Netherlands B.V. (1)
Borchwerf 10D, 4704 RG, Roosendaal, Netherlands
Tel.: (31) 850711140
Metal Packaging Product Mfr
N.A.I.C.S.: 332439
Rene Willems (Dir-Ops)

SARTHAK INDUSTRIES LIMITED
Room No 4 Anna Bhuvan 3rd Floor 87C Devji Ratansi Marg, Dana Bunder, Mumbai, 400009, Maharashtra, India
Tel.: (91) 2266102209
Web Site:
https://www.sarthakindustries.com
531930—(BOM)
Rev.: $7,391,571
Assets: $8,264,229
Liabilities: $3,610,743
Net Worth: $4,653,486
Earnings: $91,002
Emp.: 26
Fiscal Year-end: 03/31/23
LPG Cylinders Mfr
N.A.I.C.S.: 325120
Yogender Mohan Sharma (Exec Dir)

SARTHAK METALS LIMITED
G E Road Khursipar Near Bhilai ITI, Bhilai, 490 011, Chhattisgarh, India
Tel.: (91) 7883290584
Web Site:
https://www.sarthakmetals.com
Year Founded: 1995
540393—(BOM)
Rev.: $35,682,660
Assets: $12,482,427
Liabilities: $5,186,173

Net Worth: $7,296,254
Earnings: $1,087,676
Emp.: 216
Fiscal Year-end: 03/31/21
Steel Product Mfr & Distr
N.A.I.C.S.: 333992
Anoop Kumar Bansal (Chm & Mng Dir)

SARTHE AUTOMOBILES
421 A Avenue Bollee, 72000, Le Mans, Sarthe, France
Tel.: (33) 243727734
Web Site: http://www.sarthe-auto.mercedes.fr
Rev.: $21,500,000
Emp.: 45
Automobile Dealership
N.A.I.C.S.: 441110
Christian Leslin Jouard (Mng Dir, Mng Dir & Chm)

SARTORIUS AG
Otto-Brenner-Strasse 20, 37079, Gottingen, Germany
Tel.: (49) 5513080
Web Site: https://www.sartorius.com
Year Founded: 1870
SRT3—(STU)
Rev.: $3,664,688,107
Assets: $10,528,059,573
Liabilities: $7,552,233,974
Net Worth: $2,975,825,599
Earnings: $312,972,156
Emp.: 14,614
Fiscal Year-end: 12/31/23
Medical Laboratories Services
N.A.I.C.S.: 811210
Lothar Kappich (Chm-Supervisory Bd)

Subsidiaries:

Analysis S.A. (1)
26 Rue de Perone App No 4, Belvedere, Casablanca, Morocco
Tel.: (212) 522222462
Biotechnology
N.A.I.C.S.: 541714

Biohit Biotech (Suzhou) Co. Ltd. (1)
Block 6 No 2 West Jinzhi Road, Suzhou, 215151, Jiangsu, China
Tel.: (86) 512 6616 0490
Biological Product Mfr
N.A.I.C.S.: 325414

Biohit France S.A.S. (1)
2 rue Anoine Laurent de Lavoisier, Zone d'Activite de la Gaudree, 91410, Dourdan, France
Tel.: (33) 1 7062 5000
Liquid Handling Systems Mfr
N.A.I.C.S.: 811210

Biohit OOO (1)
Uralskaya Street Line 5 68 Building 4 Letter D, Saint Petersburg, 199155, Russia
Tel.: (7) 812 327 5327
Web Site: http://www.sartorius.ru
Emp.: 50
Weighing & Balancing Equipment Mfr
N.A.I.C.S.: 334516
Alexander Krasnikov (Gen Mgr)

CellGenix Inc. (1)
1 New Hampshire Ave Ste 125, Portsmouth, NH 03801
Tel.: (603) 373-0408
Pharmaceutical Mfr & Distr
N.A.I.C.S.: 325412

Distribo GmbH (1)
Groner Siekanger 1, 37081, Gottingen, Germany
Tel.: (49) 55 130 8430
Web Site: https://www.distribo.de
Emp.: 110
Logistics & Consulting Services
N.A.I.C.S.: 541614

Essen BioScience, Inc (1)
300 W Morgan Rd, Ann Arbor, MI 48108 (100%)
Tel.: (734) 769-1600

Web Site: https://www.intellicyt.com
Sales Range: $10-24.9 Million
Emp.: 55
Develops & Manufactures Cell & Bead Based Screening Solutions
N.A.I.C.S.: 334516
Thomas Duensing *(CTO)*

Essen BioScience, Inc. (1)
300 West Morgan Road, Ann Arbor, MI 48108
Tel.: (734) 769-1600
Web Site: http://www.essenbioscience.com
Nonhazardous Waste Treatment & Disposal
N.A.I.C.S.: 562219
Ashley Moseby *(Dir-Global Sls Ops)*

LLC Sartorius Stedim (1)
5th Line of V O 70 lit A, 199178, Saint Petersburg, Russia
Tel.: (7) 8123275323
Electronic Equipment & Component Mfr
N.A.I.C.S.: 334419

Life Science Factory Management GmbH (1)
Annastrasse 27, 37075, Gottingen, Germany
Tel.: (49) 1607014221
Web Site: https://lifescience-factory.com
Biotechnology Research & Development Services
N.A.I.C.S.: 541714

Life Science Factory gGmbH (1)
Annastrasse 27, 37075, Gottingen, Germany
Tel.: (49) 171 262 4634
Web Site: https://www.lifescience-factory.com
Event Management Services
N.A.I.C.S.: 561920
Irina Reimer *(Mgr-Life Science Community)*

Meditec (1)
Nombakele, BP 14389, Libreville, Gabon
Tel.: (241) 766631
Biotechnology
N.A.I.C.S.: 541714

Sartogosm ZAO (1)
Rasstannya str Building 2 Letter A, Saint Petersburg, 192007, Russia
Tel.: (7) 8123275327
Weighing & Balancing Equipment Mfr
N.A.I.C.S.: 334516

Sartoma S.A. (1)
28 Rue de Provins, 05, Casablanca, Morocco
Tel.: (212) 305774
Web Site: http://www.sartorius-stedim.com
Biotechnology
N.A.I.C.S.: 541714

Sartorius (Thailand) Co. Ltd. (1)
No 129 Rama IX Road, Huaykwang, Bangkok, 10310, Thailand
Tel.: (66) 2643 8361
Weighing & Balancing Equipment Mfr
N.A.I.C.S.: 334516

Sartorius Argentina S.A. (1)
Cuyo 2889, Martinez, B1640GIQ, Buenos Aires, Argentina
Tel.: (54) 113 989 8710
Web Site: http://www.sartoarg.com.ar
Emp.: 45
Biological Product Mfr
N.A.I.C.S.: 325414
Maria Victoria Cattaneo *(Mgr-Admin & RRHH)*

Sartorius Australia Pty. Ltd. (1)
Unit 5 7-11 Rodeo Drive, Dandenong South, 3175, VIC, Australia
Tel.: (61) 38 762 1800
Web Site: http://www.sartorius.com
Emp.: 20
Weighing & Balancing Equipment Mfr
N.A.I.C.S.: 334516

Sartorius Austria GmbH (1)
Franzosengraben 12, Vienna, 1030, Austria
Tel.: (43) 1796 57600
Emp.: 504
Weighing & Balancing Equipment Mfr
N.A.I.C.S.: 811210
Wolgang Berns *(Gen Mgr)*

Sartorius Belgium N.V. (1)
Rue Colonel Bourg 105, 1030, Vilvoorde, Belgium
Tel.: (32) 2756 0671
Weighing & Balancing Equipment Mfr
N.A.I.C.S.: 811210

Sartorius Biohit Liquid Handling Oy (1)
Laippatie 1, Helsinki, 00880, Finland
Tel.: (358) 975 5951
Web Site: http://www.sartorius.fi
Emp.: 60
Weighing & Balancing Equipment Mfr
N.A.I.C.S.: 811210
Jussi Heinio *(CEO)*

Sartorius Canada Inc. (1)
1173 North Service Road West D4, Oakville, L6M 2V9, ON, Canada **(100%)**
Tel.: (905) 569-7977
Web Site: http://www.sartorius.ca
Sales Range: $25-49.9 Million
Emp.: 6
Biotechnology
N.A.I.C.S.: 541714

Sartorius Corporate Administration GmbH (1)
Otto-Brenner-Strasse 20, 37079, Gottingen, Germany
Tel.: (49) 5513080
Web Site: https://www.sartorius.com
Emp.: 100
Biological Product Mfr
N.A.I.C.S.: 325414
Petra Kirchhoff *(VP-Corp Comm & IR)*

Sartorius Corporation (1)
5 Orville Dr Ste 200, Bohemia, NY 11716
Tel.: (631) 254-4249
Electronic Equipment & Component Mfr
N.A.I.C.S.: 334419

Sartorius France S.A.S. (1)
Zone Industrielle les Paluds, Aveue de Jouques, Aubagne, 13781, France
Tel.: (33) 4 4284 6551
Weighing & Balancing Equipment Mfr
N.A.I.C.S.: 811210

Sartorius Hong Kong Ltd. (1)
Unit 1012 Lu Plaza 2 Wing Yip Street, Kwun Tong, Kowloon, China (Hong Kong)
Tel.: (852) 2 774 2678
Web Site: http://www.sartorius.com
Emp.: 10
Weighing & Balancing Equipment Mfr
N.A.I.C.S.: 334516

Sartorius Hungary Kft. (1)
Kagylo u 5, Budakeszi, 2092, Hungary
Tel.: (36) 23 457 227
Weighing & Balancing Equipment Mfr
N.A.I.C.S.: 811210

Sartorius ICR OOO (1)
70A 5th Line of V O, Saint Petersburg, 199155, Russia
Tel.: (7) 8123275327
Web Site: http://www.sartorius.ru
Emp.: 25
Weighing & Balancing Equipment Mfr
N.A.I.C.S.: 334516
Alexandra Krasnikova *(Gen Mgr)*

Sartorius India Pvt. Ltd. (1)
69/2-69/3 Jakkasandra Kunigal Road, Nelamangala, Bengaluru, 562 123, India
Tel.: (91) 8068148600
Electronic Equipment & Component Mfr
N.A.I.C.S.: 334419

Sartorius Intec (1)
Parc d'affaires Tecnopolis Batiment Sigma 3, Avenue du Canada, 91978, Les Ulis, France
Tel.: (33) 1 69 19 21 00
Web Site: http://www.sartorius-france.fr
Laboratory Equipment Mfr
N.A.I.C.S.: 334516

Sartorius Ireland Ltd. (1)
Unit 41 The Business Centre Stadium Business Park, Ballycoolin Road, Dublin, 11, Ireland
Tel.: (353) 1 808 9050
Weighing & Balancing Equipment Mfr
N.A.I.C.S.: 811210

Sartorius Italy S.r.l. (1)
Viale Alfonso Casati 4, 20835, Muggio, Italy
Tel.: (39) 039 46591
Weighing & Balancing Equipment Mfr
N.A.I.C.S.: 811210

Sartorius Japan K.K. (1)
4th Floor Daiwa Shinagawa North Building, 1-8-11 Kita-Shinagawa Shinagawa-Ku, Tokyo, 140-0001, Japan
Tel.: (81) 3 3740 5407
Weighing & Balancing Equipment Mfr
N.A.I.C.S.: 334516

Sartorius Korea Biotech Co. Ltd. (1)
8th Fl Solid Space 220 Pangyoyeok-Ro, Bundang-Gu, Seongnam, 463-400, Gyeonggi-Do, Korea (South)
Tel.: (82) 31 622 5700
Emp.: 80
Biological Product Mfr
N.A.I.C.S.: 325414

Sartorius Korea Ltd. (1)
8th floor Solidspace 220 Pangyoyeok-ro, Bundang-Gu, Seongnam, 13493, Gyeonggi-do, Korea (South)
Tel.: (82) 31 622 5700
Web Site: https://www.sartorius.co.kr
Emp.: 100
Weighing & Balancing Equipment Mfr
N.A.I.C.S.: 334516

Sartorius Lab Holding GmbH (1)
Weender Landtrasse 94-108, Gottingen, 37075, Germany
Tel.: (49) 551 3080
Web Site: http://www.sartorius.com
Emp.: 50
Weighing & Balancing Equipment Mfr
N.A.I.C.S.: 811210

Sartorius Lab Instruments GmbH & Co. KG (1)
Otto-Brenner-Strasse 20, 37079, Gottingen, Germany
Tel.: (49) 5513080
Electronic Equipment & Component Mfr
N.A.I.C.S.: 334419

Sartorius Malaysia Sdn. Bhd. (1)
Lot L3-E-3B Enterprise 4 Technology Park Malaysia, Bukit Jalil, 57000, Kuala Lumpur, Malaysia
Tel.: (60) 389960622
Web Site: https://www.sartorius.com
Emp.: 20
Weighing & Balancing Equipment Mfr
N.A.I.C.S.: 334516

Sartorius Mechatronics Australia Pty. Ltd. (1)
Unit 5 7-11 Rodeo Drive, Dandenong South, Melbourne, 3175, VIC, Australia
Tel.: (61) 387621800
Laboratory Equipment Mfr
N.A.I.C.S.: 334516

Sartorius Mechatronics Austria GmbH (1)
Franzosengraben 12, 1030, Vienna, Austria
Tel.: (43) 1 7965760 0
Emp.: 1
Laboratory Equipment Mfr
N.A.I.C.S.: 334516

Sartorius Mechatronics Belgium N.V. (1)
Rue Colonel Boerg 105, 1800, Brussels, Belgium
Tel.: (32) 27560671
Web Site: http://www.sartorius.be
Sales Range: $25-49.9 Million
Emp.: 6
Medical Instrument Distr
N.A.I.C.S.: 423450

Sartorius Mechatronics C&D GmbH & Co. KG (1)
Am Gut Wolf 11, 52070, Aachen, Germany
Tel.; (49) 24118270
Laboratory Instrument Mfr
N.A.I.C.S.: 334516
Wolf Stolze *(Gen Mgr)*

Sartorius Mechatronics Hong Kong Ltd. (1)
Unit 1012 Lu Plaza 2 Wing Yip Street, Kwun Tong, Hong Kong, China (Hong Kong)
Tel.: (852) 2774 2678
Web Site: http://www.sartorius.com
Emp.: 10
Laboratory Equipment Mfr
N.A.I.C.S.: 334516

Subsidiary (Non-US):

PT. Sartorius Mechatronics Indonesia (2)
Prisma Kedoya Plaza Blok C no 5 Jl Raya Pejuangan, Kebon Jeruk, Jakarta Barat, 11530, Indonesia
Tel.: (62) 215 365 1248
Web Site: http://www.sartorius.co.id
Laboratory Measurement Equipment Mfr
N.A.I.C.S.: 334513

Sartorius Mechatronics Japan K.K. (2)
4th Floor Daiwa Shinagawa North Bldg 1-8-11 Kita-Shinagawa, Shinagawa-Ku, Tokyo, 140-0001, Japan
Tel.: (81) 3 3740 5408
Web Site: http://www.sartorius.co.jp
Emp.: 8
Laboratory Equipment Mfr
N.A.I.C.S.: 334516

Sartorius Mechatronics Korea Ltd. (2)
BunDang-Gu SeongNam-Si PanGyoYeok-Ro 220 Solid Space Building, Seocho-Ku, 137-893, Seoul, Korea (South)
Tel.: (82) 2 575 6945
Laboratory Equipment Mfr
N.A.I.C.S.: 334516

Sartorius Mechatronics Philippines Inc. (2)
20-A World Centre Building 330 Sen Gil Puyat Avenue, Makati, 1209, Philippines
Tel.: (63) 2 864 0929
Web Site: http://www.sartorius-mechatronics.com.ph
Sales Range: $25-49.9 Million
Software Development Services
N.A.I.C.S.: 541511

Sartorius de Mexico S.A. de C.V. (2)
Circuito Circunvalacion Poniente No 149, 53100, Mexico, Mexico
Tel.: (52) 55 5562 1102
Laboratory Equipment Distr
N.A.I.C.S.: 423490

Sartorius do Brasil Ltda. (2)
Av D Pedro I 241 Vila Pires, Santo Andre, 09110-001, Brazil
Tel.: (55) 11 4451 6226
Web Site: http://www.sartorius.com
Sales Range: $25-49.9 Million
Biological Product Mfr
N.A.I.C.S.: 325414

Sartorius Mechatronics Hungaria Kft. (1)
Kagylo U 5, 2092, Budakeszi, Hungary
Tel.: (36) 23 457 227
Web Site: http://www.sartorius.hu
Sales Range: $25-49.9 Million
Emp.: 10
Laboratory Equipment Mfr
N.A.I.C.S.: 334516

Sartorius Mechatronics Italy S.r.l. (1)
Uffici Di Milano Viale A Casati 4, 20053, Muggio, Italy
Tel.: (39) 03946591
Web Site: http://www.sartorius-mechatronics.com
Laboratory Equipment Mfr
N.A.I.C.S.: 334516

Sartorius Mechatronics Spain S.A. (1)
Avenida Industria 32 Alcobendas, 28108, Madrid, Spain
Tel.: (34) 91 358 60 94
Web Site: http://www.sartorius.es
Sales Range: $25-49.9 Million
Emp.: 25
Electrochemical Equipment Mfr
N.A.I.C.S.: 335999

Sartorius Mechatronics Switzerland AG (1)
Ringstrasse 24a, 8317, Tagelswangen, Switzerland
Tel.: (41) 44 746 50 00
Laboratory Equipment Mfr
N.A.I.C.S.: 334516

SARTORIUS AG

Sartorius AG—(Continued)

Sartorius Netherlands B.V. (1)
Edisonbaan 24, 3439 MN, Nieuwegein, Netherlands
Tel.: (31) 30 605 3001
Weighing & Balancing Equipment Mfr
N.A.I.C.S.: 811210

Sartorius Nordic A/S (1)
Horskaetten 6D, 2630, Taastrup, Denmark
Tel.: (45) 70234400
Weighing & Balancing Equipment Mfr
N.A.I.C.S.: 811210

Sartorius North America Inc. (1)
565 Johnson Ave, Bohemia, NY 11716
Tel.: (631) 254-4249
Web Site: http://www.sartorius.com
Sales Range: $50-74.9 Million
Emp.: 100
Biotechnology
N.A.I.C.S.: 423440

Subsidiary (Domestic):

Sartorius Corporation (2)
565 Johnson Ave, Bohemia, NY 11716
Tel.: (631) 254-4249
Web Site: http://www.sartorius.com
Sales Range: $25-49.9 Million
Emp.: 80
Laboratory Instrument Mfr
N.A.I.C.S.: 334516

Subsidiary (Non-US):

Sartorius Mechatronics Canada Inc. (2)
2179 Dunwin Drive 4, Mississauga, L5L 1X2, ON, Canada
Tel.: (905) 569-7977
Laboratory Equipment Distr
N.A.I.C.S.: 423490

Subsidiary (Domestic):

Sartorius Stedim SUS Inc. (2)
1910 Mark Ct, Concord, CA 94520
Tel.: (925) 689-6650
Medical Instrument Mfr & Whslr
N.A.I.C.S.: 423450

Sartorius TCC Company (2)
6542 Fig St, Arvada, CO 80004
Tel.: (303) 403-4690
Web Site: http://www.sartorius.com
Laboratory Apparatus Mfr
N.A.I.C.S.: 339113

Sartorius Poland Sp. z o.o. (1)
Ul Wrzesinska 70, 62-025, Kostrzyn, Poland
Tel.: (48) 61 647 3830
Weighing & Balancing Equipment Mfr
N.A.I.C.S.: 334516

Sartorius S.A. (1)
4 Rue Emile Baudot, 91127, Palaiseau, France (100%)
Tel.: (33) 0169192100
Web Site: http://www.saratorius.com
Sales Range: $25-49.9 Million
Emp.: 130
Biotechnology
N.A.I.C.S.: 541714

Sartorius Scientific Instruments (Beijing) Co. Ltd (1)
No 33 Yu An Road Zone B Tianzhu Airport Industry Park, 101300, Beijing, China
Tel.: (86) 10 8042 6300
Web Site: http://www.sartorius.com.cn
Laboratory Equipment Mfr
N.A.I.C.S.: 334516

Sartorius Singapore Pte. Ltd. (1)
Mapletree Business City 30 Pasir Panjang Road 06-31A/32, Singapore, 117440, Singapore
Tel.: (65) 68723966
Emp.: 35
Electronic Components Mfr
N.A.I.C.S.: 334419

Sartorius Singapore Pte. Ltd. (1)
10 Science Park Rd The Alpha 02-13/14, Singapore Science Park II, Singapore, 117684, Singapore
Tel.: (65) 6 872 3966
Web Site: http://www.sartorius.com
Emp.: 10

Sartorius Spain S.A. (1)
C/Isabel Colbrand 10-12 Oficina 69/70, Poligono Industrial de Fuencarral, 28050, Madrid, Spain
Tel.: (34) 91 358 6095
Weighing & Balancing Equipment Mfr
N.A.I.C.S.: 334516

Sartorius Stedim Biooutsource Ltd. (1)
1 Technology Terrace Todd Campus West of Scotland Science Park, Glasgow, G20 0XA, United Kingdom
Tel.: (44) 141 946 4222
Web Site: http://www.biooutsource.com
Biopharmaceutical Mfr
N.A.I.C.S.: 325412
Hugo De Wit (Mng Dir)

Sartorius Stedim Biotech S.A. (1)
Z I Les Paluds Avenue de Jouques C S 91051, 13781, Aubagne, Cedex, France (70%)
Tel.: (33) 442845600
Web Site: https://sartorius.com
Rev.: $3,063,803,952
Assets: $8,543,879,017
Liabilities: $5,593,001,436
Net Worth: $2,950,877,581
Earnings: $344,519,263
Emp.: 10,662
Fiscal Year-end: 12/31/2023
Biopharmaceutical Equipment & Products Supplier
N.A.I.C.S.: 423450
Joachim Kreuzburg (Chm-Exec Bd & CEO)

Subsidiary (Domestic):

Sartorius Stedim Aseptics S.A. (2)
Z de Saux Rue Ampere, 65100, Lourdes, France
Tel.: (33) 56 242 7373
Web Site: https://www.sartorius.com
Emp.: 25
Biological Product Mfr
N.A.I.C.S.: 325414

Subsidiary (Non-US):

Sartorius Stedim Biotech GmbH (2)
August-Spindler-Strasse 11, Gottingen, 37079, Germany
Tel.: (49) 551 308 0
Emp.: 100
Biological Product Mfr
N.A.I.C.S.: 325414

Subsidiary (Non-US):

Sartorius Stedim Belgium N.V. (3)
Colonel Urg 105, Brussels, 1030, Belgium
Tel.: (32) 2 756 06 80
Sales Range: $25-49.9 Million
Emp.: 15
Biological Product Mfr
N.A.I.C.S.: 325414
Dominique Michaud (Mgr-Sls)

Subsidiary (Domestic):

Sartorius Stedim Systems GmbH (3)
Robert-Bosch-Strasse 5-7, Guxhagen, 34302, Melsungen, Germany
Tel.: (49) 5 665 4070
Web Site: http://www.sartorius-stedim.com
Sales Range: $50-74.9 Million
Biological Product Mfr
N.A.I.C.S.: 325414

Subsidiary (Non-US):

Sartorius Stedim Australia Pty. Ltd. (4)
Unit 5 7-11 Rodeo Drive, Dandenong South, Melbourne, 3175, VIC, Australia
Tel.: (61) 3 8762 1800
Sales Range: $25-49.9 Million
Emp.: 1
Medical Instrument Mfr
N.A.I.C.S.: 339112
Lambert Schroeder (CEO)

Sartorius Stedim Austria GmbH (4)
Franzosengraben 12, 1030, Vienna, Austria
Tel.: (43) 1 796 576 345
Biological Product Mfr
N.A.I.C.S.: 325414

INTERNATIONAL PUBLIC

Wolfgang Berns (Gen Mgr)

Sartorius Stedim Bioprocess S.A.R.L. (4)
Km 24 Route de Zaghouan Bourbiaa, BP 87, Tunis, Tunisia
Tel.: (216) 79 397 014
Biological Product Mfr
N.A.I.C.S.: 325414

Sartorius Stedim Biotech (Beijing) Co. Ltd. (4)
No 33 Yu'an Road Airport Industrial Zone B, Shunyi District, Beijing, 101300, China
Tel.: (86) 10 80426516
Web Site: http://www.sartorius-stedim.com.cn
Biological Product Mfr
N.A.I.C.S.: 325414

Sartorius Stedim Filters Inc. (4)
Tel.: (787) 856-5020
Web Site: http://www.sartorius-stedim.com
Sales Range: $25-49.9 Million
Emp.: 200
Industrial Filter Mfr
N.A.I.C.S.: 333413

Sartorius Stedim Hungaria Kft. (4)
Kagylo u 5, 2092, Budakeszi, Hungary
Tel.: (36) 23457227
Web Site: http://www.sartoriusstedim.com
Emp.: 3
Biological Product Mfr
N.A.I.C.S.: 325414

Sartorius Stedim India Pvt. Ltd. (4)
No 69/2 & 69/3 NH 48 Kunigal Road, Nelamangala, Bengaluru, 562 123, India
Tel.: (91) 80 43505250
Emp.: 400
Medical Device Mfr
N.A.I.C.S.: 339112
Amit Chatterjee (Mng Dir)

Sartorius Stedim Ireland Ltd. (4)
Unit 41 The Business Centre Stadium Business Park, Ballycoolin Road, Dublin, 11, Ireland
Tel.: (353) 1 808 9050
Weighing & Balancing Equipment Mfr
N.A.I.C.S.: 811210

Sartorius Stedim Italy S.p.A. (4)
Via dell'Antella 76/A, Antella, 50012, Bagno a Ripoli, Florence, Italy
Tel.: (39) 055 6340 41
Web Site: http://www.sartorius.it
Laboratory Equipment Mfr
N.A.I.C.S.: 334516

Sartorius Stedim Lab Ltd. (4)
Binbrook Hill, Binbrook, Lincoln, LN8 6BL, United Kingdom
Tel.: (44) 1472 398888
Biological Product Mfr
N.A.I.C.S.: 325414

Sartorius Stedim Netherlands B.V. (4)
Databankweg 26, 3821 AL, Amersfoort, Netherlands
Tel.: (31) 30 602 5080
Web Site: http://www.sartorius-stedim.com
Medical Equipment Mfr
N.A.I.C.S.: 339112

Subsidiary (US):

Sartorius Stedim North America Inc. (4)
565 Johnson Ave, Bohemia, NY 11716
Tel.: (631) 254-4249
Web Site: http://www.sartorius.com
Emp.: 300
Medical Instrument Mfr
N.A.I.C.S.: 334510

Subsidiary (Domestic):

Sartorius Stedim Plastics GmbH (4)
Karl-Arnold-Strasse 21, 37079, Gottingen, Germany
Tel.: (49) 551 3080
Web Site: http://www.toha-plast.de
Biotechnology Plastic Component Mfr
N.A.I.C.S.: 326199

Subsidiary (Non-US):

Sartorius Stedim Poland Sp. z o.o. (4)

Ul Wrzesinska 70, 62-025, Kostrzyn, Poland
Tel.: (48) 61 647 3840
Weighing & Balancing Equipment Mfr
N.A.I.C.S.: 334516

Sartorius Stedim Spain S.A. (4)
Calle Jose Bardasano Baos 9 3 C D, 28016, Madrid, Spain
Tel.: (34) 90 211 0935
Web Site: http://www.sartorius-stedim.com
Sales Range: $10-24.9 Million
Emp.: 2
Medical Instrument Mfr
N.A.I.C.S.: 339112

Sartorius Stedim Switzerland AG (4)
Ringstrasse 24A, 8317, Tagelswangen, Switzerland
Tel.: (41) 52 354 3636
Web Site: http://www.sartorius-stedim.com
Sales Range: $10-24.9 Million
Emp.: 40
Biotechnology Products & Services
N.A.I.C.S.: 541714

Sartorius Stedim UK Ltd. (4)
Longmead Business Centre Blenheim Road, Epsom, KT19 9QQ, Surrey, United Kingdom
Tel.: (44) 137 273 7100
Web Site: https://www.sartorius.com
Biological Product Mfr
N.A.I.C.S.: 325414

Sartorius Stedim France S.A.S (1)
ZI des Paluds Avenue de Jouques, CS 71058, 13781, Aubagne, Cedex, France
Tel.: (33) 44 284 5600
Web Site: http://www.sartorius-france.fr
Biological Products Mfr & Distr
N.A.I.C.S.: 325414

Sartorius Stedim Japan K.K. (1)
4th Floor Daiwa Shinagawa North Bldg 8-11 Kita-Shinagawa 1-chome, Koto-ku, Tokyo, 140-0001, Japan
Tel.: (81) 3 5639 9981
Emp.: 2
Biological Product Mfr
N.A.I.C.S.: 325414

Sartorius Stedim Malaysia Sdn. Bhd. (1)
Lot L3-E-3B Enterprise 4 Technology Park Malaysia, Bukit Jalil, 57000, Kuala Lumpur, Malaysia
Tel.: (60) 389960622
Web Site: http://www.sartorius.com
Emp.: 22
Biological Product Mfr
N.A.I.C.S.: 325414

Sartorius Stedim Singapore Pte. Ltd. (1)
10 Science Park Road The Alpha Unit 02-13/14 Singapore Science Park Ii, Singapore, 117684, Singapore
Tel.: (65) 6872 3966
Emp.: 25
Medical Instrument Mfr
N.A.I.C.S.: 339112
Peter Ernandez (CEO)

Sartorius Technologies N.V. (1)
Rue Colonel Bourg 105, 1800, Brussels, Belgium (100%)
Tel.: (32) 27560680
Web Site: http://www.sartorius.com
Sales Range: $25-49.9 Million
Emp.: 30
Biotechnology
N.A.I.C.S.: 541714
Domnique Michaud (Mgr-Sls)

Sartorius UK Limited (1)
Longmead Business CentreBlenheim Road, Epsom, KT19 9QQ, Surrey, United Kingdom
Tel.: (44) 1372737100
Web Site: http://www.sartorius-mechatronics.co.uk
Laboratory Equipment Mfr
N.A.I.C.S.: 334516
Gareth Owen Jones (Mgr-Sls-Mass Comparators & Metrology)

Sartorius UK Ltd. (1)
Longmead Business CentreBlenheim Road, Epsom, KT19 9QQ, Surrey, United Kingdom

AND PRIVATE COMPANIES

Tel.: (44) 137 273 7100
Web Site: http://www.sartorius.co.uk
Weighing & Balancing Equipment Mfr
N.A.I.C.S.: 334516

Sartorius Vietnam Co. Ltd. (1)
Unit 202 City View Building 12 Mac Dinh Chi Street, Dakao Ward District 1, Ho Chi Minh City, Vietnam
Tel.: (84) 838233156
Electronic Equipment & Component Mfr
N.A.I.C.S.: 334419

Sartorius Weighing India Pvt. Ltd. (1)
No 69/2 et 69/3 Jakkasandra Kunigal Road, Nelamangala, Bengaluru, 562123, India
Tel.: (91) 80 435052 50
Web Site: http://www.sartorius.com
Emp.: 400
Weighing & Balancing Equipment Mfr
N.A.I.C.S.: 334516

Sartorius Weighing Technology GmbH (1)
Weender Landstrasse 94-108, Gottingen, 37075, Germany
Tel.: (49) 551 3080
Weighing & Balancing Equipment Mfr
N.A.I.C.S.: 811210

TechnoScient Hussein Nagui & Co. (1)
13 Abdel Salam Aref Str, Cairo, 11511, Egypt
Tel.: (20) 223930022
Sales Range: $25-49.9 Million
Emp.: 50
Biotechnology
N.A.I.C.S.: 541714
Hussam Nagui *(Mng Dir)*

ViroCyt, Inc. (1)
100 Technology Dr Suite 325, Broomfield, CO 80021 (100%)
Tel.: (720) 599-3700
Web Site: http://www.virocyt.com
Emp.: 80
Development of Life Science Instrumentation & Assays Products for the Analysis of Viruses & Microorganisms
N.A.I.C.S.: 541715

ZAO Sartogosm (1)
Naberejnaya reki Volkovki str 9 letter A, 192102, Saint Petersburg, Russia
Tel.: (7) 8123802569
Web Site: http://www.sartogosm.ru
Sales Range: $25-49.9 Million
Emp.: 60
Laboratory Equipment Mfr
N.A.I.C.S.: 334516

SARTRA INTERNATIONAL LTD
177-179 Forest Road, Ilford, IG6 3HY, United Kingdom
Tel.: (44) 2085009933
Web Site: http://www.sartra.com
Year Founded: 1983
Rev.: $35,992,853
Emp.: 27
Electrical Component Distr
N.A.I.C.S.: 423610
Brian Groves *(Mgr-Sls-Middle East & Worldwide)*

SARUP INDUSTRIES LIMITED
P O Ramdaspura, Jalandhar, 144003, Punjab, India
Tel.: (91) 1812271556
Web Site:
  https://www.sarupindustries.com
Year Founded: 1979
514412—(BOM)
Rev.: $1,162,736
Assets: $7,675,283
Liabilities: $8,364,990
Net Worth: ($689,707)
Earnings: ($299,419)
Emp.: 101
Fiscal Year-end: 03/31/23
Footwear Product Mfr & Whslr
N.A.I.C.S.: 316210
Atamjit Singh Bawa *(Mng Dir)*

SARVAMANGAL MERCANTILE COMPANY LIMITED
1076 Dr E Moses Road, Worli, Mumbai, 400018, India
Tel.: (91) 2224964656
Web Site:
  https://sarvamangalmercantile.in
Year Founded: 1983
506190—(BOM)
Rev.: $186,234
Assets: $5,923,977
Liabilities: $1,508,005
Net Worth: $4,415,971
Earnings: $27,645
Emp.: 3
Fiscal Year-end: 03/31/23
Financial Investment Services
N.A.I.C.S.: 523999
Nupur Somani *(Mng Dir)*

SARVESHWAR FOODS LTD.
Village Seora Baba Fareed Nagar PO Dharap Bishnah-Kunjwani Road, Jammu, 181132, Jammu & Kashmir, India
Tel.: (91) 1923220962
Web Site:
  https://www.sarveshwarfoods.com
Year Founded: 1890
543688—(BOM)
Rev.: $83,613,249
Assets: $67,195,048
Liabilities: $41,556,058
Net Worth: $25,638,990
Earnings: $948,624
Emp.: 35
Fiscal Year-end: 03/31/23
Rice Product Distr
N.A.I.C.S.: 424490
Rohit Gupta *(Mng Dir)*

SARVOTTAM FINVEST LIMITED
3 Bentinck Street 2nd Floor, Kolkata, 700 001, West Bengal, India
Tel.: (91) 7383625975
Web Site:
  https://www.sarvottamfinvest.in
Year Founded: 1978
539124—(BOM)
Rev.: $280,194
Assets: $3,602,549
Liabilities: $19,342
Net Worth: $3,583,207
Earnings: ($7,972)
Emp.: 16
Fiscal Year-end: 03/31/21
Financial Support Services
N.A.I.C.S.: 523999
Dilip Kumar Gupta *(CEO & Mng Dir)*

SARYTOGAN GRAPHITE LIMITED
Suite 8 110 Hay Street, Subiaco, 6008, WA, Australia
Tel.: (61) 893888290 AU
Web Site:
  https://www.sarytogangraphite.com
Year Founded: 2004
SGA—(ASX)
Rev.: $151,708
Assets: $16,002,210
Liabilities: $94,373
Net Worth: $15,907,837
Earnings: ($1,328,824)
Fiscal Year-end: 06/30/23
Graphite Product Mfr
N.A.I.C.S.: 335991
Ian Hobson *(CFO)*

SAS AB
Frosundaviks Alle 1, Solna, 195 87, Stockholm, Sweden
Tel.: (46) 87970000 SE
Web Site: https://www.sas.se
Year Founded: 2000

SAS—(OMX)
Rev.: $4,173,665,368
Assets: $5,543,709,269
Liabilities: $6,150,257,218
Net Worth: ($606,547,948)
Earnings: ($565,945,966)
Emp.: 8,099
Fiscal Year-end: 10/31/23
Scheduled Passenger Air Transportation
N.A.I.C.S.: 481111
Freja Annamatz *(Head-Media Rels-Sweden)*

Subsidiaries:

Scandinavian Airlines System SAS (1)
Frosundaviks Alle 1, 19587, Stockholm, Sweden (100%)
Tel.: (46) 770727727
Web Site: http://www.sas.no
Sales Range: $1-4.9 Billion
Emp.: 5,000
Integrated Travel Business; Airline Operations, Ground Transportation, Hotel Operations, Airport Services, Tour Operations & Other Peripheral Businesses
N.A.I.C.S.: 481111
Hans W. Dyhrfort *(Gen Mgr-SAS UK & Ireland)*

Subsidiary (Domestic):

SAS Airline (2)
Frosundaviks Alle 1, S 195 87, Stockholm, Sweden (100%)
Tel.: (46) 87970000
Web Site: http://www.sas.se
Sales Range: $5-14.9 Billion
International Passenger Air Carrier Operations
N.A.I.C.S.: 481111
Mats Johnsson *(Pres)*

SAS Trading (2)
Frosundaviks Alle 1, S 195 87, Solna, Sweden
Tel.: (46) 87974239
Web Site: http://www.sas.se
Development & Operations of Wholesale Trading, Retail Sales on Air Flights & Cruise Ships & At Airports & Media Production in Conjunction with SAS Travel Systems Services
N.A.I.C.S.: 561599

SAS DOMAINE ROLLAN DE BY
18 Route de By, 33340, Begadan, France
Tel.: (33) 5 56 41 58 59
Web Site: http://www.domaines-rollandeby.com
Year Founded: 1989
Wine Mfr
N.A.I.C.S.: 312130
Jean Guyon *(Owner)*

Subsidiaries:

Chateau Greysac (1)
18 Route de By, 33340, Begadan, France (100%)
Tel.: (33) 556732656
Web Site: http://www.greysac.com
Sales Range: $1-9.9 Million
Emp.: 32
Vineyard
N.A.I.C.S.: 111332
Brandino Brandolini d'Abba *(Pres)*

SAS EAUDISSE
Zac Du Maudarin 2 Boulevard De La Leze, Eaunes, 31600, Toulouse, France
Tel.: (33) 562115860
Sales Range: $25-49.9 Million
Emp.: 69
Grocery Stores
N.A.I.C.S.: 445110
Serge Bruliere *(Pres)*

SAS EUROPE AUTO

290 Bret Auto Cannet Espace Avenue Du Campon, Le Cannet, 06110, Cannes, France
Tel.: (33) 493468646
Rev.: $27,900,000
Emp.: 30
New & Used Car Dealers
N.A.I.C.S.: 441110
Philippe Jehlen *(Pres)*

SAS FRIGNIDIS
208 Avenue de Champagne, 51300, Frignicourt, France
Tel.: (33) 326740010
Sales Range: $25-49.9 Million
Emp.: 79
Grocery Store Operator
N.A.I.C.S.: 445110
Stephane Lorey *(Pres)*

SAS INTERNATIONAL
28 Suttons Business Park London Road, Reading, RG6 1AZ, Berkshire, United Kingdom
Tel.: (44) 1189290900 UK
Web Site: http://www.sasint.co.uk
Year Founded: 1968
Sales Range: $50-74.9 Million
Emp.: 300
Precision Engineered Metal System for Suspended Ceiling Fiber Ceiling & Partitioning Mfr
N.A.I.C.S.: 337215
Eddie McElhinney *(Chm & CEO)*

Subsidiaries:

Program Lighting Ltd. (1)
27/28 Suttons Industrial Park, London Road, Reading, RG6 1AZ, Berks, United Kingdom
N.A.I.C.S.: 332119

SAS International (1)
31 Suttons Bus Pk, London Rd, Reading, RG6 1AZ, Berkshire, United Kingdom (100%)
Tel.: (44) 189290900
Sales Range: $25-49.9 Million
Emp.: 70
Precision Engineered Metal System for Suspended Ceiling Fiber Ceiling & Partitioning Mfr
N.A.I.C.S.: 332323

SAS International Apollo Park Factory (1)
Rounds Green Road, Oldbury, B69 2DA, West Midlands, United Kingdom
Tel.: (44) 1215111300
Interior Design Product Mfr
N.A.I.C.S.: 337212

SAS International Bridgend Factory (1)
Parc Crescent Waterton Industrial Estate, Bridgend, CF31 3XU, Mid Glamorgan, United Kingdom
Tel.: (44) 1656664600
Interior Design Product Mfr
N.A.I.C.S.: 337212

SAS Maybole (1)
Murray Gardens, Maybole, KA19 7AZ, Ayrshire, United Kingdom
Tel.: (44) 1655882555
Sales Range: $50-74.9 Million
Emp.: 150
N.A.I.C.S.: 332119
David Arnott *(Gen Mgr)*

SAS MICHEZ
27 Rue Louis Quinquet, 54260, Longuyon, Meurthe Et Moselle, France
Tel.: (33) 382392254
Web Site: http://www.michez-nissan.fr
Sales Range: $10-24.9 Million
Emp.: 24
Automobile Dealers
N.A.I.C.S.: 441110
Mireille Muller *(Mgr-HR)*

SAS MURUETS

SAS Michez—(Continued)

SAS MURUETS
Rue Gerard De Nerval, 60600, Clermont, Oise, France
Tel.: (33) 344682323
Rev.: $30,400,000
Emp.: 58
Supermarket Operations
N.A.I.C.S.: 445110
Marie-Chantal De Bosschere (Gen Mgr)

SAS SOJAY
3 rue de L'Industrie ZAC Champs Saint-Ange, 38760, Varces-Allieres-et-Risset, Isere, France
Tel.: (33) 476728233
Rev.: $18,700,000
Emp.: 45
Supermarket
N.A.I.C.S.: 445110
Pierre Maurin (Pres)

SASA POLYESTER SANAYI AS
Sarihamzali Mah Turhan Cemal Beriker Bulvari No 559, Seyhan, 01355, Adana, Turkiye
Tel.: (90) 3224410053
Web Site: https://www.sasa.com.tr
Year Founded: 1966
SASA—(IST)
Rev.: $1,159,133,203
Assets: $2,018,489,135
Liabilities: $1,114,391,036
Net Worth: $904,098,099
Earnings: $411,394,233
Emp.: 4,743
Fiscal Year-end: 12/31/22
Plastic Materials Mfr
N.A.I.C.S.: 325211

SASAKURA ENGINEERING CO., LTD.
7-32 Takejima 4-chome, Nishiyodogawa-ku, Osaka, 555-0011, Japan
Tel.: (81) 664732131
Web Site: http://www.sasakura.co.jp
Year Founded: 1949
6303—(TKS)
Rev.: $98,561,760
Assets: $291,484,160
Liabilities: $76,191,280
Net Worth: $215,292,880
Earnings: $5,372,400
Emp.: 473
Fiscal Year-end: 03/31/22
Marine Engineering Services
N.A.I.C.S.: 541330
Toshihiko Sasakura (Pres & Exec Officer)

Subsidiaries:

ACWA Power Sasakura Ltd. (1)
SWEC Building Second Floor Maisaloon Street Al-Hamra District, PO Box 1745, Jeddah, 21441, Saudi Arabia
Tel.: (966) 126617484
Web Site: https://www.acwasasakura.com
Sewage Treatment Services
N.A.I.C.S.: 562219
Baraa AlZaeem (Mgr-HR & Admin)

P.T. Sasakura Indonesia (1)
Jl Pulokambing II-7 Pulogadung Industrial Estate, Jakarta Timur, 13260, Indonesia
Tel.: (62) 214604014
Sewage Treatment Services
N.A.I.C.S.: 562219

Sasakura International (H.K.) Co., Ltd. (1)
Room No 4 148-150 Queens Road Stag Building UG-4 Upper Ground Floor, Central, China (Hong Kong)
Tel.: (852) 28506139
Sewage Treatment Services
N.A.I.C.S.: 562219

Sasakura Taiwan Co., Ltd. (1)

1F No 5 Lane29 Linyi St, Taipei, Taiwan
Tel.: (886) 223223370
Sewage Treatment Services
N.A.I.C.S.: 562219

SASATOKU PRINTING CO., LTD.
7 Owaki Sakae-cho, Toyoake, 470-1196, Aichi-ken, Japan
Tel.: (81) 562971111
Web Site: https://www.sasatoku.co.jp
Year Founded: 1950
3958—(TKS)
Rev.: $80,567,660
Assets: $95,875,080
Liabilities: $37,002,780
Net Worth: $58,872,300
Earnings: $2,463,120
Emp.: 418
Fiscal Year-end: 06/30/24
Book Mfr & Distr
N.A.I.C.S.: 323111

SASBADI HOLDINGS BERHAD
12 Jalan Teknologi 3/4 Taman Sains Selangor 1, Kota Damansara, 47810, Petaling Jaya, Selangor, Malaysia
Tel.: (60) 61451188   MY
Web Site: https://www.sasbadiholdings.com
SASBADI—(KLS)
Rev.: $20,347,513
Assets: $39,648,677
Liabilities: $7,241,058
Net Worth: $32,407,619
Earnings: $2,151,958
Emp.: 400
Fiscal Year-end: 08/31/23
Holding Company; Books & Educational Materials Publisher
N.A.I.C.S.: 551112
King Hui Law (Co-Founder & Grp Mng Dir)

Subsidiaries:

Distinct Motion Sdn. Bhd. (1)
Lot 12 Jalan Teknologi 3/4 Taman Sains Selangor 1, Kota Damansara, 47810, Petaling Jaya, Selangor, Malaysia
Tel.: (60) 12 969 1230
Web Site: https://www.littlebotz.com
Educational Support Services
N.A.I.C.S.: 611710

Mindtech Education Sdn. Bhd. (1)
L1-9 10 Cova Square Jalan Teknologi Taman Sains Selangor 1, Kota Damansara, 47810, Petaling Jaya, Selangor Darul Ehsan, Malaysia
Tel.: (60) 361451188
Online Learning Services
N.A.I.C.S.: 516210

Pinko Creative Sdn. Bhd. (1)
62-1 Jalan Temenggung 17/9, Bandar Mahkota, 43200, Cheras, Selangor, Malaysia
Tel.: (60) 390748682
Web Site: https://www.i-pinko.com
Comic Book Publishing Services
N.A.I.C.S.: 513120

The Malaya Press Sdn. Bhd. (1)
No 1 Jalan TSB 10 Taman Perindustrian Sg Buloh, 47000, Sungai Buloh, Selangor, Malaysia
Tel.: (60) 361573158
Books Publishing Services
N.A.I.C.S.: 513130
Kuan Shaw Ping (Gen Mgr)

United Publishing House (M) Sdn. Bhd. (1)
Web Site: http://www.uph.com.my
Books Publishing Services
N.A.I.C.S.: 513130

SASFIN HOLDINGS LIMITED
29 Scott Street, Waverley, 2090, South Africa
Tel.: (27) 118097500
Web Site: http://www.sasfin.com

SFN—(JSE)
Rev.: $71,814,531
Assets: $823,195,496
Liabilities: $723,798,373
Net Worth: $99,397,123
Earnings: $8,237,954
Emp.: 771
Fiscal Year-end: 06/30/22
Financial Services
N.A.I.C.S.: 541611
Howard Brown (Head-Grp Legal)

Subsidiaries:

Sasfin Asia Limited (1)
Ste 3833-34 38th Fl Sun Hung Kai Ctr 30 Harbour Rd, Wanchai, China (Hong Kong)
Tel.: (852) 31073067
Finance & Banking Services
N.A.I.C.S.: 522110

Sasfin Asset Managers (Pty) Limited (1)
29 Scott Street, Waverley, Johannesburg, 2090, Gauteng, South Africa
Tel.: (27) 118097500
Web Site: http://www.sasfin.com
Sales Range: $400-449.9 Million
Portfolio & Asset Management Services
N.A.I.C.S.: 523940

Sasfin Bank Limited (1)
Sasfin Pl 29 Scott St, Waverley, 2090, Gauteng, South Africa
Tel.: (27) 118097500
Sales Range: $200-249.9 Million
Emp.: 300
Banking & Financial Services
N.A.I.C.S.: 522110
Roland Sassoon (CEO)

Sasfin Financial Advisory Services (Pty) Limited (1)
Lord Charles Ofc Park, Pretoria, 0181, Gauteng, South Africa
Tel.: (27) 118097500
Insurance Advisory Services
N.A.I.C.S.: 524298

Subsidiary (Domestic):

Sasfin Insurance Brokers (Pty) Limited (2)
29 Scott Street Waverly, Waverley, Johannesburg, 2090, Gauteng, South Africa
Tel.: (27) 118097749
Emp.: 500
Insurance Brokerage Services
N.A.I.C.S.: 524210
Roland Sassoon (CEO)

Sasfin Wealth (Pty.) Ltd. (1)
140 West Street, Sandown Sandton, Johannesburg, South Africa
Tel.: (27) 118097500
Web Site: https://sasfin.com
Investment Services
N.A.I.C.S.: 523999

SASHWAT TECHNOCRATS LIMITED
Office No 14 First Floor, Plumber House 557 JSS Road Chira Bazar, Mumbai, 400 002, Maharashtra, India
Tel.: (91) 2222016021
Web Site: https://sashwattechnocrats.com
Year Founded: 1975
506313—(BOM)
Rev.: $46,200
Assets: $575,146
Liabilities: $449,537
Net Worth: $125,609
Earnings: ($721,105)
Fiscal Year-end: 03/31/21
Information Technology Services
N.A.I.C.S.: 541512
Prakhar Singh Taunk (Sec)

SASINI PLC
3rd Floor Rivaan Centre Brookside Grove Muguga Green, PO Box 30151, 00100, Nairobi, Kenya
Tel.: (254) 20342166

Web Site: https://www.sasini.co.ke
SASN—(NAI)
Rev.: $43,459,774
Assets: $123,869,950
Liabilities: $13,372,397
Net Worth: $110,497,553
Earnings: $4,123,393
Emp.: 2,300
Fiscal Year-end: 09/30/23
Tea & Coffee Producer
N.A.I.C.S.: 111998
James Kieu (Gen Mgr-Coffee Ops)

SASKATCHEWAN MINERALS INC.
120 Railway Ave, PO Box 120, Chaplin, S0H 0V0, SK, Canada
Tel.: (306) 395-2561   Ca
Web Site: http://www.saskatchewanmineral.com
Year Founded: 1948
Sales Range: $10-24.9 Million
Emp.: 35
Sodium Sulphate Production
N.A.I.C.S.: 325180
Brent Avery (Gen Mgr)

SASKEN TECHNOLOGIES LIMITED
139/25 Ring Road Domlur, Bengaluru, 560 071, India
Tel.: (91) 8066943000
Web Site: https://www.sasken.com
Year Founded: 1989
532663—(BOM)
Rev.: $64,051,383
Assets: $105,267,476
Liabilities: $16,058,925
Net Worth: $89,208,551
Earnings: $17,505,593
Emp.: 1,324
Fiscal Year-end: 03/31/22
Telecommunication Software Services
N.A.I.C.S.: 541511
Rajiv C. Mody (Chm & Mng Dir)

SASOL LIMITED
Sasol Place 50 Katherine str, Sandton, Johannesburg, 2196, South Africa
Tel.: (27) 103445000   SA
Web Site: https://www.sasol.com
Year Founded: 1950
SSL—(NYSE)
Rev.: $13,776,319,300
Assets: $24,613,494,890
Liabilities: $14,210,398,560
Net Worth: $10,403,096,330
Earnings: $718,598,360
Emp.: 28,949
Fiscal Year-end: 06/30/21
Synthetic Fuel Producer; Oil & Natural Gas Explorer
N.A.I.C.S.: 325110
Vuyo Dominic Kahla (Exec VP-Strategy-Sustainability-Integrated Svcs)

Subsidiaries:

Sasol Chemical Industries Ltd. (1)
1 Sturdee Ave Rosebank, Rosebank, 2196, Johannesburg, South Africa (100%)
Tel.: (27) 114413111
Web Site: http://www.sasol.com
Sales Range: $50-74.9 Million
Emp.: 250
Coal Producer
N.A.I.C.S.: 324199

Affiliate (Non-US):

Sasol Augusta S.P.A. (2)
Viale enrico Forlanini 23 Bldg, I-20134, Milan, Italy
Tel.: (39) 02584531
Provider of Crude Petroleum & Natural Gas
N.A.I.C.S.: 211120
Filippo Carletti (Mng Dir)

AND PRIVATE COMPANIES — SASTASUNDAR VENTURES LIMITED

Subsidiary (Non-US):

Sasol Chemicals Europe Limited (2)
1 Hockley Ct 2401 Stratford Rd Hockley Heat, Solihull, B94 6NW, West Mid, United Kingdom (100%)
Tel.: (44) 1564783060
Web Site: http://www.sasol.com
Sales Range: $25-49.9 Million
Emp.: 13
Marketing of Sasol's Petrochemical Products in Europe
N.A.I.C.S.: 325110
Jonathan Ward (Sr Mgr-Sls & Mktg)

Sasol Chemicals Pacific Limited (2)
2409 Shiuon Ctr 628 Harbour Rd, Hong Kong, China (Hong Kong) (100%)
Tel.: (852) 28276600
Web Site: http://www.sasol.com
Sales Range: $25-49.9 Million
Emp.: 5
Responsible for the Development of the Group's Petrochemical Business in the Asia Pacific Region
N.A.I.C.S.: 325110
Pauline Yip (Mgr-Sls & Mktg-South China, Hong Kong & Taiwan)

Sasol Chemie GmbH (2)
Anckelmannsplatz 1, PO Box 261805, 20537, Hamburg, Germany
Tel.: (49) 40636841000
Sales Range: $50-74.9 Million
Emp.: 200
Laboratory Producer & Supplier of N-Paraffins, N-Olefins, Alcohols & Derivatives
N.A.I.C.S.: 325199

Affiliate (Non-US):

Sasol Chimica D.A.C. S.p.A. (2)
Via Madici Basello 26, I 20138, Lodi, Italy
Tel.: (39) 0258453361
Providers of Chemicals & Chemical Preparation Services
N.A.I.C.S.: 325998

Sasol Nanjing Chemical Company (2)
Web Site: http://www.sasolos.com
Sales Range: $50-74.9 Million
Emp.: 130
Providers of Chemicals & Chemical Preparation Services
N.A.I.C.S.: 325998

Division (Domestic):

Sasol Nitro (2)
15 Baker Street Rose Bank, Johannesburg, 2000, South Africa (100%)
Tel.: (27) 114413511
Web Site: http://www.sasol.com
Sales Range: $100-124.9 Million
Mfr & Market Commercial Explosives & Blasting Accessories for the Mining & Construction Industries
N.A.I.C.S.: 325920

Sasol Oil (2)
32 Hill St, Randburg, 2125, Johannesburg, South Africa (100%)
Tel.: (27) 118897600
Web Site: http://www.sasol.com
Mfr & Market Coke & Tar Products
N.A.I.C.S.: 324199

Sasol Solvent Olefins & Surfactants (2)
No 1 Synfuels, PO Box X1000, Secunda, 2302, South Africa (50%)
Tel.: (27) 0176103881
Web Site: http://www.sasol.com
Mfr & Market Acrylonitrile
N.A.I.C.S.: 325199

Sasol Solvente (2)
No 2 Ftusdee Ave Rosebank, PO Box 55, Saxonwold, 2196, Johannesburg, South Africa (100%)
Tel.: (27) 0112800000
Mfr & Market Flotation Reagents & Associated Products for the Mining Industry
N.A.I.C.S.: 333131

Sasol Solvents & Olefins Surfactants (2)
6 Sturdee Rd, Rosebank, 2196, South Africa (100%)
Tel.: (27) 00114413203
Web Site: http://www.sasol.com
Sales Range: $50-74.9 Million
Emp.: 120
Mfr & Market Alpha Olefin Chemicals
N.A.I.C.S.: 325998

Sasol Solvents O&S South Africa (2)
2 Sturdee Ave Rosebank, Rosebank, 2196, Johannesburg, South Africa (100%)
Tel.: (27) 0114413111
Web Site: http://www.sasol.com
N.A.I.C.S.: 211120

Sasol Synfuels International (Pty) Limited (2)
Baker Square E 33 Baker St, Rosebank, 2000, South Africa (100%)
Tel.: (27) 114413111
Web Site: http://www.sasol.investorreports.com
Sales Range: $50-74.9 Million
Emp.: 25
International Ventures Development & Implementation
N.A.I.C.S.: 211120

Subsidiary (Non-US):

Sloveca spol. s.r.o. (2)
Paulinyho 12, SK 81102, Bratislava, Slovakia (100%)
Tel.: (421) 254430219
Web Site: http://www.sk.sasol.com
Emp.: 12
Providers of Crude Petroleum & Natural Gas
N.A.I.C.S.: 211120

Sasol Financing (Pty) Ltd (1)
1 Sturdee Avenue, Johannesburg, 2196, South Africa
Tel.: (27) 114413111
Web Site: http://www.sasol.com
Emp.: 16
Financial Management Services
N.A.I.C.S.: 523999

Sasol Gas Holdings (Pty) Ltd (1)
1 Sturdee Avenue, Rosebank, 2000, South Africa
Tel.: (27) 118899000
Investment Management Service
N.A.I.C.S.: 523999

Sasol Germany GmbH (1)
Anckelmannsplatz 1, 20537, Hamburg, Germany
Tel.: (49) 40636841000
Rev.: $1,321,390,000
Emp.: 150
Chemical Products Mfr & Distr
N.A.I.C.S.: 325998
Christian Schindler (Chm-Supervisory Bd)

Subsidiary (Non-US):

Sasol Wax International AG (2)
(100%)
Tel.: (49) 40781150
Web Site: http://www.sasolwax.com
Sales Range: $600-649.9 Million
Mfr & Market a Comprehensive Range of Waxes & Liquid Paraffins
N.A.I.C.S.: 324110

Subsidiary (Non-US):

Sasol Wax Pty. Ltd. (3)
(100%)
Tel.: (27) 0169609111
Web Site: http://www.sasol.com
Sales Range: $150-199.9 Million
Emp.: 400
N.A.I.C.S.: 211120

Sasol Group Services (Pty) Ltd (1)
1 Sturdee Avenue, Rosebank, 2196, South Africa
Tel.: (27) 11 344 2275
Business Support Services
N.A.I.C.S.: 561499

Sasol Investment Company (Pty) Ltd (1)
1 Sturdy Avenue, Johannesburg, 2196, South Africa
Tel.: (27) 114413111
Investment Management Service
N.A.I.C.S.: 523999

Sasol Italy SpA (1)
Viale Forlanini 23, 20138, Milan, Italy
Tel.: (39) 02584531
Web Site: http://www.sasolos.com
Emp.: 80
Cyclic Crude & Intermediate Mfr
N.A.I.C.S.: 325194

Sasol Mining (1)
Private Bag 810151, PO Box X1015, Secunda, 2302, South Africa (100%)
Tel.: (27) 76141111
Web Site: http://www.sasol.com
Sales Range: $1-4.9 Billion
Emp.: 80,000
Coal Mining
N.A.I.C.S.: 212115

Division (Domestic):

National Petroleum Refiners of South Africa (Pty) Ltd. (2)
Industrial Zone 2, Sasolburg, 2000, Free State, South Africa (64%)
Tel.: (27) 730058690
Web Site: http://www.natref.co.za
Sales Range: $300-349.9 Million
Emp.: 600
Crude Oil Refinery
N.A.I.C.S.: 211120

Subsidiary (Domestic):

Sasol Mining Holdings (Pty) Ltd. (2)
1 Sturdee Avenue, Johannesburg, Gauteng, South Africa
Tel.: (27) 114413359
Investment Management Service
N.A.I.C.S.: 523999

Sasol North America Inc. (1)
12120 Wickchester Ln, Houston, TX 77079-2990 (100%)
Tel.: (281) 588-3000
Web Site: http://www.sasolnorthamerica.com
Sales Range: $25-49.9 Million
Emp.: 100
Mfr of Industrial Chemicals
N.A.I.C.S.: 325211
Josh Stuart (Sls Mgr-Alkylates & Surfactants)

Sasol Oil (Pty) (1)
32 Hill St, PO Box 4211-2125, Ferndale, 2194, Johannesburg, South Africa (100%)
Tel.: (27) 118897600
Web Site: http://www.sasol.com
Sales Range: $200-249.9 Million
Emp.: 500
Marketers of Automotive Fuels & a Comprehensive Range of Lubricants
N.A.I.C.S.: 211120

Division (Domestic):

Sasol Fuel Oil (2)
13 Commercial Road, Alrode, 1422, Gauteng, South Africa (100%)
Tel.: (27) 118657782
Web Site: http://www.sasol.com
Sales Range: $125-149.9 Million
Emp.: 500
Supplier of Industrial Fuel Oils
N.A.I.C.S.: 424690

Sasol Gas Limited (2)
1 Sturdee Avenue, PO Box 5486, Rosebank, 2000, Johannesburg, South Africa (100%)
Tel.: (27) 114413111
Web Site: http://www.sasol.com
Sales Range: $25-49.9 Million
Emp.: 32
Pipeline Gas Supplier
N.A.I.C.S.: 486210

Sasol Petroleum International (Pty) Ltd. (1)
Block 24 Tyrwhitt Avenue Rosebank, Johannesburg, 2196, South Africa (100%)
Tel.: (27) 114413946
Web Site: http://www.sasol.com
Sales Range: $50-74.9 Million
Emp.: 55
Oil Exploration & Production Activities
N.A.I.C.S.: 211120

Sasol Polymers International Investments (Pty) Ltd (1)
56 Grosvenor Road, Bryanston, 2191, South Africa
Tel.: (27) 117901111
Web Site: http://www.sasol.com
Emp.: 30
Plastic Material & Resin Mfr
N.A.I.C.S.: 325211

Sasol Synfuels (Pty) Ltd (1)
Synfuels Road, Secunda, 2302, Mpumalanga, South Africa
Tel.: (27) 176101111
Industrial Gas Mfr
N.A.I.C.S.: 325120
Stephan Schoeman (Mng Dir)

Sasol Synthetic Fuels (Pty.) Ltd. (1)
Synfuels Road, PO Box X1000, Secunda, 2302, South Africa (100%)
Tel.: (27) 176141111
Web Site: http://www.sasol.com
Sales Range: $1-4.9 Billion
Emp.: 6,000
Coal Conversion Into Fuels & Chemical Feedstocks
N.A.I.C.S.: 325110

Sasol Technology (Pty) Ltd. (1)
Klasie Havenga Street, PO Box 1, Sasolburg, 1947, South Africa (100%)
Tel.: (27) 00169602900
Web Site: http://www.sasol.com
Sales Range: $350-399.9 Million
Emp.: 550
Energy & Chemical Operations
N.A.I.C.S.: 211120

Plant (Domestic):

Sasol Technology Pty Ltd (2)
80 Ander Building Synfuels Rd, PO Box X1034, Secunda, 2302, South Africa (100%)
Tel.: (27) 176190111
Web Site: http://wwwsasol.com
Sales Range: $300-349.9 Million
Provides Conceptual Process Design, Engineering Support & Project Management
N.A.I.C.S.: 541330

SASSEUR REAL ESTATE INVESTMENT TRUST

7 Temasek Boulevard 06-05 Suntec Tower One, Singapore, 038987, Singapore
Tel.: (65) 62552953 SG
Web Site: https://www.sasseurreit.com
Year Founded: 2017
CRPU—(SES)
Rev.: $95,982,731
Assets: $1,323,699,159
Liabilities: $551,441,339
Net Worth: $772,257,820
Earnings: $47,277,891
Fiscal Year-end: 12/31/23
Real Estate Investment Trust Services
N.A.I.C.S.: 531190

SASSY GOLD CORPORATION

400 1681 Chestnut Street, Vancouver, V6J 4M6, BC, Canada
Tel.: (604) 833-6999
Web Site: https://www.sassygold.com
SASY—(CNSX)
Rev.: $73,776
Assets: $10,595,185
Liabilities: $312,208
Net Worth: $10,282,977
Earnings: ($9,892,045)
Fiscal Year-end: 06/30/24
Mineral Exploration Services
N.A.I.C.S.: 213115
Mark Scott (Pres & CEO)

SASTASUNDAR VENTURES LIMITED

Azimganj House 2nd Floor 7, Abanindra Nath Thakur Sarani, Kolkata, 700 017, India

SASTASUNDAR VENTURES LIMITED

Sastasundar Ventures Limited—(Continued)
Tel.: (91) 3322829330
Web Site:
https://www.sastasundar.com
533259—(BOM)
Rev.: $53,037,894
Assets: $43,067,170
Liabilities: $9,458,222
Net Worth: $33,608,948
Earnings: ($7,115,922)
Emp.: 3
Fiscal Year-end: 03/31/20
Financial & Investment Services
N.A.I.C.S.: 525990
Banwari Lal Mittal (Co-Founder, Chm & Mng Dir)

Subsidiaries:

Genu Path Labs Limited (1)
Innovation Tower Sastasundar Premises no 16-315 Plot no DH 6/32, Action Area -1D Newtown Rajarhat, Kolkata, 700156, India
Tel.: (91) 8069506950
Web Site: https://www.genupathlabs.com
Diagnostic Services
N.A.I.C.S.: 621511

Retailer Shakti Supply Chain Private Limited (1)
Innovation Tower Premises No 16-315 Plot No DH6/32, Action Area-1D Newtown Rajarhat, Kolkata, 700156, West Bengal, India
Tel.: (91) 6292002002
Web Site: https://www.retailershakti.com
Household Appliance Retailer
N.A.I.C.S.: 423720

SAT CO., LTD.
25 MTV 58 Beon-gil, Siheung, 429-926, Gyeonggi-do, Korea (South)
Tel.: (82) 31 433 4711
Web Site: http://www.sateng.co.kr
Year Founded: 2003
158300—(KRS)
Sales Range: $10-24.9 Million
Emp.: 40
Special Industrial Machinery Mfr
N.A.I.C.S.: 333248
Jinseok So (Chm & CEO)

SAT COSTA DE NIJAR
Ctra a Campohermoso Km 9, San Isidro, 04117, Almeria, Spain
Tel.: (34) 950612700
Web Site: http://www.costanijar.com
Year Founded: 1997
Sales Range: $25-49.9 Million
Emp.: 250
Agricultural Products Including Fruits & Vegetables
N.A.I.C.S.: 424480
Rafael Castilla (Mgr-Comml)

SAT INDUSTRIES LTD.
121 B Wing Mittal Towers, Nariman Point, Mumbai, 400 021, India
Tel.: (91) 2266107025
Web Site: https://www.satgroup.in
511076—(BOM)
Rev.: $47,977,320
Assets: $51,720,969
Liabilities: $22,825,967
Net Worth: $28,895,003
Earnings: $5,283,437
Emp.: 13
Fiscal Year-end: 03/31/22
Steel Trader
N.A.I.C.S.: 331110
Harikant K. Turgalia (CFO)

Subsidiaries:

Aeroflex Finance Private Limited (1)
121 B-Wing Mittal Towers 12th Floor, Nariman Point, Mumbai, 400021, India
Tel.: (91) 2266107025
Web Site: https://aeroflexfinance.com
Financing Information Services
N.A.I.C.S.: 541611

Aeroflex Industries Limited (1)
Plot No 41 And 42/13 14 18 Near Taloja MIDC, Chal Panvel Raigad, Taloja, 410 208, Maharashtra, India
Tel.: (91) 2261467100
Web Site: https://www.aeroflexindia.com
Steel Products Mfr
N.A.I.C.S.: 331210

Sah Polymers Limited (1)
E-'260-261 Opp UCCI Madri, Mewar Industrial Area, Udaipur, 313003, Rajasthan, India
Tel.: (91) 2942490534
Web Site: https://www.sahpolymers.in
Chemicals Mfr
N.A.I.C.S.: 325998
Lalit Kumar Bolia (CFO)

SATA CONSTRUCTION CO., LTD.
1-1-7 Motosojacho, Maebashi, 371-0846, Gunma, Japan
Tel.: (81) 272511551
Web Site: https://www.sata.co.jp
Year Founded: 1949
1826—(TKS)
Rev.: $172,408,630
Assets: $173,823,170
Liabilities: $73,053,720
Net Worth: $100,769,450
Earnings: $495,750
Emp.: 372
Fiscal Year-end: 03/31/24
Construction Engineering Services
N.A.I.C.S.: 541330
Miyuki Tsuchiya (Chm & Pres)

SATA GMBH & CO. KG
Domertalstrasse 20, 70806, Kornwestheim, Germany
Tel.: (49) 71548110
Web Site: https://www.sata.com
Wet Paint Manufacturer & Distributor
N.A.I.C.S.: 325510
Mike Carlos Wolf (Mng Dir)

Subsidiaries:

Dan-Am Co. (1)
1 Sata Dr, Spring Valley, MN 55975
Tel.: (507) 346-7102
Web Site: http://www.danamair.com
Rev.: $6,404,600
Emp.: 30
Other Miscellaneous Durable Goods Merchant Whslr
N.A.I.C.S.: 423990
Knud Jorgensen (Pres & CEO)

SATCHMO HOLDINGS LIMITED
No 110 A Wing Level 1 Andrews Building M G Road, Bengaluru, 560001, Karnataka, India
Tel.: (91) 8040174000
Web Site:
http://www.niteshestates.com
Rev.: $6,396,716
Assets: $200,037,804
Liabilities: $146,908,184
Net Worth: $53,129,620
Earnings: ($14,878,472)
Emp.: 674
Fiscal Year-end: 03/31/18
Real Estate Services
N.A.I.C.S.: 531390
Nitesh Shetty (Founder, Chm & Mng Dir)

SATELLITE CHANNELS INC.
Asahi Shimbun Annex 5-3-2 Tsukiji, Chuo-ku, Tokyo, 104-8443, Japan
Tel.: (81) 355506111
Web Site: http://www.asahi-newstar.com
Year Founded: 1986
Sales Range: $10-24.9 Million
Emp.: 40
Television Broadcasting Services
N.A.I.C.S.: 516120
Masaru Takahashi (Pres & CEO)

SATELLITE CHEMICAL CO., LTD.
Bujiao Road Jiaxing Industrial Park, Jiaxing, 314050, Zhejiang, China
Tel.: (86) 57382229096
Web Site: http://www.satlpec.com
Year Founded: 2005
002648—(SSE)
Rev.: $5,200,977,403
Assets: $7,916,513,333
Liabilities: $4,946,992,105
Net Worth: $2,969,521,228
Earnings: $429,903,817
Emp.: 1,000
Fiscal Year-end: 12/31/22
Chemicals Mfr
N.A.I.C.S.: 325998
Yang Weidong (Chm & Pres)

SATELLOS BIOSCIENCE INC.
6th Floor 777 Hornby Street, Vancouver, V6Z 2T3, BC, Canada
Tel.: (604) 800-9860
Web Site:
http://www.icotherapeutics.com
ICO—(OTCIQ)
Assets: $1,123,585
Liabilities: $618,023
Net Worth: $505,562
Earnings: ($1,483,215)
Emp.: 4
Fiscal Year-end: 12/31/19
Pharmaceuticals Product Mfr
N.A.I.C.S.: 325412
William Jarosz (Chm & CEO)

SATHOSA MOTORS PLC
Tel.: (94) 112432858
Web Site:
https://www.sathosamotorsplc.com
SMOT—(COL)
Rev.: $6,427,820
Assets: $11,931,904
Liabilities: $4,928,617
Net Worth: $7,003,287
Earnings: ($182,881)
Emp.: 117
Fiscal Year-end: 03/31/23
Motor Vehicle Parts Sales & Services
N.A.I.C.S.: 423120
Sumal Joseph Sanjeewa (Chm)

SATIA INDUSTRIES LIMITED
VPO Rupana Distt, Muktsar, 152 026, Punjab, India
Tel.: (91) 1633262215
Web Site:
https://www.satiagroup.com
Year Founded: 1984
539201—(BOM)
Rev.: $81,238,753
Assets: $136,700,669
Liabilities: $75,911,049
Net Worth: $60,789,620
Earnings: $6,763,384
Emp.: 1,415
Fiscal Year-end: 03/31/21
Paper Products Mfr
N.A.I.C.S.: 322299
Ajay Satia (Chm & Co-Mng Dir)

SATIN CREDITCARE NETWORK LIMITED
5th Floor Kundan Bhawan, Azadpur Commercial Complex Azad Pur, New Delhi, 110033, India
Tel.: (91) 1147545000
Web Site:
https://www.satincreditcare.com
Year Founded: 1990
SATIN—(NSE)
Rev.: $188,394,133
Assets: $1,098,103,011

INTERNATIONAL PUBLIC

Liabilities: $895,241,543
Net Worth: $202,861,468
Earnings: ($1,908,570)
Emp.: 10,612
Fiscal Year-end: 03/31/21
Microfinance Services
N.A.I.C.S.: 522291
H. P. Singh (Chm & Mng Dir)

Subsidiaries:

Satin Housing Finance Limited (1)
Tel.: (91) 1800120405060
Web Site:
http://www.satinhousingfinance.com
Housing Finance Services
N.A.I.C.S.: 925110
Sachin Sharma (CFO)

Taraashna Financial Services Limited (1)
Ground Floor Building 97 Sector - 44, Gurgaon, 122003, Haryana, India
Tel.: (91) 1244715400
Web Site: http://www.taraashna.in
Commercial Finance Services
N.A.I.C.S.: 522299
Partho Sengupta (CEO)

SATIS GROUP SA
Bekasow Street 74, 02-803, Warsaw, Poland
Tel.: (48) 223804757
Web Site:
https://www.satisgroupsa.pl
STS—(WAR)
Assets: $600,864
Liabilities: $2,767,530
Net Worth: ($2,166,667)
Earnings: ($2,313,770)
Fiscal Year-end: 12/31/23
Holding Company
N.A.I.C.S.: 551112
Andrzej Wrona (Chm-Mgmt Bd)

SATISFIED BRAKE PRODUCTS INC.
805 Education Rd, Cornwall, K6H 6C7, ON, Canada
Tel.: (613) 933-3300
Sales Range: $50-74.9 Million
Emp.: 200
Brake Products Mfr
N.A.I.C.S.: 336340
Eric Laframboise (CEO)

SATIVA WELLNESS GROUP INC.
503 905 West Pender St, Vancouver, V6C 1L6, BC, Canada
Web Site: http://www.stillcanna.com
GDBYF—(OTCEM)
Rev.: $22,978,913
Assets: $14,606,968
Liabilities: $5,085,049
Net Worth: $9,521,918
Earnings: ($3,117,701)
Emp.: 45
Fiscal Year-end: 12/31/21
Cannabidiol Product Mfr
N.A.I.C.S.: 325411
Joel Leonard (CFO)

Subsidiaries:

Olimax NT SP. Z .O.O. (1)
Ul Bukowa 2, Bilcza, Kielce, Poland
Tel.: (48) 600454787
Web Site: http://www.olimax.pl
Cannabis Product Distr
N.A.I.C.S.: 459999

SATIXFY COMMUNICATIONS LTD.
12 Hamada St, Rehovot, 670315, Israel
Tel.: (972) 89393200
Web Site: https://www.satixfy.com
Year Founded: 2012

SATO HOLDINGS CORPORATION

SATX—(NYSE)
Rev.: $10,626,000
Assets: $76,325,000
Liabilities: $107,947,000
Net Worth: ($31,622,000)
Earnings: ($397,789,000)
Emp.: 191
Fiscal Year-end: 12/31/22
Telecommunication Servicesb
N.A.I.C.S.: 517810
Ido Gur *(CEO)*

SATKAR FINLEASE LIMITED
829 Laxmideep Building 8th Floor District Centre, Next to V3S Mall Laxmi Nagar, Delhi, 110092, India
Tel.: (91) 11 32937170
Web Site:
http://www.satkarfinlease.in
Rev.: $118,100
Assets: $8,796,084
Liabilities: $1,612,265
Net Worth: $7,183,819
Earnings: $8,589
Emp.: 4
Fiscal Year-end: 03/31/18
Financial Services
N.A.I.C.S.: 525990
Roop Singh *(Chm & CFO)*

SATO FOODS CO., LTD.
13-5 Takaramachi Niigatahigashi-ku, Niigata, 950-8730, Japan
Tel.: (81) 252751110
Web Site:
http://www.satosyokuhin.co.jp
Year Founded: 1961
2923—(TKS)
Rev.: $281,460,410
Assets: $289,101,570
Liabilities: $153,028,110
Net Worth: $136,073,460
Earnings: $15,169,950
Emp.: 202
Fiscal Year-end: 04/30/24
Rice Product Mfr & Whslr
N.A.I.C.S.: 311423
Hajime Sato *(Pres)*

SATO FOODS INDUSTRIES CO.,LTD.
4-154 Horinouchi, Komaki, 485-8523, Aichi, Japan
Tel.: (81) 568777316
Web Site: https://www.sato-foods.co.jp
Year Founded: 1950
2814—(TKS)
Sales Range: $50-74.9 Million
Emp.: 205
Tea Mfr
N.A.I.C.S.: 311920
Zinichi Sato *(Chm & Pres)*

SATO HOLDINGS CORPORATION
Tamachi Station Tower N 3-1-1 Shibaura, Minato-ku, Tokyo, 108-0023, Japan
Tel.: (81) 366282400
Web Site: https://www.sato-global.com
Year Founded: 1940
6287—(TKS)
Rev.: $948,178,060
Assets: $875,540,770
Liabilities: $385,838,920
Net Worth: $489,701,850
Earnings: $23,564,650
Emp.: 5,744
Fiscal Year-end: 03/31/24
Investment Management Service
N.A.I.C.S.: 523940
Maria Olcese *(Exec Officer, Head-South America & Gen Mgr-Achernar SA)*

Subsidiaries:

ARGOX INFORMATION CO., LTD. (1)
Tel.: (886) 289121121
Printer Mfr & Distr
N.A.I.C.S.: 334118

Okil-Holding, JSC (1)
pos Metallostroy Severny proezd 15 letter A, 196641, Saint Petersburg, Russia
Tel.: (7) 8123275737
Web Site: https://www.okil.ru
Label Specialties Mfr & Distr
N.A.I.C.S.: 322220

Okil-Sato X-Pack Co., Ltd. (1)
Industrial Area d 12 lit I pos Metallostroy, 196641, Saint Petersburg, Russia
Tel.: (7) 8124490131
Flexible Packaging Mfr & Distr
N.A.I.C.S.: 326112

PT. Sato Label Solutions (1)
Kawasan MM2100 Jl Aru Blok L-2 Desa Suka Sejati Kec, Cikarang Selatan, Bekasi, 17530, Jawa Barat, Indonesia
Tel.: (62) 212 808 0270
Automatic Identification Solution Distr
N.A.I.C.S.: 423110

Prakolar Rotulos Autoadesivos Ltda. (1)
Rua Manuel Ramos Paiva 70, Sao Paulo, 03021-060, Brazil
Tel.: (55) 112 618 6171
Web Site: https://www.prakolar.com.br
Label Specialties Mfr & Distr
N.A.I.C.S.: 322220

SATO AUTO-ID (THAILAND) CO., LTD. (1)
292/1 Moo 1 Theparak Road, Tumbol Theparak Amphur Muang, Samut Prakan, 10270, Thailand
Tel.: (66) 27364460
Web Site: https://satoasiapacific.com
Printer Distr
N.A.I.C.S.: 423430

SATO America, Inc. (1)
14125 S Bridge Cir, Charlotte, NC 28273
Tel.: (704) 644-1650
Printer Distr
N.A.I.C.S.: 423430

Subsidiary (Non-US):

Achernar S.A. (2)
Gral Hornos 1304, C1272ADB, Buenos Aires, Argentina
Tel.: (54) 1153009100
Web Site: https://www.achernar.com.ar
Label Distr
N.A.I.C.S.: 424310

SATO AUTO-ID DO BRASIL LTDA. (2)
Rua Cidade de Bagda 479, Vila Santa Catarina, Sao Paulo, 04377-036, SP, Brazil
Tel.: (55) 1150335572
Printer Distr
N.A.I.C.S.: 423430

SATO Argentina S.A. (2)
Gral Hornos 1304, C1272ADB, Buenos Aires, Argentina
Tel.: (54) 1145283064
Web Site: https://www.satosudamerica.com
Printer Distr
N.A.I.C.S.: 423430

SATO PRINT CONNECT HONG KONG LTD. (2)
Unit 4 3/F Wah Shing Centre 11 Shing Yip Street, Kwun Tong, Kowloon, China (Hong Kong)
Tel.: (852) 2343 0220
Commercial Printing Services
N.A.I.C.S.: 323113

SATO Asia Pacific Pte Ltd. (1)
No 11 Ubi Road 1 03-01 Meiban Industrial Building, Singapore, 408723, Singapore
Tel.: (65) 62715300
Web Site: https://satoasiapacific.com
Printer Distr
N.A.I.C.S.: 423430

SATO Australia Pty Ltd. (1)
6 Federation Way, Chifley Business Park, Mentone, 3194, VIC, Australia
Tel.: (61) 388145300
Web Site: https://satoasiapacific.com
Printer Distr
N.A.I.C.S.: 423430

SATO Auto-ID India Private Limited (1)
Unit No 106 Tower B Unitech Cyber Park Sector 39, Sohna Road, Gurgaon, 122 003, Haryana, India
Tel.: (91) 124 449 8555
Web Site: https://www.satoasiapacific.com
Printer Distr
N.A.I.C.S.: 423430

SATO Auto-ID Malaysia Sdn. Bhd. (1)
No 38 Jalan Pemberita U1/49 Temasya Industrial Park Section U1, 40150, Shah Alam, Selangor Darul Ehsan, Malaysia
Tel.: (60) 376208901
Web Site: https://satoasiapacific.com
Printer Distr
N.A.I.C.S.: 423430

SATO Benelux B.V. (1)
Zeemanlaan 6, 3401 MV, IJsselstein, Netherlands
Tel.: (31) 348444437
Web Site: https://www.satoeurope.com
Printer Distr
N.A.I.C.S.: 423430

SATO CORPORATION (1)
Tamachi Tamachi Station Tower N 3-1-1 Shibaura, Minato-ku, Tokyo, 108-0023, Tottori, Japan
Tel.: (81) 366282400
Emp.: 5,637
Industrial Supplies Distr
N.A.I.C.S.: 423840
Nobuo Watanabe *(VP)*

SATO Germany GmbH (1)
Waldhofer Strasse 104, 69123, Heidelberg, Germany
Tel.: (49) 622158500
Printer Distr
N.A.I.C.S.: 423430

SATO IBERIA S. A, U. (1)
Dels Corrals Nous 35-39 Pol Can Roqueta, 08202, Sabadell, Barcelona, Spain
Tel.: (34) 902 636 018
Web Site: http://www.satoeurope.com
Industrial Supplies Distr
N.A.I.C.S.: 423840

SATO INTERNATIONAL EUROPE N. V. (1)
Leonardo Da Vincilaan 19 Stockholm Building, 1831, Diegem, Belgium
Tel.: (32) 2 719 03 90
Web Site: http://www.satoeurope.com
Emp.: 2
Investment Management Service
N.A.I.C.S.: 523940
Makoto Hayama *(Mng Dir)*

Subsidiary (Non-US):

SATO France S.A.S. (2)
Parc d'Activites Rue Jacques Messager, 59175, Templemars, France
Tel.: (33) 320629640
Web Site: https://www.satoeurope.com
Printer Distr
N.A.I.C.S.: 423430

SATO LABELLING POLAND SP. Z O. O. (2)
Panattoni Park II Ul Ryszarda Chomicza 3, Nowa Wies Katy, 55-080, Wroclaw, Poland
Tel.: (48) 717760460
Printer Mfr
N.A.I.C.S.: 334118
Emil Solecki *(Mgr-Production)*

SATO LOGISTICS CO., LTD. (1)
321-28 Ikezawacho, Yamatokoriyama, Nara, 639-1032, Japan
Tel.: (81) 743583640
Logistics Consulting Servies
N.A.I.C.S.: 541614
Kazuyoshi Onishi *(Gen Mgr)*

SATO New Zealand Ltd. (1)
30 Apollo Drive, Mairangi Bay, Auckland, New Zealand
Tel.: (64) 94772222
Web Site: https://satoasiapacific.com
Printer Distr
N.A.I.C.S.: 423430

SATO Shanghai Co., Ltd. (1)
Room 803 Changfang International Plaza 555 Loushanguan Road, Changning District, Shanghai, 200051, China
Tel.: (86) 4008206875
Web Site: https://www.satochina.com
Emp.: 130
Printer Mfr & Distr
N.A.I.C.S.: 334118
Sindy Chen *(Sr Mgr-Mktg)*

SATO TECHNO LAB EUROPE AB (1)
Molndalsvagen 91, 412 63, Gothenburg, Sweden
Tel.: (46) 313511500
Web Site: http://www.satoeurope.com
Printer Distr
N.A.I.C.S.: 423430

SATO UK Ltd. (1)
Valley Road, Harwich, CO12 4RR, Essex, United Kingdom
Tel.: (44) 1255240000
Web Site: http://www.satoeurope.com
Printer Distr
N.A.I.C.S.: 423430

SATO VICINITY Pty. Ltd. (1)
32 Burrows Road, Annandale, Saint Peters, 2044, NSW, Australia
Tel.: (61) 295629800
Web Site: https://www.satovicinity.com
Printer Mfr & Distr
N.A.I.C.S.: 334419

SATO Vietnam Co., Ltd. (1)
Plot B-2 Thang Long Industrial Park, Kim Chung Commune Dong Anh Dist, Hanoi, Vietnam
Tel.: (84) 2439516297
Web Site: https://satoasiapacific.com
Printer Mfr
N.A.I.C.S.: 334118

SATO Vietnam Solutions Co., Ltd. (1)
6th Floor Saigon Finance Center Building 9 Dinh Tien Hoang, Da Kao Ward District 1, Ho Chi Minh City, Vietnam
Tel.: (84) 2839101350
Web Site: https://satoasiapacific.com
Printer Distr
N.A.I.C.S.: 423430

Sato Argox India Pvt. Ltd. (1)
Unit No 106 Tower B Unitech Cyber Park Sector 39, Gurgaon, 122 003, Haryana, India
Tel.: (91) 124 449 8555
Web Site: https://www.satoasiapacific.com
Software Services
N.A.I.C.S.: 541511

Sato Europe GmbH (1)
Waldhofer Strasse 104, 69123, Heidelberg, Germany
Tel.: (49) 62 215 8500
Web Site: https://www.satoeurope.com
Electronic & Electrical Product Distr
N.A.I.C.S.: 423690
Laurent Lassus *(Mng Dir)*

Sato Healthcare Co., Ltd. (1)
Tamachi Station Tower N 3-1-1, Shibaura, Minato-ku, Tokyo, 108-0023, Japan
Tel.: (81) 36 636 9430
Automatic Identification Solution Distr
N.A.I.C.S.: 423110

Sato Impress Co., Ltd. (1)
2750 Yamazaki, Noda, Chiba, Japan
Tel.: (81) 47 124 8171
Mechatronic Product Mfr & Distr
N.A.I.C.S.: 333248

Sato Malaysia Electronics Manufacturing Sdn. Bhd. (1)
Lot 20 Jalan 223, 46100, Petaling Jaya, Selangor, Malaysia
Tel.: (60) 3 7844 9400
Web Site: http://www.satomalaysia.com
Emp.: 379
Printer Mfr
N.A.I.C.S.: 334118

SATO HOLDINGS CORPORATION

SATO Holdings Corporation—(Continued)
Daisuke Inagaki (Mng Dir)

Sato Productivity Solutions Mexico S.A. De C.V. (1)
Avenida Mina De Guadalupe Numero 950-L Parque Industrial Santa Fe IV, Puerto Interior Silao, 36275, Guanajuato, Mexico
Tel.: (52) 472 688 2092
Web Site: https://www.satoamerica.com
Printing Machinery & Equipment Mfr
N.A.I.C.S.: 333248

Sato Solution Architects Co., Ltd. (1)
3-1-1 Shibaura msb Tamachi Tamachi Station Tower N, Minato-ku, Tokyo, 108-0023, Japan
Tel.: (81) 36 636 9425
Web Site: https://www.sato-sa.com
Management Consulting Services
N.A.I.C.S.: 541611

Stafford Press, Inc
14612 NE 91st St, Redmond, WA 98052-3436
Tel.: (425) 861-5856
Web Site: http://www.westhort.com
Paper Bag & Coated & Treated Paper Mfr
N.A.I.C.S.: 322220
David Long (Owner)

WUXI SONGXING ELECTRONIC COMPONENTS CO., LTD (1)
No 507 Datong Road Binhu Economic & Technical Development Area, Wuxi, 214124, Jiangsu, China
Tel.: (86) 510 8865 7160
Electronic Components Distr
N.A.I.C.S.: 423690

SATO PHILIPPINES AIDC SOLUTIONS INC.
Bldg 8 Panorama Compound 6 LT3 BLK5 LTI Annex Binan, Laguna, Philippines
Tel.: (63) 495449459   PH
Electric Equipment Mfr
N.A.I.C.S.: 334419

SATO PHILIPPINES AUTO-ID SP INC.
2A Kabihasnan St Barangay, San Dionisio, Paranaque, Philippines
Tel.: (63) 495449459   PH
Electric Equipment Mfr
N.A.I.C.S.: 334419

SATO S.A.
250-254 Kifisias Avenue, Elefsina, 152 31, Athens, Greece
Tel.: (30) 2130181600
Web Site: https://www.sato.gr
SATOK—(ATH)
Sales Range: $100-124.9 Million
Emp.: 576
Office & Home Furniture & Accessories Mfr
N.A.I.C.S.: 337211

SATO SCHNEIDSYSTEME ANTON HUBERT E. K.
Tomphecke 51, 41169, Monchengladbach, Germany
Tel.: (49) 216199420
Web Site: http://www.sato-cuttingsystems.com
Year Founded: 1988
Rev.: $18,127,200
Emp.: 43
Cutting Machines & Equipment Mfr
N.A.I.C.S.: 333517
Anton W. Hubert (Owner)

SATO SHOJI CORPORATION
16F Marunouchi Trust Tower North 1-8-1 Marunouchi, Chiyoda-ku, Tokyo, 100-8285, Japan
Tel.: (81) 352185311
Web Site: https://www.satoshoji.co.jp
Year Founded: 1930
8065—(TKS)
Rev.: $1,810,974,750
Assets: $1,142,670,700
Liabilities: $711,685,480
Net Worth: $430,985,220
Earnings: $42,819,580
Emp.: 1,018
Fiscal Year-end: 03/31/24
Iron & Steel Product Whslr
N.A.I.C.S.: 423390
Yoshiaki Taura (Sr Mng Exec Officer & Dir)

Subsidiaries:

Daito Kogyo Co., Ltd. (1)
19 Kiriharacho, Fujisawa, 252-0811, Kanagawa, Japan
Tel.: (81) 466512990
Industrial Tools Distr
N.A.I.C.S.: 423830

Fuji Jidosha Kogyo Co., Ltd. (1)
4-3-3 Ohnodai, Minami-ku, Sagamihara, 252-0331, Kanagawa, Japan
Tel.: (81) 427596711
Web Site: https://www.fujijiko.co.jp
Emp.: 104
Automobile Parts Mfr
N.A.I.C.S.: 336110

Hanshin Special Steel Co., Ltd. (1)
6-1-1 Himejima, Nishiyodogawa-ku, Osaka, 555-0033, Japan
Tel.: (81) 664719731
Web Site: https://hanshintokusyukou.jimdofree.com
Emp.: 22
Iron & Steel Product Distr
N.A.I.C.S.: 423390

Metal Act Co., Ltd. (1)
3F Nagoya Intercity Bldg 1-11-11, Nishiki Naka-ku, Nagoya, 460-0003, Japan
Tel.: (81) 522015600
Web Site: https://www.metalact.co.jp
Emp.: 30
Iron & Steel Product Distr
N.A.I.C.S.: 423390

Nihon Yoshokki Co.,Ltd. (1)
1949 Yoshida Hokado, Tsubame, 959-0214, Niigata, Japan
Tel.: (81) 256923131
Web Site: https://www.nihon-yoshokki.co.jp
Metal Products Mfr
N.A.I.C.S.: 332510

PS Device & Material Inc. (1)
12F-1 NO 5 Taiyuan 1st, Chupei, 302, Hsinchu, Taiwan
Tel.: (886) 35601556
Electronic Material Distr
N.A.I.C.S.: 423690

PT.Sato-Shoji Indonesia (1)
Summitmas 1 18th Floor Jl Jend Sudirman kav, Jakarta, 12190, Indonesia
Tel.: (62) 212521262
Nonferrous Metal Distr
N.A.I.C.S.: 423510

Polyhose Sato Shoji Metal Works Private Limited (1)
3rd Floor Polyhose Tower No 86 Mount Road, Guindy, Chennai, 600032, India
Tel.: (91) 4445200900
Industrial Tools Distr
N.A.I.C.S.: 423830

Sato Chemical Glass (Suzhou) Co., Ltd. (1)
No 569 Fanfeng Road, Xukou Town Wuzhong District, Suzhou, China
Tel.: (86) 51267425221
Industrial Tools Distr
N.A.I.C.S.: 423830

Sato Chemiglass Corporation (1)
15-1 Imai, Mihara-ku Sakai-shi, Osaka, 587-0061, Japan
Tel.: (81) 723627778
Industrial Tools Distr
N.A.I.C.S.: 423830

Sato Genetec Corporation (1)
Marunouchi Trust Tower N Building 16F 1-8-1 Marunouchi, Chiyoda-ku, Tokyo, 100-0005, Japan
Tel.: (81) 332861501
Web Site: https://www.coin-park.net
Automobile Parts Distr
N.A.I.C.S.: 423110

Sato Shoji (shenzhen) Co., Ltd. (1)
Room 1701 1726 17/F Kerry Centre Renmin Nan Road, Luohu, Shenzhen, 518000, China
Tel.: (86) 75582306889
Electronic Equipment Distr
N.A.I.C.S.: 423690

Sato Shoji Asia Pacific Pte. Ltd. (1)
10 Anson Road 29-11 International Plaza, Singapore, 079903, Singapore
Tel.: (65) 69708074
Electronic Material Distr
N.A.I.C.S.: 423690

Sato Shoji Hong Kong Co., Ltd. (1)
Rm 1012 10/F Chinachem Golden Plaza 77 Mody Road Tsim Sha Tsui East, Kowloon, China (Hong Kong)
Tel.: (852) 23689200
Electronic Equipment Distr
N.A.I.C.S.: 423690

Sato Shoji Korea Co., Ltd. (1)
A3412 Gwanggyo SK View Lake Tower Beopjo-ro 25, Yeongtong-gu, Suwon, Gyeonggi-do, Korea (South)
Tel.: (82) 27850885
Electronic Equipment Distr
N.A.I.C.S.: 423690

Sato Shoji Shanghai Co., Ltd. (1)
Room7D1 Jinlinghaixin Building 666 Fuzhou Road, Shanghai, 200001, China
Tel.: (86) 2163917575
Iron & Steel Product Distr
N.A.I.C.S.: 423390

Sato Techno Service (Thailand) Co., Ltd. (1)
499 Moo 10 Sriracha Building Project Nongkham, Sriracha Chonburi, Bangkok, 20230, Thailand
Tel.: (66) 988299271
Web Site: https://www.shoeitechno.co.th
Robot Maintenance & Repair Services
N.A.I.C.S.: 811412
Tsuyoshi Udaka (Mng Dir)

Sato shoji (Guangzhou) Co., Ltd. (1)
Room 609 Poly Central Pivot Plaza No 157 Linhe Xi Road, Tianhe District, Guangzhou, 510610, China
Tel.: (86) 2038824479
Iron & Steel Product Distr
N.A.I.C.S.: 423390

Sato-Shoji (Cambodia) Co., Ltd. (1)
P2-061 062 Phnom Pehn Special Economic Zone National Road No 4, Sangkat Kantouk Sangkat Beung Thom Phleung Chhes Rotes Khan Posenchey, Phnom Penh, Cambodia
Tel.: (855) 23900512
Iron & Steel Product Distr
N.A.I.C.S.: 423390

Sato-Shoji (vietnam) Co., Ltd (1)
Room 503 5th Floor Centec Tower 72-74 Nguyen Thi Minh Khai St, Vo Thi Sau Ward District 3, Ho Chi Minh City, Vietnam
Tel.: (84) 838279141
Nonferrous Metal Distr
N.A.I.C.S.: 423510

Sato-Shoji India Private Limited (1)
Suite no 908 9th Floor Olympia Platina Plot No 33-B, South Phase Guindy Industrial Estate, Chennai, 600 032, India
Tel.: (91) 4466108016
Nonferrous Metal Distr
N.A.I.C.S.: 423510

Sato-Shoji(Thailand) co., ltd. (1)
1 Empire Tower3 24th Floor Unit 2406-7 South Sathorn Road, Yannawa Sathorn, Bangkok, 10120, Thailand
Tel.: (66) 26595784
Web Site: http://www.satoshoji.co.th
Emp.: 58
Steel Products Mfr
N.A.I.C.S.: 331221
Yohei Toda (Mng Dir)

Sekine Kozai K.K. (1)
2-4-2 Tekkoudori, Urayasu, 279-0025, Japan
Tel.: (81) 473839503
Industrial Tools Distr
N.A.I.C.S.: 423830

Shonan Kakou K.K. (1)
3004-1 Kuzuhara, Fujisawa, 252-0822, Kanagawa, Japan
Tel.: (81) 466481711
Industrial Tools Distr
N.A.I.C.S.: 423830

Sogabe (Suzhou) Gear Reducer Co., Ltd. (1)
1st Floor No 328-12 Su Wang Road Wuzhong Economic Development Zone, Suzhou, Jiangsu, China
Tel.: (86) 51266500318
Industrial Tools Distr
N.A.I.C.S.: 423830

Yuasa Sato (Thailand) Co., Ltd. (1)
7/158 Moo 4 Mabyangporn Sub-district, Pluakdaeng District, Rayong, 21140, Thailand
Tel.: (66) 38025815
Industrial Tools Distr
N.A.I.C.S.: 423830

INTERNATIONAL PUBLIC

SATO TAIWAN CO., LTD.
7F No 128 Lane 235 Baoqiao Rd, Xindian Dist, New Taipei City, Taiwan
Tel.: (886) 289121288   TW
Electric Equipment Mfr
N.A.I.C.S.: 334419

SATOH & CO., LTD.
5-6-22 Ogimachi, Miyagino-ku, Sendai, 983-8556, Miyagi, Japan
Tel.: (81) 222365600
Web Site: https://www.satoh-web.co.jp
Year Founded: 1950
9996—(TKS)
Rev.: $314,542,363
Assets: $244,955,333
Liabilities: $77,707,279
Net Worth: $167,248,054
Earnings: $8,107,034
Fiscal Year-end: 03/31/24
Food Product Whslr
N.A.I.C.S.: 445298
Masayuki Sato (Chm)

SATORI ELECTRIC CO., LTD.
14-10 Shiba 1-chome, Minato-ku, Tokyo, 105-0014, Japan
Tel.: (81) 334511040
Web Site: https://www.satori.co.jp
Year Founded: 1947
7420—(TKS)
Rev.: $979,026,930
Assets: $551,895,340
Liabilities: $321,497,180
Net Worth: $230,398,160
Earnings: $14,251,160
Emp.: 793
Fiscal Year-end: 05/31/24
Electronic Components & Equipment Distr
N.A.I.C.S.: 423690
Hiroyuki Satori (Pres)

Subsidiaries:

Hong Kong Satori Co., Ltd. (1)
Units 1101-1102 1113B 11/F Office Tower 1 The Harbourfront, 18 Tak Fung Street Hunghom, Kowloon, China (Hong Kong)
Tel.: (852) 27224368
Emp.: 40
Electronic Component Sales
N.A.I.C.S.: 423610

KOREA SATORI CO., LTD. (1)
3F Dansan Segyung Bldg 20 Seolleung-ro 111-gil, Gangnam-gu, Seoul, 06103, Korea (South)
Tel.: (82) 222022450
Sales Range: $25-49.9 Million
Emp.: 16
Electronic Component Support Services
N.A.I.C.S.: 811210

AND PRIVATE COMPANIES — SATURDAY CO., LTD.

Bum Jin Cho *(Mgr)*

SATORI PINICS (THAILAND) CO., LTD. (1)
7th Fl Rm LL704 The Ofc At Central World
999 9 Ramal Rd, Pathumwan, Bangkok, 10330, Thailand
Tel.: (66) 22645945
Sales Range: $50-74.9 Million
Emp.: 7
Electronic Component Sales
N.A.I.C.S.: 423690

SHENZHEN SATORI CO., LTD. (1)
Rm 5104-05 51/Fl Shun Hing Square Di Wang Commercial Centre 5002, Shen Nan Dong Rd, Shenzhen, Guangdong, China
Tel.: (86) 75582461511
Web Site: http://www.hkfatoi.com
Sales Range: Less than $1 Million
Emp.: 15
Electronic Products Support Services
N.A.I.C.S.: 238210
Alan Hui *(Sr Mgr-Sls)*

Satori E-Technology (America) Inc. (1)
33533 W 12 Mile Rd Ste 305, Farmington Hills, MI 48331-5602
Tel.: (248) 536-2207
Web Site: http://www.satori-usa.com
Sales Range: $50-74.9 Million
Emp.: 4
Electronic Component Sales
N.A.I.C.S.: 423690
Jay Tanaka *(Pres)*

Satori Electric Germany GmbH (1)
Fellnerstr 7-9, 60322, Frankfurt am Main, Germany
Tel.: (49) 6992887790
Sales Range: $50-74.9 Million
Emp.: 2
Electronic Component Sales
N.A.I.C.S.: 423690
Masaki Akira *(Dir)*

Satori Pinics (Singapore) Pte Ltd. (1)
91 Bencoolen St No 09-01 06 Sunshine Plz, Singapore, 189652, Singapore
Tel.: (65) 63338650
Sales Range: $50-74.9 Million
Emp.: 4
Electronic Component Sales
N.A.I.C.S.: 423690

Satori Pinics Co., Ltd. (1)
14-10 1-Chome Shiba, Minato-Ku, Tokyo, 108-0014, Japan
Tel.: (81) 334538831
Sales Range: $25-49.9 Million
Emp.: 40
Electrical Control Components Sales
N.A.I.C.S.: 423610

Satori Pinics Hong Kong Co., Ltd (1)
Rm 1202A E Ocean Ctr 98 Granville Rd, Tsimshatsui E, Kowloon, China (Hong Kong)
Tel.: (852) 2 722 4368
Electronic Component Sales
N.A.I.C.S.: 423690

Satori SP Technology Co., Ltd. (1)
14-10 1-Chome Shiba, Minato-Ku, Tokyo, Japan
Tel.: (81) 334527757
Electronic Parts Distr
N.A.I.C.S.: 423690

Shanghai Satoril Co., Ltd. (1)
Rm 2020 Tomsom Intl Trade Bldg No 1 Jilong Rd Shanghai Wai, Gao Qiao Trade Zone, Shanghai, China
Tel.: (86) 2158690018
Electronic Component Sales
N.A.I.C.S.: 423610

Singapore Satori Pte.Ltd. (1)
91 Bencoolen St No 09-01 06 Sunshine Plz, Singapore, 189652, Singapore
Tel.: (65) 63338681
Sales Range: $25-49.9 Million
Emp.: 16
Electronic Components Marketing & Distr
N.A.I.C.S.: 423610
Vincent Goh *(Mng Dir)*

Star Electronics Co., Ltd. (1)
1-14-10 Shiba, Minato-Ku, Tokyo, 105-0014, Japan
Tel.: (81) 334525710
Web Site: https://www.satori.co.jp
Sales Range: $25-49.9 Million
Emp.: 20
Electrical & Control Components Sales
N.A.I.C.S.: 423610

Taiwan Satori Co., Ltd. (1)
6F-1 No 760 Selection 4 Bade Road, Taipei, Taiwan
Tel.: (886) 227627128
Electronic Parts Distr
N.A.I.C.S.: 423690

Thai Satori Co., Ltd. (1)
18/8 Fico Place Building Unit 601-602 6th FL Sukhumvit 21 Asoke Rd, Klongtoey Nua Wattana, Bangkok, 10110, Thailand
Tel.: (66) 22606140
Electronic Parts Distr
N.A.I.C.S.: 423690

SATORI RESOURCES INC.
401 Bay Street Suite 2702, PO Box 86, Toronto, M5H 2Y4, ON, Canada
Tel.: (416) 904-2714   BC
Web Site: https://www.satoriresources.ca
Year Founded: 2011
STRRF—(OTCQB)
Assets: $2,963,455
Liabilities: $935,813
Net Worth: $2,027,642
Earnings: ($349,889)
Fiscal Year-end: 12/31/20
Metal Mining
N.A.I.C.S.: 212290
Jennifer L. Boyle *(Founder, Pres & CEO)*

SATOSANGYO CO., LTD.
226 Nishifujicho, Onomichi, Hiroshima, 729-0142, Japan
Tel.: (81) 849332623
Web Site: https://www.satosangyo.com
Year Founded: 1969
3450—(TKS)
Emp.: 34
Engineeering Services
N.A.I.C.S.: 541330
Tomohiko Sato *(Pres)*

Subsidiaries:

Sato Sangyo Vietnam Co., Ltd. (1)
Lot D-8H-CN and LOT D-8G-CN DE6 Street My Phuoc 3 Industrial Zone, Ben Cat, Binh Duong, Vietnam
Tel.: (84) 2743767600
Emp.: 400
Furniture Mfr & Distr
N.A.I.C.S.: 337121

SATRA PROPERTIES (INDIA) LTD.
F-27 First Floor Prime Mall Beside Irla Church Irla Road, Vile Parle West, Mumbai, 400056, Maharashtra, India
Tel.: (91) 9370935454
Web Site: https://www.satraproperties.in
508996—(BOM)
Rev.: $82
Assets: $40,966,476
Liabilities: $32,751,551
Net Worth: $8,214,925
Earnings: ($253,344)
Emp.: 30
Fiscal Year-end: 03/31/21
Real Estate Services
N.A.I.C.S.: 531390
Praful Nanji Satra *(Chm & Mng Dir)*

SATREC INITIATIVE CO., LTD.
441 Expo-ro, Yuseong-gu, Daejeon, 34051, Korea (South)
Tel.: (82) 423657474

Web Site: https://www.satreci.com
Year Founded: 1999
099320—(KRS)
Rev.: $70,071,251
Assets: $198,484,495
Liabilities: $105,550,517
Net Worth: $92,933,978
Earnings: ($1,743,763)
Emp.: 250
Fiscal Year-end: 12/31/22
Satellite System Mfr
N.A.I.C.S.: 334220
Bongki Jeon *(CFO)*

Subsidiaries:

SI Detection Co., Ltd (1)
21 Yuseong-daero 1628beon-gil, Yuseong-gu, Daejeon, 34054, Korea (South)
Tel.: (82) 7078500372
Web Site: https://www.sidetection.com
Radiation Detector Mfr & Distr
N.A.I.C.S.: 334519

SI Imaging Services Co., Ltd (1)
169-84 Gwahak-ro, Yuseong-gu, Daejeon, 34133, Korea (South)
Tel.: (82) 7078050372
Web Site: https://www.si-imaging.com
Remote Sensing Image Distribution Services
N.A.I.C.S.: 541360
Moon-Gyu Kim *(Pres & CEO)*

SATS ASA
Nydalsveien 28, 0484, Oslo, Norway
Tel.: (47) 23307000   NO
Web Site: https://www.satsgroup.com
Year Founded: 2011
2S0—(DEU)
Rev.: $377,055,237
Assets: $801,311,657
Liabilities: $721,873,268
Net Worth: $79,438,389
Earnings: ($22,723,074)
Emp.: 2,462
Fiscal Year-end: 12/31/22
Physical Exercise & Training Services
N.A.I.C.S.: 713940
Sondre Gravir *(CEO)*

Subsidiaries:

Fresh Fitness AS (1)
PO Box 4949, Nydalen, 0423, Oslo, Norway
Tel.: (47) 33308781
Web Site: https://www.freshfitness.no
Health & Fitness Services
N.A.I.C.S.: 713940

SATTLER AG
Sattlerstrasse 45, 8077, Gossendorf, Austria
Tel.: (43) 316 4104 0
Web Site: http://www.sattler.com
Year Founded: 1875
Rev.: $89,321,453
Emp.: 500
Technical Textiles Mfr
N.A.I.C.S.: 313999
Herbert Pfeilstecher *(Chm-Mgmt Bd)*

Subsidiaries:

CENO Membrane Technology GmbH (1)
Am Eggenkamp 14, 48268, Greven, Germany
Tel.: (49) 25719690
Apparels Mfr
N.A.I.C.S.: 315250

Sattler Ceno Biogas GmbH (1)
Sattlerstrabe 1, 7571, Rudersdorf, Austria
Tel.: (43) 33827330
Apparels Mfr
N.A.I.C.S.: 315250

Sattler Corporation (1)
447 Main St, Hudson, NC 28638
Tel.: (828) 759-2105
Apparels Mfr
N.A.I.C.S.: 315250
Steve Fredrickson *(Sls Dir-Awning & Marine Div)*

Sattler GmbH (1)
Miramstrabe 74, 34123, Kassel, Germany
Tel.: (49) 561861840
Apparels Mfr
N.A.I.C.S.: 315250

Sattler Italia s.r.l. (1)
Via Bagni 17, 25128, Brescia, Italy
Tel.: (39) 0303385249
Apparels Mfr
N.A.I.C.S.: 315250

Sattler Romania s.r.l. (1)
Horea Nr 17a, Timis, 300342, Timisoara, Romania
Tel.: (40) 256471015
Apparels Mfr
N.A.I.C.S.: 315250

Sattler Schweiz GmbH (1)
Falkenweg 9b, 9300, Wittenbach, Switzerland
Tel.: (41) 712901222
Apparels Mfr
N.A.I.C.S.: 315250

Sattler Textiles SARL (1)
Zac de Cremerieux 15 rue des Metiers, 42600, Savigneux, France
Tel.: (33) 31641040
Apparels Mfr
N.A.I.C.S.: 315250

SATU HOLDINGS LIMITED
Unit 2504 25/F Nanyang Plaza 57 Hung To Road, Kwun Tong, China (Hong Kong)
Tel.: (852) 2 342 5588   Ky
Web Site: http://www.bnc.cc
8392—(HKG)
Rev.: $7,819,413
Assets: $5,272,058
Liabilities: $1,114,258
Net Worth: $4,157,799
Earnings: ($946,455)
Emp.: 28
Fiscal Year-end: 03/31/21
Household Goods Mfr & Distr
N.A.I.C.S.: 327110

Subsidiaries:

B & C Industries Limited (1)
Unit 2504 25/F Nanyang Plaza 57 Hung To Road, Kwun Tong, Kowloon, China (Hong Kong)
Tel.: (852) 23425588
Web Site: https://www.bnc.cc
Durable Goods Whslr
N.A.I.C.S.: 423990

SATUDORA HOLDINGS CO., LTD.
Higashi-ku Kita 8-jo Higashi 4-chome 1-20, Sapporo, 060-0908, Japan
Tel.: (81) 117885166
Web Site: https://www.satudora-hd.co.jp
Year Founded: 2016
3544—(TKS)
Rev.: $631,387,200
Assets: $296,822,050
Liabilities: $235,745,650
Net Worth: $61,076,400
Earnings: $3,106,700
Emp.: 1,107
Fiscal Year-end: 05/31/24
Pharmaceutical Products Distr
N.A.I.C.S.: 424210
Hiroki Tomiyama *(Pres & CEO)*

SATURDAY CO., LTD.
No B-3 Jianping Road Nanhai Guicheng Tech Park, Foshan, 528200, China
Tel.: (86) 757 86250323
Sales Range: $250-299.9 Million
Emp.: 400
Shoe Mfr & Retailer
N.A.I.C.S.: 458210
Zemin Zhang *(Chm & Gen Mgr)*

SATURDAY GROUP LTD

Saturday Co., Ltd.—(Continued)

SATURDAY GROUP LTD
Biscuit Building 3rd Floor 10 Redchurch Street, London, E2 7DD, United Kingdom
Tel.: (44) 20 7749 4500
Web Site: http://www.saturday-group.com
Year Founded: 2003
Sales Range: $10-24.9 Million
Emp.: 50
Advertising & Marketing Services
N.A.I.C.S.: 541890
Jens Grede *(Mng Partner & CEO)*

Subsidiaries:

Industrie Magazine (1)
Biscuit Building 3rd Floor 10 Redchurch Street, London, E2 7DD, United Kingdom
Tel.: (44) 20 7033 7717
Web Site: http://www.industriemagazine.com
Magazine
N.A.I.C.S.: 513120
Lynette Nylander *(Mng Editor)*

Tomorrow Ltd (1)
188 St Johns Street, London, EC1V 4JY, United Kingdom
Tel.: (44) 20 7253 5753
Web Site: http://www.tomorrowltd.com
Fashion Sales Consulting
N.A.I.C.S.: 541613
Stefano Martinetto *(CEO)*

Wednesday London Ltd (1)
Biscuit Building 3rd Floor 10 Redchurch Street, London, E2 7DD, United Kingdom
Tel.: (44) 20 7033 7730
Web Site: http://www.wednesday-london.com
Advertising Related Services
N.A.I.C.S.: 541890
Oliver Walsh *(Mng Partner)*

SATURN METALS LIMITED
9 Havelock Street, West Perth, 6005, WA, Australia
Tel.: (61) 862341114 AU
Web Site: https://www.saturnmetals.com.au
Year Founded: 2017
STN—(ASX)
Rev.: $74,613
Assets: $29,989,749
Liabilities: $1,404,552
Net Worth: $28,585,197
Earnings: ($1,852,620)
Fiscal Year-end: 06/30/24
Mineral Exploration & Development Services
N.A.I.C.S.: 212220
Ian Bamborough *(Mng Dir)*

SATURN OIL & GAS INC.
525 - 8th Avenue SW Suite 2800, Calgary, T2P 1G1, AB, Canada
Tel.: (403) 268-7800
Web Site: https://www.saturnoil.com
Year Founded: 2001
SOIL—(TSX)
Rev.: $241,325,032
Assets: $434,848,622
Liabilities: $331,515,686
Net Worth: $103,332,936
Earnings: $55,811,990
Emp.: 107
Fiscal Year-end: 12/31/22
Mineral Exploration Services
N.A.I.C.S.: 213114
John Jeffrey *(Chm & CEO)*

SATYA DEVELOPERS PVT. LTD.
Plot No-8 Sector-44, Gurgaon, 122 002, Haryana, India
Tel.: (91) 1244989300
Web Site: http://www.satyagroups.in
Year Founded: 1958

Real Estate Services
N.A.I.C.S.: 531390
Nawal Kishore Agarwal *(Founder & Chm)*

SATYA MINERS & TRANSPORTERS LIMITED
Chamber No- A Room No-103 1st Floor 155 Lenin Sarani, Kolkata, 700013, India
Tel.: (91) 33 32902535
Web Site: http://www.satyaminers.com
Year Founded: 1975
Sales Range: Less than $1 Million
Non Banking Financial Services
N.A.I.C.S.: 523999
Ananda Halder *(Mng Dir)*

SATYAM SILK MILLS LIMITED
82 Maker Chambers III, Nariman Point, Mumbai, 400 021, Maharashtra, India
Tel.: (91) 2222042554
Web Site: https://satyamsilkmill.com
503893—(BOM)
Rev.: $4,204
Assets: $1,677,355
Liabilities: $90,424
Net Worth: $1,586,932
Earnings: ($44,846)
Emp.: 3
Fiscal Year-end: 03/31/21
Securities Trading Services
N.A.I.C.S.: 523150
Apoorva Jain *(Sec)*

SAU SAN TONG HOLDINGS LIMITED
Room 2303 23rd Floor China Insurance Group Building 141 Des Voeux Road, Central, China (Hong Kong)
Tel.: (852) 2 700 9142 Ky
Web Site: http://www.sst-holding.com
Year Founded: 2002
8200—(HKG)
Rev.: $201,383,697
Assets: $123,975,189
Liabilities: $18,210,299
Net Worth: $105,764,890
Earnings: $1,791,790
Emp.: 225
Fiscal Year-end: 03/31/22
Holding Company
N.A.I.C.S.: 551112
Wai Sum Mui *(Exec Dir)*

SAUDEE GROUP BERHAD
Plot 331 Taman Perindustrian Sungai Petani Fasa 3, 8000, Sungai Petani, Kedah Darul Aman, Malaysia
Tel.: (60) 44426800 MY
Web Site: https://www.saudee.com
Year Founded: 1985
SAUDEE—(KLS)
Rev.: $20,229,165
Assets: $33,070,719
Liabilities: $4,251,753
Net Worth: $28,818,966
Earnings: ($1,559,149)
Emp.: 220
Fiscal Year-end: 07/31/23
Food Products Mfr
N.A.I.C.S.: 311412
Khang Khim Tan *(Founder & Mng Dir)*

SAUDI ADVANCED INDUSTRIES COMPANY
Takhasusi Street with Othman bin Affan Road, PO Box 51743, Jarir Plaza Building Second Floor Office No 203, Riyadh, 11553, Saudi Arabia
Tel.: (966) 114105589
Web Site: https://www.saic.com.sa
Year Founded: 1988

2120—(SAU)
Rev.: $30,941,901
Assets: $242,397,942
Liabilities: $2,114,358
Net Worth: $240,283,584
Earnings: $26,718,403
Fiscal Year-end: 12/31/22
Investment Management Service
N.A.I.C.S.: 523940

SAUDI ARABIAN AIRLINES
Prince Fahad Street, PO Box 620, Jeddah, 21231, Saudi Arabia
Tel.: (966) 26860000
Web Site: http://www.saudiairlines.com
Year Founded: 1945
Sales Range: $1-4.9 Billion
Emp.: 24,000
Oil Transportation Services
N.A.I.C.S.: 481111
Saleh Nasser Al-Jasser *(Dir Gen)*

Subsidiaries:

CATRION Catering Holding Company (1)
Prince Sultan Road - Al Muhammadiyah District 5, PO Box 9178, Jeddah, 21413, Saudi Arabia
Tel.: (966) 126860011
Web Site: https://www.catrion.com
Rev.: $484,737,067
Assets: $541,579,744
Liabilities: $242,972,577
Net Worth: $298,607,167
Earnings: $68,551,697
Emp.: 4,500
Fiscal Year-end: 12/31/2022
Airline Catering Services
N.A.I.C.S.: 722320
Sami Abdulmohsen Al-Hokair *(Vice Chm)*

Saudi Airlines Cargo (1)
Saudi Arabian Airlines Main Building Ground Floor, Jeddah, Saudi Arabia
Tel.: (966) 68661654
Web Site: http://www.saudiairlines.com
Air Freight Transportation Services
N.A.I.C.S.: 481112

SAUDI ARABIAN AMIANTIT COMPANY
8162 - Industrial Area No 1 Building No 101, Dammam, 32234-3361, Saudi Arabia
Tel.: (966) 38471500
Web Site: http://www.amiantit.com
Year Founded: 1968
2160—(SAU)
Rev.: $117,444,425
Assets: $599,949,400
Liabilities: $555,009,145
Net Worth: $44,940,255
Earnings: ($104,886,782)
Emp.: 1,179
Fiscal Year-end: 12/31/20
Rubber & Concrete Piping Products Mfr
N.A.I.C.S.: 326220
Solaiman Abdulaziz Al-Twaijri *(CEO & Mng Dir)*

Subsidiaries:

Amitech Germany Gmbh (1)
Am Fuchso Och 19, Mochau, D 04720, Germany (100%)
Tel.: (49) 343171820
Web Site: http://www.amitech-germany.de
Sales Range: $50-74.9 Million
Emp.: 160
Mfr & Retailer of FRP Pipe & Fiberglass Products
N.A.I.C.S.: 326122
Nick Crofts *(Gen Mgr)*

Bondstrand Ltd. (1)
PO Box 589, Dammam, 31421, Saudi Arabia
Web Site: http://www.amiantit.com

INTERNATIONAL PUBLIC

Sales Range: $25-49.9 Million
Emp.: 250
Fiberglass Pipe & Fittings Mfr
N.A.I.C.S.: 326199

Flowtite Technology (1)
Velolvien 1, PO Box 2059, 3222, Sandefjord, Norway (100%)
Tel.: (47) 33449155
Web Site: http://www.flowtite.com
Sales Range: $25-49.9 Million
Emp.: 15
Mfr of Pipe Systems
N.A.I.C.S.: 326122

Subsidiary (Non-US):

Flowtite Andercol S.A. (2)
Carrera 33 5G 73, El Poblado, Medellin, 62159, Antioquia, Colombia (100%)
Tel.: (57) 43127222
Web Site: http://www.flowtite.com
Sales Range: $25-49.9 Million
Mfr of Converted Paper Products
N.A.I.C.S.: 322299

Joint Venture (Non-US):

Subor Boru Sanayi ve Ticaret A.S. (2)
Acibadem Mahallesi Sokullu Sokak No 12, Kadikoy, 34718, Istanbul, Turkiye (100%)
Tel.: (90) 2164741900
Web Site: http://www.subor.com.tr
Sales Range: $25-49.9 Million
Mfr of Plastic Products; Joint Venture of The Saudi Arabian Amiantit Group (50%) & Yapi Merkezi (50%)
N.A.I.C.S.: 325211

SAUDI ARABIAN COOPERATIVE INSURANCE COMPANY
Platinum Center Salahuddin St, PO Box 58073, Riyadh, 11594, Saudi Arabia
Tel.: (966) 118749666
Web Site: https://www.saico.com.sa
Year Founded: 1952
8100—(SAU)
Rev.: $277,142,426
Assets: $389,710,792
Liabilities: $320,940,202
Net Worth: $68,770,590
Earnings: ($9,919,935)
Fiscal Year-end: 12/31/22
Insurance Underwriting Company Services
N.A.I.C.S.: 524113
Ahmad Khalid Al Saud *(Chm)*

SAUDI ARABIAN MARKETS LTD.
PO Box 65, Jeddah, 21411, Saudi Arabia
Tel.: (966) 126510444
Web Site: http://www.samltd.com
Year Founded: 1947
Sales Range: $50-74.9 Million
Emp.: 250
Holding Company; Oil & Lubricants Whslr & Car Dealer
N.A.I.C.S.: 551112
Mohamed Ahmed Ashmawi *(Founder)*

Subsidiaries:

Peninsular Aviation Services Co. Ltd. (1)
Web Site: http://www.shell.com
Sales Range: $25-49.9 Million
Emp.: 90
Aviation Services; Owned 50% by Saudi Arabian Markets Ltd., 25% by BP plc & 25% by The Shell Petroleum Co. Ltd.
N.A.I.C.S.: 488119

SAUDI ARABIAN MILITARY INDUSTRIES
Alkhalidiha District Building 7252 Unit 1, Riyadh, Saudi Arabia
Tel.: (966) 920000977
Web Site: http://www.sami.com.sa
Holding Company

AND PRIVATE COMPANIES

SAUDI ARABIAN OIL COMPANY

N.A.I.C.S.: 551112
Andreas Schwer (CEO)

Subsidiaries:

Advanced Electronics Company (1)
King Khaled Air Port Industrial, PO Box 90916, Riyadh, 11623, Saudi Arabia
Tel.: (966) 12201350
Web Site: http://www.aecl.com
Military & Commercial Electronic Components Mfr
N.A.I.C.S.: 334419

SAUDI ARABIAN MINING COMPANY - MA'ADEN

PO Box 68861, Riyadh, 11537, Saudi Arabia
Tel.: (966) 118748000   SA
Web Site: https://www.maaden.com.sa
Year Founded: 1997
1211—(SAU)
Gold, Phosphate & Bauxite Exploration, Mining & Aluminum Production
N.A.I.C.S.: 212220
Suliman Abdulrahman Al-Gwaiz (Deputy Chm)

Subsidiaries:

Agora Limited (1)
Suite 10 Lynnwood Office 474 Lynnwood Road, Lynnwood, Pretoria, South Africa
Tel.: (27) 128070454
Web Site: http://www.agoraafrica.com
Construction Consulting Services
N.A.I.C.S.: 541611

Farmers World Limited (1)
38 Lavender Rd Old Warmbath Road Bon Accord, Pretoria, 0009, South Africa
Tel.: (27) 837000000
Web Site: http://www.farmworld.co.za
Farming Equipment Distr
N.A.I.C.S.: 423820

Grain Securities Limited (1)
GSL Silo Complex Off Salima Road, Kaneng, Lilongwe, Malawi
Tel.: (265) 1710437
Farm Grain Food Distr
N.A.I.C.S.: 424910

MCFI (Africa) Ltd. (1)
Chaussee Tromelin Fort George, Port Louis, Mauritius
Tel.: (230) 2163965
Web Site: http://www.mcfi.mu
Chemical & Fertilizer Product Mfr
N.A.I.C.S.: 325320
Yannis Fayd'herbe (Mng Dir)

Meridian Group Services Limited (1)
218 Grand Bay Business Park Coastal Road, Grand Baie, Mauritius
Tel.: (230) 52507382
Web Site: http://www.meridian.africa
Fertilizer Product Mfr
N.A.I.C.S.: 325320

Optichem (2000) Limited (1)
Ali Hassan Mwinyi Road, PO Box 30055, Blantyre, Malawi
Tel.: (265) 1870754
Web Site: http://www.optichem2000.com
Emp.: 250
Fertilizer Product Mfr
N.A.I.C.S.: 325320

SAUDI ARABIAN MONETARY AGENCY

PO Box 2992, Riyadh, 11169, Saudi Arabia
Tel.: (966) 14633000
Web Site: http://www.sama.gov.sa
Sales Range: $400-449.9 Million
Emp.: 2,600
Depository Banking Services
N.A.I.C.S.: 522320

SAUDI ARABIAN OIL COMPANY

PO Box 5000, Dhahran, 31311, Saudi Arabia
Tel.: (966) 138720115   SA
Web Site: https://www.aramco.com
Year Founded: 1933
2222—(SAU)
Rev.: $604,285,561,925
Assets: $664,691,107,852
Liabilities: $220,444,474,070
Net Worth: $444,246,633,782
Earnings: $161,046,527,130
Emp.: 70,496
Fiscal Year-end: 12/31/22
Oil Exploration Services
N.A.I.C.S.: 213112
Ibrahim A. Al-Assaf (Deputy Chm)

Subsidiaries:

ARLANXEO Holding B.V. (1)
Stationsplein 6-8, 6221 BT, Maastricht, Netherlands (100%)
Tel.: (31) 46 702 0677
Web Site: http://www.arlanxeo.com
Sales Range: $1-4.9 Billion
Emp.: 3,800
Holding Company; Elastomer & Other Synthetic Rubber Products Mfr & Whslr
N.A.I.C.S.: 551112
Jan Paul de Vries (Chm-Exec Bd & CEO)

Subsidiary (Non-US):

ARLANXEO Belgium N.V. (2)
Canadastraat 21 Haven 1009, 2070, Zwijndrecht, Belgium
Tel.: (32) 32521511
Rubber Products Mfr
N.A.I.C.S.: 326299

ARLANXEO Canada Inc. (2)
1265 Vidal Street South, PO Box 3001, Sarnia, N7T 7M2, ON, Canada
Tel.: (519) 337-8251
Web Site: https://www.arlanxeo.com
Sales Range: $125-149.9 Million
Emp.: 500
Synthetic Rubber Mfr
N.A.I.C.S.: 326299
John Sawaya (Chm)

ARLANXEO Elastomeres France S.A.S. (2)
Zone Industrielle de Port Jerome, BP 80041, Zone Industrielle, F-76170, Lillebonne, France
Tel.: (33) 235394700
Synthetic Rubber Mfr
N.A.I.C.S.: 325212

ARLANXEO Emulsion Rubber France S.A.S (2)
Rue du Ried, Zone Industrielle rue de Ried, 67610, La Wantzenau, France
Tel.: (33) 388592000
Emp.: 300
Synthetic Rubber Mfr & Distr
N.A.I.C.S.: 325212

Subsidiary (Domestic):

ARLANXEO Netherlands B.V. (2)
Urmonderbaan 24, 6167 RD, Geleen, Netherlands
Tel.: (31) 467020673
Sales Range: $500-549.9 Million
Emp.: 420
Rubber Mfr
N.A.I.C.S.: 325212

Subsidiary (US):

ARLANXEO USA LLC (2)
111 RIDC Park W Dr, Pittsburgh, PA 15275-1112
Tel.: (412) 809-1000
Web Site: http://www.arlanxeo.com
Synthetic Rubber Mfr
N.A.I.C.S.: 325212
John Sawaya (Pres & CEO)

Aramco Asia India Private Limited (1)
2A-0801 8th Floor Two Horizon Center DLF 5 Sector 43, Gurgaon, 122002, Haryana, India
Tel.: (91) 1246473600
Web Site: https://india.aramco.com
Engineeering Services
N.A.I.C.S.: 541330
Amin H. Nasser (Pres & CEO)

Aramco Asia Japan K.K. (1)
Marunouchi Building 26F 2-4-1 Marunouchi, Chiyoda-Ku, Tokyo, 100-6326, Japan
Tel.: (81) 363673737
Web Site: https://japan.aramco.com
Emp.: 75
Oil & Gas Exploration Services
N.A.I.C.S.: 213112

Aramco Asia Singapore Pte. Ltd. (1)
OUE Bayfront 50 Collyer Quay 13-01, Singapore, 049321, Singapore
Tel.: (65) 62242228
Web Site: https://www.singapore.aramco.com
Engineeering Services
N.A.I.C.S.: 541330

Aramco Far East (Beijing) Business Services Company (1)
43/F 45/F20-26 China World Tower 3 No 1 Jianguomenwai Avenue, Chaoyang District, Beijing, 100004, China
Tel.: (86) 1085905900
Emp.: 100
Petroleum Production & Exploration Services
N.A.I.C.S.: 324191

Aramco Overseas Company (1)
Landmark III 19th Floor 90A Nizami Street, AZ1010, Baku, Azerbaijan
Tel.: (994) 12 525 4800
Chemical Products Mfr
N.A.I.C.S.: 325998

Aramco Overseas Company UK, Limited (1)
10 Portman Square, London, W1H 6AZ, United Kingdom
Tel.: (44) 2074674100
Chemical Products Mfr
N.A.I.C.S.: 325998

Aramco Overseas Malaysia Sdn. Bhd. (1)
Level 49 P1-01 Permata Sapura Kuala Lumpur City Center, 50088, Kuala Lumpur, Malaysia
Tel.: (60) 327206999
Web Site: https://malaysia.aramco.com
Oil & Gas Distr
N.A.I.C.S.: 424720

Aramco Services Company (1)
1200 Smith St, Houston, TX 77002 (100%)
Tel.: (713) 432-4000
Web Site: https://americas.aramco.com
Sales Range: $100-124.9 Million
Emp.: 281
Purchasing & Sale of Crude Oil
N.A.I.C.S.: 541611

Subsidiary (Domestic):

Aramco Associated Company (2)
16875 John F Kennedy Blvd, Houston, TX 77032
Tel.: (713) 432-5300
Emp.: 25
Aircraft Charter Rental & Leasing Services
N.A.I.C.S.: 532411
Ed Mcmanus (Pres)

Subsidiary (Non-US):

Aramco Overseas Company BV (2)
Schuttersveld 14, 2316 ZB, Leiden, Netherlands (100%)
Tel.: (31) 715160600
Web Site: http://www.aramcooverseas.com
Sales Range: $75-99.9 Million
Emp.: 90
Support Services
N.A.I.C.S.: 221210

Subsidiary (Non-US):

AOC B.V. UK Ltd. (3)
10 Portman Square, London, W1H 6AZ, United Kingdom
Tel.: (44) 20 7467 4100
Oil & Gas Exploration Services
N.A.I.C.S.: 213112

Subsidiary (Domestic):

Team Terminal BV (3)
Rijndwarsweg 3, Europoort, Rotterdam, Netherlands
Tel.: (31) 181 286 600
Web Site: http://www.team-terminal.nl
Curde Oil Stoage Services
N.A.I.C.S.: 213112

Subsidiary (US):

VGP Holdings LLC (3)
100 Valvoline Way Ste 200, Lexington, KY 40509
Tel.: (859) 357-7777
Web Site: https://www.valvolineglobal.com
Holding Company
N.A.I.C.S.: 551112
Jamal K. Muashsher (Pres)

Subsidiary (Domestic):

Valvoline International, Inc. (4)
3499 Blazer Pkwy, Lexington, KY 40509
Tel.: (859) 357-7777
Web Site: http://www.valvoline.com
Sales Range: Less than $1 Million
Holding Company; Motor Oil & Industrial Lubricant Products Mfr & Distr
N.A.I.C.S.: 551112
Jamal K. Muashsher (Pres)

Subsidiary (Non-US):

Lubrival S. A. (5)
Av Galo Plaza Laso y Calle Publica Km 2 Via a las Esclusas, Guayaquil, Guayas, Ecuador
Tel.: (593) 42480980
Web Site: http://www.valvoline.ec
Lubricant Mfr & Distr
N.A.I.C.S.: 324191

Shanghai VC Lubricating Oil Co., Ltd. (5)
12B United Power Mansion 1566 Yan'an Road West, Shanghai, 200052, China
Tel.: (86) 2162807700
Emp.: 50
Lubricant Mfr & Distr
N.A.I.C.S.: 324191
John Fei (Gen Mgr)

Valvoline (Australia) Pty. Ltd. (5)
30 Davis Rd, Wetherill Park, 2164, NSW, Australia
Tel.: (61) 296097999
Web Site: http://www.valvoline.com
Sales Range: $75-99.9 Million
Emp.: 150
Automotive, Industrial & Marine Lubricants & Rust Preventatives Mfr
N.A.I.C.S.: 336340

Valvoline (Thailand) Ltd. (5)
6/69 Yan Phaholyothin Rd Samsen Nai, Phyathai, Bangkok, 10400, Thailand
Tel.: (66) 261827905
Web Site: http://www.valvoline.co.th
Lubricant Mfr & Distr
N.A.I.C.S.: 324191

Valvoline Cummins Argentina S.A. (5)
Valentin Virasoro 2656 Planta baja of 3, Beccar, 1643, San Isidro, Buenos Aires, Argentina
Tel.: (54) 1147190770
Web Site: http://www.valvoline.com.ar
Lubricant Mfr & Distr
N.A.I.C.S.: 324191

Valvoline Do Brasil Lubrificantes Ltda. (5)
Rua dos Pinheiros 1 060 cj 92, 05422-002, Sao Paulo, Sao Paulo, Brazil
Tel.: (55) 1130606420
Web Site: http://www.valvoline.com.br
Diesel Engine Mfr
N.A.I.C.S.: 333618

Valvoline de Colombia S.A.S. (5)
Calle 11 B 41 53, Medellin, Antioquia, Colombia
Tel.: (57) 46040433
Lubricant Distr
N.A.I.C.S.: 457210

Subsidiary (Domestic):

Saudi Refining, Inc. (2)
9009 W Loop S, Houston, TX 77096-1799
Tel.: (713) 432-4000
Web Site: http://www.aramcoservices.com

SAUDI ARABIAN OIL COMPANY

Saudi Arabian Oil Company—(Continued)

Purchase, Contracting, Shipping & Recruitment For Oil Distribution
N.A.I.C.S.: 424720

Subsidiary (Domestic):

Aramco Financial Services Company (3)
1011 Center Rd Ste 320, Wilmington, DE 19805
Tel.: (302) 388-0118
Investment Advisory Services
N.A.I.C.S.: 523940

Joint Venture (Domestic):

Motiva Enterprises LLC (3)
500 Dallas St, Houston, TX 77002 **(50%)**
Tel.: (713) 277-8000
Web Site: http://www.motivaenterprises.com
Sales Range: $10-24.9 Million
Petroleum Products Whsl
N.A.I.C.S.: 457120
J. Travis Capps (Exec VP-Comml)

Aramco Trading Company (1)
Al-Midra Tower Building Floor 3 East Wing, Dhahran, 31311, Saudi Arabia
Tel.: (966) 138744055
Web Site: http://www.aramcotrading.com
Bulk Petrochemical Mfr
N.A.I.C.S.: 325110
Ibrahim Al-Buainain (CEO)

Aramco Trading Fujairah FZE (1)
14th Floor Al Hilal Business Tower F-1, PO Box 7575 5, Fujairah, 7575, United Arab Emirates
Tel.: (971) 92033300
Bulk Petrochemical Mfr
N.A.I.C.S.: 325110
Abdullah Al Dossary (Mng Dir)

Aramco Trading Limited (1)
10 Portman Square, London, W1H 6AZ, United Kingdom
Tel.: (44) 2074674100
Bulk Petrochemical Mfr
N.A.I.C.S.: 325110
Mohammed Kadi (Mng Dir)

Aramco Trading Singapore Pte. Ltd. (1)
OUE Bayfront 50 Collyer Quay 13-025, Singapore, 049321, Singapore
Tel.: (65) 62242228
Bulk Petrochemical Mfr
N.A.I.C.S.: 325110
Mohammad Khatir (Mng Dir)

Aurora Capital Holdings LLC (1)
11611 San Vicente Blvd Ste 800, Los Angeles, CA 90049
Tel.: (310) 551-0101
Web Site: https://www.auroracap.com
Industrial Technology Services
N.A.I.C.S.: 541519
Robert West (CFO)

International Maritime Industries Company (1)
Al-Turki Business Park 7244 King Saud Road, Dhahran, 34455, Saudi Arabia
Tel.: (966) 92 002 2342
Web Site: https://www.imi-ksa.com
Maritime Maintenance Services
N.A.I.C.S.: 488390
Fathi K. Al-Saleem (CEO)

Johns Hopkins Aramco Healthcare Company (1)
6th Street, Dhahran, Saudi Arabia
Tel.: (966) 135703708
Web Site: https://www.jhah.com
Healtcare Services
N.A.I.C.S.: 622110
Michael Walsh (CEO)

S-Oil Corporation (1)
192 Baekbeom-ro, Mapo-gu, Seoul, 04196, Korea (South)
Tel.: (82) 237725151
Web Site: https://www.s-oil.com
Rev.: $26,518,039,577
Assets: $16,014,817,481
Liabilities: $9,306,709,915
Net Worth: $6,708,107,566
Earnings: $704,279,798
Emp.: 3,242

Fiscal Year-end: 12/31/2023
Refined Petroleum Distr
N.A.I.C.S.: 486910

S-Oil Singapore Pte. Ltd. (1)
50 Collyer Quay OUE Bayfront 13-03, Singapore, 049321, Singapore
Tel.: (65) 63360030
Petroleum Product Mfr & Distr
N.A.I.C.S.: 324199

SABIC Sales Europe B.V. (1)
Europaboulevard 1, 6135 LD, Sittard, Netherlands
Tel.: (31) 467222222
Petroleum Product Distr
N.A.I.C.S.: 424720

Sadara Chemical Company (1)
Jubail Industrial City, PO Box 11811, Jubail, 31961, Saudi Arabia
Tel.: (966) 133513999
Web Site: https://www.sadara.com
Chemical Products Mfr
N.A.I.C.S.: 325998
John M. Sampson (Vice Chm)

Saudi Aramco Lubricating Oil Refining Company (1)
PO Box 5518, Jeddah, 21432, Saudi Arabia
Tel.: (966) 22296611
Web Site: http://www.luberef.com
Sales Range: $25-49.9 Million
Emp.: 45
Joint Venture of Saudi Arabian Oil Company (70%) & Exxon Mobil Corporation (30%)
N.A.I.C.S.: 324110

Saudi Aramco Mobil Refinery Company Ltd. (1)
PO Box 30078, Yanbu Al-Sinaiyah, Yanbu, Saudi Arabia
Tel.: (966) 143964000
Web Site: https://www.samref.com.sa
Sales Range: $100-124.9 Million
Joint Venture of Saudi Arabian Oil Company & Exxon Mobil Corporation
N.A.I.C.S.: 324110

Saudi Aramco Product Trading Company (1)
Saudi Arabian Oil Company Building, Dhahran, 5000, Saudi Arabia
Tel.: (966) 13 872 0115
Fuel Distr
N.A.I.C.S.: 457210
Mohammed Y. Al Qahtani (Sr VP-Upstream)

Saudi Aramco Shell Refinery Company (1)
PO Box 10088, Al Jubayl, 31961, Saudi Arabia **(50%)**
Tel.: (966) 33572000
Web Site: https://www.sasref.com.sa
Sales Range: $25-49.9 Million
Emp.: 100
Oil Refining Services
N.A.I.C.S.: 324110

Saudi Aramco Total Refining and Petrochemical Company (1)
Saeed Tower Dammam Khobar Highway, PO Box 151, Al Khobar, Saudi Arabia
Tel.: (966) 38106999
Web Site: http://www.satorp.com
Petrochemical Refining Services
N.A.I.C.S.: 324110
Sulaiman Mansour Ababtain (Pres & CEO)

SAUDI ARABIAN REFINERIES COMPANY

Adham Center Al-Ruwais, Jeddah, 23215, Saudi Arabia
Tel.: (966) 26517016
Web Site: https://www.almasafi.sa
2030—(SAU)
Rev.: $4,561,453
Assets: $138,101,849
Liabilities: $2,735,167
Net Worth: $135,366,681
Earnings: $3,563,094
Emp.: 5
Fiscal Year-end: 12/31/20
Financial Investment Services
N.A.I.C.S.: 523999

Mohammed Khalid Turki Al Saud (Chm)

SAUDI AUTOMOTIVE SERVICES CO.

Makkah Road Khurais Building No 4870 7277 King Abdulaziz District, Riyadh, 12411, Saudi Arabia
Tel.: (966) 920000581
Web Site: https://www.sasco.com.sa
Year Founded: 1981
4050—(SAU)
Rev.: $2,430,049,221
Assets: $1,590,413,602
Liabilities: $1,323,373,660
Net Worth: $267,039,942
Earnings: $34,693,622
Emp.: 3,717
Fiscal Year-end: 12/31/23
Car Service Center Operator
N.A.I.C.S.: 561613
Riyadh Saleh Almalik (CEO)

Subsidiaries:

Ostool Al-Naqil Co. (1)
Unit No 2 6235 Al Ihsa 3210, Al Zahra Dist, Riyadh, 12815, Saudi Arabia
Tel.: (966) 112447781
Web Site: http://www.ostoolalnaqil.com.sa
Emp.: 150
Transportation Services
N.A.I.C.S.: 484110

Saudi Automobile & Touring Association Co. (1)
Unit No 4 6235 Al Ihsa 3210, Al Zahra Dist, Riyadh, Saudi Arabia
Tel.: (966) 114763131
Web Site: http://www.sataclub.com.sa
Automotive Products Mfr
N.A.I.C.S.: 336110

SAUDI BASIC INDUSTRIES CORPORATION

PO Box 5101, Riyadh, 11422, Saudi Arabia
Tel.: (966) 112258000
Web Site: https://www.sabic.com
Year Founded: 1976
2010—(SAU)
Rev.: $37,742,244,009
Assets: $78,499,361,536
Liabilities: $26,425,405,344
Net Worth: $52,073,956,192
Earnings: $984,683,624
Emp.: 32,000
Fiscal Year-end: 12/31/23
Basic Chemicals, Intermediates, Polymers, Fertilizers & Metals Mfr
N.A.I.C.S.: 325998
Ahmed Al-Shaikh (Exec VP-Mfg)

Subsidiaries:

AR-RAZI Saudi Methanol Co. (1)
PO Box 10065, Al Jubail, 31961, Saudi Arabia
Tel.: (966) 33577800
Web Site: http://www.sabic.com
Mfr of Chemicals
N.A.I.C.S.: 325998

Al-Jubail Fertilizer Co. (1)
PO Box 10040, Al Jubayl, 31961, Saudi Arabia
Tel.: (966) 33477200
Web Site: http://www.sabic.com
Sales Range: $25-49.9 Million
Emp.: 80
Mfr of Chemicals
N.A.I.C.S.: 325998

Al-Jubail Petrochemical Co. (1)
PO Box 10084, Al Jubayl, 31961, Saudi Arabia
Tel.: (966) 33576000
Web Site: http://www.kemya.com
Mfg. Low & High Density Polyethylene
N.A.I.C.S.: 325211

Arabian Petrochemical Co. (1)
Tareeg 272, PO Box 10002, Al Jubayl, 31961, Saudi Arabia **(100%)**

INTERNATIONAL PUBLIC

Tel.: (966) 33587000
Web Site: http://www.sabic.com
Sales Range: $900-999.9 Million
Emp.: 1,200
Mfr of Chemicals
N.A.I.C.S.: 325998

BV Snij-Unie HiFi (1)
Zoutketen 23, 1601 EX, Enkhuizen, Netherlands
Tel.: (31) 228317944
Web Site: http://www.snijunie.nl
Plastic Film Distr
N.A.I.C.S.: 424610

Black Diamonds Structures, LLC (1)
12310 Trail Driver St, Austin, TX 78737
Tel.: (512) 900-3822
Web Site: http://www.blackdiamond-structures.com
Chemical Products Mfr
N.A.I.C.S.: 325998
Paul Everill (VP-R&D)

Eastern Petrochemical Co. (1)
PO Box 10035, Al Jubayl, 31961, Saudi Arabia
Tel.: (966) 33575000
Web Site: http://www.sabic.com
Mfr of Chemicals
N.A.I.C.S.: 325998

HADEED Saudi Iron & Steel Co. (1)
PO Box 10053, Al Jubayl, 31961, Saudi Arabia
Tel.: (966) 33571100
Web Site: http://www.hadeed.com.sa
Mfr of Iron & Steel
N.A.I.C.S.: 331110

IBN SINA National Methanol Co. (1)
Juvail 167, PO Box 10003, Al Jubayl, 31961, Saudi Arabia
Tel.: (966) 33405500
Web Site: http://www.sabic.com
Sales Range: $25-49.9 Million
Emp.: 50
Mfr of Chemicals
N.A.I.C.S.: 325998

Ibn Hayyan Plastic Products Co. (1)
PO Box 10273, Al Jubail, 31961, Al Finaiyah, Saudi Arabia **(99%)**
Tel.: (966) 33584000
Web Site: http://www.sabic.com
Mfr of Chemicals
N.A.I.C.S.: 325998

Jubail United Petrochemical Company (1)
Jubail Industrial City Madinat Al Jubail Al Sinaiyah, PO Box 10085, Al Jubail, 31961, Saudi Arabia
Tel.: (966) 33595000
Petrochemical Mfr
N.A.I.C.S.: 325110

National Chemical Carriers Ltd. Co. (1)
Sitteen St Malaz Area, PO Box 8931, Riyadh, Saudi Arabia
Tel.: (966) 014773934
Web Site: http://www.nscsa.com
Sales Range: $25-49.9 Million
Emp.: 20
Petrochemical Transportation Services; Owned 80% by National Shipping Company of Saudi Arabia & 20% by Saudi Basic Industries Corporation
N.A.I.C.S.: 488330

National Chemical Fertilizer Co. (1)
PO Box 10283, Al Jubayl, 31961, Saudi Arabia
Tel.: (966) 33477200
Web Site: http://www.sabic.com
Mfr of Chemicals
N.A.I.C.S.: 325998

National Plastic Co. (1)
PO Box 10002, Al Jubayl, 31961, Saudi Arabia
Tel.: (966) 33586000
Web Site: http://www.sabic.com
Mfr of Chemicals
N.A.I.C.S.: 325998

Petrochemical Pipeline Services B.V. (1)
Sanderboutlaan 21, 6181 DN, Elsloo, Netherlands

Tel.: (31) 467224030
Web Site: https://www.pps-pipelines.com
Petrochemical Pipeline Services
N.A.I.C.S.: 237120

SABIC (China) Research & Development Co., Ltd. (1)
Shanghai Technology Center 2550 Xiupu Road, Pudong, Shanghai, 201319, China
Tel.: (86) 2120378188
Chemical Products Mfr
N.A.I.C.S.: 325998

SABIC Americas, Inc. (1)
2500 CityWest Blvd Ste100, Houston, TX 77042
Tel.: (713) 430-2301
Web Site: http://www.sabicamericas.com
Sales Range: $50-74.9 Million
Emp.: 53
Mfr of Chemicals
N.A.I.C.S.: 424720

Subsidiary (Domestic):

SABIC Innovative Plastics (2)
1 Plastics Ave, Pittsfield, MA 01201
Tel.: (413) 448-7110
Sales Range: $5-14.9 Billion
Emp.: 300
Engineering Thermoplastic Material Solutions
N.A.I.C.S.: 322220
Timothy J. O'Brien (VP-Americas)

Plant (Domestic):

SABIC Innovative Plastics (3)
9930 Kincey Ave, Huntersville, NC 28078
Tel.: (704) 992-4820
Web Site: http://www.sabic-ip.com
Sales Range: $50-74.9 Million
Plastic Resin Mfr
N.A.I.C.S.: 424610

Subsidiary (Non-US):

SABIC Innovative Plastics BV (3)
Plasticslaan 1, 4600 AC, Bergen-op-Zoom, Netherlands
Tel.: (31) 0164292911
Web Site: http://www.cevic.com
Sales Range: $550-599.9 Million
Plastic Resins, Sheets & Film, Silicone Rubber Products & Electrical Insulating Materials Mfr
N.A.I.C.S.: 325211

SABIC Innovative Plastics Iberica S.A. (3)
S A C/ Frederic Mompou 5 2 1 Sant Just Desvern, Edificio D Planta 3, 08960, Barcelona, Spain
Tel.: (34) 934703060
Web Site: http://www.sabic.com
Sales Range: $250-299.9 Million
Plastic Resins, Sheets & Film, Silicone Rubber Products & Electrical Insulating Materials Mfr
N.A.I.C.S.: 325211

Subsidiary (Domestic):

SABIC Petrochemicals (2)
State Route 892, Washington, WV 26181
Tel.: (304) 863-7779
Web Site: http://www.sabic.com
Styrene Monomer Mfr
N.A.I.C.S.: 325180

SABIC Technology Center (2)
1600 Industrial Blvd, Sugar Land, TX 77478
Tel.: (281) 207-5500
Specialty Chemicals Research & Development Services
N.A.I.C.S.: 541715

SABIC Asia Pacific Ltd. (1)
Hung Tai Ctr Unit D 5F No 170, Tun Hwa N Rd, Taipei, 104, Taiwan (100%)
Tel.: (886) 225450300
Sales Range: $25-49.9 Million
Emp.: 4
Mfr of Chemicals
N.A.I.C.S.: 325998

SABIC Asia Pacific Pte. Ltd. (1)
One Temasek Avenue 06-01 Millenia Tower, Singapore, 039192, Singapore
Tel.: (65) 65572555
Web Site: http://www.sabic.com
Sales Range: $50-74.9 Million
Emp.: 2,400
Mfr of Chemicals
N.A.I.C.S.: 325998

Representative Office (Non-US):

SABIC Asia Pacific Pte. Ltd. - Philippines Office
Phillipines Representative Office 38 Fl Philamlife Twr, Makati, 1226, Philippines
Tel.: (63) 28850497
Web Site: http://www.sabic.com
Sales Range: $25-49.9 Million
Emp.: 4
Mfr of Chemicals
N.A.I.C.S.: 325998

SABIC Australia Pty. Ltd. (1)
Suite 2 Level 4 1C Grand Avenue, Rosehill, Sydney, 2142, NSW, Australia
Tel.: (61) 800649112
Chemical Products Mfr
N.A.I.C.S.: 325998

SABIC Capital B.V. (1)
WTC Tower Ten Strawinskylaan 1475, 1077 XX, Amsterdam, Netherlands
Tel.: (31) 203333030
Investment Management Service
N.A.I.C.S.: 523999

SABIC Deutschland GmbH (1)
Ernst-Gnob-Str 24, 40039, Dusseldorf, Germany
Tel.: (49) 211171400
Chemical Products Mfr
N.A.I.C.S.: 325998

SABIC Eastern Europe OOO (1)
Kosmodamianskaya Naberezhnaya 52 bld 1 10th floor, Moscow, 115054, Russia
Tel.: (7) 4952879203
Sales Range: $25-49.9 Million
Emp.: 7
Plastic Resin Mfr
N.A.I.C.S.: 325211

SABIC Euro B.V. (1)
Europaboulevard 1, PO Box 5151, 6130 PD, Sittard, Netherlands (100%)
Tel.: (31) 464767000
Trust Management
N.A.I.C.S.: 523991

Subsidiary (Non-US):

SABIC Polyolesene GmbH (2)
Pawikerstrasse 30, 45896, Gelsenkirchen, Germany (100%)
Tel.: (49) 20993390
Web Site: http://www.sabic-gelsenkirchen.de
Sales Range: $100-124.9 Million
Emp.: 400
Producer of Polyolefin for Plastics
N.A.I.C.S.: 326199

SABIC Europe B.V (1)
Europaboulevard 1, 6135 LD, Sittard, Netherlands
Tel.: (31) 467222222
Plastic Resin Mfr
N.A.I.C.S.: 325211

SABIC Far East Ltd. (1)
Suite 2106, Jin Mao Tower Pudong New Area, 888 Century Boulevard, 200120, Shanghai, China
Tel.: (86) 2150475688
Web Site: http://www.sabic.com
Sales Range: $25-49.9 Million
Emp.: 85
Mfr of Chemicals
N.A.I.C.S.: 325998

SABIC France SAS (1)
32 rue de la Bienfaisance, La Defense 5, 75008, Paris, Cedex, France
Tel.: (33) 144693020
Chemical Products Mfr
N.A.I.C.S.: 325998

SABIC Greece MEPE (1)
Business Center Cosmos Offices Aglou Georgiou 5 Patriarchiko Pylea, 57001, Thessaloniki, Greece
Tel.: (30) 2313 080 310
Sales Range: $50-74.9 Million
Emp.: 5
Plastic Material Distr
N.A.I.C.S.: 424610

Roy V. Armes (Acct Mgr & Mgr-Sls-Greece)

SABIC Hong Kong Ltd (1)
1418 2 Pacific Pl, 88 Queensway, Hong Kong, China (Hong Kong) (100%)
Tel.: (852) 25246161
Sales Range: $25-49.9 Million
Emp.: 15
Mfr of Chemicals
N.A.I.C.S.: 325998

SABIC Hungary Kft. (1)
Nagyenyed utca 8-14, H-1123, Budapest, Hungary
Tel.: (36) 18893336
Plastic Resin Mfr
N.A.I.C.S.: 325211
Cosmin Ticu (Acct Mgr-Romania & Moldavia)

SABIC India Pvt. Ltd. (1)
10th Floor Ambience Corporate Tower II, Ambience Island, Gurgaon, 122001, India
Tel.: (91) 1244746100
Mfr & Sales of Chemicals
N.A.I.C.S.: 325998

SABIC Industrial Investment Co. (1)
PO Box 5101, Riyadh, 11422, Saudi Arabia
Tel.: (966) 112258000
Web Site: http://www.sabic.com
Venture Capital
N.A.I.C.S.: 523910

SABIC Innovative Plastics (China) Co., Ltd. (1)
2/F No 3 Jinsha Road, Nansha District Nan-Sha, Guangdong, 518052, China
Tel.: (86) 2039307800
Chemical Products Mfr
N.A.I.C.S.: 325998

SABIC Innovative Plastics (Chongqing) Co., Ltd. (1)
Chongqing Plant No 2 West 2 Road, Shapingba District, Chongqing, China
Tel.: (86) 2363462028
Chemical Products Mfr
N.A.I.C.S.: 325998

SABIC Innovative Plastics (SEA) Pte. Ltd. (1)
23 Benoi Road, Singapore, 629895, Singapore
Tel.: (65) 62104100
Plastic Resin Mfr
N.A.I.C.S.: 325211

SABIC Innovative Plastics ABS UK Ltd. (1)
96 Dukesway, Teesside Industrial Estate Thornaby, Stockton-on-Tees, TS17 9LT, United Kingdom
Tel.: (44) 1642765166
Chemical Products Mfr
N.A.I.C.S.: 325998

SABIC Innovative Plastics Argentina SRL (1)
Descartes 3668, B1661AYF, Tortuguitas, Buenos Aires, Argentina
Tel.: (54) 2320552800
Chemical Products Mfr
N.A.I.C.S.: 325998

SABIC Innovative Plastics Australia Pty Ltd. (1)
Ste 14 Level 1 Bldg 3 195 Wellington Rd, Clayton, Melbourne, 3168, VIC, Australia
Tel.: (61) 385 613 600
Web Site: http://www.sabic-ip.com
Sales Range: $25-49.9 Million
Emp.: 12
Plastics Product Mfr
N.A.I.C.S.: 326199
Frances Mongan (Office Mgr)

SABIC Innovative Plastics Austria GmbH (1)
Universitatsring 10, 1010, Vienna, Austria
Tel.: (43) 26223900
Chemical Products Mfr
N.A.I.C.S.: 325998

SABIC Innovative Plastics Canada, Inc. (1)
1 Structured Products Drive, Long Sault, K0C 1P0, ON, Canada
Tel.: (905) 534-8199
Chemical Products Mfr
N.A.I.C.S.: 325998

SABIC Innovative Plastics Czech, s.r.o. (1)
Anglicka 140/20, Vinhorady, 120 00, Prague, 2, Czech Republic
Tel.: (420) 220511400
Emp.: 8
Plastic Resin Mfr
N.A.I.C.S.: 325211

SABIC Innovative Plastics Denmark ApS (1)
Kogle Alle 2, DK-2970, Horsholm, Denmark
Tel.: (45) 45828245
Chemical Products Mfr
N.A.I.C.S.: 325998

SABIC Innovative Plastics Espana ScpA (1)
Ctra de Cartagena Alhama de Murcia Km 13 La Aljorra, 30390, Murcia, Spain
Tel.: (34) 968129100
Chemical Products Mfr
N.A.I.C.S.: 325998

SABIC Innovative Plastics Finland Oy (1)
Italahdenkatu 22B, FIN-00210, Helsinki, Finland
Tel.: (358) 96211010
Chemical Products Mfr
N.A.I.C.S.: 325998

SABIC Innovative Plastics France SAC (1)
32 rue de la Bienfaisance, 75008, Paris, France
Tel.: (33) 144693020
Sales Range: $25-49.9 Million
Emp.: 17
Plastic Resin Mfr
N.A.I.C.S.: 325211

SABIC Innovative Plastics GP B.V. (1)
Plasticslaan 1, 4612 PX, Bergen-op-Zoom, Netherlands
Tel.: (31) 164292911
Plastic Resin Mfr
N.A.I.C.S.: 325211

SABIC Innovative Plastics Hong Kong Limited (1)
Room 1701 Tower One The Gateway Harbour City 25 Canton Road, Tsimshatsui, Kowloon, China (Hong Kong)
Tel.: (852) 26290888
Polymer Plastic Resin Mfr
N.A.I.C.S.: 325211

SABIC Innovative Plastics IP B.V. (1)
Plasticslaan 1, PO Box 117, 4612 PX, Bergen-op-Zoom, Netherlands
Tel.: (31) 164 292 911
Web Site: http://www.sabic-ip.com
Plastic Resin Mfr
N.A.I.C.S.: 325211

SABIC Innovative Plastics IP Licensing B.V. (1)
Plasticslaan 1, 4612 PX, Bergen-op-Zoom, Netherlands
Tel.: (31) 164 292 911
Web Site: http://www.sabic-ip.com
Plastic Resin Mfr
N.A.I.C.S.: 325211

SABIC Innovative Plastics India Private Ltd. (1)
10th Floor Ambience Corporate Tower II, Ambience Island, Gurgaon, 122001, India
Tel.: (91) 1244746100
Sales Range: $25-49.9 Million
Emp.: 5
Plastic Resin Mfr
N.A.I.C.S.: 325211
K. Venugopal (CEO)

SABIC Innovative Plastics Kereskedelmi Kft. (1)
Nagyenyed utca 8-14, H-1123, Budapest, Hungary
Tel.: (36) 18893345
Sales Range: $25-49.9 Million
Emp.: 2
Plastic Resin Mfr
N.A.I.C.S.: 325211

SAUDI BASIC INDUSTRIES CORPORATION

Saudi Basic Industries Corporation—(Continued)

SABIC Innovative Plastics Ltd. (1)
Papermill Drive, Redditch, B98 8QJ,
Worcestershire, United Kingdom
Tel.: (44) 1527590570
Chemical Products Mfr
N.A.I.C.S.: 325998

SABIC Innovative Plastics Malaysia Sdn. Bhd. (1)
Suite 3B-11-3 Level 11 Block 3B Plaza Sentral Jalan Stesen Sentral 5, KL Sental, 50470, Kuala Lumpur, Malaysia
Tel.: (60) 322746198
Chemical Products Mfr
N.A.I.C.S.: 325998

SABIC Innovative Plastics Management (Shanghai) Co., Ltd. (1)
2550 Xiupu Road, Pudong, Shanghai, 201319, China
Tel.: (86) 2120378188
Chemical Products Mfr
N.A.I.C.S.: 325998

SABIC Innovative Plastics Mt. Vernon, LLC (1)
1 Lexan Ln, Mount Vernon, IN 47620
Tel.: (812) 831-7000
Chemical Products Mfr
N.A.I.C.S.: 325998

SABIC Innovative Plastics Poland Sp. z.o.o (1)
17 Stycznia Street 45A IV Pictro 4th Floor, 02-146, Warsaw, Poland
Tel.: (48) 224323722
Sales Range: $50-74.9 Million
Emp.: 8
Plastic Material Distr
N.A.I.C.S.: 424610

SABIC Innovative Plastics Rus. OOO (1)
Kosmodamianskaya Naberezhnaya 52 - Bld 4, Moscow, 115054, Russia
Tel.: (7) 4952879209
Thermoplastic Products Whslr
N.A.I.C.S.: 424610

SABIC Innovative Plastics Servicios Mexico, S. de R.L. de C.V. (1)
Km 4 8 Blvd De Los Rios, Altamira, 89608, Mexico
Tel.: (52) 8332292500
Plastic Resin Mfr
N.A.I.C.S.: 325211

SABIC Innovative Plastics Shanghai Co., Ltd. (1)
Shanghai Plant No 58 Aidu Road Waigaoqiao Free Trade, Shanghai, 200131, China
Tel.: (86) 2150460000
Chemical Products Mfr
N.A.I.C.S.: 325998

SABIC Iran (1)
Units D3 & E3 3rd Floor No 1643 Opposite Of Gas Station Shariati St, Tehran, 1643, Iran
Tel.: (98) 21 22648053 5
Petrochemical Mfr
N.A.I.C.S.: 325110

SABIC Italia S.p.A. (1)
Via Simone Schiaffino 11/19, 20158, Milan, Italy (100%)
Tel.: (39) 02859741
Sales Range: $25-49.9 Million
Emp.: 13
Mfr of Chemicals
N.A.I.C.S.: 325998

SABIC Japan Ltd. (1)
TOKYO OFFICE Tokyo Club Building Kasumigaseki 3-2-6, Chiyoda-ku, Tokyo, 100-0013, Japan (100%)
Tel.: (81) 335934700
Web Site: http://www.sabic.co.jp
Sales Range: $25-49.9 Million
Emp.: 6
Mfr of Chemicals
N.A.I.C.S.: 325998

Plant (Domestic):

SABIC Japan Ltd. - Moka Plant (2)
321-4392, 321-4392, Mooka, Tochigi, Japan
Tel.: (81) 285 802 111
Plastics Product Mfr
N.A.I.C.S.: 326199

SABIC Korea Ltd. (1)
SEOUL OFFICE Donghoon Tower 20F 317 Teheran-ro, Gangnam-gu, Seoul, 06151, Korea (South) (100%)
Tel.: (82) 25106000
Web Site: http://www.sabic.co.kr
Sales Range: $25-49.9 Million
Emp.: 4
Mfr of Chemicals
N.A.I.C.S.: 325998

SABIC Lebanon (1)
Mina El Hosn Park Avenue Bertus Bldg 1344 Daouk Street 5th Floor, PO Box 11-2153, 2011-8403, Beirut, Lebanon
Tel.: (961) 1 973 444
Sales Range: $25-49.9 Million
Emp.: 23
Petrochemical Mfr
N.A.I.C.S.: 325110
Khaled Al-Habardi (Gen Mgr)

SABIC Marketing Iberica S.A. (1)
Edificio Euro-3 C/Frederic Mompou 5 5 4 - 4a, E-08960, Sant Just Desvern, Barcelona, Spain
Tel.: (34) 934703060
Web Site: https://www.sabic.eu
Polyethylene Resins Mfr
N.A.I.C.S.: 325211

SABIC Marketing Iberica S.L. (1)
Edificio Euro-3 Frederic Mompou 5 5 4-4a, Sant Just Desvern, 08960, Sant Just Desvern, Spain
Tel.: (34) 934703060
Sales Range: $25-49.9 Million
Emp.: 14
Chemical Distr
N.A.I.C.S.: 424690

SABIC Morocco (1)
23 Rue Bani Ritoune Km 4 2 Avenue Mohammed 6, Hay Souissi, Rabat, Morocco
Tel.: (212) 537 751 702
Petrochemical Mfr
N.A.I.C.S.: 325110

SABIC Nordic A/S (1)
Kogle Alle 2, DK-2970, Horsholm, Denmark
Tel.: (45) 33324918
Plastic Resin Mfr
N.A.I.C.S.: 325211

SABIC Pakistan Pvt. Ltd. (1)
M-123 - 126 Mezzanine Floor Business Arcade Movenpick Movenpick Hotel, Club Road, Karachi, 75530, Pakistan
Tel.: (92) 2135633229
Chemical Products Mfr
N.A.I.C.S.: 325998
Ather Khan (Mgr-Sls Acct)

SABIC Petrokemya Ticaret Limited (1)
Saray Mah Dr Adnan Buyukdeniz Cad Akkom Ofis Park Cessas Plaza B Block, 20-21 Floor Umraniye, Istanbul, Turkiye
Tel.: (90) 2166365000
Chemical Products Mfr
N.A.I.C.S.: 325998

SABIC Poland Sp z.o.o (1)
ul 17 Stycznia 45A, 02-146, Warsaw, Poland
Tel.: (48) 224323737
Sales Range: $25-49.9 Million
Emp.: 4
Plastic Resin Mfr
N.A.I.C.S.: 325211
Piotr Kwiecien (Mng Dir)

SABIC Polymerland Muhendislik Plastikleri San. Tic. A.S. (1)
Akkom Ofis Park Cessas Plaza B Block 20-21 Floor, Umraniye, Istanbul, Turkiye
Tel.: (90) 216 636 5000
Plastic Polymer Resin Mfr
N.A.I.C.S.: 325211

SABIC Polymershapes Mexico, S. de R.L. de C.V. (1)
Calle E No 24 Col Cerveceria Model, 53330, Naucalpan, Mexico
Tel.: (52) 55 5371 0300
Plastic Material Distr

N.A.I.C.S.: 327910

SABIC Polyolefine GmbH (1)
Pawikerstr 30, 45896, Gelsenkirchen, Germany
Tel.: (49) 20993391
Chemical Products Mfr
N.A.I.C.S.: 325998

SABIC South Africa (Pty) Ltd (1)
1101b 11th Floor Portside Towers 4 Bree Street, PO Box 719, Cape Town, 8001, South Africa
Tel.: (27) 214096100
Sales Range: $25-49.9 Million
Emp.: 13
Petrochemical Mfr
N.A.I.C.S.: 325110

SABIC Tunisia SARL (1)
3 Avenue Hassib Ben Ammar, Les Berges du lac, 1053, Tunis, Tunisia
Tel.: (216) 71860231
Chemical Products Mfr
N.A.I.C.S.: 325998

SABIC Turkey (1)
Saray Mah Dr Adnan Buyukdeniz Cad Akkom Ofis Park Cessas Plaza, 2nd Block 20-21 Floor, 34768, Istanbul, Turkiye
Tel.: (90) 216 636 5000
Plastic Material Distr
N.A.I.C.S.: 424610
Fahad Al-Harthi (Gen Mgr)

SABIC United Kingdom Ltd. (1)
DSM House Papermill Drive no 3, Redditch, B98 8QJ, Worcs, United Kingdom
Tel.: (44) 1527 590570
Web Site: http://www.sabic.com
Sales Range: $25-49.9 Million
Emp.: 11
Plastic Resin Mfr
N.A.I.C.S.: 325211

SABIC Vietnam Company Limited (1)
Suite 21-02 East Tower Lotte Center Hanoi 54 Lieu Giai Street, Dong Da, 100000, Hanoi, Vietnam
Tel.: (84) 2435772518
Chemical Products Mfr
N.A.I.C.S.: 325998

SABIC innovative Plastics SIT Holding Limited (1)
Room 1701 Tower One The Gateway Harbour City 25 Canton Road, Tsimshatsui, Kowloon, China (Hong Kong)
Tel.: (852) 26290888
Investment Management Service
N.A.I.C.S.: 523999

SABTANK - SABIC Terminal Service Co. (1)
PO Box 10135, Al Jubayl, 31961, Saudi Arabia
Tel.: (966) 33579000
Web Site: http://www.sabic.com
Mfr of Chemicals
N.A.I.C.S.: 325998

SABTANK SABIC Terminal Services Co. (1)
Sadaf Administration Building Road 121, PO Box 10135, Al Jubayl, 31961, Saudi Arabia
Tel.: (966) 3 345 3646
Sales Range: $75-99.9 Million
Emp.: 400
General Warehousing & Storage Services
N.A.I.C.S.: 493190

SADAF Saudi Petrochemical Co. (1)
PO Box 10025, Al Jubayl, 31961, Saudi Arabia (50%)
Tel.: (966) 33573000
Web Site: http://www.sabic.com
Mfr of Chemicals
N.A.I.C.S.: 325998

SHARQ Eastern Petrochemical Co. (1)
Eastern Petrochemical Company Building Jubail Industrial City Exit 218, PO Box 10035, Al Jubayl, 31961, Saudi Arabia
Tel.: (966) 3 357 5000
Petrochemical Mfr
N.A.I.C.S.: 325110

INTERNATIONAL PUBLIC

Saudi Innovative Plastics Sweden AB (1)
Solna Strandvag 78, 171 54, Solna, Sweden
Tel.: (46) 4533324918
Chemical Products Mfr
N.A.I.C.S.: 325998

Saudi Yanpet Petrochemical Co. (1)
PO Box 30333, Yanbu, 21441, Saudi Arabia
Tel.: (966) 43965000
Web Site: http://www.sabic.com
Sales Range: $200-249.9 Million
Emp.: 1,000
Mfr of Chemicals
N.A.I.C.S.: 325998

Scientific Design Company, Inc. (1)
49 Industrial Ave, Little Ferry, NJ 07643-1922 (50%)
Tel.: (201) 641-0500
Web Site: https://www.scidesign.com
Sales Range: $25-49.9 Million
Emp.: 70
Process Technology Licensor
N.A.I.C.S.: 325180
Darren S. Adams (Pres & CEO)

SAUDI CEMENT COMPANY

3964-King Saud -Al-Amamrah Area
Unit No 1, Dammam, 32415-7102,
Eastern, Saudi Arabia
Tel.: (966) 138358000
Web Site:
 https://www.saudicement.com.sa
Year Founded: 1955
3030—(SAU)
Rev.: $378,568,458
Assets: $873,910,412
Liabilities: $262,535,395
Net Worth: $611,375,017
Earnings: $106,342,621
Emp.: 800
Fiscal Year-end: 12/31/22
Cement Mfr
N.A.I.C.S.: 327310
Mohammed Ali Al-Garni (CEO)

SAUDI CERAMIC COMPANY

King Fahad Rd Al Olaya, PO Box 3893, Riyadh, 11481, Saudi Arabia
Tel.: (966) 118298888   SA
Web Site:
 https://www.saudiceramics.com
Year Founded: 1977
2040—(SAU)
Rev.: $395,936,009
Assets: $816,161,845
Liabilities: $339,832,822
Net Worth: $476,329,023
Earnings: $45,395,281
Emp.: 5,000
Fiscal Year-end: 12/31/22
Ceramic Products Producer & Marketer
N.A.I.C.S.: 327120
Abdulkarim Ibrahim Alnafee (Deputy Chm)

Subsidiaries:

Ceramic Pipes Company (1)
2nd Industrial City New Saniya Nr Al Fanar City New Kharj Road, PO Box 17952, Riyadh, 11494, Saudi Arabia
Tel.: (966) 114998840
Web Site: https://cpc.com.sa
Clay Pipe Mfr
N.A.I.C.S.: 327120
Mubarak Al Hitrish (Mgr-IT)

SAUDI CHEMICAL HOLDING COMPANY

7632 Al-Ihsa Rd Al-Malaz, PO Box 2665, Riyadh, 12831-2892, Saudi Arabia
Tel.: (966) 114767432
Web Site:
 https://www.saudichemical.com
Year Founded: 1972

2230—(SAU)
Rev.: $985,433,409
Assets: $1,236,411,678
Liabilities: $791,708,572
Net Worth: $444,703,106
Earnings: $21,593,654
Fiscal Year-end: 12/31/22
Explosives Mfr
N.A.I.C.S.: 325920

Subsidiaries:

AJA Pharma Company (1)
Office 7 Building C2 Business Gate Complex Eastern Ring Road Exit 8, Riyadh, Saudi Arabia
Tel.: (966) 112687988
Web Site: http://www.ajapharma.com
Pharmaceuticals Product Mfr
N.A.I.C.S.: 325412

Suez International Nitrate Company (1)
Sheraton Residences Ministers Square Square 1157 No 3 Fifth Floor, PO 114, Before Semadco Company Ataka, Suez, Egypt
Tel.: (20) 222695101
Web Site: http://www.sinco.com.eg
Chemical Products Mfr
N.A.I.C.S.: 325998

SAUDI COMPANY FOR HARDWARE SJSC
Prince Sultan Ibn Abdul Aziz street extended between, PO Box 86387, Al-Takhasusi street and Prince Turki Ibn Abdulaziz Road, 11622, Riyadh, Saudi Arabia
Tel.: (966) 114993500
Web Site: http://www.saco-ksa.com
4008—(SAU)
Rev.: $303,036,436
Assets: $361,058,409
Liabilities: $250,734,233
Net Worth: $110,324,176
Earnings: ($37,995,197)
Emp.: 2,035
Fiscal Year-end: 12/31/22
Hardware Retailer & Distr
N.A.I.C.S.: 444140
Sameer Mohammed Abdul Aziz Al Hamidi *(CEO & Mng Dir)*

Subsidiaries:

Medscan Terminal Company Limited (1)
King Abdulaziz Road King Abdulaziz Seaport Causeway, PO Box 825, Logistics Support Zone, Dammam, 31421, Saudi Arabia
Tel.: (966) 138140470
Web Site: https://www.medscansa.com
Logistics & Warehousing Services
N.A.I.C.S.: 541614

SAUDI CONSULTING SERVICES
PO Box 2341, Riyadh, 11451, Saudi Arabia
Tel.: (966) 14659975
Web Site:
http://www.saudconsult.com
Year Founded: 1965
Sales Range: $125-149.9 Million
Emp.: 2,500
Engineering & Architectural Consulting Services
N.A.I.C.S.: 541330
Tarek M. A. Al-Shawaf *(Chm)*

Subsidiaries:

Saudi Consulting SA (1)
PO Box 2341, 11451, Riyadh, Saudi Arabia
Tel.: (966) 14659975
Engineering & Architectural Consulting Services
N.A.I.C.S.: 541330

Saudi Consulting Services (1)
8 Langland Manions 228 Finchley Road, NW3 6QA, London, United Kingdom - England

Tel.: (44) 171 4311790
Engineering & Architectural Consulting Services
N.A.I.C.S.: 541330

Saudi Servicing (1)
PO Box 1239, 31431, Dammam, Saudi Arabia
Tel.: (966) 3 8955004
Engineering & Architectural Consulting Services
N.A.I.C.S.: 541330

SAUDI DAIRY & FOODSTUFF CO. LTD.
PO Box 5043, Jeddah, 21422, Saudi Arabia
Tel.: (966) 126293366
Web Site: https://www.sadafco.com
Year Founded: 1976
2270—(SAU)
Rev.: $577,958,080
Assets: $608,873,646
Liabilities: $193,085,076
Net Worth: $415,788,570
Earnings: $55,670,548
Emp.: 2,700
Fiscal Year-end: 03/31/22
Dairy & Food Product Producer
N.A.I.C.S.: 445298
Mussad Abdullah Abdul Aziz Al-Nassar *(Exec Dir)*

Subsidiaries:

Egyptian Dairy and Foodstuff Company (1)
3rd Industrial Zone A1, PO Box 458, EL-Asher, 10th of Ramadan City, 1488, Egypt
Tel.: (20) 55 441 0497
Web Site: https://edafco.com
Emp.: 1,000
Milk & Food Products Producer
N.A.I.C.S.: 311999

Foodexo Sp. z o.o. (1)
ul Lotewska 5a, 03-918, Warsaw, Poland
Tel.: (48) 226161805
Web Site: https://foodexo.pl
Skimmed Milk Mfr
N.A.I.C.S.: 311514

SADAFCO For Foodstuff UAE (1)
Al Quoz Industrial Area Interchange #3, PO Box 52953, Near Kanoo Office, Dubai, United Arab Emirates
Tel.: (971) 43403383
Web Site: http://www.sadafco.com
Sales Range: $25-49.9 Million
Emp.: 20
Food Marketer, Distr & Sales
N.A.I.C.S.: 424420

SADAFCO Jordan Foodstuff Co. (1)
10 Abdel Hammeed Shuouman Street Matalqa Building 3rd Floor, Al-Shemesani, Amman, Jordan
Tel.: (962) 65676867
Web Site: http://www.wanadoo.jo
Sales Range: $25-49.9 Million
Emp.: 30
Food Producer & Distr
N.A.I.C.S.: 311999

SADAFCO Qatar LLC (1)
PO Box 15027, PO Box 15027, Doha, Qatar
Tel.: (974) 460 4726
Web Site: http://www.sadafco.com
Dairy Product Marketer, Distr & Sales
N.A.I.C.S.: 424430

SAUDI ELECTRIC SUPPLY COMPANY
Al Raqa St, PO Box 3298, 31952, Al Khobar, Saudi Arabia
Tel.: (966) 3 882 9546
Web Site: http://www.sesco-gex.com
Year Founded: 1976
Sales Range: $50-74.9 Million
Emp.: 300
Electrical Supply Distr
N.A.I.C.S.: 423610
Tarek Ali Abdullah Tamimi *(Chm)*

SAUDI ELECTRICITY COMPANY
At the crossing of Al-Olaya Street with Rihana Bint Zaid Street, PO Box 22955, Al-Arid district, Riyadh, 11416, Saudi Arabia
Tel.: (966) 118077202
Web Site: https://www.se.com.sa
Year Founded: 2000
5110—(SAU)
Rev.: $19,218,617,251
Assets: $127,844,696,974
Liabilities: $59,306,975,603
Net Worth: $68,537,721,370
Earnings: $4,035,521,664
Emp.: 32,200
Fiscal Year-end: 12/31/22
Electric Power Distr
N.A.I.C.S.: 335311
Najm Abdullah Al-Zaid *(Vice Chm)*

SAUDI ENAYA COOPERATIVE INSURANCE COMPANY
Prince Mohammed Bin Abdul Aziz Road, PO Box 8583, 21492, Jeddah, Saudi Arabia
Tel.: (966) 2 6675621
Web Site:
http://www.saudienaya.com
Health Insurance
N.A.I.C.S.: 524114
Faisal Tamr *(Chm)*

SAUDI FISHERIES COMPANY
8705 Nasr Bin Ghanem - Al Malaz, Riyadh, 12641-2640, Saudi Arabia
Tel.: (966) 920000527
Web Site:
https://www.alasmak.com.sa
Year Founded: 1980
6050—(SAU)
Rev.: $13,015,736
Assets: $82,942,101
Liabilities: $28,824,838
Net Worth: $54,117,263
Earnings: ($18,342,049)
Emp.: 212
Fiscal Year-end: 12/31/22
Fish & Seafood Production & Sales
N.A.I.C.S.: 445250
Sarah Al-Suhaimi *(Chm)*

SAUDI GROUND SERVICES COMPANY LIMITED
JETA6649 King Abdul Aziz Road - Al Basatin Dist Unit No 3, Jeddah, 23719 - 4358, Saudi Arabia
Tel.: (966) 26909999
Web Site: https://www.saudiags.com
4031—(SAU)
Rev.: $527,139,581
Assets: $1,165,333,422
Liabilities: $604,866,818
Net Worth: $560,466,604
Earnings: ($65,188,108)
Emp.: 8,000
Fiscal Year-end: 12/31/22
Airport Operations
N.A.I.C.S.: 488119
Omar Abdullah Jafri *(Vice Chm)*

SAUDI INDUSTRIAL DEVELOPMENT COMPANY
Jeddah - Prince Mohammed Bin Abdulaziz Street - Altahliya, PO Box 12105, Jeddah, 21473, Saudi Arabia
Tel.: (966) 126102222
Web Site: https://sidc.com.sa
Year Founded: 1992
2130—(SAU)
Rev.: $41,420,407
Assets: $73,686,053
Liabilities: $27,026,474
Net Worth: $46,659,578
Earnings: ($10,171,117)
Emp.: 209

Fiscal Year-end: 12/31/22
Building Construction Services
N.A.I.C.S.: 236210
E. Bandar Abdullah Ibrahim ALHomaidhi *(Deputy Chm)*

SAUDI INDUSTRIAL EXPORT COMPANY
Plaza AL-Ghadeer Building 3rd floor Office No 21-20, PO Box 13311, Al-Ghadeer District King Abdulaziz Road View, Riyadh, 4199, Saudi Arabia
Tel.: (966) 112002939
Web Site: https://www.siec.com.sa
Year Founded: 1990
4140—(SAU)
Rev.: $71,065
Assets: $44,978,602
Liabilities: $2,311,830
Net Worth: $42,666,772
Earnings: ($5,624,052)
Fiscal Year-end: 12/31/22
Marketing Services
N.A.I.C.S.: 541613
Hazim Fahad Aldosary *(CEO & Mng Dir)*

SAUDI INDUSTRIAL INVESTMENT GROUP
Office 203-Rubeen Plaza Northern Ring Road, PO Box 99833, Hittin Dist, Riyadh, 11625, Saudi Arabia
Tel.: (966) 112792522
Web Site: https://www.siig.com.sa
Year Founded: 1996
2250—(SAU)
Rev.: $12,148,514
Assets: $2,947,396,614
Liabilities: $97,917,611
Net Worth: $2,849,479,003
Earnings: $104,968,138
Fiscal Year-end: 12/31/22
Petrochemical Products Mfr
N.A.I.C.S.: 324110
Sulaiman Mohammed Almandeel *(Mng Dir)*

Subsidiaries:

National Petrochemical Company (1)
PO Box 99833, Riyadh, 11625, Saudi Arabia
Tel.: (966) 112192522
Web Site: http://www.petrochem.com.sa
Rev.: $1,474,503
Assets: $2,512,645,156
Liabilities: $81,397,524
Net Worth: $2,431,247,632
Earnings: $363,979,373
Emp.: 7
Fiscal Year-end: 12/31/2021
Petrochemical Mfr
N.A.I.C.S.: 325110

Saudi Polymers Company (1)
Jubail Industrial City, PO Box 11221, Jubail, 31961, Saudi Arabia
Tel.: (966) 3 356 8222
Web Site: https://www.saudipolymers.com
Polyethylene Mfr
N.A.I.C.S.: 326111
Fayez Al-Anazi *(Gen Mgr-Polymers)*

SAUDI INDUSTRIAL RESINS LTD.
Jameel Square Office No 201 2nd Floor Tahliya Street, PO Box 7764, Jeddah, 21472, Saudi Arabia
Tel.: (966) 126518920
Web Site: http://www.sir-ltd.com
Year Founded: 1977
Sales Range: $10-24.9 Million
Emp.: 150
Polyester Plastic & Related Hydro-Carbon Product Mfr
N.A.I.C.S.: 325211
Mohammed Sadique Kaki *(Mgr-Admin)*

SAUDI INTEGRATED TELECOM COMPANY

Saudi Industrial Resins Ltd.—(Continued)

SAUDI INTEGRATED TELECOM COMPANY
PO Box 8732, Riyadh, 11492, Saudi Arabia
Tel.: (966) 11 4062399
Year Founded: 2011
Telecommunication Servicesb
N.A.I.C.S.: 517810
Ian Charles Stone *(Mgr)*

SAUDI INVESTMENT BANK
8081- Sheikh Abdul Rahman bin Hassan - Al-Wizarat, Al Maather Unit No 2, Riyadh, 12622 - 3144, Saudi Arabia
Tel.: (966) 114183100   SA
Web Site: https://www.saib.com.sa
Year Founded: 1976
1030—(SAU)
Rev.: $1,976,885,922
Assets: $34,653,780,522
Liabilities: $30,058,915,392
Net Worth: $4,594,865,130
Earnings: $469,644,426
Emp.: 1,488
Fiscal Year-end: 12/31/23
Banking Services
N.A.I.C.S.: 522110
Abdallah Salih Jum'ah *(Chm)*

Subsidiaries:

SAIB BNP Paribas Asset Management Co., Ltd. (1)
PO Box 5556, Riyadh, 11432, Saudi Arabia
Tel.: (966) 14742121
Web Site: http://www.saibbnpp.com
Asset Management & Investment Services; Owned by Saudi Investment Bank & by BNP Paribas S.A.
N.A.I.C.S.: 523940

SAUDI KAYAN PETROCHEMICAL COMPANY
PO Box 10302, Jubail Industrial City, Jubail, 31961, Saudi Arabia
Tel.: (966) 133563300
Web Site: https://www.saudikayan.com
2350—(SAU)
Rev.: $2,974,807,359
Assets: $7,538,524,730
Liabilities: $3,411,798,694
Net Worth: $4,126,726,037
Earnings: ($331,659,779)
Emp.: 1,300
Fiscal Year-end: 12/31/22
Petrochemical & Chemical Products Mfr
N.A.I.C.S.: 324110
Omar A. Al-Amoudi *(Chm)*

SAUDI LIME INDUSTRIES COMPANY
2nd Industrial Area Al-Kharj Road Street 198, Riyadh, 14333, Saudi Arabia
Tel.: (966) 112652929
Web Site: https://saudilime.com
Year Founded: 1977
Limestone Products Supplier
N.A.I.C.S.: 212312

Subsidiaries:

Astra Mining Company Limited (1)
Riyadh - Malaz Salaheddin Ayyoubi Street, King Abdulaziz Building No 8128, Riyadh, Saudi Arabia
Tel.: (966) 112388830
Web Site: https://www.astramining.sa
Ore & Mineral Services
N.A.I.C.S.: 213114

SAUDI MARKETING COMPANY
Saudi Arabia Eastern Region Al Dammam Company, PO Box 4605, Dammam, 31412, Saudi Arabia
Tel.: (966) 138535800
Web Site: https://www.farm.com.sa
Year Founded: 1978
4006—(SAU)
Rev.: $479,584,051
Assets: $621,085,985
Liabilities: $445,369,894
Net Worth: $175,716,091
Earnings: $6,064,614
Emp.: 5,000
Fiscal Year-end: 12/31/22
Supermarket Owner & Operator
N.A.I.C.S.: 445110
Abdaljaleel Mahoud Atieh Daoud *(CFO)*

SAUDI NETWORKERS SERVICES COMPANY
Riyadh Building 8228 King Abdulaziz Road, PO Box 25141, Al Sulimaniyah, Riyadh, 11466, Saudi Arabia
Tel.: (966) 112939595
Web Site:
https://www.saudinetworkers.com
Year Founded: 2001
9543—(SAU)
Rev.: $147,903,751
Assets: $56,522,271
Liabilities: $29,782,907
Net Worth: $26,739,364
Earnings: $9,864,269
Fiscal Year-end: 12/31/23
Management Consulting Services
N.A.I.C.S.: 541618

SAUDI PAK LEASING COMPANY LIMITED
6th Floor Lakson Square Building 1 Sarwar Shaheed Road, Karachi, 74200, Pakistan
Tel.: (92) 2135655181
Web Site:
https://www.saudipakleasing.com
Year Founded: 1991
SPLC—(PSX)
Rev.: $116,694
Assets: $2,919,677
Liabilities: $4,964,624
Net Worth: ($2,044,947)
Earnings: $52,457
Emp.: 22
Fiscal Year-end: 06/30/23
Financial Services
N.A.I.C.S.: 522220
Ahsanullah Khan *(CEO)*

Subsidiaries:

Saudi Pak Industrial & Agultural Investment Company Limited (1)
Saudi Pak Tower 61 A- Jinnah Avenue, Islamabad, Pakistan
Tel.: (92) 51111222003
Web Site: https://www.saudipak.com
Management Consulting Services
N.A.I.C.S.: 541611

SAUDI PAPER MANUFACTURING COMPANY
2598 Industrial City 2 Unit No 2, PO Box 2598, Dammam, 34326-7169, Saudi Arabia
Tel.: (966) 920003558
Web Site:
https://www.saudipaper.com
Year Founded: 1989
2300—(SAU)
Rev.: $184,472,709
Assets: $282,124,920
Liabilities: $174,859,156
Net Worth: $107,265,764
Earnings: $12,537,480
Emp.: 965
Fiscal Year-end: 12/31/22
Tissue Paper Mfr
N.A.I.C.S.: 322291
Abdullah Owdah Suleiman Al Enazi *(Mng Dir)*

SAUDI PHARMACEUTICAL INDUSTRIES & MEDICAL APPLIANCES CORPORATION
PO Box 20001, Riyadh, 11455, Saudi Arabia
Tel.: (966) 112523333   SA
Web Site:
https://www.spimaco.com.sa
Year Founded: 1986
2070—(SAU)
Rev.: $380,305,849
Assets: $1,021,664,327
Liabilities: $570,230,350
Net Worth: $451,433,978
Earnings: ($45,656,106)
Emp.: 1,200
Fiscal Year-end: 12/31/22
Pharmaceuticals Mfr
N.A.I.C.S.: 325412
Mohammed Talal AlNahas *(Chm)*

SAUDI PUBLIC TRANSPORT COMPANY
Building No 7995 Al-Takhassusi Street, PO Box 10667, Al-Nakhil District, Riyadh, 11443, Saudi Arabia
Tel.: (966) 920026888   SA
Web Site: https://www.saptco.com.sa
Year Founded: 1979
4040—(SAU)
Rev.: $418,563,778
Assets: $1,076,295,849
Liabilities: $830,518,399
Net Worth: $245,777,450
Earnings: ($6,447,028)
Emp.: 3,181
Fiscal Year-end: 12/31/23
Bus Transportation Services
N.A.I.C.S.: 485210
Abdullah Ali Al Igail *(Deputy Chm)*

SAUDI REAL ESTATE CO.
PO Box 3572, Riyadh, 11481, Saudi Arabia
Tel.: (966) 920003938
Web Site: https://www.al-akaria.com
Year Founded: 1976
4020—(SAU)
Rev.: $133,111,386
Assets: $2,007,512,669
Liabilities: $1,251,415,601
Net Worth: $756,097,068
Earnings: ($37,479,328)
Emp.: 146
Fiscal Year-end: 12/31/20
Real Estate Development Services
N.A.I.C.S.: 531390
Aiman Mohammed Almudaifer *(Chm)*

Subsidiaries:

Al Widyan Company (1)
Al Akaria Plaza Gate D 4th Floor Suite 438 Olaya St Al Olaya, Riyadh, 12244, Saudi Arabia
Tel.: (966) 114600025
Web Site: http://www.alwidyan.com
Real Estate Services
N.A.I.C.S.: 531390
Aiman Mohamed Al Mudaifer *(Chm)*

Saudi Real Estate Construction Company (1)
Akaria 2 Olaya Street, PO Box 50438, Riyadh, 11523, Saudi Arabia
Tel.: (966) 114653111
Web Site: http://www.saudiconstruction.com
Real Estate Services
N.A.I.C.S.: 531390
Ibrahim Mohammed Alalwan *(Chm)*

Saudi Real Estate Infrastructure Company (1)
Office No 605 Al Akaria 2 Commercial Building Olaya St, PO Box 2567, Riyadh, 12244, Saudi Arabia
Tel.: (966) 114190728
Web Site: https://www.binyah.com.sa
Real Estate Services
N.A.I.C.S.: 531390
Shabbir Ahmed Khan *(Mgr-Logistics)*

INTERNATIONAL PUBLIC

SAUDI REINSURANCE COMPANY
Northern Ring Rd Al Wadi, Riyadh, 13313, Saudi Arabia
Tel.: (966) 115102000
Web Site: https://www.saudire.net
Year Founded: 2008
8200—(SAU)
Rev.: $167,245,416
Assets: $717,300,124
Liabilities: $411,489,063
Net Worth: $305,811,060
Earnings: $33,180,314
Emp.: 74
Fiscal Year-end: 12/31/23
Life & Non Life Reinsurance Products Services
N.A.I.C.S.: 524113
Mishari Al-Hussain *(Vice Chm)*

SAUDI STEEL PIPE COMPANY
PO Box 11680, Dammam, 31463, Saudi Arabia
Tel.: (966) 38122222
Web Site: http://www.sspipe.com
Sales Range: $900-999.9 Million
Emp.: 400
Steel Pole Mfr
N.A.I.C.S.: 332919
Ahmed Mubarak Al Dabasi *(Chm)*

Subsidiaries:

Titanium & Steel Manufacturing Company Limited (1)
Damman 2nd Industrial City, PO Box 661, Dammam, 31421, Saudi Arabia
Tel.: (966) 13 812 5353
Web Site: http://www.tsmarabia.com
Process Equipment Mfr
N.A.I.C.S.: 332410
Ayman A. Alhoti *(Gen Mgr)*

SAUDI SUDANESE BANK
2 Al-Muk Namer Street South, Khartoum, Sudan
Tel.: (249) 183 485675
Web Site: http://www.saudisb.sd
Year Founded: 1984
SSBA—(KHAR)
Sales Range: Less than $1 Million
Banking Services
N.A.I.C.S.: 522110

SAUDI TELECOM COMPANY
PO Box 87912, Riyadh, 11652, Saudi Arabia
Tel.: (966) 114527000   SA
Web Site: https://www.stc.com.sa
7010—(SAU)
Rev.: $17,979,348,354
Assets: $36,587,117,984
Liabilities: $16,316,329,556
Net Worth: $20,270,788,428
Earnings: $3,302,738,835
Fiscal Year-end: 12/31/22
Telecommunications Solutions & Services
N.A.I.C.S.: 517111
Ameen Fahad Alshiddi *(CFO)*

Subsidiaries:

Aqalat Company Limited (1)
PO Box 3386, Riyadh, 12461, Saudi Arabia
Tel.: (966) 920020071
Web Site: https://www.aqalat.com.sa
Real Estate Services
N.A.I.C.S.: 531390

Arabian Internet and Communications Services Company (1)
Akaria Commercial Center III, Olaya Street, Riyadh, Saudi Arabia (100%)
Tel.: (966) 1 460 0111
Web Site: http://www.awalnet.com
Sales Range: $50-74.9 Million
Emp.: 150
Internet & Telecommunications Services
N.A.I.C.S.: 517810

AND PRIVATE COMPANIES — SAVA D.D.

Saudi Digital Payments Company (1)
Pavilions Community, Ad Diriyah, Riyadh, 13714, Saudi Arabia
Tel.: (966) 92 001 1444
Web Site: https://stcpay.com.sa
Digital Bank Services
N.A.I.C.S.: 522110
Khalid Aljasser (Chm)

Stc Bahrain B.S.C. (1)
shop 201 Building 1069 Road 362 Al Hadrami Avenue, PO Box 21529, Manama, Bahrain
Tel.: (973) 33128128
Web Site: https://www.stc.com.bh
Telecom Services
N.A.I.C.S.: 517111

SAUDI TOP TRADING COMPANY
Al Noor District, Riyadh, Saudi Arabia
Tel.: (966) 112420001
Web Site: https://www.stp.com.sa
Year Founded: 2006
9552—(SAU)
Rev.: $37,909,068
Assets: $35,543,612
Liabilities: $17,381,634
Net Worth: $18,161,979
Earnings: $1,139,987
Emp.: 100
Fiscal Year-end: 12/31/23
Plastic Fabrication Product Mfr
N.A.I.C.S.: 315990

SAUDI UNITED COOPERATIVE INSURANCE COMPANY
Rabiah & Nasser Building Dhahran St, PO Box 31616, Al Khobar, 31952, Saudi Arabia
Tel.: (966) 38652200
Web Site: http://www.walaa.com
Sales Range: $150-199.9 Million
Emp.: 500
Insurance Services
N.A.I.C.S.: 524126

SAUDI VITRIFIED CLAY PIPE CO.
PO Box 6415, Riyadh, 11442, Saudi Arabia
Tel.: (966) 114769192
Web Site: https://www.svcp-sa.com
Year Founded: 1977
2360—(SAU)
Rev.: $20,357,258
Assets: $79,836,171
Liabilities: $8,191,894
Net Worth: $71,644,277
Earnings: ($2,336,402)
Emp.: 452
Fiscal Year-end: 12/31/22
Clay Pipe Mfr & Whslr
N.A.I.C.S.: 327120
Faisal Abdulaziz Faisal Al Saud (Chm)

SAUIPE S.A.
Web Site: http://www.costadosauipe.com.br
Hotel Operator
N.A.I.C.S.: 721120

SAUMYA CONSULTANTS LIMITED
A-402 Mangalam, 24/26 Hemanta Basu Sarani, Kolkata, 700 001, India
Tel.: (91) 3322436242
Web Site: https://www.saumyaconsultants.com
Year Founded: 1993
539218—(BOM)
Rev.: $2,367,307
Assets: $11,165,853
Liabilities: $649,726
Net Worth: $10,516,127
Earnings: ($138,203)
Fiscal Year-end: 03/31/23
Financial Support Services
N.A.I.C.S.: 523999
Arun Kumar Agarwalla (Mng Dir)

SAUNDERS INTERNATIONAL LIMITED
Suite 101 Level 1 3 Rider Boulevard, 1 Homebush Bay Dr, Rhodes, 2138, NSW, Australia
Tel.: (61) 297922444 AU
Web Site: https://saundersint.com
Year Founded: 1951
SND—(ASX)
Rev.: $144,283,520
Assets: $75,586,939
Liabilities: $41,335,470
Net Worth: $34,251,469
Earnings: $6,252,003
Emp.: 505
Fiscal Year-end: 06/30/24
Engineeering Services
N.A.I.C.S.: 237990
Robert Patterson (Mgr & Gen Mgr)

Subsidiaries:

Saunders PlantWeave Pty. Ltd. (1)
Unit 10 46-48 Buffalo Rd, Gladesville, NSW, Australia
Tel.: (61) 298484800
Web Site: https://plantweave.com.au
Automation & Electrical System Services
N.A.I.C.S.: 541511

SAURAMPS & CIE S A
Le Triangle Allee Jules Milhau, 34000, Montpellier, Herault, France
Tel.: (33) 467067879
Web Site: http://www.sauramps.com
Sales Range: $25-49.9 Million
Emp.: 106
Online Book Stores
N.A.I.C.S.: 459210
Jean-Marie Sevestre (Pres)

SAURASHTRA CEMENT LTD.
N K Mehta International House 2nd Floor Agrima Business Centre, 178 Backbay Reclamation Babubhai Chinai Marg, Mumbai, 400 020, India
Tel.: (91) 2266365444
Web Site: https://www.hathi-sidheecements.com
502175—(BOM)
Rev.: $93,640,761
Assets: $99,208,432
Liabilities: $27,667,881
Net Worth: $71,540,551
Earnings: $9,880,088
Emp.: 364
Fiscal Year-end: 03/31/21
Cement Mfr
N.A.I.C.S.: 327310
Mohinderpal Singh Gilotra (Mng Dir)

Subsidiaries:

Agrima Consultants International Limited (1)
N K Mehta International House 4th Floor 178 Backbay Reclamation, Mumbai, 400020, India
Tel.: (91) 2266365444
Management Consultancy Services
N.A.I.C.S.: 541611

SAVA A.D.
Mladena Stojanovica Bb, 78400, Gradiska, Bosnia & Herzegovina
Tel.: (387) 51813086
SVGR-R-A—(BANJ)
Rev.: $8,077
Assets: $978,319
Liabilities: $602,549
Net Worth: $375,770
Earnings: ($139,789)
Emp.: 4
Fiscal Year-end: 12/31/12
Hotel Operator
N.A.I.C.S.: 721110
Nebojsa Dmitrovic (Chm-Supervisory Bd)

SAVA A.D.
Cara Dusana 2, Sabac, Serbia
Tel.: (381) 15354630
Web Site: http://www.savasabac.co.rs
Year Founded: 1951
SAVA—(BEL)
Sales Range: Less than $1 Million
Home Management Services
N.A.I.C.S.: 721110
Alexandar Jovicic (Exec Dir)

SAVA A.D.
Vojvode Stepe 17, Hrtkovci, Serbia
Tel.: (381) 22 455 022
Web Site: http://www.sava.rs
Year Founded: 2003
Sales Range: $1-9.9 Million
Emp.: 71
Lumber & Wood Product Whslr
N.A.I.C.S.: 423310
Ilija Jauz (CEO)

SAVA D.D.
Dunajska 152, 1000, Ljubljana, Slovenia
Tel.: (386) 42065510
Web Site: http://www.sava.si
Year Founded: 1920
Rev.: $717,156
Assets: $171,680,591
Liabilities: $130,713,465
Net Worth: $40,967,126
Earnings: $630,228
Emp.: 1,030
Fiscal Year-end: 12/31/18
Holding Company; Management, Business Operations & Investment Services
N.A.I.C.S.: 551112
Gregor Rovansek (CEO)

Subsidiaries:

ENERGETIKA CRNOMELJ d.o.o. (1)
6 Skofjeloska Cesta, Kranj, 4000, Slovenia
Tel.: (386) 42065777
Rubber Products Mfr
N.A.I.C.S.: 326299

ENSA BH d.o.o. (1)
Prijebljezi Bb, Razboj, 78429, Srbac, Bosnia & Herzegovina
Tel.: (387) 51 75 75 40
Web Site: http://www.ensabh.com
Sales Range: $25-49.9 Million
Emp.: 42
Wood Products Mfr
N.A.I.C.S.: 321999
Stanko Cvenkel (Mng Dir)

Grand Hotel Toplice Bled d.o.o. (1)
Cesta svobode 12, 4260, Bled, Slovenia (98.88%)
Tel.: (386) 45791000
Web Site: http://www.sava-hotels-resorts.com
Sales Range: $10-24.9 Million
Emp.: 55
Hotels & Motels Services
N.A.I.C.S.: 721110
Mojca Krasovec (Dir-Hotel)

SAVA IT d.o.o. (1)
davcna ulica 1, Ljubljana, SI 1000, Slovenia
Tel.: (386) 14304150
Sales Range: $25-49.9 Million
Emp.: 17
Real Estate Devlopment
N.A.I.C.S.: 541513

SAVA TURIZEM d.d. (1)
Cankarjeva 6, Bled, 4260, Slovenia
Tel.: (386) 4 206 60 21
Tour Operating Services
N.A.I.C.S.: 561520
Andrej Prebil (CEO)

SAVATECH d.o.o. (1)
6 Skofjeloska Cesta, Kranj, 4000, Slovenia
Tel.: (386) 42066080
Web Site: http://www.savatech.si
Emp.: 900
Industrial Rubber Product Mfr
N.A.I.C.S.: 326299
Matej Zinko (Mgr-Sls)

Subsidiary (Non-US):

SAVA TRADE GmbH (2)
Kobellstr 4, Munich, 80336, Germany
Tel.: (49) 895441430
Web Site: http://www.sava-trade.de
Sales Range: $25-49.9 Million
Emp.: 10
Conveyor Belt Distr
N.A.I.C.S.: 423830

Subsidiary (US):

SAVATECH CORP. (2)
413 Oak Pl Ste J, Port Orange, FL 32127-4375
Tel.: (386) 760-0706
Web Site: http://www.savatech.com
Sales Range: $25-49.9 Million
Emp.: 6
Fire Department Equipment Whslr
N.A.I.C.S.: 423850
Jim Jeager (Gen Mgr)

Sava - Gti d.o.o. (1)
6 Skofjeloska Cesta, 4000, Kranj, Slovenia (100%)
Tel.: (386) 27879331
Web Site: http://www.sava.se
Sales Range: $50-74.9 Million
Emp.: 100
Holding Company
N.A.I.C.S.: 551112
Aleksander Mlakar (Gen Mgr)

Sava IP, d.o.o. (1)
Davcna ulica 1, PO Box 146, 1000, Ljubljana, Slovenia (100%)
Tel.: (386) 14304150
Sales Range: $50-74.9 Million
Emp.: 22
Investment Advice
N.A.I.C.S.: 523940
Mitha Selamanya (Gen Mgr)

Sava Medical In Storitve d.o.o. (1)
Skofjeloska cesta 6, 4000, Kranj, Slovenia (100%)
Tel.: (386) 42065319
Web Site: http://www.savatech.si
Sales Range: $25-49.9 Million
Emp.: 95
Management Consulting Services
N.A.I.C.S.: 541618

Sava Trade Inc (1)
1300 N Nova Rd, Daytona Beach, FL 32117 (95%)
Tel.: (386) 760-0706
Web Site: http://www.savatrade.com
Emp.: 10
Holding Company
N.A.I.C.S.: 551112
Dave Lander (VP)

Sava Trade Sp Z.o.o. (1)
Chrzanow Maly 44, Grodzisk Mazowiecki, 05-825, Warsaw, Poland (100%)
Tel.: (48) 227558011
Web Site: http://www.savatrade.com.pl
Rubber Products Mfr
N.A.I.C.S.: 326299

Sava Trade Vertriebsges. mbH (1)
Kobellstr 4, Munich, 80336, Germany (100%)
Tel.: (49) 895441430
Web Site: http://www.sava-trade.de
Sales Range: $25-49.9 Million
Emp.: 10
Rubber Products Mfr
N.A.I.C.S.: 326299
Marko Rozman (Mng Dir)

Sava Trade spol.s.r.o (1)
Uelekpry No 650-50 Park 9, 1900, Prague, Czech Republic (100%)
Tel.: (420) 224941966
Web Site: http://www.savatrade.cz
Sales Range: $25-49.9 Million
Emp.: 12
Holding Company

SAVA D.D.

Sava d.d.—(Continued)
N.A.I.C.S.: 551112
Milan Vik (Mng Dir)

Sava-Rol d.o.o. (1)
Fallerovo Setaliste 22, 10000, Zagreb,
Croatia (76%)
Tel.: (385) 13667489
Sales Range: $25-49.9 Million
Emp.: 10
Ball & Roller Bearing Mfr
N.A.I.C.S.: 332991

Savatech Trade Ltd. (1)
Bourne House 475 Godstone Road, Whyteleafe, CR3 0BL, Surrey, United
Kingdom (100%)
Tel.: (44) 1883621106
Web Site: http://www.savatech.co.uk
Management Consulting Services
N.A.I.C.S.: 541618
Ales Ribic (Gen Mgr)

Terme 3000 Moravske Toplice d.d. (1)
Kranjceva ulica 12, Moravske Toplice, 9226,
Murska Sobota, Slovenia (96.65%)
Tel.: (386) 25122200
Web Site: http://www.sava-hotels-resorts.com
Sales Range: $150-199.9 Million
Emp.: 300
Hotel & Resort Services
N.A.I.C.S.: 721120
Ivanka Ajlec (Gen Mgr)

Terme Lendava d.d.o. (1)
Tomsiceva 2a, 9220, Lendava,
Slovenia (93.8%)
Tel.: (386) 25774100
Web Site: http://www.sava-hotels-resorts.com
Sales Range: $25-49.9 Million
Emp.: 110
Hotel & Resort
N.A.I.C.S.: 721110

Terme Ptuj d.o.o. (1)
Pot v toplice 9, 2251, Ptuj,
Slovenia (72%)
Tel.: (386) 27494580
Web Site: http://www.sava-hotels-resorts.com
Sales Range: $10-24.9 Million
Emp.: 25
Hotels & Motels
N.A.I.C.S.: 721110
Barbara Stopinsek (Mgr-PR)

Terme Radenci d.o.o. (1)
Zdravilisko naselje 12, Radenci, Radenci,
9252, Slovenia (100%)
Tel.: (386) 25201000
Web Site: http://www.terme-radenci.si
Sales Range: $25-49.9 Million
Emp.: 200
Hotels & Motels
N.A.I.C.S.: 721110

SAVA KOVACEVIC A.D.

Vinogradska kosa bb, 21460, Vrbas,
Serbia
Tel.: (381) 21 795 4200
Web Site: http://www.savakovacevic.rs
Year Founded: 1946
Sales Range: $10-24.9 Million
Emp.: 268
Milk Production Services
N.A.I.C.S.: 112120
Doka Vujicic (Dir)

SAVAL

287 Avenue De Romans, 26000, Valence, Drome, France
Tel.: (33) 475781480
Web Site: http://www.group36grem.com
Rev.: $25,200,000
Emp.: 48
New & Used Car Dealers
N.A.I.C.S.: 441110
Frederic Zamith (Gen Mgr)

SAVANI FINANCIALS LIMITED

91 Marol Co-op Industrial Estate M V
Road, Andheri East, Mumbai, 400
059, Maharashtra, India
Tel.: (91) 2267604100
Web Site: https://savanifinancials.co.in
511577—(BOM)
Rev.: $17,427
Assets: $297,359
Liabilities: $2,420
Net Worth: $294,938
Earnings: $6,216
Fiscal Year-end: 03/31/21
Non Banking Financial Services
N.A.I.C.S.: 523999
Praful Sheth (CFO, Compliance Officer & Sec)

SAVANNA CAPITAL CORP.

198 Davenport Rd, Toronto, M5R
1J2, ON, Canada
Tel.: (604) 862-5190
Year Founded: 2017
SAC.P—(TSXV)
Assets: $486
Liabilities: $54,091
Net Worth: ($53,605)
Earnings: ($31,467)
Fiscal Year-end: 12/31/23
Business Consulting Services
N.A.I.C.S.: 541611
Alexandros Tzilios (Pres, CEO & Sec)

SAVANNAH ENERGY PLC

40 Bank Street, London, E14 5NR,
United Kingdom
Tel.: (44) 2038179844
Web Site: https://www.savannah-energy.com
Year Founded: 2014
Rev.: $17,758,000
Assets: $1,145,013,000
Liabilities: $913,608,000
Net Worth: $231,405,000
Earnings: ($96,847,000)
Emp.: 169
Fiscal Year-end: 12/31/19
Crude Petroleum Extraction Services
N.A.I.C.S.: 211120
Stephen Jenkins (Chm)

SAVANNAH GOLDFIELDS LIMITED

Office address Level 21 110 Mary
Street, Brisbane, 4000, QLD, Australia
Tel.: (61) 731083500 AU
Web Site: https://savannahgoldfields.com
Year Founded: 2000
SVG—(ASX)
Rev.: $15,753,330
Assets: $33,530,110
Liabilities: $20,462,411
Net Worth: $13,067,699
Earnings: ($9,821,732)
Emp.: 5
Fiscal Year-end: 06/30/23
Gold & Coking Coal Mining Services
N.A.I.C.S.: 212220
Paul Marshall (CFO & Sec)

SAVANNAH RESOURCES PLC

Salisbury House London Wall, London, EC2M 5PS, United Kingdom
Tel.: (44) 2071172489 UK
Web Site: https://www.savannahresources.com
SAV—(STU)
Rev.: $43,796
Assets: $33,285,654
Liabilities: $1,405,395
Net Worth: $31,880,259
Earnings: ($3,609,432)
Emp.: 17

Fiscal Year-end: 12/31/22
Support Activities for Metal Mining
N.A.I.C.S.: 213114
Christopher Michael McGarty (CFO)

SAVANT INFOCOMM LIMITED

16 Corporation Shopping Complex
Third Avenue Indira Nagar, Adyar,
Chennai, 600 020, India
Tel.: (91) 25300993
Web Site: https://www.savant-infocomm.com
517320—(BOM)
Assets: $2,188
Liabilities: $120,333
Net Worth: ($118,145)
Earnings: ($26,760)
Fiscal Year-end: 03/31/21
Integrated Training Providing Services
N.A.I.C.S.: 611430
Harsh P. Parikh (Chm & CFO)

SAVAR REFRACTORIES PLC

108 Airport Road Tejgaon 1st Floor,
Dhaka, 1215, Bangladesh
Tel.: (880) 28121264
Web Site: https://www.savarref.com
Year Founded: 1983
SAVAREFR—(DHA)
Rev.: $357,756
Assets: $1,982,964
Liabilities: $813,991
Net Worth: $1,168,973
Earnings: ($62,677)
Fiscal Year-end: 06/30/23
Refractory Products Mfr
N.A.I.C.S.: 327120
Lutful Tahmina Khan (Chm)

SAVARIA CORPORATION

4350 Autoroute Chomedey, Laval,
H7R 6E9, QC, Canada
Tel.: (450) 437-9414 AB
Web Site: https://www.savaria.com
Year Founded: 1979
SIS—(TSX)
Rev.: $277,315,131
Assets: $354,613,782
Liabilities: $135,788,945
Net Worth: $218,824,838
Earnings: $20,701,476
Fiscal Year-end: 12/31/20
Stairlift, Inclined & Vertical Wheelchair Platform Lift & Residential Elevator Mfr
N.A.I.C.S.: 333921
Jean-Marie Bourassa (CFO)

Subsidiaries:

Garaventa (Canada) Ltd. (1)
18920 36th Avenue, Surrey, V3S 0L5, BC,
Canada
Tel.: (604) 594-0422
Residential Elevator Mfr
N.A.I.C.S.: 333922

Garaventa USA, Inc. (1)
735 E Industrial Park Dr C, Manchester, NH
03109
Tel.: (603) 669-6553
Residential Elevator Mfr
N.A.I.C.S.: 333922

HES Elevator Services Inc. (1)
801 E 64th Ave, Denver, CO 80229
Tel.: (303) 322-3271
Web Site: http://www.heselevatorservices.com
Elevator, Dumbwaiters & Lifts Installation & Services
N.A.I.C.S.: 333921

Handicare Group AB (1)
Torshamnsgatan 39, 164 40, Kista, Sweden
Tel.: (46) 852328100
Web Site: http://www.handicare.com
Emp.: 950
Supplier of Medical Supplies & Equipment
for Elderly & Physically Disabled
N.A.I.C.S.: 423450

INTERNATIONAL PUBLIC

Asbjorn Eskild (CEO)

Subsidiary (Non-US):

Handicare AS (2)
Valerveien 159, 1599, Moss, Norway
Tel.: (47) 69244400
Web Site: http://auto.handicare.no
Sales Range: $300-349.9 Million
Emp.: 1,000
Healthcare Equipment Distr
N.A.I.C.S.: 532283
Peter J. Byloos (CEO)

Prism Medical Ltd. (2)
485 Millway Avenue Unit 2, Concord, L4K
3V4, ON, Canada
Tel.: (416) 260-2145
Web Site: http://www.prismmedical.ca
Sales Range: $25-49.9 Million
Medical Equipment Mfr
N.A.I.C.S.: 339112
Eva Salinas Redondo (VP-Ops & Admin)

Subsidiary (US):

Prism Medical Inc. (3)
10888 Metro Ct, Maryland Heights, MO
63043
Tel.: (314) 692-9135
Web Site: http://www.prismmedicalinc.com
Patient Handling Equipments Distr
N.A.I.C.S.: 339112
Steven Clark (COO)

Premier Lifts Holdings, Inc. (1)
10927 McCormick Rd, Hunt Valley, MD
21031
Tel.: (410) 561-7006
Web Site: http://www.premierlifts.com
Elevator & Lift Products Whslr & Installation Services
N.A.I.C.S.: 423830
Matt Aird (Branch Mgr)

Savaria Concord Lifts Inc. (1)
2 Walker Drive, Brampton, L6T 5E1, ON,
Canada
Tel.: (905) 791-5555
Web Site: http://www.savaria.com
Elevators & Moving Stairways Mfr
N.A.I.C.S.: 333921
Marcel Bourassa (Pres & CEO)

Span-America Medical Systems, Inc. (1)
70 Commerce Ctr, Greenville, SC 29615
Tel.: (864) 288-8877
Web Site: http://www.spanamerica.com
Sales Range: $50-74.9 Million
Medical Mattress Products, Foam Pads & Pillows; Packaging Services for Consumer & Medical Products Mfr
N.A.I.C.S.: 326150
James D. Ferguson (Pres & CEO)

SAVATRANSPORT A.D.

Karadjordjeva 53, 11000, Belgrade,
Serbia
Tel.: (381) 11 246 0823
Year Founded: 1962
Sales Range: Less than $1 Million
Emp.: 51
Cargo Handling Services
N.A.I.C.S.: 488320

SAVDEN GROUP CORP.

1005 10th Floor Tower A New Mandarin Plaza, Tsimshatsui, Kowloon,
China (Hong Kong)
Tel.: (852) 93744584 NV
Year Founded: 2014
SVDN—(OTCBB)
Liabilities: $142,473
Net Worth: ($142,473)
Earnings: ($44,245)
Fiscal Year-end: 05/31/19
Software Devolepment
N.A.I.C.S.: 541519
Yingzhi Dong (Pres, CEO, CFO, Treas & Sec)

SAVE THE CHILDREN JAPAN

Yamada Building 4th Floor 2-8-4

AND PRIVATE COMPANIES

Uchikanda, Chiyoda-ku, Tokyo, 101-0047, Japan
Tel.: (81) 368590070
Web Site:
 https://www.savechildren.or.jp
Year Founded: 1986
Social Organization Services
N.A.I.C.S.: 813920

SAVEENE GROUP CORP.
30 Eglinton Avenue West Ste 808, Mississauga, M5H 2W9, ON, Canada
Tel.: (416) 874-9500 DE
Web Site: http://www.saveene.com
Year Founded: 2008
Holding Company; Real Estate Services
N.A.I.C.S.: 551112
Keith Roberts *(CEO, CFO & COO)*

SAVELEND GROUP AB
Kammakargatan 7, 111 40, Stockholm, Sweden
Tel.: (46) 812446067
Web Site:
 https://www.savelendgroup.se
Year Founded: 2014
YIELD—(OMX)
Rev.: $14,027
Assets: $29,691
Liabilities: $19,917
Net Worth: $9,774
Earnings: ($2,576)
Emp.: 76
Fiscal Year-end: 12/31/22
Investment Management Service
N.A.I.C.S.: 523999
Jacob Gevcen *(CIO)*

SAVEN TECHNOLOGIES LIMITED
No 302 My Home Sarovar Plaza 5-9-22 Secretariat Road, Hyderabad, 500 063, Telangana, India
Tel.: (91) 4023233358
Web Site: https://www.saven.in
532404—(BOM)
Rev.: $1,880,954
Assets: $2,241,532
Liabilities: $104,226
Net Worth: $2,137,306
Earnings: $447,275
Emp.: 61
Fiscal Year-end: 03/31/23
Information Technology Enabled Services
N.A.I.C.S.: 519290
Sampath Srinivasa Rangaswamy *(Chm)*

Subsidiaries:

Medha Services Inc. (1)
771 W Meryls Ct, Palatine, IL 60074
Tel.: (847) 380-3069
Software Development Services
N.A.I.C.S.: 541511

SAVENCIA FROMAGE & DAIRY
42 Rue Rieussec, 78220, Viroflay, France
Tel.: (33) 134586300 FR
Web Site: https://www.savencia-fromagedairy.com
Year Founded: 1956
SAVE—(EUR)
Rev.: $7,070,166,199
Assets: $4,945,228,793
Liabilities: $2,973,264,623
Net Worth: $1,971,964,170
Earnings: $73,436,218
Emp.: 21,797
Fiscal Year-end: 12/31/22
Cheese & Related Dairy Products Mfr & Distr
N.A.I.C.S.: 311513
Alex Bongrain *(Chm)*

Subsidiaries:

BC-USA, Inc. (1)
400 S Custer Ave, New Holland, PA 17557-9220 (55.01%)
Tel.: (717) 355-8500
Web Site: http://www.alouettecheese.com
Rev.: $120,000,000
Emp.: 500
Cheese Products Mfr
N.A.I.C.S.: 311513

Subsidiary (Domestic):

Advanced Food Products LLC (2)
402 S Custer Ave, New Holland, PA 17557
Tel.: (717) 355-8667
Web Site: https://www.afpllc.com
Sales Range: $25-49.9 Million
Emp.: 200
Aseptically Canned Puddings, Cheese Sauces & Nutritional Beverages Mfr
N.A.I.C.S.: 311999

Subsidiary (Domestic):

Advanced Food Products LLC (3)
600 1st Ave W, Clear Lake, WI 54005-8510
Tel.: (715) 263-2956
Web Site: http://www.afpllc.com
Sales Range: $25-49.9 Million
Emp.: 85
Natural, Processed & Imitation Cheese
N.A.I.C.S.: 311422
Penny O'Connell *(Mgr-Customer Svc)*

Bongrain Europe SAS (1)
42 Rue Rieussec, Viroflay, 78220, France
Tel.: (33) 134586300
Dairy Products Mfr & Sales
N.A.I.C.S.: 311514

Bongrain International (1)
42 Rue Rieussec, 78229, Viroflay, France (100%)
Tel.: (33) 134586300
Web Site: http://www.bongrain.com
Sales Range: $50-74.9 Million
Emp.: 250
Whslr of Dairy Products
N.A.I.C.S.: 445298

Bongrain-Gerard SAS (1)
4 Rue Eugene Gerard, BP 1, 88530, Le Tholy, France (99.96%)
Tel.: (33) 329238200
Web Site: http://www.capricedesdieux.com
Sales Range: $150-199.9 Million
Emp.: 300
Dairy Products & Gourmet Foods Producer & Distr
N.A.I.C.S.: 311513
Christopher Trouvost *(Mgr-Mktg-Export)*

Compagnie Laitiere Europeenne S.A (1)
Conde Sur Vire, Paris, 50890, France
Tel.: (33) 2 33 06 65 00
Dairy Products Mfr
N.A.I.C.S.: 311514

Fruisec S.A.S. (1)
La Morelie, 24120, Terrasson, France (100%)
Tel.: (33) 553514400
Web Site: http://www.fruisec.com
Sales Range: $25-49.9 Million
Trading & Processing of Nuts
N.A.I.C.S.: 311911
Allan Chaumont *(Mng Dir)*

Mantequerias Arias S. A. (1)
Pza Carlos Trias Bertran 4 Floor 2, 28020, Madrid, Spain (100%)
Tel.: (34) 914174740
Web Site: http://arias.es
Sales Range: $150-199.9 Million
Milk, Butter & Cheese Producer
N.A.I.C.S.: 311512

Mleczarnia Turek Sp. z o.o. (1)
Ul Postepu21 D, 02-676, Warsaw, Poland
Tel.: (48) 224300390
Dairy Products Mfr
N.A.I.C.S.: 311511

Pareco S.N.C. (1)
Immeuble I Alliance, 42 Rue Rieussec, Viroflay, 78222, France (100%)
Tel.: (33) 134586541

Sales Range: $25-49.9 Million
Emp.: 37
Mfr & Distribution of Dairy Products
N.A.I.C.S.: 445298

Savencia Fromage & Dairy Czech Republic, A.S. (1)
BB C building BETA Vyskocilova 1481/4, 140 00, Prague, Czech Republic
Tel.: (420) 237838888
Dairy Products Mfr
N.A.I.C.S.: 311511

Savencia Fromage & Dairy Deutschland GmbH (1)
Dwight-D Eisenhower-Strasse 6, 65197, Wiesbaden, Germany
Tel.: (49) 61 188 0701
Web Site: https://www.savencia-fd.de
Grocery Products Retailer
N.A.I.C.S.: 445110

SAVERA INDUSTRIES LIMITED
146 Dr Radhakrishnan Road, Mylapore, Chennai, 600004, India
Tel.: (91) 4428114700
Web Site:
 https://www.saverahotel.com
512634—(BOM)
Rev.: $2,834,682
Assets: $9,369,756
Liabilities: $1,450,790
Net Worth: $7,918,966
Earnings: ($559,377)
Emp.: 576
Fiscal Year-end: 03/31/21
Home Management Services
N.A.I.C.S.: 721110
A. Ravikumar Reddy *(Mng Dir)*

Subsidiaries:

Savera Hotel (1)
146 Radhakrishnan Road, Mylapore, Chennai, 600004, India
Tel.: (91) 44 2811 4700
Web Site: http://www.saverahotel.com
Sales Range: $100-124.9 Million
Home Management Services
N.A.I.C.S.: 721110
A. Ravikumar Reddy *(Mng Dir)*

SAVERDIS
Lieu Dit Le Petit Joffrery Z I 14 Boulevard De Joffrery, Muret, 31600, Toulouse, France
Tel.: (33) 388031414
Sales Range: $25-49.9 Million
Emp.: 97
Grocery Stores
N.A.I.C.S.: 445110
Michel Moreno *(Pres)*

SAVERONE 2014 LTD.
Em Hamoshavot 94, Petah Tikva, Israel
Tel.: (972) 39094177
Web Site: https://www.saver.one
Year Founded: 2014
SVRE—(NASDAQ)
Rev.: $737,487
Assets: $7,317,933
Liabilities: $4,451,494
Net Worth: $2,866,439
Earnings: $9,173,852)
Emp.: 51
Fiscal Year-end: 12/31/23
Automotive Services
N.A.I.C.S.: 811111
Jacob Tenenboem *(Chm)*

SAVEX TECHNOLOGIES PVT. LTD.
124 Maker Chambers III 12th Floor Nariman Point, Mumbai, 400 021, Maharashtra, India
Tel.: (91) 2222 79 9999
Web Site: http://www.savex.in
Information & Communication Technology Services
N.A.I.C.S.: 518210

Jayant Goradia *(CEO)*

Subsidiaries:

Inflow Technologies Pvt Limited (1)
Inflow House 33 & 34 Indiranagar 1st stage Off 100 feet road, Bengaluru, 560 038, India
Tel.: (91) 8041265151
Web Site:
 http://www.inflowtechnologies.com
Information Technology Consulting Services
N.A.I.C.S.: 541512
Byju Pillai *(Mng Dir)*

Subsidiary (Non-US):

Inflow Technologies Singapore Pte Limited (2)
1003 Bukit Merah Central 06-46 Technopreneur Centre, Singapore, 159836, Singapore
Tel.: (65) 96534067
Web Site:
 http://www.inflowtechnologies.com
Information Technology Consulting Services
N.A.I.C.S.: 541512

SAVEZONE I&C CORPORATION
57 Hangeulbiseok-ro, Nowon-gu, Seoul, Korea (South)
Tel.: (82) 323209032
Web Site: http://www.savezone.co.kr
Year Founded: 2002
067830—(KRS)
Rev.: $91,541,661
Assets: $439,927,844
Liabilities: $83,954,961
Net Worth: $355,972,882
Earnings: $7,040,607
Emp.: 361
Fiscal Year-end: 12/31/22
Discount Department Store Operator
N.A.I.C.S.: 455110
Seok-Bong Yong *(Chm & CEO)*

SAVIA, S.A. DE C.V.
Rio Sena 500 Pte Col Del Valle, Garza Garcia, 66220, Nuevo Leon, Mexico
Tel.: (52) 8181735500
Year Founded: 1971
Emp.: 3,877
Food Products Distr
N.A.I.C.S.: 424480
Alfonso Romo Garza *(Chm)*

SAVILLE RESOURCES INC.
Suite 1450-789 West Pender Street, Vancouver, V6C 1H2, BC, Canada
Tel.: (604) 681-1568 Ca
Web Site: https://www.savilleres.com
Year Founded: 1989
S0J0—(DEU)
Rev.: $43,345
Assets: $2,350,871
Liabilities: $497,398
Net Worth: $1,853,473
Earnings: ($1,853,473)
Fiscal Year-end: 04/30/23
Mineral Exploration Services
N.A.I.C.S.: 212290
Mike Hodge *(Pres & CEO)*

SAVILLS PLC
33 Margaret Street, London, W1G 0JD, United Kingdom
Tel.: (44) 2074998644 UK
Web Site: https://www.savills.co.uk
Year Founded: 1855
SVLPF—(OTCIQ)
Rev.: $2,825,044,181
Assets: $2,728,098,965
Liabilities: $1,777,833,880
Net Worth: $950,265,085
Earnings: $49,861,146
Emp.: 42,080
Fiscal Year-end: 12/31/23
Offices of Other Holding Companies
N.A.I.C.S.: 551112

SAVILLS PLC

Savills plc—(Continued)

Simon Shaw *(CFO-Grp & Member-Exec Bd)*

Subsidiaries:

Cordea Savills GmbH (1)
Oberanger 24 4 Stock, Munich, 80231, Germany
Tel.: (49) 89203020200
Web Site: http://www.cordeasavills.com
Sales Range: $25-49.9 Million
Emp.: 20
Management Consulting Services
N.A.I.C.S.: 541618

Cordea Savills Investment Management Ltd. (1)
33 Margaret Street, London, W1G 0JD, United Kingdom
Tel.: (44) 2074998644
Web Site: http://www.cordeasavills.com
Sales Range: $50-74.9 Million
Emp.: 45
Securities Brokerage
N.A.I.C.S.: 523150

Guardian Property Management Limited (1)
7/F Cityplaza One 1111 King S Road, Taikoo Shing, Hong Kong, China (Hong Kong)
Tel.: (852) 25086777
Web Site: https://en.savillsguardian.com.hk
Property Management Services
N.A.I.C.S.: 531311

Macro Consultants LLC (1)
1040 Avenue of the Americas, New York, NY 10018-4796
Tel.: (212) 575-2200
Web Site: http://www.macropm.com
Administrative Management & General Management Consulting Services
N.A.I.C.S.: 541611
Michael Fromm *(Pres)*

Prime Purchase Limited (1)
Suite 5 121 Sloane Street, London, SW1X 9BW, United Kingdom
Tel.: (44) 2078812388
Web Site: https://www.prime-purchase.com
Sales Range: $50-74.9 Million
Property Buying Advisory Services
N.A.I.C.S.: 531390

Savills (Dormant 1) Ltd. (1)
20 Grosvenor Hill, Berkeley Sq, London, W1K3HQ, United Kingdom
Tel.: (44) 2074998644
Web Site: http://www.savills.co.uk
Real Estate Agents & Brokers
N.A.I.C.S.: 531210

Savills (L&P) Ltd. (1)
20 Grosvenor Hill, London, W1K 3HQ, United Kingdom
Tel.: (44) 2074998644
Web Site: http://www.savills.co.uk
Sales Range: $75-99.9 Million
Emp.: 150
Real Estate Agents & Brokers
N.A.I.C.S.: 531210

Savills (Overseas Holdings) Ltd. (1)
33 Margaret Street Berkeley Sq, London, W1G 0JD, United Kingdom
Tel.: (44) 2074998644
Web Site: http://www.savills.co.uk
Sales Range: $50-74.9 Million
Emp.: 800
Land Subdivision
N.A.I.C.S.: 237210

Savills (Singapore) Pte Limited (1)
30 Cecil Street 20-03 Prudential Tower, Singapore, 049712, Singapore
Tel.: (65) 68366888
Web Site: https://www.savills.com.sg
Real Estate Management Services
N.A.I.C.S.: 531390
Christopher J. Marriott *(CEO-South East Asia)*

Subsidiary (Domestic):

Woodleigh Gardens Pte Ltd (2)
14 Woodleigh Close, Singapore, 357909, Singapore
Tel.: (65) 65478768

Apartment & Condominiums Leasing Services
N.A.I.C.S.: 531110

Savills (Vietnam) Limited (1)
18th Floor Ruby Tower 81-85 Ham Nghi Street, District 1, Ho Chi Minh City, Vietnam
Tel.: (84) 2838239205
Web Site: http://www.savills.com.vn
Real Estate Management Services
N.A.I.C.S.: 531390

Savills Agency B.V. (1)
Vinoly Building Claude Debussylaan 48, PO Box 75849, 1082 MD, Amsterdam, Netherlands
Tel.: (31) 206722211
Web Site: http://www.savills.nl
Sales Range: $50-74.9 Million
Emp.: 60
Real Estate Agents & Brokers
N.A.I.C.S.: 531210
Clive Pritchard *(Mng Dir)*

Savills Aguirre Newman Barcelona SAU (1)
Av Diagonal 615-7, Barcelona, Spain
Tel.: (34) 934395454
Residential Property Services
N.A.I.C.S.: 531311

Savills Asia Pacific Limited. (1)
23rd Fl Exchange Sq Twr 2, Central, Hong Kong, China (Hong Kong) (100%)
Tel.: (852) 28424400
Web Site: http://www.savills.com
Holding Company
N.A.I.C.S.: 551112
Henkey Lai *(Asst Mgr-Investment)*

Subsidiary (Non-US):

Savills (Aust) Pty. Limited (2)
Level 25 1 Farrer Place, Sydney, 2000, NSW, Australia (100%)
Tel.: (61) 282158888
Web Site: https://www.savills.com.au
Sales Range: $75-99.9 Million
Real Estate Agents & Brokers
N.A.I.C.S.: 531210

Branch (Domestic):

Savills (ACT) Pty. Limited (3)
Ground Floor 10 National Circuit, Barton, 2600, Australia (100%)
Tel.: (61) 282158837
Emp.: 5
Real Estate Agents & Brokers
N.A.I.C.S.: 531210
Philip Harding *(Mng Dir)*

Savills (NSW) Pty. Limited (3)
L 7 50 Bridge St, Sydney, 2000, NSW, Australia (100%)
Tel.: (61) 282158888
Web Site: http://www.savills.com.au
Sales Range: $75-99.9 Million
Emp.: 118
Real Estate Agents & Brokers
N.A.I.C.S.: 531210

Savills (QLD) Pty. Limited (3)
Level 2 66 Eagle St, Brisbane, 4000, QLD, Australia (100%)
Tel.: (61) 732218355
Sales Range: $50-74.9 Million
Emp.: 100
Real Estate Agents & Brokers
N.A.I.C.S.: 531210
Anthony Ott *(Mng Dir)*

Savills (SA) Pty. Limited (3)
Level 2 50 Hindmarsh Square, Adelaide, 5000, SA, Australia (100%)
Tel.: (61) 882375000
Sales Range: $25-49.9 Million
Emp.: 50
Real Estate Agents & Brokers
N.A.I.C.S.: 531210
Rino Carpinelli *(Mng Dir)*

Savills (VIC) Pty. Limited (3)
Level 29 South Tower 80 Collins Street, Melbourne, 3000, VIC, Australia (100%)
Tel.: (61) 386868000
Web Site: https://www.savills.com.au
Sales Range: $50-74.9 Million
Real Estate Agents & Brokers
N.A.I.C.S.: 531210
Kosta Filinis *(Dir-South-East)*

Savills (WA) Pty. Limited (3)
Level 27 108 St Georges Terrace, Perth, 6000, WA, Australia
Tel.: (61) 894884111
Web Site: https://www.savills.com.au
Sales Range: $25-49.9 Million
Real Estate Agents & Brokers
N.A.I.C.S.: 531210

Subsidiary (Domestic):

Savills (Hong Kong) Limited (2)
23/F Two Exchange Square 8 Connaught Place, Central, China (Hong Kong) (100%)
Tel.: (852) 28424400
Web Site: https://www.savills.com.hk
Sales Range: $75-99.9 Million
Property Sales & Management
N.A.I.C.S.: 531210

Subsidiary (Non-US):

Savills (Macao) Limited. (2)
Suite 1309-1310 13/F Macau Landmark 555 Avenida da Amizade, Macau, China (Macau)
Tel.: (853) 28780623
Web Site: https://www.savills.com.mo
Sales Range: $25-49.9 Million
Real Estate Agents & Brokers
N.A.I.C.S.: 531210
Franco Liu *(Mng Dir)*

Savills (Taiwan) Limited (2)
21F Cathay Landmark No 68 Sec 5 Zhongxiao E Rd, Xinyi District, Taipei, 110, Taiwan
Tel.: (886) 287895828
Web Site: https://en.savills.com.tw
Sales Range: $25-49.9 Million
Real Estate Agents & Brokers
N.A.I.C.S.: 531210

Savills (Thailand) Limited. (2)
26/F Abdulrahim Place 990 Rama IV Road Silom, Bangrak, 10500, Thailand
Tel.: (66) 26360300
Web Site: http://www.savills.co.th
Sales Range: $25-49.9 Million
Real Estate Agents & Brokers
N.A.I.C.S.: 327910

Subsidiary (Domestic):

Savills Engineering Limited. (2)
8/F Cityplaza One 1111 King's Road, Taikoo Shing, China (Hong Kong)
Tel.: (852) 25341688
Web Site: http://www.savills.com.hk
Real Estate Agents & Brokers
N.A.I.C.S.: 531210
Angel Kam *(Deputy Mng Dir-Property Mgmt)*

Savills Guardian (Holdings) Limited. (2)
1111 Kings Road 7th Floor Cityplaza 1, Taikoo Shing, China (Hong Kong)
Tel.: (852) 25121838
Web Site: http://www.savillsguardian.com.hk
Sales Range: $150-199.9 Million
Emp.: 300
Real Estate Agents & Brokers
N.A.I.C.S.: 531210
Peter Ho *(Mng Dir)*

Subsidiary (Non-US):

Savills Japan Limited KK (2)
Yurakucho ITOCiA 15F 2-7-1 Yurakucho, Chiyoda-ku, Tokyo, 100-0006, Japan
Tel.: (81) 367775100
Web Site: http://www.savills.co.jp
Management Consulting Services
N.A.I.C.S.: 541618

Subsidiary (Domestic):

Savills Management Services Limited. (2)
23/F Two Exchange Square 8 Connaught Place, Central District, Hong Kong, China (Hong Kong) (100%)
Tel.: (852) 28424400
Web Site: http://www.savills.com.hk
Management Consulting Services
N.A.I.C.S.: 541618
Raymond Lee *(CEO-Greater China)*

Savills Project Consultancy Limited. (2)

INTERNATIONAL PUBLIC

1111 Kings Road Ph 1, Rm 805-813 8th Floor Cityplaza, Taikoo Shing, China (Hong Kong)
Tel.: (852) 25341688
Web Site: https://www.savills.com.hk
Emp.: 26
Real Estate Agents & Brokers
N.A.I.C.S.: 531210

Savills Property Management Holdings Limited. (2)
1111 Kings Road Ph 1, Rm 805-813 8th Floor Cityplaza, Taikoo Shing, China (Hong Kong)
Tel.: (852) 25341688
Web Site: https://www.savills.com.hk
Real Estate Agents & Brokers
N.A.I.C.S.: 531210

Subsidiary (Non-US):

Savills Property Services (Chengdu) Company Ltd. (2)
Zongfu Rd 2, Rm 1806 Blk A Times Plz, 610016, Chengdu, China
Tel.: (86) 2886721063
Web Site: http://www.savills-china.com
Sales Range: $50-74.9 Million
Emp.: 60
Real Estate Property Lessors
N.A.I.C.S.: 531190

Subsidiary (Domestic):

Savills Realty Limited. (2)
23rd Floor Exchange Sq Twr 2, Central District, Hong Kong, China (Hong Kong) (100%)
Tel.: (852) 28424400
Real Estate Agents & Brokers
N.A.I.C.S.: 531210
Raymond Lee *(CEO)*

Subsidiary (Non-US):

Savills Residential (S) Pte. Ltd. (2)
101 Thomson Road United Square 13-03, Singapore, 307591, Singapore (100%)
Tel.: (65) 67357555
Web Site: http://www.savills.com.sg
Sales Range: $50-74.9 Million
Real Estate Agents & Brokers
N.A.I.C.S.: 531210
Marcus Loo *(CEO)*

Subsidiary (Domestic):

Savills Showcase Limited. (2)
7th Floor Tung Sun Commercial Ctr, Wanchai, China (Hong Kong)
Tel.: (852) 25986028
Graphic Design Services
N.A.I.C.S.: 327910

Savills Valuation and Professional Services Ltd. (2)
23rd Floor Two Exchange Square, Central District, Hong Kong, China (Hong Kong)
Tel.: (852) 28016100
Web Site: http://www.savills.com.hk
Sales Range: $50-74.9 Million
Emp.: 70
Real Estate Agents & Brokers
N.A.I.C.S.: 531210
Charles Chan *(Mng Dir)*

Subsidiary (Non-US):

Shenzhen Savills Property Consultancy Limited. (2)
Unit 01-03 9/F China Resources Tower 2666 Keyuan South Road, Nanshan District, Shenzhen, 518000, China
Tel.: (86) 75584367000
Web Site: http://www.savills-china.com
Business Services
N.A.I.C.S.: 561499

Savills Asset Advisory Company Ltd. (1)
Yurakucho ITOCiA 15F 2-7-1 Yurakucho, Chiyoda-ku, Tokyo, 100-0006, Japan
Tel.: (81) 367775252
Portfolio & Asset Management Services
N.A.I.C.S.: 523940

Savills B.V. (1)
Vinoly Building Claude Debussylaan 48, PO Box 75849, 1082 MD, Amsterdam, Netherlands

AND PRIVATE COMPANIES — SAVILLS PLC

Tel.: (31) 206722211
Sales Range: $25-49.9 Million
Emp.: 70
Real Estate Agents & Brokers
N.A.I.C.S.: 531210
Clive Pritchard *(Mng Dir)*

Savills Belux Group SA (1)
Avenue Louise 81, Bruxelles, 1050, Brussels, Belgium
Tel.: (32) 25424050
Web Site: https://www.savills.be
Property Management Services
N.A.I.C.S.: 531311
John Defauw *(Mng Dir & Head-Country)*

Savills Catering Ltd. (1)
10 Towerfield Road, Shoeburyness, Southend-on-Sea, SS3 9QE, Essex, United Kingdom
Tel.: (44) 1702293892
Web Site: http://www.savillscatering.com
Restaurant
N.A.I.C.S.: 722511

Savills Commercial (Leeds) Ltd. (1)
3 Wellington Place, Leeds, LS1 4AP, United Kingdom (100%)
Tel.: (44) 1132440100
Web Site: http://www.savills.co.uk
Sales Range: $25-49.9 Million
Real Estate Agents & Brokers
N.A.I.C.S.: 531210

Savills Commercial Ltd. (1)
20 Grosvenor Hill, Berkeley Sq, London, W1K3HQ, United Kingdom
Tel.: (44) 2074998644
Web Site: http://www.savills.co.uk
Sales Range: $300-349.9 Million
Emp.: 1,000
Real Estate Agents & Brokers
N.A.I.C.S.: 531210

Savills Consultancy B.V. (1)
Vinoly Building Claude Debussylaan 48, PO Box 75849, 1082 MD, Amsterdam, Netherlands
Tel.: (31) 203012000
Web Site: http://www.savills.nl
Sales Range: $25-49.9 Million
Emp.: 50
Real Estate Agents & Brokers
N.A.I.C.S.: 531210

Savills Consultores Inmobiliarios SA (1)
Paseo de la Castellana 81, 28046, Madrid, Spain
Tel.: (34) 913191314
Web Site: http://www.savills-aguirrenewman.es
Sales Range: $25-49.9 Million
Land Subdivision
N.A.I.C.S.: 327910

Savills Finance Holdings Plc (1)
33 Margaret Street, Berkeley Sq, London, W1G 0JD, United Kingdom
Tel.: (44) 2074998644
Web Site: http://www.savills.co.uk
Sales Range: $250-299.9 Million
Emp.: 800
Holding Company
N.A.I.C.S.: 551112
Jeremy Helsby *(CEO)*

Savills Finance Ltd. (1)
20 Grosvenor Hill, Berkeley Sq, London, W1K 3HQ, United Kingdom
Tel.: (44) 2074998644
Web Site: http://www.savills.com
Sales Range: $50-74.9 Million
Emp.: 100
Real Estate Property Lessors
N.A.I.C.S.: 531190

Savills Financial Services PLC (1)
20 Grosvenor Hill, Berkeley Sq, London, W1K 3HQ, United Kingdom
Tel.: (44) 2074998644
Web Site: http://www.savills.co.uk
Sales Range: $150-199.9 Million
Emp.: 350
Holding Company
N.A.I.C.S.: 551112

Savills Fund Management GmbH (1)
Rotfeder-Ring 7, 60327, Frankfurt am Main, Germany

Tel.: (49) 6915340186
Web Site: https://www.savillsim-publikumsfonds.de
Investment Management Service
N.A.I.C.S.: 523940

Savills Hellas Ltd. (1)
64 Louise Riencourt Street Apollo Tower 14th Floor, 11523, Athens, Greece
Tel.: (30) 2106996311
Web Site: http://www.savills.gr
Sales Range: $50-74.9 Million
Real Estate Agents & Brokers
N.A.I.C.S.: 531210

Savills Holdings B.V. (1)
Vinoly Building Claude Debussylaan 48, PO Box 75849, 1082 MD, Amsterdam, Netherlands
Tel.: (31) 206722211
Web Site: http://www.savills.nl
Sales Range: $50-74.9 Million
Emp.: 70
Real Estate Agents & Brokers
N.A.I.C.S.: 531210

Savills Hungary LLC (1)
7th Floor E W Business Ctr, Rakoczi ut 1-3, 1088, Budapest, Hungary
Tel.: (36) 12357720
Web Site: http://www.savills.hu
Sales Range: $50-74.9 Million
Emp.: 6
Real Estate Agents & Brokers
N.A.I.C.S.: 531210

Savills Immobilien-Beratungs GmbH (1)
Taunusanlage 18, 60325, Frankfurt am Main, Germany
Tel.: (49) 30726165130
Web Site: http://www.savills.de
Sales Range: $50-74.9 Million
Open-End Investment Funds
N.A.I.C.S.: 525910

Subsidiary (Domestic):

Savills Immobilien-Beratungs GmbH (2)
Zoofenster Hardenbergstrasse 27, 10623, Berlin, Germany
Tel.: (49) 30726165165
Web Site: http://www.savills.de
Management Investment, Retail Agency & Consulting Services
N.A.I.C.S.: 541618

Savills Investment Management (KVG) GmbH (1)
Rotfeder-Ring 7, 60327, Frankfurt, Germany
Tel.: (49) 69247429600
Investment Management Service
N.A.I.C.S.: 523940

Savills Investment Management (KVG) GmbH (1)
Rotfeder-Ring 7, Frankfurt, 60327, Germany
Tel.: (49) 69272991000
Real Estate Services
N.A.I.C.S.: 531390

Savills Investment Management (Luxembourg) S.a.r.l. (1)
10 rue C M Spoo, 2546, Luxembourg, Luxembourg
Tel.: (352) 26649955
Investment Management Service
N.A.I.C.S.: 523940

Savills Investment Management AB (1)
Regeringsgatan 48, 111 56, Stockholm, Sweden
Tel.: (46) 850597300
Investment Services
N.A.I.C.S.: 523999

Savills Investment Management Pte Ltd (1)
83 Amoy Street, Singapore, 069902, Singapore
Tel.: (65) 69086226
Investment Services
N.A.I.C.S.: 523999

Savills Investment Management S.L. (1)
Paseo de la Castellana no 81 7th Floor, Madrid, 28046, Spain

Tel.: (34) 915232367
Investment Services
N.A.I.C.S.: 523999

Savills Investment Management Sp Zoo (1)
Gdanski Business Center building B 3rd floor Inflancka 4 St, Warsaw, 00-189, Poland
Tel.: (48) 223759618
Investment Services
N.A.I.C.S.: 523999

Savills Investments B.V. (1)
Vinoly Building Claude Debussylaan 48, PO Box 75849, 1082MD, Amsterdam, Netherlands
Tel.: (31) 206722211
Web Site: http://www.savills.nl
Sales Range: $50-74.9 Million
Emp.: 70
Real Estate Agents & Brokers
N.A.I.C.S.: 531210
Clive Pritchard *(Mng Dir)*

Savills Italy Srl (1)
Via Manzoni 37, 20121, Milan, Italy
Tel.: (39) 026328141
Web Site: https://en.savills.it
Sales Range: $50-74.9 Million
Real Estate Agents & Brokers
N.A.I.C.S.: 531210

Savills Japan Company Ltd. (1)
Yurakucho ITOCiA 15F 2-7-1 Yurakucho, Chiyoda-ku, Tokyo, 100-0006, Japan
Tel.: (81) 367775100
Investment Advisory Services
N.A.I.C.S.: 523940
Christian Mancini *(CEO)*

Savills Korea Co. Limited (1)
13/F Seoul Finance Center 136 Sejongdaero, Jung-gu, Seoul, 04520, Korea (South)
Tel.: (82) 221244200
Web Site: https://www.savills.co.kr
Real Estate Manangement Services
N.A.I.C.S.: 531390

Savills LLC (1)
399 Park Ave 11th Fl, New York, NY 10022 (100%)
Tel.: (212) 326-1000
Web Site: http://www.savills.us.com
Sales Range: $50-74.9 Million
Investment Banking & Securities Dealing
N.A.I.C.S.: 523150
Mitchell S. Steir *(Chm/CEO-North America)*

Savills Management Resources Ltd. (1)
33 Margaret Street, Berkeley Sq, London, W1K 3HQ, United Kingdom
Tel.: (44) 2074998644
Web Site: http://www.savills.co.uk
Sales Range: $75-99.9 Million
Emp.: 350
Court Reporting & Stenotype Services
N.A.I.C.S.: 561492

Savills Nederland Holding BV (1)
Claude Debussylaan 48, Amsterdam, 1082 MD, North Holland, Netherlands
Tel.: (31) 206722111
Sales Range: $50-74.9 Million
Emp.: 60
Investment Management Service
N.A.I.C.S.: 523999
Dave Hendriks *(Mgr-Taxation)*

Savills Netherland B.V. (1)
Claude Debussylaan 48, PO Box 75849, Amsterdam, 1082, Netherlands
Tel.: (31) 206722211
Web Site: http://www.savills.nl
Sales Range: $50-74.9 Million
Emp.: 70
Real Estate Agents & Brokers
N.A.I.C.S.: 531210
Eri Mitsostergiou *(Dir-European Res)*

Savills Private Finance Ltd. (1)
20 Grosvenor Hill, Berkeley Sq, London, W1K 3HQ, United Kingdom
Tel.: (44) 2074998644
Web Site: http://www.savills.co.uk
Sales Range: $50-74.9 Million
Emp.: 100
Depository Credit Intermediation

N.A.I.C.S.: 522180

Savills Property Management Limited (1)
Rm 805-13 8/F Cityplaza One 1111 King'S Rd, Tai Koo Shing, Hong Kong, China (Hong Kong)
Tel.: (852) 25341688
Property Management Services
N.A.I.C.S.: 531311

Savills Property Services (Shanghai) Company Ltd. (1)
25/F Two ICC No 288 South Shaanxi Road, Shanghai, 200031, China
Tel.: (86) 2163916688
Web Site: http://www.savillsresidence.com.cn
Property Management Services
N.A.I.C.S.: 531311
Louisa Zhu *(Dir-Savills Residence)*

Savills Residential (Ireland) Limited (1)
33 Molesworth Street, Dublin, 2, Ireland
Tel.: (353) 16634300
Sales Range: $75-99.9 Million
Emp.: 15
Property Management Services
N.A.I.C.S.: 531311
Catherine McAuliffe *(Dir-Residential)*

Savills S.A.S. (1)
21 Boulevard Haussmann, 75009, Paris, France
Tel.: (33) 144517300
Web Site: http://www.savills.fr
Sales Range: $50-74.9 Million
Real Estate Agents & Brokers
N.A.I.C.S.: 531210

Savills SA (1)
21 Boulevard Haussmann, 75009, Paris, France
Tel.: (33) 144517300
Web Site: http://www.savills.fr
Sales Range: $50-74.9 Million
Real Estate Manangement Services
N.A.I.C.S.: 531390
Boris Cappelle *(Head-Transaction Dept-Investment)*

Savills Sp. z o.o (1)
Q22 al Jana Pawla II 22, 00-133, Warsaw, Poland
Tel.: (48) 222224000
Web Site: http://www.savills.pl
Sales Range: $25-49.9 Million
Real Estate Property Lessors
N.A.I.C.S.: 531190

Savills Spolka z Organiczona (1)
al Jana Pawla II 22, 00-133, Warsaw, Poland
Tel.: (48) 22 222 4000
Web Site: http://www.savills.pl
Sales Range: $25-49.9 Million
Real Estate Manangement Services
N.A.I.C.S.: 531390

Savills Sweden AB (1)
Regeringsgatan 48, 111 56, Stockholm, Sweden (100%)
Tel.: (46) 854585890
Web Site: https://www.savills.se
Sales Range: $50-74.9 Million
Real Estate Agents & Brokers
N.A.I.C.S.: 531210

Savills Valuation SAS (1)
21 Boulevard Haussmann, 75009, Paris, France
Tel.: (33) 144517300
Web Site: http://www.savills.fr
Property Rental & Lease Services
N.A.I.C.S.: 531110
David Poole *(CEO-MRICS)*

Savills-Studley, LLC (1)
399 Park Ave Fl 11th, New York, NY 10022
Tel.: (212) 326-1000
Web Site: http://www.savills-studley.com
Sales Range: $200-249.9 Million
Emp.: 100
Real Estate Brokers & Advisors
N.A.I.C.S.: 531210
Richard Schuham *(Vice Chm)*

Subsidiary (Domestic):

KLG, Inc. (2)

SAVILLS PLC

Savills plc—(Continued)
399 Park Ave 11th Fl, New York, NY 10022
Tel.: (212) 514-4600
Web Site: http://www.klgadvisors.com
Real Estate Consulting Service
N.A.I.C.S.: 541618
Doane Kelly (CEO)

Savills Studley Occupier Services, Inc. (2)
3000 Bayport Dr Ste 485, Tampa, FL 33607
Tel.: (813) 864-1688
Web Site: http://www.savills-studley.com
Real Estate Brokerage & Consulting
N.A.I.C.S.: 531210
Jerry Thornbury (Mng Dir)

Swan Hygiene Services Ltd. (1)
7/F Cityplaza One 1111 King's Road, Taikoo Shing, China (Hong Kong)
Tel.: (852) 25121618
Web Site: http://www.swanservices.com.hk
Housekeeping & Cleaning Services
N.A.I.C.S.: 561720

SAVIMEX CORPORATION
No 162 HT17 Hiep Thanh Ward, District 12, Ho Chi Minh City, Vietnam
Tel.: (84) 2873008007
Web Site: https://www.savimex.com
Year Founded: 1985
SAV—(HOSE)
Rev.: $32,501,485
Assets: $25,338,536
Liabilities: $11,588,159
Net Worth: $13,750,376
Earnings: ($419,581)
Fiscal Year-end: 12/31/23
Wood Furniture Whslr
N.A.I.C.S.: 423210
Bui Ngoc Qudi (Exec Dir)

SAVINO DEL BENE S.P.A.
Via del Botteghino 24/26, 50018, Scandicci, Florence, Italy
Tel.: (39) 055 52 191
Web Site: http://www.savinodelbene.com
Year Founded: 1898
Sales Range: $1-4.9 Billion
Emp.: 3,100
Freight Forwarding & Transportation Services
N.A.I.C.S.: 488510
Paolo Nocentini (Pres)

Subsidiaries:

Albatrans SpA (1)
Via del Botteghino 19, 50018, Scandicci, Italy
Tel.: (39) 055 7311071
Web Site: http://www.albatrans.com
Logistic Services
N.A.I.C.S.: 541614

Subsidiary (Non-US):

Albatrans France S.a.r.l (2)
Batiment 5 extension Zone de Bordeaux Fret, 33521, Bordeaux, France (90%)
Tel.: (33) 556439180
Web Site: http://www.albatrans.com
Freight Transportation Arrangement
N.A.I.C.S.: 488510
Maryline Faure (Gen Mgr)

Albatrans GmbH (2)
Wilh Theodor Roemfeld Strasse 20, 55130, Mainz, Germany (50%)
Tel.: (49) 61312750510
Web Site: http://www.albatrans.com
Activities for Transportation
N.A.I.C.S.: 488999
Tanja Schott (Branch Mgr)

Subsidiary (US):

Albatrans Inc (2)
149-10 183rd Ave, Jamaica, NY 11413 (100%)
Tel.: (718) 917-6795
Web Site: http://www.albatrans.com
Freight Transportation Arrangement
N.A.I.C.S.: 488510

Connie Paris (Gen Mgr)

Subsidiary (Non-US):

Albatrans Pty Ltd. (2)
Unit 11 1 Graphix Row 160 Bourke Rd, PO Box 7383, Alexandria, 2015, NSW, Australia (100%)
Tel.: (61) 283380477
Web Site: http://www.albatrans.com
Emp.: 7
Business Support Services
N.A.I.C.S.: 561499
George Mamari (Dir-Fin)

Albatrans Spain S.L (2)
Ronda Universitat 33 1 1a A, Barcelona, 08007, Spain (90%)
Tel.: (34) 934871838
Web Site: http://www.albatrans.com
Activities for Transportation
N.A.I.C.S.: 488999
Abel Zurron (Mgr)

Albatrans UK Ltd. (2)
4th Floor Afton House 26 West Nile Street, Glasgow, G1 2PF, United Kingdom (70%)
Tel.: (44) 1412485577
Web Site: http://www.albatrans.com
Emp.: 8
Activities for Transportation
N.A.I.C.S.: 488999
Ron Crawford (Mng Dir)

Alpha Line SARL (1)
3 Rue Des 4 Vents, Paris, France (100%)
Tel.: (33) 143256564
Restaurant
N.A.I.C.S.: 722511

Brewer Enterprises Inc (1)
1501 1st St E, Roundup, MT 59072 (100%)
Tel.: (406) 323-1280
Activities for Nonmetallic Minerals
N.A.I.C.S.: 213115

CDC S.p.A. (1)
Via Paleocapa 1/5, 57123, Livorno, Italy
Tel.: (39) 0586 241111
Web Site: http://www.cdcitalia.it
Freight Transportation Arrangement
N.A.I.C.S.: 488510

Subsidiary (US):

CDC Caribe Inc. (2)
2000 Kennedy Ave Ste 207 MAI Bldg, San Juan, PR 00920
Tel.: (787) 775-6688
Web Site: http://www.cdccaribe.com
Sales Range: $25-49.9 Million
Emp.: 6
Freight Transportation Arrangement
N.A.I.C.S.: 488510
Richard M. Pujol (VP)

Do Ca Srl (1)
Via Trieste 1, Livorno, 57124, Italy (62.4%)
Tel.: (39) 0586249111
Web Site: http://www.doca.it
Emp.: 21
Medical Laboratories
N.A.I.C.S.: 621511
Claudyo Capelly (Mng Dir)

Fiorino Shipping S.r.l (1)
Via Arno 102, Osmannoro-Sesto Fiorentino, 50019, Florence, Italy (60%)
Tel.: (39) 055340068
Deep Sea Freight Transportation
N.A.I.C.S.: 483111

General Freight Inc (1)
692 Grange Rd, Teaneck, NJ 07666-4211 (100%)
Tel.: (201) 836-1503
General Freight Trucking, Local
N.A.I.C.S.: 484110

General Noli S.L. (1)
Dr JJ Domine 18 - Esc A 1, 46011, Valencia, Spain (100%)
Tel.: (34) 963241350
Web Site: http://www.generalnoli.com
Sales Range: $25-49.9 Million
Emp.: 30
Activities for Transportation
N.A.I.C.S.: 488999

General Noli Spedizioni Internazionali SpA (1)
Via Sallustio 3 Ph, Modena, 41123, Italy (100%)
Tel.: (39) 059380311
Web Site: http://www.generalnoli.com
Sales Range: $25-49.9 Million
Emp.: 37
Deep Sea Freight Transportation
N.A.I.C.S.: 483111
Nicola Karrabita (Mng Dir)

Leonardi & C Spa (1)
Via Henry Dunant 10 12 14, Sassuolo, 41049, MO, Italy (58.88%)
Tel.: (39) 0536688511
Web Site: http://www.leonardi-group.it
Sales Range: $25-49.9 Million
Emp.: 70
Freight Transportation Arrangement
N.A.I.C.S.: 488510
Angelo Bulgarelli (Mng Dir)

Leonardi & Co. USA Inc. (1)
1 Cross Island Plz Ste 312, Rosedale, NY 11422 (100%)
Tel.: (718) 276-2562
Freight Transportation Arrangement
N.A.I.C.S.: 488510

Leonardi Iberia S.A. (1)
Dr JJ Domine 18 Bajo Pasaje, 46011, Valencia, Spain (100%)
Tel.: (34) 902520402
Web Site: http://www.leonardi-group.it
Activities for Transportation
N.A.I.C.S.: 488999

Novibrama S.r.l (1)
Via of Cateratte 120, Livorno, Italy (100%)
Tel.: (39) 0586426567
Sales Range: $25-49.9 Million
Emp.: 100
Activities for Transportation
N.A.I.C.S.: 488999

PT Savino Del Bene (1)
Ruko Mega Grosir Cempaka Mas Blok D1 No 12 Jl Let Jend Suprapto, Cempaka Puthi, 10640, Jakarta, Pusat, Indonesia (100%)
Tel.: (62) 2142880251
Web Site: http://www.savinodelbene.com
Sales Range: $25-49.9 Million
Emp.: 11
Activities for Transportation
N.A.I.C.S.: 488999

SDB Information Technology (1)
Via Benozzo Gozzoli 5/2, 50018, Scandicci, Florence, Italy
Tel.: (39) 055 3811222
IT & Logistics Services
N.A.I.C.S.: 488999

Sacid S.r.l (1)
Services Bldg 2nd Fl W Entrance, 00054, Fiumicino, Italy (51%)
Tel.: (39) 0665011617
Web Site: http://www.sacid.it
Transportation Services
N.A.I.C.S.: 488999

Savino Del Bene (JB) Sdn Bhd (1)
Unit No 13A-07 Menara Landmark Jalan Ngee Heng, Mail Box 108, Menara Landmark No 12 Jalan Ng, 80000, Johor Bahru, Malaysia
Tel.: (60) 72277085
Web Site: http://www.savinodelbene.com
Sales Range: $25-49.9 Million
Emp.: 10
Transportation Services
N.A.I.C.S.: 488999
Mauro Bazurro (Mng Dir)

Savino Del Bene (Malaysia) Sdn. Bhd. (1)
Suite 13-07 Crown House 217, Persiaran Raja Muda Musa, Kelang, 42000, Malaysia (100%)
Tel.: (60) 330010013
Web Site: http://www.savinodelbene.com
Sales Range: $25-49.9 Million
Emp.: 11
Transportation Services
N.A.I.C.S.: 488999
Elia Broccoli (Gen Mgr)

Savino Del Bene (S) Pte Ltd. (1)

INTERNATIONAL PUBLIC

43 Changi South Ave 2, Singapore, 486164, Singapore (100%)
Tel.: (65) 62211600
Web Site: http://www.savinodelbene.com
Sales Range: $25-49.9 Million
Emp.: 25
Freight Transportation Arrangement
N.A.I.C.S.: 488510
Nicola Genovese (Mng Dir)

Savino Del Bene (Texas), Inc. (1)
1065 E NW Hwy Ste 250, Grapevine, TX 76051
Tel.: (817) 481-0602
Web Site: http://www.savinodelbene.com
Sales Range: $25-49.9 Million
Emp.: 15
Freight Transportation Arrangement Services
N.A.I.C.S.: 488510

Savino Del Bene (U.K.) Ltd (1)
Frontier House Pier Road, North Feltham Trading Estate, London, TW14 0TW, United Kingdom (100%)
Tel.: (44) 2088448550
Web Site: http://www.savinodelbene.com
Sales Range: $25-49.9 Million
Emp.: 15
Activities for Transportation
N.A.I.C.S.: 488999
David Bryant (Mng Dir)

Savino Del Bene Argentina S.A. (1)
Lima 355-369 2nd floor, C1073AAG, Buenos Aires, Argentina (100%)
Tel.: (54) 1143831768
Web Site: http://www.savinodelbene.com
Sales Range: $25-49.9 Million
Emp.: 25
Activities for Transportation
N.A.I.C.S.: 488999

Savino Del Bene Australia Pty Ltd (1)
Ste 1 247 Kings St Mascot, Port Botany, Mascot, 2020, NSW, Australia
Tel.: (61) 292893400
Web Site: http://www.savinodelbene.com
Sales Range: $25-49.9 Million
Emp.: 25
Transportation Services
N.A.I.C.S.: 488999

Savino Del Bene Bulgaria EAD (1)
Rakovski Street 123, 1000, Sofia, Bulgaria (100%)
Tel.: (359) 29881430
Web Site: http://www.savinodelbene.com
Sales Range: $25-49.9 Million
Emp.: 30
Activities for Transportation
N.A.I.C.S.: 488999
Paolo Rovai (Branch Mgr)

Savino Del Bene Chile S.A. (1)
Edificio Pionero Ciudad, Empresarial Ave del parque, Santiago, Chile (100%)
Tel.: (56) 24659707
Web Site: http://www.savino.com
Sales Range: $25-49.9 Million
Emp.: 26
Activities for Transportation
N.A.I.C.S.: 488999

Savino Del Bene China Ltd (1)
Rm No:1201 A5, Hui Qi Row, Shanshai Rd City, Foshan, China (99.99%)
Tel.: (86) 75783211660
Web Site: http://www.savinodelbene.com
Sales Range: $25-49.9 Million
Emp.: 4
Activities for Transportation
N.A.I.C.S.: 488999
Marco Chan (Gen Mgr)

Savino Del Bene Colombia Ltda (1)
Carrera 103 No 25 B-96 Oficina 301, Bogota, Colombia
Tel.: (57) 14159000
Web Site: http://www.savinodelbene.com
Sales Range: $25-49.9 Million
Emp.: 15
Transportation Services
N.A.I.C.S.: 488999

Savino Del Bene Corp. Canada (1)
7615 Kimbel Street Suite 8 and 9, L4V1T1, Mississauga, ON, Canada (100%)
Tel.: (905) 672-5212

Web Site: http://www.sdb.it
Sales Range: $25-49.9 Million
Emp.: 9
Freight Transportation Arrangement
N.A.I.C.S.: 488510
Giusi Miglietta *(Mgr-Pricing)*

Savino Del Bene Costa Rica S.A. (1)
200 Mts al N del Hampton Inn Hotel Ofc Centro Santa Maria B1, Alajuela, Costa Rica
Tel.: (506) 24300402
Web Site: http://www.savinodelbene.com
Sales Range: $25-49.9 Million
Emp.: 6
Transportation Services
N.A.I.C.S.: 488999
Luca Sagot *(Gen Mgr)*

Savino Del Bene D.O.O. (1)
Turkovo 1B, 51000, Rijeka, Croatia
Tel.: (385) 51681768
Sales Range: $25-49.9 Million
Emp.: 4
Transportation Services
N.A.I.C.S.: 488999

Savino Del Bene Do Brasil Ltda. (1)
Av Gomes de Carvalho 1581 3 Andar, Vila Olimpia, Sao Paulo, 4547006, Brazil **(100%)**
Tel.: (55) 1121460700
Web Site: http://www.savinodelbene.com
Sales Range: $25-49.9 Million
Emp.: 50
Activities for Transportation
N.A.I.C.S.: 488999
Alfredo Lima *(Dir-Comml)*

Savino Del Bene Florida, Inc. (1)
11701 NW 101 Rd Ste 3, Miami, FL 33178
Tel.: (305) 463-8844
Web Site: http://www.savinodelbene.com
Sales Range: $25-49.9 Million
Emp.: 16
Freight Transportation Arrangement
N.A.I.C.S.: 488510
Umberto Cella *(COO)*

Savino Del Bene France S.A. (1)
14 Rue de la Belle Borne, Entrepot n 5 - Quai 1, 95723, Roissy-en-France, France **(99.94%)**
Tel.: (33) 141843400
Web Site: http://www.scb.it
Sales Range: $25-49.9 Million
Emp.: 25
Activities for Transportation
N.A.I.C.S.: 488999

Savino Del Bene Freight Forwarders (India) Pvt. Ltd. (1)
N409 1st FL Sawera Apartments 5th Cross 1st Stage 3rd Block, HBR Layout, Bengaluru, 560043, India **(100%)**
Tel.: (91) 8043441000
Web Site: http://www.savinodelbene.com
Sales Range: $50-74.9 Million
Emp.: 10
Freight Forwarding Service
N.A.I.C.S.: 488510
Dilleswar Rao *(Branch Mgr)*

Savino Del Bene GmbH (1)
Poppenbuetteler-Bogen 17A, 22399, Hamburg, Germany **(100%)**
Tel.: (49) 406067440
Web Site: http://www.savinodelbene.com
Freight Transportation Arrangement
N.A.I.C.S.: 488510

Savino Del Bene India Pvt. Ltd. (1)
704 CNB Square Sangam Complex 127 Andheri-Kurla Road, Chakala Andheri East, Mumbai, 400059, India
Tel.: (91) 226 140 0100
Logistic Services
N.A.I.C.S.: 488510

Savino Del Bene Israel Ltd. (1)
7 Ha Melacha St North Indust Zone, 7152013, Lod, Israel
Tel.: (972) 73 211 8710
Logistic Services
N.A.I.C.S.: 488510

Savino Del Bene Japan Co Ltd
3F Kawara-Machi Takada Bldg 2/6/11 Kawara-Machi, 2-Chome Chuo-ku, Osaka, 5410048, Japan **(100%)**
Tel.: (81) 662274181
Web Site: http://www.savinodelbene.com
Sales Range: $50-74.9 Million
Emp.: 200
Deep Sea Freight Transportation
N.A.I.C.S.: 483111
Flavio Gori *(Pres)*

Savino Del Bene Korea Co. Ltd (1)
9th Floor Ryuag San Bldg 134-1 Gayngdong Gangseongu, 4ga Jung-ku, Seoul, 157-801, Korea (South)
Tel.: (82) 22188702
Emp.: 30
Transportation Services
N.A.I.C.S.: 488999
Pung Sic Cho *(Gen Mgr)*

Savino Del Bene Mexico, S.A.de C.V. (1)
Calle Libra 356 2A Col Juan Manuel Vallarta, 45120, Guadalajara, Zapopan, Mexico
Tel.: (52) 3338117280
Transportation Services
N.A.I.C.S.: 488999

Savino Del Bene Nakliyat Ltd Sti (1)
Abidei Hurriyet Caddesi, Celil Aga Ishani Kat 12 Daire, 34387, Istanbul, Turkiye **(100%)**
Tel.: (90) 2122174352
Web Site: http://www.spb.it
Sales Range: $25-49.9 Million
Emp.: 17
Activities for Water Transportation
N.A.I.C.S.: 488390

Savino Del Bene Netherlands B.V. (1)
Prestwickweg 28, Schiphol Zuidoost, 1118 LB, Amsterdam, Netherlands
Tel.: (31) 20 405 4910
Logistic Services
N.A.I.C.S.: 488510

Savino Del Bene Panama SA (1)
World Trade Ctr Bldg, Fl 11 Ofc 1104, 55-0122, Panama, Panama
Tel.: (507) 2144093
Web Site: http://www.sdbpty.net
Sales Range: $25-49.9 Million
Emp.: 10
Transportation Services
N.A.I.C.S.: 488999

Savino Del Bene Poland Sp.z o.o. (1)
Ul Slaska 17, 81-319, Gdynia, Poland **(100%)**
Tel.: (48) 586286450
Sales Range: $25-49.9 Million
Emp.: 60
Deep Sea Freight Transportation
N.A.I.C.S.: 483111
Anna Dobbek *(Dir-Fin)*

Savino Del Bene Portuguesa Lda (1)
Centro Empresarial AAA Rua Ponte da Pedra 240 Edificio Losa-Espaço, DE-8-3 Piso Gueifaes, 4470-108, Maia, Portugal **(100%)**
Tel.: (351) 229997300
Web Site: http://www.savinodelbene.com
Sales Range: $25-49.9 Million
Emp.: 21
Activities for Transportation
N.A.I.C.S.: 488999
Dugo Weirs *(Mgr-Comml)*

Savino Del Bene Quebec Inc. (1)
9157 Champ d'Eau Suite 101, St Leonard, Montreal, H1P 3M3, QC, Canada
Tel.: (514) 312-7075
Freight Transportation Services
N.A.I.C.S.: 484110
Paolo Nocentini *(Gen Dir)*

Savino Del Bene Russia, LLC (1)
Prospect Stachek n 48 Bld 2 3rd Floor - Office 304, Business Center Imperial, 198097, Saint Petersburg, Russia
Tel.: (7) 8126803016
Logistic Services
N.A.I.C.S.: 488510

Savino Del Bene S.A. (1)
Via alla Rossa Zona Industriale, Rancate, CH 6862, Mendrisio, Switzerland **(98.8%)**
Tel.: (41) 916409860
Sales Range: $25-49.9 Million
Emp.: 6
Transportation & Logistics Services
N.A.I.C.S.: 488999
Simoni Fieni *(Branch Mgr)*

Savino Del Bene S.L. (1)
Dracma 65/66, 3114, Alicante, Alicante, Spain **(100%)**
Tel.: (34) 965106522
Web Site: http://www.savinodelbene.com
Activities for Road Transportation
N.A.I.C.S.: 488490

Savino Del Bene Shanghai Co., Ltd (1)
Room A Floor 29 East Tower - Shanghai Hi-Tech King World N 668, Beijing Road East Huangpu, Shanghai, 200001, China **(100%)**
Tel.: (86) 2153080977
Web Site: http://www.savinodelbene.com
Sales Range: $25-49.9 Million
Emp.: 1
Activities for Transportation
N.A.I.C.S.: 488999
Marco Leporati *(Mng Dir)*

Savino Del Bene South Africa (Pty) Ltd. (1)
118 Cape Road Mill Park, Port Elizabeth, 1619, South Africa
Tel.: (27) 41 373 1559
Web Site: https://southafrica.savinodelbene.com
Logistic Services
N.A.I.C.S.: 488510

Savino Del Bene Switzerland AG (1)
Hohenrainstrasse 10, PO Box 1839, 4133, Pratteln, Switzerland
Tel.: (41) 61 825 6800
Logistic Services
N.A.I.C.S.: 488510

Savino Del Bene U.S.A. Inc. (1)
149-10 183rd St, Jamaica, NY 11413
Tel.: (718) 656-5971
Web Site: http://www.savinodelbene.com
Transportation Services
N.A.I.C.S.: 488999

Savino Del Bene U.S.A. Inc. (1)
1905 S Mount Prospect Rd, Des Plaines, IL 60018
Tel.: (847) 390-3600
Web Site: http://www.savinodelbene.com
Logistics & Supply Chain Management
N.A.I.C.S.: 541614
Mark Irwin *(CEO)*

Savino Del Bene Uruguay S.A. (1)
Colonia 810 Office 702, 11000, Montevideo, Uruguay
Tel.: (598) 82 903 5236
Freight Forwarding Services
N.A.I.C.S.: 488510

Savino Del Bene del Peru S.A.C (1)
Calle Grau 273 Oficina 501, Lima, Miraflores, Peru
Tel.: (51) 1 44 43 444
Web Site: http://www.savinodelbene.com
Transportation Services
N.A.I.C.S.: 488999
Jose Antonio Arias Schreiber *(Gen Mgr)*

Savitransport Triveneto S.r.l (1)
Via Feltrina S 189-G -Montebelluna, Treviso, Italy **(100%)**
Tel.: (39) 0423603712
Web Site: https://www.savitransport.com
Sales Range: $25-49.9 Million
Emp.: 25
Freight Transportation Arrangement
N.A.I.C.S.: 488510
Dino Piva *(Gen Mgr)*

SAVIOR LIFETEC CORP.
29 KeJhong Rd Chen, Miaoli, Chunan, 35053, Taiwan
Tel.: (886) 37580100
Web Site: https://www.saviorlifetec.com.tw
Year Founded: 2004
4167—(TPE)
Rev.: $39,575,681
Assets: $137,847,481
Liabilities: $32,574,211
Net Worth: $105,273,270
Earnings: $1,135,291
Emp.: 338
Fiscal Year-end: 12/31/22
Pharmaceuticals Product Mfr
N.A.I.C.S.: 325412
Yung-Fa Chen *(Gen Mgr)*

SAVITA OIL TECHNOLOGIES LIMITED
66/67 Nariman Bhavan Nariman Point, Mumbai, 400 021, India
Tel.: (91) 2222883061
Web Site: https://www.savita.com
524667—(BOM)
Rev.: $438,028,164
Assets: $271,410,095
Liabilities: $97,673,569
Net Worth: $173,736,527
Earnings: $27,060,416
Emp.: 420
Fiscal Year-end: 03/31/23
Petroleum Products Sales & Mfr
N.A.I.C.S.: 324199
G. N. Mehra *(Chm & Mng Dir)*

Subsidiaries:

Savita Oil Technologies Limited - LUBES DIVISION (1)
74 Maker Chamber VI, Nariman Point, Mumbai, 400 021, India
Tel.: (91) 22 22027452
Web Site: http://www.savita.com
Sales Range: $25-49.9 Million
Emp.: 80
Lubricant Mfr
N.A.I.C.S.: 324191

SAVO-SOLAR OY
Insinoorinkatu 7, 50150, Mikkeli, Finland
Tel.: (358) 102710810
Web Site: http://www.savosolar.com
SAVOS—(HEL)
Rev.: $9,318,561
Assets: $69,470,406
Liabilities: $31,261,827
Net Worth: $38,208,579
Earnings: ($4,388,722)
Emp.: 172
Fiscal Year-end: 12/31/22
Solar Thermal Collectors Mfr
N.A.I.C.S.: 333414
Feodor Aminoff *(Chm)*

Subsidiaries:

Savosolar ApS (1)
Haervejen 9, Bov, 6330, Padborg, Denmark
Tel.: (45) 29110371
Solar Thermal Energy Services
N.A.I.C.S.: 221114
Torben Frederiksen *(CTO)*

Savosolar GmbH (1)
Kuhnehofe 3, 22761, Hamburg, Germany
Tel.: (49) 4050034970
Solar Thermal Energy Services
N.A.I.C.S.: 221114
Torsten Lutten *(Sls Dir)*

SAVOLA GROUP
Headquarters Savola Tower Ashati District Jeddah Prince Faisal Bin, Fahd Road Savola Group 2444 Taha Khusaifan Ashati Unit No 15, Jeddah, 23511-7333, Saudi Arabia
Tel.: (966) 122687755
Web Site: https://www.savola.com
Year Founded: 1979
2050—(SAU)
Rev.: $7,480,256,766
Assets: $7,882,855,086
Liabilities: $5,398,734,835
Net Worth: $2,484,120,251
Earnings: $230,605,253
Emp.: 24,668
Fiscal Year-end: 12/31/22

SAVOLA GROUP

Savola Group—(Continued)

Owner of Edible Oils Factories, Sugar Factories, Packaging & Retail Stores
N.A.I.C.S.: 551112
Sulaiman Abdulkader Al-Muhaidib *(Chm)*

Subsidiaries:

Bayara FZE Limited (1)
Dubai Investment Park 2, Dubai, United Arab Emirates
Tel.: (971) 48857478
Web Site: https://www.bayara.com
Food & Beverage Mfr & Distr
N.A.I.C.S.: 311421

Bayara Holding Limited (1)
Dubai Investment Park 2, Dubai, United Arab Emirates
Tel.: (971) 48857478
Web Site: https://www.bayara.com
Food & Beverage Mfr
N.A.I.C.S.: 311421

Behshahr Industrial Company (1)
km 8 of Fatah highway old Karaj road, Tehran, Iran (81.2%)
Tel.: (98) 2166250435
Web Site: https://www.behshahr-ind.com
Fats & Oils Refining & Blending
N.A.I.C.S.: 311225

GYMA Food Industries FZ-LLC (1)
Dubai Investment Park 2, PO Box 16886, Dubai, United Arab Emirates
Tel.: (971) 547939001
Food Mfr & Distr
N.A.I.C.S.: 311423

Herfy Food Services Company Ltd. (1)
Riyadh Mourouj Quarter, PO Box 86958, Riyadh, 11632, Saudi Arabia (70%)
Tel.: (966) 114509767
Web Site: https://www.herfy.com
Rev.: $331,645,986
Assets: $531,795,760
Liabilities: $250,085,881
Net Worth: $281,709,880
Earnings: $945,502
Emp.: 5,718
Fiscal Year-end: 12/31/2022
Fast Food Restaurant Owner & Operator
N.A.I.C.S.: 722513
Ahmed Hamad Al Said *(Founder)*

Savola Edible Oils (Sudan) Ltd. (1)
Al Mochala, Khartoum, Sudan (100%)
Tel.: (249) 183252774
Vegetable & Melon Farming
N.A.I.C.S.: 111219

Savola Edible Oils Company Ltd. (1)
Industrial Area Phase 3, Jeddah, Saudi Arabia (90.6%)
Tel.: (966) 2657333
Oilseed Processing
N.A.I.C.S.: 311224

Savola Gida Sanayi Ve Ticaret Anonim Sirketi (1)
Palladium Tower Barbaros Mah Kardelen Sok No 2 Kat 36 D 123, Atasehir, 34746, Istanbul, Türkiye
Tel.: (90) 2165786800
Web Site: https://www.savolagida.com.tr
Edible Oil Mfr
N.A.I.C.S.: 311224

Variety Food Factory Company (1)
King Abdullah Economic City, Rabigh, 23989 -3973, Saudi Arabia
Tel.: (966) 122900553
Frozen Food Product Mfr
N.A.I.C.S.: 311412

SAVOR GROUP LIMITED

Level 4 Seafarers Building 52 Tyler St, Britomart, Auckland, 1010, New Zealand
Tel.: (64) 99720218 NZ
Web Site: https://www.savor.co.nz
Year Founded: 2003
SVR—(NZX)
Rev.: $32,977,189
Assets: $35,512,588
Liabilities: $24,605,398
Net Worth: $10,907,190
Earnings: ($1,469,486)
Emp.: 601
Fiscal Year-end: 03/31/23
Beer Mfr
N.A.I.C.S.: 312120
Geoff Ross *(Chm)*

SAVOREAT LTD.

4 Oppenheimer St Science Park, Rehovot, Israel
Tel.: (972) 86378883
Web Site: https://www.savoreat.com
Year Founded: 2018
SVRT—(TAE)
Assets: $5,737,533
Liabilities: $442,603
Net Worth: $5,294,930
Earnings: ($3,664,318)
Fiscal Year-end: 12/31/23
Food Mfr
N.A.I.C.S.: 311999
Shai Sultan *(VP-R&D Sys)*

SAVOX COMMUNICATIONS OY AB

Sinikalliontie 3B, 02630, Espoo, Finland
Tel.: (358) 9 417 411 00 FI
Web Site: http://www.savox.com
Year Founded: 1982
Professional Communication Device & Equipment Designer, Mfr & Whslr
N.A.I.C.S.: 334290
Jerry Kettunen *(CEO)*

Subsidiaries:

Savox Communications Ltd. (1)
Suite 115-4400 Dominion Street, Burnaby, V5G 4G3, BC, Canada
Tel.: (604) 244-9323
Web Site: http://www.savox.com
Professional Communication Device & Equipment Designer, Mfr & Whslr
N.A.I.C.S.: 334290
Bryan Price *(VP-Sls-Americas & Gen Mgr)*

SAVREMENA A.D.

Sarajevska br 15, 11000, Belgrade, Serbia
Tel.: (381) 112641337
Web Site: https://savremena.weebly.com
Year Founded: 1954
SAVR—(BEL)
Sales Range: $1-9.9 Million
Book Shop Operator
N.A.I.C.S.: 459210

SAW GMBH

Klotzbachstrasse 2, 73560, Bobingen, Germany
Tel.: (49) 717371670
Web Site: http://www.saw-gmbh.de
Sales Range: $25-49.9 Million
Emp.: 30
Blast Furnaces Mfr
N.A.I.C.S.: 333994
Gernot Trausner *(Mng Dir)*

SAWACA BUSINESS MACHINES LIMITED

45 Chinubhai Towers Opp Handloom House Ashram Road, Ahmedabad, 380009, Gujarat, India
Tel.: (91) 7926587363
Web Site: https://www.sawacabusiness.com
531893—(BOM)
Rev.: $501,527
Assets: $1,794,492
Liabilities: $106,236
Net Worth: $1,688,256
Earnings: $29,777
Emp.: 11
Fiscal Year-end: 03/31/21
Software Development Services
N.A.I.C.S.: 541511
Shetal S. Shah *(Chm & Mng Dir)*

SAWAFUJI ELECTRIC CO., LTD.

3 Nittahayakawa-cho, Ota, 370-0344, Gunma, Japan
Tel.: (81) 276567111
Web Site: https://www.sawafuji.co.jp
Year Founded: 1919
6901—(TKS)
Rev.: $176,764,620
Assets: $176,691,910
Liabilities: $86,029,150
Net Worth: $90,662,760
Earnings: $3,417,370
Emp.: 724
Fiscal Year-end: 03/31/24
Automobile Parts Mfr & Distr
N.A.I.C.S.: 335312
Masao Inoue *(Pres)*

Subsidiaries:

Engel Distribution Pty Ltd. (1)
6 Ernest Clark Road, Canning Vale, 6155, WA, Australia
Tel.: (61) 894555099
Web Site: http://www.engelaustralia.com.au
Emp.: 24
Refrigerator Distr
N.A.I.C.S.: 423620
Naoyuki Watabe *(CEO)*

Sawafuji Software Development Co., Ltd. (1)
478 Nittahayakawa-cho, Ota, 370-0344, Japan
Tel.: (81) 276567116
Web Site: http://www.ssd1988.com
Emp.: 32
Software Development Services
N.A.I.C.S.: 541511
Masahiro Osada *(Pres)*

SAWAI GROUP HOLDINGS CO., LTD.

5-2-30 Miyahara, Yodogawa-ku, Osaka, 532-0003, Japan
Tel.: (81) 661055818 JP
Web Site: https://global.sawaigroup.holdings
Year Founded: 2021
4887—(TKS)
Rev.: $1,169,057,820
Assets: $2,525,178,640
Liabilities: $1,084,000,340
Net Worth: $1,441,178,300
Earnings: $90,523,950
Emp.: 3,037
Fiscal Year-end: 03/31/24
Holding Company
N.A.I.C.S.: 551112
Masatoshi Ohara *(Dir-External)*

Subsidiaries:

Sawai Pharmaceutical Co., Ltd. (1)
5-2-30 Miyahara, Yodogawa-ku, Osaka, 532-0003, Japan
Tel.: (81) 661055818
Web Site: http://www.sawai.co.jp
Pharmaceutical Products & Health Care Foods Mfr
N.A.I.C.S.: 325412
Mitsuo Sawai *(Chm & CEO)*

Subsidiary (Domestic):

Kaken Shoyaku Inc. (2)
3-37-10 Shimorenjaku, Mitaka, 181-0013, Tokyo, Japan
Tel.: (81) 422440106
Pharmaceuticals Product Mfr
N.A.I.C.S.: 325412

Medisa Shinyaku Inc. (2)
2-27 Miyahara 5-Chome, Yodogawa-Ku, Osaka, 532-0003, Japan
Tel.: (81) 661501105
Web Site: http://www.medisa.co.jp

INTERNATIONAL PUBLIC

Sales Range: $50-74.9 Million
Emp.: 200
Pharmaceuticals Product Mfr
N.A.I.C.S.: 325412
Takashi Iwasa *(Pres)*

Trust Pharmatech Co., Ltd. (1)
5-15 Yaji, Awara, 919-0603, Japan
Tel.: (81) 776430127
Web Site: https://www.trustpharmatech.co.jp
Emp.: 403
Pharmaceuticals Product Mfr
N.A.I.C.S.: 325412

SAWANG EXPORT PUBLIC COMPANY LIMITED

307-307/1-4 56 305 Suriyawong Road, Kwaeng Suriyawong Khet Bangrak, Bangkok, 10500, Thailand
Tel.: (66) 22665571
Web Site: https://www.sawangexport.com
Year Founded: 1972
SAWANG—(THA)
Rev.: $3,499,825
Assets: $9,797,701
Liabilities: $796,649
Net Worth: $9,001,052
Earnings: ($396,135)
Emp.: 200
Fiscal Year-end: 12/31/23
Jewelry Products Mfr & Distr
N.A.I.C.S.: 423940
Sawang Maneepairoj *(Founder)*

SAXA HOLDINGS INC.

NBF Platinum Tower 1-17-3 Shirokane, Minato ku, Tokyo, 1088050, Japan
Tel.: (81) 357915511
Web Site: https://www.saxa.co.jp
6675—(TKS)
Rev.: $270,666,280
Assets: $274,136,530
Liabilities: $86,624,050
Net Worth: $187,512,480
Earnings: $18,508,000
Emp.: 1,098
Fiscal Year-end: 03/31/24
Communication Equipments Mfr & Sales
N.A.I.C.S.: 334220
Marui Taketo *(Pres & CEO)*

Subsidiaries:

SAXA Advanced Support Inc. (1)
1-6-3 Higashigotanda, Shinagawa-ku, Tokyo, 141-0022, Japan
Tel.: (81) 354206393
Web Site: http://www.saxa-as.co.jp
Communication Equipment Maintenance Services
N.A.I.C.S.: 811210

SAXA Business System Inc. (1)
Fujiwa Higashigotanda Building 6F 1-7-6 Higashigotanda, Shinagawa-ku, Tokyo, 141-0022, Japan
Tel.: (81) 334450393
Web Site: https://www.saxa.biz
Sales Range: $25-49.9 Million
Emp.: 51
Communication Equipment Whslr
N.A.I.C.S.: 423690

SAXA Inc. (1)
NBF Platinum Tower 1-17-3 Shirokane, Minato-ku, Tokyo, 108-8050, Japan
Tel.: (81) 357915511
Web Site: http://www.saxa.co.jp
Sales Range: $250-299.9 Million
Emp.: 662
Communications Equipments Mfr & Whslr
N.A.I.C.S.: 423690

Subsidiary (Domestic):

SAXA Proassist Inc. (2)
3-14-15 Miyashimo, Chuo-ku, Sagamihara, 252-5221, Kanagawa, Japan
Tel.: (81) 427727893

Sales Range: $25-49.9 Million
Emp.: 20
Communication Equipment Whslr
N.A.I.C.S.: 423690

SAXA Techno Inc. (2)
4-3146-13 Hachimanpara, Yonezawa, 992-1128, Yamagata, Japan
Tel.: (81) 238286111
Web Site: http://www.saxa.co.jp
Sales Range: $150-199.9 Million
Emp.: 370
Telecom Equipment Leasing Services
N.A.I.C.S.: 532490

SAXA Precision Inc. (1)
Web Site: http://www.saxa-precision.co.jp
Electric Equipment Mfr
N.A.I.C.S.: 334416

System K Corporation (1)
2-24 Higashi 1 Kita 15, Higashi-ku, Sapporo, 065-0015, Hokkaido, Japan
Tel.: (81) 117044321
Web Site: http://www.systemk-corp.com
Sales Range: $25-49.9 Million
Emp.: 50
Network Camera System Development Services
N.A.I.C.S.: 541511
Takahiro Narumi *(Pres)*

SAXLUND GROUP AB
Fannys vag 3, 131 54, Nacka, Sweden
Tel.: (46) 44218400
SAXG—(OMX)
Rev.: $23,419,221
Assets: $17,776,092
Liabilities: $14,178,538
Net Worth: $3,597,554
Earnings: ($956,288)
Emp.: 76
Fiscal Year-end: 12/31/22
Material Handling Equipment Mfr
N.A.I.C.S.: 333922
Viktor Wahlin *(COO)*

SAY YENILENEBILIR ENERJI EKIPMANLARI SANAYI VE TICARET A.S.
Kemalpasa OSB Mah 519 Street Outer Door No 317, Kemalpasa, Izmir, Turkiye
Tel.: (90) 2328787800
Web Site: https://sayas-re.com
Year Founded: 1989
SAYAS—(IST)
Rev.: $19,253,955
Assets: $12,677,148
Liabilities: $4,949,097
Net Worth: $7,728,051
Earnings: $4,730,646
Fiscal Year-end: 12/31/22
Sign Board Mfr
N.A.I.C.S.: 339950
Erkan Guldogan *(Chm)*

SAYAJI HOTELS LIMITED
Sayaji Indore H/1 Scheme No 54 Vijay Nagar, Near Best Price Hare Krishna Vihar Nipania, Indore, 452 010, Madhya Pradesh, India
Tel.: (91) 7314006666
Web Site:
 https://www.sayajihotels.com
Year Founded: 1982
523710—(BOM)
Rev.: $11,867,433
Assets: $44,846,993
Liabilities: $30,202,167
Net Worth: $14,644,826
Earnings: ($7,173,075)
Emp.: 1,085
Fiscal Year-end: 03/31/21
Home Management Services
N.A.I.C.S.: 721110
Amit Kumar Sarraf *(Compliance Officer & Sec)*

Subsidiaries:

Barbeque-Nation Hospitality Limited (1)
First Floor Plot No 20 Beverley Park Sector 6 Palm Beach Road, Above ICICI Bank Nerul, Navi Mumbai, 400706, India
Tel.: (91) 22 6060 0001
Hotel Operator
N.A.I.C.S.: 721110
Birju Raika *(Bus Mgr)*

Sayaji Hotels(Pune) Limited (1)
135/136 Mumbai-Bangalore Bypass Highway Wakad, Pune, 411057, Maharashtra, India
Tel.: (91) 2042121212
Hotel & Resort Management Services
N.A.I.C.S.: 721110

SAYAJI INDUSTRIES LIMITED
Maize Products P O Kathwada-Maize Products, Ahmedabad, 382 430, Gujarat, India
Tel.: (91) 7922901581
Web Site: https://www.sayajigroup.in
Year Founded: 1941
540728—(BOM)
Rev.: $76,511,840
Assets: $48,805,575
Liabilities: $35,983,748
Net Worth: $12,821,827
Earnings: $2,253,629
Emp.: 771
Fiscal Year-end: 03/31/21
Chemical Preparation Mfr & Distr
N.A.I.C.S.: 325612
Priyam Bipin Mehta *(Chm & Mng Dir)*

Subsidiaries:

Maize Products Limited (1)
6th Floor Vanijya Bhavan Kankaria, Ahmedabad, 380022, India
Tel.: (91) 7925454981
Web Site: http://www.maizeproducts.com
Corn Mfr
N.A.I.C.S.: 311221

N.B.Commercial Enterprises Ltd. (1)
Plot 155 Behind C L High School Opposite, Singarva Village Kathwada, Ahmedabad, 382413, India
Tel.: (91) 7922901416
Web Site: http://www.nbcplastics.com
Barrel Mfr
N.A.I.C.S.: 326199

Varun Travels Private Limited (1)
609-613 6th Floor Ten-11 Complex Besides Mardia Plaza C G Road, Navrangpura, Ahmedabad, 380009, Gujarat, India
Tel.: (91) 7926476000
Web Site: http://www.varuntravels.com
Tour & Travel Services
N.A.I.C.S.: 561510

SAYLOR ADVERTISING, INC.
2-7-20 Ogi-machi, Takamatsu, 760-8502, Kagawa, Japan
Tel.: (81) 878231155
Web Site: https://www.saylor.co.jp
Year Founded: 1951
2156—(TKS)
Rev.: $13,550,500
Assets: $27,008,460
Liabilities: $14,251,160
Net Worth: $12,757,300
Earnings: ($489,140)
Emp.: 220
Fiscal Year-end: 03/31/24
Advertising Services
N.A.I.C.S.: 541810

SAYONA MINING LIMITED
Tel.: (61) 733697058
Web Site:
 https://www.sayonamining.com.au
SYA—(ASX)
Rev.: $134,130,937
Assets: $636,031,031
Liabilities: $104,755,051
Net Worth: $531,275,979

Earnings: ($79,475,750)
Emp.: 231
Fiscal Year-end: 06/30/24
Mineral Exploration Services
N.A.I.C.S.: 213115
Paul A. Crawford *(CFO & Sec)*

Subsidiaries:

Sayona Quebec Inc. (1)
1100 Rene-Levesque Blvd W Suite 1230, Montreal, QC, Canada
Tel.: (819) 734-5000
Web Site: https://www.sayona.ca
Lithium Concentrate Mfr
N.A.I.C.S.: 325180

SAYWELL CONTRACTING LTD.
2599 McCullough Road, Nanaimo, V9S 4M9, BC, Canada
Tel.: (250) 729-0197
Web Site:
 https://www.saywellcontracting.com
Year Founded: 1998
General Contracting Services
N.A.I.C.S.: 238190

SAYWELL INTERNATIONAL
Aviation Center Downlands Business Park, BN14 9LA, Worthing, West Sussex, United Kingdom - England
Tel.: (44) 1903705700
Web Site: http://www.saywell.co.uk
Year Founded: 1946
Sales Range: $50-74.9 Million
Emp.: 60
Aircraft Parts Distr
N.A.I.C.S.: 423860
Peter Saywell *(Mng Dir)*

SB SIMPSON GROUP.
3210 Mainway, Burlington, L7M 1A5, ON, Canada
Tel.: (905) 335-6575
Web Site:
 https://www.sbsimpson.com
Year Founded: 1960
Rev.: $36,047,224
Emp.: 120
Industrial Supplies & Professional Solutions
N.A.I.C.S.: 541990
Scott Simpson *(Pres)*

SBAEK INVEST PLC
Almadeneh Almnawreh St Khalf Washti Complex First Floor, PO Box 588, Alharmen Intersection, Amman, 11821, Jordan
Tel.: (962) 65544595
Web Site:
 https://www.sabaekinvest.com
Year Founded: 2007
SABK—(AMM)
Rev.: $504,574
Assets: $9,054,569
Liabilities: $609,524
Net Worth: $8,445,045
Earnings: ($131,813)
Emp.: 5
Fiscal Year-end: 12/31/20
Financial Services
N.A.I.C.S.: 523940

Subsidiaries:

Sabaek for Financial Services LLC (1)
Al Madina Al Munawara Street Khalaf Washti Complex First Floor, Amman, Jordan
Tel.: (962) 65563111
Stocks & Bonds Sales Services
N.A.I.C.S.: 812990

SBAS (HONG KONG) LTD.
Unit 1804 Westlands Centre 20

Westlands Road, Quarry Bay, China (Hong Kong)
Tel.: (852) 28119662
Web Site: http://www.sbas.com.hk
Predictive Analytics & Data Mining Software Distr & Technical Consulting Services
N.A.I.C.S.: 423430
Raymond Poon *(Dir)*

SBC CORPORATION BERHAD
C-01 Concourse Level PJX-HM Shah Tower No 16A Persiaran Barat, 46050, Petaling Jaya, Selangor, Malaysia
Tel.: (60) 340418118
Web Site:
 https://www.sbcgroup.com.my
SBCCORP—(KLS)
Rev.: $28,728,315
Assets: $147,758,243
Liabilities: $44,970,255
Net Worth: $102,787,988
Earnings: $3,470,198
Emp.: 82
Fiscal Year-end: 03/31/22
Construction Services
N.A.I.C.S.: 236220
Chee Jing Kan *(Co-Sec)*

SBC EXPORTS LTD.
49/95 Site-Iv Sahibabad Industrial Area, Ghaziabad, 201010, Uttar Pradesh, India
Tel.: (91) 8303300100
Web Site:
 https://www.sbcexportslimited.com
Year Founded: 2011
SBC—(NSE)
Rev.: $23,718,191
Assets: $13,838,216
Liabilities: $9,636,931
Net Worth: $4,201,285
Earnings: $826,488
Emp.: 450
Fiscal Year-end: 03/31/23
Textile Products Distr
N.A.I.C.S.: 424310
Govindji Gupta *(Mng Dir)*

Subsidiaries:

Mauji Trip Limited (1)
G - 227 Sector 63, Noida, 201301, Uttar Pradesh, India
Tel.: (91) 8470009000
Web Site: https://www.maujitrip.com
Travel Agency Operator
N.A.I.C.S.: 561510

SBC SVERIGES BOSTADSRATTSCENTRUM AB
Luntmakargatan 18, Box 1353, Stockholm, 11183, Sweden
Tel.: (46) 850115000
Web Site: http://www.sbc.se
Year Founded: 1999
Real Estate Manangement Services
N.A.I.C.S.: 531390
Ola Gunnersson *(Pres & CEO)*

SBD CAPITAL CORP.
65 Queen Street West Suite 520, Toronto, M5H 2M5, ON, Canada
Tel.: (416) 985-7810
Web Site:
 http://www.sbdcapitalcorp.com
SBD—(CNSX)
Rev.: $9,025
Assets: $54,135
Liabilities: $422,135
Net Worth: ($368,000)
Earnings: ($62,272)
Fiscal Year-end: 03/31/24
Financial Support Services
N.A.I.C.S.: 541611
John Dyer *(CEO & CFO)*

SBE BIOENERGIE HANDELS GMBH

SBD Capital Corp.—(Continued)

SBE BIOENERGIE HANDELS GMBH
Berliner Promenade 16, 66111, Saarbrucken, Germany
Tel.: (49) 681938270
Web Site: http://www.sbe-bioenergie.de
Rev.: $142,664,289
Emp.: 8
Biodiesel Mfr
N.A.I.C.S.: 324199
Rolf Sieber *(Gen Mgr)*

SBE-VARVIT S.P.A.
Via Lazzaretti 2/A, 42122, Reggio Emilia, Italy
Tel.: (39) 05225088
Web Site: https://www.sbe.it
Year Founded: 2006
VARV—(ITA)
Electrical Equipment Mfr & Distr
N.A.I.C.S.: 331110

SBEC SUGAR LTD
Loyan Malakpur, Baraut Dist Baghpat, New Delhi, 250611, Uttar Pradesh, India
Tel.: (91) 1142504878
Web Site: https://www.sbecsugar.com
532102—(BOM)
Rev.: $79,265,257
Assets: $98,503,761
Liabilities: $95,043,928
Net Worth: $3,459,834
Earnings: $3,705,643)
Emp.: 257
Fiscal Year-end: 03/31/21
Sugar Mfr
N.A.I.C.S.: 311313
Umesh K. Modi *(Chm & Pres)*

SBEC SYSTEMS (INDIA), LTD.
1400 Hemkunt Tower 98 Nehru Palace, New Delhi, 110019, India
Tel.: (91) 1142504878
Web Site: https://www.sbecsystems.in
Year Founded: 1987
517360—(BOM)
Rev.: $378,095
Assets: $161,765
Liabilities: $2,077,405
Net Worth: ($1,915,641)
Earnings: $132,618
Emp.: 3
Fiscal Year-end: 03/31/23
Machine Construction Services
N.A.I.C.S.: 532412
Vijay K. Modi *(Chm)*

SBF AG
Zaucheweg 4, 04316, Leipzig, Germany
Tel.: (49) 34165235894
Web Site: https://www.sbf-ag.com
Year Founded: 1862
CY1K—(DEU)
Rev.: $37,487,581
Assets: $50,104,868
Liabilities: $13,091,953
Net Worth: $37,012,915
Earnings: ($3,709,019)
Emp.: 220
Fiscal Year-end: 12/31/23
Electric Equipment Mfr
N.A.I.C.S.: 333414

SBFC FINANCE LIMITED
103 1st Floor C&B Square Sangam Complex Andheri Kurla Road, Village Chakala Andheri East, Mumbai, 400059, India
Tel.: (91) 2267875300
Web Site: https://www.sbfc.com

Year Founded: 2017
543959—(BOM)
Rev.: $90,027,898
Assets: $698,767,104
Liabilities: $488,731,315
Net Worth: $210,035,789
Earnings: $18,207,898
Emp.: 2,822
Fiscal Year-end: 03/31/23
Financial Investment Services
N.A.I.C.S.: 523910
Aseem Dhru *(Mng Dir)*

SBI FUNDS MANAGEMENT LIMITED
9th Floor Crescenzo C-38 & 39 G Block, Bandra-Kurla Complex, Mumbai, 400 051, India
Tel.: (91) 2262511600
Web Site: https://www.sbimf.com
Emp.: 100
Financial Services
N.A.I.C.S.: 523999
Shamsher Singh *(CEO & Mng Dir)*

SBI HOLDINGS, INC.
19F Izumi Garden Tower 1-6-1 Roppongi, Minato-ku, Tokyo, 106-6019, Japan
Tel.: (81) 362290100   JP
Web Site: https://www.sbigroup.co.jp
Year Founded: 1999
ZOF—(DEU)
Rev.: $8,001,431,440
Assets: $179,391,374,510
Liabilities: $166,783,817,450
Net Worth: $12,607,557,060
Earnings: $576,676,230
Emp.: 18,586
Fiscal Year-end: 03/31/24
Holding Company; Online Investment, Asset Management, Lending & Other Financial & Business Support Services
N.A.I.C.S.: 551112
Yoshitaka Kitao *(Chm, Pres & CEO)*

Subsidiaries:

ARUHI Corporation (1)
1-6-1 Izumi Garden Tower 22 Floor, Minato-ku, Tokyo, 106 6022, Japan   (51%)
Tel.: (81) 362290777
Web Site: http://www.aruhi.jp
Housing Loans
N.A.I.C.S.: 522310
Noriaki Maruyama *(Pres, CEO & COO)*

Autoc one K.K. (1)
Shiba-koen STK Bldg 2-25-15 Shiba Minato-ku, Tokyo, Japan   (54%)
Tel.: (81) 362290100
Web Site: http://www.autoc-one.jp
Internet Support Services for Automobile Purchasers
N.A.I.C.S.: 561499
Yoshikuni Kato *(Pres & CEO)*

B2C2 Ltd. (1)
86-90 Paul Street, London, EC2A 4NE, United Kingdom
Tel.: (44) 208 133 7817
Web Site: https://b2c2.com
Financial Transaction Services
N.A.I.C.S.: 522320
Max Boonen *(Co-Founder)*

CEM Corporation (1)
Shinjuku Sumitomo Building 24F, 2-6-1 Nishi-Shinjuku, Shinjuku-ku, Tokyo, Japan   (79.7%)
Tel.: (81) 3 3342 3770
Real Estate Secured Loans
N.A.I.C.S.: 522292

Finance All Solutions Co., Ltd. (1)
418 419 HausD biz Seonyu-ro 3-gil 10, Yeongdeungpo-gu, Seoul, 07285, Korea (South)   (85.71%)
Tel.: (82) 232741646
Web Site: https://www.fasol.co.kr
System Development Solutions for Online Financial Services

N.A.I.C.S.: 541519
Jang Jeong Yeol *(CEO)*

Homeostyle Inc. (1)
Shibadaimon Center Building 9F 1-10-11, Shibadaimon Minato-ku, Tokyo, 105-0012, Japan   (49.3%)
Tel.: (81) 368951140
Web Site: http://www.homeostyle.com
Sales Range: $100-124.9 Million
Emp.: 329
Sales & Services for Beauty Care & Health Food Products
N.A.I.C.S.: 456191

Money Tap Co., Ltd. (1)
1-6-1 Roppongi, Minato-ku, Tokyo, 106-6017, Japan
Tel.: (81) 36 229 0085
Web Site: https://moneytap.jp
Remittance Services
N.A.I.C.S.: 522320

NX Development Corp. (1)
870 Corporate Dr Ste 403, Lexington, KY 40503
Web Site: https://nxdevcorp.com
Research & Development Services
N.A.I.C.S.: 541715
William F. Grieco *(Chief Compliance Officer & VP)*

Photonics Healthcare B.V. (1)
Koningin Wilhelminalaan 8, 3527 LD, Utrecht, Netherlands
Tel.: (31) 30 207 6002
Web Site: https://www.photonicshealthcare.com
Research Photonics Healthcare Services
N.A.I.C.S.: 541715
F. Michael Munker *(CEO)*

Quark Pharmaceuticals, Inc. (1)
495 N. Whisman Rd Ste. 100, Mountain view, CA 94043
Tel.: (510) 402-4020
Web Site: http://www.quarkpharma.com
Biopharmaceutical Mfr
N.A.I.C.S.: 325412
Tomer Natan *(CFO)*

Subsidiary (Non-US):

QBI Enterprises, Ltd. (2)
Weizmann Science Park, PO Box 4071, Tel Aviv, 70400, Israel
Tel.: (972) 8 9305 111
Pharmaceutical Research
N.A.I.C.S.: 541715
Hagit Ashush *(VP-Res Ops)*

SBI (China) Co., Ltd.
Suite 1420 Shanghai World Financial Center No 100 Century Avenue, Pudong District, Shanghai, 200120, China
Tel.: (86) 216 877 6855
Sales Financing Services
N.A.I.C.S.: 522220

SBI ALApromo Co., Ltd. (1)
Izumi Garden Tower 17F 1-6-1, Roppongi Minato-ku, Tokyo, 106-6017, Japan   (100%)
Tel.: (81) 120952755
Web Site: https://www.5-ala.jp
Cosmetics & Health Foods Mfr
N.A.I.C.S.: 311999
Kazuhito Uchio *(Dir)*

SBI Arsnova Research Co., Ltd. (1)
18F Izumi Garden Tower 1-6-1, Roppongi Minato-ku, Tokyo, 106-6018, Japan   (99%)
Tel.: (81) 362290824
Web Site: http://www.arsnova-cr.com
Sales Range: $50-74.9 Million
Emp.: 3
Designs, Operates & Manages Alternative Financial Solutions & Services
N.A.I.C.S.: 523999
Hirofumi Takeuchi *(CEO)*

SBI Asset Management Co., Ltd. (1)
Izumi Garden Tower Roppongi 1-chome No 6 No 1, Minato-ku, Tokyo, 106-6015, Japan   (100%)
Tel.: (81) 362290170
Web Site: http://www.sbiam.co.jp
Emp.: 23
Asset Management & Investment Advisory Services

N.A.I.C.S.: 523940

SBI AutoSupport Co., Ltd. (1)
1-6-1 Izumi Garden Tower 15F, Roppongi Minato-ku, Tokyo, 106-6019, Japan
Tel.: (81) 3 6229 2181
Web Site: http://www.sbiautosupport.jp
Automobile Financing Services
N.A.I.C.S.: 522220

SBI Bank LLC (1)
Leningradsky Prospekt 72 72 bldg 2, 125315, Moscow, Russia
Tel.: (7) 4956516512
Web Site: http://www.sbibankllc.ru
Rev.: $13,080,736
Assets: $228,279,744
Liabilities: $159,348,173
Net Worth: $68,931,571
Earnings: ($18,698,993)
Fiscal Year-end: 12/31/2019
Commercial Banking Services
N.A.I.C.S.: 522110
Karyakin Andrey Dmitrievich *(Chm-Mgmt Bd)*

SBI Benefit Systems Co., Ltd. (1)
Izumi Garden Tower 15F 1-6-1, Roppongi Minato-ku, Tokyo, 106-6019, Japan   (87%)
Tel.: (81) 362290823
Web Site: http://www.benefit401k.com
Defined-Contribution Pension Plans, Personnel & Public Welfare Services & Systems Outsourcing
N.A.I.C.S.: 525110

SBI Biotech Co., Ltd. (1)
Izumi Garden Tower 15F 1-6-1, Roppongi Minato-ku, Tokyo, 106-6015, Japan   (60.1%)
Tel.: (81) 362290787
Web Site: https://www.sbibiotech.jp
Sales Range: $25-49.9 Million
Emp.: 20
Pharmaceutical Cancer Research & Development Solutions
N.A.I.C.S.: 325412
Takeshi Irie *(Pres)*

SBI Bits Co., Ltd. (1)
Roppongi T-Cube 3-1-1 Roppongi, Minato-ku, Tokyo, 106-0032, Japan
Tel.: (81) 34 510 7000
Web Site: https://www.sbibits.com
Emp.: 398
Computer Programming Services
N.A.I.C.S.: 541511

SBI Business Solutions Co., Ltd. (1)
1-chome No 6 No 1 Izumi Garden Tower, Minato-ku Roppongi, Tokyo, 106-6013, Japan   (71.4%)
Tel.: (81) 362290809
Web Site: http://www.sbi-bs.co.jp
Sales Range: $10-24.9 Million
Emp.: 30
Back Office Support Services
N.A.I.C.S.: 561499
Masataka Natsukawa *(Pres)*

SBI Business Support Co., Ltd. (1)
8-17-1 Nishi-Shinjuku Sumitomo Realty & Development Shinjuku Grand, Tower 34F Shinjuku-ku, Tokyo, 160-0023, Japan   (100%)
Tel.: (81) 3 6863 7370
Web Site: http://www.sbibs.co.jp
Sales Range: $75-99.9 Million
Emp.: 938
Call Center & Business Staffing Services
N.A.I.C.S.: 561320
Naoki Iwayoshi *(Pres)*

SBI Capital Co., Ltd. (1)
Izumi Garden Tower 1-6-1 Roppongi, Minato-ku, Tokyo, Japan   (100%)
Tel.: (81) 362290100
Buyout & Value Up Fund Management
N.A.I.C.S.: 525910
Yoshitaka Kitao *(Pres)*

SBI Capital Solutions Co., Ltd. (1)
1-6-1 Roppongi Izumi Garden Tower, Minato-Ku, Tokyo, 106-0032, Japan
Tel.: (81) 362291020
Web Site: http://www.sbics.co.jp
Sales Range: $50-74.9 Million
Emp.: 20
Fund Management Services

SBI HOLDINGS, INC.

N.A.I.C.S.: 523940

SBI Card Co., Ltd. (1)
18F Izumi Garden Tower 1-6-1 Roppongi, Minato-ku, Tokyo, 106-6018, Japan (100%)
Tel.: (81) 362290690
Web Site: http://www.sbicard.jp
Sales Range: $50-74.9 Million
Emp.: 30
Credit Card Services
N.A.I.C.S.: 522210

SBI Equal Credit Co., Ltd. (1)
Izumi Garden Tower 19 F 1-6-1 Roppongi, Minato-ku, Tokyo, 106-0032, Japan (100%)
Tel.: (81) 3 6229 0126
Web Site: http://www.sbigroup.co.jp
Sales Range: $25-49.9 Million
Emp.: 30
Personal Credit Services
N.A.I.C.S.: 522299
Yoshitaka Kitao (Pres)

SBI Estate Management Co., Ltd. (1)
1-6-1 Roppongi, Minato-Ku, Tokyo, 1066017, Japan
Tel.: (81) 362290675
Real Estate Manangement Services
N.A.I.C.S.: 531390

SBI FinTech Solutions Co., Ltd. (1)
Shibuya 2-1-1 Aoyama First Building 9F, Shibuya-ku, Tokyo, 150-0002, Japan (77.48%)
Tel.: (81) 334985011
Web Site: https://www.sbi-finsol.co.jp
Rev.: $40,782,797
Assets: $360,887,667
Liabilities: $324,647,546
Net Worth: $36,240,121
Earnings: $2,731,854
Emp.: 221
Fiscal Year-end: 03/31/2023
Credit Card Transaction Services
N.A.I.C.S.: 522390
Masataka Sammonji (CEO)

SBI Fund Bank Co., Ltd. (1)
Izumi Garden Tower 1-6-1 Roppongi, Minato-ku, Tokyo, 176-6017, Japan (100%)
Tel.: (81) 362290100
Web Site: http://www.fundbank.jp
Consulting Sales of Investment Trusts
N.A.I.C.S.: 541613
Yoshinobu Uemura (Pres)

SBI Futures Co., Ltd. (1)
Izumi Garden Tower 20F 1-6-1 Roppongi, Minato-ku, Tokyo, 169-8050, Japan (100%)
Tel.: (81) 1 2015 6817
Online Foreign Exchange Brokerage & Dealing Services
N.A.I.C.S.: 518210

SBI Fxtrade Co., Ltd. (1)
1-6-1 Roppongi Izumi Garden Tower, Minato-ku, Tokyo, 106-6019, Japan
Tel.: (81) 12 098 2417
Web Site: https://www.sbifxt.co.jp
Foreign Exchange Services
N.A.I.C.S.: 523160

SBI Global Asset Management Co., Ltd. (1)
15F Izumi Garden Tower 1-6-1 Roppongi, Minato-ku, Tokyo, 106-6015, Japan (52.62%)
Tel.: (81) 362290812
Web Site: https://sbiglobalam.co.jp
Rev.: $67,005,570
Assets: $123,111,250
Liabilities: $16,624,150
Net Worth: $106,487,100
Earnings: $10,503,290
Emp.: 122
Fiscal Year-end: 03/31/2024
Investment Research & Information Services
N.A.I.C.S.: 518210
Tomoya Asakura (Pres & CEO)

Subsidiary (US):

Carret Asset Management, LLC (2)
360 Madison Ave 20th Fl, New York, NY 10017
Tel.: (212) 593-3800
Web Site: http://www.carret.com
Portfolio Management
N.A.I.C.S.: 523940
John H. Dunn (Mng Dir & Portfolio Mgr)

Subsidiary (Domestic):

Gomez Consulting Co., Ltd. (2)
Nomura Real Estate Nishi-Shinjuku Joint Building 4F 8-5-1, Nishi-Shinjuku-ku, Tokyo, 160-0023, Japan
Tel.: (81) 353387436
Web Site: https://www.gomez.co.jp
Sales Range: $25-49.9 Million
Emp.: 20
Evaluation, Advisory & Construction Services for Web Sites
N.A.I.C.S.: 541519
Yoshitaka Kitao (Chm)

Morningstar Asset Management Co., Ltd. (2)
1-6-1 Roppongi Izumi Garden Tower, Minato-ku, Tokyo, 106-6015, Japan
Tel.: (81) 362290811
Web Site: http://morningstarasset.jp
Asset Management Consulting; Financial Institutions Investment Advisory
N.A.I.C.S.: 523940

SBI Guarantee Co., Ltd. (1)
9th floor of Hirakawacho Court 1-1-1, Hirakawacho Chiyoda-ku, Tokyo, 102-0093, Japan (100%)
Tel.: (81) 352260565
Web Site: http://www.sbigt.co.jp
Emp.: 30
Rent Payment Guarantee Services
N.A.I.C.S.: 561499

SBI Ikiiki SSI Inc. (1)
Roppongi 1-chome Station on the Namboku Line 16th Floor, Izumi Garden Tower 1-6-1 Roppongi Minato-ku, Tokyo, 106-6016, Japan
Tel.: (81) 12 074 8164
Web Site: https://www.i-sedai.com
Insurance Agencies & Brokerages Services
N.A.I.C.S.: 524210

SBI Insurance Co., Ltd. (1)
Izumi Garden Tower 1-6-1 Roppongi, Minato-ku, Tokyo, Japan (65.5%)
Tel.: (81) 3 6229 0060
Web Site: http://www.sbisonpo.co.jp
Sales Range: $50-74.9 Million
Emp.: 70
Online Non-Life Insurance; Owned 65.5 % by SBI Holdings, Inc., 33.4% by Aioi Insurance Co., Ltd. & 1.1% by SoftBank Corporation
N.A.I.C.S.: 524128

SBI Insurance Group Co., Ltd. (1)
16th Floor Izumi Garden Tower 1-6-1 Roppongi, Minato-ku, Tokyo, 106-6016, Japan
Tel.: (81) 362290881
Web Site: https://www.sbiig.co.jp
Rev.: $722,730,790
Assets: $1,389,851,650
Liabilities: $1,125,484,700
Net Worth: $264,366,950
Earnings: $118,980
Fiscal Year-end: 03/31/2024
Fire Insurance Services
N.A.I.C.S.: 524113
Tatsuyoshi Otobe (Chm & Pres)

SBI Investment Co., Ltd. (1)
Izumi Garden Tower 1-6-1 Roppongi, Minato-ku, Tokyo, 106-6019, Japan (100%)
Tel.: (81) 36229012
Web Site: http://www.sbinvestment.co.jp
Sales Range: $75-99.9 Million
Emp.: 100
Venture Capital Fund Management Services
N.A.I.C.S.: 523940
Yoshitaka Kitao (CEO)

SBI Investment Korea Co., Ltd. (1)
14F NC Tower 509 Teheran-ro, Gangnam-gu, Seoul, Korea (South)
Tel.: (82) 221399200
Web Site: https://www.sbik.co.kr
Rev.: $13,366,319
Assets: $102,600,069
Liabilities: $9,677,310
Net Worth: $92,922,759
Earnings: ($11,858,012)
Emp.: 41
Fiscal Year-end: 12/31/2022
Financial Investment Services
N.A.I.C.S.: 523999
Yoshimi Dakahashi (CEO)

SBI Japannext Co., Ltd. (1)
Roppongi T-Cube Building 20F 3-1-1, Roppongi Minato-ku, Tokyo, 106-0032, Japan (45.7%)
Tel.: (81) 345774040
Web Site: http://www.japannext.co.jp
Operation of Proprietary Trading System; Owned 45.7% by SBI Holdings, Inc. & 35.7% by Goldman Sachs Group, Inc.
N.A.I.C.S.: 523150

SBI Korea Holdings Co., Ltd. (1)
NC Tower 1 Samseong-dong 14F 509 Teheran-ro, Gangnam-gu, Seoul, 14340, Korea (South)
Tel.: (82) 221399200
Web Site: http://www.sbigroup.co.kr
Sales Range: $50-74.9 Million
Emp.: 25
Investment Management Service
N.A.I.C.S.: 523999
Takahashi Yoshimi (CEO)

SBI Lease Co., Ltd. (1)
Izumi Garden Tower 1-6-1 Roppongi, Minato-ku, Tokyo, 106-6019, Japan (100%)
Tel.: (81) 362290821
Web Site: http://www.weblease.co.jp
Develops Lease Related Products & Services for IT Industry
N.A.I.C.S.: 561499

SBI Life Insurance Co., Ltd. (1)
Izumi Garden Tower 1-6-1, Roppongi Minato-ku, Tokyo, 106-6016, Japan
Tel.: (81) 12 027 2811
Web Site: https://www.sbilife.co.jp
Fire Insurance Services
N.A.I.C.S.: 524113

SBI Liquidity Market Co., Ltd. (1)
6-1 Izumi Garden Tower 19th floor Roppongi 1-chome, Minato-ku, Tokyo, 106-6019, Japan
Tel.: (81) 362290955
Web Site: http://www.sbilm.co.jp
Liquidity, Trading Services
N.A.I.C.S.: 522320

SBI Ly Hour Bank Plc. (1)
Building 219 Street 128 and 169, Sangkat Mittapheap Khan Prampir Makara, Phnom Penh, Cambodia
Tel.: (855) 2 398 0888
Web Site: https://www.sbilhbank.com.kh
Financial Services
N.A.I.C.S.: 523999
Neak Oknha Hour Ly (Chm)

SBI METROPOL Fund Management Company (1)
Fred Roeskestraat 123, 1076 EE, Amsterdam, Netherlands
Tel.: (31) 20 5771177
Financial Holdings Company; Fund Management
N.A.I.C.S.: 551112

SBI Marketing Co., Ltd. (1)
15 F Garden Tower Izumi 6-1 Roppongi, Minato-ku, Tokyo, 106-6015, Japan
Tel.: (81) 362290869
Web Site: http://www.sbimarketing.co.jp
Emp.: 40
Marketing Plans & Solutions
N.A.I.C.S.: 541613
Tadahiro Sonoda (Pres & CEO)

SBI Money Plaza Co., Ltd. (1)
Izumi Garden Tower 17th Floor 1-6-1 Roppongi Minato-ku, Tokyo, 106-6017, Japan
Tel.: (81) 36 229 0872
Web Site: https://www.sbi-moneyplaza.co.jp
Financial Services
N.A.I.C.S.: 523999

SBI Neo Mobile Securities Co., Ltd. (1)
1-6-1 Roppongi, Minato-ku, Tokyo, Japan
Tel.: (81) 36 880 1581
Web Site: https://www.sbineomobile.co.jp
Smartphone Security Services
N.A.I.C.S.: 561612

SBI Neotrade Securities Co., Ltd. (1)
Izumi Garden Tower 29th Floor 1-6-1 Roppongi, Minato-ku, Tokyo, 106-6029, Japan
Tel.: (81) 12 044 1250
Web Site: https://www.sbineotrade.jp
Financial Instruments Business Operator
N.A.I.C.S.: 523150

SBI Net Systems Co., Ltd. (1)
Sumitomo Ichigaya Bldg 16th Floor 1-1 Ichigaya-honmuracho Shinjuku-ku, Tokyo, 162-0845, Japan (100%)
Tel.: (81) 362290100
Web Site: http://www.sbins.co.jp
Sales Range: $10-24.9 Million
Emp.: 301
Information Security Products Developer & Distr
N.A.I.C.S.: 513210
Masaaki Uchiyama (Pres)

SBI Nihon SSI Co., Ltd. (1)
3-1 Grand Front Osaka Tower B 13F Ofukacho, Kita-ku, Osaka, 530-0011, Japan
Tel.: (81) 12 008 0828
Web Site: https://www.n-ssi.co.jp
Insurance Agencies & Brokerages Services
N.A.I.C.S.: 524210

SBI Pharmaceuticals Co., Ltd. (1)
Izumi Garden Tower 20F 1-6-1 Direct link with Roppongi 1-chome Station, Roppongi Minato-ku, Tokyo, 106-6020, Japan
Tel.: (81) 36 229 0095
Web Site: https://www.sbipharma.co.jp
Pharmaceutical Preparation Mfr
N.A.I.C.S.: 325412
Yoshitaka Kitao (Pres)

SBI Point Union Co., Ltd. (1)
Izumi Garden Tower 1-6-1 Roppongi, Minato-ku, Tokyo, 106 6019, Japan (92.5%)
Tel.: (81) 362290967
Web Site: http://sbipu.co.jp
Plans & Develops Rewards Point Programs
N.A.I.C.S.: 541519

SBI Prism SSI Co., Ltd. (1)
2-1-1-1 Ichibancho Sendai Bank Building 7th Floor, Aoba-ku, Sendai, Miyagi, Japan
Tel.: (81) 12 039 1212
Web Site: https://www.animalclub.jp
Insurance Agencies & Brokerages Services
N.A.I.C.S.: 524210

SBI Property Advisors Co., Ltd. (1)
4-5 Gbancho, Chiyoda-ku, Tokyo, Japan
Tel.: (81) 3 6229 0100
Property Advisory Services
N.A.I.C.S.: 523940

SBI R3 Japan Co., Ltd. (1)
1-6-1 Izumi Garden Tower 19F Roppongi, Minato-ku, Tokyo, Japan
Tel.: (81) 36 229 0038
Web Site: https://sbir3japan.co.jp
Consulting Services
N.A.I.C.S.: 541614

SBI Receipt Co., Ltd. (1)
1-6-1 Roppongi, Minato-Ku, Tokyo, 106-6018, Japan
Tel.: (81) 362290886
Payment Receivable Services
N.A.I.C.S.: 522299

SBI Remit Co., Ltd. (1)
Izumi Garden Tower 1-6-1, Roppongi Minato-ku, Tokyo, 106-6018, Japan
Tel.: (81) 356526759
Web Site: http://www.remit.co.jp
Money Transfer Services
N.A.I.C.S.: 522320

SBI Resta SSI Co., Ltd. (1)
16th Floor of Izumi Garden Tower 1-6-1 Roppongi, Minato-ku, Tokyo, 106-6016, Japan
Tel.: (81) 36 229 1014
Web Site: https://www.jishin.co.jp
Insurance Agencies & Brokerages Services
N.A.I.C.S.: 524210

SBI Ripple Asia Co., Ltd. (1)
1-6-1 Roppongi, Minato-ku, Tokyo, Japan
Tel.: (81) 36 229 1159

SBI HOLDINGS, INC.

SBI Holdings, Inc.—(Continued)

Web Site: https://ripple.com
Consulting Services
N.A.I.C.S.: 541611

SBI Royal Securities Plc. (1)
13Ath Floor Prince Phnom Penh Tower N
445 Preah Monivong Blvd, Sangkat Boeung
Pralit Khan 7 Makara, Phnom Penh, Cambodia
Tel.: (855) 2 399 9595
Web Site: https://sbiroyal.com
Security Services
N.A.I.C.S.: 561612
Seng Chan Thoeun (CEO)

SBI Securities Co., Ltd. (1)
Izumi Garden Tower 1-6-1 Roppongi,
Minato-ku, Tokyo, 106-6012,
Japan (100%)
Tel.: (81) 362290100
Web Site: http://www.netbk.co.jp
Online Securities Brokerage & Dealing Services
N.A.I.C.S.: 523150
Yoshitaka Kitao (Chm)

SBI Servicer Co., Ltd. (1)
Izumi Garden Tower 18th Floor 1-6-1 Roppongi, Minato-ku, Tokyo, 106 6018,
Japan (100%)
Tel.: (81) 362290136
Manages, Collects & Purchases Debt; Consulting, Office Services & Bill Collecting Services
N.A.I.C.S.: 522390

SBI Social Lending Co., Ltd. (1)
1-6-1 Roppongi Tokyo Izumi Garden Tower
14F, Minato-ku, Tokyo, 106-6013, Japan
Tel.: (81) 355492637
Web Site: https://www.sbi-sociallending.co.jp
Money Lending Operating Services
N.A.I.C.S.: 522299

SBI Sumishin Net Bank, Ltd. (1)
Sumitomo Fudosan Roppongi Grand Tower
2-1 Roppongi 3-chome, Minato-ku, Tokyo,
Japan (50%)
Tel.: (81) 353637381
Web Site: http://www.netbk.co.jp
Rev.: $783,429,138
Assets: $70,541,235,547
Liabilities: $69,539,530,889
Net Worth: $1,001,704,658
Earnings: $164,155,930
Fiscal Year-end: 03/31/2024
Internet Banking
N.A.I.C.S.: 522110

Subsidiary (Domestic):

NetMove Corporation (2)
KDC Shibuya Bldg 5F 3-9-10 Shibuya,
Shibuya-ku, Tokyo, 150-0002, Japan
Tel.: (81) 357667835
Web Site: http://www.netmove.co.jp
Sales Range: $25-49.9 Million
Emp.: 30
Corporate Website Communication & Support Services
N.A.I.C.S.: 541519

SBI Thai Online Securities Co., Ltd. (1)
1768 Thai Summit Tower 31st Fl New
Petchburi Rd, Bangkapi Huaykwang, Bangkok, 10310, Thailand
Tel.: (66) 2 022 1499
Web Site: https://www.sbito.co.th
Financial Services
N.A.I.C.S.: 523999
Hiroaki Morita (Chm)

SBI Trans-Science Co., Ltd. (1)
1-6-1 Roppongi, Minato-ku, Tokyo, 106-6019, Japan
Tel.: (81) 3 6229 0129
Asset Management Services
N.A.I.C.S.: 523940

SBI VC Trade Co., Ltd. (1)
Izumi Garden Tower 1-6-1, Roppongi
Minato-ku, Tokyo, 106-6021, Japan
Tel.: (81) 36 779 5110
Web Site: https://www.sbivc.co.jp
Foreign Exchange Services
N.A.I.C.S.: 523160

SBI Ven Holdings Pte. Ltd. (1)
1 Raffles Place 18-03, Singapore, 48616, Singapore
Tel.: (65) 65366123
Web Site: http://www.sbivencapital.com.sg
Sales Range: $50-74.9 Million
Emp.: 10
Holding Company; Overseas Investments
N.A.I.C.S.: 551112
Yoshitaka Kitao (CEO)

Subsidiary (Domestic):

SBI Ven Capital Pte. Ltd. (2)
1 Raffles Place 18-03 One Raffles Place,
Singapore, 048616, Singapore
Tel.: (65) 65366123
Web Site: http://www.sbivencapital.com.sg
Sales Range: $50-74.9 Million
Emp.: 10
Overseas Investments
N.A.I.C.S.: 523999
Yoshitaka Kitao (CEO)

SBI Ventures Malaysia Sdn. Bhd. (1)
Suite No 6 1 Level 6 Menara IMC No 8,
Jalan Sultan Ismail, 50250, Kuala Lumpur, Malaysia
Tel.: (60) 32 020 1823
Sales Financing Services
N.A.I.C.S.: 522220

SBI Wellness Bank Co., Ltd. (1)
9th floor of Pacific Century Place
Marunouchi 1-11-1, Marunouchi Chiyoda-ku, Tokyo, 100-6209, Japan (100%)
Tel.: (81) 352202481
Web Site: http://www.sbi-wellnessbank.co.jp
Healthcare Services for Members & Public;
Consulting Services Involving Wellness
N.A.I.C.S.: 621999
Yoshitaka Kitao (Chm)

SBI artfolio Co., Ltd. (1)
7F TFT Building East Wing 3-6-11 Ariake,
Koto-ku, Tokyo, 135-0063, Japan (100%)
Tel.: (81) 335276691
Web Site: http://www.artfolio.co.jp
Emp.: 15
Artwork Brokerage & Sales
N.A.I.C.S.: 459920
Yoshitaka Kitao (CEO)

SBI-Hikari P.E. Co., Ltd. (1)
Izumi Garden Tower 1-6-1 Roppongi,
Minato-ku, Tokyo, Japan (85.09%)
Tel.: (81) 3 6629 0100
Web Site: http://www.sbigroup.co.jp
Operates & Manages Venture Capital Funds
N.A.I.C.S.: 523999

Searchina Co. Ltd. (1)
1-6-1 Izumi Garden Tower 15F, Roppongi
Minato-ku, Tokyo, 106-6015,
Japan (75.7%)
Tel.: (81) 362290810
Web Site: http://searchina.ne.jp
Sales Range: $25-49.9 Million
Emp.: 30
Information Retrieval Services
N.A.I.C.S.: 519290

Subsidiary (Non-US):

Shanghai Searchina Information Consulting Co., Ltd. (2)
Room 921 1279 West Zhongshan Road No 6, Chang Ning District, Shanghai, China
Tel.: (86) 2162787487
Online Information Retrieval & Consulting Services
N.A.I.C.S.: 519290

The Global Ltd. (1)
18F Shinjuku NS Building 2-4-1 Nishi-Shinjuku, Shinjuku-ku, Tokyo, 163-0818,
Japan (51.95%)
Tel.: (81) 333456111
Web Site: https://www.the-g.co.jp
Rev.: $168,170,140
Assets: $304,792,440
Liabilities: $255,299,900
Net Worth: $49,492,540
Earnings: $16,881,080
Fiscal Year-end: 06/30/2024
Real Estate Services
N.A.I.C.S.: 531210
Keiji Okada (Pres)

SBI HOME FINANCE LTD.
4th Floor SBI Ballygunge Branch
Premises 50A Gariahat Road, Kolkata, 700019, West Bengal, India
Tel.: (91) 3324865029
Housing Finance Services
N.A.I.C.S.: 624229

SBI SHINSEI BANK, LIMITED
2-4-3 Nihonbashi-Muromachi, Chuo-ku, Tokyo, 103-8303, Japan
Tel.: (81) 359547530 JP
Web Site:
https://www.sbishinseibank.co.jp
Year Founded: 1952
8303—(TKS)
Rev.: $4,083,537,040
Assets: $132,565,964,080
Liabilities: $123,210,186,000
Net Worth: $9,355,778,080
Earnings: $414,023,280
Emp.: 5,548
Fiscal Year-end: 03/31/23
Commercial Banking Services
N.A.I.C.S.: 522110
Katsuya Kawashima (Pres & CEO)

Subsidiaries:

Alpha Servicer Co., Ltd. (1)
Sumitomo Fudosan Akihabara Building 17th Floor 3-12-8 Sotokanda, Chiyoda-ku, Tokyo, 101-0021, Japan
Tel.: (81) 36 837 6903
Web Site: https://www.alpha-servicer.co.jp
Brokerage Services
N.A.I.C.S.: 523150

Financial Japan, Co., Ltd. (1)
Sumitomo Fudosan Akihabara Building 10th Floor 3-12-8 Sotokanda, Chiyoda-ku, Tokyo, 101-0021, Japan
Tel.: (81) 36 260 8805
Web Site: https://www.financialjapan.jp
Non Life Insurance Agency Services
N.A.I.C.S.: 524210

Shinsei Capital (USA), Ltd. (1)
7 Times Sq 25th Fl, New York, NY 10036
Tel.: (212) 888-7079
Web Site: http://www.shinseibank.com
Credit Card Issuer
N.A.I.C.S.: 522210

Shinsei Financial Co., Ltd. (1)
3-12-8 Sotokanda, Chiyoda-ku, Tokyo, 101-8603, Japan
Tel.: (81) 335259000
Web Site: https://shinseifinancial.co.jp
Sales Range: $1-4.9 Billion
Emp.: 1,528
Personal & Commercial Lending & Credit Services
N.A.I.C.S.: 522291

Subsidiary (Domestic):

APLUS FINANCIAL Co., Ltd. (2)
3-12-8 Sumitomo Fudosan Akihabara Building Sotokanda, Chiyoda-ku, Tokyo,
Japan (93.3%)
Tel.: (81) 352293702
Web Site: http://www.aplusfinancial.co.jp
Rev.: $693,588,300
Assets: $13,085,294,580
Liabilities: $12,355,593,120
Net Worth: $729,701,460
Earnings: $22,505,040
Emp.: 1,100
Fiscal Year-end: 03/31/2019
Consumer Credit Services
N.A.I.C.S.: 523999

Shinsei Investment Management Co., Ltd. (1)
4-3 Nihonbashi-Muromachi 2-Chome, Chuo-ku, Tokyo, 103-0022, Japan
Tel.: (81) 36 880 6400
Web Site: https://www.shinsei-investment.com
Asset Management Services
N.A.I.C.S.: 523940
Haruko Hirai (Pres & CEO)

Shinsei Personal Loan Co., Ltd. (1)
3-12-8 Sotokanda Sumitomo Realty and Development Akihabara Building, Chiyoda-ku, Tokyo, Japan
Tel.: (81) 33 525 9400
Web Site: https://www.noloan.com
Consumer Finance Services
N.A.I.C.S.: 522291

Shinsei Securities Co., Ltd. (1)
Nihonbashi Muromachi Nomura Building 4-3
Nihonbashi-muromachi 2-chome, Chuo-ku, Tokyo, 103-0022, Japan
Tel.: (81) 36 880 6000
Web Site: https://www.shinsei-sec.co.jp
Bond Underwriting Services
N.A.I.C.S.: 523150
Yasuhiro Iwamoto (Pres)

Showa Leasing Co., Ltd. (1)
2-4-3 Nihonbashi-muromachi, Chuo-ku, Tokyo, 112-0004, Japan
Tel.: (81) 342841111
Web Site: https://www.s-l.co.jp
General Leasing Services Provider
N.A.I.C.S.: 532490

Subsidiary (Domestic):

Shinko Lease Co., Ltd. (2)
2-4-2 Wakihama Kaigandori, Chuo-ku,
Kobe, 651-0073, Japan (80%)
Tel.: (81) 782616641
Web Site: http://www.shinkolease.co.jp
Leasing of Construction Equipment
N.A.I.C.S.: 532412

UDC Finance Ltd. (1)
Victoria Street West, PO Box 91145, Auckland, 1142, New Zealand (100%)
Tel.: (64) 800500832
Web Site: https://www.udc.co.nz
Earnings: $44,000,000
Emp.: 225
Fiscal Year-end: 09/30/2019
International Banking
N.A.I.C.S.: 522299
Bruce Gadsby (CIO)

SBL INFRATECH LIMITED
Shop no 160 1st floor Vardhmaan
Fourtune Mall GTK Ind Area, Dwarka,
Delhi, 110033, India
Tel.: (91) 9873732329
Web Site: https://www.sblinfra.com
Year Founded: 2005
543366—(BOM)
Real Estate Services
N.A.I.C.S.: 531210
Ankit Sharma (Mng Dir)

SBM HOLDING BEOMEDICINA A.D.
Bulevar Vojvode Bojovica 4, Belgrade, Serbia
Tel.: (381) 11 2185 402
Year Founded: 1992
Sales Range: Less than $1 Million
Trucks Mfr
N.A.I.C.S.: 336120

SBM OFFSHORE N.V.
Evert van de Beekstraat 1-77, 1118
CL, Amsterdam, Netherlands
Tel.: (31) 202363000
Web Site:
https://www.sbmoffshore.com
Year Founded: 1969
IHCB—(DEU)
Rev.: $4,963,000,000
Assets: $17,176,000,000
Liabilities: $11,645,000,000
Net Worth: $5,531,000,000
Earnings: $614,000,000
Emp.: 5,717
Fiscal Year-end: 12/31/23
Management Holding Company that
Supplies Engineering, Supply & Offshore Installation of SPM (Single
Point Mooring) Systems
N.A.I.C.S.: 333132
Bruno Chabas (CEO & Member-Mgmt Bd)

AND PRIVATE COMPANIES

Subsidiaries:

CADEMO Corporation (1)
810 N Farrell Dr, Palm Springs, CA 92262
Tel.: (760) 776-3535
Web Site: https://cademo.net
Wind Electric Power Generation Services
N.A.I.C.S.: 221115

Llyr Floating Wind Limited (1)
Office 20 Bridge Innovation Centre, Pembrokeshire Science and Technology Park, Pembroke Dock, United Kingdom
Tel.: (44) 1646689275
Web Site: http://www.llyrwind.com
Wind Electric Power Generation Services
N.A.I.C.S.: 221115

NKI Group B.V. (1)
Industriestraat 3-5, 5107 NC, Dongen, Netherlands
Tel.: (31) 0162384800
Web Site: http://www.nkigroup.com
Sales Range: $25-49.9 Million
Emp.: 44
Design, Fabrication, Installation & Project Management of Interior Specialities for Airport Terminals
N.A.I.C.S.: 541330

SBM Offshore (1)
1255 Enclave Pkwy, Houston, TX 77077
Tel.: (281) 848-6000
Web Site: http://www.sbmoffshore.com
Sales Range: $25-49.9 Million
Emp.: 600
Design, Procurement, Fabrication & Supply of Tanker Mooring Systems
N.A.I.C.S.: 541330
Stein Rasmussen (Pres)

SBM Offshore USA, Inc. (1)
1255 Enclave Pkwy, Houston, TX 77077-1846
Tel.: (281) 848-6000
Web Site: http://www.sbmoffshore.com
Emp.: 300
Floating Production Systems, Drilling & Engineering Services
N.A.I.C.S.: 541330

Division (Domestic):

GustoMSC Inc. (2)
10353 Richmond Ave Fl 22, Houston, TX 77042-4103
Tel.: (713) 380-2600
Web Site: http://www.gustomsc.com
Engineering Consulting Services for the Offshore Industry
N.A.I.C.S.: 541330

Sbm Malaysia Sdn Bhd
Ste 2B-9-1 Level 9 block 2B Plz Sentral Jalan Stesen Sentral 5, Kuala Lumpur, 50470, Malaysia
Tel.: (60) 327735300
Web Site: http://www.sbmoffshore.com
Offshore Oil & Gas Production Services
N.A.I.C.S.: 213112
Gunther Leyen (Gen Mgr)

Single Buoy Moorings (1)
5 route de Fribourg, PO Box 152, 1723, Marly, Switzerland
Tel.: (41) 264399920
Web Site: http://www.singlebuoy.com
Sales Range: $25-49.9 Million
Emp.: 67
Design, Fabrication, Installation & Servicing of Loading & Offloading Mooring Terminals, as well as Tanker-Based Floating Production & Storage Systems for the Offshore Oil & Gas Industry
N.A.I.C.S.: 541330

SBS HOLDINGS INC.
8-17-1 Nishi-Shinjuku Sumitomo Realty & Development, Shinjuku Grand Tower 25th floor Shinjuku-ku, Tokyo, 160-6125, Japan
Tel.: (81) 367728200
Web Site: https://www.sbs-group.co.jp
Year Founded: 1987
2384—(TKS)
Rev.: $3,062,248,990
Assets: $2,136,337,530
Liabilities: $1,408,960,250
Net Worth: $727,377,280
Earnings: $71,297,040
Emp.: 23,562
Fiscal Year-end: 12/31/23
Logistics & Other Business Support Services
N.A.I.C.S.: 541614
Yasuhito Tanaka (Operating Officer)

Subsidiaries:

Asahi New Transport Development Co., Ltd. (1)
4-5-41 2nd NK Building 7F, Yodogawa-ku Miyahara, Osaka, 532-0003, Japan
Tel.: (81) 663992580
Logistics Management Services
N.A.I.C.S.: 541614

Atlas Logistics Pvt. Ltd. (1)
138 Second Floor Maruthi Tower Old Airport Rd Kodihalli, Bengaluru, 560008, Karnataka, India
Tel.: (91) 8041985000
Web Site: https://atlaslogistics.co.in
Freight Forwarding Services
N.A.I.C.S.: 541614

Furukawa Logistics (Shanghai) Co., Ltd. (1)
155 C6F No 1 West FuTe Road Shanghai WaiGaoQiao Free Trade Zone, Shanghai, China
Tel.: (86) 2158680394
Industrial & Domestic Waste Disposal Services
N.A.I.C.S.: 562211

Hinomaru Express Co., Ltd. (1)
6-7-30 Asahimachi, Takamatsu, 760-0065, Kagawa, Japan
Tel.: (81) 878211626
Web Site: https://www.hinomaru-k.com
Emp.: 173
Logistics System Development Services
N.A.I.C.S.: 541614

Hong Kong Tokhe Logistics Co., Ltd. (1)
4th Floor Warehouse 2 CTS Xie Kee Warehouse 1 Cheong Hang Road, Hung Hom, Kowloon, China (Hong Kong)
Tel.: (852) 35720338
Industrial & Domestic Waste Disposal Services
N.A.I.C.S.: 562211

I and I Co., Ltd. (1)
2-203-2 Samukawa-cho, Chuo-ku, Chiba, 260-0832, Japan
Tel.: (81) 432909495
Cargo Transportation Services
N.A.I.C.S.: 811310

Japan Logistics Future Investment Limited (1)
Sumitomo Realty & Development Shinjuku Grand Tower 25th Floor, 8-17-1 Nishi-Shinjuku Shinjuku-ku, Tokyo, 160-6125, Japan
Tel.: (81) 338293473
Freight Forwarding Services
N.A.I.C.S.: 541614

Jas Co., Ltd. (1)
926 Kamiyabe-cho, Totsuka-ku, Yokohama, 963-0547, Kanagawa, Japan
Tel.: (81) 458110141
Web Site: https://www.ja-seating.co.jp
Emp.: 135
Industrial Vehicle Seat Mfr
N.A.I.C.S.: 336360

K2 Corporate Partners Co., Ltd. (1)
8-17-1 Nishi, Shinjuku-ku Sumitomo Fudosan Shinjuku Grand Tower 25th Floor, Tokyo, 160-6125, Japan
Tel.: (81) 344058882
Web Site: https://www.k2-cp.jp
Advertising Services
N.A.I.C.S.: 541810

Marketing Partner Co., Ltd. (1)
25F Sumitomo Fudosan Shinjuku Grand Tower 8-17-1 Nishi-Shinjuku, Shinjuku-ku, Tokyo, 160-6125, Japan
Tel.: (81) 367728214
Web Site: https://www.marketing-partner.jp

SBS HOLDINGS INC.

Marketing Consulting Services
N.A.I.C.S.: 541613
Yasuhito Tanaka (Pres & CEO)

Ricoh International Logistics (HK) ltd. (1)
Units 1-2 18/F Tower 1 Ever Gain Plaza 88 Container Port Road, Kwai Chung N T, Hong Kong, China (Hong Kong)
Tel.: (852) 23697128
Emp.: 22
Truck Transportation Services
N.A.I.C.S.: 532411

Ricon International Freight Agency (Shenzhen) Co., Ltd. (1)
Room 1804-1805 Trillion Financial Building No 319 Fuhua Road, Futian District, Shenzhen, 518038, China
Tel.: (86) 75582800650
Emp.: 108
Freight Forwarding Services
N.A.I.C.S.: 541614

SBS Asset Management Co., Ltd. (1)
Sumitomo Fudosan Shinjuku Grand Tower 25th floor 8-17-1 Nishi-Shinjuku, Shinjuku-ku, Tokyo, 130-0012, Japan
Tel.: (81) 367728216
Emp.: 17
Vehicle Leasing & Insurance Services
N.A.I.C.S.: 522220

SBS Driving School Co., Ltd. (1)
341 Naganuma-cho, Inage-ku, Chiba, 263-0005, Japan
Tel.: (81) 432596371
Web Site: https://www.sbs-drivingschool.co.jp
Driving School Services
N.A.I.C.S.: 611692

SBS Finance Co., Ltd. (1)
Vehicle Leasing & Insurance Services
N.A.I.C.S.: 522220

SBS Flec Co., Ltd. (1)
Sumitomo Fudosan Shinjuku Grand Tower 25F 8-17-1 Nishi, Shinjuku-ku, Tokyo, 160-6125, Japan
Tel.: (81) 367728208
Web Site: https://www.sbs-flec.co.jp
Emp.: 280
Food Product Mfr & Distr
N.A.I.C.S.: 311999

SBS Fleck Net Co., Ltd. (1)
Sumitomo Fudosan Shinjuku Grand Tower 25F 8-17-1 Nishi, Shinjuku-ku, Tokyo, 160-6125, Japan
Tel.: (81) 367728209
Web Site: https://www.sbs-flec.co.jp
Emp.: 3,047
Freight Forwarding Services
N.A.I.C.S.: 541614

SBS Freight Service Co., Ltd. (1)
5-32 Sugita, Shishi-ku, Yokohama, 235-0033, Kanagawa, Japan
Tel.: (81) 453707305
Freight & Truck Transportation Services
N.A.I.C.S.: 488510

SBS Furukawa Logistics Co., Ltd. (1)
Sumitomo Fudosan Shinjuku Grand Tower 25F 8-17-1 Nishi, Shinjuku-ku, Tokyo, 160-6125, Japan
Tel.: (81) 367728219
Web Site: https://www.sbs-furukawa-logis.co.jp
Emp.: 145
Industrial & Domestic Waste Disposal Services
N.A.I.C.S.: 562211

SBS Kamata Zaidan (1)
Taira 4-1-3 Olinas Tower, Sumida-ku, Tokyo, 130-0012, Tokyo Prefecture, Japan
Tel.: (81) 338232367
Web Site: http://www.sbs-kamatazaidan.or.jp
Freight & Truck Transportation Services
N.A.I.C.S.: 488510

SBS Logicom Co., Ltd. (1)
362 Tsutsumisaki, Saitama, Ageo, 362-0054, Japan
Tel.: (81) 487252302

Web Site: http://www.sbs-logicom.co.jp
Logistics Consulting Servies
N.A.I.C.S.: 541614

Subsidiary (Non-US):

SBS Global Network Co., Ltd. (2)
Emp.: 100
Logistics Consulting Servies
N.A.I.C.S.: 541614

SBS Logicom Kanto Co., Ltd. (1)
8-17-1 Nishi, Shinjuku-ku, Tokyo, 160-6125, Japan
Tel.: (81) 367728206
Web Site: https://www.sbs-logicom-kanto.co.jp
Freight Forwarding Services
N.A.I.C.S.: 541614

SBS Logistics Hong Kong Ltd. (1)
Units 1-2 18/F Tower 1 Ever Gain Plaza 88 Container Port Road, Kwai Chung, China (Hong Kong)
Tel.: (852) 24332199
Freight & Truck Transportation Services
N.A.I.C.S.: 488510

SBS Logistics Singapore Pte. Ltd. (1)
No 61 Ubi Avenue 1 05-10 UB Point, Singapore, 408941, Singapore
Tel.: (65) 68487420
Freight & Truck Transportation Services
N.A.I.C.S.: 488510

Subsidiary (Non-US):

SBS Logistics (Thailand) Co., Ltd. (2)
140 Room No 1811 18th Floor One Pacific Place Between Soi4 Soi6, Sukhumvit Rd Kwaeng Klongtoey Khet Klongtoey, Bangkok, 10110, Thailand
Tel.: (66) 265334013
Freight & Truck Transportation Services
N.A.I.C.S.: 488510

SBS Total Logistics Malaysia Sdn. Bhd. (2)
B-3-B 3rd Floor North Tower Tower B BBT One The Towers, Lebuh Batu Nilam Bandar Bukit Tinggi Klang, 41200, Kuala Selangor, Malaysia
Tel.: (60) 333251520
Freight & Truck Transportation Services
N.A.I.C.S.: 488510

TAS Logistics Co., Ltd. (2)
TAC House 4th Floor No 1 Soi Ruam Rudi Ploenchit Road, Lumpini Patunmwan, Bangkok, 10330, Thailand
Tel.: (66) 22537212
Warehouse Management Services
N.A.I.C.S.: 541614

SBS Ricoh Logistics Co., Ltd. (1)
8-17-1 Nishi-Sumitomo Realty & Development Grand Tower 25th Floor, Shinjuku-ku, Tokyo, 160-6125, Japan
Tel.: (81) 367728202
Web Site: https://www.sbs-ricohlogistics.co.jp
Emp.: 4,029
Packaging Material Mfr & Distr
N.A.I.C.S.: 326112

SBS Ricoh Logistics System Co., Ltd. (1)
Orinas Tower 4-1-3 Taihei, Sumida-ku, Tokyo, 130-0012, Japan
Tel.: (81) 342145500
Freight & Truck Transportation Services
N.A.I.C.S.: 488510

SBS San-ai Logistics Co., Ltd. (1)
25th floor Sumitomo Fudosan Shinjuku Grand Tower 8-17-1 Nishi-Shinjuku, Shinjuku-ku, Tokyo, 160-6125, Japan
Tel.: (81) 367728203
Emp.: 1,660
Medical Equipment Mfr & Distr
N.A.I.C.S.: 339114

SBS Sokuhai Support Co., Ltd. (1)
1-5-29 Shinsuna, Koto-ku, Tokyo, 136-0075, Japan
Tel.: (81) 356339024
Web Site: https://www.sbs-sokuhaisupport.co.jp
Emp.: 599

SBS HOLDINGS INC.

SBS Holdings Inc.—(Continued)
Transportation & Delivery Services
N.A.I.C.S.: 532411

SBS Staff Co., Ltd. (1)
4-3-8 Taihei SD Building 3F, Sumida-ku, Tokyo, 130-0012, Japan
Tel.: (81) 338292975
Web Site: http://www.sbs-staff.co.jp
Temporary Staffing Services
N.A.I.C.S.: 561320

SBS Support Logi Co., Ltd. (1)
1-4 Koazamatsukasa Yamashirochoka-mikoma, Kyoto, 619-0204, Japan
Tel.: (81) 774860666
Web Site: http://www.sbs-supportlogi.co.jp
Logistics Consulting Servies
N.A.I.C.S.: 541614

SBS Toshiba Logistics Co., Ltd. (1)
25th Floor Sumitomo Fudosan Shinjuku Grand Tower, 8-17-1 Nishi-Shinjuku, Shinjuku-ku, Tokyo, 160-6125, Japan
Tel.: (81) 367728201
Web Site: https://www.sbs-toshibalogistics.co.jp
Emp.: 722
Freight Forwarding Services
N.A.I.C.S.: 541614

SBS Vietnam Co., Ltd. (1)
146-148 Athena Building 6F, Cong Hoa St Ward 12 Tan Binh Dist, Ho Chi Minh City, Vietnam
Tel.: (84) 2838110222
Emp.: 18
Truck Transportation Services
N.A.I.C.S.: 532411

SBS Zentsu Co., Ltd. (1)
25th floor Sumitomo Fudosan Shinjuku Grand Tower 8-17-1 Nishi, Shinjuku-ku, Tokyo, 160-6125, Japan
Tel.: (81) 367728210
Web Site: https://www.sbs-zentsu.co.jp
Emp.: 3,654
Transportation & Delivery Services
N.A.I.C.S.: 532411

TL Forwarding Service (Philippines) Corporation (1)
Perry's Logistics Centre Ninoy Aquino Avenue, San Dionisio, Paranaque, Philippines
Tel.: (63) 28081394
Warehouse & Storage Management Services
N.A.I.C.S.: 531130

TL Logistics Service Co., Ltd. (1)
8-17-1 Nishi 25th Floor Sumitomo Fudosan Shinjuku Grand Tower, Shinjuku-ku, Tokyo, 160-6125, Japan
Tel.: (81) 5017549111
Emp.: 1,307
Logistics Management Services
N.A.I.C.S.: 541614

Toshiba Logistics (Dalian) Co., Ltd. (1)
No18 Nangang Road, Tianhai District DFTZ, Dalian, China
Tel.: (86) 41187328866
Warehouse & Storage Managing Services
N.A.I.C.S.: 531130

Toshiba Logistics (Hangzhou) Co., Ltd. (1)
M12-19-1 Hangzhou Export Processing Zone Of Zhejiang, Hangzhou, China
Tel.: (86) 57186714411
Warehouse & Storage Managing Services
N.A.I.C.S.: 531130

Toshiba Logistics (Hong Kong) Co., Ltd. (1)
Unit 1117-1118 Level 11 Tower 1 Grand Century Place, 193 Prince Edward Road West Mong Kok, Kowloon, China (Hong Kong)
Tel.: (852) 21105555
Heavy Cargo Handling Services
N.A.I.C.S.: 811310

Toshiba Logistics (Philippines) Corporation (1)
103 East Main Ave Extension Special Export Processing Zone, Laguna Technopark, Binan, Laguna, Philippines
Tel.: (63) 495434942
Warehouse & Storage Management Services
N.A.I.C.S.: 531130

Toshiba Logistics (Singapore) Pte. Ltd. (1)
47 Pandan Road Block B 05-00, Singapore, 609288, Singapore
Tel.: (65) 62732217
Web Site: https://singapore.sbs-tlog.com
Warehouse & Storage Management Services
N.A.I.C.S.: 531130

Toshiba Logistics Malaysia Sdn. Bhd. (1)
1-04-03 Menara IJM Land 1 Lebuh Tunku Kudin 3, 11700, Gelugor, Penang, Malaysia
Tel.: (60) 46099288
Web Site: https://malaysia.sbs-tlog.com
Emp.: 10
Industrial Machinery Transportation Services
N.A.I.C.S.: 532411

Toshiba logistics Vietnam Co., Ltd. (1)
Room 1702 17th Floor Centec Tower 72-74 Nguyen Thi Minh Khai, Ward Vo Thi Sau District 3, Ho Chi Minh City, Vietnam
Tel.: (84) 838256417
Warehouse & Storage Management Services
N.A.I.C.S.: 531130

SBS PHILIPPINES CORPORATION
10 Resthaven St SFDM, Metro Manila, Quezon City, Philippines
Tel.: (63) 283711111
Web Site: https://www.sbsph.com
SBS—(PHI)
Rev.: $18,683,188
Assets: $156,899,877
Liabilities: $37,741,989
Net Worth: $119,157,888
Earnings: $1,084,056
Fiscal Year-end: 12/31/23
Chemical Products Distr
N.A.I.C.S.: 424690
Esmeraldo A. Tepace *(COO & Exec VP)*

SBW INC.
390 Toegye-ro, Jung-gu, 4611, Seoul, Korea (South)
Tel.: (82) 234856000
Web Site: http://www.sbw.co.kr
Year Founded: 2008
102280—(KRS)
Rev.: $79,211,903
Assets: $128,661,196
Liabilities: $22,314,617
Net Worth: $106,346,579
Earnings: ($73,624,759)
Emp.: 215
Fiscal Year-end: 12/31/22
Apparel Product Mfr & Distr
N.A.I.C.S.: 315250
Se-Ho Kim *(CEO & VP)*

SC ARTECA JILAVA SA
Prel Sos Giurgiului no 33A sector 4, Jilava, Ilfov, Romania
Tel.: (40) 723323182
Web Site: https://www.arteca.ro
Year Founded: 1935
ARJI—(BUC)
Rev.: $3,043,950
Assets: $6,974,363
Liabilities: $1,196,656
Net Worth: $5,777,707
Earnings: $160,183
Emp.: 57
Fiscal Year-end: 12/31/23
Rubber Products Mfr
N.A.I.C.S.: 326299

SC ASAM S.A.
Aurel Vlaicu 77, 700381, Iasi, Romania
Tel.: (40) 232 215 515
Web Site: http://www.asam.ro
Year Founded: 1924
Motor Vehicle Parts Mfr
N.A.I.C.S.: 336350

SC ASSET CORPORATION PCL
1010 Viphavadi Rangsit Road Chatuchak, Bangkok, 10900, Thailand
Tel.: (66) 29492000
Web Site: http://www.scassset.com
Sales Range: $250-299.9 Million
Residential Real Estate Management Services
N.A.I.C.S.: 531390

SC BRICOMAT SA
Sos Alba Iulia nr 112, 550052, Sibiu, Romania
Tel.: (40) 269253025
Web Site: https://www.bricomat.ro
Year Founded: 2002
COBL—(BUC)
Rev.: $173,511
Assets: $3,211,739
Liabilities: $215,828
Net Worth: $2,995,911
Earnings: ($151,993)
Emp.: 5
Fiscal Year-end: 12/31/23
Household Appliance Whslr
N.A.I.C.S.: 423620

SC BTT SA
Sos Calea Victoriei Nr 155 Bl D1 sc 6, 10073, Bucharest, Romania
Tel.: (40) 213124469
Web Site: https://www.btt.ro
Year Founded: 1968
BIBU—(BUC)
Rev.: $1,172,969
Assets: $12,951,629
Liabilities: $3,872,720
Net Worth: $9,078,908
Earnings: $184,650
Emp.: 20
Fiscal Year-end: 12/31/22
Accommodation Services
N.A.I.C.S.: 721110

SC CEPROHART SA
B-dul Al I Cuza nr 3, Braila, 810019, Romania
Tel.: (40) 239619741
Web Site: http://www.ceprohart.ro
Year Founded: 1956
CPHA—(BUC)
Rev.: $1,577,499
Assets: $1,523,232
Liabilities: $223,893
Net Worth: $1,299,339
Earnings: $66,937
Emp.: 45
Fiscal Year-end: 12/31/22
Paper Mfr
N.A.I.C.S.: 322120

SC COCOR SA
Bd I C Bratianu Nr 29-33 Sector 3, 030173, Bucharest, Romania
Tel.: (40) 213131403
Web Site: https://www.cocor.ro
COCR—(BUC)
Rev.: $3,096,624
Assets: $29,359,872
Liabilities: $5,281,680
Net Worth: $24,078,191
Earnings: $658,286
Emp.: 24
Fiscal Year-end: 12/31/23
Shopping Center Leasing Services
N.A.I.C.S.: 531120

INTERNATIONAL PUBLIC

SC COMES SA SAVINESTI
Str Uzinei Nr 3, Savinesti, 617410, Neamt, Romania
Tel.: (40) 233 280 601
Web Site: http://www.comes.ro
Year Founded: 1977
Pressure Vessel & Equipment Mfr
N.A.I.C.S.: 339999
Petru Cozma *(Exec Dir)*

SC DORNA TURISM SA
Str Republicii Nr 5, 725700, Vatra Dornei, Suceava, Romania
Tel.: (40) 230375314
Web Site: https://www.dornaturism.ro
Year Founded: 1991
DOIS—(BUC)
Rev.: $3,787,076
Assets: $4,493,844
Liabilities: $1,376,565
Net Worth: $3,117,279
Earnings: ($180,988)
Emp.: 135
Fiscal Year-end: 12/31/23
Hotel & Motel Services
N.A.I.C.S.: 721110
Alexandru Vezeteu *(Pres & Gen Mgr)*

SC DUMBRAVA SA
Strada Armatei nr 3, Falticeni, 5750, Suceava, Romania
Tel.: (40) 230 542329
Web Site: http://www.dumbrava.ro
Emp.: 16
Furniture Mfr
N.A.I.C.S.: 337121
Ioan Paius *(Pres & Gen Mgr)*

SC EMAILUL SA
Str Carpati nr 19, Sibiu, Medias, Romania
Tel.: (40) 269843330
Web Site: https://www.emailul-medias.ro
Year Founded: 1921
Sales Range: $10-24.9 Million
Emp.: 861
Fabricated Metal Products Mfr
N.A.I.C.S.: 332215

SC ENERGOUTILAJ SA
Str Actiunii nr 26 Sector 4, 41102, Bucharest, Romania
Tel.: (40) 21 450 30 02
Web Site: http://www.energoutilaj.ro
Year Founded: 1949
Emp.: 50
Cranes Rental & Heavy Equipment Transport Services
N.A.I.C.S.: 532412
Dorel Bajaliu *(Gen Mgr)*

SC ENGINEERING CO., LTD.
7th and 8th floors Cricket Holdings Building 396 Gonghang-daero, Gangseo-gu, Seoul, Korea (South)
Tel.: (82) 221679090
Web Site: https://www.sc-eng.com
Year Founded: 1971
023960—(KRS)
Rev.: $105,251,431
Assets: $81,690,505
Liabilities: $50,047,638
Net Worth: $31,642,867
Earnings: $4,187,357
Emp.: 139
Fiscal Year-end: 12/31/22
Heavy Construction Engineering Services
N.A.I.C.S.: 237990
Cheong-Ho Chang *(Chm & CEO)*

SC ESTATE BUILDER BHD
D-8-06 Block D Level 8 Capital 4 Oasis Square No 2 Jalan PJU 1A/7A,

Ara Damansara, 47301, Petaling Jaya, Selangor, Malaysia
Tel.: (60) 376104388
Web Site:
https://www.scestatebuilder.com.my
Year Founded: 1984
SCBUILD—(KLS)
Rev.: $523,540
Assets: $8,874,511
Liabilities: $1,631,679
Net Worth: $7,242,832
Earnings: ($843,600)
Fiscal Year-end: 01/31/23
Building Construction Services
N.A.I.C.S.: 236210
Cheng-Lai Hock *(Chm)*

SC FAIMAR SA
Str Oborului nr 1, 430392, Baia Mare, 430392, Maramures, Romania
Tel.: (40) 729885419
Web Site: https://www.faimar.ro
Year Founded: 1979
Sales Range: $1-9.9 Million
Emp.: 320
Ceramic Household Product Mfr
N.A.I.C.S.: 327110

SC FONDUL PROPRIETATEA SA
Premium Point Buzesti Street 76-80 7th-8th floor, 1st District, 11017, Bucharest, Romania
Tel.: (40) 212009600
Web Site:
https://www.fondulproprietatea.ro
Year Founded: 2005
FP—(BUC)
Rev.: $2,522,566,112
Assets: $636,389,628
Liabilities: $132,142,106
Net Worth: $504,247,522
Earnings: ($194,642,962)
Fiscal Year-end: 12/31/23
Investment Management Service
N.A.I.C.S.: 523999
Piotr Rymaszewski *(Chm)*

SC GERMINA AGRIBUSINESS S.A.
Splaiul Unirii nr 16 Etaj 5 Camera 502 sector 4, Bucharest, Romania
Tel.: (40) 213225480
Web Site: https://www.germina.ro
SEOM—(BUC)
Rev.: $709,331
Assets: $3,819,198
Liabilities: $708,999
Net Worth: $3,110,199
Earnings: $119,693
Emp.: 10
Fiscal Year-end: 12/31/23
Grain Whslr
N.A.I.C.S.: 424510

SC GLOBAL DEVELOPMENTS LIMITED
200 Newton Rd 09-01, Singapore, 307983, Singapore
Tel.: (65) 67349119
Web Site: http://www.scglobal.com.sg
Sales Range: $600-649.9 Million
Property Management Services
N.A.I.C.S.: 531311
Simon Cheong *(Chm & CEO)*

Subsidiaries:

Astidvale Pte Ltd (1)
200 Newton Road 09-01, Singapore, 307983, Singapore
Tel.: (65) 67349119
Investment Management Service
N.A.I.C.S.: 523999

Avjennings Limited (1)
Level 4 108 Power Street, Hawthorn, 3122, VIC, Australia
Tel.: (61) 131878
Web Site: https://www.avjennings.com.au
Rev.: $213,505,608
Assets: $576,384,880
Liabilities: $271,485,042
Net Worth: $304,899,838
Earnings: $682,425
Fiscal Year-end: 06/30/2024
Real Estate Support Services
N.A.I.C.S.: 531190
Peter Summers *(CEO & Mng Dir)*

Seven Palms Resorts Management Pte Ltd (1)
200 Newton Road 09-01, Singapore, 307983, Singapore
Tel.: (65) 67349119
Web Site: http://www.scglobal.com.sg
Resort Management Services
N.A.I.C.S.: 721110

SC GROUP THAI
SC Building 88 The Parkland Road, Bangna, Bangkok, 10260, Thailand
Tel.: (66) 23419000
Web Site:
http://www.scgroupthai.com
Year Founded: 1985
Holding Company; Logistics & Supply Chain Solutions
N.A.I.C.S.: 551112
Nuttaphob Ratanasuwanthawee *(Chm & Pres)*

Subsidiaries:

NFC Public Company Limited (1)
88 SC Group Building 3rd Floor, The Parkland Road Bangna Nuea, Bangkok, 10260, Thailand
Tel.: (66) 23480580
Web Site: https://www.nfc.co.th
Rev.: $52,625,084
Assets: $226,369,891
Liabilities: $185,169,053
Net Worth: $41,200,838
Earnings: $5,285,040
Emp.: 77
Fiscal Year-end: 12/31/2023
Chemical Fertilizer Mfr & Whslr
N.A.I.C.S.: 325311
Nuttaphob Ratanasuwanthawee *(Vice Chm & CEO)*

SC HELIOS SA
nr 236, 417020, Astileu, Bihor, Romania
Tel.: (40) 756151648
Web Site: https://www.heliossa.ro
Year Founded: 1885
HEAL—(BUC)
Rev.: $7,620,353
Assets: $11,381,193
Liabilities: $2,625,851
Net Worth: $8,755,342
Earnings: $590,702
Emp.: 73
Fiscal Year-end: 12/31/23
Brick & Tile Mfr
N.A.I.C.S.: 327120

SC HIDROMECANICA SA BRASOV
13 Decembrie nr 94A Str, Brasov, 500164, Romania
Tel.: (40) 368884929
Web Site: http://www.hidromecanica-brasov.ro
Sales Range: $1-9.9 Million
Emp.: 139
Engine & Turbine Mfr
N.A.I.C.S.: 333618
Valeriu Calbeaza *(Gen Mgr)*

SC ILVAS SA
Str Stefan cel Mare nr 9, 730187, Vaslui, Romania
Tel.: (40) 31 235 44 14
Web Site: http://www.ilvas.ro
Sales Range: $1-9.9 Million
Emp.: 145
Milk Production Services
N.A.I.C.S.: 112120

SC IMOTRUST S.A.
Str Mihai Eminescu Nr 5 Ap 2 Arad, 310086, Arad, Romania
Tel.: (40) 733800400
Web Site:
https://www.imotrustarad.ro
ARCV—(BUC)
Rev.: $8,278,891
Assets: $22,662,983
Liabilities: $4,977,031
Net Worth: $17,685,952
Earnings: $488,098
Emp.: 30
Fiscal Year-end: 12/31/23
Industrial & Residential Real Estate Services
N.A.I.C.S.: 531210

SC INCERTRANS SA
Calea Grivitei 391-393 Sector 1, 010719, Bucharest, Romania
Tel.: (40) 213162337
Web Site: https://www.incertrans.ro
Year Founded: 1993
INCT—(BUC)
Rev.: $1,515,685
Assets: $1,923,939
Liabilities: $258,824
Net Worth: $1,665,115
Earnings: $10,776
Emp.: 41
Fiscal Year-end: 12/31/23
Natural Sciences & Engineering Research & Development Services
N.A.I.C.S.: 541715

SC KINGFLEX CORPORATION
No 99 Xiyuan Rd, Zhongli Dist, Taoyuan, 320, Taiwan
Tel.: (886) 34514015
Web Site:
http://www.sckingflex.com.tw
Year Founded: 1979
Sales Range: $25-49.9 Million
Emp.: 110
Rubber Hoses & Related Product Mfr
N.A.I.C.S.: 326220

SC LACTATE NATURA SA
Bd Independentei nr 23, Targoviste, Romania
Tel.: (40) 245615651
Web Site: http://www.lactatenatura.ro
INBO—(BUC)
Rev.: $625,485
Assets: $3,022,800
Liabilities: $113,833
Net Worth: $2,908,967
Earnings: ($544,879)
Emp.: 5
Fiscal Year-end: 12/31/22
Cheese Mfr
N.A.I.C.S.: 311513

SC LINE S.A.
Av Roberto Motta y Boulevard, Panama, Panama
Tel.: (507) 830 5000
Web Site: http://www.scline.com
Freight Transportation
N.A.I.C.S.: 488510
Jose Maria Sola Matas *(CEO)*

Subsidiaries:

SC LINE VENEZUELA (1)
Av Henry Ford, Valencia, Carabobo, Venezuela
Tel.: (58) 4144001812
Marine Transportation Services
N.A.I.C.S.: 483111

SC LINE Zona Franca S.A.S. (1)
Usuario Industrial de Servicios Zona Franca Las Americas Km 16 Via, Alterna al Puerto Ruta del Sol II, Santa Marta, Colombia
Tel.: (57) 3178929116
Marine Transportation Services
N.A.I.C.S.: 483111

SC Line Colombia SAS (1)
Calle Real Con Callejon Porto 25 29 Manga, Cartagena, Bolivar, Colombia
Tel.: (57) 56601115
Marine Transportation Services
N.A.I.C.S.: 483111

SC Line USA Corporation (1)
8669 NW 36th ST Ste 335, Doral, FL 33166
Tel.: (305) 767-1900
Marine Transportation Services
N.A.I.C.S.: 483111

SC MECANICA CEAHLAU SA
Str Dumbravei 6, 610202, Piatra Neamt, Romania
Tel.: (40) 233211104
Web Site:
https://www.mecanicaceahlau.ro
Year Founded: 1921
MECF—(BUC)
Rev.: $4,740,713
Assets: $13,731,162
Liabilities: $1,692,545
Net Worth: $12,038,617
Earnings: ($589,058)
Emp.: 101
Fiscal Year-end: 12/31/20
Agricultural Machine & Equipment Mfr
N.A.I.C.S.: 333111
Trifa Aurelian Mircea Radu *(Chm)*

SC METAL LEMN SA
Bd Decebal Nr 85, Dolj, Craiova, Romania
Tel.: (40) 251439087
Web Site: https://www.metallemn.ro
Year Founded: 1976
MELE—(BUC)
Rev.: $1,655,127
Assets: $13,069,788
Liabilities: $2,072,773
Net Worth: $10,997,015
Earnings: $535,548
Emp.: 11
Fiscal Year-end: 12/31/23
Furniture Mfr
N.A.I.C.S.: 337214

SC NAPOCHIM SA
Str Luncii Nr 19, Cluj-Napoca, Romania
Tel.: (40) 264532015
Web Site: http://www.napochim.ro
NACH—(BUC)
Rev.: $986,234
Assets: $6,699,174
Liabilities: $8,153,895
Net Worth: ($1,454,722)
Earnings: ($343,433)
Emp.: 62
Fiscal Year-end: 12/31/19
Plastics Product Mfr
N.A.I.C.S.: 326199

SC ORIZONT TURISM SA
Str Trei Brazi nr 6, Predeal, 505300, Brasov, Romania
Tel.: (40) 268 455150
Web Site:
http://www.orizontturismsa.ro
Sales Range: $1-9.9 Million
Emp.: 107
Home Management Services
N.A.I.C.S.: 721110
Adrian Gheorghe Pintea *(Pres)*

SC PALACE SA
Str Octavian Goga 4, Sinaia, Romania
Tel.: (40) 244312052
Web Site: http://www.palacesinaia.ro
Year Founded: 1911
PACY—(BUC)
Rev.: $3,125,575
Assets: $6,256,377
Liabilities: $2,775,703
Net Worth: $3,480,674

SC PALACE SA

SC Palace SA—(Continued)
Earnings: $109,175
Emp.: 46
Fiscal Year-end: 12/31/23
Home Management Services
N.A.I.C.S.: 721110

SC PRACTIC SA
Str. Biserica Amzei nr.21-23 Corp C3 etaj 1 si 2 Sector 1, Bucharest, Romania
Tel.: (40) 213150955
Web Site: http://www.practicsa.ro
Year Founded: 1991
PRBU—(BUC)
Rev.: $10,321,650
Assets: $104,545,024
Liabilities: $9,662,438
Net Worth: $94,882,586
Earnings: $5,836,640
Emp.: 21
Fiscal Year-end: 12/31/23
Commercial Property Rental Services
N.A.I.C.S.: 531190
Mihai Ene *(Chm & Gen Mgr)*

SC PREMIUM SA
Str Trandafirilor nr 69, 107080, Brazi, Prahova, Romania
Tel.: (40) 244526606
Web Site: https://www.premiumgrup.ro
Year Founded: 1962
Engineeering Services
N.A.I.C.S.: 541330

SC SEMROM OLTENIA S.A.
Str Eugeniu Carada Nr 7 Loc, Jud Dolj, Craiova, Romania
Tel.: (40) 251461138
Web Site: https://www.semromoltenia.ro
SEOL—(BUC)
Rev.: $3,584,503
Assets: $4,463,211
Liabilities: $651,014
Net Worth: $3,812,197
Earnings: ($418,844)
Emp.: 27
Fiscal Year-end: 12/31/23
Agriculture Product Distr
N.A.I.C.S.: 424910
Laurentiu Parghel *(Pres & Gen Mgr)*

SC SINTEROM S.A.
12 Muncii Blvd, Cluj County, 400641, Cluj-Napoca, Romania
Tel.: (40) 264415086
Web Site: http://www.sinterom.ro
SIRM—(BUC)
Rev.: $1,576,611
Assets: $13,858,686
Liabilities: $739,619
Net Worth: $13,119,067
Earnings: $22,544
Emp.: 22
Fiscal Year-end: 12/31/22
Metal Parts Mfr
N.A.I.C.S.: 332117
Attila-Iosif Bogna *(Pres)*

SC SMR SA
Str Nicolae Balcescu Nr 208, Bals, 235100, Olt, Romania
Tel.: (40) 249 450860
Web Site: http://www.smr.ro
Year Founded: 1989
Locomotive & Rolling Stock Mfr
N.A.I.C.S.: 336510

SC SOMPLAST SA
Str George Cosbuc 147, Nasaud, Bistrita, 425200, Romania
Tel.: (40) 263360028
Web Site: http://www.somplast.ro
Year Founded: 1978

SOPL—(BUC)
Rev.: $492,479
Assets: $3,212,575
Liabilities: $1,180,059
Net Worth: $2,032,516
Earnings: ($288,899)
Emp.: 16
Fiscal Year-end: 12/31/22
Plastics Product Mfr
N.A.I.C.S.: 326199

SC STIMAS SA
Traian Vuia No 11, 720021, Suceava, Romania
Tel.: (40) 230523050
Web Site: http://www.stimas.ro
Sales Range: Less than $1 Million
Emp.: 7
Glassware Mfr
N.A.I.C.S.: 327212
Tetel Mircea *(Pres)*

SC TRAMECO S.A.
14/A Borsului Street, 410605, Oradea, Romania
Tel.: (40) 259467636
Web Site: http://www.selina.ro
Year Founded: 1991
TRAM—(BUC)
Rev.: $31,755,479
Assets: $28,167,643
Liabilities: $25,818,326
Net Worth: $2,349,317
Earnings: $294,323
Emp.: 43
Fiscal Year-end: 12/31/19
Freight Transport Services
N.A.I.C.S.: 484220
Beneamin Rus *(Pres & Gen Mgr)*

SC TREFO SA
Zona Libera Perimetrul III, Braila, 810118, Romania
Tel.: (40) 339107000
Web Site: http://www.trefo.ro
Year Founded: 1955
Wire & Chain Product Mfr
N.A.I.C.S.: 339999

SC TURISM FELIX SA
Str Victory no 24, 417500, Baile Felix, Bihor, Romania
Tel.: (40) 259318338
Web Site: https://www.felixspa.com
Year Founded: 1995
TUFE—(BUC)
Rev.: $21,527,651
Assets: $102,995,583
Liabilities: $55,642,006
Net Worth: $47,353,577
Earnings: $1,875,701
Emp.: 704
Fiscal Year-end: 12/31/22
Home Management Services
N.A.I.C.S.: 721110
Mihai I. Fercala *(Chm-Mgmt Bd & Pres)*

SC URBANA SA
Str Nicolae Titulescu Nr 50, Bistrita Nasaud, 420044, Bistrita, 420044, Romania
Tel.: (40) 263233585
Web Site: https://urbana.ro
URBA—(BUC)
Rev.: $2,515,496
Assets: $938,807
Liabilities: $650,608
Net Worth: $288,199
Earnings: ($69,502)
Emp.: 78
Fiscal Year-end: 12/31/23
Waste Disposal Services
N.A.I.C.S.: 562998

SC VITROMETAN SA
Soseaua Sibiului 31-33 Medias,

551129, Sibiu, Romania
Tel.: (40) 269 841455
Web Site: http://www.vitrometan.ro
Year Founded: 1922
Sales Range: $1-9.9 Million
Emp.: 216
Glassware Mfr
N.A.I.C.S.: 327215

SC. RESEARCH INSTITUTE FOR ADVANCED COATINGS - ICAA S.A.
49A Theodor Pallady, 032258, Bucharest, Romania
Tel.: (40) 213452730
Web Site: http://www.icaaro.com
ICEV—(BUC)
Rev.: $87,409
Assets: $1,138,493
Liabilities: $18,807
Net Worth: $1,119,685
Earnings: $36,713
Emp.: 3
Fiscal Year-end: 12/31/23
Natural Science & Engineering Research Services
N.A.I.C.S.: 541715
Mihai Prundianu *(Pres)*

SCA CAPSOM
2 Quai Du Canal, Corbie, 80800, Amiens, France
Tel.: (33) 322480835
Rev.: $26,300,000
Emp.: 24
Farm Supplies
N.A.I.C.S.: 424910
Eric Bridoux *(Dir)*

SCA QUALIS
21 Avenue George V, 75008, Paris, France
Tel.: (33) 156899500
Web Site: http://www.qualis-sca.com
Year Founded: 1996
Sales Range: $1-4.9 Billion
Emp.: 2,500
Investment Holding Company
N.A.I.C.S.: 551112
Herve de Galbert *(Co-Founder)*

Subsidiaries:

Erard Sas (1)
ZI de Chavanoz 4 Route de la Plaine, 38230, Pont-de-Cheruy, France
Tel.: (33) 4 72 46 16 26
Web Site: http://www.erard.com
Household Furniture Mfr
N.A.I.C.S.: 337126
Pascal Marchand *(Mgr)*

EuroCave S.A. (1)
24 Rue Francis de Pressense, 69100, Villeurbanne, France (100%)
Tel.: (33) 426101811
Web Site: http://www.eurocave.com
Sales Range: $25-49.9 Million
Emp.: 35
Wine Cabinet Mfr
N.A.I.C.S.: 335220
Pascal Marchand *(Chm)*

MASA Group S.A. (1)
8 Rue de la Michodiere, 75002, Paris, France
Tel.: (33) 1 55 43 13 20
Web Site: http://www.masasim.com
Software Development Services
N.A.I.C.S.: 541511
Remy Gilet *(VP)*

Subsidiary (US):

MASA Group Inc. (2)
4560 S Blvd Ste 295, Virginia Beach, VA 23452
Tel.: (757) 271-3382
Software Development Services
N.A.I.C.S.: 541511

SCALA DEVELOPMENT S.A.

INTERNATIONAL PUBLIC

Str Somesului no 34-36 ground floor, RO-400145, Cluj-Napoca, Romania
Tel.: (40) 754320320
Web Site: https://scaladevelopment.ro
NCHI—(BUC)
Rev.: $3,589,904
Assets: $25,167,225
Liabilities: $11,767,444
Net Worth: $13,399,781
Earnings: $1,324,305
Emp.: 1
Fiscal Year-end: 12/31/23
Engineeering Services
N.A.I.C.S.: 541330

SCALA INC.
32F Shibuya Hikarie 2-21-1, Shibuya-ku, Tokyo, 150-8510, Japan JP
Tel.: (81) 364183960
Web Site: https://scalagrp.jp
Year Founded: 1987
4845—(TKS)
Rev.: $66,641,080
Assets: $78,987,780
Liabilities: $50,568,600
Net Worth: $28,419,180
Earnings: ($17,957,140)
Fiscal Year-end: 06/30/24
Application Hosting Services
N.A.I.C.S.: 518210
Nori Keno *(Pres & CEO)*

Subsidiaries:

Grit Group Holdings Co., Ltd. (1)
Shibuya Hikarie 32F 2-21-1, Shibuya-ku, Tokyo, 150-8510, Japan
Tel.: (81) 359378462
Web Site: https://www.gritgroup.co.jp
Employment Placement Services
N.A.I.C.S.: 561311

J-Phoenix Research Inc. (1)
1-8-1 Nihonbashi Kayabacho 1 - chome Heiwa Building 9F, Chuo - ku, Tokyo, 103-0025, Japan
Tel.: (81) 355327647
Web Site: https://www.j-phoenix.com
Information Technology Services
N.A.I.C.S.: 541511

Leoconnect Inc. (1)
2-21-1 Shibuya Hikarie 17F, Shibuya-ku, Tokyo, 150-8510, Japan
Tel.: (81) 368038691
Web Site: https://www.leoconnect.co.jp
Business Consulting Services
N.A.I.C.S.: 541618

Scala Communications, Inc. (1)
Shibuya Hikarie 17F 2-21-1, Shibuya-ku, Tokyo, 150-8510, Japan
Tel.: (81) 364183973
Web Site: https://www.scala-com.jp
Software Development Services
N.A.I.C.S.: 541511

Scala Next Inc. (1)
Shibuya Hikarie 17F 2-21-1, Shibuya-ku, Tokyo, 150-8510, Japan
Tel.: (81) 364183972
Web Site: https://www.scala-next.jp
Business Consulting Services
N.A.I.C.S.: 541618

Scala Partners, Inc. (1)
2-21-1 Shibuya Hikarie 17F, Shibuya-ku, Tokyo, 150-8510, Japan
Tel.: (81) 364183976
Web Site: https://www.scala-partners.com
Software Development Services
N.A.I.C.S.: 541511

Scala Service, Inc. (1)
1-8-1 3rd Nishi-Aoyama Building B1F, Shibuya-ku, Tokyo, 150-0002, Japan
Tel.: (81) 364186653
Web Site: https://www.scala-service.jp
Construction Services
N.A.I.C.S.: 236220

SCALES CORPORATION LIMITED

52 Cashel Street, Christchurch, 8013, New Zealand
Tel.: (64) 33797720 NZ
Web Site:
https://www.scalescorporation.co.nz
Year Founded: 1897
SCL—(NZX)
Rev.: $338,439,771
Assets: $421,484,990
Liabilities: $149,411,795
Net Worth: $272,073,195
Earnings: $19,111,739
Emp.: 2,500
Fiscal Year-end: 12/31/20
Horticulture Services
N.A.I.C.S.: 111331
Andrew Borland (Mng Dir)

Subsidiaries:

Meateor Foods Limited (1)
50 Johnston Way Hawkes Bay, PO Box 5, Whakatu, Hastings, 4172, New Zealand
Tel.: (64) 274412722
Web Site: https://www.meateor.co.nz
Meat Product Distr
N.A.I.C.S.: 424470

Mr Apple New Zealand Limited (1)
2 Station Road Hawkes Bay, PO Box 42, Whakatu, Hastings, 4180, New Zealand
Tel.: (64) 68731030
Web Site: https://www.mrapple.com
Apple Distr
N.A.I.C.S.: 424480

Scales Logistics Australia Pty. Ltd. (1)
Level 1 Suite 111 189E South Centre Road, Tullamarine, 3043, VIC, Australia
Tel.: (61) 393143481
Logistics Consulting Servies
N.A.I.C.S.: 541614

Scales Logistics Limited (1)
52 Cashel Street, PO Box 1152, Christchurch, 8140, New Zealand
Tel.: (64) 33712288
Freight Logistics Services
N.A.I.C.S.: 488510

Shelby Properties LLC (1)
915 W Main St, Shelbyville, IL 62565
Tel.: (217) 774-3675
Web Site: http://www.shelbyproperties.com
Real Estate Agency Services
N.A.I.C.S.: 531210

SCAN ASSOCIATES BERHAD
Level 7 Menara Atlan 161-B Jalan Ampang, Petaling Jaya, 47301, Malaysia
Tel.: (60) 378878776
SCN—(KLS)
Rev.: $11,843,077
Assets: $27,852,793
Liabilities: $19,092,083
Net Worth: $8,760,710
Earnings: ($1,046,805)
Emp.: 245
Fiscal Year-end: 06/30/19
Information Solution Provider
N.A.I.C.S.: 541512
Teh Chee Hoe (CEO)

SCAN ENERGY A/S
Flauenskjoldvej 30-34, 9352, Dybvad, Denmark
Tel.: (45) 70258565
Web Site: http://www.scan-energy.com
Sales Range: $125-149.9 Million
Emp.: 32
Renewable Power Producer
N.A.I.C.S.: 221111
Jens Bigum (Chm)

Subsidiaries:

Scan Energy Iberica SLU (1)
Pl Colon Tower 2 Fl19, 28046, Madrid, Spain
Tel.: (34) 917001812
Solar Power Generation Services

N.A.I.C.S.: 221118
Anayeli Banuelos (Controller-Fin)

SCAN INTER PUBLIC COMPANY LIMITED
355 Bond Street, Bang Phut Subdistrict Pak Kret District, Nonthaburi, 11120, Thailand
Tel.: (66) 25034116
Web Site: https://www.scan-inter.com
SCN—(THA)
Rev.: $54,827,570
Assets: $179,907,046
Liabilities: $86,006,958
Net Worth: $93,900,088
Earnings: $5,188,989
Emp.: 651
Fiscal Year-end: 12/31/23
Natural Gas Operations
N.A.I.C.S.: 213112
Narissara Kitpipit (Exec VP-Strategic)

SCAN PROJECTS LIMITED
Village-Jorian Delhi Road, Yamunanagar, 135001, Haryana, India
Tel.: (91) 1732650495
Web Site: https://www.scanprojects.in
Year Founded: 1992
531797—(BOM)
Rev.: $701,613
Assets: $682,552
Liabilities: $109,417
Net Worth: $573,135
Earnings: $9,505
Emp.: 15
Fiscal Year-end: 03/31/23
Construction Machinery Mfr
N.A.I.C.S.: 333120
Sunil Chandra (CEO & Mng Dir)

SCAN STEELS LIMITED
Office no 104 105 E Square Building Subash Road, Opp Havmore Ice Cream Vile Parle E, Mumbai, 400057, India
Tel.: (91) 2226185461
Web Site:
https://www.scansteels.com
Year Founded: 1994
511672—(BOM)
Rev.: $131,499,934
Assets: $67,814,687
Liabilities: $23,935,064
Net Worth: $43,879,624
Earnings: $1,836,700
Emp.: 2,002
Fiscal Year-end: 03/31/23
Iron & Steel Product Mfr
N.A.I.C.S.: 332111
Prabir Kumar Das (Compliance Officer & Sec)

SCANA ASA
Wernersholmvegen 49, PO Box 878, 5232, Paradis, Norway
Tel.: (47) 51869400 NO
Web Site: https://scana.no
Year Founded: 1987
SCI—(OSL)
Rev.: $157,878,183
Assets: $146,985,965
Liabilities: $89,850,971
Net Worth: $57,134,994
Earnings: $7,038,654
Emp.: 537
Fiscal Year-end: 12/31/23
Investment Services
N.A.I.C.S.: 523999
Kjetil Flesja (CFO)

Subsidiaries:

Leshan Scana Machinery Co. (1)
Guan'e Street, Shawan District, Leshan, 614900, Sichuan, China (100%)
Tel.: (86) 333445725
Web Site: http://www.scana.no

Sales Range: $10-24.9 Million
Hardware Producer
N.A.I.C.S.: 332510
Wang Shibin (Deputy Mng Dir)

Scana Bjorneborg AB (1)
Kaistinie Hann Vagan 2, SE 68071, Bjorneborg, Sweden (100%)
Tel.: (46) 55025100
Web Site: http://www.scana-industrier.com
Sales Range: $200-249.9 Million
Emp.: 270
N.A.I.C.S.: 332510

Scana Korea Hydraulic (1)
1500 8 Songjung Dong Kangseo Ku, Pusan, 618 270, Korea (South) (100%)
Tel.: (82) 518310541
Web Site: http://www.scana.co.kr
Sales Range: $50-74.9 Million
Emp.: 60
N.A.I.C.S.: 332510

Scana Shanghai (1)
10 Heng Shan Rd, Shanghai, 20031, China (100%)
Tel.: (86) 2164330818
Web Site: http://www.scana-industrier.com
Sales Range: $50-74.9 Million
Emp.: 12
N.A.I.C.S.: 332510

Scana Skarpenord AS (1)
Saheimsveien 2, PO Box 3, 3361, Rjukan, Norway
Tel.: (47) 35 09 18 00
Sales Range: $25-49.9 Million
Emp.: 50
Industrial Valve Distr
N.A.I.C.S.: 423840

Scana Stavanger AS (1)
Scana 4100 St, NO 4100, Jorpeland, Norway (100%)
Tel.: (47) 51743400
Web Site: http://www.scana.nl
Sales Range: Less than $1 Million
Emp.: 250
N.A.I.C.S.: 332510
Erik Odegard (Asst Mgr)

Scana Steel Bjorneborg AB (1)
Kristinehamnsvagen 2, 680 71, Bjorneborg, Sweden
Tel.: (46) 55025100
Web Site: http://www.scana.no
Emp.: 260
Steel Products Mfr
N.A.I.C.S.: 331110
Marten Lund (Mgr-Quality)

Scana Steel Stavanger AS (1)
Direktor Poulssonsgate 1, 4100, Jorpeland, Norway
Tel.: (46) 51 74 34 00
Web Site: http://www.scana.no
Sales Range: $75-99.9 Million
Emp.: 200
Steel Product Distr
N.A.I.C.S.: 423510
Helge Skjellevik (Mng Dir-Jorpeland)

Scana Subsea AB (1)
Kristinehamnsvagen 2, 680 71, Bjorneborg, Sweden
Tel.: (46) 55025390
Emp.: 10
Marine Engineering Services
N.A.I.C.S.: 541330
Peter Jansson (Mng Dir)

Scana Volda AS (1)
Hamnegata 24, Volda, 6100, Norway
Tel.: (47) 70059000
Web Site: http://www.scana.no
Sales Range: $50-74.9 Million
Emp.: 150
Ship Engine & Propeller Mfr
N.A.I.C.S.: 333618
Kirsti Gjorvad (Dir-Sls & Mktg)

Scana do Brasil Industrias Ltda. (1)
Lauro Muller 116 Suite 2401 Torre do Rio Sul, Botafogo, Rio de Janeiro, 22290-160, Brazil
Tel.: (55) 21 3544 0000
Marine Engineering Services
N.A.I.C.S.: 541330

Stavanger Staal Svenska AB (1)
Storgatan 1, PO Box 36, SE 85 102,

Sundsvall, Sweden (100%)
Tel.: (46) 60140450
Web Site: http://www.stavangerstaal.se
Sales Range: $50-74.9 Million
Emp.: 2
N.A.I.C.S.: 332510

SCANCELL HOLDINGS PLC
Unit 202 Bellhouse Building Sanders Road, Oxford Science Park, Oxford, OX4 4GD, United Kingdom
Tel.: (44) 1865582006
Web Site: https://www.scancell.co.uk
Year Founded: 1997
SCLP—(AIM)
Rev.: $6,540,597
Assets: $37,568,097
Liabilities: $45,300,150
Net Worth: ($7,732,053)
Earnings: ($14,818,734)
Fiscal Year-end: 04/30/23
Biopharmaceutical Mfr, Developer & Researcher
N.A.I.C.S.: 325412
Lindy Durrant (CEO & Chief Scientific Officer)

Subsidiaries:

Scancell Limited (1)
Department of Clinical Oncology City Hospital Hucknall Road, Nottingham, NG5 1PB, Nottinghamshire, United Kingdom
Tel.: (44) 115 823 1863
Sales Range: $25-49.9 Million
Cancer Treatment Vaccines Mfr
N.A.I.C.S.: 325414

SCANDAL MEDIA GROUP S.R.O.
Ovocny trh 17, 110 00, Prague, Czech Republic
Tel.: (420) 224 815 429 CZ
Web Site:
http://www.scandalgroup.cz
Year Founded: 2013
Holding Company; Marketing Services
N.A.I.C.S.: 551112
Karel Vagner (Co-Founder & Co-Owner)

Subsidiaries:

Fruit Factory s.r.o. (1)
Ovocny trh 17, 110 00, Prague, Czech Republic
Tel.: (420) 224 815 429
Web Site: http://www.fruitfactory.cz
Public Relation Agency Services
N.A.I.C.S.: 541820
Vitek Koldinsky (CEO)

Scandal Media s.r.o. (1)
Ovocny trh 17, 110 00, Prague, 1, Czech Republic
Tel.: (420) 224 815 429
Web Site: http://www.scandalmedia.cz
Media Marketing & Consulting Services
N.A.I.C.S.: 541613

SCANDBOOK HOLDING AB
Lovasvagen 24, SE-791 45, Falun, Sweden
Tel.: (46) 23765900
Web Site:
https://www.scandbook.com
SBOK—(OMX)
Rev.: $36,285,556
Assets: $29,466,970
Liabilities: $6,263,171
Net Worth: $23,203,799
Earnings: $3,060,871
Emp.: 177
Fiscal Year-end: 12/31/22
Books Publishing Services
N.A.I.C.S.: 513130
Odd Rune Austgulen (Chm)

SCANDI STANDARD AB
Strandbergsgatan 55, PO Box 30174,

SCANDI STANDARD AB

Scandi Standard AB—(Continued)

104 25, Stockholm, Sweden
Tel.: (46) 104561300
Web Site:
https://www.scandistandard.com
SCST—(OMX)
Rev.: $1,291,917,349
Assets: $660,353,020
Liabilities: $422,399,594
Net Worth: $237,953,426
Earnings: $27,101,079
Emp.: 3,125
Fiscal Year-end: 12/31/23
Chicken Production
N.A.I.C.S.: 112320
Per Harkjaer (Chm)

Subsidiaries:

Danpo A/S (1)
Tykhojetvej 44 Farre, 7323, Give, Denmark
Tel.: (45) 72115555
Web Site: https://www.danpo.dk
Emp.: 1,030
Food Production Mfr
N.A.I.C.S.: 311999
Bo Maagaard (Head-Export)

Den Stolte Hane AS (1)
Naeringsvegen 23, Naerbo, 4365, Rogaland, Norway
Tel.: (47) 51798580
Web Site: https://www.denstoltehane.no
Food Production Mfr
N.A.I.C.S.: 311999

Kronfagel AB (1)
Strandbergsgatan 55 van 9, Box 30174, 104 25, Stockholm, Sweden
Tel.: (46) 104561300
Web Site: https://www.kronfagel.se
Food Production Mfr
N.A.I.C.S.: 311999

Naapurin Maalaiskana Oy (1)
Tiemestarintie 6, Lieto, 21360, Turku, Finland
Tel.: (358) 405196394
Web Site:
https://www.naapurinmaalaiskana.fi
Emp.: 300
Food Production Mfr
N.A.I.C.S.: 311999

SCANDIDOS AB

Uppsala Science Park, 751 83, Uppsala, Sweden
Tel.: (46) 184723030
Web Site: https://www.scandidos.com
SDOS—(OMX)
Rev.: $5,764,890
Assets: $6,782,995
Liabilities: $2,881,977
Net Worth: $3,901,018
Earnings: ($854,197)
Emp.: 34
Fiscal Year-end: 04/30/23
Medical Software
N.A.I.C.S.: 513210
Gorgen Nilsson (Pres & CEO)

Subsidiaries:

ScandiDos Inc. (1)
PO Box 930273, Verona, WI 53593-0273
Tel.: (608) 630-9415
Medical Device Mfr
N.A.I.C.S.: 339112

ScandiDos SAS (1)
59 rue des Petits Champs, 75001, Paris, France
Tel.: (33) 674088049
Clinical Services
N.A.I.C.S.: 621610

SCANDINAVIAN BRAKE SYSTEMS A/S

Kuopiovej 11, DK-5700, Svendborg, Denmark
Tel.: (45) 63211515   DK
Web Site: http://uk.sbs.dk
Year Founded: 1964

SBS—(CSE)
Rev.: $824,760
Assets: $33,178,510
Liabilities: $26,537,020
Net Worth: $6,641,490
Earnings: ($1,982,318)
Emp.: 253
Fiscal Year-end: 12/31/22
Car & Motorcycle Brake Components Mfr & Supplier
N.A.I.C.S.: 336340
Carsten Schmidt (CFO)

Subsidiaries:

SBS Deutschland GmbH (1)
Eichrodter Weg 57, 99817, Eisenach, Germany
Tel.: (49) 36912570
Web Site: https://uk.sbs-automotive.de
Sales Range: $25-49.9 Million
Automotive Spare Parts Services
N.A.I.C.S.: 441330

SBS France SAS (1)
B P 29 Z I d Angean, 60 240, Chaumont, France
Tel.: (33) 344494716
Sales Range: $25-49.9 Million
Emp.: 26
Braking Parts & Other Wear Parts Suppliers
N.A.I.C.S.: 441330

SCANDINAVIAN CHEMOTECH AB

Scheelevagen 2, Medicon Village, 223 63, Lund, Sweden
Tel.: (46) 102189300
Web Site: https://www.chemotech.se
Year Founded: 2006
CMOTEC.B—(OMX)
Rev.: $15,870
Assets: $1,952,059
Liabilities: $824,040
Net Worth: $1,128,019
Earnings: ($1,423,453)
Emp.: 7
Fiscal Year-end: 12/31/20
Medical Equipment Mfr
N.A.I.C.S.: 339112
Ingalill Forslund Larsson (Chm)

SCANDINAVIAN ENVIRO SYSTEMS AB

Frihamnen 16B, 417 70, Gothenburg, Sweden
Tel.: (46) 317990720
Web Site: https://envirosystems.se
SES—(OMX)
Rev.: $1,313,326
Assets: $36,095,512
Liabilities: $4,505,267
Net Worth: $31,590,245
Earnings: ($8,737,590)
Emp.: 52
Fiscal Year-end: 12/31/23
Recycling Services
N.A.I.C.S.: 562920
Thomas Sorensson (CEO)

SCANDINAVIAN INVESTMENT GROUP A/S

Lyskaer 8, 2730, Herlev, Denmark
Tel.: (45) 28126609   DK
Web Site: https://www.sca-inv-group.dk
Year Founded: 2001
Rev.: $51,182,730
Assets: $15,851,025
Liabilities: $4,027,845
Net Worth: $11,823,180
Earnings: $1,990,950
Emp.: 29
Fiscal Year-end: 12/31/18
Timber & Forest Products Producer
N.A.I.C.S.: 321920
Soren Dal Thomsen (Chm)

Subsidiaries:

DLH Cote d'Ivoire S.A (1)
01 Abidjan 01 Rue Saint Jean, BP 2648, Cocody, Abidjan, 2648, Cote d'Ivoire
Tel.: (225) 22 40 47 40
Web Site: http://www.dlh.com
Sales Range: $25-49.9 Million
Emp.: 17
Wood Panels & Veneer Whslr
N.A.I.C.S.: 423310

DLH Finland Oy (1)
Heidehofintie 4, 01300, Vantaa, Finland
Tel.: (358) 20 7902770
Web Site: http://www.dlh-finland.fi
Timber Products Mfr & Distr
N.A.I.C.S.: 321215

DLH France S.A.S. (1)
Rue de l'Ile Botty ZI de Chevire, Bouguenais, 44340, Nantes, Cedex 04, France   (100%)
Tel.: (33) 240652510
Sales Range: $25-49.9 Million
Emp.: 14
Door Distr
N.A.I.C.S.: 423310

DLH Nederland B.V. (1)
Eemweg 8, 3742 LB, Baarn, Netherlands
Tel.: (31) 356930720
Web Site: http://www.dlh-nederland.nl
Sales Range: $50-74.9 Million
Emp.: 8
Wood Whslr
N.A.I.C.S.: 423310

DLH Norge AS (1)
Hvamveien 4, N-2013, Skjetten, Norway
Tel.: (47) 2207 0550
Web Site: http://www.dlh-norge.no
Wood Products Whslr
N.A.I.C.S.: 423310
Kim Martens Meyer (Mgr-Sls)

DLH Procurement Cameroun S.A.R.L. (1)
BP 4385, Douala, Cameroon
Tel.: (237) 999 111 93
Wood Panels & Veneer Whslr
N.A.I.C.S.: 423310

East Asiatic Timber (Holland) B.V. (1)
, Amsterdam, Netherlands
N.A.I.C.S.: 425120

Indufor N.V. (1)
Noorderlaan 125, Antwerp, 2030, Belgium
Tel.: (32) 35426370
Web Site: http://www.dlh-belgium.com
Sales Range: $50-74.9 Million
Emp.: 15
Industrial Machinery Sls
N.A.I.C.S.: 425120

SCANDINAVIAN MEDICAL SOLUTIONS A/S

Gasvaerksvej 48 1st Floor, 9000, Aalborg, Denmark
Tel.: (45) 50808009
Web Site: https://www.scandinavian-medical.com
Year Founded: 2018
SMSMED—(CSE)
Rev.: $28,309,999
Assets: $24,278,398
Liabilities: $13,254,296
Net Worth: $11,024,102
Earnings: $1,810,071
Emp.: 20
Fiscal Year-end: 09/30/23
Medical Equipment Distr
N.A.I.C.S.: 423450
Jens Krohn (Founder)

SCANDINAVIAN PRIVATE EQUITY A/S

Sankt Annae Plads 13 3, DK 1250, Copenhagen, K, Denmark
Tel.: (45) 70251055
Web Site: http://www.speas.dk
Assets: $32,899,683
Liabilities: $47,477

Net Worth: $32,852,207
Earnings: ($1,448,799)
Emp.: 1
Fiscal Year-end: 01/31/19
Investment Services
N.A.I.C.S.: 523940
Ole Mikkelsen (CEO-IR)

SCANDINAVIAN REAL HEART AB

Kopparbergsvagen 6, 722 13, Vasteras, Sweden
Tel.: (46) 214755550
Web Site: https://www.realheart.se
Year Founded: 2007
Research & Development Services
N.A.I.C.S.: 541720
Azad Najar (Founder & CEO)

SCANDION ONCOLOGY A/S

Fruebjergvej 3, 2100, Copenhagen, Denmark
Tel.: (45) 26144708
Web Site:
https://www.scandiononcology.com
Year Founded: 2017
SCOL—(NASDAQ)
Emp.: 4
Research & Development Services
N.A.I.C.S.: 541720
Nils Brunner (CEO)

SCANFIL (HANGZHOU) CO., LTD

No 1 Industrial Zone Huanghu Town, Yuhang District, Hangzhou, 311118, Zhejiang, China
Tel.: (86) 57188519180
Sales Range: $200-249.9 Million
Emp.: 400
Contract Electronics Manufacturing Services
N.A.I.C.S.: 334419
Petri Paananen (Gen Mgr)

SCANFIL PLC

Yritystie 6, 85410, Sievi, Finland
Tel.: (358) 84882111
Web Site: https://www.scanfil.com
SCANFL—(HEL)
Rev.: $910,593,568
Assets: $567,120,656
Liabilities: $322,577,164
Net Worth: $244,543,492
Earnings: $37,819,987
Emp.: 3,497
Fiscal Year-end: 12/31/22
Contract Electronics Manufacturing Services
N.A.I.C.S.: 334419
Harri Takanen (Chm)

Subsidiaries:

Scanfil (Suzhou) Co., Ltd (1)
No 9 Binteli Road Loufeng Suzhou Industry Park, Suzhou, 215021, Jiangsu, China
Tel.: (86) 51267168867
Contract Electronics Manufacturing Services
N.A.I.C.S.: 334419

Scanfil EMS Oy (1)
Yritystie 6, 85410, Sievi, Finland
Tel.: (358) 84882111
Web Site: http://www.scanfilems.fi
Emp.: 250
Contract Electronics Manufacturing Services
N.A.I.C.S.: 334419
Marjo Nurkkala (Dir-Fin)

Scanfil Kft (1)
Rozalia Park 5-7, Biatorbagy, Hungary   (100%)
Tel.: (36) 23 531 700
Web Site: https://www.scanfil.com
Contract Electronics Manufacturing Services
N.A.I.C.S.: 334419

Scanfil Malmo Ab (1)
Bronsyxegatan 6B, 21375, Malmo, Sweden
Tel.: (46) 708649759

AND PRIVATE COMPANIES — SCATEC ASA

Electronic Components Mfr
N.A.I.C.S.: 334419

Scanfil Ou (1)
Tel.: (372) 4426800
Web Site: http://www.scanfilems.fi
Sales Range: $100-124.9 Million
Emp.: 375
Contract Electronics Manufacturing Services
N.A.I.C.S.: 334419

Scanfil Sweden AB (1)
Bronsyxegatan 6B, 213 75, Malmo, Sweden
Tel.: (46) 708649759
Sales Range: $250-299.9 Million
Contract Manufacturing Services
N.A.I.C.S.: 339999

Subsidiary (Non-US):

Scanfil Atvidaberg AB (2)
Tel.: (46) 12081000
Web Site: http://www.scanfil.com
Medical Technology Products Mfr
N.A.I.C.S.: 334510

Scanfil Poland Sp. z o.o. (2)
Wojska Polskiego 107, 98-200, Sieradz, Lodz, Poland
Tel.: (48) 43 827 8630
Web Site: https://www.scanfil.com
Electronics Assembling & Designing Services
N.A.I.C.S.: 541490

Scanfil Vantaa Oy (2)
Myllynkivenkuja 1, 01620, Vantaa, Uusimaa, Finland
Tel.: (358) 8 4882 111
Web Site: http://www.scanfil.com
Electronic Components Mfr
N.A.I.C.S.: 334419

Subsidiary (Domestic):

Scanfil Vellinge AB (2)
Bronsyxegatan 6B, 21375, Malmo, Sweden
Tel.: (46) 70 827 8061
Web Site: https://www.scanfil.com
Electronic Components Mfr
N.A.I.C.S.: 335999

Subsidiary (US):

Scanfil, Inc. (2)
4345 Hamilton Mill Rd Ste 400, Buford, GA 30518
Tel.: (770) 680-0000
Web Site: https://www.scanfil.com
Contract Manufacturing Services
N.A.I.C.S.: 334419

SCANLON PRINTING CO. PTY LIMITED
84 Pritchard Rd, Virginia, 4014, QLD, Australia
Tel.: (61) 738653700
Year Founded: 1993
Sales Range: $1-9.9 Million
Emp.: 60
Printing Services
N.A.I.C.S.: 323120
Tony Scanlon (Mng Dir)

SCANPOINT GEOMATICS LTD.
10th Floor Swati Clover Shilaj Circle Sardar Patel Ring Road Thaltej, Ahmedabad, 380 059, Gujarat, India
Tel.: (91) 7949391735
Web Site: https://www.sgligis.com
526544—(BOM)
Rev.: $5,977,059
Assets: $15,740,714
Liabilities: $7,865,894
Net Worth: $7,874,820
Earnings: $276,329
Emp.: 171
Fiscal Year-end: 03/31/21
Software Services
N.A.I.C.S.: 541511
Rameshchandra K. Sojitra (Chm & Mng Dir)

SCANTECH LTD
143 Mooringe Avenue, Camden Park, 5038, SA, Australia
Tel.: (61) 883500200   AU
Web Site: http://www.scantech.com.au
Year Founded: 1981
Rev.: $14,672,235
Assets: $14,756,053
Liabilities: $8,109,992
Net Worth: $6,646,061
Earnings: $1,849,647
Emp.: 33
Fiscal Year-end: 06/30/19
Industrial Instrument Developer & Mfr
N.A.I.C.S.: 334513
Peter Pedler (Chm)

Subsidiaries:

Scantech International Pty Ltd. (1)
143 Mooringe Avenue, Camden Park, 5038, SA, Australia (100%)
Tel.: (61) 883500200
Web Site: http://www.scantech.com.au
Industrial Instrument Developer & Services
N.A.I.C.S.: 333248

Subsidiary (Domestic):

Scantech Applications Pty. Ltd. (2)
143 Mooringe Ave, Camden Park, 5038, SA, Australia
Tel.: (61) 883500200
Process Control Device Mfr
N.A.I.C.S.: 334513

SCANWOLF CORPORATION BERHAD
No 19 19A 19B 19C Jalan Pusat Perniagaan Falim 5, Pusat Perniagaan Falim, 30200, Ipoh, Perak, Malaysia
Tel.: (60) 52850063
Web Site: https://www.scanwolf.com
SCNWOLF—(KLS)
Rev.: $7,735,440
Assets: $22,573,919
Liabilities: $10,426,608
Net Worth: $12,147,311
Earnings: ($2,199,100)
Emp.: 200
Fiscal Year-end: 06/30/23
Plastic Mfr
N.A.I.C.S.: 326199
Sin Keat Tan (Exec Dir)

Subsidiaries:

Scanwolf Plastic Industries Sdn. Bhd. (1)
Lot PT 404 Jalan Bota, Mukim Belanja, 31750, Teronoh, Perak, Malaysia
Tel.: (60) 53677866
Building Product Mfr
N.A.I.C.S.: 339999

SCAPE LIVING PLC
8 Sackville St, London, W1S 3DG, United Kingdom
Tel.: (44) 2034191400
Web Site: http://www.scape.com
Year Founded: 2012
Student Accommodation
N.A.I.C.S.: 721310
Adam Brockley (Founder & Chief Dev Officer)

Subsidiaries:

GCP Student Living plc (1)
Beaufort House 51 New North Road, Exeter, EX4 4EP, United Kingdom
Tel.: (44) 1392477500
Web Site: http://www.graviscapital.com
Sales Range: $25-49.9 Million
Emp.: 128
Real Estate Investment Trust Services
N.A.I.C.S.: 531190
Robert Peto (Chm)

SCAPE TECHNOLOGIES A/S
Osterbro 5C, 5000, Odense, Denmark
Tel.: (45) 70253113

Web Site: https://www.scapetechnologies.com
Year Founded: 2004
SCAPE—(CSE)
Rev.: $421,368
Assets: $2,102,661
Liabilities: $1,512,189
Net Worth: $590,473
Earnings: ($2,674,872)
Emp.: 21
Fiscal Year-end: 12/31/23
Software Development Services
N.A.I.C.S.: 541511
Jens Munch (Chm)

SCARBOROTOWN CHRYSLER DODGE JEEP RAM
4960 Sheppard Avenue East, Toronto, M1S 4A7, ON, Canada
Tel.: (416) 298-7600
Web Site: http://www.scarborotowndodge.com
New & Used Car Dealers
N.A.I.C.S.: 441110
Lance Hanson (Owner)

SCARBOROUGH NISSAN LTD
1941 Eglinton Ave E, Scarborough, M1L 2M4, ON, Canada
Tel.: (416) 751-3511
Web Site: http://www.scarboroughnissan.ca
Year Founded: 1989
Rev.: $10,700,800
Emp.: 40
New & Used Car Dealers
N.A.I.C.S.: 441110
Ryan Chiu (Bus Mgr)

SCARLET B.V.
Ketelmeerstraat 198, 8226 JX, Lelystad, Netherlands
Tel.: (31) 320294421   NI
Web Site: http://www.scarlet.nl
Telecommunication Servicesb
N.A.I.C.S.: 517111
M. Kamp (Mng Dir)

SCARNA CONSTRUCTION SAS
9 Rue De Santes, Haubourdin, 59320, Lille, France
Tel.: (33) 320074602
Web Site: http://www.groupe-scarna.fr
Nonresidential Construction
N.A.I.C.S.: 236220

SCARNOSE INTERNATIONAL LIMITED
503 Sun Square Off C G Road, Navrangpura, Ahmedabad, 380006, Gujarat, India
Tel.: (91) 7948975503
Web Site: https://www.scarnose.com
Year Founded: 2011
543537—(BOM)
Garment Product Mfr
N.A.I.C.S.: 314999

SCAT INC.
1-6-33 Joto, Oyama, 323-0807, Tochigi, Japan
Tel.: (81) 285235151
Web Site: https://www.scat.inc
Year Founded: 1969
3974—(TKS)
Rev.: $19,440,780
Assets: $21,099,840
Liabilities: $8,025,880
Net Worth: $13,073,960
Earnings: $1,113,130
Emp.: 138
Fiscal Year-end: 10/31/23
Information Technology Support Services

N.A.I.C.S.: 541512
Hideo Nagashima (Pres & CEO)

SCATEC AS
Karenslyst Alle 9C, 278, Oslo, Norway
Tel.: (47) 974 14 000   NO
Web Site: http://www.scatec.no
Year Founded: 1987
Investment Holding Company
N.A.I.C.S.: 551112
John Andersen Jr. (CEO)

Subsidiaries:

Keep-it Technologies AS (1)
Stromsveien 323A inngang C, 1081, Oslo, Norway
Tel.: (47) 2230 8350
Web Site: http://www.keep-it.no
Sales Range: $1-9.9 Million
Food & Medicine Shelf Life Indicator Developer, Mfr & Whslr
N.A.I.C.S.: 334513
Kristen A. Hovland (CEO)

SCATEC ASA
Askekroken 11, 0277, Oslo, Norway
Tel.: (47) 48085500   NO
Web Site: https://www.scatec.com
Year Founded: 2001
SCATC—(OSL)
Rev.: $346,480,695
Assets: $3,392,758,175
Liabilities: $2,579,623,130
Net Worth: $813,135,045
Earnings: ($113,430,630)
Emp.: 778
Fiscal Year-end: 12/31/22
Solar Power Producer
N.A.I.C.S.: 221114
John Andersen Jr. (Chm)

Subsidiaries:

Atlas Capital Energy LLC (1)
18 Likarnyana Street h 18 Nova Zburyivka, Holopristanskiy, 75631, Kherson, Ukraine
Tel.: (380) 671389278
Web Site: http://www.atlascapitalenergy.com
Solar Power Services
N.A.I.C.S.: 221114

Gigawatt Global Rwanda Ltd. (1)
Kingsfordweg 151, 1043 GR, Amsterdam, Netherlands
Tel.: (31) 202623893
Web Site: https://www.gigawattglobal.com
Solar Power Services
N.A.I.C.S.: 221114
Howie Rodenstein (Chm)

Release Africa B.V. (1)
Strawinskylaan 557 Tower 10 5th Floor, 1077 XX, Amsterdam, Netherlands
Tel.: (31) 48085500
Renewable Energy Distr
N.A.I.C.S.: 221114

SN Power AS (1)
Lilleakerveien 2A, 0283, Oslo, Norway
Tel.: (47) 66 71 70 00
Web Site: http://scatec.com
Hydro Power
N.A.I.C.S.: 221111
Jarl Kosberg (Exec VP-Project Dev)

Subsidiary (Non-US):

Bujagali Energy Limited (2)
8 Kms Kayunga Road, PO Box 186, Kikubamutwe, Jinja, Uganda (65%)
Tel.: (256) 434132532
Web Site: http://www.bujagali-energy.com
Hydroelectric Power Generation Services
N.A.I.C.S.: 221114

Scatec Hybrid EPC (Pty.) Ltd. (1)
3 Dock Road 2nd Floor North Wing Waterway House V & A Waterfront, Cape Town, 8001, South Africa
Tel.: (27) 212021230
Renewable Energy Distr
N.A.I.C.S.: 221114

Scatec Kenhardt 1 (Pty.) Ltd. (1)
3 Dock Road 2nd Floor North Wing Water-

SCATEC ASA

Scatec ASA—(Continued)
way House V & A Waterfront, Cape Town, 8001, South Africa
Tel.: (27) 212021230
Renewable Energy Distr
N.A.I.C.S.: 221114

Scatec Kenhardt 3 (Pty.) Ltd. (1)
3 Dock Road 2nd Floor North Wing Waterway House V & A Waterfront, Cape Town, 8001, South Africa
Tel.: (27) 212021230
Renewable Energy Distr
N.A.I.C.S.: 221114

Scatec Solar Solutions Egypt LLC (1)
Tel.: (20) 48085500
Web Site: http://www.scatecsolar.com
Solar Power Services
N.A.I.C.S.: 221114

SCB X PUBLIC COMPANY LIMITED

Floor 9 Zone C SCB Park Plaza 9 Rutchadapisek Rd, Bangkok, Bangkok, 10900, Thailand
Tel.: (66) 25444210 TH
Web Site: https://www.scbx.com
Year Founded: 2021
SCB—(THA)
Rev.: $4,705,418,420
Assets: $94,566,507,989
Liabilities: $81,263,609,026
Net Worth: $13,302,898,963
Earnings: $1,203,652,366
Emp.: 28,042
Fiscal Year-end: 12/31/23
Commercial Banking Services
N.A.I.C.S.: 522110
Anucha Laokwansatit (Chief Risk Officer)

Subsidiaries:

Auto X Co., Ltd. (1)
SCB Park Plaza Bldg Tower West A 6th Floor 18 Rutchadapisek Rd, Jatujak, Bangkok, 10900, Thailand
Tel.: (66) 29379220
Auto Loan & Insurance Brokerage Services
N.A.I.C.S.: 524210

Card X Asset Management Co., Ltd. (1)
SCB Park Plaza Bldg Tower East D 5th Floor 19 Rutchadapisek Rd, Jatujak, Bangkok, 10900, Thailand
Tel.: (66) 29993000
Asset Management Services
N.A.I.C.S.: 531390

Card X Co., Ltd. (1)
9 Ratchadapisek Rd, Bangkok, 10900, Thailand
Tel.: (66) 29993000
Web Site: https://www.cardx.co.th
Credit Card & Loan Services
N.A.I.C.S.: 522210

InnovestX Securities Co., Ltd. (1)
SCB Park Plaza No 18 Tower 1 2nd Fl 19 Tower 3, 2nd Fl and 20th Fl Ratchadapisek Rd Chatuchak, Bangkok, 10900, Thailand
Tel.: (66) 29491999
Web Site: https://innovestxonline.settrade.com
Fund Management Services
N.A.I.C.S.: 525910

Mahisom Co., Ltd. (1)
SCB Park Plaza 18-19 Rutchadapisek Rd, Jatujak, Bangkok, 10900, Thailand
Tel.: (66) 29375400
Property Management Services
N.A.I.C.S.: 531311

SCC HOLDINGS BERHAD

19 21 Jalan Hujan Taman Overseas Union, 58200, Kuala Lumpur, Malaysia
Tel.: (60) 377828384
Web Site: https://www.scchldg.com.my

SCC—(KLS)
Rev.: $12,049,848
Assets: $11,754,680
Liabilities: $1,389,421
Net Worth: $10,365,259
Earnings: $361,341
Fiscal Year-end: 12/31/23
Holding Company; Veterinary Chemicals & Feed Supplements
N.A.I.C.S.: 551112
Long Sing Chee (Co-Founder & Chm)

Subsidiaries:

Anitox (M) Sdn. Bhd. (1)
No 21 Jalan Hujan Taman Overseas Union, 58200, Kuala Lumpur, Malaysia
Tel.: (60) 37 782 8384
Web Site: https://www.anitox.com.my
Emp.: 80
Non Antibiotic Animal Health Products Distr
N.A.I.C.S.: 456199

SCC Corporation Sdn. Bhd. (1)
No 19-21 Jalan Hujan, Taman Overseas Union, 58200, Kuala Lumpur, Federal Territory, Malaysia
Tel.: (60) 37 782 8384
Web Site: https://www.scc.com.my
Sales Range: $25-49.9 Million
Emp.: 68
Animal Health Products & Food Service Equipment Distr
N.A.I.C.S.: 456199

SCEMI SA

11 Avenue General Leclerc, 92100, Boulogne-Billancourt, France
Tel.: (33) 33147790122
Web Site: https://www.scemi.fr
Year Founded: 2003
MLCMI—(EUR)
Sales Range: $1-9.9 Million
Business, Marketing, Outsourcing & Technical Consulting Services
N.A.I.C.S.: 561499
Alexandre Lemaire (CEO)

SCENAPPS M INC

10F 318 Hakdong-ro Gangnam-gu, Seoul, Korea (South)
Tel.: (82) 234201600
Web Site:
http://www.scenappsm.com
Online Video Network Services
N.A.I.C.S.: 516210

SCENTRE GROUP LIMITED

85 Castlereagh St, Sydney, 2000, NSW, Australia
Tel.: (61) 293587172 AU
Web Site:
https://www.scentregroup.com
Year Founded: 1960
SCG—(OTCIQ)
Rev.: $1,636,760,775
Assets: $23,258,459,933
Liabilities: $11,506,813,588
Net Worth: $11,751,646,345
Earnings: $114,103,149
Emp.: 2,964
Fiscal Year-end: 12/31/23
Real Estate Development Services
N.A.I.C.S.: 551112
Brian M. Schwartz (Executives)

Subsidiaries:

Scentre (New Zealand) Limited (1)
Level 2 Office Tower 277 Broadway, Newmarket, 1023, Auckland, New Zealand
Tel.: (64) 9 978 5050
Web Site: http://www.scentregroup.com
Retail Shopping Center Property Investment, Development & Management
N.A.I.C.S.: 531390
Tonya Carter (Gen Mgr-Leasing & BrandSpace-New Zealand)

Scentre Limited (1)
Level 30 85 Castlereagh Street, Sydney, 2000, NSW, Australia
Tel.: (61) 2 9358 7000
Web Site: http://www.scentregroup.com
Retail Shopping Center Property Investment, Development & Management
N.A.I.C.S.: 531390
Peter Leslie (Dir-Leasing)

SCEPTRE VENTURES INC.

Suite 1450 789 West Pender St, Vancouver, V6C 1H2, BC, Canada
Tel.: (604) 681-1568 BC
Year Founded: 2008
SVP.H—(TSXV)
Assets: $3,841
Liabilities: $481,541
Net Worth: ($477,700)
Earnings: ($100,349)
Fiscal Year-end: 06/30/22
Investment Services
N.A.I.C.S.: 523999
Mitchell Smith (CEO)

SCGJWD LOGISTICS PUBLIC COMPANY LIMITED

36 Krungthep Kreetha Road Huamark, Bangkapi, Bangkok, 10240, Thailand
Tel.: (66) 27104000 TH
Web Site: https://www.scgjwd.com
Year Founded: 1979
SJWD—(THA)
Rev.: $176,373,443
Assets: $419,994,574
Liabilities: $287,434,660
Net Worth: $132,559,915
Earnings: $18,546,188
Fiscal Year-end: 12/31/21
Business Logistics & Supply Chain Management
N.A.I.C.S.: 541614
Charvanin Bunditkitsada (CEO)

Subsidiaries:

DataSafe (Cambodia) Ltd. (1)
No 423 Phum Sre Nhor, Sangkat Pong Tuek Khan Dangkor, Phnom Penh, Cambodia
Tel.: (855) 23901910
Information Technology Services
N.A.I.C.S.: 541519

DataSafe Co., Ltd. (1)
99 Moo11 Suwintawong Road Khlong Nakhon Nueang Khet, Chachoengsao, 24000, Thailand
Tel.: (66) 27104050
Web Site: http://www.datasafe.co.th
Information Technology Services
N.A.I.C.S.: 541519

Dynamic IT Solutions Co., Ltd. (1)
No 36 Krungthep Kreetha Road, Huamark Bang Kapi, Bangkok, 10240, Thailand
Tel.: (66) 27104040
Web Site: http://www.dits.co.th
Information Technology Services
N.A.I.C.S.: 541519

JWD Art Space Co., Ltd. (1)
188/72 Chulalongkorn Soi 16 jarusmuang Road, Wang Mai Pathumwan, Bangkok, 10330, Thailand
Tel.: (66) 27104060
Web Site: http://www.jwd-artspace.com
Art Gallery Services
N.A.I.C.S.: 459920

JWD Bok Seng Logistics (Thailand) Co., Ltd. (1)
36 Krungthep Kreetha Road, Huamark Bangkapi, Bangkok, 10240, Thailand
Tel.: (66) 27104065
Logistic Services
N.A.I.C.S.: 488510

JWD Express Co., Ltd. (1)
36 Krungthep Kreetha Road, Huamark Subdistrict Bang Kapi District, Bangkok, 10240, Thailand
Tel.: (66) 906788205
Web Site: http://www.jwdexpress.com
Logistic Services
N.A.I.C.S.: 488510

SCGM BERHAD

PTD109444 Jalan Sengkang, 81000, Kulai, Johor, Malaysia
Tel.: (60) 76522288 MY
Web Site:
https://www.scgmberhad.com
Year Founded: 1984
SCGM—(KLS)
Rev.: $72,919,657
Assets: $26,214,207
Liabilities: $1,968,411
Net Worth: $24,245,796
Earnings: $72,148,084
Emp.: 610
Fiscal Year-end: 04/30/23
Holding Company; Plastic Mfr
N.A.I.C.S.: 551112
Hock Seng Lee (Chm)

Subsidiaries:

LSSPI Sdn. Bhd (1)
Lot 3304 Batu 241/2 Jalan Kulai - Air Hitam, 81000, Kulai, Johor, Malaysia
Tel.: (60) 76522288
Web Site:
http://www.leesoonsengplastic.com
Food Container Plastic Products Mfr
N.A.I.C.S.: 326140
Lee Hok Seng (CEO)

SCHAEFER SOUTH-EAST EUROPE SRL

Odobesti Street 1 Building C4 Office 1101, Galati, 800509, Romania
Tel.: (40) 213135655 RO
Analytical Laboratory Instrument Mfr
N.A.I.C.S.: 334516

SCHAEFER WERKZEUG- UND SONDERMASCHINENBAU GMBH

Dr Alfred-Weckesser-Strasse 6, 76669, Bad Schonborn, Germany
Tel.: (49) 7253 9421 0
Web Site: http://www.schaefer.biz
Year Founded: 1986
Wire Processing Machinery Mfr
N.A.I.C.S.: 333248
Bernhard Schaefer (Founder)

Subsidiaries:

Schaefer Megomat USA, Inc. (1)
W233 N2830 Roundy Circle W, Pewaukee, WI 53072
Tel.: (262) 524-1100
Web Site: http://www.schaefer.biz
Sales Range: $1-9.9 Million
Emp.: 32
Industrial Machinery & Equipment Merchant Whslr
N.A.I.C.S.: 423830
Todd Miller (Gen Mgr)

Schaefer Megomat do Brasil Ltda (1)
Av Eng Antonio F Paula Souza 4101, 13045-137, Campinas, Brazil
Tel.: (55) 1932767500
Industrial Machinery & Tool Distr
N.A.I.C.S.: 423830

Schaefer Romania SRL (1)
62 Petru Rares Str, 02900, Arad, Romania
Tel.: (40) 257206311
Industrial Machinery & Tool Distr
N.A.I.C.S.: 423830

Schaefer Technologies LLC (1)
751 N Raddant Rd, Batavia, IL 60510
Tel.: (630) 406-9377
Industrial Machinery Repair & Maintenance Services
N.A.I.C.S.: 811310

Schaefer Trading (Shanghai) Co., Ltd. (1)
Room 103 Building 5 Tai Hong R&D Office Park No 59 Shen Nan Road, Minhang, 201108, Shanghai, China
Tel.: (86) 2134635025
Industrial Machinery & Tool Distr
N.A.I.C.S.: 423830

Frank Leymann *(Dir-Comml)*

Schaefer Tunisie SARL (1)
Cite Echabeb Avenue Essalem 18, 4061, Sousse, Tunisia
Tel.: (216) 73334644
Industrial Machinery & Tool Distr
N.A.I.C.S.: 423830

Schafer Megomat AG (1)
Chollerstrasse 23, 6300, Zug, Switzerland
Tel.: (41) 417485800
Industrial Machinery & Tool Distr
N.A.I.C.S.: 423830

SCHAEFF MASCHINEN GMBH & CO. KG
Karl-Kurz-Strasse 6, 74523, Schwabisch Hall, Germany
Tel.: (49) 79149949670
Web Site: http://www.schaeffequity.de
Emp.: 339
Holding Company
N.A.I.C.S.: 551112
Alexander Schaeff *(Mng Dir)*

Subsidiaries:

FIMA Maschinenbau GmbH (1)
Oberfischacher Strasse 58, Obersontheim, 74423, Germany
Tel.: (49) 79736930
Web Site: http://www.fima-sha.de
Rev.: $25,200,476
Emp.: 180
Compressors & Radial Blowers Mfr
N.A.I.C.S.: 423830
Stephan Jakob *(Mng Dir)*

Subsidiary (Non-US):

FIMA GREATALL TURBO MACHINERY CO., LTD (2)
Room A Floor No 10 No 138 Pudong Avenue, Pudong, Shanghai, 200120, China
Tel.: (86) 2158219228
Chemical Industry Equipment Distr
N.A.I.C.S.: 423830

FIMA India Pvt Ltd. (2)
Western Edge II A 206 Western Express Highway Borivali East, Mumbai, 400066, India
Tel.: (91) 2228709136
Chemical Industry Equipment Distr
N.A.I.C.S.: 423830

Nuova Fima do Brasil Ltda. (2)
Pc Ocavo Bilac 28, Rio de Janeiro, 20041-010, Brazil
Tel.: (55) 2122246455
Chemical Industry Equipment Distr
N.A.I.C.S.: 423830

Papierfabrik Scheufelen GmbH + Co. KG (1)
Adolf-Scheufelen Strasse 26, 73252, Lenningen, Germany
Tel.: (49) 7026 66 0
Web Site: http://www.scheufelen.com
Coated Paper Mfr
N.A.I.C.S.: 322220
Stefan Radlmayr *(Mgmt Bd)*

SCHAEFFLER INDIA LIMITED
Maneja, Vadodara, 390 013, Gujarat, India
Tel.: (91) 2656602000
Web Site: https://www.schaeffler.co.in
Year Founded: 1962
SCHAEFFLER—(NSE)
Rev.: $768,889,485
Assets: $668,340,855
Liabilities: $169,614,900
Net Worth: $498,725,955
Earnings: $85,874,880
Emp.: 2,922
Fiscal Year-end: 12/31/21
Global Automotive & Industrial Supplier; Ball & Roller Bearings Mfr
N.A.I.C.S.: 336310
Satish Patel *(CFO & Fin Dir)*

SCHAFERROLLS GMBH & CO. KG
Benzstrasse 40, Renningen, 71272, Germany
Tel.: (49) 7159 806 0
Web Site: http://www.schaeferrolls.com
Roll Cover Mfr
N.A.I.C.S.: 326291

Subsidiaries:

SchaeferRolls Inc. (1)
23 Plank Industrial Dr, Farmington, NH 03835
Tel.: (603) 335-1786
Sales Range: $25-49.9 Million
Emp.: 31
Rubber Products Mfr
N.A.I.C.S.: 326299

SchaferRolls d.o.o. (1)
Skofjeloska c 6, Kranj, 4000, Slovenia (100%)
Tel.: (386) 42065363
Web Site: http://www.schaferrolls.si
Sales Range: $25-49.9 Million
Emp.: 4
Rubber Products Mfr
N.A.I.C.S.: 326299
Gregor Azman *(Mng Dir)*

SCHAFFER CORPORATION LIMITED
1305 Hay Street, West Perth, 6005, WA, Australia
Tel.: (61) 894831222
Web Site: https://www.schaffer.com.au
Year Founded: 1955
SFC—(ASX)
Rev.: $151,059,695
Assets: $279,157,985
Liabilities: $120,135,550
Net Worth: $159,022,435
Earnings: $20,279,113
Emp.: 900
Fiscal Year-end: 06/30/24
Building Material Mfr & Whslr
N.A.I.C.S.: 327120
John M. Schaffer *(Mng Dir & Chm)*

Subsidiaries:

Delta Corporation Limited (1)
218 Campersic Road, Herne Hill, 6056, WA, Australia
Tel.: (61) 892965000
Web Site: https://www.deltacorp.com.au
Concrete Element Mfr & Distr
N.A.I.C.S.: 327390

Howe & Co Pty Ltd (1)
57 Northgate Drive, Thomastown, 3074, VIC, Australia
Tel.: (61) 39 464 5011
Web Site: https://www.howe.com.au
Leather Product Mfr & Distr
N.A.I.C.S.: 316990

Howe Leather (Shanghai) Co. Ltd. (1)
118 Lane 2600 BaoAn Road, Malu Town Jiading District, Shanghai, China
Tel.: (86) 21 6915 7531
Leather Product Mfr & Distr
N.A.I.C.S.: 316990
Jessica Li *(Program Mgr)*

Howe Slovensko S.R.O. (1)
Magnezitarska 10, 040 01, Kosice, Slovakia
Tel.: (421) 55 7979079
Leather Product Mfr
N.A.I.C.S.: 316990
Richard Duda *(Gen Mgr)*

Limestone Resources Australia Pty Ltd (1)
27 Jandakot Rd, Jandakot, 6164, WA, Australia
Tel.: (61) 894172444
Web Site: http://www.limestone-resources.com.au
Limestone Product Mfr & Distr
N.A.I.C.S.: 327991

Schaffer Properties Pty Ltd (1)
PO Box 770, West Perth, 6872, WA, Australia
Tel.: (61) 894831222
Web Site: http://www.schaffer.com.au
Emp.: 4
Real Estate Manangement Services
N.A.I.C.S.: 531390

SCHAPPE TECHNIQUES
8 Rue D Alsace, 88520, La Croix-aux-Mines, Vosges, France
Tel.: (33) 329522323
Web Site: http://www.schappe.com
Sales Range: $25-49.9 Million
Emp.: 130
Technical Threads Producer
N.A.I.C.S.: 313110
Jean-Louis Guevel *(Dir)*

SCHAUB & CO. GMBH & CO. KG.
Billwerder Ring 15, 21035, Hamburg, Germany
Tel.: (49) 407347460
Web Site: http://www.schaubtripas.de
Year Founded: 1867
Rev.: $12,782,297
Emp.: 30
Sheep & Hog Casings Mfr
N.A.I.C.S.: 339999
Philipp Ahrens *(Gen Mgr)*

SCHAUFLER TOOLING GMBH & CO. KG
Goethestrasse 72, Laichingen, 89150, Germany
Tel.: (49) 733396080
Web Site: http://www.schaufler.de
Year Founded: 1961
Tool Mfr
N.A.I.C.S.: 333517
Siegfried Heinrich *(Mng Dir)*

Subsidiaries:

Fischer Tool & Die Corp. (1)
7155 Industrial Dr, Temperance, MI 48182
Tel.: (734) 847-4788
Web Site: http://www.fischertool.com
Sales Range: $1-9.9 Million
Emp.: 75
Special Die & Tool, Die Set, Jig & Fixture Mfr
N.A.I.C.S.: 333514
Michael Fischer *(Founder & CEO)*

SCHEER GROUP GMBH
Uni-Campus Nord, 66123, Saarbrucken, Germany
Tel.: (49) 681967770 De
Web Site: http://www.scheer-group.com
Emp.: 800
Holding Company; Information Technology Products & Services
N.A.I.C.S.: 551112
Rudolf Keul *(CFO & Member-Mgmt Bd)*

Subsidiaries:

Scheer GmbH (1)
Uni-Campus Nord, 66123, Saarbrucken, Germany
Tel.: (49) 681967770
Web Site: http://www.scheer-group.com
Sales Range: $75-99.9 Million
Emp.: 500
SAP Consulting Services
N.A.I.C.S.: 541690
Josef Bommersbach *(CEO)*

Subsidiary (Non-US):

IDS Scheer Consulting Austria GmbH (2)
Guglgasse 7-9, 1030, Vienna, Austria
Tel.: (43) 43 1 329 50 0
Information Technology Consulting Services
N.A.I.C.S.: 541512

Scheer Management BV (1)
Lage Biezenweg 5c, 4131 LV, Vianen, Netherlands
Tel.: (31) 347 322 875

Business Management & Consulting Services
N.A.I.C.S.: 541611

Scheer Management Danismanlik A.S. (1)
Uphill Towers A blok Kat 2 D 11 Dereboyu Cad, Feslegen Sok Atasehir, 34746, Istanbul, Turkiye
Tel.: (90) 216 455 41 22
Web Site: http://www.scheer-management.com
Business Management & Consulting Services
N.A.I.C.S.: 541611

SCHEERD.V KERCHOVE N.V.
Aerschotstraat 114, 9100, Saint-Niklaas, Belgium
Tel.: (32) 37604900
Web Site: https://www.svk.be
Year Founded: 1905
SCHD—(EUR)
Sales Range: $50-74.9 Million
Emp.: 425
Cement & Clay Products Mfr & Distr
N.A.I.C.S.: 327310

SCHELCHER-PRINCE GESTION
72 Rue Pierre Charron, 75008, Paris, France
Tel.: (33) 153293185
Web Site: http://www.spgestion.fr
Sales Range: $1-4.9 Billion
Emp.: 17
Inheritance Trust Management
N.A.I.C.S.: 523999
Nathalie Gauquelin *(Mgr)*

SCHELLING ANLAGENBAU GMBH
Gebhard-Scharrzler-Strasse 34, Schwarzach, 6858, Salzburg, Austria
Tel.: (43) 5572 3960
Web Site: http://www.schelling.at
Year Founded: 1960
Cutting Machine Mfr
N.A.I.C.S.: 333515
Stefan Gritsch *(Mng Dir)*

Subsidiaries:

IMA Klessmann GmbH (1)
Industriestrasse 3, 32312, Lubbecke, Germany
Tel.: (49) 57413310
Web Site: http://www.ima.de
Sales Range: $200-249.9 Million
Emp.: 700
Industrial Machinery Mfr
N.A.I.C.S.: 333248

Subsidiary (Non-US):

IMA (DongGuan) Int'l Trading Co., Ltd. (2)
Room 1103 11th Fl No 2 of Dongxi Xi Road, Xi Tou Village Houjie Town, 523000, Dongguan, Gungdong, China
Tel.: (86) 769 850 819 80
Web Site: http://www.ima-cn.cn
Industrial Machinery Distr
N.A.I.C.S.: 423830
Hans-Joachim Ferchland *(Pres & Mng Dir)*

IMA (Klessmann) UK Ltd. (2)
Scraptoft Business Centre - Unit 4 Main Street, Leicester, LE7 9TD, United Kingdom
Tel.: (44) 116 243 218 1
Industrial Machinery Distr
N.A.I.C.S.: 423830

Subsidiary (US):

IMA America Corporation (2)
301 Kitty Hawk Dr, Morrisville, NC 27560
Tel.: (919) 246-0350
Web Site: http://www.imaamerica.com
Industrial Machinery Distr
N.A.I.C.S.: 423830
Peter Tuenker *(Mng Dir-Schelling Grp)*

SCHELLING ANLAGENBAU GMBH

Schelling Anlagenbau GmbH—(Continued)
Subsidiary (Non-US):

IMA Austria GmbH (2)
Flurgasse 2, 4611, Buchkirchen, Austria
Tel.: (43) 7242 289 88
Industrial Machinery Distr
N.A.I.C.S.: 423830

IMA Canada Corporation (2)
3400 Ridgeway Drive Unit 8, Mississauga,
L5L 0A2, ON, Canada
Tel.: (905) 565-0001
Web Site: https://www.imaschelling.com
Industrial Machinery Distr
N.A.I.C.S.: 423830
Murat Dogan (Pres & Mng Dir)

IMA Espana, S.L (2)
Parq Emp Inbisa Alcala I C/Rumania 5 -
Nave D 2, 28802, Alcala de Henares, Spain
Tel.: (34) 918 865 240
Web Site: http://www.ima-spain.de
Industrial Machinery Distr
N.A.I.C.S.: 423830

IMA France (2)
Z A des Nations 10 Rue de Suede, 67380,
Benfeld, France
Tel.: (33) 388 587 380
Web Site: http://www.ima.fr
Emp.: 15
Industrial Machinery Distr
N.A.I.C.S.: 423830
Christian Zelus (Gen Mgr)

IMA Polska sp. z o.o. (2)
ul Pradzynskiego 26, Sroda Wielkopolska,
63-000, Poland
Tel.: (48) 612864700
Web Site: http://www.ima-polska.pl
Industrial Machinery Distr
N.A.I.C.S.: 423830

IMA RUS (2)
Enissejskaja Strasse 1 of 310, 129344,
Moscow, Russia
Tel.: (7) 495 225 96 22
Web Site: http://www.ima-rus.ru
Industrial Machinery Distr
N.A.I.C.S.: 423830

SCHERDEL HERCKELBOUT DAWSON S.A.R.L.
56 Rue du Tilloy, 60000, Beauvais,
Oise, France
Tel.: (33) 3 44 105200
Web Site: http://www.scherdel.de
Rev.: $18,600,000
Emp.: 100
Mfr of Cold Formed Technical Springs
N.A.I.C.S.: 332613
Walter Bach (Gen Mgr)

SCHERZER & CO. AG
Friesenstrasse 50, 50670, Cologne,
Germany
Tel.: (49) 221820320
Web Site: https://www.scherzer-ag.de
Year Founded: 1880
PZS—(DEU)
Rev.: $22,077
Assets: $97,582,515
Liabilities: $15,962,027
Net Worth: $81,620,488
Earnings: ($916,216)
Emp.: 3
Fiscal Year-end: 12/31/23
Financial Investment Services
N.A.I.C.S.: 523940
Rolf Hauschildt (Deputy Chm-
Supervisory Bd)

SCHEUCH GMBH
Weierfing 68, 4971, Aurolzmunster,
Austria
Tel.: (43) 77529050
Web Site: http://www.scheuch.com
Wood Based Panel Industry
N.A.I.C.S.: 321999
Stefan Scheuch (Mng Dir)

Subsidiaries:

Schust Development, Inc. (1)
701 North St, Auburn, IN 46706
Tel.: (260) 925-6550
Web Site:
  http://www.schustengineering.com
Plumbing & Heating Equipment & Supplies,
Hydronics, Merchant Whslr
N.A.I.C.S.: 423720
John Luttman (Pres)

SCHEUERMANN + HEILIG GMBH
Buchener Strasse 29, Hainstadt,
74722, Buchen, Germany
Tel.: (49) 62819070
Web Site: http://www.sh-gmbh.de
Year Founded: 1957
Rev.: $63,452,400
Emp.: 400
Precision Component Mfr
N.A.I.C.S.: 339999
Steffen Scheuermann (Exec Dir)

Subsidiaries:

SCHEUERMANN + HEILIG do Brasil
Ltda (1)
Tecnologia em Pecas Estampadas Rodovia
D Pedro I km 725, Bairro da Ponte, 12953-
900, Atibaia, Sao Paulo, Brazil
Tel.: (55) 1144141444
Web Site: http://www.shdobrasil.com.br
Industrial Machinery & Equipment Distr
N.A.I.C.S.: 423830
Anton Scheuermann (Co-Founder)

SCHIAVELLO GROUP PTY LTD
1 Sharps Road, Tullamarine, 3043,
VIC, Australia
Tel.: (61) 393308888
Web Site: http://www.schiavello.com
Sales Range: $75-99.9 Million
Emp.: 1,300
Furniture Product Mfr
N.A.I.C.S.: 337211
Antonino Schiavello (Chm)

Subsidiaries:

Schiavello Singapore Pty. Ltd. (1)
No 1 Magazine Rd Corner Havelock Rd
01-05 Central Mall, Singapore, 059567,
Singapore
Tel.: (65) 6 533 8011
Web Site: http://www.schiavello.com
Emp.: 12
Furniture Distr
N.A.I.C.S.: 423210
Bonnie Tin (Mgr-Mktg)

Schiavello Systems International Pty.
Ltd. (1)
Level 20 Sultan International Tower Cor-
niche Road, PO Box 3486, Abu Dhabi,
United Arab Emirates
Tel.: (971) 2 622 4411
Interior Design Services
N.A.I.C.S.: 541410

SCHIBSTED ASA
Akersgata 55, NO-0180, Oslo, Nor-
way
Tel.: (47) 23106600 NO
Web Site: https://www.schibsted.com
Year Founded: 1839
SBSNY—(OTCIQ)
Rev.: $1,421,663,880
Assets: $5,270,695,220
Liabilities: $1,246,166,530
Net Worth: $40,245,286,900,549
Earnings: $1,525,518,610
Emp.: 6,088
Fiscal Year-end: 12/31/23
Media Group; Newspaper Publishing,
Television & Internet Production; Film
Rights Distr
N.A.I.C.S.: 513110
Ole Jacob Sunde (Chm)

Subsidiaries:

A Vendre A Louer SAS (1)
LBC France 85-87 rue du Faubourg Saint
Martin, 75010, Paris, France
Tel.: (33) 140066150
Web Site: http://www.avendrealouer.fr
Real Estate Advertisement Services
N.A.I.C.S.: 541810
Antoine Jouteau (Dir-Publication)

Add Health Media AB (1)
Isafjordsgatan 32B, 164 40, Kista, Sweden
Tel.: (46) 8 648 4900
Web Site: https://www.addhealthmedia.com
Healthcare Media Services
N.A.I.C.S.: 621999

Aftenposten AS (1)
Akersgata 55, 0180, Oslo, Norway (100%)
Tel.: (47) 2 286 3000
Web Site: https://www.aftenposten.no
Sales Range: $200-249.9 Million
Emp.: 790
Mfg Newspapers
N.A.I.C.S.: 513110

Subsidiary (Domestic):

Aftenposten Distribusjon AS (2)
Sinsenveien 53d, Oslo, 0585, Norway
Tel.: (47) 22863000
Sales Range: $350-399.9 Million
Newspaper Publishing Services
N.A.I.C.S.: 513110

Subsidiary (Non-US):

Distribution Innovation AS (2)
Tel.: (47) 2 282 7800
Web Site: https://www.di.no
Sales Range: $25-49.9 Million
Emp.: 25
Newspaper & Magazine Publishing Services
N.A.I.C.S.: 513110
Tone Loyland (CEO)

Aftonbladet Gruppen (1)
Vastra Jarnvagsgatan 21, Stockholm,
10518, Sweden
Tel.: (46) 8 725 2000
Web Site: https://www.aftonbladet.se
Sales Range: $200-249.9 Million
Emp.: 600
Newspaper Publication
N.A.I.C.S.: 513110

Aftonbladet Hierta AB (1)
Vastra Jarnvagsgatan 21, Stockholm,
10518, Sweden
Tel.: (46) 87252000
Web Site: http://www.aftonbladet.se
Emp.: 20
Newspaper Publishing Services
N.A.I.C.S.: 513110
Jan Helin (Dir-Media)

Bergens Ringen DA (1)
Krinkelkroken 1, 5014, Bergen, Norway
Tel.: (47) 98 21 74 44
Sales Range: $25-49.9 Million
Emp.: 2
Online Advertising Services
N.A.I.C.S.: 541810

Bladkompaniet AS (1)
St Olvas, PO Box 6974, Oslo, 6974,
Norway (100%)
Tel.: (47) 24146800
Web Site: http://www.bladkompaniet.com
Sales Range: $25-49.9 Million
Emp.: 55
N.A.I.C.S.: 513110

Bygdanytt AS (1)
Oyrane Torg, Pb 134, Indre Arna, 5888,
Bergen, Norway
Tel.: (47) 55535770
Sales Range: $25-49.9 Million
Emp.: 12
Newspaper Publishing Services
N.A.I.C.S.: 513110

Byt Bil Nordic AB (1)
Sankt Eriksgatan 46 C, Stockholm, 112 34,
Sweden
Tel.: (46) 87322800
Sales Range: $25-49.9 Million
Emp.: 3
Online Automotive Engine Retailer
N.A.I.C.S.: 441330

INTERNATIONAL PUBLIC

Mikael Bjurek (Mng Dir)

Carrie & Serena S.L. (1)
Condesa de Venadito 1 Segundo, 28027,
Madrid, Spain
Tel.: (34) 629 358 769
Advertising Agencies
N.A.I.C.S.: 541810

Compricer AB (1)
Luntmakargatan 18, 111 37, Stockholm,
Sweden
Tel.: (46) 858612270
Web Site: http://www.compricer.se
Loan & Mortgage Services
N.A.I.C.S.: 522310

Diario 20 Minutos SL (1)
Calle Condesa De Venadito 1 - Plt 1, Ma-
drid, 28027, Spain
Tel.: (34) 917015600
Emp.: 100
Magazine Publishing Services
N.A.I.C.S.: 513120

Dicopay AB (1)
Malmskillnadsgatan 32, 111 51, Stockholm,
Sweden
Tel.: (46) 104102530
Web Site: http://www.dicopay.com
Invoice Paid Services
N.A.I.C.S.: 541214

Editora Anuntis Segundamano Online
do Brazil Ltda (1)
Rua Sete de Setembro 99 Salas 401/501,
Rio de Janeiro, 20050-005, Brazil
Tel.: (55) 1128580469
Sales Range: $25-49.9 Million
Emp.: 82
Online Advertising Services
N.A.I.C.S.: 541890

Faedrelandsvennen AS (1)
Radhusgata 14a, 4611, Kristiansand, Nor-
way
Tel.: (47) 38361800
Web Site: http://www.fvn.no
News Broadcasting Services
N.A.I.C.S.: 516210

Finn.no AS (1)
PO Box 747, Sentrum, 0106, Oslo, Norway
Tel.: (47) 22864410
Web Site: http://www.finn.no
Car Retailer
N.A.I.C.S.: 441110

FundingPartner AS (1)
Gaustadalleen 21, 0349, Oslo, Norway
Tel.: (47) 2 269 9001
Web Site: https://www.fundingpartner.no
Corporate Loan Services
N.A.I.C.S.: 522291

HB Svenska Dagbladets AB &
Co (1)
Vastra Jarnvagsgatan 21, 105 18, Stock-
holm, Sweden
Tel.: (46) 8135000
Newspaper Publishing Services
N.A.I.C.S.: 513110
Anna Careborg (Gen Mgr)

Hygglo AB (1)
Birger Jarlsgatan 57c, 113 56, Stockholm,
Sweden
Tel.: (46) 5590276662
Web Site: http://www.hygglo.se
Insurance Services
N.A.I.C.S.: 524210

Hypoteket Bolan Sverige AB (1)
Barnhusgatan 20, 111 23, Stockholm, Swe-
den
Tel.: (46) 101507000
Web Site: http://hypoteket.com
Mortgage Services
N.A.I.C.S.: 522310

InfoJobs S.A. (1)
Calle Numancia 46 Sexta Pis, Barcelona,
08029, Spain
Tel.: (34) 935 52 22 27
Online Employment Advertising Services
N.A.I.C.S.: 541810

Kundkraft AB (1)
Vastra Jarnvagsgatan 21, 105 18, Stock-
holm, Sweden
Tel.: (46) 770175400

AND PRIVATE COMPANIES — SCHIBSTED ASA

Web Site: http://www.kundkraft.se
Electric Power Distribution Services
N.A.I.C.S.: 221122

Lendo AS (1)
Hagegata 22, 0653, Oslo, Norway
Tel.: (47) 22007070
Web Site: http://www.lendo.no
Mortgage Loan Services
N.A.I.C.S.: 522310

Lendo ApS (1)
Gothersgade 8F, 1123, Copenhagen, Denmark
Tel.: (45) 7 050 0010
Web Site: https://www.lendo.dk
Car Loan & Financial Services
N.A.I.C.S.: 522220
Louise Hubertz Wright *(Head-Mktg)*

Lendo Oy (1)
Keskuskatu 1B, 00100, Helsinki, Finland
Tel.: (358) 96 899 8000
Web Site: https://www.lendo.fi
Mortgage Loan Services
N.A.I.C.S.: 522310
Juha Mantynen *(Country Mgr)*

Lendo Sp. z.o.o (1)
Postepu 14, 02-676, Warsaw, Poland
Tel.: (48) 224444777
Web Site: http://www.lendopolska.pl
Car Loan & Financial Services
N.A.I.C.S.: 522220

Lendo Topco AS (1)
Hagegata 22, 0653, Oslo, Norway
Tel.: (47) 22007070
Web Site: https://www.lendo.no
Loan Services
N.A.I.C.S.: 522390

Media Norge AS (1)
Krinkelkroken 1, PO Box 6113, Bergen, 5892, Norway
Tel.: (47) 55 70 61 50
Web Site: http://www.medianorge.no
Sales Range: $350-399.9 Million
Emp.: 2,000
Regional Media Operating Services
N.A.I.C.S.: 541840

Subsidiary (Domestic):

Askoyvaeringen AS (2)
AV-construido, PO Box 4, Kleppesto, 5321, Askoy, Hordaland, Norway
Tel.: (47) 56152800
Newspaper Publishing Services
N.A.I.C.S.: 513110

Bergens Tidende AS (2)
Krinkelkroken 1, Bergen, 5020, Norway
Tel.: (47) 55 21 45 00
Sales Range: $100-124.9 Million
Emp.: 32
Newspaper Printing & Publishing Services
N.A.I.C.S.: 513110

Duplo Media AS (2)
Storgata 38, 3182, Horten, Norway
Tel.: (47) 90 04 06 70
Online Publication Advertising Services
N.A.I.C.S.: 541810

Faedrelandsvennen Distribusjon AS (2)
Svanedamsveien 10, PO Boks 369, 4664, Kristiansand, Norway
Tel.: (47) 38 11 31 40
Postal Couriers & Delivery Services
N.A.I.C.S.: 492110

Fanaposten AS (2)
Ostre Nesttunvegen 6, PB 374, Nesttun, Bergen, 5221, Norway
Tel.: (47) 55118010
Sales Range: $25-49.9 Million
Emp.: 12
Newspaper Publishing Services
N.A.I.C.S.: 513110

Forlaget Strilen AS (2)
Kvassnesvegen 23, Isdalsto, Lindas, 5914, Norway
Tel.: (47) 56343030
Newspaper Publishing Services
N.A.I.C.S.: 513110

Lindesnes AS (2)
Bryggegata 30, 4514, Mandal, Norway

Tel.: (47) 38271000
Web Site: http://www.l-a.no
Sales Range: $25-49.9 Million
Emp.: 25
Newspaper Publishing Services
N.A.I.C.S.: 513110
Per Henrik Didriksen *(Mng Dir)*

Media Norge Trykk Oslo AS (2)
Sandakerveien 121, 484, Oslo, Norway
Tel.: (47) 23 39 10 00
Web Site: http://www.strykk.no
Sales Range: $50-74.9 Million
Emp.: 22
Newspaper Printing Services
N.A.I.C.S.: 323111
Knut L. Tiseth *(Mng Dir)*

Mediatrykk AS (2)
Kokstadflaten 40, 5257, Bergen, Norway
Tel.: (47) 55 11 51 00
Web Site: http://www.mediatrykk.no
Sales Range: $25-49.9 Million
Emp.: 14
Newspaper Printing Services
N.A.I.C.S.: 323111
Espen Pedersen *(Gen Mgr)*

Schibsted Vekst AS (2)
Akersgata 55, Oslo, 180, Norway
Tel.: (47) 23 10 66 00
Web Site: http://www.schibstedvekst.no
Online Advertising Services
N.A.I.C.S.: 541810

Sogne og Songdalen Budstikke AS (2)
Linnegrovan 24, 4640, Sogne, Norway
Tel.: (47) 38 16 80 00
Newspaper Publishing Services
N.A.I.C.S.: 513110

Vestnytt AS (2)
Skjenet 2, 5353, Straume, Norway
Tel.: (47) 56 33 65 00
Newspaper Publishing Services
N.A.I.C.S.: 513110

WoldCam AS (2)
Lagerveien 19, 4033, Stavanger, Norway
Tel.: (47) 46866000
Web Site: https://www.woldcam.no
Sales Range: $25-49.9 Million
Emp.: 12
Motion Picture Production Services
N.A.I.C.S.: 512110
Orjan Richardsen *(Editor & Engr-Sys)*

Mini Media Sweden AB (1)
Livdjursgatan 4, Johanneshov, 121 62, Stockholm, Sweden
Tel.: (46) 86007700
Advertising Agencies
N.A.I.C.S.: 541810

Motesplatsen i Norden AB (1)
Box 72, 432 22, Varberg, Sweden
Tel.: (46) 3 40 64 65 90
Online Dating Services
N.A.I.C.S.: 516210

Nettbil AS (1)
Sandakerveien 138, 0484, Oslo, Norway
Tel.: (47) 21624949
Web Site: http://www.nettbil.no
Car Distr
N.A.I.C.S.: 441110

Omnipunktse AB (1)
Vastra jarnvagsgatan 21, 111 64, Stockholm, Sweden
Tel.: (46) 87252100
Web Site: http://www.omni.se
Online News Publishing Services
N.A.I.C.S.: 513110

Penger.no AS (1)
Grensen 5-7 3 Etg, Pb 747, Sentrum, 106, Oslo, Norway
Tel.: (47) 22 82 79 90
Online Financial Advertising Services
N.A.I.C.S.: 541810

SCM Suomi Oy (1)
Mannerheimintie 12 B, 100, Helsinki, Finland
Tel.: (358) 40 549 3218
Advertising Services
N.A.I.C.S.: 541890

Sandrew Metronome AB (1)
Floragatan 4, PO Box 5612, S 114 86, Stockholm, Sweden
Tel.: (46) 87621700
Web Site: http://www.sandrewmetronome.com
Sales Range: $50-74.9 Million
Emp.: 20
N.A.I.C.S.: 513110
Verner Bach *(Chm & CEO)*

Subsidiary (Non-US):

Sandrew Metronome Denmark A/S (2)
Boulevarden 6, 9000, Aalborg, Denmark
Tel.: (45) 96303600
Web Site: http://www.sandrewmetronome.com
Sales Range: $25-49.9 Million
Emp.: 20
Distr of Video Tapes & DVDs
N.A.I.C.S.: 423990

Subsidiary (Domestic):

Sandrew Metronome International AB (2)
Floragatan 4, 114 31, Stockholm, Sweden
Tel.: (46) 87621700
Motion Picture Distribution Services
N.A.I.C.S.: 512120

Scanpix Scandinavia AB (1)
Gjorwellsgatan 30, 112 88, Stockholm, Sweden
Tel.: (46) 8 738 38 45
Web Site: http://www.scanpix.com
Newspaper & Magazine Picture Agencies
N.A.I.C.S.: 516210

Schibsted Eiendom AS (1)
Apotekergatan 10, PO Box 490, N 0105, Oslo, Norway (100%)
Tel.: (47) 23106600
Web Site: http://www.schibsted.no
Sales Range: $1-9.9 Million
Emp.: 210
N.A.I.C.S.: 513110

Schibsted Finans AS (1)
Apotekergatan 10, 0180, Oslo, Norway (100%)
Tel.: (47) 23106600
Web Site: http://www.schibsted.com
Sales Range: $25-49.9 Million
Emp.: 70
Financial
N.A.I.C.S.: 513110

Schibsted Payment AS (1)
Apotekergata 10, 180, Oslo, Norway
Tel.: (47) 23 10 66 00
Web Site: http://www.schibsted.no
Sales Range: $50-74.9 Million
Emp.: 8
Online Payment Services
N.A.I.C.S.: 522320

Schibsted Sverige AB (1)
Vastra Jarnvagsgatan 21, 111 64, Stockholm, 111 64, Sweden
Tel.: (46) 7252000
Mobile Internet Services
N.A.I.C.S.: 517810

Subsidiary (Domestic):

Aftonbladet Kolportage AB (2)
Arenavagen 63, Johanneshov, 121 77, Stockholm, Sweden
Tel.: (46) 87252000
Newspaper Publishing Services
N.A.I.C.S.: 513110
Olivia Svensson *(Mgr-News)*

Kundkraft i Sverige AB (2)
Parkvagen 2A, Solna, 169 35, Sweden
Tel.: (46) 2 01 40 40 00
Online Advertising & Trading Services
N.A.I.C.S.: 541890

Lendo AB (2)
Vastra Jarnvagsgatan 21, 111 64, Stockholm, Sweden
Tel.: (46) 771 13 13 10
Online Financial Services
N.A.I.C.S.: 513199

Prisjakt Sverige AB (2)
Strogatan 47, 262 32, Angelholm, Sweden
Tel.: (46) 87252500

Web Site: http://www.prisjakt.nu
Online Price Comparison Services
N.A.I.C.S.: 513199

Svenska Dagbladets AB (2)
Vastra Jarnvagsgatan 21, 105 17, Stockholm, Sweden
Tel.: (46) 8135000
Web Site: https://www.svd.se
Emp.: 150
Newspaper Publishing Services
N.A.I.C.S.: 513110
Gunilla Asker *(CEO)*

TVNU Sweden AB (2)
Vastra Jarnvagsgatan 21, Stockholm, 111 64, Sweden
Tel.: (46) 87 25 20 00
Online Television Programming Services
N.A.I.C.S.: 516210

Schibsted Tech Polska sp. z.o.o. (1)
High 5ive Building A ul Pawia 23, 31-154, Krakow, Poland
Tel.: (48) 12 222 0048
Web Site: https://www.schibsted.pl
Emp.: 249
Software Development Services
N.A.I.C.S.: 541511

Schibsted Tillvaxtmedier Annonsforsaljning AB (1)
Vastra Jarnvagsgatan 21, 105 18, Stockholm, Sweden
Tel.: (46) 8 7252000
Web Site: http://www.schibsted.com
Emp.: 1,300
Advertising Agencies
N.A.I.C.S.: 541810

Schibsted Trykk Oslo AS (1)
Sandakerveien 121, N 0483, Oslo, Norway (100%)
Tel.: (47) 23391000
Web Site: http://www.strykk.no
Sales Range: $125-149.9 Million
Emp.: 200
Media Services & Publishing
N.A.I.C.S.: 513110
Terge Drausvoll *(Gen Mgr)*

ServiceFinder Sverige AB (1)
stureplan 4C, Stockholm, 114 35, Sweden (100%)
Tel.: (46) 86530000
Web Site: http://www.servicefinder.se
Advertising Agencies
N.A.I.C.S.: 541810

Sibmedia Interactive S.R.L. (1)
3 Str Somesului, Sibiu, 550183, Romania
Tel.: (40) 724759603
Newspaper Publishing Services
N.A.I.C.S.: 513110
Stefan Tocca *(Gen Mgr)*

Suredo AB (1)
Vastra Jarnvagsgatan 21, 111 64, Stockholm, Sweden
Tel.: (46) 771 11 20 20
Web Site: http://www.suredo.se
Sales Range: $50-74.9 Million
Emp.: 1
General Insurance Services
N.A.I.C.S.: 524210
Jonas Hultin *(Gen Mgr)*

Svenska Dagbladet Annons AB (1)
Waestra jaernvegatan 21, Stockholm, 10517, Sweden
Tel.: (46) 8135000
Web Site: http://www.svd.se
Emp.: 100
Newspaper Publishing Services
N.A.I.C.S.: 513110
Daniela Ling-Vannerus *(Mgr-Intl Sls)*

Svenska Dagbladet Digitala Medier AB (1)
Vastra Jarnvagsgatan 21 Stockholm, Stockholm, 11164, Sweden
Tel.: (46) 8135000
Web Site: http://www.sddm.se
Emp.: 150
Newspaper Publishing Services
N.A.I.C.S.: 513110
Gunilla Asker *(CEO)*

Svenska Dagbladet Distribution AB (1)

SCHIBSTED ASA

Schibsted ASA—(Continued)
vaster jarvagatan 21, Stockholm, 10517, Sweden
Tel.: (46) 8135000
Web Site: http://www.svd.se
Advertising Agencies
N.A.I.C.S.: 541810
Raul Grunthal (Mgr)

Svenska Dagbladet Holding AB (1)
Vastra Jarnvagsgatan 21, 111 64, Stockholm, Sweden (100%)
Tel.: (46) 8135000
Web Site: http://www.svd.se
Sales Range: $400-449.9 Million
Emp.: 1,200
Newspaper Publishers
N.A.I.C.S.: 513110
Raoul Gru:Nphal (Gen Mgr)

Tesked AB (1)
Box 72, 432 38, Varberg, Sweden
Tel.: (46) 340646590
Newspaper Publishing Services
N.A.I.C.S.: 513110

Verdens Gang AS (1)
Akersgata 55, 0180, Oslo, Norway (100%)
Tel.: (47) 22000000
Web Site: http://www.vg.no
Sales Range: $125-149.9 Million
Emp.: 450
Newspaper Publishing Services
N.A.I.C.S.: 513110

Subsidiary (Domestic):

Avisretur AS (2)
Haraldrudv 5, 0581, Oslo, Norway
Tel.: (47) 22 91 69 60
Newspaper Publishing Services
N.A.I.C.S.: 513110

Dine Penger AS (2)
Akersgata 55, Oslo, 0180, Norway
Tel.: (47) 22000050
Web Site: http://www.dinepenger.no
Sales Range: $25-49.9 Million
Emp.: 27
Magazine Publishing Services
N.A.I.C.S.: 513120
Per Valebrokk (Gen Mgr)

E24 Naeringsliv AS (2)
Akersgata 55, 180, Oslo, Norway
Tel.: (47) 22 86 40 25
Web Site: http://www.e24.no
Online Business Newspaper Publishing Services
N.A.I.C.S.: 513110
Hanne Pedersen (Acct Mgr)

Mittanbud.no AS (2)
Akersgaten 55, PO Box 1185, Sentrum, 0107, Oslo, Norway
Tel.: (47) 22 00 09 30
Sales Range: $25-49.9 Million
Emp.: 6
Online Job Portal Operator
N.A.I.C.S.: 519290
Havard Bungum (CEO)

WebTraffic Norge AS (1)
Apotekergata 10, 180, Oslo, Norway
Tel.: (47) 40 00 42 75
Web Site: http://www.webtraffic.no
Sales Range: $25-49.9 Million
Emp.: 2
Internet Advertising Services
N.A.I.C.S.: 541810
Anette Solli (Dir-Sls)

Yepstr AB (1)
Skeppsbron 28, 111 30, Stockholm, Sweden
Tel.: (46) 851519000
Web Site: http://www.yepstr.com
Job Employment Services
N.A.I.C.S.: 561211

SCHIESSL & CO. GMBH

Nibelungenstr 20-22, 86343, Konigsbrunn, Germany
Tel.: (49) 8231 9603 0
Web Site: http://www.schiessl-druck.de
Year Founded: 1963
Printing Services
N.A.I.C.S.: 323111
Volker Schiessl (Chm)

Subsidiaries:

VS Broschek Druck GmbH (1)
Spenglerstrasse 90, 23556, Lubeck, Germany (100%)
Tel.: (49) 451890930
Web Site: http://www.vsbroschek.de
Sales Range: $50-74.9 Million
Emp.: 150
Commercial Printing
N.A.I.C.S.: 323111
Holger Jordan (Mgr)

SCHILDERWERK BEUTHA GMBH

Fabrikweg 1, 09366, Stollberg, Germany
Tel.: (49) 371775151333
Web Site: http://www.sw-beutha.de
Year Founded: 1953
LED Signs Mfr
N.A.I.C.S.: 339950
Karl-Heinz Kiess (Founder)

SCHILL + SEILACHER AG

Moorfleeter Strasse 28, 22113, Hamburg, Germany
Tel.: (49) 40733620
Web Site: http://www.struktol.de
Year Founded: 1877
Sales Range: $150-199.9 Million
Emp.: 600
Chemical Additives for Rubber Products
N.A.I.C.S.: 325998

Subsidiaries:

SNS Nano Fiber Technology LLC (1)
5633 Hudson Industrial Pkwy, Hudson, OH 44236
Tel.: (330) 655-0030
Web Site: http://www.snsnano.com
Nano Fiber Mfr
N.A.I.C.S.: 313230
Woraphon Kataphinan (Head-Matls & R&D)

Schill + Seilacher Chemie GmbH (1)
Alt-Neundorf 13, 01796, Pirna, Germany
Tel.: (49) 3501 7883 0
Silicone Mfr
N.A.I.C.S.: 325199

Struktol Company of America (1)
201 E Steels Corners Rd, Stow, OH 44224-4921 (100%)
Tel.: (330) 928-5188
Web Site: http://www.struktol.com
Sales Range: $25-49.9 Million
Emp.: 80
Mfr of Chemical Additives for the Rubber Industry
N.A.I.C.S.: 325199
Michael S. Fulmer (Territory Mgr-West Coast & Product Mgr-Plastics)

SCHINDLER FENSTER + FASSADEN GMBH

Mauthstrasse 15, Roding, 93426, Germany
Tel.: (49) 94614090
Web Site: http://www.schindler-roding.de
Year Founded: 1931
Rev.: $46,875,036
Emp.: 300
Wood Cutting & Precision Services
N.A.I.C.S.: 337212
Michael Schindler (Mng Dir)

SCHINDLER HOLDING AG

Seestrasse 55, 6052, Hergiswil, Switzerland
Tel.: (41) 416328550 CH
Web Site: http://www.schindler.com
Year Founded: 1874
SCHN—(SWX)
Rev.: $12,049,480,800
Assets: $12,317,876,190
Liabilities: $7,781,201,370
Net Worth: $4,536,674,820
Earnings: $842,557,680
Emp.: 66,674
Fiscal Year-end: 12/31/20
Holding Company
N.A.I.C.S.: 551112
Pius Baschera (Vice Chm)

Subsidiaries:

A.S. Latvijas Lifts Schindler (1)
Ventspils iela 50 k-6, Riga, LV-1002, Lettland, Latvia (97%)
Tel.: (371) 67311311
Web Site: https://www.schindler.com
Sales Range: $50-74.9 Million
Emp.: 140
Elevators, Escalators & Passenger Conveyors
N.A.I.C.S.: 333921

A/S Elif (1)
Pae 25, 11411, Tallinn, Estonia
Tel.: (372) 6012222
Web Site: http://www.elif.ee
Elevator & Escalator Installation Services
N.A.I.C.S.: 238290

AR Sultan Ltd (1)
122 Wilkinson Road, Freetown, Sierra Leone
Tel.: (232) 33285454
Escalator & Elevator Distr
N.A.I.C.S.: 423830

AS Aufzuge AG (1)
Zurcher Strasse 501, 9015, Saint Gallen, Switzerland (100%)
Tel.: (41) 717882525
Web Site: https://www.lift.ch
Sales Range: $75-99.9 Million
Emp.: 400
Elevators, Escalators & Passenger Conveyors
N.A.I.C.S.: 333921

Afrique Ascenseurs (1)
Cite Sica Villa no3 Sud Foire, Dakar, Senegal
Tel.: (221) 8672774
Web Site: http://www.schindler.com
Escalator & Elevator Installation Services
N.A.I.C.S.: 238290

Altra Electricals Ltd (1)
No 67 Osu Badu Str Airport West, Cantonments, Accra, DTD-192, Ghana
Tel.: (233) 302 766 888
Web Site: http://www.altraelectricals.com
Electrical Products Distr
N.A.I.C.S.: 423610
Tarek Awayda (Mng Dir)

Ascensores Andino SAS (1)
CL 17 43 F 311, Medellin, Colombia
Tel.: (57) 4 3565500
Escalator & Elevator Distr
N.A.I.C.S.: 423830

Ascensores Schindler (Chile) S.A. (1)
Av Nueva Providencia 1901 Piso 14, Santiago, Providencia, Chile (99.6%)
Tel.: (56) 227537700
Web Site: https://www.schindler.cl
Sales Range: $100-124.9 Million
Emp.: 400
Provider of Elevators, Escalators & Passenger Conveyors
N.A.I.C.S.: 333921

Ascensores Schindler S.A. (1)
Esteban Echeverria 1288, Florida Oeste, B1604ABH, Vicente Lopez, Buenos Aires, Argentina (90%)
Tel.: (54) 1153535003
Web Site: https://www.schindler.ar
Sales Range: $25-49.9 Million
Emp.: 60
Elevators, Escalators & Passenger Conveyors
N.A.I.C.S.: 333921

Ascensores Schindler S.A. (1)
Calle Colonia 950 Oficina 202, Montevideo, 11200, Uruguay (100%)
Tel.: (598) 29015594
Web Site: https://www.schindler.com
Sales Range: $25-49.9 Million
Emp.: 12
Elevators, Escalators & Passenger Conveyors
N.A.I.C.S.: 333921

Ascensores Schindler de Colombia S.A. (1)
Calle 17 43f 311, Medellin, Colombia (100%)
Tel.: (57) 6043565500
Web Site: https://www.schindler.co
Sales Range: $25-49.9 Million
Emp.: 100
Elevators, Escalators & Passenger Conveyors
N.A.I.C.S.: 333921

Ascensores Schindler del Peru S.A. (1)
Calle Los Halcones N 506 Surquillo, Lima, 100, Peru (100%)
Tel.: (51) 14428383
Web Site: https://www.schindler.com
Sales Range: $1-9.9 Million
Emp.: 130
Elevators, Escalators & Passenger Conveyors
N.A.I.C.S.: 333921

BME Lift Ltd. (1)
Nobel Avenue 25E Baku White City Office Building, AZ1025, Baku, Azerbaijan
Tel.: (994) 12404535455
Web Site: http://www.bme.az
Emp.: 160
Elevator & Escalator Installation Services
N.A.I.C.S.: 238290

BuildingMinds GmbH (1)
Friedrichstrasse 76, 10117, Berlin, Germany
Tel.: (49) 30992738150
Web Site: https://buildingminds.com
Real Estate Services
N.A.I.C.S.: 531390

Caribbean Lifts Limited (1)
Cor Clare St Eastern Main Road, PO Box 717, Laventille, Trinidad & Tobago
Tel.: (868) 6251226
Web Site: https://www.caribbeanlifts.com
Sales Range: $25-49.9 Million
Emp.: 35
Elevator & Escalator Installation & Maintenance Services
N.A.I.C.S.: 238290

Chanic S.A (1)
Av De La Montagne, 2297, Kinshasa, Congo, Democratic Republic of
Tel.: (243) 3226781835
Elevator & Escalator Distr
N.A.I.C.S.: 423830

Coastal Steel Industries Ltd. (1)
Nyerere Road, Dar es Salaam, 5331, Tanzania
Tel.: (255) 22 286 5662
Web Site: http://www.schindler.com
Elevator & Escalator Installation Services
N.A.I.C.S.: 238290

Elevadores Atlas Schindler S.A. (1)
Avenida do Estado 6116-Cambuci, Sao Paulo, 01516-900, Brazil
Tel.: (55) 8000551918
Web Site: https://www.schindler.com.br
Elevator & Escalator Distr
N.A.I.C.S.: 423830

Elevadores Schindler S.A. de C.V. (1)
Camino a San Mateo N 2 Fraccionamiento Anexo Jardines de San Mateo, 53240, Naucalpan, Estado de Mexico, Mexico (100%)
Tel.: (52) 5550801400
Web Site: https://www.schindler.mx
Sales Range: $100-124.9 Million
Emp.: 500
Elevators & Escalators Mfr
N.A.I.C.S.: 333921

Elevator Car System (1)
39 Rue De Mulhouse, PO Box 4, 68110, Illzach, France (100%)
Tel.: (33) 389366500
Web Site: http://www.fr.schindle.com
Sales Range: $50-74.9 Million
Emp.: 200
Elevators, Escalators & Passenger Conveyors

AND PRIVATE COMPANIES — SCHINDLER HOLDING AG

N.A.I.C.S.: 333921
Pastori Antonio *(Mng Dir)*

Elevator Escalator Services Limited (1)
48A Mere-Barthelemy Street, Port Louis, Mauritius
Tel.: (230) 2122000
Web Site: http://www.schindler.com
Sales Range: $25-49.9 Million
Emp.: 40
Elevator Sales & Maintenance Services
N.A.I.C.S.: 423830

Haushahn Aufzug GmbH (1)
Wienerbergstrasse 25, 1100, Vienna, Austria **(100%)**
Tel.: (43) 5724466
Web Site: http://www.haushahn.com
Sales Range: $50-74.9 Million
Emp.: 150
Installation of Elevators
N.A.I.C.S.: 333921

Haushahn GmbH & Co. (1)
Heilbronner Strasse 364, 70469, Stuttgart, Germany **(100%)**
Tel.: (49) 71189540
Web Site: https://www.haushahn.de
Sales Range: $100-124.9 Million
Emp.: 300
Elevators, Escalators & Passenger Conveyors
N.A.I.C.S.: 333921

Hedinn Schindler Lyftur h.f. (1)
Gjotuhrauni 4, 220, Hafnarfjordur, Iceland **(51%)**
Tel.: (354) 5653181
Web Site: https://www.schindler.is
Sales Range: $1-9.9 Million
Emp.: 15
Elevators, Escalators & Passenger Conveyors
N.A.I.C.S.: 333921
Eyjolfur Ingimarsson *(Mng Dir & Engr-Mechanical)*

Inventio AG (1)
Seestrasse 55, PO Box 442, CH 6052, Hergiswil, Switzerland **(100%)**
Tel.: (41) 416328510
Web Site: http://www.inventio.com
Sales Range: $25-49.9 Million
Emp.: 30
Elevators
N.A.I.C.S.: 333921

Jardine Schindler Lifts (Macao) Ltd. (1)
No 398 Alameda Dr Carlos D Assumpcao Edificio CNAC 9-andar-G and H, Macau, China (Macau)
Tel.: (853) 28757953
Elevator & Moving Stairway Mfr
N.A.I.C.S.: 333921

Mass International Co. LLC (1)
Office No 22 2nd Floor Building No 777 Way No 4508 Block No 245, PO Box 2204, Al Kuleliah Street Al Kuwair, 112, Ruwi, Oman
Tel.: (968) 24487628
Web Site: http://www.schindler.com.sa
Sales Range: $25-49.9 Million
Emp.: 54
Elevator & Escalator Installation Services
N.A.I.C.S.: 238290

PT Berca Schindler Lifts (1)
Jl Puri Lingkar Luar Blok P Puri Indah, Kembangan, Jakarta, 11610, Indonesia
Tel.: (62) 2180668222
Web Site: https://www.schindler.co.id
Elevator & Moving Stairway Mfr
N.A.I.C.S.: 333921
Thibaut Le Chatelier *(CEO)*

Reber Schindler Heis A/S (1)
Driveienn 24, PO Box 126, 4702, Vennesla, Norway **(100%)**
Tel.: (47) 38151100
Web Site: http://www.schindler.no
Sales Range: $100-124.9 Million
Emp.: 300
Elevators, Escalators & Passenger Conveyors
N.A.I.C.S.: 333921
Herald Porsae *(Mng Dir)*

Roux Combaluzier Schindler (1)
Rue De Woitine 1, PO Box 64, Velizy-Villacoublay, 78141, France **(100%)**
Tel.: (33) 130707070
Web Site: http://www.schindler.fr
Elevators, Escalators & Passenger Conveyors
N.A.I.C.S.: 333921

S.A. Schindler N.V. (1)
Boulevard de l'Humanite 241 A, 1620, Drogenbos, Belgium **(100%)**
Tel.: (32) 25358211
Web Site: https://www.schindler.be
Sales Range: $50-74.9 Million
Emp.: 120
Elevators, Escalators & Passenger Conveyors
N.A.I.C.S.: 333921

S.T.A.S. (1)
25 Place Moncef Bey, 1001, Tunis, Tunisia
Tel.: (216) 22182451
Elevator & Escalator Installation Services
N.A.I.C.S.: 238290

Schinac B.V. (1)
, Hague, Netherlands **(100%)**
Elevators, Escalators & Passenger Conveyors
N.A.I.C.S.: 333921

Schindler - Ascensores e Escadas Rolantes, S.A. (1)
Avenida Jose Gomes Ferreira n 15 - 1 Miraflores, 1495-139, Alges, Portugal
Tel.: (351) 214243800
Elevator & Moving Stairway Mfr
N.A.I.C.S.: 333921

Schindler AS (1)
Drivensveien 24, PO Box 126, 4702, Vennesla, Norway
Tel.: (47) 38151100
Elevator & Moving Stairway Mfr
N.A.I.C.S.: 333921
Harald Torsoe *(Mng Dir)*

Schindler Aufzuge & Fahrtreppen GmbH (1)
Heerdterbuschstrasse 13, 41460, Neuss, Germany **(100%)**
Tel.: (49) 21312950
Web Site: http://www.schindler.de
Sales Range: $100-124.9 Million
Emp.: 300
Elevators, Escalators & Passenger Conveyors
N.A.I.C.S.: 333921
Hans-Dieter Hartges *(Gen Mgr)*

Schindler Aufzuge AG (1)
Zugerstrasse 13, 6030, Ebikon, Switzerland **(100%)**
Tel.: (41) 413698282
Web Site: http://www.schindler.ch
Sales Range: $800-899.9 Million
Emp.: 3,000
Freight Elevators, Traffic Control Systems, Passenger Elevators
N.A.I.C.S.: 333921

Schindler Aufzuge GmbH (1)
Hanauer Landstrasse 523, 60386, Frankfurt, Germany **(100%)**
Tel.: (49) 69420930
Web Site: http://www.schindler.com
Sales Range: $25-49.9 Million
Emp.: 400
Elevators, Escalators & Passenger Conveyors
N.A.I.C.S.: 333921

Schindler Aufzuge GmbH (1)
Fuhlsbuttler Strasse 431, 22309, Hamburg, Germany **(100%)**
Tel.: (49) 40539010
Sales Range: $25-49.9 Million
Emp.: 80
Elevators, Escalators & Passenger Conveyors
N.A.I.C.S.: 333921
Frank Schazh *(Mng Dir)*

Schindler Aufzuge und Fahrtreppen AG (1)
Wienerbergstrasse 25, 1100, Vienna, Austria **(97%)**
Tel.: (43) 5724463
Web Site: https://www.schindler.at
Sales Range: $50-74.9 Million
Emp.: 700

Schindler Aufzuge und Fahrtreppen GmbH (1)
Schindler-Platz, 12105, Berlin, Germany **(100%)**
Tel.: (49) 3070290
Web Site: http://www.schindler.de
Sales Range: $50-74.9 Million
Emp.: 200
Elevators, Escalators & Passenger Conveyors
N.A.I.C.S.: 333921

Schindler BH d.o.o. (1)
Fra Andela Zvizdovica 1, 71000, Sarajevo, Bosnia & Herzegovina
Tel.: (387) 33295210
Web Site: https://www.schindler.ba
Elevator & Escalator Installation Services
N.A.I.C.S.: 238290

Schindler BV (1)
Verheeskade 4, 2521 BN, Hague, Netherlands **(100%)**
Tel.: (31) 703843700
Web Site: http://www.schindler.com
Sales Range: $100-124.9 Million
Emp.: 370
Mfr of Elevators
N.A.I.C.S.: 333921

Schindler Bulgaria EOOD (1)
260 Botevgradsko Shosse Blvd, Sofia, 1839, Bulgaria
Tel.: (359) 29456425
Web Site: http://www.schindler.com
Sales Range: $25-49.9 Million
Emp.: 25
Elevator & Escalator Installation Services
N.A.I.C.S.: 238290

Schindler CZ, a.s. (1)
Walterovo namesti 329/3, 158 00, Prague, Czech Republic **(100%)**
Tel.: (420) 257293132
Web Site: https://www.schindler-cz.cz
Sales Range: $25-49.9 Million
Emp.: 450
Sales, Installation & Maintenance of Elevators
N.A.I.C.S.: 423830

Schindler Deutschland Holding GmbH (1)
Schindler-Platz, 12105, Berlin, Germany **(100%)**
Tel.: (49) 3070290
Web Site: http://www.schindler.de
Elevators, Escalators & Passenger Conveyors
N.A.I.C.S.: 333921

Schindler Deve Lifts Australia (1)
Sir Joseph Banks Corporate Park Building D / 36-38 Lord St, Botany, 2019, NSW, Australia **(100%)**
Tel.: (61) 299319900
Web Site: http://www.schindler.com
Sales Range: $25-49.9 Million
Emp.: 100
Elevators, Escalators & Passenger Conveyors
N.A.I.C.S.: 333921

Schindler Elevator Corporation (1)
20 Whippany Rd, Morristown, NJ 07960
Tel.: (973) 397-6500
Web Site: http://www.us.schindler.com
Sales Range: $900-999.9 Million
Emp.: 5,000
Mfr of Elevators & Escalators
N.A.I.C.S.: 333921
Greg Ergenbright *(Pres-Ops-US)*

Subsidiary (Domestic):

Schindler Corporation of Puerto Rico (2)
Calle 19 Lote 1A Palmas Industrial Park, Catano, PR 00962 **(100%)**
Tel.: (787) 641-8181
Web Site: http://www.us.schindler.com
Emp.: 43
Elevators, Escalators & Passenger Conveyors
N.A.I.C.S.: 423830

Subsidiary (Non-US):

Schindler Elevator Corporation (2)
3640A McNicoll Avenue, Toronto, M1X 1G5, ON, Canada **(100%)**
Tel.: (416) 332-8280
Web Site: http://www.ca.schindler.com
Sales Range: $25-49.9 Million
Emp.: 50
Elevators, Escalators & Passenger Conveyors
N.A.I.C.S.: 333921

Subsidiary (Domestic):

Schindler Enterprises, Inc. (2)
20 Whippany Rd, Morristown, NJ 07960
Tel.: (973) 397-6500
Elevator Mfr
N.A.I.C.S.: 333921

Schindler Elevatorer A/S (1)
Industrie Parken 16, Ballerup, 2750, Denmark **(100%)**
Tel.: (45) 70131060
Web Site: https://www.schindler.dk
Sales Range: Less than $1 Million
Emp.: 40
Elevators, Escalators & Passenger Conveyors
N.A.I.C.S.: 333921
Jan Bruhn-Hansen *(Mng Dir)*

Schindler Eskalatory s.r.o. (1)
Kracanska cesta 49, Dunajska Streda, Slovakia
Tel.: (421) 31550 57 31
Elevator & Escalator Distr
N.A.I.C.S.: 423830

Schindler Fahrtreppen International GmbH (1)
Wienerbergstrasse 21-25, Vienna, 1100, Austria
Tel.: (43) 1 60188
Web Site: http://www.schindler.com
Sales Range: $50-74.9 Million
Emp.: 200
Elevator & Escalator Installation Services
N.A.I.C.S.: 238290

Schindler France (1)
5 rue Dewoitine, 78140, Velizy-Villacoublay, France
Tel.: (33) 130707070
Web Site: https://www.schindler.fr
Sales Range: $50-74.9 Million
Emp.: 250
Escalator & Elevator Installation Services
N.A.I.C.S.: 238290
Pierre Vanstoflegatte *(Mng Dir, Acting Dir & Publication)*

Schindler Hellas SA (1)
Lalechou 1 & Olympionokon L Kifissias 194, New Psychico, 154 51, Athens, Greece **(99.8%)**
Tel.: (30) 2107459510
Web Site: http://www.schindler.gr
Sales Range: $25-49.9 Million
Emp.: 70
Elevators, Escalators & Passenger Conveyors
N.A.I.C.S.: 333921

Schindler Hiss AB (1)
Bjornstigen 85, Box 4095, 169 04, Solna, Sweden **(100%)**
Tel.: (46) 86224000
Web Site: https://www.schindler.se
Sales Range: $25-49.9 Million
Emp.: 30
Elevators, Escalators & Passenger Conveyors
N.A.I.C.S.: 333921

Schindler Hiss AB (1)
PO Box 547, SE 182 15, Danderyd, Sweden **(100%)**
Web Site: http://www.schindler.se
Elevators, Escalators & Passenger Conveyors
N.A.I.C.S.: 333921

Schindler Hrvatska d.o.o. (1)
Kovinska 4A / II kat, Zagreb, 10090, Croatia
Tel.: (385) 13040630
Web Site: https://www.schindler.hr
Sales Range: $25-49.9 Million
Emp.: 37
Elevator & Escalator Installation Services

SCHINDLER HOLDING AG

Schindler Holding AG—(Continued)
N.A.I.C.S.: 238290

Schindler Hungaria KFT (1)
Budafoki ut 60, PO Box 500, 1117, Budapest, Hungary (100%)
Tel.: (36) 12069000
Web Site: https://hu.schindler.com
Sales Range: $25-49.9 Million
Emp.: 120
Elevators, Escalators & Passenger Conveyors
N.A.I.C.S.: 333921

Schindler Iberica Management, S.A. (1)
Poligono Empresarium Albardin 58, La Cartuja Baja, 50720, Zaragoza, Spain
Tel.: (34) 976 70 40 00
Elevator & Escalator Installation Services
N.A.I.C.S.: 238290
Julio Arce *(Gen Mgr)*

Schindler Informatik AG (1)
Zugerstrasse 13, CH 6030, Ebikon, Switzerland (100%)
Tel.: (41) 414453434
Web Site: http://www.schindlerinformatik.com
Sales Range: $50-74.9 Million
Emp.: 150
Elevators, Escalators & Passenger Conveyors
N.A.I.C.S.: 333921

Schindler Korea Co. Ltd. (1)
7th floor Wonter Building 32 Mullae- dong 3-ga, Yeongdeungpo-gu, Seoul, 150-834, Korea (South)
Tel.: (82) 234702500
Web Site: https://www.schindler.com
Elevator & Escalator Mfr
N.A.I.C.S.: 333921

Schindler Latin America Operations (1)
Av Nossa Senhora de Fatima 25 Fatima, Barra da Tijuca, Rio de Janeiro, 20240-050, Brazil
Tel.: (55) 8000551918
Web Site: http://www.schindler.com
Sales Range: $200-249.9 Million
Emp.: 1,000
Elevators, Escalators & Passenger Conveyors
N.A.I.C.S.: 333921

Schindler Lebanon S.A.L. (1)
3rd Floor Centre Hage Main Internal Street, Antelias, 1201, Lebanon
Tel.: (961) 4417750
Web Site: https://www.schindler.ae
Emp.: 100
Elevator & Escalator Installation Services
N.A.I.C.S.: 238290
Elie Bsaibes *(Gen Mgr)*

Schindler Liegenschaftsverwaltungs GmbH (1)
Wienerbergstrasse 25, Vienna, 1100, Austria
Tel.: (43) 1 60188 0
Web Site: http://www.schindler.at
Elevator & Escalator Installation Services
N.A.I.C.S.: 238290
Michael Uher *(Mgr-Mktg)*

Schindler Liften B.V. (1)
Verheeskade 4, 2521 BN, Hague, Netherlands (100%)
Tel.: (31) 703843700
Web Site: http://www.schindler.com
Sales Range: $50-74.9 Million
Emp.: 350
Elevators, Escalators & Passenger Conveyors
N.A.I.C.S.: 333921

Schindler Lifts (Botswana) (PTY) Ltd. (1)
Plot 20650 Block 3 Broadhurst Industrial, Gaborone, Botswana
Tel.: (267) 3930283
Web Site: https://www.schindler.com
Elevator & Escalator Installation Services
N.A.I.C.S.: 238290

Schindler Lifts (Namibia) (PTY) Ltd. (1)
84 Frans Indongo Street, PO Box 3534, Windhoek West, Windhoek, 10005, Namibia (100%)
Tel.: (264) 61240362
Web Site: http://www.schindler.co.za
Sales Range: $1-9.9 Million
Emp.: 11
Elevators, Escalators & Passenger Conveyors
N.A.I.C.S.: 333921

Schindler Lifts (Zimbabwe) (Pvt) Ltd. (1)
70 Simon Mazorodze Road, Harare, Zimbabwe (100%)
Tel.: (263) 33265522
Web Site: http://www.schindler.co.za
Sales Range: Less than $1 Million
Emp.: 40
Elevators, Escalators & Passenger Conveyors
N.A.I.C.S.: 333921

Schindler Lifts SA Investments Holding (PTY) Ltd. (1)
27 Hippo Road, Johannesburg, 2190, Gauteng, South Africa
Tel.: (27) 116818888
Investment Management Service
N.A.I.C.S.: 523940
Jorge Ramos *(Mng Dir)*

Schindler Lifts South Africa (Pty.) Ltd. (1)
27 Hippo Road, PO Box 3615, Johannesburg, 2190, South Africa (100%)
Tel.: (27) 116818888
Web Site: http://www.schindler.co.za
Sales Range: $100-124.9 Million
Emp.: 500
Elevators, Escalators & Passenger Conveyors
N.A.I.C.S.: 333921

Schindler Ltd. (1)
400 Dashwood Lang Road Bourne Business Park, Addlestone, KT15 2HJ, Surrey, United Kingdom (100%)
Tel.: (44) 1932758100
Web Site: https://www.schindler.com
Sales Range: $25-49.9 Million
Emp.: 80
Elevators, Escalators & Passenger Conveyors
N.A.I.C.S.: 333921

Schindler Ltd. (1)
Unit 12d Joyce Way Parkwest Business Park Nangor Road, Dublin, D12 YOA6, Ireland (100%)
Tel.: (353) 18832700
Web Site: https://www.schindler.ie
Sales Range: $25-49.9 Million
Emp.: 50
Elevators, Escalators & Passenger Conveyors Installer
N.A.I.C.S.: 333921

Schindler Ltd. (1)
Longonot Place 1st Floor Kijabe Street 10, Nairobi, 00100, Kenya (100%)
Tel.: (254) 20340669
Web Site: http://www.schindler.com
Elevators, Escalators & Passenger Conveyors
N.A.I.C.S.: 333921

Schindler Ltd. (1)
2 Triq Roger Debattista, Hamrun, HMR 1271, Malta
Tel.: (356) 21442914
Web Site: https://www.schindler.mt
Escalator & Elevator Installation Services
N.A.I.C.S.: 238290

Schindler Ltd., Egypt (1)
1 Aly Rashed St Star Capital 1 First Floor City Stars, Helipolis, Cairo, Egypt (100%)
Tel.: (20) 224801939
Web Site: https://www.schindler.eg
Sales Range: $50-74.9 Million
Emp.: 250
Elevators, Escalators & Passenger Conveyors Mfr
N.A.I.C.S.: 333921

Schindler Management AG (1)
Zugerstrasse 13, 6030, Ebikon, Lucerne, Switzerland (100%)
Tel.: (41) 414453232

Web Site: http://www.schindler.com
Emp.: 1,000
Elevators, Escalators & Passenger Conveyors
N.A.I.C.S.: 333921

Schindler Management AP (Shanghai) Co. Ltd. (1)
40 Wenshui Road, Shanghai, 200072, China
Tel.: (86) 21 5665 0991
Elevator & Escalator Distr
N.A.I.C.S.: 423830

Schindler Management Asia/Pacific Ltd. (1)
29 Fl Top Glory Tower 262 Gloucester Rd, Causeway Bay, China (Hong Kong) (100%)
Tel.: (852) 25743881
Web Site: https://www.schindler.com
Sales Range: $25-49.9 Million
Emp.: 20
Elevators, Escalators & Passenger Conveyors
N.A.I.C.S.: 333921

Subsidiary (Non-US):

Antah Schindler Sdn. Bhd. (2)
8/F Bangunan TH Uptown 3 No 3 Jalan SS 21/39, Damansara Uptown, 47400, Petaling Jaya, Selangor, Malaysia (70%)
Tel.: (60) 377251818
Web Site: https://www.schindler.my
Sales Range: $25-49.9 Million
Elevators, Escalators & Passenger Conveyors
N.A.I.C.S.: 333921

Schindler China Elevator Co. Ltd. (2)
555 Xingshun Road, Jiading District, Shanghai, 201815, China (100%)
Tel.: (86) 2167096666
Web Site: http://www.schindler.com
Sales Range: $25-49.9 Million
Emp.: 50
Elevators, Escalators & Passenger Conveyors
N.A.I.C.S.: 333921

Subsidiary (Domestic):

Schindler Electronics (Suzhou) Co. Ltd. (3)
12 Baiyu Rd Suzhou Industrial Pk, 215021, Suzhou, China (100%)
Tel.: (86) 51262527810
Sales Range: $25-49.9 Million
Elevators, Escalators & Passenger Conveyors
N.A.I.C.S.: 333921

Suzhou Esca Step Co. Ltd. (3)
57 Huang Pu Street, Suzhou New District, Suzhou, 215011, China (100%)
Tel.: (86) 51268250519
Web Site: http://www.schindler.com.cn
Elevators, Escalators & Passenger Conveyors
N.A.I.C.S.: 333921

Subsidiary (Non-US):

Schindler Elevator K.K (2)
8-17-5 Ginza, Chuo-ku, Tokyo, 104-0061, Japan (96.7%)
Tel.: (81) 345777820
Web Site: http://www.schindler.com
Sales Range: $25-49.9 Million
Elevators, Escalators & Passenger Conveyors
N.A.I.C.S.: 333921

Schindler India Pvt. Ltd. (2)
Schindler House Main Street, Hiranandani Gardens Powai, Mumbai, 400 076, India (100%)
Tel.: (91) 2261314444
Web Site: https://www.schindler.in
Sales Range: $25-49.9 Million
Emp.: 150
Elevators, Escalators & Passenger Conveyors
N.A.I.C.S.: 333921
Uday Kulkarni *(Pres)*

Subsidiary (Domestic):

Schindler Lifts (Hong Kong) Ltd. (2)

INTERNATIONAL PUBLIC

29th Floor Devon House Taikoo Place 979 King's Road, 979 Kings Rd, Quarry Bay, China (Hong Kong) (100%)
Tel.: (852) 25168168
Web Site: https://www.jardineschindler.com
Sales Range: $50-74.9 Million
Lift Installation & Maintenance
N.A.I.C.S.: 238290

Joint Venture (Domestic):

Jardine Schindler Group (3)
29 F Devon House Taikoo Place 979 King's Road, Quarry Bay, China (Hong Kong)
Tel.: (852) 25168168
Web Site: https://www.jardineschindler.com
Holding Company; Lift, Escalator & Moving Walkway Designer, Mfr, Installation & Maintenance Services
N.A.I.C.S.: 551112

Subsidiary (Non-US):

Jardine Schindler (Thai) Ltd. (4)
Times Square Building 20th Floor 246 Sukhumvit Road, Klongtoey, Bangkok, 10110, Thailand
Tel.: (66) 26851600
Web Site: https://www.schindler.com
Sales Range: $25-49.9 Million
Elevators, Escalators & Passenger Conveyors
N.A.I.C.S.: 333921

Jardine Schindler Elevator Corporation (4)
20th/F Tower 1 Insular Life Corporate Centre Insular Life Drive, Filinvest Corporate City Alabang, Muntinlupa, 1781, Philippines
Tel.: (63) 286836800
Web Site: https://www.schindler.ph
Sales Range: $25-49.9 Million
Elevators, Escalators & Passenger Conveyors
N.A.I.C.S.: 333921

Myanmar Jardine Schindler Ltd. (4)
No 1/4 Parami Road, Hlaing Township, Yangon, 11051, Myanmar
Tel.: (95) 1654855
Web Site: https://www.schindler.com
Sales Range: $25-49.9 Million
Emp.: 250
Elevators, Escalators & Passenger Conveyors
N.A.I.C.S.: 333921

Subsidiary (Non-US):

Schindler Lifts (Singapore) Pte. Ltd. (2)
1 Kaki Bukit View 04-18 Techview, Singapore, 415941, Singapore (100%)
Tel.: (65) 68547888
Web Site: https://www.schindler.com
Sales Range: $75-99.9 Million
Emp.: 480
Elevators, Escalators & Passenger Conveyors
N.A.I.C.S.: 333921

Schindler Lifts Australia Pty. Ltd. (2)
Level 6 241 O'Riordan St, Mascot, Sydney, 2020, NSW, Australia (100%)
Tel.: (61) 299319900
Web Site: https://au.schindler.com
Sales Range: $75-99.9 Million
Emp.: 1,000
Elevators, Escalators & Passenger Conveyors Mfr
N.A.I.C.S.: 333921

Schindler Lifts NZ Ltd. (2)
25 Nugent Street, PO Box 724, Grafton, Auckland, 1023, New Zealand (100%)
Tel.: (64) 93537500
Web Site: https://www.schindler.com
Sales Range: $25-49.9 Million
Emp.: 100
Elevators, Escalators & Passenger Conveyors
N.A.I.C.S.: 333921

Schindler Vietnam Ltd. (2)
8th Floor President Place Building 93 Nguyen Du Street, Ben Nghe Ward District 1, Ho Chi Minh City, Vietnam (70%)
Tel.: (84) 2835214890
Web Site: https://www.schindler.vn

AND PRIVATE COMPANIES

Sales Range: $25-49.9 Million
Elevators, Escalators & Passenger Conveyors
N.A.I.C.S.: 333921

Schindler Maroc S.A. (1)
Lotissement 1 Mederssa Zone Indus Immeuble 3 1er Etage, Sidi Maarouf, Casablanca, 20250, Morocco
Tel.: (212) 802002025
Web Site: https://www.schindler.com
Sales Range: $50-74.9 Million
Emp.: 25
Elevator Sales & Maintenance Services
N.A.I.C.S.: 423830

Schindler Monaco (98%)
7 Rue Du Gabian Gildo Pastor Ctr, Fontvieille, 98000, Monaco
Tel.: (377) 92056655
Web Site: http://www.schindler.fr
Sales Range: $25-49.9 Million
Emp.: 16
Elevators, Escalators & Passenger Conveyors
N.A.I.C.S.: 333921

Schindler Nechushtan Elevators Ltd. (1)
Granite 9 Kiryat Aryeh, PO Box 9715, Petah Tiqwa, 40350, Israel (100%)
Tel.: (972) 37214400
Web Site: https://www.schindler.com
Sales Range: $100-124.9 Million
Emp.: 370
Elevators, Escalators & Passenger Conveyors
N.A.I.C.S.: 333921

Schindler Olayan Elevator Company Ltd. (1)
Hail Street AL-Ruweis, PO Box 1150, Jeddah, 21431, Saudi Arabia
Tel.: (966) 126515244
Elevator & Escalator Installation Services
N.A.I.C.S.: 238290

Schindler Oy (1)
Ohrahuhdantie 2 B, FIN 00680, Helsinki, Finland (100%)
Tel.: (358) 9756730
Web Site: https://www.schindler.fi
Sales Range: $25-49.9 Million
Emp.: 150
Elevators, Escalators & Passenger Conveyors
N.A.I.C.S.: 333921

Schindler Pars International Ltd. (1)
Ruby 2 Building 1st Floor Umm Al Sheif SheikhZayed Road, PO Box 115117, Al Safa 2, Dubai, United Arab Emirates
Tel.: (971) 43760000
Web Site: http://www.schindler.com
Emp.: 100
Elevator & Escalator Mfr
N.A.I.C.S.: 333921

Schindler Polska sp. zoo. (1)
ul Postepu 12A, 02-676, Warsaw, Poland (100%)
Tel.: (48) 225492100
Web Site: https://www.schindler.com
Sales Range: $25-49.9 Million
Emp.: 200
Elevators, Escalators & Passenger Conveyors
N.A.I.C.S.: 333921

Schindler Romania S.R.L. (1)
Str Preciziei 6R etaj 1 Sector 6, 062203, Bucharest, Romania
Tel.: (40) 213367058
Web Site: https://www.schindler.com
Sales Range: $50-74.9 Million
Emp.: 100
Escalator Sales & Maintenance Services
N.A.I.C.S.: 423830

Schindler S.A. (1)
Avda Europa 22 Parque Empresarial La Moraleja, Alcobendas, 28108, Madrid, Spain (99%)
Tel.: (34) 916576000
Web Site: http://www.schindler.es
Sales Range: $25-49.9 Million
Emp.: 100
Elevators, Escalators & Passenger Conveyors
N.A.I.C.S.: 333921

Schindler S.a.r.l. (1)
7 rue de l'Innovation Building F Luxite 2, PO Box 1842, 1896, Kockelscheuer, Luxembourg (100%)
Tel.: (352) 4858581
Web Site: https://www.schindler.lu
Sales Range: $25-49.9 Million
Emp.: 80
Elevators, Escalators & Passenger Conveyors
N.A.I.C.S.: 333921

Schindler S.p.A. (1)
Via Monza 1, 20863, Concorezzo, Monza & Brianza, Italy (100%)
Tel.: (39) 03966521
Web Site: https://www.schindler.com
Emp.: 1,500
Elevators, Escalators & Passenger Conveyors
N.A.I.C.S.: 333921

Schindler Scandinavian Holding AB (1)
Rinkebyvagen 25, Danderyd, 182 15, Sweden (100%)
Tel.: (46) 86224000
Web Site: http://www.schindler.se
Sales Range: $25-49.9 Million
Emp.: 30
Elevators, Escalators & Passenger Conveyors
N.A.I.C.S.: 333921

Schindler Slovenija d.o.o. (1)
Grska ulica 13, Ljubljana, 1000, Slovenia
Tel.: (386) 15862800
Web Site: https://www.schindler.si
Emp.: 40
Elevator & Escalator Installation Services
N.A.I.C.S.: 238290

Schindler Stahl Heiser A/S (1)
Midttunlia 17 Slatthaug, PO Box 280, NO 5851, Bergen, Norway (100%)
Tel.: (47) 055925640
Web Site: http://www.stahl.no
Sales Range: $25-49.9 Million
Emp.: 75
Elevator Installations
N.A.I.C.S.: 333921
Jan Henrik Skjelbred *(Mng Dir)*

Schindler Technik AG (1)
Hohenrainstr 10, CH 4133, Pratteln, Switzerland (100%)
Tel.: (41) 618256211
Web Site: http://www.schindler.com
Sales Range: $25-49.9 Million
Emp.: 12
Mfr of Tramways
N.A.I.C.S.: 485119

Schindler Turkeli Asansor san a.s. (1)
Barbaros Mahallesi Ihlamur Bulvari Agaoglu My Newwork No 3/166, Atasehir, Istanbul, 34746, Turkiye (100%)
Tel.: (90) 2122768600
Web Site: https://www.schindler.com.tr
Sales Range: $25-49.9 Million
Emp.: 30
Elevators, Escalators & Passenger Conveyors
N.A.I.C.S.: 333921
Gaetano Conca *(Mng Dir)*

Schindler UK (1)
400 Dashwood Lang Road Bourne Business Park, Addlestone, KT15 2HJ, Surrey, United Kingdom (100%)
Tel.: (44) 1932758100
Web Site: https://www.schindlerlifts.co.uk
Sales Range: $75-99.9 Million
Emp.: 30
Mfr of Elevators & Escalators
N.A.I.C.S.: 333921

Schindler Vytahy a eskalatory a.s. (1)
Karadzicova 8, 821 08, Bratislava, Slovakia (100%)
Tel.: (421) 232724111
Web Site: https://www.schindler.sk
Sales Range: $25-49.9 Million
Emp.: 90
Elevators, Escalators & Passenger Conveyors
N.A.I.C.S.: 333921

Schindler d.o.o. Beograd (1)
Bulevar Zorana Dindica 64a GTC HOUSE, Novi Beograd, 11070, Serbia
Tel.: (381) 112608881
Web Site: https://www.schindler.com
Emp.: 30
Escalator & Elevator Mfr
N.A.I.C.S.: 333921
Tanja Milovanovic *(Mng Dir)*

Schindler for Importation Services LTD (1)
Diplomats Tower 4 El Nile Street, Cairo, Egypt
Tel.: (20) 237763900
Elevator & Escalator Installation Services
N.A.I.C.S.: 238290

Schindler, S.A. (1)
Avenida Jose Gomes Ferreira n 15 - 1 Miraflores, 1495-139, Alges, Portugal (100%)
Tel.: (351) 214243800
Web Site: http://www.schindler.com
Elevators, Escalators & Passenger Conveyors
N.A.I.C.S.: 333921

Schinvest (Jersey) Ltd. (1)
Zugerstrasse 13, Jersey, CH-6031, Ebikon, Switzerland (100%)
Tel.: (41) 4453232
Web Site: http://www.schindler.com
Mfr of Escalators & Elevators
N.A.I.C.S.: 333921

Sociedade Portuguesa dos Ascensores Schindler Lda. (1)
Av D Joao 2 n 1 16 05 H-Piso 2, Parque das Nacoes, 1990 083, Lisbon, Portugal (100%)
Mfr of Elevators, Escalators & Passenger Conveyors
N.A.I.C.S.: 333921

Societe Oranaise de Maintenance Industrielle (1)
10 Rue des Freres Belhadj, Oran, Algeria
Tel.: (213) 41414270
Web Site: http://www.schindler.com
Elevator & Escalator Installation Services
N.A.I.C.S.: 238290

Tamkin Foulad Asanbar Co. (1)
No 6 21st Ave Argentine Square, 15139-14133, Tehran, Iran
Tel.: (98) 21 8855 23 67
Web Site: http://www.schindler.com.sa
Sales Range: $50-74.9 Million
Emp.: 200
Elevator & Escalator Installation Services
N.A.I.C.S.: 238290

Tana Engineering Plc (1)
PO Box 3046, Addis Ababa, Ethiopia
Tel.: (251) 113720172
Web Site: https://tanaengineering.net
Emp.: 100
Elevator & Escalator Distr
N.A.I.C.S.: 423830

Tecnel Elevadores, LDA (1)
Av Zedequias Manganhela 1320, Maputo, 2577, Mozambique
Tel.: (258) 214 29433
Web Site: http://www.tecnelevadores.com
Sales Range: $25-49.9 Million
Emp.: 22
Elevator & Escalator Installation Services
N.A.I.C.S.: 238290
Luis Pinto *(Gen Mgr)*

Ternitz Druckguss GmbH (1)
Werkstrasse 15, 2630, Ternitz, Austria (80%)
Tel.: (43) 263035131
Web Site: http://www.tedg.com
Sales Range: $25-49.9 Million
Emp.: 70
Escalators & Moving Walkways
N.A.I.C.S.: 333921

Trade Promoters Ltd. (1)
No 272/25 Sudharshana Mawatha, 10115, Malabe, Sri Lanka
Tel.: (94) 117607800
Web Site: https://tpl.lk
Elevator & Escalator Installation Services
N.A.I.C.S.: 238290
Rohan M. Fernando *(Founder & CEO)*

UAB Schindler Liftas (1)
AP Kavoliuko g 4, 04326, Vilnius, Lithuania (100%)
Tel.: (370) 52106500
Web Site: https://www.schindler.lt
Sales Range: $50-74.9 Million
Emp.: 79
Elevators, Escalators & Passenger Conveyors
N.A.I.C.S.: 333921

ZAO Schindler (1)
Raketny Boulevard 16, 129164, Moscow, Russia
Tel.: (7) 495 775 44 11
Web Site: http://www.schindler.ru
Sales Range: $25-49.9 Million
Emp.: 115
Elevator & Escalator Installation Services
N.A.I.C.S.: 238290

SCHIPHOL GROUP NV

Evert van der Beekstraat 202, 1118 CP, Schiphol, Netherlands
Tel.: (31) 206012570
Web Site: http://www.schiphol.nl
Airport Operator
N.A.I.C.S.: 488119
Herman J. Hazewinkel *(Vice Chm-Supervisory Bd)*

Subsidiaries:

Avioport SpA (1)
Via del Gregge 100, 21015, Lonate Pozzolo, Italy
Tel.: (39) 0331 302 290
Web Site: http://www.wtc-airport.com
Tour Operator
N.A.I.C.S.: 561520

Eindhoven Airport N.V. (1)
Luchthavenweg 13, 5657 EA, Eindhoven, Netherlands
Tel.: (31) 900 9505
Web Site: http://www.eindhovenairport.com
Tour Operator
N.A.I.C.S.: 561520
Fons Latour *(Head-Route Dev)*

Luchthaven Lelystad Vastgoed B.V. (1)
Arendweg 7, 8218 PE, Lelystad, Netherlands
Tel.: (31) 320 284770
Web Site: http://www.lelystadairport.nl
Tour Operator
N.A.I.C.S.: 561520

Rotterdam Airport B.V. (1)
Rotterdam Airportplein 60, 3045 AP, Rotterdam, Netherlands
Tel.: (31) 10 446 34 44
Tour Operator
N.A.I.C.S.: 561520

Schiphol Airport Retail B.V. (1)
Snipweg 7, Schiphol, 1118DN, Netherlands
Tel.: (31) 20 601 9111
Web Site: http://www.schipholairport.com
Emp.: 1,700
Tour Operator
N.A.I.C.S.: 561520
Jos Nijhuis *(Gen Mgr)*

Schiphol Real Estate B.V. (1)
Evert van de Beekstraat 202, Schiphol, 1118 CP, Netherlands
Tel.: (31) 20 601 2888
Web Site: http://www.schiphol.nl
Emp.: 70
Tour Operator
N.A.I.C.S.: 561520
Walter Pronk *(Controller-Fin)*

Schiphol Telematics CV (1)
Tristar 3 Sta Spein No 991, 1117 BR, Schiphol, Netherlands (100%)
Tel.: (31) 203163500
Web Site: http://www.st.nl
Sales Range: $25-49.9 Million
Emp.: 90
Telecommunications Operator
N.A.I.C.S.: 517111

SCHIVO MEDICAL LIMITED

Units 1-4 IDA Business Park Cork Road, Waterford, X91 RP71, Ireland

SCHIVO MEDICAL LIMITED

Schivo Medical Limited—(Continued)
Tel.: (353) 51372010
Web Site:
http://www.schivomedical.com
Medical Devices & Life Sciences Equipment Design & Mfr
N.A.I.C.S.: 339112
Graham Reeves (CEO)

SCHJAERVEN REKLAMEBYRA
Bygdoy Alle 23, 0262, Oslo, Norway
Tel.: (47) 23086500
Web Site: http://www.schjaerven.no
Year Founded: 1962
Sales Range: $10-24.9 Million
Emp.: 100
N.A.I.C.S.: 541810
Stale Schjaerven (Mng Dir)

Subsidiaries:

Schjaerven 3D (1)
Bygdoy Alle 23, 0262, Oslo, Norway
Tel.: (47) 23 08 65 00
Web Site: http://www.schjarven.no
N.A.I.C.S.: 541810
Stale A. Osthaug (Dir-Admin)

Schjaerven Film (1)
Bygdoy Alle 23, PO Box 1186, Sentrum, 0262, Oslo, Norway
Tel.: (47) 23 08 65 00
Web Site: http://www.schjarven.no
Emp.: 12
N.A.I.C.S.: 541810
Fredrik Kiosterud (Dir-Admin)

Schjaerven Interactive (1)
Bygdoy Alle 23, 0262, Oslo, Norway
Tel.: (47) 23 08 65 00
Web Site: http://www.schjarven.no
Emp.: 40
N.A.I.C.S.: 541810
Trond Sonju (Exec-Interactive)

Schjaerven PR (1)
Bygdoy Alle 23, PO Box 1186, Sentrum, 0107, Oslo, Norway
Tel.: (47) 23 08 65 00
Web Site: http://www.schjarven.no
N.A.I.C.S.: 541820
Stig Fossum (Gen Mgr)

SCHLATTER INDUSTRIES AG
Brandstrasse 24, 8952, Schlieren, Switzerland
Tel.: (41) 447327111 CH
Web Site:
https://www.schlattergroup.com
Year Founded: 1967
STRN—(SWX)
Rev.: $96,385,536
Assets: $33,158,272
Liabilities: $2,986,304
Net Worth: $30,171,968
Earnings: $514,880
Emp.: 344
Fiscal Year-end: 12/31/19
Resistance Welding Systems Mfr
N.A.I.C.S.: 333992
Werner Schmidli (CEO)

Subsidiaries:

H.A. Schlatter AG (1)
Brandstrasse 24, Schlieren, 8952, Switzerland
Tel.: (41) 447327111
Web Site: http://www.schlattergroup.com
Sales Range: $100-124.9 Million
Resistance Welding Systems Mfr
N.A.I.C.S.: 333992
Werner Schmidli (CFO)

Subsidiary (US):

H.A. Schlatter, Inc. (2)
4640 Colt Rd, Rockford, IL 61109-2645 (100%)
Tel.: (815) 874-9471
Web Site: http://www.schlattergroup.com
Sales Range: $25-49.9 Million
Emp.: 8
Distribution & Marketing of Welding Equipment
N.A.I.C.S.: 423830

Schlatter France S.a.r.l. (1)
Immeuble Atria, 2 Rue Du Ctr, F 93885, Noisy-le-Grand, Cedex, France (100%)
Tel.: (33) 143054545
Web Site: http://www.schlatter.ch
Emp.: 3
N.A.I.C.S.: 333992

Schlatter International GmbH (1)
Dahlweg 105, 48153, Munster, Germany (100%)
Tel.: (49) 251871390
Web Site: http://www.schlatter.ch
Sales Range: $25-49.9 Million
Emp.: 11
N.A.I.C.S.: 333992

Schlatter Italiana S.r.l. (1)
Centro Svizzero, Via Palestro 4, I 20121, Milan, Italy (100%)
Tel.: (39) 0276003065
Web Site: http://www.schlatter.ch
Electric Resistance Welding Systems
N.A.I.C.S.: 333992

Schlatter Ltd. (1)
16 Fulwith Road, Harrogate, HG2 8HL, North Yorkshire, United Kingdom (100%)
Tel.: (44) 7831437873
Web Site: http://www.schlattergroup.com
Sales Range: $25-49.9 Million
Emp.: 2
Electric & Gas Welding Equipment
N.A.I.C.S.: 333992
Geoff Addy (Mgr-Customer Support)

Schlatter Maquinas de Soldar Ltda. (1)
Rua Silva Bueno 107, Alvinopolis, 09891-470, Sao Bernardo do Campo, SP, Brazil (100%)
Tel.: (55) 141254443
Sales Range: $25-49.9 Million
Emp.: 10
Electric Resistance Welding
N.A.I.C.S.: 333992

Schlatter North America (1)
4640 Colt Rd, Rockford, IL 61109
Tel.: (815) 874-9471
Web Site: http://www.schlattergroup.com
Welding & Weaving Machine Mfr
N.A.I.C.S.: 333992
Ronnie L. Meiers (Mng Dir)

Schlatter South East Asia Sdn. Bhd. (1)
C-3-6 And C-3-7 Greentown Square Jalan Dato Seri Ahmad Said, 30450, Ipoh, Perak Darul Ridzuan, Malaysia
Tel.: (60) 5 255 06 00
Welding & Weaving Machine Mfr
N.A.I.C.S.: 333992
Friedhelm Niemann (Mng Dir)

SCHLEICHER ELECTRONIC GMBH & CO. KG
Wilhelm-Kabus-Str 21-35, 10829, Berlin, Germany
Tel.: (49) 30330050 De
Web Site: http://www.schleicher.berlin
Year Founded: 1937
Emp.: 60
Automation & Safety Systems Mfr
N.A.I.C.S.: 333248
Sven Dubbers (CEO)

Subsidiaries:

Schleicher Beteiligungs GmbH (1)
Trompeterallee 192-194, Monchengladbach, 41189, Germany
Tel.: (49) 216655920
Investment Management Service
N.A.I.C.S.: 523999

Schleicher Electronic Verwaltungs-GmbH (1)
Pichelswerderstr 3-5, Berlin, 13597, Germany
Tel.: (49) 30330050
Web Site: http://www.schleicher-electronic.com
Business Management Consulting Services
N.A.I.C.S.: 541611

SCHLEUPEN AG
Otto Hahn Strasse 20, D 76275, Ettlingen, Germany
Tel.: (49) 7243 321 0 De
Web Site: http://www.schleupen.de
Year Founded: 1970
Sales Range: $50-74.9 Million
Emp.: 430
IT Services
N.A.I.C.S.: 541512
Volker Kruschinski (CEO)

SCHLOSS WACHENHEIM AG
Niederkircher Strasse 27, 54294, Trier, Germany
Tel.: (49) 65199880 De
Web Site: https://www.schloss-wachenheim.com
Year Founded: 1888
SWA—(DEU)
Rev.: $473,914,930
Assets: $504,807,958
Liabilities: $292,861,179
Net Worth: $211,946,779
Earnings: $10,165,287
Emp.: 1,743
Fiscal Year-end: 06/30/24
Wine Mfr & Distr
N.A.I.C.S.: 312130

Subsidiaries:

Ambra Brands Sp. Z o.o. (1)
ul Pulawska 336, 02-819, Warsaw, Poland
Tel.: (48) 225663300
Winery Product Retailer
N.A.I.C.S.: 445320

PH Vinex Slaviantsi Poland Sp. Z o.o. (1)
ul Lelewela 33, 87-100, Torun, Poland
Tel.: (48) 566559016
Web Site: http://www.vinex.pl
Winery Product Retailer
N.A.I.C.S.: 445320

Rindchen's Weinkontor GmbH & Co. KG (1)
Ellerhorst 1 a, Bonningstedt, 25474, Pinneberg, Germany
Tel.: (49) 405562020
Web Site: https://www.rindchen.de
Winery Product Retailer
N.A.I.C.S.: 445320

Subsidiary (Domestic):

Vino Weinhandels GmbH (2)
Burg Layen 1, Rummelsheim, 55452, Stromberg, Germany
Tel.: (49) 6721305770
Web Site: https://www.vino24.de
Winery Product Retailer
N.A.I.C.S.: 445320

Soare Sekt A.S. (1)
Videnska 101/119, 619 00, Brno, Czech Republic
Tel.: (420) 519351102
Web Site: http://www.soaresekt.cz
Winery Product Retailer
N.A.I.C.S.: 445320

Subsidiary (Non-US):

Soare Sekt Slovakia s.r.o. (2)
Orechova 2/536, Trebatice, 922 10, Trnava, Slovakia
Tel.: (421) 337914541
Winery Product Retailer
N.A.I.C.S.: 445320

Veuve Amiot SAS (1)
19-21 rue Ackerman Saint-Hilaire-Saint Florent, Saumur, France
Tel.: (33) 241831414
Web Site: https://www.veuveamiot.fr
Winery Product Retailer
N.A.I.C.S.: 445320

Winezja Sp. Z o.o. (1)
Pulawska 336, 02-819, Warsaw, Poland
Tel.: (48) 225663480
Web Site: http://www.winezja.pl
Winery Product Retailer
N.A.I.C.S.: 445320

INTERNATIONAL PUBLIC

SCHLOTT GRUPPE AG
Wittlensweiler Str 3, 72250, Freudenstadt, Germany
Tel.: (49) 74415310
Web Site:
http://www.schlottgruppe.de
Sales Range: $500-549.9 Million
Emp.: 2,426
Printing & Digital Media Services
N.A.I.C.S.: 323111
Bernd Rose (Chm-Mgmt Bd, CEO & Head-Mktg & Strategic Dev)

Subsidiaries:

Schlott Vertrieb GmbH (1)
Mainstrasse 20, 90451, Nuremberg, Germany (100%)
Tel.: (49) 70023423400
Web Site: http://www.schlottgruppe.de
Book Periodical & Newspaper Whslr
N.A.I.C.S.: 424920
Bernd Rose (Gen Mgr)

Subsidiary (Non-US):

ZAMORA S.R.O (2)
Ke Karlovu 1102/7, Plzen, 30100, Czech Republic
Tel.: (420) 377679111
Commercial Printing Services
N.A.I.C.S.: 323111

Sebaldus Beteiligungs GmbH (1)
Innere Cramer-Klett-Str 4-8, 90403, Nuremberg, Germany (100%)
Tel.: (49) 91153250
Sales Range: $350-399.9 Million
Emp.: 2,000
Media Buying Agencies
N.A.I.C.S.: 541830

Sebaldus GmbH (1)
Innere Cramer-Klett-Strasse 4-8, 90403, Nuremberg, Germany (100%)
Tel.: (49) 91153250
Sales Range: $50-74.9 Million
Emp.: 100
Holding Company
N.A.I.C.S.: 551112

SCHMALE GMBH & CO. KG
Schutzenstrasse 14, 58511, Ludenscheid, Germany
Tel.: (49) 23518770
Web Site: http://www.schmale.de
Year Founded: 1910
Rev.: $10,345,500
Emp.: 58
Fittings & Fastening Machines Mfr
N.A.I.C.S.: 333248
Christiane Schmale (Mng Dir)

SCHMID TELECOM AG
Binzstrasse 35, 8045, Zurich, Switzerland
Tel.: (41) 444561111 CH
Web Site: http://www.schmid-telecom.com
Year Founded: 1967
Sales Range: $50-74.9 Million
Emp.: 120
Fiscal Year-end: 12/31/14
Telecommunications, Digital Subscriber Line Networking & Integrated Voice Communications Systems Products & Services
N.A.I.C.S.: 517111
Peter Schmid (Pres & CEO)

Subsidiaries:

Schmid Telecom Beijing Ltd. (1)
Room 1030 Block A Ling Long Tian Di Building 160 Xisihuan North Road, 8A Guanghua Road, 100026, Beijing, China
Tel.: (86) 1085324382
Web Site: http://www.schmid-telecom.ch
Emp.: 6
DSL Systems Mfr & Communications Solutions

AND PRIVATE COMPANIES

N.A.I.C.S.: 517810
Zhu Junbao *(Gen Mgr)*

Schmid Telecom Brazil Ltda (1)
Itapeva 366 cj 131, 01414 001, Sao Paulo, Brazil
Tel.: (55) 01132886877
Web Site: http://www.schmid-telecom.ch
Sales Range: $25-49.9 Million
Emp.: 6
DSL Systems Mfr & Communications Solutions for Air Traffic Control Systems
N.A.I.C.S.: 517810
Rogerio Cascaes *(Pres & CEO)*

Schmid Telecom France Ltd. (1)
Za de L'Observatoire, 4 Avenue des 3 Peuples, Montigny-le-Bretonneux, France
Tel.: (33) 139303800
Web Site: http://www.schmid-france.fr
Sales Range: $10-24.9 Million
Emp.: 7
Electronic Parts & Equipment
N.A.I.C.S.: 423690

Schmid Telecom India Pvt. Ltd. (1)
24 Okhla Phase III Lane B Okhla Phase III, Okhla Industrial Area, 110020, New Delhi, 110020, India
Tel.: (91) 11 4323 8721
DSL Systems Mfr & Communications Solutions
N.A.I.C.S.: 517810
Rajan Mehra *(Mng Dir)*

Schmid Telecom Russia Ltd. (1)
Kulakova 20, 123529, Moscow, Russia
Tel.: (7) 4959250578
Emp.: 12
DSL Systems Mfr & Communications Solutions
N.A.I.C.S.: 517810

Schmid Telecom Singapore Pte. Ltd. (1)
51 Goldhill Plaza, 08-06 Goldhill Plaza, Singapore, 308900, Singapore
Tel.: (65) 62556838
Web Site: http://www.schmid-telecom.com
Sales Range: $25-49.9 Million
Emp.: 5
Communication Service
N.A.I.C.S.: 517810
Y. L. Loo *(Mng Dir)*

SCHMIDT ELECTRONICS GROUP LTD.
Unit 1105 11/F AXA Tower Landmark East 100 How Ming Street, Kwun Tong, Kowloon, China (Hong Kong)
Tel.: (852) 2507 0222 HK
Web Site: http://www.schmidtelectronics.com
Emp.: 400
Computer Technology Solution & Equipment Distr
N.A.I.C.S.: 423430
Daniel Lin *(CFO)*

Subsidiaries:

Schmidt & Co. (Hong Kong) Ltd. (1)
Unit 1105 11/F AXA Tower Landmark East 100 How Ming Street, Kwun Tong, Kowloon, China (Hong Kong) (100%)
Tel.: (852) 2507 0222
Web Site: http://www.schmidthk.com
Sales Range: $75-99.9 Million
Emp.: 200
Computer Equipment Mfr
N.A.I.C.S.: 334118

SCHMIDT KOMMUNAL-FAHRZEUGE GMBH
Industriestrasse 4, 68649, Gross-Rohrheim, Germany
Tel.: (49) 6245907800
Web Site: http://www.schmidt-kommunal.de
Rev.: $26,175,311
Emp.: 72
New & Used Vehicles Distr
N.A.I.C.S.: 423860
Fiorangela Schlosser *(VP & Mgr-Export)*

SCHMITZ & KRIEGER GMBH
Kolner Strasse 89, Cologne, 50859, Germany
Tel.: (49) 2234946680
Web Site: http://www.schmitz-krieger.de
Year Founded: 1911
Rev.: $10,021,524
Emp.: 50
Industrial Equipment Mfr
N.A.I.C.S.: 333248
Christo Majchrowicz *(Mng Dir)*

SCHNEIDER ELECTRIC INFRASTRUCTURE LIMITED
10th Floor DLF Cyber city Building Number 10 C, DLF Cyber City Phase II, Gurgaon, 122002, India
Tel.: (91) 1247152300
Web Site: https://infra-in.se.com
Year Founded: 2011
SCHNEIDER—(NSE)
Rev.: $179,586,498
Assets: $156,849,693
Liabilities: $156,365,664
Net Worth: $484,029
Earnings: ($138,001)
Emp.: 1,206
Fiscal Year-end: 03/31/21
Electrical Equipment Mfr & Distr
N.A.I.C.S.: 335999
Vinod Kumar Dhall *(Chm)*

SCHNEIDER ELECTRIC SE
35 rue Joseph Monier, 92500, Rueil-Malmaison, France
Tel.: (33) 141297000 FR
Web Site: http://www.schneider-electric.com
Year Founded: 1871
SBGSF—(OTCIQ)
Rev.: $35,502,277,200
Assets: $66,996,807,280
Liabilities: $32,472,209,120
Net Worth: $34,524,598,160
Earnings: $4,020,029,520
Emp.: 166,025
Fiscal Year-end: 12/31/20
Holding Company; Electrical Distribution, Industrial Control & Automation Equipment Mfr
N.A.I.C.S.: 551112
Herve Coureil *(Chief Governance Officer & Sec)*

Subsidiaries:

AVEVA Group plc (1)
High Cross Madingley Road, Cambridge, CB3 0HB, United Kingdom (100%)
Tel.: (44) 1223556655
Web Site: http://www.aveva.com
Rev.: $1,609,305,516
Assets: $9,056,671,260
Liabilities: $1,984,036,236
Net Worth: $7,072,635,024
Earnings: ($84,993,272)
Emp.: 6,500
Fiscal Year-end: 03/31/2022
Engineering Software for Plant, Power & Marine Industries
N.A.I.C.S.: 541330
Peter Herweck *(CEO)*

Subsidiary (Non-US):

AVEVA AB (2)
Drottninggatan 18, PO Box 50555, 202 15, Malmo, Sweden
Tel.: (46) 406680300
Web Site: http://www.aveva.com
Internet-Based Service Linking Shipyards
N.A.I.C.S.: 541512

AVEVA AS (2)
Kanalsletta 2, N-4033, Stavanger, Norway
Tel.: (47) 51 64 71 00
Web Site: http://www.aveva.com
Computer Software Development Services
N.A.I.C.S.: 541511

AVEVA Asia Pacific - Shanghai (2)
37th Floor China Life Finance Centre, 88 Yincheng Road Pudong New Area, Shanghai, 200127, China
Tel.: (86) 2160722999
Web Site: http://www.aveva.com
Computer Technology Solutions for Ships & Submarines
N.A.I.C.S.: 541512

AVEVA Asia Pacific Sdn Bhd (2)
Level 39, Menara 3 PETRONAS Persiaran KLCC, Kuala Lumpur City Centre, 50088, Kuala Lumpur, Malaysia
Tel.: (60) 327180888
Web Site: http://www.aveva.com
Engineering Software Development Services
N.A.I.C.S.: 541511

AVEVA Denmark A/S (2)
Indkildepark 6D, 9210, Aalborg, Denmark
Tel.: (45) 88741551
Web Site: http://www.aveva.com
Computer Software Development Services
N.A.I.C.S.: 541511

AVEVA GmbH (2)
Niederlassung Bochum, Alte Wittener Strabe 50, D-44803, Bochum, Germany (100%)
Tel.: (49) 234964170
Web Site: http://www.aveva.com
Internet-Based Service Linking Shipyards
N.A.I.C.S.: 541512

AVEVA Information Technology India Private Limited (2)
Unit No 202 Wing A Supreme Business Park Behind Lake Castle, Hiranandani Gardens Powai, Mumbai, 400 076, India
Tel.: (91) 2267368400
Web Site: http://www.aveva.com
Computer Software Development Services
N.A.I.C.S.: 541511

AVEVA Pty Limited (2)
Level 9 25 King Street, Bowen Hills, 4006, QLD, Australia
Tel.: (61) 1300841647
Web Site: http://www.aveva.com
Computer Software Development Services
N.A.I.C.S.: 541511

AVEVA SA (2)
5 Sq Felix Nadar Bat C, 94300, Vincennes, France
Tel.: (33) 158641440
Web Site: http://www.aveva.com
Computer Software Development Services
N.A.I.C.S.: 541511

AVEVA Software Singapore Pte. Ltd. (2)
15 Changi Business Park Central 1 03-01, Singapore, 486057, Singapore (100%)
Tel.: (65) 68562453
Web Site: http://www.aveva.com
Computer Systems for Submarines & Ships
N.A.I.C.S.: 541512

Subsidiary (Domestic):

AVEVA Solutions Limited (2)
High Cross Madingley Road, Cambridge, CB3 0HB, United Kingdom
Tel.: (44) 1223556655
Web Site: http://www.aveva.com
Software Development Services
N.A.I.C.S.: 541511

Subsidiary (Non-US):

AVEVA do Brasil Informatica Ltda (2)
Praia do Flamengo 154 Suite 701, Flamengo, Rio de Janeiro, 22210-906, Brazil
Tel.: (55) 21 3094 9850
Web Site: http://www.aveva.com
Computer Software Development Services
N.A.I.C.S.: 541511

Subsidiary (Domestic):

Cadcentre Property Limited (2)
High Cross Madingley Road, Cambridge, CB3 0HB, Cambridgeshire, United Kingdom
Tel.: (44) 1223 556655
Computer Software Development Services
N.A.I.C.S.: 541511

Tribon Solutions (UK) Ltd. (2)
High Cross Madingley Road, Cambridge, CB3 0HB, United Kingdom
Tel.: (44) 1912010000
Computer Systems for Submarines & Ships
N.A.I.C.S.: 541512

Behar securite SA (1)
55 Avenue de l Europe, 92400, Courbevoie, France
Tel.: (33) 147883131
Web Site: http://www.beharsecurite.com
Security & Emergency Lighting Services
N.A.I.C.S.: 561621

Eurotherm Ltda (1)
Avenida Selma Parada 201 Conjunto 403, Campinas, Brazil
Tel.: (55) 1931125333
Temperature Control & Measurement Equipment Mfr
N.A.I.C.S.: 334513

Foxboro (Malaysia) Sdn. Bhd. (1)
Suite 5 01B Mercu Picorp Lot 10 Jalan Astaka U8/84, Bukit Jelutong, 40150, Shah Alam, Selangor, Malaysia
Tel.: (60) 374551920
Web Site: http://www.foxmay.com.my
Distributed Control System Mfr
N.A.I.C.S.: 335314

IGE+XAO SA (1)
16 boulevard Deodat de Severac, CS 90 312, 31773, Colomiers, Cedex, France (67.9%)
Tel.: (33) 562743636
Web Site: http://www.ige-xao.com
Rev.: $41,165,692
Assets: $85,187,042
Liabilities: $24,924,674
Net Worth: $60,262,367
Earnings: $9,886,104
Emp.: 370
Fiscal Year-end: 12/31/2020
Computer Aided Design Software Editor, Producer, Seller & Maintenance
N.A.I.C.S.: 541512
Alain Di Crescenzo *(Pres & CEO)*

Subsidiary (Non-US):

IGE+XAO BV (2)
Beersdalweg 84a, Heerlen, 6412 PE, Netherlands
Tel.: (31) 45 561 16 36
Emp.: 7
Software Publishing Services
N.A.I.C.S.: 513210

IGE+XAO Espana (2)
Parque Empresarial Neisa Sur Av Andalucia Km 10 5, Madrid, 28021, Spain
Tel.: (34) 91 797 90 71
Web Site: http://www.ige-xao.es
Software Publishing Services
N.A.I.C.S.: 513210

Subsidiary (Domestic):

IGE+XAO Lille (2)
Synergie Club - Synergie Park 10 Rue Louis Neel, 59 260, Lezennes, France
Tel.: (33) 3 59 57 77 20
Software Publishing Services
N.A.I.C.S.: 513210

Subsidiary (Non-US):

IGE+XAO Ltd (2)
Unit 308 15 Paternoster Row, Sheffield, S12 BX, South Yorkshire, United Kingdom
Tel.: (44) 114273 1155
Web Site: http://www.ige-xao.co.uk
Software Publishing Services
N.A.I.C.S.: 513210

IGE+XAO Madagascar SARL (2)
Immeuble Santa Lot IV 24 Rue Naka Rabemanantsoa, Antanimena, Antananarivo, Madagascar
Tel.: (261) 20 22 249 19
Software Development Services
N.A.I.C.S.: 541511

Subsidiary (Domestic):

IGE+XAO Marseille (2)
Centre Etoile Valentine Bat 4 20 Traverse de la Montre CS 30035, Traverse de la Montre Bat 20, 13396, Marseilles, Cedex, France

SCHNEIDER ELECTRIC SE

Schneider Electric SE—(Continued)
Tel.: (33) 491444946
Web Site: http://www.ige-xao.fr
Software Editor, Conceiver, Producer, Seller & Maintenance of Computer Aided Designs
N.A.I.C.S.: 541512

IGE+XAO Nantes (2)
3 Rue De Lorraine, 44 240, La Chapelle-sur-Erdre, France
Tel.: (33) 2 51 89 72 12
Web Site: http://www.ige-xao.com
Software Publishing Services
N.A.I.C.S.: 513210

Subsidiary (Non-US):

IGE+XAO Polska Sp. z o.o. (2)
Pl Na Stawach 3, Krakow, 30-107, Poland
Tel.: (48) 12 630 30 30
Web Site: http://www.ige-xao.pl
Emp.: 15
Software Publishing Services
N.A.I.C.S.: 513210

IGE+XAO Software Vertriebs GmbH (2)
Lochfeldstrasse 23, Rastatt, D-76437, Germany
Tel.: (49) 722277473
Sales Range: $25-49.9 Million
Emp.: 7
Software Editor, Conceiver, Producer, Seller & Maintenance of Computer Aided Design
N.A.I.C.S.: 541512

IGE+XAO Switzerland Gmbh (2)
Paul-Emile-Brandt Str 4, 2502, Biel/Bienne, Switzerland
Tel.: (41) 323659393
Emp.: 7
Software Publishing Services
N.A.I.C.S.: 513210
Alain Di Crefcenzo (CEO)

Subsidiary (Domestic):

IGE+XAO, Inc. (2)
Immeuble Vectuer Sud, 72 Avenue de la Republique, Chatillon, 92320, France
Tel.: (33) 155481777
Web Site: http://www.ige-xao.com
Sales Range: $75-99.9 Million
Emp.: 15
Software Editor, Conceiver, Producer, Seller & Maintenance of Computer Aided Design
N.A.I.C.S.: 541512

IGE-XAO Nantes (2)
3 rue de Lorraine, 44240, La Chapelle-sur-Erdre, France
Tel.: (33) 251897212
Web Site: http://www.ige-xao.fr
Computer Software & Systems Desgin Services
N.A.I.C.S.: 541512

Subsidiary (Non-US):

IGE-XAO SRL (2)
Via Canovine 46, 24126, Bergamo, Italy
Tel.: (39) 035 4596167
Web Site: http://www.ige-xao.it
Software Publishing Services
N.A.I.C.S.: 513210

Ige Xao A/S (2)
Bistrupvej 22, Birkerod, Denmark
Tel.: (45) 45942100
Sales Range: $25-49.9 Million
Emp.: 6
Software Editor, Conceiver, Producer, Seller & Maintenance of Computer Aided Design
N.A.I.C.S.: 541512

Subsidiary (Domestic):

CAE Development Aps (3)
Bistrupvej 22, Birkerod, Denmark
Tel.: (45) 45 91 21 00
Software Editor, Conceiver, Producer, Seller & Maintenance of Computer Aided Design
N.A.I.C.S.: 541512

Subsidiary (Non-US):

Ige Xao China, Inc. (2)
Room 801 Block B Gun lin Guoji 5 Guang Jhou Road, 210008, Nanjing, China
Tel.: (86) 2586890716

Web Site: http://www.ige-xao.com.cn
Sales Range: $25-49.9 Million
Emp.: 8
Software Editor, Conceiver, Producer, Seller & Maintenance of Computer Aided Design
N.A.I.C.S.: 541512

Ige Xao Group Inc. (2)
Via delle Canovine 46, Bergamo, 24126, Italy
Tel.: (39) 0354596167
Web Site: http://www.ige-xao.it
Sales Range: $25-49.9 Million
Emp.: 16
Software Editor, Conceiver, Producer, Seller & Maintenance of Computer Aided Design
N.A.I.C.S.: 541512
Paolo Ppis (Gen Mgr)

Ige Xao North America, Inc. (2)
7777 Boul Louis H Lafontaine Suite 201, Boucherville, H1K 4E4, QC, Canada
Tel.: (450) 449-3355
Web Site: http://www.ige-xao.ca
Sales Range: $25-49.9 Million
Emp.: 5
Software Editor, Conceiver, Producer, Seller & Maintenance of Computer Aided Design
N.A.I.C.S.: 541512

Subsidiary (US):

Ige Xao North America, Inc. (2)
545 E John Carpenter Frwy Ste 300, Irving, TX 75062-3958
Tel.: (972) 719-9083
Web Site: http://www.ige-xao.us
Sales Range: $25-49.9 Million
Emp.: 1
Software Editor, Conceiver, Producer, Seller & Maintenance of Computer Aided Design
N.A.I.C.S.: 541512

Subsidiary (Non-US):

Ige Xao, Inc. (2)
205 Stanboliyski Blvd 6th Floor, 1359, Sofia, Bulgaria
Tel.: (359) 28101145
Web Site: http://www.igexao.com
Sales Range: $25-49.9 Million
Emp.: 50
Software Editor, Conceiver, Producer, Seller & Maintenance of Computer Aided Design
N.A.I.C.S.: 541512

Subsidiary (Domestic):

Ige Xao, Inc. (2)
106 Rue de la Liberte, 38180, Seyssins, France
Tel.: (33) 476701642
Web Site: http://www.ige-xao.fr
Sales Range: $75-99.9 Million
Emp.: 350
Software Editor, Conceiver, Producer, Seller & Maintenance of Computer Aided Design
N.A.I.C.S.: 541512

Ige Xao, Inc. (2)
16 Blvd Deodat de Severac cs 90312, Coloniers, Paris, 31773, France
Tel.: (33) 562743636
Web Site: http://www.ige-xao.com
Sales Range: $25-49.9 Million
Emp.: 80
Software Editor, Conceiver, Producer, Seller & Maintenance of Computer Aided Design
N.A.I.C.S.: 541512

Subsidiary (Non-US):

Ige Xao, Inc. (2)
Lochfeldstr 28 C, Rastatt, 76437, Germany
Tel.: (49) 722277473
Web Site: http://www.ige-xao.de
Sales Range: $25-49.9 Million
Emp.: 8
Software Editor, Conceiver, Producer, Seller & Maintenance of Computer Aided Design
N.A.I.C.S.: 541512
Alain Di Crescenzo (CEO)

Ige Xao, Inc. (2)
Marie Bermays 19A, Koblenz, Germany
Tel.: (49) 2166133910
Web Site: http://www.ige-xao.de
Sales Range: $25-49.9 Million
Emp.: 10
Software Editor, Conceiver, Producer, Seller & Maintenance of Computer Aided Design

N.A.I.C.S.: 541512
Thomas Steffan (Gen Mgr)

Ige Xao, Inc. (2)
Koestraat 87, Hoensbroek, 6431 XL, Netherlands
Tel.: (31) 455234300
Web Site: http://www.ige-xao.nl
Sales Range: $25-49.9 Million
Emp.: 7
Software Editor, Conceiver, Producer, Seller & Maintenance of Computer Aided Design
N.A.I.C.S.: 541512

Ige Xao, Inc. (2)
Pl Na Stawach 3, Krakow, Poland
Tel.: (48) 126303030
Web Site: http://www.ige-xao.com.pl
Software Editor, Conceiver, Producer, Seller & Maintenance of Computer Aided Design
N.A.I.C.S.: 541512

Ige Xao, Inc. (2)
Parque Empresarial Neisa Sur, Av Andalucia, Madrid, Spain
Tel.: (34) 917979071
Web Site: http://www.ige-xao.es
Sales Range: $25-49.9 Million
Software Editor, Conceiver, Producer, Seller & Maintenance of Computer Aided Design
N.A.I.C.S.: 541512

NXT Control GmbH (1)
Aumuhlweg 3/B14, 2544, Leoberdorf, Austria
Tel.: (43) 2256627030
Web Site: http://www.nxtcontrol.com
Industrial Control Product Mfr
N.A.I.C.S.: 335314

Operation Technology, Inc. (1)
17 Goodyear Ste 100, Irvine, CA 92618 (80%)
Tel.: (949) 462-0100
Web Site: http://www.etap.com
Sales Range: $1-9.9 Million
Emp.: 45
Custom Computer Programming Services
N.A.I.C.S.: 541511
Farrokh Shokooh (Founder & CEO)

RIB Software GmbH (1)
Vaihinger Strasse 151, 70567, Stuttgart, Germany (87.64%)
Tel.: (49) 71178730
Web Site: https://www.rib-software.com
Sales Range: $300-349.9 Million
Holding Company; Project Management Software Solutions
N.A.I.C.S.: 513210
Tobias Hamacher (CFO)

Subsidiary (Non-US):

A2K Technologies Limited (2)
Unit 5 Level 1 74 France Street South, Eden Terrace Newton, Auckland, 1010, New Zealand
Tel.: (64) 508232797
Software Services
N.A.I.C.S.: 541511
Dominic Wan (Mgr-Bus Dev)

A2K Technologies Pty. Ltd. (2)
Ground Floor 62 Brandl Street, Eight Mile Plains, 4113, QLD, Australia
Tel.: (61) 1800223562
Web Site:
http://www.a2ktechnologies.com.au
Software Services
N.A.I.C.S.: 541511
Jay Howarth (Acct Mgr-Strategic)

Subsidiary (US):

Building Systems Design Inc. (2)
2 Piedmont Ctr Ste 300 3565 Piedmont Rd NE, Atlanta, GA 30305 (60%)
Web Site: http://www.bsdspeclink.com
Custom Computer Programming Services
N.A.I.C.S.: 541511
Daimon Bridge (CEO)

Subsidiary (Non-US):

Construction Computer Software (Australia) (Pty) Limited (2)
8 Help St, Chatswood, 2067, NSW, Australia
Tel.: (61) 290561710
Construction & Engineering Services

N.A.I.C.S.: 541330

Construction Computer Software (Gulf) LLC (2)
The One Tower - Sheikh Zayed Rd, Dubai, United Arab Emirates
Tel.: (971) 43466456
Construction & Engineering Services
N.A.I.C.S.: 541330
Gejo Joshua (Reg Mgr)

Construction Computer Software Limited (2)
3000 Hillswood Drive Hillswood Business Park, Chertsey, KT16 0RS, United Kingdom
Tel.: (44) 1932895110
Construction & Engineering Services
N.A.I.C.S.: 541330

Subsidiary (Domestic):

Datapine GmbH (2)
Friedelstrasse 27, 12047, Berlin, Germany
Tel.: (49) 3069209427
Web Site: https://www.datapine.com
Software Programming Services
N.A.I.C.S.: 541511
Martin Blumenau (Co-Founder & Mng Partner)

Subsidiary (Non-US):

Exactal Europe Limited (2)
1 Hammersmith Grove, London, W6 0NB, United Kingdom
Tel.: (44) 2031786670
Software Services
N.A.I.C.S.: 541511
Geoff Hussey (Mgr-Channels-Intl)

Exactal Malaysia Sdn., Bhd. (2)
A-9-1 9th Floor BBT One The Towers South Tower Lebuh Batu Nilam 1, Bandar Bukit Tinggi, 41200, Klang, Selangor, Malaysia
Tel.: (60) 340657060
Software Services
N.A.I.C.S.: 541511
Andy Ang (Sls Mgr-Asia)

Guangzhou RIB Software Company Limited (2)
No 2817 Kaichuang Avenue, Huangpu District, Guangzhou, 510530, Guangdong, China
Tel.: (86) 2028069700
Software Consulting Services
N.A.I.C.S.: 541512
Lucy Cen (Sr Dir)

Subsidiary (Domestic):

IMS Gesellschaft fur Informations-und Managementsysteme mbH (2)
Erlenstrasse 80, 46539, Dinslaken, Germany
Tel.: (49) 206449860
Web Site: http://www.imsware.de
Emp.: 70
Software Programming Services
N.A.I.C.S.: 541511
Michael Heinrichs (Mng Dir)

Kirus GmbH (2)
Erlenstrasse 80, 46539, Dinslaken, Germany
Tel.: (49) 2064970650
Web Site: http://www.kirus.de
Software Programming Services
N.A.I.C.S.: 541511

Subsidiary (Non-US):

Levtech Consulting DMCC (2)
Office 1005 BB1 Mazaya Business Avenue Jumeriah Lake Towers, PO Box 62901, Dubai, United Arab Emirates
Tel.: (971) 45836802
Web Site: http://www.levtechconsulting.com
Software Consulting Services
N.A.I.C.S.: 541512
Anilesh Kumar (CEO)

Levtech Consulting LLC (2)
Office 102 1st Floor Sheikh Jabor Bin Yousef Bin Jassem Al Thani, PO Box 55991, Building Old Airport Road, Doha, Qatar
Tel.: (974) 44442150
Software Consulting Services
N.A.I.C.S.: 541512

AND PRIVATE COMPANIES

Levtech Consulting Saudi Co. Ltd. (2)
5th Floor Al Shablan Tower Dammam Highway, PO Box 3140, Al Khobar, 31952, Saudi Arabia
Tel.: (966) 138873041
Software Consulting Services
N.A.I.C.S.: 541512

Levtech Consulting Services India Private Ltd. (2)
Office 621 2nd Floor NMH Complex 80ft Road 4th Block, Koramangala, Bengaluru, 560 034, India
Tel.: (91) 8041229072
Software Consulting Services
N.A.I.C.S.: 541512
Roopa Rakesh (Mgr-HR)

Subsidiary (Domestic):

MTWO AG
Vaihingerstrasse 151, 70567, Stuttgart, Germany
Tel.: (49) 71178730
Web Site: http://www.itwocity.com
Digital Technology Development Services
N.A.I.C.S.: 541511

Subsidiary (Non-US):

Phoenx PLM Pty. Ltd. (2)
Brisbane Tech Park 62 Brandl Street, Eight Mile Plains, 4113, QLD, Australia
Tel.: (61) 1300519144
Web Site: http://www.phoenxplm.com.au
Software Consulting Services
N.A.I.C.S.: 541512

RIB A/S (2)
Ryesgade 19C 3rd floor, 2200, Copenhagen, Denmark
Tel.: (45) 35245250
Web Site: https://www.rib-software.dk
Software Consulting Services
N.A.I.C.S.: 541512
Liselotte Walther Jorgensen (Mgr-Strategic Marketing)

RIB Asia Ltd. (2)
Suite 1207 12/F ICBC Tower 3 Garden Road, Central, China (Hong Kong)
Tel.: (852) 28108799
Software Development Services
N.A.I.C.S.: 541511

RIB CADX PTY Limited (2)
3 / 11 Orion Road, Lane Cove, 2066, NSW, Australia
Tel.: (61) 1300 653 420
Software Development Services
N.A.I.C.S.: 541511
Flora Zhang (Mgr-Fin)

RIB Cosinus AG
Eichwaldstrasse 15, 6005, Lucerne, Switzerland
Tel.: (41) 41 31085 55
Software Development Services
N.A.I.C.S.: 541511

Subsidiary (Domestic):

RIB Cosinus GmbH (2)
Gundelfinger Strasse 2, 79108, Freiburg, Germany
Tel.: (49) 761 51004 0
Web Site: http://www.rib-cosinus.com
Information Technology Consulting Services
N.A.I.C.S.: 541512

RIB Deutschland GmbH (2)
Vaihinger Strasse 151, D-70567, Stuttgart, Germany (100%)
Tel.: (49) 71178730
Web Site: http://www.rib-software.com
Project Management Software Publisher
N.A.I.C.S.: 513210

RIB Leipzig GmbH (2)
Spenglerallee 26-30, 04442, Zwenkau, Germany
Tel.: (49) 34203432300
Web Site: http://www.rib-leipzig.com
Software Programming Services
N.A.I.C.S.: 541511
Hartmut Stumpf (Product Mgr-Sls)

Subsidiary (US):

RIB MC2 Incorporated (2)
5100 Poplar Ave Ste 3400, Memphis, TN 38137-3400
Tel.: (901) 685-6061
Web Site: http://www.ribmc2.com
Emp.: 40
Software Development Services
N.A.I.C.S.: 541511
Drew Mullady (CFO)

Subsidiary (Non-US):

RIB PTE. Limited (2)
9 Temasek Boulevard 31st Floor Suntec Tower Two, Singapore, 038989, Singapore
Tel.: (65) 6559 5318
Software Development Services
N.A.I.C.S.: 541511

RIB SAA Software Engineering GmbH (2)
Gudrunstrasse 184/3, 1100, Vienna, Austria
Tel.: (43) 164142470
Web Site: https://www.rib-saa.com
Software Consulting Services
N.A.I.C.S.: 541512
Christian Hanser (Mng Partner)

Subsidiary (US):

RIB Software (Americas) Inc. (2)
3200 SW Freeway Ste 3300, Houston, TX 77027
Tel.: (840) 840-6088
Project Management Software Solutions
N.A.I.C.S.: 513210

Subsidiary (Non-US):

RIB Software (UK) Ltd. (2)
3rd Floor Abbey House 74-76 St John Street, London, EC1M 4DZ, United Kingdom
Tel.: (44) 2035977566
Web Site: http://www.rib-software.com
Project Management Software Solutions
N.A.I.C.S.: 513210

RIB Software DMCC (2)
44th Floor Mazaya Business Avenue BB2 First Al Khail St Jumeirah, PO Box 5002257, Lake Towers, Dubai, United Arab Emirates
Tel.: (971) 44264272
Software Consulting Services
N.A.I.C.S.: 541512
Neil Hanks (Sls Mgr)

RIB Software NZ Limited (2)
Level 3 19 Great South Rd, Epsom, Auckland, 1051, New Zealand
Tel.: (64) 294208266
Software Consulting Services
N.A.I.C.S.: 541512
Tony Shaw (Dir-Product Solutions)

RIB Software Pty. Ltd. (2)
3/11 Orion Road, Lane Cove, 2066, NSW, Australia
Tel.: (61) 294208266
Software Consulting Services
N.A.I.C.S.: 541512

RIB Spain SA (2)
Calle de Rodriguez San Pedro 10 Comunidad de Madrid, Gaztambide, 28015, Madrid, Spain
Tel.: (34) 914483800
Software Consulting Services
N.A.I.C.S.: 541512

RIB Stavebni Software s.r.o. (2)
Zeleny Pruh 1560/99, 140 00, Prague, Czech Republic
Tel.: (420) 608953721
Web Site: http://www.rib.cz
Project Management Software Solutions
N.A.I.C.S.: 513210

Subsidiary (US):

RIB U.S. Cost Incorporated (2)
600 Northpark Town Ctr 1200 Abernathy Rd NE Bldg 600 Ste 950, Atlanta, GA 30328
Tel.: (770) 481-1600
Web Site: http://www.uscost.com
Software Development Services
N.A.I.C.S.: 541511
Glenn Wilcox (Sr VP-Project Controls)

Subsidiary (Non-US):

RIB iTWO Software Private Limited (2)
Level 1 Crescenzo Building C 38 and 39 G block Behind MCA, Bandra Kurla Complex Bandra E, Mumbai, 400 051, India
Tel.: (91) 22 61554889
Software Development Services
N.A.I.C.S.: 541511

RIB iTWO Software, Inc. (2)
21/F One World Place Building 32nd Street, Bonifacio Global City, Taguig, 1634, Philippines
Tel.: (63) 27962736
Software Consulting Services
N.A.I.C.S.: 541512

Redstack Pty. Ltd. (2)
Level 1 145 O Connell Street, Adelaide, 5006, SA, Australia
Tel.: (61) 1300667263
Web Site: http://www.redstack.com.au
Software Consulting Services
N.A.I.C.S.: 541512
John Lawrence (Sr Acct Mgr)

Subsidiary (US):

SaaSplaza Inc. (2)
5963 La Pl Ct Ste 302, Carlsbad, CA 92008
Tel.: (858) 385-8900
Software Consulting Services
N.A.I.C.S.: 541512

Subsidiary (Non-US):

SaaSplaza Inc. (2)
800 Steeles Ave W B10182, Thornhill, L4J 7L2, ON, Canada
Tel.: (416) 988-0366
Software Consulting Services
N.A.I.C.S.: 541512

SaaSplaza International B.V. (2)
Prins Mauritslaan 29-35, 1171 LP, Badhoevedorp, Netherlands
Tel.: (31) 205478060
Software Consulting Services
N.A.I.C.S.: 541512

SaaSplaza Pte. Ltd. (2)
10 Anson Road 16-23 International Plaza 16th Floor, Singapore, 079903, Singapore
Tel.: (65) 62226591
Software Consulting Services
N.A.I.C.S.: 541512
O. Lionel (Dir-Ops)

SaaSplaza Pty. Ltd. (2)
Manly PO Central Ave, PO Box 616, Sydney, 1655, NSW, Australia
Tel.: (61) 283105568
Software Consulting Services
N.A.I.C.S.: 541512

Subsidiary (US):

U.S. Cad, Inc. (2)
18831 Bardeen Ave 200, Irvine, CA 92612 (60%)
Tel.: (877) 648-7223
Web Site: http://www.uscad.com
Electronics Stores
N.A.I.C.S.: 449210
Daniel Counts (CEO)

Subsidiary (Domestic):

xTWO GmbH (2)
Giessener Strasse 42, 35410, Hungen, Germany
Tel.: (49) 6402898900
Web Site: https://www.xtwostore.de
Bathroom Accessory Retailer
N.A.I.C.S.: 449129

Schneider Electric Industries SAS (1)
35 Rue Joseph Monier, F-92506, Rueil-Malmaison, France (100%)
Tel.: (33) 141298500
Web Site: http://www.schneider-electric.com
Electrical Distribution, Industrial Control & Automation Equipment Mfr
N.A.I.C.S.: 335314
Jean-Pascal Tricoire (CEO)

Subsidiary (Non-US):

7-Technologie A/S (2)
Bistruphave 3, 3460, Birkerod, Denmark
Tel.: (45) 45 900 700
Web Site: http://www.7t.dk

SCHNEIDER ELECTRIC SE

Sales Range: $25-49.9 Million
Software Development Services
N.A.I.C.S.: 541511

APC Australia Pty. Limited (2)
Level 13 65 Berry Street, North Sydney, Sydney, 2060, NSW, Australia
Tel.: (61) 2 8923 9300
Inverter Mfr
N.A.I.C.S.: 335999

APC Brasil Ltda (2)
Av das Nacoes Unidas, Barueri, 06455-030, Sao Paulo, Brazil
Tel.: (55) 1146898600
Inverter Mfr
N.A.I.C.S.: 335999

APC Holdings BV (2)
Lange Dreef 15 Le Palmier, 4131 NJ, Vianen, Netherlands
Tel.: (31) 347325200
Sales Range: $50-74.9 Million
Emp.: 78
Investment Management Service
N.A.I.C.S.: 523940

APC India Private Ltd (2)
No 187/3 & 188/3 Jigani Village Jigani Hobli Anekal Taluk, Bengaluru, 562106, India
Tel.: (91) 80 2781 2070
Sales Range: $800-899.9 Million
Emp.: 3,000
Uninterruptible Power Supply System Mfr
N.A.I.C.S.: 335999

APC International Corporation BV (2)
Lange Dreef 15 Le Palmier, 4131 NJ, Vianen, Netherlands
Tel.: (31) 347325200
Power Transmission Equipment Mfr
N.A.I.C.S.: 333613

APC International Holdings BV (2)
Lange Dreef 15, 4131 NJ, Vianen, Netherlands
Tel.: (31) 347325200
Investment Management Service
N.A.I.C.S.: 523940

APC Japan, Inc. (2)
Shiba Park 2-4-1 Shiba Parkville b-13 Floor, Minato-ku, Tokyo, 105-0011, Japan
Tel.: (81) 364022001
Web Site: http://www.apc.com
Power Supply Product Mfr
N.A.I.C.S.: 335999

APC Power and Cooling, UK Ltd (2)
100 New Bridge Street, London, EC4V 6JA, United Kingdom
Tel.: (44) 1179 557767
Electric Equipment Mfr
N.A.I.C.S.: 335999

APC UK Ltd (2)
IIPSI Building University Road, Coventry, CV4 7AL, United Kingdom
Tel.: (44) 2476528700
Web Site: https://www.apcuk.co.uk
Sales Range: $25-49.9 Million
Emp.: 3
Uninterruptible Power Supply System Mfr
N.A.I.C.S.: 335999
Andy Connor (Dir-Channel)

APW President Systems Ltd. (2)
R 2 Ground Fl Technopolis Knowledge Park, Mahakali Caves Rd Andheri E, 400093, Mumbai, Maharashtra, India
Tel.: (91) 2266448888
Web Site: http://www.apwpresident.com
Sales Range: $25-49.9 Million
Emp.: 386
Enclosure Systems Mfr & Designer
N.A.I.C.S.: 332322
V. Dharani Babu (VP-Mfg Ops)

Ajasto Paper Products Ltd (2)
Pohjoisesplanadi 35 A, PO Box 317, 00101, Helsinki, Finland
Tel.: (358) 207872700
Web Site: http://www.ajasto.fi
Sales Range: $50-74.9 Million
Emp.: 180
Publishing
N.A.I.C.S.: 513199

Subsidiary (Non-US):

Emil Moestue as (3)

SCHNEIDER ELECTRIC SE — INTERNATIONAL PUBLIC

Schneider Electric SE—(Continued)
Ostre Aker Vei 61, PO Box 234, Alnabru,
0614, Oslo, Norway
Tel.: (47) 22974000
Web Site: http://www.emil-moestue.no
Sales Range: $25-49.9 Million
Emp.: 25
N.A.I.C.S.: 459410

Subsidiary (Domestic):

Alombard SAS (2)
10 Rue Saint Santin, Saint-Pryve-Saint-Mesmin, 45750, France
Tel.: (33) 2 38 56 91 13
Electric Equipment Mfr
N.A.I.C.S.: 335999

Subsidiary (Non-US):

American Power Conversion Corp (A.P.C.) BV (2)
Lange Dreef 15e, 4131 NJ, Vianen, Netherlands
Tel.: (31) 347 325 270
Power Supply Product Mfr & Distr
N.A.I.C.S.: 335999

Automatismo Crouzet De Mexico, S.A. de C.V. (2)
Calzada Zavaleta 2505 - C Col Sta Cruz Buenavista, 72150, Puebla, Mexico
Tel.: (52) 2224097000
Automation Control Component Mfr
N.A.I.C.S.: 334114

Subsidiary (Domestic):

BCV Technologies SAS (2)
ZI Allee des Justices, 85200, Fontenay-le-Comte, France
Tel.: (33) 2 51 53 22 00
Web Site: http://www.bcv-technologies.com
Rev.: $22,884,890
Emp.: 142
Transformer Mfr
N.A.I.C.S.: 334416

Subsidiary (Non-US):

Beijing Leader & Harvest Electric Technologies Co. Ltd (2)
South Zone of Industrial Park Yangfang, Changping Dist, Beijing, 102205, China
Tel.: (86) 10 69764466
Web Site: http://www.ld-harvest.com
Sales Range: $200-249.9 Million
Emp.: 700
Electric Equipment Mfr
N.A.I.C.S.: 334419

Beijing Merlin Great Wall Computer Room Equipment & Engineering Co. Ltd (2)
3/F Hengtong Guangsha No 10 Jiuxianqiao Road, Chaoyang District, Beijing, 100016, China
Tel.: (86) 1059236088
Electric Equipment Mfr
N.A.I.C.S.: 335999

Subsidiary (Domestic):

Boissiere Finance SNC (2)
35 Rue Joseph Monier, 92500, Rueil-Malmaison, France
Tel.: (33) 141298410
Financial Investment Services
N.A.I.C.S.: 523999

Subsidiary (Non-US):

C-Matic Systems Ltd (2)
Warren Court Park Road, Crowborough, TN6 2QX, United Kingdom
Tel.: (44) 1892 600300
Web Site: http://www.cmatic.co.uk
Sales Range: $25-49.9 Million
Emp.: 50
Electric Meter Mfr & Distr
N.A.I.C.S.: 334519
Paul Christie *(Gen Mgr)*

CBS Group Ltd (2)
Unit 8 Riverside Park Dogflud Way, Farnham, GU9 7UG, Surrey, United Kingdom
Tel.: (44) 1252 714100
Web Site: http://www.cbsgroupuk.com
Sales Range: $25-49.9 Million
Emp.: 24

Uninterruptible Power Supply System Installation Services
N.A.I.C.S.: 238210
Stuart Robinson *(Mng Dir)*

CLS Systems FZCO (2)
Jebel Ali, Dubai, 61314, United Arab Emirates
Tel.: (971) 4 8837013
Electric Equipment Mfr
N.A.I.C.S.: 335999

CST Latino America Comercio E Representacao de Produtos Electricos E Elestronicos Ltda (2)
Alameda Rio Negro 1030 18 andar - Conjunto 1803, 06454-000, Barueri, Sao Paulo, Brazil
Tel.: (55) 11 2505 7500
Sensor Mfr
N.A.I.C.S.: 334413

CST Sensors India Private Limited (2)
4th Floor Trident Towers No 23 100 Ft - Ashoka Pillar Road, 2nd Block Jayanagar, Bengaluru, 560011, Karnataka, India
Tel.: (91) 80 4113 2204
Web Site: http://www.cstsensors.tradeindia.com
Sales Range: $25-49.9 Million
Emp.: 22
Electrical Products Mfr
N.A.I.C.S.: 335999
Viang Jay *(VP-India)*

Cimac FZCO (2)
Plot No TP010110 Technopark Jebel Ali, PO Box 61314, Dubai, United Arab Emirates
Tel.: (971) 48142600
Web Site: http://www.cimac.ae
Automation Control Component Mfr
N.A.I.C.S.: 334419

Cimac Software Systems Private Ltd (2)
Unit No 8 & 9 Innovator 2nd Fl Building International Tech Park, 560066, Bengaluru, India
Tel.: (91) 80 40703456
Sales Range: $25-49.9 Million
Emp.: 40
Software Development Services
N.A.I.C.S.: 541511
Naseer Shindoli *(Mgr-Engrg)*

Clipsal Integrated Systems Pty. Limited (2)
33-37 Port Wakefield Road, Gepps Cross, 5094, SA, Australia
Tel.: (61) 137328137328
Web Site: http://www.clipsal.com
Emp.: 1,000
Electric Equipment Mfr
N.A.I.C.S.: 335999

Clipsal Manufacturing (Huizhou) Ltd (2)
No 3 Lejin Road Zhongkai Hi-Tech Industrial Development Zone, Huizhou, 516001, China
Tel.: (86) 7522633070
Socket & Switch Mfr
N.A.I.C.S.: 335313

Clipsal Manufacturing (M) Sdn Bhd (2)
No 1 Jalan Kawat 15/18, Shah Alam, 40200, Malaysia
Tel.: (60) 355192994
Web Site: http://www.schneider-electric.com.my
Emp.: 300
Electric Equipment Mfr
N.A.I.C.S.: 335999
David Beresford *(Mgr)*

Clipsal Middle East FZC (2)
E2-05 Sharjah Airport International Free Zone, PO Box 8181, Sharjah, United Arab Emirates
Tel.: (971) 6 5570 777
Web Site: http://www.clipsal.com.au
Electric Equipment Mfr
N.A.I.C.S.: 335999

Compagnie Financiere, Miniere et Industrielle SA (2)

Avenue Winston Churchill 22, 1180, Brussels, Belgium
Tel.: (32) 2 340 67 67
Investment Management Service
N.A.I.C.S.: 523940

Subsidiary (Domestic):

Construction Electrique du Vivarais SAS (2)
Zi Du Lac Boulevard Du Vivarais, 07000, Privas, France
Tel.: (33) 475665900
Electric Equipment Mfr
N.A.I.C.S.: 334419

Subsidiary (Non-US):

Control Microsystems BV (2)
Delftse Jaagpad 1B, 2324 AA, Leiden, Netherlands
Tel.: (31) 71 57 91 650
Web Site: http://www.controlmicrosystems.com
Automation Control Equipment Distr
N.A.I.C.S.: 423830

Custom Sensors & Technologies Asia (Shangai) Ltd (2)
11th floor Chang Feng International Tower 89 Yunling Road East, Putuo District, Shanghai, 200062, China
Tel.: (86) 21 6065 6888
Web Site: http://www.cstsensors.com
Emp.: 50
Sensor Mfr
N.A.I.C.S.: 334413
Sébastien Nobiron *(VP)*

Subsidiary (Domestic):

D5X S.A.S. (2)
4 Rue Alexis de Tocqueville, 92160, Antony, 92160, France
Tel.: (33) 1 55 59 02 90
Web Site: http://www.schnider-electric.fr
Sales Range: $25-49.9 Million
Emp.: 40
Room Control System Software Development Services
N.A.I.C.S.: 541511
Gerard Petit *(Gen Mgr)*

Subsidiary (Non-US):

DESEA Sdn Bhd (2)
No 11 Jalan U1/19 Section U1 Hicom Glenmarie Industrial Park, Shah Alam, 40150, Selangor, Malaysia
Tel.: (60) 378809564
Sales Range: $25-49.9 Million
Emp.: 2
Electrical Component Mfr
N.A.I.C.S.: 335999

DIN Elektro Kraft OOO (2)
st Dvintsev 12 building 1 building A business center Dvintsev, Moscow, 127018, Russia
Tel.: (7) 4957779988
Web Site: https://www.dek.ru
Electrical Products Mfr
N.A.I.C.S.: 335999

DMR Demirbag Elektrik Malzemeleri Ticaret Anonim Sirketi (2)
Mesrutiyet Caddesi No 94/A Beyoglu, Istanbul, Turkiye
Tel.: (90) 212 217 17 37
Web Site: http://www.dmrdemirbag.com
Switch Mfr
N.A.I.C.S.: 335313

Delixi Electric Algerie SARL (2)
12 cooperative CIC 3 lot 12 Ouled Fayet, Algiers, Algeria
Tel.: (213) 560 06 00 10
Electric Equipment Mfr
N.A.I.C.S.: 335999

Delixi Electric SEE EOOD (2)
20 Tsar Samuil str 1rst Floor, Sofia, Bulgaria
Tel.: (359) 885 750 232
Electric Equipment Mfr
N.A.I.C.S.: 335999

Delixi Electric South Africa (Pty) Ltd (2)
3 Springbok Road Bartlett Extension 8, Boksburg, South Africa

Tel.: (27) 11 230 5712
Web Site: http://www.delixi-electric.co.za
Electric Equipment Mfr
N.A.I.C.S.: 335999

Dexson Electric SA (2)
Calle 19 No 70 - 41 zona industrial Montevideo, Bogota, Colombia
Tel.: (57) 1412 23 22
Electric Equipment Mfr
N.A.I.C.S.: 335999

Subsidiary (Domestic):

Dinel SAS (2)
Zone Industrielle 8 Avenue de l'Europe, BP 82, 76220, Gournay-en-Bray, France
Tel.: (33) 232899310
Web Site: http://www.dinel.com
Sales Range: $25-49.9 Million
Emp.: 25
Optoelectronic Device Mfr
N.A.I.C.S.: 334413

Subsidiary (Non-US):

EFI Electronics Europe SL (2)
Albert Einstein 43, Cornella de Llobregat, Barcelona, Spain
Tel.: (34) 934 800 630
Electronic Product Distr
N.A.I.C.S.: 423690

ELKO AS (2)
Sandstuveien 68, 0680, Oslo, Norway
Tel.: (47) 67793900
Web Site: https://www.elko.no
Sales Range: $75-99.9 Million
Electrical Equipment Distr
N.A.I.C.S.: 423610

EPS Electrical Power Distribution Board & Switchgear Ltd (2)
PO Box 89249, 11682, Riyadh, Saudi Arabia
Tel.: (966) 14981575
Switchboard Mfr
N.A.I.C.S.: 335313

Subsidiary (Domestic):

Elau SARL (2)
36 avenue Carnot, Massy, 91300, France
Tel.: (33) 1 64 53 96 98
Electric Equipment Mfr
N.A.I.C.S.: 335999

Subsidiary (Non-US):

Elda Eltra S.A. (2)
Ul Glinki 146, Bydgoszcz, 85-861, Poland
Tel.: (48) 94 372 81 91
Web Site: http://www.elda.pl
Emp.: 500
Electric Equipment Mfr
N.A.I.C.S.: 335999
Robert Wielicki *(Gen Mgr)*

Elektriska AB Delta (2)
Hammarvagen 10, Arlov, 232 37, Skane, Sweden
Tel.: (46) 40227500
Web Site: http://www.schneider-electric.com
Emp.: 60
Eletric Power Generation Services
N.A.I.C.S.: 221118
Camilla Eriksson *(Gen Mgr)*

Elko AB (2)
Hammarby Kaj 14, PO Box 5115, Johanneshov, 121 17, Stockholm, Sweden
Tel.: (46) 8 449 27 27
Web Site: http://www.elko.se
Sales Range: $25-49.9 Million
Emp.: 20
Communication Equipment Mfr
N.A.I.C.S.: 334290

Subsidiary (Domestic):

Energy Pool Developpement SAS (2)
20 rue du Lac Majeur Batiment C Parc Ouragan, BP 90324, 73377, Le Bourget du Lac, Cedex, France
Tel.: (33) 488131660
Web Site: https://www.energy-pool.eu
Emp.: 100
Electric Power Distribution Services
N.A.I.C.S.: 221122
Olivier Baud *(Founder)*

AND PRIVATE COMPANIES — SCHNEIDER ELECTRIC SE

Energy Pool International (2)
59 Blvd Vivier-Merle, 69007, Lyon, France
Tel.: (33) 4 37 65 77 73
Electric Power Distribution Services
N.A.I.C.S.: 221122

Epsys SAS (2)
652 Route De Plaimpalais, 73230, Saint-Alban-Leysse, France
Tel.: (33) 4 79 75 61 50
Electrical Products Mfr
N.A.I.C.S.: 335999

Subsidiary (Non-US):

Etablissements Crouzet NV (2)
Dieweg 3 B, 1180, Brussels, Belgium
Tel.: (32) 24 62 07 30
Industrial Automation Equipments Mfr
N.A.I.C.S.: 333248

Feller AG (2)
Bergstrasse 70, 8810, Horgen, Switzerland
Tel.: (41) 447287777
Web Site: https://www.feller.ch
Sales Range: $100-124.9 Million
Emp.: 450
Switchboard & Socket Mfr
N.A.I.C.S.: 335313

Gutor Electronic Asia Pacific Sdn Bhd (2)
No 19 Jln Juruukur U1/19 Seksyen U1 Hicom Glenmarie Industrial Park, 40150, Shah Alam, Selangor, Malaysia
Tel.: (60) 355690331
Web Site: http://www.gutor.com
Sales Range: $50-74.9 Million
Emp.: 140
Uninterruptible Power Supply System Mfr
N.A.I.C.S.: 335999

Industrias Electronicas Pacifico, S.A. de C.V. (2)
Blvd Tlc 1000, Apodaca, 66600, Mexico
Tel.: (52) 8182886500
Electronic Components Mfr
N.A.I.C.S.: 334419

Subsidiary (Domestic):

Infraplus SAS (2)
3 Rue Des Marronniers Zac Du Plateau, 94240, Paris, France
Tel.: (33) 1 45 60 40 09
Telecommunications Equipment Mfr
N.A.I.C.S.: 334290

Subsidiary (Non-US):

Invensys Limited (2)
3rd Floor 40 Grosvenor Place, London, SW1X 7AW, United Kingdom
Tel.: (44) 2031551200
Web Site: http://www.invensys.com
Sales Range: $1-4.9 Billion
Emp.: 20,818
Holding Company
N.A.I.C.S.: 551112
Emmanuel Babeau *(Deputy CEO)*

Subsidiary (Non-US):

Elektronika Slovensko a.s. (3)
Chovatelska 8, Trnava, 91700, Slovakia
Tel.: (421) 33 5919 111
Web Site: http://www.toolbox.invensyscontrols.com
Sales Range: $50-74.9 Million
Emp.: 130
Washing Machine Equipment Mfr
N.A.I.C.S.: 335220
Jiri Hudec *(Mng Dir)*

Eliwell Controls Srl (3)
Via dell'Industria 15 ZI Paludi, 32016, Pieve d'Alpago, Belluno, Italy
Tel.: (39) 04371660000
Web Site: https://www.eliwell.com
Air Conditioning Equipment Mfr
N.A.I.C.S.: 333415

Subsidiary (Domestic):

Eurotherm Limited (3)
Faraday Close, Durrington, Worthing, BN13 3PL, West Sussex, United Kingdom (100%)
Tel.: (44) 1903 268500
Web Site: http://www.eurotherm.com
Sales Range: $10-24.9 Million
Electronic Measuring & Testing Equipment Mfr
N.A.I.C.S.: 334513

Subsidiary (Non-US):

EMSR Eurotherm GmbH (4)
Geiereckstrasse 18/1, 1110, Vienna, Austria (100%)
Tel.: (43) 17987601
Web Site: https://www.eurotherm.at
Industrial Control Mfr
N.A.I.C.S.: 334513
Wolfgang Obereder *(Mng Dir)*

Elcotherma Finland Oy Ab (4)
Taksvarkinkuja 4, 25700, Kimitoon, Finland (100%)
Tel.: (358) 2 250 6030
Web Site: http://www.elcotherma.fi
Temperature & Process Controllers Mfr
N.A.I.C.S.: 334513

Eurotherm AB (4)
Nordfeldts Vag 9, 645 51, Strangnas, Sweden
Tel.: (46) 46239000
Web Site: https://www.eurotherm.com
Sales Range: $25-49.9 Million
Industrial Equipment Distr
N.A.I.C.S.: 423830

Eurotherm Automation SAS (4)
6 chemin des joncs, CS 20214, 69574, Dardilly, Cedex, France (100%)
Tel.: (33) 478664500
Web Site: https://www.eurotherm.com
Temperature & Process Controllers Mfr
N.A.I.C.S.: 334513
Xavier Picavet *(Mng Dir-Southern Europe)*

Eurotherm BV (4)
Genielaan 4, 2404 CH, Alphen aan den Rijn, South Holland, Netherlands
Tel.: (31) 172411752
Web Site: http://www.eurotherm.nl
Temperature & Process Controllers Mfr
N.A.I.C.S.: 334513
Frank Kraan *(Dir-Svc & Delivery-Central & Eastern Europe)*

Subsidiary (US):

Eurotherm Inc. (4)
44621 Guilford Dr Ste 100, Ashburn, VA 20147 (100%)
Tel.: (703) 724-7300
Web Site: http://www.eurotherm.com
Emp.: 60
Mfr of Electronic Components for Control, Measurement & Data Recording Solutions for Industrial Automation
N.A.I.C.S.: 334512

Unit (Domestic):

Action Instruments (5)
44621 Guilford Dr Ste 100, Ashburn, VA 20147
Tel.: (703) 724-7300
Web Site: http://www.eurotherm.com
Electronic Instrumentation for Measurement & Control
N.A.I.C.S.: 334513

Subsidiary (Non-US):

Eurotherm India Private Limited (4)
Ground Floor Tamarai Tech Park SP Plot 16-20 20A, Thiru Vi Ka Industrial Estate Inner Ring Road Guindy, Chennai, 600 032, India (50%)
Tel.: (91) 4442240000
Web Site: https://www.eurotherm.com
Industrial Controls Whslr
N.A.I.C.S.: 423830
Kamlesh Patel *(Sls Mgr-Natl)*

Eurotherm Korea Co., Ltd. (4)
2208 Building B Hyundai Knowledge Industry Center 70 Doosan-ro, Geumcheon-gu, Seoul, 121-904, Korea (South) (100%)
Tel.: (82) 220640888
Web Site: https://www.eurotherm.com
Industrial Controls
N.A.I.C.S.: 334513

Branch (Non-US):

Eurotherm Ltd. (4)
Maynooth Business Campus, Maynooth, Kildare, Ireland (100%)
Tel.: (353) 1 4691800
Web Site: http://www.eurotherm.ie
Industrial Controls Distr
N.A.I.C.S.: 423830
Rory Lynch *(Coord-Sales)*

Subsidiary (Non-US):

Eurotherm Srl (4)
Via XXIV Maggio 2, 22070, Guanzate, Como, Italy (100%)
Tel.: (39) 031 975111
Web Site: http://www.eurotherm.com
Industrial Controls
N.A.I.C.S.: 334513

Invensys Eurotherm Sp.z o.o. (4)
Turynska 101, 43-100, Tychy, Poland
Tel.: (48) 32 7839500
Web Site: http://www.eurotherm.com
Sales Range: $50-74.9 Million
Emp.: 90
Investment Management Service
N.A.I.C.S.: 523999
Ben Jaoko *(Mng Dir)*

Division (Non-US):

Schneider Electric Systems Iberica, S.L.U. - Eurotherm Division (4)
Calle Valgrande 6, 28108, Alcobendas, Madrid, Spain (100%)
Tel.: (34) 916616001
Web Site: http://www.eurotherm.es
Emp.: 20
Temperature & Process Controllers Mfr
N.A.I.C.S.: 334513
Xavier Picavet *(Mng Dir)*

Subsidiary (Domestic):

Invensys Controls UK Limited (3)
401 Southway Drive, Plymouth, PL6 6QT, Devon, United Kingdom (100%)
Tel.: (44) 1752 737166
Web Site: http://www.schneider-electric.co.uk
Sales Range: $200-249.9 Million
Emp.: 550
Electronic Control System Mfr
N.A.I.C.S.: 334512

Subsidiary (Non-US):

Invensys SAM (3)
5 rue du Gabian Le Triton, Monaco, 98000, Monaco
Tel.: (377) 97984444
Electronic Components Mfr
N.A.I.C.S.: 334419

Invensys Systems France SAS (3)
Parc Saint Christophe 10 avenue de l'enterprise, 95861, Cergy-Pontoise, France
Tel.: (33) 1 34 43 25 25
Web Site: http://www.iom.invensys.com
Software Development Services
N.A.I.C.S.: 541511

Invensys Systems Mexico SA (3)
Calle De La Amargura No 60 Piso 3, Huixquilucan, Mexico
Tel.: (52) 55 5263 0100
Web Site: http://iom.invensys.com
Instrument Systems & Services for Industrial Process Automation
N.A.I.C.S.: 334513

Division (US):

Schneider Electric - Process Automation (3)
10900 Equity Dr, Houston, TX 77041
Tel.: (713) 329-1600
Web Site: http://www.invensys.com
Emp.: 300
Corporate Office; Operations Management & Business Optimization Services
N.A.I.C.S.: 551114
Gary Freburger *(Pres-Process Automation)*

Subsidiary (Domestic):

Applied Instrument Technologies, Inc. (4)
2121 Avation Dr, Upland, CA 91786-2195
Tel.: (909) 204-3700
Web Site: http://www.aitanalyzers.com
Instruments & Related Products Mfr
N.A.I.C.S.: 334513
Joseph LaConte *(Pres)*

Invensys Systems, Inc. (4)
33 Commercial St, Foxboro, MA 02035
Tel.: (508) 549-2424
Web Site: http://www.invensys.com
Emp.: 4,000
Instrument Systems & Services for Industrial Process Automation
N.A.I.C.S.: 334513
Gary Freburger *(Pres-Process Automation)*

Subsidiary (Domestic):

InduSoft, Inc. (5)
11044 Research Blvd Ste A100, Austin, TX 78759-5240
Tel.: (512) 349-0334
Web Site: http://www.indusoft.com
Sales Range: $1-9.9 Million
Emp.: 35
Custom Software Mfr
N.A.I.C.S.: 513210

Subsidiary (Non-US):

Invensys Systems Canada Inc. (5)
4 Lake Street, Dollard des Ormeaux, H9B 3H9, QC, Canada (100%)
Tel.: (514) 421-4210
Web Site: http://iom.invensys.com
Sales Range: $50-74.9 Million
Emp.: 180
Relays & Industrial Controls Mfr
N.A.I.C.S.: 335314
Mark Levell *(Sr Dir-Fin & Controller-Global Process)*

Subsidiary (Domestic):

Schneider Electric Software (5)
26561 Rancho Pkwy S, Lake Forest, CA 92630 (100%)
Tel.: (949) 639-8700
Web Site: http://software.schneider-electric.com
Sales Range: $100-124.9 Million
Prepackaged Software for Industrial Automation Process Control Applications
N.A.I.C.S.: 513210

Unit (Domestic):

Schneider Electric Software - SimSci (6)
26521 Rancho Pkwy S, Lake Forest, CA 92630
Computer Software Development Services
N.A.I.C.S.: 513210

Subsidiary (Non-US):

Schneider Electric Systems (Australia) Pty Limited (3)
Level 1 Building 2 195 Wellington Road, Sydney, 2113, NSW, Australia
Tel.: (61) 385629800
Web Site: http://www.schneider-electric.com.au
Air Conditioning Equipment Mfr
N.A.I.C.S.: 333415

Schneider Electric Systems Italia SpA (3)
Via Carducci 125, 20099, Sesto San Giovanni, MI, Italy
Tel.: (39) 02262971
Web Site: http://iom.invensys.com
Sales Range: $25-49.9 Million
Emp.: 100
Instrument Systems & Services for Industrial Process Automation
N.A.I.C.S.: 334513
Vittorio Panzeri *(Mgr)*

Schneider Electric Systems Netherlands N.V. (3)
Baarnsche Dijk 10, 3741 LS, Baarn, Netherlands
Tel.: (31) 355484211
Web Site: https://www.se.com
Emp.: 150
Instrument Systems & Services for Industrial Process Automation
N.A.I.C.S.: 334513
Raheem Fischer *(Gen Mgr)*

Subsidiary (Domestic):

Schneider Electric Systems UK Limited (3)

SCHNEIDER ELECTRIC SE

INTERNATIONAL PUBLIC

Schneider Electric SE—(Continued)
2nd Floor 80 Victoria Street, London, SW1E 5JL, United Kingdom
Tel.: (44) 3706088608
Web Site: http://www.se.com
Emp.: 100
Software Development Services
N.A.I.C.S.: 541511

Subsidiary (Non-US):

Inversiones Schneider Electric Uno Limitada (2)
Avda Presidente Eduardo Frei Montalva 6001-31, Conchali, Santiago, Chile
Tel.: (56) 2 4657100
Investment Management Service
N.A.I.C.S.: 523999

JO-EL Electric Oy (2)
Kalkkipellontie 6, 02650, Espoo, Finland
Tel.: (358) 10 446 6800
Web Site: http://www.jo-el.com
Sales Range: $25-49.9 Million
Emp.: 5
Electric Equipment Mfr
N.A.I.C.S.: 335999
Erkki Flinkman (Mgr-Sls)

Kell Systems Ltd (2)
Unit 1 Ground Floor 250 South Oak Way Green Park, Reading, RG2 6UG, Berkshire, United Kingdom
Tel.: (44) 118 903 7850
Web Site: http://www.kellsystems.co.uk
Portable Computer Server Mfr
N.A.I.C.S.: 334118
David O'Coimin (Mng Dir)

L&T Electrical & Automation FZE (2)
Jebel Ali Free Zone, PO Box 262158, Dubai, 262158, United Arab Emirates
Tel.: (971) 4 8131900
Sales Range: $25-49.9 Million
Emp.: 150
Architectural Systems Integration Services
N.A.I.C.S.: 541310
Mudit Goel (CEO)

Lexel AB (2)
Tillverkarvagen 2, Nykoping, 611 45, Sweden
Tel.: (46) 155265000
Communication Equipment Mfr
N.A.I.C.S.: 334290

Lexel Fabrika SIA (2)
Bukultu 7, Riga, 1037, Latvia
Tel.: (371) 67388917
Web Site: http://www.schneiderelectric.lv
Sales Range: $50-74.9 Million
Emp.: 180
Communication Equipment Mfr
N.A.I.C.S.: 334290

Lexel Holdings (UK) Ltd (2)
Stafford Park 5, Telford, TF3 3BL, Shropshire, United Kingdom
Tel.: (44) 870 608 8608
Emp.: 550
Investment Management Service
N.A.I.C.S.: 523999

Luminous Power Technologies Private Ltd (2)
C-56 Mayapuri Industrial Area Phase-II Mayapur, New Delhi, 110 064, India   **(100%)**
Tel.: (91) 8906008008
Web Site: http://www.luminousindia.com
Sales Range: $900-999.9 Million
Inverter Mfr & Distr
N.A.I.C.S.: 335999

MGE USV-Systeme GmbH (2)
Gothaer Str 29, 40880, Ratingen, Germany
Tel.: (49) 2102 404 9560
Web Site: http://www.mgeups.de
Inverter Mfr
N.A.I.C.S.: 335999

Manufacturas Electricas SA (2)
Pol Industrial Trobika - Martintxone Bidea 4, 48100, Munguia, BIZKAIA, Spain
Tel.: (34) 846600530
Web Site: https://www.mesa.es
Sales Range: $125-149.9 Million
Switchgear Mfr & Distr
N.A.I.C.S.: 335313

Subsidiary (Domestic):

Merlin Gerin Ales SAS (2)
1 rue Maurice Ravel Z I de Croupillac, PO Box 229, 30319, Ales, France
Tel.: (33) 466784141
Web Site: http://www.se.com
Electronic Product Distr
N.A.I.C.S.: 423690

Merlin Gerin Alpes SAS (2)
Parc d Activites Alpespace Voie Isaac Newton Alpespace, 73800, Francin, France
Tel.: (33) 4 79 75 48 00
Web Site: http://www.schneider-electric.fr
Electrical Equipment Distr
N.A.I.C.S.: 423610

Merlin Gerin Loire SAS (2)
Rue Des Petites Granges, Zi St Laurent Des Levees, 49412, Saumur, Cedex, France
Tel.: (33) 241832626
Web Site: http://www.schneider-electric.com
Emp.: 150
Electrical Equipment Distr
N.A.I.C.S.: 423610

Subsidiary (Non-US):

Merten Czech s.r.o. (2)
Kvitkovicka 1533, 763 61, Napajedla, Czech Republic
Tel.: (420) 577 921 296
Switchboard Mfr
N.A.I.C.S.: 335313

Merten GmbH (2)
Fritz-Kotz-Strasse 8 Industriegebiet Bomig-West, 51674, Wiehl, Germany
Tel.: (49) 226170201
Web Site: http://www.merten.com
Switch Mfr
N.A.I.C.S.: 334419
Clemens Blum (Mng Dir)

Merten Holding GmbH (2)
Fritz-Kotz-Str 8, 51674, Wiehl, Germany
Tel.: (49) 226170201
Investment Management Service
N.A.I.C.S.: 523999

Subsidiary (Domestic):

Newlog SAS (2)
22 Rue Des Garinnes Zac De Chesnes Nord, 38070, Saint-Quentin-Fallavier, France
Tel.: (33) 474958200
Sales Range: $50-74.9 Million
Emp.: 200
Electrical Products Mfr
N.A.I.C.S.: 335999

Subsidiary (Non-US):

OOO Schneider Electric Buildings (2)
Ul Dvintsev 12 Building 1 Building A, 127018, Moscow, Russia
Tel.: (7) 4957779990
Construction Management Services
N.A.I.C.S.: 236210

OOO Schneider Electric Kaliningrad (2)
Gvardeysky Prospect 15, 236040, Kaliningrad, Russia
Tel.: (7) 4012535953
Sales Range: $25-49.9 Million
Emp.: 2
Electric Equipment Mfr
N.A.I.C.S.: 335999
Lina Oleshkevich (Gen Mgr)

Orbaekvej 280 A/S (2)
Industriparken 32, 2750, Ballerup, Denmark
Tel.: (45) 44207000
Electric Equipment Mfr
N.A.I.C.S.: 335999

P.T. Schneider Electric Manufacturing Batam (2)
Jalan Beringin Batamindo, Industrial Park Block 4, Muka Kuning, 29433, Batam, Indonesia   **(100%)**
Tel.: (62) 770611133
Web Site: http://www.sniderelectric.com.sg
Sales Range: $250-299.9 Million
Emp.: 735
N.A.I.C.S.: 334220

PT Clipsal Manufacturing Jakarta (2)
Ventura Bld 7th Fl JL RA Kartini Kav 26 Cilandak, Jakarta, 12430, Indonesia
Tel.: (62) 21 750 4406
Web Site: http://www.schneider-electric.co.id
Semiconductor Devices Mfr
N.A.I.C.S.: 334413
Xavier Denoly (Pres & Gen Mgr)

PT Schneider Electric IT Indonesia (2)
Ventura Building-7th Floor Jalan R A Kartini Kav 26 Cilandak, 12430, Jakarta, Indonesia
Tel.: (62) 217504406
Software Development Services
N.A.I.C.S.: 541511

PT Schneider Electric Indonesia (2)
CIBIS 9 Building 16th Floor Jl TB Simatupang No 2 RT 13/RW 5, Cilandak Timur Kota Selatan Daerah Khusus Ibukota, 12560, Jakarta, Indonesia
Tel.: (62) 211500055
Web Site: http://www.se.com
Electric Power Distribution Services
N.A.I.C.S.: 221122

Pelco Europe BV (2)
Beemdstraat 42, Eindhoven, 5652 AB, Netherlands
Tel.: (31) 40 251 9870
Web Site: http://www.pelco.com
Sales Range: $25-49.9 Million
Emp.: 25
Video Security System Mfr
N.A.I.C.S.: 333310
Marco Wigman (Mgr-EMEA Tech Sls & Support)

Pelco Sweden AB (2)
Husargatan 18, Malmo, 21375, Sweden
Tel.: (46) 40 663 9840
Emp.: 300
Video Security System Mfr
N.A.I.C.S.: 333310
Henrik Olsson (Mng Dir)

Pelco UK Ltd (2)
Indigo House Mulberry Business Park Fishponds Road, Wokingham, RG41 2GY, Berkshire, United Kingdom
Tel.: (44) 118 978 9276
Web Site: http://www.pelco.com
Sales Range: $25-49.9 Million
Emp.: 20
Video Security System Mfr
N.A.I.C.S.: 333310
Matt Rosam (Mgr-Sls)

Pele Security AB (2)
Bergkallavagen 34, 192 79, Sollentuna, Sweden
Tel.: (46) 8 505 260 00
Web Site: http://www.pele.se
Fire Alarm & Security System Installation Services
N.A.I.C.S.: 238210

Pisara AB (2)
Brunnsgatan 17, 553 17, Jonkoping, Sweden
Tel.: (46) 36139760
Electric Equipment Mfr
N.A.I.C.S.: 335999

Power Measurement Ltd (2)
Warren Ct, Crowborough, TN6 2QX, East Sussex, United Kingdom
Tel.: (44) 1892665688
Environmental Control Equipment Mfr
N.A.I.C.S.: 334512

Powerman Ltd (2)
Stafford Park 5, Telford, TF3 3BL, Shropshire, United Kingdom
Tel.: (44) 870 608 8 608
Electronic Products Mfr
N.A.I.C.S.: 334419

Pro-face China International Trading Co., Ltd. (2)
Unit 1110 550 Yanan Road East, Shanghai, 200001, China
Tel.: (86) 2163615175
Web Site: http://www.proface.com.cn
Emp.: 60
Industrial Automation Equipments Mfr
N.A.I.C.S.: 333248
Chao Wang (Pres)

Pro-face Deutschland GmbH (2)
Albertus-Magnus-Strasse 11, 42719, Solingen, Germany
Tel.: (49) 212 258 260
Web Site: http://www.proface.de
Industrial Automation Equipment Distr
N.A.I.C.S.: 423830

Pro-face Espana SL (2)
Bac de Roda 52 Edificio A, 08019, Barcelona, Spain
Tel.: (34) 93 846 07 45
Web Site: http://www.proface.es
Sales Range: $25-49.9 Million
Emp.: 8
Industrial Automation Equipments Mfr
N.A.I.C.S.: 333248

Pro-face Europe B.V. (2)
Taurusavenue 133, 2132 JC, Hoofddorp, Netherlands
Tel.: (31) 235544094
Web Site: http://www.proface.eu
Sales Range: $25-49.9 Million
Emp.: 30
Industrial Automation Equipments Mfr
N.A.I.C.S.: 333248

Subsidiary (Domestic):

Pro-face France S.A.S. (2)
1 rue Henri Becquerel Immeuble Le Vinci 4, 77290, Mitry-Mory, France
Tel.: (33) 1 60 21 22 91
Web Site: http://www.proface.fr
Industrial Automation Equipments Mfr
N.A.I.C.S.: 333248

Subsidiary (Non-US):

Pro-face Korea Co., Ltd. (2)
6F Daebang Construction Building 248 Gonghang-daero, Gangseo-gu, Seoul, 07085, Korea (South)
Tel.: (82) 215882630
Web Site: http://www.proface.com
Industrial Automation Equipments Mfr
N.A.I.C.S.: 333248
Yoshihiko Yasumura (Pres)

Pro-face Northern Europe ApS (2)
Ledreborg Alle 118, Roskilde, 4000, Denmark
Tel.: (45) 70 22 01 22
Web Site: http://www.proface.dk
Sales Range: $25-49.9 Million
Emp.: 6
Industrial Automation Equipments Mfr
N.A.I.C.S.: 333248
Klaus Boje (Mgr-Sls)

Pro-face Schweiz GmbH (2)
Pumpwerkstr 23, 8105, Regensdorf, Switzerland
Tel.: (41) 43 343 7272
Web Site: http://www.proface.ch
Industrial Automation Equipments Mfr
N.A.I.C.S.: 333248

Pro-face Singapore (2)
10 Ang Mo Kio Street 65 01-01/03 Techpoint, Singapore, 569059, Singapore
Tel.: (65) 6832 5533
Web Site: http://www.proface.sg
Industrial Automation Equipments Mfr
N.A.I.C.S.: 333248

Pro-face Sweden AB (2)
Produktvagen 8B, Malmo, 246 21, Loddekopinge, Sweden
Tel.: (46) 46 540 90 70
Web Site: http://www.proface.se
Industrial Automation Equipments Mfr
N.A.I.C.S.: 333248

Pro-face Taiwan Co., Ltd. (2)
2F No 39 Ji-Hu Road, Nei-Hu Dist, Taipei, 114, Taiwan
Tel.: (886) 2 2657 1121
Web Site: http://www.proface.com.tw
Emp.: 100
Industrial Automation Equipments Mfr
N.A.I.C.S.: 333248

Subsidiary (Domestic):

Prodipact SAS (2)
35 Rue Joseph Monier, BP 29, 92506, Rueil-Malmaison, France
Tel.: (33) 4 79 75 46 00
Web Site: http://www.schneider-electric.fr

AND PRIVATE COMPANIES — SCHNEIDER ELECTRIC SE

Sales Range: $50-74.9 Million
Emp.: 200
Electric Equipment Mfr
N.A.I.C.S.: 335999
Jean-Pierre Rave *(Gen Mgr)*

Subsidiary (Non-US):

Proface China International Trading (Shanghai) Co. Ltd (2)
Room 1110 Ocean Building No 550 Yan'an East Road, Shanghai, 200001, China
Tel.: (86) 2163615175
Web Site: https://www.proface.com.cn
Industrial Automation Equipments Mfr
N.A.I.C.S.: 333248

Ram Do Brasil, Ltda (2)
Travessao Vitor Emanuel 2889 Bairro Pedancino, 95001-970, Caxias do Sul, Rio Grande do Sul, Brazil
Tel.: (55) 54 3224 9600
Web Site: http://www.schneider-electric.com.br
Emp.: 100
Automation Control Component Mfr
N.A.I.C.S.: 334519

Ram Tech Manufacturing de Mexico S de R.L. de C.V. (2)
Blvd Apodaca No 900-B Apodaca Technology Park, Apodaca, 66600, Mexico
Tel.: (52) 8110894099
Automation Control Component Mfr
N.A.I.C.S.: 334519

Ram Tech Services de Mexico S de R.L. de C.V. (2)
Boulevard Apodaca No 900-B, Apodaca, 66600, Nuevo Leon, Mexico
Tel.: (52) 8110894100
Sales Range: $100-124.9 Million
Emp.: 300
Electric Equipment Mfr
N.A.I.C.S.: 335999

Subsidiary (Domestic):

Rectiphase SAS (2)
399 Rue De La Gare, 74370, Pringy, France
Tel.: (33) 450669500
Web Site: https://www.schneider-electric.fr
Electronic Capacitor Mfr
N.A.I.C.S.: 334416

Subsidiary (Non-US):

SARL Schneider Electric Algerie (2)
Route d'Ouled Fayet N 2Bis, Delly Ibrahim, 16320, Algiers, Algeria
Tel.: (213) 21368900
Eletric Power Generation Services
N.A.I.C.S.: 221118

Sandas Montage BV (2)
Albionstraat 60, 5047 SN, Tilburg, Netherlands
Tel.: (31) 6 2239 1101
Web Site: http://www.schneider-electric.nl
Electrical Cable Installation Services
N.A.I.C.S.: 238210

Subsidiary (Domestic):

Sarel - Appareillage Electrique SAS (2)
57 rue de Phalsbourg, BP 106, Sarre-Union, 67269, France
Tel.: (33) 388016200
Web Site: http://www.sarel.fr
Electric Equipment Mfr
N.A.I.C.S.: 334419

Subsidiary (Non-US):

Sarel Ltd (2)
Unit C Stirling Court Stirling Road South Marston Industrial Estate, Swindon, SN3 4TQ, Wiltshire, United Kingdom
Tel.: (44) 1793 837 430
Steel Enclosure System Mfr
N.A.I.C.S.: 332322

Subsidiary (Domestic):

Scanelec SAS (2)
1 Bis Village D Entreprises, 78680, Epone, France
Tel.: (33) 130900900
Electric Equipment Mfr
N.A.I.C.S.: 335999

Subsidiary (Non-US):

Schneider (Beijing) Medium & Low Voltage Co., Ltd (2)
No 2 Liang Shui He 2nd Street BJ Economic, Technological Development Area, Beijing, 100176, China
Tel.: (86) 10 6503 9999
Emp.: 1,000
Electrical Circuit Breaker Mfr
N.A.I.C.S.: 334515
Chal Toa *(Gen Mgr)*

Schneider (Shanghai) Supply Co. Ltd (2)
No 669 Suide Rd, Shanghai, 200233, China
Tel.: (86) 2163635678
Electrical Equipment Distr
N.A.I.C.S.: 423610

Schneider (Suzhou) Drives Company Ltd (2)
555 Fengting Avenue Sip Weiting Town, Suzhou, 215121, Jiangsu, China
Tel.: (86) 51262877266
Electrical Equipment Distr
N.A.I.C.S.: 423610

Schneider (Suzhou) Transformers Co. Ltd (2)
No 128 Shenhu Road Suzhou Industrial Park, Suzhou, 215123, Jiangsu, China
Tel.: (86) 51262580808
Electric Power Transformer Mfr
N.A.I.C.S.: 335311

Schneider (Thailand) Ltd. (2)
1st 10th 11th Floor Rungrojthanakul Building 1st 10th, 46 Ratchadaphisek Rd Huaykwang, Bangkok, 10310, Thailand (100%)
Tel.: (66) 26175555
Web Site: https://www.se.com
Sales Range: $100-124.9 Million
Mfr of Industrial Controls
N.A.I.C.S.: 335314

Subsidiary (Domestic):

Schneider Automation SAS (2)
245 Route Des Lucioles Sophia Antipolis, Valbonne, 06560, France
Tel.: (33) 4 92 38 20 00
Electric Equipment Mfr
N.A.I.C.S.: 334419

Subsidiary (Non-US):

Schneider Busway (Guangzhou) Ltd (2)
85 Jun Ye Lu Northern Part of Eastern Section of Guangzhou, Economic & Tec, Guangzhou, 510530, China
Tel.: (86) 2028202828
Electrical Equipment Installation Services
N.A.I.C.S.: 238210

Schneider Egypt & North East Africa (2)
Land Plot No 291 & 292 Second District Fifth Settlement, 11835, Cairo, Egypt
Tel.: (20) 2 26 189 189
Web Site: http://www.schneider.com.eg
Sales Range: $25-49.9 Million
Emp.: 100
Electric Equipment Mfr
N.A.I.C.S.: 334419

Schneider Electric (2)
2nd Floor 80 Victoria Street, London, SW1E 5JL, United Kingdom
Tel.: (44) 3706088608
Web Site: http://www.se.com
System Integration Services
N.A.I.C.S.: 221118
Martin Walder *(VP-Industry)*

Schneider Electric (China) Co., Ltd. (2)
Building A No 6 Wangjing East Road, Chaoyang District, Beijing, 100102, China
Tel.: (86) 4008101315
Commercial & Industrial Electrical Lighting Fixture Mfr
N.A.I.C.S.: 335132
Jing Li *(Dir-Energy Solution)*

Schneider Electric (China) Investment Co. Ltd
Schneider Building No 6 Wang Jing East Road, Chaoyang District, Beijing, 100016, China
Tel.: (86) 10 8434 6699
Eletric Power Generation Services
N.A.I.C.S.: 221118

Subsidiary (Domestic):

Schneider Wingoal (Tianjin) Electric Equipment Co. Ltd (3)
Unit A 4F Block C,Xinmao Science and Technology Park No16, Rongyuan Road Huanyuan Industrial Area, Tianjin, China
Tel.: (86) 2283712900
Web Site: http://www.wgats.com
Switchgear Mfr
N.A.I.C.S.: 335313

Subsidiary (Non-US):

Schneider Electric (Hong Kong) Limited (2)
11/F Kerry Centre 683 Kings Road, Quarry Bay, China (Hong Kong)
Tel.: (852) 35807188
Web Site: https://www.se.com
Energy Consulting Services
N.A.I.C.S.: 541690

Schneider Electric (Philippines) Inc. (2)
24th Floor Fort Legend Tower Block 7 Lot 3 3rd Ave corner 31st Street, Fort Bonifacio Global City, Taguig, Philippines
Tel.: (63) 29769999
Web Site: https://www.se.com
Electric Power Distribution Services
N.A.I.C.S.: 221122

Schneider Electric (Schweiz) AG (2)
Schermenwaldstrasse 11, Ittigen, 3063, Bern, Switzerland
Tel.: (41) 319173333
Web Site: http://www.se.com
Sales Range: $25-49.9 Million
Electrical Equipment & Component Mfr
N.A.I.C.S.: 334419

Schneider Electric (UK) Ltd (2)
120 New Cavendish Street, London, W1W 6XX, United Kingdom
Tel.: (44) 870 608 8608
Web Site: http://www.schneider-electric.co.uk
Electric Power Distribution Services & Automation Control Equipment Mfr
N.A.I.C.S.: 221122

Schneider Electric (Xiamen) Switchgear Co. Ltd (2)
No 24 Huo Ju Bei Lu, Xiamen, 361006, China
Tel.: (86) 59257753160
Switchgear Mfr
N.A.I.C.S.: 335313

Schneider Electric A.E. (2)
19th km National Road Athens-Lamia, Athens, 14671, New Erythrea, Greece
Tel.: (30) 2106295200
Web Site: http://www.schneider-electric.com.gr
All Other Miscellaneous Electrical Equipment & Component Manufacturing
N.A.I.C.S.: 334419

Schneider Electric A/S (2)
Lautrupvang 1, 2750, Ballerup, Denmark
Tel.: (45) 88302000
Web Site: http://www.se.com
Sales Range: $50-74.9 Million
All Other Miscellaneous Electrical Equipment & Component Manufacturing
N.A.I.C.S.: 334419

Subsidiary (Domestic):

Schneider Electric Buildings Denmark A/S (3)
Latrupvang 1, 2750, Ballerup, Denmark (100%)
Tel.: (45) 88204060
Web Site: http://www.schneider-electric.com.com
Sales Range: $75-99.9 Million
Emp.: 300
Energy & Heating Technology Services
N.A.I.C.S.: 333415
Thomas Holst *(Mng Dir)*

Subsidiary (Non-US):

Schneider Electric AB (2)
Frosundaviks Alle 1, Solna, 169 70, Sweden
Tel.: (46) 86238400
Web Site: http://www.schneider-electric.se
Sales Range: $25-49.9 Million
Emp.: 300
All Other Miscellaneous Electrical Equipment & Component Manufacturing
N.A.I.C.S.: 334419
Marc Nezet *(CEO)*

Subsidiary (Domestic):

Schneider Electric Buildings Sweden AB (3)
Jagershillgatan 18, Malmo, 213 75, Sweden (100%)
Tel.: (46) 40316800
Web Site: http://www.tac.com
Sales Range: $75-99.9 Million
Heating, Water & Sanitary Fittings, Fire-Fighting Equipment, Controls for Heating, Ventilation & Energy Conservation Services
N.A.I.C.S.: 333414
Peter Yuhansen *(Gen Mgr)*

Subsidiary (Non-US):

Schneider Electric AS (2)
Cizovska 447, 397 01, Pisek, Czech Republic
Tel.: (420) 382 760 111
Web Site: http://www.se.com
Electrical Products Mfr
N.A.I.C.S.: 335999

Schneider Electric Administracion, S.A. de C.V. (2)
Avenida de los Insurgentes 2590 Burocrata 1ra Secc, 32330, Ciudad Juarez, Chihuahua, Mexico
Tel.: (52) 6566160683
Electric Equipment Mfr
N.A.I.C.S.: 335999

Schneider Electric Argentina SA (2)
Av San Martin 5020 or at Av De los Constituyentes, Buenos Aires, Argentina
Tel.: (54) 8104447246
Web Site: http://www.se.com
Sales Range: $200-249.9 Million
Automation Power Control Equipment Mfr
N.A.I.C.S.: 334519

Schneider Electric Asia Pacific Limited (2)
13/F East Wing Warwick House Taikoo Place 979 King's Road, Quarry Bay, China (Hong Kong)
Tel.: (852) 25650621
Energy Consulting Services
N.A.I.C.S.: 541690

Schneider Electric Australia Holdings Pty Ltd (2)
2 Solent Circuit NW Bus Pk, Baulkham Hills, 2153, NSW, Australia (100%)
Tel.: (61) 298512800
Web Site: http://www.schneiderelectric.com.au
Sales Range: $100-124.9 Million
Emp.: 450
Switchgear Mfr
N.A.I.C.S.: 335313
Mauro DelleMonache *(Dir-Indus)*

Subsidiary (Domestic):

Schneider Electric Australia Pty Ltd (3)
78 Water Loo Rd, Macquarie Park, 2113, NSW, Australia
Tel.: (61) 137328
Web Site: http://www.se.com
All Other Miscellaneous Electrical Equipment & Component Manufacturing
N.A.I.C.S.: 334419

Schneider Electric Buildings Australia Pty. Ltd. (3)
Level 3/2A Lord Street, Botany, 2019, NSW, Australia
Tel.: (61) 283366100
Web Site: http://www.tac.com
Sales Range: $25-49.9 Million
Emp.: 273

SCHNEIDER ELECTRIC SE

INTERNATIONAL PUBLIC

Schneider Electric SE—(Continued)
Computer & Information Products Mfr & Distr
N.A.I.C.S.: 334419

Subsidiary (Non-US):

Schneider Electric Austria Ges.mbH (2)
At Euro Platz 2/Stiege 6/3rd floor, 1120, Vienna, Austria
Tel.: (43) 16147111
Web Site: http://www.se.com
Sales Range: $25-49.9 Million
All Other Miscellaneous Electrical Equipment & Component Manufacturing
N.A.I.C.S.: 334419

Schneider Electric Automation (2)
Taurusavenue 133, 2132 LS, Hoofddorp, Netherlands
Tel.: (31) 23 5124 124
Web Site: http://www.se.com
Electrical Software Development Services
N.A.I.C.S.: 334111

Schneider Electric Automation Deutschland GmbH (2)
Schneiderplatz 1, 97828, Marktheidenfeld, Germany
Tel.: (49) 93 91 6060
Web Site: http://www.se.com
Automatic Control Equipment Mfr
N.A.I.C.S.: 334519

Schneider Electric BV (2)
Taurusavenue 133, 2132 LS, Hoofddorp, Netherlands
Tel.: (31) 23 5 124 124
Web Site: http://www.se.com
Sales Range: $75-99.9 Million
Energy Consulting Services
N.A.I.C.S.: 541690

Schneider Electric Bel Ltd. (2)
St Moscow 22-9, 220007, Minsk, Belarus
Tel.: (375) 172369623
Commercial & Industrial Electrical Lighting Fixture Mfr
N.A.I.C.S.: 335132

Schneider Electric Belgium SA/NV (2)
Dieweg 3, Uccle, 1180, Brussels, Belgium
Tel.: (32) 23737501
Web Site: http://www.se.com
Sales Range: $100-124.9 Million
All Other Miscellaneous Electrical Equipment & Component Manufacturing
N.A.I.C.S.: 334419
David Orgaz (Dir)

Schneider Electric Benin (2)
Rue Pierre et Marie Curie, 18 BP 2027, Ivory Coast, Abidjan, Benin
Tel.: (229) 21750010
All Other Miscellaneous Electrical Equipment & Component Manufacturing
N.A.I.C.S.: 334419

Schneider Electric Bilgi Teknolojileri Ticaret Ve Pazarlama A.S (2)
1 Bayraktar Sok Ayyildiz Plaza No 16 / B, 34750, Istanbul, Turkiye
Tel.: (90) 216 655 88 88
Sales Range: $25-49.9 Million
Emp.: 20
Information Technology Consulting Services
N.A.I.C.S.: 541512

Schneider Electric Buildings AB (2)
Raseborgsgatan 13, Kista, 164 74, Sweden
Tel.: (46) 87752700
Emp.: 300
Building Security System Installation Services
N.A.I.C.S.: 238210
Marc Nezet (Gen Mgr)

Schneider Electric Buildings Finland OY
Sokerilinnantie 11C, Espoo, 2600, Finland
Tel.: (358) 9 5842 500
Web Site: http://www.schneider-electric.fi
Air Conditioning Equipment Installation Services
N.A.I.C.S.: 238220

Schneider Electric Buildings Ireland Ltd (2)
Block A Maynooth Business Campus, Maynooth; Ireland
Tel.: (353) 1 6012200
Web Site: http://www.se.com
Sales Range: $25-49.9 Million
Building Security System Installation Services
N.A.I.C.S.: 238210

Schneider Electric Buildings Norway AS (2)
Luhrtoppen 2, 1470, Lorenskog, Norway
Tel.: (47) 48 15 05 08
Web Site: http://www.schneider-electric.no
Building Security Management Services
N.A.I.C.S.: 561621

Schneider Electric Buildings Polska Sp. z.o.o. (2)
ul Rzymowskiego 55, 02-697, Warsaw, Poland
Tel.: (48) 22 313 24 10
Web Site: http://www.schneider-electric.pl
Sales Range: $25-49.9 Million
Emp.: 25
Electrical Equipment Installation Services
N.A.I.C.S.: 238210

Schneider Electric Buildings UK Ltd (2)
Braywick House East Windsor Road, Maidenhead, SL6 1DN, Berkshire, United Kingdom
Tel.: (44) 1628741050
Web Site: http://www.se.com
Sales Range: $100-124.9 Million
Building Security System Installation Services
N.A.I.C.S.: 238210

Schneider Electric Bulgaria EOOD (2)
Business Park Sofia Building 4 Floor 6 Mladost 4, 1715, Sofia, Bulgaria
Tel.: (359) 70011020
Web Site: http://www.se.com
All Other Miscellaneous Electrical Equipment & Component Manufacturing
N.A.I.C.S.: 334419

Schneider Electric CPCS (Thailand) Co. Ltd. (2)
Rungrojthanakul Building 13th Floor 44/1 Ratchadapisek Road, Huaykwang, Bangkok, 10310, Thailand
Tel.: (66) 26175500
Eletric Power Generation Services
N.A.I.C.S.: 221118

Schneider Electric CZ s.r.o. (2)
U Trezorky 921/2, 15800, Prague, Czech Republic
Tel.: (420) 281088111
Web Site: http://www.se.com
All Other Miscellaneous Electrical Equipment & Component Manufacturing
N.A.I.C.S.: 334419

Schneider Electric Canada Inc. (2)
5985 McLaughlin Rd, Mississauga, L5R 1B8, ON, Canada
Tel.: (905) 366-3999
Web Site: http://www.se.com
Sales Range: $100-124.9 Million
Automation Control System Installation Services
N.A.I.C.S.: 238210
Xavier Biot (VP-Power Distr & Digital Energy)

Schneider Electric Centroamerica Limitada (2)
San Rafael de Centro Corporativo Cedral Torre Cuatro Piso 2, Escazu, Costa Rica (100%)
Tel.: (506) 22109400
Web Site: https://www.se.com
Electrical Circuit Breaker Mfr
N.A.I.C.S.: 335313

Schneider Electric Chile S.A. (2)
Av Sta Clara 085, Huechuraba, Chile
Tel.: (56) 224657100
Web Site: http://www.se.com
All Other Miscellaneous Electrical Equipment & Component Manufacturing
N.A.I.C.S.: 334419

Subsidiary (Domestic):

Schneider Electric Consulting SAS (2)
57 rue de la Verrerie, 38120, Saint Egreve, France
Tel.: (33) 4 76 39 46 81
Web Site: http://consulting.schneider-electric.com
Emp.: 18
Management Consulting Services
N.A.I.C.S.: 541611
Goi Arnaud (Gen Mgr)

Subsidiary (Non-US):

Schneider Electric DMS NS (2)
Narodnog fronta 25 a b c d, 21000, Novi Sad, Serbia
Tel.: (381) 214883600
Web Site: https://www.schneider-electric-dms.com
Emp.: 1,000
Electricity Distribution Management Services
N.A.I.C.S.: 221122
Nenad Katic (Head-Sls Sector)

Schneider Electric Danmark A/S (2)
Orbaekvej 280, 5220, Odense, Denmark
Tel.: (45) 88 30 20 00
Web Site: http://www.se.com
Sales Range: $25-49.9 Million
Emp.: 50
Electric Equipment Mfr
N.A.I.C.S.: 335999

Schneider Electric Deutschland Energy GmbH (2)
Gothaer Strasse 29, Ratingen, 40880, Germany
Tel.: (49) 18 05 75 35 75
Energy Consulting Services
N.A.I.C.S.: 541690

Schneider Electric Distribution Centre AB (2)
Lastgatan 2, 702 27, Orebro, Sweden
Tel.: (46) 104782000
Electric Power Distribution Services
N.A.I.C.S.: 221122

Schneider Electric East Mediterranean SAL (2)
Tabaris Square Charles Malek Avenue Tabaris Center 1063 10th Floor, PO Box 166223, Beirut, 166223, Lebanon
Tel.: (961) 1204502
Web Site: https://www.se.com
Energy Management Consulting Services
N.A.I.C.S.: 541618

Schneider Electric Eesti AS (2)
Parnu road 139E/2, 11317, Tallinn, Estonia
Tel.: (372) 6580700
Web Site: http://www.se.com
Electric Equipment Mfr
N.A.I.C.S.: 334419

Schneider Electric Egypt SA (2)
Land Plot No 291 & 292, PO Box 11835, 2nd District Fifth Settlement, New Cairo, 11835, Egypt
Tel.: (20) 226189189
Web Site: https://www.se.com
Emp.: 700
Energy Consulting Services
N.A.I.C.S.: 541690

Schneider Electric Energy Austria AG (2)
Kochlergang 14, 4060, Leonding, Austria
Tel.: (43) 7326933
Web Site: http://www.se.com
Sales Range: $125-149.9 Million
Electric Power Distribution Services
N.A.I.C.S.: 221122

Schneider Electric Energy Belgium SA (2)
Dieweg 3, 1180, Ukkel, Belgium
Tel.: (32) 23737501
Web Site: http://www.se.com
Sales Range: $250-299.9 Million
Electric Power Distribution Services
N.A.I.C.S.: 221122

Subsidiary (Domestic):

Schneider Electric Energy France SAS (2)
Route Departementale 613, 34690, Fabregues, France
Tel.: (33) 899696191
Electric Equipment Mfr
N.A.I.C.S.: 335999

Subsidiary (Non-US):

Schneider Electric Energy GmbH (2)
Rathenaustrasse 2, 93055, Regensburg, Germany
Tel.: (49) 6966320
Electric Power Distribution Services
N.A.I.C.S.: 221122

Schneider Electric Energy Malaysia Sdn Bhd (2)
Unit TB-18-2 Level-18 Tower B Plz 33 1 Jalan Kemujuan Section 13, 46200, Petaling Jaya, Selangor, Malaysia
Tel.: (60) 37883 6333
Web Site: http://www.se.com
Electric Power Distribution Services
N.A.I.C.S.: 221122
Soo Powleong (Mng Dir)

Schneider Electric Energy Manufacturing Italia Srl (2)
V Autostrada 4, 26862, Guardamiglio, Italy
Tel.: (39) 03774171
Electric Equipment Mfr
N.A.I.C.S.: 335999

Schneider Electric Energy Netherlands BV (2)
Diakenhuisweg 29--35, 2033 AP, Haarlem, Netherlands
Tel.: (31) 704141600
Web Site: http://www2.schneider-electric.com
Sales Range: $75-99.9 Million
Emp.: 100
Electric Power Distribution Services
N.A.I.C.S.: 221122

Schneider Electric Energy Poland Sp. z.o.o. (2)
Ul Strzegomska 23/27, Swiebodzice, 58-160, Poland
Tel.: (48) 74 854 84 10
Web Site: http://www.schneider-energy.pl
Sales Range: $125-149.9 Million
Emp.: 200
Electric Power Distribution Services
N.A.I.C.S.: 221122
Arthur Ostaszewski (Mgr-Market Dev)

Schneider Electric Energy Spain SL (2)
C/Bac de Roda 52 Edificio A, 08019, Barcelona, Spain
Tel.: (34) 93 484 3100
Web Site: http://www.se.com
Electric Power Distribution Services
N.A.I.C.S.: 221122

Schneider Electric Energy UK Ltd (2)
2nd Floor 80 Victoria Street, London, SW1E 5JL, United Kingdom
Tel.: (44) 08706088608
Electric Equipment Mfr
N.A.I.C.S.: 335999

Schneider Electric Equipment an Engineering (X'ian) Co., Ltd. (2)
Xian High-tech Zone No 211 Eight-Day Central Valley, Science and Technology Park Building C and P Industrial Floors 1-4, Xi'an, 710077, China
Tel.: (86) 2965692599
Commercial & Industrial Electrical Lighting Fixture Mfr
N.A.I.C.S.: 335132

Schneider Electric Espana S.A. (2)
C/Bac de Roda 52 Edificio A, 08019, Barcelona, Spain
Tel.: (34) 934843100
Web Site: http://www.schneider-electric.es
Sales Range: $550-599.9 Million
Emp.: 2,350
Miscellaneous Electrical Equipment & Component Manufacturing
N.A.I.C.S.: 423610

Schneider Electric Export Services Pte. Ltd (2)
TechPoint 02-01/06 10 Ang Mo Kio Street 65, Singapore, 569059, Singapore
Tel.: (65) 64847877
Electrical Equipment Distr
N.A.I.C.S.: 423610

AND PRIVATE COMPANIES — SCHNEIDER ELECTRIC SE

Schneider Electric FZE (2)
Customer Care Center, PO Box 17192, KC 5 & 6 Jebel Ali Free Zone, Dubai, United Arab Emirates
Tel.: (971) 47099100
Web Site: http://www.schneider-electric.ae
Electrical Distribution, Industrial Control & Automation Equipment Distr
N.A.I.C.S.: 423610

Schneider Electric Finland Oy (2)
Sokerilinnantie 11 C, 02600, Espoo, Finland
Tel.: (358) 10446615
Web Site: http://www.se.com
All Other Miscellaneous Electrical Equipment & Component Manufacturing
N.A.I.C.S.: 334419

Subsidiary (Domestic):

Schneider Electric Fonciere SAS (2)
35 Rue Joseph Monier, Rueil-Malmaison, 92506, France
Tel.: (33) 1 41 29 85 00
Web Site: http://www.schneider-electric.fr
Emp.: 40
Electric Equipment Mfr
N.A.I.C.S.: 335999
Christian Montagnon *(Dir-Fin & Control)*

Schneider Electric France SAS (2)
35 Rue Joseph Monier, 92500, Rueil-Malmaison, France
Tel.: (33) 141297000
Electric Equipment Mfr
N.A.I.C.S.: 335999
Jean Pascan *(Pres)*

Subsidiary (Non-US):

Schneider Electric GmbH (2)
Gothaer Strasse 29, 40880, Ratingen, Germany (100%)
Tel.: (49) 21173743000
Web Site: https://www.se.com
Sales Range: $200-249.9 Million
Holding Company; Industrial Control & Other Electronic Component Mfr
N.A.I.C.S.: 551112

Subsidiary (Domestic):

Ircon GMBH (2)
Grillparzerstrasse 40, PO Box 1361, 65221, Taunusstein, Germany
Tel.: (49) 612892740
Assembly of Non-Contact Infrared Radiation Thermometers & Pyrometers; Sales & Marketing
N.A.I.C.S.: 339112

Schneider Electric Buildings Germany GmbH (3)
Essener Strasse 5, D-46047, Oberhausen, Germany (100%)
Tel.: (49) 208824860
Web Site: http://www.tac.com
Sales Range: $25-49.9 Million
Emp.: 35
Automated Building Systems
N.A.I.C.S.: 334512

Schneider Electric Deutschland GmbH (3)
Gothaer Strasse 29, Ratingen, 40880, Germany
Tel.: (49) 21024040
Web Site: http://www.schneider-electric.com
All Other Miscellaneous Electrical Equipment & Component Manufacturing
N.A.I.C.S.: 334419

Subsidiary (Domestic):

Eberle Controls GmbH (4)
Klingenhofstrasse 71, 90411, Nuremberg, Germany
Tel.: (49) 91156930
Web Site: https://www.eberle.de
Electrical Component Mfr
N.A.I.C.S.: 335999

Schneider Electric Systems Germany GmbH (4)
Hermann-klammt-str 1-3, 41460, Neuss, Germany
Tel.: (49) 64312980
Software Development Services
N.A.I.C.S.: 541511

Harald Konermann *(Sr VP-Ops-Process Automation)*

Unit *(Domestic):*

Schneider Electric Systems Germany - Eurotherm (5)
Ottostrasse 1, 65549, Limburg, Germany (100%)
Tel.: (49) 6431 298 0
Web Site: http://www.eurotherm.com
Industrial Controls & Process Automation Systems Mfr
N.A.I.C.S.: 334513

Subsidiary (Domestic):

Schneider Electric Motion Deutschland GmbH (3)
Breslauer Strasse 7, 77933, Lahr, Germany (100%)
Tel.: (49) 782194601
Web Site: http://www.schneider-electric-motion.com
Sales Range: $75-99.9 Million
Emp.: 300
Automatic Environmental Control Device Mfr
N.A.I.C.S.: 334512

Subsidiary (Domestic):

Schneider Electric Holding Amerique du Nord SAS (2)
35 Rue Joseph Monier, 92500, Rueil-Malmaison, France
Tel.: (33) 1 41 29 85 00
Web Site: http://www.schneider-electric.com
Investment Management Service
N.A.I.C.S.: 523940

Schneider Electric Holding Europe SAS (2)
35 Rue Joseph Monier, 92500, Rueil-Malmaison, France
Tel.: (33) 141298500
Web Site: http://www.schneiderelectric.com
Investment Management Service
N.A.I.C.S.: 523940

Subsidiary (Non-US):

Schneider Electric Huadian Switchgear (Xiamen) Co., Ltd (2)
No 22-24 Torch N Rd Torch Park Torch Hi-New Zone, Xiamen, 361006, Fujian, China
Tel.: (86) 5925775316
Switchgear Mfr
N.A.I.C.S.: 335313

Schneider Electric Hungaria Villamassagi ZRT (2)
Vaci ut 96-98, 1133, Budapest, Hungary
Tel.: (36) 13822800
Web Site: http://www.se.com
Sales Range: $25-49.9 Million
Emp.: 100
Miscellaneous Electrical Equipment
N.A.I.C.S.: 335999
Zoltan Lerch *(Dir-HR-Natl)*

Schneider Electric II IT Portugal LDA (2)
Avenida Marechal Craveiro Lopes 6 Piso 4, Lisbon, 1749-111, Portugal
Tel.: (351) 218504100
Software Development Services
N.A.I.C.S.: 541511

Schneider Electric IT (China) Co., Ltd (2)
Schneider Electric Building No 6 East Wangjing Road, Chaoyang District, Beijing, 100102, China
Tel.: (86) 1084346699
Software Development Services
N.A.I.C.S.: 541511

Schneider Electric IT (Xiamen) Co., Ltd (2)
Jixian Road 1678, Tongan District, Xiamen, 361100, Fujian, China
Tel.: (86) 5927572721
Commercial & Industrial Electrical Lighting Fixture Mfr
N.A.I.C.S.: 335132
William Qiu *(Mgr-Supply Chain)*

Schneider Electric IT Denmark ApS (2)
R&D Center Silcon Alle, 6000, Kolding, Denmark
Tel.: (45) 75542255
Web Site: http://www.apc.com
Emp.: 200
Software Development Services
N.A.I.C.S.: 541511
Morten Stoevring *(Gen Mgr)*

Schneider Electric IT Greece ABEE (2)
Athinon - Lamias National Rd 19th km, 14671, Nea Erythraia, Greece
Tel.: (30) 2106295200
Software Development Services
N.A.I.C.S.: 541511

Schneider Electric IT Hong Kong Limited (2)
13/F East Wing Taikoo Place Warwick House 979 King s Road, Quarry Bay, China (Hong Kong)
Tel.: (852) 25792088
Web Site: http://www.schneider-electric.com
Software Development Services
N.A.I.C.S.: 541511

Schneider Electric IT Logistics Asia Pacific Pte. Ltd (2)
10 Ang Mo Kio St 65 03-06 Tech Pt, Singapore, 569059, Singapore
Tel.: (65) 62911487
Software Development Services
N.A.I.C.S.: 541511

Schneider Electric IT Logistics Europe Ltd (2)
City E Business Park Ballybrit, Galway, H91HT73, Ireland
Tel.: (353) 91702000
Sales Range: $75-99.9 Million
Emp.: 270
Electrical Equipment & Computer Logistics Services
N.A.I.C.S.: 541614
Rachel Hand *(Mgr-Credit)*

Schneider Electric IT Malaysia Sdn Bhd (2)
Suite 30C 3rd Floor Wisma TCL No 470 Jalan Ipoh 3rd Mile, Kuala Lumpur, 51200, Malaysia
Tel.: (60) 355695295
Software Development Services
N.A.I.C.S.: 541511

Schneider Electric IT Morocco, SA (2)
Lot la Colline Imm les 4 Temps 1 et sidi Maarouf, Casablanca, 20190, Morocco
Tel.: (212) 5 22 97 79 00
Software Development Services
N.A.I.C.S.: 541511
Leila Jebbari *(Gen Mgr-Ops)*

Schneider Electric IT Norway AS (2)
Gjerdrums Vei 19, 0484, Oslo, Norway
Tel.: (47) 23005550
Sales Range: $25-49.9 Million
Emp.: 20
Electrical Software Development Services
N.A.I.C.S.: 541511
Arild Bjorkedal *(Country Mgr)*

Schneider Electric IT Poland Sp. z.o.o. (2)
Ul Iizecka 24, Warsaw, 02-135, Poland
Tel.: (48) 22 666 00 11
Web Site: http://www.apc.com
Electrical Software Development Services
N.A.I.C.S.: 541511

Schneider Electric IT Singapore Pte. Ltd (2)
10 Ang Mo Kio Street 65 No 03-06/10 Tech Point, Singapore, 569059, Singapore
Tel.: (65) 64802003
Software Development Services
N.A.I.C.S.: 541511

Schneider Electric IT South Africa (Pty) Ltd (2)
80 Kyalami Boulevard Kyalami Bus Park, Halfway House, Midrand, 1683, Gauteng, South Africa
Tel.: (27) 115576600
Emp.: 400
Software Development Services
N.A.I.C.S.: 541511

Hope Mashele *(Dir-Eco Bus)*

Schneider Electric IT Sweden AB (2)
Djupdals v 17-19, Box 954, 191 29, Sollentuna, Sweden
Tel.: (46) 200 89 52 83
Web Site: http://www.apc.com
Software Development Services
N.A.I.C.S.: 541511

Schneider Electric IT Switzerland AG (2)
Hardstrasse 72, Wettingen, 5430, Switzerland
Tel.: (41) 56 437 62 62
Sales Range: $25-49.9 Million
Emp.: 40
Software Development Services
N.A.I.C.S.: 541511
Oliver Laufmann *(Head-Svcs)*

Schneider Electric IT UK Ltd (2)
Unit 59 Dunlop Commercial Pk, Bangor, BT19 7QY, United Kingdom
Tel.: (44) 2891470470
Software Development Services
N.A.I.C.S.: 541511

Schneider Electric IT, Spain SL (2)
Bac de Roda 52 Edificio A 8 Pl, 08019, Barcelona, Spain
Tel.: (34) 934951950
Sales Range: $25-49.9 Million
Emp.: 100
Software Development Services
N.A.I.C.S.: 541511

Schneider Electric India Ltd. (2)
9th Floor DLF Building No 10 Tower C DLF Cyber City Phase II, Gurgaon, 122002, India
Tel.: (91) 1243940400
Web Site: https://www.se.com
Miscellaneous Electrical Equipment
N.A.I.C.S.: 335999
Anil Chaudhry *(Mng Dir & Pres-Country)*

Schneider Electric Industrie Italia Spa (2)
Via E Greco 9, Rieti, Italy
Tel.: (39) 07462231
Switchgear Mfr
N.A.I.C.S.: 335313

Schneider Electric Industries (M) Sdn Bhd (2)
Unit TB-18-2 Level 18 Tower B Plaza 33 No 1, Petaling Jaya, 46200, Selangor, Malaysia
Tel.: (60) 37883 6333
Energy Consulting Services
N.A.I.C.S.: 541690
Soo Pow Leong *(Gen Mgr)*

Schneider Electric Industries Polska SP (2)
ul Mostowa 19, 32-332, Bukowno, Malopolskie, Poland
Tel.: (48) 326111102
Web Site: https://www.se.com
Electric Equipment Mfr
N.A.I.C.S.: 335999

Subsidiary (Domestic):

Schneider Electric International SAS (2)
35 Rue Joseph Monier, 92500, Rueil-Malmaison, 92506, France
Tel.: (33) 141297000
Electrical Contractor
N.A.I.C.S.: 238210
Jean Pascal Tricoire *(CEO)*

Subsidiary (Non-US):

Schneider Electric Ireland (2)
Block A Maynooth Business Campus, Co Kildare, Maynooth, W23 Y7X0, Ireland
Tel.: (353) 1800805800
Web Site: https://www.se.com
Sales Range: $25-49.9 Million
Electrical Equipment & Component Mfr
N.A.I.C.S.: 334419

Schneider Electric Japan Holdings Ltd (2)
Schneider Electric Osaka Building 4-4-9 Kitahama, Chuo-ku, Osaka, 541-0041, Japan
Tel.: (81) 662083133

SCHNEIDER ELECTRIC SE

Schneider Electric SE—(Continued)
Web Site: https://jpn.proface.co.jp
Holding Company; Industrial Control & Other Electronic Component Mfr
N.A.I.C.S.: 551112

Subsidiary (Domestic):

Digital Electronics Corporation (3)
8-2-52 Nanko Higashi, Suminoe-Ku, Osaka, 559-0031, Japan (100%)
Tel.: (81) 66133116
Web Site: http://www.pro-face.com
Sales Range: $75-99.9 Million
Electronic Control System Mfr
N.A.I.C.S.: 335314
Yoshihiko Yasumura *(Pres)*

Subsidiary (Non-US):

Pro-Face (UK) Ltd. (4)
11 The Cobalt Centre Siskin Pkwy E, Coventry, CV3 4PE, United Kingdom (100%)
Tel.: (44) 2476511288
Web Site: http://www.profaceuk.com
Rev.: $9,999
Emp.: 8
N.A.I.C.S.: 334111
Stuart Pambrook *(Gen Mgr)*

Subsidiary (US):

Pro-Face America, Inc. (4)
750 N Maple Rd, Saline, MI 48176
Tel.: (734) 429-4971
Web Site: http://www.profaceamerica.com
Rev.: $30,000,000
Emp.: 30
Mfr of Microcomputers & Computer Interface Equipment
N.A.I.C.S.: 334118

Subsidiary (Non-US):

Pro-Face Italia SpA (4)
Via G di Vittorio 26, Bovisio Masciago, 20813, Milan, MI, Italy
Tel.: (39) 036259961
Web Site: http://www.proface.it
Industrial Automation Equipments Mfr
N.A.I.C.S.: 333248

Pro-face South-East Asia Pacific Co., Ltd. (4)
13th Floor Rungrojthanakul Building 44/1 Ratchadapisek Road, Huaykwang, Bangkok, 10310, Thailand
Tel.: (66) 2 617 5678
Web Site: http://www.proface.co.th
Sales Range: $25-49.9 Million
Emp.: 12
Industrial Automation Equipments Mfr
N.A.I.C.S.: 333248

Subsidiary (US):

Xycom Automation, Inc. (4)
750 N Maple Rd, Saline, MI 48176-1641
Tel.: (734) 429-4971
Web Site: http://www.profaceamerica.com
Sales Range: $125-149.9 Million
Emp.: 290
Mfr of Electronic Computer Products
N.A.I.C.S.: 334111

Subsidiary (Non-US):

Schneider Electric Korea Ltd (2)
6F Daebang Tower 248 Gangseodae-ro, Gangseo-gu, Seoul, 150-037, Korea (South)
Tel.: (82) 15882630
Web Site: https://www.schneider-electric.com
Energy Management Consulting Services
N.A.I.C.S.: 541618

Schneider Electric LLP (2)
151/115 Abay Ave 12 floor, 50050, Almaty, Kazakhstan
Tel.: (7) 7273572357
Web Site: https://ccc.www.se.com
Energy Consulting Services
N.A.I.C.S.: 541690

Schneider Electric Lanka (Private) Limited (2)
Level 2B 46/7 Valiant Towers Nawam Mawatha, 02, Colombo, Sri Lanka
Tel.: (94) 117750505

Web Site: https://www.se.com
Energy Management Consulting Services
N.A.I.C.S.: 541618

Schneider Electric Latvija SIA (2)
Katlakalna street 9A, Riga, LV-1035, Latvia
Tel.: (371) 67147228
Web Site: https://www.se.com
All Other Miscellaneous Electrical Equipment & Component Manufacturing
N.A.I.C.S.: 334419

Schneider Electric Limited (2)
Stirling Rd S Marston Indus Est, Swindon, SN3 4TQ, Wilts, United Kingdom
Tel.: (44) 1793837430
Web Site: http://www.schneider-electric.co.uk
Sales Range: $50-74.9 Million
Emp.: 150
Mfr of Industrial Controls
N.A.I.C.S.: 335314

Schneider Electric Logistic Centre BV (2)
Macroweg 21, 5804CL, Venray, Netherlands
Tel.: (31) 478558110
Logistics Consulting Servies
N.A.I.C.S.: 541614

Schneider Electric Low Voltage (Tianjin) Co., Ltd. (2)
Haitai Innovation 6th Road 11 Building 2 5th Floor Outside The Ring, High-tech Industrial Development Zone, Tianjin, 300392, China
Tel.: (86) 2223748000
Commercial & Industrial Electrical Lighting Fixture Mfr
N.A.I.C.S.: 335132

Schneider Electric Madagascar (2)
Fitaratra building 1st floor, Antananarivo, 101, Madagascar
Tel.: (261) 202249565
Web Site: http://www.se.com
Electric Equipment Mfr
N.A.I.C.S.: 334419

Schneider Electric Manufacturing (Chongqing) Co., Ltd. (2)
No 4 56 Corporate Avenue Office Building 10-Story Units 5 6 7, Shui Tin Road Building, Chongqing, 400043, China
Tel.: (86) 2363839700
Commercial & Industrial Electrical Lighting Fixture Mfr
N.A.I.C.S.: 335132

Schneider Electric Manufacturing (Wuhan) Co., Ltd. (2)
B11 Financial Port 77 Guanggu Avenue Donghu High-tech Zone, Wuhan, 430205, China
Tel.: (86) 2759373000
Commercial & Industrial Electrical Lighting Fixture Mfr
N.A.I.C.S.: 335132

Subsidiary (Domestic):

Schneider Electric Manufacturing Bourguebus SAS (2)
3 Boulevard de l'Europe, 14540, Bourguebus, France
Tel.: (33) 476576060
Electric Equipment Mfr
N.A.I.C.S.: 335999
Jean-Pascal Tricoire *(CEO)*

Subsidiary (Non-US):

Schneider Electric Manufacturing The Netherlands BV (2)
Electronweg 1, 1627 LB, Hoorn, Netherlands
Tel.: (31) 22 928 1200
Electric Equipment Mfr
N.A.I.C.S.: 335999

Schneider Electric Maroc (2)
Immeuble Les 4 temps 4eme etage Lot La Colline - Sidi Maarouf, Casablanca, Morocco
Tel.: (212) 22977900
Web Site: http://www.schneider.ma
Electric Equipment Mfr
N.A.I.C.S.: 334419
Brahim Chamar *(Project Dir)*

Schneider Electric Mexico, S.A. de C.V. (2)
Calzada Javier Rojo Gomez 1121-A Col Guadalupe del Moral, CP 09300, Ixtapalapa, Moral, Mexico (100%)
Tel.: (52) 5556863000
Web Site: https://www.se.com
Sales Range: $400-449.9 Million
Emp.: 2,500
Mfr of Industrial Controls
N.A.I.C.S.: 334513
Enrique Gonzales *(Gen Mgr)*

Schneider Electric New Zealand Limited (2)
Level 2 Building 6 60 Highbrook Drive, Highbrook, Auckland, 2013, New Zealand
Tel.: (64) 98290490
Web Site: https://www.se.com
Sales Range: $100-124.9 Million
Electrical Equipment Sales
N.A.I.C.S.: 423610
Ray Dunn *(CEO)*

Branch (Domestic):

Schneider Electric New Zealand (3)
17e Mahia Street, Ahuriri, Napier, 4110, New Zealand (100%)
Tel.: (64) 6 843 5855
Web Site: http://www.se.com
Sales Range: $25-49.9 Million
Emp.: 150
Electronic Products Sales
N.A.I.C.S.: 423690

Schneider Electric New Zealand Limited (3)
11 Moncur Place, Addington, Christchurch, 8140, New Zealand (100%)
Tel.: (64) 9 829 0490
Web Site: https://www.schneider-electric.co.nz
Sales Range: $100-124.9 Million
Emp.: 100
Developer & Producer of Hi-Tech Electronic & Electrical Products
N.A.I.C.S.: 334513
Riy Dunn *(CEO)*

Subsidiary (Non-US):

Schneider Electric Nigeria Ltd (2)
1 Tunde Gafar Close, Off Adeniyi Jones Ikeja, Lagos, Nigeria
Tel.: (234) 14483380
Web Site: https://www.se.com
Emp.: 200
All Other Miscellaneous Electrical Equipment & Component Manufacturing
N.A.I.C.S.: 334419

Schneider Electric Norway AS (2)
Sandstuveien 68, 0680, Oslo, Norway
Tel.: (47) 2 319 1200
Web Site: https://www.se.com
All Other Miscellaneous Electrical Equipment & Component Manufacturing
N.A.I.C.S.: 334419

Schneider Electric Pakistan (Private) Limited (2)
5 F Gulberg II, 54000, Lahore, Pakistan
Tel.: (92) 47099333
Web Site: http://www.schneider-electric.ae
Energy Consulting Services
N.A.I.C.S.: 541690

Schneider Electric Peru S.A. (2)
Av Juan de Aliaga 425, Magdalena del Mar, 15076, Peru
Tel.: (51) 6184400
Web Site: http://www.se.com
All Other Miscellaneous Electrical Equipment & Component Manufacturing
N.A.I.C.S.: 334419

Schneider Electric Polska Sp. z o.o. (2)
Konstruktorska 12, PL - 02-673, Warsaw, Poland
Tel.: (48) 801171500
Web Site: https://www.se.com
Miscellaneous Electrical Equipment
N.A.I.C.S.: 335999

Schneider Electric Portugal Lda. (2)
Av do Forte n 3 Parq Suecia Edf IV - Piso 3, 2794-038, Carnaxide, Portugal
Tel.: (351) 217507100

INTERNATIONAL PUBLIC

Web Site: https://www.se.com
Sales Range: $25-49.9 Million
All Other Miscellaneous Electrical Equipment & Component Manufacturing
N.A.I.C.S.: 334419

Schneider Electric Power Drives GmbH (2)
Ruthnergasse 1, 1210, Vienna, Austria (100%)
Tel.: (43) 1291910
Web Site: http://www.se.com
Sales Range: $25-49.9 Million
Emp.: 100
Engineeering Services
N.A.I.C.S.: 541330
Paul Richter *(Mgr-Sales)*

Schneider Electric President Systems Ltd. (2)
5C/1 KIADB Industrial Area, Attibele Bangalore Rural, Bengaluru, 562107, Karnataka, India
Tel.: (91) 8067888300
Web Site: https://www.apwpresident.com
Server & Network Rack Mfr
N.A.I.C.S.: 334111
Ranjan Pant *(Chm)*

Subsidiary (Domestic):

Schneider Electric Protection et Controle SAS (2)
Font de la Banquiere Avenue de Figuieres, 34970, Lattes, France
Tel.: (33) 4 67 20 54 54
Security Consulting Services
N.A.I.C.S.: 561621

Subsidiary (Non-US):

Schneider Electric RAK FZE (2)
Jebel Ali Free Zone, PO Box 17192, Dubai, United Arab Emirates
Tel.: (971) 4 7099333
Management Consulting Services
N.A.I.C.S.: 541611
Ziad Mortaja *(Pres-Saudi Arabia & Yemen)*

Schneider Electric Romania SRL (2)
4 Gara Herastrau Green Court Building A 2nd Floor, 2nd District, 020334, Bucharest, Romania
Tel.: (40) 212030606
Web Site: https://www.se.com
Electrical Equipment & Component Manufacturing
N.A.I.C.S.: 334419

Schneider Electric SAS (2)
Str Belorusskaya 15-9, 220006, Minsk, Belarus
Tel.: (375) 172260674
Sales Range: $25-49.9 Million
Emp.: 12
Electric Equipment Mfr
N.A.I.C.S.: 334419

Schneider Electric Sachsenwerk GmbH (2)
Rathenaustrasse 2, 93055, Regensburg, Germany
Tel.: (49) 94146200
Energy Management Consulting Services
N.A.I.C.S.: 541618

Schneider Electric Services International SPRL (2)
Place du Champs de Mars 5 Tour Bastion 14th Floor, Brussels, 1050, Belgium
Tel.: (32) 22133111
Sales Range: $25-49.9 Million
Emp.: 50
Inverter Mfr
N.A.I.C.S.: 335999
Stephen Manetta *(Gen Mgr)*

Schneider Electric Singapore Private Limited (2)
50 Kallang Avenue Schneider Electric Building, Singapore, 339505, Singapore (100%)
Tel.: (65) 64847877
Web Site: http://www.schneider-electric.com.sg
Sales Range: $50-74.9 Million
Emp.: 100
Sales & Service of Industrial Controls
N.A.I.C.S.: 423830
Damien Dhellemmes *(Pres)*

AND PRIVATE COMPANIES — SCHNEIDER ELECTRIC SE

Schneider Electric Slovakia Spol S.R.O. (2)
Karadzicova 16, SK - 821 08, Bratislava, Slovakia
Tel.: (421) 245524010
Web Site: https://www.se.com
All Other Miscellaneous Electrical Equipment & Component Manufacturing
N.A.I.C.S.: 334419

Schneider Electric South Africa Pty. Ltd. (2)
1 River View Office Park Janadel Avenue Halfway Gardens, Midrand, 1685, South Africa
Tel.: (27) 112546400
Web Site: https://www.se.com
Sales Range: $25-49.9 Million
Emp.: 100
All Other Miscellaneous Electrical Equipment & Component Manufacturing
N.A.I.C.S.: 334419
Albert Fuchet *(Pres-Cluster)*

Schneider Electric Spa (2)
Via Circonvallazione Est 1, 24040, Stezzano, Bergamo, Italy
Tel.: (39) 035 415 1111
Web Site: http://www.se.com
Electrical Component Distr
N.A.I.C.S.: 423610

Schneider Electric Sverige AB (2)
Eskilstunavagen 7, 611 65, Nykoping, Sweden
Tel.: (46) 771360370
Sales Range: $125-149.9 Million
Electronic Parts & Equipment Mfr & Distr
N.A.I.C.S.: 334419

Schneider Electric Taiwan Co., Ltd. (2)
5F No 189 Jiouzong Rd, Neihu Dist, Taipei, 11494, Taiwan
Tel.: (886) 266111000
Web Site: http://www.proface.com.tw
All Other Miscellaneous Electrical Equipment & Component Manufacturing
N.A.I.C.S.: 334419

Subsidiary (Domestic):

Schneider Electric Telecontrol SAS (2)
839 Chemin des Batteress Z I Ouest, Saint Maurice, 01700, France
Tel.: (33) 478551313
Web Site: http://www.schneider-electric.com
Sales Range: $50-74.9 Million
Emp.: 120
Telecontrol Product Mfr
N.A.I.C.S.: 334513
Patrick Bourges *(Engr-Technical Sls)*

Subsidiary (Non-US):

Schneider Electric Transformers Poland Sp. Z.o.o. (2)
Ul Zwirki i Wigury 52, 43-190, Mikolow, Poland
Tel.: (48) 327728222
Voltage Transformer Mfr
N.A.I.C.S.: 335311
Marek Papala *(Mgr-IT)*

Schneider Electric Tunisia (2)
Rue Platon Zone Industrielle Kheireddine, Le Kram, 2015, Tunis, Tunisia
Tel.: (216) 31300310
Web Site: http://www.se.com
Sales Range: $25-49.9 Million
All Other Miscellaneous Electrical Equipment & Component Manufacturing
N.A.I.C.S.: 334419

Schneider Electric Turkey (2)
Bayraktar Sok 9, Kucukbakkalkoy Kadkoy, 34750, Istanbul, Turkiye
Tel.: (90) 2166558888
Web Site: http://www.schneiderelectric.com.tr
Sales Range: $50-74.9 Million
Emp.: 200
Electric Equipment Mfr
N.A.I.C.S.: 334419
Onur Basat *(Mgr-HR)*

Subsidiary (US):

Schneider Electric USA, Inc. (2)
800 Federal St, Andover, MA 01810 (100%)
Tel.: (978) 975-9598
Web Site: http://www2.schneider-electric.com
Sales Range: $1-4.9 Billion
Electrical Distribution Equipment, Industrial Control Products, Power Surge Protectors & Lighting Fixtures Mfr
N.A.I.C.S.: 335313
Carlos Villa *(VP-Industry Bus)*

Subsidiary (Domestic):

ASCO Power Technologies, L.P. (3)
160 Park Ave, Florham Park, NJ 07932 (100%)
Tel.: (973) 966-2000
Web Site: https://www.ascopower.com
Fluid & Electric Power Control Mfr
N.A.I.C.S.: 334419

Branch (Domestic):

ASCO Power Technologies, L.P. - Anaheim (4)
120 S Chaparral Ct #110, Anaheim, CA 92808
Tel.: (714) 283-4006
Switchgear Mfr
N.A.I.C.S.: 334419
Alex Lotz *(Mgr-Sls)*

ASCO Power Technologies, L.P. - Houston (4)
16203 Park Row, Houston, TX 77084
Tel.: (281) 829-2900
Electrical Equipment Repair Services
N.A.I.C.S.: 423610
Gary Ellis *(Engr-Field Sls)*

ASCO Power Technologies, L.P. - Woodbridge (4)
1460 Rte 9 N Ste 209, Woodbridge, NJ 07095
Tel.: (732) 596-1733
Power Distr
N.A.I.C.S.: 334419
Jerry Sawczak *(Reg Dir-Sls)*

Subsidiary (Domestic):

ASCO Valve Manufacturing, LLC (4)
1561 Columbia Hwy N, Aiken, SC 29801-8742
Tel.: (803) 641-9200
Solenoid Valves Mfr
N.A.I.C.S.: 332912
Scott Baker *(Dir-Mfg)*

Asco Power Technologies Load Bank (4)
6255 Halle Dr, Cleveland, OH 44125
Tel.: (216) 573-7600
Web Site: http://www.ascopower.com
Power Test Equipment Mfr
N.A.I.C.S.: 334515
Gary S. Brown *(Acct Mgr)*

Firetrol, LLC (4)
3412 Apex Peakway, Apex, NC 27502
Tel.: (919) 460-5200
Web Site: http://www.ascopower.com
Fire Pump Control Systems Mfr
N.A.I.C.S.: 334519
Matt Rodgers *(VP & Gen Mgr)*

Subsidiary (Domestic):

Instep Software LLC (3)
225 W Wacker Dr Fl 6, Chicago, IL 60606
Tel.: (312) 894-7837
Web Site: http://www.instepsoftware.com
Emp.: 70
Software Publisher
N.A.I.C.S.: 513210
Sean Gregerson *(Dir-Sls & Mktg)*

Palatine Hills Leasing Inc. (3)
1415 S Roselle Rd, Palatine, IL 60067-7337
Tel.: (847) 397-2600
Electric Equipment Mfr
N.A.I.C.S.: 335999

Renewable Choice Energy, Inc. (3)
4041 Hanover Ave Ste 200, Boulder, CO 80305
Tel.: (303) 468-0405
Web Site: http://www.renewablechoice.com
Sales Range: $1-9.9 Million
Emp.: 15
Home Center Operator
N.A.I.C.S.: 444110
Quayle Hodek *(Co-Founder)*

SNA Holdings Inc. (3)
1105 N Market St, Wilmington, DE 19801-1216
Tel.: (302) 427-0726
Investment Management Service
N.A.I.C.S.: 523940

Schneider Automation, Inc. (3)
1 High St, North Andover, MA 01845-2601 (100%)
Tel.: (978) 794-0800
Web Site: http://www.schneiderautomation.com
Programmable Control Systems & Industrial Automation Equipment Mfr
N.A.I.C.S.: 334512

Schneider Electric Buildings Americas, Inc. (3)
1650 W Crosby Rd, Carrollton, TX 75006
Tel.: (972) 323-1111
Web Site: http://www.tacamericas.com
Sales Range: $100-124.9 Million
Emp.: 400
Automated Building Systems
N.A.I.C.S.: 334512
Jana Gerber *(Dir-Mktg & Bus Dev)*

Branch (Domestic):

Schneider Electric Buildings Americas - Cincinnati (4)
1770 Mason Morrow Rd, Lebanon, OH 45036-9688
Tel.: (513) 398-9800
Web Site: http://www.tac.com
Rev.: $30,000,000
Emp.: 215
Indoor Climate Control
N.A.I.C.S.: 334512
Jeannie H. Birdwell *(Mgr-Comm)*

Subsidiary (Domestic):

Schneider Electric Buildings Critical Systems, Inc. (4)
8989 Herrmann Dr Ste 300, Columbia, MD 21045-4910
Tel.: (410) 381-7655
Environmental Control Product Mfr
N.A.I.C.S.: 334512
William Ryan *(Pres & CEO)*

Subsidiary (Domestic):

Schneider Electric Engineering Services, LLC (3)
4917 Waters Edge Dr Ste 270, Raleigh, NC 27606
Tel.: (919) 227-3907
Electrical Products Mfr
N.A.I.C.S.: 335999

Schneider Electric IT Corporation (3)
132 Fairgrounds Rd, West Kingston, RI 02892 (100%)
Tel.: (401) 789-5735
Electrical Power Protection Products & Services
N.A.I.C.S.: 423610
David R. Johnson *(Exec VP-IT Div)*

Subsidiary (Non-US):

APC Sweden AB (4)
Djupdals v 17-19, PO Box 954, 191 29, Sollentuna, Sweden
Tel.: (46) 200895283
Web Site: http://www.apc.com
Sales Range: $25-49.9 Million
Emp.: 10
Electrical Power Products & Services
N.A.I.C.S.: 335999

Branch (Non-US):

APC-MGE (4)
Elensenheimerstr 47a, Munich, 80687, Germany
Tel.: (49) 8951417000
Web Site: http://www.apc.com
Sales Range: $25-49.9 Million
Emp.: 100
Electrical Power Protection Products & Services
N.A.I.C.S.: 335999

APC-MGE (4)
Ul Powstancow Slaskich 44, Warsaw, 01 381, Poland
Tel.: (48) 226660011
Sales Range: $25-49.9 Million
Emp.: 20
Electrical Power Products & Services
N.A.I.C.S.: 335999
Gariusz Koseski *(Pres)*

APC-MGE (4)
Doemsky Proezd 42 Building 5, Moscow, 119334, Russia
Tel.: (7) 4956209095
Web Site: http://www.apc.com
Electrical Power Products & Services
N.A.I.C.S.: 335999

APC-MGE (4)
Calle de las hilanderas 25, Aravaca, Getafe, 28906, Spain
Tel.: (34) 917616500
Web Site: http://www.apc.com
Sales Range: $25-49.9 Million
Emp.: 13
Electrical Power Products & Services
N.A.I.C.S.: 335999

APC-MGE (4)
10 Ang Mo Kio Street 65 #03-06 10 Techpoint, Singapore, 569095, Singapore
Tel.: (65) 63981000
Web Site: http://www.apcc.com
Sales Range: $50-74.9 Million
Emp.: 160
Electrical Power Protection & Management Solutions
N.A.I.C.S.: 335999

APC-MGE (4)
140 Ave Jean Kuntzmann, 38334, Saint Ismier, France
Tel.: (33) 476183000
Web Site: http://www.schneider-electric.com
Sales Range: $150-199.9 Million
Emp.: 600
Power Product Mfr
N.A.I.C.S.: 335999
Claude Graff *(CEO)*

Subsidiary (Domestic):

Schneider Electric IT America Corp. (4)
132 Fairgrounds Rd, West Kingston, RI 02892-1517
Tel.: (401) 789-5735
Web Site: http://www.schneiderelectric.com
Emp.: 350
Electric Equipment Mfr
N.A.I.C.S.: 335999

Schneider Electric IT USA, Inc. (4)
132 Fairgrounds Rd, West Kingston, RI 02892-1517
Tel.: (401) 789-5735
Web Site: http://www.schneider-electric.com
Electrical Equipment Distr
N.A.I.C.S.: 423610
Laurent J. Vernerey *(CFO)*

Branch (Domestic):

Schneider Electric USA, Inc. - Bordentown (3)
90 United States Hwy 130 A, Bordentown, NJ 08505-2244
Tel.: (609) 298-6332
Web Site: http://www.schneider-electric.us
Sales Range: $25-49.9 Million
Emp.: 10
Mfr of Switchgear Apparatus
N.A.I.C.S.: 334513
Kurt Christensen *(Mgr)*

Schneider Electric USA, Inc. - Cedar Rapids (3)
3700 6th St SW, Cedar Rapids, IA 52404-3911
Tel.: (319) 368-3036
Sales Range: $75-99.9 Million
Emp.: 400
Mfr of Circuit Breakers
N.A.I.C.S.: 335313
D. C. Murphy *(Plant Mgr)*

Schneider Electric USA, Inc. - Cincinnati (3)

SCHNEIDER ELECTRIC SE

INTERNATIONAL PUBLIC

Schneider Electric SE—(Continued)
9870 Crescent Park Dr, West Chester, OH 45069-3800
Tel.: (513) 777-4445
Web Site: http://www.schneider-electric.com
Sales Range: $50-74.9 Million
Emp.: 105
Power Transformers Electric
N.A.I.C.S.: 335313

Schneider Electric USA, Inc. - Columbia (3)
4800 Paris Rd, Columbia, MO 65202-9396
Tel.: (573) 474-8421
Web Site: http://www.schneider-electric.us
Sales Range: $75-99.9 Million
Emp.: 345
Circuit Breaker Mfr
N.A.I.C.S.: 335313
Lori Swiatek (Gen Mgr)

Schneider Electric USA, Inc. - Dallas (3)
204 Airline Dr Ste 300, Coppell, TX 75019
Tel.: (972) 236-0300
Web Site: http://www.schneider-electric.us
Sales Range: $25-49.9 Million
Emp.: 70
Mfr of Electrical Equipment
N.A.I.C.S.: 335313

Schneider Electric USA, Inc. - Green Bay (3)
1903 Progress Way, Green Bay, WI 54130
Tel.: (920) 766-8007
Web Site: http://www.schneider-electric.us
Sales Range: $25-49.9 Million
Mfr of Isolating Systems
N.A.I.C.S.: 423610

Schneider Electric USA, Inc. - Greensboro (3)
235 Burgess Rd, Greensboro, NC 27409
Tel.: (336) 605-4800
Web Site: http://www.schneider-electric.us
Sales Range: $25-49.9 Million
Electronic Equipment Repair
N.A.I.C.S.: 811210

Schneider Electric USA, Inc. - Hopkins (3)
8821 Garners Ferry Rd, Hopkins, SC 29061
Tel.: (803) 776-7500
Web Site: http://www.schneider-electric.us
Rev.: $145,000,000
Emp.: 600
Mfr of Motor Control; Medium Voltage Starters; Crane Control
N.A.I.C.S.: 335313

Schneider Electric USA, Inc. - Huntington (3)
6 Commercial Rd, Huntington, IN 46750-8805
Tel.: (260) 356-2060
Web Site: http://www.schneider-electric.us
Sales Range: $75-99.9 Million
Emp.: 180
Coil Engineering
N.A.I.C.S.: 423610

Schneider Electric USA, Inc. - Kennesaw (3)
225 Townpark Dr NW Ste 400, Kennesaw, GA 30144-5875
Tel.: (770) 792-4830
Web Site: http://www.schneider-electric.us
Electrical Apparatus & Equipment Distr
N.A.I.C.S.: 334513

Schneider Electric USA, Inc. - Lexington (3)
1601 Mercer Rd, Lexington, KY 40511-1025
Tel.: (859) 243-8000
Web Site: http://www.schneider-electric.us
Sales Range: $150-199.9 Million
Emp.: 600
Mfr of Service Entrance Equipment, Safety Switches, Molded Case Circuit Breakers
N.A.I.C.S.: 335313

Schneider Electric USA, Inc. - Lincoln (3)
1717 Center Park Rd, Lincoln, NE 68512-1231
Tel.: (402) 423-6721
Web Site: http://www.schneider-electric.us
Sales Range: $100-124.9 Million
Emp.: 300
Mfr Miniature Circuit Breakers
N.A.I.C.S.: 335313

Schneider Electric USA, Inc. - Milwaukee (3)
11950 W Lake Park Dr Ste 240, Milwaukee, WI 53224
Tel.: (414) 247-6200
Web Site: http://www.squared.com
Sales Range: $25-49.9 Million
Emp.: 12
Mfr Control Systems & Automation Products, Services, Support
N.A.I.C.S.: 423610

Schneider Electric USA, Inc. - Nashville (3)
330 Weakley Ln, Smyrna, TN 37167-2024
Tel.: (615) 459-5026
Web Site: http://www.schneider-electric.us
Sales Range: $75-99.9 Million
Emp.: 495
Mfr of Switchboards, Motor Control Centers, Unit Substations & Switchgears
N.A.I.C.S.: 335314

Schneider Electric USA, Inc. - Norcross (3)
2979 Pacific Dr Ste E, Norcross, GA 30071-2537
Tel.: (770) 447-0351
Web Site: http://www.schneider-electric.us
Sales Range: $25-49.9 Million
Emp.: 20
Distribution of Electric Products
N.A.I.C.S.: 811210

Schneider Electric USA, Inc. - Oxford (3)
5735 College Corner Pike, Oxford, OH 45056-9715
Tel.: (513) 523-4171
Web Site: http://www.schneider-electric.us
Sales Range: $100-124.9 Million
Emp.: 320
Underfloor Duct, Busway, Wireways, Cable Tray
N.A.I.C.S.: 335931
Tom Mcdonald (Mgr)

Schneider Electric USA, Inc. - Peru (3)
252 North Tippecanoe St, Peru, IN 46970-1478
Tel.: (765) 472-3381
Web Site: http://www.schneider-electric.us
Sales Range: $150-199.9 Million
Emp.: 475
Mfr of Switchgear & Switchboard Apparatus
N.A.I.C.S.: 335313
Tony Hartley (Mgr-Ops)

Schneider Electric USA, Inc. - Puerto Rico (3)
Buchanan Ofc Ctr Ste 310 40 Rd 165, Guaynabo, PR 00968-8001
Tel.: (787) 783-2835
Electrical Equipment & Component Whslr
N.A.I.C.S.: 423610

Schneider Electric USA, Inc. - Raleigh (3)
8001 Knightdale Blvd, Knightdale, NC 27545
Tel.: (919) 266-3671
Web Site: http://www.schneider-electric.com
Sales Range: $100-124.9 Million
Emp.: 450
Mfr of Starters, Relays, Sensors, Programmable Controllers, LANs & Factory Automation Systems, Control Systems & Automation Products, Services & Support
N.A.I.C.S.: 335313

Schneider Electric USA, Inc. - Salisbury (3)
105 Summit Pk Dr, Salisbury, NC 28146
Tel.: (704) 637-9662
Web Site: http://www.schneider-electric.us
Sales Range: $25-49.9 Million
Emp.: 110
Electric Control Panels
N.A.I.C.S.: 335313

Schneider Electric USA, Inc. - Seattle (3)
7525 SE 24th St Ste 470, Mercer Island, WA 98040-2300
Tel.: (206) 236-4120
Web Site: http://www.schneider-electric.us
Sales Range: $25-49.9 Million
Mfr & Distributor of Electrical Apparatus & Equipment
N.A.I.C.S.: 423610

Schneider Electric USA, Inc. - Seneca (3)
1990 Sandifer Blvd, Seneca, SC 29678-0910
Tel.: (864) 882-2414
Sales Range: $200-249.9 Million
Emp.: 630
Mfr of Motor Control Centers & Switchboards
N.A.I.C.S.: 335313

Schneider Electric USA, Inc. - Tampa (3)
5110 Sun Forest Dr Ste 105, Tampa, FL 33634
Tel.: (813) 882-6623
Web Site: http://www.schneider-electric.us
Sales Range: $25-49.9 Million
Instrument Transformers & Electrical Supply Services
N.A.I.C.S.: 423610

Schneider Electric USA, Inc. - York (3)
3570 Concord Rd, York, PA 17402-8698
Tel.: (717) 757-7930
Sales Range: $25-49.9 Million
Emp.: 13
Mfr of Electrical Apparatus & Equipment & Wiring Supplies
N.A.I.C.S.: 423610

Subsidiary (Domestic):

Square D Investment Company (3)
1415 Roselle Rd, Palatine, IL 60067
Tel.: (847) 397-2600
Financial Investment Services
N.A.I.C.S.: 523999

Summit Energy Services, Inc.
10350 Ormsby Park Pl, Louisville, KY 40223
Tel.: (502) 429-3800
Sales Range: $25-49.9 Million
Emp.: 180
Energy Management Consulting Services
N.A.I.C.S.: 541618
Steve Wilhite (Pres)

Division (Non-US):

M&C Energy Group Ltd. (4)
Claymore House, Enterprise Way, Dunfermline, KY11 8PY, Fife, United Kingdom
Tel.: (44) 1795416850
Web Site: http://www.mcenergygroup.co.uk
Sales Range: $50-74.9 Million
Emp.: 500
Energy, Environmental & Clean Technology Consulting
N.A.I.C.S.: 541620
Simon P. Northrop (Dir-Strategic Client)

Branch (US):

Scheider Electric - Professional Services (5)
20830 N Tatum Blvd Ste 330, Phoenix, AZ 85050
Tel.: (480) 346-5800
Web Site: http://www.scheiderelectric.com
Sales Range: $25-49.9 Million
Emp.: 22
Scientific & Technical Consulting Services
N.A.I.C.S.: 541690
Elin Guenther (Dir)

Subsidiary (Domestic):

Telvent Farradyne Engineering, PC (3)
4035 NW 43rd St, Gainesville, FL 32606-4598
Tel.: (352) 374-6635
Construction Engineering Services
N.A.I.C.S.: 541330

Subsidiary (Non-US):

Schneider Electric Ukraine LLC (2)
13-V lit A Stepana Bandery Av, 04073, Kiev, Ukraine
Tel.: (380) 445381470
Web Site: https://www.se.com
Electric Equipment Mfr
N.A.I.C.S.: 334419

Schneider Electric Uruguay S.A. (2)
Ramon Masini 3190, 11300, Montevideo, Uruguay
Tel.: (598) 94992000
All Other Miscellaneous Electrical Equipment & Component Manufacturing
N.A.I.C.S.: 334419

Schneider Electric Venezuela SA (2)
Avenida Intercomunal Guarenas Guatire Sector Vega Arriba Parcela, Industrial 9C, Guatire, Estado Miranda, Venezuela
Tel.: (58) 2123400811
Web Site: http://www.schneider-electric.com.ve
Energy Management Consulting Services
N.A.I.C.S.: 541618

Schneider Electric Vietnam Co. Ltd (2)
Unit 7 2 7th Floor e-Town Building 364 Cong Hoa Street, Tan Binh, Ho Chi Minh City, Vietnam
Tel.: (84) 838103103
Web Site: https://www.se.com
Electrical Distribution, Industrial Control & Automation Equipment Distr
N.A.I.C.S.: 423610

Schneider Electric d.o.o. (2)
Dolenjska Cesta 242c, SI-1000, Ljubljana, Slovenia
Tel.: (386) 12363555
Web Site: http://www.se.com
All Other Miscellaneous Electrical Equipment & Component Manufacturing
N.A.I.C.S.: 334419

Schneider Electric d.o.o. (2)
Fallerovo setaliste 22, 10000, Zagreb, Croatia
Tel.: (385) 8007788
Web Site: http://www.se.com
All Other Miscellaneous Electrical Equipment & Component Manufacturing
N.A.I.C.S.: 334419

Schneider Electric d.o.o. (2)
Borekova 10, 821 06, Bratislava, Slovakia
Tel.: (421) 2 4552 4010
Energy Management Consulting Services
N.A.I.C.S.: 541618

Schneider Electric de Colombia S.A.S (2)
Carrera 69 F # 20-91, Bogota, Colombia
Tel.: (57) 14269700
Web Site: http://www.se.com
All Other Miscellaneous Electrical Equipment & Component Manufacturing
N.A.I.C.S.: 334419

Schneider Elektrik Sanayi Ve Ticaret A.S. (2)
Kucukbakkalkoy Mah Elvan Sok No 16-18B, Atasehir, 34750, Istanbul, Turkiye
Tel.: (90) 2166558888
Web Site: http://www.schneider-electric.com.tr
Energy Management Consulting Services
N.A.I.C.S.: 541618

Schneider Enerji Endustrisi Sanayi Ve Ticaret A.S (2)
Tosb 1 Cadde No 6, 41420, Cayirova, Kocaeli, Turkiye
Tel.: (90) 2626480400
Web Site: http://www.schneider-enerji.com.tr
Power Distribution Transformer Mfr
N.A.I.C.S.: 335311

Schneider Industrial Tlaxcala, S.A. de C.V. (2)
Via corta Km 17 5 Santa Ana Chiautempan, Acuamanala de Miguel Hidalgo, Tlaxcala, Mexico
Tel.: (52) 2464979700
Electric Equipment Mfr
N.A.I.C.S.: 335999

Schneider R&D, S.A. de C.V. (2)
Blvd Apodaca No 100, Apodaca, 66600, Nuevo Leon, Mexico
Tel.: (52) 5558045342
Electrical Equipment Research & Development Services

AND PRIVATE COMPANIES — SCHNEIDER ELECTRIC SE

N.A.I.C.S.: 541715

Schneider Recursos Humanos, S.A. de C.V. (2)
Calz J Rojo Gomez No 1121-A Guadalupe del Moral, Iztapalapa, Mexico, Mexico
Tel.: (52) 5558045079
Human Resource Consulting Services
N.A.I.C.S.: 541612

Schneider Shanghai Apparatus Parts Manufacturing Co. Ltd (2)
No 833 Kangqiao Rd Kangqiao Industrial Zone, Nanhui Dist, Shanghai, 201315, China
Tel.: (86) 2158122222
Electric Equipment Mfr
N.A.I.C.S.: 335999

Schneider Shanghai Industrial Control Co. Ltd (2)
No 629 SuiDe Road, Putuo District, Shanghai, 200331, China
Tel.: (86) 2163636868
Industrial Electric Parts Mfr
N.A.I.C.S.: 335999
Vhu Janny (Gen Mgr)

Schneider Switchgear (Suzhou) Co, Ltd (2)
No 285 Jinfeng Road, Suzhou, 215129, Jiangsu, China
Tel.: (86) 51266651318
Switchgear Mfr
N.A.I.C.S.: 335313

Serck Control and Safety Ltd (2)
11 Bilton Court Bilton Way, Luton, LU1 1LX, Bedfordshire, United Kingdom
Tel.: (44) 1582 509 900
Sales Range: $25-49.9 Million
Emp.: 12
Control System Equipment Mfr
N.A.I.C.S.: 334519

Serck Controls Ltd (2)
Rowley Drive, Coventry, CV3 4FH, United Kingdom
Tel.: (44) 24 7630 5050
Web Site: http://www.serck-controls.co.uk
Automation Engineering Services
N.A.I.C.S.: 541330

Serck Controls Pty. Ltd (2)
Newcastle 76 Munibung Road, Cardiff, 2285, NSW, Australia
Tel.: (61) 2 4941 1211
Electric Equipment Mfr
N.A.I.C.S.: 335999

Shanghai Tayee Electric Co., Ltd. (2)
Room 1702 No 889 Yishan Rd, Shanghai, China
Tel.: (86) 2154012233
Web Site: http://www.tayee-electric.com
Emp.: 500
Alarm Lamp & Sealed Box Mfr
N.A.I.C.S.: 335931

Subsidiary (Domestic):

Societe Francaise Gardy SA (2)
Centre d, BP 141, 71530, Champforgeuil, France
Tel.: (33) 385476565
Electric Equipment Mfr
N.A.I.C.S.: 335999

Societe Francaise de Construction Mecanique et Electrique SA (2)
Z I de la Ballastiere 18 avenue de la Ballastiere, BP 100, 33501, Libourne, France
Tel.: (33) 557550200
Web Site: http://www.schneiderelectric.com
Electric Equipment Mfr
N.A.I.C.S.: 335999
Marc Jaclot (Gen Mgr)

Societe d'Application et d'Ingenierie Industrielle et Informatique SAS (2)
37 Rue Helene Muller, 94320, Thiais, France
Tel.: (33) 1 57 02 17 00
Web Site: http://www.saei.com
Emp.: 70
Electric Equipment Mfr
N.A.I.C.S.: 335999
Philippe Schneider (Gen Mgr)

Societe pour l'equipement des industries chimiques SA (2)
35 Rue Joseph Monier, 92500, Rueil-Malmaison, France
Tel.: (33) 1 41 29 85 00
Electric Equipment Mfr
N.A.I.C.S.: 335999

Subsidiary (Non-US):

Softbrasil Automacao Ltda (2)
Rua Miguel Sutil 349 Bairro Brooklin, Sao Paulo, 04583-050, Brazil
Tel.: (55) 11 3488 8787
Web Site: http://www.softbrasil.com.br
Electric Equipment Mfr
N.A.I.C.S.: 334419

Square D Company Mexico, S.A. de C.V. (2)
Javier Rojo Gomez No 1121-a, Iztapalapa, Guadalupe, Mexico
Tel.: (52) 5558045204
Switchgear Mfr
N.A.I.C.S.: 335313

Steck Electric SA (2)
Belisario Hueyo 165 Avellaneda, B1870BNA, Buenos Aires, Argentina
Tel.: (54) 11 42011489
Web Site: http://www.steck.com.br
Electric Equipment Mfr
N.A.I.C.S.: 335931

Summit Energy International BVBA (2)
Holstraat 61 A1, 8790, Waregem, 8790, Belgium
Tel.: (32) 56 60 04 04
Web Site: http://www.summitenergy.com
Sales Range: $25-49.9 Million
Emp.: 55
Energy Management Consulting Services
N.A.I.C.S.: 541618
Ben van Bemmel (Gen Mgr)

Summit Energy Services BV (2)
Hofstraat 1, 4797 AC, Willemstad, Noord-Brabant, Netherlands
Tel.: (31) 168471811
Energy Management Consulting Services
N.A.I.C.S.: 541618

Sunten Electric Equipment Co., Ltd. (2)
No 23 Xinyue Road Wusha Community, Daliang Town Shunde District, Foshan, 528300, Guangdong, China
Tel.: (86) 75722338222
Web Site: http://www.sunten.com.cn
Electricity Equipment Distr
N.A.I.C.S.: 423610

Subsidiary (Domestic):

Systemes Equipements Tableaux Basse Tension SAS (2)
13 Boulevard Joseph Marechal, 35131, Chartres, France
Tel.: (33) 2 99 41 21 25
Sales Range: $50-74.9 Million
Emp.: 130
Electric Equipment Mfr
N.A.I.C.S.: 335999

Subsidiary (Non-US):

TRIO Datacom Pty. Ltd. (2)
41 Aster Avenue, Carrum Downs, Melbourne, 3201, VIC, Australia
Tel.: (61) 3 8773 0100
Web Site: http://www.trio.com.au
Sales Range: $25-49.9 Million
Emp.: 35
Wireless Communication Product Mfr
N.A.I.C.S.: 334290

Subsidiary (Non-US):

Trio Datacom Inc. (3)
48 Steacie Drive, Kanata, K2K 2A9, ON, Canada
Tel.: (613) 287-0786
Web Site: http://www.triodatacom.com
Emp.: 150
Wireless Communication Product Mfr
N.A.I.C.S.: 334290
Dave Jeffrey (Dir-Ops)

Subsidiary (Non-US):

Tamco Switchgear (Malaysia) Sdn. Bhd. (2)
Sublot 24 Lot 16505 Kawasan Perindustrian Selatan 41050 Jalan Keluli 1, Seksyen 7, 40000, Shah Alam, Malaysia
Tel.: (60) 333618200
Web Site: https://www.tamco.com.my
Emp.: 700
Medium & Low Voltage Switchgear Mfr
N.A.I.C.S.: 335313
Bipin Paul (Sr Mgr-Sales)

Subsidiary (Non-US):

PT Tamco Indonesia (3)
Jalan Jababeka Raya Blok F 36 Cikarang Utara, Bekasi, 17550, Jawa Barat, Indonesia
Tel.: (62) 218970540
Web Site: https://en.tamcoindonesia.web.com
Sales Range: $50-74.9 Million
Emp.: 100
Switchgear & Power Distributions Mfr
N.A.I.C.S.: 335313

Tamco Electrical Industries Australia Pty Limited (3)
31 Kitchen Road, Dandenong, 3175, VIC, Australia
Tel.: (61) 397067288
Web Site: http://www.tamcoaustralia.com.au
Sales Range: $25-49.9 Million
Emp.: 20
Switchgear Mfr
N.A.I.C.S.: 335313
Claude Corso (CEO)

Subsidiary (Non-US):

Telemantenimiento de Alta Tension, SL (2)
Paseo de la Riera 226 Nave 4 E, 08191, Rubi, Barcelona, Spain
Tel.: (34) 930285890
Web Site: https://www.telemat.es
Emp.: 29
Electric Power Distribution Services
N.A.I.C.S.: 221122
Francesc Vilalta (Gen Mgr)

Toshiba Schneider Inverter Corp. (2)
Mazak Art Plaza 13F 1-19-30 Aoi, Higashi-ku, Nagoya, 461-0004, Aichi Prefecture, Japan
Tel.: (81) 522179041
Web Site: https://www.inverter.co.jp
Industrial Inverter Mfr
N.A.I.C.S.: 335999

Subsidiary (Domestic):

Transfo Services SAS (2)
2 boulevard Laennec, Chateaubourg, 35220, Chateaugiron, France
Tel.: (33) 299623380
Web Site: https://www.transfo-services.fr
Oil Treatment Services
N.A.I.C.S.: 115112

Subsidiary (Non-US):

UAB Schneider Electric Lietuva (2)
Zirmunu g 139, 09120, Vilnius, Lithuania
Tel.: (370) 52477777
Sales Range: $25-49.9 Million
Emp.: 20
Energy Consulting Services
N.A.I.C.S.: 541690

Uniflair GmbH (2)
Georg-Wimmer-Ring 18, 85604, Zorneding, Germany
Tel.: (49) 810699370
Air Conditioning Equipment Mfr & Distr
N.A.I.C.S.: 333415

Uniflair Iberica SA (2)
Cami De Can Calders No 8, 08173, Sant Cugat del Valles, Barcelona, Spain
Tel.: (34) 935890090
Air Conditioning Equipment Mfr & Distr
N.A.I.C.S.: 333415

Uniflair South Africa (Pty) Ltd (2)
PO Box 10371, Edenglen, 1613, South Africa
Tel.: (27) 11 974 0053
Air Conditioning Equipment Mfr & Distr
N.A.I.C.S.: 333415

Uniflair Spa (2)
Viale della Tecnica 2, Conselve, 35026, Padova, Italy
Tel.: (39) 049 5388211
Web Site: http://www.uniflair.com
Sales Range: $125-149.9 Million
Emp.: 281
Precision Air Conditioning Product Mfr & Distr
N.A.I.C.S.: 333415
Anna Marie Gignac (Gen Mgr)

Subsidiary (Non-US):

Uniflair (Zhuhai) Electr. Appli. Manuf. Co. Ltd (3)
No 5 ChuangYe West Rd Liangang Ind Park, Jin Wan Dist, Zhuhai, 519 045, Guangdong, China
Tel.: (86) 7563386718
Web Site: http://www.uniflair.com
Precision Air Conditioning Product Mfr
N.A.I.C.S.: 333415
Frank Xu (Gen Mgr)

Subsidiary (Non-US):

Vamp OY (2)
Yrittajankatu 15, PO Box 810, Vaasa, 65101, Finland
Tel.: (358) 20 753 3200
Web Site: http://www.vamp.fi
Sales Range: $25-49.9 Million
Emp.: 40
Relay Sensor & Monitoring Unit Mfr
N.A.I.C.S.: 335314

Subsidiary (Non-US):

Vamp Solutions (Pty) Ltd (3)
182 Nigel Road Selcourt, Springs, 1559, South Africa
Tel.: (27) 11 818 2190
Web Site: http://www.vamp.co.za
Sales Range: $25-49.9 Million
Emp.: 4
Industrial Relay Mfr
N.A.I.C.S.: 335314

Subsidiary (Non-US):

Verwaltung SVEA Building Control Systems GmbH (2)
Fritz Kotz Strasse 8, 51674, Wiehl, Germany
Tel.: (49) 226170202
Web Site: http://www.schneiderelectric.com
Emp.: 500
Building Automation System Mfr
N.A.I.C.S.: 335999

Wuxi Proface Electronic Co. Ltd (2)
20 Hanjiang Road National Hi-Tech Industrial Development Zone, Wuxi, 214028, Jiangsu, China
Tel.: (86) 510 8521 2101
Web Site: http://www.pro-face.com
Industrial Automation Equipments Mfr
N.A.I.C.S.: 333248

ZAO Schneider Electric (2)
St Dvintsev 12 Building 1 Building A, 127018, Moscow, Russia
Tel.: (7) 495 777 9990
Web Site: http://www.se.com
All Other Miscellaneous Electrical Equipment & Component Manufacturing
N.A.I.C.S.: 334419

Schneider Electric Systems USA, Inc (1)
1602 Mustang Dr, Maryville, TN 37801-3766
Tel.: (865) 981-3100
Web Site: http://www.robertshawindustrial.com
Industrial Valves, Vibration Detection & Monitoring Systems Mfr
N.A.I.C.S.: 332911
Philip Scheuneman (Sr Products Mgr)

Stewart Warner Corporation (1)
1090 N Charlotte St, Lancaster, PA 17603
Tel.: (717) 581-1000
Web Site: https://www.stewartwarner.com
Gauges Mfr
N.A.I.C.S.: 332420

SCHNEIDER ELECTRIC SE

Schneider Electric SE—(Continued)

Uplight, Inc. (1)
2560 55th St, Boulder, CO 80301
Web Site: http://uplight.com
Software Development Services
N.A.I.C.S.: 541511
Thomas R. McDaniel (Chm)

Subsidiary (Domestic):

Simple Energy, Inc. (2)
1215 Spruce St Ste 301, Boulder, CO 80302
Tel.: (303) 953-4735
Web Site: http://www.simpleenergy.com
Software Development Services
N.A.I.C.S.: 513210
Yoav Lurie (Founder & CEO)

Veris Industries LLC (1)
12345 SW Leveton Dr, Tualatin, OR 97062
Tel.: (503) 598-4564
Web Site: https://www.veris.com
Sensor & HVAC Control Peripheral Distr
N.A.I.C.S.: 423690

SCHNEIDER FAHRZEUG- UND CONTAINERTECHNIK GMBH
Brockhagener Strasse 92, 33649, Bielefeld, Germany
Tel.: (49) 5214173120
Web Site: http://www.schneider-fc.com
Year Founded: 1983
Sales Range: $10-24.9 Million
Commercial, Construction & Automotive Components Mfr
N.A.I.C.S.: 423390
Horst Schneider (Founder & Mng Dir)

SCHNEIDER SCHREIBGERATE GMBH
Schwarzenbach 9, 78144, Schramberg, Germany
Tel.: (49) 77298880
Web Site:
http://www.schneiderpen.com
Year Founded: 1938
Rev.: $101,755,984
Emp.: 251
Writing Instruments Mfr
N.A.I.C.S.: 339940

Subsidiaries:

MEDISTAR Arzneimittelvertrieb GmbH (1)
Ludinghauser Str 23, 59387, Ascheberg, Germany
Tel.: (49) 2593958860
Web Site: http://www.medistar-gmbh.de
Pharmaceutical Products Distr
N.A.I.C.S.: 424210

MTP Medical Technologies GmbH (1)
Kunstseidenstr 4, 01796, Pirna, Germany
Tel.: (49) 350146590
Web Site: http://www.mtp-pirna.de
Medical Equipment Mfr
N.A.I.C.S.: 339112

Schneider Novus Vertriebs GmbH (1)
Holzhofring 20, 82362, Weilheim, Germany
Tel.: (49) 88162929100
Web Site: http://www.snv.de
Wiring Product Distr
N.A.I.C.S.: 423610

SCHNELLECKE GROUP AG & CO. KG
Stellfelder Strasse 39, 38442, Wolfsburg, Germany
Tel.: (49) 5361 301 0   De
Web Site:
http://www.schnellecke.com
Year Founded: 1939
Sales Range: $1-4.9 Billion
Emp.: 18,374
Holding Company; Integrated Logistics Services

N.A.I.C.S.: 551112
Nikolaus Kulps (Chm-Mgmt Bd & CEO)

Subsidiaries:

Dalian Schnellecke Logistics Co. Ltd. (1)
Automobile Parts Industrial Park Block No 48, Economic & Technological Development Zone, Dalian, 116620, China
Tel.: (86) 411 87338596
Freight Forwarding & Shipping Services
N.A.I.C.S.: 488510

Logtrans Spedition und Logistik GmbH (1)
Rudolf-Diesel-Strasse 2, 14974, Ludwigsfelde, Germany
Tel.: (49) 3378 898 0
Web Site: http://www.logtrans-ludwigsfelde.de
Logistics Consulting Servies
N.A.I.C.S.: 541614

OOO Schnellecke Rus (1)
Monastyrka 17, 603016, Nizhniy Novgorod, Russia
Tel.: (7) 915 955 4345
Freight Forwarding Services
N.A.I.C.S.: 488510

Schnellecke Bohemia Services s.r.o. (1)
Husova 623, 29441, Prague, Czech Republic
Tel.: (420) 326 373411
Freight Forwarding Services
N.A.I.C.S.: 488510

Schnellecke Brasil Ltda. (1)
Rodovia Luiz Augusto de Oliveira km 148 8, 13560-340, Sao Carlos, Brazil
Tel.: (55) 19 3826 8686
Warehouse Management Services
N.A.I.C.S.: 493110

Schnellecke Hungary Kft. (1)
Gesztenyefa u 4, 9027, Gyor, Hungary
Tel.: (36) 30 2378104
Logistics Consulting Servies
N.A.I.C.S.: 541614

Schnellecke Italia s.r.l. (1)
Via F Lamborghini snc, 40019, Sant'Agata Bolognese, Italy
Tel.: (39) 051 6817 834
Logistics Consulting Servies
N.A.I.C.S.: 493110
Michela Di Girolamo (Mgr-HR)

Schnellecke Jeena Logistics India Pvt. Ltd. (1)
Elphinstone Building 1st Floor 10 Veer Nariman Road, Mumbai, 400 001, India
Tel.: (91) 961 923 5115
Web Site: http://www.schnellecke.com
Packaging & Logistics Services
N.A.I.C.S.: 561910

Schnellecke Logistic Services (Pty) Ltd. (1)
103 Algoa Road, PO Box 80, Uitenhage, 6230, South Africa
Tel.: (27) 41 994 5164
Web Site: http://www.schnellecke.co.za
Emp.: 1,375
Freight Forwarding Services
N.A.I.C.S.: 488510

Schnellecke Logistics Dingolfing GmbH (1)
Landshuter Strasse 56, 84130, Dingolfing, Germany
Tel.: (49) 8731 3251 0
Warehouse Management Services
N.A.I.C.S.: 493110

Schnellecke Logistics Espana, S.A. (1)
Calle Galileo N 1-9, Sant Esteve Sesrovires, 08635, Barcelona, Spain
Tel.: (34) 93 7037700
Logistics Consulting Servies
N.A.I.C.S.: 541614

Schnellecke Logistics Germany GmbH (1)
Richard-Seiffert-Str 15, 47249, Duisburg, Germany

Tel.: (49) 203 34808 101
Logistics Consulting Servies
N.A.I.C.S.: 541614

Schnellecke Logistics Sachsen GmbH (1)
Potthoffstrasse 11, 01159, Dresden, Germany
Tel.: (49) 351 420 4630
Logistics Consulting Servies
N.A.I.C.S.: 541614

Schnellecke Logistics USA LLC (1)
8007 Volkswagen Dr Ste 173, Chattanooga, TN 37416
Tel.: (423) 987-3460
Logistics Consulting Servies
N.A.I.C.S.: 541614
Rene Deij (Mgr-Comml)

Schnellecke Logistics Wolfsburg GmbH (1)
Amerikaring 2, 27580, Bremerhaven, Germany
Tel.: (49) 471 96919 5101
Web Site: http://www.schnellecke.com
Emp.: 120
Logistics Consulting Servies
N.A.I.C.S.: 541614
Andreas Zitzea (Gen Mgr)

Schnellecke Modul GmbH (1)
Adam-Opel-Strasse 29, 99817, Eisenach, Germany
Tel.: (49) 3691 796 0
Logistics Consulting Servies
N.A.I.C.S.: 541614

Schnellecke Modul- und Lieferantenzentrum GmbH (1)
Am Exer 13, 04158, Leipzig, Germany
Tel.: (49) 341 68100 0
Logistics Consulting Servies
N.A.I.C.S.: 541614
Eric Avassis (Project Mgr)

Schnellecke Polska Sp. z o.o. (1)
ul Gorzyslawa 27, 61-057, Poznan, Poland
Tel.: (48) 61 626 22 60
Web Site: http://www.schnellecke.com
N.A.I.C.S.: 541614
Marcin Brylczak (Mgr-Sls & Mktg)

Schnellecke Portugal Lda. (1)
Edificio Schnellecke Quinta da Marquesa, 2950-557, Lisbon, Portugal
Tel.: (351) 210 817300
Web Site: http://www.schnellecke.pt
Logistics Consulting Servies
N.A.I.C.S.: 541614

Schnellecke Sachsen GmbH (1)
Buttenstrasse 4, 08058, Zwickau, Germany
Tel.: (49) 375 2711 500
Logistics Consulting Servies
N.A.I.C.S.: 541614

Unit (Domestic):

Schnellecke Sachsen GmbH - Logistik BMW Leipzig Unit (2)
BMW-Allee 1, 4349, Leipzig, Germany
Tel.: (49) 341 2009 040
Logistics Consulting Servies
N.A.I.C.S.: 541614

Schnellecke Sachsen GmbH - Logistik Porsche Leipzig Unit (2)
Porschestrasse 1, 04158, Leipzig, Germany
Tel.: (49) 341 99913 235
Logistics Consulting Servies
N.A.I.C.S.: 541614

Schnellecke Slovakia s.r.o. (1)
Westpoint Logistics Park Hala DC6b, 900 55, Lozorno, Slovakia
Tel.: (421) 2 602 62 111
Web Site: http://www.schnellecke.sk
Logistics Consulting Servies
N.A.I.C.S.: 541614
Konopeus Lubos (Mgr-IT)

Schnellecke Transport Slovakia s.r.o. (1)
Automobilovy priemysleny park Hala C, 900 55, Lozorno, Slovakia
Tel.: (421) 2 602 62 120
Logistics Consulting Servies
N.A.I.C.S.: 541614

INTERNATIONAL PUBLIC

Schnellecke Transportlogistik GmbH (1)
Hansestrasse 60, 38112, Braunschweig, Germany
Tel.: (49) 531 31909 0
Logistics Consulting Servies
N.A.I.C.S.: 541614

Seglo, S.A. de C.V. (1)
Privada 15 de Mayo No 10, Colonia San Rafael Poniente, 72029, Puebla, Mexico
Tel.: (52) 222 273 6200
Web Site: http://www.seglo.mx
Sales Range: $150-199.9 Million
Emp.: 1,000
Integrated Logistics Services
N.A.I.C.S.: 488510

SCHNORR GMBH
Stuttgarter Strasse 37, 71069, Sindelfingen, Germany
Tel.: (49) 70313020
Web Site: http://www.schnorr-group.com
Year Founded: 1908
Rev.: $36,486,432
Emp.: 240
Spring Mfr
N.A.I.C.S.: 332613
Andy Haunholter (Mng Dir)

Subsidiaries:

SCHNORR Group Mexico S.DE R.L.DE C.V. (1)
Real De Zimapan 440 Colonia Villas Del Parque, 76140, Queretaro, Mexico
Tel.: (52) 4422461000
Web Site: http://www.schnorr.com.mx
Spring Distr
N.A.I.C.S.: 423510

Schnorr Espana S.L.U. (1)
c/ Caserna 15 - bajo, 17600, Figueres, Spain
Tel.: (34) 972513681
Web Site: http://www.schnorr.es
Spring Distr
N.A.I.C.S.: 423510

Schnorr Group France S.A.R.L. (1)
2 Rue Jacquard, 91280, Saint-Pierre-du-Perray, France
Tel.: (33) 160761632
Web Site: http://www.schnorr-group-france.fr
Spring Distr
N.A.I.C.S.: 423510

Schnorr Italia s.r.l. (1)
Viale Europa 72 Strada C/2, 20090, Cusago, Milan, Italy
Tel.: (39) 0248409301
Web Site: http://www.schnorr.it
Spring Distr
N.A.I.C.S.: 423510

Schnorr Korea Co. Ltd (1)
1414 Anyang Geonsul Tower 1112-1 Bisandong, Dongan-gu, Anyang, Gyeonggi-do, Korea (South)
Tel.: (82) 313860094
Web Site: http://www.schnorrkorea.com
Spring Distr
N.A.I.C.S.: 423510

Schnorr Shanghai Trading Co., Ltd. (1)
Rm 2611 Bldg A No 325 Tianyaoqiao Rd, Xuhui District, Shanghai, 200030, China
Tel.: (86) 2133632270
Spring Distr
N.A.I.C.S.: 423510

SCHOBRUNN PARIS SA
121 Avenue des Champs Elysees, 75008, Paris, France
Tel.: (33) 172 718 599
Web Site:
http://www.schobrunnparis.com
MLSCH—(EUR)
Sales Range: Less than $1 Million
Hair Care Product Mfr & Distr
N.A.I.C.S.: 326299
Patrick Ilardi (CEO)

SCHOELLER HOLDINGS LTD.

AND PRIVATE COMPANIES

Columbia House 21 Spyrou Kyprianou, PO Box 51624, Limassol, 4042, Cyprus
Tel.: (357) 25320900
Web Site: http://www.schoeller-holdings.com
Year Founded: 1978
Sales Range: $1-4.9 Billion
Emp.: 8,000
Holding Company; Ship Management, Ship Owning & Liner Services; Other Various Interests Including Restaurants & Hotels
N.A.I.C.S.: 551112
Heinrich Schoeller *(Chm)*

Subsidiaries:

Columbia Beach Resort Pissouri (1)
PO Box 54042, 3779, Limassol, Cyprus
Tel.: (357) 25833000
Web Site: http://www.columbia-hotels.com
Sales Range: $75-99.9 Million
Emp.: 300
Hotel & Resort Operations
N.A.I.C.S.: 721110
Stelios Kizis *(Gen Mgr)*

Columbia Beachotel Pissouri (1)
PO Box 54042, 3779, Limassol, Cyprus
Tel.: (357) 25833333
Web Site: http://www.columbia-hotels.com
Sales Range: $10-24.9 Million
Emp.: 30
Hotel Operations
N.A.I.C.S.: 721110
Stelios Kizis *(Gen Mgr)*

Columbia Hotel Casino Travemuende (1)
Kaiserallee 2, Lubeck, 23570, Travemuende, Germany
Tel.: (49) 45023080
Web Site: http://www.columbia-hotels.de
Sales Range: $10-24.9 Million
Emp.: 50
Hotel & Casino Operations
N.A.I.C.S.: 721120
Marco Steinberg *(Mgr-Mktg)*

Columbia Hotel Ruesselsheim (1)
Stahlstrasse 2-4, 65428, Russelsheim, Germany
Tel.: (49) 61428760
Web Site: http://www.columbia-hotels.de
Sales Range: $10-24.9 Million
Emp.: 40
Hotel Operations
N.A.I.C.S.: 721110
Mike Hoffmann *(Gen Mgr)*

Columbia Objekt Gmbh (1)
Frankenstrasse 35, Hamburg, 20097, Germany
Tel.: (49) 40 36 13 04 888
Web Site: http://www.columbia-objekt.de
Sales Range: $50-74.9 Million
Emp.: 10
Apartment Rentals & Sales
N.A.I.C.S.: 531110
Carsten Sommerhage *(Gen Mgr)*

Columbia Projektentwicklung GmbH (1)
Grosse elb str 275, Hamburg, 22767, Germany
Tel.: (49) 40361304860
Web Site: http://www.columbia-objekt.de
Sales Range: $50-74.9 Million
Emp.: 10
Apartment Rentals & Sales
N.A.I.C.S.: 531110
Carsten Sommerhage *(Gen Mgr)*

Columbia Shipmanagement Ltd. (1)
21 Spyrou Kyprianou Ave Yermasoyia, Limassol, 4042, Cyprus
Tel.: (357) 25320900
Web Site: http://www.columbia-shipmanagement.com
Sales Range: $75-99.9 Million
Emp.: 250
Ship Management Services
N.A.I.C.S.: 488390
Dirk Fry *(Mng Dir)*

Subsidiary (Non-US):

Austral Asia Line - Australia (2)
Ground Floor South Tower, 527 Gregory Terrace, Bowen Hills, 4006, QLD, Australia
Tel.: (61) 733328555
Web Site: http://www.aalshipping.com
Sales Range: $25-49.9 Million
Emp.: 20
Line Management Services
N.A.I.C.S.: 488390
Frank O. Mueller *(Gen Mgr-Oceania)*

Austral Asia Line BV (2)
Uitstraat 12, 3201 EN, Spijkenisse, Netherlands
Tel.: (31) 0181624370
Sales Range: $25-49.9 Million
Emp.: 2
Line Management Services
N.A.I.C.S.: 488390

Subsidiary (Domestic):

Bengal Tiger Line Ltd. (2)
Columbia House Dodekanison Street, 4043, Limassol, Cyprus
Tel.: (357) 25320900
Web Site: http://www.btl-feeders.com
Sales Range: $50-74.9 Million
Emp.: 330
Container Vessel Operator
N.A.I.C.S.: 483111
Heinrich Schoeller *(Chm)*

Subsidiary (Non-US):

CSM Baltija Sia (2)
20 Katrinas Dambis Business Centre Katrinas Osta 5th Floor, 1045, Riga, Latvia
Tel.: (371) 67325007
Web Site: http://www.csmlv.com
Sales Range: $25-49.9 Million
Emp.: 30
Ship Distr
N.A.I.C.S.: 488390
Elena Kononova *(Dir)*

CSM Cruise Services GmbH (2)
Grosse Elbstrasse 275, Hamburg, 227675, Germany
Tel.: (49) 40361304290
Web Site: http://www.csm-cruise-services.de
Sales Range: $25-49.9 Million
Emp.: 120
Cruise Ship Services
N.A.I.C.S.: 561520

Columbia Shipmanagement (Deutschland) GmbH (2)
Grosse Elbstrasse 275, Hamburg, 22767, Germany
Tel.: (49) 403613040
Web Site: http://www.csm-d.com
Sales Range: $25-49.9 Million
Emp.: 70
Ship Management Services
N.A.I.C.S.: 488390
C. Sommerhage *(Mng Dir)*

Columbia Shipmanagement (Netherlands) B.V. (2)
Raadhuislaan 41, 3201 EM, Spijkenisse, Netherlands
Tel.: (31) 0181614700
Sales Range: $125-149.9 Million
Ship Management Services
N.A.I.C.S.: 488390

Columbia Shipmanagement (Singapore) Pte. Ltd. (2)
9 Temesak Blvd Suntec Tower Two, X20 03 Suntec Tower 2, Singapore, 038989, Singapore
Tel.: (65) 67324144
Web Site: http://www.csmsg.com
Sales Range: $25-49.9 Million
Emp.: 29
Ship Management Services
N.A.I.C.S.: 488390

Columbia Shipmanagement (St. Petersburg) Ltd. (2)
Neptun International Business Centre 93a, Obvodny Kanal, 191119, Saint Petersburg, Russia
Tel.: (7) 8123202616
Web Site: http://csmru.com
Sales Range: $25-49.9 Million
Emp.: 10
Ship Management Services
N.A.I.C.S.: 488390
Andreas Hadjipetrou *(Co-Mng Dir)*

Columbia Shipmangement (TCM) SA (2)
367 Syngrou Ave, 17564, Palaion Faliron, Greece
Tel.: (30) 210 94 74 000
Web Site: http://www.tcsm.gr
Ship Management Services
N.A.I.C.S.: 483111
Sokratis Dimakopoulos *(Deputy Mng Dir)*

Hanse Bereederung GmbH (2)
Grosse Elbstrasse 275, 22767, Hamburg, Germany
Tel.: (49) 403613040
Web Site: http://www.hanse-bereederung.de
Sales Range: $25-49.9 Million
Emp.: 15
Container & Dry Cargo Chartering Services; Ship Sales & Purchasing
N.A.I.C.S.: 488390
Axel Schulz *(Mng Dir)*

UPT United Product Tankers GmbH & Co. KG (2)
Reodingsmarkt 20, Hamburg, 20459, Germany
Tel.: (49) 40339570
Web Site: http://www.uptankers.com
Sales Range: $25-49.9 Million
Emp.: 20
Commercial Management, Marketing, Chartering & Commercial Operations Services To the Tanker Shipping Industry
N.A.I.C.S.: 488390
Stefan Ciegelski *(Mng Dir)*

Columbia Shipmanagement Rijeka d.o.o (1)
Rikarda Katalinica Jeretova 1, 51000, Rijeka, Croatia
Tel.: (385) 51 214 701
Web Site: http://www.csm-r.com
Ship Management Services
N.A.I.C.S.: 483111
Mario Stipanicic *(Gen Mgr)*

Londa Hotel (1)
Georgiou A St, PO Box 52000, 3509, Limassol, Cyprus
Tel.: (357) 25865555
Web Site: http://www.londahotel.com
Sales Range: $10-24.9 Million
Emp.: 100
Hotel Operations
N.A.I.C.S.: 721110

Thermenhotel Viktoria Bad Griesbach (1)
Passauer Strasse 39a, 94086, Bad Griesbach, Germany
Tel.: (49) 85323090
Web Site: http://www.viktoria-badgriesbach.de
Hotel Operations
N.A.I.C.S.: 721110

trans-o-flex Schnell-Lieferdienst GmbH (1)
Hertzstrasse 10, D-69469, Weinheim, Germany (50%)
Tel.: (49) 62019880
Web Site: http://www.trans-o-flex.com
Emp.: 1,700
Freight Transportation Arrangement
N.A.I.C.S.: 488510
Wolfgang P. Albeck *(CEO & Mgmt Bd)*

SCHOELLER-BLECKMANN OILFIELD EQUIPMENT AG

Hauptstrasse 2, A-2630, Ternitz, Austria
Tel.: (43) 2630315100
Web Site: https://www.sbo.at
SBO—(VIE)
Rev.: $540,944,313
Assets: $974,635,226
Liabilities: $515,951,867
Net Worth: $458,683,359
Earnings: $81,154,759
Emp.: 1,450
Fiscal Year-end: 12/31/22
Oil Service Industry Components Mfr
N.A.I.C.S.: 333132
Norbert Zimmermann *(Chm-Supervisory Bd)*

Subsidiaries:

Accudrill L. L. C. (1)
112 Seidel St Mirion, San Antonio, TX 78124
Tel.: (210) 693-8243
Drilling Equipment Mfr
N.A.I.C.S.: 333132

BICO Drilling Tools Inc. (1)
1604 Greens Rd, Houston, TX 77032 (100%)
Tel.: (281) 590-6966
Sales Range: $50-74.9 Million
Emp.: 20
Drilling Oil & Gas Wells
N.A.I.C.S.: 213111
Sam Claytor *(Pres)*

BICO Faster Drilling Tools Inc. (1)
2107 7th Street, Nisku, T9E 7Y3, AB, Canada (100%)
Tel.: (780) 955-5969
Web Site: http://www.bicodrilling.com
Sales Range: $25-49.9 Million
Emp.: 14
Oil & Gas Field Machinery & Equipment Mfr
N.A.I.C.S.: 333132
Bude Fagerie *(Mng Dir)*

DSI FZE (1)
10 ROUNDABOUT ROAD 911, PO Box 30576, Jebel Ali Free Zone, Dubai, United Arab Emirates
Tel.: (971) 48808228
Web Site: https://www.dsi-pbl.com
Oil Service Industry Components Mfr
N.A.I.C.S.: 333132

Darron Holdings Limited (1)
West Bawtry Road, Rotherham, S60 2XL, United Kingdom (100%)
Tel.: (44) 1709722638
Web Site: http://www.darron-sbo.com
Sales Range: $75-99.9 Million
Emp.: 120
Holding Company
N.A.I.C.S.: 551112

Darron Oil Tools Limited (1)
West Bawtry Road, Rotherham, S60 2XL, United Kingdom (100%)
Tel.: (44) 1709722600
Web Site: http://www.darron-sbo.com
Sales Range: $25-49.9 Million
Emp.: 100
Oil & Gas Field Machinery & Equipment Mfr
N.A.I.C.S.: 333132

Darron Tool & Engineering Limited (1)
West Bawtry Road, Canklow Meadow Ind Est, Rotherham, S60 2XL, United Kingdom (100%)
Tel.: (44) 1709722600
Web Site: http://www.darron-sbo.com
Sales Range: $25-49.9 Million
Emp.: 100
Oil & Gas Field Machinery & Equipment Mfr
N.A.I.C.S.: 333132

Godwin-SBO L.P. (1)
28825 Katy Brookshire Rd, Katy, TX 77494-8296 (100%)
Tel.: (281) 371-5400
Sales Range: $50-74.9 Million
Emp.: 150
Commercial & Service Industry Machinery Mfr
N.A.I.C.S.: 333310
Mike Corliss *(Pres & Gen Mgr)*

Knust-SBO Ltd. (1)
3110 Dunvale Rd, Houston, TX 77063-4410 (100%)
Tel.: (713) 785-1060
Web Site: http://www.knust.com
Sales Range: $50-74.9 Million
Emp.: 170
Commercial & Service Industry Machinery Mfr
N.A.I.C.S.: 333310
Bo Jakobsen *(Controller)*

Subsidiary (Non-US):

Knust-SBO Far East Pte Ltd. (2)
9 Tuas Loop, Singapore, 637340, Singapore
Tel.: (65) 6681 9500
Web Site: http://www.knust.com.sj
Emp.: 30
Oil Service Industry Components Mfr

SCHOELLER-BLECKMANN OILFIELD EQUIPMENT AG

Schoeller-Bleckmann Oilfield Equipment AG—(Continued)
N.A.I.C.S.: 333132
John Clark (Mng Dir)

SB Darron Pte. Ltd. (1)
14 Gul St 3, 629268, Singapore, Singapore (100%)
Tel.: (65) 68614302
Web Site: http://www.sbdarron.co.sg
Sales Range: $25-49.9 Million
Emp.: 26
Oil & Gas Field Machinery & Equipment Mfr
N.A.I.C.S.: 333132
Steve Geste (Mng Dir)

Schoeller-Bleckmann America Inc. (1)
1105 Northmarket St, Wilmington, DE 19801 (100%)
Tel.: (302) 478-6160
Oil & Gas Field Machinery & Equipment Mfr
N.A.I.C.S.: 333132

Schoeller-Bleckmann Darron (Aberdeen) Limited (1)
Howemoss Terrace Kirkhill Industrial Estate, Dyce, Aberdeen, AB21 0GR, United Kingdom
Tel.: (44) 1224 799600
Web Site: http://www.sbdl.co.uk
Sales Range: $25-49.9 Million
Emp.: 50
Drilling Equipment Mfr
N.A.I.C.S.: 333132

Schoeller-Bleckmann Darron Limited (1)
Howemoss Terrace Kirkhill Industrial Estate Dyce, Aberdeen, AB21 0GR, United Kingdom (100%)
Tel.: (44) 1224799600
Web Site: http://www.sbdl.co.uk
Sales Range: $25-49.9 Million
Emp.: 50
Oil & Gas Field Machinery & Equipment Mfr
N.A.I.C.S.: 333132

Schoeller-Bleckmann Darron Ltd. (1)
Industrial Zone Panel XI Noyabrsk, 629800, Yamala, Nenetsky, Russia
Tel.: (7) 3496342601
Web Site: http://sbdr.ru
Oil Service Industry Components Mfr
N.A.I.C.S.: 333132

Schoeller-Bleckmann Energy Services L.L.C. (1)
712 Saint Etienne Rd, Broussard, LA 70518-6013 (100%)
Tel.: (337) 837-2030
Web Site: https://www.sbesllc.com
Sales Range: $25-49.9 Million
Emp.: 75
Mining Machinery & Equipment Mfr
N.A.I.C.S.: 333131

Schoeller-Bleckmann Oilfield Equipment Middle East FZE (1)
Roundabout 10 Road 911 Jebel Ali Free Zone, Jebel Ali FZE, Dubai, United Arab Emirates (100%)
Tel.: (971) 48834228
Web Site: https://www.sboe.ae
Sales Range: $50-74.9 Million
Emp.: 7
Oil & Gas Operations Services
N.A.I.C.S.: 213112
Paul Wright (Mng Dir)

Schoeller-Bleckmann Oilfield Equipment Vietnam L.L.C. (1)
Lot B2 6 Street D3 Dong An 2 Industrial Zone, Thu Dau Mot, Binh Duong, Vietnam
Tel.: (84) 2743589590
Web Site: https://www.sobevn.com
Oil Service Industry Components Mfr
N.A.I.C.S.: 333132
Tom Dorfmeister (Gen Dir)

Schoeller-Bleckmann Oilfield Technology GmbH & Co. KG (1)
Hauptstrasse 2, 2630, Ternitz, Austria (100%)
Tel.: (43) 26303150
Web Site: https://sbot.co.at
Emp.: 350
Oil & Gas Field Machinery & Equipment Mfr
N.A.I.C.S.: 333132

Schoeller-Bleckmann Sales Co. L.P. (1)
11525 Brittmoore Park Dr, Houston, TX 77041 (100%)
Tel.: (713) 856-6500
Web Site: https://www.sbsaleshouston.com
Sales Range: $25-49.9 Million
Emp.: 12
Oil & Gas Field Machinery & Equipment Mfr
N.A.I.C.S.: 333132

Schoeller-Bleckmann de Mexico S.A. de C.V. (1)
Calle C Num 517-5, Parque Industrial Almacentro, 66600, Apodaca, Mexico (100%)
Tel.: (52) 8113443343
Web Site: http://www.sbmex.com
Sales Range: $25-49.9 Million
Emp.: 85
Oil & Gas Field Machinery & Equipment Mfr
N.A.I.C.S.: 333132
Ezequiel Villarrdal (Mgr-Ops)

Schoeller-Bleckmann do Brasil Ltda. (1)
Rua Projetada 02 Area 06, Fazend Bela Vista Imboassica, 27901-000, Macae, RJ, Brazil
Tel.: (55) 22 2773 3947
Oil Service Industry Components Mfr
N.A.I.C.S.: 333132

Techman Engineering Limited (1)
Techman House Broombank Park Chesterfield Trading Estate, Sheepbridge, Chesterfield, S41 9RT, United Kingdom
Tel.: (44) 1246261385
Web Site: http://www.techman-engineering.co.uk
Emp.: 125
Oil Service Industry Components Mfr
N.A.I.C.S.: 333132
Simon Oxstring (Mng Dir)

SCHOFFEL SPORTBEKLEIDUNG GMBH
Ludwig Schoffel Strasse 15, Schwabmunchen, 86830, Germany
Tel.: (49) 823250060
Web Site: http://www.schoeffel.de
Sales Range: $100-124.9 Million
Emp.: 150
Outdoor Equipment Mfr
N.A.I.C.S.: 339920
Peter Schoffel (Mng Dir)

SCHOLAR EDUCATION GROUP
Room 2601 Building 2-A InJoy Shangmeilin, Shenzhen, 518049, Guangdong, China
Tel.: (86) 75588240666   Ky
Web Site: http://www.skledu.com
Year Founded: 2012
1769—(HKG)
Rev.: $127,428,587
Assets: $116,526,623
Liabilities: $67,875,554
Net Worth: $48,651,069
Earnings: ($4,138,509)
Emp.: 1,552
Fiscal Year-end: 12/31/21
Educational Support Services
N.A.I.C.S.: 611710
Qiyuan Chen (Founder & Chm)

SCHOLARIS INTERNATIONAL LIMITED
1A Newlyn Street, 6104, Belmont, WA, Australia
Tel.: (61) 862412500
Web Site: http://www.scholarislg.com
Sales Range: $10-24.9 Million
Emp.: 20
Educational Software Producer
N.A.I.C.S.: 513210
Justin Cantrell (CEO)

SCHOLIUM GROUP PLC
94 New Bond Street, London, W1S 1SJ, United Kingdom
Tel.: (44) 2074930876   UK
Web Site: https://www.scholiumgroup.com
Year Founded: 1979
SCHO—(AIM)
Rev.: $8,185,694
Assets: $16,155,510
Liabilities: $3,634,616
Net Worth: $12,520,894
Earnings: ($593,324)
Emp.: 17
Fiscal Year-end: 03/31/21
Rare & Antiquarian Books & Works on Paper Retailer & Distr
N.A.I.C.S.: 459210
Bernard J. Shapero (Founder, CEO & Mng Dir-Shapero Rare Books)

Subsidiaries:

Mayfair Philatelics Limited (1)
Vintage House 37 Albert Embankment, Lambeth, London, SE1 7TL, United Kingdom
Tel.: (44) 2030193630
Web Site: http://www.mpastamps.com
Book Retailer
N.A.I.C.S.: 459210

Shapero Rare Books Limited (1)
106 New Bond Street 1st Floor, London, W1S 1DN, United Kingdom
Tel.: (44) 2074930876
Web Site: https://www.shapero.com
Book Retailer
N.A.I.C.S.: 459210

SCHOLS & VOLKMER GMBH
Schwalbacher Strasse 72, 65183, Wiesbaden, Germany
Tel.: (49) 611 180 99 0
Web Site: http://www.s-v.de
Sales Range: $10-24.9 Million
Emp.: 100
Computer Software & Applications
N.A.I.C.S.: 513210
Peter Post (Mng Dir)

SCHOLZ INDUSTRIES PTY LTD.
203 Princes Highway, PO Box 5023, Hallam, 3803, VIC, Australia
Tel.: (61) 3 8781 0000
Web Site: http://www.scholzgroup.com.au
Ventilation & Lighting Equipment Mfr
N.A.I.C.S.: 333413
Erik Scholz (Mng Dir)

Subsidiaries:

Rayson RTK Pty Ltd. (1)
203 Princes Hwy, Hallam, 3803, Victoria, Australia
Tel.: (61) 300 669 916
Web Site: http://www.aysonrtk.com.au
Sales Range: $25-49.9 Million
Emp.: 20
Laser Welding Equipment Mfr
N.A.I.C.S.: 333992
Frank McCarthy (Gen Mgr)

SCHON TEXTILES LIMITED
Schon Centre I I Chundrigar Road, Karachi, Pakistan
Tel.: (92) 21 2636000
Textile Products Mfr
N.A.I.C.S.: 313110

SCHOOLNET INDIA LIMITED
IL&FS Financial Ctr 3rd Fl plot Number C 22 G Block Bandra Kurla Comp, Bandra East, Mumbai, 400 051, India
Tel.: (91) 2266947575
Web Site: http://www.schoolnetindia.com
Sales Range: $25-49.9 Million
Emp.: 150
Educational Materials Via Internet & E-Commerce
N.A.I.C.S.: 611710

Subsidiaries:

IL&FS Cluster Development Initiative Limited (1)
IL FS Cluster NTBCL Building DND Toll Plaza, Rao Tula Ram Marg, Noida, 201301, India
Tel.: (91) 1202459200
Web Site: http://www.ilfsclusters.com
Business Management Consulting Services
N.A.I.C.S.: 541611
R. C. M. Reddy (CEO & Mng Dir)

SCHOONER CAPITAL, CORP.
1110 8 King St E, Toronto, M5C 1B5, ON, Canada
Tel.: (416) 804-9032
Web Site: http://www.roomlinx.com
Year Founded: 2014
Asset Management Services
N.A.I.C.S.: 523940
Marc Blythe (Pres)

SCHORGHUBER STIFTUNG & CO. HOLDING KG
Denninger Strasse 165, 81925, Munich, Germany
Tel.: (49) 89923803   De
Web Site: http://www.sug-munich.com
Sales Range: $1-4.9 Billion
Emp.: 6,300
Holding Company Services
N.A.I.C.S.: 551112
Klaus N. Naeve (Chm-Exec Bd)

Subsidiaries:

Arabella Hospitality GmbH & Co. KG (1)
Englschalkinger Strasse 12, 81925, Munich, Germany
Tel.: (49) 89930010
Web Site: http://www.arabella.de
Sales Range: $50-74.9 Million
Emp.: 100
Holding Company; Hotel & Golf Course Owner & Operator
N.A.I.C.S.: 551112

Subsidiary (Domestic):

Bavaria Sport & Freizeit GmbH (2)
Englschalkinger Strasse 12, D-81925, Munich, Germany
Tel.: (49) 89 93001 6494
Web Site: http://www.arabellagolf.de
Golf & Country Club Operator
N.A.I.C.S.: 713910

Bavaria International Aircraft Leasing GmbH & Co. KG (1)
Ludwig-Ganghofer-Strasse 6, 82031, Grunwald, Germany
Tel.: (49) 899238237
Web Site: http://www.bavaria-ial.com
Sales Range: $50-74.9 Million
Emp.: 4
Aircraft Leasing & Sales Financing Services
N.A.I.C.S.: 532411
Karsten Sensen (Mng Dir)

Bayerische Bau und Immobilien GmbH & Co. KG (1)
Denninger Strasse 165, D-81925, Munich, Germany
Tel.: (49) 89923804
Web Site: http://www.bbikg.de
Sales Range: $650-699.9 Million
Emp.: 600
Holding Company; Residential & Commercial Real Estate Development, Construction & Property Management
N.A.I.C.S.: 551112
Jurgen Bullesbach (Chm-Mgmt Bd & CEO)

Subsidiary (Domestic):

Bayerische Hausbau GmbH (2)
Denninger Strasse 165, 81925, Munich, Germany
Tel.: (49) 89923804
Web Site: http://www.hausbau.de

AND PRIVATE COMPANIES — SCHRODERS PLC

Residential Real Estate Development & Construction Services
N.A.I.C.S.: 236116
Jurgen Bullesbach *(Chm-Mgmt Bd)*

Bayerische Hausverwaltung GmbH (2)
Englschalkinger Strasse 12, Munich, D-81925, Germany
Tel.: (49) 8993001200
Web Site: http://www.bhv-verwaltung.de
Residential & Commercial Property Management Services
N.A.I.C.S.: 531311
Jurgen Bullesbach *(Chm-Mgmt Bd)*

Bayerische Immobilien GmbH & Co. KG (2)
Denninger Strasse 169, Munich, D-81925, Germany
Tel.: (49) 89923804
Web Site: http://www.bayerische-immobilien.de
Commercial Property Acquisition & Leasing Services
N.A.I.C.S.: 531120

Bayerische Hausbau Immobilien GmbH & Co. KG (1)
Inselkammerstrasse 14, 82008, Unterhaching, Germany
Tel.: (49) 8992387976
Real Estate Services
N.A.I.C.S.: 531390

Brau Holding International GmbH & Co. KGaA (1)
Denninger Strasse 165, D-81925, Munich, Germany (50.1%)
Tel.: (49) 89923808
Web Site: http://www.brauholdinginternational.com
Holding Company; Beer Breweries Owner & Operator
N.A.I.C.S.: 551112

Subsidiary (Domestic):

Furstlich Furstenbergische Brauerei GmbH & Co. KG (2)
Postplatz 1-4, D-78166, Donaueschingen, Germany
Tel.: (49) 771860
Web Site: http://www.fuerstenberg.de
Beer Brewer & Whslr
N.A.I.C.S.: 312120
Dirk Wagenfuhrer *(Dir-Sls-Intl Div)*

Subsidiary (Domestic):

Privat-Brauerei Schmucker GmbH & Co. KG (3)
Hauptstrasse 89, 64756, Mossautal, Germany
Tel.: (49) 60617020
Web Site: http://www.schmucker-bier.de
Beer Brewer & Whslr
N.A.I.C.S.: 312120
Willy Schmidt *(Mng Dir)*

Subsidiary (Domestic):

Kulmbacher Brauerei AG (2)
Lichtenfelser Strasse 9, Kulmbach, 95326, Germany
Tel.: (49) 92217050
Web Site: http://www.kulmbacher.de
Sales Range: $75-99.9 Million
Emp.: 500
Beer Brewer & Whslr; Bottled Water Mfr
N.A.I.C.S.: 312120

Holding (Domestic):

Paulaner Brauerei GmbH & Co. KG (2)
Hochstrasse 75, Munich, 81541, Germany (50%)
Tel.: (49) 89480050
Web Site: http://www.paulaner.de
Sales Range: $150-199.9 Million
Emp.: 800
Beer Brewer & Whslr
N.A.I.C.S.: 312120
Andreas Steinfatt *(Mng Dir)*

Subsidiary (Domestic):

Privatbrauerei Hoepfner GmbH (2)
Haid-und-Neu-Strasse 18, Karlsruhe,
76131, Germany
Tel.: (49) 72161830
Web Site: http://www.hoepfner.de
Emp.: 80
Beer Brewery Mfr
N.A.I.C.S.: 312120
Christian Lorenz *(Mgr-Logistics)*

SCHORN & GROH GMBH
Printzstrasse 15-17, 76139, Karlsruhe, Germany
Tel.: (49) 721962450
Web Site: http://www.sg-veneers.com
Year Founded: 1961
Sales Range: $25-49.9 Million
Wood Product Distr
N.A.I.C.S.: 423310
Axel Groh *(Co-Mng Dir)*

SCHOTT MUSIC GMBH & CO. KG
Weihergarten 5, 55116, Mainz, Germany
Tel.: (49) 61312460
Web Site: http://www.de.schott-music.com
Year Founded: 1770
Sales Range: $25-49.9 Million
Emp.: 180
Music Publishing Services
N.A.I.C.S.: 512230
Peter Hanser-Strecker *(CEO)*

Subsidiaries:

Bienvenido a Schott Music S.L. (1)
Alcala 70, 28009, Madrid, Spain
Tel.: (34) 915770751
Musical Instrument Distr
N.A.I.C.S.: 459140
Carlos Perez Cancio *(Pres)*

Schott Music Co. Ltd. (1)
Hiratomi Bldg 1-10-1 Uchikanda, Chiyoda-ku, Tokyo, 101-0047, Japan
Tel.: (81) 366952450
Web Site: http://www.schottjapan.com
Musical Instrument Distr
N.A.I.C.S.: 459140
Yuki Yokota *(Pres-Editorial & Promotion)*

Schott Music Corporation (1)
254 W 31st St Fl 15, New York, NY 10001
Tel.: (212) 461-6940
Musical Instrument Distr
N.A.I.C.S.: 459140
Norman Ryan *(VP)*

Schott Music Ltd (1)
48 Great Marlborough Street, London, W1F 7BB, United Kingdom
Tel.: (44) 20 7534 0710
Web Site: http://www.schott-music.co.uk
Musical Instrument Distr
N.A.I.C.S.: 459140
Heike Hoeffner *(Head-Acct)*

Schott Music Publishers (Canada) Ltd. (1)
28 Tarlton Road, Toronto, M5P 2M4, ON, Canada
Tel.: (416) 489-4155
Musical Instrument Distr
N.A.I.C.S.: 459140

WEGA-VERLAG GmbH (1)
Weihergarten 5, 55116, Mainz, Germany
Tel.: (49) 6131246451
Musical Instrument Distr
N.A.I.C.S.: 459140
Ute Maren Schubert *(Head-Production)*

SCHRAMEK GMBH
A-1230 Vienna, Sulzengasse 12, Germany
Tel.: (43) 917860
Web Site: https://schramek.at
Management Services
N.A.I.C.S.: 926150

SCHRAUBEN UND DRAHT UNION GMBH
Wallbaumweg 45-49, 44894, Bochum, Germany
Tel.: (49) 2342690
Web Site: http://www.schrauben-und-draht-union.de
Rev.: $33,121,400
Emp.: 76
Bolt Nut Screw Rivet & Washer Mfr
N.A.I.C.S.: 332722
Frederik Mischo *(Chm & Mng Partner)*

Subsidiaries:

SDU TECHNIKA ZLACZENIOWA SLASK Sp. z o.o. (1)
ul Zagorska 56, 42-500, Bedzin, Poland
Tel.: (48) 322 601616
Fastener Distr
N.A.I.C.S.: 423710

SCHREDER S.A.
Rue de Lusambo 71, 1190, Brussels, Belgium
Tel.: (32) 2 332 01 06
Web Site: http://www.schreder.com
Emp.: 2,600
Outdoor Lighting Equipment Mfr
N.A.I.C.S.: 335132
Andre Papoular *(CEO)*

SCHREIBER-RELIUS
10 Rue Michael Faraday, Ostwald, 67540, France
Tel.: (33) 3 88 67 45 42
Web Site: http://www.schreiberrelius.com
Paint Mfr & Distr
N.A.I.C.S.: 325510
Pierre Schreiber *(Pres)*

SCHRODER ASIAN TOTAL RETURN INVESTMENT COMPANY PLC
1 London Wall Place, London, EC2Y 5AU, United Kingdom
Tel.: (44) 2076583206
ATR—(LSE)
Rev.: $21,203,513
Assets: $819,692,222
Liabilities: $70,577,001
Net Worth: $749,115,221
Earnings: $49,300,171
Fiscal Year-end: 12/31/21
Investment Management Service
N.A.I.C.S.: 523940
Sarah MacAulay *(Chm)*

SCHRODER REAL ESTATE INVESTMENT TRUST LIMITED
Trafalgar Court Les Banques St Peter Port, London, GY1 2JA, United Kingdom
Tel.: (44) 32038609400 GY
Year Founded: 2004
SREI—(LSE)
Rev.: $32,019,504
Assets: $714,551,552
Liabilities: $226,549,136
Net Worth: $488,002,416
Earnings: $117,181,944
Fiscal Year-end: 03/31/22
Other Activities Related to Real Estate
N.A.I.C.S.: 531390

SCHRODER UK MID CAP FUND PLC
Schroder Unit Trusts Limited 1 London Wall Place, London, EC2Y 5AU, United Kingdom
Tel.: (44) 2076586000
Web Site: http://www.schroders.com
SCP—(LSE)
Rev.: $11,867,600
Assets: $300,238,066
Liabilities: $28,025,462
Net Worth: $272,212,605
Earnings: $42,231,700
Fiscal Year-end: 09/30/23
Other Financial Vehicles
N.A.I.C.S.: 525990
Andy Brough *(Mgr-Fund)*

SCHRODERS PLC
1 London Wall Place, London, EC2Y 5AU, United Kingdom
Tel.: (44) 2076586000 UK
Web Site: https://www.schroders.com
Year Founded: 1804
SDR—(OTCIQ)
Rev.: $2,279,816,280
Assets: $16,820,198,640
Liabilities: $13,288,403,160
Net Worth: $3,531,795,480
Earnings: $383,320,080
Emp.: 5,934
Fiscal Year-end: 12/31/22
Investment & Asset Management Banking Services
N.A.I.C.S.: 523150
Graham Staples *(Sec)*

Subsidiaries:

Aspect8 Limited (1)
Holmwood House Broadlands Business Campus Langhurstwood Road, Horsham, RH12 4QP, West Sussex, United Kingdom
Tel.: (44) 140 333 1400
Web Site: https://www.aspect8.co.uk
Financial Services
N.A.I.C.S.: 541611
Tracy Waller *(Mgr)*

Best Practice IFA Group Limited (1)
Holmwood House Broadlands Business Campus Langhurstwood Road, Horsham, RH12 4QP, West Sussex, United Kingdom
Tel.: (44) 1403334411
Web Site: http://www.bestpractice.co.uk
Financial Services
N.A.I.C.S.: 541611

Champain Financial Services Limited (1)
Bawtry Selsfield Road, Ardingly, Haywards Heath, RH17 6TJ, West Sussex, United Kingdom
Tel.: (44) 1444229520
Web Site: https://www.champain.co.uk
Emp.: 500
Pension Financial Services
N.A.I.C.S.: 525110

City Capital Analysis Limited (1)
Orchard House Park Lane, Reigate, RH2 8JX, Surrey, United Kingdom
Tel.: (44) 2070787777
Web Site: http://www.city-cap.co.uk
Financial Services
N.A.I.C.S.: 541611
John Breen *(Dir-Wealth Mgmt)*

Consultora Schroders, S.A. de C.V. (1)
Montes Urales 760 Desp 101 Col Lomas De Chapultepec, DF 11000, Mexico, Mexico
Tel.: (52) 5511001030
Investment Management Service
N.A.I.C.S.: 523999

Evolution Wealth Network Limited (1)
Holmwood House Broadlands Business Campus Langhurstwood Road, Horsham, RH12 4QP, West Sussex, United Kingdom
Tel.: (44) 1403334411
Web Site: http://www.evowealth.co.uk
Financial Services
N.A.I.C.S.: 541611

Fusion Wealth Limited (1)
Holmwood House Broadlands Business Campus Langhurstwood Road, Horsham, RH12 4QP, West Sussex, United Kingdom
Tel.: (44) 140 333 4411
Web Site: https://www.fusionwealth.co.uk
Financial Services
N.A.I.C.S.: 541611

Korea Schroder Fund Management Limited (1)
33 Gutter Lane, London, EC2V 8AS, United Kingdom
Tel.: (44) 171 658 6000

SCHRODERS PLC

Schroders plc—(Continued)
Web Site: http://www.schroders.com
Investment & Asset Management Banking
N.A.I.C.S.: 523150

PT Schroder Investment Management Indonesia (1) (85%)
Tel.: (62) 2129655100
Web Site: https://www.schroders.com
Sales Range: $50-74.9 Million
Emp.: 40
Investment & Asset Management Banking
N.A.I.C.S.: 523150

Redbourne Wealth Management Ltd. (1)
Belmont House Shrewsbury Business Park, Shrewsbury, SY2 6LG, United Kingdom
Tel.: (44) 174 327 3273
Web Site: https://www.redbournewm.com
Financial Services
N.A.I.C.S.: 541611
Michelle Charlton (Mgr-Client Support)

Schroder & Co Bank AG (1)
Tel.: (41) 442501111
Web Site: https://www.schroders.com
Emp.: 500
Commercial Banking Services
N.A.I.C.S.: 522110

Schroder & Co Banque SA (1) (100%)
Rue de Jargonnant 2, PO Box 3655, 1207, Geneva, Switzerland
Tel.: (41) 228184111
Web Site: http://www.schroder.com
Sales Range: $50-74.9 Million
Emp.: 40
Investment & Asset Management Banking
N.A.I.C.S.: 523150

Schroder & Co. (1) (100%)
31 Gresham St, London, EC2V 7QA, United Kingdom
Tel.: (44) 2076586000
Web Site: http://www.schroders.com
Sales Range: $700-749.9 Million
Emp.: 1,200
Investment & Asset Management Banking
N.A.I.C.S.: 523150

Schroder & Co. (Asia) Limited (1)
138 Market Street 23-02 CapitaGreen, Singapore, 048946, Singapore
Tel.: (65) 68007100
Sales Range: $50-74.9 Million
Emp.: 20
Commercial Banking Services
N.A.I.C.S.: 522110

Schroder AIDA SAS (1)
1 Rue Euler, 75008, Paris, France
Tel.: (33) 153858585
Investment Fund Services
N.A.I.C.S.: 525910

Schroder Adveq Management AG (1)
Affolternstrasse 56, 8050, Zurich, Switzerland
Tel.: (41) 58 445 5555
Web Site: http://www.schroderadveq.com
Sales Range: $50-74.9 Million
Emp.: 60
Private Equity Firm & Alternative Investment Services
N.A.I.C.S.: 523940
Tim Creed (Head-Investments-Europe)

Subsidiary (Non-US):

Adveq (Shanghai) Equity Investment Management Co., Ltd. (2)
Unit 832 Level 8 Shanghai International Finance Center Tower, 2 8 Century Avenue Pudong, Shanghai, 200120, China
Tel.: (86) 21 6062 7191
Real Estate Manangement Services
N.A.I.C.S.: 531390

Adveq Investment Management (Beijing) Co., Ltd. (2)
1902 19th Floor Beijing Excel Centre 6 Wudinghou Street, Xicheng District, Beijing, 100033, China
Tel.: (86) 10 8801 3000
Real Estate Manangement Services
N.A.I.C.S.: 531390

Adveq Management (Deutschland) GmbH (2)
An der Welle 4, 60322, Frankfurt am Main, Germany
Tel.: (49) 69 759 38 586
Real Estate Manangement Services
N.A.I.C.S.: 531390

Adveq Management (Hong Kong) Limited (2)
Suite 616 100 Queen's Road, Central, China (Hong Kong)
Tel.: (852) 8208 2780
Real Estate Manangement Services
N.A.I.C.S.: 531390

Adveq Management (UK) Limited (2)
42 Brook Street, London, W1K 5DB, United Kingdom
Tel.: (44) 203 008 7179
Real Estate Manangement Services
N.A.I.C.S.: 531390

Subsidiary (US):

Adveq Management US, Inc. (2)
100 Park Ave 28th Fl, New York, NY 10017
Tel.: (212) 488-5330
Web Site: http://www.adveq.com
Real Estate Manangement Services
N.A.I.C.S.: 531390

Schroder Cayman Bank and Trust Company Limited (1) (100%)
Harbour Center, PO Box 1040, Georgetown, Grand Cayman, Cayman Islands
Tel.: (345) 9492849
Web Site: http://www.schroders.com
Sales Range: $50-74.9 Million
Emp.: 6
Investment & Asset Management Banking
N.A.I.C.S.: 523150

Schroder Executor & Trustee Company Limited (1) (100%)
1 London Wall Place, London, EC2Y 5AU, United Kingdom
Tel.: (44) 2076586000
Web Site: http://www.schroders.com
Sales Range: $700-749.9 Million
Emp.: 1,500
Investment & Asset Management Banking
N.A.I.C.S.: 523150

Schroder Fund Advisors LLC (1)
7 Bryant Pk, New York, NY 10018-3706
Tel.: (212) 641-3800
Investment Fund Services
N.A.I.C.S.: 525910

Schroder Investment Management (Australasia) Limited (1) (100%)
Level 20 Angel Place 123 Pitt Street, Sydney, 2000, NSW, Australia
Tel.: (61) 29 210 9200
Web Site: https://www.schroders.com
Sales Range: $50-74.9 Million
Emp.: 70
Investment & Asset Management Banking
N.A.I.C.S.: 523150

Schroder Investment Management (Europe) S.A. (1)
5 Rue Hohenhof, 1736, Senningerberg, Luxembourg
Tel.: (352) 341342444
Web Site: https://www.schroders.com
Investment Management Service
N.A.I.C.S.: 523940

Schroder Investment Management (Hong Kong) Limited (1) (100%)
33/F Tower Two Pacific Place 88 Queensway, Hong Kong, China (Hong Kong)
Tel.: (852) 25211633
Web Site: https://www.schroders.com
Sales Range: $100-124.9 Million
Emp.: 130
Investment & Asset Management Banking
N.A.I.C.S.: 523150
Jason Yu (Head-Multiasset Product-North Asia)

Schroder Investment Management (Japan) Limited (1)
21st Floor Marunouchi Trust Tower Main Building 1-8-3 Marunouchi, Chiyoda-ku, Tokyo, 100-0005, Japan
Tel.: (81) 352931500
Web Site: https://www.schroders.com
Investment & Asset Management Banking Services
N.A.I.C.S.: 523150

Schroder Investment Management (Luxembourg) S.A. (1) (100%)
5 Rue Hohenhof, 1736, Senningerberg, Luxembourg
Tel.: (352) 341342202
Web Site: http://www.schroders.lu
Sales Range: $100-124.9 Million
Emp.: 240
Investment & Asset Management Banking
N.A.I.C.S.: 523150

Schroder Investment Management (Singapore) Ltd. (1) (100%)
Tel.: (65) 68007000
Web Site: https://www.schroders.com
Sales Range: $100-124.9 Million
Emp.: 139
Investment & Asset Management Banking
N.A.I.C.S.: 523150

Schroder Investment Management (Taiwan) Limited (1)
9F 108 Sec 5 Hsin-Yi Road, Hsin-YI District, Taipei, 11047, Taiwan
Tel.: (886) 287236888
Investment Management Service
N.A.I.C.S.: 523999

Schroder Investment Management (UK) Limited (1) (100%)
1 London Wall Place, London, EC2Y 5AU, United Kingdom
Tel.: (44) 207 658 6000
Web Site: http://www.schroders.com
Sales Range: $700-749.9 Million
Emp.: 1,100
Investment & Asset Management Banking
N.A.I.C.S.: 523150

Schroder Investment Management A/S (1)
Bredgade 45c 2, 1260, Copenhagen, Denmark
Tel.: (45) 3315 1822
Web Site: http://www.schroders.com
Investment Management Service
N.A.I.C.S.: 523999

Schroder Investment Management Benelux N.V. (1) (100%)
Aert Van Nesstraat 25 R, 3012 CA, Rotterdam, Netherlands
Tel.: (31) 102757111
Web Site: http://www.schroders.nl
Sales Range: $50-74.9 Million
Emp.: 5
Investment & Asset Management Banking
N.A.I.C.S.: 523150

Schroder Investment Management Brasil Dtzm SA (1) (100%)
Avenida Presidente Juscelino Kubitschek 1327 Faria Lima, Itaim Bibi 12 Andar-cj 121, Sao Paulo, 04543-011, Brazil
Tel.: (55) 113 054 5155
Web Site: https://www.schroders.com
Sales Range: $50-74.9 Million
Emp.: 19
Investment & Asset Management Banking
N.A.I.C.S.: 523150
Daniel Celano (Head-Country)

Schroder Investment Management Fondsmaeglerselskab A/S (1)
21 Storestrant St, 1255, Copenhagen, Denmark
Tel.: (45) 33151822
Web Site: http://www.schroders.com
Sales Range: $50-74.9 Million
Emp.: 6
Investment & Asset Management Banking
N.A.I.C.S.: 523150
Lars K. Jelgren (Sr Dir-Client)

Schroder Investment Management GmbH (1)
Taunustor 1, 60311, Frankfurt am Main, Germany
Tel.: (49) 69 97 57 17 0
Sales Range: $50-74.9 Million
Emp.: 35
Investment Management Service
N.A.I.C.S.: 523999
Achim Kuessner (Mng Dir)

Schroder Investment Management North America International Inc. (1) (100%)
Monte Pelvoux 111 Despacho 404, Lomas de Chapultepec, 11000, Mexico, Mexico
Tel.: (52) 5526230203
Web Site: http://www.schroder.com.mx
Sales Range: $50-74.9 Million
Emp.: 2
Investment & Asset Management Banking
N.A.I.C.S.: 523150

Schroder Investment Management SA (1) (100%)
Ing Enrique Butty 220, C1001AFB, Buenos Aires, Argentina
Tel.: (54) 1143171300
Web Site: https://www.schroders.com
Sales Range: $50-74.9 Million
Emp.: 19
Investment & Asset Management Banking
N.A.I.C.S.: 523150

Schroder Property Investment Management Limited (1) (100%)
31 Gresham St, London, EC2V 7QA, United Kingdom
Tel.: (44) 2076586000
Web Site: http://www.schroder.com
Sales Range: $700-749.9 Million
Emp.: 1,200
Investment & Asset Management Banking
N.A.I.C.S.: 523150

Schroder Property Kapitalanlagegesellschaft MbH (1)
Taunustor 1 Taunusturm, 60311, Frankfurt am Main, Germany
Tel.: (49) 69 975717 800
Asset Management Services
N.A.I.C.S.: 523940

Schroder Real Estate Kapitalverwaltungsgesellschaft mbH (1)
Tel.: (49) 69975717700
Investment Fund Services
N.A.I.C.S.: 525910

Schroder Real Estate Managers (Jersey) Limited (1)
Tel.: (44) 756650
Investment Fund Services
N.A.I.C.S.: 525910

Schroder S.A. Sociedad Gerente de Fondos Comunes de Inversion (1)
Ing Enrique Butty 220 Piso 12, C1001AFB, Buenos Aires, Argentina
Tel.: (54) 1143171312
Web Site: https://www.schroder-socger.com.ar
Financial Services
N.A.I.C.S.: 541611

Schroder Trust AG (1) (100%)
Central 2, PO Box 1820, 8021, Zurich, Switzerland
Tel.: (41) 12501111
Web Site: http://www.schroder.com
Sales Range: $50-74.9 Million
Emp.: 100
Investment & Asset Management Banking
N.A.I.C.S.: 523150

Schroder US Holdings Inc. (1)
Tel.: (212) 641-3800
Investment Management Service
N.A.I.C.S.: 523999

Subsidiary (Domestic):

Schroder Investment Management North America Inc. (2) (100%)
7 Bryant Park, New York, NY 10018-3706
Tel.: (212) 641-3800
Web Site: http://www.schroderfunds.com
Sales Range: $50-74.9 Million
Emp.: 100
Investment Management Service
N.A.I.C.S.: 523150

Subsidiary (Domestic):

STW Fixed Income Management LLC (3)

6185 Carpinteria Ave, Carpinteria, CA 93013
Tel.: (805) 745-2300
Web Site: http://www.stw.com
Sales Range: $50-74.9 Million
Emp.: 40
Investment Management Service
N.A.I.C.S.: 523150

Schroder Unit Trusts Limited (1)
(100%)
Tel.: (44) 2076586000
Sales Range: $700-749.9 Million
Emp.: 1,500
Investment & Asset Management Banking
N.A.I.C.S.: 523150

Schroders (Bermuda) Limited (1)
Wellesley House 2nd Floor 90 Pitts Bay Road, Pembroke, HM 08, Bermuda (100%)
Tel.: (441) 4412924995
Web Site: https://www.schroders.com
Sales Range: $50-74.9 Million
Emp.: 6
Investment & Asset Management Banking
N.A.I.C.S.: 523150

Schroders (C.I.) Limited (1)
Regency Court Glategny Esplanade, PO Box 334, Saint Peter Port, GY1 3UF, Guernsey (100%)
Tel.: (44) 1481703700
Web Site: https://www.schroders.com
Sales Range: $50-74.9 Million
Emp.: 38
Investment & Asset Management Banking
N.A.I.C.S.: 523150
Giles Neville *(CEO)*

Schroders (Shanghai) Financial Advisory Co. Limited (1)
Rm 1505 Shanghai Overseas Chinese Mansion, 129 Yanan Xi Lu, Shanghai, 200040, China (100%)
Tel.: (86) 2162481550
Web Site: http://www.schroders.com
Investment & Asset Management Banking
N.A.I.C.S.: 523150

Schroders Capital Management (France) S.A.S. (1)
1 Rue Euler, 75008, Paris, France
Tel.: (33) 153858585
Advisory & Asset Management Services
N.A.I.C.S.: 523940

Schroders Chile SpA (1)
Tel.: (56) 224245510
Investment Fund Services
N.A.I.C.S.: 525910

Schroders France (1)
1 rue Euler, 75008, Paris, France
Tel.: (33) 1 53 85 85 85
Web Site: http://www.schroders.com
Sales Range: $50-74.9 Million
Investment Management Service
N.A.I.C.S.: 523999

Schroders Italy SIM S.p.A. (1)
Via della Spiga 30, 20121, Milan, Italy
Tel.: (39) 02 763771
Web Site: http://www.schroders.com
Commercial Banking Services
N.A.I.C.S.: 522110

Schroders Korea Limited (1)
Tel.: (82) 263905000
Web Site: https://www.schroders.com
Commercial Banking Services
N.A.I.C.S.: 522110

Schroders Property Managers (Jersey) Limited (1)
47 Esplanade, PO Box 490, Saint Helier, JE1 0BD, Jersey
Tel.: (44) 1534835600
Web Site: http://www.schroders.com
Property Fund Management Services
N.A.I.C.S.: 523940

Schroders Taiwan Limited (1)
9th Floor No 108 Section 5 Xinyi Road, Xinyi, Taipei, Taiwan (100%)
Tel.: (886) 22 722 1868
Web Site: https://www.schroders.com
Sales Range: $50-74.9 Million
Emp.: 75
Investment & Asset Management Banking

N.A.I.C.S.: 523150
Francine Wu *(CEO)*

Unique Financial Planning Limited (1)
Shrivenham Hundred Business Park Majors Rd, Watchfield, Swindon, SN6 8TZ, United Kingdom
Tel.: (44) 1793784211
Web Site: https://www.uniquefp.com
Financial Investment Services
N.A.I.C.S.: 523999

SCHUKAT ELECTRONIC VERTRIEBS GMBH
Daimlerstrasse 26, Monheim, 40789, Germany
Tel.: (49) 21739505
Web Site: http://www.schukat.com
Year Founded: 1964
Rev.: $59,262,532
Emp.: 144
Electromechanical Devices Mfr
N.A.I.C.S.: 334413
Hans-Georg Schukat *(Founder)*

SCHULTE ELEKTROTECHNIK GMBH & CO KG
Jungerstrasse 21, 58515, Ludenscheid, Germany
Tel.: (49) 235194810
Web Site: http://www.evoline.com
Year Founded: 1964
Rev.: $21,298,385
Emp.: 150
Switch Distr
N.A.I.C.S.: 423690
Siegfried Schulte *(Founder & Owner)*

Subsidiaries:

EVOline B.V. (1)
Valkenlaar 51, 4854 GR, Breda, Netherlands
Tel.: (31) 765617795
Web Site: http://www.evoline.nl
Electronic Products Mfr
N.A.I.C.S.: 334419

EVOline Chile (1)
Fernando de Arguello 8096, Vitacura, 7650469, Santiago, Chile
Tel.: (56) 975778844
Electronic Product Distr
N.A.I.C.S.: 423690

EVOline Espana (1)
Calle escuela 5 - bajo, 12429, El Toro, Castellon, Spain
Tel.: (34) 964123142
Web Site: http://www.evoline.es
Electronic Product Distr
N.A.I.C.S.: 423690

EVOline Ireland (1)
1 Maple Grove Carpenterstown Park, Castelknock, Dublin, Ireland
Tel.: (353) 834088579
Web Site: http://www.evoline.ie
Electronic Product Distr
N.A.I.C.S.: 423690

EVOline NZ Ltd (1)
PO Box 69031, Glendene, Waitakere, 0645, New Zealand
Tel.: (64) 800386546
Web Site: http://www.evoline.co.nz
Electronic Product Distr
N.A.I.C.S.: 423690

EVOline Norge AS (1)
Drammensveien 37, 0271, Oslo, Norway
Tel.: (47) 22446152
Web Site: http://www.evoline.no
Electronic Product Distr
N.A.I.C.S.: 423690
Espen Bjornes *(Mgr-Sls)*

SCHULTE-HENKE GMBH
Im Schlahbruch 21, 59872, Meschede, Germany
Tel.: (49) 2912070
Web Site: http://www.stabau.com
Year Founded: 1974
Rev.: $22,784,067

Emp.: 160
Forklift Mfr
N.A.I.C.S.: 333924
Jurgen Keller *(CEO)*

SCHULZ S/A
Rua Dona Francisca 6901A, Zona Industrial Norte, Joinville, 89219-600, SC, Brazil
Tel.: (55) 4734516000
Web Site: https://www.schulz.com.br
Year Founded: 1963
SHUL4—(BRAZ)
Rev.: $396,859,762
Assets: $490,491,498
Liabilities: $222,950,849
Net Worth: $267,540,648
Earnings: $57,267,800
Emp.: 3,400
Fiscal Year-end: 12/31/23
Auto Mobile Parts Mfr & Whslr
N.A.I.C.S.: 336390
Waldir Carlos Schulz *(Chm & Exec VP)*

SCHUNK GMBH
Rodheimer Strasse 59, 35452, Heuchelheim, Germany
Tel.: (49) 6416080   De
Web Site: http://www.schunk-group.com
Year Founded: 1945
Sales Range: $800-899.9 Million
Emp.: 7,120
Automation System Products Mfr
N.A.I.C.S.: 333310
Arno Roth *(CEO)*

Subsidiaries:

Climats S.A.S. (1)
Zone du Bedat, CS 50067, 33652, Saint-Medard-de-Eyrans, Cedex, France
Tel.: (33) 556202525
Web Site: http://www.climats-tec.com
Industrial Machinery Mfr
N.A.I.C.S.: 333998
David Dany *(Mgr-Sls)*

Envirotronics Beijing Industry and Trade Inc. (1)
Rm 417 Shenzhou Building No 31 Zhongguancun South Street, Haidian, 100081, Beijing, China
Tel.: (86) 1068118738
Industrial Machinery Distr
N.A.I.C.S.: 423830

Gerhard Prazisionspresstechnik GmbH (1)
Ringstrasse 23, 91619, Obernzenn, Germany
Tel.: (49) 984497110
Web Site: http://www.gerhard-obernzenn.de
Sales Range: $25-49.9 Million
Emp.: 40
Industrial Machinery
N.A.I.C.S.: 333248
Andreas Gerhard *(Mng Dir)*

Jiangsu Seung Lim Electric Co. Ltd. (1)
Xinba Avenue Xinba Scientific & Technologic, Yangzhong, Jiangsu, China
Tel.: (86) 51158120862
Industrial Machinery Distr
N.A.I.C.S.: 423830

K-Tec Verwaltungsgesellschaft mbH (1)
Rodheimer Strasse 59, 35452, Heuchelheim, Germany
Tel.: (49) 6416080
Web Site: http://www.schunk.com
Sales Range: $400-449.9 Million
Emp.: 2,000
Industrial Machinery
N.A.I.C.S.: 333248
Gerald Hinz *(Dir-Controlling)*

OOO NPP Soyuzkarbon (1)
UL Uralskaja 100/1, 350058, Krasnodar, Russia
Tel.: (7) 8612006230

Industrial Machinery Distr
N.A.I.C.S.: 423830

OOO Schunk Carbon Technology (1)
Sinichkina 2-ja Street 9A Building 4 Office 35, 111020, Moscow, Russia
Tel.: (7) 4993725157
Ceramic & Sintered Metal Product Mfr & Distr
N.A.I.C.S.: 332999

OOO Schunk Karbon Moskau (1)
2-ya Sinichkina Street 9A building 4 office 35, 111020, Moscow, Russia
Tel.: (7) 4993725157
Industrial Machinery Distr
N.A.I.C.S.: 423830

OOO Weiss Klimatechnik (1)
Letnikowskaja 10, 115114, Moscow, Russia
Tel.: (7) 4957872043
Industrial Machinery Distr
N.A.I.C.S.: 423830

OptoTech AG (1)
Luterbachstrasse 10, 4528, Zuchwil, Switzerland
Tel.: (41) 326133800
Optical Equipment Mfr
N.A.I.C.S.: 333310
Volker Harnickell *(Mng Dir)*

OptoTech Asia Ltd. (1)
Room 2322 Metro Centre II 21 Lam Hing Street, Kowloon Bay, China (Hong Kong)
Tel.: (852) 35683243
Ceramic & Sintered Metal Product Mfr & Distr
N.A.I.C.S.: 332999

OptoTech India Pvt. Ltd. (1)
505 5th Floor Station Road, Vidyavihar W, Mumbai, 400 086, India
Tel.: (91) 2266710393
Ceramic & Sintered Metal Product Mfr & Distr
N.A.I.C.S.: 332999

OptoTech Optical Machinery Inc. (1)
PO Box 7, Palm, PA 18070
Tel.: (215) 679-2091
Optical Equipment Mfr
N.A.I.C.S.: 333310
Heidi Hofke *(Gen Mgr)*

OptoTech Technologies Inc. (1)
PO Box 665, Germantown, WI 53022
Tel.: (262) 345-2850
Optical Equipment Mfr
N.A.I.C.S.: 333310

Pichit Industrial Works Co. Ltd. (1)
52/3 Moo 13 Krumbthep Kritha Rd, Sapansoong, Bangkok, 10250, Thailand
Tel.: (66) 21388205
Web Site: http://www.pic.co.th
Sales Range: $100-124.9 Million
Emp.: 300
Carbon & Graphite Products
N.A.I.C.S.: 335991
Anton Hermans *(Mng Dir)*

SIRMA Elektrik Komurleri SAN. VE TIC. A.S. (1)
4 Levent oto sanayii sitesi celik cad 57/2, Seyrantepe, 34418, Istanbul, Turkiye
Tel.: (90) 2122789970
Web Site: http://www.sirmaschunk.com
Industrial Machinery Distr
N.A.I.C.S.: 423830

STAPLA Ultrasonics Corporation (1)
250 Andover St, Wilmington, MA 01887
Tel.: (978) 658-9400
Web Site: http://www.staplaultrasonics.com
Emp.: 100
Industrial Machinery Mfr
N.A.I.C.S.: 333998
Edwin Zijlstra *(Pres)*

Sapratin Technologies S.A.S. (1)
73 avenue du Gros Chene, 95615, Eragny-sur-Oise, France
Tel.: (33) 182310430
Industrial Machinery Distr
N.A.I.C.S.: 423830

Schunk (Aust) Pty. Ltd. (1)
44 Jellico Dr, Scoresby, 3178, VIC, Australia

Schunk GmbH—(Continued)
Tel.: (61) 397533588
Web Site: http://www.schunk.com.au
Sales Range: $50-74.9 Million
Emp.: 10
Industrial Machinery
N.A.I.C.S.: 423830

Schunk AG (1)
Soodring 13 A, 8134, Adliswil, Switzerland
Tel.: (41) 447164646
Industrial Machinery Distr
N.A.I.C.S.: 423830

Schunk Bahn- und Industrietechnik GmbH (1)
Hauptstrasse 97, 35435, Wettenberg, Germany
Tel.: (49) 6418030
Web Site: http://www.schunk-sbi.com
Industrial Machinery Mfr
N.A.I.C.S.: 333998

Schunk Bahntecknik GmbH (1)
Aupoint 23, 5105, Bergheim, Austria
Tel.: (43) 662459200
Web Site: http://www.schunk-group.at
Sales Range: $25-49.9 Million
Emp.: 35
Industrial Machinery
N.A.I.C.S.: 423830

Schunk Benelux B.V. (1)
Jufferstraat 10, 3011 XM, Rotterdam, Netherlands
Tel.: (31) 0104144766
Web Site: http://www.schunkbenelux.com
Sales Range: $25-49.9 Million
Emp.: 7
Industrial Machinery
N.A.I.C.S.: 333248

Schunk Carbon Processing GmbH (1)
Rodheimer Strasse 59, 35452, Heuchelheim, Germany
Tel.: (49) 6416080
Ceramic & Sintered Metal Product Mfr & Distr
N.A.I.C.S.: 332999

Schunk Carbon Technology (Suzhou) Co., Ltd. (1)
No 389 Panlong Road Wujiang Economic & Technological Development Zone, Wujiang, Suzhou, 215200, Jiangsu, China
Tel.: (86) 2034634888
Carbon Product Mfr & Distr
N.A.I.C.S.: 335991

Schunk Carbon Technology Co. Ltd. (1)
11 Krungthep-Kritha Road, Sapansoong, Bangkok, 10250, Thailand
Tel.: (66) 273603234
Ceramic & Sintered Metal Product Mfr & Distr
N.A.I.C.S.: 332999

Schunk Carbon Technology Co., Ltd. (1)
Krungthep-Kritha road 11, Sapansoong, 10250, Bangkok, Thailand
Tel.: (66) 273603234
Carbon & Graphite Product Mfr
N.A.I.C.S.: 335991

Schunk Carbon Technology Japan KK (1)
Shin Yokohama 3-19-5, Kohoku-ku, Yokohama, 222-0033, Japan
Tel.: (81) 454702551
Industrial Machinery Distr
N.A.I.C.S.: 423830

Schunk Carbon Technology Kft. (1)
Ady utca 49, 8973, Czesztreg, Hungary
Tel.: (36) 92500900
Web Site: http://www.schunk-carbontechnology.hu
Industrial Machinery Distr
N.A.I.C.S.: 423830

Schunk Carbon Technology Limited (1)
Unit 1705 17/F Tower 1 Enterprise Square 9 Sheung Yuet Road, Kowloon Bay, China (Hong Kong)
Tel.: (852) 24086688
Ceramic & Sintered Metal Product Mfr & Distr
N.A.I.C.S.: 332999

Schunk Carbon Technology Limited (1)
Richardshaw Drive, Grangefield Industrial Estate Pudsey, Leeds, LS28 6QR, West Yorkshire, United Kingdom
Tel.: (44) 1132363496
Ceramic & Sintered Metal Product Mfr & Distr
N.A.I.C.S.: 332999

Schunk Carbon Technology Ltd. (1)
38 Sandanro 67-gil, Danwon-gu, 425-851, Ansan, Gyeonggi-do, Korea (South)
Tel.: (82) 314912722
Industrial Machinery Distr
N.A.I.C.S.: 423830

Schunk Carbon Technology Pty Ltd (1)
Jellico Drive 44, Scoresby, 3179, VIC, Australia
Tel.: (61) 397533588
Industrial Machinery Distr
N.A.I.C.S.: 423830

Schunk Carbon Technology S.A.S. (1)
78-82 Rue Alfred Dequeant, 92737, Nanterre, Cedex, France
Tel.: (33) 141195252
Ceramic & Sintered Metal Product Mfr & Distr
N.A.I.C.S.: 332999
Gilles Garnier *(Mng Dir & Dir Gen)*

Schunk Carbon Technology S.r.l. (1)
Via Murri 22/28, 20013, Magenta, MI, Italy
Tel.: (39) 029721901
Ceramic & Sintered Metal Product Mfr & Distr
N.A.I.C.S.: 332999

Schunk Carbon Technology SRL (1)
Str Atomistilor nr 45-49, 077125, Magurele, Ilfov, Romania
Tel.: (40) 213372859
Web Site: http://www.schunk.ro
Industrial Machinery Distr
N.A.I.C.S.: 423830

Schunk Carbon Technology s.r.o. (1)
V Ochozu 1789/8, 110 00, Prague, Czech Republic
Tel.: (420) 377454126
Ceramic & Sintered Metal Product Mfr & Distr
N.A.I.C.S.: 332999

Schunk Carbon Technology s.r.o. Sp. z o.o. (1)
Ul Bonifraterska 17, 00-203, Warsaw, Poland
Tel.: (48) 538272388
Ceramic & Sintered Metal Product Mfr & Distr
N.A.I.C.S.: 332999

Schunk Dienstleistungsges. mbH (1)
Rodheimer Strasse 59, 35452, Heuchelheim, Germany
Tel.: (49) 6416080
Web Site: http://www.schunk-group.com
Sales Range: $25-49.9 Million
Emp.: 130
Business Management Services
N.A.I.C.S.: 561499
Arno Roth *(CEO)*

Schunk Electro Carbon, S.A. de C.V. (1)
Acueducto del Alto Lerma No 6A, Zona Industrial Ocoyoacac, Ocoyoacac, CP 52740, Mexico
Tel.: (52) 7282827890
Web Site: http://www.schunk.com.mx
Sales Range: $100-124.9 Million
Emp.: 300
Carbon & Graphite Products
N.A.I.C.S.: 335991
Matthias Fritz Butte Facca *(Mng Dir)*

Schunk Electrographite SAS (1)
78-82 rue Alfred Dequeant, BP 717, 92737, Nanterre, Cedex, France
Tel.: (33) 0141195252

Sales Range: $25-49.9 Million
Emp.: 40
Carbon & Graphite Products
N.A.I.C.S.: 335991

Schunk General Carbon (Panyu) Co., Ltd. (1)
Weichongcun Zhongcunzhen, 511495, Panyu, Guangzhou, China
Tel.: (86) 2084714761
Web Site: http://www.schunkchina.com
Sales Range: $25-49.9 Million
Emp.: 70
Carbon & Graphite Products
N.A.I.C.S.: 335991

Schunk General Carbon Ltd. (1)
Unit 1004 Tsuen Wan Industrial Center 220 Texaco Road, Tsuen Wan, NT, China (Hong Kong)
Tel.: (852) 24086688
Web Site: http://www.schunkhk.com
Sales Range: $25-49.9 Million
Emp.: 25
Carbon & Graphite Products
N.A.I.C.S.: 335991

Schunk Gerhard Carbon Technology GmbH (1)
Ringstrasse 23, 91619, Obernzenn, Germany
Tel.: (49) 984497110
Web Site: http://www.gerhard-obernzenn.de
Industrial Machinery Mfr
N.A.I.C.S.: 333998
Andreas Gerhard *(CEO)*

Schunk Hoffmann Carbon Technology AG (1)
Au 62, 4822, Bad Goisern am Hallstattersee, Austria
Tel.: (43) 61354000
Web Site: http://www.hoffmann.at
Industrial Machinery Distr
N.A.I.C.S.: 423830

Schunk Iberica S.A. (1)
C/El Horcajo, 6- Apdo.52 Poligono Industrial Las Arenas, Pinto, 28320, Madrid, Spain
Tel.: (34) 916912511
Web Site: http://www.schunk.es
Sales Range: $25-49.9 Million
Emp.: 120
Industrial Machinery
N.A.I.C.S.: 333248
Emilio Munoz Miranda *(Mng Dir)*

Subsidiary (Non-US):

Schunk Portugal Lda. (2)
Rua Nova da Pedrulheira s n, Apartado 680, 2430-90, Marinha Grande, Portugal
Tel.: (351) 2445724800
Web Site: http://www.schunk.com
Sales Range: $25-49.9 Million
Emp.: 12
Industrial Machinery
N.A.I.C.S.: 333248

Schunk Ingenieurkeramik GmbH (1)
Hans Martin Schleyer Strasse 5, 47877, Willich, Germany
Tel.: (49) 21544970
Web Site: http://www.schunk-sik.com
Sales Range: $50-74.9 Million
Emp.: 180
Semiconductors
N.A.I.C.S.: 334413
Joachim Heym *(Mng Dir)*

Schunk Italia S.r.l. (1)
Via Murri 22-28, Magenta, 20013, Milan, Italy
Tel.: (39) 029721901
Web Site: http://www.schunk-group.com
Sales Range: $25-49.9 Million
Emp.: 50
Industrial Machinery
N.A.I.C.S.: 333248
Ivano Marinelli *(Gen Mgr)*

Schunk Metal & Carbon (I) Pvt. Ltd. (1)
Whitefield Road 54, Mahadevapura, 560 048, Bengaluru, India
Tel.: (91) 8067038501
Web Site: http://sgroup.cms.schunk-group.com
Sales Range: $25-49.9 Million
Emp.: 65
Carbon & Graphite Product Mfr

N.A.I.C.S.: 335991

Schunk Nordiska AB (1)
Industrigatan 15, Box 34, 360 73, Lenhovda, Sweden
Tel.: (46) 47429500
Web Site: http://www.schunk.se
Sales Range: $25-49.9 Million
Emp.: 60
Industry Machinery
N.A.I.C.S.: 333248
Dan Karlsson *(Mgr-Mktg)*

Schunk Praha s r.o. (1)
Vyrobni zavod Pizen Skladova 17, Pizen, 326 00, Prague, Czech Republic
Tel.: (420) 377454111
Web Site: http://www.schunk.cz
Sales Range: $50-74.9 Million
Emp.: 220
Industrial Machinery
N.A.I.C.S.: 333248

Schunk Sintermetal SA de CV (1)
Acueducto del Alto Lerma No 6-A Zona Ind de, Ocoyoacac, 52740, Edo de Mexico, Mexico
Tel.: (52) 7282875014
Ceramic & Sintered Metal Product Mfr & Distr
N.A.I.C.S.: 332999
Jesus Gonzalez *(Sls Mgr)*

Schunk Sintermetalltechnik GmbH (1)
Rodheimer Strasse 59-61, 35452, Heuchelheim, Germany
Tel.: (49) 6416080
Web Site: http://www.sintermetalltechnik.com
Sales Range: $400-449.9 Million
Emp.: 1,700
Industrial Machinery
N.A.I.C.S.: 333248

Schunk Sonosystems Innovations GmbH (1)
Thuringer Strasse 19, 61279, Gravenwiesbach, Germany
Tel.: (49) 60861818
Ceramic & Sintered Metal Product Mfr & Distr
N.A.I.C.S.: 332999
Stefan Trube *(Mng Dir)*

Schunk UK Ltd. (1)
Richardshaw Dr, Grangefield Industrial Estate, Pudsey, LS28 6QR, W Yorkshire, United Kingdom
Tel.: (44) 01132567238
Sales Range: $25-49.9 Million
Emp.: 77
Carbon & Graphite Products Mfr
N.A.I.C.S.: 335991
Willfried Otto Seidt *(Mng Dir)*

Schunk Ultraschalltechnik GmbH (1)
Hauptstrasse 95, 35435, Wettenberg, Germany
Tel.: (49) 6418030
Web Site: http://www.sut.biz
Sales Range: $25-49.9 Million
Emp.: 64
Industrial Machinery
N.A.I.C.S.: 333248

Schunk Wien Gesellschaft m.b.H. (1)
Oberlaaer Strasse 316, 1230, Vienna, Austria
Tel.: (43) 16166807
Web Site: http://www.schunk-materials.at
Sales Range: $25-49.9 Million
Emp.: 50
Industrial Machinery Sales
N.A.I.C.S.: 423830
Conrad Reeaan *(Gen Mgr)*

Subsidiary (Domestic):

Hoffmann & Co. Elektrokohle AG (2)
Au 62, Postfach 2, 4823, Steeg, Austria
Tel.: (43) 61354000
Web Site: http://www.hoffmann.at
Sales Range: $75-99.9 Million
Industrial Machinery
N.A.I.C.S.: 333248

Schunk Wien Gesellschaft m.b.H. (1)

Dusan Corluka Milosa Matijevica-Mrse 9,
11060, Belgrade, Serbia
Tel.: (381) 112083506
Industrial Machinery Distr
N.A.I.C.S.: 423830

Schunk Wien Gesellschaft m.b.H. (1)
Roman Tomat Pod Plevno 10, 4220, Skofja Loka, Slovenia
Tel.: (386) 45139848
Industrial Machinery Distr
N.A.I.C.S.: 423830

Schunk Xycarb (Shanghai) Precision Ceramics Technology Co., Ltd. (1)
Room 404 B1 No 1599 Xinjinqiao Rd, Pudong, Shanghai, China
Tel.: (86) 2150315123
Ceramic & Sintered Metal Product Mfr & Distr
N.A.I.C.S.: 332999

Schunk Xycarb Technology B.V. (1)
Zuiddijk 23, 5705 CS, Helmond, Netherlands
Tel.: (31) 492758787
Web Site: http://www.schunk-xycarbtechnology.com
Silicon Consumable Product Distr
N.A.I.C.S.: 424990
Renate Van Alten *(Mgr-Customer Svc-Global)*

Schunk Xycarb Technology Co. Ltd. (1)
1404 Parkview Office Tower 248 Jeongjailro, Bundang-gu, Seongnam, 13554, Gyeonggi, Korea (South)
Tel.: (82) 317177260
Ceramic & Sintered Metal Product Mfr & Distr
N.A.I.C.S.: 332999

Schunk Xycarb Technology Co. Ltd. (1)
No 372-6 Sec 4 Zhongxing Rd, Zhudong Township, Hsinchu, 310, Taiwan
Tel.: (886) 35836019
Ceramic & Sintered Metal Product Mfr & Distr
N.A.I.C.S.: 332999
Rinie Coort *(Dir-Bus Dev-Asia)*

Schunk Xycarb Technology Pte. Ltd. (1)
2 Bukit Batok Street 23 01-10, Singapore, 659554, Singapore
Tel.: (65) 6360672
Ceramic & Sintered Metal Product Mfr & Distr
N.A.I.C.S.: 332999

Schunk do Brasil Eletrografites Ltda. (1)
Estrada do Embu Bairro Moinho Velho 2777, 06713-100, Cotia, Sao Paulo, Brazil
Tel.: (55) 1146133202
Industrial Machinery Distr
N.A.I.C.S.: 423830

Schunk do Brasil Ltda. (1)
Estrada do Embu 2777 Bairro Moinho Velho, Cotia, 06713-100, Sao Paulo, Brazil
Tel.: (55) 1146133202
Web Site: http://www.schunk.se
Sales Range: $50-74.9 Million
Emp.: 130
Industrial Machinery
N.A.I.C.S.: 333248

Schunk of North America, Inc. (1)
W146 N9300 Held Dr, Menomonee Falls, WI 53051-1643
Tel.: (262) 253-8720
Web Site: http://www.schunkgraphite.com
Sales Range: $75-99.9 Million
Emp.: 110
Holding Company
N.A.I.C.S.: 551112
Sherry Farrel *(CFO)*

Division (Domestic):

Schunk Graphite Technology, LLC (2)
W 146 S 9300 Held Dr, Menomonee Falls, WI 53051-1643
Tel.: (262) 253-8720
Web Site: http://www.schunkgraphite.com

Sales Range: $25-49.9 Million
Emp.: 100
Carbon, Ceramic & Graphic Products Mfr
N.A.I.C.S.: 335991
David DaRin *(Pres)*

Weiss Environmental Technology Inc. (2)
W146 N9300 Held Dr, Menomonee Falls, WI 53051
Tel.: (586) 873-2009
Web Site: http://www.weiss-et.com
Sales Range: $25-49.9 Million
Emp.: 100
Pollution Control Equipment Sales
N.A.I.C.S.: 334512

Xycarb Ceramics Inc. (2)
101 SE Inner Loop Rd, Georgetown, TX 78626
Tel.: (512) 863-0033
Web Site: http://www.xycarb.com
Sales Range: $25-49.9 Million
Emp.: 50
Semiconductor Mfr
N.A.I.C.S.: 334413
John Neff *(Gen Mgr)*

Sintermetal S.A. de C.V. (1)
Acueducto del Alto Lerma No 6A Zona Industrial Ocoyoacac, Ocoyoacac, Mexico
Tel.: (52) 7282827890
Web Site: http://www.schunk.com.mx
Sales Range: $50-74.9 Million
Emp.: 140
Industrial Machinery
N.A.I.C.S.: 333248
Matthias Fritz Butte Facca *(Mng Dir)*

Stapla Ultraschalltechnik GmbH (1)
Hauptstrasse 95, 35429, Wettenberg, Germany
Tel.: (49) 641803350
Web Site: http://www.sonostems.com
Sales Range: $25-49.9 Million
Emp.: 35
Industrial Machinery
N.A.I.C.S.: 333248

Unique Engineering Australia Pty. Ltd. (1)
76-78 Cyber Loop, Dandenong South, 3175, VIC, Australia
Tel.: (61) 397028833
Industrial Machinery Distr
N.A.I.C.S.: 423830

Votsch Industrietechnik GmbH (1)
Beethovenstr 34, 72336, Balingen, Germany
Tel.: (49) 74333030
Web Site: http://www.v-it.com
Industrial Machinery Distr
N.A.I.C.S.: 423830

Weiss Envirotronics Inc. (1)
3881 N Greenbrooke S E, Grand Rapids, MI 49512
Tel.: (616) 554-5020
Web Site: http://www.envirotronics.com
Industrial Machinery Mfr
N.A.I.C.S.: 333998
Jim Weiss *(Acct Mgr)*

Subsidiary (Non-US):

Envirotronics Asia Sdn. Bhd. (2)
Block K No 68-G Persiaran Bayan Indah Bayan Bay, 11950, Penang, Malaysia
Tel.: (60) 46456020
Industrial Machinery Distr
N.A.I.C.S.: 423830

Envirotronics Singapore Pte. Ltd. (2)
68 Kallang Pudding Road 03-04 S Y H Logistics Building, Singapore, 349327, Singapore
Tel.: (65) 67468768
Industrial Machinery Distr
N.A.I.C.S.: 423830

Weiss Pharmatechnik GmbH (1)
Georg-Bolts-Strasse 2-8, 26135, Oldenburg, Germany
Tel.: (49) 441570540
Surgical Appliance Mfr
N.A.I.C.S.: 339113
Bernd Weber *(Mng Dir)*

Weiss Technik AG (1)
Brugglistr 2, 8852, Altendorf, Switzerland

Tel.: (41) 552561066
Web Site: http://www.weiss-technik.ch
Industrial Machinery Distr
N.A.I.C.S.: 423830

Weiss Technik India Private Limited (1)
3-6-271 2nd Floor Sudheer Tapani Tower, Himayath Nagar, Hyderabad, 500 029, India
Tel.: (91) 4023224910
Heating Equipment Mfr
N.A.I.C.S.: 333414
Girish Malik *(Mng Dir)*

Weiss Technik Italia S.r.l. (1)
Via Murri 22/28, 20013, Magenta, Milan, Italy
Tel.: (39) 0297291616
Web Site: http://www.weissitalia.it
Industrial Machinery Distr
N.A.I.C.S.: 423830

Weiss Technik Malaysia Sdn. Bhd. (1)
Block K No 68-G Persiaran Bayan, Bayan Bay, Penang, Malaysia
Tel.: (60) 124338708
Air Conditioning Repair Services
N.A.I.C.S.: 238220

Weiss Technik Singapore Pte. Ltd. (1)
No 68 Kallang Pudding Road 03-04 Syh Logistics Building, Singapore, 349327, Singapore
Tel.: (65) 124338708
Air Conditioning Product Retailer
N.A.I.C.S.: 423730
Jay Chan *(Sls Mgr)*

Weiss Umwelttechnik GmbH (1)
Greizer Strasse 41-49, 35447, Reiskirchen, Germany
Tel.: (49) 6408840
Web Site: http://www.wut.com
Sales Range: $200-249.9 Million
Emp.: 930
Environmental Control Mfr
N.A.I.C.S.: 334512
Arno Roth *(Mng Dir)*

Subsidiary (Domestic):

Weiss GWE GmbH (2)
Wiechmann Allee 3, 27798, Hude, Germany
Tel.: (49) 44841890
Web Site: http://www.gwe.de
Sales Range: $25-49.9 Million
Emp.: 80
Environmental Cleaning Products Mfr
N.A.I.C.S.: 334512
Wolfgang Koenig *(Mng Dir)*

Weiss Klimatechnik GmbH (2)
Greizer Strasse 41-49, 35447, Reiskirchen, Germany
Tel.: (49) 6408846500
Web Site: http://www.wkt.com
Sales Range: $25-49.9 Million
Emp.: 217
Climate-Control Equipment
N.A.I.C.S.: 333415

Subsidiary (Non-US):

Weiss Technik Belgium B.V.B.A. (2)
Nijverheldszone Begljinenmeers 63, Liedekerke, 1770, Gent, Belgium
Tel.: (32) 53681010
Web Site: http://www.weisstechnik.be
Sales Range: $25-49.9 Million
Emp.: 25
Pollution Control Equipment
N.A.I.C.S.: 334512

Weiss Technik France E.u.r.l. (2)
283 route d'Andresy, 78955, Poissy, France
Tel.: (33) 134011100
Web Site: http://www.weissfr.com
Sales Range: $25-49.9 Million
Emp.: 10
Pollution Control Equipment
N.A.I.C.S.: 334512

Subsidiary (Domestic):

Servathin S.A. (3)
283 route d'Andresy, PO Box 4015, 78955, Poissy, Cedex, France
Tel.: (33) 0134011111

Web Site: http://www.servathin.com
Sales Range: $25-49.9 Million
Climate Control Product Mfr
N.A.I.C.S.: 333415

Subsidiary (Domestic):

Secasi Technologies S.A. (4)
ZI du Bedat, Saint Medard dEyrans, 33650, Bordeaux, France
Tel.: (33) 556466930
Web Site: http://www.secasi.com
Sales Range: $10-24.9 Million
Emp.: 35
Climate-Control Products
N.A.I.C.S.: 333415

Subsidiary (Non-US):

Weiss Technik Nederland B.V. (2)
Newtonstraat 5, 4004 KD, Tiel, Netherlands
Tel.: (31) 344670400
Web Site: http://www.weissenet.nl
Sales Range: $25-49.9 Million
Emp.: 28
Air Conditioning & Environmental Products
N.A.I.C.S.: 333415
Dirk Van Manen *(Mng Dir)*

Subsidiary (US):

Weiss Technik North America, Inc. (2)
3881N Greenbrooke Dr SE, Grand Rapids, MI 49512
Tel.: (616) 554-5020
Environmental Test Chamber Solutions
N.A.I.C.S.: 334515
Edward Smith *(VP-Sls & Mktg)*

Subsidiary (Domestic):

Cincinnati Sub-Zero Products, LLC (3)
12011 Mosteller Rd, Cincinnati, OH 45241-1528
Tel.: (513) 772-8810
Web Site: http://www.genthermcsz.com
Production Chilling Chambers; Environmental Test Equipment; Cryogenic Equipment; Hyperthermia & Hypothermia Equipment; Disposable Blankets & Pads Mfr
N.A.I.C.S.: 334513
Marc Wolfrum *(VP & Gen Mgr)*

Division (Domestic):

Cincinnati Sub-Zero Products, Inc. - CSZ Testing Services Laboratories Division (4)
11901 Mosteller Rd, Cincinnati, OH 45241
Tel.: (513) 793-7774
Web Site: http://www.csztesting.com
Laboratory Testing Services
N.A.I.C.S.: 541380
Bryan Kanter *(CFO & VP)*

Subsidiary (Domestic):

Vacuum Technology Associates, Inc. (3)
110 Indus Pk Rd, Hingham, MA 02043-4369
Tel.: (781) 740-8600
Web Site: http://www.dynavac.com
Sales Range: $50-74.9 Million
Emp.: 60
Mfr of Vacuum Deposition Coating Equipment & Other Vacuum Items
N.A.I.C.S.: 333248
Joel Smolka *(COO)*

Subsidiary (Non-US):

Weiss Technik UK Limited (2)
32 Rassau Industrial Estate, Ebbw Vale, Gwent, NP23 5SD, United Kingdom
Tel.: (44) 1495305555
Web Site: http://www.weiss-uk.com
Sales Range: $25-49.9 Million
Emp.: 125
Environmental Services
N.A.I.C.S.: 541620
Malcolm Youll *(Mng Dir)*

Weiss Umwelttechnik Ges. m.b.H. (2)
Oberlaaer Strasse 316, 1230, Vienna, Austria
Tel.: (43) 16166697
Web Site: http://www.wut.com

SCHUNK GMBH

Schunk GmbH—(Continued)

Sales Range: $25-49.9 Million
Emp.: 8
Pollution Control Equipment
N.A.I.C.S.: 334512
Conrad Reynvaan (Mgr)

Weiss-Voetsch Environmental Testing Instruments (Taicang) Co. Ltd. (2)
No 102 Changsheng Road Taicang Economy, Development Area, Taicang, 215400, Jiangsu, China
Tel.: (86) 51253443110
Web Site: http://www.weiss-voetsch.com
Sales Range: $25-49.9 Million
Emp.: 25
Pollution Control Equipment
N.A.I.C.S.: 334512

Xycarb Ceramics B.V. (1)
Zuiddijk 4, 5705 CS, Helmond, Netherlands
Tel.: (31) 492578787
Web Site: http://www.xycarb.com
Sales Range: $50-74.9 Million
Emp.: 150
Semiconductor Mfr
N.A.I.C.S.: 334413
Jacques Devries (Mgr-Pur)

Subsidiary (Non-US):

Xycarb Ceramics Singapore Pte Ltd (2)
No 107 Gul Circle, Singapore, 629593, Singapore
Tel.: (65) 63630672
Construction Materials Whslr
N.A.I.C.S.: 423320
K.L. Yue (Asst Mgr)

Xycarb Ceramics Taiwan Ltd. (2)
N0 372-6 Sec 4 Zhongxing Rd, Zhudong, Hsin-chu, 31061, Taiwan
Tel.: (886) 35836019
Construction Materials Whslr
N.A.I.C.S.: 423320
Rinie Coort (VP-Worldwide Sls)

SCHUR INTERNATIONAL A/S

J W Schurs Vej 1, 8700, Horsens, Denmark
Tel.: (45) 76272727
Web Site: http://www.schur.com
Year Founded: 1846
Sales Range: $300-349.9 Million
Emp.: 850
Mfr of Packaging Equipment & Products
N.A.I.C.S.: 333993
Hans Schur (CEO & Dir-Sls)

Subsidiaries:

Schur Conference Center a/s (1)
Soborgvej 20, Glud, 7130, Juelsminde, Denmark
Tel.: (45) 7568 3099
Property Leasing Services
N.A.I.C.S.: 531120

Schur Consumer Products Inc. (1)
2664 Vista Pacific Dr, Oceanside, CA 92056
Tel.: (760) 650-3815
Packaging Material Distr
N.A.I.C.S.: 423840

Schur Consumer Products a/s (1)
Niels Finsensvej 11, 7100, Vejle, Denmark
Tel.: (45) 76 42 88 88
Packaging Material Distr
N.A.I.C.S.: 423840

Schur Pack Sweden AB (1)
Vastra Bangatan 50, PO Box 104, 692 22, Kumla, Sweden
Tel.: (46) 19 58 72 00
Packaging Material Distr
N.A.I.C.S.: 423840

Subsidiary (Non-US):

Schur Pack Germany GmbH (2)
Parkstrasse 1, 21514, Buchen, Germany
Tel.: (49) 41 55 12 30
Packaging Material Distr
N.A.I.C.S.: 423840
Klaus Madsen (Mng Dir)

Subsidiary (Non-US):

Schur Pack Norway a/s (3)
Angedalen, Forde, 6800, Norway
Tel.: (47) 57 72 22 00
Packaging Material Distr
N.A.I.C.S.: 423840

Schur Packaging Systems AB (1)
Telegatan 2, 575 36, Eksjo, Sweden
Tel.: (46) 381 66 33 00
Web Site: http://www.schur.com
Sales Range: $25-49.9 Million
Emp.: 50
Develop, Produce & Sell Unique, Operationally Secure Handling Technology Solutions for Post-Press Mailroom, Direct Mail Handling & Palletising in Printed Media
N.A.I.C.S.: 333248
Ola Johansson (Reg Mgr-Sls)

Subsidiary (US):

Schur Packaging Systems Inc. (2)
3200 Lionshead Ave Ste 110, Carlsbad, CA 92010
Tel.: (760) 421-6404
Web Site: http://www.schurstarusa.com
Packaging Machinery Distr
N.A.I.C.S.: 423830

Subsidiary (Non-US):

Schur Wamac France SAS (3)
ZAC du Gue Langlois Avenue du Gue Langlois, 77600, Bussy-Saint-Martin, France
Tel.: (33) 1 60 54 30 00
Web Site: http://www.schur-wamac.fr
Packaging Machinery Distr
N.A.I.C.S.: 423830

Schur Star Systems GmbH (1)
Liebigstrasse 7, 24941, Flensburg, Germany
Tel.: (49) 461 99 750
Packaging Material Distr
N.A.I.C.S.: 423840

Schur Technology a/s (1)
Fuglevangsvej 41, 8700, Horsens, Denmark
Tel.: (45) 79 28 29 28
Packaging Material Distr
N.A.I.C.S.: 423840

SCHUSSLER NOVACHEM GMBH

Otto-Stomps-Str 101, 06116, Halle, Germany
Tel.: (49) 345 6868 0 De
Web Site: http://www.novachem.de
Sales Range: $10-24.9 Million
Inorganic Salt Mfr
N.A.I.C.S.: 325180
Daniel F. Schussler (Mng Dir)

Subsidiaries:

CFL Chemische Fabrik Lehrte GmbH & Co. KG (1)
Kothenwaldstrasse 2 6, 31275, Lehrte, Germany
Tel.: (49) 513285990
Web Site: http://www.cfl-lehrte.de
Chemicals Company
N.A.I.C.S.: 325998
Regine Hoft (Mgr-Sls)

SCHUSTER THOMSEN ROEHLE

Shooting Strasse 61, 40549, Dusseldorf, Germany
Tel.: (49) 211695600 De
Web Site: http://www.schuster-thomsen-roehle.de
Year Founded: 1969
Rev.: $463,000,000
Emp.: 18
N.A.I.C.S.: 541810
Werner Schuster (Acct Dir)

SCHWABO CAPITAL CORPORATION

Suite 1000 409 Granville Street, Vancouver, V6C 1T2, BC, Canada
Tel.: (604) 602-0001 AB

Year Founded: 2007
SBO.H—(TSXV)
Assets: $76
Liabilities: $94,566
Net Worth: ($94,490)
Earnings: $15,964
Fiscal Year-end: 10/31/22
Investment Services
N.A.I.C.S.: 523999
Jordan Shapiro (CEO)

SCHWAGER ENERGY S.A.

Isidora Goyenechea 2939 of 702, Las Condes, Santiago, Chile
Tel.: (56) 938605309
Web Site: https://www.schwager.cl
Year Founded: 1847
SCHWAGER—(SGO)
Sales Range: Less than $1 Million
Engineeering Services
N.A.I.C.S.: 541330
Alex Acosta Maluenda (CEO)

SCHWALBCHEN MOLKEREI JAKOB BERZ AG

JakobBerzStrasse 1, 65307, Schwalbach, Germany
Tel.: (49) 61245030
Web Site: https://www.schwaelbchen-molkerei.de
Year Founded: 1938
SMB—(DEU)
Rev.: $247,875,041
Assets: $84,799,647
Liabilities: $45,082,239
Net Worth: $39,717,408
Earnings: $7,263,495
Emp.: 385
Fiscal Year-end: 12/31/23
Frozen Food Product Distr
N.A.I.C.S.: 424420

SCHWAN-STABILO COSMETICS GMBH & CO. KG

Schwanweg 1, 90562, Heroldsberg, Germany
Tel.: (49) 911 567 0
Web Site: http://www.schwancosmetics.com
Year Founded: 1855
Sales Range: $50-74.9 Million
Emp.: 3,000
Cosmetics Mfr
N.A.I.C.S.: 456120
Jorg Karas (Mng Dir)

Subsidiaries:

COSMA International Ltd. (1)
Skladochnaya Str 6 Office 105, 127018, Moscow, Russia
Tel.: (7) 495 981 92 89
Cosmetics Mfr
N.A.I.C.S.: 456120

COSMETIC COLORS, S.A. DE C.V. (1)
Boulevard Miguel Aleman KM 2 Colonia Reforma San Pedro Totoltepec, Toluca, 50226, Mexico
Tel.: (52) 55 5096 8402
Cosmetic Product Distr
N.A.I.C.S.: 456120

Cosmolab Div. (1)
1100 Garrett Pkwy, Lewisburg, TN 37091-3541 (100%)
Tel.: (931) 359-6253
Web Site: http://www.cosmolab.com
Mfr of Cosmetic Pencils, Powder & Other Cosmetic Products
N.A.I.C.S.: 325620

Creative Colors S.A. (1)
Carrera 106 15-25, Int 26 Manzana 07, Bogota, Colombia
Tel.: (57) 1 571 0809 0
Cosmetics Mfr
N.A.I.C.S.: 456120

Deuter Sport GmbH & Co. KG (1)

INTERNATIONAL PUBLIC

Daimlerstrasse 23, 86368, Gersthofen, Germany
Tel.: (49) 821 49 87 327
Web Site: http://www.deuter.com
Backpack Mfr
N.A.I.C.S.: 314910

ORTOVOX Sportartikel GmbH (1)
Rotwandweg 5, 82024, Taufkirchen, Germany
Tel.: (49) 89 666 74 0
Web Site: http://www.ortovox.com
Backpack Mfr
N.A.I.C.S.: 314910
Christian Schneidermeier (CEO)

Subsidiary (Non-US):

ORTOVOX CANADA LTD (2)
Suite 110 4520 - 16th Ave NW, Calgary, T3B 0M6, AB, Canada
Tel.: (403) 283-8944
Backpack Distr
N.A.I.C.S.: 424990

ORTOVOX Vertriebs GmbH (2)
Salzburger Siedlung 258, 8970, Vienna, Austria
Tel.: (43) 3687 22 551
Backpack Distr
N.A.I.C.S.: 424990
Alexander Helpferer (Gen Mgr)

PT Kirana Anindita (1)
Taman Tekno, Sektor XI Blok G1 No 62, Tangerang, Indonesia
Tel.: (62) 21 758 752
Cosmetics Mfr
N.A.I.C.S.: 456120

SDK Agencis C.C. (1)
Unit G Alphen West 338 George Street, Randjespark, Midrand, 1682, Gauteng, South Africa
Tel.: (27) 11 314 0020
Web Site: http://www.sdkagencies.com
Emp.: 10
Cosmetics Mfr
N.A.I.C.S.: 456120
Levi Singer (Gen Mgr)

Schwan Cosmetics CR, s.r.o. (1)
Prumyslova 176, 38101, Cesky Krumlov, Czech Republic
Tel.: (420) 380 708 160
Cosmetics Mfr
N.A.I.C.S.: 456120

Schwan Cosmetics Kunststofftechnik GmbH & Co. KG (1)
Augsburger Str 52, 91781, Weissenburg, Germany
Tel.: (49) 91419080
Cosmetics Products Mfr
N.A.I.C.S.: 325620
Gunter Lurz (Exec Dir)

Schwan Cosmetics USA Inc. (1)
21 Gordon Rd, Piscataway, NJ 08854
Tel.: (732) 777-6800
Web Site: http://www.schwancosmetics.com
Emp.: 125
Cosmetics Mfr
N.A.I.C.S.: 456120
Carol Rosenbloom (Mgr-Quality Assurance)

Schwan Cosmetics do Brasil Ltda. (1)
Avenida das Torres 1500, Sao Jose dos Pinhais, 83 040 300, Parana, Brazil
Tel.: (55) 41 3388 8800
Cosmetics Mfr
N.A.I.C.S.: 456120

Schwan-STABILO Creative Colors de Mexico, S.A. de C.V. (1)
Avenida de las Torres 485 Col Nueva Industrial Vallejo, Delegacion Gustavo A Madero, 7700, Mexico, Mexico
Tel.: (52) 55 2062 0140
Web Site: http://www.schwancosmetics.com
Emp.: 60
Cosmetics Mfr
N.A.I.C.S.: 456120
Adriana Tinoco (Office Mgr)

Schwan-STABILO Promotion Products GmbH & Co. KG (1)
Schwanweg 1, 90562, Heroldsberg, Germany

Tel.: (49) 911 567 3455
Web Site: http://www.stabilo-promotion.com
Stationery Product Distr
N.A.I.C.S.: 424120
Harry Saffer *(Mng Dir)*

Tianjin Schwan Cosmetics Co. Ltd. (1)
Jinna Economic, Development Area, 300350, Tianjin, China
Tel.: (86) 22 2859 4859
Cosmetics Mfr
N.A.I.C.S.: 456120

SCHWARZ UNTERNEHMEN-STREUHAND KG
Stiftsbergstrasse 1, 74172, Neckarsulm, Germany
Tel.: (49) 713230788600 De
Web Site: https://gruppe.schwarz
Emp.: 100
Diversified Holding Company
N.A.I.C.S.: 551112
Gerd Chrzanowski *(CEO)*

Subsidiaries:

Lidl Stiftung & Co. KG (1)
Sekretariat Immobilien Rotelstrasse 30, 74166, Neckarsulm, Germany
Tel.: (49) 7132306060
Web Site: http://www.lidl.de
Sales Range: $25-49.9 Billion
Emp.: 80,000
Discount Department Stores
N.A.I.C.S.: 445110
Johannes Fieber *(Pres/CEO-US)*

Subsidiary (Non-US):

Lidl Limited (2)
19 Worple Rd, London, SW19 4JS, Wimbleton, United Kingdom
Tel.: (44) 8704441234
Web Site: http://www.lidl.co.uk
Sales Range: $1-9.9 Billion
Discount Department Stores
N.A.I.C.S.: 455110
Johannes Fieber *(Pres/CEO-US)*

PreZero Stiftung & Co. KG (1)
Stiftsbergstrasse 1, 74172, Neckarsulm, Germany
Tel.: (49) 7132 3077 3344
Web Site: http://www.prezero-international.com
Environmental Services
N.A.I.C.S.: 541620
Thomas Kyriakis *(CEO)*

Subsidiary (Non-US):

CESPA S.A. (2)
Avenida de la Catedral 6 y 8, 08002, Barcelona, Spain
Tel.: (34) 932 479 100
Web Site: http://www.cespa.es
Sales Range: $1-4.9 Billion
Emp.: 16,000
Waste Collection & Disposal Services
N.A.I.C.S.: 562219

Schwarz Unternehmenskommunikation GmbH & Co. KG (1)
Stiftsbergstrasse 1, 74172, Neckarsulm, Germany
Tel.: (49) 7132 3078 860
Web Site: http://www.gruppe.schwarz
Public Relations & Communications Agency
N.A.I.C.S.: 541820
Gerd Chrzanowski *(CEO)*

SCHWEITER TECHNOLOGIES AG
Hinterbergstrasse 20, 6312, Steinhausen, Switzerland
Tel.: (41) 417577700
Web Site: https://www.schweiter.ch
Year Founded: 1942
SWTQ—(SWX)
Rev.: $1,327,827,051
Assets: $1,202,106,430
Liabilities: $367,516,630
Net Worth: $834,589,800
Earnings: $32,261,641
Emp.: 4,255
Fiscal Year-end: 12/31/22
Holding Company; Textile Machinery & Coating Business
N.A.I.C.S.: 551112
Heinz O. Baumgartner *(CEO)*

Subsidiaries:

3A Composites (China) Ltd. (1)
F1902-03 Hongkong Prosperity Tower 763 Mengzi Road, Shanghai, 200023, China
Tel.: (86) 2163158550
Emp.: 40
Aluminium Composite Material & Plastic Sheet Mfr
N.A.I.C.S.: 325211

3A Composites Asia Pacific Pte. Ltd. (1)
300 Beach Road The Concourse, Singapore, 199555, Singapore
Tel.: (65) 63039750
Panel Mfr
N.A.I.C.S.: 321992

3A Composites Germany GmbH (1)
Tel.: (49) 77319410
Emp.: 350
Aluminium Composite Material & Plastic Sheet Mfr
N.A.I.C.S.: 325211
Joachim Werner *(Exec Dir)*

3A Composites Holding AG (1)
Tel.: (41) 417577000
Web Site: http://www.3acomposites.com
Sales Range: $600-649.9 Million
Emp.: 3,000
Aluminum Composite, Plastic & Foam Materials Mfr
N.A.I.C.S.: 331315

Subsidiary (Non-US):

3A Composites GmbH (2)
Alusingenplatz 1, 78224, Singen, Germany
Tel.: (49) 77319413500
Web Site: http://www.display.3acomposites.com
Sales Range: $450-499.9 Million
Forged Aluminum, Aluminum Sheet & Composite Materials Mfr
N.A.I.C.S.: 331315

3A Composites GmbH (2)
Kiefernweg 10, 49090, Osnabruck, Germany
Tel.: (49) 541121930
Web Site: https://www.display.3acomposites.com
Sales Range: $50-74.9 Million
Emp.: 90
Polyurethane Composite Materials Mfr
N.A.I.C.S.: 326160
Joachim Werner *(Exec Dir)*

3A Composites USA Inc. (2)
Tel.: (704) 658-3500
Web Site: https://3acompositesusa.com
Emp.: 330
Aluminum Composite, Plastic & Foam Materials Mfr
N.A.I.C.S.: 331315

Subsidiary (Domestic):

Airex AG (2)
Industrie Nord 26, 5643, Sins, Switzerland
Tel.: (41) 417896600
Web Site: http://www.airexag.ch
Sales Range: $50-74.9 Million
Emp.: 180
Structural Core Materials Mfr
N.A.I.C.S.: 326140

Subsidiary (US):

Baltek Inc. (2)
5240 National Ctr Dr, Colfax, NC 27235
Tel.: (336) 398-1900
Web Site: http://www.3accorematerials.com
Sales Range: $200-249.9 Million
Emp.: 100
Structural Core Materials Mfr
N.A.I.C.S.: 541310

Subsidiary (Non-US):

Polycasa N.V. (2)
Van Doornelaan 2A, 2440, Geel, Belgium
Tel.: (32) 14576711
Emp.: 30
Plastic Extrusion Products Mfr
N.A.I.C.S.: 326199

Subsidiary (Non-US):

Polycasa GmbH (3)
Gassnerallee 40, 55120, Mainz, Germany
Tel.: (49) 61316310
Emp.: 100
Acrylic Sheet Plastics Mfr
N.A.I.C.S.: 326113

Polycasa Spain S.A.U. (3)
Calle Alimentacio 6-12, Poligono Industrial La Ferreria Montcada i Reixac, 08110, Barcelona, Spain
Tel.: (34) 935751990
Emp.: 80
Acrylic Cast Sheets Mfr
N.A.I.C.S.: 326113

Polycasa s.r.o. (3)
Obecnicka 520, 261 01, Pribram, VI, Czech Republic
Tel.: (420) 318493911
Emp.: 90
Industrial Sheet Plastic Products Mfr
N.A.I.C.S.: 326113

3A Composites India Pte. Ltd. (1)
Tel.: (91) 2242564500
Aluminium Composite Material & Plastic Sheet Mfr
N.A.I.C.S.: 325211

3A Composites International AG (1)
Hinterbergstrasse 20, 6312, Steinhausen, Switzerland
Tel.: (41) 417577000
Emp.: 12
Aluminium Composite Material & Plastic Sheet Mfr
N.A.I.C.S.: 325211

3A Composites Mobility AG (1)
Park Altenrhein, 9423, Altenrhein, Switzerland
Tel.: (41) 718584848
Aluminium Composite Material Mfr & Distr
N.A.I.C.S.: 331315

3A Composites Mobility SA (1)
ul Inwestorow 6, 39-300, Mielec, Poland
Tel.: (48) 177737800
Emp.: 250
Aluminium Composite Material & Plastic Sheet Mfr
N.A.I.C.S.: 325211

Alucobond (Far East) Pte. Ltd. (1)
6 Shenton Way 40-05 OUE Downtown 1, Singapore, 068809, Singapore
Tel.: (65) 63039750
Lumber Plywood Mfr
N.A.I.C.S.: 321912

Alucobond Asia Pacific Management (Shanghai) Ltd. (1)
298 East Kangqiao Road, Shanghai, 201319, China
Tel.: (86) 2158135353
Lumber Plywood Mfr
N.A.I.C.S.: 321912

Alucobond Composites (Jiangsu) Ltd. (1)
10 South Hehuan Road, Zhonglou, Changzhou, 213023, China
Tel.: (86) 51981665766
Lumber Plywood Mfr
N.A.I.C.S.: 321912

Athlone Extrusions (UK) Ltd. (1)
Tel.: (44) 1217644848
Emp.: 3
Thermoplastic Sheet Product Mfr
N.A.I.C.S.: 326199

Athlone Extrusions Ltd. (1)
Grace Road, Westmeath, Athlone, N37 H594, Ireland
Tel.: (353) 906483200
Emp.: 8
Thermoplastic Sheet Product Mfr
N.A.I.C.S.: 326199

Foamalite Ltd. (1)
Loch Gowna, Cavan, H12 VW 84, Ireland
Tel.: (353) 436683525
Emp.: 80
Plastics Product Mfr & Distr
N.A.I.C.S.: 326199

JMB Wind Brasil Ltda. (1)
R Joao Eusebio da Silva 989 Catole, Belo Horizonte, CE 62887-350, Brazil
Tel.: (55) 8521358669
Wind Blade Product Mfr
N.A.I.C.S.: 333611

JMB Wind Ltda. (1)
Zona Industrial da Palhaca Lote 10, 3770-355, Palhaca, Portugal
Tel.: (351) 234244222
Wind Blade Product Mfr
N.A.I.C.S.: 333611

PT. Alucobond Far East Indonesia (1)
Jl Jalur Sutera Timur Kav 7A No 6 Alam Sutera, Tangerang, 15143, Banten, Indonesia
Tel.: (62) 2129779583
Emp.: 2
Lumber Plywood Mfr
N.A.I.C.S.: 321912

Perspex International Limited (1)
Duckworth Street, Darwen, BB3 1AT, Lancs, United Kingdom
Tel.: (44) ()12548740
Web Site: http://www.perspex.com
Acrylic Sheet Products Mfr
N.A.I.C.S.: 326130

Subsidiary (Domestic):

Perspex Distribution Limited (2)
2-3 Lonebarn Link, Springfield Business Park, Chelmsford, CM2 5AR, Essex, United Kingdom
Tel.: (44) 1245232800
Web Site: https://www.perspex.co.uk
Sales Range: $25-49.9 Million
Emp.: 52
Acrylic Sheet Products Distr
N.A.I.C.S.: 424610
Keith Piggot *(Mng Dir)*

Polycasa France SA (1)
57 rue d Amsterdam, 75008, Paris, France
Tel.: (33) 14576711
Acrylic Sheet Product Mfr
N.A.I.C.S.: 326113

Polycasa Nischwitz GmbH (1)
Manfred-von-Ardenne-Str 1 OT Nischwitz, Thallwitz, 04808, Leipzig, Germany
Tel.: (49) 3425985300
Emp.: 60
Ore Material & Sandwich Constructions Services
N.A.I.C.S.: 423390

Polycasa Slovakia sro (1)
M R Stefanika 71, 01039, Zilina, Slovakia
Tel.: (421) 417071411
Emp.: 100
Acrylic Sheet Product Mfr
N.A.I.C.S.: 326113

SCHWEIZER ELECTRONIC AG
Einsteinstrasse 10, 78713, Schramberg, Germany
Tel.: (49) 74225120
Web Site: https://www.schweizer.ag
SCE—(MUN)
Rev.: $153,923,633
Assets: $117,142,684
Liabilities: $88,673,877
Net Worth: $28,468,807
Earnings: $36,306,284
Emp.: 533
Fiscal Year-end: 12/31/23
Printed Circuit Board Mfr
N.A.I.C.S.: 334412
Marc Bunz *(Deputy Chm-Exec Bd & CFO)*

Subsidiaries:

Schweizer Electronic (Jiangsu) Co., Ltd. (1)
No 2268 Baita Road, Jintan District, Changzhou, 213200, China
Tel.: (86) 51982768888
Information Technology Services
N.A.I.C.S.: 541519

SCHWEIZER ELECTRONIC AG

Schweizer Electronic AG—(Continued)

Schweizer Electronic Singapore Pte. Ltd. (1)
51 Goldhill Plaza 08-10, Singapore, 308900, Singapore
Tel.: (65) 62597588
Information Technology Services
N.A.I.C.S.: 541519

SCHWEIZERISCHE BUNDES-BAHNEN SBB AG
Hilfikerstrasse 1, 3000, Bern, Switzerland
Tel.: (41) 512201111   CH
Web Site: http://www.sbb.ch
Local Train Service
N.A.I.C.S.: 485999
Andreas Meyer *(CEO)*

Subsidiaries:

ChemOil Logistics AG (1)
Guterstrasse 97, 4053, Basel, Switzerland   **(100%)**
Tel.: (41) 612266060
Web Site: http://www.chemoil.ch
Sales Range: $25-49.9 Million
Emp.: 30
Rail Transportation Services
N.A.I.C.S.: 488210

Elvetino AG (1)
Limmatstrasse 23, 8005, Zurich, Switzerland   **(100%)**
Tel.: (41) 512229222
Web Site: http://www.elvetino.ch
Hotels & Motels
N.A.I.C.S.: 721110

Etzelwerk AG (1)
Letzistrasse 27, 8852, Altendorf, Switzerland   **(100%)**
Tel.: (41) 51 223 8410
Web Site: http://www.sbb.ch
Electric Power Distribution
N.A.I.C.S.: 221122

RailAway AG (1)
Zentralstrasse 7, 6002, Lucerne, Switzerland   **(86%)**
Tel.: (41) 512273640
Web Site: http://www.railaway.ch
Sales Range: $25-49.9 Million
Emp.: 70
Travel Agencies
N.A.I.C.S.: 561510
Rene Kamer *(CEO)*

RegionAlps SA (1)
Rue de la Poste 3, Case postale 727, 1920, Martigny, Switzerland   **(70%)**
Tel.: (41) 277204747
Web Site: http://www.regionalps.ch
Sales Range: $25-49.9 Million
Emp.: 50
Railroad Rolling Stock Mfr
N.A.I.C.S.: 336510
Praz Gregoire *(Gen Mgr)*

SBB Cargo Deutschland GmbH (1)
Schifferstrasse 200, 47059, Duisburg, Germany   **(100%)**
Tel.: (49) 2036078303
Local Freight Trucking
N.A.I.C.S.: 484110

SBB Cargo GmbH (1)
Schifferstrasse 166, 47059, Duisburg, Germany   **(100%)**
Tel.: (49) 2036078407
Web Site: http://www.sbbcargo.com
Sales Range: $25-49.9 Million
Emp.: 100
Line-Haul Railroads
N.A.I.C.S.: 482111

SBB Cargo Italia S.r.l. (1)
Via Damiano Chiesa 2, 21013, Gallarate, Italy   **(100%)**
Tel.: (39) 0331248511
Web Site: http://www.sbbcargo.com
Line-Haul Railroads
N.A.I.C.S.: 482111

STC Switzerland Travel Centre AG (1)
Binzstrasse 38, 8045, Zurich, Switzerland   **(67%)**
Tel.: (41) 432105500
Web Site: http://www.switzerlandtravelcentre.com
Emp.: 120
Travel Agencies
N.A.I.C.S.: 561510
Michael Maeder *(Mgr)*

STC Switzerland Travel Centre Ltd. (1)
30 Bedford St 1st Fl, London, WC2E9ED, United Kingdom   **(67%)**
Tel.: (44) 2074204900
Sales Range: $25-49.9 Million
Emp.: 20
Travel Agencies
N.A.I.C.S.: 561510
Helmut Kolb *(Mgr-Ops)*

Schweizerische Bodensee-Schifffahrtsges. AG (1)
Friedrichshafenerstrasse 55a, 8590, Romanshorn, Switzerland   **(97.39%)**
Tel.: (41) 714667888
Web Site: http://www.sbsag.ch
Sales Range: $25-49.9 Million
Emp.: 60
Inland Water Passenger Transportation
N.A.I.C.S.: 483212
Andrea Ruf *(Mgr-Sls)*

Schweizerische Bundesbahnen SBB Cargo AG (1)
Bahnhostrasse 12, 400065, Olten, Switzerland   **(100%)**
Tel.: (41) 512291111
Web Site: http://www.sbbcargo.com
Line-Haul Railroads
N.A.I.C.S.: 482111
Peter Imfeld *(Mgr-Content)*

Securitrans Public Transport Security AG (1)
Bubenbergplatz 10 A, 3001, Bern, Switzerland   **(51%)**
Tel.: (41) 512204600
Web Site: http://www.securitrans.ch
Sales Range: $10-24.9 Million
Emp.: 30
Security System Services
N.A.I.C.S.: 561621
Martin Graf *(CEO)*

Sensetalbahn AG (1)
Zwyssigstrasse 45, 3007, Bern, Switzerland   **(65.47%)**
Tel.: (41) 313819740
Web Site: http://www.stb-bus.ch
Line-Haul Railroads
N.A.I.C.S.: 482111

Thurbo AG (1)
Bahnhofstrasse 31, 8280, Kreuzlingen, Switzerland   **(90%)**
Tel.: (41) 512234900
Web Site: http://www.thurbo.ch
Sales Range: $125-149.9 Million
Emp.: 400
Line-Haul Railroads
N.A.I.C.S.: 482111

SCHWEIZERISCHE MOBILIAR VERSICHERUNGSGESELL-SCHAFT AG
Bundesgasse 35, 3001, Bern, Switzerland
Tel.: (41) 313898844
Web Site: http://www.mobi.ch
Sales Range: $600-649.9 Million
Emp.: 380
Fire Insurance Services
N.A.I.C.S.: 524298
Marcus Hongelr *(CEO)*

SCHWEIZERISCHE NATIONAL-BANK
Boersenstrasse 15, PO Box, CH-8022, Zurich, Switzerland
Tel.: (41) 586310000
Web Site: http://www.snb.ch
Year Founded: 1907
SWZNF—(OTCIQ)
Assets: $880,980,155,211
Liabilities: $811,596,674,058
Net Worth: $69,383,481,153
Earnings: ($58,994,235,033)
Emp.: 999
Fiscal Year-end: 12/31/23
International Banking Services
N.A.I.C.S.: 522110
Olivier Steimer *(Vice Chm-Supervisory Bd)*

Subsidiaries:

Landqart AG (1)
Kantonsstrasse 16, 7302, Landqart, Switzerland
Tel.: (41) 813079090
Web Site: http://www.landqart.com
Emp.: 210
Paper Mfr
N.A.I.C.S.: 322120
Axel Wappler *(CEO)*

LiPro (LP) AG (1)
Schweizerische Nationalbank Bundesplatz 1, Bern, 3011, Switzerland
Tel.: (41) 313270211
Commercial Banking Services
N.A.I.C.S.: 522110

StabFund (GP) AG (1)
Schweizerische Nationalbank Bundesplatz 1, Bern, 3011, Switzerland
Tel.: (41) 313270211
Web Site: http://www.snb.ch
Commercial Banking Services
N.A.I.C.S.: 522110

Swiss Interbank Clearing AG (1)
Hardturmstrasse 201, 8021, Zurich, Switzerland
Tel.: (41) 442793111
Web Site: http://www.six-interbank-clearing.com
Sales Range: $50-74.9 Million
Emp.: 100
Commericial Banking
N.A.I.C.S.: 522110

SCHWEPPES ZIMBABWE LTD.
67a Woolwich Road, PO Box 506, Willovale, Harare, Zimbabwe
Tel.: (263) 2426202326
Web Site: http://www.schweppes.co.zw
Sales Range: $25-49.9 Million
Emp.: 500
Soft Drink Mfr & Distr
N.A.I.C.S.: 312111
Sternford Moyo *(Chm)*

SCHWEVERS & RAAB STAHL - HOCHBAU GMBH
Wohrmannstrasse 27, 47546, Kalkar, Germany
Tel.: (49) 2824997490   De
Web Site: http://www.schwevers.de
Year Founded: 1937
Sales Range: $10-24.9 Million
Emp.: 45
Industrial & Commercial Metal Modular Building Mfr
N.A.I.C.S.: 332311
Heinz Schwevers *(Co-Owner & Co-CEO)*

SCI ELECTRIC PUBLIC COMPANY LIMITED
No 107/1 Moo1 Bangna-Trad Km 27 Road T Bangpleang A Bangbor, Samut Prakan, 10560, Thailand
Tel.: (66) 23381414
Web Site: https://investor.sci-mfgr.com
Year Founded: 1987
SCI—(THA)
Rev.: $46,934,956
Assets: $50,638,911
Liabilities: $30,908,154
Net Worth: $19,730,757
Earnings: ($16,857,469)
Emp.: 583
Fiscal Year-end: 12/31/23
Electric Power Utility
N.A.I.C.S.: 221121

INTERNATIONAL PUBLIC

Noppol Milinthanggoon *(Chm)*

Subsidiaries:

Ajikawa & SCI Metal Tech Co., Ltd. (1)
No 1 Soi Udomsuk 45 Sukhumvit 103, Bangna, Bangkok, 10260, Thailand
Tel.: (66) 2361801417
Web Site: https://www.agscimt-wcp.com
Telecommunication Tower Equipment Mfr
N.A.I.C.S.: 334290

SCI INFORMATION SERVICE INC.
23 Gukhoi-daero 70-gil, Yeongdeungpo-gu, Seoul, 04081, Korea (South)
Tel.: (82) 234455000
Web Site: http://www.sci.co.kr
Year Founded: 1992
036120—(KRS)
Rev.: $31,369,716
Assets: $29,774,904
Liabilities: $6,458,202
Net Worth: $23,316,703
Earnings: $1,816,740
Emp.: 195
Fiscal Year-end: 12/31/22
Credit Information Services
N.A.I.C.S.: 561450
Wuk Seong Kang *(CEO)*

SCI JOINT STOCK CO.
3rd Floor - Tower C Golden Palace Building Me Tri Street, Nam Tu Liem District, Hanoi, Vietnam
Tel.: (84) 437684495
Web Site: https://scigroup.vn
Year Founded: 1998
Sales Range: $1-9.9 Million
Civil Engineering Construction Services
N.A.I.C.S.: 237990
Phuc Van Nguyen *(Chm-Mgmt Bd & Gen Dir)*

SCI LTD.
7030 Woodbine Avenue 6th Floor, Markham, L3R 6G2, ON, Canada
Tel.: (905) 479-1595
Web Site: http://www.scitorque.com
Year Founded: 1994
Sales Range: $10-24.9 Million
Emp.: 130
Enterprise Retail Process Management Solutions
N.A.I.C.S.: 513210
Paul D. Damp *(Chm)*

SCI-TEK INSTRUMENTS LTD.
Berrybrook House Stilebrook Road, Olney, MK46 5EA, Buckinghamshire, United Kingdom
Tel.: (44) 1234240765
Web Site: http://www.scitekuk.com
Year Founded: 1983
Sales Range: $1-9.9 Million
Emp.: 10
Laboratory Instruments Distr
N.A.I.C.S.: 423450
D. Martin *(Mng Dir)*

SCIBASE HOLDING AB
Landsvagen 39 Sundbyberg, 172 63, Stockholm, Sweden
Tel.: (46) 841062000
Web Site: https://www.scibase.se
Year Founded: 1998
SCIB—(OMX)
Rev.: $1,675,611
Assets: $4,669,046
Liabilities: $2,305,019
Net Worth: $2,364,026
Earnings: ($4,043,384)
Emp.: 26
Fiscal Year-end: 12/31/22
Medical Device Mfr

AND PRIVATE COMPANIES

N.A.I.C.S.: 339112
Stig Ollmar (Founder & Chief Scientific Officer)

SCICOM (MSC) BERHAD
25th Floor Menara TA One, 22 Jalan P Ramlee, 50250, Kuala Lumpur, Malaysia
Tel.: (60) 321621088
Web Site: https://www.scicom-intl.com
Year Founded: 1997
SCICOM—(KLS)
Rev.: $65,600,275
Assets: $40,831,071
Liabilities: $13,077,357
Net Worth: $27,753,714
Earnings: $7,782,814
Emp.: 3,790
Fiscal Year-end: 06/30/22
Business Process Outsourcing Services
N.A.I.C.S.: 561499
Krishnan Menon (Chm)

SCIDEV LTD
Unit 1 8 Turbo Road, Kings Park, 2148, NSW, Australia
Tel.: (61) 296225185
Web Site: https://scidevltd.com
Year Founded: 2001
SDV—(ASX)
Rev.: $72,940,705
Assets: $48,086,271
Liabilities: $14,541,266
Net Worth: $33,545,005
Earnings: $1,452,324
Emp.: 89
Fiscal Year-end: 06/30/24
Mineral Exploration Services
N.A.I.C.S.: 212290
Heath Roberts (Gen Counsel & Sec)

Subsidiaries:

Intec Envirometals Pty Ltd (1)
20 River Road, PO Box 666, Burnie, 7320, TAS, Australia
Tel.: (61) 364319867
Mineral Exploration Services
N.A.I.C.S.: 212290
Brian Banister (Mng Dir)

Science Developments Pty Ltd (1)
Unit 1 8 Turbo Road, Kings Park, 2148, NSW, Australia (50%)
Tel.: (61) 296225185
Web Site: http://www.scidev.com.au
Chemical Research & Development Services
N.A.I.C.S.: 541715

SCIENCE GROUP PLC
Harston Mill, Harston, Cambridge, CB22 7GG, United Kingdom
Tel.: (44) 1223875200 UK
Web Site: https://www.sciencegroup.com
SAG—(AIM)
Rev.: $108,938,399
Assets: $160,661,449
Liabilities: $61,950,265
Net Worth: $98,711,184
Earnings: $13,323,656
Emp.: 436
Fiscal Year-end: 12/31/22
Holding Company; Diversified Investments in Engineering Materials, Telecommunications, Life Sciences & Medical Products
N.A.I.C.S.: 551112
Martyn Ratcliffe (Chm)

Subsidiaries:

Frontier Smart Technologies Group Limited (1)
137 Euston Road, London, NW1 2AA, United Kingdom
Tel.: (44) 2073910620
Web Site: http://www.frontiersmart.com
Rev.: $41,754,000
Assets: $33,876,000
Liabilities: $14,928,000
Net Worth: $18,948,000
Earnings: ($2,955,000)
Emp.: 130
Fiscal Year-end: 12/31/2018
Investment Holding Company
N.A.I.C.S.: 551112
Anthony Sethill (CEO)

Subsidiary (Domestic):

Toumaz Healthcare Limited (2)
115 Olympic Avenue Building 3, Abingdon, OX14 4SA, United Kingdom (100%)
Tel.: (44) 1235 438 950
Web Site: http://www.toumaz.com
Emp.: 60
Medical Application Semiconductor & Electronic Components Mfr
N.A.I.C.S.: 334413

Toumaz Microsystems Limited (2)
Building 3 115 Milton Park, Abingdon, OX14 4RZ, United Kingdom (75%)
Tel.: (44) 1235 438 950
Web Site: http://www.toumaz.com
Sales Range: $25-49.9 Million
Emp.: 1
Semiconductor Chips & Other Electronic Components Mfr
N.A.I.C.S.: 334413

Subsidiary (Domestic):

Frontier Silicon Limited (3)
137 Euston Road, London, NW1 2AA, United Kingdom
Tel.: (44) 207 391 0620
Web Site: http://www.toumaz.com
Sales Range: $25-49.9 Million
Emp.: 20
Semiconductor & Modular Solutions for Digital Media Products Developer
N.A.I.C.S.: 334413

Sagentia Catella AB (1)
Veddestavagen 7, 17562, Jarfalla, Sweden
Tel.: (46) 84457960
Web Site: http://www.sagentiacatella.com
Sales Range: $25-49.9 Million
Emp.: 11
Scientific & Technical Consulting Services
N.A.I.C.S.: 541690

Sagentia Inc (1)
8161 Maple Ln Blcd, Fulton, MD 20759
Tel.: (410) 654-0090
Web Site: http://www.sagentia.com
Professional Scientific & Technical Services
N.A.I.C.S.: 541990

Sagentia Ltd. (1)
Harston Mill Royston Road, Harston, Cambridge, CB22 7GG, United Kingdom
Tel.: (44) 01223875200
Sales Range: $25-49.9 Million
Consultancy & Intellectual Property Exploitation
N.A.I.C.S.: 561499

Sagentia SGAI Ltd. (1)
Unit 5 & 6 10th Floor Blk B, Veristrong Ind Ctr 36 Au Pui W, Fotan, China (Hong Kong)
Tel.: (852) 28668701
Web Site: http://www.sgaitech.com
Administrative Management & General Management Consulting Services
N.A.I.C.S.: 541611

Sagentia Technology Advisory Limited (1)
Harston Mill Harston, Cambridge, CB22 7GG, United Kingdom
Tel.: (44) 1223875200
Web Site: http://www.sagentia.com
Technology Consulting Services
N.A.I.C.S.: 541690

TP Group Plc (1)
Cody Technology Park old Ively Road, Farnborough, GU14 0LX, Hampshire, United Kingdom
Tel.: (44) 1753285810
Web Site: http://www.tpgroupglobal.com
Rev.: $80,166,577
Assets: $83,107,399
Liabilities: $46,459,821
Net Worth: $36,647,578
Earnings: ($13,575,842)
Emp.: 461
Fiscal Year-end: 12/31/2020
Air Compressor Technology Developer
N.A.I.C.S.: 333912
Phil Cartmell (CEO)

SCIENCE IN SPORT PLC
16-18 Hatton Garden, Farringdon, London, EC1N 8AT, United Kingdom
Tel.: (44) 2074003700 UK
Web Site: https://www.scienceinsport.com
Year Founded: 2013
SIS—(AIM)
Rev.: $80,501,136
Assets: $95,562,989
Liabilities: $44,703,358
Net Worth: $50,859,631
Earnings: ($13,771,775)
Emp.: 229
Fiscal Year-end: 12/31/22
Holding Company; Sports Supplements & Nutrition Products Mfr & Distr
N.A.I.C.S.: 551112
Stephen N. Moon (CEO)

Subsidiaries:

SiS (Science in Sport) Limited (1)
2nd Floor 16-18 Hatton Garden, Farringdon, London, EC1N 8AT, United Kingdom (100%)
Tel.: (44) 2074003700
Sports Supplements & Nutrition Products Mfr & Distr
N.A.I.C.S.: 325412

SCIENCENOW LIMITED
Middlesex House 34-42 Cleveland Street, London, W1T 4LB, United Kingdom
Tel.: (44) 20 7323 0323 UK
Web Site: http://www.sciencenavigation.com
Year Founded: 2006
Emp.: 100
Holding Company; Biomedical Journal, Website & Software Publisher & Information Services
N.A.I.C.S.: 551112
Vitek Tracz (Chm)

Subsidiaries:

Faculty of 1000 Ltd. (1)
Middlesex House 34-42 Cleveland Street, London, W1T 4LB, United Kingdom
Tel.: (44) 2073230323
Web Site: http://www.f1000.com
Emp.: 80
Biological & Medical Publication Peer Reviews & Information Publisher
N.A.I.C.S.: 519290
Vitek Tracz (Chm)

Global Data Point Ltd. (1)
Ha-Pardes 9, Tel Aviv, Israel
Tel.: (972) 3 758 5840
Web Site: http://www.gdp.co.il
Events Database Publisher
N.A.I.C.S.: 513140

SCIENCESOFT, INC.
2 Bedy St, 220040, Minsk, Belarus
Tel.: (375) 172933736
Web Site: http://www.scnsoft.com
IT Services
N.A.I.C.S.: 519290
Nikolay Kurayev (CEO)

SCIENJOY HOLDING CORP.
Room 1118 11th Floor Building 3 99 Wangzhou Road, Liangzhu Sub district Yuhang District, Hangzhou, Zhejiang, China
Tel.: (86) 18610932235 VG
Web Site: https://www.scienjoy.com
Year Founded: 2018
SJ—(NASDAQ)
Rev.: $299,258,505
Assets: $230,125,710
Liabilities: $52,021,230
Net Worth: $178,104,480
Earnings: $29,620,549
Emp.: 277
Fiscal Year-end: 12/31/22
Computer Processing & Data Preparation Services
N.A.I.C.S.: 513210
Yongsheng Liu (Vice Chm)

SCIENS INTERNATIONAL INVESTMENTS & HOLDINGS S.A.
Solonos 10 - Kolonaki, Athens, 10673, Greece
Tel.: (30) 2103392760
Web Site: http://www.sciens.gr
Sales Range: $1-9.9 Million
Emp.: 10
Business Consulting & Financial Management Services
N.A.I.C.S.: 523940
Ioannis P. Rigas (Pres & CEO)

SCIENTECH CORPORATION
11F No 208 Ruiguang Rd, Neihu Dist, Taipei, 114673, Taiwan
Tel.: (886) 287512323 TW
Web Site: https://www.scientech.com.tw
Year Founded: 1979
3583—(TAI)
Rev.: $226,036,847
Assets: $618,818,349
Liabilities: $488,361,079
Net Worth: $130,457,270
Earnings: $21,266,293
Fiscal Year-end: 12/31/23
Semiconductor Devices Mfr
N.A.I.C.S.: 334413
H. L. Hsieh (Chm)

Subsidiaries:

Scientech Corporation - Huko Factory (1)
30352 Zhonghua Road Hsinchu Industrial Zone Hukou Township, Hsinchu, Taiwan
Tel.: (886) 35986199
Semiconductor Devices Mfr
N.A.I.C.S.: 334413

SCIENTECHNIC LLC
PO Box 25490, Dubai, United Arab Emirates
Tel.: (971) 4 2035777
Web Site: http://www.scientechnic.com
Year Founded: 1973
Electronic Equipment Distr
N.A.I.C.S.: 423690
Vijith Mukundan (Sr Mgr-Traffic Mgmt Div)

SCIENTEX BERHAD
No 9 Persiaran Selangor Seksyen 15, 40200, Shah Alam, Selangor Darul Ehsan, Malaysia
Tel.: (60) 355191325
Web Site: https://scientex.com.my
Year Founded: 1968
SCIENTX—(KLS)
Rev.: $862,835,132
Assets: $1,165,124,868
Liabilities: $401,877,249
Net Worth: $763,247,619
Earnings: $95,013,968
Emp.: 3,990
Fiscal Year-end: 07/31/23
Holding Company; Plastic Resins & Plastic Products Mfr
N.A.I.C.S.: 551112
Peng Jin Lim (Mng Dir)

Subsidiaries:

Scientex Industries Group Sdn. Bhd. (1)

SCIENTEX BERHAD

Scientex Berhad—(Continued)
No 9 Persiaran Selangor Seksyen 15,
40200, Shah Alam, Selangor, Malaysia
Tel.: (60) 355248888
Synthetic & Plastic Material Mfr
N.A.I.C.S.: 325211
Lim Peng Jin *(CEO & Mng Dir)*

Scientex Packaging (Ayer Keroh) Berhad (1)
No 9 Persiaran Selangor Seksyen 15,
40200, Shah Alam, Selangor,
Malaysia (71.9%)
Tel.: (60) 355191325
Web Site:
 https://scientexpackagingak.com.my
Rev.: $168,283,085
Assets: $131,353,872
Liabilities: $46,335,059
Net Worth: $85,018,813
Earnings: $6,108,098
Emp.: 1,386
Fiscal Year-end: 07/31/2023
Plastic Packaging Mfr
N.A.I.C.S.: 326112
Geoff Jin Wei Low *(Exec Dir)*

Subsidiary (Non-US):

Daibochi Australia Pty. Ltd. (2)
18 Capital Court, Braeside, 3195, VIC, Australia
Tel.: (61) 385860400
Web Site: http://www.daibochi.com.au
Sales Range: $25-49.9 Million
Emp.: 4
Flexible Packaging Products Mfr
N.A.I.C.S.: 326112

Subsidiary (Domestic):

Daibochi Land Sdn. Bhd. (2)
D8/08 Plz Jayamuda Jalan Pelanduk Putih,
75300, Melaka, Malaysia
Tel.: (60) 62835442
Sales Range: $50-74.9 Million
Emp.: 5
Residential Property Development Services
N.A.I.C.S.: 531390

Scientex Packaging Film Sdn. Bhd. (1)
Scientex Berhad No 9 Persiaran Selangor
Seksyen 15, Shah Alam, 40200, Selangor
Darul Ehsan, Malaysia
Tel.: (60) 355191325
Web Site: http://www.scientex.com.my
Emp.: 1,000
Plastic Packaging Film Mfr
N.A.I.C.S.: 326112

Subsidiary (Domestic):

Great Wall Plastic Industries Berhad (2)
Lot 1608 Rawang Integrated Industrial
Park, Jalan Rawang Batang Berjuntai,
48000, Rawang, Selangor Darul Ehsan,
Malaysia
Tel.: (60) 3 6092 3333
Web Site: http://www.gwpi.com.my
Sales Range: $100-124.9 Million
Emp.: 300
Plastic Film, Printing & Converting Flexible
Packaging Products Mfr
N.A.I.C.S.: 326112
Yong Chee Ming *(Gen Mgr)*

Pan Pacific Straptex Sdn. Bhd. (2)
Lot 2379 Mukim Tanjung Kling, Melaka,
76400, Malaysia
Tel.: (60) 63518533
Emp.: 100
Plastics Product Mfr
N.A.I.C.S.: 326199
Chua Chun Seng *(Mgr)*

Scientex Quatari Sdn. Bhd. (1)
35 Jalan Rusa 1Taman Scientex, Pasir Gudang, 81700, Johor, Malaysia
Tel.: (60) 72899883
Investment Management Service
N.A.I.C.S.: 523940

Subsidiary (Domestic):

Scientex (Skudai) Sdn. Bhd. (2)
Pejabat Jualan Taman Scientex Utama PTD
113011, Jalan Persiaran Scientex Utama 1
Senai Johor Darul Takzim, 81400, Johor

Bahru, Malaysia
Tel.: (60) 197017515
Emp.: 30
Property Development Services
N.A.I.C.S.: 531311
Choo Chee Meng *(Sr Gen Mgr)*

SCIENTIA SCHOOL, S.A.
Oficina 2 Calle Conde de Penalver
45, 28006, Madrid, Spain ES
Web Site:
 https://www.scientiaschool.com
Year Founded: 2014
MLSCI—(EUR)
Rev.: $10,091,733
Assets: $45,632,420
Liabilities: $34,540,255
Net Worth: $11,092,165
Earnings: $1,966,329
Emp.: 401
Fiscal Year-end: 12/31/22
Educational Support Services
N.A.I.C.S.: 611710
Estanislao Martinez *(Chm)*

Subsidiaries:

Ieducnado Mexico S.A.P.I de C.V. (1)
Avenida Revolucion 1267 Int 19-A Col, Alvaro Obregon, 01010, Los Alpes, Mexico
Tel.: (52) 5576980366
Web Site: https://www.ieducando.mx
Educational Consulting Services
N.A.I.C.S.: 611710

Scientia Alhucema, S.L. (1)
Avenida De Las Provincias 51, Fuenlabrada, 28941, Madrid, Spain
Tel.: (34) 916098087
Web Site:
 https://www.alhucema.scientiaschool.com
Educational Support Services
N.A.I.C.S.: 611710

Scientia Denia, S.L. (1)
Cami de Santa Llucia 12, Alicante, 03700,
Denia, Spain
Tel.: (34) 943456600
Web Site:
 https://www.denia.scientiaschool.com
Educational Support Services
N.A.I.C.S.: 611710

Scientia Karmelo, S.L. (1)
Illunbe Kalea 8, Donostia, 20011, Guipuzcoa, Spain
Tel.: (34) 943456600
Web Site:
 https://www.karmelo.scientiaschool.com
Education Services
N.A.I.C.S.: 611710

Scientia Lalin, S.L. (1)
Penatoares 1, Lalin, 36500, Pontevedra, Spain
Tel.: (34) 886448940
Web Site:
 https://www.lalin.scientiaschool.com
Educational Support Services
N.A.I.C.S.: 611710

Tilin Talan Spain, S.L. (1)
Avenida de Tolosa 107, Donostia Gipuzkoa,
20018, San Sebastian, Spain
Tel.: (34) 943535679
Web Site: https://www.tilintalan.es
Education Services
N.A.I.C.S.: 624410

SCIENTIFIC & MEDICAL EQUIPMENT HOUSE COMPANY
King Fahad Road, PO Box 5561, AL-Mutammarat district, Riyadh, 11432,
Saudi Arabia
Tel.: (966) 114646699
Web Site: https://smeh.com.sa
Year Founded: 1979
4014—(SAU)
Rev.: $190,326,916
Assets: $248,242,459
Liabilities: $123,291,545
Net Worth: $124,950,914
Earnings: $4,163,694

Emp.: 6,890
Fiscal Year-end: 12/31/22
Medical Equipment Distr
N.A.I.C.S.: 423450
Saud Mohammad Nasser Al-Arifi *(Founder)*

SCIENTIFIC BRAIN TRAINING SA
52 Quai Rambaud, 69002, Lyon, Cedex, France
Tel.: (33) 4 78 89 75 40
Web Site: http://www.sbt-corp.com
Year Founded: 2000
MLSBT—(EUR)
Sales Range: $10-24.9 Million
Cognitive Research & Development Services
N.A.I.C.S.: 541720

Subsidiaries:

Arnava Sas (1)
114 Boulevard Malesherbes, 75017, Paris, France
Tel.: (33) 142611601
Web Site: http://www.arnava.com
Education Training & Skill Providing Services
N.A.I.C.S.: 611710

HAPPYneuron Inc. (1)
900 E Hamilton Ave Ste 450, Campbell, CA 95008
Tel.: (800) 560-0966
Web Site: http://www.happy-neuron.com
Research & Development Services
N.A.I.C.S.: 541720

OSE Consulting SARL (1)
5 rue de Rome, 75008, Paris, France
Tel.: (33) 1 40 15 01 02
Web Site: http://www.oseconsulting.com
Emp.: 18
Cognitive Research & Development Services
N.A.I.C.S.: 541720
Edouard Blanchard *(Gen Mgr)*

Symetrix SARL (1)
34 avenue de l'Europe, 38100, Grenoble, France
Tel.: (33) 4 76 61 91 50
Web Site: http://www.symetrix.fr
Software Development Services
N.A.I.C.S.: 541511

SCIES B.G.R. INC.
2341 avenue de la Rotonde, Levis,
G6X 2M2, QC, Canada
Tel.: (418) 832-2918
Web Site: http://www.sciesbgr.com
Year Founded: 1968
Circular & Band Saws Mfr
N.A.I.C.S.: 333243
Sylvain Saint-Hilaire *(Pres)*

Subsidiaries:

Simonds International, LLC (1)
950 International Way, Springfield, OR 97477
Tel.: (800) 426-6226
Web Site: http://www.simondsint.com
Industrial Cutting Tool Mfr
N.A.I.C.S.: 333515
David Miles *(Pres-Simonds Saw)*

Branch (Domestic):

Simonds International Corporation-Portland (2)
2700 SE Tacoma St, Portland, OR 97202
Tel.: (503) 228-8381
Web Site: http://www.simondsint.com
Saw Blades Mfr
N.A.I.C.S.: 332216
George H. Jacobson *(Chm)*

Subsidiary (Domestic):

U.S. Blades Sub LLC (2)
600 Grantham Ave, W Monroe, LA 71292
Tel.: (800) 633-2710
Web Site: http://www.usblades.net

Industrial Knives, Blades, Saws & Ancillary
Materials Mfr
N.A.I.C.S.: 423830

INTERNATIONAL PUBLIC

SCIGINEER INC.
1-24-2 Ooi Shinagawa-ku, Tokyo,
140-0014, Japan
Tel.: (81) 357433147
Web Site: http://www.scigineer.co.jp
6031—(TKS)
Rev.: $10,816,580
Assets: $16,439,460
Liabilities: $9,473,060
Net Worth: $6,966,400
Earnings: $1,940,640
Emp.: 27
Fiscal Year-end: 06/30/24
Internet Marketing Services
N.A.I.C.S.: 541613
Shinichiro Yoshii *(Pres)*

SCIM S.A. CONSTANTA
Popas 3 Mamaia Km 2, Loc Navodari
Jud, 905750, Constanta, Romania
Tel.: (40) 341439153
Web Site: http://www.scimct.ro
Year Founded: 1965
Construction & Contract Services
N.A.I.C.S.: 236220

SCINAI IMMUNOTHERAPEUTICS LTD.
Jerusalem BioPark Hadassah Ein
Kerem campus, Jerusalem, Israel
Tel.: (972) 89302529
Web Site: https://www.scinai.com
Year Founded: 2003
SCNI—(NASDAQ)
Assets: $17,472,000
Liabilities: $22,041,000
Net Worth: ($4,569,000)
Earnings: ($6,500,000)
Emp.: 31
Fiscal Year-end: 12/31/23
Biopharmaceutical Product Mfr
N.A.I.C.S.: 325412
Mark S. Germain *(Chm)*

SCINEX CORPORATION
5315 Uehonmachi, Tennoji-ku,
Osaka, 543-0001, Japan
Tel.: (81) 667663333
Web Site: https://www.scinex.co.jp
Year Founded: 1966
2376—(TKS)
Rev.: $101,727,900
Assets: $98,766,620
Liabilities: $46,818,630
Net Worth: $51,947,990
Earnings: $2,491,970
Fiscal Year-end: 03/31/24
Commercial Printing & Media Services
N.A.I.C.S.: 323113
Yoshimasa Murata *(Pres)*

SCINOPHARM TAIWAN, LTD.
No 1 Nan-Ke 8th Road Shan-Hua,
T'ainan, 741014, Taiwan
Tel.: (886) 65052888
Web Site:
 https://www.scinopharm.com
Year Founded: 1997
1789—(TAI)
Rev.: $104,191,860
Assets: $383,321,415
Liabilities: $44,381,960
Net Worth: $338,939,455
Earnings: $9,387,357
Emp.: 740
Fiscal Year-end: 12/31/23
Pharmaceuticals Mfr
N.A.I.C.S.: 325412
Portia Lin *(Co-Chief Strategy Officer & VP-Mktg & Sls)*

AND PRIVATE COMPANIES

Subsidiaries:

SPT International, Ltd. (1)
98/15 Baankung Muang Ramkhamheng 39, Bangkok, Thailand
Web Site: http://steelexinternational.net
Shot Blasting & Painting System Mfr
N.A.I.C.S.: 332999

Subsidiary (Non-US):

Scianda (Changshu) Pharmaceuticals, Ltd. (2)
No 16 Dongzhou Road, Economic Development Zone, Changshu, 215513, Jiangsu, China
Tel.: (86) 51251921000
Web Site: https://spc.scianda.com.cn
Pharmaceuticals Mfr
N.A.I.C.S.: 325412

Scianda Shanghai Biochemical Technology, Ltd. (2)
Room 209 Block B Uni-President Building No 568 Tianshan west Road, Changning District, Shanghai, 200335, China
Tel.: (86) 2162372266
Pharmaceuticals Mfr
N.A.I.C.S.: 325412

SCINTILLA COMMERCIAL & CREDIT LTD.
9/12 Lal Bazar Street Merchantile Building Block-E 2nd Floor, Kolkata, 700 001, India
Tel.: (91) 3322485664
Web Site: http://www.scintilla.co.in
Year Founded: 1990
Rev.: $132,597
Assets: $1,685,897
Liabilities: $9,268
Net Worth: $1,676,629
Earnings: ($166)
Emp.: 3
Fiscal Year-end: 03/31/19
Commercial Banking Services
N.A.I.C.S.: 522110
Jitendra Kumar Goyal (Exec Dir)

SCINTREX LTD.
222 Snidercroft Road, Concord, L4K 2K1, ON, Canada
Tel.: (905) 669-2280
Web Site: http://www.scintrexltd.com
Year Founded: 1967
Sales Range: $25-49.9 Million
Emp.: 130
Measuring Device Mfr
N.A.I.C.S.: 334519
Radka Tamchyna (Mgr-Intl Sls)

SCINTRONIX CORPORATION LTD.
18 Kaki Bukit Road 3 #02-11, Entrepreneur Business Centre, Singapore, 415978, Singapore
Tel.: (65) 6744 3323
Sales Range: $10-24.9 Million
Industrial Products Mfr
N.A.I.C.S.: 333248
Wei Min Yang (Chm)

Subsidiaries:

Scintronix Engineering Pte. Ltd. (1)
8 Kallang Way 4, Singapore, 349068, Singapore
Tel.: (65) 67443323
Emp.: 3
Investment Management Service
N.A.I.C.S.: 523999

Scintronix Manufacturing Pte. Ltd. (1)
8 Kallang Way 4, Singapore, 415978, Singapore
Tel.: (65) 67443323
Emp.: 3
Electronic Components Mfr
N.A.I.C.S.: 334419

Scintronix Technology Pte. Ltd. (1)
8 Kallang Way 4, Singapore, Singapore

Tel.: (65) 67443323
Investment Management Service
N.A.I.C.S.: 523999

Subsidiary (Non-US):

TTL Promex Manufacturing (Shanghai) Co., Ltd. (2)
88 A 879 Lane Shuangbai Rd Meilong Town, Minhang District, Shanghai, China
Tel.: (86) 2154405099
Injection Molded Plastic Products Mfr
N.A.I.C.S.: 326121

TTL Promex Precision Engineering (Shanghai) Co., Ltd. (2)
88 C 879 Lane Shuangbai Rd Meilong Town, Minhang District, Shanghai, China
Tel.: (86) 2154408906
Injection Molded Plastic Products Mfr
N.A.I.C.S.: 326121

TTL Manufacturing (Shanghai) Co., Ltd. (1)
No 376 Debao Road West Wing 3rd Floor No 30 Building Waigaoqiao, Free Trade Zone Pudong, Shanghai, 200131, China
Tel.: (86) 2158652273
Injection Molded Plastic Products Mfr
N.A.I.C.S.: 326121

SCIO AUTOMATION GMBH
Durkheimer Strasse 130, D-67227, Frankenthal, Germany
Tel.: (49) 6233600065
Web Site: https://www.scio-automation.com
Emp.: 100
Industrial Automation & Labelling; Other Technical Support Services
N.A.I.C.S.: 541690

SCISPARC LTD.
20 Raul Wallenberg St Tower A 2nd Floor, Tel Aviv, 6971916, Israel
Tel.: (972) 36103100 IL
Web Site: https://www.scisparc.com
Year Founded: 2004
SPRC—(NASDAQ)
Rev.: $2,879,000
Assets: $11,182,000
Liabilities: $1,595,000
Net Worth: $9,587,000
Earnings: ($5,883,000)
Emp.: 4
Fiscal Year-end: 12/31/23
Pharmaceutical Product Research & Development Services
N.A.I.C.S.: 325412
Adi Zuloff-Shani (Chief Technologies Officer)

SCITEK AUSTRALIA PTY LTD.
Unit 1 12 Chaplin Drive, Lane Cove, 2066, NSW, Australia
Tel.: (61) 290465500 AU
Web Site: http://www.scitek.com.au
Year Founded: 1989
Vacuum Product Distr
N.A.I.C.S.: 423830

SCIUKER FRAMES SPA
Via Fratte Contrada, 83020, Avellino, Italy
Tel.: (39) 082574984
Web Site: https://www.sciuker.it
SCK—(ITA)
Rev.: $55,836,881
Assets: $107,642,552
Liabilities: $74,440,830
Net Worth: $33,201,722
Earnings: $7,342,092
Emp.: 154
Fiscal Year-end: 12/31/22
Aluminum Window & Door Mfr
N.A.I.C.S.: 321911
Marco Cipriano (Chm & CEO)

SCIVISION BIOTECH INC.

No 1 South 1st Rd, Qianzhen Dist, Kaohsiung, 806, Taiwan
Tel.: (886) 78232258
Web Site: https://www.scivision.com.tw
1786—(TAI)
Rev.: $23,316,262
Assets: $70,642,268
Liabilities: $17,452,009
Net Worth: $53,190,259
Earnings: $5,817,718
Emp.: 103
Fiscal Year-end: 12/31/23
Biotechnology Products Mfr
N.A.I.C.S.: 325414
Tony Han (Gen Mgr)

SCM DMA (PTY) LTD.
48 7th Ave Parktown North, Johannesburg, South Africa
Tel.: (27) 10 201 6300 ZA
Web Site: http://www.dma.co.za
Investment Banking Services
N.A.I.C.S.: 523150

SCM LIFESCIENCE CO., LTD.
310 Junsgsuk building A, 366 Seohaedaero, Incheon, 22332, Jung-gu, Korea (South)
Tel.: (82) 328813600
Web Site: http://www.scmlifescience.co.kr
Year Founded: 2014
Stem cell Therapy, Stem cell Storage, CMO, Contract Research & Consulting & Cosmetic Businesses
N.A.I.C.S.: 622110

Subsidiaries:

Coimmune, Inc. (1)
4233 Technology Dr, Durham, NC 27704
Tel.: (919) 287-6300
Web Site: https://www.coimmune.com
Biopharmaceutical Researcher, Developer & Mfr
N.A.I.C.S.: 325412
Lori R. Harrelson (CFO)

Subsidiary (Domestic):

Formula Pharmaceuticals, Inc. (2)
1055 Westlakes Dr 3rd Fl, Berwyn, PA 19312
Tel.: (610) 727-4172
Web Site: http://www.formulapharma.com
Chemicals Mfr
N.A.I.C.S.: 325412
Eric L. Steager (Treas & Sr VP-Fin)

SCM STIFTUNG CHRISTLICHE MEDIEN
Bodenborn 43, Witten, 58452, Germany
Tel.: (49) 2302 93093611
Web Site: http://www.stiftung-christliche-medien.de
Private Investment Firm
N.A.I.C.S.: 523999

Subsidiaries:

Gerth Medien GmbH (1)
Dillerberg 1, 35614, Asslar, Germany
Tel.: (49) 6443680
Web Site: http://www.gerth.de
Magazine Publisher
N.A.I.C.S.: 513120

SCO-PAK S.A.
Ul Prosta 28, 00-838, Warsaw, Poland
Tel.: (48) 82 5654017
Web Site: http://www.scopak.com.pl
SCO—(WAR)
Sales Range: $10-24.9 Million
Emp.: 220
Corrugated Board, Paper, Packaging & Paperboard Mfr
N.A.I.C.S.: 322211
Grzegorz Pleskot (Chm-Mgmt Bd)

SCOMI GROUP BERHAD

SCODER
Zi Oree Du Bois, 25480, Pirey, Doubs, France
Tel.: (33) 381482122
Web Site: http://www.scoder.fr
Rev.: $24,400,000
Emp.: 50
Metal Stamping Mfr
N.A.I.C.S.: 332119
Sylvain Giampiccolo (Dir)

SCODIX LTD.
13 Amal Street Park Afek, Rosh Ha'Ayin, 4809249, Israel
Tel.: (972) 39033371
Web Site: https://www.scodix.com
Year Founded: 2007
SCDX—(TAE)
Rev.: $26,061,000
Assets: $23,193,000
Liabilities: $14,363,000
Net Worth: $8,830,000
Earnings: ($2,741,000)
Fiscal Year-end: 06/30/23
Digital Printing Services
N.A.I.C.S.: 323120
Dov Ofer (Chm)

Subsidiaries:

Scodix B.V. (1)
Wim Duisenbergplantsoen 31, 6221 SE, Maastricht, Netherlands
Tel.: (31) 850212829
Printing Services
N.A.I.C.S.: 323111

Scodix Inc. (1)
Park 80 W Plz 1 250 Pehle Ave Ste 101, Saddle Brook, NJ 07663
Printing Services
N.A.I.C.S.: 323111

SCOM D.O.O.
Marsala Tita 15/1, Feketic, Srbobran, Serbia
Tel.: (381) 21 730 630
Web Site: http://www.scomdoo.com
Year Founded: 2003
Consumer Products Mfr & Supplier
N.A.I.C.S.: 926140

SCOMI GROUP BERHAD
Level 15 Menara TSR No 12 Jalan PJU 7/3 Mutiara Damansara, 47810, Petaling Jaya, Selangor Darul Ehsan, Malaysia
Tel.: (60) 37 717 3000 MY
Web Site: http://www.scomigroup.com.my
SCOMI—(KLS)
Assets: $2,974,950
Liabilities: $64,522,013
Net Worth: ($61,547,063)
Earnings: ($4,151,070)
Emp.: 2,000
Fiscal Year-end: 06/30/21
Holding Company
N.A.I.C.S.: 551112
Sharifah Norizan Shahabudin (Head-Legal & Corp Secretarial)

Subsidiaries:

Scomi Energy Services Berhad (1)
Level 15 Menara TSR No 12 Jalan PJU 7/3, Mutiara Damansara, 47810, Petaling Jaya, Selangor Darul Ehsan, Malaysia
Tel.: (60) 377173000
Web Site: https://www.scomienergy.com.my
Assets: $79,008,683
Liabilities: $84,323,250
Net Worth: ($5,314,568)
Earnings: ($9,293,130)
Emp.: 2,000
Fiscal Year-end: 06/30/2022
Oil, Gas & Coal Industry Support Services
N.A.I.C.S.: 561499
Stephen Fredrick Bracker (Chm)

Scomi Group Berhad—(Continued)

Subsidiary (Non-US):

PT. Rig Tenders Indonesia Tbk. (2)
18th floor Unit D Kawasan Rasuna Epicentrum, Jl HR Rasuna Said, Jakarta, 12940, Indonesia (80.54%)
Tel.: (62) 212527402
Web Site: https://www.rigtenders.co.id
Rev.: $34,170,706
Assets: $69,865,935
Liabilities: $1,954,713
Net Worth: $67,911,222
Earnings: $6,251,229
Emp.: 44
Fiscal Year-end: 06/30/2023
Holding Company; Coal, Oil & Gas Barge & Supply Vessel Chartering Services
N.A.I.C.S.: 551112
Degdo Suprayitno (Mgr-Operation-Offshore)

Subsidiary (US):

Scomi Equipment Inc. (2)
6818 N Sam Houston Pkwy W, Houston, TX 77064
Tel.: (281) 260-6016
Web Site: http://www.scomiequipment.com
Oil Industry Support Services
N.A.I.C.S.: 213112

Holding (Non-US):

Scomi Marine Services Pte Ltd (2)
390 Jalan Ahmad Ibrahim, Singapore, 629155, Singapore
Tel.: (65) 68079960
Holding Company
N.A.I.C.S.: 551112

Subsidiary (Domestic):

Scomi Oiltools Sdn. Bhd. (2)
Level 17 1 First Avenue, Bandar Utama, 47800, Petaling Jaya, Selangor Darul Ehsan, Malaysia
Tel.: (60) 3 7717 3000
Web Site: http://www.scomigroup.com.my
Oil Industry Support Services
N.A.I.C.S.: 213112

Scomi Sosma Sdn. Bhd. (2)
Level 17 First Avenue, Bandar Utama, 47800, Petaling Jaya, Selangor Darul Ehsan, Malaysia
Tel.: (60) 377173000
Oil Industry Support Services
N.A.I.C.S.: 213112

SCOOBEE DAY GARMENTS (INDIA) LIMITED
666-12 Anna Aluminium Building Kizhakkambalam Aluva, Kochi, 683 562, India
Tel.: (91) 4842680701 In
Web Site: https://scoobeedaygarments.com
Year Founded: 1994
531234—(BOM)
Rev.: $6,329,869
Assets: $7,578,568
Liabilities: $7,641,148
Net Worth: ($62,579)
Earnings: $939,708
Fiscal Year-end: 03/31/23
Paper Product Mfr & Distr
N.A.I.C.S.: 322130
Kalpathy Lakshminarayanan Venkitanarayanan (Mng Dir)

SCOOTERS INDIA LIMITED
3/481 1st Floor Vikalp Khand, PO Box No 23, Gomti Nagar, Lucknow, 226 010, Uttar Pradesh, India
Tel.: (91) 94507715176
Web Site: https://www.scootersindialtd.com
505141—(BOM)
Rev.: $1,280,780
Assets: $13,888,083
Liabilities: $13,819,506
Net Worth: $68,578
Earnings: ($6,640,220)
Emp.: 75
Fiscal Year-end: 03/31/21
3-Wheeled Vehicle Mfr
N.A.I.C.S.: 423110
Renati Sreenivasulu (Chm & Mng Dir)

SCOPE CARBON CORP.
Guinness Tower Suite 1000-1055 W Hastings St, Vancouver, V6E 2E9, BC, Canada
Tel.: (604) 683-0911 BC
Web Site: https://www.scopecarboncorp.com
Year Founded: 2018
SCPCF—(OTCQB)
Rev.: $1,222
Assets: $907,455
Liabilities: $96,762
Net Worth: $810,693
Earnings: ($275,322)
Fiscal Year-end: 09/30/22
Software Development Services
N.A.I.C.S.: 541511
Alan Tam (CFO)

SCOPE FLUIDICS SPOLKA AKCYJNA
Ogrodowa 58 9th floor, 00-876, Warsaw, Poland
Tel.: (48) 223762114
Web Site: https://www.scopefluidics.com
Year Founded: 2010
SCP—(WAR)
Health Care Products Mfr
N.A.I.C.S.: 325412
Piotr Garstecki (Pres)

SCOPE INDUSTRIES BERHAD
Lot 6181 Jln Perusahaan 2 Kawasan Perindustrian Parit Buntar, 34200, Parit Buntar, Perak, Malaysia
Tel.: (60) 57169605 MY
Web Site: https://www.scope.com.my
Year Founded: 1991
SCOPE—(KLS)
Rev.: $36,570,515
Assets: $48,027,937
Liabilities: $4,038,695
Net Worth: $43,989,242
Earnings: $284,692
Fiscal Year-end: 06/30/23
Electronic Component Mfr & Distr
N.A.I.C.S.: 334419
Chiow Hoo Lim (Founder & Mng Dir)

Subsidiaries:

Scope Manufacturers (M) Sdn. Bhd. (1)
Lot 6181 Jalan Perusahaan 2 Kawasan Perusahaan, 34200, Parit Buntar, Perak, Malaysia
Tel.: (60) 57169605
Electronic Components Mfr
N.A.I.C.S.: 334419

SCOPE METALS GROUP LTD.
75 Hamerkava St Reem Industrial Park, PO Box 3, Bne Ayish, 6086000, Tel Aviv, 6086000, Israel
Tel.: (972) 88631040 Il
Web Site: https://www.scope-metal.com
Year Founded: 1980
SCOP—(TAE)
Rev.: $452,494,813
Assets: $585,986,729
Liabilities: $313,897,771
Net Worth: $272,088,958
Earnings: $42,521,342
Emp.: 600
Fiscal Year-end: 12/31/23
Metal Service Centers & Other Metal Merchant Wholesalers
N.A.I.C.S.: 423510
Shmuel Shiloh (Chm)

Subsidiaries:

Alinox SP.Z.O.O. (1)
Ul Partyzantow 7, 41-400, Myslowice, Poland
Tel.: (48) 327 658 112
Web Site: http://www.alinox.pl
Sales Range: $25-49.9 Million
Stainless Steel Coils Mfr
N.A.I.C.S.: 331221

Buymetal.com, Inc. (1)
555 State Rd, Bensalem, PA 19020
Web Site: https://store.buymetal.com
Metal Alloy Mfr & Distr
N.A.I.C.S.: 332999

Dalian Best Metals (1)
Building 6-5 Guangshen Mould & Die Garden III B1-1-1 Free Trade Zone, 6 Huanghai Middle Road, Dalian, 116600, DDA, China
Tel.: (86) 41187187155
Web Site: http://www.scope-metal.com
Sales Range: $50-74.9 Million
Emp.: 3
Seal Products Distr
N.A.I.C.S.: 423510

Gilinox S.R.L. (1)
Str Maramures 38, Otopeni, Romania
Tel.: (40) 312240800
Web Site: https://www.gilinox.ro
Emp.: 23
Seal Products Distr
N.A.I.C.S.: 423510

Hadco Metal Trading Co., LLC (1)
120 Spagnoli Rd, Melville, NY 11747
Tel.: (631) 270-9800
Web Site: http://www.hadco-metal.com
Sales Range: $10-24.9 Million
Emp.: 100
Aluminum Products Whslr
N.A.I.C.S.: 423510

Material Technology Solutions LLC (1)
18 Elm St, Morristown, NJ 07960
Tel.: (973) 401-0711
Web Site: https://www.materialtech.com
Metal Alloy Mfr & Distr
N.A.I.C.S.: 332999

Materials Technology Solutions, LLC (1)
18 Elm St, Morristown, NJ 07960
Tel.: (973) 401-0711
Web Site: http://www.materialtech.com
Sales Range: $50-74.9 Million
Emp.: 7
Seal Products Distr
N.A.I.C.S.: 423510
Boaz Leshem (CEO)

Primapol-Metal-Spot s.r.o. (1)
Druzstevni 2, 273 51, Pleteny Ujezd, Czech Republic
Tel.: (420) 31 581 7111
Web Site: https://www.primapol.cz
Sales Range: $25-49.9 Million
Seal Products Distr
N.A.I.C.S.: 423510

SCOR SE
5 Avenue Kleber, 75795, Paris, Cedex 16, France
Tel.: (33) 158447000 FR
Web Site: https://www.scor.com
Year Founded: 1970
SCRYY—(OTCIQ)
Rev.: $20,926,753,120
Assets: $56,765,568,080
Liabilities: $49,178,729,600
Net Worth: $7,586,838,480
Earnings: $282,495,200
Emp.: 3,123
Fiscal Year-end: 12/31/20
Financial Investment Services
N.A.I.C.S.: 523999
Frieder Knupling (Chief Risk Officer)

Subsidiaries:

ReMark International BV (1)
World Trade Center 26th Floor Zuidplein 214, 1077 XV, Amsterdam, Netherlands
Tel.: (31) 20 54 55 101
Web Site: http://www.remarkgroup.com
Sales Range: $100-124.9 Million
Emp.: 150
Marketing, Product, Technology & Financing Solutions for Insurance Industry
N.A.I.C.S.: 524298

Subsidiary (Non-US):

ReMark Hong Kong (2)
625 King's Road Suite 1303, North Point, Hong Kong, China (Hong Kong) (100%)
Tel.: (852) 29680808
Marketing, Product, Technology & Financing Solutions for Insurance Industry
N.A.I.C.S.: 524298
Benedict Ho (Controller-Fin)

SCOR AFRICA Ltd (1)
4th Floor Blend On Baker 17 Baker Street, Rosebank, 2196, South Africa
Tel.: (27) 115073900
Sales Range: $50-74.9 Million
Emp.: 8
General Insurance Services
N.A.I.C.S.: 524210
Richard Wolfaardt (Gen Mgr)

SCOR Asia House Limited Partnership (1)
10 Lime Street, London, EC3M 7AA, United Kingdom
Tel.: (44) 2032078500
Reinsurance Services
N.A.I.C.S.: 524130
Julia Brewster (Head-Gen Svcs)

SCOR Brasil Ltda (1)
Rua de gloria 344 Sl 601/603, 20241-180, Rio de Janeiro, Brazil
Tel.: (55) 21 2252 8498
Reinsurance & Insurance Services
N.A.I.C.S.: 524130

SCOR Canada Reinsurance Company (1)
199 Bay St Ste 2800 Commerce Ct W, PO Box 615, 161 Bay St Ste 5000, Toronto, M5L 1G1, ON, Canada (100%)
Tel.: (416) 869-3670
Web Site: http://www.scor.com
Sales Range: $50-74.9 Million
Emp.: 35
Reinsurance Services
N.A.I.C.S.: 524130

SCOR Global Investment SE (1)
5 Avenue Kleber, 79795, Paris, France
Tel.: (33) 158447000
Emp.: 60
Investment Management Service
N.A.I.C.S.: 523999

SCOR Global Life (1)
Immueble SCOR 1 avenue du General de Gaulle, 92074, Paris, Cedex, La Defense, France (100%)
Tel.: (33) 146987497
Web Site: http://www.scor.com
Sales Range: $50-74.9 Million
Emp.: 100
Life Reinsurance
N.A.I.C.S.: 524130
Paolo De Martin (CEO)

Subsidiary (Non-US):

ReMark Group BV (2)
Zuidplein 214, Amsterdam, 1077 XV, Netherlands
Tel.: (31) 205455101
Web Site: http://www.remarkgroup.com
Sales Range: $25-49.9 Million
Emp.: 35
Insurance Management Services
N.A.I.C.S.: 524298
Stephen Collins (CEO)

Revios Sweden Reinsurance Company (2)
Drotrinngatan 82, 11136, Stockholm, Sweden
Tel.: (46) 84408250
Web Site: http://www.revios.com
Sales Range: $50-74.9 Million
Emp.: 21
Insurance Agents
N.A.I.C.S.: 524298
Svein Borre Solvang (CEO)

AND PRIVATE COMPANIES

SCOR Global Life Ruckversicherung Schweiz AG (2)
General-Guisan-Quai 26, Zurich, 8002, Switzerland
Tel.: (41) 44 639 93 93
Web Site: http://www.scor.com
General Insurance Services
N.A.I.C.S.: 524210
Gabriele Hollmann *(Gen Mgr)*

SCOR Services Belux SPRL (2)
Brand Whitlocklaan 87, 1200, Brussels, Belgium
Tel.: (32) 27402565
Insurance Management Services
N.A.I.C.S.: 524298

SCOR Global Life Australia Pty Ltd. (1)
Level 33 1 O'Connell Street, Sydney, 2000, NSW, Australia
Tel.: (61) 292763501
Reinsurance Services
N.A.I.C.S.: 524130

SCOR Global Life Chile Ltda. (1)
Edificio Manatiales 3120 Oficina 8B Piso8 Ave Isidora Goyenechea, Las Condes, Santiago, Chile
Tel.: (56) 23349940
Sales Range: $50-74.9 Million
Emp.: 3
Reinsurance Services
N.A.I.C.S.: 524130

SCOR Global Life Reinsurance Ireland Ltd. (1)
36 Lower Baggot Street, Dublin, 2, Ireland
Tel.: (353) 16145151
Web Site: http://www.scor.com
Sales Range: $50-74.9 Million
Emp.: 6
Reinsurance Services
N.A.I.C.S.: 524130

SCOR Global Life Reinsurance Ltd. (1)
Golden Anchorage Complex, First Floor Sunset Crest, Saint James, BB 24014, Barbados
Tel.: (246) 432 6467
Web Site: http://www.usarisk.com
Sales Range: $50-74.9 Million
Emp.: 7
Reinsurance Services
N.A.I.C.S.: 524130
Martin Hole *(Pres)*

SCOR Global P&C (1)
Avenue Kleber, 75795, Paris, Cedex 16, France
Tel.: (33) 146987000
Web Site: http://www.scor.com
Sales Range: $50-74.9 Million
Emp.: 60
Property & Casualty Insurance Services
N.A.I.C.S.: 524126
Laurent Rousseau *(Deputy CEO)*

SCOR Global South Africa (Pty) Ltd. (1)
2nd Floor West Tower Maude Street, Nelson Mandela Square, Sandton, 2196, South Africa
Tel.: (27) 11 881 5584
Insurance Services
N.A.I.C.S.: 524298

SCOR Holding (Switzerland) Ltd (1)
General Guisan Quai 26, 8022, Zurich, Switzerland
Tel.: (41) 44 639 9393
Web Site: http://www.scor.com
Sales Range: $1-4.9 Billion
Emp.: 514
Reinsurance Services
N.A.I.C.S.: 524130
Benjamin Gentsch *(Deputy CEO)*

Subsidiary (Non-US):

SCOR Global P&C Deutschland (2)
Goebenstrasse 1, Cologne, 50672, Germany
Tel.: (49) 221 2928 0
Web Site: http://www.scor.com
Sales Range: $75-99.9 Million
Emp.: 200
Reinsurance Services
N.A.I.C.S.: 524130

Marc von Harpke *(CEO)*

SCOR Italia Riassicurazioni S.p.A. (1)
Via Della Moscova 3, 20121, Milan, Italy **(100%)**
Tel.: (39) 0265591000
Web Site: http://www.scor.com
Sales Range: $50-74.9 Million
Emp.: 30
Reinsurance
N.A.I.C.S.: 524130
Denis Kessler *(Chm)*

SCOR Perestrakhovaniye O.O.O. (1)
10 Nikolskaya Street, 109012, Moscow, Russia
Tel.: (7) 4956609386
Reinsurance Services
N.A.I.C.S.: 524130

SCOR Reinsurance Asia-Pacific Pte Ltd. (1)
143 Cecil Street No 20-01 GB Building, Singapore, 069542, Singapore **(100%)**
Tel.: (65) 64168900
Sales Range: $50-74.9 Million
Emp.: 70
Reinsurance Services
N.A.I.C.S.: 524130
Ben Ho *(Mng Dir)*

SCOR Reinsurance Co. (Asia) Ltd. (1)
1603-06 Shui On Ctr 6-8 Harbour Rd, Wanchai, China (Hong Kong)
Tel.: (852) 28643535
Sales Range: $50-74.9 Million
Emp.: 14
Reinsurance Services
N.A.I.C.S.: 524130

SCOR Reinsurance Company (1)
199 Water St 2100, New York, NY 10038-3526
Tel.: (212) 480-1900
Web Site: http://www.scor.com
Reinsurance Services
N.A.I.C.S.: 524130

Subsidiary (Domestic):

SCOR Global Life Reinsurance Company of America (2)
101 S Tryon St, Charlotte, NC 28280
Tel.: (704) 344-2700
Reinsurance Services
N.A.I.C.S.: 524130
Scott Boug *(Sr VP & Deputy Head-Fin Solutions-Americas)*

SCOR Global Life Reinsurance Company of Texas (2)
3900 Dallas Pkwy Ste 200, Plano, TX 75093
Tel.: (469) 246-9500
Reinsurance Services
N.A.I.C.S.: 524130

SCOR Representaciones S.A. (1)
Avenida del Libertador 498 5o, C1001 ABR, Buenos Aires, Argentina
Tel.: (54) 11 5032 5400
Reinsurance & Insurance Services
N.A.I.C.S.: 524130

SCOR Services Asia Pacific Pte Ltd (1)
143 Cecil Street 20-01 Gb Building, Singapore, 69542, Singapore
Tel.: (65) 64168900
Web Site: http://www.scor.com
Sales Range: $50-74.9 Million
Emp.: 110
General Insurance Services
N.A.I.C.S.: 524210
Ben Ho *(Mng Dir)*

SCOR Services Japan Co. Ltd. (1)
5th Fl Kioicho Bldg 3-12 Kioi-cho, Chiyoda-ku, Tokyo, 102-0094, Japan
Tel.: (81) 332220721
Web Site: http://www.scor.com
Sales Range: $50-74.9 Million
Emp.: 9
Insurance Services
N.A.I.C.S.: 524298
Yasunari Hirabayashi *(Mgr)*

SCOR Services Switzerland AG (1)
General Guisan-Quai 26, Zurich, 8002, Switzerland
Tel.: (41) 446399393
Web Site: http://www.scor.com
General Insurance Services
N.A.I.C.S.: 524210

SCOR Switzerland AG (1)
General-Guisan-Quai 26, Zurich, 8002, Switzerland
Tel.: (41) 446399393
Reinsurance Services
N.A.I.C.S.: 524130

Subsidiary (Non-US):

SCOR Services (UK) Ltd (2)
10 Lime Street, London, EC3M 7AA, United Kingdom
Tel.: (44) 2032078725
Sales Range: $75-99.9 Million
Emp.: 20
Reinsurance Management Services
N.A.I.C.S.: 524130
Malcolm Newman *(Gen Mgr)*

SCOR U.S. Corporation (1)
199 Water St, New York, NY 10038-3526 **(100%)**
Tel.: (212) 480-1900
Web Site: http://www.scor.com
Sales Range: $50-74.9 Million
Emp.: 100
Reinsurance
N.A.I.C.S.: 524130
Jean-Paul Conoscente *(Pres & CEO)*

SCOR UK Company Ltd. (1)
10 Lime Streetourt, London, EC3M 7AA, United Kingdom **(100%)**
Tel.: (44) 20 3207 8500
Web Site: http://www.scor.com
Sales Range: $150-199.9 Million
Emp.: 200
Reinsurance Services
N.A.I.C.S.: 524130
Laurent Thabault *(Mng Dir)*

SCOR Underwriting Ltd. (1)
10 Lime Street, London, EC3M 7AA, United Kingdom
Tel.: (44) 2032078725
Sales Range: $100-124.9 Million
Emp.: 20
Reinsurance Services
N.A.I.C.S.: 524130

SCORPIO GOLD CORPORATION
Suite 750-1095 West Pender Street, Vancouver, V6E 2M6, BC, Canada
Tel.: (604) 536-2711 BC
Web Site: https://www.scorpiogold.com
SRCRF—(OTCIQ)
Assets: $14,689,068
Liabilities: $11,918,730
Net Worth: $2,770,338
Earnings: ($2,273,057)
Fiscal Year-end: 12/31/23
Gold & Silver Mining Services
N.A.I.C.S.: 212220
Peter J. Hawley *(Founder)*

SCORPIO TANKERS INC.
9 Boulevard Charles III, 98000, Monaco, 98000, Monaco
Tel.: (377) 97985716 MH
Web Site: https://www.scorpiotankers.com
STNG—(NYSE)
Rev.: $1,562,873,000
Assets: $4,559,163,000
Liabilities: $2,052,355,000
Net Worth: $2,506,808,000
Earnings: $637,251,000
Emp.: 24
Fiscal Year-end: 12/31/22
Crude Oil & Other Petroleum Products Water Transporter
N.A.I.C.S.: 486110
Emanuele A. Lauro *(Founder, Chm & CEO)*

SCOTIA CHRYSLER INC.

SCORPION MINERALS LIMITED
Tel.: (61) 862411877 AU
Web Site: https://www.scorpionminerals.com.au
SCN—(ASX)
Rev.: $735,542
Assets: $4,283,261
Liabilities: $1,458,977
Net Worth: $2,824,284
Earnings: ($722,935)
Fiscal Year-end: 06/30/22
Uranium, Gold & Base Metals Exploration Services
N.A.I.C.S.: 212290

SCOTCH CREEK VENTURES, INC.
1140-625 Howe Street, Vancouver, V6C 2T6, BC, Canada
Tel.: (604) 862-2793
Web Site: https://www.scotch-creek.com
SCV—(DEU)
Assets: $8,045,122
Liabilities: $100,744
Net Worth: $7,944,378
Earnings: ($1,600,758)
Fiscal Year-end: 12/31/21
Mineral Exploration Services
N.A.I.C.S.: 213115
Logan Anderson *(CFO)*

SCOTGEMS PLC
23 St Andrew Square, Edinburgh, EH2 1BB, United Kingdom
Tel.: (44) 1314732900 UK
Web Site: http://www.scotgems.com
Year Founded: 2017
SGEM—(LSE)
Rev.: $1,183,932
Assets: $63,127,191
Liabilities: $720,949
Net Worth: $62,406,242
Earnings: ($839,071)
Fiscal Year-end: 12/31/20
Investment Management Service
N.A.I.C.S.: 523940
William Salomon *(Chm)*

SCOTGOLD RESOURCES LIMITED
4/189 Stirling Highway, Nedlands, 6009, WA, Australia
Tel.: (61) 419790875
Web Site: http://www.scotgoldresources.com
Year Founded: 2007
SGZ—(AIM)
Rev.: $13,624,533
Assets: $40,799,945
Liabilities: $22,467,724
Net Worth: $18,332,221
Earnings: ($8,263,347)
Emp.: 96
Fiscal Year-end: 06/30/22
Gold Mining & Exploration Services
N.A.I.C.S.: 212220
Richard Barker *(Sec)*

Subsidiaries:

Scotgold Resources Limited - Scotland (1)
Upper Tyndrum Station, Crianlarich, FK20 8RY, United Kingdom
Tel.: (44) 1838 400306
Web Site: http://www.scotgoldresources.com.au
Mineral Exploration Services
N.A.I.C.S.: 212390

SCOTIA CHRYSLER INC.
325 Welton Street, Sydney, B1P5S3, NS, Canada
Tel.: (902) 539-2280

SCOTIA CHRYSLER INC.

Scotia Chrysler Inc.—(Continued)
Web Site:
http://www.scotiachrysler.com
Year Founded: 1993
Rev.: $18,205,000
Emp.: 45
New & Used Car Dealers
N.A.I.C.S.: 441110
Robert J. Hawkins (Pres)

SCOTIA FUELS LTD.
6380 Lady Hammond Road, Halifax, B3K 2S2, NS, Canada
Tel.: (902) 453-2121
Web Site:
https://www.scotiafuels.com
Year Founded: 1971
Rev.: $10,172,559
Emp.: 35
Oil Dealers
N.A.I.C.S.: 457210
J. Gordon Lawley (Pres)

SCOTIAN GOLD COOPERATIVE LIMITED
2900 Lovett Rd, Coldbrook, B4R 1A6, NS, Canada
Tel.: (902) 679-2191
Web Site:
https://www.scotiangold.com
Year Founded: 1912
Sales Range: $10-24.9 Million
Fruit & Vegetable Mfr
N.A.I.C.S.: 311411
Dave Parrish (CEO)

SCOTOIL GROUP PLC
Davidson House Miller St, Aberdeen, AB11 5AN, Scotland, United Kingdom
Tel.: (44) 1224571491 UK
Web Site: http://www.scotoil.co.uk
Year Founded: 1982
Holding Company; Land Remediation Services
N.A.I.C.S.: 551112
Craig Smith (Gen Mgr)

Subsidiaries:

Scotoil Services Limited (1)
Davidson House Miller St, Aberdeen, AB11 5AN, United Kingdom (100%)
Tel.: (44) 1224571491
Web Site: http://www.scotoil.co.uk
Service to Industry & Oil Business (Wet Blast, Dry Blast, etc.) & Chemical Handling Storage
N.A.I.C.S.: 333310

SCOTSBURN CO-OPERATIVE SERVICES LIMITED
PO Box 340, Scotsburn, B0K 1R0, NS, Canada
Tel.: (902) 485-8023 Ca
Web Site: http://www.scotsburn.com
Year Founded: 1900
Sales Range: $150-199.9 Million
Emp.: 700
Dairy Products Processor & Distr
N.A.I.C.S.: 311512
Jennifer Swinemar (Dir-HR)

SCOTT PLASTICS LTD.
2065 Henry Ave W, Sidney, V8L 5Z6, BC, Canada
Tel.: (250) 656-8102
Web Site:
http://www.scottplasticsltd.com
Year Founded: 1952
Plastic Molding Mfr
N.A.I.C.S.: 326199
Robin Richardson (VP-Ops)

SCOTT SPORTS SA
Route du Crochet 17, 1762, Givisiez, Switzerland
Tel.: (41) 264601616

Web Site: http://www.scott-sports.com
Holding Company; Bicycle & Bicycle Accessories Mfr
N.A.I.C.S.: 551112

Subsidiaries:

Moto Palic s.r.o. (1)
Pod Jehlicnou 304, Krhova, 756 63, Czech Republic
Tel.: (420) 571633127
Web Site: http://www.motopalic.cz
Motor Cycle Distr
N.A.I.C.S.: 423110
Ruda Kavsky (Mng Dir)

SCOTT ITALIA S.R.L. (1)
Via Provinciale n 110, Albino, 24021, Bergamo, Italy
Tel.: (39) 035756104156
Sporting Goods Distr
N.A.I.C.S.: 423910

SCOTT JAPAN INC. (1)
31-21 Senju Miyamoto-cho, Adachi-ku, Tokyo, 120-0043, Japan
Tel.: (81) 368062751
Sporting Goods Distr
N.A.I.C.S.: 423910

SCOTT Sports AB (1)
Box 2055, 75002, Uppsala, Sweden
Tel.: (46) 18562800
Sporting Goods Distr
N.A.I.C.S.: 423910
Calle Friberg (Coord-Mktg)

SCOTT Sports AG (1)
Niederlassung Osterrech Grabenweg 69, 6020, Innsbruck, Austria
Tel.: (43) 512343531
Sporting Goods Distr
N.A.I.C.S.: 423910

SCOTT Sports AG (1)
Gutenbergstrasse 27, 85748, Garching, Germany
Tel.: (49) 8989878360
Sporting Goods Distr
N.A.I.C.S.: 423910

SCOTT Sports Africa (Pty) Ltd (1)
2 Hereford Drive Longmeadow Business Estate West, Edenvale, Johannesburg, South Africa
Tel.: (27) 112014000
Sporting Goods Distr
N.A.I.C.S.: 423910

SCOTT Sports SA (1)
11 rue du Pre Faucon PAE, Les Glaisins, 74940, Annecy-le-Vieux, France
Tel.: (33) 450642400
Sporting Goods Distr
N.A.I.C.S.: 423910

SCOTT Sports, Inc. (1)
2733 E Parleys Way Ste 204, Salt Lake City, UT 84109
Tel.: (208) 622-1000
Sporting Goods Distr
N.A.I.C.S.: 423910

Scott (China) Co., Ltd. (1)
21st Floor Block A Wanda Plaza No 93 Jianguo Road, Chaoyang District, Beijing, China
Tel.: (86) 1058203228
Web Site: http://www.scott-sports.com.cn
Sporting Goods Distr
N.A.I.C.S.: 423910

Scott Korea Ltd. (1)
133-2 Sangdaewon-dong, Jungwon-gu, Seongnam, Gyeonggi, Korea (South)
Tel.: (82) 317495544
Web Site: http://www.scott-korea.com
Sporting Goods Distr
N.A.I.C.S.: 423910

Scott Sports India Private Limited (1)
202 Lodha Supremus Road, No 22 Wagle Industrial Estate, Thane, 400604, India
Tel.: (91) 2225871652
Web Site: http://www.scott-sports.com
Sporting Goods Distr
N.A.I.C.S.: 423910
Shrikant Nikalje (Mgr-Sls-West Zone)

Scott USA (1)
110 Lindsay Cir, Ketchum, ID 83340
Tel.: (208) 622-1000
Web Site: http://www.scott-sports.com
Sales Range: $50-74.9 Million
Emp.: 35
Mfr & Distr of Sporting Goods & Athletic Apparel
N.A.I.C.S.: 339920

SCOTTIE RESOURCES CORP.
905 - 1111 West Hastings Street, PO Box 48202, Bentall, Vancouver, V6E 2J3, BC, Canada
Tel.: (250) 217-2321 BC
Web Site:
https://www.scottieresources.com
SCTSF—(OTCQB)
Rev.: $41
Assets: $17,644,569
Liabilities: $619,571
Net Worth: $17,024,998
Earnings: ($4,999,796)
Fiscal Year-end: 08/31/21
Metal Mining
N.A.I.C.S.: 212290
Bradley Rourke (Pres & CEO)

Subsidiaries:

AUX Resources Corporation (1)
905 - 1111 West Hastings Street, Vancouver, V6E 2J3, BC, Canada
Tel.: (604) 638-2545
Rev.: $14,043
Assets: $2,601,882
Liabilities: $329,544
Net Worth: $2,272,337
Earnings: ($417,024)
Fiscal Year-end: 12/31/2019
Metal Exploration Services
N.A.I.C.S.: 213114

SCOTTISH BUILDING SOCIETY
SBS House 193 Dalry Road, Edinburgh, EH11 2EF, United Kingdom
Tel.: (44) 131 313 7755
Web Site: http://www.scottishbs.co.uk
Year Founded: 1848
Rev.: $13,936,378
Assets: $539,456,595
Liabilities: $495,726,166
Net Worth: $43,730,429
Earnings: $1,054,556
Emp.: 58
Fiscal Year-end: 01/31/19
Mortgage Lending & Other Financial Services
N.A.I.C.S.: 522310
John Ogston (Vice Chm)

SCOTTISH ENTERPRISE
Atrium Court 50 Waterloo Street, Glasgow, G2 6HQ, United Kingdom
Tel.: (44) 3000133385 UK
Web Site: http://www.scottish-enterprise.com
Year Founded: 1991
Sales Range: $800-899.9 Million
Emp.: 1,200
Regional Economic Development Services
N.A.I.C.S.: 561499
Carolyn Stewart (Dir-People Svcs)

Subsidiaries:

Careers Trust Scotland Limited (1)
5 Atlantic Quay 150 Broomielaw, Glasgow, G28LU, United Kingdom
Tel.: (44) 1412482700
Sales Range: $150-199.9 Million
Emp.: 600
Administrative Management & General Management Consulting Services
N.A.I.C.S.: 541611
John Ward (Chm)

GDA Fund Partner Limited (1)
Atrium Ct, 50 Waterloo St, Glasgow, G2

INTERNATIONAL PUBLIC

6HQ, United Kingdom (100%)
Tel.: (44) 0845 607 8787
Web Site: http://www.scottish-enterprise.com
Management Consulting Services
N.A.I.C.S.: 541618

GDA International Limited (1)
Atrium Court, 50 Waterloo St, Glasgow, G26 HQ, United Kingdom (100%)
Tel.: (44) 845 607 8787
Web Site: http://www.scottish-enterprise.com
Management Consulting Services
N.A.I.C.S.: 541618

Glasgow Science Centre (Trading) Limited (1)
50 Pacific Quay, Glasgow, G51 1EA, United Kingdom
Tel.: (44) 1414205000
Web Site:
http://www.glasgowsciencecentre.org
Emp.: 100
Museums
N.A.I.C.S.: 712110

Glasgow Science Centre Limited (1)
50 Pacific Quay, Glasgow, G51 1EA, United Kingdom (100%)
Tel.: (44) 1414205010
Web Site:
http://www.glasgowsciencecentre.org
Sales Range: $75-99.9 Million
Emp.: 200
Museums
N.A.I.C.S.: 712110
Stephen Breslin (CEO)

ITI Scotland Limited (1)
191 W George St, Glasgow, G22LB, United Kingdom (50%)
Tel.: (44) 1412048000
Web Site: http://www.itiscotland.com
Sales Range: $25-49.9 Million
Emp.: 100
Management Consulting Services
N.A.I.C.S.: 541618

Investors in People (Scotland) Limited (1)
Ocean Point 1 94 Ocean Drive Leith, Edinburgh, EH66JH, United Kingdom (50%)
Tel.: (44) 1316250155
Web Site: http://www.iipscotland.co.uk
Sales Range: $25-49.9 Million
Emp.: 18
Management Consulting Services
N.A.I.C.S.: 541618
Peter Russian (CEO)

Matchmaker Services Limited (1)
5 Atlantic Quay 150 Broomielaw, Glasgow, G28LU, United Kingdom (100%)
Tel.: (44) 1412482700
Sales Range: $200-249.9 Million
Emp.: 600
Software Reproducing
N.A.I.C.S.: 334610

SSTRIC Limited (1)
The Scottish Microelectronics Center, The kings Bldg W Mains Road, Edinburgh, EH93JF, United Kingdom
Tel.: (44) 1316507474
Web Site: http://www.scotmicrocentre.co.uk
Sales Range: $25-49.9 Million
Emp.: 10
Administrative Management & General Management Consulting Services
N.A.I.C.S.: 541611
Iain Hyslop (CEO)

Scotland Europa Limited (1)
5 Atlantic Quay 150 Broomielaw, Glasgow, G2 8LU, United Kingdom (100%)
Tel.: (44) 1412482700
Web Site: http://www.scotlandeuropa.com
Sales Range: $150-199.9 Million
Emp.: 20
Management Consulting Services
N.A.I.C.S.: 541618

Scottish Development International (1)
Atlantic Quay 150 Broomielaw, Glasgow, G2 8LU, United Kingdom
Tel.: (44) 01412482700
Web Site: http://www.sdi.co.uk

Sales Range: $150-199.9 Million
Emp.: 300
Promoter of Business
N.A.I.C.S.: 711310

Subsidiary (US):

Scottish Development
International (2)
28 State St Ste 2300, Boston, MA 02109
Tel.: (617) 725-0340
Web Site:
http://www.scottishdevelopment.com
Sales Range: $25-49.9 Million
Emp.: 10
American Corporate Investment in Scotland
N.A.I.C.S.: 541910

Scottish Development
International (2)
2570 N 1st St Ste 440, San Jose, CA 95131
Tel.: (408) 436-5520
Web Site:
http://www.scottishdevelopment.com
Sales Range: $25-49.9 Million
Emp.: 6
Administrative Management & General Management Consulting Service
N.A.I.C.S.: 541611
Alex Simonini *(Mgr)*

Scottish Enterprise Ayrshire Ltd. (1)
17-19 Hill St, Kilmarnock, KA31HA, Ayrshire, United Kingdom (100%)
Tel.: (44) 1563526623
Web Site: http://www.scotent.co.uk
Sales Range: $25-49.9 Million
Emp.: 55
Management Consulting Services
N.A.I.C.S.: 541618
Neil Francis *(Sr Dir-Technical Sector Delivery)*

Scottish Enterprise Borders Ltd. (1)
Bridge St, Galashiels, TD1 1SW, United Kingdom (100%)
Tel.: (44) 1896758991
Web Site: http://www.scotent.co.uk
Sales Range: $25-49.9 Million
Emp.: 60
Management Consulting Services
N.A.I.C.S.: 541618

Scottish Enterprise Dumfries & Galloway Ltd. (1)
Solway House Dumfries Enterprise Park, Tinwald Downs Rd, Dumfries, DG13SJ, United Kingdom (100%)
Tel.: (44) 1387245000
Sales Range: $25-49.9 Million
Emp.: 40
Management Consulting Services
N.A.I.C.S.: 541618

Scottish Enterprise Dunbartonshire Ltd. (1)
Spectrum House 1 A North Ave, Clydebank Business Park, Clydebank, G812DR, United Kingdom (100%)
Tel.: (44) 1419512121
Web Site: http://www.scottish-enterprise.com
Sales Range: $25-49.9 Million
Emp.: 70
Management Consulting Services
N.A.I.C.S.: 541618

Scottish Enterprise Edinburgh & Lothian Ltd. (1)
Apex House 99 Haymarket Ter, Edinburgh, EH12 5HD, United Kingdom (100%)
Tel.: (44) 1313134000
Web Site: http://www.scottish-enterprise.com
Sales Range: $25-49.9 Million
Emp.: 200
Management Consulting Services
N.A.I.C.S.: 541618
Jim McFaylen *(Mng Dir)*

Scottish Enterprise Fife Ltd. (1)
Kingdom House Saltire Ctr Fife, Glenrothes, KY62AQ, United Kingdom (100%)
Tel.: (44) 1592623000
Sales Range: $25-49.9 Million
Emp.: 20
Management Consulting Services
N.A.I.C.S.: 541618

Scottish Enterprise Forth Valley Ltd. (1)
Laurel House, Laurelhill Business Park, Stirling, FK79JQ, United Kingdom (100%)
Tel.: (44) 1786451919
Web Site:
http://www.scottishenterprise.co.uk
Sales Range: $25-49.9 Million
Emp.: 50
Management Consulting Services
N.A.I.C.S.: 541618
Lena C. Wilson *(CEO)*

Scottish Enterprise Glasgow Ltd. (1)
Atrium Court, 50 Waterloo St, Glasgow, G2 6HQ, United Kingdom (100%)
Tel.: (44) 1412041111
Web Site: http://www.scottish-enterprise.com
Sales Range: $75-99.9 Million
Emp.: 400
Management Consulting Services
N.A.I.C.S.: 541618
Lena C. Wilson *(CEO)*

Scottish Enterprise Grampian Ltd. (1)
41 Albine Pl, Aberdeen, AB10 1YN, United Kingdom (100%)
Tel.: (44) 1224252000
Web Site:
http://www.scottish.enterprise.com
Sales Range: $25-49.9 Million
Emp.: 60
Management Consulting Services
N.A.I.C.S.: 541618
Lena C. Wilson *(CEO)*

Scottish Enterprise Renfrewshire Ltd. (1)
27 Causeyside St, Paisley, PA1 1UL, United Kingdom (100%)
Tel.: (44) 1418480101
Web Site: http://www.scottish-enterprise.com
Sales Range: $25-49.9 Million
Emp.: 100
Management Consulting Services
N.A.I.C.S.: 541618
Jim Reid *(Dir-Ops)*

Scottish Enterprise Tayside Ltd. (1)
Enterprise House, 3 Greenmarket, Dundee, DD14QB, United Kingdom (100%)
Tel.: (44) 1382223100
Web Site: http://www.scotnet.co.uk
Sales Range: $25-49.9 Million
Emp.: 59
Management Consulting Services
N.A.I.C.S.: 541618

Scottish Stem Cell Network Limited (1)
15 Hill Place, Edinburgh, EH89DS, United Kingdom (100%)
Tel.: (44) 1315273442
Web Site: http://www.sscn.co.uk
Management Consulting Services
N.A.I.C.S.: 541618

The Enterprise Europe Network Ltd. (1)
5 Atlantic Quay 150 Broomielaw, Glasgow, G28LU, United Kingdom (100%)
Tel.: (44) 1412282797
Web Site: http://www.enterprise-europe-scotland.com
Sales Range: $50-74.9 Million
Emp.: 7
Financial Investment Activities
N.A.I.C.S.: 523999

SCOTTISH EQUITY PARTNERS LLP
17 Blythswood Square, Glasgow, G2 4AD, United Kingdom
Tel.: (44) 141 273 4000
Web Site: http://www.sep.co.uk
Sales Range: $25-49.9 Million
Emp.: 35
Privater Equity Firm
N.A.I.C.S.: 523999
Calum Paterson *(Mng Partner)*

SCOTTISH LEATHER GROUP LTD.

Locher House Kilbarchan Road Renfrewshire, Bridge of Weir, PA11 3RN, United Kingdom
Tel.: (44) 1505691730
Web Site:
http://www.scottishleathergroup.com
Year Founded: 1965
Sales Range: $50-74.9 Million
Emp.: 450
Leather Mfr
N.A.I.C.S.: 316110
Jonathan A. M. Muirhead *(Chm)*

Subsidiaries:

Andrew Muirhead & Son Limited (1)
Dalmarnock Leather Works 273-289 Dunn Street, Glasgow, G40 3EA, United Kingdom
Tel.: (44) 141 554 3724
Web Site: http://www.muirhead.co.uk
Leather Mfr
N.A.I.C.S.: 316110

Bridge of Weir Leather Company Limited (1)
Baltic Works Kilbarchan Road, Renfrewshire, Bridge of Weir, PA11 3RH, Scotland, United Kingdom
Tel.: (44) 1505 612132
Web Site: http://www.bowleather.co.uk
Leather Mfr
N.A.I.C.S.: 316110

NCT Leather Limited (1)
Locher Works, Bridge of Weir, PA11 3RL, United Kingdom
Tel.: (44) 1505 612182
Web Site: http://www.nctleather.co.uk
Emp.: 550
Leather Mfr
N.A.I.C.S.: 316110
Paul McDonald *(Mng Dir)*

SLG Technology Limited (1)
Locher Works Kilbarchan Road, Renfrewshire, Bridge of Weir, PA11 3RL, Scotland, United Kingdom
Tel.: (44) 1505 691700
Web Site: http://www.slgtechnology.com
Thermal Power Generation Services
N.A.I.C.S.: 221116

SCOTTISH MORTGAGE INVESTMENT TRUST PLC
Calton Square 1 Greenside Row, Edinburgh, EH1 3AN, United Kingdom
Tel.: (44) 1312752000 UK
Web Site:
https://www.scottishmortgage.com
Year Founded: 1909
SMT—(LSE)
Assets: $16,564,428,027
Liabilities: $2,294,260,227
Net Worth: $14,270,167,800
Earnings: $3,626,667,954)
Fiscal Year-end: 03/31/23
Investment Trust
N.A.I.C.S.: 525990
Fiona McBain *(Chm)*

SCOTTISH WATER BUSINESS STREAM LIMITED
7 Lochside View, Edinburgh, EH12 9DH, Scotland, United Kingdom
Tel.: (44) 03031231113
Web Site: http://www.business-stream.co.uk
Water Mfr & Dist
N.A.I.C.S.: 488390
Dame Susan Rice *(Chm)*

SCOTTS GARMENTS LTD.
No 481 B 4th Phase Peenya Industrial Area, Bengaluru, 560 058, India
Tel.: (91) 80 4085 8585
Web Site:
http://www.scottsgarments.com
Sales Range: $100-124.9 Million
Woven, Knitted & Denim Garments Mfr
N.A.I.C.S.: 313210
Naseer Ahmed *(Mng Dir)*

SCOUT GAMING GROUP AB
c/o Ace of Spades, box 3696, 10359, Stockholm, Sweden
Tel.: (46) 707581668
Web Site:
https://www.scoutgaminggroup.com
Year Founded: 2013
SCOUT—(OMX)
Rev.: $2,394,935
Assets: $8,102,691
Liabilities: $2,276,921
Net Worth: $5,825,770
Earnings: ($6,036,509)
Emp.: 37
Fiscal Year-end: 12/31/22
Software Development Services
N.A.I.C.S.: 541511
Andreas Ternstrom *(CEO)*

SCOUT SECURITY LIMITED
Level 8 210 George St, Sydney, 2000, NSW, Australia
Tel.: (61) 861413500
Web Site: http://www.scoutalarm.com
SCT—(ASX)
Rev.: $1,313,427
Assets: $355,837
Liabilities: $5,585,688
Net Worth: ($5,229,850)
Earnings: ($2,397,949)
Fiscal Year-end: 06/30/24
Security System Mfr
N.A.I.C.S.: 334290
Daniel Roberts *(Co-Founder, CEO & Exec Dir)*

SCOUT24 SE
Invalidenstr 65, 10557, Berlin, Germany
Tel.: (49) 4989262024920 De
Web Site: https://www.scout24.com
Year Founded: 1998
G24—(DEU)
Rev.: $561,991,256
Assets: $2,229,166,117
Liabilities: $631,634,414
Net Worth: $1,597,531,703
Earnings: $197,349,879
Emp.: 1,073
Fiscal Year-end: 12/31/23
Internet Marketing Services
N.A.I.C.S.: 541613
Tobias Hartmann *(CEO & Member-Mgmt Bd)*

Subsidiaries:

AutoScout24 Belgium S.A (1)
Boulevard International 55 Riverside Business Park building G, 1070, Brussels, Belgium
Tel.: (32) 25590010
Web Site: http://www.autoscout24.be
Car Distr
N.A.I.C.S.: 441110

AutoScout24 France SAS (1)
88 ter avenue du General Leclerc, 92100, Boulogne-Billancourt, France
Tel.: (33) 155648539
Web Site: http://www.autoscout24.fr
Car Distr
N.A.I.C.S.: 441110

AutoScout24 Italia S.R.L. (1)
Via Battaglia 71 / C, 35020, Albignasego, Padua, Italy
Tel.: (39) 0497801121
Web Site: http://www.autoscout24.it
Car Distr
N.A.I.C.S.: 441110

AutoScout24 Nederland B.V. (1)
Fred Roeskestraat 115, 1076 EE, Amsterdam, Netherlands
Tel.: (31) 887300100
Web Site: http://www.autoscout24.nl
Car Distr
N.A.I.C.S.: 441110

FFG Finanzcheck Finanzportale GmbH (1)

SCOUT24 SE

Scout24 SE—(Continued)
Admiralitatstrasse 60, 20459, Hamburg, Germany
Tel.: (49) 40524769759
Web Site: http://www.finanzcheck.de
Mortgage Lending Services
N.A.I.C.S.: 522310

Flow Fact Schweiz AG (1)
Bahnhofstrasse 100, 8001, Zurich, Switzerland
Tel.: (41) 447982940
Web Site: http://www.flowfact.ch
Software Development Services
N.A.I.C.S.: 541511

FlowFact GmbH (1)
Holweider Strasse 2a, 51065, Cologne, Germany
Tel.: (49) 221995900
Web Site: https://www.flowfact.de
Emp.: 120
Software Development Services
N.A.I.C.S.: 541511

Immobilien Scout Osterreich GmbH (1)
Opernring 5, 1010, Vienna, Austria
Tel.: (43) 8004005959
Web Site: https://www.immobilienscout24.at
Property Rental Services
N.A.I.C.S.: 531110

Scout24 Holding GmbH (1)
Dingolfinger Strasse 1-15, 81673, Munich, Germany (70%)
Tel.: (49) 89444560
Web Site: http://www.scout24.com
Sales Range: $75-99.9 Million
Emp.: 500
Holding Company; Online Marketplace Search Portals Developer & Operator
N.A.I.C.S.: 551112
Christian Gisy (CFO)

finanzcheckPRO GmbH (1)
Admiralitatstrasse 60, 20459, Hamburg, Germany
Tel.: (49) 40524769700
Web Site: http://www.finanzcheckpro.de
Credit Financial Services
N.A.I.C.S.: 522320

SCOZINC MINING LTD.
Purdy's Wharf Tower 1 1959 Upper Water Street Suite 1301, Halifax, B3J 3N2, NS, Canada
Tel.: (902) 482-4481   Ca
Web Site: https://www.edmresources.com
SWNLF—(OTCIQ)
Rev.: $36,757
Assets: $18,862,744
Liabilities: $11,137,833
Net Worth: $7,724,912
Earnings: ($1,775,315)
Fiscal Year-end: 12/31/23
Zinc & Lead Mining & Production
N.A.I.C.S.: 212230
Victor Lazarovici (Chm)

Subsidiaries:

ScoZinc Limited (1)
Purdy's Wharf Tower 1 Suite 1301 1959 Upper Water Street, Halifax, B3J 3N2, NS, Canada
Tel.: (902) 482-4481
Web Site: https://www.edmresources.co
Sales Range: $50-74.9 Million
Emp.: 15
Lead Mining Services
N.A.I.C.S.: 212230

SCP MANAGEMENT SDN BHD
Lot 2.67, 2nd Floor, South City Plaza, Persiaran Serdang Perdana, 43300, Seri Kembangan, Selangor, Malaysia
Tel.: (60) 389481888
Sales Range: $10-24.9 Million
Emp.: 100
Management Consulting Services
N.A.I.C.S.: 541618
Low Chean Khow (Mgr-Building)

SCP SAMLIP CO., LTD.
101 Gongdan 1-daero, Siheung, 15085, Gyeonggi-do, Korea (South)
Tel.: (82) 222765035   KR
Web Site: https://spcsamlip.co.kr
Year Founded: 1968
005610—(KRS)
Rev.: $2,542,257,764
Assets: $993,571,482
Liabilities: $695,124,972
Net Worth: $298,446,510
Earnings: $40,832,655
Emp.: 2,992
Fiscal Year-end: 12/31/22
Bakery Products Mfr
N.A.I.C.S.: 311812
Jong Hyun Hwang (CEO)

SCR SIBELCO SA
Plantin en Moretuslei 1A, 2018, Antwerp, Dessel, Belgium
Tel.: (32) 32236611
Web Site: http://www.sibelco.com
Year Founded: 1872
Sales Range: $125-149.9 Million
Emp.: 300
Quartz Sand Extraction & Refining Services
N.A.I.C.S.: 212322
Hilmar Rode (CEO)

Subsidiaries:

Krynicki Recykling S.A. (1)
ul Iwaszkiewicza 48/23, 10-089, Olsztyn, Poland
Tel.: (48) 89 535 32 92
Web Site: http://www.krynicki.pl
Sales Range: $1-9.9 Million
Emp.: 80
Recycling Services
N.A.I.C.S.: 423930
Adam Krynicki (CEO)

PT Sibelco Lautan Minerals (1)
Jl Jababeka XVI Blok W No 30-35 Kawasan Industri Jababeka 1, Cikarang, Bekasi, 17530, Indonesia
Tel.: (62) 21 893 7465
Industrial Minerals Mining & Distr
N.A.I.C.S.: 212322

Sibelco Australia Limited (1)
Level 16 111 Pacific Highway, North Sydney, 2060, NSW, Australia
Tel.: (61) 2 9458 2929
Web Site: http://www.sibelco.com.au
Emp.: 100
Mineral Exploration Services
N.A.I.C.S.: 213115
Carly Clifford (Mgr-Health & Safety)

Sibelco Benelux B.V. (1)
Koolkoelenweg 40, Heerlen, 6414 XP, Limburg, Netherlands
Tel.: (31) 433523131
Sand Mining Services
N.A.I.C.S.: 212321

Sibelco Gilfair Xinhui Minerals Co., Ltd. (1)
Cangshan Yamen, Xinhui, Jiangmen, Guangdong, China
Tel.: (86) 750 645 5239
Sand Mining Services
N.A.I.C.S.: 212322

Sibelco India Minerals Pvt. Ltd. (1)
Shriman Chambers 8-2-293/k/311& 312 Kamalapuri Colony Phase 3, Near Srinagar Colony, Hyderabad, 500 073, India
Tel.: (91) 40 2360 7274
Web Site: http://www.sibelcoindia.com
Sand Mining Services
N.A.I.C.S.: 212322
R. M. Shanmugam (CFO)

Sibelco Italia S.p.A (1)
Via A Ressi 10, 20125, Milan, Italy
Tel.: (39) 02 67 71 351
Web Site: http://www.sibelco-italia.com
Sand Mining Services
N.A.I.C.S.: 212322

Sibelco Japan Ltd. (1)
9F Nisshin Kasai Nagoya Building 2-4-11 Nishiki, Naka-ku, Nagoya, 460-0003, Japan
Tel.: (81) 52 687 2020
Sand Mining Services
N.A.I.C.S.: 212322
Eigaku Iwasaki (Country Mgr-Sls)

Sibelco Korea Co., Ltd. (1)
26 Saneopdanjiro 4-gil Sungdong-myon, Nonsan, 320-944, Chungcheongnam-do, Korea (South)
Tel.: (82) 41 734 9800
Sand Mining Services
N.A.I.C.S.: 212322

Sibelco Malaysia Sdn Bhd (1)
Unit No 201D Level 2 Tower D Uptown 5 5 Jalan SS21/39 Damansara Uptown, 47400, Petaling Jaya, Selangor, Malaysia
Tel.: (60) 3 7729 9822
Sand Mining Services
N.A.I.C.S.: 212322
Ng Yinchoo (Mgr-Sls)

Sibelco Maoming Kaolin Co., Ltd. (1)
Jinshan Development Zone, 1st District, Gaozhou, 525259, Guangdong, China
Tel.: (86) 668 613 7769
Sand Mining Services
N.A.I.C.S.: 212322

Sibelco Nordic Oy Ab (1)
Kaappolantie 264, 39940, Kantti, Finland
Tel.: (358) 2 544 3261
Sand Mining Services
N.A.I.C.S.: 212322
Juhani Saure (Mgr-HR & TQM)

Sibelco Shanghai Minerals Co., Ltd. (1)
Room 310-317 Longement Yes Tower No 369 Kaixuan Road, Changning District, Shanghai, 200051, China
Tel.: (86) 21 5289 5000
Sand Mining Services
N.A.I.C.S.: 212322

WBB Minerals (1)
Brookside Hall, Sandbach, CW11 4TF, Cheshire, United Kingdom (100%)
Tel.: (44) 270752752
Web Site: http://www.wbbminerals.com
Sales Range: $50-74.9 Million
Emp.: 120
Production, Processing, Marketing & Distribution of Ball Clays, Kaolins & Other Ceramic Raw Materials
N.A.I.C.S.: 327120

Subsidiary (Non-US):

Sibelco Asia Pte Ltd. (2)
180 Clemenceau Avenue #05-01 Haw Par Centre, Singapore, 239922, Singapore (100%)
Tel.: (65) 65380355
Web Site: http://www.sibelcoasia.com
Sales Range: $50-74.9 Million
Emp.: 25
Ceramic Raw Material Products
N.A.I.C.S.: 212323
Bruno Wauters (CEO)

Affiliate (Non-US):

Clays & Minerals (Thailand) Ltd. (3)
134 7 Moo 5 Bangkadi Industrial Park, Tiwanon Road, Amphur Muang, Pathumthani, 12000, Thailand
Tel.: (66) 2963721118
Web Site: http://www.sibelcoasia.com
Sales Range: $50-74.9 Million
Production & Processing of Thai Ball Clays & Kaolins; Production of Ceramic-Grade Feldspar; Joint Venture of Watts Blake Bearne & Co, Plc (80%) & WBB Pacific Clays Ltd. (20%)
N.A.I.C.S.: 212323

Subsidiary (Non-US):

Sibelco GmbH (2)
Saelzerstrasse 20, Ransbach-Baumbach, 56235, Germany (100%)
Tel.: (49) 2623830
Web Site: http://www.sibelco.com
Production of Kaolins, Plastic Clays & Prepared Ceramics
N.A.I.C.S.: 327120

Subsidiary (Domestic):

Kaolin-Und Tonwerke Seilitz-Lothain GmbH (3)
OT Mehren Nummer 11, D 01665, Kaebschuetztal, Sachsen, Germany (100%)
Tel.: (49) 3521 416370
Web Site: http://www.sibelco.de
Sales Range: $50-74.9 Million
Emp.: 40
Production of Kaolins & Other Ceramic Raw Materials
N.A.I.C.S.: 212323

SCREEN HOLDINGS CO., LTD.
Tenjinkita-machi 1-1 Teranouchi-agaru 4-chome Horikawa-dori, Kamigyo-ku, Kyoto, 602 8585, Japan
Tel.: (81) 754147111   JP
Web Site: https://www.screen.co.jp
Year Founded: 1943
7735—(TKS)
Rev.: $3,337,494,760
Assets: $4,473,700,880
Liabilities: $2,015,369,170
Net Worth: $2,458,331,710
Earnings: $466,527,190
Emp.: 6,264
Fiscal Year-end: 03/31/24
Electronic Component & Semiconductor Component & Inspection Systems Developer, Mfr & Whslr
N.A.I.C.S.: 334413
Kimito Ando (Mng Dir)

Subsidiaries:

DNS Electronics, LLC (1)
820 Kifer Rd Ste B, Sunnyvale, CA 94086
Tel.: (408) 523-9140
Web Site: http://www.dnse.com
Semiconductor Products Sales, Marketing, Engineering & Service
N.A.I.C.S.: 811210
James Beard (Pres)

DNS Feats (Taiwan) Co., Ltd (1)
2F-1 No 20 Taiyuan St, Jhubei, 30288, Hsinchu, Taiwan
Tel.: (886) 35526288
Printing Machinery Mfr
N.A.I.C.S.: 333248

DS Finance Co., Ltd. (1)
Tenjinkita-machi 1-1 Teranouchi-agaru 4-chome Horikawa-dori, Kamigyo-ku, Kyoto, 602 8585, Japan
Tel.: (81) 754418131
Accounting & Lease Mediation Services
N.A.I.C.S.: 541219

Dainippon Screen (Australia) Pty. Ltd. (1) (100%)
Tel.: (61) 290163400
Web Site: http://www.screenaust.com.au
Sales Range: $25-49.9 Million
Emp.: 11
Sales & Maintenance of Graphic Arts Equipment
N.A.I.C.S.: 811210
Peter Scott (Mng Dir)

Dainippon Screen (China) Ltd. (1) (100%)
Tel.: (852) 29530038
Web Site: http://www.screenchina.com
Sales Range: $25-49.9 Million
Emp.: 45
Sales & Maintenance of Electronics & Graphic Arts Equipment
N.A.I.C.S.: 811210

Dainippon Screen (Deutschland) GmbH (1)
Fraunhoferstrasse 7, 85737, Ismaning, Germany (100%)
Tel.: (49) 89324951600
Web Site: https://www.screen-spe.com
Sales Range: $25-49.9 Million
Emp.: 30
Sales & Maintenace of Electronics Equipment & Graphic Arts Equipment
N.A.I.C.S.: 811210
Satoshi Kitano (Gen Mgr)

AND PRIVATE COMPANIES

SCREEN HOLDINGS CO., LTD.

Dainippon Screen (Korea) Co., Ltd. (1)
K-TOWER 11F 88 Iljik-ro, Manan-gu, Anyang, 13901, Gyeonggi-do, Korea (South)
Tel.: (82) 27270800 **(100%)**
Web Site: https://www.screen-korea.com
Sales Range: $25-49.9 Million
Emp.: 150
Sales & Maintenance of Graphic Arts Equipment
N.A.I.C.S.: 811210

Dainippon Screen (Nederland) B.V. (1)
Tel.: (31) 204567800 **(100%)**
Web Site: http://www.screeneurope.com
Sales Range: $25-49.9 Million
Emp.: 25
Sales & Maintenance of Graphic Arts Equipment
N.A.I.C.S.: 811210

Dainippon Screen Electronics (Shanghai) Co., Ltd (1)
South Unit 3rd Floor Building 4 Lujiazui Software Park, 1215 Dongfang Road Pudong New Area, Shanghai, 200127, China
Tel.: (86) 2158313033
Web Site: https://www.screen-spesh.com.cn
Sales Range: $25-49.9 Million
Emp.: 40
Semiconductor Devices Mfr
N.A.I.C.S.: 334413

Dainippon Screen Electronics (Taiwan) Co., Ltd (1)
No 311 Gaocui Road, Hsinchu, Taiwan
Tel.: (886) 35631066
Web Site: https://www.screen.com.tw
Sales Range: $50-74.9 Million
Emp.: 150
Printing Machinery Mfr
N.A.I.C.S.: 333248

Dainippon Screen Electronics France Sarl (1)
Rousset Parc Club-Z I Num 205, 13106, Rousset, France
Tel.: (33) 442290820
Sales Range: $25-49.9 Million
Emp.: 13
Semiconductor Devices Mfr
N.A.I.C.S.: 334413
Herve Busseire *(Gen Mgr)*

Dainippon Screen Graphics (USA), LLC (1)
5110 Tollview Dr, Rolling Meadows, IL 60008
Tel.: (847) 870-7400
Web Site: http://www.screenusa.com
Sales Range: $25-49.9 Million
Emp.: 45
Electronic Component & Semiconductor Component & Inspection Systems Developer, Mfr & Whslr
N.A.I.C.S.: 334413

Dainippon Screen Mfg. Co., Ltd. - Hikone Plant (1)
Takamiya-cho 480-1, Hikone, 522-0292, Shiga, Japan
Tel.: (81) 749248300
Web Site: http://www.screen.co.jp
Printing Machinery Mfr
N.A.I.C.S.: 333248

Dainippon Screen Mfg. Co., Ltd. - Kuze Plant (1)
304-1 Shinkaichi Sayama Kumiyamacho, Kuse-Gun, Kyoto, 613-0034, Japan
Tel.: (81) 774467900
Web Site: http://www.screen.co.jp
Printing Machinery Mfr
N.A.I.C.S.: 333248

Dainippon Screen Mfg. Co., Ltd. - Rakusai Plant (1)
Furukawa-cho 322 Hazukashi, Fushimi-ku, Kyoto, 612-8486, Japan
Tel.: (81) 759317771
Semiconductor Machinery Mfr
N.A.I.C.S.: 333242

Dainippon Screen Mfg. Co., Ltd. - Taga Plant (1)
Suwa 976-5 Shide Taga-cho, Inugami-gun, Shiga, 522-0314, Japan
Tel.: (81) 749488200
Semiconductor Devices Mfr
N.A.I.C.S.: 334413

Dainippon Screen Singapore Pte. Ltd. (1)
29 Kaki Bukit View, Kaki Bukit Techpark II, Singapore, 415963, Singapore **(100%)**
Tel.: (65) 67493833
Web Site: https://www.screen-spe.com
Sales Range: $75-99.9 Million
Emp.: 84
Sales & Maintenance of Electronics & Graphic Arts Equipment
N.A.I.C.S.: 811210

Dainippon Screen Unterstuetzungskasse GmbH (1)
Mundelheimer Weg 39, Dusseldorf, 40472, Germany
Tel.: (49) 211472701
Web Site: http://www.screen-tse.de
Emp.: 23
Inkjet Printer Mfr
N.A.I.C.S.: 333248
Satoshi Kitano *(Co-Mng Dir)*

FASSE Co., Ltd. (1)
Iwatsubo Industrial Park 23-25 Iwatsubo, Takaoka, Toyama, 933-0974, Japan
Tel.: (81) 766252010
Web Site: https://www.screen-wk.co.jp
Emp.: 294
Assembly, Inspection, Installation & Setup of Semiconductor Manufacturing Equipment
N.A.I.C.S.: 333242

FEBACS Co., Ltd. (1)
480-1 Takamiya-cho, Shimogyo-ku, Hikone, 522-0292, Shiga, Japan
Tel.: (81) 749248310
Sales Range: $25-49.9 Million
Emp.: 53
Maintenance for Semiconductor Manufacturing Equipment
N.A.I.C.S.: 811310
Toshiki Takemura *(Pres)*

Gerant Co., Ltd. (1)
480-1 Takamiya-cho, Hikone, Shiga, 522 0292, Japan
Tel.: (81) 749 24 8303
Facility Management, Including Building & Environmental Control
N.A.I.C.S.: 561210

INITOUT Japan Co., Ltd. (1)
2nd Floor Keihan Bus Jujo Bldg 5 Minami-Ishida-cho Higashi-Kujo, Minami-ku, Kyoto, 601 8033, Japan
Tel.: (81) 75 662 6633
Sales Range: $25-49.9 Million
Emp.: 32
Information Technology Services
N.A.I.C.S.: 541519

Inca Digital Printers Ltd (1)
515 Coldhams Lane, Cambridge, CB1 3JS, United Kingdom
Tel.: (44) 1223577800
Web Site: https://www.incadigital.com
Emp.: 180
Inkjet Printer Mfr
N.A.I.C.S.: 333248

Link Ring Co., Ltd. (1)
Tenjinkita-machi 1-1 Teranouchi-agaru 4-chome Horikawa-dori, Kamigyo-ku, Kyoto, 602 8585, Japan
Tel.: (81) 754143850
Web Site: http://www.link-ring.co.jp
Emp.: 96
Personnel Staffing Services
N.A.I.C.S.: 561320
Fukai Jiro *(Pres)*

MEBACS Co., Ltd. (1)
8th Floor Yasukuni-Kudan-Minami Bldg 3-14 Kudan-Minami 2-chome, Chiyoda-ku, Tokyo, 102 0074, Japan
Tel.: (81) 3 3237 3117
Web Site: http://www.mebacs.co.jp
Maintenance for PCB Production Equipment
N.A.I.C.S.: 811310

MT Service Japan East Co., Ltd. (1)
6th Fl Otsuka-Higashiikebukuro Bldg 32-22 Gugasgu-Ikebukuro 2-chome, Toshima-ku, Tokyo, 170 0013, Japan
Tel.: (81) 359526011
Web Site: http://www.mtsej.co.jp
Maintenance for Graphic Arts Equipment
N.A.I.C.S.: 811310

MT Service Japan West Co., Ltd. (1)
6th Floor Nihonseimei Sakaisuji-honmachi Bldg 8-12 Honmachi 1-chome, Chuo-ku, Osaka, 541 0053, Japan
Tel.: (81) 6 7637 0280
Web Site: http://www.mtswj.co.jp
Sales Range: $10-24.9 Million
Emp.: 1,117
Graphic Arts Equipment Maintenance
N.A.I.C.S.: 811310

Media Technology Japan Co., Ltd. (1)
1st Floor Yamatane Fukagawa Building No 1 1-1 Etchujima 1-chome, Koto-ku, Tokyo, 135-0044, Japan
Tel.: (81) 332373101
Web Site: http://www.mtjn.co.jp
Sales Range: $75-99.9 Million
Emp.: 100
Domestic Sales of Graphic Arts Equipment
N.A.I.C.S.: 423690
Katsu Kitani *(Pres)*

Quartz Lead Co., Ltd. (1)
Koriyama-Seibu-Industrial Park 2 1-chome 15-4 Machiikedai, Koriyama, 963-0215, Fukushima, Japan
Tel.: (81) 249631711
Web Site: http://www.qld.co.jp
Sales Range: $25-49.9 Million
Emp.: 78
Quartz Glass Parts & Semiconductor Equipment Mfr
N.A.I.C.S.: 334413

S. Ten Nines Kyoto Co., Ltd. (1)
Nishikyogokushinmei cho 13-1, Ukyo-ku, Kyoto, 615 0864, Japan **(100%)**
Tel.: (81) 75 325 6116
Web Site: http://www.st-kyoto.co.jp
Emp.: 118
Software Publisher & Semiconductor Equipment Mfr
N.A.I.C.S.: 513210
Ohara Setsuo *(Pres)*

SCREEN GP TAIWAN Co., Ltd. (1)
103 4th Floor No 126-1 Minzu West Road, Taipei, Taiwan
Tel.: (886) 225862711
Web Site: https://www.screen-gptw.com.tw
Emp.: 11
Electronics & Graphic Arts Equipment Services
N.A.I.C.S.: 811210

SEBACS Co., Ltd. (1)
13-1 Shinmei-cho Nishikyogoku, Ukyo-ku, Kyoto, 615-0864, Japan
Tel.: (81) 753232080
Web Site: http://www.sebacs.co.jp
Maintenance for Semiconductor Manufacturing Equipment
N.A.I.C.S.: 811310

Scientific and Semiconductor Manufacturing Equipment Recycling Co., Ltd. (1)
Tsukiyama-cho 557-1, Kuze Minami-ku, Kyoto, 601-8203, Japan
Tel.: (81) 759348151
Web Site: http://www.sserc.co.jp
Sales Range: $25-49.9 Million
Emp.: 20
Sales & Maintenance of Second-Hand Electronic Equipment
N.A.I.C.S.: 449210

Screen Business Expert Co., Ltd. (1)
1-1 Tenjin Kitamachi 4-chome Teranouchi-dori Horikawa-dori, Kamigyo-ku, Kyoto, 602-8585, Japan
Tel.: (81) 75 414 7118
Web Site: https://www.screen-bex.co.jp
Business Consulting Services
N.A.I.C.S.: 541618

Screen Electronics Sha Co., Ltd. (1)
South Unit 3rd Floor Building 4 Lujiazui Software Park, 1215 Dongfang Road Pudong, Shanghai, 200127, China
Tel.: (86) 215 831 3033
Web Site: https://www.screen-spesh.com.cn
Semiconductor Product Mfr
N.A.I.C.S.: 334413

Screen FT Changshu Co., Ltd. (1)
No 59 Huangpujiang Road, Changshu, 215500, Jiangsu, China
Tel.: (86) 5128 339 9000
Display Production Equipment Mfr
N.A.I.C.S.: 334419

Screen FT Taiwan Co., Ltd. (1)
1st Floor No 20 Taiyuan Street, Hsinchu County, Zhubei, Taiwan
Tel.: (886) 3 552 6288
Web Site: https://www.screen-fttw.com.tw
Display Production Equipment Mfr
N.A.I.C.S.: 334419

Screen Finetech Solutions Co., Ltd. (1)
Tenjinkita-machi 1-1 Teranouchi-agaru 4-chome Horikawa-dori, Kamigyo-ku, Kyoto, 602-8585, Japan
Tel.: (81) 75 417 2570
Web Site: https://www.screen.co.jp
Display Production Equipment Mfr
N.A.I.C.S.: 334419
Yasumasa Shima *(Pres)*

Screen Finetech Solutions Shanghai Co., Ltd. (1)
Room 301 Aetna Building No 107 Zunyi Road, Changning District, Shanghai, 200051, China
Tel.: (86) 216 266 5881
Web Site: https://www.screen-ftsh.com.cn
Display Production Equipment Mfr
N.A.I.C.S.: 334419

Screen GP China Co., Ltd. (1)
Room 2001 - 2003 20/F Cable TV Tower 9 Hoi Shing Road, Tsuen Wan, China (Hong Kong)
Tel.: (852) 2 953 0038
Web Site: https://www.screenchina.com
Graphic Art Equipment Mfr
N.A.I.C.S.: 333248

Screen GP Europe B.V. (1)
Bouwerij 46, 1185 XX, Amstelveen, Netherlands
Tel.: (31) 20 456 7800
Web Site: https://www.screeneurope.com
Printing Equipment Mfr
N.A.I.C.S.: 333248

Screen GP Hangzhou Co., Ltd. (1)
7 Chunhui Road Qiaonan Block, Xiaoshan Economic and Technology Development Zone, Hangzhou, 311231, Zhejiang, China
Tel.: (86) 5712 286 1088
Graphic Art Equipment Mfr
N.A.I.C.S.: 333248

Screen GP IJC Ltd. (1)
515 Coldhams Lane, Cambridge, CB1 3JS, United Kingdom
Tel.: (44) 122 357 7800
Web Site: https://www.screen-ijc.com
Printing Equipment Mfr
N.A.I.C.S.: 333248

Screen GP Japan Co., Ltd. (1)
1-1-1 Etchujima Yamatane Fukagawa Building No 1 5th Floor, Koto-ku, Tokyo, 135-0044, Japan
Tel.: (81) 35 621 8266
Graphic Art Equipment Mfr
N.A.I.C.S.: 333248

Screen GP Service Japan East Co., Ltd. (1)
1-1-1 Etchujima Yamatane Fukagawa Building No 1, Koto-ku, Tokyo, 135-0044, Japan
Tel.: (81) 35 639 0031
Printing & Plate Making Related System Maintenance Services
N.A.I.C.S.: 811210

Screen GP Service Japan West Co., Ltd. (1)
2-1-1 Awaza Osaka Honmachi Nishi Daiichi Building, Nishi-ku, Osaka, 550-0011, Japan
Tel.: (81) 67 637 0280
Printing & Plate Making Related System Maintenance Services
N.A.I.C.S.: 811210

Screen GP Shanghai Co., Ltd. (1)
Room 1202-1203 Executive Mansion No

SCREEN HOLDINGS CO., LTD.

Screen Holdings Co., Ltd.—(Continued)
597 Lan Gao Road, Shanghai, 200333, China
Tel.: (86) 213 126 5122
Printed Circuit Board Equipment Mfr
N.A.I.C.S.: 334419

Screen HD Korea Co., Ltd. (1)
11th Floor K-Tower Main Building 88 Iljik-ro, Manan-gu, Anyang, Gyeonggi, Korea (South)
Tel.: (82) 2 727 0800
Web Site: https://www.screen-korea.com
Semiconductor Product Mfr
N.A.I.C.S.: 334413

Screen Holdings Co., Ltd. - Yasu Plant (1)
Mikami 2426-1, Yasu, 520-2323, Shiga, Japan
Tel.: (81) 775865111
Web Site: https://www.screen.co.jp
Semiconductor Devices Mfr
N.A.I.C.S.: 334413

Screen Holdings Singapore Pte. Ltd. (1)
02-00 29 Kaki Bukit View Kaki Bukit Techpark II, Singapore, 415963, Singapore
Tel.: (65) 6 845 3288
Web Site: https://www.screensp.com.sg
Graphic Art Equipment Mfr
N.A.I.C.S.: 333248

Screen Laminatech Co., Ltd. (1)
480-1 Takamiya Cho, Hikone, 522-0292, Shiga, Japan
Tel.: (81) 74 924 8440
Web Site: https://www.screen-lamina.co.jp
Emp.: 19
Energy Related Device Mfr & Distr
N.A.I.C.S.: 335999
Shigeki Minami *(Pres)*

Screen Media Technology Ltd (1)
Room A06 1/F Building No 1 No 40Wen Shui Road, Shanghai, 200072, China
Tel.: (86) 2131265122
Emp.: 2
Inkjet Printer Mfr
N.A.I.C.S.: 333248

Screen PE Engineering Co., Ltd. (1)
2-32-22 Higashiikebukuro 3rd Floor Otsuka Higashiikebukuro Building, Toshima-ku, Tokyo, 170-0013, Japan
Tel.: (81) 35 953 2661
Web Site: https://www.screen-peeg.co.jp
Electronic Equipment Maintenance Services
N.A.I.C.S.: 811210

Screen PE Solutions Co., Ltd. (1)
Tenjinkita-machi 1-1 Teranouchi-agaru 4-chome Horikawa-dori, Kamigyo-ku, Kyoto, 602-8585, Japan
Tel.: (81) 75 417 2703
Web Site: https://www.screen.co.jp
Printed Circuit Board Equipment Mfr
N.A.I.C.S.: 334419
Masato Suemori *(Pres)*

Screen SPE Germany GmbH (1)
Fraunhoferstrasse 7, 85737, Ismaning, Germany
Tel.: (49) 8932 495 1600
Web Site: https://www.screen-spe.com
Semiconductor Product Mfr
N.A.I.C.S.: 334413
Keiho Nishida *(Mng Dir)*

Screen SPE Korea Co., Ltd. (1)
M Tower 2F 201-207 51-9 Dongtancheomdansaneop 1-ro, Hwaseong, 18469, Gyeonggi, Korea (South)
Tel.: (82) 31 282 0713
Web Site: https://www.screen-spe.com
Semiconductor Product Mfr
N.A.I.C.S.: 334413
Miyajima Yoshihiro *(Pres)*

Screen SPE Quartz Co., Ltd. (1)
Koriyama-Seibu-Industrial Park 2 1-chome 15-4 Machiikedai, Koriyama, 963-0215, Fukushima, Japan
Tel.: (81) 24 963 1711
Web Site: https://www.screen-qt.co.jp
Emp.: 106
Semiconductor Product Mfr
N.A.I.C.S.: 334413
Ito Yuichi *(Pres)*

Screen SPE Singapore Pte. Ltd. (1)
29 Kaki Bukit View Kaki Bukit Techpark II, Singapore, 415963, Singapore
Tel.: (65) 6 749 3833
Web Site: https://www.screen-spe.com
Semiconductor Product Mfr
N.A.I.C.S.: 334413
Kenichiro Arai *(Pres)*

Screen SPE Taiwan Co., Ltd. (1)
No 311 Kao-tsui Rd, Hsinchu, 30064, Taiwan
Tel.: (886) 3 563 1066
Web Site: https://www.screen-spe.com
Semiconductor Product Mfr
N.A.I.C.S.: 334413

Screen SPE Works Co., Ltd. (1)
Iwatsubo Industrial Area 23-25 Iwatsubo, Takaoka, 933-0974, Toyama, Japan
Tel.: (81) 76 625 2010
Semiconductor Product Mfr
N.A.I.C.S.: 334413

Screen Semiconductor Solutions Co., Ltd. (1)
Tenjinkita-machi 1-1 Teranouchi-agaru 4-chome Horikawa-dori, Kamigyo-ku, Kyoto, 602-8585, Japan
Tel.: (81) 75 417 2502
Web Site: https://www.screen.co.jp
Semiconductor Product Mfr
N.A.I.C.S.: 334413
Masato Goto *(Pres)*

Subsidiary (Non-US):

Laser Systems & Solutions of Europe SASU (2)
14-38 Rue Alexandre Bldg D, 92230, Gennevilliers, France
Tel.: (33) 14 111 2720
Web Site: https://www.screen.co.jp
Semiconductor Product Mfr
N.A.I.C.S.: 334413

Silicon Light Machines Corp. (1)
3939 N 1st St, San Jose, CA 95134-1506
Tel.: (408) 240-4700
Web Site: http://www.siliconlight.com
Sales Range: $25-49.9 Million
Emp.: 30
Digital Display & Telecommunications Component Mfr
N.A.I.C.S.: 334419
Ken Fukui *(Sr VP-Ops)*

Sokudo Co., Ltd. (1)
5th Floor K-I Shijo Building 88 Kankobokocho Shimogyo-ku, Shijodori-Muromachi-Higashiiru, Kyoto, 600 8009, Japan (81%)
Tel.: (81) 752568245
Web Site: http://www.sokudo.com
Sales Range: $100-124.9 Million
Emp.: 300
Development, Sales & Service Related to Coat/Develop Track Equipment for Semiconductor Production
N.A.I.C.S.: 334413
Tadahiro Suhara *(Pres & CEO)*

TRANSUP Japan Co., Ltd. (1)
Dainippon Screen Gojo Bldg 12-2 Chudoji-Bojo-cho, Shimogyo-ku, Kyoto, 600 8811, Japan
Tel.: (81) 753422277
Installation, Transport, Packing, Supply Chain Management & Related Services
N.A.I.C.S.: 488991

Tec Communications Co., Ltd. (1)
13-1 Shinmei-cho Nishikyogoku, Ukyo-ku, Kyoto, 615 0864, Japan (100%)
Tel.: (81) 753256221
Web Site: http://www.k-tecs.co.jp
Sales Range: $25-49.9 Million
Emp.: 10
Planning & Production of Technical Documents
N.A.I.C.S.: 513140

Tech In Tech Co., Ltd. (1)
Furukawa-cho 322 Hazukashi, Fushimi-ku, Kyoto, 612-8486, Japan (100%)
Tel.: (81) 759317781
Web Site: https://www.screen-tc.co.jp
Sales Range: $50-74.9 Million
Emp.: 200

Development & Production of Semiconductor & Graphic Arts Equipment
N.A.I.C.S.: 334413

SCRIBBLERS' CLUB
288 Frederick St, Kitchener, N2H 2N5, ON, Canada
Tel.: (519) 570-9402
Web Site: http://www.scribblersclub.com
Year Founded: 1990
Sales Range: $10-24.9 Million
Emp.: 6
Advertising Agencies
N.A.I.C.S.: 541810
Eric E. Sweet *(Chief Creative Officer)*

SCROCCA OPTION TRADING B.V.
Naritaweg 185, 1043 BW, Amsterdam, Netherlands
Tel.: (31) 205810880
Web Site: http://www.scrocca.nl
Options Trading
N.A.I.C.S.: 523150
Maurizio Scrocca *(CEO)*

SCROLL CORPORATION
2-24-1 Sato, Naka-ku, Hamamatsu, 430-0807, Shizuoka, Japan
Tel.: (81) 534641111
Web Site: https://www.scroll.jp
Year Founded: 1943
8005—(TKS)
Rev.: $527,649,860
Assets: $352,035,380
Liabilities: $131,373,750
Net Worth: $220,661,630
Earnings: $24,119,890
Emp.: 886
Fiscal Year-end: 03/31/24
Online Shopping Services
N.A.I.C.S.: 541860
Mamoru Horita *(Chm & CEO)*

Subsidiaries:

AXES Co., Ltd. (1)
2-2-24 Higashishinagawa Tennozu Central Tower 4F, Shinagawa, 140-0002, Japan
Tel.: (81) 568343898
Web Site: https://www.axes-net.jp
Electronic Shopping Services
N.A.I.C.S.: 425120

Himax Corporation (1)
2-24-17 Midorigaoka, Meguro-Ku, Tokyo, 152-0034, Japan
Tel.: (81) 357012833
Web Site: http://www.himax.co.jp
Sales Range: $25-49.9 Million
Emp.: 12
Industrial Machinery Mfr
N.A.I.C.S.: 333248
Robert Saborit *(CEO)*

Mutow Credit Co., Ltd (1)
2-24-1 Sato, Naka-Ku, Hamamatsu, 430-0807, Shizuoka, Japan
Tel.: (81) 534661001
Web Site: http://www.mutow-c.com
Financial Management Services
N.A.I.C.S.: 523999

Naturum Co., LTD. (1)
10th floor Oe Building 1-1-22 Noninbashi, Chuo-ku, Osaka, 540-0011, Japan
Tel.: (81) 669100031
Sporting Goods, Health Foods & Beauty Products Electronic Shopping
N.A.I.C.S.: 423910
Mamuro Hotta *(Chm, Pres & CEO)*

Scroll360 Corporation (1)
2-24-1 Sato, Naka-Ku, Hamamatsu, 430-0807, Shizuoka, Japan
Tel.: (81) 343263207
Web Site: https://www.scroll360.jp
Emp.: 343
Online Shopping Services
N.A.I.C.S.: 425120

SCRYB INC.

65 International Blvd Suite 202, Toronto, M9W 6L9, ON, Canada
Tel.: (647) 872-0082 BC
Web Site: https://www.scryb.ai
SCYRF—(OTCQB)
Rev.: $907,317
Assets: $14,132,699
Liabilities: $946,129
Net Worth: $13,186,571
Earnings: ($13,496,896)
Fiscal Year-end: 09/30/21
Point of Care Testing Medical Device Developer & Mfr
N.A.I.C.S.: 334516
Chris Hopkins *(CFO)*

SCS UPHOLSTERY LTD.
45-49 Villiers St, Sunderland, SR1 1HA, Tyne & Wear, United Kingdom
Tel.: (44) 1915146000
Web Site: http://www.scssofas.co.uk
Sales Range: $350-399.9 Million
Emp.: 1,300
Furniture Retailer
N.A.I.C.S.: 449110
David Knight *(CEO)*

SCULLY ROYALTY LTD.
Unit 803 Dina House Ruttonjee Centre, 11 Duddell Street, Hong Kong, China (Hong Kong) Ky
Web Site: https://www.scullyroyalty.com
Year Founded: 2017
SRL—(NYSE)
Rev.: $49,822,631
Assets: $371,956,148
Liabilities: $111,842,572
Net Worth: $260,113,576
Earnings: ($18,303,787)
Emp.: 71
Fiscal Year-end: 12/31/22
Commodities Trading & Investment Services
N.A.I.C.S.: 523160
Michael J. Smith *(Chm & Mng Dir)*

Subsidiaries:

F.J. Elsner Trading Gesellschaft mbH (1)
Millennium Tower 21st Floor, Handelskai 94-96, A-1200, Vienna, Austria (100%)
Tel.: (43) 1 24025 411
Web Site: http://www.elsner.at
Sales Range: $1-9.9 Million
Emp.: 30
Agricultural Commodities & Foodstuffs Trading Whslr
N.A.I.C.S.: 425120

MFC Resources Inc. (1)
1 Maynard Dr, Park Ridge, NJ 07656-1878 (100%)
Tel.: (201) 307-1500
Web Site: http://www.accr.com
Global Commodity Supply Chain Solutions
N.A.I.C.S.: 523160

Possehl Mexico, S.A. de C.V. (1)
Bosques de Alisos No 47 B Oficina A1-01 Bosques de las Lomas, Cuajimalpa, 05120, Mexico, Mexico (100%)
Tel.: (52) 5591777440
Web Site: https://www.possehl.mx
Emp.: 49
Global Commodity Supply Chain Solutions
N.A.I.C.S.: 523160
Alfonso Loera *(Dir-Comml)*

SCUT SA
Tel.: (40) 234584325
Web Site: https://www.sut.ro
SCBC—(BUC)
Rev.: $3,213,331
Assets: $4,911,802
Liabilities: $670,229
Net Worth: $4,241,573
Earnings: $12,557
Emp.: 41
Fiscal Year-end: 12/31/23

Construction Machinery Leasing Services
N.A.I.C.S.: 532412
Fratila Constantin *(Pres & Gen Mgr)*

SCUTUM CAPITAL AG
Nymphenburger Strasse 70, 80335, Munich, Germany
Tel.: (49) 8985633558
Sales Range: Less than $1 Million
Emp.: 15
Financial Services
N.A.I.C.S.: 523999
Niels Raeder *(Mng Dir)*

SCYTL SECURE ELECTRONIC VOTING SA
C/Enric Granados 84, 08008, Barcelona, Spain
Tel.: (34) 934 230 324
Web Site: http://www.scytl.com
Year Founded: 2001
Sales Range: $25-49.9 Million
Emp.: 150
Electoral Security Technology Services
N.A.I.C.S.: 561621
Pere Valles *(Chm)*

Subsidiaries:

Scytl Australia Pty. Ltd. (1)
104/4 Columbia Court, Baulkham Hills, 2153, NSW, Australia
Tel.: (61) 320929388
Data Protection & Security Services
N.A.I.C.S.: 561621

Scytl Canada Inc. (1)
380 Wellington St Tower B 6th Floor, London, N6A 5B5, ON, Canada
Tel.: (705) 358-1860
Data Protection & Security Services
N.A.I.C.S.: 561621
Susan Crutchlow *(Gen Mgr)*

Scytl META FZE (1)
Technohub Building Office G-18 Dubai Silicon Oasis DSO, PO Box 6009, Dubai, United Arab Emirates
Tel.: (971) 504818455
Data Protection & Security Services
N.A.I.C.S.: 561621

Scytl Mexico, SRL de CV. (1)
Av Santa Fe 94 Torre A Piso 8 Col Zedec, Santa Fe, Mexico, Mexico
Tel.: (52) 5591712010
Data Protection & Security Services
N.A.I.C.S.: 561621

Scytl Peru S.A.C. (1)
Calle Dean Valdivia 148 Piso 13, San Isidro, 15046, Lima, Peru
Tel.: (51) 14420022
Data Protection & Security Services
N.A.I.C.S.: 561621
Alex Freitas *(Gen Mgr)*

Scytl USA LLC (1)
4334 NW Expressway, Oklahoma City, OK 73116
Tel.: (813) 490-7150
Data Protection & Security Services
N.A.I.C.S.: 561621

Soe Software Corporation (1)
5426 Bay Center Dr, Tampa, FL 33609
Tel.: (813) 490-7132
Web Site: http://www.soesoftware.com
Sales Range: $1-9.9 Million
Emp.: 41
Software Publisher
N.A.I.C.S.: 513210
Marc Fratello *(CEO)*

SD BIOSENSOR, INC.
C-4&5 Floor 16 Deogyeong-Daero 1556Beon-Gil, Yeongtong-Gu, Suwon, 16690, Gyeonggi-do, Korea (South)
Tel.: (82) 313000400
Web Site: https://www.sdbiosensor.com
Year Founded: 1999
137310—(KRS)
Electro-Diagnostic Mfr
N.A.I.C.S.: 334515
Hyo-Keun Lee *(Vice Chm & Co-CEO)*

Subsidiaries:

SD Biosensor Healthcare Pvt. Ltd. (1)
Unit 202 A-D 2nd Floor Tower-A Unitech Signature Towers South City-I, Gurgaon, 122001, Haryana, India
Tel.: (91) 706 555 5601
Web Site: https://www.sdbiosensor.co.in
Rapid Diagnostic Test Equipment Mfr
N.A.I.C.S.: 325413
Sung Ho Kim *(Mng Dir)*

SD SYSTEM CO., LTD
613 31 Galmachi-ro 244beon-gil, Jungwon-gu, Seongnam, 13212, Gyeonggi-Do, Korea (South)
Tel.: (82) 317396500
Web Site: https://www.sdsystem.co.kr
Year Founded: 2001
121890—(KRS)
Rev.: $17,254,898
Assets: $10,230,653
Liabilities: $3,038,812
Net Worth: $7,191,840
Earnings: ($462,219)
Emp.: 62
Fiscal Year-end: 12/31/22
Traffic Management Systems
N.A.I.C.S.: 516210

SD WORX GROUP
Brouwersvliet 2, 2000, Antwerp, Belgium
Tel.: (32) 3 220 2111
Web Site: http://www.sdworx.com
Sales Range: $450-499.9 Million
Emp.: 3,900
Payroll & HR Services
N.A.I.C.S.: 541214
Kobe Verdonck *(CEO)*

Subsidiaries:

SD Worx UK Limited (1)
100 Longwater Avenue, GreenPark, Reading, RG2 6GP, Berkshire, United Kingdom
Tel.: (44) 118 922 3600
Web Site: http://www.sdworx.co.uk
Emp.: 4,100
Human Resources & Payroll Services
N.A.I.C.S.: 541214
Iain McGregor *(COO)*

SDAI LIMITED
Level 39 Marina Bay Financial Centre Tower 2, 10 Marina Boulevard, Singapore, 18983, Singapore
Tel.: (65) 64716776
Web Site: https://www.sdai.com.sg
5TI—(CAT)
Rev.: $4,301,216
Assets: $3,476,004
Liabilities: $3,588,044
Net Worth: ($112,040)
Earnings: ($19,049,193)
Emp.: 18
Fiscal Year-end: 12/31/22
Kitchen Appliances Sales & Distr
N.A.I.C.S.: 449210
Wee Li Lim *(Chm & CEO)*

Subsidiaries:

Haus Furnishings & Interiors Pte. Ltd. (1)
2 Leng Kee Road 01-07 Thye Hong Centre, Singapore, 159086, Singapore
Tel.: (65) 66619582
Web Site: http://www.haus.com.sg
Furniture Distr
N.A.I.C.S.: 449110

KHL Marketing Asia-Pacific Pte. Ltd. (1)
9 Raffles Place 52-02 Republic Plaza, Singapore, 048619, Singapore
Tel.: (65) 6 904 6426
Web Site: https://www.khlmktg.com
Kitchen Systems & Appliances Retailer
N.A.I.C.S.: 449210
Lim Wee-Li *(CEO)*

Kitchen Culture Pte. Ltd. (1)
2 Leng Kee Road 06-09 Thye Hong Centre, Singapore, 159086, Singapore
Tel.: (65) 6 471 6776
Web Site: https://www.kitchenculture.com
Kitchen Cabinet Distr
N.A.I.C.S.: 423440

Kitchen Culture Sdn. Bhd. (1)
Unit G8 Lot PT 317 Jalan Anggerik, Kampung Sungai Kayu Ara, Petaling Jaya, Selangor, Malaysia
Tel.: (60) 37 732 7766
Web Site: https://www.kitchenculture.com
Kitchen Cabinet Distr
N.A.I.C.S.: 423440

SDB INTERNATIONAL B.V.
De Beverspijken 20, PO Box 2197, 's-Hertogenbosch, 5202, Netherlands
Tel.: (31) 736339133
Web Site: http://www.sdb.nu
Sales Range: $1-9.9 Million
Emp.: 30
Display Case & Cabinet Mfr
N.A.I.C.S.: 337215
Bianca Van Wagensveld *(Mng Dir)*

Subsidiaries:

sdb uk Ltd (1)
Imperial House 6th Floor 15-19 Kingsway, London, WC2B 6UN, United Kingdom
Tel.: (44) 115 951 9500
Web Site: http://www.sdb-international.co.uk
Display Cabinet Mfr
N.A.I.C.S.: 337215

SDBIOTECH CO., LTD.
66 Magokjungang 8-ro 1-gil, Gangseo-gu, Seoul, 07793, Korea (South)
Tel.: (82) 25831846
Web Site: https://www.sdbiotech.co.kr
Year Founded: 2008
217480—(KRS)
Rev.: $71,849,258
Assets: $85,874,119
Liabilities: $64,136,207
Net Worth: $21,737,913
Earnings: ($38,638,476)
Emp.: 239
Fiscal Year-end: 12/31/22
Cosmetic Product Mfr & Distr
N.A.I.C.S.: 325620
Sul-Woong Park *(CEO)*

Subsidiaries:

SD BIOTECHNOLOGIES COSMETICS Co., Ltd. (1)
90 Tran Dinh Xu Street, Co Glang Ward District 1, Ho Chi Minh City, Vietnam
Tel.: (84) 862913966
Cosmetic Product Distr
N.A.I.C.S.: 424210

SD BIOTECHNOLOGIES U.S Corporation (1)
3303 E Miraloma Ave Ste 188, Anaheim, CA 92806
Cosmetic Product Distr
N.A.I.C.S.: 424210

SD COSMETICS (Qingdao) Co., Ltd. (1)
No 206 Chongyang Road Chengyang District, Qingdao, Shandong, China
Tel.: (86) 53280967187
Cosmetic Product Distr
N.A.I.C.S.: 424210

SD COSMETICS (Shanghai) Co., Ltd. (1)
3B No 1235 Wuzhong Road, Minchang District, Shanghai, China
Tel.: (86) 2160719360
Cosmetic Product Distr
N.A.I.C.S.: 424210

SDC TECHMEDIA LTD
33/1 Wallajah Road, Chepauk, Chennai, 600002, India
Tel.: (91) 4428545757
Web Site: https://www.sdctech.in
Year Founded: 2008
535647—(BOM)
Rev.: $1,372,903
Assets: $3,459,097
Liabilities: $2,879,144
Net Worth: $579,953
Earnings: $39,770
Emp.: 61
Fiscal Year-end: 03/31/23
Media & Entertainment Distr & Marketer
N.A.I.C.S.: 512120
Fayaz Usman Faheed *(Mng Dir)*

SDCL ENERGY EFFICIENCY INCOME TRUST PLC
One Vine Street, London, W1J 0AH, United Kingdom
Tel.: (44) 2072877700
Web Site: https://www.seeitplc.com
Year Founded: 2018
SEIT—(LSE)
Rev.: $252,461
Assets: $1,242,741,734
Liabilities: $3,282,000
Net Worth: $1,239,459,734
Earnings: ($71,067,912)
Emp.: 50
Fiscal Year-end: 03/31/24
Portfolio Management & Investment Advice
N.A.I.C.S.: 523940
Tony Roper *(Chm)*

Subsidiaries:

Primary Energy Recycling Corporation (1) (100%)
2215 So York Rd Ste 202, Oak Brook, IL 60523
Tel.: (630) 230-1313
Web Site: https://www.primaryenergy.com
Sales Range: $50-74.9 Million
Emp.: 7
Eletric Power Generation Services
N.A.I.C.S.: 221118
Joseph Powell *(CFO & Exec VP)*

SDI CORPORATION
260 Chang-Nan Rd Sec 2, Chang-Hua, Taiwan
Tel.: (886) 47383991
Web Site: https://www.sdi.com.tw
Year Founded: 1967
2351—(TAI)
Rev.: $355,032,231
Assets: $397,181,548
Liabilities: $164,442,651
Net Worth: $232,738,897
Earnings: $25,534,516
Emp.: 2,428
Fiscal Year-end: 12/31/23
Semiconductor Mfr
N.A.I.C.S.: 334413
Jau Shyong Chen *(Chm)*

Subsidiaries:

Chao Shin Metal Ind. Corp. (1)
No 134 Jen Ho Road Nan Kang Industrial District, Nant'ou, 54012, Taiwan
Tel.: (886) 492254708
Web Site: http://www.csmtw.com
Sales Range: $25-49.9 Million
Emp.: 50
Steel Products Mfr
N.A.I.C.S.: 331110

SDI China Co., Ltd. (1)
Shanghai Rd Zhangjiagang Free Trade Zone, Jiangsu, China
Tel.: (86) 51258320292
Electronic Components Mfr
N.A.I.C.S.: 334419

SDI GROUP PLC

SDI Corporation—(Continued)

SDI GROUP PLC
Beacon House Nuffield Road, Cambridge, CB4 1TF, United Kingdom
Tel.: (44) 1223727144
Web Site: https://sdigroup.com
Year Founded: 2007
SDI—(AIM)
Rev.: $83,873,538
Assets: $105,481,089
Liabilities: $49,097,916
Net Worth: $56,383,173
Earnings: $4,840,290
Fiscal Year-end: 04/30/23
Digital Imaging Services
N.A.I.C.S.: 323111
Michael John Creedon (CEO)

Subsidiaries:

Perseu Comercio de Equipamento Para Informatica e Astronomica S.A. (1)
R Dr Agostinho Neto 1-lj C Santa Iria de Azoia, 2690-576, Santa Iria de Azoia, Portugal
Tel.: (351) 21 086 8596
Camera Mfr
N.A.I.C.S.: 333310

SDI LIMITED
3-15 Brunsdon Street, Bayswater, 3153, VIC, Australia
Tel.: (61) 387277111
Web Site: https://www.sdi.com.au
SDI—(ASX)
Rev.: $74,256,143
Assets: $93,924,278
Liabilities: $31,174,546
Net Worth: $62,749,733
Earnings: $6,958,467
Emp.: 260
Fiscal Year-end: 06/30/24
Dental Restorative Materials Mfr
N.A.I.C.S.: 339114
Samantha Jane Cheetham (CEO & Mng Dir)

Subsidiaries:

SDI (North America) Inc. (1)
1279 Hamilton Pkwy, Itasca, IL 60143
Tel.: (630) 361-9200
Emp.: 6
Dental Product Distr
N.A.I.C.S.: 423450
Robert Zeeman (Gen Mgr)

SDI Brasil Industria e Comercio Ltda (1)
Av Paulista 2300-PilotisBela Vista, Sao Paulo, 01310-300, Brazil
Tel.: (55) 1130927100
Sales Range: $25-49.9 Million
Emp.: 20
Dental Product Distr
N.A.I.C.S.: 423450
Moacir Lacerda (Mgr-Sls & Mktg)

SDI Dental Limited (1)
Block 8 St Johns Ct Swords Rd, Santry, Dublin, 9, Leinster, Ireland
Tel.: (353) 18869575
Web Site: http://www.sdi.com.au
Sales Range: $25-49.9 Million
Emp.: 5
Dental Product Mfr
N.A.I.C.S.: 339114
Peggy Rochford (Office Mgr)

Southern Dental Industries GmbH (1)
Dieselstrasse 14, 50859, Cologne, Nordrhein-Westfalen, Germany
Tel.: (49) 2234933460
Sales Range: $50-74.9 Million
Emp.: 5
Dental Product Distr
N.A.I.C.S.: 423450

SDIC CAPITAL CO., LTD.
SDIC Financial Building Building 2
Fuchengmen North Street, Xicheng District, Beijing, 100034, China
Tel.: (86) 1083325163
Web Site: https://www.sdiccapital.com
600061—(SHG)
Rev.: $2,417,369,683
Assets: $38,784,064,383
Liabilities: $30,641,542,257
Net Worth: $8,142,522,126
Earnings: $326,322,469
Fiscal Year-end: 12/31/23
Asset Management Services
N.A.I.C.S.: 523999
Duan Wenwu (Acting Gen Mgr)

Subsidiaries:

Beijing Tongyizhong Specialty Fiber Technology & Development Co. Ltd. (1)
No 17 Jingsheng South 2nd Street Majuqiao Town, Tongzhou District, Beijing, China
Tel.: (86) 1056710323
Web Site: http://www.bjtyz.com
Polyethylene Fiber Mfr
N.A.I.C.S.: 325220

SDIC POWER HOLDINGS CO., LTD.
No 147 Xizhimen Nanxiao Street, Xicheng District, Beijing, 100034, China
Tel.: (86) 1088006378
Web Site: https://www.sdicpower.com
600886—(SHG)
Rev.: $7,088,689,801
Assets: $36,258,925,482
Liabilities: $23,114,054,934
Net Worth: $13,144,870,548
Earnings: $572,744,348
Fiscal Year-end: 12/31/22
Holding Company
N.A.I.C.S.: 551112
Jiwei Zhu (Chm & Pres-Interim)

Subsidiaries:

Red Rock Power Limited (1)
5th Floor 40 Princes Street, Edinburgh, EH2 2BY, United Kingdom
Tel.: (44) 131 557 7101
Web Site: https://www.redrockpower.co.uk
Energy Renewable Services
N.A.I.C.S.: 221118
David Bruce (Mgr-Asset)

SDIC ZHONGLU FRUIT JUICE CO., LTD.
21F Block B Wantong New World Plaza, No 2 Fuchengmenwai St Xicheng District, Beijing, 100037, China
Tel.: (86) 1088009088
Web Site: https://www.sdiczl.com
Year Founded: 1991
600962—(SHG)
Rev.: $242,404,952
Assets: $319,276,536
Liabilities: $193,031,495
Net Worth: $126,245,040
Earnings: $12,931,556
Fiscal Year-end: 12/31/22
Beverage Mfr & Distr
N.A.I.C.S.: 311421
He Jun (Chm)

Subsidiaries:

Zhongxin Fruit & Juice Limited (1)
25 International Business Park 02-53 German Centre, Singapore, 609916, Singapore
Tel.: (65) 65572308
Web Site: https://www.newlakeside.net
Rev.: $15,858,025
Assets: $32,244,545
Liabilities: $13,585,096
Net Worth: $18,659,448
Earnings: $826,180
Emp.: 90
Fiscal Year-end: 06/30/2023
Fruit Juice Mfr & Distr
N.A.I.C.S.: 311411
Jiming Zhang (Chm)

SDIPTECH AB
Stureplan 13, Stockholm, 111 45, Sweden
Tel.: (46) 761612191
Web Site: http://www.sdiptech.com
Engineeering Services
N.A.I.C.S.: 541330
Jakob Holm (CEO)

Subsidiaries:

Unipower, LLC (1)
3900 Coral Ridge Dr, Coral Springs, FL 33065
Tel.: (954) 346-2442
Web Site: http://www.unipowerco.com
Power Electronics Mfr
N.A.I.C.S.: 335311
Christopher Statis (Sr VP-Ops)

SDIPTECH AB
Nybrogatan 39, 114 39, Stockholm, Sweden
Tel.: (46) 707983639
Web Site: https://www.sdiptech.com
SDIP-B—(OMX)
Rev.: $257,967,248
Assets: $470,337,616
Liabilities: $256,001,760
Net Worth: $214,335,856
Earnings: $26,882,016
Emp.: 1,499
Fiscal Year-end: 12/31/20
Venture Management, Technical Services & Corporate Services
N.A.I.C.S.: 523999
Jakob Holm (CEO)

Subsidiaries:

Agrosistemi S.R.L. (1)
Via del Capitolo 54, 29122, Piacenza, PC, Italy
Tel.: (39) 0523490772
Web Site: https://www.agrosistemi.it
Biological Sludge Treatment Services
N.A.I.C.S.: 562998

Alerter Group Ltd. (1)
4 Mallard Way Pride Park, Derby, DE24 8GX, United Kingdom
Tel.: (44) 1332363981
Web Site: https://alertergroup.com
Information Communication Services
N.A.I.C.S.: 335929

Auger Site Investigations Ltd. (1)
14a Cross Lane, Wirral, Wallasey, CH45 8RH, United Kingdom
Tel.: (44) 1516305886
Web Site: https://www.auger.co.uk
Sewage Treatment Services
N.A.I.C.S.: 221320

CERTUS Port Automation B.V. (1)
Rietlanden 3, 3361 AN, Sliedrecht, Netherlands
Tel.: (31) 850068800
Web Site: https://certusautomation.com
Software Development Services
N.A.I.C.S.: 541511

Castella Entreprenad AB (1)
Molnbackavagen 1, 177 71, Jarfalla, Sweden
Tel.: (46) 86129550
Web Site: https://castella.se
Building Construction Services
N.A.I.C.S.: 236220

Centralbyggarna i Akersberga AB (1)
Bathamnsvagen 12, 184 40, Akersberga, Sweden
Tel.: (46) 812855200
Web Site: https://centralbyggarna.se
Electric Equipment Mfr
N.A.I.C.S.: 335999

Centralmontage i Nykoping AB (1)
Oldenburgs Alle 20, 611 38, Nykoping, Sweden
Tel.: (46) 155120700

INTERNATIONAL PUBLIC

Web Site: https://centralmontage.se
Cable Distr
N.A.I.C.S.: 423610

Cliff Models AB (1)
Flygfaltsgatan 21, 423 37, Torslanda, Sweden
Tel.: (46) 31923500
Web Site: https://www.cliffmodels.com
Elevator Installation Services
N.A.I.C.S.: 238290
David Halling (CEO & Partner)

ELM Kragelund AS (1)
Herredsvej 19, 8723, Losning, Denmark
Tel.: (45) 75893500
Web Site: https://e-l-m.com
Forklift Whslr
N.A.I.C.S.: 423830

Eurotech AB (1)
Mallslingan 20, 187 66, Taby, Sweden
Tel.: (46) 84730880
Web Site: http://www.eurotech-ups.se
Uninterruptible Power System Distr
N.A.I.C.S.: 423610

Eurotech Sire System AB (1)
Mallslingan 20 A, 187 66, Taby, Sweden
Tel.: (46) 84730880
Web Site: https://eurotech-ups.se
Battery Distr
N.A.I.C.S.: 423610

Ficon Oy (1)
Rekkatie 9, 80100, Joensuu, Finland
Tel.: (358) 458061067
Web Site: https://ficon.fi
Automobile Maintenance Services
N.A.I.C.S.: 811198

Frigotech AB (1)
Elektravagen 33, 126 30, Hagersten, Sweden
Tel.: (46) 86120770
Web Site: https://www.frigotech.se
Refrigeration Installation Services
N.A.I.C.S.: 238220

GAH Europe GmbH (1)
Habichtshohe 85, 48282, Emsdetten, Germany
Tel.: (49) 25729592491
Web Site: https://gaheurope.com
Refrigerator System Mfr
N.A.I.C.S.: 334419

GAP Experten AB (1)
Gamla Krokeksvagen 35, 618 33, Kolmarden, Sweden
Tel.: (46) 114600799
Web Site: https://www.gapexperten.se
Plastic Product Distr
N.A.I.C.S.: 424610

Hilltip GmbH (1)
Goerdelerstrasse 66, 36100, Petersberg, Germany
Tel.: (49) 15157170370
Road Maintenance Equipment Mfr & Distr
N.A.I.C.S.: 333120

Hilltip Inc. (1)
4519 Allen Martin Dr, Fort Wayne, IN 46806
Tel.: (859) 760-7211
Road Maintenance Equipment Mfr & Distr
N.A.I.C.S.: 333120

Hydrostandard Matteknik Nordic AB (1)
Herrgardsgatan 26, Borlange, Sweden
Tel.: (46) 243248500
Web Site: https://hydrostandard.se
Water Meter Distr
N.A.I.C.S.: 423830

IDE Systems Ltd. (1)
Unit 3 Swaffield Park Hyssop Close, Cannock, WS11 7FU, Staffordshire, United Kingdom
Tel.: (44) 1543574111
Web Site: https://idesystems.co.uk
Temporary Power Product Mfr & Distr
N.A.I.C.S.: 336320

Linesense Fire Detection Ltd. (1)
PO Box 3122, Reading, RG1 9QW, United Kingdom
Tel.: (44) 3450304223
Web Site: https://www.linesense.co.uk
Heat Deduction Cable Mfr

Mecno Services S.r.l. (1)
Via Terraglio 212, Mestre-I, 30174, Venice, Italy
Tel.: (39) 0415745203
Web Site: http://www.mecnoservice.com
Biological Sludge Treatment Services
N.A.I.C.S.: 562998

Metus d.o.o. (1)
Poloznica 5, 10431, Sveta Nedelja, Croatia
Tel.: (385) 13874647
Web Site: http://www.metus.hr
Emp.: 350
Elevator Installation Services
N.A.I.C.S.: 238290

Multitech Site Services Ltd. (1)
Multitech House, Flitch Industrial Estate, Great Dunmow, CM6 1XJ, Essex, United Kingdom
Tel.: (44) 1371877060
Web Site: http://www.temporary-electrics.co.uk
Construction Services
N.A.I.C.S.: 236220
Sam Scilly *(Fin Dir)*

Optyma Security Systems Ltd. (1)
6 Harcourt Road, Bexley, DA6 8AQ, Kent, United Kingdom
Tel.: (44) 2083048635
Web Site: https://www.optyma.co.uk
Security Services
N.A.I.C.S.: 561612

Patol Ltd. (1)
Archway House Bath Rd, Padworth, Reading, RG7 5HR, Berkshire, United Kingdom
Tel.: (44) 1189701701
Web Site: https://www.patol.co.uk
Safety Product Mfr
N.A.I.C.S.: 335921

Polyproject Environment AB (1)
Gamla Krokeksvagen 35, 618 33, Kolmarden, Sweden
Tel.: (46) 11320100
Web Site: https://polyproject.com
Environmental Services
N.A.I.C.S.: 541620

Pure Water Scandinavia AB (1)
Ryckepungsvagen 7, 791 77, Falun, Sweden
Tel.: (46) 23797990
Web Site: https://www.en.purewater.se
Sewage Treatment Services
N.A.I.C.S.: 221320
Jenny Jansson *(CEO)*

RedSpeed International Ltd. (1)
Coppice Trading Estate, Kidderminster, DY11 7QY, United Kingdom
Tel.: (44) 1562825556
Web Site: https://www.redspeed-int.com
Camera Mfr
N.A.I.C.S.: 333310

Rolec Services Ltd. (1)
Ralphs Lane, Boston, PE20 1QU, United Kingdom
Tel.: (44) 1205724754
Web Site: https://www.rolecserv.com
Electrical Equipment Mfr & Distr
N.A.I.C.S.: 336320

St. Eriks Hiss AB (1)
Box 90253, 120 24, Stockholm, Sweden
Tel.: (46) 8194200
Web Site: http://www.sterikshiss.se
Elevator Installation Services
N.A.I.C.S.: 238290

Stockholm Hiss & Elteknik AB (1)
Vastberga Alle 36C, 126 30, Hagersten, Sweden
Tel.: (46) 806026560
Web Site: http://www.hiss-elteknik.se
Elevator Installation Services
N.A.I.C.S.: 238290

Stockholmradio AB (1)
Box 1242, 131 28, Nacka, Sweden
Tel.: (46) 86017920
Web Site: https://stockholmradio.se
Radio Broadcasting Services
N.A.I.C.S.: 516110

Storadio AB (1)
PO Box 1242, 13128, Nacka, Sweden
Tel.: (46) 86017900
Web Site: https://storadio.aero
Radio Broadcasting Services
N.A.I.C.S.: 516110

Storadio Aero AB (1)
PO Box 1242, 131 28, Nacka, Sweden
Tel.: (46) 86017900
Web Site: https://storadio.aero
Telecommunication Servicesb
N.A.I.C.S.: 517810

Temperature Electronics Ltd. (1)
Unit 2 Wren Nest Road, Glossop, SK13 8HB, Derbyshire, United Kingdom
Tel.: (44) 1457865635
Web Site: https://tel-uk.com
Research Laboratory Services
N.A.I.C.S.: 541715

Thors Trading AB (1)
Saltangsvagen 37A, 72132, Vasteras, Sweden
Tel.: (46) 21123910
Web Site: http://www.thorstrading.com
Motor Vehicle Parts Mfr
N.A.I.C.S.: 336390

Topas Vatten Service AB (1)
Sagvagen 5, 184 40, Akersberga, Sweden
Tel.: (46) 854063099
Waste Water Treatment Services
N.A.I.C.S.: 221320

Topas VattenAB (1)
Vasavagen 82 3tr, 181 41, Lidingo, Sweden
Tel.: (46) 87670030
Web Site: http://www.topasvatten.se
Sewage Treatment Services
N.A.I.C.S.: 221320

Unipower AB (1)
Metallgatan 4C, 441 32, Alingsas, Sweden
Tel.: (46) 322638020
Web Site: https://www.unipower.se
Measuring Instrument Distr
N.A.I.C.S.: 423610

Vera Klippan AB (1)
Brannerigatan 5, 264 39, Klippan, Sweden
Tel.: (46) 43514090
Web Site: https://www.veraklippan.se
Pipe Product Mfr
N.A.I.C.S.: 332996
Anders Alm *(Mgr-Site & Sls)*

Water Treatment Products Holding Ltd. (1)
Unit 1 Gilchrist Thomas Industrial Estate, Blaenavon, Pontypool, NP4 9RL, Torfaen, United Kingdom
Tel.: (44) 1495792790
Web Site: https://www.watertreatmentproducts.co.uk
Waste Treatment Services
N.A.I.C.S.: 221310

Water Treatment Products Limited (1)
Unit 1 Gilchrist Thomas Industrial Estate, Blaenavon, Pontypool, NP4 9RL, Torfaen, United Kingdom
Tel.: (44) 1495792790
Web Site: https://www.watertreatmentproducts.co.uk
Chemical Product Mfr & Distr
N.A.I.C.S.: 325998
Steve Jones *(Gen Mgr)*

SDL SUDDEUTSCHE LEASING AG
Donaustrasse 1, D-89275, Elchingen, Germany
Tel.: (49) 73117662690
Web Site: http://www.sueddeutsche-leasing.com
Financial Services
N.A.I.C.S.: 523999

SDM EDUCATION GROUP HOLDINGS LIMITED
Room 202B 2/F Liven House 61-63 King Yip Street, Kwun Tong, China (Hong Kong)
Tel.: (852) 25282222   Ky
Web Site: https://www.sdm.hk
Year Founded: 2014
8363—(HKG)
Rev.: $21,016,080
Assets: $46,435,373
Liabilities: $76,694,183
Net Worth: ($30,258,810)
Earnings: ($4,692,255)
Emp.: 564
Fiscal Year-end: 12/31/22
Holding Company
N.A.I.C.S.: 551112
Richard Chi Ngon Chun *(CEO)*

SDM SE
Ranertstr 5, 81477, Munich, Germany
Tel.: (49) 8955291150
Web Site: https://www.s-d-m.de
Year Founded: 1999
75S—(MUN)
Rev.: $55,193
Assets: $15,365,870
Liabilities: $7,738,129
Net Worth: $7,627,742
Earnings: $827,902
Fiscal Year-end: 12/31/23
Software Development Services
N.A.I.C.S.: 541511

SDM-BANK PJSC
73 Volokolamskoe Shosse, 125424, Moscow, Russia
Tel.: (7) 4957059090   RU
Web Site: http://www.sdm.ru
Year Founded: 1991
Rev.: $80,353,056
Assets: $969,486,600
Liabilities: $852,344,281
Net Worth: $117,142,320
Earnings: $17,028,095
Emp.: 700
Fiscal Year-end: 12/31/18
Banking Services
N.A.I.C.S.: 522110
Anatoly Landsman *(Chm)*

SDN COMPANY LTD.
1281 Daewangpangyo-ro, Sujeong-gu, Seongnam, 13100, Gyeonggi-do, Korea (South)
Tel.: (82) 24466691
Web Site: http://www.sdn-i.com
Year Founded: 1994
099220—(KRS)
Rev.: $80,129,340
Assets: $136,235,998
Liabilities: $57,876,205
Net Worth: $78,359,792
Earnings: $583,413
Emp.: 95
Fiscal Year-end: 12/31/22
Engineeering Services
N.A.I.C.S.: 541330
Kim Yoon Hwan *(Exec Dir)*

Subsidiaries:

SDN Company Ltd. - Korea Renewable Energy Laboratory & Gwangju Advanced Science Factory (1)
959-70 Daechon-dong, Book-gu, 500-470, Gwangju, Jeunlanam-do, Korea (South)
Tel.: (82) 62 973 5770
Web Site: http://www.sdn-i.com
Eletric Power Generation Services
N.A.I.C.S.: 221118

SDP JOINT STOCK COMPANY
Alley 795 Quang Trung Street Phu La Ward, Ha Dong District, Hanoi, Vietnam
Tel.: (84) 2432216425   VN
Web Site: https://www.sdp.com.vn
Year Founded: 2003
SDP—(HNX)
Rev.: $2,221,916
Assets: $9,547,482
Liabilities: $11,884,634
Net Worth: ($2,337,152)
Earnings: ($278,141)
Emp.: 15
Fiscal Year-end: 12/31/23
Industrial Building Construction & Civil Construction Services
N.A.I.C.S.: 236210
Pham Truong Tam *(Gen Dir)*

SDS GROUP BERHAD
5 Jalan Selatan 8 Off Jalan Kempas Lama Kawasan Perusahaan, Ringan Pulai, 81200, Johor Bahru, Johor, Malaysia
Tel.: (60) 72888305   MY
Web Site: https://www.sdsgroups.com
Year Founded: 1987
SDS—(KLS)
Rev.: $43,010,055
Assets: $34,407,203
Liabilities: $16,520,130
Net Worth: $17,887,073
Earnings: $1,751,805
Fiscal Year-end: 03/31/21
Bakery Product Distr
N.A.I.C.S.: 424490
Kim Seng Tan *(Mng Dir)*

Subsidiaries:

Daily Bakery Sdn. Bhd. (1)
5 Jalan Selatan 8 Taman Perusahaan Ringan Pulai, 81200, Johor Bahru, Johor, Malaysia
Tel.: (60) 72888031
Web Site: http://www.dailysbakery.com.my
Bakery Product Mfr & Distr
N.A.I.C.S.: 311812

SDS GROUP LIMITED
Office Suite 2 Courtlands Farm Turnden Road, Cranbrook, TN17 2QL, Kent, United Kingdom
Tel.: (44) 1580715038   UK
Web Site: http://www.sdsgroupltd.co.uk
Year Founded: 1975
Sales Range: $50-74.9 Million
Security Equipment Whslr & Training Services
N.A.I.C.S.: 423610

SDS HOLDINGS CO., LTD.
1F Izumi Shibadaimon Bldg 2-2-11 Shibadaimon, Minato-Ku, Tokyo, 105-0021, Japan
Tel.: (81) 368210004
Web Site: https://www.shodensya.com
Year Founded: 1986
1711—(TKS)
Rev.: $27,332,350
Assets: $25,051,900
Liabilities: $19,882,880
Net Worth: $5,169,020
Earnings: ($694,050)
Emp.: 35
Fiscal Year-end: 03/31/24
Holding Company; Renewable Energy Structure Construction Services
N.A.I.C.S.: 551112

SDX ENERGY PLC
38 Welbeck Street, W1G 8DP, London, W1G 8DP, United Kingdom - England
Tel.: (44) 2032195640   Ca
Web Site: https://www.sdxenergygroup.com
Year Founded: 2006
SDX—(AIM)
Rev.: $43,760,000
Assets: $78,510,000
Liabilities: $37,100,000
Net Worth: $41,410,000
Earnings: ($36,180,000)
Fiscal Year-end: 12/31/22
Oil & Gas Exploration Services

SDX ENERGY PLC

SDX Energy plc—(Continued)
N.A.I.C.S.: 213112
Mark Reid (CEO)

SE CORPORATION
43F Shinjuku I-Land Tower 6-5-1
Nishi-shinjuku, Shinjuku-ku, Tokyo,
163-1343, Japan
Tel.: (81) 333405500
Web Site: https://www2.se-corp.com
Year Founded: 1967
3423—(TKS)
Rev.: $174,993,140
Assets: $174,715,520
Liabilities: $101,846,880
Net Worth: $72,868,640
Earnings: $6,405,090
Emp.: 526
Fiscal Year-end: 03/31/24
Construction Equipment Mfr
N.A.I.C.S.: 333120
Mineo Morimoto (Pres)

Subsidiaries:

Ingerosec Corporation
Shinjuku i-LAND Tower 43F 6-5-1 Nishi-
Shinjuku, Shinjuku, 163-1343, Tokyo, Japan
Tel.: (81) 353240211
Web Site: http://www.ingerosec.com
Emp.: 37
Engineering Consulting Services
N.A.I.C.S.: 541330
Mineo Morimoto (Pres & CEO)

SE A&K Corporation (1)
46-1 Namegawanakatsusawa Sugakawa,
Fukushima, 962-0403, Japan
Tel.: (81) 248760215
Web Site: http://www.se-ak.jp
Reinforcing Material Distr
N.A.I.C.S.: 423510

SE Repair Co., Ltd. (1)
5-15-24 Osa, Minami-ku, Fukuoka, 811-
1313, Japan
Tel.: (81) 925855133
Web Site: http://www.se-r.jp
Building Inspection Services
N.A.I.C.S.: 541350

Vietnam-Japan Engineering Consultants Co., Ltd. (1)
20th Floor ICON4 Tower 243A De La
Thanh, Dang Da Dist, Hanoi, Vietnam
Tel.: (84) 436288886
Web Site: http://www.vjec.vn
Building Construction & Design Services
N.A.I.C.S.: 236220

WIROP INDUSTRIAL Co., Ltd. (1)
806 Fengping 1st Road, Daliao District, Kaohsiung, 83141, Taiwan
Tel.: (886) 77019369
Web Site: https://www.wirop.com.tw
Swaging Machine Mfr
N.A.I.C.S.: 333517

SE GYUNG HI TECH CO., LTD.
128 Sanup-ro 155beon-gil,
Gwonseon-gu, Suwon, Gyeonggi-do,
Korea (South)
Tel.: (82) 312047200
Web Site: https://www.sghitech.co.kr
Year Founded: 2006
148150—(KRS)
Rev.: $199,916,362
Assets: $160,149,460
Liabilities: $26,548,955
Net Worth: $133,600,505
Earnings: $12,673,175
Emp.: 196
Fiscal Year-end: 12/31/22
Information Technology Services
N.A.I.C.S.: 541512
Nakhee Kwon (Mng Dir)

SE HOLDINGS & INCUBATIONS CO., LTD.
5 Funacho, Shinjuku-Ku, Tokyo, 160-0006, Japan
Tel.: (81) 353623700

Web Site: https://www.sehi.co.jp
Year Founded: 1985
9478—(TKS)
Rev.: $48,371,980
Assets: $95,633,480
Liabilities: $39,283,230
Net Worth: $56,350,250
Earnings: $4,818,690
Emp.: 301
Fiscal Year-end: 03/31/24
Holding Company
N.A.I.C.S.: 551112

Subsidiaries:

SE Plus Co., Ltd. (1)
2nd floor Kowa Nibancho Building 11-19
Nibancho, Chiyoda-ku, Tokyo, 102-0084,
Japan
Tel.: (81) 366855420
Information Technology Services
N.A.I.C.S.: 541512

SHOEISHA Academy Co., Ltd. (1)
8th floor Yotsubashi Grand Building 1-4-26
Shinmachi, Nishi-ku, Osaka, 550-0013, Japan
Tel.: (81) 643938961
Web Site:
  https://www.shoeishaacademy.co.jp
Educational Support Services
N.A.I.C.S.: 611710

SE SPEZIAL-ELECTRONIC AG
Friedrich-Bach-Strasse 1, 31675,
Buckeburg, Germany
Tel.: (49) 57222030
Web Site: http://www.spezial.com
Year Founded: 1970
Sales Range: $50-74.9 Million
Electronic Components Distr
N.A.I.C.S.: 423690
Christopher Wuttke (CEO)

SE SWISS ESTATES AG
Badenerstrasse 296, Postfach 224,
CH-8040, Zurich, Switzerland
Tel.: (41) 58 252 6000
Web Site: http://www.swiss-estates.ch
WAG—(DEU)
Rev.: $6,568,326
Assets: $183,460,140
Liabilities: $134,084,448
Net Worth: $49,375,692
Earnings: $3,510,657
Fiscal Year-end: 12/31/20
Real Estate Investment Services
N.A.I.C.S.: 531390
Udo Roessig (CEO & VP)

SE-EDUCATION PUBLIC CO., LTD.
1858/87-90 Interlink Tower 19th Floor
Bangna Tai, Bangna Tai Bangna,
Bangkok, 10260, Thailand
Tel.: (66) 28268000
Web Site: https://www.se-ed.com
Year Founded: 1947
SE.ED—(THA)
Rev.: $63,374,378
Assets: $76,382,037
Liabilities: $37,085,175
Net Worth: $39,296,862
Earnings: $1,559,186
Emp.: 973
Fiscal Year-end: 12/31/23
Educational Products & Services
N.A.I.C.S.: 611710
Kasemsant Weerakul (Chm)

SEA & AIR FREIGHT INTERNATIONAL
No 209 Nguyen Van Thu Street
Dakao Ward District 1, Ho Chi Minh
City, Vietnam
Tel.: (84) 838238799
Web Site: https://www.safi.com.vn
Year Founded: 1992

SFI—(HOSE)
Rev.: $41,922,112
Assets: $36,703,720
Liabilities: $6,434,904
Net Worth: $30,268,816
Earnings: $4,248,544
Fiscal Year-end: 12/31/23
Freight Transportation Services
N.A.I.C.S.: 483111
Nguyen Hoang Anh (CEO)

SEA BIOGAS CORPORATION
4202 Tower One Lippo Center, 89
Queensway Rd, Hong Kong, China
(Hong Kong)
Tel.: (852) 6101 7023
Year Founded: 2009
Biodiesel Products & Services
N.A.I.C.S.: 324199
Douglas Fletcher (Pres, CEO, CFO, Treas & Sec)

SEA FISH INDUSTRY AUTHORITY
18 Logie Mill, Edinburgh, EH7 4HS,
United Kingdom
Tel.: (44) 1315583331
Web Site: http://www.seafish.org
Year Founded: 1981
Trade Association for the U.K. Fishing Industry
N.A.I.C.S.: 445250
Marcus Coleman (CEO)

SEA HOLDINGS LIMITED
26th Floor Everbright Centre 108
Gloucester Road, Wanchai, China
(Hong Kong)
Tel.: (852) 28286363
Web Site:
  http://www.seagroup.com.hk
0251—(HKG)
Rev.: $47,394,428
Assets: $1,757,722,268
Liabilities: $1,160,036,948
Net Worth: $597,685,320
Earnings: ($48,916,523)
Emp.: 170
Fiscal Year-end: 12/31/22
Investment Holding Property & Asset Management Services
N.A.I.C.S.: 523940
Jesse Wing Chi Lu (Chm)

Subsidiaries:

High Team International Limited (1)
7/F Palace International Hotel Office Building No 28 Donghua 2nd Road, Jiangmen, Guangdong, China
Tel.: (86) 7503373186
Web Site: https://www.profixxer.com
Motorcycle Product Mfr & Distr
N.A.I.C.S.: 336991

Leighton Road Hotel Management Services Limited (1)
8 Leighton Road Causeway Bay, Wanchai, China (Hong Kong)
Tel.: (852) 39803980
Web Site: http://www.cphongkong.com
Home Management Services
N.A.I.C.S.: 561110

SEA KAY HOLDINGS LTD.
7 Patton Street, Duncanville, 1930,
Vereeniging, South Africa
Tel.: (27) 164222067
Web Site: http://www.seakay.co.za
Year Founded: 1998
Sales Range: $25-49.9 Million
Residential Property Development Services
N.A.I.C.S.: 236116
Pieter van der Schyf (Acting CEO)

Subsidiaries:

Sea Kay Engineering Services (Pty) Limited (1)

INTERNATIONAL PUBLIC

7 Patton St, Vereeniging, 1939, Gauteng, South Africa
Tel.: (27) 164222066
Construction Engineering Services
N.A.I.C.S.: 541330

Sea Kay Engineering Services Gauteng Province (Pty) Limited (1)
7 Patton Street Duncanville, Vereeniging, 1939, Gauteng, South Africa
Tel.: (27) 164222066
Construction Engineering Services
N.A.I.C.S.: 541330

Sea Kay Engineering Services Western Cape (Pty) Limited (1)
9 Fairway Business Park Niblick Street, Somerset West, 7130, Western Cape, South Africa
Tel.: (27) 218527971
Construction Engineering Services
N.A.I.C.S.: 541330

Sea Kay Property Development (Pty) Limited (1)
10 Fairway Office Park Niblick Street Somerset Mall, Somerset West, 7130, South Africa
Tel.: (27) 16 422 2066
Real Estate Development Services
N.A.I.C.S.: 531390

Sea Kay Property Development Western Cape (Pty) Limited (1)
9 Fairway Off Prk Nibleck Str Somerset Mall, Somerset West, 7130, Western Cape, South Africa
Tel.: (27) 218527971
Construction Engineering Services
N.A.I.C.S.: 541330

SEA LIMITED
1 Fusionopolis Place 17-10, Galaxis,
Singapore, 138522, Singapore
Tel.: (65) 62708100
Web Site: https://www.sea.com
Year Founded: 2009
SE—(NYSE)
Rev.: $12,449,705,000
Assets: $17,002,796,000
Liabilities: $11,191,972,000
Net Worth: $5,810,824,000
Earnings: ($1,651,421,000)
Emp.: 63,800
Fiscal Year-end: 12/31/22
Online Game Development Services
N.A.I.C.S.: 541511
Forrest Xiaodong Li (Co-Founder, Chm & CEO)

Subsidiaries:

AirPay (Thailand) Co., Ltd (1)
89 AIA Capital Center Building Floor 24 Ratchadapisek Road, Din Daeng Subdistrict Din Daeng District, Bangkok, 10400, Thailand
Tel.: (66) 21189170
Web Site: http://www.airpay.in.th
Information Technology Services
N.A.I.C.S.: 541511

PT. Garena Indonesia (1)
Gama Tower LT 23-26 JI H R Rasuna Said Kav C22, Karet Kuningan Setiabudi, Jakarta, 12940, Selatan, Indonesia
Tel.: (62) 2180864211
Web Site: https://www.garena.co.id
Ecommerce Services
N.A.I.C.S.: 513210

PT. Shopee International Indonesia (1)
JI Agung karya VII No1 Kawasan Pergudangan Dunex Gudang G Sunter, Jakarta, 14340, Utara, Indonesia
Tel.: (62) 2180647100
Web Site: http://shopee.co.id
Ecommerce Services
N.A.I.C.S.: 423620

Shopee Singapore Private Limited (1)
5 Science Park Drive Shopee Building, Singapore, Singapore
Tel.: (65) 62066610
Web Site: http://shopee.sg

AND PRIVATE COMPANIES

Ecommerce Services
N.A.I.C.S.: 423620

SEA MECHANICS CO., LTD.
80 1gongdan-ro 10-gi, Gumi, 39379, Gyeongsangbuk-do, Korea (South)
Tel.: (82) 544672000
Web Site:
   https://www.seamechanics.com
Year Founded: 1999
396300—(KRS)
Rev.: $67,218,902
Assets: $60,567,914
Liabilities: $11,671,121
Net Worth: $48,896,793
Earnings: $2,935,851
Emp.: 197
Fiscal Year-end: 12/31/22
Electronic Parts Mfr & Distr
N.A.I.C.S.: 334419
Chang-su Kim *(CEO)*

SEA OIL PUBLIC COMPANY LIMITED
88 Soi Banga-Trad 30 Debaratna Road, Bangna, Bangkok, 10260, Thailand
Tel.: (66) 23989850
Web Site:
   https://www.seaoilthailand.com
SEAOIL—(THA)
Rev.: $403,660,694
Assets: $90,408,816
Liabilities: $19,297,877
Net Worth: $71,110,938
Earnings: $10,006,423
Emp.: 231
Fiscal Year-end: 12/31/23
Marine Bunker Fuels Supplier
N.A.I.C.S.: 457210
Apisit Rujikeatkamjorn *(Chm)*

Subsidiaries:

Sea Oil Petroleum Pte. Ltd. (1)
7 Temasek Boulevard Suntec City Tower One 08-02/2A, Singapore, 038987, Singapore
Tel.: (65) 66610860
Web Site: http://www.seaoilpetroleum.com
Sea Oil Petroleum Distr
N.A.I.C.S.: 211120
Koh Kuan Hua *(Head-Trading)*

SEA STAR CAPITAL PLC
Strovolou Avenue 117 1st floor 102 Office, Strovolos, 2042, Cyprus
Tel.: (357) 22766006
Tourism Management Services
N.A.I.C.S.: 561520

SEA SWIFT PTY. LTD.
41-45 Tingira St, Cairns, 4870, QLD, Australia
Tel.: (61) 7 4035 1234 AU
Web Site: http://www.seaswift.com.au
Sales Range: $25-49.9 Million
Emp.: 400
Water Freight Transportation Services
N.A.I.C.S.: 483211
Fred White *(CEO)*

SEA TV NETWORK LIMITED
148 Manas Nagar, Shahganj, Agra, 282010, India
Tel.: (91) 5624036666
Web Site:
   https://www.seatvnetwork.com
533268—(BOM)
Rev.: $1,865,507
Assets: $3,006,032
Liabilities: $11,883,598
Net Worth: $(8,877,566)
Earnings: $(1,178,344)
Emp.: 208
Fiscal Year-end: 03/31/21
Cable Television Programming
N.A.I.C.S.: 516210

Neeraj Jain *(Chm & Mng Dir)*

SEA-INVEST GROUP
Skaldenstraat 1, 9042, Gent, Belgium
Tel.: (32) 9 255 02 11
Web Site: http://www.sea-invest.com
Sales Range: $1-9.9 Million
Emp.: 5,500
Marine Cargo Handling
N.A.I.C.S.: 488320
Erik Loontjens *(Mng Dir)*

Subsidiaries:

Antwerp Bulk Terminal NV (1)
Nieuwe Westweg 14, 2040, Antwerp, Belgium
Tel.: (32) 35601211
Marine Cargo Handling Services
N.A.I.C.S.: 488320
Bart Laureys *(Gen Mgr)*

Belfruco NV (1)
Rostockweg/Kade 214-216, 2030, Antwerp, Belgium
Tel.: (32) 35405955
Marine Cargo Handling Services
N.A.I.C.S.: 488320
Luc Buelens *(Gen Mgr)*

Port Polnocny Sp. z o.o. (1)
Ul Budowniczych Portu Polnocnego 23, 80-601, Gdansk, Poland
Tel.: (48) 587376003
Web Site: http://www.port-polnocny.pl
Marine Cargo Handling Services
N.A.I.C.S.: 488320

Rotterdam Fruit Wharf B.V. (1)
Marconistraat 80, 3029 AK, Rotterdam, Netherlands
Tel.: (31) 102215000
Marine Cargo Handling Services
N.A.I.C.S.: 488320
Fred Krijnen *(Gen Mgr)*

SEA -TANK FRANCE, SA (1)
Quai Alfred de Vial, 33530, Bassens, France
Tel.: (33) 556749744
Marine Cargo Handling Services
N.A.I.C.S.: 488320

SEA INVEST SHIPPING AGENCY N.V. (1)
Rostockweg 25 - Haven 300, 2030, Antwerp, Belgium
Tel.: (32) 35436605
Web Site: http://www.sea-invest-sa.com
Sea Freight Transportation Services
N.A.I.C.S.: 483113
Fredien Claes *(Dir-Comml)*

SEA-Tankers (1)
7 Ru du Golf, Parc Innolin, 33700, Merignac, France
Tel.: (33) 556161514
Web Site: http://www.sea-tankers.fr
Sales Range: $25-49.9 Million
Emp.: 28
Oil Products Transportation
N.A.I.C.S.: 483111
Laurent Bach *(Dir-Admin)*

Sogatra NV (1)
Skaldenstraat 1, 9042, Gent, Belgium
Tel.: (32) 92550336
Marine Cargo Handling Services
N.A.I.C.S.: 488320

SEABIRD EXPLORATION NORWAY AS
Sandviksbodene 68, PO Box 1302, 5035, Bergen, Norway
Tel.: (47) 977236371
Web Site: https://www.sbexp.com
Rev.: $19,880,000
Assets: $58,346,000
Liabilities: $20,837,000
Net Worth: $37,509,000
Earnings: $(11,976,000)
Emp.: 325
Fiscal Year-end: 12/31/18
Seismic Management Services
N.A.I.C.S.: 541360
Kjell Mangeroy *(VP-Bus Dev)*

Subsidiaries:

SeaBird Exploration Americas Inc (1)
1155 N Dairy Ashford Ste 206, Houston, TX 77079
Tel.: (281) 556-1666
Web Site: http://www.sbexp.com
Sales Range: $50-74.9 Million
Emp.: 5
Oil & Gas Exploration Services
N.A.I.C.S.: 211120

SeaBird Exploration FZ LLC (1)
Al Shatha Tower 35/F Dubai Media City, PO Box 500549/500347, Dubai, United Arab Emirates
Tel.: (971) 44271700
Web Site: http://www.sbexp.com
Seismic Management Services
N.A.I.C.S.: 561990

SEABOARD TRANSPORT GROUP
721 Wilkinson Ave, Dartmouth, Nova Scotia, B3B 0H4, BC, Canada
Tel.: (902) 468-4447
Web Site:
   http://seaboardtransportgroup.com
Freight Transportation Arrangement
N.A.I.C.S.: 488510

SEABRIDGE GOLD INC.
106 Front Street East Suite 400, Toronto, M5A 1E 1, ON, Canada
Tel.: (416) 367-9292 Ca
Web Site:
   https://www.seabridgegold.com
Year Founded: 1979
SA—(NYSE)
Rev.: $2,185,690
Assets: $857,080,831
Liabilities: $277,776,676
Net Worth: $579,304,155
Earnings: $(5,784,178)
Fiscal Year-end: 12/31/22
Gold, Silver & Copper Exploration & Mining Services
N.A.I.C.S.: 213114
Rudi P. Fronk *(CEO & Chm)*

Subsidiaries:

KSM Mining ULC (1)
106 Front Street East Suite 400, Toronto, ON, Canada
Tel.: (416) 367-9292
Web Site: http://ksmproject.com
Mineral Exploration & Mining Services
N.A.I.C.S.: 213114

SEAC LIMITED
Unit 2-4 Chartwell Drive, Wigston, LE18 2FL, Leicester, United Kingdom
Tel.: (44) 116 2887719 UK
Web Site: http://www.seac.co.uk
Year Founded: 1916
Sales Range: $10-24.9 Million
Emp.: 45
Specialty Fastener Building Product Mfr
N.A.I.C.S.: 339993
Richard Beer *(Dir-Fin)*

SEACERA GROUP BERHAD
DF2-11-01 Unit 1 Level 11 Persoft Tower, 6B Persiaran Tropicana Tropicana Golf Country Resort, 47410, Petaling Jaya, Selangor, Malaysia
Tel.: (60) 376887517
Web Site:
   https://www.seacera.com.my
Year Founded: 1987
SEACERA—(KLS)
Rev.: $11,017,816
Assets: $178,751,552
Liabilities: $27,393,112
Net Worth: $151,358,440
Earnings: $1,600,775
Emp.: 21

Fiscal Year-end: 06/30/23
Ceramic Tile Mfr
N.A.I.C.S.: 327120

Subsidiaries:

Seacera Care Sdn. Bhd. (1)
No 5 5A 5B and 5C Jalan PS 8/3 Taman Prima Selayang, 68100, Batu Caves, Selangor, Malaysia
Tel.: (60) 172019394
Personal Protective Equipment Product Distr
N.A.I.C.S.: 423450

SeaceraMart Sdn. Bhd. (1)
No 5 5A 5B and 5C Jalan PS 8/3 taman prima selayang, 68100, Batu Caves, Selangor, Malaysia
Tel.: (60) 172019394
Facilities Support Services
N.A.I.C.S.: 455219

SEACH MEDICAL GROUP LTD.
Arie Shenkar 14, Mailbox 52520, Ramat Gan, 4672514, Israel
Tel.: (972) 7700009
Web Site: http://seach.co.il
SEMG—(TAE)
Rev.: $41,531,703
Assets: $36,164,110
Liabilities: $11,577,290
Net Worth: $24,586,821
Earnings: $(3,279,735)
Fiscal Year-end: 12/31/23
Other Activities Related to Real Estate
N.A.I.C.S.: 531390

Subsidiaries:

Eybna Technologies Ltd. (1)
23 Pa'amei Aviv St, Givat Hen, 43905, Givatayim, Israel
Tel.: (972) 33741976
Web Site: http://www.eybna.com
Pharmaceuticals Mfr
N.A.I.C.S.: 325412

SEACOAST SHIPPING SERVICES LTD.
Address D 1202 Swati Crimson and Clover Shilaj Circle S P Ring Road, SG Highway Bodakdev, Ahmedabad, 380054, Gujarat, India
Tel.: (91) 9824256765
Web Site:
   https://www.seacoastltd.com
Year Founded: 2005
542753—(BOM)
Rev.: $33,190,717
Assets: $20,303,754
Liabilities: $14,148,268
Net Worth: $6,155,486
Earnings: $1,514,530
Fiscal Year-end: 03/31/21
Logistic Services
N.A.I.C.S.: 541614
Manish Raichand Shah *(Chm & Mng Dir)*

SEACON SHIPPING GROUP HOLDINGS LIMITED
23 / F Tower B Hisense Chuangzhi Valley No 20 Zhuzhou Road, Laoshan District, Qingdao, Shandong, China
Tel.: (86) 53281929800 Ky
Web Site: https://www.seacon.com
Year Founded: 2012
2409—(HKG)
Rev.: $359,101,000
Assets: $287,247,000
Liabilities: $178,237,000
Net Worth: $109,010,000
Earnings: $58,929,000
Emp.: 191
Fiscal Year-end: 12/31/22
Holding Company
N.A.I.C.S.: 551112

SEACON SHIPPING GROUP HOLDINGS LIMITED

Seacon Shipping Group Holdings Limited—(Continued)

Subsidiaries:

Golden Bridge Ships Limited (1)
Room 2205-2206 China Insurance Group Bldg 141 Des Voeux Road C, Hong Kong, China (Hong Kong)
Tel.: (852) 28542318
Web Site: https://www.gbship.com
Ship Management Services
N.A.I.C.S.: 532411

SEACREST PETROLEO BERMUDA LIMITED

Seacrest Petroleo 99 Front Street, Hamilton, HM12, Bermuda
Tel.: (441) 7949714756 BM
Web Site:
https://www.seacrestpetroleo.com
Year Founded: 2020
SEAPT—(OSL)
Rev.: $177,431,000
Assets: $811,262,000
Liabilities: $651,162,000
Net Worth: $160,100,000
Earnings: ($79,338,000)
Emp.: 314
Fiscal Year-end: 12/31/23
Oil & Gas Exploration Services
N.A.I.C.S.: 237120
Michael Stewart (CEO)

SEADRAGON LTD.

12 Nayland Road Stoke, Nelson, 7011, New Zealand
Tel.: (64) 3 547 0336 NZ
Web Site:
http://www.seadragon.co.nz
Year Founded: 1996
Rev.: $3,274,046
Assets: $7,731,223
Liabilities: $1,827,624
Net Worth: $5,903,599
Earnings: ($6,415,441)
Emp.: 21
Fiscal Year-end: 03/31/19
Pharmaceuticals Mfr
N.A.I.C.S.: 325412
Matthew McNamara (Chief Investment Officer)

SEADRILL LIMITED

Park Place 55 Par la Ville Road, Hamilton, HM 11, Bermuda
Tel.: (441) 2956935 BM
Web Site: https://www.seadrill.com
SDRL—(NYSE)
Rev.: $1,502,000,000
Assets: $4,218,000,000
Liabilities: $1,235,000,000
Net Worth: $2,983,000,000
Earnings: $300,000,000
Emp.: 2,505
Fiscal Year-end: 12/31/23
Offshore Drilling Services
N.A.I.C.S.: 213111
Julie Johnson Robertson (Chm)

Subsidiaries:

Aquadrill LLC (1)
2nd Floor Building 11 Chiswick Business Park 566 Chiswick High Road, London, W4 5YS, United Kingdom
Tel.: (44) 2088114700
Web Site: http://www.seadrillpartners.com
Rev.: $538,100,000
Assets: $927,200,000
Liabilities: $2,992,400,000
Net Worth: ($2,065,200,000)
Earnings: ($2,550,900,000)
Emp.: 569
Fiscal Year-end: 12/31/2020
Offshore Drilling Services
N.A.I.C.S.: 333132
Steven L. Newman (Chm & CEO)

North Atlantic Crew AS (1)
Lokkeveien 111, Stavanger, 4007, Rogaland, Norway

Tel.: (47) 51 30 97 97
Drilling Services
N.A.I.C.S.: 213111

North Atlantic Drilling Ltd. (1)
Par-la-Villa Place 4th Floor 14 Par-la-Villa Road, Hamilton, HM08, Bermuda
Tel.: (441) 295 69 35
Web Site: http://www.nadlcorp.com
Rev.: $257,500,000
Assets: $2,621,200,000
Liabilities: $2,529,900,000
Net Worth: $91,300,000
Earnings: $286,400,000
Emp.: 631
Fiscal Year-end: 12/31/2017
Offshore Drilling Company
N.A.I.C.S.: 213111

North Atlantic Drilling Management AS (1)
Finnestadveien 28, PO Box 109, 4001, Stavanger, Norway
Tel.: (47) 51 30 90 00
Web Site: http://www.seadrill.com
Offshore Drilling Services
N.A.I.C.S.: 213111

North Atlantic Management AS (1)
Finnestadveien 28, PO Box 109, Stavanger, 4029, Rogaland, Norway
Tel.: (47) 51 30 90 00
Business Management Consulting Services
N.A.I.C.S.: 541618

Seadrill Americas Inc. (1)
11025 Equity Dr Ste 150, Houston, TX 77041
Tel.: (713) 329-1150
Web Site: http://www.seadrill.com
Sales Range: $50-74.9 Million
Emp.: 75
Offshore Drilling Services
N.A.I.C.S.: 213111

Seadrill Asia Ltd. (1)
6th Floor Sindhorn Tower 2 130-132 Wireless Road Lumpini Pathumwan, Bangkok, 10330, Thailand
Tel.: (66) 2 263 3320
Web Site: http://www.seadrill.com
Offshore Drilling Services
N.A.I.C.S.: 213111

Seadrill Deepwater Units Pte Ltd (1)
10 Hoe Chiang Road 18-01 Keppel Towers, Singapore, 089315, Singapore
Tel.: (65) 6411 5000
Offshore Drilling Services
N.A.I.C.S.: 213111

Seadrill Management (S) Pte Ltd (1)
10 Hoe Chiang Road 18-01 Keppel Towers, Singapore, 089315, Singapore
Tel.: (65) 6411 5000
Web Site: http://www.seadrill.com
Offshore Drilling Services
N.A.I.C.S.: 213111

Seadrill Management A.M.E LDT (1)
Arenco Building 21th Floor Sheikh Zayed Road Media City, PO Box 487828, Dubai, United Arab Emirates
Tel.: (971) 4 455 1300
Web Site: http://www.seadrill.com
Offshore Drilling Services
N.A.I.C.S.: 213111

Seadrill Management AS (1)
Lokkeveien 107, PO Box 110, Stavanger, 4001, Norway
Tel.: (47) 51309000
Web Site: http://www.seadrill.com
Offshore Drilling Services
N.A.I.C.S.: 213111

Subsidiary (Non-US):

Seadrill Management (S) Pte. Ltd. (2)
10 Hoe Chiang Road 09-01 Keppel Towers, Singapore, 89315, Singapore
Tel.: (65) 64115000
Web Site: http://www.seadrill.com
Sales Range: $150-199.9 Million
Emp.: 300
Oil Drilling Services
N.A.I.C.S.: 213111

Seadrill Rig Holding Company Ltd (1)

Par la Ville Place 4th Floor 14 Par la Ville Road, Hamilton, HM08, Bermuda
Tel.: (441) 2959500
Holding Company
N.A.I.C.S.: 551112

Subsidiary (Domestic):

Asia Offshore Drilling Limited (2)
Par-la-Ville Place 4th Floor, 14 Par-la-Ville Road, Hamilton, Bermuda (100%)
Tel.: (441) 295 9500
Sales Range: Less than $1 Million
Offshore Drilling Services
N.A.I.C.S.: 213111
Erling Lind (Chm)

Seadrill Sdn. Bhd. (1)
No 20 Lot 3862 Jalan Pandan Lima A, Kuala Belait, KA1931, Brunei Darussalam
Tel.: (673) 3 333 910
Web Site: http://www.seadrill.com
Offshore Drilling Services
N.A.I.C.S.: 213111

Seadrill Servicos de Petroleo Ltda. (1)
Republica Do tela No 230 Fl 22, Rio de Janeiro, 20021170, Brazil
Tel.: (55) 21 3506 2750
Web Site: http://www.seadrill.com
Emp.: 200
Offshore Drilling Services
N.A.I.C.S.: 213111

Seadrill Tender Rig Pte. Ltd. (1)
10 Hoe Chiang Road, 089315, Singapore
Tel.: (65) 64115000
Sales Range: $200-249.9 Million
Emp.: 300
Oil Well Drilling Services
N.A.I.C.S.: 213111

Smedvig Holding AS (1)
Par-la-Ville Place 14 Pa-la-Ville Road, Hamilton, HM 08, Bermuda
Tel.: (441) 295 6935
Web Site: https://www.seadrill.com
Emp.: 5
Holding Company
N.A.I.C.S.: 551112

Subsidiary (Non-US):

Smedvig ASA (2)
Lokkeveien 103, PO Box 900, N 4004, Stavanger, Norway
Tel.: (47) 51509600
Web Site: http://www.smedvig.no
Sales Range: $650-699.9 Million
Offshore Drilling Contractor
N.A.I.C.S.: 213111
John Fredriksen (Chm)

SEAFARMS GROUP LIMITED

Level 10 490 Upper Edward Street, Spring Hill, 4000, QLD, Australia
Tel.: (61) 732480222 AU
Web Site:
https://www.seafarms.com.au
Year Founded: 1990
SFG—(ASX)
Rev.: $17,032,627
Assets: $21,410,945
Liabilities: $11,526,341
Net Worth: $9,884,604
Earnings: ($12,895,340)
Fiscal Year-end: 06/30/24
Environmental Engineering Services
N.A.I.C.S.: 541330
Ian Norman Trahar (Chm)

SEAFCO PUBLIC COMPANY LIMITED

144 Prayasuren Road Bangchan Khlong Sam Wah, Bangkok, 10510, Thailand
Tel.: (66) 29190090
Web Site: https://www.seafco.co.th
Year Founded: 1974
SEAFCO—(THA)
Rev.: $52,532,410
Assets: $74,899,881
Liabilities: $28,282,932

INTERNATIONAL PUBLIC

Net Worth: $46,616,949
Earnings: $4,945,412
Fiscal Year-end: 12/31/23
Deep Foundation Services
N.A.I.C.S.: 238190
Somjai Phagaphasvivat (Chm)

Subsidiaries:

Seafco (Myanmar) Co., Ltd. (1)
60 B/C Myintzu Street Sub-Street 2 Parami Avenue, Yankin Township, Yangon, Myanmar
Tel.: (95) 1664880
Web Site: http://www.seafcomyanmar.com
Construction Building Services
N.A.I.C.S.: 236220

SEAFIELD RESOURCES LTD.

36 Toronto Street Suite 1000, Toronto, M5C 2C5, ON, Canada
Tel.: (416) 361-3434
Web Site:
http://www.sffresources.com
Sales Range: Less than $1 Million
Gold Exploration Services
N.A.I.C.S.: 212220
Stephanie Ashton (CFO)

SEAFIRE AB

Master Samuelsgatan 9, Box 5321, 111 44, Stockholm, Sweden
Tel.: (46) 854440450
Web Site: https://www.seafireab.com
Year Founded: 2016
SEAF—(NYSE)
Financial Investment Services
N.A.I.C.S.: 523999
Johan Bennarsten (Pres)

SEAFOOD JOINT STOCK COMPANY NO.4

320 Hung Phu 9 Ward, District 8, Ho Chi Minh City, Vietnam
Tel.: (84) 839543361
Web Site:
https://www.seafoodno4.com
Year Founded: 2001
TS4—(HOSE)
Rev.: $3,839,390
Assets: $39,999,593
Liabilities: $37,192,117
Net Worth: $2,807,476
Earnings: ($2,106,601)
Emp.: 34
Fiscal Year-end: 12/31/21
Seafood Product Mfr
N.A.I.C.S.: 311710
Nguyen Van Luc (Gen Dir)

SEAFORT CAPITAL, INC.

CIBC Building Suite 701 1809 Barrington Street, Halifax, B3J 3K8, NS, Canada
Tel.: (902) 407-4188 Ca
Web Site:
http://www.seafortcapital.com
Year Founded: 2012
Privater Equity Firm
N.A.I.C.S.: 523999
Rob Normandeau (Pres)

Subsidiaries:

G. Cooper Equipment Rentals Ltd. (1)
6335 Edwards Blvd, Mississauga, L5T 2W7, ON, Canada
Tel.: (877) 329-6531
Web Site: http://www.cooperequipment.ca
Emp.: 300
Construction Equipment Rental Services
N.A.I.C.S.: 532412
Darryl Cooper (Pres)

Jardine Transport Ltd. (1)
Tel.: (506) 453-1811
Web Site: http://jardinetransport.ca
Long Haul Transportation
N.A.I.C.S.: 488510
Dion Cull (Pres)

AND PRIVATE COMPANIES

Subsidiary (Domestic):

R.E.M. Transport Ltd. (2)
4 Hall Rd, Old Ridge, Saint Stephen, E3L
5E1, NB, Canada
Tel.: (506) 466-2918
Web Site: http://www.jardinetransport.ca
Tractors & Trailors Transportation Services
N.A.I.C.S.: 484110
Samantha Kinney *(Controller)*

SEAFRESH INDUSTRY PUBLIC COMPANY LIMITED

31 Flr Chartered Square
Building152/25 North Sathon Road
Silom, Bangrak, Bangkok, 10500,
Thailand
Tel.: (66) 26378888
Web Site: https://www.seafresh.com
Year Founded: 1982
CFRESH—(THA)
Rev.: $192,519,196
Assets: $153,009,527
Liabilities: $72,413,208
Net Worth: $80,596,318
Earnings: $2,459,209
Emp.: 2,142
Fiscal Year-end: 12/31/23
Frozen Seafood Mfr & Distr
N.A.I.C.S.: 311710
Narit Chia-Apar *(Chm & CEO)*

Subsidiaries:

Blue Earth Foods Limited (1)
Ocean House Oxleasow Road, Redditch,
B98 0RE, Worcestershire, United Kingdom
Tel.: (44) 152 751 9900
Web Site: https://www.blueearthfoods.co.uk
Frozen Food Distr
N.A.I.C.S.: 424460

Seafresh Group (Holdings)
Limited (1)
Atlantic House Oxleasow Road, Redditch,
B98 0RE, Worcestershire, United Kingdom
Tel.: (44) 152 746 0460
Web Site: https://www.seafresh-group.com
Emp.: 4,000
Aquaculture Farming Services
N.A.I.C.S.: 112519

Subsidiary (Domestic):

Sea Farms Nutrition Limited (1)
Atlantic House Oxleasow Road East Moons
Moat, Redditch, B98 0RE, Worcestershire,
United Kingdom
Tel.: (44) 1527460460
Animal Feed Mfr & Retailer
N.A.I.C.S.: 311119
OddGeir Oddsen *(Mng Dir)*

Subsidiary (US):

Sea Farms, Inc. (2)
536 Mill Point Rd, Hudgins, VA 23076
Tel.: (804) 725-9113
Web Site: http://www.seafarmsva.com
Seafood Processing Services
N.A.I.C.S.: 311710

Seafresh Industry Public Company
Limited - Chumphon Factory (1)
402 Moo 8 Chumphon-Pak Nam Road Pak-Nam, Mueang, Chumphon, 86120, Thailand
Tel.: (66) 7 752 1321
Web Site: http://www.seafresh.com
Emp.: 2,004
Frozen Food Mfr & Distr
N.A.I.C.S.: 311710
Pairoj Yangthong *(COO & Member-Exec Bd)*

SEAFRONT RESOURCES CORPORATION

7th Floor JMT Building ADB Ave Ortigas Center, Pasig, 1600, Philippines
Tel.: (63) 286372917
Web Site:
https://www.seafrontresources.com
SPM—(PHI)
Rev.: $57,330
Assets: $12,087,619
Liabilities: $1,108,938
Net Worth: $10,978,681
Earnings: $21,564
Fiscal Year-end: 12/31/22
Oil Exploration & Production Services
N.A.I.C.S.: 211120
Samuel V. Torres *(Gen Counsel & Sec)*

SEAGATE TECHNOLOGY HOLDINGS PLC

38/39 Fitzwilliam Square, Dublin, D02
NX53, Ireland
Tel.: (353) 12343136   IE
Web Site: http://www.seagate.com
Year Founded: 1979
STX—(NASDAQ)
Rev.: $7,384,000,000
Assets: $7,556,000,000
Liabilities: $8,755,000,000
Net Worth: ($1,199,000,000)
Earnings: ($529,000,000)
Emp.: 33,400
Fiscal Year-end: 06/30/23
Holding Company
N.A.I.C.S.: 551112
Ban Seng Teh *(Exec VP-Sls Ops & Sls-Global)*

Subsidiaries:

Nippon Seagate Inc. (1)
Tennoz Parkside Bldg 3rd Fl 2-5-8 Hagashi,
Shinagawa-Ku, Tokyo, 140 0002,
Japan (100%)
Tel.: (81) 354622900
Web Site: http://www.seagate.com
Sales Range: $25-49.9 Million
Emp.: 50
Computer Peripherals Distr & Sales
N.A.I.C.S.: 541611
BanSeng Teh *(Mng Dir & VP)*

Penang Seagate Industries (M) Sdn.
Bhd. (1)
88A Lebuhraya Kampung Jawa Bayan
Lepas, Penang, 11900, Malaysia
Tel.: (60) 46157000
Web Site: http://www.penengseagate.com
Sales Range: $800-899.9 Million
Emp.: 3,000
Computer Storage Device Mfr
N.A.I.C.S.: 334112

Seagate International (Johor) Sdn.
Bhd. (1)
Plo 55 Jalan Persiaran Teknologi Taman
Teknologi, Senai, 81400, Malaysia
Tel.: (60) 75556888
Electronic Components Mfr
N.A.I.C.S.: 334419

Seagate Singapore International
Headquarters Pte. Ltd. (1)
7000 Ang Mo Kio Ave 5, Singapore,
569877, Singapore (100%)
Tel.: (65) 64853888
Web Site: http://www.seagate-asia.com
Computer Peripherals Sales & Marketer
N.A.I.C.S.: 334118

Seagate Technology (Ireland) (1)
1 Disc Dr, Londonderry, BT48 0BF, United
Kingdom
Tel.: (44) 2871274000
Data Storage Device Mfr
N.A.I.C.S.: 334112

Seagate Technology (Marlow)
Limited (1)
Atlas House 3rd Avenue Globe Park, Marlow, SL7 1AY, Bucks, United
Kingdom (100%)
Tel.: (44) 1628890366
Web Site: http://www.seagate.com
Sales Range: $25-49.9 Million
Emp.: 25
Computer Peripherals Sales
N.A.I.C.S.: 541611

Seagate Technology (Netherlands)
B.V. (1)
Koolhovenlaan 1, 1119 NB, Schiphol-Rijk,
Netherlands
Tel.: (31) 203167300

Sales Range: $25-49.9 Million
Emp.: 100
Hard Disk Mfr
N.A.I.C.S.: 334118
Donna de Smet *(Mng Dir)*

Seagate Technology (Thailand)
Limited (1)
1627 Moo 7 Theparak Road, Ban Thepharak, 10270, Thailand
Tel.: (66) 27152999
Web Site: http://www.seagate.com
Sales Range: $1-4.9 Billion
Emp.: 10,000
Information Management & Storage Mfr
N.A.I.C.S.: 334112

Seagate Technology (US) Holdings,
Inc. (1)
10200 S De Anza Blvd, Cupertino, CA
95014
Tel.: (408) 658-1000
Holding Company
N.A.I.C.S.: 551112

Subsidiary (Domestic):

LaCie Ltd (2)
7555 SW Tech Center Dr, Tigard, OR
97223
Tel.: (971) 246-8200
Web Site: http://www.lacie.com
Software Development Services
N.A.I.C.S.: 541511

Subsidiary (Non-US):

LaCie S.A.S. (2)
17 rue Ampere, 91349, Massy, Cedex,
France (92.1%)
Tel.: (33) 169328350
Web Site: http://www.lacie.com
Sales Range: $350-399.9 Million
Emp.: 475
Crossplatform, High-End, Mass Storage,
Digital & Color Management Peripherals Mfr
& Distr
N.A.I.C.S.: 334112
Philippe Pardonnet *(CTO)*

Subsidiary (Non-US):

LaCie AB (3)
Sveavagen 905, 11359, Stockholm,
Sweden (100%)
Tel.: (46) 84110602
Web Site: http://www.lacie.com
Sales Range: $50-74.9 Million
Emp.: 10
Computer & Computer Peripheral Equipment & Software Whslr
N.A.I.C.S.: 423430

LaCie Asia Limited (3)
25 F Winsan Tower 98 Thomson Road,
Wanchai, China (Hong Kong)
Tel.: (852) 35280628
Web Site: http://www.lacie.com
Computer Peripheral Equipment Mfr
N.A.I.C.S.: 334118

LaCie Electronique D2, S.A. (3)
Calle Acanto 22 Oficina 4, Madrid, 28045,
Spain
Tel.: (34) 913238300
Web Site: http://www.lacie.com
Office Equipment Distr
N.A.I.C.S.: 423420

Subsidiary (US):

LaCie Limited (3)
22985 NW Evergreen Pkwy, Hillsboro, OR
97124-7165
Tel.: (503) 844-4500
Web Site: http://www.lacie.com
Emp.: 150
Computer Components
N.A.I.C.S.: 334118

Subsidiary (Non-US):

LaCie Peripherals Inc. (3)
235 Dufferin St, Toronto, M6K 1Z5, ON,
Canada (100%)
Tel.: (416) 530-2545
Web Site: http://www.lacie.com
Sales Range: $25-49.9 Million
Emp.: 20
Computer & Computer Peripheral Equipment & Software Whslr
N.A.I.C.S.: 423430

SEAGATE TECHNOLOGY HOLDINGS PLC

LaCie Pty Ltd. (3)
6/151 Beauchamp Road, Matraville, 2036,
NSW, Australia
Tel.: (61) 296696900
Web Site: http://www.lacie.com
Computer & Computer Peripheral Equipment & Software Whslr
N.A.I.C.S.: 423430

Subsidiary (Domestic):

LaCie S.A.S. (3)
17 Rue Ampere, 91349, Massy,
France (100%)
Tel.: (33) 1 69 32 07 60
Web Site: http://www.lacie.com
Sales Range: $50-74.9 Million
Emp.: 200
Computer & Computer Peripheral Equipment & Software Whslr
N.A.I.C.S.: 423430

Subsidiary (Non-US):

LaCie Sprl (3)
Bld du Souverain 165, B-1160, Brussels,
Belgium (100%)
Tel.: (32) 26391470
Web Site: http://www.lacie.com
Sales Range: $25-49.9 Million
Emp.: 11
Computer Peripheral Equipment Mfr
N.A.I.C.S.: 334118

LaCie Srl. (3)
Milano Business Park Edificio B1, Via dei
Missaglia 97, 20142, Milan, Italy
Tel.: (39) 02202021209
Web Site: http://www.lacie.com
Computer & Computer Peripheral Equipment & Software Whslr
N.A.I.C.S.: 423430

Subsidiary (Domestic):

SandForce, Inc. (2)
691 S Milpitas Blvd Ste 100, Milpitas, CA
95035-5476
Tel.: (408) 372-9000
Web Site: http://www.sandforce.com
Sales Range: $25-49.9 Million
Emp.: 190
Flash Storage Processors Mfr
N.A.I.C.S.: 334112

Seagate Cloud Systems, Inc. (2)
1351 S Sunset St, Longmont, CO 80501
Tel.: (303) 845-3200
Web Site: http://www.dothill.com
Sales Range: $200-249.9 Million
Data Storage System Designer & Mfr
N.A.I.C.S.: 334112
Bill Wuertz *(Sr VP-Solutions & Products)*

Seagate Systems (US) Holdings
Inc. (2)
10200 S De Anza Blvd, Cupertino, CA
95014
Tel.: (831) 438-6550
Holding Company
N.A.I.C.S.: 551112

Seagate Technology LLC (2)
10200 S De Anza Blvd, Cupertino, CA
95014
Tel.: (408) 658-1000
Web Site: https://www.seagate.com
Data Protection & Management Solutions
N.A.I.C.S.: 334118
Terry Noonan *(CTO & VP-R&D)*

Unit (Domestic):

Seagate Recording Media (3)
47010 Kato Rd, Fremont, CA 94538-7332
Tel.: (510) 490-3222
Web Site: http://www.seagate.com
Computer Hard Disk Drives Mfr
N.A.I.C.S.: 334112

Seagate Recovery Services (3)
3101 Jay St Ste 110, Santa Clara, CA
95054
Tel.: (408) 625-5850
Web Site: http://www.seagate.com
Digital Media Data Recovery
N.A.I.C.S.: 541511

Branch (Domestic):

Seagate Technology LLC -
Bloomington (3)

SEAGATE TECHNOLOGY HOLDINGS PLC

Seagate Technology Holdings PLC—(Continued)
7801 Computer Ave, Bloomington, MN 55435-5412
Tel.: (952) 402-8000
Web Site: http://www.seagate.com
Hard Disk Drive Mfr
N.A.I.C.S.: 334112

Seagate Technology LLC - Oklahoma City (3)
10321 W Reno Ave, Oklahoma City, OK 73127-7140
Tel.: (405) 324-3000
Web Site: http://www.seagate.com
Hard Disk Drive Mfr
N.A.I.C.S.: 334112

Subsidiary (Non-US):

Seagate Technology Taiwan Ltd. (2)
Room B 14th Fl 363 Fu Hsin N Rd, Taipei, 105, Taiwan (100%)
Tel.: (886) 225451305
Web Site: http://www.seagate.com
Sales Range: $25-49.9 Million
Emp.: 30
Computer Peripherals Sales & Marketer
N.A.I.C.S.: 541611

Subsidiary (Domestic):

Seagate US LLC (2)
10200 S De Anza Blvd, Cupertino, CA 95014
Tel.: (408) 658-1000
Web Site: http://www.seagate.com
Hard Disk Drive Mfr
N.A.I.C.S.: 332510

Seagate Technology Korea, Inc. (1)
2nd Fl Bonsol Building 144-27 Samsung Dong, Seoul, 135 528, Korea (South) (100%)
Tel.: (82) 25627201
Web Site: http://www.seagate-asia.com
Sales Range: $25-49.9 Million
Emp.: 15
Peripherals Sales & Marketer
N.A.I.C.S.: 423430

Seagate Technology UK Ltd. (1)
60 Norden Road, Maidenhead, SL6 4AY, Berkshire, United Kingdom
Tel.: (44) 1628777977
Sales Range: $25-49.9 Million
Emp.: 3
Hard Disk Drive Mfr
N.A.I.C.S.: 332510
Mark Whitby *(VP)*

SEAGULL SHIPPING COMPANY
12 Doan Nhu Hai Ward 12, District 4, Ho Chi Minh City, Vietnam
Tel.: (84) 83267282
Web Site:
http://www.seagullshipping.com.vn
Emp.: 100
Marine Transportation Services
N.A.I.C.S.: 483111
Ton V. Tran *(Chm)*

SEAH HOLDINGS CORP.
SeAH Tower 45 Yanghwa-ro, Mapo-gu, Seoul, 04036, Korea (South)
Tel.: (82) 269700110   KR
Web Site: https://www.seah.co.kr
Year Founded: 1960
058650—(KRS)
Rev.: $5,174,029,747
Assets: $4,540,608,480
Liabilities: $2,236,086,041
Net Worth: $2,304,522,440
Earnings: $119,708,064
Emp.: 46
Fiscal Year-end: 12/31/22
Holding Company; Steel Mfr
N.A.I.C.S.: 551112
Cheon Jung Chull *(CEO)*

Subsidiaries:

Foshan SeAH Precision Metal Co., Ltd. (1)
No 48 Sanhe Road, Hecheng Sub-district Gaoming District, Foshan, 528511, Guangdong, China
Tel.: (86) 75783311009
Fluid Component Mfr
N.A.I.C.S.: 333996

India Seah Precision Metal Pvt. Ltd. (1)
A-39 Sector-80 Phase-2, Noida, Uttar Pradesh, India
Tel.: (91) 9871729991
Emp.: 200
Automotive Parts Mfr & Distr
N.A.I.C.S.: 336390

POS-SeAH Steel Wire (Thailand) Co., Ltd. (1)
390/15 Moo 2 T Khaokhansong, A Siracha, Chon Buri, 20110, Thailand
Tel.: (66) 33143470
Automobile Parts Mfr
N.A.I.C.S.: 336390

POS-SeAH Steel Wire (Tianjin) Co., Ltd. (1)
Automobile Parts Mfr
N.A.I.C.S.: 336390

Pos-Seah Steel Wire (Nantong) Co. Ltd. (1)
No 92 Jianghai Road, Nantong E T Development Area, Jiangsu, China
Tel.: (86) 51381055800
Automobile Parts Mfr
N.A.I.C.S.: 336390

Qingdao SeAH Precision Metal Co., Ltd. (1)
The west side of the 6th way The south of the 35th way, Fuyuan Industrial Garden Development District, Qingdao, 266426, Shandong, China
Tel.: (86) 53283166123
Fluid Component Mfr
N.A.I.C.S.: 333996

SeAH Aerospace & Defense Co., Ltd. (1)
48 Jeongdong-ro, Seongsan-gu, Changwon, Korea (South)
Tel.: (82) 552699500
Web Site: https://eng.seahaerospace.com
Aerospace Parts Mfr
N.A.I.C.S.: 336413

SeAH Automotive (Nantong) Co. Ltd. (1)
No 90 Jianghai Road, Nantong E and T Development Area, Jiangsu, China
Tel.: (86) 51381055901
Automobile Parts Mfr
N.A.I.C.S.: 336390

SeAH Besteel Holdings Corporation (1)
29F SeAH Tower 45 Yanghwa-ro, Mapo-gu, Seoul, 04036, Korea (South)
Tel.: (82) 269702021
Web Site:
https://www.seahbesteelholdings.co.kr
Rev.: $3,364,317,218
Assets: $2,928,715,908
Liabilities: $1,416,387,687
Net Worth: $1,512,328,221
Earnings: $67,734,225
Emp.: 25
Fiscal Year-end: 12/31/2022
Steel Products Mfr
N.A.I.C.S.: 339999
Chul Hee Kim *(Co-CEO)*

Subsidiary (Domestic):

SeAH E & T Corporation (2)
765 Daegak-Ri Daesong-Myeon, Nam-Gu, 790-841, Pohang, Kyungbuk, Korea (South)
Tel.: (82) 54 727 2301
Web Site: http://www.seahent.co.kr
Sales Range: $25-49.9 Million
Emp.: 20
Industrial Machinery Mfr & Distr
N.A.I.C.S.: 333248
Sang Eul Ahn *(CEO)*

SeAH Metal Co. Ltd (2)
280 Gongdan-ro, Seongsan-gu, 641-290, Changwon, Gyeongsangnam-do, Korea (South)
Tel.: (82) 552668777
Web Site: https://www.seahmetal.co.kr

Sales Range: $25-49.9 Million
Steel Products Mfr
N.A.I.C.S.: 331110
DoHoon Park *(CEO)*

SeAH Networks Co., Ltd. (1)
3F SeAH Tower 45 Yanghwa-ro, Mapo-gu, Seoul, 121-841, Korea (South)
Tel.: (82) 269701500
Web Site: https://www.seahnetworks.com
Sales Range: $1-9.9 Million
Emp.: 200
Software & Network Integration Services
N.A.I.C.S.: 541512
Jae-Mo Park *(CEO)*

SeAH CSS Corp. (1)
147 Jeokhyeon-ro, Seongsan-gu, Changwon, Gyeongsangnam-do, Korea (South)
Tel.: (82) 552696114
Web Site: https://www.seahss.co.kr
Stainless Steel Wire Mfr
N.A.I.C.S.: 332996

SeAH Changwon Integrated Special Steel Corporation (1)
147 Jeokhyeon-ro, Seongsan-gu, Changwon, Gyeongsangnam-do, Korea (South)
Tel.: (82) 552696114
Steel Products Mfr
N.A.I.C.S.: 332999
Lee Sang Eun *(CEO)*

SeAH FS Co., Ltd. (1)
19 Silli-gil Jinwi-myeon, Pyeongtaek, Gyeonggi-do, Korea (South)
Tel.: (82) 316623335
Web Site: https://www.seahfs.co.kr
Fluid Component Mfr
N.A.I.C.S.: 333996
Jin-Gun Lee *(Pres & CEO)*

SeAH Global Inc. (1)
11750 Katy Fwy Ste 810, Houston, TX 77079
Tel.: (832) 855-3510
Automobile Parts Mfr
N.A.I.C.S.: 336390
Dongpil Kang *(CEO)*

SeAH Precision Metal (Thailand) Co., Ltd. (1)
700/809 Moo 1 Amata Nakorn Industrial Estate Phase 8, T Pantong A Pantong, Chon Buri, 20160, Thailand
Tel.: (66) 384473348
Fluid Component Mfr
N.A.I.C.S.: 333996

SeAH Precision Mexico S.A de C.V. (1)
AV Bentio Juarez121 B-2 Col Parque Industrial Queretaro, Santa Rosa Jauregui, 76220, Queretaro, Mexico
Tel.: (52) 4422409390
Fluid Component Mfr
N.A.I.C.S.: 333996

SeAH Special Steel Co., Ltd. (1)
24F SeAH Tower 45 Yanghwa-ro, Mapo-gu, Seoul, 04036, Korea (South)
Tel.: (82) 269700200
Web Site: https://www.seahsp.co.kr
Rev.: $824,030,325
Assets: $529,377,353
Liabilities: $260,900,839
Net Worth: $268,476,514
Earnings: $13,803,785
Emp.: 340
Fiscal Year-end: 12/31/2022
Steel Wires, Cold Drawn Bars & Stainless Steel Bars Mfr
N.A.I.C.S.: 331222
Kang Dong-Kyun *(Dir)*

SeAH Steel Corporation (1)
SeAH Tower 25/26/27th floor 45 Yanghwa-ro, Mapo-gu, Seoul, 121-841, Korea (South) (100%)
Tel.: (82) 269701000
Web Site: https://www.seahsteel.co.kr
Emp.: 500
Steel Mfrs
N.A.I.C.S.: 331513
Soon-Hyung Lee *(Chm)*

Subsidiary (US):

SeAH Steel America, Inc. (2)

INTERNATIONAL PUBLIC

2100 Main St Ste 100, Irvine, CA 92614
Tel.: (949) 655-8000
Web Site: https://www.seahusa.com
Emp.: 15
Provider of Metal Products & Services
N.A.I.C.S.: 423510

Subsidiary (Domestic):

PanMeridian Tubular (3)
14550 Torrey Chase Blvd Ste 345, Houston, TX 77014
Tel.: (281) 873-7800
Web Site: http://www.consultec-inc.com
Sales Range: $25-49.9 Million
Emp.: 10
Provider of Metal Products & Services
N.A.I.C.S.: 423510
Gene Lee *(Exec VP)*

State Pipe & Supply Inc. (3)
183 S Cedar Ave, Rialto, CA 92376-9011
Tel.: (562) 695-5555
Web Site: http://www.statepipe.com
Sales Range: $50-74.9 Million
Pipe Products & Services
N.A.I.C.S.: 423510
Gary Knoroski *(VP & Gen Mgr)*

Seah Engineering Co. (1)
40 Sinildong-ro 67 beon-gil, Daedeok-gu, Daejeon, Korea (South)
Tel.: (82) 42 931 8240
Web Site: https://www.seaheng.co.kr
Industrial Equipment Mfr
N.A.I.C.S.: 333248
Won Sik Park *(CEO)*

Seah Esab Co. Ltd. (1)
56 Jeongdong-ro 62 Beon-gil, Seongsan-gu, Changwon, Gyeongsangnam-do, Korea (South)
Tel.: (82) 552898111
Web Site: https://www.seahesab.co.kr
Industrial Welding Services
N.A.I.C.S.: 811310
Kyu-Hwan Cho *(CEO)*

Seah Global Thailand Co., Ltd. (1)
399 Interchange 21 Building 20th Floor Unit 2007-2009 Sukhumvit Road, Klongtoey-nua Wattana, Bangkok, 10110, Thailand
Tel.: (66) 22590371
Web Site: https://www.seah.co.th
Automobile Parts Mfr
N.A.I.C.S.: 336390
Dongkook Kang *(CEO)*

Seah M&S corp. (1)
188 Sandanjungang-ro, Yeosu, Jeollanam-do, Korea (South)
Tel.: (82) 618077114
Web Site: https://eng.seahmns.co.kr
Metal Mining Services
N.A.I.C.S.: 212290
Ma Jung Rak *(CEO)*

Seah Precision Metal Indonesia, PT (1)
Jl Akasia 3 Delta Silicon Blok A-6 No 7 Sukaresmi Cikarang Selatan, Bekasi, 17550, Jawa Barat, Indonesia
Tel.: (62) 2189906073
Fluid Component Mfr
N.A.I.C.S.: 333996

Suzhou SeAH Precision Metal Co., Ltd. (1)
No 2008 Dongtaihu RD, Wangshan Industry Park Wuzhong Economic Development Zone, Suzhou, 215103, Jiangsu, China
Tel.: (86) 51266300173
Fluid Flow Component Mfr
N.A.I.C.S.: 333996

SEAHAWK GOLD CORP.
909 Bowron Street, Coquitlam, V3J 7W3, BC, Canada
Tel.: (604) 939-1848   BC
Web Site:
https://seahawkgoldcorp.com
Year Founded: 2010
SEAG—(OTCIQ)
Assets: $1,896,722
Liabilities: $630,287
Net Worth: $1,266,435
Earnings: ($116,872)
Fiscal Year-end: 05/31/22
Investment Services

N.A.I.C.S.: 523999
Bruno Gasbarro *(CFO)*

SEAL INCORPORATED BERHAD
Level 3A ELIT Avenue Business Park 1-3A-18 Jalan Mayang Pasir 3, Bayan Baru, 11950, Penang, Malaysia
Tel.: (60) 46183333
Web Site: https://www.sib.com.my
SEAL—(KLS)
Rev.: $2,360,553
Assets: $110,809,660
Liabilities: $32,929,306
Net Worth: $77,880,355
Earnings: $1,126,372
Emp.: 32
Fiscal Year-end: 06/30/22
Property Development Services
N.A.I.C.S.: 531312
Teng Choon Koay *(Exec Dir)*

SEALAND CAPITAL GALAXY LIMITED
Floor 2 Willow House, PO Box 709, Cricket Square Grand Cayman, Georgetown, KY1-1107, Cayman Islands
Tel.: (345) 9494544   Ky
Web Site: https://www.scg-ltd.com
Year Founded: 2015
SCGL—(LSE)
Rev.: $160,144
Assets: $195,390
Liabilities: $1,809,742
Net Worth: ($1,614,351)
Earnings: ($543,661)
Emp.: 5
Fiscal Year-end: 12/31/23
Investment Management Service
N.A.I.C.S.: 523940
Nelson Law *(CEO & Chm)*

SEALAND SECURITIES CO., LTD.
Guohai Building No 46 Binhu Road, Nanning, 530028, Guangxi, China
Tel.: (86) 7715539300
Web Site: https://www.ghzq.com.cn
Year Founded: 1988
000750—(SSE)
Rev.: $507,779,836
Assets: $10,367,253,318
Liabilities: $7,652,457,451
Net Worth: $2,714,795,867
Earnings: $34,994,124
Fiscal Year-end: 12/31/22
Securities Brokerage Services
N.A.I.C.S.: 523150
He Chunmei *(Chm)*

SEALINK INTERNATIONAL BHD
Lot 1035 Block 4 MCLD Piasau Industrial Area, 98000, Miri, Sarawak, Malaysia
Tel.: (60) 85651778
Web Site: https://www.asiasealink.com
SEALINK—(KLS)
Rev.: $13,819,118
Assets: $69,943,362
Liabilities: $24,581,137
Net Worth: $45,362,225
Earnings: ($4,269,820)
Emp.: 75
Fiscal Year-end: 12/31/22
Shipping & Transportation Services
N.A.I.C.S.: 488390
Puay Huang Yeo *(Sec)*

Subsidiaries:

Era Sureway Sdn. Bhd.   (1)
Lot 1035 Block 4 MCLD Piasau Industrial Area, 98000, Miri, Sarawak, Malaysia
Tel.: (60) 8 565 1778
Web Site: https://www.erasureway.com
Marine Services
N.A.I.C.S.: 488390
Andrew Victor Nub *(Exec Dir)*

Seagood Pte Ltd.   (1)
545 Orchard Road 09-07 Far East Shopping Centre, Singapore, 23882, Singapore
Tel.: (65) 6737 7911
Web Site: http://www.asiasealink.com
Emp.: 5
Shipping Services
N.A.I.C.S.: 488510

Sealink Engineering and Slipway Sdn Bhd   (1)
Lot 816 Block 1 Kuala Baram, Land District Kuala Baram, 98100, Miri, Sarawak, Malaysia
Tel.: (60) 85605767
Ship Building Services
N.A.I.C.S.: 336611

Sealink Shipyard Sdn Bhd   (1)
Lot 1339 Jalan Cattleya 1 MCLD, Krokop, 98000, Miri, Sarawak, Malaysia
Tel.: (60) 85651778
Emp.: 106
Ship Building Services
N.A.I.C.S.: 336611
Anders Hii *(Sr Mgr-HR)*

SEALMATIC INDIA LIMITED
Building A Indiplex IV Survey No 12 Hissa No 9A, Village Ghodbunder Shanti Vidya Nagri Road Mira Road East, Thane, 401107, India
Tel.: (91) 8928136160
Web Site: https://www.sealmaticindia.com
Year Founded: 2009
543782—(BOM)
Software Development Services
N.A.I.C.S.: 541511
Umar A. K. Balwa *(Mng Dir)*

SEALORD GROUP LTD.
149 Vickerman Street, PO Box 11, Nelson, 7010, New Zealand
Tel.: (64) 35483069
Web Site: http://www.sealord.com
Year Founded: 1961
Fresh & Frozen Seafood Processing
N.A.I.C.S.: 424460
Steve Young *(CEO)*

Subsidiaries:

Petuna Pty. Ltd.   (1)
134 Tarleton Street, Devonport, 7310, TAS, Australia
Tel.: (61) 364219111
Web Site: http://www.petuna.com.au
Seafood Distr
N.A.I.C.S.: 424460
Tim Hess *(Gen Mgr-Sls & Logistics)*

SEALSQ CORP.
Avenue Louis-Casai 58, 1216, Cointrin, Switzerland
Tel.: (41) 225943000   VG
Web Site: https://www.sealsq.com
Year Founded: 2022
LAES—(NASDAQ)
Semiconductor Product Mfr & Distr
N.A.I.C.S.: 334413
Carlos Moreira *(Chm)*

SEALY OF AUSTRALIA
1299 Boundary Road, Wacol, 4076, QLD, Australia
Tel.: (61) 733315200
Web Site: http://www.sealy.com.au
Year Founded: 1923
Mattress Mfr & Distr
N.A.I.C.S.: 337910
Daniel Green *(Mgr-R&D)*

SEAMLESS DISTRIBUTION SYSTEMS AB
Hangovagen 29, 115 41, Stockholm, Sweden
Tel.: (46) 858633469   SE
Web Site: http://www.seamless.se
Year Founded: 2001
SEAM—(OMX)
Rev.: $26,154,992
Assets: $36,325,737
Liabilities: $28,619,424
Net Worth: $7,706,314
Earnings: ($7,063,512)
Emp.: 154
Fiscal Year-end: 12/31/22
Mobile Monetary Transaction Software
N.A.I.C.S.: 513210
Sandipan Mukherjee *(COO)*

Subsidiaries:

eServGlobal Holdings SAS   (1)
244 avenue Pierre Brossolette, 92245, Malakoff, France
Tel.: (33) 146125885
Web Site: http://www.eservglobal.com
Telecommunication Servicesb
N.A.I.C.S.: 517810

Subsidiary (Non-US):

eServGlobal (HK) Limited   (2)
Level 19 2 Intl Fin Ctr, 8 Fin St, Central, China (Hong Kong)
Tel.: (852) 22511953
Web Site: http://www.eservglobal.com
Telecommunication Servicesb
N.A.I.C.S.: 517810

eServGlobal (NZ) Pty Limited   (2)
Suite 5 30 Florence Street, Newlands, QLD 4006, Australia
Tel.: (61) 733020194
Web Site: http://www.eservglobal.com
Sales Range: $25-49.9 Million
Emp.: 65
Telecommunication Servicesb
N.A.I.C.S.: 517810

eServGlobal NVSA   (2)
Gossetlaan 54, 1702, Dilbeek, Groot Bijgaarden, Belgium
Tel.: (32) 2 304 3918
Web Site: http://www.eservglobal.com
Sales Range: $25-49.9 Million
Emp.: 50
Telecommunication Servicesb
N.A.I.C.S.: 517810

Subsidiary (Domestic):

eServGlobal SAS   (2)
244 avenue Pierre Brossolette, Malakoff, 92240, France
Tel.: (33) 1 4612 5885
Web Site: http://www.eservglobal.com
Mobile Payment Solutions
N.A.I.C.S.: 561499

Subsidiary (Non-US):

P.T. eServGlobal Indonesia   (3)
Manara Rajalawali, Kawasan Mega Kuningan, Jakarta, 12950, Indonesia
Tel.: (62) 2157950220
Web Site: http://www.eservglobal.com
Sales Range: $25-49.9 Million
Emp.: 12
Software Programming Services
N.A.I.C.S.: 541511

eServGlobal Telecom Romania Srl   (3)
Calea Floreasca N 167 Sector 1, Bucharest, 014459, Romania
Tel.: (40) 21 233 2115
Business Support Services
N.A.I.C.S.: 561499

Subsidiary (Non-US):

eServGlobal UK Limited   (2)
Atrium Court The Ring, Bracknell, RG12 1BW, Berks, United Kingdom
Tel.: (44) 1344393228
Web Site: http://www.eservglobal.com
Sales Range: $25-49.9 Million
Emp.: 6
Telecommunication Servicesb
N.A.I.C.S.: 517810

John Conoley *(Chm)*

SEAMLESS GREEN CHINA (HOLDINGS) LIMITED
Room 1604 Seaview Commercial Building 21-24 Connaught Road West, Sheung Wan, China (Hong Kong)
Tel.: (852) 24161168   BM
Year Founded: 2001
8150—(HKG)
Rev.: $14,134,650
Assets: $15,159,878
Liabilities: $11,844,623
Net Worth: $3,315,255
Earnings: ($1,580,108)
Emp.: 76
Fiscal Year-end: 12/31/22
Holding Company
N.A.I.C.S.: 551112
Kin Hong Wong *(Chm)*

SEANERGY MARITIME HOLDINGS CORP.
154 Vouliagmenis Avenue, 166 74, Glyfada, Greece
Tel.: (30) 2130181507   MH
Web Site: https://www.seanergymaritime.com
Year Founded: 2006
SHIP—(NASDAQ)
Rev.: $110,234,000
Assets: $477,877,000
Liabilities: $249,432,000
Net Worth: $228,445,000
Earnings: $2,282,000
Emp.: 81
Fiscal Year-end: 12/31/23
Shipping & Sea Transportation Investment Services
N.A.I.C.S.: 523999
Stamatis Tsantanis *(Chm & CEO)*

SEAOIL PHILIPPINES INC.
19th Floor The Taipan Place F Ortigas Jr Road, Ortigas Center, Pasig, 1605, Philippines
Tel.: (63) 23971010
Web Site: http://www.seaoil.com.ph
Year Founded: 1978
Sales Range: $75-99.9 Million
Emp.: 400
Gas Station Owner, Operator & Franchiser
N.A.I.C.S.: 457120
Francis Glenn Yu *(Pres & CEO)*

SEAPRODEX REFRIGERATION INDUSTRY CORPORATION
20th Floor TTC Tower 253 Hoang Van Thu Ward 2, Tan Binh District, Ho Chi Minh City, Vietnam
Tel.: (84) 2838227260
Web Site: https://searefico.com
Year Founded: 1977
SRF—(HOSE)
Rev.: $118,560,842
Assets: $173,056,469
Liabilities: $130,157,588
Net Worth: $42,898,880
Earnings: ($14,133,014)
Emp.: 521
Fiscal Year-end: 12/31/22
Machinery Mfr
N.A.I.C.S.: 333248
Pham Ngoc Son *(Member-Mgmt Bd & Deputy Gen Dir)*

SEARCH INVESTMENT OFFICE LIMITED
57th Floor Cheung Kong Center, 2 Queen's Road, Central, China (Hong Kong)
Tel.: (852) 25251211
Web Site: http://www.searchgroup.com

SEARCH INVESTMENT OFFICE LIMITED

Search Investment Office Limited—(Continued)

Year Founded: 1973
Investment Holding Company
N.A.I.C.S.: 551112
Robert W. Miller *(Founder & Chm)*

Subsidiaries:

SAIL Advisors Limited (1)
57th Fl Cheung Kong Ctr, 2 Queen's Rd,
Central, China (Hong Kong)
Tel.: (852) 25251211
Web Site: http://www.sailfunds.com
Emp.: 25
Hedge Fund Portfolio Management Services
N.A.I.C.S.: 523940
Harold Yoon *(CIO)*

Subsidiary (US):

SAIL Advisors Research Inc. (2)
45 Rockefeller Plz Ste 2301, New York, NY 10111
Tel.: (917) 338-8560
Financial Investment Services
N.A.I.C.S.: 523999

SEARCH MINERALS INC.
108 901 West 3rd Street, North Vancouver, V7P 3P9, BC, Canada
Tel.: (604) 998-3432
Web Site:
http://www.searchminerals.ca
Year Founded: 2006
SHCMF—(OTCIQ)
Rev.: $30,868
Assets: $22,254,344
Liabilities: $2,870,731
Net Worth: $19,383,613
Earnings: ($1,166,840)
Emp.: 5
Fiscal Year-end: 11/30/23
Mineral Exploration Services
N.A.I.C.S.: 213114
David B. Dreisinger *(VP-Metallurgy)*

SEARCHLIGHT ELECTRIC LTD.
Sidney House 900 Oldham Road, Manchester, M40 2BS, United Kingdom
Tel.: (44) 161 203 3300
Web Site:
http://www.searchlightelectric.com
Year Founded: 1945
Sales Range: $25-49.9 Million
Emp.: 200
Lighting Product Whslr
N.A.I.C.S.: 423220
Herzl Hamburger *(Chm)*

Subsidiaries:

Illuma Lighting Limited (1)
Sills Road Willow Farm Business Park, Castle Donington, DE74 2US, Derbyshire, United Kingdom
Tel.: (44) 1332818200
Web Site: http://www.illuma.co.uk
Lighting Fixture Mfr
N.A.I.C.S.: 335132
Daniel Hamburger *(Mng Dir)*

SEARCHLIGHT PHARMA, INC.
1600 Notre-Dame Street West Suite 312, Montreal, H3J 1M1, QC, Canada
Tel.: (514) 613-1513
Web Site:
http://searchlightpharma.com
Privater Equity Firm
N.A.I.C.S.: 523940
Mark Nawacki *(Pres & CEO)*

Subsidiaries:

Nuvo Pharmaceuticals Inc. (1)
6733 Mississauga Rd Suite 610, Mississauga, L5N 6J5, ON, Canada
Tel.: (905) 673-6980

Web Site:
http://www.nuvopharmaceuticals.com
Rev.: $53,219,381
Assets: $124,803,757
Liabilities: $106,367,595
Net Worth: $18,436,162
Earnings: $2,571,972
Emp.: 91
Fiscal Year-end: 12/31/2019
Drug Research & Development
N.A.I.C.S.: 541715
Kelly Demerino *(CFO-Interim)*

Subsidiary (Domestic):

Dimethaid Immunology Inc. (2)
7560 Airport Road Unit 10, Mississauga, ON, Canada
Tel.: (905) 673-6980
Web Site: http://www.nuvoresearch.com
Pharmaceuticals
N.A.I.C.S.: 325412

Dimethaid Management Inc. (2)
7560 Airport Road, Unit 10, Mississauga, L4T 4H4, ON, Canada
Tel.: (905) 673-6980
Web Site: http://www.nuvoresearch.com
Pharmaceuticals
N.A.I.C.S.: 325412

Subsidiary (Non-US):

Nuvo Manufacturing GmbH (2)
Vor Dem Schlostor 9, Wanzleben-Borde, 39164, Germany
Tel.: (49) 3920969390
Pharmaceuticals
N.A.I.C.S.: 325412

Nuvo Research GmbH (2)
Deutscher Platz 5c D, 04103, Leipzig, Germany
Tel.: (49) 341 35 53 45 40
Pharmaceutical Products Research Services
N.A.I.C.S.: 541715

Subsidiary (US):

ZARS Pharma, Inc. (2)
1142 W 2320 S, Salt Lake City, UT 84119
Tel.: (801) 350-0202
Sales Range: $1-9.9 Million
Topically Applied Pharmaceutical Mfr & Marketer
N.A.I.C.S.: 325412

fqubed, Inc. (2)
4025 Sorrento Valley Blvd, San Diego, CA 92121-1404
Tel.: (858) 677-6733
Pharmaceuticals
N.A.I.C.S.: 325412

SEARCHLIGHT RESOURCES INC.
408 - 1199 West Pender St, Vancouver, V6E 2R1, BC, Canada
Tel.: (604) 331-9326 NV
Web Site:
https://searchlightresources.com
Year Founded: 2000
CNYCF—(OTCIQ)
Assets: $184,564
Liabilities: $365,314
Net Worth: ($180,750)
Earnings: ($415,830)
Fiscal Year-end: 06/30/19
Copper Mining Services
N.A.I.C.S.: 212230
Brian Crawford *(CFO)*

SEASCOPE INSURANCE SERVICES LTD.
57 Mansell Street, London, E1 8AN, United Kingdom
Tel.: (44) 20 7488 3288 UK
Web Site: http://www.seains.com
Insurance & Reinsurance Brokerage Services
N.A.I.C.S.: 524210
Alexander Stephen Voyvoda *(Chm)*

SEASHORE ORGANIC MEDICINE INC.
Suite 101 5682 Wharf Street, Sechelt, V0N 3A0, BC, Canada
Tel.: (604) 885-5500 BC
Web Site:
http://www.seashoremedicine.com
Year Founded: 2014
Medical Cannabis Mfr
N.A.I.C.S.: 325411
Len Werden *(Pres & CEO)*

SEASIDE CHEVROLET LTD.
13 Harbour View Drive, Shediac, E4P 8T8, NB, Canada
Tel.: (506) 532-6666
Web Site:
http://www.seasidechev.com
Sales Range: $10-24.9 Million
New & Used Car Dealers
N.A.I.C.S.: 441110
Francis Goguen *(Bus Mgr)*

SEASIF EXPLORATION INC.
Suite 1700 Park Place 666 Burrard Street, Vancouver, V6C 2X8, BC, Canada
Tel.: (604) 256-4777
Web Site: https://seasifx.com
SAF—(TSXV)
Assets: $3,773,033
Liabilities: $305,730
Net Worth: $3,467,303
Earnings: ($509,830)
Fiscal Year-end: 12/31/23
Gold Mining Services
N.A.I.C.S.: 212220
Susan Rubin *(CFO)*

SEASON GROUP INTERNATIONAL CO., LTD.
Unit 3 5/F Sun Fung Industrial Building 8 Ma Kok Street, Tsuen Wan, New Territories, China (Hong Kong)
Tel.: (852) 2407 3761
Web Site:
http://www.seasongroup.com
Year Founded: 1975
Sales Range: $100-124.9 Million
Emp.: 1,800
Electronic Products Mfr
N.A.I.C.S.: 334419
Carl Hung *(Pres & CEO)*

Subsidiaries:

Canada Tools & Molding Supplies, Inc. (1)
145 West Beaver Creek Road Unit 3, Richmond Hill, L4B 1C6, ON, Canada
Tel.: (905) 761-1171
Web Site: https://www.canadatools-inc.com
Electronic Components Distr
N.A.I.C.S.: 423690

DSP Design Ltd (1)
Floor 4 Wards Exchange 199 Ecclesall Road, Sheffield, S11 8HW, United Kingdom
Tel.: (44) 1143980400
Web Site:
http://www.seasondesigntechnology.com
Electronic Components Distr
N.A.I.C.S.: 423690
Patrick Hung *(Chm)*

Outsource Electronics Limited (1)
600 Nest Business Park Martin Rd, Havant, PO9 5TL, United Kingdom
Tel.: (44) 2392 452222
Web Site:
http://www.outsourceelectronics.co.uk
Emp.: 70
Electronics Mfr
N.A.I.C.S.: 334419
Steve Wilks *(VP-Sls)*

Patrick Plastics Inc. (1)
18 Basaltic Road, Vaughan, L4K 1G6, ON, Canada
Tel.: (905) 660-9066
Web Site: http://www.ppi-stech.com
Electronic Components Distr

INTERNATIONAL PUBLIC

N.A.I.C.S.: 423690
Eric Cho *(Engr-Quality)*

Season Components Co., Ltd. (1)
18 Basaltic Road, Vaughan, L4K 1G6, ON, Canada
Tel.: (905) 660-9066
Electronic Components Mfr
N.A.I.C.S.: 334419
Linda Young *(Gen Mgr)*

Season Group MX S. de R.L. de C.V. (1)
Ave Primero de Mayo Lote 3 Suite B Parque Industrial Reynosa, 88780, Reynosa, Tamaulipas, Mexico
Tel.: (52) 8999580240
Electronic Components Distr
N.A.I.C.S.: 423690

Season Group USA LLC (1)
3503 Crosspoint Ste 2, San Antonio, TX 78217
Tel.: (210) 824-0323
Electronics Mfr
N.A.I.C.S.: 334419
Alex Colquhoun *(Gen Mgr)*

Xytronics, Ltd. (1)
8001 Mainland Dr, San Antonio, TX 78250
Tel.: (210) 522-1116
Web Site: http://www.xytronics.com
Rev.: $10,000,000
Emp.: 100
Electronic Components Mfr
N.A.I.C.S.: 334419
Tom Mansour *(VP-Sls & Mktg)*

SEASONS FURNISHINGS LTD.
Kh No 432 Pillar No 88 Near Sultanpur Metro Station MG Road, New Delhi, 110030, India
Tel.: (91) 9810863157
Web Site:
https://www.seasonsfurnishings.com
521182—(BOM)
Rev.: $567,906
Assets: $1,715,363
Liabilities: $1,835,930
Net Worth: ($120,568)
Earnings: $6,704
Emp.: 12
Fiscal Year-end: 03/31/22
Fabric Products Marketing Services
N.A.I.C.S.: 313310
Mandeep Singh Wadhwa *(Chm & Mng Dir)*

SEASONS TEXTILES LIMITED
Seasons House B-18 Sector-5, Noida, 201301, UP, India
Tel.: (91) 1204690000
Web Site:
https://www.seasonsworld.com
Year Founded: 1986
514264—(BOM)
Rev.: $2,343,048
Assets: $9,075,551
Liabilities: $4,188,787
Net Worth: $4,886,764
Earnings: ($108,858)
Emp.: 110
Fiscal Year-end: 03/31/21
Textile Product Mfr & Whslr
N.A.I.C.S.: 314999
Inderjeet Singh Wadhwa *(Founder, Chm & Mng Dir)*

SEASPAN CORPORATION
Unit 2 2nd Floor Bupa Centre 141 Connaught Road West, Hong Kong, China (Hong Kong)
Tel.: (852) 2540 1686 MH
Web Site:
http://www.seaspancorp.com
Rev.: $1,096,331,000
Assets: $7,477,997,000
Liabilities: $5,018,018,000
Net Worth: $2,459,979,000
Earnings: $278,798,000
Emp.: 4,300
Fiscal Year-end: 12/31/18

AND PRIVATE COMPANIES — SEB S.A.

Holding Company; Marine Transportation Services
N.A.I.C.S.: 551112
Kyle R. Washington (Founder)
Subsidiaries:

Seaspan Advisory Services Limited (1)
Units 1401-05 Jardine House 1 Connaught Place, Central, China (Hong Kong)
Tel.: (852) 2160 5161
Web Site: http://www.seaspancorp.com
Business Support Services
N.A.I.C.S.: 561499

Seaspan Crew Management (India) Pvt. Ltd. (1)
502 Centre Point JB Nagar, Andheri Kurla Road, Andheri East, Mumbai, 400 059, India
Tel.: (91) 22 2837 4961
Freight Transportation Arrangement
N.A.I.C.S.: 488510

Seaspan Management Services Limited (1)
Units 1401-05 Jardine House 1 Connaught Place, Central, China (Hong Kong)
Tel.: (852) 2160 5161
Web Site: http://www.seaspancorp.com
Sales Range: $25-49.9 Million
Emp.: 40
Business Support Services Related to Shipping
N.A.I.C.S.: 561499

Subsidiary (Non-US):

Seaspan Ship Management Ltd. (2)
2600-200 Granville St, Vancouver, V6C 1S4, BC, Canada
Tel.: (604) 638-2575
Web Site: http://www.seaspanshipmanagement.com
Sales Range: $25-49.9 Million
Financial, Technical, Strategic & Administrative Services
N.A.I.C.S.: 561499

SEATECH VENTURES CORP.
Unit 305306 3F New East Ocean Centre 9 Science Museum Road, Tsim Sha Tsui, Hong Kong, China (Hong Kong)
Tel.: (852) 83311767   NV
Web Site: https://www.seatech-ventures.com
Year Founded: 2018
SEAV—(OTCIQ)
Rev.: $548,095
Assets: $261,258
Liabilities: $186,372
Net Worth: $74,886
Earnings: ($94,157)
Emp.: 3
Fiscal Year-end: 12/31/22
Investment Advisory Services
N.A.I.C.S.: 523940
Chee Seong Chin (Pres, CEO, Treas & Sec)

SEATWIRL AB
Lilla Bommen 1, 411 04, Gothenburg, Sweden
Tel.: (46) 769385051
Web Site: https://www.seatwirl.com
Year Founded: 2012
STW—(OMX)
Assets: $10,258,788
Liabilities: $1,708,393
Net Worth: $8,550,395
Earnings: ($1,876,048)
Emp.: 14
Fiscal Year-end: 12/31/22
Solar Electric Power Generation Services
N.A.I.C.S.: 221114
Peter Schou (Mng Dir)

SEAVUS AB
Skeppsbron 5, 211 20, Malmo, Sweden
Tel.: (46) 40 300 940
Web Site: http://www.seavus.com
Year Founded: 1999
Sales Range: $10-24.9 Million
Emp.: 500
Software Development & Consulting
N.A.I.C.S.: 513210
Kocha Boshku (CEO)

SEAWAY CHEVROLET CADILLAC BUICK GMC LTD
2695 Brookdale Avenue, PO Box 938, Cornwall, K6H 5V1, ON, Canada
Tel.: (613) 933-3000
Web Site: http://www.seawaygm.com
Year Founded: 2002
Sales Range: $10-24.9 Million
Emp.: 40
Car Dealer
N.A.I.C.S.: 441110
Mike McParlan (Gen Mgr-Sls)

SEAZEN GROUP LIMITED
Seazen Holdings Tower Building NO 5 Lane 388 Zhongjiang Road, Putuo District, Shanghai, China
Tel.: (86) 2122835888
Year Founded: 1996
1030—(HKG)
Rev.: $16,540,696,998
Assets: $52,210,976,407
Liabilities: $39,679,222,281
Net Worth: $12,531,754,126
Earnings: $108,630,372
Emp.: 22,361
Fiscal Year-end: 12/31/23
Real Estate Manangement Services
N.A.I.C.S.: 531190
Xiaoping Lv (CEO)

Subsidiaries:

Seazen Holdings Co., Ltd. (1)
Seazen Holdings Tower Building No 6 Lane 388 Zhongjiang Road, Putuo District, Shanghai, 200062, China
Tel.: (86) 2122835888
Web Site: https://www.seazen.com.cn
Rev.: $16,210,118,307
Assets: $64,290,144,906
Liabilities: $51,729,832,988
Net Worth: $12,560,311,918
Earnings: $195,694,223
Fiscal Year-end: 12/31/2022
Holding Company
N.A.I.C.S.: 551112
Zhicheng Liang (Co-Pres)

SEB BANK JSC
11 Mikhailova Street, Saint Petersburg, 195009, Russia
Tel.: (7) 812 334 0360
Web Site: http://www.sebbank.ru
Year Founded: 1995
Financial Investment Services
N.A.I.C.S.: 523999
Carl Johan Alexander Christensson (Chm)

SEB S.A.
Campus SEB 112 chemin du Moulin Carron CS90229, 69134, Ecully, Cedex, France
Tel.: (33) 472181818   FR
Web Site: https://www.groupeseb.com
Year Founded: 1973
SK—(EUR)
Rev.: $8,590,222,318
Assets: $9,850,852,579
Liabilities: $6,128,750,270
Net Worth: $3,722,102,310
Earnings: $341,247,572
Emp.: 30,886
Fiscal Year-end: 12/31/22
Holding Company; Cookware, Small Kitchen Appliance, Home & Personal Care Products Mfr & Whslr
N.A.I.C.S.: 551112
Nathalie Lomon (CFO & Sr Exec VP-Fin)

Subsidiaries:

All-Clad Metalcrafters LLC (1)
424 Morganza Rd, Canonsburg, PA 15317-5707
Tel.: (724) 745-8300
Web Site: http://www.allclad.com
Sales Range: $125-149.9 Million
Emp.: 400
Metal Cookware Mfr
N.A.I.C.S.: 331221
Dan Taylor (Gen Mgr)

Subsidiary (Domestic):

All-Clad USA, Inc. (2)
1105 N Market St, Wilmington, DE 19801-1216
Tel.: (302) 427-0199
Household Kitchen Appliances Mfr
N.A.I.C.S.: 332215

Clad Holdings Corp. (2)
1105 N Market St Ste 1300, Wilmington, DE 19801-1241
Tel.: (302) 427-7833
Investment Management Service
N.A.I.C.S.: 523999

Calor S.A.S. (1)
112 Chemin Du Moulin Carron, PO Box 8353, 69355, Ecully, France (100%)
Tel.: (33) 478786666
Web Site: http://www.calor.fr
Sales Range: $50-74.9 Million
Emp.: 200
Mfr of Small Household Electrical Appliances
N.A.I.C.S.: 335220
Thierry Delaunoy de La Tour d'Artaise (Chm)

Groupe SEB USA (1)
2121 Eden Rd, Millville, NJ 08332-4060
Tel.: (856) 825-6300
Web Site: http://www.groupeseb.com
Household Appliance Distr
N.A.I.C.S.: 423620
Volker Lixfeld (CEO)

Lagostina SpA (1)
Via IV Novembre 45, Omegna, 28887, Verbano-Cusio-Ossola, Italy
Tel.: (39) 03236521
Household Stainless Steel Appliances Mfr
N.A.I.C.S.: 332215

Subsidiary (Domestic):

Casa Lagostina s.r.l. (2)
Via IV Novembre 37, 28887, Omegna, Italy
Tel.: (39) 0323865058
Web Site: https://www.casalagostina.it
Furniture Product Distr
N.A.I.C.S.: 423210

S.A.S. SEB (1)
Rue La Patenee, 21261, Selongey, France
Tel.: (33) 380754444
Web Site: http://www.seb.com
Sales Range: $200-249.9 Million
Emp.: 600
Kitchen Appliances, Including Pressure Cookers, Electric Fryers, Mini-Grinders, Grills, Mini-Ovens, Toasters, Coffee Makers, Food Processors Mfr
N.A.I.C.S.: 335220

Subsidiary (Non-US):

Groupe SEB Australia Ltd. (2)
U 1 10 Hill Rd, Homebush Bay, Sydney, 2169, NSW, Australia
Tel.: (61) 297487944
Home Appliance Mfr
N.A.I.C.S.: 335220

Groupe SEB Belgium SA (2)
Ave De l Esperance ZI 25, 6220, Fleurus, Belgium (99.8%)
Tel.: (32) 71825260
Web Site: http://www.seb.be
Sales Range: $25-49.9 Million
Emp.: 73
Distribution of Electrical Appliances & Cookware
N.A.I.C.S.: 449210

Groupe SEB Bulgaria EOOD (2)
81B Bulgaria Boulevard, 1680, Sofia, Bulgaria
Tel.: (359) 28589198
Web Site: http://www.groupeseb.com
Sales Range: $25-49.9 Million
Emp.: 13
Home Appliance Distr
N.A.I.C.S.: 449210
Ivo Grozdanov (Country Mgr)

Groupe SEB CR s.r.o. (2)
Futurama Business Park building A Sokolovska 651 / 136a, 18600, Prague, Czech Republic (100%)
Tel.: (420) 731010111
Web Site: http://www.groupseb.com
Sales Range: $25-49.9 Million
Emp.: 50
Electrical Appliances & Cookware Distr
N.A.I.C.S.: 449210

Groupe SEB Canada Inc. (2)
36 Newmill Gate Unit 2, Scarborough, M1V 0E2, ON, Canada (100%)
Tel.: (416) 297-4131
Web Site: https://www.t-fal.ca
Sales Range: $25-49.9 Million
Emp.: 55
Distribution of Electrical Appliances
N.A.I.C.S.: 449210

Groupe SEB Central Europe Kft (2)
Puskas Tivadar ut 14, 2040, Budaors, Hungary
Tel.: (36) 618018434
Web Site: http://www.groupeseb.com
Sales Range: $25-49.9 Million
Emp.: 40
Household Kitchen Appliances Mfr
N.A.I.C.S.: 332215

Groupe SEB Colombia S.A. (2)
Vi Cajica Zipaquira Km 1, Cundinamarca, Colombia
Tel.: (57) 1 5923838
Home Appliance Distr
N.A.I.C.S.: 423620

Groupe SEB Danmark AS (2)
Tempovej 27, 2750, Ballerup, Denmark (100%)
Tel.: (45) 44663155
Web Site: http://www.tefal.com
Sales Range: $10-24.9 Million
Emp.: 30
Distribution of Electrical Appliances & Cookware
N.A.I.C.S.: 449210

Groupe SEB Deutschland GmbH (2)
Theodor-Stern-Kai 1, 60596, Frankfurt am Main, Germany (100%)
Tel.: (49) 6985040
Web Site: http://www.tefal.de
Sales Range: $100-124.9 Million
Distribution of Electrical Appliances & Cookware
N.A.I.C.S.: 449210

Groupe SEB Hellados S.A. (2)
7 Frangokklissias, 15125, Maroussi, Greece
Tel.: (30) 2106371000
Household Appliance Distr
N.A.I.C.S.: 423620

Groupe SEB Iberica S.A. (2)
Carrer dels Almogavers 119, 08018, Barcelona, Spain (100%)
Tel.: (34) 932922122
Emp.: 60
Distribution of Electrical Appliances & Cookware
N.A.I.C.S.: 449210
Ingrid Herrlein (Mgr-HR)

Groupe SEB Istanbul EV Aletleri Tic AS (2)
Dereboyu Cad Bilim Sok, Sun Plaza No 5 Kat 2 Maslak, 34398, Sariyer, Turkiye (100%)
Tel.: (90) 4444050
Web Site: http://www.tefal.com.tr
Sales Range: $25-49.9 Million
Emp.: 56
Distribution of Electrical Appliances

SEB S.A.

SEB S.A.—(Continued)
N.A.I.C.S.: 449210

Groupe SEB Italia SpA (2)
Via Marconi, 2, Assago, I 20090, Milan, Italy (100%)
Tel.: (39) 02457751
Web Site: http://www.tefal.it
Sales Range: $25-49.9 Million
Emp.: 35
Electrical Appliances & Cookware Marketer & Distr
N.A.I.C.S.: 449210

Groupe SEB Magyarorszag Kft. (2)
Edison Utca 2, 2040, Budapest, Hungary (100%)
Tel.: (36) 12368400
Web Site: http://www.tefal.hu
Sales Range: $25-49.9 Million
Emp.: 22
Distribution of Electrical Appliances
N.A.I.C.S.: 449210

Groupe SEB Mexicana SA de CV (2)
Goldsmith 38 Desp 401 Col Polanco, 11560, Mexico, Mexico (99.9%)
Tel.: (52) 5552839300
Web Site: http://www.t-fal.com.mx
Sales Range: $25-49.9 Million
Emp.: 74
Distribution of Electrical Appliances & Cookware
N.A.I.C.S.: 449210

Subsidiary (Domestic):

Groupe SEB Moulinex SAS (2)
Immeuble le Monge 22 Place des Vosges, 92979, Paris, Cedex 5, France
Tel.: (33) 144194199
Web Site: http://www.moulinex.com
Sales Range: $1-4.9 Billion
Emp.: 21,524
Mfr, Designer & Marketer of Cooking, Cooling & Washing Machines, Microwave Ovens & Small Domestic Appliances
N.A.I.C.S.: 335220
Alain Grimm-Hecker (Mktg)

Subsidiary (Non-US):

Krups GmbH (3)
Nummener Feld 10, 42719, Solingen, Germany (100%)
Tel.: (49) 212387400
Web Site: http://www.krups.com
Sales Range: $25-49.9 Million
Emp.: 27
Household Cooking Equipment Mfr
N.A.I.C.S.: 335220

Subsidiary (US):

Krups North America, Inc. (3)
2199 Eden Rd, Millville, NJ 08332-4060
Tel.: (856) 825-6300
Web Site: http://www.groupeseb.com
Emp.: 250
Household Cooking Equipment Mfr
N.A.I.C.S.: 423620

Subsidiary (Non-US):

Groupe SEB Nederland BV (2)
Generatorstraat 6, Postbus 238, NL-3900 AE, Veenendaal, Netherlands (100%)
Tel.: (31) 8582424
Web Site: http://www.moulinex.com
Emp.: 60
Distribution of Electrical Appliances & Cookware
N.A.I.C.S.: 449210

Groupe SEB Nederland BV (2)
De Schutterij 27, 3903 LJ, Veenendaal, Netherlands
Tel.: (31) 318582424
Sales Range: $50-74.9 Million
Emp.: 10
Household Appliance Distr
N.A.I.C.S.: 423620
Rob Poppelen (Gen Mgr)

Groupe SEB Nordik AS (2)
Tempovej 27, Ballerup, 2750, Denmark
Tel.: (45) 44 66 31 55
Cooking Appliances Distr
N.A.I.C.S.: 423720

Groupe SEB Peru S.R.L. (2)
Av Camino Real 111 Of 805-B, San Isidro, Lima, 2727, Peru
Tel.: (51) 14414455
Home Appliance Distr
N.A.I.C.S.: 423620

Groupe SEB Polska Sp. z o.o. (2)
Ul Ostrobramska 79, 4175, Warsaw, Poland (100%)
Tel.: (48) 225142233
Web Site: http://www.tesoa.pl
Sales Range: $25-49.9 Million
Emp.: 50
Distribution of Electrical Appliances & Cookware
N.A.I.C.S.: 449210

Groupe SEB Portugal Lda (2)
Rua Projectada A Rua 1 3 B D, Urb de Matinha, 796, Lisbon, Portugal (100%)
Tel.: (351) 218684735
Emp.: 30
Distribution of Electrical Appliances & Cookware
N.A.I.C.S.: 449210
Jose Roma Abrantes (Gen Mgr)

Groupe SEB SR, s.r.o. (2)
Rybnicna 40, 831 07, Bratislava, Slovakia (100%)
Tel.: (421) 233595224
Web Site: http://www.groupeseb.sk
Sales Range: $25-49.9 Million
Emp.: 6
Appliances & Cookware Distr
N.A.I.C.S.: 449210

Groupe SEB Schweiz GmbH (2)
Thurgauerstrasse 105, Opfikon, 8152, Zurich, Switzerland
Tel.: (41) 448094000
Household Appliance Distr
N.A.I.C.S.: 423620

Groupe SEB Servicios Mexico (2)
Goldsmith No 38-4011 Piso 4 Chapultepec Polanco, Miguel Hidalgo, Mexico, 11560, Mexico
Tel.: (52) 5552839300
Household Appliance Retailer
N.A.I.C.S.: 449210
Carlos A. Gorbea (Gen Mgr)

Groupe SEB Singapore Pty Ltd. (2)
3A International Business Park 12-04/05, Singapore, 609935, Singapore
Tel.: (65) 65508900
Electronic Appliance Distr
N.A.I.C.S.: 423620

Groupe SEB Thailand Co., Ltd. (2)
2034/66 Italthai Tower Building 14th Floor New Petchaburi Road, Huai Khwang District, Bangkok, 10320, Thailand
Tel.: (66) 27656565
Household Appliances Mfr
N.A.I.C.S.: 335220

Groupe SEB UK Ltd. (2)
Ditton Park Riding Court Road, Datchet, Slough, SL3 9LL, Berks, United Kingdom (99.9%)
Tel.: (44) 3456021454
Web Site: https://www.groupeseb.co.uk
Sales Range: $25-49.9 Million
Emp.: 100
Sales & Marketing of Household Appliances
N.A.I.C.S.: 449210

Groupe SEB d.o.o. (2)
Posrednistvo Pri Prodaji Gregorciceva Ulica 6, 2000, Maribor, Slovenia
Tel.: (386) 22349490
Sales Range: $50-74.9 Million
Emp.: 7
Household Cooking Alliances Distr
N.A.I.C.S.: 423440
Romana Kancler (Reg Mgr)

Grupo SEB do Brasil (2)
Alvaro Guimaraes 1 100, Sao Bernardo do Campo, 09890 003, Sao Paulo, Brazil
Tel.: (55) 1143906999
Electric Household Appliances Mfr
N.A.I.C.S.: 335210

Subsidiary (Domestic):

Lojas SEB (3)
R Joao Cachoeira 1262 Vila Nova Conceicao 04535-005, 04535-005, Sao Caetano do Sul, Sao Paulo, Brazil
Tel.: (55) 11 3045 6594
Cooking Equipment Distr
N.A.I.C.S.: 423440

Rowenta Werke GmbH (2)
Carl Benz Strasse 14 18, Erbach, 64711, Germany (100%)
Tel.: (49) 6062660
Web Site: http://www.rowenta.de
Sales Range: $25-49.9 Million
Emp.: 190
Mfr of Household Appliances; Coffee Makers, Toasters, Dental Hygiene Accessories & Steam Irons
N.A.I.C.S.: 335220

Subsidiary (US):

Rowenta (USA), Inc. (3)
2121 Eden Rd, Millville, NJ 08332 (100%)
Tel.: (781) 396-0600
Web Site: http://www.rowentausa.com
Sales Range: $25-49.9 Million
Emp.: 32
Marketing & Distribution of Household Appliances
N.A.I.C.S.: 423620
John Crisostamo (CFO)

Subsidiary (Non-US):

Rowenta France S.A. (3)
Chemin Du Virolet, PO Box 815, 27200, Vernon, France (99.9%)
Tel.: (33) 232646704
Web Site: https://www.rowenta.fr
Sales Range: $50-74.9 Million
Household Appliances Mfr
N.A.I.C.S.: 335220

Subsidiary (Non-US):

SEB Asia (2)
Room 901 and 903 9/F South Block Skyway House 3 Sham Mong Road, Tai Kok Tsui, Kowloon, China (Hong Kong) (99.9%)
Tel.: (852) 23953331
Emp.: 300
Distribution of Electrical Appliances
N.A.I.C.S.: 449210

Subsidiary (Domestic):

SEB Developpement S.A. (2)
112 Chemin du Moulin Carron, CS 90229, 69134, Ecully, Cedex, France (100%)
Tel.: (33) 472181818
Sales Range: $75-99.9 Million
Emp.: 450
Group Research & Administrative Services
N.A.I.C.S.: 561110
Thierry De La Tour D'Artaise (Pres)

Subsidiary (Non-US):

SEB Oesterreich Handels GmbH (2)
Deutschstrasse 5, A 1230, Vienna, Austria (100%)
Tel.: (43) 1610490
Sales Range: $25-49.9 Million
Emp.: 15
Distribution of Electrical Appliances & Cookware
N.A.I.C.S.: 449210

SSEAC Co. Ltd. (1)
No 398 Shennan Rd, Shanghai, 201108, China
Tel.: (86) 2164896969
Household Appliances Mfr
N.A.I.C.S.: 335220

Supor (Vietnam) Co. Ltd. (1)
My Phuoc 1 Industrial Zone Lot A-1-Cn My Phuoc Townlet, Ben Cat, Binh Duong, Vietnam
Tel.: (84) 6503559848
Home Appliance Distr
N.A.I.C.S.: 423620

Tefal S.A.S. (1)
15 Avenue des Alpes, BP 89, 74150, Rumilly, Cedex, France (100%)
Tel.: (33) 450885555
Web Site: http://www.tefal.fr

Sales Range: $400-449.9 Million
Emp.: 2,000
Cooking Utensils & Products Mfr
N.A.I.C.S.: 335220
Patrick Lollebrogh (Mng Dir)

Subsidiary (US):

T-Fal Corporation (2)
1 Boland Dr Ste 101, West Orange, NJ 07052 (100%)
Tel.: (973) 736-0300
Web Site: http://www.t-falusa.com
Sales Range: $50-74.9 Million
Emp.: 240
Mfr & Distributor of Household Appliances
N.A.I.C.S.: 332215

Subsidiary (Non-US):

Tefal India Household Appliances Pvt. Ltd. (2)
A 10 Green Park, New Delhi, 110 016, India (100%)
Tel.: (91) 1126863301
Sales Range: $25-49.9 Million
Emp.: 10
Marketing of Non-Stick Cookware
N.A.I.C.S.: 423220

WMF Group GmbH (1)
WMF Platz 1, 73312, Geislingen, Germany
Tel.: (49) 73 31 25 1
Web Site: http://www.wmf.com
Emp.: 6,000
Tableware & Kitchenware Products Mfr & Whslr
N.A.I.C.S.: 332215
Bernd Stoeppel (Mng Dir)

Subsidiary (US):

WMF Americas, Inc. (2)
3512 Faith Church Rd, Indian Trail, NC 28079-9321 (100%)
Tel.: (800) 966-3009
Web Site: http://www.wmfamericas.com
Tableware & Kitchenware Products Whslr
N.A.I.C.S.: 423710
Anne-Mari Kelly (Head-North American Digital Sls)

Wilbur Curtis Co., Inc. (1)
6913 Acco St, Montebello, CA 90640
Tel.: (323) 837-2300
Web Site: https://www.wilburcurtis.com
Filter Coffee & Cappuccino Machines Marketer & Mfr
N.A.I.C.S.: 333241

Wuhan Supor Co. Ltd. (1)
No 368 Pengjialing, Hanyang Dist, Wuhan, 430050, China
Tel.: (86) 2784680325
Household Appliances Mfr
N.A.I.C.S.: 335220

Zhejiang Lesu Metal Material Co. Ltd. (1)
Nanyou Industrial Zone Damaiyu, Yuhuan County, Taizhou, 317604, China
Tel.: (86) 57687337620
Sales Range: $25-49.9 Million
Emp.: 80
Home Appliance Mfr
N.A.I.C.S.: 335220
John Wu (Gen Mgr)

Zhejiang Supor Electrical Appliances Manufacturing Co. Ltd. (1)
No 501 Bin'an Road Hi-tech Development Zone, Hangzhou, Zhejiang, China
Tel.: (86) 571 86850316
Household Cooking Appliance Mfr
N.A.I.C.S.: 335220
Wang Feng (Gen Mgr)

SEBANG CO., LTD.

433 Seolleung-ro, Gangnam-gu Yeoksam-dong SEBANG Building, Seoul, 06212, Korea (South)
Tel.: (82) 234690300
Web Site: https://www.sebang.com
Year Founded: 1965
Rev.: $586,514,025
Assets: $890,036,815
Liabilities: $155,824,468
Net Worth: $734,212,347

Earnings: $39,074,087
Emp.: 778
Fiscal Year-end: 12/31/18
Road Freight Transportation Services
N.A.I.C.S.: 484121
Jeong Ho Cheol *(Chm)*

Subsidiaries:

ENS Global Co., Ltd. (1)
433 Seolleung-ro Yeoksam-dong 3rd Floor of Sebang Building, Gangnam-gu, Seoul, Korea (South)
Tel.: (82) 25640313
Web Site: http://www.ensglobal.co.kr
Management Consulting Services
N.A.I.C.S.: 541611

Gunsan Port Pier 7 Operation Co., Ltd. (1)
145 Oehangan-gil, Soryong-dong, Gunsan, 54007, North Jeolla, Korea (South)
Tel.: (82) 634646792
Transportation Services
N.A.I.C.S.: 488490

INTC Co., Ltd. (1)
41 Wonseok-ro, Seo-gu, Incheon, 22848, Korea (South)
Tel.: (82) 325729300
Transportation Services
N.A.I.C.S.: 488490

Mokpo Daebul Pier Operation Co., Ltd. (1)
629 Daebul-ro Samho-eup, Yeongam, 526-892, South Jeolla, Korea (South)
Tel.: (82) 614628167
Transportation Services
N.A.I.C.S.: 488490

Pyeongtaek Dangjin Central Pier Co., Ltd. (1)
792 Seodongdae-ro Poseung-eup, Pyeongtaek, 17961, Gyeonggi, Korea (South)
Tel.: (82) 316849211
Transportation Services
N.A.I.C.S.: 488490

Sebang Busan New Port Container Depot Co., Ltd. (1)
320 Sinhangbuk-ro, Jinhae-gu, Changwon, 51611, South Gyeongsang, Korea (South)
Tel.: (82) 555448360
Transportation Services
N.A.I.C.S.: 488490

Sebang Busan New Port Logistics Co., Ltd. (1)
96-17 Sinhang-ro, Gangseo-gu Seongbuk-dong, Busan, 618-410, Korea (South)
Tel.: (82) 519419671
Transportation Services
N.A.I.C.S.: 488490

Sebang Estates Co., Ltd. (1)
148 Beolmal-ro 3F Gwanyang-dong Sebang R and D Center, Dongan-gu, Anyang, 14057, Gyeonggi, Korea (South)
Tel.: (82) 234516040
Transportation Services
N.A.I.C.S.: 488490

Sebang Express Co., Ltd. (1)
433 Seolleung-ro Yeoksam-dong Sebang Building Main Building, New Hall 8F Gangnam-gu, Seoul, 135-919, Korea (South)
Tel.: (82) 23460700
Transportation Services
N.A.I.C.S.: 488490

Sebang Gwangyang International Logistics Co., Ltd. (1)
45 Taein 4-gil, Gwangyang, 545-885, South Jeolla, Korea (South)
Tel.: (82) 617987428
Transportation Services
N.A.I.C.S.: 488490

Sebang Industrial Co., Ltd. (1)
236 Sonjae-ro, Gwangsan-gu, Gwangju, 506-250, Korea (South)
Tel.: (82) 629514271
Transportation Services
N.A.I.C.S.: 488490

Sebang Land Transport Co., Ltd. (1)
326 Sinseon-ro, Nam-gu Yongdang-dong, Busan, 48560, Korea (South)

Tel.: (82) 516115940
Transportation Services
N.A.I.C.S.: 488490

Sebang Vina Co., Ltd. (1)
5th Floor Licogi 13 Building Khuat Duy Tien Street, Nhan Chinh Ward Thanh Xuan District, Hanoi, Vietnam
Tel.: (84) 432222108
Web Site: http://www.sebangvina.com
Logistics Consulting Servies
N.A.I.C.S.: 541614
Nguyen Thu Ngan *(Sls Mgr)*

SEBANG GLOBAL BATTERY CO., LTD.
Sebang Bldg 708-8 Yeoksam-Dong, Kangnam-Gu, Seoul, Korea (South)
Tel.: (82) 234516201
Web Site: https://www.gbattery.com
Year Founded: 1952
004490—(KRS)
Rev.: $1,129,900,511
Assets: $1,286,245,180
Liabilities: $330,544,734
Net Worth: $955,700,445
Earnings: $32,734,244
Emp.: 1,139
Fiscal Year-end: 12/31/22
Battery Mfr
N.A.I.C.S.: 335910

Subsidiaries:

Sebang Batteries Europe GmbH (1)
Mergenthalerallee 79-81, 65760, Eschborn, Germany
Tel.: (49) 61967730743
Web Site: https://www.sebang-europe.com
Battery Mfr
N.A.I.C.S.: 335910

Sebang Global (M) Sdn Bhd (1)
5 Jalan 51/203A Kawasan Perindustrian Tiong Nam, 46050, Petaling Jaya, Selangor Darul Ehsan, Malaysia
Tel.: (60) 377729595
Web Site: https://www.sebangglobal.my
Battery Mfr
N.A.I.C.S.: 335910

SEBASTIANI VENTURES CORP.
1600 - 609 Granville Street, Pacific Centre, Vancouver, V7Y 1C3, BC, Canada
Tel.: (778) 331-8505   ON
Year Founded: 2011
SBS—(TSXV)
Assets: $104,198
Liabilities: $16,053
Net Worth: $88,145
Earnings: ($69,275)
Fiscal Year-end: 12/31/20
Gold Mining Services
N.A.I.C.S.: 212220
Scott Ackerman *(CEO & CFO)*

SEBATA HOLDINGS
38 Wierda Rd E Wierda Valley Sandton 21, Sandton, 2196, South Africa
Tel.: (27) 836483031   ZA
Web Site: https://sebataholdings.com
SEB—(JSE)
Rev.: $1,750,599
Assets: $24,758,394
Liabilities: $6,400,997
Net Worth: $18,357,397
Earnings: ($5,952,376)
Fiscal Year-end: 03/31/24
Investment Holding Services
N.A.I.C.S.: 523940
Ian Gregory Morris *(CEO)*

Subsidiaries:

Deltec Batteries (1)
22 C Trotter Rd, Pinetown, Durban, 3610, Kwazulu-Natal, South Africa
Tel.: (27) 31 701 7761
Batteries Whslr
N.A.I.C.S.: 423610

Essential Power Services (Proprietary) Limited (1)
49 Pickering St, Newton Park, Port Elizabeth, 6045, Eastern Cape, South Africa
Tel.: (27) 41 364 0323
Batteries Distr
N.A.I.C.S.: 423610

MECS Africa (Proprietary) Limited (1)
66 Park Lane, Sandton, 2146, Gauteng, South Africa
Tel.: (27) 11 218 8060
Web Site: http://www.mecs.co.za
Human Resource Consulting & Payroll Processing Services
N.A.I.C.S.: 541214
Roland Glass *(Mng Dir)*

Subsidiary (Domestic):

NOSA Employment Agency (2)
3 Chislehurston Office Park 19 Impala Road, Sandton, 2196, Gauteng, South Africa
Tel.: (27) 11 883 1106
Recruiting Services
N.A.I.C.S.: 561311

Subsidiary (Non-US):

Petrolmecs Lda (2)
Mdumduma 52B Miramar Sambizamga, Luanda, Angola
Tel.: (244) 222 447 412
Sales Range: $50-74.9 Million
Emp.: 4
Offshore Oil Operation Services
N.A.I.C.S.: 211120

MICROmega National Certification Authority (Proprietary) Limited (1)
58 Brown St, Nelspruit, 1201, Mpumalanga, South Africa
Tel.: (27) 137551160
Web Site: http://www.nosa.co.za
Sales Range: $25-49.9 Million
Emp.: 8
Health & Safety Certification Services
N.A.I.C.S.: 541611

MICROmega Technologies (Proprietary) Limited (1)
Postnet Ste 389, Private Bag X 1, Jukskei Park, Johannesburg, 2153, Gauteng, South Africa
Tel.: (27) 114621516
Business Optimisation Software Development Services
N.A.I.C.S.: 541511

MICROmega Traeasury Solutions (Proprietary) Limited (1)
10 Cradock Ave, Johannesburg, 2196, Gauteng, South Africa
Tel.: (27) 117834000
Securities Trading Services
N.A.I.C.S.: 523150

NOSA (1)
Block A Ground Fl Centurion Ofc Park Embankment Rd, Centurion, 157, Gauteng, South Africa
Tel.: (27) 126830200
Web Site: http://www.nosa.co.za
Sales Range: $25-49.9 Million
Emp.: 200
Business Consulting Services
N.A.I.C.S.: 541611
Justin Hobday *(Mng Dir)*

Subsidiary (Domestic):

EMPOWERisk (Proprietary) Limited (2)
66 Park Ln, Sandton, 2196, Gauteng, South Africa
Tel.: (27) 118838775
Web Site: http://www.empowerisk.co.za
Sales Range: $25-49.9 Million
Emp.: 6
Safety & Health Administration Services
N.A.I.C.S.: 926150
Karl Bailey *(Mgr)*

NQA Africa (2)
Block A Ground Fl Centurion Office Park Embankment Road, Centurion, 157, Gauteng, South Africa
Tel.: (27) 126830200

Web Site: http://www.nqa-africa.co.za
Sales Range: $25-49.9 Million
Emp.: 5
International Organization for Standardization Certification Services
N.A.I.C.S.: 561499
Mike Timberlake *(Mgr)*

SA Meter Reading Services (Proprietary) Limited (1)
Fern Glen Fernridge Ofc Park, Ferndale, Randburg, 2194, Gauteng, South Africa
Tel.: (27) 117834000
Electrical, Gas & Water Meter Reading Services
N.A.I.C.S.: 561990

Sebata Municipal Solutions (Proprietary) Limited (1)
66 Park Ln, Johannesburg, 2196, Gauteng, South Africa
Tel.: (27) 126829800
Web Site: http://www.sebata.co.za
Sales Range: $25-49.9 Million
Emp.: 30
Financial Management Software Solutions
N.A.I.C.S.: 541511
Dylan Strydom *(Mng Dir)*

SEBINO S.P.A.
Via Enrico Mattei 28, 24040, Madone, BG, Italy
Tel.: (39) 035292811
Web Site: https://www.sebino.eu
Year Founded: 1982
SEB—(EUR)
Emp.: 70
Software Development Services
N.A.I.C.S.: 541511
Franco Amigoni *(Chm)*

Subsidiaries:

Sebino Fire RO S.r.l. (1)
23 Venus Street 1st floor, 300693, Timisoara, Romania
Tel.: (40) 214403363
Software Development Services
N.A.I.C.S.: 541512

Sebino Security S.r.l. (1)
Via Portico 51, Orio al Serio, 24050, Bergamo, Italy
Tel.: (39) 035219429
Software Development Services
N.A.I.C.S.: 541512

Sebino Service S.r.l. (1)
Via per Abbiategrasso snc, Cisliano, 20046, Milan, Italy
Tel.: (39) 0225566501
Software Development Services
N.A.I.C.S.: 541512

SEBITCHEM CO., LTD.
98 Gongdan-ro, Gimcheon, 39541, Gyeongsangbuk-do, Korea (South)
Tel.: (82) 544313586
Web Site: https://www.sebitchem.com
Year Founded: 1993
107600—(KRS)
Chemical Product Mfr & Distr
N.A.I.C.S.: 325312
Yongjin Park *(Dir)*

SEBO MANUFACTURING ENGINEERING CORP.
Insan Building 341 Hyoryeong-ro, Seocho-gu, Seoul, Korea (South)
Tel.: (82) 220467922
Web Site: https://www.sebomec.com
Year Founded: 1978
011560—(KRS)
Rev.: $791,520,580
Assets: $338,931,916
Liabilities: $198,288,167
Net Worth: $140,643,749
Earnings: $18,119,836
Emp.: 465
Fiscal Year-end: 12/31/22
Air Conditioning & Heating Facility Construction Services

SEBO MANUFACTURING ENGINEERING CORP.

Sebo Manufacturing Engineering Corp.—(Continued)
N.A.I.C.S.: 237990
Woo-young Kim (Pres & CEO)

Subsidiaries:

SBTA Incorporation (1)
4201 W Parmer Ln Ste C125, Austin, TX 78727
Tel.: (512) 371-7500
Web Site: https://www.sbta-inc.com
Building Equipment Mfr
N.A.I.C.S.: 333120

SEC CARBON, LIMITED
6th Floor Amagasaki Front Bldg 1-2-6 Shioe, Amagasaki, 661-0976, Hyogo, Japan
Tel.: (81) 664918600
Web Site: https://www.sec-carbon.com
Year Founded: 1934
5304—(TKS)
Rev.: $246,599,270
Assets: $580,344,780
Liabilities: $98,515,440
Net Worth: $481,829,340
Earnings: $48,246,390
Emp.: 268
Fiscal Year-end: 03/31/24
Graphite Product Mfr
N.A.I.C.S.: 335991
Tamiaki Otani (Chm)

Subsidiaries:

OTANI STEEL CORPORATION Inc. (1)
8-4 Nagonoe, Imizu, 934-8567, Toyama, Japan
Tel.: (81) 766846151
Web Site: http://www.e-osc.co.jp
Emp.: 257
Steel Product Mfr & Distr
N.A.I.C.S.: 331221
Hisakazu Otani (Pres)

SEC Carbon, Limited - Kyoto Plant (1)
3-26 Osadano-cho, Fukuchiyama, 620-0853, Kyoto, Japan
Tel.: (81) 773272411
Carbon & Graphite Product Mfr
N.A.I.C.S.: 335991

SEC Carbon, Limited - Okayama Plant (1)
4700-2 Masaki, Higashi-ku, Okayama, 704-8147, Japan
Tel.: (81) 869461500
Carbon & Graphite Product Mfr
N.A.I.C.S.: 335991

SEC ELECTRIC MACHINERY CO., LTD.
NO 777 Gaolang East Road, Binhu District, Wuxi, 214131, Jiangsu, China
Tel.: (86) 51085628590
Web Site: https://www.sec-motor.com
Year Founded: 2003
603988—(SHG)
Rev.: $120,736,250
Assets: $165,489,017
Liabilities: $76,572,138
Net Worth: $88,916,878
Earnings: $7,242,450
Emp.: 900
Fiscal Year-end: 12/31/22
Motor Mfr
N.A.I.C.S.: 335312
Xiong Xiaobing (Chm)

SEC NEWGATE S.P.A.
Palazzo Aporti-Via Ferrante Aporti 8, Milan, 20125, Italy
Tel.: (39) 02 6249991
Web Site: http://www.secnewgate.com
Year Founded: 2019

SECG—(AIM)
Rev.: $80,243,376
Assets: $84,511,510
Liabilities: $60,527,667
Net Worth: $23,983,842
Earnings: $1,690,058
Emp.: 570
Fiscal Year-end: 12/31/20
Communications Agency
N.A.I.C.S.: 541820
Fiorenzo Tagliabue (CEO)

Subsidiaries:

UKFH Limited (1)
Sky Light City Tower 50 Basinghall Street, London, EC2V 5DE, United Kingdom
Tel.: (44) 20 7680 6500
Web Site: http://www.secnewgate.com
Public Relations, Advertising & Media Buying Agencies
N.A.I.C.S.: 541810

Subsidiary (Domestic):

Newgate Communications LLP (2)
Sky Light City Tower 50 Basinghall Street, London, EC2V 5DE, United Kingdom
Tel.: (44) 2037576767
Web Site: http://www.newgatecomms.com
Public Relations Services
N.A.I.C.S.: 541820

Newgate Threadneedle Limited (2)
Sky Light City Tower 50 Basinghall Street, London, EC2V5DE, United Kingdom
Tel.: (44) 20 7653 9850
Web Site: http://www.newgatethreadneedle.com
Emp.: 20
Investor & Corporate Communications Services
N.A.I.C.S.: 541820

Twenty20 Media Group Limited (2)
Vale House, Clarence Road, Tunbridge Wells, TN1 1HE, Kent, United Kingdom (90%)
Tel.: (44) 844 324 2020
Web Site: http://www.ttmv.co.uk
Emp.: 20
Media Planning & Buying Services
N.A.I.C.S.: 541830

SECITS HOLDING AB
Vastberga Alle 26, Hagersten, 126 30, Stockholm, Sweden
Tel.: (46) 87124230
Web Site: https://www.secits.se
SECI—(OMX)
Rev.: $8,089,578
Assets: $17,041,783
Liabilities: $13,004,955
Net Worth: $4,036,828
Earnings: ($3,392,434)
Emp.: 134
Fiscal Year-end: 12/31/22
Commercial Banking Services
N.A.I.C.S.: 522110
Daniel Faldt (CFO)

SECKLER AG
Moosstrasse 3, PO Box 307, 2542, Pieterlen, Switzerland
Tel.: (41) 323760730
Web Site: http://www.seckler.ch
Year Founded: 1975
Sales Range: $25-49.9 Million
Emp.: 30
Automation Machinery Mfr
N.A.I.C.S.: 333310
Jacques Hess (CEO)

SECLA, SOCIEDADE DE EXPORTACAO E CERAMICA, S.A.
Rua S Jaoa de Deus Apartado 37, 2504 909, Caldas da Rainha, Portugal
Tel.: (351) 262842151
Web Site: http://www.secla.pt
Year Founded: 1947

Sales Range: $150-199.9 Million
Emp.: 600
Mfr of Utility & Decorating Earthenware Products
N.A.I.C.S.: 327110
Antonio Galvao Lucas (Mng Dir)

SECMARK CONSULTANCY LIMITED
36/227 Rdp 10 Sector Vi Charkop, Kandivali W, Mumbai, 400067, Maharashtra, India
Tel.: (91) 9869265949
Web Site: https://www.secmark.in
Year Founded: 2011
543234—(BOM)
Rev.: $1,107,286
Assets: $3,187,018
Liabilities: $344,355
Net Worth: $2,842,663
Earnings: $214,713
Emp.: 62
Fiscal Year-end: 03/31/21
Management Consulting Services
N.A.I.C.S.: 541611
Jignesh Mehta (CEO & Mng Dir)

Subsidiaries:

Sutra Software Private Limited (1)
23 Electronic Co-Operative Estate Ltd Pune-Satara Road, Pune, 411 009, India
Tel.: (91) 2024223463
Web Site: https://www.sutrasys.com
Software Development Services
N.A.I.C.S.: 541511

SECO S.P.A.
Via A Grandi 20, Arezzo, 52100, Italy
Tel.: (39) 0575 26979
Web Site: http://www.seco.com
Year Founded: 1979
Electronic Embedded Solutions Provider
N.A.I.C.S.: 334419
Daniele Conti (Pres & CEO)

Subsidiaries:

Inhand Electronics, Inc. (1)
30 W Gude Dr Ste 550, Rockville, MD 20850-1178
Tel.: (240) 558-2014
Web Site: http://www.inhand.com
Circuit Boards & Custom Devices Mfr
N.A.I.C.S.: 334412
Rodney Feldman (VP-Sls)

SECO/WARWICK S.A.
8 Sobieskiego Str, 66-200, Swiebodzin, Poland
Tel.: (48) 683820500
Web Site: https://www.secowarwick.com
Year Founded: 1985
SWG—(WAR)
Rev.: $105,007,703
Assets: $121,466,045
Liabilities: $70,451,789
Net Worth: $51,014,256
Earnings: $3,805,545
Emp.: 754
Fiscal Year-end: 12/31/20
Heat Treatment Furnace Mfr
N.A.I.C.S.: 333994
Jaroslaw Talerzak (Vice Chm-Mgmt Bd, Deputy CEO & VP-Bus Segment Thermal)

SECODI
15 Rue Marcel Sembat, BP 78553, 44185, Nantes, France
Tel.: (33) 2 4095 1313
Web Site: http://www.secodi.fr
Year Founded: 1978
Rev.: $20,400,000
Emp.: 100
Engines & Parts Technical Support
N.A.I.C.S.: 333618
Marie-Paule Fetis (Gen Mgr)

INTERNATIONAL PUBLIC

SECOM CO., LTD.
5-1 Jingumae 1-chome, Shibuya-ku, Tokyo, 150-0001, Japan
Tel.: (81) 357758100 JP
Web Site: https://www.secom.co.jp
Year Founded: 1962
XSC—(DEU)
Rev.: $8,799,855,720
Assets: $16,328,807,430
Liabilities: $6,036,329,790
Net Worth: $10,292,477,640
Earnings: $872,560,320
Emp.: 15,923
Fiscal Year-end: 03/31/23
Security Systems & Products
N.A.I.C.S.: 561621
Yasuo Nakayama (Chm)

Subsidiaries:

ADT Alarm Monitoring Hong Kong Ltd. (1)
2701 SAXON Tower 7 Cheung Shun Street, Lai Chi Kok, Kowloon, China (Hong Kong)
Tel.: (852) 2 155 0222
Web Site: https://www.adt.com.hk
Home Security Services
N.A.I.C.S.: 561621

ADT Integrated Security Solutions Pte. Ltd. (1)
81 Toh Guan Road East SECOM Centre 06-01, Singapore, 608606, Singapore
Tel.: (65) 6 881 1111
Web Site: https://www.secomsmart.com.sg
Security Services
N.A.I.C.S.: 561621

AT TOKYO Corporation (1)
3rd floor Toyosu Prime Square 5-6-36 Toyosu, Koto-ku, Tokyo, 135-0061, Japan (50.9%)
Tel.: (81) 363723000
Web Site: https://www.attokyo.co.jp
Data Facilities
N.A.I.C.S.: 541513
Akira Nakamura (Pres & CEO)

Anbao Corp. (1)
1302-1312 Tower A Jinming International No 3 Liupanshan Road, ETDZ, Qinhuangdao, 066000, China
Tel.: (86) 335 389 3600
Web Site: https://www.anbao.net
Steel Pole Mfr
N.A.I.C.S.: 331222

Beijing Jingdun Secom Electronic Security Co., Ltd (1)
No 100 Xili Balizhuang, Chaoyang District, Beijing, 100025, China
Tel.: (86) 1085862933
Electronic Security System Mfr
N.A.I.C.S.: 334419

BiOS, Inc. (1)
Sumitomo Fudosan Nishi Shinjuku 20F 7-20-1 Nishi Shinjuku, Shinjuku-ku, Tokyo, 160-0023, Japan
Tel.: (81) 34 588 2228
Web Site: https://www.biosjp.com
Information Technology Solutions Services
N.A.I.C.S.: 541511
Mina Tsuchiya (CEO)

ClearLight Partners, LLC (1)
100 Bayview Cir Ste 5000, Newport Beach, CA 92660
Tel.: (949) 725-6610
Web Site: https://www.clearlightpartners.com
Privater Equity Firm
N.A.I.C.S.: 523999
Michael S. Kaye (Founder & Mng Partner)

Holding (Domestic):

Katzkin Leather Inc. (2)
6868 W Acco St, Montebello, CA 90640
Tel.: (323) 725-1243
Web Site: https://katzkin.com
Sales Range: $75-99.9 Million
Automotive Leather Mfr
N.A.I.C.S.: 336360
Brooks Mayberry (Pres)

Moore Landscapes, LLC (2)
1869 Techny Rd, Northbrook, IL 60062

AND PRIVATE COMPANIES — SECOM CO., LTD.

Tel.: (847) 564-9393
Web Site:
https://www.moorelandscapes.com
Commercial or Multi-family Landscape Maintenance & Construction & Snow Removal Services
N.A.I.C.S.: 561730
Christopher Coe *(Div Mgr-Construction)*

Paul Fredrick MenStyle Inc. (2)
223 W Poplar St, Fleetwood, PA 19522
Tel.: (610) 944-0909
Web Site: http://www.paulfredrick.com
Men's Clothing Mfr
N.A.I.C.S.: 458110
Lyle Croft *(Pres & CEO)*

Dalian Secom Security Co., Ltd. (1)
The Mountains 147 SenMao Building 6th Floor Room 602, Xigang District, Dalian, 116011, China
Tel.: (86) 4118 360 3411
Professional Security Services
N.A.I.C.S.: 561621

FM-International Oy FINNMAP (1)
Malminkaari 5, Helsinki, 700, Finland
Tel.: (358) 925221700
Web Site: http://www.finnmap.com
Sales Range: $10-24.9 Million
Emp.: 30
Forest Mapping Services
N.A.I.C.S.: 115310
Leena-Maija Jarvinen *(Sec-Project)*

Fujian Secom Security Co., Ltd. (1)
The Streets of Pu Ning Road the center of R and F Block A Room 611, Taijiang District, Fuzhou, 350004, Fujian, China
Tel.: (86) 5918 801 3800
Professional Security Services
N.A.I.C.S.: 561621

GIS Hokkaido Co., Ltd. (1)
5th Floor 3rd Koyasu Building 1-73 Minami 7- Jonishi, Chuo-ku, Sapporo, 064-0807, Japan
Tel.: (81) 11 521 6711
Web Site: https://www.gish.co.jp
Geographic Information Consulting Services
N.A.I.C.S.: 541618

GIS Kanto Co., Ltd. (1)
4-74-6 Higashiomiya, Minuma-ku, Saitama, 337-0051, Japan
Tel.: (81) 48 664 3726
Web Site: https://www.gis-kanto.co.jp
Construction Services
N.A.I.C.S.: 236220

Guangdong Secom Security Co., Ltd. (1)
706-707 Building B Poly Zhongke Plaza 101 Lanyue Road, Huangpu District, Guangzhou, 510700, China
Tel.: (86) 203 206 8989
Professional Security Services
N.A.I.C.S.: 561621

ICS Solutions Group (1)
111 Grant Ave Ste 103, Endicott, NY 13760
Tel.: (833) 706-2225
Web Site: https://icscomplete.com
IT Services
N.A.I.C.S.: 513210
Kevin Blake *(CEO)*

Subsidiary (Domestic):

Infosera, Inc. (2)
3525 Hyland Ave Ste 235, Costa Mesa, CA 92626
Web Site: http://www.techmd.com
Sales Range: Less than $1 Million
Emp.: 36
Information Technology Consulting Services
N.A.I.C.S.: 541511
Sebastian Igreti *(Pres)*

Japan Safety Guard Co., Ltd. (1)
5th Floor Yamamoto Building 71 Kyomachi, Chuo-ku, Kobe, 650-0034, Hyogo, Japan
Tel.: (81) 78 391 1101
Web Site: https://www.ankei.co.jp
Machine Security Services
N.A.I.C.S.: 561621

Jiangsu Secom Security Co., Ltd. (1)
No 89 Zijin Innovation Research Center Building 4 Room 1403, Shengli Road Jiangning District, Nanjing, 211106, Jiangsu, China
Tel.: (86) 255 218 1606
Professional Security Services
N.A.I.C.S.: 561621

Jie Sheng Communication Services (Shanghai), Inc. (1)
Free Trade Pilot Area No 55 Keelung Road 11th Floor, Shanghai, China
Tel.: (86) 212 601 5000
Corporate Management Consulting Services
N.A.I.C.S.: 541618

Kumalift Co., Ltd. (1)
1-12-20 Kyomachibori, Nishi-ku, Osaka, 550-0003, Japan
Tel.: (81) 66 445 6700
Web Site: https://www.kumalift.co.jp
Lift Equipment Mfr
N.A.I.C.S.: 333921
Tomoya Kumagai *(Pres)*

Liaoning Secom Security Co., Ltd. (1)
167 North Main Street Youth Media Center 25th Floor, River District, Shenyang, 110014, China
Tel.: (86) 242 318 0777
Professional Security Services
N.A.I.C.S.: 561621

Nittan Asean Co., Ltd. (1)
Standard Factory No 9 C and D Plot No H-1, Thang Long Industrial Park II Di Su Commune My Hao District, Hung Yen, Vietnam
Tel.: (84) 221 358 9998
Fire Alarm Security Services
N.A.I.C.S.: 561621

Nittan Co., Ltd. (1)
54-5 1-chome, Sasazuka Shibuya-ku, Tokyo, 151-8535, Japan
Tel.: (81) 35 333 7021
Web Site: https://www.nittan.com
Emp.: 1,225
Fire Protection Systems
N.A.I.C.S.: 922160
Hideki Itakura *(Pres)*

Subsidiary (Non-US):

Nittan Europe Limited (2)
Hipley Street, Old Woking, GU22 9LQ, Surrey, United Kingdom
Tel.: (44) 148 376 9555
Web Site: https://www.nittan.co.uk
Sales Range: $25-49.9 Million
Emp.: 40
Fire Protection Systems
N.A.I.C.S.: 922160

Nittan Denko Co., Ltd. (1)
54-5 1-chome Sasazuka, Shibuya-ku, Tokyo, 151-8535, Japan
Tel.: (81) 35 333 7075
Electrical & Pipe Installation Services
N.A.I.C.S.: 238290

Pasco Corporation (1)
PASCO Meguro Sakura Bldg 1-7-1 Shimomeguro, Meguro-ku, Tokyo, 153-0064, Japan **(71.55%)**
Tel.: (81) 354353571
Web Site: https://www.pasco.co.jp
Rev.: $401,253,440
Assets: $489,939,810
Liabilities: $272,655,890
Net Worth: $217,283,920
Earnings: $33,658,120
Emp.: 2,838
Fiscal Year-end: 03/31/2024
Aerial Photographic Surveying, Measurement & Research, Construction Consulting, Geographical Information System Business, Land Development, Real Estate
N.A.I.C.S.: 541360
Norimitsu Takahashi *(Pres & CEO)*

Subsidiary (Non-US):

Base Aerofotogrametria E Projetos S.A (2)
Rua Marques De Lages 1027, Sao Paulo, 04162-001, Brazil
Tel.: (55) 112 948 9900
Web Site: https://www.baseaerofoto.com.br
Sales Range: $25-49.9 Million
Emp.: 100
Geographic Information Services
N.A.I.C.S.: 519290
Antonio Cobo *(CEO)*

PT. Nusantara Secom InfoTech (2)
Menara Jamsostek 17th Fl Jl Jend Gatot Subroto No 38, Jakarta, 12710, Indonesia **(51%)**
Tel.: (62) 212501248
Web Site: https://www.nsi.co.id
Sales Range: $25-49.9 Million
Emp.: 85
Supplier of Computer-Aided Engineering (CAE) Software & Comprehensive Finite Element (FEA) Program
N.A.I.C.S.: 334610
Yoichi Suzuki *(Pres)*

Pasco China Corporation (2)
Room 1105 Building B Cyber Tower No 2 South Street, Guancun, Haidian District, Beijing, 100086, China
Tel.: (86) 1051626630
Geophysical Mapping Services
N.A.I.C.S.: 541360

Subsidiary (Domestic):

Pasco Engineering Co., Ltd. (2)
1-1-2 Higashiyama, Meguro-ku, Tokyo, 153 0043, Japan
Tel.: (81) 357227600
Rev.: $250,000
Emp.: 50
Sales, Planning & Supervision of Water Treatment Facilities
N.A.I.C.S.: 423850

Subsidiary (Non-US):

Pasco Philippines Corporation (2)
2302 Raffles Corporate Center F Ortigas Jr Road, Ortigas Center, Pasig, 1605, Philippines
Tel.: (63) 27 914 4329
Web Site: https://www.pascoph.com
Emp.: 350
Geophysical Mapping Services
N.A.I.C.S.: 541360

Pasco Thailand Co., Ltd. (2)
42 Tower BLD 18 FL 65 Sukhumvit Soi 42, Prakanong Klongtoey, Bangkok, 10110, Thailand
Tel.: (66) 271 365 3036
Web Site: https://www.pascoth.com
Sales Range: $25-49.9 Million
Emp.: 140
Geographic Mapping Services
N.A.I.C.S.: 541360
Yoshihiro Kani *(Mng Dir)*

Pitakkij Thailand Co., Ltd. (1)
87/2 Wireless Road 14th Floor CRC Tower All Seasons Place Lumpinee, 10330, Bangkok, Phatumwan, Thailand
Tel.: (66) 26853999
Web Site: http://www.secom.co.th
Emp.: 1,550
Security Consultancy Services, Design, Installation & Maintenance of Systems
N.A.I.C.S.: 561621

Qingdao Secom Security Co., Ltd. (1)
No 1902 Suite A Huishang Guoji No 467 Changjiangshen Road, Qingdao, 266071, Shandong, China
Tel.: (86) 53285018595
Electronic Security System Mfr
N.A.I.C.S.: 334419

Scan Alarms & Security Systems (UK) Ltd. (1)
52 Trench Road Mallusk, County Antrim, Newtownabbey, BT36 4TY, United Kingdom
Tel.: (44) 289 034 2233
Web Site: https://www.scanalarms.co.uk
Security Services
N.A.I.C.S.: 561621

Scan Alarms Ltd. (1)
Wolseley Business Park 14 Railton Road, Bedford, MK42 7PN, United Kingdom
Tel.: (44) 158 273 3271
Fire Security Services
N.A.I.C.S.: 561621

Secom (China) Co., Ltd (1)
Unit 801 Block E Phase II Ocean International Center No 210 Beili, Ciyun Temple Chaoyang District, Beijing, 100025, China
Tel.: (86) 105 086 8588
Web Site: https://www.secom.cn
Security System Mfr
N.A.I.C.S.: 334419

Subsidiary (Domestic):

Guangdong Jinpeng Secom Security Co., Ltd (2)
Science City Shenzhou Road 9, Guangzhou, 510663, China
Tel.: (86) 2032068989
Web Site: http://www.secom.cn
Electronic Security Device Mfr
N.A.I.C.S.: 334419

Secom (Malaysia) Sdn Bhd (1)
No 15 and 17 Jalan Astaka U8/84, Bukit Jelutong Business and Technology Park, 40150, Shah Alam, Selangor, Malaysia
Tel.: (60) 37 843 2000
Web Site: https://www.secom.com.my
Sales Range: $75-99.9 Million
Emp.: 878
Security Network Systems Services
N.A.I.C.S.: 561621

Secom Alpha Co., Ltd. (1)
MSD20 Building 5-17-14 Sendagaya, Shibuya-ku, Tokyo, 151-0051, Japan
Tel.: (81) 33 351 5338
Web Site: https://www.secom-alpha.co.jp
Water Treatment Equipment Distribution Services
N.A.I.C.S.: 221310

Secom Australia Pty. Ltd. (1)
Level 2 69 Christie St, Saint Leonards, 2065, NSW, Australia **(100%)**
Tel.: (61) 29 461 0000
Web Site: https://www.secom.com.au
Emp.: 500
Security System Services
N.A.I.C.S.: 561621
Nick Soleas *(Mgr-Natl-Ops)*

Secom Engineering Co., Ltd. (1)
4-8-15 Kaisei, Koriyama, 963-8851, Fukushima, Japan
Tel.: (81) 24 935 3555
Web Site: https://www.secom-tep.co.jp
Construction Services
N.A.I.C.S.: 236220

Secom Guardall NZ Ltd. (1)
12 Triton Drive, Albany, Auckland, 0632, New Zealand
Tel.: (64) 9 970 5330
Web Site: https://secom.co.nz
Security Services
N.A.I.C.S.: 561621

Secom Hokuriku Co., Ltd. (1)
2-4-30 Korinbo Korinbo Ramoda, Kanazawa, 920-0961, Ishikawa, Japan
Tel.: (81) 76 222 2296
Web Site: https://www.secom-hokuriku.co.jp
Security Services
N.A.I.C.S.: 561621

Secom Jastic Co., Ltd. (1)
Secom Mejirodai Building 2-7-8 Mejirodai, Bunkyo-ku, Tokyo, 112-0015, Japan
Tel.: (81) 35 319 3361
Web Site: https://www.secom-jastic.co.jp
Security Services
N.A.I.C.S.: 561621

Secom Jastic Hokuriku Co., Ltd. (1)
2-15-10 Kitayasue 3rd Floor Secom Hokuriku Kanazawa Building, Kanazawa, 920-0022, Ishikawa, Japan
Tel.: (81) 76 222 3395
Web Site: https://www.secom-hokuriku.co.jp
Security Services
N.A.I.C.S.: 561621

Secom Jastic Kochi Co., Ltd. (1)
4-2-12 Kitahonmachi, Kochi, 780-0056, Japan
Tel.: (81) 88 861 3131
Web Site: https://www.secom-kochi.co.jp
Facility Security Services
N.A.I.C.S.: 561621

Secom Jastic Miyazaki Co., Ltd. (1)
4-3-4 Tachibanadorinishi, Miyazaki, 880-0001, Japan
Tel.: (81) 98 531 7524
Business Security Services
N.A.I.C.S.: 561621

SECOM CO., LTD.

SECOM Co., Ltd.—(Continued)

Secom Jastic Sanin Co., Ltd. (1)
34 Hokuryo-cho, Matsue, 690-0816, Shimane, Japan
Tel.: (81) 85 223 8124
Web Site: https://www.secom-sanin.co.jp
Security Services
N.A.I.C.S.: 561621

Secom Jastic Yamanashi Co., Ltd. (1)
3-12-25 Tokugyo Secom Yamanashi Building, Kofu, 400-0047, Yamanashi, Japan
Tel.: (81) 55 220 7365
Resident Security Services
N.A.I.C.S.: 561621

Secom Joshinetsu Co., Ltd. (1)
1-10 Shinko-cho, Chuo-ku, Niigata, 950-8557, Japan (100%)
Tel.: (81) 252815000
Web Site: http://www.secom-joshinetsu.co.jp
Rev.: $235,659,600
Assets: $539,882,640
Liabilities: $69,279,760
Net Worth: $470,602,880
Earnings: $29,756,320
Emp.: 1,765
Fiscal Year-end: 03/31/2021
Security System Services
N.A.I.C.S.: 561621

Secom Medical System Co., Ltd. (1)
5-1 Jingumae 1-chome, Shibuya-ku, Tokyo, 150-0001, Japan
Tel.: (81) 35 775 8150
Web Site: https://medical.secom.co.jp
Medical Care Services
N.A.I.C.S.: 621610
Tatsuro Fuse (Chm)

Secom Medipharma Co., Ltd. (1)
1-5-1 Jingumae Secom Headquarters Building 14th Floor, Shibuya-ku, Tokyo, 150-0001, Japan
Tel.: (81) 35 775 8158
Web Site: https://medipharma.secom.co.jp
Medical Consulting Services
N.A.I.C.S.: 541618

Secom Mie Co., Ltd. (1)
14-15 Kotobukicho Secom Tsu Building, Tsu, 514-0015, Mie, Japan
Tel.: (81) 59 226 2552
Web Site: https://www.secom-mie.co.jp
Online Security System Services
N.A.I.C.S.: 561621

Secom Miyazaki Co., Ltd. (1)
4-3-4 Tachibanadorinishi, Miyazaki, 880-0001, Japan
Tel.: (81) 98 532 2111
Web Site: https://www.secom-miyazaki.co.jp
Security Services
N.A.I.C.S.: 561621

Secom Plc (1)
Secom House 52 Godstone Road, Kenley, CR8 5JF, Surrey, United Kingdom (100%)
Tel.: (44) 333 060 6361
Web Site: https://www.secom.plc.uk
Sales Range: $25-49.9 Million
Emp.: 70
Security System Services
N.A.I.C.S.: 561621
Minoru Takezawa (Mng Dir)

Secom Sanin Co., Ltd. (1)
34 Hokuryo-cho, Matsue, 690-0816, Shimane, Japan
Tel.: (81) 85 223 6000
Web Site: https://www.secom-sanin.co.jp
Security Services
N.A.I.C.S.: 561621

Secom Singapore Pte Ltd (1)
81 Toh Guan Road East 01-01 Secom Centre, Singapore, 608606, Singapore
Tel.: (65) 3 157 3700
Web Site: https://www.secom.com.sg
Sales Range: $25-49.9 Million
Emp.: 100
Security Management Services
N.A.I.C.S.: 561621

Secom Static Ryukyu Co., Ltd. (1)
1-7-1 Kumoji Ryukyu Lease General Building 3rd Floor, Naha, 900-0015, Okinawa, Japan
Tel.: (81) 98 941 4303

Human Security Services
N.A.I.C.S.: 561621

Secom Tech Sanin Co., Ltd. (1)
Time Plaza Building 5F 2-10-14 Gakuenminami, Matsue, 690-0826, Shimane, Japan
Tel.: (81) 85 225 8900
Web Site: https://www.secom-sanin.co.jp
Security System Installation Services
N.A.I.C.S.: 561621

Secom Tosec Co., Ltd. (1)
1-2-4 Isago Kawasaki Isago Building, Kawasaki-ku, Kawasaki, 210-0006, Kanagawa, Japan
Tel.: (81) 44 221 6650
Web Site: https://www.secom-tosec.co.jp
Resident Security Services
N.A.I.C.S.: 561621

Secom Trust Systems Co., Ltd. (1)
1-5-1 Jingumae, Shibuya-Ku, Tokyo, 150-0001, Japan
Tel.: (81) 42 291 8501
Web Site: https://www.secomtrust.net
Telecommunication Networking Services
N.A.I.C.S.: 517810

Secom Vietnam Security Service JSC (1)
4th Floor VPI Tower 167 Trung Kinh Street, Yen Hoa Ward Cau Giay Dist, Hanoi, Vietnam
Tel.: (84) 243 782 4976
Web Site: https://www.secom.vn
Security Consulting Services
N.A.I.C.S.: 541618

Secom Yamanashi Co., Ltd. (1)
3-12-25 Tokugyo Secom Yamanashi Building, Kofu, 400-0047, Yamanashi, Japan
Tel.: (81) 55 220 7700
Web Site: https://www.secom-yamanashi.co.jp
Online Security System Services
N.A.I.C.S.: 561621

Secomfort Co., Ltd. (1)
1-23-6 Azamino, Aoba-ku, Yokohama, 225-0011, Kanagawa, Japan
Tel.: (81) 45 905 2271
Web Site: https://www.secomfort.com
Medical Care Services
N.A.I.C.S.: 621610

Secomfort Tama Co., Ltd. (1)
1461 Shimooyamadamachi, Machida, 194-0202, Tokyo, Japan
Tel.: (81) 42 797 6611
Web Site: https://www.royal-tama.co.jp
Medical Care Services
N.A.I.C.S.: 621610

Secomfort West Co., Ltd. (1)
3-11-14 Shinohara Kitamachi, Nada-ku, Kobe, 657-0068, Japan
Tel.: (81) 78 861 8989
Web Site: https://www.secomfortwest.com
Medical Care Services
N.A.I.C.S.: 621610

Shaanxi Secom Security Co., Ltd. (1)
High-tech Zone in Xi'an High-tech Four No 1 Tech Tower A 16th Floor, Xi'an, 710075, China
Tel.: (86) 298 832 0242
Professional Security Services
N.A.I.C.S.: 561621

Sichuan Secom Security Co., Ltd. (1)
409 Block A Oriental Hope Building No 3 Gaopeng Avenue, High-tech Zone, Chengdu, 610093, Sichuan, China
Tel.: (86) 288 555 7571
Professional Security Services
N.A.I.C.S.: 561621

TMJ, Inc. (1)
Sumitomo Fudosan Nishi-Shinjuku Building, 7-20-1 Nishi Shinjuku, 7-20-1 Nishi-Shinjuku, Shinjuku, Tokyo, 160-0023, Japan (100%)
Tel.: (81) 36 758 2000
Web Site: https://www.tmj.jp
Emp.: 2,208
Telemarketing Services
N.A.I.C.S.: 561422
Hideki Maruyama (Pres)

Tianjin Secom Security Co., Ltd. (1)

Tianjin Hongqi Road intersection with 5th Floor, Chamber of Commerce jointly building Lingbin Road Nankai District, Tianjin, 300381, China
Tel.: (86) 225 866 0200
Professional Security Services
N.A.I.C.S.: 561621

Value Communication Services (Shanghai), Inc. (1)
Yi Peak Center No 1781 Xinhua Road, Baoshan District, Shanghai, 200436, China
Tel.: (86) 212 601 5000
Web Site: https://www.vcs-china.com
Call Center Consulting Services
N.A.I.C.S.: 541611

Zhejiang Secom Security Co., Ltd. (1)
No 68 Ting Names are Given Room 604-607 An Road, Hangzhou, 310009, Zhejiang, China
Tel.: (86) 5718 775 6505
Professional Security Services
N.A.I.C.S.: 561621

SECOMAK LIMITED

330 Centennial Park, Elstree, WD6 3TJ, Herts, United Kingdom
Tel.: (44) 2087321300
Web Site: http://www.secomak.com
Year Founded: 1930
Sales Range: $10-24.9 Million
Emp.: 35
Air Movement Technology & Solutions for Drying & Shrink Wrap
N.A.I.C.S.: 333413
John Moore (Owner & CEO)

Subsidiaries:

Secomak Limited - Beckair Division (1)
330 Centennial Park, Elstree, WD6 3TJ, Hertfordshire, United Kingdom
Tel.: (44) 2087321300
Web Site: http://www.beck-air.com
Emp.: 30
Compressed Air Driven Product Mfr
N.A.I.C.S.: 332999
David Palmer (Mng Dir)

SECOND CHANCE PROPERTIES LTD.

60 Paya Lebar Road 0720 Paya Lebar Square, Singapore, 400845, Singapore
Tel.: (65) 67456911
Web Site: https://secondchance.com.sg 528—(SES)
Rev.: $31,053,293
Assets: $280,103,690
Liabilities: $70,185,310
Net Worth: $209,918,379
Earnings: $14,565,224
Emp.: 37
Fiscal Year-end: 08/31/23
Apparels Retailing Services
N.A.I.C.S.: 458110
Jainulabedeen Raj Mohamed (Mgr-Accounts)

Subsidiaries:

Another Chance Properties Pte Ltd (1)
Tanjong Katong Complex 04-22 845 Geylang Road, Singapore, 400845, noisy, Singapore
Tel.: (65) 67456911
Property Management Services
N.A.I.C.S.: 531311

Best Chance Properties Pte Ltd (1)
845 Geylang Road 04-22 Tanjong Katong Complex, Singapore, 400845, Singapore
Tel.: (65) 6745 6911
Web Site: http://www.secondchance.com.sg
Emp.: 50
Commercial Property Leasing Services
N.A.I.C.S.: 531110

Better Chance Properties Pte Ltd (1)
Tanjong Katong Complex 04-22 845 Geylang Road, Singapore, Singapore
Tel.: (65) 67456911
Commercial Property Leasing Services
N.A.I.C.S.: 531120

Double Chance Properties Pte Ltd (1)
845 Geylang Rd 04-22 Tanjong Katong Complex, Singapore, 400845, Singapore
Tel.: (65) 67456911
Web Site: http://www.secondchance.com.sg
Emp.: 8
Commercial Property Leasing Services
N.A.I.C.S.: 531120

Equal Chance Properties Pte Ltd (1)
845 Geylang Road 04-22 Tanjong Katong Complex, Singapore, 400845, Singapore
Tel.: (65) 67456911
Property Management Services
N.A.I.C.S.: 531311

Fair Chance Properties Pte Ltd (1)
845 Geylang Road 04-22 Tanjong Katong Complex, Singapore, Singapore
Tel.: (65) 400845
Residential Property Development Services
N.A.I.C.S.: 236115

Golden Chance Goldsmith Pte Ltd (1)
845 Geylang Road 04-22 Tanjong Katong Complex, Singapore, 400845, Singapore
Tel.: (65) 67453577
Web Site: http://www.secondchance.com.sg
Jewelry Retailer
N.A.I.C.S.: 458310

Good Chance Properties Pte Ltd (1)
845 Geylang Rd 04-22 Tanjong Katong Complex, Singapore, 400845, Singapore
Tel.: (65) 67456911
Web Site: http://www.secondchance.com.sg
Sales Range: $75-99.9 Million
Emp.: 150
Commercial Property Leasing Services
N.A.I.C.S.: 531110

Second Chance Investments Pte Ltd (1)
845 Geylang Road 04-22 Tanjong Katong Complex, Singapore, 400845, Singapore
Tel.: (65) 67456911
Web Site: http://www.secondchance.com.sg
Emp.: 50
Investment Management Service
N.A.I.C.S.: 523999

Super Chance Properties Pte Ltd (1)
845 Geylang Road 04-22 Tanjong Katong Complex, Singapore, 400845, Singapore
Tel.: (65) 67456911
Sales Range: $50-74.9 Million
Emp.: 11
Real Estate Manangement Services
N.A.I.C.S.: 531390
Mohamed Salleh (CEO)

Top Chance Properties Pte Ltd (1)
845 Geylang Rd 04-22 Tanjong Katong Complex, Singapore, 400845, Singapore
Tel.: (65) 67456911
Web Site: http://www.secondchance.com.sg
Emp.: 45
Real Estate Investment & Development Services
N.A.I.C.S.: 531210

Winning Chance Investments Pte Ltd (1)
Tanjong Katong Complex 04-22 845 Geylang Road, Singapore, Singapore
Tel.: (65) 67436485
Investment Management Service
N.A.I.C.S.: 523999

SECOND CITY CAPITAL PARTNERS

Suite 2600 1075 West Georgia Street, Vancouver, V6E 3C9, BC, Canada
Tel.: (604) 806-3350
Web Site: http://www.secondcitycapital.com
Sales Range: $50-74.9 Million
Emp.: 20
Private Equity; Real Estate & Energy Investment

N.A.I.C.S.: 523999
Ryan Chan *(CFO)*

SECOO HOLDING LIMITED
Secoo Tower Sanlitun Road A No 3 Courtyard Building 2, Chaoyang District, Beijing, 100027, China
Tel.: (86) 106 588 0135 Ky
Web Site: http://www.secoo.com
Year Founded: 2011
SECO—(NASDAQ)
Rev.: $479,796,113
Assets: $684,983,218
Liabilities: $412,325,953
Net Worth: $272,657,266
Earnings: ($86,602,412)
Emp.: 509
Fiscal Year-end: 12/31/21
Online Shopping Services
N.A.I.C.S.: 423940
Richard Rixue Li *(Co-Founder, Chm & CEO)*

SECOS GROUP LIMITED
1/247 Ferntree Gully Road, Mount Waverley, Melbourne, 3149, VIC, Australia
Tel.: (61) 385666800
Web Site:
 https://www.secosgroup.com.au
MCO—(ASX)
Rev.: $9,648,104
Assets: $12,054,621
Liabilities: $2,683,627
Net Worth: $9,370,994
Earnings: ($6,292,735)
Fiscal Year-end: 06/30/24
Packaging & Waste Management Services
N.A.I.C.S.: 326112
Richard Tegoni *(Chm)*

Subsidiaries:

Cardia Bioplastics (Australia) Pty Ltd (1)
1/247 Ferntree Gully Road, Mount Waverley, 3149, VIC, Australia
Tel.: (61) 385666800
Web Site:
 https://www.cardiabioplastics.com.au
Emp.: 8
Resins Mfr & Whslr
N.A.I.C.S.: 325211

P-Fuel Limited (1)
Suite 5 310 Whitehorse Road, Balwyn, 3103, VIC, Australia
Tel.: (61) 398307946
Web Site: http://www.p-fuel.com
Bio-fuel Mfr
N.A.I.C.S.: 324199

SECTOR AVIATION HOLDINGS LTD. (SAH)
The Saint Botolph Building, 138 Houndsditch, London, EC3A 7AR, United Kingdom
Tel.: (44) 1224 401900
Investment Holding Company
N.A.I.C.S.: 551112
Stephen Bond *(Partner)*

Subsidiaries:

British Midland Regional Ltd. (1)
Aberdeen Airport East Wellheads Drive, Dyce, Aberdeen, AB21 7EU, United Kingdom
Tel.: (44) 330 333 7998
Web Site: http://www.bmiregional.com
Sales Range: $150-199.9 Million
Emp.: 400
Passenger & Freight Air Transportation
N.A.I.C.S.: 481111
Colin Lewis *(Dir-Mktg)*

SECTRA AB
Teknikringen 20, 583 30, Linkoping, Sweden
Tel.: (46) 13235200
Web Site: https://www.sectra.com
SECT—(OMX)
Rev.: $225,537,198
Assets: $256,321,429
Liabilities: $134,872,948
Net Worth: $121,448,481
Earnings: $35,119,185
Emp.: 1,093
Fiscal Year-end: 04/30/23
Cutting Edge Products Developer & Seller
N.A.I.C.S.: 811210
Jan-Olof Bruer *(Chm)*

Subsidiaries:

Columbitech Inc. (1)
2 Enterprise Dr Ste 507, Shelton, CT 06484
Tel.: (203) 925-0899
Emp.: 100
Medical Information Technology Services
N.A.I.C.S.: 621999

Sectra Communications AB (1)
Teknikringen 20, 583 30, Linkoping, Ostergotland, Sweden
Tel.: (46) 13235200
Web Site: http://www.sectra.se
Sales Range: $50-74.9 Million
Emp.: 200
Secure Voice & Data Communication Products Mfr
N.A.I.C.S.: 517112

Subsidiary (Non-US):

Sectra Communications BV (2)
Prinsessegracht 3, 2514 AN, Hague, Netherlands
Tel.: (31) 703023000
Web Site: http://www.sectra.nl
Secure Voice & Data Communication Products Mfr
N.A.I.C.S.: 517112
Jeroen de Muijnck *(Mng Dir)*

Sectra Communications Oy (1)
Kirjatyontekijankatu 14, 00170, Helsinki, Finland
Tel.: (358) 400545486
Security System Services
N.A.I.C.S.: 561621

Sectra Imtec AB (1)
Teknikringen 20, 583 30, Linkoping, Ostergotland, Sweden
Tel.: (46) 13235200
Web Site: http://www.sectra.com
Sales Range: $25-49.9 Million
Emp.: 300
Custom Computer Programming Services
N.A.I.C.S.: 541511

Subsidiary (Non-US):

Sectra A/S (2)
Niels Bohrs Alle 185, 5220, Odense, Denmark
Tel.: (45) 45 65 06 00
Web Site: http://www.sectra.com
Emp.: 3
Mammography & Orthopedic Imaging Solutions
N.A.I.C.S.: 621512

Sectra GmbH (2)
Technologiezentrum am Europaplatz, 52068, Aachen, Nordrhein-Westfalen, Germany
Tel.: (49) 2419632650
Web Site: http://www.sectra.com
Sales Range: $10-24.9 Million
Emp.: 30
Mammography & Orthopedic Imaging Solutions Provider
N.A.I.C.S.: 621512

Sectra Italia S.r.l. (2)
Via Cesare Pavese 11/13, 20090, Opera, MI, Italy
Tel.: (39) 0257607050
Web Site: http://www.andra.it
Sales Range: $10-24.9 Million
Emp.: 25
Mammography & Orthopedic Imaging Solutions
N.A.I.C.S.: 621512

Sectra Ltd (2)
Baird House Seebeck Pl, Knowlhill, Milton Keynes, MK5 8FR, Buckinghamshire, United Kingdom
Tel.: (44) 1908673107
Web Site: http://www.sectra.se
Sales Range: $10-24.9 Million
Emp.: 52
Mammography & Orthopedic Imaging Solutions Provider
N.A.I.C.S.: 621512

Sectra Medical Systems S.L. (2)
Calle General Oraa 26 1 izda, 28006, Madrid, Spain
Tel.: (34) 930010333
Web Site: http://www.sectra.com
Mammography Orthopedic Imaging Solutions
N.A.I.C.S.: 621512

Subsidiary (US):

Sectra NA, Inc. (2)
2 Enterprise Dr Ste 507, Shelton, CT 06484
Tel.: (203) 925-0899
Web Site: http://www.sectra.com
Sales Range: $10-24.9 Million
Emp.: 95
Mammography & Orthopedic Imaging Solutions Provider
N.A.I.C.S.: 621512
Mikael Anden *(Pres)*

Subsidiary (Domestic):

Sectra Skandinavien AB (2)
Teknikringen 20, 583 30, Linkoping, Ostergotland, Sweden
Tel.: (46) 13235200
Web Site: http://www.sectra.com
Sales Range: $125-149.9 Million
Emp.: 300
Computer Peripherals & Software Whslr
N.A.I.C.S.: 423430
Ann-Sofi Mikaelsson *(Mgr)*

Subsidiary (Non-US):

Sectra imaXperts B.V. (2)
Televisieweg 37A, 1322 AJ, Almere, Flevoland, Netherlands
Tel.: (31) 365401970
Sales Range: $10-24.9 Million
Emp.: 30
Mammography & Orthopedic Imaging Solutions Provider
N.A.I.C.S.: 621512
Niels Wijdogen *(Mgr-Sls)*

Sectra Inc. (1)
2 Enterprise Dr Ste 507, Shelton, CT 06484
Tel.: (203) 925-0899
Health Care Srvices
N.A.I.C.S.: 621610

Sectra Medical Systems GmbH (1)
Gustav-Heinemann-Ufer 74 c, 50968, Cologne, Germany
Tel.: (49) 221474570
Medical Equipment Installation Services
N.A.I.C.S.: 532490

Sectra Pty. Ltd. (1)
Level 5 Pinnacle Office Building B 4 Drake Avenue, PO Box 1945, North Ryde, 2113, NSW, Australia
Tel.: (61) 294201620
Medical Information Technology Services
N.A.I.C.S.: 621999

Sectra Secure Transmission AB (1)
Teknikringen 20, 583 30, Linkoping, Ostergotland, Sweden
Tel.: (46) 13212050
Data Transmission Services
N.A.I.C.S.: 517112

SECUAVAIL INC.
Higashitenma 1-1-19 Urban Ace Higashitenma Building, Kita-ku, Osaka, 530-0044, Japan
Tel.: (81) 661360020
Web Site: https://www.secuavail.com
Year Founded: 2001
3042—(TKS)
Rev.: $7,257,780
Assets: $9,796,020
Liabilities: $2,227,570
Net Worth: $7,568,450
Earnings: $1,507,080
Emp.: 62
Fiscal Year-end: 03/31/24
Security Support Provider
N.A.I.C.S.: 561621
Masaomi Yoneima *(Pres & CEO)*

SECUCEN CO LTD
79-10 Daerim-3dong, Yeongdeungpo-gu, Seoul, 150-073, Korea (South)
Tel.: (82) 234950700
Web Site: http://www.secucen.com
Year Founded: 2011
Information Security Services
N.A.I.C.S.: 518210
Lee Jung Ju *(Dir)*

SECULETTER CO., LTD.
14F PangyoInnovationLab 4221 Gumto dong, Sujeong-gu, Seongnam, 422-1, Gyeonggi-do, Korea (South)
Tel.: (82) 316088866
Web Site:
 https://global.seculetter.com
Year Founded: 2015
418250—(KRS)
Software Development Services
N.A.I.C.S.: 541511
Chasung Lim *(Founder)*

SECUNDERABAD HEALTHCARE LIMITED
6 220/1/1 Supriya Nivas 2nd Floor Plot No 47, Hyderabad, 500034, India
Tel.: (91) 40 65881177
Rev.: $463,778
Assets: $28,383,524
Liabilities: $5,156,458
Net Worth: $23,227,066
Earnings: $16,188
Fiscal Year-end: 03/31/16
Pharmaceuticals Product Mfr
N.A.I.C.S.: 325412
Vinay Madhukar Ganu *(Compliance Officer)*

SECUR CREDENTIALS LTD.
8th Floor A Wing Prism Tower Mindspace, Malad West, Mumbai, 400 064, India
Tel.: (91) 2269047100
Web Site: https://www.secur.co.in
SECURCRED—(NSE)
Rev.: $6,006,481
Assets: $11,488,885
Liabilities: $5,796,356
Net Worth: $5,692,530
Earnings: ($294,857)
Emp.: 142
Fiscal Year-end: 03/31/21
Business Management Consulting Services
N.A.I.C.S.: 541611
Rahul Belwalkar *(Mng Dir)*

SECURA GROUP LIMITED
38 Alexandra Terrace, Singapore, 119932, Singapore
Tel.: (65) 68349500
Web Site:
 https://www.securagroup.com.sg
43B—(CAT)
Rev.: $45,199,576
Assets: $44,879,194
Liabilities: $11,722,336
Net Worth: $33,156,858
Earnings: $784,670
Emp.: 1,071
Fiscal Year-end: 12/31/23
Investment Holding Company
N.A.I.C.S.: 551112
Tat Kin Ho *(Chm)*

Subsidiaries:

Red Sentry Pte. Ltd. (1)
38 Alexandra Terrace Level 5, Singapore, 119932, Singapore

SECURA GROUP LIMITED

Secura Group Limited—(Continued)
Tel.: (65) 68139515
Web Site: https://www.redsentry.net
Cyber Security Services
N.A.I.C.S.: 561621

Secura Singapore Pte. Ltd.
8 Pioneer Road North, Singapore, 628460, Singapore
Tel.: (65) 62654911
Security & Investigation Services
N.A.I.C.S.: 561611

Secura Training Academy Pte. Ltd. (1)
38 Alexandra Terrace, Singapore, 119932, Singapore
Tel.: (65) 68139564
Training Academy Services
N.A.I.C.S.: 611519
Jingquan Yang (Mgr)

Soverus Kingdom Systems Pte. Ltd. (1)
38 Alexandra Terrace, Singapore, 119932, Singapore
Tel.: (65) 62758600
Security & Investigation Services
N.A.I.C.S.: 561611
Philip Lee (Deputy Gen Mgr)

SECURE EARTH TECHNOLOGIES LIMITED
407 Dalamal Tower Free Press Journal Road, Nariman Point, Mumbai, 400 021, India
Tel.: (91) 22 6610 0300
Software Development Services
N.A.I.C.S.: 513210

SECURE ELECTRONIC TECHNOLOGY PLC.
107 Bamgbose Street, Lagos, Nigeria
Tel.: (234) 08084177472
Web Site: https://setplc.com
Year Founded: 2001
NSLTECH—(NIGE)
Rev.: $9,693,821
Assets: $7,709,685
Liabilities: $1,880,015
Net Worth: $5,829,670
Earnings: ($91,162)
Fiscal Year-end: 12/31/22
Public Finance Activities
N.A.I.C.S.: 921130
Odunlami B. A. Kola-Daisi (Vice Chm)

SECURE ENERGY SERVICES INC.
Brookfield Place 2300 225 6 Ave SW, Calgary, T2P 1N2, AB, Canada
Tel.: (403) 984-6100 AB
Web Site: https://www.secure-energy.com
Year Founded: 2007
SES—(TSX)
Rev.: $2,946,066,480
Assets: $2,297,556,360
Liabilities: $1,432,354,680
Net Worth: $865,201,680
Earnings: ($159,585,120)
Emp.: 2,050
Fiscal Year-end: 12/31/21
Energy Services Company; Solids Processing & Recycling & Water Disposal Facilities; Drilling Services
N.A.I.C.S.: 213112
Rene Amirault (Chm, Pres & CEO)

Subsidiaries:

Secure Energy Services Inc. - Emerson Class Ib Water Disposal Facility (1)
RR1 Box 14 Site 14, PO Box 14, Sexsmith, T0H 3C0, AB, Canada
Tel.: (780) 882-4303
Web Site: http://www.secureenergy.ca

Sales Range: $25-49.9 Million
Emp.: 2
Hazardous Waste Disposal Services
N.A.I.C.S.: 562211

Secure Energy Services Inc. - Fox Creek Full Service Terminal (FST) (1)
Box 329, Fox Creek, T0H 1P0, AB, Canada
Tel.: (780) 225-2000
Web Site: http://www.secure-energy.com
Emp.: 30
Oilfield Waste Disposal Services
N.A.I.C.S.: 562213
Shaun Craig (Mgr-Facility)

Secure Energy Services Inc. - Kotcho Class Ib Fluids Separation/Disposal Facility (1)
PO Box 3040, Fort Nelson, V0C 1R0, BC, Canada
Tel.: (250) 263-7060
Sales Range: $25-49.9 Million
Emp.: 7
Oil Fluids Separation & Disposal Services
N.A.I.C.S.: 562213

Secure Energy Services Inc. - Nosehill Class Ib Water Disposal Facility (1)
PO Box 6869, Edson, T7E 1V2, AB, Canada
Tel.: (866) 765-0798
Web Site: http://www.secure-energy.ca
Sales Range: $25-49.9 Million
Emp.: 20
Hazardous Waste Disposal Services
N.A.I.C.S.: 562211
Rene Besler (Gen Mgr)

Secure Energy Services Inc. - Obed Class Ib Water Disposal Facility (1)
Box 6132, PO Box 6869, Hinton, T7B 1X5, AB, Canada
Tel.: (780) 517-4600
Web Site: http://www.secure-energy.com
Sales Range: $25-49.9 Million
Emp.: 11
Oilfield Waste Disposal Services
N.A.I.C.S.: 562998
Rene Besler (Gen Mgr)

Secure Energy Services Inc. - Pembina Class I & Class II Oilfield Landfill (1)
3149-50 Street, Drayton Valley, T7A 1R9, AB, Canada
Tel.: (780) 542-4733
Sales Range: $10-24.9 Million
Emp.: 50
Hazardous Waste Disposal Services
N.A.I.C.S.: 562211

Secure Energy Services Inc. - South Grande Prairie Class II Oilfield Landfill (1)
Box 382, Grovedale, Grande Prairie, T0H 1X0, AB, Canada
Web Site: http://www.secureenergy.ca
Emp.: 30
Oilfield Solid Waste Disposal Services
N.A.I.C.S.: 562212

Secure Energy Services Inc. - Willesden Green Class II Oilfield Landfill (1)
PO Box 1299, Rocky Mountain House, T4T 1A9, AB, Canada
Tel.: (866) 942-2609
Web Site: http://www.secure-energy.com
Sales Range: $25-49.9 Million
Emp.: 10
Oilfield Solid Waste Disposal Services
N.A.I.C.S.: 562212

Tervita Corporation (1)
140-10th Avenue SE Suite 1600, Calgary, T2G 0R1, AB, Canada
Tel.: (403) 233-7565
Web Site: http://www.tervita.com
Industrial, Mining, Oil & Gas Industries Environmental Remediation, Waste Management & Regulatory Support Services
N.A.I.C.S.: 541990
Kelly Sansom (Mgr-Comm)

SECURE INC.
20F Shinjuku Sumitomo Building

2-6-1, Nishi-Shinjuku Shinjuku-ku, Tokyo, 163-0220, Japan
Tel.: (81) 369110660
Web Site: https://www.secureinc.co.jp
Year Founded: 2002
4264—(TKS)
Rev.: $34,297,985
Assets: $18,163,198
Liabilities: $11,410,638
Net Worth: $6,752,560
Earnings: $1,110,010
Fiscal Year-end: 12/31/23
Software Development Services
N.A.I.C.S.: 541511
Fumiaki Yokoi (Sr Mng Dir)

SECURE PROPERTY DEVELOPMENT & INVESTMENT LIMITED
Prytysko-Mykilska 5, 4070, Kiev, Ukraine
Tel.: (380) 444593000 CY
Web Site: https://www.secure-property.eu
Year Founded: 2005
SPDI—(AIM)
Rev.: $1,234,354
Assets: $32,522,417
Liabilities: $17,973,897
Net Worth: $14,548,520
Earnings: ($12,566,242)
Emp.: 10
Fiscal Year-end: 12/31/22
Real Estate Investment Services
N.A.I.C.S.: 523999
Lambros G. Anagnostopoulos (CEO)

SECURE TRUST BANK PLC
Yorke House Arleston Way, Shirley, Solihull, B90 4LH, United Kingdom
Tel.: (44) 1216939100
Web Site: https://www.securetrustbank.com
Year Founded: 1952
STB—(AIM)
Rev.: $256,248,422
Assets: $4,266,978,036
Liabilities: $3,854,329,715
Net Worth: $412,648,321
Earnings: $42,539,763
Emp.: 940
Fiscal Year-end: 12/31/22
Banking & Financial Services
N.A.I.C.S.: 522110
Paul Anthony Lynam (CEO)

SECURE2GO GROUP LIMITED
96 Hay Street, Subiaco, 6008, WA, Australia
Tel.: (61) 1300001246 AU
Web Site: http://www.secure2go.com
Year Founded: 2014
Software Development Services
N.A.I.C.S.: 513210
Wesley Lawrence (CEO)

SECUREKLOUD TECHNOLOGIES LTD.
No 37 38 ASV Ramana Towers 5th Floor, Venkat Narayana Road T Nagar, Chennai, 600 017, India
Tel.: (91) 4466028000
Web Site: https://www.securekloud.com
SECURKLOUD—(NSE)
Rev.: $52,748,309
Assets: $33,145,039
Liabilities: $28,877,981
Net Worth: $4,267,058
Earnings: ($92,070,833)
Emp.: 201
Fiscal Year-end: 03/31/20
Software Developer
N.A.I.C.S.: 513210
Suresh Venkatachari (Founder, Chm, CEO & Mng Dir)

INTERNATIONAL PUBLIC

Subsidiaries:

Cornerstone Advisors Group, LLC (1)
20 Thunderlake Dr, Wilton, CT 06897
Tel.: (203) 774-3323
Web Site: http://www.cornerstone-advisors.com
Health Information Technology Consulting & Executive Advisory Services
N.A.I.C.S.: 513210
Kristi Lane (VP)

Devcool Inc. (1)
7901 Stoneridge Dr Ste 220, Pleasanton, CA 94588
Tel.: (408) 372-4313
Web Site: https://www.devcool.com
Information Technology Management Services
N.A.I.C.S.: 541512

NexAge Technologies USA, Inc. (1)
75 Lincoln Hwy Ste 101, Iselin, NJ 08830
Tel.: (732) 494-4944
Web Site: http://www.nexageusa.com
IT Consulting Services
N.A.I.C.S.: 541613
Suresh U. Kumar (Founder)

SecureKloud Technologies Inc. (1)
666 Plainsboro Rd Ste 448, Plainsboro, NJ 08536
Cloud Network Security Services
N.A.I.C.S.: 541519

SECUREMETRIC BERHAD
Unit 2-12-01 Level 12 Ho Hup Tower No 1 Persiaran Jalil 1, Bandar Bukit Jalil, 57000, Kuala Lumpur, Malaysia
Tel.: (60) 348188225 MY
Web Site: https://www.securemetric.com
Year Founded: 2007
SMETRIC—(KLS)
Rev.: $6,324,903
Assets: $12,109,214
Liabilities: $3,449,261
Net Worth: $8,659,953
Earnings: ($380,398)
Emp.: 129
Fiscal Year-end: 12/31/22
Software Development Services
N.A.I.C.S.: 541511
Nioo Yu Siong (COO)

Subsidiaries:

PT Securemetric Technology (1)
Ketapang Business Center Block C No 11 Jl KH Zainul Arifin No 20, Jakarta, 11140, Indonesia
Tel.: (62) 2122634496
Digital Security Services
N.A.I.C.S.: 561621

PT Softkey Indonesia (1)
Ketapang Business Center Blok C No 11 Jl KH Zainul Arifin No 20, Tamansari Krukut, Jakarta Barat, 11140, Jakarta, Indonesia
Tel.: (62) 2122634771
Electronic Identification Product Distr
N.A.I.C.S.: 423690

Securemetric Technology Pte. Ltd. (1)
50 Ubi Crescent 01-08 Ubi TechPark, Singapore, 408568, Singapore
Tel.: (65) 68274452
Electronic Identification Product Distr
N.A.I.C.S.: 423690

Securemetric Technology, Inc. (1)
Unit 7D Athenaeum Building, 160 L P Leviste Street Salcedo Village, Makati, 1227, Philippines
Tel.: (63) 27766003
Electronic Identification Product Distr
N.A.I.C.S.: 423690

Signing Cloud Sdn. Bhd. (1)
Level 5-E-6 Enterprise 4 Technology Park Malaysia Lebuhraya, Sg Besi - Puchong Bukit Jalil, 57000, Kuala Lumpur, Malaysia
Tel.: (60) 389968225
Web Site: https://www.signingcloud.com
Digital Signature Services

AND PRIVATE COMPANIES

N.A.I.C.S.: 541519

SECURIGUARD SERVICES LIMITED
1445 West Georgia St 4th Floor, Vancouver, V6G 2T3, BC, Canada
Tel.: (604) 685-6011
Web Site: http://www.securiguard.com
Year Founded: 1974
Security Guard Services
N.A.I.C.S.: 561612
David Long *(Gen Mgr)*

SECURITAG ASSEMBLY GROUP CO., LTD.
No 99 Renhuagong 2nd Rd, Dali District, Taichung, 41280, Taiwan
Tel.: (886) 424925298
Web Site: https://www.sag.com
Year Founded: 1999
6417—(TPE)
Rev.: $35,324,603
Assets: $47,032,717
Liabilities: $17,283,641
Net Worth: $29,749,076
Earnings: $3,412,479
Fiscal Year-end: 12/31/20
Communication Equipment Mfr
N.A.I.C.S.: 334290
Yu-Chi Chang *(VP)*

SECURITAS AB
Lindhagensplan 70, PO Box 12307, SE-102 28, Stockholm, Sweden
Tel.: (46) 104703000
Web Site: https://www.securitas.com
SCTBY—(OTCIQ)
Rev.: $13,148,016,000
Assets: $7,735,355,040
Liabilities: $5,196,091,040
Net Worth: $2,539,264,000
Earnings: $382,598,720
Emp.: 345,000
Fiscal Year-end: 12/31/21
Security & Cash Handling Services
N.A.I.C.S.: 561621
Bart Adam *(CFO)*

Subsidiaries:

AB Jourmontor (1)
Box 12516, 102 29, Stockholm, Sweden
Tel.: (46) 8 657 77 00
Web Site: http://www.securitas.se
Sales Range: $25-49.9 Million
Emp.: 40
Real Estate Manangement Services
N.A.I.C.S.: 531390

Alarm West Group d.o.o (1)
Bacici 15, 71 000, Sarajevo, Bosnia & Herzegovina
Tel.: (387) 33 789 000
Web Site: http://www.awg.ba
Sales Range: $300-349.9 Million
Emp.: 1,500
Property Protection Security Services
N.A.I.C.S.: 561612

B.I.G.A. d.o.o. (1)
Bacici 15, 71000, Sarajevo, Bosnia & Herzegovina
Tel.: (387) 33 789 000
Web Site: http://www.securitas.com
Security Guard Services
N.A.I.C.S.: 561612

Bren Security (PVT) LTD (1)
50A Sarasavi Lane Off Castle Street, Colombo, 00800, Sri Lanka
Tel.: (94) 11 2698661
Web Site: http://www.securitas.com
Security System Services
N.A.I.C.S.: 561621

Certas AG (1)
Schweizerische Alarm- und Einsatzzentrale Kalkbreitestrasse 51, PO Box 8021, 8003, Zurich, Switzerland
Tel.: (41) 446373737
Web Site: https://www.certas.ch

Sales Range: $25-49.9 Million
Emp.: 170
Alarm Systems & Services; Joint Venture Between Siemans AG (50%) & Securitas AB (50%)
N.A.I.C.S.: 561621

Dansikring A/S (1)
Sydvestvej 98, Glostrup, 2600, Denmark
Tel.: (45) 4343 4388
Web Site: http://www.securitas.dk
Sales Range: $25-49.9 Million
Emp.: 400
Security Consulting Services
N.A.I.C.S.: 541618
Tom Laursen *(Gen Mgr)*

Grupo Securitas Mexico SA de CV (1) (99.98%)
Tel.: (52) 8183215010
Web Site: http://www.securitas.com.mx
Sales Range: $1-4.9 Billion
Emp.: 7,000
Security Services
N.A.I.C.S.: 561621

Protectas SA (1) (100%)
Tel.: (41) 216232000
Web Site: http://www.protectas.com
Sales Range: $150-199.9 Million
Emp.: 975
Security & Cash Handling Services Provider
N.A.I.C.S.: 561621
Frank Dantand *(COO & Member-Mgmt Bd)*

SAIT Zenitel sa (1)
Z 1 Research Park 110, Zellik, 1731, Belgium
Tel.: (32) 23705311
Web Site: http://www.saitzenitel.com
Sales Range: $10-24.9 Million
Wireless & ICT Solutions
N.A.I.C.S.: 541512
Alain Van den Broeck *(CEO)*

Subsidiary (Non-US):

SAIT bv (2)
Manuscriptstraat 1, 1321 NP, Almere, Netherlands
Tel.: (31) 365462600
Web Site: http://sait.nu
Wireless Communications & Security Systems Services
N.A.I.C.S.: 334220

Seccredo Holding AB (1)
Platsejagan Plaseaholms Gaten 4, Box 5318, 102 47, Stockholm, Sweden
Tel.: (46) 8 545 322 30
Investment Management Service
N.A.I.C.S.: 523999

Subsidiary (Domestic):

Seccredo AB (2)
Blasieholmsgatan 4A, Stockholm, 111 48, Sweden
Tel.: (46) 8 545 322 30
Web Site: http://www.seccredo.se
Security Consulting Services
N.A.I.C.S.: 541690

Securitas (1)
Groenezoom 1, Badhoevedorp, 1171 JA, Netherlands (100%)
Tel.: (31) 883221100
Web Site: http://www.securitas.nl
Security Services
N.A.I.C.S.: 561621

Securitas - Servicos e Tecnologia de Seguranca, S.A (1)
Rua Rodrigues Lobo n 2 Edificio Securitas, Linda-a-Velha, 2799553, Portugal
Tel.: (351) 214 154 600
Security Guard Services
N.A.I.C.S.: 561612
Jorge Couto *(Pres-Div)*

Securitas Alert Services Polska Sp.z o.o. (1)
ul Cybernetyki 21, Warsaw, Poland (100%)
Tel.: (48) 224570800
Web Site: http://www.alert-services.pl
Security Services
N.A.I.C.S.: 561612

Dariusz Janusz Bak *(Pres)*

Securitas Asia Holding AB (1)
Lindhagensplan 70, 112 43, Stockholm, Sweden
Tel.: (46) 104703000
Holding Company
N.A.I.C.S.: 551112

Securitas BH d.o.o. (1)
Bacici 3, 71000, Sarajevo, Bosnia & Herzegovina
Tel.: (387) 33789000
Security & Cash Handling Services
N.A.I.C.S.: 561621

Securitas CR, s.r.o. (1)
Katerinska 466/40, 120 00, Prague, 2, Czech Republic (100%)
Tel.: (420) 284018372
Web Site: https://www.securitas.cz
Emp.: 35,000
Cash Handling & Security Services Provider
N.A.I.C.S.: 561621

Securitas Canada Limited (1)
235 Yorkland Blvd Suite 400, North York, M2J 4Y8, ON, Canada (100%)
Tel.: (416) 774-2500
Web Site: https://www.securitas.ca
Rev.: $67,861,616
Emp.: 8,100
Detective, Uniformed Security & Armored Car Services
N.A.I.C.S.: 561613

Securitas Deutschland Holding GmbH & Co. KG (1)
Hallesches Ufer 74-76, 10963, Berlin, Germany (100%)
Tel.: (49) 30 50 1000 0
Web Site: http://www.securitas.de
Security & Cash Handling Services
N.A.I.C.S.: 561621
Manfred Buhl *(Chm-Mgmt Bd)*

Subsidiary (Domestic):

SECURITAS Akademie GmbH (2)
Wahlerstrasse 2a, 40472, Dusseldorf, Germany
Tel.: (49) 211 640030
Security Guard Training Services
N.A.I.C.S.: 611519

SECURITAS GmbH (2)
Hallesches Ufer 74-76, 10963, Berlin, Germany
Tel.: (49) 30 501000613
Web Site: http://www.securitas.com
Security Guard Services
N.A.I.C.S.: 561612

SECURITAS Personalmanagement GmbH (2)
Hallesches Ufer 74-76, 10963, Berlin, Germany
Tel.: (49) 30 5010000
Human Resource Consulting Services
N.A.I.C.S.: 541612

SECURITAS Safety Cooperation Service GmbH & Co. KG (2)
Keniastrasse 12, 47269, Duisburg, Germany
Tel.: (49) 203998070
Emp.: 17
Fire Prevention & Protection Services
N.A.I.C.S.: 922160
Mansred Buhl *(Gen Mgr)*

SGB SECURITAS Gleisbausicherung GmbH & Co. KG (2)
Zweigniederlassung Bous Saarbrucker Strasse 115, 66359, Bous, Germany
Tel.: (49) 6834 92330
Emp.: 4
Security Guard Services
N.A.I.C.S.: 561612
Manfred Buhl *(Mng Dir)*

Securitas Alert Services GmbH (2)
Besselstrasse 13, 68219, Mannheim, Germany
Tel.: (49) 621878880
Web Site: http://www.securitas.com
Security Alarm Services
N.A.I.C.S.: 561612

Securitas Aviation Service GmbH & Co. KG (2)

SECURITAS AB

Schutzenstrasse 10, 12526, Berlin, Germany
Tel.: (49) 30652141712
Web Site: http://www.securitas.com
Aviation Security Services
N.A.I.C.S.: 561612

Securitas Flugverkehr Services GmbH (2)
Hahnstrasse 70, 60528, Frankfurt, Hesse, Germany
Tel.: (49) 69257564520
Web Site: http://www.securitas24.de
Sales Range: $100-124.9 Million
Emp.: 300
Airport Operation Services
N.A.I.C.S.: 488119

Securitas GmbH Mobil (2)
Verkehrshof 17, Potsdam, 14478, Brandenburg, Germany
Tel.: (49) 3318699677
Web Site: http://www.securitas.com
Sales Range: $125-149.9 Million
Emp.: 800
Data Protection & Security Services
N.A.I.C.S.: 561621

Securitas Sicherheit & Service GmbH & Co. KG (2)
Ruhrallee 201, 45136, Essen, Germany
Tel.: (49) 20143751871
Security Consulting Services
N.A.I.C.S.: 541690

Securitas Sicherheitsdienste GmbH & Co. KG (2)
Hallesches Ufer 74-76, Berlin, Germany
Tel.: (49) 305010000
Web Site: http://www.securitas.com
Security Services
N.A.I.C.S.: 561612
Manfred Buhl *(Country Mgr)*

Securitas Eesti AS (1)
Lootsa 12, 11415, Tallinn, Estonia (100%)
Tel.: (372) 6139200
Web Site: http://www.securitas.ee
Sales Range: $50-74.9 Million
Emp.: 800
Security & Cash Handling Services
N.A.I.C.S.: 561621
Ergo Oolup *(Mgr-Project)*

Securitas Egypt LLC (1)
20 El Farik Mohamed Ebrahim, Nasr City, Cairo, Egypt (80%)
Tel.: (20) 123920091
Web Site: http://www.securitas.com
Security Services
N.A.I.C.S.: 561612
Ahmed Emam *(Pres)*

Securitas Electronic Security Inc. (1)
3800 Tabs Dr, Uniontown, OH 44685
Tel.: (855) 331-0359
Web Site: http://www.securitases.com
Electronic Security Solutions
N.A.I.C.S.: 561621
Tony Byerly *(Pres & CEO)*

Subsidiary (Domestic):

F.E. Moran Security Solutions, LLC (2)
201 W University Ave, Champaign, IL 61820
Tel.: (217) 403-6444
Web Site: http://www.femoransecurity.com
Security Services
N.A.I.C.S.: 561621
Brett Bean *(Founder, Pres & CEO)*

Subsidiary (Domestic):

MidCo Inc. (3)
221 Shore Ct, Burr Ridge, IL 60527
Tel.: (630) 887-1800
Web Site: http://www.midcosystems.com
Communications Specialization
N.A.I.C.S.: 238210
Michael Kielbasa *(Mgr-Sls)*

Subsidiary (Domestic):

Kratos Public Safety & Security Solutions, Inc. (2)
4820 Eastgate Mall Ste 200, San Diego, CA 92121
Tel.: (858) 812-7300

SECURITAS AB

Securitas AB—(Continued)

Video Surveillance Equipment Designer, Mfr & Whslr
N.A.I.C.S.: 334310
Ben Goodwin (Pres)

Securitas France S.A.R.L. (1)
253 Battle Dock of Stalingrad CS20169, 92137, Issy-les-Moulineaux, Cedex, France (100%)
Tel.: (33) 141338400
Web Site: http://www.securitas.fr
Sales Range: $75-99.9 Million
Emp.: 500
Security & Cash Handling Services
N.A.I.C.S.: 561621

Securitas Guarding Services (Singapore) Pte Ltd. (1)
19 Tai Seng Avenue 05-10, Singapore, 534054, Singapore
Tel.: (65) 6338 8217
Sales Range: $10-24.9 Million
Emp.: 600
Security Guard Services
N.A.I.C.S.: 561612
David Amos Seth (Pres-Country)

Securitas Hrvatska d.o.o (1)
Oreskoviceva 6n/2, 10010, Zagreb, Croatia
Tel.: (385) 16173000
Web Site: https://www.securitas.com.hr
Emp.: 2,300
Security & Cash Handling Services
N.A.I.C.S.: 561612

Securitas Invest AB (1)
PO Box 12307, 102 28, Stockholm, Sweden
Tel.: (46) 86577400
Security Consulting Services
N.A.I.C.S.: 541618

Securitas N.V. (1)
Tel.: (32) 22635555
Web Site: https://www.securitas.be
Sales Range: $75-99.9 Million
Emp.: 5,500
Security Services
N.A.I.C.S.: 561612

Securitas Oy (1)
Elimaenkatu 30, 00520, Helsinki, Finland (100%)
Tel.: (358) 204911
Web Site: http://www.securitas.fi
Sales Range: $650-699.9 Million
Emp.: 3,000
Uniformed Security Services
N.A.I.C.S.: 561621
Jarmo Mikkonen (Mng Dir)

Securitas Polska Sp. z o.o. (1)
ul Postepu 6, 02-676, Warsaw, Poland (100%)
Tel.: (48) 224570700
Web Site: https://www.securitas.pl
Emp.: 6,000
Security & Cash Handling Services
N.A.I.C.S.: 561621

Securitas S.A. (1)
Rua Rodrigues Lobo 2 Edificio Securitas, 2799 553, Linda-a-Velha, Portugal (100%)
Tel.: (351) 214154600
Web Site: http://www.securitas.pt
Sales Range: $25-49.9 Million
Emp.: 220
Cash Handling & Security System Services
N.A.I.C.S.: 561621

Securitas SA (1)
Sint Lendriksborre 3 Font St Landry, Neder-Over-Heembeek, 1120, Belgium (100%)
Tel.: (32) 22635555
Web Site: http://www.securitas.be
Sales Range: $1-4.9 Billion
Emp.: 5,500
Uniformed Security Services
N.A.I.C.S.: 561621

Securitas SA Holdings Pty. Ltd. (1)
Grayston Ridge Office Park Block C 144 Katherine Street, Sandton, 2146, Gauteng, South Africa
Tel.: (27) 861100900
Web Site: http://www.securitas.com
Security Services
N.A.I.C.S.: 561612

Securitas Security Services USA, Inc. (1)
9 Campus Dr, Parsippany, NJ 07054-4400 (100%)
Tel.: (973) 267-5300
Web Site: http://www.securitasinc.com
Sales Range: $1-4.9 Billion
Emp.: 200
Security Services
N.A.I.C.S.: 561612
Santiago Galaz (Pres)

Subsidiary (Domestic)

Pinkerton Government Services, Inc. (2)
6850 Versar Ctr, Springfield, VA 22151
Tel.: (703) 750-1098
Web Site: http://www.pgs-usa.com
Sales Range: $75-99.9 Million
Investigation Services
N.A.I.C.S.: 561611
Kevin M. Sandkuhler (Pres)

Subsidiary (Domestic)

Paragon Systems, Inc. (3)
14160 Newbrook Dr, Chantilly, VA 20151 (100%)
Tel.: (703) 263-7176
Web Site: http://www.parasys.com
Security Guard Services
N.A.I.C.S.: 561612
Grady Baker (VP-Ops)

Subsidiary (Domestic)

Security Consultants Group, Inc. (4)
102 Mitchell Rd Ste 100, Oak Ridge, TN 37830
Tel.: (865) 482-7440
Web Site: http://www.scgincorp.com
Sales Range: $100-124.9 Million
Emp.: 2,000
Security Guard & Patrol Services
N.A.I.C.S.: 561612
Joe Singh Rodriguez (CEO)

Branch (Domestic)

Securitas Security Services USA, Inc. (2)
3605 Vartan Way, Harrisburg, PA 17110
Tel.: (717) 657-0734
Web Site: http://www.securitasinc.com
Sales Range: $25-49.9 Million
Security Services
N.A.I.C.S.: 561612

Unit (Domestic)

Securitas Security Services USA, Inc. - Western Operations Center (2)
4330 Park Terrace Dr, Westlake Village, CA 91361-4630
Tel.: (818) 706-6800
Web Site: http://www.securitasinc.com
Sales Range: $25-49.9 Million
Emp.: 150
Security Guard Service, Private Investigation, Security Systems Integration, Pre-Employment Screenings
N.A.I.C.S.: 561612
David Glass (Mgr-Shreveport)

Securitas Seguridad Holding SL (1)
Calle Entrepenas 27, 28051, Madrid, Spain
Tel.: (34) 912776000
Web Site: https://www.securitas.es
Security Solution Services
N.A.I.C.S.: 561612

Subsidiary (Non-US)

Securitas Argentina S.A. (2)
Tel.: (54) 8001227328
Web Site: https://securion.com.ar
Sales Range: $250-299.9 Million
Security Services
N.A.I.C.S.: 561612

Subsidiary (Domestic)

Securitas Seguridad Espana, S.A. (2)
Calle Entrepenas 27, Poligono Las Mercedes, 28051, Madrid, Spain (100%)
Tel.: (34) 912776000
Web Site: https://www.securitas.es

Sales Range: $25-49.9 Million
Emp.: 400
Cash Handling & Security Services
N.A.I.C.S.: 561621

Securitas Services Holding U.K. Ltd. (1)
Tel.: (44) 800716586
Web Site: http://www.securitas.uk.com
Security Services
N.A.I.C.S.: 561612

Subsidiary (Domestic):

Securitas UK (2)
271 High St, Uxbridge, UB8 1LQ, United Kingdom (100%)
Tel.: (44) 2083926000
Web Site: http://www.securitas.uk.com
Cash Handling Security Services
N.A.I.C.S.: 561621

Securitas Services International B.V. (1)
Groenezoom 1, 1171 JA, Badhoevedorp, Netherlands
Tel.: (31) 206584700
Web Site: https://www.securitas.nl
Security Services
N.A.I.C.S.: 561612

Securitas Services Romania SRL (1)
Tel.: (40) 743057052 (100%)
Web Site: https://www.securitas.com.ro
Sales Range: $650-699.9 Million
Security Services
N.A.I.C.S.: 561612

Securitas Services d.o.o. (1)
Milentija Popovic 9 Sava Centar-Delegate Units 13 27 28, Belgrade, 11070, Serbia (100%)
Tel.: (381) 112284050
Web Site: https://www.securitas.rs
Sales Range: $300-349.9 Million
Emp.: 1,800
Security Services
N.A.I.C.S.: 561612
Marko Novakovic (Mgr-Comm)

Securitas Sicherheitsdienstleistungen GmbH (1)
Franzosengraben 8, A-1030, Vienna, Austria (100%)
Tel.: (43) 1211960
Web Site: https://www.securitas.at
Sales Range: $300-349.9 Million
Emp.: 2,400
Security & Secure Cash Handling Services
N.A.I.C.S.: 561621

Securitas Sverige AB (1)
Lindhagensplan 70, PO Box 12516, 102 29, Stockholm, Sweden (100%)
Tel.: (46) 104701000
Web Site: http://www.securitas.com
Sales Range: $10-24.9 Million
Emp.: 45
Security Alarm Systems & Services
N.A.I.C.S.: 561621

Securitas Toolbox Ltd (1)
Groenezoom 1, 1171 JA, Badhoevedorp, Netherlands
Tel.: (31) 20 658 47 00
Security System Services
N.A.I.C.S.: 561621

Securitas Treasury Ireland Ltd. (1)
Lagouche House IFSC, Dublin, Ireland
Tel.: (353) 14350100
Web Site: http://www.securitas.com
Sales Range: $25-49.9 Million
Emp.: 9
Detective, Uniformed Security & Armored Car Services
N.A.I.C.S.: 561613

Securitas Uruguay SA (1)
Avda Italia 3888, 11400, Montevideo, Uruguay
Tel.: (598) 2509 7328
Security Guard Services
N.A.I.C.S.: 561612

Securitas nv/sa (1)
Sint Lendriksborre 3 Font St Landry, Neder-Over-Heembeek, 1120, Belgium

Tel.: (32) 2 263 55 55
Web Site: http://www.securitas.com
Sales Range: $75-99.9 Million
Emp.: 5,500
Security Guard Services
N.A.I.C.S.: 561612

Supreme Security Systems, Inc. (1)
1565 Union Ave, Union, NJ 07083
Tel.: (908) 810-8822
Web Site: http://www.supremesecurity.com
Security System Services
N.A.I.C.S.: 561621
David B. Bitton (Pres)

SECURITAS AG

Alpenstrasse 20, 3052, Zollikofen, Switzerland
Tel.: (41) 319101111 CH
Web Site: http://www.swiss-securitas.com
Year Founded: 1907
Security Services
N.A.I.C.S.: 561612
Armin Berchtold (CEO)

Subsidiaries:

Securitas (Liechtenstein) AG (1)
Landstrasse 38, Postfach 626, Vaduz, 9490, Liechtenstein
Tel.: (423) 239 65 55
Security Alarm Services
N.A.I.C.S.: 561612

Securitas Direct S.A. (1)
Chemin De Bere 50, PO Box 217, 1010, Lausanne, Switzerland (100%)
Tel.: (41) 216511655
Web Site: http://www.securitas-direct.ch
Sales Range: $10-24.9 Million
Emp.: 40
Security Alarm Systems & Services
N.A.I.C.S.: 561621
Serjy Luke (Office Mgr)

SECURITIES & COMMODITIES AUTHORITY

P.O. Box 33733, PO Box 33733, Abu Dhabi, United Arab Emirates
Tel.: (971) 26277888
Web Site: http://www.sca.ae
Sales Range: $50-74.9 Million
Emp.: 200
Stock Exchange Services
N.A.I.C.S.: 523210
Sultan Saeed Al-Mansoori (Chm)

SECURITIES & INVESTMENT COMPANY BSC

East Tower 16th floor Isa AlKabeer Avenue 365 Block 316, PO Box 1331, Bahrain World Trade Center, Manama, Bahrain
Tel.: (973) 17515000 BH
Web Site: https://sicobank.com
Year Founded: 1995
SICO-C—(BAH)
Rev: $38,304,024
Assets: $742,638,126
Liabilities: $557,014,403
Net Worth: $185,623,724
Earnings: $9,564,733
Emp.: 146
Fiscal Year-end: 12/31/22
Investment Banking Services
N.A.I.C.S.: 523150
Hussain Al Hussaini (Vice Chm)

Subsidiaries:

SICO Capital Company Ltd. (1)
CMC Tower 5th Floor - 7702 King Fahd Road, Al Malqa District, Riyadh, 13524, Saudi Arabia
Tel.: (966) 115213835
Web Site: https://www.sicocapital.com
Investment Banking & Financial Services
N.A.I.C.S.: 522320

SICO Funds Services Co. BSC (C) (1)
Bmb Building Second Floor, PO Box 20233,

AND PRIVATE COMPANIES

Manama, Bahrain
Tel.: (973) 1751 6060
Web Site: http://www.sicobahrain.com
Emp.: 90
Securities Brokerage Services
N.A.I.C.S.: 523150
Najla Al Shirawi *(Gen Mgr)*

SICO Funds Services Company BSC (1)
Bahrain World Trade Center East Tower, 16th floor Isa AlKabeer Avenue 365 Block 316, Manama, Bahrain
Tel.: (973) 17516060
Custody & Administration Services
N.A.I.C.S.: 523991

SECURITY & INTELLIGENCE SERVICES (INDIA) LIMITED
A-28/29 Okhla Industrial Area Phase-I, New Delhi, 110 020, India
Tel.: (91) 1146464444
Web Site: https://www.sisindia.com
Year Founded: 1985
SIS—(NSE)
Rev.: $413,645,232
Assets: $275,616,842
Liabilities: $164,814,195
Net Worth: $110,802,647
Earnings: $7,793,195
Emp.: 134,306
Fiscal Year-end: 03/31/21
Security Services
N.A.I.C.S.: 561612
Ravindra Kishore Sinha *(Founder & Chm)*

Subsidiaries:

Safety Direct Solutions Pty. Ltd. (1)
143 Balcatta Road, Balcatta, 6021, WA, Australia
Tel.: (61) 1300955097
Web Site: https://www.sdsaus.com.au
Training & Medical Services
N.A.I.C.S.: 611519

Uniq Security Solutions Private Limited (1)
Vayudooth Chambers 15-16 7th Floor Opposite Trinity Church MG Road, Bengaluru, 560040, Karnataka, India
Tel.: (91) 9591990099
Web Site: https://uniqsec.com
Security Management Services
N.A.I.C.S.: 561612

SECURITY INVESTMENT BANK LIMITED
Office No 01st Floor Junaid Plaza I10 Markaz, Near MCB Bank, Islamabad, Pakistan
Tel.: (92) 514102926
Web Site: https://sibl.com.pk_us
Year Founded: 1991
SIBL—(PSX)
Rev.: $471,527
Assets: $5,312,968
Liabilities: $1,199,823
Net Worth: $4,113,146
Earnings: $272,651
Emp.: 26
Fiscal Year-end: 12/31/19
Investment Banking Services
N.A.I.C.S.: 523150
Jan Muhammad *(Chm)*

Subsidiaries:

SIBL Exchange Company (Pvt.) Ltd. (1)
Shop 2 Mezzanine Fl Al-Rahim Tower, I I Chundrigar Rd, Karachi, Pakistan
Tel.: (92) 212440770
Investment Management Service
N.A.I.C.S.: 541618

SECURITY LEASING CORPORATION LIMITED
Block B 5th Floor Lakson Square Building No 3 Sarwar Shaheed Road, Karachi, 74200, Pakistan
Tel.: (92) 356603078
Web Site: https://www.seclease.com
SLCL—(KAR)
Rev.: $61,407
Assets: $4,229,630
Liabilities: $3,475,042
Net Worth: $754,588
Earnings: ($177,830)
Fiscal Year-end: 06/30/19
Corporate, Operating & Automobile Leasing
N.A.I.C.S.: 532490
M. R. Khan *(Chm)*

SECURITY PAPERS LIMITED
Jinnah Avenue Malir Halt, Karachi, 75100, Pakistan
Tel.: (92) 2199248285
Web Site: https://www.security-papers.com
SEPL—(KAR)
Rev.: $28,731,423
Assets: $43,686,236
Liabilities: $8,230,707
Net Worth: $35,455,529
Earnings: $5,543,204
Emp.: 372
Fiscal Year-end: 06/30/19
Paper Mfr
N.A.I.C.S.: 322120
Faizul Islam *(Gen Mgr-SCM)*

SECURITY RESEARCH GROUP PLC
Vicarage House, 58-60 Kensington Church Street, London, W8 4DB, United Kingdom
Tel.: (44) 20 7368 3317
Web Site: http://www.srgroupplc.com
Sales Range: $1-9.9 Million
Emp.: 56
Investment Services
N.A.I.C.S.: 525910
Jonathan Philip Mervis *(Chm)*

Subsidiaries:

Audiotel International Ltd (1)
Corby Road Weldon, Corby, NN1748Z, United Kingdom
Tel.: (44) 1536266677
Web Site: http://www.audiotel-int.com
Sales Range: $25-49.9 Million
Emp.: 30
Counter Surveillance Equipment Mfr
N.A.I.C.S.: 334511
Bernie Connor *(Mng Dir)*

Moore, Buckle (Flexible Packaging) Ltd. (1)
Sutton Fold Industrial Park, Saint Helens, WA9 3GL, United Kingdom
Tel.: (44) 1744733066
Web Site: http://www.mooreandbuckle.com
Sales Range: $25-49.9 Million
Emp.: 150
Packaging Services
N.A.I.C.S.: 561910
Derek Hewitt *(Mng Dir)*

PSG Franchising Ltd. (1)
Wellington Mills 70 Plover Road Lindley, Huddersfield, HD3 3HR, United Kingdom
Tel.: (44) 01484311649
Web Site: http://www.psgonline.co.uk
Private Property Search
N.A.I.C.S.: 531210

Subsidiary (Domestic):

PSG Energy Limited (2)
6 Great Cliffe Court Great Cliffe Road, Dodworth, Barnsley, S75 3SP, South Yorkshire, United Kingdom
Tel.: (44) 1226320070
Web Site: http://www.psgenergy.co.uk
Sales Range: $25-49.9 Million
Emp.: 25
Building Survey & Auditing Services
N.A.I.C.S.: 541370
Samanthj Horn *(Mgr)*

Patersons Financial Services Ltd. (1)
Signet House 49-51 Farringdon Road, London, EC1M 3JP, United Kingdom
Tel.: (44) 2074046136
Insurance Services
N.A.I.C.S.: 524298

SECUVE CO., LTD.
801 111 Digital-ro 26-gil, Guro-gu, Seoul, 152-848, Korea (South)
Tel.: (82) 262619300
Web Site: http://www.secuve.com
Year Founded: 2000
131090—(KRS)
Rev.: $10,510,044
Assets: $35,858,093
Liabilities: $3,826,006
Net Worth: $32,032,087
Earnings: $3,701,514
Emp.: 66
Fiscal Year-end: 12/31/22
Information Security Software, Products & Services
N.A.I.C.S.: 513210
Kyu-Ho Lee *(CEO)*

SEDANA MEDICAL AB
Vendevagen 89, 182 32, Danderyd, Sweden
Tel.: (46) 812405200
Web Site: https://www.sedanamedical.com
Year Founded: 2005
SEDANA—(OMX)
Rev.: $11,507,769
Assets: $101,303,586
Liabilities: $4,910,974
Net Worth: $96,392,612
Earnings: ($6,884,805)
Emp.: 85
Fiscal Year-end: 12/31/22
Medical Equipment Mfr
N.A.I.C.S.: 339112
Thomas Eklund *(Chm)*

Subsidiaries:

Sedana Medical Ltd. (1)
Unit 2A The Village Centre Two Mile House, Naas, Kildare, W91 PWH5, Ireland
Tel.: (353) 45879081
Medical Device Mfr & Retailer
N.A.I.C.S.: 339112

Sedana Medical Sarl (1)
3 Rue du Colonel Moll, 75017, Paris, France
Tel.: (33) 153817710
Medical Device Mfr & Retailer
N.A.I.C.S.: 339112
Didier Doreau *(Country Mgr)*

SEDANIA INNOVATOR BERHAD
Level 10 Kelana Parkview Tower Jalan SS6/2, 47301, Petaling Jaya, Selangor Darul Ehsan, Malaysia
Tel.: (60) 378802001
Web Site: https://www.sedaniainnovator.com
SEDANIA—(KLS)
Rev.: $8,116,947
Assets: $12,224,067
Liabilities: $3,455,857
Net Worth: $8,768,209
Earnings: $285,992
Emp.: 84
Fiscal Year-end: 12/31/22
Telecommunications & IT Products
N.A.I.C.S.: 334290
Noor Azrin Mohd Noor *(Founder & Mng Dir)*

Subsidiaries:

Offspring Inc Sdn. Bhd. (1)
11th Floor Kelana Parkview Tower Jalan SS 6/2 No 6, Petaling Jaya, Selangor, Malaysia
Tel.: (60) 378871919
Web Site: https://offspringinc.com
Pulp & Paper Mfr
N.A.I.C.S.: 322130

SEDLABANKI ISLANDS

SEDCO CAPITAL REIT FUND
South Tower of the Red Sea Mall King Abdulaziz Mailk Road, PO Box 13396, Jeddah, 21491, Saudi Arabia
Tel.: (966) 126906555
Web Site: https://www.sedcocapital.com
Year Founded: 1976
4344—(SAU)
Rev.: $43,335,989
Assets: $635,816,320
Liabilities: $226,968,931
Net Worth: $408,847,389
Earnings: $8,949,424
Fiscal Year-end: 12/31/23
Real Estate Investment Services
N.A.I.C.S.: 531190
Ahmed Suleiman Banaja *(Chm-SEDCO Capital)*

SEDEX MINING CORP.
675 Hastings Street Suite 711, Vancouver, V6B 1N2, BC, Canada
Tel.: (604) 685-2222
Web Site: http://www.sedexmining.com
Mineral Exploration Services
N.A.I.C.S.: 213114

SEDIBELO PLATINUM MINES LIMITED
6 EcoFusion Office Park Block B 324 Witch-Hazel Avenue, Highveld Park X59, Centurion, 0157, South Africa
Tel.: (27) 126614280
Web Site: http://www.platmin.com
Rev.: $170,584,000
Assets: $1,090,244,000
Liabilities: $98,325,000
Net Worth: $991,919,000
Earnings: ($31,412,000)
Emp.: 604
Fiscal Year-end: 12/31/18
Platinum Mining & Exploration Services
N.A.I.C.S.: 212290
Arne H. Frandsen *(Chm)*

Subsidiaries:

Boynton Platinum (Pty) Ltd. (1)
Ground Fl S Solar Pl Highveld Technopark, Centurion, 46, Gauteng, South Africa
Tel.: (27) 126654360
Platinum Exploration Services
N.A.I.C.S.: 213115

SEDILEC S.C.R.L.
Ave Jean Monnet 2, 1348, Louvain, La Neuve, Belgium
Tel.: (32) 10486611
Web Site: http://www.sedilec.be
Sales Range: $150-199.9 Million
Emp.: 350
Electricity & Natural Gas Distr
N.A.I.C.S.: 221210
J. Conel *(Mgr)*

SEDIVIO S.A.
ul Okopowa 47/23, 01-059, Warsaw, Poland
Tel.: (48) 226022530
Web Site: https://sedivio.com
Year Founded: 2012
Software Development Services
N.A.I.C.S.: 541511
Jakub Budziszewski *(CEO)*

SEDLABANKI ISLANDS
Kalkofnsvegi 1, 101, Reykjavik, Iceland
Tel.: (354) 5699600
Web Site: http://www.sedlabanki.is
Emp.: 115
Central Bank
N.A.I.C.S.: 521110
Sturla Palsson *(Principal & Dir-Treasury & Market Ops)*

SEDLMAYR GRUND UND IMMOBILIEN AG

Sedlabanki Islands—(Continued)

SEDLMAYR GRUND UND IMMOBILIEN AG
Marsstrasse 46-48, 80335, Munich, Germany
Tel.: (49) 8951220
Web Site: https://www.sedlmayr-ag.de
Year Founded: 1937
SPB—(STU)
Rev.: $139,618,059
Assets: $1,291,731,979
Liabilities: $1,052,003,533
Net Worth: $239,728,447
Earnings: $14,063,362
Emp.: 63
Fiscal Year-end: 12/31/23
Real Estate Investment Services
N.A.I.C.S.: 531190
Hermann Brandstetter *(Chm)*

SEE HUP CONSOLIDATED BERHAD
No 1062 Mukim 6 Jalan Perusahaan, Kawasan Perusahaan Perai, 13600, Perai, Penang, Malaysia
Tel.: (60) 46882688
Web Site: https://www.seehup.com.my
SEEHUP—(KLS)
Rev.: $26,706,916
Assets: $30,332,874
Liabilities: $11,573,231
Net Worth: $18,759,643
Earnings: ($1,290,441)
Emp.: 407
Fiscal Year-end: 03/31/23
Transportation Services
N.A.I.C.S.: 481112
Muhadzir Mohd Isa *(Exec Dir)*

SEEC MEDIA GROUP LIMITED
Room 1408 14/F Wing On Kowloon Centre, 345 Nathan Road, Kowloon, China (Hong Kong)
Tel.: (852) 23569880
Web Site: http://www.seec-media.com.hk
0205—(HKG)
Rev.: $9,328,283
Assets: $54,467,235
Liabilities: $28,253,618
Net Worth: $26,213,618
Earnings: ($11,381,033)
Emp.: 46
Fiscal Year-end: 12/31/22
Advertising Agency Services
N.A.I.C.S.: 541810
Zhifang Zhang *(Exec Dir)*

SEED CO., LTD.
2-40-2 Hongo, Bunkyo-ku, Tokyo, 113-8402, Japan
Tel.: (81) 338131111
Web Site: https://www.seed.co.jp
Year Founded: 1957
7743—(TKS)
Rev.: $214,137,560
Assets: $327,684,140
Liabilities: $211,017,640
Net Worth: $116,666,500
Earnings: $12,982,040
Emp.: 1,337
Fiscal Year-end: 03/31/24
Contact Lens Mfr & Whslr
N.A.I.C.S.: 339115
Masahiro Urakabe *(Pres & CEO)*

Subsidiaries:

SEED CONTACT LENS ASIA PTE. LTD. (1)
34 Boon Leat Terrace 04-20A, Singapore, 119866, Singapore
Tel.: (65) 65436251
Web Site: https://www.seedasiacontactlens.com.sg
Contact Lens Distr
N.A.I.C.S.: 423460

SEED CONTACT LENS TAIWAN CO., LTD. (1)
No 97 Section 1 Xintai 5th Road No 12 26th Floor, Xizhi Dist, New Taipei City, 11475, Taiwan
Tel.: (886) 800200686
Web Site: https://www.seed-taiwan.com
Contact Lens Distr
N.A.I.C.S.: 423460

SEED Contact Lens (M) Sdn Bhd (1)
No 38 Jalan Puteri 5/8, Bandar Puteri Puchong, 47100, Puchong, Selangor, Malaysia
Tel.: (60) 380519889
Contact Lens Distr
N.A.I.C.S.: 423460
Low Khun Keong *(Gen Mgr)*

SEED Trading (Shanghai) Co., Ltd. (1)
Block A 14th Floor Jiushi Fuxing Building No 918 Huaihai Middle Road, Huangpu, Shanghai, 200020, China
Tel.: (86) 2154669790
Web Site: http://www.seed-china.com.cn
Contact Lens Whslr
N.A.I.C.S.: 423460

SEED INNOVATIONS LIMITED
Suite 8 Upper House 16-20 Smith Street, Saint Peter Port, GY1 2JQ, Guernsey
Tel.: (44) 1481810100   GY
Web Site: https://seedinnovations.co
Year Founded: 2006
SEED—(AIM)
Rev.: $143,903
Assets: $17,207,776
Liabilities: $35,345
Net Worth: $17,172,431
Earnings: ($2,676,092)
Emp.: 351
Fiscal Year-end: 03/31/24
Energy Operations
N.A.I.C.S.: 221118
Edward McDermott *(CEO)*

SEEDHEIWA CO., LTD.
SEED Yamashina Chuo Bldg 8-1 Nagitsuji Chuzaike-cho, Yamashina-ku, Kyoto, 607-8161, Japan
Tel.: (81) 75 5951311
Web Site: http://www.seed-kyoto.co.jp
Year Founded: 1993
17390—(JAS)
Sales Range: $200-249.9 Million
Emp.: 70
Construction Engineering Services
N.A.I.C.S.: 541330
Shinzo Koike *(Pres)*

SEEEN PLC
27-28 Eastcastle Street, London, W1W 8DH, United Kingdom
Tel.: (44) 2078619000   UK
Web Site: http://www.seeen.com
SEEN—(AIM)
Rev.: $2,050,000
Assets: $4,370,000
Liabilities: $1,120,000
Net Worth: $3,250,000
Earnings: ($5,140,000)
Fiscal Year-end: 12/31/23
Software Development Services
N.A.I.C.S.: 541511
Adrian Hargrave *(CEO)*

Subsidiaries:

GTChannel, Inc. (1)
1730 E Holly St, El Segundo, CA 90245
Tel.: (310) 753-1040
Web Site: http://www.creatorformula.io
Automotive Engineering Consulting Services
N.A.I.C.S.: 541330

SEEF PROPERTIES B.S.C.
Office 2001 Building 2102 Road 2825, PO Box 20084, Seef District 428, Manama, Bahrain
Tel.: (973) 77911111
Web Site: https://www.seef.com.bh
Year Founded: 1999
SEEF—(BAH)
Rev.: $36,945,452
Assets: $475,714,615
Liabilities: $46,227,933
Net Worth: $429,486,682
Earnings: $16,309,801
Emp.: 139
Fiscal Year-end: 12/31/22
Commercial Real Estate Management Services
N.A.I.C.S.: 531390
Essa Mohammed Najibi *(Chm)*

Subsidiaries:

Fraser Suites Seef SPC (1)
Rd 2825 Block 428 Al Seef, 428 Bldg 2109, Manama, 11873, Bahrain
Tel.: (973) 17569333
Web Site: http://www.frasershospitality.com
Sales Range: $25-49.9 Million
Emp.: 45
Serviced Apartments
N.A.I.C.S.: 531110

SEEGENE, INC.
KT Bldg 209 Jamsil-ro, Songpa-gu, Seoul, 05552, Korea (South)
Tel.: (82) 222404000
Web Site: https://www.seegene.com
Year Founded: 2000
096530—(KRS)
Rev.: $654,681,357
Assets: $1,066,726,387
Liabilities: $184,462,413
Net Worth: $882,263,974
Earnings: $139,925,620
Emp.: 1,016
Fiscal Year-end: 12/31/22
In-Vitro Diagnostic Substance & Pharmaceutical Mfr
N.A.I.C.S.: 325413
Jun Hyuk Lee *(VP)*

Subsidiaries:

Biotron Healthcare (India) P. Ltd. (1)
301 Coral Classic 20th Road, Chembur, Mumbai, 400 071, Maharashtra, India
Tel.: (91) 2261406400
Web Site: https://www.biotronhealthcare.com
Sales Range: $25-49.9 Million
Diagnostic Equipment Distr
N.A.I.C.S.: 423450

SEEING MACHINES LIMITED
80 Mildura Street, Fyshwick, Canberra, 2609, ACT, Australia
Tel.: (61) 261034700
Web Site: https://www.seeingmachines.com
SEE—(LSE)
Rev.: $45,155,582
Assets: $87,003,873
Liabilities: $62,309,028
Net Worth: $24,694,845
Earnings: ($20,884,081)
Emp.: 421
Fiscal Year-end: 06/30/24
Eye Tracking & Face Tracking Devices Mfr
N.A.I.C.S.: 334118
Tim Edwards *(Co-Founder & CTO)*

Subsidiaries:

Seeing Machines Incorporated (1)
6875 N Oracle Rd Ste 105, Tucson, AZ 85704
Web Site: https://www.seeingmachines.com
Seeing Machine Component Mfr
N.A.I.C.S.: 334419

INTERNATIONAL PUBLIC

SEEK LIMITED
60 Cremorne St, Cremorne, 3121, VIC, Australia
Tel.: (61) 385174100   AU
Web Site: https://www.seek.com.au
Year Founded: 1997
SKLTF—(OTCIQ)
Rev.: $584,832,827
Assets: $3,524,933,714
Liabilities: $2,054,844,961
Net Worth: $1,470,088,753
Earnings: $576,328,118
Emp.: 1,030
Fiscal Year-end: 06/30/21
Holding Company; Online Job Advertising, Career Training & Human Resources Consulting Services
N.A.I.C.S.: 551112
Andrew R. Bassat *(Founder & CEO)*

Subsidiaries:

Job Adder Operations Pty. Ltd. (1)
Level 1 Bond Street, Sydney, 2000, NSW, Australia
Tel.: (61) 25 632 9231
Web Site: https://www.jobadder.com
Software Development Services
N.A.I.C.S.: 541511

Jobs DB Recruitment (Thailand) Limited (1)
1 Empire Tower III 26th Floor Unit 2607-2608 South Sathorn Road, Yannawa Sathorn, Bangkok, 10120, Thailand
Tel.: (66) 2 667 0700
Web Site: https://www.th.jobsdb.com
Recruitment Services
N.A.I.C.S.: 561311

PT. Prestige Indonesia (1)
Pluit Karang Ayu C1 Utara No 11 RT 4/RW 3 Pluit Kec Penjaringan Kota, Jakarta Utara, 14450, Jakarta, Indonesia
Tel.: (62) 21 669 0444
Web Site: https://www.prestigecorp.co.id
Emp.: 300
Hotel Laundry Services
N.A.I.C.S.: 812320

SEEK Commercial Pty Ltd (1)
60 Cremorne St, Cremorne, Melbourne, 3121, VIC, Australia
Tel.: (61) 383939962
Web Site: https://www.seekbusiness.com.au
Sales Range: $200-249.9 Million
Emp.: 600
Business Directory Services
N.A.I.C.S.: 513140
Nick Anderson *(Mgr-Display, Agency & Comml Sls)*

SEEK Learning Pty Ltd (1)
Level 14 100 Pacific Highway, North Sydney, 2060, NSW, Australia
Tel.: (61) 130 065 8700
Web Site: https://www.seek.com.au
Sales Range: $10-24.9 Million
Emp.: 25
Education Training Services
N.A.I.C.S.: 611710

Subsidiary (Domestic):

Dynamic Web Training Pty Ltd (2)
Level 11 32 Walker street, North Sydney, 2060, NSW, Australia
Tel.: (61) 130 088 8724
Web Site: https://www.dynamicwebtraining.com.au
Sales Range: $10-24.9 Million
Emp.: 8
Web Designing Training Services
N.A.I.C.S.: 611420

Subsidiary (Non-US):

JobStreet.com Pte. Ltd. (2)
1 Wallich Street 24-03 Guoco Tower, Singapore, 078881, Singapore
Tel.: (65) 6 538 0060
Web Site: https://www.jobstreet.com
Emp.: 800
Online Human Resource Consulting Services
N.A.I.C.S.: 541612
Isar Mazer *(Mng Dir-Intl Ops)*

AND PRIVATE COMPANIES — SEFALANA HOLDINGS COMPANY LIMITED

Subsidiary (Non-US):

JobStreet.com Philippines Inc. (3)
20th Floor Cybergate Center Tower 3 Robinson's Pioneer Complex, Pioneer Street, Mandaluyong, 1550, Philippines
Tel.: (63) 28 286 6222
Web Site: https://www.jobstreet.com
Online Recruitment Services
N.A.I.C.S.: 561311
Philip A. Gioca *(Country Mgr)*

PT. JobStreet Indonesia (3)
Prudential Tower 15th Floor Jl Jend Sudirman Kav 79, Jakarta, 12910, Indonesia
Tel.: (62) 218 082 5888
Web Site: https://www.jobstreet.com
Online Recruitment Services
N.A.I.C.S.: 541612

SEEK NZ Limited (1)
Level 10 2 Commerce Street, Auckland, 1010, New Zealand
Tel.: (64) 508733569
Online Job Advertising, Career Training & Human Resources Consulting Services
N.A.I.C.S.: 541810

Zhaopin Limited (1)
5th Floor First Open Plaza No 10 Furong Street, Wangjing Chaoyang District, Beijing, 100020, China
Tel.: (86) 1058692828
Web Site: https://special.zhaopin.com
Online Career-Related Website Publisher & Data Services
N.A.I.C.S.: 518210
Evan Sheng Guo *(CEO)*

SEEKA LIMITED
34 Young Road, PO Box 47, Te Puke, New Zealand
Tel.: (64) 75730303
Web Site: https://www.seeka.co.nz
SEK—(NZX)
Rev.: $159,196,614
Assets: $247,494,454
Liabilities: $143,358,141
Net Worth: $104,136,313
Earnings: $4,626,668
Emp.: 423
Fiscal Year-end: 12/31/19
Kiwi Fruit Orchard Management & Leasing Services
N.A.I.C.S.: 111339
Michael Franks *(CEO)*

Subsidiaries:

Verified Lab Services Limited (1)
234 Jellicoe Street, Industrial Park, Te Puke, New Zealand
Tel.: (64) 75738920
Web Site: http://www.vls.net.nz
Lab Services
N.A.I.C.S.: 541380

SEELEY INTERNATIONAL
112 OSullivan Beach Road, Lonsdale, 5160, SA, Australia
Tel.: (61) 883283850
Web Site: http://www.seeleyinternational.com
Year Founded: 1972
Sales Range: $25-49.9 Million
Emp.: 650
Portable & Ducted Climate Control Solutions Mfr
N.A.I.C.S.: 333415
Frank Seeley *(Founder & Chm)*

Subsidiaries:

Seeley International (Europe) Limited (1)
Hucknall Business Centre 5 Papplewick Lane, Hucknall, NG15 7TN, Nottingham, United Kingdom
Tel.: (44) 845 868 2017
Air Conditioning Equipment Installation Services
N.A.I.C.S.: 238220
Chris Ashton *(Mgr-Fin)*

Seeley International Americas (1)
1002 S 56th Ave Ste 101, Phoenix, AZ 85043
Tel.: (602) 353-8066
Web Site: http://www.convaircooler.com
Sales Range: $25-49.9 Million
Emp.: 30
Evaporative Coolers Mfr
N.A.I.C.S.: 423730
Matt Sculley *(VP)*

Seeley International Europe (ITALY) s.r.l. (1)
Via Rigutino est 194, 52100, Rigutino, Arezzo, Italy
Tel.: (39) 05759 7189
Air Conditioning Equipment Installation Services
N.A.I.C.S.: 238220
Mauro Ercoli *(Mgr-Sls-Europe, Middle East & Africa)*

Seeley International France S.A.R.L. (1)
320 avenue Berthelot, 69871, Lyon, Cedex, France
Tel.: (33) 472 7847 80
Air Conditioning Equipment Installation Services
N.A.I.C.S.: 238220

SEEN TEC CO., LTD.
64 Jungang-daero, Seongsan-gu, Changwon, Gyeongsannam-do, Korea (South)
Tel.: (82) 55 210 7000
Web Site: http://www.hansolseentec.com
Year Founded: 2001
Rev.: $119,955,644
Assets: $193,416,700
Liabilities: $152,183,812
Net Worth: $41,232,888
Earnings: $(43,086,045)
Emp.: 286
Fiscal Year-end: 12/31/17
Power Boiler Mfr
N.A.I.C.S.: 332410
Jeon Goo-Soo *(Mng Dir)*

Subsidiaries:

Hansol SeenTec Co., Ltd. - No 1 Factory (1)
531 Daebu-ro, Chilseo, Haman Gyeongsanam-do, Korea (South)
Tel.: (82) 555895800
Boiler Mfr
N.A.I.C.S.: 332410

Hansol SeenTec Co., Ltd. - No 2 Factory (1)
48 Gongdanan-gil, Chilseo, Haman Gyeongsanam-do, Korea (South)
Tel.: (82) 555895900
Boiler Mfr
N.A.I.C.S.: 332410

Hansol SeenTec Co., Ltd. - No 3 Factory (1)
80-113 Yulchonsandan 1-ro Haeryongmyeon, Suncheon, Jeollanam-do, Korea (South)
Tel.: (82) 618065319
Boiler Mfr
N.A.I.C.S.: 332410

SEERA GROUP HOLDING CO.
3730 Imam Saud bin Abdulaziz, PO Box 12476, Riyadh, 11573, Saudi Arabia
Tel.: (966) 112909303
Web Site: https://www.seera.sa
1810—(SAU)
Rev.: $605,441,168
Assets: $2,273,333,764
Liabilities: $826,162,037
Net Worth: $1,447,171,728
Earnings: $(12,196,873)
Emp.: 4,111
Fiscal Year-end: 12/31/22
Travel, Tourism, Hospitality & Cargo Services
N.A.I.C.S.: 561599

Nasser Aqeel Al Tayyar *(Founder)*

Subsidiaries:

Al Sarh Co. for Travel & Tourism Ltd. (1)
King Abdullah Road, Al Rahmaniyah Area, Riyadh, Saudi Arabia
Tel.: (966) 11 494 1111
Web Site: https://www.alsarh.com.sa
Travel & Tourism Services
N.A.I.C.S.: 561510

Al Tayyar Holiday Travel Group (1)
5 Al Obour Building Salah Salem Avenue, Cairo, Egypt
Tel.: (20) 224042118
Web Site: http://www.altayyareg.com
Tour Operator
N.A.I.C.S.: 561520

Al-Tayyar Travel & Tourism (1)
PO Box 28060, Dubai, United Arab Emirates
Tel.: (971) 4 2249240
Web Site: http://www.altayyardubai.com
Emp.: 30
Tour Operator
N.A.I.C.S.: 561520

Belantara Holidays Sdn Bhd (1)
Unit B-15-2 Block B Megan Avenue II No12 Jalan Yap Kwan Seng, 50450, Kuala Lumpur, Malaysia
Tel.: (60) 3 2166 2299
Web Site: http://www.belantaraholidays.com.my
Emp.: 20
Tour Operator
N.A.I.C.S.: 561520
Michelle Ng *(Exec Dir & Mgr-Acct & Admin)*

Elaa for Travel, Tourism & Shipping Ltd. (1)
Seera Group Takhasussi Street, Riyadh, Saudi Arabia
Tel.: (966) 92 001 2333
Web Site: https://www.elaa.sa
Travel Management Services
N.A.I.C.S.: 561599
Abdulrahman Mutrib *(Exec VP)*

Elegant Resorts Ltd. (1)
Elegant House Sandpiper Way Chester Business Park, Chester, CH4 9QE, United Kingdom
Tel.: (44) 1244757567
Web Site: https://www.elegantresorts.co.uk
Travel & Tourism Services
N.A.I.C.S.: 561510
Jemma Rigby *(Sls Mgr)*

Ian Allan Ltd. (1)
Terminal House Station Approach, Shepperton, TW17 8AS, Surrey, United Kingdom
Tel.: (44) 193 223 9200
Web Site: https://www.ianallan.com
Travel & Tourism Services
N.A.I.C.S.: 561510

If Only Holidays Ltd. (1)
Abbey House 2nd Floor 10 Bothwell Street, Glasgow, G2 6LU, United Kingdom
Tel.: (44) 1419554000
Web Site: https://www.ifonly.net
Emp.: 70
Travel Agency Services
N.A.I.C.S.: 561510
Annika Rieley *(Mktg Mgr)*

Lena Tours and Travel (1)
37 Main Office St Georges Center Ground Floor, Sin El Fil, Beirut, Lebanon
Tel.: (961) 1 496696
Web Site: http://www.lenatours.com
Tour Operator
N.A.I.C.S.: 561520

SEERS BHD
No 4 Jalan Utarid U5/18A Seksyen U5, 40150, Shah Alam, Selangor, Malaysia
Tel.: (60) 378422871
Web Site: https://www.seers.com.my
Year Founded: 2008
3009—(KLS)
Rev.: $2,353,805
Assets: $1,544,801
Liabilities: $610,784
Net Worth: $934,017
Earnings: $415,246
Fiscal Year-end: 06/30/22
Inverter Mfr
N.A.I.C.S.: 335312
Ken Foo *(Chm)*

SEETEC GROUP LTD.
Main Road, Hockley, SS5 4RG, Essex, United Kingdom
Tel.: (44) 1702 201 070
Web Site: http://www.seetec.co.uk
Year Founded: 1984
Sales Range: $25-49.9 Million
Emp.: 932
Employment & Skills Training
N.A.I.C.S.: 561311
John Baumback *(CEO)*

SEFALANA HOLDINGS COMPANY LIMITED
Plot 10038 Corner of Nelson Mandela Drive and Kubu Road, Broadhurst Industrial Site, Gaborone, Botswana
Tel.: (267) 3913661   BW
Web Site: https://www.sefalana.com
Year Founded: 1986
SEFA—(BOT)
Rev.: $665,021,082
Assets: $260,111,977
Liabilities: $89,352,213
Net Worth: $170,759,764
Earnings: $21,925,636
Emp.: 6,623
Fiscal Year-end: 04/30/23
Holding Company; Supermarket Retail Stores
N.A.I.C.S.: 551112
Chandra Chauhan *(Mng Dir)*

Subsidiaries:

Foods Botswana (Pty) Limited - Beverages (1)
Plot 25433 Block 3 Industrial, Gaborone, Botswana
Tel.: (267) 3913056
Beverage Mfr & Distr
N.A.I.C.S.: 311999

Foods Botswana (Pty.) Limited - Milling (1)
Plot 98, NewTown, Serowe, Botswana
Tel.: (267) 4630268
Nutritional Food Mfr
N.A.I.C.S.: 311919

Kgalagadi Soap Industries (Pty) Ltd. (1)
Plot 10247/50 Corner Lejara & Noko Roads, Private Bag BR 33, Broadhurst Industrial Site, Gaborone, 10247, Botswana
Tel.: (267) 3912791
Sales Range: $25-49.9 Million
Emp.: 50
Toilet & Laundry Soaps & Vegetable Cooking Oil Mfr
N.A.I.C.S.: 325611

MF Holdings (Pty) Ltd. (1)
Plot 10243 Legolo Road, Broadhurst Industrial Site, Gaborone, Botswana
Tel.: (267) 397 4336
Holding Company
N.A.I.C.S.: 551112

Holding (Domestic):

Mechanised Farming (Pty) Ltd. (2)
Plot 10243 Legolo Road, PO Box 2276, Broadhurst Industrial Site, Gaborone, Botswana
Tel.: (267) 3974336
Agricultural Supplies
N.A.I.C.S.: 424910

Refined Oil Products (Pty.) Ltd. (1)
Plot 10247/50 Corner Lejara & Noko Roads, Private Bag BR33, Broadhurst Industrial Site, Gaborone, Botswana
Tel.: (267) 3912791

SEFALANA HOLDINGS COMPANY LIMITED

Sefalana Holdings Company Limited—(Continued)
Sales Range: $50-74.9 Million
Emp.: 50
Refining & Production of Edible Oils
N.A.I.C.S.: 311224

Sefalana Cash & Carry (Namibia) (Proprietary) Limited (1)
11 Van Der Bijl Street, Northern Industrial, Windhoek, Namibia
Tel.: (264) 84 000 2000
Consumer Goods Whslr
N.A.I.C.S.: 424490
Bryan Davis (Mng Dir)

Sefalana Catering (Pty.) Limited (1)
Plot 1217 Ext 6 Nkrumah Road, Gaborone, Botswana
Tel.: (267) 3911800
Food Products Distr
N.A.I.C.S.: 424490

Sefalana Lesotho (Proprietary) Limited (1)
2 Lioli Road West Station Area, Maseru West, Maseru, Lesotho
Tel.: (266) 2 232 6223
Logistic Services
N.A.I.C.S.: 541614
Devin Serfontein (Head)

SEFAR HOLDING AG

Freibach, 9425, Thal, Switzerland
Tel.: (41) 718863232
Web Site: http://www.sefar.com
Year Founded: 1830
Sales Range: $200-249.9 Million
Emp.: 1,600
Synthetic Fabric for Screen Printing & Filtration Mfr
N.A.I.C.S.: 313230
Christoph Tobler (CEO)

Subsidiaries:

Sefar (International) AG (1)
223 Hing Fong Road Metroplaza Tower 1, Unit 3113-3116 Level 31, Kwai Fong, China (Hong Kong)
Tel.: (852) 26500581
Web Site: http://www.sefar.com
Sales Range: $25-49.9 Million
Emp.: 7
Management Consulting Services
N.A.I.C.S.: 541618
Daniel Ng (Mng Dir)

Sefar AG (1)
Hinterbissaustrasse 12, Heiden, 9410, Switzerland
Tel.: (41) 718985700
Sales Range: $200-249.9 Million
Emp.: 700
Fabricated Metal Products Mfr
N.A.I.C.S.: 332999
Christoph Tobler (Gen Mgr)

Sefar America, Inc. (1)
120 Mt Holly By-Pass, Lumberton, NJ 08048
Tel.: (609) 613-5000
Web Site: http://www.sefar.us
Sales Range: $50-74.9 Million
Emp.: 190
Synthetic Fabrics, Wire Meshes & Supplies Mfr
N.A.I.C.S.: 332618

Subsidiary (Domestic):

Sefar America Inc. (2)
4221 NE 34th St, Kansas City, MO 64177-3120 **(100%)**
Tel.: (816) 452-1520
Web Site: http://www.sefar.us
Sales Range: $75-99.9 Million
Sifting Screens & Supplies Sales & Distr
N.A.I.C.S.: 423840

Sefar Asia Pacific Co. Ltd. (1)
24th Floor Lao Peng Nguan (LPN) Tower 1 333 Soi Choei Phuang, Vibhavadi Rangsit Road Chomphon, 10900, Bangkok, Chatuchak, Thailand
Tel.: (66) 2618 8778
Web Site: http://www.sefar.com

Sales Range: $25-49.9 Million
Emp.: 16
Food & Beverages, Healthcare, Industrial & Appliances & Transportation Mfr
N.A.I.C.S.: 423830

Sefar B.V. (1)
Aalsvoort 71, PO Box 77, 7241 MB, Lochem, Netherlands
Tel.: (31) 573744111
Web Site: http://www.sefar.com
Industrial Supplies Whslr
N.A.I.C.S.: 423840

Sefar BDH Inc. (1)
200 rue Clement Gilbert, Saguenay, G7H 5B1, QC, Canada
Tel.: (418) 690-0888
Web Site: http://www.sefar.ca
Emp.: 50
Chemical Products Distr
N.A.I.C.S.: 424690
Yves Trembley (Gen Mgr)

Sefar Co. Ltd. (1)
Ohgimachi Matsushima Bldg 7th Fl, 3-13 Suehiro-cho Kita-ku, 530-0053, Osaka, Japan **(100%)**
Tel.: (81) 647091070
Web Site: http://www.sefar.com
Sales Range: $50-74.9 Million
Emp.: 6
Acoustic, Chemical & Life Sciences, Screen Printing & Transportation Services
N.A.I.C.S.: 323113

Sefar Fabrication (M) Sdn Bhd (1)
No 1 Jalan Desa Tropika 1 Taman Perindustrian Tropika, Ulu Tiram, 81800, Johor, Malaysia
Tel.: (60) 7 861 0023
Chemical Products Distr
N.A.I.C.S.: 424690
Yong Seng Yap (Mgr-Ops)

Sefar Filter Specialists Ltd (1)
24G Allright Pl, PO Box 1061, Onehunga, Auckland, 1061, Mount Wellington, New Zealand
Tel.: (64) 9 622 3330
Web Site: http://www.sefar.inz.com
Emp.: 8
Chemical Products Distr
N.A.I.C.S.: 424690
Karen Good (Office Mgr)

Sefar Filtrasyon Sanayi & Ticaret Ltd. Sirketi (1)
Tepe Prime B Blok 17 Kat No 125 Eskisehir-Devlet Yolu 9 Km, Ankara, 06800, Turkiye
Tel.: (90) 312 287 3414
Chemical Products Distr
N.A.I.C.S.: 424690

Sefar Filtration Solutions (Suzhou) Co., Ltd. (1)
2 Jingdong Road Weiting Town Suzhou Industrial Park, Weiting, Suzhou, 215121, Jiangsu, China
Tel.: (86) 512 6283 6383
Chemical Products Distr
N.A.I.C.S.: 424690

Sefar Fyltis S.A.S. (1)
89 Rue de la Villette, Postale 3175, Lyon, 69211, France
Tel.: (33) 472 13 14 15
Chemical Products Distr
N.A.I.C.S.: 424690

Sefar GmbH (1)
Am Gewerbering 22, Edling, 9456, Bavaria, Germany **(100%)**
Tel.: (49) 8071904000
Web Site: http://www.sefar.de
Sales Range: $25-49.9 Million
Emp.: 14
Weft Knit Fabric Mills
N.A.I.C.S.: 313240
Hermann Pauker (Mng Dir)

Sefar Inc. (1)
111 Calumet St, Buffalo, NY 14043
Tel.: (800) 995-0531
Chemical Products Distr
N.A.I.C.S.: 424690

Sefar India Private Limited (1)
A4 11 16 Prerana Complex Anjur Mankoli Road Val Village, Bhiwandi, 421 302, Thane, MH, India

Tel.: (91) 2522294034
Web Site: http://www.sefar.com
Nonwoven Fabric Mfr
N.A.I.C.S.: 313230
Satish Kanade (Mng Dir)

Sefar Italia SRL (1)
Via Nazione Unite 44, Collegno, 10093, Italy
Tel.: (39) 011 42 001
Chemical Products Distr
N.A.I.C.S.: 424690

Sefar Ltd. (1)
Kay Street, The Bury Business Center, Bury, BL9 6BU, Lancashire, United Kingdom **(100%)**
Tel.: (44) 1617051878
Web Site: http://www.sefar.co.uk
Sales Range: $50-74.9 Million
Emp.: 7
Industrial Supplies Whslr
N.A.I.C.S.: 423840
Joeaj Stoeckle (Mng Dir)

Sefar Maissa S.A. (1)
Avda del Valles 59-61 Sector P-2, Poligono Industrial Sud, Barcelona, 08440, Spain
Tel.: (34) 938444710
Industrial Machinery & Equipment Whslr
N.A.I.C.S.: 423830
Miguel Sancho (Mgr)

Sefar Printing Solutions Inc. (1)
120 Mt Holly By-Pass PO Box 679, Lumberton, NJ 08048
Tel.: (609) 613-5000
Web Site: http://www.sefar.com
Industrial Machinery & Equipment Whslr
N.A.I.C.S.: 423830

Sefar Printing Solutions Ltda (1)
Ave Robert Kennedy 625 Planalto, 09895-003, Sao Bernardo do Campo, Brazil **(100%)**
Tel.: (55) 1143906300
Web Site: http://www.sefar.com
Sales Range: $25-49.9 Million
Emp.: 60
Broadwoven Fabric Mills
N.A.I.C.S.: 313210
Marcel Wust (Mng Dir)

Sefar Pty Ltd (1)
PO Box 1015, Blacktown, 2148, NSW, Australia
Tel.: (61) 2 8822 1700
Web Site: http://www.sefar.com.au
Chemical Products Distr
N.A.I.C.S.: 424690

Sefar SA de CV (1)
Pablo Valdez N 1623 La Huerta 2a Seccion, 44370, Guadalajara, Mexico
Tel.: (52) 33 3543 4163
Chemical Products Distr
N.A.I.C.S.: 424690

Sefar Singapore Pte. Ltd. (1)
8 Kallang Avenue #04-03 Aperia Tower 1, Singapore, 339509, Singapore **(100%)**
Tel.: (65) 62999092
Web Site: http://www.sefar.com
Sales Range: $25-49.9 Million
Emp.: 17
Acoustic, Chemical & Life Sciences, Environmental, Mining & Refining Services
N.A.I.C.S.: 541620
Victor Pang (Reg Mgr-Sls)

Sefar Trading (Shenzhen) Co. Ltd. (1)
Room 2804-2805 28/F Tower 3A Excellence Century Center FuHua 3rd Road, Shenzhen, China
Tel.: (86) 755 2382 0322
Chemical Products Distr
N.A.I.C.S.: 424690

Sefar sp. z o.o. (1)
Garbary 56, 61-758, Poznan, Poland
Tel.: (48) 618551645
Web Site: http://www.sefar.pl
Chemical Products Distr
N.A.I.C.S.: 424690
Paawel Kwiatkowski (Gen Mgr)

SEFTON RESOURCES, INC.

1 Northumberland Avenue Trafalgar

INTERNATIONAL PUBLIC

Square, London, WC2N 5BW, United Kingdom
Tel.: (44) 2078725570 VG
Web Site: http://www.seftonresources.com
Oil & Gas Exploration & Production Services
N.A.I.C.S.: 211120
Daniel Levi (CEO)

SEGA SAMMY HOLDINGS, INC.

Sumitomo Fudosan Osaki Garden Tower 1-1-1 Nishi-Shinagawa, Shinagawa-ku, Tokyo, 141-0033, Japan
Tel.: (81) 362159955 JP
Web Site: https://www.segasammy.co.jp
Year Founded: 2004
6460—(TKS)
Rev.: $3,092,792,560
Assets: $4,322,900,340
Liabilities: $1,958,490,120
Net Worth: $2,364,410,220
Earnings: $218,493,550
Emp.: 516
Fiscal Year-end: 03/31/24
Holding Company
N.A.I.C.S.: 551112
Hajime Satomi (Chm)

Subsidiaries:

AG SQUARE, LTD. (1)
6-5-1 Nishishinjuku Shinjuku Island Tower, Shinjuku-ku, Tokyo, 160-0023, Japan
Tel.: (81) 353259113
Amusement Park Construction Services
N.A.I.C.S.: 237990

Atlus Co. Ltd. (1)
12th floor Sumitomo Fudosan Osaki Garden Tower 1-1-1 Nishi-Shinagawa, Shinagawa-ku, Tokyo, 141-0033, Japan **(62.2%)**
Tel.: (81) 368642306
Web Site: https://www.atlus.co.jp
Sales Range: $125-149.9 Million
Emp.: 325
Game Software Mfr
N.A.I.C.S.: 541512

BAKUGAN Limited (1)
Ebisu Prime Square Tower 8F 1-1-39 Hiroo, Shibuya-ku, Tokyo, 150-0021, Japan
Tel.: (81) 354254891
Web Site: http://www.bakugan.jp
Toy Mfr
N.A.I.C.S.: 339930

Butterfly Corporation (1)
Shinjuku Square Bldg 7F 27-56 Shinjuku 6-chome, Shinjuku-ku, Tokyo, 160-0022, Japan
Tel.: (81) 3 5155 5110
Web Site: http://www.butterfly-corp.jp
Sales Range: $25-49.9 Million
Emp.: 96
Mobile & Computer Games Software Development Services
N.A.I.C.S.: 541511
Atsushi Kitagawa (Exec VP)

DARTSLIVE Co., Ltd (1)
Ebisu Business Tower 18th Floor 1-19-19 Ebisu, Shibuya-ku, Tokyo, 150-0013, Japan
Tel.: (81) 334487422
Web Site: http://www.dartslive.co.jp
Gaming Machine Software Development Services
N.A.I.C.S.: 541511
Kikuo Masumoto (Pres)

Hivecreation Co., Ltd. (1)
2-1-14 Kakyoin Kakyoin Building 8F, Aoba-ku, Sendai, 980-0013, Miyagi, Japan
Tel.: (81) 22 716 8850
Web Site: https://www.hivecreation.co.jp
Dart Distr
N.A.I.C.S.: 423910

Japan Multimedia Services Corporation (1)

AND PRIVATE COMPANIES

Sales Range: $150-199.9 Million
Emp.: 900
Business Process Outsourcing Services
N.A.I.C.S.: 561990
Takatoshi Akiba *(Pres & CEO)*

MARZA ANIMATION PLANET INC (1)
Tennoz Ocean Square 18F 2-2-20 Higashi-Shinagawa, Shinagawa-ku, Tokyo, 140-0002, Japan
Tel.: (81) 363810555
Web Site: http://www.marza.com
Sales Range: $25-49.9 Million
Emp.: 150
Animated Film Production Services
N.A.I.C.S.: 512199
Akira Sugano *(Deputy COO)*

OASIS PARK Co., Ltd. (1)
1564-1 Kawashima Kasada-cho, Kakamigahara, 501-6021, Gifu, Japan
Tel.: (81) 586896766
Web Site: https://www.oasispark.co.jp
Amusement Park Operating Services
N.A.I.C.S.: 713110

Phoenix Resort Co., Ltd. (1)
3083 Hamayama O-Aza Shioji Aza Hamayama, Miyazaki, 880-8545, Japan
Tel.: (81) 98 521 1111
Web Site: https://www.seagaia.co.jp
Hotel & Resort Services
N.A.I.C.S.: 721110
Koichi Katagiri *(Pres)*

REALUS INC (1)
NBF Minami-Aoyama Bldg 8F 3-3-31, Minato-ku, Tokyo, 107-0062, Japan
Tel.: (81) 357713670
Web Site: http://www.realus.co.jp
Internet Advertising Services
N.A.I.C.S.: 541810

RODEO Co., Ltd (1)
Tel.: (81) 359581006
Web Site: http://www.rodeo.ne.jp
Emp.: 8
Gaming Machinery Mfr & Distr
N.A.I.C.S.: 333310

Rovio Entertainment Oyj (1)
Keilaranta 17, 02150, Espoo, Finland (97.7%)
Tel.: (358) 207888300
Web Site: http://www.rovio.com
Sales Range: $150-199.9 Million
Emp.: 224
Mobile Videogame Developer & Publisher
N.A.I.C.S.: 513210
Ville Heijari *(Chief Mktg Officer)*

SEGA Bee LINK Co., LTD. (1)
2-12-14 Higashikojiya Sega Honsha 3 Gokan, Ota-ku, Tokyo, 144-0033, Japan
Tel.: (81) 357367660
Web Site: http://www.bee-style.jp
Darts Bar Operating Services
N.A.I.C.S.: 722410

SEGA LOGISTICS SERVICE CO., LTD (1)
Web Site: http://www2.sls-net.co.jp
Sales Range: $25-49.9 Million
Emp.: 200
Logistics Consulting Servies
N.A.I.C.S.: 541614

SEGA SAMMY GOLF ENTERTAINMENT INC (1)
26 Rankoshi Chitose, Hokkaido, 066-0068, Japan
Tel.: (81) 123272121
Web Site: https://www.the-north.co.jp
Sales Range: $50-74.9 Million
Emp.: 100
Golf Club Operating Services
N.A.I.C.S.: 713910
Ota Yasuhiro *(Co-Pres)*

SEGA TOYS CO., LTD (1)
CS Tower 4th floor 5-20-8 Asakusabashi, Taito-ku, Tokyo, 111-0053, Japan
Tel.: (81) 358257200
Web Site: http://www.segatoys.co.jp
Sales Range: $50-74.9 Million
Emp.: 100
Game Toys Mfr
N.A.I.C.S.: 339930
Junichi Kimura *(Exec VP)*

Sammy Corporation (1)
Sun Shine 60 29F 3-1-1 Higashi-Ikebukuro, Toshima-ku, Tokyo, 170-6029, Japan (100%)
Tel.: (81) 359503790
Web Site: http://www.sammy.co.jp
Sales Range: $200-249.9 Million
Emp.: 982
Pachinko, Pachislot, Arranged-Ball, Jankyu Machines & Related Equipment Mfr & Marketer
N.A.I.C.S.: 334310
Hajime Satomi *(Chm)*

Sega Corporation (1) (100%)
Tel.: (81) 357367111
Web Site: http://www.sega.co.jp
Sales Range: $25-49.9 Million
Emp.: 100
Amusement Centers & Amusement Video Machines Mfr & Developer of Software & Games for PC's & Wireless Devices
N.A.I.C.S.: 334310

Subsidiary (Domestic):

SEGA Networks Co., Ltd. (2)
Izumi Garden Tower 9F 1-6-1 Roppongi, Minato-ku, Tokyo, 106-6009, Japan
Tel.: (81) 3 6837 1955
Web Site: http://www.sega-net.com
Mobile Video Game Developer
N.A.I.C.S.: 513210
Haruki Satomi *(CEO)*

Subsidiary (US):

Sega Networks Inc. (3)
612 Howard St, San Francisco, CA 94105
Tel.: (415) 615-9596
Mobile Video Game Publisher
N.A.I.C.S.: 513210
Chris Olson *(COO)*

Subsidiary (Domestic):

Three Rings Design, Inc. (4)
612 Howard St Ste 500, San Francisco, CA 94105
Tel.: (415) 615-9596
Web Site: http://www.threerings.net
Sales Range: $1-9.9 Million
Emp.: 20
Computer Software, Supplies & Services
N.A.I.C.S.: 513210

Subsidiary (Domestic):

Sammy NetWorks Co., Ltd. (2)
NBF Minami-Aoyama Bldg 3F 3-1-31 Minami-Aoyama, Minato-ku, Tokyo, 107-0062, Japan (54.74%)
Tel.: (81) 354143030
Web Site: http://www.sammy-net.jp
Sales Range: $100-124.9 Million
Distribution of Music & Game-Related Contents to Mobile Phones & PCs, Internet Advertising, E-Commerce & System Development
N.A.I.C.S.: 513210
Hajime Satomi *(Chm)*

Subsidiary (Non-US):

Sega Europe Ltd. (2)
27 Great West Road, Brentford, TW8 9BW, Middlesex, United Kingdom (100%)
Tel.: (44) 8081965711
Web Site: http://www.sega.co.uk
Mfr of Amusement Centers & Amusement Video Machines
N.A.I.C.S.: 334310
Mike Hayes *(CEO)*

Subsidiary (Domestic):

Sega Rosso Co., Ltd. (2)
4th Floor 2-12-14 Higashi-Koujiya, Ohta-ku, Tokyo, 144-0033, Japan
Web Site: http://www.segarosso.com
Sales Range: $25-49.9 Million
Emp.: 42
Game Software
N.A.I.C.S.: 334610

Subsidiary (US):

Sega of America Inc. (2)
6400 Oak Canyon Ste 100, Irvine, CA 92618
Tel.: (949) 788-0455
Sales Range: $125-149.9 Million
Emp.: 100
Video Games Mfr & Distr
N.A.I.C.S.: 423430
Ian Curran *(Pres & COO)*

Sega Publishing Europe Ltd. (1)
27 Great West Road, Brentford, TW8 9BW, Middlesex, United Kingdom
Tel.: (44) 845 301 5502
Web Site: https://www.sega.co.uk
Game Publishing Services
N.A.I.C.S.: 513210

Sega Sammy Creation Inc. (1)
Sumitomo Fudosan Osaki Garden Tower, 1-1-1 Nishi-Shinagawa Shinagawa-ku, Tokyo, 141-0033, Japan
Tel.: (81) 354358006
Web Site: https://www.segasammycreation.com
Casino Equipment & Software Mfr
N.A.I.C.S.: 713290

TMS ENTERTAINMENT, LTD. (1)
3-31-1 Nakano, Nakano-ku, Tokyo, 164-0001, Japan
Tel.: (81) 363826140
Web Site: http://www.tms-e.co.jp
Emp.: 225
Computer Gaming Software Development Services
N.A.I.C.S.: 541511
Hideki Okamura *(Chm)*

TMS MUSIC, CO., LTD (1)
3-31-1 Nakano, Nakano-Ku, Tokyo, 164-0001, Japan
Tel.: (81) 333191131
Gaming Machine Software Development Services
N.A.I.C.S.: 541511

TOCSIS INC (1)
18th floor Tennozu Ocean Square 2-2-20 Higashi-Shinagawa, Shinagawa-ku, Tokyo, 140-0002, Japan
Tel.: (81) 368229700
Web Site: https://www.tocsis.com
Game Machine Software Development Services
N.A.I.C.S.: 541511

TOMS PHOTO CO., LTD. (1)
5-49-4 Chuo TMS Studio Building, Nakanoku, Tokyo, 164-0011, Japan
Tel.: (81) 368788951
Web Site: https://www.tms-e.co.jp
Emp.: 41
Gaming Machine Software Development Services
N.A.I.C.S.: 541511

Taiyo Elec Co., Ltd. (1)
Uchikanda Mid Square 1-16-8, Uchikanda Chiyoda-ku, Tokyo, 101-0047, Japan
Tel.: (81) 33 293 3061
Web Site: http://www.taiyo-electric.co.jp
Electric Equipment & Machinery Mfr
N.A.I.C.S.: 335999
Shinzo Yamada *(Pres)*

Telecom Animation Film Co., Ltd. (1)
7-16-22 Shimorenjaku, Mitaka, Tokyo, Japan
Tel.: (81) 422424541
Web Site: http://www.telecom-anime.com
Sales Range: $25-49.9 Million
Emp.: 70
Animation Film Production Services
N.A.I.C.S.: 512199
Koji Takeuchi *(Pres)*

WAVEMASTER, INC (1)
Megurosumiya Bldg 4F 3-9-13 Shimomeguro, Meguro-ku, Tokyo, 153-0064, Japan
Tel.: (81) 354371517
Web Site: http://www.wave-master.com
Sales Range: $25-49.9 Million
Emp.: 15
Music Publishers
N.A.I.C.S.: 512230
Takatoshi Akiba *(Mgr)*

SEGAFREDO ZANETTI S.P.A.

Via Puccini 1, Rastignano, Bologna, 40067, Italy
Tel.: (39) 0516202111   IT
Web Site: http://www.segafredo.it
Year Founded: 1985
Sales Range: $800-899.9 Million
Emp.: 3,000
Coffee & Related Products Mfr, Marketer & Distr
N.A.I.C.S.: 311920

Subsidiaries:

BONCAFE (CAMBODIA) Ltd (1)
28A Street 21 Sangkat Tonle Basac Khan, Chamkarmorn, Phnom Penh, Cambodia
Tel.: (855) 23212316
Web Site: http://www.boncafe.com.kh
Tea & Coffee Product Distr
N.A.I.C.S.: 424490
Chan Thy *(Mng Dir)*

BONCAFE (EAST MALAYSIA) Sdn Bhd (1)
Lot 16 House No 12 Hing Industrial Estate Jalan Undan, Inanam, 88450, Kota Kinabalu, Sabah, Malaysia
Tel.: (60) 88383148
Coffee Product Distr
N.A.I.C.S.: 424490

BONCAFE (THAILAND) Ltd (1)
21st Fl Muang Thai-Phatra Tower 2 252/110-111 107 114 Rachadaphisek, Huai Khwang, Bangkok, Thailand
Tel.: (66) 26932570
Web Site: http://www.boncafe.co.th
Emp.: 50
Coffee Product Mfr & Distr
N.A.I.C.S.: 311920
Paranee Thupklang *(Mgr-Bus Dev)*

BONCAFE INTERNATIONAL Pte Ltd (1)
208 Pandan Loop, Singapore, 128401, Singapore
Tel.: (65) 6776 2216
Web Site: http://www.boncafe.com
Coffee Product Mfr & Distr
N.A.I.C.S.: 311920
Steve Lum *(Mgr-Sls)*

Subsidiary (Non-US):

Boncafe (Hong Kong) Limited (2)
410-11 Nan Fung Commercial Centre 19 Lam Kok St Kowloon Bay, Kowloon, Hong Kong, China (Hong Kong)
Tel.: (852) 24137238
Coffee Product Distr
N.A.I.C.S.: 424490
Yeung Gavin *(Mgr-Sls)*

BONCAFE MALAYSIA Sdn Bhd (1)
2 Jalan Cahaya 15 Taman Cahaya, 68000, Ampang, Selangor, Malaysia
Tel.: (60) 392853678
Coffee Product Distr
N.A.I.C.S.: 424490
Bennie Teoh *(Gen Mgr)*

BONCAFE MIDDLE EAST LLC (1)
220 Sheikh Zayed Rd, PO Box 74044, Dubai, United Arab Emirates
Tel.: (971) 47059000
Web Site: http://www.boncafeme.ae
Emp.: 200
Coffee Product Mfr & Distr
N.A.I.C.S.: 311920
Aparna Barretto *(CFO)*

Brodies Melrose Drysdale & Co. Ltd. (1)
Newhailes Industriale Estate, Newhailes Road, Musselburgh, EH21 6SY, United Kingdom
Tel.: (44) 1316534010
Coffee & Related Products Mfr, Marketer & Distr
N.A.I.C.S.: 311920

Brulerie Des Cafes Corsica S.A.S. (1)
ZI. Baleone BP 5333, 20503, Ajaccio, France
Tel.: (33) 4 9523 1303
Coffee & Related Products Mfr, Marketer & Distr
N.A.I.C.S.: 311920

Cofiroasters S.A. (1)
Cours de Rive 4, Geneva, 1204, Switzerland

SEGAFREDO ZANETTI S.P.A.

Segafredo Zanetti S.p.A.—(Continued)
Tel.: (41) 227352122
Coffee & Related Products Mfr, Marketer & Distr
N.A.I.C.S.: 311920

Distribuidora Cafe Montana S.A. (1)
Apdo: 1385-4050, Alajuela, Costa Rica
Tel.: (506) 24420000
Coffee & Related Products Mfr, Marketer & Distr
N.A.I.C.S.: 311920

KAUAI COFFEE LLC. (1)
PO Box 530, Kalaheo, HI 96741
Tel.: (808) 335-3324
Web Site: http://www.kauaicoffee.com
Emp.: 200
Coffee Product Mfr & Distr
N.A.I.C.S.: 311920
Faith Soto *(Mgr-ECommerce)*

La San Marco S.p.A. (1)
Via Padre e Figlio Venuti 10, Gradisca D'Isonzo, 34072, Gorizia, Italy
Tel.: (39) 0481967111
Web Site: http://www.lasanmarco.com
Espresso Coffee Machine & Equipment Mfr
N.A.I.C.S.: 333248

Massimo Zanetti Beverage Mexico, S.A. de C.V. (1)
Carretera Federal Libre Mazatlan-Villa Union Km 1192, 82180, Mazatlan, Sinaloa, Mexico
Tel.: (52) 6699849311
Coffee Product Distr
N.A.I.C.S.: 424490

Massimo Zanetti Beverage S.A. (1)
67 Rue De Rhone, CH 1207, Geneva, Switzerland
Tel.: (41) 227188050
Coffee & Related Products Mfr, Marketer & Distr
N.A.I.C.S.: 311920

Massimo Zanetti Beverage USA, Inc. (1)
200 Port Center Pkwy, Portsmouth, VA 23704
Tel.: (757) 215-7300
Web Site: http://www.mzb-usa.com
Sales Range: $75-99.9 Million
Emp.: 200
Coffee & Tea Products Processing, Packaging, Distr & Marketer
N.A.I.C.S.: 424490
Sarah Nolan *(Mgr)*

Meira Eesti Ou (1)
Narva Mnt 4, 10117, Tallinn, Estonia
Tel.: (372) 6616310
Web Site: http://www.meira.ee
Sales Range: $25-49.9 Million
Emp.: 5
Coffee & Related Products Mfr, Marketer & Distr
N.A.I.C.S.: 311920
Marek Lage *(Mgr)*

Meira Oy Ltd. (1)
Aleksis Kiven Katu 15, 00510, Helsinki, Finland
Tel.: (358) 207443500
Web Site: http://www.meira.fi
Emp.: 150
Coffee & Related Products Mfr, Marketer & Distr
N.A.I.C.S.: 311920
Raimo Sinisalo *(CEO)*

Nossa Senhora Da Guia Exportadora De Cafe Ltda. (1)
Rua Getulio Vargas 1528, 37925-000, Gerais, Brazil
Tel.: (55) 37 3371 1555
Coffee & Related Products Mfr, Marketer & Distr
N.A.I.C.S.: 311920

Puccino's Worldwide Ltd. (1)
Newhailes Industriale Estate, Newhailes Road, Musselburgh, EH21 6SY, United Kingdom
Tel.: (44) 1316533960
Web Site: http://www.puccinosworldwide.com
Sales Range: $25-49.9 Million
Emp.: 3

Coffee & Related Products Mfr, Marketer & Distr
N.A.I.C.S.: 311920
Ralph Lotton *(Mng Dir)*

SEGAFREDO ZANETTI NEW ZEALAND Ltd (1)
1A Arthur Brown Pl, PO Box 67141, Mount Wellington, Auckland, 1060, New Zealand
Tel.: (64) 96230063
Web Site: http://www.segafredo.co.nz
Coffee Product Distr
N.A.I.C.S.: 424490
Leesa Brewer *(Mgr-Ops)*

SEGAFREDO ZANETTI PORTUGAL - SUCURSAL EM ESPANHA Comercializacao E Distribuicao De Cafe, Sa (1)
Avenida del Sistema Solar 21 Nave 1 San Fernando de Henares, 28830, Madrid, Spain
Tel.: (34) 915982410
Coffee Product Distr
N.A.I.C.S.: 424490

SEGAFREDO ZANETTI spol. S.r.o. (1)
Trnavska cesta 50, 821 02, Bratislava, Slovakia
Tel.: (421) 244632341
Coffee Product Distr
N.A.I.C.S.: 424490

Santa Laura Exportadora de Cafe S.L.E.C SA (1)
PO. Box 73, Alajuela, Sarchi, Costa Rica
Tel.: (506) 454 1919
Web Site: http://www.segafredo.it
Coffee & Related Products Mfr, Marketer & Distr
N.A.I.C.S.: 311920

Segafredo Zanetti Argentina S.A. (1)
Avenida Triumvirato 2716/24, C1427AAN, Buenos Aires, Argentina
Tel.: (54) 11 4555 4955
Web Site: http://www.segafredoargentina.com.ar
Coffee & Related Products Mfr, Marketer & Distr
N.A.I.C.S.: 311920

Segafredo Zanetti Australia Pty Ltd. (1)
Unit 9 4 Huntley St, Alexandria, 2015, NSW, Australia
Tel.: (61) 293103664
Web Site: http://www.segafredo.com.au
Emp.: 20
Coffee & Related Product Mfr
N.A.I.C.S.: 311920

Segafredo Zanetti Austria Ges.m.b.H. (1)
Hallwanger Landestrasse 10, Salzburg, 5300, Austria
Tel.: (43) 662661.382
Web Site: http://www.segafredo.at
Sales Range: $25-49.9 Million
Emp.: 30
Coffee & Related Products Mfr, Marketer & Distr
N.A.I.C.S.: 311920

Segafredo Zanetti Belgium NV/SA (1)
Bvd Paepsem 10 A, 1070, Brussels, Belgium
Tel.: (32) 2522.0116
Web Site: http://www.segafredo.be
Sales Range: $25-49.9 Million
Emp.: 7
Coffee & Related Products Mfr, Marketer & Distr
N.A.I.C.S.: 311920
John Henrard *(Gen Mgr)*

Segafredo Zanetti Brasil (1)
Commercializacao e Distribuicao de Cafe SA, Rua Continental 400, Contagem, Brazil
Tel.: (55) 31 3326 0200
Coffee & Related Products Mfr, Marketer & Distr
N.A.I.C.S.: 311920

Segafredo Zanetti Chile S.A. (1)
Av Americo Vespucio 2760-G Conchali, Santiago, Chile

Tel.: (56) 2 5960470
Web Site: http://www.segafredochile.cl
Coffee & Related Products Mfr, Marketer & Distr
N.A.I.C.S.: 311920

Segafredo Zanetti Coffee System S.p.A. (1)
Via Preschiere 51, Conscio di Casale sul Sile, 31032, Treviso, Italy
Tel.: (39) 0422786811
Web Site: http://www.szcoffeesystem.com
Sales Range: $25-49.9 Million
Coffee Tea Hot Chocolate & Freeze-Dried Coffee Mfr
N.A.I.C.S.: 311920

Segafredo Zanetti Czech Republic spol.S.r.o. (1)
Trnavska cesta 50, 821 02, Bratislava, Slovakia
Tel.: (421) 244632341
Coffee & Related Products Mfr, Marketer & Distr
N.A.I.C.S.: 311920

Segafredo Zanetti Danmark ApS (1)
Cort Adelers Gade 1 St, 1053, Copenhagen, Denmark
Tel.: (45) 33911515
Web Site: http://www.segafredo.dk
Sales Range: $25-49.9 Million
Emp.: 5
Coffee & Related Products Mfr, Marketer & Distr
N.A.I.C.S.: 311920
Kristian Kohm *(Gen Mgr)*

Segafredo Zanetti Deutschland GmbH (1)
Furstenrieder Strasse 61, 80686, Munich, Germany
Tel.: (49) 898299250
Web Site: http://www.segafredo.de
Coffee & Related Products Mfr, Marketer & Distr
N.A.I.C.S.: 311920

Segafredo Zanetti Espania S.A. (1)
Avenida del Sistema Solar 21 Nave 1, San Fernando de Henares, 28830, Madrid, Spain
Tel.: (34) 915982410
Sales Range: $25-49.9 Million
Emp.: 50
Coffee & Related Products Mfr, Marketer & Distr
N.A.I.C.S.: 311920
Massimo Zatti *(Owner)*

Segafredo Zanetti Espresso Worldwide Japan Inc. (1)
YTT Bldg Annex, 6-14-10 Futako Takatsu-Ku, Kawasaki, 213 0002, Kanagawa, Japan
Tel.: (81) 448295277
Coffee & Related Products Mfr, Marketer & Distr
N.A.I.C.S.: 311920

Segafredo Zanetti France SAS (1)
14 Bd Industriel, PO Box 10047, 76301, Sotteville-les-Rouen, Cedex, France
Tel.: (33) 235581800
Web Site: http://www.segafredo.fr
Emp.: 260
Coffee & Related Products Marketer Mfr
N.A.I.C.S.: 311920

Segafredo Zanetti Hellas SA (1)
Protomagias 1 14568 Krioneri, Athens, 14568, Greece
Tel.: (30) 2106221428
Coffee & Related Products Mfr, Marketer & Distr
N.A.I.C.S.: 311920

Segafredo Zanetti Hungary (1)
Stefania ut 101-103, 1143, Budapest, Hungary
Tel.: (36) 14733470
Web Site: http://www.segafredo.hu
Sales Range: $25-49.9 Million
Emp.: 19
Coffee & Related Products Mfr, Marketer & Distr
N.A.I.C.S.: 311920

Segafredo Zanetti Poland (1)
Ul Partyzantow 7, 32-700, Tarnow, Poland
Tel.: (48) 1416154100

INTERNATIONAL PUBLIC

Coffee & Related Products Mfr, Marketer & Distr
N.A.I.C.S.: 311920

Segafredo Zanetti Portugal (1)
Avenida da Boavista 1681, Av Da Boavista 1681 8th Floor, Porto, 4100-132, Portugal
Tel.: (351) 226059900
Web Site: http://www.segafredo.pt
Sales Range: $25-49.9 Million
Emp.: 20
Coffee & Related Products Mfr, Marketer & Distr
N.A.I.C.S.: 311920
George Mota *(CEO)*

Segafredo Zanetti d.o.o. (1)
Spruha 44, 1236, Trzin, Slovenia
Tel.: (386) 14304975
Web Site: http://www.segafredo.se
Emp.: 6
Coffee & Related Products Mfr, Marketer & Distr
N.A.I.C.S.: 311920
Mitaja Grasez *(Gen Mgr)*

Tiktak/Segafredo Zanetti Nederland B.V. (1)
Rouaanstraat 10, 9723 CD, Groningen, Netherlands
Tel.: (31) 503176300
Web Site: http://www.tiktak-segafredo.nl
Sales Range: $25-49.9 Million
Emp.: 50
Espresso Coffee Mfr & Distr
N.A.I.C.S.: 311920
Guidof Vanas *(Gen Mgr)*

SEGECO
45 Avenue Victor Hugo Batiment 216A, 93534, Aubervilliers, France
Tel.: (33) 1 53 56 12 48
Web Site: http://www.segeco.fr
Year Founded: 1989
Rev.: $14,300,000
Emp.: 28
Women's Clothing Mfr
N.A.I.C.S.: 315250
Laurent Mouquet *(Mng Dir)*

SEGEPO COMPOSANTS MECANIQUES
Cidex 614 bis, 379 Route de Charentay, Saint-Lager, 69220, France
Tel.: (33) 474667700
Web Site: http://www.segepo.fr
Rev.: $23,200,000
Emp.: 50
Turning, Machining, Assembling, Cutting, Plastic Injection Moulding & Soldered Sub-Assembly
N.A.I.C.S.: 332721
Philippe Chapeaux *(Dir)*

Subsidiaries:

SEGEPO-REFA Sp zo.o (1)
Strefowa 2A, 58 160, Swiebodzice, Poland
Tel.: (48) 74 641 91 70
Web Site: http://www.segepo-refa.pl
Machine Tools Mfr
N.A.I.C.S.: 332721

SEGI RETECH CO.,LTD.
Geumho-eup Ogyegongdan-gil 1-67, Yeongcheon, Gyeongsangbuk-do, Korea (South)
Tel.: (82) 543348383
Web Site: http://www.sgretech.com
Year Founded: 2010
Pig Lead Mfr & Distr
N.A.I.C.S.: 331529
Chan Doo Chung *(CEO)*

SEGO RESOURCES INC.
310- 744 West Hastings Street, Vancouver, V6C 1A5, BC, Canada
Tel.: (604) 682-2933
Web Site: https://www.segoresources.com
Year Founded: 2005
SGOZF—(OTCIQ)
Assets: $4,803,526

Liabilities: $282,822
Net Worth: $4,520,704
Earnings: ($160,604)
Fiscal Year-end: 06/30/24
Mineral Exploration Services
N.A.I.C.S.: 213114
John Paul Stevenson *(CEO)*

SEGRO PLC
1 New Burlington Place, London,
W1S 2HR, United Kingdom
Tel.: (44) 2074519100
Web Site: https://www.segro.com
SGRO—(EUR)
Rev.: $945,468,316
Assets: $21,845,493,562
Liabilities: $8,081,292,603
Net Worth: $13,764,200,959
Earnings: ($319,363,797)
Emp.: 460
Fiscal Year-end: 12/31/23
Real Estate Manangement Services
N.A.I.C.S.: 531390
Phil Redding *(Chief Investment Officer)*

Subsidiaries:

Allnatt London Properties plc (1)
258 Bath Rd, Slough, SL1 4BX, Berkshire,
United Kingdom
Tel.: (44) 1753537171
Web Site: http://www.segro.com
Real Estate Manangement Services
N.A.I.C.S.: 531390

Bilton Plc (1)
Uxbridge Rd Ealing, London, W52TL,
United Kingdom **(100%)**
Tel.: (44) 2085677777
Real Estate Property Lessors
N.A.I.C.S.: 531190

Farnborough Business Park
Limited (1)
Pinehurst Rd, Farnborough, GU147BD,
Hampshire, United Kingdom **(100%)**
Tel.: (44) 1252543408
Real Estate Agents & Brokers
N.A.I.C.S.: 531210

HelioSlough Limited (1)
2 BerKeley Square, London, W1J 6EB,
United Kingdom
Tel.: (44) 2074958810
Web Site: http://www.helioslough.com
Sales Range: $50-74.9 Million
Emp.: 25
Real Estate Property Lessors
N.A.I.C.S.: 531190

Ozarow Biznes Park Sp.z.o.o. (1)
Ozarowska 40/42, 05-830, Ozarow, Poland
Tel.: (48) 227399000
Web Site: https://www.cbo.tk1.pl
Telecommunication Support Services
N.A.I.C.S.: 541618

Quail West Ltd. (1)
6289 Burnham Rd, Naples, FL 34119
Tel.: (239) 593-4100
Web Site: http://www.quailwest.com
Sales Range: $75-99.9 Million
Emp.: 170
Resort
N.A.I.C.S.: 713910

SEGRO (KNBC) Limited (1)
42 Imperial Court Kings Norton Business
Centre, Kings Norton, B30 3ES, Birmingham, United Kingdom
Tel.: (44) 121 486 1086
Web Site:
   http://www.kingsnortonbusinesscentre.com
Sales Range: $50-74.9 Million
Emp.: 12
Real Estate Development Services
N.A.I.C.S.: 531390

SEGRO (Slough Estates CR
S.r.o.) (1)
Na Prikope 9-11, 110 00, Prague, 1, Czech
Republic
Tel.: (420) 224234963
Sales Range: $50-74.9 Million
Emp.: 5
Real Estate Property Lessors

N.A.I.C.S.: 531190
Magdalena Szulc *(Reg Dir)*

SEGRO (Slough Estates Mainland
B.V.) (1)
Zandsteen 11, 2132 MZ, Hoofddorp, Netherlands
Tel.: (31) 203160160
Web Site: http://www.segro.com
Sales Range: $50-74.9 Million
Emp.: 4
Commercial Property Investment & Development
N.A.I.C.S.: 531312
Ernest Sweens *(Reg Dir)*

SEGRO BV (1)
Zandsteen 11, 2132 MZ, Hoofddorp, Netherlands
Tel.: (31) 20 3160 160
Real Estate Development Services
N.A.I.C.S.: 531390

SEGRO Belgium NV (1)
De Kleetlaan 4, Bus 8, 1831, Diegem, Belgium
Tel.: (32) 2 714 0600
Real Estate Development Services
N.A.I.C.S.: 531390

SEGRO Czech Republic s.r.o. (1)
Na Prikope 9 a 11, 110 00, Prague, Czech
Republic
Tel.: (420) 221466437
Real Estate Investment Services
N.A.I.C.S.: 531210

SEGRO France S.A. (1)
20 Rue Brunel, 75017, Paris, France
Tel.: (33) 156893131
Real Estate Investment Services
N.A.I.C.S.: 531210

SEGRO Germany GmbH (1)
Berliner Allee 51-53, 40212, Dusseldorf,
Germany **(100%)**
Tel.: (49) 21149765200
Sales Range: $50-74.9 Million
Emp.: 23
Real Estate Property Lessors
N.A.I.C.S.: 531190

SEGRO ITALY SRL (1)
Parco Tecnologico Energy Park - Building
03 Via Monza 7/a, 20871, Vimercate,
Monza and Brianza, Italy
Tel.: (39) 0 39 9633 050
Sales Range: $50-74.9 Million
Emp.: 3
Real Estate Development Services
N.A.I.C.S.: 531390
Mario Ferroni *(Gen Mgr)*

SEGRO N.V. (1)
De Kleetlaan 4 Bus 8, 1831, Diegem,
Belgium **(100%)**
Tel.: (32) 27140600
Sales Range: $50-74.9 Million
Emp.: 12
Real Estate Agents & Brokers
N.A.I.C.S.: 531210

SEGRO Poland Sp. z o.o (1)
Pl Andersa 5, 61-894, Poznan, Poland
Tel.: (48) 61 850 5300
Emp.: 20
Land Subdivision & Property Development
N.A.I.C.S.: 237210
Waldemar Witczak *(Reg Dir)*

SEGRO Properties Limited (1)
258 Bath Road, Slough, SL1 4DX, Berkshire, United Kingdom
Tel.: (44) 1753 537171
Web Site: http://www.segro.com
Real Estate Development Services
N.A.I.C.S.: 531390

Segro Developments (France)
SA (1)
20 rue Brunel, 75017, Paris,
France **(100%)**
Tel.: (33) 156893131
Web Site: http://www.segro.com
Sales Range: $25-49.9 Million
Emp.: 30
Real Estate Property Lessors
N.A.I.C.S.: 531190
Andrew Gulliford *(COO)*

Segro Estates Hungary Kft (1)
Madach Trade Ctr Bldg B 3rd Fl, 1075 Madach 13-14, 1075, Budapest, Hungary
Tel.: (36) 12146636
Real Estate Property Lessors
N.A.I.C.S.: 531190

Segro Management N.V. (1)
De Kleetlaan 4 Bus 8, 1831, Diegem,
Belgium **(100%)**
Tel.: (32) 27140600
Sales Range: $50-74.9 Million
Emp.: 4
Real Estate Agents & Brokers
N.A.I.C.S.: 531210
G. Kist *(Mng Dir)*

Slough BV (1)
Hoogbrugstraat 11, PO Box 3013, 6221 CN,
Maastricht, Netherlands **(100%)**
Tel.: (31) 433242424
Real Estate Property Lessors
N.A.I.C.S.: 531190

Sofibus Patrimoine (1)
43 rue Taitbout, 75009, Paris,
France **(96.37%)**
Tel.: (33) 1 53 20 39 99
Web Site: http://www.sofibus.fr
Sales Range: $10-24.9 Million
Commercial Real Estate Management Services
N.A.I.C.S.: 531210
Jean-Marc Costes *(CEO)*

Vailog S.R.L. (1)
Strada 3 Palazzo B3, Assago Milanofiori,
20057, Milan, Italy
Tel.: (39) 0289209009
Web Site: https://www.vailog.com
Real Estate Development Services
N.A.I.C.S.: 531210

SEGUE GROUP CO., LTD.
Sumitomo R&D Kayabacho Building
1-16-3 Shinkawa Chuo-ku, Tokyo,
104-0033, Japan
Tel.: (81) 362283822
Web Site: http://www.segue-g.jp
Year Founded: 2014
3968—(TKS)
Rev.: $123,670,870
Assets: $83,881,790
Liabilities: $55,422,530
Net Worth: $28,459,260
Earnings: $4,679,400
Emp.: 570
Fiscal Year-end: 12/31/23
Infrastructure Services
N.A.I.C.S.: 541512
Yasuyuki Aisu *(Founder, Pres & CEO)*

Subsidiaries:

J's Communication Co., Ltd. (1)
Sumitomo Real Estate Kayabacho Building
8F 1-16-3 Shinkawa, Chuo-ku, Tokyo, 104-0033, Japan
Tel.: (81) 36 222 5858
Web Site: https://www.jscom.jp
Emp.: 210
System Integration Services
N.A.I.C.S.: 541512

SEGULA TECHNOLOGIES SA
17-23 rue dArras, 92000, Nanterre,
France
Tel.: (33) 141394400
Web Site: http://www.segula.fr
Sales Range: $600-649.9 Million
Emp.: 12,000
Engineering & Innovation Consulting
Services
N.A.I.C.S.: 541330
Franck Ghrenassia *(CEO)*

Subsidiaries:

Aura Engineering Solution Co.,
Ltd. (1)
Suite 1506 Hongnan Investment Building
No 939 Jinqiao Road, Pudong, Shanghai,
China
Tel.: (86) 2161761778
Industrial Engineering Services

N.A.I.C.S.: 541330

Segula Matra Technologies (1)
8 rue Jean d'Alembert, Parc d'Activites de
Pissaloup, 78190, Trappes, Cedex, France
Tel.: (33) 1 30 68 30 68
Sales Range: $75-99.9 Million
Emp.: 400
Automotive Engineering Services
N.A.I.C.S.: 541330

Segula Technologies Canada,
Inc. (1)
50 rue Lauzon suite 500, Boucherville, J4B
1E6, QC, Canada
Tel.: (450) 857-1330
Web Site:
   http://canada.segulatechnologies.com
Industrial Engineering Services
N.A.I.C.S.: 541330

Segula Technologies Hungary
Kft. (1)
Budafoki u 187-189 Lokomotiv House B
Building, 1117, Budapest, Hungary
Tel.: (36) 709085334
Web Site:
   http://hungary.segulatechnologies.com
Industrial Engineering Services
N.A.I.C.S.: 541330

Segula Technologies Israel Ltd. (1)
HaOman 17, Hadera, 3850100, Israel
Tel.: (972) 547006305
Web Site:
   http://israel.segulatechnologies.com
Industrial Engineering Services
N.A.I.C.S.: 541330

Segula Technologies Italia Srl (1)
Via Olivetti 24/26, 00131, Rome, Italy
Tel.: (39) 0645653990
Industrial Engineering Services
N.A.I.C.S.: 541330

Segula Technologies Nederland
BV (1)
De witbogt 2, 5652 AG, Eindhoven, Netherlands
Tel.: (31) 408517500
Web Site:
   http://netherlands.segulatechnologies.com
Industrial Engineering Services
N.A.I.C.S.: 541330

Segula Technologies Russia,
LLC (1)
2-nd Khutorskaya str 38A building 9 office
316, 127287, Moscow, Russia
Tel.: (7) 8482423996
Web Site:
   http://russia.segulatechnologies.com
Industrial Engineering Services
N.A.I.C.S.: 541330

Segula Technologies Switzerland
GmbH (1)
Lerchenfeldstrasse 3, 9014, Saint Gallen,
Switzerland
Tel.: (41) 797756753
Web Site:
   http://switzerland.segulatechnologies.com
Industrial Engineering Services
N.A.I.C.S.: 541330

Segula Technologies, Inc. (1)
14841 Keel St, Plymouth, MI 48170
Tel.: (248) 686-4616
Engineering & Innovation Consulting
N.A.I.C.S.: 541330
Nick Andreou *(CEO)*

Subsidiary (Domestic):

Griswold Engineering, Inc. (2)
14841 Keel St, Plymouth, MI 48170
Tel.: (734) 404-0160
Web Site: http://griswoldengineering.com
Engineeering Services
N.A.I.C.S.: 541330
John Flannery *(Dir-Engrg)*

Technicon Design Corp. (1)
18004 Sky Park Cir, Irvine, CA 92614
Tel.: (949) 863-9618
Web Site: http://www.techniconims.com
Sales Range: $1-9.9 Million
Emp.: 35
Professional Recruitment & Associated
Technical Services

SEGULA TECHNOLOGIES SA

Segula Technologies SA—(Continued)
N.A.I.C.S.: 561330
David Shall (Pres)

SEGULAH ADVISOR AB
Besok Ostermalmstorg 1, Box 5483,
Stockholm, 114 42, Sweden
Tel.: (46) 84028700
Web Site: http://www.segulah.se
Sales Range: $10-24.9 Million
Emp.: 13
Privater Equity Firm
N.A.I.C.S.: 523999
Sebastian Ehrnrooth (Chm)

Subsidiaries:

PMC Technology A/S (1)
Lammefjordsvej 2, 6715, Esbjerg, Denmark
Tel.: (45) 7514 4444
Industrial Machinery & Equipment Mfr
N.A.I.C.S.: 333248
Ralph Timm Barfoed (Key Acct Mgr)

Segulah IV L.P. (1)
Stureplan 3, Stockholm, 114 84, Sweden
Tel.: (46) 84 02 87 00
Web Site: http://www.segulah.se
Emp.: 17
Capital Market Investment Services
N.A.I.C.S.: 523940
Sebastian Ann (Gen Mgr)

Holding (Non-US):

Balco Balcony Systems Ltd (2)
MIOC Manchester Airport Suite 15B Styal Road, Manchester, M22 5WB, United Kingdom
Tel.: (44) 1619 740462
Web Site: http://www.balcouk.com
Balcony Installation Services
N.A.I.C.S.: 238190
Micael Bengtsson (Mng Dir)

Subsidiary (Non-US):

Balco A/S (3)
Industriholmen 15 B, 2650, Hvidovre, Denmark
Tel.: (45) 57 83 13 50
Web Site: http://www.balco.dk
Balcony Installation Services
N.A.I.C.S.: 238190

Balco AB (3)
Algvagen 4, 352 45, Vaxjo, Sweden
Tel.: (46) 470 53 30 00
Web Site: http://www.balco.se
Balcony Installation Services
N.A.I.C.S.: 238190

Balco Balkonkonstruktionen GmbH (3)
Ernst-Ruska-Ufer 2, 12489, Berlin, Germany
Tel.: (49) 30 634 998 25
Web Site: http://www.balco.de
Balcony Installation Services
N.A.I.C.S.: 238190

Balco Balkonsystemen B.V. (3)
Ommeloseweg 44d, 5721 WV, Asten, Netherlands
Tel.: (31) 493 698098
Web Site: http://www.balco.nl
Balcony Installation Services
N.A.I.C.S.: 238190

Holding (Domestic):

Docu i Sverige AB (2)
Lojtnantsgatan 9, 827 81, Ljusdal, Sweden
Tel.: (46) 651 760 420
Web Site: http://www.byggfaktadocu.se
Holding Company
N.A.I.C.S.: 551112

Holding (Non-US):

KP Komponenter A/S (2)
Birkevej 2, 6971, Spjald, Denmark
Tel.: (45) 97 38 16 11
Web Site: http://www.kp-components.com
Holding Company
N.A.I.C.S.: 551112
Lars Old Jensen (CFO)

Subsidiary (US):

KP Components Inc. (3)
117 Sheriff Mill Rd, Easley, SC 29642
Tel.: (864) 644-8522
Machine Parts Whslr
N.A.I.C.S.: 332710
Stig Skov Laursen (CEO & Mng Dir)

Holding (Non-US):

Oglaend Industrier AS (2)
Engelsvollveien 264, PO Box 133, 4358, Klepp, Norway
Tel.: (47) 51 78 81 00
Web Site: http://www.oglaend-system.com
Holding Company
N.A.I.C.S.: 551112

Subsidiary (Non-US):

Oglaend Industries (Suzhou) Co., Ltd (3)
No 168 Wei Xin Road North gate, Suzhou Industrial Park, 215122, Suzhou, China
Tel.: (86) 512 62625453
Ship Building Services
N.A.I.C.S.: 336611
James Foo (Mng Dir)

Oglaend Industries Middle East LLC (3)
DIRC Offices Plot 597-201 Office G-9 Dubai Investments Park DIRC, PO Box 90456, Warehouses Unit W9-C2, Dubai, United Arab Emirates
Tel.: (971) 4 887 8134
Ship Building Services
N.A.I.C.S.: 336611
David Dickie (Mng Dir & Dir-Sls)

Oglaend Industries Snd Bhd (3)
Jalan Hulu Tinggi 26/6 Section 26 Sector A, Hicom Industrial Park, Shah Alam, Selangor, Malaysia
Tel.: (60) 3 51922049
Metal Products Mfr
N.A.I.C.S.: 332312
Fraser Campbell (Mng Dir)

Oglaend System BV (3)
Brouwerstraat 38, 2984 AR, Ridderkerk, Netherlands
Tel.: (31) 1804 14204
Ship Building Services
N.A.I.C.S.: 336611
John Witte (Mng Dir)

Oglaend System Korea Co Ltd (3)
1754 Songjung-dong, Gangseo-gu, Busan, Korea (South)
Tel.: (82) 51 832 0760
Ship Building Services
N.A.I.C.S.: 336611
Jeong-Ho Lee (Mng Dir)

Oglaend System Russia LLC (3)
Gorskoye shosse 169 k 2 lit B office 83, Levashovo, 194361, Saint Petersburg, Russia
Tel.: (7) 8123131580
Ship Building Services
N.A.I.C.S.: 336611
Oleg Veryuzhsky (CEO & Gen Mgr)

Oglaend System Singapore Pte Ltd (3)
705 Sims Drive 05-03 Shun Li Industrial Complex, Singapore, 387384, Singapore
Tel.: (65) 6748 8278
Cable Tray & Ladder Whslr
N.A.I.C.S.: 423510
Tay Kay Hong (Mng Dir)

Oglaend System UK Limited (3)
Unit 6 The Woodsbank Estate Woden Road West, Wednesbury, WS10 7SU, West Midlands, United Kingdom
Tel.: (44) 121 502 3452
Steel Product Distr
N.A.I.C.S.: 423510
Andy Foulkes (Mng Dir)

Subsidiary (US):

Oglaend System US LLC (3)
283 Lockhaven Dr Ste 201, Houston, TX 77073
Tel.: (281) 209-0678
Ship Building Services
N.A.I.C.S.: 336611

Mark Edgar (Mng Dir)

Subsidiary (Non-US):

Ogland System AB (3)
Bradgardsvagen 28, PO Box 2292, 236 32, Hollviken, Sweden
Tel.: (46) 40 45 74 60
Oil & Gas Pipeline Construction Services
N.A.I.C.S.: 237120
Bjorn Slettebo (Mgr-Bus Dev-Infrastructure)

Semantix Holdings AB (1)
Linnegatan 89E, PO Box 10059, SE 100 55, Stockholm, Sweden (94%)
Tel.: (46) 8 506 225 50
Web Site: http://www.semantix.se
Emp.: 350
Holding Company; Professional Language & Communications Services
N.A.I.C.S.: 551112
Karl Jansson (CIO)

Subsidiary (Non-US):

Semantix Finland Oy (2)
Elimaenkatu 15, FI-00510, Helsinki, Finland
Tel.: (358) 10 346 7500
Web Site: http://www.semantix.fi
Emp.: 500
Language Translation & Interpretation Services
N.A.I.C.S.: 541930
Kalle Toivonen (CEO & Country Mgr)

SEGUROS DE CREDITO Y GARANTIA S.A.
Av Victor Andres Belaunde No 147 Via Principal No 103 Office 601, Building Real Diez Centro Empresarial Real San Isidro, Lima, 18, Peru
Tel.: (51) 13993500
Web Site: http://www.secrex.com.pe
Year Founded: 1980
Credit Insurance Services
N.A.I.C.S.: 524113

SEGUROS VIDA SECURITY PREVISION SA
Apoquindo 3150, Santiago, Chile
Tel.: (56) 25842400
Web Site: http://www.vidasecurity.cl
PREVISION—(SGO)
Sales Range: Less than $1 Million
Insurance Services
N.A.I.C.S.: 524210
Francisco Silva Silva (Pres)

SEI INDUSTRIES LTD.
7400 Wilson Avenue, Delta, V4G 1H3, BC, Canada
Tel.: (604) 946-3131
Web Site: https://www.sei-ind.com
Year Founded: 1978
Rev.: $12,259,238
Emp.: 90
Industrial Fabric Products Mfr
N.A.I.C.S.: 333248

SEIBU ELECTRIC & MACHINERY CO., LTD.
3-3-1 Eki-Higashi, Koga, 811-3193, Fukuoka, Japan
Tel.: (81) 929411500
Web Site: https://www.seibudenki.co.jp
Year Founded: 1927
6144—(FKA)
Rev.: $254,806,640
Assets: $418,679,360
Liabilities: $154,231,440
Net Worth: $264,447,920
Earnings: $18,798,560
Emp.: 568
Fiscal Year-end: 03/31/22
Industrial Machinery Mfr & Distr
N.A.I.C.S.: 333248
Keishiro Miyaji (Pres)

Subsidiaries:

Seibu Paint Co., Ltd. (1)

INTERNATIONAL PUBLIC

1367-1 Wakiyama, Sawara-Ku, Fukuoka, 811-1111, Japan
Tel.: (81) 928347817
Painting Services
N.A.I.C.S.: 238320

Seiden Kousan Co., Ltd. (1)
Ekihigashi 3-3-1, Koga-Shi, Koga, 811-3102, Fukuoka, Japan
Tel.: (81) 929435411
Industrial Machinery Distr
N.A.I.C.S.: 423830
Hideo Takahara (Pres)

SEIBU ELECTRIC INDUSTRY CO., LTD.
3-7-1 Hakataeki Higashi, Hakata-ku, Fukuoka, 812-8565, Japan
Tel.: (81) 92 4183111
Web Site: http://www.seibu-denki.co.jp
Year Founded: 1947
Rev.: $481,118,400
Assets: $425,369,760
Liabilities: $162,299,760
Net Worth: $263,070,000
Earnings: $8,924,400
Emp.: 1,268
Fiscal Year-end: 03/31/18
Construction Engineering Services
N.A.I.C.S.: 541330
Kazumi Miyakawa (Chm)

SEIBU GIKEN CO., LTD.
3108-3 Aoyagi, Koga, 811-3134, Fukuoka, Japan
Tel.: (81) 929423511
Web Site: https://www.seibu-giken.com
Year Founded: 1965
6223—(TKS)
Rev.: $203,660,250
Assets: $278,878,060
Liabilities: $88,901,510
Net Worth: $189,976,550
Earnings: $24,325,790
Emp.: 348
Fiscal Year-end: 12/31/23
Air Conditioning Product Mfr & Distr
N.A.I.C.S.: 333415

SEIBU HOLDINGS INC.
11615 Minamilkebukuro, Toshima-ku, Tokyo, 171-0022, Japan
Tel.: (81) 367093100
Web Site: https://www.seibuholdings.co.jp
Year Founded: 2006
9024—(TKS)
Rev.: $3,156,922,780
Assets: $10,807,475,590
Liabilities: $7,951,076,460
Net Worth: $2,856,399,130
Earnings: $178,403,900
Emp.: 323
Fiscal Year-end: 03/31/24
Holding Company; Urban Transportation, Hotels, Leisure, Real Estate & Construction
N.A.I.C.S.: 551112
Takashi Goto (Pres & CEO)

Subsidiaries:

Izuhakone Railway Co., Ltd. (1)
300 Diba, Shizuoka, 411-8533, Japan
Tel.: (81) 559771201
Railway Freight Transportation Services
N.A.I.C.S.: 482111

Leisure Inn Penny Royal Pty. Ltd. (1)
147 Paterson St, Launceston, 7250, TAS, Australia
Tel.: (61) 36 335 6600
Web Site: https://www.leisureinnpennyroyal.com.au
Hotel Operator
N.A.I.C.S.: 721110

AND PRIVATE COMPANIES   SEIKA CORPORATION

Leisure Inn Pokolbin Resort Pty. Limited (1)
485 McDonalds Rd, Pokolbin, 2320, NSW, Australia
Tel.: (61) 24 998 7000
Web Site: https://www.leisureinnpokolbinhill.com.au
Hotel Operator
N.A.I.C.S.: 721110

Leisure Inn Spires Resort Pty. Limited (1)
100 Leura Mall, Leura, Sydney, 2780, NSW, Australia
Tel.: (61) 24 784 4999
Web Site: https://www.leisureinnspires.com.au
Hotel Operator
N.A.I.C.S.: 721110

Mauna Kea Resort Service LLC. (1)
62-100 Kauna'oa Dr Kohala Coast, Kamuela, HI 96743
Tel.: (808) 880-3490
Web Site: https://maunakearesidences.com
Resort Operator
N.A.I.C.S.: 721110
Wallene Blizzard *(Mgr-Golf & Membership Sls)*

Ohmi Railway Co., Ltd. (1)
15-1 Ekihigashimachi, Hikone, Shiga, Japan
Tel.: (81) 749223301
Web Site: https://www.ohmitetudo.co.jp
Emp.: 555
Railway Transportation Services
N.A.I.C.S.: 482112

Park Regis Cairns Pty. Ltd. (1)
6 Lake Street, Cairns, 4870, QLD, Australia
Tel.: (61) 74 042 6400
Web Site: https://www.parkregiscityquays.com.au
Hotel Operator
N.A.I.C.S.: 721110

Park Regis Griffin Pty. Ltd. (1)
604 St Kilda Road, Melbourne, 3004, VIC, Australia
Tel.: (61) 38 530 1800
Web Site: https://www.parkregisgriffinsuites.com.au
Hotel Operator
N.A.I.C.S.: 721110

Prince Hotels, Inc. (1)
3-1-5 Higashi Ikebukuro, Toshima-ku, Tokyo, 170-8440, Japan
Tel.: (81) 367419155
Web Site: https://www.princehotels.com
Home Management Services
N.A.I.C.S.: 721110
Shigeyoshi Akasaka *(Pres)*

SEIBU Railway Co., Ltd. (1)
1-11-1 Kusunokidai, Tokorozawa, 359 8520, Saitama, Japan
Tel.: (81) 429262691
Web Site: https://www.seiburailway.jp
Railway & Other Transportation
N.A.I.C.S.: 482111
Kimio Kitamura *(Pres)*

Subsidiary (Domestic):

Seibu Construction Co., Ltd. (2)
1-15-29 Jigyo, Chuo-ku, Fukuoka, 810-0064, Japan   (100%)
Tel.: (81) 927711766
Web Site: https://www.seibuken.co.jp
Real Estate Services
N.A.I.C.S.: 531390
Makoto Sato *(Pres & CEO)*

Seibu Lions Inc. (2)
2135 Kami-Yamaguchi, Tokorozawa, 359 1189, Saitama Ken, Japan
Tel.: (81) 429241155
Web Site: http://www.seibulions.co.jp
Professional Basketball Team
N.A.I.C.S.: 711211
Hajime Igo *(Pres)*

Yokohama Arena Co., Ltd. (2)
3-10 Shin-yokohama, Kohoku-ku, Yokohama, 222-0033, Kanagawa, Japan   (63%)
Tel.: (81) 45 474 4000
Web Site: http://www.yokohama-arena.co.jp
Event Organizing Services
N.A.I.C.S.: 711310

Seibu Bus Co., Ltd. (1)
546-1 Kume, Tokorozawa, 359-1131, Japan
Tel.: (81) 429958116
Bus Transportation Services
N.A.I.C.S.: 541614

Seibu Construction Supply Co., Ltd. (1)
5-2019-7 Miharacho, Tokorozawa, 359-0045, Japan
Tel.: (81) 429913260
Railway Construction Services
N.A.I.C.S.: 237990

Seibu Landscape Co., Ltd. (1)
Floor 2 of the Higashi Nagasaki Seibu Bldg 5-1-34, Toshima-ku, Nagasaki, 171-0051, Japan
Tel.: (81) 359265790
Web Site: https://www.seibu-la.co.jp
Industrial Construction Services
N.A.I.C.S.: 236210

Seibu Lions, Inc. (1)
Seibu Dome Kyujo 2135 kamiyamaguchi, Tokorozawa, 359-1153, Japan
Tel.: (81) 429241155
Home Management Services
N.A.I.C.S.: 721110

Seibu Properties, Inc. (1)
1-16-15 Minamiikebukuro Diamond Gate Ikebukuro 14th floor, Toshima-ku, Tokyo, 171-0022, Saitama, Japan
Tel.: (81) 367093500
Web Site: http://www.seibupros.jp
Property Construction Services
N.A.I.C.S.: 236116

Seibu Travel, Inc. (1)
3F Sunshine City Prince Hotel 3-1-5 Higashi-Ikebukuro, Toshima-ku, Tokyo, 170-0013, Japan
Tel.: (81) 5033549062
Web Site: https://www.seibutravel.co.jp
Travel Tour Operator
N.A.I.C.S.: 561520

StayWell Holdings Pty. Ltd. (1)
Level 10/80 Clarence Street, Sydney, 2000, NSW, Australia
Tel.: (61) 28 198 9299
Web Site: https://www.staywellgroup.com
Hotel Operator
N.A.I.C.S.: 721110
Simon Wan *(Pres)*

Yokohama Hakkeijima Inc. (1)
Hakkeijima, Kanazawa Ward, Yokohama, 236-0006, Kanagawa, Japan
Tel.: (81) 45 788 8888
Web Site: https://www.seaparadise.co.jp
Leisure Facility Services
N.A.I.C.S.: 713990

SEIGAKUSYA CO., LTD.
Kaijo Umeda Bldg 3-1-2 Nakazaki-Nishi, Kita-ku, Osaka, 530-0015, Japan
Tel.: (81) 663731529
Web Site: http://www.kaisei-group.co.jp
Year Founded: 1987
2179—(TKS)
Rev.: $86,567,534
Assets: $58,559,614
Liabilities: $35,606,201
Net Worth: $22,953,413
Earnings: $2,860,918
Fiscal Year-end: 03/31/24
Education Services
N.A.I.C.S.: 923110
Akihiro Ohta *(Pres)*

SEIHYO CO., LTD.
2434-10 Shimami-cho, Kita-ku, Niigata, 950-3102, Japan
Tel.: (81) 0252574711   JP
Web Site: https://www.seihyo.co.jp
Year Founded: 1916
2872—(TKS)
Sales Range: $25-49.9 Million
Emp.: 81
Confectioneries & Ice-Cream Mfr
N.A.I.C.S.: 311351
Sugawara Kenji *(Mng Dir)*

SEIKA CORPORATION
Shin Tokyo Building 3-3-1 Marunouchi, Chiyoda-ku, Tokyo, 100-0005, Japan
Tel.: (81) 352217101
Web Site: https://www.seika.com
Year Founded: 1947
8061—(TKS)
Rev.: $573,648,850
Assets: $783,569,230
Liabilities: $498,149,430
Net Worth: $285,419,800
Earnings: $29,672,290
Emp.: 1,040
Fiscal Year-end: 03/31/24
Industrial Machinery Mfr & Distr
N.A.I.C.S.: 333248
Masaaki Yamashita *(Sr Mng Exec Officer)*

Subsidiaries:

Ao Machinery Service GmbH (1)
Wahlerstr 10, 40472, Dusseldorf, Germany
Tel.: (49) 2114792325
Industrial Equipment Mfr
N.A.I.C.S.: 333248

Asahi Sunac Machinery Service (Thailand) Co., Ltd. (1)
57 Park Ventures Ecoplex 12F Room No 1210 Wireless Road Lumpini, Patumwan, Bangkok, 10330, Thailand
Tel.: (66) 21164600
Industrial Equipment Mfr
N.A.I.C.S.: 333248

Hydreutes, S.A.U. (1)
Avenida de San Pablo 31 Nave 18, Coslada, 28823, Madrid, Spain
Tel.: (34) 916735515
Web Site: https://hydreutes.es
Industrial Equipment Distr
N.A.I.C.S.: 423830

Japan Ejector Engineering Co., Ltd. (1)
1-2-11 Nipponbashi nishi, Naniwa-ku, Osaka, 556-0004, Japan
Tel.: (81) 666432244
Web Site: https://www.ejector.co.jp
Industrial Equipment Mfr
N.A.I.C.S.: 333248

Marine Motors & Pumps N.V. (1)
Ter Stratenweg 39, 2520, Ranst, Belgium
Tel.: (32) 34702020
Industrial Pump Mfr
N.A.I.C.S.: 333914

Ndv (Thailand) Co., Ltd. (1)
700/691 Moo 1 Tambon Phanthong, Amphur Phanthong Amata City Industrial Estate Chonburi, Chon Buri, 20160, Thailand
Tel.: (66) 38109341
Industrial Equipment Mfr
N.A.I.C.S.: 333248

Nippon Daiya Valve Co., Ltd. (1)
1-3-22 Hiromachi, Shinagawa-ku, Tokyo, 140-0005, Japan
Tel.: (81) 354345330
Emp.: 60
Semiconductor Product Mfr
N.A.I.C.S.: 334413
Hirohisa Masuda *(Pres & CEO)*

Obart Pumps Limited (1)
Obart House Liphook Way 20/20, Industrial Estate, Maidstone, ME16 0FZ, Kent, United Kingdom
Tel.: (44) 1622355000
Web Site: https://www.obartpumps.uk
Industrial Pump Mfr
N.A.I.C.S.: 333914
Mattew Hill *(Mng Dir)*

SEIKA Digital Image Corporation (1)
Koraku Kokusai Building 2F 1-5-3 Koraku, Bunkyo-ku, Tokyo, 107-0052, Japan
Tel.: (81) 338302300
Digital Equipment Distr
N.A.I.C.S.: 423990

Seika Daiya Engine Co., Ltd. (1)
8F Daiyafugen Bldg 1-1-19 Kitashinjuku, Shinjuku-ku, Tokyo, 169-0074, Japan
Tel.: (81) 359370430
Industrial Equipment Mfr
N.A.I.C.S.: 333248

Seika Machinery, Inc. (1)
21241 S Western Ave Ste 140, Torrance, CA 90501
Tel.: (310) 540-7310
Electric Equipment Mfr
N.A.I.C.S.: 334419

Seika Sangyo (Thailand) Co., Ltd. (1)
57 Park Ventures Ecoplex 12th Fl Room 1210 Wireless Rd, Lumpini Patumwan, Bangkok, 10330, Thailand
Tel.: (66) 21089818
Industrial Machinery Distr
N.A.I.C.S.: 423830
Eiji Hayashida *(Chm)*

Seika Sangyo (Vietnam) Company Limited (1)
Room 03 34th floor Bitexco Financial Tower No 02 Hai Trieu Street, Ben Nghe Ward District 1, Ho Chi Minh City, Vietnam
Tel.: (84) 2838278623
Industrial Equipment Mfr
N.A.I.C.S.: 333248
Hayashida Eiji *(Chm)*

Seika Sangyo GmbH (1)
Wahlerstr 10, 40472, Dusseldorf, Germany
Tel.: (49) 21141580
Industrial Machinery Distr
N.A.I.C.S.: 423830
Osamu Kawamoto *(Mng Dir)*

Seika Shanghai Co., Ltd. (1)
Room 2209 Building B Far East International Plaza No 317 Xianxia Road, Changning Qu, Shanghai, 200051, China
Tel.: (86) 216 235 0060
Web Site: https://www.seikachina.com
Emp.: 30
Industrial Machinery Distr
N.A.I.C.S.: 423830

Seika Trading (Shenzhen) Co., Ltd. (1)
15-F Shenfubao Building Ronghua Road, Futian Free Trade Zone, Shenzhen, 518038, China
Tel.: (86) 755 83593620
Industrial Machinery Distr
N.A.I.C.S.: 423830

Seika Ykc Circuit (Thailand) Co., Ltd. (1)
144 Moo 6 T Srimahaphot A Srimahaphot, Prachin Buri, 25140, Thailand
Tel.: (66) 37210488
Industrial Equipment Mfr
N.A.I.C.S.: 333248

Shikishimakiki Corporation (1)
18-1-35 Kita 7 Johigashi, Higashi-ku, Sapporo, 065-0007, Japan
Tel.: (81) 117119121
Emp.: 92
Industrial Equipment Distr
N.A.I.C.S.: 423830

Takemoto & Company Limited (1)
3-9-22 Sumiyoshimiyamachi Takemoto Building, Higashinada-ku, Kobe, 658-0053, Hyogo, Japan
Tel.: (81) 788415511
Industrial Equipment Mfr
N.A.I.C.S.: 333248

Ten Feet Wright Inc. (1)
2-16-11 Nihonbashi Nihonbashi Central Square 7th Floor, Chuo-ku, Tokyo, 103-0027, Japan
Tel.: (81) 368953048
Emp.: 50
Industrial Equipment Mfr
N.A.I.C.S.: 333248

Tianjin Daiya Valve Co., Ltd. (1)
No B3 Hongtai Industrial Resident No 87 Taifeng Str TEDA, Hongtai Industrial Resident, Tianjin, China
Tel.: (86) 2259813960
Industrial Equipment Mfr
N.A.I.C.S.: 333248

Tozai Jitsugyo Co., Ltd. (1)

6685

SEIKA CORPORATION

Seika Corporation—(Continued)
3F Shin Tokyo Bldg 3-3-1 Marunouchi,
Chiyoda-ku, Tokyo, 100-0005, Japan
Tel.: (81) 352217105
Industrial Equipment Mfr
N.A.I.C.S.: 333248

Tsurumi France S.A.S. (1)
994 Route de la gare, 13770, Venelles,
France
Tel.: (33) 442540876
Web Site: https://tsurumi-france.fr
Industrial Pump Mfr
N.A.I.C.S.: 333914

Tsurumi-Intec Pump AB (1)
Produktionsvagen 4, 262 96, Angelholm,
Sweden
Tel.: (46) 102065010
Industrial Pump Mfr
N.A.I.C.S.: 333914

SEIKAGAKU CORPORATION
10F Marunouchi Center Building
1-6-1 Marunouchi, Chiyoda-ku, To-
kyo, 100-0005, Japan
Tel.: (81) 352208950
Web Site:
https://www.seikagaku.co.jp
Year Founded: 1947
4548—(TKS)
Rev.: $239,367,930
Assets: $540,664,950
Liabilities: $62,880,930
Net Worth: $477,784,020
Earnings: $14,449,460
Emp.: 988
Fiscal Year-end: 03/31/24
Pharmaceutical Product Mfr & Distr
N.A.I.C.S.: 325412
Ken Mizutani *(Pres & CEO)*

Subsidiaries:

Associates of Cape Cod, Inc. (1)
Falmouth Technology Park 124 Bernard E
Saint Jean Dr, East Falmouth, MA 02536-
4445
Tel.: (508) 540-3444
Web Site: https://www.acciusa.com
Pharmaceutical Product Mfr & Distr
N.A.I.C.S.: 325412

Seikagaku Corporation - Kurihama Plant (1)
3-1 Kurihama 9-chome, Yokosuka, 239-
0831, Kanagawa, Japan
Tel.: (81) 468353311
Medicinal Ingredient Mfr
N.A.I.C.S.: 325411

Seikagaku Corporation - Takahagi Plant (1)
258-5 Aza-Matsukubo Oaza-Akahama,
Takahagi, 318-0001, Ibaraki, Japan
Tel.: (81) 293231181
Medicinal Ingredient Mfr
N.A.I.C.S.: 325411

SEIKITOKYU KOGYO CO., LTD.
2-9-3 Shibakoen, Minato-ku, Tokyo,
105-8509, Japan
Tel.: (81) 367704029
Web Site:
https://www.seikitokyu.co.jp
Year Founded: 1950
1898—(TKS)
Rev.: $581,924,570
Assets: $502,637,620
Liabilities: $234,714,490
Net Worth: $267,923,130
Earnings: $18,111,400
Emp.: 995
Fiscal Year-end: 03/31/24
Pavement Construction Services
N.A.I.C.S.: 237310
Kiichi Taira *(Pres & CEO)*

Subsidiaries:

ST Services CO., Ltd. (1)
92b Chittaranjan Avenue 2nd Floor, Kol-
kata, 700 012, West Bengal, India
Tel.: (91) 3322360095
Web Site: https://www.stservices.org.in
Cash & Financial Services
N.A.I.C.S.: 541611

SEIKO CORPORATION
2-8-1 Tenjin, Shimizu-ku, Shizuoka,
424-0809, Shizuoka, Japan
Tel.: (81) 543661030
Web Site: https://www.seiko-co.com
Year Founded: 1939
6286—(TKS)
Rev.: $238,533,134
Assets: $187,400,014
Liabilities: $86,818,608
Net Worth: $100,581,406
Earnings: $5,147,009
Fiscal Year-end: 03/31/24
Packaging Machinery Mfr
N.A.I.C.S.: 333993
Hiroyuki Suzuki *(Vice Chm)*

Subsidiaries:

SEIKO CORPORATION - Fujikawa Plant (1)
837-6 Kitamatsuno, Fuji, 421-3301, Shi-
zuoka, Japan
Tel.: (81) 545851122
Electric Power Tool Mfr
N.A.I.C.S.: 333991

SEIKO CORPORATION - Mishima Plant (1)
270 Matsumoto, Mishima, 411-0822, Shi-
zuoka, Japan
Tel.: (81) 559771515
Packaging Machinery Mfr
N.A.I.C.S.: 333993

SEIKO ELECTRIC CO., LTD.
2-7-25 Toko, Hakata-ku, Fukuoka,
812-0008, Japan
Tel.: (81) 924738831
Web Site: https://www.seiko-denki.co.jp
Year Founded: 1921
6653—(TKS)
Rev.: $191,933,390
Assets: $203,872,950
Liabilities: $110,199,870
Net Worth: $93,673,080
Earnings: $8,522,180
Emp.: 990
Fiscal Year-end: 12/31/23
Electronic Equipment Mfr & Distr
N.A.I.C.S.: 335999
Naonori Tsuchiya *(Chm)*

Subsidiaries:

Beijing Seiko Electric Group Co., Ltd. (1)
Beijing Fortune Building No 5 North Street
East 3rd Ring Road, Chaoyang District, Bei-
jing, China
Tel.: (86) 1065287656
Control Device Mfr & Distr
N.A.I.C.S.: 335314
Hirohumi Yamaguchi *(Gen Mgr)*

Dalian Seiko Electric Control Co., Ltd. (1)
No 12 North-East 4th St Dalian Economic
Technical Development Zone, Dalian,
116600, China
Tel.: (86) 41166775900
Switchgear Mfr & Distr
N.A.I.C.S.: 335313
Hidehiro Goto *(Gen Mgr)*

Seiko Electric Co., Ltd. - Koga Factory (1)
20-1 3-Chome Tenjin, Koga, 811-3197, Fu-
kuoka, Japan
Tel.: (81) 929437181
Electronic Control Device Mfr
N.A.I.C.S.: 334513

Seiko Electric Construction Co., Ltd. (1)
24-25 Wakahisa 5-chome, Minami-ku, Fu-
kuoka, 815-0042, Japan
Tel.: (81) 925115101
Electrical & Machinery Services
N.A.I.C.S.: 238210
Yukihiro Okuhata *(Pres)*

Seiko IT Solution Co., Ltd. (1)
7-25 Toko 2chome, Hakata-ku, Fukuoka,
812-0008, Japan
Tel.: (81) 924732282
Software Publishing Services
N.A.I.C.S.: 513210
Katsutoshi Arie *(Pres)*

Seiko IT Solutions Philippines Inc. (1)
Antel Global Corporate Center 3 Dona Julia
Vargas Avenue, Ortigas Center, Pasig, Phil-
ippines
Tel.: (63) 2687692
System Integration Services
N.A.I.C.S.: 541512

Seiko Service & Engineering Co., Ltd. (1)
2-7-25 Toko, Hakata-ku, Fukuoka, 812-
0008, Japan
Tel.: (81) 924114761
Web Site: https://www.seiko-se.co.jp
Emp.: 43
Industrial Machinery Equipment Distr
N.A.I.C.S.: 423610

Trytec Corporation (1)
Tel.: (81) 932456386
Electronic Control Device Mfr
N.A.I.C.S.: 334513
Hiroaki Matsuo *(Pres)*

SEIKO EPSON CORPORATION
3-3-5 Owa Suwa, Nagano, 392-8502,
Japan
Tel.: (81) 266523131   JP
Web Site: https://global.epson.com
Year Founded: 1942
SE7—(DEU)
Rev.: $9,538,473,270
Assets: $9,619,092,750
Liabilities: $4,403,082,660
Net Worth: $5,216,010,090
Earnings: $538,115,670
Emp.: 79,906
Fiscal Year-end: 03/31/23
Development, Manufacturing, Sales,
Marketing & Servicing of Information-
Related Equipment, Electronic De-
vices & Other Products
N.A.I.C.S.: 334111
Minoru Usui *(Chm)*

Subsidiaries:

Epmall Co, Ltd. (1)
10F No 287 Nanking E Rd, Sec 3, 105, Tai-
pei, Taiwan
Tel.: (886) 2 27177370
Computer & Software Sales
N.A.I.C.S.: 449210

Epsodecua Cia, Ltda. (1)
Shyris N36-120 y Suecia Edificio Allure
Park Of 18 en el PH, Quito, Ecuador
Tel.: (593) 2 602 3070
Computer Peripheral Product Mfr
N.A.I.C.S.: 334118

Epson (China) Co., Ltd. (1)
4th Floor Building 1 China Central Place No
81 Jianguo Road, Chaoyang District, Bei-
jing, 100025, China
Tel.: (86) 108 522 1199
Web Site: https://www.epson.com.cn
Emp.: 16,000
Electronic Components Distr & Mfr
N.A.I.C.S.: 334118
Qingwen Xiaochi *(Chm)*

Epson (Shanghai) Information Equipment Co., Ltd. (1)
2 F No 140 Hedan Road, Shanghai Wai
Gao Qiao, Shanghai, 200131, China
Tel.: (86) 400 8109 9779
Computer & Software Sales
N.A.I.C.S.: 449210

Epson (Thailand) Co., Ltd. (1)
195 24th Floor Empire Tower Building
South Sathorn Road, Yannawa Sathorn,
Bangkok, 10120, Thailand
Tel.: (66) 2 6700680
Computer & Software Sales
N.A.I.C.S.: 449210

Epson (U.K.) Ltd. (1)
Westside London Road, Hemel Hempstead,
HP3 9TD, Hertfordshire, United
Kingdom   (100%)
Tel.: (44) 3439037766
Web Site: http://www.epson.co.uk
Sales Range: $750-799.9 Million
Emp.: 250
Office Products Sales & Service
N.A.I.C.S.: 449210
Phil McMullin *(Mgr-Sls-Pro Graphics Bus Unit)*

Epson America Inc. (1)
3131 Katella Ave, Los Alamitos, CA 90720
Tel.: (562) 981-3840
Web Site: https://www.epson.com
Sales Range: $1-4.9 Billion
Emp.: 500
Printer, Scanner & Component Product
Marketer & Distr
N.A.I.C.S.: 423430
Keith Kratzberg *(Pres & CEO)*

Division (Domestic):

Epson America Robotics Division (2)
18300 Central Ave, Carson, CA 90746-4008
Tel.: (562) 290-5900
Web Site: http://www.epson.com
Sales Range: $25-49.9 Million
Emp.: 25
Warehouse of Precision Assembly Robots
N.A.I.C.S.: 493110

Subsidiary (Non-US):

Epson Canada Limited (2)
185 Renfrew Drive, Markham, L3R 6G3,
ON, Canada   (100%)
Tel.: (416) 498-9955
Web Site: http://www.epson.ca
Emp.: 90
Computer Printers & Accessories Mfr
N.A.I.C.S.: 449210
Andrea Zoeckler *(CFO & COO)*

Subsidiary (Domestic):

Epson Electronics of America Inc. (2)
2580 Orchard Pkwy, San Jose, CA
95131   (100%)
Tel.: (408) 922-0200
Web Site: http://www.eea.epson.com
Sales Range: $25-49.9 Million
Emp.: 44
Sales & Technical Support for Semiconduc-
tors in the U.S.
N.A.I.C.S.: 423690

Epson Portland Inc. (2)
3950 NE Aloclek Dr, Hillsboro, OR 97124-
7100
Tel.: (503) 645-1118
Web Site: http://www.epi.epson.com
Sales Range: $75-99.9 Million
Emp.: 320
Mfr of Computers
N.A.I.C.S.: 334118
Toru Ushiyama *(Pres)*

Epson Research & Development Inc. (2)
169 Myers Corners Rd, Wappingers Falls,
NY 12590
Tel.: (845) 296-1590
Sales Range: $25-49.9 Million
Emp.: 15
Electronic Components Mfr
N.A.I.C.S.: 334419

K-Sun Corporation (2)
370 SMC Dr, Somerset, WI 54025
Tel.: (715) 247-4440
Web Site: http://www.ksun.com
Sales Range: $1-9.9 Million
Emp.: 25
Office Equipments Mfr
N.A.I.C.S.: 339940
Linda Law *(Pres)*

Epson Argentina, SRL (1)
Centro EPSON de Servicios, Av Belgrano
970, 1092, Buenos Aires, Argentina

AND PRIVATE COMPANIES — SEIKO EPSON CORPORATION

Tel.: (54) 11 5167 0300
Computer & Software Sls
N.A.I.C.S.: 449210

Epson Australia Pty. Ltd. (E.A.L.) (1)
Level 1 3 Talavera Road, Macquarie Park, 2113, NSW, Australia
Tel.: (61) 28 899 3666 **(100%)**
Web Site: https://www.epson.com.au
Sales Range: $300-349.9 Million
Emp.: 110
Sales & Service for Epson Brand & OEM in Australia & New Zealand
N.A.I.C.S.: 449210
Craig Heckenberg *(Mng Dir)*

Epson Chile S.A. (1)
La Concepcion 322, Piso 3, Santiago, Chile
Tel.: (56) 2 484 3400
Computer & Software Sls
N.A.I.C.S.: 449210

Epson Colombia Ltda. (1)
Calle 100 No 19-54 Piso 7, Bogota, Colombia
Tel.: (57) 1523 5000
Computer & Software Sls
N.A.I.C.S.: 449210

Epson Costa Rica, S.A. (1)
Pavas San Jose 1361-1200, San Jose, Costa Rica
Tel.: (506) 2210 9555
Computer & Software Sales
N.A.I.C.S.: 449210

Epson Deutschland GmbH (1)
Otto-Hahn-Str 4, 40670, Meerbusch, Germany **(100%)**
Tel.: (49) 21595380
Web Site: http://www.epson.de
Sales Range: $50-74.9 Million
Emp.: 200
Sales & Service for Epson Brand & OEM Products
N.A.I.C.S.: 449210

Epson Europe B.V. (1)
Azie Building Atlas Arena, Hoogoorddreef 5, 1101, Amsterdam, Netherlands
Tel.: (31) 203145000
Computer & Software Sales
N.A.I.C.S.: 449210
Rob Clark *(Sr VP)*

Epson Europe Electronics GmbH (1)
Riesstrasse 15, 80992, Munich, Germany
Tel.: (49) 8 914 0050
Web Site: https://www.epson-electronics.de
Emp.: 49
Electronic Device Mfr & Distr
N.A.I.C.S.: 334419
Hideki Nakamura *(Pres)*

Epson France S.A. (E.F.S.) (1)
150 rue Victor Hugo, BP 320, 92305, Levallois-Perret, Cedex, France
Tel.: (33) 821017017
Web Site: http://www.epson.fr
Sales Range: $50-74.9 Million
Emp.: 120
Computer & Software Sales
N.A.I.C.S.: 449210

Epson Hong Kong Ltd. (1)
Unit 715-723 Trade Square 681 Cheung Sha Wan Road, Kowloon, China (Hong Kong) **(100%)**
Tel.: (852) 25854600
Web Site: http://www.epson.com.hk
Sales Range: $50-74.9 Million
Emp.: 150
Sales & Service for Epson Brand & OEM Products in Hong Kong, China & the Philippines
N.A.I.C.S.: 449210

Epson Iberica, S.A. (1)
Avda. de Roma 18-26 08290 Cerdanyola del Valles, Barcelona, Spain
Tel.: (34) 3 582 1500
Computer & Software Sls
N.A.I.C.S.: 449210

Epson India Pvt. Ltd. (1)
304 3rd Floor Windfall Sahar Plaza Complex J B Nagar, Andheri East, Mumbai, 400059, India
Tel.: (91) 223 079 8200
Web Site: https://www.epson.co.in
Computer & Software Sales

N.A.I.C.S.: 327910
Samba Moorthy *(Pres)*

Epson Italia S.p.A. (1)
V le F Lli Casiraghi, Sesto Giovanni Mi, 427 20099, Milan, Italy
Tel.: (39) 02 262331
Computer & Software Sls
N.A.I.C.S.: 449210

Epson Korea Co., Ltd. (1)
27/F Star Tower, 737 Yeoksam-dong, 135984, Seoul, Korea (South)
Tel.: (82) 2 558 4270
Computer & Software Sales
N.A.I.C.S.: 449210

Epson Malaysia Sdn. Bhd. (1)
3rd Floor East Tower Wisma Consplant 1 No 2 Jalan SS 16/4, 47500, Subang Jaya, Malaysia
Tel.: (60) 3 56 288 288
Web Site: http://www.epson.com.my
Emp.: 80
Computer & Software Sales
N.A.I.C.S.: 449210

Epson Malaysia Sdn. Bhd. (1)
Wisma Kyoei Prince 16th Floor, Jl Jend Sudirman Kav 3, Jakarta, 10220, Indonesia
Tel.: (62) 21 5723161
Computer & Software Sales
N.A.I.C.S.: 449210

Epson Mexico, S.A. de C.V. (1)
Boulevard Manuel Avila Camacho No 389 Conjunto Legaria Edificio, 1 Col Irrigacion, Mexico, 11510, Mexico
Tel.: (52) 5513232000
Computer & Software Sales
N.A.I.C.S.: 449210

Epson New Zealand Ltd. (1)
Level 2 7-9 Fanshawe Street, Auckland, 1010, New Zealand
Tel.: (64) 9 366 6855
Web Site: http://www.epson.co.nz
Computer & Software Sales
N.A.I.C.S.: 449210

Epson Paulista Ltda. (1)
Tucunare 720 Bloco 1, Tambore, Barueri, 6460020, Brazil
Tel.: (55) 114196 6409
Computer & Software Sales
N.A.I.C.S.: 449210

Epson Peru, S.A. (1)
Av Canaval y Moreyra 590, Lima, Peru
Tel.: (51) 1418 0210
Computer & Software Sales
N.A.I.C.S.: 449210

Epson Philippines Corporation (1)
8th Floor Anson's Center, 23 ADB Avenue Ortigas Center, Pasig, 1605, Philippines
Tel.: (63) 2 7062609
Computer & Software Sales
N.A.I.C.S.: 449210

Epson Precision (Hong Kong) Ltd. (1)
21-33 Tai Lin Pai Road, Hong Kong, China (Hong Kong)
Tel.: (852) 489 9119
Computer & Software Sales
N.A.I.C.S.: 449210

Epson Precision (Johor) Sdn. Bhd. (1)
No. 31 A, Jalan Kempas, Kempas Baru, Johor, 81200, Malaysia
Tel.: (60) 7 237 0933
Emp.: 1,500
Computer & Software Sls
N.A.I.C.S.: 449210
Sheko Epson *(COO)*

Epson Precision (Philippines) Inc. (1)
Lot 1 Blk 3 T5 Ampere St, Cabuyao, Philippines
Tel.: (63) 2 843 0358
Computer & Software Sls
N.A.I.C.S.: 449210

Epson Precision Malaysia Sdn. Bhd. (1)
3rd Floor East Tower Wisma Consplant 1 No 2 Jalan SS 16/4, 47500, Subang Jaya, Malaysia

Tel.: (60) 35 628 8288
Web Site: https://www.epson.com.my
Emp.: 1,921
Printer Mfr
N.A.I.C.S.: 333248

Epson Singapore Pte., Ltd. (ESP) (1)
1 HarbourFront Place 03-02 HarbourFront Tower 1, Singapore, 098633, Singapore **(100%)**
Tel.: (65) 65865500
Web Site: http://www.epson.com.sg
Sales Range: $50-74.9 Million
Emp.: 180
Sales & Service for Epson Brand & OEM Products in Singapore, Malaysia, Indonesia, Thailand & India
N.A.I.C.S.: 449210

Epson Taiwan Technology & Trading Ltd. (1)
15th Floor No 100 Songren Road, Xinyi District, Taipei, 110, Taiwan
Tel.: (886) 287866688
Web Site: http://www.epson.com.tw
Sales Range: $50-74.9 Million
Emp.: 200
Sales & Service for Epson Brand Products in Taiwan
N.A.I.C.S.: 449210

Epson Telford Ltd. (1)
Hortonwood 30, Telford, TF1 7YD, United Kingdom
Tel.: (44) 1952 670066
Computer & Software Sls
N.A.I.C.S.: 449210

Epson Toyocom Corporation (1)
421 8 Hino, Hino Shi, Tokyo, 191 8501, Japan **(100%)**
Tel.: (81) 425811707
Web Site: http://www.epsontoyocom.co.jp
Sales Range: $350-399.9 Million
Emp.: 1,700
Digital Telecommunications & Electrical Products Mfr
N.A.I.C.S.: 334220

Subsidiary (US):

Epson Electronics America (2)
1827 Walden Office Sq, Schaumburg, IL 60173
Tel.: (847) 925-8350
Sales Range: $25-49.9 Million
Emp.: 4
Mfr of Electronic Components
N.A.I.C.S.: 423690

Subsidiary (Non-US):

Epson Toyocom (Thailand) Ltd. (2)
239-239/1 Moo 7 Gateway City Industrial Estate, T. Huasamrong A Pleang Yao, 24190, Chachoengsao, Thailand
Tel.: (66) 3857 5440 44
Computer & Software Sls
N.A.I.C.S.: 449210

Epson Toyocom (Wuxi) Co.,Ltd. (2)
No 36 Changjiang Road Wuxi State, High&Technology Industrial Dev, Wuxi, China
Tel.: (86) 51085221818
Computer & Software Sls
N.A.I.C.S.: 449210

Epson Toyocom Malaysia Sdn.Bhd (2)
Lot 1,Jalan Persiaran Industri Taman Perindustrian, Sri Damansara Sungai Buloh, 52200, Kuala Lumpur, Malaysia
Tel.: (60) 3 6273 3550
Computer & Software Sls
N.A.I.C.S.: 449210

Oriental Electronics Device Co., Ltd. (2)
Bangchan Industrial Estate 30 1 Moo 14 Serithai Rd, T Minburi A Minburi, Bangkok, 10510, Thailand
Tel.: (66) 29199929
Sales Range: $50-74.9 Million
Emp.: 150
N.A.I.C.S.: 334220

P.T. Toyocom Indonesia (2)
Lot 293 Jalan Bungur, Batamindo Industrial Park, Muka Kuning, 29433, Batam, Indonesia
Tel.: (62) 770612112
Sales Range: $200-249.9 Million
Emp.: 600
N.A.I.C.S.: 334220

Toyocom Asia Pte. Ltd. (2)
1 Harbour Frnt Pl, 03 02 Harbour Frnt, Singapore, 347719, Singapore
Tel.: (65) 65865500
Sales Range: $1-9.9 Million
Emp.: 5
Electronic Components Manufacturing
N.A.I.C.S.: 334220

Subsidiary (Domestic):

Toyocom Engineering Co., Ltd. (2)
8-31 Ichinomiya 5-chome Samukawamachi, Koza, 253-0111, Kanagawa, Japan
N.A.I.C.S.: 334220

Subsidiary (Non-US):

Toyocom Europe GmbH (2)
Bollenhohe 5, D 40822, Mettmann, Germany
Tel.: (49) 210491890
Sales Range: $10-24.9 Million
Emp.: 12
N.A.I.C.S.: 334220

Subsidiary (Domestic):

Toyocom Trading Co., Ltd. (2)
484 Tsukagoshi 3 Chome, Saiwai Ku, Kawasaki, 212 0024, Kanagawa, Japan
Tel.: (81) 445426500
Sales Range: $200-249.9 Million
Emp.: 550
N.A.I.C.S.: 334220

Epson Venezuela, S.A. (1)
calle 4 Con Calle 11, La Urbina Sur, Caracas, Venezuela
Tel.: (58) 2241 0433
Computer & Software Sales
N.A.I.C.S.: 449210

Epson Vietnam Co., Ltd. (1)
10th Floor Savico Tower 66-68 Nam Ky Khoi Nghia, Nguyen Thai Binh Ward District 1, Ho Chi Minh City, Vietnam
Tel.: (84) 283 925 5545
Web Site: https://www.epson.com.vn
Printer Mfr
N.A.I.C.S.: 333248

Epson de Mexico, S.A. de C.V. (1)
Boulevard Manuel Avila Camacho No 389 Conjunto Legaria Edificio 1, Col Irrigacion, 11510, Mexico, Mexico
Tel.: (52) 1 323 2000
Web Site: https://www.epson.com.mx
Computer Peripheral Product Mfr
N.A.I.C.S.: 334118

Epson do Brasil Industria e Comercio Ltda. (1)
Av Tucunare 720, 06460 020, Barueri, Brazil
Tel.: (55) 114196 6350
Computer & Software Sls
N.A.I.C.S.: 449210

P.T.Epson Batam (1)
Perum Muka Kuning Indah Blok BL 22, Batam, Indonesia
Tel.: (62) 812 70491387
Computer & Software Sls
N.A.I.C.S.: 449210

PT. Epson Indonesia (1)
CIBIS Tower 9 3rd Floor CIBIS Business Park Jl T B Simatupang No 2, Jakarta Selatan, 12560, Indonesia
Tel.: (62) 218 086 6766
Web Site: https://www.epson.co.id
Printer Mfr
N.A.I.C.S.: 333248

Philippines Epson Optical Inc. (1)
SEPZ Gateway Business Park, General Trias, Cavite, Philippines
Tel.: (63) 4 643 3000
Computer & Software Sls
N.A.I.C.S.: 449210

Shanghai Epson Magnetics Co., Ltd. (1)

SEIKO EPSON CORPORATION

Seiko Epson Corporation—(Continued)

No 3210 North Road, Jiading, Shanghai, 201807, China
Tel.: (86) 2159927369
Web Site: http://en.semag-sh.com.cn
Emp.: 800
Computer & Software Sls
N.A.I.C.S.: 449210

Singapore Epson Industrial Pte. Ltd. (1)
86 & 88 Second Lok Yang Road, Jurong, Singapore, 628162, Singapore
Tel.: (65) 62682164
Web Site: http://www.epson-plating.com.sg
Emp.: 197
Computer & Software Sls
N.A.I.C.S.: 449210
John Loh Kwong Yong *(Gen Mgr-Plating Div)*

Suzhou Epson Co., Ltd. (1)
186 Jinfeng Road, New Area, Suzhou, China
Tel.: (86) 51268257002
Computer & Software Sls
N.A.I.C.S.: 449210

Tianjin Epson Co., Ltd. (1)
214 Hong Qi Road, Tianjin, 300190, Nankai, China
Tel.: (86) 2227633924
Computer & Software Sls
N.A.I.C.S.: 449210

Time Tech (Hong Kong) Ltd. (1)
7/F Ying Tung Bldg 802, Lai Chi Rd, Hong Kong, China (Hong Kong)
Tel.: (852) 2208 5307
Computer & Software Sales
N.A.I.C.S.: 449210

epService Co., Ltd. (1)
5F-1 No 700 Zhongzheng Road, Taipei, 235, Taiwan
Tel.: (886) 2 82273300
Computer & Software Sales
N.A.I.C.S.: 449210

SEIKO GROUP CORPORATION

26-1 Ginza 1-chome, Chuo-ku, Tokyo, 104-8110, Japan
Tel.: (81) 335632111 JP
Web Site: https://www.seiko.co.jp
Year Founded: 1881
8050 (TKS)
Rev.: $1,829,694,270
Assets: $2,487,091,820
Liabilities: $1,486,774,080
Net Worth: $1,000,317,740
Earnings: $66,437,110
Emp.: 11,740
Fiscal Year-end: 03/31/24
Watches, Clocks & Precision Products Mfr
N.A.I.C.S.: 423940
Shinji Hattori *(Chm & CEO)*

Subsidiaries:

Asian Electronic Technology Pte. Ltd. (1)
2 Marsiling Lane, Singapore, 739144, Singapore
Tel.: (65) 63680098
Watch Whslr
N.A.I.C.S.: 423510

CRONOS INC. (1)
7F Kanda Kajicho Building 1-8-8 Kajicho, Chiyoda-ku, Tokyo, 101-0044, Japan
Tel.: (81) 335258100
Web Site: https://www.cronos.co.jp
Emp.: 486
Watches & Jewelry Retailer
N.A.I.C.S.: 458310

Chino Watch Co., Ltd. (1)
2-6-15 Dogenzaka Shibuya, Tokyo, 150-0043, Japan
Tel.: (81) 33 464 1848
Web Site: https://www.c-watch.co.jp
Watch Whslr
N.A.I.C.S.: 423510
Toku Chino *(CEO)*

City Service Co., Ltd. (1)
8 Nakase 1-chome, Mihama-ku, Chiba, 261-8507, Japan
Tel.: (81) 432111435
Watch Whslr
N.A.I.C.S.: 423510

Dalian Seiko Instruments Inc. (1)
No 9 Dongbei Third Street, Dalian Economic and Technical Development Zone, Dalian, 116600, China
Tel.: (86) 41187613000
Watch Mfr
N.A.I.C.S.: 316990

IIM Corporation (1)
Seiko Kyobashi East Building 3-6-1 Hatchobori, Chuo-ku, Tokyo, 104-0032, Japan
Tel.: (81) 368584710
Web Site: https://www.iim.co.jp
Emp.: 153
Computer System Operation Services
N.A.I.C.S.: 541513

Muang Thong Seiko Ltd. (1)
1091 286 New Petchburi Rd, Makkasan Rajthevi, Bangkok, 10400, Thailand
Tel.: (66) 22551250
Web Site: http://www.seiko.co.th
Sales Range: $50-74.9 Million
Emp.: 120
Provider of Watches & Clocks
N.A.I.C.S.: 334519
Puripurik Mahagun *(Gen Mgr)*

SEIKO CLOCK INC. (1)
Fukuzumi 2-4-3, Koto-ku, Tokyo, 135-8610, Japan
Tel.: (81) 3 5639 6500
Web Site: http://www.seiko-clock.co.jp
Emp.: 170
Clocks Mfr & Whslr
N.A.I.C.S.: 334519
Kenji Hagiwara *(Pres)*

SEIKO NPC CORPORATION (1)
2-9-4 Taito, Taito-ku, Tokyo, 110-0016, Japan
Tel.: (81) 367475300
Web Site: http://www.npc.co.jp
Sales Range: $100-124.9 Million
Emp.: 214
Semiconductor Equipment Mfr
N.A.I.C.S.: 334413
Kimio Yomogida *(Sr VP)*

Unit (Domestic):

SEIKO NPC CORPORATION - Nasushiobara Unit (2)
531-1 Shimotano, Nasushiobara, 329-2811, Tochigi, Japan
Tel.: (81) 287353111
Semiconductor Product Mfr
N.A.I.C.S.: 334413
Tatsuo Mori *(Pres)*

SEIKO OPTICAL PRODUCTS CO., LTD. (1)
Higashinari Building 18-10 Nihonbashi Hakozakicho, Chuo-ku, Tokyo, 103-0015, Japan
Tel.: (81) 367472001
Web Site: https://www.seiko-opt.co.jp
Emp.: 486
Optical Lenses & Frames Whslr
N.A.I.C.S.: 423460

SEIKO SERVICE CENTER CO., LTD. (1)
1-12-13 Shinohashi, Koto-ku, Tokyo, 135-0007, Japan
Tel.: (81) 356242111
Watch Repair Services
N.A.I.C.S.: 811490

SEIKO TIME SYSTEMS INC. (1)
Fukuzumi 2-4-3, Koto-ku, Tokyo, 135-8610, Japan
Tel.: (81) 356461500
Web Site: http://www.seiko-sts.co.jp
Emp.: 120
Sports Counting Device Mfr
N.A.I.C.S.: 334514
Ryozo Suenaga *(Exec VP)*

SII Crystal Technology Inc. (1)
1110 Hirai-cho, Tochigi, 328-0054, Japan
Tel.: (81) 28 224 1212
Web Site: http://www.sii.co.jp
Electronic Components Mfr

N.A.I.C.S.: 334419
Kazuhisa Onishi *(Pres)*

Seiko (Thailand) Co., Ltd. (1)
2032 Ital-Thai Tower Building 2nd Floor New Petchburi Road, Bangkapi Huaykwang, Bangkok, 10310, Thailand
Tel.: (66) 22551245
Web Site: http://www.seiko.co.th
N.A.I.C.S.: 423510

Seiko Australia Pty. Ltd. (1)
89 Epping Road, Macquarie Park, 2113, NSW, Australia (100%)
Tel.: (61) 29 805 4666
Web Site: https://www.seiko.com.au
Sales Range: $25-49.9 Million
Emp.: 50
Distr of Watches & Clocks
N.A.I.C.S.: 423940
Garry Manou *(Mgr-Ops)*

Seiko Belgium S.A. (1)
Blvd Paepsem 18 A, 1070, Brussels, Belgium (100%)
Tel.: (32) 24681323
Web Site: http://www.seiko.be
Sales Range: $25-49.9 Million
Emp.: 14
Provider of Clocks & Watches
N.A.I.C.S.: 334519

Seiko Clock (Shenzhen) Co., Ltd. (1)
Unit 501 5/F Sail Plaza No 1052 Nan Hai Road, Nan Shan District, Shenzhen, Guang Dong, China
Tel.: (86) 75586608700
Clock Mfr
N.A.I.C.S.: 316990

Seiko Corporation of America (1)
1111 McArthur Blvd, Mahwah, NJ 07430-2038 (100%)
Tel.: (201) 529-5730
Web Site: http://www.seikousa.com
Sales Range: $75-99.9 Million
Emp.: 245
Distr of Watches & Clocks
N.A.I.C.S.: 423940
Yosh Kawada *(Pres & CEO)*

Seiko France S.A. (1)
9 Chemin De Palente, 25075, Besancon, Cedex 9, France (100%)
Tel.: (33) 381542420
Web Site: https://www.seikowatches.com
Sales Range: $25-49.9 Million
Emp.: 60
Provider of Watches & Clocks
N.A.I.C.S.: 334519
Arvi Lorenzo *(Mgr)*

Seiko Hong Kong Ltd (1)
Ying Tung Industrial Building 8th Floor, 802 Lai Chi Kok Road, Kowloon, China (Hong Kong) (100%)
Tel.: (852) 25211111
Web Site: http://www.seiko.com
Sales Range: $75-99.9 Million
Emp.: 200
Distr of Watches
N.A.I.C.S.: 423940
S. Sato *(Mng Dir)*

Seiko Instruments (Shanghai) Inc. (1)
2701-2703 Shanghai Square No 138 Mid Huaihai Rd, Shanghai, 200021, China
Tel.: (86) 2163756611
Watch Mfr
N.A.I.C.S.: 316990

Seiko Instruments (Thailand) Ltd. (1)
60/83 Moo 19 Nava-Nakorn, Industrial Estate Zone 3 Klong Nueng Klong Luang, Pathumthani, 12120, Thailand
Tel.: (66) 25292420
Emp.: 1,016
Watch Whslr
N.A.I.C.S.: 423510

Seiko Instruments Technology (Shanghai) Inc. (1)
3F 168 Meisheng Road, Wai Gaoqiao Free Trade Zone, Shanghai, 200131, China
Tel.: (86) 2158660322
Watch Whslr
N.A.I.C.S.: 423510

INTERNATIONAL PUBLIC

Seiko Instruments Trading (H.K.) Ltd. (1)
4-5/F Wyler Centre 2 200 Tai Lin Pai Rd, Kwai Chung N T, Kowloon, China (Hong Kong)
Tel.: (852) 24945111
Electronic Components Mfr
N.A.I.C.S.: 334419

Seiko Instruments, Inc. (1)
8 Nakase 1-chome, Mihama-ku, Chiba, 261-8507, Japan
Tel.: (81) 432111111
Web Site: https://www.sii.co.jp
Emp.: 3,313
N.A.I.C.S.: 334419
Shinji Nureki *(Exec VP)*

Subsidiary (Domestic):

Morioka Seiko Instruments Inc. (2)
61-1 Itabashi Shizukuishi-ch, Iwate-gun, Iwate, 020-0596, Japan (100%)
Tel.: (81) 196923511
Web Site: https://www.morioka-seiko.co.jp
Sales Range: $10-24.9 Million
Emp.: 750
Watch Component Mfr
N.A.I.C.S.: 334519

Subsidiary (Domestic):

Ninohe Tokei Kogyo Co., Ltd. (3)
67-12 Uwanotai Shimotomai, Ninohe-shi, Iwate, 028-6102, Japan (100%)
Tel.: (81) 195254621
Watch Component Factory
N.A.I.C.S.: 334519

Tono Seiki Co., Ltd. (3)
11-14 Shimokumi-cho, Tono-shi, Iwate, 028-0526, Japan (100%)
Tel.: (81) 198622327
Web Site: http://www.sii.co.jp
Watch Component Mfr
N.A.I.C.S.: 334519

Subsidiary (Domestic):

SII Printek Inc. (2)
563 Takatsuka-shinden, Matsudo, Chiba, 270-2222, Japan
Tel.: (81) 473923795
Sales Range: $1-9.9 Million
Inkjet Printer Cartridge Research & Mfr
N.A.I.C.S.: 333248
Yoshihiro Takeda *(Pres)*

Seiko I Infotech Inc. (2)
8 Nakase 1-chome Mihama-ku, Chiba, 261-8507, Japan
Tel.: (81) 432111363
Sales Range: $125-149.9 Million
Emp.: 347
Network Computer Peripherals & Consumables Mfr, Sls & Maintenance
N.A.I.C.S.: 334118
Satoshi Sakata *(Pres)*

Subsidiary (Non-US):

Seiko Instruments (H.K.) Ltd. (2)
4-5/F Wyler Centre 2 200 Tai Lin Pai Road, Kwai Chung, 999077, NT, China (Hong Kong)
Tel.: (852) 24945111
Web Site: http://www.sih.com.hk
Sales Range: $50-74.9 Million
Emp.: 200
Batteries, CMOS IC, LCD/LCD Module, Micro Printer, Fiber Optics, Quartz Crystals
N.A.I.C.S.: 334419
Marianna Yeung *(Gen Mgr)*

Seiko Instruments GmbH (2)
Siemensstr 9, 63263, Neu-Isenburg, Germany
Tel.: (49) 6 102 2970
Web Site: https://www.seiko-instruments.de
Sales Range: $25-49.9 Million
Emp.: 50
CMOS IC, LCD/LCD Module, Micro Printer, Fiber Optics, Batteries, Quartz Crystals
N.A.I.C.S.: 334419
Frank Kuehn *(Mng Dir)*

Seiko Instruments Singapore Pte. Ltd. (2)
2 Marsiling Lane, Singapore, 739144, Singapore

Tel.: (65) 6 269 6906
Web Site: http://www.sii.com.sg
Sales Range: $50-74.9 Million
Emp.: 554
Batteries, LCD/LCD Module, Fiber Optics, Quartz Crystals, Micro Printer
N.A.I.C.S.: 334419
Hiroshi Nakahara *(Mng Dir)*

Subsidiary (Non-US):

Instruments Technology (Johor) Sdn. Bhd. (3)
No 16 Jalan Petaling, Larkin Industrial Estate, 80350, Johor Bahru, Johor, Malaysia
Tel.: (60) 72363166
Emp.: 682
Watch Component Mfr
N.A.I.C.S.: 334519
Hidekazu Kazama *(Gen Mgr)*

Subsidiary (Non-US):

Seiko Instruments Taiwan, Inc. (2)
2F No 143 Changchun Rd, Taipei, 10491, Taiwan
Tel.: (886) 225635001
Web Site: http://www.sii.com.tw
Sales Range: $25-49.9 Million
Emp.: 40
Batteries, LCD/LCD Module, Micro Printer, Fiber Optics, Quartz Crystals
N.A.I.C.S.: 334419

Subsidiary (US):

Seiko Instruments USA, Inc. (2)
21221 S Western Ave Ste 250, Torrance, CA 90501
Tel.: (310) 517-7700
Web Site: http://www.seikoinstruments.com
Sales Range: $25-49.9 Million
Emp.: 35
Watch & Electronic Components Mfr
N.A.I.C.S.: 334519

Seiko Italia- sede secondaria italiana di Seiko France SAS (1)
Via Giovanni da Udine 34, 20156, Milan, Italy
Tel.: (39) 0238093471
Watch Whslr
N.A.I.C.S.: 423510

Seiko Manufacturing (H.K.) Ltd. (1)
4-5/F Wyler Centre 2 200 Tai Lin Pai Rd, Kwai Chung, China (Hong Kong)
Tel.: (852) 24945111
Web Site: https://www.timemodule.com
Watch Mfr
N.A.I.C.S.: 316990

Seiko Manufacturing (Singapore) Pte. Ltd. (1)
2 Marsiling Lane, Singapore, 739144, Singapore
Tel.: (65) 6 269 6906
Web Site: https://www.seiko-mfg.sg
Emp.: 498
Watch Mfr
N.A.I.C.S.: 316990
Hiroyuki Kihara *(Mng Dir)*

Seiko NPC Corporation (1)
Rm N513 5F No 9 Lane 3 Minsheng West Road, Zhongshan District, Taipei, 104-49, Taiwan
Tel.: (886) 225232281
Watch Mfr & Whslr
N.A.I.C.S.: 316990

Seiko Nederland B.V. (1)
Daniel Pichotstraat 17-31, 3115 JB, Schiedam, Netherlands (100%)
Tel.: (31) 104009899
Web Site: http://www.seiko.nl
Sales Range: $25-49.9 Million
Emp.: 70
Watches & Clocks Service Provider
N.A.I.C.S.: 334519
P. Daniels *(Dir-Comml)*

Seiko Panama S.A. (1)
Torre de las Americas Lobby Punta Pacifica, PO Box 081906949, Panama, El Dorado, Panama (100%)
Tel.: (507) 2042000
Web Site: http://www.seikowatches.com
Sales Range: $25-49.9 Million
Emp.: 17
Provider of Watches & Clocks

N.A.I.C.S.: 334519
Shingo Sato *(Gen Mgr)*

Seiko Precision (Thailand) Co., Ltd. (1)
104 Moo 18 Nava Nakorn Industrial Estate Zone 3, Klongnueng Klongluang, Pathumthani, 12120, Thailand
Tel.: (66) 25292162
Web Site: https://www.seiko-spt.co.th
Clock Mfr
N.A.I.C.S.: 316990

Seiko Precision Hong Kong Ltd. (1)
Unit 903-907 9/F Laws Commercial Plz 788, Cheung Sha Wan Rd, Kowloon, China (Hong Kong)
Tel.: (852) 23102812
Web Site: http://www.seiko-precision.com.hk
Sales Range: $25-49.9 Million
Emp.: 20
Distr of Watch & Clock Movements
N.A.I.C.S.: 423940

Seiko S.A. (1)
Rue De La Marbrerie 3, PO Box 1336, Carouge, CH 1227, Geneva, Switzerland (100%)
Tel.: (41) 223089850
Mfr & Distributor of Clocks & Watches
N.A.I.C.S.: 334519

Seiko Solutions Inc. (1)
1-8 Nakase, Mihama-ku, Chiba, 261-8507, Japan
Tel.: (81) 432733111
Web Site: https://www.seiko-sol.co.jp
Emp.: 1,864
Information Technology Consulting Services
N.A.I.C.S.: 541512

Seiko Taiwan Co., Ltd. (1)
7F No 90 Sec 1 Jianguo N Road, Jian Guo N Rd, Taipei, 10491, Taiwan (100%)
Tel.: (886) 225046969
Web Site: http://www.seiko.com.tw
Sales Range: $25-49.9 Million
Emp.: 54
Provider of Watches & Clocks
N.A.I.C.S.: 334519

Seiko Time Labs Co., Ltd. (1)
1-12-13 Shinohashi, Koto-ku, Tokyo, 135-0007, Japan
Tel.: (81) 356246500
Web Site: http://www.seiko-stl.co.jp
Watch Whslr
N.A.I.C.S.: 423510

Seiko UK Limited (1)
SC House Vanwall Road, Maidenhead, SL6 4UW, Berkshire, United Kingdom (100%)
Tel.: (44) 1628770001
Web Site: http://www.seikowatches.com
Sales Range: $75-99.9 Million
Emp.: 150
Distr of Watches & Clocks
N.A.I.C.S.: 423940
Mark Brion *(Mgr-Sls)*

Branch (Non-US):

Seiko Deutschland GmbH (2)
Siemensring 44m, 47877, Willich, Germany (100%)
Tel.: (49) 2154943701
Web Site: http://seiko-boutique.de
Sales Range: $25-49.9 Million
Emp.: 50
Watches & Clocks Distr
N.A.I.C.S.: 423940

Seiko Wach Europe B.V. (1)
Daniel Pichotstraat 17-31, 3115 JB, Schiedam, Netherlands
Tel.: (31) 80076873
Watch Mfr & Distr
N.A.I.C.S.: 334519

Seiko Watch (Shanghai) Co., Ltd. (1)
16/F Tower 2 Enterprise Centre No 209 Gong He Road, Jing'an District, Shanghai, 200070, China
Tel.: (86) 2162720688
Watch Whslr
N.A.I.C.S.: 423510

Seiko Watch Corporation (1)
26-1 Ginza 1-chome, Chuo-ku, Tokyo, 104-8118, Japan (100%)

Tel.: (81) 33 564 2111
Web Site: https://www.seikowatches.com
Emp.: 6,057
Mfr of Watches & Clocks
N.A.I.C.S.: 334519
Atsushi Kaneko *(Sr VP)*

Seiko Watch India Pvt. Ltd. (1)
Temple Vista 874 Sree Krishna Temple Road Indiranagar 1st Stage, Bengaluru, 560038, India
Tel.: (91) 8041493900
Watch Whslr
N.A.I.C.S.: 423510

Seiko Watch of America LLC (1)
1111 Macarthur Blvd, Mahwah, NJ 07430
Tel.: (201) 529-5730
Watch Whslr
N.A.I.C.S.: 423510

WAKO CO., LTD. (1)
4-5-11 Ginza, Chuo-ku, Tokyo, 104-8105, Japan
Tel.: (81) 335622111
Web Site: http://www.wako.co.jp
Emp.: 300
Jewelry & Gift Accessories Distr

SEIKO PMC CORPORATION
Wakamatsu Building 8th Floor 3-6 Nihonbashi Honcho 3-chome, Chuoku, Tokyo, 103-0023, Japan
Tel.: (81) 362027331 JP
Web Site: http://www.seikopmc.co.jp
Year Founded: 1968
4963—(TKS)
Rev.: $232,437,060
Assets: $333,813,690
Liabilities: $110,769,330
Net Worth: $223,044,360
Earnings: $11,808,990
Emp.: 711
Fiscal Year-end: 12/31/22
Paper Making Chemicals Mfr
N.A.I.C.S.: 325998
Seido Kan *(Pres)*

Subsidiaries:

KJ Chemicals Corporation (1)
2nd floor Wakasue Building 3-3-6 Nihonbashi Honmachi, Chuo-Ku, Tokyo, 100-0023, Japan
Tel.: (81) 332423018
Web Site: https://www.kjchemicals.co.jp
Emp.: 116
Chemical Product Mfr & Distr
N.A.I.C.S.: 325199

Plant (Domestic):

KJ Chemicals Corporation - Yatsushiro Plant (2)
1-3 Koukokumachi, Yatsushiro, 866-0881, Kumamoto, Japan
Tel.: (81) 965339752
Chemical Products Mfr
N.A.I.C.S.: 325998

Seiko PMC (Shanghai) Commerce & Trading Corp. (1)
Room 905 No 1065 Zhaojiabang Road, Xuhui District, Shanghai, 200030, China
Tel.: (86) 2152283211
Papermaking Chemical Mfr
N.A.I.C.S.: 325180

Seiko PMC (Zhangjiagang) Corporation (1)
68-Nanhai Road, Jiangsu Yangtze River International Chemicals Park, Zhangjiagang, 215633, Jiangsu, China
Tel.: (86) 51258937260
Papermaking Chemical Mfr
N.A.I.C.S.: 325180

Seiko PMC Corporation - Akashi Plant (1)
1-1 Tateishi 1-chome, Akashi, 673-0032, Hyogo, Japan
Tel.: (81) 789258626
Chemical Products Mfr
N.A.I.C.S.: 325998

Seiko PMC Corporation - Chiba Plant (1)

12 Yahatakaigan-dori, Ichihara, 290-0067, Chiba, Japan
Tel.: (81) 436412346
Chemical Products Mfr
N.A.I.C.S.: 325998

Seiko PMC Corporation - Harima Plant (1)
47-2 Niijima, Harimacho Kakogun, Hyogo, 675-0155, Japan
Tel.: (81) 794377687
Chemical Products Mfr
N.A.I.C.S.: 325998

Seiko PMC Corporation - Iwai Plant (1)
28 Koujindaira, Bando, 306-0608, Ibaraki, Japan
Tel.: (81) 297359910
Chemical Products Mfr
N.A.I.C.S.: 325998

Seiko PMC Corporation - Mizushima Plant (1)
8252-40 Tamashima-otoshima, Shinminato, Kurashiki, 713-8103, Okayama, Japan
Tel.: (81) 865227822
Chemical Products Mfr
N.A.I.C.S.: 325998

Seiko PMC Corporation - Ryugasaki Plant (1)
3-1 Koyodai 5-chome, Ryugasaki, 301-0852, Ibaraki, Japan
Tel.: (81) 297642331
Chemical Products Mfr
N.A.I.C.S.: 325998

Seiko PMC Corporation - Shizuoka Plant (1)
4386-1 Utsubusa, Fujinomiya, 419-0317, Shizuoka, Japan
Tel.: (81) 544652310
Chemical Products Mfr
N.A.I.C.S.: 325998

Total Acrylic Polymer Industry Corporation (1)
No 7 Kung-Yeh 5th Rd Ping-Zhen Industrial Park, Taoyuan, 32459, Taiwan
Tel.: (886) 34692301
Papermaking Chemical Mfr
N.A.I.C.S.: 325180

SEIKOH GIKEN CO., LTD.
296-1 Matsuhidai Matsudo City, Chiba, 270-2214, Japan
Tel.: (81) 473115111
Web Site: https://www.seikoh-giken.co.jp
Year Founded: 1972
6834—(TKS)
Rev.: $104,338,850
Assets: $213,013,860
Liabilities: $33,314,400
Net Worth: $179,699,460
Earnings: $5,030,210
Emp.: 752
Fiscal Year-end: 03/31/24
Mold Mfr
N.A.I.C.S.: 333511
Masatoshi Ueno *(Pres & CEO)*

Subsidiaries:

Fuji Electronics Industries Co., Ltd. (1)
4-8-1 Toshinden, Suruga-ku, Shizuoka, 421-0112, Japan
Tel.: (81) 542572804
Web Site: https://www.fuji-ele.co.jp
Automotive & Electronic Precision Compound Molding & Precision Press Molding Components Mfr
N.A.I.C.S.: 332999
Masaharu Hirata *(Pres)*

Seikoh Giken Dalian Co., Ltd. (1)
No 36 Fuan Street Economic Technological, Development Area, Dalian, 116600, China
Tel.: (86) 41187304777
Fiber Optic Products Mfr
N.A.I.C.S.: 333248

Seikoh Giken Europe GmbH (1)
Siemensstrasse 9, 63263, Neu-Isenburg, Germany

SEIKOH GIKEN CO., LTD.

Seikoh Giken Co., Ltd.—(Continued)
Tel.: (49) 6102297700
Compact Disc Whslr
N.A.I.C.S.: 423990

Seikoh Giken Hangzhou Co., Ltd. (1)
526 Binkang Road, Binjiang District, Hangzhou, 310052, Zhejiang, China
Tel.: (86) 57187774098
Compact Disc Whslr
N.A.I.C.S.: 423990

Seikoh Giken USA, Inc. (1)
4465 Commerce Dr Ste 103, Buford, GA 30518
Tel.: (770) 279-6602
Compact Disc Whslr
N.A.I.C.S.: 423990

SEILON, INC.
1881 Steeles Avenue Suite 364, Toronto, M3H 0A1, ON, Canada
Tel.: (307) 459-1908
Year Founded: 1998
SEIL—(OTCIQ)
Sales Range: Less than $1 Million
Television Broadcasting Services
N.A.I.C.S.: 516120

SEINO HOLDINGS CO., LTD.
1 Taguchicho, Ogaki, 503-8501, Gifu, Japan
Tel.: (81) 584823881 JP
Web Site: http://www.seino.co.jp
Year Founded: 1930
9076—(TKS)
Rev.: $4,248,980,710
Assets: $4,557,760,250
Liabilities: $1,678,596,280
Net Worth: $2,879,163,970
Earnings: $96,248,210
Fiscal Year-end: 03/31/24
Transportation Services
N.A.I.C.S.: 485999
Yoshitaka Taguchi *(Chm, Pres & CEO)*

Subsidiaries:

Asahi Create Co., Ltd. (1)
Kagano 4-1-16 Seino Softopia Building 4F, Ogaki, 503-0006, Gifu, Japan
Tel.: (81) 584823555
Web Site: https://www.asahicreate.co.jp
Commercial Printing
N.A.I.C.S.: 323111

Asahi Enterprise Co., Ltd. (1)
Hakata Mitsui Building, 2go-Kan 2nd Floor, 812-0025, Fukuoka, Japan
Tel.: (81) 922910038
Parking Lots & Garages
N.A.I.C.S.: 812930

Box Charter Co., Ltd. (1)
Arte Building Shibadaimon 4f, Minato-Ku, Tokyo, Japan
Tel.: (81) 462924003
General Freight Trucking, Long-Distance, Truckload
N.A.I.C.S.: 484121

Central Logistics Co., Ltd. (1)
Logistics Consulting Servies
N.A.I.C.S.: 541614

Cosmo Hokuriku Haiso Center Co., Ltd. (1)
1-33-6 Higashikagatsumemachi, Kanazawa, 920-0209, Ishikawa, Japan
Tel.: (81) 762377230
Freight Trucking Services
N.A.I.C.S.: 484121

Eco Alliance Co., Ltd. (1)
5-7-10 Kotobashi, Sumida-ku, Tokyo, 503-0853, Gifu, Japan
Tel.: (81) 336338077
Web Site: https://www.seino.co.jp
Transportation Services
N.A.I.C.S.: 488999

Enshu Seino Transportation Co., Ltd. (1)
245 Shiratori-cho, Higashi-ku, Hamamatsu, 435-0002, Shizuoka Prefecture, Japan
Tel.: (81) 534216471
Local Freight Trucking
N.A.I.C.S.: 484110

Gifu Hino Motor Co., Ltd. (1)
4522-1 Maki Anpachi-cho, Anpachi-gun, Gifu, 503-0125, Japan
Tel.: (81) 584646888
Web Site: https://www.gifuhino.co.jp
Automobile & Motor Vehicle Whslr
N.A.I.C.S.: 423110
Takao Taguchi *(Pres)*

Hinomaru Seino Transportation Co., Ltd. (1)
3-40 Higashi Koyamacho, Tottori, Tottori Prefecture, Japan
Tel.: (81) 857282221
Local Freight Trucking
N.A.I.C.S.: 484110

Hokkaido Seino Transportation Co., Ltd. (1)
15-14-4-1 Hassamu, Nishi-ku, Sapporo, 063-0835, Hokkaido, Japan
Tel.: (81) 116643112
Web Site: https://www.hokkaido-seino.co.jp
Couriers
N.A.I.C.S.: 492110
Shoji Okada *(Mgr)*

Kanto Seino Transportation Co., Ltd. (1)
16-1 Itahana, Annaka, Annaka, Japan
Tel.: (81) 273823311
Local Freight Trucking
N.A.I.C.S.: 484121

Kyushu Seino Transportation Co., Ltd. (1)
1-1-56 Iaida, Hakata Ward, Fukuoka, 812-0881, Fukuoka Prefecture, Japan
Tel.: (81) 925911650
Web Site: https://www.kyushu-seino.co.jp
Emp.: 1,672
Local Freight Trucking
N.A.I.C.S.: 484110

Living Pro-Seed, Ltd. (1)
3-23 Kioicho Bungeishunju Bldg Shinkan, Chiyoda-ku, Tokyo, 102-0094, Japan
Tel.: (81) 352169411
Web Site: http://www.lps.co.jp
Newspaper Publishing Services
N.A.I.C.S.: 513110

Mie Seino Transportation Co., Ltd. (1)
Emp.: 2
Logistics Consulting Servies
N.A.I.C.S.: 541614
Hironori Matsutara *(Mgr)*

Mitsubishi Electric Logistics Corporation (1)
(66.6%)
Web Site: http://www.mdlogis.co.jp
Emp.: 997
Logistic & Delivery Support Services
N.A.I.C.S.: 541614
Shoichiro Hara *(Pres & CEO)*

Miyagi Seino Transportation Co., Ltd. (1)
51-1 Azagakkomae, Kanomata Ishinomaki, Miyagi, Japan
Tel.: (81) 225865781
Sales Range: $25-49.9 Million
Emp.: 130
Couriers
N.A.I.C.S.: 492110

Netz Toyota Centro Gifu Co., Ltd. (1)
4-81 Miyake Ginan-cho, Hashima-gun, Gifu, 501-6002, Japan
Tel.: (81) 120246851
Web Site: http://www.netzgifu.jp
Emp.: 595
Motor Vehicle Dealers
N.A.I.C.S.: 441227

Netz Toyota Gifu Co., Ltd. (1)
4-81 Miyake Ginancho, Hashima-Gun, Gifu, Japan
Tel.: (81) 582463111
Motor Vehicle Dealers
N.A.I.C.S.: 441227

Nohi Seino Transportation Co., Ltd. (1)
1 Ikeda-cho, Seki, 501-3247, Gifu, Japan (100%)
Tel.: (81) 575231711
Web Site: https://www.nouhi-seino.co.jp
Emp.: 1,394
Local Freight Trucking
N.A.I.C.S.: 484110
Yoshitaka Taguchi *(CEO)*

Okinawa Seino Transportation Co., Ltd. (1)
7-8-8 Oyama, Ginowan, 901-2223, Okinawa, Japan
Tel.: (81) 988988804
Sales Range: $25-49.9 Million
Emp.: 62
Couriers
N.A.I.C.S.: 492110
Yuto Weihara *(Gen Mgr)*

Seino Auto Lease Co., Ltd. (1)
4522-1 Maki Ampacho, Gifu, 503-0125, Japan
Tel.: (81) 584646328
Automobile Rental & Leasing Services
N.A.I.C.S.: 532411

Seino Auto Service Kanto Co., Ltd. (1)
400-3 Idoimachi, Maebashi, 379-2111, Gunma, Japan
Tel.: (81) 272685521
Automotive Repair & Maintenance Services
N.A.I.C.S.: 811198

Seino Business Support Co., Ltd. (1)
1 Taguchicho, Ogaki, 503-8501, Gifu, Japan
Tel.: (81) 584825174
Business Support Services
N.A.I.C.S.: 561499

Seino Customs Clearance Service Co., Ltd. (1)
12-9 Nihombashinakasu, Chuo-Ku, Tokyo, 103-0008, Japan
Tel.: (81) 3 3664 1101
Customs Brokerage Services
N.A.I.C.S.: 488510

Seino Ecotrading Inc. (1)
1-12-9 Nihonbashi Hamacho Building 5F, Nihonbashi Hamacho Chuo-ku, Tokyo, 103-0007, Japan
Tel.: (81) 336675901
Web Site: https://www.seino.co.jp
Environmental Consulting Services
N.A.I.C.S.: 541620

Seino Engineering Co., Ltd. (1)
1 Taguchi-cho, Ogaki, 503-0853, Gifu, Japan
Tel.: (81) 584815178
Web Site: https://www.seino.co.jp
Building Finishing Contractors
N.A.I.C.S.: 327910

Seino Express Co., Ltd. (1)
253-1 Nakashiro Niremata Shinden Wanouchi-cho, Anpachi-gun, Gifu, 503-0203, Japan
Tel.: (81) 584694555
Web Site: https://exp-seino.com
Local Freight Trucking
N.A.I.C.S.: 484110

Seino Family Co., Ltd. (1)
1 Taguchi-cho, Ogaki, 503-0853, Gifu, Japan
Tel.: (81) 120110848
Web Site: https://www.seino.co.jp
Emp.: 9
Insurance Agencies & Brokerages
N.A.I.C.S.: 524210

Seino Hikkoshi Co., Ltd. (1)
2-28 Fukujuchoasahira, Hashima, Gifu, Japan
Tel.: (81) 583941022
Local Freight Trucking
N.A.I.C.S.: 484110

Seino Hokkaido Express Co., Ltd. (1)
1-703-6 Shinko Nishi, Ishikari, Ishikari, 061-3241, Japan

INTERNATIONAL PUBLIC

Tel.: (81) 133728888
Local Freight Trucking
N.A.I.C.S.: 484110

Seino Hokuriku Express Co., Ltd. (1)
16-8 Hayashifujishimacho, Fukui, 910-0829, Japan
Tel.: (81) 776570300
Freight Trucking Services
N.A.I.C.S.: 484110

Seino Information Service Co., Ltd. (1)
1 Taguchi-cho, Ogaki, 503-8512, Gifu, Japan
Tel.: (81) 584738888
Web Site: https://www.seino.co.jp
Emp.: 473
Information Services
N.A.I.C.S.: 519290

Seino Logistics Hokkaido Co., Ltd. (1)
2165-1 Kawashimo, Shiroishi-Ku, Hokkaido, Japan
Tel.: (81) 118797558
Water Transportation Services
N.A.I.C.S.: 488390

Seino Logix Co., Ltd. (1)
11th fl Queen's Tower A 2-3-1 Minatomirai, Nishi-ku, Yokohama, 220-6011, Japan
Web Site: http://www.logix.co.jp
Logistics Consulting Servies
N.A.I.C.S.: 541614
Hiroshi Nakayama *(Pres)*

Seino Nippon Express Co., Ltd. (1)
2-7-5 Tomae, Ogaki, 503-0835, Gifu, Japan
Tel.: (81) 584896171
Web Site: http://www.seino.co.jp
Emp.: 155
Local Freight Trucking
N.A.I.C.S.: 484121
Kazunori Kawakami *(Mng Dir)*

Seino Osaka Express Co., Ltd. (1)
2-20-48 Tamadenishi, Nishinari Ward, Osaka, 557-0045, Osaka Prefecture, Japan
Tel.: (81) 666554010
General Freight Trucking, Long-Distance, Truckload
N.A.I.C.S.: 484121

Seino Sangyo Co., Ltd. (1)
3-96-1 Oi, Ogaki, 503-0836, Gifu, Japan
Tel.: (81) 584811323
Web Site: https://www.seino.co.jp
Emp.: 70
Motor Vehicle Supplies & New Parts Whslr
N.A.I.C.S.: 423120
Takahashi Akira *(Pres)*

Seino Staff Service Co., Ltd. (1)
1 Taguchi-cho, Ogaki, 503-0853, Gifu, Japan
Tel.: (81) 584818848
Web Site: https://www.seino.co.jp
Human Resource Consulting & Staffing Outsourcing Services
N.A.I.C.S.: 541612

Seino Super Express Co., Ltd. (1)
3-10-23 Tatsumi, Koto-Ku, Tokyo, 135-0053, Japan
Tel.: (81) 3 6384 7851
Web Site: http://www.seino.co.jp
Emp.: 2,028
Logistics Consulting Servies
N.A.I.C.S.: 541614

Seino Tokyo Express Co., Ltd. (1)
5-7-10 Kotobashi, Sumida-ku, Tokyo, 130-0022, Japan
Tel.: (81) 336327880
General Freight Trucking, Long-Distance, Truckload
N.A.I.C.S.: 484121

Seino Trading Co., Ltd. (1)
1 Taguchi-cho, Ogaki, 503-8509, Gifu, Japan (100%)
Tel.: (81) 584826111
Web Site: http://www.seino-shoji.co.jp
Emp.: 214
Packaging Material Distr
N.A.I.C.S.: 423840

Seino Transportation Co., Ltd. (1)
1 Taguchi-cho, Ogaki, 503-8501, Japan

AND PRIVATE COMPANIES

Tel.: (81) 584 81 1111
Logistics Consulting Servies
N.A.I.C.S.: 541614

Subsidiary (Domestic):

Kanagawa Seino Transportation Co., Ltd. (2)
2-10-1 Sachiura, Kanazawa-Ku, Yokohama, 236-0003, Kanagawa, Japan
Tel.: (81) 457810081
Web Site: http://www.seino.co.jp
Freight Trucking Services
N.A.I.C.S.: 484110

Subsidiary (US):

Seibu Transportation Co., Ltd (2)
5343 W Imperial Hwy 900, Los Angeles, CA 90045
Tel.: (310) 641-4949
Web Site: http://www.seibutrans.com
Emp.: 15
Logistics Consulting Services
N.A.I.C.S.: 541614
Akinori Koga *(Pres)*

Shiga Hino Motor Co., Ltd. (1)
2-30 Ogaki 3-chome, Ritto, 520-3024, Shiga, Japan
Tel.: (81) 77 552 2533
Motor Vehicle Distr
N.A.I.C.S.: 423110

Shikoku Seino Transportation Co., Ltd. (1)
980 Ko Uemura, Toon, 791-0288, Japan
Tel.: (81) 899901311
Web Site: http://www.seino.co.jp
Emp.: 899
Local Freight Trucking
N.A.I.C.S.: 484110

Suito Travel Co., Ltd. (1)
3-11 Asahimachi, Ogaki, 503-0824, Gifu, Japan
Tel.: (81) 584787155
Travel Agency Services
N.A.I.C.S.: 561510

Takuma Seino Transportation Co., Ltd. (1)
2-29-47 Oyama, Kumamoto, 862-0930, Japan
Tel.: (81) 963806037
Web Site: http://www.tkm.seino.co.jp
Sales Range: $25-49.9 Million
Emp.: 50
Local Freight Trucking
N.A.I.C.S.: 484110
Kenzo Matsumur *(Mng Dir)*

Tokai Seino Transportation Co., Ltd. (1)
5-60 Otowacho, Tajimi, Gifu, Japan
Tel.: (81) 572233333
Local Freight Trucking
N.A.I.C.S.: 484110

Toyo Co., Ltd. (1)
1209 Amida Amidacho, Takasago, 676-0827, Hyogo, Japan
Tel.: (81) 794471271
Transportation Services
N.A.I.C.S.: 488999

Toyota Corolla Gifu Co., Ltd. (1)
4-1-3 Rokujoomizo, Gifu, Japan
Tel.: (81) 582723111
Motor Vehicle Dealers
N.A.I.C.S.: 441227

Toyota Home Gifu Co., Ltd. (1)
2-1-1 Ichihashi, Gifu, 500-8381, Gifu Prefecture, Japan
Tel.: (81) 582748300
Web Site: https://gifu.toyotahome.co.jp
Emp.: 70
Building Finishing Contractors
N.A.I.C.S.: 238390

Toyota Rent-A-Lease Gifu Co., Ltd. (1)
9-2 Kanazonocho, Gifu, 500-8113, Japan
Tel.: (81) 582400100
Web Site: http://www.trl-gifu.co.jp
Used Car Dealers
N.A.I.C.S.: 441120

United-seino Transportation (Malaysia) Sdn. Bhd. (1)
Lot 21, Lion Industrial Park, 40300, Shah Alam, Selangor, Malaysia
Tel.: (60) 35 191 5881
Transportation Services
N.A.I.C.S.: 485210

SEIREN CO., LTD.

13F Shin Aoyama Bldg East 1-1-1 Minamiaoyama, Minato-ku, Tokyo, 107-0062, Japan
Tel.: (81) 368347453   JP
Web Site: https://www.seiren.com
Year Founded: 1889
3569—(TKS)
Rev.: $938,058,150
Assets: $1,239,097,380
Liabilities: $414,903,090
Net Worth: $824,194,290
Earnings: $80,351,160
Emp.: 6,718
Fiscal Year-end: 03/31/24
Automotive Interior Materials Mfr & Supplier, Textile Store Management, Medical Equipment & Housing Products Developer
N.A.I.C.S.: 423110
Tatsuo Kawada *(Chm & CEO)*

Subsidiaries:

Alma Japan Corporation (1)
71-1-2 Sakaichonagaya, Sakai, Japan
Tel.: (81) 776665020
Web Site: http://www.seiren.com
Sales Range: $25-49.9 Million
Emp.: 59
Textile Product Mills
N.A.I.C.S.: 314999

BMD Private Limited (1)
Bhilwara Towers A-12 Sector 1, Noida, 201301, Uttar Pradesh, India
Tel.: (91) 1204390300
Web Site: https://www.bmdtextiles.in
Sales Range: $25-49.9 Million
Emp.: 25,000
Automotive Furnishing Fabric Mfr
N.A.I.C.S.: 313240
Shekhar Agarwal *(Chm)*

Borgstena Textile Portugal, Lda (1)
EN 234 - km 877 Floor of Pisco Apartado 35, 3521-909, Nelas, Portugal
Tel.: (351) 232 427 660
Web Site: http://www.borgstena.com
Sales Range: $25-49.9 Million
Emp.: 250
Textile Products Mfr
N.A.I.C.S.: 314999
Jorge Machado *(CEO)*

Depro Co., Ltd. (1)
2-27-11F Minami-Osawa, Hachioji, 192-0364, Tokyo, Japan
Tel.: (81) 426702801
Web Site: https://www.de-pro.co.jp
Sales Range: $25-49.9 Million
Emp.: 44
Periodical Publishers
N.A.I.C.S.: 513120

Gunsen Co., Ltd. (1)
552 Ko Yasaka-cho, Isesaki, 372-0044, Gunma, Japan
Tel.: (81) 270242706
Sales Range: $25-49.9 Million
Emp.: 102
Textile & Fabric Dyeing Mills
N.A.I.C.S.: 313310

KB Seiren Dty, Ltd. (1)
13-23 Shimorokujo-cho, Fukui, 918-8135, Japan
Tel.: (81) 77 641 1231
Web Site: https://www.kbseiren-dty.com
Textile Product Mfr & Distr
N.A.I.C.S.: 314999

KB Seiren Ltd. (1)
14-15F Umeda Daibiru Building 3-3-10 Umeda, Kita-ku, Osaka, 530-0001, Japan
Tel.: (81) 663455454
Sales Range: $250-299.9 Million
Emp.: 600
Manufacturing, Processing & Sales of Textiles & Raw Materials
N.A.I.C.S.: 314999

Tatsuo Kawada *(Pres)*

Plant (Domestic):

KB Seiren Co., Ltd. - Hokuriku Synthetic Fibers Plant (2)
6-1-1 Shimokobata-cho, Sabae, 916-0038, Fukui, Japan
Tel.: (81) 778515350
Web Site: https://www.kbseiren.com
Polyester Resin Mfr
N.A.I.C.S.: 325211

KB Seiren Co., Ltd. - Nagahama Plant (2)
1-11 Kanebo-cho, Nagahama, 526-0068, Shiga, Japan
Tel.: (81) 749630700
Textile Products Mfr
N.A.I.C.S.: 314999

Nagoya Seiren Co., Ltd. (1)
10-1 Keya 1-chome, Fukui, 918-8560, Japan   **(81.2%)**
Tel.: (81) 776352110
Web Site: http://www.seiren.com
Sales Range: $75-99.9 Million
Emp.: 150
Real Estate Leasing & Management
N.A.I.C.S.: 531390

PT. Seiren Indonesia (1)
Jalan Science Timur 2 Block B1G Jababeka Science Park Jababeka Phase 5, Kawasan Industri Desa Jayamukti-Kecamatan Cikarang Pusat, Bekasi, 17530, Indonesia
Tel.: (62) 212 957 4606
Textile Product Mfr & Distr
N.A.I.C.S.: 314999

Saha Seiren Co., Ltd. (1)
Tel.: (66) 21163945
Web Site: http://www.saha-seiren.co.th
Sales Range: $150-199.9 Million
Emp.: 630
Knitted Fabric Mfr
N.A.I.C.S.: 313240

Plant (Domestic):

Saha Seiren Co., Ltd. - Factory II (2)
127 Mu 1 Suwannasorn Rd Nontri, Kabinburi, Prachin Buri, 25110, Thailand
Tel.: (66) 372901315
Web Site: http://www.saha-seiren.co.th
Emp.: 919
Knitted Fabric Mfr
N.A.I.C.S.: 313240

Seiren Alma Co., Ltd. (1)
1-2 Nagaya 71-Aza Sakai-cho, Sakai, 919-0503, Fukui, Japan
Tel.: (81) 77 666 5020
Women's Clothing Mfr
N.A.I.C.S.: 315250

Seiren Aucus Co., Ltd. (1)
18-1 Futsukaichi-cho, Fukui, 910-0108, Japan
Tel.: (81) 776551111
Web Site: http://www.seiren.com
Sales Range: $50-74.9 Million
Emp.: 126
Vehicle Parts Mfr
N.A.I.C.S.: 336390

Seiren Co., Ltd - Nitta No.3 Plant (1)
60-1 Nittazuka 1-Chome, Fukui, 910-0067, Japan
Tel.: (81) 776 23 5203
Web Site: http://www.seiren.com
Sales Range: $200-249.9 Million
Emp.: 800
Chemical Products Mfr
N.A.I.C.S.: 325998

Seiren Co., Ltd - Nitta Plat Plant (1)
1-60-1 Nittazuka, Fukui, 910-0067, Japan
Tel.: (81) 776 23 5281
Electric Equipment Mfr
N.A.I.C.S.: 334419

Seiren Co., Ltd. - Honsya-Plant (1)
1-10-1 Keya, Fukui, 918-8560, Japan
Tel.: (81) 776352100
Web Site: http://www.seiren.com
Sales Range: $450-499.9 Million
Emp.: 2,000
Industrial Chemicals Mfr
N.A.I.C.S.: 325998

SEIREN CO., LTD.

Seiren Co., Ltd. - Nitta No.1 Plant (1)
60-1 Nittazuka 1-Chome, Fukui, 910-0067, Japan
Tel.: (81) 776235201
Chemical Products Mfr
N.A.I.C.S.: 325998

Seiren Co., Ltd. - Nitta No.2 Plant (1)
1-60-1 Nittazuka, Fukui, 910-0067, Japan
Tel.: (81) 776235202
Electric Equipment Mfr
N.A.I.C.S.: 334419

Seiren Co., Ltd. - Nitta No.5 Plant (1)
60-1 Nittazuka 1-Chome, Fukui, 910-0067, Japan
Tel.: (81) 776235205
Web Site: http://www.seiren.com
Industrial Machinery Mfr
N.A.I.C.S.: 333248

Seiren Co., Ltd. - Nitta No.6 Plant (1)
1-60-1 Nittazuka, Fukui, 910-0067, Japan
Tel.: (81) 776 23 5206
Web Site: http://www.seiren.com
Chemical Products Mfr
N.A.I.C.S.: 325998

Seiren Co., Ltd. - Sabae Plant (1)
3-1 Torii-machi, Sabae, 916-0063, Fukui, Japan
Tel.: (81) 778622222
Web Site: http://www.seiren.com
Emp.: 63
Electronic Components Mfr
N.A.I.C.S.: 334419

Seiren Cosmo Co., Ltd. (1)
1-1-1 Kasuga, Fukui, 918-8108, Japan   **(100%)**
Tel.: (81) 776351611
Web Site: http://www.seirencosmo.co.jp
Employment Placement Services
N.A.I.C.S.: 561311

Seiren Design Center North America, LLC (1)
5 Park Plz Ste 1560, Irvine, CA 92614
Tel.: (949) 442-0630
Automotive Upholstery Material Distr
N.A.I.C.S.: 423120

Seiren Electronics (Suzhou) Co., Ltd. (1)
No 5 Factory Building No 58 Xinting Road, Suzhou New District, Suzhou, 215129, Jiangsu, China
Tel.: (86) 5126 662 8186
Web Site: https://www.seiren-e.com
Textile Machinery Mfr & Distr
N.A.I.C.S.: 333248

Seiren Electronics Co., Ltd. (1)
Tel.: (81) 776501400
Sales Range: $25-49.9 Million
Emp.: 40
Planning, Mfg & Sales of Dyeing & Finishing Machinery; Electronic & Electrical Equipment & Components
N.A.I.C.S.: 333248

Seiren Guangdong Co., Ltd. (1)
No 6 Kuangzongyou Road, Yongle Village Huashan Town Huadu District, Guangzhou, Guangdong, China
Tel.: (86) 203 947 4549
Automobile Interior Material Mfr & Distr
N.A.I.C.S.: 336390

Seiren Hebei Co., Ltd. (1)
No 25 Industrial Road, Wuji, Shijiazhuang, 052460, Hebei, China
Tel.: (86) 3118 735 2008
Automotive Airbag Distr
N.A.I.C.S.: 423120

Seiren Housing Co., Ltd. (1)
4-6-7 Ninomiya, Fukui, Japan
Tel.: (81) 776277880
Web Site: http://www.seiren.com
Sales Range: $25-49.9 Million
Emp.: 44
Real Estate Agents & Brokers
N.A.I.C.S.: 531210

Seiren KP Co., Ltd. (1)

SEIREN CO., LTD.

Seiren Co., Ltd.—(Continued)
1-1 Tomyoji-cho, Fukui, 910-0062, Japan
Tel.: (81) 776235207
Web Site: http://www.seirenkp.co.jp
Woven Textile Fabrics Mfr
N.A.I.C.S.: 313210

Seiren KST Corp. (1)
13-23 Shimorokujo-cho, Fukui, 918-8135, Japan
Tel.: (81) 77 641 7333
Web Site: https://www.kst.seiren.com
Semiconductor & Optical Communication Distr
N.A.I.C.S.: 423690
Masahiro Kawasaki *(Pres & CEO)*

Seiren Produtos Automotivos Ltda (1)
Av Ireno da Silva Venancio 196 Bairro Protestantes, Votorantim, 18111-100, SP, Brazil
Tel.: (55) 1533537500
Web Site: http://www.seiren.com
Textile Products Mfr
N.A.I.C.S.: 314999

Seiren Shanghai Co., Ltd. (1)
Room 904 Building B Arch Shanghai No 533 Loushanguan Road, Changning District, Shanghai, China
Tel.: (86) 216 270 2397
Web Site: https://www.seirenshop.com
Textile Products Distr
N.A.I.C.S.: 424310

Seiren Shoji Co., Ltd (1)
1-10-1 Keya Building 3F, Fukui, 918-8003, Japan
Tel.: (81) 776338822
Web Site: https://www.seirensyouji.jp
Emp.: 60
Insurance Management Services
N.A.I.C.S.: 524210

Seiren Suzhou Co., Ltd. (1)
No 50 Lushan Road High-tech Zone, Suzhou, China
Tel.: (86) 5126 665 5266
Web Site: https://www.seiren.cn
Automotive Airbag Mfr & Distr
N.A.I.C.S.: 336390

Seiren System Service Co., Ltd (1)
2-3-1 Techno Port Mikuni-cho, Sakai, 913-0038, Fukui, Japan
Tel.: (81) 776507200
Web Site: http://www.srnss.co.jp
Rev.: $11,909,520
Emp.: 69
Information Technology Consulting Services
N.A.I.C.S.: 541512

Seiren Viscotec Mexico S.A. de C.V. (1)
Av Miguel Hidalgo 200 Carr Federal 90 Km 36 125, Parque Industrial Marabis Abasolo, 36987, Guanajuato, Mexico
Tel.: (52) 462 166 4001
Textile Product Mfr & Distr
N.A.I.C.S.: 314999

Viscotec Automotive Products, LLC (1)
1500 E Union St, Morganton, NC 28655
Tel.: (828) 430-3456
Web Site: http://www.seiren-na.com
Emp.: 200
Automotive Upholstery Materials Mfr & Whslr
N.A.I.C.S.: 314999

SEIRYO ELECTRIC CORPORATION

JRE Dojima Tower 2-4-27 Dojima, Kita-ku, Osaka, 530-0003, Japan
Tel.: (81) 663454160
Web Site: https://www.seiryodenki.co.jp
Year Founded: 1966
4341—(TKS)
Rev.: $122,212,290
Assets: $77,079,210
Liabilities: $40,882,850
Net Worth: $36,196,360
Earnings: $1,877,240
Emp.: 429
Fiscal Year-end: 03/31/24

Telecommunication Equipment Maintenance Services
N.A.I.C.S.: 811210
Nobuaki Nishioka *(CEO)*

Subsidiaries:

Tottori Seiryo Electric Corporation (1)
5F Tottori Ekimae Building 102 Higashishinajicho, Tottori, 680-0835, Japan
Tel.: (81) 857298741
Web Site: https://www.tottori.seiryodenki.co.jp
Emp.: 17
Software Design Services
N.A.I.C.S.: 541511

SEISLAND SURVEYS LTD.

7235 Flint Road SE, Calgary, T2H 1G2, AB, Canada
Tel.: (403) 255-2770
Web Site: http://www.seisland.com
Year Founded: 1980
Rev.: $46,428,603
Emp.: 100
Seismic Surveying Services
N.A.I.C.S.: 541370
Garvin Geck *(Pres)*

SEIWA CHUO HOLDINGS CORPORATION

3-1-20 Kujo-Minami, Nishi-ku, Osaka, 550-0025, Japan
Tel.: (81) 665812141
Web Site: https://www.seiwa-chuo-holdings.co.jp
Year Founded: 1954
7531—(TKS)
Rev.: $443,670,930
Assets: $281,841,680
Liabilities: $168,344,960
Net Worth: $113,496,720
Earnings: $730,270
Emp.: 234
Fiscal Year-end: 12/31/23
Holding Company
N.A.I.C.S.: 551111
Masaaki Sakagami *(Pres)*

SEIWA ELECTRIC MFG. CO., LTD.

36 Terada Shinike, Joyo, 610-0192, Kyoto, Japan
Tel.: (81) 774558181
Web Site: https://www.seiwa.co.jp
Year Founded: 1949
6748—(TKS)
Rev.: $168,458,400
Assets: $198,087,510
Liabilities: $87,150,280
Net Worth: $110,937,230
Earnings: $5,622,370
Fiscal Year-end: 12/31/23
Information & Lighting Equipment Mfr & Whslr
N.A.I.C.S.: 334290
Teruaki Masuyama *(Pres)*

Subsidiaries:

SEIWA ELECTRIC (VIETNAM) Co., Ltd. (1)
Tan Thuan Export Processing Zone Road No 18-Dist 7, Ho Chi Minh City, Vietnam
Tel.: (84) 837701180
Lighting Equipment Distr
N.A.I.C.S.: 423610

SEIWA TECHNOLOGY Co., Ltd. (1)
InterOne Place Karasuma 2 3F 680 Ohmandokoro-Cho, Bukkoji-Sagaru Karasuma-dori Shimogyo-ku, Kyoto, 600-8413, Japan
Tel.: (81) 753449191
Web Site: https://www.seiwatec.co.jp
Emp.: 36
Computer Equipment Distr
N.A.I.C.S.: 423430
Kazuyuki Fukuzono *(Pres & CEO)*

Seiwa Electric Mfg. Co., Ltd. - Overseas Business Promotion Division (1)
Yanagibashi First Bldg 2-19-6 Yanagibashi Taito-ku, Tokyo, 111-0052, Japan
Tel.: (81) 358338948
Lighting Equipment Mfr
N.A.I.C.S.: 335139

SEIWA HOLDINGS CO., LTD.

1-17-26 Nishiki Round Terrace Fushimi 4th Floor, Naka-ku, Nagoya, 460-0003, Japan
Tel.: (81) 52 265 8467
Web Site: http://www.seiwaholdings.co.jp
Year Founded: 2021
Holding Company
N.A.I.C.S.: 551112
Yudai Nomiyama *(Pres)*

Subsidiaries:

Mie Kogyo Co., Ltd. (1)
6381-1 Karasu-cho, Tsu, 514-0315, Mie, Japan
Tel.: (81) 592922811
Metal Products Mfr
N.A.I.C.S.: 332999

Seiwa Kogyo Co., Ltd. (1)
1-1-2 Uchisaiwai-cho Udhibiya Bldg 8F, Chiyoda-ku, Tokyo, 100-0011, Japan
Tel.: (81) 335808901
Automobile Parts Mfr
N.A.I.C.S.: 336390

SEJAL GLASS LTD.

173 174 Sejal Encasa 3rd Floor S V Road, Kandivali West, Mumbai, 400067, India
Tel.: (91) 2228665100
Web Site: https://www.sejalglass.co.in
Year Founded: 1998
532993—(BOM)
Rev.: $534,720
Assets: $7,491,736
Liabilities: $25,629,694
Net Worth: ($18,137,958)
Earnings: ($2,935,147)
Emp.: 72
Fiscal Year-end: 03/31/20
Glass Processing Services
N.A.I.C.S.: 327211
Amrut S. Gada *(Chm & Mng Dir)*

Subsidiaries:

Sejal Glass & Glass Manufacturing Products LLC (1)
Plot 41 & 43 Al Ghali Industrial Zone, Ras al Khaimah, United Arab Emirates
Tel.: (971) 72331592
Laminated Flat Glass Mfr
N.A.I.C.S.: 327211

Sejal Glass House Ltd (1)
No 7 Krishna Kunj S V Road, Malad W, Mumbai, 400064, Maharashtra, India
Tel.: (91) 2228886208
Web Site: http://www.sejalglass.co.in
Sales Range: $125-149.9 Million
Emp.: 20
Glass Mfr & Retailer
N.A.I.C.S.: 327215

Sejal Insurance Broking Ltd. (1)
Abhilasha 6th Floor S V Road, Kandivali W, Mumbai, 400067, Maharashtra, India
Tel.: (91) 22 28616132
Web Site: http://www.sejalinsurance.com
Sales Range: $50-74.9 Million
Emp.: 20
Life & Non Life Insurance Solutions
N.A.I.C.S.: 524113
Amurth Gada *(Mng Dir)*

Sejal International Ltd. (1)
Plot No 250/10/1 near Alok Rubplast opp Sun Pharma Village Dadra, Silvassa, 396191, India
Tel.: (91) 260 2669981
Web Site: http://www.sejalglass.co.in
Glass Mfr & Trading Services

N.A.I.C.S.: 327212

SEJIN HEAVY INDUSTRIES CO., LTD

216-18 Dangwol-ro Onsan-eup 1213 Wonsan-ri, Ulju-gun, Ulsan, 45011, Korea (South)
Tel.: (82) 522318000
Web Site: https://www.sejinheavy.com
Year Founded: 1999
075580—(KRS)
Rev.: $314,511,162
Assets: $423,268,316
Liabilities: $262,700,461
Net Worth: $160,567,855
Earnings: $10,245,252
Emp.: 291
Fiscal Year-end: 12/31/22
Ship Component Mfr
N.A.I.C.S.: 336611
Lim Soo-Han *(Dir)*

SEJIN TS CO., LTD

51-43 Jimoon-Ri Wongok-Myun, Aasung, 456-812, GyungGi-Do, Korea (South)
Tel.: (82) 316503700
Web Site: https://www.sejints.co.kr
Year Founded: 1990
067770—(KRS)
Rev.: $12,674,719
Assets: $35,998,309
Liabilities: $1,487,488
Net Worth: $34,510,821
Earnings: ($491,286)
Emp.: 51
Fiscal Year-end: 12/31/22
Electronic Components Mfr
N.A.I.C.S.: 334419
In Shik Kim *(CEO)*

Subsidiaries:

SEJIN TS Co., Ltd - Cheonan Plant (1)
460 Chonhung-Ri Songgo-Ub, Cheonan, 330-836, Chungchong Nam-Do, Korea (South)
Tel.: (82) 41 556 9964
Plastics Films Mfr
N.A.I.C.S.: 326113

SKC-SEJIN OPTO ELECTRONICS (SUZHOU) Co., Ltd (1)
No 1 Tongxing Road Wujang Economy Developement Zone, Suzhou, Jangsu, China
Tel.: (86) 512 6340 6332
Plastics Films Mfr
N.A.I.C.S.: 326113
Kim In Shik *(CEO)*

SEJONG MATERIALS CO., LTD.

604 Building 29 Banwol Industrial Complex 641-7 Seongkok-dong, Danwon-gu, Ansan, Gyeonggi-do, Korea (South)
Tel.: (82) 31 491 1850
Web Site: http://www.sejongmaterials.co.kr
Year Founded: 2000
Sales Range: $25-49.9 Million
Emp.: 185
Metal Components for Electronics
N.A.I.C.S.: 332999
Jae-Bok Seong *(CEO)*

SEJONG MEDICAL CO., LTD.

11 Sinchon 2-ro, Paju, 10880, Gyeonggi-do, Korea (South)
Tel.: (82) 319458191
Web Site: https://www.sejongmedical.com
Year Founded: 1996
258830—(KRS)
Rev.: $12,335,604
Assets: $105,999,111
Liabilities: $85,544,391

Net Worth: $20,454,720
Earnings: ($70,077,448)
Emp.: 137
Fiscal Year-end: 12/31/22
Surgical Medical Equipment Mfr
N.A.I.C.S.: 339112
Seong Hwan Cho *(CEO)*

SEJONG TELECOM INC.
12 Gwacheon-daero 7-gil, Gangdong-gu, Gwacheon, Gyeonggi-do, Korea (South)
Tel.: (82) 234154935
Web Site: https://www.sejongtelecom.net
Year Founded: 1992
036630—(KRS)
Rev.: $248,713,899
Assets: $331,197,464
Liabilities: $89,157,451
Net Worth: $242,040,013
Earnings: ($29,308,998)
Emp.: 410
Fiscal Year-end: 12/31/22
Integrated Communication Services
N.A.I.C.S.: 517810
Ki-Yoon Yoo *(CEO)*

SEJOONG CO., LTD.
143 Changgyeonggung-ro, Jongno-gu, Seoul, 03136, Korea (South)
Tel.: (82) 221267777
Web Site: http://www.sejoong.com
Year Founded: 1995
039310—(KRS)
Rev.: $32,309,162
Assets: $99,507,308
Liabilities: $31,460,768
Net Worth: $68,046,540
Earnings: $2,825,714
Emp.: 168
Fiscal Year-end: 12/31/22
Tour Arrangement Services
N.A.I.C.S.: 561599
Se-Jeon Chun *(Pres & CEO)*

SEKAR LAUT TBK
Jl Raya Darmo 23-25, Surabaya, 60265, East Java, Indonesia
Tel.: (62) 315671371
Web Site: https://www.sekarlaut.com
SKLT—(INDO)
Rev.: $116,524,784
Assets: $83,301,090
Liabilities: $30,248,761
Net Worth: $53,052,329
Earnings: $5,071,138
Emp.: 2,143
Fiscal Year-end: 12/31/23
Seafood Product Mfr
N.A.I.C.S.: 311710
John Canfi Gozal *(Fin Dir)*

Subsidiaries:

PT Pangan Lestari (1)
Jl Jenggololi/17, Sidoarjo, 61219, Indonesia
Tel.: (62) 315671371
Web Site: http://www.panganlestari.co.id
Food Products Distr
N.A.I.C.S.: 424490

SEKAWAN INTIPRATAMA TBK
Menara Global Lt 15/20 Jln Jend Gatot Subroto Kav 27, Jakarta Selatan, 12950, Indonesia
Tel.: (62) 21 5279660
Web Site: http://www.siaptbk.com
Rev.: $64,459
Assets: $15,905,768
Liabilities: $16,707,769
Net Worth: ($802,001)
Earnings: ($740,905)
Emp.: 30
Fiscal Year-end: 12/31/17
Coal Mining Services
N.A.I.C.S.: 212115

Sebastian Jaafar *(Dir-Operation & Bus Dev)*

SEKERBANK T.A.S.
Emniyet Evleri Mah Eski Buyukdere Cad No 1 / 1A, 34415, Istanbul, Kagthane, Turkiye
Tel.: (90) 2123197000
Web Site: https://www.sekerbank.com.tr
Year Founded: 1953
SKBNK—(IST)
Rev.: $280,178,190
Assets: $2,130,667,820
Liabilities: $1,919,474,757
Net Worth: $211,193,063
Earnings: $60,791,154
Emp.: 3,418
Fiscal Year-end: 12/31/22
Commercial Banking Services
N.A.I.C.S.: 522110
Hasan Basri Goktan *(Chm)*

Subsidiaries:

Seker Bilisim Sanayi A.S. (1)
Bilkent Mahallesi 2 cad Cyberpark A Blok 4 kat Bilkent, 06533, Ankara, Turkiye
Tel.: (90) 3122650204
Web Site: http://www.sekerbilisim.com.tr
Sales Range: $25-49.9 Million
Emp.: 6
Financial Software Development Services
N.A.I.C.S.: 541511

Seker Faktoring A.S. (1)
Buyukdere Cad No 171 Metrocity A Blok Kat 7, Esentepe Sisli, 34340, Istanbul, Turkiye
Tel.: (90) 2122927410
Web Site: https://www.sekerfactoring.com
Real Estate Financial Services
N.A.I.C.S.: 522292

Seker Faktoring Hizmetleri A.S. (1)
MetroCity A Block No 7 Fl, 34330, Esentepe, Turkiye
Tel.: (90) 2122927410
Web Site: http://www.sekerfactoring.com
Commercial Banking Services
N.A.I.C.S.: 522110

Seker Finansal Kiralama A.S. (1)
Buyukdere Cad No 171 Metro City Business Center A Block Floor8, Esentepe/Sisli, 34394, Istanbul, Turkiye
Tel.: (90) 2123623400
Web Site: https://www.sekerleasing.com.tr
Rev.: $18,280,107
Assets: $78,480,491
Liabilities: $61,088,694
Net Worth: $17,391,797
Earnings: $6,482,965
Emp.: 33
Fiscal Year-end: 12/31/2023
Financial Lending Services
N.A.I.C.S.: 522220
Hasan Basri Goktan *(Chm)*

Seker Finansman A.S. (1)
Barbaros Blv 149/7, Balmumcu Besiktas, Istanbul, 34349, Turkiye
Tel.: (90) 212 340 0800
Web Site: https://www.sekerfinans.com.tr
Mortgage Lending Services
N.A.I.C.S.: 522292

Seker Gayrimenkul Yatirim Ortakligi A.S. (1)
Emniyet Evleri Mah Akarsu Cad Seker Kule Kat 11 No 3/51, Kagthane, 34415, Istanbul, Turkiye
Tel.: (90) 2123983800
Web Site: https://www.sekergyo.com.tr
Real Estate Trust Services
N.A.I.C.S.: 525920
Emin Erdem *(Chm)*

Seker Yatirim Menkul Degerler A.S. (1)
Buyukdere Cad No 171 Metrocity A Blok Floor 4-5, 3-4 Gumussuyu, 34394, Istanbul, Turkiye
Tel.: (90) 2123343333
Sales Range: $25-49.9 Million
Emp.: 100
Financial Management Services

N.A.I.C.S.: 541611
Osman Goktan *(Mng Dir)*
Sekerbank International Banking Unit Ltd. (1)
Ataturk Cad Muhtar Yusuf Galleria F Blok K 3, Nicosia, Cyprus
Tel.: (357) 3922289134
Commercial Banking Services
N.A.I.C.S.: 522110

Sekerbank Kibris Ltd. (1)
Ataturk Street Muhtar Yusuf Galleria F Block Floor 2 and 3, Nicosia, Cyprus
Tel.: (357) 3926007000
Web Site: https://www.sekerbankkibris.com
Commercial Banking Services
N.A.I.C.S.: 522110

SEKI CO., LTD.
7-7-1 Minato-machi, Matsuyama, 790-8686, Ehime, Japan
Tel.: (81) 899450111
Web Site: https://www.seki.co.jp
Year Founded: 1949
7857—(TKS)
Rev.: $79,207,114
Assets: $122,735,347
Liabilities: $19,993,387
Net Worth: $102,741,960
Earnings: $2,411,628
Fiscal Year-end: 03/31/24
Commercial Printing & Paper Distr
N.A.I.C.S.: 424110
Keizo Seki *(Chm)*

SEKICHU CO., LTD.
4531-1 Kuragano-machi, Takasaki, 370-1201, Gunma, Japan
Tel.: (81) 273451111
Web Site: https://www.sekichu.co.jp
Year Founded: 1952
9976—(TKS)
Sales Range: $25-49.9 Billion
Home Center Operator
N.A.I.C.S.: 444110
Tadahiro Sekiguchi *(Pres & CEO)*

SEKIDO CO., LTD.
6th Fl Nishishinjuku-Matsuya bldg 4-31-6 Yoyogi, Shibuya Ward, Tokyo, 151-0053, Japan
Tel.: (81) 362732020
Web Site: http://www.sekido.com
Year Founded: 1956
9878—(TKS)
Rev.: $56,052,800
Assets: $35,125,540
Liabilities: $28,945,190
Net Worth: $6,180,350
Earnings: $310,670
Emp.: 62
Fiscal Year-end: 03/31/24
Apparel Accessory Store Operator
N.A.I.C.S.: 458110
Masami Sekido *(Pres)*

SEKISUI CHEMICAL CO., LTD.
2-4-4 Nishitemma, Kita-ku, Osaka, 530-8565, Japan
Tel.: (81) 663654122   JP
Web Site: https://www.sekisuichemical.com
Year Founded: 1947
SUI—(DEU)
Rev.: $8,908,875,570
Assets: $8,805,699,270
Liabilities: $3,553,495,020
Net Worth: $5,252,204,250
Earnings: $496,615,710
Emp.: 26,838
Fiscal Year-end: 03/31/23
Mfr of Prefabricated Houses, Chemical & Plastic Products
N.A.I.C.S.: 325998
Teiji Koge *(Chm)*

Subsidiaries:

AIM Aerospace, Inc. (1)
705 SW 7th St, Renton, WA 98057
Tel.: (425) 235-2750
Web Site: http://www.aim-aerospace.com
Sales Range: $25-49.9 Million
Emp.: 150
Aircraft Parts & Equipment Mfr
N.A.I.C.S.: 336413
Daniele Cagnatel *(Pres & CEO)*

Subsidiary (Domestic):

AIM Aerospace Auburn, Inc. (2)
1502 20th St NW, Auburn, WA 98001-3428
Tel.: (253) 804-3355
Aircraft Parts & Equipment Mfr
N.A.I.C.S.: 336413
Nicolette Pratt *(Mgr-Production)*

AIM Aerospace Sumner, Inc. (2)
1516 Fryar Ave, Sumner, WA 98390
Tel.: (253) 863-7868
Emp.: 334
Aircraft Parts & Equipment Mfr
N.A.I.C.S.: 336413

Quatro Composites, LLC (2)
403 14th St SE, Orange City, IA 51041
Tel.: (712) 707-9200
Web Site: http://www.quatrocomposites.com
Carbon & Graphite Product Mfr
N.A.I.C.S.: 335991
Steve Roesner *(Pres)*

Chu-Shikoku Sekisui Shoji Co., Ltd. (1)
2-5-21 Minamikan-On, Nishi-Ku, Hiroshima, 733-0035, Japan
Tel.: (81) 822345100
Chemical Product Whslr
N.A.I.C.S.: 424690

Dalian Sekisui Housing Technology Co., Ltd. (1)
Unit3 Unit4 36F Eton Place Dalian ST2 Office Block 280 Changjiang Road, Zhongshan District, Dalian, 116001, Liaoning, China
Tel.: (86) 4118 253 9771
Web Site: http://www.sekisuichemical.com
Construction Machinery Mfr
N.A.I.C.S.: 333120

Gunma Sekisui Heim Co., Ltd. (1)
Sekisui Heim Building 3-35-3 Minami-cho, Maebashi, 371-0805, Gunma, Japan
Tel.: (81) 27 220 1211
Web Site: https://gs816.jp
Emp.: 322
Apartment Rental Services
N.A.I.C.S.: 531110

Hanyu Plastics Industries Ltd. (1)
392 Kamiiwase, Hanyu, 348-0044, Saitama, Japan   (100%)
Tel.: (81) 485612251
Plastic Extrusion Molding Products Mfr & Whslr
N.A.I.C.S.: 326199

Hinomaru Co., Ltd. (1)
5-7-29 Kuhonji, Kumamoto, 862-0976, Japan
Tel.: (81) 963724747
Synthetic Resin Products Whslr
N.A.I.C.S.: 424610

Hiroseki Kako Co., Ltd. (1)
2-5-1 Minatomachi, Otake, 739-0621, Hiroshima, Japan
Tel.: (81) 827577171
Plastics Product Mfr
N.A.I.C.S.: 326199

Hokkaido Sekisui Fami S Co., Ltd. (1)
4-1-10 Kita12jonishi Heim Bldg, Kita-Ku, Sapporo, 001-0012, Hokkaido, Japan
Tel.: (81) 117171825
Chemical Product Whslr
N.A.I.C.S.: 424690

Hokkaido Sekisui Shoji Co., Ltd. (1)
29-6-15 Kita37johigashi, Higashi-Ku, Sapporo, 007-0837, Hokkaido, Japan
Tel.: (81) 117853311
Metal Merchant Whslr
N.A.I.C.S.: 423510

Kyushu Sekisui Kenzai Co., Ltd. (1)
4-17-15 Noma, Minami-Ku, Fukuoka, 815-0041, Japan

SEKISUI CHEMICAL CO., LTD.

Sekisui Chemical Co., Ltd.—(Continued)
Tel.: (81) 92 562 5511
Web Site: http://www.sekisui-kenzai.co.jp
Construction Materials Distr
N.A.I.C.S.: 423320
Kataoka Hiroshi (Pres)

M&S Pipe Systems Co., Ltd. (1)
Shimbashi TS Bldg 1-22-5 Nishi Shimbashi, Minato-ku, Tokyo, 105-0003, Japan (100%)
Tel.: (81) 351572050
Sales Range: $25-49.9 Million
Emp.: 2
Plastic Pipe & Pipe Fitting Manufacturing & Distribution Consulting Services
N.A.I.C.S.: 541614

Naseki Seimitsukako Co., Ltd. (1)
4-1-1 Sanjooji, Nara, 630-8013, Japan
Tel.: (81) 742348856
Plastics Product Mfr
N.A.I.C.S.: 326199

Osaka Sekisui Heim Real Estate Co., Ltd. (1)
1-6-1 Miyahara Shinosaka Blic Bldg 11f, Yodogawa-Ku, Osaka, 532-0003, Japan
Tel.: (81) 663948717
Real Estate Manangement Services
N.A.I.C.S.: 531390

PT. Sekisui Polymatech Indonesia (1)
MM2100 Block O-9, Industrial Town Cikarang Barat, Bekasi, 17520, Jawa Barat, Indonesia
Tel.: (62) 21 898 0170
Emp.: 428
Consumer Electronic Component Mfr & Distr
N.A.I.C.S.: 334419
Koichiro Mashimo (Pres)

PT. Sekisui Polymatech Trading Indonesia (1)
MM2100 Block O-9, Industrial Town Cikarang Barat, Bekasi, 17520, Jawa Barat, Indonesia
Tel.: (62) 218 998 3236
Consumer Electronic Component Mfr & Distr
N.A.I.C.S.: 334419

Ryuseki Jubi Co., Ltd. (1)
4-1-1 Sanjooji, Nara, 630-8013, Japan
Tel.: (81) 742333445
Synthetic Resin Mfr
N.A.I.C.S.: 325211

S & L Specialty Polymers Co., Ltd. (1)
5 Phangmuang Chapoh 3-1 Road, Huaypong, Muang Rayong, 21150, Rayong, Thailand
Tel.: (66) 3 801 0210
Chlorinated Polyvinyl Chloride Resin Mfr & Distr
N.A.I.C.S.: 325211
Yuki Goto (CEO)

Sanin Sekisui Shoji Co., Ltd. (1)
975 Naoe Kaminaoe, Hikawa-cho, Izumo, 699-0624, Shimane, Japan (100%)
Tel.: (81) 853723881
Web Site: http://www.sanin-sekisui.co.jp
Sales Range: $25-49.9 Million
Emp.: 41
Synthetic Resin Distr
N.A.I.C.S.: 424690
Motoharu Moriki (Mng Dir)

Sekisui (Dalian) Housing Technology Co., Ltd. (1)
Unit3 Unit4 36F Eton Place Dalian ST2 Office Block 280 Changjiang Road, Zhongshan District, Dalian, 116001, Liaoning, China
Tel.: (86) 4118 253 9771
Consumer Electronic Component Mfr & Distr
N.A.I.C.S.: 334419
Hideo Uraki (Pres & CEO)

Sekisui (Hong Kong) Ltd. (1)
8/F 111 Leighton Road, Causeway Bay, China (Hong Kong) (100%)
Tel.: (852) 2 890 9161
Web Site: https://www.sekisui.hk

Sales Range: $25-49.9 Million
Emp.: 83
Importer & Exporter of Plastic Products
N.A.I.C.S.: 424130
Yasuhiro Hirayama (Pres & CEO)

Sekisui (Qingdao) Plastic Co., Ltd. (1)
Room801 Excellence Mansion NO 128 Yanji Road, Shibei, Qingdao, 266034, Shandong, China
Tel.: (86) 5328 596 9080
Web Site: http://www.sekisui-qd.com
Plastic Pipe Mfr & Whslr
N.A.I.C.S.: 326122

Plant (Domestic):

Sekisui (Qingdao) Plastic Co., Ltd. - Huangdao Plant (2)
273 Yanhe Rd, Qingdao Economic & Technology Development Zone, Qingdao, 266500, China
Tel.: (86) 5328 683 7875
Web Site: http://www.sekisuichemical.com
Plastic Tank Mfr
N.A.I.C.S.: 326122

Sekisui (Shanghai) Environmental Technology Co., Ltd. (1)
No 4159 Baoan Road, Anting Town Jiading District, Shanghai, 201814, China
Tel.: (86) 215 950 8999
Plastic Product Mfr & Distr
N.A.I.C.S.: 326199
Wu Weiliang (Pres & CEO)

Sekisui (Shanghai) International Trading Co., Ltd. (1)
Room 702-706 Metro Building No 30 Tianyaoqiao Road, Shanghai, 200030, China (100%)
Tel.: (86) 216 482 0638
Web Site: https://www.sekisui.com.cn
Sales Range: $50-74.9 Million
Emp.: 78
Trading Office
N.A.I.C.S.: 522299
Yasuhiro Hirayama (Pres & CEO)

Sekisui (Wuxi) Plastics Technology Co., Ltd. (1)
Block 82-A, Wuxi National High and New Technology Industrial Development Zone, Wuxi, 214028, Jiangsu, China
Tel.: (86) 5108 520 4282
Electro Fusion Joint Product Mfr & Distr
N.A.I.C.S.: 333992
Shinichi Takeda (Pres)

Sekisui Accounting Center Co., Ltd. (1)
2-4-4 Nishitemma Dojima Kanden Bldg, Kita-Ku, Osaka, 530-0047, Japan
Tel.: (81) 663654085
General Accounting Services
N.A.I.C.S.: 541219

Sekisui Amagasaki Kako Co., Ltd. (1)
5-8-6 Shioe, Amagasaki, 661-0976, Hyogo, Japan
Tel.: (81) 664294301
Plastics Product Mfr
N.A.I.C.S.: 326199

Sekisui America Corporation (1)
333 Meadowlands Pkwy, Secaucus, NJ 07094
Tel.: (201) 423-7960
Web Site: https://www.sekisui-corp.com
Sales Range: $50-74.9 Million
Emp.: 3
Corporate Planning, Administration & Technology Research
N.A.I.C.S.: 326150
Ian Moran (Pres)

Subsidiary (Domestic):

Allen Extruders, LLC (2)
1305 Lincoln Ave, Holland, MI 49423
Tel.: (616) 394-3808
Web Site: http://www.allenx.com
Custom Thermoplastic Sheet Distr
N.A.I.C.S.: 424610
Michael Angell (Mgr-Mfg)

KYDEX, LLC (2)

6685 Low St, Bloomsburg, PA 17815 (100%)
Tel.: (570) 389-5814
Web Site: https://kydex.com
Sales Range: $25-49.9 Million
Sales & Marketing of Acrylic PVC Alloy Sheets
N.A.I.C.S.: 325211
Michael Karr (Dir-Ops)

Sekisui Products, LLC (2)
50 W Big Beaver Rd, Troy, MI 48084
Tel.: (248) 307-0000
Web Site: http://www.sekisui-corp.com
Sales Range: $25-49.9 Million
Emp.: 10
Mfr of Prefabricated Houses; Chemical & Plastic Products
N.A.I.C.S.: 325998
Takashi Ito (Pres)

Sekisui S-Lec American, LLC (2)
1200 Rolling Hills Ln, Winchester, KY 40391-6014 (100%)
Tel.: (614) 527-5250
Web Site: http://www.s-lecfilm.com
Sales Range: $25-49.9 Million
Sales & Marketing of Polyvinyl Butyral Interlayer Film
N.A.I.C.S.: 336370

Sekisui SPR Americas, LLC (2)
5000 Austell Powder Springs Rd Ste 138, Austell, GA 30106 (100%)
Tel.: (678) 510-1820
Web Site: https://sekisui-spr.com
Trenchless Sewer Pipeline Replacement Materials Mfr, Whslr & Installation Services
N.A.I.C.S.: 339999

Sekisui Specialty Chemicals America, LLC (2)
1603 W LBJ Freeway Ste 200, Dallas, TX 75234
Tel.: (972) 277-2900
Polyvinyl Alcohol Products Mfr
N.A.I.C.S.: 325211

Sekisui TA Industries, Inc. (2)
100 South Puente St, Brea, CA 92821
Tel.: (714) 255-7888
Web Site: http://www.sta-tape.com
Sales Range: $50-74.9 Million
Mfg., Sales & Marketing of Adhesive Tape
N.A.I.C.S.: 322220

Sekisui Aqua Systems Co., Ltd. (1)
1-1-30 Oyodonaka Umeda Sky Building Tower West 21st Floor, Kita-ku, Osaka, 531-0076, Japan
Tel.: (81) 66 440 2500
Web Site: https://www.sekisuia.co.jp
Emp.: 192
Industrial Plant Construction Services
N.A.I.C.S.: 236210
Katsunori Nishizaki (Mng Dir)

Sekisui Board Co., Ltd. (1)
1259 Minakuchichoizumi, Koka, 528 0056, Shiga, Japan
Tel.: (81) 748 62 0073
Web Site: http://www.sekisui-board.com
Exterior Wall Tiles Mfr
N.A.I.C.S.: 327120

Sekisui Chemical (China) Co., Ltd. (1)
Room 706 Metro Tower No 30 Tianyaoqiao Road, Shanghai, 200030, China
Tel.: (86) 216 482 0638
Consumer Electronic Component Mfr & Distr
N.A.I.C.S.: 334419
Tomoyuki Miyano (Pres & CEO)

Sekisui Chemical (Taiwan) Co., Ltd. (1)
Room A 10F No 2 SEC 2 Nanjing E Rd, Taipei, 104, Taiwan
Tel.: (886) 2 2523 5335
Emp.: 32
Chemical Product Whslr
N.A.I.C.S.: 424690
Toyoma Shigeo (Pres)

Sekisui Chemical (Thailand) Co., Ltd. (1)
968 12th Floor U-Chuliang Building Rama 4 Road Silom, Bangrak, Bangkok, 10500, Thailand

Tel.: (66) 26324561
Web Site: http://www.sekisuichemical.com
Sales Range: $25-49.9 Million
Emp.: 11
Chemical Products Mfr
N.A.I.C.S.: 325998

Sekisui Chemical Co., Ltd. - Amagasaki Plant (1)
8-6 Shioe 5-chome, Amagasaki, 661-8564, Hyogo, Japan
Tel.: (81) 6 6429 4301
Plastic Tank Mfr
N.A.I.C.S.: 326199

Sekisui Chemical Co., Ltd. - Gunma Plant (1)
54 Sakaishimofuchina, Isesaki, 370-0103, Gunma, Japan
Tel.: (81) 270 76 3355
Pipe Products Mfr
N.A.I.C.S.: 327332

Sekisui Chemical Co., Ltd. - Musashi Plant (1)
3535 Kurohama, Hasuda, 349-0198, Saitama, Japan
Tel.: (81) 48 768 1131
Plastic Tank Mfr
N.A.I.C.S.: 326199

Sekisui Chemical Co., Ltd. - Tokyo Plant (1)
15-1 Negishidai 3-chome, Asaka, 351-8511, Saitama, Japan
Tel.: (81) 48 463 5111
Molded Plastic Product Mfr
N.A.I.C.S.: 326199

Sekisui Chemical Hokkaido Co., Ltd. (1)
234 Higashicho, Iwamizawa, 068-8668, Hokkaido, Japan
Tel.: (81) 126220801
Plastics Product Mfr
N.A.I.C.S.: 326199

Sekisui Chemical India Pvt. Ltd. (1)
310 A Rectangle One D-4, Saket District Centre Saket, New Delhi, 110017, India
Tel.: (91) 11 4265 8451
Web Site: http://www.sekisuichemical.com
Sales Range: $50-74.9 Million
Emp.: 1
Electronic Film Distr
N.A.I.C.S.: 423410

Sekisui Chemical Singapore (Pte.) Ltd. (1)
2 Jurong E St Rd 21 05 17 IMM Bldg, Singapore, 609601, Singapore (100%)
Tel.: (65) 625081
Web Site: http://www.sekisuichemical.com
Sales Range: $50-74.9 Million
Emp.: 10
Importer & Exporter of Plastic Products
N.A.I.C.S.: 424130

Sekisui DLJM Molding Private Ltd. (1)
Plot No 889 3rd and 4th Floor Udyog Vihar Phase-1, Gurgaon, 122 016, Haryana, India
Tel.: (91) 729 004 5557
Web Site: https://www.sekisuidljm.in
Emp.: 950
Chrome Plating Mfr & Distr
N.A.I.C.S.: 332813
Hirokazu Kinoshita (CEO)

Sekisui Engineering Co., Ltd. (1)
2-2 Kamichoshicho Kamitoba, Minami-Ku, Kyoto, 601-8105, Japan
Tel.: (81) 756930511
Engineering Services
N.A.I.C.S.: 541330

Sekisui Europe B.V. (1)
Metaalweg 5, 6045 JB, Roermond, Netherlands
Tel.: (31) 475 349963
Industrial Chemicals Mfr
N.A.I.C.S.: 325998
Nagafusa Isamu (Gen Mgr)

Subsidiary (Non-US):

Sekisui Alveo AG (2)
Ebikonerstrasse 75, 6043, Adligenswil, Switzerland
Tel.: (41) 2289292

SEKISUI CHEMICAL CO., LTD.

Web Site: https://www.sekisuialveo.com
Polyolefin Foam Products Mfr & Whslr
N.A.I.C.S.: 326150
Kenichi Takaki *(Pres)*

Subsidiary (Non-US):

Sekisui Alveo (Benelux) B.V. (3)
Gutenbergweg, 4102 DG, Culemborg, Netherlands
Tel.: (31) 345533939
Sales Range: $50-74.9 Million
Emp.: 4
Polyolefin Foam Products Whslr
N.A.I.C.S.: 424610

Sekisui Alveo BS G.m.b.H. (3)
Haystrasse 14-20, 55566, Sobernheim, Germany
Tel.: (49) 6751 8530 0
Polyethylene Mfr & Whslr
N.A.I.C.S.: 325211
Markus Romer *(Pres)*

Sekisui Alveo GmbH (3)
Frankfurter Strasse 151C, 63303, Dreieich, Germany (100%)
Tel.: (49) 61 039 4830
Web Site: https://www.sekisuialveo.com
Polyolefin Foam Products Whslr
N.A.I.C.S.: 424610
Manfred Werner *(Mng Dir)*

Sekisui Alveo Ltd. (3)
Merthyr Indus Pk Cardiff Rd, Merthyr Tydfil, CF48 4DR, United Kingdom (100%)
Tel.: (44) 1443690940
Web Site: http://www.sekisuialveo.com
Sales Range: $25-49.9 Million
Mfr of Polyolefin Foam Products
N.A.I.C.S.: 326140

Sekisui Alveo Representacoes Ltda. (3)
Avenida Vitoria Rossi Martini 612 Distrito Industrial Vitoria Martini, Indaiatuba, 13347-613, SP, Brazil (100%)
Tel.: (55) 19 3936 5579
Web Site: http://www.sekisuialveo.com
Emp.: 4
Polyethylene Foam Whslr
N.A.I.C.S.: 424610
Elias Fries *(Mgr)*

Sekisui Alveo S.a.r.l. (3)
8 allee des Chevreuils, Lissieu, 69380, Lyon, France (100%)
Tel.: (33) 478339797
Web Site: http://www.sekisuialveo.com
Sales Range: $50-74.9 Million
Emp.: 4
Polyolefin Foam Products Whslr
N.A.I.C.S.: 424610
Thierry Loysel *(Reg Mgr-Sls)*

Sekisui Alveo S.r.l. (3)
Viale Italia 5/A, 20045, Lainate, MI, Italy (100%)
Tel.: (39) 029 357 0283
Web Site: https://www.sekisuialveo.com
Sales Range: $25-49.9 Million
Emp.: 9
Sales of Polyolefin Foam Products
N.A.I.C.S.: 326140

Subsidiary (US):

Sekisui Voltek LLC (3)
100 Shepard St, Lawrence, MA 01843-1024
Tel.: (978) 685-2557
Web Site: http://www.voltek.com
Sales Range: $50-74.9 Million
Mfr Sales & Marketing of Polyolefin Foam Products
N.A.I.C.S.: 326150
Neil Beckhusen *(Pres)*

Subsidiary (Non-US):

Sekisui-Alveo B.V. (3)
Montageweg 6, 6045 JA, Roermond, Netherlands (100%)
Tel.: (31) 88 966 4354
Web Site: https://www.sekisuialveo.com
Sales Range: $125-149.9 Million
Emp.: 270
Mfr of Polyolefin Foam Products
N.A.I.C.S.: 326140

Sekisui-Alveo S.A. (3)
Miquel Torello i Pages 60 Poligono Industrial el Pla 42, PO Box 42, Apartado de Correos, 08750, Molins de Rei, Barcelona, Spain (100%)
Tel.: (34) 93 680 2842
Web Site: https://www.sekisuialveo.com
Sales Range: $25-49.9 Million
Emp.: 5
Sales of Polyolefin Foam Products
N.A.I.C.S.: 326140
Eiji Tateo *(Pres)*

Subsidiary (Non-US):

Sekisui Chemical GmbH (2)
Konigsallee 106, 40215, Dusseldorf, Germany (100%)
Tel.: (49) 21 136 9770
Web Site: https://www.sekisui.de
Sales Range: $25-49.9 Million
Emp.: 15
Exporter & Importer of Plastic Products
N.A.I.C.S.: 424130
Koji Yamaguchi *(Pres)*

Subsidiary (Domestic):

Sekisui Eslon B.V. (2)
Metaalweg 7, 6045 JB, Roermond, Netherlands (100%)
Tel.: (31) 47 532 2851
Web Site: https://www.eslon.nl
Mfr, Sales & Marketing of PVC Rain Gutters
N.A.I.C.S.: 326199
R. Vernaus *(Gen Mgr)*

Sekisui S-Lec B.V. (2)
Metaalweg 5, 6045 JB, Roermond, Netherlands (100%)
Tel.: (31) 475349900
Web Site: http://www.s-lec.nl
Sales Range: $50-74.9 Million
Emp.: 180
Mfr of Polyvinyl Butyral Interlayer Film
N.A.I.C.S.: 326113
Naoya Nishimoto *(Pres)*

Sekisui Exterior Co., Ltd. (1)
7F Iidabashi Masumoto Building 1-21 Yangbacho, Shinjyuku-ku, Tokyo, 162-0824, Japan
Tel.: (81) 3 6685 7030
Web Site: http://www.sekisui-exterior.co.jp
Construction Engineering Services
N.A.I.C.S.: 541330

Sekisui Fami S Kyushu Co., Ltd. (1)
2-8-1 Takasago, Chuo-ku, Fukuoka, 810-0011, Japan
Tel.: (81) 12 038 0816
Web Site: https://www.sekisuiheim-owner.jp
Emp.: 361
Residential Remodeling Services
N.A.I.C.S.: 236118

Sekisui Fami S Shinetsu Co., Ltd. (1)
6-11 Ryoshima, Matsumoto, 390-0848, Nagano, Japan
Tel.: (81) 263288300
Chemical Product Whslr
N.A.I.C.S.: 424690

Sekisui Fami-S Chushikoku Co., Ltd. (1)
2-chome 2 5 (Nissei Okayama Square Building 7th floor, Kita-Ku, Okayama, 700-0907, Japan
Tel.: (81) 862353030
Web Site: http://www.sekisui-fs.jp
Residential Remodeling Services
N.A.I.C.S.: 236118
Takayuki Ikeda *(Pres)*

Sekisui Famis Kinki Co., Ltd. (1)
Shin-Osaka Brick Building 11F 1-6-1 Miyahara, Yodogawa-Ku, Osaka, 532-0003, Japan
Tel.: (81) 66 394 8778
Web Site: https://www.famis-kinki.jp
Emp.: 474
Residential Remodeling Services
N.A.I.C.S.: 236118

Sekisui Film Co., Ltd. (1)
2-4-4 Nishitemma Dojimakanden Bldg, Kita-Ku, Osaka, 530-8565, Japan
Tel.: (81) 663654220
Web Site: http://www.sekisui.co.jp

Sales Range: $125-149.9 Million
Emp.: 343
Polyolefin Film Mfr & Whslr
N.A.I.C.S.: 325220
Takeshi Inoue *(Pres)*

Sekisui Heim Chubu Co., Ltd. (1)
1-13-3 Higashisakura, Higashi-ku, Nagoya, 461-0005, Japan
Tel.: (81) 52 955 8160
Web Site: https://www.816chubu.jp
Emp.: 680
Construction Engineering Services
N.A.I.C.S.: 541330

Sekisui Heim Chushikoku Co., Ltd. (1)
2-2-5 Shimoishi, Okayama, 700-0907, Japan (100%)
Tel.: (81) 862353322
Web Site: http://www.oka816.jp
Sales Range: $400-449.9 Million
Emp.: 971
Construction Engineering Services
N.A.I.C.S.: 541330
Ikeda Takayuki *(Pres)*

Sekisui Heim Kinki Co., Ltd. (1)
1-6-1 Miyahara Shinosaka Brick Bldg 11f, Yodogawa-Ku, Osaka, 532-0003, Japan
Tel.: (81) 663948161
Condominium Building Construction Services
N.A.I.C.S.: 236117

Sekisui Heim Kyushu Co., Ltd. (1)
2-8-1 Takasago Onuki Takasago Bldg 6f, Chuo-Ku, Fukuoka, 810-0011, Japan
Tel.: (81) 925338071
Construction Engineering Services
N.A.I.C.S.: 237990

Sekisui Heim Shinetsu Co., Ltd. (1)
6-11 Ryoshima Matsumoto, Nagano, 390-0848, Japan
Tel.: (81) 263288300
Construction Engineering Services
N.A.I.C.S.: 541330

Sekisui Heim Supply Co., Ltd. (1)
MPR Higashiueno Building 5F 6-2-1 Higashiueno, Taito-Ku, Tokyo, 110-0015, Japan
Tel.: (81) 36 895 2931
Web Site: https://www.sekisuiheim-supply.com
Sales Range: $1-9.9 Million
Emp.: 60
Construction Materials Whslr
N.A.I.C.S.: 423320
Ichiro Matsuhashi *(Pres & CEO)*

Sekisui Heim Tohoku Co., Ltd. (1)
14th floor Azeria Hills 3-4-1 Tsutsujigaoka, Miyagino-ku, Sendai, 983-0852, Miyagi, Japan
Tel.: (81) 22 369 3816
Web Site: https://www.heim-tohoku.co.jp
Emp.: 536
Construction Engineering Services
N.A.I.C.S.: 541330

Sekisui High Performance Packaging (Langfang) Co., Ltd. (1)
No 12 Hui Yuan Road Langfang E&T Zone, Langfang, 065001, Hebei, China (100%)
Tel.: (86) 316 608 9731
Web Site: http://www.sekisuichemical.com
Mfr of Packaging Tapes
N.A.I.C.S.: 561910
Noriaki Narita *(Pres & CEO)*

Sekisui Home Techno Co., Ltd. (1)
Nissei Shin-Osaka Building 17th Floor 3-4-30 Miyahara, Yodogawa-Ku, Osaka, 532-0003, Japan
Tel.: (81) 66 397 7341
Web Site: https://www.sekisui-hometechno.co.jp
Emp.: 409
Construction Materials Whslr
N.A.I.C.S.: 423320

Sekisui Industrial Piping Co., Ltd. (1)
No 18 Ching 1st Road, Wuqi Dist, Taichung, 435059, Taiwan
Tel.: (886) 22 964 1478
Web Site: https://www.eslon.com.tw
Sales Range: $75-99.9 Million
Emp.: 230
Plastic Valves & Pipes Mfr & Whslr

N.A.I.C.S.: 326199
Hiroyuki Hatayama *(CEO)*

Sekisui Korea Co., Ltd. (1)
16F Sanhak foundation Bldg Seocho-dong 329 Gangnam-daero, Seocho-gu, 06627, Seoul, Korea (South) (100%)
Tel.: (82) 2 319 9471
Web Site: http://www.sekisui.co.kr
Sales Range: $25-49.9 Million
Emp.: 13
Specialty Chemicals Mfr
N.A.I.C.S.: 325998

Sekisui Kosan Co., Ltd. (1)
2-4-4 Nishitemma, Kita-Ku, Osaka, 530-0047, Japan
Tel.: (81) 663654147
Real Estate Manangement Services
N.A.I.C.S.: 531390

Sekisui Kydex, LLC (1)
6685 Low St, Bloomsburg, PA 17815
Tel.: (570) 389-5814
Web Site: https://www.kydex.com
Plastic Sheet Mfr
N.A.I.C.S.: 326112

Sekisui Medical Co., Ltd. (1)
Urbannet Nihonbashi 2-chome Building 2-1-3 Nihonbashi, Chuo-ku, Tokyo, 103-0027, Japan (100%)
Tel.: (81) 33 272 0671
Web Site: https://www.sekisuimedical.jp
Sales Range: $350-399.9 Million
Emp.: 1,100
Pharmaceuticals & Medical Diagnostics Products Developer, Mfr & Marketer
N.A.I.C.S.: 325413
Hideo Tagashira *(Pres & CEO)*

Subsidiary (US):

Sekisui Diagnostics, LLC (2)
1 Wall St, Burlington, MA 01803
Tel.: (781) 652-7800
Web Site: https://www.sekisuidiagnostics.com
Sales Range: $25-49.9 Million
Emp.: 100
Mfr & Marketer of Diagnostic Products
N.A.I.C.S.: 339112
Robert T. Schruender *(Pres & CEO)*

Unit (Domestic):

Sekisui Diagnostics (3)
6659 Top Gun St, San Diego, CA 92121
Tel.: (858) 777-2600
Web Site: https://sekisuidiagnostics.com
Sales Range: $25-49.9 Million
Mfr of Monoclonal & Polyclonal Antibodies, Antigens, Elisa Test Kits & Rapid Test Systems
N.A.I.C.S.: 325414

Subsidiary (Non-US):

Sekisui Diagnostics (UK) Limited (3)
50 Gibson Drive Kings Hill, West Malling, ME19 4AF, Kent, United Kingdom
Tel.: (44) 1732 220022
Sales Range: $25-49.9 Million
Emp.: 50
Diagnostic Reagents & Enzymes Developer, Mfr & Marketer
N.A.I.C.S.: 339112

Division (Domestic):

Sekisui Diagnostics - Coagulation Division - Stamford (3)
500 West Ave, Stamford, CT 06902
Tel.: (203) 602-7777
Web Site: http://sekisuidxcoag.com
Diagnostic Reagent Mfr & Whslr
N.A.I.C.S.: 325412

Subsidiary (Non-US):

Sekisui Diagnostics GmbH (4)
Uhlandstr 9, 64297, Darmstadt, Germany
Tel.: (49) 6151 359 8520
Web Site: http://www.sekisuidiagnostics.com
Diagnostic Reagent Distr
N.A.I.C.S.: 423450

Subsidiary (Non-US):

Sekisui Diagnostics P.E.I. Inc. (3)
70 Watts Avenue, Charlottetown, C1E 2B9, PE, Canada

SEKISUI CHEMICAL CO., LTD.

Sekisui Chemical Co., Ltd.—(Continued)
Tel.: (902) 566-1396
Web Site: http://www.sekisuidiagnostics.com
Sales Range: $50-74.9 Million
Emp.: 100
Diagnostic Products Marketer
N.A.I.C.S.: 423450

Subsidiary (Non-US):

Sekisui Virotech G.m.b.H. (2)
Lowenplatz 5, 65428, Russelsheim, Germany
Tel.: (49) 61 42 69 09 0
Web Site: http://www.sekisuivirotech.com
Sales Range: $50-74.9 Million
Emp.: 13
Diagnostic Products Mfr
N.A.I.C.S.: 325413
Klaus Ackermann *(Gen Mgr)*

Sekisui Medical Technology (China) Ltd. (1)
Tianzhu Road 17 Zone A, Tianzhu Airport Industrial Zone Shunyi District, Beijing, 101312, China
Tel.: (86) 108 048 6940
Web Site: http://www.sekisuitrank.com
Sales Range: $50-74.9 Million
Emp.: 170
Producer of Vacuum Blood Collection Tubes
N.A.I.C.S.: 339112
Wang Qiang *(Pres & CEO)*

Sekisui Medical Technology (Suzhou) Co., Ltd. (1)
Unit B Plant 6 78th Xinglin Street, Emerging Industry Industrial Workshop Suzhou Industrial Park, Suzhou, 215026, China
Tel.: (86) 5126 788 1190
Clinical Diagnostic Reagent Mfr & Distr
N.A.I.C.S.: 325413
Hisashi Komine *(Pres & CEO)*

Sekisui Minakuchi Kako Co., Ltd. (1)
C/O Sekisui Kagaku Kogyo K K Shiga Minakuchi Kojo, 1259 Minakuchichoizumi, Koka, 528-0056, Shiga, Japan
Tel.: (81) 748623857
Film Products Mfr
N.A.I.C.S.: 326113

Sekisui Musashi Kako Co., Ltd. (1)
Kurohama 3535, Hasuda, 349-0198, Saitama, Japan (100%)
Tel.: (81) 48 768 1181
Web Site: https://www.sekisui.co.jp
Emp.: 367
Adhesive Tape Mfr
N.A.I.C.S.: 326113
Hisashiko Kashiwabara *(Pres & CEO)*

Sekisui Nuvotec Co., Ltd. (1)
1720-23 Taejang-Dong, Wonju, Kangwon-Do, Korea (South)
Tel.: (82) 2531300
Pipe Products Mfr & Whslr
N.A.I.C.S.: 332996

Sekisui Pilon Pty. Ltd. (1)
1-5 Parraweena Rd, PO Box 2898, Taren Point, 2229, NSW, Australia (100%)
Tel.: (61) 29 525 9880
Web Site: https://www.sekisuifoam.com.au
Sales Range: $25-49.9 Million
Emp.: 50
Polystyrene Foam Product Manufacturing
N.A.I.C.S.: 326140
Rocco Romiti *(Mng Dir)*

Sekisui Polymatech (Shanghai) Co., Ltd. (1)
718 Guangzhong Road, Xinzhuang Industry Park Minhang, Shanghai, 201108, China
Tel.: (86) 216 442 2002
Emp.: 2,390
Consumer Electronic Component Mfr & Distr
N.A.I.C.S.: 334419
Masayuki Itakura *(Pres)*

Sekisui Polymatech (Shanghai) Trading Co., Ltd. (1)
718 Guangzhong Road, Xinzhuang Industry Park Minhang, Shanghai, 201108, China
Tel.: (86) 216 219 4374
Consumer Electronic Component Mfr & Distr
N.A.I.C.S.: 334419

Sekisui Polymatech (Thailand) Co., Ltd. (1)
222 Moo 2 Klongjik, Bangpa-in Industrial Estate, Ayutthaya, 13160, Thailand
Tel.: (66) 3 525 8193
Emp.: 319
Consumer Electronic Component Mfr & Distr
N.A.I.C.S.: 334419
Masatsugu Kato *(Pres)*

Sekisui Polymatech Co., Ltd. (1)
8-10-1 Tajima, Sakura-ku, Saitama, 338-0837, Japan
Tel.: (81) 48 611 6601
Web Site: https://polymatech.co.jp
Emp.: 189
Plastic Film Mfr & Whslr
N.A.I.C.S.: 326113

Sekisui Polymatech Trading (Thailand) Co., Ltd. (1)
222 Moo 2 Klongjik, Bangpa-in Industrial Estate, Ayutthaya, 13160, Thailand
Tel.: (66) 3 526 8130
Consumer Electronic Component Mfr & Distr
N.A.I.C.S.: 334419

Sekisui Refresh Co., Ltd. (1)
383 1 OiRyong Ri Buknae-Myun Yeoju-gun, Gyeonggi-do, 469-852, Seoul, Korea (South)
Tel.: (82) 318813741
Web Site: http://www.sekisuichemical.com
Pipeline Renewal Materials Mfr
N.A.I.C.S.: 237120

Sekisui Roof System Co., Ltd. (1)
2-4-4 Nishitemma, Kita-Ku, Osaka, 530-0047, Japan
Tel.: (81) 663654128
Roofing Material Mfr & Whslr
N.A.I.C.S.: 327390

Sekisui S-Lec (Suzhou) Co., Ltd. (1)
No 25 Tazhou Road, New District Suzhou, Suzhou, 215129, China (100%)
Tel.: (86) 5126 661 8181
Web Site: https://www.sekisuichemical.com
Sales Range: $50-74.9 Million
Emp.: 120
Film Mfr
N.A.I.C.S.: 325992
Zhang Jun *(Pres & CEO)*

Sekisui S-Lec (Thailand) Co., Ltd. (1)
64/31 Moo4 Eastern Seaboard Industrial Estate, T Pluakdaeng A Plukdaeng, Rayong, 21140, Thailand
Tel.: (66) 3 895 5430
Web Site: https://www.s-lec.th
Mfr of PVB Interlayer Film
N.A.I.C.S.: 325992

Sekisui S-Lec Korea Ltd. (1)
Soon Hwa Bldg 5 2, Seoul, 100 130, Korea (South) (100%)
Tel.: (82) 23199471
Web Site: http://www.sekisui.co.kr
Sales Range: $25-49.9 Million
Emp.: 11
Sales of Polyvinyl Butyral Interlayer Film; Provider of Technical Services
N.A.I.C.S.: 325992
Chooncat Lee *(CEO)*

Sekisui S-Lec Mexico S.A. de C.V. (1)
Calle 21 Este No 524 CIVAC, 62578, Jiutepec, Morelos, Mexico (71%)
Tel.: (52) 7773290601
Web Site: https://www.sekisuichemical.com
Sales Range: $25-49.9 Million
Emp.: 70
Polyvinyl Butyral Interlayer Film Mfr & Sales
N.A.I.C.S.: 326113
P. Cordoba Najera *(Pres)*

Sekisui SPR Asia Pte. Ltd. (1)
11-302 The Plaza 7500A Beach Road, Singapore, 199591, Singapore
Tel.: (65) 629 637 88
Pipeline Products Mfr
N.A.I.C.S.: 332996

Subsidiary (Non-US):

Sekisui Rib Loc Australia Pty. Ltd. (2)
587 Grand Junction Road, Gepps Cross, 5094, SA, Australia
Tel.: (61) 882608000
Web Site: http://www.ribloc.com.au
Sales Range: $25-49.9 Million
Emp.: 50
Pipe Relining Mfr
N.A.I.C.S.: 326122
John Taylor *(Pres)*

Sekisui Singapore Pte. Ltd. (1)
7500A Beach Road 12-306 The Plaza, Singapore, 199591, Singapore
Tel.: (65) 6 296 3788
Water Infrastructure Related Material Distr
N.A.I.C.S.: 423390
Yuichi Kamio *(Pres)*

Sekisui Southeast Asia Co., Ltd. (1)
Unit 14C 14th Floor President Tower 973 Phloen Chit Road, Lumpini Pathum Wan, Bangkok, 10330, Thailand
Tel.: (66) 2 656 0274
Plastic Product Mfr & Distr
N.A.I.C.S.: 326199
Kazutora Taira *(Pres)*

Sekisui Speciality Chemicals (Thailand) Co., Ltd. (1)
968 12 Floor U Chu Liang Building Rama 4 Road, Silom Bangrak, Bangkok, 10500, Thailand
Tel.: (66) 2 632 4561
Web Site: https://www.sekisui-ssct.com
Emp.: 108
Chlorinated Polyvinyl Chloride Resin Mfr & Distr
N.A.I.C.S.: 325211
Toshiyuki Nakajima *(Mng Dir)*

Sekisui Speciality Chemicals Europe S.L. (1)
Apartado 1388, 43080, Tarragona, Spain
Tel.: (34) 97 754 9899
Polyvinyl Alcohol Product Mfr & Distr
N.A.I.C.S.: 325211

Sekisui Specialty Chemicals Mexico S, de R.L. de C.V. (1)
Avenida Rio Magdalena 326 Oficina 103, La Otra Banda, 01090, Mexico, Mexico
Tel.: (52) 555 550 2885
Poly Vinyl Acetate Resin Distr
N.A.I.C.S.: 424610
Cory Sikora *(Pres)*

Sekisui Techno Shoji Higashi Nihon Co., Ltd. (1)
Nihonbashi Koamicho Nihonbashi Soyic Bldg 3-11, Chuo-Ku, Tokyo, 103-0016, Japan
Tel.: (81) 356235651
Resin Products Whslr
N.A.I.C.S.: 424610

Sekisui Techno Shoji Nishi Nihon Co., Ltd. (1)
2-4-4 Nishitemma Doshima Kanden Bldg 5f, Kita-Ku, Osaka, 530-8565, Japan
Tel.: (81) 663654321
Synthetic Resin Products Whslr
N.A.I.C.S.: 424610

Sekisui Unidea Co., Ltd. (1)
4-27-3 Higashiueno, Taito-Ku, Tokyo, 110-0015, Japan
Tel.: (81) 358068228
Web Site: http://www.unidea.co.jp
Chemical Products Mfr
N.A.I.C.S.: 325998

Sekisui Vietnam Co., Ltd. (1)
Room1414 CornerStone Building 16 Phan Chu Trinh St, Hoan Kiem District, Hanoi, Vietnam
Tel.: (84) 243 939 2677
Water Infrastructure Related Material Distr
N.A.I.C.S.: 423390
Noboru Kobayashi *(Pres)*

Sekisui Xenotech, LLC (1)
1101 W Cambridge Circle Dr, Kansas City, KS 66103
Tel.: (913) 438-7450
Web Site: https://www.xenotech.com
Pharmaceuticals Product Mfr
N.A.I.C.S.: 325412
Darren Warren *(Pres & CEO)*

Sekisui Youngbo HPP (Wuxi) Co., Ltd. (1)
No 1219 Lianfu Road, Xishan District, Wuxi, Jiangsu, China
Tel.: (86) 5108 878 5933
Polyolefin Foam Product Mfr & Distr
N.A.I.C.S.: 326150
Takanobu Sugiyama *(Gen Mgr)*

Sekisui-SCG Industry Co., Ltd. (1)
Hemaraj Saraburi Industrial Land Soi 6 33 Moo 1 Tambon Bua Loi, Amphoe Nongkhae, Saraburi, 18140, Thailand
Tel.: (66) 3 637 3476
Web Site: https://www.sekisuichemical.com
Modular Housing Construction Services
N.A.I.C.S.: 326117
Masaya Fujiwara *(Pres)*

Seksui Eslon B.V. (1)
Metaalweg 7, 6045 JB, Roermond, Netherlands
Tel.: (31) 47 532 2851
Web Site: https://www.eslon.nl
Polyvinyl Chloride Building Product Mfr
N.A.I.C.S.: 326199

Senseki Kako Co., Ltd. (1)
163-1 Azaohara Okumanakaizumi Wataricho, Watari-Gun, Miyagi, 989-2301, Japan
Tel.: (81) 223344641
Plastics Films Mfr
N.A.I.C.S.: 326113

Thai Sekisui Foam Co., Ltd. (1)
700/379 Moo 6 Tumbol Donhua-Ioh, Amphur Muang, Chon Buri, 20000, Thailand
Tel.: (66) 3 821 3219
Web Site: https://www.thaisekisui.co.th
Sales Range: $25-49.9 Million
Emp.: 51
Mfg., Sales & Marketing of Polyolefin Foam Products
N.A.I.C.S.: 326140
Rocco Romiti *(Pres)*

Tohoku Sekisui Shoji Co., Ltd. (1)
4-1 Izai, Wakabayashi-Ku, Sendai, Miyagi, Japan
Tel.: (81) 222873911
Construction Materials Whslr
N.A.I.C.S.: 423390

Toto Sekisui Co., Ltd. (1)
2-8-13 Shibadaimon Success Shibadaimon Bldg 3f, Minato-Ku, Tokyo, 105-0012, Japan
Tel.: (81) 334382270
Resin Products Whslr
N.A.I.C.S.: 424610

Toyo Plastics Industries Corp. (1)
300 Kamijo Araimachi, Kofu, 400-0052, Yamanashi, Japan (100%)
Tel.: (81) 552413101
Sales Range: $50-74.9 Million
Emp.: 90
Molded Plastic Products Mfr & Whslr
N.A.I.C.S.: 326199
Chinami Hanakawa *(Pres)*

Vantec Co., Ltd. (1)
321 Nikucho, Nasushiobara, Tochigi287363398, Japan
Tel.: (81) 287363398
Plastics Product Mfr
N.A.I.C.S.: 326199

Vantec Shoji Co., Ltd. (1)
1-6-3 Ohashi Nichibei Bldg Vantec Nai, Meguro-Ku, Tokyo, 153-0044, Japan
Tel.: (81) 357844716
Resin Products Whslr
N.A.I.C.S.: 424610

Veredus Laboratories Pte. Ltd. (1)
83 Science Park Drive 04-02 The Curie, Singapore, 118258, Singapore
Tel.: (65) 6 496 8600
Web Site: https://www.vereduslabs.com
Diagnostic Reagent Mfr & Distr
N.A.I.C.S.: 325413
Rosemary Tan *(CEO)*

Wuxi SSS-Diamond Plastics Co., Ltd. (1)
Wuxi National High & New Technology Industrial Development Zone, Block 82-A, Wuxi, 214028, Jiangsu, China (100%)
Tel.: (86) 51085204282
Sales Range: $75-99.9 Million
Emp.: 150
Polyethylene Electro-Fusion Fittings Mfr & Distr

AND PRIVATE COMPANIES SEKISUI HOUSE, LTD.

N.A.I.C.S.: 326199
Tsutomu Nakamura *(Pres & CEO)*

Yongchang Sekisui Composites Co., Ltd. (1)
High Technical Industrial Zone, Midong, Xinjiang, 831400, Urumqi, China **(100%)**
Tel.: (86) 991 653 9999
Web Site: http://www.sekisuichemical.com
Mfr of Plastic Composites
N.A.I.C.S.: 326199

Youngbo Chemical Co., Ltd. (1)
230-23 Seobu-ro Gangnae-myeon, Heungdeok-gu, Cheongju, 465 810, Chungcheongbuk-do, Korea (South)
Tel.: (82) 43 249 2000
Web Site: https://www.youngbo.com
Sales Range: $125-149.9 Million
Emp.: 296
Mfr of Cross-Linked Polyolefin Foam Products
N.A.I.C.S.: 326140
Young-Sik Lee *(CEO)*

Youngbo Hpp (Langfang) Co., Ltd. (1)
No 7 Xinyuan East Road, LangFang Economic and Technical Development Zone, Hebei, 065001, China
Tel.: (86) 316 591 8520
Polyolefin Foam Product Mfr & Distr
N.A.I.C.S.: 326150
Choi Hyun Ho *(Gen Mgr)*

SEKISUI HOUSE, LTD.
1-1-88 Oyodonaka, Kita-Ku, Osaka, 531-0076, Japan
Tel.: (81) 664403111   JP
Web Site:
https://www.sekisuihouse.co.jp
Year Founded: 1960
1928—(TKS)
Rev.: $20,530,175,091
Assets: $22,152,613,148
Liabilities: $10,298,949,455
Net Worth: $11,853,663,693
Earnings: $1,336,802,114
Emp.: 14,932
Fiscal Year-end: 01/31/24
Real Estate Manangement Services
N.A.I.C.S.: 236115
Takashi Uchida *(Exec VP)*

Subsidiaries:

Almetax Manufacturing Co., Ltd. (1)
1-1-30 Oyodonaka Umeda Sky Building Tower West 30th floor, Kita-ku, Osaka, 531-6130, Japan
Tel.: (81) 664403838
Web Site: https://www.almetax.co.jp
Sales Range: $75-99.9 Million
Building Material Mfr & Whslr
N.A.I.C.S.: 332321
Tatsuya Hikima *(Chm)*

Ekisui House Real Estate Chubu, Ltd. (1)
4-24-16 Meieki Hirokoji Garden Avenue, Nakamura-ku, Nagoya, 450-0002, Japan
Tel.: (81) 525412101
Web Site: https://www.sekisuihouse-f-chubu.co.jp
Emp.: 1,043
Real Estate Services
N.A.I.C.S.: 531210

Greentechno Sekiwa Kansai, Ltd (1)
1-1-93 Oyodonaka Shinumeda City Garden Six 5f, Kita-ku, Osaka, 531-0076, Japan
Tel.: (81) 664403655
Residential Property Development Services
N.A.I.C.S.: 236115

Greentechno Sekiwa, Ltd (1)
2-8-15 Shakujimachi, Nerima-ku, Tokyo, 177-0041, Japan
Tel.: (81) 353727311
Real Estate Manangement Services
N.A.I.C.S.: 531390

Konoike Construction Co., Ltd. (1)
3-6-1 Kitakyuhojimachi, Chuo-ku, Osaka, 541-0057, Japan
Tel.: (81) 662456300
Web Site: https://www.konoike.co.jp

Emp.: 1,907
Construction Materials Mfr & Distr
N.A.I.C.S.: 324122

Landtech Sekiwa Chubu, Ltd (1)
1504 Yabutacho Moriyama-ku, Nagoya, 463-0026, Aichi, Japan
Tel.: (81) 527681300
Land Surveying Services
N.A.I.C.S.: 541370

Landtech Sekiwa, Ltd (1)
3498-1 Honcho, Moriya, 302-0109, Ibaraki, Japan
Tel.: (81) 297211171
Construction Engineering Services
N.A.I.C.S.: 541330

M.D.C. Holdings, Inc. (1)
4350 S Monaco St Ste 500, Denver, CO 80237
Tel.: (303) 773-1100
Web Site: http://www.mdcholdings.com
Rev.: $4,520,296,000
Assets: $5,631,085,000
Liabilities: $2,253,200,000
Net Worth: $3,377,885,000
Earnings: $401,005,000
Emp.: 1,760
Fiscal Year-end: 12/31/2023
Homebuilding & Financial Services
N.A.I.C.S.: 236117
Larry A. Mizel *(Exec Chm)*

Subsidiary (Domestic):

American Home Title & Escrow Company (2)
4704 Harlan St Ste 620, Denver, CO 80212 **(100%)**
Tel.: (303) 426-0990
Web Site: http://www.ahteco.com
Sales Range: $50-74.9 Million
Emp.: 10
General Contractors
N.A.I.C.S.: 236118
Patrick A. Rice *(Pres)*

HomeAmerican Mortgage Corp. (2)
4350 S Monaco St Ste 100, Denver, CO 80237 **(100%)**
Web Site:
http://www.homeamericanmortgage.com
Sales Range: $75-99.9 Million
Mortgage Lending & Origination Services
N.A.I.C.S.: 236115

M.D.C. Land Corporation (2)
4350 S Monaco St, Denver, CO 80237
Tel.: (303) 773-1100
Web Site:
http://www.mdcholdings.com
Residential Building Construction Services
N.A.I.C.S.: 236115

Richmond American Homes of Arizona, Inc. (2)
3091 W Ina Rd, Tucson, AZ 85741 **(100%)**
Tel.: (520) 544-2700
Web Site:
http://www.richmondamerican.com
Sales Range: $100-124.9 Million
Emp.: 50
Single Family Home Construction
N.A.I.C.S.: 236220

Richmond American Homes of Arizona, Inc. (2)
16427 N Scottsdale Rd Ste 175, Scottsdale, AZ 85254 **(100%)**
Tel.: (480) 624-0238
Web Site:
http://www.richmondamerican.com
Sales Range: $75-99.9 Million
Residential Construction
N.A.I.C.S.: 236115

Richmond American Homes of California, Inc. (2)
5171 California Ave Ste 120, Irvine, CA 92617
Tel.: (760) 653-7011
Web Site:
http://www.richmondamerican.com
Sales Range: $50-74.9 Million
Emp.: 70
Residential Construction
N.A.I.C.S.: 236115

Richmond American Homes of California, Inc. (South) (2)
5171 California Ave Ste 110, Irvine, CA 92617 **(100%)**
Tel.: (909) 579-3301
Web Site:
http://www.richmondamerican.com
Sales Range: $50-74.9 Million
Emp.: 40
Residential Construction
N.A.I.C.S.: 236115

Richmond American Homes of Colorado, Inc. (2)
2060 Briar Gate Pkwy Ste 240, Colorado Springs, CO 80920 **(100%)**
Tel.: (719) 260-0684
Web Site:
http://www.richmondamerican.com
Sales Range: $50-74.9 Million
Emp.: 25
General Contractors-Single Family Houses
N.A.I.C.S.: 236115

Richmond American Homes of Colorado, Inc. (2)
4350 S Monaco St, Denver, CO 80237 **(100%)**
Tel.: (303) 694-9109
Web Site:
http://www.richmondamerican.com
Sales Range: $300-349.9 Million
Residential Construction
N.A.I.C.S.: 236115

Richmond American Homes of Florida, LP (2)
10255 Fortune Pkwy Ste 150, Jacksonville, FL 32256
Tel.: (904) 637-8610
Web Site:
https://www.richmondamerican.com
Sales Range: $25-49.9 Million
Residential Building Construction Services
N.A.I.C.S.: 236117

Richmond American Homes of Maryland, Inc. (2)
6210 Old Dobbin Ln Ste 190, Columbia, MD 21045 **(100%)**
Tel.: (703) 349-7381
Web Site:
http://www.richmondamerican.com
Sales Range: $50-74.9 Million
Home Building of Single Family Homes
N.A.I.C.S.: 236115

Richmond American Homes of Nevada, Inc. (2)
7770 S Dean Martin Dr, Las Vegas, NV 89139 **(100%)**
Tel.: (702) 638-4470
Web Site:
http://www.richmondamerican.com
Sales Range: $300-349.9 Million
General Contractors-Single Family Houses
N.A.I.C.S.: 236115

Richmond American Homes of Virginia, Inc. (2)
12200 Sunrise Valley Dr Ste 400, Reston, VA 20191 **(100%)**
Tel.: (703) 390-0900
Web Site:
http://www.richmondamerican.com
Sales Range: $50-74.9 Million
Building Construction Services
N.A.I.C.S.: 236115

Richmond American Homes of Washington, Inc. (2)
20829 72nd Ave S Ste 115, Kent, WA 98032
Tel.: (253) 693-4777
Web Site:
http://www.richmondamerican.com
Emp.: 60
Residential Building Construction Services
N.A.I.C.S.: 236115

North America Sekisui House, LLC (1)
2101 Wilson Blvd Ste 1004, Arlington, VA 22201
Tel.: (703) 740-0232
Web Site: http://www.nashcommunities.com
Sales Range: $25-49.9 Million
Emp.: 5
Construction Engineering Services
N.A.I.C.S.: 541330

SGM Operation Co., Ltd. (1)

1-30 Oyodonaka 1-chome, Kita-ku, Osaka, 531-0076, Hyogo, Japan
Tel.: (81) 788570008
Real Estate Services
N.A.I.C.S.: 531190

Sekisui House Asset Management, Ltd. (1)
4-15-1 Akasaka, Minato-ku, Tokyo, 107-0052, Japan
Tel.: (81) 364474870
Web Site: https://sekisuihouse-am.co.jp
Real Estate Asset Management Services
N.A.I.C.S.: 531390

Sekisui House Australia Holdings Pty Limited (1)
Sekisui House Ground floor 68 Waterloo Rd, Macquarie Park, 2113, NSW, Australia
Tel.: (61) 288171400
Web Site: https://www.sekisuihouse.com.au
Real Estate Manangement Services
N.A.I.C.S.: 531390

Sekisui House Changcheng (Suzhou) Real Estate Development Co. Ltd. (1)
1-88 Oyodonaka 1-Chome, Kita-ku, Osaka, 531-0076, Japan
Tel.: (81) 664403111
Real Estate Manangement Services
N.A.I.C.S.: 531390

Sekisui House Financial Services Co, Ltd. (1)
1-90 Oyodonaka 1-chome, Kita-ku, Osaka, 531-0076, Japan
Tel.: (81) 531 0076
Financial Investment Services
N.A.I.C.S.: 327910

Sekisui House REIT, Inc. (1)
1-6-6 Motoakasaka, Minato-ku, Tokyo, 107-0051, Japan
Tel.: (81) 364474870
Web Site: http://www.sekisuihouse-reit.co.jp
Sales Range: $125-149.9 Million
Real Estate Investment Trust
N.A.I.C.S.: 525990
Atsuhiro Kida *(Exec Dir)*

Sekisui House Real Estate Chugoku & Shikoku, Ltd (1)
1-25 Komachi, Naka-ku, Hiroshima, 730-0041, Japan
Tel.: (81) 822492105
Web Site: https://www.sekisuihouse-f-chugokushikoku.co.jp
Real Estate Services
N.A.I.C.S.: 531210

Sekisui House Real Estate Kansai, Ltd (1)
1-1-30 Oyodonaka Umeda Sky Building Tower West 25th floor, Kita-ku, Osaka, 531-6125, Japan
Tel.: (81) 664403800
Web Site: https://www.sekisuihouse-f-kansai.co.jp
Emp.: 531
Real Estate Services
N.A.I.C.S.: 531210
Yasushi Sawada *(Pres)*

Sekisui House Real Estate Kyushu, Ltd (1)
3-26-29 Hakata Ekimae 5th floor Kusou Hakata Building, Hakata-ku, Fukuoka, 812-8567, Japan
Tel.: (81) 924416310
Web Site: https://www.sekisuihouse-f-kyushu.co.jp
Real Estate Services
N.A.I.C.S.: 531210
Hironao Murasaki *(Pres)*

Sekisui House Real Estate Tohoku, Ltd (1)
MetLife Sendai Honmachi Building 2F
2-16-10 Honmachi, Aoba-ku, Sendai, 980-8431, Miyagi, Japan
Tel.: (81) 222622251
Web Site: https://www.sekisuihouse-f-tohoku.co.jp
Real Estate Services
N.A.I.C.S.: 531210
Yasuyuki Tsukada *(Pres)*

Sekisui House Remodeling, Ltd (1)

SEKISUI HOUSE, LTD.

Sekisui House, Ltd.—(Continued)
1-1-90 Oyodonaka, Kita-Ku, Osaka, 531-0076, Japan
Tel.: (81) 664403375
Web Site:
http://www.sekisuihousereform.co.jp
Residential Property Remodeling Services
N.A.I.C.S.: 236118

Sekisui House SI Asset Management, Ltd (1)
2-12 Kojimachi, Chiyoda-Ku, Tokyo, 102-0083, Japan
Tel.: (81) 352158973
Web Site: http://www.shsiam.co.jp
Sales Range: $50-74.9 Million
Emp.: 30
Asset Management Services
N.A.I.C.S.: 523999
Junichi Inoue (Pres)

Sekisui House Umeda Operation Co., Ltd. (1)
1-1-88 Oyodonaka Umeda Sky Building, Kita-ku, Osaka, 531-6039, Japan
Tel.: (81) 664403899
Web Site: https://www.skybldg.co.jp
Residential Property Development Services
N.A.I.C.S.: 236115

Sekiwa Construction Higashi-Tokyo, Ltd. (1)
1-24-4 Akitsucho Higashi Murayama, Tokyo, 189-0001, Japan
Tel.: (81) 423901011
Web Site: http://www.sekisuihouse.co.jp
Construction Engineering Services
N.A.I.C.S.: 541330

Sekiwa Construction, Ltd (1)
84-3 Otorinishimachi Nishi-ku, Sakai, 593-8326, Osaka, Japan
Tel.: (81) 722658525
Construction Engineering Services
N.A.I.C.S.: 236220

Sekiwa Real Estate Sapporo Ltd. (1)
Sapporo 55 Building Kita 5 Jonishi 5 Chome 7 Banchi, Chuo-ku, Sapporo, 060 0005, Hokkaido, Japan
Tel.: (81) 112218711
Web Site: http://www.sekiwasapporo.co.jp
Real Estate Services
N.A.I.C.S.: 531210

Sekiwa Wood, Ltd (1)
2-27-3 Ariso Imizu, Toyama, 933-0251, Japan
Tel.: (81) 766863610
Real Estate Manangement Services
N.A.I.C.S.: 531390

Sumainotoshokan, Ltd (1)
4-15-1 Akasaka Garden City,11 F, Minato-ku, Tokyo, 107-0052, Japan
Tel.: (81) 355751720
Web Site: http://www.sekisuihouse.co.jp
Emp.: 4
Construction Engineering Services
N.A.I.C.S.: 236220

The Mortgage Corporation of Japan, Ltd (1)
9th Floor Shinjuku Maynds Tower 2-1-1 Yoyogi, Shibuya-ku, Tokyo, 151-0053, Japan
Tel.: (81) 367017700
Web Site: https://www.mc-j.co.jp
Sales Range: $25-49.9 Million
Emp.: 193
Business Management Consulting Services
N.A.I.C.S.: 541611

Woodside Homes, Inc. (1)
460 W 50 N Ste 205, Salt Lake City, UT 84101
Tel.: (801) 869-4000
Web Site: https://www.woodsidehomes.com
Housing Construction Services
N.A.I.C.S.: 236115
Joel Shine (CEO)

SEKISUI JUSHI CORPORATION
2-4-4 Nishitenma, Kita-ku, Osaka, 530-8565, Japan
Tel.: (81) 663653204
Web Site:
https://www.sekisuijushi.co.jp
4212—(TKS)
Rev.: $415,041,900
Assets: $880,908,090
Liabilities: $227,648,400
Net Worth: $653,259,690
Earnings: $30,875,310
Emp.: 1,521
Fiscal Year-end: 03/31/24
Traffic & Road Safety & Construction Products & Residential Building Materials Mfr
N.A.I.C.S.: 325211
Yaichiro Fukui (Chm & CEO)

Subsidiaries:

WEMAS Absperrtechnik GmbH (1)
Edisonstrasse 20, 33334, Gutersloh, Germany
Tel.: (49) 524193700
Web Site: http://www.wemas.de
Holding Company
N.A.I.C.S.: 551112

SEKISUI KASEI CO., LTD.
2-4-4 Nishitenma Kita-ku, Osaka, 530 8565, Japan
Tel.: (81) 663653014   JP
Web Site:
http://www.sekisuikasei.com
4228—(TKS)
Rev.: $861,051,650
Assets: $968,186,530
Liabilities: $592,599,720
Net Worth: $375,586,810
Earnings: $7,158,630
Emp.: 3,460
Fiscal Year-end: 03/31/24
Plastic Mfr
N.A.I.C.S.: 315210
Masato Kashiwabara (Pres & CEO)

Subsidiaries:

Proseat GmbH & Co. KG (1)
Hessenring 32, Morfelden-Walldorf, 64546, Morfelden, Germany (75%)
Tel.: (49) 610520060
Upholstery & Moulded Foam Mfr
N.A.I.C.S.: 424610

Subsidiary (Non-US):

Proseat Mlada Boleslav S.r.o. (2)
Plazy 115, 293 01, Mlada Boleslav, Czech Republic (100%)
Tel.: (420) 326377326
Plastics Material & Resin Mfr
N.A.I.C.S.: 325211

Proseat SAS (2)
71 Avenue de Verdun, 77470, Trilport, France
Tel.: (33) 160233820
Sales Range: $50-74.9 Million
Seating Components Development & Production
N.A.I.C.S.: 326199

Proseat Sp. z o.o. (2)
ul Szklana 164, 43 300, Bielsko-Biala, Poland (100%)
Tel.: (48) 535850346
Mattress Mfr
N.A.I.C.S.: 337910

Sekisui Plastics (H.K.) Co., Ltd. (1)
Room 1003 10/F Yue Shing Commercial Building, 15-16 Queen Victoria Street, Central, China (Hong Kong)
Tel.: (852) 21179831
Web Site: http://www.sekisuiplastics.com.hk
Sales Range: $25-49.9 Million
Emp.: 2
Resin Product Mfr
N.A.I.C.S.: 325211

Sekisui Plastics (Shanghai) International Trading Co., Ltd. (1)
Room 04 06F Regus Shanghai Eco City 1788 West Nanjing Road, Jing an District, Shanghai, 200040, China
Tel.: (86) 2158681661

Sales Range: $25-49.9 Million
Emp.: 36
Foam Plastic Products Mfr
N.A.I.C.S.: 326150

Sekisui Plastics Co., Ltd. - Chemicals Business Division (1)
2-7-1 Daichi Seimei bldg, Shinju ku, Tokyo, Japan
Tel.: (81) 333479617
Web Site: http://www.sekisuplastics.co.jp
Sales Range: $250-299.9 Million
Emp.: 503
Chemical Product Whslr
N.A.I.C.S.: 424690

Sekisui Plastics Creative Design (Thailand) Co., Ltd. (1)
11th Fl Ramaland Bldg 952 Rama 4 Rd Surawong, Bangkok, 10500, Thailand
Tel.: (66) 26329434
Web Site: http://www.sekisuiplastics.co.th
Sales Range: $25-49.9 Million
Emp.: 10
Foam Plastic Products Mfr
N.A.I.C.S.: 326150

Sekisui Plastics Europe B.V. (1)
Bedrijvenpark Twente 449 7602 KM, Almelo, Netherlands
Tel.: (31) 546473979
Sales Range: $25-49.9 Million
Emp.: 4
Plastics Product Mfr
N.A.I.C.S.: 326199

Sekisui Plastics Industrial Materials (Thailand) Co., Ltd. (1)
14th Fl Ramaland Bldg 952 Rama 4 Rd Surawong, Bangkok, 10500, Thailand
Tel.: (66) 26329434
Web Site: http://www.sekisuiplastics.com
Sales Range: $25-49.9 Million
Emp.: 10
Foam Plastic Products Mfr
N.A.I.C.S.: 326150
Tatsuya Eguchi (Mng Dir)

Sekisui Plastics U.S.A. Inc. (1)
110 Clifton Way, Mount Pleasant, TN 38474
Tel.: (931) 379-0300
Web Site: https://www.sekisuikaseiusa.com
Sales Range: $25-49.9 Million
Emp.: 12
Plastics Product Mfr
N.A.I.C.S.: 326199
Michelle Williams (Pres)

Sekiwoo Co., Ltd. (1)
15th floor 329 Gangnam-daero, Seocho-gu, Seoul, 152-887, Korea (South)
Tel.: (82) 25214100
Web Site: http://www.sekiwoo.co.kr
Sales Range: $25-49.9 Million
Emp.: 3
Foam Plastic Products Mfr
N.A.I.C.S.: 326150
Young-Mi Hong (Mgr-Customer Svc)

Taiwan Sekisui Centex Co., Ltd. (1)
4F-A No 183 Zhouzi St Taipei Neihu Tech Park, Taipei, 114, Taiwan
Tel.: (886) 287978355
Web Site: http://www.sekisuiplastics.com.tw
Sales Range: $25-49.9 Million
Emp.: 9
Foam Plastic Products Mfr
N.A.I.C.S.: 326150

Taiwan Sekisui Yunchu Co., Ltd. (1)
No 7 Tzu Chiang Rd Hsinchu Indust Park, 30352, Hsin-chu, Taiwan
Tel.: (886) 35983001
Web Site: http://www.sekisuiplastics.com
Sales Range: $25-49.9 Million
Emp.: 30
Foam Plastic Products Mfr
N.A.I.C.S.: 326150
Lin Kayslin (Gen Mgr)

SEKO S.A.
ul Zakladowa 3, 89-620, Chojnice, Poland
Tel.: (48) 525108140
Web Site: https://www.sekosa.pl
Year Founded: 1992
SEK—(WAR)
Rev.: $66,334,603

Assets: $35,779,217
Liabilities: $12,477,134
Net Worth: $23,302,083
Earnings: $3,795,224
Emp.: 650
Fiscal Year-end: 12/31/23
Fish Product Mfr
N.A.I.C.S.: 311710
Bogdan Nogalski (Chm-Supervisory Bd)

SEKONIC CORPORATION
3-1-3 Ikejiri Setagaya-ku, Tokyo, 154-0001, Japan
Tel.: (81) 354333611   JP
Web Site: http://www.sekonic.co.jp
Year Founded: 1951
7758—(TKS)
Rev.: $56,763,520
Assets: $67,934,240
Liabilities: $14,258,640
Net Worth: $53,675,600
Earnings: $1,210,000
Fiscal Year-end: 03/31/21
Holding Company; Optomechatronics Equipment Mfr
N.A.I.C.S.: 551112

Subsidiaries:

Huizhou Sekonic Technologies Co., Ltd. (1)
No 39 Guangtai Road Huinan Hi-Tech Industrial Park, Zhongkai Hi-Tech Industrial Development ZONE, Huizhou, Guang Dong, China
Tel.: (86) 752 2595008
Office Equipment Mfr & Distr
N.A.I.C.S.: 339940

Sekonic (Hong Kong) Co., Ltd. (1)
Suites 1008-8A 10th Floor Ocean Centre Harbour City, Kowloon, China (Hong Kong)
Tel.: (852) 2735 3055
Office Equipment Mfr & Distr
N.A.I.C.S.: 339940

Sekonic Corporation (1)
2nd Floor SEKONIC building 7-24-14, Oizumi-Gakuen-cho, Nerima-ku, Tokyo, 178-8686, Japan
Tel.: (81) 33 978 2325
Web Site: https://www.sekonic.co.jp
Office Equipment Mfr & Distr
N.A.I.C.S.: 339940

Sekonic Electronics (Changshu) Co., Ltd. (1)
YuBang Road 8 Yushan Hightech Industrial Park of Changshu, Economic Development Zone, Changshu, Jiangsu, China
Tel.: (86) 512 5233 0308
Electronic Equipment Mfr & Distr
N.A.I.C.S.: 334419

Sekonic Electronics, Inc. (1)
50-2 Akaiwaotu Sawada-Shimogou-machi, Minamiaizu-Gun, Fukushima, 969-5344, Japan
Tel.: (81) 241 67 3285
Electronic Equipment Mfr & Distr
N.A.I.C.S.: 334419

Shenzhen Sekonic Technologies Co., Ltd. (1)
Nan Ling Community Nan Wan Street Dong, Long Shan Industrial Zone, Shenzhen, Guangdong, China
Tel.: (86) 755 2872 8680
Office Equipment Mfr & Distr
N.A.I.C.S.: 339940

SEKONIX CO., LTD.
Tel.: (82) 318601000
Web Site: https://www.sekonix.com
053450—(KRS)
Rev.: $367,865,605
Assets: $231,899,748
Liabilities: $147,221,371
Net Worth: $84,678,376
Earnings: ($1,660,583)
Emp.: 739
Fiscal Year-end: 12/31/22
Optical Electronic Components Mfr

N.A.I.C.S.: 333310
Won-hee Park *(Chm & CEO)*

Subsidiaries:

SEKONIX Poland Sp. Z o.o. (1)
Jana Pawla II 71, 44-240, Zory, Poland
Tel.: (48) 885504223
Web Site: https://poland.sekonix.co.kr
Optical Lens Distr
N.A.I.C.S.: 423460

Weihai Sekonix Optical Electronics Co., Ltd. (1)
No 60-2 Qilu Road ETDZ, Weihai, Shandong, China
Tel.: (86) 6313635808
Web Site: http://www.shigaoguang.com
Optical Lens Mfr
N.A.I.C.S.: 333310

SEKTKELLEREI J OPPMANN AG
Im Kreuz 3, 97076, Wurzburg, Germany
Tel.: (49) 931355740
Web Site: https://www.oppmann.de
Year Founded: 1865
Alcoholic Beverage Distr
N.A.I.C.S.: 424820

SEKUR PRIVATE DATA LTD.
First Canadian Place 100 King Street West Suite 5600, Toronto, M5X 1C9, ON, Canada
Tel.: (416) 644-8690
Web Site: https://sekurprivatedata.com
SWIS—(CNSX)
Rev.: $20,931
Assets: $2,498,462
Liabilities: $67,895
Net Worth: $2,430,567
Earnings: ($1,032,215)
Fiscal Year-end: 12/31/20
Software Development Services
N.A.I.C.S.: 541511

SEKUR PRIVATE DATA LTD.
MNP TOWER, 900 - 1021 WEST HASTINGS STREET, VANCOUVER, British Columbia, Canada
Tel.: (604) 558-5134 BC
SWISF—(OTCQB)
N.A.I.C.S.: 517111

SEKURO PLASTIK AMBALAJ SANAYI AS
BORSAB Bozuyuk Organize Sanayi Bolgesi, Poyra Mevkii 4 Cad No 6 Bozuyuk, 11302, Bilecik, Turkiye
Tel.: (90) 2283254426
Web Site: http://www.sekuro.com.tr
SEKUR—(IST)
Rev.: $22,281,176
Assets: $33,008,883
Liabilities: $23,316,430
Net Worth: $9,692,452
Earnings: ($746,593)
Emp.: 110
Fiscal Year-end: 12/31/23
Paper Coated & Laminated Packaging Mfr
N.A.I.C.S.: 326112
Tugba Tanrikulu Cil *(Vice Chm)*

SEL MANUFACTURING COMPANY LIMITED
274 Dhandari Khurd G T Road, Ludhiana, 141014, India
Tel.: (91) 161 7111117
Web Site: http://www.selindia.in
SELMCL—(NSE)
Emp.: 5,036
Yarn Sales & Mfr
N.A.I.C.S.: 313110
Ram Saran Saluja *(Chm)*

Subsidiaries:

SEL Textiles Ltd. (1)
Plot No 274 G T Road Dhandari Khurd, Ludhiana, 141010, India
Tel.: (91) 16 1661 1111
Cotton Yarn Mfr & Distr
N.A.I.C.S.: 313110

SELAN EXPLORATION TECHNOLOGY LTD.
Unit no 455457 4th Floor JMD Megapolis Sector48 Sohna Road, Gurgaon, 110043, Delhi, India
Tel.: (91) 1244200325
Web Site: https://www.selanoil.com
530075—(BOM)
Rev.: $7,950,620
Assets: $51,276,362
Liabilities: $6,720,837
Net Worth: $44,555,525
Earnings: $851,637
Emp.: 26
Fiscal Year-end: 03/31/21
Crude Oil & Natural Gas Extraction
N.A.I.C.S.: 211120
Rohit Kapur *(Chm)*

SELANGOR DREDGING BERHAD
18th Floor West Block Wisma Golden Eagle Realty 142-C Jalan Ampang, 50450, Kuala Lumpur, Malaysia
Tel.: (60) 321613377
Web Site: https://www.sdb.com.my
SDRED—(KLS)
Rev.: $29,151,958
Assets: $293,585,397
Liabilities: $111,406,349
Net Worth: $182,179,048
Earnings: $1,322,963
Emp.: 213
Fiscal Year-end: 03/31/23
Property Development Services
N.A.I.C.S.: 531312
Fei San Seow *(Co-Sec)*

Subsidiaries:

SDB Asia Pte. Ltd. (1)
60 Paya Lebar Road 06-03 Paya Lebar Square, Singapore, 409501, Singapore
Tel.: (65) 62382288
Residential Property Development Services
N.A.I.C.S.: 531390

SDB Properties Sdn. Bhd. (1)
12th Floor South Block Wisma Golden Eagle Realty 142-A Jalan Ampang, 50450, Kuala Lumpur, Malaysia
Tel.: (60) 392128333
Residential Property Development Services
N.A.I.C.S.: 531390

SuperGreen Solutions Sdn. Bhd. (1)
B-1-07 Block B 19 Sentral Jalan Harapan Seksyen 19, 46300, Petaling Jaya, Selangor, Malaysia
Tel.: (60) 379312290
Web Site: https://www.supergreen.com.my
Green Energy Generation Services
N.A.I.C.S.: 221114

SELANGOR PROPERTIES BERHAD
Level 2 Block D Kompleks Pejabat Damansara Jalan Dungun, Damansara Heights, 50490, Kuala Lumpur, Wilayah Persekutuan, Malaysia
Tel.: (60) 320941122
Web Site: http://www.selangorproperties.com.my
SPB—(KLS)
Sales Range: $25-49.9 Million
Emp.: 61
Commercial Property Development Services
N.A.I.C.S.: 531312
Chiu Chi Wen *(Chm)*

Subsidiaries:

Wenworth Hotel (K.L.) Sdn. Bhd. (1)
Jalan Yew Off Jalan Pudu, 55100, Kuala Lumpur, Malaysia
Tel.: (60) 392002133
Web Site: http://www.wenworthhotel.com.my
Hotel Operator
N.A.I.C.S.: 721110

SELCODIS SA
68 rue Singer, 75016, Paris, France
Tel.: (33) 158847100
Web Site: https://www.selcodis.fr
Year Founded: 1969
Real Estate Brokerage Services
N.A.I.C.S.: 531210
Jimenez Michel *(Chm)*

SELCUK ECZA DEPOSU TICARET VE SANAYI AS
Yesilbaglar Mah Altin Yayla Street No 2, 34893, Istanbul, Turkiye
Tel.: (90) 2165540600
Web Site: https://selcukecza.com.tr
Year Founded: 1958
SELEC—(IST)
Rev.: $1,381,050,786
Assets: $667,018,623
Liabilities: $470,093,489
Net Worth: $196,925,134
Earnings: $73,555,016
Emp.: 6,116
Fiscal Year-end: 12/31/22
Pharmaceutical Products Distr
N.A.I.C.S.: 424210

Subsidiaries:

As Ecza Deposu Ticaret A.S. (1)
Mahmutbey Mah Bilici Sok N 5/1, Bagcilar, Istanbul, Turkiye
Tel.: (90) 2124470555
Web Site: http://www.asecza.com.tr
Pharmaceutical Products Distr
N.A.I.C.S.: 424210

SELCUK GIDA ENDUSTRI IHRACAT ITHALAT A.S.
Akdeniz Mah Ataturk Caddesi No92 Kat4 Daire, Izmir, Turkiye
Tel.: (90) 2324454400
Web Site: https://www.selcukfood.com
SELGD—(IST)
Rev.: $2,192,058
Assets: $4,879,633
Liabilities: $1,193,408
Net Worth: $3,686,224
Earnings: $1,367,029
Fiscal Year-end: 12/31/23
Dried Food Product Mfr
N.A.I.C.S.: 311423

SELECT GROUP LIMITED
24A Senoko South Road, Singapore, 758099, Singapore
Tel.: (65) 68523333
Web Site: http://select.com.sg
Year Founded: 1991
Sales Range: $100-124.9 Million
Home Management Services
N.A.I.C.S.: 721110
Jack Choh Peng Tan *(Co-Founder)*

Subsidiaries:

Lerk Thai Restaurant Pte Ltd (1)
36 Senoko Crescent, Singapore, 758282, Singapore
Tel.: (65) 63343323
Web Site: http://www.lerkthai.com.sg
Emp.: 2,000
Restaurant Operating Services
N.A.I.C.S.: 722511

PG Holdings Pte Ltd (1)
401 Havelock Road, Singapore, 169631, Singapore
Tel.: (65) 62529833
Web Site: http://www.peachgarden.com.sg
Sales Range: $25-49.9 Million
Emp.: 200
Restaurant Operating Services
N.A.I.C.S.: 722511

Subsidiary (Domestic):

Peach Garden @33 Pte Ltd (2)
65 Chulia St 33-01, Singapore, 49513, Singapore
Tel.: (65) 65357833
Web Site: http://www.peachgarden.com
Emp.: 50
Restaurant Operating Services
N.A.I.C.S.: 722511
Veronica Tan *(Gen Mgr)*

Peach Garden Restaurant Pte Ltd (2)
401 Havelock Rd, Singapore, 169631, Singapore
Tel.: (65) 62529833
Web Site: http://www.peachgarden.com.sg
Sales Range: $50-74.9 Million
Emp.: 300
Restaurant Operating Services
N.A.I.C.S.: 722511
T. C. Ho *(Gen Mgr)*

Peach Garden @OCC Pte Ltd (1)
1 Orchid Club Road 02-35, Singapore, 769162, Singapore
Tel.: (65) 6759 3833
Restaurant Operating Services
N.A.I.C.S.: 722511
Danny Lee *(Mng Dir)*

SCS Food Services Pte Ltd (1)
36 Senoko Crescent, Singapore, Singapore
Tel.: (65) 68221828
Restaurant Operating Services
N.A.I.C.S.: 722511

Select Catering Services Pte Ltd (1)
36 Senoko Crescent, Singapore, 758282, Singapore
Tel.: (65) 68523333
Web Site: http://www.selectcatering.com.sg
Banquet & Industrial Catering Services
N.A.I.C.S.: 722310
Vincent Tan *(Mng Dir)*

Select Offshore Services Pte Ltd (1)
36 Senoko Crescent, Singapore, 758282, Singapore
Tel.: (65) 68492321
Web Site: http://www.selectoffshore.com.sg
Marine Catering & Housekeeping Services
N.A.I.C.S.: 561720

Stamford Catering Services Pte Ltd (1)
36 Senoko Crescent, Singapore, 758282, Singapore
Tel.: (65) 68523338
Web Site: http://www.stamfordcs.com.sg
Emp.: 100
Catering Services
N.A.I.C.S.: 722320
Vincent Tan *(Mng Dir)*

SELECT HARVESTS LIMITED
4444B Hattah-Robinvale Road, PO Box 5, Wemen, 3549, VIC, Australia
Tel.: (61) 394743544
Web Site: https://www.selectharvests.com.au
SHV—(ASX)
Rev.: $137,527,603
Assets: $609,685,700
Liabilities: $334,951,610
Net Worth: $274,734,090
Earnings: ($76,591,745)
Emp.: 476
Fiscal Year-end: 06/30/23
Almonds, Other Nuts & Related Products Grower, Processor, Packager & Distr
N.A.I.C.S.: 111335
Laurence Van Driel *(Gen Mgr)*

Subsidiaries:

Kyndalyn Park Pty Ltd (1)
2267 Murray Valley Hwy, Robinvale, 3549, VIC, Australia
Tel.: (61) 350269216

SELECT HARVESTS LIMITED

Select Harvests Limited—(Continued)
Food Marketing Services
N.A.I.C.S.: 722310

Select Harvests Food Products Pty Ltd (1)
360 Settlement Rd, PO Box 5, Thomastown, 3074, VIC, Australia
Tel.: (61) 394743544
Web Site: http://www.selectharvests.com
Sales Range: $10-24.9 Million
Emp.: 100
Food Marketing Services
N.A.I.C.S.: 722310

SELECT HUMANEROFORRAS KFT.
Lonyay utca 34, 1093, Budapest, Hungary
Tel.: (36) 614560700
Web Site: http://www.select.hu
Sales Range: $10-24.9 Million
Emp.: 4
Staffing Services
N.A.I.C.S.: 561320
Noemi Csaposs *(Mng Dir)*

SELECT SANDS CORP.
Suite 310 850 West Hastings St, Vancouver, V6C 1E1, BC, Canada
Tel.: (604) 639-4533 BC
Web Site:
https://www.selectsands.com
Year Founded: 2006
ROG—(DEU)
Rev.: $22,297,548
Assets: $20,907,770
Liabilities: $14,856,330
Net Worth: $6,051,440
Earnings: ($868,130)
Emp.: 33
Fiscal Year-end: 12/31/22
Metal Exploration Services
N.A.I.C.S.: 212290
Darren Charles Urquhart *(CFO)*

SELECTED ENERGY S.A.
15th km of Parnithos Avenue, PO Box 46577, 13610, Athens, Greece
Tel.: (30) 2102404240
Web Site:
https://www.selectedenergy.gr
Renewable Energy Consulting Services
N.A.I.C.S.: 541690

SELECTED TEXTILES S.A.
15th km of Avenue Parnithos, 13671, Axarnai, Greece
Tel.: (30) 2102404240
Web Site: https://www.stiafilco.com
Year Founded: 1970
EPIL—(ATH)
Sales Range: Less than $1 Million
Emp.: 198
Cotton & Yarn Mfr
N.A.I.C.S.: 111920
Apostolos Dontas *(Exec Dir)*

SELECTIRENTE SA
303 Sq des Champs Elysees, 91026, Evry, Cedex, France
Tel.: (33) 169870200
Web Site:
https://www.selectirente.com
Year Founded: 1997
SELER—(EUR)
Rev.: $32,360,084
Assets: $671,064,135
Liabilities: $265,157,302
Net Worth: $405,906,833
Earnings: $14,566,729
Emp.: 2,800
Fiscal Year-end: 12/31/23
Malls & Storefront Shops Investor & Manager
N.A.I.C.S.: 531312

Jerome Grumler *(Chm)*

SELECTOUR VOYAGES
6 B Rue Laferriere, 75009, Paris, France
Tel.: (33) 142820089
Web Site: http://www.selectour.com
Rev.: $28,800,000
Emp.: 39
Travel Agencies
N.A.I.C.S.: 561510
Bernard Saur *(Dir-Tourism, Mktg, Comm & eCommerce)*

SELECTPART PARTICIPACOES S.A.
R Iguatemi 354 - Cj 301, 1451010, Sao Paulo, Brazil
Tel.: (55) 21 3231 8200
Year Founded: 1998
Assets: $8,163
Liabilities: $22,370
Net Worth: ($14,207)
Fiscal Year-end: 12/31/15
Investment Management Service
N.A.I.C.S.: 523940
Luiz Marcelo Pimpao Ferraz *(COO)*

Subsidiaries:

LONGDIS S.A. (1)
R Iguatemi 354 - Cj 301, 1451010, Sao Paulo, Brazil
Tel.: (55) 2132318200
Sales Range: Less than $1 Million
Financial Investment Services
N.A.I.C.S.: 523999
Joedir Dilson Do Lago *(CFO)*

SELEKSI JUANG SDN BHD
Level 2A No. 88 Jalan Perdana, Taman Tasek Perdana, Kuala Lumpur, 50480, Malaysia
Tel.: (60) 321421611
Sales Range: $10-24.9 Million
Holding Company
N.A.I.C.S.: 551112
Lui Meng Chia *(CEO)*

Subsidiaries:

United Malayan Land Bhd (1)
Suasana Bukit Ceylon No 2, Persiran Raja Chulan, Kuala Lumpur, 50200, Malaysia
Tel.: (60) 320368188
Web Site: http://www.umland.com.my
Sales Range: $100-124.9 Million
Emp.: 280
Property Development Services
N.A.I.C.S.: 531312
Ng Eng Tee *(Deputy Chm)*

Subsidiary (Domestic):

Dynasty View Sdn. Bhd. (2)
Seri Austin Off Jalan Setia 1, Johor Bahru, 81100, Johor, Malaysia
Tel.: (60) 73541111
Real Estate Property Development Services
N.A.I.C.S.: 531312
Wong Kuen Kong *(CEO)*

Seri Alam Properties Sdn. Bhd. (2)
Galleria Seri Alam 8 Jalan Suria Bandar Saeri Salam, Bandar Seri Alam, 81750, Johor Bahru, Johor, Malaysia
Tel.: (60) 73881111
Emp.: 90
Real Estate Property Development Services
N.A.I.C.S.: 531311
Freddie Lee *(Exec Dir)*

UM Development Sdn. Bhd. (2)
Suite 1 1 1st Floor Kompleks Antarabangsa Jalan Sultan Ismail, 50250, Kuala Lumpur, Federal Territory, Malaysia
Tel.: (60) 321421611
Real Estate Property Development Services
N.A.I.C.S.: 531311

UM Residences Sdn. Bhd. (2)
Suasana Bukit Ceylon No 2 Persiaran Raja Chulan, 50250, Kuala Lumpur, Malaysia
Tel.: (60) 321421611
Residential Property Development Services

N.A.I.C.S.: 531210

SELENA FM S.A.
ul Legnicka 48A, 54-202, Wroclaw, Poland
Tel.: (48) 717838290
Web Site: https://www.selena.com
Year Founded: 1992
SEL—(WAR)
Rev.: $493,218,359
Assets: $294,200,623
Liabilities: $113,762,498
Net Worth: $180,438,125
Earnings: $28,282,420
Emp.: 1,872
Fiscal Year-end: 12/31/22
Construction Materials Whslr
N.A.I.C.S.: 423390
Krzysztof Domarecki *(Chm-Mgmt Bd)*

Subsidiaries:

Carina Silicones Sp. z o.o. (1)
ul Polna 14-18, Siechnice, 55-011, Wroclaw, Poland
Tel.: (48) 713902130
Web Site: https://www.carina.pl
Silicone & Sealant Mfr
N.A.I.C.S.: 325212
Wojciech Mikos *(Dir-Sls & Mktg)*

Orion PU Sp. z o.o. (1)
ul Pieszycka 4 Zaklad 1, 58-200, Dzierzoniow, Poland
Tel.: (48) 746450201
Web Site: http://www.orion.biz.pl
Polyurethane Foam Mfr
N.A.I.C.S.: 326150

Selena Bohemia s.r.o. (1)
Na Strzi 65/1702, 140 00, Prague, Czech Republic
Tel.: (420) 416532004
Web Site: https://www.tytan.cz
Building Materials Whslr
N.A.I.C.S.: 423390
Katerina Travnickova *(Mktg Mgr)*

Selena Bulgaria Ltd. (1)
67 Gurmazovsko shose str, Bozhurishte Municipality Gurmazovo Village, Sofia, Bulgaria
Tel.: (359) 24900344
Web Site: http://www.tytan.bg
Building Materials Whslr
N.A.I.C.S.: 423390
Zlati Velev *(Area Mgr-Sls)*

Selena Deutschland GmbH (1)
Malmkestr 5, 58099, Hagen, Germany
Tel.: (49) 23314733337
Construction Chemical Mfr & Distr
N.A.I.C.S.: 325998

Selena Hungaria Kft. (1)
Kozraktar u1, 7630, Pecs, Hungary
Tel.: (36) 703190203
Web Site: http://www.tytan.hu
Building Materials Whslr
N.A.I.C.S.: 423390

Selena Iberia Slu (1)
C/ Marie Curie 17-19 Floor 6 1, 28521, Rivas-Vaciamadrid, Spain
Tel.: (34) 900923295
Web Site: https://www.quilosa.com
Sealant Mfr
N.A.I.C.S.: 325212

Selena Italia Srl (1)
Via G Battista Ricci 6, 35131, Padova, Italy
Tel.: (39) 049767336
Web Site: http://www.tytan-italia.it
Building Materials Whslr
N.A.I.C.S.: 423390

Selena Romania Srl (1)
Str Drumul Mare Nr 26-28, Sat Olteni Comuna Clinceni Jud Ilfov, 077060, Bucharest, Romania
Tel.: (40) 721207657
Web Site: https://www.tytan.ro
Building Materials Whslr
N.A.I.C.S.: 423390

Subsidiary (Domestic):

Euro MGA Product Srl (2)
Str Drumul Mare Nr 26-28, Sat Olteni Co-

INTERNATIONAL PUBLIC

muna Clinceni, Bucharest, Romania
Tel.: (40) 213529288
Construction Chemical Mfr & Distr
N.A.I.C.S.: 325998

Selena S.A. (1)
ul Wyscigowa 56 E, 53-012, Wroclaw, Poland
Tel.: (48) 717838301
Web Site: http://www.selena.pl
Construction Chemical Mfr & Distr
N.A.I.C.S.: 325998

Selena Sulamericana Ltda. (1)
Rua Carneiro Lobo 468-6th floor-Agua Verde, Curitiba, 80240-240, Parana, Brazil
Tel.: (55) 4130260306
Web Site: https://www.tytanpro.com.br
Building Materials Whslr
N.A.I.C.S.: 423390
Sebastian Woldanski *(Owner & Gen Dir)*

Selena USA, Inc. (1)
486 Century Ln, Holland, MI 49423
Web Site: http://www.selenausa.com
Emp.: 1,700
Construction Chemical Mfr & Distr
N.A.I.C.S.: 325998
Drew Robinson *(Mktg Dir)*

Selena Ukraine Ltd. (1)
119x V Lobanovskyi Avenue, 03039, Kiev, Ukraine
Tel.: (380) 443649927
Web Site: https://tytan.com
Construction Chemical Mfr & Distr
N.A.I.C.S.: 325998

Selena Vostok Moscow Srl (1)
Chermiansky Projezd 5, 127282, Moscow, Russia
Tel.: (7) 4956603553
Construction Chemical Mfr & Distr
N.A.I.C.S.: 325998
Vasiliy Yakimov *(Mgr-Category)*

Taurus Sp. z o.o. (1)
ul Sierpecka 1i, 09-402, Plock, Poland
Tel.: (48) 242641278
Web Site: https://www.taurus-plock.pl
Transport Services
N.A.I.C.S.: 485999
Adam Pikala *(Mgr-Transport)*

SELFDOCTOR BEIJING TECHNOLOGY CO. LTD.
Room 1005 Timeson Tower No B12, Chao Yang Men North Street, 100020, Beijing, China
Tel.: (86) 1084539720 CN
Web Site:
http://www.selfdoctor.com.cn
Digital Healthcare Management Services
N.A.I.C.S.: 561499
Sa Ren *(Owner)*

SELFWEALTH LIMITED
Level 7 130 Lonsdale Street, Surrey Hills, Melbourne, 3000, VIC, Australia
Tel.: (61) 398245254 AU
Web Site:
https://www.selfwealth.com.au
Year Founded: 2012
SWF—(ASX)
Rev.: $18,403,629
Assets: $266,110,475
Liabilities: $256,893,704
Net Worth: $9,216,771
Earnings: $2,281,259
Fiscal Year-end: 06/30/24
Electronic Trading Services
N.A.I.C.S.: 523150
Brendan Mutton *(Head-Sales & Gen Mgr-Sls)*

SELIC CORP PCL
270 Liapkhlong Pacharoenfangtai Road, Nongkhaem, Bangkok, 10160, Thailand
Tel.: (66) 280733479
Web Site: https://www.seliccorp.com
Year Founded: 1979

AND PRIVATE COMPANIES

SELIC—(THA)
Rev.: $55,623,839
Assets: $88,885,462
Liabilities: $58,758,765
Net Worth: $30,126,697
Earnings: $2,339,736
Fiscal Year-end: 12/31/23
Adhesive Product Mfr
N.A.I.C.S.: 325520
Athvudhi Hirunburana (Chm)

Subsidiaries:

PMC Label Materials (Malaysia) Sdn. Bhd. (1)
No 10 Jalan PBS 14/1A, 43300, Seri Kembangan, Selangor Darul Ehsan, Malaysia
Tel.: (60) 127992652
Adhesive Label Distr
N.A.I.C.S.: 424310

PMC Label Materials Co., Ltd. (1)
30/28 M 2 T Khokkham A Muang, Samut Sakhon, Thailand
Tel.: (66) 34452000
Web Site: https://www.pmclabel.com
Adhesive Label Mfr & Distr
N.A.I.C.S.: 323111

PMC Label Materials Pte. Ltd. (1)
30 Loyang Way 02-19 and 20, Singapore, Singapore
Tel.: (65) 96436516
Adhesive Label Distr
N.A.I.C.S.: 424310

SELIGDAR OJSC

12 Piket-26 ulitsa, Aldan ulus, Aldan, 678900, Russia
Tel.: (7) 4114547075
Web Site: https://www.seligdar.ru
Year Founded: 2008
SELG—(MOEX)
Sales Range: Less than $1 Million
Gold Mining Services
N.A.I.C.S.: 212220
Sergey Mikhailovich Tatarinov (Chm-Mgmt Bd & CEO)

Subsidiaries:

Rusolovo OAO (1)
6 Leninsky Ave Building 7 Prem III Room 47 3rd Floor, 119049, Moscow, Russia
Tel.: (7) 4957894347
Web Site: http://www.rus-olovo.ru
Holding Company
N.A.I.C.S.: 551112

SELINA HOSPITALITY PLC

200 Aldersgate c/o Fti Consulting LLP, Barbican, London, EC1A 4HD, United Kingdom
Tel.: (44) 7929847360   UK
Web Site: https://www.selina.com
Year Founded: 2014
SLNAF—(NASDAQ)
Rev.: $183,935,000
Assets: $638,291,000
Liabilities: $801,845,000
Net Worth: ($163,554,000)
Earnings: ($198,082,000)
Emp.: 132
Fiscal Year-end: 12/31/22
Restaurant Operators
N.A.I.C.S.: 722511

Subsidiaries:

BOA Acquisition Corp. (1)
2600 Virginia Ave NW Ste T23 Management Office, Washington, DC 20037
Investment Services
N.A.I.C.S.: 523999

SELKIRK CHRYSLER (MB) LTD.

1011 Manitoba Ave, Selkirk, R1A 3T7, MB, Canada
Tel.: (204) 482-5808
Web Site: http://www.selkirkchrysler.com
Year Founded: 1995
Rev.: $10,796,631
Emp.: 24
New & Used Car Dealers
N.A.I.C.S.: 441110
Andy Rewucki (Pres)

SELLA CAPITAL REAL ESTATE LTD.

7 Jabotinsky Floor 26, Moshe Aviv Tower, Ramat Gan, 52520, Israel
Tel.: (972) 35759222
Web Site: https://www.sellacapital.com
SLARL—(TAE)
Rev.: $97,693,050
Assets: $1,483,056,753
Liabilities: $845,031,621
Net Worth: $638,025,132
Earnings: $49,730,625
Emp.: 13
Fiscal Year-end: 12/31/23
Other Activities Related to Real Estate
N.A.I.C.S.: 531390
Gadi Elikam (CEO)

SELLING-WARE CO., LTD.

2F-16 No 5Tai Yuan 1 Street, Hsin-Chu County, Zhubei, 302, Taiwan
Tel.: (886) 35601066   TW
Web Site: http://www.sellingware.com.tw
Year Founded: 1990
Semiconductor Equipment Mfr
N.A.I.C.S.: 333242

SELLWIN TRADERS LIMITED

126/B Old China Bazar Street, Kolkata, 700001, West Bengal, India
Tel.: (91) 9714787932
Web Site: https://www.sellwinindia.com
Year Founded: 1980
538875—(BOM)
Rev.: $6,825
Assets: $216,820
Liabilities: $33,949
Net Worth: $182,871
Earnings: ($28,289)
Fiscal Year-end: 03/31/21
Real Estate Support Services
N.A.I.C.S.: 531390
Navin Chandra Sharma (Mng Dir)

SELMERBRIDGE PRINT VEHICLES LIMITED

9 Hedera Road, Ravensbank Business Park, Redditch, B98 9EY, Worcs, United Kingdom
Tel.: (44) 1527508000   UK
Year Founded: 2017
Holding Company
N.A.I.C.S.: 551112
Kouadjo Landry Kouakou (Owner)

Subsidiaries:

SP Group Limited (1)
9 Hedera Road Ravensbank Business Park, Redditch, B98 9EY, Worcs, United Kingdom
Tel.: (44) 1527 50 8000
Business Consulting Services
N.A.I.C.S.: 541611

Service Graphics Limited (1)
Crown Industrial Estate Priorswood Unit E Venture Way, Taunton, Somerset, TA2 8QY, United Kingdom
Tel.: (44) 695 725 486
Web Site: http://www.servicegraphics.co.uk
Commercial Printing Services
N.A.I.C.S.: 323111

SELONDA AQUACULTURE SA

Navarhou Nikodimou 30, 105 56, Athens, Greece
Tel.: (30) 2103724900
Web Site: http://www.selonda.com
Year Founded: 1981
Sales Range: $100-124.9 Million
Emp.: 654
Farmed Fish Producer
N.A.I.C.S.: 114119
Leonidas Kolioulis (Chm & CEO)

Subsidiaries:

Fjord Marin Turkey AS (1)
Dorttepe Koyu Pulluk Mevki Milas, Mugla, Turkiye
Tel.: (90) 2525223284
Web Site: http://www.fjord-marin.com.tr
Sales Range: $25-49.9 Million
Emp.: 180
Fish Farming Services
N.A.I.C.S.: 112511

SELTECH ELECTRONICS INC.

342 Bronte Street Unit 6, Milton, L9T 5B7, ON, Canada
Tel.: (905) 875-2985
Web Site: https://www.seltech.net
Electronic Parts Whslr
N.A.I.C.S.: 423690
Ron Armstrong (Pres)

SELVAAG BOLIG ASA

Silurveien 2, 0380, Oslo, Norway
Web Site: http://www.selvaagbolig.no
0Q92—(LSE)
Rev.: $267,539,165
Assets: $549,562,073
Liabilities: $332,872,344
Net Worth: $216,689,728
Earnings: $31,299,926
Emp.: 84
Fiscal Year-end: 12/31/22
Residential Property Developer
N.A.I.C.S.: 237210
Olav Hindahl Selvaag (Chm)

Subsidiaries:

Selvaag Eiendomsoppgjor AS (1)
Silurveien 2 Inngang A, N-0380, Oslo, Norway
Tel.: (47) 48448488
Web Site: https://selvaageiendom.no
Property Leasing Services
N.A.I.C.S.: 531120

Selvaag Pluss Service AS (1)
Silurveien 2, Pb 13, 0380, Oslo, Norway
Tel.: (47) 2224
Web Site: http://www.plusservice.no
Property Leasing Services
N.A.I.C.S.: 531120
Anders Haavik (Gen Mgr)

SELVAS AI CO., LTD.

20F Daerung Techno Town 18 19 Gasan digital 1-ro, Geumcheon-gu, Seoul, 08594, Korea (South)
Tel.: (82) 28527788
Web Site: http://www.selvasai.com
Year Founded: 1999
108860—(KRS)
Rev.: $39,016,683
Assets: $81,746,824
Liabilities: $26,878,545
Net Worth: $54,868,279
Earnings: $5,065,501
Emp.: 176
Fiscal Year-end: 12/31/22
Software Development Services
N.A.I.C.S.: 541511
Eun Joo Kim (CFO)

Subsidiaries:

HIMS International Corporation (1)
174 Gajeong-ro, Yuseong-gu, Daejeon, 305-350, Korea (South)
Tel.: (82) 42 864 4460
Web Site: http://www.himsintl.com
Blind & Visually Impaired Assistive Technology Products Mfr
N.A.I.C.S.: 339112
Yangtaek Yoon (CEO)

SELVAS HEALTHCARE, INC.

18th 20th Floor Daeryung Technotown 19th Gasan Digital 1-ro, Geumcheon-gu, Seoul, Korea (South)
Tel.: (82) 25874056
Web Site: https://selvashealthcare.com
Year Founded: 2014
208370—(KRS)
Rev.: $21,234,940
Assets: $34,597,315
Liabilities: $9,367,110
Net Worth: $25,230,206
Earnings: $2,032,830
Emp.: 122
Fiscal Year-end: 12/31/22
Financial Investment Management Services
N.A.I.C.S.: 523940

SELVITA S.A.

Ul Podole 79 30394, 30-348, Krakow, Poland
Tel.: (48) 122974700   PL
Web Site: https://selvita.com
Year Founded: 2007
SLV—(WAR)
Rev.: $89,393,292
Assets: $161,651,422
Liabilities: $78,554,116
Net Worth: $83,097,307
Earnings: $17,753,557
Emp.: 847
Fiscal Year-end: 12/31/23
Laboratory Information Management Systems Development Services
N.A.I.C.S.: 541512
Piotr Romanowski (Chm-Supervisory Bd)

Subsidiaries:

Fidelta d.o.o. (1)
Prilaz Baruna Filipovica 29, 10000, Zagreb, 10000, Croatia
Tel.: (385) 18886300
Web Site: http://wwwfidelta.eu
Emp.: 181
Medical Research & Development Services
N.A.I.C.S.: 541715
Adrijana Vinter (Mng Dir)

SELWOOD GROUP LIMITED

Bournemouth Road Chandlers Ford, Eastleigh, SO53 3ZL, Hampshire, United Kingdom
Tel.: (44) 23 8026 6311
Web Site: http://www.selwood.co.uk
Year Founded: 1946
Sales Range: $75-99.9 Million
Emp.: 420
Pumping Equipment Contract Services
N.A.I.C.S.: 238290
Chris Garrett (CEO)

Subsidiaries:

Selwood Group Limited - Bristol Plant (1)
115b Burcott Road, Severnside Trading Estate, Avonmouth, BS11 8AD, United Kingdom
Tel.: (44) 1179823257
Pumps Mfr
N.A.I.C.S.: 333914

SEM FIRE AND RESCUE PTY LTD.

17 Trewin Street, Wendouree, 3355, VIC, Australia
Tel.: (61) 353390222
Web Site: http://www.semfirerescue.com.au
Year Founded: 1955
Emp.: 200
Design, Mfr & Service of Special Purpose Vehicles
N.A.I.C.S.: 336211
Jon Julian (Product Mgr-Vehicles)

SEM HOLDINGS LIMITED

SEM Fire and Rescue Pty Ltd.—(Continued)

SEM HOLDINGS LIMITED
Unit B 5/F Wing Sing Commercial Centre Nos 12-16 Wing Lok Street, Sheung Wan, China (Hong Kong)
Tel.: (852) 21165111 Ky
Web Site: http://www.semhld.com
Year Founded: 2006
9929—(HKG)
Rev.: $36,999,863
Assets: $35,306,280
Liabilities: $6,752,528
Net Worth: $28,553,753
Earnings: ($885,488)
Emp.: 79
Fiscal Year-end: 12/31/22
Holding Company
N.A.I.C.S.: 551112
Chu Fai Woo (CEO)

SEMAC CONSULTANTS LTD.
Pollachi Road Malumachampatti P O, Coimbatore, 641050, Tamilnadu, India
Tel.: (91) 4226655100
Web Site: https://www.semacconsultants.com
Year Founded: 1977
505368—(BOM)
Rev.: $18,835,376
Assets: $42,363,144
Liabilities: $16,139,869
Net Worth: $26,223,274
Earnings: $355,992
Emp.: 201
Fiscal Year-end: 03/31/21
Mining Equipment & Accessories Mfr
N.A.I.C.S.: 333131
Abhishek Dalmia (Chm)

Subsidiaries:

SEMAC Private Limited (1)
24 Palace Cross Road, Bengaluru, 560020, India
Tel.: (91) 80 23446284
Web Site: http://www.semacindia.com
Sales Range: $50-74.9 Million
Emp.: 139
Architectural & Engineering Services
N.A.I.C.S.: 541310
Ashok Pavate (Co-Founder & Chm)

Subsidiary (Non-US):

Semac & Partners LLC (2)
Al Wasl Building 483 Way No 3109, PO Box 3784, Ruwi, 112, Oman
Tel.: (968) 24705956
Sales Range: $25-49.9 Million
Emp.: 79
Architectural & Engineering Services
N.A.I.C.S.: 541310
Ragavendra Bhat (Dir-Technical)

SEMAFONE LIMITED
3 The Billings Walnut Tree Close, Guildford, GU1 4UL, Surrey, United Kingdom
Tel.: (44) 845 543 0822
Web Site: http://www.semafone.com
Year Founded: 2009
Sales Range: $1-9.9 Million
Emp.: 30
Call Center Solutions
N.A.I.C.S.: 561422
Mandy Pattenden (Mgr-Mktg Comm)

SEMANA, S.L.
Av de Burgos 16, Madrid, 28036, Spain
Tel.: (34) 915472300 ES
Web Site: http://www.semana.es
Sales Range: $10-24.9 Million
Emp.: 33
Magazine Publisher
N.A.I.C.S.: 513120
Charo Montiel (CEO)

SEMANTIX, INC.
Av Eusebio Matoso 1375 10 andar, Pinheiros, Sao Paulo, 05423-180, SP, Brazil
Tel.: (55) 1150822656 Ky
Web Site: https://www.semantix.ai
Year Founded: 2010
STIX—(NASDAQ)
Rev.: $53,336,129
Assets: $142,967,094
Liabilities: $57,207,106
Net Worth: $85,759,988
Earnings: ($67,120,405)
Emp.: 683
Fiscal Year-end: 12/31/22
Software Development Services
N.A.I.C.S.: 541511
Leonardo Dos Poca D'gua Santos (Founder)

SEMAT AS
Fararske 6922, 917 01, Trnava, Czech Republic
Tel.: (420) 335536472
Web Site: http://www.semat.sk
1SEA01AE—(BRA)
Sales Range: Less than $1 Million
Grain & Oil Seed Farm Services
N.A.I.C.S.: 111191
Jens Peter Gadensgaard (Chm-Mgmt Bd)

SEMBA CORPORATION
1-2-3 Shibaura Seavans S Building 9F, Minato-ku, Tokyo, 105-0023, Japan
Tel.: (81) 368651008 JP
Web Site: https://www.semba1008.co.jp
Year Founded: 1947
6540—(TKS)
Rev.: $176,441,740
Assets: $138,779,660
Liabilities: $51,955,520
Net Worth: $86,824,140
Earnings: $7,323,970
Emp.: 517
Fiscal Year-end: 12/31/23
Interior Design Services
N.A.I.C.S.: 541410
Hirokazu Kuriyama (Chm)

Subsidiaries:

Hong Kong Semba Ltd. (1)
Room603 6/F East Ocean Centre 98 Granville Road, TsimShaTsui East, Kowloon, China (Hong Kong)
Tel.: (852) 2 369 7311
Web Site: https://hksemba.byethost3.com
Emp.: 6
Interior Design Services
N.A.I.C.S.: 541410

Idea Corporation (1)
9F Seavans South Building 1-2-3 Shibaura, Minato, Tokyo, 105-0023, Japan
Tel.: (81) 368651118
Real Estate Manangement Services
N.A.I.C.S.: 531210

Nonscale Corporation (1)
3-3-10-202 Jingumae, Shibuya-ku, Tokyo, 150-0001, Japan
Tel.: (81) 334708828
Web Site: https://www.nonscale.com
Interior Design Services
N.A.I.C.S.: 541410
Shigeru Kuriyama (Pres, CEO & Dir-Creative)

ReRiya Corporation (1)
2FOkayasu Building 1-7-15 Shibaura, Minato-ku, Tokyo, 105-0023, Japan
Tel.: (81) 368093340
Web Site: http://www.reriya.co.jp
Interior Design Services
N.A.I.C.S.: 541410

Semba (Shanghai) Co., Ltd. (1)
3 Floor 3 Building No 225 Xikang Road, Jing'an District, Shanghai, China
Tel.: (86) 2162722213

Interior Design Services
N.A.I.C.S.: 541410
Saegusa Nobumasa (Exec Gen Mgr)

Semba Malaysia Design & Construction Sdn. Bhd. (1)
Unit no A2-13A-3 Soho Suites No 20 Jalan Perak, 50450, Kuala Lumpur, Malaysia
Tel.: (60) 321810585
Real Estate Manangement Services
N.A.I.C.S.: 531210

Semba Singapore Pte. Ltd. (1)
No 73A Tanjong Pagar Road, Singapore, 088494, Singapore
Tel.: (65) 63391318
Web Site: https://www.semba1008-sg.com
Emp.: 12
Interior Design Services
N.A.I.C.S.: 541410
Keiichiro Kurita (Mng Dir)

Semba Vietnam Co., Ltd. (1)
3F Secoin Building No 9 D2 Street Saigon Pearl 92 Nguyen Huu Canh, Ward 22 Binh Thanh Dist, Ho Chi Minh City, Vietnam
Tel.: (84) 838247160
Emp.: 13
Interior Design Services
N.A.I.C.S.: 541410

Sobi Co., Ltd. (1)
Seavans S building 9th floor 1-2-3 Shibaura, Minato-ku, Tokyo, 105-0023, Japan
Tel.: (81) 368651260
Web Site: https://www.sobi1008.co.jp
Emp.: 70
Interior Design Services
N.A.I.C.S.: 541410

Sobi Co., Ltd. - IZUMO Factory (1)
516-32 Nagahama-cho, Izumo, 693-0043, Japan
Tel.: (81) 853281771
Real Estate Manangement Services
N.A.I.C.S.: 531210

Sobi Co., Ltd. - KUMAMOTO Factory (1)
431-23 Itera, Kashima-machi, Kumamoto, 861-3103, Japan
Tel.: (81) 962354321
Real Estate Manangement Services
N.A.I.C.S.: 531210

Taiwan Semba Co., Ltd. (1)
Room 1105 11th Floor No 136 Section 3 Renai Road, Daan District, Taipei, 94043, Taiwan
Tel.: (886) 227411464
Web Site: https://www.sembatw.com.tw
Emp.: 21
Interior Design Services
N.A.I.C.S.: 541410

SEMBA TOHKA INDUSTRIES CO., LTD.
2-1-10 Namiki-cho, Mooka, 321-4361, Tochigi, Japan
Tel.: (81) 285822171
Web Site: https://www.sembatohka.co.jp
Year Founded: 1947
2916—(TKS)
Rev.: $126,441,986
Assets: $152,005,243
Liabilities: $67,988,088
Net Worth: $84,017,155
Earnings: $3,270,564
Fiscal Year-end: 03/31/24
Food Mfr & Distr
N.A.I.C.S.: 311999
Mitsuo Kobayashi (Pres & CEO)

SEMBCORP INDUSTRIES LTD.
30 Hill Street No 05-04, Singapore, 179360, Singapore
Tel.: (65) 67233113 SG
Web Site: https://www.sembcorp.com
Year Founded: 1998
SCRPF—(OTCIQ)
Rev.: $4,112,321,590
Assets: $10,238,903,140
Liabilities: $7,614,627,420

INTERNATIONAL PUBLIC

Net Worth: $2,624,275,720
Earnings: ($846,321,370)
Emp.: 16,482
Fiscal Year-end: 12/31/20
Holding Company; Engineering & Technology Services
N.A.I.C.S.: 551112
Chiap Khiong Koh (Head-Energy-SEA & China)

Subsidiaries:

Aguas de Panama S.A (1)
Via Hacia Rio Congo Nuevo Emperador Arraijan, Calle Miguel Brostella Plaza, Panama, Panama
Tel.: (507) 2489648
Emp.: 29
Environmental Consulting Services
N.A.I.C.S.: 541620

Fuzhou Sembcorp Water Co Ltd (1)
No 180 Gongheli, Mawei District, Fuzhou, 350015, Fujian, China
Tel.: (86) 5918 302 2599
Web Site: https://www.sembcorp-fuzhou.com
Emp.: 102
Water Utility Services
N.A.I.C.S.: 237110

P.T. Adhya Tirta Batam (50%)
Batam Centre Square Block D2-5 Jl Engku Putri, Batam, 29461, Indonesia
Tel.: (62) 778 460 955
Web Site: http://www.atbbatam.com
Water Treatment & Distribution Services
N.A.I.C.S.: 221310

Qinzhou Sembcorp Water Co Ltd (1)
Guoying Road Opposite Power Plant, Qinzhou Port Economic Zone, Qinzhou, 535008, Guangxi, China
Tel.: (86) 777 531 3388
Web Site: http://www.sembcorp.com
Water Utility Services
N.A.I.C.S.: 488390

SITA Australia (1)
Level 3 3-5 Rider Boulevard, Rhodes, NSW, Australia
Tel.: (61) 287540000
Web Site: http://www.sita.com.au
Sales Range: $75-99.9 Million
Emp.: 60
Water Supplier; Owned 60% by SUEZ Environment & 40% by SembCorp Industries Ltd.
N.A.I.C.S.: 221310
Manfred Giggacher (Dir-Bus Analysis & Optimization)

Safe & Mansfield Travel Group Pte Ltd. (1)
3 Lim Teck Kim Rd 02-01 Singapore Technologies Bldg, Singapore, 088934, Singapore
Tel.: (65) 62208866
Web Site: http://www.safe2travel.com
Travel Agency
N.A.I.C.S.: 561510

Sanhe Yanjiao Sembcorp Water Co Ltd (1)
No 4 North Shenwei Road, Yanjiao Development Zone, Sanhe, 065201, Hebei, China
Tel.: (86) 316 5996861
Web Site: http://www.sembcorp.com
Sales Range: $25-49.9 Million
Emp.: 35
Water Utility Services
N.A.I.C.S.: 237110

Seatrium Limited (1)
80 Tuas South Boulevard, Singapore, 637051, Singapore (60.7%)
Tel.: (65) 62651766
Web Site: https://www.seatrium.com
Rev.: $1,442,901,074
Assets: $6,744,637,273
Liabilities: $3,937,381,993
Net Worth: $2,807,255,280
Earnings: ($196,783,994)
Emp.: 9,713
Fiscal Year-end: 12/31/2022
Holding Company; Marine Engineering & Construction Services

AND PRIVATE COMPANIES

SEMBCORP INDUSTRIES LTD.

N.A.I.C.S.: 551112
Weng Sun Wong *(Pres & CEO)*

Subsidiary (Domestic):

Jurong Shipyard Pte Ltd. (2)
29 Tanjong Kling Road, Singapore, 628054, Singapore
Tel.: (65) 6265 1766
Ship Repair Services
N.A.I.C.S.: 336611
Weng Sun Wong *(CEO)*

Keppel Offshore & Marine Ltd. (2)
50 Gul Road, Singapore, 629351, Singapore
Tel.: (65) 68637200
Web Site: http://www.keppelom.com
Sales Range: $1-4.9 Billion
Emp.: 3,000
Offshore & Marine Services
N.A.I.C.S.: 213112
Chin Hua Loh *(Chm)*

Subsidiary (Domestic):

Alpine Engineering Services Pte Ltd (3)
51 Pioneer Sector 1, Singapore, 628437, Singapore
Tel.: (65) 68611813
Marine Engineering Services
N.A.I.C.S.: 541330

Blastech Abrasives Pte Ltd (3)
51 Pioneer Sector 1, Singapore, 628437, Singapore
Tel.: (65) 6861 1126
Web Site: http://www.blastechabrasives.com
Sales Range: $75-99.9 Million
Emp.: 20
Steel Blasting Services
N.A.I.C.S.: 213114
Ronald Tan *(Mgr-Sls-Tuas Plant)*

FELS Offshore Pte Ltd (3)
50 Gul Road, Singapore, 629351, Singapore
Tel.: (65) 68637200
Marine Engineering Services
N.A.I.C.S.: 541330
David Yong Soon Lee *(Controller-Fin)*

Subsidiary (Non-US):

KV Enterprises BV (3)
Professor Gerbrandyweg 25 Botlek, Rotterdam, 3197 KK, South Holland, Netherlands
Tel.: (31) 181234300
Web Site: http://www.keppelverolme.nl
Sales Range: $125-149.9 Million
Emp.: 30
Marine Vessels Construction, Repair & Maintenance
N.A.I.C.S.: 336611
Harold Linssen *(Gen Mgr)*

Subsidiary (Non-US):

Keppel FELS Brasil SA (4)
Rua Quitanda 86, 20091-005, Rio de Janeiro, Brazil
Tel.: (55) 21 2102 9400
Ship Building & Repairing Services
N.A.I.C.S.: 336611

Subsidiary (Domestic):

Keppel FELS Ltd. (3)
50 Gul Road, Singapore, 629351, Singapore (100%)
Tel.: (65) 68637200
Web Site: http://www.keppelfels.com
Sales Range: $700-749.9 Million
Offshore Construction & Specialized Ship Building
N.A.I.C.S.: 336611
Leong Peng *(Mng Dir)*

Subsidiary (Non-US):

Arya Offshore Services Pvt. Ltd. (4)
Empire Industries Complex 414 Senapati Bapat Marg Lower Parel West, Mumbai, 400 013, India
Tel.: (91) 22 3346 6666
Web Site: http://www.aryaoffshore.com
Oil & Gas Support Services
N.A.I.C.S.: 213112

Joint Venture (Domestic):

Asian Lift Pte Ltd (4)
23 Gul Rd, Singapore, 629356, Singapore
Tel.: (65) 66684222
Web Site: http://www.asianlift.com.sg
Sales Range: $25-49.9 Million
Emp.: 10
Marine Heavy Lift Consulting Services
N.A.I.C.S.: 541620

Subsidiary (Non-US):

Caspian Shipyard Company Limited (4)
S Bay Sabayil, Baku, 1023, Azerbaijan
Tel.: (994) 124499930
Sales Range: $150-199.9 Million
Emp.: 700
N.A.I.C.S.: 541330
Chandru Rajwani *(CEO)*

FELS Baku Ltd. (4)
153 Azadlig Avenue, Baku, 4361041, Azerbaijan
Tel.: (994) 124361078
Web Site: http://www.felsbaku.com
Hotel Services
N.A.I.C.S.: 721110

Subsidiary (US):

Keppel AmFELS Inc. (4)
20000 S Hwy 48, Brownsville, TX 78523-3107 (100%)
Tel.: (956) 831-8220
Sales Range: $250-299.9 Million
Emp.: 1,000
Offshore & Marine Services
N.A.I.C.S.: 237120
Simon Lee *(Pres & CEO)*

Subsidiary (Non-US):

Keppel FELS Baltech Ltd. (4)
54 Debar St, Varna, 9000, Bulgaria (100%)
Tel.: (359) 52684250
Web Site: http://www.fels.bg
Sales Range: $25-49.9 Million
Emp.: 150
Marine & Offshore Engineering Services
N.A.I.C.S.: 541330

Subsidiary (US):

Keppel Marine Agencies Inc. (4)
5177 Richmond Ave Ste 1065, Houston, TX 77056
Tel.: (713) 840-1188
Sales Range: $25-49.9 Million
Emp.: 20
Marketing Office for Off Shore Drilling Rigs
N.A.I.C.S.: 561110
Michael J. Holcomb *(Pres)*

Branch (Domestic):

Keppel Marine Agencies Inc. (5)
15 Huddy Ave, Highlands, NJ 07732-0417
Tel.: (732) 872-8800
Sales Range: $25-49.9 Million
Emp.: 1
Marketing Office for Off Shore Drilling Rigs
N.A.I.C.S.: 561499

Subsidiary (US):

Keppel Offshore & Marine USA, Inc. (4)
5177 Richmond Ave Ste 1065, Houston, TX 77056
Tel.: (713) 840-8811
Web Site: http://www.keppelom.com
Sales Range: $25-49.9 Million
Emp.: 17
Engineering Services; Solutions for Offshore Structures
N.A.I.C.S.: 541330
Simon Kim Foong Lee *(Pres)*

Subsidiary (Non-US):

Keppel Prince Engineering Pty Ltd (4)
Level 7 3 Bowen Crescent, Melbourne, 3004, VIC, Australia (100%)
Tel.: (61) 398209033
Web Site: http://www.keppelprince.com

Sales Range: $50-74.9 Million
Emp.: 200
Provider of Metal Fabrication Services
N.A.I.C.S.: 423510

Subsidiary (Non-US):

Keppel FELS Offshore & Engineering Services Mumbai Pte Ltd (4)
Unit Number 3 & 4 8th Floor Prism Tower A Mindspace Link Road, Goregaon W, Mumbai, 400062, Maharashtra, India
Tel.: (91) 22 40018888
Emp.: 15
Offshore Engineering Services
N.A.I.C.S.: 541330
Kabir Ahmed *(Gen Mgr)*

Keppel LeTourneau Middle East FZE (3)
Office No LB16504, Jebel Ali, Dubai, United Arab Emirates
Tel.: (971) 8880250
Web Site: http://www.keppelletourneau.com
Oil & Gas Pressure Control Equipment Mfr
N.A.I.C.S.: 333132

Subsidiary (Domestic):

Keppel Offshore & Marine Technology Centre Pte Ltd (3)
31 Shipyard Road, Singapore, 628130, Singapore
Tel.: (65) 65915450
Web Site: http://www.keppelom.com
Sales Range: $25-49.9 Million
Emp.: 70
Ship Building & Repair Services
N.A.I.C.S.: 336611

Subsidiary (Non-US):

Keppel Philippines Marine Inc (3)
Unit 3-B Country Space 1 Building Sen Gil Puyat Avenue, Salcedo Village, 1200, Makati, Philippines
Tel.: (63) 2 892 1816
Web Site: http://www.keppelphilippinesmarine.com
Ship Building & Repairing Services
N.A.I.C.S.: 336611
Chor How Jat *(Chm)*

Subsidiary (Domestic):

Keppel Batangas Shipyard Inc (4)
Barrio San Miguel, 4201, Bauan, Batangas, Philippines
Tel.: (63) 437271532
Ship Building & Repairing Services
N.A.I.C.S.: 336611

Keppel Subic Shipyard Inc. (4)
Subic Shipyard - Special Economic Zone Cabangaan Point Cawag, 2209, Subic, Zambales, Philippines
Tel.: (63) 472322380
Web Site: https://www.keppelom.com
Ship Building Mfr
N.A.I.C.S.: 336611

Subsidiary (Domestic):

Keppel Shipyard Ltd. (3)
51 Pioneer Sector 1, Singapore, 628437, Singapore
Tel.: (65) 68614141
Web Site: http://www.keppelshipyard.com
Sales Range: $400-449.9 Million
Emp.: 2,000
Ship Building & Repair
N.A.I.C.S.: 336611

Keppel Singmarine Pte Ltd (3)
15 Benoi Road, Singapore, 629888, Singapore
Tel.: (65) 68616622
Web Site: http://www.keppelsingmarine.com
Emp.: 500
Ship Building & Repairing Services
N.A.I.C.S.: 336611

Subsidiary (Non-US):

Keppel Nantong Shipyard Company Limited (4)
No 9 Yan Jiang Road, Nantong, 226005, Jiangsu, China
Tel.: (86) 513 8530 0000
Specialized Vessel Construction Engineering Services

N.A.I.C.S.: 237990

Subsidiary (Domestic):

PPL Shipyard Pte Ltd (2)
21 Pandan Road, Singapore, 609273, Singapore
Tel.: (65) 62650477
Web Site: http://www.ppl.com.sg
Sales Range: $350-399.9 Million
Emp.: 1,200
Drilling Rigs Mfr
N.A.I.C.S.: 333132
Woon Kee Soon *(Mgr-Mktg)*

SMOE Pte. Ltd. (2)
60 Admiralty Road West 02-01, Singapore, 759947, Singapore (100%)
Tel.: (65) 6752 2222
Web Site: http://www.smoe.com
Offshore Oil & Gas Platform Engineering & Construction Services
N.A.I.C.S.: 541330

Subsidiary (Non-US):

PT SMOE Indonesia (3)
Kawasan Industrial Kabil Indonusa Estate Jalan Hang Kesturi VI Lot 5-1, Batu Besar Nongsa, Batam, 29466, Indonesia (90%)
Tel.: (62) 77 871 1223
Web Site: http://www.smoe.com
Offshore Oil & Gas Platform Engineering & Construction Services
N.A.I.C.S.: 541330

Sembmarine SLP Limited (3)
Hamilton Dock Hamilton Road, Lowestoft, NR32 1XF, Suffolk, United Kingdom (70%)
Tel.: (44) 1502 548 000
Web Site: http://www.sembmarineslp.com
Emp.: 100
Offshore Oil & Gas Platform Engineering & Construction Services
N.A.I.C.S.: 541330

Subsidiary (Domestic):

Sembawang Shipyard Pte Ltd (2)
Admiralty Road West, Singapore, 759956, Singapore
Tel.: (65) 67522222
Web Site: http://www.sembship.com
Ship Repair & Maintenance Services
N.A.I.C.S.: 336611
Ong Poh Kwee *(Mng Dir)*

SembRamky Environmental Management Pvt Ltd (1)
6 3 1089 G 10&11 Gulmohar Avenue Raj Bhavan Road, Somajiguda, Hyderabad, 500 082, India
Tel.: (91) 4044422222
Web Site: http://www.sembcorp.com
Environmental Consulting Services
N.A.I.C.S.: 541620

SembWaste Pte Ltd (1)
4543 Jalan Bukit Merah, Singapore, 159470, Singapore
Tel.: (65) 68611218
Web Site: http://www.sembcorp.com
Waste Management Services
N.A.I.C.S.: 562998

Sembcorp (Antigua) Water Ltd (1)
Crabbs Peninsula, PO Box 2500, Crabbs, Antigua & Barbuda
Tel.: (268) 463 4200
Web Site: http://www.sembcorp.com
Water Irrigation Services
N.A.I.C.S.: 221310

Sembcorp Aguas Santiago S.A. (1)
Joaquin Montero 3000 Piso 4, Vitacura, Santiago, Chile
Tel.: (56) 2 873 0100
Web Site: http://www.sembcorp.com
Waste Treatment Services
N.A.I.C.S.: 221310

Sembcorp Air Products (HYCO) Pte. Ltd. (1)
71 Sakra Avenue, Singapore, 627876, Singapore
Tel.: (65) 6867 7040
Industrial Gas & Hydrogen Mfr
N.A.I.C.S.: 325120

Sembcorp Cogen Pte Ltd (1)

SEMBCORP INDUSTRIES LTD.

Sembcorp Industries Ltd.—(Continued)
51 Sakra Avenue, Jurong Island, Singapore, 627894, Singapore
Tel.: (65) 62675287
Web Site: http://www.sembcorp.com
Sales Range: $50-74.9 Million
Emp.: 60
Electric Utility Services
N.A.I.C.S.: 926130

Sembcorp Development Ltd. (1)
30 Hill Street 03-01, Singapore, 179360, Singapore
Tel.: (65) 67233900
Integrated Services
N.A.I.C.S.: 541512
Alfred Tsang (VP)

Sembcorp Environment Pte. Ltd (1)
30 Hill Street 02-01, Singapore, 179360, Singapore
Tel.: (65) 67233200
Web Site: http://www.sembcorp.com
Sales Range: $75-99.9 Million
Emp.: 300
Environmental Consulting Services
N.A.I.C.S.: 541620
Meng Poh Ng (Head-Ops-Global)

Sembcorp Green Infra Limited (1)
5th floor Tower C Building No 8, DLF Cybercity, Gurgaon, 122 002, Haryana, India
Tel.: (91) 1243896700
Integrated Services
N.A.I.C.S.: 541512
Sougato Dasgupta (Sr Mgr)

Sembcorp Huiyang New Energy (Shenzhen) Co., Ltd. (1)
Room 1606 16th Floor Dinghe Building 100 Fuhua 3rd Road, Futian District, Shenzhen, 518046, China
Tel.: (86) 75583227275
Environmental Consulting Services
N.A.I.C.S.: 541690

Sembcorp Myingyan Power Company Limited (1)
Myanmar Centre Tower 1 20-01/03 192 Kaba Aye Pagoda Road, Bahan Township, Yangon, Myanmar
Tel.: (95) 19345233
Integrated Services
N.A.I.C.S.: 541512
Dennis Foo (Mng Dir)

Sembcorp Newater Pte. Ltd (1)
10 Changi East Close, Singapore, 498785, Singapore
Tel.: (65) 65423727
Engineeering Services
N.A.I.C.S.: 541330

Sembcorp North-West Power Company Ltd. (1)
Level-10 111 Bir Uttam CR Dutta Road, Monem Business District, Dhaka, 1205, Bangladesh
Tel.: (880) 296323256
Environmental Consulting Services
N.A.I.C.S.: 541620

Sembcorp Power Pte. Ltd. (1)
30 Hill Street 05-04, Singapore, 179360, Singapore
Tel.: (65) 67233384
Web Site: http://www.sembcorp.com
Electric Utility Services
N.A.I.C.S.: 926130

Sembcorp Silulumanzi (Pty) Limited (1)
Bateleur building 16 Nel Street, PO Box 12753, Nelspruit, 1200, South Africa
Tel.: (27) 13 752 6839
Web Site: http://www.silulumanzi.com
Sanitation Services
N.A.I.C.S.: 221320

Sembcorp Siza Water Co (Pty) Ltd (1)
Reypark House Rey's Place, PO Box 1635, Avondale, Ballito, 4420, South Africa
Tel.: (27) 32 9467200
Water Supply Services
N.A.I.C.S.: 221310
Shyam Misra (Mng Dir)

Sembcorp Tianjin Lingang Industrial Area Wastewater Treatment Co Ltd (1)
No 2328 Huanghe Road Lingang Industrial Area, Tanggu District, Tianjin, 300452, China
Tel.: (86) 2266619797
Water Utility Services
N.A.I.C.S.: 237110

Sembcorp Utilities (Chile) S.A. (1)
Joaquin Montero 3000 Piso 4, Vitacura, Santiago, Chile (100%)
Tel.: (56) 28730100
Web Site: http://www.sembcorp-utilities.cl
Sales Range: $75-99.9 Million
Emp.: 13
Waste Treatment Services
N.A.I.C.S.: 221310

Sembcorp Utilities (South Africa) Pty Limited (1)
16 Nel Street, PO Box 12753, Nelspruit, 1200, South Africa
Tel.: (27) 13 7526839
Web Site: http://www.sembcorp.com
Emp.: 256
Water Supply Services
N.A.I.C.S.: 221310

Sembcorp Utilities (UK) Limited (1)
Wilton International, PO Box 1985, Middlesbrough, TS10 8WS, United Kingdom
Tel.: (44) 1642 212000
Web Site: http://www.sembcorp.co.uk
Industrial Engineering Services
N.A.I.C.S.: 541330

Subsidiary (Domestic):

Sembcorp Bournemouth Water Limited (2)
George Jessel House Francis Avenue, Bournemouth, BH11 8NX, Dorset, United Kingdom (100%)
Tel.: (44) 1202591111
Web Site: http://www.bwhwater.co.uk
Water Treatment & Distribution Services
N.A.I.C.S.: 221310

Unit (Domestic):

AquaCare (3)
Knapp Mill Site Mill Road, Christchurch, BH23 2JY, Dorset, United Kingdom (100%)
Tel.: (44) 1202591100
Web Site: http://www.aquacare247.co.uk
Sales Range: $1-9.9 Million
Emp.: 50
Plumbing, Heating, Drainage & Water Hygiene Contractor Services
N.A.I.C.S.: 238220

Subsidiary (Domestic):

Sembcorp Utilities Services Ltd (1)
Leatherhead House Station Road, Leatherhead, KT22 7FG, Surrey, United Kingdom
Tel.: (44) 1372384200
Web Site: http://www.sembcorp.com
Business Management Consulting Services
N.A.I.C.S.: 541611

Sembcorp Utilities Pte Ltd (1)
30 Hill Street 05-04, Singapore, 179360, Singapore
Tel.: (65) 6723 3113
Web Site: http://www.sembcorp.com
Sales Range: $75-99.9 Million
Emp.: 500
Waste Management Services
N.A.I.C.S.: 562998

Subsidiary (Domestic):

Sembcorp Gas Pte Ltd (2)
80 Sakra Road, Jurong Island, Singapore, 627863, Singapore (100%)
Tel.: (65) 67969918
Sales Range: $25-49.9 Million
Emp.: 30
Gas Utility Services
N.A.I.C.S.: 926130
Emmy Teo (Gen Mgr)

Shenyang Sembcorp Water Co Ltd (1)
No 9 7th Road Shenyang Economic & Technological Development Zone, Shenyang, Liaoning, China
Tel.: (86) 2425369257

Water Utility Services
N.A.I.C.S.: 237110

Singapore Precision Industries Pte. Ltd. (1)
20 Teban Gardens Crescent, Singapore, 608928, Singapore
Tel.: (65) 65662626
Integrated Services
N.A.I.C.S.: 541512

Subic Water & Sewerage Company Inc. (1)
Rizal Avenue, Sub Com Area Subic Bay Freeport Zone, Subic, 2222, Philippines (30%)
Tel.: (63) 472522965
Web Site: http://www.subicwater.com.ph
Water Treatment & Distribution Services
N.A.I.C.S.: 221310

SEMBCORP SALALAH POWER & WATER COMPANY SAOG
PO Box 1466, 211, Salalah, 211, Oman
Tel.: (968) 23238510
Web Site:
https://www.sembcorpsalalah.com
Year Founded: 2009
SSPW—(MUS)
Rev.: $186,254,381
Assets: $834,942,074
Liabilities: $551,857,476
Net Worth: $283,084,598
Earnings: $47,475,396
Emp.: 2
Fiscal Year-end: 12/31/20
Electric Power Generation Services
N.A.I.C.S.: 221111
Kalat Al-Bulooshi (Deputy Chm)

SEMBERIJA PD A.D.
Novo Selo 31, 76300, Bijeljina, Bosnia & Herzegovina
Tel.: (387) 55209340
SEMB—(BANJ)
Sales Range: $1-9.9 Million
Emp.: 185
Cereal Crop Farming Services
N.A.I.C.S.: 111998
Bosko Radic (Pres)

SEMBIOSYS GENETICS INC.
110 2985 23rd Avenue NE, Calgary, T1Y 7L3, AB, Canada
Tel.: (403) 250-5424
Web Site: http://www.sembiosys.ca
Sales Range: Less than $1 Million
Emp.: 21
Biotechnology Products
N.A.I.C.S.: 325414
Maurice Moloney (Founder & Chief Scientific Officer)

SEMCNS CO., LTD.
150 Maeyeong-ro, Yeongtong-gu, Suwon, Gyeonggi-do, Korea (South)
Tel.: (82) 315467000
Web Site: https://www.semcns.com
Year Founded: 2016
252990—(KRS)
Rev.: $38,440,956
Assets: $153,603,471
Liabilities: $67,731,986
Net Worth: $85,871,485
Earnings: $11,610,587
Emp.: 201
Fiscal Year-end: 12/31/22
Electronic Component Mfr & Distr
N.A.I.C.S.: 334419

SEMCOGLAS HOLDING GMBH
Langebrugger Str 10, 26655, Westerstede, Germany
Tel.: (49) 44888400
Web Site: http://www.semcoglas.com
Rev.: $119,865,090
Emp.: 1,100

INTERNATIONAL PUBLIC

Interior Design Services
N.A.I.C.S.: 541410
Bernhard Feldmann (Mng Dir-Comml)

SEMENCES PROGRAIN INC.
145 Rang du Bas de la Riviere Nord, Saint-Cesaire, J0L 1T0, QC, Canada
Tel.: (450) 469-5744
Web Site:
http://www.semencesprograin.com
Year Founded: 1980
Rev.: $19,933,274
Emp.: 55
Soybeans Distr & Mfr
N.A.I.C.S.: 311224
Alan Letourneau (Pres)

SEMICAN INC.
366 rang 10, Plessisville, G6L 2Y2, QC, Canada
Tel.: (819) 362-8823
Web Site: http://www.semican.ca
Year Founded: 1982
Rev.: $15,482,000
Emp.: 50
Seed Supplier
N.A.I.C.S.: 111191

SEMICONDUCTOR MANUFACTURING INTERNATIONAL CORPORATION
No 18 Zhangjiang Road Pudong New Area, Shanghai, 201203, China
Tel.: (86) 2138610000 Ky
Web Site: https://www.smics.com
Year Founded: 2000
688981—(SHG)
Rev.: $6,265,289,239
Assets: $46,862,981,419
Liabilities: $16,613,999,640
Net Worth: $30,248,981,779
Earnings: $667,757,809
Emp.: 20,233
Fiscal Year-end: 12/31/23
Semiconductor Product Mfr
N.A.I.C.S.: 334413
Yonggang Gao (CFO, Sec & Exec VP-Strategic Plng)

Subsidiaries:

SJ Semiconductor (HK) Limited (1)
Suite 3003 30th Floor No 9 Queen's Road, Central, China (Hong Kong)
Tel.: (852) 2 537 8588
Semiconductor Product Mfr & Distr
N.A.I.C.S.: 334413

SMIC Americas (1)
1732 N 1st St Ste 200, San Jose, CA 95112
Tel.: (408) 550-8888
Web Site: http://www.smics.com
Sales Range: $25-49.9 Million
Emp.: 22
Integrated Circuits Mfr
N.A.I.C.S.: 334419

SMIC Beijing (1)
18 Wenchang Road, Beijing Economic-Technological Development Area, Beijing, 100176, China
Tel.: (86) 1067855000
Web Site: http://www.smics.com
Integrated Circuits Mfr
N.A.I.C.S.: 334419

SMIC Europe (1)
Via Archimede 31, 20040, Agrate Brianza, Italy
Tel.: (39) 0396892181
Integrated Circuits Mfr
N.A.I.C.S.: 334419

SMIC Hong Kong (1)
Suite 3003 30th Floor No 9 Queen's Road Central, Hong Kong, China (Hong Kong)
Tel.: (852) 25378588
Web Site: http://www.smics.com
Emp.: 10
Integrated Circuits Mfr
N.A.I.C.S.: 334419

AND PRIVATE COMPANIES

SMIC Japan (1)
Shinagawa Grand Central Tower 9F, 2-16-4 Konan Minato-ku, Tokyo, 108-0075, Japan
Tel.: (81) 364331411
Sales Range: $25-49.9 Million
Emp.: 5
Integrated Circuits Mfr
N.A.I.C.S.: 334419

SMIC Shanghai (1)
No 18 Zhangjiang Rd, Pudong New Area, Shanghai, 201203, China
Tel.: (86) 2138610000
Emp.: 6,000
Integrated Circuits Mfr
N.A.I.C.S.: 334419

SMIC Tianjin (1)
19 Xing Hua Ave Xi Qing, Tianjin, 300385, China
Tel.: (86) 2223700000
Integrated Circuits Mfr
N.A.I.C.S.: 334419

Semiconductor Manufacturing International (Beijing) Corporation (1)
18 Wenchang Road, Beijing Economic-Technological Development Area, Beijing, 100176, China
Tel.: (86) 106 785 5000
Semiconductor Product Mfr & Distr
N.A.I.C.S.: 334413

Semiconductor Manufacturing International (Shenzhen) Corporation (1)
No 18 Gaoxin Road Export Processing Zone, Pingshan New Area, Shenzhen, 518118, China
Tel.: (86) 7552 861 0000
Semiconductor Product Mfr & Distr
N.A.I.C.S.: 334413

Semiconductor Manufacturing International (Tianjin) Corporation (1)
No 19 Xinghua Avenue, Xiqing Economic Development Area, Tianjin, 300385, China
Tel.: (86) 222 370 0000
Semiconductor Product Mfr & Distr
N.A.I.C.S.: 334413

SEMIKRON INTERNATIONAL GMBH
Sigmundstr 200, 90431, Nuremberg, Germany
Tel.: (49) 91165590 De
Web Site: http://www.semikron.com
Year Founded: 1951
Sales Range: $700-749.9 Million
Emp.: 2,800
Power Semiconductor & Power Supply Module Mfr
N.A.I.C.S.: 334413
Dirk Heidenreich *(Chm)*

Subsidiaries:

Bongiorno Srl (1)
Via Galvani 9, 35030, Rubano, Italy
Tel.: (39) 0498974236
Semiconductor Mfr
N.A.I.C.S.: 334413

Compel JSC (1)
1 2 Derbenevskaya Str Bldg 1, 115114, Moscow, Russia
Tel.: (7) 4952347762
Semiconductor Mfr
N.A.I.C.S.: 334413
Boris Rogachev *(Sls Dir)*

Corporation IP Ltd. (1)
131 Plakhotnogo Str, 630136, Novosibirsk, Russia
Tel.: (7) 88005553361
Semiconductor Mfr
N.A.I.C.S.: 334413

HK China Group Limited (1)
News Road East Wing 1 Electric Razor Information Building, 1717 1721 Room 1717 Futian, Shenzhen, 510800, China
Tel.: (86) 75583733223
Semiconductor Mfr
N.A.I.C.S.: 334413

Hongzhi Mech. & Elect. (SZ) Co., Ltd. (1)
Room 2608 West Gate Shengtang Business Building Tairan Ninth Road, Futian, Shenzhen, China
Tel.: (86) 75583479091
Semiconductor Mfr
N.A.I.C.S.: 334413

Incomtech-Project Ltd. (1)
Hertsenastr 17 25 Office 9, 04050, Kiev, Ukraine
Tel.: (380) 442300181
Semiconductor Mfr
N.A.I.C.S.: 334413

SEMIC Slovakia, s.r.o. (1)
Sladkovicova 63, 018 51, Nova Dubnica, Slovakia
Tel.: (421) 251551204
Semiconductor Mfr
N.A.I.C.S.: 334413

SEMIKRON (HONG KONG) CO. Ltd. (1)
Infinitus Plaza 199 Des Voeux Road, Central, China (Hong Kong)
Tel.: (852) 3426 3366
Power Supply Equipment Mfr
N.A.I.C.S.: 335999

SEMIKRON AB (1)
Ostra Kopmansgatan 18, 44430, Stenungsund, Sweden
Tel.: (46) 303 816 16
Power Supply Equipment Mfr
N.A.I.C.S.: 335999
Tobias Jacobsson *(Mgr-Sls)*

SEMIKRON AG (1)
8304, 8304, Wallisellen, Switzerland
Tel.: (41) 449141333
Power Supply Equipment Mfr
N.A.I.C.S.: 335999
Roland Muhlemann *(Mng Dir)*

SEMIKRON B.V. (1)
Linie 502, 7325 DZ, Apeldoorn, Netherlands
Tel.: (31) 555295295
Power Supply Equipment Mfr
N.A.I.C.S.: 335999

SEMIKRON CO. Ltd. (1)
Unit 1602 16th Floor Infinitus Plaza 199 Des Voeux Road, Central, China (Hong Kong)
Tel.: (852) 34263366
Power Supply Equipment Mfr
N.A.I.C.S.: 335999

SEMIKRON Co., Ltd. (1)
Sosa-gu, Sosa-gu, Bucheon, 422-233, Gyeonggi-do, Korea (South)
Tel.: (82) 323462830
Power Supply Equipment Mfr
N.A.I.C.S.: 335999

SEMIKRON DE MEXICO S.A. de C.V. (1)
Ave Morelos No 28 Col Parque Industrial, Naucalpan, 53470, Estado de Mexico, Mexico
Tel.: (52) 5553001151
Web Site: http://www.semikron.com
Industrial Machinery Distr
N.A.I.C.S.: 423830

SEMIKRON ELECTRONICS S.L. (1)
C/ de la Ciencia 35 Nave 3, 8850, Gava, Spain
Tel.: (34) 936335890
Power Supply Equipment Mfr
N.A.I.C.S.: 335999

SEMIKRON Electronics (Zhu Hai) Co. Ltd. (1)
Ground Floor Block B2 Western Park Zhuhai Southern Software, Tangjia Zhuhai, 519080, Zhuhai, China
Tel.: (86) 7563396707
Power Supply Equipment Mfr
N.A.I.C.S.: 335999

SEMIKRON Electronics Private Limited (1)
EL 148 TTC Industrial Area MIDC Electronic Zone Mahape, Navi Mumbai, 400710, India
Tel.: (91) 2227628600
Web Site: http://www.semikron.com
Emp.: 60
Power Supply Equipment Mfr
N.A.I.C.S.: 335999
Sharad Shanbhag *(Deputy Gen Mgr)*

SEMIKRON Gleichrichterelemente Ges.m.b.H. (1)
Hirschstettner Strasse 19 21, 1220, Vienna, Austria
Tel.: (43) 158636580
Semiconductor Mfr
N.A.I.C.S.: 334413

SEMIKRON GmbH (1)
Hirschstettner Strasse 19-21, 1220, Vienna, Austria
Tel.: (43) 158636580
Power Supply Equipment Mfr
N.A.I.C.S.: 335999

SEMIKRON K. K. (1)
Sarugakucho Kikuhide Bldg 4F 2-8-4, Chiyoda-ku Sarugakucho, Tokyo, 101-0064, Japan
Tel.: (81) 3 6895 1396
Web Site: http://www.semikron.com
Power Supply Equipment Mfr
N.A.I.C.S.: 335999

SEMIKRON Ltd. (1)
9 Harforde Court John Tate Road Foxholes Business Park, Hertford, SG13 7NW, United Kingdom
Tel.: (44) 1992584677
Web Site: http://www.semikron.com
Emp.: 6
Power Supply Equipment Mfr
N.A.I.C.S.: 335999
Nigel Roe *(Mgr-Ops)*

SEMIKRON Ltd. (1)
B Pushkarskaya 41, 197101, Saint Petersburg, Russia
Tel.: (7) 8122329825
Power Supply Equipment Mfr
N.A.I.C.S.: 335999
Frank Thom *(Gen Mgr)*

SEMIKRON OY (1)
Tuupakantie 3, 01740, Vantaa, Finland
Tel.: (358) 103217950
Power Supply Equipment Mfr
N.A.I.C.S.: 335999

SEMIKRON Pty. Ltd. (1)
Route 21 Corporate Park Cnr Regency Sovereign Sts 62, Irene, Centurion, South Africa
Tel.: (27) 123456060
Power Supply Equipment Mfr
N.A.I.C.S.: 335999

SEMIKRON Pty. Ltd. (1)
8/8 Garden Road, Clayton, Melbourne, 3168, VIC, Australia
Tel.: (61) 385615600
Power Supply Equipment Mfr
N.A.I.C.S.: 335999

SEMIKRON S.A.R.L (1)
130 route de Cormeilles, PO Box 70, 78501, Sartrouville, Cedex, France
Tel.: (33) 130868000
Web Site: http://www.semikron.com
Emp.: 100
Power Supply Equipment Mfr
N.A.I.C.S.: 335999
Christian Meyer *(Gen Mgr)*

SEMIKRON S.r.l. (1)
via Laurentina km 24 200, 00071, Pomezia, Italy
Tel.: (39) 069114241
Power Supply Equipment Mfr
N.A.I.C.S.: 335999
Alfonso Gargano *(Gen Mgr)*

SEMIKRON Semicondutores Ltda. (1)
Av Inocencio Serafico 6300, 06366-900, Carapicuiba, Brazil
Tel.: (55) 1141869500
Power Supply Equipment Mfr
N.A.I.C.S.: 335999

SEMIKRON Sp. z o.o. (1)
Ul Pozaryskiego 28 skr pcztowa 14, 4703, Warsaw, Poland
Tel.: (48) 226157984
Power Supply Equipment Mfr
N.A.I.C.S.: 335999

SEMIKRON s.r.o. (1)
Teslova 3, 30100, Plzen, Czech Republic
Tel.: (420) 378051400

SEMILEDS CORPORATION

Power Supply Equipment Mfr
N.A.I.C.S.: 335999

SEMIKRON s.r.o. (1)
Steruska ul 3, 92203, Vrbove, Slovakia
Tel.: (421) 378051400
Power Supply Equipment Mfr
N.A.I.C.S.: 335999

Semcor (Qingdao) Electronic Co., Ltd. (1)
No 192 Zhuzhou Rd Hi Tech Park, Qingdao, China
Tel.: (86) 53288701773
Semiconductor Mfr
N.A.I.C.S.: 334413

Semic Trade, s.r.o. (1)
Volutova 2521 18 Praha 5, 158 00, Prague, Czech Republic
Tel.: (420) 251551204
Semiconductor Mfr
N.A.I.C.S.: 334413
Jaroslav Kubr *(Sls Mgr)*

Semikron Inc. (1)
11 Executive Dr, Hudson, NH 03051-0066 (100%)
Tel.: (603) 883-8102
Web Site: http://www.semikronusa.com
Sales Range: $25-49.9 Million
Emp.: 40
Power Semiconductor & Power Supply Module Mfr & Distr
N.A.I.C.S.: 423690
Thomas Oreilly *(Pres & CEO)*

SindoPower GmbH (1)
Vershofenstrasse 7, 90431, Nuremberg, Germany
Tel.: (49) 911309196663
Web Site: http://www.sindopower.com
Electronic Product Distr
N.A.I.C.S.: 423690

Subsidiary (Non-US):

Zhuhai SindoPower Electronics Company Limited (2)
Unit No 406 Fourth Floor Zhuhai Int Science and Technology Building, No 288 Hongshan Road Xiangzhou, Zhuhai, 519075, China
Tel.: (86) 756 3396622
Web Site: http://www.sindopower.com.cn
Emp.: 10
Electronic Product Distr
N.A.I.C.S.: 423690
Leilani Wu *(Mgr-Mktg & Sls)*

Technoservicedrive Ltd. (1)
Peremogy Ave 56 of 335, 03057, Kiev, Ukraine
Tel.: (380) 443662462
Semiconductor Mfr
N.A.I.C.S.: 334413
Ivan Shapoval *(Sr Engr)*

Totem Electro SRL (1)
Viale Lombardia 66, 20131, Milan, Italy
Tel.: (39) 022885111
Semiconductor Mfr
N.A.I.C.S.: 334413

Vremeplov d.o.o. (1)
Vidikovacki Venac 104g Lokal 75, 11190, Novi Beograd, Serbia
Tel.: (381) 112322161
Semiconductor Mfr
N.A.I.C.S.: 334413

Weltronics Component Limited (1)
Rm 611 622 6 F Chang Ping Commercial Bldg 99 Hong Hua Road, Futian Free Trade Zone, Shenzhen, 518038, China
Tel.: (86) 75583480330
Semiconductor Mfr
N.A.I.C.S.: 334413
Cano Wong *(Mgr-Bus Dev)*

SEMILEDS CORPORATION
3F No 11 Ke Jung Rd Chu-Nan Site Hsinchu Science Park Chu-Nan 350, Miao-li, 350, Taiwan
Tel.: (886) 37586788 DE
Web Site: https://www.semileds.com
Year Founded: 2005
LEDS—(NASDAQ)
Rev.: $5,979,000

SEMILEDS CORPORATION

SemiLEDs Corporation—(Continued)
Assets: $13,455,000
Liabilities: $12,261,000
Net Worth: $1,194,000
Earnings: ($2,690,000)
Emp.: 152
Fiscal Year-end: 08/31/23
LED Chip & Component Mfr
N.A.I.C.S.: 334413
Trung Tri Doan *(Chm, Pres & CEO)*

SEMITEC CORPORATION
7-7 Kinshi 1-Chome, Sumida-ku, Tokyo, 130-8512, Japan
Tel.: (81) 336212704
Web Site: https://www.semitec.co.jp
Year Founded: 1958
6626—(TKS)
Rev.: $149,881,750
Assets: $186,739,110
Liabilities: $45,311,550
Net Worth: $141,427,560
Earnings: $14,198,280
Emp.: 3,646
Fiscal Year-end: 03/31/24
Electronic Components Mfr & Sales
N.A.I.C.S.: 334419
Jiro Ishizuka *(Chm & Co-CEO)*

Subsidiaries:

SEMITEC KOREA Co., Ltd. (1)
1408 Daeryung Technotown12 14 Gasan digital 2-ro, Gumcheon-gu, Seoul, Korea (South)
Tel.: (82) 232811155
Sales Range: $50-74.9 Million
Emp.: 60
Thermistor Resistor Distr
N.A.I.C.S.: 423690

Semitec USA Corp. (1)
2377 Crenshaw Blvd Ste 310, Torrance, CA 90501
Tel.: (310) 540-2330
Electronic Components Mfr & Sales
N.A.I.C.S.: 334419
Joseph Sgambato *(Pres & COO)*

SEMITRONIX CORPORATION
Building A1 No 188 Lianchuang Street, Yuhang District, Hangzhou, 311121, Zhejiang, China
Tel.: (86) 57188158085
Web Site:
https://www.semitronix.com
Year Founded: 2003
301095—(CHIN)
Rev.: $66,129,791
Assets: $490,886,450
Liabilities: $39,857,097
Net Worth: $451,029,353
Earnings: $17,833,850
Fiscal Year-end: 12/31/23
Software Development Services
N.A.I.C.S.: 541511
Yongjun Zheng *(Chm)*

SEMPERIT AG HOLDING
Am Belvedere 10, 1100, Vienna, Austria
Tel.: (43) 1797770 AT
Web Site:
https://www.semperitgroup.com
Year Founded: 1824
SEM—(VIE)
Rev.: $857,194,043
Assets: $909,688,107
Liabilities: $349,419,383
Net Worth: $560,268,724
Earnings: ($5,966,976)
Emp.: 6,528
Fiscal Year-end: 12/31/22
Holding Company; Rubber Products Mfr
N.A.I.C.S.: 551112
Walter Koppensteiner *(Chm-Supervisory Bd)*

Subsidiaries:

Hartereitechnik Rosenblattl GmbH (1)
Am Thalbach 7, Thalheim, 4600, Wels, Austria
Tel.: (43) 7242206699
Web Site: https://www.htr-rosenblattl.at
Metal & Plastic Mold Mfr
N.A.I.C.S.: 333511

Latexx Partners Berhad (1)
Lot 18374 Jalan Perusahaan 3, Kamunting Industrial Estate, 34600, Kamunting, Perak Darul Ridzuan, Malaysia **(85.26%)**
Tel.: (60) 605 829 5555
Web Site: http://www.latexx.com.my
Emp.: 2,119
Examination Glove Mfr
N.A.I.C.S.: 339113

Subsidiary (Domestic):

Latexx Manufacturing Sdn. Bhd. (2)
Lot 18374 Jalan Perusahaan 3, Kamunting Industrial Estate, 34600, Perak, Malaysia
Tel.: (60) 58295555
Web Site: http://www.latexx.com.my
Sales Range: $200-249.9 Million
Latex Rubber Mfr
N.A.I.C.S.: 325212

Medtexx Manufacturing Sdn. Bhd. (2)
PT 4004 Kamunting Industrial Estate, 34600, Taiping, Perak, Malaysia
Tel.: (60) 58911111
Sales Range: $150-199.9 Million
Emp.: 1,000
Latex Gloves Mfr
N.A.I.C.S.: 339112

RICO Group GmbH (1)
Am Thalbach 8, Thalheim, 4600, Wels, Austria
Tel.: (43) 724276460
Web Site: https://www.rico-group.net
Plastic & Elastomer Mfr
N.A.I.C.S.: 325211

Semperform Kft. (1)
Somfalvi ut 29, 9400, Sopron, Hungary
Tel.: (36) 301852100
Medical Device Mfr & Distr
N.A.I.C.S.: 339112

Semperit Technische Produkte Ges.mbH (1)
Triester Bundesstrasse 26, 2632, Wimpassing, Austria **(100%)**
Tel.: (43) 26303100
Web Site: http://www.semperit.at
Emp.: 900
Rubber Products Mfr
N.A.I.C.S.: 326299

Division (Domestic):

Semperit Technische Produkte Ges.mbH - Semperflex Division (2)
Triester Bundesstrasse 26, 2632, Wimpassing, Austria
Tel.: (43) 2630310201
Web Site: http://www.semperflex.com
Sales Range: $125-149.9 Million
Emp.: 600
Industrial & Hydraulic Rubber Hoses & Rubber Sheeting Mfr
N.A.I.C.S.: 326220

Joint Venture (Non-US):

Semperflex Shanghai Ltd. (3)
1255 Cang Gong Road, Shanghai Chemical Industrial Park Fengxian Subzone, Shanghai, 201417, China **(50%)**
Tel.: (86) 2137581133
Rubber Products Mfr
N.A.I.C.S.: 326299

Division (Domestic):

Semperit Technische Produkte Ges.mbH - Semperform Division (2)
Triester Bundesstrabe 26, Wimpassing, 2632, Austria
Tel.: (43) 26303100
Web Site: http://www.semperitgroup.com
Sales Range: $200-249.9 Million
Emp.: 750
Molded Plastic & Rubber Products Mfr
N.A.I.C.S.: 326299

Semperit Technische Produkte Ges.mbH - Sempermed Division (2)
Modecenterstrasse 22, 1031, Vienna, Austria
Tel.: (43) 1 79777 520
Web Site: http://www.semperitgroup.com
Sales Range: $25-49.9 Million
Emp.: 4
Medical Latex Gloves Mfr
N.A.I.C.S.: 326299

Subsidiary (US):

Sempermed USA Inc. (3)
13900 49th St N, Clearwater, FL 33762
Tel.: (727) 787-7250
Web Site: http://www.sempermedusa.com
Sales Range: $25-49.9 Million
Emp.: 50
Hand Protection Products Mfr
N.A.I.C.S.: 326299
Brian Eye *(CEO)*

Sempermed Kft. (1)
Somfalvi ut 14, 9400, Sopron, Hungary
Tel.: (36) 307743711
Medical Device Mfr & Distr
N.A.I.C.S.: 339112

Sempertrans France Belting Technology SAS (1)
1bis Rue Collange, CS 20001, 92593, Levallois-Perret, Cedex, France **(100%)**
Tel.: (33) 15 590 5620
Web Site: http://www.sempertrans.com
Sales Range: $50-74.9 Million
Conveyor Belt Developer, Mfr & Installation Services
N.A.I.C.S.: 333922

Subsidiary (Non-US):

Semperit Industrial Products Inc. (2)
Tel.: (201) 797-7794
Web Site: http://www.semperit.at
Sales Range: $25-49.9 Million
Emp.: 20
Mfr of Rubber Handrails
N.A.I.C.S.: 423840

Silcoplast AG (1)
Luchten 75, 9427, Wolfhalden, Switzerland
Tel.: (41) 718985060
Web Site: https://www.silcoplast.ch
Plastic Material Mfr & Distr
N.A.I.C.S.: 325211

SEMPIO COMPANY
2 Chungmuro, Jung-gu, Seoul, 04557, Korea (South)
Tel.: (82) 233935500
Web Site: https://www.sempio.com
Year Founded: 1946
007540—(KRS)
Rev.: $285,191,705
Assets: $357,360,569
Liabilities: $106,349,113
Net Worth: $251,011,456
Earnings: $8,005,674
Emp.: 2
Fiscal Year-end: 12/31/22
Sauce Products Mfr
N.A.I.C.S.: 311941
Jin-Sun Park *(Pres & CEO)*

Subsidiaries:

Sempio China Co., Ltd. (1)
Room 810 No 1888 Yishan Road, Shanghai, 201104, China
Tel.: (86) 2161679990
Sauce Product Distr
N.A.I.C.S.: 424490

Sempio Food Service. Inc. (1)
12928 Moore St, Cerritos, CA 90703
Tel.: (562) 207-9540
Sauce Product Distr
N.A.I.C.S.: 424490
John Lee *(COO)*

SEMTEK CO., LTD.
15 Mongae-ro 122 beon-gil, Danwon-gu, Ansan, 15598, Gyeonggi-do, Korea (South)
Tel.: (82) 31 492 9817
Web Site: http://www.semtek.co.kr
Year Founded: 2004
Semiconductor Inspection Devices & Precision Tools Mfr
N.A.I.C.S.: 334515
Myung-Bae Choi *(Chm & CEO)*

Subsidiaries:

DD Diamond Corporation (1)
778 Seongjusan-ro Seongju-myeon, Boryeong, 33486, Chungcheongnam-do, Korea (South)
Tel.: (82) 529348454
Industrial Diamond Tools Mfr & Whslr
N.A.I.C.S.: 333515
Myung-Bae Choi *(Chm & CEO)*

SEMYUNG ELECTRIC MACHINERY CO., LTD.
188 Daedong-ro, Sasang-gu, Busan, Korea (South)
Tel.: (82) 513166886
Web Site: https://www.semyung-elec.com
Year Founded: 1962
017510—(KRS)
Rev.: $10,712,046
Assets: $63,649,706
Liabilities: $6,336,726
Net Worth: $57,312,980
Earnings: $1,728,553
Emp.: 57
Fiscal Year-end: 12/31/22
Electrical Fitting Mfr
N.A.I.C.S.: 335932
Cheol-Hyun Kwon *(CEO)*

Subsidiaries:

Semyung Electric Machinery Co., Ltd. - Busan Mieum Plant (1)
10 Mieumsandan 5-ro 42beon-gil, Gangseo-gu, Busan, Korea (South)
Tel.: (82) 513166887
Vehicle Parts & Electronic Equipment Mfr
N.A.I.C.S.: 336390

Semyung Electric Machinery Co., Ltd. - Changwon Plant (1)
654-11 Ungnam-ro, Seongsan-gu, Changwon, Gyeongsangnam-do, Korea (South)
Tel.: (82) 552859832
Vehicle Parts & Electronic Equipment Mfr
N.A.I.C.S.: 336390

SEN YU INTERNATIONAL HOLDINGS, INC.
308 Baowei Road 6th Floor, Qianjin District, Jiamusi, China
Tel.: (86) 454 844 2728 DE
Sales Range: $75-99.9 Million
Emp.: 96
Hog Research, Breeding & Sales
N.A.I.C.S.: 112210
Zhenyu Shang *(Chm & CEO)*

SENA DEVELOPMENT PUBLIC COMPANY LIMITED
448 Thanyalakpark Building Ratchadapisek 26, Khwaeng Samsen Nok Khet Huai Khwang, Bangkok, 10310, Thailand
Tel.: (66) 25414642
Web Site: https://www.sena.co.th
SENA—(THA)
Rev.: $106,877,181
Assets: $744,160,381
Liabilities: $444,444,269
Net Worth: $299,716,112
Earnings: $12,924,045
Emp.: 1,548
Fiscal Year-end: 12/31/23
Residential Property Development & Construction Services

AND PRIVATE COMPANIES

N.A.I.C.S.: 236116
Vichien Ratanabirabongse *(Chm)*

Subsidiaries:

Acute Realty Co., Ltd. (1)
484 524 Ratchadaphisek Road, Samsen Nok Sub-district Huai Khwang District, Bangkok, 10310, Thailand
Tel.: (66) 856645000
Web Site: https://www.acuterealty.com
Real Estate Manarigement Services
N.A.I.C.S.: 531210

Sena Solar Energy Co., Ltd. (1)
448 Thanyalakpark Building Ratchadapisek 26 Khwaeng Samsen Nok, Khet Huai Khwang, Bangkok, 10310, Thailand
Tel.: (66) 25414642
Web Site: https://www.senasolarenergy.com
Solar Farm Operator
N.A.I.C.S.: 221114

Sena Vanij Development Co., Ltd. (1)
No 448 3rd Floor, Samsennok Subdistrict Huay Kwang, Bangkok, 10310, Thailand
Tel.: (66) 205929379
Web Site: http://www.proudvanich.com
Real Estate Development Services
N.A.I.C.S.: 531210

Victory Asset Management Co., Ltd. (1)
448 Thanyalakpark Building Ratchadapisek 26 Khwaeng Samsen Nok, Khet Huai Khwang, Bangkok, 10310, Thailand
Tel.: (66) 25415014
Web Site: http://www.victory-assets.co.th
Property Management Services
N.A.I.C.S.: 531210

SENATA GMBH

GuteAnger11, 85356, Freising, Germany
Tel.: (49) 8161988220
Web Site: http://www.senata.de
Sales Range: $10-24.9 Million
Emp.: 5
Holding Company
N.A.I.C.S.: 551112
Werner Folger *(Co-CEO)*

Subsidiaries:

Fiberpachs S.A. (1)
Poligon Industrial La Xarmada S/N, Paos del Penedes, 8796, Barcelona, Spain
Tel.: (34) 93890 0288
Web Site: http://www.fiberpachs.com
Engineered Composites Mfr
N.A.I.C.S.: 333248
Cesar Alvarez *(Mng Dir)*

MITRAS Composites Systems GmbH (1)
Bahnhofstrasse 32, 1471, Radeburg, Germany
Tel.: (49) 35 208 8330
Web Site: http://www.mitras-composites.de
Glass Fiber Reinforced Composites Mfr
N.A.I.C.S.: 333248
Stefan Ott *(Mng Dir)*

Subsidiary (Non-US):

MITRAS Automotive (UK) Ltd. (2)
Road 1 Winsford Industrial Estate, Winsford, CW7 3PZ, Cheshire, United Kingdom
Tel.: (44) 1606 550339
Web Site: http://www.mitras.co.uk
Engineered Composite Components & Modules for Automotive Industry
N.A.I.C.S.: 336390
Cesar Alvarez *(Mng Dir)*

MITRAS Materials GmbH (1)
Friedrich-Ochs-Strasse 2, 92637, Weiden, Germany
Tel.: (49) 96 189 308
Web Site: http://www.mitras-materials.com
Plastics Product Mfr
N.A.I.C.S.: 326199

Menzolit GmbH (1)
Werner-von-Siemens-Str. 2-6, 69120, Bruchsal, Germany
Tel.: (49) 72513219730
Web Site: http://www.menzolit.com
Compression Moulded Parts Mfr
N.A.I.C.S.: 327212
Christian Gromer *(Mgr-Sls)*

Subsidiary (Non-US):

Menzolit Ltd. (UK) (2)
Perseverance Works Halifax Road, Eastwood, Todmorden, OL14 6EG, Lancs, United Kingdom
Tel.: (44) 1706 814 714
Web Site: http://www.menzolit-uk.co.uk
Compression Moulded Parts Mfr
N.A.I.C.S.: 327212

Menzolit S.r.l. (2)
Via Isonzo 39, Turate, I 22078, Italy
Tel.: (39) 02 96 71 52 17
Web Site: http://www.menzolit.com
Compression Moulded Parts Mfr
N.A.I.C.S.: 327212
Adamo Nicolo *(Mgr-Sls)*

Menzolit Vitroplast S.L. (2)
Poligono Ind Can Jane Coll de la Manya, Granollers, E 08403, Spain
Tel.: (34) 938443386
Web Site: http://www.menzolit.com
Compression Moulded Parts Mfr
N.A.I.C.S.: 327212
Joan Montobbio *(Mng Dir-Granollers Plant)*

United Trading System (2)
140-L Leninskiy Av, Saint Petersburg, Russia
Tel.: (7) 8123895555
Web Site: http://www.utsrus.com
Compression Moulded Parts Mfr
N.A.I.C.S.: 327212
Andrey Shkola *(Gen Mgr)*

OPTIPLAN GmbH (1)
Am Johannisberg 9-13, 08606, Oelsnitz, Germany
Tel.: (49) 374214940
Web Site: http://www.optiplan.eu
Glass Fiber Reinforced Plastics Mfr
N.A.I.C.S.: 326199
Alexandra Semrau *(Mng Dir)*

QANTOS GmbH (1)
Am Forst 13, Weiden, 92637, Germany
Tel.: (49) 961 6346830
Web Site: http://www.qantos.de
Plastics Product Mfr
N.A.I.C.S.: 326199
Franz Kern *(Mng Dir)*

RCS GmbH Rail Components and Systems (1)
Hockendorfer Str 91, 01936, Konigsbruck, Germany
Tel.: (49) 357953450
Web Site: http://www.railcomsys-gmbh.de
Emp.: 200
Component & Module for Railway Industry Mfr
N.A.I.C.S.: 326199

ZSO GmbH (1)
Im Moos 2, Oberstaufen, 87534, Germany
Tel.: (49) 8386 4980
Web Site: http://www.zso.de
Emp.: 150
Metal Cutting Services
N.A.I.C.S.: 423510
Carsten Binder *(Mng Dir)*

SENATOR INTERNATIONAL LTD

Altham Business Park, Accrington, BB5 5YE, Lancashire, United Kingdom
Tel.: (44) 1282725000
Web Site: http://www.senator.co.uk
Year Founded: 1977
Rev.: $158,594,161
Emp.: 887
Office Furniture Mfr
N.A.I.C.S.: 337214
Colin Mustoe *(Founder & Chm)*

SENBA SENSING TECHNOLOGY CO., LTD.

Senba Sensing Industrial Park Zhengzhou Road, Sheqi County, Nanyang, 473300, Henan, China
Tel.: (86) 75582594732
Web Site: https://www.senbasensor.com
Year Founded: 2005
300701—(CHIN)
Rev.: $41,544,848
Assets: $171,388,534
Liabilities: $49,508,564
Net Worth: $121,879,970
Earnings: $7,950,151
Emp.: 1,000
Fiscal Year-end: 12/31/23
Electronic Component Mfr & Distr
N.A.I.C.S.: 334413
Shan Senlin *(Chm)*

SENBO INDUSTRIES LIMITED

87 Lenin Sarani, Kolkata, 700 013, West Bengal, India
Tel.: (91) 33 2217 8915
Web Site: http://www.senboengineering.com
Year Founded: 1994
Rev.: $15,049
Assets: $445,512
Liabilities: $3,183,525
Net Worth: ($2,738,013)
Earnings: ($36,527)
Fiscal Year-end: 03/31/18
Intravenous Fluid Mfr
N.A.I.C.S.: 325199
Kajal Sengupta *(CEO)*

SENCHUK FORD SALES LTD.

118 Souris Avenue N, Estevan, S4A 1J6, SK, Canada
Tel.: (306) 634-3696
Web Site: http://www.senchuk.com
Rev.: $16,848,000
Emp.: 24
New & Used Car Dealers
N.A.I.C.S.: 441110
Blaine Dirks *(Mgr-Parts)*

SENCI ELECTRIC MACHINERY CO., LTD.

No 46 Jiade Avenue, Caijiagang Town Beibei, Chongqing, 400700, China
Tel.: (86) 2386021111
Web Site: https://www.senci.cn
Year Founded: 1993
603109—(SHG)
Rev.: $365,075,325
Assets: $410,039,674
Liabilities: $176,654,116
Net Worth: $233,385,558
Earnings: $28,821,565
Emp.: 3,500
Fiscal Year-end: 12/31/22
Electrical Equipment Mfr & Distr
N.A.I.C.S.: 335999
Chun Ai *(Chm & Gen Mgr)*

SENCO GOLD LIMITED

41A AJC Bose Road Diamond Prestige 10TH Floor, Kolkata, 700017, West Bengal, India
Tel.: (91) 1800103001
Web Site: https://www.sencogold.com
Year Founded: 1994
SENCO—(NSE)
Rev.: $429,946,092
Assets: $254,542,422
Liabilities: $166,555,222
Net Worth: $87,987,200
Earnings: $15,647,162
Emp.: 1,862
Fiscal Year-end: 03/31/22
Jewelry Product Distr
N.A.I.C.S.: 423940
Ranjana Sen *(Chm)*

Subsidiaries:

Senco Global Jewellery Trading LLC (1)

Senco Gold Artisanship Private Limited (1)

SENER INGENIERIA Y SISTEMAS, SA

Avda Zugazarte n 56, Getxo, 48930, Las Arenas, Vizcaya, Spain
Tel.: (34) 944 817 500
Web Site: http://www.ingenieriayconstruc.com
Engineering, Construction, Energy, Environment & Aerospace Industries
N.A.I.C.S.: 237990

SENERGY HOLDING COMPANY K.P.S.C.

East Ahmadi Block 8 Plot 42 Mezzanine, PO Box 9920, Hawally, Ahmadi, 61010, Kuwait
Tel.: (965) 23970097
Web Site: https://www.senergyholding.com
Year Founded: 1983
SENERGY—(KUW)
Rev.: $10,809,386
Assets: $44,024,226
Liabilities: $6,597,458
Net Worth: $37,426,767
Earnings: ($606,819)
Emp.: 12
Fiscal Year-end: 12/31/22
Oil & Gas Investment Services
N.A.I.C.S.: 523999
Naser Bader Al Sharhan *(Vice Chm)*

Subsidiaries:

Eastern Industrial & Oilfield Services Company (1)
Mushtan Bldg Ofc 54 Bldg 2415, Rd 2831 Block 428 Al-Seef, Manama, Bahrain
Tel.: (973) 17565522
Web Site: http://www.eiosholding.com
Sales Range: $25-49.9 Million
Emp.: 30
Engineering Solutions & Services
N.A.I.C.S.: 541330

Eastern National Oilfield Services Co. (1)
PO Box 9377, Ahmadi, 61004, Kuwait
Tel.: (965) 23970000
Web Site: http://www.eastern-national.com
Sales Range: $50-74.9 Million
Emp.: 40
Wireline & Perforation Services
N.A.I.C.S.: 213112

Emirates Western Petroleum Services (1)
PO Box 8107, Abu Dhabi, United Arab Emirates
Tel.: (971) 26725637
Web Site: http://www.ewpsco.ae
Sales Range: $100-124.9 Million
Offshore Drilling Fluid Services
N.A.I.C.S.: 213111

SENETAS CORPORATION LIMITED

312 Kings Way, South Melbourne, 3205, VIC, Australia
Tel.: (61) 398684555
Web Site: https://www.senetas.com
SEN—(ASX)
Rev.: $20,864,887
Assets: $23,328,822
Liabilities: $24,394,152
Net Worth: ($1,065,330)
Earnings: ($8,947,580)
Emp.: 77
Fiscal Year-end: 06/30/24
IT Products & Services
N.A.I.C.S.: 541512
Andrew R. Wilson *(CEO)*

Subsidiaries:

Senetas Security Pty Ltd (1)
312 Kings Way, Melbourne, 3205, VIC, Australia

SENETAS CORPORATION LIMITED

Senetas Corporation Limited—(Continued)
Tel.: (61) 398684555
Web Site: http://www.senetas.com
Sales Range: $50-74.9 Million
Financial Services
N.A.I.C.S.: 551112

Subsidiary (US):

CTAM Inc (2)
120 Waterfront St Ste 200, Oxon Hill, MD 20745-1142
Tel.: (703) 549-4200
Web Site: http://www.ctam.com
Cable Mfr & Distr
N.A.I.C.S.: 335921
Vicki Lins (Pres & CEO)

SENG FONG HOLDINGS BERHAD
12 Tingkat Bawah Taman Sri Jeram, Jalan Bakri, 84000, Muar, Johor, Malaysia
Tel.: (60) 69864268
Web Site: https://www.sengfongholdings.com
Year Founded: 1986
SENFONG—(KLS)
Rev.: $241,361,821
Assets: $82,764,901
Liabilities: $34,752,314
Net Worth: $48,012,586
Earnings: ($3,699,643)
Emp.: 154
Fiscal Year-end: 06/30/24
Holding Company
N.A.I.C.S.: 551112
Hock Lai Er (Mng Dir)

SENGER HOLDING GMBH
Oldenburger Strasse 1-11, 48429, Rheine, Germany
Tel.: (49) 597179137270 De
Web Site: http://www.auto-senger.de
Year Founded: 1953
Sales Range: $400-449.9 Million
Emp.: 1,100
Holding Company; New Car Dealerships Owner & Operator
N.A.I.C.S.: 551112
Andreas Senger (Mng Dir)

Subsidiaries:

Egon Senger GmbH (1)
Oldenburger Strasse 1-11, 48429, Rheine, Germany
Tel.: (49) 5971 7913 4137
Web Site: http://www.auto-senger.de
New & Used Car Dealerships Operator
N.A.I.C.S.: 441110
Andreas Senger (CEO & Mng Dir)

SENHENG NEW RETAIL BERHAD
42B 44B Jalan Pandan 3/2, Pandan Jaya, 55100, Kuala Lumpur, Selangor, Malaysia
Tel.: (60) 162991398 MY
Web Site: https://www.senheng.com
Year Founded: 1989
SENHENG—(KLS)
Rev.: $330,628,284
Assets: $179,987,190
Liabilities: $68,003,731
Net Worth: $111,983,458
Earnings: $12,808,988
Emp.: 1,837
Fiscal Year-end: 12/31/22
Electronic Product Distr
N.A.I.C.S.: 449210
Teng Kean Kheng (VP)

Subsidiaries:

Senheng Electric (KL) Sdn. Bhd. (1)
44B Jalan Pandan 3/2, Pandan Jaya, 55100, Kuala Lumpur, Malaysia
Tel.: (60) 162991398
Web Site: https://www.senheng.com.my
Electrical & Electronic Product Retailer

N.A.I.C.S.: 423610

SENI JAYA CORPORATION BERHAD
A-01-01 Block Allamanda 10 Boulevard Lebuhraya SPRINT, Damansara Heights, 47400, Petaling Jaya, Selangor, Malaysia
Tel.: (60) 377291795
Web Site: https://www.senijayacorp.com
SJC—(KLS)
Rev.: $8,027,516
Assets: $14,897,880
Liabilities: $3,907,231
Net Worth: $10,990,648
Earnings: $1,616,733
Fiscal Year-end: 12/31/22
Media Services
N.A.I.C.S.: 541850
Anne Teo (Chm)

SENIOR PLC
59/61 High Street, Rickmansworth, WD3 1RH, Hertfordshire, United Kingdom
Tel.: (44) 1923775547 UK
Web Site: https://www.seniorplc.com
Year Founded: 1933
SNR—(LSE)
Rev.: $1,021,897,800
Assets: $1,176,676,050
Liabilities: $635,373,750
Net Worth: $541,302,300
Earnings: $23,849,100
Fiscal Year-end: 12/31/22
Holding Company; Commercial & Industrial Equipment & Systems Mfr
N.A.I.C.S.: 551112
Michael Sheppard (CEO)

Subsidiaries:

Industrias Traterh, S.A. (1)
Pol Industrial Aproin, Alcotanes 32, 28320, Pinto, Madrid, Spain (100%)
Tel.: (34) 916920810
Web Site: http://www.aamtlastgroup.com
Sales Range: $25-49.9 Million
Emp.: 20
Flexible Hose & Braiding; Bellows Expansion Joints; Drawn Seamless & Welded Tubing in Carbon, Alloy & Stainless Steel; Manipulated Tube; Steel Processing Equipment & Tools; Heat Treatment Services
N.A.I.C.S.: 332999

Lymington Precision Engineers Co., Ltd. (1)
Gosport Street, Lymington, SO41 9EE, Hampshire, United Kingdom
Tel.: (44) 1590 677 944
Web Site: http://www.lymingtonprecision.co.uk
Machinery Component Mfr
N.A.I.C.S.: 333248

Senior Aerospace (Thailand) Limited (1)
789/198 Moo 1, Nhongkham Sriracha, Chon Buri, 20230, Thailand
Tel.: (66) 330472815
Web Site: http://www.senior-thailand.com
Emp.: 7,470
Hard Metal Structural Parts Mfr
N.A.I.C.S.: 332312
Jadsada Kingkaew (Dir-Technical Svcs)

Senior Aerospace Bosman B.V (1)
Bergen 6, 2993 LR, Barendrecht, Netherlands
Tel.: (31) 180656800
Web Site: http://www.sabosman.nl
Aircraft Ducting Component Mfr
N.A.I.C.S.: 336412

Senior Aerospace Ermeto SAS (1)
ZA Euro Val de Loire 8 rue du Clos Thomas, 41330, Fosse, France
Tel.: (33) 254335060
Web Site: http://www.senior-aerospace-ermeto.com

INTERNATIONAL PUBLIC

Sales Range: $50-74.9 Million
Emp.: 150
Hydraulic & Pneumatic Components Mfr
N.A.I.C.S.: 332912

Senior Aerospace Mexico (1)
Parque Industrial La Angostura KM 4 5 Carretera Saltillo-Zacatecas, 25086, Saltillo, Coahuila, Mexico
Tel.: (52) 8444116611
Web Site: http://www.senioraerospacemexico.com
Aerospace Fabricated Component Mfr
N.A.I.C.S.: 332312

Senior Automotive Blois SAS (1)
22 boulevard de l'Industrie, BP 702, 41007, Blois, France (100%)
Tel.: (33) 254553500
Web Site: http://www.senioautomotive.sr
Sales Range: $50-74.9 Million
Emp.: 200
Automotive Components Mfr
N.A.I.C.S.: 336340
Cavelier Syluain (Mng Dir)

Senior Calorstat SAS (1)
Rue Des Soufflets, PO Box 58, F 91416, Dourdan, France (100%)
Tel.: (33) 160815454
Sales Range: $50-74.9 Million
Emp.: 84
Distr of Flexible Tubes
N.A.I.C.S.: 423690

Senior Flexonics Czech s.r.o (1)
Prumyslova 9, Olomouc, 779 00, Holice, Czech Republic
Tel.: (420) 585 151 170
Aircraft Equipment Mfr
N.A.I.C.S.: 336413

Senior Flexonics GmbH (1)
Frankurter Strasse 199, D 34070, Kassel, Germany (100%)
Tel.: (49) 56120020
Web Site: http://www.berghofer.de
Sales Range: $100-124.9 Million
Emp.: 270
Flexible Hose & Braiding; Bellows Expansion Joints; Drawn Seamless & Welded Tubing in Carbon, Alloy & Stainless Steel; Manipulated Tube; Steel Processing Equipment & Tools; Heat Treatment Services
N.A.I.C.S.: 332999
Andreas Brand (Mng Dir)

Senior Flexonics SA (Pty) Limited (1)
11 Thor Circle, Thornton, Cape Town, 7460, South Africa
Tel.: (27) 21 532 5300
Web Site: http://flexonics.co.za
Automotive Exhaust Connector Mfr
N.A.I.C.S.: 336390

Senior India Private Limited (1)
Plot No 89 Sector 8 IMT Manesar, Gurgaon, 122050, Haryana, India
Tel.: (91) 1244387704
Web Site: http://www.senioauto.co.in
Auto Parts Mfr
N.A.I.C.S.: 336390
Sidharth Yadav (Head-HR)

Senior Operations (Canada) Limited (1)
134 Nelson Street West, Brampton, L6X 1C9, ON, Canada
Tel.: (905) 451-1250
Web Site: http://www.flexonics.ca
Sales Range: $25-49.9 Million
Emp.: 10
Cryogenic Equipment Mfr & Distr
N.A.I.C.S.: 332420

Senior Operations LLC (1)
300 E Devon Ave, Bartlett, IL 60103-1811
Tel.: (630) 837-1811
Commercial & Industrial Equipment & Systems Mfr
N.A.I.C.S.: 332999
Michael Sheppard (CEO-Flexonics)

Unit (Domestic):

Senior Aerospace AMT (2)
20100 71st Ave NE, Arlington, WA 98223
Tel.: (360) 435-1119
Web Site: http://www.amtnw.com

Sales Range: $10-24.9 Million
Emp.: 300
Aircraft Parts & Auxiliary Equipment Mfr
N.A.I.C.S.: 336413

Senior Aerospace Absolute Manufacturing (2)
20350 71st Ave NE Ste C, Arlington, WA 98223
Tel.: (360) 435-1116
Web Site: http://www.absolutemfg.com
Aerospace Machine Tools Mfr
N.A.I.C.S.: 334511

Senior Aerospace Capo Industries (2)
5498 Vine St, Chino, CA 91710
Tel.: (909) 627-2723
Web Site: http://www.capoindustriesinc.com
Sales Range: $1-9.9 Million
Emp.: 95
Aircraft Engine & Engine Parts Mfr
N.A.I.C.S.: 336412
Manuel Perez (CFO)

Senior Aerospace Composites (2)
2700 S Custer, Wichita, KS 67217
Tel.: (316) 942-3208
Web Site: http://www.seniorcomposites.com
Aircraft Ducting Component Mfr
N.A.I.C.S.: 336412

Senior Aerospace Damar (2)
14767 172nd Dr SE, Monroe, WA 98272
Tel.: (360) 794-4448
Web Site: http://www.damaraerosystems.com
Sales Range: $25-49.9 Million
Aerospace Fabricated Component Mfr
N.A.I.C.S.: 332312
Charles Elder (CEO)

Senior Aerospace Ketema (2)
790 Greenfield Dr, El Cajon, CA 92021-3101 (100%)
Tel.: (619) 442-3451
Web Site: http://www.senioraerospace.com
Sales Range: $100-124.9 Million
Emp.: 350
Jet Engine & Aerospace Components Mfr
N.A.I.C.S.: 332312

Senior Aerospace Metal Bellows (2)
1075 Providence Hwy, Sharon, MA 02067
Tel.: (781) 784-1400
Web Site: http://www.metalbellows.com
Emp.: 200
Metal Bellows Mfr
N.A.I.C.S.: 332999

Senior Aerospace SSP (2)
2980 N San Fernando Blvd, Burbank, CA 91504
Tel.: (818) 260-2900
Web Site: http://www.seniorplc.com
Aircraft Ducting Component Mfr
N.A.I.C.S.: 336412

Senior Aerospace Sterling Machine (2)
4 Peerless Way, Enfield, CT 06082
Tel.: (860) 741-2546
Web Site: http://www.seniorplc.com
Aerospace Machined Component Mfr
N.A.I.C.S.: 334511

Senior Flexonics Bartlett (2)
300 E Devon Ave, Bartlett, IL 60103-4608
Tel.: (630) 837-1811
Web Site: http://www.seniorflexonics.com
Sales Range: $150-199.9 Million
Emp.: 300
Flexible Metal Hose, Expansion Joints, Compensators, Flexible Ducting & Connectors, Fabricated Metal Components Mfr
N.A.I.C.S.: 332999

Unit (Domestic):

Senior Flexonics GAMFG Precision (3)
5215 W Airways Ave, Franklin, WI 53132
Tel.: (414) 423-6400
Web Site: http://www.seniorflexonicsgaprecision.com
Sales Range: $25-49.9 Million
Machined Component Mfr
N.A.I.C.S.: 336390

Senior Flexonics Pathway (3)

2400 Longhorn Industrial Dr, New Braunfels, TX 78130
Tel.: (830) 629-8080
Web Site: http://www.sfpathway.com
Industrial Metal Bellows Mfr
N.A.I.C.S.: 333994

Unit (Domestic):

Senior Flexonics Pathway - Metroflex Dampers (4)
29 Lexington St, Lewiston, ME 04240
Tel.: (207) 784-2338
Web Site: http://www.sfpathway.com
Rev.: $45,400,000
Emp.: 70
Fabricated Structural Metal Mfr
N.A.I.C.S.: 332312

Senior UK Limited (1)
Adlington Business Park Adlington, Macclesfield, SK10 4NL, Cheshire, United Kingdom
Tel.: (44) 1625 870700
Web Site: http://www.bwt.co.uk
Sales Range: $100-124.9 Million
Emp.: 300
Aircraft Ducting Component Mfr
N.A.I.C.S.: 336412
Nick Parr *(Dir-Comml)*

Unit (Domestic):

Senior Aerospace BWT (2)
Adlington Business Park, Adlington, Macclesfield, SK10 4NL, Cheshire, United Kingdom
Tel.: (44) 1625870700
Web Site: http://www.senioraerospacebwt.co.uk
Sales Range: $75-99.9 Million
Aircraft Ducting Component Mfr
N.A.I.C.S.: 336412

Senior Aerospace Bird Bellows (2)
Radnor Park Estate, Congleton, CW12 4UQ, Cheshire, United Kingdom
Tel.: (44) 1260 271411
Web Site: http://www.sabirdbellows.co.uk
Emp.: 180
Aerospace Products Mfr
N.A.I.C.S.: 336412

Senior Flexonics Crumlin (2)
Pen-y-Fan Industrial Estate, Crumlin, NP11 3HY, United Kingdom
Tel.: (44) 1495241500
Web Site: http://www.sabirdbellows.co.uk
Automotive Exhaust Component Mfr
N.A.I.C.S.: 336390

Senior do Brasil Ltda. (1)
Praca Faustino Roncoroni n 01 - Portao B - Distrito Industrial, Caixa Postal 01001, Aracariguama, 18147-000, Sao Paulo, Brazil
Tel.: (55) 11 4136 4514
Web Site: http://www.seniorbrazil.com.br
Emp.: 120
Industrial Supplies Whslr
N.A.I.C.S.: 423840
Francesco Ferrero *(Mng Dir)*

Steico Industries, Inc. (1)
1814 Ord Way, Oceanside, CA 92056
Tel.: (760) 438-8015
Web Site: http://www.steicoindustries.com
Metal Stamping Services
N.A.I.C.S.: 332119
Troy Steiner *(Founder)*

Upeca Aerotech Sdn. Bhd. (1)
Lot 2-22 Jalan SU 6A Section 22 Lion Industrial Park Darul Ehsan, 40400, Shah Alam, Selangor, Malaysia
Tel.: (60) 323339299
Web Site: http://www.upeca.com
Aerospace Component Mfr
N.A.I.C.S.: 336412
Kavan Jeet Singh *(CEO)*

Upeca Flowtech Sdn. Bhd. (1)
Lot 2827 Jalan Sri Gambut Off Jalan Kebun Seksyen 32, 40460, Shah Alam, Selangor, Malaysia
Tel.: (60) 351617363
Oil & Gas Equipment Mfr
N.A.I.C.S.: 333132
Bryant Liew *(Program Mgr)*

Upeca Technologies Sdn. Bhd. (1)
Lot 2827 Jalan Sri Gambut Off Jalan Kebun Seksyen 32, 40460, Shah Alam, Selangor, Malaysia
Tel.: (60) 351617363
Web Site: http://www.upeca.com
Precision Turned Product Mfr
N.A.I.C.S.: 332721
Eugene Ang *(CEO)*

SENIOR TRUST RETIREMENT VILLAGE LISTED FUND

44 Constellation Drive Rosedale, Auckland, New Zealand
Tel.: (64) 800609600
Web Site: http://www.seniortrust.co.nz
Rev.: $3,082,630
Assets: $29,780,973
Liabilities: $785,372
Net Worth: $28,995,601
Earnings: $1,419,443
Fiscal Year-end: 03/31/19
Investment Management Service
N.A.I.C.S.: 525990
John Jackson *(Exec Dir)*

Subsidiaries:

Senior Trust Capital Limited (1)
PO Box 113120, Newmarket, Auckland, 1149, New Zealand
Tel.: (64) 800609600
Web Site: http://www.seniortrustcapital.co.nz
Trust Management Services
N.A.I.C.S.: 523991
John Jackson *(Founder & Exec Dir)*

SENKO GROUP HOLDINGS CO., LTD.

Shiomi SIF Bldg 2-8-10 Shiomi, Koto-ku, Tokyo, 135-0052, Japan
Tel.: (81) 664405156
Web Site: https://www.senkogrouphd.co.jp
Year Founded: 1946
9069—(TKS)
Rev.: $5,145,025,700
Assets: $4,528,643,200
Liabilities: $3,178,973,740
Net Worth: $1,349,669,460
Earnings: $105,389,840
Emp.: 25,574
Fiscal Year-end: 03/31/24
Holding Company;Petroleum-Related Products Distr & Seller, Information Processing & Software Development & Sales, Freight Forwarding Services, Truck Transport & Warehouse Management Services
N.A.I.C.S.: 551112
Yasuhisa Fukuda *(Pres)*

Subsidiaries:

Anzen Yuso Co., Ltd. (1)
2026 Kamiyabe-cho, Totsuka-ku, Yokohama, 245-0053, Kanagawa, Japan
Tel.: (81) 45 812 6088
Web Site: https://www.anzen-yuso.co.jp
Freight Transportation Services
N.A.I.C.S.: 484121

Aphrodite Co., Ltd. (1)
1-1 Tadei Town, Sakai Ward, Sakai, 590-0014, Osaka, Japan
Tel.: (81) 72 242 8865
Freight Transportation Services
N.A.I.C.S.: 484121

Atsugi Senko Transport Co., Ltd. (1)
1902 Sakai, Atsugi, 243-0022, Kanagawa, Japan
Tel.: (81) 46 230 6270
Web Site: https://www.atsugi-senko.com
Freight Transportation Services
N.A.I.C.S.: 484121

Aya Construction Co., Ltd. (1)
174 Kawarasakimachi, Nobeoka, 882-0033, Miyazaki, Japan
Tel.: (81) 98 221 2188
Industrial Waste Transportation Services
N.A.I.C.S.: 562112

Best Global Logistics Co., Ltd. (1)
77/141-142 Sinnsathorn Tower 33rd Krungthon Rd, Klongtonsai Klongsarn, Bangkok, 10600, Thailand
Tel.: (66) 2 400 4999
Web Site: https://www.bestgloballogistics.com
Freight Forwarding Services
N.A.I.C.S.: 488510
Stefan Der Sluys *(Pres & CEO)*

Blue Earth Japan Co., Ltd. (1)
1040-1 Osatomachi, Kofu, 400-0053, Yamanashi, Japan
Tel.: (81) 55 220 2007
Web Site: https://www.blueearth.co.jp
Fitness Services
N.A.I.C.S.: 713940

Chiba Senko Transport Co., Ltd. (1)
8934-2 Goi, Ichihara, 290-0056, Chiba, Japan
Tel.: (81) 436218741
Web Site: https://chibasenko.senko.co.jp
Emp.: 162
Vehicle Maintenance, Trucking Services, In-Factory Work & Moving Services
N.A.I.C.S.: 484110

Chuo Kagaku Co., Ltd. (1)
3-5-1 Miyaji, Konosu, 365-8603, Saitama, Japan (70.64%)
Tel.: (81) 485422511
Web Site: http://www.chuo-kagaku.co.jp
Rev.: $461,406,880
Assets: $361,518,960
Liabilities: $259,578,880
Net Worth: $101,940,080
Earnings: $5,972,560
Emp.: 2,110
Fiscal Year-end: 03/31/2022
Plastic Food Container Mfr & Whslr
N.A.I.C.S.: 326199
Yasumasa Kondo *(Pres)*

Chushikoku Logistics K.K. (1)
6-571-1 Asahimachi, Takamatsu, 760-0065, Kagawa, Japan
Tel.: (81) 878226697
Web Site: http://chushikoku-logi.co.jp
Trucking, Warehousing & In-Factory Work & Logistics
N.A.I.C.S.: 493110

Crefeel Koto Co., Ltd. (1)
22-3 Hirayanagicho, Higashi-omi, 527-0102, Shiga, Japan
Tel.: (81) 749453880
Web Site: https://www.crefeel.co.jp
Hotel Management & Educational Training Services
N.A.I.C.S.: 561110

Daito Senko Apollo Co., Ltd. (1)
1100 Naka, Kakegawa, 437-1405, Shizuoka, Japan
Tel.: (81) 537 74 4130
Web Site: http://group.senko.co.jp
Supply Chain Management & In-Factory Services
N.A.I.C.S.: 541614

Dalian Tri-Enterprise Logistics Co., Ltd. (1)
Tel.: (86) 41187595928
Freight Forwarding & Warehousing Services
N.A.I.C.S.: 488510

Delivery Ace Co., Ltd. (1)
441-1 Imaizumi, Fuji, 417-8501, Shizuoka, Japan
Tel.: (81) 54 553 7744
Freight Transportation Services
N.A.I.C.S.: 484121

EIKO Shipping Co., Ltd. (1)
5-22-10 Shinbashi, Minato Ward, Tokyo, 105-0004, Japan
Tel.: (81) 36 450 1167
Freight Transportation Services
N.A.I.C.S.: 484121

Eikichi Kaiun Co., Ltd. (1)
5-10-16 Hibi, Tamano, 706-0027, Okayama, Japan
Tel.: (81) 86 381 7111
Web Site: https://www.eikichikaiun.jp
Freight Transportation Services
N.A.I.C.S.: 484121

Esaka Logistics Service Co., Ltd. (1)
1-2-5 Naruohama, Nishinomiya, 663-8142,
Hyogo, Japan
Tel.: (81) 798406868
Web Site: http://www.senko.co.jp
General Freight Trucking Services
N.A.I.C.S.: 484110

Fuji Senko Transport Co., Ltd. (1)
154-1 Ono Shinden Higashifuji PD Center 2F, Gokanjima, Fuji, 417-0845, Shizuoka, Japan
Tel.: (81) 545389816
Web Site: https://group.senko.co.jp
Sales Range: $125-149.9 Million
Emp.: 500
General Trucking Services
N.A.I.C.S.: 484110

Fukuoka Senko Transport Co., Ltd. (1)
2-2-41 Hakozaki Pier, Higashi Ward, Fukuoka, 812-0051, Japan
Tel.: (81) 926517455
Web Site: https://www.f-senko.co.jp
Emp.: 165
General Freight Trucking Services
N.A.I.C.S.: 484110

Guangzhou Senko Logistics Co., Ltd. (1)
Tel.: (86) 2082225446
Sales Range: $25-49.9 Million
Emp.: 11
Freight Forwarding & Warehousing Services
N.A.I.C.S.: 488510

Hanshin Senko Transport Co., Ltd. (1)
7F Solar Building 2-1-7 Nunobiki-cho, Chuo-ku, Kobe, 651-0097, Hyogo, Japan
Tel.: (81) 782310153
Web Site: https://www.hanshinsenko.com
Emp.: 228
General Freight Trucking Services
N.A.I.C.S.: 484110

Hanshin Transportation Co., Ltd. (1)
1-2-5 Naruohama, Nishinomiya, 663-8142, Hyogo, Japan
Tel.: (81) 79 840 6877
Freight Transportation Services
N.A.I.C.S.: 484121

Harcob Co., Ltd. (1)
859 Kuchi Asa-cho, Asakita-ku, Hiroshima, 731-3362, Japan
Tel.: (81) 82 837 3333
Web Site: https://www.harcob.co.jp
Freight Transportation Services
N.A.I.C.S.: 484121

Hokkaido Senko Co., Ltd. (1)
2-1-1 Yonesato, Shiroishi-ku, Sapporo, 003-0872, Japan
Tel.: (81) 11 879 7030
Web Site: https://www.hokkaidosenko.co.jp
Freight Transportation Services
N.A.I.C.S.: 484121

Hokuriku Senko Transport Co., Ltd. (1)
17-1-1 Futsukaichi Town, Fukui, 910-0109, Japan
Tel.: (81) 776552235
Web Site: http://group.senko.co.jp
General Trucking Services
N.A.I.C.S.: 484110

Hososhimako Niyaku Shinko Co., Ltd. (1)
17731-2 Oaza Hichiya, Hyuga, 883-0062, Miyazaki, Japan
Tel.: (81) 982524527
Cargo Handling Services
N.A.I.C.S.: 488320

Ienonaka Company, Ltd. (1)
2-14-12 Hirakawacho Well Building 2nd Floor, Chiyoda-ku, Tokyo, 102-0093, Japan
Tel.: (81) 36 380 9146
Web Site: https://www.service.ienonaka.jp
Real Estate Property Management Services
N.A.I.C.S.: 531311

JCN Kanto Co., Ltd. (1)
2061-1 Kamiyabe-cho, Totsuka-ku, Yokohama, 236-0002, Kanagawa, Japan
Tel.: (81) 45 779 2577
Web Site: https://www.jcn-kanto.co.jp
Freight Transportation Services
N.A.I.C.S.: 484121

SENKO GROUP HOLDINGS CO., LTD.

Senko Group Holdings Co., Ltd.—(Continued)

KO-Senko Logistics Co., Ltd. (1)
1190 Nammun-dong, Jinhae-gu, Changwon, Gyeongsangnam-do, Korea (South)
Tel.: (82) 51 631 5218
Web Site: https://www.ks.kplg.co.kr
Logistic Services
N.A.I.C.S.: 541614
Kook-Dong Lee (CEO)

Kan-etsu Senko Logistics Co., Ltd. (1)
600-1 Nitta Ocho, Ota, 370-0351, Gunma, Japan
Tel.: (81) 27 657 9228
Freight Transportation Services
N.A.I.C.S.: 484121

Kanagawa Senko Transport Co., Ltd. (1)
Tel.: (81) 442887557
Web Site: http://kanasen.com
Emp.: 207
General Trucking Services
N.A.I.C.S.: 484110

Kanto Senko Transport Co., Ltd. (1)
836-3 Kuno, Koga, 306-0212, Ibaraki Prefecture, Japan
Tel.: (81) 280926679
Web Site: https://group.senko.co.jp
Emp.: 445
Trucking, Warehousing, In-Factory Work, Vehicle Maintenance & Moving Services
N.A.I.C.S.: 484110

Kashiwa Senko Transport Co., Ltd. (1)
9-18 Kashiwa Inter Minami, Kashiwa, 277-0873, Chiba, Japan
Tel.: (81) 471570188
Web Site: https://www.kashiwa-senko.co.jp
Emp.: 800
General Trucking Services
N.A.I.C.S.: 484110

Keihanna Helper Station Co., Ltd. (1)
3-952-1 Nimyo, Nara, 631-0072, Japan
Tel.: (81) 74 252 6570
Web Site: https://www.khs91918.com
Home Visit Nursing Care Services
N.A.I.C.S.: 621610

Kitanihonunyu Corporation (1)
29-3 Kashimamachi, Hakusan, 929-0201, Ishikawa, Japan
Tel.: (81) 76 278 6600
Web Site: https://www.kitanihonunyu.co.jp
Freight Transportation Services
N.A.I.C.S.: 484121

Kyoto Senko Transport Co., Ltd. (1)
6 Kotari Tanatsugu, Nagaokakyo, 617-0833, Kyoto, Japan
Tel.: (81) 75 959 3118
Web Site: https://www.kyotosenko.com
Freight Transportation Services
N.A.I.C.S.: 484121

Life-eat Co., Ltd. (1)
7-3-18 Nishifukatsu-cho, Fukuyama, 721-0975, Hiroshima, Japan
Tel.: (81) 84 922 3003
Web Site: https://www.susi-maru.co.jp
Restaurant Management Services
N.A.I.C.S.: 722511

Logi Factoring Co., Ltd. (1)
Logistics Consulting & Credit Collecting Services
N.A.I.C.S.: 541614

Logi Solution Co., Ltd. (1)
2-8-10 Shiomi SIF building 5F, Koto-ku, Tokyo, 135-0052, Japan
Tel.: (81) 368627180
Emp.: 70
Logistics Consulting Servies
N.A.I.C.S.: 541614

M-Senko Logistics Co., Ltd. (1)
62/3 Moo 1, Sisa Chorakhe Yai Subdistrict, Bang Sao Thong, 10570, Samut Prakan, Thailand
Tel.: (66) 64 003 2816
Web Site: https://www.m-senko.com
Logistic Services
N.A.I.C.S.: 541614

Marufuji Co., Ltd. (1)
Inside the Kobe Minato Warehouse 2-1 Nadahama-cho, Nada-ku, Kobe, 657-0853, Hyogo, Japan
Tel.: (81) 788067300
Web Site: https://www.marufuji.co.jp
Emp.: 130
Consumer Household Products Whslr
N.A.I.C.S.: 423820

Subsidiary (Domestic):

OKUMURA CORPORATION (2)
2-2-2 Matsuzakicho, Abeno-ku, Osaka, 545-8555, Japan
Tel.: (81) 666211101
Web Site: https://www.okumuragumi.co.jp
Rev.: $1,904,645,060
Assets: $2,543,197,500
Liabilities: $1,276,899,970
Net Worth: $1,266,297,530
Earnings: $82,578,730
Emp.: 2,265
Fiscal Year-end: 03/31/2024
Construction Services
N.A.I.C.S.: 237990
Takanori Okumura (Pres)

Subsidiary (Domestic):

Okumura Machinery Corporation (3)
3-5-26 Himejima, Nishiyodogawa-ku, Osaka, 555-0033, Japan
Tel.: (81) 664723461
Web Site: www.okumuragumi.co.jp
Sales Range: $50-74.9 Million
Emp.: 71
Construction Machinery Mfr & Distr
N.A.I.C.S.: 333120
Kenji Arakawa (Pres)

Taihei Real Estate Corporation (3)
Shiba Building 4F 5-16-7 Shiba, Minato-ku, Tokyo, 108-0014, Japan
Tel.: (81) 354395401
Web Site: https://www.taiheifudousan-okumuragumi.com
Real Estate Manangement Services
N.A.I.C.S.: 531390

Mexicana de Paqueteria Urgente, S.A.de C.V. (1)
Eje 116 Esquina Carretera 57, S/N Zona Industrial, San Luis Potosi, Mexico
Tel.: (52) 444 824 9550
Web Site: https://www.mexpur.pw
Freight Transportation Services
N.A.I.C.S.: 484121

Mie Senko Logistics Co., Ltd. (1)
303 Iinoji Kecho, Iinojike Town, Suzuka, 513-0802, Mie, Japan (97%)
Tel.: (81) 593690064
Web Site: http://www.mie-senkologi.com
Emp.: 60
General Freight Trucking Services
N.A.I.C.S.: 484110

Minami Kyushu Senko Co., Ltd. (1)
1-3-12 Minatomachi, Minamata, 867-0052, Kumamoto, Japan (100%)
Tel.: (81) 966634111
Web Site: https://www.m-kyusyu.senko.co.jp
Sales Range: $10-24.9 Million
Emp.: 154
General Freight Trucking Services
N.A.I.C.S.: 484110
Ryoji Takahashi (Pres & CEO)

Minami Osaka Senko Transport Co., Ltd. (1)
2934-5 Wada, Minami-ku, Sakai, 590-0152, Osaka, Japan
Tel.: (81) 72 297 7310
Web Site: https://www.minamiosakasenko.com
Freight Transportation Services
N.A.I.C.S.: 484121

Miyazaki Senko Apollo Co., Ltd. (1)
Tel.: (81) 982310954
Web Site: http://www.miyazaki-senkoapollo.co.jp
General Freight Trucking Services
N.A.I.C.S.: 484110

Miyazaki Senko Transport Co., Ltd. (1)
6-1711 Totoro Town, Nobeoka, 889-0513, Miyazaki, Japan
Tel.: (81) 982373568
Web Site: http://miyazaki-senko.jp
Vehicle Maintenance & Trucking Services
N.A.I.C.S.: 484110

Moriyama Hoso Co., Ltd. (1)
515 Kojima, Moriyama, 524-0002, Shiga, Japan
Tel.: (81) 77 583 3983
Freight Transportation Services
N.A.I.C.S.: 484121

NH-Senko Logistics Co., Ltd. (1)
15 Sinhang 6-ro, Jinhae-gu, Changwon, 51619, Gyeongsangnam-do, Korea (South)
Tel.: (82) 55 542 1005
Web Site: https://www.nh-senko.com
Freight Transportation Services
N.A.I.C.S.: 484121
Fujiwara Shoki (CEO)

Nankai Tsuun Co., Ltd. (1)
1-23 Rinkai-cho, Izumiotsu, 595-0075, Osaka, Japan
Tel.: (81) 72 532 3241
Web Site: https://www.nantsu.jp
Freight Transportation Services
N.A.I.C.S.: 484121

Nara Senko Logistics Co., Ltd. (1)
Tel.: (81) 743569572
Web Site: http://group.senko.co.jp
General Freight Trucking Services
N.A.I.C.S.: 484110

Nichiei Koun Co., Ltd. (1)
1-25-13 Kobayashinishi, Taisho Ward, Osaka, 551-0013, Japan
Tel.: (81) 66 554 1521
Freight Transportation Services
N.A.I.C.S.: 484121

Nishikanto Senko Logi Co., Ltd. (1)
4022-2 Sakuradai Aikawa-cho GLP Atsugi II 2F, Aiko-gun, Nakatsu, 243-0303, Kanagawa, Japan
Tel.: (81) 46 284 3250
Web Site: https://www.nishikanto-senkologi.jp
Freight Transportation Services
N.A.I.C.S.: 484121

Noda Senko Logi Service Co., Ltd. (1)
1-1-6 Izumi, Noda, 270-0239, Chiba, Japan
Tel.: (81) 47 128 1518
Freight Transportation Services
N.A.I.C.S.: 484121

Obata Co., Ltd. (1)
71 Kamishinohai, Niida, Odate, 018-5751, Akita, Japan
Tel.: (81) 18 649 3927
Web Site: https://www.kabuobata.co.jp
Daily Miscellaneous Goods Distr
N.A.I.C.S.: 459999

Okayama Senko Transport Co., Ltd (1)
1-13-30 Higashizuka, Kurashiki, 712-8044, Okayama, Japan
Tel.: (81) 864551050
Sales Range: $50-74.9 Million
Emp.: 215
General Freight Trucking Services
N.A.I.C.S.: 484110

Osaka Senko Transport Co., Ltd. (1)
1-51-2 Shibocho, Takatsuki, 569-0823, Osaka, Japan (100%)
Tel.: (81) 726791156
Web Site: www.osakasenko.com
Emp.: 389
General Freight Trucking Services
N.A.I.C.S.: 484121
Miyazu Junji (Pres)

Prettyporters Co., Ltd. (1)
22-8 Futamatashinmachi Ichikawa Fashion Logistics Center Inner East 5F, Ichikawa, 272-0002, Chiba, Japan
Tel.: (81) 47 712 8205
Web Site: https://www.prettyporters.co.jp
Freight Transportation Services
N.A.I.C.S.: 484121

Procare Co., Ltd. (1)
1-30-4 Takadanobaba 30 Sankyo Building 3F, Shinjuku-ku, Tokyo, 169-0075, Japan
Tel.: (81) 36 233 7800
Web Site: https://www.procare.co.jp

INTERNATIONAL PUBLIC

Nursery School Services
N.A.I.C.S.: 624410

Qingdao Senko Logistics Co., Ltd. (1)
No 45 Xiangtan Road, Li Cang District, Qingdao, 266047, Shandong, China
Tel.: (86) 5326 691 9100
Freight Transportation Services
N.A.I.C.S.: 484121

Runtec Corporation (1)
4-26 Komondomachi, Hakata-ku, Fukuoka, 812-0029, Japan
Tel.: (81) 92 282 2331
Web Site: https://www.runtec.co.jp
Freight Transportation Services
N.A.I.C.S.: 484121

S-TAFF Co., Ltd (1)
Tel.: (81) 663635310
Cargo Handling & Facility Management Services
N.A.I.C.S.: 488490

SENKO (U.S.A.) Inc. (1)
1253 Hamilton Pkwy, Itasca, IL 60143
Tel.: (224) 265-8440
Web Site: http://www.senko-usa.com
Sales Range: $25-49.9 Million
Emp.: 10
Logistics & Warehousing Services
N.A.I.C.S.: 493110
Ryuzo Uchimoto (Pres)

SENKO International Trading Co., Ltd. (1)
2-8-10 Shiomi, Koto Ward, Tokyo, 135-0052, Japan
Tel.: (81) 36 862 7103
Freight Transportation Services
N.A.I.C.S.: 484121

SENKO Logistics Vietnam Co., Ltd. (1)
R202A V-Tower 649 Kim Ma Street, Ba Dinh District, Hanoi, 100000, Vietnam
Tel.: (84) 243 232 1158
Freight Transportation Services
N.A.I.C.S.: 484121

SERIO Holdings Co., Ltd. (1)
1-5-17 Dojima, Kita-Ku, Osaka, 530-0003, Japan
Tel.: (81) 664420500
Web Site: http://www.serio-corp.com
Rev.: $64,697,721
Assets: $33,049,224
Liabilities: $18,817,311
Net Worth: $14,231,913
Earnings: $898,579
Fiscal Year-end: 05/31/2023
Holding Company
N.A.I.C.S.: 551112

Saitama Minami Senko Logi Co., Ltd. (1)
2-2-1 Ryutsudanchi, Koshigaya, 343-0824, Saitama, Japan
Tel.: (81) 48 990 5668
Freight Transportation Services
N.A.I.C.S.: 484121

Saitama Senko Logiservice Co., Ltd. (1)
7 Nakanome, Kazo, 347-0124, Saitama, Japan
Tel.: (81) 48 053 9703
Web Site: https://www.saitama-senkologiservice.jp
Logistic Services
N.A.I.C.S.: 541614

Saitama Senko Transport Co., Ltd. (1)
1916-1 Oazadaimon, Midori-ku, Saitama, 336-0963, Japan
Tel.: (81) 488780823
Web Site: http://www.senko.co.jp
General Trucking & Vehicle Maintenance Services
N.A.I.C.S.: 484110

Samurai Farm Saito Co., Ltd. (1)
Shimosanzai 8127-48, Oaza Shimosanzai, Saito, 881-0113, Miyazaki, Japan
Tel.: (81) 98 344 5586
Web Site: https://www.samurai.ocnk.net
Grocery Product Distr
N.A.I.C.S.: 445110

Sankyo Butsuryu Niyaku Co., Ltd. (1)
1-18 Higashimemurokita, Memuro Town Kasai County, Hokkaido, 082-0004, Japan
Tel.: (81) 15 561 3372
Freight Transportation Services
N.A.I.C.S.: 484121

Sankyo Freight Co., Ltd. (1)
3-4-11 Tomonishi, Asaminami Ward, Hiroshima, 731-3169, Japan
Tel.: (81) 828496001
Web Site: https://group.senko.co.jp
Emp.: 243
General Freight Trucking Services
N.A.I.C.S.: 484110

Sanyo Senko Transport Co., Ltd. (1)
601-8 Asada, Yamaguchi, 753-0871, Japan
Tel.: (81) 839851008
Web Site: https://group.senko.co.jp
Emp.: 97
General Freight Trucking Services
N.A.I.C.S.: 484110

Sapologi Co., Ltd. (1)
5-1-40 Hakozaki Wharf 2nd PD Center Office 2F, Higashi-ku, Fukuoka, 812-0051, Japan
Tel.: (81) 92 631 3003
Web Site: https://www.sapologi.com
Freight Transportation Services
N.A.I.C.S.: 484121

Sapporo Senko Transport Co., Ltd. (1)
2 2 11 Yonesato Shiroishi-ku, Sapporo, 003 0872, Hokkaido, Japan
Tel.: (81) 11 879 7030
Web Site: http://www.senko.co.jp
General Trucking & Freight Services
N.A.I.C.S.: 484122

Senko (Thailand) Co., Ltd. (1)
1 Empire Tower 29th Floor Unit 2905/2 South Sathorn Road, Yannawa Sathorn, Bangkok, 10120, Thailand
Tel.: (66) 2 670 1099
Freight Forwarding Services
N.A.I.C.S.: 488510

Senko A Line Amano Co., Ltd. (1)
2-3-5 Nishishinozaki, Edogawa-ku, Tokyo, 133-0055, Japan
Tel.: (81) 356640600
Web Site: https://www.senko-ala.co.jp
Emp.: 707
Warehousing & Trucking Services
N.A.I.C.S.: 484121

Senko Asset Management Co., Ltd. (1)
Umeda Sky Building Tower West 14F 1-1-30 Oyodonaka, Kita-ku, Osaka, 531-6114, Japan
Tel.: (81) 66 440 5160
Web Site: https://www.senkoam.com
Asset Management Services
N.A.I.C.S.: 523940
Hiroshi Yamamoto *(Pres & CEO)*

Senko Business Support Co., Ltd. (1)
1176-13 Tenkacho, Claire Park Nobeoka Industrial Park, Nobeoka, 882-0071, Miyazaki, Japan
Tel.: (81) 982235760
Web Site: https://www.sbs.senko.jp
Emp.: 430
Business Support Services
N.A.I.C.S.: 561439

Senko Creative Management Co., Ltd. (1)
2-8-10 Shiomi SIF Building 1F, Shiomi Koto-ku, Tokyo, 135-0052, Japan
Tel.: (81) 36 684 1145
Web Site: https://www.scm-senko.jp
Restaurant Management Services
N.A.I.C.S.: 722511

Senko Facilities Co., Ltd. (1)
2-8-10 Shiomi, Koto Ward, Tokyo, 135-0052, Japan
Tel.: (81) 36 862 7140
Freight Transportation Services
N.A.I.C.S.: 484121

Senko Fashion Logistics Co., Ltd. (1)
22-8 Futamatashinmachi, Ichikawa, 272-0002, Chiba, Japan
Tel.: (81) 473273422
Web Site: http://senko-sfb.co.jp
General Trucking & Warehousing Services
N.A.I.C.S.: 484110

Senko Foods Co., Ltd. (1)
2-8-10 Shiomi, Koto Ward, Tokyo, 135-0052, Japan
Tel.: (81) 368627123
Sales Range: $10-24.9 Million
Emp.: 100
Restaurant Services
N.A.I.C.S.: 722511

Senko Forwarding Co., Ltd. (1)
2-8-10 Shiomi, Koto Ward, Tokyo, 135-0052, Japan
Tel.: (81) 36 862 7102
Web Site: https://www.senko-forwarding.co.jp
Emp.: 86
Freight Forwarding Services
N.A.I.C.S.: 488510
Kenji Takahashi *(Pres)*

Senko Housing Logistics Co., Ltd. (1)
3470-1 Kurohama, Hasuda, 349-0101, Saitama, Japan
Tel.: (81) 487656511
Web Site: https://group.senko.co.jp
Emp.: 177
Warehousing & Trucking Services
N.A.I.C.S.: 484110

Senko Information System Co., Ltd. (1)
2F Honmachi Center Building 2-6-10 Honmachi, Chuo-ku, Osaka, 541-0053, Japan
Tel.: (81) 677091100
Web Site: https://www.sis.senko.co.jp
Emp.: 195
Software Development & Consulting Services
N.A.I.C.S.: 541511

Senko Insurance Services Co., Ltd. (1)
2-8-10 Shiomi, Koto Ward, Tokyo, 135-0052, Japan
Tel.: (81) 368627088
General Insurance Services
N.A.I.C.S.: 524126

Senko International Logistics (Hong Kong) Co., Ltd. (1)
Room 1002 10th FL Fareast Consortium Bldg 204-206 Nathan Road, Kowloon, China (Hong Kong)
Tel.: (852) 3 580 0064
Freight Forwarding Services
N.A.I.C.S.: 488510

Senko International Logistics (Hong Kong) Ltd. (1)
Room 1002 10th FL Fareast Consortium Bldg 204-206 Nathan Road, Far East development building, Kowloon, China (Hong Kong)
Tel.: (852) 35800064
Sales Range: $50-74.9 Million
Emp.: 6
Freight Forwarding & Warehousing Services
N.A.I.C.S.: 488510

Senko International Logistics Pte. Ltd (1)
20 Sakra Road Jurong Island, Singapore, 627889, Singapore **(100%)**
Tel.: (65) 63161896
Transportation Services
N.A.I.C.S.: 488999

Senko Line Co., Ltd. (1)
2-8-10 Shiomi SIF Building 2F, Koto-ku Shiomi, Tokyo, 135-0052, Japan
Tel.: (81) 36 862 7201
Web Site: https://www.senko-line.co.jp
Freight Transportation Services
N.A.I.C.S.: 484121

Senko Living Plaza Co., Ltd. (1)
2-8-10 Shiomi SIF Building 2F, Koto-ku, Tokyo, 135-0062, Japan
Tel.: (81) 36 684 1134
Web Site: https://www.plaza.senko.co.jp
Freight Transportation Services
N.A.I.C.S.: 484121

Senko Logistics (Shanghai) Co., Ltd. (1)
2F-56 Warehouse No 273 De Bao Road, Wai Gao Qiao Free Trade Zone Pu Dong New Area, Shanghai, China
Tel.: (86) 2158684271
Web Site: https://www.china.senko.co.jp
Customs Clearing & Freight Forwarding Services
N.A.I.C.S.: 561990

Senko Logistics (Thailand) Co., Ltd. (1)
188/10 Moo 2 Tambon Krongtumru, Tong Grow Industrial Estate Amphur Muang, Chon Buri, 20000, Thailand
Tel.: (66) 3 825 4052
Emp.: 134
Cross Boarder Trucking Services
N.A.I.C.S.: 484230

Senko Logistics Australia Pty Ltd (1)
6 Macdonald Road, Ingleburn, 2565, NSW, Australia
Tel.: (61) 296058640
Web Site: http://www.senko.co.jp
Sales Range: $25-49.9 Million
Emp.: 2
Logistics & Freight Charter Services
N.A.I.C.S.: 481212

Senko Logistics Distribution (Thailand) Co., Ltd. (1)
Pinthong Land1 130/11-13 Moo 9 Tumbol Nongkham, Aumphur Sriracha, Chon Buri, 20110, Thailand
Tel.: (66) 3 819 0111
Freight Forwarding Services
N.A.I.C.S.: 488510

Senko Logistics Mexico S.A. de C.V. (1)
36275 Plaza de la Paz No 100-101 Puerto Interior, 36275, Silao, Guanajuato, Mexico
Tel.: (52) 472 748 9319
Freight Transportation Services
N.A.I.C.S.: 484121

Senko Medical Logistics Co., Ltd. (1)
Umeda Sky Building 1-1-30, Oyodonaka Kita Ward, Osaka, 531-6114, Japan
Tel.: (81) 664405917
Web Site: http://www.senko.co.jp
Medical Logistics Services
N.A.I.C.S.: 541614

Senko Moving Plaza Co., Ltd. (1)
Keihin Truck Terminal 2-1-1 Heiwajima, Otaku, Tokyo, 143-0006, Japan
Tel.: (81) 337667771
Web Site: http://www.plaza.senko.co.jp
General Freight Trucking Services
N.A.I.C.S.: 484110

Senko Nagase Logistics Co., Ltd. (1)
2-4-45 Higashitsukaguchi-cho, Amagasaki, 661-0011, Hyogo, Japan
Tel.: (81) 66 427 8651
Web Site: https://www.senko-nagase-logi.co.jp
Freight Transportation Services
N.A.I.C.S.: 484121

Senko Plantec Co., Ltd. (1)
39-25 Odakemachi Nobeoka Iron Works Complex, Nobeoka, 882-0024, Miyazaki, Japan
Tel.: (81) 98 231 1050
Web Site: https://www.senkoplantech.com
Freight Transportation Services
N.A.I.C.S.: 484121

Senko Private REIT Inc. (1)
Umeda Sky Building 1-1-30 Oyodonaka, Kita Ward, Osaka, 531-6119, Japan
Tel.: (81) 66 440 5151
Freight Transportation Services
N.A.I.C.S.: 484121

Senko Real Estate Co., Ltd. (1)
2-8-10 Shiomi, Koto Ward, Tokyo, 135-0052, Japan
Tel.: (81) 36 684 1147
Freight Transportation Services
N.A.I.C.S.: 484121

Senko SMI Myanmar Co., Ltd. (1)
No 74 Lann Thit Road, Nant Thar Kone Ward Insein TSP, Yangon, Myanmar
Tel.: (95) 996 970 1702
Web Site: https://www.senkosmi.com
Logistic Services
N.A.I.C.S.: 541614

Senko School Farm Tottori Co., Ltd. (1)
1350 Hawai Nagase, Yurihama-cho Tohakugun, Tottori, 682-0722, Japan
Tel.: (81) 858355238
Web Site: https://www.senko-sf.jp
Emp.: 22
Fresh Vegetables Whslr
N.A.I.C.S.: 424480

Senko Shoji Co., Ltd. (1)
2-8-10 Shiomi SIF Building 4F, Koto-ku, Tokyo, 135-0052, Japan
Tel.: (81) 36 862 7050
Web Site: https://www.senko-shoji.co.jp
General Freight Trucking Services
N.A.I.C.S.: 484121
Hiroshi Yoneji *(Pres)*

Senko Trading Co., Ltd. (1)
Shiomi-SIF Bldg 4F 2-8-10, Shiomi Koto-ku, Tokyo, 135-0052, Japan
Tel.: (81) 368627064
Web Site: http://www.senko-shoji.co.jp
Sales Range: $50-74.9 Million
Emp.: 100
Food & Petroleum Products Distr
N.A.I.C.S.: 424420

Shanghai Senko International Freight Co., Ltd. (1)
Li Hang Road 369, Pu Dong New Area, Shanghai, China
Tel.: (86) 2163562211
Web Site: https://www.china.senko.co.jp
Customs Clearing & Freight Forwarding Services
N.A.I.C.S.: 561990

Shanghai Senko International Freight Forwarding Inc. (1)
No 369 Li Hang Road, Pu Dong New Area, Shanghai, China
Tel.: (86) 216 356 2211
Freight Forwarding Services
N.A.I.C.S.: 488510

Shenyang Senko Logistics Co., Ltd. (1)
Economic and Technological Development Zone Huizhou Xixiang No 15, Shenyang, 110141, Liaoning, China
Tel.: (86) 248 590 5405
Freight Transportation Services
N.A.I.C.S.: 484121

Shiga Senko Transport Co., Ltd. (1)
79-2 Anamura-cho, Kusatsu, 525-0012, Shiga, Japan
Tel.: (81) 775682600
Web Site: https://shiga-senko.co.jp
Emp.: 356
General Freight Trucking Services
N.A.I.C.S.: 484110

Skylift Consolidator (Pte) Ltd. (1)
62 Ubi Road 1 Oxley Bizhub 2 09-18, Singapore, 408734, Singapore
Tel.: (65) 6 542 6777
Web Site: https://www.skylift.com.sg
Emp.: 80
Freight Forwarding Services
N.A.I.C.S.: 488510

Skylift Districentre (Pte)Ltd. (1)
No 2 Tuas View Place 01-03, Singapore, 637431, Singapore
Tel.: (65) 6 791 6777
Freight Forwarding Services
N.A.I.C.S.: 488510

Smile Corp. (1)
2-8-10 Shiomi SIF Building 4F, Koto-ku, Tokyo, 135-0052, Japan
Tel.: (81) 36 743 7072
Web Site: https://www.smilecorp.jp
Alcoholic Beverages Whslr
N.A.I.C.S.: 424820

Smilecorp Vietnam Co., Ltd. (1)
2Floor The Landmark No 5B Ton Duc Thang Street, Ben Nghe Ward District 1, Ho Chi Minh City, Vietnam
Tel.: (84) 283 520 8001

SENKO GROUP HOLDINGS CO., LTD.

Senko Group Holdings Co., Ltd.—(Continued)
Web Site: https://www.smilecorp.com.vn
Emp.: 7
Consumer Daily Product Distr
N.A.I.C.S.: 424490

Takano Machinery Works Co., Ltd. (1)
Aqua Hakusan Building 6F 1-13-7 Hakusan, Bunkyo-ku, Tokyo, 113-0001, Japan
Tel.: (81) 35 801 0725
Web Site: https://www.takanokikai.co.jp
Printing Machine Mfr & Distr
N.A.I.C.S.: 333248

Terauchi Co., Ltd. (1)
1-9-13 Minamikyuhojimachi, Chuo-ku, Osaka, 541-0058, Japan
Tel.: (81) 66 262 2161
Web Site: https://www.fanbi.co.jp
Daily Miscellaneous Goods Distr
N.A.I.C.S.: 459999

Tohoku Senko Transport Co., Ltd. (1)
General Trucking & Warehousing Services
N.A.I.C.S.: 484110

Tokai Senko Transport Co., Ltd. (1)
480-1 Takazasa Kawachiya Nitta, Oguchi-Cho, Komaki, 485-0085, Aichi, Japan
Tel.: (81) 568656791
Web Site: https://tokai-senko.com
Emp.: 144
General Trucking Services
N.A.I.C.S.: 484110

Tokyo Nohin Daiko Co., Ltd. (1)
22-8 Futamatashinmachi, Ichikawa, 272-0002, Chiba, Japan
Tel.: (81) 473289870
Web Site: http://www.tndc.co.jp
Sales Range: $150-199.9 Million
Emp.: 600
Warehousing & Logistics Services
N.A.I.C.S.: 493110

Tokyo Nohin Daiko West Japan Co., Ltd. (1)
5-2-10 Nankohigashi, Suminoe Ward, Osaka, 559-0031, Japan
Tel.: (81) 66 616 6181
Freight Transportation Services
N.A.I.C.S.: 484121

Toyohashi Senko Transport Co., Ltd. (1)
33-12 Akemicho, Toyohashi, 441-8074, Aichi, Japan
Tel.: (81) 532254928
Web Site: https://www.toyohashi-senko.jp
Emp.: 47
General Trucking Services
N.A.I.C.S.: 484110

UACJbutsuryu.Co., Ltd. (1)
3-1-12 Chitose, Minato-ku, Nagoya, 455-0011, Aichi, Japan
Tel.: (81) 52 654 0003
Web Site: https://www.ulogi.uacj-group.com
Freight Transportation Services
N.A.I.C.S.: 484121

SENKON LOGISTICS CO.,LTD.
672-1 Nakani Shimoyoda, Natori City, Miyagi, 981-1223, Japan
Tel.: (81) 223826127
Web Site: https://www.senkon.co.jp
Year Founded: 1959
9051—(TKS)
Rev.: $115,959,230
Assets: $119,171,690
Liabilities: $81,098,090
Net Worth: $38,073,600
Earnings: $2,531,630
Emp.: 448
Fiscal Year-end: 03/31/24
Transportation Services
N.A.I.C.S.: 488999
Haruo Kubota (Chm & CEO)

Subsidiaries:

SENKON Enterprise Co., Ltd. (1)
981-1224 5-10-7 Masuda, Natori, Miyagi, Japan
Tel.: (81) 22 383 0983

Funeral Services
N.A.I.C.S.: 812210
Haruo Kubota (Mng Dir)

SENKON Ltd. (1)
office145B 1 Nijneportovaya str, 690091, Vladivostok, Russia
Tel.: (7) 4232302660
Logistics Consulting Servies
N.A.I.C.S.: 541614
Haruo Kubota (Chm)

SENKON Trading Shanghai Ltd. (1)
No 2005 Yang Gao Road North Xinyi Bldg 2F-233, Pu Dong New District, Shanghai, 200131, China
Tel.: (86) 21 6401 9055
Trading Services
N.A.I.C.S.: 523160
Haruo Kubota (Pres & CEO)

SENKRON GUVENLIK VE ILETISIM SISTEMLERI AS
Esentepe Mah Buyukdere Cad LOFT Residence Apt No 201/6, Sisli, 34373, Istanbul, Turkiye
Tel.: (90) 2129426396
Web Site:
https://senkronguvenlik.com.tr
Year Founded: 1997
SNKRN—(IST)
Rev.: $458,799
Assets: $948,651
Liabilities: $697,102
Net Worth: $251,549
Earnings: $207,614
Fiscal Year-end: 12/31/20
Financial Consulting Services
N.A.I.C.S.: 541611

SENLIS AUTOMOBILES CAMIONS LOISIRS INDUSTRIE
64 Ave General De Gaulle, 60300, Senlis, Oise, France
Tel.: (33) 344539700
Rev.: $29,500,000
Emp.: 100
New & Used Car Dealers
N.A.I.C.S.: 441110
Igor Zachcial (Dir)

SENMIAO TECHNOLOGY LIMITED
16F Shihao Square Middle Jiannan Blvd, High-Tech Zone Chengdu, Sichuan, 610000, China
Tel.: (86) 2861554399   NV
Web Site:
https://www.senmiaotech.com
Year Founded: 2014
AIHS—(NASDAQ)
Rev.: $6,814,428
Assets: $9,861,484
Liabilities: $5,573,116
Net Worth: $4,288,368
Earnings: ($4,234,214)
Emp.: 55
Fiscal Year-end: 03/31/24
Online Lending Services
N.A.I.C.S.: 459999
Xi Wen (Chm, Pres, CEO & Sec)

SENNEN POTASH CORPORATION
1095 West Pender Street Suite 305, Vancouver, V6E2M6, BC, Canada
Tel.: (604) 331-1213
Web Site:
http://www.sennenpotash.com
SN—(TSXV)
Rev.: $33
Assets: $377,394
Liabilities: $1,409,793
Net Worth: ($1,032,399)
Earnings: ($481,884)
Fiscal Year-end: 01/31/23
Potash Exploration Services
N.A.I.C.S.: 212390
Pawitter Sidhu (CEO & CFO)

SENNHEISER ELECTRONIC GMBH & CO. KG
Am Labor 1, 30900, Wedemark, Germany
Tel.: (49) 51306000
Web Site: http://www.en-in.sennheiser.com
Year Founded: 1945
Sales Range: $700-749.9 Million
Emp.: 2,728
Microphones, Headphones & Wireless Transmission Systems Mfr
N.A.I.C.S.: 334310
Daniel Sennheiser (Co-CEO & Member-Mgmt Bd)

Subsidiaries:

Sennheiser (Schweiz) AG (1)
In der Luberzen 29, 8902, Urdorf, Switzerland
Tel.: (41) 44 751 75 75
Web Site: http://www.sennheiser.ch
Audio Equipment Whslr
N.A.I.C.S.: 423620
Bjoern Grefer (Gen Mgr-Fin & Ops)

Sennheiser Audio Ltd. (1)
Semenovskaya square 1A 22 floor, 107023, Moscow, Russia
Tel.: (7) 4956204963
Web Site: http://ru-ru.sennheiser.com
Audio Equipment Whslr
N.A.I.C.S.: 423620
Andrey Alekhin (Dir-Mktg & Sls Admin)

Sennheiser Australia Pty Limited (1)
Unit 3 31 Gibbes Street, Chatswood, 2067, NSW, Australia
Tel.: (61) 2 9910 6700
Web Site: http://www.sennheiser.com.au
Audio Equipment Whslr
N.A.I.C.S.: 423620
Bjorn Rennemo Henriksen (Mng Dir)

Sennheiser Austria GmbH (1)
Zimbagasse 5, 1140, Vienna, Austria
Tel.: (43) 19790000
Web Site: http://www.sennheiser.at
Product Distribution Services
N.A.I.C.S.: 541870

Sennheiser Belux bvba (1)
Doornveld 22, Asse, 1731, Zellik, Belgium
Tel.: (32) 2 4664410
Web Site: http://www.sennheiser.be
Emp.: 17
Audio Equipment Whslr
N.A.I.C.S.: 423620

Sennheiser Canada Inc. (1)
221 Labrosse Ave, Pointe-Claire, H9R 1A3, QC, Canada
Tel.: (514) 426-3013
Web Site: http://www.sennheiser.ca
Emp.: 50
Audio Equipment Whslr
N.A.I.C.S.: 423620
Gilles Marcotte (Dir-Sls)

Sennheiser Communications A/S (1)
Industriparken 27, 2750, Solrod, Denmark
Tel.: (45) 56180000
Web Site:
http://www.sennheisercommunications.com
Sales Range: $25-49.9 Million
Emp.: 80
Wireless & Wired Headset Mfr; Joint Venture of Sennheiser Electronic GmbH & Co. KG (50%) & William Demant Holding A/S (50%)
N.A.I.C.S.: 334310
Jane Craven (Dir-Sls-UK Telecom)

Sennheiser Electronic (Beijing) Co. Ltd (1)
1608 Room 16th Floor Tower 2 ZhuBang 2000 Business Center, Chaoyang District, Beijing, 100025, China
Tel.: (86) 10 5731 9666
Web Site: http://www.sennheiser.com.cn
Audio Equipment Whslr
N.A.I.C.S.: 423620
Nico Zhang (Mgr-HR & Ops)

Sennheiser Electronic Corp. (1)
1 Enterprise Dr, Old Lyme, CT 06371
Tel.: (860) 434-9190

INTERNATIONAL PUBLIC

Web Site: http://www.sennheiserusa.com
Sales Range: $50-74.9 Million
Emp.: 100
Microphone Headphone & Wireless Transmission System Mfr
N.A.I.C.S.: 423690
Greg Beebe (Dir-Professional Audio)

Division (Domestic):

Neumann (USA) (2)
1 Enterprise Dr, Old Lyme, CT 06371-1537
Tel.: (860) 434-9190
Web Site: http://www.sennheiserusa.com
Sales Range: $25-49.9 Million
Emp.: 100
Professional Microphones, Headphones & Accessories
N.A.I.C.S.: 334417
Marcus Warlitz (Head-Ops)

Sennheiser France SARL (1)
Parc da Activites Mure 128 bis Av Jean Jaures, 94851, Ivry-sur-Seine, Cedex, France
Tel.: (33) 1 49870300
Web Site: http://www.sennheiser.fr
Audio Equipment Whslr
N.A.I.C.S.: 423620
Didier Chagnon (Gen Mgr)

Sennheiser Hong Kong Limited (1)
Unit 2310 23/F No 1 Hung To Road, Kwun Tong, Kowloon, China (Hong Kong)
Tel.: (852) 3412 8400
Web Site: http://www.sennheiser.com.hk
Audio Equipment Whslr
N.A.I.C.S.: 423620

Sennheiser Japan K.K. (1)
1-1-1 Minamiaoyama, Minato-ku, Tokyo, 107-0062, Japan
Tel.: (81) 3 6406 8911
Web Site: http://www.sennheiserindia.co.jp
Emp.: 35
Audio Equipment Whslr
N.A.I.C.S.: 423620
Shozo Kubo (Mng Dir)

Sennheiser Nederland BV (1)
Tunerstraat 2, 1322 CA, Almere, Netherlands
Tel.: (31) 36 5358444
Web Site: http://www.sennheiser.nl
Emp.: 38
Audio Equipment Whslr
N.A.I.C.S.: 423620
Eddie Demoortel (Gen Mgr)

Sennheiser New Zealand Ltd (1)
Unit A 26-30 Vestey Drive Mt Wellington, Auckland, 1060, New Zealand
Tel.: (64) 9 580 0489
Web Site: http://www.sennheiser.co.nz
Audio Equipment Whslr
N.A.I.C.S.: 423620

Sennheiser Nordic A/S (1)
Skovlytoften 33, 2840, Holte, Denmark
Tel.: (45) 70 26 66 33
Web Site: http://www.sennheisernordic.com
Audio Equipment Whslr
N.A.I.C.S.: 423620
Jorgen Wengel (Mng Dir)

Sennheiser electronic (SA) (Pty) Ltd. (1)
2nd Floor JCC House 27 Owl Street Milpark, Johannesburg, 2001, South Africa
Tel.: (27) 11 482 2501
Web Site: http://www.sennheiser.co.za
Audio Equipment Whslr
N.A.I.C.S.: 423620
Gerald Newport (Gen Mgr)

Sennheiser electronic ASIA Pte Ltd (1)
438B Alexandra Road 01-06/08 Alexandra TechnoPark, Singapore, 119968, Singapore
Tel.: (65) 6273 5202
Web Site: http://www.sennheiserasia.com
Audio Equipment Whslr
N.A.I.C.S.: 423620
Martin Low (VP-Sls & Mktg)

Sennheiser electronics India Pvt. Ltd (1)
102 A First Floor Time Tower Sec-28 M G Road, Gurgaon, 122 002, Haryana, India
Tel.: (91) 124 4187800

Web Site: http://www.sennheiserindia.com
Emp.: 30
Audio Equipment Whslr
N.A.I.C.S.: 423620
Vipin Pungalia *(VP-Sls & Mktg)*

SENSAS SA
25 Rue Jean Riedberger, 28630, Fontenay-sur-Eure, Eure-et-Loir, France
Tel.: (33) 237334450
Web Site: http://www.sensas.com
Rev.: $30,300,000
Emp.: 155
Fishing Bait Mfr
N.A.I.C.S.: 311119
Gerome Vangheluwe *(Mgr-Pur)*

SENSEN NETWORKS LIMITED
Unit 2 570 City Rd, South Melbourne, 3205, VIC, Australia
Tel.: (61) 394175368   AU
Web Site: https://sensen.ai
SNNSF—(OTCIQ)
Rev.: $4,238,975
Assets: $7,807,076
Liabilities: $2,975,902
Net Worth: $4,831,174
Earnings: ($2,315,232)
Fiscal Year-end: 06/30/21
Artificial Intelligence & IoT Analytics Services
N.A.I.C.S.: 513210
David Smith *(Bd of Dirs & Sec)*

Subsidiaries:

PT Orpheus Energy (1)
Menera Anugrah Lt 27 Kantor Taman E 3 3 Kawasan Mega, Kuningan, Jakarta, 12950, Indonesia
Tel.: (62) 2157948860
Emp.: 50
Coal Distr
N.A.I.C.S.: 423520
Ardiansyah Ahmad Situmorang *(Accountant)*

SENSERA LIMITED
Level 14 440 Collins Street, Melbourne, 3000, VIC, Australia
Tel.: (61) 7814046500   AU
Web Site: http://www.sensera.com
Year Founded: 2016
SE1—(ASX)
Rev.: $2,951,429
Assets: $3,786,261
Liabilities: $5,222,987
Net Worth: ($1,436,726)
Earnings: ($4,465,014)
Fiscal Year-end: 06/30/21
Electronic Component Mfr & Distr
N.A.I.C.S.: 334413
Ralph Schmitt *(Mng Dir)*

Subsidiaries:

Sensera Inc. (1)
15 Presidential Way, Woburn, MA 01801
Tel.: (781) 404-6500
Web Site: http://www.sensera.com
Electronic Components Mfr
N.A.I.C.S.: 334419
Tim Stucchi *(COO)*

SENSETIME GROUP INC.
No 1900 Hongmei Road, Xuhui District, Shanghai, 200233, China   Ky
Web Site:
  https://www.sensetime.com
Year Founded: 2014
0020—(HKG)
Rev.: $583,501,817
Assets: $5,734,189,598
Liabilities: $1,288,976,107
Net Worth: $4,445,213,491
Earnings: ($933,506,998)
Emp.: 5,098
Fiscal Year-end: 12/31/22
Software Development Services
N.A.I.C.S.: 541511

Bing Xu *(Sec)*

Subsidiaries:

Beijing SenseTime Technology Development Co., Ltd. (1)
Rooms 1101-1107 No 58 Northwest 4th Ring Road, Haidian, China
Tel.: (86) 4009005986
Software Development Services
N.A.I.C.S.: 541511

SENSHU ELECTRIC CO., LTD.
1-4-21 Minami-Kaneden, Suita, 564-0044, Osaka, Japan
Tel.: (81) 663841101
Web Site: https://www.senden.co.jp
Year Founded: 1947
9824—(TKS)
Rev.: $886,016,030
Assets: $718,692,030
Liabilities: $359,129,770
Net Worth: $359,562,260
Earnings: $41,972,800
Emp.: 820
Fiscal Year-end: 10/31/23
Electric Cable Whslr
N.A.I.C.S.: 423610
Motohide Nishimura *(Pres)*

Subsidiaries:

NBS Co., Ltd. (1)
NBS Daiichi Bldg 113-1 Shirane, Isehara, 259-1147, Kanagawa, Japan
Tel.: (81) 463737900
Web Site: https://www.nbs-grp.com
Electrical Cable Distr
N.A.I.C.S.: 423610

SENSHU ELECTRIC (THAILAND) CO., LTD. (1)
Rojana Industrial Park 68 Moo 9 Tambol Thanu Amphur, U-Thai, Ayutthaya, Thailand
Tel.: (66) 3 533 0202
Electrical Cable Distr
N.A.I.C.S.: 423610

SENSHU ELECTRIC INTERNATIONAL CO., LTD. (1)
90 Cyberworld Tower 17th Floor Room 1704B Ratchadapisek Rd, Huay Kwang, Bangkok, 10310, Thailand
Tel.: (66) 2 168 3224
Web Site: http://www.senshu.co.th
Emp.: 16
Electrical Cable Distr
N.A.I.C.S.: 423610
Motohide Nishimura *(Pres)*

SHANGHAI SENSHU ELECTRIC INTERNATIONAL Co., LTD. (1)
Room 2101 Xin Da Building No 322 Xian Xia Road, Chang Ning, Shanghai, China
Tel.: (86) 2162780502
Web Site: http://www.senden.com.cn
Electrical Cable Distr
N.A.I.C.S.: 423610

STEC Co., Ltd. (1)
STEC Building 3-10-12 Tarumi-cho, Suita, 564-0062, Osaka, Japan
Tel.: (81) 663391151
Web Site: https://www.stec.ne.jp
Electrical Cable Distr
N.A.I.C.S.: 423610

SENSHU IKEDA HOLDINGS, INC.
18-14 Chayamachi Kita-ku, Osaka, 530 0013, Japan
Tel.: (81) 648020181
Web Site: https://www.senshuikeda-hd.co.jp
Year Founded: 2009
8714—(TKS)
Rev.: $563,297,590
Assets: $42,582,327,270
Liabilities: $40,964,034,020
Net Worth: $1,618,293,250
Earnings: $41,312
Emp.: 159
Fiscal Year-end: 03/31/24
Bank Holding Company

N.A.I.C.S.: 522110
Hiroo Maeno *(Sr Mng Exec Officer)*

Subsidiaries:

Bank Computer Service Corporation (1)
1-5 Rinku Orakita, Izumisano, 598-0048, Osaka, Japan
Tel.: (81) 724612931
Web Site: http://www.senshuikeda-hd.co.jp
Computer Software Development & Sales
N.A.I.C.S.: 541511

Ikeda Bank Lease Co., Ltd. (1)
3-3-6 Kyutaroumachi, Chuo-ku, Osaka, 541-0056, Japan
Tel.: (81) 6 4704 5135
Credit Card Processing Services
N.A.I.C.S.: 522320

Ikeda Investment Management Co., Ltd. (1)
3-1-22 Toyosaki, Kita-ku, Osaka, 541-0056, Japan
Tel.: (81) 661202051
Investment Advisory Services
N.A.I.C.S.: 523940

Ikegin Capital Co., Ltd. (1)
18-14 Chayamachi, Kita-Ku, Osaka, 530-0013, Japan
Tel.: (81) 663757204
Venture Capital Services
N.A.I.C.S.: 523999

Ikegin Office Service Co., Ltd. (1)
2-1-11 Jonan, Ikeda, 563-0025, Osaka, Japan
Tel.: (81) 727536751
Financial Support Services
N.A.I.C.S.: 523999

J. I. Co., Ltd. (1)
8-6 Kawadacho Tokyo Joshi Ika Daigaku No 2 Bekkan, Shinjuku-Ku, Tokyo, 162-0054, Japan
Tel.: (81) 333536204
Credit Card Services
N.A.I.C.S.: 522320

Sengin General Leasing Company Limited (1)
27-1 Miyamotocho Senshu Building 3F, Kishiwada, 596-0054, Osaka, Japan
Tel.: (81) 724392821
Web Site: http://www.sg-lease.co.jp
Emp.: 90
Equipment Leasing Services
N.A.I.C.S.: 532490
Takitoshi Yokota *(Mgr)*

The Senshu Ikeda Bank, Ltd. (1)
18-14 Chayamachi, Kita-ku, Osaka, 530 0013, Japan
Tel.: (81) 6 6375 1005
Web Site: http://www.sihd-bk.jp
Emp.: 2,280
Banking Services
N.A.I.C.S.: 522110

Subsidiary (Domestic):

Senshu Ikeda Business Service Co., Ltd. (2)
18-14 Chayamachi, Kita-ku, Osaka, 563-0025, Japan (100%)
Tel.: (81) 727533734
Cash Payment & Printing Services
N.A.I.C.S.: 522390

Vui I Co., Ltd. (1)
8-10 Kurehacho, Ikeda, 563-0048, Osaka, Japan
Tel.: (81) 727500610
Credit Card Services
N.A.I.C.S.: 522320

SENSHUKAI CO., LTD.
1-6-23 Doshin, Kita-ku, Osaka, 530-0035, Japan
Tel.: (81) 668813220   JP
Web Site:
  https://www.senshukai.co.jp
Year Founded: 1955
8165—(TKS)
Rev.: $349,012,340
Assets: $225,525,810
Liabilities: $103,017,700

Net Worth: $122,508,110
Earnings: ($33,904,380)
Emp.: 910
Fiscal Year-end: 12/31/23
Fashion Wear, Home Furnishings, Household Products, General Goods, Sportswear, Publications, Infants & Children Items
N.A.I.C.S.: 459999
Kenji Kajiwara *(Pres & CEO)*

Subsidiaries:

Pet First Co., Ltd. (1)
5-8-1 Futago Takatsu Inoue Bldg 3rd Fl, Takatsu-ku, 213 0002, Kawasaki, Japan
Tel.: (81) 448505121
Web Site: http://www.petfirst.jp
Sales Range: $50-74.9 Million
Emp.: 150
Mail Order Business
N.A.I.C.S.: 513199

RG Marketing Co., Ltd. (1)
5-9-11 Kitashinagawa MT Bldg, Osaki Shinagawa-ku, 141 0001, Tokyo, Japan
Tel.: (81) 334419161
Web Site: http://www.restgenol.jp
Sales Range: $25-49.9 Million
Emp.: 8
Mail Order Business
N.A.I.C.S.: 513199

Senshu Logisco Co.,Ltd. (1)
Tel.: (81) 662428617
Web Site: http://www.senshulogisco.jp
Rev.: $65,075,200
Emp.: 1,223
Logistic Services
N.A.I.C.S.: 541614

Senshukai General Services Co., Ltd. (1)
1-6-23 Doshin, Kita-ku, Osaka, 530-0035, Japan
Tel.: (81) 668813220
Web Site: http://www.senshukai.co.jp
Travel Services
N.A.I.C.S.: 561599

Senshukai Iihana Co., Ltd. (1)
Tel.: (81) 334403541
Mail Order Shopping Solutions
N.A.I.C.S.: 513199

WellServe Co., Ltd. (1)
3-15-12-5F Kotobuki, Taito-ku, Tokyo, 111-0042, Japan
Tel.: (81) 366837639
Web Site: https://wellserve.co.jp
Mail Order Services
N.A.I.C.S.: 561431

SENSIBLE MEATS INC.
Sensible Meats Inc, Calgary, T2G 4Y8, AB, Canada
Tel.: (825) 800-0115   AB
Web Site:
  https://www.sensiblehotdogs.com
Year Founded: 2020
OX4—(DEU)
Rev.: $72,027
Assets: $7,971,317
Liabilities: $177,649
Net Worth: $7,793,667
Earnings: ($803,569)
Fiscal Year-end: 11/30/22
Meat Product Distr
N.A.I.C.S.: 424470

SENSIRION HOLDING AG
Laubisruetistrasse 50, Staefa, 8712, Zurich, Switzerland
Tel.: (41) 443064000   CH
Web Site: https://www.sensirion.com
Year Founded: 1998
SENS—(SWX)
Rev.: $356,681,818
Assets: $396,870,288
Liabilities: $59,680,710
Net Worth: $337,189,579
Earnings: $70,487,805
Emp.: 947
Fiscal Year-end: 12/31/22

SENSIRION HOLDING AG

Sensirion Holding AG—(Continued)

Sensor Module Component Mfr & Distr
N.A.I.C.S.: 334413
Moritz Lechner (Co-Founder & Co-Chm)

Subsidiaries:

Sensirion Automotive Solutions (Shanghai) Co., Ltd. (1)
4F Building 2 No 800 Jiuxin Highway, Jiuting Town Songjiang District, Shanghai, 201615, China
Tel.: (86) 2157638872
Digital Micro Sensor & System Mfr
N.A.I.C.S.: 334111

Sensirion Automotive Solutions Inc. (1)
44765 Ellery Ln, Novi, MI 48377
Tel.: (248) 308-9149
Digital Micro Sensor & System Mfr
N.A.I.C.S.: 334111

Sensirion Automotive Solutions Korea Co., Ltd. (1)
14F Hanshin IT Tower 272 Digital-ro, Guro-gu, Seoul, 08389, Korea (South)
Tel.: (82) 221087899
Digital Micro Sensor & System Mfr
N.A.I.C.S.: 334111

Sensirion China Co. Ltd. (1)
Room 1706 Tower 1 Excellence Meilin Center Plaza ZhongKang Road, Shangmeilin Futian District, Shenzhen, 518049, China
Tel.: (86) 75582521501
Digital Micro Sensor & System Mfr
N.A.I.C.S.: 334111

Sensirion Japan Co. Ltd. (1)
Takanawa Kaneo Bldg 4F 3-25-22, Takanawa Minato-ku, Tokyo, 108-0074, Japan
Tel.: (81) 334444940
Digital Micro Sensor & System Mfr
N.A.I.C.S.: 334111

Sensirion Korea Co. Ltd. (1)
1809-1813 Gumkang Penterium A 282 Hagui-Ro, Dongan-gu, Anyang, 14056, Gyeonggi-Do, Korea (South)
Tel.: (82) 3133777003
Digital Micro Sensor & System Mfr
N.A.I.C.S.: 334111

Sensirion Taiwan Co. Ltd. (1)
15F-2 No 223 Fuxing 2nd Rd, Hsinchu County, 30271, Zhubei, Taiwan
Tel.: (886) 35506701
Digital Micro Sensor & System Mfr
N.A.I.C.S.: 334111

SENSODETECT AB
Arenagatan 31, 215 32, Malmo, Sweden
Tel.: (46) 46157904
Web Site: https://www.sensodetect.com
Year Founded: 2005
Medical Equipment & Device Mfr
N.A.I.C.S.: 339112
Soren Nielzen (Founder)

SENSONOR AS
Knudsrodveien 7, PO Box 1004, 3194, Horten, Norway
Tel.: (47) 3303 5000
Web Site: http://www.sensonor.com
Year Founded: 1985
Sales Range: $50-74.9 Million
Emp.: 140
Sensors & Automotive Mfr
N.A.I.C.S.: 334513
Sverre Hormgvedt (Pres & CEO)

SENSOR TECHNOLOGIES CORP.
2455 Cawthra Road Suite 75, Mississauga, L5A3P1, ON, Canada
Tel.: (905) 232-1700
Web Site: https://www.sensetekinc.com
Year Founded: 1999

MOOIF—(OTCIQ)
Rev.: $77,624
Assets: $723,801
Liabilities: $527,157
Net Worth: $196,645
Earnings: $101,493
Fiscal Year-end: 12/31/22
Oil & Gas Exploration Services
N.A.I.C.S.: 213112
Alan Myers (CFO)

SENSORION SA
375 Rue du Professeur Joseph Blayac, 34080, Montpellier, France
Tel.: (33) 330664799751
Web Site: https://www.sensorion.com
ALSEN—(EUR)
Rev.: $6,289,755
Assets: $51,333,274
Liabilities: $14,601,246
Net Worth: $36,732,028
Earnings: ($24,355,231)
Emp.: 57
Fiscal Year-end: 12/31/23
Pharmaceuticals Mfr
N.A.I.C.S.: 325412
Pierre Attali (Dir-Medical)

SENSORVIEW CO., LTD.
705 Samwhan Hipex A 240 Pangyoyeok-ro, Bundang-gu, Seongnam, 13493, Gyeonggi-do, Korea (South)
Tel.: (82) 220387765
Web Site: https://www.sensor-view.com
Year Founded: 2015
321370—(KRS)
Emp.: 106
Electric Equipment Mfr
N.A.I.C.S.: 333414

SENSTAR TECHNOLOGIES LTD.
7 Menachem Begin Road 10th Floor Gibor Sport Tower, PO Box 70, Ramat Gan, 5268102, Israel
Tel.: (972) 747945200
Year Founded: 1969
SNT—(NASDAQ)
Rev.: $35,558,000
Assets: $51,886,000
Liabilities: $14,199,000
Net Worth: $37,687,000
Earnings: $3,831,000
Emp.: 158
Fiscal Year-end: 12/31/22
Perimeter Security & Bomb Detection Systems Mfr
N.A.I.C.S.: 561621

Subsidiaries:

Magal China (1)
Room A508 Dongyu Building No A1 Shuguang Xili, Chaoyang District, Beijing, 100028, China
Tel.: (86) 10 58221966
Web Site: http://www.magal-china.com
Mfr of Perimeter Security & Bomb Detection Systems
N.A.I.C.S.: 561621

Magal S3 Espana, S.L. (1)
Chile 4 Edificio II, Las Rozas, 28290, Madrid, Spain
Tel.: (34) 91 630 1555
Web Site: https://www.ms3.es
Security System Services
N.A.I.C.S.: 561621

Magal Security Systems (India) Limited (1)
225 Second Floor D-21 Corporate Park Sector 21, Dwarka, New Delhi, 110075, India
Tel.: (91) 981 101 7044
Security System Services
N.A.I.C.S.: 561621

Magal-S3 Canada Inc. (1)

5-2710 Carp Road, Carp, K0A 1L0, ON, Canada
Tel.: (613) 831-4500
Security System Services
N.A.I.C.S.: 561621

SENSYNE HEALTH PLC
Schrodinger Building Heatley Road Oxford Science Park, Oxford, OX4 4GE, United Kingdom
Tel.: (44) 3300581845 UK
Web Site: http://www.sensynehealth.com
Year Founded: 2018
SENS—(AIM)
Rev.: $12,348,463
Assets: $84,170,494
Liabilities: $12,572,487
Net Worth: $71,598,006
Earnings: ($37,365,812)
Emp.: 144
Fiscal Year-end: 04/30/21
Pharmaceutical Product Mfr & Distr
N.A.I.C.S.: 325412
Lorimer Headley (Co-CFO)

SENSYS GATSO GROUP AB
Vasavagen 3c, 554 54, Jonkoping, Sweden
Tel.: (46) 36342980
Web Site: https://www.sensysgatso.com
Year Founded: 1982
SGG—(OMX)
Rev.: $46,322,834
Assets: $77,575,562
Liabilities: $18,936,844
Net Worth: $58,638,718
Earnings: $1,878,389
Emp.: 284
Fiscal Year-end: 12/31/22
Traffic Safety Systems Mfr & Distr
N.A.I.C.S.: 339999
Jorgen Andersson (Gen Mgr-Sensys Gatso Sweden AB)

Subsidiaries:

Gatso Australia Pty Ltd. (1)
Unit 8 11-12 Phillip Court, Port Melbourne, 3207, VIC, Australia
Tel.: (61) 3 9647 6470
Web Site: http://www.gatso.com.au
Traffic Safety Systems Mfr
N.A.I.C.S.: 339999

Gatso Deutschland GmbH (1)
Hofstr 64, 40723, Hilden, Germany
Tel.: (49) 2103 9689 760
Web Site: http://www.gatso-de.com
Traffic Safety Systems Mfr
N.A.I.C.S.: 339999

Gatsometer BV (1)
Claes Tillyweg 2, 2031 CW, Haarlem, Netherlands
Tel.: (31) 23 5255050
Web Site: http://www.gatso.com
Traffic Safety Systems Mfr
N.A.I.C.S.: 339999

Sensys Gatso Australia Ltd. (1)
Unit 7A 256 New Line Road, Dural, 2158, NSW, Australia
Tel.: (61) 280916470
Information Technology Services
N.A.I.C.S.: 541511

Sensys Gatso Deutschland GmbH (1)
Hofstr 64, 40723, Hilden, Germany
Tel.: (49) 21039689760
Information Technology Services
N.A.I.C.S.: 541511

Sensys Gatso Group B.V. (1)
Claes Tillyweg 2, 2031 CW, Haarlem, Netherlands
Tel.: (31) 235255050
Automated Traffic System Mfr
N.A.I.C.S.: 334512

Sensys Gatso Netherlands B.V. (1)
Claes Tillyweg 2, 2031 CW, Haarlem, Netherlands

INTERNATIONAL PUBLIC

Tel.: (31) 235255050
Information Technology Services
N.A.I.C.S.: 541511

Sensys Gatso Software B.V. (1)
Joan Muyskenweg 22, 1096 CJ, Amsterdam, Netherlands
Tel.: (31) 235255050
Information Technology Services
N.A.I.C.S.: 541511

Sensys Gatso Sweden AB (1)
Vasavagen 3c, 55454, Jonkoping, Sweden
Tel.: (46) 36342980
Automated Traffic System Mfr
N.A.I.C.S.: 334512

Sensys Gatso USA Inc. (1)
900 Cummings Ctr Ste 316U, Beverly, MA 01915
Tel.: (978) 922-7294
Information Technology Services
N.A.I.C.S.: 541511

SENTA - PROMET A.D.
Novosadski put bb, 24400, Senta, Serbia
Tel.: (381) 24 815 879
Web Site: http://www.spmarketi.com
Year Founded: 1956
SNPR—(BEL)
Sales Range: $10-24.9 Million
Emp.: 410
Supermarket Store Operator
N.A.I.C.S.: 445110
Zoran Samardzic (Mng Dir)

SENTAGE HOLDINGS INC.
501 Platinum Tower 233 Taicang Road, HuangPu, Shanghai, 200001, China
Tel.: (86) 2153860209
Web Site: https://sentageholdings.com
Year Founded: 2019
SNTG—(NASDAQ)
Rev.: $161,372
Assets: $14,658,834
Liabilities: $483,870
Net Worth: $14,174,964
Earnings: ($2,561,907)
Emp.: 21
Fiscal Year-end: 12/31/22
Holding Company
N.A.I.C.S.: 551112
Qiaoling Lu (Chm & CEO)

SENTELIC CORP.
6th Floor No 88 Zhouzi Street, Neihu District, Taipei, Taiwan
Tel.: (886) 287525880
Web Site: https://www.sentelic.com
Year Founded: 2000
4945—(TPE)
Rev.: $16,120,595
Assets: $24,006,566
Liabilities: $2,850,108
Net Worth: $21,156,458
Earnings: $2,787,137
Fiscal Year-end: 12/31/22
Integrated Circuits Mfr
N.A.I.C.S.: 334413
Eric Lee (Chm)

SENTHIL INFOTEK LIMITED
157 Dhanalakshmi Society Mahendra Hills, East Marredpally, Secunderabad, 500 026, AP, India
Tel.: (91) 4027731375
Web Site: https://www.senthilinfo.com
Year Founded: 1994
Rev.: $19,660
Assets: $681,537
Liabilities: $645
Net Worth: $680,892
Earnings: $1,090
Fiscal Year-end: 03/31/19
Information Technology Services
N.A.I.C.S.: 541512
Chellamani Pitchandi (Mng Dir)

SENTICA PARTNERS OY
Kasarmikatu 21 B 7th Floor, 00130, Helsinki, Finland
Tel.: (358) 207 529 610 FI
Web Site: http://www.sentica.fi
Year Founded: 2004
Privater Equity Firm
N.A.I.C.S.: 523999
Mika Uotila (Mng Partner)
Subsidiaries:

Tammermatic Group Oy (1)
Tesoman valtatie 28, 33300, Tampere, Finland
Tel.: (358) 40 199 3550
Web Site: http://www.tammermatic.com
Holding Company; Vehicle Washing Equipment Designer & Mfr
N.A.I.C.S.: 551112
Juha Soutolahti (CEO)

Subsidiary (Domestic):

Tammermatic Oy (2)
Tesoman valtatie 28, 33300, Tampere, Finland
Tel.: (358) 40 199 3550
Web Site: http://www.tammermatic.com
Vehicle Washing Equipment Designer & Mfr
N.A.I.C.S.: 333310
Juha Soutolahti (CEO)

SENTIEN PRINTING FACTORY CO., LTD.
No 85 Keji 5th Rd, Annan Dist, Tainan City, 709, Taiwan
Tel.: (886) 63842811
Web Site: https://www.sentien.com.tw
Year Founded: 1956
8410—(TPE)
Rev.: $32,680,174
Assets: $63,596,723
Liabilities: $16,803,427
Net Worth: $46,793,296
Earnings: $699,559
Emp.: 230
Fiscal Year-end: 12/31/22
Label Foil Mfr
N.A.I.C.S.: 322220
Chang-Shan Huang (Chm)

SENTIS PTY LTD
Building 5 Ground Level 747 Lytton Road, Murarrie, 4172, QLD, Australia
Tel.: (61) 1300653042
Web Site: http://www.sentis.com.au
Year Founded: 2003
Sales Range: $750-799.9 Million
Emp.: 90
Safety Services
N.A.I.C.S.: 922190
Joseph Condon (Mgr-ICT)
Subsidiaries:

Sentis USA, Inc. (1)
6205 S Main St Ste 260, Aurora, CO 80316
Tel.: (720) 226-9550
Web Site: http://www.sentis.net
Safety Services
N.A.I.C.S.: 922190
Michelle Brown (Mgr-Bus Dev)

SENTON ENERGY CO., LTD.
No 5000 Heping Road, Economic Development Zone Longkou, Yantai, 265700, Shandong, China
Tel.: (86) 5358882717
Web Site: https://www.senton.cn
Year Founded: 2012
001331—(SSE)
Rev.: $724,056,447
Assets: $242,390,688
Liabilities: $19,684,010
Net Worth: $222,706,678
Earnings: $24,160,973
Fiscal Year-end: 12/31/22
Natural Gas Distribution Services
N.A.I.C.S.: 221210
Wei Zhang (Chm & Gen Mgr)

SENTON PRINTING & PACKAGING INCORPORATED
1669 Oxford Street East, London, N5V 2Z5, ON, Canada
Tel.: (519) 455-5500
Web Site: http://www.senton.com
Year Founded: 1984
Rev.: $14,780,642
Emp.: 110
Commercial Printing Services
N.A.I.C.S.: 323111
John Thain (Pres)

SENTORIA GROUP BERHAD
56 and 58 Jalan Dagang SB 4/2 Taman Sungai Besi Indah, 43300, Seri Kembangan, Selangor, Malaysia
Tel.: (60) 389438388
Web Site: https://www.sentoria.com.my
Year Founded: 1998
SNTORIA—(KLS)
Rev.: $8,367,619
Assets: $172,611,852
Liabilities: $146,709,418
Net Worth: $25,902,434
Earnings: ($14,966,561)
Fiscal Year-end: 09/30/23
Property Development Services
N.A.I.C.S.: 237210
Leh Kiah Tan (Co-Sec)
Subsidiaries:

Bukit Gambang Resort City (1)
Gambang, 26300, Kuantan, Pahang, Malaysia
Tel.: (60) 95488000
Web Site: https://www.bgrc.com.my
Resort Hotel
N.A.I.C.S.: 721110

Datasonic Corporation Sdn. Bhd. (1)
No 2D Jalan Kilang 51/206 Petaling Jaya, 46050, Kuala Selangor, Malaysia
Tel.: (60) 377819868
Property Development Services
N.A.I.C.S.: 531390

Sempurna Resort Sdn. Bhd. (1)
Jalan TIS1 Taman Indera Sempurna, 25150, Kuantan, Pahang Darul Makmur, Malaysia
Tel.: (60) 95173000
Web Site: http://www.sempurna.com.my
Theme Park
N.A.I.C.S.: 713110

Sentoria Borneo Land Sdn. Bhd. (1)
Sublot No 43 Survey Lot 7677 Lot 5569 Block 9, Salak Land District Bandar Samariang Commercial Centre, 93050, Kuching, Sarawak, Malaysia
Tel.: (60) 82882211
Property Development Services
N.A.I.C.S.: 531390

SENTRAL REIT
G27A Level 3A Block B Platinum Sentral Jalan Stesen Sentral 2, Kuala Lumpur Sentral, 50470, Kuala Lumpur, Malaysia
Tel.: (60) 327868080 MY
Web Site: https://www.sentralreit.com
Year Founded: 2006
5123—(KLS)
Rev.: $35,286,327
Assets: $569,448,121
Liabilities: $274,828,756
Net Worth: $294,619,364
Earnings: $15,826,812
Emp.: 7
Fiscal Year-end: 12/31/23
Real Estate Investment Trust Services
N.A.I.C.S.: 531120
Shirley Soot Lee Tam (CFO & Gen Mgr-Fin)

SENTREX COMMUNICATIONS INC.
25 Milvan Drive North York, Toronto, M9L 1Y8, ON, Canada
Tel.: (416) 749-7400
Web Site: http://www.sentrexco.com
Communication Network Design Services
N.A.I.C.S.: 541512
Tony Bellisario (VP)
Subsidiaries:

Bethlehem WM Trenching Ltd (1)
1154 Pettit Rd, Burlington, L7O 2T5, ON, Canada
Tel.: (905) 319-3003
Excavating Contract Services
N.A.I.C.S.: 238910

SENVEST CAPITAL, INC.
1000 Sherbrook St West Suite 2400, Montreal, H3A 3G4, QC, Canada
Tel.: (514) 281-8082
Web Site: https://www.senvest.com
SEC—(TSX)
Rev.: $1,941,756,641
Assets: $5,134,809,257
Liabilities: $3,714,460,228
Net Worth: $1,420,349,029
Earnings: $575,657,948
Emp.: 27
Fiscal Year-end: 12/31/21
Business Activities in Merchant Banking, Asset Management, Real Estate, Printing & Electronic Security
N.A.I.C.S.: 561499
Richard Mashaal (Founder)
Subsidiaries:

Pennsylvania Properties, Inc. (1)
1000 Sherbrook W Ste 2400, Montreal, H3A 3G4, QC, Canada (100%)
Tel.: (514) 281-8082
Sales Range: $25-49.9 Million
Emp.: 15
Business Services
N.A.I.C.S.: 561499
George Malikotsis (Mng Dir)

Senvest Blends Inc. (1)

Senvest International L.L.C. (1)
540 Madison Avenue 32nd Fl, New York, NY 10022-5429
Tel.: (212) 977-2466
Web Site: http://www.senvest.com
Sales Range: $50-74.9 Million
Business Services
N.A.I.C.S.: 523150
Richard Mashaal (Pres)

SENYSOFT INFO-TECH (DALIAN) CO., LTD.
Room 1002 10th Floor Cyber Building 133 Guangxian Road High-Tech Park, Dalian, China
Tel.: (86) 41139683465 CN
Web Site: http://www.senysoft.com
Software Development Services
N.A.I.C.S.: 541511

SENZAGEN AB
Bldg 401, Medicon Village, 223 63, Lund, Sweden
Tel.: (46) 462756200
Web Site: https://www.senzagen.com
SENZA—(OMX)
Rev.: $4,950,662
Assets: $9,646,793
Liabilities: $2,935,255
Net Worth: $6,711,537
Earnings: ($2,193,599)
Emp.: 34
Fiscal Year-end: 12/31/23
Pharmaceutical Products Distr
N.A.I.C.S.: 424210
Carl Borrebaeck (Founder & Chm)
Subsidiaries:

VitroScreen s.r.l. (1)
Via Mose Bianchi 103, 20149, Milan, Italy
Tel.: (39) 0289077608
Web Site: https://www.vitroscreen.com
Biotechnology Research Services
N.A.I.C.S.: 541714

SENZIME AB
Verkstadsgatan 8 hus 1, 756 51, Uppsala, Sweden
Tel.: (46) 18515640
Web Site: https://www.senzime.com
SEZI—(NASDAQ)
Rev.: $719,218
Assets: $20,122,346
Liabilities: $2,579,368
Net Worth: $17,542,979
Earnings: ($3,609,057)
Emp.: 12
Fiscal Year-end: 12/31/19
Medical Device Mfr
N.A.I.C.S.: 339112
Philip Siberg (Chm)

SEOAM MACHINERY INDUSTRY CO., LTD.
738-5 Anchung-dong, Gwangsan-gu, Gwangju, 560258, Korea (South)
Tel.: (82) 629605000
Web Site: https://www.smiltd.co.kr
Year Founded: 1978
100660—(KRS)
Rev.: $38,670,763
Assets: $58,020,965
Liabilities: $8,831,027
Net Worth: $49,189,938
Earnings: $1,670,029
Emp.: 165
Fiscal Year-end: 12/31/22
Gears, Cylinders, Transmissions & Other Industrial Machinery Equipment Mfr
N.A.I.C.S.: 333612
Kwon Hyeong Rok (Co-CEO)
Subsidiaries:

Heacheon Machinery Co., Ltd. (1)
1022-7 Bangbae-dong, Seocho-gu, Seoul, Korea (South)
Tel.: (82) 25237766
Machine Tools Mfr
N.A.I.C.S.: 332710

SEOBU T&D CO., LTD.
167 Sinjeong-ro, Yangcheon-gu, Seoul, Korea (South)
Tel.: (82) 226890035
Web Site: http://www.seobutt.com
Year Founded: 1979
006730—(KRS)
Rev.: $103,760,528
Assets: $1,584,402,138
Liabilities: $957,910,149
Net Worth: $626,491,989
Earnings: $12,808,023
Emp.: 474
Fiscal Year-end: 12/31/22
Oil Distribution Services
N.A.I.C.S.: 457120
Won Jae Chun (VP)

SEOHAN CO., LTD.
415 Myeongdeok-ro, Suseong-gu, Daegu, Korea (South)
Tel.: (82) 537419980
11370—(KRS)
Rev.: $446,417,424
Assets: $499,768,665
Liabilities: $207,432,304
Net Worth: $292,336,361
Earnings: $16,718,092
Emp.: 375
Fiscal Year-end: 12/31/20
Construction & Engineering Services
N.A.I.C.S.: 541330
Jong-Su Jo (CEO)

SEOHAN CONST. & ENG. CO., LTD
415 Myeongdeok-ro Daegu Seohan

SEOHAN CONST. & ENG. CO., LTD

SEOHAN Const. & Eng. Co., Ltd---(Continued)
Building, Suseong-gu, Daegu, Korea (South)
Tel.: (82) 537419980
Web Site: https://www.seo-han.co.kr
Year Founded: 1976
011370—(KRS)
Rev.: $559,935,440
Assets: $803,668,557
Liabilities: $499,686,544
Net Worth: $303,982,013
Earnings: $30,188,611
Emp.: 434
Fiscal Year-end: 12/31/22
Civil Engineering Services
N.A.I.C.S.: 237990

SEOHEE CONSTRUCTION CO., LTD.
Sunaedong 4-4, Bundang-gu, Seongnam, Gyeong-gido, Korea (South)
Tel.: (82) 234166644
Web Site: http://www.seohee.co.kr
Year Founded: 1994
035890—(KRS)
Rev.: $1,102,692,114
Assets: $1,239,505,367
Liabilities: $659,766,981
Net Worth: $579,738,387
Earnings: $76,780,156
Emp.: 912
Fiscal Year-end: 12/31/22
Construction Engineering Services
N.A.I.C.S.: 236220
Bong-Kwan Lee (Chm & CEO)

SEOHO ELECTRIC CO., LTD
900-3 Hogye-dong, Dongan-gu, Anyang, 14042, Kyungki-do, Korea (South)
Tel.: (82) 314686611
Web Site: https://www.seoho.com
Year Founded: 1981
065710—(KRS)
Rev.: $46,150,785
Assets: $78,084,159
Liabilities: $8,948,097
Net Worth: $69,136,063
Earnings: $8,639,914
Emp.: 80
Fiscal Year-end: 12/31/22
Control System Device Mfr
N.A.I.C.S.: 334519
Seung Nam Kim (CEO)

SEOJEON ELECTRIC MACHINERY CO., LTD.
38-19 Daewol-ro 667 beon-gil, Daewol-myeon, Icheon, 17401, Gyeonggi-do, Korea (South)
Tel.: (82) 316325520
Web Site: https://www.sjem.co.kr
Year Founded: 1998
189860—(KRS)
Rev.: $38,890,813
Assets: $39,124,527
Liabilities: $12,973,512
Net Worth: $26,151,015
Earnings: ($2,448,970)
Emp.: 119
Fiscal Year-end: 12/31/22
Heavy Electric & Electronic Equipment Mfr
N.A.I.C.S.: 335999
Hansoo Kim (CEO)

SEOJIN SYSTEM CO., LTD.
20-22 Saneom-ro Ojeong-gu, Bucheon, Gyeonggi-do, Korea (South)
Tel.: (82) 325062760
Web Site: https://www.seojinsystem.net
Year Founded: 1996
178320—(KRS)
Rev.: $604,088,389
Assets: $1,062,152,222
Liabilities: $648,302,252
Net Worth: $413,849,970
Earnings: $1,235,783
Emp.: 311
Fiscal Year-end: 12/31/22
Communication Equipment Mfr & Distr
N.A.I.C.S.: 334220
Kwangok Choi (Mng Dir)

Subsidiaries:

Texon Co., Ltd (1)
98 Sandan-ro, Uijeongbu, Gyeonggi-do, Korea (South)
Tel.: (82) 31 852 3366
Web Site: http://www.texon.co.kr
Emp.: 190
Telecommunication Equipment Mfr & Distr
N.A.I.C.S.: 334220
Hyun-Cheol Han (CEO)

Subsidiary (US):

Texon USA Co., Ltd. (2)
2735 Villa Creek Rd Farmers Branch, Dallas, TX 75234
Tel.: (469) 878-9948
Telecommunication Equipment Distr
N.A.I.C.S.: 423690

SEONDO ELECTRIC CO., LTD.
444 Sihwa Venture-ro, Danwon-gu, Ansan, Gyeonggi-do, Korea (South)
Tel.: (82) 314912284
Web Site: https://www.seondo.co.kr
Year Founded: 1972
007610—(KRS)
Rev.: $63,924,565
Assets: $101,044,088
Liabilities: $54,871,150
Net Worth: $46,172,938
Earnings: ($7,633,884)
Emp.: 184
Fiscal Year-end: 12/31/22
Electric Equipment Mfr
N.A.I.C.S.: 335313
Ha Bongsu (CEO)

Subsidiaries:

Seondo Electric Co., Ltd. - The 2nd Factory (1)
647 Choji-dong, Danwon-gu, Ansan, Kyonggi-do, Korea (South)
Tel.: (82) 31 494 0608
Electric Equipment Mfr
N.A.I.C.S.: 335313

SEONG AN CO LTD
740 Geomdan-dong, Buk-gu, Daegu, Korea (South)
Tel.: (82) 267106900
Web Site: https://www.startex.co.kr
Year Founded: 1953
011300—(KRS)
Rev.: $55,576,821
Assets: $95,010,209
Liabilities: $77,970,684
Net Worth: $17,039,524
Earnings: ($2,225,787)
Emp.: 59
Fiscal Year-end: 12/31/22
Polyester Fabric Product Mfr & Distr
N.A.I.C.S.: 313110

Subsidiaries:

Seong-An Synthetics Co. Ltd. (1)
29 Namgumi-ro Gondan-dong, Gumi, Gyeongsangbuk-do, Korea (South)
Tel.: (82) 54 460 0114
Web Site: http://www.sasyn.co.kr
Polyester Yarn Mfr & Distr
N.A.I.C.S.: 325220
Sang-won Park (CEO)

Subsidiary (Domestic):

Seong An Dyeing Co., Ltd (2)
2041-124 Bisan-dong Seo-gu, Daegu, Korea (South)
Tel.: (82) 533585151
Emp.: 160

Polyester Yarn Mfr & Distr
N.A.I.C.S.: 325220

Seong-An Trade Corporation (1)
Rm 1509 Munjeong Daemyung Valeon 127 Beopwon-ro Song Pa Gu, Seoul, Korea (South)
Tel.: (82) 267106900
Fabric Product Mfr
N.A.I.C.S.: 315990

SEOSAN CO LTD,.
143 Hanam Industrial Complex 4-beon-ro, Gwangsan-gu, Gwangju, Korea (South)
Tel.: (82) 629505000
Web Site: https://www.seo-san.co.kr
Year Founded: 1974
079650—(KRS)
Rev.: $37,708,342
Assets: $85,621,037
Liabilities: $5,271,042
Net Worth: $80,349,995
Earnings: $966,767
Emp.: 61
Fiscal Year-end: 12/31/22
Concrete Product Mfr & Distr
N.A.I.C.S.: 327320
Hong-Sub Youm (Chm & CEO)

SEOUL AUCTION
98 Pyeongchang-Dong, Jongno-Gu, Seoul, Korea (South)
Tel.: (82) 220754324
Web Site: https://www.seoulauction.com
Year Founded: 1998
063170—(KRS)
Rev.: $42,290,091
Assets: $149,059,925
Liabilities: $53,824,311
Net Worth: $95,235,614
Earnings: $3,483,929
Emp.: 140
Fiscal Year-end: 12/31/22
Auction Services
N.A.I.C.S.: 459920
Yong-Gyeon Kim (Dir)

Subsidiaries:

SeoulAuction Hong Kong Limited (1)
11F H Queens 80 Queens Road, Central, China (Hong Kong)
Tel.: (852) 2537 1880
Web Site: http://www.seoulauction.com
Emp.: 50
Auction Services
N.A.I.C.S.: 459920

SEOUL CITY GAS CO., LTD.
607 Gonghang-daero, Gangseo-gu, Seoul, 157-864, Korea (South)
Tel.: (82) 28108000
Web Site: http://www.seoulgas.co.kr
Year Founded: 1983
017390—(KRS)
Rev.: $1,322,654,687
Assets: $1,435,319,657
Liabilities: $627,692,617
Net Worth: $807,627,040
Earnings: $13,744,042
Emp.: 515
Fiscal Year-end: 12/31/22
Natural Gas Distr
N.A.I.C.S.: 221210
Hwang Sung Soo (Deputy Gen Mgr)

Subsidiaries:

SCG Solutions Co., Ltd. (1)
5F 11 Beobwon-ro 6-gil, Songpa-gu, 05855, Seoul, Korea (South)
Tel.: (82) 2 827 0020
Web Site: http://www.scgs.co.kr
Communication Equipment Distr
N.A.I.C.S.: 423690
Minyong Kim (CEO)

Subsidiary (Non-US):

SCG Solutions Thailand Limited (2)

INTERNATIONAL PUBLIC

195/5 Lake Rajada Office Complex Tower 2 4th Floor Rajadapisek Road, Klongtoey Sub-District Klongtoey District, Bangkok, 10110, Thailand
Tel.: (66) 21197570
Web Site: http://www.scgs.co.th
Communication Equipment Distr
N.A.I.C.S.: 423690
Surakiat Thirasak (Sr Mgr-Bus Dev)

SEOUL ELECTRONICS & TELECOM CO., LTD.
4(Saebeol-ro, Bupyeong-gu, Incheon, 21315, Korea (South)
Tel.: (82) 327234111
Web Site: https://www.seoulset.co.kr
Year Founded: 1983
027040—(KRS)
Rev.: $39,758,368
Assets: $99,100,295
Liabilities: $57,443,398
Net Worth: $41,656,897
Earnings: ($7,949,388)
Emp.: 87
Fiscal Year-end: 12/31/22
Transformers & Power Parts, AC Adaptors, Switching Transformers & Coils & Battery Chargers Mfr & Sales
N.A.I.C.S.: 335311
Jong-man Son (CEO)

Subsidiaries:

Seoul Electronics & Telecommunications (M) Sdn. Bhd. (1)
Lot 9 and 10 Puncak Perusahaan 1, Prai Industrial Estates, Prai, Penang, Malaysia
Tel.: (60) 43983100
Electronic Components Mfr
N.A.I.C.S.: 335999

Set Vina Co., Ltd. (1)
Slot C5 D1 Street, Chau Son Industrial Park, Phu Ly, Ha Nam, Vietnam
Tel.: (84) 3513682569
Electronic Components Mfr
N.A.I.C.S.: 335999

SEOUL FOOD INDUSTRIAL. CO., LTD.
862 Chungwondearo, Chungju, Choong Chung Buk Do, Korea (South)
Tel.: (82) 437207000
Web Site: http://www.seoul-food.co.kr
Year Founded: 1955
004410—(KRS)
Rev.: $49,355,994
Assets: $54,344,529
Liabilities: $32,624,024
Net Worth: $21,720,505
Earnings: $518,464
Emp.: 230
Fiscal Year-end: 12/31/22
Bakery Product Mfr & Whslr
N.A.I.C.S.: 311821
Sung Hoon Suh (CEO)

Subsidiaries:

think coffee KOREA (1)
Tel.: (82) 260166860
Coffeeshop Operator
N.A.I.C.S.: 445298

SEOUL PHARMA CO., LTD.
124-31 Osongsaengmyeong 6-ro, Osong-eup Heungdeok-gu, Cheongju, 06710, Chungcheongbuk-do, Korea (South)
Tel.: (82) 234702300
Web Site: http://www.seoulpharma.com
Year Founded: 1976
018680—(KRS)
Rev.: $38,393,508
Assets: $47,882,329
Liabilities: $20,713,902
Net Worth: $27,168,428
Earnings: $655,857
Emp.: 180

Fiscal Year-end: 12/31/22
Pharmaceuticals Product Mfr
N.A.I.C.S.: 325412
Dong Hyun Yoon (CEO)

SEOUL SEMICONDUCTOR CO., LTD.
97-11 Sandan-ro 163 beon-gil, Danwon-gu, Ansan, 15429, Gyeonggi-do, Korea (South)
Tel.: (82) 15662771
Web Site:
https://www.seoulsemicon.com
Year Founded: 1987
046890—(KRS)
Rev.: $850,930,865
Assets: $989,331,790
Liabilities: $394,470,088
Net Worth: $594,861,702
Earnings: ($41,667,831)
Emp.: 630
Fiscal Year-end: 12/31/22
Electronic Components Mfr
N.A.I.C.S.: 334413
Chung-hoon Lee (Founder, Pres & Co-CEO)

Subsidiaries:

China Seoul Semiconductor (1)
Rm A-1006 Fairmont Tower No33 Guangshunbei street, Chaoyang District, Beijing, 100102, China
Tel.: (86) 10 6474 6900
Semiconductor Device Whslr
N.A.I.C.S.: 423690

Japan Seoul Semiconductor Co., Ltd (1)
KS Bldg No2 5F 1-11-17 Shinjuku, Shinjuku-ku, Tokyo, 160-0022, Japan
Tel.: (81) 353607620
Semiconductor Device Whslr
N.A.I.C.S.: 423690

Nitek, Inc. (1)
1895 Beaver Ridge Cir Ste G, Norcross, GA 30071
Web Site: http://www.nitekusa.com
Semiconductor Product Mfr
N.A.I.C.S.: 334413

Nitek, Inc. (1)
1895 Beaver Ridge Cir Ste G, Norcross, GA 30071
Web Site: http://www.nitekusa.com
Semiconductor Product Mfr
N.A.I.C.S.: 334413

North America Seoul Semiconductor Inc. (1)
11145 Knott Ave Ste G, Cypress, CA 90360
Tel.: (678) 762-9610
Semiconductor Product Mfr
N.A.I.C.S.: 334413

Seoul Semiconductor Europe GmbH (1)
Claudius-Keller-Strasse 3B, 81669, Munich, Germany
Tel.: (49) 89 450 3690 0
Web Site: http://www.seoulsemicon.com
Semiconductor Device Whslr
N.A.I.C.S.: 423690
J. H. Andrew Kim (Dir-Sls)

Seoul Viosys Co., Ltd. (1)
65-16 Sandan-ro 163beon-gil, Danwon-gu, Ansan, Gyeonggi-do, Korea (South)
Tel.: (82) 15662771
Web Site: https://www.seoulviosys.com
Semiconductor Product Mfr
N.A.I.C.S.: 334413
Lee Chung-Hoon (Founder)

Subsidiary (US):

Sensor Electronic Technology, Inc. (2)
1195 Atlas Rd, Columbia, SC 29209 (62.2%)
Tel.: (803) 647-9757
Web Site: http://www.s-et.com
Semiconductor Machinery Mfr
N.A.I.C.S.: 333242

WAVE ELECTRONICS JAPAN CO., LTD. (1)
201 Apri Shinyokohama Building 2-5-19 Shinyokohama Kouhoku, Yokohama, Kanagawaken, Japan
Tel.: (81) 45 624 8019
Electronic Components Mfr
N.A.I.C.S.: 334419

SEOULIN BIOSCIENCE CO., LTD.
4F A Korea Bio Park 700 Daewangpangyo-ro, Bundang-gu, Seongnam, 463-400, Gyeonggi-do, Korea (South)
Tel.: (82) 3116705911
Web Site: https://www.seoulin.co.kr
Year Founded: 1984
038070—(KRS)
Rev.: $78,545,570
Assets: $103,444,343
Liabilities: $35,819,507
Net Worth: $67,624,835
Earnings: $7,652,560
Emp.: 106
Fiscal Year-end: 12/31/22
Bio Research Equipment Mfr
N.A.I.C.S.: 334510
Mi-Ok Kang (Pres & Co-CEO)

SEOWON CO., LTD.
94 Sandan-ro 67beon-gil, Danwon-gu, 15999, Ansan, Gyeonggi-do, Korea (South)
Tel.: (82) 313658700
Web Site: https://www.swbrass.co.kr
Year Founded: 1988
021050—(KRS)
Rev.: $211,445,956
Assets: $204,200,602
Liabilities: $99,707,358
Net Worth: $104,493,243
Earnings: $212,001
Emp.: 149
Fiscal Year-end: 12/31/22
Non Ferrous Metal Mfr
N.A.I.C.S.: 331410
Kyung Ho Cho (Co-CEO)

Subsidiaries:

Seowon Co., Ltd. - Hwaseong Factory (1)
35 Madogongdan-ro 4-gil Mado-myeon, Hwaseong, Gyeonggi-do, Korea (South)
Tel.: (82) 313559591
Non Ferrous Metal Mfr
N.A.I.C.S.: 331491

Taewoo Co., Ltd.: (1)
664-10 Seonggok-dong, Ansan, Gyeonggi-do, Korea (South)
Tel.: (82) 314988145
Web Site: https://www.taewoometal.co.kr
Copper Product Mfr
N.A.I.C.S.: 331420

SEOWON INTECH CO., LTD.
32-15 Gongdan-ro 140beon-gil, Gunpo, 15809, Gyeonggi-do, Korea (South)
Tel.: (82) 314289500
Web Site:
https://www.seowonintech.co.kr
Year Founded: 1983
093920—(KRS)
Rev.: $242,977,871
Assets: $183,365,903
Liabilities: $31,719,483
Net Worth: $151,646,420
Earnings: $17,619,905
Emp.: 214
Fiscal Year-end: 12/31/22
Cellular Phone Parts Mfr
N.A.I.C.S.: 334220
Jae-Yoon Kim (CEO)

SEOYEON CO., LTD.
41-22 Burim-ro 170 Beon-gil Dongan-gu, Anyang, Korea (South)
Tel.: (82) 314203000
Web Site: http://www.seo-yon.com
Year Founded: 1972
007860—(KRS)
Rev.: $2,493,937,839
Assets: $1,782,157,747
Liabilities: $1,012,161,357
Net Worth: $769,996,390
Earnings: $76,042,001
Emp.: 21
Fiscal Year-end: 12/31/22
Motor Vehicle Seating & Interior Trim Mfr
N.A.I.C.S.: 336360
Yang Seok Yoo (Chm & CEO)

Subsidiaries:

Seoyon Autovision Co., Ltd. (1)
895-19 Nambu-ro, Sunseong-myeon, Dangjin, Chungcheongnam-do, Korea (South)
Tel.: (82) 413541010
Auto Part Mfr & Retailer
N.A.I.C.S.: 336390

Seoyon CNF Co., Ltd. (1)
13 Jeoneup Duseo-myeon Nongong-gil, Ulju-gun, Ulsan, Korea (South)
Tel.: (82) 522558000
Web Site: http://www.seoyoncnf.com
Auto Part Mfr & Retailer
N.A.I.C.S.: 336390

Seoyon Intech Co., Ltd. (1)
Tel.: (82) 638304900
Web Site: http://www.seoyonintech.com
Car Interior Part Mfr
N.A.I.C.S.: 336360

SEOYON CO., LTD.
41-22 Bulim-ro 170beon-gil, Dongan-gu, Anyang, Gyeonggi-do, Korea (South)
Tel.: (82) 314203200
Web Site: https://seo-yon.com
7860—(KRS)
Rev.: $1,894,270,278
Assets: $1,905,211,320
Liabilities: $1,212,906,042
Net Worth: $692,305,277
Earnings: ($81,980,554)
Fiscal Year-end: 12/31/19
Automobile Equipment Mfr
N.A.I.C.S.: 336110
Yang-Seok Ryu (Chm & CEO)

SEOYON E-HWA CO., LTD.
41-22 Burim-ro 170beon-gil, Dongan-gu, Anyang, Gyeonggi-do, Korea (South)
Tel.: (82) 2314203200
Web Site: https://www.seoyoneh.com
Year Founded: 1972
200880—(KRS)
Rev.: $2,182,309,335
Assets: $1,480,564,856
Liabilities: $900,033,007
Net Worth: $580,531,849
Earnings: $46,384,306
Emp.: 896
Fiscal Year-end: 12/31/22
Automotive Exterior Parts Mfr
N.A.I.C.S.: 336360
Keun Sik Kim (CEO)

Subsidiaries:

SEOYON E-HWA AUTOMOTIVE INDIA PRIVATE LIMITED (1)
A-8 Sipcot Irrungattukottai, Sriperumbudur, Kanchipuram, India
Tel.: (91) 44 6717 2400
Web Site: http://www.seoyoneh.in
Automotive Interior Parts Distr
N.A.I.C.S.: 441330
R. Senthil Arumugam (Engr-R&D)

Seoyon E-HWA Automotive Poland Sp. z o.o. (1)
Ul Cieszynska 1D, 43-440, Bazanowice, Poland
Tel.: (48) 334321719

Automobile Parts Mfr
N.A.I.C.S.: 336390
Bartlomiej Czauderna (Officer)

Seoyon E-HWA Automotive Slovakia s.r.o. (1)
Tel.: (421) 422818414
Automobile Parts Mfr
N.A.I.C.S.: 336390
Jong Myung Kim (Pres & CEO)

SEOYON TOPMETAL CO., LTD.
40 410beongil Cheongneung-daero, Namdong-gu, Incheon, Korea (South)
Tel.: (82) 328203200
Web Site:
https://www.seoyontop.com
Year Founded: 1987
019770—(KRS)
Rev.: $125,924,666
Assets: $101,588,135
Liabilities: $42,521,035
Net Worth: $59,067,100
Earnings: $2,142,212
Emp.: 190
Fiscal Year-end: 12/31/22
Automobile Parts Mfr
N.A.I.C.S.: 336390
W. J. Choi (CEO)

Subsidiaries:

Top Metal Works Co., Ltd. - Incheon Facility (1)
663-6 Gojan-Dong, Namdong-Gu, Incheon, Korea (South)
Tel.: (82) 32 820 3230
Automobile Parts Mfr
N.A.I.C.S.: 336390

SEP ANALYTICAL (SHANGHAI) CO., LTD.
Building 25 & 34 No 1288 Zhongchun Road, Minhang District, Shanghai, 201109, China
Tel.: (86) 2164881367
Web Site: https://www.sepchina.cn
Year Founded: 2008
301228—(CHIN)
Rev.: $52,652,394
Assets: $173,932,211
Liabilities: $45,371,479
Net Worth: $128,560,732
Earnings: ($13,174,422)
Emp.: 1,200
Fiscal Year-end: 12/31/23
Testing Laboratory Services
N.A.I.C.S.: 541380
Jin Yang (Chm & Gen Mgr)

SEPAH INVESTMENT COMPANY
Africa Blvd Anahita Plak 18 Alley Old 23, PO Box 775-14335, 1917644151, Tehran, Iran
Tel.: (98) 2188887349
Web Site: https://www.sinco.ir
Year Founded: 1991
SPAH1—(THE)
Sales Range: Less than $1 Million
Investment Management Service
N.A.I.C.S.: 523999
Mohammad Javad Salimi (CEO)

SEPAHAN CEMENT
Argentina Square-Alvand Street- No 11- 3rd Floor-Sepahan Cement, Company Unit, 1514944349, Tehran, Iran
Tel.: (98) 2186087972
Web Site:
https://www.sepahancement.com
Year Founded: 1970
SSEP1—(THE)
Sales Range: Less than $1 Million
Cement Mfr
N.A.I.C.S.: 327310
Mohammad Reza Soleimian (Chm)

SEPAHAN INDUSTRIAL GROUP CO.

Sepahan Cement—(Continued)

SEPAHAN INDUSTRIAL GROUP CO.
No 1 Sepahan Bldg Ahmad Ghasir Ave, 1514613138, Tehran, Iran
Tel.: (98) 2188739010
Web Site: https://www.sepahan.com
Year Founded: 1973
SEPA1—(THE)
Sales Range: Less than $1 Million
Steel Pipe & Tube Mfr
N.A.I.C.S.: 331210

Subsidiaries:

Sepahan Rolling & Tube Profile Co. (1)
No 1 Bokharest St Dr Beheshti Ave, Tehran, Iran
Tel.: (98) 2188738983
Web Site: http://www.sepahantubeco.com
Steel Precision Pipe Mfr & Distr
N.A.I.C.S.: 331210

SEPATU BATA TBK
JL RA Kartini Kav No 28 Cilandak Barat Selatan, Jakarta, 12430, Indonesia
Tel.: (62) 217505353
Web Site: https://www.bata.com
Year Founded: 1931
BATA—(INDO)
Rev.: $39,588,172
Assets: $38,037,944
Liabilities: $29,508,072
Net Worth: $8,529,872
Earnings: ($12,374,972)
Emp.: 366
Fiscal Year-end: 12/31/23
Footwear Product Mfr
N.A.I.C.S.: 316210

SEPC LIMITED
Old No 56/L New No 10/1 4th Floor BASCON FUTURA SV IT Park, Venkatnarayana Road Parthasarathy Puram T Nagar, Chennai, 600 017, Tamil Nadu, India
Tel.: (91) 4449005555
Web Site:
https://www.shriramepc.com
532945—(BOM)
Rev.: $47,824,243
Assets: $240,012,421
Liabilities: $109,553,624
Net Worth: $130,458,797
Earnings: ($587,950)
Emp.: 251
Fiscal Year-end: 03/31/23
Renewable Energy Projects, Process & Metallurgical Plants Design, Engineering, Procurement & Construction Services
N.A.I.C.S.: 335311
T. Shivaraman (CEO & Co-Mng Dir)

Subsidiaries:

Blackstone Group Technologies Pvt Limited (1)
No 31 A SP Kochar Tehnology Park, Ambattur Industrial Estate, Chennai, 600 058, India
Tel.: (91) 4445985100
Web Site: http://www.bgtek.in
Sales Range: $25-49.9 Million
Emp.: 200
Engineeering Services
N.A.I.C.S.: 541310

Leitner Shriram Manufacturing Limited (1)
18/3 4th Floor Sigappi Achi Building Rukmini Lakshmipathi Salai, Marshalls Road Egmore, Chennai, 600 008, Tamil Nadu, India
Tel.: (91) 2792 6000
Web Site: http://www.leitwind.in
Wind Power Development Services
N.A.I.C.S.: 221118

Orient Green Power Ltd. (1)
Bascon Futura SV 4th Floor No 10/1 Venkatanarayana Road, T Nagar, Chennai, 600017, India
Tel.: (91) 4449015678
Web Site:
https://www.orientgreenpower.com
Rev.: $34,795,276
Assets: $202,878,724
Liabilities: $141,137,821
Net Worth: $61,740,903
Earnings: $3,996,163
Emp.: 4
Fiscal Year-end: 03/31/2023
Renewable Energy Producer
N.A.I.C.S.: 221118
N. Rangachary (Chm)

SEPHAKU HOLDINGS LTD.
Southdowns Office Park Block A First Floor, Cnr John Vorster & Karee St, Irene, 0062, South Africa
Tel.: (27) 126120210
Web Site:
https://www.sephakuholdings.com
SEP—(JSE)
Rev.: $53,614,526
Assets: $95,658,656
Liabilities: $17,379,691
Net Worth: $78,278,966
Earnings: $3,041,526
Fiscal Year-end: 03/31/22
Minerals Exploration Development & Investment Services
N.A.I.C.S.: 213115
Neil Robus Crafford-Lazarus (Dir-Fin)

Subsidiaries:

Metier Mixed Concrete Proprietary Limited (1)
Romead Business Park 23 Malone Road Maxmead, Durban, 3610, South Africa
Tel.: (27) 317163600
Web Site: https://www.metiersa.co.za
Readymix Concrete Mfr
N.A.I.C.S.: 327320

SEPLAT ENERGY PLC
16A Temple Road, Lagos, Nigeria
Tel.: (234) 12770400 NG
Web Site:
https://www.seplatenergy.com
Year Founded: 2009
SEPLAT—(NIGE)
Rev.: $298,975,566
Assets: $1,170,705,927
Liabilities: $588,248,618
Net Worth: $582,457,309
Earnings: $32,889,215
Emp.: 596
Fiscal Year-end: 12/31/22
Oil & Gas Exploration Services
N.A.I.C.S.: 213112
Effiong Okon (Exec Dir-Ops)

Subsidiaries:

Eland Oil & Gas PLC (1)
Seabrokers House Prospect Road, Westhill, Aberdeen, AB32 6FE, Scotland, United Kingdom
Tel.: (44) 1224737300
Web Site: http://www.elandoilandgas.com
Sales Range: $150-199.9 Million
Oil & Gas Exploration
N.A.I.C.S.: 211120
Pieter van der Groen (Dir-Bus Dev)

Subsidiary (Non-US):

Eland Oil & Gas (Nigeria) Limited (2)
Atlantic House 121 Louis Solomon Close Victoria Island, Lagos, Nigeria
Tel.: (234) 16310920
Oil & Gas Retailer
N.A.I.C.S.: 457210
Dayo Balogun (Mgr-Facility Engrg)

Seplat Energy UK Limited (1)
4th Floor 50 Pall Mall, London, SW1Y 5JH, United Kingdom
Tel.: (44) 2037256500

Oil & Gas Resources Distr
N.A.I.C.S.: 424710

SEPPALA OY
Tikkurilantie 146, PO Box 234, FIN 01530, Vantaa, Finland
Tel.: (358) 9825981 FI
Web Site: http://www.seppala.fi
Sales Range: $100-124.9 Million
Emp.: 600
Women's Fashion Stores
N.A.I.C.S.: 455110
Eveliina Melentjeff (CEO)

SEPROD LIMITED
3 Felix Fox Boulevard, Kingston, Jamaica
Tel.: (876) 9221220
Web Site: https://www.seprod.com
Year Founded: 1940
SEP—(JAM)
Rev.: $727,578,574
Assets: $678,374,730
Liabilities: $426,436,782
Net Worth: $251,937,949
Earnings: $29,606,921
Fiscal Year-end: 12/31/23
Oil, Fat, Corn, Grain & Cereal Mfr & Sales
N.A.I.C.S.: 311225
Paul B. Scott (Chm)

Subsidiaries:

Caribbean Products Company Limited (1)
3 Felix Fox Boulevard, Kingston, Jamaica
Tel.: (876) 922 1220
Web Site: https://www.seprod.com
Cooking Oil Mfr & Whslr
N.A.I.C.S.: 424490

International Biscuits Limited (1)
2 Valentine Dr, Kingston, 19, Jamaica
Tel.: (876) 9259418
Web Site: http://www.seprod.com
Sales Range: $25-49.9 Million
Emp.: 200
Biscuit Mfr
N.A.I.C.S.: 311812
Rupert Ashman (Plant Mgr)

SEPTENI HOLDINGS CO., LTD.
Sumitomo Fudosan Shinjuku Grand Tower 30th Floor 8-17-1 Nishishinjuku, Shinjuku-ku, Tokyo, 160-6130, Japan
Tel.: (81) 368635623
Web Site: https://www.septeni-holdings.co.jp
Year Founded: 1990
4293—(TKS)
Rev.: $242,953,030
Assets: $663,666,540
Liabilities: $197,818,090
Net Worth: $465,848,450
Earnings: $30,621,710
Emp.: 1,735
Fiscal Year-end: 12/31/23
Holding Company; Web-Based & Conventional Marketing Programs
N.A.I.C.S.: 551112
Koki Sato (Pres & CEO)

Subsidiaries:

ACRESS Ltd (1)
12th Flr Edobori Center Building 2-1-1 Edobori, Nishi-ku, Osaka, 550-0002, Osaka, Japan
Tel.: (81) 120 34 3471
Web Site: http://www.acress.jp
Mail Order Business Services
N.A.I.C.S.: 541490
Kondo Takashi (Dir)

ADspace Inc. (1)
Septeni Gaien Building 24 Daikyo-cho, Shinjuku, Tokyo, 160-0015, Japan
Tel.: (81) 3 5919 2510
Web Site: http://www.adspace.jp
Internet Advertising Services

INTERNATIONAL PUBLIC

N.A.I.C.S.: 541810

ASP CO.,LTD. (1)
6th floor Shinagawa Intercity Building B 2-15-2 Konan, Minato-ku, Tokyo, 108-6106, Japan
Tel.: (81) 367121011
Web Site: https://www.asp.co.jp
Emp.: 120
Electronic Marketing Services
N.A.I.C.S.: 513210

Cytech,Inc. (1)
1-14-5 Shinjuku KM Building 4F, Shinjuku-ku, Tokyo, Japan
Tel.: (81) 3 5312 9876
Web Site: http://www.cytech.co.jp
Gaming Software Development Services
N.A.I.C.S.: 541511

Dentsu Direct Inc. (1)
1-8-1 Higashi-Shimbashi, Minato-ku, Tokyo, 105-7001, Japan
Tel.: (81) 362171400
Web Site: http://www.ddir.co.jp
Advertising Communication Services
N.A.I.C.S.: 541810

GRP Co.,Ltd. (1)
Septeni Gaien Building 24 Daikyo-cho, Tokyo, Tokyo, 160-0015, Japan
Tel.: (81) 3 6685 7550
Web Site: http://www.grpcorp.jp
Television Advertising Services
N.A.I.C.S.: 541840

HighScore,Inc. (1)
Sumitomo Fudosan Shinjuku Grand Tower 8-17-1 Nishi-Shinjuku, Shinjuku-ku, Tokyo, 160-0023, Japan
Tel.: (81) 353637227
Web Site: https://www.highscore.co.jp
Business Support Services
N.A.I.C.S.: 561499

MANGO Inc. (1)
Miyazaki Office 6F/1F Koa Miyazaki Building 2-5-16, Hiroshima, Miyazaki, 880-0806, Japan
Tel.: (81) 985356166
Web Site: https://www.10005.co.jp
Email Marketing Services
N.A.I.C.S.: 541860

Media Grow CO., LTD. (1)
Septeni Gaien Building 24 Daikyo-cho, Shinjuku-ku, Tokyo, 160-0015, Japan
Tel.: (81) 3 3359 4350
Web Site: http://www.media-grow.co.jp
Email Marketing Services
N.A.I.C.S.: 541860

SEPTENI CO., LTD. (1)
Sumitomo Shinjuku Grand Tower 28F 8-17-1 Nishi-Shinjuku, Shinjuku-ku, Tokyo, 160-6128, Japan
Tel.: (81) 353637320
Web Site: https://www.septeni.co.jp
Internet Advertising Services
N.A.I.C.S.: 541810
Koki Sato (Pres)

SEPTENI CROSSGATE CO.,LTD. (1)
27F Sumitomo Fudosan Shinjuku Grand Tower 8-17-1 Nishi-Shinjuku, Shinjuku-ku, Tokyo, 160-6127, Japan
Tel.: (81) 353620920
Web Site: https://www.cgate.jp
Emp.: 47
Advertising Agencies Services
N.A.I.C.S.: 541810

Tricorn Corporation (1)
Sumitomo Fudosan Shinjuku Grand Tower 27F 8-17-1 Nishi-Shinjuku, Tokyo, 160-0023, Japan
Tel.: (81) 368635638
Web Site: https://www.tricorn.co.jp
Sales Range: $25-49.9 Million
Emp.: 60
Email Marketing Services
N.A.I.C.S.: 541860

Vasara Inc. (1)
4th and 5th floors reception 3-14-3 Sotokanda, Fukuei Akihabara Building Chiyoda-ku, Tokyo, 160-0015, Japan
Tel.: (81) 332510836
Web Site: https://vasara-h.co.jp
Internet Advertising Services

AND PRIVATE COMPANIES

SEQUOIA FINANCIAL GROUP LIMITED

N.A.I.C.S.: 541810

SEQUA PETROLEUM NV
Fifth Floor 23 Savile Row, London, W1S 2ET, United Kingdom
Tel.: (44) 2037284450
Web Site: https://www.sequa-petroleum.com
MLSEQ—(EUR)
Sales Range: Less than $1 Million
Oil & Gas Support Services
N.A.I.C.S.: 213112
Jacob Broekhuijsen *(CEO & Mng Dir)*

SEQUANA MEDICAL NV
Kortrijksesteenweg 1112, 9051, Gent, Belgium
Tel.: (32) 92928065
Web Site: https://www.sequanamedical.com
2SE—(DEU)
Rev.: $786,150
Assets: $11,150,275
Liabilities: $32,637,386
Net Worth: ($21,487,111)
Earnings: ($35,946,102)
Emp.: 62
Fiscal Year-end: 12/31/23
Health Care Srvices
N.A.I.C.S.: 621399
Ian Crosbie *(CEO)*

Subsidiaries:

Sequana Medical GmbH (1)
Rundfunkplatz 2, 80335, Munich, Germany
Tel.: (49) 8938038405
Medical Device Mfr
N.A.I.C.S.: 339112

SEQUANA SA
8 rue de Seine, 92517, Boulogne-Billancourt, Cedex, France
Tel.: (33) 158042280   FR
Web Site: http://www.sequana.com
Year Founded: 1848
Holding Company; Paper Products Mfr
N.A.I.C.S.: 551112
Antoine Courteault *(Sec)*

Subsidiaries:

Antalis Groupe SAS (1)
122 rue Edouard Vaillant, 92300, Levallois-Perret, France
Tel.: (33) 141497300
Web Site: http://www.antalis.com
Sales Range: $1-4.9 Billion
Emp.: 6,900
Print, Office & Packaging Paper Distr
N.A.I.C.S.: 424110
Pascal Lebard *(CEO)*

Subsidiary (Non-US):

1st Class Packaging Ltd (2)
Units 1-3 Osyth Close Brackmills Industrial Estate, Northampton, NN4 7DY, United Kingdom
Tel.: (44) 1604 750730
Web Site: http://www.1stclasspackaging.co.uk
Emp.: 20
Packaging Paper Material Distr
N.A.I.C.S.: 424110
Barry Hancock *(Mng Dir)*

Donnington Packaging Supplies Ltd (2)
Pudding Lane Wardentree Lane, Pinchbeck, Spalding, PE11 3TJ, Lincolnshire, United Kingdom
Tel.: (44) 1775 723522
Web Site: http://www.donningtonpackaging.co.uk
Emp.: 11
Packaging Paper Material Distr
N.A.I.C.S.: 424130
Adrian Griggs *(Gen Mgr)*

Parkside Packaging Ltd (2)
Willenhall Lane, Binley, Coventry, CV3 2AS, United Kingdom
Tel.: (44) 2476455455
Web Site: http://www.parkside-pkg.co.uk
Emp.: 30
Packaging Paper Products Distr
N.A.I.C.S.: 424110
Keith Hobbs *(Mng Dir)*

SEQUANS COMMUNICATIONS S.A.
15-55 Boulevard Charles de Gaulle, 92700, Colombes, France
Tel.: (33) 170721600   FR
Web Site: https://www.sequans.com
Year Founded: 2003
SQNS—(NYSE)
Rev.: $33,616,000
Assets: $109,172,000
Liabilities: $115,243,000
Net Worth: ($6,071,000)
Earnings: ($40,990,000)
Emp.: 264
Fiscal Year-end: 12/31/23
Fabless 4G Semiconductor Mfr & Distr
N.A.I.C.S.: 334413
Georges Karam *(Co-Founder, Chm, Pres & CEO)*

Subsidiaries:

Sequans Communications (Israel) Ltd. (1)
10 Ahaliav Street, Ramat Gan, 5252263, Israel
Tel.: (972) 722502100
Communication Chip Mfr
N.A.I.C.S.: 334413
Ronen Cohen *(Engr-Algorithm)*

Sequans Communications Inc (1)
14500 Burnhaven Dr Ste 192, Burnsville, MN 55306
Tel.: (952) 500-8789
Semiconductor Devices Mfr
N.A.I.C.S.: 334413

Sequans Communications Ltd. (1)
155 Wharfedale Road Winnersh Triangle, Wokingham, Reading, RG41 5RB, United Kingdom
Tel.: (44) 1189904020
Sales Range: $25-49.9 Million
Emp.: 20
Semiconductor Devices Mfr
N.A.I.C.S.: 334413

Sequans Communications Ltd. Pte (1)
173B Thomson Rd Goldhill Ctr, Singapore, 307623, Singapore
Tel.: (65) 62584806
Semiconductor Devices Mfr
N.A.I.C.S.: 334413

SEQUENT SCIENTIFIC LIMITED
301/A 3rd Floor Dosti Pinnacle Plot No E7 Road No 22, Wagle Industrial Area Thane W, Mumbai, 400604, Maharashtra, India
Tel.: (91) 2241114777   In
Web Site: https://www.sequent.in
Year Founded: 1991
512529—(NSE)
Rev.: $187,001,997
Assets: $190,084,304
Liabilities: $84,117,170
Net Worth: $105,967,134
Earnings: $14,257,698
Emp.: 504
Fiscal Year-end: 03/31/21
Pharmaceutical Ingredient Mfr
N.A.I.C.S.: 325412
Manish Gupta *(CEO & Co-Mng Dir)*

Subsidiaries:

Alivira Animal Health Limited (1)
301/A Dosti Pinnacle Plot No E7 Road No 22, Wagle Industrial Area Thane West, Mumbai, 400604, Maharashtra, India
Tel.: (91) 2241114777
Web Site: https://alivira.co
Veterinary Laboratory Services
N.A.I.C.S.: 541940

Alivira Italia S.R.L. (1)
Via Giorgio Rizzi 12, 44123, Ferrara, FE, Italy
Tel.: (39) 03401965303
Web Site: https://alivira.it
Pharmaceutical Ingredient Mfr & Distr
N.A.I.C.S.: 325412

Bremer Pharma GmbH (1)
Tel.: (49) 564298090
Web Site: https://www.bremer-pharma.de
Veterinary Pharmaceutical Mfr
N.A.I.C.S.: 325412
Mohit Kumar *(Mng Dir)*

Fendigo S.A. (1)
Av Herrmann Debroux 17, 1160, Brussels, Belgium
Tel.: (32) 27344821
Web Site: https://www.fendigo.com
Veterinary Laboratory Services
N.A.I.C.S.: 541940

Laboratorios Karizoo, S.A. (1)
P I La Borda Borges Blanques 21-25, Caldes de Montbui, 08140, Barcelona, Spain
Tel.: (34) 938654148
Web Site: https://alivira.es
Animal Health Nutrition Product Mfr & Distr
N.A.I.C.S.: 311119

Laboratorios Karizoo, S.A. de C.V. (1)
Av de Las Fuentes 70 Int Bodega 5, Parque Industrial Finsa, 76246, El Marques, Qro, Mexico
Tel.: (52) 4429620947
Web Site: https://www.karizoo.com.mx
Veterinary Laboratory Services
N.A.I.C.S.: 541940

N-Vet AB (1)
Uppsala Science Park Husaren Dag Hammarskjolds Vag 36B, 751 83, Uppsala, Sweden
Tel.: (46) 18572430
Web Site: https://n-vet.se
Veterinary Laboratory Services
N.A.I.C.S.: 541940

Phytotherapic Solutions S.L. (1)
P I La Borda Mas Pujades 11-12, Caldes de Montbui, 08140, Barcelona, Spain
Tel.: (34) 938654148
Web Site: https://www.phytosolutions.es
Animal Health Nutrition Product Mfr & Distr
N.A.I.C.S.: 311119

Provet Veteriner Urunleri San. Ve Tic. A.S. (1)
Cavusoglu Mah Baskumandan Caddesi No 28, Kartal, 34873, Istanbul, Turkiye
Tel.: (90) 2164420281
Web Site: https://en.provet.com.tr
Veterinary Laboratory Services
N.A.I.C.S.: 541940

SeQuent Research Limited (1)
Tel.: (91) 7619516304
Biotechnology Research & Development Services
N.A.I.C.S.: 541714

SeQuent Scientific Ltd. (1)
Plot No 236 Industrial Area Baikampady, Mangalore, 575011, Karnataka, India
Tel.: (91) 7619516304
Web Site: http://www.sequent.in
Sales Range: $125-149.9 Million
Emp.: 300
Pharmaceutical Preparation Mfr
N.A.I.C.S.: 325412
K. Ravi Shankar *(Mng Dir)*

SEQUOIA ECONOMIC INFRASTRUCTURE INCOME FUND LTD.
85 Fleet St, London, EC4Y 1AE, United Kingdom
Tel.: (44) 2073534200
Web Site: https://www.seqi.fund
SEQI—(LSE)
Rev.: $11,864,916
Assets: $2,350,209,015
Liabilities: $342,295,380
Net Worth: $2,007,913,635
Earnings: ($22,277,745)
Fiscal Year-end: 03/31/23
Other Financial Vehicles
N.A.I.C.S.: 525990
Robert Jennings *(Mgr-Fund)*

SEQUOIA FINANCIAL GROUP LIMITED
Suite 7 01 Level 7 1 Castlereagh Street, Sydney, 2000, NSW, Australia
Tel.: (61) 81142290
Web Site: https://www.sequoia.com.au
SEQ—(ASX)
Rev.: $83,166,898
Assets: $53,010,867
Liabilities: $15,166,913
Net Worth: $37,843,954
Earnings: ($2,098,367)
Fiscal Year-end: 06/30/24
Investment Advisory Services
N.A.I.C.S.: 523940
Garry Crole *(CEO & Head-Sequoia Wealth Grp)*

Subsidiaries:

Bourse Data Pty. Ltd. (1)
Level 8 525 Flinders St, Melbourne, 3000, VIC, Australia
Tel.: (61) 385483333
Web Site: https://www.boursedata.com.au
Sales Range: $50-74.9 Million
Emp.: 15
Financial Independent Supplier Services
N.A.I.C.S.: 523999

Docscentre Pty. Ltd. (1)
Level 8 525 Flinders St, Melbourne, VIC, Australia
Tel.: (61) 1800799666
Web Site: https://www.docscentre.com
Document Digitization Services
N.A.I.C.S.: 561410

Finance TV Pty Ltd (1)
Level 7 7 Macquarie Place, Sydney, 2000, NSW, Australia
Tel.: (61) 28 294 4301
Web Site: https://www.finnewsnetwork.com.au
Broadcast Media Services
N.A.I.C.S.: 516120
Matt Wilson *(Mng Dir)*

InterPrac Financial Planning Pty Ltd (1)
Level 8 525 Flinders Street, Melbourne, 3000, VIC, Australia
Tel.: (61) 39 209 9777
Web Site: https://www.interprac.com.au
Financial Planning Services
N.A.I.C.S.: 523940
Garry Crole *(Mng Dir)*

PantherCorp CST Pty Ltd (1)
Level 1 18 Richardson St, West Perth, 6006, WA, Australia
Tel.: (61) 89 388 0551
Web Site: https://www.panthercorp.com.au
Professional Services
N.A.I.C.S.: 541990
Zoey McCormick *(Office Mgr)*

Sequoia Home Loans Pty. Ltd. (1)
Level 7 7 Macquarie Place, Sydney, NSW, Australia
Tel.: (61) 281142225
Web Site: https://www.sequoiahomeloans.com
Mortgage Banking Services
N.A.I.C.S.: 522310

Sequoia Premium Funding Pty. Ltd. (1)
Suite 10A 3 Male Street, Brighton, VIC, Australia
Tel.: (61) 395550544
Web Site: https://sequoiafunding.com.au
Insurance Maintaining Services
N.A.I.C.S.: 524298

Sequoia Specialist Investments Pty Ltd (1)

SEQUOIA FINANCIAL GROUP LIMITED

Sequoia Financial Group Limited—(Continued)
Level 7 7 Macquarie Place, Sydney, 2000, NSW, Australia
Tel.: (61) 28 114 2222
Web Site: https://www.sequoiasi.com.au
Financial Advice Services
N.A.I.C.S.: 523940

Sequoia Superannuation Pty Ltd (1)
Level 7 7 Macquarie Place, Sydney, 2000, NSW, Australia
Tel.: (61) 28 114 2290
Web Site: https://www.sequoiasuper.com.au
Mortgage Broker Services
N.A.I.C.S.: 522310
Jenna Alderson *(Officer-Client Service)*

Sequoia Wealth Management Pty Ltd
Level 7 7 Macquarie Place, Sydney, 2000, NSW, Australia
Tel.: (61) 281142288
Web Site: https://www.sequoiawm.com.au
Custom Computer Programming Services
N.A.I.C.S.: 541511

Sequoia Wealth Management Pty Ltd (1)
Level 7 7 Macquarie Place, Sydney, 2000, NSW, Australia
Tel.: (61) 28 114 2288
Web Site: https://www.sequoiawm.com.au
Wealth Management Services
N.A.I.C.S.: 523940

Trader Dealer Online Pty. Ltd. (1)
Level 37 Rialto South Tower, 525 Collins St, Melbourne, 3000, Victoria, Australia
Tel.: (61) 293003500
Web Site: http://www.traderdealer.com.au
Sales Range: $25-49.9 Million
Emp.: 30
Online Trading Services
N.A.I.C.S.: 238990

SEQUOIA INSURANCE BROKERS PTY. LTD.
Suite 10A 3 Male Street, Brighton, VIC, Australia
Tel.: (61) 395550544   AU
Web Site: https://www.sequoiainsurance.com
Year Founded: 1994
Insurance Brokerage Services
N.A.I.C.S.: 524210

SER EDUCACIONAL S.A.
Rua Treze de Maio n 254, Santo Amaro, Recife, 50100-160, Pernambuco, Brazil
Tel.: (55) 8134126285   BR
Web Site: https://www.sereducacional.com
Year Founded: 1993
SEER3—(BRAZ)
Rev.: $327,297,322
Assets: $623,680,826
Liabilities: $407,473,220
Net Worth: $216,207,606
Earnings: $5,013,139)
Fiscal Year-end: 12/31/23
Professional & Management Development Training Services
N.A.I.C.S.: 611430
José Janguie Bezerra Diniz *(Chm)*

SER INDUSTRIES LIMITED
107-108 Mittal Chamber, Nariman Point, Mumbai, 400021, India
Tel.: (91) 2222813137
Web Site: https://www.serindustries.co.in
Year Founded: 1963
Rev.: $1,034
Assets: $233,026
Liabilities: $64,530
Net Worth: $168,496
Earnings: ($50,144)
Fiscal Year-end: 03/31/16
Freight Transportation Services
N.A.I.C.S.: 484220

SER SOLUTIONS DEUTSCHLAND GMBH
Innovationspark Rahms, D 53577, Neustadt, Germany
Tel.: (49) 26839840
Web Site: http://www.ser.de
Year Founded: 1996
Sales Range: $25-49.9 Million
Emp.: 340
Document Management & Archiving Solutions
N.A.I.C.S.: 541512
Oswald Freisberg *(Mng Partner)*

Subsidiaries:

S.E.R. Solutions Polska Sp. z o.o. (1)
Ul Grzybowska 2/81, 00-131, Warsaw, Poland
Tel.: (48) 22 4365695
Web Site: http://www.ser-solutions.pl
Software Development Services
N.A.I.C.S.: 541511

SER Banking Software Solutions GmbH (1)
Friedrich-Ebert-Anlage 35-37, 60327, Frankfurt am Main, Germany
Tel.: (49) 69 713770 0
Web Site: http://www.ser.de
Sales Range: $25-49.9 Million
Emp.: 20
Banking Software Development Services
N.A.I.C.S.: 541511
Stefan Girmann *(Mng Dir)*

SER HealthCare Solutions GmbH (1)
Innovationspark Rahms, 53577, Neustadt, Wied, Germany
Tel.: (49) 2683 984 0
Web Site: http://www.ser-healthcare.de
Healthcare Software Development Services
N.A.I.C.S.: 541511

SER Solutions France SARL (1)
65 Rue de la Garenne, 92310, Sevres, France
Tel.: (33) 1 55 38 96 41
Web Site: http://www.ser-solutions.fr
Software Development Services
N.A.I.C.S.: 541511

SER Solutions Schweiz AG (1)
Ausserfeldstrasse 9, 5036, Oberentfelden, Switzerland
Tel.: (41) 627 3781 11
Web Site: http://www.ser.ch
Sales Range: $25-49.9 Million
Emp.: 18
Software Development Services
N.A.I.C.S.: 541511
Albert Baumberger *(CEO)*

SER Solutions United Kingdom Ltd. (1)
25 Southampton Buildings, London, WC2A 1AL, United Kingdom
Tel.: (44) 203178 6882
Software Development Services
N.A.I.C.S.: 541511

SER Storage & Imaging Technology GmbH (1)
Heuweg 6, 53577, Neustadt, Wied, Germany
Tel.: (49) 2683 946 8 0
Web Site: http://www.ser-storage.de
Sales Range: $25-49.9 Million
Emp.: 10
Software Development Services
N.A.I.C.S.: 541511

SER eGovernment Europe GmbH (1)
Kurfurstendamm 21, Berlin, 10719, Germany
Tel.: (49) 30 498582 0
Web Site: http://www.prodea.de
Emp.: 21
Software Development Services
N.A.I.C.S.: 541511
Sweifgrug Dirk *(Mgr)*

TRIADE InformationSystems GmbH (1)
Hellersbergstr 2, 41460, Neuss, Germany
Tel.: (49) 2131 36010 0
Web Site: http://www.triade.de
Software Development Services
N.A.I.C.S.: 541511

SERABI GOLD PLC
66 Lincoln 's Inn Fields, London, WC2A 3LH, United Kingdom
Tel.: (44) 2072466830   UK
Web Site: https://www.serabigold.com
Year Founded: 2004
SRB—(AIM)
Rev.: $58,710,000
Assets: $100,240,000
Liabilities: $18,720,000
Net Worth: $81,520,000
Earnings: ($980,000)
Fiscal Year-end: 12/31/22
Gold Mining Services
N.A.I.C.S.: 212220
Ulisses Melo *(Gen Mgr)*

SERAFIN UNTERNEHMENSGRUPPE GMBH
Lowengrube 18, 80333, Munich, Germany
Tel.: (49) 89 30 90 66 9 0   De
Web Site: http://www.serafin-gruppe.de
Year Founded: 2010
Holding Company
N.A.I.C.S.: 551112
Falk Daum *(Founder)*

Subsidiaries:

BHS tabletop AG (1)
Ludwigsmuhle 1, 95100, Selb, Germany (100%)
Tel.: (49) 9287730
Web Site: http://www.bhs-tabletop.de
Porcelain Tableware Products Mfr
N.A.I.C.S.: 327110
Rainer Schwarzmeier *(Member-Mgmt Bd)*

CLG Holdings Limited (1)
Brunel House Jessop Way, Newark, NG24 2ER, Notts, United Kingdom
Tel.: (44) 1636 642461
Web Site: http://www.playtop.com
Sales Range: $10-24.9 Million
Emp.: 50
Synthetic Playground Surface Mfr
N.A.I.C.S.: 326199
Nigel Allen *(Mng Dir)*

CONICA AG (1)
Industriestrasse 26, 8207, Schaffhausen, Switzerland
Tel.: (41) 52 644 36 00
Web Site: http://www.conica.com
Sales Range: $50-74.9 Million
Emp.: 100
Synthetic Sports Surface Mfr
N.A.I.C.S.: 326199
James Wright *(Dir-Comml)*

Subsidiary (US):

CONICA Corporation (2)
2548 Main St, Elgin, SC 29045-8844
Tel.: (803) 518-9444
Flooring Product Distr
N.A.I.C.S.: 423310

Subsidiary (Non-US):

CONICA LTD (2)
Jessop Way, Newark, NG24 2ER, Notting-hamshire, United Kingdom
Tel.: (44) 1636642460
Flooring Product Distr
N.A.I.C.S.: 423310

KCB Interlight Sp. z o.o. (2)
ul Inowroclawska 4, Gniewkowo, Poland
Tel.: (48) 523558207
Candle Distr
N.A.I.C.S.: 424990

KCB UMA GmbH (2)
Werner-von-Siemens-Str 7 - 9, 50226, Frechen, Germany
Tel.: (49) 223418610
Web Site: http://www.kcb.pl

INTERNATIONAL PUBLIC

Candle Mfr
N.A.I.C.S.: 339999

Roos - KCB Holland BV (2)
De Boorn 15, 8253 RA, Dronten, Netherlands
Tel.: (31) 320212931
Candle Distr
N.A.I.C.S.: 424990

Gersthofer Backbetriebe GmbH (1)
Siemensstrasse 7, 86368, Gersthofen, Germany
Tel.: (49) 821297620
Web Site: http://www.gersthofer-backbetriebe.de
Emp.: 400
Food Products Distr
N.A.I.C.S.: 424450

Heller Tools GmbH (1)
Steinfelder Str 11, 49413, Dinklage, Germany
Tel.: (49) 444396210
Web Site: http://www.hellertools.com
Emp.: 100
Drill Bit Mfr
N.A.I.C.S.: 332216
Frank Schubert *(Mng Dir)*

Nextrusion GmbH (1)
Max-Fischer-Strasse 11, D-86399, Bobingen, Germany
Tel.: (49) 8234 99 2000
Web Site: http://www.nextrusion.de
Sales Range: $50-74.9 Million
Emp.: 210
Monofilament Mfr
N.A.I.C.S.: 325220
Christlorenz Bundi *(Mng Dir)*

Perga-Plastic GmbH (1)
Richard-Rohlf-Strasse 1, D 74731, Walldurn, Germany
Tel.: (49) 62 85 82 0
Web Site: http://www.perga.de
Sales Range: $50-74.9 Million
Emp.: 240
Plastic Film & Packaging Mfr
N.A.I.C.S.: 326112
Martin Wilhelms *(Mng Dir)*

Perlon-Monofil GmbH (1)
Building F 18, PO Box 10 01 42, Dormagen, 41519, Germany
Tel.: (49) 21 33 51 43 37
Web Site: http://www.perlon-monofil.com
Sales Range: $25-49.9 Million
Emp.: 100
Polyester Resin Mfr
N.A.I.C.S.: 325211
Frank Winkes *(Mng Dir)*

Vollmar GmbH (1)
Werner-von-Siemens-Strasse 7-9, 50226, Frechen, Germany
Tel.: (49) 222684100
Web Site: http://www.vollmar.de
Sales Range: $50-74.9 Million
Emp.: 180
Candle Mfr
N.A.I.C.S.: 339999

suki.international GmbH (1)
Suki-Strasse 1, 54526, Landscheid, Germany
Tel.: (49) 6575 710
Web Site: http://www.suki.com
Sales Range: $75-99.9 Million
Emp.: 450
Tool Packaging & Display Product Mfr
N.A.I.C.S.: 337215
Sebastian Laus *(Mng Dir)*

Subsidiary (Non-US):

Suki International GesmbH (2)
1/E1/11 on Concordepark, 2320, Schwechat, Austria
Tel.: (43) 17079860
Web Site: http://www.suki.at
Emp.: 11
Hardware Merchant Whslr
N.A.I.C.S.: 423710
Jens Stilling *(Mgr)*

SERAKU CO., LTD.
6F Nishishinjuku Prime Square Bldg 7525 Nishishinjuku, Shinjuku-Ku, Tokyo, 160-0023, Japan

Tel.: (81) 332272321
Web Site: https://www.seraku.co.jp
6199—(TKS)
Rev.: $138,214,620
Assets: $74,963,440
Liabilities: $26,683,800
Net Worth: $48,279,640
Earnings: $9,796,500
Emp.: 3,387
Fiscal Year-end: 08/31/24
Information Technology Consulting Services
N.A.I.C.S.: 541512
Tatsumi Miyazaki *(CEO & Gen Mgr-Sls Div)*

Subsidiaries:

SERAKU Business Solutions Co., Ltd. (1)
Nishi-Shinjuku Prime Square 6F 7-5-25, Nishi-Shinjuku Shinjuku-ku, Tokyo, 160-0023, Japan
Tel.: (81) 366983737
Web Site: https://www.bs-seraku.co.jp
Information & Communication Technology Services
N.A.I.C.S.: 541512

SERAPHIM CAPITAL (GENERAL PARTNER) LLP
The Clubhouse 11-14 Grafton Street, London, W1S 4EW, United Kingdom
Tel.: (44) 203 674 2805 UK
Web Site: http://www.seraphimcapital.co.uk
Venture Capital Investment Firm
N.A.I.C.S.: 523999
Kit Hunter Gordon *(Chm & Mng Partner)*

SERAPHINE GROUP PLC
2nd Floor 265 Tottenham Court Road, London, W1T 7RQ, United Kingdom UK
Web Site: https://www.seraphine.com
Year Founded: 2002
BUMP—(LSE)
Rev.: $62,477,617
Assets: $63,535,948
Liabilities: $35,855,738
Net Worth: $27,680,210
Earnings: ($46,054,640)
Emp.: 81
Fiscal Year-end: 04/30/22
Medical Product Distr
N.A.I.C.S.: 423450
Lee Williams *(CFO)*

SERBA DINAMIK HOLDINGS BERHAD
Menara Serba Dinamik Presint 3 4 Persiaran Perbandaran Seksyen 14, 40000, Shah Alam, Selangor Darul Ehsan, Malaysia
Tel.: (60) 355166100 MY
Web Site: http://www.e-serbadk.com
Year Founded: 1993
5279—(KLS)
Rev.: $1,101,270,055
Assets: $1,560,731,672
Liabilities: $967,400,438
Net Worth: $593,331,234
Earnings: $121,099,506
Emp.: 1,725
Fiscal Year-end: 12/31/19
Engineering Solution Provider
N.A.I.C.S.: 541330
Muhammad Abdul Karim Abdullah *(CEO & Mng Dir-Grp)*

Subsidiaries:

KB Engineering Coating Sdn. Bhd. (1)
No 22 Jalan TS 6/9, Taman Industri Subang, 47510, Subang Jaya, Selangor, Malaysia
Tel.: (60) 35 879 8762
Web Site: https://www.kbengineering.com.my
Protective Coating Component Distr
N.A.I.C.S.: 424950

Materials Technology Education Sdn. Bhd. (1)
13-2 Pusat Dagangan Shah Alam Lot 13 Persiaran Damai Seksyen 11, 40100, Shah Alam, Selangor, Malaysia
Web Site: https://www.mte.com.my
Education Training Services
N.A.I.C.S.: 611710

Quantum Offshore Limited (1)
Tregoniggie Industrial Estate Cornwall, Falmouth, TR11 4SN, United Kingdom
Tel.: (44) 1326377705
Web Site: http://www.quantumoffshore.co.uk
Oil & Gas Equipment Mfr
N.A.I.C.S.: 333132
Leon Whotton *(Project Engr)*

Quantum Pump Systems Limited (1)
Kirkhill Industrial Estate Dyce, Aberdeen, AB21 0EU, United Kingdom
Tel.: (44) 122 472 4478
Web Site: https://www.quantum-pumps.com
Fire Pump Mfr
N.A.I.C.S.: 333996

Wellahead Engineering Limited (1)
Kirkhill Drive Dyce, Kirkhill Industrial Estate, Aberdeen, AB21 0EU, United Kingdom
Tel.: (44) 122 472 4478
Web Site: https://www.wellaheadengineering.com
Precision Turned Product Mfr & Distr
N.A.I.C.S.: 332721
John Stevenson *(Mgr-Operations-Sales)*

SERCO GROUP PLC
Serco House 16 Bartley Wood Business Park, Bartley Way, Hook, RG27 9UY, Hampshire, United Kingdom
Tel.: (44) 1256745900 UK
Web Site: https://www.serco.com
Year Founded: 1929
SCGPY—(OTCIQ)
Rev.: $5,461,203,000
Assets: $3,312,615,900
Liabilities: $2,072,342,250
Net Worth: $1,240,273,650
Earnings: $172,243,500
Fiscal Year-end: 12/31/22
Holding Company; Engineering & Business Support Services
N.A.I.C.S.: 551112
Mark Irwin *(CEO-Asia Pacific)*

Subsidiaries:

Serco Australia Pty Limited (1)
Level 10 90 Arthur Street, North Sydney, 2060, NSW, Australia
Tel.: (61) 299649733
Web Site: http://www.serco-ap.com.au
Facilities Management & Support Services
N.A.I.C.S.: 561210

Serco Belgium S.A. (1)
Parc Serenitas Av Edmond Van Niewenhuyse 6, Parc Serenitas, 1160, Brussels, Belgium
Tel.: (32) 27745360
Sales Range: $25-49.9 Million
Emp.: 25
Information & Communication Technology Consulting Services
N.A.I.C.S.: 541512
Alain Istace *(Mgr-Contract)*

Serco DES, Inc. (1)
5000 Yonge St Ste 1402, North York, M2N 7E9, ON, Canada
Tel.: (416) 225-3788
Web Site: http://www.serco-des.ca
Driver Examination & License Issuing Services
N.A.I.C.S.: 611692

Serco Facilities Management B.V. (1)
Ambachtsweg 20a, 2222 AL, Katwijk aan Zee, South Holland, Netherlands
Tel.: (31) 714016070

Sales Range: $25-49.9 Million
Emp.: 12
Facilities Management Services
N.A.I.C.S.: 561210
Michael Alner *(Principal)*

Serco Gestion de Negocios SL (1)
Calle Valle Del Roncal 12 - Plt 2 Oficina 5, Las Rozas De Madrid, 28232, Madrid, Spain
Tel.: (34) 916266231
Sales Range: $25-49.9 Million
Emp.: 21
Facilities Management Services
N.A.I.C.S.: 561210

Serco Group (HK) Limited (1)
1101 Sino Plaza 255 Gloucester Road, Causeway Bay, China (Hong Kong)
Tel.: (852) 29070118
Web Site: http://www.serco-hk.com
Sales Range: $25-49.9 Million
Emp.: 20
Facilities Management Services
N.A.I.C.S.: 561210

Serco Group Pty Limited (1)
Level 24 60 Margaret Street, Sydney, 2000, NSW, Australia
Tel.: (61) 299649733
Building Construction Services
N.A.I.C.S.: 541330

Serco Leisure Operating Limited (1)
7 Merus Court Meridian Business Park, Leicester, LE19 1RJ, Leicestershire, United Kingdom
Tel.: (44) 1162407500
Web Site: http://www.serco.com
Sales Range: $25-49.9 Million
Emp.: 100
Leisure Facilities Management Services
N.A.I.C.S.: 561210

Serco Nederland B.V. (1)
Kapteynstraat 1, 2201 BB, Noordwijk, Netherlands
Tel.: (31) 207083242
Building Construction Services
N.A.I.C.S.: 541330
Martijn Jordans *(Mgr-Fin)*

Serco S.p.A. (1)
Via Sciadonna 24/26, 00044, Frascati, Rome, Italy
Tel.: (39) 0698354400
Web Site: http://www.serco.it
Sales Range: $25-49.9 Million
Emp.: 220
Facilities Management Services
N.A.I.C.S.: 561210

Serco SARL (1)
Le Technoparc Gessein 15 R Louis Et Auguste Lumiere, 01630, Saint-Genis-Pouilly, Ain, France
Tel.: (33) 450991250
Web Site: http://www.serco.uk.com
Sales Range: $25-49.9 Million
Emp.: 80
Information & Communication Technology Consulting Services
N.A.I.C.S.: 541690

Serco Services GmbH (1)
Lise-Meitner-Strasse 10, 64293, Darmstadt, Germany
Tel.: (49) 6151812780
Building Construction Services
N.A.I.C.S.: 541330

Serco Services Ireland Limited (1)
Unit 30 Airways Industrial Estate, Clonshaugh, Dublin, 17, Ireland
Tel.: (353) 18621541
Web Site: http://www.serco.com
Sales Range: $25-49.9 Million
Emp.: 22
Facilities Management Services
N.A.I.C.S.: 561210

Serco Solutions (1)
Laburnum House Laburnum Road, Bournville, Birmingham, B30 2BD, United Kingdom
Tel.: (44) 1214591155
Web Site: http://www.serco.com
Sales Range: $300-349.9 Million
Emp.: 2,260
IT, Application & Business Process Services & E-Business Solutions to Commercial & Public Sectors

N.A.I.C.S.: 541214

Serco, Inc. (1)
12930 Worldgate Dr Ste 600, Reston, VA 20170
Tel.: (703) 263-6000
Web Site: http://www.serco-na.com
Business Process Management & IT Services
N.A.I.C.S.: 561499
David J. Dacquino *(Chm)*

Subsidiary (Domestic):

Serco Services Inc. (2)
8000 Towers Crescent Dr Ste 1350, Vienna, VA 22182
Tel.: (706) 903-6996
Web Site: http://www.serco-na.com
Sales Range: $25-49.9 Million
Emp.: 200
Business Process Management & IT Services
N.A.I.C.S.: 561499

Whitney, Bradley & Brown, Inc. (2)
11790 Sunrise Valley Dr, Reston, VA 20191
Tel.: (703) 215-8614
Web Site: http://www.wbbinc.com
Analytical & Development Solution Services
N.A.I.C.S.: 611430

Subsidiary (Domestic):

BRTRC Federal Solutions, Inc. (3)
8521 Leesburg Pike Ste 500, Vienna, VA 22182
Tel.: (703) 204-9277
Web Site: https://w7th.com
Professional Services to Federal Government Agencies
N.A.I.C.S.: 541990
Terri Thomas *(CEO)*

Decisive Analytics Corporation (3)
1400 Crystal Dr Ste 1400, Arlington, VA 22202
Tel.: (703) 414-5001
Web Site: http://www.dac.us
Computer Systems Design & Related Services
N.A.I.C.S.: 541512
John Donnellon *(CEO)*

Serco-IAL Limited (1)
Abu Dhabi Islamic Bank Building Najda Street, PO Box 72484, Abu Dhabi, United Arab Emirates
Tel.: (971) 26335547
Sales Range: $125-149.9 Million
Emp.: 300
Air Traffic Control & Telecommunication Engineering Services
N.A.I.C.S.: 238210

SERCOMM CORPORATION
8F No 3-1 YuanQu St Nankang Software Park, Taipei, 115, Taiwan
Tel.: (886) 226553988
Web Site: https://www.sercomm.com
Year Founded: 1992
5388—(TAI)
Rev.: $2,046,649,355
Assets: $1,562,004,225
Liabilities: $1,129,807,178
Net Worth: $432,197,047
Earnings: $78,118,673
Emp.: 5,208
Fiscal Year-end: 12/31/23
Broadband & Wireless Networking Equipment Mfr
N.A.I.C.S.: 517112
Paul Por-Yuan Wang *(Bd of Dirs, Co-Founder & Chm)*

Subsidiaries:

Sercomm Deutschland GmbH (1)
Prinzenallee 7, 40549, Dusseldorf, Germany
Tel.: (49) 6943052122
IT Products Distr
N.A.I.C.S.: 423690

Sercomm France SARL (1)
1 rue de Stockholm, 75008, Paris, France
Tel.: (33) 177706303
IT Products Distr

SERCOMM CORPORATION

SerComm Corporation—(Continued)
N.A.I.C.S.: 423690

Sercomm Japan Corp. (1)
Tennozu First Tower 24F 2-2-4 Higashishi-nagawa, Shinagawa-Ku, Tokyo, 140-0002, Japan
Tel.: (81) 357963266
Web Site: https://www.sercomm.co.jp
IT Products Distr
N.A.I.C.S.: 423690

Sercomm Philippines Inc. (1)
Lot 15 Road 3 Carmelray Industrial Park CIP I Brgy. Canlubang Laguna, Calamba, Philippines
Tel.: (63) 495598190
Communication Equipment Mfr
N.A.I.C.S.: 334210

Sercomm Russia LLC (1)
Otradnaya Street 2B/9 3rd Floor, 127273, Moscow, Russia
Tel.: (7) 4957717276
IT Products Distr
N.A.I.C.S.: 423690

Sercomm USA Inc. (1)
42808 Christy St Ste 231, Fremont, CA 94538
Tel.: (510) 870-1598
IT Products Distr
N.A.I.C.S.: 423690

Sernet Technology Mexico S. de R.L. de C.V. (1)
Bahia de las Palmas 1 INT 2 Col Veronica Anzures alcaldia, Alcaldia Miguel Hidalgo, 11300, Mexico, Mexico
Tel.: (52) 5513156256
Communication Equipment Mfr
N.A.I.C.S.: 334210

Servercom (India) Private Limited (1)
B1/H3 Mohan Co-operative Industrial Area Mathura Road Block B, New Delhi, 110044, India
Tel.: (91) 1139595578
Communication Equipment Mfr
N.A.I.C.S.: 334210

Smart Trade Inc. (1)
12-19 Higashimine-cho, Ota-ku, Tokyo, 101-0047, Japan
Tel.: (81) 365554270
Web Site: https://smarttrade.co.jp
IT Products Distr
N.A.I.C.S.: 423690

Subsidiary (Non-US):

Dwnet Technology (Suzhou) Limited (2)
No 26 Xinghai Street, Suzhou Industrial Park, Jiangsu, China
Tel.: (86) 51267615551
IT Products Distr
N.A.I.C.S.: 423690

SERDIKA PROPERTIES REIT
19 Karnigradska street, Sofia, 1000, Bulgaria
Tel.: (359) 29320040
Web Site: http://www.serdicaproperties.bg
Year Founded: 2006
SPRO—(BUL)
Sales Range: Less than $1 Million
Real Estate Investment Services
N.A.I.C.S.: 531210
Desislava Hristova Toteva (Exec Dir)

SERENDIB LAND PLC
Level 4 No 464A TB Jayah Mawatha, 10, Colombo, Sri Lanka
Tel.: (94) 112332155
Year Founded: 1980
SLND.N0000—(COL)
Rev.: $82,763
Assets: $2,397,019
Liabilities: $374,718
Net Worth: $2,022,301
Earnings: $88,420
Fiscal Year-end: 03/31/23

Commercial Property Leasing Services
N.A.I.C.S.: 531120
J. M. Swaminathan (Chm)

SERENDIPITY CAPITAL ACQUISITION CORP.
Level 11 Asia Square Tower 2 12 Marina View, Singapore, 018961, Singapore
Tel.: (65) 6678 6680   Ky
Year Founded: 2021
SCAC.U—(NYSE)
Investment Services
N.A.I.C.S.: 523999
Stephen Roder (Chm)

SERES GROUP CO., LTD.
No 7 Wuyunhu Road Shapingba District, Chongqing, 400033, China
Tel.: (86) 2365155666   CN
Web Site: https://seres.cn
Year Founded: 1986
601127—(SHG)
Rev.: $5,048,163,069
Assets: $7,217,559,288
Liabilities: $6,203,482,348
Net Worth: $1,014,076,941
Earnings: ($345,026,351)
Emp.: 10,000
Fiscal Year-end: 12/31/23
Automobile Mfr
N.A.I.C.S.: 336310
Zhang Xinghai (Chm)

Subsidiaries:

SF Motors, Inc. (1)
3303 Scott Blvd, Santa Clara, CA 95054
Tel.: (408) 617-7878
Vehicle Mfr
N.A.I.C.S.: 423110
John Zhang (Founder & CEO)

SERESCO SA
Avda de Filipinas 1 Bis 2nd floor, 28003, Madrid, Spain
Tel.: (34) 915989110
Web Site: https://www.seresco.es
Year Founded: 1969
SCO—(BAR)
Information Technology Services
N.A.I.C.S.: 541512
Carlos Suarez (CEO)

SERGE FERRARI SAS
Zone Industrielle, Saint Jean de Soudain, 38110, La Tour-du-Pin, France
Tel.: (33) 474974133
Web Site: https://www.sergeferrari.com
Year Founded: 1973
SEFER—(EUR)
Rev.: $239,876,500
Assets: $374,027,330
Liabilities: $249,598,020
Net Worth: $124,429,310
Earnings: $926,093
Fiscal Year-end: 12/31/20
Flexible Composite Materials Mfr
N.A.I.C.S.: 325998
Sebastien Ferrari (Chm & CEO)

Subsidiaries:

VERSEIDAG-INDUTEX GmbH (1)
Industriestrasse 56, 47803, Krefeld, Germany
Tel.: (49) 2151 876 0
Web Site: http://www.verseidag.de
Textile Products Mfr
N.A.I.C.S.: 314999
Markus Simon (Mng Dir)

SERGEN - SERVICOS GERAIS DE ENGENHARIA S.A.
Rua Visconde de Inhauma 50 - 10 andar, Centro, Rio de Janeiro, 20091-007, Brazil

Tel.: (55) 21 3981 2100
Web Site: http://www.sergen.com.br
Year Founded: 1961
Sales Range: $1-9.9 Million
Civil Engineering Construction Services
N.A.I.C.S.: 237310
Antonio de Padua Coimbra Tavares Pais (Dir-IR)

SERGIO TACCHINI FRANCE SA
10 Rue Galvani, 91300, Massy, Essonne, France
Tel.: (33) 164531570
Rev.: $38,900,000
Emp.: 58
N.A.I.C.S.: 424350
Jean Guerin (Gen Mgr)

SERGIOLIN SPA
Via Dell'artigianato 2, Ozzano dell'Emilia, 40064, Italy
Tel.: (39) 051796922
Web Site: http://www.sergiolin.it
Leather Goods Mfr
N.A.I.C.S.: 316990
Enrico Massari (CFO)

SERI INDUSTRIAL SPA
Piazza Oberdan 2/A, 20129, Milan, Italy
Tel.: (39) 0262231400
Web Site: http://www.krenergy.it
Year Founded: 1991
SERI—(ITA)
Sales Range: $150-199.9 Million
Emp.: 21
Holding Company; Renewable Energy
N.A.I.C.S.: 551112
Luca Lelli (Mgr-IR)

Subsidiaries:

F&F S.R.L. (1)
Via degli Artigiani 1, 26025, Pandino, CR, Italy
Tel.: (39) 0373980495
Web Site: https://www.f-f-srl.it
Air Filtration Services
N.A.I.C.S.: 238990

FIB S.P.A. (1)
Centro Az Quercete snc, 81016, San Potito Sannitico, CE, Italy
Tel.: (39) 08231442200
Web Site: https://faam.com
Electric Battery Mfr & Distr
N.A.I.C.S.: 335910

ICS Poland Sp. z o.o. (1)
UI Fabryczna 6/H/2, 05-077, Warsaw, Poland
Tel.: (48) 507323324
Web Site: https://ics-poland.eu
Plastic Material Mfr & Distr
N.A.I.C.S.: 325211

Seri Plast S.p.A. (1)
Centro Aziendale Quercete n a, 81016, San Potito Sannitico, CE, Italy
Tel.: (39) 08231442200
Web Site: https://www.seriplastsrl.it
Plastic Material Mfr & Distr
N.A.I.C.S.: 325211

SERIA CO., LTD.
2-38 Sobutsu, Ogaki, 503-0934, Gifu, Japan
Tel.: (81) 584898858
Web Site: https://www.seria-group.com
Year Founded: 1987
2782—(TKS)
Sales Range: Less than $1 Million
Emp.: 440
Retail Store Operator
N.A.I.C.S.: 459999
Eiji Kawai (Pres)

INTERNATIONAL PUBLIC

SERIAL SYSTEM LTD.
8 Ubi View No 05-01 Serial System Building, Singapore, 408554, Singapore
Tel.: (65) 65102408
Web Site: https://serialsystem.com
Year Founded: 1988
S69—(SES)
Rev.: $758,951,000
Assets: $399,478,000
Liabilities: $267,645,000
Net Worth: $131,833,000
Earnings: ($17,326,000)
Emp.: 800
Fiscal Year-end: 12/31/23
Semiconductor Component Distr
N.A.I.C.S.: 423690
Lawrence Ho (Pres-Serial Microelectronics HK Limited-Hong Kong & China)

Subsidiaries:

Achieva Technology Pte Ltd (1)
8 Ubi View #05-01, Singapore, 408554, Singapore   (100%)
Tel.: (65) 65102408
Web Site: www.serialdistribution.com
Computer & Computer Peripheral Equipment & Software Whslr
N.A.I.C.S.: 423430

Subsidiary (Non-US):

Achieva Technology Australia Pty. Ltd. (2)
New South Wales Unit 8 5 Dunlop Street, Strathfield, 2136, NSW, Australia
Tel.: (61) 297423288
Web Site: http://www.achieva.com.my
Computer & Computer Peripheral Equipment & Software Merchant Whslr
N.A.I.C.S.: 423430

Achieva Technology Sdn. Bhd (1)
2 03 2nd Floor Wisma Academy No 4A Jalan 19/1, 46300, Petaling Jaya, Selangor Darul Ehsan, Malaysia
Tel.: (60) 379551768
Web Site: https://www.achieva.com.my
Computer Peripheral Products Distr
N.A.I.C.S.: 423430

Newstone Technology (Shenzhen) Company Limited (1)
Room A1012-1013 Yousong Tech Mansion Donghuan 1st Road New Area, Longhua, Shenzhen, Guangdong, China
Tel.: (86) 75523240549
Electric Device Mfr
N.A.I.C.S.: 334419
Zhu William (Mgr)

Print-IQ Singapore Pte. Ltd. (1)
8 Ubi View Serial System Building 03-01, Singapore, 408554, Singapore
Tel.: (65) 61007746
Web Site: https://www.print-iq.com.sg
Printer Accessory Distr
N.A.I.C.S.: 424110
Chin Teng Wein Ong (Mng Partner)

SCE Enterprise Pte. Ltd. (1)
230 Victoria Street 06-02 Bugis Junction Towers, Singapore, 188024, Singapore
Tel.: (65) 66901550
Web Site: https://www.sce.org.sg
International Affair Services
N.A.I.C.S.: 928120
Seah Moon Ming (Chm)

Serial I-Tech (Far East) Pte. Ltd. (1)
11 Changi North Way, Singapore, 498796, Singapore
Tel.: (65) 62485333
Web Site: http://www.serial-itech.com
Emp.: 40
Consumer Electronics Distr
N.A.I.C.S.: 423620

Subsidiary (Non-US):

GSH Distribution (Cambodia) Pte. Ltd. (2)
Unit 2 1st Floor Mao Tse Tong Blvd Intercontinenetal Hotel Complex B, Sangkat Tomnoubteouk Khan Chamkamon, Phnom

Penh, Cambodia
Tel.: (855) 23 424 042
Electronic Products Sales
N.A.I.C.S.: 423620

JEL Trading (Bangladesh) Ltd. (2)
34 Kemal Ataturk Avenue 1st Floor West Side Awal Centre, Banani C/A, Dhaka, 1213, Bangladesh
Tel.: (880) 288 61271
Consumer Electronics Distr
N.A.I.C.S.: 423620

Serial I-Tech (Middle East) Pte. Ltd. (2)
RA08NB02 Jebel Ali Free Zone, PO Box 17470, Dubai, United Arab Emirates
Tel.: (971) 48861350
Emp.: 9
Consumer Electronic Products Distr
N.A.I.C.S.: 423620
Yeo Csuenseng *(Mgr)*

Serial Microelectronics (Beijing) Co., Ltd. (1)
Floor 9 Boya C-Center Building 11 Life Science Park Beiqing Road, Changping District, Beijing, China
Tel.: (86) 1052801437
Semiconductor Equipment Mfr
N.A.I.C.S.: 333242

Serial Microelectronics (Shenzhen) Co., Ltd. (1)
Room 513-525 Building B3 Futian Plaza No 3 Shihua Road, Futian Free Trade Zone Futian District, Shenzhen, 518038, China
Tel.: (86) 75526935923
Semiconductor Equipment Mfr
N.A.I.C.S.: 333242

Serial Microelectronics Inc. (1)
3B No 199 Ruihu St, Nei Hu, Taipei, 114, Taiwan
Tel.: (886) 227955333
Web Site: https://www.serialsystem.com
Sales Range: $50-74.9 Million
Emp.: 53
Semiconductor Distr
N.A.I.C.S.: 423690

Serial Microelectronics Pte Ltd (1)
8 Ubi View 04-01 Serial System Building, Singapore, 408554, Singapore
Tel.: (65) 65102408
Web Site: http://www.serialsytem.com.sg
Sales Range: $25-49.9 Million
Emp.: 50
Electronic Components Distr
N.A.I.C.S.: 423690
Ng Teck Cheng *(Sr VP-Ops & Asset Mgmt)*

Subsidiary (Non-US):

Serial Microelectronics (HK) Limited (2)
Room 601 02 6/6F 909 Cheung Sha Wan Road, Kowloon, China (Hong Kong)
Tel.: (852) 27908220
Web Site: http://www.serialsystem.com
Electronic Components Distr
N.A.I.C.S.: 423690

Serial Microelectronics Korea Limited (2)
5F Dongsan Building 890-38 Daechi-Dong, Gangnam-Gu, Seoul, 135-280, Korea (South)
Tel.: (82) 552896623
Web Site: http://www.serialsystem.com
Electronic Components Distr
N.A.I.C.S.: 423690

Subsidiary (Domestic):

Bona Technology Inc. (3)
5F Dongsan Building 890-38 Daechi-Dong, Gangnam-Gu, Seoul, Korea (South)
Tel.: (82) 5 788 44 44
Sales Range: $50-74.9 Million
Emp.: 10
Semiconductor Distr
N.A.I.C.S.: 423690

Subsidiary (Non-US):

Unitron Tech Co., Limited (2)
5F Dongsan Building 890-38 Daechi-Dong, Gangnam-Gu, Seoul, 135-280, Korea (South)
Tel.: (82) 2 573 6800
Web Site: http://www.serialsystem.com
Sales Range: $25-49.9 Million
Emp.: 15
Electronic Components Distr
N.A.I.C.S.: 423690

Serial Microelectronics Sdn. Bhd. (1)
No 14 Jalan Sultan Azlan Shah, 11700, Gelugor, Penang, Malaysia
Tel.: (60) 46570204
Semiconductor Equipment Mfr
N.A.I.C.S.: 333242

Serial Multivision Pte Ltd (1)
8 Ubi View 05-01 Serial System Building, Singapore, 408554, Singapore
Tel.: (65) 65102408
Web Site: https://www.serialmultivision.com
Sales Range: $25-49.9 Million
Outdoor Media Consulting Services
N.A.I.C.S.: 541850

SerialTec (Japan) Co., Ltd. (1)
3F Iwamotocho TUC Building 2-16-5 Iwamotocho, Chiyoda-Ku, Tokyo, 101-0032, Japan
Tel.: (81) 5088818639
Web Site: https://www.serial-tec.com
Electronic Device Distr
N.A.I.C.S.: 423690

URG Pte. Ltd. (1)
8 Ubi View 04-01 Serial System Building, Singapore, 408554, Singapore
Tel.: (65) 65102408
Web Site: https://www.unitedretailersgroup.com
Logistic Services
N.A.I.C.S.: 488510

SERICA ENERGY PLC
72 Welbeck Street 4th Floor, London, W1G 0AY, United Kingdom
Tel.: (44) 2074877300
Web Site: https://www.serica-energy.com
Year Founded: 2004
SQZ—(AIM)
Rev.: $1,025,527,645
Assets: $1,088,591,265
Liabilities: $572,655,895
Net Worth: $515,935,370
Earnings: $224,433,224
Emp.: 175
Fiscal Year-end: 12/31/22
Oil & Gas Exploration Services
N.A.I.C.S.: 211120
Antony Craven Walker *(Chm)*

Subsidiaries:

Serica Energy Corporation (1)
48 George Street, London, W1U 7DY, United Kingdom
Tel.: (44) 207 487 7300
Web Site: https://www.serica-energy.com
Sales Range: $50-74.9 Million
Emp.: 152
Oil & Gas Exploration Services
N.A.I.C.S.: 211120

Serica Holdings UK Ltd (1)
52 George St, London, W1U 7EI, United Kingdom
Tel.: (44) 2074877300
Sales Range: $50-74.9 Million
Oil & Gas Exploration Services
N.A.I.C.S.: 211120

Subsidiary (Domestic):

Serica Energy (UK) Ltd (2)
52 George Street, London, W1U 7EA, United Kingdom
Tel.: (44) 2074877300
Sales Range: $50-74.9 Million
Oil & Gas Exploration Services
N.A.I.C.S.: 211120
Paul Ellis *(CEO)*

SERIM B&G CO., LTD.
154-51 Oseongbuk-ro Oseongmyeon, Pyeongtaek, Gyeonggi-do, Korea (South)
Tel.: (82) 316849935

Web Site: https://www.serimbng.co.kr
Year Founded: 2003
340440—(KRS)
Rev.: $41,332,830
Assets: $36,035,995
Liabilities: $13,046,443
Net Worth: $22,989,553
Earnings: $1,729,951
Emp.: 83
Fiscal Year-end: 12/31/22
Packaged Food Mfr
N.A.I.C.S.: 327213
Na Sang Soo *(CEO)*

SERIPLAST SA
25 Rue De Tamas, 01100, Oyonnax, Ain, France
Tel.: (33) 474817060
Web Site: http://www.seriplast.fr
Rev.: $12,800,000
Emp.: 113
Plastics Product Mfr
N.A.I.C.S.: 326199
Danielle Tartaglione *(Mgr-Comml)*

SERIPRESS
18 Ave De Romans, 38160, Saint-Marcellin, Isere, France
Tel.: (33) 476366115
Web Site: http://www.seripress.com
Rev.: $10,400,000
Emp.: 35
Mfr of Heat Transfer Designs
N.A.I.C.S.: 541430
Victor Tomas *(Gen Mgr)*

SERKO LIMITED
Level 1 125 The Strand, Parnell, Auckland, 1010, New Zealand
Tel.: (64) 93094754 NZ
Web Site: https://www.serko.com
Year Founded: 1994
SKO—(NZX)
Rev.: $28,723,086
Assets: $84,279,904
Liabilities: $8,962,919
Net Worth: $75,316,986
Earnings: ($18,265,550)
Emp.: 364
Fiscal Year-end: 03/31/23
Software Development Services
N.A.I.C.S.: 513210
Simon Botherway *(Chm)*

SERMA TECHNOLOGIES SA
14 rue Galilee, CS 10055, 33600, Pessac, Gironde, France
Tel.: (33) 5 57 26 08 88
Web Site: http://www.serma-technologies.com
Year Founded: 1991
ALSER—(EUR)
Sales Range: $75-99.9 Million
Emp.: 150
Engineering Consulting Services
N.A.I.C.S.: 541330
Philippe Berlie *(Chm-Exec Bd)*

SERMATI
763 Avenue Robert Destic, PO Box 10, 46400, Saint-Cere, France
Tel.: (33) 565380380
Web Site: http://www.sermati.com
Year Founded: 1949
Rev.: $22,100,000
Emp.: 210
Industrial Inspection Tool Mfr
N.A.I.C.S.: 334513
Xavier Mielvaque *(Mgr-Publication)*

Subsidiaries:

SERMATI Canada Inc. (1)
1200 Ave McGill College 1100, Montreal, H3B 4G7, QC, Canada
Tel.: (514) 735-7333
Automobile Parts Distr
N.A.I.C.S.: 423120

SERMES DISTRIBUTION
14 Rue Des Freres Eberts, 67100, Strasbourg, Bas Rhin, France
Tel.: (33) 388407200
Web Site: http://www.sermes.fr
Sales Range: $10-24.9 Million
Emp.: 29
Electrical Products Systems Sales & Business Consulting
N.A.I.C.S.: 423620
Pierre Schmittheisler *(Pres)*

SERMSANG POWER CORPORATION PLC
325/14 Lanlaung Rd Mahanak Square, Dusit, Bangkok, 10300, Thailand
Tel.: (66) 26280991
Web Site: https://www.sermsang.com
Year Founded: 2010
SSP—(THA)
Rev.: $91,156,966
Assets: $614,991,050
Liabilities: $367,826,597
Net Worth: $247,164,453
Earnings: $24,244,270
Emp.: 63
Fiscal Year-end: 12/31/23
Solar Power Generation Services
N.A.I.C.S.: 221114
Varut Tummavaranukub *(CEO)*

Subsidiaries:

Sermsang Infinite Company Limited (1)
325/14 Lanlaung Rd Mahanak Square, Dusit, Bangkok, 10300, Thailand
Tel.: (66) 262809912
Web Site: https://www.sermsanginfinite.com
Solar Panels Installation Services
N.A.I.C.S.: 221114

SERN KOU RESOURCES BERHAD
Lot PTD 6019 Lot 8804 Jalan Perindustrian, 1 Kawasan Perindustrian Bukit Bakri Mukim Bakri, 84200, Muar, Johor, Malaysia
Tel.: (60) 69865562
Web Site: https://www.sernkou.com
SERNKOU—(KLS)
Rev.: $80,556,979
Assets: $73,310,227
Liabilities: $23,193,288
Net Worth: $50,116,939
Earnings: $265,134
Emp.: 671
Fiscal Year-end: 06/30/23
Furniture Mfr
N.A.I.C.S.: 337121
Peng Sian Chua *(Mng Dir)*

Subsidiaries:

S.K. Furniture Sdn. Bhd. (1)
No 15 Tingkat Bawah Jalan Sinar Bakri 2 Pusat Perniagaan Sinar Bakri, Bukit Bakri, 84200, Muar, Malaysia
Tel.: (60) 126656689
Web Site: https://skfurniture.com.my
Home Furniture Mfr & Distr
N.A.I.C.S.: 337121

SERNEKE GROUP AB
Kvarnbergsgatan 2, 411 05, Gothenburg, Sweden
Tel.: (46) 317129700
Web Site: http://www.serneke.se
Year Founded: 2002
SRNKE.B—(OMX)
Rev.: $838,811,680
Assets: $731,503,360
Liabilities: $493,935,680
Net Worth: $237,567,680
Earnings: ($43,704,640)
Emp.: 1,184
Fiscal Year-end: 12/31/20
Construction Engineering Services

SERNEKE GROUP AB

Serneke Group AB—(Continued)
N.A.I.C.S.: 541330
Neil Wood *(CFO-Interim)*

Subsidiaries:

Serneke International AB (1)
Kvarnbergsgatan 2, 411 05, Gothenburg, Sweden
Tel.: (46) 317129700
Construction Services
N.A.I.C.S.: 238120

SERNOVA CORP.
700 Collip Circle Ste 114, London, N6G 4X8, ON, Canada
Tel.: (519) 858-5184 Ca
Web Site: https://www.sernova.com
Year Founded: 1998
SVA—(TSX)
Rev.: $451,599
Assets: $41,057,904
Liabilities: $3,814,598
Net Worth: $37,243,306
Earnings: ($19,103,697)
Emp.: 25
Fiscal Year-end: 10/31/22
Biotechnology Pharmaceutical Research Services
N.A.I.C.S.: 541714
Philip M. Toleikis *(Pres & CEO)*

Subsidiaries:

Sernova (US) Corp. (1)

SERODUS ASA
c/o Arnstein Endresen Bygdoy Alle 89, N-0268, Oslo, Norway
Tel.: (47) 959 34 199
Web Site: http://www.serodus.com
Rev.: $9,879
Assets: $2,558,387
Liabilities: $525,768
Net Worth: $2,032,619
Earnings: ($2,853,593)
Emp.: 3
Fiscal Year-end: 12/31/19
Pharmaceuticals Mfr
N.A.I.C.S.: 325412
Eva Steiness *(CEO)*

SEROJA INVESTMENTS LIMITED
15 Scotts Rd Thong Teck Building 08-05, Singapore, 228218, Singapore
Tel.: (65) 64384221
Web Site: http://seroja.com.sg
Year Founded: 1983
IW5—(SES)
Assets: $1,054,000
Liabilities: $45,000
Net Worth: $1,009,000
Earnings: ($442,000)
Emp.: 102
Fiscal Year-end: 12/31/22
Marine Cargo & Coal Transportation Services
N.A.I.C.S.: 488320
Edwin Soeryadjaya *(Chm)*

SERONICS CO., LTD.
36 Suchul-daero 9 gil, Gumi, 730-902, Gyeongsangbuk, Korea (South)
Tel.: (82) 544637945
Web Site: http://www.seronics.co.kr
Year Founded: 1968
042600—(KRS)
Rev.: $167,717,560
Assets: $267,102,320
Liabilities: $110,351,530
Net Worth: $156,750,790
Earnings: $69,096,329
Emp.: 65
Fiscal Year-end: 12/31/22
Electronic Components Mfr
N.A.I.C.S.: 334419
Jae-Hong Hur *(CEO)*

SEROYAL INTERNATIONAL INC.
490 Elgin Mills Road E, Richmond Hill, L4C 0L8, ON, Canada
Tel.: (905) 508-2050 ON
Web Site: http://www.seroyal.com
Year Founded: 1984
Homeopathic Pharmaceutical & Botanical Products Mfr
N.A.I.C.S.: 325411

SERRA ENERGY METALS CORP.
907 - 1030 West Georgia St, Vancouver, V6E 2Y3, BC, Canada
Tel.: (604) 288-8082
Web Site: https://serrametals.com
SEEM—(CNSX)
Assets: $10,718,079
Liabilities: $257,030
Net Worth: $10,461,049
Earnings: ($2,002,822)
Fiscal Year-end: 04/30/21
Mineral Exploration Services
N.A.I.C.S.: 213115
Patrick Donnelly *(Pres)*

SERRANDER COMPANY
Styrmansgatan 2, 11454, Stockholm, Sweden
Tel.: (46) 8661 1440
Web Site: http://www.serrander.se
Year Founded: 1990
Rev.: $10,000,000
Emp.: 8
N.A.I.C.S.: 541810
Oyvind Serrander *(Mng Dir)*

SERRANO RESOURCES LTD.
401 West Georgia Street Suite 2020, Vancouver, V6B 5A1, BC, Canada
Tel.: (604) 684-6264
Oil & Gas Exploration Services
N.A.I.C.S.: 213112
Byron Coulthard *(CEO)*

SERRUYA PRIVATE EQUITY INC.
210 Shields Court, Markham, L3R 8V2, ON, Canada
Tel.: (905) 479-8762
Web Site: http://www.serruyaprivateequity.com
Privater Equity Firm
N.A.I.C.S.: 523999
Michael Serruya *(Chm & CEO)*

SERSOL BERHAD
28 Jalan Canggih 1 Taman Perindustrian Cemerlang, 81800, Johor, Malaysia
Tel.: (60) 78611112 MY
Web Site: https://www.sersol.com.my
Year Founded: 2002
0055—(KLS)
Rev.: $4,040,162
Assets: $6,456,418
Liabilities: $942,299
Net Worth: $5,514,120
Earnings: ($3,303,887)
Fiscal Year-end: 12/31/22
Painting Contractor Services
N.A.I.C.S.: 238160
Fie Jen Tan *(Mng Dir-Acting)*

Subsidiaries:

Multi Square Sdn. Bhd. (1)
No 28 Jalan Canggih 1, Taman Perindustrian Cemerlang, 81800, Ulu Tiram, Johor, Malaysia
Tel.: (60) 78611112
Web Site: http://www.multisquare.com
Furniture Mfr
N.A.I.C.S.: 337127

Subsidiary (Non-US):

Multi Square Coating (Thailand) Co., Ltd. (2)
19/37 MOO 10 Tambul Klong Neung, Klong Luang, Amphur Muang, 12120, Pathhumthani, Thailand
Tel.: (66) 25296240
Furniture Mfr
N.A.I.C.S.: 337127

SERSTECH AB
Aldermansgatan 13, 227 64, Lund, Sweden
Tel.: (46) 46255112
Web Site: https://www.serstech.com
SERT—(OMX)
Rev.: $2,099,057
Assets: $4,921,558
Liabilities: $2,428,653
Net Worth: $2,492,905
Earnings: ($2,769,208)
Emp.: 22
Fiscal Year-end: 12/31/22
Spectrometer Mfr
N.A.I.C.S.: 334516
Thomas Pileby *(Chm)*

SERT-MST PLC.
Tetron Point William Nadin Way, Swadlincote, DE11 0BB, Derbyshire, United Kingdom
Tel.: (44) 84 5226 5000
Web Site: http://www.sert-mst.com
Year Founded: 2002
Sales Range: $150-199.9 Million
Emp.: 123
Toiletries Whslr
N.A.I.C.S.: 424210
Sabir Tayub *(CEO)*

SERTEC GROUP HOLDINGS LTD.
Wincaster House Highway Point Gorsey Lane, Birmingham, B46 1JU, West Midlands, United Kingdom
Tel.: (44) 1675436600
Web Site: http://www.sertec.co.uk
Year Founded: 1962
Sales Range: $125-149.9 Million
Emp.: 564
Automobile Parts Mfr
N.A.I.C.S.: 336390
Grant Adams *(CEO)*

Subsidiaries:

Presslite Ltd (1)
Essex Works Holborn Hill, Aston, Birmingham, B6 7QT, United Kingdom
Tel.: (44) 1213271428
Automobile Parts Mfr
N.A.I.C.S.: 336390

Sertec China (1)
Chang Qing south road No 303 Diwang Plaza Room 2102, Changan Town 4 areas, Dongguan, Guangdong, China
Tel.: (86) 75583457851
Automobile Parts Mfr
N.A.I.C.S.: 336390

Sertec Tube & Pressings Limited (1)
Redfern Parkway, Tyseley, Birmingham, B11 2BF, United Kingdom
Tel.: (44) 1217060330
Automobile Parts Mfr
N.A.I.C.S.: 336390

SERUMWERK BERNBURG AG
Hallesche Landstrasse 105 b, 06406, Bernburg, Germany
Tel.: (49) 3471860420
Web Site: http://www.serumwerk.com
Year Founded: 1954
Sales Range: $75-99.9 Million
Emp.: 268
Medicinal Products & Devices Mfr & Distr
N.A.I.C.S.: 423450
Frank Kilian *(CEO)*

INTERNATIONAL PUBLIC

SERVAL SAS
La Creuse, BP 4, Sainte-Eanne, 79800, La Mothe-Saint-Heray, France
Tel.: (33) 549062829
Web Site: http://www.serval.fr
Sales Range: $250-299.9 Million
Emp.: 200
Dairy Product Mfr & Milk Replacer Services
N.A.I.C.S.: 311119
Gerard Lemaitre *(Chm)*

Subsidiaries:

Serval Canada Foods Ltd. (1)
303 Saint-Marc Street, Louiseville, J5V 2G2, QC, Canada
Tel.: (819) 228-5551
Web Site: http://www.servalcanada.com
Sales Range: $25-49.9 Million
Emp.: 26
Animal Food Product Mfr
N.A.I.C.S.: 311119
Yves Desaulniers *(Dir-Plant)*

Subsidiary (US):

NRV, Inc. (2)
N 8155 American St, Ixonia, WI 53036-0347
Tel.: (920) 261-7000
Web Site: http://www.nrvmilk.com
Sales Range: $10-24.9 Million
Producer of Dry Veal Feed Milk Replacer Supplier Mfr
N.A.I.C.S.: 311119
Duane Kleve *(Mng Dir)*

VTF QUEST (1)
38 bis bd du General Leclerc, 53100, Mayenne, France
Tel.: (33) 2 43 32 28 90
Dairy Products Distr
N.A.I.C.S.: 424430

Veau des Terroirs Bretons (1)
35 rue Marcelin Berthelot, ZI de Kerivin, 29600, Saint-Martin-des-Champs, France
Tel.: (33) 2 98 62 29 00
Web Site: http://www.serval.fr
Veal Calves Production & Sales
N.A.I.C.S.: 112990
Marcel Cann *(Chm)*

Veau des Terroirs de France (1)
BP 4, 79800, La Mothe-Saint-Heray, France
Tel.: (33) 549068728
Sales Range: $25-49.9 Million
Emp.: 100
Veal Calves Production & Sales
N.A.I.C.S.: 112990

SERVCORP LIMITED
Level 63 MLC Centre 19-29 Martin Place, Sydney, 2000, NSW, Australia
Tel.: (61) 292317500 AU
Web Site: http://www.servcorp.com.au
Year Founded: 1978
SRV—(ASX)
Rev.: $211,680,688
Assets: $450,289,127
Liabilities: $320,336,537
Net Worth: $129,952,590
Earnings: $26,067,040
Emp.: 674
Fiscal Year-end: 06/30/24
Executive Suite & Virtual Office Leasing Services
N.A.I.C.S.: 531120
Alfred George Moufarrige *(CEO, Founder & Mng Dir)*

Subsidiaries:

Servcorp Is Merkezi Isletmeciligi Limited Sirketi (1)
Tesvikiye Bostani Sok Orjin Apt No 15 Kat 5-6 Nisantasi, Istanbul, Türkiye
Tel.: (90) 2123101893
Information Technology Services
N.A.I.C.S.: 541512

Servcorp Marina Pte. Ltd. (1)
Level 39 Marina Bay Financial Centre

Tower 2 10 Marina Boulevard, Singapore, Singapore
Tel.: (65) 68186100
Web Site: https://www.servcorp.com.sg
Information Technology Services
N.A.I.C.S.: 541512

Servcorp Mayfair Limited (1)
Level 1 Devonshire House One Mayfair Place, London, United Kingdom
Tel.: (44) 2032057100
Web Site: https://www.servcorp.co.uk
Information Technology Services
N.A.I.C.S.: 541512

Servcorp Southbank Pty. Ltd. (1)
Level 2 1 Southbank Boulevard, Southbank, 3006, VIC, Australia
Tel.: (61) 399824500
Information Technology Services
N.A.I.C.S.: 541512

SERVERWORKS CO., LTD.
2nd Floor Iidabashi Masumoto Building 121 Agebacho, Shinjuku-ku, Tokyo, 162-0824, Japan
Tel.: (81) 355798029
Web Site:
  https://www.serverworks.co.jp
Year Founded: 2000
4434—(TKS)
Rev.: $195,045,900
Assets: $128,017,040
Liabilities: $52,388,010
Net Worth: $75,629,030
Earnings: $4,523,420
Emp.: 403
Fiscal Year-end: 02/29/24
Application Development Services
N.A.I.C.S.: 541511
Ryo Oishi (Pres)

SERVET GAYRIMENKUL YATIRIM ORTAKLIGI A.S.
Dikilitas Neighborhood Yenidogan Street 36/1 Sinpas Headquarters Fl 8, Besiktas, 34349, Istanbul, Turkiye
Tel.: (90) 2123105334
Web Site:
  https://www.servetgyo.com.tr
Year Founded: 1986
SRVGY—(IST)
Rev.: $33,387,828
Assets: $647,424,763
Liabilities: $129,069,106
Net Worth: $518,355,657
Earnings: $170,756,272
Fiscal Year-end: 12/31/23
Real Estate Investment Services
N.A.I.C.S.: 523999
Avni Celik (Chm)

SERVICE ALIMENTAIRE DESCO INC.
97 rue Prevost, Boisbriand, J7G 3A1, QC, Canada
Tel.: (450) 437-7182
Web Site:
  http://www.groupedesco.com
Rev.: $23,822,916
Emp.: 160
Meat & Poultry Products Mfr
N.A.I.C.S.: 424440
Guy Chevalier (Pres)

SERVICE FABRICS LIMITED
OffIslamabadice No 17 1st Floor Anique Arcade I-8Markaz, Islamabad, Pakistan
Tel.: (92) 514861780
SERF—(KAR)
Assets: $108,751
Liabilities: $1,417,369
Net Worth: ($1,308,617)
Earnings: ($13,947)
Emp.: 2
Fiscal Year-end: 06/30/20
Textile Mill Operator
N.A.I.C.S.: 314999

Aftab Ahmad Chaudhry (Chm)

SERVICE INDUSTRIES LIMITED
Servis House 2 Main Gulberg, Lahore, 54662, Pakistan
Tel.: (92) 4235751990 PK
Web Site:
  https://www.servisgroup.com
Year Founded: 1941
SRVI—(KAR)
Rev.: $193,575,587
Assets: $146,895,260
Liabilities: $107,070,693
Net Worth: $39,824,567
Earnings: $8,752,018
Emp.: 7,238
Fiscal Year-end: 12/31/19
Footwear Distr
N.A.I.C.S.: 424340
Chaudhary Ahmed Javed (Chm)

Subsidiaries:

Service Global Footwear Limited (1)
Servis House 2 Main Gulberg, Lahore, 54662, Pakistan
Tel.: (92) 42357519906
Web Site:
  https://www.serviceglobalfootwear.com
Footwear Mfr
N.A.I.C.S.: 316210
Hassan Javed (Chm & CEO)

Service Shoes Lanka (Private) Limited (1)
60B Ring Road Phase 2 Katukayake EPZ, Katunayake, Sri Lanka
Tel.: (94) 112253138
Web Site: https://www.ssl.lk
Footwear Mfr
N.A.I.C.S.: 316210

SERVICE INNOVATION GROUP
Denmark House The Broadway Staples Corner, London, WD17 1HP, United Kingdom
Tel.: (44) 2084576400 UK
Web Site: http://www.sigeurope.co.uk
Year Founded: 1980
Sales Range: $25-49.9 Million
Emp.: 100
Advertising Agencies
N.A.I.C.S.: 541810

SERVICE NEPTUN 2002 SA
Cladirea Serviciul Tehnic, Neptun, Constanta, Romania
Tel.: (40) 241701471
SECE—(BUC)
Rev.: $38,822
Assets: $1,682,118
Liabilities: $525,335
Net Worth: $1,156,783
Earnings: ($10,969)
Emp.: 1
Fiscal Year-end: 12/31/22
Textile Product Drycleaning Services
N.A.I.C.S.: 812320
Maria Durbac (Gen Mgr)

SERVICE STREAM LIMITED
357 Collins Street, Melbourne, 3000, VIC, Australia
Tel.: (61) 396778888
Web Site:
  https://www.servicestream.com.au
Year Founded: 1996
SSM—(ASX)
Rev.: $1,530,174,273
Assets: $700,159,586
Liabilities: $379,454,459
Net Worth: $320,705,127
Earnings: $21,566,506
Emp.: 5,200
Fiscal Year-end: 06/30/24
Telecommunication Industry Support Services
N.A.I.C.S.: 517810

Ashley Haynes (Exec Gen Mgr)
Subsidiaries:

AMRS (Aust) Pty Ltd (1)
11 Garden Blvd, Dingley, 3172, VIC, Australia
Tel.: (61) 395524600
Web Site: http://www.servicestream.com.au
Sales Range: $25-49.9 Million
Emp.: 20
Construction Engineering Services
N.A.I.C.S.: 541330
Leigh Mackender (Mgr)

Comdain Infrastructure Pty. Ltd. (1)
40 Willandra Drive, Epping, 3076, VIC, Australia
Tel.: (61) 38 405 0000
Web Site:
  https://www.comdaininfrastructure.com.au
Asset Management Services
N.A.I.C.S.: 523940

Service Stream Holdings Pty Ltd (1)
L 1 355 Spencer St, West Melbourne, Melbourne, 3003, VIC, Australia
Tel.: (61) 396778888
Sales Range: $75-99.9 Million
Emp.: 500
Construction Engineering Services
N.A.I.C.S.: 541330

Subsidiary (Domestic):

RADHAZ Consulting Pty Ltd. (2)
2/13 Compark Circuit 13 Compark Circuit, Mulgrave, 3170, VIC, Australia
Tel.: (61) 385695800
Web Site: https://www.radhaz.com.au
Sales Range: $25-49.9 Million
Emp.: 5
Electromagnetic Energy Management & Compliance Services
N.A.I.C.S.: 541618
Jo Olava (Gen Mgr)

Service Stream Communications Pty Ltd (2)
2 Coal Street, Silverwater, 2128, NSW, Australia
Tel.: (61) 287564100
Construction Engineering Services
N.A.I.C.S.: 541330

Subsidiary (Domestic):

Milcom Communications Pty Ltd (3)
Unit 12/1866 Princes Highway, Clayton, Melbourne, 3168, VIC, Australia
Tel.: (61) 130 036 9320
Web Site: https://milcom.edu.au
Computer Training Services
N.A.I.C.S.: 611420

Service Stream Infrastructure Services Pty Ltd (3)
L 4 357 Collins Street, West Melbourne, Melbourne, 3000, VIC, Australia
Tel.: (61) 396778888
Web Site: http://www.servicestream.com.au
Sales Range: $125-149.9 Million
Emp.: 500
Construction Engineering Services
N.A.I.C.S.: 237130

Service Stream Limited (3)
Level 4 357 Collins Street, St Leonards, Melbourne, 3000, VIC, Australia
Tel.: (61) 396778888
Web Site:
  https://www.servicestream.com.au
Sales Range: $25-49.9 Million
Emp.: 100
Telecommunication Structures Installation & Maintenance Services
N.A.I.C.S.: 517810

Subsidiary (Non-US):

TCI Renewables Ltd. (2)
Willow Court Minns Business Park 7 West Way, Oxford, OX2 0JB, United Kingdom
Tel.: (44) 1865261300
Web Site: http://www.tcirenewables.com
Sales Range: $25-49.9 Million
Emp.: 15
Renewable Energy Services
N.A.I.C.S.: 237130
Brett O'Connor (Co-Founder)

Service Stream Solutions Pty Ltd (1)
Level 3 355 Spencer Street, Melbourne, 3003, VIC, Australia
Tel.: (61) 396778888
Construction Engineering Services
N.A.I.C.S.: 541330

TechSafe Australia Pty. Ltd. (1)
Level 4 357 Collins Street, Melbourne, 3000, VIC, Australia
Tel.: (61) 39 677 8888
Web Site: https://www.techsafe.com.au
Electrical Testing Services
N.A.I.C.S.: 541380
Ashley Haynes (Mng Dir)

SERVICEPLAN AGENTURGRUPPE FUR INNOVATIVE KOMMUNIKATION GMBH & CO. KG
Brienner Strasse 45 AD, 80250, Munich, Germany
Tel.: (49) 89 20 50 20 De
Web Site: http://www.serviceplan.de
Year Founded: 1970
Sales Range: $150-199.9 Million
Emp.: 900
Advetising Agency
N.A.I.C.S.: 541810
Peter Haller (Mng Dir)

Subsidiaries:

Serviceplan Austria GmbH (1)
Gregor-Mendel-Str 50, 1190, Vienna, Austria
Tel.: (43) 1 26110 0
Web Site: http://www.serviceplan.at
Advertising Agency Services
N.A.I.C.S.: 541810
Birgit Schondorfer (Dir-Acct)

Serviceplan India Pvt. Ltd. (1)
DLF Cyber City Phase III Building No 9 Tower B 14th Floor, Gurgaon, 122 002, Haryana, India
Tel.: (91) 85 27 297 302
Web Site: http://www.serviceplan.in
Advertising Agency Services
N.A.I.C.S.: 541810
Andreas Wochenalt (Exec Dir-Creative)

Serviceplan Italia S.R.L. (1)
Via Solferino 40, 20121, Milan, Italy
Tel.: (39) 02 9929 7600
Web Site: http://www.serviceplan-group.it
Sales Range: $10-24.9 Million
Emp.: 60
Advetising Agency
N.A.I.C.S.: 541810
Stefania Siani (CEO & Chief Creative Officer)

Serviceplan Suisse AG (1)
Haus der Kommunikation Kirchenweg 8, 8008, Zurich, Switzerland
Tel.: (41) 44 446 21 21
Web Site: http://www.serviceplan.ch
Advertising Agency Services
N.A.I.C.S.: 541810
Manuela Brunner (Grp Dir-Acct)

SERVICEWARE SE
Kreisel 1 65510 Idstein, Bad Camberg, 65520, Limburg, Germany
Tel.: (49) 643494500
Web Site: https://serviceware-se.com
Year Founded: 1998
SJJ—(DEU)
Rev.: $101,036,270
Assets: $137,697,491
Liabilities: $86,638,354
Net Worth: $51,059,137
Earnings: ($4,353,372)
Emp.: 479
Fiscal Year-end: 11/30/23
Software Development Services
N.A.I.C.S.: 541511
Dirk K. Martin (Co-Founder, CEO & Mng Dir)

Subsidiaries:

Catenic AG (1)

SERVICEWARE SE

Serviceware SE—(Continued)
Hauptstrasse 1, 82008, Unterhaching, Germany
Tel.: (49) 89200018050
Software Development Services
N.A.I.C.S.: 541511
Dirk K. Martin (VP-Customer Svc & Logistics)

Cubus AG (1)
Bahnhofstrasse 29, 71083, Herrenberg, Germany
Tel.: (49) 703294510
Web Site: http://www.cubus.eu
Software Development Services
N.A.I.C.S.: 541511
Dirk Fleischmann (Dir)

Subsidiary (Non-US):

Cubus Schweiz GmbH (2)
Leutschenbachstrasse 95, 8050, Zurich, Switzerland
Tel.: (41) 443083612
Web Site: http://www.cubus-schweiz.ch
Business Management Consulting Services
N.A.I.C.S.: 541611

HelpLine GmbH (1)
Carl-Zeiss-Strasse 16, Bad Camberg, 65520, Weilburg, Germany
Tel.: (49) 6434930760
Software Development Services
N.A.I.C.S.: 541511
Alexander Becker (Mng Dir)

Subsidiary (Non-US):

HelpLine BV (2)
Dellaertweg 9 F, 2316 WZ, Leiden, Netherlands
Tel.: (31) 715232604
Software Development Services
N.A.I.C.S.: 541511
Roderick A. Schipper (Mng Dir)

HelpLine IT solutions GmbH (1)
Karl-Farkas-Gasse 22/ Top 1b/ 15, 1030, Vienna, Austria
Tel.: (43) 171541800
Software Development Services
N.A.I.C.S.: 541511

PMCS. HelpLine Software S.L. (1)
Gremi de Sabaters 21 2nd Floor-Office A21
Illes Balears, 07009, Palma de Mallorca, Spain
Tel.: (34) 912582853
Software Development Services
N.A.I.C.S.: 541511

Sabio GmbH (1)
Schutzenstr 5, 22761, Hamburg, Germany
Tel.: (49) 408519270
Web Site: https://www.getsabio.com
Computer Software Services
N.A.I.C.S.: 541511
Constantin Gaul (Mng Dir)

Serviceware SE UK Ltd. (1)
Building B Watchmoor Park Riverside Way, Camberley, GU15 3YL, Surrey, United Kingdom
Tel.: (44) 1276402345
Software Development Services
N.A.I.C.S.: 541511

Strategic Service Consulting GmbH (1)
Lennestrasse 3, 10785, Berlin, Germany
Tel.: (49) 64349450880
Web Site: https://www.strategic-sc.de
Management Consulting Services
N.A.I.C.S.: 541611

SERVICII TEHNICE COMUNALE SA

Str Praidului Nr 108B, 545 500, Sovata, Mures, Romania
Tel.: (40) 265 570 508
Web Site: http://www.stc-sovata.ro
Sales Range: $1-9.9 Million
Emp.: 96
Water & Sewer Treatment
N.A.I.C.S.: 221320

SERVICIOS & SOLUCIONES ELECTROMECANICOS S.A. DE C.V.

Paseo de la Reforma 155 Floor 1 Local B Col Lomas de Chapultepec, 1st Sec Del Miguel Hidalgo, Mexico, 11000, Mexico
Tel.: (52) 5552621900
Web Site: http://www.seselec.mx
Year Founded: 1979
Emp.: 105
Electrical & Industrial Infrastructure Services
N.A.I.C.S.: 238210
Jesus Franco (Dir Gen)

SERVICIOS CORPORATIVOS JAVER, S.A.B. DE C.V.

Av Juarez 1102 Pabellon M Piso 34 Colonia Centro, 64000, Monterrey, Nuevo Leon, Mexico
Tel.: (52) 8111336699
Web Site: https://www.ri.javer.com.mx
Year Founded: 1973
JAVER—(MEX)
Rev.: $537,741,174
Assets: $578,437,730
Liabilities: $412,878,867
Net Worth: $165,558,864
Earnings: $34,093,885
Fiscal Year-end: 12/31/23
Housing Construction Services
N.A.I.C.S.: 236117
Rene Martinez Martinez (CEO)

SERVIZI ITALIA SPA

Via S Pietro 59 B Castellina di, 43019, Soragna, Parma, Italy
Tel.: (39) 0524598511
Web Site: https://www.servizitaliagroup.com
Year Founded: 1986
SRI—(ITA)
Rev.: $294,974,118
Assets: $465,622,099
Liabilities: $319,970,031
Net Worth: $145,652,069
Earnings: $3,628,221
Emp.: 3,656
Fiscal Year-end: 12/31/20
Hospital Sanitation Services
N.A.I.C.S.: 812332
Ilaria Eugeniani (Vice Chm)

Subsidiaries:

Ankateks Turizm Insaat Tekstil Temizleme Sanayi ve Ticaret Ltd. (1)
Hurel 28 Cd No 4, Mamak, 06350, Ankara, Turkiye
Tel.: (90) 3126401280
Industrial Laundery Services
N.A.I.C.S.: 812320

Lavsim Higienizacao Textil S.A. (1)
Rodovia Raposo Tavares km 58 2, Sao Roque, 18131-220, SP, Brazil
Tel.: (55) 1147122299
Web Site: http://www.lavsim.com.br
Industrial Laundery Services
N.A.I.C.S.: 812320
Plinio Rodrigues (CEO)

Maxlav Lavanderia Especializada S.A. (1)
Av Vigatto 520-Vila Sao Francisco, Jaguariuna, 13820-000, SP, Brazil
Tel.: (55) 1938374656
Industrial Laundery Services
N.A.I.C.S.: 812320

SAS Sterilizasyon Servisleri A.S. (1)
Fulya Mahallesi Vefa Deresi Sokak No 4, Istanbul, Turkiye
Tel.: (90) 2122725200
Web Site: http://www.sassterilizasyon.com
Surgical Instrument Sterilization Services
N.A.I.C.S.: 812332

Shubhram Hospital Solutions Private Ltd. (1)
485-486 Phasell Barhi Textile Park, HSIIDC Industrial Area Barhi National Highway 1, Sonipat, 131101, Haryana, India
Tel.: (91) 1302345678
Web Site: http://www.shubhram.com
Industrial Laundery Services
N.A.I.C.S.: 812320
Parveen Rohilla (Mgr-Trng)

Vida Lavanderias Especializada S.A. (1)
Joaquim Justo da Silva 201, Jardim Villaca, Sao Roque, 18135-165, SP, Brazil
Tel.: (55) 1155551377
Industrial Laundery Services
N.A.I.C.S.: 812320

SERVOCA PLC

Audrey House 16-20 Ely Place, London, EC1N 6SN, United Kingdom
Tel.: (44) 207 747 3030
Web Site: http://www.servoca.com
Year Founded: 1991
Rev.: $100,493,776
Assets: $32,113,323
Liabilities: $13,332,803
Net Worth: $18,780,520
Earnings: $2,699,410
Emp.: 248
Fiscal Year-end: 09/30/17
Outsourced Business Services
N.A.I.C.S.: 561499
John Foley (Chm)

Subsidiaries:

Academics Limited (1)
4th Floor Arodene House 41-55 Perth Road, Ilford, IG2 6BX, Essex, United Kingdom
Tel.: (44) 2085183550
Web Site: http://www.academicsltd.co.uk
Sales Range: $75-99.9 Million
Teacher Recruitment Services
N.A.I.C.S.: 561311
Andy Church (CEO)

Global Medics Ltd. (1)
85 Uxbridge Road Ealing, London, W5 5TH, United Kingdom
Tel.: (44) 2085664111
Web Site: http://www.globalmedics.com
Sales Range: $25-49.9 Million
Emp.: 25
Medical Staffing Services
N.A.I.C.S.: 561320

Servoca Nursing & Care Limited (1)
Queensgate 121 Suffolk Street Queensway, Birmingham, B1 1LX, United Kingdom
Tel.: (44) 8453710223
Web Site: http://www.servocahealth.com
Medical Staff Recruitment Services
N.A.I.C.S.: 561311

The Locum Partnership Limited (1)
Suite T2 Bates Business Centre Church Road Harold Wood, Romford, RM3 0JA, Essex, United Kingdom
Tel.: (44) 8456801599
Web Site: http://www.thelocumpartnership.com
Medical Staff Recruitment Services
N.A.I.C.S.: 561311

Triple West Medical Limited (1)
87 Paine's Lane Pinner, London, HA5 3BZ, United Kingdom
Tel.: (44) 8450740614
Web Site: http://www.triplewestmedical.com
Medical Staff Recruitment Services
N.A.I.C.S.: 561311

SERVOPRAX GMBH

Am Marienbusch 9, 46485, Wesel, Germany
Tel.: (49) 281952830
Web Site: http://www.servoprax.de
Rev.: $99,191,656
Emp.: 136
Medical & Hospital Equipment Whslr
N.A.I.C.S.: 423450

SERVOTEACH INDUSTRIES LIMITED

INTERNATIONAL PUBLIC

502 Triveni Krupa Carter Road No 3 Opp Ambaji Mata Temple, Borivali East, Mumbai, 400 066, India
Tel.: (91) 2241014400
Web Site: https://www.servoteachengineering.in
Year Founded: 1994
531944—(BOM)
Assets: $20,398
Liabilities: $55,647
Net Worth: ($35,249)
Earnings: ($10,564)
Fiscal Year-end: 03/31/21
Solvent Extraction Plant Mfr & Whslr
N.A.I.C.S.: 333248

SERVOTECH POWER SYSTEMS LTD.

806 8th Floor Crown Height Hotel Crown Plaza Sector- 10 Rohini, New Delhi, 110085, India
Tel.: (91) 1141183117
Web Site: http://www.servotech.in
SERVOTECH—(NSE)
Rev.: $33,408,465
Assets: $19,991,919
Liabilities: $10,139,728
Net Worth: $9,852,191
Earnings: $1,326,671
Emp.: 251
Fiscal Year-end: 03/31/23
Solar Panel Mfr
N.A.I.C.S.: 335132
Raman Bhatia (Founder & Mng Dir)

SERVUS CREDIT UNION, LTD.

151 Karl Clark Road NW, Edmonton, AB, Canada
Tel.: (780) 496-2000
Web Site: https://www.servus.ca
Year Founded: 1938
Emp.: 2,200
Credit Card Services
N.A.I.C.S.: 522210

Subsidiaries:

Connect First Credit Union Ltd. (1)
200 -2850 Sunridge Boulevard NE Suite 200, Calgary, T1Y 6G2, AB, Canada
Tel.: (866) 923-4778
Web Site: https://www.connectfirstcu.com
Financial Services
N.A.I.C.S.: 523999

Subsidiary (Domestic):

SugarBud Craft Growers Corp. (2)
suite 620 634 6th Avenue SW, Calgary, T2P 0S4, AB, Canada
Tel.: (403) 532-4466
Web Site: http://www.sugarbud.ca
Assets: $12,624,490
Liabilities: $3,783,933
Net Worth: $8,840,557
Earnings: ($5,402,868)
Fiscal Year-end: 12/31/2019
Oil & Gas Exploration Services
N.A.I.C.S.: 213112
Daniel T. Wilson (Chm)

SES S.A.

Chateau de Betzdorf, L-6815, Luxembourg, Luxembourg
Tel.: (352) 7107251
Web Site: https://www.ses.com
Year Founded: 1985
SESG—(LUX)
Rev.: $3,295,367,920
Assets: $16,066,607,440
Liabilities: $9,025,107,520
Net Worth: $7,041,499,920
Earnings: $547,795,040
Emp.: 102
Fiscal Year-end: 12/31/21
Telecommunications Satellites Owner & Operator
N.A.I.C.S.: 517410
Tsega Gebreyes (Vice Chm)

AND PRIVATE COMPANIES — SES S.A.

Subsidiaries:

AOS Inc. (1)
17817 Davenport Rd Ste 225, Dallas, TX 75252
Tel.: (972) 735-0101
Web Site: http://www.aosusa.com
Satellite Communication Services
N.A.I.C.S.: 517410

ASTRA Benelux B.V. (1)
Mozartlaan 27d, 1217 CM, Hilversum, Netherlands
Tel.: (31) 35 625 44 90
Sales Range: $25-49.9 Million
Emp.: 3
Satellite Communication Services
N.A.I.C.S.: 517410

HD Plus GmbH (1)
Beta-Str 1-10, D-85774, Unterfohring, Germany
Tel.: (49) 8990409797
Web Site: https://www.hd-plus.de
Satellite Communication Services
N.A.I.C.S.: 517410

Nahuelsat S.A. (1)
Bouchard 1680 12th Fl, Capital Federal, 1106, Buenos Aires, Argentina
Tel.: (54) 158112600
Web Site: http://www.nahuelsat.com.ar
Sales Range: $25-49.9 Million
Emp.: 50
Communication Equipment Mfr
N.A.I.C.S.: 334290

New Skies Satellites Australia Pty Ltd (1)
12 Park Way, Mawson Lakes, Adelaide, 5095, SA, Australia
Tel.: (61) 883596157
Web Site: http://www.ses.com
Sales Range: $25-49.9 Million
Emp.: 1
Satellite Communication Services
N.A.I.C.S.: 517410
Glenn Tindell (Dir)

New Skies Satellites, Inc. (1)
4 Research Way, Princeton, NJ 08540-6618
Tel.: (609) 987-4504
Satellite Communication Services
N.A.I.C.S.: 517410

Redu Space Services S.A. (1)
rue devant les Hetres 2B, Galaxia, 6890, Transinne, Belgium
Tel.: (32) 61550603
Web Site: https://www.reduspaceservices.com
Satellite Communication Services
N.A.I.C.S.: 517410

SES AMERICOM Colorado, Inc. (1)
4 Research Way, Princeton, NJ 08540
Tel.: (609) 987-4000
Satellite Communication Services
N.A.I.C.S.: 517410
Mike Kononenko (Gen Mgr)

SES AMERICOM do Brasil Servicos de Telecomunicacoes, Ltda (1)
Av Das Nacoes Unidas 12551 9 Andar, Sao Paulo, Brazil
Tel.: (55) 1134437452
Sales Range: $25-49.9 Million
Emp.: 5
Telecommunication Servicesb
N.A.I.C.S.: 517810

SES AMERICOM, Inc. (1)
4 Research Way, Princeton, NJ 08540-6684 (100%)
Tel.: (609) 987-4000
Web Site: http://www.ses.com
Owner & Operator of Satellite System
N.A.I.C.S.: 517410

Subsidiary (Domestic):

AMERICOM Government Services, Inc. (2)
2 Research Way, Princeton, NJ 08540
Tel.: (609) 987-4500
Web Site: http://www.americom-gs.com
Satellite Telecommunications
N.A.I.C.S.: 517410

SES ASTRA CEE Sp. z.o.o (1)
Pl Pilsudskiego 2 Building 2, 00-073, Warsaw, Poland
Tel.: (48) 22 332 78 50
Web Site: http://www.ses.com
Sales Range: $25-49.9 Million
Emp.: 10
Satellite Telecommunication Services
N.A.I.C.S.: 517410
Martin O. Kubacki (Gen Mgr)

SES ASTRA S.A. (1)
Chateau de Betzdorf, 6815, Betzdorf, Luxembourg (100%)
Tel.: (352) 7107251
Web Site: http://www.ses.com
Sales Range: $800-899.9 Million
Satellite Communications
N.A.I.C.S.: 517410

Subsidiary (Non-US):

ASTRA (GB) Limited (2)
15 Fetter Lane, London, EC4A 1BW, United Kingdom
Tel.: (44) 2076327920
Web Site: http://www.ses-astra.com
Satellite Communication Services
N.A.I.C.S.: 517410

ASTRA Deutschland GmbH (2)
Betastrasse 1-10 Haus B, 85774, Unterfohring, Germany
Tel.: (49) 8918962120
Sales Range: $50-74.9 Million
Emp.: 200
Satellite Communication Services
N.A.I.C.S.: 517410

ASTRA France S.A. (2) (100%)
Tel.: (33) 142680009
Web Site: http://www.ses-astra.com
Sales Range: $25-49.9 Million
Emp.: 5
N.A.I.C.S.: 516210

ASTRA Marketing GmbH (2)
Mergenthalerallee 79 81, D 65760, Eschborn, Germany (100%)
Tel.: (49) 6196470625
Web Site: http://www.astra.de
Sales Range: $25-49.9 Million
Emp.: 9
N.A.I.C.S.: 516210

ASTRA Marketing Ltd. (2)
Fl 7 Wellington House, 125 Strand, London, WC2 0AP, United Kingdom
Tel.: (44) 2074203600
Sales Range: $25-49.9 Million
Emp.: 5
Marketing Consulting
N.A.I.C.S.: 541613

ASTRA Platform Services GmbH (2)
Beta-Strasse 1-10 B, 85774, Unterfohring, Germany (100%)
Tel.: (49) 8918962100
Web Site: http://de.astra.ses
Sales Range: $25-49.9 Million
Emp.: 60
Satellite Telecommunications
N.A.I.C.S.: 517410

ASTRA Polska (2)
Plac Pitsudskiego 2, 00073, Warsaw, Poland (100%)
Tel.: (48) 22331890
Web Site: http://www.ses-astra.com
N.A.I.C.S.: 516210

MX1 GmbH (2)
Bareket Building 1, Hanegev Street, Airport City, 7019900, Israel (100%)
Tel.: (972) 3 928 0808
Web Site: http://www.mx1.com
Satellite Network for Television & Radio Broadcasting Industries
N.A.I.C.S.: 517410
Ziv Mor (CTO)

SES ASTRA (Romania) S.a r.l. (2)
Nicolae Titulescu No 4-8 America House Bldg W Wing, Bucharest, 11141, Romania
Tel.: (40) 21 222 17 51
Sales Range: $25-49.9 Million
Emp.: 2
Satellite Communication Services
N.A.I.C.S.: 517410
Mihai Ursoi (Gen Mgr)

SES ASTRA (U.K.) Ltd (2)
15 Fetter Lane Fleet Street, London, EC4A 1BW, United Kingdom
Tel.: (44) 2076327900
Emp.: 9
Telecommunication Servicesb
N.A.I.C.S.: 517810

Subsidiary (Domestic):

SES ASTRA 1KR S.a r.l. (2)
Chateau De Betzdorf, 6815, Betzdorf, Luxembourg
Tel.: (352) 710 7251
Web Site: http://www.ses.com
Emp.: 40
Satellite Telecommunication Services
N.A.I.C.S.: 517410
Roman Bauch (Mgr)

SES ASTRA 1L S.a r.l. (2)
Chateau De Betzdorf, 6815, Betzdorf, Luxembourg
Tel.: (352) 7107251
Satellite Communication Services
N.A.I.C.S.: 517410
Roman Bausch (CEO)

SES ASTRA 1M S.a r.l. (2)
Chateau De Betzdorf, Betzdorf, 6815, Luxembourg
Tel.: (352) 710 725 1
Satellite Communication Services
N.A.I.C.S.: 517410
Roman Bausch (Pres)

SES ASTRA 1N S.a r.l. (2)
Chateau de Betzdorf, Betzdorf, 6815, Luxembourg
Tel.: (352) 710 725 1
Web Site: http://www.ses.com
Satellite Communication Services
N.A.I.C.S.: 517410

SES ASTRA 2G S.a r.l. (2)
Chateau De Betzdorf, Betzdorf, 6815, Luxembourg
Tel.: (352) 7107251
Web Site: http://www.ses.com
Emp.: 40
Satellite Communication Services
N.A.I.C.S.: 517410
Karim Sadag (Mng Dir)

SES ASTRA 5B S.a r.l. (2)
Chateau De Betzdorf, 6815, Betzdorf, Luxembourg
Tel.: (352) 710 725 1
Web Site: http://www.ses.com
Emp.: 40
Satellite Telecommunication Services
N.A.I.C.S.: 517410
Andrew Ross (Gen Mgr)

Subsidiary (Non-US):

SES ASTRA AB (2)
Kista Science Tower Farogatan 33, 164 51, Kista, Sweden
Tel.: (46) 850564500
Satellite Communication Services
N.A.I.C.S.: 517410

SES ASTRA Iberica S.A. (2)
Calle Velazquez 47, 28001, Madrid, Spain (100%)
Tel.: (34) 117469141
Web Site: http://es.ses.com
Communication Satellite Services
N.A.I.C.S.: 516210

Subsidiary (Domestic):

SES ENGINEERING (Luxembourg) S.a r.l. (2)
Chateau De Betzdorf, 6815, Betzdorf, Luxembourg
Tel.: (352) 7107251
Web Site: http://www.ses.com
Satellite Communication Services
N.A.I.C.S.: 517410

SES ASTRA TechCom Belgium S.A. (1)
Rue Devant les Hetres 2, Transinne, 6890, Libin, Belgium
Tel.: (32) 61229645
Satellite Communication Services
N.A.I.C.S.: 517410

SES Belgium S.p.r.l (1)
Avenue de Tervueren 55, 1040, Brussels, Belgium
Tel.: (32) 27335839
Web Site: http://www.ses.com
Sales Range: $25-49.9 Million
Emp.: 2
Telecommunication Servicesb
N.A.I.C.S.: 517810
Christine Leurquin (VP)

SES Digital Distribution Services AG (1)
Lowenstrasse 32, Zurich, 8001, Switzerland
Tel.: (41) 442269900
Television Broadcasting Services
N.A.I.C.S.: 516120

SES ENGINEERING (Netherlands) B.V. (1)
Rooseveltplantsoen 4, 2517 KR, Hague, Netherlands
Tel.: (31) 703064100
Satellite Telecommunication Services
N.A.I.C.S.: 517410

SES Finance S.a r.l. (1)
Lowenstrasse 32, 8001, Zurich, Switzerland
Tel.: (41) 442269900
Financial Management Services
N.A.I.C.S.: 523999

SES GLOBAL-Americas Finance Inc. (1)
4 Research Way, Princeton, NJ 08540-6618
Tel.: (609) 987-4000
Financial Management Services
N.A.I.C.S.: 523999

SES Global South America Holding S.L. (1)
Paseo Castellana 91 - PLT 4 B, Madrid, 28046, Spain
Tel.: (34) 914111746
Investment Management Service
N.A.I.C.S.: 523999

SES Government Solutions (1)
11790 Sunrise Valley Dr Ste 300, Reston, VA 20191
Tel.: (703) 610-1000
Web Site: http://www.ses-gs.com
Sales Range: $25-49.9 Million
Satellite Communication Services
N.A.I.C.S.: 517410
William Flynn (VP-Programs)

SES Latin America S.A. (1)
Chateau de Betzdorf, 6815, Betzdorf, Luxembourg
Tel.: (352) 710 7251
Satellite Telecommunication Services
N.A.I.C.S.: 517410

SES New Skies (1)
Level 31 ABN AMRO Tower 88 Phillip St, Sydney, 2000, NSW, Australia
Tel.: (61) 282112744
Sales Range: $25-49.9 Million
Emp.: 1
Satellite Telecommunications
N.A.I.C.S.: 517410
Glen Tindall (Dir-Mktg)

SES New Skies BV (1)
Rooseveltplantsoen 4, 2517 KR, Hague, Netherlands (100%)
Tel.: (31) 703064100
Web Site: http://www.ses-newskies.com
Sales Range: $150-199.9 Million
Emp.: 200
Telecommunications Satellites Owner & Operator
N.A.I.C.S.: 517410
Simon Gatty Saunt (VP-Sls-Europe)

SES Participations S.A. (1)
Chateau De Betzdorf, Luxembourg, 6815, Luxembourg
Tel.: (352) 710 725 1
Web Site: http://www.ses.com
Satellite Communication Services
N.A.I.C.S.: 517410
Aurelie Notermans (Mgr-HR)

SES Platform Services GmbH (1)
Betastrasse 1-10, Postfach 11 27, 85774, Unterfohring, Germany
Tel.: (49) 8918962100
Web Site: http://www.ses-ps.com
Sales Range: $50-74.9 Million
Television Broadcasting Services
N.A.I.C.S.: 516120

SES S.A.

SES S.A.—(Continued)

SES Sirius AB (1)
Kista Science Tower, 16451, Kista, Sweden
Tel.: (46) 850564500
Web Site: http://www.ses-astra.com
Sales Range: $25-49.9 Million
Emp.: 50
Satellite Telecommunications
N.A.I.C.S.: 517410
Benny Norling (Sr Mgr-Mktg Dev)

SES Space & Defense, Inc. (1)
11790 Sunrise Valley Dr Ste 300, Reston, VA 20191
Tel.: (703) 610-1000
Satellite Communication Services
N.A.I.C.S.: 517410

SES TechCom S.A. (1)
Chateau de Betzdorf, 6815, Betzdorf, Luxembourg
Tel.: (352) 710725259
Sales Range: $25-49.9 Million
Emp.: 80
Technical Consulting Services
N.A.I.C.S.: 541690
Nicole Robinson (Mng Dir)

SES World Skies Singapore Pty Ltd (1)
Tel.: (65) 65933600
Web Site: http://www.ses.com
Sales Range: $25-49.9 Million
Electronic Parts Distr
N.A.I.C.S.: 423690

Star One S.A. (1)
Praia de Botafogo 228 3o andar, 22250-906, Rio de Janeiro, RJ, Brazil **(19.99%)**
Tel.: (55) 2121219381
Web Site: http://www.starone.com.br
Telecommunications Services; Owned 80% by Embratel & 20% by SES Global S.A.
N.A.I.C.S.: 517111

Virtual Planet Group GmbH (1)
Domagkstrasse 34, Munich, 80807, Germany
Tel.: (49) 894120070
Web Site: http://www.virtualplanet.de
Satellite Communication Services
N.A.I.C.S.: 517410

SESA S.P.A.
Via Piovola 138, Empoli, 50053, Florence, Italy
Tel.: (39) 0571997444 **IT**
Web Site: https://www.sesa.it
Year Founded: 1973
SES—(ITA)
Rev.: $3,415,148,925
Assets: $2,289,719,400
Liabilities: $1,774,561,836
Net Worth: $515,157,564
Earnings: $89,637,384
Emp.: 5,691
Fiscal Year-end: 04/30/24
Information Technology Services
N.A.I.C.S.: 519290
Moreno Gaini (Vice Chm & Exec VP)

Subsidiaries:

A Plus S.R.L. (1)
Via Leonardo da Vinci 20, 50132, Florence, Italy
Tel.: (39) 0571920442
Web Site: https://www.aplus.srl
Automatic Security Services
N.A.I.C.S.: 561621

ABS Technology S.p.A. (1)
Via Policarpo Petrocchi 24, 50127, Florence, FI, Italy
Tel.: (39) 0559073699
Web Site: https://www.abstechnology.it
Information Technology Services
N.A.I.C.S.: 541511

Adacto S.R.L. (1)
Via Vigevano 15, 20144, Milan, Italy
Tel.: (39) 0236685010
Web Site: https://www.adacto.it
Emp.: 70
Software Development Services
N.A.I.C.S.: 541511

Addfor Industriale Srl (1)
Via Cavour 1, 10123, Turin, Italy
Tel.: (39) 0111 971 6290
Web Site: https://www.add-for.com
Information Technology Services
N.A.I.C.S.: 541519

Adiacent Apac Limited (1)
R 603 6/F Shun Kwong Com Bldg 8 Des Voeux Road West, Sheung Wan, Hong Kong, China (Hong Kong)
Tel.: (852) 62863211
Digital Architect Development Services
N.A.I.C.S.: 541310

Albalog s.r.l. (1)
Via del Ponte all Asse 2, 50019, Sesto Fiorentino, Italy
Tel.: (39) 055300311
Web Site: https://extraerp.it
Software Development Services
N.A.I.C.S.: 541512

Aldebra S.P.A. (1)
Via Linz 13 Spini di Gardolo, 38121, Trento, Italy
Tel.: (39) 0461302400
Web Site: https://www.aldebra.com
Emp.: 50
Software Development Services
N.A.I.C.S.: 541512

Alfasap S.R.L. (1)
Via Fiume Giallo 3, 00144, Rome, Italy
Tel.: (39) 0652244040
Web Site: https://alfasap.com
Software Development Services
N.A.I.C.S.: 541512

Amaeco S.R.L. (1)
Via Radici in Piano 1, 41042, Fiorano-Modenese, Italy
Tel.: (39) 0595961360
Web Site: https://www.amaeco.it
Software Development Services
N.A.I.C.S.: 541512

Analytics Network Srl (1)
Via Isonzo 55/2, 40033, Casalecchio di Reno, BO, Italy
Tel.: (39) 051252573
Web Site: https://www.analyticsnetwork.co
Information Technology Services
N.A.I.C.S.: 541511

Assist Informatica S.R.L. (1)
Via delle Querce 15/17, 06083, Bastia Umbra, Italy
Tel.: (39) 0758001062
Web Site: https://www.assistinformatica.com
Software Development Services
N.A.I.C.S.: 541512

Ausilia S.R.L. (1)
Via Magazzini Posteriori, 48122, Ravenna, Italy
Tel.: (39) 0544200378
Web Site: https://www.ausilia.pro
Environment & Energy Management Services
N.A.I.C.S.: 541620

Base Digitale Group S.R.L. (1)
Via Leonardo da Vinci 20, 50132, Florence, Italy
Tel.: (39) 0559073600
Web Site: https://basedigitalegroup.com
Emp.: 150
Software Development Services
N.A.I.C.S.: 541512

Beenear Srl (1)
Moara de Foc 35 floor 7-8-9, 700520, Iasi, Romania
Tel.: (40) 232211896
Web Site: https://www.beenear.com
Software Development Services
N.A.I.C.S.: 541511

Cadlog Gmbh (1)
Breslauer Str 3, 85386, Eching, Germany
Tel.: (49) 893700390
Software Development Services
N.A.I.C.S.: 541511

Cadlog Group Srl (1)
Via Derna 26, 20132, Milan, Italy
Tel.: (39) 0284947211
Web Site: https://www.cadlog.com
Information Technology Services
N.A.I.C.S.: 541519

Cadlog S.A.S. (1)
HUBSTART Center Roissypole-Batiment Aeronef 5 rue de Copenhague CDG, CS 13918, Roissy, 95731, Tremblay-en-France, Cedex, France
Tel.: (33) 486870213
Software Development Services
N.A.I.C.S.: 541511

Cadlog S.L. (1)
Calle Bahia de Pollensa 5 oficina 35, 28042, Madrid, Spain
Tel.: (34) 911238431
Software Development Services
N.A.I.C.S.: 541511

Cimtec GmbH (1)
Ringstrasse 5, Grossheirath, 96269, Coburg, Germany
Tel.: (49) 956594600
Web Site: https://cimtec.de
Computer Training Services
N.A.I.C.S.: 611420

DI.Tech S.p.A. (1)
Via Giambologna 18, 40138, Bologna, Italy
Tel.: (39) 0516033311
Web Site: https://www.ditechonline.it
Information Technology Consulting Services
N.A.I.C.S.: 541512

Datef S.p.a. (1)
Business Park Luigi Negrellistrasse 13/B, I-39100, Bolzano, Italy
Tel.: (39) 0471066500
Web Site: https://datef.it
Emp.: 75
Information Technology Services
N.A.I.C.S.: 541512

Digital Storm Srl (1)
Via Montefeltro 6, 20156, Milan, Italy
Tel.: (39) 029105777
Web Site: https://www.digitalstorm.it
Information Technology Services
N.A.I.C.S.: 541511

Durante S.p.A. (1)
Via Prealpi 8, Cormano, 20032, Milan, Italy
Tel.: (39) 02663291
Web Site: https://www.durante.it
Information Technology Consulting Services
N.A.I.C.S.: 541512

Dvr Italia S.R.L. (1)
Via Giuseppe Frua 14, 20146, Milan, Italy
Tel.: (39) 0236697323
Web Site: https://www.dvritalia.it
Information Technology Consulting Services
N.A.I.C.S.: 541690

Dynamics Business Solutions S.R.L. (1)
Via Cesare Battisti 5, 8110, Caserta, Italy
Tel.: (39) 0823355774
Web Site: http://www.dynamicsbs.it
Information Technology Services
N.A.I.C.S.: 541512

Emmedi S.R.L. (1)
Via Gemona 104, 33100, Udine, Italy
Tel.: (39) 043226558
Web Site: https://www.emmedi.com
Scanner Machinery Mfr & Distr
N.A.I.C.S.: 334118

Endurance S.R.L. (1)
Via Regione Pozzo 26, 10034, Chivasso, Italy
Tel.: (39) 0119592455
Fleet Management Services
N.A.I.C.S.: 532112

Eurolab S.R.L. (1)
Viale Mare ionio 4, 89040, Marina di Caulonia, Italy
Tel.: (39) 096482185
Web Site: http://www.eurolab-srl.it
Microbiological Research & Development Services
N.A.I.C.S.: 541714

Ever Green Mobility Rent S.R.L. (1)
Via Ilio Barontini 26/A, 50055, Scandicci, Italy
Tel.: (39) 0555277182
Web Site: https://www.evergreenrent.it
Software Development Services
N.A.I.C.S.: 541512

Evotre Srl (1)
via G Brodolini 12, 60035, Jesi, AN, Italy
Tel.: (39) 073122911
Web Site: https://www.evotre.it
Information Technology Services
N.A.I.C.S.: 541511

ITF Srl (1)
Via E Mattei 20, Mesero, 20010, Milan, Italy
Tel.: (39) 02 97 28 96 96
Web Site: https://www.itf.it
Financial Services
N.A.I.C.S.: 523940

Icos Deutschland GmbH (1)
Paul-Heyse-Str 28, 80336, Munich, Germany
Tel.: (49) 893267640
Web Site: https://www.icosvad.de
Information Technology Services
N.A.I.C.S.: 541511

Ifm Infomaster S.p.A. (1)
Via V maggio 81, 16147, Genoa, GE, Italy
Tel.: (39) 0103747811
Web Site: https://www.ifmgroup.it
Information Technology Services
N.A.I.C.S.: 541511

Incos Italia Srl (1)
Via L Giuntini 40, Empoli, 50053, Florence, Italy
Tel.: (39) 0571 99 33 55
Web Site: http://www.incos.it
Computer Product Maintenance & Repair Services
N.A.I.C.S.: 811210

Infolog S.p.A. (1)
Via Pier Paolo Pasolini 23, 41123, Modena, MO, Italy
Tel.: (39) 059822446
Web Site: https://www.infolog.it
Information Technology Services
N.A.I.C.S.: 541511

Kolme S.R.L. (1)
Viale Famagosta 75, 20142, Milan, Italy
Tel.: (39) 0287124000
Web Site: https://www.kolme.it
Telecommunication Servicesb
N.A.I.C.S.: 423620

MF Services s.r.l. (1)
Via Vettigano 8/M, Campagnola Emilia, 42012, Reggio Emilia, Italy
Tel.: (39) 0522 1847499
Web Site: https://www.mfservices.it
Computer Maintenance & Repair Services
N.A.I.C.S.: 811210

Mediamente Consulting S.R.L. (1)
Corso Francesco Ferrucci 122, 10141, Rivalta di Torino, Italy
Tel.: (39) 05719988
Web Site: https://www.mediamenteconsulting.it
Emp.: 50
Information Technology Services
N.A.I.C.S.: 541512

Mr Fleet S.R.L. (1)
Via di Santo Spirito 11, 50125, Florence, Italy
Tel.: (39) 0550351747
Web Site: https://www.mrfleet.it
Car Rental Services
N.A.I.C.S.: 532111

Next Step Solution S.R.L. (1)
Via R Luxemburg 10, 43044, Collecchio, Italy
Tel.: (39) 0521305707
Web Site: http://www.nextstepsolution.it
Information Technology Services
N.A.I.C.S.: 541512

Omigrade Servizi S.R.L. (1)
Via Ferdinando Santi 1, Lemignano, 43044, Collecchio, Italy
Tel.: (39) 0521334811
Web Site: https://www.omigrade.it
Software Development Services
N.A.I.C.S.: 541512

Pal Ifm S.R.L. (1)
Via A Lombardi 6/B, 88100, Catanzaro, Italy
Tel.: (39) 0961715011
Web Site: https://www.palifm.it
Emp.: 3,400
Software Development Services
N.A.I.C.S.: 541512

AND PRIVATE COMPANIES — SET POINT GROUP LIMITED

Palitalsoft Srl (1)
Via Brodolini 12, 60035, Jesi, AN, Italy
Tel.: (39) 073122911
Web Site: https://www.palitalsoft.it
Information Technology Services
N.A.I.C.S.: 541511

Pbu Cad-systeme Gmbh (1)
Robert-Bosch-Str 8, 86551, Aichach, Germany
Tel.: (49) 825181910
Web Site: https://www.pbu-cad.de
Emp.: 3,400
Software Development Services
N.A.I.C.S.: 541512

Pragma Progetti S.R.L. (1)
Via Guido Rossa 3, 10024, Moncalieri, Italy
Tel.: (39) 0116813947
Web Site: https://www.pragmaprogetti.it
Information Technology Services
N.A.I.C.S.: 541512

Sailing Srl (1)
Via Emidio Villa 1/1, 42124, Reggio Emilia, Italy
Tel.: (39) 0522513285
Web Site: https://www.sailingweb.it
Information Technology Services
N.A.I.C.S.: 541519

Service Technology Srl (1)
Via dei Frati 16, 52100, Arezzo, Italy
Tel.: (39) 057 584 9396
Web Site: https://www.servicetechnology.it
Information Technology Services
N.A.I.C.S.: 541511

Sinapsi Informatica Srl (1)
Via Silvio Travaglia 14, Monselice, PD, Italy
Tel.: (39) 042 978 2088
Web Site: https://www.sinapsinet.it
Information Technology Services
N.A.I.C.S.: 541519

Sirio Informatica E Sistemi SpA (1)
Via Caduti Di Marcinelle 5, 20134, Milan, Italy
Tel.: (39) 02 365835 1
Web Site: http://www.sirio-is.it
Software Development Services
N.A.I.C.S.: 541511

Sirio Nord Srl (1)
Viale Europa 80, Cusago, 20090, Milan, Italy
Tel.: (39) 029 039 4370
Web Site: https://www.sirionord.it
Information Technology System Services
N.A.I.C.S.: 541512

Sisthema S.p.A. (1)
Via Gaetano Sbodio 2, 20134, Milan, Italy
Tel.: (39) 023658351
Web Site: https://sisthemaspa.it
Software Development Services
N.A.I.C.S.: 541512

Skeeller Srl (1)
Via Bruno Simonucci 18, 06135, Perugia, Italy
Tel.: (39) 0755173485
Web Site: https://www.magespecialist.it
Information Technology Services
N.A.I.C.S.: 541519
Tommaso Galmacci *(Project Mgr, CEO & Co-Founder)*

Sps S.R.L. (1)
Via Marche 1, 41049, Sassuolo, Modena, Italy
Tel.: (39) 0536885021
Web Site: https://www.spssrl.it
Ceramic Tile Mfr & Distr
N.A.I.C.S.: 327110

Ssa Informatica Srl (1)
Via Marsure 11, 33170, Pordenone, PN, Italy
Tel.: (39) 043 424 1045
Web Site: https://www.ssainformatica.com
Information Technology Services
N.A.I.C.S.: 541519

Superre Solution S.R.L. (1)
Via Della Piovola 138, Empoli, 50053, Florence, Italy
Tel.: (39) 0571998292
Web Site: https://www.superresolution.it
Digital & Video Production Services
N.A.I.C.S.: 512120

T&O s.r.l. (1)
Via Pacini 93, 20131, Milan, Italy
Tel.: (39) 0245373600
Web Site: https://teobiz.com
Software Development Services
N.A.I.C.S.: 541512

Tech Value Iberica Srl (1)
Via Ercole Oldofredi 47, 20124, Milan, Italy
Tel.: (39) 028 324 2006
Web Site: https://www.tech-value.com
Information Technology Services
N.A.I.C.S.: 541519

Technology Consulting S.R.L. (1)
Via G mo Leopardi nr 66, Palermo, Italy
Tel.: (39) 0916191900
Web Site: https://www.ntcitalia.it
Telecommunication Servicesb
N.A.I.C.S.: 517810

Var 4 Advisory S.p.A. (1)
Via Della Piovola 138, Empoli, 50053, Florence, Italy
Tel.: (39) 0800646543
Web Site: https://www.var4advisory.it
Information Technology Consulting Services
N.A.I.C.S.: 541512

Var Bms S.p.A. (1)
Via Privata Gaetano Sbodio 2, 20134, Milan, Italy
Tel.: (39) 0221082038
Web Site: https://www.varbms.it
Information Technology Services
N.A.I.C.S.: 541511

Var Business Engineering Srl (1)
Via Danubio N 14, Sesto Fiorentino, 50019, Florence, Italy
Tel.: (39) 055 34 24 674
Web Site: http://www.var-be.it
Software Development Services
N.A.I.C.S.: 541511

Var Group Suisse S.A. (1)
Via Cantonale 19, 6900, Lugano, Switzerland
Tel.: (41) 800445003
Web Site: https://www.vargroup.ch
Emp.: 3,700
Cyber Security Services
N.A.I.C.S.: 541690

Var Hub Srl (1)
Via Piovole 138, Empoli, 50053, Florence, Fl, Italy
Tel.: (39) 05719988
Web Site: https://www.varhub.it
Information Technology Services
N.A.I.C.S.: 541519

Var One Nord Est S.R.L. (1)
Via Silvio Travaglia 14, 35043, Monselice, Italy
Tel.: (39) 0429782088
Web Site: https://var-one-nordest.it
Emp.: 3,700
Information Technology Services
N.A.I.C.S.: 541512

Var Prime Srl (1)
Via Della Piovola 138, Empoli, 50053, Florence, Fl, Italy
Tel.: (39) 0221082874
Web Site: https://www.varprime.com
Emp.: 200
Information Technology Services
N.A.I.C.S.: 541519

Var4Team Srl (1)
Via Zanica 58, 24126, Bergamo, BG, Italy
Tel.: (39) 0354202111
Web Site: https://www.var4team.it
Information Technology Services
N.A.I.C.S.: 541511

Weelgo Srl (1)
Via Provinciale 21, 24040, Lallio, BG, Italy
Tel.: (39) 03 569 3771
Web Site: https://www.weelgo.it
Information Technology Services
N.A.I.C.S.: 541519

Wss It Sagl (1)
Casella Postale 351, Camorino, 6528, Bellinzona, Switzerland
Tel.: (41) 918200203
Information Technology Services
N.A.I.C.S.: 541519

Xautomata Technology Gmbh (1)
Lakeside B01 Lakeside Park, 9020, Klagenfurt, Austria
Tel.: (43) 6643543555
Web Site: https://www.xautomata.com
Software Development Services
N.A.I.C.S.: 541512

Yarix Srl (1)
Vicolo Boccacavalla 12, 31044, Montebelluna, Italy
Tel.: (39) 0423614249
Web Site: https://www.yarix.com
Information Technology Services
N.A.I.C.S.: 541519

Yoctoit S.R.L. (1)
Via Sempione 11, 20900, Monza, MB, Italy
Tel.: (39) 0396777623
Web Site: https://www.yoctoit.it
Information Technology Services
N.A.I.C.S.: 541512

Zero12 Srl (1)
Via Salborro 22 / B, 35124, Padua, PD, Italy
Tel.: (39) 049 941 4411
Web Site: https://www.zero12.it
Information Technology Services
N.A.I.C.S.: 541512

SESCOM SA
al Grunwaldzka 82, 80-244, Gdansk, Poland
Tel.: (48) 587612960
Web Site: https://www.sescom.eu
Year Founded: 2008
SES—(WAR)
Rev.: $58,275,406
Assets: $43,204,522
Liabilities: $26,581,047
Net Worth: $16,623,476
Earnings: $5,102,642
Emp.: 500
Fiscal Year-end: 09/30/23
Information Technology Services
N.A.I.C.S.: 541519
Adam Kabat *(COO & Member-Mgmt Bd)*

SESHACHAL TECHNOLOGIES LIMITED
Seshachal Technologies Ltd Plot No 57 Text Book Colony, Banjara Hills, Hyderabad, 500034, India
Tel.: (91) 4023547119
Web Site: https://www.seshachal.com
Rev.: $24,572
Assets: $160,546
Liabilities: $61,722
Net Worth: $98,824
Earnings: ($373)
Fiscal Year-end: 03/31/16
Software Development Services
N.A.I.C.S.: 541511
Anita Chitturi *(Mng Dir)*

SESHASAYEE PAPER & BOARDS LTD
Pallipalayam Cauvery R S P O, Erode, 638 007, India
Tel.: (91) 4288240221
Web Site: https://www.spbltd.com
Year Founded: 1960
SESHAPAPER—(NSE)
Rev.: $1,092,682,500
Assets: $207,089,610
Liabilities: $51,106,965
Net Worth: $155,982,645
Earnings: $145,195,050
Emp.: 1,256
Fiscal Year-end: 03/31/21
Pulp Paper Mfr
N.A.I.C.S.: 322110
K. S. Kasi Viswanathan *(Mng Dir)*

Subsidiaries:

Esvin Advanced Technologies Ltd (1)
Esvin House No 13 Old Mahabalipuram Road, Perungudi, Chennai, 600 096, Tamil Nadu, India
Tel.: (91) 4439279300
Web Site: http://www.esvintech.in
Sales Range: $50-74.9 Million
Emp.: 3
Biofertilizer & Biopesticides Whslr
N.A.I.C.S.: 424910
T. S. Venktaraman *(Mng Dir)*

High Energy Batteries (India) Ltd (1)
Pakkudi Road, Mathur Industrial Estate Pudukottai District, Tiruchirappalli, 622 515, Tamil Nadu, India
Tel.: (91) 4339250444
Web Site: http://www.highenergy.co.in
Sales Range: $50-74.9 Million
Emp.: 150
Batteries Mfr
N.A.I.C.S.: 335910
G. A. Pathanjali *(Mng Dir)*

Ponni Sugars Erode Limited (1)
Esvin House No 13 Rajiv Gandhi Salai OMR, Seevaram Village Perungudi, Chennai, 600 096, Tamil Nadu, India
Tel.: (91) 442 496 1920
Web Site: https://www.ponnisugars.com
Sales Range: $100-124.9 Million
Emp.: 380
Sugar Mfr
N.A.I.C.S.: 311314
K. Yokanathan *(Pres & CFO)*

SPB-PC Ltd. (1)
Esvin House Rajiv Gandhi Salai, Perungudi, Chennai, 600096, Tamil Nadu, India
Tel.: (91) 4461279400
Web Site: http://www.spbpc.com
Sales Range: $25-49.9 Million
Emp.: 100
Newsprint & Paper Mfr
N.A.I.C.S.: 322120

SESHIN BUFFALO CO., LTD.
48 Ungnam-dong, Changwon, 641-290, Gyeongnam, Korea (South)
Tel.: (82) 55 269 0600
Web Site: http://www.seshinbuffalo.co.kr
Emp.: 100
Hand Tools, Cutting Tools & Parts Mfr
N.A.I.C.S.: 333991
Byung-Cheol Moon *(CEO)*

SESODA CORPORATION
23rd Floor No 99 Section 2 Dunhua South Road, Taipei, Taiwan
Tel.: (886) 227047272
Web Site: https://www.sesoda.com.tw
Year Founded: 1957
1708—(TAI)
Rev.: $192,262,101
Assets: $427,648,991
Liabilities: $219,448,633
Net Worth: $208,200,358
Earnings: ($930,639)
Emp.: 188
Fiscal Year-end: 12/31/23
Fertilizers Mfr & Distr
N.A.I.C.S.: 325312
Frank Chen *(CEO)*

Subsidiaries:

East Tender Optoelectronics Corporation (1)
14 Te Hsing 7th Rd, Su-ao, 27051, Yilan, Taiwan
Tel.: (886) 39908671
Web Site: http://www.east-tender.com
Sales Range: $25-49.9 Million
Optoelectronic Product Mfr
N.A.I.C.S.: 333310

Sesoda Steamship Corporation (1)
Salduba Building Top Floor Urbanizacion Obarrio, Panama, Panama
Tel.: (507) 227047272
Ship Operation & Chartering Services
N.A.I.C.S.: 532411

SET POINT GROUP LIMITED
11 Avalon Road West Lake View EXT 11, PO Box 856, Johannesburg, Isando, 1600, Gauteng, South Africa

SET POINT GROUP LIMITED

Set Point Group Limited—(Continued)
Tel.: (27) 119237000
Web Site: http://www.setpoint.co.za
Sales Range: $25-49.9 Million
Emp.: 400
Industrial Technology Service Providers
N.A.I.C.S.: 236210
Martyn Evers *(CFO)*

Subsidiaries:

African Mineral Standards (1)
D1 Isando Business Park off Hulley Road Isando Ext 3, Ekuruleni, Johannesburg, South Africa
Tel.: (27) 119230800
Web Site: http://www.amis.co.za
Mineral Exploration Services
N.A.I.C.S.: 213115
Raksha Nagaser *(Ops Mgr)*

Brubin Pumps (Pty) Ltd (1)
PO Box 1199, Edenvale, Johannesburg, 1610, South Africa
Tel.: (27) 116091940
Web Site: http://www.brubin.com
Industrial Pump Mfr
N.A.I.C.S.: 333914

Letaba Dewatering (1)
Platinum Industrial Park Unit 6 Van Belkum Str, Rustenburg, South Africa
Tel.: (27) 145965700
Web Site: http://www.letabapumps.co.za
Industrial Pump Mfr
N.A.I.C.S.: 333914

Letaba Group (1)
34 Cadle Street, PO Box 14012, Sidwell, Port Elizabeth, 6061, South Africa
Tel.: (27) 451 2822
Web Site: http://www.letabapumps.co.za
N.A.I.C.S.: 423810
Steen kamp *(Mgr-Ops)*

Letaba Industrial Pumps (Pty) Ltd (1)
378 Bergseering Str Building C Ext 3, Steelpoort, 1133, South Africa
Tel.: (27) 132309990
Web Site: http://www.letabapumps.co.za
Industrial Pump Mfr
N.A.I.C.S.: 333914

Meter Systems Trading (Pty) Ltd (1)
4 Mopedi Street Sebenza, Edenvale, Gauteng, South Africa
Tel.: (27) 114517000
Web Site: http://www.metersystems.co.za
Mechanical Equipment Distr
N.A.I.C.S.: 423840
Warren Erasmus *(Mng Dir)*

North West GoPro (1)
4 Uraan Street, PO Box 734, Stilfontein, Klerksdorp, 2551, South Africa
Tel.: (27) 184843292
Web Site: http://www.nwgopro.com
Locomotive Wheel Mfr
N.A.I.C.S.: 331110

Pneumax Southern Africa (Pty) Limited (1)
449 Pretoria street cnr Republic Ave, Silverton, Pretoria, 0184, South Africa
Tel.: (27) 128463340
Web Site: http://www.pneumax.co.za
Automation Engineering Services
N.A.I.C.S.: 541330

RENG (1)
1a Escom Stree, PO Box 6190, Rustenburg, 0300, South Africa
Tel.: (27) 145973566
Web Site: http://www.nwgopro.com
Locomotive Wheel Mfr
N.A.I.C.S.: 331110

Set Point Laboratories (1)
30 Electron Avenue, Isando, Johannesburg, 1610, South Africa
Tel.: (27) 119237100
Web Site: http://www.setpointlabs.co.za
Laboratory Testing Services
N.A.I.C.S.: 621511
Kevin Gerber *(Mng Dir)*

Tuscany (1)
Unit 2 Brand Park 20 Brand Road, Durban, KwaZulu-Natal, South Africa
Tel.: (27) 317009974
Web Site: http://www.tuscanypumps.co.za
Industrial Pump Distr
N.A.I.C.S.: 423840

Wearcheck Africa (Pty) Ltd. (1)
9 Le Mans Place Westmead, Pinetown, 3610, South Africa
Tel.: (27) 317005460
Web Site: http://www.wearcheck.co.za
Oil Exploration Services
N.A.I.C.S.: 213112
Neil Robinson *(Mng Dir)*

SETA S.P.A.

Via Verga 40, 10036, Settimo Torinese, Italy
Tel.: (39) 0118015711
Web Site: http://www.setaspa.com
Year Founded: 2002
Sales Range: $450-499.9 Million
Emp.: 1,134
Waste Management Services
N.A.I.C.S.: 562111
Alessandro Di Benedetto *(Pres)*

SETCO AUTOMOTIVE LTD

54A Tardeo Road Next to Film Center Building, Mumbai, 400 034, Maharashtra, India
Tel.: (91) 2240755555
Web Site: https://www.setcoauto.com
505075—(BOM)
Rev.: $65,950,495
Assets: $68,873,173
Liabilities: $120,514,514
Net Worth: ($51,641,340)
Earnings: $18,280,918
Emp.: 1,000
Fiscal Year-end: 03/31/23
Clutch Product Mfr
N.A.I.C.S.: 336350
Harish K. Sheth *(Chm & Mng Dir)*

Subsidiaries:

Setco Automotive (NA) Inc., USA (1)
1731 Mineral Wells Ave, Paris, TN 38242
Tel.: (731) 642-4215
Web Site: https://setcoauto.com
Sales Range: $25-49.9 Million
Emp.: 38
Clutches Mfr
N.A.I.C.S.: 336350

Setco Automotive (UK) Limited (1)
York Avenue, Haslingden, BB4 4HU, Lancashire, United Kingdom **(100%)**
Tel.: (44) 1706228321
Web Site: https://setcoauto.com
Sales Range: $25-49.9 Million
Emp.: 25
Automobile Parts Mfr
N.A.I.C.S.: 336390

SETTLEMENTS SA

33 Boulevard de la Cambre, 1000, Brussels, Belgium
Tel.: (32) 23247405
Web Site: http://www.settlements-sa.net
Year Founded: 2008
STTL—(EUR)
Sales Range: Less than $1 Million
Financial Management Services
N.A.I.C.S.: 523999
Marco Mennella *(Chm & CEO)*

SETUBANDHAN INFRASTRUCTURE LIMITED

The Exchange Near VedMandir Tidke Colony, Trimbak Road, Nashik, 422 002, Maharashtra, India
Tel.: (91) 2532315269
Web Site: https://www.prakashconstro.com
533605—(NSE)
Rev.: $7,862,837
Assets: $24,875,801
Liabilities: $17,289,882
Net Worth: $7,585,919
Earnings: ($3,901,047)
Emp.: 700
Fiscal Year-end: 03/31/21
Construction Services
N.A.I.C.S.: 236220

Subsidiaries:

Atal Buildwell Pvt. Ltd. (1)
501-Vijayraj Appts Shrirang Nagar Gangapur Road, Nasik, 422002, Maharashtra, India
Tel.: (91) 253 2597724
Sales Range: $25-49.9 Million
Emp.: 35
Marble & Granite Whslr
N.A.I.C.S.: 444180
Krishnan Ganpat Trichur *(Mng Dir)*

Jaikumar Real Estates Private Limited (1)
Godavari Housing Society Near Boys Town School Off College Road, Nasik, 422005, India
Tel.: (91) 253 3194040
Web Site: http://www.parksyde.com
Residential Building Construction Services
N.A.I.C.S.: 236116

Unique Vastu Nirman Private Limited (1)

SETUZA A.S.

Zukovova 100, 401 29, Usti nad Labem, Czech Republic
Tel.: (420) 475291111
Web Site: http://www.setuza.cz
Sales Range: $300-349.9 Million
Emp.: 1,300
Oil Seed Processor; Edible Plant Oil & Fat Producer
N.A.I.C.S.: 311224
Radovan Macek *(Dir Gen)*

Subsidiaries:

CINERGETIKA Usti n. L. (1)
Zukovova 100, Usti nad Labem, 400 03, Czech Republic
Tel.: (420) 472 707 011
Web Site: http://cinergetika.czechtrade.us
Natural Gas Production Services
N.A.I.C.S.: 211130

SEUNG IL CORPORATION

10 4sandan 1-gil Jiksan-eup, Seobuk-gu, Cheonan, Chungcheongnam-do, Korea (South)
Tel.: (82) 325781811
Web Site: http://www.seungilcan.kr
Year Founded: 1961
049830—(KRS)
Rev.: $121,906,516
Assets: $135,631,181
Liabilities: $24,014,760
Net Worth: $111,616,421
Earnings: $1,006,591
Emp.: 331
Fiscal Year-end: 12/31/22
Aerosol Can Product Mfr
N.A.I.C.S.: 332431
Chang-soo Hyun *(CEO)*

SEUNGIL CORP.

Web Site: http://www.seungilcan.com
Year Founded: 1961
49830—(KRS)
Rev.: $117,506,780
Assets: $147,043,498
Liabilities: $26,203,295
Net Worth: $120,840,203
Earnings: ($503,919)
Emp.: 362
Fiscal Year-end: 12/31/19
Aerosol Can Product Mfr
N.A.I.C.S.: 332431
Chang Soo Hyun *(Pres)*

SEV.EN ENERGY AG

Zollstrasse 82, 9494, Schaan, Liechtenstein
Tel.: (423) 233 11 31   LI
Web Site: http://www.7energy.com
Year Founded: 2016
Sales Range: $700-749.9 Million
Emp.: 2,700
Portfolio Management
N.A.I.C.S.: 523940
Lubos Pavlas *(CEO)*

Subsidiaries:

Alpiq Generation (CZ) s.r.o. (1)
Dubska 257, 272 03, Kladno, Czech Republic **(100%)**
Tel.: (420) 312644853
Web Site: http://generation.alpiq.cz
Electricity & Heat Distribution
N.A.I.C.S.: 221122
Milan Prajzler *(CEO & Mng Dir)*

SEVEN & I HOLDINGS CO., LTD.

8-8 Nibancho, Chiyoda-ku, Tokyo, 102-8452, Japan
Tel.: (81) 362383000   JP
Web Site: https://www.7andi.com
Year Founded: 2005
SVNDF—(OTCIQ)
Rev.: $81,334,728,770
Assets: $75,098,109,530
Liabilities: $47,442,685,370
Net Worth: $27,655,424,160
Earnings: $1,592,577,070
Emp.: 167,248
Fiscal Year-end: 02/29/24
Holding Company
N.A.I.C.S.: 551112
Katsuhiro Goto *(VP)*

Subsidiaries:

7dream.com Co., Ltd. (1)
8-8 Nibancho, Chiyoda-ku, Tokyo, 102-8466, Japan
Tel.: (81) 362383691
Web Site: https://www.7dream.com
Emp.: 79
Online Shopping Services
N.A.I.C.S.: 561499

Akachan Honpo Co., Ltd. (1)
3-3-21 Minamihonmachi, Chuo Ward, Osaka, 541-0054, Japan
Tel.: (81) 662510625
Web Site: https://www.akachan.jp
Emp.: 3,768
Toys & Baby Apparel Retailer
N.A.I.C.S.: 459120

Barneys Japan Co., Ltd. (1)
MFPR Kojimachi Building 5F 5-7-2 Kojimachi, Chiyoda-ku, Tokyo, 100-0001, Japan
Tel.: (81) 5036153600
Web Site: https://www.barneys.co.jp
Emp.: 635
Departmental Store Operator
N.A.I.C.S.: 455110

Gottsuobin Co., Ltd. (1)
Kojimachi Hachiman Building 5F 2-4 Kojimachi, Chiyoda-ku, Tokyo, 102-0083, Japan **(100%)**
Tel.: (81) 352136111
Web Site: https://www.gottsuobin.co.jp
Emp.: 24
Food Product Retailer
N.A.I.C.S.: 445298
Masanori Yamada *(CEO)*

IY Foods K.K. (1)
2-717-8 Toyonodai, Kazo, 349-1148, Saitama, Japan **(100%)**
Tel.: (81) 480727311
Web Site: https://www.iyfoods.co.jp
Emp.: 310
Processed Food Mfr & Whslr
N.A.I.C.S.: 311991
Hideto Fukuda *(Pres & Dir)*

Ikebukuro Shopping Park Co., Ltd. (1)
1-29-1 Minamiikebukuro, Toshima-ku, Tokyo, 171-8532, Japan

AND PRIVATE COMPANIES

Tel.: (81) 339822111
Web Site: https://www.web-isp.co.jp
Shopping Mall Operation Services
N.A.I.C.S.: 531120

Ito-Yokado Co., Ltd. (1)
8-8 Nibancho, Chiyoda-ku, Tokyo, 102-8450, Japan
Tel.: (81) 362382111
Web Site: http://www.itoyokado.co.jp
Sales Range: $5-14.9 Billion
Emp.: 26,083
Supermarkets & Hypermarkets Operator
N.A.I.C.S.: 445110

Subsidiary (Non-US):

Hua Tang Yokado Commercial Co., Ltd. (2)
Qianhe Home 108 North Fourth Ring East Road, Chaoyang District, Beijing, 100012, China
Tel.: (86) 1064910099
Web Site: http://www.ht-store.com
Sales Range: $150-199.9 Million
Emp.: 500
General Merchandise Stores
N.A.I.C.S.: 455219

K.K. Terre Verte (1)
222-1 Tomisato, Kitami, 099-0876, Hokkaido, Japan
Tel.: (81) 157332211
Food Product Retailer
N.A.I.C.S.: 445298

K.K. York Keibi (1)
8-8 Nibancho, Chiyoda-ku, Tokyo, Japan
Tel.: (81) 36 238 2802
Web Site: https://www.yorkkeibi.co.jp
Security System Services
N.A.I.C.S.: 561621

Life Foods Co., Ltd. (1)
Esaka-cho 1-13-41 Esaka NK Building 2nd floor, Suita, 564-0063, Osaka, Japan
Tel.: (81) 663388331
Web Site: https://www.meshiya.co.jp
Restaurant Operators
N.A.I.C.S.: 722511
Tsuyoshi Ohira (Pres, Chief Dir-Sls & Dir-FF Bus)

Mall & SC Development Inc. (1)
8-8 Nibancho, Chiyoda-ku, Tokyo, 102-8452, Japan
Tel.: (81) 362382691
Web Site: https://www.createlink.jp
Real Estate Manangement Services
N.A.I.C.S.: 531390
Kamei Atsushi (Chm)

Marron Style Co., Ltd. (1)
801 Shimano Building 2-1-4 Nakazaki, Kita-ku, Osaka, 530-0016, Japan
Tel.: (81) 64 256 7359
Web Site: https://www.marron-style.jp
Ecommerce Services
N.A.I.C.S.: 424350

Marudai Co., Ltd. (1)
225-4 Toyoda nishinoshima, Shizuoka, Iwata, 438-0835, Japan
Tel.: (81) 538351331
Web Site: https://www.marudai1.com
Super Market Stores Operating Services
N.A.I.C.S.: 445110

Nissen Holdings Co., Ltd. (1)
26 Nishikujoin-cho, Minami-ku, Kyoto, 601-8412, Japan (100%)
Tel.: (81) 756822010
Web Site: https://www.nissen-hd.co.jp
Sales Range: $1-4.9 Billion
Emp.: 1,319
Holding Company; Mail Order Retailer
N.A.I.C.S.: 551112

Seven & i Create Link Co., Ltd. (1)
8-8 Nibancho, Chiyoda-ku, Tokyo, 102-8452, Japan
Tel.: (81) 36 238 2690
Web Site: https://www.createlink.jp
Real Estate Services
N.A.I.C.S.: 531390

Seven & i Food Systems Co., Ltd. (1)
4-5 Nibancho, Chiyoda-ku, Tokyo, 102-8415, Japan
Tel.: (81) 362383570

Web Site: https://www.7andi-fs.co.jp
Emp.: 11,343
Restaurant Operating Services
N.A.I.C.S.: 722513
Masami Komatsu (Pres & CEO)

Seven & i Netmedia Co., Ltd. (1)
Sumitomo Fudosan Nibancho First Building 2F 4-5 Nibancho, Chiyoda-ku, Tokyo, 102-8436, Japan
Tel.: (81) 368665711
Web Site: https://www.7andinm.co.jp
Emp.: 253
Information Technology Business Management Services
N.A.I.C.S.: 541611

Seven & i Publishing Co., Ltd. (1)
Royal Building 2nd Floor, Chiyoda-Ku, Tokyo, 102-0084, Japan
Tel.: (81) 362382888
Web Site: http://www.7andi-pub.co.jp
Magazine Publishing Services
N.A.I.C.S.: 513120

Seven CS Card Service Co., Ltd. (1)
4-5 Nibancho, Chiyoda-ku, Tokyo, 102-8436, Japan
Tel.: (81) 35 996 9125
Web Site: https://www.7cs-card.jp
Credit Card Issuing Services
N.A.I.C.S.: 522210

Seven Card Service Co., Ltd. (1)
4-5 Nibancho, Chiyoda-ku, Tokyo, 102-8435, Japan
Tel.: (81) 362382952
Web Site: https://www.7card.co.jp
Sales Range: $50-74.9 Million
Emp.: 350
Credit Card Processing Services
N.A.I.C.S.: 522320

Seven Culture Network Co., Ltd. (1)
8-8 Nibancho, Chiyoda-ku, Tokyo, 102-0084, Japan
Tel.: (81) 359493844
Web Site: https://www.7cn.co.jp
Culture & Classroom Management Services
N.A.I.C.S.: 561499

Seven Financial Service Co., Ltd. (1)
4-5 Nibancho, Chiyoda-ku, Tokyo, 102-8435, Japan
Tel.: (81) 362382946
Web Site: https://www.7fin.jp
Emp.: 1,074
Financial Management Services
N.A.I.C.S.: 523999

Seven Health Care Co., Ltd. (1)
8-8 Nibancho, Chiyoda-ku, Tokyo, 1028450, Japan
Tel.: (81) 362382366
Web Site: http://www.7healthcare.co.jp
Emp.: 60
Pharmaceuticals Product Mfr
N.A.I.C.S.: 325412
Yasuhiro Nagakura (Mgr)

Seven Internet Lab. Co., Ltd. (1)
5-4 Kojimachi Kojimachidaito Bldg, Chiyoda-Ku, Tokyo, 102-0083, Japan
Tel.: (81) 368665541
Web Site: http://www.7inetlab.jp
Business Software Development Services
N.A.I.C.S.: 541511

Seven Net Shopping Co., Ltd. (1)
5-4 Kojimachi JPR Kojimachi Building, Chiyoda-Ku, Tokyo, 102-0083, Japan
Tel.: (81) 368665729
Web Site: https://company.7netshopping.jp
Online Shopping Services
N.A.I.C.S.: 425120

Seven Pay Co., Ltd. (1)
4-5 Nibancho, Chiyoda-ku, Tokyo, Japan
Tel.: (81) 34 500 8805
Web Site: https://www.7pay.co.jp
Payment Processing Services
N.A.I.C.S.: 522320

Seven-Eleven Japan Co., Ltd. (1)
8-8 Nibancho, Chiyoda-ku, Tokyo, 102-8455, Japan
Tel.: (81) 362383711
Web Site: https://www.sej.co.jp
Emp.: 8,930
Convenience Store Operator

N.A.I.C.S.: 445131
Kazuki Furuya (Chm)

Subsidiary (US):

7-Eleven, Inc. (2)
1722 Routh St, Dallas, TX 75201-2506 (100%)
Tel.: (214) 965-0990
Web Site: http://www.7-eleven.com
Sales Range: $5-14.9 Billion
Convenience Store Operator & Franchisor
N.A.I.C.S.: 445131
Joseph Michael DePinto (Pres & CEO)

Subsidiary (Non-US):

7-Eleven Canada, Inc. (3)
10416 King George Blvd, Surrey, V3T 2W8, BC, Canada (100%)
Tel.: (604) 585-8160
Web Site: https://stores.7-eleven.ca
Sales Range: $600-649.9 Million
Emp.: 5,400
Convenience Store Operator & Franchisor
N.A.I.C.S.: 445131

Subsidiary (Domestic):

Handee Marts, Inc. (3)
714 Warrendale Rd, Gibsonia, PA 15044-6145
Tel.: (724) 625-2711
Web Site: http://www.handeemarts.com
Sales Range: $100-124.9 Million
Emp.: 248
Provider of Gasoline Service Stations
N.A.I.C.S.: 533110

Seven-Eleven Hawaii, Inc. (3)
1755 Nuuanu Ave 2nd Fl, Honolulu, HI 96817
Tel.: (808) 526-1711
Web Site: http://7elevenhawaii.com
Convenience Store Operator & Franchisor
N.A.I.C.S.: 445131

Speedway LLC (3)
500 Speedway Dr, Enon, OH 45323
Tel.: (937) 864-3000
Web Site: http://www.speedway.com
Gasoline Stations, Convenience Stores & Truck Stops
N.A.I.C.S.: 457110
Glenn M. Plumby (COO & Sr VP)

Subsidiary (Non-US):

Seven-Eleven (Beijing) Co., Ltd. (2)
No 5 Dongzhimen Inner Street, Dongcheng District, Beijing, 100007, China
Tel.: (86) 1084060177
Web Site: https://www.7-11bj.com
Convenience Stores Operating Services
N.A.I.C.S.: 445131

Seven-Meal Service Co., Ltd. (1)
8-8 Nibancho Seven Eleven Japan Nai, Chiyoda-Ku, Tokyo, 102-0084, Japan
Tel.: (81) 362383711
Web Site: http://www.7meal.jp
Meal Delivery Services
N.A.I.C.S.: 624210

Shell Garden Co., Ltd. (1)
8-8 Nibancho, Chiyoda-ku, Tokyo, 102-8452, Japan
Tel.: (81) 332615931
Web Site: https://www.garden.co.jp
Emp.: 1,010
Fresh Foods Retailer
N.A.I.C.S.: 445298

Terube Ltd. (1)
222-1 Tomisato, Kitami, 099-0876, Hokkaido, Japan
Tel.: (81) 15 733 2211
Web Site: https://terube.jp
Mushroom Farming Services
N.A.I.C.S.: 111411

The Loft Co., Ltd. (1)
3rd 4th 6th and 7th floor 4-2-6 Kudankita, Chiyoda-ku, Tokyo, 102-0073, Japan
Tel.: (81) 352106210
Web Site: https://www.loft.co.jp
Emp.: 5,085
Household Lifestyle Products Retailer
N.A.I.C.S.: 459999

SEVEN BANK LTD.

Yatsugatake Kogen Lodge Co., Ltd. (1)
2244-1 Uminokuchi Minamimaki-mura, Minamisaku-gun Yatsugatake Highlands, 384-1302, Japan
Tel.: (81) 267983131
Web Site: https://www.yatsugatake.co.jp
Emp.: 75
Home Management Services
N.A.I.C.S.: 721110

York Co., Ltd. (1)
8-8 Nibancho, Chiyoda-ku, Tokyo, Japan
Tel.: (81) 362383266
Web Site: https://www.york-inc.com
Sales Range: $800-899.9 Million
Emp.: 7,503
Supermarket
N.A.I.C.S.: 445110

York-Benimaru Co., Ltd. (1)
18 2 Asahi 2 Chome, Koriyama, Fukushima, 963 8543, Japan
Tel.: (81) 249243111
Web Site: http://www.yorkbeni.co.jp
Sales Range: $1-4.9 Billion
Emp.: 10,000
Supermarket
N.A.I.C.S.: 445110
Nobutake Sato (Chm)

SEVEN BANK LTD.

1 Kanda Aioicho, Chiyoda-ku, Tokyo, 101-0029, Japan
Tel.: (81) 332113041
Web Site:
https://location.sevenbank.co.jp
Year Founded: 2001
SVNBY—(OTCIQ)
Rev.: $1,500,245,120
Assets: $12,702,802,640
Liabilities: $10,241,740,080
Net Worth: $2,461,062,560
Earnings: $182,506,720
Emp.: 549
Fiscal Year-end: 03/31/23
Banking Services
N.A.I.C.S.: 522110
Yasuaki Funatake (Pres)

Subsidiaries:

Bank Business Factory Co., Ltd. (1)
134 Kobe-cho Kanagawa Yokohama Business Park East Tower 2F, Hodogaya-ku, Yokohama, 240-0005, Japan
Tel.: (81) 45 348 8884
Web Site:
https://www.bankbusinessfactory.co.jp
Emp.: 600
Financial Services
N.A.I.C.S.: 523999

Fcti, Inc. (1)
11766 Wilshire Blvd Ste 300, Los Angeles, CA 90025
Web Site: https://fcti.com
ATM Network & Services Provider
N.A.I.C.S.: 522390
Robel Gugsa (CEO & CTO)

Financial Consulting & Trading International, Inc. (1)
1801 Avenue of the Stars Ste 1225, Century City, CA 90067
Tel.: (310) 201-2535
Web Site: http://www.fcti.net
Sales Range: $25-49,9 Million
Emp.: 35
Automated Teller Machine Distr & Support Services
N.A.I.C.S.: 423420
Robel Gugsa (CEO & CTO)

PT. Abadi Tambah Mulia Internasional (1)
Bellezza Office Tower GP Tower 16th Floor Units 1 and 2 Jl, Permata Hijau Artery RT 4/RW 2 North Grogol Kebayoran Lama, Jakarta, 12210, Indonesia
Tel.: (62) 215 085 8600
Web Site: https://www.atm-intl.com
Financial Services
N.A.I.C.S.: 523999
Jo Watabe (Pres)

Seven Payment Services, Ltd. (1)

SEVEN BANK LTD.

Seven Bank Ltd.—(Continued)

1-6-1 Marunouchi, Chiyoda-ku, Tokyo, 100-0005, Japan
Tel.: (81) 12 058 8789
Web Site: https://www.7ps.jp
Financial Services
N.A.I.C.S.: 523999

SEVEN GROUP HOLDINGS LIMITED

Level 30 175 Liverpool Street, Sydney, 2000, NSW, Australia
Tel.: (61) 287777574 AU
Web Site:
https://www.sevengroup.com.au
Year Founded: 2010
SGH—(ASX)
Rev.: $7,089,676,787
Assets: $9,083,934,258
Liabilities: $6,334,268,136
Net Worth: $2,749,666,121
Earnings: $348,624,464
Emp.: 13,731
Fiscal Year-end: 06/30/24
Holding Company; Media Products & Services; Construction & Engineering Equipment Dealer & Services
N.A.I.C.S.: 551112
Warren Walter Coatsworth (Sec)

Subsidiaries:

AllightPrimax FZCO (1)
Plot S 50119 Jebel Ali Free Zone South JAFZA, Dubai, United Arab Emirates
Tel.: (971) 4 889 4805
Lighting Tower Mfr & Distr
N.A.I.C.S.: 335139

Boral Limited (1)
Level 18 15 Blue Street, North Sydney, 2060, NSW, Australia **(100%)**
Tel.: (61) 292206300
Web Site: https://www.boral.com
Rev.: $2,264,781,021
Assets: $3,371,925,571
Liabilities: $1,918,080,046
Net Worth: $1,453,845,525
Earnings: $736,002,114
Emp.: 4,749
Fiscal Year-end: 06/30/2022
Construction Materials Mfr & Distr
N.A.I.C.S.: 327331
Kylie FitzGerald (Dir-IR & Grp Comm)

Subsidiary (Domestic):

Alsafe Premix Concrete Pty Ltd (2)
26 Encore Avenue, Somerton, 3062, VIC, Australia
Tel.: (61) 393086300
Web Site: https://www.alsafepremix.com.au
Concrete Distr
N.A.I.C.S.: 423320

Boral Building Materials Pty Ltd (2)
Level 18 15 Blue St, North Sydney, 2060, NSW, Australia
Tel.: (61) 292206300
Web Site: http://www.boral.com.au
Emp.: 80
Construction Materials Mfr
N.A.I.C.S.: 327120
Stephen Dadd (Exec Gen Mgr)

Subsidiary (Domestic):

Boral Concrete Products Pty. Ltd. (3)
Level 3 40 Mount St, North Sydney, 2060, NSW, Australia **(100%)**
Tel.: (61) 292206300
Web Site: http://www.boral.com.au
Sales Range: $1-4.9 Billion
Mfr & Distribution of Concrete Masonry Products & Manufacturer of Precast Concrete Floor & Wall Panels
N.A.I.C.S.: 238140

Boral International Pty Ltd (3)
Level 18 15 Blue St, North Sydney, 2060, NSW, Australia
Tel.: (61) 292206300
Web Site: http://www.boral.com.au
Emp.: 80
Construction Materials Mfr

N.A.I.C.S.: 327120
David Marinar (Pres)

Subsidiary (Non-US):

Boral Concrete (Thailand) Ltd (4)
12 Floor PB Tower 1000/51 Sukhumvit 71 North Klongton, Watana, Bangkok, 10110, Thailand
Tel.: (66) 22788800
Web Site: http://www.boral.co.th
Concrete Product Distr
N.A.I.C.S.: 423320

Subsidiary (Domestic):

Boral Construction Materials Ltd (2)
Greystanes House Clunies Ross Street, Prospect, NSW, Australia
Tel.: (61) 363361333
Construction Materials Distr
N.A.I.C.S.: 423320

Subsidiary (Domestic):

Bayview Pty Ltd (3)
251 Salmon St, Port Melbourne, 3207, VIC, Australia
Tel.: (61) 292206300
Web Site: http://www.boral.com.au
Sales Range: $125-149.9 Million
Emp.: 40
Construction Material Mfr & Sales
N.A.I.C.S.: 327331

Boral Bricks Pty. Ltd. (3)
L 3 40 Mount St, North Sydney, 2060, NSW, Australia
Tel.: (61) 292206300
Web Site: http://www.boral.com.au
Emp.: 70
Clay Brick Mfr
N.A.I.C.S.: 327120

Boral Building Products Ltd (3)
Level 3 40 Mount St, North Sydney, 2060, NSW, Australia
Tel.: (61) 292206300
Web Site: http://www.boral.com.au
Emp.: 80
Construction Materials Mfr & Distr
N.A.I.C.S.: 327331
Mike Kane (CEO & Mng Dir)

Boral Contracting Pty Ltd (3)
2 Craig Rd, Kalgoorlie, 6430, WA, Australia
Tel.: (61) 893333400
Web Site: http://www.borel.com
Sales Range: $25-49.9 Million
Emp.: 10
Construction Materials Mfr
N.A.I.C.S.: 327331

Boral Masonry Ltd (3)
Clunies Ross St, Prospect, 2145, NSW, Australia
Tel.: (61) 298402333
Construction Materials Distr
N.A.I.C.S.: 423320

Boral Recycling Pty Ltd (3)
End Of Reconciliation Road, Prospect, 2148, NSW, Australia
Tel.: (61) 290335000
Web Site: http://www.boral.com.au
Emp.: 30
Building Materials Distr
N.A.I.C.S.: 423320
Charlie Bounassif (Gen Mgr)

Boral Shared Business Services Pty Ltd (3)
L 3 40 Mount St, North Sydney, 2060, NSW, Australia
Tel.: (61) 292206300
Web Site: http://www.boral.com.au
Sales Range: $50-74.9 Million
Emp.: 70
Construction Materials Mfr & Distr
N.A.I.C.S.: 327331

Boral Windows Systems Ltd (3)
188 Canterbury Road, Bayswater, 3153, VIC, Australia
Tel.: (61) 3 9721 0700
Glass Products Mfr
N.A.I.C.S.: 327211

De Martin & Gasparini Pty Ltd (3)
Unit B 7 Worth Street, Chullora, 2190, NSW, Australia

Tel.: (61) 297485100
Web Site:
https://www.demartinandgasparini.com.au
Emp.: 400
Building Materials Distr
N.A.I.C.S.: 423320
Louie Mazzarolo (Mng Dir)

Subsidiary (Domestic):

De Martin & Gasparini Concrete Placers Pty Ltd (4)
Bennelong Rd, Homebush, 2140, NSW, Australia
Tel.: (61) 297485100
Concrete Products Mfr
N.A.I.C.S.: 327320

De Martin & Gasparini Contractors Pty Ltd (4)
16 Hill Road Homebush Way, PO Box 524, Sydney, 2127, NSW, Australia
Tel.: (61) 297485100
Concrete Products Mfr
N.A.I.C.S.: 327320

De Martin & Gasparini Pumping Pty Ltd (4)
16 Hill Rd, Homebush Bay, 2127, NSW, Australia
Tel.: (61) 297485100
Concrete Products Mfr
N.A.I.C.S.: 327320

Pro Concrete Group Pty Limited (4)
4 Ern Harley Drive, PO Box 963, Burleigh Heads, 4220, QLD, Australia
Tel.: (61) 755937860
Web Site: http://www.proconcrete.com.au
Concrete Distr
N.A.I.C.S.: 423320

Subsidiary (Domestic):

Midland Brick Limited (3)
321 Great Northern Highway, Middle Swan, Perth, 6056, WA, Australia
Tel.: (61) 131540
Web Site: http://www.midlandbrick.com.au
Sales Range: $25-49.9 Million
Emp.: 100
Construction Materials Mfr
N.A.I.C.S.: 327331
Jonnene Fowler (Gen Mgr)

Road Surfaces Group Pty Ltd (3)
18 Oak St, Barcaldine, 4725, QLD, Australia
Tel.: (61) 746511585
Sales Range: $1-4.9 Billion
Emp.: 2
Construction Materials Distr
N.A.I.C.S.: 423320
Kevin MacDonald (Mgr)

Subsidiary (US):

Boral Industries Inc. (2)
200 Manville Ct E Ste 310, Roswell, GA 30076 **(100%)**
Tel.: (770) 645-4500
Web Site: http://www.boralbricks.com
Holding Company
N.A.I.C.S.: 327120

Subsidiary (Domestic):

Boral Lifetile Inc. (3)
7575 Irvine Ctr Dr Ste 100, Irvine, CA 92618-2930 **(100%)**
Tel.: (949) 756-1605
Sales Range: $300-349.9 Million
Emp.: 800
Concrete Roof Tile Mfr & Whslr
N.A.I.C.S.: 327390
Christian Doelle (VP-Sls & Mktg)

Subsidiary (Domestic):

Boral Roofing LLC (4)
7575 Irvine Ctr Dr Ste 100, Irvine, CA 92618
Web Site: http://www.boralroof.com
Building Materials Mfr
N.A.I.C.S.: 327120
Darren Schulz (Pres & CEO)

Subsidiary (Domestic):

Boral Timber Inc (3)
6 Campbell CtCt, Novato, CA 94947-3858
Tel.: (415) 209-6192

INTERNATIONAL PUBLIC

Timber Logging Services
N.A.I.C.S.: 113110

Krestmark Industries, LP (3)
3950 Bastille Rd Ste 100, Dallas, TX 75212
Tel.: (214) 237-5055
Metal Window & Door Mfr
N.A.I.C.S.: 332321
Steve Rosenthal (Gen Counsel & VP)

Division (Domestic):

LA Ash, Inc. (3)
2651 E Napoleon St, Sulphur, LA 70663
Tel.: (337) 426-0826
Web Site: http://www.laash.net
Coke Fired CFB Calcined Limestone Products Marketer
N.A.I.C.S.: 212322

Subsidiary (Non-US):

Boral Investments (2)
Nieuwe Stationsstraat 10, 6811 KS, Arnhem, Netherlands
Tel.: (31) 263201169
Real Estate Manangement Services
N.A.I.C.S.: 531390

Subsidiary (Domestic):

Boral Investments Pty Ltd (2)
Level 3 40 Mount Street, Sydney, 2060, NSW, Australia
Tel.: (61) 292206300
Web Site: http://www.boral.com.au
Sales Range: $50-74.9 Million
Emp.: 100
Investment Management Service
N.A.I.C.S.: 523999

Boral Resources Ltd. (2)
Clunies Ross Street, Prospect, 2148, NSW, Australia **(100%)**
Tel.: (61) 290335000
Web Site: http://www.boralresources.com.au
Sales Range: $100-124.9 Million
Emp.: 480
Quarrying, Sand Extraction, Premixed Concrete
N.A.I.C.S.: 212321
Mike Kane (CEO)

Subsidiary (Domestic):

Boral Resources (Qld) Pty Ltd (3)
Level 6 88 Musk Avenue, Kelvin Grove, 4059, QLD, Australia
Tel.: (61) 738677600
Web Site: http://www.boral.com.au
Emp.: 100
Construction Material Mfr & Whslr
N.A.I.C.S.: 327331

Subsidiary (Domestic):

Allens Asphalt Pty Ltd (4)
22 Piper Street, PO Box 1106, Caboolture, 4510, QLD, Australia
Tel.: (61) 413546529
Web Site: http://www.allensasphalt.com.au
Emp.: 100
Road Construction Equipment Rental Services
N.A.I.C.S.: 532120
Glenn Ducat (Mgr-Sys & Safety)

Q-Crete Premix Pty Ltd (4)
PO Box 1278, Stafford, 4053, QLD, Australia
Tel.: (61) 300727383
Web Site: https://www.qcrete.com.au
Concrete Distr
N.A.I.C.S.: 423320

Subsidiary (Domestic):

Boral Resources (SA) Ltd (3)
Level 1/ 49 The Pde, Norwood, 5067, SA, Australia
Tel.: (61) 884250400
Web Site: https://www.boral.com.au
Construction Materials Distr
N.A.I.C.S.: 423320

Boral Resources (Vic) Pty Ltd (3)
251 7th St, Port Melbourne, 3207, VIC, Australia
Tel.: (61) 395087111
Web Site: https://www.boral.com.au

AND PRIVATE COMPANIES

Construction Materials Mfr
N.A.I.C.S.: 327120

Subsidiary (Domestic):

Bayview Quarries Pty Ltd (4)
Level 3 40 Mount Street, Sydney, 2060, NSW, Australia
Tel.: (61) 292206300
Web Site: http://www.boral.com.au
Emp.: 70
Construction Materials Mfr
N.A.I.C.S.: 327120
Mike Kane *(CEO)*

Subsidiary (Non-US):

CMI Springs (2)
7a Carmont Place, Mount Wellington, Auckland, 1060, New Zealand (100%)
Tel.: (64) 95794089
Web Site: https://www.cmisprings.com
Sales Range: $25-49.9 Million
Emp.: 50
Mfr & Maintainance of Elevators & Escalators; Scaffolding & Material Handling Systems
N.A.I.C.S.: 238290
Barry Agnew *(Gen Mgr-Product Mfg)*

Joint Venture (Non-US):

Caribbean Roof Tile Company Limited (2)
C/o ABS ANSA Centre 1st Floor Guardian Media Ltd Building, Uriah Butler Highway & Endeavour Road, Chaguanas, Trinidad & Tobago (50%)
Tel.: (868) 2354227
Web Site: https://www.ansamcal.com
Piece Goods Notions & Dry Goods Whslr
N.A.I.C.S.: 424310

Subsidiary (Domestic):

Concrite Pty Ltd (2)
Level 1 36 Eton Street, Sutherland, 2232, NSW, Australia
Tel.: (61) 295456111
Web Site: https://www.concrite.com.au
Concrete Mfr & Distr
N.A.I.C.S.: 327320
Donn Jeffrey Eagleson *(Pres)*

Found Concrete Pty. Ltd. (2)
T2/39 Delhi Rd, North Ryde, 2113, NSW, Australia
Tel.: (61) 1300980626
Web Site: https://hello.foundconcrete.com.au
Concrete Product Distr
N.A.I.C.S.: 424690

Subsidiary (US):

Headwaters Incorporated (2)
10701 S River Front Pkwy Ste 300, South Jordan, UT 84095 (100%)
Tel.: (801) 984-9400
Web Site: http://www.headwaters.com
Sales Range: $900-999.9 Million
Construction Materials & Energy Industry Products & Services
N.A.I.C.S.: 423320
Sharon Madden *(VP-IR)*

Subsidiary (Domestic):

Boral Building Products Inc. (3)
29797 Beck Rd, Wixom, MI 48393
Tel.: (248) 668-6400
Construction Materials Mfr
N.A.I.C.S.: 423390

Boral Materials LLC (3)
10701 S River Frnt Pkwy Ste 300, South Jordan, UT 84095
Tel.: (801) 984-9400
Chemicals & Allied Products Supplier
N.A.I.C.S.: 424690

Dutch Quality Stone, Inc. (3)
18012 Dover Rd, Mount Eaton, OH 44659
Tel.: (330) 359-7866
Web Site: http://www.dutchqualitystone.com
Commercial Building Materials Distr
N.A.I.C.S.: 444180

Eldorado Stone, LLC (3)
3817 Ocean Ranch Blvd Ste 114, Oceanside, CA 92056
Tel.: (760) 736-3232
Web Site: https://www.eldoradostone.com
Stone Veneers Mfr
N.A.I.C.S.: 327390

Subsidiary (Domestic):

Eldorado Stone Operations LLC (4)
3817 Ocean Ranch Blvd Ste 114, Oceanside, CA 92056
Tel.: (760) 736-3232
Cut Stone & Stone Product Mfr
N.A.I.C.S.: 327991

Subsidiary (Domestic):

Headwaters Energy Services Corp. (3)
10701 S River Front Pkwy Ste 300, South Jordan, UT 84095
Tel.: (801) 984-9400
Construction Materials & Energy Industry Products Mfr
N.A.I.C.S.: 423320

Palestine Concrete Tile Company, L.P. (3)
2500 W Reagan St, Palestine, TX 75801
Tel.: (903) 729-2217
Concrete Products Mfr
N.A.I.C.S.: 327331

Subsidiary (Non-US):

Piedras Headwaters, S. de RL de CV (3)
Camino Martin 2500 BC Avenida Baja California 2, Las Palmas, Tijuana, Mexico
Tel.: (52) 6646380088
Construction Materials Whslr
N.A.I.C.S.: 423320

Subsidiary (Domestic):

Synthetic Materials LLC (3)
6009 Brownsboro Park Blvd, Louisville, KY 40207
Tel.: (502) 895-2810
Web Site: https://synmat.com
Mechanical & Industrial Engineering Services
N.A.I.C.S.: 541330

Joint Venture (Domestic):

USG Boral Building Products Pty Limited (2)
Level 3 40 Mount Street, Sydney, NSW 2060, Australia (50%)
Tel.: (61) 2 9220 6300
Web Site: http://www.usgboral.com
Plasterboard & Construction Materials Mfr
N.A.I.C.S.: 423320
Frederic de Rougemont *(CEO)*

Subsidiary (Domestic):

Lympike Pty Ltd (3)
71 Milperra Rd, Revesby, 2212, NSW, Australia
Tel.: (61) 297923022
Sales Range: $25-49.9 Million
Emp.: 20
Construction Materials Distr
N.A.I.C.S.: 423320
Mark Nuner *(Gen Mgr)*

Coates Group Holdings Pty. Limited (1)
36 Doody Street, Alexandria, 2015, NSW, Australia (100%)
Tel.: (61) 296993122
Web Site: http://www.coatesgroup.com
Holding Company; Commercial Construction Vehicles, Equipment & Support Facilities Rental, Training & Technical Consulting Services
N.A.I.C.S.: 551112
Leo Coates *(CEO)*

Subsidiary (Domestic):

Coates Hire Operations Pty. Limited (2)
Level 6 241 O'Riordan St, Mascot, 2020, NSW, Australia
Tel.: (61) 297013300
Web Site: http://www.coateshire.com.au
Commercial Construction Vehicles, Equipment & Support Facilities Rental, Training & Technical Consulting Services
N.A.I.C.S.: 532412
Ben Waterhouse *(CIO)*

PT AllightSykes (1)
Duta Indah Iconic Blok E9-10 JL M H Thamrin Kebon Nanas, Panunggan Utara - Pinang, Tangerang, 15143, Indonesia
Tel.: (62) 212 259 4438
Web Site: https://allightsykes.co.id
Construction Equipment Distr
N.A.I.C.S.: 423810

SGH Energy Pty Limited (1)
Level 23 530 Collins Street, Melbourne, 3000, VIC, Australia (100%)
Tel.: (61) 396602500
Oil & Gas Exploration Company
N.A.I.C.S.: 211120
Susan Robutti *(CFO & Sec)*

Sitech (WA) Pty Limited (1)
1/8 Hasler Road, Osborne Park, 6017, WA, Australia
Tel.: (61) 89 392 7700
Web Site: https://www.sitechwa.com.au
Construction Technology Services
N.A.I.C.S.: 236220

Sitech Solutions Pty Limited (1)
2 Voyager Circuit, Glendenning, 2761, NSW, Australia
Tel.: (61) 26 788 2155
Web Site: https://www.sitechsolutions.com.au
Construction Technology Services
N.A.I.C.S.: 236220

Unwired Australia Pty. Limited (1)
Level 21 1 Market Street, Sydney, 2000, NSW, Australia (100%)
Tel.: (61) 292316055
Web Site: http://www.unwired.com.au
Fixed Wireless Telecommunications Network Development & Broadband Internet Services
N.A.I.C.S.: 517810

WesTrac Holdings Pty. Limited (1)
128-136 Great Eastern Highway, Guildford, 6055, WA, Australia (100%)
Tel.: (61) 893779444
Web Site: http://www.westrac.com.au
Holding Company; Construction, Mining & Engineering Vehicle Dealerships Operator, Rental Services & Parts Retailer
N.A.I.C.S.: 551112

Subsidiary (Domestic):

National Hire Group Limited (2)
12 Hoskins Road, Landsdale, Perth, 6065, WA, Australia (100%)
Tel.: (61) 893020000
Web Site: http://www.nationalhire.com.au
Holding Company; Construction Equipment Rental Services & Utility Equipment Distr
N.A.I.C.S.: 551112
Richard Court *(Chm)*

Subsidiary (Domestic):

Allight Pty Ltd (3)
12 Hoskins Road, Landsdale, Perth, WA, Australia (100%)
Tel.: (61) 893027000
Web Site: https://allight.com
Sales Range: $100-124.9 Million
Emp.: 120
Lighting Tower Mfr & Commercial Utility Equipment Distr
N.A.I.C.S.: 237130
Craig Dettman *(CEO)*

National Hire Trading Pty Limited (3)
12 Hoskins Road, Perth, 6065, Landsdale, Australia (100%)
Tel.: (61) 893020000
Web Site: http://www.nationalhire.com.au
Office Machinery & Equipment Rental & Leasing
N.A.I.C.S.: 532420

Subsidiary (Domestic):

WesTrac Pty. Limited (2)
128-136 Great Eastern Hwy South, Guildford, 6055, WA, Australia
Tel.: (61) 893779444

Web Site: https://www.westrac.com.au
Sales Range: $25-49.9 Million
Emp.: 100
Construction, Mining & Engineering Vehicle Dealerships Operator & Parts Retailer
N.A.I.C.S.: 441227
Peter Hansen *(CFO)*

Subsidiary (Non-US):

WesTrac (China) Machinery Equipment Limited (3)
Sky Centre Tower A No 22 Wanyuan Street, Econ-Tech Development Area, Beijing, 100176, China (100%)
Tel.: (86) 1059021666
Web Site: http://www.westrac.com.au
Construction, Mining & Engineering Vehicle Dealerships Operator & Parts Retailer
N.A.I.C.S.: 441227

SEVEN HILL INDUSTRIES LIMITED

Ground Floor Daya Sarita C Wing Gokul Dham Opp RBI Quarters, Goregaon East, Mumbai, 400063, India
Tel.: (91) 2267300585
Web Site: https://www.sevenhillsindustries.com
511760—(BOM)
Rev.: $29,423
Assets: $2,624,087
Liabilities: $2,622,145
Net Worth: $1,942
Earnings: $17,601
Fiscal Year-end: 03/31/23
Financial Management Services
N.A.I.C.S.: 523999

SEVEN INDUSTRIES CO., LTD.

1006 Makino, Minokamo, 505-0016, Gifu, Japan
Tel.: (81) 574287800
Web Site: https://www.seven-gr.co.jp
Year Founded: 1961
7896—(TKS)
Sales Range: $100-124.9 Million
Emp.: 392
Building Construction Material Mfr & Distr
N.A.I.C.S.: 332323
Yoshiaki Eikichi *(Pres)*

SEVEN PRINCIPLES AG

Ettore-Bugatti-Strasse 6-14, 51149, Cologne, Germany
Tel.: (49) 221920070
Web Site: https://www.7p-group.com
T3T1—(STU)
Sales Range: Less than $1 Million
Information Technology Management Services
N.A.I.C.S.: 541611
Michael Pesch *(CEO)*

SEVEN SQUARED

Sea Containers House 20 Upper Ground, London, SE1 9PD, United Kingdom
Tel.: (44) 2077757775
Web Site: http://www.sevensquared.co.uk
Year Founded: 2007
Emp.: 200
Advertising Agencies
N.A.I.C.S.: 541810
Michael Potter *(Chm)*

SEVEN TECHNOLOGIES LTD.

Unit 23/24 Crescent Business Park, Lisburn, BT28 2GN, Co Antrim, United Kingdom
Tel.: (44) 2892 605200
Web Site: http://www.seventechgroup.com
Sales Range: $25-49.9 Million
Emp.: 100
Software Engineering Services

SEVEN TECHNOLOGIES LTD.

Seven Technologies Ltd.—(Continued)
N.A.I.C.S.: 513210

SEVEN UTILITIES AND POWER PUBLIC CO., LTD.
73 Mahachol Building Soi Sukhumvit 62 Sukhumvit Road Phrakhanong Tai, Prakanong, Bangkok, 10260, Thailand
Tel.: (66) 27415700
Web Site: http://www.sevenup.co.th
Year Founded: 1995
7UP—(THA)
Rev.: $29,140,732
Assets: $108,346,443
Liabilities: $24,039,045
Net Worth: $84,307,398
Earnings: ($5,975,457)
Emp.: 47
Fiscal Year-end: 12/31/23
LPG Distr
N.A.I.C.S.: 424710
Sita Divari (Chm)

Subsidiaries:

Asia Recycle Technology Company Limited (1)
No 73 Mahachon Building 4th Floor Soi Sukhumvit 62 Sukhumvit Road, South Phra Khanong Subdistrict Phra Khanong District, Bangkok, 10260, Thailand
Tel.: (66) 20 069 8789
Web Site: https://www.asiarecycle.com
Industrial Waste Disposal Services
N.A.I.C.S.: 562998

SEVEN VIEW CHRYSLER DODGE JEEP RAM
2685 Highway 7 West, Toronto, L4K 1V8, ON, Canada
Tel.: (888) 293-6586
Web Site: http://www.sevenviewchrysler.ca
Year Founded: 1979
New & Used Car Dealers
N.A.I.C.S.: 441110
Mark A. Pompa (Mgr-Parts)

SEVEN WEST MEDIA LIMITED
Newspaper House 50 Hasler Road, Osborne Park, Perth, 6017, WA, Australia
Tel.: (61) 894823111 **AU**
Web Site: https://www.sevenwestmedia.com
SWM—(ASX)
Rev.: $945,492,785
Assets: $986,846,283
Liabilities: $717,423,875
Net Worth: $269,422,408
Earnings: $30,249,065
Emp.: 1,154
Fiscal Year-end: 06/30/24
Newspaper & Magazine Publisher; Broadcasting Services
N.A.I.C.S.: 513110
Kerry Matthew Stokes (Chm)

Subsidiaries:

Channel Seven Adelaide Pty. Limited (1)
40 Port Road, Hindmarsh, 5007, SA, Australia
Tel.: (61) 88 342 7777
Web Site: http://www.sevenwestmedia.com.au
Television Broadcasting Station
N.A.I.C.S.: 516120
Andy Kay (Gen Mgr)

Channel Seven Brisbane Pty. Limited (1)
Sir Samuel Griffitth Drive, Mount Coot-tha, Brisbane, 4006, QLD, Australia
Tel.: (61) 733697777
Web Site: http://www.yahoo7.com.au
Sales Range: $50-74.9 Million
Emp.: 200
Television Broadcasting Station

N.A.I.C.S.: 516120
Ben Roberts-Smith (Gen Mgr)

Channel Seven Melbourne Pty. Limited (1)
160 Harbour Esplanade, Docklands, Melbourne, 3008, VIC, Australia
Tel.: (61) 396977777
Web Site: http://www.sevenwestmedia.com.au
Emp.: 400
Television Broadcasting Station
N.A.I.C.S.: 516120
Lewis Martin (Gen Mgr)

Channel Seven Perth Pty. Limited (1)
Off Dianella Drive, Dianella, Perth, 6059, WA, Australia
Tel.: (61) 893440777
Web Site: http://www.sevenwestmedia.com.au
Television Broadcasting Station
N.A.I.C.S.: 516120
Dan Stinton (Head-Digital)

Channel Seven Queensland Pty. Limited (1)
140-142 Horton Parade, Maroochydore, 4558, QLD, Australia
Tel.: (61) 754301777
Web Site: http://www.seven.com.au
Emp.: 100
Television Broadcasting Station
N.A.I.C.S.: 516120

Channel Seven Sydney Pty. Limited (1)
Martin Pl, Sydney, 2000, NSW, Australia
Tel.: (61) 298777777
Web Site: http://www.sevenwestmedia.com.au
Sales Range: $800-899.9 Million
Emp.: 5,000
Television Broadcasting Station
N.A.I.C.S.: 516120

Great Southern Television Limited (1)
Level 2 4 Galatos Street, Newton, Auckland, New Zealand
Tel.: (64) 9 374 2900
Web Site: https://greatsouthern.tv
Television Services
N.A.I.C.S.: 516120
Philip Smith (CEO)

PRT Company Limited (1)
363 Antill Street, Watson, 2602, ACT, Australia
Tel.: (61) 262423700
Web Site: http://www.primemedia.com.au
Rev.: $136,885,973
Assets: $80,957,934
Liabilities: $18,975,462
Net Worth: $61,982,472
Earnings: $14,975,184
Emp.: 512
Fiscal Year-end: 06/30/2021
Television Broadcasting Services
N.A.I.C.S.: 516120
Dave Walker (Gen Mgr-Sls & Mktg)

Subsidiary (Domestic):

Golden West Network Pty Limited (2)
Roberts Cres, 6231, Bunbury, WA, Australia (100%)
Tel.: (61) 897214466
Web Site: http://www.igwn.com.au
Sales Range: $25-49.9 Million
Emp.: 30
Television Broadcasting
N.A.I.C.S.: 516120

Hot 91 Pty Limited (2)
NAB Building 17 Carnaby Street, PO Box 1195, Maroochydore Post Office, Maroochydore, 4558, QLD, Australia
Tel.: (61) 754751911
Sales Range: $25-49.9 Million
Emp.: 60
Radio Broadcasting Services
N.A.I.C.S.: 516210
David Graham (Gen Mgr)

Prime Digitalworks Pty Limited (2)
363 Antill Street, Watson, Canberra, 2602, ACT, Australia

Tel.: (61) 262423700
Radio & Television Broadcasting Services
N.A.I.C.S.: 516210

Prime Television (Holdings) Pty Limited (2)
363 Antill St, Watson, 2602, ACT, Australia
Tel.: (61) 262423700
Web Site: http://www.prime7.com.au
Sales Range: $50-74.9 Million
Emp.: 150
Television Broadcasting Services
N.A.I.C.S.: 516120

Prime Television (Investments) Pty Limited (2)
363 Antill St Watson, Canberra, VIC, Australia (100%)
Tel.: (61) 262423700
Sales Range: $25-49.9 Million
Emp.: 100
Television Broadcasting
N.A.I.C.S.: 516120
D. Edwards (CEO)

Prime Television (Northern) Pty Limited (2)
Se 4b 225-227 Victoria Street, Taree, 2430, NSW, Australia
Tel.: (61) 265528777
Television Broadcasting Services
N.A.I.C.S.: 516120

Prime Television (Southern) Pty Limited (2)
363 Antill St Watson, 2604, Canberra, Australia (100%)
Tel.: (61) 262423700
Web Site: http://www.primetelevision.com
Sales Range: $25-49.9 Million
Emp.: 100
Television Broadcasting
N.A.I.C.S.: 516120

Prime Television (Victoria) Pty Limited (2)
Ballarat Mail Centre 7777, Ballarat, 3354, VIC, Australia (100%)
Tel.: (61) 353371777
Web Site: http://www.iprime.com.au
Sales Range: $25-49.9 Million
Emp.: 8
Television Broadcasting
N.A.I.C.S.: 516120
Andrew Schiltz (Mng Dir)

Radio Mackay Pty Ltd (2)
37 Sydney Street, MacKay, 4740, QLD, Australia
Tel.: (61) 749519800
Web Site: https://www.star1019.com.au
Sales Range: $25-49.9 Million
Emp.: 15
Radio Broadcasting Services
N.A.I.C.S.: 516210
Justine Price (Gen Mgr)

Telepro Pty Limited (2)
L 4 434 St Kilda Road, Melbourne, 3004, VIC, Australia
Tel.: (61) 392435622
Television Broadcasting Services
N.A.I.C.S.: 516120

Seven Studios Distribution Pty Ltd (1)
Media City 8 Central Avenue, Eveleigh, Sydney, 2015, NSW, Australia
Tel.: (61) 28 777 7231
Media Services
N.A.I.C.S.: 541840

SEVENS ATELIER LIMITED
31 Joo Chiat Place, Singapore, 427755, Singapore
Tel.: (65) 63153777
Web Site: https://sevensatelier.com
Year Founded: 1979
5EW—(CAT)
Rev.: $5,032,975
Assets: $13,431,641
Liabilities: $5,410,152
Net Worth: $8,021,489
Earnings: ($3,059,652)
Emp.: 18
Fiscal Year-end: 12/31/22
Ductile Iron Pipes Mfr

INTERNATIONAL PUBLIC

N.A.I.C.S.: 332919
Eddie Koh (CEO & Mng Dir)

Subsidiaries:

Duvalco Valves & Fittings Pte. Ltd. (1)
2 Kallang Avenue 05-19 CT Hub, Singapore, 339407, Singapore
Tel.: (65) 62658128
Butterfly Valve Mfr
N.A.I.C.S.: 332911

Subsidiary (Non-US):

Duvalco B.V. (2)
Zernikestraat 25, 3316 BZ, Dordrecht, Netherlands
Tel.: (31) 78 654 5250
Web Site: https://www.duvalco.net
Butterfly Valve Mfr
N.A.I.C.S.: 332911
Hans Liefaard (Gen Mgr)

Sacha Inchi Pte. Ltd. (1)
2 Kallang Avenue CT Hub 05-18, Singapore, 339407, Singapore
Tel.: (65) 6 268 7227
Web Site: https://www.incarich.com
Organic Health Supplement Retailer
N.A.I.C.S.: 456191

SEVER HOLDING AD
Tsar Asen I 5 et 3, 9000, Varna, Bulgaria
Tel.: (359) 896023443
Web Site: https://sever-holding.com
Year Founded: 1996
SEVA—(BUL)
Sales Range: Less than $1 Million
Holding Company
N.A.I.C.S.: 551112

SEVERCOOP GAMZA HOLDING AD
Simeonovsko Shose Blvd No 85z Entrance A Office 9, Lozenets district, 1700, Sofia, Bulgaria
Tel.: (359) 29440699
Web Site: https://severcoop.com
Year Founded: 1996
GAMZ—(BUL)
Sales Range: Less than $1 Million
Financial Services
N.A.I.C.S.: 523999

SEVERFIELD PLC
Severs House Dalton Airfield Industrial Estate, Dalton, Thirsk, YO7 3JN, North Yorkshire, United Kingdom
Tel.: (44) 1845577896
Web Site: https://www.severfield.com
Year Founded: 1978
SFR—(LSE)
Rev.: $590,025,464
Assets: $481,744,114
Liabilities: $200,711,649
Net Worth: $281,032,465
Earnings: $20,243,157
Emp.: 1,894
Fiscal Year-end: 03/30/24
Holding Company; Structural Steel Engineering & Construction
N.A.I.C.S.: 551112
Ian R. S. Cochrane (COO)

Subsidiaries:

Engineering Construction Training Ltd (1)
Lostock Lane, Lostock, Bolton, BL6 4BL, Lancashire, United Kingdom
Tel.: (44) 1204 675298
Web Site: http://www.sfrplc.co.uk
Emp.: 200
Construction Engineering Services
N.A.I.C.S.: 541330
John Dodd (Gen Mgr)

Fisher Engineering Ltd (1)
Main Street Ballinamallard Co, Enniskillen, BT94 2FY, Fermanagh, United Kingdom
Tel.: (44) 28 66 388521

AND PRIVATE COMPANIES

Web Site: http://www.sfrplc.co.uk
Sales Range: $100-124.9 Million
Emp.: 285
Steel Products Mfr
N.A.I.C.S.: 331110
Brian Keyf *(Gen Mgr)*

Rowen Structures Limited (1)
Maisies Way The Village, South Normanton, DE55 2DS, Derbyshire, United Kingdom
Tel.: (44) 1773860086
Web Site: http://www.sfrplc.com
Sales Range: $25-49.9 Million
Emp.: 100
Fabricated Structural Metal Mfr
N.A.I.C.S.: 332311

Severfield (Design & Build) Ltd. (1)
Ward House, Sherburn, Malton, YO17 8PZ, North Yorkshire, United Kingdom
Tel.: (44) 1 944 710421
Web Site: http://www.severfield.com
Sales Range: $50-74.9 Million
Emp.: 200
Portal Frame & Low Rise Design & Build Steelwork Contractor
N.A.I.C.S.: 332311

Severfield-Reeve International Limited (1)
Dalton Airfield Industrial Estate Dalton, Thirsk, YO73JN, N Yorkshire, United Kingdom **(100%)**
Tel.: (44) 1845578082
Web Site: http://www.sfrplc.com
Sales Range: $25-49.9 Million
Emp.: 10
Fabricated Structural Metal Mfr
N.A.I.C.S.: 332311
John Dodds *(Chm)*

Severfield-Reeve Projects Limited (1)
Dalton Airfield Industrial Estate, Dalton, Thirsk, YO7 3JN, N Yorkshire, United Kingdom **(100%)**
Tel.: (44) 1845578082
Sales Range: $25-49.9 Million
Emp.: 35
Fabricated Structural Metal Mfr
N.A.I.C.S.: 332311

Severfield-Reeve Structures Limited (1)
Dalton Airfield Industrial Estate, Dalton, Thirsk, YO7 3JN, N Yorkshire, United Kingdom **(100%)**
Tel.: (44) 1845577896
Web Site: http://www.severfield-rowen.com
Sales Range: $100-124.9 Million
Emp.: 395
Fabricated Structural Metal Mfr
N.A.I.C.S.: 332311
Fraser Darrington *(Mgr-Sls)*

Steelcraft Erection Services Limited (1)
Dalton Airfield Industrial Estate Dalton, Thirsk, YO7 3JN, N Yorkshire, United Kingdom **(100%)**
Tel.: (44) 1845577896
Web Site: http://www.steelcraft.com
Sales Range: $25-49.9 Million
Emp.: 40
Fabricated Structural Metal Mfr
N.A.I.C.S.: 332311

Watson Steel Structures Ltd. (1)
Lostock Ln, PO Box 9, Bolton, BL6 4TB, United Kingdom
Tel.: (44) 204699999
Sales Range: $100-124.9 Million
Emp.: 252
Heavy Construction
N.A.I.C.S.: 237990
Peter Emerson *(Mng Dir & COO)*

SEVERGROUP OOO
2 Klara Tsetkin Street, Moscow, RU-127299, Russia
Tel.: (7) 495926 77 66
Web Site: http://severgroup.ru
Year Founded: 1993
Investment Managment Company
N.A.I.C.S.: 523999
Mordashov Alexey *(CEO)*

Subsidiaries:

Lenta Ltd. (1)
112B Savushkina str, Saint Petersburg, 197374, Russia **(78.73%)**
Tel.: (7) 8123806131
Web Site: http://www.lentainvestor.com
Rev.: $6,471,115
Assets: $4,593,194
Liabilities: $3,162,057
Net Worth: $1,431,137
Earnings: $166,976
Emp.: 75,000
Fiscal Year-end: 12/31/2021
Supermarket & Retail Chains Operator
N.A.I.C.S.: 445110
Sergey Prokofiev *(Dir-Legal & Govt Rels)*

SEVERN GLOCON LTD.
Olympus Park Quedgeley, Gloucester, GL2 4NF, United Kingdom
Tel.: (44) 8452232040
Web Site:
http://www.severnglocon.com
Year Founded: 1961
Sales Range: $125-149.9 Million
Emp.: 800
Industrial Valve Mfr
N.A.I.C.S.: 332911
Ron Baker *(Dir-Sls)*

SEVERN TRENT PLC
Severn Trent Centre 2 St Johns Street, Coventry, CV1 2LZ, United Kingdom
Tel.: (44) 2477715000
Web Site: http://www.severntrent.com
Year Founded: 1974
STRNY—(OTCIQ)
Rev.: $2,688,621,180
Assets: $15,086,131,480
Liabilities: $13,880,840,400
Net Worth: $1,205,291,080
Earnings: $164,165,960
Emp.: 8,369
Fiscal Year-end: 03/31/23
Water & Waste Water Utility Services
N.A.I.C.S.: 221310
Sarah Bentley *(Chief Customer Officer)*

Subsidiaries:

Charles Haswell and Partners Limited (1)
3900 Park Side Burghingam Business Park, London, B37 7YJ, United Kingdom **(100%)**
Tel.: (44) 1217177744
Web Site: http://www.haswell.com
Sales Range: $75-99.9 Million
Emp.: 400
Engineering Design Consultants
N.A.I.C.S.: 541330

Severn Trent CAS Ltd (1)
80 Lockhurst Ln, Coventry, CV6 5PZ, W Midlands, United Kingdom **(100%)**
Tel.: (44) 2476584800
Sales Range: $25-49.9 Million
Emp.: 175
Environmental Lab Services
N.A.I.C.S.: 541380

Severn Trent Green Power Group Limited (1)
The Stables Radford, Chipping Norton, OX7 4EB, Oxfordshire, United Kingdom
Tel.: (44) 1608677700
Web Site: https://www.stgreenpower.co.uk
Food Waste Composting Services
N.A.I.C.S.: 562219

Severn Trent Laboratories Limited - Coventry (1)
STS CoventryTorrington Avenue, Coventry, CV4 9GU, United Kingdom **(100%)**
Tel.: (44) 2476421213
Web Site: http://www.stsanalytical.com
Sales Range: $75-99.9 Million
Emp.: 300
Environmental Lab Services
N.A.I.C.S.: 541380

Division (Domestic):

Severn Trent Laboratories Limited - Runcorn (2)
Howard Ct Manor Pk Runcorn, Mersey, WA7 1SJ, Cheshire, United Kingdom
Tel.: (44) 1928594000
Sales Range: $25-49.9 Million
Emp.: 22
Environmental Lab Services
N.A.I.C.S.: 541380

Severn Trent Laboratories Limited - Scotland (2)
1 & 2 Cumbelnauld Bus Pk Waldpark Rd Cumbelnauld, Glasgow, G67 3JZ, Lanarkshire, United Kingdom **(100%)**
Tel.: (44) 1236868790
Sales Range: $25-49.9 Million
Emp.: 6
Environmental Lab Services
N.A.I.C.S.: 541380

Severn Trent Metering Services Limited (1)
Direct 2 Business Park Units 7 15 Roway Lane, Oldbury, B69 3EH, West Midlands, United Kingdom **(100%)**
Tel.: (44) 1217226333
Sales Range: $75-99.9 Million
Emp.: 70
Water Processing
N.A.I.C.S.: 221310

Severn Trent Overseas Holdings Limited (1)
2297 Coventry Rd, Birmingham, B26 3PU, W Midlands, United Kingdom **(100%)**
Tel.: (44) 217226000
Web Site: http://www.severntrent.com
Sales Range: $75-99.9 Million
Emp.: 150
Holding Company
N.A.I.C.S.: 551112

Severn Trent Retail and Utility Services Limited (1)
Pure Offices Sherwood Business Park Lake View Drive, Nottingham, NG15 0DT, United Kingdom **(100%)**
Tel.: (44) 1159713550
Web Site:
https://www.severntrentaffinity.co.uk
Water Processing Services
N.A.I.C.S.: 561990

Severn Trent Water International Limited (1)
2308 Coventry Rd, Birmingham, B26 3JZ, United Kingdom **(100%)**
Tel.: (44) 1217226130
Web Site:
http://www.stwaterinternational.com
Sales Range: $75-99.9 Million
Emp.: 20
Water & Waste Management
N.A.I.C.S.: 221310
Sarah Bentley *(Chief Customer Officer)*

Subsidiary (Domestic):

Severn Trent Water Limited (2)
Severn Trent, PO Box 407, Darlington, DL1 9WD, United Kingdom **(100%)**
Tel.: (44) 3457500500
Web Site: https://www.stwater.co.uk
Water Processing
N.A.I.C.S.: 221310
Tony Wray *(CEO)*

Subsidiary (Non-US):

C2C Services Limited (3)
2308 Coventry Rd, B26 3JZ, Birmingham, United Kingdom - England
Tel.: (44) 1217224000
Sales Range: $50-74.9 Million
Emp.: 50
Water & Wastewater Services
N.A.I.C.S.: 221310

Subsidiary (Domestic):

Dee Valley Group Limited (3)
Packsaddle Wrexham Road, Rhostyllen, Wrexham, LL14 4EH, United Kingdom
Tel.: (44) 1978846946
Web Site: http://www.deevalleygroup.com
Holding Company; Water Supply Services
N.A.I.C.S.: 551112

Subsidiary (Domestic):

Dee Valley Plc (4)

SEVERN TRENT PLC

Packsaddle Wrexham Road Rhostyllen, Wrexham, LL14 4EH, United Kingdom
Tel.: (44) 1978846946
Web Site: http://www.deevalleygroup.com
Water Distribution Services
N.A.I.C.S.: 221310
Vaughn Bradley Walton *(Sec)*

Dee Valley Water (Holdings) Limited (4)
Packsaddle Wrexham Road, Rhostyllen, Wrexham, LL144EH, United Kingdom
Tel.: (44) 1978846946
Water Supply & Irrigation Systems
N.A.I.C.S.: 221310
Gemma Louise Eagle *(Sec)*

Dee Valley Water Plc (4)
Packsaddle Wrexham Rd Rhostyllen, Wrexham, LL14 4EH, United Kingdom
Tel.: (44) 1978846946
Web Site: http://www.ulproductlibrary.com
Water Supply Services
N.A.I.C.S.: 221310
Ian Plendeleith *(CEO)*

Subsidiary (Domestic):

Genera Technologies Limited (3)
Lynx Business Pk Fordham Road Newmarket, Unit 5F, Cambridge, CB8 7NY, United Kingdom **(56%)**
Tel.: (44) 1638723011
Water Processing Services
N.A.I.C.S.: 221310

Severn Trent Engineering Ltd (3)
Alpha House Gallows Hill, Warwick Technology Park, Warwick, CV34 6DA, United Kingdom **(100%)**
Tel.: (44) 1217224000
Web Site: http://www.stwater.co.uk
Engineeering Services
N.A.I.C.S.: 541330

Branch (Domestic):

Severn Trent Water Limited-Barlaston (3)
Strongford Sewage Treatment Works, Barlaston Old Rd, Barlaston, Stoke-on-Trent, ST12 9EX, United Kingdom **(100%)**
Tel.: (44) 1782654253
Web Site: http://www.stwater.co.uk
Sales Range: $75-99.9 Million
Emp.: 100
Sewage Processing
N.A.I.C.S.: 221320

Severn Trent Water Limited-Birmingham (3)
2297 Coventry Rd, Birmingham, B26 3PU, United Kingdom **(100%)**
Tel.: (44) 1217224000
Web Site: http://www.stwater.co.uk
Sales Range: $450-499.9 Million
Water Processing
N.A.I.C.S.: 221310

Severn Trent Water Limited-Carsington (3)
Big Lane, Ashbourne, DE6 1ST, Derbyshire, United Kingdom **(100%)**
Tel.: (44) 3306780701
Web Site: http://www.stwater.co.uk
Emp.: 9
Water Processing
N.A.I.C.S.: 221310

Severn Trent Water Limited-Coventry (3)
2 St John s Street, PO Box 5309, Coventry, CV1 2LZ, United Kingdom **(100%)**
Tel.: (44) 3457500500
Web Site: http://www.stwater.co.uk
Sales Range: $250-299.9 Million
Emp.: 300
Water Processing
N.A.I.C.S.: 221310
Liv Garfield *(CEO)*

Severn Trent Water Limited-Derby (3)
Raynesway, PO Box 51, Derby, DE21 7JA, Derbyshire, United Kingdom **(100%)**
Tel.: (44) 332683031
Web Site: http://www.stwater.co.uk
Sales Range: $450-499.9 Million
Water Processing
N.A.I.C.S.: 221310

SEVERN TRENT PLC

Severn Trent Plc—(Continued)

Severn Trent Water Limited-Gloucester (3)
Staverton Depot Cheltenham Rd E, Gloucester, GL2 9QY, United Kingdom **(100%)**
Tel.: (44) 1217224000
Web Site: http://www.stwater.co.uk
Water Processing
N.A.I.C.S.: 221310

Severn Trent Water Limited-Leamington (3)
2 Saint Thomas St Coventry, Black Ln, Birmingham, CV1 2LZ, United Kingdom **(100%)**
Tel.: (44) 1217224339
Web Site: http://www.stwater.co.uk
Water Processing
N.A.I.C.S.: 221310

Severn Trent Water Limited-Leicester (3)
Leicester Water Centre Gorse Hill, Anstey, Leicester, LE7 7GU, United Kingdom **(100%)**
Tel.: (44) 1162340340
Web Site: http://www.stwater.co.uk
Water Processing
N.A.I.C.S.: 221310

Severn Trent Water Limited-Minworth (3)
Park Ln, Minworth, Sutton Coldfield, B76 9BL, United Kingdom **(100%)**
Tel.: (44) 1213134617
Web Site: http://www.stwater.co.uk
Water Processing
N.A.I.C.S.: 221310

Severn Trent Water Limited-Nottingham (3)
Hucknall Rd, Nottingham, NG5 1FH, United Kingdom **(100%)**
Tel.: (44) 1217224000
Web Site: http://www.stwater.co.uk
Sewer Processing
N.A.I.C.S.: 221320

Severn Trent Water Limited-Shrewsbury (3)
STC 2 St.John St, PO Box 5310, Coventry, CV1 2LZ, United Kingdom **(100%)**
Tel.: (44) 2477715000
Web Site: http://www.stwater.co.uk
N.A.I.C.S.: 334513
Liv Garfield *(CEO)*

Severn Trent Water Limited-Stock Bardolph (3)
Stoke Bardolph Sewage Treatment Works, Stoke Ln, Nottingham, United Kingdom **(100%)**
Tel.: (44) 2477715000
Web Site: http://www.stwater.co.uk
Sewage Processing
N.A.I.C.S.: 221320

Severn Trent Water Limited-Stoke on Trent (3)
Westport Rd, Burslem, Stoke-on-Trent, ST6 4JT, United Kingdom **(100%)**
Tel.: (44) 1782836336
Web Site: http://www.stwater.co.uk
Water Processing
N.A.I.C.S.: 221310

Severn Trent Water Limited-Wanlip (3)
Wanlip Sewage Treatment Works Fillingate, Wanlip, LE7 4PF, Leicestershire, United Kingdom **(100%)**
Tel.: (44) 1217224000
Web Site: http://www.stwater.co.uk
Sewage Processing
N.A.I.C.S.: 221320

Severn Trent Water Limited-Warwick (3)
Longbridge Gate 2, Stratford Rd, Warwick, CV34 6QW, United Kingdom **(100%)**
Tel.: (44) 1217224000
Web Site: http://www.stwater.co.uk
Water Processing
N.A.I.C.S.: 221310

Severn Trent Water Limited-Wolverhampton (3)
Regis Rd, Tettenhall, Wolverhampton, WV6 8RU, United Kingdom **(100%)**
Tel.: (44) 1902754144
Web Site: http://www.stwater.co.uk
Water Processing
N.A.I.C.S.: 221310

Severn Trent Water Limited-Worcester (3)
Bromwich Rd, Lower Wick, Worcester, WR2 4BN, United Kingdom **(100%)**
Tel.: (44) 1905748484
Web Site: http://www.stwater.co.uk
Water Processing
N.A.I.C.S.: 221310

SEVERNI BANAT A.D.

Put za pristaniste bb, Kikinda, Serbia
Tel.: (381) 230426625
Year Founded: 1974
SEVB—(BEL)
Assets: $1,297,793
Liabilities: $900,711
Net Worth: $397,082
Earnings: ($76,151)
Fiscal Year-end: 12/31/23
Building Construction Services
N.A.I.C.S.: 236116
Dejan Canji *(Exec Dir)*

SEVERTRANS A.D.

Filipa Kljajica bb, Sombor, Serbia
Tel.: (381) 25424577
Web Site: https://www.severtrans.rs
Year Founded: 1947
SVRT—(BEL)
Rev.: $7,030,679
Assets: $5,462,358
Liabilities: $6,999,834
Net Worth: ($1,537,476)
Earnings: ($454,104)
Fiscal Year-end: 12/31/23
Passenger Transportation Services
N.A.I.C.S.: 485999
Nenad Celic *(Exec Dir)*

SEVES S.P.A.

Via R Giuliani, 50141, Florence, Italy
Tel.: (39) 0554495
Web Site: http://www.seves.com
Year Founded: 2002
Sales Range: $350-399.9 Million
Emp.: 1,850
Glass & Composite Insulators
N.A.I.C.S.: 327215

Subsidiaries:

Electro Vidro S.A. (1)
Av Lucio Thome Feteira 312 Cep, 24415-000, Sao Goncalo, Brazil
Tel.: (55) 2126249507
Glass Product Distr
N.A.I.C.S.: 449129

PPC Insulators Holding GmbH (1)
Stattermayergasse 28, Vienna, 1100, Austria
Tel.: (43) 198258500
Web Site: http://www.ppcinsulators.com
Sales Range: $125-149.9 Million
Emp.: 12
Electrical Porcelain Insulator Products Mfr
N.A.I.C.S.: 327110
Vienna Vittel *(Mng Dir)*

Subsidiary (Non-US):

Elektrokeramik Sonneberg GmbH (2)
Werkringstrasse 11, 96515, Sonneberg, Germany
Tel.: (49) 36758730
Web Site: http://www.ppcinsulators.com
Sales Range: $50-74.9 Million
Porcelain Electrical Insulator Mfr
N.A.I.C.S.: 327110

Subsidiary (US):

Seves USA (2)
981 Tyber Rd, Tiffin, OH 44883
Tel.: (419) 447-3460
Web Site: http://www.seves.com
Porcelain Electrical Insulator Mfr
N.A.I.C.S.: 327110

Sediver Insulators (Shanghai) Co., Ltd. (1)
338 Minle Road Spark Zone, Pudong, Shanghai, 201419, China
Tel.: (86) 2157505111
Glass Product Distr
N.A.I.C.S.: 449129
Jie Fang *(Mgr-Plng)*

Sediver S.A. (1)
95 avenue Francois Arago, 92017, Nanterre, France
Tel.: (33) 146141516
Web Site: http://www.sediver.com
Emp.: 5,000
Technical Consulting Services
N.A.I.C.S.: 541380

Seves Canada Inc. (1)
378 McArthur, Saint Laurent, H4T 1X8, QC, Canada
Tel.: (514) 739-3385
Glass Product Distr
N.A.I.C.S.: 449129
Sarkis Minassian *(Project Mgr)*

Seves S.p.A. - Nusco Factory (1)
Area Industriale F2, Nusco, 83051, Avellino, Italy
Tel.: (39) 0827607016
Glass Products Mfr
N.A.I.C.S.: 327215

Shanghai Seves Glass Co., Ltd. (1)
9485 Puxing Highway Spark Zone, Pudong, Shanghai, 201419, China
Tel.: (86) 2157505784
Glass Product Distr
N.A.I.C.S.: 449129
He Zhi *(Mgr-Quality)*

Zigong Sediver Toughened Glass Insulator Co., Ltd. (1)
162 Hutou Street, Gongjing, Zigong, 643020, China
Tel.: (86) 8133302615
Glass Product Distr
N.A.I.C.S.: 449129
Min Liu *(Asst Mgr-Fin)*

SEVKAZENERGO JSC

Zhambyl St 215, Petropavl, 150009, Kazakhstan
Tel.: (7) 152314324
Web Site: http://www.sevkazenergo.kz
Year Founded: 2009
SKEN—(KAZ)
Rev.: $24,155,777
Assets: $300,920,702
Liabilities: $148,384,031
Net Worth: $152,536,671
Earnings: $9,685,757
Fiscal Year-end: 12/31/19
Electric Power Distribution Services
N.A.I.C.S.: 221122
Igor Vitalyevich Tatarov *(Gen Dir)*

Subsidiaries:

North Kazakhstan Electric Distribution Company, Joint-Stock Company (1)
A Shazhimbayev St 144, Petropavl, Kazakhstan
Tel.: (7) 7152411451
Electric Power Distr
N.A.I.C.S.: 221122

Petropavlovsk Heating Networks LLP (1)
Stroitelnaya St 23, North Kazakhstan region, Petropavl, Kazakhstan
Tel.: (7) 7152411451
Electric Power Distr
N.A.I.C.S.: 221122

Sevkazenergosbyt LLP (1)
Zhumabayev St 68, North Kazakhstan region, Petropavl, Kazakhstan
Tel.: (7) 7152366156
Electric Power Distr
N.A.I.C.S.: 221122

SEVKO AD

Tel.: (359) 898557176

INTERNATIONAL PUBLIC

SEVK—(BUL)
Sales Range: Less than $1 Million
Real Estate Services
N.A.I.C.S.: 531390

SEWHA P&C INC.

1203 Building A Hyundai Knowledge Industry Center 11 Beobwon-ro 11-gil, Songpa-gu, Seoul, Korea (South)
Tel.: (82) 25554019 **KR**
Web Site: https://www.sewha.co.kr
Year Founded: 2016
252500—(KRS)
Rev.: $29,083,674
Assets: $31,229,652
Liabilities: $2,740,595
Net Worth: $28,489,057
Earnings: $1,012,648
Emp.: 104
Fiscal Year-end: 12/31/22
Hair Care Products Mfr
N.A.I.C.S.: 325620
Hoon Ku Lee *(CEO)*

Subsidiaries:

Sewha P&C Inc. - Jincheon-gun Factory/Head Office (1)
36 Eunam-gil, Chopyeong-myeon, Jincheon, Chungcheongbuk-do, Korea (South)
Tel.: (82) 43 838 1010
Hair Care Products Mfr
N.A.I.C.S.: 325620

SEWON CO LTD

56 Sandan-ro 64beon-gil, Pyeongtaek, Gyeonggi-do, Korea (South)
Tel.: (82) 316686611
Web Site: http://www.sewonmfg.co.kr
Year Founded: 1991
234100—(KRS)
Rev.: $135,560,444
Assets: $200,783,301
Liabilities: $41,803,762
Net Worth: $158,979,539
Earnings: $1,419,686
Emp.: 209
Fiscal Year-end: 12/31/22
Automobile Parts Mfr
N.A.I.C.S.: 336320
Hyun-Woo Cho *(Pres & CEO)*

SEWON CORPORATION CO., LTD.

554 Dalseo-daero, Dalseo-gu, Daegu, Korea (South)
Tel.: (82) 535825161
Web Site: https://www.se-won.com
Year Founded: 1985
024830—(KRS)
Rev.: $131,259,498
Assets: $238,207,409
Liabilities: $51,584,963
Net Worth: $186,622,446
Earnings: $12,483,786
Emp.: 547
Fiscal Year-end: 12/31/22
Automobile Parts Mfr
N.A.I.C.S.: 336110
Moon Ki Kim *(Chm & CEO)*

Subsidiaries:

Chongqing Sungwoo Automotive Technology Co., Ltd. (1)
Myungdo 2 Rd, Chongqing, Jangsugu, China
Tel.: (86) 2340885161
Automobile Parts Mfr & Distr
N.A.I.C.S.: 336214

Huanghua Sewon Automotive Technology Co., Ltd. (1)
The intersection of the Xinhai Rd & New 205 national Rd, Korea Industrial Park Tengzhuangzi Village, Huanghua, Hebei, China
Tel.: (86) 3175555617
Automobile Parts Mfr & Distr
N.A.I.C.S.: 336214

AND PRIVATE COMPANIES

Samha Sewon Automotive Technology Co., Ltd. (1)
Shenwei North Road Yanjiao Economic & Technological Development Zone, South of Xiaozhuang Village, Sanhe, Hebei, China
Tel.: (86) 3163385011
Automobile Parts Mfr & Distr
N.A.I.C.S.: 336214

Sewon E&I Co., Ltd. (1)
35 Donamgongdan 2-gil, Yeongcheon, Gyeongsangbuk-do, Korea (South)
Tel.: (82) 543385161
Automobile Parts Mfr
N.A.I.C.S.: 336330

Sewon Technology Co., Ltd. (1)
172 Hyudae-gil, Baebang-eup, Asan, Chungcheongnam-do, Korea (South)
Tel.: (82) 415325161
Automobile Parts Mfr
N.A.I.C.S.: 336330

SEWON E&C CO., LTD.
211 Gongdan-ro, Seongsan-gu, Changwon, 51562, Gyeongsangnam-do, Korea (South)
Tel.: (82) 552697039
Web Site: https://www.sewonenc.com
Year Founded: 1971
091090—(KRS)
Rev.: $97,123,158
Assets: $216,832,556
Liabilities: $88,435,683
Net Worth: $128,396,873
Earnings: ($66,240,339)
Emp.: 233
Fiscal Year-end: 12/31/22
Process & Hydraulic Equipment Mfr
N.A.I.C.S.: 333998
Jong-In Lee (CEO)

Subsidiaries:

SEWONCELLONTECH CORP. - CHANGWON HYDRAULICE PLANT (1)
44-1 Woongnam-dong, Seongsan-gu, Changwon, 641-290, Gyeongsangnam-do, Korea (South)
Tel.: (82) 55 239 6400
Hydraulic Equipment Mfr
N.A.I.C.S.: 333998

SEWONCELLONTECH CORP. - PROCESS EQUIPMENT 1ST PLANT (1)
72 Shinchon-dong, Seongsan-gu, Changwon, 641-370, Gyeongsangnam-do, Korea (South)
Tel.: (82) 55 269 7000
Heat Exchanger Mfr
N.A.I.C.S.: 332410

SEWONCELLONTECH CORP. - RMS PLANT (1)
4 5th Fl Techno Center 273-15 Sungsoo2-ga 3-dong, Seongdong-gu, Seoul, Korea (South)
Tel.: (82) 2 460 3127
Hydraulic Equipment Mfr
N.A.I.C.S.: 333998

SEWON PRECISION INDUSTRY CO., LTD.
554 Dalseo-daero, Dalseo-gu, Daegu, Korea (South)
Tel.: (82) 535825161
Web Site: https://www.se-won.com
Year Founded: 1989
021820—(KRS)
Rev.: $122,583,582
Assets: $519,043,030
Liabilities: $71,512,827
Net Worth: $447,530,203
Earnings: ($24,079,441)
Emp.: 181
Fiscal Year-end: 06/30/23
Automobile Parts Mfr
N.A.I.C.S.: 336110
Moon Ki Kim (Chm)

Subsidiaries:

Chongqing Sungwon Automative Techhnology Co., Ltd. (1)
Myungdo 2 Rd, Chongqing, Jangsugu, China
Tel.: (86) 2340885161
Automotive Parts Mfr & Distr
N.A.I.C.S.: 336211

Huanghua Sewon Automative Tech-hnology Co., Ltd. (1)
The intersection of the Xinhai Rd & New 205 national Rd, Korea Industrial Park Tengzhuangzi Village, Huanghua, China
Tel.: (86) 3175555617
Auto Body Module Mfr
N.A.I.C.S.: 336390

Samha Sewon Automative Techhnology Co., Ltd. (1)
Shenwei North Road Yanjiao Economic & Technological Development Zone, South of Xiaozhuang village, Sanhe, China
Tel.: (86) 3163385011
Automobile & Auto Body Parts Mfr
N.A.I.C.S.: 336211

Sewon Precision Co., Ltd. (1)
554 Dalseo-daero, Dalseo-gu, Daegu, Korea (South)
Tel.: (82) 535825161
Automotive Parts Mfr & Distr
N.A.I.C.S.: 336211

SEWOO GLOBAL CO., LTD.
26-48 Yeomjeon-ro 261beon-gil, Michuhol-gu, Incheon, Korea (South)
Tel.: (82) 328681100
Web Site: https://www.sewooglobal.co.kr
Year Founded: 1978
013000—(KRS)
Rev.: $21,526,489
Assets: $38,264,649
Liabilities: $3,091,109
Net Worth: $35,173,540
Earnings: $1,167,520
Emp.: 22
Fiscal Year-end: 12/31/22
Plastic Material Whslr
N.A.I.C.S.: 424610
Baek-Soon Ahn (CEO)

Subsidiaries:

Sewoo Global Vietnam Ltd. (1)
Dong Lang Industrial Park, PhuNinh, Viet Tri, Phu Tho, Vietnam
Tel.: (84) 210736102
Plastic Material & Basic Form Whslr
N.A.I.C.S.: 424610

SEWOONMEDICAL CO. LTD
60 Dorim-gil Ipjang-myeon, Seobuk-gu, Cheonan, Chungcheongnam-Do, Korea (South)
Tel.: (82) 415842903
Web Site: http://www.sewoonmedical.co.kr
100700—(KRS)
Rev.: $46,109,060
Assets: $101,611,148
Liabilities: $5,717,781
Net Worth: $95,893,367
Earnings: $8,160,189
Emp.: 202
Fiscal Year-end: 12/31/22
Medical Equipment Mfr
N.A.I.C.S.: 339113
Jae-Hee Lee (CEO)

Subsidiaries:

Qingdao Sewoon Medical Co., Ltd. (1)
West Side of Shuangyuan Road Liuting Street Airport Industrial Park, Chengyang District, Qingdao, Shandong, China
Tel.: (86) 53284716927
Web Site: http://www.sewoonmedical.cn
Medical Instrument Mfr
N.A.I.C.S.: 339112

SEYA INDUSTRIES LTD.
5th Floor Ghanshyam Chambers Link Road, Andheri W, Mumbai, 400053, Maharashtra, India
Tel.: (91) 2226732894
Web Site: https://www.seya.in
524324—(BOM)
Rev.: $36,442,033
Assets: $242,035,931
Liabilities: $109,403,945
Net Worth: $132,631,986
Earnings: $6,418,203
Emp.: 131
Fiscal Year-end: 03/31/20
Benzene-based Chemical Products Mfr
N.A.I.C.S.: 325998
Ashok G. Rajani (Chm & Mng Dir)

SEYCHELLES TRADING COMPANY LTD.
Latanier Rd, PO Box 634, Victoria, Mahe, Seychelles
Tel.: (248) 285000
Web Site: http://www.stcl.sc
Sales Range: $50-74.9 Million
Emp.: 433
Durable & Non-Durable Products Importer, Exporter & Marketer
N.A.I.C.S.: 425120
Christine Joubert (Deputy CEO)

SEYFERT LTD.
3-27-11 Yushin Building 2nd floor, Tokyo, 150-0002, Japan
Tel.: (81) 354643690
Web Site: https://www.seyfert.co.jp
Year Founded: 1991
9213—(TKS)
Rev.: $15,356,940
Assets: $12,882,530
Liabilities: $5,019,720
Net Worth: $7,862,810
Earnings: $872,070
Emp.: 128
Fiscal Year-end: 12/31/23
Advertising Agency Services
N.A.I.C.S.: 541810

Subsidiaries:

Seyfert International USA Inc. (1)
2543-D Pacific Coast Hwy, Torrance, CA 90505
Tel.: (310) 326-0815
Web Site: https://www.seyfertusa.com
Beauty Product Mfr & Distr
N.A.I.C.S.: 335210

SEYITLER KIMYA SANAYI AS
1 OSB 2007 Cd No 5-7, Turgutlu, 45400, Manisa, Turkiye
Tel.: (90) 2363148383
Web Site: https://www.seyitler.com
Year Founded: 1991
SEYKM—(IST)
Sales Range: Less than $1 Million
Surgical Appliance Mfr
N.A.I.C.S.: 339113
Seyit Sanli (Chm)

SEYLAN BANK PLC
Seylan Towers No 90 Galle Road, 3, Colombo, Sri Lanka
Tel.: (94) 112008888
Web Site: https://www.seylan.lk
Year Founded: 1987
SEYB.N0000—(COL)
Rev.: $322,347,505
Assets: $2,239,722,965
Liabilities: $2,048,429,503
Net Worth: $191,293,462
Earnings: $15,238,408
Emp.: 2,834
Fiscal Year-end: 12/31/22
Banking Services
N.A.I.C.S.: 522110

Chitral de Silva (Deputy Gen Mgr-Branches Zone I)

Subsidiaries:

Seylan Developments PLC (1)
Level 15 Seylan Towers No 90 Galle Road, Colombo, Sri Lanka
Tel.: (94) 112452697
Web Site: https://www.seylandevelopments.com
Property Management Services
N.A.I.C.S.: 531312

Seylan Merchant Bank Ltd. (1)
Seylan Towers No 90, Galle Rd, Colombo, Sri Lanka (51.84%)
Tel.: (94) 112573363
Web Site: https://www.smblk.com
Commercial Banking
N.A.I.C.S.: 522110

SF DIAMOND CO., LTD.
No 109 10th Street Economic and Technological Development Area, Zhengzhou, 450016, Henan, China
Tel.: (86) 37166728026
Web Site: https://www.sf-diamond.com
Year Founded: 1997
300179—(CHIN)
Rev.: $72,137,520
Assets: $198,581,760
Liabilities: $37,527,516
Net Worth: $161,054,244
Earnings: $21,620,196
Emp.: 279
Fiscal Year-end: 12/31/22
Polycrystalline Diamond Mfr
N.A.I.C.S.: 333514

Subsidiaries:

SFD Europe Srl (1)
SeL Unipersonale Str Valsalice 68/8, 10131, Turin, Italy
Tel.: (39) 0116603313
Industrial Diamond Distr
N.A.I.C.S.: 423840

SF MARKETING INC.
325 boul Bouchard, Dorval, H9S 1A9, QC, Canada
Tel.: (514) 780-2070
Web Site: http://www.sfm.ca
Year Founded: 1978
Rev.: $36,516,879
Emp.: 135
Audio & Lighting Equipment Distr
N.A.I.C.S.: 335139
Sol Fleising (Founder & Pres)

SF URBAN PROPERTIES AG
Seefeldstrasse 275, 8008, Zurich, Switzerland
Tel.: (41) 433446131
Web Site: https://www.sfurban.ch
SFPN—(SWX)
Rev.: $28,864,173
Assets: $706,442,134
Liabilities: $377,681,986
Net Worth: $328,760,148
Earnings: $19,101,018
Fiscal Year-end: 12/31/19
Financial & Property Investment Services
N.A.I.C.S.: 525990
Hans-Peter Bauer (Chm)

SFA ENGINEERING CORP.
25 Dongtansunhwan-daero 29-gil, Hwaseong, 18472, Gyeonggi-do, Korea (South)
Tel.: (82) 313797512
Web Site: https://www.sfa.co.kr
Year Founded: 1998
056190—(KRS)
Rev.: $1,291,909,018
Assets: $1,476,741,020
Liabilities: $393,114,908
Net Worth: $1,083,626,112

SFA ENGINEERING CORP.

SFA Engineering Corp.—(Continued)
Earnings: $59,182,490
Emp.: 685
Fiscal Year-end: 12/31/22
Electronic Components Mfr
N.A.I.C.S.: 334413
Young Min Kim *(Pres & CEO)*

Subsidiaries:

CI Solid Co., Ltd. (1)
529 Dalseo-daero, Dalseo-gu, Daegu, 42709, Korea (South)
Tel.: (82) 535846700
Web Site: https://www.cisolid.com
Automation Machinery Mfr
N.A.I.C.S.: 333131

SFA Semicon China (Suzhou) Corporation (1)
No 288 Jiangxing East Road, Wujiang District, Suzhou, Jiangsu, China
Tel.: (86) 51285168000
Web Site: https://www.sfasemicon.com.cn
Semiconductor Packaging Distr
N.A.I.C.S.: 423690

SFA SEMICON CO., LTD.
16 Baekseokgongdan 7-ro, Seobuk-gu, Cheonan, 31094, Chungcheongnam-do, Korea (South)
Tel.: (82) 415206400
Web Site: https://www.sfasemicon.com
Year Founded: 1998
036540—(KRS)
Rev.: $536,449,089
Assets: $517,628,620
Liabilities: $146,463,792
Net Worth: $371,164,828
Earnings: $32,902,685
Emp.: 628
Fiscal Year-end: 12/31/22
Semiconductor Mfr
N.A.I.C.S.: 334413
Yeong Min Kim *(CEO)*

Subsidiaries:

SFA Semicon Philippines Corporation (1)
Panday Pira Avenue Creekside Road, Clark Freeport Zone, Pampanga, Philippines
Tel.: (63) 454991713
Web Site: https://www.sfasemicon.com.ph
Rev.: $347,017,869
Assets: $194,536,357
Liabilities: $56,734,120
Net Worth: $137,802,237
Earnings: $12,735,245
Emp.: 695
Fiscal Year-end: 12/31/2021
Semiconductor Packaging & Testing Solutions
N.A.I.C.S.: 334413
Joon Sang Kang *(Pres)*

SFAKIANAKIS S.A.
Sidirokastrou 5-7 & Pydnas, 11855, Athens, Greece
Tel.: (30) 2103499000
Web Site: http://www.sfakianakis.gr
Sales Range: $250-299.9 Million
Emp.: 1,248
Motor Vehicle Spare Parts Import & Export Services
N.A.I.C.S.: 423110
Stavros P. Taki *(Pres & CEO)*

Subsidiaries:

Executive Lease S.A. (1)
Sidirokastrou 9, 118 55, Athens, Greece
Tel.: (30) 2103463588
Car Rental Services
N.A.I.C.S.: 532111

Panergon S.A.
Thesi Patima, 193 00, Magoula, Attica, Greece
Tel.: (30) 210 5538260
Web Site: http://www.daftrucks.gr
Sales Range: $25-49.9 Million
Emp.: 36
Automobile Dealers
N.A.I.C.S.: 441110
Nicolas Kyriakidis *(Mgr)*

Personal Best S.A. (1)
4 Aeroporias Avenue, Alimos, 17455, Athens, Greece
Tel.: (30) 2109967727
Web Site: http://www.personalbest.com
Emp.: 30
Automotive Repair & Maintenance Services
N.A.I.C.S.: 811111
Christos Konstantinidis *(Gen Mgr)*

SFC CO., LTD.
682 Naepo-ro Guhang-myeon, Hongseong, Chungcheongnam-do, Korea (South)
Tel.: (82) 41 640 0001
Web Site: http://www.sfcltd.co.kr
Year Founded: 1988
Rev.: $31,965,905
Assets: $124,734,030
Liabilities: $39,299,429
Net Worth: $85,434,601
Earnings: ($5,339,160)
Emp.: 96
Fiscal Year-end: 12/31/18
Laminated Film Mfr
N.A.I.C.S.: 322220
Pyeong-jik Cho *(CEO)*

Subsidiaries:

SFC Co., Ltd. - Boryeong Factory (1)
71 Yoam-dong, Boryeong, 355-110, Chungnam, Korea (South)
Tel.: (82) 41 936 1500
Photovoltaic Backsheet Mfr
N.A.I.C.S.: 326113

SFC EKA-INVEST LLP
50 Zhibek Zholy st Office 812, Almaty, 050044, Kazakhstan
Tel.: (7) 273562144
Web Site: http://www.eka.kz
EKAI—(KAZ)
Sales Range: Less than $1 Million
Financial Investment Services
N.A.I.C.S.: 523940

SFC ENERGY AG
Eugen-Saenger-Ring 7, 85649, Brunnthal, Germany
Tel.: (49) 896735920
Web Site: https://www.sfc.com
F3C—(DEU)
Rev.: $130,422,240
Assets: $194,722,668
Liabilities: $53,250,689
Net Worth: $141,471,979
Earnings: $23,269,580
Emp.: 388
Fiscal Year-end: 12/31/23
Methanol Fuel Cell Mfr
N.A.I.C.S.: 335999
Peter Podesser *(Chm-Mgmt Bd & CEO)*

Subsidiaries:

PBF Group B. V. (1)
Twentepoort oost 54, 7609 RG, Almelo, Netherlands
Tel.: (31) 546540030
Web Site: http://www.pbfgroup.nl
Power Supply Product Mfr & Distr
N.A.I.C.S.: 335999

Subsidiary (Non-US):

PBF Power Srl (2)
Taieutra Turcului 47/15N, Tetarom 1 Industrial Park, 400221, Cluj-Napoca, Romania
Tel.: (40) 264287481
Semiconductor Machinery Mfr
N.A.I.C.S.: 333242
Aniela Costea *(Fin Mgr)*

SFC Energy Power S.R.L.
Tetarom 1 Industrial Park Taieutra Turcului 47/15N, 400221, Cluj-Napoca, Romania
Tel.: (40) 264287468
Methanol Fuel Cells Distr
N.A.I.C.S.: 424690

SFC Smart Fuel Cell, Inc. (1)
7632 Standish Place, Derwood, MD 20855
Tel.: (240) 328-6688
Web Site: http://www.sfc.com
Fuel Cell Mfr
N.A.I.C.S.: 334413

SFC WHOLESALE LTD
8 Westminster Chambers 106 Lord Street, Southport, PR8 1LF, United Kingdom
Tel.: (44) 1704 548 641
Web Site: http://www.sfcltd.co.uk
Year Founded: 2003
Chicken Products Mfr & Distr
N.A.I.C.S.: 112320
Tony Nuttall *(Grp Mng Dir)*

SFINKS POLSKA S.A.
ul Swietojanska 5a, Piaseczno, 05-500, Warsaw, Poland
Tel.: (48) 227027101
Web Site: http://www.sfinks.pl
Year Founded: 2006
SFS—(WAR)
Rev.: $25,429,878
Assets: $30,162,602
Liabilities: $48,166,158
Net Worth: ($18,003,557)
Earnings: ($86,128)
Fiscal Year-end: 12/31/23
Restaurant Operators
N.A.I.C.S.: 722511
Sylwester Eugeniusz Cacek *(Chm-Mgmt Bd & Pres)*

SFL INTERNATIONAL LIMITED
101-104 Gcp Business Centre Opp Memnagar Fire Station Office No 107, Vijay Cross Road, Ahmedabad, 380014, Gujarat, India
Tel.: (91) 8162210090
Web Site: http://www.sfl.net.in
Year Founded: 1992
Assets: $373,375
Liabilities: $16,827
Net Worth: $356,548
Earnings: ($8,574)
Fiscal Year-end: 03/31/18
Financial Services
Mayank Bhandari *(Exec Dir-Professional)*

SFP HOLDINGS CO., LTD.
2-24-7 Tamagawa Setagaya-ku, Tokyo, 158-0094, Japan
Web Site: http://www.sfpdining.jp
3198—(TKS)
Rev.: $206,170,110
Assets: $94,318,270
Liabilities: $39,413,310
Net Worth: $54,904,960
Earnings: $12,272,790
Emp.: 1,000
Fiscal Year-end: 02/29/24
Restaurant Operators
N.A.I.C.S.: 722511

SFP TECH HOLDINGS BERHAD
Plot 350 A & B Lorong Perindustrian Bukit Minyak 20, Penang Science Park MK13 Kawasan Perindustrian Bukit Minyak, 14100, Pulau Penang, Malaysia
Tel.: (60) 45062184
Web Site: https://www.sfptechholdings.com
Year Founded: 2012
SFPTECH—(KLS)
Rev.: $26,757,772
Assets: $63,512,901

INTERNATIONAL PUBLIC

Liabilities: $20,582,715
Net Worth: $42,930,185
Earnings: $8,518,387
Emp.: 432
Fiscal Year-end: 12/31/23
Holding Company
N.A.I.C.S.: 551112
Beng Huat Keoh *(Mng Dir)*

SFS GROUP AG
Rosenbergsaustrasse 8, CH-9435, Heerbrugg, Switzerland
Tel.: (41) 717275151   CH
Web Site: https://www.sfs.com
SFSN—(SWX)
Rev.: $3,036,252,772
Assets: $2,853,880,266
Liabilities: $1,408,647,450
Net Worth: $1,445,232,816
Earnings: $295,676,275
Emp.: 13,282
Fiscal Year-end: 12/31/22
Holding Company
N.A.I.C.S.: 551112
Heinrich Spoerry *(Chm)*

Subsidiaries:

GESIPA Blindniettechnik GmbH (1)
Nordendstr 13-39, 64546, Moerfelden-Walldorf, Germany
Tel.: (49) 61059620
Web Site: https://eri.gesipa.de
Rivet & Nut Mfr
N.A.I.C.S.: 332722

Garant Productions GmbH (1)
Otto-Knecht-Str 3, Mittelstadt, 72766, Reutlingen, Germany
Tel.: (49) 712797800
Power Tool Mfr & Distr
N.A.I.C.S.: 333991

HECO Schrauben GmbH & Co. KG (1)
Dr Kurt-Steim-Strasse 28, D-78713, Schramberg, Germany
Tel.: (49) 74229890
Web Site: https://www.heco-schrauben.com
Screw Mfr
N.A.I.C.S.: 332722

HECO Schrauben S.R.L. (1)
Strada Laminoristilor 159, 405100, Campia Turzii, Romania
Tel.: (40) 769223256
Building Material Mfr & Distr
N.A.I.C.S.: 321992

Hoffmann Austria Qualitaetswerkzeuge GmbH (1)
Mondseer Strasse 2, 4893, Zell am See, Austria
Tel.: (43) 5088770
Power Tool Mfr & Distr
N.A.I.C.S.: 333991

Hoffmann Danmark ApS (1)
Kongens Nytorv 26 3, 1050, Copenhagen, Denmark
Tel.: (45) 70264150
Power Tool Mfr & Distr
N.A.I.C.S.: 333991

Hoffmann Engineering Services GmbH (1)
Haberlandstrasse 55, 81241, Munich, Germany
Tel.: (49) 8983910
Industrial Equipment Mfr & Whslr
N.A.I.C.S.: 333514

Hoffmann Essen Qualitaetswerkzeuge GmbH (1)
Frohnhauser Strasse 69, 45127, Essen, Germany
Tel.: (49) 20172220
Power Tool Mfr & Distr
N.A.I.C.S.: 333991

Hoffmann France S.A.S. (1)
1 Rue Gay Lussac, CS 80836, 67410, Drusenheim, France
Tel.: (33) 390551200
Power Tool Mfr & Distr
N.A.I.C.S.: 333991

AND PRIVATE COMPANIES — SFS GROUP AG

Hoffmann GmbH (1)
Herbert-Ludwig-Str 4, 28832, Achim, Germany
Tel.: (49) 42025270
Power Tool Mfr & Distr
N.A.I.C.S.: 333991

Hoffmann Goppingen Qualitatswerkzeuge GmbH (1)
Ulmer Strasse 70, 73037, Goppingen, Germany
Tel.: (49) 71616220
Power Tool Mfr & Distr
N.A.I.C.S.: 333991

Hoffmann Group System GmbH (1)
Morungenstr 10, 81241, Munich, Germany
Tel.: (49) 8983910
Tool Equipment Mfr & Distr
N.A.I.C.S.: 333515

Hoffmann Hungary Quality Tools Kft. (1)
Zugligeti ut 41, 1121, Budapest, Hungary
Tel.: (36) 13920290
Power Tool Mfr & Distr
N.A.I.C.S.: 333991

Hoffmann Iberia Quality Tools S.L. (1)
Parque Empresarial San Fernando Avenida de Castilla 2 Edificio Atenas, San Fernando de Henares, 28830, Madrid, Spain
Tel.: (34) 900900728
Power Tool Mfr & Distr
N.A.I.C.S.: 333991

Hoffmann Industrial Tools S.R.L. (1)
Str Aristide Pascal Nr 18 Sector 3, 031443, Bucharest, Romania
Tel.: (40) 213224544
Power Tool Mfr & Distr
N.A.I.C.S.: 333991

Hoffmann Italia S.p.A. (1)
Via San Crispino 114, 35129, Padova, Italy
Tel.: (39) 0497960211
Power Tool Mfr & Distr
N.A.I.C.S.: 333991

Hoffmann Nurnberg GmbH (1)
Poststrasse 15, 90471, Nuremberg, Germany
Tel.: (49) 91165810
Industrial Equipment Mfr & Whslr
N.A.I.C.S.: 333514

Hoffmann Qualitatswerkzeuge CZ s.r.o (1)
Zemska 211/I, 337 01, Ejpovice, Czech Republic
Tel.: (420) 371707250
Tool Equipment Mfr & Distr
N.A.I.C.S.: 333515

Hoffmann Qualitatswerkzeuge SK s.r.o. (1)
Karpatska 8, 81105, Bratislava, Slovakia
Tel.: (421) 262520495
Industrial Equipment Mfr & Whslr
N.A.I.C.S.: 333514

Hoffmann Quality Tools (Malaysia) Sdn. Bhd. (1)
Level 9-03 Wisma Conlay No 1 Jalan USJ 10/1, 47620, Subang Jaya, Selangor, Malaysia
Tel.: (60) 1800888469
Power Tool Mfr & Distr
N.A.I.C.S.: 333991

Hoffmann Quality Tools B.V. (1)
Morseltoven 2, Postbus 71, 7621 HB, Borne, Netherlands
Tel.: (31) 742077000
Power Tool Mfr & Distr
N.A.I.C.S.: 333991

Hoffmann Quality Tools India Pvt. Ltd. (1)
No 512 5th Floor Tower 2 World Trade Centre, Kharadi, Pune, 411014, India
Tel.: (91) 18002667708
Power Tool Mfr & Distr
N.A.I.C.S.: 333991

Hoffmann Quality Tools Mexico S. de R.L. de C.V. (1)
Avenida Ebano Lote C Parque Industrial Finsa Puebla, 72710, Cuautlancingo, Puebla, Mexico
Tel.: (52) 2226891400
Power Tool Mfr & Distr
N.A.I.C.S.: 333991

Hoffmann Quality Tools Trading Co., Ltd. (1)
Unit 04-08 5/F Building 16 No 2177 Shenkun Road, Portmix Minhang District, Shanghai, 201106, China
Tel.: (86) 2154544660
Industrial Equipment Mfr & Whslr
N.A.I.C.S.: 333514

Hoffmann Supply Chain GmbH (1)
Poststrasse 15, 90471, Nuremberg, Germany
Tel.: (49) 91165810
Power Tool Mfr & Distr
N.A.I.C.S.: 333991

Hoffmann kvalitetna orodja d.o.o. (1)
Celovska Cesta 150, 1000, Ljubljana, Slovenia
Tel.: (386) 15072002
Power Tool Mfr & Distr
N.A.I.C.S.: 333991

Jevith A/S (1)
Navervej 26, 4000, Roskilde, Denmark
Tel.: (45) 46414182
Web Site: https://jevith.dk
Emp.: 10
Building Materials Whslr
N.A.I.C.S.: 423390

Nvelope Rainscreen Systems Ltd. (1)
Unit A City Park Watchmead, Welwyn Garden City, AL7 1LT, Herts, United Kingdom
Tel.: (44) 1707333396
Web Site: http://www.nvelope.com
Rainscreen Cladding Product Mfr
N.A.I.C.S.: 326199
Nick Eckers *(Mgr-Technical)*

Proserve Vertriebs- und Beratungs GmbH (1)
Haberlandstr 55, 81241, Munich, Germany
Tel.: (49) 15116175686
Web Site: https://www.proserve-gmbh.de
Technical Consulting Services
N.A.I.C.S.: 541330

SFS Group Austria GmbH (1)
Wiener Str 29, 2100, Korneuburg, Austria
Tel.: (43) 2262905000
Fastening System Product Mfr
N.A.I.C.S.: 332722

SFS Group CZ s.r.o. (1)
Vesecko 500, 511 01, Turnov, Czech Republic
Tel.: (420) 481354400
Web Site: http://www.sfsintec.biz
Screw Mfr
N.A.I.C.S.: 332722

SFS Group Canada Inc. (1)
40 Innovation Drive, Dundas, L9H 7P3, ON, Canada
Tel.: (905) 847-5400
Web Site: https://ca.sfs.com
Building Material Mfr & Distr
N.A.I.C.S.: 321992

SFS Group Fastening Technology Mexico S.A. (1)
Autopista Mexico - Queretaro Km 201 JGN Business Park de, Conin Modules 30/32 Col Cumbres de Conin El Marques, 76240, Queretaro, Mexico
Tel.: (52) 4423251465
Web Site: https://gesipa.mx
Building Material Mfr & Distr
N.A.I.C.S.: 321992

SFS Group Finland Oy (1)
Allika Tee 2, Harjumaa, 75312, Peetri, Estonia
Tel.: (372) 6610600
Web Site: https://ee.sfs.com
Building Material Mfr & Distr
N.A.I.C.S.: 321992

SFS Group Germany GmbH (1)
In den Schwarzwiesen 2, 61440, Oberursel, Germany
Tel.: (49) 617170020
Web Site: https://de.sfs.com
Fabricated Metal Product Mfr & Distr
N.A.I.C.S.: 332999

SFS Group Hungary Kft. (1)
Vasarter 18, 9241, Janossomorja, Hungary
Tel.: (36) 308477477
Building Material Mfr & Distr
N.A.I.C.S.: 321992

SFS Group India Pvt. Ltd. (1)
Gat 378/387/389, Urawade, Pune, 412115, India
Tel.: (91) 2066740512
Industrial Equipment Mfr & Whslr
N.A.I.C.S.: 333514

SFS Group Italy S.R.L. (1)
Via Castelfranco Veneto N 71, 33170, Pordenone, Italy
Tel.: (39) 04349951
Web Site: https://it.sfs.com
Building Material Mfr & Distr
N.A.I.C.S.: 321992

SFS Group Pazarlama A.S. (1)
Celal Umur Caddesi No 9, Torbali, Izmir, Turkiye
Tel.: (90) 2328532000
Fabricated Metal Product Mfr & Distr
N.A.I.C.S.: 332999

SFS Group S.A.S. (1)
39 Rue Georges Melies, BP 55, 26902, Valence, Cedex 9, France
Tel.: (33) 75754422
Web Site: https://fr.sfs.com
Emp.: 300
Building Material Mfr & Distr
N.A.I.C.S.: 321992

SFS Group Schweiz AG (1)
Rosenbergsaustrasse 4, 9435, Heerbrugg, Switzerland
Tel.: (41) 717275151
Web Site: https://www.sfs.ch
Fabricated Metal Product Mfr & Distr
N.A.I.C.S.: 332999

SFS Group Sp. z o.o. (1)
Ul Torowa 6, 61-315, Poznan, Poland
Tel.: (48) 616604900
Web Site: https://pl.sfs.com
Fabricated Metal Product Mfr & Distr
N.A.I.C.S.: 332999

SFS Group Sweden AB (1)
Olivehallsvagen 10, 645 42, Strangnas, Sweden
Tel.: (46) 152715000
Web Site: https://se.sfs.com
Building Material Mfr & Distr
N.A.I.C.S.: 321992

SFS Group TR San. ve Tic. A.S. (1)
Celal Umur Caddesi no 9, Torbali, 35860, Izmir, Turkiye
Tel.: (90) 5343549042
Industrial Equipment Mfr & Whslr
N.A.I.C.S.: 333514

SFS Group USA, Inc (1)
1045 Spring St, Wyomissing, PA 19610
Tel.: (610) 376-5751
Web Site: https://us.sfs.com
Fabricated Metal Product Mfr & Distr
N.A.I.C.S.: 332999

SFS Group the Netherlands B.V. (1)
Grasbeemd 14, 5705 DG, Helmond, Netherlands
Tel.: (31) 492597414
Web Site: https://bnl.sfs.com
Building Material Mfr & Distr
N.A.I.C.S.: 321992

SFS Intec (China) Advanced Precision Parts Manufacturing Co., Ltd. (1)
Huangge Motor City Huangge East 2nd Road District A3, Nansha District, Guangzhou, 511455, China
Tel.: (86) 2082221305
Fastening System Product Mfr
N.A.I.C.S.: 332722

SFS Intec GmbH (1)
Division Construction In den Schwarzwiesen 2, 61440, Oberursel, Germany
Tel.: (49) 617170020
Fastening System Product Mfr
N.A.I.C.S.: 332722

SFS Intec Oy (1)
Ratastie 18, 03100, Nummela, Finland
Tel.: (358) 931549810
Fastening System Product Mfr
N.A.I.C.S.: 332722

SFS intec AG (1)
Rosenbergsaustrasse 10, 9435, Heerbrugg, Switzerland
Tel.: (41) 717276262
Sales Range: $650-699.9 Million
Emp.: 2,952
Precision Cold Formed Components, Special Fasteners & Mechanical Fastening Systems Developer, Mfr & Supplier
N.A.I.C.S.: 332722

Subsidiary (Non-US):

Unisteel Fastening Systems (Shanghai) Co., Ltd. (2)
No 988 Shang Xue Lu, Ma Lu Town, Shanghai, 201801, China
Tel.: (86) 261802888
Fastening System Product Mfr
N.A.I.C.S.: 332722

Unisteel Precision (Suzhou) Co., Ltd. (2)
Unit A4-6 BLK A Flatted Factory Weiting SIP, Suzhou, 215122, Jiangsu, China
Tel.: (86) 51288186788
Fastening System Product Mfr
N.A.I.C.S.: 332722

Unisteel Technology Limited (2)
67 Ubi Avenue 1 02-10, Starhub Green, Singapore, 408942, Singapore
Tel.: (65) 66346366
Web Site: https://www.unisteeltech.com
Sales Range: $150-199.9 Million
Holding Company; Precision Fastener, Stamped Component, Spring & Engineered Plastic Component Mfr
N.A.I.C.S.: 551112

SFS intec, Inc. (1)
Spring St & Van Reed Rd, Wyomissing, PA 19610
Tel.: (610) 376-5751
Web Site: http://www.sfsintecusa.com
Sales Range: $100-124.9 Million
Emp.: 200
Bolts, Nuts, Rivets & Washers
N.A.I.C.S.: 332722

Simple System GmbH (1)
Haberlandstrasse 55, 81241, Munich, Germany
Tel.: (49) 89998298700
Web Site: https://www.simplesystem.com
Information Technology Consulting Services
N.A.I.C.S.: 541512

Stamm AG (1)
Roemerstrasse 27, 8215, Hallau, Switzerland
Tel.: (41) 525443900
Web Site: https://www.stamm.ch
Injection Mould Mfr
N.A.I.C.S.: 333511

Sunil SFS intec Automotive Parts (Tianjin) Co., Ltd. (1)
No 2 of 3rd Road, Jinghai Economic Development Area, Tianjin, 301600, China
Tel.: (86) 2259583555
Web Site: https://www.sunilsfs.com
Machine Tool Mfr & Distr
N.A.I.C.S.: 333517

Tegra Medical Costa Rica S.A. (1)
Tel.: (506) 40525640
Surgical & Medical Instrument Mfr
N.A.I.C.S.: 339112

Tegra Medical, LLC (1)
16 Forge Park, Franklin, MA 02038
Tel.: (508) 541-4200
Web Site: https://www.tegramedical.com
Medical Instrument Mfr & Sales
N.A.I.C.S.: 339112
Mike Treleaven *(Sr VP-Engrg)*

Triangle Fastener Corporation (1)
1925 Preble Ave, Pittsburgh, PA 15233-2243
Tel.: (412) 321-5000
Web Site: http://www.trianglefastener.com
Distr of Hardware

SFS GROUP AG

INTERNATIONAL PUBLIC

SFS Group AG—(Continued)
N.A.I.C.S.: 423710
Mary Helt (Supvr-Acctg)

Unisteel Technology (China) Co., Ltd. (1)
8 Yun Tai Shan Lu Sutong Science Technology Park, Nantong, 226017, China
Tel.: (86) 51369920000
Fastening System Product Mfr
N.A.I.C.S.: 332722

Unisteel Technology (M) Sdn. Bhd. (1)
No 2 4 6 8 10 & 12 Jalan Mega 1, 79200, Iskandar Puteri, Johor, Malaysia
Tel.: (60) 75555333
Precision Metal Machined Parts Mfr
N.A.I.C.S.: 332119

SFS GROUP PUBLIC COMPANY LIMITED
Ellinas House 6 Theotoki Street, PO Box 22379, 1521, Nicosia, Cyprus
Tel.: (357) 22554200
Web Site: http://www.sfsnet.com
SFS—(CYP)
Sales Range: $10-24.9 Million
Emp.: 295
Financial Services
N.A.I.C.S.: 523150
Christodoulos Ellinas (Co-Founder, Chm & CEO)

Subsidiaries:

CyVenture Capital Public Company Ltd (1)
Ellina House Theotoki 6, 22379, Nicosia, Cyprus
Tel.: (357) 22 55 40 00
Venture Capital Management Services
N.A.I.C.S.: 541618

Sharelink Securities & Financial Services Ltd (1)
Ellinas House, Theotoki 6, 1055, Nicosia, Cyprus
Tel.: (357) 22554000
Web Site: http://www.sharelinksecurities.com
Asset Management & Brokerage Services
N.A.I.C.S.: 523150
Loizos Loizou (Mng Dir)

Triena Investments Public Company Ltd (1)
6 Thoetoki St Ellinas House, 22379, Nicosia, Cyprus
Tel.: (357) 22554000
Sales Range: $25-49.9 Million
Emp.: 50
Investment Management Service
N.A.I.C.S.: 541618

White Knight Holdings Public Company Ltd (1)
Ellinas House 6 Theotokis St, PO Box 22379, Nicosia, 1055, Cyprus
Tel.: (357) 22554000
Web Site: http://www.sfsnet.com
Sales Range: $25-49.9 Million
Emp.: 83
Investment Management Service
N.A.I.C.S.: 541618
Christiulos Ellinas (Chm)

SFUND INTERNATIONAL HOLDINGS LIMITED
Suites 904-5 Great Eagle Centre 23 Harbour Road, Wanchai, China (Hong Kong)
Tel.: (852) 25118339   Ky
Web Site: http://www.1367.com.hk
Rev.: $8,260,615
Assets: $26,305,816
Liabilities: $41,761,757
Net Worth: ($15,455,941)
Earnings: ($16,105,311)
Emp.: 175
Fiscal Year-end: 12/31/19
Holding Company; Financial Services Business, Money Lending Business, Securities Investment & Apparel Trading

N.A.I.C.S.: 551112
Kwan Sing Lam (CEO)

SG ALLIED BUSINESSES LIMITED
B-40 SITE, Karachi, Pakistan
Tel.: (92) 2132953410   PK
Web Site: https://www.sgabl.com.pk
Year Founded: 1968
SGABL—(PSX)
Rev.: $76,821
Assets: $5,282,774
Liabilities: $1,072,672
Net Worth: $4,210,102
Earnings: ($29,007)
Emp.: 21
Fiscal Year-end: 06/30/23
Filamenr Yarn Mfr
N.A.I.C.S.: 313110
Sohail Ahmed (CEO)

SG COMPANY S.P.A.
Piazza Guglielmo Oberdan 2/a, 20129, Milan, Italy
Tel.: (39) 0283450000
Web Site: https://www.sg-company.it
Year Founded: 2000
SGC—(ITA)
Sales Range: Less than $1 Million
Digital Marketing Services
N.A.I.C.S.: 541613
Davide Verdesca (Chm & CEO)

SG CORPORATION
35 Digital-ro 10-gil, Geumcheon-gu, Seoul, Korea (South)
Tel.: (82) 28505191
Web Site: http://www.sgsegye.com
Year Founded: 1964
004060—(KRS)
Rev.: $123,720,770
Assets: $233,026,619
Liabilities: $44,785,579
Net Worth: $188,241,040
Earnings: $1,360,831
Emp.: 111
Fiscal Year-end: 12/31/22
Men's & Women's Apparel Mfr
N.A.I.C.S.: 315210
Eui-Bum Lee (Chm & CEO)

Subsidiaries:

Myanmar Segye International Ltd. (1)
G-F Pyay Rd Pyin Ma Pin Indust Zone Pyin Ma Pin Ward, Mingaladon, Yangon, Myanmar
Tel.: (95) 1600161
Sales Range: $150-199.9 Million
Emp.: 1,000
Clothing Mfr
N.A.I.C.S.: 315250

SGWICUS BANGLADESH LTD. (1)
Plot No 73-80 Depz Ganakbari, Savar, Dhaka, Bangladesh
Tel.: (880) 27701056
Menswear Mfr
N.A.I.C.S.: 315210

SGWICUS Corporation - Garment Export Division (1)
60-9 Karibong-dong, Kuro-gu, Seoul, 152-020, Korea (South)
Tel.: (82) 28505960
Sales Range: $100-124.9 Million
Emp.: 300
Garments Mfr
N.A.I.C.S.: 315990

Division (Domestic):

SGWICUS Corporation - Casual Wear Export Division 1 (2)
60-9 Gasan-dong, Geumcheon-gu, Seoul, 153023, Korea (South)
Tel.: (82) 28505239
Sales Range: $25-49.9 Million
Emp.: 250
Leather Garment Mfr
N.A.I.C.S.: 316990

Y. K. Na (Mgr)

SGWICUS Corporation - Casual Wear Export Division 2 (2)
60-9 Karibong-dong, Kuro-gu, Seoul, 153-801, Korea (South)
Tel.: (82) 28505992
Sales Range: $10-24.9 Million
Emp.: 50
Garments Export Services
N.A.I.C.S.: 315210

SGWICUS Corporation - Ladies Garment Division (1)
60-9 Gasan-dong, Geumcheon-gu, Seoul, 153023, Korea (South)
Tel.: (82) 28505230
Sales Range: $25-49.9 Million
Emp.: 250
Ladies Garment Mfr
N.A.I.C.S.: 315210
B. H. Ahn (Exec VP)

SGWICUS USA, INC (1)
141 W 26th St 17th Fl, New York, NY 10018
Tel.: (212) 805-8400
Textile Designing Services & Mfr
N.A.I.C.S.: 314999

SG FINSERVE LIMITED
37 Hargobind Enclave, Vikas Marg, New Delhi, 110092, India
Tel.: (91) 1141450121
Web Site: https://www.sgfinserve.com
Year Founded: 1994
539199—(BOM)
Rev.: $5,031,089
Assets: $129,396,319
Liabilities: $60,686,170
Net Worth: $68,710,149
Earnings: $2,206,858
Emp.: 33
Fiscal Year-end: 03/31/23
Stock Brokerage Services
N.A.I.C.S.: 523150
Mohd. Javed Qureshi (CFO)

SG GLOBAL CO.,LTD.
7F Sgtower 47 daewangpanggyo-ro, Bundang-gu, Seongnam, South Choongcheong, Korea (South)
Tel.: (82) 217241702
Web Site: https://www.sgchoongbang.com
Year Founded: 1954
001380—(KRS)
Rev.: $51,896,382
Assets: $142,612,489
Liabilities: $49,682,621
Net Worth: $92,929,868
Earnings: ($1,875,812)
Emp.: 112
Fiscal Year-end: 12/31/22
Textile Mfr
N.A.I.C.S.: 313310
E. B. Lee (CEO)

SG HOLDINGS CO., LTD.
68 Kamitobatsunoda-cho, Minami-ku, Kyoto, 601-8104, Japan
Tel.: (81) 756718600   JP
Web Site: https://www.sg-hldgs.co.jp
Year Founded: 2006
9143—(TKS)
Rev.: $8,704,973,400
Assets: $5,929,493,890
Liabilities: $2,027,868,680
Net Worth: $3,901,625,210
Earnings: $385,224,190
Emp.: 94,087
Fiscal Year-end: 03/31/24
Holding Company
N.A.I.C.S.: 551112
Eiiichi Kuriwada (Chm & CEO)

Subsidiaries:

SG Fielder Co., Ltd. (1)
1-6-35 Shinsuna East Square Tokyo 2nd Floor, Koto-ku, Tokyo, Japan
Tel.: (81) 368342733
Human Resource Consulting Services
N.A.I.C.S.: 541612

SG Holdings Global Pte. Ltd. (1)
150 Beach Road 28-03 Gateway West, Singapore, 189720, Singapore
Tel.: (65) 65895400
Logistics Transportation Services
N.A.I.C.S.: 541614

SG Motors Co., Ltd. (1)
SGH Building Shinsuna II 3F 1-8-2 Shinsuna, Koto-ku, Tokyo, 136-0075, Japan
Tel.: (81) 120134960
Web Site: https://www.sg-motors.co.jp
Emp.: 851
Automotive Truck & Spare Part Mfr
N.A.I.C.S.: 336211

SG Moving Co., Ltd. (1)
3-2-9 Shinsuna, Koto-ku, Tokyo, 136-0075, Japan
Web Site: http://www.sagawa-mov.co.jp
Vehicles Transportation Services
N.A.I.C.S.: 488490

SG Realty Co., Ltd. (1)
68 Kamitoba Tsunoda-cho, Minami-ku, Kyoto, Japan
Tel.: (81) 756922304
Real Estate Services
N.A.I.C.S.: 531210

SG Systems Co., Ltd. (1)
Kamitobatsunoda-cho 25, Minami-ku, Kyoto, 601-8104, Japan
Tel.: (81) 756611178
Web Site: http://www.sg-systems.co.jp
Logistics Transportation Services
N.A.I.C.S.: 541614

SGH Global Japan Co., Ltd. (1)
X Frontier West 5F 3-2-9 Shinsuna, Koto-ku, Tokyo, Japan
Web Site: http://www.sgh-globalj.com
Emp.: 290
Logistics Transportation Services
N.A.I.C.S.: 541614
Akira Oyama (Pres)

Sagawa Advance Co., Ltd. (1)
4F SGH Building Shinsuna 1-8-10 Shinsuna, Koto-ku, Tokyo, 136-0075, Japan
Web Site: http://www.sg-advance.co.jp
Logistics Transportation Services
N.A.I.C.S.: 541614

Sagawa Global Logistics Co., Ltd. (1)
1-1-1 Katsushima, Shinagawa-ku, Tokyo, Japan
Tel.: (81) 337688501
Logistic Transportation & Warehousing Services
N.A.I.C.S.: 541614

SG MART LTD.
Kintech House 8 Shivalik Plaza, Opp AMA IIM Road, Ahmedabad, 380 015, Gujarat, India
Tel.: (91) 7926303064
Web Site: https://sgmart.co.in
512329—(BOM)
Rev.: $309,754
Assets: $1,460,692
Liabilities: $1,774
Net Worth: $1,458,917
Earnings: $23,632
Emp.: 3
Fiscal Year-end: 03/31/23
Textile Product Mfr & Whslr
N.A.I.C.S.: 314999
Jigar Shah (Chm & Mng Dir)

SG MICRO CORP.
87 Xi San Huan North Road the IFEC Building D-1106, Haidian District, Beijing, 100089, China
Tel.: (86) 1088825716
Web Site: https://www.sg-micro.com
Year Founded: 2007
300661—(CHIN)
Rev.: $368,423,655
Assets: $662,960,273

AND PRIVATE COMPANIES

Liabilities: $121,557,592
Net Worth: $541,402,681
Earnings: $39,546,215
Fiscal Year-end: 12/31/23
Integrated Circuit Mfr & Distr
N.A.I.C.S.: 334413

SG POWER LIMITED
B-40 SITE, Karachi, Pakistan
Tel.: (92) 2132953410
Web Site: https://www.sgabl.com.pk
Year Founded: 1994
SGPL—(PSX)
Rev.: $12,045
Assets: $45,517
Liabilities: $18,867
Net Worth: $26,650
Earnings: ($10,449)
Fiscal Year-end: 06/30/23
Power Generation Services
N.A.I.C.S.: 221118
Asim Ahmed (CEO)

SG PRIVATE EQUITY CO., LTD.
402 OPULENCE Building, 254 Seocho-daero, Seocho-gu, Seoul, 06647, Korea (South)
Tel.: (82) 260901300
Web Site: https://www.sgpef.com
Year Founded: 2012
Emp.: 100
Private Equity
N.A.I.C.S.: 523940

Subsidiaries:

Dongsung TCS Co., Ltd. (1)
81 Gomo-ro 134beon-gil, Jillye-myeon, Gimhae, Gyeongsangnam, Korea (South)
Tel.: (82) 553456861
Web Site: https://dongsungtcs.com
Construction Machinery Mfr
N.A.I.C.S.: 333120
Gyung-Ku Gwak (CEO)

SG&G CORPORATION
254 Beotkkot-ro, Geumcheon-gu, Seoul, Korea (South)
Tel.: (82) 221051310
Web Site: https://www.sgng.com
Year Founded: 1993
040610—(KRS)
Rev.: $32,765,782
Assets: $289,654,972
Liabilities: $49,562,623
Net Worth: $240,092,349
Earnings: $31,696,238
Emp.: 69
Fiscal Year-end: 12/31/22
Automobile Seats Mfr
N.A.I.C.S.: 336360
Eui-Bum Lee (CEO)

SGA CLOUD SERVICE CO., LTD.
25 Beobwon-ro 11-gil, Songpa-gu, Seoul, Korea (South)
Tel.: (82) 7074109348
Software Development Services
N.A.I.C.S.: 541512
Eun You-Jin (CEO)

SGA CO., LTD.
1004 4 Jeongui-ro 8-gil, Songpa-gu, Seoul, Korea (South)
Tel.: (82) 7073089319
Web Site: http://www.sgacorp.kr
Year Founded: 1997
049470—(KRS)
Rev.: $42,154,292
Assets: $56,106,475
Liabilities: $20,690,148
Net Worth: $35,416,327
Earnings: ($5,371,328)
Emp.: 180
Fiscal Year-end: 12/31/22
Software Developing Services
N.A.I.C.S.: 513210

You-Jin Eun (Board of Directors & CEO)

Subsidiaries:

SGA Systems Co., Ltd. (1)
20 Cheomdan-ro 8-gil Dong-gu, Daegu, 41069, Korea (South) **(74.52%)**
Tel.: (82) 7074109300
Web Site: http://www.sgasys.kr
Educational Software Development Services
N.A.I.C.S.: 541511
Kim Byung-Chun (CEO)

SGA SOLUTIONS CO., LTD.
5th floor Quantum B-dong, Songpa-gu, Uiwang, 05836, Korea (South)
Tel.: (82) 5746856
Web Site: https://sgasol.kr
Year Founded: 2002
184230—(KRS)
Rev.: $28,627,310
Assets: $72,793,825
Liabilities: $29,023,831
Net Worth: $43,769,993
Earnings: $3,699,306
Emp.: 126
Fiscal Year-end: 12/31/22
Investment Services
N.A.I.C.S.: 523999
Yeong Cheol Choi (CEO)

SGC ETEC E&C CO., LTD.
4 8 13F Songam Building 246 Yangjae-daero, Seocho-gu, Seoul, 137-170, Korea (South)
Tel.: (82) 24899000
Web Site: https://www.etecnc.com
Year Founded: 1967
016250—(KRS)
Rev.: $1,168,396,770
Assets: $746,694,172
Liabilities: $557,773,124
Net Worth: $188,921,047
Earnings: $39,880,919
Emp.: 1,022
Fiscal Year-end: 12/31/22
Construction Services
N.A.I.C.S.: 237990
Chan-Kyu Ahn (Pres)

Subsidiaries:

PT. eTEC Indonesia (1)
11Fl Menara Prima B/D Jl Lingkar Mega Kuningan Sub-Block 6 2, Jakarta Selatan, 12950, Indonesia
Tel.: (62) 2157948252
Construction Engineering Services
N.A.I.C.S.: 541330

eTEC Arabia Limited (1)
No 8 3055 Prince Sultan Street, PO Box 4621, Al Andalus, Al Khobar, 34437, Saudi Arabia
Tel.: (966) 138817790
Construction Engineering Services
N.A.I.C.S.: 541330

eTEC E&C (Nanjing) Co., Ltd. (1)
Rm911 31 Building No 9 Shanhuxilu, Nanjing, China
Tel.: (86) 2152067077
Construction Services
N.A.I.C.S.: 237990

eTEC E&C (Shanghai) Co., Ltd. (1)
D/6F Liaoshen International Building 1068 Wuzhong Rd, Shanghai, 201103, China
Tel.: (86) 2152067077
Construction Engineering Services
N.A.I.C.S.: 541330

eTEC Malaysia Sdn. Bhd. (1)
1-21-3 Suntech Penang Cybercity Lintang Mayang Pasir 3, 11905, Bayan Baru, Penang, Malaysia
Tel.: (60) 46438989
Construction Engineering Services
N.A.I.C.S.: 541330

SGC SOLUTIONS CO., LTD.
Yangjaedaero 246, Seocho-gu, Seoul, Korea (South)
Tel.: (82) 262833200
Web Site: https://www.glasslock.co.kr
Year Founded: 1967
005090—(KRS)
Rev.: $2,230,433,912
Assets: $2,412,946,119
Liabilities: $1,728,421,201
Net Worth: $684,524,919
Earnings: $117,245,186
Emp.: 227
Fiscal Year-end: 12/31/22
Glass Products Mfr & Sales
N.A.I.C.S.: 327215
Moon Byeong Do (CEO)

Subsidiaries:

Samkwang Glass Co., Ltd. - Cheonan Plant (1)
1112-84 Manghyang Ipjang-myeon, Seobuk-gu, Cheonan, 330-820, South Chungcheong, Korea (South)
Tel.: (82) 416237300
Web Site: http://www.glasslock.co.kr
Glass Container Mfr
N.A.I.C.S.: 327213

SGF CAPITAL PUBLIC COMPANY LIMITED
No 121 WTH Holding Building 4th Floor Vibhavadi Rangsit Road, Samsennai, Bangkok, 10400, Thailand
Tel.: (66) 22321789   TH
Web Site: http://www.sgf.co.th
Year Founded: 1985
SGF—(THA)
Rev.: $16,661,484
Assets: $85,858,815
Liabilities: $34,811,042
Net Worth: $51,047,773
Earnings: ($914,209)
Emp.: 304
Fiscal Year-end: 12/31/23
Financial Services
N.A.I.C.S.: 522320
Pinit Wuthipand (Chm)

SGIS SONGSHAN CO., LTD.
Shaogang office, Qujiang District, Shaoguan, 512123, China
Tel.: (86) 7518787265
Web Site: http://www.sgss.com.cn
000717—(SSE)
Rev.: $5,518,245,559
Assets: $2,826,462,066
Liabilities: $1,536,121,581
Net Worth: $1,290,340,486
Earnings: ($182,195,241)
Emp.: 5,458
Fiscal Year-end: 12/31/22
Iron & Steel Product Mfr
N.A.I.C.S.: 331221

SGL CARBON SE
Sohnleinstrasse 8, 65201, Wiesbaden, Germany
Tel.: (49) 61160290   De
Web Site: https://www.sglcarbon.com
Year Founded: 1992
SGL—(DUS)
Rev.: $1,202,224,817
Assets: $1,625,558,962
Liabilities: $957,386,451
Net Worth: $668,172,511
Earnings: $45,258,670
Emp.: 4,784
Fiscal Year-end: 12/31/23
Carbon & Graphite Products Mfr
N.A.I.C.S.: 335991
Helmut Jodl (Deputy Chm-Supervisory Bd)

Subsidiaries:

Gelter-Ringsdorff, S.A. (1)
C-San Dalmacio 33, 28021, Madrid, 28021, Spain **(64%)**
Tel.: (34) 917231000
Web Site: http://www.sglgroup.com
Sales Range: $25-49.9 Million
Emp.: 45
Motor Vehicle Body Mfr
N.A.I.C.S.: 336211
Silvia Gil (Mng Dir)

P. G. Lawton (Industrial Services) Ltd. (1)
Unit 1 Caldene Business Park, Burnley Road Mytholmroyd, Hebden Bridge, HX75QJ, West Yorkshire, United Kingdom **(100%)**
Tel.: (44) 1422883903
Web Site: http://www.sglcarbon.com
Sales Range: $25-49.9 Million
Emp.: 45
Textile Machinery Mfr
N.A.I.C.S.: 333248
David Collinge (Mgr)

SGL Automotive Carbon Fibers GmbH & Co. KG (1)
Anton-Ditt-Bogen 5, 80939, Munich, Germany **(51%)**
Tel.: (49) 89 316 0568 0
Web Site: http://www.sgl-acf.com
Non-Crimp Carbon Fiber Fabrics Mfr
N.A.I.C.S.: 335991
Andreas Wullner (Mng Dir)

SGL Brakes GmbH (1)
Werner-von-Siemens-Strasse 18, Meitingen, 86405, Augsburg, 86405, Germany **(100%)**
Tel.: (49) 8271830
Web Site: http://www.sglgroup.com
Industrial Supplies Whslr
N.A.I.C.S.: 423840

SGL Carbon (Pty) Ltd. (1)
Kelvin Street Powerville 1380, Vereeniging, South Africa
Tel.: (27) 164212980
Industrial Supplies Whslr
N.A.I.C.S.: 423840

SGL Carbon Asia-Pacific Sdn. Bhd. (1)
Ste 19 02 Level 19 Menara Citibank, 165 Jalan Ampang, 50450, Kuala Lumpur, Malaysia **(100%)**
Tel.: (60) 327155240
Carbon & Graphite Product Mfr
N.A.I.C.S.: 335991

SGL Carbon Far East Ltd. (1)
151 Huan Cheng Dong Lu Shanghai Fengpu Industrial Development Zone, Shanghai Oriental Plz, Shanghai, 200041, China **(100%)**
Tel.: (86) 2160976888
Emp.: 280
Carbon & Graphite Product Mfr
N.A.I.C.S.: 335991

SGL Carbon Fibers America LLC (1)
8781 Randolph Rd NE, Moses Lake, WA 98837
Tel.: (509) 762-4600
Emp.: 180
Carbon Products Mfr
N.A.I.C.S.: 335991

SGL Carbon Fibers Ltd. (1)
Ross-Shire, Muir of Ord, IV6 7UA, United Kingdom
Tel.: (44) 1463274100
Carbon & Graphite Product Mfr
N.A.I.C.S.: 335991

SGL Carbon GmbH (1)
Werner-von-Siemens-Strasse 18, Meitingen, 86405, Augsburg, Germany **(100%)**
Tel.: (49) 8271830
Web Site: http://www.sglcarbon.com
Sales Range: $450-499.9 Million
Nonclay Refractory Mfr
N.A.I.C.S.: 327120

Subsidiary (Domestic):

Dr Schnabel GmbH (2)
Offheimer Weg 21, 65549, Limburg, Germany
Tel.: (49) 643191060
Emp.: 50
Carbon & Graphite Product Mfr
N.A.I.C.S.: 335991

SGL CARBON SE

SGL Carbon SE—(Continued)

Subsidiary (Non-US):

SGL Gelter S.A. (2)
San Dalmacio 33, 28021, Madrid, Spain
Tel.: (34) 917231000
Carbon & Graphite Product Mfr
N.A.I.C.S.: 335991

SGL Graphite Verdello S.r.l. (2)
Stabilimento di Verdello Viale Friuli 2/L,
24049, Verdello, Italy
Tel.: (39) 0354187811
Carbon & Graphite Product Mfr
N.A.I.C.S.: 335991

SGL Carbon Gmbh & Co. Kg (1)
Steeg 64, 4822, Steeg, Austria **(100%)**
Tel.: (43) 613586410
Carbon & Graphite Product Mfr
N.A.I.C.S.: 335991

SGL Carbon Graphite Technic Co. Ltd. (1)
151 Huan Cheng Dong Lu Shanghai
Fengpu Industrial Development Zone,
Shanghai, 201401, China **(100%)**
Web Site: http://www.sglgroup.com.cn
Pump & Pumping Equipment Mfr
N.A.I.C.S.: 333914

SGL Carbon Holding S.L. (1)
Carretera Coruna A Arteixo Km 1, 15008,
La Coruna, Spain **(100%)**
Tel.: (34) 981173171
Web Site: http://www.sglgroup.com
Emp.: 150
Holding Company
N.A.I.C.S.: 551112

SGL Carbon Holdings B.V. (1)
Schouwburgplein 30-34, Rotterdam,
Netherlands **(100%)**
Tel.: (31) 102245333
Carbon & Graphite Product Mfr
N.A.I.C.S.: 335991

Subsidiary (Non-US):

SGL Graphite Solutions Polska sp. z o.o. (2)
ul Wegierska 188, 33-300, Nowy Sacz, Poland
Tel.: (48) 18442301
Carbon & Graphite Product Mfr
N.A.I.C.S.: 335991

SGL Carbon Japan Ltd. (1)
2-2 Wakita-Honcho Kawagoe, Saitama,
350-1123, Japan **(100%)**
Tel.: (81) 492380557
Electrical Apparatus & Equipment
N.A.I.C.S.: 423610

SGL Carbon Korea Ltd. (1)
189 Cheonggyesan-ro, Seocho-gu, Seoul,
06802, Korea (South) **(70%)**
Tel.: (82) 1052013048
Web Site: http://www.sglcarbon.com.cn
Sales Range: $25-49.9 Million
Emp.: 5
Carbon & Graphite Product Mfr
N.A.I.C.S.: 335991

SGL Carbon Ltd. (1)
4 Arden Court Arden Road, Alcester, B49
6HN, Warwickshire, United Kingdom
Tel.: (44) 1789400221
Web Site: http://www.sglcarbon.co.uk
Sales Range: $25-49.9 Million
Emp.: 6
Engineering Services
N.A.I.C.S.: 541330

SGL Carbon Polska S.A. (1)
ul Wegierska 188, 33-300, Nowy Sacz,
Poland **(100%)**
Tel.: (48) 184497920
Web Site: http://www.sglgroup.com
Automotive & Mechanical Applications
N.A.I.C.S.: 811114

SGL Carbon S.A. (1)
Zona Industria Dav la Apdo De Correos
478, La Coruna, 15008, Spain **(99.9%)**
Tel.: (34) 981173171
Web Site: http://www.sglgroupe.com
Electrical Equipment & Component Mfr
N.A.I.C.S.: 335999

SGL Carbon S.A.S. (1)
131 Place Aristide Berges, 74190, Passy,
France **(100%)**
Tel.: (33) 476597242
Web Site: http://www.sglgroup.com.cn
Sales Range: $50-74.9 Million
Emp.: 200
Nonmetallic Mineral Product Mfr
N.A.I.C.S.: 327999

SGL Carbon S.P.A. (1)
Via Lepetit 8, 20020, Lainate, MI,
Italy **(99.7%)**
Tel.: (39) 0233627305
Web Site: http://www.sglgroup.com
Sales Range: $25-49.9 Million
Emp.: 30
Petroleum & Coal Products Mfr
N.A.I.C.S.: 324199

SGL Carbon Technic S.A.S. (1)
18 Avenue Marcel Cachin, Saint-Martin-
d'Heres, 38400, Grenoble, France **(100%)**
Tel.: (33) 476259638
Web Site: http://www.sglgroup.sr
Sales Range: $50-74.9 Million
Emp.: 130
Refrigeration & Heating Equipment
N.A.I.C.S.: 333415

SGL Carbon, LLC (1)
10715 David Taylor Dr Ste 460, Charlotte,
NC 28262
Tel.: (704) 593-5100
Web Site: http://www.sglgroup.com
Carbon & Graphite Products Mfr
N.A.I.C.S.: 335991

Subsidiary (Domestic):

HITCO Carbon Composites, Inc. (2)
1600 W 135th St, Gardena, CA
90249-2506 **(100%)**
Tel.: (310) 527-0700
Web Site: http://www.hitco.com
Metal Stamping
N.A.I.C.S.: 332119

SGL Carbon Technic LLC (2)
21945 Drake Rd, Strongsville, OH
44149 **(100%)**
Tel.: (440) 572-3600
Web Site: http://www.sglcarbon.com
Carbon & Graphite Product Mfr
N.A.I.C.S.: 335991

Plant (Domestic):

SGL Carbon, LLC - Saint Marys (2)
900 Theresia St, Saint Marys, PA 15857
Tel.: (814) 781-2600
Web Site: http://www.sglcarbon.com
Electronic Applications
N.A.I.C.S.: 449210

SGL Carbon, LLC - Sinking Spring (2)
796 Fritztown Rd, Sinking Spring, PA
19608-2193
Tel.: (610) 670-4040
Emp.: 40
Carbon & Graphite Product Mfr
N.A.I.C.S.: 335991
Bill Pichler *(Plant Mgr)*

Subsidiary (Domestic):

SGL Technic Inc. (2)
28176 No Ave Stanford, Valencia, CA
91355-1119 **(100%)**
Tel.: (661) 257-0500
Web Site: http://www.sglgroup.com
Carbon & Graphite Product Mfr
N.A.I.C.S.: 335991

SGL Technologies LLC (2)
10715 David Taylor Dr Ste 460, Charlotte,
NC 28262
Tel.: (704) 593-5100
Carbon & Graphite Product Mfr
N.A.I.C.S.: 335991

SGL Composites GmbH (1)
Fischerstrasse 8, 4910, Ried im Innkreis,
Austria
Tel.: (43) 7752825000
Carbon & Graphite Product Mfr
N.A.I.C.S.: 335991

SGL Composites S.A. (1)
Parque Industrial Da Quimiparque, 2836-
908, Barreiro, Portugal
Tel.: (351) 212066000
Carbon & Graphite Product Mfr
N.A.I.C.S.: 335991

SGL Process Technology Pte. Ltd. (1)
151 Huan Cheng Dong Lu Shanghai
Fengpu Industrial Development Zone,
Shanghai, 201401, China
Tel.: (86) 2160976888
Emp.: 280
Carbon & Graphite Product Mfr
N.A.I.C.S.: 335991

Subsidiary (Non-US):

Graphite Chemical Engineering Co. Ltd. (2)
1226-1 Ogasawara Minami-Alps, Yama-
nashi, 400-0306, Japan
Tel.: (81) 552846013
Carbon & Graphite Product Mfr
N.A.I.C.S.: 335991

SGL Quanhai Carbon (Shanxi) Co., Ltd. (1)
Xincun Zhangzhuang Town, Pingding
County, Yangquan, 045210, China
Tel.: (86) 3536029581
Carbon & Graphite Product Mfr
N.A.I.C.S.: 335991

SGL Quanhai High-Tech Materials (Shanxi) Co. Ltd. (1)
Xincun, Zhangzhuang Town Pingding
County, Yangquan, 45210, China
Tel.: (86) 3536029581
Emp.: 140
Carbon Product Mfr & Distr
N.A.I.C.S.: 335991

SGL Technic Ltd. (1)
Great North Road Muir of Ord Industrial Es-
tate, Edinburgh, IV67UA, United
Kingdom **(100%)**
Tel.: (44) 1463870000
Web Site: http://www.sgl.com
Sales Range: $50-74.9 Million
Emp.: 200
Carbon & Graphite Product Mfr
N.A.I.C.S.: 335991

SGL Technologies GmbH (1)
Werner-von-Siemens-Strasse 18, Meitingen,
86405, Augsburg, Germany **(100%)**
Tel.: (49) 8271830
Web Site: http://www.sglcarbon.com
Sales Range: $200-249.9 Million
Nonclay Refractory Mfr
N.A.I.C.S.: 327120

Subsidiary (Domestic):

SGL Composites GmbH & Co. KG (2)
Oskar-Von-Miller-Strasse 18, 92442, Wack-
ersdorf, Germany
Tel.: (49) 94317983100
Carbon & Graphite Product Mfr
N.A.I.C.S.: 335991

SGL Epo GmbH (2)
Siemensring 24, 47877, Willich, Germany
Tel.: (49) 215492380
Emp.: 90
Carbon & Graphite Product Mfr
N.A.I.C.S.: 335991

SGL Tokai Carbon Ltd. (1)
12th-Floor 31 Wujiang Rd, Shanghai Orien-
tal Plz, 200041, Shanghai, China **(100%)**
Tel.: (86) 2152110333
Carbon Black Mfr
N.A.I.C.S.: 325180

T. Kylberg Norden AB (1)
PO Box 70, 18205, Djursholm, Sweden
Tel.: (46) 87536900
Petroleum Product Whslr
N.A.I.C.S.: 424720

SGN GROUP OY

Juurakkokuja 4, 01510, Vantaa, Fin-
land
Tel.: (358) 58) 306 5050
Web Site: http://www.sgn.fi
Sports & Leisure, Agricultural & In-
dustrial Products Whslr

INTERNATIONAL PUBLIC

N.A.I.C.S.: 423830
Sam Nieminem *(CEO)*

SGN TELECOMS LIMITED

Plot no E- 58 59 industrial area
phase - 8, Ropar, Mohali, 160055,
Punjab, India
Tel.: (91) 1725063378
Web Site: https://sgntelecomsltd.com
Year Founded: 1986
531812—(BOM)
Rev.: $14,735
Assets: $427,630
Liabilities: $292,061
Net Worth: $135,569
Earnings: ($18,708)
Emp.: 5
Fiscal Year-end: 03/31/23
Wire & Cable Mfr & Whslr
N.A.I.C.S.: 332618
Surinder Singh *(Chm, Mng Dir, Com-
pliance Officer & Exec Dir)*

SGS SA

1 Place des Alpes, PO Box 2152,
1211, Geneva, Switzerland
Tel.: (41) 227399111 CH
Web Site: https://www.sgs.com
Year Founded: 1878
SGSN—(SWX)
Rev.: $5,973,044,001
Assets: $6,098,422,001
Liabilities: $5,622,166,001
Net Worth: $476,256,000
Earnings: $538,494,000
Emp.: 103,193
Fiscal Year-end: 12/31/23
Holding Company; Inspection, Verifi-
cation, Testing & Certification Ser-
vices
N.A.I.C.S.: 551112
Jeffery McDonald *(Head-Bus Assur-
ance)*

Subsidiaries:

African Assay Laboratories (Tanzania) Ltd. (1)
OFive Plaza 2nd Floor Plot No 1046 Haile
Selassie Road, PO Box 2249; 2249,
Mwanza, Tanzania
Tel.: (255) 222345800
Web Site: https://www.sgs.co.tz
Testing Laboratory Services
N.A.I.C.S.: 541380

Gearhart Australia Limited (1)
28th Reid Rd 3rd A Fort, Newburn, Perth,
6105, WA, Australia
Tel.: (61) 893733500
Sales Range: $150-199.9 Million
Emp.: 30
Verification & Certification Services
N.A.I.C.S.: 926150
Henry Wang *(Gen Mgr)*

Subsidiary (Non-US):

Redback Drilling Tools Ltd (2)
Unit 20 Howe Moss Drive, Kirkhill, Ind Est,
Dyce, AB21 0GL, Aberdeen, United King-
dom
Tel.: (44) 1224774000
Web Site:
https://www.redbackdrillingtools.com
Sales Range: $25-49.9 Million
Industrial Machine Tool Distr
N.A.I.C.S.: 423830
Tamer El Mahdy *(Reg Mgr-Middle East & Africa)*

General de Servicios ITV, S.A (1)
Calle de Trespaderne 29, Madrid, 28027,
Spain
Tel.: (34) 91 404 42 78
Web Site: http://www.serviciositv.es
Sales Range: $25-49.9 Million
Emp.: 17
Public Vehicle Inspection Services
N.A.I.C.S.: 926150
Jorge Soriano *(Gen Mgr)*

Ghana Community Network Services Limited (1)

AND PRIVATE COMPANIES · SGS SA

Cocoshe Building Block B 4th Floor Agostinho Neto Close, PO Box OS 756, Osu Airport Residential Area, Accra, Ghana
Tel.: (233) 302610840
Web Site: https://www.gcnet.com.gh
Sales Range: $25-49.9 Million
Emp.: 250
Information Technology Consulting Services
N.A.I.C.S.: 541512

ITV SA (1)
Tronador 4890- 3 Piso, Buenos Aires, Argentina
Tel.: (54) 114 124 2000
Medical Laboratory Services
N.A.I.C.S.: 621511

Malagasy Community Network Services SA (1)
Immeuble Ariane 5A Enceinte Galaxy Andraharo, 101, Antananarivo, Madagascar
Tel.: (261) 202356410
Web Site: https://gasynet.com
Medical Laboratory Services
N.A.I.C.S.: 621511

P.T. SGS Indonesia (1)
The Garden Centre 2nd Floor, Cilandak Commercial Estate, South Jakarta, 12560, Jakarta, Indonesia
Tel.: (62) 2129780600
Web Site: https://www.sgs.co.id
Emp.: 400
Medical Laboratory Services
N.A.I.C.S.: 621511

Qualitest Algerie SPA (1)
Cooperative ElBadr Villa No 04 Boulevard du 11 Decembre 1960 El Biar, El Biar, 16000, Algiers, Algeria
Tel.: (213) 21 79 20 20
Investigation & Verification Services
N.A.I.C.S.: 926150

Ryobi Geotechnique International Pte Ltd (1)
70 Sungei Kadut Loop, Singapore, 729511, Singapore
Tel.: (65) 6 369 7100
Web Site: https://www.ryobi-g.com
Geotechnical & Surveying Services
N.A.I.C.S.: 541360
Joseph Wang Hou (CEO)

SGS (Cambodia) Ltd. (1)
No 1076A-D Street 371 Sangkat Stung Meanchey, Khan Meanchey, Phnom Penh, 12352, Cambodia
Tel.: (855) 23967888
Medical Laboratory Services
N.A.I.C.S.: 621511

SGS (Jordan) Private Shareholding Company (1)
Amman Al-Jbeiha Yajouz Street, Caracas Building Entrance No1 3rd Floor Office 311, Amman, 11193, Jordan
Tel.: (962) 6 537 7355
Medical Laboratory Services
N.A.I.C.S.: 621511

SGS (Liban) S.A.L. (1)
2/F Tanios Saba Building Ibrahim Pacha Street, PO Box 16, Medawar, Beirut, 2038 3054, Lebanon
Tel.: (961) 1580030
Web Site: http://www.sgs.com
Inspection & Verification Services
N.A.I.C.S.: 926150

SGS (Malaysia) Sdn. Bhd (1)
Unit 10-1 10th Floor Bangunan Malaysian RE No 17 Lorong Dungun, Damansara Heights, 50490, Kuala Lumpur, Malaysia
Tel.: (60) 327838588
Web Site: http://www.sgs.com
Inspection & Testing Services
N.A.I.C.S.: 926150

SGS (Mauritius) LTD (1)
SGS House, Valentina, Phoenix, 73553, Mauritius
Tel.: (230) 6968808
Web Site: https://www.sgs.mu
Sales Range: $50-74.9 Million
Inspection & Testing Services
N.A.I.C.S.: 926150
Cedric Catlin (Mng Dir)

SGS (Moldova) S.A. (1)
7 M Eminescu Street, MD-2009, Chisinau, Moldova
Tel.: (373) 22228383
Web Site: https://www.us.sgs.com
Inspection & Testing Services
N.A.I.C.S.: 926150

SGS (Myanmar) Limited (1)
79 D Bo Chein Street 6 1/2 Mile, PO Box 975, Hlaing Township, 11051, Yangon, Myanmar
Tel.: (95) 1654795
Web Site: https://www.sgs-myanmar.com
Testing Laboratory Services
N.A.I.C.S.: 541380

SGS (Thailand) Limited (1)
100 Nanglinchee Road Chongnonsee, Yannawa, 10120, Bangkok, Thailand
Tel.: (66) 26781813
Web Site: http://www.sgs.co.th
Sales Range: $250-299.9 Million
Inspection & Testing Services
N.A.I.C.S.: 926150
Vichan Satjasenee (Mgr-Industrial Svc)

SGS ADRIATICA, D.O.O. (1)
Karlovacka cesta 4i, 10000, Zagreb, Croatia
Tel.: (385) 16140961
Web Site: https://www.sgsgroup.hr
Sales Range: $25-49.9 Million
Inspection & Verification Services
N.A.I.C.S.: 926150

SGS Argentina S.A. (1)
Tronador 4890 - Piso 3, C1430DNN, Buenos Aires, Argentina
Tel.: (54) 1141242000
Web Site: https://www.sgsgroup.com.ar
Sales Range: $25-49.9 Million
Emp.: 600
Inspection & Testing Services
N.A.I.C.S.: 926150

SGS Aster SA (1)
3-5 rue Eugene Millon, 75015, Paris, France
Tel.: (33) 153680868
Laboratory Testing Services
N.A.I.C.S.: 541380

SGS Australia Pty Ltd. (1)
28 Reid Road, Perth International Airport, Perth, 6105, WA, Australia
Web Site: https://www.sgs.com.au
Sales Range: $300-349.9 Million
Emp.: 300
Holding Company; Laboratory Services to the Mining & Environmental Industries
N.A.I.C.S.: 551112
Yvonne Dickson (Mng Dir)

Subsidiary (Domestic):

SGS Scientific Services Pty Ltd. (2)
28 Reid Rd, Perth, 6105, WA, Australia
Tel.: (61) 893733500
Web Site: http://www.au.sgs.com
Sales Range: $75-99.9 Million
Emp.: 400
Laboratory Services to the Mining & Environmental Industries
N.A.I.C.S.: 541380

Subsidiary (Domestic):

Gearhart United Pty Ltd. (3)
104 Francis Road, Wingfield, Adelaide, 5013, SA, Australia
Tel.: (61) 88 413 5300
Web Site: https://www.sgs.com.au
Sales Range: $50-74.9 Million
Emp.: 50
Technical Services & Products Whslr to the Oil & Gas Industries
N.A.I.C.S.: 213112

SGS Austria Controll-Co. Ges.m.b.H (1)
Grunbergstrasse 15, 1120, Vienna, Austria
Tel.: (43) 151225670
Web Site: https://www.sgsgroup.at
Emp.: 100
Verification & Testing Services
N.A.I.C.S.: 926150
Thomas Koestinger (Mng Dir)

SGS Automotive Albania sh.p.k. (1)
Rr Irfan Tomini Pallati G and P Kati 1, Tirana, 2408, Albania
Tel.: (355) 4 450 0480

Medical Laboratory Services
N.A.I.C.S.: 621511

SGS Bangladesh Limited (1)
Noor Tower 2nd 6th - 10th 13th Floor 110 Bir Uttam C R Dutta Road, Dhaka, 1205, Bangladesh
Tel.: (880) 29676500
Web Site: https://www.sgs.com
Inspection & Certification Services
N.A.I.C.S.: 926150
Akther Zaman (Mgr-Fin)

SGS Belgium N.V. (1)
SGS House - Noorderlaan 87, 2030, Antwerp, Belgium
Tel.: (32) 35454400
Web Site: https://www.sgs.be
Inspection & Testing Services
N.A.I.C.S.: 926150
Dirk Hellemans (Mng Dir)

SGS Beograd d.o.o. (1)
Jurija Gagarina 7b, 11070, Belgrade, Serbia
Tel.: (381) 117155275
Web Site: https://www.sgs.rs
Inspection & Certification Services
N.A.I.C.S.: 926150
Marinjou Ukropina (Mng Dir)

SGS Bolivia S.A. (1)
Calle 15 de Agosto N 16 Final Av Brasil y 4to Anillo, Santa Cruz, Bolivia
Tel.: (591) 33464145
Inspection & Testing Services
N.A.I.C.S.: 926150

SGS Bulgaria Ltd. (1)
Megapark Business Centre Floor 6 Office C, 115G Tsarigradsko Shosse Blvd, 1784, Sofia, Bulgaria
Tel.: (359) 291015
Web Site: https://www.sgs.bg
Sales Range: $150-199.9 Million
Emp.: 330
Inspection & Testing Services
N.A.I.C.S.: 926150
Dimitar Marikin (Mng Dir)

SGS Burkina SA (1)
Zone Industrielle de Kossodo 11, BP 565, Ouagadougou, Burkina Faso
Tel.: (226) 25412104
Medical Laboratory Services
N.A.I.C.S.: 621511

SGS Cameroun SA (1)
176 Rue Victoria - Bonanjo, Douala, 13144, Cameroon
Tel.: (237) 33421030
Medical Laboratory Services
N.A.I.C.S.: 621511

SGS Central America SA (1)
6a Calle 14-08 Zona 13 Ground, 1013, Guatemala, Guatemala
Tel.: (502) 23278900
Medical Laboratory Services
N.A.I.C.S.: 621511

SGS Colombia SAS (1)
Carrera 100 No 25C - 11, Bogota, Colombia
Tel.: (57) 16069292
Web Site: https://www.sgs.co
Commercial Support Services
N.A.I.C.S.: 561499

SGS Congo S.A. (1)
Immeuble CNSS Avenue du General De Gaulle, BP 744, Pointe Noire, Congo, Republic of
Tel.: (242) 222944843
Web Site: https://www.us.sgs.com
Inspection & Verification Services
N.A.I.C.S.: 926150

SGS Czech Republic s.r.o. (1)
K Hajum 1233/2, 155 00, Prague, Czech Republic
Tel.: (420) 234708111
Web Site: http://www.cz.sgs.com
Sales Range: $75-99.9 Million
Inspection Verification & Testing Services
N.A.I.C.S.: 926150
Jan Chochol (Mng Dir)

SGS Danmark A/S (1)
Cph Business Park Stamholmen 153 2, 2650, Hvidovre, Denmark
Tel.: (45) 3 693 3300
Web Site: http://www.sgsgroup.dk

Inspection & Verification Services
N.A.I.C.S.: 926150

SGS Egypt Ltd (1)
9G Ahmed Kamel St off Laselky Street, New Maadi, 11728, Cairo, Egypt
Tel.: (20) 227263000
Web Site: https://www.sgs.com
Sales Range: $75-99.9 Million
Emp.: 400
Inspection & Testing Services
N.A.I.C.S.: 926150
Ziad Otey (Mng Dir)

SGS Espanola de Control S.A. (1)
Poligono Industrial Las Salinas de Levante C/ Doctor Pariente Nave 12, El Puerto de Santa Maria, 11500, Cadiz, Spain **(100%)**
Tel.: (34) 956560820
Web Site: https://www.sgs.es
Emp.: 4,100
Inspection & Testing Services
N.A.I.C.S.: 926150
Jose Maria Hernandez-Sampelayo (Dir Gen)

SGS Estonia Ltd. (1)
Vana-Narva Mnt 27A, Maardu, 74114, Tallinn, Estonia
Tel.: (372) 6348300
Web Site: https://www.sgs.ee
Emp.: 110
Inspection & Verification Services
N.A.I.C.S.: 926150
Nikolai Salnikov (Mng Dir)

SGS Fimko Oy (1)
Takomotie 8, PO Box 30, 00380, Helsinki, Finland
Tel.: (358) 9696361
Web Site: https://fi-onlinestore.sgs.com
Sales Range: $75-99.9 Million
Emp.: 135
Inspection & Certification Services
N.A.I.C.S.: 926150
Sixten Lokfors (Project Mgr-Installation Components & Cables)

SGS France SAS (1)
29 Avenue Aristide Briand, 94111, Arcueil, Cedex, France
Tel.: (33) 141248888
Web Site: https://www.sgsgroup.fr
Medical Laboratory Services
N.A.I.C.S.: 621511

SGS Georgia Ltd. (1)
104 Gorgasali Street, 4400, Poti, Georgia
Tel.: (995) 493223031
Medical Laboratory Services
N.A.I.C.S.: 621511

SGS Germany GmbH (1)
Heidenkampsweg 99, 20097, Hamburg, Germany
Tel.: (49) 40301010
Web Site: https://www.sgs-cqe.de
Inspection & Verification Services
N.A.I.C.S.: 926150

SGS Ghana Limited (1)
Cocoshe Building Block B 4th Floor Street No B28a, PO Box 732, Agostinho Neto Close Airport Residential Area, Accra, Ghana
Tel.: (233) 30 277 3994
Web Site: https://www.sgs-ghana.com
Sales Range: $25-49.9 Million
Inspection & Testing Services
N.A.I.C.S.: 926150

SGS Global Trade Solutions Philippines, Inc. (1)
20th Floor Citibank Tower 8741 Paseo De Roxas, Makati, 1200, Philippines
Tel.: (63) 28480777
Web Site: http://www.sgs.com
Emp.: 70
Inspection & Testing Services
N.A.I.C.S.: 926150

SGS Gottfeld NDT Services GmbH (1)
Baukauer Str 98, 44653, Herne, Germany
Tel.: (49) 2323 9265 0
Web Site: http://www.sgsgroup.de
Inspection & Testing Services
N.A.I.C.S.: 926150
Steffan Steenart (Gen Mgr)

SGS Greece SA (1)

SGS SA

SGS SA—(Continued)
2 Parnassou Street 217 Kifissias Avenue, Maroussi, 15124, Athens, Greece
Tel.: (30) 2105720777
Web Site: https://www.sgsgroup.gr
Laboratory Testing Services
N.A.I.C.S.: 541380

SGS Group Management SA (1)
1 Place des Alpes, PO Box 2152, 1211, Geneva, Switzerland
Tel.: (41) 22 739 91 11
Web Site: http://www.sgs.com
Sales Range: $150-199.9 Million
Inspection & Certification Services
N.A.I.C.S.: 926150

SGS Guam Inc. (1)
810 W Marine Corps Dr, Hagatna, GU 96910
Tel.: (671) 588-2923
Medical Laboratory Services
N.A.I.C.S.: 621511

SGS Guinee Conakry SA (1)
Cite Chemin de Fer C/Kaloum Immeuble Kankan, Conakry, 4559, Guinea
Tel.: (224) 3 045 4790
Medical Laboratory Services
N.A.I.C.S.: 621511

SGS Hong Kong Limited (1)
Units 303 305 3/F Building 22E Phase 3, Hong Kong Science Park Pak Shek Kok, Hong Kong, New Territories, China (Hong Kong)
Tel.: (852) 23344481
Web Site: https://www.sgsgroup.com.hk
Sales Range: $550-599.9 Million
Inspection & Certification Services
N.A.I.C.S.: 926150
Raymond Wong *(Asst Mgr-Technical)*

SGS Horizon B.V. (1)
Prinses Margrietplantsoen 81, 2595 BR, Hague, Netherlands
Tel.: (31) 70 312 4960
Web Site: http://www.horizon-ep.com
Sales Range: $50-74.9 Million
Emp.: 55
Oil & Gas Integrated Reservoir & Field Services
N.A.I.C.S.: 213112
Arie Vliegenthart *(Mgr-Bus Dev & Sls)*

SGS Hungaria Kft. (1)
Siraly utca 4, 1124, Budapest, Hungary
Tel.: (36) 13093300
Web Site: https://www.sgs.hu
Sales Range: $50-74.9 Million
Inspection & Verification Services
N.A.I.C.S.: 926150
Ferenc Petik *(Deputy Mng Dir & Mgr-Bus Dev-Sys & Svcs Certification)*

SGS India Private Ltd (1)
SGS House 4B Adi Shankaracharya Marg, Vikhroli West, Mumbai, 400 083, Maharashtra, India
Tel.: (91) 2266408888
Web Site: https://www.sgs.com
Sales Range: $1-4.9 Billion
Inspection & Testing Services
N.A.I.C.S.: 926150

SGS Industrial - Instalacaoes, Testes e Comissionamentos Ltda. (1)
Av Sagitario 743 - Cj 11, Alphaville Barueri, Sao Paulo, 06473-073, Brazil
Tel.: (55) 113 883 8800
Medical Laboratory Services
N.A.I.C.S.: 621511

SGS Inspection Services Nigeria Limited (1)
13/15 Wharf Road, Apapa, Lagos, 101251, Nigeria
Tel.: (234) 7007 476 4583
Web Site: https://www.sgs.com.ng
Testing Laboratories Services
N.A.I.C.S.: 541380

SGS Inspection Services Oy (1)
Sarkiniementie 3, PO Box 128, 210, Helsinki, Finland
Tel.: (358) 96963701
Web Site: http://www.fi.sgs.com
Sales Range: $75-99.9 Million
Emp.: 16
Inspection & Testing Services
N.A.I.C.S.: 926150
Mika Richardt *(Gen Mgr)*

SGS Inspection Services Saudi Arabia Ltd. (1)
SGS Building Road 112 Cross 293 Third Support Industries, PO Box 725, Jubail Industrial Area, 31951, Jubail, Saudi Arabia
Tel.: (966) 133400044
Web Site: https://www.sgs-me.com
Inspection & Verification Services
N.A.I.C.S.: 926150

SGS Institut Fresenius GmbH (1)
Im Maisel 14, 65232, Taunusstein, Germany
Tel.: (49) 61287440
Web Site: https://sgs-institut-fresenius.de
Laboratory Testing Services
N.A.I.C.S.: 541380
Stefan Steinhardt *(Mng Dir)*

SGS Iran (Private Joint Stock) Limited (1)
No 47 Ahmad Ghasir St Arjantine Square, 1514843133, Tehran, Iran
Tel.: (98) 2188542400
Medical Laboratory Services
N.A.I.C.S.: 621511

SGS Ireland (Holdings) Limited (1)
Hazel House Millennium Park, County Kildare, Naas, W91 PXP3, Ireland
Tel.: (353) 1 295 0654
Web Site: https://www.sgs.ie
Emp.: 220
Commercial Support Services
N.A.I.C.S.: 561499

SGS Italia S.p.A (1)
Via Caldera 21, 20153, Milan, Lombardy, Italy
Tel.: (39) 0273931
Web Site: https://www.sgsgroup.it
Emp.: 1,000
Inspection & Verification Services
N.A.I.C.S.: 926150

SGS Japan Inc. (1)
134 Yokohama Business Park North Square I, Hodogaya-ku Godo-cho, Yokohama, 240-0005, Japan
Tel.: (81) 453305000
Emp.: 284
Inspection & Verification Services
N.A.I.C.S.: 926150

SGS Kazakhstan Limited (1)
151 Mynbayeva Street, Verum Business Center, 050040, Almaty, Kazakhstan
Tel.: (7) 7272588250
Inspection & Testing Services
N.A.I.C.S.: 926150
Azer Mammadov *(Mng Dir)*

SGS Kenya Limited (1)
Abdalla Ndovu Mwidau Street, 80100, Mombasa, Kenya
Tel.: (254) 709967000
Web Site: https://www.sgs.co.ke
Logistics Consulting Servies
N.A.I.C.S.: 541614

SGS Klaipeda Ltd (1)
Silutes pl 119, 95112, Klaipeda, Lithuania
Tel.: (370) 46320770
Sales Range: $50-74.9 Million
Inspection & Certification Services
N.A.I.C.S.: 926150

SGS Korea Co., Ltd (1)
12FL Chongryong Bldg 257 Hangangdaero, Yongsan-gu, Seoul, 04322, Korea (South)
Tel.: (82) 27094500
Web Site: https://www.sgsgroup.kr
Inspection & Verification Services
N.A.I.C.S.: 926150

SGS Kuwait W.L.L. (1)
7th Floor Hammoudah Tower Gulf Road, Fahaheel, Kuwait, 61008, Kuwait
Tel.: (965) 2 392 0847
Medical Laboratory Services
N.A.I.C.S.: 621511

SGS Lanka (Private) Limited (1)
3rd Floor AEC House 140 Vauxhall Street 02, Colombo, 200, Sri Lanka
Tel.: (94) 115376280
Web Site: https://www.sgs.lk
Emp.: 200

SGS Latvija Limited (1)
Katrinas iela 5, Riga, LV-1045, Latvia
Tel.: (371) 67326163
Web Site: https://www.sgs.lv
Emp.: 150
Inspection & Verification Services
N.A.I.C.S.: 926150

SGS Liberia Inc (1)
Old Road, Sinkor, Monrovia, Liberia
Tel.: (231) 6874352
Web Site: https://www.us.sgs.com
Inspection & Certification Services
N.A.I.C.S.: 926150

SGS Luxembourg S.A (1)
Rue des Champs 2, 8218, Mamer, Luxembourg
Tel.: (352) 31 99 13
Sales Range: $25-49.9 Million
Emp.: 3
Inspection & Testing Services
N.A.I.C.S.: 926150

SGS M-Scan Limited (1)
3 Millars Business Centre Fishponds Close, Wokingham, RG41 2TZ, Berkshire, United Kingdom
Tel.: (44) 118 989 6940
Web Site: http://www.m-scan.co.uk
Sales Range: $25-49.9 Million
Emp.: 45
Chemical Testing Services
N.A.I.C.S.: 541380

Subsidiary (Domestic):

SGS Correl Rail Ltd (2)
Gee House Holborn Hill, Birmingham, B7 5PA, United Kingdom
Tel.: (44) 121 326 9900
Web Site: http://www.sgs.co.uk
Professional Scientific & Technical Services
N.A.I.C.S.: 541690

Subsidiary (Non-US):

SGS Gulf Limited (2)
S3A1SR01 JAFZA Business Showroom, PO Box 18556, Dubai, 1243, United Arab Emirates
Tel.: (971) 48809393
Inspection & Verification Services
N.A.I.C.S.: 926150

SGS MCNET Mocambique Limitada (1)
Avenida da Namaacha km 1 5 n 8274 Cidade de, Maputo, 1116, Mozambique
Tel.: (258) 843262030
Web Site: https://www.sgs.co.mz
Consultancy Services
N.A.I.C.S.: 541618

SGS Mali Sarlu (1)
Zone Industrielle Sotuba Rue 947 Porte 213, BPE 2514, Bamako, Mali
Tel.: (223) 20211610
Medical Laboratory Services
N.A.I.C.S.: 621511

SGS Maroc SA (1)
67 Avenue des FAR, 20000, Casablanca, Morocco
Tel.: (212) 522307491
Web Site: https://www.sgsgroup.ma
Industrial Services
N.A.I.C.S.: 811310

SGS Minerals RDC SARL (1)
760 Avenue du 30 Juin, Lubumbashi, Congo, Democratic Republic of
Tel.: (243) 81 066 4362
Medical Laboratory Services
N.A.I.C.S.: 621511

SGS Minsk Ltd (1)
29-107 V Khoruzhey St, 220123, Minsk, Belarus
Tel.: (375) 172886780
Web Site: https://sgsminsk.by
Sales Range: $25-49.9 Million
Emp.: 3
Inspection & Verification Services
N.A.I.C.S.: 926150
Iouri Iasinski *(Gen Mgr)*

SGS Mocambique, Limitada (1)
Avenida da Namaacha km 1 5 n 8274, Cidade de Maputo, Maputo, 1116, Maputo, Mozambique
Tel.: (258) 84 326 2030
Web Site: https://www.sgs.co.mz
Inspection & Verification Services
N.A.I.C.S.: 926150

SGS Mongolia LLC (1)
Uildveriin Toirgiin 101toot, Bayangol Duureg 20th khoroo, Ulaanbaatar, 17060, Mongolia
Tel.: (976) 70144415
Emp.: 15
Inspection & Verification Services
N.A.I.C.S.: 926150

SGS Nederland B.V. (1)
Malledijk 18, Postbus 200, 3208 LA, Spijkenisse, Netherlands
Tel.: (31) 882143333
Web Site: http://www.sgs.nl
Sales Range: $550-599.9 Million
Inspection & Verification Services
N.A.I.C.S.: 926150

SGS New Zealand Limited (1)
Level 1 7 Albert Street, Penrose Onehunga, Auckland, 1061, New Zealand
Tel.: (64) 96346367
Web Site: http://www.sgs.co.nz
Sales Range: $75-99.9 Million
Emp.: 800
Inspection & Verification Services
N.A.I.C.S.: 926150
Phil Schunk *(Gen Mgr-Industrial Regulatory)*

SGS Norge A/S (1)
Nordic House Litlas 18, 5954, Mongstad, Norway
Tel.: (47) 5 616 8100
Web Site: https://www.sgs.com
Inspection & Testing Services
N.A.I.C.S.: 926150

SGS North America Inc. (1)
201 Route 17 N 7th and 8th Fl, Rutherford, NJ 07070
Tel.: (201) 508-3000
Web Site: http://www.us.sgs.com
Sales Range: $75-99.9 Million
Holding Company; Regional Managing Office
N.A.I.C.S.: 551112
Jeffrey McDonald *(COO)*

Subsidiary (Domestic):

CyberMetrix, Inc. (2)
2860 N National Rd, Columbus, IN 47201
Tel.: (812) 378-5903
Web Site: http://www.cybermetrix.com
Sales Range: $10-24.9 Million
Emp.: 50
Instrument Manufacturing for Measuring & Testing Electricity & Electrical Signals
N.A.I.C.S.: 334515
Pete Palladino *(Pres)*

Environmental Testing Corp. (2)
2022 Helena St, Aurora, CO 80011
Tel.: (303) 344-5470
Web Site: http://www.sgs.com
Sales Range: $10-24.9 Million
Emp.: 40
Vehicle & Engine Emission Laboratory Services
N.A.I.C.S.: 541380
Mark Van Horck *(Mgr-Bus Ops)*

Galson Laboratories, Inc. (2)
6601 Kirkville Rd, East Syracuse, NY 13057
Tel.: (315) 671-3926
Web Site: https://www.sgsgalson.com
Emp.: 120
Industrial Hygiene Air Testing Services
N.A.I.C.S.: 541380
Joe Unangst *(Pres & CEO)*

Subsidiary (Domestic):

INALAB, Inc. (3)
3615 Harding Ave, Honolulu, HI 96816
Tel.: (808) 735-0422
Web Site: http://www.inalab.com
Sales Range: $10-24.9 Million
Research & Development in Biotechnology
N.A.I.C.S.: 541714

Subsidiary (Domestic):

Integrated Paper Services, Inc. (2)

AND PRIVATE COMPANIES — SGS SA

3211 E Capitol Dr, Appleton, WI 54911
Tel.: (920) 749-3040
Web Site: https://www.ipstesting.com
Sales Range: $25-49.9 Million
Emp.: 60
Laboratory Testing Services
N.A.I.C.S.: 541380

Maine Pointe LLC (2)
PO Box 271, Duxbury, MA 02331-0271
Tel.: (403) 444-5995
Web Site: http://www.mainepointe.com
Custom Computer Programming Services
N.A.I.C.S.: 541511
Stephen Ottley (VP)

SGS Accutest Inc (2)
2235 United States Hwy 130 B, Dayton, NJ 08810
Tel.: (201) 508-3000
Web Site: http://www.accutest.com
Emp.: 155
Testing Laboratories
N.A.I.C.S.: 541715
Matt Cordova (Mgr-Customer Svcs)

SGS Advanced Testing & Engineering Inc. (2)
12255 Delta St, Taylor, MI 48180
Tel.: (734) 442-0200
Web Site: https://www.atande.com
Sales Range: $1-9.9 Million
Testing & Certification Services
N.A.I.C.S.: 541380

Subsidiary (Non-US):

SGS Canada Inc. (2)
6755 Mississauga Road Suite 204, Mississauga, L5N 7Y2, ON, Canada
Tel.: (905) 364-3771
Web Site: https://www.sgs.ca
Sales Range: $50-74.9 Million
Emp.: 200
Raw Materials, Bulk, Containerized & Finished Products Auditing, Monitoring & Testing Services
N.A.I.C.S.: 325998

Subsidiary (Domestic):

SGS Canada Inc. (3)
3260 Production Way, Burnaby, V5A 4W4, BC, Canada
Tel.: (604) 638-2349
Web Site: https://www.sgs.ca
Sales Range: $25-49.9 Million
Emp.: 7
Inspection & Testing Laboratory Services
N.A.I.C.S.: 541380

Subsidiary (Domestic):

SGS Chemical Solutions Laboratories Inc. (2)
931 North Seventh St, Harrisburg, PA 17102
Tel.: (717) 697-7536
Web Site: http://www.chemicalsolutionsltd.com
Research & Development in Biotechnology
N.A.I.C.S.: 541714
Mark Hartman (Mgr-Sls)

SGS Control Services, Inc. (2)
201 Route 17, Rutherford, NJ 07070 (100%)
Tel.: (201) 508-3000
Sales Range: $25-49.9 Million
Emp.: 200
Petroleum, Chemicals, Agricultural Products & Environmental Inspection & Laboratory Testing
N.A.I.C.S.: 541990
Jeff McDonald (CEO)

SGS Environmental Services Inc. (2)
5500 Business Dr, Wilmington, NC 28405
Tel.: (910) 350-1903
Web Site: http://www.sgsgroup.us.com
Sales Range: $10-24.9 Million
Environmental Testing Services
N.A.I.C.S.: 541715

SGS IBR Laboratories, Inc. (2)
11599 Morrissey Rd, Grass Lake, MI 49240
Tel.: (517) 522-8453
Web Site: https://www.ibr-usa.com
Testing Laboratories Operator

N.A.I.C.S.: 541380
Mark A. Ferrone (Dir-Ops-US & UK)

SGS Intermodal Transportation Services Inc. (2)
201 Route 17 N 7th and 8th Fl, Rutherford, NJ 07070 (100%)
Tel.: (201) 508-3000
Sales Range: $25-49.9 Million
Emp.: 100
Transportation Inspection & Loss Control Services
N.A.I.C.S.: 541990

SGS International Certification Services, Inc. (2)
201 Route 17 7th and 8th Fl, Rutherford, NJ 07070 (100%)
Tel.: (201) 508-3000
Web Site: http://www.sgsgroup.us.com
Sales Range: $25-49.9 Million
Emp.: 60
ISO 9000 Systems Assessments & Certifications
N.A.I.C.S.: 541611

Unit (Domestic):

SGS Life Science Services - Northview Laboratory (2)
616 Heathrow Dr, Lincolnshire, IL 60069
Tel.: (847) 821-8900
Web Site: http://www.pharmardqc.sgs.com
Sales Range: $25-49.9 Million
Emp.: 60
Life Sciences Testing Laboratory
N.A.I.C.S.: 541380
Haris Jamil (Mgr-Biologics)

SGS North America Inc. - Governments & Institutions Services (2)
7769 NW 48th St Ste 250, Miami, FL 33166
Tel.: (305) 592-0410
Web Site: http://www.us.sgs.com
Rev: $13,202,000
Emp.: 25
Inspection & Testing Services
N.A.I.C.S.: 541380

Division (Domestic):

SGS North America Inc. - Minerals Services Division (2)
1919 S Highland Ave Ste 140 D, Lombard, IL 60148-6133
Tel.: (630) 953-9300
Sales Range: $25-49.9 Million
Emp.: 10
Coal, Precious Metals, Minerals, Environmental Inspection & Laboratory Services
N.A.I.C.S.: 541715

Branch (Domestic):

SGS North America Inc. - Mineral Services Division, Denver (3)
4665 Paris St Ste 100-106 200-210, Denver, CO 80239-3126
Tel.: (303) 373-4772
Web Site: http://www.sgs.com
Sales Range: $10-24.9 Million
Mineral Research Services
N.A.I.C.S.: 541715
Marc Rademacher (Reg Mgr-Western Ops)

Subsidiary (Domestic):

SGS Petroleum Service Corporation (2)
6700 Jefferson Hwy Bldg 8, Baton Rouge, LA 70806
Tel.: (225) 343-8262
Loading Vessels, Process or Storage
N.A.I.C.S.: 488320
Houston Haymon (Sr VP)

SGS Testcom, Inc. (2)
2691 Route 9 Ste 201, Malta, NY 12020-4319 (100%)
Tel.: (518) 580-0555
Web Site: http://www.sgstestcom.com
Sales Range: $10-24.9 Million
Emp.: 40
Vehicle Emissions Testing Services
N.A.I.C.S.: 541715
Kelly Bertrand (Mgr-Ops)

SGS U.S. Testing Company Inc. (2)
291 Fairfield Ave, Fairfield, NJ 07004-3833 (100%)

Tel.: (973) 575-5252
Web Site: http://www.sgs.com
Sales Range: $25-49.9 Million
Emp.: 150
Specializes in the Testing Certification & Inspections of Industrial & Consumer Products
N.A.I.C.S.: 541715
Nicolas Bachere (Mng Dir-Consumer Testing Svcs)

Thomas J. Stephens & Associates, Inc. (2)
1801 N Glenville Dr Ste 200, Richardson, TX 75081
Tel.: (972) 392-1529
Web Site: http://www.stephens-associates.com
Testing Laboratories
N.A.I.C.S.: 541380
Brooke Stephens (Dir-Bus Dev)

SGS Oil, Gas & Chemicals, SAS (1)
29 Aristide Briand, 94111, Arcueil, France
Tel.: (33) 1 41 24 84 43
Sales Range: $50-74.9 Million
Emp.: 2
Oil & Gas Industry Inspection & Testing Services
N.A.I.C.S.: 926130

SGS PNG Pty. Limited (1)
C/O PNG Forest authority HQ Frangipani St, PO Box 1260, Hohola, 121, Port Moresby, Papua New Guinea
Tel.: (675) 3231433
Web Site: http://www.sgs.com
Sales Range: $150-199.9 Million
Inspection & Testing Services
N.A.I.C.S.: 926150

SGS Pakistan (Private) Limited (1)
Plot 04 Sector 24 Korangi Industrial Area Near Shan Chowrangi, Karachi, 74900, Pakistan
Tel.: (92) 21111222747
Web Site: https://www.sgsgroup.pk
Inspection & Testing Services
N.A.I.C.S.: 926150
Syed Farukh Mazhar (Mng Dir)

SGS Panama Control Services Inc. (1)
Ovidio Saldana St 235 First Floor Office A City of Knowledge, Clayton, Panama, Panama
Tel.: (507) 3174800
Web Site: http://www.pa.sgs.com
Sales Range: $25-49.9 Million
Inspection & Testing Services
N.A.I.C.S.: 926150
Willem Van Strien (Mng Dir)

SGS Paraguay S.A. (1)
Av Peru 809 e/ Herminio Gimenez, Asuncion, 1224, Paraguay
Tel.: (595) 21201720
Web Site: http://www.py.sgs.com
Sales Range: $25-49.9 Million
Verification & Inspection Services
N.A.I.C.S.: 926150
Arnaldo de Marzi (Mng Dir)

SGS Philippines, Inc (1)
3/F Alegria Bldg 2229 Chino Roces Avenue, Makati, 1231, Metro Manila, Philippines
Tel.: (63) 282888787
Web Site: http://www.sgs.ph
Emp.: 1,000
Verification & Certification Services
N.A.I.C.S.: 926150
Ariel Miranda (Mng Dir)

SGS Polska Sp. z.o.o. (1)
Al Jerozolimskie 146A, 02-305, Warsaw, Poland
Tel.: (48) 223292222
Web Site: https://www.sgs.pl
Sales Range: $75-99.9 Million
Inspection & Testing Services
N.A.I.C.S.: 926150
Jaroslaw Sawicki (Mng Dir)

SGS Portugal - Sociedade Geral de Superintendencia SA (1)
Polo Tecnologico de Lisboa Rua Cesina Adaes Bermudes Lote 11, 1600-604, Lisbon, Portugal
Tel.: (351) 808200747
Web Site: https://www.sgs.pt

Emp.: 300
Testing Laboratory Services
N.A.I.C.S.: 541380

SGS Qualitest Algerie SpA (1)
14 bis Rue Cesaree Hydra, 16000, Algiers, Algeria
Tel.: (213) 23230899
Web Site: https://www.sgs-algeria.com
Medical Laboratory Services
N.A.I.C.S.: 621511

SGS Qualitest Industrie SAS (1)
Domaine de Corbeville Ouest, 91400, Orsay, France
Tel.: (33) 1 69 336 933
Web Site: http://www.fr.sgs.com
Inspection & Testing Services
N.A.I.C.S.: 926150

SGS RDC SPRL (1)
Bd Du 30 Juin N 64 Imeuble Ex-Ericsson, Kinshasa, Congo, Democratic Republic of
Tel.: (243) 819363751
Inspection & Verification Services
N.A.I.C.S.: 926150

SGS Romania S.A. (1)
38 Calea Serban Voda Sector 4, 040212, Bucharest, Romania
Tel.: (40) 213354683
Sales Range: $50-74.9 Million
Emp.: 60
Inspection & Verification Services
N.A.I.C.S.: 926150
Dan Marinescu (Gen Mgr)

SGS Scanning Nigeria Limited (1)
7B Etim Inyang Crescent Off Muri Okunola Street, Victoria Island, Lagos, PMB 80048, Nigeria
Tel.: (234) 1 2805096
Web Site: http://www.be.sgs.com
Inspection & Verification Services
N.A.I.C.S.: 926150
Andy Hunger (Gen Mgr)

SGS Senegal S.A. (1)
26-28 Rue Felix Faure, BP 2734, Dakar, 2734, Senegal
Tel.: (221) 338494343
Web Site: http://www.fr.sgs.com
Inspection & Testing Services
N.A.I.C.S.: 926150

SGS Slovakia spol.s.r.o. (1)
Kysucka 14, 040 11, Kosice, Slovakia
Tel.: (421) 557836111
Sales Range: $25-49.9 Million
Emp.: 3
Inspection & Testing Services
N.A.I.C.S.: 926150

SGS Slovenija d.o.o. (1)
Verovskova ulica 60a PE Koper Sermin 74d, Koper, 1000, Ljubljana, Slovenia
Tel.: (386) 5 610 9000
Web Site: https://www.sgs.si
Sales Range: $25-49.9 Million
Inspection & Testing Services
N.A.I.C.S.: 926150

SGS Societe Generale de Surveillance SA (1)
Technoparkstrasse 1, 8005, Zurich, Switzerland
Tel.: (41) 444451680
Web Site: http://www.ch.sgs.com
Inspection & Testing Services
N.A.I.C.S.: 926150
Elvera Beire (Mgr)

SGS South Africa (Proprietary) Limited (1)
Building No 1 Harrowdene Office Park Western Service Road, Woodmead Sandton Western Service Road, Woodmead, 2191, South Africa
Tel.: (27) 11 800 1000
Web Site: https://www.sgs.co.za
Inspection & Testing Services
N.A.I.C.S.: 926150

SGS Supervise Gozetme Etud Kontrol Servisleri Anonim Sirketi (1)
Baglar Mah Osmanpasa Cad No 95 Is Istanbul Plaza A Girisi, Gunesli, 34209, Istanbul, Turkiye
Tel.: (90) 2123684000
Web Site: https://www.sgs.com.tr

SGS SA

SGS SA—(Continued)
Sales Range: $250-299.9 Million
Inspection & Testing Services
N.A.I.C.S.: 926150

SGS Sweden AB (1)
Maskingatan 5, 417 64, Gothenburg, Sweden
Tel.: (46) 31 755 0500
Medical Laboratory Services
N.A.I.C.S.: 621511

SGS Taiwan Limited (1)
No 134 Wu Kung Rd New Taipei Industrial Park, Wu Ku Dist, Taipei, 248016, Taiwan
Tel.: (886) 222993279
Web Site: https://www.sgs.com.tw
Sales Range: $600-649.9 Million
Inspection & Testing Services
N.A.I.C.S.: 926150
Dennis Yang *(Mng Dir)*

SGS Tanzania Superintendence Co. Limited (1)
Plot No 127 Mafinga Street Kingsway Kinondoni road, PO Box 2249, Dar es Salaam, 2249, Tanzania
Tel.: (255) 22 234 5800
Web Site: https://www.sgs.co.tz
Emp.: 485
Inspection & Testing Services
N.A.I.C.S.: 926150

SGS Tashkent Ltd. (1)
16 Sharaf Rashidov Street floor 12, 100017, Tashkent, Uzbekistan
Tel.: (998) 781206831
Sales Range: $50-74.9 Million
Emp.: 10
Inspection & Verification Services
N.A.I.C.S.: 926150
Tulkun Samukov *(Mgr-Ops)*

SGS Tecnos, S.A. (1)
C/ Trespaderne 29 Edif Barajas I, Barrio Aeropuerto, 28042, Madrid, Spain
Tel.: (34) 913138000
Web Site: https://www.sgs.es
Sales Range: $600-649.9 Million
Inspection & Testing Services
N.A.I.C.S.: 926150
Hernandez Jose Marla *(Mng Dir)*

SGS Tecnos, SA, Sociedad Unipersonal (1)
C/ Trespaderne 29, Edif Barajas I Barrio Aeropuerto, 28042, Madrid, Spain
Tel.: (34) 91 313 8000
Web Site: https://www.sgs.es
Emp.: 4,100
Testing Laboratories Services
N.A.I.C.S.: 541380

SGS Testing & Control Services Singapore Pte Ltd. (1)
30 Boon Lay Way 03-01, Singapore, 609957, Singapore
Tel.: (65) 63790111
Web Site: https://www.sgs.sg
Inspection & Testing Services
N.A.I.C.S.: 926150

SGS Togo S.A. (1)
Rue des Hydrocarbures Tokoin Centre, BP 3626, Lome, Togo
Tel.: (228) 22233330
Web Site: http://www.hk.sgs.com
Inspection & Testing Services
N.A.I.C.S.: 926150

SGS Turkmen Ltd. (1)
82 Ataturk 1972 Street Berkarar Business Center 6th Floor Office F7, Ashgabat, 744017, Turkmenistan
Tel.: (993) 12468324
Medical Laboratory Services
N.A.I.C.S.: 621511

SGS Uganda Limited (1)
1st Floor Block B Plot 1 Hill Drive, PO Box 63, Kololo, Kampala, Uganda
Tel.: (256) 392739966
Web Site: http://www.sgs.ug
Inspection & Testing Services
N.A.I.C.S.: 926150

SGS Ukraine, Foreign Enterprise (1)
vul Chornomorsky Cossacks 103, 65003, Odessa, Ukraine
Tel.: (380) 487869600

Web Site: http://www.ua.sgs.com
Sales Range: $150-199.9 Million
Emp.: 1,000
Inspection & Testing Services
N.A.I.C.S.: 926150
Alexey Katok *(Bus Mgr)*

SGS United Kingdom Limited (1)
Inward Way Rossmore Business Park, Cheshire, Ellesmere Port, CH65 3EN, United Kingdom
Tel.: (44) 1513506666
Web Site: http://www.sgs.co.uk
Sales Range: $550-599.9 Million
Emp.: 1,500
Inspection & Certification Services
N.A.I.C.S.: 926150

SGS Uruguay Limitada (1)
Avenida Alfredo Arocena 1964, 11500, Montevideo, Uruguay
Tel.: (598) 26003600
Sales Range: $25-49.9 Million
N.A.I.C.S.: 561110

SGS Vietnam Ltd. (1)
198 Nguyen Thi Minh Khai Street, District 3, Ho Chi Minh City, Vietnam
Tel.: (84) 2839351920
Web Site: https://www.sgs.vn
Emp.: 600
Testing Laboratories Services
N.A.I.C.S.: 541380

SGS de Mexico, S.A. de C.V (1)
Volcan 150 Piso 5 Col Lomas de Chapultepec Tercera Seccion, Miguel Hidalgo, 11000, Mexico, Mexico
Tel.: (52) 5553872100
Web Site: https://www.sgs.mx
Sales Range: $75-99.9 Million
Inspection & Testing Services
N.A.I.C.S.: 926150

SGS del Ecuador S.A. (1)
Km 5 5 Via Daule Avenida Martha Bucaram de Roldos, Junto al Colegio Dolores Sucre, 90112, Guayaquil, Ecuador
Tel.: (593) 4 373 2110
Web Site: http://www.ec.sgs.com
Sales Range: $50-74.9 Million
Inspection & Verification Services
N.A.I.C.S.: 926150

SGS do Brasil Ltda. (1)
Alameda Xingu 512 - 19th floor Alphaville Industrial, Barueri, 06455-030, Brazil
Tel.: (55) 113 883 8880
Web Site: https://www.sgsgroup.com.br
Sales Range: $550-599.9 Million
Inspection & Verification Services
N.A.I.C.S.: 926150

SGS-CSTC Standards Technical Services Co. Ltd. (1)
A-16/F Century Yuhui Mansion No 73 Fucheng Road, Haidian District Beijing Municipality, Beijing, 100142, China
Tel.: (86) 1058352655
Web Site: https://www.sgsgroup.com.cn
Medical Laboratory Services
N.A.I.C.S.: 621511

SGS-IMME Mongolia LLC (1)
Uildveriin Toirgiin 101toot Bayangol Duureg 20th Khoroo, Ulaanbaatar, 17060, Mongolia
Tel.: (976) 70144415
Medical Laboratory Services
N.A.I.C.S.: 621511

Securitest S.A (1)
1 Place du Gue de Maulny, 72019, Le Mans, France
Tel.: (33) 243414141
Inspection & Testing Services
N.A.I.C.S.: 926150

Sociedad Uruguaya de Control Tecnico de Automotores Sociedad Anonima (1)
Ruta 5 km 16 no 7350, Montevideo, 12600, Uruguay
Tel.: (598) 2322 7910
Web Site: http://www.suta.com.uy
Sales Range: $50-74.9 Million
Automotive Testing & Verification Services
N.A.I.C.S.: 926150
Arnaldo de Marzi *(Mng Dir)*

Societe Generale de Surveillance Azeri Ltd. (1)

3001 Tbilisi Prospect Moscow Ave, Baku, 1102, Azerbaijan
Tel.: (994) 12 430 3380
Medical Laboratory Services
N.A.I.C.S.: 621511

SGSG SCIENCE&TECHNOLOGY CO LTD ZHUHAI
9-15F Building 1 No 199 Dingxing Road High-tech Zone, Zhuhai, 519085, Guangdong, China
Tel.: (86) 7563236673
Web Site: http://www.sgsg.cc
Year Founded: 2005
300561—(CHIN)
Rev.: $19,603,207
Assets: $95,472,595
Liabilities: $5,108,911
Net Worth: $90,363,684
Earnings: $736,786
Fiscal Year-end: 12/31/23
Banking Software Development Services
N.A.I.C.S.: 513210
Zhe Chen *(Founder & Chm)*

SH ENERGY & CHEMICAL CO, LTD.
14th Fl 445 Teheran Road 445, Gangnam-gu, Seoul, Korea (South)
Tel.: (82) 220400600
Web Site:
   https://www.shinhochem.com
Year Founded: 1958
002360—(KRS)
Rev.: $128,361,956
Assets: $95,230,944
Liabilities: $23,055,118
Net Worth: $72,175,826
Earnings: $1,413,085
Emp.: 157
Fiscal Year-end: 12/31/22
Acetal Resin Mfr
N.A.I.C.S.: 325211
Kevin Chung *(CEO)*

SH GROUP (HOLDINGS) LIMITED
Units 603-606 6/F Tower I Cheung Sha Wan Plaza 833 Cheung Sha Wan Road, Kowloon, China (Hong Kong)
Tel.: (852) 23872882
Web Site:
   https://www.shunhingeng.com
Year Founded: 1987
1637—(HKG)
Rev.: $97,164,116
Assets: $65,536,415
Liabilities: $28,024,387
Net Worth: $37,512,027
Earnings: $1,513,322
Emp.: 207
Fiscal Year-end: 03/31/22
Electrical & Mechanical Engineering Services
N.A.I.C.S.: 541330
Cheung Choy Yu *(Founder, Chm & Exec Dir)*

SHAANXI AEROSPACE POWER HIGH-TECH CO., LTD.
No 78 Jinye Road, Hi-Tech District, Xi'an, 710077, Shaanxi, China
Tel.: (86) 2981881826
Web Site: https://www.china-htdl.com
Year Founded: 1999
600343—(SHG)
Rev.: $179,049,396
Assets: $441,892,110
Liabilities: $172,886,552
Net Worth: $269,005,558
Earnings: $(5,610,707)
Emp.: 2,000
Fiscal Year-end: 12/31/22

INTERNATIONAL PUBLIC

Fuel Pump & Torque Converter Mfr
N.A.I.C.S.: 336310
Sun Yantang *(Chm)*

Subsidiaries:

Baoji Aerospace Power Pump Co., Ltd. (1)
No 3 Renmin Road, Baoji, 721001, Shaanxi, China
Tel.: (86) 917 3514088
Web Site: http://www.htdl-bjb.com
Emp.: 370
Industrial Pump Mfr & Distr
N.A.I.C.S.: 333914

Huawei Chemical & Biologic Engineering Co., Ltd. (1)
No 58 Mail box 8 points, Xi'an, Shaanxi, China
Tel.: (86) 29 85206007
Industrial Machinery & Equipment Mfr
N.A.I.C.S.: 333998

Jiangsu Aerospace Hydraulic Equipments co., Ltd. (1)
No 8 Bosideng Avenue Development Zone, Gaoyou, 225600, Jiangsu, China
Tel.: (86) 51480955141
Web Site: https://www.pumpcj.com
Pump Product Mfr
N.A.I.C.S.: 333914

Jiangsu Aerospace Power Electric Co., Ltd. (1)
No 88 Dazhong Road Ji City, Jingjiang, Jiangsu, China
Tel.: (86) 52384549688
Web Site: http://www.motor-htdl.com
Emp.: 290
Industrial Motor Mfr
N.A.I.C.S.: 333996

Xi'an Aerospace Fire Engineering Co., Ltd. (1)
YuHang Road, Chang'an Area, Xi'an, 710110, Shaanxi, China
Tel.: (86) 29 85602523
Industrial Motor Mfr
N.A.I.C.S.: 333996

Yantai Aerospace YiHua Science and Technology Co., Ltd. (1)
Fengcheng Industrial Park Haiyang, Yantai, 265100, Shandong, China
Tel.: (86) 535 3315109
Torque Converter Mfr
N.A.I.C.S.: 336350

SHAANXI BAOGUANG VACUUM ELECTRONIC APPARATUS CO., LTD.
No 53 Baoguang Road, Weibin District, Baoji, 721006, Shaanxi, China
Tel.: (86) 9173561512
Web Site:
   http://www.baoguang.com.cn
Year Founded: 1997
600379—(SHG)
Rev.: $172,488,350
Assets: $210,881,362
Liabilities: $115,758,901
Net Worth: $95,122,460
Earnings: $8,077,521
Emp.: 1,400
Fiscal Year-end: 12/31/22
Electronic Components Mfr
N.A.I.C.S.: 334419
Xie Hongtao *(Chm & Sec-Party Committee)*

SHAANXI BEIYUAN CHEMICAL INDUSTRY GROUP CO., LTD.
Tel.: (86) 9128493288
Web Site: http://www.sxbychem.com
Year Founded: 2003
601568—(SHG)
Rev.: $1,767,575,516
Assets: $2,349,989,591
Liabilities: $432,938,605
Net Worth: $1,917,050,986
Earnings: $203,131,211

Fiscal Year-end: 12/31/22
Chemical Product Mfr & Distr
N.A.I.C.S.: 325520
Shi Yanyong (Chm)

SHAANXI BROADCAST & TV NETWORK INTERMEDIARY (GROUP) CO., LTD.
14-16 18-19 and 22-24F Shouzuo Mansion, Administrative And Business Zone Qujiang New District, Xi'an, 710061, Shaanxi, China
Tel.: (86) 2958000831
Web Site: http://www.600831.com
Year Founded: 1992
600831—(SHG)
Rev.: $421,044,002
Assets: $1,632,476,079
Liabilities: $1,097,532,816
Net Worth: $534,943,263
Earnings: $4,726,075
Fiscal Year-end: 12/31/22
Cable Television Network Operator
N.A.I.C.S.: 516120
Han Pu (Chm, Sec-Party Committee & Gen Mgr)

SHAANXI COAL INDUSTRY COMPANY LIMITED
19-22F Shaanxi Coal Chemical Group Bldg No 2 Jinye 1st Road, Yanta District, Xi'an, 710077, China
Tel.: (86) 2981772602
Web Site: http://www.shxcoal.com
601225—(SHG)
Rev.: $23,425,420,730
Assets: $30,222,480,623
Liabilities: $10,858,915,136
Net Worth: $19,363,565,487
Earnings: $4,931,261,352
Fiscal Year-end: 12/31/22
Coal Mfr & Distr
N.A.I.C.S.: 333131
Long Min (Chm)

SHAANXI CONSTRUCTION ENGINEERING GROUP CORPORATION LIMITED
No 199 North Street, Xi'an, 710003, Shaanxi, China
Tel.: (86) 2987370168   CN
Web Site: https://www.sxjgkg.com
Year Founded: 1950
600248—(SHG)
Rev.: $24,999,306,519
Assets: $48,002,814,065
Liabilities: $42,811,341,230
Net Worth: $5,191,472,835
Earnings: $548,571,874
Fiscal Year-end: 12/31/23
Petroleum Project Construction Services
N.A.I.C.S.: 237120
Yong Mo (CEO)

Subsidiaries:

Shaanxi Construction Engineering Installation Group Co., Ltd.   (1)
No 111 North Huanguang Road, Stele Forest, Xi'an, Shaanxi, China
Tel.: (86) 2988420234
Web Site: http://en.sxaz.com
Construction & Engineering Services
N.A.I.C.S.: 237990

SHAANXI CONSTRUCTION MACHINERY CO., LTD.
No 418 Jinhua North Road, Xincheng District, Xi'an, 710032, Shaanxi, China
Tel.: (86) 2982592288
Web Site: https://www.scmc-xa.com
Year Founded: 1954
600984—(SHG)
Rev.: $545,828,559
Assets: $2,526,025,708
Liabilities: $1,682,209,746
Net Worth: $843,815,962
Earnings: ($6,274,659)
Fiscal Year-end: 12/31/22
Construction Machinery Mfr & Whslr
N.A.I.C.S.: 333120
Yang Hongjun (Chm)

Subsidiaries:

CRMA Road Machinery Alliance (Beijing) Engineering Equipment Co., Ltd.   (1)
Room 2606 22nd Floor No 1 Building No 93 Yard Jianguo Road, Chaoyang District, Beijing, China
Tel.: (86) 1058208101
Construction Management Services
N.A.I.C.S.: 541330

Mechanized Engineering Company   (1)
No 418 Jinhua North Road, Xi'an, 710032, China
Tel.: (86) 2982592360
Construction Management Services
N.A.I.C.S.: 541330

SHAANXI FENGHUO ELECTRONICS CO., LTD.
No 72 Qingjiang Road, Baoji, 721006, Shaanxi, China
Tel.: (86) 9173626561
Web Site: http://www.fenghuo.cn
Year Founded: 1956
000561—(SSE)
Rev.: $224,642,204
Assets: $605,050,809
Liabilities: $333,294,395
Net Worth: $271,756,415
Earnings: $13,713,795
Fiscal Year-end: 12/31/22
Electrical Equipment Mfr & Distr
N.A.I.C.S.: 335999
Zhao Gangqiang (Chm)

SHAANXI HEIMAO COKING CO., LTD.
Coal Chemical Industrial Park, Hancheng, 715403, Shaanxi, China
Tel.: (86) 9135326936
Web Site: http://www.heimaocoking.com
Year Founded: 2003
601015—(SHG)
Rev.: $3,257,282,274
Assets: $2,998,026,051
Liabilities: $1,453,744,956
Net Worth: $1,544,281,095
Earnings: $39,021,470
Fiscal Year-end: 12/31/22
Coking & Chemical Product Mfr & Whslr
N.A.I.C.S.: 324199
Zhang Linxing (Chm)

SHAANXI INTERNATIONAL TRUST CO., LTD.
Block C Jinqiao International Square No 50 Keji Road, Hi-tech Zone, Xi'an, 710075, Shaanxi, China
Tel.: (86) 2981870262
Web Site: http://www.siti.com.cn
Year Founded: 1993
000563—(SSE)
Rev.: $270,398,340
Assets: $3,201,158,610
Liabilities: $924,191,270
Net Worth: $2,276,967,340
Earnings: $117,652,631
Fiscal Year-end: 12/31/22
Asset Management Services
N.A.I.C.S.: 523940
Yao Weidong (Chm)

SHAANXI JINYE SCIENCE TECHNOLOGY & EDUCATION GROUP CO., LTD.
19F Tower B City Gate No 1 Jinye Road, Hi-tech Zone, Xi'an, 710065, Shaanxi, China
Tel.: (86) 2981778550
Web Site: http://www.jinyegroup.cn
Year Founded: 1998
000812—(SSE)
Rev.: $181,166,488
Assets: $569,709,701
Liabilities: $318,428,815
Net Worth: $251,280,886
Earnings: $8,799,219
Emp.: 2,000
Fiscal Year-end: 12/31/22
Packaging Material Printing Services
N.A.I.C.S.: 561910
Hanyuan Yuan (Chm & Pres)

SHAANXI KANGHUI PHARMACEUTICAL CO., LTD.
Caihong 2nd Road High-tech Industrial Development Zone, Qindu District, Xianyang, 712000, Shaanxi, China
Tel.: (86) 2933347561
Web Site: http://www.sxkh.com
Year Founded: 2009
603139—(SHG)
Rev.: $69,008,172
Assets: $255,766,512
Liabilities: $111,723,876
Net Worth: $144,042,636
Earnings: ($8,853,048)
Emp.: 800
Fiscal Year-end: 12/31/22
Pharmaceutical Product Mfr & Distr
N.A.I.C.S.: 325412
Wang Yanling (Chm & Gen Mgr)

SHAANXI MEINENG CLEAN ENERGY CORP., LTD.
Room B1605 Chuangye Plaza No 48 Keji Road, High-tech Zone, Xi'an, 710016, Shaanxi, China
Tel.: (86) 2983279777
Web Site: https://www.meinenggas.com
Year Founded: 2008
001299—(SSE)
Rev.: $77,205,623
Assets: $227,298,642
Liabilities: $54,758,892
Net Worth: $172,539,750
Earnings: $13,226,396
Fiscal Year-end: 12/31/22
Natural Gas Distribution Services
N.A.I.C.S.: 221210
Liqun Yan (Chm)

SHAANXI NORTHWEST NEW TECHNOLOGY INDUSTRY COMPANY LIMITED
No 6 Gao Xin Yi Road Xian National Hi-tech Ind Dev zone, Xi'an, 710075, Shaanxi, China
Tel.: (86) 2988375006   CN
Web Site: http://www.xibeishiye.com
Year Founded: 1999
Rev.: $5,475,387
Assets: $25,286,520
Liabilities: $2,988,782
Net Worth: $22,297,737
Earnings: $1,647,414
Emp.: 74
Fiscal Year-end: 12/31/18
Gasoline Additive Mfr & Distr
N.A.I.C.S.: 325998
Cong Wang (Chm)

SHAANXI PANLONG PHARMACEUTICAL GROUP LIMITED BY SHARE LTD.
Panlong Ecological Industrial Park, Zhashui County Shangluo, Shaanxi, 710025, Shaanxi, China
Tel.: (86) 2983338888
Web Site: http://www.pljt.com
Year Founded: 1997
002864—(SSE)
Rev.: $136,790,751
Assets: $271,082,495
Liabilities: $138,038,935
Net Worth: $133,043,559
Earnings: $14,203,355
Fiscal Year-end: 12/31/22
Pharmaceutical Product Mfr & Distr
N.A.I.C.S.: 325412
Xie Xiaolin (Chm)

SHAANXI PROVINCIAL NATURAL GAS CO., LTD.
No 2 Kaiyuan Road, A1 Area Economic Tech Dev Zone, Xi'an, 710016, Shaanxi, China
Tel.: (86) 2986520111
Web Site: https://www.shaanxigas.com
Year Founded: 1991
002267—(SSE)
Rev.: $1,194,195,689
Assets: $1,824,916,785
Liabilities: $899,793,203
Net Worth: $925,123,582
Earnings: $86,536,593
Fiscal Year-end: 12/31/22
Natural Gas Distr
N.A.I.C.S.: 486910
Hongbo Liu (Chm)

SHAANXI XINGHUA CHEMISTRY CO., LTD.
Yingbin Road, Dongcheng District, Xingping, 713100, Shaanxi, China
Tel.: (86) 2938838546
Web Site: https://www.snxhchem.com
Year Founded: 1997
002109—(SSE)
Rev.: $457,378,581
Assets: $704,646,624
Liabilities: $45,700,902
Net Worth: $658,945,722
Earnings: $55,294,153
Fiscal Year-end: 12/31/22
Chemical Fertilizer Mfr & Distr
N.A.I.C.S.: 325311
Fan Mingxi (Chm)

SHAANXI YANCHANG PETROLEUM GROUP CO., LTD.
75 Second Keji Road, Xi'an, 710075, Shaanxi, China
Tel.: (86) 2988899666   CN
Year Founded: 1905
Sales Range: $25-49.9 Billion
Emp.: 126,793
Oil & Gas Exploration & Production
N.A.I.C.S.: 211120
Hao Shen (Chm)

Subsidiaries:

Beijing Petrochemical Engineering Co., Ltd.   (1)
Bldg 7 Tianjuyuan Olympic Media Village, Chaoyang Dist, Beijing, 100107, China
Tel.: (86) 1052243333
Petrochemical Engineering Services
N.A.I.C.S.: 325110

Shaanxi Yanchang Petroleum Material Corp. Ltd.   (1)
No 2 East Zaoyuan Road, Xi'an, China
Tel.: (86) 2984622219
Oil & Gas Exploration Services
N.A.I.C.S.: 211120

SHAANXI ZHONGTIAN ROCKET TECHNOLOGY CO., LTD.
Languan Street, Lantian County, Xi'an, 710500, Shaanxi, China
Tel.: (86) 2982829481
Web Site: http://www.zthj.com

Shaanxi Zhongtian Rocket Technology Co., Ltd.—(Continued)
Year Founded: 2002
003009—(SSE)
Rev.: $173,497,840
Assets: $417,894,057
Liabilities: $202,615,480
Net Worth: $215,278,577
Earnings: $20,258,077
Fiscal Year-end: 12/31/22
Information Technology Services
N.A.I.C.S.: 541512
Li Shuhai *(Chm)*

SHABA CHEMICALS LIMITED
101 Rajani Bhawan 569/2 M G Road, Indore, 452 001, Madhya Pradesh, India
Tel.: (91) 731 4299232
Web Site: http://www.shabachemicals.com
Rev.: $1,451
Assets: $4,984
Liabilities: $7,650
Net Worth: ($2,666)
Earnings: $78
Fiscal Year-end: 03/31/18
Commodity Trading Services
N.A.I.C.S.: 523160
Sangeeta Neema *(Mng Dir & Compliance Officer)*

SHABBIR TILES & CERAMICS LTD
15th Milestone National Highway, Landhi, Karachi, 75120, Pakistan
Tel.: (92) 2138183610
Web Site: https://www.stile.com.pk
Year Founded: 1978
STCL—(KAR)
Rev.: $44,649,016
Assets: $35,979,726
Liabilities: $22,425,767
Net Worth: $13,553,959
Earnings: $1,509,156
Emp.: 869
Fiscal Year-end: 06/30/19
Tiles Mfr
N.A.I.C.S.: 327120
Ovais Jamani *(Sec & Head-Fin)*

Subsidiaries:

Shabbir Tiles & Ceramics Ltd - Unit I (1)
15th Milestone National Hwy, Landhi, Karachi, 75120, Sindh, Pakistan
Tel.: (92) 2135015024
Ceramics & Sanitary Mfr
N.A.I.C.S.: 327120
Haroon Afaq *(Mgr-HR)*

SHACKS MOTOR GROUP PTY. LTD.
64 Queen Victoria Street, Fremantle, 6160, WA, Australia
Tel.: (61) 894329432
Web Site: http://www.shacks.com.au
Year Founded: 1906
Automotive Retailer
N.A.I.C.S.: 441110
Doug Kerr *(Chm & Mng Dir)*

SHADAB TEXTILE MILLS LIMITED
A-601 6-K City Towers Main Boulevard Gulberg II, Lahore, Pakistan
Tel.: (92) 4235788714
Web Site: https://www.shadabtextile.com
Year Founded: 1979
SHDT—(LAH)
Rev.: $20,200,427
Assets: $5,593,421
Liabilities: $2,079,859
Net Worth: $3,513,562
Earnings: $560,363
Emp.: 1,092
Fiscal Year-end: 06/30/19
Yarn Spinning Mills
N.A.I.C.S.: 313110
Aamir Naseem *(CEO)*

SHADMAN COTTON MILLS LTD.
2-E Block G Mushtaq Ahmed Gurmani Road Gulberg II, Lahore, Pakistan
Tel.: (92) 4235959121
Web Site: https://www.shadman.com.pk
Year Founded: 1979
SHCM—(PSX)
Rev.: $1,255,995
Assets: $6,005,478
Liabilities: $2,686,192
Net Worth: $3,319,286
Earnings: $337,131
Emp.: 159
Fiscal Year-end: 06/30/23
Yarn Spinning Mill Operator
N.A.I.C.S.: 313110
Ghazala Shahid *(Chm)*

SHAFFI CHEMICAL INDUSTRIES LIMITED
23-km Multan Road, Mohlanwal, Lahore, Pakistan
Tel.: (92) 4237540336
Web Site: https://scil.com.pk
Year Founded: 1994
SHCI—(PSX)
Rev.: $67,694
Assets: $207,977
Liabilities: $377,652
Net Worth: ($169,675)
Earnings: $11,260
Emp.: 8
Fiscal Year-end: 06/30/23
Chemical Products Mfr
N.A.I.C.S.: 325199
Zahoor Ahmad *(Sec)*

SHAFTESBURY CAPITAL PLC
Regal House 14 James Street, London, WC2E 8BU, United Kingdom
Tel.: (44) 2032149150
Web Site: https://www.shaftesburycapital.com
Year Founded: 2010
SHCE—(JSE)
Rev.: $93,536,986
Assets: $2,967,937,390
Liabilities: $996,718,001
Net Worth: $1,971,219,389
Earnings: ($267,356,728)
Emp.: 57
Fiscal Year-end: 12/31/22
Property Development Services
N.A.I.C.S.: 531190
Ian Hawksworth *(CEO)*

Subsidiaries:

Capco Covent Garden Limited (1)
1st Floor Regal House 14 James Street, London, WC2E 8BU, United Kingdom
Tel.: (44) 2073951350
Web Site: http://www.coventgarden.london
All Grocery & Food Product Retailer
N.A.I.C.S.: 445110

SHAFTESBURY PLC
22 Ganton Street, London, W1F 7FD, United Kingdom
Tel.: (44) 207 333 8118
Web Site: http://www.shaftesbury.co.uk
Year Founded: 1986
SHB—(LSE)
Rev.: $153,015,044
Assets: $4,557,322,952
Liabilities: $1,335,860,708
Net Worth: $3,221,462,244
Earnings: $264,619,628)
Emp.: 54
Fiscal Year-end: 09/30/21
Real Estate Investment Services
N.A.I.C.S.: 525990
Brian Bickell *(CEO)*

Subsidiaries:

Shaftesbury Carnaby Limited (1)
22 Ganton Street, Carnaby, London, W1F 7FD, United Kingdom (100%)
Tel.: (44) 2073338118
Web Site: https://www.carnaby.co.uk
Sales Range: $50-74.9 Million
Emp.: 20
Other Real Estate Property Lessors
N.A.I.C.S.: 531190

Shaftesbury Charlotte Street Limited (1)
22 Ganton Street, Carnaby, London, W1F 7FD, United Kingdom
Tel.: (44) 2073338118
Web Site: http://www.shaftesbury.co.uk
Sales Range: $50-74.9 Million
Emp.: 17
Residential Property Management Services
N.A.I.C.S.: 531311

Shaftesbury Chinatown Limited (1)
22 Ganton street, London, W1F 7FD, United Kingdom (100%)
Tel.: (44) 2073338118
Web Site: http://www.shaftesbury.co.uk
Sales Range: $50-74.9 Million
Emp.: 25
Other Real Estate Property Lessors
N.A.I.C.S.: 531190
Brian Bickell *(CEO)*

Shaftesbury Covent Garden Limited (1)
22 Ganton Street, London, W1F 7FD, United Kingdom (100%)
Tel.: (44) 2073338118
Web Site: http://www.shaftesbury.co.uk
Sales Range: $50-74.9 Million
Emp.: 25
Other Real Estate Property Lessors
N.A.I.C.S.: 531190

SHAGRIR GROUP VEHICLE SERVICES LTD.
8 HaNafh St, Holon, 5881804, Israel
Tel.: (972) 35578888
Web Site: https://www.shagrir.co.il
Year Founded: 1984
SHGR—(TAE)
Rev.: $90,900,675
Assets: $133,707,416
Liabilities: $90,799,833
Net Worth: $42,907,583
Earnings: $2,555,325
Fiscal Year-end: 12/31/23
Motor Vehicle Towing
N.A.I.C.S.: 488410
Yosef Ben Shalom *(Chm)*

SHAH ALLOYS LIMITED
Shah Alloys Corporate House Sola-Kalol road Santej Ta Kalol, Gandhinagar, 382721, Gujarat, India
Tel.: (91) 2764661100
Web Site: https://www.shahalloys.com
513436—(BOM)
Rev.: $75,287,956
Assets: $36,071,219
Liabilities: $32,415,143
Net Worth: $3,656,076
Earnings: ($385,013)
Emp.: 682
Fiscal Year-end: 03/31/23
Stainless Steel Products Sales & Mfr
N.A.I.C.S.: 331221
Ashok A. Sharma *(CFO)*

SHAH CONSTRUCTION COMPANY LIMITED
11 Shah Industrial Estate New Link Road Opp Anna temple, Andheri W, Mumbai, 400 053, Maharashtra, India
Tel.: (91) 2266920678
Web Site: https://shah-construction.in
Year Founded: 1944
509870—(BOM)
Rev.: $257,177
Assets: $5,370,047
Liabilities: $16,583,256
Net Worth: ($11,213,209)
Earnings: ($657,188)
Fiscal Year-end: 03/31/21
Construction Engineering Services
N.A.I.C.S.: 237990
Mehul Jadavji Shah *(Chm & Mng Dir)*

SHAH FOODS LTD
Block no 453/1 Chhatral Kalol-Mehsana Highway Taluka Kalol, Gandhinagar, Gujarat, 382729, India
Tel.: (91) 2764233931
Web Site: http://www.shahfoods.com
Year Founded: 1982
519031—(BOM)
Rev.: $13,894
Assets: $157,466
Liabilities: $153,795
Net Worth: $3,671
Earnings: ($75,462)
Emp.: 1
Fiscal Year-end: 03/31/21
Biscuit Mfr
N.A.I.C.S.: 311821
Nirav Janakbhai Shah *(Mng Dir)*

SHAH METACORP LIMITED
2nd Floor Mrudul Tower B/h Times of India, Ashram Road, Ahmedabad, 380009, India
Tel.: (91) 7966614508
Web Site: https://www.gyscoal.com
Year Founded: 1999
533275—(BOM)
Rev.: $3,129,099
Assets: $11,880,168
Liabilities: $16,174,472
Net Worth: ($4,294,304)
Earnings: ($768,782)
Emp.: 49
Fiscal Year-end: 03/31/22
Steel Mfrs
N.A.I.C.S.: 331110
Viral Mukundbhai Shah *(Chm & Mng Dir)*

SHAH TRADING COMPANY LIMITED
3401 Douglas B Floreani Ville, Saint Laurent, H4S 1Y6, QC, Canada
Tel.: (514) 336-2462
Web Site: http://www.shahtrading.com
Year Founded: 1974
Rev.: $17,601,840
Emp.: 110
Food Products Distr
N.A.I.C.S.: 445298
Kamal Shah *(VP)*

SHAHDAAB
PO Box 185, 57189-85643, Urmia, West Azarbaydjan, Iran
Tel.: (98) 441 2355585
Web Site: http://www.shahdaab.com
Year Founded: 1987
Fruit Juices Mfr
N.A.I.C.S.: 311411
Ahmad Afshar *(Bus Mgr)*

SHAHDIRAN INC.
Km 5 Mashhad-Ghouchan Rd, PO Box 91775-1174, 9187381731, Mashhad, Iran
Tel.: (98) 5136514300
Web Site: https://shahdiran.ir
Year Founded: 2000
SHAD—(THE)
Sales Range: Less than $1 Million
Food Industry Complex
N.A.I.C.S.: 311999

SHAHE INDUSTRIAL CO., LTD.
Shahe Century Building No 2222 Baishi Road, Nanshan District, Shenzhen, 518053, Guangdong, China
Tel.: (86) 75586091298
Web Site: http://www.shahe.cn
Year Founded: 1992
000014—(SSE)
Rev.: $107,209,693
Assets: $419,888,734
Liabilities: $248,691,545
Net Worth: $171,197,189
Earnings: $34,914,489
Fiscal Year-end: 12/31/22
Real Estate Development Services
N.A.I.C.S.: 531390
Yong Chen *(Chm)*

SHAHED COMPANY
No 21 Kooh-e-Noor st Ostad Motahari Ave, Tehran, Iran
Tel.: (98) 21 88735941
Web Site: http://www.shahed.co.ir
Year Founded: 1985
SAHD1—(THE)
Sales Range: Less than $1 Million
Holding Company
N.A.I.C.S.: 551112

SHAHEEN INSURANCE COMPANY LTD.
10th Floor Shaheen Complex M R Kayani Road, Karachi, Pakistan
Tel.: (92) 32630370
Web Site: https://www.shaheeninsurance.com
SHNI—(KAR)
Rev.: $1,901,021
Assets: $7,561,901
Liabilities: $3,561,941
Net Worth: $3,999,959
Earnings: $386,401
Emp.: 110
Fiscal Year-end: 12/31/19
General Insurance Services
N.A.I.C.S.: 524126
Naveed Y. Butt *(Head-Bus & Mktg)*

SHAHI SHIPPING LIMITED
404 Abhay Steel House Baroda Street, Mumbai, 400050, India
Tel.: (91) 2240151972
Web Site: https://www.shahilogistics.com
Year Founded: 1985
Rev.: $2,800,367
Assets: $6,075,923
Liabilities: $2,678,909
Net Worth: $3,397,014
Earnings: $170,471
Emp.: 51
Fiscal Year-end: 03/31/18
Marine Transportation Services
N.A.I.C.S.: 488390
Nungavaram Vaidyanathan Agandeswaran *(Compliance Officer & Sec)*

SHAHID BAHONAR COPPER IND. CO.
Km 12 Kerman Baghin Road Kerman, 7613836183, Tehran, Iran
Tel.: (98) 2182166700
Web Site: https://www.csp.ir
BAHN1—(THE)
Sales Range: Less than $1 Million
Copper Mines Services
N.A.I.C.S.: 212230
M. Ziaie *(CEO)*

SHAHIN PLASTIC MANUFACTURING COMPANY
No 464 km 1 Saveh Road, PO Box 11365/933, 136961413, Tehran, Iran
Tel.: (98) 21 66249694
Web Site: http://www.shahinplastic.com
Year Founded: 1956
Emp.: 236
Plastics Product Mfr
N.A.I.C.S.: 325211
Alireza Sharifi Sari *(Chm)*

SHAHJALAL ISLAMI BANK PLC
Shahjalal Islami Bank Tower Plot No 4 Block CWNC Gulshan Avenue, Dhaka, 1212, Bangladesh
Tel.: (880) 2222834573
Web Site: https://www.sjiblbd.com
Year Founded: 2001
SHAHJABANK—(DHA)
Rev.: $129,776,799
Assets: $3,672,077,308
Liabilities: $3,439,407,775
Net Worth: $232,669,533
Earnings: $30,303,294
Emp.: 2,741
Fiscal Year-end: 12/31/21
Banking Services
N.A.I.C.S.: 522110
Md. Sanaullah Shahid *(Chm)*

Subsidiaries:

Shahjalal Islami Bank Securities Limited (1)
DSL Building 3rd floor 1/C DIT Avenue Dainik Bangla Motijheel, Dhaka, 1000, Bangladesh
Tel.: (880) 24 711 0035
Web Site: https://www.shahjalalbanksecurities.com
Emp.: 144
Bank Security Services
N.A.I.C.S.: 561612
Alhaj Mohammed Younus *(Chm)*

SHAHLON SILK INDUSTRIES LTD.
3rd Floor Dawer Chamber Ring Road, Surat, 395 002, Gujarat, India
Tel.: (91) 261 419 0200
Web Site: http://www.shahlon.com
542862—(BOM)
Rev.: $29,328,922
Assets: $37,752,651
Liabilities: $25,188,673
Net Worth: $12,563,979
Earnings: $473,751
Emp.: 1,731
Fiscal Year-end: 03/31/21
Synthetic Fabric Mfr
N.A.I.C.S.: 313310
Dhirajlal Raichand Shah *(Chm)*

SHAHMURAD SUGAR MILLS LIMITED
96-A Sindhi Muslim Housing Society, Karachi, 7440, Pakistan
Tel.: (92) 2134550161
Web Site: https://www.shahmuradsugar.co
Year Founded: 1952
SHSML—(PSX)
Rev.: $82,326,970
Assets: $81,296,486
Liabilities: $31,584,312
Net Worth: $49,712,174
Earnings: $13,769,846
Emp.: 370
Fiscal Year-end: 09/30/23
Sugar Mfr & Distr
N.A.I.C.S.: 311314
Ismail H. Zakaria *(Chm)*

SHAHTAJ SUGAR MILLS LIMITED
72-C-1 MM Alam Road Gulberg III, Lahore, 54660, Pakistan
Tel.: (92) 4235710482
Web Site: https://www.shahtajsugar.com
SHJS—(KAR)
Rev.: $33,096,497
Assets: $34,031,326
Liabilities: $16,369,761
Net Worth: $17,661,565
Earnings: $238,685
Emp.: 459
Fiscal Year-end: 09/30/19
Sugar Mfr
N.A.I.C.S.: 311314
Ijaz Ahmad *(Exec Dir)*

Subsidiaries:

Information System Associates Limited (1)
6th. Floor Ilaco House Abdullah Haroon Road, Saddar, Karachi, Pakistan
Tel.: (92) 21111566111
Web Site: https://www.comstar.com.pk
Information Technology Services
N.A.I.C.S.: 541511
Aisha Tahir *(Engr-Network)*

Shahnawaz (Private) Limited (1)
19 West Wharf, Karachi, 74000, Pakistan
Tel.: (92) 21323139348
Web Site: https://www.shahnawazltd.com
Car Distr
N.A.I.C.S.: 423120

SHAHTAJ TEXTILE LIMITED
Shahnawaz Building 19-Dockyard Road, West Wharf, Karachi, 74000, Pakistan
Tel.: (92) 2132313934
Web Site: https://shahtaj.com
Year Founded: 1990
STJT—(PSX)
Rev.: $29,086,475
Assets: $17,017,867
Liabilities: $10,584,249
Net Worth: $6,433,618
Earnings: $550,483
Emp.: 481
Fiscal Year-end: 06/30/23
Textile Mill Operator
N.A.I.C.S.: 314999
Muhammad Naeem *(CEO)*

SHAHZAD TEXTILE MILLS LTD.
19-A Off Zafar Ali Road, Gulberg-V, Lahore, Pakistan
Tel.: (92) 4235754024
Web Site: https://shahzadtex.com
SZTM—(PSX)
Rev.: $30,214,106
Assets: $18,508,991
Liabilities: $7,676,736
Net Worth: $10,832,255
Earnings: ($968,592)
Emp.: 1,999
Fiscal Year-end: 06/30/23
Home Textile Mfr
N.A.I.C.S.: 313210
Humayun Bakht *(CFO)*

SHAILJA COMMERCIAL TRADE FRENZY LTD.
E-55 Roy Mullick Colony 21 Parsee Church Cabin No 7, Kolkata, 700 030, India
Tel.: (91) 3365039584
Web Site: http://www.sctfl.org
Rev.: $11,693,082
Assets: $8,984,821
Liabilities: $7,967,502
Net Worth: $1,017,319
Earnings: $513,308
Fiscal Year-end: 03/31/18
Textile Product Trading Services
N.A.I.C.S.: 523160
Kushal Damodar Vaishnav *(Compliance Officer)*

SHAILY ENGINEERING PLASTICS LIMITED
Survey No 363/364/366 Rania Ta Savli, Vadodara, 391780, Gujarat, India
Tel.: (91) 2667244307
Web Site: https://www.shaily.com
Year Founded: 1987
501423—(BOM)
Rev.: $49,573,674
Assets: $63,751,342
Liabilities: $38,926,701
Net Worth: $24,824,641
Earnings: $3,005,839
Emp.: 762
Fiscal Year-end: 03/31/21
Plastic Product Mfr & Whslr
N.A.I.C.S.: 326199
Mahendra Sanghvi *(Chm)*

SHAIVAL REALITY LTD.
A-1/B-1 Maharaja Palace Near Vijay Char Rasta Navarangpura, Ahmedabad, 380009, Gujarat, India
Tel.: (91) 7926407802
Web Site: https://www.shaivalgroup.ooo
Year Founded: 1996
SHAIVAL—(NSE)
Rev.: $1,231,821
Assets: $1,640,353
Liabilities: $51,676
Net Worth: $1,588,677
Earnings: $804,218
Emp.: 3
Fiscal Year-end: 03/31/23
Bulk Cargo Transportation Services
N.A.I.C.S.: 484230
Mayur Mukundbhai Desai *(Mng Dir)*

SHAKARGANJ LIMITED
Executive Floor IT Tower 73 E 1 Hali Road Gulberg 3, Lahore, Pakistan
Tel.: (92) 42111111765
Web Site: https://www.sml.com.pk
SML—(LAH)
Rev.: $40,262,281
Assets: $85,980,331
Liabilities: $35,363,219
Net Worth: $50,617,112
Earnings: ($4,839,873)
Emp.: 1,469
Fiscal Year-end: 09/30/19
Sugar Mills
N.A.I.C.S.: 311314
Anjum M. Saleem *(CEO)*

Subsidiaries:

Safeway Fund Limited (1)
9th Floor Lakson Square Building Number 1 Molana Deen Muhammad, Wafai Road, Karachi, Sindh, Pakistan
Tel.: (92) 21 35620971
Web Site: http://www.safewayfund.com
Sales Range: $75-99.9 Million
Emp.: 10
Investment Advisory & Asset Management Services
N.A.I.C.S.: 523940
Nihal Cassim *(CEO)*

Shakarganj Mills Limited - Crescent Ujala (1)
Management House Toba Road, Jhang, Jhang, Punjab, Pakistan
Tel.: (92) 477652801
Cotton Yarn Mfr
N.A.I.C.S.: 313110

SHAKER RESOURCES INC.
101 6th Avenue SW Suite 1545, Calgary, T2P 3P4, AB, Canada
Tel.: (403) 264-8900
Year Founded: 1996
Rev.: $28,400,000
Emp.: 95
Oil & Natural Gas Distr
N.A.I.C.S.: 211120
Christina M. Fehr *(CEO)*

SHAKEY'S PIZZA ASIA VENTURES, INC.
KM 15 East Service Road corner Marian Road 2, Barangay San Martin

SHAKEY'S PIZZA ASIA VENTURES, INC.

Shakey's Pizza Asia Ventures, Inc.—(Continued)
de Porres, Paranaque, 1700, Philippines
Tel.: (63) 288390011
Web Site:
https://www.shakeyspizza.ph
Year Founded: 1954
PIZZA—(PHI)
Rev.: $231,541,444
Assets: $336,335,611
Liabilities: $192,628,663
Net Worth: $143,706,948
Earnings: $19,489,872
Emp.: 2,269
Fiscal Year-end: 12/31/23
Restaurant Operators
N.A.I.C.S.: 722511
Jesher Vidon *(Gen Mgr-Acctg)*

SHAKLEE GLOBAL GROUP, INC.
21F Shinjuku Sumitomo Bldg 2-6-1 Nishi Shinjuku, Shinjuku-Ku, Tokyo, 163-0221, Japan
Tel.: (81) 3 33403601
Web Site: http://www.shaklee.co.jp
Year Founded: 1975
Rev.: $229,870,320
Assets: $316,130,580
Liabilities: $185,267,940
Net Worth: $130,862,640
Earnings: ($516,420)
Fiscal Year-end: 03/31/19
Nutraceutical & Personal Care Product Mfr & Distr
N.A.I.C.S.: 311999
Roger Barnett *(Chm, Pres & CEO)*

SHAKTI PRESS LIMITED
Plot No 49 Khasra No 69 Kanholibara Road Vill Mondha Tah Hingna, Nagpur, 441110, Maharashtra, India
Tel.: (91) 9371162925
Web Site:
https://www.shaktipresslimited.com
Rev.: $2,669,832
Assets: $4,889,589
Liabilities: $4,665,802
Net Worth: $223,787
Earnings: $211,453
Emp.: 30
Fiscal Year-end: 06/30/18
Printing & Packaging Services
N.A.I.C.S.: 323111
Raghav K. Sharma *(Chm & Mng Dir)*

SHAKTI PUMPS (INDIA) LTD.
Plot No 401 402 413 Industrial Area Sector3, Dhar Dist, Pithampur, 454774, MP, India
Tel.: (91) 7292410500
Web Site:
https://www.shaktipumps.com
SHAKTIPUMP—(NSE)
Rev.: $127,413,550
Assets: $91,520,506
Liabilities: $45,027,323
Net Worth: $46,493,183
Earnings: $10,317,544
Emp.: 544
Fiscal Year-end: 03/31/21
Stainless Steel Water Pumps Mfr
N.A.I.C.S.: 331210
Dinesh Patidar *(Mng Dir)*

Subsidiaries:

Shakti EV Mobility Pvt. Ltd. (1)
Plot No - 4 Pithampur Sector-5 Dhar Road, Integrated Industrial Area District-Dhar, Pithampur, 454774, MP, India
Tel.: (91) 7292410500
Web Site: https://shaktievmobility.com
Power Electronics Equipment Mfr
N.A.I.C.S.: 335311

Shakti Energy Solutions Pvt. Ltd. (1)
Plot No. 155 - 156 Sector 3 Industrial Growth Centre, Pithampur, 454774, Madhya Pradesh, India
Tel.: (91) 7292410500
Web Site: https://www.sespl.org
Motor Pump Mfr & Distr
N.A.I.C.S.: 333996

Shakti Pumps (Bangladesh) Ltd. (1)
Unique Trade Centre 19th Floor 8 Panthapath, Karwanbazar, Dhaka, 1215, Bangladesh
Tel.: (880) 1763069219
Motor Pump Mfr & Distr
N.A.I.C.S.: 333996

Shakti Pumps FZE (1)
Q4 - 267 Sharjah Airport International Free Zone, PO Box 8521, Sharjah, United Arab Emirates
Tel.: (971) 508831589
Pump & Motor Mfr & Whslr
N.A.I.C.S.: 423830

Shakti Pumps USA LLC (1)
740 Florida Central Pkwy Ste 1008, Longwood, FL 32750
Tel.: (407) 574-4001
Web Site: https://www.shaktipumps.us
Pump & Motor Whslr
N.A.I.C.S.: 423830
Ashish Rathi *(Head-Sales-Natl)*

SHALAG INDUSTRIES, LTD.
Upper Galilee, Shamir, 12135, Israel
Tel.: (972) 46947856
Web Site: http://www.shalag.co.il
Nonwoven Product Mfr
N.A.I.C.S.: 313230
Ilan Pickman *(CEO)*

SHALAMUKA CAPITAL (PTY) LTD.
1st Floor 8 Melville Road, Illovo, 2196, South Africa
Tel.: (27) 113808314
Year Founded: 2008
Private Equity Firm
N.A.I.C.S.: 523999

Subsidiaries:

MineRP (1)
Ground Floor 267 West Avenue, Centurion, 0157, South Africa
Tel.: (27) 879803100
Web Site: http://www.minerp.com
Sales Range: $150-199.9 Million
Emp.: 200
Mining Management Software Solutions
N.A.I.C.S.: 541511

Subsidiary (Non-US):

GIJIMAAST Americas Incorporated (2)
432 Westmount Ave Unit AB, Sudbury, P3A 5Z8, ON, Canada
Tel.: (705) 525-4774
Web Site: http://www.gijimaast.ca
Sales Range: $25-49.9 Million
Emp.: 10
Mining Software Consulting Services
N.A.I.C.S.: 541511

GijimaAst (Pty) Limited (2)
2 44 Denis St, Subiaco, 6008, WA, Australia
Tel.: (61) 863801719
Sales Range: $25-49.9 Million
Emp.: 6
Mining Software Consulting Services
N.A.I.C.S.: 541512

SHALBY LIMITED
Opposite Karnawati Club Sarkhej Gandhinagar Highway, Near Prahlad Nagar Garden, Ahmedabad, 380 015, Gujarat, India
Tel.: (91) 7940203000
Web Site: https://www.shalby.org
Year Founded: 1994
SHALBY—(NSE)
Rev.: $60,054,267
Assets: $136,038,767
Liabilities: $22,106,994
Net Worth: $113,931,773
Earnings: $5,782,413
Emp.: 2,228
Fiscal Year-end: 03/31/21
Healtcare Services
N.A.I.C.S.: 622310
Vikram I. Shah *(Founder, Chm & Mng Dir)*

Subsidiaries:

Shalby Advanced Technologies Inc. (1)
1115 Windfield Way, El Dorado Hills, CA 95762
Tel.: (916) 355-7127
Web Site: https://www.shalbytech.com
Orthopaedic Machinery Mfr & Distr
N.A.I.C.S.: 339112

Shalby Global Technologies Pte. Limited (1)
Regus One Fullerton 1 Fullerton Road 02-01 One Fullerton, Singapore, 049213, Singapore
Tel.: (65) 64083922
Orthopaedic Equipment Mfr & Distr
N.A.I.C.S.: 339113

Slaney Healthcare Private Limited (1)
B-301-302 Mondeal Heights, Ahmedabad, 380015, Gujarat, India
Tel.: (91) 9904403664
Web Site: https://slaneyhealthcare.com
Pharmaceutical Mfr & Distr
N.A.I.C.S.: 325412

SHALIBHADRA FINANCE LIMITED
3 Kamat Industrial Estate, 396 Veer Savarkar Marg Prabhadevi, Mumbai, 400 025, Maharashtra, India
Tel.: (91) 2224224575
Web Site:
https://www.shalibhadrafinance.com
511754—(BOM)
Rev.: $2,890,046
Assets: $15,281,875
Liabilities: $9,105,423
Net Worth: $6,176,451
Earnings: $479,765
Fiscal Year-end: 03/31/21
Vehicle Financing Services
N.A.I.C.S.: 522220
Minesh M. Doshi *(Mng Dir)*

SHALIMAR AGENCIES LTD.
11-12 1st Floor Pavadai naicker Street Opp kalaimagal Kalvi nilayam, Erode, 638001, Tamil Nadu, India
Tel.: (91) 9944446886
Web Site:
https://www.shalimaragencies-erode.com
Year Founded: 1982
539895—(BOM)
Assets: $492,132
Liabilities: $149,383
Net Worth: $342,750
Earnings: ($10,281)
Fiscal Year-end: 03/31/23
Pharmaceutical Products Distr
N.A.I.C.S.: 424210
V. Purusothaman *(Chm)*

SHALIMAR PAINTS LTD
Stainless Centre 4th Floor Plot No 50 Sector 32, Gurgaon, 122001, Haryana, India
Tel.: (91) 1244616600
Web Site:
https://www.shalimarpaints.com
Year Founded: 1902
509874—(BOM)
Rev.: $45,420,102
Assets: $68,651,310
Liabilities: $38,202,050
Net Worth: $30,449,260
Earnings: ($6,806,313)

INTERNATIONAL PUBLIC

Emp.: 611
Fiscal Year-end: 03/31/21
Paints Mfr
N.A.I.C.S.: 325510
Mohit Kumar Donter *(CFO)*

SHALIMAR PRODUCTIONS LIMITED
A9 Shree Sidhdhivinayak Plaza Plot B-31 Off-link Road, Andheri W, Mumbai, 400 053, India
Tel.: (91) 2265501200
Web Site:
https://www.shalimarpro.com
Year Founded: 1985
512499—(BOM)
Rev.: $609,473
Assets: $14,414,226
Liabilities: $594,553
Net Worth: $13,819,673
Earnings: $8,026
Fiscal Year-end: 03/31/21
Film Production Services
N.A.I.C.S.: 512110
Tilokchand Kothari *(Chm)*

SHALIMAR WIRES INDUSTRIES LTD.
25 Ganesh Chandra Avenue, Kolkata, 700013, West Bengal, India
Tel.: (91) 3322349308
Web Site:
https://www.shalimarwires.com
Year Founded: 1962
532455—(BOM)
Rev.: $12,402,704
Assets: $25,403,346
Liabilities: $21,814,802
Net Worth: $3,588,544
Earnings: ($2,277,257)
Emp.: 389
Fiscal Year-end: 03/31/21
Paper Products Mfr
N.A.I.C.S.: 322299
D. Khaitan *(Pres-Paper Machine Wire Unit-Nasik)*

SHAMARAN PETROLEUM CORP.
1055 Dunsmuir Street Suite 2800, Vancouver, V7X 1L2, BC, Canada
Tel.: (604) 689-7842
Web Site:
https://www.shamaranpetroleum.com
SHASF—(OTCIQ)
Rev.: $82,886,000
Assets: $450,411,000
Liabilities: $310,980,000
Net Worth: $139,431,000
Earnings: ($26,706,000)
Emp.: 7
Fiscal Year-end: 12/31/23
Oil & Gas Exploration Services
N.A.I.C.S.: 211120
Chris Bruijnzeels *(Chm)*

Subsidiaries:

ShaMaran Petroleum BV (1)
Amaliastraat 5, Hague, 2514 JC, Zuid-Holland, Netherlands
Tel.: (31) 7037178111
Oil & Gas Exploration Services
N.A.I.C.S.: 213112

SHAMAYM IMPROVE LTD.
30 Habarzel St, Tel Aviv, 6971042, Israel
Tel.: (972) 35094700
Web Site: https://www.shamaym.com
SHMM—(TAE)
Rev.: $765,414
Assets: $913,725
Liabilities: $1,415,596
Net Worth: ($501,871)
Earnings: ($1,622,201)
Fiscal Year-end: 06/30/23

Software Development Services
N.A.I.C.S.: 541511
Ofir Paldi (Chm & CEO)

SHAMROCK INDUSTRIAL CO., LTD.
83 E Hansraj Pragji Building Off Dr E Moses Road Worli, Mumbai, 400 018, India
Tel.: (91) 2224904433
Pharmaceutical Ingredient Mfr
N.A.I.C.S.: 325412
Kamlesh Khokhani (Mng Dir)

SHAMROCK VALLEY ENTERPRISES LTD.
Highway 41 South of Elk Point, PO Box 505, Elk Point, T0A 1A0, AB, Canada
Tel.: (780) 724-3177
Web Site:
http://www.shamrockvalley.ca
Year Founded: 1985
Heavy Civil Construction Services
N.A.I.C.S.: 237990
Murry Nielsen (Owner & Pres)

SHAMS TEXTILE MILLS LTD.
7-B-3 Aziz Avenue Gulberg 5, Lahore, Pakistan
Tel.: (92) 4235711138
Web Site: https://shams.com.pk
Year Founded: 1968
STML—(PSX)
Rev.: $11,482,279
Assets: $8,529,555
Liabilities: $5,254,912
Net Worth: $3,274,642
Earnings: ($531,923)
Emp.: 386
Fiscal Year-end: 06/30/23
Yarn Mfr
N.A.I.C.S.: 313110
Asif Bashir (Exec Dir)

SHAN DONG KEXING BIO-PRODUCTS CO., LTD.
No 2666 Chuangye Road, Mingshui Development Zone Zhangqiu District, Jinan, 250200, Shandong, China
Tel.: (86) 75586967773
Web Site: http://www.kexing.com
Year Founded: 1997
688136—(SHG)
Rev.: $184,748,934
Assets: $443,483,123
Liabilities: $189,943,074
Net Worth: $253,540,048
Earnings: $12,677,446)
Fiscal Year-end: 12/31/22
Pharmaceutical Product Mfr & Distr
N.A.I.C.S.: 325412
Xueqin Deng (Chm)

Subsidiaries:

Kexing Biopharm Co., Ltd. (1)
Mingshui Development Zone, Zhangqiu District, Jinan, Shandong, China
Tel.: (86) 4008889496
Pharmaceutical Preparation Mfr
N.A.I.C.S.: 325412

Shenzhen Kexing Pharmaceutical Co., Ltd. (1)
Floor 15-19 Building B Chuangyi Technology Building No 198, Keji Middle 1st Road Nanshan District, Shenzhen, Guangdong, China
Tel.: (86) 4008889496
Pharmaceutical Preparation Mfr
N.A.I.C.S.: 325412

Shenzhen Tong'an Pharmaceutical Co., Ltd. (1)
Yonghe Road Fuyong Street, Baoan District, Shenzhen, Guangdong, China
Tel.: (86) 4008889496
Pharmaceutical Preparation Mfr
N.A.I.C.S.: 325412

SHAN-LOONG TRANSPORTATION CO., LTD.
1th Floor No 1-2 DWC 1 Mn-Sheng Rd, Banqiao Dist, Taipei, 22069, Taiwan
Tel.: (886) 229599611
Web Site: https://w3.slc.com.tw
Year Founded: 1976
2616—(TAI)
Rev.: $537,097,138
Assets: $358,193,387
Liabilities: $191,924,549
Net Worth: $166,268,838
Earnings: $2,703,031
Emp.: 1,200
Fiscal Year-end: 12/31/23
Transportation Services
N.A.I.C.S.: 488490
Jen-Hao Cheng (Chm & Dir)

Subsidiaries:

Shan-Loong International & Customs Broker Co., Ltd. (1)
14-1F No 133 Sec 14 Minsheng Rd, Banqiao Dist, New Taipei City, 220, Taiwan
Tel.: (886) 229596668
Web Site: http://w3.slc.com.tw
Sales Range: $25-49.9 Million
Transportation Management & Customs Brokerage Services
N.A.I.C.S.: 488510
Cheng Wen Ming (Pres)

Shan-Loong Transportation Co., Ltd. - Chung Li Plant (1)
No 5-3 Ji Lin Road Chung Li Industrial Zone, Chung-li, 32063, Taoyuan Hsien, Taiwan
Tel.: (886) 34617151
Gasoline Stations Operation Services
N.A.I.C.S.: 424710

Shan-Loong Transportation Co., Ltd. - Kaohsiung Plant (1)
No 26-3 Yanhai 3rd Rd Neighborhood 1, Fengming Vil Xiaogang Dist, Kaohsiung, 812, Taiwan
Tel.: (886) 7 871 6691
Web Site: http://www.slc.com.tw
Gasoline Stations Operation Services
N.A.I.C.S.: 424710

Shan-Loong Transportation Co., Ltd. - Miao Li Plant (1)
No 1 Zhonglong 1st Rd, Zhongping Vil Tongluo Township, Miao-li, Taiwan
Tel.: (886) 37234529
Web Site: http://www.slc.com.tw
Gasoline Stations Operation Services
N.A.I.C.S.: 424710

Shan-Loong Transportation Co., Ltd. - Taichung Plant (1)
No 568 Tzi Li Road, Wu Chi Town, Taichung, 435, Taiwan
Tel.: (886) 426392151
Logistics & Vehicles Repair & Maintenance Services
N.A.I.C.S.: 541611

Shanghai Shan Tong Co., Ltd. (1)
No 399 Xiupu Rd, Pudong New District, Shanghai, China
Tel.: (86) 2168194520
Paper & Cardboard Mfr
N.A.I.C.S.: 322220

SHANAYA LIMITED
3A Tuas South Street 15, Singapore, 636845, Singapore
Tel.: (65) 63162023 SG
Web Site:
https://www.shanayagroup.com
Year Founded: 1981
SES—(CAT)
Rev.: $5,725,083
Assets: $16,964,061
Liabilities: $13,872,545
Net Worth: $3,091,515
Earnings: ($1,058,170)
Fiscal Year-end: 12/31/22
Holding Company
N.A.I.C.S.: 551112

Tung Kheng Choo (Mng Dir)

Subsidiaries:

Circuits Plus (M) Sdn. Bhd. (1)
Plo 146 Jalan Angkasa Mas Utama Kawasan Perindustrian Tebrau II, 81100, Johor Bahru, Johor, Malaysia
Tel.: (60) 2073515520
Automobile Equipment Mfr
N.A.I.C.S.: 336110

Circuits Plus Pte. Ltd. (1)
8 First Lok Yang Rd Jurong, Singapore, 629731, Singapore
Tel.: (65) 62686622
Semiconductor Product Mfr
N.A.I.C.S.: 334413

Shanaya Environmental Services Pte. Ltd. (1)
27 Kian Teck Drive, Singapore, 628844, Singapore
Tel.: (65) 63162023
Web Site: https://www.shanayagroup.com
Waste Management Services
N.A.I.C.S.: 562119

SHANDA GAMES LIMITED
No 1 Office Building No 690 Bibo Road, Pudong New Area, Shanghai, 201203, China
Tel.: (86) 2150504740 Ky
Web Site:
http://www.shandagames.com
Sales Range: $600-649.9 Million
Online Game Producer
N.A.I.C.S.: 541511
Yingfeng Zhang (Chm & Co-CEO)

SHANDA GROUP PTE. LTD.
8 Stevens Road, Singapore, 257819, Singapore
Tel.: (65) 6361 0060 SG
Web Site: http://www.shanda.com
Year Founded: 1999
Privater Equity Firm
N.A.I.C.S.: 523999
Tianqiao Chen (Chm & CEO)

SHANDA INTERACTIVE ENTERTAINMENT LIMITED
208 Juli Road, Pudong New Area, Shanghai, 201203, China
Tel.: (86) 2150504740 Ky
Web Site: http://www.shanda.com.cn
Year Founded: 1999
Sales Range: $800-899.9 Million
Emp.: 8,431
Online Computer Games Designer & Operator
N.A.I.C.S.: 541511
Tianqiao Chen (Chm, Pres & CEO)

Subsidiaries:

Actoz Soft Co. Ltd. (1)
1F 5F TNS Building 33 Seoae-ro, Jung-gu, Seoul, 6210, Korea (South)
Tel.: (82) 236710000
Web Site: https://www.actoz.com
Rev.: $45,296,220
Assets: $243,247,045
Liabilities: $85,940,418
Net Worth: $157,306,627
Earnings: $1,945,416
Emp.: 161
Fiscal Year-end: 12/31/2022
Online Gambling Services
N.A.I.C.S.: 541511

Cloudary Corporation (1)
35 Boxia Road, Pudong New Area, Shanghai, 201203, China
Tel.: (86) 2161870500
Web Site: http://www.cloudary.com.cn
Sales Range: $200-249.9 Million
Emp.: 829
Online Literature Library
N.A.I.C.S.: 519210
Tianqiao Chen (Chm)

Shengqu Information Technology (Shanghai) Co., Ltd. (1)
Zhangjiang High-Tech Park No 1 Building

No 690 Bibo Road, Shanghai, China
Tel.: (86) 2150504740
Sales Range: $350-399.9 Million
Emp.: 2,000
Computer Related Services
N.A.I.C.S.: 541519
Tianqiao Chen (Chm & CEO)

SHANDERS PROPERTIES PVT. LTD.
Old No 1097 New No 58 18th B Main 5th Block Rajajinagar, Bengaluru, 560 010, India
Tel.: (91) 8023156466
Web Site:
http://www.shandersproperties.com
Year Founded: 1983
Real Estate Support Services
N.A.I.C.S.: 531390
Sriram Chitturi (CEO)

SHANDONG AIRLINES CO., LTD.
Shandong Aviation Mansion No 5746 2nd Ring East Road, Jinan, 250014, Shandong, China
Tel.: (86) 05318569866
Web Site: https://www.sda.cn
Year Founded: 1994
200152—(SSE)
Rev.: $1,613,975,424
Assets: $3,432,441,767
Liabilities: $3,038,650,700
Net Worth: $393,791,067
Earnings: ($364,949,284)
Fiscal Year-end: 12/31/20
Oil Transportation Services
N.A.I.C.S.: 481211
Chuanyu Xu (Chm & Pres)

SHANDONG AOFU ENVIRONMENTAL TECHNOLOGY CO., LTD.
East Side of South Head Fumin Road, Economic Development Zone Linyi County, Dezhou, 251500, Shandong, China
Tel.: (86) 5344260688
Web Site: https://www.sdaofu.com
Year Founded: 2009
688021—(SHG)
Rev.: $28,609,561
Assets: $202,282,606
Liabilities: $71,303,811
Net Worth: $130,978,795
Earnings: ($1,100,357)
Fiscal Year-end: 12/31/22
Ceramic Products Mfr
N.A.I.C.S.: 327110
Jiqing Pan (Chm & Gen Mgr)

SHANDONG BAILONG CHUANGYUAN BIO-TECH CO., LTD.
Dexin Road, Yucheng National High-tech Industrial Development Zone, Dezhou, 251200, Shandong, China
Tel.: (86) 5348215088
Web Site:
https://www.chinabailong.com
Year Founded: 2005
605016—(SHG)
Rev.: $101,353,861
Assets: $206,662,257
Liabilities: $17,829,831
Net Worth: $188,832,426
Earnings: $21,172,531
Emp.: 500
Fiscal Year-end: 12/31/22
Food Product Mfr & Distr
N.A.I.C.S.: 311421
Baode Dou (Chm)

SHANDONG BOAN BIOTECHNOLOGY CO., LTD.
No 39 Keji Avenue High-Tech Indus-

SHANDONG BOAN BIOTECHNOLOGY CO., LTD.

Shandong Boan Biotechnology Co., Ltd.—(Continued)
trial Development Zone, Yantai, Shandong, China
Tel.: (86) 5354379111 CN
Web Site: https://www.boan-bio.com
Year Founded: 2013
6955—(HKG)
Rev.: $79,050,232
Assets: $337,454,064
Liabilities: $120,144,524
Net Worth: $217,309,540
Earnings: ($50,827,264)
Emp.: 745
Fiscal Year-end: 12/31/22
Information Technology Services
N.A.I.C.S.: 541512
Changlin Dou (COO)

Subsidiaries:

Nanjing Boan Biotechnology Co., Ltd. (1)
28 Gaoxin Road, Jiangbei new district, Nanjing, China
Tel.: (86) 53528993200
Pharmaceutical Product Mfr & Distr
N.A.I.C.S.: 325412

SHANDONG BOHUI PAPER CO., LTD.

North end of Gongye Road, Maqiao Town, 256405, Zibo, 256405, Huantai, China
Tel.: (86) 5338539966
Web Site: http://en.bohui.net
Year Founded: 1994
600966—(SHG)
Rev.: $2,577,994,305
Assets: $3,198,113,825
Liabilities: $2,282,975,099
Net Worth: $915,138,727
Earnings: $32,021,295
Emp.: 5,000
Fiscal Year-end: 12/31/22
Paper Products Mfr
N.A.I.C.S.: 322299
Lin Xinyang (Chm)

Subsidiaries:

Shandong Bohui Pulp Co., Ltd. (1)
North Head of Gongye Road Maqiao Town Huantai County, Zibo, 256405, Shandong, China
Tel.: (86) 5338533827
Paper Products Mfr
N.A.I.C.S.: 322299

SHANDONG CAOPU ARTS & CRAFTS CO., LTD.

No 2888 Qinghe Road, Development Zone Cao County, Beijing, 274400, Shandong, China
Tel.: (86) 530 343 1658 CN
Web Site: http://en.caopu.cc
Sales Range: $75-99.9 Million
Household Furniture Designer, Mfr & Distr
N.A.I.C.S.: 337122
Jinliang Li (CEO)

SHANDONG CHENMING PAPER HOLDINGS LIMITED

No 2199 Neosun Street, Shouguang, 262705, Shandong, China
Tel.: (86) 5362158073 CN
Web Site: https://www.chenmingpaper.com
Year Founded: 1958
200488—(SSE)
Rev.: $4,493,413,169
Assets: $11,835,862,843
Liabilities: $8,504,416,009
Net Worth: $3,331,446,834
Earnings: $26,576,330
Emp.: 13,677
Fiscal Year-end: 12/31/22
Paper Mfr

N.A.I.C.S.: 322120
Hu Changqing (Exec Dir & Exec Dir)

Subsidiaries:

Chenming GmbH (1)
Friedrich-Ebert-Str 31-33, 40210, Dusseldorf, Germany
Tel.: (49) 2119365690
Web Site: https://www.chenmingpaper.de
Paper Products Mfr
N.A.I.C.S.: 322299

SHANDONG CHIWAY INDUSTRY DEVELOPMENT CO., LTD.

No 1 Lipeng Road Subdistrict Office Jianggezhuang, Muping District, Yantai, 264114, Shandong, China
Tel.: (86) 2122192955
Web Site: http://www.lp.com.cn
Year Founded: 1995
002374—(SSE)
Rev.: $118,021,293
Assets: $541,636,047
Liabilities: $355,718,367
Net Worth: $185,917,680
Earnings: ($96,471,859)
Emp.: 1,300
Fiscal Year-end: 12/31/22
Aluminum Plates, Bottle Caps & Plastics Molded Products Mfr
N.A.I.C.S.: 331315
Qian Jianrong (Chm)

Subsidiaries:

Bozhou Lipeng Caps Making Co., Ltd. (1)
The North of Huatuo Road Economic Development Zone, Bozhou, 236800, Anhui, China
Tel.: (86) 5585316028
Aluminum Sheet Mfr
N.A.I.C.S.: 331315

Chengdu Seariver Closures Co., Ltd. (1)
No 277 Industry Road North, Pujiang, Chengdu, 611630, Sichuan, China
Tel.: (86) 2888550077
Aluminum Sheet Mfr
N.A.I.C.S.: 331315

Chongqing Huayu Landscape & Architecture Co., Ltd. (1)
No 506 Beibin 1st Road, Jiangbei District, Chongqing, 400021, China
Tel.: (86) 2363670488
Aluminum Sheet Mfr
N.A.I.C.S.: 331315

Daye Jinpeng Caps Making Co., Ltd. (1)
Luoqiao Office, Shilipu Village, Daye, 435100, Hubei, China
Tel.: (86) 7148754058
Aluminum Sheet Mfr
N.A.I.C.S.: 331315

Sichuan Luzhou Lipeng Caps Making Co., Ltd. (1)
No F006 Juyuan Road Liquor Concentration Zones, Jiangyang, Luzhou, 646015, Sichuan, China
Tel.: (86) 8303652377
Aluminum Sheet Mfr
N.A.I.C.S.: 331315

Xinjiang Junpeng Caps Making Co., Ltd. (1)
Production and Construction Corps Agri Division 4 Regiment 72, Xinjiang, 835811, China
Tel.: (86) 9995266330
Aluminum Sheet Mfr
N.A.I.C.S.: 331315

SHANDONG CYNDA CHEMICAL CO., LTD.

Youyun Building No 324 Zhongshan North Road, Gulou Ditrict, Nanjing, 256500, Jiangsu, China
Tel.: (86) 5432328187
Web Site: http://www.cynda.cn
Year Founded: 1998

603086—(SHG)
Rev.: $438,879,659
Assets: $470,734,482
Liabilities: $164,515,792
Net Worth: $306,218,690
Earnings: $53,520,340
Emp.: 1,400
Fiscal Year-end: 12/31/22
Pesticide Mfr & Distr
N.A.I.C.S.: 325320
Xianquan Wang (Founder & Chm)

SHANDONG DAWN POLYMER CO.,LTD.

Industrial Park Dawn Economic Zone Zhenxing Road North En, Longkou, 265700, Shandong, China
Tel.: (86) 5358866557
Web Site: http://www.dawnprene.com
Year Founded: 2002
002838—(SSE)
Rev.: $635,407,887
Assets: $694,217,586
Liabilities: $257,937,812
Net Worth: $436,279,774
Earnings: $21,386,697
Emp.: 100
Fiscal Year-end: 12/31/22
Plastic Product Mfr & Distr
N.A.I.C.S.: 325211
Yu Xiaoning (Chm)

Subsidiaries:

KPIC Dawn Polymer (Shanghai) Co., Ltd. (1)
No 568 Yungong Road, Fengxian District Shanghai Chemical Industry Park, Shanghai, 201424, China
Tel.: (86) 2137586622
Web Site: http://www.kpicdawn.com
Plastics Product Mfr
N.A.I.C.S.: 326199

SHANDONG DAYE CO., LTD.

Xinxing Economic Industrial Park, Zhucheng, Shandong, China
Tel.: (86) 5366528821
Web Site: https://www.sddaye.com
603278—(SHG)
Rev.: $731,909,398
Assets: $1,011,202,976
Liabilities: $723,264,394
Net Worth: $287,938,582
Earnings: ($35,835,205)
Emp.: 2,000
Fiscal Year-end: 12/31/22
Steel Product Mfr & Distr
N.A.I.C.S.: 314994
Dou Yong (Pres & Gen Mgr)

SHANDONG DELISI FOOD CO., LTD.

Delisi Industrial Park, Zhucheng, Weifang, 262216, Shandong, China
Tel.: (86) 4006030536
Web Site: https://www.delisi.com.cn
Year Founded: 2003
002330—(SSE)
Rev.: $431,707,101
Assets: $487,119,064
Liabilities: $150,873,363
Net Worth: $336,245,701
Earnings: $4,442,158
Emp.: 6,500
Fiscal Year-end: 12/31/22
Meat Packing & Production
N.A.I.C.S.: 311611
Zheng Simin (Chm)

SHANDONG DENGHAI SEEDS CO., LTD.

Chengshan Road West Side Academy of Agricultural Science, Laizhou City, Yantai, 261448, Shandong, China
Tel.: (86) 5352788889
Web Site: http://www.sddhzy.com

INTERNATIONAL PUBLIC

Year Founded: 2000
002041—(SSE)
Rev.: $186,141,478
Assets: $649,726,581
Liabilities: $146,128,938
Net Worth: $503,597,643
Earnings: $35,552,102
Fiscal Year-end: 12/31/22
Hybrid Seeds Distr
N.A.I.C.S.: 424910
Tang Shiwei (Chm)

SHANDONG DONGHONG PIPE INDUSTRY CO., LTD.

No 1 Donghong Road, Qufu, 273100, Shandong, China
Tel.: (86) 5374640989
Web Site: http://www.dhguanye.com
Year Founded: 2008
603856—(SHG)
Rev.: $400,345,489
Assets: $552,796,597
Liabilities: $255,112,781
Net Worth: $297,683,816
Earnings: $20,947,736
Emp.: 156
Fiscal Year-end: 12/31/22
Plastic Pipeline System Mfr
N.A.I.C.S.: 333998
Ni Liying (Chm)

SHANDONG DONGYUE ORGANOSILICON MATERIALS CO., LTD.

3799 Gongye Road, Tangshan Town Huantai County, Zibo, 256401, Shandong, China
Tel.: (86) 5338514338
Web Site: https://www.dyyjg.com
Year Founded: 2006
300821—(SSE)
Rev.: $945,453,628
Assets: $1,040,086,191
Liabilities: $304,294,339
Net Worth: $735,791,851
Earnings: $71,761,051
Fiscal Year-end: 12/31/22
Silicone Material Mfr
N.A.I.C.S.: 325211
Weidong Wang (Chm)

SHANDONG ENERGY GROUP CO., LTD.

No 10777 Jingshi Road, Jinan, 250014, Shandong, China
Tel.: (86) 531 6659 7812
Web Site: http://www.snjt.com
Year Founded: 2011
Sales Range: Less than $1 Million
Emp.: 200,000
Holding Company; Coal Mining, Coal By-Product Chemical Mfr & Clean Energy Development
N.A.I.C.S.: 551112
Weimin Li (Chm & Sec)

Subsidiaries:

Shandong Energy Linyi Mining Group Co., Ltd. (1)
No 69 Shangye Street, Luozhuang District, Linyi, 276017, Shandong, China (100%)
Tel.: (86) 539 710 8019
Web Site: http://www.lykyjt.com
Coal Mining
N.A.I.C.S.: 212115

Shandong Energy Longkou Mining Group Co., Ltd. (1)
No 369 South Road, Longgang Development Zone, Longkou, 265700, Shandong, China (100%)
Tel.: (86) 535 865 8222
Web Site: http://www.lkjt.com
Coal Mining
N.A.I.C.S.: 212115

Shandong Energy Xinwen Mining Group Co., Ltd. (1)

AND PRIVATE COMPANIES

Xinwen, Xintai, 271233, Shandong, China **(100%)**
Tel.: (86) 538 787 2147
Web Site: http://www.xwky.cn
Coal Mining
N.A.I.C.S.: 212115

Shandong Energy Zaozhuang Mining Group Co., Ltd. **(1)**
No 118 Taishan South Road, Xuecheng District, Zaozhuang, 277100, Shandong, China **(100%)**
Tel.: (86) 632 408 1104
Web Site: http://www.zkjt.com.cn
Coal Mining
N.A.I.C.S.: 212115

Shandong Energy Zibo Mining Group Co., Ltd. **(1)**
No 133 Zikuang Road, Zichuan District, Zibo, 255120, China
Tel.: (86) 53 3585 1605
Web Site: http://www.zbcoal.com
Emp.: 20,000
Coal Mining Services
N.A.I.C.S.: 212115

SHANDONG FENGXIANG CO., LTD.
Liumiao Village, Anle Town Yanggu County, Liaocheng, Shandong, China
Tel.: (86) 6357138018 **CN**
Web Site: https://www.fengxiang.com
Year Founded: 2010
9977—(HKG)
Poultry Meat Product Mfr & Distr
N.A.I.C.S.: 311615
Zhiguang Liu (Chm)

SHANDONG FENGYUAN CHEMICAL CO LTD
Yushan Road Economic Development Zone, Taierzhuang District, Zaozhuang, 277400, Shandong, China
Tel.: (86) 6326611799
Web Site: https://www.fengyuanhuaxue.com
002805—(SSE)
Rev.: $243,696,843
Assets: $696,341,740
Liabilities: $265,791,366
Net Worth: $430,550,373
Earnings: $21,186,922
Fiscal Year-end: 12/31/22
Acid Mfr & Distr
N.A.I.C.S.: 325199

Subsidiaries:

Qingdao Fengyuan Unite International Trade Co., Ltd. **(1)**
Room 701 Guohua Tower A No 2 Minjiang Road, Shinan District, Qingdao, Shandong, China
Tel.: (86) 53280971681
Web Site: http://www.fengyuanchem.com.cn
Oxalic Acid Mfr
N.A.I.C.S.: 325199

SHANDONG FIBERGLASS GROUP CO., LTD.
Industrial Park, Yishui County, Linyi, 276400, Shandong, China
Tel.: (86) 5397369857
Web Site: http://www.glasstex.com
Year Founded: 2008
605006—(SHG)
Rev.: $390,501,259
Assets: $708,458,358
Liabilities: $309,841,459
Net Worth: $398,616,899
Earnings: $75,224,832
Emp.: 1,000
Fiscal Year-end: 12/31/22
Fiberglass Product Mfr & Distr
N.A.I.C.S.: 337126
Zhang Shanjun (Chm)

SHANDONG GOLD MINING CO., LTD.
Building 3 Shuntai Square No 2000 Shunhua Road, Jinan, 250101, Shandong, China
Tel.: (86) 53167710376
Web Site: https://www.sd-gold.com
Year Founded: 1996
600547—(SHG)
Rev.: $8,322,248,540
Assets: $18,897,736,385
Liabilities: $11,420,116,105
Net Worth: $7,477,620,279
Earnings: $326,816,170
Fiscal Year-end: 12/31/23
Gold Exploration & Production Services
N.A.I.C.S.: 212220
Xiaoping Li (Chm-Supervisory Bd)

Subsidiaries:

Cardinal Resources Limited **(1)**
Suite 1 28 Ord Street, West Perth, 6005, WA, Australia **(95.51%)**
Tel.: (61) 865580573
Web Site: http://www.cardinalresources.com.au
Rev.: $257,279
Assets: $14,650,990
Liabilities: $27,408,603
Net Worth: ($12,757,613)
Earnings: ($19,022,777)
Emp.: 101
Fiscal Year-end: 06/30/2019
Gold Mining
N.A.I.C.S.: 212220
Archie Koimtsidis (Co-Founder, CEO & Mng Dir)

SHANDONG GOLD PHOENIX CO., LTD.
999 Fule Road, Laoling, 253600, Shandong, China
Tel.: (86) 5342119777
Web Site: https://www.chinabrake.com
Year Founded: 1999
603586—(SHG)
Rev.: $256,768,953
Assets: $399,992,805
Liabilities: $88,284,194
Net Worth: $311,708,611
Earnings: $27,133,507
Fiscal Year-end: 12/31/22
Braking Friction Product Mfr & Distr
N.A.I.C.S.: 336340

Subsidiaries:

Jinan Gold Phoenix Brake Systems Co., Ltd. **(1)**
No 6 Anshun Street, Jiyang, Jinan, 251400, Shandong, China
Tel.: (86) 53181173976
Braking Friction Product Mfr
N.A.I.C.S.: 336340

SHANDONG HAIHUA CO., LTD.
Binhai Economic Development Zone, Weifang, 262737, Shandong, China
Tel.: (86) 5365329379
Web Site: http://www.chinahaihua.com
Year Founded: 1998
000822—(CHIN)
Rev.: $1,363,616,762
Assets: $968,663,980
Liabilities: $389,304,237
Net Worth: $579,359,744
Earnings: $155,566,415
Fiscal Year-end: 12/31/22
Cement Product Mfr & Distr
N.A.I.C.S.: 327310
Sun Lingbo (Chm)

Subsidiaries:

Shandong Haihua Hualong new material Co., Ltd. **(1)**
No 02600 Chlor-alkali Road Binhai Economic Development Zone, Weifang, Shandong, China

Tel.: (86) 5365329070
Chemical Product Mfr & Distr
N.A.I.C.S.: 325998

Shandong Haihua Ocean Engineering Co., Ltd. **(1)**
No 14065 Yihe Street, Binhai Economic & Technological Development Zone, Weifang, Shandong, China
Tel.: (86) 5365329339
Emp.: 259
Housing Construction Services
N.A.I.C.S.: 236220

Shandong Haihua Plastic knitting Co., Ltd. **(1)**
Economic Development Zone Yihe Street No 14020, Binhai, Weifang, China
Tel.: (86) 5365329380
Emp.: 497
Chemical Product Mfr & Distr
N.A.I.C.S.: 325998

SHANDONG HAIWANG CHEMICAL CO., LTD.
Haiwang Avenue, Economic Tech Dev Zone, Weifang, 261108, Shandong, China
Tel.: (86) 5367579292 **VG**
Web Site: http://www.sdhwchem.com
Sales Range: $50-74.9 Million
Emp.: 669
Holding Company; Bromine & Crude Salt Chemical Mfr & Sales
N.A.I.C.S.: 551112
Chunbin Yang (Chm)

SHANDONG HEAD GROUP CO., LTD.
No 999 Heda Road, Zhoucun District, Zibo, 255300, Shandong, China
Tel.: (86) 5333190661
Web Site: https://www.sdhead.com
Year Founded: 1992
002810—(SSE)
Rev.: $241,977,055
Assets: $467,720,515
Liabilities: $203,525,188
Net Worth: $264,195,327
Earnings: $49,673,366
Emp.: 1,800
Fiscal Year-end: 12/31/22
Cellulose Ether Mfr & Distr
N.A.I.C.S.: 325998
Jack Bee (Chm)

Subsidiaries:

Shandong Head Europe BV **(1)**
De Bouw 1a, 3991 SX, Houten, Netherlands
Tel.: (31) 307603653
Web Site: http://www.sdhead.eu
Emp.: 739
Organic Chemical Distr
N.A.I.C.S.: 424690

Shandong Healsee Capsule Ltd. **(1)**
No 1111 Head Road, Zhoucun District, Zibo, Shandong, China **(100%)**
Tel.: (86) 13561623550
Web Site: http://www.healsee.net
Pharmaceutical Product Mfr & Distr
N.A.I.C.S.: 325412

SHANDONG HEAVY INDUSTRY GROUP CO., LTD.
Economic Development Zone, Linyi, 220022, China
Tel.: (86) 539 2771028 **CN**
Web Site: http://www.shig.com.cn
Sales Range: $1-4.9 Billion
Emp.: 20,000
Holding Company; Construction & Agricultural Equipment Mfr & Distr
N.A.I.C.S.: 551112
Xuguang Tan (Chm & CEO)

Subsidiaries:

Shandong Shantui Machinery Co., Ltd. **(1)**
6666 Chongwen Avenue High-tech Development Zone, Jining, 27200, Shandong, China
Tel.: (86) 537 2908585
Web Site: http://www.shantuimachinery.com
Forklift Mfr
N.A.I.C.S.: 333924
Xiu Wen Zhang (Gen Mgr)

Strong Construction Machinery Co., Ltd **(1)**
66 Binhe East Road Linyi Economic & Technological Development Zone, Linyi, 276006, Shandong, China
Tel.: (86) 539 8152370
Web Site: http://www.strongest.cn
Construction Machinery Mfr
N.A.I.C.S.: 333120

Weichai Group Holdings Limited **(1)**
197 Jia Fushou East Street High Tech Development Zone, Weifang, Shandong, China
Tel.: (86) 5368197777
Web Site: https://en.weichai.com
Sales Range: $10-24.9 Million
Holding Company; Construction, Commercial & Industrial Machinery Mfr & Distr
N.A.I.C.S.: 551112
Xuguang Tan (Chm & CEO)

Subsidiary (US):

MAT Holding, Inc. **(2)**
6700 Wildlife Way, Long Grove, IL 60047
Tel.: (847) 821-9630
Web Site: http://www.matholdingsinc.com
Automotive & Consumer Products Mfr, Distr & Marketer
N.A.I.C.S.: 423120

Affiliate (Domestic):

Weichai Power Co., Ltd. **(2)**
197 A Fushou East Street High-Tech Development Zone, Weifang, Shandong, China **(16.83%)**
Tel.: (86) 5362297072
Web Site: https://en.weichaipower.com
Rev.: $30,257,609,899
Assets: $41,481,633,546
Liabilities: $29,158,443,056
Net Worth: $12,323,190,489
Earnings: $1,410,624,387
Emp.: 95,000
Fiscal Year-end: 12/31/2020
Automobile Parts Mfr & Distr
N.A.I.C.S.: 336310
Kui Jiang (Sr President)

Subsidiary (Domestic):

Baoji Fast Gear Co., Ltd. **(3)**
Caijiapo Town Qishan County, Baoji, 722405, Shaanxi, China
Tel.: (86) 9178730624
Automotive Gears Mfr
N.A.I.C.S.: 333612

Subsidiary (Non-US):

Ferretti S.p.A. **(3)**
Via Ansaldo 9B, Forli, 47122, Italy **(75%)**
Tel.: (39) 0543474411
Web Site: http://www.ferrettigroup.com
Sales Range: $700-749.9 Million
Emp.: 3,000
Yacht Builder
N.A.I.C.S.: 336612
Norberto Ferretti (Chm)

Subsidiary (US):

Allied Marine LLC **(4)**
3660 Northwest 21st St, Miami, FL 33142
Tel.: (305) 633-9761
Web Site: http://www.alliedmarine.com
Rev.: $17,600,000
Emp.: 80
Boat Dealers
N.A.I.C.S.: 441222
Bruce Schattenburg (Dir-Luxury Yacht Charters)

Allied Richard Bertram Marine Group Inc. **(4)**
1445 SE 16th St, Fort Lauderdale, FL 33316
Tel.: (954) 462-5527
Web Site: http://www.alliedmarine.com

SHANDONG HEAVY INDUSTRY GROUP CO., LTD.

Shandong Heavy Industry Group Co., Ltd.—(Continued)
Sales Range: $25-49.9 Million
Emp.: 175
Boat & Yacht Sales & Services
N.A.I.C.S.: 441222
Jessica Cortada (Dir-PR)

Subsidiary (Domestic):

Searock Inc. (5)
1445 SE 16th St, Fort Lauderdale, FL 33316-1712
Tel.: (954) 462-5557
Sales Range: $25-49.9 Million
Emp.: 80
Marketer of Boats & Related Services
N.A.I.C.S.: 441222

Subsidiary (Non-US):

Linde Hydraulics LP (3)
Grossostheimer Strasse 198, 63741, Aschaffenburg, Germany (70%)
Tel.: (49) 6021 99 0
Web Site: http://www.linde-hydraulics.com
Hydraulic Equipment Mfr
N.A.I.C.S.: 332912

Subsidiary (US):

Linde Hydraulics Corporation (4)
5089 Western Reserve Rd, Canfield, OH 44406
Tel.: (330) 533-6801
Web Site: http://www.lindeamerica.com
Sales Range: $25-49.9 Million
Emp.: 55
High Pressure Hydraulic Piston Pumps, Motors & Power Units Distr
N.A.I.C.S.: 333996

Subsidiary (Non-US):

Linde Hydraulics Ltd. (4)
12-13 Eyston Way, Abingdon, OX14 1TR, Oxon, United Kingdom
Tel.: (44) 1235 522828
Web Site: http://www.lindehydraulics.co.uk
Sales Range: $10-24.9 Million
Emp.: 15
High Pressure Hydraulic Piston Pumps, Motors & Power Units Distr
N.A.I.C.S.: 333996
John Chapman (Mng Dir)

Subsidiary (Domestic):

Shaanxi Hande Axle Co., Ltd. (3)
Jingwei Industrial Park Economic And Technology Development Zone, Xi'an, 710201, Shaanxi, China
Tel.: (86) 29 86957527
Web Site: http://www.hdcq.com
Sales Range: $800-899.9 Million
Emp.: 450
Automobile Parts Mfr
N.A.I.C.S.: 336390
Fang Hongwei (Chm)

Weichai Power (Weifang) Casting and Forging Co., Ltd. (3)
Cangshang Village, Weifang, 261100, Shandong, China
Tel.: (86) 5362208350
Aluminium Casting & Forging Services
N.A.I.C.S.: 331523

Zhuzhou Torch Sparkplugs Co., Ltd. (3)
No 68 Hongqi Road, Zhuzhou, 412-0001, Hunan, China
Tel.: (86) 731 28450437
Web Site: http://www.torchsparkplug.com
Emp.: 1,500
Automotive Spark Plug Mfr
N.A.I.C.S.: 336320
Chen Guangyun (Mng Dir)

SHANDONG HENGYUAN PETROCHEMICAL CO. LTD.

111 Hengyuan Road, Linyi, 251500, Shandong, China
Tel.: (86) 5344233715
Web Site: http://www.es.hyshjt.com
Petroleum Product Mfr
N.A.I.C.S.: 324199

Subsidiaries:

Shell Refining Company (Federation of Malaya) Berhad (1)
Batu 1 Jalan Pantai, 71000, Port Dickson, Negeri Sembilan, Malaysia (51.02%)
Tel.: (60) 66412000
Web Site: https://hrc.com.my
Sales Range: $1-9.9 Million
Petroleum Mfr
N.A.I.C.S.: 324110
Wang YouDe (Chm)

SHANDONG HI-SPEED GROUP CO., LTD.

No 8 Long Ao North Road, Lixia District, Jinan, 250098, Shandong, China
Tel.: (86) 53188275566 CN
Web Site: http://www.sdhsg.com
Sales Range: $5-14.9 Billion
Emp.: 70,000
Holding Company; Civil Infrastructure Development, Engineering & Construction Services
N.A.I.C.S.: 551112
Liang Sun (Chm & Pres)

Subsidiaries:

Shandong Hi-Speed Road & Bridge Co., Ltd. (1)
No 14677 Jingshi Road, Lixia District, Jinan, 250014, Shandong, China
Tel.: (86) 53168906079
Web Site: http://www.sdlqgf.com
Rev.: $9,128,658,657
Assets: $14,468,221,488
Liabilities: $11,245,723,960
Net Worth: $3,222,497,529
Earnings: $351,651,288
Fiscal Year-end: 12/31/2022
Road & Bridges Construction Services
N.A.I.C.S.: 237310
Lin Cunyou (Chm)

Shandong Hi-speed Company Limited (1)
No 5006 Olympic Sports Center Road, Jinan, 250014, Shandong, China
Tel.: (86) 53189260052
Web Site: https://www.sdecl.com.cn
Rev.: $2,595,484,284
Assets: $19,241,304,886
Liabilities: $11,904,822,900
Net Worth: $7,336,481,986
Earnings: $400,878,939
Fiscal Year-end: 12/31/2022
Toll Collection Services
N.A.I.C.S.: 488490
Fu Baixian (Chm)

SHANDONG HI-SPEED HOLDINGS GROUP LIMITED

Rooms 1405-1410 14/F China Resources Building 26 Harbour Road, Wanchai, China (Hong Kong)
Tel.: (852) 39030988
Web Site: http://www.cifg.com.hk
0412—(HKG)
Rev.: $137,448,956
Assets: $2,960,149,170
Liabilities: $1,849,308,533
Net Worth: $1,110,840,637
Earnings: $1,426,261
Emp.: 163
Fiscal Year-end: 12/31/21
Property Investment Services
N.A.I.C.S.: 531311
Wang Zhenjiang (VP)

SHANDONG HIGH SPEED RENEWABLE ENERGY GROUP LIMITED

No 4 12F Building No 8 Renhe Chuntian Garden No 9 1st Section, Yinghua South Road Shunqing District, Nanchong, 250000, Sichuan, China
Tel.: (86) 53183178628
Web Site: http://www.000803.cn
Year Founded: 1988
000803—(SSE)
Rev.: $251,438,148
Assets: $783,843,372
Liabilities: $576,132,804
Net Worth: $207,710,568
Earnings: $11,931,192
Fiscal Year-end: 12/31/22
Silk Product Mfr
N.A.I.C.S.: 313110
Xie Xin (Chm)

SHANDONG HIKING INTERNATIONAL CO., LTD.

Xinhuajin Development Building No 131 Songling Road, Laoshan District, Qingdao, 266101, Shandong, China
Tel.: (86) 53285967330
Web Site: https://www.hikinginternational.com
Year Founded: 2007
600735—(SHG)
Rev.: $261,869,433
Assets: $326,676,009
Liabilities: $110,117,335
Net Worth: $216,558,674
Earnings: $7,304,984
Fiscal Year-end: 12/31/22
Textile Products Mfr
N.A.I.C.S.: 315250
Zhang Hang (Chm)

Subsidiaries:

Hiking Group Shandong Haishun International Co., Ltd. (1)
12f golden Plaza 20 Hongkong Middle Road, Qingdao, 266071, China
Tel.: (86) 53285025111
Commodity Trading Services
N.A.I.C.S.: 523160

Hiking Textile (Shandong) Co., Ltd. (1)
FL 10 CITIC Building No 22 Hong Kong Road M, Qingdao, China
Tel.: (86) 53266062788
Web Site: http://www.hikingtextile.cn
Textile Product Mfr & Distr
N.A.I.C.S.: 313210
Peter Wang (Pres)

SHANDONG HOMEY AQUATIC DEVELOPMENT CO., LTD.

Shazuizi Haodangjia Industrial Park, Hushan Town Rongcheng, Weihai, 264305, Shandong, China
Tel.: (86) 6317438073
Web Site: https://www.sdhaodangjia.com
Year Founded: 1978
600467—(SHG)
Rev.: $167,493,774
Assets: $928,360,672
Liabilities: $455,896,827
Net Worth: $472,463,845
Earnings: $8,371,589
Fiscal Year-end: 12/31/22
Aquaculture & Food Processing Services
N.A.I.C.S.: 311710
Chuanqin Tang (Chm, Pres & Gen Mgr)

SHANDONG HONGYU AGRICULTURAL MACHINERY CO., LTD.

No 3 Hongyu Road Hutouya Economic & Technological Industrial Park, Laizhou, 261400, Shandong, China
Tel.: (86) 4006668287
Web Site: https://www.sdhynj.net
Year Founded: 1999
002890—(SSE)
Rev.: $55,819,530
Assets: $103,806,284
Liabilities: $22,262,287
Net Worth: $81,543,997
Earnings: $3,174,612

INTERNATIONAL PUBLIC

Fiscal Year-end: 12/31/22
Agricultural Machinery Parts Mfr & Distr
N.A.I.C.S.: 333111
Qiujie Liu (Gen Mgr)

SHANDONG HUALU-HENGSHENG CHEMICAL CO., LTD.

No 24 Tianqu West Road, Dezhou, 253024, Shandong, China
Tel.: (86) 5342465426
Web Site: http://www.hl-hengsheng.com
Year Founded: 2000
600426—(SSE)
Rev.: $4,246,437,789
Assets: $4,914,764,576
Liabilities: $994,675,678
Net Worth: $3,920,088,898
Earnings: $883,028,208
Fiscal Year-end: 12/31/22
Chemical Product Mfr & Distr
N.A.I.C.S.: 325998
Chang Huaichún (Chm)

SHANDONG HUATAI PAPER INDUSTRY SHAREHOLDING CO., LTD.

Huatai Industrial Park, Guangrao County, Dongying, 257335, Shandong, China
Tel.: (86) 5466888808
Web Site: https://www.huataipaper.com
Year Founded: 1993
600308—(SHG)
Rev.: $2,130,486,729
Assets: $2,163,717,682
Liabilities: $885,617,760
Net Worth: $1,278,099,922
Earnings: $59,815,777
Fiscal Year-end: 12/31/22
Paper Products Mfr
N.A.I.C.S.: 322120
Xiaoliang Li (Chm)

SHANDONG HUIFA FOODSTUFF CO., LTD.

No 139 Shungeng Road, Zhucheng, 262200, Shandong, China
Tel.: (86) 5366857000
Web Site: https://www.huifafoods.com
Year Founded: 2005
603536—(SHG)
Rev.: $221,903,183
Assets: $225,571,975
Liabilities: $154,308,600
Net Worth: $71,263,376
Earnings: $(16,830,422)
Fiscal Year-end: 12/31/22
Meat Product Mfr & Distr
N.A.I.C.S.: 311612
Zengyu Hui (Chm & Gen Mgr)

SHANDONG HUMON SMELTING CO., LTD.

Shuidao Town, Mouping District, Yantai, 264109, Shandong, China
Tel.: (86) 5354631769
Web Site: http://www.hbyl.cn
Year Founded: 1994
002237—(SSE)
Rev.: $7,026,567,463
Assets: $2,790,280,004
Liabilities: $1,640,012,316
Net Worth: $1,150,267,688
Earnings: $70,075,156
Emp.: 5,000
Fiscal Year-end: 12/31/22
Chemical Products Mfr
N.A.I.C.S.: 325180
Shengli Qu (Vice Chm, Pres & Gen Mgr)

SHANDONG INTERNATIONAL TRUST CO., LTD.
1/F 2/F 13/F 32-35/F & 40/F Tower A
No 2788 Aoti West Rd, Lixia District,
Jinan, 250101, Shangdong, China
Tel.: (86) 53186566888
Web Site: http://www.sitic.com.cn
Year Founded: 1987
1697—(HKG)
Rev.: $202,905,518
Assets: $2,029,921,733
Liabilities: $495,339,062
Net Worth: $1,534,582,670
Earnings: $39,372,232
Emp.: 377
Fiscal Year-end: 12/31/22
Finance Management Services
N.A.I.C.S.: 531390
Jiguang Fu *(Chief Risk Mgmt Officer)*

SHANDONG IRON AND STEEL COMPANY LTD.
No 99 Fuqian Street, Gangcheng District, Jinan, 271104, Shandong, China
Tel.: (86) 53177920789
Year Founded: 2000
600022—(SHG)
Rev.: $14,361,434,568
Assets: $9,689,212,297
Liabilities: $5,222,614,054
Net Worth: $4,466,598,243
Earnings: $77,943,509
Fiscal Year-end: 12/31/22
Iron & Steel Product Mfr
N.A.I.C.S.: 331110
Guo Yunyi *(Sec)*

SHANDONG JINCHENG PHARMACEUTICAL GROUP CO., LTD.
No 1 Shuangshan Road Zichuan Economic Development Zone, Zibo, Shandong, China
Tel.: (86) 5335414988
Web Site: https://www.jinchengpharm.com
Year Founded: 2004
300233—(CHIN)
Rev.: $492,203,088
Assets: $817,981,632
Liabilities: $304,214,508
Net Worth: $513,767,124
Earnings: $38,379,744
Emp.: 3,800
Fiscal Year-end: 12/31/22
Pharmaceutical & Chemical Mfr
N.A.I.C.S.: 325412
Yeqing Zhao *(Chm)*

Subsidiaries:

Shandong Jincheng Zhonghua Biopharmaceutical Co., Ltd. (1)
Zichuan Economic Development Zone, Zibo, 255130, Shandong, China
Tel.: (86) 533 5415882
Pharmaceuticals Product Mfr
N.A.I.C.S.: 325412
Yang Hui *(Gen Mgr)*

SHANDONG JINDU TALIN FOODS CO., LTD.
2 Xinhui Rd, Zhaoyuan Development Zone, Yantai, 265400, Shandong, China
Tel.: (86) 5358038818
Web Site: http://www.jdtl.cn
Year Founded: 1990
Sales Range: $25-49.9 Million
Emp.: 300
Pea Product Manufacturing
N.A.I.C.S.: 311999
Xuehua Chen *(Mktg Dir)*

SHANDONG JINJING SCIENCE & TECHNOLOGY CO., LTD.
Wangzhuang Hi-tech Development Zone, Baoshi Town, Zibo, 255086, Shandong, China
Tel.: (86) 5333586666
Web Site: http://www.cnggg.cn
Year Founded: 1999
600586—(SHG)
Rev.: $1,047,182,456
Assets: $1,609,131,476
Liabilities: $846,095,833
Net Worth: $763,035,643
Earnings: $49,974,510
Fiscal Year-end: 12/31/22
Glass Product Mfr & Distr
N.A.I.C.S.: 327211
Gang Wang *(Chm)*

Subsidiaries:

Jinjing Technology Malaysia Sdn. Bhd. (1)
No 1 Jalan Hi-Tech 16 Zon Industri Fasa 4, Kulim Hi-Tech Park, 09090, Kulim, Kedah, Malaysia
Tel.: (60) 123389689
Optical Glass Mfr & Distr
N.A.I.C.S.: 327211

Qingdao Jinjing Co., Ltd. (1)
Jiangshan Bei Road 201, QingDao Economic and Technical Development Aras, Qingdao, 266500, Shandong, China
Tel.: (86) 53286907666
Web Site: https://www.jinjing.com.cn
Flat Glass Mfr
N.A.I.C.S.: 327211
Deng Wenji *(Asst Gen Mgr)*

Shandong Haitian Bio-Chemical Co., Ltd. (1)
No 1 Jinjing Avenue, Coastal Economic Development Zone Changyi City, Weifang, 261300, Shandong, China
Tel.: (86) 5367857088
Flat Glass Mfr
N.A.I.C.S.: 327211

Shandong Hualiang Glass Technology Ltd. (1)
No 216 Shuangshan Str, Boshan District, Zibo, 255200, Shandong, China
Tel.: (86) 5334192809
Web Site: http://www.cnggg.cn
Emp.: 100
Flat Glass Mfr
N.A.I.C.S.: 327211
Sun Chenghai *(Dir)*

Shandong Jinjing Science & Technology Stock Co., Ltd. (1)
High-new Technology Development Zone, Zibo, 255086, Shandong, China
Tel.: (86) 5333581586
Flat Glass Mfr
N.A.I.C.S.: 327211

Zibo Jinjing New Energy Co., Ltd. (1)
No 216 Shuangshan Str, Boshan district, Zibo, 255200, Shandong, China
Tel.: (86) 5334192822
Glass Product Mfr & Distr
N.A.I.C.S.: 327211

SHANDONG JINLING MINING CO., LTD.
Zhongbu Town, Zhangdian District, Zibo, 255081, China
Tel.: (86) 5333088888
000655—(SSE)
Rev.: $192,734,198
Assets: $495,471,516
Liabilities: $59,924,896
Net Worth: $435,546,620
Earnings: $28,517,051
Fiscal Year-end: 12/31/22
Mineral Mining Services
N.A.I.C.S.: 212210

SHANDONG JINTAI GROUP CO., LTD.
No 29 Hung House Road, Jinan, 250100, Shandong, China
Tel.: (86) 5318 890 2341
600385—(SHG)
Rev.: $7,522,611
Assets: $20,862,606
Liabilities: $19,007,233
Net Worth: $1,855,373
Earnings: ($1,397,275)
Fiscal Year-end: 12/31/20
Gold Jewelry Whslr
N.A.I.C.S.: 423940
Yun Lin *(Chm & Pres)*

SHANDONG KAISHENG NEW MATERIALS CO., LTD.
East of Zhangbo Highway, Shuangyang Town Zichuan District, Zibo, 255185, Shandong, China
Tel.: (86) 5332275366
Web Site: https://www.ksxc.cn
Year Founded: 2005
301069—(CHIN)
Rev.: $141,871,392
Assets: $234,261,612
Liabilities: $34,768,656
Net Worth: $199,492,956
Earnings: $32,926,608
Fiscal Year-end: 12/31/22
Chemical Product Mfr & Distr
N.A.I.C.S.: 327120
Jiarong Wang *(Chm)*

SHANDONG KUNTAI NEW MATERIAL TECHNOLOGY CO., LTD.
No 75 Baiyunshan Road, Fushan District, Yantai, 264000, Shandong, China
Tel.: (86) 5356362388
Web Site: https://www.chinakuntai.com
Year Founded: 2009
001260—(SSE)
Rev.: $63,103,384
Assets: $100,250,570
Liabilities: $40,225,344
Net Worth: $60,025,226
Earnings: $9,028,029
Fiscal Year-end: 12/31/22
Automotive Interior Product Mfr
N.A.I.C.S.: 314110
Ming Zhang *(Chm)*

SHANDONG LIANCHENG PRECISION MANUFACTURING CO., LTD.
No 6 North Ring Road Yanzhou Economic Development Zone, Jining, 272100, Shandong, China
Tel.: (86) 5376050926
Web Site: https://www.lmc-ind.cn
Year Founded: 1995
002921—(SSE)
Rev.: $172,662,923
Assets: $318,033,238
Liabilities: $139,319,018
Net Worth: $178,714,219
Earnings: $3,618,894
Emp.: 1,800
Fiscal Year-end: 12/31/22
Motor Vehicle Product Mfr & Distr
N.A.I.C.S.: 336390
Guo Yuanqiang *(Chm & Gen Mgr)*

Subsidiaries:

Shandong Liancheng Agricultural Equipment Co., Ltd. (1)
Liancheng Industrial Park, Yanzhou District, Jining, 272100, China
Tel.: (86) 53760509266
Web Site: https://www.lmc-t.com
Agricultural Machinery Mfr & Distr
N.A.I.C.S.: 333111

Shanghai Siwei Cleaning Equipment Technology Co., Ltd. (1)
No 1 Room 906 168 Lane Taihong Road, Minhang District, Shanghai, China
Tel.: (86) 4001011077
Web Site: https://www.swpclean.com
Cleaning & Sanitation Machine Equipment Mfr
N.A.I.C.S.: 325612

SHANDONG LINGLONG TYRE CO., LTD.
No 777 Jinlong Road, Zhaoyuan, 265406, Shandong, China
Tel.: (86) 5358238901
Web Site: https://en.linglong.cn
Year Founded: 1975
601966—(SHG)
Rev.: $2,387,626,352
Assets: $5,248,461,877
Liabilities: $2,546,036,303
Net Worth: $2,702,425,574
Earnings: $40,942,999
Fiscal Year-end: 12/31/22
Tire Mfr & Distr
N.A.I.C.S.: 326211
Wang Feng *(Chm & Pres)*

Subsidiaries:

Linglong International Tire (Thailand) Co., Ltd. (1)
Charn Issara Tower II 2922/1 New Phetchaburi Rd Huai Khwang, Bang Kapi, Bangkok, 10310, Thailand
Tel.: (66) 38109088
Web Site: https://linglongtireth.com
Car Radial Tire Mfr
N.A.I.C.S.: 326199

SHANDONG LINK SCIENCE & TECHNOLOGY CO., LTD.
No 577 Luxing Road, Qingzhou, Weifang, 262500, Shandong, China
Tel.: (86) 5363532728
Web Site: https://www.sdlkgroup.com
Year Founded: 2001
001207—(SSE)
Rev.: $263,744,135
Assets: $323,865,448
Liabilities: $82,203,228
Net Worth: $241,662,220
Earnings: $23,193,346
Emp.: 500
Fiscal Year-end: 12/31/23
Chemical Product Mfr & Distr
N.A.I.C.S.: 327120
Xiaolin Wu *(Chm)*

Subsidiaries:

Shandong Link Advanced Materials Co., Ltd. (1)
No 4888 Donghong Road Dongcheng Street, Linqu County, Weifang, China
Tel.: (86) 5363353538
Web Site: https://www.sdlkxcl.com
Emp.: 155
Rubber Products Mfr
N.A.I.C.S.: 326299

SHANDONG LINUO TECHNICAL GLASS CO., LTD.
Yuhuangmiao Town, Shanghe County, Jinan, 251604, Shandong, China
Tel.: (86) 53184759599
Web Site: https://www.linuoglass.com
Year Founded: 1995
301188—(CHIN)
Rev.: $115,411,608
Assets: $230,254,596
Liabilities: $29,308,500
Net Worth: $200,946,096
Earnings: $16,377,660
Fiscal Year-end: 12/31/22
Pharmaceutical Product Mfr & Distr
N.A.I.C.S.: 325412
Qingfa Sun *(Chm & Chm-Supervisory Bd)*

Subsidiaries:

Linuo Group Holdings Co.,Ltd. (1)
No 30099 East Jingshi Road, Jinan, 250103, Shandong, China

SHANDONG LINUO TECHNICAL GLASS CO., LTD.

Shandong Linuo Technical Glass Co., Ltd.—(Continued)

Tel.: (86) 53188729999
Web Site: https://www.linuo.com
Emp.: 7,500
Pharmaceuticals Product Mfr
N.A.I.C.S.: 325411

SHANDONG LIULIUSHUN FOOD CO., LTD
No 669 Jincheng Road, Zhaoyuan, 265400, Shandong, China
Tel.: (86) 535 8130866 CN
Web Site: http://en.liuliushun.com
Year Founded: 2001
Emp.: 100
Production of Vermicelli & Noodle Products
N.A.I.C.S.: 311999
Gi Fong (Mgr-Sls)

SHANDONG LONGDA MEISHI CO., LTD.
No 17 Taishan Road, Laiyang, 265200, Shandong, China
Tel.: (86) 4006582266
Web Site: https://www.longdameishi.com
Year Founded: 1996
002726—(SSE)
Rev.: $2,262,729,517
Assets: $1,119,988,434
Liabilities: $628,066,034
Net Worth: $491,922,400
Earnings: $10,582,734
Emp.: 6,000
Fiscal Year-end: 12/31/22
Pig Farming, Slaughtering & Processing
N.A.I.C.S.: 112210
Yang Xiaochu (Chm & Gen Mgr)

SHANDONG LONGERTEK TECHNOLOGY CO., LTD.
20th Floor Building G2 288 Ningxia Road, Qingdao Software Park, Qingdao, 266071, China
Tel.: (86) 53285922957
Web Site: https://www.longertek.com
Year Founded: 2000
300594—(SSE)
Rev.: $108,210,099
Assets: $243,848,489
Liabilities: $117,561,244
Net Worth: $126,287,245
Earnings: ($8,142,091)
Emp.: 800
Fiscal Year-end: 12/31/22
Air Conditioner Product Mfr
N.A.I.C.S.: 333415
Jingmao Li (Chm)

SHANDONG LONGHUA NEW MATERIAL CO., LTD.
289 WeiGao Road, Gaoqing, Zibo, 256300, Shandong, China
Tel.: (86) 15653393017
Web Site: https://www.longhuapu.com.cn
Year Founded: 2011
301149—(CHIN)
Rev.: $707,184,829
Assets: $372,577,083
Liabilities: $112,897,802
Net Worth: $259,679,281
Earnings: $34,933,732
Fiscal Year-end: 12/31/23
Chemical Product Mfr & Distr
N.A.I.C.S.: 327120
Zhigang Han (Chm)

SHANDONG LONGJI MACHINERY CO., LTD.
Longkou Economic Development Zone, Longkou, 265716, Shandong, China
Tel.: (86) 5358841279
Web Site: https://www.sdljjx.com.cn
Year Founded: 1994
002363—(SSE)
Rev.: $319,323,149
Assets: $502,111,944
Liabilities: $194,457,019
Net Worth: $307,654,926
Earnings: $6,399,053
Emp.: 1,300
Fiscal Year-end: 12/31/22
Automobile Brake Parts & Components Mfr
N.A.I.C.S.: 336340
Zhang Haiyan (Chm & Gen Mgr)

SHANDONG LONGLIVE BIO-TECHNOLOGY CO., LTD.
High-Tech Development Zone, Yucheng, 251200, Shandong, China
Tel.: (86) 532 81926176
Web Site: http://www.en.longlive.cn
Year Founded: 2001
Rev.: $124,453,840
Assets: $217,067,270
Liabilities: $687,258,530
Net Worth: ($470,191,260)
Earnings: ($408,255,120)
Fiscal Year-end: 12/31/18
Functional & Starch Sugar Mfr
N.A.I.C.S.: 325199

SHANDONG LONGQUAN PIPELINE ENGINEERING CO., LTD.
No 333 Xiwaihuan Road, Boshan District, Zibo, 255200, Shandong, China
Tel.: (86) 51968196652
Web Site: https://www.lq-pipe.cn
Year Founded: 2000
002671—(CHIN)
Rev.: $139,909,049
Assets: $371,324,781
Liabilities: $150,509,418
Net Worth: $220,815,364
Earnings: ($89,962,648)
Emp.: 400
Fiscal Year-end: 12/31/22
Prestressed Concrete Cylinder Pipes Mfr
N.A.I.C.S.: 327332
Fu,Bo (Chm & Pres)

Subsidiaries:

Anhui Longquan Pipeline Engineering Co., Ltd. (1)
Jade Lake Road Hefei Modern Industrial Park, Yingzhou District, Fuyang, China
Tel.: (86) 5582264678
Concrete Pipe Mfr
N.A.I.C.S.: 327332

Changzhou Longquan Pipeline Engineering Co., Ltd. (1)
No 98 Binjiang No 2 Road Jiangbian Industrial Park, Xinbei District, Changzhou, 213127, Jiangsu, China
Tel.: (86) 51985720898
Concrete Pipe Mfr
N.A.I.C.S.: 327332

SHANDONG LUBEI CHEMICAL CO., LTD.
Lubei High-tech Development Zone, Wudi County, Binzhou, 251909, Shandong, China
Tel.: (86) 5436451577
Web Site: https://www.lubeichem.com
Year Founded: 1996
600727—(SHG)
Rev.: $687,672,040
Assets: $1,073,374,272
Liabilities: $624,563,349
Net Worth: $448,810,924
Earnings: ($12,397,629)
Emp.: 2,000
Fiscal Year-end: 12/31/22
Chemical Product Mfr & Distr
N.A.I.C.S.: 325180
Chen Shuchang (Chm)

SHANDONG LUKANG PHARMACEUTICAL CO., LTD.
88 Deyuan Road High-Tech Zone, Jining, 272104, Shandong, China
Tel.: (86) 5372983821
Web Site: https://www.lkpc.com
Year Founded: 1966
600789—(SHG)
Rev.: $789,250,443
Assets: $1,225,364,222
Liabilities: $732,957,765
Net Worth: $492,406,457
Earnings: $19,377,039
Emp.: 6,000
Fiscal Year-end: 12/31/22
Pharmaceutical Product Mfr & Whslr
N.A.I.C.S.: 325412
Wang Chaoran (Mgr)

Subsidiaries:

Shandong Lukang Biological Pesticides Co., Ltd. (1)
North of Jinneng Avenue, Qihe, Dezhou, Shandong, China
Tel.: (86) 5345337908
Web Site: https://en.lkbp.com
Emp.: 300
Biological Pesticide Mfr
N.A.I.C.S.: 325320

Shandong Lukang Zerun Pharma Co., Ltd. (1)
16 North Ji'anqiao Road, Jining, Shandong, China
Tel.: (86) 5372985814
Animal Pharmaceutical Mfr & Distr
N.A.I.C.S.: 325412

SHANDONG LUOXIN PHARMACEUTICAL GROUP STOCK CO., LTD.
National New & Hi-Tech Industrial Development Zone, No 18 Huxi Rd, Linyi, 276017, Shandong, China
Tel.: (86) 5398241226 CN
Web Site: http://www.luoxin.cn
Sales Range: $550-599.9 Million
Pharmaceutical Product Mfr & Distr
N.A.I.C.S.: 325412
Minghua Li (CEO & Gen Mgr)

SHANDONG MEICHEN ECOLOGY & ENVIRONMENT CO.,LTD.
No 12001 Mizhou East Road, Zhucheng, Weifang, 262200, Shandong, China
Tel.: (86) 5366151511 CN
Web Site: https://www.meichen.cc
Year Founded: 2004
300237—(CHIN)
Rev.: $237,191,794
Assets: $1,174,455,372
Liabilities: $1,105,020,041
Net Worth: $69,435,332
Earnings: ($195,890,884)
Fiscal Year-end: 12/31/23
Ecological Gardening, Water Management & Soil Repair
N.A.I.C.S.: 541620
Sun Laihua (Chm)

SHANDONG MINHE ANIMAL HUSBANDRY CO., LTD.
No 2-3 Nanguan Road, Penglai District, Yantai, 265600, Shandong, China
Tel.: (86) 5355637723
Web Site: http://www.minhe.cn
Year Founded: 1997
002234—(SSE)
Rev.: $225,853,561

INTERNATIONAL PUBLIC

Assets: $555,256,265
Liabilities: $180,481,855
Net Worth: $374,774,409
Earnings: ($63,469,252)
Fiscal Year-end: 12/31/22
Animal Breeding Services
N.A.I.C.S.: 311611
Sun Xianfa (Chm, Vice Chm & Gen Mgr)

SHANDONG MINING MACHINERY GROUP CO., LTD.
Mining Machinery Industrial Park Economic Development Zone, Changle County, Shandong, China
Tel.: (86) 5366231141
Web Site: https://www.sdkjjt.com
Year Founded: 1955
002526—(SSE)
Rev.: $337,661,775
Assets: $612,636,902
Liabilities: $203,579,565
Net Worth: $409,057,338
Earnings: $16,194,298
Emp.: 2,000
Fiscal Year-end: 12/31/22
Coal Mining Machinery Mfr
N.A.I.C.S.: 333131

Subsidiaries:

Beijing Sankuangtong Technology Co., Ltd. (1)
Room 307 Block B Technology Fortune Center No 8 Xueqing Road, Haidian, Beijing, 100192, China
Tel.: (86) 1082734669
Mining Product Mfr
N.A.I.C.S.: 333131

Changle Jieyuan Mental Surface Treatment Co., Ltd. (1)
West of Rentuan Road South of Keji Street Economic Development Zone, Changle, Weifang, Shandong, China
Tel.: (86) 5366852016
Mining Product Mfr
N.A.I.C.S.: 333131

Shandong Changkongyan Aviation Technology Company (1)
No 2407 Donghuan Road Economic Development Zone, Changle, Weifang, Shandong, China
Tel.: (86) 5366228015
High End Composite Material Mfr
N.A.I.C.S.: 325211

Shandong Mining Machinery Cosmec Construction Materials Machinery Co., Ltd. (1)
Economic Development Zone, Mine Machinery Industrial Park Changle County, Weifang, shandong, China
Tel.: (86) 18866180070
Web Site: http://en.chinacosmec.cn
Automation Machinery Equipment Mfr
N.A.I.C.S.: 333998

Xinjiang Changmei Mining Machinery Co., Ltd. (1)
20th Floor Building B NAGA Shangyuan No 887 Northwest Road, Urumqi, Xinjiang, China
Tel.: (86) 9914537966
Mining Product Mfr
N.A.I.C.S.: 333131

Yulin Tianning Mining Service Co., Ltd. (1)
No 4 Row 2 North District North East Ring Road, Liusha Xing High-tech Industrial Park Company, Yulin, China
Tel.: (86) 9127997034
Mining Product Mfr
N.A.I.C.S.: 333131

SHANDONG MOLONG PETROLEUM MACHINERY COMPANY LIMITED
No 99 XingShang Road, Shouguang, 262700, Shandong, China
Tel.: (86) 5365103360 CN

Web Site:
https://www.molonggroup.com
Year Founded: 2001
002490—(SSE)
Rev.: $388,296,600
Assets: $567,020,226
Liabilities: $439,206,637
Net Worth: $127,813,589
Earnings: ($59,665,746)
Emp.: 2,501
Fiscal Year-end: 12/31/22
Petroleum Extraction Machinery Mfr
N.A.I.C.S.: 333132
Liu Min (Exec Dir)

SHANDONG NANSHAN ALUMINIUM CO., LTD.
Qiansong Village Dongjiang Town, Longkou, Yantai, 265706, Shandong, China
Tel.: (86) 5358616188
Web Site: http://www.600219.com.cn
Year Founded: 1993
600219—(SHG)
Rev.: $4,907,151,639
Assets: $9,087,529,698
Liabilities: $2,064,944,751
Net Worth: $7,022,584,947
Earnings: $493,579,443
Fiscal Year-end: 12/31/22
Aluminum Product Mfr & Distr
N.A.I.C.S.: 331313
Lv Zhengfeng (Chm)

SHANDONG NANSHAN ZHISHANG SCI-TECH CO., LTD.
Nanshan Industrial Park, Dongjiang Town Longkou, Yantai, 265706, Shandong, China
Tel.: (86) 535123456
Web Site:
http://www.nanshanchina.com
Year Founded: 2007
300918—(SSE)
Rev.: $229,378,250
Assets: $449,827,658
Liabilities: $195,350,637
Net Worth: $254,477,022
Earnings: $26,215,628
Fiscal Year-end: 12/31/22
Textile Product Mfr & Distr
N.A.I.C.S.: 313310
Liang Zhao (Chm & Gen Mgr)

SHANDONG NEW BEIYANG INFORMATION TECHNOLOGY CO., LTD.
No126 Kunlun Road, Huancui District, Weihai, 264203, Shandong, China
Tel.: (86) 6315673777
Web Site: https://www.snbc.com.cn
Year Founded: 2002
002376—(SSE)
Rev.: $319,623,998
Assets: $821,656,195
Liabilities: $320,136,079
Net Worth: $501,520,116
Earnings: ($3,603,801)
Emp.: 5,000
Fiscal Year-end: 12/31/22
Printer Mfr & Distr
N.A.I.C.S.: 334118
Qiangzi Cong (Board of Directors & Chm)

Subsidiaries:

SNBC Europe B.V.   (1)
Meerheide 115, Eersel, Netherlands
Tel.: (31) 497331080
Web Site: http://www.snbc.com.cn
Emp.: 10
Printer Distr
N.A.I.C.S.: 423430
Raina Tu (Mgr-Fin)

Shandong Hualing Electronics Co., Ltd.   (1)
159 Torch Road Hi-Tech IDZ, Weihai, 264209, Shandong, China
Tel.: (86) 631 5684114
Web Site: http://www.shecl.com.cn
Emp.: 700
Thermal Print Head Mfr & Distr
N.A.I.C.S.: 334118
Katagiri Jo (Pres)

Weihai Hualing Opto Electronics Co., Ltd.   (1)
No 179 KeJi Road Hi-Tech IDZ, Weihai, Shandong, China
Tel.: (86) 6315698128
Web Site: https://www.w-hec.com
Emp.: 400
Electronics Mfr
N.A.I.C.S.: 334419
Cong Qiangzi (Chm)

SHANDONG ORIENTAL OCEAN SCI-TECH CO., LTD.
No 18 Aucma Street, Laishan District, Yantai, 264003, Shandong, China
Tel.: (86) 5356729111
Web Site: http://en.dfhy.cc
Year Founded: 2001
002086—(SSE)
Rev.: $88,354,043
Assets: $281,075,437
Liabilities: $443,079,908
Net Worth: ($162,004,471)
Earnings: ($222,520,718)
Fiscal Year-end: 12/31/22
Aquatic Products Mfr
N.A.I.C.S.: 112990
Zhang Le (Chm)

Subsidiaries:

Avioq Inc.   (1)
104 T.W. Alexander Dr, Research Triangle Park, NC 27709   (100%)
Tel.: (919) 314-5535
Web Site: http://www.avioq.com
Sales Range: $1-9.9 Million
Emp.: 60
Medical Products & Highly Flexible Contract Manufacturing Services
N.A.I.C.S.: 339112
Chamroen Chetty (Pres & CEO)

SHANDONG PHARMACEUTICAL GLASS CO., LTD.
Yaobo Rd, Yiyuan County, Zibo, 256100, Shandong, China
Tel.: (86) 5333259167
Web Site:
https://www.pharmglass.com
Year Founded: 1970
600529—(SHG)
Rev.: $587,894,014
Assets: $1,233,309,051
Liabilities: $255,889,249
Net Worth: $977,419,802
Earnings: $86,807,509
Fiscal Year-end: 12/31/22
Pharmaceutical Glass Product Mfr
N.A.I.C.S.: 327910
Hu Yonggang (Chm)

SHANDONG POLYMER BIO-CHEMICALS CO., LTD.
No 892 XiSi Road, Dongying District, Dongying, 257081, Shandong, China
Tel.: (86) 5467775226
Web Site: https://en.slcapam.com
Year Founded: 1996
002476—(SSE)
Rev.: $83,156,786
Assets: $146,011,634
Liabilities: $23,918,993
Net Worth: $122,092,640
Earnings: $4,160,108
Emp.: 500
Fiscal Year-end: 12/31/22
Chemicals Mfr
N.A.I.C.S.: 325998

SHANDONG PUBLISHING & MEDIA CO., LTD.
No 189 Yingxiongshan Road, Jinan, 250002, Shandong, China
Tel.: (86) 53182098193
Web Site: https://en.sdcbcm.com
Year Founded: 2011
601019—(SHG)
Rev.: $1,574,589,412
Assets: $2,887,511,356
Liabilities: $1,011,656,889
Net Worth: $1,875,854,467
Earnings: $235,934,506
Emp.: 10,000
Fiscal Year-end: 12/31/22
Books Publishing Services
N.A.I.C.S.: 513130
Tao Xucheng (Chm)

SHANDONG RIKE CHEMICAL CO., LTD.
No 3999 Yingxuan Street, Changle County, Weifang, 262400, Shandong, China
Tel.: (86) 5366295617
Web Site: https://www.rikechem.com
Year Founded: 2003
300214—(CHIN)
Rev.: $387,436,608
Assets: $427,797,396
Liabilities: $73,156,824
Net Worth: $354,640,572
Earnings: $27,588,600
Emp.: 1,500
Fiscal Year-end: 12/31/22
Plastic Materials & Resins Mfr
N.A.I.C.S.: 325211
Dongri Zhao (Founder & Vice Chm)

Subsidiaries:

Shandong Rike Plastic Co., Ltd.   (1)
East Of Gaoxin 2nd Road South Of Jiankang East St Export Proc, Weifang, 261000, Shandong, China
Tel.: (86) 5367522336
Plastics Product Mfr
N.A.I.C.S.: 326199

SHANDONG RUIFENG CHEMICAL CO., LTD.
Dongling Road, Economic Development Zone Yiyuan, Zibo, 256100, Shandong, China
Tel.: (86) 5333231093
Web Site:
https://www.ruifengchemical.com
Year Founded: 1994
300243—(CHIN)
Rev.: $257,146,812
Assets: $272,586,600
Liabilities: $141,243,804
Net Worth: $131,342,796
Earnings: $8,584,056
Emp.: 400
Fiscal Year-end: 12/31/22
Polyvinyl Chloride (PVC) Additives Mfr & Sales
N.A.I.C.S.: 325998
Zhou Shibin (Chm)

SHANDONG RUYI WOOLEN GARMENT GROUP CO., LTD.
Ruyi Industrial Park No 96 Hongxing East Road, Hi-Tech Zone, Jining, 272073, China
Tel.: (86) 5372933069
Web Site:
http://www.shandongruyi.com
021930—(SSE)
Sales Range: $75-99.9 Million
Emp.: 3,809
Worsted Fabric Product Mfr & Distr
N.A.I.C.S.: 313210
Ya Fu Qiu (Chm)

SHANDONG SACRED SUN POWER SOURCES COMPANY LIMITED
No 1 Shengyang Road, Qufu, Jining, 273100, Shandong, China
Tel.: (86) 5374422313
Web Site:
https://www.sacredsun.com
Year Founded: 1991
002580—(SSE)
Rev.: $392,594,918
Assets: $425,559,996
Liabilities: $144,828,076
Net Worth: $280,731,920
Earnings: $19,129,374
Emp.: 1,400
Fiscal Year-end: 12/31/22
Battery Mfr
N.A.I.C.S.: 335910
Li Wei (Chm)

Subsidiaries:

FnS Power Technology Inc.   (1)
B611 Block B HengYu center No 21 Dengliand Road, Nanshan District, Shenzhen, 515054, Guangdong, China
Tel.: (86) 75526452336
Web Site: http://www.fnspower.com
Battery Mfr & Distr
N.A.I.C.S.: 335910

Sacred Sun Asia Pacific Pte Ltd.   (1)
6 Genting Road 03-00 Jubilee Industrial Building, Singapore, 349471, Singapore
Tel.: (65) 86601585
Battery Distr
N.A.I.C.S.: 423120

Sacred Sun Europe SPRL   (1)
Paul Dejaerlaan 4b, 1060, Brussels, Belgium
Tel.: (32) 674444555
Battery Distr
N.A.I.C.S.: 423120

SHANDONG SAHNDA OUMASOFT CO., LTD.
No 128 Bole Road, High-tech Zone, Jinan, 250101, Shandong, China
Tel.: (86) 53166680735
Web Site: https://www.oumasoft.com
Year Founded: 2005
301185—(CHIN)
Rev.: $31,136,113
Assets: $149,838,577
Liabilities: $4,368,606
Net Worth: $145,469,971
Earnings: $10,794,042
Fiscal Year-end: 12/31/23
Software Development Services
N.A.I.C.S.: 541511
Lei Ma (Chm)

SHANDONG SANXING GROUP CO., LTD.
Handian Industrial Park, Zouping, 256209, Shandong, China
Tel.: (86) 5434610263
Web Site: http://www.chinasanxing.cn
Year Founded: 2003
Emp.: 4,000
Holding Company; Oil Machinery Repair Services
N.A.I.C.S.: 551112

Subsidiaries:

Changshouhua Food Company Limited   (1)
Handian Industrial Park, Zouping County, Shandong, China   (52.14%)
Tel.: (86) 5434610263
Web Site: http://www.chinacornoil.com
Rev.: $429,796,700
Assets: $551,943,998
Liabilities: $77,779,429
Net Worth: $474,164,569
Earnings: $45,869,846
Emp.: 4,301
Fiscal Year-end: 12/31/2019
Edible Corn Oil Refiner & Whslr
N.A.I.C.S.: 311225

SHANDONG SANXING GROUP CO., LTD.

Shandong Sanxing Group Co., Ltd.—(Continued)

Mingxing Wang *(Co-Founder, Chm & CEO)*

SHANDONG SANYUAN BIO-TECHNOLOGY CO., LTD

No 89 Zhangfu Road, Binbei, Binzhou, 256600, Shandong, China
Tel.: (86) 5433529851
Web Site:
https://www.sanyuanbz.com
Year Founded: 2007
301206—(CHIN)
Rev.: $70,352,225
Assets: $677,524,843
Liabilities: $38,366,746
Net Worth: $639,158,097
Earnings: $8,292,169
Fiscal Year-end: 12/31/23
Biotechnology Research & Development Services
N.A.I.C.S.: 541714
Zaijian Nie *(Chm)*

SHANDONG SHENGLI CO., LTD.

Jinan Pharmaceutical Valley North Section of Gangxing 3rd Road, Hi-tech Zone, Jinan, 250101, Shandong, China
Tel.: (86) 53188725656
Web Site: https://www.vicome.com
Year Founded: 1994
000407—(SSE)
Rev.: $652,192,721
Assets: $1,004,981,206
Liabilities: $570,370,591
Net Worth: $434,610,615
Earnings: $21,300,884
Emp.: 2,000
Fiscal Year-end: 12/31/22
Agrochemical Product Mfr
N.A.I.C.S.: 325998
Xu Tieliang *(Chm)*

SHANDONG SHIDA SHENGHUA CHEMICAL GROUP CO., LTD.

No 198 Tongxing Road, Kenli District, Dongying, 257503, Shandong, China
Tel.: (86) 5462169377
Web Site: http://www.sinodmc.com
603026—(SHG)
Rev.: $1,167,580,861
Assets: $899,341,326
Liabilities: $274,166,170
Net Worth: $625,175,156
Earnings: $125,029,991
Fiscal Year-end: 12/31/22
Organic Chemical Product Mfr & distr
N.A.I.C.S.: 325199
Tianming Guo *(Pres & CEO)*

SHANDONG SHUANGYI TECHNOLOGY CO., LTD.

No 1 Shuangyi Rd Xinhua Industrial Park Dezhou, Shandong, 253007, China
Tel.: (86) 13375511202
Web Site:
https://www.shuangyitec.com
Year Founded: 2000
300690—(CHIN)
Rev.: $105,530,891
Assets: $250,849,765
Liabilities: $50,454,597
Net Worth: $200,395,169
Earnings: $12,386,180
Emp.: 2,000
Fiscal Year-end: 12/31/23
Composite Product Mfr & Distr
N.A.I.C.S.: 335991

SHANDONG SINO-AGRI UNITED BIOTECHNOLOGY CO., LTD.

14th Floor Block A Golden Times Square No 9999 Jingshi Road, Pilot Free Trade Zone, Jinan, 250014, Shandong, China
Tel.: (86) 53188977085
Web Site: https://www.sdznlh.com
Year Founded: 2006
003042—(SSE)
Rev.: $271,452,702
Assets: $496,563,575
Liabilities: $260,807,279
Net Worth: $235,756,296
Earnings: $10,268,561
Fiscal Year-end: 12/31/22
Agricultural Chemical Mfr & Distr
N.A.I.C.S.: 325320
Xu Hui *(Gen Mgr)*

SHANDONG SINOBIOWAY BIOMEDICINE CORP., LTD.

No 28 Nanzhi 1st Road Xingyuan Road, Zibo Science and Technology Industrial Park Zhangdian District, Zibo, 255068, Shandong, China
Tel.: (86) 5332988888
Year Founded: 2000
002581—(SSE)
Rev.: $50,134,102
Assets: $401,251,378
Liabilities: $54,680,128
Net Worth: $346,571,250
Earnings: $(2,062,448)
Fiscal Year-end: 12/31/22
Chemical Products Mfr; Trimethyl Orthoformate & Triethyl Orthoformate Supplier & Mfr
N.A.I.C.S.: 325998

SHANDONG SINOCERA FUNCTIONAL MATERIAL CO., LTD.

No 24 Liaohe Road, Dongying District, Dongying, 257091, Shandong, China
Tel.: (86) 5468073788
Web Site: https://www.en.sinocera.cn
Year Founded: 2005
300285—(SSE)
Rev.: $444,631,356
Assets: $1,053,249,912
Liabilities: $167,984,388
Net Worth: $885,265,524
Earnings: $69,784,416
Emp.: 370
Fiscal Year-end: 12/31/22
Electronic Components
N.A.I.C.S.: 334419
Zhang Xi *(Chm)*

SHANDONG SUN PAPER INDUSTRY CO., LTD.

No 1 Youyi Road, Yanzhou District, Jining, 272100, Shandong, China
Tel.: (86) 5377925888
Web Site:
http://www.sunpapergroup.com
Year Founded: 1982
002078—(SSE)
Rev.: $5,583,276,382
Assets: $6,741,160,307
Liabilities: $3,487,573,613
Net Worth: $3,253,586,694
Earnings: $394,350,620
Emp.: 14,000
Fiscal Year-end: 12/31/22
Paper Products Mfr
N.A.I.C.S.: 322120
Hongxin Li *(Chm & Gen Mgr)*

SHANDONG SUNWAY CHEMICAL GROUP CO., LTD.

No 22 Lianchang Middle Road, Linzi, Zibo, 255434, Shandong, China
Tel.: (86) 5337993801
Web Site:
https://www.sdsunway.com.cn
Year Founded: 1969
002469—(SSE)
Rev.: $366,423,445
Assets: $469,759,586
Liabilities: $88,470,182
Net Worth: $381,289,405
Earnings: $38,437,055
Fiscal Year-end: 12/31/22
Chemical Engineering Design Services
N.A.I.C.S.: 541330
Siqiu Qu *(Chm & Sec)*

SHANDONG SWAN COTTON INDUSTRIAL MACHINERY STOCK CO., LTD

No 99 East Road of Dawei Village, Tianqiao District, Jinan, 250032, Shandong, China
Tel.: (86) 53158675811
Web Site: https://www.sdmj.com.cn
Year Founded: 1946
603029—(SHG)
Rev.: $90,875,669
Assets: $262,294,873
Liabilities: $150,187,663
Net Worth: $112,107,210
Earnings: $8,057,261
Fiscal Year-end: 12/31/22
Cotton Industrial Machinery Mfr & Distr
N.A.I.C.S.: 333111
Wang Xinting *(Chm, Pres & Gen Mgr)*

Subsidiaries:

Shandong Swan USA, Inc. (1)
5320 Perimeter Pkwy Ct, Montgomery, AL 36116
Tel.: (334) 356-8824
Web Site: https://www.usaswan.com
Blade Mfr & Distr
N.A.I.C.S.: 332216
Fred Peek *(Dir-Ops)*

SHANDONG TAIHE WATER TREATMENT TECHNOLOGIES CO., LTD.

No 1 Shiliquan East Road, Shizhong, Zaozhuang, 277100, Shandong, China
Tel.: (86) 6325113066
Web Site: https://www.thwater.net
Year Founded: 2006
300801—(SSE)
Rev.: $382,873,060
Assets: $408,253,084
Liabilities: $74,904,102
Net Worth: $333,348,982
Earnings: $55,826,985
Fiscal Year-end: 12/31/22
Chemical Products Mfr
N.A.I.C.S.: 325520
Zhongfa Cheng *(Chm)*

SHANDONG TONGDA ISLAND NEW MATERIALS CO., LTD.

No 522 Tongda Street, Changyi City, Weifang, 261300, Shandong, China
Tel.: (86) 5367191939
Web Site: https://www.td300321.com
Year Founded: 2002
300321—(SSE)
Rev.: $65,197,548
Assets: $96,600,816
Liabilities: $8,263,944
Net Worth: $88,336,872
Earnings: $1,599,156
Emp.: 600
Fiscal Year-end: 12/31/22
Synthetic Leather Product Mfr
N.A.I.C.S.: 313320
Zhang Zhenjiang *(Chm)*

SHANDONG WEIDA MACHINERY CO., LTD.

2 Zhonghan Rd, Manshan Town

INTERNATIONAL PUBLIC

Wendeng City, Weihai, 264414, Shandong, China
Tel.: (86) 6313909518
Web Site:
https://www.weidapeacock.com
Year Founded: 1998
002026—(SSE)
Rev.: $346,391,595
Assets: $708,886,185
Liabilities: $244,481,679
Net Worth: $464,404,506
Earnings: $28,976,117
Emp.: 5,000
Fiscal Year-end: 12/31/22
Industrial Machinery Mfr
N.A.I.C.S.: 333998
Zhang Hongjiang *(Sec)*

Subsidiaries:

Shandong Weida Saw Blade Co., Ltd. (1)
No 121 Longshan Road Wendeng, Shandong, 264400, China
Tel.: (86) 6313909399
Saw Blades Mfr
N.A.I.C.S.: 332216

WEIHAI WEIDA PRECISION CASTING CO., LTD (1)
No 1 Wenming Rd Erlongshan Industrial Zone Wendeng, Shandong, 264414, China
Tel.: (86) 6313909886
Saw Blades Mfr
N.A.I.C.S.: 332216

SHANDONG WEIFANG RAINBOW CHEMICAL CO., LTD.

30th floor Hanyu Financial Centre Building A5-5 No 7000 Jingshi Road, Jinan, 250101, Shandong, China
Tel.: (86) 53188875231
Web Site:
https://www.rainbowagro.com
Year Founded: 2000
301035—(CHIN)
Rev.: $1,617,576,418
Assets: $2,098,303,388
Liabilities: $1,134,966,490
Net Worth: $963,336,899
Earnings: $108,608,563
Emp.: 4,400
Fiscal Year-end: 12/31/23
Agricultural Chemical Product Mfr & Distr
N.A.I.C.S.: 325320
Wencai Wang *(Chm)*

SHANDONG WEIGAO GROUP MEDICAL POLYMER COMPANY LIMITED

No 18 Xinshan Road Torch Hi-Tech Industry Development Zone, Weihai, 264210, China
Tel.: (86) 6315621999 CN
Web Site:
http://www.weigaogroup.com
Year Founded: 1988
SHWGF—(OTCIQ)
Rev.: $2,014,974,868
Assets: $4,652,536,956
Liabilities: $1,449,306,542
Net Worth: $3,203,230,415
Earnings: $371,783,676
Emp.: 11,123
Fiscal Year-end: 12/31/21
Medical Devices Mfr & Distr
N.A.I.C.S.: 339112
Phillis Miu Ling Wong *(Sec)*

Subsidiaries:

Argon Medical Devices, Inc. (1)
7800 Dallas Pkwy Ste 200, Plano, TX 75024
Tel.: (903) 675-9321
Web Site: https://www.argonmedical.com
Emp.: 1,000
Medical Instrument Mfr
N.A.I.C.S.: 339112

George A. Leondis (CEO)

Plant (Domestic):

Argon Medical Devices, Inc. - Gainesville Plant (2)
3600 SW 47th Ave, Gainesville, FL 32608
Tel.: (352) 338-0440
Medical Supplies Mfr
N.A.I.C.S.: 339113

Subsidiary (Domestic):

Matrex Mold & Tool, Inc. (2)
1200 Northport Road, Portage, WI 53901
Tel.: (608) 742-6565
Web Site: http://www.matrexmold.com
Rev.: $2,333,333
Emp.: 20
Industrial Mold Mfr
N.A.I.C.S.: 333511
Edward Palmer (Plant Mgr)

Rad Source Technologies, Inc. (1)
4907 Golden Pkwy Ste 400, Buford, GA 30518
Tel.: (678) 765-7900
Web Site: https://radsource.com
Radiation Equipment Mfr & Distr
N.A.I.C.S.: 334517

Shandong Weigao Orthopaedic Device Company Limited (1)
No 26 Xiangjiang Road Tourist Resorts, Weihai, Shandong, China
Tel.: (86) 631 5788927
Web Site: http://en.wegortho.com
Orthopedic Equipment Mfr & Distr
N.A.I.C.S.: 339112
Gong Jianbo (Exec Dir)

Weigao Nikkiso (Weihai) Dialysis Equipment Co., Ltd. (1)
No 20 Xingshan Road Chucun Weigao Industry Park, Weihai, Shandong, China
Tel.: (86) 6315716298
Medical Product Mfr & Distr
N.A.I.C.S.: 336340

SHANDONG WEIQIAO GROUP CO., LTD.

No 1 Weifang Road, Zouping economic development zone, Shandong, 256200, China
Tel.: (86) 5434161111
Web Site: https://www.weiqiaocy.com
Sales Range: $25-49.9 Billion
Cotton Yarn Mfr
N.A.I.C.S.: 313110
Zhang Shiping (Chm)

Subsidiaries:

Weiqiao Textile Company Limited (1)
No 1 Weifang Road Zouping Economic Development Zone, Zouping, 256200, Shandong, China
Tel.: (86) 5434161066
Web Site: https://www.wqfz.com
Rev.: $2,170,478,122
Assets: $3,495,430,576
Liabilities: $858,564,941
Net Worth: $2,636,865,635
Earnings: $3,086,309
Emp.: 50,000
Fiscal Year-end: 12/31/2019
Cotton Yarn, Grey Fabric & Denim Mfr
N.A.I.C.S.: 313110
Yanhong Zhang (Exec Dir)

SHANDONG WIT DYNE HEALTH CO., LTD.

4th Floor Walter Plaza No 17703 Jingshi Road, Jinan, 250061, Shandong, China
Tel.: (86) 53185198090
Web Site: https://www.sd-wit.com
Year Founded: 1993
000915—(SSE)
Rev.: $328,687,014
Assets: $658,545,189
Liabilities: $88,315,447
Net Worth: $570,229,742
Earnings: $73,971,706
Fiscal Year-end: 12/31/22

Pharmaceuticals Mfr
N.A.I.C.S.: 325412
Xiaoping Zhu (Chm)

SHANDONG WOHUA PHARMACEUTICAL CO., LTD.

No 3517 Liyuan Street High-tech Industrial Development Zone, Weifang, 261205, Shandong, China
Tel.: (86) 5368553373
Web Site: https://www.wohua.cn
Year Founded: 2003
002107—(SSE)
Rev.: $142,480,517
Assets: $154,438,779
Liabilities: $43,552,192
Net Worth: $110,886,586
Earnings: $15,076,980
Fiscal Year-end: 12/31/22
Pharmaceuticals Mfr
N.A.I.C.S.: 325412
Yingzi Zeng (Pres)

SHANDONG XIANTAN CO., LTD.

Muping Industrial Park, Yantai, 264117, Shandong, China
Tel.: (86) 5354658757
Web Site: https://en.sdxiantan.com
Year Founded: 2001
002746—(SSE)
Rev.: $716,348,473
Assets: $852,369,046
Liabilities: $208,647,485
Net Worth: $643,721,561
Earnings: $18,021,084
Emp.: 10,000
Fiscal Year-end: 12/31/22
Chicken Production
N.A.I.C.S.: 112320
Wang Shouchun (Pres)

SHANDONG XINCHAO ENERGY CORPORATION LIMITED

10th Floor Building A Gemdale Center No 91 Jianguo Road, Chaoyang District, Beijing, 264003, China
Tel.: (86) 1087934800
Web Site: https://xinchaoenergy.com
Year Founded: 1985
600777—(SHG)
Rev.: $1,313,718,518
Assets: $4,397,117,512
Liabilities: $2,025,352,106
Net Worth: $2,371,765,406
Earnings: $439,167,901
Fiscal Year-end: 12/31/22
Real Estate Property Development Services
N.A.I.C.S.: 531390
Ke Liu (Chm & Pres)

SHANDONG XINHUA PHARMACEUTICAL COMPANY LIMITED

Chemical Industrial Section Hi-tech Industrial Development Zone, Zibo, 255086, Shandong, China
Tel.: (86) 5332166666
Web Site: http://www.xhzy.com
Year Founded: 1993
000756—(SSE)
Rev.: $1,053,419,389
Assets: $1,160,424,435
Liabilities: $549,697,744
Net Worth: $610,726,690
Earnings: $57,731,595
Emp.: 6,781
Fiscal Year-end: 12/31/22
Chemical Products Mfr & Whslr
N.A.I.C.S.: 325320
Daiming Zhang (Chm)

Subsidiaries:

Shandong Xinhua Pharmaceutical (USA) Co., Ltd. (1)
2025 Mountain View Rd, South El Monte, CA 91733
Tel.: (626) 401-1048
Web Site: http://www.sxpharmusa.com
Nutraceutical Products Distr
N.A.I.C.S.: 424210
Zhang Daiming (Chm)

Shandong Xinhua Wanbo Chemical Industry Co., Ltd. (1)
No 9 Dongjiao Thermal Circuit, Zhangdian District, Zibo, Shandong, China
Tel.: (86) 5332065066
Web Site: https://www.xhwbhg.com
Emp.: 177
Chemical Products Mfr
N.A.I.C.S.: 325110

Xinhua Pharmaceutical (Gaomi) Co., Ltd. (1)
2998 Mishui Avenue west Mishui Street, Gaomi, Shandong, China
Tel.: (86) 5362219169
Pharmaceutical Product Mfr & Distr
N.A.I.C.S.: 325412

Xinhua Pharmaceutical (Shouguang) Co., Ltd. (1)
Hou Town Project Park, Shouguang, Weifang, Shandong, China
Tel.: (86) 5365396305
Web Site: https://www.xinhuashouguang.com
Emp.: 430
Pharmaceutical Product Mfr & Distr
N.A.I.C.S.: 325412
Du Deping (Chm)

SHANDONG XINJUFENG TECHNOLOGY PACKAGING CO., LTD.

Xiaoxie Town Development Zone, Xintai, 271221, Shandong, China
Tel.: (86) 1084447866
Web Site: https://www.xinjufengpack.com
Year Founded: 2007
301296—(CHIN)
Rev.: $225,758,988
Assets: $403,595,244
Liabilities: $70,781,256
Net Worth: $332,813,988
Earnings: $23,800,608
Fiscal Year-end: 12/31/22
Packaging Products Mfr
N.A.I.C.S.: 322220
Xunjun Yuan (Chm)

SHANDONG XINNENG TAISHAN POWER GENERATION CO., LTD.

No 6 Changcheng West Road, TaishanDaiyue District, Tai'an, 210000, Shandong, China
Tel.: (86) 2587730881
Web Site: http://www.xntsgs.com
Year Founded: 1994
000720—(SSE)
Rev.: $559,302,902
Assets: $782,568,779
Liabilities: $410,592,682
Net Worth: $371,976,097
Earnings: $(18,786,250)
Fiscal Year-end: 12/31/22
Eletric Power Generation Services
N.A.I.C.S.: 221111
Zhang Tong (Chm)

SHANDONG YABO TECHNOLOGY CO., LTD.

17 Donghai Road, Shizhong District, Zaozhuang, 277116, Shandong, China
Tel.: (86) 632312119
Web Site: https://yaboo-cn.com
Year Founded: 2009
002323—(SSE)
Rev.: $98,317,627
Assets: $163,769,229
Liabilities: $70,215,360

Net Worth: $93,553,869
Earnings: $4,440,248
Fiscal Year-end: 12/31/22
Transformer Mfr
N.A.I.C.S.: 335311

SHANDONG YANGGU HUATAI CHEMICAL CO., LTD.

No 399 Qinghe West Road, Yanggu County, Liaocheng, 252300, Shandong, China
Tel.: (86) 6355106655
Web Site: https://en.yghuatai.com
Year Founded: 1994
300121—(SSE)
Rev.: $493,814,880
Assets: $497,191,500
Liabilities: $106,979,184
Net Worth: $390,212,316
Earnings: $72,357,948
Emp.: 1,800
Fiscal Year-end: 12/31/22
Chemicals Mfr
N.A.I.C.S.: 325998
Wang Wenbo (Chm & Gen Mgr)

Subsidiaries:

Shandong Yanggu Huatai Import & Export Co., Ltd. (1)
No 217 Nanhuan Road, Yanggu County, Liaocheng, 252300, Shandong, China
Tel.: (86) 6356381194
Rubber Additives Mfr
N.A.I.C.S.: 325998

SHANDONG YISHENG LIVESTOCK & POULTRY BREEDING CO., LTD.

No 1 Yisheng Road South of Konggang Road, Fushan District, Yantai, 265508, Shandong, China
Tel.: (86) 5352119065
Web Site: https://www.yishenggufen.com
Year Founded: 1989
002458—(SSE)
Rev.: $296,468,949
Assets: $833,179,511
Liabilities: $432,822,593
Net Worth: $400,356,918
Earnings: $(51,533,666)
Fiscal Year-end: 12/31/22
Poultry Farming Services
N.A.I.C.S.: 311615
Jisheng Sheng Cao (Chm & Pres)

SHANDONG YONGTAI CHEMICAL GROUP CO. LTD.

Dawang Rubber Industry Area, Dongying, 257335, Guangrao, China
Tel.: (86) 54 6687 9801   CN
Web Site: http://www.yongtaigroup.net
Tiles Mfr
N.A.I.C.S.: 326211

Subsidiaries:

UYT Ltd. (1)
Renown Avenue Coventry Business Park, Canley, Coventry, CV5 6UF, United Kingdom
Tel.: (44) 2476 671 400
Web Site: http://www.uyt.ltd.uk
Sales Range: $100-124.9 Million
Emp.: 300
Automobile Parts Mfr
N.A.I.C.S.: 336390
Carol Henderson (Head-Admin & Procurement)

SHANDONG YULONG GOLD CO., LTD.

Room 1101-1 Building No A4-4 Hanyu Jingu No 7000 Jingshi East Road, Pilot Free Trade Zone, Jinan, 250101, Shandong, China
Tel.: (86) 53186171227

SHANDONG YULONG GOLD CO., LTD.

Shandong Yulong Gold Co., Ltd.—(Continued)
Web Site:
  http://www.yulongsteelpipe.com
Year Founded: 1999
601028—(SHG)
Rev.: $1,535,394,590
Assets: $831,491,524
Liabilities: $424,531,917
Net Worth: $406,959,607
Earnings: $40,899,152
Emp.: 1,000
Fiscal Year-end: 12/31/22
Steel Pipe & Tube Mfr
N.A.I.C.S.: 331210
Niu Lei *(Chm)*

SHANDONG YUMA SUN-SHADING TECHNOLOGY CORP., LTD.

1966 Jinguang West Street, Shouguang, 262702, Shandong, China
Tel.: (86) 5365207653
Web Site: https://www.yuma.cn
Year Founded: 2014
300993—(SSE)
Rev.: $76,744,802
Assets: $190,413,190
Liabilities: $11,989,177
Net Worth: $178,424,013
Earnings: $21,994,194
Fiscal Year-end: 12/31/22
Window Product Mfr & Distr
N.A.I.C.S.: 337920
Chengzhi Sun *(Founder, Chm & Gen Mgr)*

SHANDONG ZHANGQIU BLOWER CO., LTD.

Mingshui Economic Development Zone, Zhangqiu District, Jinan, 250200, Shandong, China
Tel.: (86) 53183250080
Web Site: https://en.blower.cn
Year Founded: 1968
002598—(SSE)
Rev.: $263,213,019
Assets: $358,072,678
Liabilities: $202,850,762
Net Worth: $155,221,916
Earnings: $15,467,966
Fiscal Year-end: 12/31/22
Root Blower Mfr
N.A.I.C.S.: 333413
Fang Rungang *(Chm)*

Subsidiaries:

Eurus Blower, Inc. (1)
PO Box 4588, Wheaton, IL 60189
Tel.: (630) 221-8282
Web Site: http://www.eurusblower.com
Emp.: 1
Blower Mfr & Distr
N.A.I.C.S.: 333413

SHANDONG ZHONGLU OCEANIC FISHERIES COMPANY LIMITED

T1 Conson Financial Center No 31 Xianxialing Road, Laoshan District, Qingdao, 266061, Shandong, China
Tel.: (86) 53255719257
Web Site: https://www.zofco.cn
Year Founded: 1999
200992—(SSE)
Rev.: $138,354,133
Assets: $258,115,446
Liabilities: $82,885,603
Net Worth: $175,229,842
Earnings: $4,245,626
Fiscal Year-end: 12/31/22
Ocean Fishing Services
N.A.I.C.S.: 114119
Lianxing Lu *(Chm)*

SHANE GLOBAL HOLDING, INC.

2F No 97 Sec 2 Dunhua S Rd, Daan Dist, Taipei, 10682, Taiwan
Tel.: (886) 277111060 Ky
Web Site:
  https://www.shaneglobal.com.tw
Year Founded: 2014
8482—(TAI)
Rev.: $118,116,056
Assets: $151,515,381
Liabilities: $42,039,830
Net Worth: $109,475,551
Earnings: $9,571,339
Emp.: 2,600
Fiscal Year-end: 12/31/23
Furniture Product Mfr
N.A.I.C.S.: 337127
Hsieh-Chih Tong Aka Jay Shane *(Chm)*

SHANE HOMES LTD.

5661 7th Street NE, Calgary, T2E 8V3, AB, Canada
Tel.: (403) 536-2200
Web Site:
  https://www.shanehomes.com
Year Founded: 1979
Rev.: $158,714,023
Emp.: 75
Residential Construction
N.A.I.C.S.: 444110
Shane Wenzel *(Pres)*

SHANG GONG GROUP CO., LTD.

No 263 Shitai Road, Baoshan District, Shanghai, 201206, China
Tel.: (86) 2168407700
Web Site:
  https://www.sgsbgroup.com
900924—(SHG)
Rev.: $467,392,148
Assets: $819,590,026
Liabilities: $335,415,558
Net Worth: $484,174,468
Earnings: $10,271,622
Emp.: 620
Fiscal Year-end: 12/31/22
Sewing Machines, Office Equipment & Photo Film Product Mfr & Whslr
N.A.I.C.S.: 335210
Min Zhang *(Chm & Pres)*

Subsidiaries:

Duerkopp Adler (DA) Trading (Shanghai) Co., Ltd (1)
1566 New JinQiao Road, Pudong, 201206, China
Tel.: (86) 21 6393 8822
Web Site: http://www.sgsbgroup.com
Sales Range: $25-49.9 Million
Emp.: 45
Sewing Machines & Spare Parts Mfr
N.A.I.C.S.: 333998

Fuji Xerox of Shanghai Limited (1)
32 Floor Hong Kong New World Tower No 300 Huaihai Road Centre, Shanghai, 200021, China
Tel.: (86) 1023022288
Sales Range: $400-449.9 Million
Multifunction Devices Mfr
N.A.I.C.S.: 333244

PFAFF Industrial Sewing Machine (Zhangjiagang) Co., Ltd. (1)
No 8 Miaoqiao Middle Road, Tangqiao Town, Zhangjiagang, 215600, Jiangsu, China
Tel.: (86) 51258910766
Sewing Equipment Mfr & Distr
N.A.I.C.S.: 333248

SMPIC Electronic Company Limited (1)
No 927 Huyi Highway, Nanxiang Jiading District, Shanghai, China
Tel.: (86) 2134040205
Electronic Wiring Product Mfr & Distr
N.A.I.C.S.: 335931

SMPIC Import & Export Co., Ltd. (1)
33 Sichuan Rd (M), 200002, Shanghai, China
Tel.: (86) 2163060610
Web Site: http://www.smpic.com
Industrial Machinery & Equipment Whslr
N.A.I.C.S.: 423830

ShangGong (Europe) Holding Corp. GmbH (1)
Potsma St 190, 33719, Bielefeld, Germany
Tel.: (49) 52192500
Industrial Machinery & Equipment Whslr
N.A.I.C.S.: 423830

Subsidiary (Domestic):

Duerkopp Adler AG (2)
Potsdamer Strasse 190, D 33719, Bielefeld, Germany (95%)
Tel.: (49) 52192500
Web Site: http://www.duerkopp-adler.com
Industrial Sewing Machines & Material Handling Systems Mfr
N.A.I.C.S.: 333248

Shanggong Export & Import Co., Ltd. (1)
No 1566 New JinQiao Road, Pudong, Shanghai, China
Tel.: (86) 2168407700
Web Site: http://www.sgsbgroup.com
Industrial Machinery & Equipment Whslr
N.A.I.C.S.: 423830

Shanghai Butterfly Imp. & Exp. Co., Ltd (1)
Room 2403 No 2018 Huashan Road, Shanghai, 20030, China
Tel.: (86) 2154070870
Web Site: http://www.pfiechshy.com
Sales Range: $25-49.9 Million
Emp.: 30
Industrial Machinery & Equipment Whslr
N.A.I.C.S.: 423830
Hu Ting Shen *(Gen Mgr)*

Shanghai Butterfly Import & Export Co., Ltd. (1)
No 1566 Xinjinqiao Rd, Shanghai, 201206, China
Tel.: (86) 2154070870
Sewing Equipment Mfr & Distr
N.A.I.C.S.: 333248

Tianjin Richpeace Ai Co., Limited (1)
No 6 Baozhong Road Baodi Economic Development Zone, Tianjin, 301800, China
Tel.: (86) 2222533456
Web Site: https://www.richpeace.com
Sewing Equipment Mfr & Distr
N.A.I.C.S.: 333248

SHANG HAI YA TONG CO., LTD.

No 1 Bayi Road, Chongming District, Shanghai, 202150, China
Tel.: (86) 2169695918
600692—(SHG)
Rev.: $172,036,121
Assets: $414,981,319
Liabilities: $276,166,365
Net Worth: $138,814,954
Earnings: $643,088
Fiscal Year-end: 12/31/22
Real Estate Manangement Services
N.A.I.C.S.: 531390
Lei Xuan *(Sec)*

SHANG PROPERTIES, INC.

Level 5 Shangri-La Plaza Shang Central EDSA corner Shaw Boulevard, Mandaluyong, 1550, Metro Manila, Philippines
Tel.: (63) 283703700
Web Site:
  https://www.shangproperties.com
SHNG—(PHI)
Rev.: $55,488,760
Assets: $1,347,843,447
Liabilities: $436,256,202
Net Worth: $911,587,244
Earnings: $110,166,235
Emp.: 783
Fiscal Year-end: 12/31/23

INTERNATIONAL PUBLIC

Property Development & Real Estate Management Services
N.A.I.C.S.: 531311
Edward Khoon Loong Kuok *(Chm)*

Subsidiaries:

Shangri-La Plaza Corporation (1)
Edsa corner Shaw Boulevard, Mandaluyong, 1550, Metro Manila, Philippines
Tel.: (63) 283702700
Web Site: https://www.shangrila-plaza.com
Shopping Mall Operation Services
N.A.I.C.S.: 531120

SHANGAR DECOR LIMITED

4 Sharad Flat Opposite Dharnidhar Derasar Behind Sales, Paldi, Ahmedabad, 380 007, Gujarat, India
Tel.: (91) 7926634458 In
Web Site:
  https://www.shangardecor.com
Year Founded: 1995
540259—(BOM)
Rev.: $1,159,079
Assets: $2,732,666
Liabilities: $1,939,152
Net Worth: $793,514
Earnings: $24,219
Fiscal Year-end: 03/31/23
Event Management Services
N.A.I.C.S.: 711310
Samir Rasiklal Shah *(Mng Dir)*

SHANGDONG HUAPENG GLASS CO., LTD.

Shidao Longyun Road No 468, Rongcheng, Shandong, China
Tel.: (86) 6317381873
Web Site:
  https://www.en.huapengglass.com
603021—(SHG)
Rev.: $107,841,872
Assets: $330,872,944
Liabilities: $257,797,355
Net Worth: $73,075,589
Earnings: $(53,322,909)
Fiscal Year-end: 12/31/22
Glass Product Mfr & Distr
N.A.I.C.S.: 327215

Subsidiaries:

Anqing Huapeng Changjiang Glass Co., Ltd. (1)
DaGuan Economic Area Industry zone, Daguan Economic Area, Anqing, 246602, Anhui, China
Tel.: (86) 5565349522
Web Site: https://www.anqingglass.com
Glass Products Mfr
N.A.I.C.S.: 327215

Huapeng Glass (Heze) Co., Ltd. (1)
No 439 Renmin South Road, Heze, Shandong, China
Tel.: (86) 5303976786
Web Site: http://www.hezeglass.com
Glass Products Mfr
N.A.I.C.S.: 327215

Liaoning Huapeng Guangyuan Glass Co., Ltd. (1)
Shencai Orefield Xinglongbao, Xinmin, Liaoning, China
Tel.: (86) 2487462585
Web Site: http://www.hpgyglass.cn
Glass Container Mfr
N.A.I.C.S.: 327213

SHANGHAI 2345 NEWORK HOLDING GROUP CO., LTD.

6F Block 85 No 700 Yishan Road, Xuhui District, Shanghai, China
Tel.: (86) 2164822345
Web Site: http://www.2345hyron.com
Year Founded: 2001
002195—(SSE)
Rev.: $93,695,322
Assets: $1,388,504,361
Liabilities: $67,589,978
Net Worth: $1,320,914,383

AND PRIVATE COMPANIES

SHANGHAI AUTOMOTIVE INDUSTRY CORPORATION

Earnings: $29,757,499
Emp.: 1,401
Fiscal Year-end: 12/31/22
Software Outsourcing Services
N.A.I.C.S.: 541519
Yubing Chen *(Chm & Pres)*

SHANGHAI ACE INVESTMENT & DEVELOPMENT CO., LTD.
36th Floor World Plaza 855 Pudong South Road, Shanghai, 200120, China
Tel.: (86) 2158369726
Web Site: https://www.aceonline.cn
Year Founded: 2004
603329—(SHG)
Rev.: $433,609,717
Assets: $300,723,953
Liabilities: $119,014,455
Net Worth: $181,709,499
Earnings: $20,878,491
Fiscal Year-end: 12/31/22
Supply Chain Logistics Services
N.A.I.C.S.: 541614
Liu Zhongyi *(Chm)*

SHANGHAI ACREL CO., LTD.
No 253 Yulu Road, Jiading District, Shanghai, 201801, China
Tel.: (86) 13611962943
Web Site: https://www.acrel.cn
Year Founded: 2003
300286—(SSE)
Rev.: $143,008,632
Assets: $221,363,064
Liabilities: $60,317,244
Net Worth: $161,045,820
Earnings: $23,953,644
Emp.: 475
Fiscal Year-end: 12/31/22
Electrical Measurement & Control Equipment Mfr
N.A.I.C.S.: 334519

SHANGHAI ACTION EDUCATION TECHNOLOGY CO., LTD.
Building A Lane168 Xinghong Road, Hongqiao Business District, Shanghai, 201206, China
Tel.: (86) 2133535658
Web Site: http://www.jiaodao.com
Year Founded: 2006
605098—(SHG)
Rev.: $63,309,098
Assets: $273,872,173
Liabilities: $123,669,304
Net Worth: $150,202,868
Earnings: $15,564,547
Fiscal Year-end: 12/31/22
Educational Support Services
N.A.I.C.S.: 611710
Jian Li *(Chm & Gen Mgr)*

SHANGHAI AEROSPACE AUTOMOBILE ELECTROMECHANICAL CO., LTD.
No 661 Rongqiao Road Pudong New Area, Pilot Free Trade Zone, Shanghai, 201109, China
Tel.: (86) 2164827176
Web Site: http://www.ht-saae.com
Year Founded: 1998
600151—(SHG)
Rev.: $1,236,146,718
Assets: $1,568,795,076
Liabilities: $759,003,172
Net Worth: $809,791,903
Earnings: ($14,580,343)
Fiscal Year-end: 12/31/22
Automobile Parts Mfr & Distr
N.A.I.C.S.: 336390
Zhang Jiangong *(Chm)*

Subsidiaries:

ERAE Automotive Systems Co.,Ltd. (1)
664 Nongong-Ro, Nongong-eup Dalseong-gun, Daegu, 42981, Korea (South)
Tel.: (82) 536101500
Web Site: https://www.erae-automotive.com
Automotive Component Mfr & Distr
N.A.I.C.S.: 336370

SDAAC Automotive Air-Conditioning Systems Co., Ltd. (1)
No 1768 Hunan Highway, Pudong New Area, Shanghai, China
Tel.: (86) 2138663051
Automotive Component Mfr & Distr
N.A.I.C.S.: 336370

Shanghai Delphi Automotive Air Conditioning Systems Co., Ltd. (1)
No 1768 Hunan Road, Pudong New Area, Shanghai, 201204, China
Tel.: (86) 2138663051
Web Site: http://www.sdaac.com
Motor Vehicle Parts Mfr
N.A.I.C.S.: 336390

SHANGHAI AIKO SOLAR ENERGY CO., LTD.
Room 201-1 Block 4 No 26 Qiuyue Road, Pudong New District, Shanghai, 201210, China
Tel.: (86) 57985912509
Web Site: http://www.shinmay.com.cn
Year Founded: 1996
600732—(SHG)
Rev.: $4,924,523,977
Assets: $3,466,438,303
Liabilities: $2,194,562,214
Net Worth: $1,271,876,089
Earnings: $326,879,463
Fiscal Year-end: 12/31/22
Real Estate Manangement Services
N.A.I.C.S.: 531390
Chen Gang *(Chm)*

SHANGHAI AILU PACKAGING CO., LTD.
No 88 Yangda Road, JinShan, Shanghai, 201508, China
Tel.: (86) 2157293030
Web Site: https://www.ailugroup.com
Year Founded: 2006
301062—(CHIN)
Rev.: $150,218,662
Assets: $388,726,055
Liabilities: $218,823,689
Net Worth: $169,902,366
Earnings: $10,602,732
Fiscal Year-end: 12/31/23
Packaging Products Mfr
N.A.I.C.S.: 322220
Ankang Chen *(Chm)*

SHANGHAI AIYINGSHI CO., LTD.
Room 3E-1157 No 2123 Pudong Avenue, Pudong New Area, Shanghai, 200127, China
Tel.: (86) 2168470177
Web Site: http://www.aiyingshi.com
Year Founded: 2005
603214—(SHG)
Rev.: $508,172,381
Assets: $384,093,010
Liabilities: $227,315,884
Net Worth: $156,777,126
Earnings: $12,067,506
Fiscal Year-end: 12/31/22
Maternal Product Distr
N.A.I.C.S.: 424350
Shi Qiong *(Chm & Pres)*

SHANGHAI AJ GROUP CO., LTD.
No 746 Zhaojiabang Road, Xuhui District, Shanghai, 200030, China
Tel.: (86) 64396500
Web Site: https://www.aj.com.cn
Year Founded: 1979
600643—(SHG)
Rev.: $422,374,994

Assets: $3,725,467,443
Liabilities: $1,975,158,390
Net Worth: $1,750,309,053
Earnings: $67,664,530
Fiscal Year-end: 12/31/22
Real Estate Investment Services
N.A.I.C.S.: 523999
Yongjin Fan *(Chm & Vice Chm)*

SHANGHAI ALADDIN BIOCHEMICAL TECHNOLOGY CO., LTD.
16F South Tower No 36 Xinjinqiao Road, Pudong New Area, Shanghai, 201206, China
Tel.: (86) 2150560989
Web Site: http://www.aladdin-e.com
Year Founded: 2009
688179—(SHG)
Rev.: $53,085,802
Assets: $207,297,329
Liabilities: $70,446,402
Net Worth: $136,850,927
Earnings: $12,963,343
Fiscal Year-end: 12/31/22
Chemical Product Mfr & Distr
N.A.I.C.S.: 325520
Jiuzhen Xu *(Chm & Gen Mgr)*

SHANGHAI ALLIED INDUSTRIAL CORP., LTD.
Room 801 No 27 Lane 99 Shouyang Road, Jingan District, Shanghai, 200443, China
Tel.: (86) 2156484208
Web Site: https://www.allied-corp.com
Year Founded: 2004
301419—(SSE)
Rev.: $55,947,912
Assets: $98,482,485
Liabilities: $41,870,790
Net Worth: $56,611,695
Earnings: $10,427,480
Fiscal Year-end: 12/31/22
Chemical Products Mfr
N.A.I.C.S.: 325998
Yaohua Zhang *(Chm)*

SHANGHAI ALLIST PHARMACEUTICALS CO., LTD.
5F Building 1 No 1118 Halei Road and No 1227 Zhangheng Road, China Shanghai Pilot Free Trade Zone, Shanghai, 201203, China
Tel.: (86) 2180423292
Web Site: http://www.allist.com.cn
Year Founded: 2004
688578—(SHG)
Rev.: $111,056,751
Assets: $483,280,977
Liabilities: $35,818,357
Net Worth: $447,462,620
Earnings: $18,325,106
Fiscal Year-end: 12/31/22
Pharmaceutical Product Mfr & Distr
N.A.I.C.S.: 325412
Jinhao Du *(Chm & Gen Mgr)*

Subsidiaries:

Jiangsu Allist Pharmaceutical Co., Ltd. (1)
No 666 Huashi Road, Qidong Economic Development Zone, Jiangsu, 226200, China
Tel.: (86) 51380926082
Pharmaceuticals Product Mfr
N.A.I.C.S.: 325412

SHANGHAI AMARSOFT INFORMATION & TECHNOLOGY CO., LTD.
Room 2308 No 11 Guotai Road, Yangpu District, Shanghai, 200433, China
Tel.: (86) 2155137223
Web Site: http://www.amarsoft.com

Year Founded: 2001
300380—(SSE)
Rev.: $109,375,812
Assets: $118,646,424
Liabilities: $60,251,256
Net Worth: $58,395,168
Earnings: ($10,181,808)
Emp.: 1,100
Fiscal Year-end: 12/31/22
Software Publisher
N.A.I.C.S.: 513210
Yong Gao *(Chm & Gen Mgr)*

SHANGHAI ANOKY GROUP CO., LTD.
No 881 Songhua Road Qingpu Export Processing Zone, Qingpu District, Shanghai, 201703, China
Tel.: (86) 2159867500
Web Site: http://anoky.com.cn
Year Founded: 1999
300067—(SSE)
Rev.: $105,499,368
Assets: $413,558,028
Liabilities: $82,552,392
Net Worth: $331,005,636
Earnings: $4,393,116
Fiscal Year-end: 12/31/22
Textile Dyeing & Finishing Solutions
N.A.I.C.S.: 325130
Ji Lijun *(Chm & Gen Mgr)*

SHANGHAI AUTOMOTIVE INDUSTRY CORPORATION
489 Weihai Road, Shanghai, 200041, China
Tel.: (86) 2122011888
600104—(SSE)
Sales Range: $15-24.9 Billion
Emp.: 64,343
Automobile Parts Mfr
N.A.I.C.S.: 336110
Chen Zhixin *(VP & Sr Engr)*

Subsidiaries:

HUAYU Automotive Systems Company Limited (1)
No 489 Weihai Road, Jing'an District, Shanghai, 200041, China
Tel.: (86) 2123102080
Web Site: http://www.huayu-auto.com
Rev.: $22,220,814,115
Assets: $22,856,690,292
Liabilities: $14,846,207,786
Net Worth: $8,010,482,505
Earnings: $1,011,318,778
Emp.: 120,000
Fiscal Year-end: 12/31/2022
Automotive Parts Mfr & Whslr
N.A.I.C.S.: 336390
Wang Xiaoqiu *(Chm)*

Subsidiary (Domestic):

Huayu Vision Technology (Shanghai) Co., Ltd. (2)
767 Ye Cheng Rd Jia Ding, Shanghai, 201821, China (100%)
Tel.: (86) 67085999
Web Site: http://www.hascovision.com
Emp.: 6,880
Mfr & Marketer of Automotive Lighting Products
N.A.I.C.S.: 336320

SAIC Europe GmbH (1)
Am Festungsgraben 5, 21079, Hamburg, Germany
Tel.: (49) 40 322291
Emp.: 2
Car Mfr & Distr
N.A.I.C.S.: 336110
Wang Chenhui *(Gen Mgr)*

SAIC GM Wuling Co., Ltd. (1)
18th Hexi Road, Guangxi, Liuzhou, 545007, China
Tel.: (86) 772 265 0233
Web Site: https://www.sgmw.com.cn
Vehicle Mfr
N.A.I.C.S.: 336110

SAIC Hong Kong Co., Ltd (1)

SHANGHAI AUTOMOTIVE INDUSTRY CORPORATION

Shanghai Automotive Industry Corporation—(Continued)

Suite 2608 Shell Tower Times Square 1 Matheson Street, Causeway Bay, China (Hong Kong)
Tel.: (852) 25042080
Car Mfr & Distr
N.A.I.C.S.: 336110

SAIC Motor Corporation Limited (1)
489 Weihai Road, Shanghai, 200041, China
Tel.: (86) 2122011888
Web Site: https://www.saicmotor.com
Rev.: $113,702,112,665
Assets: $140,863,535,380
Liabilities: $93,362,104,742
Net Worth: $47,501,430,637
Earnings: $3,130,239,638
Fiscal Year-end: 12/31/2020
Car Mfr & Sales
N.A.I.C.S.: 336110
Xiaoqiu Wang (Pres)

Subsidiary (Domestic):

Nanjing Automobile Group Corporation (2)
331 Zhongyang Road, Gulou District, Nanjing, 210037, China
Tel.: (86) 25 8343 2417
Web Site: http://www.nanqi.cn
Motor Vehicles & Engines Designer & Mfr
N.A.I.C.S.: 336110

Subsidiary (Non-US):

MG Motor UK Limited (3)
Main Gate Lowhill Lane, Longbridge, Birmingham, B31 2BQ, United Kingdom
Tel.: (44) 845 303 6464
Web Site: http://www.mg.co.uk
Automobile Mfr
N.A.I.C.S.: 336110
Daniel Gregorious (Head-Sls & Mktg)

Subsidiary (Domestic):

Shanghai New Power Automotive Technology Co Ltd. (2)
NO 2636 Jungong Road, Shanghai, 200438, China
Tel.: (86) 2160652315
Web Site: https://www.sdeciepower.com
Rev.: $1,394,036,374
Assets: $3,102,403,412
Liabilities: $1,985,894,202
Net Worth: $1,116,509,210
Earnings: ($226,250,093)
Emp.: 2,000
Fiscal Year-end: 12/31/2022
Diesel Engine Mfr
N.A.I.C.S.: 333618
Lan Qingsong (Chm)

Joint Venture (Domestic):

Shanghai-Volkswagen Automotive Company Ltd. (2)
63 Anting Luo Pu Road, Shanghai, 201805, China
Tel.: (86) 2159561888
Web Site: http://www.csvw.com
Automobile Mfr
N.A.I.C.S.: 336110

SAIC Motor-CP Co., Ltd. (1)
No 191 Silom Complex 25th Floor Silom Road Khwaeng Silom, Bangrak, Bangkok, Thailand
Tel.: (66) 2 6258666
Web Site: http://www.mgthai.com
Emp.: 600
Car Mfr & Distr
N.A.I.C.S.: 336110
Zhang Haibo (Mng Dir)

Joint Venture (Non-US):

Pan Asia Technical Automotive Center Co., Ltd. (2)
No 2199 Jufeng Road, 201201, Shanghai, Pudong, China
Tel.: (86) 2150165016
Web Site: http://www.patac.com.cn
Automotive Engineering & Design Services
N.A.I.C.S.: 541490

SAIC USA Inc. (1)
1301 W Longlake Rd, Troy, MI 48098

Tel.: (248) 267-9117
Rev.: $31,216,532
Emp.: 20
Sales of Automotive Supplies & Parts
N.A.I.C.S.: 423120
Amy Jiang (Asst Pres & Mgr-Treasury)

Shanghai Hydrogen Propulsion Technology Co., Ltd. (1)
1788 Xiechun Rd, Jiading, Shanghai, China
Tel.: (86) 213 996 2400
Web Site: https://www.shpt.com
Engineeering Services
N.A.I.C.S.: 541330

SHANGHAI BAIRUN INVESTMENT HOLDING GROUP CO., LTD.
No 558 East Kangqiao Road, Kangqiao Industrial Zone, Shanghai, 201319, China
Tel.: (86) 2158135000
Web Site: https://www.bairun.net
Year Founded: 1997
002568—(SSE)
Rev.: $364,114,441
Assets: $906,732,066
Liabilities: $377,935,347
Net Worth: $528,796,719
Earnings: $73,187,403
Fiscal Year-end: 12/31/22
Flavors & Fragrances Mfr
N.A.I.C.S.: 311930
Xiaodong Liu (Chm, Pres & Gen Mgr)

SHANGHAI BAOLONG AUTOMOTIVE CORPORATION
No 5500 Shenzhuan Road, Songjiang, Shanghai, 201619, China
Tel.: (86) 2131273333
Web Site: https://en.baolong.biz
Year Founded: 1997
603197—(SHG)
Rev.: $670,791,088
Assets: $928,754,410
Liabilities: $537,522,004
Net Worth: $391,232,406
Earnings: $30,064,835
Fiscal Year-end: 12/31/22
Automobile Parts Mfr & Distr
N.A.I.C.S.: 336390
Holley Chen (Co-Founder)

Subsidiaries:

Dill Air Controls Products, LLC (1)
1500 Williamsboro St, Oxford, NC 27565 (90%)
Tel.: (919) 692-2300
Web Site: http://www.dillvalves.com
Rev.: $7,900,000
Emp.: 95
Valve System Mfr & Distr
N.A.I.C.S.: 332911
Richard Buhr (Mgr-Quality Assurance)

Longway Poland Sp. z o.o. (1)
ul Przejazdowa 22, 05-800, Pruszkow, Poland
Tel.: (48) 224072418
Web Site: http://www.longway.com.pl
Automotive Valve Mfr
N.A.I.C.S.: 332912

MMS Modular Molding Systems GmbH (1)
Leobersdorferstrasse 26, A-2560, Berndorf, Austria
Tel.: (43) 26728324714
Web Site: https://www.mms-technology.com
Modular Moulding Product Mfr
N.A.I.C.S.: 326150

PEX Automotive GmBH (1)
Muhleweg 11, 72800, Eningen, Germany
Tel.: (49) 7121994220
Web Site: https://pex.de
Automotive Component Mfr & Distr
N.A.I.C.S.: 334419

Shanghai Longan Automotive Electronics Co., Ltd. (1)
Pudong, Shanghai, 201300, China
Tel.: (86) 2158182999

Web Site: https://www.lgsensor.com
Automotive Component Mfr & Distr
N.A.I.C.S.: 334419

Tesona Gmbh & Co. Kg (1)
Am Kunkelhof 4, 99820, Horselberg-Hainich, Germany
Tel.: (49) 36920716790
Web Site: https://www.tesona.de
Consumer Electronics Product Mfr
N.A.I.C.S.: 334310

Valor Europe GmbH (1)
Hombergstr 33, 45549, Sprockhovel, Germany
Tel.: (49) 23243444980
Web Site: https://www.endrohre.net
Stainless Steel Component Distr
N.A.I.C.S.: 423510
Axel Buer (Mng Dir)

Valor HK Co. (1)
4320 Harvester Road, Burlington, L7L 5S4, ON, Canada
Tel.: (905) 631-6800
Automotive Valve Mfr
N.A.I.C.S.: 332912

SHANGHAI BAOSTEEL PACKAGING CO., LTD.
No 1818 LuoDong Road, Baoshan, Shanghai, 200949, China
Tel.: (86) 2156766307
Web Site: http://www.baosteelpack.cn
Year Founded: 2004
601968—(SHG)
Rev.: $1,199,490,229
Assets: $1,165,230,060
Liabilities: $609,954,602
Net Worth: $555,275,457
Earnings: $37,688,597
Fiscal Year-end: 12/31/22
Steel Products Mfr
N.A.I.C.S.: 331110
Cao Qing (Chm & Pres)

Subsidiaries:

Wuhan Baosteel Metal Decorating Co., Ltd. (1)
Luo Han Industrial Park, Huangpi District, Wuhan, 432200, China
Tel.: (86) 2761655888
Metal Tank Mfr
N.A.I.C.S.: 332431

SHANGHAI BEITE TECHNOLOGY CO., LTD.
No 666 Huaye Road, Jiading District, Shanghai, 201816, China
Tel.: (86) 21399007706035
Web Site: https://www.sh-beite.com
Year Founded: 2002
603009—(SHG)
Rev.: $239,452,579
Assets: $448,418,309
Liabilities: $219,329,131
Net Worth: $229,089,178
Earnings: $6,450,664
Emp.: 1,000
Fiscal Year-end: 12/31/22
Automobile Parts Mfr
N.A.I.C.S.: 336350
Kun Jin (Chm)

Subsidiaries:

Changchun Beite Automobile Parts Co., Ltd (1)
Bingyi Street & Yiliu Road Interchange, Automobile industry development district, Changchun, 130000, Jilin, China
Tel.: (86) 43185982271
Automobile Parts Mfr
N.A.I.C.S.: 336330

Tianjin Beit Auto Parts Co., Ltd. (1)
No 16 Central Avenue Jinghai Economic Development District, Tianjin, 301600, China
Tel.: (86) 2259591618
Automobile Parts Mfr
N.A.I.C.S.: 336330

INTERNATIONAL PUBLIC

SHANGHAI BELLING CO., LTD.
810 YiShan Road, Shanghai, 200233, China
Tel.: (86) 2124261000
Web Site: https://www.belling.com.cn
Year Founded: 1998
600171—(SHG)
Rev.: $287,015,003
Assets: $698,632,632
Liabilities: $105,134,384
Net Worth: $593,498,248
Earnings: $56,024,500
Fiscal Year-end: 12/31/22
Integrated Circuits Mfr
N.A.I.C.S.: 334413
Yang Kun (Chm)

Subsidiaries:

Miaxis Biometrics Co., Ltd. (1)
5 Floor Science and technology Building East Software Park, No 90 Wensan Rd, Hangzhou, 310012, China
Tel.: (86) 57189986377
Web Site: https://www.miaxis.net
Biometric Device Mfr & Distr
N.A.I.C.S.: 334118

SHANGHAI BIO-HEART BIOLOGICAL TECHNOLOGY CO., LTD.
Room 301 Building 6 Building 6 No 590 Ruiqing Road Pudong New Area, Shanghai, China
Tel.: (86) 2168798511
Web Site: https://www.bio-heart.com
Year Founded: 2014
2185—(HKG)
Rev.: $1,186,171
Assets: $113,244,766
Liabilities: $6,097,973
Net Worth: $107,146,793
Earnings: ($26,143,664)
Emp.: 32
Fiscal Year-end: 12/31/23
Information Technology Services
N.A.I.C.S.: 541512
Bradley Stewart Hubbard (Chief Medical Officer)

SHANGHAI BRIGHT POWER SEMICONDUCTOR CO., LTD.
Room 504-511 5F No 2 Lane 666 Zhangheng Road, China Pilot Free Trade Zone, Shanghai, 201203, China
Tel.: (86) 2151870166
Web Site: http://www.bpsemi.com
Year Founded: 2008
688368—(SHG)
Rev.: $151,547,732
Assets: $353,291,342
Liabilities: $138,955,818
Net Worth: $214,335,525
Earnings: ($28,903,699)
Fiscal Year-end: 12/31/22
Semiconductor Product Mfr & Distr
N.A.I.C.S.: 334413
Liqiang Hu (Chm & Gen Mgr)

SHANGHAI BROADBAND TECHNOLOGY CO., LTD.
Room 1601 Building 1 No 299 Jiangchang West Road, Shanghai, 200436, China
Tel.: (86) 2161079899
Web Site: https://www.600608.net
Year Founded: 1991
600608—(SHG)
Rev.: $51,495,210
Assets: $27,737,929
Liabilities: $17,780,481
Net Worth: $9,957,449
Earnings: $564,240
Fiscal Year-end: 12/31/22
Iron & Steel Pipe Mfr & Distr
N.A.I.C.S.: 331210

AND PRIVATE COMPANIES

Zhang Lu *(Chm)*

SHANGHAI CARTHANE CO.,LTD
No 813 Jianye Road Pudong New Area, Shanghai, 201201, China
Tel.: (86) 2158386588
Web Site: https://www.carthane.com
Year Founded: 2000
603037—(SHG)
Rev.: $90,139,510
Assets: $154,491,148
Liabilities: $30,382,462
Net Worth: $124,108,686
Earnings: $10,957,743
Fiscal Year-end: 12/31/22
Automotive Parts Mfr & Distr
N.A.I.C.S.: 336390
Benjamin Hetzel *(Dir-Bus Dev Europe)*

Subsidiaries:

Shanghai Kaizhong Materials Science & Technology Co., Ltd. (1)
No 813 Jianye Road, Pudong New Area, Shanghai, China
Tel.: (86) 2158386588
Chemical Engineering Services
N.A.I.C.S.: 541330

SHANGHAI CDXJ DIGITAL TECHNOLOGY CO., LTD.
7F Building A No 289 Linhong Road, Changning District, Shanghai, 200135, China
Tel.: (86) 2152806755
Web Site: http://www.shcd.cc
Year Founded: 1997
603887—(SHG)
Rev.: $376,773,663
Assets: $1,188,481,058
Liabilities: $708,732,096
Net Worth: $479,748,962
Earnings: $364,226
Fiscal Year-end: 12/31/22
Construction Engineering Services
N.A.I.C.S.: 541330
Zhang Yang *(Chm & Pres)*

SHANGHAI CENTURY ACQUISITION CORPORATION
23rd Floor Shun Ho Tower 24-30 Ice House Street, Central, China (Hong Kong)
Tel.: (852) 2845 8989   Ky
Web Site: http://www.shanghaicentury.com
Year Founded: 2005
Sales Range: $25-49.9 Million
Emp.: 2
Holding Company
N.A.I.C.S.: 551112
Anthony Kai Yiu Lo *(Chm & Co-CEO)*

SHANGHAI CEO ENVIRONMENTAL PROTECTION TECHNOLOGY CO., LTD.
8F Building A7 Wangu Science and Technology Park Lane 1688, Guoquan North Road Yangpu District, Shanghai, 200438, China
Tel.: (86) 2155081682
Web Site: http://www.ceo.sh.cn
Year Founded: 2011
688335—(SHG)
Rev.: $110,841,967
Assets: $216,838,632
Liabilities: $44,249,629
Net Worth: $172,589,003
Earnings: $16,190,128
Fiscal Year-end: 12/31/22
Protection Equipment Mfr
N.A.I.C.S.: 335999
Wenjun Huang *(Chm)*

SHANGHAI CHALLENGE TEXTILE CO., LTD.
No 1918 Tingfeng Road Tinglin, Jin Shan District, Shanghai, 201504, China
Tel.: (86) 2137330000
Web Site: https://www.challenge-21c.com
Year Founded: 2001
002486—(SSE)
Rev.: $191,669,363
Assets: $182,225,286
Liabilities: $35,816,208
Net Worth: $146,409,078
Earnings: $13,079,973
Emp.: 3,934
Fiscal Year-end: 12/31/22
Fabric Product Mfr
N.A.I.C.S.: 313310
Xi Yang *(Chm)*

SHANGHAI CHENGTOU HOLDING CO., LTD.
No 1540 Bei'ai Road, Pudong New Area, Shanghai, 200080, China
Tel.: (86) 2166981556
Web Site: http://www.sh600649.com
Year Founded: 1992
600649—(SHG)
Rev.: $1,188,927,193
Assets: $10,014,613,264
Liabilities: $6,984,576,729
Net Worth: $3,030,036,535
Earnings: $109,870,764
Emp.: 2,011
Fiscal Year-end: 12/31/22
Holding Company; Real Estate, Environmental & Venture Capital Investment Services
N.A.I.C.S.: 551112
Zhang Chen *(Chm)*

Subsidiaries:

Shanghai City Land (Group) Co., Ltd. (1)
No 701 Guohao Road, Shanghai, 200438, China
Tel.: (86) 21 6590 6677
Web Site: http://www.sh600649.com
Real Estate Development Services
N.A.I.C.S.: 237210

Shanghai Environment Group Co., Ltd. (1)
No 1881 Hongqiao Road, Changning District, Shanghai, 200120, China (60%)
Tel.: (86) 2168907088
Web Site: http://www.sh600649.com
Environmental Waste Management Services
N.A.I.C.S.: 562998
Wang Selan *(Chm)*

SHANGHAI CHICMAX COSMETIC CO., LTD.
25 Floor Building B No 3300 Zhongshan North Road, Putuo, Shanghai, China
Tel.: (86) 2152035333   CN
Web Site: https://www.chicmaxgroup.com
Year Founded: 2003
2145—(HKG)
Rev.: $409,887,463
Assets: $481,947,641
Liabilities: $220,472,561
Net Worth: $261,475,080
Earnings: $21,002,027
Emp.: 2,572
Fiscal Year-end: 12/31/22
Cosmetic Product Distr
N.A.I.C.S.: 456120
Ming Lian *(Sec)*

SHANGHAI CHINAFORTUNE CO., LTD.
Huaxin Haixin Building No 666 Fuzhou Road, Huangpu District, Shanghai, 200001, China
Tel.: (86) 2154967665
Web Site: http://www.shchinafortune.com
Year Founded: 1952
600621—(SHG)
Rev.: $343,030,601
Assets: $4,918,981,209
Liabilities: $3,861,092,538
Net Worth: $1,057,888,672
Earnings: $49,442,632
Fiscal Year-end: 12/31/22
Electronic Component Mfr & Distr
N.A.I.C.S.: 334412
Yang Yu *(Pres, Gen Mgr & Dir)*

SHANGHAI CHLOR-ALKALI CHEMICAL CO., LTD.
16th Floor No 560 Xujiahui Road, Huangpu District, Shanghai, 200025, China
Tel.: (86) 2123530000
Web Site: https://www.scacc.com
Year Founded: 1992
600618—(SHG)
Rev.: $893,537,036
Assets: $1,568,374,465
Liabilities: $405,546,509
Net Worth: $1,162,827,956
Earnings: $192,418,495
Fiscal Year-end: 12/31/22
Chemical Product Mfr & Distr
N.A.I.C.S.: 325180
Gu Chunlin *(Chm)*

SHANGHAI CHONGYANG INVESTMENT MANAGEMENT CO., LTD.
Level 51 North Tower IFC 8 Century Avenue, Shanghai, 200120, China
Tel.: (86) 21 2021 6666   CN
Web Site: http://www.chongyang.net
Year Founded: 2001
Investment Management Service
N.A.I.C.S.: 523940
Jianqing He *(Partner & Chief Res Officer)*

SHANGHAI CHUANGLI GROUP CO., LTD.
No 889 Xinkang Road, Qingpu District, Shanghai, 201706, China
Tel.: (86) 2159869999
Web Site: https://www.shclkj.com
Year Founded: 2003
603012—(SHG)
Rev.: $366,150,718
Assets: $877,003,167
Liabilities: $403,138,340
Net Worth: $473,864,826
Earnings: $56,767,398
Fiscal Year-end: 12/31/22
Coal Mining Support Services
N.A.I.C.S.: 213113

SHANGHAI CHURUI ENERGY TECHNOLOGY CO., LTD.
B3-3002 No 171Huayuan Rd, Shanghai, 200083, China
Tel.: (86) 21 66293936
Web Site: http://www.atfss.com
Energy Generation & Storage Services
N.A.I.C.S.: 221118

Subsidiaries:

Solutronic Energy GmbH (1)
Kuferstrasse 18, 73257, Kongen, Germany
Tel.: (49) 7024961280
Web Site: http://www.solutronic.de
Sales Range: $1-9.9 Million
Emp.: 35
Grid-Connected Photovoltaic Inverter Mfr & Sales
N.A.I.C.S.: 335999
Karl-Friedrich Kaupp *(Chm-Supervisory Bd)*

SHANGHAI COMMERCIAL BANK LIMITED
Shanghai Commercial Bank Tower 12 Queens Road, Central, China (Hong Kong)
Tel.: (852) 2818 0282   HK
Web Site: http://www.shacombank.com.hk
Year Founded: 1950
Rev.: $866,266,829
Assets: $28,587,290,889
Liabilities: $24,654,829,149
Net Worth: $3,932,461,740
Earnings: $388,052,837
Emp.: 1,858
Fiscal Year-end: 12/31/19
Banking Services
N.A.I.C.S.: 522110
David Sek-chi Kwok *(Deputy Chm, CEO & Mng Dir)*

Subsidiaries:

Infinite Financial Solutions Limited (1)
17/F Fortis Tower 77 - 79 Gloucester Road, Wanchai, China (Hong Kong)
Tel.: (852) 21341291
Web Site: http://www.ifshk.com
Information Technology Consulting Services
N.A.I.C.S.: 541512

Paofoong Insurance Company (Hong Kong) Limited (1)
20/F 666 Nathan Road, Mongkok, Kowloon, China (Hong Kong)
Tel.: (852) 2207 2015
General Insurance Services
N.A.I.C.S.: 524210

Shacom Futures Limited (1)
Room 303 Houston Centre 63 Mody Road Tsimshatsui East, Mongkok, Kowloon, China (Hong Kong)
Tel.: (852) 22903860
Web Site: http://www.shacomfutures.com.hk
Online Trading Services
N.A.I.C.S.: 561990

Shacom Insurance Brokers Limited (1)
20/F Shacombank Building 666 Nathan Road, Mongkok, Kowloon, China (Hong Kong)
Tel.: (852) 22072028
General Insurance Services
N.A.I.C.S.: 524210
Mo Joysse *(Gen Mgr)*

Shanghai Commercial Bank Trustee Limited (1)
11/F Mongkok, Kowloon, China (Hong Kong)
Tel.: (852) 22072218
Financial Services
N.A.I.C.S.: 522320

SHANGHAI CONSTRUCTION GROUP CO., LTD.
No 666 Daming Road E, Shanghai, 200080, China
Tel.: (86) 2155885959
Web Site: https://www.scg.com.cn
Year Founded: 1998
600170—(SHG)
Rev.: $42,769,721,484
Assets: $53,643,703,310
Liabilities: $46,453,897,442
Net Worth: $7,189,805,867
Earnings: $218,724,021
Emp.: 30,000
Fiscal Year-end: 12/31/23
Construction Engineering Services
N.A.I.C.S.: 541330
Yongshen Xue *(VP & Dir-Risk Control)*

Subsidiaries:

Broadway Elite LLC (1)
400 S Broadway, Los Angeles, CA 90013
Tel.: (213) 568-6677
Web Site: https://perlabroadway.com
Construction Services

SHANGHAI CONSTRUCTION GROUP CO., LTD.

Shanghai Construction Group Co., Ltd.—(Continued)
N.A.I.C.S.: 236220

China SFECO Group (1)
No 681 Xiaomuqiao Road, Shanghai, 200032, China
Tel.: (86) 21 61952888
Web Site: http://www.sfeco.net.cn
Civil Engineering Services
N.A.I.C.S.: 541330
Zhang Linfa *(Chm)*

SCG America Group Inc. (1)
1500 Broadway 33rd Fl, New York, NY 10036
Tel.: (212) 789-0000
Web Site: https://www.scgamerica.com
Real Estate Services
N.A.I.C.S.: 531210

SCG E-commerce Co., Ltd. (1)
No 150 Wuyi Road, Shanghai, 200050, China
Tel.: (86) 2162516006
Construction Services
N.A.I.C.S.: 236220

Shanghai Building Decoration Engineering Group Co., Ltd. (1)
Building 3 Lane 318 Yonghe Road, Shanghai, 200072, China
Tel.: (86) 2126079955
Construction Services
N.A.I.C.S.: 236220

Shanghai Construction Building Materials Technology Group Co., Ltd. (1)
No 848 Siping Road, Shanghai, 200086, China
Tel.: (86) 2125252898
Construction Services
N.A.I.C.S.: 236220

Shanghai Construction Design & Research General Institute Co., Ltd. (1)
Building 1 No 51 Wuzhong Road, Xuhui District, Shanghai, 200050, China
Tel.: (86) 2151628833
Web Site: https://scdri.scg.com.cn
Emp.: 2,000
Construction Services
N.A.I.C.S.: 236220

Shanghai Construction Design & Research Institute Co., Ltd. (1)
Wuyi Road No 150, Changning district, Shanghai, 200050, China
Tel.: (86) 21 62108117
Web Site: http://www.scdri.com
Civil Engineering Services
N.A.I.C.S.: 541330

Shanghai Construction No.1 (Group) Co., Ltd. (1)
33 Fushan Road, 200120, Shanghai, China
Tel.: (86) 21 5888 5866
Web Site: http://www.sc1gc.cn
Civil Engineering Services
N.A.I.C.S.: 541330

Shanghai Construction No.2 (Group) Co., Ltd. (1)
No 289 Wuzhou Road, Shanghai, 200080, China
Tel.: (86) 21 6541 8128
Web Site: http://www.scg2.com
Civil Engineering Services
N.A.I.C.S.: 541330

Shanghai Construction No.4 (Group) Co., Ltd. (1)
No 928 Guilin Road, Shanghai, 201103, China
Tel.: (86) 2162530177
Web Site: http://www.scc4.cn
Civil Engineering Services
N.A.I.C.S.: 541330

Shanghai Construction No.5 (Group) Co., Ltd. (1)
No 1000 Caoyang Road, Shanghai, 200063, China
Tel.: (86) 2162549070
Web Site: http://www.scgwj.com
Civil Engineering Services
N.A.I.C.S.: 541330

Shanghai Construction No.7 (Group) Co., Ltd. (1)

No 150 Wuyi Road, Shanghai, 200050, China
Tel.: (86) 21 62527188
Web Site: http://www.shqj.com.cn
Civil Engineering Services
N.A.I.C.S.: 541330

Shanghai Foundation Engineering Group Co., Ltd. (1)
No 406 Jiangxi Road M, Shanghai, 200002, China
Tel.: (86) 2163292888
Web Site: http://www.sfeg.cc
Civil Engineering Services
N.A.I.C.S.: 541330
Xudong Lee *(Engr-Project)*

Shanghai Garden & Landscape (Group) Co., Ltd. (1)
No 130 Zhizaoju Road, Shanghai, 200023, China
Tel.: (86) 63127878
Web Site: http://www.sggc.com.cn
Civil Engineering Services
N.A.I.C.S.: 541330

Shanghai Hua Dong Construction Machinery Co., Ltd. (1)
No 1058 Heng an road pudong new area, Shanghai, 200137, China
Tel.: (86) 21 50675858
Web Site: http://www.huajian.com.cn
Transportation Equipment Mfr
N.A.I.C.S.: 336360

Shanghai Huadong Construction Machinery Factory Co., Ltd. (1)
No 1058 Heng'an Road, Shanghai, 200137, China
Tel.: (86) 2150675858
Construction Services
N.A.I.C.S.: 236220

Shanghai Installation Engineering Group Co., Ltd. (1)
No 390 Tanggu Road, Shanghai, 200080, China
Tel.: (86) 2163246340
Web Site: http://www.siec.cn
Civil Engineering Services
N.A.I.C.S.: 541330

Shanghai Jianhao Engineering Consultancy Co., Ltd. (1)
Room 402 Xinda Science and Technology Park No 499 Northwest Road, Shayibake District, Urumqi, 200030, Xinjiang, China
Tel.: (86) 215 407 1998
Web Site: https://sjhec.scg.com.cn
Engineering Consulting Services
N.A.I.C.S.: 541330

Shanghai Mechanized Construction Corporation Ltd. (1)
No 701 Luochuan Road N, Zhabei District, Shanghai, 200072, China
Tel.: (86) 21 56653131
Web Site: http://www.chinasmcc.com
Civil Engineering Services
N.A.I.C.S.: 541330

Shanghai Mechanized Construction Group Co., Ltd. (1)
No 701 Luochuan Road N, Shanghai, 200072, China
Tel.: (86) 2156036232
Construction Services
N.A.I.C.S.: 236220

Shanghai Municipal Construction Co., Ltd. (1)
No 2100 Songhu Road, Shanghai, 200438, China
Tel.: (86) 2165909091
Civil Engineering Services
N.A.I.C.S.: 541330

Shanghai Municipal Engineering Design Institute (Group) Co., Ltd. (1)
901 North Zhongshan Road 2nd, Yangpu District, Shanghai, 200092, China
Tel.: (86) 2155000000
Web Site: https://www.smedi.com
Civil Engineering Services
N.A.I.C.S.: 541330

Tianjin House Construction Development Group Co., Ltd. (1)
No 66 MaChang Road, Tianjin, 300050, China

Tel.: (86) 222 302 3665
Construction Services
N.A.I.C.S.: 236220

SHANGHAI COOLTECH POWER CO., LTD.
No 1633 Tianchen Road Pingpu Park Zhangjian High-tech Zone, Qingpu District, Shanghai, 201712, China
Tel.: (86) 2159758000
Web Site: https://www.cooltechsh.com
Year Founded: 2002
300153—(CHIN)
Rev.: $122,878,080
Assets: $212,701,788
Liabilities: $99,303,516
Net Worth: $113,398,272
Earnings: $3,945,240
Emp.: 300
Fiscal Year-end: 12/31/22
Generator Mfr
N.A.I.C.S.: 333611
Songfeng Xie *(Chm)*

Subsidiaries:

Cooltech Power International Pte Ltd (1)
22 Boon Lay Way 01-64 Tradehub 21, Singapore, 609968, Singapore
Tel.: (65) 67957003
Web Site: https://www.coolpower.com.sg
Emp.: 6
Generator Distr
N.A.I.C.S.: 423610

SHANGHAI DAIMAY AUTOMOTIVE INTERIOR CO., LTD.
1299 Lianxi Road Beicai Industrial Park, Pudong New District, Shanghai, 201204, China
Tel.: (86) 2150421228
Web Site: https://en.daimay.com
Year Founded: 2001
603730—(SHG)
Rev.: $722,469,913
Assets: $816,889,615
Liabilities: $218,603,614
Net Worth: $598,286,001
Earnings: $80,001,535
Fiscal Year-end: 12/31/22
Car Interior Material Mfr & Distr
N.A.I.C.S.: 336360

SHANGHAI DASHENG AGRICULTURE FINANCE TECHNOLOGY CO., LTD.
706 Renhe Building 2056 Pudong Road, Pudong New Area, Shanghai, 200135, China
Tel.: (86) 2164669450   CN
Web Site: http://www.dsgd-sh.co
1103—(HKG)
Rev.: $131,546,376
Assets: $1,117,444
Liabilities: $310,316,713
Net Worth: ($309,199,270)
Earnings: ($157,937,083)
Emp.: 24
Fiscal Year-end: 12/31/21
Investment Services
N.A.I.C.S.: 523999

Subsidiaries:

Donghua (Hong Kong) Limited (1)
Room 703 7/F New Victory House 93-103 Wing Lok Street, Hong Kong, China (Hong Kong)
Tel.: (852) 35431976
Asphalt & Fuel Oil Dist
N.A.I.C.S.: 423320

Nantong Road and Bridge Engineering Co., Ltd. (1)
Room 1803 Building No 17 No 8 Taoyuan Road, Nantong, 226008, China
Tel.: (86) 513 83562244
Web Site: http://www.ntrb.net.cn
Road & Bridge Construction Services

INTERNATIONAL PUBLIC

N.A.I.C.S.: 237310
Shanghai Taihua Petrochemical Co., Ltd. (1)
4 Floor ShiHua Building No 1525 Pudong Avenue, Shanghai, 200135, China
Tel.: (86) 21 50936990
Fuel Oil Distr
N.A.I.C.S.: 424720

Wuhan Hualong Highway Resources Company Limited (1)
No A0301 3 Floor Xingcheng Building No 176 Fazhan Avenue, Wuhan, 430000, China
Tel.: (86) 27 65681492
Asphalt Distr
N.A.I.C.S.: 423320

Zhengzhou Huasheng Petroleum Products Co. Ltd. (1)
Room 1505 Unit A No 16 East Nongye Road, Zhengzhou, 451450, China
Tel.: (86) 371 62169370
Fuel Oil Distr
N.A.I.C.S.: 424720

SHANGHAI DATA PORT CO., LTD
No 166 Jiangchang Third Road, Jing'an District, Shanghai, 200436, China
Tel.: (86) 2131762188   CN
Web Site: https://www.athub.com
603881—(SHG)
Rev.: $204,337,570
Assets: $1,045,521,018
Liabilities: $621,347,655
Net Worth: $424,173,363
Earnings: $16,133,083
Fiscal Year-end: 12/31/22
Web Hosting Services
N.A.I.C.S.: 518210
Sun Zhongfeng *(Chm)*

SHANGHAI DATUN ENERGY RESOURCES CO., LTD.
No 256 Pudong South Road, Pudong New Area, Shanghai, 200120, China
Tel.: (86) 2168864621
Web Site: http://www.sdtny.com
Year Founded: 1999
600508—(SHG)
Rev.: $1,773,793,158
Assets: $2,715,371,479
Liabilities: $1,011,267,658
Net Worth: $1,704,103,821
Earnings: $244,271,893
Fiscal Year-end: 12/31/22
Coal Mining Services
N.A.I.C.S.: 212115
Mao Zhonghua *(Chm)*

SHANGHAI DAZHONG PUBLIC UTILITIES (GROUP) CO., LTD.
10 F No 2121 Longteng Avenue, Shanghai, 200232, China
Tel.: (86) 2164280679   CN
Web Site: https://www.dzug.cn
Year Founded: 1991
600635—(SHG)
Rev.: $821,840,077
Assets: $3,311,049,802
Liabilities: $1,966,499,824
Net Worth: $1,344,549,979
Earnings: ($46,695,790)
Emp.: 3,208
Fiscal Year-end: 12/31/22
Natural Gas Transmission & Distribution Services
N.A.I.C.S.: 486210
Guoping Yang *(Chm)*

Subsidiaries:

Shenzen Capital Group Co., Ltd. (1)
Fl 11 Investment Building No 4009 Shennan Rd, Futian Center District, Shenzhen, 518048, China
Tel.: (86) 75582912888
Web Site: http://www.szvc.com.cn

AND PRIVATE COMPANIES

Financial Investment Services
N.A.I.C.S.: 523999

Songz Automobile Air Conditioning Co., Ltd. (1)
No 4999 Huaning Road, Xinzhuang Industrial Park, Shanghai, 201108, China
Tel.: (86) 2154424998
Web Site: http://www.shsongz.com.cn
Automobile Air-Conditioning Mfr & Distr
N.A.I.C.S.: 333415

SHANGHAI DOBE CULTURAL & CREATIVE INDUSTRY DEVELOPMENT (GROUP) CO., LTD.
8th Floor Building A Dobe E-Manor No 492 Anhua Road, Changning District, Shanghai, 200050, China
Tel.: (86) 2132508752
Web Site:
 https://www.dobechina.com
Year Founded: 2011
300947—(CHIN)
Rev.: $109,350,512
Assets: $865,995,371
Liabilities: $677,492,703
Net Worth: $188,502,669
Earnings: $4,562,144
Fiscal Year-end: 12/31/22
Information Technology Services
N.A.I.C.S.: 541512
Bo Jia *(Chm)*

SHANGHAI DOWELL TRADING CO. LTD.
Dowell Business Building, No.288 Luban Road, Huangpu District, Shanghai, China
Tel.: (86) 21 53027777
Web Site:
 http://www.dowellgroup.com.cn
Electrical Power Distr & Mfr
N.A.I.C.S.: 221117
Chen Cunwu *(Chm)*

Subsidiaries:

Beijing Fraser Suites Real Estate Management Co., Ltd (1)
12 Jin Tong Xi Road, Chaoyang, Beijing, 100020, China
Tel.: (86) 1059086000
Web Site:
 http://beijing.frasershospitality.com
Real Estate Manangement Services
N.A.I.C.S.: 531390

SHANGHAI DRAGON CORPORATION
4F Block 10 No 584 Zhizaoju Road, Huangpu District, Shanghai, 201315, China
Tel.: (86) 2163159108
Web Site:
 http://www.shanghaidragon.com.cn
Year Founded: 1992
600630—(SHG)
Rev.: $308,088,453
Assets: $239,084,450
Liabilities: $138,300,711
Net Worth: $100,783,739
Earnings: $73,314,395)
Fiscal Year-end: 12/31/22
Textile Products Mfr
N.A.I.C.S.: 315250
Ni Guohua *(Chm)*

SHANGHAI DRAGONNET TECHNOLOGY CO., LTD.
Building 6 Phase 3 Technology Oasis No 1016 Tianlin Road, Minhang District, Shanghai, 200233, China
Tel.: (86) 2123521259
Web Site: http://www.dnt.com.cn
Year Founded: 2001
300245—(SSE)
Rev.: $83,999,916
Assets: $243,248,616
Liabilities: $38,197,224
Net Worth: $205,051,392
Earnings: ($432,432)
Emp.: 400
Fiscal Year-end: 12/31/22
IT Services
N.A.I.C.S.: 541519
Su Bo *(Chm)*

SHANGHAI DZH LIMITED
Building 1 Youyou Century Plaza Lane 428 Yanggao South Road, Pudong New District, Shanghai, 200127, China
Tel.: (86) 2120219997
Web Site: https://www.gw.com.cn
Year Founded: 2000
601519—(SHG)
Rev.: $109,547,577
Assets: $328,048,826
Liabilities: $100,715,603
Net Worth: $227,333,223
Earnings: ($12,393,852)
Fiscal Year-end: 12/31/22
Internet Financial Information Services
N.A.I.C.S.: 513199

Subsidiaries:

Aastocks.com Ltd. (1)
43/F Axa Tower Landmark East 100 How Ming Street, Kwun Tong, Kowloon, China (Hong Kong)
Tel.: (852) 21218803
Web Site: http://www.aastocks.com
Software Development Services
N.A.I.C.S.: 513210

SHANGHAI ELECTRIC GROUP COMPANY LIMITED
No 110 Middle Sichuan Road, Shanghai, 200002, China
Tel.: (86) 2133261888   CN
Web Site: https://www.shanghai-electric.com
Year Founded: 1880
2727—(HKG)
Rev.: $16,514,285,767
Assets: $40,438,127,621
Liabilities: $27,213,266,574
Net Worth: $13,224,861,047
Earnings: ($500,734,354)
Emp.: 41,739
Fiscal Year-end: 12/31/22
Electric Industrial Products Mfr
N.A.I.C.S.: 335999
Liping Tong *(Chief Legal Officer)*

Subsidiaries:

Shanghai Boiler Works Ltd. (1)
No250 Huaning Road, Minhang District, Shanghai, 200245, PRC, China
Tel.: (86) 2164302391
Web Site: http://www.shanghai-electric.com
Sales Range: $25-49.9 Million
Emp.: 1,800
Design & Manufacture of Utility Boilers
N.A.I.C.S.: 332410

Shanghai Cyeco Environmental Technology Co., Ltd. (1)
2478 pudong avenue, Shanghai, 200129, China
Tel.: (86) 2158852405
Web Site: http://www.cyeco.com
Electric Equipment Mfr
N.A.I.C.S.: 335311

Shanghai Electric Automation Group (1)
No 360 Mengzi Road, Huangpu District, Shanghai, 200003, China
Tel.: (86) 2163893999
Electric Equipment Mfr
N.A.I.C.S.: 335999

Shanghai Electric Digital Technology Co., Ltd. (1)
Building L 115 Caobao Road, Xuhui District, Shanghai, 200233, China
Tel.: (86) 2154587000
Software & Digital Development Services
N.A.I.C.S.: 541810

Shanghai Electric Economy Group (1)
No 212 Jiangning Road Catic Building, Shanghai, 200041, China
Tel.: (86) 2152895577
Financial Services
N.A.I.C.S.: 522291

Subsidiary (Domestic):

Shanghai Electric Group Finance Co., Ltd. (2)
No 212 Jiangning Road Catic Building, Shanghai, 200041, China
Tel.: (86) 2152895555
Electric Equipment Mfr
N.A.I.C.S.: 335999

Shanghai Electric Environmental Protection Group (1)
No 1287 West Beijing Road, Jing'An District, Shanghai, 200040, China
Tel.: (86) 2162472277
Electric Industrial Products Mfr
N.A.I.C.S.: 335999

Shanghai Electric Group Nuclear Power Corporation (1)
No 77 Cenglin Road, Pudong New District, Shanghai, 201306, China
Tel.: (86) 2138220121
Nuclear Device Mfr
N.A.I.C.S.: 334519

Subsidiary (Domestic):

SEC-KSB Pump Co., Ltd. (2)
No 1400 Jiangchuan Road, Minhang District, Shanghai, 200245, China
Tel.: (86) 2164302888
Electric Equipment Mfr
N.A.I.C.S.: 335999

Shanghai Electric Nuclear Power Equipment Co., Ltd. (2)
No77 Cenglin Road Lingang, Pudon New District, Shanghai, 201306, China
Tel.: (86) 2138220100
Nuclear Device Mfr
N.A.I.C.S.: 334519

Shanghai No 1 Machine Tool Works Co., Ltd. (2)
No 185 Yitian Road, Pudong New District, Shanghai, 201308, China
Tel.: (86) 2138221000
Electric Equipment Mfr
N.A.I.C.S.: 335999

Shanghai Electric Heavy Industry Group (1)
No 3988 Dongchuan Road, Minhang District, Shanghai, 200245, China
Tel.: (86) 2167287000
Rolling Mill Machinery Product Mfr
N.A.I.C.S.: 333519

Subsidiary (Domestic):

Shanghai Institute of Machinery Building Technology Co., Ltd. (2)
No 960 Zhongxin Road, Zhabei District, Shanghai, 200070, China
Tel.: (86) 2156977377
Electric Equipment Mfr
N.A.I.C.S.: 335999

Shanghai Ship-use Crankshaft Co., Ltd. (2)
177 Yitian Road Lingang New City, Pudong New District, Shanghai, 201308, China
Tel.: (86) 2138220800
Electric Equipment Mfr
N.A.I.C.S.: 335999

Shanghai Electric Lingang Heavy Machinery Equipment Co., Ltd. (1)
No 77 Cenglin Road Lingang New Town, Pudong New Area, Shanghai, 201306, China
Tel.: (86) 2138220000
Electric Equipment Mfr
N.A.I.C.S.: 335999

Shanghai Electric Power Electronics Co., Ltd. (1)
No 66 Fuqiao Rd, Baoshan, Shanghai, 201906, China
Tel.: (86) 2133713200
Electric Equipment Mfr.
N.A.I.C.S.: 335999

Shanghai Electric Power Generation Group (1)
No 188 Linchun Road, Minhang District, Shanghai, 201199, PRC, China
Tel.: (86) 2134059888
Power Generating Equipment Mfr
N.A.I.C.S.: 333611

Subsidiary (Domestic):

SEC - IHI Power Generation Environment Protection Engineering Co., Ltd. (2)
3/F No 333 Yindu W Road, Minhang District, Shanghai, 201612, China
Tel.: (86) 2137018128
Electric Equipment Mfr
N.A.I.C.S.: 335999

SEPG Service Co., Ltd. (2)
F4-7 Building A No 333 West Yindu Road, Shanghai, 201612, China
Tel.: (86) 2167686999
Electric Equipment Mfr
N.A.I.C.S.: 335999

Shanghai Electric - SPX Engineering & Technologies Co., Ltd. (2)
Floor 3 Building C No621 Long Chang Road, Yangpu District, Shanghai, 200090, China
Tel.: (86) 2160703766
Electric Equipment Mfr
N.A.I.C.S.: 335999

Shanghai Electric Desalination Engineering Technology Co., Ltd. (2)
No 2218 Yangshupu Road, Shanghai, 200090, China
Tel.: (86) 2160703802
Electric Equipment Mfr
N.A.I.C.S.: 335999

Shanghai Electric Fuji Electric Power Technology Co., Ltd. (2)
1F No 188 LinChun Road, Minhang District, Shanghai, 201199, China
Tel.: (86) 2163816698
Emp.: 200
Electric Equipment Mfr
N.A.I.C.S.: 335999

Shanghai Electric Group Shanghai Electric Machinery Co., Ltd. (2)
No 555 Jiangchuan Road, Minhang District, Shanghai, 200240, China
Tel.: (86) 2164638221
Emp.: 2,300
Electric Equipment Mfr
N.A.I.C.S.: 335999

Shanghai Electric Power Generation Engineering Company (2)
No 188 Linchun Rd, Minhang District, Shanghai, 201199, China
Tel.: (86) 2134059888
Electric Equipment Mfr
N.A.I.C.S.: 335999

Plant (Domestic):

Shanghai Electric Power Generation Group - SEPG Lingang Works (2)
Zone 5-6 No 77 Lingang Cengling Road, Pudong New Area, Shanghai, 201308, China
Tel.: (86) 2138220600
Electric Equipment Mfr
N.A.I.C.S.: 335999

Shanghai Electric Power Generation Group - SEPG Shanghai Generator Works (2)
No 555 Jiangchuan Road, Minhang District, Shanghai, 200240, China
Tel.: (86) 2164626666
Electric Equipment Mfr
N.A.I.C.S.: 335999

Subsidiary (Domestic):

Shanghai Electric SHMP Pulverizing & Special Equipment Co., Ltd. (2)
No 1800 Jiangchuan Rd, Minghang, Shanghai, 200245, China

SHANGHAI ELECTRIC GROUP COMPANY LIMITED / INTERNATIONAL PUBLIC

Shanghai Electric Group Company Limited—(Continued)
Tel.: (86) 2134097557
Electric Equipment Mfr
N.A.I.C.S.: 335999

Shanghai Electric Wind Power Group Co., Ltd. (2)
No 115 Caobao Road, Minhang District, Shanghai, 200233, China
Tel.: (86) 2134290800
Wind Power Equipment Mfr
N.A.I.C.S.: 333611

Shanghai Power Station Auxiliary Equipment Works Co., Ltd. (2)
No 1900 Yangshupu Road, Shanghai, 200090, China
Tel.: (86) 2165431040
Electric Equipment Mfr
N.A.I.C.S.: 335999

Shanghai Turbine Works Co., Ltd. (2)
No 333 Jiangchuan Road, Minhang District, Shanghai, 200240, China
Tel.: (86) 2164358331
Gas Turbine Mfr
N.A.I.C.S.: 336412

Shanghai Electric Power T&D Group (1)
Floor 30 Wandu Centre No 8 Xingyi Road, Changning District, Shanghai, 200336, China
Tel.: (86) 2122306230
Power Transmission Equipment Mfr & Distr
N.A.I.C.S.: 333613

Subsidiary (Domestic):

Shanghai Dahua Electrical Equipment Co., Ltd.
No 2000 Xiangjiang Highway, Jiading District, Shanghai, 201812, China
Tel.: (86) 69132663
Electric Equipment Mfr
N.A.I.C.S.: 335999

Shanghai Electric Power T&D Engineering Co., Ltd. (2)
4th Floor No 1395 Yuyuan Road, Changning District, Shanghai, 200050, China
Tel.: (86) 2152371666
Electric Equipment Mfr
N.A.I.C.S.: 335999

Shanghai Electric Power T&D Testing Center Co., Ltd. (2)
No 110 Middle Sichuan Road, Huang Pu District, Shanghai, 200233, China
Tel.: (86) 2133261888
Web Site: http://en.setc-sh.com
Testing Laboratory Services
N.A.I.C.S.: 541380

Shanghai Feihang Electric Wire & Cable Co., Ltd. (2)
688 Yuyang Road, Songjiang District, Shanghai, 201600, China
Tel.: (86) 2157705569
Electric Equipment Mfr
N.A.I.C.S.: 335999

Shanghai Huapu Cable Co., Ltd. (2)
2800 Guanghua Road, Minhang District, Shanghai, 201111, China
Tel.: (86) 2154981381
Emp.: 598
Electric Equipment Mfr
N.A.I.C.S.: 335999

Shanghai Najie Complete Electric Co., Ltd. (2)
Qizhong Forest Sports City Economic Park, Minhang District, Shanghai, 201111, China
Tel.: (86) 2154982864
Emp.: 210
Electric Equipment Mfr
N.A.I.C.S.: 335999

Shanghai Nan Qiao Transformer Co., Ltd. (2)
6 Fengpu Avenue Shanghai Fengpu Industrial Park, Shanghai, 201400, China
Tel.: (86) 2167100854
Electric Equipment Mfr
N.A.I.C.S.: 335999

Wujiang Transformer Co., Ltd. (2)
No 18 Wubian Avenue Friendship Industrial Zone, Songling Town Wujiang District, Suzhou, 215200, China
Tel.: (86) 51263422090
Web Site: https://en.wbelec.com
Electric Equipment Mfr
N.A.I.C.S.: 335999

Shanghai Heavy Machinery Plant Co., Ltd. (1)
1800 Jiangchuan Road, Minhang District, Shanghai, 200245, China (99.77%)
Tel.: (86) 21 5472 1141
Web Site: http://www.shanghai-electric.com
Mining Machinery & Equipment Mfr
N.A.I.C.S.: 333131

Shanghai Jiejin New Electric Materials Co., Ltd. (1)
Building 2 585 Chuanzhan Road, Pudong New District, Shanghai, 201299, China
Tel.: (86) 2158599559
Electric Equipment Mfr
N.A.I.C.S.: 335999

Shanghai Machine Tool Works Ltd. (2)
1146 Jungong Road, Yangpu District, Shanghai, 200093, China
Tel.: (86) 2165483006
Electric Equipment Mfr
N.A.I.C.S.: 335999

Shanghai Mechanical & Electrical Industry Co., Ltd. (2)
No 2188 Xinzhu Road, Minhang District, Shanghai, 200237, China
Tel.: (86) 2168547168
Web Site: https://www.chinasec.cn
Rev.: $3,309,161,858
Assets: $5,265,933,211
Liabilities: $3,077,887,691
Net Worth: $2,188,045,520
Earnings: $137,798,950
Fiscal Year-end: 12/31/2022
Elevator & Moving Stairway Mfr
N.A.I.C.S.: 333921
Wu Lei (Chm & Sec-Party)

Shanghai Neles-Jamesbury Valve Co., Ltd. (1)
No 333 Lane QinQiao Road, Pudong District, Shanghai, China
Tel.: (86) 2161006611
Web Site: http://www.snjvalve.com
Electric Equipment Mfr
N.A.I.C.S.: 335311

Shanghai Power Transmission & Distribution Co., Ltd. (1)
No 212 Qin Jiang Road, 200233, Shanghai, PRC, China (83.57%)
Tel.: (86) 2152392068
Web Site: http://www.shanghai-electric.com
Power Distribution & Specialty Transformer Mfr
N.A.I.C.S.: 335311

Shanghai Prime Machinery Company Limited (1)
2747 Songhuajiang Road, Shanghai, 200437, China
Tel.: (86) 2164729900
Web Site: http://www.pmcsh.com
Rev.: $1,201,282,715
Assets: $1,380,097,040
Liabilities: $781,315,840
Net Worth: $598,781,201
Earnings: $18,878,897
Emp.: 4,488
Fiscal Year-end: 12/31/2019
Cutting Tool Mfr & Distr
N.A.I.C.S.: 333515
Zhiyan Zhou (Chm)

Subsidiary (Non-US):

Koninklijke Nedschroef Holding B.V. (2)
Kanaaldijk NW 75, 5707 IC, Helmond, Netherlands
Tel.: (31) 492548556
Web Site: http://www.nedschroef.com
Fasteners & Machine Tools Mfr & Distr
N.A.I.C.S.: 332722
Paul Raedts (CFO)

Subsidiary (Domestic):

Shanghai Biaowu High Tensile Fasteners Company Limited (2)

No 175 Gongxiang Road, Baoshan District, Shanghai, 201901, China (100%)
Tel.: (86) 21 66734516
Web Site: http://www.pmcsh.com
Industrial Products Mfr
N.A.I.C.S.: 333248

Shanghai Fastener & Welding Material Technology Research Centre Company Limited (2)
No 175 Baoshan District Road, Shanghai, 201901, China (100%)
Tel.: (86) 21 5585564
Web Site: http://www.sh-jhs.com
Industrial Research Services
N.A.I.C.S.: 541715

Affiliate (Domestic):

Shanghai General Bearing Company Limited (2)
No 1201 Humin Road Minhang District, Shanghai, 200240, China (40%)
Tel.: (86) 21 6435 9876
Industrial Bearing Mfr
N.A.I.C.S.: 332991

Subsidiary (Domestic):

Shanghai High Strength Bolt Factory Company Limited (2)
No 2866 Jiangshan Road Lingang Heavy Equipment Zone, Shanghai, 201306, China (100%)
Tel.: (86) 21 63831141
Web Site: http://www.shsg.cn
Industrial Bolt Mfr
N.A.I.C.S.: 332722

Shanghai Tian An Bearing Company Limited (2)
No 4399 Yindu Road, Shanghai, 201108, China (100%)
Tel.: (86) 2134707698
Web Site: http://www.pmcsh.com
Industrial Bearing Mfr
N.A.I.C.S.: 332991

Shanghai Tool Works Company Limited (2)
1060 Jun Gong Road, Shanghai, 200093, China (100%)
Tel.: (86) 2165386538
Web Site: https://stwc.cncmachinetool.com
Industrial Tools Mfr
N.A.I.C.S.: 333515

Shanghai United Bearing Company Limited (2)
No 1111 Humin Road, Shanghai, 200240, China (90%)
Tel.: (86) 2164358201
Web Site: http://www.subc.com.cn
Industrial Products Mfr
N.A.I.C.S.: 332991

Shanghai Zhenhua Bearing Factory Company Limited (2)
No 5291 Jiading Huyi Road, Shanghai, 210806, China (100%)
Tel.: (86) 21 67073865
Web Site: http://www.sbczhbearing.com
Industrial Bearing Mfr
N.A.I.C.S.: 332991

WuXi Turbine Blade Company Limited (2)
No 1800 Huishan Avenue, Huishan Economic Development District, Wuxi, 214174, JiangSu, China (100%)
Tel.: (86) 51085727135
Web Site: https://www.turblade.com
Turbine Blade Mfr
N.A.I.C.S.: 333611

SHANGHAI ELECTRIC POWER COMPANY LIMITED
No 268 Zhongshan South Road, Shanghai, 200010, China
Tel.: (86) 2123108718
Web Site: http://www.shanghaipower.com
Year Founded: 1998
600021—(SHG)
Rev.: $5,498,220,041
Assets: $22,602,303,702
Liabilities: $16,416,363,717
Net Worth: $6,185,939,985
Earnings: $45,035,827
Emp.: 6,150
Fiscal Year-end: 12/31/22
Electric Power
N.A.I.C.S.: 221122
Hua Lin (Chm)

Subsidiaries:

Shanghai Electric Power Fuel Co., Ltd. (1)
No 310 Chongqing S Road, Huangpu, Shanghai, 200025, China
Tel.: (86) 2164673583
Electric Power Distr
N.A.I.C.S.: 221122

Shanghai Waigaoqiao Power Generation Co., Ltd. (1)
1001 Haixu Road, Pudong New Zone, Shanghai, 200000, China
Tel.: (86) 2158695869
Electric Power Generation Services
N.A.I.C.S.: 221118

SHANGHAI EMPEROR OF CLEANING HI-TECH CO., LTD.
Floor 5-6 Block B Cypress Mansion No 1230 Zhongshan North 1st Road, Shanghai, 200437, China
Tel.: (86) 4006596586
Web Site: https://www.china-xiba.com
Year Founded: 1994
603200—(SHG)
Rev.: $84,939,164
Assets: $192,783,970
Liabilities: $59,288,617
Net Worth: $133,495,353
Earnings: $5,934,806
Fiscal Year-end: 12/31/22
Waste Treatment Services
N.A.I.C.S.: 562219
Wei Wang (Chm & Pres)

SHANGHAI FEILO ACOUSTICS CO., LTD.
F11-13 Building 1 No 406 Guilin Road, Xuhui District, Shanghai, 200233, China
Tel.: (86) 2134239651
Web Site: https://facs.inesa.com
Year Founded: 1984
600651—(SHG)
Rev.: $468,085,695
Assets: $666,359,179
Liabilities: $318,385,908
Net Worth: $347,973,271
Earnings: $43,724,589
Fiscal Year-end: 12/31/22
Electrical Equipment Mfr & Whslr
N.A.I.C.S.: 335999
Li Li Xin (Chm & Sec-Party)

Subsidiaries:

Inesa Europa Kft. (1)
30 Pallag Street, Dunakeszi, Hungary
Tel.: (36) 27200988
Web Site: http://inesaeuropa.com
Light Emitting Diode Distr
N.A.I.C.S.: 423610
Miroslav Rasonja (Reg Mgr-Sls)

SHANGHAI FENGHWA GROUP CO., LTD.
Room 901 Youyou International Plaza No 76 Pujian Road Pudong New Area, Shanghai, 200127, China
Tel.: (86) 2150903399
Web Site: http://www.fenghwa.sh.cn
600615—(SHG)
Rev.: $21,397,058
Assets: $98,204,114
Liabilities: $8,780,111
Net Worth: $89,424,003
Earnings: $1,131,441
Fiscal Year-end: 12/31/22
Magnesium Alloy Product Mfr

SHANGHAI FENGYUZHU CULTURE TECHNOLOGY CO., LTD.
No 191 Jiangchang 3rd Road, Jing'an District, Shanghai, 200436, China
Tel.: (86) 2156206468
Web Site: http://www.fengyuzhu.com.cn
Year Founded: 2003
603466—(SHG)
Rev.: $450,423,611
Assets: $674,697,005
Liabilities: $323,156,660
Net Worth: $351,540,345
Earnings: $67,234,676
Fiscal Year-end: 12/31/21
Digital Entertainment Services
N.A.I.C.S.: 512131
Hui Li *(Chm & Gen Mgr)*

SHANGHAI FILM CO., LTD
Building C Shanghai Film Plaza No 595 Caoxi North Road, Xuhui District, Shanghai, 200030, China
Tel.: (86) 2133991000
Web Site: https://www.sh-sfc.com
Year Founded: 1994
601595—(SHG)
Rev.: $51,715,680
Assets: $407,997,233
Liabilities: $172,799,940
Net Worth: $235,197,294
Earnings: ($47,005,316)
Fiscal Year-end: 12/31/22
Movie Theatre Operator
N.A.I.C.S.: 512131
Jianer Wang *(Chm)*

SHANGHAI FLYCO ELECTRICAL APPLIANCE CO., LTD.
No 555 Fulin East Road, Songjiang District, Shanghai, 201613, China
Tel.: (86) 2152858888
Web Site: https://www.flyco.com
Year Founded: 1999
603868—(SHG)
Rev.: $649,649,586
Assets: $610,253,725
Liabilities: $128,943,023
Net Worth: $481,310,702
Earnings: $115,545,999
Fiscal Year-end: 12/31/22
Hair Dryer Mfr & Distr
N.A.I.C.S.: 335210
Li Gaiteng *(Chm & Pres)*

SHANGHAI FOREIGN SERVICE HOLDING GROUP CO.,LTD.
12F Building T3 Greenland Bund Center No 55 Huiguan Street, Huangpu District, Shanghai, 200011, China
Tel.: (86) 2165670587
Web Site: http://www.62580000.com.cn
Year Founded: 1992
600662—(SHG)
Rev.: $2,058,783,943
Assets: $2,063,370,601
Liabilities: $1,468,870,879
Net Worth: $594,499,721
Earnings: $76,703,174
Emp.: 3,000,000
Fiscal Year-end: 12/31/22
Holding Company
N.A.I.C.S.: 551112
Chen Weiquan *(Chm & Pres)*

SHANGHAI FORTUNE TECH-GROUP CO., LTD
3F Building A2 China Fortune Properties No 200 Tianlin Road, Xuhui District, Shanghai, 200233, China
Tel.: (86) 2154644699
Web Site: https://www.fortune-co.com
Year Founded: 2000
300493—(CHIN)
Rev.: $295,055,444
Assets: $223,687,344
Liabilities: $79,865,262
Net Worth: $143,822,082
Earnings: $7,597,297
Fiscal Year-end: 12/31/22
Semi Conductor Chip Distr
N.A.I.C.S.: 423690
Lang Xiaogang *(Chm)*

SHANGHAI FOSUN PHARMACEUTICAL (GROUP) CO., LTD.
No 1289 Yishan Road, Building A Fosun Technology Park, Shanghai, 200233, China
Tel.: (86) 2133987000   CN
Web Site: https://www.fosunpharma.com
Year Founded: 1994
SFOSF—(OTCIQ)
Rev.: $5,711,190,873
Assets: $15,705,475,604
Liabilities: $7,871,807,432
Net Worth: $7,833,668,171
Earnings: $402,553,722
Emp.: 40,370
Fiscal Year-end: 12/31/23
Pharmaceuticals Product Mfr
N.A.I.C.S.: 325412
Guan Xiaohui *(Co-Pres & CFO)*

Subsidiaries:

Ambrx, Inc.   (1)
10975 N Torrey Pines Rd, La Jolla, CA 92037
Tel.: (858) 875-2400
Web Site: http://www.ambrx.com
Biopharmaceutical Developer
N.A.I.C.S.: 325412
Feng Tian *(Chm, Pres & CEO)*

Beijing United Family Hospital Management Co., Ltd.   (1)
2 Jiangtai Road, Chaoyang, Beijing, 100015, China
Tel.: (86) 1059277000
Web Site: http://beijing.ufh.com.cn
Holding Company; Hospital, Clinic & Clinical Research Facilities Operator; Home Health Care Services
N.A.I.C.S.: 551112

Affiliate (Domestic):

Beijing United Family Hospital Co., Ltd.   (2)
No 2 Jiangtai Road, Chaoyang District, Beijing, 100015, China
Tel.: (86) 10 5927 7200
Web Site: http://beijing.ufh.com.cn
Emp.: 350
Hospital Operator
N.A.I.C.S.: 622110

Chindex Medical Limited   (1)
28F Fosun International Center No 237 Chaoyang North Road, Chaoyang District, Beijing, 100020, China   (100%)
Tel.: (86) 1065528822
Web Site: https://www.chindexmedical.com
Emp.: 1,500
Medical Device Mfr
N.A.I.C.S.: 339112

Subsidiary (Non-US):

Alma Lasers Ltd.   (2)
Halamish 14, 38900, Caesarea, Israel
Tel.: (972) 46275357
Web Site: https://www.almalasers.com
Sales Range: $25-49.9 Million
Emp.: 138
Developer & Mfr of Laser, Light-Based, Radiofrequency & Ultrasound Devices for Aesthetic & Medical Applications
N.A.I.C.S.: 339112

Subsidiary (US):

Alma Lasers, Inc.   (3)
485 Half Day Rd Ste 100, Buffalo Grove, IL 60089
Tel.: (224) 377-2000
Web Site: http://www.almainc.com
Sales Range: $25-49.9 Million
Laser, Light-Based & Radiofrequency Devices for Aesthetic & Medical Applications Whslr
N.A.I.C.S.: 423450
Avi Farbstein *(CEO-North America)*

Subsidiary (Domestic):

Chindex (Shanghai) Int'l Trading Co., Ltd.   (2)
317 Mei Gui Bei Lu, Waigaoqiao Free Trade Zone, Shanghai, 200131, China
Tel.: (86) 2150643566
Sales Range: $50-74.9 Million
Emp.: 130
Medical & Hospital Equipment Importer
N.A.I.C.S.: 423450

Subsidiary (Non-US):

Chindex Hong Kong Limited   (2)
Room 903 9th Fl 148 Electric Road, North Point, China (Hong Kong)
Tel.: (852) 25471536
Web Site: http://www.chindexmedical.com
Emp.: 10
Medical & Hospital Equipment Importer
N.A.I.C.S.: 423450

Foshan Fosun Chancheng Hospital Company Limited   (1)
No 3 Sanyou South Road, Chancheng District, Foshan, China
Tel.: (86) 75782263333
Web Site: https://www.fsccyy.com
Emp.: 2,800
Healthcare & Medical Technology Services
N.A.I.C.S.: 621999

Fosun Kite Biotechnology Co., Ltd.   (1)
No 777 Shengrong Road Zhangjiang Pudong New Area, Shanghai, China
Tel.: (86) 2152212192
Web Site: https://www.fosunkitebio.com
Pharmaceutical Products Research and Development
N.A.I.C.S.: 541714

Human Design Medical LLC   (1)
119 Braintree St, Boston, MA 02134
Tel.: (434) 980-8189
Web Site: http://www.hdmusa.com
Medical Device Mfr
N.A.I.C.S.: 339112

Subsidiary (Non-US):

BREAS Medical AB   (2)
Foretagsvagen 1, Molnlycke, SE-435 33, Gothenburg, Sweden
Tel.: (46) 31 86 88 00
Web Site: http://www.breas.com
Home Care Ventilation & Sleep Therapy Products Mfr
N.A.I.C.S.: 339112
Ola Jensell *(CFO & Sr VP)*

Subsidiary (Non-US):

BREAS Medical GmbH   (3)
Bahnhofstrasse 26, DE-822 11, Herrsching am Ammersee, Germany
Tel.: (49) 815237210
Web Site: http://www.breas.com
Home Care Ventilation & Sleep Therapy Products Distr
N.A.I.C.S.: 423450

BREAS Medical Limited   (3)
Unit A2 The Bridge Business Centre Timothy's Bridge Road, Stratford-Upon-Avon, CV37 9HW, Warks, United Kingdom
Tel.: (44) 1789 293 460
Web Site: http://www.breas.com
Home Care Ventilation & Sleep Therapy Products Distr
N.A.I.C.S.: 423450

BREAS Medical S.R.L.   (3)
C/Minas 32, Alcorcon, 28923, Madrid, Spain
Tel.: (34) 91 752 66 18
Web Site: http://www.breas.com
Home Care Ventilation & Sleep Therapy Products Distr
N.A.I.C.S.: 423450

BREAS Medical SARL   (3)
Parc Technologique de Lyon 8 allee Irene Joliot Curie, Batiment B8, 69800, Saint Priest, France
Tel.: (33) 472472992
Web Site: http://www.breas.com
Home Care Ventilation & Sleep Therapy Products Distr
N.A.I.C.S.: 423450

YaoPharma Co., Ltd.   (1)
100 Xingguang Avenue Renhe Town, Yubei District, Chongqing, 401121, China
Tel.: (86) 23 632 11443
Web Site: http://en.yaopharma.com
Pharmaceuticals Product Mfr
N.A.I.C.S.: 325412

Subsidiary (Domestic):

GlaxoSmithKline Pharmaceuticals (Suzhou) Ltd.   (2)
40 Su Hong Xi Road Suzhou Industrial Park, Suzhou, 215021, China
Tel.: (86) 512 6257 1660
Pharmaceuticals Product Mfr
N.A.I.C.S.: 325412
Herve Gisserot *(Gen Mgr)*

SHANGHAI FRIENDESS ELECTRONICS TECHNOLOGY CO., LTD.
No 1000 Lanxianghu South Road, Minhang District, Shanghai, 200240, China
Tel.: (86) 2164306968
Web Site: http://www.fscut.com
Year Founded: 2007
688188—(SSE)
Rev.: $126,148,263
Assets: $632,474,580
Liabilities: $28,087,554
Net Worth: $604,387,026
Earnings: $67,325,085
Fiscal Year-end: 12/31/22
Electronic Product Mfr & Distr
N.A.I.C.S.: 334419
Ye Tang *(Chm)*

SHANGHAI FUDAN FORWARD S&T CO., LTD.
No 525 Guoquan Road, Yangpu District, Shanghai, 200433, China
Tel.: (86) 2163872288
Web Site: https://www.forwardgroup.com
Year Founded: 1984
600624—(SHG)
Rev.: $110,776,358
Assets: $261,201,424
Liabilities: $121,682,012
Net Worth: $139,519,411
Earnings: ($506,802)
Fiscal Year-end: 12/31/22
Pharmaceutical Product Mfr & Distr
N.A.I.C.S.: 325412
Song Zheng *(Chm)*

SHANGHAI FUDAN MICROELECTRONICS GROUP CO., LTD.
Building 4 127 Guotai Road, Shanghai, 200433, China
Tel.: (86) 2165659100   CN
Web Site: https://www.fmsh.com
Year Founded: 1998
1385—(HKG)
Rev.: $496,862,807
Assets: $857,968,683
Liabilities: $134,463,702
Net Worth: $723,504,981
Earnings: $156,863,973
Emp.: 1,691
Fiscal Year-end: 12/31/22
Integrated Circuits Mfr
N.A.I.C.S.: 334413
Guoxing Jiang *(Chm)*

SHANGHAI FUDAN MICROELECTRONICS GROUP CO., LTD.

Shanghai Fudan Microelectronics Group Co., Ltd.—(Continued)

Subsidiaries:

Beijing Fudan Microelectronics Technology Co., Ltd. (1)
Gehua Buiding B 423 North Street, Dongcheng District, Beijing, China
Tel.: (86) 1084186608
Smart Meter & Analogue Circuit Mfr
N.A.I.C.S.: 334513

Fudan Microelectronics (USA) Inc. (1)
97 E Brokaw Rd Ste 320, San Jose, CA 95112
Tel.: (408) 335-6936
Smart Meter & Analogue Circuit Mfr
N.A.I.C.S.: 334513

Shanghai Fudan - Microelectronics (HK) Limited (1)
Unit 506 5/F East Ocean Centre 98 Granville Road Tsimshatsui East, Kowloon, China (Hong Kong)
Tel.: (852) 21163288
Smart Meter & Analogue Circuit Mfr
N.A.I.C.S.: 334513

Shenzhen Fudan Microelectronics Company Limited (1)
Room 1303 Century Bldg Shengtingyuan Hotel Huaqiang Rd North, Shenzhen, China
Tel.: (86) 75583351011
Smart Meter & Analogue Circuit Mfr
N.A.I.C.S.: 334513

Sino IC Technology Co., Ltd. (1)
Building 2 No 351 Guo Shoujing Road, Pudong New Area, Shanghai, China
Tel.: (86) 2150278215
Web Site: http://www.sinoictest.com.cn
Integrated Circuit Testing Services
N.A.I.C.S.: 541990
Zhang Zhiyong (Gen Mgr)

SHANGHAI FUDAN-ZHANGJIANG BIO-PHARMACEUTICAL CO., LTD.
308 Cailun Road ZJ Hi-Tech Park, Pudong New District, Shanghai, 201210, China
Tel.: (86) 2158953355
Web Site: http://www.fd-zj.com
Year Founded: 1996
1349—(HKG)
Rev.: $144,774,841
Assets: $417,831,421
Liabilities: $101,507,223
Net Worth: $316,324,198
Earnings: $19,273,017
Emp.: 897
Fiscal Year-end: 12/31/22
Pharmaceuticals Mfr
N.A.I.C.S.: 325412
Da Jun Zhao (Co/Co-Founder, Deputy Gen Mgr, Deputy Gen Mgr & Exec Dir)

SHANGHAI FUKONG INTERACTIVE ENTERTAINMENT CO., LTD.
No 2 Building No 437 Guangyue Road, Hongkou District, Shanghai, 200434, China
Tel.: (86) 21 65929055
Web Site: http://www.zpzchina.com
Sales Range: $250-299.9 Million
Digital Technology Services
N.A.I.C.S.: 541519
Xiaoqiang Wang (Chm)

SHANGHAI FULLHAN MICROELECTRONICS CO., LTD.
No 717 Yishan Road Block 2 Floor 6, Xuhui District, Shanghai, 200233, China
Tel.: (86) 2161121575
Web Site: https://www.fullhan.com
Year Founded: 2004

300613—(SSE)
Rev.: $296,324,028
Assets: $484,043,040
Liabilities: $131,804,712
Net Worth: $352,238,328
Earnings: $55,897,452
Fiscal Year-end: 12/31/22
Video Surveillance Product Mfr & Distr
N.A.I.C.S.: 334511
Yang Xiaoqi (Chm & Gen Mgr)

Subsidiaries:

Molchip Technology(Shanghai) Co., Ltd. (1)
8F No 298 Xiangke Road Zhangjiang Hi-Tech Park Pudong New Area, Shanghai, China
Tel.: (86) 2158993277
Web Site: https://www.molchip.com
Optical Chip Mfr
N.A.I.C.S.: 334413

Shanghai Yangge Technology Co., Ltd. (1)
Room 601 West Building 10 Guiping Road 471, Shanghai, China
Tel.: (86) 18602186243
Semiconductor Mfr & Distr
N.A.I.C.S.: 334413

SHANGHAI GANGLIAN E-COMMERCE HOLDINGS CO., LTD.
68 Yuanfeng Road, Boshan District, Shanghai, 200444, China
Tel.: (86) 2166896815
Web Site: https://www.mysteel.net
300226—(CHIN)
Rev.: $10,749,956,256
Assets: $1,944,284,472
Liabilities: $1,387,643,400
Net Worth: $556,641,072
Earnings: $28,519,452
Fiscal Year-end: 12/31/22
Business-to-Business Electronic Commerce for the Steel Industry
N.A.I.C.S.: 425120
Junhong Zhu (Chm)

SHANGHAI GENCH EDUCATION GROUP LIMITED
N510 Library 1111 Hucheng Ring Road, Pudong New Area, Shanghai, China
Tel.: (86) 2168197868
Web Site: https://www.genchedugroup.com
Year Founded: 2018
1525—(HKG)
Rev.: $128,750,138
Assets: $526,487,317
Liabilities: $226,056,851
Net Worth: $300,430,466
Earnings: $39,234,188
Emp.: 1,793
Fiscal Year-end: 12/31/23
Educational Support Services
N.A.I.C.S.: 611710
Bangyong Wang (Deputy CEO)

SHANGHAI GENERAL HEALTHY INFORMATION & TECHNOLOGY CO., LTD.
518 Zhongchen Road, Songjiang District, Shanghai, 201613, China
Tel.: (86) 2157860888
Web Site: https://www.g-healthy.com
Year Founded: 2014
605186—(SHG)
Rev.: $45,259,316
Assets: $168,317,712
Liabilities: $16,227,966
Net Worth: $152,089,746
Earnings: $16,241,683
Fiscal Year-end: 12/31/22
Information Technology Services
N.A.I.C.S.: 541512

Jianwei Dai (Chm & Gen Mgr)

SHANGHAI GENEXT MEDICAL TECHNOLOGY CO., LTD.
Building 2 2nd Floor Ming Pu Square No 3279 San Lu Road, Shanghai, 201112, China
Tel.: (86) 21 5187 3629
Web Site: http://www.genext.com.cn
Medical Devices
N.A.I.C.S.: 424210

Subsidiaries:

Lifeline Scientific, Inc.
1 Pierce Pl Ste 475W, Itasca, IL 60143
Tel.: (847) 294-0300
Web Site: http://www.lifeline-scientific.com
Organ Recovery & Preservation System Developer Mfr
N.A.I.C.S.: 339113
David Kravitz (Founder & CEO)

SHANGHAI GENTECH CO., LTD.
No 55 Chunyong Road, Minhang District, Shanghai, 201108, China
Tel.: (86) 2154428800
Web Site: http://www.gentechindustries.com
Year Founded: 2009
688596—(SSE)
Rev.: $379,745,861
Assets: $835,941,740
Liabilities: $497,149,240
Net Worth: $338,792,501
Earnings: $36,318,068
Fiscal Year-end: 12/31/22
Energy Distribution Services
N.A.I.C.S.: 221122
Dong Lei Yu (Chm & Gen Mgr)

SHANGHAI GOLDEN BRIDGE INFOTECH CO., LTD.
Building No 25 Baoshiyuan No 487 Tianlin Road, Xuhui District, Shanghai, 200233, China
Tel.: (86) 2133674997
Web Site: http://www.shgbit.com
Year Founded: 1994
603918—(SHG)
Rev.: $121,270,261
Assets: $234,189,755
Liabilities: $82,519,454
Net Worth: $151,670,301
Earnings: $2,518,495
Emp.: 454
Fiscal Year-end: 12/31/22
Multimedia Information System Applied Solutions & Services
N.A.I.C.S.: 541519
Jin Shiping (Chm & Gen Mgr)

SHANGHAI GOLDEN UNION COMMERCIAL MANAGEMENT CO., LTD.
18-19F Jinhe Center No 68 Hongcao Road, Xuhui District, Shanghai, 200233, China
Tel.: (86) 2152341623
Web Site: https://www.iyuejie.com
Year Founded: 2007
603682—(SHG)
Rev.: $123,797,532
Assets: $738,934,803
Liabilities: $566,238,942
Net Worth: $172,695,861
Earnings: $13,624,051
Fiscal Year-end: 12/31/22
Investment Management Service
N.A.I.C.S.: 523940
Minjun Yu (Chm & Gen Mgr)

SHANGHAI GREENCOURT INVESTMENT GROUP CO., LTD.
New Commercial Building 5th Floor

INTERNATIONAL PUBLIC

1800 Pine Lane, Songjiang Road, Songjiang, 200233, China
Tel.: (86) 213 422 5027
Web Site: http://www.greencourtinvestment.com
Year Founded: 1985
900919—(SHG)
Rev.: $3,926,772
Assets: $147,179,654
Liabilities: $45,184,693
Net Worth: $101,994,961
Earnings: ($3,307,804)
Fiscal Year-end: 12/31/20
Food Product Mfr & Distr
N.A.I.C.S.: 311999

SHANGHAI GUANGDIAN ELECTRIC (GROUP) CO., LTD.
No 1 Lane 123 East Ring Road, Fengxian, Shanghai, 201401, China
Tel.: (86) 2167101666
Web Site: https://www.sgeg.cn
Year Founded: 1986
601616—(SHG)
Rev.: $138,126,615
Assets: $429,652,712
Liabilities: $64,649,623
Net Worth: $365,003,089
Earnings: $8,334,776
Fiscal Year-end: 12/31/22
Electrical Product Mfr & Distr
N.A.I.C.S.: 335999
Zhao Shu Wen (Chm & Pres)

SHANGHAI GUAO ELECTRONIC TECHNOLOGY CO., LTD
No 6 Alley 1225 Tongpu Road, Putuo District, Shanghai, 200333, China
Tel.: (86) 4000059090
Web Site: https://en.gooao.cn
Year Founded: 1990
300551—(CHIN)
Rev.: $80,050,562
Assets: $215,128,318
Liabilities: $75,597,237
Net Worth: $139,531,081
Earnings: ($10,573,243)
Fiscal Year-end: 12/31/23
Integrated Equipment Mfr & Distr
N.A.I.C.S.: 333310
Hou Yaoqi (Chm)

SHANGHAI GUIJIU CO., LTD.
No 1 Lane 65 Hufa Road, Nanqiao Town Fengxian District, Shanghai, 564510, China
Tel.: (86) 85122292688
Web Site: http://www.sh600696.com
Year Founded: 1989
600696—(SHG)
Rev.: $153,229,794
Assets: $213,675,939
Liabilities: $124,877,488
Net Worth: $88,798,451
Earnings: $5,229,058
Fiscal Year-end: 12/31/22
Real Estate Development Services
N.A.I.C.S.: 531390
Han Xiao (Chm & Gen Mgr)

SHANGHAI GUOSHENG (GROUP) CO., LTD.
No 1320 Yuyuan Road, Changning District, Shanghai, 200050, China
Tel.: (86) 21 5238 8000
Web Site: http://www.sh-gsg.com
Year Founded: 2007
Investment Holding Company
N.A.I.C.S.: 551112
Liping Zhang (Chm)

Subsidiaries:

Arcplus Group PLC (1)
Number 258 Shi Men Er Road, Shanghai, 200041, China
(71.93%)

Tel.: (86) 2152524567
Web Site: https://www.arcplus.com.cn
Rev.: $1,128,769,092
Assets: $2,179,503,093
Liabilities: $1,493,664,902
Net Worth: $685,838,191
Earnings: $54,093,158
Emp.: 8,000
Fiscal Year-end: 12/31/2022
Industrial Products Mfr
N.A.I.C.S.: 333998
Yun Qin *(Chm)*

Subsidiary (Domestic):

Shanghai Pulong Concrete Products Co., Ltd. (2)
1453 Chuanbei Highway Pudong, Shanghai, 201203, China (100%)
Tel.: (86) 2158551571
Sales Range: $50-74.9 Million
Emp.: 124
Readymix Concrete Mfr
N.A.I.C.S.: 327320

SHANGHAI HAISHUN NEW PHARMACEUTICAL PACKAGING CO., LTD.

No 18 Caojiabang Road, Dongjing Songjiang, Shanghai, 201103, China
Tel.: (86) 2133887378
Web Site:
http://www.haishunpackaging.com
300501—(CHIN)
Rev.: $143,789,821
Assets: $420,661,652
Liabilities: $149,823,370
Net Worth: $270,838,282
Earnings: $12,034,463
Emp.: 800
Fiscal Year-end: 12/31/23
Pharmaceutical Packaging Product Mfr
N.A.I.C.S.: 326112
Wuhui Lin *(Chm & Pres)*

Subsidiaries:

Suzhou Haishun Packaging Material Co., Ltd. (1)
No 8 Laixiu Rd, Fenhu, Suzhou, China
Tel.: (86) 2137017627
Packing Product Mfr & Distr
N.A.I.C.S.: 333993

SHANGHAI HAIXIN GROUP CO., LTD.

No 688 Changxing Road, Dongjing Town Songjiang District, Shanghai, 200001, China
Tel.: (86) 2157698100
Web Site: http://www.haixin.com.cn
Year Founded: 1986
600851—(SHG)
Rev.: $202,188,734
Assets: $692,181,000
Liabilities: $127,934,698
Net Worth: $564,246,301
Earnings: $23,033,476
Fiscal Year-end: 12/31/22
Textile Products Mfr
N.A.I.C.S.: 314999
Fei Minhua *(Chm)*

Subsidiaries:

Nanhai Haixin Plush Co., Ltd. (1)
No 2 East Hegui Road, Lishui Town Nanhai Hegui Industrial District, Foshan, Guangdong, China
Tel.: (86) 757 85100993
Web Site: http://www.hxplush.com
Textile Products Mfr
N.A.I.C.S.: 314999

Subsidiary (Non-US):

HAIXIN (H.K.) INT'L TRADING CO., LTD (2)
Unit 11 11/Fl Concordia Plaza 1 Science Museum Road, Tsimshatsui East, Kowloon, China (Hong Kong)
Tel.: (852) 27238938
Textile Products Mfr

N.A.I.C.S.: 314999

Shanghai HaiHuang Garment Co., Ltd. (1)
Dongjing Town Songjiang, Shanghai, China
Tel.: (86) 21 57612847
Textile Products Mfr
N.A.I.C.S.: 314999

Shanghai Haixin Biotechnology Co., Ltd. (1)
Room 1206 Wujiao Fengda Business Plaza No 48 Zhengyi Road, Yangpu District, Shanghai, China
Tel.: (86) 21605050357
Web Site: http://www.hisunbio.com
Bio Technology Services
N.A.I.C.S.: 541715

Shanghai Haixin Pharmaceutical Co., Ltd. (1)
18th Floor 1 Yitaili Building No446 Zhaojiabang Road, Xuhui District, Shanghai, 200031, China
Tel.: (86) 2154651284
Web Site: http://www.shhxyy.com
Pharmaceuticals Product Mfr
N.A.I.C.S.: 325412

Xi'an Haixin Pharmaceutical Co., Ltd. (1)
No 20 Tuanjie South Road High-tech Development Zone, Xi'an, 710075, China
Tel.: (86) 2988384898
Web Site: http://www.xianhaixin.com
Pharmaceuticals Product Mfr
N.A.I.C.S.: 325412

SHANGHAI HAJIME ADVANCED MATERIAL TECHNOLOGY CO., LTD.

No 633 Qinwan Road, Jinshanwei Town Jinshan, Shanghai, 201515, China
Tel.: (86) 2157930288
Web Site: https://www.hps-sh.com
Year Founded: 2011
301000—(SSE)
Rev.: $75,056,506
Assets: $179,325,338
Liabilities: $22,408,219
Net Worth: $156,917,119
Earnings: $13,224,725
Fiscal Year-end: 12/31/22
Automotive Parts Mfr & Distr
N.A.I.C.S.: 336390
Xionghui Shao *(Chm & Gen Mgr)*

SHANGHAI HANBELL PRECISE MACHINERY CO., LTD.

NO 8289 Tingfeng Road Fengjing Town, Jinshan District, Shanghai, China
Tel.: (86) 2157350280   CN
Web Site:
https://www.hanbell.com.cn
002158—(SSE)
Rev.: $458,509,040
Assets: $778,354,687
Liabilities: $346,729,397
Net Worth: $431,625,290
Earnings: $90,470,390
Emp.: 1,000
Fiscal Year-end: 12/31/22
Screw Compressor Mfr & Distr
N.A.I.C.S.: 333241
Yuxuan Yu *(Chm)*

Subsidiaries:

Anhui Hanyang Precise Machinery Co., Ltd. (1)
The Intersection of Xingang Avenue & Lianyi Road, Ningguo Port Ecological Industrial Park, Anhui, China
Tel.: (86) 5634802026
Food Machinery Mfr & Distr
N.A.I.C.S.: 333241

Denair Energy Saving Technology (Shanghai) Co., Ltd. (1)
No 6767 Tingfeng Rd, Jinshan District, Shanghai, China

Tel.: (86) 2137831829
Web Site: https://www.denair.net
Emp.: 500
Air Compressor Product Mfr & Distr
N.A.I.C.S.: 333912

HANBELL PRECISE MACHINERY CO., LTD. (1)
No 5 Konsan Rd Kuan-Yin Industrial Park, Taoyuan, 328, Taiwan
Tel.: (886) 34836215
Web Site: http://www.hanbell.com.tw
Sales Range: $100-124.9 Million
Emp.: 40
Refrigerant Screw Compressor Mfr
N.A.I.C.S.: 333415

Hanbell Precise Machinery Korea Co., Ltd. (1)
1st Floor No 112 2nd Industrial Park 2nd Industrial Park, Northwest District, Cheonan, Chungcheongnam-do, Korea (South)
Tel.: (82) 415625888
Food Machinery Mfr & Distr
N.A.I.C.S.: 333241

Hermes Viet Nam Machinery Company (1)
Plot 28-30-32 11 Str Tan Duc IP, Huu Thanh Commune, Duc Hoa, Long An, Vietnam
Tel.: (84) 2723769688
Web Site: https://www.hanbell-vn.com
Industrial Machinery Mfr & Distr
N.A.I.C.S.: 333248

P.T. Ilthabi Hanbell Indonesia (1)
Rukan Sunter Permai Blok B No 1, Jl Danau Sunter Utara Sunter, Jakarta, Indonesia
Tel.: (62) 2165307798
Web Site: https://hanbellindonesia.com
Industrial Equipment Mfr
N.A.I.C.S.: 333248

Qingdao Century Dongyuan High Tech Mechanical And Electrical Co., Ltd. (1)
Room 810 8th Floor Oriental Jinshi No 288 Zhuhai East Road, Huangdao District, Qingdao, Shandong, China
Tel.: (86) 53286619986
Food Machinery Mfr & Distr
N.A.I.C.S.: 333241

Shanghai Hanbell Vacuum Technology Co., Ltd. (1)
3rd Floor Building 7 No 108 Jiangong Road, Fengjing Town Jinshan District, Shanghai, China
Tel.: (86) 57350280
Food Machinery Mfr & Distr
N.A.I.C.S.: 333241

Zhejiang Hanson Precise Machinery Co., Ltd. (1)
No 588 Hongqiao North Road, Xindai Town, Pinghu, Zhejiang, China
Tel.: (86) 57359502388
Food Machinery Mfr & Distr
N.A.I.C.S.: 333241

SHANGHAI HAOHAI BIOLOGICAL TECHNOLOGY CO., LTD.

23/F WenGuang Plaza No 1386 Hongqiao Road, Changning District, Shanghai, China
Tel.: (86) 2152293555
Web Site:
https://www.3healthcare.com
6826—(HKG)
Rev.: $295,322,695
Assets: $967,692,820
Liabilities: $138,998,246
Net Worth: $828,694,573
Earnings: $26,722,472
Emp.: 1,990
Fiscal Year-end: 12/31/22
Biological Product Mfr
N.A.I.C.S.: 325414
Yongtai Hou *(Chm)*

Subsidiaries:

Contamac Limited (1)
Carlton House Shire Hill, Essex, Saffron Walden, CB11 3AU, United Kingdom

Tel.: (44) 1799514800
Web Site: https://www.contamac.com
Emp.: 80
Intraocular Lens Mfr & Distr
N.A.I.C.S.: 339113

Henan Universe Intraocular Lens Research and Manufacture Co., Ltd. (1)
Block A Torch Building 8 Guohuai Street Zhengzhou High-tech Industrial, Zhengzhou, China
Tel.: (86) 37163921018
Web Site: https://www.universeiol.com
Intraocular Lens Mfr & Distr
N.A.I.C.S.: 339113

SHANGHAI HAOYUAN CHEMEXPRESS CO., LTD.

No 3 Building No 1999 Zhangheng Road, Pudong New Area, Shanghai, 201203, China
Tel.: (86) 58950125
Web Site:
https://www.chemexpress.com
Year Founded: 2006
688131—(SHG)
Rev.: $190,670,782
Assets: $505,123,328
Liabilities: $177,715,358
Net Worth: $327,407,970
Earnings: $27,187,547
Fiscal Year-end: 12/31/22
Pharmaceutical Product Mfr & Distr
N.A.I.C.S.: 325412
Baofu Zheng *(Chm & Gen Mgr)*

SHANGHAI HEARTCARE MEDICAL TECHNOLOGY CORPORATION LIMITED

Floor 1 & 3 Building 38 No 356 Zhengbo Road, Lingang New District Pilot Free Trade Zone, Shanghai, China
Tel.: (86) 2158975056   CN
Web Site:
https://www.heartcare.com.cn
Year Founded: 2016
6609—(HKG)
Rev.: $32,169,916
Assets: $166,322,137
Liabilities: $17,390,480
Net Worth: $148,931,657
Earnings: ($13,016,726)
Emp.: 368
Fiscal Year-end: 12/31/23
Information Technology Services
N.A.I.C.S.: 541512
Guohui Wang *(Founder)*

SHANGHAI HENLIUS BIO-TECH, INC.

11/F B8 Building No188 Yizhou Rd, Xuhui, Shanghai, 200233, China
Tel.: (86) 2133395800   CN
Web Site: https://www.henlius.com
Year Founded: 2010
2696—(HKG)
Rev.: $451,348,092
Assets: $1,252,972,843
Liabilities: $1,023,231,830
Net Worth: $229,741,013
Earnings: ($97,614,364)
Emp.: 3,406
Fiscal Year-end: 12/31/22
Pharmaceutical Product Mfr & Distr
N.A.I.C.S.: 325412
Scott Kau-Shi Liu *(Co-Founder & Co-CEO)*

SHANGHAI HI-ROAD FOOD TECHNOLOGY CO., LTD.

No 666 Jindou Road, Jinhui Town Fengxian District, Shanghai, 201404, China
Tel.: (86) 2137560135
Web Site: http://www.hiroad.sh.cn
Year Founded: 2003

SHANGHAI HI-ROAD FOOD TECHNOLOGY CO., LTD.

Shanghai Hi-Road Food Technology Co., Ltd.—(Continued)
300915—(CHIN)
Rev.: $121,890,155
Assets: $241,796,501
Liabilities: $37,768,723
Net Worth: $204,027,778
Earnings: $13,100,977
Fiscal Year-end: 12/31/22
Dairy Products Mfr
N.A.I.C.S.: 333241
Haixiao Huang *(Chm)*

SHANGHAI HI-TECH CONTROL SYSTEM CO., LTD.
XinJun Ring Road 777 Caohejing Pujiang Hi-Tech Park, Minhang District, Shanghai, 201114, China
Tel.: (86) 60572333
Web Site: https://www.hite.com.cn
Year Founded: 1994
002184—(SSE)
Rev.: $379,872,460
Assets: $439,392,920
Liabilities: $221,792,688
Net Worth: $217,600,232
Earnings: $19,890,679
Fiscal Year-end: 12/31/22
Industrial Electrical Product Distr
N.A.I.C.S.: 423610
Xu Hong *(Chm)*

Subsidiaries:

Chengdu Hi-Tech Control System Co., Ltd. (1)
Wangfujiang Business Building C 18th floor A3&A4, 610016, Chengdu, China
Tel.: (86) 2886512441
System Integration Services
N.A.I.C.S.: 541512

Fujian Hi-Tech Automation Control System Co., Ltd. (1)
Fuzhou Software Park Zone D Building 20 Software Road 89, Gulou District, 350003, Fuzhou, China
Tel.: (86) 59188595980
System Integration Services
N.A.I.C.S.: 541512

Hangzhou Hi-Tech Control Technology Co., Ltd. (1)
Yuda Building Room 301 Tiyuchang Road 8, 310004, Hangzhou, China
Tel.: (86) 57186772988
System Integration Services
N.A.I.C.S.: 541512

Jilin Hi-Tech Renewable Energy Co., Ltd. (1)
Chenguang Garden Building C Room 902 Qianjin Road, 130021, Changchun, Jilin, China
Tel.: (86) 43185535908
System Integration Services
N.A.I.C.S.: 541512

Jinan Hi-Tech Control System Co., Ltd. (1)
Yike industry base C-501 Shunhua Road Jinan High-tech Development Zone, 250101, Jinan, China
Tel.: (86) 53183175333
System Integration Services
N.A.I.C.S.: 541512

Shanghai Hi-Tech Control System Assembling Co., Ltd. (1)
Meigui North Road 317 Build No 3 Waigaoqiao Free Trade Zone, 201131, Shanghai, China
Tel.: (86) 2150464305
System Integration Services
N.A.I.C.S.: 541512

Zhejiang Hi-tech Electric Assembling Co., Ltd. (1)
Erhuannan Road 1320 Economic Development Zone Industry Zone 3, Tongxiang, 314500, Zhejiang, China
Tel.: (86) 80881302
Web Site: http://www.assembling.hite.com.cn
System Integration Services

N.A.I.C.S.: 541512

SHANGHAI HIGHLY (GROUP) CO., LTD.
No 888 Ningqiao Road China Shanghai Pilot Free Trade Zone, Shanghai, 201206, China
Tel.: (86) 2158547777
Web Site: https://www.highly.cc
Year Founded: 1954
600619—(SHG)
Rev.: $2,316,997,543
Assets: $2,837,701,283
Liabilities: $1,800,752,092
Net Worth: $1,036,949,191
Earnings: $4,978,050
Emp.: 14,000
Fiscal Year-end: 12/31/22
Refrigeration Equipment Mfr & Distr
N.A.I.C.S.: 333415
Dong Jianhua *(Chm)*

Subsidiaries:

Anhui Highly Precision Casting Co., Ltd. (1)
Hanshan County Economic Development Zone, Baochanshan Intersection Tiangu Road, Ma'anshan, 238101, Anhui, China
Tel.: (86) 5554959858
Heating & Cooling Product Mfr
N.A.I.C.S.: 333415

Hangzhou Fusheng Electrical Appliance Co., Ltd. (1)
Dongzhou Industrial Area, Fuyang, Hangzhou, 311401, China
Tel.: (86) 57163409888
Web Site: http://www.hzfs.com.cn
Industrial Motor Mfr
N.A.I.C.S.: 333618

Shanghai Highly Electrical Appliances Co., Ltd. (1)
888 Ningqiao Road, Jinqiao Pudong, Shanghai, 201206, China (75%)
Tel.: (86) 2150554560
Heating & Cooling Product Mfr
N.A.I.C.S.: 333415

Shanghai Highly New Energy Technology Co., Ltd. (1)
888 Ningqiao Road, Pilot Free Trade Zone, Shanghai, 201206, China
Tel.: (86) 2158996688
Heating & Cooling Product Mfr
N.A.I.C.S.: 333415

SHANGHAI HILE BIO-TECHNOLOGY CO., LTD.
No 6720 JinHai Road Economic Development Zone, Fengxian District, Shanghai, 201403, China
Tel.: (86) 2160890888
Web Site: https://www.hile-bio.com
Year Founded: 1981
603718—(SHG)
Rev.: $42,118,835
Assets: $212,601,051
Liabilities: $56,616,202
Net Worth: $155,984,849
Earnings: $17,073,735
Fiscal Year-end: 12/31/22
Animal Health Product Provider
N.A.I.C.S.: 115210
Zhang Haiming *(Chm)*

SHANGHAI HIUV NEW MATERIALS CO., LTD.
No 29 Shande Road, Shanyang Town Jinshan District, Shanghai, 201203, China
Tel.: (86) 2158964211
Web Site: https://www.hiuv.net
Year Founded: 2005
688680—(SSE)
Rev.: $745,081,698
Assets: $909,487,023
Liabilities: $561,044,802
Net Worth: $348,442,221
Earnings: $7,033,113

Fiscal Year-end: 12/31/22
Film Material Mfr
N.A.I.C.S.: 325992
Xiaoyu Li *(Chm & Deputy Gen Mgr)*

SHANGHAI HOLLYWAVE ELECTRONIC SYSTEM CO., LTD.
1-2F Building No 16 No 498 Guoshoujing Road, China Pilot Free Trade Zone, Shanghai, 201203, China
Tel.: (86) 2150806021
Web Site: http://www.holly-wave.com
Year Founded: 2007
688682—(SSE)
Rev.: $47,202,452
Assets: $126,960,561
Liabilities: $32,012,211
Net Worth: $94,948,350
Earnings: $7,077,845
Fiscal Year-end: 12/31/22
Electronic Product Mfr & Distr
N.A.I.C.S.: 334419
Jianhua Zhou *(Chm & CTO)*

SHANGHAI HOLYSTAR INFORMATION TECHNOLOGY CO., LTD.
8th Floor Building A3 No 1528 Gumei Road, Xuhui District, Shanghai, 200233, China
Tel.: (86) 2133266008
Web Site: https://www.holystar.com.cn
Year Founded: 2011
688330—(SHG)
Rev.: $150,438,951
Assets: $582,738,778
Liabilities: $86,778,095
Net Worth: $495,960,683
Earnings: $44,709,636
Fiscal Year-end: 12/31/22
Information Technology Services
N.A.I.C.S.: 541512
Hui Zhang *(Chm)*

SHANGHAI HONGDA NEW MATERIAL CO., LTD.
Room 3603 Zhongganghui No 15 Dapu Road, Huangpu District, Shanghai, 200023, Jiangsu, China
Tel.: (86) 51188226078
Web Site: http://www.hongda-chemical.com
Year Founded: 1992
002211—(SSE)
Rev.: $51,190,907
Assets: $48,445,048
Liabilities: $35,440,287
Net Worth: $13,004,761
Earnings: $5,559,742
Fiscal Year-end: 12/31/22
Rubber Products Mfr
N.A.I.C.S.: 325212

Subsidiaries:

Dongguan New Orient Technology Co., Ltd. (1)
Beimen Xiang, TianXinVillage HuangJiang Town, Dongguan, China
Tel.: (86) 76983639068
Web Site: http://www.dg-neworient.com
Emp.: 400
Silicone Rubber Mfr
N.A.I.C.S.: 325212

SHANGHAI HONGHUA OFFSHORE OIL & GAS EQUIPMENT CO., LTD.
3rd floor No 11 Building 27 Xinjinqiao Road Pudong, Pudong New District, Shanghai, 201206, China
Tel.: (86) 21 5190 1600
Oil & Gas Equipment Mfr
N.A.I.C.S.: 333132

INTERNATIONAL PUBLIC

Daniel Park *(Gen Mgr)*

SHANGHAI HUACE NAVIGATION TECHNOLOGY LTD
577 Songying Road, Shanghai, 201706, China
Tel.: (86) 2154260273
Web Site: https://www.chcnav.com
Year Founded: 2003
300627—(CHIN)
Rev.: $377,244,344
Assets: $621,437,242
Liabilities: $192,745,915
Net Worth: $428,691,328
Earnings: $63,261,482
Emp.: 1,700
Fiscal Year-end: 12/31/23
Navigation Device Mfr & Distr
N.A.I.C.S.: 334511
Yanping Zhao *(Chm)*

Subsidiaries:

CHC Navigation Europe Kft. (1)
Infopark Building A 1/a Neumann Janos street, 1117, Budapest, Hungary
Tel.: (36) 202358248
Web Site: http://www.chcnav.com
Emp.: 6
Global Positioning System Device Distr
N.A.I.C.S.: 423690
Xunye Mao *(VP)*

CHC Navigation USA LLC (1)
1545 S 1100 E Ste 2, Salt Lake City, UT 84105
Tel.: (801) 923-4883
Global Positioning System Device Distr
N.A.I.C.S.: 423690

CHC Navtech (Thailand) Co., Ltd. (1)
16th floor SJ Infinite I 349, Chom Phon Chatuchak, Bangkok, 10900, Thailand
Tel.: (66) 20141600
Web Site: http://www.chcthailand.com
Global Positioning System Device Distr
N.A.I.C.S.: 423690

SHANGHAI HUAFON ALUMINIUM CORPORATION
No 1111 Yuegong Road, Jinshan, Shanghai, China
Tel.: (86) 2167271999
Web Site: https://www.huafonal.com
Year Founded: 2008
601702—(SHG)
Rev.: $1,199,685,245
Assets: $882,414,337
Liabilities: $358,362,899
Net Worth: $524,051,438
Earnings: $93,474,319
Fiscal Year-end: 12/31/22
Aluminium Products Mfr
N.A.I.C.S.: 331313
Guozhen Chen *(Chm)*

SHANGHAI HUAHONG JITONG SMART SYSTEM CO., LTD.
No 9 10 Building 2777 Fairview Road, Shanghai, 201206, China
Tel.: (86) 2131016900
Web Site: http://www.huahongjt.com
300330—(CHIN)
Rev.: $49,693,664
Assets: $98,920,037
Liabilities: $40,605,246
Net Worth: $58,314,790
Earnings: $900,875
Emp.: 170
Fiscal Year-end: 12/31/20
Integrated Circuits Mfr
N.A.I.C.S.: 334413

SHANGHAI HUAMING INTELLIGENT TERMINAL EQUIPMENT CO., LTD.
No 895 Rongmei Road Rongbei Industrial Estate, Songjiang District, Shanghai, 201613, China

Tel.: (86) 2157784382
Web Site:
  https://www.hmmachine.com
Year Founded: 2001
300462—(SSE)
Rev.: $87,584,328
Assets: $329,604,444
Liabilities: $107,340,012
Net Worth: $222,264,432
Earnings: $8,530,704
Emp.: 470
Fiscal Year-end: 12/31/22
Ticket Vending Machine, Automatic Gate Machine, Ticket Checking Machine & Add Value Machine Mfr
N.A.I.C.S.: 333310
Zhang Liang *(Chm & Gen Mgr)*

SHANGHAI HUAYI GROUP CORPORATION LTD.
No 809 Changde Road, Jing An District, Shanghai, 200040, China
Tel.: (86) 2123530152
Web Site:
  http://www.doublecoinholdings.com
Year Founded: 1990
600623—(SHG)
Rev.: $5,466,820,423
Assets: $8,311,805,153
Liabilities: $4,654,373,892
Net Worth: $3,657,431,260
Earnings: $179,882,095
Emp.: 2,000
Fiscal Year-end: 12/31/22
Holding Company
N.A.I.C.S.: 551112
Lili Gu *(Chm & Pres)*

SHANGHAI HUGONG ELECTRIC (GROUP) CO., LTD
7177 Waiqingsong Road Qingpu District, Shanghai, 201700, China
Tel.: (86) 2151215999
Web Site:
  http://www.hugongwelds.com
Year Founded: 1958
603131—(SHG)
Rev.: $139,208,734
Assets: $325,795,280
Liabilities: $148,136,180
Net Worth: $177,659,099
Earnings: ($17,769,796)
Emp.: 1,000
Fiscal Year-end: 12/31/22
Welding Equipment Mfr & Distr
N.A.I.C.S.: 333992
Shu Zhenyu *(Chm & Gen Mgr)*
Subsidiaries:
Shanghai Gas Welding Equipment Co., Ltd. (1)
7177 Waiqingsong Road, Qingpu District, Shanghai, 201700, China
Tel.: (86) 2131117888
Web Site: http://www.hugongwelds.com
Laser Cutting Machinery Mfr
N.A.I.C.S.: 333517

SHANGHAI HUIDE SCIENCE & TECHNOLOGY SHARES CO., LTD.
No 180 Chunhua Rd, Jinshan District, Shanghai, 201512, China
Tel.: (86) 2137285599
Web Site: https://www.shhdsz.com
Year Founded: 1997
603192—(SHG)
Rev.: $423,623,079
Assets: $321,675,902
Liabilities: $125,715,325
Net Worth: $195,960,576
Earnings: $8,672,101
Emp.: 500
Fiscal Year-end: 12/31/22
Polyurethane Resin Product Mfr & Distr
N.A.I.C.S.: 325211

Jianzhong Qian *(Chm & Gen Mgr)*
Subsidiaries:
Shanghai Hongde Polyurethane Co., Ltd. (1)
No 8 Lane 3736 Hunan Road, Zhoupu Town Pudong New District, Shanghai, 201318, China
Tel.: (86) 2168070384
Web Site: http://www.hoardpu.com
Polyurethane Products Mfr
N.A.I.C.S.: 326150

SHANGHAI HUILI BUILDING MATERIALS CO., LTD.
Room 213 Block 1 No 406 Hengqiao Road, Zhoupu Town Pudong New Area, Shanghai, 201318, China
Tel.: (86) 2158138717
Web Site: http://www.huili.com
Year Founded: 1996
900939—(SHG)
Rev.: $2,065,087
Assets: $20,586,473
Liabilities: $3,606,890
Net Worth: $16,979,583
Earnings: $1,068,669
Fiscal Year-end: 12/31/22
Wood Product Mfr & Distr
N.A.I.C.S.: 321999
Zhan Lin *(Sec, VP & Deputy Gen Mgr)*

SHANGHAI HUITONG ENERGY CO., LTD.
Unit 209 No 373 Zhongxing Road, Jing'an District, Shanghai, 200335, China
Tel.: (86) 2162560000
Web Site:
  http://www.huitongenergy.com
Year Founded: 1991
600605—(SHG)
Rev.: $15,231,126
Assets: $321,264,136
Liabilities: $162,418,749
Net Worth: $158,845,387
Earnings: $1,301,227
Fiscal Year-end: 12/31/22
Wind Power Generation
N.A.I.C.S.: 221115
Lu Xiangqian *(Chm)*

SHANGHAI HYP- ARCH ARCHITECTURAL DESIGN CONSULTANT CO., LTD
5/6/10F China Enterprise Fortune Century Building, No 469 Binjiang Avenue Pudong New Area, Shanghai, 200120, China
Tel.: (86) 2158783137
Web Site: https://www.hyp-arch.com
Year Founded: 2008
301024—(SSE)
Rev.: $18,805,176
Assets: $111,752,784
Liabilities: $18,471,024
Net Worth: $93,281,760
Earnings: ($24,991,200)
Fiscal Year-end: 12/31/22
Architectural Services
N.A.I.C.S.: 541310
Gong Jun *(Chm & Gen Mgr)*

SHANGHAI INDUSTRIAL HOLDINGS LIMITED
26F Harcourt House 39 Gloucester Road, Wanchai, China (Hong Kong)
Tel.: (852) 25295652
Web Site: https://www.sihl.com.hk
Year Founded: 1996
SGHIY—(OTCIQ)
Rev.: $4,006,363,439
Assets: $24,784,816,287
Liabilities: $14,970,521,681
Net Worth: $9,814,294,606

Earnings: $425,546,027
Emp.: 17,905
Fiscal Year-end: 12/31/22
Infrastructure Facilities, Medicine, Consumer Products & Information Technology Investment Services
N.A.I.C.S.: 523999
Cherie Yat Ying Chan *(Asst CEO & Controller-Fin)*
Subsidiaries:
Nanyang Brothers Tobacco Co Ltd (1)
No 9 Tsing Yeung Street, Tuen Mun, New Territories, China (Hong Kong) (100%)
Tel.: (852) 27613321
Web Site: https://www.nbt-hk.com
Sales Range: $100-124.9 Million
Emp.: 450
Cigarette Mfr
N.A.I.C.S.: 312280
Qiu Hua Yang *(Chm)*

Shanghai Industrial Development Co., Ltd. (1)
20F Golden Bell Plaza No 98 Huaihai Middle Road, Shanghai, 200021, China
Tel.: (86) 2153858859
Web Site: http://www.sidlgroup.com
Rev.: $736,811,295
Assets: $6,366,465,673
Liabilities: $4,820,626,699
Net Worth: $1,545,838,974
Earnings: $17,221,731
Fiscal Year-end: 12/31/2022
Real Estate Manangement Services
N.A.I.C.S.: 531390
Jixing Yuan *(CFO & VP)*

Shanghai Industrial Pharmaceutical Investment Co Ltd (1)
16th Floor Jinzhong Atrium, 98 Huaihai Rd, Shanghai, China
Tel.: (86) 2153858898
Web Site: http://www.siph.com.cn
Pharmaceutical Preparation Mfr
N.A.I.C.S.: 325412

The Wing Fat Printing Co., Ltd. (1)
9/F 6 Luk Hop Street, San Po Kong, Kowloon, China (Hong Kong) (93.44%)
Tel.: (852) 25874888
Web Site: https://www.wingfat.com
Sales Range: $1-4.9 Billion
Emp.: 150
Commercial Printing Services
N.A.I.C.S.: 323111
Lou Jun *(Chm)*

SHANGHAI INDUSTRIAL URBAN DEVELOPMENT GROUP LIMITED
11/F Henley Building No 5 Queen s Road, Central, China (Hong Kong)
Tel.: (852) 25448000
Web Site: http://www.siud.com
0563—(HKG)
Rev.: $1,405,368,240
Assets: $7,324,465,343
Liabilities: $4,668,477,908
Net Worth: $2,655,987,435
Earnings: $38,887,628
Emp.: 774
Fiscal Year-end: 12/31/22
Real Estate Investment & Development Services
N.A.I.C.S.: 531390
Weiqi Qi Ye *(VP)*

SHANGHAI INSULATING MATERIALS CO., LTD.
No 188 Tongqiang Road Laogang Town, Pudong New Area, Shanghai, 201302, China
Tel.: (86) 21 5885 5650 CN
Web Site: http://www.shangjue.com
Insulating Materials Mfr
N.A.I.C.S.: 326130

SHANGHAI INTERNATIONAL AIRPORT CO., LTD.
No 900 Qihang Road Pudong International Airport, Shanghai, 201207, China
Tel.: (86) 2196990
Web Site: https://www.shairport.com
Year Founded: 1998
600009—(SHG)
Rev.: $769,454,843
Assets: $9,515,623,872
Liabilities: $3,800,854,184
Net Worth: $5,714,769,687
Earnings: ($420,490,966)
Fiscal Year-end: 12/31/22
Airport Services
N.A.I.C.S.: 488119
Zhihong Hu *(Chm-Supervisory Bd & Interim & Pres)*

SHANGHAI INTERNATIONAL PORT (GROUP) CO., LTD.
358 East Daming Road, Shanghai, 200080, China
Tel.: (86) 2155333388 CN
Web Site:
  https://www.portshanghai.com.cn
600018—(SHG)
Rev.: $5,199,320,171
Assets: $28,186,685,202
Liabilities: $9,330,569,188
Net Worth: $18,856,116,014
Earnings: $1,828,081,732
Emp.: 5,000
Fiscal Year-end: 12/31/23
Holding Company; Port Logistics Services
N.A.I.C.S.: 551112
Gu Jinshan *(Chm)*
Subsidiaries:
SIPG Logistics Co., Ltd. (1)
53 Huangpu Road 15/F Panorama Mansions, Hongkou District, Shanghai, 200080, China
Tel.: (86) 2153930088
Web Site: http://www.sipgl.com
Emp.: 200
Port Logistics Services
N.A.I.C.S.: 488510

SIPG Luojing Subsidiary Co. Ltd. (1)
8 Shigang Road Yuepu Town Chengqiao, Baoshan District, Shanghai, 200942, China
Tel.: (86) 2156150090
Handling Bulk Cargo Services
N.A.I.C.S.: 488390

SIPG Passenger Transport Corporation Ltd. (1)
8 Yangshupu Road, Shanghai, 200082, China
Tel.: (86) 2165460730
Passenger Transportation & Domestic Freight Services
N.A.I.C.S.: 483212

Shanghai Container Terminals Co., Ltd. (1)
4333 Yixian Road, Shanghai, 200940, China
Tel.: (86) 2156441988
Web Site: http://www.sctport.com.cn
Shipping Container Terminal Operator
N.A.I.C.S.: 488310

Shanghai East Container Terminals Co., Ltd. (1)
1 Gangjian Road, Pudong New Area, Shanghai, 200137, China
Tel.: (86) 2168685966
Web Site: http://www.sect.com.cn
Sales Range: $200-249.9 Million
Emp.: 1,000
Shipping Container Terminal Operator
N.A.I.C.S.: 488310

Shanghai Guandong International Container Terminal Co., Ltd. (1)
No 1 Tonghui Road Luchao Gang Town, Nanhui District, Shanghai, 201306, China
Tel.: (86) 21 3803 3737
Web Site: http://www.sgict.com.cn
Container Terminal Operation Services
N.A.I.C.S.: 488310

SHANGHAI INTERNATIONAL PORT (GROUP) CO., LTD.

Shanghai International Port (Group) Co., Ltd.—(Continued)

Shanghai Haihua Shipping Co., Ltd. (1)
F7 8 358 E Daming Rd, Shanghai, 200080, China
Tel.: (86) 21 35308880
Sales Range: $50-74.9 Million
Emp.: 20
Marine Shipping Services
N.A.I.C.S.: 483111

Shanghai Haitong International Automobile Logistics Co., Ltd. (1)
1919 Gangjian Road, Pudong, Shanghai, 200137, China
Tel.: (86) 21 20300600
Web Site: http://www.haitongauto.com
Automotive Shipping Container Terminal Operator
N.A.I.C.S.: 488310

Shanghai Haitong International Automobile Terminal Co., Ltd. (1)
3988 Zhou Hai Road, Pudong, Shanghai, 200137, China
Tel.: (86) 21 686 85858
Web Site: http://www.haitongauto.com
Shipping Container Terminal Operations
N.A.I.C.S.: 488310

Shanghai Harbor Fuxing Shipping Co. Ltd.
6 27 28/F Jinan Building 908 Dongdeming Road, Shanghai, 200082, China
Tel.: (86) 2165952255
Port Tugboat Services
N.A.I.C.S.: 488390

Shanghai Harbour Engineering Company Ltd.
210 Yangshupu Road, Shanghai, 200082, China
Tel.: (86) 2165417500
Port Facility Construction Services
N.A.I.C.S.: 237990

Shanghai Jihai Shipping Co., Ltd. (1)
22-24/F Gang Yun Mansions 18 Yangshupu Road, Shanghai, 200082, China
Tel.: (86) 2165456600
Web Site: http://www.shjsco.com
Container Shipping ervices
N.A.I.C.S.: 483211

Shanghai Mingdong Container Terminals Ltd.
No 999 Gangjian Road, Pudong New Area, Shanghai, 200137, China
Tel.: (86) 2138984888
Web Site: http://www.smct.com.cn
Emp.: 900
Shipping Container Terminal Operator
N.A.I.C.S.: 488310

Shanghai Ocean Shipping Tally Co., Ltd. (1)
1322 Yuhang Road East, Hongkou District, Shanghai, China
Tel.: (86) 2165868388
Port Operation Services
N.A.I.C.S.: 488310

Shanghai Port International Cruise Terminal Development Co., Ltd. (1)
1 Taiping Road, Shanghai, China
Tel.: (86) 2195950959
Port Facility Construction Services
N.A.I.C.S.: 236210

Shanghai Port Skilled Labor Service Co., Ltd. (1)
2/F 110 Huangpu Road, Shanghai, 200080, China
Tel.: (86) 2163073123
Web Site: http://www.portshanghai.com.cn
Labor Management Services
N.A.I.C.S.: 813930

Shanghai Pudong International Container Terminals Ltd. (1)
88 Yanggao No 1 Road N, Pudong New Area, Shanghai, 200131, China
Tel.: (86) 21 5861 3635
Web Site: http://www.spict.com
Shipping Container Terminal Operator
N.A.I.C.S.: 488310

Shanghai Puyuan Shipping Co., Ltd. (1)
12th Floor Chuanyan Mansion 600 Minsheng Rd, Pudong New Area, Shanghai, 2000135, China
Tel.: (86) 2150281188
Coastal & Offshore Shipping Service
N.A.I.C.S.: 488510

Shanghai Shengdong International Container Terminals Co., Ltd. (1)
1 Tonghui Road Luchaogang Town, Nanhui District, Shanghai, 201308, China
Tel.: (86) 2168288888
Web Site: http://www.shsict.com
Sales Range: $200-249.9 Million
Emp.: 1,000
Shipping Container Terminal Operator
N.A.I.C.S.: 488310

SHANGHAI INTERNATIONAL SHANGHAI GROWTH INVESTMENT LIMITED
Room 1501 15/F Shanghai Industrial Investment Building, 48-62 Hennesy Road, Wanchai, China (Hong Kong)
Tel.: (852) 28401608 Ky
Web Site:
  https://www.shanghaigrowth.com
770—(HKG)
Rev.: $12,237
Assets: $3,745,621
Liabilities: $94,117
Net Worth: $3,651,504
Earnings: ($555,856)
Emp.: 2
Fiscal Year-end: 12/31/19
Investment Management Service
N.A.I.C.S.: 523940
Ching Wang (Exec Dir)

SHANGHAI JIAODA ONLLY CO., LTD.
11th Floor Building 13 No 99 Tianzhou Road, Xuhui District, Shanghai, 200030, China
Tel.: (86) 2154271688
Web Site: https://www.onlly.com.cn
Year Founded: 1990
600530—(SHG)
Rev.: $52,951,902
Assets: $124,229,556
Liabilities: $72,240,812
Net Worth: $51,988,744
Earnings: ($69,978,505)
Fiscal Year-end: 12/31/22
Healthcare Food & Biological Product Mfr
N.A.I.C.S.: 311999
Ji Min (Chm)

Subsidiaries:

Shanghai JTU Venture Capital Co., Ltd. (1)
6F Shentongxinxi Square 55 West Huaihai Road, Shanghai, 200030, China
Tel.: (86) 21 5298 9040
Web Site: http://www.sjtu-vc.com
Financial Management Services
N.A.I.C.S.: 523999

Shanghai Novanat Bioresources Co., Ltd. (1)
3/F Building 12 No 99 Tianzhou Rd, Shanghai, 200233, China
Tel.: (86) 21 5445 0909
Web Site: http://www.novanat.com
Food Products Mfr
N.A.I.C.S.: 325199

Shanghai Onlly Advertising Co., Ltd. (1)
St Jiahua Business Center Hongqiao Road 808, Shanghai, China
Tel.: (86) 21 62810808
Advetising Agency
N.A.I.C.S.: 541810

SHANGHAI JIAODA WITHUB INFORMATION INDUSTRIAL COMPANY LIMITED
2nd Floor Block 7 471 Gui Ping Road, Shanghai, China
Tel.: (86) 2164078333 CN
Web Site: http://www.withub.com.cn
Year Founded: 1998
8205—(HKG)
Rev.: $5,054,797
Assets: $6,675,813
Liabilities: $3,076,398
Net Worth: $3,599,415
Earnings: ($3,066,091)
Emp.: 101
Fiscal Year-end: 12/31/22
Application Software Development Services
N.A.I.C.S.: 541511
Ling Shang (CEO)

SHANGHAI JIAOYUN GROUP CO., LTD.
No 288 Hengfeng Road, Shanghai, 200070, China
Tel.: (86) 2162116009
Web Site: http://www.cnsjy.com
Year Founded: 1993
600676—(SHG)
Rev.: $834,390,601
Assets: $1,101,124,964
Liabilities: $325,014,263
Net Worth: $776,110,702
Earnings: $3,813,390
Fiscal Year-end: 12/31/22
Automobile Spare Parts Mfr
N.A.I.C.S.: 336390
Chen Xiaolong (Chm)

SHANGHAI JIELONG INDUSTRY GROUP CO., LTD.
5F No 2112 Middle Yanggao Rd Pudong New Area, Shanghai, 200135, China
Tel.: (86) 2158600836
Web Site: http://www.jielongcorp.com
Year Founded: 1968
600836—(SHG)
Rev.: $72,214,291
Assets: $289,330,479
Liabilities: $124,182,157
Net Worth: $165,148,322
Earnings: ($11,372,512)
Emp.: 2,500
Fiscal Year-end: 12/31/22
Commercial Printing Services
N.A.I.C.S.: 323113
Fei Junde (Chm)

Subsidiaries:

Shanghai Jielong Art Printing Co., Ltd. (1)
No 7077 Chuanzhou Rd, Pudong, Shanghai, 201205, China
Tel.: (86) 2158925888
Web Site: http://www.jielongart.com
Commercial Printing Services
N.A.I.C.S.: 323113

SHANGHAI JIN JIANG CAPITAL COMPANY LIMITED
26/F Union Building No 100 Yan'an East Road, Shanghai, China
Tel.: (86) 2163264000
Web Site:
  http://www.jinjianghotels.com
2006—(HKG)
Rev.: $2,175,744,709
Assets: $9,455,074,622
Liabilities: $6,413,374,737
Net Worth: $3,041,699,886
Earnings: $74,566,847
Emp.: 50,233
Fiscal Year-end: 12/31/20
Hotel Operator
N.A.I.C.S.: 721110

Subsidiaries:

Kunming Jin Jiang Hotel Company Limited (1)

INTERNATIONAL PUBLIC

98 Beijing Road, Beijing, China
Tel.: (86) 8716 313 8888
Web Site:
  https://www.jinjianghotelkunming.com
Hotel Services
N.A.I.C.S.: 721110

Louvre Hotels Group (1)
Tour Voltaire 1 place des Degres, La Defense, 92800, Paris, France
Tel.: (33) 14 291 4600
Web Site: https://www.louvrehotels.com
Sales Range: $1-4.9 Billion
Hotels & Motels Owner, Operator & Franchiser
N.A.I.C.S.: 721110
Pierre-Frederic Roulot (Chm & CEO)

Shanghai Hua Ting Guest House Company Limited (1)
2525 Zhongshan Road West, Shanghai, 200030, China
Tel.: (86) 2151801133
Web Site: http://www.huatinghotels.com
Hotel Services
N.A.I.C.S.: 721110

Wuhan Jin Jiang International Hotel Company Limited (1)
No 707 Jianshe Avenue, Hankou District, Wuhan, China
Tel.: (86) 2785786888
Web Site:
  http://www.jinjianghotelwuhan.com
Hotel Services
N.A.I.C.S.: 721110

SHANGHAI JIN JIANG INTERNATIONAL HOTELS CO LTD
25F No 100 Yan'an East Road, Pudong New Area, Shanghai, 200002, China
Tel.: (86) 2163741122
Web Site:
  http://www.jinjianghotels.sh.cn
Year Founded: 1994
600754—(SHG)
Rev.: $1,545,470,269
Assets: $6,659,321,961
Liabilities: $4,251,421,512
Net Worth: $2,407,900,449
Earnings: $15,933,406
Fiscal Year-end: 12/31/22
Restaurant Operators
N.A.I.C.S.: 722511

Subsidiaries:

Shanghai Jinhua Hotel Co., Ltd. (1)
No 1121 Pujian Road Huamu Subdistrict Pudong New District, Shanghai, 201204, China
Tel.: (86) 2150590938
Home Management Services
N.A.I.C.S.: 721110

Shanghai Jinpan Hotel Co., Ltd. (1)
No 711 Pangu Rd Baoshan Dist, Shanghai, 201900, China
Tel.: (86) 2160255500
Home Management Services
N.A.I.C.S.: 721110

SHANGHAI JIN JIANG ONLINE NETWORK SERVICE CO., LTD.
No 1 Pudong Avenue Pilot Free Trade Zone, Shanghai, 200002, China
Tel.: (86) 2163218800 CN
Year Founded: 1993
600650—(SHG)
Rev.: $266,993,866
Assets: $705,448,092
Liabilities: $131,510,509
Net Worth: $573,937,581
Earnings: $20,899,562
Fiscal Year-end: 12/31/23
Automobile Transportation Services
N.A.I.C.S.: 488510
Xian Zhang (CEO)

SHANGHAI JINFENG WINE COMPANY LIMITED

Haitang Building No 777 Ningxia Road, Putuo District, Shanghai, 200063, China
Tel.: (86) 2150812727
Web Site: http://www.jinfengwine.com
Year Founded: 1992
600616—(SHG)
Rev.: $92,889,440
Assets: $317,331,195
Liabilities: $51,368,611
Net Worth: $265,962,584
Earnings: $726,135
Fiscal Year-end: 12/31/22
Rice Wine Product Mfr
N.A.I.C.S.: 311213
Zhu Yong *(Chm)*

SHANGHAI JINJIANG INTERNATIONAL TRAVEL CO., LTD.
27F Lianyi Building No 100 Yan'an East Road, Shanghai, 200002, China
Tel.: (86) 2163299090
Web Site: http://www.jjtravel.com
Year Founded: 1994
900929—(SHG)
Rev.: $28,027,364
Assets: $137,834,401
Liabilities: $40,683,174
Net Worth: $97,151,226
Earnings: ($10,762,123)
Fiscal Year-end: 12/31/22
Travel Agency Services
N.A.I.C.S.: 561510
Sha Deyin *(Chm)*

SHANGHAI JINQIAO EXPORT PROCESSING ZONE DEVELOPMENT CO., LTD.
Building 18 No 27 Xinjinqiao Road, Pudong New District, Shanghai, 201206, China
Tel.: (86) 2168811818
Web Site: https://shpdjq.com
Year Founded: 1992
900911—(SHG)
Rev.: $709,510,501
Assets: $4,850,494,132
Liabilities: $2,708,391,170
Net Worth: $2,142,102,961
Earnings: $222,333,776
Fiscal Year-end: 12/31/22
Real Estate Support Services
N.A.I.C.S.: 531390
Yan Shaoyun *(Sec)*

SHANGHAI JOIN BUY CO., LTD.
14th Floor Dongzhan Commercial Building No 669 Beijing West Road, Jing'an District, Shanghai, 200041, China
Tel.: (86) 2162729898
Web Site: https://www.shjb600838.com
Year Founded: 1939
600838—(SHG)
Rev.: $9,623,479
Assets: $218,596,440
Liabilities: $17,636,655
Net Worth: $200,959,785
Earnings: $7,342,878
Fiscal Year-end: 12/31/22
Departmental Store Operator
N.A.I.C.S.: 455110

SHANGHAI JUNSHI BIOSCIENCES CO., LTD.
15F Building 7 Crystal Plaza No 6 Lane 100 Pingjiaqiao Road, Pudong New Area, Shanghai, 200126, China
Tel.: (86) 2161058800 CN
Web Site: https://www.junshipharma.com
Year Founded: 2012
1877—(HKG)
Rev.: $204,070,417

Assets: $1,765,710,554
Liabilities: $390,597,854
Net Worth: $1,375,112,700
Earnings: ($362,526,138)
Emp.: 2,961
Fiscal Year-end: 12/31/22
Biopharmaceutical Product Mfr
N.A.I.C.S.: 325412
Jun Xiong *(Chm)*

Subsidiaries:

Shanghai Junshi Biotechnology Co., Ltd. (1)
No 1069 Xinyang Hwy, Lin-Gang Special Area Pilot Free Trade Zone, Shanghai, 201413, China
Tel.: (86) 2161040024
Pharmaceuticals Product Mfr
N.A.I.C.S.: 325412

Suzhou Junmeng Biosciences Co., Ltd. (1)
No 7 Yunchuang Road, Wujiang District, Suzhou, 215200, Jiangsu, China
Tel.: (86) 51286850000
Pharmaceuticals Product Mfr
N.A.I.C.S.: 325412

Suzhou Union Biopharm Biosciences Co., Ltd. (1)
No 7 Yunchuang Road, Wujiang District, Suzhou, 215200, Jiangsu, China
Tel.: (86) 51286850000
Pharmaceuticals Product Mfr
N.A.I.C.S.: 325412

Suzhou Union Biopharm Co., Ltd. (1)
No 7 Yunchuang Road, Wujiang District, Suzhou, 215200, Jiangsu, China
Tel.: (86) 51286850000
Pharmaceutical Mfr & Distr
N.A.I.C.S.: 325412

TopAlliance Biosciences Inc. (1)
9430 Key W Ave Ste 125, Rockville, MD 20850
Tel.: (301) 640-5166
Web Site: https://www.topalliancebio.com
Pharmaceuticals Product Mfr
N.A.I.C.S.: 325412
Hui Feng *(COO)*

SHANGHAI KAI KAI INDUSTRIAL CO., LTD.
No 678 Changping Road, Jing'an District, Shanghai, 200040, China
Tel.: (86) 2162712002
Web Site: https://www.chinesekk.com
Year Founded: 1992
600272—(SHG)
Rev.: $125,541,735
Assets: $169,498,672
Liabilities: $88,312,176
Net Worth: $81,186,497
Earnings: $5,608,896
Fiscal Year-end: 12/31/22
Pharmaceutical Product Mfr & Distr
N.A.I.C.S.: 325412
Zhuang Qianyun *(Chm)*

SHANGHAI KAIBAO PHARMACEUTICAL CO., LTD.
No 88 Chengpu Road Shanghai Industrial Development Zone, Shanghai, 201401, China
Tel.: (86) 2137572069
Web Site: http://www.xykb.com
Year Founded: 2000
300039—(SSE)
Rev.: $157,086,540
Assets: $598,001,508
Liabilities: $69,952,896
Net Worth: $528,048,612
Earnings: $26,788,320
Emp.: 250
Fiscal Year-end: 12/31/22
Pharmaceuticals Mfr
N.A.I.C.S.: 325412
Jingwei Mu *(Chm)*

SHANGHAI KAICHUANG MARINE INTERNATIONAL CO., LTD.
3/F Building 3 No 661 Anpu Road, Yangpu District, Shanghai, 200082, China
Tel.: (86) 2165688761
Web Site: https://www.skmic.sh.cn
Year Founded: 2008
600097—(SHG)
Rev.: $272,504,915
Assets: $482,196,724
Liabilities: $183,553,204
Net Worth: $298,643,520
Earnings: $14,896,889
Fiscal Year-end: 12/31/22
Fish Market Operator
N.A.I.C.S.: 445250
Wang Haifeng *(Chm)*

SHANGHAI KARON ECOVALVE MANUFACTURING CO., LTD.
No 815 Deyuan Road, Nanxiang Town Jiading District, Shanghai, 201804, China
Tel.: (86) 2131229378
Web Site: https://www.karon-valve.com
Year Founded: 1991
301151—(SSE)
Rev.: $131,041,203
Assets: $369,553,355
Liabilities: $87,532,436
Net Worth: $282,020,918
Earnings: $14,293,703
Fiscal Year-end: 12/31/22
Industry Machinery Mfr
N.A.I.C.S.: 333310
Zhenghong Li *(Chm & Gen Mgr)*

SHANGHAI KAYTUNE INDUSTRIAL CO., LTD.
Room 2401 Building 2 No 857 Tiangong Road, Jinshan Industrial Zone, Shanghai, 200030, China
Tel.: (86) 2155080030
Web Site: http://www.kaytune.com.cn
Year Founded: 2008
301001—(SSE)
Rev.: $107,331,588
Assets: $144,183,261
Liabilities: $29,203,186
Net Worth: $114,980,075
Earnings: ($831,772)
Fiscal Year-end: 12/31/22
E Commerce Site Operator
N.A.I.C.S.: 333248
Li Wang *(Chm & Gen Mgr)*

SHANGHAI KEHUA BIO-ENGINEERING CO., LTD.
No 1189 North Qinzhou Road Caohejing Hi-Tech Park, Xuhui District, Shanghai, 200233, China
Tel.: (86) 2164950625
Web Site: https://www.skhb.com
Year Founded: 1981
002022—(SSE)
Rev.: $978,568,709
Assets: $1,237,367,243
Liabilities: $415,745,713
Net Worth: $821,621,530
Earnings: $136,306,652
Emp.: 2,000
Fiscal Year-end: 12/31/22
Biological Product Mfr
N.A.I.C.S.: 325414
Li Ming *(Chm & Pres)*

Subsidiaries:

Technogenetics S.r.l. (1)
Corso Vittorio Emanuele II 15, 20122, Milan, Italy
Tel.: (39) 03711921800
Web Site: http://www.technogenetics.it

Biotechnology Research & Development Services
N.A.I.C.S.: 541713
Salvatore Cincotti *(CEO)*

SHANGHAI KELAI MECHATRONICS ENG CO LTD
No 1555 Luo Dong Road Baoshan District, Shanghai, 200949, China
Tel.: (86) 2133850620
Web Site: https://www.sh-kelai.com
603960—(SHG)
Rev.: $95,089,508
Assets: $181,007,611
Liabilities: $40,468,671
Net Worth: $140,538,940
Earnings: $9,044,905
Fiscal Year-end: 12/31/22
Automotive Product Mfr & Distr
N.A.I.C.S.: 336110
Shi Li Tan *(Chm & Pres)*

SHANGHAI KINDLY ENTERPRISE DEVELOPMENT GROUP CO., LTD
No 658 Gaochao Road, Jiading District, Shanghai, 201803, China
Tel.: (86) 2169116128
Web Site: https://en.kdlchina.com
Year Founded: 1987
603987—(SHG)
Rev.: $437,883,985
Assets: $580,876,527
Liabilities: $222,974,365
Net Worth: $357,902,162
Earnings: $43,763,901
Fiscal Year-end: 12/31/22
Medical Device Mfr & Distr
N.A.I.C.S.: 339113
Zhang Xianmiao *(Chm)*

Subsidiaries:

Guangzhou Kindly Medical Devices Co., Ltd (1)
No 6 Dengyun Big Rd Tangbu East County Nanchun Town Panyu District, Guangzhou, 511442, China
Tel.: (86) 2034826660
Medical Equipment Distr
N.A.I.C.S.: 423450

Nanchang Kindly Medical Devices Co., Ltd (1)
No 929 Gangkou Avenue Economic and Technological Development Zone, Nanchang, 330013, Jiangxi, China
Tel.: (86) 7913717890
Medical Equipment Distr
N.A.I.C.S.: 423450

Shanghai Kindly Enterprise Development Group Medical Instruments Co., Ltd (1)
No 925 Jinyuanyi Road, Shanghai, 201803, China
Tel.: (86) 2159140056
Web Site: http://en.kdl-interv.com
Medicinal Product Mfr
N.A.I.C.S.: 339113

Shanghai Kindly Enterprise Development Group Pharmaceutical Co., Ltd (1)
Area 2 No 658 Gaochao Rd Jiading District, Shanghai, 201803, China
Tel.: (86) 2159140797
Disposable Blood Bag Mfr & Distr
N.A.I.C.S.: 326111

Shanghai Kindly International Trade Co., Ltd (1)
Building 8 No 171 Huajiang Rd Jiangqiao Town, Shanghai, 201803, China
Tel.: (86) 2159140058
Medical Device Distr
N.A.I.C.S.: 423450

Shanghai Kindly Tube Co., Ltd (1)
No 171 Huajiang Rd, Shanghai, 201803, China
Tel.: (86) 2159117628
Medical Puncture Needle Product Mfr & Distr

SHANGHAI KINDLY ENTERPRISE DEVELOPMENT GROUP CO., LTD

Shanghai Kindly Enterprise Development Group Co., Ltd—(Continued)
N.A.I.C.S.: 339112

Wenzhou Kindly Medical Devices Co., Ltd (1)
No 252 Yongqiang Rd Yongzhong Town Longwan District, Wenzhou, 325024, Zhejiang, China
Tel.: (86) 57786960626
Disposable Medical Product Distr
N.A.I.C.S.: 423450

Zhejiang Kindly Medical Devices Co., Ltd (1)
No 758 Binhai 5th Avenue, Binhai Industrial Park Longwan, Wenzhou, Zhejiang, China
Tel.: (86) 57786862296
Web Site: https://www.zjkdl.com
Medical Puncture Needle Product Mfr
N.A.I.C.S.: 339112

Zhuhai Kindly Medical Devices Co., Ltd (1)
No 288 Airport EastRoad, Jinwan District, Zhuhai, 519040, Guangdong, China
Tel.: (86) 7567770688
Web Site: http://zhkdl.diytrade.com
Disposable Syringe Mfr
N.A.I.C.S.: 339112

SHANGHAI KINDLY MEDICAL INSTRUMENTS CO., LTD.
No 925 Jinyuan 1st Road, Jiading District, Shanghai, China
Tel.: (86) 2159140056 CN
Web Site: https://sh-intmedical.com
Year Founded: 2006
1501—(HKG)
Rev.: $71,192,857
Assets: $248,436,909
Liabilities: $28,133,186
Net Worth: $220,303,723
Earnings: $21,517,578
Emp.: 1,189
Fiscal Year-end: 12/31/21
Medical Instrument Mfr
N.A.I.C.S.: 339112
Dongke Liang (Chm)

SHANGHAI KINETIC MEDICAL CO., LTD.
Building 23 Lane 528 Ruiqing Road Zhangjiang Hi-tech East Zone, Pudong New Area, Shanghai, 201201, China
Tel.: (86) 2150785060
Web Site: https://www.kmcglobal.com.cn
Year Founded: 2005
300326—(CHIN)
Rev.: $163,712,016
Assets: $479,065,860
Liabilities: $83,881,980
Net Worth: $395,183,880
Earnings: ($2,987,712)
Emp.: 90
Fiscal Year-end: 12/31/22
Surgical Product Mfr
N.A.I.C.S.: 339112
Jay Qin (Chm)

Subsidiaries:

Jiangsu Ideal Medical Science & Technology Co., Ltd (1)
East area Jinfeng Industry Park, Zhangjiagang, 215625, China
Tel.: (86) 51258552580
Web Site: https://www.idealmedical.com.cn
Surgical Instrument Mfr
N.A.I.C.S.: 339112

SHANGHAI KINLITA CHEMICAL CO., LTD.
No 139 Chugong Rd Shanghai Chemicals Park, Shanghai, 201417, China
Tel.: (86) 2131156999
Web Site: https://www.knt.cn
Year Founded: 1993

300225—(CHIN)
Rev.: $90,824,760
Assets: $157,229,748
Liabilities: $49,113,324
Net Worth: $108,116,424
Earnings: ($14,892,228)
Emp.: 170
Fiscal Year-end: 12/31/22
Automobile Paints & Coatings Mfr
N.A.I.C.S.: 325510

SHANGHAI LABWAY CLINICAL LABORATORY CO., LTD.
Floor 4-9 Building 1 Lane 268 Linxin Road, Changning District, Shanghai, 200335, China
Tel.: (86) 2131778162
Web Site: https://www.labway.cn
Year Founded: 2007
301060—(CHIN)
Rev.: $589,583,124
Assets: $526,060,548
Liabilities: $206,966,448
Net Worth: $319,094,100
Earnings: $86,671,728
Fiscal Year-end: 12/31/22
Medical Laboratory Services
N.A.I.C.S.: 621511
Tsang Wai-Hung (Chm)

SHANGHAI LAIMU ELECTRONIC LIMITED
No 88 Lane 651 Dongxue Road, Dongjing Town Songjiang District, Shanghai, 201619, China
Tel.: (86) 2167679190
Web Site: https://www.laimu.com.cn
Year Founded: 2003
603633—(SHG)
Rev.: $130,659,343
Assets: $404,511,789
Liabilities: $143,445,178
Net Worth: $261,066,612
Earnings: $9,596,466
Fiscal Year-end: 12/31/22
Electronic Component Mfr & Distr
N.A.I.C.S.: 334419
Zhu Xinai (Chm)

SHANGHAI LAIYIFEN CO., LTD
Laiyifen Qingnian Building No 68 Lane 1399 Husong Highway, Songjiang District, Shanghai, 201615, China
Tel.: (86) 2151760952
Web Site: http://www.lyfen.com
Year Founded: 1999
603777—(SHG)
Rev.: $615,287,991
Assets: $517,889,156
Liabilities: $263,567,234
Net Worth: $254,321,922
Earnings: $14,324,942
Fiscal Year-end: 12/31/22
Snack Food Mfr & Distr
N.A.I.C.S.: 311911
Ruifen Yu (Pres)

SHANGHAI LIANGXIN ELECTRICAL CO., LTD.
No 2000 South Shen Jiang Rd, Pudong New Area, Shanghai, 201315, China
Tel.: (86) 2168586719
Web Site: https://www.sh-liangxin.com
Year Founded: 1999
002706—(SSE)
Rev.: $583,652,347
Assets: $800,918,736
Liabilities: $275,339,928
Net Worth: $525,578,808
Earnings: $59,216,143
Emp.: 1,060
Fiscal Year-end: 12/31/22

Low Voltage Electrical Components Mfr
N.A.I.C.S.: 334419
Ren Silong (Chm)

Subsidiaries:

Shanghai Liangxin (Nader) Electrical U.S. Co. Inc. (1)
100 E Campus View Blvd Ste 250, Columbus, OH 43235
Tel.: (323) 613-0946
Electrical Apparatus & Equipment Whslr
N.A.I.C.S.: 423610

SHANGHAI LIANMING MACHINERY CO., LTD.
No 950 Shiwan 6th Road Pudong New Area, Shanghai, China
Tel.: (86) 2158560801
Web Site: https://www.shanghailmjx.com
Year Founded: 2003
603006—(SHG)
Rev.: $172,855,594
Assets: $321,578,295
Liabilities: $79,880,103
Net Worth: $241,698,193
Earnings: $20,779,186
Fiscal Year-end: 12/31/22
Automobile Parts Mfr
N.A.I.C.S.: 336370
Taoming Xu (Chm)

SHANGHAI LIKANG DISINFECTANT HIGH-TECH CO., LTD.
F5 Building E No 3100 Hutai Road, Shanghai, 200444, China
Tel.: (86) 2156200588
Web Site: http://www.en.lkgk.com
Year Founded: 1988
Chemicals Mfr
N.A.I.C.S.: 325998
Wensheng Sun (COO)

SHANGHAI LILI & BEAUTY COSMETICS CO., LTD.
No 876 Panyu Road, Xuhui, Shanghai, China
Tel.: (86) 2154489668
Web Site: https://www.lrlz.com
Year Founded: 2010
605136—(SHG)
Rev.: $455,110,966
Assets: $446,672,365
Liabilities: $95,724,790
Net Worth: $350,947,575
Earnings: ($19,560,851)
Emp.: 950
Fiscal Year-end: 12/31/22
Cosmetic Product Distr
N.A.I.C.S.: 456120
Tao Huang (Chm & CEO)

SHANGHAI LINGANG HOLDINGS CO., LTD.
3F No 668 Shenzhuan Highway, Songjiang District, Shanghai, 201306, China
Tel.: (86) 2164855827 CN
Web Site: http://www.saic.sh.cn
Year Founded: 1994
600848—(SHG)
Rev.: $842,317,080
Assets: $9,310,454,164
Liabilities: $5,461,071,773
Net Worth: $3,849,382,391
Earnings: $141,645,334
Emp.: 14,000
Fiscal Year-end: 12/31/22
Real Estate Development Services
N.A.I.C.S.: 531390
Weng Kaining (Chm)

SHANGHAI LINGYUN INDUSTRIES DEVELOPMENT CO., LTD.

INTERNATIONAL PUBLIC

Room 501 12F No 1088 Yuanshen Road Pudong New Area, Shanghai, 200122, China
Tel.: (86) 2168400880
Web Site: http://www.elingyun.com
Year Founded: 1998
900957—(SHG)
Rev.: $16,835,827
Assets: $149,729,103
Liabilities: $70,132,720
Net Worth: $79,596,382
Earnings: $5,685,624
Fiscal Year-end: 12/31/22
Building Materials Whslr
N.A.I.C.S.: 423390
Aiqin Lian (Vice Chm & Pres)

SHANGHAI LONGYUN MEDIA GROUP CO., LTD.
15th Floor No 118 Min Sheng Road Vanke Center, Riverside Pudong New Area, Shanghai, 200120, China
Tel.: (86) 2158822988
Web Site: http://www.obm.com.cn
Year Founded: 2003
603729—(SHG)
Rev.: $56,283,004
Assets: $95,462,523
Liabilities: $21,898,118
Net Worth: $73,564,405
Earnings: ($26,821,651)
Fiscal Year-end: 12/31/22
Television Media Advertising Services
N.A.I.C.S.: 541890

SHANGHAI LONYER FUELS CO., LTD.
25 F No 710 Dongfang Road Pudong New Area, Shanghai, 200122, China
Tel.: (86) 2158300945
Web Site: http://www.lyrysh.com
Year Founded: 1997
603003—(SHG)
Rev.: $1,401,775,488
Assets: $624,308,607
Liabilities: $116,124,587
Net Worth: $508,184,020
Earnings: $4,550,252
Fiscal Year-end: 12/31/22
Fuel Oil Distr
N.A.I.C.S.: 424720
Zeng Zeng Xu (Chm)

SHANGHAI LUJIAZUI FINANCE & TRADE ZONE DEVELOPMENT
Floor 18-21 Building D Qiantan World Trade Center Phase II, No 6 Lane 227 Dongyu Road Pudong New District, Shanghai, 200126, China
Tel.: (86) 2133848788 CN
Web Site: https://www.ljz.com.cn
Year Founded: 1992
900932—(SHG)
Rev.: $1,651,427,271
Assets: $17,647,817,719
Liabilities: $12,360,496,183
Net Worth: $5,287,321,536
Earnings: $152,297,454
Fiscal Year-end: 12/31/22
Property Development & Leasing Services
N.A.I.C.S.: 237210
Hui Zhou (CFO)

Subsidiaries:

Lujiazui International Trust Company (1)
30/28F Lujiazui Square No 1600 Century Avenue, Pudong, Shanghai, 200122, China
Tel.: (86) 21 5058 7808
Web Site: http://en.lujiazui.gov.cn
Investment Trust
N.A.I.C.S.: 525990

Joint Venture (Domestic):

Shanghai Krupp Stainless Co., Ltd. (2)

AND PRIVATE COMPANIES

21 Tong Yao Road Pudong New Area,
Shanghai, 200126, China (55%)
Tel.: (86) 2138874887
Web Site: http://ww.skschina.com
Cold Rolled Steel Mfr
N.A.I.C.S.: 331221

SHANGHAI LUOMAN LIGHTING TECHNOLOGIES, INC.
Block B Shanjin Financial Plaza No 1198 Yangshupu Road, Yangpu, Shanghai, 200082, China
Tel.: (86) 2165031217
Web Site: http://www.shluoman.cn
Year Founded: 1999
605289—(SHG)
Rev.: $43,846,611
Assets: $264,048,567
Liabilities: $90,386,108
Net Worth: $173,662,459
Earnings: ($2,121,135)
Fiscal Year-end: 12/31/22
Construction Services
N.A.I.C.S.: 236220
Kaijun Sun (Chm & Gen Mgr)

SHANGHAI M&G STATIONERY INC.
Building 3 No 3469 Jinqian Highway, Fengxian District, Shanghai, 201612, China
Tel.: (86) 2157475621
Web Site: http://www.mg-pen.net
Year Founded: 1997
603899—(SHG)
Rev.: $2,807,482,710
Assets: $1,828,372,113
Liabilities: $810,166,308
Net Worth: $1,018,205,805
Earnings: $180,056,935
Emp.: 10,000
Fiscal Year-end: 12/31/22
Stationery Product Mfr & Distr
N.A.I.C.S.: 322230
Chen Huwen (Chm)

SHANGHAI MATERIAL TRADING CO., LTD.
7F No 325 South Suzhou Road, Huangpu District, Shanghai, 200063, China
Tel.: (86) 2163231818 CN
Web Site: http://www.600822sh.com
Year Founded: 1993
600822—(SHG)
Rev.: $705,100,551
Assets: $487,238,095
Liabilities: $337,012,510
Net Worth: $150,225,585
Earnings: $8,414,200
Emp.: 1,500
Fiscal Year-end: 12/31/22
Trading of Metal, Oil Products & Automobiles Materials
N.A.I.C.S.: 423510
Ning Bin (Chm)

SHANGHAI MEDICILON, INC.
No 585 Chuanda Road, Pudong New Area, Shanghai, 201299, China
Tel.: (86) 2158591500
Web Site: https://www.medicilon.com
Year Founded: 2004
688202—(SHG)
Rev.: $232,913,814
Assets: $327,073,158
Liabilities: $102,042,186
Net Worth: $225,030,972
Earnings: $47,488,377
Fiscal Year-end: 12/31/22
Pharmaceutical Product Mfr & Distr
N.A.I.C.S.: 325412
Chunlin Chen (Founder & CEO)

SHANGHAI MENON ANIMAL NUTRITION TECHNOLOGY CO., LTD.
No 151 Lihong Road, Jiading District, Shanghai, 201807, China
Tel.: (86) 2159546881
Web Site: https://www.sinomenon.com
Year Founded: 1997
301156—(CHIN)
Rev.: $69,841,036
Assets: $116,141,975
Liabilities: $5,499,363
Net Worth: $110,642,612
Earnings: $8,729,134
Fiscal Year-end: 12/31/23
Animal Feed Mfr & Distr
N.A.I.C.S.: 311119
Hong Wei (Chm)

SHANGHAI METERSBONWE FASHION & ACCESSORIES CO., LTD.
No 208 Huanqiao Road, Kangqiao Town Pudong New Area, Shanghai, 201315, China
Tel.: (86) 2168182996
Web Site: http://www.metersbonwe.com
Year Founded: 1995
002269—(SSE)
Rev.: $202,086,074
Assets: $531,536,976
Liabilities: $496,849,851
Net Worth: $34,687,126
Earnings: ($115,523,338)
Fiscal Year-end: 12/31/22
Casual Wear & Accessories Design, Mfr & Sales
N.A.I.C.S.: 458110
Zhou Chengjian (Chm & Pres)

SHANGHAI MILKGROUND FOOD TECH CO., LTD.
Jintai Building No 1398 Jinqiao Road, Pudong New District, Shanghai, 201206, China
Tel.: (86) 4006886918
Web Site: https://milkground.cn
Year Founded: 1988
600882—(SHG)
Rev.: $678,067,135
Assets: $1,044,125,007
Liabilities: $359,461,782
Net Worth: $684,663,225
Earnings: $19,010,511
Fiscal Year-end: 12/31/22
Holding Company; Investment Services
N.A.I.C.S.: 551112

Subsidiaries:

Brownes Foods Operations Pty. Ltd. (1)
22 Geddes Street, Balcatta, 6021, WA, Australia
Tel.: (61) 800 675 484
Web Site: http://www.brownesdairy.com.au
Milk, Dairy & Juice Products Mfr & Distr
N.A.I.C.S.: 311511
Julie Fairweather (Dir-HR)

SHANGHAI MOONS' ELECTRIC CO., LTD.
No 168 Mingjia Road Minhang District, Shanghai, 201107, China
Tel.: (86) 2152634688
Web Site: http://www.moonsindustries.com
Year Founded: 1994
603728—(SHG)
Rev.: $415,578,721
Assets: $542,722,434
Liabilities: $161,290,579
Net Worth: $381,431,854
Earnings: $34,712,945
Emp.: 3,000
Fiscal Year-end: 12/31/22
Industrial Automation Equipments Mfr
N.A.I.C.S.: 335314

Subsidiaries:

Applied Motion Products Inc. (1)
18645 Madrone Pkwy, Morgan Hill, CA 95037
Tel.: (408) 612-4375
Web Site: http://www.applied-motion.com
Mfr & Designer of Motion Control Products
N.A.I.C.S.: 423610
Dennis Joyce (VP-Sls & Mktg)

Lin Engineering, Inc. (1)
16245 Vineyard Blvd, Morgan Hill, CA 95037
Tel.: (408) 919-0200
Web Site: https://www.linengineering.com
Industrial Control Product Mfr & Distr
N.A.I.C.S.: 335314

Moons' Industries (America), Inc. (1)
1113 N Prospect Ave, Itasca, IL 60143
Tel.: (630) 833-5940
Web Site: http://www.moons.com
Emp.: 11
Industrial Machinery & Equipment Whslr
N.A.I.C.S.: 423830

Moons' Industries (Europe) S.R.L. (1)
Via Torri Bianche 1, 20871, Vimercate, Italy
Tel.: (39) 039 626 0521
Web Site: https://www.moonsindustries.eu
Stepper Motor Mfr
N.A.I.C.S.: 335312

Moons' Industries (South-East Asia) Pte. Ltd. (1)
33 Ubi Avenue 3 08-23 Vertex, Singapore, 408868, Singapore
Tel.: (65) 66341198
Web Site: http://www.moonsindustries.com
Emp.: 5
Industrial Machinery & Equipment Whslr
N.A.I.C.S.: 423830
Daniel Sung (Gen Mgr)

Moons' Industries Europe Head Quarter S.R.L. (1)
Via Torri Bianche 1, 20871, Vimercate, MB, Italy
Tel.: (39) 039 626 0521
Web Site: https://www.moonsindustries.eu
Industrial Control Product Mfr
N.A.I.C.S.: 335314
Mario Manganini (Mng Dir)

Moons' Industries Japan Co., Ltd. (1)
Room 602 6F Shin Yokohama Koushin Building 2-12-1, Shin-Yokohama Kohoku-ku, Yokohama, 222-0033, Kanagawa, Japan
Tel.: (81) 454755788
Web Site: http://www.moons.com.cn
Emp.: 5
Industrial Machinery & Equipment Whslr
N.A.I.C.S.: 423830
Masanory Iwanaga (Mgr)

TECHNOSOFT SA (1)
Avenue des Alpes 20, 2000, Neuchatel, Switzerland
Tel.: (41) 327325500
Web Site: https://technosoftmotion.com
Stepper Motor Development, Design & Mfr
N.A.I.C.S.: 335312

SHANGHAI MORN ELECTRIC EQUIPMENT CO., LTD.
No 2829 Jiangshan Road Pudong New Area, Shanghai, 201306, China
Tel.: (86) 2168099820
Web Site: https://www.mornelectric.com
Year Founded: 1997
002451—(SSE)
Rev.: $151,419,603
Assets: $230,870,713
Liabilities: $111,432,883
Net Worth: $119,437,831
Earnings: $2,059,233
Fiscal Year-end: 12/31/22
Electric Wires & Cables Mfr
N.A.I.C.S.: 335921

SHANGHAI NAR INDUSTRIAL CO., LTD.
No 26 Xinhan Road, Pudong District, Shanghai, 201316, China
Tel.: (86) 2131272888
Web Site: https://www.nar.com.cn
Year Founded: 2002
002825—(SSE)
Rev.: $227,211,398
Assets: $276,433,012
Liabilities: $80,228,814
Net Worth: $196,204,198
Earnings: $49,418,006
Fiscal Year-end: 12/31/22
Adhesive Product Mfr & Distr
N.A.I.C.S.: 322220
Aiguo You (Founder, Chm & Gen Mgr)

Subsidiaries:

Shanghai NAR Industrial Co., Ltd. - Nantong Factory (1)
No 628 West Jinqiao Rd Tongzhou Economic Development Zone, Nantong, 226300, Jiangsu, China
Tel.: (86) 51386557156
Printing Material Mfr
N.A.I.C.S.: 325910

SHANGHAI NATIONAL CENTER OF TESTING & INSPECTION FOR ELECTRIC CABLE & WIRE CO., LTD.
888 Zhenchen Road, Baoshan, Shanghai, 200444, China
Tel.: (86) 2165493333
Web Site: https://www.ticw.com.cn
Year Founded: 1983
301289—(SSE)
Rev.: $29,298,630
Assets: $164,086,898
Liabilities: $29,436,545
Net Worth: $134,650,353
Earnings: $10,334,633
Emp.: 200
Fiscal Year-end: 12/31/22
Testing Laboratory Services
N.A.I.C.S.: 541380

SHANGHAI NENGHUI TECHNOLOGY CO., LTD.
i288 Tongxie Road, Putuo, Shanghai, 200335, China
Tel.: (86) 2150896255
Web Site: https://www.nhet.energy
Year Founded: 2009
301046—(CHIN)
Rev.: $53,586,468
Assets: $163,469,124
Liabilities: $56,277,936
Net Worth: $107,191,188
Earnings: $3,670,056
Fiscal Year-end: 12/31/22
Eletric Power Generation Services
N.A.I.C.S.: 221116
Chuankui Luo (Chm)

SHANGHAI NEW CENTURION NETWORK CO., LTD.
3F Zhongqi Building No 2000 Zhongshan North Road, Putuo, Shanghai, 200063, China
Tel.: (86) 2152908588
Web Site: http://www.shsnc.com
Year Founded: 2014
605398—(SHG)
Rev.: $86,091,371
Assets: $173,206,454
Liabilities: $30,196,516
Net Worth: $143,009,938
Earnings: $7,999,866
Fiscal Year-end: 12/31/22
Information Technology Services
N.A.I.C.S.: 541512
Xingyan Sun (Chm)

Shanghai New Centurion Network Co., Ltd.—(Continued)

SHANGHAI NEW CULTURE MEDIA GROUP CO., LTD.
Room 238 North District 444 Dongjiangwan Road, Hongkou District, Shanghai, 200081, China
Tel.: (86) 02165871976
Web Site: http://www.ncmedia.com.cn
300336—(CHIN)
Rev.: $51,916,741
Assets: $218,422,304
Liabilities: $171,783,648
Net Worth: $46,638,656
Earnings: ($256,262,110)
Emp.: 60
Fiscal Year-end: 12/31/20
Movie & Television Production, Distribution & Other Related Business
N.A.I.C.S.: 512110

SHANGHAI NEW HUANGPU GROUP CO. LTD.
32F East Building No 668 Beijing East Road, Shanghai, 200001, China
Tel.: (86) 2163238888
Web Site: https://600638.com
600638—(SHG)
Rev.: $663,516,037
Assets: $3,443,190,042
Liabilities: $2,799,255,453
Net Worth: $643,934,589
Earnings: $7,929,230
Fiscal Year-end: 12/31/22
Real Estate Development Services
N.A.I.C.S.: 236115
Xu Jun (Sec)

SHANGHAI NEW WORLD CO., LTD.
No 2-88 Nanjing West Road, Shanghai, 200003, China
Tel.: (86) 2163871786
Web Site: http://www.newworld-china.com
Year Founded: 1988
600628—(SHG)
Rev.: $119,342,246
Assets: $802,461,718
Liabilities: $211,164,254
Net Worth: $591,297,464
Earnings: ($7,304,057)
Fiscal Year-end: 12/31/22
Departmental Store Operator
N.A.I.C.S.: 455110
Chen Yong (Chm)

SHANGHAI NEWTOUCH SOFTWARE CO., LTD.
4-6F No 98 Lane 91 Eshan Road Building No 1, Software Park Pilot Free Trade Zone, Shanghai, 200127, China
Tel.: (86) 2151105633
Web Site: http://www.newtouch.cn
Year Founded: 1994
688590—(SHG)
Rev.: $184,684,561
Assets: $334,180,599
Liabilities: $134,934,172
Net Worth: $199,246,428
Earnings: ($7,292,264)
Fiscal Year-end: 12/31/22
Software Development Services
N.A.I.C.S.: 541511
Wei Guo (Chm)

Subsidiaries:

Beijing Newtouch Junyang Information Technology Co., Ltd. (1)
13F Chengming Building 2 Nandajie Xizhimen, Xicheng District, Beijing, 100035, China
Tel.: (86) 105 377 9500
Software Development Services

N.A.I.C.S.: 541511

Chengdu Newtouch Software Co., Ltd. (1)
Room 2A 10F Unit 2 Buidling 2 10 Keyuan 2 Road Hi-tech Zone, Chengdu, 610093, China
Tel.: (86) 288 337 8392
Software Development Services
N.A.I.C.S.: 541511

Chengdu Newtouch Yuanri Software Co., Ltd. (1)
Room 2A 10F Unit 2 Buidling 2 10 Keyuan 2 Road Hi-tech Zone, Chengdu, 610093, China
Tel.: (86) 288 337 8392
Software Development Services
N.A.I.C.S.: 541511

Dalian Eland Information Technology Co., Ltd. (1)
Room 201 DLSP Building 16 269 Wuyi Road, Shahekou District, Dalian, 116021, Liaoning, China
Tel.: (86) 4118 476 8331
Software Development Services
N.A.I.C.S.: 541511

Dalian Newtouch Software Co., Ltd. (1)
Chambre 301C Batiment 12 21 Rue Ruanjianyuandong, Dalian, 116023, China
Tel.: (86) 4118 476 8350
Software Development Services
N.A.I.C.S.: 541511

Eland Co., Ltd. (1)
7F Grace Takanawa Building 2-14-17, Takanawa Minato-ku, Tokyo, Japan
Tel.: (81) 35 791 5198
Software Development Services
N.A.I.C.S.: 541511

Newtouch Software (Kunshan)Co., Ltd. (1)
8 Zhaofeng Road, Huaqiao Town, Kunshan, 200127, China
Tel.: (86) 215 110 5660
Software Development Services
N.A.I.C.S.: 541511

Nihon Newtouch Software Co., Ltd. (1)
2F Minami Shinagawa JN Building 2-2-13 Minami Shinagawa, Shinagawa-ku, Tokyo, Japan
Tel.: (81) 36 809 4521
Software Development Services
N.A.I.C.S.: 541511

Seio Technology Co., Ltd. (1)
2F Minami Shinagawa JN Building 2-2-13 Minami Shinagawa, Shinagawa-ku, Tokyo, 140-0004, Japan
Tel.: (81) 36 433 1695
Software Development Services
N.A.I.C.S.: 541511

Shanghai CAI-Newtouch Software Co., Ltd. (1)
Room 231 Zone B 227 Rushan Road, Pilot Free Trade Zone, Shanghai, 200127, China
Tel.: (86) 215 110 5660
Software Development Services
N.A.I.C.S.: 541511

Shanghai Freesky Technology Co., Ltd. (1)
Room 206 Building C 200 Tianlin road, Xuhui District, Shanghai, 200127, China
Tel.: (86) 215 110 5660
Software Development Services
N.A.I.C.S.: 541511

Shanghai Newtouch Information Technology Co., Ltd. (1)
E-03 6F Building 1 198 Huashen Road, Pilot Free Trade Zone, Shanghai, 200127, China
Tel.: (86) 215 110 5660
Software Development Services
N.A.I.C.S.: 541511

Shenzhen Newtouch Software Co., Ltd. (1)
Room 2629 26F Anlian Building 4018 Jintian road, Futian District, Shenzhen, 518026, China
Software Development Services

N.A.I.C.S.: 541511

Xi'an Newtouch Information Technology Co., Ltd. (1)
Room 601 Qinfeng Mansion Xian Software Park No 68, Kejier Road High-tech Zone, Xi'an, 710075, China
Tel.: (86) 28 766 9728
Software Development Services
N.A.I.C.S.: 541511

SHANGHAI NO.1 PHARMACY CO., LTD.
No 616 Nanjing East Road, Huangpu District, Shanghai, 200032, China
Tel.: (86) 2164337282
Web Site: http://www.dyyy.com.cn
Year Founded: 1992
600833—(SHG)
Rev.: $372,889,553
Assets: $286,289,949
Liabilities: $151,691,544
Net Worth: $134,598,405
Earnings: $20,155,305
Fiscal Year-end: 12/31/22
Pharmaceutical Product Whslr
N.A.I.C.S.: 424210
Zhang Haibo (Chm)

SHANGHAI ORIGINAL ADVANCED COMPOUNDS CO., LTD.
No 268 North Hengsha Road Xinzhuang Industry Park, Shanghai, China
Tel.: (86) 2164095566
Web Site: http://www.sh-original.com
603991—(SHG)
Rev.: $18,185,156
Assets: $56,634,033
Liabilities: $14,406,584
Net Worth: $42,227,448
Earnings: ($2,361,612)
Fiscal Year-end: 12/31/22
Cable Mfr & Distr
N.A.I.C.S.: 332618
Hai Liang Hou (Chm)

SHANGHAI PHARMACEUTICALS HOLDING CO., LTD.
Shanghai Pharma Building 200 Taicang Road, Shanghai, 200020, China
Tel.: (86) 2163730908
Web Site: https://www.sphchina.com
SHPMF—(OTCIQ)
Rev.: $29,402,402,404
Assets: $22,856,734,969
Liabilities: $14,469,907,725
Net Worth: $8,386,827,243
Earnings: $688,865,866
Emp.: 48,136
Fiscal Year-end: 12/31/20
Holding Company
N.A.I.C.S.: 551112
Bo Shen (CFO & VP)

Subsidiaries:

Changzhou Pharmaceutical Factory Co., Ltd. (1)
No 518 Laodong East Road, Changzhou, 213018, Jiangsu, China
Tel.: (86) 51988821493
Web Site: https://www.czpharma.com
Pharmaceuticals Product Mfr
N.A.I.C.S.: 325412

Ningbo Pharmaceutical Co., Ltd. (1)
No 26 Chejiao Street, Ningbo, 315000, China
Web Site: https://www.nbyyz.com
Pharmaceutical Products Distr
N.A.I.C.S.: 424210

Shanghai Medical Instruments Co., Ltd. (1)
No 588 Shenwang Road, Minhang District, Shanghai, 201108, China
Tel.: (86) 2165289166
Web Site: https://www.jzsf.com

Medical Instrument Mfr & Distr
N.A.I.C.S.: 339112

Shanghai Zhonghua Pharmaceutical Co., Ltd. (1)
3F No 685 Dingxi Road, Shanghai, 200052, China
Tel.: (86) 2162816563
Web Site: https://www.en.zhpharm-sh.com
Pharmaceutical Products Distr
N.A.I.C.S.: 424210

SHANGHAI PHOENIX ENTERPRISE (GROUP) CO., LTD.
4F Block 6 No 518 Fuquan North Road, Changning District, Shanghai, 200335, China
Tel.: (86) 2132795555
Web Site: http://www.jskfjs.com
Year Founded: 1993
600679—(SHG)
Rev.: $226,029,328
Assets: $423,607,298
Liabilities: $125,102,156
Net Worth: $298,505,142
Earnings: ($43,248,914)
Fiscal Year-end: 12/31/22
Bicycle Mfr & Distr
N.A.I.C.S.: 336991
Hu Wei (Chm)

SHANGHAI PIONEER HOLDING LTD.
No 15 Lane 88 Wuwei Road, Pudong New District, Shanghai, 200331, China
Tel.: (86) 2150498986
Web Site: http://www.pioneer-pharma.com
Year Founded: 1996
1345—(HKG)
Rev.: $219,828,772
Assets: $203,535,961
Liabilities: $63,963,796
Net Worth: $139,572,165
Earnings: $21,574,726
Emp.: 250
Fiscal Year-end: 12/31/21
Pharmaceuticals & Medical Products Distr
N.A.I.C.S.: 424210
Wenfei Huang (Gen Mgr-Ophthalmology Bus Unit)

Subsidiaries:

Covex, S.A. (1)
Tel.: (34) 918450200
Pharmaceuticals Product Mfr
N.A.I.C.S.: 325412

Pioneer Pharma (Hong Kong) Company Limited (1)
Room 1106 11/F Golden Gate Commercial Building 136-138 Austin Road, Tsimshatsui, Kowloon, (Hong Kong)
Tel.: (852) 2628 7422
Investment Holding Services
N.A.I.C.S.: 523940

SHANGHAI POTEVIO CO., LTD.
No 700 Yishan Road, Xuhui District, Shanghai, 200233, China
Tel.: (86) 21 64360900
Web Site: http://www.shpte.com
Rev.: $98,319,507
Assets: $319,007,918
Liabilities: $260,675,486
Net Worth: $58,332,432
Earnings: ($53,844,912)
Fiscal Year-end: 12/31/17
Communication Device Mfr & Whslr
N.A.I.C.S.: 334210
Zhongyao Li (Sec & VP)

SHANGHAI PRET COMPOSITES CO., LTD.
No 558 Xinye Road Qingpu Industrial Park, Shanghai, 201707, China

Tel.: (86) 2131115900
Web Site: https://www.pret.com.cn
Year Founded: 1993
002324—(SSE)
Sales Range: $25-49.9 Million
Emp.: 900
Plastic & Polymer Mfr
N.A.I.C.S.: 325998
Xiangfu Zhang *(Vice Chm, Deputy Gen Mgr & Chief Engr)*

Subsidiaries:

Wellman Plastics Recycling LLC (1)
520 Kingsburg Highway, Johnsonville, SC 29555
Tel.: (843) 386-8054
Web Site: http://www.wellmanpr.com
Sales Range: $100-124.9 Million
Plastics Recycler Mfr
N.A.I.C.S.: 326130
Tim Carter *(Mgr-IT)*

SHANGHAI PROSOLAR RESOURCES DEVELOPMENT CO., LTD.

Room A 3rd Floor No 1388 Kangqiao Road, Pudong New Area, Shanghai, 310000, China
Tel.: (86) 4000960980
600193—(SHG)
Rev.: $37,017,106
Assets: $102,037,244
Liabilities: $57,325,769
Net Worth: $44,711,475
Earnings: $873,962
Fiscal Year-end: 12/31/22
Iron Ore Mining Services
N.A.I.C.S.: 212210

SHANGHAI PUDONG DEVELOPMENT BANK CO., LTD.

No 12 Zhongshan Dong Yi Road, Shanghai, China
Tel.: (86) 2161618888 CN
Web Site: https://eng.spdb.com.cn
Year Founded: 1992
600000—(SHG)
Rev.: $26,482,528,800
Assets: $1,222,133,000,400
Liabilities: $1,122,901,790,400
Net Worth: $99,231,210,000
Earnings: $7,184,408,400
Emp.: 60,000
Fiscal Year-end: 12/31/22
Banking Services
N.A.I.C.S.: 522110
Xinyi Liu *(Exec VP)*

Subsidiaries:

SPDB International Holding, Ltd. (1)
33/F SPD Bank Tower One Hennessy 1 Hennessy Road, Hong Kong, China (Hong Kong)
Tel.: (852) 28090300
Web Site: http://www.spdbi.com
Financial Investment Services
N.A.I.C.S.: 523999

SHANGHAI PUDONG ROAD & BRIDGE CONSTRUCTION CO., LTD.

11th-12th Floor No 7 Lane 188 Zouping Road, Pudong New District, Shanghai, 201206, China
Tel.: (86) 2158206677
Web Site: https://www.pdjs.com.cn
Year Founded: 1998
600284—(SHG)
Rev.: $1,977,433,867
Assets: $3,804,457,593
Liabilities: $2,784,003,731
Net Worth: $1,020,453,862
Earnings: $79,682,911
Fiscal Year-end: 12/31/22
Road & Bridge Construction Services
N.A.I.C.S.: 237310
Yang Ming *(Chm)*

SHANGHAI PUDONG SCIENCE & TECHNOLOGY INVESTMENT CO., LTD.

46F Building 1 Lujiazui Century Financial Plaza, No 729 South Yanggao Road Pudong, Shanghai, 201203, China
Tel.: (86) 2150276328
Web Site: http://www.pdsti.com
Emp.: 70
Investment Management Service
N.A.I.C.S.: 523999
Xudong Zhu *(Chm & CEO)*

Subsidiaries:

Montage Technology Group Limited (1)
6/F Block A Technology Building 900 Yishan Road, Shanghai, 200233, China
Tel.: (86) 2154679038
Web Site: http://www.montage-tech.com
Rev.: $279,404,481
Assets: $1,289,942,402
Liabilities: $53,499,400
Net Worth: $1,236,443,003
Earnings: $169,094,813
Emp.: 446
Fiscal Year-end: 12/31/2020
Fabless Analog & Mixed-Signal Semiconductor Products Mfr
N.A.I.C.S.: 334413
Stephen Tai *(Gen Mgr)*

SHANGHAI PUTAILAI NEW ENERGY TECHNOLOGY CO., LTD.

Building 116-117 G4 Zone 456 Dieqiao Rd, Pudong New District, Shanghai, 201315, China
Tel.: (86) 2161902901 CN
Web Site: https://www.putailai.com
Year Founded: 2012
603659—(SHG)
Rev.: $2,171,132,402
Assets: $5,011,902,212
Liabilities: $3,050,623,864
Net Worth: $1,961,278,348
Earnings: $435,862,534
Emp.: 700
Fiscal Year-end: 12/31/22
Battery Product Mfr & Distr
N.A.I.C.S.: 335910
Liang Feng *(Chm)*

Subsidiaries:

Dongguan Advanced Electronic Technology Co. Ltd. (1)
Dongxing Industrial Park, Dongguan, Guanddong Province, China
Tel.: (86) 88328600
Lithium-Ion Anode Material Mfr
N.A.I.C.S.: 335910

Dongguan Advanced Material Technology Co. Ltd. (1)
Onxing Industrial Park Kangle Road, Hengli Town, Dongguan, Guanddong Province, China
Tel.: (86) 3794955274
Lithium-Ion Anode Material Mfr
N.A.I.C.S.: 335910

Jiangxi Zhichen Technology Co. Ltd. (1)
Fengxin Industrial Park, Fengxin, 330700, Jiangxi, China
Tel.: (86) 7957182588
Web Site: http://www.jxzichen.com
Lithium-Ion Anode Material Mfr
N.A.I.C.S.: 335910
William Chen *(Chm)*

Shenzhen Katop Automation Technology Co., Ltd. (1)
B Building No 6 Road Twenty-one Lanjin, Pingshan New District, Shenzhen, 518118, China
Tel.: (86) 75528318788
Lithium-Ion Anode Material Mfr
N.A.I.C.S.: 335910

The Hongkong Excellen Science & Technology Ltd. (1)
Room 15C Chinese Centre No 678 Nathan Road, Kowloon Bay, China (Hong Kong)
Tel.: (852) 13918512630
Lithium-Ion Anode Material Mfr
N.A.I.C.S.: 335910

Zhejiang Keaton Technology Co., Ltd. (1)
Building 2 No 8 Fengshan Road, Chengtan Town Xinchang County, Shaoxing, Zhejiang, China
Tel.: (86) 57586333297
Lithium-Ion Anode Material Mfr
N.A.I.C.S.: 335910

SHANGHAI QIFAN CABLE CO., LTD.

No 238 Zhenkang Road, Zhangyan Town Jinshan, Shanghai, 201514, China
Tel.: (86) 2157220171
Web Site: https://www.qifancable.com
Year Founded: 1994
605222—(SHG)
Rev.: $2,898,445,273
Assets: $1,715,333,574
Liabilities: $1,126,846,525
Net Worth: $588,487,049
Earnings: $51,428,829
Emp.: 4,500
Fiscal Year-end: 12/31/22
Wire & Cable Mfr
N.A.I.C.S.: 331491
Guihua Zhou *(Chm)*

SHANGHAI QINGPU FIRE-FIGHTING EQUIPMENT CO. LTD

1988 Jihe Road Hua Xin Town, Qingpu District, Shanghai, 201708, China
Tel.: (86) 59796330 CN
Web Site: https://www.shanghaiqingpu.com
Year Founded: 2000
8115—(HKG)
Rev.: $8,732,599
Assets: $25,461,400
Liabilities: $4,386,377
Net Worth: $21,075,023
Earnings: $1,286,906
Emp.: 90
Fiscal Year-end: 12/31/22
Pressure Vessel Mfr & Distr
N.A.I.C.S.: 332420
Jun Luo *(Mgr-Technical)*

SHANGHAI RAAS BLOOD PRODUCTS CO., LTD.

No 2009 Wangyuan Road, Fengxian District, Shanghai, 201401, China
Tel.: (86) 2122130888
Web Site: https://www.raas-corp.com
Year Founded: 1988
002252—(SSE)
Rev.: $922,034,683
Assets: $4,276,297,514
Liabilities: $230,904,381
Net Worth: $4,045,393,133
Earnings: $263,964,650
Fiscal Year-end: 12/31/22
Blood Product Research & Development Services
N.A.I.C.S.: 541715
Tan Lixia *(Chm)*

Subsidiaries:

Tonrol Bio-Pharmaceutical Co., Ltd. (1)
No 376 Yanzihe Road High-tech Zone, Hefei, 230088, China
Tel.: (86) 55163638855
Web Site: http://www.tonrol.com
Emp.: 300
Pharmaceuticals Product Mfr
N.A.I.C.S.: 325412

SHANGHAI REALWAY CAPITAL ASSETS MANAGEMENT CO., LTD.

Room 706-707 Block 1 Shiji Hui No 1198 Shiji Avenue, Pudong New Area, Shanghai, 200122, China
Tel.: (86) 2152126818 CN
Web Site: https://www.realwaycapital.com
Year Founded: 2010
1835—(HKG)
Rev.: $5,160,121
Assets: $50,878,854
Liabilities: $4,480,164
Net Worth: $46,398,690
Earnings: ($4,859,665)
Emp.: 91
Fiscal Year-end: 12/31/22
Asset Management Services
N.A.I.C.S.: 531390
Ping Zhu *(Co-Founder, Chm, CEO & Dir)*

SHANGHAI RIGHTONGENE BIOTECHNOLOGY CO., LTD.

Building 3 No 6055 Jinhai Road, Fengxian, Shanghai, 201403, China
Tel.: (86) 2133282601
Web Site: http://www.rightongene.com
Year Founded: 2012
688217—(SHG)
Rev.: $59,571,453
Assets: $152,042,375
Liabilities: $15,654,726
Net Worth: $136,387,649
Earnings: $5,682,493
Fiscal Year-end: 12/31/22
Medical Product Mfr & Distr
N.A.I.C.S.: 339112
Hui Xiong *(Chm & Gen Mgr)*

SHANGHAI RONGTAI HEALTH TECHNOLOGY CORPORATION LIMITED

NO 1226 Zhufeng Rd, Qingpu District, Shanghai, 201714, China
Tel.: (86) 2159833669
Web Site: https://www.rotai.com
Year Founded: 1997
603579—(SHG)
Rev.: $281,476,826
Assets: $480,705,058
Liabilities: $218,144,352
Net Worth: $262,560,706
Earnings: $23,057,597
Fiscal Year-end: 12/31/22
Massage Product Mfr & Distr
N.A.I.C.S.: 335210
Lin Guangrong *(Chm)*

SHANGHAI RUNDA MEDICAL TECHNOLOGY CO., LTD.

8th Floor Building 1 Xinghui Center No 89 Zhapu Road, Shanghai, 200085, China
Tel.: (86) 2151096821 CN
Web Site: https://www.rundamedical.com
Year Founded: 1999
603108—(SHG)
Rev.: $1,473,416,385
Assets: $2,038,448,267
Liabilities: $1,335,065,285
Net Worth: $703,382,982
Earnings: $58,651,609
Emp.: 3,000
Fiscal Year-end: 12/31/22
In-Vitro Diagnostic & Medical Laboratory Products Developer, Mfr & Whslr
N.A.I.C.S.: 325413
Hui Liu *(Vice Chm & Gen Mgr)*

SHANGHAI RURAL COMMERCIAL BANK CO., LTD.

SHANGHAI RURAL COMMERCIAL BANK CO., LTD.

Shanghai Rural Commercial Bank Co., Ltd.—(Continued)
Shanghai Rural Commercial Bank Building No 70 Zhongshan Road East-2, Huangpu District, Shanghai, 200002, China
Tel.: (86) 21962999 CN
Web Site: https://www.shrcb.com
Year Founded: 2005
601825—(SHG)
Rev.: $3,657,205,084
Assets: $192,763,305,826
Liabilities: $176,652,526,169
Net Worth: $16,110,779,658
Earnings: $1,681,152,802
Fiscal Year-end: 12/31/23
Commercial Banking Services
N.A.I.C.S.: 522110
Gu Jianzhong (Vice Chm & Pres)

SHANGHAI RYCHEN TECHNOLOGIES CO., LTD.
Block C Building 3 No 358 Shenxia Road, Jiading, Shanghai, 201822, China
Tel.: (86) 2155789678
Web Site: https://www.richenenergy.com.cn
Year Founded: 2010
301273—(CHIN)
Rev.: $61,585,056
Assets: $178,595,820
Liabilities: $39,728,988
Net Worth: $138,866,832
Earnings: $7,069,140
Fiscal Year-end: 12/31/22
Pump Product Mfr & Distr
N.A.I.C.S.: 333914
Wandong Chen (Chm & Gen Mgr)

SHANGHAI SANMAO ENTERPRISE (GROUP) CO., LTD.
No 791 Xietu Road, Huangpu District, Shanghai, 200023, China
Tel.: (86) 2163028180
Web Site: https://www.600689.com
Year Founded: 1993
600689—(SHG)
Rev.: $145,126,538
Assets: $112,351,113
Liabilities: $52,636,339
Net Worth: $59,714,774
Earnings: ($1,813,364)
Fiscal Year-end: 12/31/22
Textile Product Mfr & Whslr
N.A.I.C.S.: 315990
Hu Yu (Chm)

Subsidiaries:

Shanghai Sanjin Import & Export Co., Ltd. (1)
791 Building B Xietu Road, Huangpu District, Shanghai, 200023, China
Tel.: (86) 2153023377
Web Site: https://www.sanjinie.com
Logistic Services
N.A.I.C.S.: 541614

SHANGHAI SANYOU MEDICAL CO., LTD.
No 385 Huirong Rd, Jiading, Shanghai, China
Tel.: (86) 2158389980
Web Site: https://www.sanyou-medical.com
Year Founded: 2005
688085—(SHG)
Rev.: $91,140,983
Assets: $307,667,786
Liabilities: $39,080,312
Net Worth: $268,587,474
Earnings: $26,790,889
Fiscal Year-end: 12/31/22
Medical Product Mfr & Distr
N.A.I.C.S.: 339112
Liu Mingyan Michael (Chm)

SHANGHAI SHEN LIAN BIO-MEDICAL CORP.
No 48 Jiangchuan East Road, Minhang, Shanghai, 200241, China
Tel.: (86) 2161255101
Web Site: http://www.shenlianbiotech.com.cn
Year Founded: 2001
688098—(SHG)
Rev.: $46,134,668
Assets: $225,353,751
Liabilities: $15,192,572
Net Worth: $210,161,180
Earnings: $8,578,187
Fiscal Year-end: 12/31/22
Medical Product Mfr & Distr
N.A.I.C.S.: 339112
Dongsheng Nie (Chm)

SHANGHAI SHENDA CO., LTD.
No 1500 Jiangning Road, Pudong New Area, Shanghai, 200060, China
Tel.: (86) 2162319898
Web Site: https://shenda.com.cn
Year Founded: 1986
600626—(SHG)
Rev.: $1,578,662,079
Assets: $1,456,232,829
Liabilities: $991,625,783
Net Worth: $464,607,047
Earnings: ($26,767,878)
Emp.: 8,000
Fiscal Year-end: 12/31/22
Textile Product Whslr
N.A.I.C.S.: 424990
Luo Qionglin (Sec)

SHANGHAI SHENG JIAN ENVIRONMENT TECHNOLOGY CO., LTD.
Sheng Jian Building No 301 Huifa Road, Jiading District, Shanghai, 201815, China
Tel.: (86) 2160712858
Web Site: http://www.sheng-jian.com
Year Founded: 2012
603324—(SHG)
Rev.: $186,518,143
Assets: $364,952,671
Liabilities: $164,926,490
Net Worth: $200,026,181
Earnings: $18,295,678
Fiscal Year-end: 12/31/22
Pollution Control Product Distr
N.A.I.C.S.: 423830
Weiming Zhang (Chm & Gen Mgr)

SHANGHAI SHENQI PHARMACEUTICAL INVESTMENT MANAGEMENT CO., LTD.
Room 613 Changfa Building No 128 Weihai Road, Shanghai, 200003, China
Tel.: (86) 2153750009
Web Site: http://www.gzsq.com
Year Founded: 1992
900904—(SHG)
Rev.: $335,361,925
Assets: $474,704,404
Liabilities: $141,510,424
Net Worth: $333,193,981
Earnings: $6,806,185
Fiscal Year-end: 12/31/22
Pharmaceutical Product Mfr & Distr
N.A.I.C.S.: 325412
Zhiting Zhang (Chm & Vice Chm)

SHANGHAI SHENTONG METRO CO., LTD.
No 489 Pudian Road Pilot Free Trade Zone, Shanghai, 201103, China
Tel.: (86) 2154259971
600834—(SHG)
Rev.: $48,175,887
Assets: $366,352,782
Liabilities: $133,708,115
Net Worth: $232,644,667
Earnings: $10,222,622
Fiscal Year-end: 12/31/22
Metro Line Operation & Maintenance Services
N.A.I.C.S.: 485111
Sun Sihui (Sec)

SHANGHAI SHIBEI HI-TECH CO., LTD.
1F No 262 Jiangchang Third Road, Shanghai, 200436, China
Tel.: (86) 2166300333
Web Site: https://www.shibeiht.com
Year Founded: 1993
600604—(SHG)
Rev.: $177,319,935
Assets: $3,097,474,572
Liabilities: $1,902,832,088
Net Worth: $1,194,642,484
Earnings: $10,994,963
Fiscal Year-end: 12/31/22
Real Estate Manangement Services
N.A.I.C.S.: 531390
Sun Yat-Feng (Chm)

SHANGHAI SHINE-LINK INTERNATIONAL LOGISTICS CO., LTD.
No 68 Ri Jing Road WaiGaoQiao Free Trade Zone, Shanghai, 200131, China
Tel.: (86) 2120895888
Web Site: https://www.chinaslc.com
Year Founded: 2001
603648—(SHG)
Rev.: $229,915,221
Assets: $321,829,064
Liabilities: $64,383,102
Net Worth: $257,445,962
Earnings: $22,755,077
Emp.: 1,600
Fiscal Year-end: 12/31/22
International Logistics Services
N.A.I.C.S.: 541614
Yin Qiang (Chm)

SHANGHAI SHUIXING HOME TEXTILE CO., LTD.
No 1487 Huhang Highway, Fengxian District, Shanghai, 201401, China
Tel.: (86) 2157435982
Web Site: http://www.shuixing.com
Year Founded: 2000
603365—(SHG)
Rev.: $514,390,654
Assets: $496,400,472
Liabilities: $107,881,029
Net Worth: $388,519,443
Earnings: $39,067,213
Fiscal Year-end: 12/31/22
Textile Goods Mfr & Distr
N.A.I.C.S.: 313230
Li Yulu (Chm & Pres)

SHANGHAI SHUNHO NEW MATERIALS TECHNOLOGY CO.,LTD.
No 200 Zhenchen Road, Putuo District, Shanghai, 200331, China
Tel.: (86) 2166959697
Web Site: https://www.shunhostock.com
Year Founded: 2004
002565—(SSE)
Rev.: $198,118,215
Assets: $408,160,884
Liabilities: $121,818,116
Net Worth: $286,342,767
Earnings: ($8,389,153)
Emp.: 2,000
Fiscal Year-end: 12/31/22
Packaging Materials Mfr; Aluminium-coated Paper, Laminating Paper, Paperboard, Acrylic Fiber & Printed Material Products Mfr

INTERNATIONAL PUBLIC

N.A.I.C.S.: 322220
Wang Zhenglin (Chm & Pres)

SHANGHAI SHYNDEC PHARMACEUTICAL CO., LTD.
No 378 Jianlu Road Pudong New Area, Shanghai, 200137, China
Tel.: (86) 2162510990
Web Site: http://www.shyndec.com
Year Founded: 1996
600420—(SHG)
Rev.: $1,819,488,598
Assets: $2,756,100,592
Liabilities: $1,049,858,466
Net Worth: $1,706,242,127
Earnings: $88,142,390
Emp.: 12,000
Fiscal Year-end: 12/31/22
Pharmaceutical Product Mfr & Distr
N.A.I.C.S.: 325412
Xu Jihui (Chm & Sec-Party)

Subsidiaries:

Shanghai Techwell Biopharmaceutical Co., Ltd. (1)
4258 Suite Jindu Road, Shanghai, 201108, China
Tel.: (86) 2154427100
Web Site: http://www.techwell-cn.com
Pharmaceuticals Product Mfr
N.A.I.C.S.: 325412

SHANGHAI SINOTEC CO., LTD.
No 218 Songxiu Road, Qingpu District, Shanghai, 201703, China
Tel.: (86) 2159786158
Web Site: https://www.sinotec.cn
Year Founded: 2006
603121—(SHG)
Rev.: $126,992,334
Assets: $307,890,742
Liabilities: $142,553,441
Net Worth: $165,337,300
Earnings: ($1,182,126)
Emp.: 500
Fiscal Year-end: 12/31/22
Automobile Parts Mfr
N.A.I.C.S.: 336110
Wu Huailei (Chm & Gen Mgr)

Subsidiaries:

Jiangsu Sinotec Co., Ltd. (1)
No 6 Huaxing Road, Rugao District, Jiangsu, Nantong, China
Tel.: (86) 51387902499
Automotive Core Part Distr
N.A.I.C.S.: 423120

SHANGHAI SINYANG SEMI-CONDUCTOR MATERIALS CO., LTD.
No 3600 Sixian Road, Songjiang District, Shanghai, 201616, China
Tel.: (86) 2157850088
Web Site: https://www.sinyang.com.cn
Year Founded: 1999
300236—(CHIN)
Rev.: $167,874,876
Assets: $789,097,140
Liabilities: $205,764,624
Net Worth: $583,332,516
Earnings: $7,473,492
Emp.: 279
Fiscal Year-end: 12/31/22
Semiconductor Product Mfr & Whslr
N.A.I.C.S.: 334413
Wang Fuxiang (Chm)

SHANGHAI SK AUTOMATION TECHNOLOGY CO., LTD.
518 Guanghua Rd, Songjiang, Shanghai, 201614, China
Tel.: (86) 2157858807
Web Site: https://www.sk1.net.cn
Year Founded: 2007

688155—(SHG)
Rev.: $253,443,846
Assets: $639,836,847
Liabilities: $447,663,940
Net Worth: $192,172,907
Earnings: ($13,258,155)
Emp.: 3,000
Fiscal Year-end: 12/31/22
Automatic Intelligent Equipment Mfr
N.A.I.C.S.: 334512
Yanqing Pan *(Chm & CTO)*

SHANGHAI SK PETROLEUM & CHEMICAL EQUIPMENT CORPORATION LTD.
No 1769 Puxing Highway, Minhang District, Shanghai, 201114, China
Tel.: (86) 2154332841
Web Site: https://www.shenkai.com
Year Founded: 1995
002278—(SSE)
Rev.: $84,795,970
Assets: $254,560,349
Liabilities: $93,279,780
Net Worth: $161,280,569
Earnings: ($3,921,035)
Fiscal Year-end: 12/31/22
Petrochemical Equipment Mfr
N.A.I.C.S.: 333132
Li Fangying *(Chm)*

SHANGHAI SMART CONTROL CO., LTD.
Building A No 470 Jiujing Road, Jiading, Shanghai, 201802, China
Tel.: (86) 2137829918
Web Site: https://www.smartsh.com
Year Founded: 2005
001266—(SSE)
Rev.: $57,178,518
Assets: $163,835,034
Liabilities: $18,967,099
Net Worth: $144,867,935
Earnings: $10,060,081
Emp.: 450
Fiscal Year-end: 12/31/22
Electronic Components Mfr
N.A.I.C.S.: 334419
Huahong Zhang *(Chm)*

SHANGHAI SMITH ADHESIVE NEW MATERIAL CO., LTD.
No 89 Dajiang Road, Yongfeng Subdistrict Songjiang, Shanghai, 201600, China
Tel.: (86) 2131167522
Web Site: http://www.smithcn.com
Year Founded: 2006
603683—(SHG)
Rev.: $198,509,370
Assets: $258,361,033
Liabilities: $115,942,699
Net Worth: $142,418,334
Earnings: $816,468
Emp.: 1,200
Fiscal Year-end: 12/31/22
Adhesive Tape Mfr & Distr
N.A.I.C.S.: 322220
Zhou Xiaonan *(Chm)*

Subsidiaries:

Anhui Smith New Material Technology Co., Ltd. (1)
New Materials Optoelectronics Industrial Park, Dingcheng Economic Development Zone Dingyang, Chuzhou, Anhui, China
Tel.: (86) 5502166470
Adhesive Tape Mfr & Distr
N.A.I.C.S.: 325520

Chengdu Smith Adhesive New Material Co., Ltd. (1)
No 399 Siwei Road Intelligent Application Industry Functional Zone, Chongzhou, Chengdu, China
Tel.: (86) 2887463415
Adhesive Tape Mfr & Distr
N.A.I.C.S.: 325520

Jiangsu Smith New Material Technology Co., Ltd. (1)
No 6 Donghai Road Yangtze River International Chemical Industrial Park, Zhangjiagang, China
Tel.: (86) 51280179088
Adhesive Tape Mfr & Distr
N.A.I.C.S.: 325520

Kunshan Smith Xingye Electronic Materials Co., Ltd. (1)
No 128 Liushijing Road Kunshan Development Zone, Jiangsu, China
Tel.: (86) 15190176866
Adhesive Tape Mfr & Distr
N.A.I.C.S.: 325520

Qingdao Smith Electronic Materials Co., Ltd. (1)
No 6 Danhui Road Xiazhuang Street, Chengyang, Qingdao, China
Tel.: (86) 53287768666
Adhesive Tape Mfr & Distr
N.A.I.C.S.: 325520

Zhejiang Smith Special Paper Co., Ltd. (1)
NO 3 Tianhu West Road Shenjia Economic Development Zone, Qujiang, Quzhou, Zhejiang, China
Tel.: (86) 5703665309
Web Site: https://www.smith-paper.com
Emp.: 180
Wet Wipes Paper Mfr & Distr
N.A.I.C.S.: 322291

SHANGHAI STEP ELECTRIC CORPORATION
No 289 Xinqin Road, Nanxiang Town Jiading District, Shanghai, 201801, China
Tel.: (86) 2169926126
Web Site: http://www.liftcontrolsystem.com
Year Founded: 1995
002527—(SSE)
Rev.: $434,860,358
Assets: $839,560,059
Liabilities: $573,174,744
Net Worth: $266,385,315
Earnings: ($148,395,991)
Emp.: 642
Fiscal Year-end: 12/31/22
Electric Elevators & Elevator Controlling Systems Mfr
N.A.I.C.S.: 333921
Ji Yi *(Chm)*

Subsidiaries:

Hong Kong International STEP Electric Holdings Co., Ltd. (1)
Room 1502 15th Floor Of The Guangdong Provincial Bank Building, 589 Nathan Road, Kowloon, China (Hong Kong)
Tel.: (852) 27592938
Web Site: http://www.stepelevator.com
Emp.: 10
Electronic Controls Mfr
N.A.I.C.S.: 335314

STEP Sigriner Elektronik GmbH (1)
Martin Moser Street 15, Bavaria, 84503, Altotting, Germany
Tel.: (49) 86713096
Web Site: http://www.step-sigriner.com
Emp.: 30
Lift Controls Mfr
N.A.I.C.S.: 334419
Anton Sigriner *(Founder)*

SHANGHAI STOCK EXCHANGE
528 South Pudong Road, Shanghai, 200120, PR, China
Tel.: (86) 21 68808888
Web Site: http://www.sse.com.cn
Year Founded: 1990
Sales Range: $125-149.9 Million
Emp.: 400
Stock Exchange
N.A.I.C.S.: 523210
Hongyuan Huang *(Pres)*

SHANGHAI SUNGLOW PACKAGING TECHNOLOGY CO., LTD.
No 299 Cuibo Road Pudong New Area, Shanghai, 201306, China
Tel.: (86) 2158066696
Web Site: https://www.sunglow-tec.com
Year Founded: 2006
603499—(SHG)
Rev.: $93,096,951
Assets: $167,356,589
Liabilities: $79,130,240
Net Worth: $88,226,349
Earnings: $1,918,440
Fiscal Year-end: 12/31/22
Packaging Products Mfr
N.A.I.C.S.: 322212
Jianjun Dong *(Chm, Pres & Gen Mgr)*

SHANGHAI TAIHE WATER TECHNOLOGY DEVELOPMENT CO., LTD.
Lanyun Cultural Center Lane 899 Panlong Road, Qingpu District, Shanghai, 201702, China
Tel.: (86) 2165661627
Web Site: https://www.shtaihe.com
Year Founded: 2010
605081—(SHG)
Rev.: $28,839,157
Assets: $268,608,492
Liabilities: $44,432,332
Net Worth: $224,176,161
Earnings: ($23,016,867)
Fiscal Year-end: 12/31/22
Information Technology Services
N.A.I.C.S.: 541512
Wenhui He *(Chm)*

SHANGHAI TAISHENG WIND POWER EQUIPMENT CO., LTD.
No 1988 Weiqing East Road, Jinshan District, Shanghai, 201508, China
Tel.: (86) 2157243692
Web Site: http://www.shtsp.com
Year Founded: 2001
300129—(CHIN)
Rev.: $438,987,276
Assets: $1,006,884,216
Liabilities: $437,103,108
Net Worth: $569,781,108
Earnings: $38,594,556
Emp.: 280
Fiscal Year-end: 12/31/22
Wind Turbine Generator Mfr
N.A.I.C.S.: 333611
Guo Chuanzhou *(Chm)*

Subsidiaries:

Jiangsu Dongtai Taisheng Power Engineering Machinery Co., Ltd. (1)
No 2 Weiliu Road Development Zone, Dongtai, 224200, Jiangsu, China
Tel.: (86) 51585718880
Wind Towers Mfr
N.A.I.C.S.: 333611

Shanghai Taisheng Power Engineering Machinery Co., Ltd. (1)
No 1988 Weiqing Road Jinshan Zui Industrial Park, Shanghai, Shanghai, China
Tel.: (86) 2113818562500
Wind Towers Mfr
N.A.I.C.S.: 333611

SHANGHAI TIANCHEN CO., LTD.
29F No 8 Xianxia Road, Changning District, Shanghai, 200336, China
Tel.: (86) 2162782233
Web Site: http://www.shstc.com
Year Founded: 1992
600620—(SHG)
Rev.: $34,220,338
Assets: $471,596,089
Liabilities: $173,963,912
Net Worth: $297,632,177
Earnings: $5,045,372
Fiscal Year-end: 12/31/22
Real Estate Property Development Services
N.A.I.C.S.: 531390
Maojing Ye *(Chm)*

SHANGHAI TIANYONG ENGINEERING CO., LTD.
No 500 Huixian Road, Waigang Town Jiading District, Shanghai, 201806, China
Tel.: (86) 2150675528
Web Site: http://www.ty-industries.com
Year Founded: 1996
603895—(SHG)
Rev.: $81,185,444
Assets: $237,749,850
Liabilities: $176,140,884
Net Worth: $61,608,966
Earnings: ($17,757,750)
Fiscal Year-end: 12/31/22
Vehicle Automatic Equipment Mfr & Distr
N.A.I.C.S.: 336350
Rong Junlin *(Chm, Pres & Gen Mgr)*

SHANGHAI TITAN SCIENTIFIC CO., LTD.
No 89 Shilong Road, Xuhui, Shanghai, 200232, China
Tel.: (86) 2160878336
Web Site: https://www.titansci-group.com
Year Founded: 2007
688133—(SHG)
Rev.: $366,148,360
Assets: $557,613,328
Liabilities: $169,172,593
Net Worth: $388,440,735
Earnings: $17,523,099
Fiscal Year-end: 12/31/22
Analytical Instrument Mfr & Distr
N.A.I.C.S.: 334516
Yingbo Xie *(Chm)*

SHANGHAI TOFFLON SCIENCE AND TECHNOLOGY CO., LTD.
No 1509 Duhui Road, Shanghai, 201108, China
Tel.: (86) 2164909699
Web Site: http://www.tofflon.com
Year Founded: 1993
300171—(CHIN)
Rev.: $767,907,972
Assets: $1,878,125,184
Liabilities: $804,904,776
Net Worth: $1,073,220,408
Earnings: $118,858,428
Emp.: 2,000
Fiscal Year-end: 12/31/22
Medical Freeze Dryers & Freeze Drying Systems Mfr
N.A.I.C.S.: 339112
Zheng Xiaodong *(Chm & Gen Mgr)*

SHANGHAI TONGDA VENTURE CAPITAL CO., LTD.
21F Lekai Building No 660 Shangcheng Road Pudong, Shanghai, 200120, China
Tel.: (86) 2161638853
Web Site: http://www.shtdcy.com
600647—(SHG)
Rev.: $14,899,673
Assets: $81,153,805
Liabilities: $30,171,645
Net Worth: $50,982,160
Earnings: $897,811
Fiscal Year-end: 12/31/21
Restaurant Operator & Outdoor Advertising Services

SHANGHAI TONGDA VENTURE CAPITAL CO., LTD.

Shanghai Tongda Venture Capital Co., Ltd.—(Continued)
N.A.I.C.S.: 722511
Shemei Liu (Chm)

SHANGHAI TONGJI SCIENCE & TECHNOLOGY INDUSTRIAL CO., LTD.
20th Floor Building B Tongji United Plaza 1398 Siping Road, Shanghai, 200092, China
Tel.: (86) 2165985860
Web Site: https://www.tjkjsy.com.cn
600846—(SHG)
Rev.: $553,562,311
Assets: $1,521,622,908
Liabilities: $1,016,263,048
Net Worth: $505,359,860
Earnings: $49,455,984
Emp.: 660
Fiscal Year-end: 12/31/22
Construction Engineering Services
N.A.I.C.S.: 541330
Mingzhong Wang (Chm)

SHANGHAI TOPCARE MEDICAL SERVICES CO., LTD.
21F Building T1 Jinkong Square No 1788-1800 Shiji Avenue, Pudong New Area, Shanghai, 200120, China
Tel.: (86) 2150342280
Web Site: http://www.hdky600532.com
600532—(SHG)
Rev.: $656,265,842
Assets: $395,140,847
Liabilities: $106,552,959
Net Worth: $288,587,888
Earnings: $3,355,299
Emp.: 1,017
Fiscal Year-end: 12/31/20
Ferrous Metal Mining; Iron Powder, Copper Powder & Iron Ore Production
N.A.I.C.S.: 212210

SHANGHAI TRENDZONE CONSTRUCTION DECORATION GROUP CO., LTD.
6335-7-461 Hu Qingping Road, Zhujiajiao Qingpu District, Shanghai, 200233, China
Tel.: (86) 2164086775
Web Site: http://www.trendzone.com.cn
603030—(SHG)
Rev.: $282,051,750
Assets: $846,863,597
Liabilities: $859,460,130
Net Worth: ($12,596,534)
Earnings: ($168,125,925)
Fiscal Year-end: 12/31/22
Residential Building Decoration Services
N.A.I.C.S.: 335131
Bin Zhu (Chm)

SHANGHAI TUNNEL ENGINEERING CO., LTD.
No 1099 South Wanping Road, Xuhui District, Shanghai, 200232, China
Tel.: (86) 58301000
Web Site: https://www.stec.net
Year Founded: 1965
600820—(SHG)
Rev.: $9,164,539,561
Assets: $20,559,479,167
Liabilities: $15,806,123,695
Net Worth: $4,753,355,471
Earnings: $394,412,242
Fiscal Year-end: 12/31/22
Construction Engineering Services
N.A.I.C.S.: 237990
Lei Yang (VP)

Subsidiaries:

STEC SUCG International Engineering Co., Ltd. (1)
1099 South Wanping Rd, Xuhui District, Shanghai, 200032, China
Tel.: (86) 2153599950
Civil Engineering Construction Services
N.A.I.C.S.: 237990

STEC Shanghai City Building Material Co., Ltd. (1)
F16 1040 Caoyang Rd, Putuo District, Shanghai, 200063, China
Tel.: (86) 2152667350
Civil Engineering Construction Services
N.A.I.C.S.: 237990

STEC Shanghai Construction Property Development Co., Ltd. (1)
161 East Nandan Rd, Xuhui District, Shanghai, 200030, China
Tel.: (86) 2164877000
Civil Engineering Construction Services
N.A.I.C.S.: 237990

STEC Shanghai Gas Engineering Design & Research Co., Ltd. (1)
887 Gushan Rd, Pudong New District, Shanghai, 200135, China
Tel.: (86) 2168706001
Civil Engineering Construction Services
N.A.I.C.S.: 237990

STEC Shanghai Infrastructure Construction & Development Co., Ltd. (1)
1099 South Wanping Rd, Xuhui District, Shanghai, 200032, China
Tel.: (86) 2158306688
Civil Engineering Construction Services
N.A.I.C.S.: 237990

STEC Shanghai Municipal Engineering Material Company (1)
92 Shunde Rd, Jingan District, Shanghai, 200041, China
Tel.: (86) 2162156098
Civil Engineering Construction Services
N.A.I.C.S.: 237990

STEC Shanghai Municipal Maintenance & Management Co., Ltd. (1)
3500 West Yanan Rd, Minghang District, Shanghai, 201103, China
Tel.: (86) 2164495547
Civil Engineering Construction Services
N.A.I.C.S.: 237990

STEC Shanghai No. 1 Gas Pipeline Engineering Co., Ltd. (1)
1277 Shuidian Rd, Hongkou District, Shanghai, 200434, China
Tel.: (86) 2165440199
Civil Engineering Construction Services
N.A.I.C.S.: 237990

STEC Shanghai No. 2 Gas Pipeline Engineering Co., Ltd. (1)
162 Weifang Rd, Pudong New District, Shanghai, 200122, China
Tel.: (86) 2158200942
Civil Engineering Construction Services
N.A.I.C.S.: 237990

STEC Shanghai Pudong Water Supply & Drainage Construction Co., Ltd. (1)
25 Yilin Rd, Pudong New District, Shanghai, 200125, China
Tel.: (86) 2158732393
Civil Engineering Construction Services
N.A.I.C.S.: 237990

STEC Shanghai Road & Bridge (Group) Co., Ltd. (1)
36 Guoke Rd, Yangpu District, Shanghai, 200433, China
Tel.: (86) 2155509050
Civil Engineering Construction Services
N.A.I.C.S.: 237990

STEC Shanghai Tap Water Pipeline Engineering Co., Ltd. (1)
18 Longjiang Rd, Yangpu District, Shanghai, 200082, China
Tel.: (86) 2155219929
Civil Engineering Construction Services
N.A.I.C.S.: 237990

STEC Shanghai Underground Space Development Company (1)
F5-F6 663 Hongqiao Rd, Xuhui District, Shanghai, 200030, China
Tel.: (86) 2162817685
Civil Engineering Construction Services
N.A.I.C.S.: 237990

STEC Shanghai Urban Construction Investment & Development Co., Ltd. (1)
1099 South Wanping Rd, Xuhui District, Shanghai, 200032, China
Tel.: (86) 2158306688
Civil Engineering Construction Services
N.A.I.C.S.: 237990

STEC Shanghai Urban Construction Municipal Engineering (Group) Co., Ltd. (1)
1565 Jiaotong Rd, Putuo District, Shanghai, 200065, China
Tel.: (86) 2156088833
Civil Engineering Construction Services
N.A.I.C.S.: 237990

STEC Shanghai Water Construction & Engineering Co., Ltd. (1)
815 Hutai Rd, Zhabei District, Shanghai, 200072, China
Tel.: (86) 2156959993
Civil Engineering Construction Services
N.A.I.C.S.: 237990

STEC The Operation Management Co., Ltd. (1)
600 Dapu Rd, Huangpu District, Shanghai, 200023, China
Tel.: (86) 2163024641
Civil Engineering Construction Services
N.A.I.C.S.: 237990

SHANGHAI TURBO ENTERPRISES LTD.
No 9 Yinghua Road Zhonglou Economic Development Zone, Changzhou, Jiangsu, China
Tel.: (86) 51983906629
Web Site: https://www.shanghaiturbo.com
AWM—(SES)
Rev.: $5,250,966
Assets: $16,212,069
Liabilities: $6,328,952
Net Worth: $9,883,117
Earnings: ($4,478,022)
Emp.: 500
Fiscal Year-end: 12/31/20
Precision Engineering Products Mfr
N.A.I.C.S.: 332216
Yoen Har Wong (Sec)

Subsidiaries:

Changzhou 3D Technological Complete Set Equipment Co., Limited (1)
No 9 Yinghua Road Zhonglou District Economic Development Zone, Changzhou, 213003, Jiangsu, China
Tel.: (86) 51983906635
Vane Product Mfr
N.A.I.C.S.: 333998
Jiang Ronglin (Gen Mgr)

SHANGHAI U9 GAME CO., LTD.
333 Lane 3 6B Shimenerlu, Shanghai, 200031, China
Tel.: (86) 216 471 0022
Web Site: http://www.sh-ace.com
600652—(SHG)
Rev.: $1,890,611
Assets: $281,097,451
Liabilities: $12,704,173
Net Worth: $268,393,278
Earnings: ($4,207,147)
Fiscal Year-end: 12/31/20
Online Game & Coal Mining Services
N.A.I.C.S.: 212115
Xinchun Wang (CFO)

SHANGHAI UNIVERSAL BIO-

INTERNATIONAL PUBLIC TECH CO., LTD.
Building 16 Lane 15 Gudan Road, Pudong New District, Shanghai, 200082, China
Tel.: (86) 2138939000
Web Site: https://www.univ-bio.com
Year Founded: 2004
301166—(CHIN)
Rev.: $167,794,848
Assets: $348,012,288
Liabilities: $45,096,480
Net Worth: $302,915,808
Earnings: $14,951,196
Fiscal Year-end: 12/31/22
Biotechnology Research & Development Services
N.A.I.C.S.: 541714
Zhaowu Leng (Chm & Gen Mgr)

SHANGHAI URBAN ARCHITECTURE DESIGN CO., LTD.
Urban Building Building No 3 Zhongshe Square No 1 Yingao Road, Baoshan, Shanghai, 200439, China
Tel.: (86) 2135322683
Web Site: http://www.uachina.com.cn
Year Founded: 2004
300983—(SSE)
Rev.: $71,345,776
Assets: $463,387,715
Liabilities: $28,728,620
Net Worth: $434,659,095
Earnings: $2,921,429
Fiscal Year-end: 12/31/22
Architectural Services
N.A.I.C.S.: 541310
Zesong Shi (Chm)

SHANGHAI WAIGAOQIAO FREE TRADE ZONE GROUP CO., LTD.,
No 889 Yanggao North Road, Pudong New Area, Shanghai, 200137, China
Tel.: (86) 2158680088
Web Site: http://www.china-ftz.com
Year Founded: 1992
900912—(SHG)
Rev.: $1,291,844,689
Assets: $5,853,312,321
Liabilities: $4,126,985,076
Net Worth: $1,726,327,245
Earnings: $174,208,783
Emp.: 2,920
Fiscal Year-end: 12/31/22
Residential Property Leasing Services
N.A.I.C.S.: 531110
Yu Yong (Chm)

SHANGHAI WANYE ENTERPRISES CO., LTD.
15th Floor Wonder Building No 1500 Puming Road, Pudong New District, Shanghai, 200127, China
Tel.: (86) 2150366699
Web Site: https://www.wanye.com.cn
Year Founded: 1991
600641—(SHG)
Rev.: $162,523,684
Assets: $1,370,609,173
Liabilities: $193,393,067
Net Worth: $1,177,216,106
Earnings: $59,470,492
Fiscal Year-end: 12/31/22
Real Estate Property Development
N.A.I.C.S.: 531311
Guang Cheng (Vice Chm)

SHANGHAI WEAVER NETWORK CO.,LTD.
Weaver Software Park No 3419 Sanlu Road, MinHang District, Shanghai, 201112, China
Tel.: (86) 2168869298
Web Site: http://www.weaver.com.cn

AND PRIVATE COMPANIES

Year Founded: 2001
603039—(SHG)
Rev.: $327,340,311
Assets: $497,199,419
Liabilities: $228,887,704
Net Worth: $268,311,715
Earnings: $31,341,043
Emp.: 8,000
Fiscal Year-end: 12/31/22
Software Development Services
N.A.I.C.S.: 513210
Wei Lidong (Chm)

SHANGHAI WEIHONG ELECTRONIC TECHNOLOGY CO., LTD
No 1590 Huhang Rd, Fengxian, Shanghai, 201401, China
Tel.: (86) 2152235036
Web Site:
 https://www.weihong.com.cn
Year Founded: 2007
300508—(CHIN)
Rev.: $62,152,063
Assets: $125,648,581
Liabilities: $26,552,155
Net Worth: $99,096,426
Earnings: $5,568,251
Fiscal Year-end: 12/31/23
Motion Control System Development Services
N.A.I.C.S.: 238210
Tang Tongkui (Chm)

SHANGHAI WELLTECH AUTOMATION CO., LTD.
Building 1 No 263 Hongzhong Road, MinHang District, Shanghai, 201103, China
Tel.: (86) 2164656465
Web Site:
 https://www.welltech.com.cn
Year Founded: 1992
002058—(SSE)
Rev.: $20,730,074
Assets: $52,391,313
Liabilities: $24,059,435
Net Worth: $28,331,878
Earnings: ($2,947,923)
Fiscal Year-end: 12/31/22
Automation Instrument Mfr
N.A.I.C.S.: 334513
Ye Pengzhi (Chm)

SHANGHAI WINNER INFORMATION TECHNOLOGY CO., INC.
No 6 Zhangjiang Artificial Intelligence Island Lane 55 Chuanhe Road, Zhangjiang Pudong New Area, Shanghai, 201210, China
Tel.: (86) 2160220636
Web Site: http://www.winnerinf.com
Year Founded: 2004
300609—(CHIN)
Rev.: $52,994,784
Assets: $195,866,095
Liabilities: $33,928,089
Net Worth: $161,938,006
Earnings: ($4,792,787)
Fiscal Year-end: 12/31/23
Data Analytic Services
N.A.I.C.S.: 518210
Zhang Baijun (Chm)

SHANGHAI WONDERTEK SOFTWARE CORP LTD
No 409 Chuanqiao Road China Shanghai Pilot Free Trade Zone, Shanghai, 201206, China
Tel.: (86) 2150306629
Web Site:
 http://www.wondertek.com.cn
Year Founded: 2009
603189—(SHG)
Rev.: $44,450,261
Assets: $262,696,276
Liabilities: $21,258,638
Net Worth: $241,437,639
Earnings: $5,143,526
Fiscal Year-end: 12/31/22
Software Development Services
N.A.I.C.S.: 541511
Da Feng (Chm & Gen Mgr)

SHANGHAI WORTH GARDEN CO., LTD.
No 5000 Yuanjiang Road, Minhang District, Shanghai, 201108, China
Tel.: (86) 2164092111
Web Site:
 http://www.worthgarden.com
300483—(CHIN)
Rev.: $190,691,167
Assets: $1,112,806,003
Liabilities: $516,099,880
Net Worth: $596,706,123
Earnings: ($34,650,762)
Fiscal Year-end: 12/31/23
Garden Machinery Mfr
N.A.I.C.S.: 333112
Hailin Wu (Chm & Gen Mgr)

SHANGHAI XIN PENG INDUSTRY LTD.
No 1698 Hualong Road, Huaxin Town Qingpu District, Shanghai, 201708, China
Tel.: (86) 2131275888
Web Site: https://www.xinpeng.com
Year Founded: 2009
002328—(SSE)
Rev.: $848,995,852
Assets: $814,594,159
Liabilities: $303,891,630
Net Worth: $510,702,529
Earnings: $43,721,206
Fiscal Year-end: 12/31/22
Communication Equipment Mfr
N.A.I.C.S.: 334290
Song Lin (Chm)

Subsidiaries:

Shanghai Xin Peng Metal Products Co., Ltd. (1)
518 Jiasong Road M Qingpu District, 201708, Shanghai, China
Tel.: (86) 2159798313
Electromechanical Parts Mfr
N.A.I.C.S.: 333517

Shanghai Xinpeng Lianzhong Automotive Co., Ltd. (1)
No 29 Huawei Street Huaxin Town Qingpu, Shanghai, 201708, China
Tel.: (86) 2169780612
Web Site: http://www.xinplz.com
Car Parts Mfr
N.A.I.C.S.: 336390

SHANGHAI XINHUA MEDIA CO., LTD.
7th-8th Floor Xinhua Center Tower A China International Plaza, No 331 Caoxi North Road, Shanghai, 200030, China
Tel.: (86) 2160376284
Web Site: https://www.xhmedia.com
Year Founded: 1992
600825—(SHG)
Rev.: $176,829,097
Assets: $556,878,825
Liabilities: $205,981,093
Net Worth: $350,897,733
Earnings: $1,232,740
Fiscal Year-end: 12/31/22
Book & Newspaper Publishing Services
N.A.I.C.S.: 513130
Hang Liu (Pres & CFO)

SHANGHAI XINTONGLIAN PACKAGING CO., LTD.
No 1238 Luobei Road, Baoshan District, Shanghai, 200072, China
Tel.: (86) 2136535008
Web Site: http://www.xtl.sh.cn
Year Founded: 1999
603022—(SHG)
Sales Range: Less than $1 Million
Paper & Wood Packaging Product Mfr & Distr
N.A.I.C.S.: 322120
Gu Yunfeng (Chm & Deputy Gen Mgr)

SHANGHAI XNG HOLDINGS LIMITED
2F East Bldg 777 Jiamusi Road, Yangpu District, Shanghai, 200433, China
Tel.: (86) 2125259999
Web Site:
 http://www.tanshglobal.com
3666—(HKG)
Rev.: $45,714,802
Assets: $53,118,374
Liabilities: $57,350,030
Net Worth: ($4,231,656)
Earnings: ($9,327,614)
Emp.: 694
Fiscal Year-end: 12/31/22
Restaurant Owner
N.A.I.C.S.: 722511
Wai Ming Lai (Chm)

Subsidiaries:

Million Rank (HK) Limited (1)
5/F Paramount Bldg, Chai Wan, China (Hong Kong)
Tel.: (852) 23674101
Web Site: http://www.pokkacafe.com
Restaurant Operators
N.A.I.C.S.: 722511

SHANGHAI XUERONG BIO-TECHNOLOGY CO., LTD.
No 999 Gaofeng Road Modern Agricultural Park, Fengxian District, Shanghai, 201401, China
Tel.: (86) 2137198681
Web Site: http://www.xuerong.com
Year Founded: 1997
300511—(CHIN)
Rev.: $361,300,561
Assets: $648,215,194
Liabilities: $446,463,907
Net Worth: $201,751,286
Earnings: ($26,488,617)
Fiscal Year-end: 12/31/23
Mushroom Mfr & Distr
N.A.I.C.S.: 311411
Yongping Yang (Chm & Gen Mgr)

SHANGHAI XUJIAHUI COMMERCIAL CO., LTD.
9th Floor No 1000 Zhaojiabang Road, Xuhui District, Shanghai, 200030, China
Tel.: (86) 64269999
Web Site: https://www.xjh-sc.com
Year Founded: 1993
002561—(SSE)
Rev.: $67,513,825
Assets: $386,258,849
Liabilities: $67,539,476
Net Worth: $318,719,372
Earnings: $3,436,164
Emp.: 1,080
Fiscal Year-end: 12/31/22
Department Store Owner & Operator
N.A.I.C.S.: 455110

SHANGHAI YAHONG MOULDING CO LTD
No 7588 Hangnan Highway, Fengxian District, Shanghai, 201415, China
Tel.: (86) 2157595726

SHANGHAI YAOHUA PILKINGTON GLASS GROUP CO., LTD.

Web Site: http://www.yahong-mould.com
Year Founded: 1997
603159—(SHG)
Rev.: $83,916,055
Assets: $89,536,197
Liabilities: $22,189,925
Net Worth: $67,346,272
Earnings: $4,243,113
Fiscal Year-end: 12/31/22
Plastic Product Mfr & Distr
N.A.I.C.S.: 325211
Sun Lin (Chm)

SHANGHAI YANHUA SMARTECH GROUP CO., LTD.
6th 7th and 17th Floors Putuo Science and Technology Building, No 1255 Xikang Road Putuo District, Shanghai, 200060, China
Tel.: (86) 2161818686
Web Site:
 http://www.chinaforwards.com
Year Founded: 2006
002178—(SSE)
Rev.: $87,886,988
Assets: $228,965,836
Liabilities: $147,526,662
Net Worth: $81,439,174
Earnings: ($20,541,531)
Fiscal Year-end: 12/31/22
Construction Engineering Services
N.A.I.C.S.: 541330
Hu Xinyu (Chm)

SHANGHAI YANPU METAL PRODUCTS CO., LTD.
No 128 Jiangkai Road, Pujiang Town Minhang, Shanghai, 201114, China
Tel.: (86) 2134308994
Web Site: https://www.shyanpu.com
Year Founded: 1999
605128—(SHG)
Rev.: $157,491,285
Assets: $304,066,091
Liabilities: $145,082,396
Net Worth: $158,983,695
Earnings: $6,422,514
Fiscal Year-end: 12/31/22
Metal Stamping Mfr & Distr
N.A.I.C.S.: 336370
Jianqing Zhou (Chm & Gen Mgr)

SHANGHAI YAOHUA PILKINGTON GLASS GROUP CO., LTD.
Building 4-5 1388 Zhangdong Road, Pudong New District, Shanghai, 201203, China
Tel.: (86) 2161633599
Web Site: https://www.sypglass.com
Year Founded: 1983
600819—(SHG)
Rev.: $667,748,929
Assets: $1,101,815,213
Liabilities: $478,660,216
Net Worth: $623,154,996
Earnings: $2,132,142
Fiscal Year-end: 12/31/22
Glass Products Mfr
N.A.I.C.S.: 327211
Yin Jun (Chm)

Subsidiaries:

AGC Flat Glass (Dalian) Co., Ltd. (1)
No 5 West Tieshan Road Development Zone, Dalian, 116600, China
Tel.: (86) 41187614190
Web Site: http://www.agc-flatglass.cn
Sales Range: $200-249.9 Million
Automotive Glass Products Mfr & Distr
N.A.I.C.S.: 811122

Changshu SYP Special Glass Co., Ltd. (1)
No 16 Xinggang Road, Changshu Economic Development Zone, Suzhou, 215536, China

SHANGHAI YAOHUA PILKINGTON GLASS GROUP CO., LTD.

Shanghai Yaohua Pilkington Glass Group Co., Ltd.—(Continued)

Tel.: (86) 512 5229 7000
Glass Products Mfr
N.A.I.C.S.: 327211

Chongqing SYP Engineering Glass Co., Ltd. (1)
Economic and Technological Development Zone Yaopi Road No 1, Wandong Town of Wansheng City, Chongqing, China
Tel.: (86) 2365966666
Flat Glass Mfr
N.A.I.C.S.: 327211

Jiangmen SYP Engineering Glass Co., Ltd. (1)
No 10 Yinyuan Road Xinhui Economical Zone, Guangdong, 529141, China
Tel.: (86) 7506398999
Flat Glass Mfr
N.A.I.C.S.: 327211

Jiangsu Huadong SYP Glass Co., Ltd. (1)
No 10 Xinggang Road Changshu Economic Development Zone, Jiangsu, 215536, China
Tel.: (86) 512 5229 7000
Web Site: http://www.sypglass.com
Glass Products Mfr
N.A.I.C.S.: 327211

Jiangsu Pilkington SYP Glass Co. Ltd. (1)
No 10 Xinggang Road Economic Development Zone, Changshu, 215536, Jiangsu, China
Tel.: (86) 512 52297000
Emp.: 400
Flat Glass Mfr
N.A.I.C.S.: 327211
Ming Quing Liu (Gen Mgr)

SYP Building Glass Co., Ltd. (1)
No 611 Kangqiao Road, Pudong New District, Shanghai, 201315, China
Tel.: (86) 21 5812 1754
Glass Products Mfr
N.A.I.C.S.: 327211

SYP Kangqiao Autoglass Co., Ltd. (1)
No 55 Kangliu Road, Pudong New District, Shanghai, China
Tel.: (86) 2168193000
Flat Glass Mfr
N.A.I.C.S.: 327211

Shanghai SYP Engineering Glass Co., Ltd. (1)
No 75 Kangliu Road, Pudong New District, Shanghai, 201315, China
Tel.: (86) 2138108108
Flat Glass Mfr
N.A.I.C.S.: 327211

Tianjin SYP Engineering Glass Co., Ltd. (1)
No 1 Huatai Road Hi-Tech Industrial Park, Beichen, Tianjin, 300409, China
Tel.: (86) 2286880202
Flat Glass Mfr
N.A.I.C.S.: 327211

Tianjin SYP Glass Co.,Ltd. (1)
No 1168 Dagang Beiweidi Road, Binhai New District, Tianjin, 300271, China
Tel.: (86) 2263203102
Collared Glazing Glass Mfr & Distr
N.A.I.C.S.: 327211

Wuhan SYP Kangqiao Autoglass Co., Ltd. (1)
No 18 Tongyong Avenue, Jiangxia District, Wuhan, China
Tel.: (86) 2786697658
Flat Glass Mfr
N.A.I.C.S.: 327211

Yizheng SYP Autoglass Co., Ltd. (1)
No 18 Wanshitong Road Economic Development Zone, Yizheng, Jiangsu, China
Tel.: (86) 51480862756
Flat Glass Mfr
N.A.I.C.S.: 327211

SHANGHAI YAOJI TECHNOLOGY CO., LTD.

No 4218 Caoan Road, Jiading District, Shanghai, 201804, China
Tel.: (86) 2169591889
Web Site: https://www.yaojikeji.com
Year Founded: 1994
002605—(SSE)
Rev.: $549,644,477
Assets: $618,513,878
Liabilities: $235,373,341
Net Worth: $383,140,536
Earnings: $48,937,641
Fiscal Year-end: 12/31/22
Playing Card Mfr
N.A.I.C.S.: 323111
Yao Shuobin (Chm & Gen Mgr)

SHANGHAI YCT ELECTRONICS GROUP CO., LTD.

4th Floor No 62 Lane 99 Chunguang Road, Minhang District, Shanghai, 201108, China
Tel.: (86) 2151516111
Web Site: https://www.yctexin.com
Year Founded: 2008
301099—(CHIN)
Rev.: $309,270,312
Assets: $299,508,300
Liabilities: $137,455,812
Net Worth: $162,052,488
Earnings: $21,646,872
Emp.: 500
Fiscal Year-end: 12/31/22
Electronic Component Mfr & Distr
N.A.I.C.S.: 334419
Lishu Xie (Chm & Gen Mgr)

SHANGHAI YIMIN COMMERCIAL GROUP CO., LTD.

Jia 7F No 809 Huaihai Middle Road, Shanghai, 200020, China
Tel.: (86) 2164721278
Web Site: http://www.yimingroup.com
Year Founded: 1993
600824—(SHG)
Rev.: $113,861,789
Assets: $451,183,838
Liabilities: $118,117,537
Net Worth: $333,066,301
Earnings: ($42,112,685)
Fiscal Year-end: 12/31/22
Departmental Store Operator
N.A.I.C.S.: 455110
Chuanhua Yang (Chm)

Subsidiaries:

Shanghai Oriental Pawn Co., Ltd. (1)
No 381 XieTu Road, Shanghai, 200023, China
Tel.: (86) 63055888
Web Site: http://www.orientalpawn.com
Pawn Services
N.A.I.C.S.: 522299

Shanghai Xinguang Optical Instrument Co., Ltd. (1)
No 95 Jianguo East Rd, Shanghai, 200000, China
Tel.: (86) 2163285642
Real Estate Manangement Services
N.A.I.C.S.: 531210

Shanghai Yimin Industry Co., Ltd. (1)
YiMinHe Road 20, HongKou District, Shanghai, China
Tel.: (86) 2165530801
Real Estate Manangement Services
N.A.I.C.S.: 531210

SHANGHAI YINDA TECHNOLOGY INDUSTRIAL CO. LTD.

National Road No 200 building 3 floor 3, Yangpu District, Shanghai, 200032, China
Tel.: (86) 21 54658856
Web Site: http://www.yindatech.com
Year Founded: 1997

Communications Technology Service Enterprises
N.A.I.C.S.: 517810

Subsidiaries:

Totm Technologies Limited (1)
APAC & International Sales 47 Scotts Road 02-03/04 Goldbell Towers, Singapore, 228233, Singapore
Tel.: (65) 69701971
Web Site: https://totmtechnologies.com
Rev.: $4,829,196
Assets: $46,845,498
Liabilities: $4,257,132
Net Worth: $42,588,366
Earnings: ($8,534,272)
Emp.: 76
Fiscal Year-end: 05/31/2024
Investment Holding Services; Communications Solutions & Services
N.A.I.C.S.: 551112
Gordon Chee Bun Tan (Exec Dir)

Subsidiary (Non-US):

Yinda Communications (Philippines), Inc. (2)
Unit 3D 3/F Country Space I Bldg Sen Gil Puyat Ave Salcedo Village, Makati, 1200, Philippines
Tel.: (63) 28935085
Telecommunications Equipment Mfr
N.A.I.C.S.: 334210

Yinda Technology (Thailand) Company Ltd. (2)
240/63 Ayothaya Tower 25th Floor Soi Ratchadapisek 18, Ratchadapisek Road Huaykwang, Bangkok, 10310, Thailand
Tel.: (66) 26927600
Telecommunication Network Services
N.A.I.C.S.: 517112

Yinda Technology Malaysia Sdn. Bhd. (2)
A6-3A Jalan Selaman 1/1 Dataran Palma, Ampang, 68000, Selangor, Malaysia
Tel.: (60) 342663810
Telecommunication Network Services
N.A.I.C.S.: 517112

SHANGHAI YIQIAN TRADING CO. LTD.

Building 2 No 116 South Tangbang Road, Shanghai, 200023, Huangpu District, China
Tel.: (86) 21 63035066
Video Equipmentt Sales
N.A.I.C.S.: 512120

SHANGHAI YONGGUAN ADHESIVE PRODUCTS CORP LTD.

15 Kanggong Road Zhujiajiao Industrial Zone, Qingpu District, Shanghai, 201713, China
Tel.: (86) 2159835246
Web Site: https://ygtape.com
Year Founded: 2002
603681—(SHG)
Rev.: $705,784,089
Assets: $906,588,255
Liabilities: $557,678,684
Net Worth: $348,909,570
Earnings: $31,957,090
Fiscal Year-end: 12/31/22
Packaging Services
N.A.I.C.S.: 561910
Xinmin Lv (Chm)

SHANGHAI YONGLI BELTING CO., LTD.

No 58 Xuwang Road, Xujing Town Qingpu District, Shanghai, 201706, China
Tel.: (86) 2159884061
Web Site: http://www.yonglibelt.com
Year Founded: 1999
300230—(SSE)
Rev.: $294,941,088
Assets: $526,369,428
Liabilities: $141,709,932

Net Worth: $384,659,496
Earnings: $34,315,164
Emp.: 600
Fiscal Year-end: 12/31/22
Conveyor Belts Mfr
N.A.I.C.S.: 326220
Shi Peihao (Chm)

Subsidiaries:

YONGLI EUROPE B.V. (1)
Koolmand 3, 1724 BC, Oudkarspel, Netherlands
Tel.: (31) 22 639 9928
Web Site: http://yonglibelting.com
Emp.: 17
Conveyor Belts Mfr
N.A.I.C.S.: 333922

SHANGHAI YONGMAOTAI AUTOMOTIVE TECHNOLOGY CO., LTD.

No 577 Zhangliantang Road, Liantang Town Qingpu District, Shanghai, China
Tel.: (86) 2159815201
Web Site: https://www.ymtauto.com
Year Founded: 2000
605208—(SHG)
Rev.: $496,168,096
Assets: $470,960,652
Liabilities: $179,890,898
Net Worth: $291,069,755
Earnings: $13,224,866
Emp.: 270
Fiscal Year-end: 12/31/22
Aluminium Products Mfr
N.A.I.C.S.: 331313
Hong Xu (Chm & Gen Mgr)

Subsidiaries:

Anhui Yongmao Tai Aluminum Co. Ltd. (1)
East Group of Liudong Village, Xinhang Town Guangde County, Xuancheng, Anhui, China
Tel.: (86) 5636683588
Aluminium Products Mfr
N.A.I.C.S.: 331315

Anhui Yongmaotai Auto Parts Co. Ltd. (1)
Jingsi Road Xinhang Economic Development Zone, Guangde County, Anhui, China
Tel.: (86) 5636855168
Aluminium Products Mfr
N.A.I.C.S.: 331315

Liaoning Yongxuetai Auto Parts Co. Ltd. (1)
No 11 Dongyue First Street, Dadong District, Shenyang, China
Tel.: (86) 2462830802
Aluminium Products Mfr
N.A.I.C.S.: 331315

Shandong Yongmaotai Auto Parts Co. Ltd. (1)
127 Jinshan Road, Fushan District, Yantai, China
Tel.: (86) 5352135127
Aluminium Products Mfr
N.A.I.C.S.: 331315

Shanghai Yongmaotai Auto Parts Co., Ltd. (1)
388 Sanfeng Road, Liantang Town Qingpu District, Shanghai, China
Tel.: (86) 2159815220
Aluminium Products Mfr
N.A.I.C.S.: 331315

Sichuan Wantai Aluminum Co. Ltd. (1)
No 55 Nanyi Road, Longquanyi District, Chengdu, Sichuan, China
Tel.: (86) 2862040099
Aluminium Products Mfr
N.A.I.C.S.: 331315

Yantai Tongtai Renewable Resources Co. Ltd. (1)
91 Hongfu Street, Fushan District, Yantai, China

Tel.: (86) 5352135653
Aluminium Products Mfr
N.A.I.C.S.: 331315

SHANGHAI YUYUAN TOURIST MART (GROUP) CO., LTD.
No 2 Fuxing East Road, Huangpu District, Shanghai, 200010, China
Tel.: (86) 2123029999 CN
Web Site:
 htttps://www.yuyuantm.com.cn
Year Founded: 1990
600655—(SHG)
Rev.: $8,050,913,948
Assets: $17,175,004,846
Liabilities: $11,683,753,655
Net Worth: $5,491,251,191
Earnings: $280,248,242
Fiscal Year-end: 12/31/23
Jewelry Retailer
N.A.I.C.S.: 458310
Xiaoliang Xu *(Chm)*

Subsidiaries:

Yuyuan Culture Promoting & Publicizing Co., Ltd (1)
3F No 10 Wenchang Road, Shanghai, China
Tel.: (86) 21 63200836
Web Site: http://www.culture-sh.com
Jewelry Store Operator
N.A.I.C.S.: 458310

SHANGHAI ZENDAI PROPERTY LIMITED
Unit 6508 65/F Central Plaza 18 Harbour Road, Wanchai, China (Hong Kong)
Tel.: (852) 21693308
Web Site: http://www.zendai.com
0755—(HKG)
Rev.: $50,569,178
Assets: $832,067,678
Liabilities: $680,436,263
Net Worth: $151,631,415
Earnings: $366,988,095
Emp.: 592
Fiscal Year-end: 12/31/22
Property Development Business & Agency Services
N.A.I.C.S.: 531190
Jian Tang *(Sr VP)*

Subsidiaries:

Heartland Properties (Pty) Limited (1)
Heartland House 1 Casino Road, PO Box 500, Modderfontein, 1645, Gauteng, South Africa
Tel.: (27) 11 579 1000
Web Site: http://www.heartland.co.za
Sales Range: $25-49.9 Million
Emp.: 40
Property Management Services
N.A.I.C.S.: 531311

SHANGHAI ZHANGJIANG HI-TECH PARK DEVELOPMENT CO., LTD.
17F No 560 Songtao Road, Pudong New Area, Shanghai, 201203, China
Tel.: (86) 2138959000
Web Site: http://www.600895.com
Year Founded: 1996
600895—(SHG)
Rev.: $267,703,404
Assets: $5,998,903,682
Liabilities: $3,852,115,376
Net Worth: $2,146,788,306
Earnings: $115,439,154
Fiscal Year-end: 12/31/22
Real Estate Development Services
N.A.I.C.S.: 531120
Ying Liu *(Chm)*

SHANGHAI ZHEZHONG GROUP CO., LTD.
Room 2501 Block 5 No 215 Lianhe North Road, Fengxian District, Shanghai, 201424, China
Tel.: (86) 2157403888
002346—(SSE)
Rev.: $101,876,065
Assets: $573,461,455
Liabilities: $192,968,512
Net Worth: $380,492,943
Earnings: $63,265,588
Fiscal Year-end: 12/31/22
Switchgear Mfr
N.A.I.C.S.: 334419

SHANGHAI ZHONGGU LOGISTICS CO., LTD.
Room 106 Comprehensive Building No 99 Shuanghui Road, Pilot Free Trade Zone, Shanghai, 200125, China
Tel.: (86) 2131761722
Web Site: http://www.zhonggu56.com
Year Founded: 2010
603565—(SHG)
Rev.: $1,994,931,877
Assets: $2,826,311,263
Liabilities: $1,515,525,280
Net Worth: $1,310,785,983
Earnings: $384,890,552
Fiscal Year-end: 12/31/22
Logistics Consulting Servies
N.A.I.C.S.: 541614
Zongjun Lu *(Board of Directors & Chm)*

SHANGHAI ZHONGZHOU SPECIAL ALLOY MATERIALS CO., LTD.
No 580 Shisheng Road, Jiading Industrial Zone, Shanghai, 201815, China
Tel.: (86) 2159962255
Web Site: https://www.alloy-china.com
Year Founded: 2002
300963—(SSE)
Rev.: $122,483,837
Assets: $190,744,393
Liabilities: $60,780,929
Net Worth: $129,963,464
Earnings: $11,232,842
Emp.: 670
Fiscal Year-end: 12/31/22
Alloy Product Mfr
N.A.I.C.S.: 331420
Mingming Feng *(Chm)*

SHANGHAI ZIJIANG ENTERPRISE GROUP CO., LTD.
No 618 Shen Fu Road, Xinzhuang Industrial Zone, Shanghai, 200336, China
Tel.: (86) 2162377118
Web Site: http://www.zijiangqy.com
Year Founded: 1999
600210—(SHG)
Rev.: $1,348,955,085
Assets: $1,695,575,532
Liabilities: $863,909,617
Net Worth: $831,665,915
Earnings: $84,688,494
Fiscal Year-end: 12/31/22
Plastic Bottle Product Mfr
N.A.I.C.S.: 326199
Shen Wen *(Chm)*

Subsidiaries:

Shanghai Zi Ri Packaging Co., Ltd (1)
No 899 Zhuanxing Road, Minhang District, Shanghai, 201108, China
Tel.: (86) 6 442 6588
Web Site: https://www.ziri.com.cn
Emp.: 300
Plastic Closure Mfr
N.A.I.C.S.: 332119
Littail Yang *(Supvr-Quality Assurance)*

SHANGHAI ZJ BIO-TECH CO., LTD.
Building 26 No 588 Xinjun Ring Road, Minhang District, Shanghai, 201114, China
Tel.: (86) 2134680598
Web Site: http://www.liferiver.com.cn
Year Founded: 2005
688317—(SSE)
Rev.: $326,606,216
Assets: $666,036,723
Liabilities: $76,298,920
Net Worth: $589,737,803
Earnings: $106,742,399
Fiscal Year-end: 12/31/22
Medical Product Mfr & Distr
N.A.I.C.S.: 339112
Junbin Shao *(Chm & Gen Mgr)*

Subsidiaries:

Liferiver Bio-Tech (United States) Corp. (1)
9855 Towne Centre Dr, San Diego, CA 92121
Tel.: (858) 352-6520
Web Site: https://www.liferiverusa.com
Infectious Pathogens Mfr
N.A.I.C.S.: 334519

SHANGRI-LA ASIA LIMITED
28/F Kerry Centre 683 Kings Road, Quarry Bay, China (Hong Kong)
Tel.: (852) 25993000
Web Site: https://www.shangri-la.com
Year Founded: 1971
SHALF—(OTCIQ)
Rev.: $1,462,145,000
Assets: $12,633,506,000
Liabilities: $7,208,991,000
Net Worth: $5,424,515,000
Earnings: ($187,452,000)
Emp.: 23,900
Fiscal Year-end: 12/31/22
Hotel Management & Investment Properties
N.A.I.C.S.: 523940
Hui Kwong Kuok *(Chm)*

Subsidiaries:

Edsa Shangri-La Hotel & Resort, Inc. (1)
1 Garden Way Ortigas Center, Mandaluyong, 1650, Manila, Philippines
Tel.: (63) 26338888
Restaurant Services
N.A.I.C.S.: 722511
Amit Oberoi *(Gen Mgr)*

Golden Sands Beach Resort Sdn Berhad (1)
Batu Feringgi Beach, 11100, Penang, Malaysia
Tel.: (60) 48861911
Restaurant Services
N.A.I.C.S.: 722511
Choong Kit Siong *(Dir-Sls)*

Harbin Songbei Shangri-La Hotel Co., Limited (1)
No 1 Songbei Avenue, Songbei District, Harbin, 150028, China
Tel.: (86) 45158629999
Restaurant Services
N.A.I.C.S.: 722511
Tyson Wang *(Gen Mgr & Area Mgr)*

Mactan Shangri-La Hotel & Resort, Inc. (1)
Punta Engano Road, Lapu-Lapu, 6015, Cebu, Philippines
Tel.: (63) 322310288
Restaurant Services
N.A.I.C.S.: 722511
Rene D. Egle *(Gen Mgr)*

Makati Shangri-La Hotel & Resort, Inc. (1)
Ayala Avenue corner Makati Avenue, Makati, 1200, Philippines
Tel.: (63) 28138888
Restaurant Services
N.A.I.C.S.: 722511

Greg Findlay *(Gen Mgr)*

Pantai Dalit Beach Resort Sdn Berhad (1)
PO Box 600, Tuaran, Kota Kinabalu, 89208, Sabah, Malaysia
Tel.: (60) 88797888
Restaurant Services
N.A.I.C.S.: 722511

SHANGRI-LA HOTEL PUBLIC COMPANY LIMITED (1)
89 SOI Watsuanphlu New Road, Bang Rak, Bangkok, 10500, Thailand
Tel.: (66) 22367777
Web Site: http://www.shangri-la.com
Rev.: $63,819,185
Assets: $229,118,305
Liabilities: $16,067,186
Net Worth: $213,051,119
Earnings: $4,072,799
Emp.: 935
Fiscal Year-end: 12/31/2023
Home Management Services
N.A.I.C.S.: 721110
Seow Chow Loong Iain *(Sec)*

Sanya Shangri-La Hotel Co., Limited (1)
No 88 North Hai Tang Road, Sanya, 572000, Hainan, China
Tel.: (86) 89888758888
Restaurant Services
N.A.I.C.S.: 722511
Rudolf Gimmi *(Gen Mgr)*

Shangri-La Hotel (Cairns) Pte. Ltd. (1)
Pierpoint Road, Cairns, 4870, QLD, Australia
Tel.: (61) 740527500
Restaurant Services
N.A.I.C.S.: 722511
Jennifer Smith *(Dir-HR)*

Shangri-La Hotel (KL) Sdn Berhad (1)
11 Jalan Sultan Ismail, 50250, Kuala Lumpur, Malaysia
Tel.: (60) 320322388
Restaurant Services
N.A.I.C.S.: 722511
Gonzalo Duarte Silva *(Gen Mgr)*

Shangri-La Hotel (Lhasa) Co., Limited (1)
19 Norbulingka Road, Tibet, Lhasa, 850000, China
Tel.: (86) 8916558888
Restaurant Services
N.A.I.C.S.: 722511
Claudia Lee *(Gen Mgr)*

Shangri-La Hotel (Nanjing) Co., Limited (1)
329 Zhongyang Road, Gulou District, Nanjing, 210037, Jiangsu, China
Tel.: (86) 2586308888
Restaurant Services
N.A.I.C.S.: 722511
Melinde Lim *(Gen Mgr)*

Shangri-La Hotel (Qufu) Co., Limited (1)
3 Chunqiu Road, Qufu, 273100, Shandong, China
Tel.: (86) 5375058888
Restaurant Services
N.A.I.C.S.: 722511
Peter Qu *(Gen Mgr)*

Shangri-La Hotel (Xiamen) Co., Limited (1)
Guanyinshan International Business Centre No 168 Taidong Road, Siming District, Xiamen, Fujian, China
Tel.: (86) 5928385888
Restaurant Services
N.A.I.C.S.: 722511
Richard H'ng *(Gen Mgr)*

Shangri-La Hotel Limited (1)
22 Orange Grove Road, Singapore, 258350, Singapore
Tel.: (65) 67373644
Restaurant Services
N.A.I.C.S.: 722511
Tane Picken *(Gen Mgr)*

Shangri-La Hotels Japan KK (1)

SHANGRI-LA ASIA LIMITED

Shangri-La Asia Limited—(Continued)

Marunouchi Trust Tower Main 1-8-3,
Marunouchi Chiyoda-ku, Tokyo, 100-8283,
Japan
Tel.: (81) 367397888
Restaurant Services
N.A.I.C.S.: 722511
Jade Woon *(Dir-Sls & Mktg)*

Shangri-La Hotels Pte. Ltd. (1)
31 St Thomas Street, London, SE1 9QU,
United Kingdom
Tel.: (44) 2072348000
Restaurant Services
N.A.I.C.S.: 722511

Shangri-La International Hotel Management GmbH (1)
An der Welle 4, 60322, Frankfurt am Main,
Germany
Tel.: (49) 6975938080
Web Site: http://www.shangri-la.com
Emp.: 4
Home Management Services
N.A.I.C.S.: 561110

Shangri-La International Marketing Company (1)
11/F Tokyo Kotsu Kaikan Bldg 2-10-1, Yurakucho Chiyoda-ku, Tokyo, 100-0006, Japan
Tel.: (81) 3 5288 5668
Web Site: http://www.shangri-la.com
Emp.: 8
Marketing Consulting Services
N.A.I.C.S.: 541613

Shangri-La Ulaanbaatar Hotel LLC (1)
19 Olympic Street, Sukhbaatar District-1,
Ulaanbaatar, 14241, Mongolia
Tel.: (976) 77029999
Restaurant Services
N.A.I.C.S.: 722511
Terence Tan *(Gen Mgr)*

Shangri-La Ulaanbaatar LLC (1)
Rm 513 Central Tower Great Chinggis
Khaan's Square-2 SBD-8, Ulaanbaatar,
14200, Mongolia
Tel.: (976) 70122888
Web Site: http://www.centraltower.mn
Emp.: 90
Building Management Services
N.A.I.C.S.: 531390

Shangri-La Yangon Company Limited (1)
223 Sule Pagoda Road, GPO Box 888,
Yangon, Myanmar
Tel.: (95) 1242828
Restaurant Services
N.A.I.C.S.: 722511
Phillip Couvaras *(Gen Mgr & Area Mgr)*

UBN Tower Sdn Bhd (1)
UBN Complex 10 Jalan P Ramlee, 50250,
Kuala Lumpur, Wilayah Persekutuan, Malaysia
Tel.: (60) 320783296
Real Estate Manangement Services
N.A.I.C.S.: 531390

SHANGRI-LA DEVELOPMENT BANK LTD.
New Road, PO Box 174, Kathmandu,
Nepal
Tel.: (977) 61 523715
Web Site:
http://www.shangrilabank.com
Banking Services
N.A.I.C.S.: 522110
Rabeendra Prasad Shrestha *(Chm)*

SHANGRI-LA DEVELOPMENT BANK LTD.
Baluwatar-4, Kathmandu, Nepal
Tel.: (977) 14522864
Web Site:
https://www.shangrilabank.com
Year Founded: 2006
SADBL—(NEP)
Rev.: $53,412,111
Assets: $439,513,541
Liabilities: $405,912,223
Net Worth: $33,601,318
Earnings: $2,026,431
Emp.: 799
Fiscal Year-end: 07/16/23
Commercial Banking Services
N.A.I.C.S.: 522110
Surendra Bahadur Bhariju *(Chm)*

SHANGRI-LA HOTELS (MALAYSIA) BERHAD
11 Jalan Sultan Ismail, 50250, Kuala
Lumpur, Malaysia
Tel.: (60) 320261018 MY
Web Site: https://www.shangri-la.com
SHANG—(KLS)
Rev.: $42,592,770
Assets: $328,861,665
Liabilities: $73,068,188
Net Worth: $255,793,478
Earnings: ($26,900,775)
Emp.: 2,204
Fiscal Year-end: 12/31/20
Hotel Services
N.A.I.C.S.: 561110
Rozina Mohammad Amin *(Sec)*

Subsidiaries:

Dalit Bay Golf & Country Club Berhad (1)
Pantai Dalit Beach, PO Box 600, Tuaran,
Kota Kinabalu, Sabah, Malaysia
Tel.: (60) 88791333
Web Site: http://www.dalitbaygolf.com.my
Golf Club Resort Services
N.A.I.C.S.: 713910
Alfons Olim *(Gen Mgr)*

Shangri-La International Hotels, Inc. - Los Angeles (1)
PO Box 451489, Los Angeles, CA 90045
Tel.: (212) 768-3190
Hotel Operator
N.A.I.C.S.: 721110

SHANGTEX HOLDING CO., LTD.
989 Gubei Road, Changning, Shanghai, 200336, China
Tel.: (86) 21 2211 0288
Web Site: http://www.shangtex.biz
Year Founded: 2001
Emp.: 58,000
Holding Company
N.A.I.C.S.: 551112
LiMin Zhan *(Dir-Res-Strategy & Policy)*

Subsidiaries:

Luen Thai Holdings Limited (1)
Rooms 1001-1005 10/F Nanyang Plaza 57
Hung To Road, Kwun Tong, Kowloon, China
(Hong Kong) **(74.5%)**
Tel.: (852) 2193 3800
Web Site: http://www.luenthai.com
Rev.: $969,789,000
Assets: $563,129,000
Liabilities: $344,436,000
Net Worth: $218,693,000
Earnings: $25,165,000
Emp.: 52,000
Fiscal Year-end: 12/31/2019
Apparel Mfr; Logistics Services
N.A.I.C.S.: 541614
Francisco Sauceda *(COO)*

Subsidiary (Non-US):

CTSI Logistics (Korea), Inc. (2)
11F Ace Tower 92 Tongil-ro, Jung-gu,
Seoul, Korea (South)
Tel.: (82) 27715521
Web Site: http://korea.ctsi-logistics.com
Freight Transportation Arrangement
N.A.I.C.S.: 488510

Subsidiary (Domestic):

CTSI Logistics Limited (2)
5F Nanyang Plaza 57 Hung To Road, Kwun
Tong, Kowloon, China (Hong Kong)
Tel.: (852) 21930252
Web Site: http://hongkong.ctsi-logistics.com

Freight Transportation Arrangement
N.A.I.C.S.: 488510
Jerry Tan *(CEO)*

Subsidiary (US):

CTSI Logistics, Inc. (2)
2517 W Rosecrans Ave, Los Angeles, CA
90059
Tel.: (310) 320-0818
Web Site: http://usa.ctsi-logistics.com
Sales Range: $25-49.9 Million
Emp.: 40
Freight Transportation Arrangement
N.A.I.C.S.: 488510

Subsidiary (Domestic):

TMS Fashion (H.K.) Limited (2)
Unit 1001-1002 10F Nanyang Plaza
57Hung To Road, Kwun Tong, Kowloon,
China (Hong Kong) **(100%)**
Tel.: (852) 29594300
Web Site: http://www.tmsfashion.com
Mens & Boys Clothing & Furnishing Distr
N.A.I.C.S.: 424350

Subsidiary (US):

Tan Holdings Corporation (2)
TSL Plz 3rd Fl Beach Rd Garapan, Saipan,
MP 96950
Tel.: (670) 233-8080
Web Site: http://www.tanholdings.com
Emp.: 4,000
Diverse Holding Company
N.A.I.C.S.: 551112
Lina Dimaano *(VP-Fin)*

SHANGYA TECHNOLOGY CO., LTD.
9F-12 No 188 Sec 5 Nanjing E Rd,
Songshan Dist, Taipei, 10571, Taiwan
Tel.: (886) 227132100
Web Site: https://www.singbao.com
6130—(TPE)
Rev.: $2,662,977
Assets: $29,357,940
Liabilities: $5,258,981
Net Worth: $24,098,959
Earnings: $39,896
Fiscal Year-end: 12/31/22
Driver & Controller IC Mfr
N.A.I.C.S.: 334419
Huang Kunjian *(Chm & Gen Mgr)*

SHANGYING GLOBAL CO., LTD.
Room 1105-1106 Tower A No 1600
Hongwell International Plaza, Zhongshan Road, Shanghai, 200235, China
Tel.: (86) 216 469 8668
Web Site: http://www.600146.net
600146—(SHG)
Rev.: $18,933,692
Assets: $219,908,441
Liabilities: $112,863,679
Net Worth: $107,044,763
Earnings: ($62,993,824)
Fiscal Year-end: 12/31/20
Industrial Plastic & Pipe Mfr & Distr
N.A.I.C.S.: 326199
Zhu Fangming *(Pres)*

Subsidiaries:

Oneworld Apparel, LLC (1)
18525 Railrod St, City of Industry, CA
91748
Tel.: (213) 743-5899
Web Site: http://www.oneworldapparel.com
Other Apparel Accessories & Other Apparel
Mfr
N.A.I.C.S.: 315990
Eileen Bushman *(VP)*

SHANIV PAPER INDUSTRIES LTD.
Bezalel 7 St, Ofakim, 80300, Israel
Tel.: (972) 89908230
Web Site: https://www.shaniv.com
Year Founded: 1988

SHAN—(TAE)
Rev.: $223,248,788
Assets: $249,813,783
Liabilities: $157,496,337
Net Worth: $92,317,446
Earnings: $5,316,204
Emp.: 250
Fiscal Year-end: 12/31/23
Sanitary Paper Product Manufacturing
N.A.I.C.S.: 322291

Subsidiaries:

Sasa Cosmetics Agricultural Cooperative Society Ltd. (1)
Bnei Yehuda Industrial Park, Bnei Yehuda,
Israel
Tel.: (972) 46600859
Cosmetics Products Mfr
N.A.I.C.S.: 325620

Sasatech Agricultural Cooperative Society Ltd. (1)
Dalton Industrial Park, Dalton, Israel
Tel.: (972) 46987720
Detergents Mfr
N.A.I.C.S.: 325611

SHANKAR ELECTRONICS LTD.
Africa Bldg Moi Avenue, PO Box
80651-80100, Mombasa, 80100, Kenya
Tel.: (254) 41 2225619
Web Site:
http://www.shankarelectronics.com
Year Founded: 1970
Air Conditioners, Refrigerators & Audio Systems Installer & Distr
N.A.I.C.S.: 423730
Akram Sheikh *(CEO)*

SHANKAR LAL RAMPAL DYE CHEM LTD.
SG 2730, Suwana, Bhilwara, 311001,
Rajasthan, India
Tel.: (91) 1482220062
Web Site:
https://www.srdyechem.com
Year Founded: 1980
542232—(BOM)
Rev.: $24,255,038
Assets: $8,912,593
Liabilities: $2,112,757
Net Worth: $6,799,836
Earnings: $1,041,858
Emp.: 9
Fiscal Year-end: 03/31/21
Chemical Products Mfr
N.A.I.C.S.: 325199
Rampal Inani *(Mng Dir)*

SHANKARA BUILDING PRODUCTS LIMITED
G2 Farah Winsford 133 Infantry
Road, Bengaluru, 560 001, India
Tel.: (91) 8040117777
Web Site:
https://www.shankarabuildpro.com
Year Founded: 1995
SHANKARA—(BOM)
Rev.: $484,074,096
Assets: $154,876,806
Liabilities: $77,772,316
Net Worth: $77,104,490
Earnings: $7,559,499
Emp.: 991
Fiscal Year-end: 03/31/23
Construction Material Retailer
N.A.I.C.S.: 423390
Sukumar Srinivas *(Founder & Mng Dir)*

SHANNON SEMICONDUCTOR TECHNOLOGY CO., LTD.
No 16 Chuangye North Road, Ningguo Economic and Technological De-

AND PRIVATE COMPANIES

velopment Zone, Xuancheng, 242300, Anhui, China
Tel.: (86) 5634186119
Web Site: http://www.ahjlcd.com
Year Founded: 1998
300475—(CHIN)
Rev.: $1,587,054,235
Assets: $640,227,703
Liabilities: $264,051,889
Net Worth: $376,175,814
Earnings: $53,193,960
Fiscal Year-end: 12/31/23
Industrial Control Equipment Mfr
N.A.I.C.S.: 335314
Fan Yongwu *(Chm)*

SHANON, INC.
4F Mita 43MT Building 3-13-16 Mita, Minato-ku, Tokyo, 108-0073, Japan
Tel.: (81) 367431551
Web Site: https://www.shanon.co.jp
Year Founded: 2000
3976—(TKS)
Rev.: $20,802,060
Assets: $14,350,160
Liabilities: $14,073,650
Net Worth: $276,510
Earnings: ($3,155,050)
Emp.: 260
Fiscal Year-end: 10/31/23
Marketing Consulting Services
N.A.I.C.S.: 541613
Kenichiro Nakamura *(Pres & CEO)*

SHANSHAN BRAND MANAGEMENT CO., LTD.
238 Yunlin Middle Road Wangchun Industrial Park, Ningbo, Zhejiang, China
Tel.: (86) 57488323975   CN
Web Site: http://www.chinafirs.com
Year Founded: 2011
1749—(HKG)
Rev.: $123,720,432
Assets: $106,504,235
Liabilities: $74,562,456
Net Worth: $31,941,778
Earnings: $2,247,288
Emp.: 352
Fiscal Year-end: 12/31/22
Apparel Mfr & Distr
N.A.I.C.S.: 315250
Yang Yong *(Deputy Gen Mgr)*

SHANTA GOLD LIMITED
11 New Street, PO Box 91, Saint Peter Port, GY1 3EG, Guernsey
Tel.: (44) 1481732153
Web Site: http://www.shantagold.com
SHG—(LSE)
Rev.: $114,055,000
Assets: $234,408,000
Liabilities: $82,441,000
Net Worth: $151,967,000
Earnings: ($2,299,000)
Emp.: 914
Fiscal Year-end: 12/31/22
Gold Exploration Services
N.A.I.C.S.: 212220
Luke Alexander Leslie *(CFO & Head-Corp Dev)*

Subsidiaries:

Shanta Mining Company Limited   (1)
Tel.: (255) 2229251480
Gold Mining Services
N.A.I.C.S.: 212220

SHANTAI INDUSTRIES LIMITED
820 Golden Point Falsawadi Near Telephone Exchange, Ring Road, Surat, 395 003, Gujarat, India
Tel.: (91) 9099211000
Web Site: https://www.shantaiindustries.com
Year Founded: 1985

512297—(BOM)
Rev.: $74,684
Assets: $933,457
Liabilities: $43,583
Net Worth: $889,875
Earnings: ($11,474)
Emp.: 4
Fiscal Year-end: 03/31/23
Textile Fabric Mfr
N.A.I.C.S.: 313310
Shailesh J. Damor *(CFO)*

SHANTHALA FMCG PRODUCTS LIMITED
7th Block Gandhinagar Bye Pass Road Virajpet, Kodagu, Karnataka, 571218, India
Tel.: (91) 8274298999
Web Site: https://www.shanthalafmcg.com
Year Founded: 1996
SHANTHALA—(NSE)
Rev.: $4,941,627
Assets: $796,539
Liabilities: $622,968
Net Worth: $173,571
Earnings: $21,489
Emp.: 26
Fiscal Year-end: 03/31/23
Grocery Product Distr
N.A.I.C.S.: 424410

SHANTHI GEARS LIMITED
304-A Shanthi Gears Road Singanallur, Coimbatore, 641 005, Tamil Nadu, India
Tel.: (91) 4224545745
Web Site: https://www.shanthigears.com
Year Founded: 1969
SHANTIGEAR—(NSE)
Rev.: $30,550,065
Assets: $44,419,830
Liabilities: $12,051,585
Net Worth: $32,368,245
Earnings: $2,753,205
Emp.: 572
Fiscal Year-end: 03/31/21
Gear Products Sales & Mfr
N.A.I.C.S.: 333612
C. Subramaniam *(Officer-Compliance & Sec)*

Subsidiaries:

Shanthi Gears Limited - A Unit   (1)
304-A Trichy Road, Singanallur, Coimbatore, 641 005, Tamil Nadu, India
Tel.: (91) 422 454 5845
Web Site: https://www.shanthigears.com
Emp.: 475
Industrial Gear Mfr
N.A.I.C.S.: 333612
Senthil Vel *(Gen Mgr-Mktg)*

Shanthi Gears Limited - B Unit   (1)
304-F Trichy Road, Singanallur, Coimbatore, 641 005, Tamil Nadu, India
Tel.: (91) 422 454 5845
Web Site: http://www.shanthigears.com
Sales Range: $800-899.9 Million
Industrial Gear Mfr
N.A.I.C.S.: 333612

Shanthi Gears Limited - C Unit   (1)
Avanashi Road Muthugoundenputhur, Coimbatore, 641 406, Tamil Nadu, India
Tel.: (91) 422 454 5745
Web Site: http://www.shanthigears.com
Industrial Gear Mfr
N.A.I.C.S.: 333612
V. C. S. Velumani *(CEO)*

Shanthi Gears Limited - F Unit   (1)
26 Trichy Road Kambanthottam Kannampalayam, Coimbatore, 641 402, Tamilnadu, India
Tel.: (91) 422 2687310
Sales Range: $400-449.9 Million
Emp.: 150
Industrial Gear Mfr
N.A.I.C.S.: 333612

V. C. S. Velumani *(CEO)*

SHANTI EDUCATIONAL INITIATIVES LTD.
1909 - 1910 D Block West Gate, Nr YMCA Club S G Highway, Ahmedabad, 380051, India
Tel.: (91) 7966177266
Web Site: https://www.seil.edu.in
Year Founded: 2009
539921—(BOM)
Rev.: $1,896,181
Assets: $8,034,494
Liabilities: $803,021
Net Worth: $7,231,473
Earnings: $403,597
Emp.: 58
Fiscal Year-end: 03/31/23
Education Training Services
N.A.I.C.S.: 611110
Jayesh Patel *(CFO)*

SHANTI GURU INDUSTRIES LIMITED
Sapna Trade Centre 10th Floor 10B/2 No 109 P H Road, Chennai, 600084, India
Tel.: (91) 4448508024
Web Site: https://shantiguruindustries.com
Sales Range: $1-9.9 Million
Food Retailer
N.A.I.C.S.: 445298

SHANTI OVERSEAS (INDIA) LTD.
203 2nd Floor NM verge 8/5 Yeshwant Niwas Road Opposite Central Bank, Indore, 452003, Madhya Pradesh, India
Tel.: (91) 7314020586
Web Site: https://www.shantioverseas.com
SHANTI—(NSE)
Rev.: $28,742,587
Assets: $9,646,400
Liabilities: $5,652,096
Net Worth: $3,994,304
Earnings: $11,234
Emp.: 44
Fiscal Year-end: 03/31/21
Soybean & Oilseed Product Mfr
N.A.I.C.S.: 311224
Mukesh Kacholia *(Founder)*

SHANTIDOOT INFRA SERVICES LIMITED
House No 221 Patliputra Colony 2nd floor, Patna, 800013, Bihar, India
Tel.: (91) 6122271960
Web Site: https://www.shantidootinfra.com
Year Founded: 2019
543598—(BOM)
Construction Services
N.A.I.C.S.: 236210

SHANTIVIJAY JEWELS LTD.
G-37 Gems and Jewellery Complex III SEEPZ, Andheri East, Mumbai, 400 096, India
Tel.: (91) 2242182222
Web Site: http://www.shantivijay.com
Year Founded: 1973
Rev.: $33,149,858
Assets: $14,582,978
Liabilities: $5,586,768
Net Worth: $8,996,210
Earnings: $1,397,514
Fiscal Year-end: 03/31/22
Jewelry Mfr
N.A.I.C.S.: 339910
Pradeepkumar Bimalchand Godha *(Chm & Mng Dir)*

SHANTUI CONSTRUCTION MACHINERY CO., LTD.

Subsidiaries:

Shantivijay Impex DMCC   (1)
22-J AU Tower Jumeirah Lake Towers Sheikh Zayed Road, PO Box 123909, Dubai, United Arab Emirates
Tel.: (971) 4 4472167
Sales Range: $25-49.9 Million
Emp.: 4
Jewelry Mfr & Whslr
N.A.I.C.S.: 339910
Pradeep Kumar Godha *(Office Mgr)*

Stern International Ltd.   (1)
15 W 47 St Ste 1206, New York, NY 10036
Tel.: (212) 719-1555
Jewelry Mfr & Whslr
N.A.I.C.S.: 339910

SHANTOU DONGFENG PRINTING CO., LTD.
Chaoshan Road, Jinyuan Ind District, Shantou, 515064, Guangdong, China
Tel.: (86) 75488118555
Web Site: https://www.dfp.com.cn
Year Founded: 1983
601515—(SHG)
Rev.: $525,658,442
Assets: $1,146,076,608
Liabilities: $303,255,941
Net Worth: $842,820,666
Earnings: $40,611,500
Fiscal Year-end: 12/31/22
Printing & Packaging Services
N.A.I.C.S.: 323120
Xie Mingyou *(Chm)*

SHANTOU WANSHUN NEW MATERIAL GROUP CO., LTD.
Wanshun Industrial Blocks Shantou Free Trade Zone, Shantou, 515078, Guangdong, China
Tel.: (86) 75483597123
Web Site: https://www.wanshun.cn
Year Founded: 1998
300057—(CHIN)
Rev.: $819,151,164
Assets: $1,447,803,396
Liabilities: $670,026,708
Net Worth: $777,776,688
Earnings: $28,707,588
Emp.: 400
Fiscal Year-end: 12/31/22
Paper Packaging Materials Mfr
N.A.I.C.S.: 322299
Chengcheng Du *(Chm)*

Subsidiaries:

Guangdong Eastcross Stationery Co., Ltd.   (1)
Rm 806 Building No 7 Nanhui Bldg West Area of Fengze Zhuang, Songshan Road South Longhu District, Shantou, Guangdong, China
Tel.: (86) 75488482730
Web Site: http://www.eastcross.cn
Paper Product Mfr & Distr
N.A.I.C.S.: 322212

Jiangsu Zhongji Lamination Materials Co., Ltd   (1)
No 2 Yabao Road, Jiangyin, Jiangsu, China
Tel.: (86) 51088616009
Web Site: http://www.zjalufoil.com
Aluminium Foil Mfr & Distr
N.A.I.C.S.: 332999

Shantou Eastcross Optoelectronic Material Co., Ltd.   (1)
No 60 Muyang GeZhou Haojiang, Shantou, 515071, Guangdong, China
Tel.: (86) 75483580838
Web Site: http://www.eastcross-gd.com
Thin Film Mfr & Distr
N.A.I.C.S.: 326113
Weiming Li *(Gen Mgr)*

SHANTUI CONSTRUCTION MACHINERY CO., LTD.
Shantui International Business Park

SHANTUI CONSTRUCTION MACHINERY CO., LTD.

Shantui Construction Machinery Co., Ltd.—(Continued)
No 58 National Highway 327, Jining, 272073, Shandong, China
Tel.: (86) 5372909999
Web Site: https://www.shantui.com
Year Founded: 1980
000680—(SSE)
Rev.: $1,403,696,020
Assets: $1,617,852,043
Liabilities: $890,665,111
Net Worth: $727,186,932
Earnings: $88,695,650
Fiscal Year-end: 12/31/22
Construction Engineering Machinery Mfr
N.A.I.C.S.: 333120

SHANXI ANTAI GROUP CO., LTD.

Antai Industrial Zone, Jiexiu, 032002, Shanxi, China
Tel.: (86) 3547531002
Web Site: https://www.antaigroup.com
Year Founded: 1993
600408—(SHG)
Rev.: $1,782,562,415
Assets: $731,235,731
Liabilities: $376,519,399
Net Worth: $354,716,332
Earnings: ($41,710,537)
Fiscal Year-end: 12/31/22
Coal & Electrical Products Mfr
N.A.I.C.S.: 423520
Yang Jinlong (Chm)

SHANXI BLUE FLAME HOLDING CO., LTD.

No 83 Heping South Road, South Middle Ring Street Xiaodian District, Taiyuan, 030006, Shanxi, China
Tel.: (86) 3515600968
000968—(SSE)
Rev.: $351,249,027
Assets: $1,604,453,826
Liabilities: $872,835,393
Net Worth: $731,618,433
Earnings: $79,089,272
Fiscal Year-end: 12/31/22
Coal Mining Services
N.A.I.C.S.: 213113

SHANXI C&Y PHARMACEUTICAL GROUP CO., LTD.

Area A No 1378 Hengan Street, Economic And Technological Development Zone, Datong, 037010, Shanxi, China
Tel.: (86) 3526116426
Web Site: http://www.cy-pharm.com
Year Founded: 2005
300254—(CHIN)
Rev.: $112,582,123
Assets: $201,848,670
Liabilities: $92,206,509
Net Worth: $109,642,161
Earnings: $3,548,800
Emp.: 1,700
Fiscal Year-end: 12/31/23
Pharmaceutical Mfr & Distr
N.A.I.C.S.: 325412
Qun Zhao (Chm & Pres)

Subsidiaries:

Hangzhou Aoyi Pollen Pharmaceutical Co., Ltd. (1)
No 668 the 23rd Avenue Economic and Technological Development Zone, Hangzhou, 310022, Zhejiang, China
Tel.: (86) 57185318271
Pharmaceuticals Product Mfr
N.A.I.C.S.: 325412

Hangzhou En's Gene Technology Developement Co., Ltd. (1)
Building 2 Huaye Science and Technology Park No 1180 Binan, Binjiang District, Hangzhou, 310051, Zhejiang, China
Tel.: (86) 57187378739
Pharmaceuticals Product Mfr
N.A.I.C.S.: 325412

Sichuan C&Y Traditional Chinese Medicine Co., Ltd. (1)
11F Tower A jiaxin Building No 153 Ther Youyh Road, Jianghan District, Wuhan, 430030, Hubei, China
Tel.: (86) 2783607900
Pharmaceuticals Product Mfr
N.A.I.C.S.: 325412

Suzhou DMD Biomed Co., Ltd. (1)
5F Building 1 Medical Park No 8 Jinfeng Road, Suzhou, 214100, Jiangsu, China
Tel.: (86) 51266801851
Pharmaceuticals Product Mfr
N.A.I.C.S.: 325412

Wuhan C&Y E-Commerce Co., Ltd. (1)
17F Tower 1 World Trade Center No 70 Optics Valley Avenue, Hongshan District, Wuhan, 430073, Hubei, China
Tel.: (86) 2750101356
Pharmaceuticals Product Mfr
N.A.I.C.S.: 325412

Wuxi Uni-King Lab Co., Ltd. (1)
Building 12 Creative Industry Park of Jiaotong University, No 59 Xiuxi Road Binhu District, Wuxi, 214100, Jiangsu, China
Tel.: (86) 51082820390
Pharmaceuticals Product Mfr
N.A.I.C.S.: 325412

Xizang C&Y Pharmaceutical Co., Ltd. (1)
Building 5 Area B, Xizang and Qinghai Industrial Park, Golmud, 816000, Qinhai, China
Tel.: (86) 9798437259
Pharmaceuticals Product Mfr
N.A.I.C.S.: 325412

SHANXI CHANGCHENG MICROLIGHT EQUIPMENT CO., LTD.

No 7 Dianzi Street Demonstration Zone, Taiyuan, Shanxi, China
Tel.: (86) 3517075474
Web Site: http://www.sxccoe.com
Year Founded: 2000
8286—(HKG)
Rev.: $2,181,114
Assets: $21,150,979
Liabilities: $34,899,790
Net Worth: ($13,748,810)
Earnings: $1,743,487
Emp.: 353
Fiscal Year-end: 12/31/22
Fiber Optic Cable Mfr & Whslr
N.A.I.C.S.: 335921
Wu Bo (Chm)

SHANXI COAL INTERNATIONAL ENERGY GROUP CO., LTD.

115 Changfeng Street, Taiyuan, 030006, Shanxi, China
Tel.: (86) 3514645546
Web Site: http://www.smgjcoal.com
600546—(SHG)
Rev.: $5,174,296,259
Assets: $5,623,785,362
Liabilities: $2,780,976,850
Net Worth: $2,842,808,512
Earnings: $589,778,979
Fiscal Year-end: 12/31/23
Coal Mining & Trading Services
N.A.I.C.S.: 212115

SHANXI COAL TRANSPORTATION AND SALES GROUP CO., LTD.

82 Kaihuasi Street, Taiyuan, 030002, China
Tel.: (86) 35 1492 4040
Web Site: http://www.sxmx.com.cn
Year Founded: 1983
Emp.: 110,691
Coal Mining, Trading & Logistics
N.A.I.C.S.: 212115
Jianzhong Liu (CEO)

SHANXI COKING CO., LTD.

Guangshengsi Town, Hongdong County Linfen, Shanghai, 041606, China
Tel.: (86) 3576625444
Web Site: https://www.sxjh.com.cn
Year Founded: 1995
600740—(SHG)
Rev.: $1,695,271,243
Assets: $3,293,374,229
Liabilities: $1,233,610,616
Net Worth: $2,059,763,612
Earnings: $362,506,510
Emp.: 8,600
Fiscal Year-end: 12/31/22
Coal Mining Services
N.A.I.C.S.: 213113
Li Feng (Chm)

Subsidiaries:

Shanxi Coking Coal Group Co., Ltd. (1)
No 1 Section 1 Xinjinci Road, Taiyuan, 030024, Shanxi, China
Tel.: (86) 3518305000
Web Site: http://www.sxcc.com.cn
Coal Coke & Chemical Product Distr
N.A.I.C.S.: 424690

SHANXI COKING COAL ENERGY GROUP CO., LTD.

Xishan Building No 318 Xikuang Street, Taiyuan, 030006, Shanxi, China
Tel.: (86) 3514645903
Web Site: http://www.xsmd.com.cn
Year Founded: 1999
000983—(SSE)
Rev.: $7,687,592,892
Assets: $12,960,167,313
Liabilities: $6,280,520,810
Net Worth: $6,679,646,503
Earnings: $937,550,966
Emp.: 81,081
Fiscal Year-end: 12/31/23
Coal Production & Sales; Electric Power Distr
N.A.I.C.S.: 324199

Subsidiaries:

XiShan Coal Electricity Group Co., Ltd. (1)
No 318 Xikuang Street, Taiyuan, 030053, ShanXi, China
Tel.: (86) 3516218271
Web Site: http://en.xsmd.com.cn
Coal Product Mfr
N.A.I.C.S.: 324199
Wang Leiying (Deputy Gen Mgr)

SHANXI GUOXIN ENERGY CORPORATION LIMITED

No 6 Zhongxin Street Hi-tech Development Zone, Taiyuan, 030032, China
Tel.: (86) 3512981617
Web Site: http://www.600617.com.cn
Year Founded: 1993
900913—(SHG)
Rev.: $2,167,510,953
Assets: $4,364,246,418
Liabilities: $3,787,790,035
Net Worth: $576,456,384
Earnings: $8,939,605
Fiscal Year-end: 12/31/22
Natural Gas Pipeline Construction Services
N.A.I.C.S.: 213112
Jun Liu (Chm)

SHANXI HI-SPEED GROUP CO., LTD.

10F Block B Qingkong Innovation Base No 529 Nanzhonghuan Street, Xiaodian District, Taiyuan, 030006, Shanxi, China
Tel.: (86) 3517773592
Web Site: http://www.sxsanwei.com
Year Founded: 1970
000755—(SSE)
Rev.: $226,535,611
Assets: $1,786,792,274
Liabilities: $1,149,332,273
Net Worth: $637,460,001
Earnings: $61,453,291
Fiscal Year-end: 12/31/22
Chemical Products Mfr
N.A.I.C.S.: 325998
Wu Yi (Chm)

SHANXI HUAXIANG GROUP CO., LTD.

Huaxiang Industrial Park, Ganting Town HongTong County, Linfen, 041609, China
Tel.: (86) 3573933778
Web Site: https://www.huaxianggroup.cn
Year Founded: 2008
603112—(SHG)
Rev.: $452,900,017
Assets: $716,023,250
Liabilities: $359,541,108
Net Worth: $356,482,143
Earnings: $36,979,549
Emp.: 4,000
Fiscal Year-end: 12/31/22
Metal Parts Mfr & Distr
N.A.I.C.S.: 332119
Chunxiang Wang (Chm)

SHANXI HUAYANG GROUP NEW ENERGY CO., LTD.

No 2 Taobei West Street, Kuang District, Yangquan, 045008, Shanxi, China
Tel.: (86) 3537078568
Web Site: http://yqmy.ymjt.com.cn
Year Founded: 1999
600348—(SHG)
Rev.: $4,919,965,526
Assets: $9,816,739,344
Liabilities: $5,659,191,238
Net Worth: $4,157,548,106
Earnings: $986,384,946
Emp.: 35,883
Fiscal Year-end: 12/31/22
Coal Production & Sales
N.A.I.C.S.: 324199
Wang Yongge (Chm)

SHANXI HUAYANG NEW MATERIAL CO., LTD.

No 87 Zhengyang Street Science and Technology Innovation City, Shanxi Transformation Comprehensive Reform Demonstration Zone, Taiyuan, 030021, Shanxi, China
Tel.: (86) 3515638598
600281—(SHG)
Rev.: $46,038,129
Assets: $150,296,894
Liabilities: $87,846,090
Net Worth: $62,450,805
Earnings: ($5,208,826)
Fiscal Year-end: 12/31/22
Chemical Product Mfr & Distr
N.A.I.C.S.: 325998
Jing Hongsheng (Sec)

SHANXI HUHUA GROUP CO., LTD.

No 1 Huagong Road Huguan Economic Development Zone, Changzhi, 047300, Shanxi, China
Tel.: (86) 3556010025

Web Site:
http://www.shanxihuhua.com
Year Founded: 1994
003002—(SSE)
Rev.: $135,324,863
Assets: $241,458,193
Liabilities: $62,361,117
Net Worth: $179,097,076
Earnings: $17,035,841
Fiscal Year-end: 12/31/22
Explosive Mfr & Distr
N.A.I.C.S.: 325920

SHANXI JINCHENG ANTHRACITE COAL MINING GROUP CO., LTD.
The City Zone, Beishidian, Jincheng, 048006, Shanxi, China
Tel.: (86) 356 366 6114   CN
Web Site: http://www.jccoal.com
Sales Range: Less than $1 Million
Holding Company; Coal Mining & Wholesale Distr
N.A.I.C.S.: 551112
Huatai Wu (CEO)

Subsidiaries:

Shanxi Jincheng Anthracite Mining Group International Trading Co., Ltd.   (1)
No 15 Zhenxing Street, Taiyuan, 030006, Shanxi, China   (100%)
Tel.: (86) 351 703 7798
Coal Wholesale Trade Distr
N.A.I.C.S.: 425120
Liting Zhang (Mgr)

SHANXI LANHUA SCI-TECH VENTURE CO., LTD.
Lanhua Technology Building No 2288 Fengtai East Street, Jincheng, 048000, Shanxi, China
Tel.: (86) 3562189600
Web Site:
https://www.chinalanhua.com
Year Founded: 1998
600123—(SHG)
Rev.: $1,987,447,812
Assets: $4,260,043,265
Liabilities: $2,111,923,602
Net Worth: $2,148,119,663
Earnings: $452,586,111
Fiscal Year-end: 12/31/22
Coal Product & Chemical Fertilizer Mfr & Whslr
N.A.I.C.S.: 212114
Liu Haishan (Chm & Gen Mgr)

SHANXI LU'AN ENVIRONMENTAL ENERGY DEVELOPMENT CO. LTD.
No 65 Chengbei East Street, High-tech Development Zone, Changzhi, 046204, Shanxi, China
Tel.: (86) 3555923838
Web Site: http://www.luanhn.com
Year Founded: 2001
601699—(SHG)
Rev.: $5,972,672,477
Assets: $12,012,950,058
Liabilities: $5,170,467,338
Net Worth: $6,842,482,720
Earnings: $1,096,809,717
Emp.: 26,600
Fiscal Year-end: 12/31/23
Coal Mining & Production Services
N.A.I.C.S.: 212115
Jinping Liu (Deputy Gen Mgr)

SHANXI LU'AN MINING (GROUP) CO., LTD.
Houbu, Xiangyuan, Changzhi, 046204, Shanxi, China
Tel.: (86) 355 592 1114   CN
Web Site: http://www.cnluan.com
Year Founded: 1959

Sales Range: $25-49.9 Billion
Emp.: 85,027
Coal Mining & Wholesale Distr
N.A.I.C.S.: 212115
Jinping Li (CEO)

SHANXI MEIJIN ENERGY CO., LTD.
Guanzhong Building, Yingze District, Taiyuan, 030002, Shanxi, China
Tel.: (86) 3514236095
000723—(SSE)
Rev.: $3,453,842,218
Assets: $5,133,677,365
Liabilities: $2,811,259,246
Net Worth: $2,322,418,120
Earnings: $310,178,588
Fiscal Year-end: 12/31/22
Coal Mining Services
N.A.I.C.S.: 324199

SHANXI ORIENTAL MATERIAL HANDLING CO., LTD.
No 51 Xinlan Road, Taiyuan, 030008, Shanxi, China
Tel.: (86) 3513633818
Web Site: http://www.omhgroup.com
Year Founded: 1995
300486—(CHIN)
Rev.: $122,817,876
Assets: $473,216,787
Liabilities: $276,236,569
Net Worth: $196,980,218
Earnings: ($34,992,182)
Fiscal Year-end: 12/31/23
Logistics Equipment Mfr & Distr
N.A.I.C.S.: 333922

SHANXI SECURITIES CO., LTD.
Shanxi International Trade Center No 69 Fuxi Street, East Tower, Taiyuan, 030002, Shanxi, China
Tel.: (86) 3518686668
Web Site: http://www.i618.com.cn
Year Founded: 1988
002500—(SSE)
Rev.: $584,141,922
Assets: $11,640,455,920
Liabilities: $9,135,293,090
Net Worth: $2,505,162,830
Earnings: $80,654,984
Fiscal Year-end: 12/31/22
Securities Brokerage Services
N.A.I.C.S.: 523150
Wei Hou (Chm & Gen Mgr)

SHANXI TAIGANG STAINLESS STEEL COMPANY LTD.
No 2 Jiancaoping Street, Taiyuan, 030003, Shanxi, China
Tel.: (86) 3512137728
Web Site: https://tgbx.tisco.com.cn
Year Founded: 1998
000825—(SSE)
Rev.: $13,710,674,531
Assets: $10,229,458,735
Liabilities: $4,985,793,596
Net Worth: $5,243,665,139
Earnings: $21,557,718
Emp.: 22,000
Fiscal Year-end: 12/31/22
Stainless Steel Mfr
N.A.I.C.S.: 331110
Zhang Zhijun (Sec)

SHANXI TOND CHEMICAL CO., LTD.
Damaokou Jiaoweicheng, Wenbi Town, Hequ, 036500, Shanxi, China
Tel.: (86) 350726396
Web Site: https://www.tondchem.com
Year Founded: 2006
002360—(SSE)
Rev.: $153,049,408
Assets: $421,411,386

Liabilities: $175,459,045
Net Worth: $245,952,341
Earnings: $25,830,483
Emp.: 790
Fiscal Year-end: 12/31/22
Chemical Mfr; Carbon Black & Explosives
N.A.I.C.S.: 325998

SHANXI XINGHUACUN FEN WINE FACTORY CO., LTD.
Xinghua Village Fenyang City, Luliang, 032205, Shanxi, China
Tel.: (86) 3587220006
Web Site: http://www.fenjiu.com.cn
600809—(SHG)
Rev.: $3,680,426,042
Assets: $5,150,780,992
Liabilities: $2,097,709,815
Net Worth: $3,053,071,176
Earnings: $1,136,657,523
Fiscal Year-end: 12/31/22
Liquor Product Distr
N.A.I.C.S.: 424820
Zhongbao Tan (Vice Chm & Gen Mgr)

SHANXI YONGDONG CHEMICAL CO., LTD.
East of Zhenxi Street, Jishan Economic And Technological Development Zone Jishan County, Yuncheng, 043205, Shanxi, China
Tel.: (86) 3595662069
Web Site: http://www.sxydhg.com
Year Founded: 2000
002753—(SSE)
Rev.: $632,364,520
Assets: $470,840,737
Liabilities: $161,507,876
Net Worth: $309,332,860
Earnings: $5,529,471
Fiscal Year-end: 12/31/22
Carbon Black & Other Chemicals Mfr
N.A.I.C.S.: 335991
Dongjie Liu (Chm)

SHANXI ZHENDONG PHARMACEUTICAL CO., LTD.
Zhendong Science and Technology Park Guangming South Road, Shangdang District, Changzhi, 047100, Shanxi, China
Tel.: (86) 3558096012
Web Site: http://www.zdjt.com
Year Founded: 1995
300158—(CHIN)
Rev.: $510,724,368
Assets: $870,523,002
Liabilities: $145,975,320
Net Worth: $724,547,682
Earnings: ($6,195,160)
Emp.: 5,000
Fiscal Year-end: 12/31/23
Pharmaceutical Product Mfr & Distr
N.A.I.C.S.: 325412
Anping Li (Chm)

SHANYING INTERNATIONAL HOLDINGS CO., LTD.
Shanying International Headquarter Building No 645 Anpu Road, Yangpu District, Shanghai, 200082, China
Tel.: (86) 2160360888
Web Site:
https://www.shanyingintl
Year Founded: 1999
600567—(SHG)
Rev.: $4,775,581,914
Assets: $7,373,428,274
Liabilities: $5,389,932,343
Net Worth: $1,983,495,932
Earnings: ($316,805,397)
Fiscal Year-end: 12/31/22
Paper Mfr
N.A.I.C.S.: 322120

Mingwu Wu (Chm & Pres)

SHANYU GROUP HOLDINGS COMPANY LIMITED
Shop Space No 66 Ground Floor Blocks 7-14 City Garden, No 233 Electric Road, Hong Kong, China (Hong Kong)
Tel.: (852) 37554882   Ky
Web Site: http://www.on-real.com
Year Founded: 2001
8245—(HKG)
Rev.: $16,274,825
Assets: $7,259,123
Liabilities: $10,877,141
Net Worth: ($3,618,018)
Earnings: ($7,796,454)
Emp.: 550
Fiscal Year-end: 03/31/22
Communication Device Mfr & Distr
N.A.I.C.S.: 334220
Lung Ming Chan (Chm)

SHANYUAN CO., LTD.
National Financial Plaza 8th Floor No 96 Section 2 Nanjing East Road, Taipei, Taipei, Taiwan
Tel.: (886) 225639136
Web Site: https://shanyuan.com.tw
4416—(TPE)
Rev.: $2,992,746
Assets: $462,924,960
Liabilities: $408,090,079
Net Worth: $54,834,881
Earnings: ($8,476,628)
Fiscal Year-end: 12/31/22
Building Construction Services
N.A.I.C.S.: 236210
Wang Ya-Lin (Chm)

SHAOYANG VICTOR HYDRAULICS CO., LTD.
Jianshe Road, Shuangqing District, Shaoyang, 422001, Hunan, China
Tel.: (86) 7395131298
Web Site: https://www.shaoyecn.com
Year Founded: 1968
301079—(CHIN)
Rev.: $38,845,887
Assets: $122,153,521
Liabilities: $54,210,605
Net Worth: $67,942,915
Earnings: $926,535
Emp.: 640
Fiscal Year-end: 12/31/23
Pump Product Mfr & Distr
N.A.I.C.S.: 333914
Wuhong Su (Chm)

SHAPE AUSTRALIA CORPORATION LIMITED
Level 11 155 Clarence Street, Sydney, 2000, NSW, Australia
Tel.: (61) 299066977   AU
Web Site: https://www.shape.com.au
Year Founded: 1989
SHA—(ASX)
Rev.: $562,278,803
Assets: $169,080,003
Liabilities: $152,167,308
Net Worth: $16,912,695
Earnings: $6,844,233
Emp.: 571
Fiscal Year-end: 06/30/23
Construction Services
N.A.I.C.S.: 237120
Greg Miles (Chm)

SHAPE ROBOTICS A/S
Lyskaer 3CD 4 th, 2730, Herlev, Denmark
Tel.: (45) 53513131
Web Site:
https://www.shaperobotics.com
Year Founded: 2017

SHAPE ROBOTICS A/S

Shape Robotics A/S—(Continued)
SHAPE—(CSE)
Rev.: $24,773,625
Assets: $39,596,446
Liabilities: $20,658,940
Net Worth: $18,937,506
Earnings: $377,219
Emp.: 9
Fiscal Year-end: 12/31/23
Educational Support Services
N.A.I.C.S.: 611710
Andre Fehrn (CEO)

Subsidiaries:

Video Technic Systems S.R.L. (1)
Strada Silozului 19 Sector 2, 021114, Bucharest, Romania
Tel.: (40) 374466297
Web Site: https://www.vtsystems.ro
Audio Visual Equipment Mfr & Distr
N.A.I.C.S.: 334310

SHAPERON INC.
218 & 606 Gangnam Ace Tower
174-10 Jagok-ro, Gangnam-gu,
Seoul, 06373, Korea (South)
Tel.: (82) 260838315
Web Site: https://www.shaperon.com
Year Founded: 2008
378800—(KRS)
Biotechnology Research & Development Services
N.A.I.C.S.: 541714

SHAPIR ENGINEERING & INDUSTRY LTD.
12 Bareket St, PO Box 7113, Petah Tiqwa, 49170, Israel
Tel.: (972) 39169500
Web Site: https://shapir.co.il
Year Founded: 1968
SPEN—(TAE)
Rev.: $1,438,596,469
Assets: $4,105,539,375
Liabilities: $3,082,746,187
Net Worth: $1,022,793,187
Earnings: $51,112,031
Emp.: 70
Fiscal Year-end: 12/31/23
Engineeering Services
N.A.I.C.S.: 541330
Yehuda Segev (Chm)

SHAPOORJI PALLONJI & CO. LTD.
SP Centre 41/44 Minoo Desai Marg Colaba, Behind Radio Club Colaba, Mumbai, 400 005, India
Tel.: (91) 2267490000
Web Site: http://www.shapoorji.in
Year Founded: 1865
Sales Range: $250-299.9 Million
Emp.: 60,000
Civil & Structural Engineering Services
N.A.I.C.S.: 237990
Pallonji P. Misitry (Chm)

Subsidiaries:

Afcons Infrastructure Limited (1)
16 Shah Industrial Estate Veera Desai Road, Andheri West Azadnagar, Mumbai, 400 053, India
Tel.: (91) 2267191000
Web Site: http://www.afcons.com
Sales Range: $125-149.9 Million
Construction Services
N.A.I.C.S.: 237110
K. Subramanian (Vice Chm & Mng Dir)

Forbes & Company Ltd. (1)
Forbes Building Charanjit Rai Marg Fort, Mumbai, 400001, India
Tel.: (91) 2261358900
Web Site: http://www.forbes.co.in
Rev.: $85,140,471
Assets: $84,059,193
Liabilities: $57,104,670
Net Worth: $26,954,523
Earnings: $22,998,693
Emp.: 520
Fiscal Year-end: 03/31/2023
Shipping & Logistics Services
N.A.I.C.S.: 541614
Shapoorji Pallonji Mistry (Chm)

Subsidiary (Domestic):

Eureka Forbes Limited (2)
B1/B2 701 7th Floor Marathon Innova Marathon NextGen, Off Ganpatrao Kadam Marg Lower Parel, Mumbai, 400 013, India (100%)
Tel.: (91) 2248821700
Web Site: http://www.eurekaforbes.com
Vacuum Cleaner Distr
N.A.I.C.S.: 423620

Subsidiary (Domestic):

Aquadiagnostics Water Research & Technology Center Limited (3)
No 57 Omshakti Complex 1st Floor G B Palya Hosur Main Road, Bengaluru, 560 068, India
Tel.: (91) 8025731181
Web Site: http://www.aquadiagnostics.com
Research & Development Services
N.A.I.C.S.: 541714
Muralidhara Rao Sakhumalla (Mng Dir)

Subsidiary (Non-US):

EFL Mauritius Limited (3)
5th Floor West Wing Barkly Wharf Le Caudan Waterfront, Port Louis, Mauritius
Tel.: (230) 2139115
Web Site: http://www.expofreight.com
Freight Air Transportation Services
N.A.I.C.S.: 481112

Lux (Deutschland) GmbH (3)
Petersberger Strase 21, 36037, Fulda, Germany
Tel.: (49) 6619021210
Web Site: http://www.luxinternational.com
Electrical Appliance Mfr
N.A.I.C.S.: 335210

Lux Hungaria Kereskedelmi Kft. (3)
Javor utca 5/a., 1145, Budapest, Hungary
Tel.: (36) 14224444
Web Site: http://www.luxinternational.com
Electrical Appliance Mfr
N.A.I.C.S.: 335210
Attila Tigyi (Mng Dir)

Lux International AG (3)
Seestrasse 39, Kusnacht, 8700, Zurich, Switzerland
Tel.: (41) 417688888
Web Site: http://www.luxinternational.com
Electrical Appliance Mfr
N.A.I.C.S.: 335210
Marzin R. Shroff (Chm)

Lux Italia S.r.l (3)
Viale delle Industrie 34, 20040, Cambiago, Monza and Brianza, Italy
Tel.: (39) 0295308160
Web Site: http://www.luxitalia.eu
Electrical Appliance Mfr
N.A.I.C.S.: 335210

Lux Norge A/S (3)
Nye Vakas vei 64, 1395, Hvalstad, Norway
Tel.: (47) 22749990
Web Site: http://www.luxinternational.com
Electrical Appliance Mfr
N.A.I.C.S.: 335210

Lux Osterreich GmbH (3)
Concorde Business Park 1/B3/31, 2320, Schwechat, Austria
Tel.: (43) 17064252
Web Site: http://www.luxinternational.com
Electrical Appliance Mfr
N.A.I.C.S.: 335210

Lux Schweiz AG (3)
Seestrasse 39, Kusnacht, 8700, Zurich, Switzerland
Tel.: (41) 627493770
Web Site: http://www.luxinternational.com
Electrical Appliance Mfr
N.A.I.C.S.: 335210

Subsidiary (Domestic):

Forbes Bumi Armada Limited (2)
6th Floor 602/Trade Centre, Opposite MTNL Office Bandra Kurla Complex Bandra East, Mumbai, 400 051, India
Tel.: (91) 2261470900
Engineeering Services
N.A.I.C.S.: 541330

Forbes Technosys Limited (2)
Wagle Industrial Estate, Mumbai Metropolitan Region, Thane, 400 604, India
Tel.: (91) 2240639595
Web Site: http://www.forbestechnosys.com
Software Development Services
N.A.I.C.S.: 513210
Rashmi Kulkarni (Project Mgr)

Shapoorji Pallonji Co .Ltd Pvt. (1)
Mail Bag Ct 463 Cantonments, Accra, Ghana
Tel.: (233) 202015290
Engineeering Services
N.A.I.C.S.: 541330
Santosh Kumar Singh (Gen Mgr)

Shapoorji Pallonji International FZE (1)
Office No 20 5w West A-Wing Dubai Airport Free Zone Authority Dafza, PO Box 54449, Dubai, United Arab Emirates
Tel.: (971) 42993880
Engineeering Services
N.A.I.C.S.: 541330
M. D. Saini (CEO & Mng Dir)

Shapoorji Pallonji Lanka (Pvt) Ltd. (1)
4 1/1 Geethanjali Place Galle Road, 00300, Colombo, Sri Lanka
Tel.: (94) 2508246
Engineeering Services
N.A.I.C.S.: 541330
Avinash Shepur (Engr-Structural Design)

Shapoorji Pallonji Mideast L.L.C. (1)
Block -C Mci Al Naboodah Building Hor-Al-Anz, PO Box 118219, Dubai, United Arab Emirates
Tel.: (971) 42690334
Engineeering Services
N.A.I.C.S.: 541330
Vivek Anandarajah (VP)

Shapoorji Pallonji Nigeria Ltd (1)
Suite 7 3rd Floor Eleganza Biro Plaza Plot 634 Adeyemo Alakija Street, Victoria Island, Lagos, Nigeria
Tel.: (234) 8052294779
Engineeering Services
N.A.I.C.S.: 541330

Shapoorji Pallonji Qatar WLL (1)
Financial Square C-21 Budg 2 1st Floor Office No 5 Al Muntaza, PO Box 22587, C-Ring Road, Doha, Qatar
Tel.: (974) 44566026
Engineeering Services
N.A.I.C.S.: 541330
Rajeev Kaul (VP)

Sterling and Wilson Pvt. Ltd. (1)
Universal Majestic 9th Floor P L Lokhande Marg, Chembur West, Mumbai, 400 043, Maharashtra, India
Tel.: (91) 2225485300
Web Site: http://www.sterlingandwilson.com
Engineeering Services
N.A.I.C.S.: 541330
Elikesh Ogra (Pres)

SHARANAM INFRAPROJECT & TRADING LTD.
C808 303 Earth Arise Nr Y M C A Club S G Highway, Makarba Vejalpur, Ahmedabad, 380051, India
Tel.: (91) 7929707666
Web Site:
  https://www.sharanaminfra.co.in
539584—(BOM)
Rev.: $63,046
Assets: $577,725
Liabilities: $74,991
Net Worth: $502,735
Earnings: $401
Emp.: 1
Fiscal Year-end: 03/31/21
Real Estate Support Services
N.A.I.C.S.: 531390

INTERNATIONAL PUBLIC

Jitendrakumar A. Parmar (CFO)

SHARAT INDUSTRIES LIMITED
Flat No 4 3rd Floor Pallavi Apartments No 57/11 Old No 29/TF4, 1st Main Road HDFC Bank Compound R A Puram, Chennai, 600 028, India
Tel.: (91) 4424357868
Web Site:
  https://www.sharatindustries.com
Year Founded: 1990
519397—(BOM)
Rev.: $34,511,818
Assets: $24,705,876
Liabilities: $16,865,914
Net Worth: $7,839,962
Earnings: $352,818
Emp.: 217
Fiscal Year-end: 03/31/21
Seafood Product Distr
N.A.I.C.S.: 424460
S. Prasad Reddy (Mng Dir)

SHARC INTERNATIONAL SYSTEMS INC.
1443 Spitfire Pl, Port Coquitlam, V3C 6L4, BC, Canada
Tel.: (604) 475-7710   BC
Web Site:
  https://www.sharcenergy.com
Year Founded: 2011
IWIA—(DEU)
Rev.: $1,434,392
Assets: $2,329,888
Liabilities: $3,767,418
Net Worth: ($1,437,530)
Earnings: ($3,559,109)
Emp.: 16
Fiscal Year-end: 12/31/22
Wastewater Heat Exchange Systems Designer & Mfr
N.A.I.C.S.: 332410
Lynn Mueller (Founder, Chm & CEO)

SHARDA CROPCHEM LIMITED
Prime Business Park 2nd Floor, Vile Parle W, Mumbai, 400056, India
Tel.: (91) 2266782800
Web Site:
  https://www.shardacropchem.com
SHARDACROP—(NSE)
Rev.: $333,270,660
Assets: $390,916,794
Liabilities: $170,522,939
Net Worth: $220,393,856
Earnings: $31,288,216
Emp.: 175
Fiscal Year-end: 03/31/21
Crop Protection Chemical Mfr
N.A.I.C.S.: 325320
Ashish Lodha (CFO)

Subsidiaries:

Sharda Cropchem Espana, S.L. (1)
Carril Condomina No 3, 30006, Murcia, Spain
Tel.: (34) 868127589
Web Site: https://sharda.es
Pesticide Mfr
N.A.I.C.S.: 325320

Sharda De Mexico S. De RL DE CV (1)
Joaquin Angulo 2776 Col Circunvalacion Vallarta, 44680, Guadalajara, Jalisco, Mexico
Tel.: (52) 3318095840
Web Site: https://shardacropchem.mx
Pesticide Mfr
N.A.I.C.S.: 325320

Sharda Del Ecuador CIA. Ltda. (1)
England E3-54 and Av Republica Ed Centrum Floor 5 Ofc 5-C, Quito, Ecuador
Tel.: (593) 23330555
Web Site: https://shardacropchem.ec
Pesticide Mfr
N.A.I.C.S.: 325320

Sharda Hungary Kft (1)

Ovutca 182/b, 1147, Budapest, Hungary
Tel.: (36) 616319093
Pesticide Mfr
N.A.I.C.S.: 325320

Sharda Peru SAC (1)
Calle Las Castanitas 138-Urb El Palomar
San Isidro, Lima, Peru
Tel.: (51) 12222695
Pesticide Mfr
N.A.I.C.S.: 325320

Sharda USA LLC (1)
34E Germantown PK Ste 227, Norristown, PA 19401
Tel.: (416) 951-0132
Web Site: https://shardausa.com
Agricultural Product Mfr & Distr
N.A.I.C.S.: 325320

Sharda Ukraine LLC (1)
st Holosiivska 7 Building 3 5th Floor, 03039, Kiev, Ukraine
Tel.: (380) 445247496
Pesticide Mfr
N.A.I.C.S.: 325320

SHARDA ISPAT LTD.
Kamptee Road, Near Transport Plaza, Nagpur, 440 026, Maharashtra, India
Tel.: (91) 7122640071
Web Site: https://shardaispat.com
Year Founded: 1960
513548—(BOM)
Rev.: $13,203,700
Assets: $5,478,660
Liabilities: $1,705,868
Net Worth: $3,772,792
Earnings: $470,980
Emp.: 40
Fiscal Year-end: 03/31/21
Iron & Steel Product Mfr
N.A.I.C.S.: 331110
Nandkishore Sarda (Chm & Mng Dir)

SHARDA MOTOR INDUSTRIES LIMITED
D-188 Okhla Industrial Area Phase - I, New Delhi, 110020, India
Tel.: (91) 1147334100
Web Site:
  https://www.shardamotor.com
535602—(BOM)
Rev.: $328,717,979
Assets: $166,527,822
Liabilities: $75,663,342
Net Worth: $90,864,481
Earnings: $24,978,598
Emp.: 646
Fiscal Year-end: 03/31/23
Automobile Parts Mfr & Whslr
N.A.I.C.S.: 336390
Kishan N. Parikh (Co-Chm)

Subsidiaries:

NDR Auto Components Limited (1)
Plot No 1 Maruti Joint Venture Complex, Gurgaon, 122015, Haryana, India
Tel.: (91) 9643339874
Web Site: http://www.ndrauto.com
Auto Parts Mfr
N.A.I.C.S.: 336390
Shymala Khera (Chm)

SHARDUL SECURITIES LTD
G-12 Tulsiani Chambers 212 Nariman Point, Mumbai, 400 021, India
Tel.: (91) 2246032806
Web Site:
  https://www.shardulsecurities.com
Year Founded: 1985
512393—(BOM)
Rev.: $20,827,745
Assets: $83,535,697
Liabilities: $3,061,335
Net Worth: $80,474,362
Earnings: $11,727,323
Emp.: 6
Fiscal Year-end: 03/31/24
Financial Services
N.A.I.C.S.: 522291
Sundaresan Ramamoorthy (Chm)

SHARE INDIA SECURITIES LIMITED
A-15 Sector-64 Gautam Buddha Nagar, Noida, 201301, Uttar Pradesh, India
Tel.: (91) 1204910000
Web Site:
  https://www.shareindia.com
Year Founded: 1994
SHAREINDIA—(NSE)
Rev.: $131,850,896
Assets: $220,469,804
Liabilities: $98,354,331
Net Worth: $122,115,473
Earnings: $39,644,758
Emp.: 2,306
Fiscal Year-end: 03/31/23
Securities Brokerage Services
N.A.I.C.S.: 523150
Saroj Gupta (Exec Dir)

Subsidiaries:

Algowire Trading Technologies Private Limited (1)
Plot No A-15 3rd Floor Sector 64, Gautam Budh Nagar, Noida, 201301, Uttar Pradesh, India
Tel.: (91) 1204627700
Web Site: https://www.algowire.in
Financial Services
N.A.I.C.S.: 521110

Share India Algoplus Private Limited (1)
1715 17th Floor Dalal Street Commercial Co-operative Society Limited, Road 5 E Block 53 Zone 5 Gift City, Gandhinagar, 382355, Gujarat, India
Tel.: (91) 2242644002
Web Site:
  https://www.shareindiaalgoplus.com
Money Trading Services
N.A.I.C.S.: 525990

SHARE MICROFIN LIMITED
1-8-437 & 445 7th Floor Splendid Towers Huda Road, Begumpet, Hyderabad, 500 016, Telangana, India
Tel.: (91) 4044648380
Web Site:
  http://www.sharemicrofin.com
Year Founded: 1989
Financial Services
N.A.I.C.S.: 522291
M. Udaia Kumar (Mng Dir)

SHAREHOLDER VALUE BETEILIGUNGEN AG
Neue Mainzer Strasse 1, 60311, Frankfurt am Main, Germany
Tel.: (49) 696698300
Web Site:
  https://www.shareholdervalue.de
SVE—(DEU)
Rev.: $17,231,483
Assets: $87,250,248
Liabilities: $2,494,757
Net Worth: $84,755,492
Earnings: ($10,873,165)
Fiscal Year-end: 12/31/23
Investment Services
N.A.I.C.S.: 523999
Frank Fischer (Member-Mgmt Bd)

SHAREHOPE MEDICINE CO., LTD.
19F No 168 Ching-Kuo Rd, Taoyuan Dist, Taoyuan, 330, Taiwan
Tel.: (886) 33469595
Web Site: https://share-hope.com
Year Founded: 2003
8403—(TPE)
Rev.: $126,668,101
Assets: $243,485,324
Liabilities: $114,133,192
Net Worth: $129,352,132
Earnings: $1,807,286
Emp.: 140
Fiscal Year-end: 12/31/23
Medical Equipment Mfr
N.A.I.C.S.: 339112
Hung-Jen Yang (Chm & CEO)

SHAREINVESTOR PTE LTD
82 Genting Ln #03 01 Media Ctr Annex, Singapore, 349567, Singapore
Tel.: (65) 65178777
Web Site:
  http://www.shareinvestor.com
Year Founded: 1999
Emp.: 100
Online Business & Investment Publisher & Other Business Services
N.A.I.C.S.: 513130
Sheila Low (Mgr-HR)

SHAREROOT LIMITED
Level 1 33 Ord Street, West Perth, 6005, WA, Australia
Tel.: (61) 8 9420 9300
Investment Services
N.A.I.C.S.: 523999
Julian Chick (Chm)

SHARETRONIC DATA TECHNOLOGY CO., LTD.
Room 1209 12th Floor Block 1 Yaohua Chuangjian Building Shennan Avenue, Futian District, Shenzhen, 518040, Guangdong, China
Tel.: (86) 75533098502
Web Site:
  https://www.sharetronic.com
Year Founded: 2005
300857—(SSE)
Rev.: $442,026,739
Assets: $394,009,546
Liabilities: $192,919,793
Net Worth: $201,089,753
Earnings: $18,379,357
Fiscal Year-end: 12/31/22
Wireless Communication Product Mfr
N.A.I.C.S.: 334220
Sihua Geng (Chm)

SHAREWEALTH SECURITIES LIMITED
20/232 Adiyat Lane M.G. Road West Fort Poothole, Thrissur, Kerala, 680004, India
Tel.: (91) 4872436500
Web Site:
  http://www.sharewealthindia.com
Year Founded: 2005
Stock Broking Services
N.A.I.C.S.: 523150
Pradeep Johnson (Sr Mgr-IT & Ops)

Subsidiaries:

SI Capital & Financial Services Ltd. (1)
No 27 First Floor New Scheme Road, Pollachi Coimbatore, Chennai, 642001, Tamil Nadu, India (60.93%)
Tel.: (91) 4442145840
Web Site: https://www.sicapital.co.in
Rev.: $135,148
Assets: $717,679
Liabilities: $322,738
Net Worth: $394,940
Earnings: $11,666
Emp.: 21
Fiscal Year-end: 03/31/2023
Financial Services
N.A.I.C.S.: 523999
Vinod Manazhy (Executives, Bd of Dirs)

SHARIKA ENTERPRISES LTD.
504 Tower C 5th Floor ATS BOUQUET Sector 132, Noida, 201301, Uttar Pradesh, India
Tel.: (91) 1202593900
Web Site: https://www.sharikaindia.com
Year Founded: 1998
540786—(BOM)
Rev.: $6,081,803
Assets: $6,073,135
Liabilities: $3,230,376
Net Worth: $2,842,759
Earnings: ($398,390)
Emp.: 56
Fiscal Year-end: 03/31/23
Engineering Consulting Services
N.A.I.C.S.: 541330
Rajinder Kaul (Chm & Mng Dir)

SHARIKAT PERMODALAN KEBANGSAAN BHD
12th Floor Menara Perak, 24 Jalan Perak, 50450, Kuala Lumpur, Malaysia
Tel.: (60) 3 2264 5555
Web Site: http://www.spkb.net
Year Founded: 1961
Sales Range: $10-24.9 Million
Emp.: 30
Holding Company
N.A.I.C.S.: 551112
Saiful Aznir Shahabudin (Grp CEO)

Subsidiaries:

S.J. Properties Sdn. Bhd. (1)
No 1 Jalan Hijau Serindit U9/68 Cahaya SPK Seksyen U9, 40150, Shah Alam, Malaysia
Tel.: (60) 378472288
Web Site: http://www.spkhomes.spkb.net
Civil Construction Services
N.A.I.C.S.: 236116

SPK Oil & Gas Supplies and Services Sdn Bhd (1)
12th Floor Menara Perak 24 Jalan Perak, 50450, Kuala Lumpur, Malaysia
Tel.: (60) 322645555
Web Site: http://www.spkoilandgas.com
Oil & Gas Field Engineering Services
N.A.I.C.S.: 333132

SHARING ECONOMY INTERNATIONAL INC
No 85 Castle Peak Road, Castle Peak Bay, Tuen Mun, China (Hong Kong)
Tel.: (852) 25832186 NV
Web Site: https://www.seii.com
Year Founded: 1987
SEII—(OTCIQ)
Rev.: $317,316
Assets: $2,983,594
Liabilities: $17,782,536
Net Worth: ($14,798,942)
Earnings: ($4,154,230)
Emp.: 2
Fiscal Year-end: 12/31/22
Textile Dyeing & Finishing Machines Mfr
N.A.I.C.S.: 332999
Ka Man Lam (CFO)

Subsidiaries:

Wuxi Huayang Electrical Power Equipment Co., Ltd (1)
No 9 Yanyu Middle Rd, Qianzhou Huishan, Wuxi, Jiangsu, China
Tel.: (86) 51083381199
Electric Power Equipment Mfr
N.A.I.C.S.: 333611

SHARINGTECHNOLOGY, INC.
JP Tower Nagoya 19F 1-1-1 Meieki, Nakamura-ku, Nagoya, 450-6319, Japan
Tel.: (81) 524145919
Web Site: https://sharing-tech.co.jp
3989—(TKS)
Rev.: $44,156,520
Assets: $29,253,340
Liabilities: $13,740,420
Net Worth: $15,512,920

SHARINGTECHNOLOGY, INC.

Sharingtechnology, Inc.—(Continued)
Earnings: $9,358,800
Emp.: 147
Fiscal Year-end: 09/30/23
Marketing Management Consulting Services
N.A.I.C.S.: 541613
Subsidiaries:

Shiotani Glass Co., Ltd. (1)
4-4-14 Nakatsu, Kita-ku, Osaka, 531-0071, Japan
Tel.: (81) 663716331
Web Site: https://www.shiotani-glass.com
Emp.: 131
Pharmaceutical Product Mfr & Distr
N.A.I.C.S.: 325412

SHARJAH AIRPORT AUTHORITY
PO Box 8, Sharjah, United Arab Emirates
Tel.: (971) 65581252
Web Site:
http://www.sharjahairport.ae
Sales Range: $300-349.9 Million
Emp.: 2,500
Oil Transportation Services
N.A.I.C.S.: 481111
Ali Salem Al Midfa *(Chm)*

SHARJAH CEMENT & INDUSTRIAL DEVELOPMENT COMPANY P.S.C.
Al Hisn Tower 14th Floor Bank Street Borj Avenue, PO Box 2083, Sharjah, United Arab Emirates
Tel.: (971) 65695666
Web Site:
https://sharjahcements.com
Year Founded: 1976
SCIDC—(ABU)
Rev.: $172,738,361
Assets: $526,857,608
Liabilities: $173,254,560
Net Worth: $353,603,048
Earnings: $1,001,361
Emp.: 1,115
Fiscal Year-end: 12/31/23
Cement & Paper Sacks Mfr; Limestone & Siltstone Quarries Operator
N.A.I.C.S.: 327310
Ahmad Abdullah Al Noman *(Chm)*
Subsidiaries:

Gulf Rope & Plastic Products LLC (1)
Sajaa Industrial Area Dhaid Road, PO Box 21422, Sharjah, United Arab Emirates
Tel.: (971) 65347926
Web Site: https://www.gulf-rope.com
Sales Range: $25-49.9 Million
Emp.: 250
Synthetic Rope Mfr
N.A.I.C.S.: 314994

Paper Sacks Factory (1)
PO Box 2083, Sharjah, United Arab Emirates
Tel.: (971) 65695666
Web Site: https://papersacksfactory.ae
Packaging Services
N.A.I.C.S.: 561910

Sharjah Cement Factory (1)
PO Box 5419, Sharjah, United Arab Emirates
Tel.: (971) 65311583
Sales Range: $200-249.9 Million
Emp.: 250
Cement Mfr
N.A.I.C.S.: 327310

SHARJAH INSURANCE COMPANY (PSC)
01 02 Floors Al Raha Tower Corniche Al Mamsar Al Khan, Sharjah, United Arab Emirates
Tel.: (971) 65195666
Web Site: https://www.shjins.com
Year Founded: 1970
SICO—(EMI)
Rev.: $13,209,392
Assets: $80,270,836
Liabilities: $27,542,765
Net Worth: $52,728,071
Earnings: $4,008,340
Fiscal Year-end: 12/31/19
Insurance Services
N.A.I.C.S.: 524298
Shafat Ali *(Mgr-Non Motor)*

SHARJAH ISLAMIC BANK PJSC
Sharjah Islamic Bank Tower Al Khan, PO Box 4, Sharjah, United Arab Emirates
Tel.: (971) 65999999
Web Site: https://www.sib.ae
Year Founded: 1975
SIB—(ABU)
Rev.: $840,977,129
Assets: $17,936,014,389
Liabilities: $15,723,472,058
Net Worth: $2,212,542,331
Earnings: $231,837,734
Emp.: 1,194
Fiscal Year-end: 12/31/23
Commercial Banking Services
N.A.I.C.S.: 522110
Abdul Rahman Mohamed Nasir Al Owais *(Chm)*
Subsidiaries:

ASAS Real Estate Company (1)
ASAS Real Estate - Industrial Area 18 Maleha Road, Muwailih, Sharjah, United Arab Emirates
Tel.: (971) 65999909
Web Site: https://www.asasproperties.ae
Real Estate Services
N.A.I.C.S.: 531210
Ahmed Hussain Al Ameeri *(Gen Mgr)*

Sharjah Islamic Financial Services LLC (1)
Al Khan Street Al Ghanim Business Center Building second floor, PO Box 66060, Office No 201, Sharjah, United Arab Emirates
Tel.: (971) 65992555
Web Site: https://www.sifs.ae
Financial Institution Services
N.A.I.C.S.: 522320
Abdulnasser Jasim Al Midfa *(Chm)*

Sharjah National Hotel Corporation (1)
Al Buhaira Corniche, PO Box 5802, Sharjah, United Arab Emirates
Tel.: (971) 65736666
Web Site:
https://www.sharjahnationalhotel.com
Hotel Services
N.A.I.C.S.: 721110

SHARKIA NATIONAL FOOD
Investment Projects Complex Bldg in front of, Agriculture Administration, Zagazig, Egypt
Tel.: (20) 55 2302188
Web Site:
http://www.elsharkyaelwatanya.com
Year Founded: 1981
SNFC.CA—(EGX)
Sales Range: Less than $1 Million
Food Products Mfr
N.A.I.C.S.: 311999
Iraqi Attia Metwalli Mohammed *(Gen Mgr)*

SHARMA EAST INDIA HOSP
Jaipur Hospital Lal Kothi Near SMS Stadium Tonk Road, Jaipur, 302015, India
Tel.: (91) 1412742557
Healthcare Medical Insurance Services
N.A.I.C.S.: 524114
Vimal Kumar Joshi *(CFO)*

SHARON BIO-MEDICINE LTD
C-312 BSEL Tech Park Sector 30A, Vashi, Navi Mumbai, 400703, India
Tel.: (91) 2267944000
Web Site: http://www.sharonbio.com
Sales Range: $25-49.9 Million
Emp.: 525
Pharmaceutical & Medicine Mfr
N.A.I.C.S.: 325412

SHARP INVESTMENTS LIMITED
14 N S Road 2nd Floor, Kolkata, 700 001, India
Tel.: (91) 3340669225 In
Web Site:
https://www.sharpinvestments.com
Year Founded: 1977
538212—(BOM)
Rev.: $1,065
Assets: $4,027,401
Liabilities: $150,433
Net Worth: $3,876,967
Earnings: ($9,959)
Emp.: 1
Fiscal Year-end: 03/31/21
Securities Investment Services
N.A.I.C.S.: 523999
Sagar Mal Nahata *(Mng Dir)*

SHARYN GOL JSC
Level 4 Land Mark Office Building, Chinggis Avenue-13 Sukhbaatar district 1st Khoroo, Ulaanbaatar, Mongolia
Tel.: (976) 11311073
Web Site: http://www.sharyngol.com
SHG—(MONG)
Rev.: $23,547,318
Assets: $29,420,024
Liabilities: $19,917,571
Net Worth: $9,502,453
Earnings: ($684,069)
Fiscal Year-end: 12/31/19
Coal Mining Services
N.A.I.C.S.: 213113
Batbaatar Badan *(CEO)*

SHASHA DENIMS LTD.
House 8 Road 4 Banani DOHS, Dhaka, 1212, Bangladesh
Tel.: (880) 2222260548
Web Site:
https://www.shashadenims.com
Year Founded: 1996
SHASHADNIM—(CHT)
Rev.: $80,997,711
Assets: $57,094,342
Liabilities: $3,799,648
Net Worth: $53,294,694
Earnings: $1,718,163
Emp.: 2,739
Fiscal Year-end: 06/30/23
Textile & Fabric Product Mfr
N.A.I.C.S.: 313310
Shams Mahmud *(Mng Dir)*

SHASHANK TRADERS LTD.
702-A Arunachal Building 19 Barakhamba Road Connaught Place, New Delhi, 110 001, India
Tel.: (91) 1143571041
Web Site:
https://www.shashankinfo.in
Year Founded: 1985
540221—(BOM)
Rev.: $88,683
Assets: $480,583
Liabilities: $92,829
Net Worth: $387,754
Earnings: ($2,282)
Emp.: 2
Fiscal Year-end: 03/31/21
Financial Consulting Services
N.A.I.C.S.: 541611
Praveen Jain *(Chm)*

INTERNATIONAL PUBLIC

SHASHIJIT INFRAPROJECTS LIMITED
Plot No 209 Shop No 23 2nd Floor Girnar Khusboo Plaza G I D C, Vapi, 396 195, Gujarat, India
Tel.: (91) 2602432963 In
Web Site:
https://www.shashijitinfraprojects.com
Year Founded: 1991
540147—(BOM)
Rev.: $4,256,013
Assets: $4,563,429
Liabilities: $3,147,786
Net Worth: $1,415,643
Earnings: $54,042
Emp.: 49
Fiscal Year-end: 03/31/23
Civil Engineering Services
N.A.I.C.S.: 541330
Aakruti Jain *(Exec Dir)*

SHASHWAT FURNISHING SOLUTIONS LIMITED
121 Mahaveer Nagar K N Nagar, Jodhpur, 342008, Rajasthan, India
Tel.: (91) 9001269000
Web Site:
https://www.handicraftsvillage.com
Year Founded: 2021
543519—(BOM)
Rev.: $549,104
Assets: $694,203
Liabilities: $198,106
Net Worth: $496,097
Earnings: $25,358
Emp.: 12
Fiscal Year-end: 03/31/23
Furniture Product Mfr & Distr
N.A.I.C.S.: 337121

SHATO HOLDINGS LTD.
4088 Cambie Street, Vancouver, V5Z 2X8, BC, Canada
Tel.: (604) 874-5533
Web Site:
https://www.shatoholdings.com
Year Founded: 1969
Sales Range: $50-74.9 Million
Emp.: 6,000
Investment Holding Company Services
N.A.I.C.S.: 551112
Sultan Thiara *(CFO & Exec VP)*

SHAVER SHOP GROUP LIMITED
Level 1 Chadstone Tower One 1341 Dandenong Road, Chadstone, 3148, VIC, Australia
Tel.: (61) 398405900 AU
Web Site:
http://www.shavershop.com.au
Year Founded: 1986
SSG—(ASX)
Rev.: $146,483,826
Assets: $85,172,583
Liabilities: $26,713,041
Net Worth: $58,459,542
Earnings: $10,097,843
Emp.: 756
Fiscal Year-end: 06/30/24
Grooming Product Distr
N.A.I.C.S.: 456120
Broderick Arnhold *(Chm)*

SHAW BROTHERS HOLDINGS LIMITED
19/F Leighton Centre 77 Leighton Road, Causeway Bay, China (Hong Kong)
Tel.: (852) 23352879 Ky
Web Site:
http://www.shawbrotherspictures.com
0953—(HKG)
Rev.: $22,611,560
Assets: $74,850,469

AND PRIVATE COMPANIES SHAWCOR LTD.

Liabilities: $13,350,776
Net Worth: $61,499,693
Earnings: ($1,056,510)
Emp.: 74
Fiscal Year-end: 12/31/22
Motion Picture Production Services
N.A.I.C.S.: 512110
Virginia Yee Ling Lok *(Exec Dir)*

SHAWCOR LTD.
25 Bethridge Road, Toronto, M9W 1M7, ON, Canada
Tel.: (416) 743-7111   Ca
Web Site: http://www.shawcor.com
Year Founded: 1968
SCL—(OTCIQ)
Rev.: $894,146,040
Assets: $991,737,035
Liabilities: $489,456,168
Net Worth: $502,280,866
Earnings: ($63,067,414)
Emp.: 4,273
Fiscal Year-end: 12/31/21
Energy Industry Products
N.A.I.C.S.: 331420
D. S. Blackwood *(Chm)*

Subsidiaries:

Bredero Shaw (Singapore) Pte. Ltd.
Unit 17-01/02 United Square, 101 Thompson Road, Singapore, 307591, Singapore **(100%)**
Tel.: (65) 67322355
Web Site: http://www.shawpipeline.com
Sales Range: $25-49.9 Million
Emp.: 10
Pipeline Inspection Services
N.A.I.C.S.: 332999

Bredero Shaw Ltd. **(1)**
Imperial Dock, Leith, Edinburgh, EH6 7DT, Scotland, United Kingdom **(100%)**
Tel.: (44) 1315539600
Web Site: http://www.brederoshaw.com
Sales Range: $450-499.9 Million
Emp.: 2,500
Mfr of Pipe Coatings
N.A.I.C.S.: 332812

Bredero Shaw Middle East Limited **(1)**
Saqr Port Authority, PO Box 6997, Ras al Khaimah, United Arab Emirates
Tel.: (971) 7 2660133
Pipe Coating Solution Mfr
N.A.I.C.S.: 325998
Stuart Lockey *(Plant Mgr)*

Bredero Shaw Norway AS **(1)**
Gronora Industriomrade, 7300, Orkanger, Norway
Tel.: (47) 72 46 60 60
Web Site: http://www.brederoshaw.com
Pipe Coating Solution Mfr
N.A.I.C.S.: 325998
Karl Pedersen *(Gen Mgr)*

Canusa Systems Limited **(1)**
Unit 3 Sterling Park Gatwick Road, Crawley, RH10 9QT, West Sussex, United Kingdom
Tel.: (44) 1293541254
Emp.: 16
Corrision Protection & Sealing Products Mfr
N.A.I.C.S.: 325998
Emerson Tacoma *(Gen Mgr)*

Canusa-CPS **(1)**
25 Bethridge Rd, Toronto, M9W 1M7, ON, Canada **(100%)**
Tel.: (416) 743-7111
Web Site: http://www.canusacps.com
Sales Range: $50-74.9 Million
Pipe Coating Solutions
N.A.I.C.S.: 332919

DSG-Canusa **(1)**
25 Bethridge Road, Toronto, M9W 1M7, ON, Canada **(100%)**
Tel.: (416) 743-7111
Web Site: http://www.dsgcanusa.com
Sales Range: $10-24.9 Million
Pipe Coating Solutions
N.A.I.C.S.: 332919

Desert NDT, LLC **(1)**
5875 North Sam Houston Pkwy W Ste 200, Houston, TX 77086 **(100%)**
Tel.: (713) 568-3513
Web Site: http://www.shawcor.com
Emp.: 100
Inspection & Testing Services for Oilfield & New Building Construction
N.A.I.C.S.: 541380
Matt McCoy *(Dev & Quality)*

Subsidiary (Domestic):

Midwest Inspection Services, Inc. **(2)**
1206 SW 9th Ave, Perryton, TX 79070-3231
Tel.: (806) 435-4043
Infrastructure Testing Services
N.A.I.C.S.: 541990
Darryl Ezzell *(Mgr)*

Flexpipe Systems Inc. **(1)**
3501 - 54th Avenue SE, Calgary, T2C 0A9, AB, Canada
Tel.: (403) 503-0548
Web Site: http://www.flexpipesystems.com
Pipe Coating Solutions Mfr & Distr
N.A.I.C.S.: 325998

Guardian A Shawcor Company **(1)**
8010 40th St SE, Calgary, T2C 2Y3, AB, Canada **(100%)**
Tel.: (403) 279-2400
Web Site: http://www.guardian.shawcor.com
Sales Range: $25-49.9 Million
Emp.: 100
N.A.I.C.S.: 332812

Guardian Inspection S.A. de C.V. **(1)**
Periferico Carlos Pellicer Camara 4002A, Col Miguel Hidalgo, Villahermosa, 86120, Tabasco, Mexico
Tel.: (52) 993 350 6762
Web Site: http://www.guardianoil.com
Emp.: 5
Drilling Equipment Inspection Services
N.A.I.C.S.: 926150

Guardian Oilfield Services **(1)**
950 78th Ave, Edmonton, T6P 1L7, AB, Canada **(100%)**
Tel.: (780) 440-1444
Web Site: http://www.guardianoil.com
Sales Range: $25-49.9 Million
Emp.: 20
Pipeline Construction Equipment Mfr
N.A.I.C.S.: 332996

Kanata Electronic Services Limited **(1)**
20 Baywood Road Unit 1, Etobicoke, M9V 4A8, ON, Canada
Tel.: (416) 745-0688
Web Site: http://www.kesl.com
Rev.: $1,478,064
Emp.: 17
Aerospace & Nuclear Products Mfr
N.A.I.C.S.: 336413
John Miller *(Mgr-Quality Assurance)*

Lake Superior Consulting **(1)**
130 W Superior St Ste 500, Duluth, MN 55802 **(100%)**
Tel.: (218) 727-3141
Web Site: https://www.lsconsulting.com
Emp.: 320
Project Management Methodologies & Engineering Services
N.A.I.C.S.: 541330
Phillip Powers *(Pres & Mng Dir)*

PT Bredero Shaw Indonesia **(1)**
Jl Hang Kesturi Kav 3A1 Kawasan Industri Terpadu Kabil, Batam, 29467, Indonesia
Tel.: (62) 778 412 275
Web Site: http://www.brederoshaw.com
Sales Range: $125-149.9 Million
Emp.: 500
Pipe Coating Solution Mfr
N.A.I.C.S.: 325998

Shaw Core Energy Services **(1)**
10502 Fallstone Rd, Houston, TX 77099-4302
Tel.: (416) 743-7111
Web Site: http://www.shawcor.com
Sales Range: $50-74.9 Million
Emp.: 200
N.A.I.C.S.: 332812

Division (Domestic):

Canusa-CPS **(2)**
3813A Helios Way Ste 900, Pflugerville, TX 78660
Tel.: (832) 933-6292
Web Site: https://www.canusacps.com
Sales Range: $25-49.9 Million
Pipe Coating Solutions
N.A.I.C.S.: 325510

DSG-Canusa **(2)**
173 Commerce Blvd, Cincinnati, OH 45140-7727 **(100%)**
Tel.: (513) 683-7800
Web Site: http://www.dsgcanusa.com
Sales Range: $25-49.9 Million
Pipe Coating Solutions
N.A.I.C.S.: 332919

Shaw Pipeline Services **(2)**
5875 N Sam Houston Pkwy W Ste 200, Houston, TX 77086 **(100%)**
Tel.: (281) 744-3495
Web Site: https://www.shawpipeline.com
Sales Range: $25-49.9 Million
Emp.: 100
Pipeline Weld Inspections Services
N.A.I.C.S.: 561499

Shaw Industries Holding GmbH **(1)**
25 BethRidge Rd, Toronto, M9W 1M7, ON, Canada **(100%)**
Tel.: (416) 743-7111
Web Site: http://www.shawcor.de
Sales Range: $125-149.9 Million
Emp.: 300
N.A.I.C.S.: 332812

Subsidiary (Non-US):

DSG-Canusa GmbH & Co. KG **(2)**
Heidestrasse 5, Meckenheim, 53340, Germany **(100%)**
Tel.: (49) 222588920
Web Site: http://www.dsgcanusa.de
Sales Range: $50-74.9 Million
Emp.: 200
N.A.I.C.S.: 332812

Subsidiary (Non-US):

DSG-Canusa Polska Sp. z.o.o. **(3)**
Zagorki Rychnowy, Czluchow, 77-300, Poland
Tel.: (48) 598323301
Electrical Wire Distr.
N.A.I.C.S.: 423610

Subsidiary (Non-US):

DSG-Canusa Italia S.r.L **(2)**
Via Alessi 8A 8, 16128, Genoa, GE, Italy **(100%)**
Tel.: (39) 0106001472
Web Site: http://www.dsgcanusa.de
Sales Range: $25-49.9 Million
Emp.: 3
N.A.I.C.S.: 332812

Shaw Pipe Protection Limited **(1)**
2 Exe Pl 18 20th Fl Crowchild NW, Calgary, T2P 4L4, AB, Canada **(100%)**
Tel.: (403) 263-2255
Web Site: http://www.brederoshaw.shawcor.com
Sales Range: $50-74.9 Million
Emp.: 40
Pipe Coating Applications
N.A.I.C.S.: 332812

ShawCor Global Services Limited **(1)**
C/O The Corporate Centre The Beach House 2nd Floor, Bridgetown, Barbados
Tel.: (246) 4198800
Sales Range: $50-74.9 Million
Emp.: 4
Investment Management Service
N.A.I.C.S.: 523999
Leslie W. J. Hutchison *(Gen Mgr)*

ShawCor Ltd. - Guardian Division **(1)**
950-78th Avenue, Edmonton, T6P 1L7, AB, Canada
Tel.: (780) 440-1444
Web Site: http://www.guardianoil.com
Sales Range: $125-149.9 Million
Emp.: 50
Tubular Management Services
N.A.I.C.S.: 322219

ShawCor UK Limited - Canusa Systems Division **(1)**
Unit 3 Sterling Park Gatwick Road, Crawley, RH10 9QT, West Sussex, United Kingdom
Tel.: (44) 1293 541 254
Web Site: http://www.shawcor.com
Emp.: 16
Corrosion Prevention & Control Services
N.A.I.C.S.: 237120

Shawflex **(1)**
25 Bethridge Road, Toronto, M9W 1M7, ON, Canada **(100%)**
Tel.: (416) 743-7111
Web Site: http://www.shawflex.com
Sales Range: $125-149.9 Million
Pipe Coating Solutions
N.A.I.C.S.: 332919

Suzhou DSG-Canusa Polymer Technologies Co. Ltd. **(1)**
Unit 4C Suchun Industrial Sq 428 Xinglong St Suzhou Industrial Park, Suzhou, 215126, Jiangsu, China
Tel.: (86) 512 82280099
Sales Range: $25-49.9 Million
Emp.: 4
Plastics Product Mfr
N.A.I.C.S.: 326199
Lily Yang *(Gen Mgr)*

ZCL Composites Inc. **(1)**
1420 Parson Road SW, Edmonton, T6X 1M5, AB, Canada
Tel.: (780) 466-6648
Web Site: http://www.zcl.com
Rev.: $149,893,544
Assets: $112,102,518
Liabilities: $23,491,439
Net Worth: $88,611,078
Earnings: $14,325,875
Emp.: 584
Fiscal Year-end: 12/31/2017
Fiberglass Reinforced Plastic & Steel Underground Storage Tanks Designer, Mfr & Supplier
N.A.I.C.S.: 326199
Anthony P. Franceschini *(Chm)*

Subsidiary (Non-US):

Parabeam b.v. **(2)**
Vossenbeemd 1C, PO Box 134, 5705 CL, Helmond, Netherlands
Tel.: (31) 492591222
Web Site: http://www.parabeam.com
Emp.: 20
3D Glass Fabrics Mfr
N.A.I.C.S.: 327215

Subsidiary (Domestic):

DWT Holding B.V **(3)**
Vossenbeemd 1c, Helmond, 5705 CL, North Brabant, Netherlands
Tel.: (31) 492591222
Web Site: http://www.parabeam3d.com
Investment Management Service
N.A.I.C.S.: 523999

Subsidiary (Non-US):

Romar-Voss B.V. **(2)**
Bevelantstraat 5, Roggel, 6088 PB, Leudal, Netherlands
Tel.: (31) 475491019
Web Site: http://www.romar-voss.nl
Composite & Floor System Mfr
N.A.I.C.S.: 325211

Subsidiary (US):

Xerxes Corporation **(2)**
7901 Xerxes Ave S, Minneapolis, MN 55431-1288 **(100%)**
Tel.: (952) 887-1890
Web Site: https://www.xerxes.com
Fiberglass Storage Tank Mfr
N.A.I.C.S.: 326199
Dave Van Eylle *(Controller)*

Division (Domestic):

ZCL Composites Inc. - ZCL Everlast **(2)**
1420 Parsons Rd SW, Edmonton, T6X 1M5, AB, Canada
Tel.: (800) 661-8265

SHAWCOR LTD.

ShawCor Ltd.—(Continued)
Fiberglass Tank Mfr
N.A.I.C.S.: 326199
Ted Redmond *(Pres)*

SHAWKWEI & PARTNERS LTD.
28/F South Island Place 8 Wong Chuk Hang Road Wong Chuk Hang, Hong Kong, China (Hong Kong)
Tel.: (852) 31628479
Web Site: http://www.shawkwei.com
Year Founded: 1999
Sales Range: $25-49.9 Million
Emp.: 10
Private Equity Firm Services
N.A.I.C.S.: 523999
Kyle Shaw *(Founder & Mng Partner)*

Subsidiaries:

Beyonics Technology Limited (1)
30 Marsiling Industrial Estate Road 8, Singapore, 739193, Singapore
Tel.: (65) 63490600
Web Site: http://www.beyonics.com
Contract Manufacturing Services
N.A.I.C.S.: 339999
Soon Fah Loo *(VP-Ops-Kota Tinggi & Kuala Lumpur)*

Subsidiary (Domestic):

Beyonics Advanced Manufacturing Pte Ltd (2)
30 Marsiling Industrial Estate Road 8, Singapore, 739193, Singapore
Tel.: (65) 6349 0600
Web Site: http://www.beyonics.com
Sales Range: $75-99.9 Million
Electronic Component & Equipment Mfr
N.A.I.C.S.: 334419
Michael Ng *(CEO)*

Beyonics International Pte Ltd (2)
30 Marsiling Industrial Estate Road 8, Singapore, 739193, Singapore
Tel.: (65) 63490600
Web Site: http://www.beyonics.com
Sales Range: $75-99.9 Million
Emp.: 300
Contract Manufacturing Services
N.A.I.C.S.: 339999
Sean Ng *(Dir-Ops)*

Beyonics Precision Engineering Pte Ltd (2)
30 Marsiling Industrial Estate Road 8, Singapore, 739193, Singapore
Tel.: (65) 63490600
Web Site: http://www.beyonics.com.sg
Sales Range: $25-49.9 Million
Engineeering Services
N.A.I.C.S.: 541330
Michael Ng *(CEO)*

Subsidiary (Non-US):

Beyonics Precision Machining Sdn Bhd (2)
Plot 6 Jalan Dewani Satu off Jalan Tampoi, Johor Bahru, 81100, Johor, Malaysia
Tel.: (60) 72763466
Web Site: http://www.beyonics.com
Sales Range: $350-399.9 Million
Contract Manufacturing Services
N.A.I.C.S.: 339999

Subsidiary (Domestic):

Beyonics Precision Stampings Pte Ltd (2)
10 Tuas Avenue 12, Singapore, 639032, Singapore
Tel.: (65) 68619300
Web Site: http://www.beyonics.com
Sales Range: $25-49.9 Million
Contract Manufacturing Services
N.A.I.C.S.: 339999
Nai Teck Lui *(Gen Mgr)*

Subsidiary (Non-US):

Beyonics Technology (KL) Sdn Bhd (2)
Lot 10 Jalan Perusahaan Utama Taman Industri Selesa Jaya, Balakong, 43300, Selangor, Malaysia
Tel.: (60) 389626970
Contract Manufacturing Services
N.A.I.C.S.: 339999

Beyonics Technology (Senai) Sdn Bhd (2)
Plot 3627 Jalan Harmoni 1 Batu 22, Kulai, 81000, Johor, Malaysia
Tel.: (60) 76612300
Web Site: http://www.beyonics.com
Sales Range: $150-199.9 Million
Contract Manufacturing Services
N.A.I.C.S.: 339999

Plant (Domestic):

Beyonics Technology (Senai) Sdn Bhd - Senai Campus (3)
Plot 171 Jalan Perindustrian 7 Kawasan Perindustrian Senai III, Senai, 81400, Johor Darul Takzim, Malaysia
Tel.: (60) 7 598 2888
Web Site: http://www.beyonics.com
Contract Manufacturing Services
N.A.I.C.S.: 339999

Subsidiary (Non-US):

Beyonics Technology (Thailand) Co., Ltd. (2)
137 Moo 1 Hi Tech Industrial Estate Tambol Ban Lane, Amphur Bangpa-in, Ayutthaya, 13160, Thailand
Tel.: (66) 35351990
Contract Manufacturing Services
N.A.I.C.S.: 339999

Beyonics Technology Electronics (Changshu) Co., Ltd (2)
18 Yinhuan Road Changshu Southeast Economic Development Zone, Changzhou, 215500, Jiangsu, China
Tel.: (86) 512 52351155
Web Site: http://www.beyonics.com
Computer Peripheral Equipment Mfr
N.A.I.C.S.: 334118
Leong Hua *(Gen Mgr)*

Beyonics Technology Electronics (Suzhou) Co., Ltd. (2)
78 Honxi Road Suzhou High Tech Economic Dev Zone Daxin Technology Park, Xushu Guan, Suzhou, 215151, China
Tel.: (86) 512 6616 1088
Web Site: http://www.beyonics.com
Contract Manufacturing Services
N.A.I.C.S.: 339999
Tc Lau *(Mgr)*

Flairis Sdn Bhd (2)
Plot 8/9 Kawasan Perindustrian Kota Tinggi Batu 2, Jalan Lombang, Kota Tinggi, 81900, Johor, Malaysia
Tel.: (60) 78836970
Web Site: http://www.beyonics.com
Sales Range: $700-749.9 Million
Contract Manufacturing Services
N.A.I.C.S.: 339999
Soon Fah Loo *(VP-Ops)*

PT Beyonics Manufacturing (2)
PANBIL Industrial Estate Lot 02-03 Sektor 2, Muka Kuning, Batam, 29433, Indonesia
Tel.: (62) 778371800
Web Site: http://www.beyonics.com
Electronic Components Mfr
N.A.I.C.S.: 334419

SHAZAND PETROCHEMICAL CORPORATION
No 68 West Taban St Vali-e-Asr Ave, PO Box 14155/6589 & 6591, 19689 13751, Tehran, Iran
Tel.: (98) 21 82120
Web Site: http://www.arpc.ir
Year Founded: 1987
PARK—(THE)
Sales Range: Less than $1 Million
Petrochemical Products Mfr
N.A.I.C.S.: 325110
E. Valadkhani *(CEO)*

SHEARWATER GROUP PLC
32 Threadneedle Street, London, EC2R 8AY, United Kingdom
Tel.: (44) 2081067785 UK
Web Site: https://www.shearwatergroup.com
Year Founded: 2004
SWG—(AIM)
Rev.: $28,578,698
Assets: $78,553,551
Liabilities: $20,512,538
Net Worth: $58,041,014
Earnings: ($2,739,213)
Fiscal Year-end: 03/31/24
Digital Resilience Services
N.A.I.C.S.: 541512
David Williams *(Chm)*

Subsidiaries:

Brookcourt Solutions Limited (1)
Kingsgate 62 High Street, Redhill, RH1 1SH, United Kingdom
Tel.: (44) 1737886111
Web Site: https://www.brookcourtsolutions.com
Information Technology Services
N.A.I.C.S.: 541511
Russell Houlbrook *(Acct Dir)*

GeoLang Limited (2)
Cardiff Business Technology Centre Senghennydd Road, Cardiff, CF24 4AY, United Kingdom
Tel.: (44) 2920647012
Web Site: http://www.geolang.com
Software Development Services
N.A.I.C.S.: 541511
Debbie Garside *(CEO)*

Pentest Limited (1)
26a The Downs, Altrincham, WA14 2PU, Cheshire, United Kingdom
Tel.: (44) 1612330100
Web Site: https://www.pentest.co.uk
Information Technology Services
N.A.I.C.S.: 541511
David Quinn *(Mktg Mgr)*

SecurEnvoy GmbH (1)
Freibadstr 30, 81543, Munich, Germany
Tel.: (49) 8925552842
Information Technology Services
N.A.I.C.S.: 541511

SecurEnvoy Limited (1)
1 King William St, London, EC4N 7AF, United Kingdom
Tel.: (44) 8452600010
Web Site: http://www.securenvoy.com
Information Technology Services
N.A.I.C.S.: 541511
Steve Watts *(CEO)*

SecurEnvoy, Inc. (1)
1700 Park St Ste 205, Naperville, IL 60563
Tel.: (312) 604-5362
Information Technology Services
N.A.I.C.S.: 541511

Xcina Consulting Limited (1)
1 King William Street, London, EC4N 7AF, United Kingdom
Tel.: (44) 2039858467
Web Site: http://www.xcinaconsulting.com
Management Consulting Services
N.A.I.C.S.: 541611
George Grey *(Mng Dir)*

SHEBA METAL CASTING
PO Box 398, Amman, 11623, Jordan
Tel.: (962) 64203189
Web Site: http://www.shebametalcasting.com
Year Founded: 1992
SHBA—(AMM)
Rev.: $9,931
Assets: $567,677
Liabilities: $125,167
Net Worth: $442,511
Earnings: ($6,517)
Fiscal Year-end: 12/31/23
Metal Mining Services
N.A.I.C.S.: 213114

SHEDE SPIRITS CO., LTD.
No 999 Tuopai avenue, Tuopai town, Shehong, 629209, Sichuan, China
Tel.: (86) 4009978989
Web Site: https://www.tuopaishede.cn
Year Founded: 1940
600702—(SHG)
Sales Range: $200-249.9 Million
Liquor Product & Purified Water Mfr
N.A.I.C.S.: 312140
Qiang Li *(Vice Chm & Chm-Supervisory Bd)*

SHEDIR PHARMA GROUP SPA
Via Bagnulo 95, Piano di Sorrento, 80063, Naples, Italy
Tel.: (39) 0818787158
Web Site: https://www.shedirpharmagroup.com
Year Founded: 2008
SHE—(ITA)
Sales Range: Less than $1 Million
Biotechnology Research & Development Services
N.A.I.C.S.: 541714
Umberto Di Maio *(Founder & Chm)*

SHEEHAN'S TRUCK CENTRE INC.
4320 Harvester Rd, Burlington, L7L 5S4, ON, Canada
Tel.: (905) 632-0300
Web Site: http://www.heavytrx.com
Year Founded: 1989
Rev.: $28,842,000
Emp.: 60
New & Used Car Dealers
N.A.I.C.S.: 441110
Lucien Lemay *(Mgr-Parts)*

SHEELA FOAM LIMITED
37/2 Site IV Sahibabad Industrial Area, Ghaziabad, 201 010, Uttar-Pradesh, India
Tel.: (91) 1204512260
Web Site: https://www.sheelafoam.com
Year Founded: 1971
540203—(BOM)
Rev.: $339,534,891
Assets: $283,353,825
Liabilities: $120,480,851
Net Worth: $162,872,974
Earnings: $32,780,666
Emp.: 1,968
Fiscal Year-end: 03/31/21
Mattress Mfr & Distr
N.A.I.C.S.: 326299
Sheela Gautam *(Founder)*

Subsidiaries:

Interplasp S.L. (1)
Carretera C-3314 de Villena a Yecla S/N, Yecla, 30510, Murcia, Spain
Tel.: (34) 968751180
Web Site: https://www.interplasp.com
Polyurethane Foam Mfr
N.A.I.C.S.: 326150

Joyce Foam Pty. Limited (1)
5-9 Bridges Road, Moorebank, 2170, NSW, Australia
Tel.: (61) 1800021304
Web Site: https://www.joyce.com.au
Foam Products Mfr
N.A.I.C.S.: 326140
Kevin Graham *(COO)*

Staqo Technologies L.L.C. (1)
908 Metropolis Tower Marasi Drive, Business Bay, Dubai, United Arab Emirates
Tel.: (971) 588870382
Information Technology Services
N.A.I.C.S.: 541519

Staqo World Pvt. Ltd. (1)
Plot No 14 Sector 135, Noida, 201 301, Uttar Pradesh, India
Tel.: (91) 1204868450
Web Site: https://www.staqo.com
Emp.: 200
Information Technology Services
N.A.I.C.S.: 541511

SHEEN TAI HOLDINGS GROUP COMPANY LIMITED
Room 1903 19/F Jubilee Centre 18 Fenwick St, Wanchai, China (Hong Kong)
Tel.: (852) 39984118 Ky
Web Site: http://www.sheentai.com
1335—(HKG)
Rev.: $40,251,878
Assets: $105,602,130
Liabilities: $6,839,738
Net Worth: $98,762,393
Earnings: $931,260
Emp.: 57
Fiscal Year-end: 12/31/22
Cigarette Packaging Material Mfr
N.A.I.C.S.: 322220
Yumin Guo *(Chm)*

SHEETAL COOL PRODUCTS LIMITED
Plot No 75 to 81 G I D C Estate, Amreli, 365 601, Gujarat, India
Tel.: (91) 2792240501
Web Site: https://www.sheetalicecream.com
Year Founded: 1987
540757—(BOM)
Rev.: $32,569,268
Assets: $24,018,233
Liabilities: $16,538,646
Net Worth: $7,479,587
Earnings: $832,048
Emp.: 449
Fiscal Year-end: 03/31/21
Dairy Product Mfr & Distr
N.A.I.C.S.: 311520
Bhupatbhai D. Bhuva *(Mng Dir)*

SHEETAL DIAMONDS LIMITED
Office No BW-2030 Bharat Diamond Bourse Bandra Kurla Complex, Bandra E, Mumbai, 400 051, Maharastra, India
Tel.: (91) 2240102666
Web Site: https://www.sheetaldiamonds.com
530525—(BOM)
Rev.: $3,123,531
Assets: $1,232,109
Liabilities: $745,656
Net Worth: $486,453
Earnings: $50,868
Emp.: 5
Fiscal Year-end: 03/31/21
Diamond Jewelry Mfr & Whslr
N.A.I.C.S.: 339910

SHEFA GEMS LTD.
Southern Industrial Zone, Barbour Center, Acre, Israel
Tel.: (972) 4 8203770
Web Site: http://www.shefayamim.com
SEFA—(TAE)
Sales Range: Less than $1 Million
Precious Stone Mining Services
N.A.I.C.S.: 212390
Abraham Taub *(CEO)*

SHEFFIELD GREEN LTD.
10 Anson Road 1713 International Plaza, Singapore, 49317, Singapore
Tel.: (65) 62502688 SG
Web Site: https://www.sheffieldgreen.com
Year Founded: 2021
SGR—(SES)
Human Resource Consulting Services
N.A.I.C.S.: 541612

SHEFFIELD RESOURCES LIMITED
Level 2 41 - 47 Colin Street, West Perth, 6005, WA, Australia
Tel.: (61) 865558777
Web Site: https://www.sheffieldresources.com
SFX—(ASX)
Rev.: $701,122
Assets: $92,532,719
Liabilities: $298,478
Net Worth: $92,234,241
Earnings: ($21,495,059)
Emp.: 119
Fiscal Year-end: 06/30/24
Talc Mining Services
N.A.I.C.S.: 212319
Will Burbury *(Chm)*

SHEH FUNG SCREWS CO., LTD.
180 E Sec Wen-an Road, Mituo, Kaohsiung, 82744, Taiwan
Tel.: (886) 76116116
Web Site: https://www.shehfung.com
Year Founded: 1973
2065—(TPE)
Rev.: $81,015,602
Assets: $94,284,464
Liabilities: $45,120,627
Net Worth: $49,163,837
Earnings: $11,574,180
Emp.: 301
Fiscal Year-end: 12/31/22
Screw Bolt & Concrete Drill Bit Mfr
N.A.I.C.S.: 332722
Terry Tu *(Chm)*

SHEH KAI PRECISION CO., LTD.
No 1 Bengong 1st Rd, Gangshan, Kaohsiung, 820110, Taiwan
Tel.: (886) 76225669
Web Site: https://www.shehkai.com
Year Founded: 1992
2063—(TPE)
Rev.: $45,351,812
Assets: $58,494,419
Liabilities: $28,126,098
Net Worth: $30,368,321
Earnings: $7,295,970
Fiscal Year-end: 12/31/22
Screw Bolt & Concrete Drill Bit Mfr
N.A.I.C.S.: 332722

SHEIKH AHMED BIN DALMOOK AL MAKTOUM PRIVATE OFFICE LLC
Sheikh Zayed Road 27th Floor Burj Al Salam Tower, Dubai, United Arab Emirates
Tel.: (971) 43422222
Web Site: https://admoffice.ae
Investment Services
N.A.I.C.S.: 523999

Subsidiaries:

Uniper Energy DMCC (1)
Dubai World Trade Centre Level 22, Dubai, United Arab Emirates
Tel.: (971) 43295467
Web Site: http://www.uniper.energy
Marine Fuel Oil Distr
N.A.I.C.S.: 457210

SHEIKH HOLDINGS GROUP (INVESTMENTS) LIMITED
Metropolitan House 7th Floor 3 Darkes Lane Potters Bar, Hertfordshire, EN6 1AG, United Kingdom
Tel.: (44) 1707661503
Web Site: http://www.sheikhholdings.co.uk
Year Founded: 2011
Emp.: 100
Holding Company
N.A.I.C.S.: 551112
Akbar Sheikh *(CEO)*

Subsidiaries:

CareTech Holdings PLC (1)
5th Floor Metropolitan House 3 Darkes Lane, Potters Bar, EN6 1AG, United Kingdom
Tel.: (44) 1707 601 800
Web Site: http://www.caretech-uk.com
Rev.: $583,773,438
Assets: $1,312,696,647
Liabilities: $818,193,300
Net Worth: $494,503,348
Earnings: $36,727,684
Emp.: 10,129
Fiscal Year-end: 09/30/2020
Holding Company; Social Care Services
N.A.I.C.S.: 551112
Haroon Sheikh *(Co-Founder & CEO)*

Subsidiary (Domestic):

Ashcroft House Limited (2)
11 Elmstead Rd, Bexhill-on-Sea, TN40 2HP, Sussex, United Kingdom
Tel.: (44) 1424736020
Web Site: http://www.caretechcommunityservice.com
Sales Range: $10-24.9 Million
Emp.: 11
Homage Services
N.A.I.C.S.: 623110

Ashring House Limited (2)
Ashring House Lewes Rd Ringmer, Lewes, BN8 5ES, Sussex, United Kingdom
Tel.: (44) 1273814400
Web Site: http://www.caretech-uk.com
Sales Range: $10-24.9 Million
Emp.: 11
Homage Services
N.A.I.C.S.: 623110

Beech Care Limited (2)
99 Dunes Rd, Greatstone, New Romney, TN28 8SW, Kent, United Kingdom
Tel.: (44) 1797362121
Sales Range: $10-24.9 Million
Emp.: 14
Physically Challenged People Caring Services
N.A.I.C.S.: 623110
Carol Foord *(Gen Mgr)*

Cambian Group PLC (2)
4th Floor Waterfront Building, Chancellors Road, London, W6 9RU, United Kingdom
Tel.: (44) 2087856150
Web Site: http://www.cambiangroup.com
Rev.: $264,362,762
Assets: $535,672,143
Liabilities: $115,517,051
Net Worth: $420,155,092
Earnings: ($15,330,051)
Emp.: 4,539
Fiscal Year-end: 12/31/2017
Behavioral Health Services
N.A.I.C.S.: 621420
Anne Marie Carrie *(COO)*

Subsidiary (Domestic):

Cambian Ansel Limited (3)
Clifton Lane, Clifton, NG11 8NB, Notts, United Kingdom
Tel.: (44) 845 200 0465
Mental Health Care Services
N.A.I.C.S.: 623220
Richard Idle *(Mgr-Svc & Registered)*

Subsidiary (Domestic):

CareTech Community Services Limited (2)
Metropoliton House 6th Floor 3 Darkes Lane, Potters Bar, EN6 1AG, Herts, United Kingdom
Tel.: (44) 1707601800
Sales Range: $10-24.9 Million
Emp.: 80
Physically Challenged People Caring Services
N.A.I.C.S.: 623110
Farouq Sheikh *(Mng Dir)*

Subsidiary (Domestic):

Applied Care & Development Limited (3)
Netherlea House Bankend Road, Dumfries, DG1 4AL, United Kingdom
Tel.: (44) 138 776 0260
Web Site: https://www.appliedcare.co.uk
Health & Social Care Services
N.A.I.C.S.: 621610

CareTech Community Services (No. 2) Limited (3)
5th FL Metropolitan House 3 Darkes Ln, Potters Bar, EN6 1AG, Herts, United Kingdom
Tel.: (44) 1707652053
Web Site: http://www.caretech-uk.com
Sales Range: $10-24.9 Million
Emp.: 50
Physically Challenged People Caring Services
N.A.I.C.S.: 623110

Complete Care & Enablement Services Limited (3)
161a Church Road, Urmston Trafford, Manchester, M41 6EA, United Kingdom
Tel.: (44) 161 747 5966
Web Site: https://www.completecareenablement.uk
Supported Living & Domiciliary Care Services
N.A.I.C.S.: 624120
Natalie Toner *(Mgr-North Wales & Cheshire)*

Daisybrook Limited (3)
49 Norton Green Ln, Norton Canes, Cannock, WS11 9PR, Staffordshire, United Kingdom
Tel.: (44) 1543274848
Sales Range: $10-24.9 Million
Emp.: 39
Physically Challenged People Caring Services
N.A.I.C.S.: 623110

Dawn Hodge Associates Limited (3)
Fiveways House Buildwas Road, Neston, CH64 3RU, United Kingdom
Tel.: (44) 151 336 6900
Web Site: https://www.dhassociates.co.uk
Training & Consultancy Services
N.A.I.C.S.: 611513
Stephen Robinson *(Head-Bus Dev)*

Huntsmans Lodge Limited (3)
33 Huntsmans Way, Leicester, LE4 7ZG, Leicestershire, United Kingdom
Tel.: (44) 1162611222
Web Site: http://www.caretechcommunityservice.com
Sales Range: $10-24.9 Million
Emp.: 5
Physically Challenged People Caring Services
N.A.I.C.S.: 623110

Kirkstall Lodge Limited (3)
56 Kirkstall Rd, Streatham, London, SW2 4HF, United Kingdom
Tel.: (44) 2086788296
Sales Range: $10-24.9 Million
Emp.: 13
Physically Challenged People Caring Services
N.A.I.C.S.: 623110

Lonsdale Midlands Limited (3)
1st Fl Court House 335- 337 High Street, West Bromwich, Birmingham, B70 8LU, W Midlands, United Kingdom
Tel.: (44) 1215005262
Web Site: http://www.caretech-uk.com
Physically Challenged People Caring Services
N.A.I.C.S.: 623110
Emma Fox *(Gen Mgr)*

Oakleaf Care (Hartwell) Limited (3)
Hilltop House Ashton Road, Hartwell, Northampton, NN7 2EY, Northamptonshire, United Kingdom
Tel.: (44) 160 486 4466
Web Site: https://www.oakleafcare.com
Health & Social Care Services
N.A.I.C.S.: 611513
Kathy Swannell *(Dir-Ops & Clinical)*

Outlook Fostering Services Limited (3)
2 Willow House 32 Kennington Road, Willsborough, Ashford, TN24 0NR, Kent, United Kingdom
Tel.: (44) 1233610661
Web Site: http://www.outlookfostering.com

SHEIKH HOLDINGS GROUP (INVESTMENTS) LIMITED

Sheikh Holdings Group (Investments) Limited—(Continued)
Children & Young People Fostering Services
N.A.I.C.S.: 624110

Park Foster Care Limited (3)
APV House Parkhouse Industrial Estate Speedwell Road, Newcastle, Newcastle-under-Lyme, ST5 7RG, Staffordshire, United Kingdom
Tel.: (44) 781 697 8058
Web Site: https://www.parkfostercare.com
Children & Young People Fostering Services
N.A.I.C.S.: 624110

Phoenix Therapy & Care Limited (3)
Dunbar Business Centre Spott Road, East Lothian, Dunbar, EH42 1RS, United Kingdom
Tel.: (44) 162 082 8566
Web Site: https://www.phoenixtherapyandcare.co.uk
Children & Young People Fostering Services
N.A.I.C.S.: 624310

ROC North West Limited (3)
Unit 2 South Preston Office Village Cuerden Way, Bamber Bridge, Preston, PR5 6BL, United Kingdom
Tel.: (44) 177 233 0187
Web Site: https://www.rocnorthwest.co.uk
Residential Care Services
N.A.I.C.S.: 623210

Roborough House Limited (3)
Tamerton Road, Woolwell, Plymouth, PL6 7BQ, Devon, United Kingdom
Tel.: (44) 175 270 0788
Web Site: https://www.roboroughhouse.com
Health & Social Care Services
N.A.I.C.S.: 611513

Rosedale Children's Services Limited (3)
2 Bullace Trees Ln, Liversedge, WF15 7PF, West Yorkshire, United Kingdom
Tel.: (44) 1924407540
Sales Range: $10-24.9 Million
Emp.: 30
Physically Challenged People Caring Services
N.A.I.C.S.: 623110

Selwyn Care Limited (3)
Matson House Matson Lane, Gloucester, GL4 6ED, United Kingdom
Tel.: (44) 145 230 2492
Web Site: https://www.selwyncare.com
Health & Social Care Services
N.A.I.C.S.: 611513

Spark of Genius Limited (3)
Trojan House Pegasus Avenue, Phoenix Business Park, Paisley, PA1 2BH, United Kingdom
Tel.: (44) 141 587 2710
Web Site: https://www.sparkofgenius.com
Health & Social Care Services
N.A.I.C.S.: 611513

St Michael's Support & Care Limited (3)
Nicholas House River Front, Enfield, EN1 3TF, United Kingdom
Tel.: (44) 2083678229
Health & Social Care Services
N.A.I.C.S.: 611513

Subsidiary (Domestic):

Fostering Support Group Limited (2)
5th Floor Yeoman House 63 Croydon Road, London, SE20 7TS, United Kingdom
Tel.: (44) 208 778 5656
Web Site: https://www.fosteringsupportgroup.com
Children & Young People Fostering Services
N.A.I.C.S.: 624110
Vevene Muhammad (Head-Svc)

Glenroyd House Limited (2)
Glenroyd House 26 High Rd N, Basildon Dist, Laindon, SS15 4DP, Essex, United Kingdom
Tel.: (44) 1268541333
Web Site: http://www.caretech.co.uk

Sales Range: $10-24.9 Million
Emp.: 17
Physically Challenged People Caring Services
N.A.I.C.S.: 623110
Barbara Childs (Gen Mgr)

One Step (Support) Limited (2)
First Floor Badgemore Park Golf Club Badgemore, Henley-on-Thames, RG9 4NR, Oxfordshire, United Kingdom
Tel.: (44) 149 141 4455
Web Site: https://www.onestepatatime.org.uk
Sales Range: $10-24.9 Million
Emp.: 10
Residential Support & Family Assessment Services
N.A.I.C.S.: 623990

Palm Care Limited (2)
12 Hardy Rd, Greatstone, New Romney, TN28 8SF, Kent, United Kingdom
Tel.: (44) 1797367006
Web Site: http://www.caretech-uk.com
Sales Range: $10-24.9 Million
Emp.: 12
Physically Challenged People Caring Services
N.A.I.C.S.: 623110
Iron Shiek (Mng Dir)

TLC (Wales) Independent Fostering Limited (2)
Tan-y-Fron Pontardulais Road, Cross Hands, Llanelli, SA14 6PG, Carmarthenshire, United Kingdom
Tel.: (44) 126 984 6371
Web Site: https://www.tlcwales.org.uk
Health & Social Care Services
N.A.I.C.S.: 611513
Judith Gibby (Head-Registered Svc)

Valeo Franklin (2)
26-28 Cambridge Road, Huddersfield, HD1 5BU, West Yorkshire, United Kingdom
Tel.: (44) 148 442 1037
Web Site: https://www.franklinhomes.co.uk
Sales Range: $10-24.9 Million
Emp.: 12
Residential & Domiciliary Support Services
N.A.I.C.S.: 624190
Dave Johnson (Mgr)

SHEKEL BRAINWEIGH LTD.
Level 7 330 Collins Street, Melbourne, 3000, VIC, Australia
Tel.: (61) 280981163
Web Site: https://www.shekelbrainweigh.com
Year Founded: 1971
SBW—(ASX)
Rev.: $27,192,000
Assets: $22,243,000
Liabilities: $27,237,000
Net Worth: ($4,994,000)
Earnings: ($5,575,000)
Fiscal Year-end: 12/31/23
Weighing Product Mfr & Distr
N.A.I.C.S.: 333993
Nir Leshem (CEO)

Subsidiaries:

Shekel (Ningbo) Scales Ltd. (1)
1177 Linyun Rd Building No 9 3 Rd, GaoXin District, Ningbo, Zhejiang, China
Tel.: (86) 57489076321
Web Site: http://en.shekel.cn
Electronic Scale Mfr
N.A.I.C.S.: 333998

Shekel EU S.A. (1)
9 Grand Rue, 1917, Luxembourg, Luxembourg
Tel.: (352) 26677142
Electronic Scale Mfr
N.A.I.C.S.: 333998

Shekel Scales (2008) Ltd. (1)
Kibbutz Beit Keshet MP, Afula, 1524700, Lower Galilee, Israel
Tel.: (972) 46629100
Web Site: http://www.shekelonline.com
Electronic Scale Mfr
N.A.I.C.S.: 333998
Nir Leshem (CEO)

Shekel USA LLC (1)
1829 Reisterstown Rd Ste 350, Pikesville, MD 21208
Electronic Scale Mfr
N.A.I.C.S.: 333998

SHEKHAWATI POLY-YARN LIMITED
Express Zone A Wing Unit No 1102/1103 Patel Vatika, Off Western Express Highway Malad East, Mumbai, 400097, India
Tel.: (91) 2266940626
Web Site: https://www.shekhawatiyarn.com
Year Founded: 1990
Rev.: $21,212,588
Assets: $20,133,604
Liabilities: $29,994,777
Net Worth: ($9,861,173)
Earnings: ($1,325,317)
Emp.: 485
Fiscal Year-end: 03/31/19
Polyester Textured Yarn Mfr
N.A.I.C.S.: 313110
Mukesh Ramniranjan Ruia (Founder, Chm & Mng Dir)

SHELDON & HAMMOND PTY LTD
22-24 Salisbury Rd, Asquith, 2077, NSW, Australia
Tel.: (61) 294826666
Web Site: http://www.sheldonhammond.com
Sales Range: $50-74.9 Million
Emp.: 96
Home Furnishing Mfr
N.A.I.C.S.: 423220
Kenneth Douglas Angus (Mng Dir)

SHELF DRILLING, LTD.
One JLT Floor 12 Jumeirah Lakes Towers, PO Box 212201, Dubai, United Arab Emirates
Tel.: (971) 45673400
Web Site: https://www.shelfdrilling.com
SHLLF—(OTCIQ)
Rev.: $695,221,000
Assets: $2,046,338,000
Liabilities: $1,730,847,000
Net Worth: $315,491,000
Earnings: ($28,805,000)
Emp.: 3,900
Fiscal Year-end: 12/31/22
Water Drilling Services
N.A.I.C.S.: 237110
David Mullen (CEO)

Subsidiaries:

Shelf Drilling Adriatic Services KFT (1)
Viale Randi 37, 48121, Ravenna, Italy
Tel.: (39) 0544422626
Oil & Gas Services
N.A.I.C.S.: 213112

SHELF SUBSEA PTY LTD
60 Howe St, Osborne Park, 6017, WA, Australia
Tel.: (61) 8 9329 5000
Web Site: http://www.shelfsubsea.com
Year Founded: 2002
Offshore & Marine Construction Services
N.A.I.C.S.: 237990
Peter Evans (Mng Dir)

Subsidiaries:

Shelf Subsea Solutions Pte (1)
23G Loyang Crescent Loyang Offshore Supply Base Blk 603, Singapore, 509023, Singapore
Web Site: http://www.shelfsubsea.com

Services to Offshore, Onshore, Marine & Construction Industries
N.A.I.C.S.: 213112
Peter Evans (Mng Dir)

SHELL OMAN MARKETING COMPANY SAOG
Mina Al-Fahal, PO Box 38, 116, Muscat, 116, Oman
Tel.: (968) 24570100
Web Site: https://www.shelloman.com.om
Year Founded: 1958
SOMS—(MUS)
Rev.: $1,349,297,382
Assets: $435,769,760
Liabilities: $296,781,734
Net Worth: $138,988,025
Earnings: $9,358,685
Emp.: 93,000
Fiscal Year-end: 12/31/23
Petroleum Product Whslr
N.A.I.C.S.: 424720
Shabib Mohammed Saif Al-Darmaki (Deputy Chm)

SHELL PLC
Shell Centre, London, SE1 7NA, United Kingdom
Tel.: (44) 2079341234
Web Site: https://www.shell.com
Year Founded: 2005
SHEL—(NYSE)
Rev.: $386,201,000,000
Assets: $443,024,000,000
Liabilities: $250,427,000,000
Net Worth: $192,597,000,000
Earnings: $42,309,000,000
Emp.: 93,000
Fiscal Year-end: 12/31/22
Oil & Gas Distribution Services
N.A.I.C.S.: 551112
Donny Ching (Dir-Legal)

Subsidiaries:

Accurasea SAS (1)
10 place de Catalogne, 75014, Paris, France
Tel.: (33) 14 007 9500
Web Site: https://www.accurasea.com
Offshore Wind Measurement Device Mfr
N.A.I.C.S.: 334519

BG Gas Services Limited (1)
Millstream Maidenhead Road, Windsor, SL4 5GD, Berkshire, United Kingdom
Tel.: (44) 207 741 4100
Web Site: https://www.britishgas.co.uk
Natural Gas Distribution Services
N.A.I.C.S.: 221210

Connected Freight Pte. Ltd. (1)
The Metropolis Tower 1 9 North Buona Vista Drive, Singapore, 138588, Singapore
Tel.: (65) 9 685 1148
Web Site: https://www.connectedfreight.com
Online Marketing Services
N.A.I.C.S.: 541613
Nir Ten Bosch (CEO)

Connected Freight Solutions Philippines, Inc. (1)
41st Floor The Finance Centre 26th Street Fort Bonifacio NCR, Fourth District, Taguig, Philippines
Tel.: (63) 27 796 9170
Online Marketing Services
N.A.I.C.S.: 541613

Enersol GmbH (1)
Einsteinstrasse 47, 71665, Vaihingen an der Enz, Germany
Tel.: (49) 7042 818 9910
Web Site: https://www.enersol.eu
Solar Energy Equipment Distr
N.A.I.C.S.: 423690

Enhanced Well Technologies AS (1)
Smalonane 16, 5343, Straume, Norway
Tel.: (47) 56154000
Drilling, Cementing & Safe Enhancement Technology
N.A.I.C.S.: 213111

AND PRIVATE COMPANIES — SHELL PLC

Kjetil Lunde *(VP-Fin & Bus Support)*

Subsidiary (Domestic):

IKM Cleandrill AS (2)
Smalonane 5, Trollhaugmyra 15, 5353, Straume, Norway
Tel.: (47) 958 27 109
Web Site: http://www.ikm.com
Collection Management & Transfer of Drilling Fluid & Cutting Services
N.A.I.C.S.: 213112
Tom Hasler *(Mng Dir)*

Gas Investments & Services Company Limited (1)
3rd Floor Continental Building 25 Church Street, Hamilton, HM 12, Bermuda
Tel.: (441) 296 0585
Oil & Gas Exploration Services
N.A.I.C.S.: 213112

Gasnor AS (1)
Helganesvegen 59, 4262, Avaldsnes, Norway
Tel.: (47) 8 152 0080
Web Site: https://www.gasnor.no
Renewable Gas Services
N.A.I.C.S.: 221210
Harald Arnoy *(Mgr)*

Greenlots Technology India LLP (1)
Platina Tower MG Road Near Sikandarpur Metro Station Sector 28, Gurgaon, 122001, Haryana, India
Tel.: (91) 981 080 4757
Software Development Services
N.A.I.C.S.: 541511

Hazira Port Private Limited (1)
Office No 2008 The Address Westgate-D Block Nr YMCA Club S G Highway, Makarba, Ahmedabad, 380051, Gujarat, India
Tel.: (91) 794 755 4100
Transportation Services
N.A.I.C.S.: 488999

Jordan Oil Shale Company B.V. (1)
Siwar Bin Amara Street, PO Box 140502, Bayadir Industrial Area, Amman, 11814, Jordan
Tel.: (962) 6 580 6333
Oil & Gas Mfr
N.A.I.C.S.: 324110

K.K. SVC Tokyo (1)
4052-2 Nakatsu Aikawa-cho, Aiko, 243-0303, Kanagawa, Japan
Tel.: (81) 46 285 0583
Web Site: https://www.svctokyo.jp
Petroleum Product Testing Services
N.A.I.C.S.: 541380

Limejump Ltd. (1)
Unit 2 13 Canterbury Court Kennington Park 1-3 Brixton Road, London, SW9 6DE, United Kingdom
Tel.: (44) 207 127 5308
Web Site: https://www.limejump.com
Renewable Energy Services
N.A.I.C.S.: 221114
Catherine Newman *(CEO)*

PT. Shell Indonesia (1)
Talavera Office Park 22nd-26th Floor Jl TB Simatupang Kav 22-26, Jakarta, 12430, Indonesia
Tel.: (62) 217 592 4700
Web Site: https://www.shell.co.id
Emp.: 270
Fuel Distr
N.A.I.C.S.: 457210
Dian Andyasuri *(Pres & Chm)*

Pertini Vista Sdn. Bhd. (1)
No 211 Jalan Tun Sambanthan, 50470, Kuala Lumpur, Malaysia
Tel.: (60) 32 385 2888
Oil Product Mfr & Distr
N.A.I.C.S.: 324199

Powermetric Metering Pty. Ltd. (1)
Level 30 275 George Street, Brisbane, 4000, QLD, Australia
Tel.: (61) 180 079 9992
Web Site: https://www.powermetric.com.au
Metering Installation Services
N.A.I.C.S.: 561990

QGC Pty Limited (1)
Level 27 275 George Street, Brisbane, 4000, QLD, Australia
Tel.: (61) 73 024 9000
Natural Gas Extraction Services
N.A.I.C.S.: 211130

Qatar Shell Service Company W.L.L. (1)
Al Mirqab Tower-1st Floor Corniche Road West Bay, PO Box 3747, Doha, Qatar
Tel.: (974) 4 495 7777
Web Site: https://www.shell.com.qa
Petroleum Product Distr
N.A.I.C.S.: 424720

Rheinland Kraftstoff GmbH (1)
Auf dem Schollbruch 24-26, 45899, Gelsenkirchen, Germany
Tel.: (49) 20 950 8020
Web Site: https://www.rheinland-kraftstoff.de
Gasoline Distr
N.A.I.C.S.: 457110

Sarawak Shell Berhad (1)
Locked Bag No 1, Lutong, 98100, Miri, Sarawak, Malaysia
Tel.: (60) 8 545 4545
Oil & Gas Extraction Services
N.A.I.C.S.: 211130

Shell & MOH Aviation Fuels A.E. (1)
151 Kifisias Ave, Marousi, 151 24, Athens, Greece
Tel.: (30) 2106 006 3801
Web Site: https://www.shell-moh.com
Aviation Fuel Distr
N.A.I.C.S.: 424720
Petsis Stamatis *(CEO)*

Shell & Turcas Petrol A.S. (1)
Karamancilar Business Center Gulbahar Mah Salih Tozan Sok No 18 B Blok, Esentepe Sisli, Istanbul, 34394, Turkiye
Tel.: (90) 212 376 0000
Oil & Gas Mfr
N.A.I.C.S.: 324110

Shell Argentina S.A. (1)
Avda RS Pena 788 4th Floor, Buenos Aires, Argentina
Tel.: (54) 810 999 7435
Web Site: https://www.shell.com.ar
Oil & Gas Exploration Services
N.A.I.C.S.: 213112

Shell Aviation Sweden AB (1)
Gustavslundsvagen 22, 167 51, Bromma, Sweden
Tel.: (46) 85 782 3050
Web Site: https://www.shellaviation.business.site
Fluid Distr
N.A.I.C.S.: 424720

Shell Bulgaria EAD (1)
48 Sitnyakovo Blvd Serdika Offices Fl 8, 1505, Sofia, Bulgaria
Tel.: (359) 2 960 1700
Web Site: https://www.shell.bg
Fuel Distr
N.A.I.C.S.: 457210

Shell Business Service Centre Sdn. Bhd. (1)
3450 Jalan Teknokrat 3, 63000, Cyberjaya, Selangor, Malaysia
Tel.: (60) 38 316 8888
Oil & Gas Extraction Services
N.A.I.C.S.: 211130

Shell Energy Australia Pty. Ltd. (1)
275 George Street, Brisbane, 4000, QLD, Australia
Tel.: (61) 132476
Web Site: https://www.shellenergy.com.au
Emp.: 350
Electricity Distribution Services
N.A.I.C.S.: 221122
Greg Joiner *(CEO)*

Shell Energy Italia S.R.L. (1)
Viale Edison 110, 20099, Sesto San Giovanni, Italy
Tel.: (39) 020 069 5000
Electricity Distribution Services
N.A.I.C.S.: 221122

Shell Energy Philippines Inc. (1)
41st Floor The Finance Centre 26th Street corner 9th Avenue Bonifacio, Global City Barangay Fort Bonifacio, Taguig, 1635, Metro Manila, Philippines
Tel.: (63) 27 502 7994
Web Site: https://www.shell.com.ph
Petroleum Product Distr
N.A.I.C.S.: 424720

Shell Energy Retail GmbH (1)
Suhrenkamp 71-77, 22335, Hamburg, Germany
Tel.: (49) 40743 090 3090
Web Site: https://www.shellenergy.de
Renewable Energy Distribution Services
N.A.I.C.S.: 221114

Shell Energy Retail Limited (1)
Shell Energy House Westwood Way Westwood Business Park, Coventry, CV4 8HS, United Kingdom
Tel.: (44) 330 094 5800
Web Site: https://www.shellenergy.co.uk
Natural Gas Distribution Services
N.A.I.C.S.: 221210

Shell Energy UK Limited (1)
3rd Floor Elder House 586-592 Elder Gate, Milton Keynes, MK9 1LR, United Kingdom
Tel.: (44) 330 088 2679
Natural Gas Distribution Services
N.A.I.C.S.: 221210

Shell Exploration & Production Tanzania Limited (1)
1st Floor Kilwa House Plot 369 Toure Drive, PO Box 105833, Oysterbay, Dar es Salaam, Tanzania
Tel.: (255) 22 221 8300
Web Site: https://www.shell.co.tz
Natural Gas Distribution Services
N.A.I.C.S.: 221210

Shell International B.V. (1)
PO Box 444, 2501 CK, Hague, Netherlands
Tel.: (31) 70 377 8743
Fuel Distr
N.A.I.C.S.: 424720

Shell Lubricants Japan K.K. (1)
12F Pacific Century Place Marunouchi 1-11-1 Marunouchi, Chiyoda-ku, Tokyo, 100-6216, Japan
Tel.: (81) 33 218 1780
Web Site: https://www.shell-lubes.co.jp
Lubricant Mfr & Distr
N.A.I.C.S.: 324191
Makoto Abe *(Pres)*

Shell Nederland B.V. (1)
Oostduinlaan 2, 2596 JM, Hague, Netherlands
Tel.: (31) 703779111
Web Site: https://www.shell.nl
Emp.: 30
Holding Company; Petroleum Refining, Chemical Mfr & Petroleum Products Distr
N.A.I.C.S.: 551112

Joint Venture (Non-US):

Petroleum Development Oman LLC (2)
Mina Alfahal, Postal Office Box 81, Muscat, 100, Oman
Tel.: (968) 24678111
Web Site: https://www.pdo.co.om
Sales Range: $1-4.9 Billion
Emp.: 8,500
Petroleum Refiner
N.A.I.C.S.: 324110
Mohammed Saif Al Rumhy *(Chm)*

Subsidiary (Domestic):

Shell Additives Holdings (II) B.V. (2)
Carel van Bylandtlaan 30, 2596 HR, Hague, Netherlands
Tel.: (31) 703779111
Investment Management Service
N.A.I.C.S.: 523940

Shell Finance (Netherlands) B.V. (2)
Carel van Bylandtlaan 30, 2596 HR, Hague, Netherlands
Tel.: (31) 703779111
Emp.: 20
Financial Management Services
N.A.I.C.S.: 523999

Shell International Finance B.V. (2)
Carel Van Bylandtlaan 30, 2596 HR, Hague, Netherlands
Tel.: (31) 703779111
Financial Management Services
N.A.I.C.S.: 523999

Shell Nederland Chemie B.V. (2)
Chemieweg 25, 4782 SJ, Moerdijk, Netherlands (100%)
Tel.: (31) 168359111
Sales Range: $800-899.9 Million
Petroleum Refiner
N.A.I.C.S.: 324110

Shell Nederland Raffinaderij B.V. (2)
Vondelingenweg 601, 3196 KK, Hoogvliet, Netherlands (100%)
Tel.: (31) 104319111
Sales Range: $400-449.9 Million
Petroleum Refiner
N.A.I.C.S.: 324110

Joint Venture (US):

Poseidon Oil Pipeline Company, LLC (3)
919 Milam Ste 2100, Houston, TX 77002
Tel.: (832) 280-3080
Web Site: https://www.poseidonoil.com
Sales Range: $10-24.9 Million
Emp.: 2
Crude Oil Pipeline Services
N.A.I.C.S.: 486110
Ray Cordova *(Pres-Bus Dev)*

Shell Nederland Verkoopmaatschappij B.V. (1)
Antwoordnummer 30295, 3030 VB, Rotterdam, Netherlands
Tel.: (31) 10 798 2810
Oil & Gas Mfr
N.A.I.C.S.: 324110

Shell Operaciones Peru S.A.C. (1)
Dean Valdivia 111 Oficina 802, Lima, Peru
Tel.: (51) 1 513 7373
Oil & Gas Mfr
N.A.I.C.S.: 324110

Shell Petroleum N.V. (2)
Afdeling Corporate Affairs, Postbus 444, 2501 CK, Hague, Netherlands (100%)
Tel.: (31) 703779111
Web Site: http://www.shell.com
Holding Company
N.A.I.C.S.: 551112

Subsidiary (Non-US):

BG Group Limited (2)
Shell Centre, London, SE1 7NA, United Kingdom (100%)
Tel.: (44) 1189353222
Natural Gas Mfr & Distr
N.A.I.C.S.: 211130

HanKook Shell Oil Co., Ltd. (2)
250 Sinseon-ro, Nam-gu, Busan, 48561, Korea (South)
Tel.: (82) 516205197
Web Site: https://www.shell.co.kr
Rev.: $231,359,567
Assets: $132,185,128
Liabilities: $45,548,070
Net Worth: $86,637,059
Earnings: $20,495,257
Emp.: 110
Fiscal Year-end: 12/31/2022
Lubricating Oil & Grease Mfr & Whslr
N.A.I.C.S.: 324191
Ramus Yerun Peter *(CEO)*

Subsidiary (Domestic):

Shell Caspian B.V. (2)
Carel van Bylandtlaan 30, 2596 HR, Hague, Zuid-Holland, Netherlands
Tel.: (31) 703779111
Crude Oil & Natural Gas Extracting Services
N.A.I.C.S.: 211120

Shell EP Middle East Holdings B.V. (2)
Carel van Bylandtlaan 30, 2596 HR, Hague, Netherlands
Tel.: (31) 703779111
Investment Management Service
N.A.I.C.S.: 523940

Shell Gas (LPG) Holdings B.V. (2)
Carel Van Bylandtlaan 30, 2596 HR, Hague, Netherlands
Tel.: (31) 703779111
Investment Management Service

SHELL PLC

Shell plc—(Continued)
N.A.I.C.S.: 523940

Shell Gas B.V. (2)
Carel Van Bylandtlaan 30, 2596 HR,
Hague, Netherlands
Tel.: (31) 703779111
Gas Exploration Services
N.A.I.C.S.: 213112

Shell Kazakhstan Development B.V. (2)
Carel van Bylandtlaan 30, 2596 HR, Hague,
Netherlands
Tel.: (31) 703779111
Petroleum Product Whslr
N.A.I.C.S.: 424720

Shell Overseas Investments B.V. (2)
Carel van Bylandtlaan 16, 2596 HR, Hague,
Netherlands (100%)
Tel.: (31) 703779111
Web Site: http://www.shell.com
Investment Holding Company
N.A.I.C.S.: 551112

Joint Venture (Non-US):

Bharat Shell Limited (3)
3rd Floor 1 Tower A B 37 Sector 1, Gautam
Budh Nagar, Noida, 201301, India
Tel.: (91) 202445001
Web Site: http://www.shell.com
Sales Range: $25-49.9 Million
Emp.: 30
Petroleum Refining; Owned 49% by Bharat
Petroleum Corporation Ltd. & 51% by Shell
International Petroleum Company
N.A.I.C.S.: 324110

SADAF Saudi Petrochemical Co. (3)
PO Box 10025, Al Jubayl, 31961, Saudi
Arabia (50%)
Tel.: (966) 33573000
Web Site: http://www.sabic.com
Mfr of Chemicals
N.A.I.C.S.: 325998

Subsidiary (US):

Shell Petroleum Inc. (2)
3333 Hwy 6 S, Houston, TX 77082-3101
Tel.: (281) 544-8665
Web Site: http://www.shell.com
Sales Range: $400-449.9 Million
Emp.: 1,500
Refinery Gas
N.A.I.C.S.: 325199

Joint Venture (Domestic):

Halliburton/WellDynamics (3)
445 Woodline Dr, Spring, TX 77386
Tel.: (281) 297-1200
Web Site: http://www.halliburton.com
Sales Range: $250-299.9 Million
Emp.: 165
Developer of Oil Well Monitoring & Analysis
Systems
N.A.I.C.S.: 213112

Subsidiary (Domestic):

Shell Chemical LP (3)
910 Louisiana St, Houston, TX 77002
Tel.: (713) 241-6161
Web Site: http://www.shellchemicals.com
Petrochemical Mfr & Marketer
N.A.I.C.S.: 325998
Sean Clarry *(Gen Mgr-Intermediates)*

Plant (Domestic):

Shell Chemical LP (4)
400 Industrial Pkwy Ext E, Saraland, AL
36571
Tel.: (251) 675-7040
Web Site: http://www.shellchemicals.com
Sales Range: $50-74.9 Million
Emp.: 136
Liquid Petroleum Gases, Gasoline, Kerosene & Heavy Olefin Plant Feed Mfr
N.A.I.C.S.: 324110
Ben Van Beurden *(CEO)*

Shell Chemical LP (4)
7594 Hwy 75, Geismar, LA 70734-3505
Tel.: (225) 201-6222
Web Site: http://www.shellchemicals.com
Sales Range: $150-199.9 Million
Emp.: 600
Alpha Olefins, Detergent Alcohols, Alcohol
Ethoxylates & Plasticiser Alcohols Mfr
N.A.I.C.S.: 325998

Shell Chemical LP Norco (4)
15536 River Rd, Norco, LA 70079 (100%)
Tel.: (504) 465-7342
Web Site: http://www.shellus.com
Sales Range: $150-199.9 Million
Emp.: 600
Ethylene, Propylene, Butadiene, Aromatic
Feedstock, Secondary Butyl Alcohol &
Olefin Cracker Feedstocks Mfr
N.A.I.C.S.: 325998

Subsidiary (Domestic):

Shell Offshore Inc (4)
1 Shell Sq 701 Poydras St, New Orleans,
LA 70161
Tel.: (504) 728-4501
Crude Oil & Natural Gas Extracting Services
N.A.I.C.S.: 211120

Shell Oil Company (3)
1 Shell Plz 910 Louisiana St, Houston, TX
77002
Tel.: (713) 241-6161
Web Site: http://www.shell.com
Lubricants, Fuel Oils, Oils & Greases,
Coke, Asphalts & Asphalt Emulsions, Road
Oils, Diesel Fuels, Industrial Chemical &
Petroleum Products Mfr & Retailer
N.A.I.C.S.: 324199
Gretchen H. Watkins *(Pres-USA)*

Subsidiary (Domestic):

Jiffy Lube International, Inc. (4)
910 Louisiana St, Houston, TX
77002 (100%)
Tel.: (713) 546-4100
Web Site: https://www.jiffylube.com
Sales Range: $500-549.9 Million
Emp.: 3,000
Oil Change Shop Owner, Operator & Franchisor
N.A.I.C.S.: 811191
Stephen Spinelli Jr. *(Co-Founder)*

Subsidiary (Domestic):

Jiffy Lube International of Maryland Inc. (5)
PO Box 4427, Houston, TX
77210-4427 (100%)
Tel.: (713) 546-4100
Web Site: http://www.jiffylube.com
Sales Range: $150-199.9 Million
Emp.: 300
Automotive Services
N.A.I.C.S.: 811111

Joint Venture (Domestic):

Motiva Enterprises LLC (4)
500 Dallas St, Houston, TX 77002 (50%)
Tel.: (713) 277-8000
Web Site: http://www.motivaenterprises.com
Sales Range: $10-24.9 Million
Petroleum Products Whsl
N.A.I.C.S.: 457120
J. Travis Capps *(Exec VP-Comml)*

Subsidiary (Domestic):

Pecten Trading Company (4)
910 Louisiana St, Houston, TX
77002 (100%)
Tel.: (713) 241-6161
Web Site: http://www.dutchshell.com
Sales Range: $25-49.9 Million
Emp.: 180
Ethylene Glycol, Glycol Gthers, Ethylene
Oxide & Triethylene Glycol Mfr
N.A.I.C.S.: 325998

Plant (Domestic):

Shell BTC (4)
3737 Bellaire Blvd, Houston, TX 77025
Tel.: (713) 245-7100
Web Site: http://www.shellus.com
Sales Range: $100-124.9 Million
Emp.: 500
Lubricants, Fuel Oils, Oils & Greases,
Coke, Asphalts & Asphalt Emulsions, Road
Oils, Diesel Fuels, Industrial Chemical &
Petroleum Products Mfr & Retailer
N.A.I.C.S.: 324199

Subsidiary (Domestic):

Shell Lubricants (4)
700 Milam St, Houston, TX 77010
Tel.: (713) 546-4100
Sales Range: $150-199.9 Million
Emp.: 800
Oil & Auto Products Whslr & Distr
N.A.I.C.S.: 324191
Troy Chapman *(Brand Dir-Pennzoil & Dir-Mktg-Quaker State)*

Subsidiary (Domestic):

T.F. Hudgins, Inc. (5)
4405 Directors Row, Houston, TX 77092
Tel.: (713) 682-3651
Web Site: http://www.tfhudgins.com
Construction & Mining Machinery & Equipment Merchant Whslr
N.A.I.C.S.: 423810
Carmen Montemayor *(VP & Mgr-Ops)*

Subsidiary (Domestic):

Allied Reliability Inc. (6)
10344 Sam Houston Park Dr Ste 110,
Houston, TX 77064
Tel.: (713) 682-3651
Web Site: http://www.alliedreliability.com
Rev.: $3,800,000
Emp.: 140
Building Maintenance & Related Services
N.A.I.C.S.: 561499

Subsidiary (Domestic):

Shell Oil Products Company LLC (3)
1 Shell Plz, Houston, TX 77054
Tel.: (713) 241-6161
Petroleum Refiner & Products Marketer
N.A.I.C.S.: 324110
Brooks Herring *(Brand Mgr)*

Subsidiary (Domestic):

Shell Lubricants (4)
700 Milam St, Houston, TX 77002-2806
Tel.: (713) 546-4000
Sales Range: $1-4.9 Billion
Emp.: 7,467
Petroleum Mfr
N.A.I.C.S.: 324191

Shell Pipeline Company LP (4)
910 Louisiana St, Houston, TX 77252-2648
Tel.: (713) 245-7600
Sales Range: $150-199.9 Million
Emp.: 540
Oil Pipeline Services
N.A.I.C.S.: 486910
Bruce Culpepper *(Pres)*

Subsidiary (Domestic):

Shell Midstream Partners, L.P. (5)
150 N Dairy Ashford, Houston, TX
77079 (68.5%)
Tel.: (832) 337-2034
Web Site:
http://www.shellmidstreampartners.com
Rev.: $788,000,000
Assets: $2,318,000,000
Liabilities: $2,811,000,000
Net Worth: ($493,000,000)
Earnings: $568,000,000
Fiscal Year-end: 12/31/2021
Crude Oil Pipelines
N.A.I.C.S.: 486110
Paul R. A. Goodfellow *(Chm)*

Subsidiary (Domestic):

Shell Philippines Exploration B.V. (2)
Carel Van Bylandtlaan 30, Hague, South
Holland, Netherlands
Tel.: (31) 703771757
Oil & Gas Exploration Services
N.A.I.C.S.: 213112

Subsidiary (Non-US):

Shell Sakhalin Holdings B.V. (2)
Tel.: (31) 703779111
Web Site: http://www.shell.com
Investment Management Service
N.A.I.C.S.: 523940

INTERNATIONAL PUBLIC

Subsidiary (Domestic):

Shell Trading Russia B.V. (2)
Carel Van Bylandtlaan 30, 2596 HR,
Hague, Netherlands
Tel.: (31) 703779111
Fuel Distr
N.A.I.C.S.: 424720

Subsidiary (Non-US):

Shell Treasury Centre Limited (2)
Shell Centre, London, SE1 7NA, United
Kingdom
Tel.: (44) 1244685000
Treasury Management Services
N.A.I.C.S.: 921130

Shell Treasury Dollar Company Limited (2)
Shell Centre, London, SE1 7NA, United
Kingdom
Tel.: (44) 2079343363
Mortgage Loan Brokerage Services
N.A.I.C.S.: 522310

ShellWestern LNG B.V. (2)
Tel.: (31) 703779111
Crude Oil & Natural Gas Extracting Services
N.A.I.C.S.: 211120

The Shell Petroleum Company Limited (2)
Shell Centre, 2 York Road, London, SE1
7NA, United Kingdom (100%)
Tel.: (44) 2079341234
Holding Company
N.A.I.C.S.: 551112

Subsidiary (Non-US):

A/S Dansk Shell (3)
Egeskovvej 265, 7000, Fredericia, Denmark
Tel.: (45) 79203522
Web Site: https://crossbridge.dk
Emp.: 240
Petroleum Refiner
N.A.I.C.S.: 324110

A/S Norske Shell (3)
Tankvegen 1, Tananger, 4098, Norway
Tel.: (47) 51693000
Web Site: http://www.shell.com
Rev: $2,246,597,888
Emp.: 200
Petroleum Refiner
N.A.I.C.S.: 324110
Torbjorn Tidemann *(CFO)*

Subsidiary (Domestic):

Enterprise Oil Norge As (4)
Tankveien 1, Tananger, 4098, Norway
Tel.: (47) 51 69 30 00
Sales Range: $250-299.9 Million
Oil & Gas Exploration Serivces
N.A.I.C.S.: 213112
Tor Arnesen *(Pres)*

Joint Venture (Non-US):

Arrow Energy Pty. Ltd. (3)
Level 39 111 Eagle Street, Brisbane, 4000,
QLD, Australia
Tel.: (61) 730124000
Web Site: https://www.arrowenergy.com.au
Sales Range: $50-74.9 Million
Coal Seam Gas Extraction Services
N.A.I.C.S.: 211130
Qian Mingyang *(CEO)*

Subsidiary (Domestic):

CH4 Operations Pty Ltd (4)
Level 19 42-60 Albert St, Brisbane, 4000,
Queensland, Australia
Tel.: (61) 732282300
Sales Range: $75-99.9 Million
Emp.: 200
Oil & Gas Supplier
N.A.I.C.S.: 213112

Affiliate (Non-US):

Basell Polyolefins (3)
Weena 737, 3013 AM, Rotterdam, Netherlands
Tel.: (31) 102755500

AND PRIVATE COMPANIES — SHELL PLC

Sales Range: $25-49.9 Million
Emp.: 20
Production of Polymeric Materials
N.A.I.C.S.: 325211

Subsidiary (Non-US):

Belgian Shell, S.A. (3)
Cantersteen 47, 1000, Brussels, Belgium
Tel.: (32) 25089111
Web Site: https://www.shell.be
Sales Range: $125-149.9 Million
Emp.: 500
Petroleum Refiner
N.A.I.C.S.: 324110

Joint Venture (Non-US):

Brunei LNG Sdn. Bhd. (3)
Jalan Utara Panaga Seria KB 3534,
Negara, 7082, Negara, Brunei Darussalam
Tel.: (673) 3236901
Sales Range: $200-249.9 Million
Emp.: 400
Liquified Natural Gas Mfr; Owned 50% by Government of Brunei, 25% by The Shell Petroleum Co. Ltd. & 25% by Mitsubishi Corporation
N.A.I.C.S.: 211120

Subsidiary (Domestic):

Brunei Shell Petroleum Co. Sdn. Bhd. (4)
Jalan Utara Panaga, Seria, KB2933, Negara, Brunei Darussalam
Tel.: (673) 3373999
Emp.: 3,500
Oil & Natural Gas Mfr
N.A.I.C.S.: 324110

Subsidiary (Non-US):

Deutsche Shell Holding GmbH (3)
Tel.: (49) 4063240
Web Site: http://www.shell.com
Investment Management Service
N.A.I.C.S.: 523940

Joint Venture (Domestic):

Infineum International Ltd. (3)
Milton Hill Business and Technology Centre, PO Box 1, Abingdon, OX13 6BB, Oxfordshire, United Kingdom
Tel.: (44) 1235549500
Web Site: http://www.infineum.com
Sales Range: $150-199.9 Million
Lubricant Additives Mfr; Owned 50% by ExxonMobil Chemical Company & 50% by The Shell Petroleum Co. Ltd.
N.A.I.C.S.: 324191

Subsidiary (Non-US):

Kenya Shell Ltd. (3)
Sales Range: $125-149.9 Million
Emp.: 307
Chemicals & Petroleum Products Mfr
N.A.I.C.S.: 325998

Affiliate (Non-US):

La Refineria Dominicana de Petroleo, S.A. (3)
Antigua Carretera Sanchez Km 17 1/2 Zoma Industrial de Haina, PO 1439, Santo Domingo, Dominican Republic (50%)
Tel.: (809) 4729999
Web Site: http://www.refidomsa.com.do
Petroleum Refiner; Owned 50% by Government of Dominican Republic & 50% by The Shell Petroleum Co. Ltd.
N.A.I.C.S.: 324110

Nederlandse Aardolie Maatschappij B.V. (3)
Tel.: (31) 592369111
Web Site: http://www.nam.nl
Sales Range: $700-749.9 Million
Emp.: 1,800
Exploration & Production in the Netherlands; Joint Venture of Exxon Mobil Corporation & Royal Dutch/Shell Group of Companies
N.A.I.C.S.: 211120

Joint Venture (Non-US):

Peninsular Aviation Services Co. Ltd. (3)
Web Site: http://www.shell.com
Sales Range: $25-49.9 Million
Emp.: 90
Aviation Services; Owned 50% by Saudi Arabian Markets Ltd., 25% by BP plc & 25% by The Shell Petroleum Co. Ltd.
N.A.I.C.S.: 488119

Subsidiary (Non-US):

Pilipinas Shell Foundation, Inc. (3)
The Finance Centre 41 ste Floor 26th Street, Bonifacio Global City, Taguig, 1635, Philippines
Tel.: (63) 9178146093
Web Site: https://pilipinasshellfoundation.org
Social Development Program Administrative Services
N.A.I.C.S.: 923130

Joint Venture (Non-US):

Pioneer Road Services Pty. Ltd. (3)
Ste 1202 Level 12 Flinders Tower, World Trade Centre, Melbourne, 3005, VIC, Australia
Tel.: (61) 39628080
Web Site: http://www.fultonhogan.com
Sales Range: $150-199.9 Million
Emp.: 1,000
Road Construction, Maintenance & Resurfacing Services; Joint Venture of Royal Dutch Shell plc (50%) & Fulton Hogan Ltd. (50%)
N.A.I.C.S.: 237310

Subsidiary (Non-US):

Sabah Shell Petroleum Co. Ltd (3)
Level 9-11 Plaza Shell 29 Jalan Tunku Abdul Rahman, 88000, Kota Kinabalu, Sabah, Malaysia
Tel.: (60) 88535714
Petroleum Product Whslr
N.A.I.C.S.: 424720

Joint Venture (Non-US):

Saudi Aramco Shell Refinery Company (3)
PO Box 10088, Al Jubayl, 31961, Saudi Arabia (50%)
Tel.: (966) 33572000
Web Site: https://www.sasref.com.sa
Sales Range: $25-49.9 Million
Emp.: 100
Oil Refining Services
N.A.I.C.S.: 324110

Subsidiary (Non-US):

Shell (China) Limited (3)
Emp.: 100
Oil & Gas Exploration Services
N.A.I.C.S.: 213112

Shell (Switzerland) AG (3)
Baarermatte, 6340, Baar, Switzerland
Tel.: (41) 7694444
Web Site: https://www.shell.ch
Rev.: $759,800,000
Emp.: 100
Oil & Natural Gas Exploration & Marketing
N.A.I.C.S.: 324110

Shell Abu Dhabi B.V. (3)
13th Floor Al Muhairy Center - office tower Zayed The First Street, PO Box 46807, Abu Dhabi, United Arab Emirates
Tel.: (971) 25469060
Oil & Gas Exploration Services
N.A.I.C.S.: 213112

Shell Adria D.O.O. (3)
Bravnicarjeva ulica 13, 1000, Ljubljana, Slovenia
Tel.: (386) 15140500
Web Site: https://www.shell.si
Petroleum & Petroleum Product Whslr
N.A.I.C.S.: 424720

Shell Australia Limited (3)
PO Box 872K, Melbourne, 3000, VIC, Australia
Tel.: (61) 3 8823 4444
Web Site: http://www.shell.com.au
Sales Range: $450-499.9 Million
Emp.: 2,250
Petroleum Product Mfr
N.A.I.C.S.: 324199
Michelle Barry *(Head-Rels)*

Subsidiary (Domestic):

The Shell Company of Australia Ltd. (4)
PO Box 872K, Melbourne, 3001, Australia
Tel.: (61) 396665444
Web Site: http://www.shell.com
Petroleum Refiner
N.A.I.C.S.: 324110

Subsidiary (Domestic):

Shell Refining Australia Pty. Ltd. (5)
PO Box 872K, Melbourne, 3000, VIC, Australia
Tel.: (61) 396665444
Web Site: http://www.shell.com.au
Sales Range: $150-199.9 Million
Emp.: 700
Toluene, Xylenes & Hydrocarbon Solvents Mfr
N.A.I.C.S.: 325998

Subsidiary (Non-US):

Shell Austria GmbH (3)
Tech Gate Donau-City-Strasse 1, 1220, Vienna, Austria
Tel.: (43) 1797970
Web Site: https://www.shell.at
Sales Range: $50-74.9 Million
Emp.: 100
Petroleum Refiner
N.A.I.C.S.: 324110

Subsidiary (Domestic):

Shell Bitumen (UK) Ltd (3)
Brabazon House Concord Business Park Threapwood Road, Wythenshawe, Manchester, M22 500, United Kingdom
Tel.: (44) 870 201 7777
Web Site: http://www.shell.com
Oil & Gas Exploration & Production Services
N.A.I.C.S.: 211120

Subsidiary (Non-US):

Shell Canada Limited (3)
400 4th Ave SW, Calgary, T2P 0J4, AB, Canada (78%)
Tel.: (403) 691-3111
Web Site: http://www.shell.ca
Sales Range: $5-14.9 Billion
Emp.: 4,500
Oil & Natural Gas Producer
N.A.I.C.S.: 211120

Subsidiary (Domestic):

Shell Americas Funding (Canada) Limited (4)
400 4 Ave Ste 3200, Calgary, T2P 0X9, AB, Canada
Tel.: (403) 691-3111
Oil & Gas Exploration Services
N.A.I.C.S.: 213112

Plant (Domestic):

Shell Canada Caroline Gas Plant (4)
Bag 500, PO Box 500, Caroline, T0M 0M0, AB, Canada
Tel.: (403) 722-7000
Web Site: http://www.shell.ca
Sales Range: $125-149.9 Million
Emp.: 130
Petroleum Refiner
N.A.I.C.S.: 324110

Subsidiary (Domestic):

Shell Canada Energy (4)
400 4th Avenue S W Station M, PO Box 100, Calgary, T2P 2H5, AB, Canada
Tel.: (403) 691-3111
Motor Oil & Lubricant Mfr
N.A.I.C.S.: 324191

Plant (Domestic):

Shell Canada Limited (4)
St Clair Parkway, approximately 10 kilometres south of Sarnia, Corunna, N0N 1G0, ON, Canada
Tel.: (519) 481-1245
Web Site: https://www.shell.ca
Emp.: 350
Petroleum Refiner
N.A.I.C.S.: 324110

Shell Canada Limited (4)
PO Bag 23, Fort Saskatchewan, T8L 3T2, AB, Canada
Tel.: (780) 992-3600
Web Site: http://www.shell.ca
Sales Range: $450-499.9 Million
Emp.: 700
Petroleum Refiner
N.A.I.C.S.: 324110

Shell Canada Limited - Montreal (4)
400 De maisonnoube W Ste 200, Montreal, H3A 164, QC, Canada
Tel.: (514) 645-1661
Web Site: http://www.shell.ca
Sales Range: $250-299.9 Million
Emp.: 450
Petroleum Refiner
N.A.I.C.S.: 324110

Shell Waterton Complex (4)
40 Km SW Pincher Creek, Pincher Creek, T0K 1W0, AB, Canada
Tel.: (403) 627-7200
Web Site: http://www.shell.ca
Sales Range: $200-249.9 Million
Emp.: 200
Crude Petroleum & Natural Gas Producer
N.A.I.C.S.: 211120

Subsidiary (Domestic):

Shell Catalysts & Technologies Limited (3)
Stuart Adams Shell Centre York Road, London, SE1 7NA, United Kingdom (100%)
Tel.: (44) 1489881881
Web Site: http://www.shell.com
Hydroprocessing Chemicals Mfr
N.A.I.C.S.: 325998

Joint Venture (US):

Zeolyst International (4)
PO Box 830, Valley Forge, PA 19482
Tel.: (610) 651-4621
Web Site: http://www.zeolyst.com
Sales Range: $25-49.9 Million
Catalysts & Adsorbents Mfr
N.A.I.C.S.: 325180

Subsidiary (Domestic):

Shell Chemicals U.K. Limited (3)
Shell Centre 2 York Rd, London, SE1 7NA, United Kingdom (100%)
Tel.: (44) 2079341234
Web Site: http://www.shell.co.uk
Petrochemical Mfr
N.A.I.C.S.: 325998
Martha Frances Keeth *(Exec VP)*

Shell China Exploration and Production Company Limited (3)
Shell Centre, London, SE1 7NA, United Kingdom
Tel.: (44) 2079344248
Crude Oil & Natural Gas Extracting Services
N.A.I.C.S.: 211120

Subsidiary (Non-US):

Shell China Holding GmbH (3)
Schulhof 6/1 Stock, Vienna, 1010, Austria
Tel.: (43) 179797
Investment Management Service
N.A.I.C.S.: 523940

Shell Colombia SA (3)
Tel.: (57) 16404000
Oil & Gas Exploration Services
N.A.I.C.S.: 213112

Shell Compania Argentina de Petroleo S.A. (3)
RS Pena 788 Piso 4, 1383, Buenos Aires, Argentina
Tel.: (54) 143280333
Web Site: https://www.shell.com.ar
Sales Range: $450-499.9 Million
Emp.: 1,130
Petroleum Refiner
N.A.I.C.S.: 324110

Shell Compania de Petroleos Ecuador S.A. (3)
Calle 9na Y Av Domingo Comin, Guayaquil, Ecuador
Tel.: (593) 4 2445345

SHELL PLC

Shell plc—(Continued)

Crude Oil & Natural Gas Extracting Services
N.A.I.C.S.: 211120

Shell Company of Turkey Ltd. (3)
Kocayol Cad Ibrahim Ag Sokak No 7, Istanbul, 34742, Istanbull, Türkiye
Tel.: (90) 2165718000
Web Site: http://www.shell.com.tr
Sales Range: $125-149.9 Million
Emp.: 500
Petroleum Fuels & Additives Mfr
N.A.I.C.S.: 324199

Shell Czech Republic a.s. (3)
Antala Staska 2027/77 4 Krc, 141 00, Prague, Czech Republic
Tel.: (420) 244 025 111
Web Site: http://www.shell.cz
Sales Range: $50-74.9 Million
Emp.: 200
Petroleum Product Mfr
N.A.I.C.S.: 324199

Shell Deutschland Oil GmbH (3)
Suhrenkamp 71-77, 22335, Hamburg, Germany
Tel.: (49) 4063245290
Web Site: https://www.shell.de
Sales Range: $350-399.9 Million
Emp.: 1,000
Natural Gas Mfr
N.A.I.C.S.: 211130

Shell Development (Australia) Proprietary Limited (3)
360 Collins Street, Melbourne, 3032, VIC, Australia
Tel.: (61) 396665444
Oil & Gas Exploration Services
N.A.I.C.S.: 213112

Shell Development Oman LLC (3)
Mina Al-Fahal, PO Box 74, 232, Muscat, Oman
Tel.: (968) 24091100
Web Site: https://www.shell.com.om
Oil & Gas Exploration Services
N.A.I.C.S.: 213112

Subsidiary (Domestic):

Shell EP Offshore Ventures Limited (3)
Shell Centre, London, SE1 7NA, United Kingdom
Tel.: (44) 20 79 34 12 34
Web Site: http://www.shell.co.uk
Oil & Gas Exploration & Production Services
N.A.I.C.S.: 211120

Subsidiary (Non-US):

Shell Eastern Petroleum (Pte) Limited (3)
The Metropolis Tower 1 9 North Buona Vista Drive 06-01, Singapore, 138588, Singapore
Tel.: (65) 63848000
Web Site: https://www.shell.com.sg
Sales Range: $450-499.9 Million
Emp.: 1,500
Petroleum Refiner
N.A.I.C.S.: 324110

Joint Venture (Domestic):

ELLBA Eastern (Pte) Ltd. (4)
61 seraya avenue, Jurong, 627879, Singapore
Tel.: (65) 63370330
Sales Range: $200-249.9 Million
Emp.: 650
Styrene Monomer & Propylene Oxide Mfr; Owned 50% by BASF SE & 50% by Royal Dutch Shell plc
N.A.I.C.S.: 325998

Subsidiary (Domestic):

Shell Chemicals Seraya (Pte) Limited (4)
61 Seraya Avenue, Singapore, 627879, Singapore
Tel.: (65) 65760400
Petrochemical Products Mfr
N.A.I.C.S.: 325998

Subsidiary (Non-US):

Shell Egypt N.V. (3)
Sales Range: $75-99.9 Million
Emp.: 250
Oil & Gas Exploration Services
N.A.I.C.S.: 213112

Shell El Salvador S.A. (3)
Boulevard de Los Proceres Frente a Reparto Los Heroes, Estacion Shell Monumental, San Salvador, El Salvador
Tel.: (503) 2528 8000
Web Site: http://www.shell.com
Specialty Gasoline Mfr & Distr
N.A.I.C.S.: 211120

Shell Energy Deutschland GmbH (3)
Suhrenkamp 71-77, 22335, Hamburg, Germany
Tel.: (49) 4063244721
Oil & Gas Exploration Services
N.A.I.C.S.: 213112

Shell Energy Holdings Australia Limited (3)
8 Redfern Road, Hawthorn East, Melbourne, 3123, VIC, Australia
Tel.: (61) 396665444
Investment Management Service
N.A.I.C.S.: 523999

Subsidiary (Domestic):

ERM Power Limited (4)
Level 52 111 Eagle St, Brisbane, 4000, QLD, Australia
Tel.: (61) 730205100
Web Site: http://www.ermpower.com.au
Rev.: $2,560,462,226
Assets: $1,061,570,205
Liabilities: $866,837,950
Net Worth: $194,732,255
Earnings: ($62,987,104)
Emp.: 336
Fiscal Year-end: 06/30/2018
Electric Power & Natural Gas Distribution & Generation Services
N.A.I.C.S.: 926130
Derek McKay (CIO & Exec Gen Mgr-Generation)

Subsidiary (Non-US):

Shell Enerji A.S. (3)
Bilkent Plaza A3 Blok Kat 4 No 37, Bilkent, 06800, Ankara, Türkiye
Tel.: (90) 312 266 02 44
Web Site: http://www.shell.com.tr
Oil & Gas Exploration Services
N.A.I.C.S.: 213112

Shell Erdoel Und Erdgas Exploration GmbH (3)
Suhrenkamp 71-77, 22335, Hamburg, Germany
Tel.: (49) 4063244516
Oil & Gas Exploration Services
N.A.I.C.S.: 213112

Shell Espana, S.A. (3)
Tel.: (34) 915370100
Sales Range: $1-4.9 Billion
Emp.: 150
Petroleum Refiner
N.A.I.C.S.: 211120

Shell Exploration NZ Limited (3)
Level 10 ASB Tower 2 Hunter Street, Wellington, 6145, New Zealand
Tel.: (64) 4 471 4519
Web Site: http://www.shell.co.nz
Emp.: 14
Oil & Gas Exploration & Production Services
N.A.I.C.S.: 211120

Shell Exploration and Production Libya GmbH (3)
Gargaresh Road km 6 2 Abunawas 2, PO Box 91791, Tripoli, Libya
Tel.: (218) 21 4843001
Web Site: http://www.shell.com
Oil & Gas Exploration Services
N.A.I.C.S.: 213112

Subsidiary (Domestic):

Shell Exploration and Production Oman Limited (3)

Shell Centre, London, SE1 7NA, United Kingdom
Tel.: (44) 2079344248
Oil & Gas Exploration & Production Serivces
N.A.I.C.S.: 211120

Subsidiary (Non-US):

Shell Gabon (3)
, BP 146, Port-Gentil, Gabon (75%)
Tel.: (241) 552662
Web Site: http://www.shell.com
Petroleum Refiner
N.A.I.C.S.: 324110

Shell Gas Vietnam Ltd. (3)
Fl 7 39 Le Duan D1, Ho Chi Minh City, Vietnam
Tel.: (84) 8 3824 0300
Gas Exploration Services
N.A.I.C.S.: 213112

Shell Ghana Ltd. (3)
Rangoon Lane, PO Box 1097, Accra, Ghana
Tel.: (233) 302428282
Chemical Products Distr
N.A.I.C.S.: 424690

Shell Global Solutions (Deutschland) GmbH (3)
Hohe Schaar Str 36, 21107, Hamburg, Germany
Tel.: (49) 4075656
Sales Range: $75-99.9 Million
Emp.: 250
Oil & Gas Exploration Services
N.A.I.C.S.: 213112

Subsidiary (US):

Shell Global Solutions (US) Inc (3)
Westhollow Technology Ctr 3333 Hwy 6 S, Houston, TX 77082-3101
Tel.: (281) 544-8844
Web Site: http://www.shell.com
Business & Operational Consultancy Services
N.A.I.C.S.: 541614

Subsidiary (Domestic):

Shell Global Solutions UK (3)
Shell Technology Centre Thornton, PO Box 1, Chester, CH1 3SH, United Kingdom
Tel.: (44) 1513735000
Web Site: http://www.shell.co.uk
Petroleum Product Mfr
N.A.I.C.S.: 324199

Subsidiary (Non-US):

Shell Guatemala SA (3)
11 calle 2-20 zone 10 Avia complex tower 3 level 19 office 1901, Guatemala, Guatemala
Tel.: (502) 22851400
Petroleum Product Mfr
N.A.I.C.S.: 324199

Shell Hellas A.E. (3)
Irodou Attikou 12A, 15124, Maroussi, Greece
Tel.: (30) 2109476000
Sales Range: $50-74.9 Million
Emp.: 250
Chemicals Whslr
N.A.I.C.S.: 424690

Shell Hong Kong Limited (3)
35/F AIA Kowloon Tower Landmark East 100 How Ming Street, Kwun Tong, Kowloon, China (Hong Kong)
Tel.: (852) 25067000
Web Site: https://www.shell.com.hk
Petroleum Product Distr
N.A.I.C.S.: 424720

Shell Hungary Rt (3)
Bocskai ut 134-146, 1113, Budapest, Hungary
Tel.: (36) 14363200
Web Site: https://www.shell.hu
Sales Range: $600-649.9 Million
Emp.: 300
Petroleum Refiner
N.A.I.C.S.: 324110

Shell India Markets Private Limited (3)
Powai Plaza 401-403 4th Floor Hiranandani

INTERNATIONAL PUBLIC

Business Park, Powai, Mumbai, 400 076, India
Tel.: (91) 22 40363888
Web Site: http://www.shell.com
Lubricant Distr
N.A.I.C.S.: 424720

Plant (Domestic):

Shell India Markets Private Limited - Eastern Processing Plant (4)
Plot No 54 WBIIDC Uluberia Industrial Growth Centre, Birshibpur, Howrah, 711 316, West Bengal, India
Tel.: (91) 33 64509267
Web Site: http://www.shell.com
Asphalt Product Mfr
N.A.I.C.S.: 324121

Shell India Markets Private Limited - Western Processing Plant (4)
Plot 745 GIDC Manjusar, Tal Savli Dist, Vadodara, 391 775, Gujarat, India
Tel.: (91) 2667 264151
Web Site: http://www.shell.com
Petroleum Product Mfr
N.A.I.C.S.: 324199

Subsidiary (Non-US):

Shell Japan Ltd. (3)
16F Pacific Century Place Marunouchi 1-11-1 Marunouchi, Chiyoda-ku, Tokyo, 100-6216, Japan
Tel.: (81) 3 3218 1771
Web Site: http://www.shell.co.jp
Sales Range: $50-74.9 Million
Emp.: 20
Oil & Gas Exploration Services
N.A.I.C.S.: 213112
Chris Gunner (Pres)

Shell Luxembourgeoise Sarl (3)
7 rue de l'Industrie, 8069, Bertrange, Luxembourg
Tel.: (352) 3111411
Web Site: https://www.shell.lu
Sales Range: $25-49.9 Million
Emp.: 12
Petroleum Product Mfr
N.A.I.C.S.: 324199

Shell MDS Sendirian Berhad (3)
Changkat Semantan, Damansara Heights, 50490, Kuala Lumpur, Malaysia (72%)
Tel.: (60) 320959144
Web Site: http://www.shell.com
Sales Range: $200-249.9 Million
Emp.: 1,000
Petroleum Refiner
N.A.I.C.S.: 324110

Shell Malaysia Trading Sdn. Bhd. (3)
Menara Shell No 211 Jalan Tun Sambanthan, Damansara Heights, 50470, Kuala Lumpur, Malaysia
Tel.: (60) 23852888
Petroleum Products Wholesale Trade Distr
N.A.I.C.S.: 425120

Subsidiary (Domestic):

Shell Marine Products Ltd. (3)
2 York Road Shell Centre, London, SE1 7NA, United Kingdom
Tel.: (44) 2079341234
Web Site: http://www.shell.com
Sales Range: $500-549.9 Million
Emp.: 1,800
Quality Fuels, Lubricants & Complementary Services & Whslr
N.A.I.C.S.: 424720

Subsidiary (Non-US):

Shell Marketing Algerie S.p.A. (3)
5 Chemin El Bekri, Ben Aknoun, 16033, Algiers, Algeria
Tel.: (213) 21 915 915
Crude Oil & Natural Gas Extracting Services
N.A.I.C.S.: 211120

Shell Markets Middle East (3)
Level 3 The Offices 4 One Central World Trade Center, Dubai, United Arab Emirates
Tel.: (971) 44054400
Sales Range: $250-299.9 Million
Emp.: 1,000
Chemicals Whslr

AND PRIVATE COMPANIES — SHELL PLC

N.A.I.C.S.: 424690

Shell New Zealand Ltd. (3)
Level 28 Majestic Centre 100 Willis Street, Wellington, New Zealand
Tel.: (64) 44714519
Web Site: http://www.shell.com
Sales Range: $25-49.9 Million
Emp.: 12
Petroleum Product Whslr
N.A.I.C.S.: 424720

Shell Nigeria Gas Limited (3)
NSC Building Plot 33 Mobolaji Johnson Way Oregun, Ikeja, Lagos, Nigeria
Tel.: (234) 8070315243
Natural Gas Distr
N.A.I.C.S.: 221210

Shell Oman Trading Limited (3)
PO Box 38, Muscat, Oman
Tel.: (968) 24570200
Fuel Distr
N.A.I.C.S.: 424720

Subsidiary (Domestic):

Shell Overseas Holdings Limited (3)
Shell Centre, London, SE1 7NA, United Kingdom
Tel.: (44) 2079344248
Investment Management Service
N.A.I.C.S.: 523940

Subsidiary (Non-US):

Shell Overseas Services Ltd. (3)
Granada Oasis Park 10th Floor Building A4 Exit 9 East ring road, Post Box 12212, Riyadh, 11473, Saudi Arabia
Tel.: (966) 115117050
Web Site: https://www.shell.sa
Sales Range: $25-49.9 Million
Emp.: 100
Petroleum Services
N.A.I.C.S.: 324110

Shell Panama S.A. (3)
Via Transistmica a 200 mts a mano izquierda, San Miguelito, Panama
Tel.: (507) 275 9000
Crude Oil & Natural Gas Extracting Services
N.A.I.C.S.: 211120

Shell Papua New Guinea Pty. Ltd. (3)
PO Box 169, Port Moresby, Papua New Guinea
Tel.: (675) 3228700
Sales Range: $25-49.9 Million
Emp.: 70
Chemicals
N.A.I.C.S.: 424690

Shell Polska Sp. z o.o. (3)
Street Bitwy Warszawskiej 1920 no 7a, 02-366, Warsaw, Poland
Tel.: (48) 225700000
Web Site: https://www.shell.pl
Petroleum Whslr
N.A.I.C.S.: 424720

Shell Portuguesa Lda (3)
Jofe Malhoa 16, PO Box 2008, 1099091, Lisbon, Portugal
Tel.: (351) 213119000
Sales Range: $1-9.9 Million
Emp.: 350
Marketing of Chemicals
N.A.I.C.S.: 424690
Antonio Victor *(Gen Mgr)*

Shell Slovakia, s.r.o. (3)
Einsteinova 23, 81104, Bratislava, Slovakia
Tel.: (421) 258245110
Web Site: http://www.shell.sk
Emp.: 30
Oil & Gas Exploration Services
N.A.I.C.S.: 213112

Shell South Africa Energy (Pty) Ltd. (3)
The Campus Twickenham 57 Sloane Street, Epsom Downs, Bryanston, 2021, South Africa
Tel.: (27) 119967000
Petroleum Refiner, Marketer & Wholesale Distr; Chemical Mfr
N.A.I.C.S.: 551114

Division (Domestic):

Shell South Africa Energy (Pty) Ltd. - Chemical Division (4)
Reunion, PO Box 193, Umbogintwini, 4120, South Africa
Tel.: (27) 319132000
Chemical Products Mfr
N.A.I.C.S.: 325998
J. Koovarjee *(Gen Mgr)*

Subsidiary (Domestic):

Shell South Africa Holdings (Pty) Limited (4)
The Campus Twickenham 57 Sloane Street, Epsom Downs, Bryanston, 2021, South Africa
Tel.: (27) 119967000
Holding Company
N.A.I.C.S.: 551112
Hloniphizwe Mtolo *(Mng Dir)*

Shell South Africa Marketing (Pty) Ltd. (4)
The Campus Twickenham 57 Sloane Street, Epsom Downs, Bryanston, 2021, South Africa
Tel.: (27) 11 996 7000
Emp.: 120
Petroleum Products Marketer & Distr
N.A.I.C.S.: 424720

Subsidiary (Non-US):

Shell Suriname Verkoop Maatschappij NV (3)
PO Box 849, Paramaribo, Suriname
Tel.: (597) 482027
Oil & Gas Exploration Services
N.A.I.C.S.: 213112
Marc Goede *(Acct Mgr)*

Shell Technology Norway AS (3)
Sentrum, PO Box 1154, Oslo, 107, Norway
Tel.: (47) 51693000
Crude Oil & Natural Gas Extracting Services
N.A.I.C.S.: 211120

Shell Thailand (3)
10 Soonthornkosa Rd, Klongtoey, Bangkok, 10110, Thailand
Tel.: (66) 22626000
Web Site: http://www.shell.co.th
Oil & Natural Gas Exploration
N.A.I.C.S.: 211120

Shell Treasury Luxembourg SARL (3)
7 Rue de l'Industrie, L-8069, Bertrange, Luxembourg
Tel.: (352) 3111411
Web Site: http://www.shell.lu
Sales Range: $25-49.9 Million
Emp.: 10
Chemicals Whslr
N.A.I.C.S.: 424690

Shell Trinidad Limited (3)
Shell Energy House 5 St Clair Avenue, PO Bag 51, St Clair, Port of Spain, Trinidad & Tobago
Tel.: (868) 6280888
Sales Range: $25-49.9 Million
Emp.: 100
Petroleum Product Mfr
N.A.I.C.S.: 324199

Subsidiary (Domestic):

Shell U.K. Ltd. (3)
Shell Centre, London, SE1 7NA, United Kingdom (100%)
Tel.: (44) 2079341234
Web Site: https://www.shell.co.uk
Sales Range: $1-4.9 Billion
Emp.: 8,000
Holding Company; Oil & Gas Exploration Services
N.A.I.C.S.: 551112
Sinead Lynch *(Chm)*

Joint Venture (Domestic):

British Pipeline Agency Ltd. (4)
5-7 Alexandra Road, Hemel Hempstead, HP2 5BS, Herts, United Kingdom
Tel.: (44) 1442242200
Web Site: http://www.bpa.co.uk
Sales Range: $25-49.9 Million
Emp.: 100
Gas Pipelines Operator & Engineering Services; Owned 50% by Shell U.K. Ltd. & 50% by BP Oil U.K.
N.A.I.C.S.: 237120
Peter Davis *(Gen Mgr)*

Subsidiary (Non-US):

Shell Uganda (3)
Vivo Energy Uganda 7th Street Industrial Area Plot 9 11, PO Box 7082, Kampala, Uganda
Tel.: (256) 312210010
Web Site: https://www.shell.co.ug
Sales Range: $50-74.9 Million
Emp.: 110
Chemicals Whslr
N.A.I.C.S.: 424690

Subsidiary (Domestic):

Shell Upstream International Ltd. (3)
1 Altens Farm Road Nigg, Aberdeen, AB12 3FY, United Kingdom
Tel.: (44) 1224 882000
Crude Oil & Natural Gas Extracting Services
N.A.I.C.S.: 211120

Plant (Domestic):

Shell Upstream International Ltd. - Bacton Gas Plant (4)
Paston Rd Bacton, Norwich, Norfolk, NR12 0JE, United Kingdom
Tel.: (44) 1263 720661
Crude Oil & Natural Gas Extracting Services
N.A.I.C.S.: 211120

Shell Upstream International Ltd. - Fife NGL Plant (4)
PO Box 16, Cowdenbeath, KY4 8EL, Fife, United Kingdom
Tel.: (44) 1383 611333
Crude Oil & Natural Gas Extracting Services
N.A.I.C.S.: 211120

Subsidiary (Non-US):

Shell Uruguay S.A. (3)
San Fructuoso 927, Montevideo, CP-11800, Uruguay
Tel.: (598) 22007853
Web Site: http://www.shell.com
Sales Range: $25-49.9 Million
Emp.: 50
Chemicals Whslr
N.A.I.C.S.: 424690

Shell Venezuela Productos, C.A. (3)
Zona Industrial Municipal Sur Av Domingo Olavarria Parcela 6-2, Planta de Lubricantes Shell, Valencia, Venezuela
Tel.: (58) 241 874 4600
Web Site: http://www.shell.com.ve
Oil & Gas Exploration Services
N.A.I.C.S.: 213112

Shell Verwaltungsgesellschaft Fur Erdgasbeteiligungen mbH (3)
Suhrenkamp 71-77, 22335, Hamburg, Germany
Tel.: (49) 4063240
Investment Management Service
N.A.I.C.S.: 523940

Shell Vietnam Ltd. (3)
7th Floor 39 Le Duan, District 1, Ho Chi Minh City, Vietnam
Tel.: (84) 2838240300
Web Site: https://www.shell.com.vn
Petroleum Services
N.A.I.C.S.: 324110

Plant (Domestic):

Shell Vietnam Ltd. - Go Dau Plant (4)
Lot 2 Go Dau Industrial Zone, Long Thanh, Dong Nai, Vietnam
Tel.: (84) 61 384 1313
Web Site: http://www.shell.com
Sales Range: $50-74.9 Million
Emp.: 80
Oil & Gas Exploration Services
N.A.I.C.S.: 213112

Subsidiary (Non-US):

Shell del Peru S.A. (3)
Las Begonias 441 4to Piso, Lima, Peru
Tel.: (51) 1 513 7373
Crude Oil & Natural Gas Extracting Services
N.A.I.C.S.: 211120

Ste des Petroles Shell SAS (3)
Immeuble Portes de la Defense 307 Rue Estienne d'Orves, Colombes, 92700, France
Tel.: (33) 1 57 60 61 00
Oil & Gas Exploration Services
N.A.I.C.S.: 213112

Syria Shell Petroleum Development BV (3)
Dummer 1st Island Alfurat Bldg, PO Box 9663, Damascus, Syria
Tel.: (963) 112217220
Web Site: http://www.shell.com
Sales Range: $75-99.9 Million
Emp.: 200
Oil & Natural Gas Exploration
N.A.I.C.S.: 211120

The Shell Co. of the Philippines Ltd. (3)
156 Valero Street, Salcedo Village, Makati, 1227, Philippines
Tel.: (63) 28166565
Sales Range: $50-74.9 Million
Emp.: 130
Petroleum Refiner
N.A.I.C.S.: 324110

The Shell Company of Sri Lanka Ltd. (3)
498 RA De Mel Mawatha, Colombo, 3, Sri Lanka
Tel.: (94) 1581131
Web Site: http://www.shell-srilanka.com
Sales Range: $900-999.9 Million
Emp.: 4,000
Petroleum Refiner
N.A.I.C.S.: 324110

The Shell Company of Thailand Ltd. (3)
Shell Building 10 Sunthonkosa Road, Khlong Toei, Bangkok, 10110, Thailand
Tel.: (66) 22626000
Sales Range: $200-249.9 Million
Emp.: 620
Petroleum Refiner
N.A.I.C.S.: 324110
Panun Prachuabmoh *(Chm & CFO)*

Vivo Energy Cote d'Ivoire (3)
15 BP 378 Abidjan 15 Rue des petroliers, BP 378, Zone Industrielle de Vridi, 15, Abidjan, Cote d'Ivoire
Tel.: (225) 21752727
Sales Range: $25-49.9 Million
Emp.: 100
Energy & Petrochemicals Producer
N.A.I.C.S.: 325120
Franck Konan Yahaut *(Exec VP/VP-West)*

Subsidiary (Non-US):

The Shell Transport & Trading Co. Ltd. (2)
Shell Centre, 2 York Road, London, SE1 7NA, United Kingdom (100%)
Tel.: (44) 2079341234
Sales Range: $500-549.9 Million
Emp.: 1,500
Holding Company
N.A.I.C.S.: 551112

Subsidiary (Non-US):

Shell International Trading & Shipping Co. Ltd. (3)
Tel.: (44) 2075465000
Web Site: http://www.shell.com
Sales Range: $150-199.9 Million
Emp.: 460
Crude Oil, Refined Products, Natural Gas, Electrical Power & Chemicals Trading Services
N.A.I.C.S.: 523160

Subsidiary (US):

Shell Energy North America (US) L.P. (4)

SHELL PLC

Shell plc—(Continued)

1000 Main St Level 12, Houston, TX 77002 **(100%)**
Tel.: (713) 241-6161
Web Site: http://www.shell.us
Sales Range: $150-199.9 Million
Emp.: 400
Holding Company; Oil & Gas Wholesale Trading & Marketing
N.A.I.C.S.: 551112

Subsidiary (Domestic):

MP2 Energy LLC (5)
21 Waterway Ave Ste 450, The Woodlands, TX 77380 **(100%)**
Tel.: (832) 510-1030
Web Site: https://shellenergy.com
Renewable Energy Supplier
N.A.I.C.S.: 221114
David Black (CEO)

Subsidiary (Non-US):

Shell Energy North America (Canada) Inc. (5)
400 - 4th Avenue SW, Calgary, T2P 0J4, AB, Canada **(100%)**
Tel.: (403) 691-3111
Web Site: http://www.shell.ca
Sales Range: $200-249.9 Million
Emp.: 125
Oil & Gas Wholesale Trading & Marketing
N.A.I.C.S.: 425120

Shell Trading (US) Company (5)
Tel.: (713) 241-6161
Web Site: http://www.shell.us
Sales Range: $200-249.9 Million
Emp.: 200
Oil & Gas Wholesale Trading & Marketing
N.A.I.C.S.: 425120

Subsidiary (Domestic):

Shell US Gas & Power LLC (5)
1301 McKinney, Houston, TX 77010
Tel.: (713) 230-3000
Web Site: http://www.shell-usgp.com
Emp.: 8
Electric Power Marketers
N.A.I.C.S.: 221122

Subsidiary (Non-US):

Shell Tankers (Singapore) Private Limited (4)
83 Clemenceau Avenue 04-00 Orchard, Singapore, 239920, Singapore
Tel.: (65) 63848000
Petroleum Product Whslr
N.A.I.C.S.: 424720

Shell Trading Rotterdam B.V. (4)
Weena 70, Rotterdam, 3012 CM, Zuid-Holland, Netherlands
Tel.: (31) 104415000
Petroleum Product Distr
N.A.I.C.S.: 424720

Shell Western Supply & Trading Ltd. (4)
Mahogany Court Wildey Business Center, Wildey, Barbados
Tel.: (246) 4314800
Petroleum Product Whslr
N.A.I.C.S.: 424720

Shell USA, Inc. (1)
Tel.: (281) 544-2600
Web Site: https://www.shell.us
Natural Gas Explorer, Extractor, Refiner & Distr
N.A.I.C.S.: 324110

Subsidiary (Domestic):

Volta Inc. (2)
155 De Haro St, San Francisco, CA 94103
Tel.: (415) 583-3805
Web Site: https://voltacharging.com
Rev.: $54,600,000
Assets: $341,312,000
Liabilities: $189,988,000
Net Worth: $151,324,000
Earnings: ($154,633,000)
Emp.: 208
Fiscal Year-end: 12/31/2022
Investment Services
N.A.I.C.S.: 523999

Brandt Hastings (Pres)

Subsidiary (Domestic):

Volta Industries, Inc. (3)
155 De Haro, San Francisco, CA 94103
Tel.: (805) 215-9915
Web Site: http://www.voltacharging.com
Electric Vehicle Charging Services
N.A.I.C.S.: 457120
Scott Mercer (Co-Founder & CEO)

Shell Ukraine Exploration & Production I LLC
St M Hrinchenko 4 Horizon Park Business Center, Kiev, 03038, Ukraine
Tel.: (380) 44 237 0077
Web Site: https://www.shell.ua
Natural Gas Distribution Services
N.A.I.C.S.: 221210

Sonnen Australia Pty Limited (1)
Lionsgate Business Park Tenancy 6/180 Philip Hwy, Elizabeth, 5112, SA, Australia
Tel.: (61) 137666
Web Site: https://www.sonnen.com.au
Home Battery Mfr
N.A.I.C.S.: 335910

Sonnen S.R.L. (1)
Via Autostrada 32, 24126, Bergamo, Italy
Tel.: (39) 035 033 1135
Web Site: https://www.sonnen.it
Electrical Equipment Distr
N.A.I.C.S.: 423610

The New Motion Deutschland GmbH (1)
Wattstrasse 11, 13355, Berlin, Germany
Electrical Equipment Distr
N.A.I.C.S.: 423610

Zeco Systems Pte. Ltd. (1)
1 Commonwealth Lane 09-30 One Commonwealth Building, Singapore, 149544, Singapore
Tel.: (65) 6 227 5944
Oil & Gas Mfr
N.A.I.C.S.: 324110

euroShell Deutschland GmbH & Co. KG (1)
Suhrenkamp 71-77, 22335, Hamburg, Germany
Tel.: (49) 4080 908 0500
Natural Gas Mfr
N.A.I.C.S.: 325120

SHELMAN SWISS-HELLENIC WOOD PRODUCT MANUFACTURERS SA

2 26 Kifissias Ave & Paradeisou Str, Marousi, 151 25, Athens, Greece
Tel.: (30) 2108172600
Web Site: http://www.shelman.gr
Year Founded: 1962
Sales Range: $100-124.9 Million
Emp.: 687
Plywood, Chipboard, Blackboard, Veneers, Melamine, Timber & Flooring Products Mfr
N.A.I.C.S.: 321211
Antonios G. Adamopoylos (Chm & CEO)

Subsidiaries:

XYLEMPORIKI PATRON S.A. (1)
Coast Dyme 167 & Agenor, PC 26333, Patras, Greece
Tel.: (30) 2610529886
Web Site: http://www.xyleboriki.gr
Wood Products Mfr
N.A.I.C.S.: 238160
Psiris Konstantinos (Mng Dir)

SHELTER INFRA PROJECTS LIMITED

Eternity DN-1 Sector-V Salt Lake City, Kolkata, 7000 91, India
Tel.: (91) 3323576255
Web Site: https://www.ccapltd.in
526839—(BOM)
Rev.: $174,702
Assets: $5,082,669
Liabilities: $4,620,874
Net Worth: $461,795
Earnings: ($48,474)
Emp.: 11
Fiscal Year-end: 03/31/23
Construction & Infrastructure Services
N.A.I.C.S.: 237990
Aparupa Das (Compliance Officer & Sec)

SHEMAROO ENTERTAINMENT LTD.

Shemaroo House Plot no 18 Marol Co-op Industrial Estate, Off Andheri-Kurla Road Andheri E, Mumbai, 400 059, India
Tel.: (91) 2240319911
Web Site: https://www.shemarooent.com
538685—(BOM)
Rev.: $67,145,962
Assets: $124,509,214
Liabilities: $54,078,520
Net Worth: $70,430,694
Earnings: $1,122,774
Emp.: 593
Fiscal Year-end: 03/31/23
Content For Satellite Channels, Physical Formats & Emerging Digital Technologies Distr
N.A.I.C.S.: 512120
Buddhichand Maroo (Founder)

Subsidiaries:

Shemaroo Contentino Media LLP (1)
Shemaroo House Plot No 18 Marol Co Op Indl Estate Off, Andheri-Kurla Road Andheri E, Mumbai, 400059, India
Tel.: (91) 2240319911
Web Site: https://www.contentino.in
Flight Entertainment Services
N.A.I.C.S.: 713940

SHEMEN INDUSTRIES LTD.

PO Box 136, Haifa, 31000, Israel
Tel.: (972) 48604600
Web Site: http://www.shemen.co.il
Edible vegetable Oil Mfr
N.A.I.C.S.: 311224
Eyal Ben Sira (CEO)

SHEMEN OIL & GAS RESOURCES LTD.

ITSKHAK SADE 17, Tel Aviv, 64239, Israel
Tel.: (972) 37615000
Year Founded: 2010
Sales Range: Less than $1 Million
Oil & Gas Exploration Services
N.A.I.C.S.: 213112
Becor Sabag (CEO)

SHEN YAO HOLDINGS LIMITED

80 Raffles Place 32-01 UOB Plaza, Singapore, 048624, Singapore
Tel.: (65) 80179198
Web Site: https://www.shenyaoholdings.com
Year Founded: 2004
A78—(SES)
Rev.: $63,022,631
Assets: $55,614,110
Liabilities: $31,432,421
Net Worth: $24,181,689
Earnings: $4,840,868
Fiscal Year-end: 06/30/22
Holding Company; Gold Ore Mining
N.A.I.C.S.: 551112
Sing Huat Ong (Sec)

Subsidiaries:

Golden Point Group Pty Ltd (1)
10 Woolshed Gully Drive, PO Box 98, Mount Clear, 3350, VIC, Australia **(100%)**
Tel.: (61) 353272555
Web Site: https://ballaratgoldmine.com.au

INTERNATIONAL PUBLIC

Sales Range: $1-9.9 Million
Emp.: 150
Gold Exploration Services
N.A.I.C.S.: 212220
Mark G. Davies (Mgr-Processing)

Golden Point Group Pty Ltd. (1)
10 Woolshed Gully Drive, Mount Clear, Ballarat, 3350, VIC, Australia
Tel.: (61) 353272555
Web Site: https://ballaratgoldmine.com.au
Gold Mining Services
N.A.I.C.S.: 212220

Shen Yao Investments Pte. Ltd. (1)
9 Temasek Boulevard 24-01 Suntec Tower 2, Singapore, 038989, Singapore
Tel.: (65) 66906860
Web Site: https://www.shenyaoholdings.com
Gold Mining Services
N.A.I.C.S.: 212220

Shenzhen Vigorhood Electronics Co. Ltd (1)
No 2 Longshan Road Eight Luotian Yanluo, Baoan, Shenzhen, 518127, Guangdong, China
Tel.: (86) 7552 765 2580
Web Site: https://www.vigorhood.com
Emp.: 27
Office Equipments Mfr
N.A.I.C.S.: 339940

Signature Metals Limited (1)
10 Woolshed Gully Drive, PO Box 98, Mount Clear, 3350, VIC, Australia **(76.22%)**
Tel.: (61) 353272616
Web Site: http://www.signaturemetals.com.au
Sales Range: Less than $1 Million
Emp.: 109
Gold Mining
N.A.I.C.S.: 212220
Catherine Officer (Sec)

SHEN'S ART PRINTING CO., LTD.

No 7 Lane365 Sec 1 Chung-Yung Road, To-Chen Taipei, Hsien, Taiwan
Tel.: (886) 222708198
8921—(TPE)
Rev.: $20,483,538
Assets: $38,897,352
Liabilities: $9,498,702
Net Worth: $29,398,649
Earnings: $486,571
Fiscal Year-end: 12/31/22
Digital Printing Services
N.A.I.C.S.: 323117
Cheng-Kang Chen (Chm, Pres & CEO)

SHENDA INTERNATIONAL ENGINEERING CO. LTD.

Rm 2702 Building 1 Kerry Everbright City No 218 West Tianmu Rd, Zhabei district, Shanghai, China
Tel.: (86) 2152182883
Web Site: http://www.shenda.com
Transformer Mfr
N.A.I.C.S.: 334416
Guoquan Jiang (VP)

Subsidiaries:

Jiangshan Shenda Electric Co. Ltd. (1)
No.17 Huatong Road, Development Zone, Quzhou, China
Tel.: (86) 57 0422 1777
Transformer Mfr
N.A.I.C.S.: 335311

Subsidiary (US):

R. E. Uptegraff Manufacturing Co. (2)
120 Uptegraff Dr, Scottdale, PA 15683
Tel.: (724) 887-7700
Web Site: http://www.uptegraff.com
Emp.: 51
Transformer Mfr
N.A.I.C.S.: 335311

SHENERGY COMPANY LIMITED
5F No 159 Hongjing Road, Shanghai, 201103, China
Tel.: (86) 2133570888
Web Site: http://www.shenergy.net.cn
Year Founded: 1993
600642—(SHG)
Rev.: $3,958,313,837
Assets: $12,621,913,345
Liabilities: $7,264,124,515
Net Worth: $5,357,788,830
Earnings: $151,978,142
Fiscal Year-end: 12/31/22
Natural Gas Distr
N.A.I.C.S.: 486910
Hua Shichao (Chm)

SHENG SIONG GROUP LIMITED
6 Mandai Link, Singapore, 728652, Singapore
Tel.: (65) 68951888
Web Site: https://corporate.shengsiong.com.sg
Year Founded: 1985
OV8—(SES)
Rev.: $1,035,915,322
Assets: $628,791,183
Liabilities: $252,378,247
Net Worth: $376,412,936
Earnings: $101,489,055
Emp.: 3,274
Fiscal Year-end: 12/31/23
Supermarkets, Chain
N.A.I.C.S.: 445110
Hock Chee Lim (Co-Founder & CEO)

Subsidiaries:
C M M Marketing Management Pte Ltd (1)
6 Mandailink, 728652, Singapore, Singapore
Tel.: (65) 62690876
Sales Range: $100-124.9 Million
Emp.: 300
Logistics & Warehousing Services
N.A.I.C.S.: 541614

Sheng Siong Supermarket Pte. Ltd. (1)
6 Mandai Link, Singapore, 728652, Singapore
Tel.: (65) 68951888
Web Site: http://www.shengsiong.com.sg
Emp.: 50
Supermarket Operating Services
N.A.I.C.S.: 445110

SHENG YI DEVELOPMENT CO., LTD.
11F No 417 Sec 2 Kung Dao Wu Rd, Hsien, Hsinchu, 300, Taiwan
Tel.: (886) 35753189
5455—(TPE)
Rev.: $18,744,802
Assets: $106,838,164
Liabilities: $88,263,390
Net Worth: $18,574,774
Earnings: $1,867,680
Fiscal Year-end: 12/31/22
Real Estate Management Services
N.A.I.C.S.: 531390
Chen Wen-Chih (Chm & CEO)

SHENG YUAN HOLDINGS LIMITED
26/F No 238 Des Voeux Road, Sheung Wan, Central, China (Hong Kong)
Tel.: (852) 35887000   BM
Web Site: http://www.shengyuan.hk
0851—(HKG)
Rev.: $7,642,350
Assets: $27,372,720
Liabilities: $32,110,110
Net Worth: $(4,737,390)
Earnings: $(739,755)
Emp.: 23
Fiscal Year-end: 12/31/22
Financial Services
N.A.I.C.S.: 523999
Liu Yang (CEO)

Subsidiaries:
Sheng Yuan Securities Limited (1)
Suites 4303-5 43/F Tower 1 Times Square 1 Matheson Street, Causeway Bay, China (Hong Kong)
Tel.: (852) 31928888
Web Site: http://www.shengyuansec.hk
Security Dealing Services
N.A.I.C.S.: 523150

SHENGDA NETWORK TECHNOLOGY, INC.
Floor 6 Building 6 ChouJiang, Lu-Gang WebMall Town YiWu, Jinhua, 32200, Zhejiang, China
Tel.: (86) 7788882886   NV
Web Site: http://www.soltrest.com
Year Founded: 2018
SDWL—(OTCEM)
Rev.: $3,957,000
Assets: $12,886,000
Liabilities: $462,000
Net Worth: $12,424,000
Earnings: $4,323,000
Emp.: 10
Fiscal Year-end: 06/30/22
Application Software Development Services
N.A.I.C.S.: 541511
HangJin Chen (Pres, CEO, CFO, Principal Acctg Officer, Treas & Sec)

SHENGDA RESOURCES CO., LTD.
2FShengda Building No 158 Nanfangzhuang, Fengtai District, Beijing, 100079, China
Tel.: (86) 1056933909
Web Site: https://www.sdjt.com
Year Founded: 1992
000603—(SSE)
Rev.: $263,841,042
Assets: $755,622,438
Liabilities: $259,149,253
Net Worth: $496,473,186
Earnings: $51,190,556
Fiscal Year-end: 12/31/22
Metal & Mineral Mining Services
N.A.I.C.S.: 212210
Zhao Mantang (Chm)

SHENGDATECH, INC.
Unit 2003 East Tower Zhong Rong Heng Rui International Plaza, 620 Zhang Yang Road, Pudong District, Shanghai, 200122, China
Tel.: (86) 21 58359979   NV
Web Site: http://www.shengdatechinc.com
Sales Range: $100-124.9 Million
Emp.: 1,063
Calcium Carbonate & Coal-Based Chemicals Developer, Mfr & Marketer
N.A.I.C.S.: 325998
Michael D. Kang (Chief Restructuring Officer)

Subsidiaries:
Shandong Haize Nano-Materials Co., Ltd. (1)
Chuangye Road, Tai'an, 271000, Shandong, China
Tel.: (86) 5388560629
Specialty Compound & Chemical Mfr
N.A.I.C.S.: 325998

SHENGFENG DEVELOPMENT LIMITED
Shengfeng Building No 478 Fuxin East Road, Jin'an District, Fuzhou, 350001, Fujian, China
Tel.: (86) 59183619860   Ky
Web Site: https://sfwl.com.cn
Year Founded: 2020
SFWL—(NASDAQ)
Rev.: $404,121,000
Assets: $265,838,000
Liabilities: $153,525,000
Net Worth: $112,313,000
Earnings: $10,308,000
Emp.: 1,341
Fiscal Year-end: 12/31/23
Supply Chain Management Services
N.A.I.C.S.: 541614
Yongxu Liu (Chm)

SHENGHE RESOURCES HOLDING CO., LTD.
Floor 7 Chengnan Tianfu Mansion 66 Ste Shenghe No 1 Road, Chengdu, 610041, Sichuan, China
Tel.: (86) 2864362930
Web Site: http://www.shengheholding.com
Year Founded: 2001
600392—(SHG)
Rev.: $2,352,812,951
Assets: $2,181,950,952
Liabilities: $775,516,936
Net Worth: $1,406,434,017
Earnings: $223,724,283
Emp.: 2,000
Fiscal Year-end: 12/31/22
Holding Company
N.A.I.C.S.: 551112

Subsidiaries:
Ganzhou Chenguang Rare Earth New Material Co., Ltd. (1)
10th Floor Tianji Huating Office Building No 2 Changzheng Avenue, Ganzhou, Jiangxi, China
Tel.: (86) 7978384180
Web Site: https://www.gzcgxt.com
Emp.: 400
Rare Earth New Material Mfr & Distr
N.A.I.C.S.: 331492

Hainan Wen-Sheng High-Tech Materials Co., Ltd. (1)
3-301 Shoudan Commercial Building No 199, Haikou, 570000, Hainan, China
Tel.: (86) 89865383348
Web Site: http://www.winsheen.net
Metal Ore Mining Services
N.A.I.C.S.: 212290

Razel Catalysts Corporation (1)
Room 2008 20 floor Palm Springs International Center 99 Tianfu Avenue, Middle Road High-Tech Zone, Chengdu, Sichuan, China
Tel.: (86) 2887578746
Web Site: http://www.rezel.com.cn
Metal Ore Mining Services
N.A.I.C.S.: 212290

SKN (Shanghai) Mining Investment Co., Ltd. (1)
No 530 Zhengding Road Pilot Free Trade Zone, Shanghai, China
Tel.: (86) 2583332600
Web Site: http://www.shskn.cn
Metal Ore Mining Services
N.A.I.C.S.: 212290

SHENGHONG HOLDING GROUP CO., LTD.
Shengze Textile Technology Demonstration Park, Wujiang District, Suzhou, Jiangsu, China
Tel.: (86) 4006212266   CN
Web Site: http://www.shenghonggroup.cn
Year Founded: 1992
Holding Company
N.A.I.C.S.: 551112
Han'gen Miao (Chm)

SHENGHUA ENTERTAINMENT COMMUNICATION CO., LTD.
4F No 176 Sing'ai Rd, Neihu district, Taipei, Taiwan
Tel.: (886) 227955112
4806—(TPE)
Rev.: $25,639
Assets: $10,361,411
Liabilities: $9,782,166
Net Worth: $579,245
Earnings: $(6,243,754)
Fiscal Year-end: 12/31/22
Film & Video Production Services
N.A.I.C.S.: 512120
Wu Yi-Ching (Chm)

SHENGHUA GROUP HOLDINGS CO., LTD.
Zhongguan Industrial Park, Deqing, Hangzhou, 313220, Zhejiang, China
Tel.: (86) 5728402928   CN
Web Site: http://www.shenghuagroup.com
Holding Company
N.A.I.C.S.: 551112
Shilin Xia (Pres)

Subsidiaries:
Zhejiang Huge Leaf Co., Ltd. (1)
Zhongguan Industrial Park, Deqing, Hangzhou, 313220, Zhejiang, China
Tel.: (86) 57187788551
Web Site: http://www.hugeleafgroup.com
Rev.: $84,532,692
Assets: $465,947,081
Liabilities: $32,345,998
Net Worth: $433,601,083
Earnings: $68,237,068
Fiscal Year-end: 12/31/2022
Bio Agrochemical Mfr & Whslr
N.A.I.C.S.: 325320

SHENGJING BANK CO., LTD.
No 109 Beizhan Road, Shenhe District, Shenyang, 110013, Liaoning, China
Tel.: (86) 4000095337   CN
Web Site: https://www.shengjingbank.com.cn
Year Founded: 2007
2066—(HKG)
Rev.: $5,313,606,419
Assets: $149,542,078,257
Liabilities: $138,479,984,908
Net Worth: $11,062,093,348
Earnings: $105,887,101
Emp.: 8,574
Fiscal Year-end: 12/31/23
Commercial Banking Services
N.A.I.C.S.: 522110
Yigong Wang (Exec Dir)

SHENGKAI INNOVATIONS, INC.
No 106 Zhonghuan South Road Airport Industrial Park, Tianjin, 300308, China
Tel.: (86) 2258838509   FL
Web Site: http://www.shengkai.com
VALV—(OTCEM)
Sales Range: $25-49.9 Million
Holding Company; Ceramic Valve Mfr
N.A.I.C.S.: 551112
Chen Wang (Chm, CEO & CTO)

SHENGLAN TECHNOLOGY CO., LTD.
No 4 Hexing Road, Changan Town Shatou South District, Dongguan, 523447, Guangdong, China
Tel.: (86) 76938928688
Web Site: https://www.jctc.com.cn
Year Founded: 2007
300843—(SSE)
Rev.: $164,322,658
Assets: $268,608,970
Liabilities: $119,482,464
Net Worth: $149,126,506
Earnings: $8,389,167
Fiscal Year-end: 12/31/22

SHENGLAN TECHNOLOGY CO., LTD.

Shenglan Technology Co., Ltd.—(Continued)
Electrical Equipment Mfr & Distr
N.A.I.C.S.: 335999
Xuelin Huang (Chm)

SHENGLI OIL & GAS PIPE HOLDINGS LIMITED
Zhongbu Town Zhangdian District, Zibo, Shandong, China
Tel.: (86) 5332272337
Web Site: http://www.slogp.com
Year Founded: 1972
1080—(HKG)
Rev.: $146,983,496
Assets: $162,358,279
Liabilities: $77,754,643
Net Worth: $84,603,636
Earnings: ($4,107,823)
Emp.: 539
Fiscal Year-end: 12/31/22
Holding Company; Oil & Gas Pipeline Mfr
N.A.I.C.S.: 551112
Bizhuang Zhang (CEO)

Subsidiaries:

Hunan Shengli Xianggang Steel Pipe Co., Ltd. (1)
No 8 Binjiang Avenue, High-tech Zone, Xiangtan, Hunan, China
Tel.: (86) 1816 390 9185
Web Site: https://www.hnslxg.cn
Oil & Gas Transmission Steel Pipe Mfr & Whslr
N.A.I.C.S.: 331210

SHENGLONG SPLENDECOR INTERNATIONAL LIMITED
No 8 Shangguafan Rd, Jinnan Subdistrict Lin an, Hangzhou, Zhejiang, China
Tel.: (86) 57163750061   Ky
Web Site: http://www.splendecor.com
Year Founded: 1993
8481—(HKG)
Rev.: $63,010,958
Assets: $81,566,222
Liabilities: $49,673,660
Net Worth: $31,892,562
Earnings: $1,692,943
Emp.: 347
Fiscal Year-end: 12/31/22
Printing Product Mfr & Distr
N.A.I.C.S.: 326113
Yingming Sheng (Founder, Chm & CEO)

Subsidiaries:

Zhejiang Shenglong Decoration Material Co., Ltd. (1)
No 8 Shangguafan Rd, Jinnan Lin'an, Hangzhou, 311301, China
Tel.: (86) 57163750061
Decorating Material Mfr
N.A.I.C.S.: 322299
Joey Wu (Reg Sls Mgr)

SHENGTAI PHARMACEUTICAL, INC.
Changda Road, East Development District, Shandong, 262400, China
Tel.: (86) 5366295802
Pharmaceuticals Product Mfr
N.A.I.C.S.: 325412
Qingtai Liu (Pres & CEO)

SHENGTAK NEW MATERIAL CO., LTD.
West of The Industrial Park, Changzhou, 213144, Jiangsu, China
Tel.: (86) 51983832158
Web Site: https://www.shengdechina.com
Year Founded: 2001
300881—(SSE)
Rev.: $169,447,328
Assets: $224,071,563
Liabilities: $106,272,635
Net Worth: $117,798,927
Earnings: $10,312,450
Fiscal Year-end: 12/31/22
Steel Pipe Mfr & Distr
N.A.I.C.S.: 331210
Wenqing Zhou (Chm)

SHENGUAN HOLDINGS (GROUP) LIMITED
29 Fudian Shangchong Xijiang Fourth Road, Wuzhou, Guangxi, China
Tel.: (86) 7742035538   Ky
Web Site: http://www.shenguan.com.hk
0829—(HKG)
Rev.: $144,914,562
Assets: $470,959,304
Liabilities: $117,229,648
Net Worth: $353,729,657
Earnings: $3,014,388
Emp.: 2,439
Fiscal Year-end: 12/31/22
Sausage Products Mfr & Sales
N.A.I.C.S.: 311613
Yaxian Zhou (Chm & Pres)

Subsidiaries:

CQRC Wealth Management Co., Ltd. (1)
20/F and 21/F Chengda-Jinjia International Building, No 10 Guihua Street Branch Road Jiangbei District, Chongqing, 400024, China
Tel.: (86) 2361111693
Wealth Management Services
N.A.I.C.S.: 523940

Jumbo Gain Developments Limited (1)
Rm 1-3 4/F Win Century Centre, Mong Kok, China (Hong Kong)
Tel.: (852) 27120211
Pharmaceutical Products Distr
N.A.I.C.S.: 424210

Yunnan Xiangyun CQRC Village and Township Bank Co., Ltd. (1)
No 16 Block 11 Yinxiang Garden Wenyuan Road North Side, Xiangcheng Town Xiangyun County, Dali, 672100, Yunnan, China
Tel.: (86) 8723997552
Banking Services
N.A.I.C.S.: 522110

SHENGYI TECHNOLOGY, CO. LTD.
No 5 West Industry Road Songshan Lake Sci & Tech Industry Park, Dongguan, Guangdong, China
Tel.: (86) 769889863188225
Web Site: https://www.syst.com.cn
Year Founded: 1985
600183—(SHG)
Rev.: $2,529,227,685
Assets: $3,537,466,635
Liabilities: $1,389,885,139
Net Worth: $2,147,581,496
Earnings: $214,922,874
Emp.: 10,000
Fiscal Year-end: 12/31/22
Copper Clad Laminates Mfr
N.A.I.C.S.: 334419
Chen Renxi (Chm & Gen Mgr)

Subsidiaries:

Shengyi Electronics Co., Ltd. (1)
No 33 Tong Zhen Road, Tongsha Technology Industrial Park Dong Cheng District, Dongguan, 523127, Guangdong, China
Tel.: (86) 76989281888
Web Site: http://www.sye.com.cn
PCB Line Card Mfr
N.A.I.C.S.: 334412

Shengyi Technology (Hong Kong) Co., Ltd.
Room 802 8/F Ruixing Center 13 Changyue Road, Kowloon, Hong Kong, China (Hong Kong)
Tel.: (852) 23312432

Aluminum Base Material Mfr
N.A.I.C.S.: 331314

SHENGYUAN ENVIRONMENTAL PROTECTION CO., LTD.
Northern Commercial Building No 6 Huli Avenue 519, Huli District, Xiamen, 361000, Fujian, China
Tel.: (86) 5925616385
Web Site: https://www.chinasyep.com
Year Founded: 1997
300867—(SSE)
Rev.: $245,915,388
Assets: $1,180,792,178
Liabilities: $708,032,581
Net Worth: $472,759,597
Earnings: $25,299,294
Fiscal Year-end: 12/31/22
Waste Management Services
N.A.I.C.S.: 562998
Yuxuan Zhu (Chm)

SHENHUA GROUP CORPORATION LIMITED
22 West Binhe Road, Andingmen Dongcheng District, Beijing, 100011, China
Tel.: (86) 1058133355   CN
Web Site: https://www.csec.com
Year Founded: 2004
Holding Company
N.A.I.C.S.: 551112
Zhang Yuzhuo (Vice Gen Mgr)

Subsidiaries:

China Shenhua Energy Company Limited (1)
22 West Riverside Road, Andingmen Dongcheng District, Beijing, 100011, China
Tel.: (86) 1058131088
Sales Range: $25-49.9 Billion
Coal Mining, Production & Transport Services & Power Generation
N.A.I.C.S.: 212115
Dong Li (Exec Dir)

Subsidiary (Domestic):

Shenhua Fujian Energy Co., Ltd. (2)
150 Wenquan East Road, 3F Heyue Town, Fuzhou, 350005, China
Tel.: (86) 59 1887 02510
Power Generation & Distribution Services
N.A.I.C.S.: 221111

Shenhua Shendong Coal Group Co., Ltd. (2)
Daliuta Town, Shenmu County, Yulin, 719315, Shanxi, China
Tel.: (86) 9128220114
Coal Product Distr
N.A.I.C.S.: 423520

Shanxi Guohua Jinjie Energy Co., Ltd. (1)
Jinjie Industrial Zone, Shenmu County, Yulin, 719319, China
Tel.: (86) 9128551062
Eletric Power Generation Services
N.A.I.C.S.: 221118

Shenhua Australia Holdings Pty Limited (1)
Suite 2401 1 York Street, Sydney, 2000, NSW, Australia
Tel.: (61) 2 8273 8888
Web Site: http://www.shenhuawatermark.com
Coal Distr
N.A.I.C.S.: 423520
Liu Xiang (Chm)

Subsidiary (Domestic):

Shenhua Watermark Coal Pty Ltd. (2)
368-370 Conadilly Street, PO Box 1026, Gunnedah, 2380, NSW, Australia
Tel.: (61) 2 6741 8800
Coal Mining Services
N.A.I.C.S.: 212115
Liu Xiang (Chm)

INTERNATIONAL PUBLIC

SHENHUA INTERNATIONAL LIMITED
Level 41 55 Collins Street, Melbourne, 3000, VIC, Australia
Tel.: (61) 39 654 1988   AU
Web Site: http://www.zjhdbl.com
Year Founded: 2008
SHU—(ASX)
Sales Range: $25-49.9 Million
Home Textile Mfr
N.A.I.C.S.: 314999
Xiaohong Chen (Chm)

SHENJI GROUP KUNMING MACHINE TOOL CO., LTD.
23 Ciba Road, Kunming, 650203, Yunnan, China
Tel.: (86) 87166166382   CN
Web Site: http://www.kmtcl.com.cn
Year Founded: 1993
Rev.: $86,049,303
Assets: $259,751,046
Liabilities: $264,435,876
Net Worth: ($4,684,830)
Earnings: ($54,070,093)
Emp.: 2,623
Fiscal Year-end: 12/31/17
Precision Machine Tools Mfr
N.A.I.C.S.: 333517

SHENKE SLIDE BEARING CORP.
No 1 Jiangong East Road, Zhuji, 311800, Zhejiang, China
Tel.: (86) 57587381698
Web Site: https://www.shenke.com
Year Founded: 1996
002633—(SSE)
Rev.: $32,104,945
Assets: $91,068,747
Liabilities: $30,516,530
Net Worth: $60,552,217
Earnings: ($5,459,384)
Emp.: 600
Fiscal Year-end: 12/31/22
Ball & Roller Bearing Mfr
N.A.I.C.S.: 332991
He Jiannan (Chm)

SHENMA INDUSTRY CO., LTD.
63 Middle Jianshe Road, Pingdingshan, 467000, Henan, China
Tel.: (86) 3753921222
Web Site: https://www.shenma.com
Year Founded: 1977
600810—(SHG)
Rev.: $1,903,661,431
Assets: $3,840,485,608
Liabilities: $2,383,620,431
Net Worth: $1,456,865,177
Earnings: $59,918,733
Fiscal Year-end: 12/31/22
Chemical Fiber Mfr & Distr
N.A.I.C.S.: 313110
Wei Wang (Sec)

SHENMAO TECHNOLOGY INC.
No 665 Datan N Rd, Guanyin Dist, Taoyuan, 328451, Taiwan
Tel.: (886) 34160177
Web Site: https://www.shenmao.com
Year Founded: 1973
3305—(TAI)
Rev.: $200,091,559
Assets: $267,270,012
Liabilities: $112,451,482
Net Worth: $154,818,530
Earnings: $7,530,396
Emp.: 630
Fiscal Year-end: 12/31/23
Metal Mfr & Processor
N.A.I.C.S.: 332999
San Lian Lee (Founder, Chm & CEO)

Subsidiaries:

DONG GUAN SHEN MAO SOLDERING TIN CO., LTD. (1)

The 2nd IInd Area Jiumen Village Hu Men Town, Dongguan, China
Tel.: (86) 769 550 8193
Solder Paste Mfr
N.A.I.C.S.: 333992

Dong Guan ShenYang Solder Material Co., Ltd. (1)
Yinhu Industrial Park, Xiegang Town, Dongguan, China
Tel.: (86) 76982126112
Web Site: http://www.shenmao.com
Electric Equipment Mfr
N.A.I.C.S.: 333992

SHENMAO America, Inc. (1)
2156 Ringwood Ave, San Jose, CA 95131
Tel.: (408) 943-1755
Solder Paste Mfr
N.A.I.C.S.: 333992
Watson Tseng (Gen Mgr)

SHENMAO SOLDER (Malaysia) SDN. BHD (1)
No 7 Lorong Jelawat Lapan Kawasan Perusahaan, Seberang Jaya, Perai, Pulau Pinang, Malaysia
Tel.: (60) 4 399 5259
Emp.: 34
Solder Paste Mfr
N.A.I.C.S.: 333992
C. C. Lee (Gen Mgr)

SHENMAO TECHNOLOGY (THAILAND) CO., LTD. (1)
322 Moo 7 304 Industrial Park Zone 3, Thatoom, Tambol, 25140, Prachinburi, Thailand
Tel.: (66) 840887055
Solder Paste Mfr
N.A.I.C.S.: 333992

Shenmao Europe GmbH (1)
Hans Urmiller Ring 16, D 82515, Wolfratshausen, Germany
Tel.: (49) 81713872311
Web Site: http://www.shenmao.com
Sales Range: $25-49.9 Million
Emp.: 4
Electric Equipment Mfr
N.A.I.C.S.: 333992

Shenmao Solder Material (Suzhou) Co., Ltd. (1)
No 1477 Chung San North Rd Wu Chiang Economic Development Area, Sung Lin Town Wu Chiang, Suzhou, 215200, China
Tel.: (86) 51263451092
Emp.: 142
Electric Equipment Mfr
N.A.I.C.S.: 334419

SHENTONG ROBOT EDUCATION GROUP COMPANY LIMITED
Units 3006 30/F West Tower Shun Tak Centre, 168-200 Connaught Road, Central, China (Hong Kong)
Tel.: (852) 3 102 8166 Ky
Web Site: http://www.srobotedu.com
Year Founded: 2002
8206—(HKG)
Rev.: $1,568,526
Assets: $35,475,691
Liabilities: $39,867,718
Net Worth: ($4,392,027)
Earnings: ($10,685,735)
Emp.: 84
Fiscal Year-end: 03/31/22
Holding Company; Electronic Smart Card Mfr & School-based Robot Teaching Services
N.A.I.C.S.: 551112
Chenguang He (Chm)

SHENTONG TECHNOLOGY GROUP CO., LTD.
No 788 Tanjialing West Road, Ningbo, Yuyao, Zhejiang, China
Tel.: (86) 57462590629
Web Site: https://www.shentongtech.com
Year Founded: 2005

605228—(SHG)
Rev.: $200,608,687
Assets: $311,266,814
Liabilities: $103,965,723
Net Worth: $207,301,091
Earnings: $6,324,992
Fiscal Year-end: 12/31/22
Automotive Parts Mfr & Distr
N.A.I.C.S.: 336390
Lifeng Fang (Chm & Sec)

SHENWAN HONGYUAN (H.K.) LIMITED
Level 6 Three Pacific Place 1 Queen's Road East, Hong Kong, China (Hong Kong)
Tel.: (852) 25098333
Web Site: https://www.swhyhk.com
0218—(HKG)
Rev.: $54,358,350
Assets: $2,105,877,083
Liabilities: $1,728,492,000
Net Worth: $377,385,083
Earnings: ($112,190,310)
Emp.: 315
Fiscal Year-end: 12/31/22
Investment Holding Company
N.A.I.C.S.: 523940
Qingli Fang (Chm)

Subsidiaries:

Shenwan Hongyuan Singapore Private Limited (1)
Unit 1202 Robinson Centre 61 Robinson Road, Singapore, 068893, Singapore
Tel.: (65) 63235211
Securities Brokerage Services
N.A.I.C.S.: 523150

SHENWAN HONGYUAN GROUP CO., LTD.
19 taipingqiao street, Xicheng District, Beijing, China
Tel.: (86) 9912301870
Web Site: https://www.swhygh.com
6806—(HKG)
Rev.: $3,784,555,965
Assets: $87,981,476,794
Liabilities: $70,148,881,812
Net Worth: $17,832,594,982
Earnings: $758,086,370
Emp.: 11,803
Fiscal Year-end: 12/31/23
Financial Investment Services
N.A.I.C.S.: 523999
Xiaoming Chu (Chm)

Subsidiaries:

Hongyuan Huizhi Investment Co., Ltd. (1)
Room 3-4 Room 104 Building 3 Balongqiao Yayuan, Qiaozi Town Huairou District, Beijing, China
Tel.: (86) 1088013705
Investment Management & Consulting Services
N.A.I.C.S.: 522320

SWS MU Fund Management Co., Ltd. (1)
11/F No 100 Zhongshan South Road, Huangpu District, Shanghai, China
Tel.: (86) 2123261188
Web Site: https://www.swsmu.com
Fund Management Services
N.A.I.C.S.: 525110

SWS Research Co., Ltd. (1)
3/F 99 East Nanjing Road, Shanghai, 200002, China
Tel.: (86) 2123297818
Web Site: https://www.swsresearch.com
Emp.: 250
Financial Advisory Services
N.A.I.C.S.: 522320

Shenwan Hongyuan (International) Holdings Limited (1)
4/F Three Pacific Place 1 Queens Road East, Hong Kong, China (Hong Kong)
Tel.: (852) 25098333

Securities Brokerage & Investment Services
N.A.I.C.S.: 523999

Shenwan Hongyuan Financing Services Co., Ltd. (1)
Room 2004 20/F Dacheng International Building No 358, Beijing South Road Urumqi Hightech Industrial Development Zone, Xinjiang, China
Tel.: (86) 2133389988
Securities Brokerage & Investment Services
N.A.I.C.S.: 523999

Shenyin & Wanguo Alternative Investment Co., Ltd. (1)
Room 201 Building A No 1 Qianwan First Road, Qianhai Shenzhen-Hong Kong Cooperation Zone, Shenzhen, China
Tel.: (86) 2161820675
Investment Management & Advisory Services
N.A.I.C.S.: 522320

Shenyin & Wanguo Investment Co., Ltd. (1)
Room 503-509 5th Floor No 989 Changle Road, Xuhui District, Shanghai, China
Tel.: (86) 2160581188
Web Site: https://www.sywgtz.com.cn
Financial Advisory Services
N.A.I.C.S.: 522320

SHENWU ENERGY SAVING CO., LTD.
Room 907 Block A Huizhi Building No 28 Ningshuang Road, Yuhuatai District, Nanjing, 121203, China
Tel.: (86) 2585499131
Web Site: https://njswes.com.cn
Year Founded: 1993
000820—(SSE)
Rev.: $22,004,415
Assets: $49,450,733
Liabilities: $32,948,258
Net Worth: $16,502,476
Earnings: ($2,234,592)
Fiscal Year-end: 12/31/22
Investment Services
N.A.I.C.S.: 523999

SHENWU ENVIRONMENTAL TECHNOLOGY CO., LTD.
7F Tower C No 15 Building No 5 Yard Jiangtai Road, Chaoyang District, Beijing, 100016, China
Tel.: (86) 10 80470099
Web Site: http://www.swet.net.cn
Year Founded: 2004
300156—(CHIN)
Sales Range: $25-49.9 Million
Emp.: 370
Industrial Kiln & Furnace Environmental Protection System Mfr
N.A.I.C.S.: 333994
Daohong Wu (Chm)

SHENYANG BLUE SILVER INDUSTRY AUTOMATIC EQUIPMENT CO., LTD.
No 3 Feiyun Road Hunnan Industry Zone, Hunnan District, Shenyang, 110168, Liaoning, China
Tel.: (86) 2423819555
Web Site: https://www.chnsbs.net
Year Founded: 1996
300293—(CHIN)
Rev.: $177,386,976
Assets: $302,567,616
Liabilities: $233,052,768
Net Worth: $69,514,848
Earnings: ($7,651,800)
Emp.: 290
Fiscal Year-end: 12/31/22
Automatic Control Equipment Mfr
N.A.I.C.S.: 334517
Guo Hongtao (Chm & Gen Mgr)

Subsidiaries:

Ecoclean GmbH (1)

Muhlenstrasse 12, 70794, Filderstadt, Germany (100%)
Tel.: (49) 71170060
Web Site: http://www.durr-ecoclean.com
Industrial Machinery Cleaning
N.A.I.C.S.: 333998

Branch (Domestic):

Durr Ecoclean GmbH (2)
Hans-Georg-Weiss-Strasse 10, 52156, Monschau, Germany (100%)
Tel.: (49) 2472830
Web Site: http://www.durr-ecoclean.com
Sales Range: $25-49.9 Million
Emp.: 200
Industry Machinery Manufacturing
N.A.I.C.S.: 811121
William Bell (Mng Dir)

SHENYANG CHEMICAL INDUSTRY CO., LTD.
No 55 Shenxisan East Road Economic and Technological Development Zone, Tiexi District, Shenyang, 110143, Liaoning, China
Tel.: (86) 2425553506
Web Site: http://www.sychem.com
Year Founded: 1938
000698—(SSE)
Rev.: $834,165,021
Assets: $957,177,955
Liabilities: $675,143,642
Net Worth: $282,034,313
Earnings: ($248,929,916)
Fiscal Year-end: 12/31/22
Petrochemical Products Mfr
N.A.I.C.S.: 325110
Zhu Bin (Chm)

SHENYANG COMMERCIAL CITY CO., LTD.
No 212 Zhongjie Road, Shenhe District, Shenyang, 110011, Liaoning, China
Tel.: (86) 2424865832
Web Site: https://www.sysyc.cn
Year Founded: 1999
600306—(SHG)
Rev.: $15,453,000
Assets: $186,322,144
Liabilities: $214,039,421
Net Worth: ($27,717,277)
Earnings: ($34,330,454)
Emp.: 500
Fiscal Year-end: 12/31/22
Departmental Store Operator
N.A.I.C.S.: 455110
Sun Zhen (Sec)

SHENYANG CUIHUA GOLD AND SILVER JEWELRY CO., LTD.
No 72 Cuihua Lane Beishuncheng Road, Dadong District, Shenyang, 110041, Liaoning, China
Tel.: (86) 2424868333
Web Site: http://www.chjd.com.cn
Year Founded: 1985
002731—(SSE)
Rev.: $590,499,332
Assets: $437,930,387
Liabilities: $254,279,044
Net Worth: $183,651,343
Earnings: $6,712,173
Emp.: 610
Fiscal Year-end: 12/31/22
Gold & Silvery Jewelry Products Mfr & Distr
N.A.I.C.S.: 339910
Chen Siwei (Chm)

SHENYANG HUITIAN THERMAL POWER CO., LTD.
No 47 Renao Road, Shenhe District, Shenyang, 110014, Liaoning, China
Tel.: (86) 2422928087
Web Site: http://www.htrd.cn

SHENYANG HUITIAN THERMAL POWER CO., LTD.

Shenyang Huitian Thermal Power Co., Ltd.—(Continued)
Year Founded: 1993
000692—(SSE)
Rev.: $280,279,327
Assets: $770,245,646
Liabilities: $1,027,383,178
Net Worth: ($257,137,532)
Earnings: ($272,176,084)
Fiscal Year-end: 12/31/22
Thermal Power Generation Services
N.A.I.C.S.: 221116
Chen Weiguo *(Chm & Gen Mgr)*

SHENYANG JINBEI AUTOMOTIVE COMPANY LIMITED
No 38 Wanliutang Road, Shenhe District, Shenyang, 110044, Liaoning, China
Tel.: (86) 2431669069
600609—(SHG)
Rev.: $790,626,377
Assets: $619,549,960
Liabilities: $441,304,185
Net Worth: $178,245,775
Earnings: $21,048,431
Fiscal Year-end: 12/31/22
Automobile Parts Mfr & Distr
N.A.I.C.S.: 336110
Sun Xuelong *(Sec)*

Subsidiaries:

Shenyang Brilliance JinBei Automobile Co., Ltd. (1)
No 39 Dongwang St, Dadong Distr, Shenyang, 110044, China (49%)
Tel.: (86) 2431666631
Sales Range: $1-4.9 Billion
Emp.: 7,000
Automobile Mfr
N.A.I.C.S.: 336110
Yumin Qi *(Chm)*

SHENYANG MACHINE TOOL CO., LTD.
No 1 Jia 17 Kaifa Road, Shenyang Economic And Technological Development Zone, Shenyang, 110142, Liaoning, China
Tel.: (86) 2425190865
Web Site: http://www.smtcl.com
Year Founded: 1949
000410—(SSE)
Rev.: $234,508,463
Assets: $506,238,062
Liabilities: $369,524,250
Net Worth: $136,713,812
Earnings: $3,616,142
Fiscal Year-end: 12/31/22
Machine Tools Mfr
N.A.I.C.S.: 333517
An Fengshou *(Chm)*

SHENYANG PUBLIC UTILITY HOLDINGS COMPANY LIMITED
Shenben Avenue, Hunnan New Town, Shenyang, China
Tel.: (86) 2424351042 CN
Web Site: https://shenyangpublic.todayir.com
Year Founded: 1999
0747—(HKG)
Rev.: $4,131,551
Assets: $105,156,932
Liabilities: $24,658,452
Net Worth: $80,498,480
Earnings: ($10,645,690)
Emp.: 49
Fiscal Year-end: 12/31/22
Holding Company
N.A.I.C.S.: 551112
Jing Ming Zhang *(Chm & Exec Dir)*

SHENYANG XINGQI PHARMACEUTICAL CO LTD
No 68 Sishui Street, Dongling District, Shenyang, 110063, Liaoning, China
Tel.: (86) 2422503989
Web Site: https://www.sinqi.com
Year Founded: 1977
300573—(CHIN)
Rev.: $206,707,220
Assets: $285,058,526
Liabilities: $47,033,167
Net Worth: $238,025,359
Earnings: $33,809,071
Fiscal Year-end: 12/31/23
Anti Bacteria Drug Mfr & Distr
N.A.I.C.S.: 325412
Jidong JidLiu Liu *(Chm & Gen Mgr)*

SHENYANG YUANDA INTELLECTUAL INDUSTRY GROUP CO., LTD.
No 27 Kaifa Avenue Economic and Technological Development Zone, Shenyang, 110027, Liaoning, China
Tel.: (86) 2425162800
Web Site: https://www.bltelevator.com.cn
Year Founded: 2001
002689—(SSE)
Rev.: $138,749,486
Assets: $276,621,780
Liabilities: $116,738,865
Net Worth: $159,882,915
Earnings: ($15,640,209)
Emp.: 2,000
Fiscal Year-end: 12/31/22
Elevators, Escalators & Moving Pavements Mfr
N.A.I.C.S.: 333921
Kang Baohua *(Chm)*

SHENYU COMMUNICATION TECHNOLOGY INC.
No 275 East Outer Ring Road, Jiangyin, 214429, Jiangsu, China
Tel.: (86) 51086279712
Web Site: https://www.shenyucable.com
Year Founded: 2003
300563—(CHIN)
Rev.: $106,342,891
Assets: $180,886,922
Liabilities: $32,754,034
Net Worth: $148,132,889
Earnings: $7,105,390
Emp.: 500
Fiscal Year-end: 12/31/23
Coaxial Cable Mfr & Distr
N.A.I.C.S.: 335929
Gu Guixin *(Sec)*

SHENZHEN ABSEN OPTOELECTRONIC COMPANY LIMITED
18-20F Building 3A Cloud Park Bantian, Longgang District, Shenzhen, 518129, China
Tel.: (86) 75589747399
Web Site: https://www.absen.com
300389—(CHIN)
Rev.: $392,555,592
Assets: $422,434,116
Liabilities: $256,237,020
Net Worth: $166,197,096
Earnings: $28,504,008
Emp.: 2,000
Fiscal Year-end: 12/31/22
LED Products Mfr
N.A.I.C.S.: 334419

Subsidiaries:

Absen Inc. (1)
7120 Lake Ellenor Dr, Orlando, FL 32809
Tel.: (407) 203-8870
Electronic Components Mfr
N.A.I.C.S.: 334419

SHENZHEN AGRICULTURAL PRODUCTS GROUP CO., LTD.
13F Times Technology Building No 7028 Shennan Avenue, Futian District, Shenzhen, 518040, Guangdong, China
Tel.: (86) 75582589021
Web Site: http://www.szap.com
Year Founded: 1994
000061—(SSE)
Rev.: $611,242,702
Assets: $2,946,653,129
Liabilities: $1,891,283,542
Net Worth: $1,055,369,587
Earnings: $28,032,348
Fiscal Year-end: 12/31/22
Agriculture Product Distr
N.A.I.C.S.: 325320
Huang Wei *(Chm)*

SHENZHEN AIRPORT CO., LTD.
Office Building A T3 Business District Bao'an International Airport, Bao'an District, Shenzhen, 518128, Guangdong, China
Tel.: (86) 75523456331
Web Site: http://www.szairport.com
Year Founded: 1998
000089—(SSE)
Rev.: $375,033,335
Assets: $3,527,941,449
Liabilities: $2,026,313,874
Net Worth: $1,501,627,575
Earnings: ($160,432,469)
Fiscal Year-end: 12/31/22
Airport Services
N.A.I.C.S.: 488119
Chen Fanhua *(Chm)*

SHENZHEN AISIDI CO., LTD.
18th Floor Nanshan Financial Building No 83 Kefa Road, Nanshan District, Shenzhen, 518055, China
Tel.: (86) 75521519888
Web Site: https://www.aisidi.com
Year Founded: 1998
002416—(SSE)
Rev.: $12,836,632,611
Assets: $2,027,576,758
Liabilities: $1,143,594,265
Net Worth: $883,982,493
Earnings: $102,530,133
Emp.: 3,300
Fiscal Year-end: 12/31/22
Electronics Wholesale Distr
N.A.I.C.S.: 423690
Zhou Youmeng *(Vice Chm & Pres)*

SHENZHEN ANCHE TECHNOLOGIES CO., LTD.
No 63 Xuefu Road, Nanshan District, Shenzhen, 518052, Guangdong, China
Tel.: (86) 75586182188
Web Site: https://www.anche.cn
Year Founded: 2006
300572—(CHIN)
Rev.: $65,115,448
Assets: $404,203,386
Liabilities: $105,500,932
Net Worth: $298,702,454
Earnings: ($8,242,824)
Emp.: 800
Fiscal Year-end: 12/31/23
Automotive Inspection Services
N.A.I.C.S.: 811198
Yunfei Li *(CFO, Sec & Deputy Gen Mgr)*

SHENZHEN AONI ELECTRONIC CO., LTD.
Building 5 Honghui Industrial Park Liuxian 2nd Road Xin'an Street, Bao'an District, Shenzhen, 523705, Guangdong, China
Tel.: (86) 75521632223

INTERNATIONAL PUBLIC

Web Site: https://www.anc.cn
Year Founded: 2005
301189—(CHIN)
Rev.: $93,795,624
Assets: $371,269,548
Liabilities: $47,564,712
Net Worth: $323,704,836
Earnings: $8,922,420
Fiscal Year-end: 12/31/22
Electronic Component Mfr & Distr
N.A.I.C.S.: 334419
Wu Shijie *(Chm & Gen Mgr)*

SHENZHEN AOTO ELECTRONICS CO., LTD.
9-10F High-Tech Zone Union Tower No 63 Xuefu Road, Nanshan District, Shenzhen, Guangdong, China
Tel.: (86) 75526983431
Web Site: https://en.aoto.com
Year Founded: 1993
002587—(SSE)
Rev.: $129,697,729
Assets: $317,319,711
Liabilities: $123,027,199
Net Worth: $194,292,512
Earnings: $2,944,132
Emp.: 1,300
Fiscal Year-end: 12/31/22
LED Display Systems Mfr
N.A.I.C.S.: 334419

Subsidiaries:

AOTO Electronics (US) LLC (1)
12 Hughes D-100, Irvine, CA 92618
Tel.: (949) 421-3104
Web Site: http://www.us.aoto.com
Electronic Components Mfr
N.A.I.C.S.: 334419
Ralph Paonessa *(VP-Sls)*

SHENZHEN ASIA LINK TECHNOLOGY DEVELOPMENT CO.,LTD.
24/F Yihua Financial Technology Building No 2388 Houhai Road, Nanshan District, Shenzhen, China
Tel.: (86) 75526520661
Web Site: https://www.asialink.com
002316—(SSE)
Rev.: $232,641,972
Assets: $127,498,279
Liabilities: $118,908,832
Net Worth: $8,589,447
Earnings: ($12,856,554)
Emp.: 260
Fiscal Year-end: 12/31/22
Energy & Traffic Network Communication Products Mfr
N.A.I.C.S.: 334290

Subsidiaries:

Shenzhen Keybridge Huaneng Communication Technology Co., Ltd. (1)
13 Floor Xihaian Building, Nanshan District, Shenzhen, China
Tel.: (86) 75526712209
Communication Equipment Mfr
N.A.I.C.S.: 334290

SHENZHEN AUSTRALIS ELECTRONIC TECHNOLOGY CO., LTD.
No 5 Furong Road, Songgang Subdistrict Baoan District, Shenzhen, 518105, Guangdong, China
Tel.: (86) 75529691606
Web Site: http://www.cnnjg.com
Year Founded: 2009
300940—(SSE)
Rev.: $90,175,185
Assets: $181,431,998
Liabilities: $66,983,352
Net Worth: $114,448,647
Earnings: ($6,393,493)
Emp.: 2,000
Fiscal Year-end: 12/31/22

Electronic Product Mfr & Distr
N.A.I.C.S.: 334419
Faming Jiang *(Chm & Gen Mgr)*

SHENZHEN AUTO ELECTRIC POWER PLANT CO., LTD.
Aotexun Power Building No 3 Songpingshan Road, High-tech Industrial Park North District Nanshan District, Shenzhen, 518057, Guangdong, China
Tel.: (86) 75526520500
Web Site: https://www.atc-a.com
Year Founded: 1993
002227—(SSE)
Rev.: $43,793,343
Assets: $218,284,864
Liabilities: $63,791,330
Net Worth: $154,493,535
Earnings: ($5,662,599)
Fiscal Year-end: 12/31/22
Electric Equipment Mfr
N.A.I.C.S.: 335999
Liao Xiaoxia *(Chm & Pres)*

SHENZHEN AV-DISPLAY CO., LTD.
No 39 Jin Yuan Road, He Ao Jin Yuan Industrial Park Yuanshan Long Gang, Shenzhen, 518115, Guangdong, China
Tel.: (86) 75588860696
Web Site: https://www.av-display.com
Year Founded: 2004
300939—(SSE)
Rev.: $154,955,717
Assets: $224,221,875
Liabilities: $43,345,664
Net Worth: $180,876,211
Earnings: $22,358,307
Emp.: 1,000
Fiscal Year-end: 12/31/22
Electronic Product Mfr & Distr
N.A.I.C.S.: 334419
Zhiyi Huang *(Chm)*

SHENZHEN BAOMING TECHNOLOGY CO., LTD.
Room 3001 Building 2 Huilong Business Center Minzhi Street, Beizhan Community Longhua District, Shenzhen, 518109, Guangdong, China
Tel.: (86) 75529841816
Web Site: https://www.bmseiko.com
Year Founded: 2006
002992—(SSE)
Rev.: $131,951,219
Assets: $290,865,262
Liabilities: $159,119,083
Net Worth: $131,746,179
Earnings: ($31,355,167)
Fiscal Year-end: 12/31/22
Electronic Product Mfr & Distr
N.A.I.C.S.: 334419
Jun Li *(Chm)*

SHENZHEN BAONENG INVESTMENT GROUP CO., LTD.
6E Futian Zhonggang City Fuqiang Road, Futian District, Shenzhen, 518048, China
Tel.: (86) 755 8383 6666
Holding Company
N.A.I.C.S.: 551112
Robert Young *(Exec Vice Gen Mgr-Hotel Bus Div)*

Subsidiaries:

Shenzhen Hualitong Investment Co., Ltd. (1)
805 Shenye Logistics Building 2088 Bao'an North Road, Luohu District, Shenzhen, 518023, Guangdong, China
Tel.: (86) 13632843008
Investment Services
N.A.I.C.S.: 523940

SHENZHEN BATIAN ECO-TYPIC ENGINEERING CO., LTD.
30th and 31st Floor Joint Headquarters Building No 63 Xuefu Road, High-tech Park Nanshan District, Shenzhen, 518057, Guangdong, China
Tel.: (86) 75526955688
Web Site: https://www.batian.com.cn
Year Founded: 1989
002170—(SSE)
Rev.: $400,890,157
Assets: $662,884,251
Liabilities: $354,459,288
Net Worth: $308,424,964
Earnings: $17,019,400
Fiscal Year-end: 12/31/22
Compound Fertilizer Mfr
N.A.I.C.S.: 325314
Peizhao Huang *(Chm & Pres)*

SHENZHEN BAUING CONSTRUCTION GROUP CO., LTD.
3F Block 303 Tairan 4th Road Chegongmiao, Futian District, Shenzhen, 518040, Guangdong, China
Tel.: (86) 75582924810
Web Site: http://www.szby.cn
Year Founded: 2001
002047—(SSE)
Rev.: $523,285,500
Assets: $1,281,752,765
Liabilities: $1,129,677,789
Net Worth: $152,074,976
Earnings: ($307,191,479)
Fiscal Year-end: 12/31/22
Architectural Services
N.A.I.C.S.: 541310
Shaobo Gu *(Vice Chm & Pres)*

Subsidiaries:

Kenneth Ko Design Co., Ltd. (1)
Rm 1405 14/F Fo Tan Industrial Centre 26-28 Au Pui Wan Street Fo Tan, Sha Tin, China (Hong Kong)
Tel.: (852) 2604 9494
Emp.: 100
Architectural Services
N.A.I.C.S.: 541310
Kenneth Ko *(Dir-Design)*

Subsidiary (Non-US):

Shanghai Kenneth Ko Designs LTD. (2)
3021 Kai Xuan Road Suite A-401 Xuhui District, Shanghai, China
Tel.: (86) 2165149494
Architectural Services
N.A.I.C.S.: 541310

Shenzhen Kenneth Ko Designs LTD. (2)
Room 107 NO F-1 Industrial Park East Overseas Chinese Town, Nanshan District, Shenzhen, Guangdong, China
Tel.: (86) 75582998288
Architectural Services
N.A.I.C.S.: 541310

Shenzhen Ninefold Construction Group Co., Ltd (1)
D Section Xiangnian Square 4060 Qiaoxiang Rd, Nanshan, Shenzhen, 518040, China
Tel.: (86) 75582950220
Web Site: http://www.szsde.com
Building Construction Services
N.A.I.C.S.: 236110

SHENZHEN BEST OF BEST HOLDINGS CO., LTD.
Rm 1501-1504 Fiyta Tech Bldg 2 No 1 Southern Road High-Tech Park, Nanshan District, Shenzhen, 518057, Guangdong, China
Tel.: (86) 75586018818
Web Site: https://www.bobholdings.com

Year Founded: 2014
001298—(SSE)
Rev.: $897,884,311
Assets: $355,990,939
Liabilities: $144,957,272
Net Worth: $211,033,668
Earnings: $13,931,064
Emp.: 500
Fiscal Year-end: 12/31/22
Holding Company
N.A.I.C.S.: 551112
Yucheng Wang *(Chm & Gen Mgr)*

SHENZHEN BESTEK TECHNOLOGY CO., LTD.
Buildings 22 23 34 & 37 the 3rd Industrial Zone Xueyuan Road, Longxi Community Longgang Subdistrict Longgang District, Shenzhen, 518116, Guangdong, China
Tel.: (86) 75584878557
Web Site: https://www.szbtk.com
Year Founded: 2010
300822—(CHIN)
Rev.: $122,089,563
Assets: $219,102,197
Liabilities: $40,746,451
Net Worth: $178,355,746
Earnings: $6,705,183
Fiscal Year-end: 12/31/23
Intelligent Control Equipment Mfr
N.A.I.C.S.: 335314
Xiao Ping *(Chm & Gen Mgr)*

SHENZHEN BINGCHUAN NETWORK CO LTD
15F United Headquarters Building Rongchao High-tech Zone No 63, Xuefu Road Nanshan District, Shenzhen, 518052, Guangdong, China
Tel.: (86) 75586384819
Web Site: http://www.q1.com
Year Founded: 2008
300533—(CHIN)
Rev.: $392,032,326
Assets: $374,926,615
Liabilities: $148,209,567
Net Worth: $226,717,047
Earnings: $38,487,572
Emp.: 1,800
Fiscal Year-end: 12/31/23
Online Game Development Services
N.A.I.C.S.: 541511
Heguo Liu *(Chm & Gen Mgr)*

SHENZHEN BIOEASY BIO-TECHNOLOGY CO., LTD.
A101 Building 2 Bioeasy Industry Park No 289 Yunchang Road, Baoan District, Shenzhen, 518126, Guangdong, China
Tel.: (86) 75527948546
Web Site: https://www.bioeasy.com
Year Founded: 2007
300942—(SSE)
Rev.: $96,440,409
Assets: $180,056,766
Liabilities: $44,612,732
Net Worth: $135,444,034
Earnings: $11,648,356
Fiscal Year-end: 12/31/22
Medical Product Mfr & Distr
N.A.I.C.S.: 339112
Xiao Zhaoli *(Chm & Gen Mgr)*

SHENZHEN BSC TECHNOLOGY CO., LTD.
No 26 Shuitian Road, Tongle Community Baolong Sub-district Longgang District, Shenzhen, 518116, Guangdong, China
Tel.: (86) 75589690666
Web Site: https://www.bsc-sz.com
Year Founded: 2016
300951—(SSE)
Rev.: $164,235,090

Assets: $367,356,488
Liabilities: $68,897,762
Net Worth: $298,458,726
Earnings: $42,924,941
Fiscal Year-end: 12/31/22
Electronic Product Mfr & Distr
N.A.I.C.S.: 334419
Sitong Xu *(Chm & Gen Mgr)*

SHENZHEN CAPCHEM TECHNOLOGY CO., LTD.
Capchem Plaza Changye Road, Pingshan District, Shenzhen, 518118, Guangdong, China
Tel.: (86) 75589923768
Web Site: https://www.capchem.com
Year Founded: 1996
300037—(CHIN)
Rev.: $1,356,363,684
Assets: $2,161,473,444
Liabilities: $933,603,840
Net Worth: $1,227,869,604
Earnings: $246,879,360
Emp.: 2,450
Fiscal Year-end: 12/31/22
Petrochemical Mfr
N.A.I.C.S.: 325110
Jiusan Qin *(Chm)*

Subsidiaries:

Nantong Capchem High Pure Chemical Co.,Ltd. (1)
Yuntaishan Pingchao Town, Tongzhou Dist, Nantong, Jiangsu, China
Tel.: (86) 51386571759
Sales Range: $75-99.9 Million
Emp.: 200
Electronic Chemicals Mfr & Distr
N.A.I.C.S.: 325199

SHENZHEN CAPOL INTERNATIONAL & ASSOCIATES CO., LTD.
Room 101 Building 3 Headquarters Building Minzhi Street, Longhua Design Industrial Park Beizhan Community Longhua District, Shenzhen, 518038, Guangdong, China
Tel.: (86) 75582739188
Web Site: https://en.capol.cn
002949—(SSE)
Rev.: $256,299,638
Assets: $452,250,064
Liabilities: $230,448,039
Net Worth: $221,802,025
Earnings: $15,749,524
Emp.: 5,000
Fiscal Year-end: 12/31/22
Engineeering Services
N.A.I.C.S.: 541330

SHENZHEN CAPSTONE INDUSTRIAL CO., LTD.
904-905 Yaohua Chuangjian Buliding No 6023, Shennan Avenue Futian District, Shenzhen, 518000, Guangdong, China
Tel.: (86) 7552 692 6508
Web Site: http://www.chinadatong.com
000038—(SSE)
Rev.: $326,374,070
Assets: $496,170,585
Liabilities: $50,617,520
Net Worth: $445,553,065
Earnings: $12,186,323
Fiscal Year-end: 12/31/20
Real Estate Development Services
N.A.I.C.S.: 531390
Shi Lijun *(Chm)*

SHENZHEN CDL PRECISION TECHNOLOGY CO., LTD.
No 9 Lanjin 6th Road Longtian Street, Nanbu Community Pingshan District, Shenzhen, 523705, China

SHENZHEN CDL PRECISION TECHNOLOGY CO., LTD.

Shenzhen CDL Precision Technology Co., Ltd.—(Continued)
Tel.: (86) 75584631291
Web Site: https://www.szcdl.com
Year Founded: 2004
300686—(CHIN)
Rev.: $195,290,441
Assets: $337,769,371
Liabilities: $168,584,323
Net Worth: $169,185,048
Earnings: ($35,799,887)
Emp.: 4,000
Fiscal Year-end: 12/31/23
Electronic Parts Mfr & Distr
N.A.I.C.S.: 326130
Wu Jiawei *(Chm & Fin Dir)*

SHENZHEN CENTER POWER TECH. CO., LTD.
Office Building Xiongtao Science and Technology Park, Tongfu Industrial Zone Dapeng Town Dapeng New District, Shenzhen, 518120, Guangdong, China
Tel.: (86) 75566851118
Web Site: https://www.vision-batt.com
Year Founded: 1994
002733—(SSE)
Rev.: $572,589,796
Assets: $793,426,374
Liabilities: $409,545,621
Net Worth: $383,880,753
Earnings: $22,027,426
Emp.: 4,000
Fiscal Year-end: 12/31/22
Storage Battery Mfr
N.A.I.C.S.: 335910
Huanong Zhang *(Chm & Chm-Vision Grp)*

Subsidiaries:

Vietnam Center Power Tech Co., Ltd. (1)
Road 5C Nhon Trach 2 Industrial Park, Nhon Trach, Dong Nai, Vietnam
Tel.: (84) 61 3569936
Web Site: http://www.vision-batt.vn
Battery Mfr & Distr
N.A.I.C.S.: 335910

Subsidiary (Domestic):

VISION TECHNOLOGY JOINT STOCK COMPANY (2)
No 343/5A To Hien Thanh Strs Ward 12 Distr 10, Ho Chi Minh City, Vietnam
Tel.: (84) 839381265
Battery Distr
N.A.I.C.S.: 423610

Vision Battery USA, Inc. (1)
1824 E 7th St Ste D, Joplin, MO 64801
Tel.: (417) 625-4842
Web Site: http://www.visionbatteryusa.com
Battery Distr
N.A.I.C.S.: 423610

Vision Europe BVBA (1)
Wijngaardveld 3, 9300, Aalst, Belgium
Tel.: (32) 53776373
Web Site: http://www.vision-batt.eu
Battery Distr
N.A.I.C.S.: 423610
Hans de Vriese *(Mgr-Sls & Mktg)*

SHENZHEN CENTRALCON INVESTMENT HOLDING CO., LTD.
38F Zhongzhou Building No 3088 Jintian Road, Futian District, Shenzhen, 518033, Guangdong, China
Tel.: (86) 75588393609
Web Site: http://www.zztzkg.com
Year Founded: 1994
000042—(SSE)
Rev.: $994,458,984
Assets: $5,150,869,444
Liabilities: $3,997,332,359
Net Worth: $1,153,537,084

Earnings: $11,184,685
Fiscal Year-end: 12/31/22
Holding Company
N.A.I.C.S.: 551112

SHENZHEN CENTURY PLAZA HOTEL CO., LTD.
No 4001 Spring Road, Luohu District, Shenzhen, 518001, Guangdong, China
Tel.: (86) 755 8232 0888
Web Site: http://www.szcphotel.com
Year Founded: 1988
Sales Range: $10-24.9 Million
Hotel Operator
N.A.I.C.S.: 722511

SHENZHEN CEREALS HOLDINGS CO., LTD.
8F Block B Building 4 Software Industry Base South Area, Technology Park Xuefu Road Yuehai Subdistrict Nanshan District, Shenzhen, 518033, Guangdong, China
Tel.: (86) 75583778690
Web Site: http://www.sbsy.com.cn
Year Founded: 1981
000019—(SSE)
Rev.: $1,167,106,323
Assets: $1,044,763,392
Liabilities: $366,282,470
Net Worth: $678,480,922
Earnings: $59,051,524
Fiscal Year-end: 12/31/22
Soft Drinks Mfr
N.A.I.C.S.: 312111
Wang Zhikai *(Chm)*

SHENZHEN CHANGFANG GROUP CO., LTD.
5F Office Building Building D No 6 Juliu Road Zhukeng Community, Longtian Subdistrict Pingshan District, Shenzhen, 518110, China
Tel.: (86) 75582828966
Web Site: https://www.cfled.com
Year Founded: 2005
300301—(SSE)
Rev.: $102,269,901
Assets: $139,735,936
Liabilities: $112,684,268
Net Worth: $27,051,668
Earnings: ($31,573,657)
Fiscal Year-end: 12/31/22
Light Emitting Diode Lighting Device Mfr
N.A.I.C.S.: 335999
Wu Taoxiang *(Chm & Gen Mgr)*

SHENZHEN CHANGHONG TECHNOLOGY CO., LTD.
No3 Jinglong Avenue Shahu Community Biling Street, Pingshan District, Shenzhen, Guangdong, China
Tel.: (86) 75589785568
Web Site: https://www.sz-changhong.com
Year Founded: 2001
300151—(CHIN)
Rev.: $131,169,577
Assets: $359,933,217
Liabilities: $121,797,066
Net Worth: $238,136,151
Earnings: $4,458,621
Emp.: 2,000
Fiscal Year-end: 12/31/23
Plastic Injection Molding Mfr
N.A.I.C.S.: 333511
Huanchang Li *(Chm & Gen Mgr)*

Subsidiaries:

Lingen Precision Medical Products (Shanghai) Co., Ltd. (1)
No 59 Yewang Road Yexie Industrial Park, Songjiang Road, Shanghai, 201609, China
Tel.: (86) 21 578 0227

Web Site: https://www.labtub.com
Medical Device Mfr
N.A.I.C.S.: 339112

Nidacon Life Science (Shanghai) Co., Ltd. (1)
5/F BLD 1 No 59 Yewang Road, Songjiang District, Shanghai, China
Tel.: (86) 18354989256
Surgical & Medical Instrument Mfr
N.A.I.C.S.: 339112

Shenzhen Boomingshing Medical Device Co., Ltd. (1)
Floor 1 to 3 Industrial Plant 4, Fuxingda Industrial Zone Lanzhu East Road Pingshan New District, Shenzhen, 518118, China
Tel.: (86) 75589318668
Web Site: https://www.boomingshing.com
Research & Development Services
N.A.I.C.S.: 541714

SHENZHEN CHENG CHUNG DESIGN CO., LTD.
4B01-4B02 Excellence Times Suqare 4068 YiTianRoad, Futian District, Shenzhen, China
Tel.: (86) 75523607755
Web Site: https://www.atgcn.com
Year Founded: 1994
002811—(SSE)
Rev.: $153,902,071
Assets: $371,821,053
Liabilities: $201,925,625
Net Worth: $169,895,429
Earnings: ($24,562,250)
Fiscal Year-end: 12/31/22
Construction Consultancy Services
N.A.I.C.S.: 541330
Zheng Zhong *(Chm)*

SHENZHEN CHENGTIAN WEIYE TECHNOLOGY CO., LTD.
Room B3401-B3404 Building 10 No 10 Gaoxin South 9th Road Yuehai Street, Nanshan District, Shenzhen, 518052, Guangdong, China
Tel.: (86) 75536900689
Web Site: https://www.ctwy.cn
Year Founded: 1997
300689—(CHIN)
Rev.: $55,534,225
Assets: $110,241,464
Liabilities: $12,845,112
Net Worth: $97,396,352
Earnings: $1,256,044
Fiscal Year-end: 12/31/23
Card Material Mfr & Distr
N.A.I.C.S.: 326199
Feng Xueyu *(Chm & Gen Mgr)*

SHENZHEN CHINA BICYCLE COMPANY (HOLDINGS) CO., LTD.
8th Floor Shuibei Jinzuo Building No 89 Beili North Road Cuizhu Street, Luohu District, Shenzhen, 518029, Guangdong, China
Tel.: (86) 75525516998
Web Site: https://www.szcbc.com
Year Founded: 1992
000017—(SSE)
Rev.: $62,444,613
Assets: $55,774,391
Liabilities: $12,973,802
Net Worth: $42,800,589
Earnings: ($1,069,343)
Fiscal Year-end: 12/31/22
Holding Company
N.A.I.C.S.: 551112
Sun Longlong *(Sec)*

SHENZHEN CHIPSCREEN BIOSCIENCES CO., LTD.
21-24F Block B Zhigu Industrial Park 3157 Shahe West Road, Nanshan

INTERNATIONAL PUBLIC

District, Shenzhen, 518057, Guangdong, China
Tel.: (86) 75536993500
Web Site: https://www.chipscreen.com
Year Founded: 2001
688321—(SHG)
Rev.: $74,403,506
Assets: $406,570,236
Liabilities: $185,341,829
Net Worth: $221,228,406
Earnings: $2,454,866
Fiscal Year-end: 12/31/22
Pharmaceutical Product Mfr & Distr
N.A.I.C.S.: 325412
Ning Zhiqiang *(Founder & Deputy Gen Mgr)*

Subsidiaries:

Chengdu Chipscreen Pharmaceutical Co., Ltd. (1)
No 298 Kangqiang Yi Road, Pidu District, Chengdu, Sichuan, China
Tel.: (86) 2864907325
Pharmaceuticals Product Mfr
N.A.I.C.S.: 325412

Shenzhen Chipscreen Pharmaceutical Co., Ltd. (1)
No 21 Jinxiu East Road Kengzi Street, Pingshan New District, Shenzhen, Guangdong, China
Tel.: (86) 75536993573
Pharmaceuticals Product Mfr
N.A.I.C.S.: 325412

SHENZHEN CHIWAN PETROLEUM SUPPLY BASE CO., LTD.
14F Chiwan Petroleum Building Shekou, Shenzhen, 518068, China
Tel.: (86) 75526694211
Web Site: http://www.chiwanbase.com
Year Founded: 1984
Rev.: $117,170,006
Assets: $1,432,476,213
Liabilities: $883,432,179
Net Worth: $549,044,034
Earnings: ($6,573,774)
Fiscal Year-end: 12/31/17
Natural Gas Exploration & Extraction Services
N.A.I.C.S.: 211130
Shiyun Wang *(Pres)*

SHENZHEN CHUANGYITONG TECHNOLOGY CO., LTD.
Building 4 Changfeng Industrial Park Phoenix Street, Dongkeng Community Guangming District, Shenzhen, 518106, Guangdong, China
Tel.: (86) 75529892530
Web Site: https://www.chysz.cn
Year Founded: 2003
300991—(SSE)
Rev.: $60,543,063
Assets: $173,791,220
Liabilities: $84,945,496
Net Worth: $88,845,724
Earnings: $1,193,891
Emp.: 1,500
Fiscal Year-end: 12/31/22
Electronic Product Mfr & Distr
N.A.I.C.S.: 334419
Jianming Zhang *(Chm & Gen Mgr)*

SHENZHEN CLICK TECHNOLOGY CO., LTD.
Building 7 Zhengzhong Industrial Park, Qiaotou Community Fuyong Town Baoan District, Shenzhen, China
Tel.: (86) 75529918117
Web Site: https://www.clickele.com
Year Founded: 2004
002782—(SSE)
Rev.: $458,782,876

AND PRIVATE COMPANIES

Assets: $524,860,802
Liabilities: $293,864,445
Net Worth: $230,996,357
Earnings: $15,618,208
Emp.: 3,500
Fiscal Year-end: 12/31/22
Electrical Equipment Mfr & Distr
N.A.I.C.S.: 334416
Xiao Keng *(Chm & Gen Mgr)*

Subsidiaries:

Click International (HK) Trading Co., Ltd. (1)
Flat 1707 17/F Sterling Centre 11 Cheung Yue Street Cheung Sha Wang, Kowloon, China (Hong Kong)
Tel.: (852) 27854822
Electrical Apparatus & Equipment Distr
N.A.I.C.S.: 423610

Click Tech Inc. (1)
599 N Ave Door 6 2nd Fl, Wakefield, MA 01880
Tel.: (859) 420-6763
Electrical Apparatus & Equipment Distr
N.A.I.C.S.: 423610

SHENZHEN CLOU ELECTRONICS CO., LTD.
Clou building Baoshen Road North District high tech Industrial Park, Nanshan District, Shenzhen, 518057, Guangdong, China
Tel.: (86) 75533309999
Web Site: https://www.szclou.com
Year Founded: 1996
002121—(SSE)
Rev.: $496,849,809
Assets: $1,235,139,727
Liabilities: $1,137,717,571
Net Worth: $97,422,156
Earnings: ($14,217,016)
Emp.: 3,000
Fiscal Year-end: 12/31/22
Power Distribution Services
N.A.I.C.S.: 221118
Liu Biao *(Chm & Pres)*

Subsidiaries:

CLOU PANAMA S.A. (1)
Ancon Calle Luis Felix Clement Edificio Barca, Panama, Panama
Tel.: (507) 3976746
Meter Equipment Distr
N.A.I.C.S.: 423830

Cloutek Gmbh (1)
Heisterbacher Str 85, 53639, Konigswinter, Germany
Tel.: (49) 22237879650
Web Site: http://www.cloutek.de
Meter Equipment Distr
N.A.I.C.S.: 423830
Felix Gall *(Mng Dir)*

SHENZHEN COLIBRI TECHNOLOGIES CO., LTD.
Colibri Tech Park Guangqiao Road, Guangming District, Shenzhen, 518107, Guangdong, China
Tel.: (86) 75526710011
Web Site: https://www.colibri.com.cn
Year Founded: 2001
002957—(SSE)
Rev.: $455,772,672
Assets: $867,307,774
Liabilities: $435,567,778
Net Worth: $431,739,996
Earnings: $43,952,557
Emp.: 3,600
Fiscal Year-end: 12/31/22
Power Automation Equipment Mfr & Distr
N.A.I.C.S.: 333613
Ming Lee Phua *(Chm)*

Subsidiaries:

Chengdu Innorev Industrial Co., Ltd. (1)
No 499 Section 2 Chuangxin Road, Chongzhou Economic Development Zone, Chengdu, 611230, China
Tel.: (86) 2882188001
Web Site: https://en.innorev.cn
Precision Turned Product Mfr
N.A.I.C.S.: 332721

Colibri Automation (Suzhou) Co., Ltd. (1)
No 7-2 9-3 Tingrong Street, Suzhou Industrial Park, Suzhou, 215021, Jiangsu, China
Tel.: (86) 51262958700
Precision Parts Mfr
N.A.I.C.S.: 332721

Colibri Automation (Thailand) Co., Ltd. (1)
19/56-58 Moo 10, Klongnueng Klongluang, Pathumthani, 12120, Thailand
Tel.: (66) 29081671
Precision Parts Mfr
N.A.I.C.S.: 332721

Colibri Precision Hong Kong Company Limited (1)
25/F OTB Building 160 Gloucester Road, Wanchai, China (Hong Kong)
Tel.: (852) 28811226
Precision Parts Mfr
N.A.I.C.S.: 332721

Colibri Precision Pte. Ltd. (1)
3018 Bedok North Street 5 06-32 Eastlink, Singapore, 486132, Singapore
Tel.: (65) 63668063
Precision Parts Mfr
N.A.I.C.S.: 332721

Philippines Innorev Automation Inc. (1)
Unit 307 and 308 Plaza B Building Northgate Avenue Northgate Cyberzone, Filinvest Corporate City Alabang NCR Fourth District, Muntinlupa, Philippines
Tel.: (63) 25708298
Precision Parts Mfr
N.A.I.C.S.: 332721

Zhongshan Colibri Automation Co., Ltd. (1)
No 18 Wugui Road, Cuiheng District, Zhongshan, 528400, Guangdong, China
Tel.: (86) 75588656716
Precision Parts Mfr
N.A.I.C.S.: 332721

SHENZHEN COMIX GROUP CO., LTD.
Comix Industrial Park No 18 Jinxiu Middle Road, Pingshan District, Shenzhen, 518118, Guangdong, China
Tel.: (86) 75566829999
Web Site: https://comix.qx.com
Year Founded: 1991
002301—(SSE)
Rev.: $1,211,531,172
Assets: $1,091,398,277
Liabilities: $659,422,605
Net Worth: $431,975,672
Earnings: $17,786,911
Emp.: 2,600
Fiscal Year-end: 12/31/22
Stationery Product Mfr & Distr
N.A.I.C.S.: 322220
Chen Qinpeng *(Chm & Gen Mgr)*

SHENZHEN CONSYS SCIENCE & TECHNOLOGY CO., LTD.
5th Floor Avic Nanhang Building No 7 Langshan Road, Nanshan District, Shenzhen, 518057, Guangdong, China
Tel.: (86) 75586111131
Web Site: https://www.consys.com.cn
Year Founded: 2004
688788—(SSE)
Rev.: $32,756,106
Assets: $399,130,075
Liabilities: $21,797,900
Net Worth: $377,332,174
Earnings: ($27,615,810)

Fiscal Year-end: 12/31/22
Telecommunication Equipment Mfr & Distr
N.A.I.C.S.: 334290
Chen Chen *(Sec)*

SHENZHEN COTRAN NEW MATERIAL CO., LTD.
Building No 2 and No 3 Fuchuan Science and Technology Industrial Park, Huanli Road Guangming District, Shenzhen, China
Tel.: (86) 75533691628 CN
Web Site: https://www.cotranglobal.com
Year Founded: 2008
300731—(CHIN)
Rev.: $78,674,697
Assets: $142,445,943
Liabilities: $51,480,478
Net Worth: $90,965,465
Earnings: $3,585,633
Fiscal Year-end: 12/31/23
Adhesive Tape Mfr & Distr
N.A.I.C.S.: 322220
Zhou Dong *(Chm & Gen Mgr)*

SHENZHEN CRASTAL TECHNOLOGY CO., LTD.
Block A 3801 Block A B and C West Area Tanglangcheng Plaza No 3333, Liuxian Avenue Fuguang Community Taoyuan Subdistrict Nanshan District, Shenzhen, 518055, Guangdong, China
Tel.: (86) 75526559930
Web Site: http://www.buydeem.com
Year Founded: 2003
300824—(SSE)
Rev.: $112,985,931
Assets: $145,887,267
Liabilities: $45,316,038
Net Worth: $100,571,230
Earnings: $6,594,616
Fiscal Year-end: 12/31/22
Kitchen Appliance Mfr & Distr
N.A.I.C.S.: 335215
George Mohan Zhang *(Chm & Gen Mgr)*

SHENZHEN DANBOND TECHNOLOGY CO., LTD.
Danbond building No 8 Langshan road 1 high-technology park North, Nanshan district, Shenzhen, 518057, China
Tel.: (86) 7552 698 1518
Web Site: http://www.danbang.com
Year Founded: 2001
002618—(SSE)
Rev.: $7,464,391
Assets: $268,100,647
Liabilities: $127,853,745
Net Worth: $140,246,902
Earnings: ($124,260,971)
Fiscal Year-end: 12/31/20
Circuit Board Mfr
N.A.I.C.S.: 334412

SHENZHEN DAS INTELLITECH CO., LTD.
Das Tower Keji Nanyi Road South District, Shenzhen High-tech Zone, Shenzhen, Guangdong, China
Tel.: (86) 75526639961
Web Site: https://www.chn-das.com
002421—(SSE)
Rev.: $504,644,760
Assets: $1,286,221,290
Liabilities: $879,279,682
Net Worth: $406,941,608
Earnings: $29,732,733
Emp.: 2,800
Fiscal Year-end: 12/31/22
Electromechanical Energy Saving Services

N.A.I.C.S.: 624229
Beng Liu *(Chm & Gen Mgr)*

Subsidiaries:

Chengdu Juya Medical Letter Technology Co., Ltd. (1)
1713 No 99 Jirui 3rd Road chengdu High-tech Zone, Sichuan Free Trade Pilot Zone, Chengdu, Sichuan, China
Telecommunication Servicesb
N.A.I.C.S.: 517810

Jiangsu Dashijiuxin Medical Technology Co., Ltd. (1)
No 103 West Hanjiang Road, Xinbei District, Changzhou, Jiangsu, China
Tel.: (86) 51985195071
Telecommunication Servicesb
N.A.I.C.S.: 517810

Shenzhen Dash Financial Leasing Co., Ltd. (1)
Das Tower Keji Nanyi Road, South District Shenzhen High-tech Zone, Shenzhen, China
Tel.: (86) 75526639961
Telecommunication Servicesb
N.A.I.C.S.: 517810

Shenzhen Dashi Internet of Things Technology Co., Ltd. (1)
Das Tower Keji Nanyi Road, South District Shenzhen High-tech Zone, Shenzhen, China
Tel.: (86) 75586368199
Telecommunication Servicesb
N.A.I.C.S.: 517810

SHENZHEN DAWEI INNOVATION TECHNOLOGY CO., LTD.
Room A1406 Bldg 12 Shenzhen Bay Science & Technology Ecological Park, No 18 Keji S Rd High-tech Zone Community Yuehai St Nanshan District, Shenzhen, 518000, Guangdong, China
Tel.: (86) 75583002213
Web Site: https://www.daweitechnology.cn
Year Founded: 2000
002213—(SSE)
Rev.: $117,637,243
Assets: $112,920,519
Liabilities: $17,255,286
Net Worth: $95,665,233
Earnings: $2,243,480
Fiscal Year-end: 12/31/22
Electromagnetic Retarder Mfr
N.A.I.C.S.: 325998
Zongmin Lian *(Chm & Gen Mgr)*

SHENZHEN DEREN ELECTRONIC CO., LTD.
Deren Building No 366 Chaofeng Road, Guangming District, Shenzhen, China
Tel.: (86) 75533260000
Web Site: https://www.deren.com
Year Founded: 1992
002055—(SSE)
Rev.: $1,088,745,152
Assets: $1,313,493,639
Liabilities: $863,823,973
Net Worth: $449,669,666
Earnings: ($35,954,966)
Fiscal Year-end: 12/31/22
Electric Appliances Mfr
N.A.I.C.S.: 335999
Liu Biao *(Vice Chm & Pres)*

Subsidiaries:

Chongqing Ruiren Electronic Co., Ltd. (1)
No 269 Jinjian Road Biquan Street, Bishan District, Chongqing, China
Tel.: (86) 2341668550
Precision Component Mfr & Distr
N.A.I.C.S.: 332721

Deren Auto Parts (Chongqing) Co., Ltd. (1)

SHENZHEN DEREN ELECTRONIC CO., LTD.

Shenzhen Deren Electronic Co., Ltd.—(Continued)

Deren Electronic Industrial Park 13 Jujin Road Biquan Street, Bishan District, Chongqing, Chongqing, China
Tel.: (86) 2341889986
Precision Component Mfr & Distr
N.A.I.C.S.: 332721

Deren Electronic (Hong Kong) Co., Limited (1)
Room 5 12/F Lladro' Centre 72 Hoi Yuen Road, Kwun Tong, Kowloon, China (Hong Kong)
Tel.: (852) 26692288
Precision Component Mfr & Distr
N.A.I.C.S.: 332721

Deren Electronic (Vietnam) Company Limited (1)
Factory No 3 Land Lot CN1, An Duong Industrial Park Hong Phong Commune An Duong District, Haiphong, Vietnam
Tel.: (84) 345906885
Precision Component Mfr & Distr
N.A.I.C.S.: 332721

Hefei Deren Electronic Device Co., Ltd. (1)
No 19 Gengyun Road, Economic and Technology Development Zone, Hefei, Anhui, China
Tel.: (86) 55163851500
Precision Component Mfr & Distr
N.A.I.C.S.: 332721

Heshan Deren Electronic Science&Technology Co., Ltd. (1)
No 13 Hongjiang Road, Heshan Industrial City, Heshan, Guangdong, China
Tel.: (86) 7508922055
Precision Component Mfr & Distr
N.A.I.C.S.: 332721

Huizhou Shenghua Science&Technology Co., Ltd. (1)
Zhongkai High-tech Development Zone, Pingnan Industrial Zone, Huizhou, Guangdong, China
Tel.: (86) 7525308120
Precision Component Mfr & Distr
N.A.I.C.S.: 332721

Liuzhou Shuangfei Auto Electric Appliances Manufacturing Co., Ltd. (1)
No 1 Chuangxin Road, Xinxing Industrial Park, Liuzhou, Guangxi, China
Tel.: (86) 772 750 7268
Web Site: https://en.lzsfdq.com
Emp.: 100
Vehicle Harness Product Mfr & Distr
N.A.I.C.S.: 336320

Meta System (Chongqing) Co., Ltd. (1)
13 Jujin Road Biquan Street, Deren Electronic Industrial Park Bishan District, Chongqing, China
Tel.: (86) 2381678000
Precision Component Mfr & Distr
N.A.I.C.S.: 332721

Meta System S.p.A. (1)
Via T Galimberti 5, 42124, Reggio Emilia, Italy
Tel.: (39) 0522364111
Web Site: https://www.metasystem.it
Emp.: 200
Electronic Components Mfr
N.A.I.C.S.: 334419

Mianyang Hongren Electronic Co., Ltd. (1)
Zone A Torch Building High Tech Zone, Mianyang, Sichuan, China
Tel.: (86) 8164682010
Precision Component Mfr & Distr
N.A.I.C.S.: 332721

PLATI Morocco sarl. (1)
Lot 101 Zone Industrielle Sud-Ouest, Mohammedia, Morocco
Tel.: (212) 523301304
Electronic Appliance Distr
N.A.I.C.S.: 423620

Qingdao Deren Electronic Co., Ltd. (1)
South of Xinhe Road and West of Taihu Road, Jiulong Sub district Office Qingdao, Jiaozhou, Shandong, China
Tel.: (86) 53287273020
Precision Component Mfr & Distr
N.A.I.C.S.: 332721

Shenzhen Deren Optics Co., Ltd. (1)
No 269 Huitong Road Fenghuang Street, Deren Industrial Park Guangming District, Shenzhen, Guangdong, China
Tel.: (86) 75533260000
Precision Component Mfr & Distr
N.A.I.C.S.: 332721

Wuhan Hanren Electronic Co., Ltd. (1)
Building 1 Gaoyuan Biotechnology Park Hannan Road, Hannan Economic Development Zone, Wuhan, Hubei, China
Tel.: (86) 2784758278
Precision Component Mfr & Distr
N.A.I.C.S.: 332721

SHENZHEN DESAY BATTERY TECHNOLOGY CO., LTD.

26F Desai Technology Building Gaoxin South 1st Road High-tech Park, Nanshan District, Shenzhen, 518057, Guangdong, China
Tel.: (86) 75586299888
Web Site: http://www.desaybattery.com
Year Founded: 1995
000049—(SSE)
Rev.: $3,053,577,304
Assets: $1,757,043,297
Liabilities: $1,163,939,756
Net Worth: $593,103,542
Earnings: $121,615,744
Fiscal Year-end: 12/31/22
Battery Mfr
N.A.I.C.S.: 335910
Liu Qi (Chm)

SHENZHEN DIWEIXUN CO., LTD.

20th Floor Building T1 Qiaochengfang No 2080 Qiaoxiang Road, Gaofa Community Shahe Street Nanshan District, Shenzhen, 518073, Xili, China
Tel.: (86) 26727755
Web Site: https://www.dvision.cn
Year Founded: 2001
300167—(CHIN)
Sales Range: $50-74.9 Million
Emp.: 250
Software & Hardware Solutions
N.A.I.C.S.: 513210

SHENZHEN DYNANONIC CO., LTD.

10/F Building 1st Chongwen Park Nanshan Zhiyuan No 3370 Liuxian Avenue, Nanshan, Shenzhen, 518071, China
Tel.: (86) 75586226896
Web Site: https://www.dynanonic.com
Year Founded: 2007
300769—(SSE)
Rev.: $3,167,013,765
Assets: $4,084,831,900
Liabilities: $2,588,260,690
Net Worth: $1,496,571,210
Earnings: $334,179,883
Fiscal Year-end: 12/31/22
Nanometer Product Mfr
N.A.I.C.S.: 334516
Lingyong Kong (Chm & Gen Mgr)

SHENZHEN EASTTOP SUPPLY CHAIN MANAGEMENT CO., LTD.

6F Dongfang Jiasheng Building No 10 Shihua Road Futian Bonded Area, Shenzhen, 518000, Guangdong, China
Tel.: (86) 75525331104
Web Site: http://www.easttop.com.cn
Year Founded: 2001
002889—(SSE)
Rev.: $397,392,498
Assets: $604,788,191
Liabilities: $305,905,233
Net Worth: $298,882,958
Earnings: $21,734,131
Fiscal Year-end: 12/31/22
Logistics Management Services
N.A.I.C.S.: 541614
Sun Weiping (Chm & Gen Mgr)

SHENZHEN ECOBEAUTY CO., LTD.

Room B1701-1703 Block B Hainabaichuan Headquarters Building, No 6 Baoxing Road Haiwang Community Xin'an Street Bao'an District, Shenzhen, 518102, Guangdong, China
Tel.: (86) 75588260210
Web Site: https://eco-beauty.cn
Year Founded: 1989
000010—(SSE)
Rev.: $86,072,683
Assets: $508,623,977
Liabilities: $382,765,865
Net Worth: $125,858,112
Earnings: ($75,225,042)
Fiscal Year-end: 12/31/22
Compressed Natural Gas Equipment Mfr
N.A.I.C.S.: 333912
Chen Meiling (Sec)

SHENZHEN EDADOC TECHNOLOGY CO., LTD.

11F Metro Financial Technology Building No 9819 Shennan Avenue, Shenda Community Yuehai Subdistrict Nanshan District, Shenzhen, 518051, Guangdong, China
Tel.: (86) 75586530851
Web Site: https://www.edadoc.com
Year Founded: 2003
301366—(CHIN)
Rev.: $110,723,295
Assets: $381,868,450
Liabilities: $68,239,507
Net Worth: $313,628,943
Earnings: $13,921,268
Emp.: 60
Fiscal Year-end: 12/31/23
Circuit Board Mfr & Distr
N.A.I.C.S.: 334412
Tang Changmao (Chm & Gen Mgr)

SHENZHEN ELLASSAY FASHION CO., LTD.

1901-1905 Building A Tianan Hightech Plaza Chegongmiao, Futian, Shenzhen, 518048, Guangdong, China
Tel.: (86) 75583438860
Web Site: http://www.ellassay.com
Year Founded: 1996
603808—(SHG)
Rev.: $336,222,184
Assets: $609,821,265
Liabilities: $207,598,922
Net Worth: $402,222,343
Earnings: $2,871,433
Fiscal Year-end: 12/31/22
Women Apparel Mfr & Distr
N.A.I.C.S.: 315990
Guoxin Xia (Chm, Pres & Gen Mgr)

Subsidiaries:

Iro Inc. (1)
19 Rue Bachaumont, 75002, Paris, France
Tel.: (33) 143160901
Web Site: http://www.iroparis.com
Clothing Accessory Distr
N.A.I.C.S.: 458110

SHENZHEN EMPEROR TECHNOLOGY CO., LTD.

29/F Block A Building 10 Shenzhen Bay Eco-Technology Park, Nanshan District, Shenzhen, 518063, China
Tel.: (86) 75583416677
Web Site: https://www.emperortech.com
Year Founded: 1995
300546—(CHIN)
Rev.: $86,684,364
Assets: $191,426,976
Liabilities: $38,503,296
Net Worth: $152,923,680
Earnings: $5,145,660
Fiscal Year-end: 12/31/22
Electronic Application Equipment Mfr
N.A.I.C.S.: 334419

Subsidiaries:

Emperor Global Resources LLC (1)
5220 Spring Valley Rd Ste 200, Dallas, TX 75254
Tel.: (214) 614-8340
Web Site: https://emperortech.us
Automatic Personalization Equipment Mfr & Distr
N.A.I.C.S.: 334118

Shenzhen Emperor Technology Co., Ltd. - Shenzhen Plant (1)
Xiongdi Building No 49 Nantong Road, Longgang District, Shenzhen, 518107, China
Tel.: (86) 75528894103
Smartcard Mfr
N.A.I.C.S.: 326199

SHENZHEN ENERGY GROUP CO., LTD.

9/F 29-31/F 34-41/F North Tower Energy Building No 2026 Jintian Road, Futian Subdistrict Futian District, Shenzhen, 518033, Guangdong, China
Tel.: (86) 75583684138
Web Site: http://www.sec.com.cn
Year Founded: 1993
000027—(SSE)
Rev.: $5,268,470,225
Assets: $19,833,845,958
Liabilities: $12,207,206,452
Net Worth: $7,626,639,506
Earnings: $308,685,181
Fiscal Year-end: 12/31/22
Electric Power Distribution Services
N.A.I.C.S.: 221122
Li Yingfeng (Chm)

Subsidiaries:

China Hydroelectric Corporation (1)
F8 West Zone No 2068 Shennan Middle Road, Futian District, Shenzhen, China (100%)
Tel.: (86) 755 83680288
Web Site: http://www.sec.com.cn
Hydroelectric Power Generation & Distribution Services
N.A.I.C.S.: 221111

Huizhou City Gas Development Co., Ltd. (1)
F13-13a Foreign Investment Building No 6 Yunshan West Road, Jiangbei, Huizhou, 519060, Guangdong, China
Tel.: (86) 7566836888
Electric Power Distribution Services
N.A.I.C.S.: 221122

Huizhou Shenzhen Energy Fengda Power Co., Ltd. (1)
Admiralty Road No 29 Huizhou Industrial Park Huiao Road, Guangdong, 516025, Huizhou, China
Tel.: (86) 7522598903
Electric Power Distribution Services
N.A.I.C.S.: 221122

Shenzhen Energy Electricity Sale Company (1)
F8 West Tower Huaneng Building No 2068 Shennan Middle Road, Futian District, Shenzhen, 518031, China

AND PRIVATE COMPANIES — SHENZHEN FENDA TECHNOLOGY CO., LTD.

Tel.: (86) 75583684096
Electric Power Distribution Services
N.A.I.C.S.: 221122

Shenzhen Energy Environment Engineering Co., Ltd. (1)
F12-13 Times Financial Center No 4001 Shennan Avenue, Futian District, Shenzhen, 518048, Guangdong, China
Tel.: (86) 75523676000
Electric Power Distribution Services
N.A.I.C.S.: 221122

Shenzhen Energy Finance Co., Ltd. (1)
No 2068 Shennan Middle Road, Futian District, Shenzhen, 518031, Guangdong, China
Tel.: (86) 75525325200
Electric Power Distribution Services
N.A.I.C.S.: 221122

Shenzhen Energy Hopewell Power (Heyuan) Co., Ltd. (1)
The Town of Po Town, Heyuan, 517025, Guangdong, China
Tel.: (86) 7623427799
Electric Power Distribution Services
N.A.I.C.S.: 221122

Shenzhen Energy Korla Power Generation Co., Ltd. (1)
Donghuan Road Korla Economic and Technological Development Zone, Xinjiang, China
Tel.: (86) 9962056889
Electric Power Distribution Services
N.A.I.C.S.: 221122

Shenzhen Energy Nanjing Holding Co., Ltd. (1)
F22 Tower C Wanda Plaza, Jianye District, Nanjing, 210000, Jiangsu, China
Tel.: (86) 2586667545
Electric Power Distribution Services
N.A.I.C.S.: 221122

Shenzhen Energy North Holdings Co., Ltd. (1)
No A29 Baizhifang East Street, Xuanwu District, Beijing, 100054, China
Tel.: (86) 75583680748
Electric Power Distribution Services
N.A.I.C.S.: 221122

Shenzhen Energy Power Service Co., Ltd. (1)
F7 Nangang Business Building Qianhai Road, Nanshan District, Shenzhen, 518052, Guangdong, China
Tel.: (86) 75586263777
Electric Power Distribution Services
N.A.I.C.S.: 221122

Shenzhen Energy Resource Comprehensive Development Co., Ltd. (1)
F20 Jinfeng Building Shangbu South Road, Futian District, Shenzhen, 518031, Guangdong, China
Tel.: (86) 26530329
Electric Power Distribution Services
N.A.I.C.S.: 221122

Shenzhen Energy Transportation Co., Ltd. (1)
Times Financial Center No 4001 Shennan Avenue, Futian District, Shenzhen, 518031, Guangdong, China
Tel.: (86) 75583635516
Electric Power Distribution Services
N.A.I.C.S.: 221122

Shenzhen Guangshen Shajiao B Power Co., Ltd. (1)
F26-27 Times Financial Center No 4001 Shennan Avenue, Futian District, Shenzhen, 518034, Guangdong, China
Tel.: (86) 75533355002
Electric Power Distribution Services
N.A.I.C.S.: 221122

Sichuan Shenzhen Energy Power Investment Holding Co., Ltd. (1)
F15 Building 1 Teda Times Center No 1288 Tianfu Avenue North Section, Gaoxin District, Chengdu, 610041, China
Tel.: (86) 2883166130
Electric Power Distribution Services
N.A.I.C.S.: 221122

Sunon (Hong Kong) International Co., Ltd. (1)
Rm 1101/1102 Great Eagle Centre No 23 Harbour Road Wan Chai, Hong Kong, China (Hong Kong)
Tel.: (852) 34723472
Electric Power Distribution Services
N.A.I.C.S.: 221122

SHENZHEN ENVICOOL TECHNOLOGY CO., LTD
Building 9 Hongxin Industrial Park Guanlan, Longhua District, Shenzhen, 518110, China
Tel.: (86) 75566833272
Web Site: https://www.envicool.com
Year Founded: 2005
002837—(SSE)
Rev.: $410,414,739
Assets: $567,543,483
Liabilities: $271,534,569
Net Worth: $296,008,914
Earnings: $39,351,719
Emp.: 4,000
Fiscal Year-end: 12/31/22
Environment Control Equipment Mfr & Distr
N.A.I.C.S.: 334512

SHENZHEN ESUN DISPLAY CO., LTD.
3F Tower East Second-Phase Shenzhen Culture Innovation Park, Xinzhou Road, Futian District, Shenzhen, China
Tel.: (86) 7558 383 1626
Web Site: http://www.es-display.com
002751—(SSE)
Rev.: $156,928,407
Assets: $628,361,705
Liabilities: $360,922,925
Net Worth: $267,438,780
Earnings: $8,135,451
Emp.: 860
Fiscal Year-end: 12/31/20
Terminal Display Mfr
N.A.I.C.S.: 337215
Menglong Liu (Pres & CEO)

SHENZHEN ETMADE AUTOMATIC EQUIPMENT CO., LTD.
401 Tower A Building 1 Xingzhan Plaza No 446 Shajing Nanhuan Road, Shatou Community Shajing Subdistrict Baoan District, Shenzhen, 518104, Guangdong, China
Tel.: (86) 75527850601
Web Site: http://www.etmade.com
Year Founded: 2007
300812—(SSE)
Rev.: $92,010,649
Assets: $221,792,576
Liabilities: $100,343,641
Net Worth: $121,448,934
Earnings: $6,218,470
Emp.: 300
Fiscal Year-end: 12/31/22
Automatic Equipment Mfr & Distr
N.A.I.C.S.: 334512
Minghua Chai (Board of Directors & Chm)

SHENZHEN EVERWIN PRECISION TECHNOLOGY CO., LTD.
11 Block No 3 Industry Area, Fuyong Qiaotou Baoan District, Shenzhen, 518103, Guangdong, China
Tel.: (86) 75527343066
Web Site: https://www.ewpt.cn
Year Founded: 2001
300115—(CHIN)
Rev.: $2,134,492,776
Assets: $2,468,335,896
Liabilities: $1,639,014,156
Net Worth: $829,321,740
Earnings: $5,974,020
Emp.: 35,000
Fiscal Year-end: 12/31/22

Precise Electronic Parts & Components Mfr
N.A.I.C.S.: 334419
Qixing Chen (Chm)

Subsidiaries:

Dongguan Everwin Precision Technology Co., Ltd. (1)
No 639 Meijing West Road, Rhinoceros Village Dalang Town, Dongguan, China
Tel.: (86) 7692 289 0087
Electronic Products Mfr
N.A.I.C.S.: 334417

Guangdong Everwin Precision Technology Co., Ltd. (1)
No 6 Industrial West 3rd Road Songshan Lake High, New Technology Industrial Development Zone, Dongguan, Guangdong, China
Tel.: (86) 7692 223 6311
Electronic Products Mfr
N.A.I.C.S.: 334417

Guangdong Tianji Industrial Intelligent System Co., Ltd. (1)
Building 3 No 6 Industrial West Third Road, Songshan Lake Park, Dongguan, Guangdong, China
Tel.: (86) 7692 289 2095
Electronic Products Mfr
N.A.I.C.S.: 334417

Guangdong Tianji Robot Co., Ltd. (1)
Room 402 Building 3 No 6 Industrial West Third Road, Songshan Lake Park, Dongguan, Guangdong, China
Tel.: (86) 7692 289 1197
Electronic Products Mfr
N.A.I.C.S.: 334417

Kunshan EWPT Precision Technology Co., Ltd. (1)
Zhang Garden Road Town 3, Kunshan, 215321, Jiangsu, China
Tel.: (86) 51257296268
Web Site: http://www.ewpt.cc
Precision Equipment Mfr
N.A.I.C.S.: 333248

Kunshan Everwin Precision Technology Co., Ltd. (1)
No 100 North Binjiang Road, Zhangpu Town, Kunshan, Jiangsu, China
Tel.: (86) 5125 729 6269
Electronic Products Mfr
N.A.I.C.S.: 334417

Kunshan Hubble Radio Electronic Technology Co., Ltd. (1)
No 100 North Binjiang Road, Zhangpu Town, Kunshan, Jiangsu, China
Tel.: (86) 5125 788 7876
Electronic Products Mfr
N.A.I.C.S.: 334417

Kunshan Just Conn. Precision Components Co., Ltd. (1)
No 1389 Zizhu Road, Yushan Town, Kunshan, Jiangsu, China
Tel.: (86) 5125 773 0489
Electronic Products Mfr
N.A.I.C.S.: 334417

Kunshan Taibo Precision Technology Co., Ltd. (1)
No 100 North Binjiang Road, Zhangpu Town, Kunshan, Jiangsu, China
Electronic Products Mfr
N.A.I.C.S.: 334417

SHENZHEN EXC-LED TECHNOLOGY CO., LTD.
Building 1 Jiancang Technology Park No 11 Songgang Avenue, Songgang Street Baoan District, Shenzhen, 518105, Guangdong, China
Tel.: (86) 75523229069
Web Site: https://www.exc-light.com
Year Founded: 2009
300889—(CHIN)
Rev.: $127,104,120
Assets: $371,148,804
Liabilities: $144,106,560
Net Worth: $227,042,244

Earnings: $5,113,368
Fiscal Year-end: 12/31/22
LCD Products Mfr
N.A.I.C.S.: 334413
Mingwu Xie (Chm)

SHENZHEN FARBEN INFORMATION TECHNOLOGY CO., LTD.
Block B WeiDa Technology Park No 15 Gaoxin North 6th Road Xili Street, Songpingshan Community Nanshan District, Shenzhen, 518067, Guangdong, China
Tel.: (86) 75523633188
Web Site: https://www.farben.com.cn
Year Founded: 2006
300925—(SSE)
Rev.: $503,450,925
Assets: $375,510,864
Liabilities: $165,315,440
Net Worth: $210,195,423
Earnings: $18,189,424
Fiscal Year-end: 12/31/22
Information Technology Services
N.A.I.C.S.: 541512
Hua Yan (Chm & Gen Mgr)

SHENZHEN FASTPRINT CIRCUIT TECH CO., LTD.
Floor 8 Block A Building 2 Zone 1, Shenzhen Bay Science and Technology Ecological Park Nanshan District, Shenzhen, 518057, China
Tel.: (86) 75526051688
Web Site: https://www.chinafastprint.com
Year Founded: 1999
002436—(SSE)
Rev.: $751,681,242
Assets: $1,669,116,660
Liabilities: $682,179,774
Net Worth: $986,936,886
Earnings: $73,798,887
Fiscal Year-end: 12/31/22
Printed Circuit Board Mfr
N.A.I.C.S.: 334412

Subsidiaries:

Guangzhou Fastprint Circuit Tech Co., Ltd. (1)
No 33 Guangpuzhong Rd, Guangzhou Science City Huangpu District, Guangzhou, 510663, China
Tel.: (86) 2032213001
PCB Board Mfr
N.A.I.C.S.: 334412

SHENZHEN FEIMA INTERNATIONAL SUPPLY CHAIN CO., LTD.
11B Huitong Building No 11 Wenxin 5th Road Haizhu Community, Yuehai Subdistrict Nanshan District, Shenzhen, 518064, Guangdong, China
Tel.: (86) 75533356399
Web Site: http://www.fmscm.com
Year Founded: 1998
002210—(SSE)
Rev.: $49,695,703
Assets: $174,573,514
Liabilities: $137,172,148
Net Worth: $37,401,367
Earnings: $12,404,579
Fiscal Year-end: 12/31/22
Logistic Services
N.A.I.C.S.: 541614
Zhao Libin (Chm)

SHENZHEN FENDA TECHNOLOGY CO., LTD.
Fenda Hi-Tech Park Zhoushi Road Shiyan, Baoan, Shenzhen, 518108, China
Tel.: (86) 75527353888
Web Site: https://www.fenda.com

SHENZHEN FENDA TECHNOLOGY CO., LTD.

Shenzhen Fenda Technology Co., Ltd.—(Continued)
002681—(SSE)
Rev.: $413,217,039
Assets: $568,024,465
Liabilities: $257,224,243
Net Worth: $310,800,223
Earnings: $11,942,719
Emp.: 4,700
Fiscal Year-end: 12/31/22
Audio Products & Personal Appliances
N.A.I.C.S.: 334310

Subsidiaries:

Epticore Microelectronics (jiangsu) Co., Ltd. (1)
Room 14506 Building 6 498 GuoShouJing Road, Shanghai, China
Tel.: (86) 2150315930
Photoelectric Sensor Mfr & Whslr
N.A.I.C.S.: 334413

Shenzhen Waveguider Optical Telecom Technology Inc. (1)
1411 14F Tower C Zhan tao Technology Building Min zhi Road, Min Zhi Stree Long Hua District, Shenzhen, 518060, China
Tel.: (86) 75533581159
Web Site: https://www.waveguider.com.cn
Health Care Srvices
N.A.I.C.S.: 524114

SHENZHEN FINE MADE ELECTRONICS GROUP CO., LTD.

101 Building 1 Intersection of Renmin East Road & Shouhe Road, Jinsha Community Kengzi Subdistrict Pingshan District, Shenzhen, 518083, Guangdong, China
Tel.: (86) 75583492887
Web Site: http://www.superchip.cn
Year Founded: 2001
300671—(CHIN)
Rev.: $108,290,885
Assets: $459,841,337
Liabilities: $155,262,393
Net Worth: $304,578,944
Earnings: ($24,242,489)
Fiscal Year-end: 12/31/22
Electrical Component Mfr
N.A.I.C.S.: 335999
Liu Jingyu *(Chm & Gen Mgr)*

SHENZHEN FLUENCE TECHNOLOGY PLC

07F 4 Building B Tian An Cyber Innovation Park, Longgang district, Shenzhen, 518172, Guangdong, China
Tel.: (86) 75589979003
Web Site: https://www.cps-lighting.com
Year Founded: 2005
300647—(CHIN)
Rev.: $89,487,625
Assets: $315,321,881
Liabilities: $176,983,574
Net Worth: $138,338,306
Earnings: ($33,732,561)
Fiscal Year-end: 12/31/23
Lighting Equipment Mfr & Distr
N.A.I.C.S.: 335139
Du Jianjun *(Chm & Gen Mgr)*

SHENZHEN FORMS SYNTRON INFORMATION CO., LTD.

Forms Syntron Building No 8 No 7 South Gaoxin Road, Nanshan District, Shenzhen, Guangdong, China
Tel.: (86) 75586336133
Web Site: https://www.formssi.com
Year Founded: 2003
300468—(SSE)
Rev.: $93,241,044
Assets: $242,208,252
Liabilities: $18,275,868
Net Worth: $223,932,384
Earnings: $5,785,884
Emp.: 1,280
Fiscal Year-end: 12/31/22
IT Services
N.A.I.C.S.: 541519

SHENZHEN FORTUNE TREND TECHNOLOGY CO., LTD.

1801 Building 5 Shenzhen New Generation Industrial Park, No 136 Zhongkang Road Meidu Community Meilin Street Futian District, Shenzhen, 518000, Guangdong, China
Tel.: (86) 2787788668
Web Site: https://www.tdx.com.cn
Year Founded: 2007
688318—(SHG)
Rev.: $45,134,065
Assets: $472,766,182
Liabilities: $27,889,210
Net Worth: $444,876,972
Earnings: $21,561,902
Fiscal Year-end: 12/31/22
Software Development Services
N.A.I.C.S.: 541511
Shan Huang *(Chm & Gen Mgr)*

SHENZHEN FOUNTAIN CORPORATION

Huale Tower Shennan East Ave 2017, Shenzhen, 518001, Guangdong, China
Tel.: (86) 75582208888
Web Site: http://www.fountain.com.cn
000005—(SSE)
Rev.: $39,837,615
Assets: $365,347,462
Liabilities: $181,635,831
Net Worth: $183,711,631
Earnings: ($21,910,459)
Fiscal Year-end: 12/31/22
Real Estate Lending Services
N.A.I.C.S.: 531110

SHENZHEN FRD SCIENCE & TECHNOLOGY CO., LTD.

Building 1 2 & 3 FRD Industrial Park, Guangming District, Shenzhen, 518132, China
Tel.: (86) 75586081680   CN
Web Site: https://www.frd.cn
Year Founded: 1993
300602—(CHIN)
Rev.: $579,081,330
Assets: $880,370,646
Liabilities: $508,070,731
Net Worth: $372,299,916
Earnings: $13,504,669
Fiscal Year-end: 12/31/22
Electromagnetic Shielding Material Mfr & Distr
N.A.I.C.S.: 334513
Ma Fei *(Chm)*

Subsidiaries:

FRD (Hong Kong) Co., Ltd (1)
Unit 503 5/F Silvercord Tower 2 30 Canton Road, Tsimshatsui, Kowloon, China (Hong Kong)
Tel.: (852) 35195726
Electronic Product Distr
N.A.I.C.S.: 423690

Kunshan FRD Electronic Materials Co., Ltd. (1)
FRD Industrial Park 258 Dongping Road, Bacheng, Kunshan, 215311, China
Tel.: (86) 51257851188
Electronic Products Mfr
N.A.I.C.S.: 334419

Tianjin FRD Science & Technology Co., Ltd. (1)
FRD Park No 160 Xiangyuan Road, Beijing-Tianjin Science and Technology Valley Wuqing Area, Tianjin, China
Tel.: (86) 2259695716
Electronic Products Mfr
N.A.I.C.S.: 334419

SHENZHEN FRIENDCOM TECHNOLOGY DEVELOPMENT CO., LTD.

3rd Floor Building 6 Guangqian Industrial Park 3rd Longzhu Road, Taoyuan Street Nanshan District, Shenzhen, 518005, Guangdong, China
Tel.: (86) 75523230588
Web Site: https://www.friendcom.cn
Year Founded: 2002
300514—(CHIN)
Rev.: $143,428,582
Assets: $153,177,888
Liabilities: $51,829,278
Net Worth: $101,348,610
Earnings: $13,865,988
Fiscal Year-end: 12/31/22
Communication Equipment Mfr & Distr
N.A.I.C.S.: 334220

SHENZHEN FUANNA BEDDING & FURNISHING CO., LTD.

Fuanna Industry Buiding Nanguang Road, Nanshan District, Shenzhen, 518054, Guangdong, China
Tel.: (86) 75526055333
Web Site: http://www.fuanna.com.cn
Year Founded: 1994
002327—(SSE)
Rev.: $432,374,548
Assets: $656,081,408
Liabilities: $126,939,375
Net Worth: $529,142,033
Earnings: $74,948,904
Fiscal Year-end: 12/31/22
Textile Products Mfr
N.A.I.C.S.: 313310
Guofang Lin *(Chm & Gen Mgr)*

SHENZHEN FUDAKIN PLASTIC & METAL LTD.

No 39 Tangkeng 2nd Road, Pingshan, Shenzhen, 518118, China
Tel.: (86) 755 84635699
Web Site: http://www.fudakin.com
Year Founded: 1997
Emp.: 400
Plastic Injection Molding, Dies & Jigs
N.A.I.C.S.: 333511
Dajun Li *(Chm & Mng Dir)*

SHENZHEN GAS CORPORATION LTD.

No 268 Meiao 1st Road, Futian District, Shenzhen, 518049, Guangdong, China
Tel.: (86) 75588660777
Web Site: http://www.szgas.com.cn
Year Founded: 1996
601139—(SHG)
Rev.: $4,220,643,417
Assets: $5,363,381,650
Liabilities: $3,202,033,709
Net Worth: $2,161,347,940
Earnings: $171,611,917
Emp.: 2,370
Fiscal Year-end: 12/31/22
Natural & Liquefied Gas Distribution & Pipeline Transportation Services
N.A.I.C.S.: 221210
Wang Wenjie *(Chm)*

SHENZHEN GENVICT TECHNOLOGIES CO., LTD.

Floor 19-20 Block A Building 11 Shenzhen Bay, Shenzhen Bay Eco Technology Park Yuehai Street Nanshan District, Shenzhen, 518000, Guangdong, China
Tel.: (86) 75526030288   CN
Web Site: https://www.genvict.com
Year Founded: 2004
002869—(SSE)
Rev.: $68,966,067
Assets: $363,699,306
Liabilities: $74,047,339
Net Worth: $289,651,967
Earnings: $2,702,124
Fiscal Year-end: 12/31/22
Transportation Management Consulting Services
N.A.I.C.S.: 541614
Luo Ruifa *(Chm)*

SHENZHEN GLORY MEDICAL CO., LTD.

Shangrong Technology Industrial Park No 2 Baolong 5th Road, Baolong Industrial City Longgang District, Shenzhen, 518116, China
Tel.: (86) 75582290988
Web Site: https://www.glory-medical.com.cn
Year Founded: 1998
002551—(SSE)
Rev.: $179,109,684
Assets: $598,170,030
Liabilities: $177,070,472
Net Worth: $421,099,558
Earnings: ($43,252,045)
Fiscal Year-end: 12/31/22
Medical Facilities Construction, Computer Systems & Equipment
N.A.I.C.S.: 236220
Lin Li *(Sec)*

SHENZHEN GONGJIN ELECTRONICS CO., LTD.

No 2 Danzi North Road Kengzi Street, Pingshan District, Shenzhen, 518118, Guangdong, China
Tel.: (86) 75589990666
Web Site: https://www.twsz.com
Year Founded: 1998
603118—(SHG)
Rev.: $1,540,698,649
Assets: $1,478,969,641
Liabilities: $755,956,380
Net Worth: $723,013,261
Earnings: $31,834,703
Emp.: 8,000
Fiscal Year-end: 12/31/22
Electronic Component Mfr & Distr
N.A.I.C.S.: 334419
Hu Zumin *(Chm)*

Subsidiaries:

Shanghai Gongjin Communications Technology Co., Ltd. (1)
Building T9 Xiexin No2 Lane 187 Xinghong Road, Minhang, Shanghai, 201106, China
Tel.: (86) 33390888
Electronic Product Distr
N.A.I.C.S.: 449210

Taicang T&W Electronics Co., Ltd. (1)
No 89 Jiangnan Road, Ludu, Taicang, 215412, China
Tel.: (86) 233026800
Electronic Product Distr
N.A.I.C.S.: 449210

SHENZHEN GOODIX TECHNOLOGY CO., LTD.

Floor 13 Phase B Tengfei Industrial Building, Futian Freetrade Zone, Shenzhen, 518000, China
Tel.: (86) 75533338828
Web Site: https://www.goodix.com
Year Founded: 2002
603160—(SHG)
Rev.: $475,106,889
Assets: $1,323,504,931
Liabilities: $231,430,797
Net Worth: $1,092,074,134
Earnings: ($104,968,923)
Emp.: 1,500
Fiscal Year-end: 12/31/22
Biometric Technology Mfr & Distr

N.A.I.C.S.: 334118
Fan Zhang (Chm & CEO)

SHENZHEN GRANDLAND GROUP CO., LTD.
No 2188 Hongling North Road, Luohu District, Shenzhen, Guangdong, China
Tel.: (86) 75525886666
Web Site: https://www.szgt.com
Year Founded: 1995
002482—(SSE)
Rev.: $500,347,383
Assets: $1,514,348,517
Liabilities: $2,218,431,000
Net Worth: ($704,082,483)
Earnings: ($745,673,933)
Fiscal Year-end: 12/31/22
Architectural Decoration Design & Construction Services
N.A.I.C.S.: 541310

Subsidiaries:

Chengdu Grandland South China Decoration Engineering Co., Ltd. (1)
F5 Block 3 Torch Power Port Phase Two No 81 Jinshi Road, Jinjiang District, Chengdu, 610021, China
Tel.: (86) 2886510799
Architectural Design Services
N.A.I.C.S.: 541310

Nanjing Grandland Bosen Industrial Co., Ltd. (1)
Xinglong Building No 188 Xinglong Street, Nanjing, 210019, China
Tel.: (86) 2583197001
Architectural Design Services
N.A.I.C.S.: 541310

Shenzhen Grandland Curtain Wall Co., Ltd. (1)
F19 Reith International Building A No 1002 Yanhe North Road, Luohu District, Shenzhen, 518003, China
Tel.: (86) 75536800555
Architectural Design Services
N.A.I.C.S.: 541310

Shenzhen Grandland Decoration Group Corp. Ltd - The 5th Division (1)
F3 Creative Park D No 808 Yaojiayuan Village Chaoyang District, Beijing, 100025, China
Tel.: (86) 1052933001
Architectural Design Services
N.A.I.C.S.: 541310

Shenzhen Grandland Fangte Facade Technology Co., Ltd. (1)
6 floor HuangFengling Industry area ShiYan town Bao'an District, Shenzhen, 518108, China
Tel.: (86) 75527633456
Web Site: http://www.fang-te.com
Building Architectural Design Services
N.A.I.C.S.: 541310
Yan Jun (Dir-Engrg)

Shenzhen Grandland Hi-Tech New Materials Co., Ltd. (1)
No 86 Xiangyang Road Yanchuan Community Songgang Bao'an District, Shenzhen, 518105, China
Tel.: (86) 75529698666
Architectural Design Services
N.A.I.C.S.: 541310

Shenzhen Grandland Intelligent Technology Co., Ltd. (1)
Room515 Block4C Software Industry Base No 1003, Sience Based Industrial Park Road South of Science & Technology Park, Guangzhou, 518003, China
Tel.: (86) 75532938666
Interior Design Services
N.A.I.C.S.: 541410

Shenzhen Grandland Soft Decoration Art Co., Ltd. (1)
F5 Yilan Center Block 802 Zhanyi Road, Luohu District, Shenzhen, 518033, China
Tel.: (86) 75522950199
Interior Decoration Services
N.A.I.C.S.: 541310

Shenzhen Xinhuafeng Environment Development Co., Ltd. (1)
F12 Wujing Building Xiangmei North Road Futian District, Shenzhen, 518034, China
Tel.: (86) 75582891137
Landscape Design Services
N.A.I.C.S.: 541320

SHENZHEN GUANGJU ENERGY CO., LTD.
22nd Floor Tianli Central Business Plaza Hyde 3rd Road, Nanshan District, Shenzhen, 518054, Guangdong, China
Tel.: (86) 75586000096
Web Site: https://www.gj000096.com
Year Founded: 1999
000096—(SSE)
Rev.: $294,874,763
Assets: $386,352,973
Liabilities: $21,157,129
Net Worth: $365,195,844
Earnings: $7,742,161
Fiscal Year-end: 12/31/22
Petroleum Product Whslr
N.A.I.C.S.: 424720
Lin Weibin (Chm)

SHENZHEN GUOHUA NETWORK SECURITY TECHNOLOGY CO., LTD.
12th Floor Cuilin Building No 10 Kaifeng Road Meilin Street, Maling Community Futian District, Shenzhen, 518049, China
Tel.: (86) 75583521713
Web Site: https://sz000004.cn
Year Founded: 1981
000004—(SSE)
Rev.: $23,371,447
Assets: $80,784,854
Liabilities: $31,291,060
Net Worth: $49,493,794
Earnings: ($83,560,857)
Fiscal Year-end: 12/31/22
Pharmaceuticals Mfr
N.A.I.C.S.: 325412

SHENZHEN H&T INTELLIGENT CONTROL CO., LTD.
Shenzhen Academy of Aerospace Technology Building D Floor 10, 6 Keji South 10th Rd Hi-Tech South Area Nanshan Dist, Shenzhen, 518000, Guangdong, China
Tel.: (86) 75586119291
Web Site: https://www.szhittech.com
Year Founded: 2000
002402—(SSE)
Rev.: $837,552,437
Assets: $1,192,090,068
Liabilities: $501,768,947
Net Worth: $690,321,121
Earnings: $61,432,245
Emp.: 750
Fiscal Year-end: 12/31/22
Electronic Control System Mfr
N.A.I.C.S.: 334419

Subsidiaries:

Shenzhen H&T Intelligent Control Co., Ltd. - Factory (1)
Building 6 2nd Industrial Park Baimang Nangang Town, Nanshan, Shenzhen, 518018, Guangdong, China
Tel.: (86) 755 81795424
Electronic Control System Whslr
N.A.I.C.S.: 423690

SHENZHEN HAN'S CNC TECHNOLOGY CO., LTD.
Hans Laser Global Intelligence Production Base No 16 Chongqqing Road, Fuhai Street Baoan, Shenzhen, 518103, Guangdong, China
Tel.: (86) 4006282600
Web Site: https://www.hanscnc.com
Year Founded: 2002
301200—(CHIN)
Rev.: $230,184,661
Assets: $842,130,420
Liabilities: $181,772,126
Net Worth: $660,358,294
Earnings: $19,090,972
Fiscal Year-end: 12/31/23
Industrial Machinery Mfr & Distr
N.A.I.C.S.: 333248
Chaohui Yang (Chm)

SHENZHEN HEKEDA PRECISION CLEANING EQUIPMENT CO., LTD.
1-3F Block 2 Hekeda Industrial Park No 294 Huarong Road, Langkou Community Dalang Subdistrict Longhua District, Shenzhen, 518109, Guangdong, China
Tel.: (86) 75527048451
Web Site: http://www.hekeda.cn
Year Founded: 2008
002816—(SSE)
Rev.: $12,110,370
Assets: $61,650,525
Liabilities: $14,182,899
Net Worth: $47,467,625
Earnings: ($11,382,298)
Fiscal Year-end: 12/31/22
Precision Cleaning Equipment Mfr & Distr
N.A.I.C.S.: 335999
Meng Yuliang (Chm & Pres)

Subsidiaries:

Shenzhen HEKEDA Water Treatment Equipment Co., Ltd. (1)
Hekeda Industrial Zone Huawang Road, Dalang Longhua Town, Shenzhen, China
Tel.: (86) 755 2704 7450
Web Site: http://www.hkdwater.com
Water Treatment Equipment Mfr
N.A.I.C.S.: 333310

Subsidiary (Domestic):

Suzhou HEKEDA Water Treatment Technology Limited (2)
Hekeda Industrial Zone Xingwang Road Huangqiao Town, Xiangcheng District, Suzhou, China
Tel.: (86) 51266185880
Water Treatment Equipment Mfr
N.A.I.C.S.: 333310

Xi'an HEKEDA Water Treatment Technology Limited (2)
1/F Building A2 Textile Industrial Zone Baqiao District, Xi'an, China
Tel.: (86) 2983381281
Water Treatment Equipment Mfr
N.A.I.C.S.: 333310

Suzhou HEKEDA Liquid Crystal Equipment Co., Ltd. (1)
Room 5 of Xingwang Rd, the 2nd Zone of Huangqiao Bridge Industrial Park Xiangcheng, Suzhou, 215132, China
Tel.: (86) 51265796801
Cleaning Equipment Mfr
N.A.I.C.S.: 335999

SHENZHEN HELLO TECH ENERGY CO., LTD.
38/39/41/42 Floors Building No 1 OCT North Station Minzhi Street, Longhua District, Shenzhen, 518109, Guangdong, China
Tel.: (86) 75529106556
Web Site: https://www.hello-tech.com
Year Founded: 2011
301327—(CHIN)
Rev.: $449,688,564
Assets: $1,059,351,696
Liabilities: $160,687,800
Net Worth: $898,663,896
Earnings: $40,249,872
Fiscal Year-end: 12/31/22
Battery Product Mfr
N.A.I.C.S.: 335910
Zhongwei Sun (Chm & Gen Mgr)

Subsidiaries:

Guangdong DX2 Technology Co., Ltd. (1)
The 26th Floor Huide Building, Longhua District, Shenzhen, China
Tel.: (86) 75529128833
Portable Power Product Mfr
N.A.I.C.S.: 333414

Jackery Japan Co., Ltd. (1)
I/O SHIMBASHI 2F 1-11-2 Shimbashi, Minato-ku, Tokyo, 105-0004, Japan
Tel.: (81) 5031989007
Web Site: https://www.jackery.jp
Portable Power & Solar Panel Distr
N.A.I.C.S.: 423720

Jackery, Inc. (1)
48531 Warm Springs Blvd Ste 408, Fremont, CA 94539
Web Site: https://www.jackery.com
Solar Electric Power Generation Distr
N.A.I.C.S.: 221114

SHENZHEN HEMEI GROUP CO., LTD.
2205 Building T7 No 1 Shenzhen Bay No 3008 Zhongxin Road, Nanshan District, Shenzhen, 518000, Guangdong, China
Tel.: (86) 75526755598
Web Site: http://www.szhnd.com
Year Founded: 1994
002356—(SSE)
Rev.: $22,796,959
Assets: $118,586,375
Liabilities: $31,991,951
Net Worth: $86,594,424
Earnings: ($8,660,055)
Fiscal Year-end: 12/31/22
Electrotechnical Instruments & Meters Mfr
N.A.I.C.S.: 334514
Zheng Ziwei (Chm)

SHENZHEN HEPALINK PHARMACEUTICAL GROUP CO., LTD.
No 21 Langshan Road Songpingshan, Nanshan District, Shenzhen, 518057, Guangdong, China
Tel.: (86) 75526980200
Web Site: https://www.hepalink.com
Year Founded: 1998
002399—(SSE)
Rev.: $1,005,181,262
Assets: $2,922,314,635
Liabilities: $1,180,281,656
Net Worth: $1,742,032,979
Earnings: $102,081,709
Emp.: 2,000
Fiscal Year-end: 12/31/22
Pharmaceuticals Mfr
N.A.I.C.S.: 325412
Yu Shan (Gen Mgr)

Subsidiaries:

Cytovance Biologics, Inc. (1)
800 Research Pkwy Ste 200, Oklahoma City, OK 73104
Tel.: (405) 319-8310
Web Site: http://www.cytovance.com
Emp.: 178
Biological Product Mfr
N.A.I.C.S.: 325414
Li Li (Founder & Chm)

Scientific Protein Laboratories, LLC (1)
700 E Main St, Waunakee, WI 53597-1440 (100%)
Tel.: (608) 849-5944
Web Site: http://www.spl-pharma.com
Sales Range: $50-74.9 Million
Emp.: 204

Shenzhen Hepalink Pharmaceutical Group Co., Ltd.—(Continued)

Pharmaceuticals, Pancreatins, Heparins & Blood Protein Products Mfr
N.A.I.C.S.: 325414
Kathy Lynch (Dir-HR)

Shenzhen Techdow Pharmaceutical Co., Ltd. (1)
No 19 Gaoxin Zhongyi Road, Nanshan District, Shenzhen, 518057, China
Tel.: (86) 75586142880
Web Site: https://www.techdow.com
Pharmaceutical Product Mfr & Distr
N.A.I.C.S.: 325412

SHENZHEN HEUNGKONG HOLDING CO., LTD.
Xiangjiang Holdings Office Building Jinxiu Xiangjiang Garden, Panyu Avenue Panyu District, Guangzhou, 511442, Guangdong, China
Tel.: (86) 2034821006
Web Site: https://www.hkhc.com.cn
Year Founded: 1993
600162—(SHG)
Rev.: $850,086,381
Assets: $3,421,868,631
Liabilities: $2,472,630,353
Net Worth: $949,238,279
Earnings: $34,175,283
Fiscal Year-end: 12/31/22
Holding Company
N.A.I.C.S.: 551112
Meiqing Zhai (Chm & Gen Mgr)

SHENZHEN HIFUTURE INFORMATION TECHNOLOGY CO., LTD.
Hifuture Technology Factory Zone South of Jinxiu Road, East of Lanjing Road Dagongye District Pingshan New District, Shenzhen, 518118, Guangdong, China
Tel.: (86) 75589921086
Web Site: http://www.hifuture.com
Year Founded: 1999
002168—(SSE)
Rev.: $34,314,869
Assets: $113,522,652
Liabilities: $106,677,563
Net Worth: $6,845,090
Earnings: ($16,127,916)
Fiscal Year-end: 12/31/22
Electric Power Distribution Services
N.A.I.C.S.: 221122
Ai Yuanpeng (Chm)

SHENZHEN HIRISUN TECHNOLOGY INC.
3a/F Area B R2 Factory Shennan Avenue, Nanshan District, Shenzhen, 518057, China
Tel.: (86) 75526972918
Web Site: http://www.hirisun.com
300277—(CHIN)
Rev.: $36,176,868
Assets: $94,719,456
Liabilities: $23,775,336
Net Worth: $70,944,120
Earnings: $1,444,716
Emp.: 370
Fiscal Year-end: 12/31/22
Custom Computer Programing
N.A.I.C.S.: 541511
Qian Yuchen (Chm)

SHENZHEN HOLIDE INDUSTRY DEVELOPMENT CO., LTD.
28 Fl 6031 Chegongmiao Shennan Rd, 518000, Shenzhen, China
Tel.: (86) 75588359999   CN
Web Site: http://www.holide.com
Year Founded: 1995
Sales Range: $25-49.9 Million
Emp.: 30
Electronic Products Mfr

N.A.I.C.S.: 335999
Michael Change (Gen Mgr & Mgr-Sls)

SHENZHEN HONGFUHAN TECHNOLOGY CO., LTD.
5 floor 27 Building Dayun software Town No 8288 Ronggang Road, Yuanshan Street Longgang District, Shenzhen, 518110, Guangdong, China
Tel.: (86) 75529808290
Web Site: https://www.hongfuhan.cn
Year Founded: 2008
301086—(CHIN)
Rev.: $100,423,908
Assets: $330,180,084
Liabilities: $65,392,704
Net Worth: $264,787,380
Earnings: $22,228,128
Fiscal Year-end: 12/31/22
Electronic Component Mfr & Distr
N.A.I.C.S.: 334419
Dingwu Zhang (Chm)

Subsidiaries:

Dongguan Hongfuhanhao New Meterial Technology Co., Ltd. (1)
No 5 Gaoli No 3 Road, Tangxia, Dongguan, China
Tel.: (86) 76982865129
Industrial Machinery Mfr
N.A.I.C.S.: 333248

Huaian Hongfu Hanhan science and Technology Co., Ltd. (1)
No 8 237 Provincial Road Economic Development Zone, Chuzhou District, Huaian, China
Tel.: (86) 51785362808
Mobile Phone Mfr & Distr
N.A.I.C.S.: 334210

Meizhou Hongfuhan Technology Co., Ltd. (1)
Dashaba shanzixia village, huliao Town Dapu county, Meizhou, China
Tel.: (86) 7535559603
Industrial Machinery Mfr
N.A.I.C.S.: 333248

USA Hongfuhan Technology Co. (1)
19925 Stevens Creek Blvd Ste 100, Cupertino, CA 95014
Tel.: (408) 725-7560
Industrial Machinery Mfr
N.A.I.C.S.: 333248

SHENZHEN HONGTAO GROUP CO., LTD.
No 17 Hongtao Road Nigangxi, Luohu District, Shenzhen, 518029, Guangdong, China
Tel.: (86) 75529999999
Web Site: http://www.szhongtao.cn
002325—(SSE)
Rev.: $186,825,731
Assets: $1,178,344,038
Liabilities: $745,397,823
Net Worth: $432,946,215
Earnings: ($99,730,262)
Fiscal Year-end: 12/31/22
Construction Services
N.A.I.C.S.: 541330
Hua Song (CFO)

SHENZHEN HONOR ELECTRONIC CO., LTD.
No 19 Building 1 Nanhang Mingzhu Garden No 175 Hangcheng Avenue, Sanwei Community Hangcheng Street Baoan District, Shenzhen, 518000, Guangdong, China
Tel.: (86) 75581453432
Web Site: https://www.aspower.ltd
Year Founded: 1996
300870—(CHIN)
Rev.: $379,518,708
Assets: $468,740,830
Liabilities: $240,177,085
Net Worth: $228,563,745

Earnings: $12,659,138
Fiscal Year-end: 12/31/22
Electronic Product Mfr & Distr
N.A.I.C.S.: 334419
Heqiu Wang (Chm & Gen Mgr)

SHENZHEN HOPEWIND ELECTRIC CO., LTD.
9-12F Daxing Jiye Building Building 1 No 33 Renda North Road, Haidian District, Beijing, 518055, China
Tel.: (86) 75586026786
Web Site: http://www.hopewindelectric.com
Year Founded: 2007
603063—(SHG)
Rev.: $394,403,649
Assets: $823,994,529
Liabilities: $343,484,655
Net Worth: $480,509,874
Earnings: $37,459,871
Fiscal Year-end: 12/31/22
Electric Drive Product Mfr & Distr
N.A.I.C.S.: 333611
Han Yu (Chm)

SHENZHEN HUAQIANG INDUSTRY CO., LTD.
5th Floor Building A Huaqiang Plaza 1019 Huaqiang North Road, Futian district, Shenzhen, China
Tel.: (86) 75583030002
Web Site: https://www.szhq000062.com
Year Founded: 1994
000062—(SSE)
Rev.: $3,361,358,506
Assets: $2,297,429,784
Liabilities: $1,199,005,681
Net Worth: $1,098,424,103
Earnings: $133,717,873
Fiscal Year-end: 12/31/22
Electronic Information Industry Support Services
N.A.I.C.S.: 519290

Subsidiaries:

Mogultech Int'l Ltd. (1)
Floors 4 7 and 12 Block B Tairan Building, Tairan 8th Road Chegongmiao Futian District, Shenzhen, China
Tel.: (86) 75583396000
Web Site: https://www.mogul-tech.com
Electronic Parts & Equipment Distr
N.A.I.C.S.: 423690

Shenzhen Electronic Commodity Trading Center Co., Ltd. (1)
Qianhai Enterprise Dream Park Qianwan 1st Road No 63 Shenzhen-hongkong, Cooperation on Modern Service Industries in Qianhai Area, Shenzhen, China
Tel.: (86) 7558 696 7213
Electronic Components Distr
N.A.I.C.S.: 423690

Shenzhen Huaqiang China Electronic Market Price Index Co., Ltd. (1)
6F Building 2 of Huaqiang Group Huangqiang Road Shennan Middle Road, Shenzhen, China
Tel.: (86) 7558 696 7213
Electronic Components Distr
N.A.I.C.S.: 423690

Shenzhen Huaqiang Electronic Commerce Co., Ltd. (1)
3C-2 Huangqiang Cloud Iindustrial Park No 1-1 Meixiu Road, Futian District, Shenzhen, China
Tel.: (86) 75583589505
Electronic Components Mfr
N.A.I.C.S.: 334419

Shenzhen Huaqiang Electronic Trading Network Co., Ltd. (1)
7F Building 2 of Huaqiang Group Huangqiang Road Shennan Middle Road, Shenzhen, China
Tel.: (86) 75583796108
Electronic Components Mfr
N.A.I.C.S.: 334419

Shenzhen Huaqiang Electronic Trading Networks Co., Ltd. (1)
Fl 6 & 7 Building 2 Huaqiang Group Intersection of Shennan Middle Rd, Huaqiang Road, Shenzhen, China
Tel.: (86) 75583796108
Web Site: https://www.hqew.com
Electronic Components Distr
N.A.I.C.S.: 423690

Shenzhen Huaqiang Electronic World Management Co., Ltd. (1)
6F Building A of Huaqiang Square No 1019 North Of Huaqiang Road, Shenzhen, China
Tel.: (86) 75583698888
Electronic Components Distr
N.A.I.C.S.: 423690

Shenzhen Huaqiang North Electronic Market Price Index Co., Ltd. (1)
6F Building 2 of Huaqiang Group Huangqiang Road Shennan Middle Road, Shenzhen, China
Tel.: (86) 75586967213
Electronic Components Mfr
N.A.I.C.S.: 334419

Shenzhen Huaqiang Square Holding Co., Ltd. (1)
5F Building A of Huaqiang Square No 1019 Huaqiang North, Futian District, Shenzhen, China
Tel.: (86) 75583320011
Electronic Components Distr
N.A.I.C.S.: 423690

Shenzhen Sanet Electronic Co., Ltd. (1)
Room 01- 05 31th Floor Tianli Centre Commercial Square, 3rd Haide Street Nanshan District, Shenzhen, China
Tel.: (86) 75586331651
Electronic Components Mfr
N.A.I.C.S.: 334419

SHENZHEN HUI CHUANG DA TECHNOLOGY CO., LTD.
Building 2-2 Tongfuyu Industrial Zone Aiqun Road Shiyan Street, Baoan, Shenzhen, 518108, Guangdong, China
Tel.: (86) 75527356897
Web Site: http://www.gb.hcdtechnology.com
Year Founded: 2004
300909—(SSE)
Rev.: $116,196,276
Assets: $267,833,147
Liabilities: $76,337,095
Net Worth: $191,496,053
Earnings: $17,972,323
Fiscal Year-end: 12/31/22
Electronic Product Mfr & Distr
N.A.I.C.S.: 334419
Ming Li (Chm & Gen Mgr)

SHENZHEN HUIJIE GROUP CO., LTD.
F31-32 BlockA InternationalInnovation Block A 1006 Shennan Road, Futian District, Shenzhen, 518040, Guangdong, China
Tel.: (86) 75588916088
Web Site: https://www.huijiegroup.com
002763—(SSE)
Rev.: $344,707,356
Assets: $380,358,061
Liabilities: $76,803,742
Net Worth: $303,554,319
Earnings: $18,910,687
Fiscal Year-end: 12/31/22
Lingerie Mfr & Distr
N.A.I.C.S.: 315250
Xingping Lu (Chm & Gen Mgr)

SHENZHEN IDREAMSKY TECHNOLOGY CO., LTD.
16/F Unit 3 Block A Kexing science Park15 Keyuan Rd, Nanshan District, Shenzhen, 518057, China

AND PRIVATE COMPANIES

Tel.: (86) 75586685111
Web Site: http://www.idreamsky.com
Year Founded: 2011
1119—(HKG)
Rev.: $492,128,599
Assets: $1,034,602,770
Liabilities: $465,298,770
Net Worth: $569,304,000
Earnings: ($86,563,037)
Emp.: 737
Fiscal Year-end: 12/31/20
Entertainment Services
N.A.I.C.S.: 711190
Chen Xiangyu (Founder, Chm & CEO)

SHENZHEN IN-CUBE AUTOMATION CO., LTD.
Floor 1 to 5 Building A Hongfa Technology Park Tangtou Road, Shiyan Town Baoan District, Shenzhen, 518108, Guangdong, China
Tel.: (86) 75533525952
Web Site: https://www.incubecn.com
Year Founded: 2011
301312—(CHIN)
Rev.: $71,350,634
Assets: $171,552,443
Liabilities: $13,937,452
Net Worth: $157,614,992
Earnings: $16,378,011
Fiscal Year-end: 12/31/22
Industrial Automation Equipment Mfr & Distr
N.A.I.C.S.: 333248
Qiu Peng (Chm)

SHENZHEN INCREASE TECHNOLOGY CO., LTD.
1001 Building 1 Increase science and technology building, No 60 Baolong second road Baolong street Longgang district, Shenzhen, 518052, Guangdong, China
Tel.: (86) 75526586000
Web Site:
https://www.szincrease.com
Year Founded: 2002
300713—(CHIN)
Rev.: $48,091,212
Assets: $145,280,304
Liabilities: $50,204,232
Net Worth: $95,076,072
Earnings: ($8,520,876)
Fiscal Year-end: 12/31/22
Power Electronic Product Mfr & Distr
N.A.I.C.S.: 335999
Wei Yin (Founder, Chm, Pres & Gen Mgr)

SHENZHEN INFINOVA CO., LTD.
Infinova Park Guanlan Shenzhen High-tech Industrial Development Zone, Longhua District, Shenzhen, 518110, China
Tel.: (86) 75586095088
Web Site:
https://www.infinova.com.cn
Year Founded: 2008
002528—(SSE)
Rev.: $257,955,432
Assets: $628,815,040
Liabilities: $455,461,854
Net Worth: $173,353,186
Earnings: ($154,411,695)
Fiscal Year-end: 12/31/22
Holding Company; Security Technologies Mfr & Distr
N.A.I.C.S.: 551112
Liu Zhaohuai (Chm & Gen Mgr)

Subsidiaries:

Infinova Corporation (1)
51 Stouts Ln, Monmouth Junction, NJ 08852
Tel.: (732) 355-9100
Web Site: http://www.infinova.com
Emp.: 25
Security Technologies Mfr & Distr
N.A.I.C.S.: 334290

March Networks Corporation (1)
303 Terry Fox Drive Suite 200, Ottawa, K2K 3J1, ON, Canada
Tel.: (613) 591-8181
Web Site: http://www.marchnetworks.com
Sales Range: $100-124.9 Million
Emp.: 165
Internet Protocol Video Management Solutions
N.A.I.C.S.: 541511
Peter Strom (Pres & CEO)

SHENZHEN INFOGEM TECHNOLOGIES CO., LTD.
12F Tower B Bojin Business Plaza Tairan 7th Road, Futian District, Shenzhen, 518042, China
Tel.: (86) 7558393008
Web Site: http://www.yinzhijie.com
Year Founded: 2007
300085—(CHIN)
Rev.: $142,983,201
Assets: $200,969,344
Liabilities: $106,821,851
Net Worth: $94,147,492
Earnings: ($16,534,720)
Fiscal Year-end: 12/31/23
Software Development Services
N.A.I.C.S.: 541512
Xiangjun Chen (Chm)

SHENZHEN INOVANCE TECHNOLOGY CO., LTD.
Unit B01 17/F MG Tower 133 Hoi Bun Road, Kwun Tong, China (Hong Kong)
Tel.: (852) 27516080
Web Site: http://www.inovance.cn
300124—(CHIN)
Rev.: $3,887,679,451
Assets: $6,256,797,590
Liabilities: $3,061,660,191
Net Worth: $3,195,137,398
Earnings: $606,012,154
Fiscal Year-end: 12/31/23
Industrial Automation Control Product Mfr
N.A.I.C.S.: 335314

Subsidiaries:

Inovance Technology Europe GmbH (1)
Gottlieb-Daimler-Strasse 17/2, 74385, Pleidelsheim, Germany
Tel.: (49) 71448990
Web Site: https://www.inovance.eu
Elevator & Escalator Mfr
N.A.I.C.S.: 333921
Alexia Batanara (Mgr-Mktg)

Ningbo EST Technology Co., Ltd. (1)
No 66 Pufeng Road, Jiangbei District, Ningbo, Zhejiang, China
Tel.: (86) 4000801890
Web Site: https://www.esto.cn
Plastic Machinery Automation Control Product Mfr
N.A.I.C.S.: 333248

Suzhou Inovance Automotive Co., Ltd. (1)
No 52 Tianedang Road Yuexi Town, Wuzhong District, Suzhou, 215104, China
Tel.: (86) 4007771260
Web Site: https://www.en.inovance-automotive.com
Electronic & Mechanical Component Mfr
N.A.I.C.S.: 334419

Suzhou Monarch Control Technology Co., Ltd. (1)
No 16 Youxiang Road, Yuexi Wuzhong District, Suzhou, 215104, China
Tel.: (86) 5126 637 6666
Web Site: https://www.szmctc.com
Escalator Integrated Controller Mfr
N.A.I.C.S.: 333921

SHENZHEN INSTITUTE OF BUILDING RESEARCH CO., LTD.
Jianke Building No 29 Meiao 3rd Road, Meilin Futian District, Shenzhen, 518049, Guangdong, China
Tel.: (86) 75523931888
Web Site: http://www.szibr.com
Year Founded: 2007
300675—(CHIN)
Rev.: $58,613,896
Assets: $201,907,292
Liabilities: $112,656,210
Net Worth: $89,251,081
Earnings: $3,327,778
Fiscal Year-end: 12/31/23
Landscape Development Services
N.A.I.C.S.: 541320
Mao Hongwei (Gen Mgr)

Subsidiaries:

Shenzhen Municpial Engineering Consulting Center Co., Ltd. (1)
17th Floor Jianyi Building 3 Zhenxing Road, Futian District, Shenzhen, China
Tel.: (86) 75583786819
Construction Consulting Services
N.A.I.C.S.: 541618

SHENZHEN INTERNATIONAL HOLDINGS LIMITED
Rooms 2205-08 22/F Greenfield Tower Concordia Plaza 1, Science Museum Road Tsimshatsui East, Hong Kong, Kowloon, China (Hong Kong)
Tel.: (852) 23660268 BM
Web Site: http://www.szihl.com
0152—(HKG)
Rev.: $1,979,985,878
Assets: $17,020,602,938
Liabilities: $9,982,708,253
Net Worth: $7,037,894,685
Earnings: $246,860,018
Emp.: 8,983
Fiscal Year-end: 12/31/22
Transportation & Logistic Services
N.A.I.C.S.: 488999
Jun Liu (Exec Dir)

Subsidiaries:

CSG Holding Co., Ltd. (1)
CSG Bldg No1the 6th Industrial Road Shekou, Shenzhen, China
Tel.: (86) 75526860666
Web Site: https://www.csgholding.com
Sales Range: $1-4.9 Billion
Glass Products Mfr
N.A.I.C.S.: 327215

Shenzhen Expressway Company Limited (1)
Podium Level 2-4 Jiangsu Building Yitian Road, Futian District, Shenzhen, 518026, Guangdong, China (30.3%)
Tel.: (86) 75582853300
Web Site: http://www.sz-expressway.com
Construction, Operation & Management of Highways & Roads
N.A.I.C.S.: 237310
Tao Tao Gong (VP)

Shenzhen International Modern Logistics Microfinance Co., Ltd. (1)
15th Floor Shen International Building No 8045 Hongqiao West Road, Futian District, Shenzhen, China
Tel.: (86) 75523961516
Web Site: http://www.szihlc.com
Logistic Services
N.A.I.C.S.: 541614

Shenzhen International West Logistics Co., Ltd. (1)
Western Logistics Center No 88 Linhai Avenue, Qianhai Shenzhen-Hong Kong Cooperation Zone, Shenzhen, China
Tel.: (86) 75586305911
Web Site: https://www.west-logistics.com
Logistic Services
N.A.I.C.S.: 541614

Shenzhen South-China International Logistics Co., Ltd. (1)
1 Minkang Road Longhua, Baoan, Shenzhen, 518000, China (66.67%)
Tel.: (86) 75529838888
Web Site: http://www.silc.com.cn
Sales Range: $25-49.9 Million
Emp.: 108
Logistic Services
N.A.I.C.S.: 561499
Chen Jun Sheng (Gen Mgr)

Shenzhen Total Logistics Services Limited (1)
(100%)
Tel.: (86) 75583434856
Web Site: http://www.56888.com
Logistics Industry Services
N.A.I.C.S.: 541614

SHENZHEN INVESTMENT LIMITED
8th Floor New Tung Hoi Commercial Centre 9 Science Museum Road, Kowloon, China (Hong Kong)
Tel.: (852) 27238113 HK
Web Site:
https://www.shenzheninvestment.com
Year Founded: 1992
SZNTF—(OTCIQ)
Rev.: $4,030,854,346
Assets: $20,891,227,651
Liabilities: $14,557,825,348
Net Worth: $6,333,402,303
Earnings: $313,794,011
Emp.: 21,205
Fiscal Year-end: 12/31/22
Mid Market Property Developer
N.A.I.C.S.: 531312
Hua Lu (Chm)

Subsidiaries:

SHUM Yip Taifu Logistics Group Holdings Co., Ltd (1)
23f Shenye Center Mansion No 5045 Shennan Road East, Shenzhen, 518001, Guangdong, China
Tel.: (86) 75582083723
Property Development Services
N.A.I.C.S.: 531312

Shenzhen Investment Holdings Bay Area Development Company Limited (1)
Rooms 49024916 49th Floor Sun Hung Kai Centre 30 Harbour Road Wanchai, Wanchai, China (Hong Kong) (71.83%)
Tel.: (852) 25284975
Web Site: https://www.sihbay.com
Rev.: $85,215,573
Assets: $673,449,584
Liabilities: $48,082,868
Net Worth: $625,366,716
Earnings: $79,739,400
Fiscal Year-end: 12/31/2019
Highway Infrastructure Development Services
N.A.I.C.S.: 237310
Tianliang Zhang (Gen Mgr)

Shenzhen Jinghua Displays Co., Ltd. (1)
3F Bd2 Jinghua Displays Park No 3 Liuhe Road Henggang Street, Longgang District, Shenzhen, 518173, China
Tel.: (86) 7552 502 3072
Web Site: https://www.china-lcd.com
LCD & Electronic Component Mfr
N.A.I.C.S.: 334419
Candice Su (Mgr-Mktg)

Shum Yip Southern Land (Holdings) Co., Ltd. (1)
Suite C 5/F Huamin Mansion No 1001 Renmin South Road, Luohu, Shenzhen, 518001, Guangdong, China
Tel.: (86) 7552345283
Property Development Services
N.A.I.C.S.: 531312

SHENZHEN INVT ELECTRIC CO., LTD.

SHENZHEN INVT ELECTRIC CO., LTD.

Shenzhen INVT Electric Co., Ltd.—(Continued)
INVT Guangming Technology Building Songbai Road Matan Street, Guangming District, Shenzhen, 518106, China
Tel.: (86) 4007009997
Web Site: https://www.invt.com.cn
Year Founded: 2002
002334—(SSE)
Rev.: $575,201,531
Assets: $686,097,524
Liabilities: $360,130,184
Net Worth: $325,967,340
Earnings: $38,602,489
Emp.: 4,500
Fiscal Year-end: 12/31/22
AC Drives & Automation Products Mfr
N.A.I.C.S.: 335311
Huang Shenli (Chm)

Subsidiaries:

INVT Electric (India) Co., Ltd. (1)
3rd Floor Maxx Avenue Plot no 91a, Near Mathadi Bhavan Chowk Opp Manu Motors Vashi, Navi Mumbai, 400 705, India
Tel.: (91) 9892543276
Automatic Control Product Mfr
N.A.I.C.S.: 334512

INVT Electric Thailand Co., Ltd. (1)
5/38 BIZ Town Soi Srinakarin 46/1 Pramoted Nongbon, Prawet, Bangkok, 10250, Thailand
Tel.: (66) 831354124
Automatic Control Product Mfr
N.A.I.C.S.: 334512

INVT Elevator Control Technology (Wuxi) Co., Ltd. (1)
4 Bldg Gaofa Technological Park Longjing, Nanshan District, Shenzhen, 518055, China
Tel.: (86) 75586312937
Web Site: http://www.invt-elevator.com
Elevator Control Mfr
N.A.I.C.S.: 333921

INVT Power System (Shenzhen) Co., Ltd. (1)
1 Bldg Gaofa Technological Park Longjing, Nanshan District, Shenzhen, China
Tel.: (86) 75526782840
Web Site: http://www.invt-power.com
Electric Power Product Distr
N.A.I.C.S.: 423610
Andy Lee (Sls Mgr)

SHENZHEN JAME TECHNOLOGY CORP., LTD.
42nd floor Building 1 Huide Building Minzhi Street, Longhua District, Shenzhen, 518000, Guangdong, China
Tel.: (86) 75533300868
Web Site: https://www.jamepda.com
Year Founded: 2006
300868—(SSE)
Rev.: $100,969,966
Assets: $292,891,304
Liabilities: $64,271,582
Net Worth: $228,619,722
Earnings: ($16,275,210)
Emp.: 2,000
Fiscal Year-end: 12/31/22
Telecommunication Products Mfr
N.A.I.C.S.: 334290
Jianping Chen (Chm & Gen Mgr)

SHENZHEN JASIC TECHNOLOGY CO., LTD.
No 3 Qinglan 1st Road, Pingshan New District, Shenzhen, 518052, Guangdong, China
Tel.: (86) 75529651666
Web Site: http://www.jasic.com.cn
Year Founded: 2005
300193—(CHIN)
Rev.: $172,986,840
Assets: $385,991,892
Liabilities: $91,684,008
Net Worth: $294,307,884
Earnings: $24,758,136
Emp.: 178
Fiscal Year-end: 12/31/22
Inverter Welding Machinery Mfr
N.A.I.C.S.: 333248
Zhang Zhiying (Chm-Supervisory Bd)

Subsidiaries:

Chongqing YUNDA Technology Co., Ltd. (1)
11-8 Jiangxi Rd Chayuan, Nan'an Dist, Chongqing, 401336, China
Tel.: (86) 2388608277
Web Site: http://www.en.cqyd.com
Welding Equipment Mfr & Distr
N.A.I.C.S.: 333992

SHENZHEN JIANG & ASSOCIATES CREATIVE DESIGN CO., LTD.
13F Unit B4 Kexing Science Park No 15 Keyuan Road, Nanshan District, Shenzhen, 518057, Guangdong, China
Tel.: (86) 75586669998
Web Site: https://www.jaid.cn
Year Founded: 2004
300668—(CHIN)
Rev.: $105,452,902
Assets: $166,031,219
Liabilities: $55,444,476
Net Worth: $110,586,744
Earnings: $8,081,142
Emp.: 800
Fiscal Year-end: 12/31/23
Architectural Design Services
N.A.I.C.S.: 541310
Frank Jiang (Chm)

Subsidiaries:

JATO Design International Limited (1)
Room 1502 Tai Tung Building 8 Fleming Road, Wanchai, China (Hong Kong)
Tel.: (852) 35431738
Web Site: https://www.jato.hk
Interior & Graphic Design Services
N.A.I.C.S.: 541410

SHENZHEN JIANYI DECORATION GROUP CO., LTD.
Jianyi Group No 8 Binglang Road Futian Free Trade Zone, Futian District, Shenzhen, Guangdong, China
Tel.: (86) 75583788033
Web Site: https://www.jyzs.com.cn
Year Founded: 1994
002789—(SSE)
Rev.: $304,050,549
Assets: $1,260,432,632
Liabilities: $1,216,180,518
Net Worth: $44,252,114
Earnings: $1,570,121
Fiscal Year-end: 12/31/22
Housing Construction & Design Services
N.A.I.C.S.: 236116

SHENZHEN JIESHUN SCIENCE & TECHNOLOGY INDUSTRY CO., LTD.
No 5 Guansheng 2nd Road, Longhua District, Shenzhen, 518049, China
Tel.: (86) 75583112288
Web Site: https://www.jieshun-tech.com
Year Founded: 1992
002609—(SSE)
Rev.: $193,141,541
Assets: $538,045,654
Liabilities: $191,436,046
Net Worth: $346,609,608
Earnings: $2,547,221
Fiscal Year-end: 12/31/22
Security System Services
N.A.I.C.S.: 561621
Tang Jian (Chm)

SHENZHEN JINGQUANHUA ELECTRONICS CO., LTD.
Jingquanhua Industrial Area Number 325 Guiyue Road Guanlan Street, Longhua District, Shenzhen, 518110, Guangdong, China
Tel.: (86) 75527040011
Web Site: https://www.everrise.net
Year Founded: 1996
002885—(SSE)
Rev.: $362,834,400
Assets: $352,106,801
Liabilities: $219,919,008
Net Worth: $132,187,793
Earnings: $19,989,310
Fiscal Year-end: 12/31/22
Electronic Component Mfr & Distr
N.A.I.C.S.: 334416

Subsidiaries:

Hk Jingquanhua Development Ltd. (1)
Flat/Rm 1101 11/F Leader Industrial Centre 57-59 Au Pui Street, Fotan, China (Hong Kong)
Tel.: (852) 85229477355
Electronic Parts & Equipment Whslr
N.A.I.C.S.: 423690

Hubei RunSheng Electronics Industrial Co., Ltd. (1)
Bldg 10-11 Xifan Industrial Area Beihuanxi Road, Macheng, Hubei, China
Tel.: (86) 7132937883
Electronic Parts & Equipment Whslr
N.A.I.C.S.: 423690

JQH Electronics India LLP (1)
1-18 Site-V UPSIDC, Kasna Industrial Area, Noida, 201308, Uttar Pradesh, India
Tel.: (91) 8448597080
Electronic Parts & Equipment Whslr
N.A.I.C.S.: 423690

JQH Inc. (1)
19 Peters Canyon Rd, Irvine, CA 92606
Tel.: (949) 299-8576
Electronic Parts & Equipment Whslr
N.A.I.C.S.: 423690

SHENZHEN JINJIA GROUP CO., LTD.
Jinjia Technology Mansion Keji Middle 2ndRoad, High-tech Industrial Park Nanshan District, Shenzhen, 518057, Guangdong, China
Tel.: (86) 75526498899
Web Site: https://www.jinjia.com
Year Founded: 1996
002191—(SSE)
Rev.: $728,485,477
Assets: $1,324,926,299
Liabilities: $246,505,208
Net Worth: $1,078,421,091
Earnings: $27,702,478
Fiscal Year-end: 12/31/22
Packaging Materials Mfr
N.A.I.C.S.: 326112
Qiao Luyu (Chm-Grp)

Subsidiaries:

Changchun Jixing Printing Co., Ltd. (1)
No 600 Linhe Street, Changchun, 130031, Jilin, China
Tel.: (86) 43184952708
Web Site: https://www.ccjxyw.com
Cigarette Label Mfr
N.A.I.C.S.: 323111

Chongqing Hongjin Printing Co., Ltd. (1)
No 3 Changdian Road, Nan an District, Chongqing, China
Tel.: (86) 2362483928
Web Site: https://www.en.hj-pack.com
Paper Bag Mfr
N.A.I.C.S.: 322220

Holotek Technology Co., Ltd. (1)
No 15 Xinghan Road, Sanzao Town Jinwan District, Zhuhai, Guangdong, China
Tel.: (86) 7566229898
Web Site: https://www.holotek.com.cn
Packaging Materials Mfr
N.A.I.C.S.: 326112

Kunming Color Printing Co., Ltd. (1)
Village Longquan Road, Kunming, 650202, Yunnan, China
Tel.: (86) 87165815796
Web Site: https://www.kmcyc.com
Tobacco Mfr
N.A.I.C.S.: 312230

Shenzhen Jinjia Technology Co., Ltd. (1)
Yanshan Avenue Songgang, Jinjia Industry Park Bao an District, Shenzhen, Guangdong, China
Tel.: (86) 75527300008
Web Site: https://www.jinjiatech.com
Tobacco Mfr
N.A.I.C.S.: 312230

Shenzhen Qianhai Blueberry Culture Communication Co., Ltd. (1)
17 Floor Jinjia Technology Building Science and Technology Mid, No 2 Road Nanshan District, Shenzhen, China
Tel.: (86) 7552660999
Web Site: http://www.szlanmei.com
Healthcare Services
N.A.I.C.S.: 621999

SHENZHEN JINXINNONG TECHNOLOGY CO., LTD.
Jinxinnong Building No 18 Guangdian North Road Guangming Street, Guangming District, Shenzhen, 518107, Shangshi, China
Tel.: (86) 75527166036
Web Site: https://www.safeed.com.cn
Year Founded: 1999
002548—(SSE)
Rev.: $557,940,642
Assets: $979,768,961
Liabilities: $673,484,999
Net Worth: $306,283,962
Earnings: $2,785,087
Emp.: 770
Fiscal Year-end: 12/31/22
Pig Feed Mfr & Distr
N.A.I.C.S.: 424910
Junhai Chen (Vice Chm)

SHENZHEN JIYIN TECHNOLOGY CO., LTD.
Fuyong Streets Huaide South Road, Tsui Kong Industrial Park 40 District 5 Bao'an District, Shenzhen, 518103, China
Tel.: (86) 75529919881
Web Site: http://www.jiyin-tech.com
Year Founded: 2002
Fitting Equipment Mfr & Distr
N.A.I.C.S.: 332913

SHENZHEN JOVE ENTERPRISE LIMITED
No 8 Xingye Road, Heyi Community Heer Industrial Zone Shajing Street Baoan District, Shenzhen, 518067, Guangdong, China
Tel.: (86) 75526683724
Web Site: https://www.jovepcb.com
Year Founded: 2004
300814—(CHIN)
Rev.: $174,806,704
Assets: $318,644,323
Liabilities: $154,973,140
Net Worth: $163,671,183
Earnings: $3,699,901
Emp.: 300
Fiscal Year-end: 12/31/23
Circuit Board Mfr & Distr
N.A.I.C.S.: 334412
Wang Changmin (Chm)

SHENZHEN JPT OPTO-ELECTRONICS CO., LTD.

Floor 1-12 Building A Komron Technology Park Guansheng 5th Road, Luhu Community Guanhu Street Longhua District, Shenzhen, 518110, China
Tel.: (86) 75529528181
Web Site: https://www.jptoe.com
Year Founded: 2006
688025—(SHG)
Rev.: $164,732,668
Assets: $343,198,814
Liabilities: $86,028,247
Net Worth: $257,170,568
Earnings: $10,764,665
Fiscal Year-end: 12/31/22
Electronic Product Mfr & Distr
N.A.I.C.S.: 334419
Chongguang Zhao *(Dir-Mfg)*

Subsidiaries:

Dongguan JPT Optical Technology Co., Ltd. (1)
Room 101 No 11 Building Xingye 4th Road Qinghu, Qingxi Town, Dongguan, China
Tel.: (86) 7698 730 1858
Laser Product Mfr & Distr
N.A.I.C.S.: 334510

JPT Electronics Pte. Ltd. (1)
12 Ang Mo Kio Street 65 04-01, Singapore, 569060, Singapore
Tel.: (65) 6 792 5919
Laser Product Mfr & Distr
N.A.I.C.S.: 334510

SHENZHEN JT AUTOMATION EQUIPMENT COMPANY LIMITED

JT Industrial Park Beiba Rd Hezhou Industrial Zone, Hangcheng Baoan, Shenzhen, 518126, China
Tel.: (86) 19129984151
Web Site: https://www.jt-int.com
Year Founded: 2004
300400—(CHIN)
Rev.: $111,081,672
Assets: $173,942,964
Liabilities: $68,272,308
Net Worth: $105,670,656
Earnings: $12,509,640
Emp.: 1,100
Fiscal Year-end: 12/31/22
Electronic Industrial Equipment Mfr
N.A.I.C.S.: 335999
Wu Siyuan *(Chm)*

Subsidiaries:

JT United (M) Sdn Bhd (1)
68 Jalan Ekoperniagaan 2 Taman Ekoperniagaan 2 Senai Airport City, 81400, Senai, Johor, Malaysia
Tel.: (60) 75520396
Industrial Machinery Distr
N.A.I.C.S.: 423830

JT Universal (M) Sdn Bhd (1)
No 7 Jalan Bertam Permai 2 Taman Bertam Permai, 76450, Melaka, Malaysia
Tel.: (60) 127833231
Industrial Machinery Distr
N.A.I.C.S.: 423830
James Teo *(Mgr-Sls)*

JT Universal Philippines Inc. (1)
5 Town & country Southville Dimaranan Compound Atlanta St, Barangay Sto Tomas, Binan, Laguna, Philippines
Tel.: (63) 24004182
Industrial Machinery Distr
N.A.I.C.S.: 423830

JT Universal Pte Ltd (1)
52 Ubi Avenue 3 02-38 Frontier, Singapore, 408867, Singapore
Tel.: (65) 65475450
Web Site: https://www.jtugroup.com
Industrial Machinery Distr
N.A.I.C.S.: 423830

JTU (Thailand) Co. Ltd (1)
19/48 Moo 3 Paholyothin Road Klong Nueng Klong Lueng, Khlong Luang, 12120, Pathum Thani, Thailand
Tel.: (66) 25165001
Industrial Machinery Distr
N.A.I.C.S.: 423830

JTU (Vietnam) Co. Ltd (1)
159 A Nguyen Huu Canh Street, Ward 22, Binh Thanh, Vietnam
Tel.: (84) 866802817
Industrial Machinery Distr
N.A.I.C.S.: 423830

PT JT Universal Indonesia (1)
Ruko Palem Permata Blok B1 No 8 Cengkareng, Jakarta Barat, 11830, Indonesia
Tel.: (62) 816900695
Industrial Machinery Distr
N.A.I.C.S.: 423830

SHENZHEN JUFEI OPTOELECTRONICS CO., LTD.

No 4 Eling Industrial Zone Eling Community, Pinghu Street Longgang District, Shenzhen, 518111, China
Tel.: (86) 75529632290
Web Site: https://www.jfled.com.cn
Year Founded: 2005
300303—(CHIN)
Rev.: $317,555,316
Assets: $693,717,804
Liabilities: $282,726,288
Net Worth: $410,991,516
Earnings: $26,414,856
Emp.: 3,000
Fiscal Year-end: 12/31/22
Optoelectronic Product Mfr
N.A.I.C.S.: 334419

SHENZHEN KAIZHONG PRECISION TECHNOLOGY CO., LTD

No 1 Guihua 4th road, Pingshan District, Shenzhen, 518125, Guangdong, China
Tel.: (86) 75527255619
Web Site: https://www.kaizhong.com
002823—(SSE)
Rev.: $373,749,461
Assets: $519,885,096
Liabilities: $322,666,044
Net Worth: $197,219,052
Earnings: $3,484,868
Fiscal Year-end: 12/31/22
Commutator Mfr & Distr
N.A.I.C.S.: 335312

Subsidiaries:

Kaizhong Vogt GmbH (1)
Erwin-Seiz-Strasse 10, 72764, Reutlingen, Germany
Tel.: (49) 71 211 4920
Web Site: https://www.kaizhong-vogt.com
Electronic Parts Mfr & Distr
N.A.I.C.S.: 335312

SHENZHEN KANGTAI BIOLOGICAL PRODUCTS CO., LTD.

No 6 Kefa Road, Nanshan District Science and Technology Industrial Park, Shenzhen, 518057, China
Tel.: (86) 75526988658   CN
Web Site: https://www.biokangtai.com
Year Founded: 1992
300601—(SSE)
Rev.: $443,299,213
Assets: $1,935,603,779
Liabilities: $674,062,295
Net Worth: $1,261,541,483
Earnings: ($18,632,189)
Emp.: 400
Fiscal Year-end: 12/31/22
Vaccine Mfr & Distr
N.A.I.C.S.: 325414
Weimin Du *(Founder & Chm)*

Subsidiaries:

Beijing Minhai Biotechnology Co., Ltd. (1)
No 35 Simiao Road Zhongguancun Science Park, Daxing Biomedical Industrial Base Daxing District, Beijing, China
Tel.: (86) 1059613639
Web Site: https://www.biominhai.com
Emp.: 1,600
Biological Vaccine Product Mfr
N.A.I.C.S.: 325414

SHENZHEN KEANDA ELECTRONIC TECHNOLOGY CORP., LTD.

14F C Block Shenzhen International Innovation Center No 1006, Shennan Avenue Futian, Shenzhen, 518026, Guangdong, China
Tel.: (86) 75586956831
Web Site: http://www.keanda.com.cn
Year Founded: 1998
002972—(SSE)
Rev.: $51,471,974
Assets: $216,663,076
Liabilities: $39,356,563
Net Worth: $177,306,513
Earnings: $17,177,280
Fiscal Year-end: 12/31/22
Electronic Product Mfr & Distr
N.A.I.C.S.: 334419
Fengming Guo *(Chm)*

Subsidiaries:

Chengdu Keanda Rail Transit Technology Co., Ltd. (1)
Unit 2 Building 2 No 666 Golden Phoenix Avenue, Jinniu District, Chengdu, China
Tel.: (86) 75583056349
Rail Transit Product Mfr & Distr
N.A.I.C.S.: 336510

Keanda (Hong Kong) International Group Co., Ltd. (1)
RM 1405A 14/F Lucky CTR 165-171 Wanchai Rd, Wanchai, China (Hong Kong)
Tel.: (852) 75583056349
Rail Transit Product Mfr & Distr
N.A.I.C.S.: 336510

Shanghai Yanshi Electronic Technology Co., Ltd. (1)
Room D3027 3rd Floor Building 2 No 7001 Zhongchun Road, Minhang District, Shanghai, China
Tel.: (86) 75583056349
Rail Transit Product Mfr & Distr
N.A.I.C.S.: 336510

Shenzhen Keanda Rail Transit Technology Co., Ltd. (1)
Floor A Building 4 Xili Street, Jiuxiangling Industrial Zone Nanshan District, Shenzhen, China
Tel.: (86) 75583056349
Rail Transit Product Mfr & Distr
N.A.I.C.S.: 336510

Shenzhen Keanda Software Co., Ltd. (1)
Woekshop on the Fourth Floor Building 2, Jiuxiangling Industrial Zone Xili Nanshan District, Shenzhen, China
Tel.: (86) 75583056349
Rail Transit Product Mfr & Distr
N.A.I.C.S.: 336510

Shenzhen Keanda Testing Technologh Co., Ltd. (1)
14A Building C No 1006 Shennan Avanue Huafu Street, Futian District, Shenzhen, China
Tel.: (86) 75583056349
Rail Transit Product Mfr & Distr
N.A.I.C.S.: 336510

Shenzhen Keanda Track Equipment Co., Ltd. (1)
Room 302 No 123 Shenshan Special Cooperation Zone, jiaohu Village Ebu Town, Shenzhen, China
Tel.: (86) 75583056349
Rail Transit Product Mfr & Distr
N.A.I.C.S.: 336510

Zhuhai Gaoping Electronic Technology Development Co., Ltd. (1)
Zone F Room 202 Second Floor Jinqiao Building, Jinhai Industrial Zone Sanzao Town Jinwan District, Zhuhai, China
Tel.: (86) 75583056349
Rail Transit Product Mfr & Distr
N.A.I.C.S.: 336510

Zhuhai Keanda Techology Development Co., Ltd. (1)
No 201 Complex Building Zhuhai Bowei Mould Co Ltd Dalin Mountain, Liangang Industrial Zone Hongqi Town Jinwan District, Zhuhai, China
Tel.: (86) 75583056349
Rail Transit Product Mfr & Distr
N.A.I.C.S.: 336510

SHENZHEN KEDALI INDUSTRY CO., LTD.

1st Floor Zhongjian Technology Factory Tongsheng Community, Dalang Street Longhua District, Shenzhen, 518000, Guangdong, China
Tel.: (86) 75526400270
Web Site: https://www.kedali.com.cn
Year Founded: 1996
002850—(SSE)
Rev.: $1,214,951,400
Assets: $1,990,062,046
Liabilities: $1,171,861,068
Net Worth: $818,200,979
Earnings: $126,526,121
Fiscal Year-end: 12/31/22
Automotive Battery Mfr & Distr
N.A.I.C.S.: 335910
Jianli Li *(Chm)*

SHENZHEN KEXIN COMMUNICATION TECHNOLOGIES CO., LTD

Kexin Science And Technology Building New Energy First Road Baolong St, Longgang District, Shenzhen, 518116, China
Tel.: (86) 75529893456
Web Site: https://www.szkexin.com.cn
Year Founded: 2001
300565—(CHIN)
Rev.: $117,105,590
Assets: $247,648,794
Liabilities: $172,287,985
Net Worth: $75,360,809
Earnings: ($1,870,535)
Emp.: 1,000
Fiscal Year-end: 12/31/22
Telecommunication Equipment Mfr & Distr
N.A.I.C.S.: 334210
Chen Dengzhi *(Chm & Gen Mgr)*

Subsidiaries:

Efore Telecom Finland Oy (1)
Linnoitustie 4B, FI-02600, Espoo, Finland
Tel.: (358) 293609006
Web Site: https://www.efore.com
AC & DC Power System Mfr
N.A.I.C.S.: 335999

SHENZHEN KING BROTHER ELECTRONICS TECHNOLOGY CO.

Floor 15 Tower 1 New Generation Industrial Park Shang Meilin, Futian District, Shenzhen, 518049, Guangdong, China
Tel.: (86) 75583105567
Web Site: https://www.kingbrother.com
Year Founded: 1997
301041—(CHIN)
Rev.: $91,493,064
Assets: $117,312,624
Liabilities: $28,105,272
Net Worth: $89,207,352
Earnings: $4,755,348
Fiscal Year-end: 12/31/22
Circuit Board Mfr & Distr

SHENZHEN KING BROTHER ELECTRONICS TECHNOLOGY CO.

Shenzhen King Brother Electronics Technology Co.—(Continued)
N.A.I.C.S.: 334412
Shoukun Wu (Chm & Gen Mgr)

SHENZHEN KING EXPLORER SCIENCE & TECHNOLOGY CORPORATION
Floor 33 High Tech Zone Union Tower No 63 Xuefu Road Nanshan District, Shenzhen, 518052, Guangdong, China
Tel.: (86) 75526970167
Year Founded: 1994
002917—(SSE)
Rev.: $167,496,484
Assets: $429,719,163
Liabilities: $191,932,865
Net Worth: $237,786,298
Earnings: $3,546,237
Fiscal Year-end: 12/31/22
Industrial Equipment Mfr & Distr
N.A.I.C.S. 325920
Ming Gang (Chm & Gen Mgr)

SHENZHEN KINGDOM SCI-TECH CO., LTD.
Jinzheng Technology Building Gaoxin South 5th Road, Nanshan District, Shenzhen, 518057, Guangdong, China
Tel.: (86) 75583172999
Web Site: https://www.szkingdom.com
Year Founded: 1998
600446—(SHG)
Rev.: $909,497,399
Assets: $936,496,024
Liabilities: $390,429,332
Net Worth: $546,066,692
Earnings: $37,795,427
Emp.: 6,000
Fiscal Year-end: 12/31/22
Software Development Services
N.A.I.C.S.: 541511
Li Jieyi (Chm)

Subsidiaries:

Shenzhen Chips Information S&T Co., Ltd. (1)
5th Floor Jinxu Technology Building Gaoxin South 5th Road, South District, Shenzhen, 518057, China
Tel.: (86) 75586393588
Web Site: http://www.chipsinfo.com.cn
Software Development Services
N.A.I.C.S.: 513210

SHENZHEN KINGKEY SMART AGRICULTURE TIMES CO., LTD.
71F Building A Kingkey 100 5016 Shennan East Road, Luohu District, Shenzhen, 518001, Guangdong, China
Tel.: (86) 75525425020
Web Site: https://www.kingkeyzn.com
000048—(SSE)
Rev.: $841,790,116
Assets: $2,462,060,830
Liabilities: $2,088,257,792
Net Worth: $373,803,038
Earnings: $108,539,576
Fiscal Year-end: 12/31/22
Animal Feed Mfr
N.A.I.C.S.: 311119

SHENZHEN KINGSUN SCIENCE & TECHNOLOGY CO., LTD.
9th Floor Block B Innovation Building No 198 Daxin Road, Nanshan District, Shenzhen, 518052, Guangdong, China
Tel.: (86) 75586336966

Web Site: http://www.kingsunsoft.com
Year Founded: 1993
300235—(CHIN)
Rev.: $15,133,716
Assets: $98,932,860
Liabilities: $3,074,760
Net Worth: $95,858,100
Earnings: $3,275,532
Emp.: 170
Fiscal Year-end: 12/31/22
Educational Software Publisher
N.A.I.C.S.: 513210
Yuanzhong Huang (Chm)

SHENZHEN KINWONG ELECTRONIC CO.,LTD.
No 166 Tiegang Reservoir Road Xixiang Street, Bao an District, Shenzhen, 518132, China
Tel.: (86) 75583896578
Web Site: https://www.kinwong.com
Year Founded: 1993
603228—(SHG)
Rev.: $1,476,164,238
Assets: $2,175,015,993
Liabilities: $1,011,036,588
Net Worth: $1,163,979,405
Earnings: $149,643,459
Emp.: 15,000
Fiscal Year-end: 12/31/22
Printed Circuit Board Mfr & Distr
N.A.I.C.S.: 334418
Liu Shaobai (Chm)

Subsidiaries:

Jiangxi Kinwong Precision Circuit Co., Ltd. (1)
Chengxi Industrial Park Jishui County, Jian, 331600, Jiangxi, China
Tel.: (86) 7968683866
Printed Circuit Board Mfr
N.A.I.C.S.: 334418

Kinwong Electronic (HongKong) Ltd. (1)
Rm 1005-6 10/F Block B Veristrong Ind Centre, 36 Au Pui Wan Street, Fotan, New Terroteris, China (Hong Kong)
Tel.: (852) 26872088
Printed Circuit Board Distr
N.A.I.C.S.: 423690

Kinwong Electronic Technology (Longchuan) Co., Ltd. (1)
Baotong Industrial Zone Dapingshan Longchuan County, Heyuan, 517333, Guangdong, China
Tel.: (86) 7626323333
Printed Circuit Board Mfr
N.A.I.C.S.: 334418

SHENZHEN KSTAR SCIENCE AND TECHNOLOGY CO., LTD.
4/F No 1 Bldg Software Park Keji C Rd, 2nd Hi-Tech Industrial Zone, Shenzhen, 518057, China
Tel.: (86) 75521389008
Web Site: https://www.kstar.com
Year Founded: 1993
002518—(SSE)
Rev.: $617,856,806
Assets: $873,318,060
Liabilities: $366,087,510
Net Worth: $507,230,549
Earnings: $92,169,413
Emp.: 3,000
Fiscal Year-end: 12/31/22
Uninterruptible Power Supplies & Storage Batteries Mfr
N.A.I.C.S.: 335910
Liu Chengyu (Chm & Gen Mgr)

SHENZHEN KTC TECHNOLOGY CO., LTD.
No 4023 Wuhe Road, Bantian Subdistrict Longgang District, Shenzhen, 518129, China
Tel.: (86) 75533610000

Web Site: https://www.ktc.cn
Year Founded: 1995
001308—(SSE)
Rev.: $1,626,820,950
Assets: $1,389,000,113
Liabilities: $556,412,431
Net Worth: $832,587,683
Earnings: $212,789,987
Emp.: 6,000
Fiscal Year-end: 12/31/22
Electronic Components Mfr
N.A.I.C.S.: 334419
Ling Bin (Chm)

SHENZHEN L & A DESIGN HOLDING LIMITED
Room 302B 303 & 404 Building 5 Huajian Industrial Building No 6, Xinghua Road Shekou Subdistrict Nanshan District, Shenzhen, 518067, Guangdong, China
Tel.: (86) 75526826690
Web Site: http://www.aoya-hk.com
Year Founded: 2001
300949—(SSE)
Rev.: $67,410,308
Assets: $207,544,685
Liabilities: $46,101,505
Net Worth: $161,443,180
Earnings: ($7,256,223)
Fiscal Year-end: 12/31/22
Holding Company
N.A.I.C.S.: 551112
Baozhang Li (Chm)

SHENZHEN LAIBAO HI-TECH CO., LTD.
No 29 Gaoxin North 2nd Road Xili Street, Nanshan District, Shenzhen, 518057, China
Tel.: (86) 75529891909
Web Site: https://www.laibao.com.cn
Year Founded: 1992
002106—(SSE)
Rev.: $863,948,536
Assets: $877,101,489
Liabilities: $177,403,024
Net Worth: $699,698,465
Earnings: $51,499,141
Fiscal Year-end: 12/31/22
Display Material Mfr
N.A.I.C.S.: 334419
Shaozong Li (Pres & Gen Mgr)

SHENZHEN LEAGUER CO., LTD.
No 1001 Longgang Road, Longgang Distict, Shenzhen, 518117, Guangdong, China
Tel.: (86) 75528482022
Web Site: https://www.beautystar.cn
Year Founded: 1984
002243—(SSE)
Rev.: $367,540,327
Assets: $2,089,297,567
Liabilities: $916,721,147
Net Worth: $1,172,576,420
Earnings: $58,508,148
Fiscal Year-end: 12/31/22
Packaging Products Mfr
N.A.I.C.S.: 326121
Chen Shou (Vice Chm)

Subsidiaries:

Guangzhou Beauty Star Co., Ltd. (1)
High-tech Industrial Base Zengjiang Street, Eastern District Zengcheng, Guangzhou, 511300, China
Tel.: (86) 2032851088
Unlaminated Plastic Profile Shape Mfr
N.A.I.C.S.: 326121

Shanghai Beauty Star Co., Ltd. (1)
Room 1116 Jh Plaza No 2008 Huqingping Road, Qingpu District, Shanghai, China
Tel.: (86) 2159898929
Unlaminated Plastic Profile Shape Mfr

INTERNATIONAL PUBLIC

N.A.I.C.S.: 326121

Suzhou Beauty Star Co., Ltd. (1)
358 Panlong Rd, Wujiang Economic and Technological Development Area, Suzhou, China
Tel.: (86) 51263788016
Unlaminated Plastic Profile Shape Mfr
N.A.I.C.S.: 326121

SHENZHEN LIANDE AUTOMATION EQUIPMENT CO.,LTD.
Liande Building Qiu Zhi East Road Guanhu Street, Longhua District, Shenzhen, 518109, China
Tel.: (86) 76989994888
Web Site: https://www.liande-china.com
Year Founded: 2002
300545—(CHIN)
Rev.: $136,877,392
Assets: $370,145,772
Liabilities: $159,559,068
Net Worth: $210,586,704
Earnings: $10,794,598
Emp.: 1,100
Fiscal Year-end: 12/31/22
Automated Equipment Mfr & Distr
N.A.I.C.S.: 334419
Quan Nie (Chm & Gen Mgr)

Subsidiaries:

Suzhou Lianpeng Automation Equipment Co., Ltd (1)
No 78 Keling Road High-Tech District, Suzhou, China
Tel.: (86) 51267374965
Auxiliary Equipment Mfr
N.A.I.C.S.: 333248

SHENZHEN LIANSHUO AUTOMATION TECHNOLOGY CO., LTD.
3/F Tianli Technology Building No 1 Lougang Road Songgang Avenue, Baoan District, Shenzhen, 518105, China
Tel.: (86) 75536693699
Vehicle Platform Mfr
N.A.I.C.S.: 333923

SHENZHEN LIANTRONICS CO., LTD.
Liantronics Building Antongda Industrial Zone, 3rd Liuxian Rd 68 Block Baoan District, Shenzhen, China
Tel.: (86) 75523001729
Web Site: https://www.liantronics.com
300269—(CHIN)
Rev.: $175,185,504
Assets: $172,025,100
Liabilities: $163,661,472
Net Worth: $8,363,628
Earnings: ($8,136,180)
Emp.: 1,300
Fiscal Year-end: 12/31/22
LCD Display Mfr
N.A.I.C.S.: 334413

Subsidiaries:

Liantronics (Hong Kong) Co. Ltd. (1)
Flat 2 14/F Block A Veristrong industrial Centre, 34 - 36 Au Pui Wan Street Fo Tan, Sha Tin, New Territories, China (Hong Kong)
Tel.: (852) 2 252 4600
Web Site: http://www.liantronics-hk.com
Light Emitting Diode Displays Mfr
N.A.I.C.S.: 334419

Shenzhen Liantronics LLC (1)
46701 Fremont Blvd, Fremont, CA 94538
Web Site: http://www.liantronics-usa.com
Light Emitting Diode Mfr
N.A.I.C.S.: 334419

SHENZHEN LIFOTRONIC TECHNOLOGY CO., LTD.

AND PRIVATE COMPANIES

1st Floor Lifotronic headquarter building No 8 Qiuzhi East Road, Guancheng Community Guanhu Street Longhua District, Shenzhen, 518110, China
Tel.: (86) 75529016066
Web Site: https://www.lifotronic.com
Year Founded: 2008
688389—(SHG)
Rev.: $138,019,490
Assets: $255,599,604
Liabilities: $52,933,103
Net Worth: $202,666,501
Earnings: $35,310,024
Emp.: 1,400
Fiscal Year-end: 12/31/22
Medical Product Mfr & Distr
N.A.I.C.S.: 339112
Xiancheng Liu (Chm)

SHENZHEN LIHEXING CO., LTD.
21F Office Building 1 Huide Building No 385 Mintang Road, Longhua District, Shenzhen, 518131, Guangdong, China
Tel.: (86) 75528191082
Web Site: https://www.lihexing.com
Year Founded: 2006
301013—(CHIN)
Rev.: $43,038,216
Assets: $193,701,456
Liabilities: $70,763,004
Net Worth: $122,938,452
Earnings: ($5,811,156)
Fiscal Year-end: 12/31/22
Power Automation Equipment Mfr & Distr
N.A.I.C.S.: 333613
Lin Yipan (Chm & Gen Mgr)

SHENZHEN LONGLI TECHNOLOGY CO., LTD.
Building G Guanghao Industrial Park Queshan Road Gaofeng Community, Dalang Street Longhua District, Shenzhen, 518000, China
Tel.: (86) 75528111999
Web Site: https://www.blbgy.com
Year Founded: 2007
300752—(CHIN)
Rev.: $175,789,449
Assets: $240,330,865
Liabilities: $131,720,711
Net Worth: $108,610,155
Earnings: ($46,314,857)
Emp.: 3,000
Fiscal Year-end: 12/31/22
Lighting Equipment Mfr & Distr
N.A.I.C.S.: 335139
Wu Xinli (Chm, Pres & Gen Mgr)

Subsidiaries:

Huizhou Longli Technology Development Co., Ltd. (1)
Debang Science & Technology Park No 68 North Lianfa Avenue, Tongqiao Town Zhongkai High-tech Zone, Huizhou, China
Tel.: (86) 7525311616
Display Module Mfr & Distr
N.A.I.C.S.: 334413

Longli Technology (India) Co., Ltd. (1)
A-164A Phase II 80 District, Noida, Uttar Pradesh, India
Tel.: (91) 8448571703
Display Module Mfr & Distr
N.A.I.C.S.: 334413

Shenzhen Longli Optoelectronics Technology Development Co., Ltd. (1)
Building 5 Fenghuang Third Industrial Zone Fuyong Street, Baoan District, Shenzhen, China
Tel.: (86) 13538196590
Display Module Mfr & Distr
N.A.I.C.S.: 334413

SHENZHEN LONGOOD INTELLIGENT ELECTRIC CO., LTD.
Building1 1701 Xinyilingyu R&D Center 30 Honglang North No 2 Ave, Xingdong Block 69 Xinan BaoAn District, Shenzhen, 518108, China
Tel.: (86) 75533236610
Web Site: https://www.longood.com
Year Founded: 2001
300543—(CHIN)
Rev.: $187,866,293
Assets: $288,921,351
Liabilities: $133,879,376
Net Worth: $155,041,976
Earnings: $5,636,690
Emp.: 4,000
Fiscal Year-end: 12/31/22
Household Appliance Mfr & Distr
N.A.I.C.S.: 335220

Subsidiaries:

Guangdong Longood Intelligent Electric Co., Ltd (1)
No 7 Tiansha Ave Tangxia, Dongguan, 523710, Guangdong, China
Tel.: (86) 76938959888
Electronic Products Mfr
N.A.I.C.S.: 334419
Franky Zhou (Engr-Sls)

Zhejiang Longood Intelligent Electric Co., Ltd (1)
No 141 Qichao Ave Chang an, Haining, 314422, Zhejiang, China
Tel.: (86) 57387979595
Electronic Products Mfr
N.A.I.C.S.: 334419

SHENZHEN LONGSYS ELECTRONICS COMPANY LIMITED
Floor 20 22 23 B Tower Horoy Qianhai Finance Centre Phase II No 5059, Tinghai Avenue Qianhai, Shenzhen, 518057, China
Tel.: (86) 75586168848
Web Site: https://www.longsys.com
Year Founded: 1999
301308—(SSE)
Rev.: $1,169,522,776
Assets: $1,258,512,423
Liabilities: $326,431,446
Net Worth: $932,080,977
Earnings: $10,220,699
Fiscal Year-end: 12/31/22
Digital Storage Product Mfr & Distr
N.A.I.C.S.: 334112
Cai Huabo (Chm & Gen Mgr)

Subsidiaries:

Powertech Technology (Suzhou) Ltd. (1)
33 Xinghai Street, Suzhou Industrial Park, Suzhou, China (70%)
Tel.: (86) 51262523333
IC Backend Chip Probing & Packaging Mfr
N.A.I.C.S.: 334413

SHENZHEN LONGTECH SMART CONTROL CO., LTD.
Building G Jianshi Industrial Park Huangpu Road 52th Xinqiao Street, Baoan Area, Shenzhen, 518125, Guangdong, China
Tel.: (86) 75523501350
Web Site: https://www.longtechcc.com
Year Founded: 2003
300916—(SSE)
Rev.: $181,302,957
Assets: $213,560,292
Liabilities: $52,770,463
Net Worth: $160,789,829
Earnings: $25,383,674
Fiscal Year-end: 12/31/22
Home Appliance Mfr
N.A.I.C.S.: 334512
Zhengliang Ouyang (Chm & Gen Mgr)

SHENZHEN MAGIC DESIGN AND DECORATION ENGINEERING CO., LTD
Floor 1-6 Building 7 Research Building Bagua 4th Road, Futian District, Shenzhen, 518029, Guangdong, China
Tel.: (86) 75583260111
Web Site: https://www.szmeizhi.com
Year Founded: 1984
002856—(SSE)
Rev.: $234,074,010
Assets: $315,815,690
Liabilities: $236,760,844
Net Worth: $79,054,845
Earnings: ($20,096,926)
Fiscal Year-end: 12/31/22
Building Decoration Engineering Services
N.A.I.C.S.: 236220
Suhua Li (Board of Directors & Chm)

SHENZHEN MASON TECHNOLOGIES CO., LTD.
No 2 Gongye West 2nd Road, Songshan Lake high-tech Industrial Development Zone, Dongguan, 518107, Guangdong, China
Tel.: (86) 76989950999
Web Site: https://www.mason-led.com
Year Founded: 2010
002654—(SSE)
Rev.: $526,170,102
Assets: $594,744,733
Liabilities: $367,130,107
Net Worth: $227,614,627
Earnings: ($24,003,303)
Emp.: 1,500
Fiscal Year-end: 12/31/22
LED Light Mfr & Supplier
N.A.I.C.S.: 335132
Gong Daoyi (Chm)

SHENZHEN MASS POWER ELECTRONIC CO. LTD.
437 Hedong Village Hengkeng Community Guanlan Street, Longhua District, Shenzhen, Baoan, China
Tel.: (86) 75529453196
Web Site: http://www.mass-power.com
Power Supply Accessory Distr
N.A.I.C.S.: 423620

SHENZHEN MAXONIC AUTOMATION CONTROL CO., LTD.
Maxonic Automation Control Mansion, North 3 Road Hi-Tech Industrial Park, Shenzhen, 518057, Guangdong, China
Tel.: (86) 75586250388
Web Site: https://www.maxonic.com.cn
Year Founded: 1994
300112—(CHIN)
Rev.: $154,136,736
Assets: $252,172,440
Liabilities: $72,800,208
Net Worth: $179,372,232
Earnings: $13,311,324
Fiscal Year-end: 12/31/22
Automation Control Systems Mfr
N.A.I.C.S.: 334513
Simon Chung Yee (Dir)

Subsidiaries:

MaxAuto Company Limited (1)
Room 803-4 Yale Ind Center 61-63 Au Pui Wan Street, Hong Kong, China (Hong Kong)
Tel.: (852) 26875000
Automation Instruments Mfr
N.A.I.C.S.: 334512

SHENZHEN MEGMEET ELECTRICAL CO.,LTD
Ningbo Jiangbei Investment and Pioneering Park, Nanshan District, Shenzhen, 518052, Zhejiang, China
Tel.: (86) 75586600637
Web Site: http://www.megmeet.com
Year Founded: 2003
002851—(SSE)
Rev.: $769,077,307
Assets: $1,186,878,546
Liabilities: $648,915,462
Net Worth: $537,963,084
Earnings: $66,366,448
Emp.: 6,000
Fiscal Year-end: 12/31/22
Smart Home Appliance Mfr & Distr
N.A.I.C.S.: 334512
Tong Yongsheng (Chm & Gen Mgr)

Subsidiaries:

Hangzhou Qianjing Technology Co., Ltd. (1)
13F Zhongzi Technology Park No 6 Xiasha Street, Jianggan District, Hangzhou, Zhejiang, China
Tel.: (86) 5718 538 6629
Web Site: https://www.qianjingtech.com
Oil Production Equipment Mfr
N.A.I.C.S.: 333132

Megmeet Germany GmbH (1)
Meisenstr 94, 33607, Bielefeld, Germany
Tel.: (49) 5215 881 3140
Electric Equipment Mfr
N.A.I.C.S.: 335129

Megmeet Sweden AB (1)
Norgegatan 2, 16432, Kista, Sweden
Tel.: (46) 70 789 6757
Electric Equipment Mfr
N.A.I.C.S.: 335999

Megmeet USA, Inc. (1)
4020 Moorpark Ave Ste 115, San Jose, CA 95117
Tel.: (408) 260-7211
Web Site: https://www.megmeetusa.com
Power Converter Product Distr
N.A.I.C.S.: 423610

Shanghai Megmeet Electrical Co., Ltd (1)
806 Room 19th Building Fenghuang Park 1515 Gumei Road, Caohejing Development Are, Shanghai, 200030, China
Tel.: (86) 2154452259
Electronic Products Mfr
N.A.I.C.S.: 334419

Shenzhen Megmeet Control Technology Co., Ltd. (1)
5th Floor Block B Unisplendour Information Harbor Langshan Road, Shenzhen, China
Tel.: (86) 7558 660 0500
Internal Gear Pump Distr
N.A.I.C.S.: 423830

Shenzhen Megmeet Energy Technology Co., Ltd. (1)
5th Floor Block B Unisplendour Information Harbor Langshan Road, Shenzhen, China
Tel.: (86) 7558 660 0500
Electric Equipment Mfr
N.A.I.C.S.: 335999

Shenzhen Megmeet Welding Technology Co., Ltd. (1)
5th Floor Block B Unisplendour Information Harbor Langshan Road, Shenzhen, China
Tel.: (86) 7558 660 0500
Welding Equipment Mfr
N.A.I.C.S.: 333992

Suzhou ANCHI Control System Co., Ltd. (1)
16 / F Business Center No 88 Nanxijiang Road, Wuzhong District, Suzhou, China
Tel.: (86) 5126 561 9888
Servo Drive Mfr
N.A.I.C.S.: 335312

Suzhou Zhiwei precision Drive Control Technology Co., Ltd. (1)
Building 3 No 521 Nanguandu Road, Wuzhong District, Suzhou, China
Tel.: (86) 1891 315 2053

SHENZHEN MEGMEET ELECTRICAL CO.,LTD

Shenzhen Megmeet Electrical Co.,Ltd—(Continued)
Web Site: https://www.zhiweijq.com
Linear Motor Mfr & Distr
N.A.I.C.S.: 335312

Xiamen Rongji Precision Technology Co., Ltd. (1)
No 285 Wengjiao Road, Haicang District, Xiamen, Fujian, China
Tel.: (86) 592 739 0581
Web Site: https://www.xmrongji.com.cn
Emp.: 300
Internal Gear Pump Mfr
N.A.I.C.S.: 333914

Zhejiang ALLEAD Precision Technology Co., Ltd. (1)
No 777 Haopai Road, Suxi Town, Yiwu, 322009, Zhejiang, China
Tel.: (86) 5798 358 6668
Web Site: https://alleaden.bce97.jhjishicn.com
Internal Gear Pump Mfr & Distr
N.A.I.C.S.: 333914

Zhejiang iKAHE Sanitary Ware Co., Ltd. (1)
No 102 Dongtaihe Road, Jiaojiang District, Taizhou, Zhejiang, China
Tel.: (86) 5768 110 7110
Web Site: https://english.ikahe.com
Emp.: 351
Smart Toilet Mfr
N.A.I.C.S.: 325620

Zhuzhou InnoPower Technology Co., Ltd. (1)
No 1728 Taishan Road, Tianyuan District, Zhuzhou, 412000, Hunan, China
Tel.: (86) 7312 250 9200
Web Site: https://www.innopwr.com
Industrial Automation Products Mfr
N.A.I.C.S.: 333998

Zhuzhou Megmeet Electric Co., Ltd (1)
Liyu Industrial Park B05 Taishan Road Tianyuan District, Zhuzhou, 412000, Hunan, China
Tel.: (86) 4008469000
Electronic Products Mfr
N.A.I.C.S.: 334419

Zhuzhou Wavelane Technology Co., Ltd. (1)
No 1728 Taishan West Road, Tianyuan District, Zhuzhou, Hunan, China
Tel.: (86) 7318 407 9668
Web Site: https://www.wavelane-tech.com
Microwave Application Equipment Distr
N.A.I.C.S.: 449210

SHENZHEN MICROGATE TECHNOLOGY CO. LTD.
Microgate Smart Park Pingshan Technology Road Zhukeng community, Longtian street Pingshan District, Shenzhen, China
Tel.: (86) 75528085000
Web Site: https://www.szmicrogate.com
Year Founded: 2001
300319—(SSE)
Rev.: $442,488,852
Assets: $791,047,296
Liabilities: $218,441,340
Net Worth: $572,605,956
Earnings: $27,988,740
Emp.: 220
Fiscal Year-end: 12/31/22
Electronic Components Mfr
N.A.I.C.S.: 334419
Qixin Liang (CTO & Deputy Gen Mgr)

SHENZHEN MINDE ELECTRONICS TECHNOLOGY LTD.
5th Floor Section 1 25th Block No 5 Kezhi Xi Road Keji Yuan, Nanshan District, Shenzhen, 518057, China
Tel.: (86) 75586141288
Web Site: https://www.mindeo.cn
Year Founded: 2004
300656—(CHIN)
Rev.: $72,754,901
Assets: $215,172,716
Liabilities: $52,469,333
Net Worth: $162,703,382
Earnings: $12,595,172
Fiscal Year-end: 12/31/22
Electronic Device Mfr & Distr
N.A.I.C.S.: 334118

SHENZHEN MINGDIAO DECORATION CO., LTD.
Room 36-40 2F Block1 Longguang Century Building Xinghua Road South, Baoan District, Shenzhen, 518000, Guangdong, China
Tel.: (86) 75523348796
Web Site: http://www.mingdiao.com.cn
002830—(SSE)
Rev.: $110,444,070
Assets: $204,686,126
Liabilities: $106,248,859
Net Worth: $98,437,267
Earnings: $5,505,366
Fiscal Year-end: 12/31/23
Decorating Services
N.A.I.C.S.: 541410
Jixiao Lan (Chm, Pres & Gen Mgr)

SHENZHEN MINGLIDA PRECISION TECHNOLOGY CO., LTD.
21st floor Block F TongFang Information Harbor No 11 Langshan Road, Nanshan District, Shenzhen, 523661, Guangdong, China
Tel.: (86) 75586660087
Web Site: https://www.minglidagroup.com
Year Founded: 2004
301268—(SSE)
Rev.: $451,940,580
Assets: $658,504,080
Liabilities: $347,860,656
Net Worth: $310,643,424
Earnings: $56,575,584
Fiscal Year-end: 12/31/22
Industrial Machinery Mfr & Distr
N.A.I.C.S.: 333248
Tao Cheng (Chm & Gen Mgr)

SHENZHEN MINGWAH AOHAN HIGH TECHNOLOGY CORPORATION LIMITED
Room 338 Build 202 Shangbu Industrial Huaqiang North Road, Futian District, Shenzhen, 518028, China
Tel.: (86) 755 83345003   CN
Web Site: http://www.mwcard.com
Year Founded: 1992
Rev.: $7,194,066
Assets: $9,252,703
Liabilities: $12,233,619
Net Worth: ($2,980,916)
Earnings: ($5,355,804)
Emp.: 17
Fiscal Year-end: 12/31/19
Electronic Products Mfr
N.A.I.C.S.: 334413
Tao Zhang (Chm, CEO & Compliance Officer)

SHENZHEN MINKAVE TECHNOLOGY CO., LTD.
Floor 20 Block A Building 10, Shenzhen Bay Science and Technology Ecological Park Nanshan District, Shenzhen, 518054, Guangdong, China
Tel.: (86) 75526490198
Web Site: https://www.minkave.com
Year Founded: 2001
300506—(CHIN)
Rev.: $17,273,145
Assets: $207,413,159
Liabilities: $134,256,293
Net Worth: $73,156,866
Earnings: ($66,677,841)
Fiscal Year-end: 12/31/22
Lighting System Mfr
N.A.I.C.S.: 335132
Zongyu Cheng (Chm & Pres)

SHENZHEN MOSO POWER SUPPLY TECHNOLOGY CO., LTD.
Xili Moso Science and Technology Park, Nanshan District, Shenzhen, 518108, China
Tel.: (86) 75527657000
Web Site: https://www.mosopower.com
Year Founded: 2006
002660—(SSE)
Rev.: $216,666,824
Assets: $267,093,183
Liabilities: $93,367,530
Net Worth: $173,725,653
Earnings: $11,927,752
Emp.: 1,800
Fiscal Year-end: 12/31/22
Switch Power Supplies Mfr
N.A.I.C.S.: 335311
Zhang Xin (Chm)

Subsidiaries:

MOSO Electronics Corp. (1)
MOSO Industrial Park, Nanshan District, Shenzhen, China
Tel.: (86) 4008890018
Electronic Lighting Mfr
N.A.I.C.S.: 335210

SHENZHEN MTC CO., LTD.
6th Floor 3rd Building MTC industry Park 1st Lilang Road, Longgang, Shenzhen, China
Tel.: (86) 75532901659
Web Site: https://www.szmtc.com.cn
002429—(SSE)
Rev.: $2,109,983,850
Assets: $3,595,369,574
Liabilities: $1,644,716,895
Net Worth: $1,950,652,679
Earnings: $160,891,282
Emp.: 8,000
Fiscal Year-end: 12/31/22
Video & Audio Equipment Mfr
N.A.I.C.S.: 334310

Subsidiaries:

Shenzhen MTC Optronics Co., Ltd. (1)
MTC Industrial Park Xialilang Community Nanwan street, Longgang District, Shenzhen, China
Tel.: (86) 755 32901233
Web Site: http://www.bmtclighting.com
Commercial Lighting Fixtures Mfr
N.A.I.C.S.: 335132

SHENZHEN NANSHAN POWER CO., LTD.
Floor 16 17 OCT Han Tang Building, Nanshan District, Shenzhen, 518053, Guangdong, China
Tel.: (86) 75526948888
Web Site: https://www.nsrd.com.cn
Year Founded: 1990
000037—(SSE)
Rev.: $97,469,569
Assets: $365,912,769
Liabilities: $170,360,967
Net Worth: $195,551,802
Earnings: ($22,486,913)
Fiscal Year-end: 12/31/22
Electric Power Generation & Distribution Services
N.A.I.C.S.: 221111
Kong Guoliang (Chm & Sec)

SHENZHEN NEOWAY TECHNOLOGY CO., LTD.
Floor 43 Huide Tower, Longhua District, Shenzhen, China
Tel.: (86) 75529672566
Web Site: https://www.neoway.com
Year Founded: 2006
688159—(SHG)
Rev.: $117,877,678
Assets: $191,955,821
Liabilities: $82,947,084
Net Worth: $109,008,736
Earnings: ($7,992,410)
Emp.: 500
Fiscal Year-end: 12/31/22
Telecommunication Device Mfr
N.A.I.C.S.: 334290
Kang Wang (Chm & Gen Mgr)

SHENZHEN NEPTUNUS BIO-ENGINEERING CO., LTD.
24F Neptunus Yinhe Technology Building No 1 Keji Middle 3rd Road, Nanshan District, Shenzhen, 518057, Guangdong, China
Tel.: (86) 75526980336
Web Site: https://www.neptunus.com
Year Founded: 1992
000078—(SSE)
Rev.: $5,312,014,161
Assets: $5,089,819,550
Liabilities: $4,231,915,080
Net Worth: $857,904,470
Earnings: ($144,243,408)
Emp.: 35,000
Fiscal Year-end: 12/31/22
Pharmaceuticals Mfr
N.A.I.C.S.: 325412
Simin Zhang (Chm)

Subsidiaries:

Shenzhen Neptunus Interlong Bio-Technique Co., Ltd. (1)
Suite 2103 21st Floor Neptunus Yinhe Technology Mansion, 1 Keji Middle 3rd Road Yuehai Sub-district Nanshan District, Shenzhen, 518000, Guangdong, China
Tel.: (86) 75526411869
Web Site: https://www.interlong.com
Rev.: $149,980,422
Assets: $199,386,760
Liabilities: $56,262,535
Net Worth: $143,124,225
Earnings: $2,045,915
Emp.: 1,444
Fiscal Year-end: 12/31/2023
Pharmaceutical Product Mfr & Distr
N.A.I.C.S.: 325412
Feng Zhang (Chm & Officer-Compliance)

SHENZHEN NEW INDUSTRIES BIOMEDICAL ENGINEERING CO., LTD.
Snibe Building No 23 Jinxiu East Road, Pingshan, Shenzhen, 518122, China
Tel.: (86) 75526501514
Web Site: https://www.snibe.com
Year Founded: 1995
300832—(SSE)
Rev.: $427,792,580
Assets: $984,843,424
Liabilities: $86,354,382
Net Worth: $898,489,042
Earnings: $186,439,743
Fiscal Year-end: 12/31/22
Medical Product Mfr & Distr
N.A.I.C.S.: 339112
Wei Rao (Chm & Gen Mgr)

SHENZHEN NEW LAND TOOL PLANNING & ARCHITECTURAL DESIGN CO., LTD.
10F Xinchengshi Building No 39 Qinglin Middle Road Center City, Longgang, Shenzhen, 518172, Guangdong, China
Tel.: (86) 75533283211
Web Site: http://www.nlt.com.cn
Year Founded: 1993

300778—(SSE)
Rev.: $65,309,180
Assets: $260,190,698
Liabilities: $94,559,681
Net Worth: $165,631,017
Earnings: $8,564,442
Emp.: 1,000
Fiscal Year-end: 12/31/22
Architectural Services
N.A.I.C.S.: 541310
Yi Hongmei *(CFO, Sec & Deputy Gen Mgr)*

SHENZHEN NEW NANSHAN HOLDING GROUP CO., LTD.
25F-26F Chiwan Headquarters Building No 8 Chiwan 6th Road, Nanshan District, Shenzhen, 518068, Guangdong, China
Tel.: (86) 75526826070 CN
Web Site: https://www.xnskg.cn
Year Founded: 1982
002314—(SSE)
Rev.: $1,705,917,957
Assets: $9,735,247,183
Liabilities: $7,176,385,495
Net Worth: $2,558,861,688
Earnings: $95,537,483
Emp.: 3,595
Fiscal Year-end: 12/31/22
Modular Houses Mfr
N.A.I.C.S.: 321991
Yang Guolin *(Chm)*

SHENZHEN NOPOSION CROP SCIENCE CO., LTD.
No 113 Xixiang Reservoir Road, Baoan District, Shenzhen, 518102, Guangdong, China
Tel.: (86) 75529977586 CN
Web Site: http://www.noposion.com
Year Founded: 2005
002215—(SSE)
Rev.: $570,383,515
Assets: $1,504,753,517
Liabilities: $918,738,494
Net Worth: $586,015,023
Earnings: $32,624,405
Emp.: 4,000
Fiscal Year-end: 12/31/23
Agricultural Product Mfr
N.A.I.C.S.: 325320
Qiang Lu Bo *(Chm & Gen Mgr)*

SHENZHEN O-FILM TECH CO., LTD.
9F Block T6 Taiziwan Business Plaza No 91 Shanghai Road Shekou, Nanshan District, Shenzhen, 518107, Guangdong, China
Tel.: (86) 75527545080
Web Site: https://www.o-film.com
Year Founded: 2002
002456—(SSE)
Rev.: $2,081,737,518
Assets: $2,559,755,222
Liabilities: $2,001,447,419
Net Worth: $558,307,803
Earnings: ($727,608,679)
Emp.: 30,000
Fiscal Year-end: 12/31/22
Precision Optoelectronic Thin-Film Component Mfr
N.A.I.C.S.: 333310

SHENZHEN OVERSEAS CHINESE TOWN CO., LTD.
Office Building of OCT Group, Nanshan District, Shenzhen, Guangdong, China
Tel.: (86) 75526600248 CN
Web Site: https://www.octholding.com
Year Founded: 1997
000069—(SSE)
Rev.: $7,718,230,948
Assets: $51,372,019,287
Liabilities: $39,459,848,042
Net Worth: $11,912,171,245
Earnings: ($898,931,380)
Emp.: 20,974
Fiscal Year-end: 12/31/23
Real Estate Manangement Services
N.A.I.C.S.: 531390

SHENZHEN PAGODA INDUSTRIAL (GROUP) CORPORATION LIMITED
Floor 11-13 Tower B Jiansheng Building No 1 Pingji Avenue, Longgang, Shenzhen, Guangdong, China
Tel.: (86) 75536865476 CN
Web Site: https://www.pagoda.com.cn
Year Founded: 2001
2411—(HKG)
Rev.: $1,733,110,754
Assets: $1,043,320,419
Liabilities: $580,704,203
Net Worth: $462,616,216
Earnings: $46,903,250
Emp.: 3,006
Fiscal Year-end: 12/31/22
Fruit Product Distr
N.A.I.C.S.: 424480

SHENZHEN PHOENIX TELECOM TECHNOLOGY CO.,LTD.
Bldg3 Runheng Industrial Park West of Fuyuan 1st Road, Fuyong Street Baoan District, Shenzhen, 518052, Guangdong, China
Tel.: (86) 75586060269
Web Site: https://www.phoenixcompany.cn
Year Founded: 1999
301191—(CHIN)
Rev.: $287,264,220
Assets: $326,958,795
Liabilities: $95,709,446
Net Worth: $231,249,349
Earnings: $19,989,034
Fiscal Year-end: 12/31/23
Telecommunications Equipment Mfr
N.A.I.C.S.: 334220
Longfa Chen *(Chm)*

SHENZHEN PREVAIL TECHNOLOGY CO., LTD.
No 25 Cai Tian Road, ShaTian Industrial Zone KengZi Town PingShan New District, Shenzhen, China
Tel.: (86) 75528618888 CN
Welding Equipment Mfr
N.A.I.C.S.: 333992

SHENZHEN PRINCE NEW MATERIALS CO., LTD.
Prince Industrial Park No 4 Fenjin Road Longhua Street, Longhua District, Shenzhen, China
Tel.: (86) 75528172222
Web Site: https://www.szwzxc.com
Year Founded: 1997
002735—(SSE)
Rev.: $245,796,946
Assets: $296,252,073
Liabilities: $139,783,419
Net Worth: $156,468,654
Earnings: $9,880,566
Emp.: 2,000
Fiscal Year-end: 12/31/22
Plastic Packaging Materials Mfr
N.A.I.C.S.: 325211
Jinjun Wang *(Chm & Pres)*

SHENZHEN PROLTO SUPPLY CHAIN MANAGEMENT CO., LTD.
21F Tower A Shenzhen International Innovation Center No 1006, Shennan Road Futian District, Shenzhen, 518048, Guangdong, China
Tel.: (86) 75582877543
Web Site: https://www.prolto.com
Year Founded: 2005
002769—(SSE)
Rev.: $210,645,504
Assets: $990,205,721
Liabilities: $796,667,803
Net Worth: $193,537,918
Earnings: ($11,629,444)
Fiscal Year-end: 12/31/22
Freight Transportation Services
N.A.I.C.S.: 484110
Shuzhi Chen *(Pres-Prolto)*

Subsidiaries:

Beihai Prolto Supply Chain Management Co., Ltd. (1)
2/F Declaration Office Administrative Committee Building, Export Processing Zone Beihai Avenue West, Beihai, China
Tel.: (86) 7793935721
Supply Chain Management Services
N.A.I.C.S.: 541614

Chengdu Hope Times Trading Co., Ltd. (1)
NO 1311 13/F Block 3 No 88 Jiaozi Avenue, Chengdu Hi-Tech Industrial Development Zone, Chengdu, China
Tel.: (86) 2865589700
Supply Chain Management Services
N.A.I.C.S.: 541614

Hongkong Raton International Co., Ltd. (1)
Unit 805 8/F Grandtech Centre NO 8 On Ping St, Sha Tin, China (Hong Kong)
Tel.: (852) 2865589700
Supply Chain Management Services
N.A.I.C.S.: 541614

Shenzhen Qianhai Prolto E-business Integrated Services Co., Ltd. (1)
Room 301 Building W6 Qianhai Bonded Bay Linhai Avenue, Nanshan, Shenzhen, China
Tel.: (86) 75582835961
Supply Chain Management Services
N.A.I.C.S.: 541614

Wuhan Prolto Supply Chain Management Co., Ltd. (1)
Special No 1 Taizhong Road Gaoqiao Industrial Park, Wujiashan Taiwanese Business Investment Zone Dongxihu, Wuhan, China
Tel.: (86) 2787490059
Supply Chain Management Services
N.A.I.C.S.: 541614

SHENZHEN PROPERTIES & RESOURCES DEVELOPMENT (GROUP) LTD.
39/F and 42/F Guomao Building Renmin South Road, Luohu District, Shenzhen, 518014, Guangdong, China
Tel.: (86) 75582211020
Web Site: http://www.szwuye.com.cn
Year Founded: 1992
200011—(SSE)
Rev.: $520,697,128
Assets: $2,218,360,379
Liabilities: $1,590,939,301
Net Worth: $627,421,078
Earnings: $75,488,124
Fiscal Year-end: 12/31/22
Real Estate Support Services
N.A.I.C.S.: 531390
Yugan Chen *(Chm)*

SHENZHEN QIANGRUI PRECISION TECHNOLOGY CO., LTD.
Building C Qiaoan Technology Park No 308 Wuhe Avenue Guanhu Street, Longhua District, Shenzhen, 518109, Guangdong, China
Tel.: (86) 75528227752
Web Site: https://www.qiangruivip.com
Year Founded: 2005
301128—(CHIN)
Rev.: $64,109,448
Assets: $138,226,608
Liabilities: $22,545,432
Net Worth: $115,681,176
Earnings: $5,405,400
Emp.: 800
Fiscal Year-end: 12/31/22
Industrial Machinery Mfr & Distr
N.A.I.C.S.: 333248
Gaobin Yin *(Chm)*

SHENZHEN QINGYI PHOTOMASK LTD.
Building QingYi Photoelectric Road Langshang Two, North of High-tech Park, Shenzhen, China
Tel.: (86) 75586352288
Web Site: https://www.supermask.com
Year Founded: 1997
688138—(SHG)
Rev.: $107,006,422
Assets: $244,722,212
Liabilities: $64,760,988
Net Worth: $179,961,224
Earnings: $13,904,037
Fiscal Year-end: 12/31/22
Electronic Products Mfr
N.A.I.C.S.: 334419
Yingmin Tang *(Chm)*

SHENZHEN QIXIN GROUP CO., LTD.
1/F-2/F Jiangnan Mingyuan, Futian District, Shenzhen, 518101, Guangdong, China
Tel.: (86) 7552 532 9819
Web Site: http://www.qxzs.com
002781—(SSE)
Rev.: $323,207,220
Assets: $584,977,229
Liabilities: $366,485,981
Net Worth: $218,491,249
Earnings: ($85,036,146)
Fiscal Year-end: 12/31/20
Housing Construction Services
N.A.I.C.S.: 236116
Hongxiao Ye *(Chm)*

SHENZHEN QUANSINHAO CO., LTD.
6th Floor Ideal Times Building No 8 Meikang Road, Futian District, Shenzhen, 518031, Guangdong, China
Tel.: (86) 13332994828
Web Site: https://www.sz000007.com
Year Founded: 1983
000007—(SSE)
Rev.: $31,005,655
Assets: $49,727,700
Liabilities: $35,367,560
Net Worth: $14,360,140
Earnings: ($752,053)
Fiscal Year-end: 12/31/22
Hotel Operator
N.A.I.C.S.: 721110
Huang Guoming *(Chm)*

SHENZHEN RAPOO TECHNOLOGY CO., LTD.
Floor 56 China Energy Storage Building No 3099 Keyuan South Road, Nanshan District, Shenzhen, 518122, Guangdong, China
Tel.: (86) 75528588566
Web Site: https://www.rapoo.com
Year Founded: 2002
002577—(SSE)
Rev.: $62,828,326
Assets: $170,580,889
Liabilities: $11,821,891
Net Worth: $158,758,999

SHENZHEN RAPOO TECHNOLOGY CO., LTD.

Shenzhen Rapoo Technology Co., Ltd.—(Continued)
Earnings: $5,228,777
Emp.: 2,500
Fiscal Year-end: 12/31/22
Computer Equipment Mfr
N.A.I.C.S.: 334118
Zeng Hao (Chm & Gen Mgr)

SHENZHEN RAYITEK HI-TECH FILM CO., LTD.
Huamei Industrial Park, Songgang Town, Shenzhen, 518105, China
Tel.: (86) 75529712221
Web Site: https://www.rayitek.cn
Year Founded: 2004
688323—(SHG)
Rev.: $42,360,309
Assets: $325,251,567
Liabilities: $180,420,178
Net Worth: $144,831,389
Earnings: $5,457,924
Fiscal Year-end: 12/31/22
Film Material Mfr
N.A.I.C.S.: 325992
Guihong Lan (Chm)

SHENZHEN REFOND OPTO-ELECTRONICS CO. LTD.
Refond Optoelectronics Building Ronghui Road, Guangming District, Shenzhen, China
Tel.: (86) 75529675000
Web Site: https://www.refond.com
Year Founded: 2000
300241—(SSE)
Rev.: $187,543,512
Assets: $511,971,408
Liabilities: $211,383,432
Net Worth: $300,587,976
Earnings: $1,926,288
Emp.: 630
Fiscal Year-end: 12/31/22
LED Component Mfr
N.A.I.C.S.: 334413
Yafang Liu (Sec)

Subsidiaries:

Shenzhen Lingtao Optoelectronics Co., Ltd. (1)
1F Building B15 Hengfeng Industrial Area Baoan District, Shenzhen, China
Tel.: (86) 75527865464
Light Emitting Diode Mfr
N.A.I.C.S.: 334413

Zhejiang Refond Optoelectronics Co., Ltd. (1)
No 505 Haopai Road Suxi Town, Yiwu, Zhejiang, China
Tel.: (86) 57989972688
Light Emitting Diode Mfr
N.A.I.C.S.: 334413

SHENZHEN RIDGE ENGINEERING CONSULTING CO., LTD.
Room A3103 A3103 A3108 Building A No 1 Yabao Road, Bantian Subdistrict Longgang, Shenzhen, 518129, Guangdong, China
Tel.: (86) 75589509995
Web Site: http://www.szridge.com
Year Founded: 2010
300977—(SSE)
Rev.: $80,284,595
Assets: $231,769,386
Liabilities: $37,434,417
Net Worth: $194,334,969
Earnings: $2,201,261
Fiscal Year-end: 12/31/22
Engineeering Services
N.A.I.C.S.: 541330
Wenhong Fan (Chm)

SHENZHEN RILAND INDUSTRY CO., LTD.
4-5th Floor Building B Feiyang Technology, No 8 Longchang Road Baocheng Zone No 67 Baoan District, Shenzhen, 518101, China
Tel.: (86) 75527345888
Web Site: https://www.riland.com.cn
Year Founded: 1993
300154—(CHIN)
Rev.: $150,602,868
Assets: $295,690,824
Liabilities: $55,262,844
Net Worth: $240,427,980
Earnings: $11,731,824
Fiscal Year-end: 12/31/22
Welding & Cutting Machinery Mfr
N.A.I.C.S.: 333992

SHENZHEN RONGDA PHOTOSENSITIVE SCIENCE & TECHNOLOGY CO., LTD.
Floor 1-3 R&D Building of Lixin Lake No 1, Science and Technology Industrial Park Fuyong Town Baoan District, Shenzhen, 518103, China
Tel.: (86) 75527312760
Web Site: https://www.szrd.com
Year Founded: 1996
300576—(SSE)
Rev.: $120,387,822
Assets: $179,923,696
Liabilities: $86,695,411
Net Worth: $93,228,285
Earnings: $6,128,400
Fiscal Year-end: 12/31/21
Printed Circuit Board Mfr & Distr
N.A.I.C.S.: 334412
Haiwang Lin (Board of Directors & Chm)

Subsidiaries:

Huizhou Rongda Ink Co., Ltd. (1)
Haibin City Development Zone, Renshan-Town Huidong Country, Huizhou, 516000, China
Tel.: (86) 7528326622
Photosensitive Chemical Material Mfr
N.A.I.C.S.: 325992

ShenZhen RongDa Photosensitive Science & Technology Co., Ltd. (1)
Quanhong RD Economic Development Zone, Wujiang, 215200, Jiangsu, China
Tel.: (86) 51263021109
Photosensitive Chemical Material Mfr
N.A.I.C.S.: 325992

SHENZHEN RUIHE CONSTRUCTION DECORATION CO., LTD.
Ruihe building No 3027 East Shennan Road, Luohu District, Shenzhen, 518001, Guangdong, China
Tel.: (86) 75533526666
Web Site: https://www.sz-ruihe.com
Year Founded: 1992
002620—(SSE)
Rev.: $301,798,884
Assets: $673,452,075
Liabilities: $549,051,778
Net Worth: $124,400,297
Earnings: $1,350,718
Fiscal Year-end: 12/31/22
Decoration Engineering
N.A.I.C.S.: 541330
Jie Ping Li (Chm)

SHENZHEN SALUBRIS PHARMACEUTICALS CO., LTD.
37F Tower B NEO Building No 6009 Shennan Road, Futian District, Shenzhen, 518040, Guangdong, China
Tel.: (86) 75583867888
Web Site: https://www.salubris.com
Year Founded: 1998
002294—(SSE)
Rev.: $488,874,401
Assets: $1,369,619,073
Liabilities: $249,712,042
Net Worth: $1,119,907,030
Earnings: $89,426,881
Fiscal Year-end: 12/31/22
Pharmaceuticals Mfr
N.A.I.C.S.: 325412
Ye Yuxiang (Chm)

Subsidiaries:

Salubris (Suzhou) Pharmaceuticals Co., Ltd. (1)
No 1 Mengxi Road Biomedical Industrial Park, Taicang, Shenzhen, China
Tel.: (86) 51282787998
Disease Research Organization Services
N.A.I.C.S.: 813212

Splendris Pharmaceuticals GmbH (1)
Frankfurter Strasse 39, 63303, Dreieich, Germany
Tel.: (49) 61038705340
Web Site: http://www.splendris-pharmaceuticals.de
Pharmaceuticals Product Mfr
N.A.I.C.S.: 325412

SHENZHEN SDG INFORMATION CO., LTD.
18th Floor Building B Special Information Port Building Kefeng Road, Central District High-tech Zone Nanshan District, Shenzhen, 518057, Guangdong, China
Tel.: (86) 75526506800
Web Site: https://www.sdgicable.com
Year Founded: 1997
000070—(SSE)
Rev.: $588,502,212
Assets: $1,105,372,443
Liabilities: $773,201,487
Net Worth: $332,170,956
Earnings: $1,863,501
Fiscal Year-end: 12/31/22
Optical Cables & Optical Transmission Equipment Mfr & Sales
N.A.I.C.S.: 335921
Gao Tianliang (Chm)

Subsidiaries:

Guangxi JICON Electronics Co., Ltd. (1)
W1-B1 Hi & New-tech Zone South, 518057, Shenzhen, China
Tel.: (86) 75526520550
Optical Fiber Cable Mfr
N.A.I.C.S.: 335921

Shenzhen SDGI Optical Fiber Co., Ltd. (1)
No 10 Langshan First Road the Fifth Industrial Zone Nanshan District, 518057, Shenzhen, China
Tel.: (86) 75526891288
Optical Fiber Cable Mfr
N.A.I.C.S.: 335921

SHENZHEN SDG SERVICE CO., LTD.
5th Floor Tefa Cultural & Creative Plaza No 1010 Qiaoxiang Road, Xiangmihu Street Futian, Shenzhen, 518000, Guangdong, China
Tel.: (86) 75583075915
Web Site: http://www.tefafuwu.com
Year Founded: 1993
300917—(SSE)
Rev.: $281,584,597
Assets: $215,889,205
Liabilities: $80,072,072
Net Worth: $135,817,133
Earnings: $16,003,859
Emp.: 12,000
Fiscal Year-end: 12/31/22
Property Management Services
N.A.I.C.S.: 531311
Baojie Chen (Chm)

SHENZHEN SEA STAR TECHNOLOGY CO., LTD.
Rm 2801 Block A Xinhao E Du Building Caitian Rd, Futian District, Shenzhen, 518116, China
Tel.: (86) 75586001058 CN
Web Site: https://www.zg-seastar.com
Year Founded: 1998
002137—(SSE)
Rev.: $89,613,656
Assets: $271,892,182
Liabilities: $53,955,215
Net Worth: $217,936,967
Earnings: $20,244,880
Emp.: 724
Fiscal Year-end: 12/31/22
Electronic Products Mfr
N.A.I.C.S.: 335131
Chen Yamei (Founder & Chm)

SHENZHEN SED INDUSTRY CO., LTD.
Floors 15-17 SED Technology Building No 1 Keji Road Technology Park, Nanshan District, Shenzhen, 518057, Guangdong, China
Tel.: (86) 75586316073
Web Site: http://www.sedind.com
Year Founded: 1993
000032—(SSE)
Rev.: $7,167,689,722
Assets: $7,418,794,098
Liabilities: $5,997,102,560
Net Worth: $1,421,691,537
Earnings: ($22,780,560)
Emp.: 24,000
Fiscal Year-end: 12/31/22
Electronic Components Mfr
N.A.I.C.S.: 335311
Si Yuncong (Chm)

SHENZHEN SEG GROUP CO., LTD.
31/F Tower A Qunxing Square Huaqiang North Road, Futian District, Shenzhen, 518028, China
Tel.: (86) 755 8374 7939 CN
Web Site: http://www.shic.com
Year Founded: 1984
Holding Company
N.A.I.C.S.: 551112
Li Wang (Gen Mgr)

Subsidiaries:

Shenzhen SEG Co., Ltd. (1)
31F Block A Qunxing Plaza Huaqiang North Road, Futian District, Shenzhen, 518028, China (30.24%)
Tel.: (86) 75583747939
Web Site: https://www.segcl.com.cn
Rev.: $256,764,068
Assets: $746,751,293
Liabilities: $402,458,439
Net Worth: $344,292,853
Earnings: $2,214,993
Fiscal Year-end: 12/31/2022
Electronics Components & Systems Mfr
N.A.I.C.S.: 334419
Zhang Liang (Chm)

Affiliate (Domestic):

Shenzhen Huakong SEG Co., Ltd. (2)
No 23 Lanzhu East Road Grand Industrial Zone, Shenzhen, 518118, China (22.45%)
Tel.: (86) 75589938888
Rev.: $155,646,008
Assets: $605,015,050
Net Worth: $59,484,054
Earnings: ($30,559,057)
Emp.: 372
Fiscal Year-end: 12/31/2022
Electronics Glass Bulbs Mfr
N.A.I.C.S.: 327215

Shenzhen SEG Hi-tech Industrial Co., Ltd. (1)
3/F Multifunctional Building Section D yitian Garden Fuqiang Road, Futian District, Shenzhen, 518038, China

Tel.: (86) 755 82842666
Web Site: www.shic.com
Electronic Parts Mfr & Whslr
N.A.I.C.S.: 423690

SHENZHEN SENIOR TECHNOLOGY MTRL CO LTD
Tianyuan Road Gongming Town, Guangming District, Shenzhen, 518106, China
Tel.: (86) 75536800999
Web Site: https://www.senior798.com
Year Founded: 2003
300568—(CHIN)
Rev.: $424,413,981
Assets: $2,527,617,985
Liabilities: $1,124,924,301
Net Worth: $1,402,693,684
Earnings: $81,176,080
Fiscal Year-end: 12/31/23
Lithium-Ion Battery Separator Mfr & Distr
N.A.I.C.S.: 335910
Xiufeng Chen *(Chm)*

Subsidiaries:

Changzhou senior new energy Material Co., Ltd. (1)
No 888 Xingdong Road, Changzhou, China
Tel.: (86) 51983593999
Lithium Battery Mfr & Distr
N.A.I.C.S.: 335910

SHENZHEN SILVER BASIS TECHNOLOGY CO., LTD.
603/606 No 1 Tangkeng Intersection Baoshi East Road Guantian Community, Shiyan Street Baoan District, Shenzhen, 518108, China
Tel.: (86) 75527642891
Web Site: https://www.silverbasis.com
Year Founded: 2000
002786—(SSE)
Rev.: $364,619,291
Assets: $562,564,169
Liabilities: $528,717,211
Net Worth: $33,846,958
Earnings: ($36,187,215)
Fiscal Year-end: 12/31/22
Automotive Components Mfr
N.A.I.C.S.: 336320
He Fei *(Chm)*

Subsidiaries:

Silver Basis (HongKong) Investment Development Co., Ltd. (1)
Rm 1733 17/F Star House 3 Salisbury Road, Tim Sha Tsui, Kowloon, China (Hong Kong)
Tel.: (852) 34602673
Automobile Parts Mfr
N.A.I.C.S.: 336390

Silver Basis Engineering Germany Gmbh (1)
Bockenheimer Landstrasse 17/19, 60325, Frankfurt am Main, Germany
Tel.: (49) 1755003227
Mold Mfr
N.A.I.C.S.: 333511
Hans-Juergen Krug *(VP)*

SHENZHEN SINE ELECTRIC CO., LTD.
Floor 5 Workshop No 7 Antuoshan High-tech Industrial Park, Shaer Community Shajing Street Baoan District, Shenzhen, China
Tel.: (86) 13243787735
Web Site: https://www.sineedrive.com
Year Founded: 2003
688395—(SHG)
Rev.: $48,790,727
Assets: $110,813,003
Liabilities: $14,961,319
Net Worth: $95,851,684
Earnings: $6,433,732
Fiscal Year-end: 12/31/22
Electrical Equipment Mfr & Distr
N.A.I.C.S.: 335999
Conghuan Tu *(Chm & Gen Mgr)*

SHENZHEN SINEXCEL ELECTRIC CO., LTD.
1002 Songbai Rd, Nanshan, Shenzhen, 518000, China
Tel.: (86) 75586511588
Web Site: https://www.sinexcel.com
Year Founded: 2007
300693—(CHIN)
Rev.: $373,389,702
Assets: $471,525,320
Liabilities: $266,543,934
Net Worth: $204,981,385
Earnings: $56,738,211
Emp.: 800
Fiscal Year-end: 12/31/23
Power Electronic Equipment Mfr & Distr
N.A.I.C.S.: 335999
Xing Fang *(Chm, Pres & Gen Mgr)*

SHENZHEN SINOVATIO TECHNOLOGY CO., LTD.
Room 1403 Building A National Engineering Laboratory Building, Gaoxin South 7th Road Nanshan District, Shenzhen, China
Tel.: (86) 4001008102
Web Site: https://www.sinovatio.com
Year Founded: 2003
002912—(SSE)
Rev.: $61,183,063
Assets: $275,813,722
Liabilities: $57,102,912
Net Worth: $218,710,810
Earnings: ($17,137,519)
Emp.: 1,000
Fiscal Year-end: 12/31/22
Network System Development Services
N.A.I.C.S.: 541512
Li Shouyu *(Chm)*

SHENZHEN SKING INTELLIGENT EQUIPMENT CO., LTD.
10th to 11th floors Block B, Specialized and Special New Headquarters Base, Shenzhen, 518103, Guangdong, China
Tel.: (86) 75527889869
Web Site: https://www.szskd.com
Year Founded: 2004
688328—(SHG)
Rev.: $82,669,486
Assets: $253,765,587
Liabilities: $140,750,186
Net Worth: $113,015,401
Earnings: ($5,032,385)
Fiscal Year-end: 12/31/22
Electronic Product Mfr & Distr
N.A.I.C.S.: 334419
Yihong Huang *(Chm & Gen Mgr)*

SHENZHEN SKYWORTH DIGITAL TECHNOLOGY CO., LTD.
Unit A 14F Skyworth Bldg Gaoxin Ave 1 S, Nanshan, Shenzhen, 518057, China
Tel.: (86) 75526010018
Web Site: http://www.skyworthdigital.com
Year Founded: 1988
000810—(SSE)
Rev.: $1,686,004,843
Assets: $1,517,736,636
Liabilities: $673,386,677
Net Worth: $844,349,959
Earnings: $115,554,549
Fiscal Year-end: 12/31/22
Digital Marketing Services
N.A.I.C.S.: 541870

Weide Lai *(Chm)*

SHENZHEN SOLING INDUSTRIAL CO., LTD.
28/F Block B Dachong Business Center, Nanshan District, Shenzhen, China
Tel.: (86) 75586702766
Web Site: http://www.szsoling.com
Year Founded: 1997
Sales Range: $100-124.9 Million
Audio & Video Equipment Mfr
N.A.I.C.S.: 334310
Xingyi Xiao *(Chm)*

SHENZHEN SONGXIN SPORTS PRODUCTS CO., LTD.
No 30 Cuibao Road, Baolong Industry Area, Longgang District, Shenzhen, Guangdong, China
Tel.: (86) 13923486636 CN
Web Site: https://szsongx.com
Swimming & Diving Products Mfr & Whslr
N.A.I.C.S.: 339920

SHENZHEN SOSEN ELECTRONICS CO., LTD.
10F Pengzhanhui No 1 Building Zhongxin Road, No 233 Xinqiao Street Baoan District, Shenzhen, 518104, China
Tel.: (86) 75529358806
Web Site: https://www.szsosen.com
Year Founded: 2011
301002—(SSE)
Rev.: $104,451,338
Assets: $228,155,251
Liabilities: $109,152,632
Net Worth: $119,002,619
Earnings: $10,944,784
Emp.: 1,400
Fiscal Year-end: 12/31/22
Electronic Product Mfr & Distr
N.A.I.C.S.: 334419
Nianbin Tian *(Chm)*

SHENZHEN SPECIAL ECONOMIC ZONE REAL ESTATE AND PROPERTIES (GROUP) CO., LTD.
47F Shenfang Square Renmin South Road, Shenzhen, 518001, Guangdong, China
Tel.: (86) 75525108837
Web Site: http://www.sfjt.com.cn
Year Founded: 1993
200029—(SSE)
Rev.: $89,067,598
Assets: $798,843,680
Liabilities: $197,013,211
Net Worth: $601,830,469
Earnings: $21,582,120
Fiscal Year-end: 12/31/22
Real Estate Support Services
N.A.I.C.S.: 531390
Tang Xiaoping *(Chm & Gen Mgr)*

SHENZHEN STOCK EXCHANGE
2012 Shennan Blvd, Futian District, Shenzhen, 518038, China
Tel.: (86) 75588668888
Web Site: http://www.szse.cn
Year Founded: 1990
Sales Range: $200-249.9 Million
Emp.: 300
Stock Exchange Services
N.A.I.C.S.: 523210
Peng Ming *(VP)*

Subsidiaries:

Shenzhen Securities Information Co., Ltd. (1)
First Floor 203 Building Shangbu Industrial Zone Hongli West Road, Futian, Shenzhen, 518028, China
Tel.: (86) 755 8324 7239
Web Site: http://www.cninfo.com.cn
Securities Information Services
N.A.I.C.S.: 519290

SHENZHEN STRONGTEAM DECORATION ENGINEERING CO., LTD.
8F Block C Shenye Tairan Building Tairan 8th Road, Chegongmiao Futian District, Shenzhen, 518000, China
Tel.: (86) 75583475153
Web Site: https://www.ztjzgf.net
Year Founded: 2000
002989—(SSE)
Rev.: $279,782,605
Assets: $508,776,143
Liabilities: $261,169,609
Net Worth: $247,606,534
Earnings: $9,455,898
Fiscal Year-end: 12/31/22
Engineeering Services
N.A.I.C.S.: 541330
Rongjian Qiao *(Board of Directors & Chm)*

SHENZHEN SUNLINE TECH CO., LTD.
5F Building 2-A Zone I Shenzhen Bay Technology & Ecological Park, West Shahe Road Nanshan District, Shenzhen, 518057, China
Tel.: (86) 75586168118
Web Site: https://www.sunline.cn
300348—(CHIN)
Rev.: $264,965,688
Assets: $348,446,124
Liabilities: $138,354,372
Net Worth: $210,091,752
Earnings: $3,149,172
Emp.: 6,000
Fiscal Year-end: 12/31/22
Software & Hardware Computer Integration
N.A.I.C.S.: 513210
Changchun Wang *(Chm)*

Subsidiaries:

PT Sunline Master International (1)
Wisma Nugra Santana 11th Floor Jl Jend Sudirman Kav 7-8, Karet Tengsin Tanah Abang, Jakarta, 10220, Indonesia
Tel.: (62) 21 570 4911
Software & Technology Services
N.A.I.C.S.: 541511

ProSticks.com Limited (1)
11th Floor Baoji Building 156-157 Connaught Road Central, Hong Kong, Sheung Wan, China (Hong Kong)
Tel.: (852) 28668635
Web Site: http://www.prosticks.com.hk
Software Development Services
N.A.I.C.S.: 513210

Sunline Holding (HK) Limited (1)
9/F Hong Kong and Macau Building 156-157 Connaught Rd Central, Sheung Wan, China (Hong Kong)
Tel.: (852) 228668630
Software Development Services
N.A.I.C.S.: 513210

Sunline Technology (Malaysia) Sdn Bhd (1)
Level 29-15 and 16 Menara Q Sentral No 2A Jalan Stesen Sentral 2, KL Sentral, 50470, Kuala Lumpur, Malaysia
Tel.: (60) 32 720 1288
Software & Technology Services
N.A.I.C.S.: 541511

Sunline Technology (Thailand) Limited (1)
98 Sathorn Square Building 37Fl Office 3711 North Sathorn Road Silom, Bangrak, Bangkok, 10500, Thailand
Tel.: (66) 2 105 6443

SHENZHEN SUNLINE TECH CO., LTD.

Shenzhen Sunline Tech Co., Ltd.—(Continued)
Software & Technology Services
N.A.I.C.S.: 541511

SHENZHEN SUNLORD ELECTRONICS CO., LTD.
Sunlord Industrial Park Dafuyuan Guanlan, Longhua District, Shenzhen, Guangdong, China
Tel.: (86) 75529832333
Web Site: https://www.sunlordinc.com
Year Founded: 2000
002138—(SSE)
Rev.: $595,044,642
Assets: $1,535,758,577
Liabilities: $679,359,615
Net Worth: $856,398,961
Earnings: $60,800,543
Emp.: 2,000
Fiscal Year-end: 12/31/22
Electronic Components Mfr
N.A.I.C.S.: 334416
Yuan Jinyu (Chm)

Subsidiaries:

Dongguan Surpass Structure Ceramics Co., Ltd. (1)
Sunlord Industrial Park 28th Tangqing West Road Shitanpu, Tangxia Town, Dongguan, Guangdong, China
Tel.: (86) 76938808000
Web Site: https://www.sgcera.com
Chip Electronic Component Mfr
N.A.I.C.S.: 334413

Guiyang Sunlord Xunda Electronics Co., Ltd. (1)
Shawen Ecological Science and Technology Industrial Park, New and High-tech Development Zone Baiyun District, Guiyang, Guizhou, China
Tel.: (86) 85184470023
Chip Electronic Component Mfr
N.A.I.C.S.: 334413

Quzhou Sunlord Electronics Co., Ltd. (1)
No 1 Zhongguancun Avenue Green Industry Cluster, Quzhou, Zhejiang, China
Tel.: (86) 18892698518
Chip Electronic Component Mfr
N.A.I.C.S.: 334413

Sunlord Electronics Japan LLC (1)
1-22-14 Niijuku, Katsushika Ku, Tokyo, 116-0014, Japan
Tel.: (81) 9089616688
Chip Electronic Component Mfr
N.A.I.C.S.: 334413

Sunlord Electronics Taiwan, Inc. (1)
1/F No 15 Lane 35 Lixin 3rd Street, Xinzhuang District, New Taipei City, Taiwan
Tel.: (886) 918270
Chip Electronic Component Mfr
N.A.I.C.S.: 334413

Sunlord Electronics USA, Inc. (1)
2060 Walsh Ave Ste 128, Santa Clara, CA 95050
Tel.: (669) 588-6786
Chip Electronic Component Mfr
N.A.I.C.S.: 334413

SHENZHEN SUNMOON MICROELECTRONICS CO., LTD.
11F Guoshi Building No 1801 Shahe West Road, Gaoxin District Yuehai Street Nanshan District, Shenzhen, 518057, Guangdong, China
Tel.: (86) 75526983905
Web Site: https://www.chinaasic.com
Year Founded: 2003
688699—(SHG)
Rev.: $96,120,072
Assets: $241,480,320
Liabilities: $27,119,973
Net Worth: $214,360,347
Earnings: $1,492,101
Fiscal Year-end: 12/31/22
Electronic Product Mfr & Distr

N.A.I.C.S.: 334419
Lekang Wang (Chm)

SHENZHEN SUNNYPOL OPTO-ELECTRONICS CO., LTD.
No 246 Gongchang Road Xinhu Street, Guangming District, Shenzhen, China
Tel.: (86) 75536676888
Web Site: https://www.sunnypol.com
Year Founded: 2007
002876—(SSE)
Rev.: $305,162,629
Assets: $532,499,348
Liabilities: $204,686,254
Net Worth: $327,813,094
Earnings: $28,981,551
Fiscal Year-end: 12/31/22
Electronic Parts Mfr & Distr
N.A.I.C.S.: 334516
Zhang Jianjun (Chm & Gen Mgr)

SHENZHEN SUNRISE NEW ENERGY CO., LTD.
No 01-06 34F Block B Building 12, Shenzhen Bay Science & Technology Ecological Park Nanshan District, Shenzhen, 518063, Guangdong, China
Tel.: (86) 75586922886
Web Site: http://en.szsunrisene.com
Year Founded: 1995
002256—(SSE)
Rev.: $42,305,707
Assets: $275,409,422
Liabilities: $102,222,895
Net Worth: $173,206,706
Earnings: ($3,183,612)
Fiscal Year-end: 12/31/22
Solar Electricity Generating Equipment Mfr
N.A.I.C.S.: 221114
Li Huachun (Chm)

SHENZHEN SUNSHINE LASER & ELECTRONICS TECHNOLOGY CO., LTD.
1/F Block C Unisplendour Information Harbor No 13 Langshan Road, Hi-tech Industry Park North Nanshan District, Shenzhen, 518057, China
Tel.: (86) 75526981000
Web Site: https://www.sunshine-laser.com
Year Founded: 1998
300227—(CHIN)
Rev.: $144,592,344
Assets: $358,323,264
Liabilities: $135,373,680
Net Worth: $222,949,584
Earnings: $11,236,212
Emp.: 490
Fiscal Year-end: 12/31/22
Semiconductor Machinery Mfr
N.A.I.C.S.: 333242
Hou Ruohong (Chm & Gen Mgr)

Subsidiaries:

Shenzhen Sunshine Laser Technology Ltd. (1)
1/F Block C Unisplendour Information Harbor NO 13 Langshan Road, Hi-tech Industry Park Nanshan District, Shenzhen, 518057, China
Tel.: (86) 75526981000
Web Site: http://sunshine-laser.com
Laser Cutting Equipment Distr
N.A.I.C.S.: 423830

SHENZHEN SUNWAY COMMUNICATION CO., LTD.
Floor 1-3 Building A SDG Info-Port No 2 Kefeng Road, High-Tech Park Nanshan District, Shenzhen, China
Tel.: (86) 75581773388 CN

Web Site: https://www.sz-sunway.com.cn
Year Founded: 2006
300136—(CHIN)
Rev.: $1,206,024,768
Assets: $1,712,082,528
Liabilities: $778,314,420
Net Worth: $933,768,108
Earnings: $91,033,956
Emp.: 10,000
Fiscal Year-end: 12/31/22
Telecommunication Equipment Mfr & Distr
N.A.I.C.S.: 334290
Peng Hao (Chm & Gen Mgr)

Subsidiaries:

Sunway Techtronic Communication Technology (Beijing) Co Ltd. (1)
No 14 Jinxiu St Beijing Economic Technology Development Zone, Beijing, 100176, China
Tel.: (86) 10 5933 3659
Web Site: http://www.sz-sunway.com
Electronic Equipment Mfr & Distr
N.A.I.C.S.: 334419

SHENZHEN SUNWIN INTELLIGENT CO., LTD.
A101-15 F Saiwei building 8 LIANLI East Road xialilang community, Nanshan District, Shenzhen, China
Tel.: (86) 75586169696
Web Site: https://www.szsunwin.com
300044—(CHIN)
Rev.: $54,225,288
Assets: $274,724,892
Liabilities: $162,302,400
Net Worth: $112,422,492
Earnings: ($31,797,792)
Fiscal Year-end: 12/31/22
Automatic Ticket Selling, Checking, Communication, Security, Passenger Information & Monitoring Systems Mfr
N.A.I.C.S.: 334419

Subsidiaries:

Hefei Sunwin Intelligent Co., Ltd (1)
NO 666 ChuangXin Road High -tech Zone, Hefei, 230022, China
Tel.: (86) 5516 271 7710
Web Site: https://www.siwill.com
Aviation Drone Mfr & Distr
N.A.I.C.S.: 336411

SHENZHEN SUNXING LIGHT ALLOY MATERIALS, CO., LTD.
1404 Zhongguo Youse Bldg 6013 Shennan Road, Shenzhen, China
Tel.: (86) 75529891365 CN
Web Site: https://www.stalloys.com
Year Founded: 1992
603978—(SHG)
Rev.: $214,012,099
Assets: $447,748,966
Liabilities: $204,532,572
Net Worth: $243,216,394
Earnings: ($6,751,120)
Fiscal Year-end: 12/31/22
Light Alloy Material Mfr & Distr
N.A.I.C.S.: 331313

SHENZHEN SUNYES ELECTRONIC MANUFACTURING HOLDING CO., LTD.
3/F Building One Excellence Meilin Central Plaza Zhongkang Rd, Futian District, Shenzhen, 518026, China
Tel.: (86) 75523818612
Web Site: http://www.sunyes.cn
Year Founded: 2003
002388—(SSE)
Rev.: $253,756,910
Assets: $356,644,628
Liabilities: $151,005,339
Net Worth: $205,639,289
Earnings: $3,440,699

INTERNATIONAL PUBLIC

Emp.: 650
Fiscal Year-end: 12/31/22
Electronic Products & Systems Mfr
N.A.I.C.S.: 334419

SHENZHEN SUOXINDA DATA TECHNOLOGY CO., LTD.
Floor 9 Building B Tongfang Information Port No 11 Langshan Road, Nanshan, Shenzhen, China
Tel.: (86) 4008880039 Ky
Web Site: https://www.datamargin.com
Year Founded: 2004
3680—(HKG)
Rev.: $57,779,474
Assets: $62,951,384
Liabilities: $47,092,158
Net Worth: $15,859,227
Earnings: ($19,001,411)
Emp.: 770
Fiscal Year-end: 12/31/22
Holding Company
N.A.I.C.S.: 551112
Xulang Chen (Chm)

SHENZHEN TAGEN GROUP CO., LTD.
19th Floor Tianjian Business Building No 7019 Hongli Road, Zijing Community Lianhua Street Futian District, Shenzhen, 518034, Guangdong, China
Tel.: (86) 75582550846
Web Site: https://www.tagen.cn
000090—(SSE)
Rev.: $3,715,544,786
Assets: $9,716,481,207
Liabilities: $7,738,494,922
Net Worth: $1,977,986,285
Earnings: $273,757,648
Emp.: 14,000
Fiscal Year-end: 12/31/22
Construction Engineering Services
N.A.I.C.S.: 541330
Han Dehong (Chm)

SHENZHEN TECHWINSEMI TECHNOLOGY CO., LTD.
Room 2301 2401 2501 Building 1 No 136 Shangmeilin Zhongkang Road, Shenzhen New Generation Industrial Park Futian District, Shenzhen, 518000, China
Tel.: (86) 75523576651
Web Site: https://twsc.com.cn
Year Founded: 2008
001309—(SSE)
Rev.: $244,370,378
Assets: $452,464,629
Liabilities: $297,904,113
Net Worth: $154,560,515
Earnings: $3,439,861
Emp.: 500
Fiscal Year-end: 12/31/23
Semiconductor Product Mfr
N.A.I.C.S.: 334413
Hu Li (Chm)

SHENZHEN TELLUS HOLDING CO., LTD.
3rd & 4th Floor Teli Building Shuibei 2nd Road, Luohu District, Shenzhen, 518031, China
Tel.: (86) 75583989333
Web Site: https://www.tellus.cn
Year Founded: 1986
000025—(SSE)
Rev.: $117,606,945
Assets: $313,376,815
Liabilities: $80,842,446
Net Worth: $232,534,369
Earnings: $11,722,852
Fiscal Year-end: 12/31/22
Automotive Distr
N.A.I.C.S.: 423110

Fu Chunlong *(Chm & Sec-Party)*

SHENZHEN TEXTILE (HOLDINGS) CO., LTD.
6/F Shenfang Building 3 Huaqiang North Road, Futian District, Shenzhen, 518031, Guangdong, China
Tel.: (86) 75583776043
Web Site: http://www.chinasthc.com
Year Founded: 1994
200045—(SSE)
Rev.: $398,453,557
Assets: $788,646,091
Liabilities: $222,687,752
Net Worth: $565,958,339
Earnings: $10,292,612
Fiscal Year-end: 12/31/22
Textile Garment Mfr
N.A.I.C.S.: 315250
Yin Kefei *(Chm)*

SHENZHEN TIANYUAN DIC INFORMATION TECHNOLOGY CO., LTD.
Guangdong Floor A24-25 Chuangzhi Cloud Center No 1 Guangxia Road, Futian District, Shenzhen, 518057, China
Tel.: (86) 75526745688
Web Site: https://www.tydic.com
Year Founded: 1993
300047—(CHIN)
Rev.: $799,221,384
Assets: $917,290,764
Liabilities: $419,586,804
Net Worth: $497,703,960
Earnings: $4,575,636
Emp.: 930
Fiscal Year-end: 12/31/22
Computer System Design Services
N.A.I.C.S.: 541512
Chen You *(Chm & Gen Mgr)*

SHENZHEN TONGYE TECHNOLOGY CO., LTD.
101 Building 3 Meitai Industrial Park No 1231 Guangguan Road, Guihua Community Guanlan Street Longhua District, Shenzhen, 518110, China
Tel.: (86) 75528083364
Web Site: https://www.sz-tongye.com.cn
Year Founded: 2000
300960—(SSE)
Rev.: $41,497,228
Assets: $126,485,560
Liabilities: $36,734,214
Net Worth: $89,751,346
Earnings: $4,128,701
Fiscal Year-end: 12/31/22
Electrical Equipment Mfr & Distr
N.A.I.C.S.: 335999
Jianying Xu *(Chm)*

SHENZHEN TONGYI INDUSTRY CO., LTD.
Baohuasen International Center, Xixiang Baoan District, Shenzhen, 518126, China
Tel.: (86) 75527872397 CN
Web Site: https://www.tongyiplastic.com
Year Founded: 1998
300538—(CHIN)
Rev.: $458,649,616
Assets: $328,709,209
Liabilities: $175,837,901
Net Worth: $152,871,308
Earnings: $3,668,509
Fiscal Year-end: 12/31/23
Engineering Plastic Distr
N.A.I.C.S.: 424610
Yunan Shao *(Chm)*

Subsidiaries:

Suzhou Chuangyi Plastic Co., Ltd (1)
3rd Floor Building 2 No 32 Tongyuan Road Suzhou Industrial Park, Suzhou, China
Tel.: (86) 51262925877
Light Emitting Diode Product Mfr & Distr
N.A.I.C.S.: 334413

SHENZHEN TOPBAND CO., LTD.
Topband Industrial Park Tangtou Avenue Shiyan Town, Banan District, Shenzhen, 518108, China
Tel.: (86) 75527651888
Web Site: https://www.topband-e.com
Year Founded: 1996
002139—(SSE)
Rev.: $1,246,063,914
Assets: $1,455,183,775
Liabilities: $637,802,493
Net Worth: $817,381,282
Earnings: $81,804,804
Emp.: 3,200
Fiscal Year-end: 12/31/22
Electronic Products Mfr
N.A.I.C.S.: 334419
Yongqiang Wu *(Chm & Gen Mgr)*

Subsidiaries:

Topband India Private Limited (1)
No 401 Konarak Epitome Viman Nagar, Pune, 411014, Maharashtra, India
Tel.: (91) 2065206668
Electronic Product Distr
N.A.I.C.S.: 423690

SHENZHEN TOPWAY VIDEO COMMUNICATION CO., LTD.
No 6001 Caitian Road, Futian District, Shenzhen, 518036, Guangdong, China
Tel.: (86) 75583066888
Web Site: https://www.topway.com.cn
Year Founded: 1995
002238—(SSE)
Rev.: $211,293,464
Assets: $566,668,257
Liabilities: $234,178,650
Net Worth: $332,489,608
Earnings: $15,420,160
Fiscal Year-end: 12/31/22
Television Program Broadcasting Services
N.A.I.C.S.: 516120
Zhang Yumin *(Chm)*

SHENZHEN TRANSSION HOLDINGS CO., LTD.
T33 Full Time Center Number 8 Xianyuan Rd, Xili Sub-district Nanshan District, Shenzhen, 518057, China
Tel.: (86) 75533979200
Web Site: https://www.transsion.com
Year Founded: 2013
688036—(SHG)
Rev.: $8,746,200,703
Assets: $6,475,388,470
Liabilities: $3,923,356,793
Net Worth: $2,552,031,678
Earnings: $777,401,146
Fiscal Year-end: 12/31/23
Holding Company
N.A.I.C.S.: 551112
Zhu Zhaojiang *(Chm & Gen Mgr)*

SHENZHEN TVT DIGITAL TECHNOLOGY CO., LTD.
23 Floor Block B4 Building No 9 Shenzhen Bay Eco-Technology Park, Nanshan District, Shenzhen, 518057, Guangdong, China
Tel.: (86) 75536995888
Web Site: https://www.tvt.net.cn
Year Founded: 2004
002835—(SSE)
Rev.: $136,283,458
Assets: $179,933,664
Liabilities: $50,237,128
Net Worth: $129,696,536
Earnings: $15,365,095
Fiscal Year-end: 12/31/22
Camera Mfr & Distr
N.A.I.C.S.: 334220
Guo Lizhi *(Chm & Gen Mgr)*

Subsidiaries:

Shenzhen TVT Digital Technology Co., Ltd. - Shenzhen Factory (1)
Building C Huilong Industrial Park Shilongzai Shiyan Street, Bao'an District, Shenzhen, Guangdong, China
Tel.: (86) 75533086095
Closed Circuit Television Equipment Mfr
N.A.I.C.S.: 334220

SHENZHEN TXD TECHNOLOGY CO LTD
14-16F Building 2 Phase 1 Zhijie Yinxing High tech Industrial Park, Guanlan Street Longhua District, Shenzhen, China
Tel.: (86) 75528065632
Web Site: https://www.txdkj.com
Year Founded: 2004
002845—(SSE)
Rev.: $1,181,994,409
Assets: $1,031,242,366
Liabilities: $658,197,685
Net Worth: $373,044,681
Earnings: ($5,641,370)
Fiscal Year-end: 12/31/22
Liquid Crystal Display Mfr & Distr
N.A.I.C.S.: 334419
Chen Li *(Sec)*

Subsidiaries:

Ganzhou Tongxingda Electronic Technology Co., Ltd. (1)
No 168 Weiyi Road Ganzhou Economic and Technological Development Zone, Ganzhou, Jiangxi, China
Tel.: (86) 7978486662
Electric Equipment Mfr
N.A.I.C.S.: 334419

Nanchang Tongxingda Intelligent Display Co., Ltd. (1)
Room 420 Office Building, Nanchang Economic and Technological Development Zone Minqiao Town, Nanchang, Jiangxi, China
Tel.: (86) 79186802845
Electric Equipment Mfr
N.A.I.C.S.: 334419

Nanchang Tongxingda Precision Optoelectronics Co., Ltd. (1)
Room 419 Office Building, Nanchang Economic and Technological Development Zone, Nanchang, Jiangxi, China
Tel.: (86) 79186802845
Electric Equipment Mfr
N.A.I.C.S.: 334419

Tongxingda (Hong Kong) Trading Co., Ltd. (1)
10th Floor Block A Yijing Center Wang Kwong Road No 1, Kowloon Bay, China (Hong Kong)
Tel.: (852) 25926208
Electric Equipment Mfr
N.A.I.C.S.: 334419

SHENZHEN UNITED WINNERS LASER CO., LTD.
101 Building 1 No 6352 Pingshan Boulevard Shatian Community, Kengzi Sub-District Pingshan District, Shenzhen, China
Tel.: (86) 75526415405
Web Site: https://www.uwlaser.com
Year Founded: 2005
688518—(SHG)
Rev.: $396,265,830
Assets: $794,835,091
Liabilities: $544,876,029
Net Worth: $249,959,062
Earnings: $37,478,474
Fiscal Year-end: 12/31/22
Welding Equipment Mfr
N.A.I.C.S.: 333992
Jinlong Han *(Chm)*

SHENZHEN UNIVERSE (GROUP) CO., LTD.
10F Dongwu Business Mansion, Shenzhen, 518057, Guangdong, China
Tel.: (86) 75586154212
Web Site: http://www.sztiandi.com
000023—(SSE)
Rev.: $50,970,479
Assets: $212,605,726
Liabilities: $177,612,037
Net Worth: $34,993,689
Earnings: ($38,009,186)
Fiscal Year-end: 12/31/22
Concrete & Construction Material Mfr
N.A.I.C.S.: 327331

SHENZHEN URBAN TRANSPORT PLANNING CENTER CO., LTD.
Building 1 Headquarters Building Longhua Design Industrial Park, Beizhan Community Minzhi Street Longhua District, Shenzhen, 518000, Guangdong, China
Tel.: (86) 75586729876
Web Site: https://www.sutpc.com
Year Founded: 2008
301091—(CHIN)
Rev.: $172,102,320
Assets: $433,875,312
Liabilities: $126,758,736
Net Worth: $307,116,576
Earnings: $22,515,948
Fiscal Year-end: 12/31/22
Transportation Services
N.A.I.C.S.: 483211
Tao Lin *(Chm)*

SHENZHEN UROVO TECHNOLOGY CO., LTD.
36F High Tech Zone Union Tower No 63 Xuefu Road Nanshan District, Shenzhen, China
Web Site: http://www.urovo.com
300531—(CHIN)
Rev.: $178,561,179
Assets: $330,259,404
Liabilities: $112,218,716
Net Worth: $218,040,687
Earnings: ($23,498,724)
Emp.: 1,300
Fiscal Year-end: 12/31/23
Mobile Application Development Services
N.A.I.C.S.: 513210
Guo Song *(Co-CEO)*

SHENZHEN V&T TECHNOLOGIES CO., LTD.
Block 2 Zhiyan Innovation Building, Tianliao Community Yutang Street Guangming District, Shenzhen, 518107, China
Tel.: (86) 75526580810
Web Site: https://www.v-t.net.cn
Year Founded: 2006
300484—(CHIN)
Rev.: $62,747,596
Assets: $138,709,387
Liabilities: $42,434,664
Net Worth: $96,274,723
Earnings: $11,746,889
Emp.: 600
Fiscal Year-end: 12/31/22
Industrial Control Equipment Mfr
N.A.I.C.S.: 335314
Qiu Wenyuan *(Chm & Gen Mgr)*

SHENZHEN VITAL NEW MATERIAL CO., LTD.
No 18 Shuitian 1st Road Tongle Community Baolong Street, Long-

Shenzhen Vital New Material Co., Ltd.—(Continued)
gang District, Shenzhen, 518116, Guangdong, China
Tel.: (86) 75561863003
Web Site: https://www.szvital.com
Year Founded: 1998
301319—(CHIN)
Rev.: $146,680,092
Assets: $170,240,616
Liabilities: $19,568,952
Net Worth: $150,671,664
Earnings: $11,613,888
Fiscal Year-end: 12/31/22
Electronic Component Mfr & Distr
N.A.I.C.S.: 334419
Gaobing Liao (Chm & Pres)

SHENZHEN WATER PLANNING & DESIGN INSTITUTE CO., LTD.
Building 4 Headquarters Building Longhua Design Industrial Park, Beizhan Community Minzhi Street Longhua District, Shenzhen, 518131, Guangdong, China
Tel.: (86) 75533181038
Web Site: https://www.swpdi.com
Year Founded: 2008
301038—(CHIN)
Rev.: $130,813,488
Assets: $256,522,032
Liabilities: $134,303,832
Net Worth: $122,218,200
Earnings: ($4,115,124)
Fiscal Year-end: 12/31/22
Architectural Services
N.A.I.C.S.: 541310
Wenbo Zhu (Chm & Gen Mgr)

SHENZHEN WEIGUANG BIOLOGICAL PRODUCTS CO., LTD.
No 3402 Guangqiao Avenue, Guangming District, Shenzhen, 518107, China
Tel.: (86) 75527400826
Web Site: https://www.szwg.com
Year Founded: 1985
002880—(SSE)
Rev.: $93,777,583
Assets: $361,633,026
Liabilities: $99,431,238
Net Worth: $262,201,788
Earnings: $16,489,081
Emp.: 700
Fiscal Year-end: 12/31/22
Biological Product Mfr & Distr
N.A.I.C.S.: 325414
Zhan Zhang (Chm & Gen Mgr)

SHENZHEN WOER HEAT-SHRINKABLE MATERIAL CO., LTD.
Woer Mansion North Lanjing Road, Pingshan, Shenzhen, China
Tel.: (86) 75528299160 CN
Web Site: https://en.woer.com
Year Founded: 1998
002130—(SSE)
Rev.: $749,855,902
Assets: $1,169,236,767
Liabilities: $495,441,737
Net Worth: $673,795,030
Earnings: $86,272,824
Emp.: 2,000
Fiscal Year-end: 12/31/22
Heat-Shrinkable & Cross-Linked Materials Mfr & Distr
N.A.I.C.S.: 325211

Subsidiaries:

LTK International Ltd. (1)
Suite 502 Concorida Plaza 1 Science Museum Road, Tsimshatsui East, Kowloon, China (Hong Kong)
Tel.: (852) 23851866
Web Site: http://www.ltkcable.com
Electronic Cable & Wiring Products Mfr
N.A.I.C.S.: 335929

Subsidiary (Non-US):

LTK Electric Wire (Huizhou) Limited (2)
DESAY 3rd Industrial Zone Zhong Kai Road, Chenjiang, Huizhou, 516229, Guangdong, China
Tel.: (86) 752 2619 200
Web Site: http://us.ltkcable.com
Wire & Cable Mfr
N.A.I.C.S.: 335929

SHENZHEN WONGTEE INTERNATIONAL ENTERPRISE CO., LTD.
28th Floor Royal Center, No 350 Fuhua Road Futian District, Shenzhen, 518048, Guangdong, China
Tel.: (86) 75522669299
Web Site: https://wongtee000056.com
Year Founded: 1983
000056—(SSE)
Rev.: $93,109,728
Assets: $1,422,610,174
Liabilities: $1,127,868,497
Net Worth: $294,741,678
Earnings: ($172,823,372)
Emp.: 487
Fiscal Year-end: 12/31/22
Real Estate Development Services
N.A.I.C.S.: 531311
Qiu Shanqin (Chm)

SHENZHEN WOTE ADVANCED MATERIALS CO., LTD.
Floor 31 Block B Building 7 International Innovation Valley Phase 3, Vanke Yuncheng Nanshan District, Shenzhen, China
Tel.: (86) 75526880866
Web Site: https://www.wotlon.com
Year Founded: 2001
002886—(SSE)
Rev.: $209,220,359
Assets: $373,296,952
Liabilities: $192,620,601
Net Worth: $180,676,351
Earnings: $2,048,253
Fiscal Year-end: 12/31/22
Plastic Material Mfr & Distr
N.A.I.C.S.: 325211
Wu Xian (Chm)

Subsidiaries:

Chongqing WOTE Zhicheng Advanced Materials Technology Co., Ltd. (1)
No 10 Huabei 2nd Road Yanjia street, Changshou District, Chongqing, China
Tel.: (86) 2340288665
Polymer Material Mfr
N.A.I.C.S.: 325211

Jiangsu WOTE Advanced Materials Technology Co., Ltd. (1)
No 11 Weiba Road Dongtai Economic Development Zone, Jiangsu, China
Tel.: (86) 51585390673
Polymer Material Mfr
N.A.I.C.S.: 325211

Shanghai Valqua Fluorocarbon Products Co., Ltd. (1)
No 255 Jiangtian East Road, Songjiang industrial Zone, Shanghai, 201613, China (51%)
Tel.: (86) 2157741130
Web Site: http://en.valqua.cn
Emp.: 180
Fluorocarbon Resins Mfr
N.A.I.C.S.: 325211

Zhejiang Kesai Advanced Materials Technology Co., Ltd. (1)
No 9 Guangming Street Fuxi street, Deqing, Huzhou, Zhejiang, China
Tel.: (86) 5728899636

Polymer Material Mfr
N.A.I.C.S.: 325211

SHENZHEN XFH TECHNOLOGY CO., LTD.
Building A7 No 11 Lane 635 Xiaoyun Road, Baoshan District, Shanghai, 200949, Guangdong, China
Tel.: (86) 2166566217
Web Site: http://www.xiangfenghua.com
Year Founded: 2009
300890—(SSE)
Rev.: $330,903,902
Assets: $617,785,876
Liabilities: $384,445,779
Net Worth: $233,340,097
Earnings: $22,552,775
Fiscal Year-end: 12/31/22
Electrical Battery Mfr & Distr
N.A.I.C.S.: 335910
Pengwei Zhou (Chm)

SHENZHEN XINHAO PHOTO-ELECTRICITY TECHNOLOGY CO., LTD
No 18 SongTang Road, Tangxiayong Community Yanluo Street Baoan District, Shenzhen, 518105, China
Tel.: (86) 75533118666
Web Site: https://www.xinhaoph.com
Year Founded: 2013
301051—(CHIN)
Rev.: $223,411,500
Assets: $661,271,364
Liabilities: $285,715,404
Net Worth: $375,555,960
Earnings: ($21,405,384)
Fiscal Year-end: 12/31/22
Optical Component Mfr
N.A.I.C.S.: 327215
Rujing Bai (Chm & Gen Mgr)

SHENZHEN XINYICHANG TECHNOLOGY CO., LTD.
Building C8 Ruiming Industrial Park Hexiu West Road Fuhai Street, Baoan District, Shenzhen, Guangdong, China
Tel.: (86) 4000688383
Web Site: https://www.szhech.com
Year Founded: 2006
688383—(SHG)
Rev.: $166,185,288
Assets: $343,242,928
Liabilities: $149,815,168
Net Worth: $193,427,760
Earnings: $28,741,972
Fiscal Year-end: 12/31/22
Semiconductor Product Mfr & Distr
N.A.I.C.S.: 334413
Xinrong Hu (Chm)

SHENZHEN XUNJIEXING TECHNOLOGY CORP. LTD.
G-I Building, Shasi Dongbao Industrial Zone Shajing Town Baoan District, Shenzhen, China
Tel.: (86) 75533653366
Web Site: https://www.jxpcb.com
Year Founded: 2005
688655—(SHG)
Rev.: $62,430,236
Assets: $146,871,317
Liabilities: $50,762,364
Net Worth: $96,108,953
Earnings: $6,506,992
Fiscal Year-end: 12/31/22
Printed Circuit Board Mfr & Distr
N.A.I.C.S.: 334418
Zhuo Ma (Chm & Gen Mgr)

SHENZHEN YAN TIAN PORT HOLDINGS CO., LTD.
18th-19th Floor Haigang Building Yantian Port, Yantian District, Shenzhen, 518081, Guangdong, China
Tel.: (86) 75525290180
Web Site: http://www.yantian-port.com
Year Founded: 1997
000088—(SSE)
Rev.: $111,984,388
Assets: $2,301,948,053
Liabilities: $777,997,088
Net Worth: $1,523,950,965
Earnings: $63,178,512
Fiscal Year-end: 12/31/22
Holding Company
N.A.I.C.S.: 551112
Li Yutian (Chm)

SHENZHEN YANMADE TECHNOLOGY, INC.
Building C No 2 Bangkai Technology City Fenghuang Street, Guangming District, Shenzhen, 518000, Guangdong, China
Tel.: (86) 75523243087
Web Site: https://www.yanmade.com
Year Founded: 2012
688312—(SHG)
Rev.: $44,630,829
Assets: $210,041,573
Liabilities: $22,592,326
Net Worth: $187,449,247
Earnings: $11,456,149
Fiscal Year-end: 12/31/22
Intelligent Test Equipment Mfr
N.A.I.C.S.: 334515
Yan Liu (Founder, Chm & Gen Mgr)

SHENZHEN YHLO BIOTECH CO., LTD.
Building 1 YHLO Biopark Baolong 2nd Road, Baolong Subdistrict Longgang District, Shenzhen, 518116, Guangdong, China
Tel.: (86) 75526601910
Web Site: https://www.szyhlo.com
Year Founded: 2008
688575—(SHG)
Rev.: $558,898,255
Assets: $591,297,001
Liabilities: $248,066,021
Net Worth: $343,230,980
Earnings: $142,139,345
Fiscal Year-end: 12/31/22
Medical Product Mfr & Distr
N.A.I.C.S.: 339112
Kunhui Hu (Chm)

SHENZHEN YINGHE TECHNOLOGY CO., LTD.
No 301 of huize Road Dongjiang Sci-tech Park, Nanshan District, Huizhou, China
Tel.: (86) 7527388333
Web Site: https://www.yhwins.com
Year Founded: 2006
300457—(CHIN)
Rev.: $1,266,382,728
Assets: $2,298,700,404
Liabilities: $1,485,483,948
Net Worth: $813,216,456
Earnings: $68,433,768
Emp.: 520
Fiscal Year-end: 12/31/22
Automation Production Equipment Mfr
N.A.I.C.S.: 334519
Jia Tinggang (Chm)

SHENZHEN YITOA INTELLIGENT CONTROL CO., LTD.
No 6 Baoxing Road Xinan Street, 5th Hi-tech Industrial Park Nanshan District, Shenzhen, 518108, China
Tel.: (86) 75526616688
Web Site: https://www.yitoa.com

AND PRIVATE COMPANIES

300131—(CHIN)
Rev.: $725,685,480
Assets: $456,716,988
Liabilities: $196,790,256
Net Worth: $259,926,732
Earnings: $8,040,708
Emp.: 700
Fiscal Year-end: 12/31/22
Electronic Controllers Mfr
N.A.I.C.S.: 335314
Qingzhou Hu *(Chm & Pres)*

SHENZHEN YSSTECH INFO-TECH CO., LTD.

37th Floor Phase II South District Shenye Shangcheng, No 5001 Huanggang Road Futian District, Shenzhen, 518048, China
Tel.: (86) 75588265110
Web Site: https://www.ysstech.com
Year Founded: 1998
300377—(CHIN)
Rev.: $192,727,080
Assets: $465,719,436
Liabilities: $47,276,892
Net Worth: $418,442,544
Earnings: $8,634,600
Emp.: 830
Fiscal Year-end: 12/31/22
Financial Software Publisher
N.A.I.C.S.: 513210
Qiu Tang *(Chm)*

SHENZHEN YUTO PACKAGING TECHNOLOGY CO., LTD.

No 1 Shihuan Road Shiyan Street, Bao an District, Shenzhen, Guangdong, China
Tel.: (86) 75533873999
Web Site: https://www.szyuto.com
Year Founded: 2002
002831—(SSE)
Rev.: $2,297,238,601
Assets: $2,957,650,493
Liabilities: $1,447,666,366
Net Worth: $1,509,984,127
Earnings: $208,897,524
Emp.: 20,000
Fiscal Year-end: 12/31/22
Paper Packaging Product Mfr & Distr
N.A.I.C.S.: 322220
Huajun Wang *(Founder & Chm)*

Subsidiaries:

Vietnam YUTO Printing & Packing Co., Ltd (1)
H-02 Workshop of Guiwu Extended Industrial Zone, Fangliu Township Guiwu County, Bac Ninh, Vietnam
Tel.: (84) 2223617926
Web Site: http://vnyuto.com
Paperboard Box Mfr & Distr
N.A.I.C.S.: 322211

Wuhan YUTO Printing & Packaging Co., Ltd. (1)
No 2 The Second Huashan Road, Happiness Village Miaoshan Office Jiangxia District, Wuhan, 430200, Hubei, China
Tel.: (86) 2750753094
Paperboard Box Mfr
N.A.I.C.S.: 322211
Wei Hone Yi *(Gen Mgr)*

SHENZHEN ZHAOWEI MACHINERY & ELECTRONICS CO., LTD.

No 88 Yanluo Street Songgang, Baoan District, Shenzhen, 518127, Guangdong, China
Tel.: (86) 75527322645
Web Site: https://www.zwgearbox.com
Year Founded: 2001
003021—(SSE)
Rev.: $161,805,187
Assets: $499,609,623
Liabilities: $85,838,103
Net Worth: $413,771,520
Earnings: $21,129,666
Fiscal Year-end: 12/31/22
Electronic Product Mfr & Distr
N.A.I.C.S.: 334419
Haizhou Li *(Chm)*

SHENZHEN ZHENYE (GROUP) CO., LTD.

Floor 42-43 Block A Building 11 No 16 Keji South Road, Shenzhen Bay Science & Technology Ecological Pk Nanshan District, Shenzhen, 518063, Guangdong, China
Tel.: (86) 75525863016
Web Site: https://www.zhenye.com
Year Founded: 1989
000006—(SSE)
Rev.: $519,453,829
Assets: $3,706,427,434
Liabilities: $2,517,315,222
Net Worth: $1,189,112,212
Earnings: $58,914,522
Fiscal Year-end: 12/31/22
Real Estate Development & Leasing Services
N.A.I.C.S.: 531110
Song Yang *(Chm)*

SHENZHEN ZHILAI SCIENCE & TECHNOLOGY CO., LTD.

3705-3709 37th Floor Building No 4 Tianan Cloud Valley II, Xuegang North Road 2018 Bantian Street Longgang District, Shenzhen, 518129, China
Tel.: (86) 75528657760
Web Site:
https://www.smartelocker.com
Year Founded: 1999
300771—(SSE)
Rev.: $122,514,528
Assets: $314,333,347
Liabilities: $31,384,707
Net Worth: $282,948,639
Earnings: $24,189,179
Fiscal Year-end: 12/31/22
Electronic Product Mfr & Distr
N.A.I.C.S.: 334419
Deyi Gan *(Chm & Gen Mgr)*

SHENZHEN ZHONGHENG HWAFA CO., LTD.

6F East Tower Huafa Mnsn Bldg 411 Huafa North Road Futian District, Shenzhen, 518031, Guangdong, China
Tel.: (86) 75586360201
Web Site: http://www.hwafa.com.cn
Year Founded: 1981
000020—(SSE)
Rev.: $93,286,688
Assets: $85,478,862
Liabilities: $35,836,454
Net Worth: $49,642,407
Earnings: $1,421,943
Fiscal Year-end: 12/31/22
Electronic Product Mfr & Distr
N.A.I.C.S.: 334419
Li Zhongqiu *(Chm & Gen Mgr)*

SHENZHEN ZHONGJIN LINGNAN NONFEMET CO., LTD.

Floors 23-26 No 6013 Shennan Avenue, Futian, Shenzhen, 518040, Guangdong, China
Tel.: (86) 75583474800
Web Site: http://www.nonfemet.com
Year Founded: 1994
000060—(SSE)
Rev.: $7,783,390,700
Assets: $4,584,368,094
Liabilities: $2,436,936,012
Net Worth: $2,147,432,082
Earnings: $170,205,432
Emp.: 10,831
Fiscal Year-end: 12/31/22
Metals Mining & Processing; Aluminum Windows & Doors Mfr; Property Development & Management
N.A.I.C.S.: 212230
Bian Wang *(Chm)*

Subsidiaries:

Perilya Limited
Level 8 251 Adelaide Terrace, Perth, 6000, WA, Australia
Tel.: (61) 863301000
Web Site: https://www.perilya.com.au
Sales Range: $350-399.9 Million
Emp.: 653
Mineral Exploration & Mining Services
N.A.I.C.S.: 212230
Minzhi Han *(Gen Mgr-Metals Mktg & Exec Dir)*

Subsidiary (Domestic):

Perilya Broken Hill Limited (2)
Wentworth Road, PO Box 5001, Broken Hill, 2880, NSW, Australia
Tel.: (61) 880888582
Web Site: http://www.perilya.com.au
Emp.: 350
Lead Ore & Zinc Ore Mining
N.A.I.C.S.: 212230

Shenzhen Jingzhou Precision Technology Corp. (1)
Longgang High-Tech Industry Park, 518116, Shenzhen, China
Tel.: (86) 755 84877666
Web Site: http://www.chinadrill.com
Drill Bit Mfr
N.A.I.C.S.: 333515

Shenzhen King Facade Decoration Engineering Co., Ltd. (1)
No 533 Building Area 5-1 Baguailing Industrial Zone Futian Dis, Shenzhen, Guangdong, China
Tel.: (86) 75582414888
Construction Engineering Services
N.A.I.C.S.: 541330

Shenzhen Nonfemet Hi-Power Battery Material Co., Ltd. (1)
No 10-11building Fuqiao Industrial Zone Fuyong Town, Baoan, Shenzhen, 518103, Guangdong, China
Tel.: (86) 755 27303666
Web Site: http://www.zjgn.com.cn
Storage Battery Mfr
N.A.I.C.S.: 335910

SHENZHEN ZHONGZHUANG DESIGN DECORATION ENGINEERING CO., LTD

Hong Long Century Plaza four Five 4002 Shennan Road Luohu District, Shenzhen, China
Tel.: (86) 75583599233
Web Site:
http://www.zhongzhuang.com
002822—(SSE)
Rev.: $731,767,706
Assets: $1,348,378,911
Liabilities: $821,422,120
Net Worth: $526,956,791
Earnings: $1,579,388
Fiscal Year-end: 12/31/22
Building Decoration Engineering Services
N.A.I.C.S.: 236220

SHENZHEN ZOWEE TECHNOLOGY CO., LTD.

No 5 Zowee Technology Building, Nanshan District, Shenzhen, 518055, China
Tel.: (86) 75526997888
Web Site: https://www.zowee.com.cn
Year Founded: 2004
002369—(SSE)
Rev.: $270,339,610
Assets: $381,835,041
Liabilities: $228,589,269
Net Worth: $153,245,772

SHENZHOU SPACE PARK GROUP LIMITED

Earnings: ($18,411,873)
Emp.: 8,500
Fiscal Year-end: 12/31/22
Electronics Manufacture Outsourcing Services
N.A.I.C.S.: 334419
Li Xingfang *(Chm & Gen Mgr)*

Subsidiaries:

Shenzhen ALL Link Technology Co., Ltd. (1)
Floor 5th Block 9th, Sunny Industrial Zone Xili Town Nanshan District, Shenzhen, 518108, China
Tel.: (86) 7552 650 8812
Web Site: https://www.link-all.com
Optical Component Mfr & Distr
N.A.I.C.S.: 333310

Tianjin Zhuoda Technology Development Co., Ltd. (1)
No 71 New Ring South Street Development Zone, Tianjin, China
Tel.: (86) 2259802369
Electronic Components Mfr
N.A.I.C.S.: 334419

SHENZHEN ZQGAME NETWORK CO., LTD.

Floor 21-24 Building 10A Phase 3, Shenzhen Bay Science & Technology Ecological Park Nanshan District, Shenzhen, 518063, Guangdong, China
Tel.: (86) 75526733925
Web Site: http://www.zqgame.com
Year Founded: 2008
300052—(CHIN)
Rev.: $38,576,304
Assets: $133,719,768
Liabilities: $57,819,528
Net Worth: $75,900,240
Earnings: ($8,241,480)
Fiscal Year-end: 12/31/22
Online Game Publisher
N.A.I.C.S.: 339930
Yilun Li *(Chm & Gen Mgr)*

SHENZHOU INTERNATIONAL GROUP HOLDINGS LIMITED

No 18 Yongjiang Road, Ningbo Economic and Technological Development Zone, Ningbo, Zhejiang, China
Tel.: (86) 57486980888 CN
Web Site:
https://www.shenzhouintl.com
2313—(HKG)
Rev.: $3,457,270,713
Assets: $6,730,607,139
Liabilities: $2,179,860,019
Net Worth: $4,550,747,120
Earnings: $630,990,114
Emp.: 92,030
Fiscal Year-end: 12/31/23
Holding Company
N.A.I.C.S.: 551112
Kenji Tak Hing Chan *(Sec)*

Subsidiaries:

Tuton Textile (Ningbo) Co., Ltd. (1)
10th Fl /Bldg C12 R and D Park 299Lane Guanghua Road, National Hi-tech Park, Ningbo, 315040, Zhejiang, China
Tel.: (86) 57487730919
Web Site: https://www.tuton-textile.com
Knitwear Products Mfr
N.A.I.C.S.: 315250

SHENZHOU SPACE PARK GROUP LIMITED

Suite no 1001B 10/F Tower 1 China Hong Kong City, 33 Canton Road, Kowloon, Tsim Sha Tsui, China (Hong Kong)
Tel.: (852) 2377 9262
Web Site: http://www.chh.hk
Rev.: $112,437,320
Assets: $212,916,355

SHENZHOU SPACE PARK GROUP LIMITED

Shenzhou Space Park Group Limited—(Continued)
Liabilities: $121,955,202
Net Worth: $90,961,153
Earnings: ($44,029,984)
Emp.: 275
Fiscal Year-end: 12/31/16
Investment Holding Company; Titanium Exploration; Textile Mfr & Sales
N.A.I.C.S.: 551112
Jianhua Zheng (Pres)

Subsidiaries:

Ching Hing Weaving Dyeing & Printing Factory Limited (1)
10 F Intl Indus Bldg 501-503 Castle Peak Rd, Kowloon, China (Hong Kong)
Tel.: (852) 22669107
Web Site: http://www.ching-hing.com.hk
Fabrics Processing Services
N.A.I.C.S.: 313210

SHEPHERD NEAME LIMITED
The Faversham Brewery 17 Court Street, Faversham, ME13 7AX, Kent, United Kingdom
Tel.: (44) 1795532206
Web Site:
https://www.shepherdneame.co.uk
SHEP—(AQSE)
Rev.: $191,232,592
Assets: $441,652,445
Liabilities: $168,712,420
Net Worth: $272,940,025
Earnings: $3,395,732
Emp.: 1,865
Fiscal Year-end: 06/29/19
Drinking Places (Alcoholic Beverages)
N.A.I.C.S.: 722410
Miles H. Templeman (Chm)

Subsidiaries:

Royal Albion Hotel (Broadstairs) Limited (1)
6-12 Albion Street, Broadstairs, CT10 1AN, Kent, United Kingdom
Tel.: (44) 1843868071
Web Site:
https://www.albionbroadstairs.co.uk
Hotel Services
N.A.I.C.S.: 721110

Village Green Restaurants Limited (1)
36 Prospect St, Ridgewood, NJ 07450-4402
Tel.: (201) 445-2914
Web Site:
https://www.villagegreenrestaurant.com
Restaurant Services
N.A.I.C.S.: 722511

SHERATON PROPERTIES & FINANCE LIMITED
301 & 302 3rd Floor Peninsula Heights CD Barfiwala Road, Andheri West, Mumbai, 400 053, India
Tel.: (91) 2226731779
Web Site:
https://sheratonproperties.in
Year Founded: 1985
512367—(BOM)
Rev.: $427,936
Assets: $14,699,215
Liabilities: $1,151
Net Worth: $14,698,064
Earnings: $304,850
Fiscal Year-end: 03/31/23
Civil Engineering Services
N.A.I.C.S.: 541330
Shailaja Karkera (CEO)

SHERBORNE INVESTORS (GUERNSEY) A LIMITED
Ogier House Saint Julian S Avenue, Saint Peter Port, GY1 1WA, Guernsey
Tel.: (44) 2127351000
Investment Management Service

N.A.I.C.S.: 525910
Talmai Morgan (Chm)

SHERBROOKE O.E.M. LTD
262 Rue Pepin, Sherbrooke, J1L 2V8, QC, Canada
Tel.: (819) 563-7374
Web Site: http://www.sherbrooke-oem.com
Year Founded: 1997
Rev.: $10,085,614
Emp.: 80
Recycling Equipment Mfr
N.A.I.C.S.: 423930
Alain Brasseur (Co-Founder)

SHERIDAN NURSERIES
12302 Tenth Line, Georgetown, L7G 4S7, ON, Canada
Tel.: (416) 798-7970
Web Site:
http://www.sheridannurseries.com
Year Founded: 1913
Rev.: $29,754,494
Emp.: 350
Plant Nursery
N.A.I.C.S.: 115112
Karl Stensson (Vice Chm & Dir-Brand Integrity)

SHERPA CAPITAL SL
Hermosilla Street 11, Madrid, Spain
Tel.: (34) 902 70 25 26
Web Site:
http://www.sherpacapital.es
Privater Equity Firm
N.A.I.C.S.: 523999
Jorge Fernandez Miret (Partner)

Subsidiaries:

Dogi International Fabrics, S.A (1)
C/ Mig s/n, El Masnou, 08320, Barcelona, Spain
Tel.: (34) 934628000
Web Site: http://www.dogi.com
Sales Range: $125-149.9 Million
Emp.: 1,500
Lingerie, Swimwear, Active Wear & Outerwear Mfr & Sales
N.A.I.C.S.: 315250
Eduardo Navarro Zamora (Chm)

Subsidiary (Non-US):

D.E.S Agencies (PTY) Ltd. (2)
27/29 Mewett Street, Ophirton, Booysens, 2091, South Africa
Tel.: (27) 11 493 7079
Web Site:
http://www.dieselelectricservices.co.za
Generator Mfr & Distr
N.A.I.C.S.: 335312
Robert Pretorius (Mgr-Technical)

Subsidiary (US):

EFA, Inc. (2)
3112 Pleasant Garden Rd, Greensboro, NC 27406
Tel.: (510) 430-8404
Web Site: http://www.efainc.com
Building Construction & Remodeling Services
N.A.I.C.S.: 236220

Iluna USA inc. (2)
110 E 40th St Ste 301, New York, NY 10016
Tel.: (212) 719-9760
Web Site: http://www.iluna.com
Clothing Retailer
N.A.I.C.S.: 458110
Odalis Tejada (Dir-Color & Quality Assurance)

Subsidiary (Non-US):

Penn Elastic Gmbh (2)
Ab Der Talle 20, 33102, Paderborn, Germany
Tel.: (49) 525140080
Web Site: http://www.penn-ts.com

Sales Range: $50-74.9 Million
Emp.: 200
Fabrics Mfr
N.A.I.C.S.: 332999
Markus Regenstein (Mng Dir)

SHERPA II HOLDINGS CORP.
918-1030 West Georgia St, Vancouver, V6E 2Y3, BC, Canada
Tel.: (604) 628-5616
Year Founded: 2018
SHRP—(TSXV)
Assets: $593,181
Liabilities: $17,058
Net Worth: $576,123
Earnings: ($99,041)
Fiscal Year-end: 06/30/24
Asset Management Services
N.A.I.C.S.: 523940
O'Neill Thomas (CEO)

SHERRITT INTERNATIONAL CORPORATION
22 Adelaide Street West Suite 4220, Bay Adelaide Centre East Tower, Toronto, M5H 4E3, ON, Canada
Tel.: (416) 924-4551
Web Site: https://www.sherritt.com
Year Founded: 1927
S—(TSX)
Rev.: $105,297,024
Assets: $1,330,063,644
Liabilities: $777,483,840
Net Worth: $552,579,804
Earnings: ($281,378,748)
Emp.: 3,308
Fiscal Year-end: 12/31/19
Oil & Natural Gas, Metal Ore & Coal Mining
N.A.I.C.S.: 211120
Elvin Saruk (Sr VP-Oil, Gas & Power)

Subsidiaries:

Royal Utilities Partnership (1)
1600 Oxford Tower 10235 101 St NW, Edmonton, T5J 3G1, AB, Canada
Tel.: (780) 420-5810
Sales Range: $75-99.9 Million
Emp.: 116
Holding Company
N.A.I.C.S.: 551112

SHERVANI INDUSTRIAL SYNDICATE LIMITED
Shervani Nagar Sulem Sarai, Harwara, Allahabad, 211015, Uttar Pradesh, India
Tel.: (91) 7311128115
Web Site:
https://sherwaniind.ssls1.com
526117—(BOM)
Rev.: $4,608,882
Assets: $25,306,158
Liabilities: $7,163,957
Net Worth: $18,142,201
Earnings: $909,472
Emp.: 24
Fiscal Year-end: 03/31/21
Real Estate Manangement Services
N.A.I.C.S.: 531390
Tahir Hasan (CFO)

SHERWOOD CHEVROLET INC.
550 Brand Rd Saskatoon Auto Mall, Saskatoon, S7J 5J3, SK, Canada
Tel.: (306) 374-6330
Web Site:
http://www.sherwoodchev.com
Sales Range: $25-49.9 Million
Emp.: 85
New & Used Car Dealers
N.A.I.C.S.: 441110
Sherwood Sharfe (Pres)

SHERWOOD CO-OPERATIVE ASSOCIATION LIMITED
B 615 Winnipeg Street N, PO Box

5044, Regina, S4R 8T5, SK, Canada
Tel.: (306) 791-9300
Web Site: http://www.sherwoodco-op.com
Year Founded: 1931
Rev.: $69,746,978
Emp.: 300
Retail Co-Operative
N.A.I.C.S.: 457110
Troy Verboom (Gen Mgr)

SHERWOOD INDUSTRIES LTD.
6782 Oldfield Rd, Saanichton, V8M 2A3, BC, Canada
Tel.: (250) 652-6080
Web Site: http://www.enviro.com
Year Founded: 1988
Rev.: $13,690,320
Emp.: 100
Commercial Products Whslr & Distr
N.A.I.C.S.: 424490
Shebil Yousief (Owner)

SHESHADRI INDUSTRIES LTD.
Surya Towers 6th Floor 105 SP Road, Baguiati Block-2, Secunderabad, 500 003, Telangana, India
Tel.: (91) 4030512700
Web Site: https://www.sheshadri.in
539111—(BOM)
Rev.: $4,187,363
Assets: $5,037,372
Liabilities: $7,045,153
Net Worth: ($2,007,781)
Earnings: $1,170,014
Emp.: 10
Fiscal Year-end: 03/31/23
Spinning Mill Operator
N.A.I.C.S.: 313110
Jeetender Kumar Agarwal (Mng Dir, Mng Dir, CFO & CFO)

SHETRON LIMITED
A-6 MIDC Road No 5 Andheri East, Mumbai, 400093, India
Tel.: (91) 2228326228
Web Site:
https://www.shetrongroup.com
Year Founded: 1980
526137—(BOM)
Rev.: $29,434,686
Assets: $18,000,120
Liabilities: $11,962,113
Net Worth: $6,038,007
Earnings: $743,361
Emp.: 211
Fiscal Year-end: 03/31/23
Metal Packaging Mfr
N.A.I.C.S.: 561910
Diwakar Sanku Shetty (Chm)

SHEUNG MOON HOLDINGS LIMITED
Office D 27/F The Globe No79 Wing Hong Street, Cheung Sha Wan, Kowloon, China (Hong Kong)
Tel.: (852) 2 473 3003 Ky
Web Site: http://www.smcl.com.hk
Year Founded: 1997
8523—(HKG)
Rev.: $60,442,608
Assets: $49,367,869
Liabilities: $25,575,573
Net Worth: $23,792,296
Earnings: $2,663,050
Emp.: 450
Fiscal Year-end: 03/31/21
Civil Engineering Services
N.A.I.C.S.: 238910
Sze Wo Tang (Chm & Compliance Officer)

SHEUNG YUE GROUP HOLDINGS LIMITED
Unit 103-105 New East Ocean Cen-

tre 9 Science Museum Road, Kowloon, China (Hong Kong)
Tel.: (852) 2 311 8982 Ky
Web Site:
http://www.simonandsons.com.hk
Year Founded: 1970
1633—(HKG)
Rev.: $27,558,512
Assets: $37,185,063
Liabilities: $15,740,590
Net Worth: $21,444,473
Earnings: $1,443,544
Emp.: 138
Fiscal Year-end: 03/31/22
Foundation Constructing Services
N.A.I.C.S.: 238910
Gary Lap Wai Chan (Chm)

SHEZAN INTERNATIONAL LIMITED
56 - Bund Road, Lahore, 54500, Pakistan
Tel.: (92) 4237466900
Web Site: https://shezan.com
Year Founded: 1964
SHEZ—(LAH)
Rev.: $55,315,416
Assets: $34,500,927
Liabilities: $18,463,822
Net Worth: $16,037,104
Earnings: $811,871
Emp.: 303
Fiscal Year-end: 06/30/19
Juices, Beverages, Pickles, Preserves & Flavorings Mfr
N.A.I.C.S.: 311411
Muneer Nawaz (Chm)

SHF COMMUNICATION TECHNOLOGIES AG
Wilhelm-von-Siemens-Str 23 D, 12277, Berlin, Germany
Tel.: (49) 307720510
Web Site: http://www.shf.de
Year Founded: 1983
Communication Equipment Mfr & Distr
N.A.I.C.S.: 334220
Frank Hieronymi (Member-Mgmt Bd)

Subsidiaries:

SHF Japan Corporation (1)
Tower Front Kamiya-cho 4th Floor 1-3-8, Higashiazabu Minatu-ku, Tokyo, 106-0044, Japan
Tel.: (81) 355451486
Optical Communication Equipment Mfr & Distr
N.A.I.C.S.: 335921

SHH RESOURCES HOLDINGS BERHAD
No 2 1st Floor Jalan Marin Taman Marin Jalan Haji Abdullah, Sungai Abong, 84000, Muar, Johor Darul Takzim, Malaysia
Tel.: (60) 69510223
Web Site: https://shh.com.my
Year Founded: 1981
SHH—(KLS)
Rev.: $17,572,097
Assets: $20,990,400
Liabilities: $4,544,956
Net Worth: $16,445,444
Earnings: $739,203
Emp.: 630
Fiscal Year-end: 06/30/23
Furniture Mfr
N.A.I.C.S.: 337121
Chan Huat Teo (Deputy Mng Dir)

SHI SHI SERVICES LIMITED
Unit 903 9 Floor Haleson Building, 1 Jubilee Street, Central, China (Hong Kong)
Tel.: (852) 2 155 4112 Ky
Web Site:
www.shishiservices.com.hk
Year Founded: 1984
8181—(HKG)
Rev.: $67,708,180
Assets: $51,306,309
Liabilities: $12,820,096
Net Worth: $38,486,213
Earnings: ($3,346,902)
Emp.: 1,801
Fiscal Year-end: 03/31/22
Investment Holding Company; Property Management Services
N.A.I.C.S.: 551112
Eric Todd (Exec Dir)

SHIAN YIH ELECTRONIC INDUSTRY CO., LTD.
No 22 Industria 24th Road, Taichung Industrial Park, Taichung, Taiwan
Tel.: (886) 423590111
Web Site:
https://www.shianyih.com.tw
Year Founded: 1979
3531—(TPE)
Rev.: $70,063,440
Assets: $86,923,866
Liabilities: $27,565,175
Net Worth: $59,358,691
Earnings: $5,763,812
Emp.: 1,500
Fiscal Year-end: 12/31/22
Semiconductor & Related Device Mfr
N.A.I.C.S.: 334413
John Teng (Chm)

Subsidiaries:

Taiwan Corporation (1)
No 22 Industry 24th Rd, Taichung Industrial Park, Taichung, Taiwan
Tel.: (886) 423590111
Electronic Mold Mfr
N.A.I.C.S.: 333511

SHIBAURA ELECTRONICS CO., LTD.
Sanshoku Bldg 2-1-24 Kamiochiai, Chuo- ku, Saitama, Japan
Tel.: (81) 486154000
Web Site:
https://www.shibauraelectronic.com
Year Founded: 1953
6957—(TKS)
Rev.: $214,170,610
Assets: $288,024,140
Liabilities: $55,603,320
Net Worth: $232,420,820
Earnings: $25,263,420
Emp.: 4,350
Fiscal Year-end: 03/31/24
Semiconductor Devices Mfr
N.A.I.C.S.: 334413
Akira Kasai (Pres)

Subsidiaries:

Dongguan Shibaura Electronics Co., Ltd. (1)
No 21 Shang Xin-Rd Xinan, Changan Town, Dongguan, Guangdong, China
Tel.: (86) 76985412371
Emp.: 350
Temperature Sensor Distr
N.A.I.C.S.: 423830

Fukushima Shibaura Electronics Co., Ltd. (1)
66-5 Higashi Sasada Nukazawa, Motomiya, Fukushima, Japan
Tel.: (81) 243443017
Emp.: 380
Temperature Sensor Mfr
N.A.I.C.S.: 334513

Iwate Shibaura Electronics Co., Ltd. (1)
Location 17 Notsuki Michinoshita Torigoe, Ichinohe-machi Ninohe-gun, Iwate, Japan
Tel.: (81) 195332981
Emp.: 130
Temperature Sensor Mfr
N.A.I.C.S.: 334513

Kakunodate Shibaura Electronics Co., Ltd (1)
60-2 Hagurodo Kawara Kakunodate-machi, Semboku, Akita, Japan
Tel.: (81) 187543210
Emp.: 130
Temperature Sensor Mfr
N.A.I.C.S.: 334513

Miharu Electronics Co., Ltd. (1)
100 Binda Umenai Sannohe-machi Sannohe-gun, Aomori, Japan
Tel.: (81) 179220089
Emp.: 60
Temperature Sensor Mfr
N.A.I.C.S.: 334513

Shanghai Shibaura Electronics Co., Ltd. (1)
88 Changxu Rd, Juyuan Subdistrict Jiading, Shanghai, China
Tel.: (86) 2159167387
Emp.: 530
Temperature Sensor Distr
N.A.I.C.S.: 423830

Shibaura Electronics Europe GmbH (1)
Trimburgstrasse 2, 81249, Munich, Germany
Tel.: (49) 8984039034
Temperature Sensor Distr
N.A.I.C.S.: 423830

Shibaura Electronics Hong Kong Co., Ltd. (1)
Room801 8/F Grand City Plaza 1-17 SaiLau KokRoad, Tsuen Wan, Hong Kong, N T, China (Hong Kong)
Tel.: (852) 23771678
Temperature Sensor Distr
N.A.I.C.S.: 423830

Shibaura Electronics Korea Co., Ltd. (1)
1205-S46 67 Yeouinaru-ro, Yeongdeungpo-gu, Seoul, Korea (South)
Tel.: (82) 2634605112
Temperature Sensor Distr
N.A.I.C.S.: 423830

Shibaura Electronics of America Corporation (1)
39555 Orchard Hill Pl Ste 435, Novi, MI 48375
Tel.: (248) 504-6090
Temperature Sensor Distr
N.A.I.C.S.: 423830

Thai Shibaura Denshi Co., Ltd. (1)
Indra Industrial Park 51 Moo 3 Tambol Namtan Amphur Inburi, Sing Buri, 16110, Thailand
Tel.: (66) 36812870
Web Site: https://www.thaishibaura.com
Emp.: 1,890
Temperature Sensor Distr
N.A.I.C.S.: 423830

SHIBUYA CORPORATION
Ko-58 Mameda-Honmachi, Kanazawa, 920-8681, Ishikawa, Japan
Tel.: (81) 762621201
Web Site: https://www.shibuya.co.jp
Year Founded: 1931
6340—(TKS)
Rev.: $717,999,480
Assets: $1,007,036,660
Liabilities: $378,636,280
Net Worth: $628,400,380
Earnings: $60,837,820
Emp.: 3,665
Fiscal Year-end: 06/30/24
Industrial Machinery Mfr
N.A.I.C.S.: 333248
Hidetoshi Shibuya (Pres & CEO)

Subsidiaries:

Kaijo Corporation (1)
3-1-5 Sakae-cho, Hamura-shi, Tokyo, 205-8607, Japan
Tel.: (81) 42 555 2244
Web Site: https://www.kaijo.co.jp
Emp.: 240
Packaging Machine Mfr & Distr
N.A.I.C.S.: 333993
Tetsuo Oikawa (Pres)

Okinawa Shibuya Co., Ltd. (1)
5192-7 Katsurenhaebaru, Uruma, 904-2311, Okinawa, Japan
Tel.: (81) 98 921 1001
Packaging Machine Mfr & Distr
N.A.I.C.S.: 333993

Shibuya Edi Co., Ltd. (1)
58 Ko Mamedahonmachi, Kanazawa, 920-8681, Ishikawa, Japan
Tel.: (81) 12 081 4145
Web Site: https://www.shibuya-edi.co.jp
Advertising Agency Services
N.A.I.C.S.: 541810

Shibuya Hoppman Corporation (1)
7849 Coppermine Dr, Manassas, VA 20109
Tel.: (540) 829-2564
Web Site:
http://www.shibuyahoppmann.com
Sales Range: $10-24.9 Million
Emp.: 130
Industrial Machinery & Equipment Mfr
N.A.I.C.S.: 333998
Gary Marsh (Exec VP-Sls)

Shibuya Packaging System Corp. (1)
2 Kawaraichi-machi, Kanazawa, 920-0172, Ishikawa, Japan
Tel.: (81) 76 256 5500
Web Site: https://www.shibuya-sps.co.jp
Emp.: 220
Packaging Machine Mfr & Distr
N.A.I.C.S.: 333993
Mitsutoshi Shibuya (Pres)

Shibuya Seiki Co., Ltd. (1)
630 Sasagase-cho, Higashi-ku, Hamamatsu, 435-0042, Japan
Tel.: (81) 53 421 1213
Web Site: https://www.shibuya-sss.co.jp
Emp.: 400
Agricultural Equipment Mfr & Distr
N.A.I.C.S.: 333111
Hisashi Kitagawa (Pres)

SHIDAX CORPORATION
Shibuya Shidax Village 1-12-13 Jinnan, Shibuya-ku, Tokyo, 150-0041, Japan
Tel.: (81) 35 784 8890
Web Site: http://www.shidax.co.jp
Year Founded: 2001
4837—(TKS)
Rev.: $1,118,282,000
Assets: $320,979,120
Liabilities: $210,907,840
Net Worth: $110,071,280
Earnings: $39,581,520
Emp.: 9,882
Fiscal Year-end: 03/31/22
Restaurant Operators
N.A.I.C.S.: 722511
Kinichi Shida (Chm & Pres)

SHIEH YIH MACHINERY INDUSTRY CO., LTD.
No 446 Nanshang Rd, Guishan, Taoyuan, 333, Taiwan
Tel.: (886) 33525466
Web Site: https://www.seyi.com
Year Founded: 1962
4533—(TPE)
Rev.: $110,954,038
Assets: $194,491,136
Liabilities: $118,634,869
Net Worth: $75,856,267
Earnings: $898,727
Emp.: 389
Fiscal Year-end: 12/31/22
Tool & Machinery Mfr
N.A.I.C.S.: 333517

Subsidiaries:

Seyi (Thailand) Co., Ltd. (1)
399/69 Moo13 Rachatewa, Bangplee, Samut Prakan, 10540, Thailand
Tel.: (66) 20063184

SHIEH YIH MACHINERY INDUSTRY CO., LTD.

Shieh Yih Machinery Industry Co., Ltd.—(Continued)
Servo Press Mfr
N.A.I.C.S.: 333519

Seyi Presses Europe GmbH (1)
Wilhelm-Gutbrod-Strasse 25, Frankfurt am Main, Germany
Tel.: (49) 69247544162
Servo Press Mfr
N.A.I.C.S.: 333519

Seyi-America Inc. (1)
17534 Von Karman Ave, Irvine, CA 92614
Tel.: (949) 387-7668
Servo Press Mfr
N.A.I.C.S.: 333519

Seyi-America, Inc.
843 Joint Park Blvd, Tullahoma, TN 37388
Tel.: (931) 455-7700
Servo Press Mfr
N.A.I.C.S.: 333519

Xie Yi Tech Machinery (China) Co., Ltd. (1)
No 88 Xing Puzhong Lu, Qiandeng, Kunshan, Jiangsu, China
Tel.: (86) 51257407900
Servo Press Mfr
N.A.I.C.S.: 333519

SHIELD CORPORATION LIMITED

Block-6 P E C H S Suite 1007 10th Floor Business Avenue, Shahrah-e-Faisal, Karachi, Pakistan
Tel.: (92) 2134385003
Web Site: https://www.shield.com.pk
Year Founded: 1975
SCL—(LAH)
Rev.: $12,771,747
Assets: $8,189,864
Liabilities: $5,110,208
Net Worth: $3,079,656
Earnings: $174,687
Emp.: 99
Fiscal Year-end: 06/30/19
Oral & Baby Care Products Mfr
N.A.I.C.S.: 325620
M. Haroon Qassim (CEO)

Subsidiaries:

Shield Corporation Limited - Factory (1)
Plot No 368/4 & 5, Landhi Industrial Area, Karachi, 75160, Sindh, Pakistan
Tel.: (92) 2135021463
Web Site: http://www.shield.com.pk
Babycare Products Mfr
N.A.I.C.S.: 325620

SHIELD THERAPEUTICS PLC

Northern Design Centre Baltic Business Quarter, Gateshead Quays, Newcastle, NE8 3DF, United Kingdom
Tel.: (44) 1915118500
Web Site: https://www.shieldtherapeutics.com
Year Founded: 2008
STX—(AIM)
Rev.: $16,664,486
Assets: $62,125,816
Liabilities: $42,991,574
Net Worth: $19,134,242
Earnings: ($42,380,500)
Emp.: 28
Fiscal Year-end: 12/31/23
Pharmaceutical Product Mfr & Distr
N.A.I.C.S.: 325412
Tim Watts (CEO)

Subsidiaries:

Shield TX (Switzerland) AG (1)
Sihleggstrasse 23, 8832, Wollerau, Switzerland
Tel.: (41) 435080781
Pharmaceuticals Product Mfr
N.A.I.C.S.: 325412

SHIFA INTERNATIONAL HOSPITALS LTD.

Pitras Bukhari Road Sector H-8/4, Islamabad, Pakistan
Tel.: (92) 518463000
Web Site: https://www.shifa.com.pk
SHFA—(KAR)
Rev.: $75,750,506
Assets: $79,721,417
Liabilities: $40,572,097
Net Worth: $39,149,320
Earnings: $4,822,530
Emp.: 4,801
Fiscal Year-end: 06/30/19
Medical Devices
N.A.I.C.S.: 622110
Muhammad Zahid (Exec Dir-Plng & Dev)

Subsidiaries:

Shifa International DWC-LLC (1)
539 Block No A-3 Business Park, Dubai South Dubai World Central, Dubai, United Arab Emirates
Tel.: (971) 564032005
Web Site: https://www.shifa.com.pk
Health Care Srvices
N.A.I.C.S.: 621999

Shifa Medical Center Islamabad (Pvt.) Limited (1)
3rd Road G-10/4, Islamabad, Pakistan
Tel.: (92) 512228231
Health Care Srvices
N.A.I.C.S.: 621999

SHIFANG HOLDING LIMITED

6/F Hua Fu Mansion No 121 Gutian Road, Fuzhou, 350005, Fujian, China
Tel.: (86) 59188347997 Ky
Web Site:
  http://www.shifangholding.com
1831—(HKG)
Rev.: $18,156,668
Assets: $36,123,376
Liabilities: $30,794,353
Net Worth: $5,329,022
Earnings: ($23,575,266)
Emp.: 106
Fiscal Year-end: 12/31/22
Printing & Digital Media Services
N.A.I.C.S.: 323111
Zhi Chen (Chm & CEO)

SHIFENG CULTURAL DEVELOPMENT CO., LTD.

Chenghua Industrial Zone Wenguan Road, Chenghai District, Shantou, 515800, China
Tel.: (86) 75485899699
Web Site:
  https://www.sunfuntoys.com
Year Founded: 1992
002862—(SSE)
Rev.: $46,127,437
Assets: $98,876,110
Liabilities: $32,507,107
Net Worth: $66,369,003
Earnings: ($5,682,367)
Emp.: 1,000
Fiscal Year-end: 12/31/22
Toy Mfr & Distr
N.A.I.C.S.: 339930
Cai Junquan (Chm & Gen Mgr)

Subsidiaries:

Shifeng (Shenzhen) Internet Technology Limited (1)
A4-902 Kexing Academy of Sciences Keyuan Road, Nanshan District, Shenzhen, China
Tel.: (86) 75586152689
Game Software Development Services
N.A.I.C.S.: 541511

Sunfun (HK) International Co., Ltd. (1)
Block A 29th Floor Ningjin Center 7 Shing Yip Street, Kwun Tong, Kowloon, China (Hong Kong)
Tel.: (852) 23662316
Game Software Development Services
N.A.I.C.S.: 541511

SHIFT, INC.

Azabudai Hills Mori JP Tower 131 Azabudai, Minato-ku, Tokyo, 106-0041, Japan
Tel.: (81) 368091128
Web Site: https://www.shiftinc.jp
Year Founded: 2005
3697—(TKS)
Rev.: $688,099,940
Assets: $390,099,740
Liabilities: $175,372,900
Net Worth: $214,726,840
Earnings: $31,889,940
Fiscal Year-end: 08/31/24
Software Testing Services
N.A.I.C.S.: 541519
Masaru Tange (Pres & CEO)

Subsidiaries:

ALH Inc. (1)
1-24-12 Meguro Orix Meguro Building 5F Reception /8F, Meguro-ku, Tokyo, Japan
Tel.: (81) 337794482
Web Site: https://www.alhinc.jp
Emp.: 1,363
Infrastructure Management Software Development Services
N.A.I.C.S.: 541511

SHIFT India Pvt. Ltd. (1)
404 Pentagon P2, West Magarpatta City Hadapsar, Pune, 411028, India
Tel.: (91) 2049102222
Web Site: http://www.shiftinc.in
Software Testing Services
N.A.I.C.S.: 541511
Masakazu Suga (Mng Dir)

Shift Asia Co., Ltd. (1)
130 Suong Nguyet Anh Street, Ben Thanh Ward District 1, Ho Chi Minh City, Vietnam
Tel.: (84) 2838223341
Web Site: https://shiftasia.com
Emp.: 200
Software Development & Software Testing Services
N.A.I.C.S.: 541511

Shift Security, Inc. (1)
Building 2-4-5 Azabudai, Minato-ku, Tokyo, Japan
Tel.: (81) 368091660
Web Site: https://www.shiftsecurity.jp
Client Information Security Services
N.A.I.C.S.: 541430

SHIFTCARBON INC.

Sea Meadow House, PO Box 116, Road Town, Tortola, VG 1110, Virgin Islands (British)
Tel.: (284) 6045677893 VG
Web Site: https://www.shiftcarbon.io
Year Founded: 1996
SHIFF—(OTCEM)
Rev.: $9,568,251
Assets: $3,172,782
Liabilities: $3,175,658
Net Worth: ($2,876)
Earnings: ($6,640,932)
Fiscal Year-end: 12/31/21
Cryptocurrencies & Alt Coins Quantity Measure Developer & Services
N.A.I.C.S.: 713290
James Passin (Chm)

SHIGEMATSU WORKS CO., LTD.

1-26-1 Nishigahara, Kita-ku, Tokyo, 114-0024, Japan
Tel.: (81) 369037525
Web Site: https://www.sts-japan.com
Year Founded: 1917
7980—(TKS)
Rev.: $124,630,000
Assets: $147,155,360
Liabilities: $76,026,720

INTERNATIONAL PUBLIC

Net Worth: $71,128,640
Earnings: $7,240,640
Emp.: 390
Fiscal Year-end: 03/31/23
Respiratory Protective Device Mfr
N.A.I.C.S.: 339112
Nobuo Shigematsu (Pres)

SHIH HER TECHNOLOGIES, INC.

No 18 Renzheng Road, Hsinchu Industrial Park Hukou Township, Hsinchu, 30352, Taiwan
Tel.: (886) 35981100
Web Site: https://sht.com.tw
Year Founded: 1977
3551—(TPE)
Rev.: $74,813,620
Assets: $149,774,411
Liabilities: $43,330,707
Net Worth: $106,443,704
Earnings: $11,354,657
Emp.: 842
Fiscal Year-end: 12/31/22
Chemical Research & Development Services
N.A.I.C.S.: 541715
Chen Syue-Sheng (Chm)

SHIH WEI NAVIGATION CO., LTD.

16th Floor No 167 Fuxing North Road, Song-Shan District, Taipei, 10547, Taiwan
Tel.: (886) 287121888
Web Site: https://www.swnav.com.tw
5608—(TAI)
Rev.: $113,186,562
Assets: $691,580,012
Liabilities: $374,244,533
Net Worth: $317,335,480
Earnings: ($18,701,984)
Emp.: 889
Fiscal Year-end: 12/31/23
Shipping Services
N.A.I.C.S.: 488510

Subsidiaries:

LANDO Co., Ltd. (1)
Onarimon Building 6F 3-24-5 Nishi Shimbashi, Minato-ku, Tokyo, 105-0003, Japan
Tel.: (81) 364027243
Sales Range: $25-49.9 Million
Emp.: 3
Marine Shipping Services
N.A.I.C.S.: 488330
Katsumi Ono (Pres)

SHIH-KUEN PLASTICS CO., LTD.

125 & 127 Ma-Gong 3rd Road Ma-Kou Li, Ma-Dou District, Tainan City, 72154, Taiwan
Tel.: (886) 65703989
Web Site: https://www.shihkuen.com
Year Founded: 1986
4305—(TPE)
Rev.: $28,444,267
Assets: $38,264,609
Liabilities: $4,316,418
Net Worth: $33,948,191
Earnings: $4,592,127
Fiscal Year-end: 12/31/22
Plastic Product Distr
N.A.I.C.S.: 424610
Chang-Fu Lin (Chm)

SHIHLIN DEVELOPMENT CO., LTD.

8th Floor No 90 Section 6 Zhongshan North Road, Shihlin Dist, Taipei, 111, Taiwan
Tel.: (886) 228348392
Web Site: https://sldc.com.tw
Year Founded: 1990
5324—(TPE)
Rev.: $14,138,542

Assets: $267,521,089
Liabilities: $219,179,283
Net Worth: $48,341,807
Earnings: ($7,134,384)
Fiscal Year-end: 12/31/22
Catering Services
N.A.I.C.S.: 722320
Xu Yushan *(Chm)*

SHIHLIN ELECTRIC & ENGINEERING CORP.
No 234 Zhonglun Village, Xinfeng Township, Hsinchu, Taiwan
Tel.: (886) 35995111
Web Site:
https://automation.seec.com.tw
Year Founded: 1955
1503—(TAI)
Rev.: $1,040,174,296
Assets: $1,757,379,606
Liabilities: $673,486,354
Net Worth: $1,083,893,252
Earnings: $80,436,309
Emp.: 3,939
Fiscal Year-end: 12/31/23
Electrical Equipment Mfr & Distr
N.A.I.C.S.: 335999
Emmet Hsu *(Chm)*

Subsidiaries:

Changzhou Shihlin Auto Parts Co., Ltd. (1)
NO 9 Xin4RD Electronics Park, New District, Changzhou, Jiansu, China
Tel.: (86) 51985106358
Electrical Equipment Mfr & Distr
N.A.I.C.S.: 334515

Shihlin Electric (Australia) Pty. Ltd. (1)
Suite 2 Building 6 Omnico Business Park 270 Ferntree Gully Road, Notting Hill, 3168, VIC, Australia
Tel.: (61) 395019588
Electric Equipment Mfr
N.A.I.C.S.: 335999

Shihlin Electric (Suzhou) Power Equipment Co., Ltd. (1)
No 38 Yongfang Road Huangqiao Industrial Park, Xiangcheng, Suzhou, 215009, China
Tel.: (86) 51265468835
Electrical Equipment Mfr & Distr
N.A.I.C.S.: 334515

Shihlin Electric Engineering Equipment Vietnam Company Limited (1)
Road 10 Ho Nai Industrial Zone, Ho Nai 3 Commune, Trang Bom, Vietnam
Tel.: (84) 2513987750
Electrical Equipment Mfr & Distr
N.A.I.C.S.: 334515

Shihlin Electric USA Company Limited (1)
80 S Lake Ave Ste 780, Pasadena, CA 91101
Tel.: (626) 535-0132
Marketing Promotion Services
N.A.I.C.S.: 541613

Suzhou Shihlin Electric & Engineering Co., Ltd. (1)
88 Guangdong Street, Suzhou, 215129, China
Tel.: (86) 51268432662
Electrical Equipment Mfr & Distr
N.A.I.C.S.: 334515

Wuling Electric Co., Ltd. (1)
No 8 Gonger Road Gonger Industrial Zone, Linkou District, New Taipei City, Taiwan
Tel.: (886) 226033339
Web Site: https://www.wuling.com.tw
Motor Product Mfr & Distr
N.A.I.C.S.: 336999

Wuxi Shihlin Electric & Electric & Engineering Co., Ltd. (1)
88 Mei Yu Road, LotB Wuxi New District, Wuxi, 214028, China
Tel.: (86) 5108658666
Electrical Equipment Mfr & Distr
N.A.I.C.S.: 334515

Xiamen Shihlin Electric & Engineering Co., Ltd. (1)
No 92-96 Sunban S Rd Northern Industry Area, Jimei, Xiamen, 361021, China
Tel.: (86) 5926100660
Electrical Equipment Mfr & Distr
N.A.I.C.S.: 334515

SHIHLIN PAPER CORPORATION
No 31 Fude Rd, Shilin Dist, Taipei, 111, Taiwan
Tel.: (886) 228811111
Web Site: https://www.shihlin.com.tw
Year Founded: 1959
1903—(TAI)
Rev.: $5,595,507
Assets: $284,807,341
Liabilities: $144,140,058
Net Worth: $140,667,283
Earnings: $2,823,899
Emp.: 50
Fiscal Year-end: 12/31/23
Paper & Paper Products Mfr
N.A.I.C.S.: 322230
Po-Ting Chen *(Chm)*

SHIJIAZHUANG CHANGSHAN TEXTILE CO., LTD.
No 260 East Heping Road, Shijiazhuang, 050011, Hebei, China
Tel.: (86) 31186046786
Web Site:
https://www.changshantex.com
Year Founded: 1991
000158—(SSE)
Rev.: $1,356,751,483
Assets: $2,324,550,627
Liabilities: $1,490,131,104
Net Worth: $834,419,524
Earnings: ($29,171,133)
Emp.: 5,054
Fiscal Year-end: 12/31/22
Textile Products Mfr
N.A.I.C.S.: 313210
Mi Yong *(Chm)*

SHIJIAZHUANG JUNLEBAO DAIRY CO., LTD.
No 36 Shitong Road, Luquan, Shijiazhuang, 050221, China
Tel.: (86) 31167362666
Web Site:
http://www.english.junlebaoruye.com
Year Founded: 1995
Emp.: 8,000
Milk Product Distr
N.A.I.C.S.: 424430

SHIJIAZHUANG KELIN ELECTRIC CO., LTD.
Nanjiangbi Hongqi Street, Luquan District, Shijiazhuang, 050222, Hebei, China
Tel.: (86) 31189176007
Web Site: https://www.kechina.com
Year Founded: 2000
603050—(SHG)
Rev.: $368,212,731
Assets: $656,544,264
Liabilities: $462,028,839
Net Worth: $194,515,425
Earnings: $16,065,761
Emp.: 2,500
Fiscal Year-end: 12/31/22
Electric Power Distribution Services
N.A.I.C.S.: 221122
Chen Weiqiang *(Chm)*

SHIJIAZHUANG SHANGTAI TECHNOLOGY CO., LTD.
West of Nansha Road, Lichengdao Village Wuji County, Hebei, 052461, China
Tel.: (86) 31186509019

Web Site:
https://www.shangtaitech.com
Year Founded: 2008
001301—(SSE)
Rev.: $671,371,206
Assets: $1,245,352,423
Liabilities: $515,731,671
Net Worth: $729,620,752
Earnings: $181,039,412
Fiscal Year-end: 12/31/22
Battery Product Mfr
N.A.I.C.S.: 335910
Yongyue Ouyang *(Chm & Gen Mgr)*

SHIJIAZHUANG TONHE ELECTRONICS TECHNOLOGIES CO., LTD.
No 350 Lijiang Road High-tech Zone, Shijiazhuang, 50035, China
Tel.: (86) 31166577110
Web Site: https://www.tonhe.com.cn
Year Founded: 1998
300491—(CHIN)
Rev.: $142,057,310
Assets: $279,239,858
Liabilities: $121,958,268
Net Worth: $157,281,589
Earnings: $14,447,125
Emp.: 500
Fiscal Year-end: 12/31/23
Electronic Products Mfr
N.A.I.C.S.: 334419
Ma Xiaofeng *(Chm & Gen Mgr)*

SHIJIAZHUANG YILING PHARMACEUTICAL CO., LTD.
238 Tianshan Street, East developing zone, Shijiazhuang, Hebei, China
Tel.: (86) 31185901712
Web Site: https://www.yiling.cn
Year Founded: 1992
002603—(SSE)
Rev.: $1,759,610,876
Assets: $2,293,590,223
Liabilities: $758,980,062
Net Worth: $1,534,610,161
Earnings: $331,597,380
Emp.: 10,000
Fiscal Year-end: 12/31/22
Pharmaceuticals Mfr
N.A.I.C.S.: 325412
Yiling Wu *(Chm)*

Subsidiaries:

Yiling Pharmaceutical Ltd. (1)
No 36 Zhujiang Street Shijiazhuang, Hebei, 50035, China
Tel.: (86) 31185901712
Pharmaceutical Preparation Mfr
N.A.I.C.S.: 325412

SHIKHAR CONSULTANTS LIMITED
A - 41 Nandjyot Industrial Estate Near Safed Pool Andheri - Kurla Road, Andheri E, Mumbai, 400072, Maharashtra, India
Tel.: (91) 2228518641
Year Founded: 1993
526883—(BOM)
Sales Range: Less than $1 Million
Financial Services
N.A.I.C.S.: 523999
Babulal Agrawal *(Chm & Compliance Officer)*

SHIKHAR INSURANCE COMPANY LTD.
Shikhar Biz Centre Thapathali Fourth to Seventh Floor, PO Box 10692, Kathmandu, Nepal
Tel.: (977) 15346101
Web Site:
https://shikharinsurance.com
SICL—(NEP)
Rev.: $40,145,523

Assets: $83,710,209
Liabilities: $46,668,519
Net Worth: $37,041,691
Earnings: $1,714,030
Emp.: 650
Fiscal Year-end: 07/16/23
Insurance Services
N.A.I.C.S.: 524298
Rajendra Prasad Shrestha *(Chm)*

SHIKHAR LEASING & TRADING LIMITED
1301 13th Floor Peninsula Business Park Tower B Senapati Bapat Marg, Lower Parel West, Mumbai, 400 013, Maharashtra, India
Tel.: (91) 2230036565
Web Site:
https://shikharleasingandtrading.in
Yarn & Fabric Distr
N.A.I.C.S.: 424310
Heena Sanjay Desai *(CFO)*

SHIKIBO LTD.
2-6 Bingomachi 3-chome, Chuo-ku, Osaka, 541-8516, Japan
Tel.: (81) 662685490
Web Site: https://www.shikibo.co.jp
Year Founded: 1892
3109—(TKS)
Rev.: $255,681,410
Assets: $550,606,390
Liabilities: $325,337,590
Net Worth: $225,268,800
Earnings: $5,288,000
Emp.: 2,198
Fiscal Year-end: 03/31/24
Textile Product Mfr & Whslr
N.A.I.C.S.: 313110
Mikio Kiyohara *(Chm & Pres)*

Subsidiaries:

HUZHOU SHIKIBO HAPPINESS TEXTILES CO., LTD. (1)
Economic Development Zone, Zhili, Huzhou, 313008, Zhejiang, China
Tel.: (86) 5723152115
Textile Products Distr
N.A.I.C.S.: 424990

P.T. MERMAID TEXTILE INDUSTRY INDONESIA (1)
Desa Lengkong Kec, Mojoanyar Kab, Mojokerto, 61364, Jawa Timur, Indonesia
Tel.: (62) 321322411
Web Site: https://www.mertex.co.id
Emp.: 620
Textile Products Distr
N.A.I.C.S.: 424990

SHIKIBO LINEN CO., LTD. (1)
1293-1 Asso, Kamitonda-Cho NishiMuro-Gun, Wakayama, 649-2105, Japan
Tel.: (81) 739470123
Textile Products Distr
N.A.I.C.S.: 424990

Shinnaigai Textile Ltd. (52.21%)
4F Shikishima Bldg 3-2-6 Bingo-machi, Chuo-ku, Osaka, 541-0051, Japan
Tel.: (81) 6 47053781
Web Site: http://www.shinnaigai-tex.co.jp
Rev.: $44,946,600
Assets: $42,029,340
Liabilities: $16,869,720
Net Worth: $25,159,620
Fiscal Year-end: 03/31/2019
Textile Product Mfr & Distr
N.A.I.C.S.: 313210
Hidetaka Nagato *(Chm)*

THAI SHIKIBO CO., LTD. (1)
311 Moo 1 Tambon Bung, Amphur, Si Racha, 20230, Chonburi, Thailand
Tel.: (66) 38 480416
Emp.: 270
Textile Products Distr
N.A.I.C.S.: 424990

shikibo (HK) Ltd. (1)
Suite 2408 24th Floor Lippo Centre Tower 2 89 Queensway Admiralty, Tsim Sha Tsui, Hong Kong, China (Hong Kong)

SHIKIBO LTD.

Shikibo Ltd.—(Continued)
Tel.: (852) 27445825
Textile Products Distr
N.A.I.C.S.: 424990

SHIKIGAKU CO., LTD.
1F Osaki West City Building 293
Osaki, Shinagawa-Ku, Tokyo, 141-0031, Japan
Tel.: (81) 368217560
Web Site:
https://www.corp.shikigaku.jp
7049—(TKS)
Rev.: $34,237,610
Assets: $32,330,400
Liabilities: $10,457,750
Net Worth: $21,872,650
Earnings: ($687,730)
Emp.: 253
Fiscal Year-end: 02/29/24
Educational Support Services
N.A.I.C.S.: 611710
Kodai Ando *(Founder & Pres)*

Subsidiaries:

Fukushima Sports Entertainment Co., Ltd. (1)
1-2 Doumaecho Ishii Building 1F, Koriyama, 963-8877, Japan
Tel.: (81) 249270777
Web Site: https://firebonds.jp
Basketball Games Goods & Ticket Distr
N.A.I.C.S.: 423910

SHIKINO HIGH-TECH CO., LTD.
829 Kichijima, Uozu, 937-0041, Toyama, Japan
Tel.: (81) 765223477
Web Site: https://www.shikino.co.jp
Year Founded: 1975
6614—(TKS)
Emp.: 342
Electronic Equipment Mfr & Distr
N.A.I.C.S.: 336320
Takashi Tsukada *(Chm & CEO)*

SHIKISHIMA BAKING CO., LTD.
5 3 Shirakabe, Higashi-ku, Nagoya, 461 8721, Japan
Tel.: (81) 0529332111
Web Site: http://www.pasconet.co.jp
Year Founded: 1920
Sales Range: $500-549.9 Million
Emp.: 4,104
Baked Goods Mfr
N.A.I.C.S.: 311812
Atsuo Morita *(Pres & CEO)*

SHIKOKU CHEMICALS CORPORATION
8-537-1 Doki-cho-higashi, Marugame, 763-8504, Kagawa, Japan
Tel.: (81) 877224111
Web Site: https://www.shikoku.co.jp
4099—(TKS)
Rev.: $417,026,759
Assets: $865,847,374
Liabilities: $291,899,571
Net Worth: $573,947,803
Earnings: $51,886,356
Emp.: 619
Fiscal Year-end: 12/31/23
Chemical Segment Mfr
N.A.I.C.S.: 325180
Naoto Tanaka *(Pres, Pres, CEO & CEO)*

Subsidiaries:

Shikoku Analytical laboratories (1)
2-14-10 Kitahirayama-cho, Marugame, 763-0015, Kagawa, Japan
Tel.: (81) 877584001
Web Site: http://www.niji.or.jp
Sales Range: $75-99.9 Million
Emp.: 12
Water Treatment Consulting Services
N.A.I.C.S.: 221310
Toshiharu Maruoka *(Pres)*

Shikoku Chemicals Corporatiion - Tokushima Plant (Kitajima) (1)
1 Ejiri Kitajima-cho, Itano-gun, Tokushima, 771 0288, Japan
Tel.: (81) 886984111
Sales Range: $25-49.9 Million
Emp.: 138
Environmental Management Services
N.A.I.C.S.: 541330

Shikoku Chemicals Corporation - Marugame Plant (1)
147-1 Minatomachi, Marugame, 763-0042, Kagawa, Japan
Tel.: (81) 877234111
Web Site: http://www.shikoku.co.jp
Environmental Management Services
N.A.I.C.S.: 541330

Shikoku Chemicals Corporation - Tokushima Plant (Yoshinari) (1)
127 Ude Yoshinari Oujin-cho, Tokushima, 771-1153, Japan
Tel.: (81) 886414111
Web Site: http://www.shikoku.co.jp
Environmental Management Services
N.A.I.C.S.: 541330

Shikoku Environmental Business Company (1)
5-4 Tarumi-cho, Marugame, 763 0095, Kagawa, Japan
Tel.: (81) 877288308
Civil Engineering Services
N.A.I.C.S.: 541330

Shikoku International Corporation (1)
301 N Rampart St Ste C, Orange, CA 92868
Tel.: (714) 978-0347
Sales Range: $50-74.9 Million
Emp.: 5
Building Materials Whslr
N.A.I.C.S.: 423390
Hirotaka Ide *(Pres & COO)*

Shikoku Keizai Corporation (1)
42 Nishiminato-machi, Tadotsu-cho Nakatado-gun, Kagawa, 764-0017, Japan
Tel.: (81) 877334111
Web Site: http://www.shikoku.co.jp
Sales Range: $200-249.9 Million
Exterior Products Mfr
N.A.I.C.S.: 321918
Yuichi Ikeda *(Officer)*

Plant (Domestic):

Shikoku Keizai Corporation - Naruto Plant (2)
52 Uashiro Dounoura, Seto-cho, Naruto, 771 0361, Tokushima, Japan
Tel.: (81) 886880456
Exterior Products Mfr
N.A.I.C.S.: 321918

Shikoku Keizai Kanto Corporation (1)
3-4 Hanamidai, Ranzan-machi Hiki-gun, Saitama, 355-0204, Japan
Tel.: (81) 493624113
Web Site: http://www.shikoku.co.jp
Sales Range: $25-49.9 Million
Emp.: 53
Shutters Mfr
N.A.I.C.S.: 321918

Shikoku Kosan Corporation (1)
Ejiri Kitajima-cho, Itanu-gun, Tokushima, 771 0205, Japan
Tel.: (81) 886986958
Packaging & Transportation Services
N.A.I.C.S.: 488999

Shikoku OM (Shanghai) Co., Ltd. (1)
Rm 2208 Mingshen Center 3131 Kaixuan Rd, Shanghai, 20030, China
Tel.: (86) 21 5407 1788
Web Site: http://www.shikoku.co.jp
Sales Range: $50-74.9 Million
Emp.: 5
Construction Materials Whslr
N.A.I.C.S.: 423320

Shikoku System Kohboh Corporation (1)
537-1 Dokichohigashi, Pottery Town, Marugame, 763-0082, Kagawa, Japan
Tel.: (81) 877255200
Web Site: http://www.kohboh.co.jp
Emp.: 27
Software Development Services
N.A.I.C.S.: 541511

SHIKOKU DOCKYARD CO., LTD.
1-3-23 Asahimachi, Takamatsu, 760-0065, Kagawa, Japan
Tel.: (81) 87 851 9021
Web Site:
https://www.shikokudock.co.jp
Year Founded: 1964
Emp.: 147
Ship Building & Repairing Services
N.A.I.C.S.: 336611

SHIKOKU ELECTRIC POWER CO., INCORPORATED
2-5 Marunouchi, Takamatsu, 760-8573, Kagawa, Japan
Tel.: (81) 878215061
Web Site: http://www.yonden.co.jp
Year Founded: 1951
9507—(TKS)
Rev.: $5,204,733,830
Assets: $10,768,046,940
Liabilities: $8,367,506,460
Net Worth: $2,400,540,480
Earnings: $400,004,150
Emp.: 2,170
Fiscal Year-end: 03/31/24
Electric Power Distr
N.A.I.C.S.: 221122
Hayato Saeki *(Co-Chm)*

Subsidiaries:

Abe Iron Works Ltd. (1)
171 Minami Hohji, Nakaono-cho, Anan, 774-0048, Tokushima, Japan
Tel.: (81) 88 422 9256
Web Site: https://www.abe-iron-works.com
Emp.: 9
High-Quality Product Mfr
N.A.I.C.S.: 334513
Nobuo Inoue *(Pres)*

Agribbon Corporation (1)
241-1 Inoe, Miki-cho Kita-gun, Kagawa, 761-0705, Japan
Tel.: (81) 87 802 7280
Web Site: https://www.agribbon.com
Agricultural Services
N.A.I.C.S.: 115116

Aitosa Corporation (1)
2-4-8 Kitakyuhojimachi, Chuo-ku, Osaka, 541-0057, Japan
Tel.: (81) 66 262 5220
Web Site: https://www.aitoz.co.jp
Wear Cloth Mfr & Distr
N.A.I.C.S.: 315250

STNet, Incorporated (1)
1735-3 Kasuga-cho, Takamatsu, 761-0195, Kagawa, Japan
Tel.: (81) 878872400
Web Site: http://www.stnet.co.jp
Emp.: 722
Telecommunication & Information System Services
N.A.I.C.S.: 517810

Sakaide LNG Co., Inc. (1)
2 Sakaide Power Plant Bannosu cho, Sakaide, 762-0065, Kagawa, Japan
Tel.: (81) 877592244
Construction of LNG Fuel Bases, Vaporization & Storage Facilities
N.A.I.C.S.: 237120
Akihiro Nakahara *(Dir-Gen Affairs)*

Shikoku Instrumentation Co., Ltd. (1)
200-1 Minamigamo Tadotsu-cho, Nakatado, Kagawa, 764-8502, Japan
Tel.: (81) 877332221
Web Site: http://www.yonkei.co.jp
Emp.: 762

INTERNATIONAL PUBLIC

Automatic Gauging Control Instruments Mfr
N.A.I.C.S.: 334513
Hiromichi Wada *(Pres)*

Yonden Business Company, Incorporated (1)
2-5 Marunouchi, Takamatsu, 760-0033, Kagawa, Japan
Tel.: (81) 878511151
Real Estate Manangement Services
N.A.I.C.S.: 531210

Yonden Consultants Company, Incorporated (1)
1007-3 Mure Mure-cho, Takamatsu, 761-0121, Kagawa, Japan
Tel.: (81) 8 7845 8881
Web Site: http://www.yon-shi.co.jp
Civil Engineering Services
N.A.I.C.S.: 541330

Yonden Energy Service Company, Incorporated (1)
7-9 Kameicho Bldg 1st & 2nd floor, Takamatsu, 760-0050, Kagawa, Japan
Tel.: (81) 878350551
Web Site: http://www.yonden-yes.co.jp
Electrical Water Heaters & Air Conditioning Systems Sales & Maintenance Services
N.A.I.C.S.: 449210

Yonden Engineering Company, Incorporated (1)
3-1-4 Kaminomachi, Kamino-Cho, Takamatsu, 761-8541, Kagawa, Japan
Tel.: (81) 878671711
Web Site: https://www.yon-e.co.jp
Emp.: 1,116
Engineeering Services
N.A.I.C.S.: 541330

Yonden Life Care Co., Inc. (1)
2-27 Momijimachi, Matsuyama, 790-0861, Ehime, Japan
Tel.: (81) 899868100
Web Site: http://www.yondenlc.co.jp
Nursing Support Services
N.A.I.C.S.: 623110

Yondenko Corporation (1)
2-3-9 Hananomiya-cho, Takamatsu, 760-0068, Kagawa, Japan
Tel.: (81) 878361111
Web Site: https://www.yondenko.co.jp
Emp.: 2,100
Electrical Engineering Services
N.A.I.C.S.: 541330

SHIKUN & BINUI LTD.
1a Ha'Yarden St, PO Box 1133, Airport City, Ben-Gurion Airport, 7010000, Israel
Tel.: (972) 36301111
Web Site:
https://www.shikunbinui.com
SKBN—(TAE)
Rev.: $2,275,452,375
Assets: $7,715,982,750
Liabilities: $6,043,928,625
Net Worth: $1,672,054,125
Earnings: $85,647,188
Emp.: 9,192
Fiscal Year-end: 12/31/23
Offices of Other Holding Companies
N.A.I.C.S.: 551112
Ronit Rosensweig *(Deputy CFO & Head-Fin Reporting)*

Subsidiaries:

Shikun & Binui Real Estate Ltd. (1)
3 Shalem Street, Ramat Gan, 52215, Israel
Tel.: (972) 3 630 1570
Real Estate Consulting Service
N.A.I.C.S.: 531390

SHILCHAR TECHNOLOGIES LTD.
Bil Road Bil, 391 410, Vadodara, 391 410, India
Tel.: (91) 2652680466
Web Site: https://www.shilchar.com
531201—(BOM)
Rev.: $16,408,583
Assets: $14,626,466

Liabilities: $5,571,643
Net Worth: $9,054,823
Earnings: $753,794
Emp.: 115
Fiscal Year-end: 03/31/21
Transformer Mfr
N.A.I.C.S.: 334416
Alay J. Shah *(Chm & Mng Dir)*

SHILP GRAVURES LTD
7786 Pramukh Industrial Estate Sola-Santej Road Rakanpu, Tal Kalol, Gandhinagar, 382721, Gujarat, India
Tel.: (91) 9925204058
Web Site:
https://www.shilpgravures.com
513709—(BOM)
Rev.: $10,608,105
Assets: $12,636,425
Liabilities: $2,217,001
Net Worth: $10,419,423
Earnings: $936,299
Emp.: 292
Fiscal Year-end: 03/31/23
Engraving Services
N.A.I.C.S.: 332813
Atul Manilal Vinchi *(COO)*

Subsidiaries:

Etone India Private Limited (1)
Bally-Durgapur N H 2 Samabayapally, Howrah, 711205, West Bengal, India
Tel.: (91) 6289671741
Base Roller Mfr
N.A.I.C.S.: 333519

SHILPA MEDICARE LTD
12-6-214/A1, Hyderabad Road, Raichur, 584 135, Karnataka, India
Tel.: (91) 8532238704
Web Site: https://www.vbshilpa.com
Year Founded: 1987
SHILPAMED—(NSE)
Rev.: $127,118,587
Assets: $360,026,203
Liabilities: $159,712,917
Net Worth: $200,313,286
Earnings: $19,956,791
Emp.: 2,350
Fiscal Year-end: 03/31/21
Pharmaceuticals Mfr & Marketer
N.A.I.C.S.: 424210
Vishnukant Chaturbhuj Bhutada *(Mng Dir)*

Subsidiaries:

FTF Pharma Private Limited (1)
Block No 193 Part 211 Part Xcelon Industrial Park, Chak-de-India Weigh Bridge Road Vasana Chacharwadi Tal Sanand, Ahmedabad, 382213, Gujarat, India
Tel.: (91) 2717617800
Web Site: https://www.ftfpharma.com
Pharmaceutical Research & Development Services
N.A.I.C.S.: 541715

INM Nuvent Paints Private
Limited (1)
B No 13-E/13 1st Phase Kumbalgodu Industrial Area, Kengri H, Bengaluru, 560074, Karnataka, India
Tel.: (91) 8062733448
Web Site: https://www.nuventpaints.in
Emp.: 37
Chemical Product Mfr & Distr
N.A.I.C.S.: 325998

Koanna Healthcare GmbH (1)
Fehrgasse 7, 2401, Fischamend Dorf, Austria
Tel.: (43) 7202727010
Web Site: https://www.koanaa.com
Pharmaceutical Research & Development Services
N.A.I.C.S.: 541715

Loba Feinchemie GmbH (1)
Fehrgasse 7, 2401, Fischamend Dorf, Austria
Tel.: (43) 2232773910

Web Site: https://www.lobabiotech.com
Emp.: 40
Chemical Products Mfr
N.A.I.C.S.: 325199
Leopold Arnberger *(Dir-Technical)*

Shilpa Biologicals Private Limited (1)
Plot 532/A Belur Industrial Area, Hubli-Dharwad, 580011, Karnataka, India
Tel.: (91) 8362485555
Web Site: https://www.shilpabio.com
Biological Research Services
N.A.I.C.S.: 541714

Sravathi AI Technology Private
Limited (1)
63-B Bommasandra Industrial Area, Bengaluru, 560099, Karnataka, India
Tel.: (91) 8049738885
Web Site: https://sravathi.ai
Pharmaceutical Research & Development Services
N.A.I.C.S.: 541715

Sravathi Advance Process Tech Private Limited (1)
113/40 2nd Main Road Rajajinagar, Industrial Town, Bengaluru, 560 010, Karnataka, India
Tel.: (91) 8049738885
Web Site: https://www.sravathi.com
Pharmaceutical Research & Development Services
N.A.I.C.S.: 541715

SHIMA SEIKI MFG., LTD.
85 Sakata, Wakayama, 641-8511, Japan
Tel.: (81) 734748210
Web Site:
https://www.shimaseiki.com
Year Founded: 1962
6222—(TKS)
Rev.: $237,365,100
Assets: $712,584,440
Liabilities: $104,953,580
Net Worth: $607,630,860
Earnings: $6,808,300
Emp.: 1,789
Fiscal Year-end: 03/31/24
Knitting Machinery Mfr & Distr
N.A.I.C.S.: 333248
Masahiro Shima *(Chm)*

Subsidiaries:

SHIMA SEIKI (THAILAND) CO.,
LTD. (1)
19 21 Soi 30 Rama 2 Rama 2 Road Bangmod, Jomthong, Bangkok, 10150, Thailand
Tel.: (66) 24520550
Knitting Machinery Distr
N.A.I.C.S.: 423830
Prapawadee Sukjun *(Mng Dir)*

SHIMA SEIKI Korea, Inc. (1)
Seojung Bldg 47 Achasan-Ro 58-Gil, Gwangjin-Gu, Seoul, 05049, Korea (South)
Tel.: (82) 222164057
Knitting Machinery Distr
N.A.I.C.S.: 423830

SHIMA SEIKI SPAIN, S.A.U. (1)
Poligono Industrial Can Salvatella Calle Comadran 35, Barbera del Valles, 08210, Barcelona, Spain
Tel.: (34) 937293727
Knitting Machinery Distr
N.A.I.C.S.: 423830

Shima Fine Press Co., Ltd. (1)
357 Kamimae, Wakayama, 640-8314, Japan
Tel.: (81) 734730321
Web Site: https://www.shimaseiki.co.jp
Emp.: 118
Knitting Machine Mfr
N.A.I.C.S.: 333248
Masahiro Shima *(Pres)*

Shima Seiki (Hong Kong) Ltd. (1)
3/F S A C C 64 Tsun Yip Street, Kwun Tong, Kowloon, China (Hong Kong)
Tel.: (852) 28988339
Knitting Machinery Distr
N.A.I.C.S.: 423830
Ikuto Umeda *(CEO)*

Shima Seiki Europe Ltd. (1)
Unit 1 1A Sills Road Willow Farm Business Park, Castle Donington, DE74 2US, Derbyshire, United Kingdom
Tel.: (44) 1332814770
Knitting Machinery Distr
N.A.I.C.S.: 423830
Richard Webster *(Mng Dir)*

Shima Seiki France SARL (1)
Espace Lumiere - Building 7 55 Boulevard de La Republique, 78400, Chatou, France
Tel.: (33) 134930580
Web Site: https://www.shimaseiki.com
Knitting Machinery Distr
N.A.I.C.S.: 423830

Shima Seiki Italia S.p.A. (1)
Via Martiri di Cefalonia 6, 20054, Segrate, MI, Italy
Tel.: (39) 02216621
Knitting Machinery Distr
N.A.I.C.S.: 423830
Nobuyuki Sasamoto *(Pres)*

Shima Seiki U.S.A. Inc. (1)
2301 E 7th St Unit A 350, Los Angeles, CA 90023
Tel.: (609) 655-4788
Web Site: http://www.shimaseikiusa.com
Knitting Machinery Distr
N.A.I.C.S.: 423830

Shima Seiki Win Win Shanghai
Ltd. (1)
Rm 103 105 Building 3 No 299 You Le Road, Shanghai, 200335, China
Tel.: (86) 2152709898
Knitting Machinery Distr
N.A.I.C.S.: 423830

Shima Seiki WinWin Dongguan
Ltd. (1)
Rm 401 No 6 Yumin Sixth Street, Xiangwei Community Dalang Town, Dongguan, 523770, Guangdong, China
Tel.: (86) 76983189234
Knitting Machinery Distr
N.A.I.C.S.: 423830

Toyoboshi Kogyo Co., Ltd. (1)
3-3-10 Tadaokahigashi Tadaoka-cho, Semboku-gun, Osaka, 595-0805, Japan
Tel.: (81) 725223190
Apparel & Accessory Mfr & Distr
N.A.I.C.S.: 315990

SHIMA TRADING CO. LTD.
1-18 Kitahama 3-chome, Chou-ku, Osaka, 5400-0041, Japan
Tel.: (81) 0662080201
Web Site: http://www.shima-tra.co.jp
Year Founded: 1904
Sales Range: $25-49.9 Billion
Emp.: 148
Chemical Product Whslr
N.A.I.C.S.: 424690
Koshi Shima *(Chm)*

Subsidiaries:

Shima American Corp. (1)
500 Park Blvd Ste 480, Itasca, IL 60143 (100%)
Tel.: (630) 760-4330
Web Site: http://www.shimaamerian.com
Sales Range: $25-49.9 Million
Emp.: 20
Chemicals Whslr
N.A.I.C.S.: 424690
Saburo Kobayashi *(Pres)*

Shima Asia Pacific (M) Sdn.
Bhd. (1)
Suite 6 03 Wisma E&C No 2 Lorong Dungun Kiri Damansara Heights, 50490, Kuala Lumpur, Malaysia
Tel.: (60) 3 2093 5233
Chemical Products Distr
N.A.I.C.S.: 424690

Shima Trading (Shanghai) Co.,
Ltd. (1)
Room 1601 Innov Tower Block A 1801 HongMei Road, Shanghai, 200233, China
Tel.: (86) 21 33678181
Chemical Products Distr
N.A.I.C.S.: 424690

Shima Trading Singapore Pte.
Ltd. (1)
9 Penang Road 08-07 ParkMall, Singapore, 238459, Singapore
Tel.: (65) 6732 8860
Chemical Products Distr
N.A.I.C.S.: 424690

SHIMACHU CO., LTD.
5-1555 Mihashi, Nishi-ku, Saitama, 331-8511, Japan
Tel.: (81) 48 6237711
Web Site: http://www.shimachu.co.jp
Year Founded: 1947
8184—(TKS)
Sales Range: $1-4.9 Billion
Emp.: 1,559
Store Operator
N.A.I.C.S.: 449110
Shigeo Yamashita *(Pres)*

SHIMADZU CORPORATION
1 Nishinokyo Kuwabara-cho, Nakagyo-ku, Kyoto, 604 8511, Japan
Tel.: (81) 758231111 JP
Web Site: https://www.shimadzu.com
Year Founded: 1875
7701—(TKS)
Rev.: $3,383,625,950
Assets: $4,454,888,820
Liabilities: $1,200,554,470
Net Worth: $3,254,334,350
Earnings: $377,014,570
Emp.: 14,219
Fiscal Year-end: 03/31/24
Analytical & Measuring Instruments, Medical Systems, Industrial & Aircraft Equipment Mfr
N.A.I.C.S.: 334513
Teruhisa Ueda *(Chm)*

Subsidiaries:

Alsachim SAS (1)
160 Rue Tobias Stimmer, 67400, Illkirch-Graffenstaden, France
Tel.: (33) 39 040 2200
Web Site: https://www.alsachim.com
Pharmaceuticals Product Mfr
N.A.I.C.S.: 325412
Jean-Francois Hoeffler *(Mng Dir)*

Beijing Shimadzu Medical Equipment Co., Ltd. (1)
No 207 Longsheng Industry Zone No 7 Rong Chang Dong Street, Beijing Economic Technology Development Area, Beijing, 100176, China
Tel.: (86) 1067880406
Web Site: http://www.shimadzu.com
Sales Range: $25-49.9 Million
Emp.: 30
Medical Equipment Mfr
N.A.I.C.S.: 339112

Infraserv Vakuumservice GmbH (1)
Gleiwitzerstrasse 8, 85386, Eching, Germany
Tel.: (49) 89 319 0103
Web Site: https://www.vakuumservice.de
Vacuum Services
N.A.I.C.S.: 811111

Kratos Analytical Inc. (1)
404 E Route 59, Nanuet, NY 10954
Tel.: (845) 426-6700
Web Site: http://www.kratos.com
Sales Range: $25-49.9 Million
Emp.: 10
Provider of Analytical Instruments
N.A.I.C.S.: 334519

Kratos Analytical Ltd. (1)
Wharfside Trafford Wharf Road, Manchester, M17 1GP, United Kingdom (100%)
Tel.: (44) 1618884400
Web Site: https://www.kratos.com
Sales Range: $25-49.9 Million
Emp.: 200
Mfr of Analytical & Measurement Instruments
N.A.I.C.S.: 334516
Kozo Shimazu *(Mgr)*

SHIMADZU CORPORATION

Shimadzu Corporation—(Continued)

Ningbo Shimadzu Vacuum Technology Development Co., Ltd. (1)
No 3 BinHai Cixi Economic Development Zone, Hangzhou Bay New Zone, Ningbo, 315336, Zhejiang, China
Tel.: (86) 5742 371 1337
Industrial Equipment Mfr
N.A.I.C.S.: 333248

SHIMADZU BENELUX B.V. (1)
Australielaan 14, 5232 BB, 's-Hertogenbosch, Netherlands
Tel.: (31) 736 430 320
Web Site: http://www.shimadzu.nl
Emp.: 50
Analytical Instrument Mfr
N.A.I.C.S.: 334516
Corwin Pigmans *(Mng Dir)*

SHIMADZU DEUTSCHLAND GmbH (1)
Keniastrasse 38, 47269, Duisburg, Germany
Tel.: (49) 203 7687 0
Web Site: http://www.shimadzu.de
Emp.: 15
Analytical Instrument Mfr
N.A.I.C.S.: 334516

SHIMADZU FRANCE SAS (1)
Le Luzard II - Bat A Bd Salvador Allende, Noisiel, 77448, Marne-la-Vallee, Cedex, France
Tel.: (33) 160951010
Web Site: https://www.shimadzu.fr
Emp.: 60
Biotechnology Equipment Mfr
N.A.I.C.S.: 325414
Mark Fernandes *(Gen Mgr)*

SHIMADZU HANDELSGESELLSCHAFT mbH (1)
Laaer Strasse 7-9, 2100, Korneuburg, Austria
Tel.: (43) 2262 62601 0
Web Site: http://www.shimadzu.eu.com
Sales Range: $25-49.9 Million
Emp.: 14
Analytical Instrument Mfr
N.A.I.C.S.: 334516
Robert Kaubek *(Mng Dir)*

SHIMADZU ITALIA S.r.l. (1)
Via G B Cassinis 7, 20139, Milan, Italy
Tel.: (39) 0257409690
Web Site: https://www.shimadzu.it
Medical Instrument Mfr
N.A.I.C.S.: 339112

SHIMADZU PHILIPPINES CORPORATION (1)
19th Floor Marajo Tower 26th St corner 4th Avenue, Bonifacio Global City, Taguig, 1634, Metro Manila, Philippines
Tel.: (63) 288699563
Web Site: http://www.shimadzu.com.ph
Sales Range: $25-49.9 Million
Emp.: 7
Medical Instrument Mfr & Distr
N.A.I.C.S.: 339112

SHIMADZU SLOVAKIA o.z. (1)
Rontgenova 28, 851 01, Bratislava, Slovakia
Tel.: (421) 248200081
Web Site: https://www.shimadzu.sk
Medical Instrument Mfr
N.A.I.C.S.: 339112

SHIMADZU d.o.o. (1)
Zavrtnica 17, 10000, Zagreb, Hrvatska, Croatia
Tel.: (385) 16185777
Web Site: https://www.shimadzu.hr
Sales Range: $25-49.9 Million
Emp.: 5
Medical Instrument Mfr
N.A.I.C.S.: 339112

Shimadzu (Asia Pacific) Pte. (1)
79 Science Park Drive 02-01/08 Cintech IV, Science Park 1, Singapore, 118264, Singapore (100%)
Tel.: (65) 67786280
Web Site: https://www.shimadzu.com.sg
Sales Range: $25-49.9 Million
Emp.: 100

Mfr of Analytical & Measurement Instruments, Medical Systems & Equipment
N.A.I.C.S.: 334516

Shimadzu (Guangzhou) Analysis & Technology Services Co., Ltd. (1)
Room 201-213 D District Guangzhou Technology Innovation Base No 80, Lan Yue Road Science City, Guangzhou, 510663, China
Tel.: (86) 203 205 8871
Industrial Equipment Mfr
N.A.I.C.S.: 333248

Shimadzu (Hong Kong) Ltd. (1)
Suite 1028 Ocean Centre Harbour City, Tsim Sha Tsui, Kowloon, 999077, China (Hong Kong) (100%)
Tel.: (852) 23754979
Web Site: http://www.shimadzu.com.cn
Sales Range: $25-49.9 Million
Emp.: 14
Provider of Medical & Analytical Instruments
N.A.I.C.S.: 334516
Take Moto *(Gen Mgr)*

Shimadzu (Shanghai) Global Laboratory Consumables Co., Ltd. (1)
Building C801 Huaxintiandi II No 180 Yizhou Road, Xuhui District, Shanghai, 200233, China
Tel.: (86) 216 280 0202
Industrial Equipment Mfr
N.A.I.C.S.: 333248

Shimadzu (Suzhou) Instruments Manufacturing Co., Ltd. (1)
183 Taishan Road, Suzhou New District, Jiangsu, 215011, China
Tel.: (86) 5126 536 4429
Industrial Equipment Mfr
N.A.I.C.S.: 333248

Shimadzu Analytical (India) Pvt. Ltd. (1)
1 A/B Rushabh Chambers Makwana Road, Marol Andheri E, Mumbai, 400 059, India
Tel.: (91) 222 920 4741
Web Site: https://www.an.shimadzu.in
Analytical Instrument Mfr & Distr
N.A.I.C.S.: 334516
Yoshiyuki Fujino *(Mng Dir)*

Shimadzu Do Brasil Comercio Ltda. (1)
Avenida Tambore 576 - Tambore, Barueri, 06460-000, SP, Brazil (100%)
Tel.: (55) 1124241700
Web Site: http://www.shimadzu.com.br
Sales Range: $25-49.9 Million
Emp.: 50
Provider of Medical & Analytic Instruments
N.A.I.C.S.: 334516

Shimadzu Europa GmbH (1)
Albert-Hahn-Strasse 6-10, 47269, Duisburg, Germany (100%)
Tel.: (49) 20376870
Web Site: https://www.shimadzu.eu
Sales Range: $50-74.9 Million
Emp.: 140
Analytical, Measurement Instruments, Medical Systems & Equipment
N.A.I.C.S.: 334516
Jiro Takashima *(Mng Dir)*

Subsidiary (Non-US):

SHIMADZU SCHWEIZ GmbH (2)
Hofackerstrasse 40B, 4132, Muttenz, BL, Switzerland
Tel.: (41) 617179333
Web Site: https://www.shimadzu.ch
Sales Range: $25-49.9 Million
Emp.: 2
Analytical Component Distr
N.A.I.C.S.: 423490
Jiro Takashima *(Mng Dir)*

Shimadzu Korea Vacuum Equipment Co., Ltd. (1)
9 Deokseongsandan 1-ro Idong-eup, Cheoin-gu, Yongin, Gyeonggi, Korea (South)
Tel.: (82) 31 283 0242
Web Site: https://www.shimadzu.kr
Vacuum Equipment Mfr
N.A.I.C.S.: 333914

Shimadzu Latin America S.A. (1)

Building 3 Office 202-007 - Zonamerica Ruta 8 Km 17 500, Montevideo, 91600, Uruguay
Tel.: (598) 2 518 2063
Web Site: https://www.shimadzu-la.com
Medical Equipment Whslr
N.A.I.C.S.: 423450

Shimadzu Malaysia Sdn. Bhd. (1)
No 6 Lorong Teknologi 3/4A Taman Sains Selangor 1, Nouvelle Industrial Park 2 Kota Damansara, 47810, Petaling Jaya, Selangor, Malaysia
Tel.: (60) 36 158 9989
Web Site: https://www.shimadzu.com.my
Emp.: 69
Analytical & Measuring Instrument Distr
N.A.I.C.S.: 423490
Ryutaro Yoshioka *(Mng Dir)*

Shimadzu Manufacturing Asia Sdn. Bhd. (1)
PT 13130 Jalan Techvalley 1/2, Techvalley, 71950, Bandar Sri Sendayan, Negeri Sembilan, Malaysia
Tel.: (60) 6 781 2200
Industrial Equipment Mfr
N.A.I.C.S.: 333248

Shimadzu Medical (India) Pvt. Ltd. (1)
1 A/B Rushabh Chambers Makwana Road, Marol Andheri East, Mumbai, 400 059, India
Tel.: (91) 222 920 1692
Web Site: https://www.med.shimadzu.in
Medical Equipment Mfr
N.A.I.C.S.: 339113

Shimadzu Medical Systems (Oceania) Pty. Ltd. (1)
Unit E 10-16 South Street, Rydalmere, 2116, NSW, Australia
Tel.: (61) 29 898 2444
Web Site: https://www.shimadzumedical.com.au
Medical Equipment Distr
N.A.I.C.S.: 423450
Genzo Shimadzu *(Founder)*

Shimadzu Medical Systems USA (1)
20101 S Vermont Ave, Torrance, CA 90502
Tel.: (310) 217-8855
Web Site: http://www.shimadzu-usa.com
Medical Instrument Mfr
N.A.I.C.S.: 339112
Fred Eans *(Mgr-Sls-Interventional X-ray Bus-Natl)*

Shimadzu Middle East & Africa FZE (1)
Warehouse No RA08UC02, PO Box 262081, Jebel Ali Free Zone, Dubai, United Arab Emirates
Tel.: (971) 4 883 6668
Web Site: https://www.shimadzumea.com
Medical Equipment Distr
N.A.I.C.S.: 423450

Shimadzu Philippines Manufacturing Inc. (1)
Phase 3 Lot 14-15 Block 15 Cavite EPZ, Rosario, Cavite, Philippines
Tel.: (63) 46 437 0431
Industrial Equipment Mfr
N.A.I.C.S.: 333248

Shimadzu Precision Instruments, Inc. (1)
3645 Lakewood Blvd, Long Beach, CA 90808 (100%)
Tel.: (562) 420-6226
Web Site: http://www.spi-inc.com
Sales Range: $50-74.9 Million
Emp.: 100
Distribution of Aircraft Equipment & Supplies & Medical Equipment
N.A.I.C.S.: 423860
Mike Ivans *(Dir-Comml Ops)*

Division (Domestic):

Shimadzu Precision Instruments, Inc.-Medical System Div. (2)
20101 S Vermont Ave, Torrance, CA 90502-1328
Tel.: (310) 217-8855
Web Site: http://www.shimadzu-usa.com
Sales Range: $25-49.9 Million
Emp.: 50
Distr of Medical Instruments

N.A.I.C.S.: 423450

Shimadzu Research Laboratory (Europe) Ltd. (1)
Wharfside Trafford Wharf Road, Manchester, M17 1GP, United Kingdom
Tel.: (44) 161 886 6550
Web Site: https://www.srlab.co.uk
Laboratory Research & Development Services
N.A.I.C.S.: 541715

Shimadzu Research Laboratory (Shanghai) Co., Ltd. (1)
3/F No 52 Building 1000 JinHai Road, Pudong New District, Shanghai, 201206, China
Tel.: (86) 215 858 7726
Web Site: https://www.srlab.com.cn
Laboratory Research & Development Services
N.A.I.C.S.: 541715

Shimadzu Scientific Instruments (Oceania) Pty Limited (1)
Unit F 10-16 South Street, Rydalmere, 2116, NSW, Australia (100%)
Tel.: (61) 296844200
Web Site: http://www.shimadzu.com.au
Sales Range: $1-9.9 Million
Emp.: 100
Provider of Analytical & Measurement Instruments, Medical Systems & Equipment
N.A.I.C.S.: 334516
John Hewatson *(Gen Mgr)*

Subsidiary (Domestic):

Shimadzu Scientific Instruments (2)
Unit 15 899 Wellington Road, Rowville, 3178, VIC, Australia (100%)
Tel.: (61) 398394200
Web Site: http://www.shimadzu.com.au
Sales Range: $25-49.9 Million
Emp.: 12
Provider of Analytical Instruments
N.A.I.C.S.: 334516
John Hewatson *(Gen Mgr)*

Shimadzu Scientific Instruments (Taiwan) Co., Ltd. (1)
11F 11F No 37 Dongxing Rd, Xinyi Dist, Taipei, 11070, Taiwan
Tel.: (886) 28 768 1880
Web Site: https://www.shimadzu.com.tw
Industrial Equipment Mfr
N.A.I.C.S.: 333248

Shimadzu Scientific Instruments, Inc. (1)
7102 Riverwood Dr, Columbia, MD 21046 (100%)
Tel.: (410) 381-1227
Web Site: http://www.ssi.shimadzu.com
Sales Range: $75-99.9 Million
Emp.: 220
Mfr of Analytical, Testing & Characterizations Instruments
N.A.I.C.S.: 423490
Samuel Velez *(Coord-Intl Sls & Svc)*

Shimadzu Scientific Korea Corporation (1)
9th Floor 609 Eonju-ro Pax Tower, Gangnam-gu Nonhyeon-dong, Seoul, 06046, Korea (South)
Tel.: (82) 2 540 5541
Web Site: https://www.shimadzu.co.kr
Laboratory Equipment Mfr
N.A.I.C.S.: 334516

Shimadzu Singapore Pte. Ltd. (1)
79 Science Park Drive 02-01/08 Cintech IV Science Park I, Singapore, 118264, Singapore
Tel.: (65) 6 778 6280
Web Site: https://www.shimadzu.com.sg
Medical Equipment Distr
N.A.I.C.S.: 423450
Tetsuya Tanigaki *(Mng Dir)*

Shimadzu Software Development Canada (1)
1600 Montgolfier St suite 201, Laval, H7T 0A2, QC, Canada (100%)
Tel.: (450) 681-5665
Web Site: https://www.shimadzu.ca
Sales Range: $25-49.9 Million
Emp.: 18
Software Developer & Publisher

AND PRIVATE COMPANIES

Shimadzu South Africa (Pty) Ltd. (1)
Wild Fig Business Park Units 37-40 1494
Cranberry Street, Roodepoort, Honeydew,
2170, South Africa
Tel.: (27) 11 795 2608
Medical Equipment Distr
N.A.I.C.S.: 423450

Shimadzu Taiwan Industrial Machinery Co., Ltd. (1)
3F No 122-7 Zhonghua Road, Hsinchu County, Hukou, 30352, Taiwan
Tel.: (886) 3 598 6008
Web Site: https://www.shimadzusti.com.tw
Semiconductor Machinery Mfr
N.A.I.C.S.: 333242

Shimadzu U.S.A. Manufacturing, Inc. (1)
1900 SE 4th Ave B14, Canby, OR 97013
Tel.: (503) 263-2133
Industrial Machinery Mfr
N.A.I.C.S.: 333248

Shimadzu UK Limited (1)
Centre of Excellence Mill Court Featherstone Road Wolverton Mill South, Milton Keynes, MK12 5RD, Buckinghamshire, United Kingdom
Tel.: (44) 190 855 2209
Web Site: https://www.shimadzu.co.uk
Medical Equipment Distr
N.A.I.C.S.: 423450
Stuart Phillips (Mng Dir)

Shimadzu Vacuum Equipment (Shanghai) Co., Ltd. (1)
West of 3rd Floor Building D No 2059 Du Hui Road, Minhang District, Shanghai, 201108, China
Industrial Equipment Mfr
N.A.I.C.S.: 333248

Shimadzu Vietnam Co., Ltd. (1)
10th Floor Detech Tower 08 Ton That Thuyet My Dinh 2, Nam Tu Liem, Hanoi, Vietnam
Tel.: (84) 243 574 0468
Web Site: https://www.shimadzu-vn.com
Industrial Equipment Mfr
N.A.I.C.S.: 333248
Yusuke Kondo (Gen Dir)

Tianjin-Shimadzu Hydraulic Equipment Co., Ltd. (1)
No 15 Xinghua Sizhi Road, Xiqing Economic Development Zone, Tianjin, 300385, China
Tel.: (86) 2283963757
Web Site: http://www.tjshimadzu.com
Emp.: 133
Hydraulic Equipment
N.A.I.C.S.: 333998
Komacsu Kodi (Pres)

Toshbro Shimadzu Private Ltd. (1)
78 83 Electronic Complex, Indore, 452010, India (60%)
Tel.: (91) 731554278
Provider of Analytical Instruments
N.A.I.C.S.: 334516

Xian Shimadzu Vacuum Equipment Co., Ltd. (1)
18 Building 2c Hi-tech Enterprises Accelerator Park, No 2 Qinling West Road Xi'an Hi-tech Zone, Xi'an, 710304, China
Tel.: (86) 298 902 5998
Industrial Equipment Mfr
N.A.I.C.S.: 333248

SHIMAMURA CO., LTD.
1-602-1 Kitabukuro-cho, Omiya-ku, Saitama, 331-9550, Japan
Tel.: (81) 486522111
Web Site: https://www.shimamura.gr.jp
Year Founded: 1953
8227—(TKS)
Rev.: $4,502,795,190
Assets: $3,784,691,630
Liabilities: $442,098,410
Net Worth: $3,342,282,720
Earnings: $284,195,560
Emp.: 19,357

Fiscal Year-end: 02/29/24
Apparel Store Operator
N.A.I.C.S.: 458110
Makoto Suzuki (Pres)

SHIMANE BANK LTD.
484-19 Asahi-cho Matsue City, Matsue, 690-0003, Shimane, Japan
Tel.: (81) 852241234
Web Site: https://www.shimagin.co.jp
7150—(TKS)
Rev.: $60,831,830
Assets: $3,531,147,930
Liabilities: $3,407,732,620
Net Worth: $123,415,310
Earnings: $33,050
Emp.: 308
Fiscal Year-end: 03/31/24
Banking Services
N.A.I.C.S.: 522110
Yoshio Suzuki (Pres)

SHIMANO, INC.
3-77 Oimatsu-cho, Sakai-ku, Sakai, 590-8577, Osaka, Japan
Tel.: (81) 722233210
Web Site: https://www.shimano.com
Year Founded: 1921
SHMDF—(OTCIQ)
Rev.: $3,659,427,200
Assets: $5,715,265,600
Liabilities: $586,946,800
Net Worth: $5,128,318,800
Earnings: $614,408,960
Emp.: 12,244
Fiscal Year-end: 12/31/20
Bicycle Components & Fishing Tackle Mfr
N.A.I.C.S.: 336991
Yozo Shimano (Pres)

Subsidiaries:

G-Loomis Products, Inc. (1)
1359 Down River Dr, Woodland, WA 98674-9546 (100%)
Tel.: (360) 225-6516
Web Site: http://www.gloomis.com
Sales Range: $25-49.9 Million
Fishing Tackle Product Distr
N.A.I.C.S.: 459110

G.Loomis, Inc. (1)
1359 Down River Dr, Woodland, WA 98674
Tel.: (360) 225-6516
Bicycle Component Mfr & Distr
N.A.I.C.S.: 336991

Innovative Textiles, Inc. (1)
559 Sandhill Ln, Grand Junction, CO 81505
Tel.: (970) 242-3002
Web Site: http://www.innotex.com
Emp.: 200
Heat Resistant Clothing Mfr
N.A.I.C.S.: 314999

Kumamoto Fishing Tackle Co., Ltd. (1)
660-1 Aza Doubaru Shicho, Kamoto-gun, Kumamoto, 861 0601, Japan (100%)
Tel.: (81) 968 32 3195
Fishing Rods & Tackle Mfr
N.A.I.C.S.: 339920

Lazer Sport N.V. (1)
Tel.: (32) 15207057
Sports Equipment Mfr
N.A.I.C.S.: 339920

Nakano Metal Press (Singapore) Pte. Ltd. (1)
70 Joo Koon Circle, Jurong, 629087, Singapore
Tel.: (65) 68612088
Sales Range: $25-49.9 Million
Emp.: 35
Mfr of Bicycle Components
N.A.I.C.S.: 336991
Hirishina Nakano (Mng Dir)

P.T. Shimano Batam (1)
Panbil Industrial Estate Factory A Lot 10-19, Jl Shimano Jaya Muka Kuning, Batam, 29433, Indonesia
Tel.: (62) 7784042200

Web Site: http://corporate.shimano.com
Bicycle Components Mfr
N.A.I.C.S.: 336991

Pro (Taiwan) Procurement Co., Ltd. (1)
5F-2 Grand Asia Plaza 138 Zhongming S Road, Taichung, 40361, Taiwan
Tel.: (886) 423233388
Sports Equipment Mfr
N.A.I.C.S.: 339920

SHIMANO (CAMBODIA) CO., LTD. (1)
St National Road 4, Trapeng Rokar Village Samraong Tong District, Trapeng Kong, Kampong Speu, Cambodia
Tel.: (855) 12985114
Emp.: 1,029
Bicycle Component Distr
N.A.I.C.S.: 423120

SHIMANO (LIANYUNGANG) INDUSTRIAL CO., LTD. (1)
15 North Taishan Road Eco Tech Dev Zone, Lianyungang, 222047, Jiangsu, China
Tel.: (86) 51882342406
Sporting Goods Distr
N.A.I.C.S.: 423910

SHIMANO (SHANGHAI) BICYCLE COMPONENTS CO., LTD. (1)
Room 1701-1703 Shenggao International Building No 137, Xianxia, Shanghai, 200051, China
Tel.: (86) 2152061212
Bicycle Components Mfr
N.A.I.C.S.: 336991
Hao Lin (Mgr-Sls)

SHIMANO (TIANJIN) BICYCLE COMPONENTS CO., LTD. (1)
172 Xijiu Road, Airport Economic Area, Tianjin, 300308, China
Tel.: (86) 2224890055
Bicycle Components Mfr
N.A.I.C.S.: 336991

SHIMANO LATIN AMERICA REPRESENTACAO COMERCIAL LTDA. (1)
Tel.: (55) 1131494949
Web Site: https://www.shimano.com
Sales Range: $25-49.9 Million
Emp.: 30
Sporting Goods Mfr & Distr
N.A.I.C.S.: 339920

SHIMANO TAIWAN CO., LTD. (1)
Tel.: (886) 423195318
Sporting Goods Mfr & Distr
N.A.I.C.S.: 339920

Shimano (Kunshan) Bicycle Components Co., Ltd. (1)
No 6 Dong Ting Hu South Road, Kunshan, 215335, Jiangsu, China (100%)
Tel.: (86) 51257310666
Sales Range: $400-449.9 Million
Emp.: 1,400
Mfr of Bicycle Components
N.A.I.C.S.: 336991

Shimano (Kunshan) Fishing Tackle Co., Ltd. (1)
No 6 Dong Ting Hu South Road, Kunshan, 215335, Jiangsu, China
Tel.: (86) 51257317000
Fishing Rod Mfr
N.A.I.C.S.: 339920

Shimano (Philippines) Inc. (1)
Lot 21-A Phase 1B First Philippine Industrial Park, Tanauan, 4232, Batangas, Philippines
Tel.: (63) 434306000
Sports Equipment Mfr
N.A.I.C.S.: 339920

Shimano (Shanghai) Sales Corporation (1)
Tel.: (86) 2152061212
Sports Equipment Mfr
N.A.I.C.S.: 339920

Shimano (Singapore) Pte. Ltd. (1) (100%)
Tel.: (65) 62654777
Web Site: http://www.shimano.com.sg
Sales Range: $200-249.9 Million
Mfr of Bicycle Components & Fishing Tackle

Shimano Argentina S.A.U. (1)
Tel.: (54) 1153552273
Sports Equipment Mfr
N.A.I.C.S.: 339920

Shimano Australia Cycling Pty. Ltd. (1)
2 Wurrook Circuit, Caringbah, 2229, NSW, Australia (100%)
Tel.: (61) 2 9526 7799
Web Site: http://www.shimano.com.au
Sales Range: $25-49.9 Million
Emp.: 15
Bicycle Component Distr
N.A.I.C.S.: 423910

Shimano Australia Fishing Pty Ltd (1)
2 Wurrook Circuit, PO Box 2082, Caringbah, 2229, NSW, Australia
Tel.: (61) 295330000
Web Site: http://www.shimanofish.com.au
Emp.: 60
Sporting Goods Mfr & Distr
N.A.I.C.S.: 339920

Shimano Balikcilik Malzemeleri Ve Ekipmanlari Satis Ticaret Anonim Sirketi (1)
Ziya Gokalp Mah Seyit Onbasi Cad No 30 Kat 6 ic kapi No 12, Basaksehir, Istanbul, Turkiye
Tel.: (90) 5380864214
Bicycle Component Mfr & Distr
N.A.I.C.S.: 336991

Shimano Belgium N.V. (1) (100%)
Tel.: (32) 15209480
Sales Range: $25-49.9 Million
Emp.: 19
Bicycle Component Distr
N.A.I.C.S.: 423910

Shimano Benelux B.V. (1)
Industrieweg 24, 8071 CT, Nunspeet, Netherlands (100%)
Tel.: (31) 341272327
Sales Range: $125-149.9 Million
Emp.: 300
Retailer of Bicycle Components & Fishing Tackle
N.A.I.C.S.: 459110

Shimano Bike & Fishing Mexico S.A. de C.V. (1)
de la Carretera Estatal 431 El Colorado Galindo, Parque Industrial Tecnologico Innovación, El Marques, Queretaro, Mexico
Tel.: (52) 4421476303
Bicycle Component Mfr & Distr
N.A.I.C.S.: 336991

Shimano Bisiklet Parca Ve Ekipmanlari Satis Servis Ticaret Anonim Sirketi (1)
Sair Esref Bulv Ismet Kaptan Mah Osman Sahin Is Mrk No 4 K 7 D 71, Cankaya Konak, Izmir, Turkiye
Tel.: (90) 2324029393
Bicycle Component Mfr & Distr
N.A.I.C.S.: 336991

Shimano Canada Ltd. (1)
427 Pido Road, Peterborough, K9J 6X7, ON, Canada (100%)
Tel.: (705) 745-3232
Sales Range: $25-49.9 Million
Emp.: 18
Retailer of Bicycle Components & Fishing Tackle
N.A.I.C.S.: 459110

Shimano Components (Malaysia) Sdn. Bhd. (1)
Lot 4550 Lorong A-16, Pekan Nanas Pontian, 81500, Johor, Malaysia
Tel.: (60) 76991599
Web Site: http://www.tradenex.com
Sales Range: $200-249.9 Million
Emp.: 1,000
Bicycle Components & Fishing Tackle Mfr
N.A.I.C.S.: 336991

Shimano Cycling World Pte. Ltd. (1)
6 Stadium Walk 01-02, Singapore, 397698, Singapore
Tel.: (65) 98305212
Web Site: https://shimanocyclingworld.com

SHIMANO, INC.

Shimano, Inc.—(Continued)

Bicycle Component Mfr & Distr
N.A.I.C.S.: 336991

Shimano Czech Republic s.r.o (1)
Detmarovicka 403/4, Stare Mesto, 733 01,
Karvina, Czech Republic
Tel.: (420) 597441111
Web Site: http://www.scrs.cz
Sporting Goods Mfr & Distr
N.A.I.C.S.: 339920

Shimano Europe B.V. (1)
Industrieweg 24, NL-8071 CT, Nunspeet,
Netherlands
Tel.: (31) 341272222
Emp.: 300
Investment Management Service
N.A.I.C.S.: 523999

Shimano Europe B.V. (1)
Industrieweg 24, 8071 CT, Nunspeet, Netherlands
Tel.: (31) 34 127 2222
Web Site: http://www.shimano.com
Sporting Bicycle Distr
N.A.I.C.S.: 423910

Shimano Europe Fishing Holding B.V. (1)
Industrieweg 24, 8071 CT, Nunspeet,
Netherlands **(100%)**
Tel.: (31) 341272222
Web Site: http://www.shimano.com
Sales Range: $25-49.9 Million
Emp.: 270
Holding Company
N.A.I.C.S.: 551112

Shimano Europe Holding B.V. (1)
Industrieweg 24, Nunspeet, 8071 CT, Netherlands
Tel.: (31) 341 272222
Web Site: http://www.shimano.com
Emp.: 300
Investment Management Service
N.A.I.C.S.: 523999

Shimano France (1)
Zone Actiparc 777 Rue Commios, PO Box
45, 62223, Saint-Laurent-Blangy, Cedex,
France **(100%)**
Tel.: (33) 321732525
Web Site: http://www.shimano-france.fr
Sales Range: $25-49.9 Million
Emp.: 50
Sales of Bicycle Components
N.A.I.C.S.: 423910

Shimano France Composants Cycles S.A.S. (1)
777 Rue Commios, 62223, Saint-Laurent-Blangy, France
Tel.: (33) 321732525
Web Site: http://www.shimano-france.com
Emp.: 250
Sporting Goods & Accessories Distr
N.A.I.C.S.: 423910

Shimano Germany Fishing GmbH (1)
Diessemer Bruch 114f, 47805, Krefeld,
Germany **(100%)**
Tel.: (49) 215155670
Sales Range: $25-49.9 Million
Retailer of Bicycle Components & Fishing Tackle
N.A.I.C.S.: 459110

Shimano Iberia, S.L. (1)
Avenida Doctor Severo Ochoa 34, Alcobendas, 28100, Madrid, Spain
Tel.: (34) 919022586
Bicycle Component Mfr & Distr
N.A.I.C.S.: 336991

Shimano Italy Bicycle Components S.R.L. (1)
Via Jucker 22, Legnano, 20025, Milan, Italy
Tel.: (39) 0331936911
Sports Equipment Mfr
N.A.I.C.S.: 339920

Shimano Italy Fishing S.R.L. (1)
Via Jucker 22, Milan, 20025, Legnano,
Italy **(100%)**
Tel.: (39) 0331742711
Web Site: http://www.shimano.com
Sales Range: $25-49.9 Million
Emp.: 16
Fishing Product Distr

Shimano Kumamoto Co., Ltd. (1)
Tel.: (81) 968321130
Sports Equipment Mfr
N.A.I.C.S.: 339920

Shimano Menat Spor Etkinlikleri Spor Malzemeleri Ve Ekipmanlari Ticaret Limited Sirketi (1)
Ziya Gokalp Mah Seyit Onbasi Cad No 30
Floor 6 Inner Door No 12, Basaksehir, Istanbul, Turkiye
Tel.: (90) 5380864214
Bicycle Component Mfr & Distr
N.A.I.C.S.: 336991

Shimano New Zealand Ltd. (1)
79 Apollo Drive North Shore City, Albany,
0632, Auckland, New Zealand
Tel.: (64) 94781969
Sports Equipment Mfr
N.A.I.C.S.: 339920
Greg McKinney (Natl Sls Mgr-Fishing)

Shimano Nordic AB (1)
Edsbrogatan 1F, 75228, Uppsala, Sweden
Tel.: (46) 1861600
Bicycle Component Mfr & Distr
N.A.I.C.S.: 336991

Shimano Nordic AS (1)
Vakasveien 7, Hvalstad, Norway
Tel.: (47) 66778010
Bicycle Component Mfr & Distr
N.A.I.C.S.: 336991

Shimano Nordic Cycle AB (1)
Edsbrogatan 1F, 752 28, Uppsala, Sweden
Tel.: (46) 18 56 16 00
Web Site: http://www.shimano-nordic.se
Sales Range: $25-49.9 Million
Emp.: 30
Sporting Cycle Mfr & Distr
N.A.I.C.S.: 339920

Shimano Nordic Cycle AS (1)
Vakasveien 7, 1395, Hvalstad, Norway
Tel.: (47) 6 677 8010
Web Site: http://www.shimano-nordic.no
Emp.: 7
Sporting Goods Mfr & Distr
N.A.I.C.S.: 339920

Shimano Nordic Cycle Oy (1)
Teknobulevardi 3-5, 01530, Vantaa, Finland
Tel.: (358) 8201550800
Sports Equipment Mfr
N.A.I.C.S.: 339920
Jyrki Niini (Mgr-Major Acct)

Shimano Nordic Denmark Aps (1)
Tel.: (45) 69911660
Sports Equipment Mfr
N.A.I.C.S.: 339920

Shimano Nordic Oy (1)
Teknobulevardi 3-5, 01530, Vantaa, Finland
Tel.: (358) 201550800
Bicycle Component Mfr & Distr
N.A.I.C.S.: 336991

Shimano North America Fishing, Inc. (1)
9560 Palmetto Commerce Pkwy, Ladson,
SC 29456
Tel.: (949) 951-5003
Sports Equipment Mfr
N.A.I.C.S.: 339920

Shimano North America Holding, Inc. (1)
1 Holland, Irvine, CA 92618-2506 **(100%)**
Tel.: (949) 951-5003
Sales Range: $75-99.9 Million
Retailer of Bicycle Components & Fishing Tackle
N.A.I.C.S.: 423910

Shimano Oceania Holdings Pty Ltd (1)
2 Wurrook Circuit, Caringbah, 2229, NSW,
Australia **(100%)**
Tel.: (61) 295267799
Web Site: http://www.shimano.com.au
Sales Range: $25-49.9 Million
Emp.: 25
Retailer of Fishing Tackle & Sporting Goods
N.A.I.C.S.: 423910

Shimano Polska Sp. z o.o. (1)

Ul Jana Gutenberga, Zerniki, 62-023,
Poznan, Poland
Tel.: (48) 616252100
Sport Equipment Distr
N.A.I.C.S.: 423910

Shimano Pte. Ltd. (1)
No 20 Benoi Sector, Jurong, 629852,
Singapore **(100%)**
Tel.: (65) 62654777
Web Site: http://www.shimano.com
Sales Range: $100-124.9 Million
Emp.: 550
Mfr of Bicycle Components
N.A.I.C.S.: 336991

Shimano Sales Co., Ltd. (1)
1-5-15 Chikko-Shinmachi, Nishi-Ku, Sakai,
592-8331, Osaka, Japan **(100%)**
Tel.: (81) 722432820
Sales Range: $25-49.9 Million
Emp.: 50
Warehousing; Service Center for Bicycle
Parts & Fishing Tackle
N.A.I.C.S.: 493110

Shimano South Asia Private Ltd. (1)
No 19 Kumarakrupa Road, Bengaluru,
560001, Karnataka, India
Tel.: (91) 8041253331
Sports Equipment Mfr
N.A.I.C.S.: 339920

Shimano U.K. Ltd. (1)
The Development Centre Fosseway, Cotgrave, Nottingham, NG12 3HG, United
Kingdom
Tel.: (44) 3303334888
Web Site: http://www.shimano.co.uk
Sales Range: $25-49.9 Million
Emp.: 16
Retailer of Fishing Tackle
N.A.I.C.S.: 459110

Shimano Uruguay S.A. (1)
Ruta 8 km 17 500 S/N Edificio Costa Park,
91600, Montevideo, Uruguay
Tel.: (598) 25182566
Sports Equipment Mfr
N.A.I.C.S.: 339920

Shimano, Inc. - Yamaguchi Factory (1)
1-4-7 Ozuki Kojima, Shimonoseki, 750-1192, Yamaguchi, Japan
Tel.: (81) 832833502
Bicycle Component Mfr & Distr
N.A.I.C.S.: 336991

Tsuriyoshi Co., Ltd. (1)
1420 Kita Harako Yoshimura Cho, Miyazaki,
880, Japan
Tel.: (81) 985298212
Sales of Fishing Tackle
N.A.I.C.S.: 459110

Wooyun Co., Ltd. (1)
188 Shinmun-ri Jangyu-myun, Kimhae,
Kyungnam, Korea (South)
Tel.: (82) 553201061
Mfr & Sale of Cycling Shoes & Snowboard Boots
N.A.I.C.S.: 339920

SHIMAO GROUP HOLDINGS LTD.

38th Floor Tower One Lippo Centre
89 Queensway, Hong Kong, China
(Hong Kong)
Tel.: (852) 25119968
Web Site: https://shimaogroup.hk
Year Founded: 2002
0813—(HKG)
Rev.: $7,581,623,280
Assets: $69,264,425,363
Liabilities: $62,729,919,038
Net Worth: $6,534,506,325
Earnings: ($3,008,925,667)
Emp.: 53,836
Fiscal Year-end: 12/31/23
Investment Holding Company
N.A.I.C.S.: 551112
Wing Mau Hui (Chm)

Subsidiaries:

Shanghai Shimao Co., Ltd. (1)
Shimao Tower No 55 Weifang West Road,
Pudong New District, Shanghai, 200120,
China
Tel.: (86) 2120203388
Web Site: https://www.shimaoco.com
Rev.: $806,821,011
Assets: $18,314,603,335
Liabilities: $12,585,111,430
Net Worth: $5,729,491,905
Earnings: ($636,132,463)
Fiscal Year-end: 12/31/2022
Real Estate Manangement Services
N.A.I.C.S.: 531390

SHIMAO SERVICES HOLDINGS CO., LTD.
26/F Shanghai Shimao Tower No 55
West Weifang Road, Shanghai,
200122, China
Tel.: (86) 2138611216   Ky
Web Site:
http://www.shimaofuwu.com
Year Founded: 2005
0873—(HKG)
Rev.: $1,212,608,264
Assets: $2,049,778,505
Liabilities: $875,019,834
Net Worth: $1,174,758,671
Earnings: ($123,084,749)
Emp.: 47,084
Fiscal Year-end: 12/31/22
Holding Company
N.A.I.C.S.: 551112
Jason Sai Tan Hui (Chm)

SHIMIZU BANK, LTD.

2-1 Fujimicho, Shimizu-ku, Shizuoka,
424-0941, Shizuoka, Japan
Tel.: (81) 543535164
Web Site:
https://www.shimizubank.co.jp
Year Founded: 1928
8364—(TKS)
Rev.: $197,665,440
Assets: $11,606,247,820
Liabilities: $11,077,910,520
Net Worth: $528,337,300
Earnings: $165,250
Emp.: 893
Fiscal Year-end: 03/31/24
Banking Services
N.A.I.C.S.: 522110
Satoshi Kobayashi (Mng Exec Officer)

Subsidiaries:

The Shimizu Card Service Co., Ltd (1)
3-3 Aioicho, Shimizu-Ku, Shizuoka, Japan
Tel.: (81) 543553100
Credit Card Issuing
N.A.I.C.S.: 522210

The Shimizu General Computer Service Co., Ltd (1)
1-8-25 Tenjin, Shimizu-ku, Shizuoka, 424-0809, Japan
Tel.: (81) 543636121
Billing Software Development Services
N.A.I.C.S.: 541511

The Shimizu JCB Card Co., Ltd (1)
3-3 Aioicho, Shimizu-Ku, Shizuoka, Japan
Tel.: (81) 543553030
Credit Card Issuing
N.A.I.C.S.: 522210

The Shimizu Regional Economy Research Center, INC (1)
2-1 Fujimi-cho Shimizu Bank Head Office
Building 4th floor, Shimizu-ku, Shizuoka,
424-0941, Japan **(100%)**
Tel.: (81) 543555510
Web Site: http://www.shimizubank.co.jp
Economic Research Services
N.A.I.C.S.: 541720
Naoki Toba (Pres)

The Shimizugin Career Up Co., Ltd (1)
3rd floor Shimizu Bank Head Office Building
2-1, Fujimi-cho Shimizu-Ku, Shizuoka, 424-0941, Japan

Tel.: (81) 543535170
Web Site: http://www.shimizugin-careerup.jp
Temporary Help Service
N.A.I.C.S.: 561320
Shiokawa Hiroyasu (Pres)

SHIMIZU CORPORATION
2-16-1 Kyobashi, Chuo-ku, Tokyo, 104-8370, Japan
Tel.: (81) 335611111   JP
Web Site: https://www.shimz.co.jp
Year Founded: 1804
XSZ—(DEU)
Rev.: $14,098,658,640
Assets: $18,475,964,320
Liabilities: $10,524,367,040
Net Worth: $7,951,597,280
Earnings: $747,063,680
Emp.: 16,586
Fiscal Year-end: 03/31/21
Engineering & Construction Services
N.A.I.C.S.: 236220
Yoichi Miyamoto (Chm)

Subsidiaries:

CSP Japan, Inc. (1)
5th Floor Oshimaya Bldg 2-22-5 Hatchobori, Chuo-ku, Tokyo, 104-0032, Japan
Tel.: (81) 364539003
Web Site: http://www.csp.co.jp
Sales Range: $25-49.9 Million
Emp.: 5
Engineeering Services
N.A.I.C.S.: 237990

Daiichi Setsubi Engineering Corporation (1)
4F Shibaura Shimizu Building 4-15-33 Shibaura, Minato-ku, Tokyo, 108-0023, Japan
Tel.: (81) 354435100
Web Site: http://www.issetsu.co.jp
Sales Range: $200-249.9 Million
Emp.: 313
Engineeering Services
N.A.I.C.S.: 237990

Jeep Construction Co., Ltd. (1)
7F 1A No 111 Sung Chiang Rd, Taipei, 104, Taiwan (100%)
Tel.: (886) 225176580
Web Site: http://www.shimizu.com.tw
Sales Range: $25-49.9 Million
Emp.: 1
N.A.I.C.S.: 236220

Kankyoryokka Co.,Ltd. (1)
2-11-20 Tamagawa, Ota-ku, Tokyo, 146-0095, Japan
Tel.: (81) 337566466
Web Site: https://www.kanryoku.co.jp
Engineering Construction Services
N.A.I.C.S.: 541330

Katayama Stratech Corp. (1)
6-2-21 Minami-Okajima Taisho-ku, Osaka, 551-0021, Japan
Tel.: (81) 665521231
Sales Range: $150-199.9 Million
Emp.: 260
Engineeering Services
N.A.I.C.S.: 237990
Yasuhisa Kitayama (Pres)

MILX Corporation (1)
Takaramachi Shimizu Building 2-18-3, Kyobashi Chuo-ku, Tokyo, 104-0031, Japan
Tel.: (81) 335677700
Web Site: http://www1.milx.co.jp
Travel Agency Services
N.A.I.C.S.: 561510

Makuhari Techno-Garden Co., Ltd. (1)
1-3 Nakase, Mihama-ku, Chiba, 261-8501, Japan
Tel.: (81) 432968111
Web Site: https://www.mtg-bld.co.jp
Real Estate Manangement Services
N.A.I.C.S.: 531210

NDIC. Co., Ltd. (1)
5-23-7 Shimbashi, Minato-ku, Tokyo, 105-0004, Japan
Tel.: (81) 354251761
Web Site: https://www.ndic.jp
Life Insurance Agency Services
N.A.I.C.S.: 524113

Nd Leasing System Co., Ltd. (1)
2-6-14 Mejirodai, Bunkyo-ku, Tokyo, 112-0015, Japan
Tel.: (81) 359408271
Web Site: https://www.ndls.co.jp
Civil Engineering & Construction Services
N.A.I.C.S.: 541330

P.T. Shimizu Bangun Cipta Kontraktor (1)
5th Fl Midplaza 2 Bldg Jl Jenderal Sudirman Kav 10-11, Jakarta, 10220, Indonesia
Tel.: (62) 215704646
Sales Range: $25-49.9 Million
Emp.: 30
Construction Contractor
N.A.I.C.S.: 236220

S.C. Properties (Singapore) Pte. Ltd. (1)
78 Shenton Way 11 01, Singapore, 079120, Singapore (100%)
Tel.: (65) 62200406
Web Site: http://www.shimz.com.sg
Sales Range: $25-49.9 Million
Emp.: 100
N.A.I.C.S.: 236220

SC Machinery Corp. (1)
25-9 Kitamachi, Yokohama, 246-0002, Kanagawa Seya-ku, Japan
Tel.: (81) 459242711
Web Site: http://www.shimz.co.jp
Sales Range: $150-199.9 Million
Emp.: 223
Engineeering Services
N.A.I.C.S.: 237990

SC PRE-CON Corp. (1)
Otakanomori Nishi 3-chome 440, Nagareyama, 270-0128, Chiba, Japan
Tel.: (81) 471586531
Web Site: http://www.sc-precon.co.jp
Emp.: 63
Engineeering Services
N.A.I.C.S.: 237990

Shimizu America, Inc. (1)
1000 Parkwood Circle Ste 820, Atlanta, GA 30339
Tel.: (770) 956-1123
Construction Services
N.A.I.C.S.: 532412

Shimizu BLC Co., Ltd. (1)
2-10-2 Kyobashi Nurihiko Building South Building, Chuo-ku, Tokyo, 104-0031, Japan
Tel.: (81) 362286130
Web Site: http://www.sblc.co.jp
Engineeering Services
N.A.I.C.S.: 237990

Shimizu Building Life Care Kansai, Co., Ltd. (1)
6th floor Higobashi Shimizu Building 1-3-7 Tosabori, Nishi-ku, Osaka, 550-0001, Japan
Tel.: (81) 664430298
Web Site: http://www.sblc.co.jp
Sales Range: $25-49.9 Million
Emp.: 100
Engineering & Construction Services
N.A.I.C.S.: 237990

Shimizu Building Life Care Kyushu, Co., Ltd. (1)
Fukuoka Fukoku Seimei Building 5th Fl, 3-6-11 Watanabedori Chuo-ku, Fukuoka, 810-8607, Japan
Tel.: (81) 927162066
Sales Range: $10-24.9 Million
Emp.: 47
Engineeering Services
N.A.I.C.S.: 237990
Noboru Matsuda (Gen Mgr)

Shimizu Canada Engineering Corporation (1)
280-8899 Odlin Crescent, Richmond, V6X 3Z7, BC, Canada
Tel.: (604) 207-1777
N.A.I.C.S.: 236220

Shimizu Corporation (1)
24 Lombard Street, London, EC3V 9AJ, United Kingdom (100%)
Tel.: (44) 2073372570
Web Site: http://www.shimz-global.com
Construction & Engineering Services
N.A.I.C.S.: 236220

Shimizu Corporation (1)
Krenova 1, Prague, 16200, Czech Republic
Tel.: (420) 235365228
Web Site: http://www.shimizu.cz
Sales Range: $25-49.9 Million
Emp.: 10
N.A.I.C.S.: 236220

Shimizu Corporation (1)
Room 1313-1315 Metroplaza Tower 1 No 223 Hing Fong Road, Kwai Fong, NT, China (Hong Kong)
Tel.: (852) 25826888
Web Site: http://www.shimz.co.jp
Commercial Construction Projects
N.A.I.C.S.: 236220

Shimizu Corporation (1)
12-3 12th Floor Faber Imperial Court Jalan Sultan Ismail, Kuala Lumpur, 50250, Malaysia
Tel.: (60) 320700000
Web Site: http://www.shimz-global.com
Sales Range: $50-74.9 Million
Emp.: 120
Heavy Duty Construction Services
N.A.I.C.S.: 236220

Shimizu Corporation (1)
Kompleks ATAL-INVEST ul Porcelanowa 10/15, 40-246, Katowice, Poland
Tel.: (48) 323538335
Construction Services
N.A.I.C.S.: 237990

Shimizu Corporation (1)
House No 2 One Sunningdale Stand No 16847 off Mwinilunga Road, Sunningdale, Lusaka, Zambia
Tel.: (260) 976155224
Building Construction Services
N.A.I.C.S.: 236220

Shimizu Corporation (1)
Saray Mahallesi kucuksu Caddesi No 64/A Antasya Residence Kat 9 No 139, Umraniye, 34768, Istanbul, Turkiye
Tel.: (90) 2165047213
Building Construction Services
N.A.I.C.S.: 236220

Shimizu Corporation (1)
Gedung Setiabudi Atrium Lantai 6 Suite 601 Jl H R Rasuna Said Kav 62, Kuningan, Jakarta, 12920, Indonesia
Tel.: (62) 2129047777
Building Construction Services
N.A.I.C.S.: 236220

Shimizu Corporation (1)
Unit 2301 23rd Floor Empire Tower 1 South Sathorn Road, Yannawa Sathorn, Bangkok, 10120, Thailand
Tel.: (66) 22300333
Building Construction Services
N.A.I.C.S.: 236220

Shimizu Corporation (1)
Room 109B Prime Hill Business Square No60 Shwe Dagon Pagoda Road, Dagon Township, Yangon, Myanmar
Tel.: (95) 19250064
Building Construction Services
N.A.I.C.S.: 236220

Shimizu Corporation (1)
3rd Floor Lang Ha Building 14 Lang Ha, Ba Dinh District, Hanoi, Vietnam
Tel.: (84) 2437720500
Building Construction Services
N.A.I.C.S.: 236220

Shimizu Corporation (1)
506 5th Floor Time Tower Sector 28 Main MG Road, Gurgaon, 122002, Haryana, India
Tel.: (91) 1244608100
Building Construction Services
N.A.I.C.S.: 236220

Shimizu Corporation (1)
Office 1C 1st Floor Albwardy Building Bur Dubai Khalid Bin Walid Road, PO Box 122372, Dubai, United Arab Emirates
Tel.: (971) 43515901
Building Construction Services
N.A.I.C.S.: 236220

Shimizu Corporation (1)
7F-2 No 111 Song Jiang Rd, Zhongshan District, Taipei, 10486, Taiwan
Tel.: (886) 225176580
Building Construction Services
N.A.I.C.S.: 236220

Shimizu Corporation (1)
5th Floor King's Court Building I 2129 Chino Roces Avenue, Metro Manila, Makati, Philippines
Tel.: (63) 28112981
Building Construction Services
N.A.I.C.S.: 236220

Shimizu Corporation (1)
52 Kuloltuprok Street, 100100, Tashkent, Uzbekistan
Tel.: (998) 711207297
Building Construction Services
N.A.I.C.S.: 236220

Shimizu Corporation (China) Ltd. (1)
Room 2001 No 4 Lane 255 Dongyu Rd, Pudong District, Shanghai, 200126, China
Tel.: (86) 2162708800
Web Site: http://www.shimz-global.com
Emp.: 300
Engineering & Construction Services
N.A.I.C.S.: 237990

Shimizu Corporation India Pte. Ltd. (1)
Prestige Emerald 5th Level No 2 Madras Bank Road-Lavelle Road, Bengaluru, 560 001, India
Tel.: (91) 80 4356 7777
Web Site: http://www.shimz-global.com
Sales Range: $25-49.9 Million
Emp.: 100
Construction Engineering Services
N.A.I.C.S.: 541330

Shimizu Corporation de Mexico (1)
Av Tecnologico Norte 950-B Piso 15-A Corporativo Blanco Col San Pablo, Queretaro, 76125, Mexico, Qro, Mexico (100%)
Tel.: (52) 4421894160
Web Site: http://www.shimz-global.com
Sales Range: $25-49.9 Million
Emp.: 10
Construction Services
N.A.I.C.S.: 236220

Shimizu Europe Ltd. (1)
Immermannstr 50 52, Dusseldorf, D 40210, Germany (100%)
Tel.: (49) 211172710
Sales Range: $25-49.9 Million
Emp.: 2
N.A.I.C.S.: 236220

Shimizu Finance Co., Ltd. (1)
1-2-3 Shibaura Seavans S Kan 22f, Minato-Ku, Tokyo, 105-0023, Japan
Tel.: (81) 337693107
Financial Management Services
N.A.I.C.S.: 523999

Shimizu Hong Kong Co., Ltd. (1)
Munich 1313 21315 Twr 1 Metro Plz, 223 Hingfong Rd Kwaifong, Kwai Chung, NT, China (Hong Kong) (100%)
Tel.: (852) 25826888
Web Site: http://www.shimz.com.hk
Sales Range: $200-249.9 Million
Emp.: 10
N.A.I.C.S.: 236220
T. Hayashi (Gen Mgr)

Shimizu International Capital (Singapore) Pte. Ltd. (1)
8 Kallang Avenue 05-01 Aperia Tower 1, Singapore, 339509, Singapore
Tel.: (65) 62200406
Building Construction Services
N.A.I.C.S.: 236220

Shimizu International Finance (U.S.A.), Inc. (1)
909 3rd Ave 28th Fl, New York, NY 10022
Tel.: (212) 223-7757
Sales Range: $25-49.9 Million
Emp.: 1
Commercial Building Construction
N.A.I.C.S.: 236220
Hitoshi Kamura (Gen Mgr)

Shimizu International Finance (UK) Ltd. (1)

SHIMIZU CORPORATION

Shimizu Corporation—(Continued)

7th Floor Crown House, 72 Hammersmith Road, London, W14 8TH, United Kingdom
Tel.: (44) 2075599808
Credit & Financial Services
N.A.I.C.S.: 522390

Shimizu Investment (Asia) Pte. Ltd. (1)
8 Kallang Avenue Ste 05-01 Aperia Tower 1, Singapore, 339509, Singapore
Tel.: (65) 6220 0406
Emp.: 1,000
Investment Management Service
N.A.I.C.S.: 523999
Sugita Hitoshi *(Gen Mgr)*

Shimizu North America LLC
1000 Parkwood Cir Ste 810, Atlanta, GA 30339 (100%)
Tel.: (770) 956-1123
Web Site: https://www.shimz-global.com
Sales Range: $25-49.9 Million
Emp.: 25
Commercial Construction Services
N.A.I.C.S.: 236115
Takeo Yoshigi *(Pres & CEO)*

Branch (Domestic):

Shimizu North America LLC - New York (2)
155 E 56th St 4th Fl, New York, NY 10022
Tel.: (212) 223-7757
Web Site: http://www.shimizu.com
General Contractors
N.A.I.C.S.: 236220

Shimizu North America LLC (1)
Av Tecnologico Norte 950-B Piso 15-A Corporativo Blanco San Pablo, 76125, Queretaro, Mexico
Tel.: (52) 4421894160
Building Construction Services
N.A.I.C.S.: 236220

Shimizu Philippine Contractors, Inc. (1)
Chino Roces Avenue 5th Floor Kings Court Building 1, Makati, 2129, Philippines (60%)
Tel.: (63) 28112981
Sales Range: $1-9.9 Million
Emp.: 150
N.A.I.C.S.: 236220
Kezuhiro Akeboshi *(Gen Mgr)*

Sonorous Corporation (1)
6th floor Akasaka Enosaka Mori Building 1-7-1 Akasaka, Minato-Ku, Tokyo, 107-0052, Japan
Tel.: (81) 355492600
Web Site: http://www.sonorous.co.jp
Emp.: 130
Nursing Homes Management Services
N.A.I.C.S.: 623312

Super Regional, Inc. (1)
1-3F Harmony Tower 1-32-2 Honcho, Nakano-ku, Tokyo, 164-0012, Japan
Tel.: (81) 363000950
Web Site: http://www.super-r.net
Emp.: 87
Business Support Services
N.A.I.C.S.: 561499

TOKYO Concrete Co., Ltd. (1)
3-11-10 Nihombashikayabacho Chiba Bldg 9f, Chuo-Ku, Tokyo, 103-0025, Japan
Tel.: (81) 336660009
Readymix Concrete Mfr
N.A.I.C.S.: 327320

TTK Corporation (1)
4-18-32 Shibaura, Minato-ku, Tokyo, 108-0023, Japan
Tel.: (81) 334511141
Structural Steel Erection Services
N.A.I.C.S.: 238120

Thai Shimizu Co., Ltd. (1)
Unit 2301 23rd Floor Empire Tower 1 South Sathorn Road, Yannawa Sathon, Bangkok, 10120, Thailand (100%)
Tel.: (66) 22300333
Web Site: http://www.shimz-global.com
Sales Range: $50-74.9 Million
Emp.: 200
Commercial Building Construction
N.A.I.C.S.: 236220

The Nippon Road Co., Ltd. (1)
7F Seavans South Building 2-3 Shibaura 1-chome, Minato-ku, Tokyo, 105-0023, Japan (50.1%)
Tel.: (81) 342353890
Web Site: https://www.nipponroad.co.jp
Rev.: $1,061,030,590
Assets: $991,010,860
Liabilities: $328,596,320
Net Worth: $662,414,540
Earnings: $33,400,330
Emp.: 1,662
Fiscal Year-end: 03/31/2024
Construction Business
N.A.I.C.S.: 236116
Hiromi Hisamatsu *(Pres)*

Subsidiary (Non-US):

Nippon Road (M) Sdn. Bhd. (2)
A-1-46 1 & 2nd Fl Block A Jln Pju 1 43 Aman Suria Damansara, 47301, Petaling Jaya, Selangor, Malaysia
Tel.: (60) 378038299
Road Building Contractors
N.A.I.C.S.: 238390

Thai Nippon Road Co., Ltd.
Na Nakorn Bldg 99/349 Chang Watana Rd 8Fl, Tungsonghong Laksi, Bangkok, 10210, Thailand
Tel.: (66) 25761510
Sales Range: $25-49.9 Million
Emp.: 100
Road Construction Services
N.A.I.C.S.: 237310

SHIMOJIMA CO., LTD.

5-29-8 Asakusabashi, Taito-ku, Tokyo, 111-0053, Japan
Tel.: (81) 338640061
Web Site:
  https://www.shimojima.co.jp
Year Founded: 1920
7482—(TKS)
Rev.: $382,018,340
Assets: $286,920,270
Liabilities: $57,183,110
Net Worth: $229,737,160
Earnings: $15,678,920
Emp.: 812
Fiscal Year-end: 03/31/24
Wrapping Paper Whslr
N.A.I.C.S.: 424130
Wako Shimojima *(CEO)*

Subsidiaries:

Heiko Pack Co., Ltd. (1)
1702-1 Ubagai Hagamachi, Hagagun, Tochigi, 321-3304, Japan
Tel.: (81) 28 677 0214
Wrapping Paper Whslr
N.A.I.C.S.: 424130

LEAD SHOJI Co., Ltd. (1)
5-7-8 Higashikojiya, Ota-ku, Tokyo, Japan
Tel.: (81) 3 5736 0361
Wrapping Paper Whslr
N.A.I.C.S.: 424130

SHIMOJIMA (Shanghai) Co., Ltd. (1)
6F Guolv Building 1277 608 Room East Beijing Road, Jingan District, Shanghai, 200040, China
Tel.: (86) 21 6245 9762
Wrapping Paper Distr
N.A.I.C.S.: 424130

SHIMOJIMA PACKAGE Co., Ltd. (1)
1 2 3F 80 Taiyuan RD, Datong, Taipei, Taiwan
Tel.: (886) 2 2559 6255
Wrapping Paper Distr
N.A.I.C.S.: 424130

Saikosha Co., Ltd. (1)
8-14-1 Machiya, Arakawa-ku, Tokyo, Japan
Tel.: (81) 3 5692 0330
Wrapping Paper Whslr
N.A.I.C.S.: 424130

Shimojima Kakoushi Co., Ltd. (1)
204 Tada-machi, Sano, Tochigi, Japan
Tel.: (81) 283 62 8011
Wrapping Paper Whslr
N.A.I.C.S.: 424130

SHIN FOONG SPECIALTY & APPLIED MATERIALS CO., LTD.

No 55 Sec 3 Jhongshan Rd, Fangliao Ping Tung, 94048, Kaohsiung, 94048, Taiwan
Tel.: (886) 88660088
Web Site:
  https://www.shinfoong.com.tw
Year Founded: 1979
6582—(TAI)
Rev.: $29,246,802
Assets: $203,923,567
Liabilities: $12,330,913
Net Worth: $191,592,654
Earnings: ($3,527,323)
Emp.: 200
Fiscal Year-end: 12/31/23
Chemical Product Mfr & Distr
N.A.I.C.S.: 325998
Sheu Chi Min *(Chm & Gen Mgr)*

SHIN HAI GAS CORP.

No 52 Section 1 Lixing Road, Sanchong District, Taipei, Taiwan
Tel.: (886) 229821131
Web Site:
  https://www.shinhaigas.com.tw
Year Founded: 1966
9926—(TAI)
Rev.: $74,871,478
Assets: $271,463,183
Liabilities: $143,846,000
Net Worth: $127,617,183
Earnings: $15,296,150
Emp.: 180
Fiscal Year-end: 12/31/23
Natural Gas Distr
N.A.I.C.S.: 221210

SHIN HEUNG ENERGY & ELECTRONICS CO., LTD.

48 Yangsan-ro, Osan, Gyeonggi-do, Korea (South)
Tel.: (82) 313788141
Web Site: http://www.shsec.co
Year Founded: 1979
243840—(KRS)
Rev.: $366,491,537
Assets: $503,393,082
Liabilities: $267,278,273
Net Worth: $236,114,808
Earnings: $15,032,411
Emp.: 3,165
Fiscal Year-end: 12/31/22
Lithium Ion Battery Mfr
N.A.I.C.S.: 335910
Hwang Man-Yong *(CEO)*

SHIN HWA CONTECH CO., LTD.

3 Iljik-ro 94beon-gil Manan-gu, Anyang, Gyeonggi-do, Korea (South)
Tel.: (82) 314321527
Web Site: http://www.sh-ct.co.kr
187270—(KRS)
Rev.: $34,474,573
Assets: $70,869,318
Liabilities: $27,014,867
Net Worth: $43,854,451
Earnings: $3,572,129
Emp.: 117
Fiscal Year-end: 12/31/22
Electronic Connector Mfr
N.A.I.C.S.: 334417
Joung-jin Lee *(CEO)*

SHIN HWA DYNAMICS CO., LTD.

31 Beonnyeong 2 -ro, Dan Won-gu, Ansan, 15410, Gyeonggi-do, Korea (South)
Tel.: (82) 314999922
Web Site:
  https://www.shinhwatp.co.kr
Year Founded: 1956

INTERNATIONAL PUBLIC

001770—(KRS)
Rev.: $96,077,482
Assets: $67,719,943
Liabilities: $28,253,214
Net Worth: $39,466,729
Earnings: $8,298,183
Emp.: 78
Fiscal Year-end: 12/31/22
Tin Plates Mfr & Sales
N.A.I.C.S.: 339999
Jong-Ho Shin *(CEO)*

SHIN HWA WORLD LIMITED

Suites 5801-5804 58/F Two International Finance Centre, No 8 Finance Street, Central, China (Hong Kong)
Tel.: (852) 36225777 Ky
Web Site: http://www.582.com.hk
0582—(HKG)
Rev.: $176,817,000
Assets: $1,282,142,805
Liabilities: $247,176,473
Net Worth: $1,034,966,333
Earnings: ($27,656,153)
Emp.: 1,418
Fiscal Year-end: 12/31/22
Paints Mfr & Trade
N.A.I.C.S.: 325510
Zhihui Yang *(Chm)*

Subsidiaries:

Jiangsu Wenrun Optoelectronic Co., Ltd. (1)
NO 88 Zhengde Road Dingmao Development Zone, Zhenjiang, 212009, Jiangsu, China
Tel.: (86) 51188891159
Web Site: https://en.wenrun.com
Light Emitting Diode Product Mfr & Distr
N.A.I.C.S.: 334413

Landing Entertainment Korea Co., Ltd (1)
38 Sinhwayeoksa-ro 304 beon-gil Andeokmyeon, Seogwipo, Jeju, Korea (South)
Tel.: (82) 649088880
Web Site: http://www.landingkorea.com
Casino Hotel Operator
N.A.I.C.S.: 721120
Joe Chew Chye Hong *(Mgr-Casino Sr Shift)*

Landing Jeju Development Co., Ltd (1)
No 217 Nokchabunjae-ro Andeok-myeon, Seogwipo, Jeju, Korea (South)
Tel.: (82) 647608288
Resort Operator
N.A.I.C.S.: 721110
Jaemin Seo *(Mgr-Recruiting)*

Les Ambassadeurs Club Limited (1)
5 Hamilton Place, London, W1Y 7ED, United Kingdom
Tel.: (44) 2074955555
Web Site: https://lesambassadeurs.com
Casino Hotel Operator
N.A.I.C.S.: 721120
Kevin McGowen *(CEO)*

SHIN KONG GROUP

8th Fl 123 Sec 2, Nan King East Rd, Taipei, Taiwan
Tel.: (886) 225071251
Web Site:
  https://www.shinkonggroup.com
Conglomerate Holding Company
N.A.I.C.S.: 551112
Tung-Chin Wu *(Chm)*

Subsidiaries:

Shin Kong Financial Holding Co., Ltd. (1)
38F No 66 Sec 1 Chung-Hsiao W Rd, Taipei, Taiwan
Tel.: (886) 223895858
Web Site: https://www.skfh.com.tw
Rev.: $4,110,070,694
Assets: $154,878,972,923
Liabilities: $147,184,875,872
Net Worth: $7,694,097,052
Earnings: ($229,006,191)
Emp.: 15,975

Fiscal Year-end: 12/31/2023
Financial Investment Services
N.A.I.C.S.: 523999
Shih-Yi Cheng *(Chm & Pres-Shin Kong Venture Capital)*

Subsidiary (Domestic):

MasterLink Securities
Corporation (2)
22F No 97 Sec 2 Dunhua S Rd, Taipei, Taiwan
Tel.: (886) 223255818
Web Site: http://www.masterlink.com.tw
Rev.: $376,959,584
Assets: $5,281,389,991
Liabilities: $4,260,636,741
Net Worth: $1,020,753,250
Earnings: $139,551,319
Emp.: 2,062
Fiscal Year-end: 12/31/2021
Trading Services
N.A.I.C.S.: 523150

Subsidiary (Domestic):

MasterLink Futures Co., Ltd. (3)
4th Floor Section 1 Fu Shing South Road 209, Taipei, 10640, Taiwan
Tel.: (886) 227213458
Web Site: http://www.masterlink.com.tw
Emp.: 90
Financial Future Brokerage Services
N.A.I.C.S.: 523160

Subsidiary (Non-US):

MasterLink Securities (HK) Corp., Ltd. (3)
Unit 2603 26th Fl The Center, Central, China (Hong Kong)
Tel.: (852) 22953228
Web Site: http://www.i-masterlink.com
Emp.: 30
Securities Brokerage Services
N.A.I.C.S.: 523150

Subsidiary (Domestic):

MasterLink Securities Investment Advisory Corp. (3)
19F 97 Tun Hua South Road Sector 2, Taipei, 10601, Taiwan
Tel.: (886) 223253299
Web Site: http://www.masterlink.com
Emp.: 50
Securities Brokerage Services
N.A.I.C.S.: 523150

Subsidiary (Non-US):

Shin Kong Investment Trust Co., Ltd. (2)
Tel.: (886) 225071123
Web Site: http://www.skit.com.tw
Sales Range: $5-14.9 Billion
Emp.: 100
Investment Services
N.A.I.C.S.: 523999

Shin Kong Life Insurance Co., Ltd. (2)
Web Site: http://www.skl.com.tw
Sales Range: $15-24.9 Billion
Emp.: 12,991
Individual & Group Life Insurance, Health Insurance & Accident Insurance
N.A.I.C.S.: 524128
Tung-Chin Wu *(Chm)*

Subsidiary (Non-US):

Shin Kong Leasing Corp. (3)
Room 801 8F No 188 Wangdun Road Suzhou Industrial Park, Suzhou, Jiangsu, China
Tel.: (86) 512 8718 5858
Financial Lending Services
N.A.I.C.S.: 522220

Subsidiary (Domestic):

Shin Kong Life Real Estate Service Company (3)
18th Floor No 66 Section 1 Zhongxiao West Road, Zhongzheng District, Taipei, 10485, Taiwan
Tel.: (886) 225021363
Web Site: https://www.skhb.com.tw
Real Estate Manangement Services

N.A.I.C.S.: 531390

Subsidiary (Domestic):

Taiwan Shin Kong Commercial Bank Co., Ltd. (2)
28th Floor No 66 Sec 1, Chunghsiao West Road, Taipei, 100, Taiwan
Tel.: (886) 226183515
Web Site: http://www.skbank.com.tw
Sales Range: $300-349.9 Million
Banking Services
N.A.I.C.S.: 522110

Shin Kong Mitsukoshi Department Store Co., Ltd. (1)
No 12 Nanjing West Road, Zhongshan, Taipei, 104, Taiwan
Tel.: (886) 225682868
Web Site: https://www.skm.com.tw
Sales Range: $100-124.9 Million
Emp.: 300
Department Store Operator; Owned by Isetan Misukoski Holdings Ltd. & Shinkong Group
N.A.I.C.S.: 455110

Shinkong Synthetic Fibers Corporation (1)
14F 123 Sec 2 Nanjing E Rd, Zhongshan Dist, Taipei, 104, Taiwan
Tel.: (886) 225071251
Web Site: https://www.shinkong.com.tw
Rev.: $1,494,868,726
Assets: $5,909,894,526
Liabilities: $4,411,442,031
Net Worth: $1,498,452,495
Earnings: $117,738,270
Emp.: 2,000
Fiscal Year-end: 12/31/2022
Polyester Products Mfr
N.A.I.C.S.: 325212

Subsidiary (Non-US):

LOFO High Tech Film GmbH (2)
Weidstrasse 2, Weil am Rhein, 79576, Germany (100%)
Tel.: (49) 76217030
Web Site: http://www.lofo.com
Sales Range: $50-74.9 Million
Emp.: 120
Film Production Services
N.A.I.C.S.: 512110

Subsidiary (Domestic):

Pan Asian Plastics Corp. (2)
14F 123 Sec 2 Nanking E Rd, Taipei, Taiwan
Tel.: (886) 225071251
Staple Fiber & Optronic Mfr
N.A.I.C.S.: 325220

Shinkong Engineering Corp. (2)
9 14F 123 Sec 2 Nanking E Rd, Taipei, Taiwan
Tel.: (886) 225071251
Staple Fiber & Optronic Mfr
N.A.I.C.S.: 325220

Shinkong International Leasing Corp. (2)
7F-2 No 202 Sec 2 Yanping N Rd, Taipei, Taiwan
Tel.: (886) 225578008
Staple Fiber & Optronic Mfr
N.A.I.C.S.: 325220

Shinkong Materials Technology Co., Ltd. (2)
8 Fl 123 Sec 2 Nanking E Road, Taipei, Taiwan (85.02%)
Tel.: (886) 225083395
Web Site: http://www.shinkongmaterials.com.tw
Polyester Film Mfr
N.A.I.C.S.: 326113

Shinkong iEcofun Corporation (2)
1F No 20 Liugu Linkou, Jinshan Dist, New Taipei City, 208-42, Taiwan
Tel.: (886) 224080095
Web Site: http://www.iecofun.com
Software Publishing Services
N.A.I.C.S.: 513210

Shinpont Industry Inc. (2)
9 14F 123 Sec 2 Nanking E Rd, Taipei, Taiwan
Tel.: (886) 225071251

Staple Fiber & Optronic Mfr
N.A.I.C.S.: 325220

TacBright Optronics Corp. (2)
No 3 Section 2 Kebei 350, Zhunan Town, Miao-li, Taiwan
Tel.: (886) 37587500
Web Site: http://www.tacbright.com
Film Mfr
N.A.I.C.S.: 326112
Macro W. C. Wang *(CTO)*

Youhui Optoelectronics Co., Ltd. (1)
No 80 Xinguang E Rd, Renshan Vil Daxi Dist, Taoyuan, 335, Taiwan
Tel.: (886) 33074830
Web Site: http://www.ubright.com.tw
Rev.: $74,247,225
Assets: $130,596,473
Liabilities: $27,794,547
Net Worth: $102,801,926
Earnings: $8,987,650
Fiscal Year-end: 12/31/2022
Optronic Technologies & Films Mfr
N.A.I.C.S.: 333310

SHIN MAINT HOLDINGS CO., LTD.

2-13-8 Higashioi Keihin Higashioi Building 3F, Shinagawa-ku, Tokyo, 140-0011, Japan
Tel.: (81) 357676461
Web Site: https://www.shin-pro.com
Year Founded: 1999
6086—(TKS)
Rev.: $158,489,860
Assets: $58,861,180
Liabilities: $32,826,700
Net Worth: $26,034,480
Earnings: $6,104,490
Emp.: 276
Fiscal Year-end: 02/29/24
Holding Company; Stores & Kitchen Equipment Maintenance Services
N.A.I.C.S.: 238990
Hideo Naito *(Chm, Pres & CEO)*

Subsidiaries:

TESCO Co., Ltd. (1)
1-12-17 Kamirenjaku, Mitaka, 181-8535, Japan (100%)
Tel.: (81) 422562411
Web Site: https://www.tesco-net.co.jp
Construction & Renovation
N.A.I.C.S.: 236220

SHIN NIPPON AIR TECHNOLOGIES CO., LTD.

Hamacho Center 2-31-1 Nihonbashi, Chuo-ku, Tokyo, 103-0007, Hamacho, Japan
Tel.: (81) 3 3639 2700
Web Site: http://www.snk.co.jp
Year Founded: 1969
Sales Range: $750-799.9 Million
Emp.: 985
Air-Conditioning, Ventilation & Drainage Engineering & Installation Services
N.A.I.C.S.: 333415
Akihiro Iwasaki *(Pres)*

SHIN NIPPON BIOMEDICAL LABORATORIES, LTD.

8-1 Akashicho St Lukes Tower 28th floor, Chuo-ku, Tokyo, 104-0044, Japan
Tel.: (81) 355655001
Web Site: https://www.snbl.co.jp.e.transer.com
Year Founded: 1957
2395—(TKS)
Rev.: $174,834,500
Assets: $504,356,220
Liabilities: $278,558,620
Net Worth: $225,797,600
Earnings: $36,559,910
Emp.: 1,341
Fiscal Year-end: 03/31/24

Biotechnology Research & Development Services
N.A.I.C.S.: 541714
Ryoichi Nagata *(Chm, Pres, Grp CEO-Finance & Fisheries, CEO & Officer-Community Health)*

Subsidiaries:

Ina Research, Inc. (1)
2148-188 Nishiminowa Ina-shi, Nagano, 399-4501, Japan
Tel.: (81) 265726616
Web Site: http://www.ina-research.co.jp
Sales Range: $100-124.9 Million
Emp.: 180
Contract Research Laboratory Services
N.A.I.C.S.: 541380
Kenshi Nakagawa *(Pres & CEO)*

Subsidiary (Non-US):

Ina Research Philippines, Inc. (2)
Phase 2 Block 7 Lot 1-A Technology Avenue Laguna Technopark, Binan, 4024, Laguna, Philippines
Tel.: (63) 495412874
Sales Range: $25-49.9 Million
Emp.: 3
Pharmaceutical Products Research & Development Services
N.A.I.C.S.: 541715
Kimio Yoneda *(Gen Mgr)*

SNBL USA, Ltd. (1)
6605 Merrill Creek Pkwy, Everett, WA 98203
Tel.: (425) 407-0121
Web Site: http://www.snblus.com
Biotechnology Research & Development Services
N.A.I.C.S.: 541714
Monica Vegarra *(Dir-Toxicology Support Svcs)*

Satsuma Pharmaceuticals, Inc. (1)
400 Oyster Point Blvd Ste 221, South San Francisco, CA 94080 (100%)
Tel.: (650) 410-3200
Web Site: https://www.satsumarx.com
Rev.: $905,000
Assets: $54,939,000
Liabilities: $8,115,000
Net Worth: $46,824,000
Earnings: ($70,055,000)
Emp.: 25
Fiscal Year-end: 12/31/2022
Biotechnology Research & Development Services
N.A.I.C.S.: 541714
Ryoichi Nagata *(Pres)*

SHIN POONG PAPER MANUFACTURING CO., LTD.

144-32 Godeok-ro Godeok-myeon, Pyeongtaek, Gyeonggi, Korea (South)
Tel.: (82) 316698271
Web Site: http://www.shinpoongpaper.com
Year Founded: 1960
2870—(KRS)
Rev.: $13,940,711
Assets: $83,441,872
Liabilities: $22,319,564
Net Worth: $61,122,308
Earnings: ($5,593,201)
Emp.: 18
Fiscal Year-end: 12/31/22
Paper Products Mfr
N.A.I.C.S.: 322120
Chung Il-hong *(Founder)*

SHIN POONG PHARMACEUTICAL CO., LTD.

161 Yeoksam-ro, Gangnam-gu, Seoul, 06246, Korea (South)
Tel.: (82) 221893400   KR
Web Site: https://www.shinpoong.co.kr
Year Founded: 1962
019170—(KRS)
Rev.: $148,619,110
Assets: $259,848,611

SHIN POONG PHARMACEUTICAL CO., LTD.

Shin Poong Pharmaceutical Co., Ltd.—(Continued)
Liabilities: $58,861,315
Net Worth: $200,987,296
Earnings: ($42,510,378)
Emp.: 821
Fiscal Year-end: 12/31/23
Pharmaceutical Product Mfr & Distr
N.A.I.C.S.: 325412
Yoo Je-Man (CEO)

Subsidiaries:

Shin Poong Daewoo Pharm Co., Ltd (1)
No 22 Yaw Min Gyi St, Dagon, Yangon, Myanmar
Tel.: (95) 1 707741
Pharmaceutical Products Distr
N.A.I.C.S.: 424210

Shin Poong Pharmaceutical Co., Ltd. - KGMP Plant 1 (1)
434-4 Moknae-dong, Ansan, Gyeonggi-do, Korea (South)
Tel.: (82) 31 491 6191
Pharmaceuticals Product Mfr
N.A.I.C.S.: 325412

SHIN SHIN CO., LTD.
No 247 Linsen North Road, Taipei, Taiwan
Tel.: (886) 25212211
Web Site: https://www.shinshinltd.com.tw
Year Founded: 1972
2901—(TAI)
Rev.: $2,788,548
Assets: $33,120,081
Liabilities: $4,330,684
Net Worth: $28,789,397
Earnings: $968,639
Emp.: 164
Fiscal Year-end: 12/31/23
Departmental Store Operator
N.A.I.C.S.: 455110
You Zhi Huang (Chm)

SHIN SHIN NATURAL GAS CO., LTD.
No 100 Sec 1 Yung-Ho Road, Yung-Ho Dist, Taipei, Taiwan
Tel.: (886) 29217811
Web Site: https://www.shinshingas.com.tw
Year Founded: 1969
9918—(TAI)
Rev.: $63,193,481
Assets: $188,025,206
Liabilities: $84,485,101
Net Worth: $103,540,105
Earnings: $11,638,215
Emp.: 144
Fiscal Year-end: 12/31/23
Natural Gas Distribution Services
N.A.I.C.S.: 221210
Ho-Chia Chen (Chm)

SHIN STEEL CO., LTD.
174 Mieumsandan 4-ro, Gangseo-gu, Busan, Korea (South)
Tel.: (82) 519727215
Web Site: https://www.shin-steel.com
Year Founded: 2008
162300—(KRS)
Steel Products Mfr
N.A.I.C.S.: 331210
Shin Seung Gon (CEO)

SHIN TAI INDUSTRY CO., LTD.
No 10 Gaonan Highway, Renwu, Kaohsiung, Hsien, Taiwan
Tel.: (886) 73425301
Web Site: https://www.goldenbrand.com.tw
Year Founded: 1972
1235—(TAI)
Rev.: $2,476,176
Assets: $141,321,751

Liabilities: $78,698,123
Net Worth: $62,623,628
Earnings: $2,780,666
Emp.: 67
Fiscal Year-end: 12/31/23
Animal, Fish & Shrimp Feeds Processing & Packaging
N.A.I.C.S.: 112210

Subsidiaries:

Hausmann International pte Ltd. (1)
Lck 113 Neo Tiew Cres Cent, Singapore, Singapore
Tel.: (65) 67921318
Web Site: http://www.hausmann-aqua.com
Animal Feed Mfr
N.A.I.C.S.: 311111

Khai Van Trading Company (1)
334 Vinh Vien St Dist 10, Ho Chi Minh City, Vietnam
Tel.: (84) 903808745
Animal Feed Mfr
N.A.I.C.S.: 311111

SHIN YANG SHIPPING CORPORATION BERHAD
Sublot 153 Parent Lot 70 Jalan Kuala Baram Kuala Baram, 98100, Miri, Sarawak, Malaysia
Tel.: (60) 85428399
Web Site: https://www.shinyanggroup.com.my
SYGROUP—(KLS)
Rev.: $198,858,067
Assets: $332,570,065
Liabilities: $73,207,683
Net Worth: $259,362,382
Earnings: $38,646,491
Emp.: 1,380
Fiscal Year-end: 06/30/23
Transportation & Ship Building Services
N.A.I.C.S.: 483211
Chiong Sing Ling (Mng Dir-Grp)

Subsidiaries:

Dynasys Technology & Engineering Sdn. Bhd. (1)
Lot 1750 Jalan Prunus 3 Piasau Utara 4, 98000, Miri, Sarawak, Malaysia
Tel.: (60) 85428399
Web Site: https://www.dynasys.com.my
Marine Equipment Repair Services
N.A.I.C.S.: 811310

Hock Leong Shipping Sdn. Bhd. (1)
3 Jalan Berangan, 42000, Port Klang, Selangor, Malaysia
Tel.: (60) 331689261
Web Site: https://www.hlship.com.my
Shipping Services
N.A.I.C.S.: 488510
Peter Hong (Co-Founder)

Piasau Gas Sdn. Bhd. (1)
Lot 314 Provisional Lease 1999 Block 1 K B L D Jalan Miri Port, Kuala Baram Industrial Estate, 98000, Miri, Sarawak, Malaysia
Tel.: (60) 85668228
Web Site: https://piasaugas.com
Industrial Gases & Medical Gases Mfr
N.A.I.C.S.: 325120

Piasau Slipways Sdn. Bhd. (1)
Lot 523, PO Box 2075, Kuala Baram Land District, 98008, Miri, Sarawak, Malaysia
Tel.: (60) 85604499
Shipbuilding & Repairing Services
N.A.I.C.S.: 488390

Shin Yang Shipyard Sdn. Bhd. (1)
Lot 211, PO Box 2075, Kuala Baram Land District, 98008, Miri, Sarawak, Malaysia
Tel.: (60) 85604999
Shipbuilding & Repairing Services
N.A.I.C.S.: 488390

Shinline Sdn. Bhd. (1)
Sublot 153, Jalan Kuala Baram, 98100, Kuala Baram, Sarawak, Malaysia
Tel.: (60) 85428399
Shipbuilding & Repairing Services
N.A.I.C.S.: 488390

SHIN ZU SHING CO., LTD.
No 174 Junying Street, Shulin District, New Taipei City, 238, Taipei, Taiwan
Tel.: (886) 226813316
Web Site: https://www.szs-group.com
3376—(TAI)
Rev.: $329,237,275
Assets: $704,799,607
Liabilities: $196,174,164
Net Worth: $508,625,443
Earnings: $26,403,871
Emp.: 4,500
Fiscal Year-end: 12/31/23
Spring Products, Stamping & Hinge Components Mfr & Distr
N.A.I.C.S.: 332613
Sheng Nan Lu (Co-Founder)

Subsidiaries:

Dongguan Chengyue Computer Fittings Co., Ltd. (1)
No 58 Shenlong Road, Shixiaxian Village, Dalang Town, Dongguan, Guangdong, China
Tel.: (86) 51265026668
Computer Hardware Parts Mfr & Distr
N.A.I.C.S.: 334118

KunShan Jeng Jea Computer Fittings Co., Ltd. (1)
No 118 Nangang Fuli Road, Zhangpu Town, Kunshan, Jiangsu, China
Tel.: (86) 51257427500
Computer Hardware Parts Mfr & Distr
N.A.I.C.S.: 334118

Redstar Precision Electorn (Fuqing) Co., Ltd. (1)
1F & 2F Building 5 Optoelectronics Technology Park, Stiger Industrial District, Fuqing, Fujian, China
Tel.: (86) 51265026668
Computer Hardware Parts Mfr & Distr
N.A.I.C.S.: 334118

SZS Precision Electronics Co., Ltd. (1)
174 Jyunying St Shulin Dist, New Taipei City, 238, Taiwan
Tel.: (886) 226813316
Spring Mfr
N.A.I.C.S.: 332613

SHIN-ETSU CHEMICAL CO. LTD.
20th Floor Marunouchi Eiraku Building 4-1 Marunouchi 1-Chome, Chiyoda-ku, Tokyo, 100-0005, Japan
Tel.: (81) 368122300   JP
Web Site: https://www.shinetsu.co.jp
Year Founded: 1926
SEH—(DEU)
Rev.: $15,962,733,570
Assets: $34,028,108,140
Liabilities: $4,784,985,610
Net Worth: $29,243,122,530
Earnings: $3,438,125,400
Emp.: 26,004
Fiscal Year-end: 03/31/24
Methanol, Chloromethane, Cellulose Derivatives, PVC, Silicone, Semiconductor Silicon & Synthetic Quartz Mfr
N.A.I.C.S.: 325180
Chihiro Kanagawa (Chm)

Subsidiaries:

Admatechs Co., Ltd. (1)
1099-20 Marune, Kurozasa-cho, Miyoshi, 470-0201, Aichi, Japan
Tel.: (81) 56 133 0215
Web Site: https://www.admatechs.co.jp
Semiconductor Silicon Product Mfr
N.A.I.C.S.: 334413
Susumu Abe (Pres)

Asia Silicones Monomer Ltd. (1)
1 Moo 2 Asia Industrial Estate Tambol Banchang, Ampher Banchang, Rayong, 21130, Thailand
Tel.: (66) 38 687 050

INTERNATIONAL PUBLIC

Sales Range: $50-74.9 Million
Emp.: 100
Silicone Monomer Mfr & Distr
N.A.I.C.S.: 325199
Atthap Hong (Mgr-Ops)

Fukui Shin-Etsu Quartz Co., Ltd. (1)
1-4 Kayadani-cho 3-chome, Echizen, 915-0037, Fukui, Japan
Tel.: (81) 778272777
Quartz Glass Product Mfr
N.A.I.C.S.: 327212

Heraeus Shin-Etsu America, Inc. (1)
4600 NW Pacific Rim Blvd, Camas, WA 98607-9401   (75%)
Tel.: (360) 834-4004
Sales Range: $125-149.9 Million
Emp.: 350
Quartz Crucibles Mfr & Whslr
N.A.I.C.S.: 327110

Human Create Co., Ltd. (1)
1-8-6 Itachibori Hoshiwa CITY BLD Honmachi Nishi 3rd floor, Nishi-ku, Osaka, 550-0012, Japan
Tel.: (81) 66 567 9140
Web Site: https://www.human-create.co.jp
Computer Peripheral Equipment Distr
N.A.I.C.S.: 423430

JAPAN VAM & POVAL Co., Ltd (1)
3-11-1 Chikkoshinmachi, Nishi-ku, Sakai, 592-8331, Osaka, Japan
Tel.: (81) 72 245 1131
Web Site: https://www.j-vp.co.jp
Emp.: 130
Specialty Chemicals Mfr
N.A.I.C.S.: 325998
Yoshiharu Koizumi (Pres)

K-Bin Inc. (1)
5618 Hwy 332 E, Freeport, TX 77541   (100%)
Tel.: (979) 233-6610
Sales Range: $25-49.9 Million
Emp.: 16
PVC Compound Mfr
N.A.I.C.S.: 325211

Maruki Chemical Ind. Co. Ltd. (1)
Naka 403-14, Shiroi, 270-1406, Chiba, Japan
Tel.: (81) 474919566
Synthetic Resin Sheet Mfr
N.A.I.C.S.: 325211

Mimasu Semiconductor Industry Co., Ltd. (1)
2174-1 Hodota-machi, Takasaki, 370-3533, Gunma, Japan   (88.37%)
Tel.: (81) 273722021
Web Site: https://www.mimasu.co.jp
Sales Range: $350-399.9 Million
Emp.: 951
Semiconductor Material Mfr
N.A.I.C.S.: 334413
Masayuki Nakazawa (Chm & Pres)

Nagano Electronics Industrial Co., Ltd (1)
1393 Yashiro, Chikuma, 387-8555, Nagano, Japan
Tel.: (81) 262613100
Sales Range: $200-249.9 Million
Emp.: 580
Semiconductor Silicon Wafer Mfr
N.A.I.C.S.: 334413

Naoetsu Electronics Co., Ltd. (1)
2 596 Jonokoshi, Kubikiku, Joetsu, 942-0193, Niigata, Japan
Tel.: (81) 25 530 2631
Web Site: https://www.naoden.co.jp
Emp.: 622
Precision Processing of Semiconductor Silicon Wafers
N.A.I.C.S.: 334413

Naoetsu Precision Co., Ltd. (1)
935-1 Azagokawari Ogatakushibukakihama, Joetsu, 949-3115, Niigata, Japan
Tel.: (81) 255344931
Photomask Glass Mfr
N.A.I.C.S.: 327212

Naoetsu Sangyo Limited (1)
28-1 Kubikikunishifukujima, Joetsu, 942-0147, Niigata, Japan
Tel.: (81) 255455880
Packaging & Warehousing Services

AND PRIVATE COMPANIES / SHIN-ETSU CHEMICAL CO. LTD.

N.A.I.C.S.: 561910

Nihon Resin Co., Ltd. (1)
KDX Hamamatsucho Center Building 5F
1-22-5 Hamamatsucho, Minato-Ku, Tokyo, 105-0013, Japan
Tel.: (81) 3 5425 2288
Web Site: http://www.nihon-resin.co.jp
Emp.: 17
Silicone Resin Distr
N.A.I.C.S.: 424610

Nissin Chemical Industry Co., Ltd. (1)
2-17-33 Kitago, Echizen, 915-0802, Fukui, Japan
Tel.: (81) 77 822 5100
Web Site: https://www.nissin-chem.co.jp
Emp.: 200
Specialty Chemicals Mfr & Whslr
N.A.I.C.S.: 325998
Yoshiyuki Miyazawa (Pres)

P.T. Shin-Etsu Magnetics Indonesia (1)
Lot 311 Jalan Beringin Batamindo Industrial Park, Muka Kuning, Batam, Indonesia
Tel.: (62) 770612070
Vinyl Chloride Monomer Mfr
N.A.I.C.S.: 325180
Hiroshi Hisano (Pres & Mng Dir)

Pacific Biocontrol Corporation (1)
14615 NE 13th Ct Ste A, Vancouver, WA 98685
Tel.: (360) 571-2247
Web Site: https://pacificbiocontrol.com
Agricultural Chemicals Whslr
N.A.I.C.S.: 424690
Nancy J. Hays (Controller)

S.E.H. Malaysia Sdn. Bhd (1)
Lot No 2 Lorong Enggang 35 Ulu Klang Free Trade Zone, 54200, Kuala Lumpur, Selangor, Malaysia
Tel.: (60) 342596600
Web Site: https://www.sehmy.com
Emp.: 400
Semiconductor Silicon Wafer Distr
N.A.I.C.S.: 423690
Shiomi Hara (Mng Dir)

Subsidiary (Domestic):

S.E.H. (Shah Alam) Sdn. Bhd. (2)
Lot No 8 Jalan Sementa 27 / 91 Seksyen 27, 40400, Shah Alam, Selangor, Malaysia
Tel.: (60) 351237000
Web Site: http://www.sehmy.com
Sales Range: $75-99.9 Million
Silicon Wafers Mfr
N.A.I.C.S.: 334413
Hara Shiomi (Mng Dir)

S.E.H. Singapore Pte. Ltd. (1)
8 temasek Boulevard 21-05 Suntec Tower Three, Singapore, 038988, Singapore
Tel.: (65) 62935160
Semiconductor Silicon Product Mfr
N.A.I.C.S.: 334413

SE Tylose GmbH & Co. KG (1)
Kasteler Str 45, 65203, Wiesbaden, Germany
Tel.: (49) 6 119 6204
Web Site: https://www.setylose.com
Sales Range: $125-149.9 Million
Emp.: 500
Cellulose Mfr
N.A.I.C.S.: 325211
Fumio Arai (Mng Dir)

Saitama Shinkoh Mold Co., Ltd. (1)
88-78 Shingo, Higashimatsuyama, 355-0071, Saitama, Japan
Tel.: (81) 493236311
Silicone Resin Product Mfr & Distr
N.A.I.C.S.: 325211

San-Ace Co., Ltd. (1)
1-406-1 Yoshinocho, Kita-Ku, Saitama, 331-0811, Japan
Tel.: (81) 486 65 0131
Finishing Process Testing & Packaging Services
N.A.I.C.S.: 541380

Se Tylose Usa, Inc. (1)
26270 Hwy 405, Plaquemine, LA 70764
Tel.: (225) 309-0110
Cellulose Product Mfr

N.A.I.C.S.: 325199

Shin-Etsu (Changting) Technology Co., Ltd. (1)
Main Road of Rare-earth Industrial Park 1 period, Changting, Longyan, 366300, Fujian, China
Tel.: (86) 5976688270
Alloy Mfr
N.A.I.C.S.: 331314

Shin-Etsu (Jiangsu) Optical Preform Co., Ltd. (1)
No 8 Runhua Road, Ligang, Jiangyin, Jiangsu, China
Tel.: (86) 51086096060
Optical Fiber Product Mfr
N.A.I.C.S.: 335921

Shin-Etsu (Jiangyin) Optical Preform Trading Co., Ltd. (1)
No 8 Runhua Road, Ligang Zhen, Jiangyin, 021-4444, Jiangsu, China
Tel.: (86) 51086096108
Optical Fiber Product Mfr
N.A.I.C.S.: 335921

Shin-Etsu (Malaysia) Sdn. Bhd. (1)
Lot 50 Jalan Serendah 26/17 HICOM Industrial Estate, Bandaraya, 40000, Shah Alam, Selangor, Malaysia
Tel.: (60) 351912233
Rare Earth Magnet Mfr & Whslr
N.A.I.C.S.: 339999

Shin-Etsu Advanced Materials Korea Co., Ltd. (1)
Keungil Tower 17F 223 Teheran-ro, Gangnam-gu, Seoul, 06142, Korea (South)
Tel.: (82) 269647750
Photo Resist Product Distr
N.A.I.C.S.: 459999

Shin-Etsu Astech Co., Ltd. (1)
2-2-1 kanda, Chiyoda-Ku, Tokyo, 101-0047, Japan
Tel.: (81) 35 298 3211
Web Site: https://www.shinetsu-astech.co.jp
Emp.: 85
Industrial Chemical Distr
N.A.I.C.S.: 424690

Shin-Etsu Chemical Co. Ltd. - Goubara Plant (1)
13-1 Isobe 2-chome, Annaka, 379-0195, Gunma, Japan
Tel.: (81) 27 385 2734
Silicone Rubber Mfr
N.A.I.C.S.: 325212

Shin-Etsu Chemical Co. Ltd. - Isobe Plant (1)
13-1 Isobe 2-chome, Annaka, 379-0195, Gunma, Japan
Tel.: (81) 27 385 2120
Web Site: https://www.shinetsu.co.jp
Semiconductor Silicon Mfr
N.A.I.C.S.: 334413

Shin-Etsu Chemical Co. Ltd. - Matsuida Plant (1)
1-10 Hitomi, Matsuida-machi, Annaka, 379-0224, Gunma, Japan
Tel.: (81) 27 384 5111
Web Site: https://www.shinetsu.co.jp
Silicone Rubber Mfr
N.A.I.C.S.: 325212

Shin-Etsu Chemical Co. Ltd. - Naoetsu Plant (1)
28-1 Nishifukushima, Kubiki-ku, Joetsu, 942-8601, Niigata, Japan
Tel.: (81) 25 545 2000
Silicone Products Mfr
N.A.I.C.S.: 325211

Shin-Etsu Chemical Co. Ltd. - Takefu Plant (1)
1-5 Kitago 2-chome, Echizen, 915-8515, Fukui, Japan
Tel.: (81) 77 821 8100
Web Site: https://www.shinetsu.co.jp
Semiconductor Silicon Mfr
N.A.I.C.S.: 334413

Shin-Etsu Chemical Co., Ltd. - Kashima Plant (1)
1 Towada, Kamisu, 314-0102, Ibaraki, Japan
Tel.: (81) 299 96 3411

Polyvinyl Chloride Mfr
N.A.I.C.S.: 325211

Shin-Etsu Electronics (Malaysia) Sdn. Bhd. (1)
Lot 50 Jalan Serendah 26/17, HICOM Industrial Estate, 40400, Shah Alam, Selangor, Malaysia
Tel.: (60) 351921081
Epoxy Moulding Compound Mfr
N.A.I.C.S.: 325211

Shin-Etsu Electronics Materials Penang Sdn. Bhd. (1)
Lot P22 Phase 4, Free Industrial Zone, 11900, Bayan Lepas, Penang, Malaysia
Tel.: (60) 46437008
Silicone Products Mfr
N.A.I.C.S.: 334413

Shin-Etsu Electronics Materials Singapore Pte. Ltd. (1)
11-20A HarbourFront Centre 1 Maritime Square, Singapore, 099253, Singapore
Tel.: (65) 629 7921
Web Site: http://www.shinetsu.co.jp
Sales Range: $25-49.9 Million
Emp.: 20
Rare Earth Magnet Whslr
N.A.I.C.S.: 423690

Shin-Etsu Electronics Materials Taiwan Co., Ltd. (1)
No 28 Kejia 6 Rd, Yunlin, Douliu, 64057, Taiwan
Tel.: (886) 55511122
Photo Resist Product Mfr
N.A.I.C.S.: 333310

Shin-Etsu Electronics Materials Vietnam Co., Ltd. (1)
Plot No A-7, Thang Long Industrial Park II Yen My District, My Hao, Hun Yen, Vietnam
Tel.: (84) 2213974880
LED Material Mfr
N.A.I.C.S.: 334413

Shin-Etsu Engineering Co., Ltd. (1)
9 Kanda Nishikicho 2-chome, Chiyoda-ku, Tokyo, 101-0054, Japan
Tel.: (81) 332961080
Emp.: 300
Mechanical Engineering Services
N.A.I.C.S.: 541330

Shin-Etsu Film Co., Ltd. (1)
Stage Uchikanda 3-8 Uchikanda 1-chome, Chiyoda-Ku, Tokyo, 101-0047, Japan (100%)
Tel.: (81) 33 259 1061
Web Site: https://www.shinetsu-film.co.jp
Polypropylene Film Mfr
N.A.I.C.S.: 326113

Shin-Etsu Handotai Co., Ltd. (1)
4 2 Marunouchi 1 Chome, Tokyo, 1000005, Japan (100%)
Tel.: (81) 332141831
Sales Range: $400-449.9 Million
Emp.: 1,760
Mfr of Semiconductor Silicon Products
N.A.I.C.S.: 334413

Joint Venture (US):

Hemlock Semiconductor, LLC (2)
1805 Salzburg Rd, Midland, MI 48640
Tel.: (989) 301-5000
Web Site: https://www.hscpoly.com
Polysilicon Material Mfr & Distr
N.A.I.C.S.: 325199
Mark R. Bassett (Chm & CEO)

Subsidiary (Domestic):

Hemlock Semiconductor Operations LLC (3)
12334 Geddes Rd, Hemlock, MI 48626-9409
Tel.: (989) 301-5000
Web Site: https://www.hscpoly.com
Polysilicon Materials Mfr & Whslr
N.A.I.C.S.: 325180
Mark R. Bassett (Chm & CEO)

Subsidiary (US):

Shin-Etsu Handotai America, Inc. (2)
4111 NE 112th Ave, Vancouver, WA 98682-6776 (100%)

Tel.: (360) 883-7000
Web Site: http://www.sehamerica.com
Emp.: 700
Mfr of Semiconductor Silicon Products
N.A.I.C.S.: 334413
Steven Shimada (Sr VP)

Subsidiary (Non-US):

Shin-Etsu Handotai Europe, Ltd. (2)
Wilson Rd Toll Roundabout Eliburn, Livingston, EH54 7DA, West Lothian, United Kingdom
Tel.: (44) 150 641 5555
Web Site: https://www.sehe.com
Sales Range: $100-124.9 Million
Emp.: 500
Semiconductor Silicon Mfr
N.A.I.C.S.: 334413

Shin-Etsu Handotai Taiwan Co., Ltd (2)
No 12 Industry East Road 9 Hsin-Chu Science Park, Hsin-chu, Taiwan
Tel.: (886) 35771188
Semiconductor Silicon Wafer Mfr & Distr
N.A.I.C.S.: 334413

Shin-Etsu International Europe B.V. (1)
World Trade Center Amsterdam Strawinskylaan B-827, 1077 XX, Amsterdam, Netherlands
Tel.: (31) 206621359
Sales Range: $50-74.9 Million
Emp.: 10
Chemical Product Whslr
N.A.I.C.S.: 424690

Subsidiary (Non-US):

CIRES, S.A. (2)
Rua da Cires n 8, Avanca, 3860-160, Estarreja, Portugal
Tel.: (351) 23 481 1200
Web Site: https://www.cires.pt
Resin Product Mfr
N.A.I.C.S.: 325211

Shin-Etsu Magnet Co., Ltd. (1)
2-1-5 Kitago, Echizen, 915-0802, Fukui, Japan
Tel.: (81) 778218175
Electronic Components Mfr
N.A.I.C.S.: 334419

Shin-Etsu Magnetic Materials Vietnam Co., Ltd. (1)
Lot CN5 2D Petro-chemical Area Dong Hai 2 Hai An, Dinh Vu Industrial Zone, Haiphong, Vietnam
Tel.: (84) 2253250518
Rare Earth Magnet Mfr
N.A.I.C.S.: 327992

Shin-Etsu Magnetics (Thailand) Ltd. (1)
60/120 122 Moo19 Tambol Klongnueng, Amphur, Khlong Luang, 12120, Pathumthani, Thailand
Tel.: (66) 2 520 4293
Web Site: http://www.set.co.th
Vinyl Chloride Monomer Mfr & Distr
N.A.I.C.S.: 325211

Shin-Etsu Magnetics Europe GmbH (1)
Gerbermuehlstrasse 7, 60594, Frankfurt am Main, Germany
Tel.: (49) 69870031611
Rare Earth Magnet Mfr
N.A.I.C.S.: 327992

Shin-Etsu Magnetics Philippines, Inc. (1)
125 East Main Ave Laguna Technopark SEPZ, Binan, Laguna, Philippines
Tel.: (63) 495413190
VCM Product Mfr
N.A.I.C.S.: 325211

Shin-Etsu Magnetics, Inc. (1)
2372 Qume Dr Ste B, San Jose, CA 95131
Tel.: (408) 383-9240
Web Site: http://www.shinetsumagnetics.com
Rare Earth Materials Distr
N.A.I.C.S.: 424690
James Peacock (Mgr-Sls)

SHIN-ETSU CHEMICAL CO. LTD.

Shin-Etsu Chemical Co. Ltd.—(Continued)

Shin-Etsu MicroSi, Inc. (1)
10028 S 51st St, Phoenix, AZ
85044-5203 (100%)
Tel.: (480) 893-8898
Web Site: https://www.microsi.com
Sales Range: $25-49.9 Million
Emp.: 25
Distr of Microlithography Materials
N.A.I.C.S.: 325998

Shin-Etsu New Materials (Thailand) Limited (1)
9/9 Moo 2 Asia Industrial Estate Tambol Banchang Amphur, Banchang, Rayong, 21130, Thailand
Tel.: (66) 38689465
Fumed Silica Mfr
N.A.I.C.S.: 325180

Shin-Etsu PVC B.V. (1)
Building Noorderhaeve Noorderweg 68, 1221 AB, Hilversum, Netherlands
Tel.: (31) 35 689 8010
Web Site: https://www.shinetsu.nl
Sales Range: $50-74.9 Million
Emp.: 200
Polyvinyl Chloride Product Mfr
N.A.I.C.S.: 325211
Paul Beaufort *(Mgr-Quality, Health, Safety & Environment)*

Plant (Non-US):

Shin-Etsu PVC B.V. - Botlek Plant (2)
Tel.: (31) 10 438 9700
Web Site: https://www.shinetsu.nl
Sales Range: $50-74.9 Million
Emp.: 250
Vinyl Chloride Monomer Mfr
N.A.I.C.S.: 325211

Shin-Etsu PVC B.V. - Pernis Plant (2)
Tel.: (31) 10 431 1818
Web Site: https://www.shinetsu.nl
Vinyl Chloride Monomer Mfr
N.A.I.C.S.: 325211

Shin-Etsu Polymer (Malaysia) Sdn. Bhd. (1)
Lot52 Jalan Sepintas 26/13 Kawasan, Perindustrian Hicom, 40000, Shah Alam, Selangor, Malaysia
Tel.: (60) 35111161
Silicone Rubber Roller Mfr
N.A.I.C.S.: 325212

Shin-Etsu Polymer (Thailand) Ltd. (1)
No 323 United Center Building 30th Floor Room No 3001 Silom Road, Silom Bangrak, Bangkok, 10500, Thailand
Tel.: (66) 2 630 4740
Web Site: https://www.shinpoly.co.th
Semiconductor Silicon Product Mfr
N.A.I.C.S.: 334413

Shin-Etsu Polymer Co., Ltd. (1)
Ote Center Building 1-1-3 Otemachi, Chiyoda-ku, Tokyo, 100-0004, Japan
Tel.: (81) 352888400
Web Site: https://www.shinpoly.co.jp
Rev.: $689,945,190
Assets: $930,542,580
Liabilities: $183,830,710
Net Worth: $746,711,870
Earnings: $57,335,140
Emp.: 4,457
Fiscal Year-end: 03/31/2024
Silicon Rubber, PVC Resin & Other Synthetic Resin Products Mfr & Marketer
N.A.I.C.S.: 325211
Toru Takayama *(Sr Dir)*

Subsidiary (Non-US):

PT. Shin-Etsu Polymer Indonesia (2)
JL Permata Raya Lot-3 Kawasan Industri KIIC, Karawang, 41361, West Java, Indonesia
Tel.: (62) 21 890 5417
Emp.: 150
Polymer Product Mfr
N.A.I.C.S.: 325211

Subsidiary (Domestic):

Shin-Etsu Finetech Co., Ltd. (2)
4-24-11 Higashi-Ueno, Taito-ku, Tokyo, 110-0015, Japan
Tel.: (81) 36 777 1060
Web Site: https://www.shinfine.co.jp
Emp.: 110
Silicone Products Mfr
N.A.I.C.S.: 334413

Subsidiary (US):

Shin-Etsu Polymer America, Inc. (2)
5600 Mowry School Rd Ste 320, Newark, CA 94560-5371 (100%)
Tel.: (510) 623-1881
Web Site: https://www.shinpoly.com
Sales Range: $25-49.9 Million
Emp.: 15
Keypads & Inter-Connectors Mfr & Marketer
N.A.I.C.S.: 325211

Subsidiary (Non-US):

Shin-Etsu Polymer Mexico S.A. de C.V. (3)
Carretera a Matamoros Brecha E-99 Norte, Parque Industrial, 88780, Reynosa, Tamaulipas, Mexico (100%)
Tel.: (52) 8999216350
Web Site: http://www.shinpoly.com
Sales Range: $125-149.9 Million
Keypads & Inter-Connectors Mfr & Marketer
N.A.I.C.S.: 325211
Yoshio Akinaga *(Pres)*

Subsidiary (Non-US):

Shin-Etsu Polymer Europe B.V (2)
Noorderpoort 49, 5916 PJ, Venlo, Netherlands
Tel.: (31) 77 323 6000
Web Site: https://www.shinetsu.info
Sales Range: $25-49.9 Million
Emp.: 21
Polymer Product Distr
N.A.I.C.S.: 424610

Subsidiary (Non-US):

Urawa Polymer Co., Ltd. (3)
1333 Koemon, Kuki, 349-1105, Saitama, Japan
Tel.: (81) 480 52 0085
Web Site: http://www.shinpoly.co.jp
Polymer Resin Mfr
N.A.I.C.S.: 325211

Subsidiary (Non-US):

Shin-Etsu Polymer Hungary Kft. (2)
Berkenyefa sor 2/A, 9027, Gyor, Hungary
Tel.: (36) 96887100
Web Site: http://www.shinetsu.hu
Sales Range: $25-49.9 Million
Emp.: 30
Telecommunications Equipment Mfr
N.A.I.C.S.: 334220

Shin-Etsu Polymer Shanghai Co., Ltd (2)
Rm 1708 Ruijin Building 205 Maoming Rd S, Shanghai, 200020, China
Tel.: (86) 216 472 7170
Web Site: http://www.shinpoly.co.jp
Sales Range: $25-49.9 Million
Emp.: 15
Rubber Product Distr
N.A.I.C.S.: 423840

Shin-Etsu Polymer Singapore Pte. Ltd.
4 Shenton way 10-02 SGX Centre 2, Singapore, 068807, Singapore (100%)
Tel.: (65) 6 735 0007
Web Site: http://www.shinpoly.com.sg
Sales Range: $25-49.9 Million
Emp.: 25
Semiconductor Materials & Electronic Equipment Sales
N.A.I.C.S.: 423430
Osamu Kowada *(Mng Dir)*

Shin-Etsu Polymer Hong Kong Co., Ltd. (1)
Suite 1602 16 / F Tower 6 China Hong Kong City 33 Canton Road, Tsim Sha Tsui, Kowloon, China (Hong Kong)
Tel.: (852) 23779131
Semiconductor Silicon Product Mfr
N.A.I.C.S.: 334413

Shin-Etsu Polymer India Pvt. Ltd. (1)
Plot No OZ-12 Hi Tech SEZ, SIPCOT Industrial Growth Centre Oragadam Sriperumbudur, Kanchipuram, 602105, Tamil Nadu, India
Tel.: (91) 446 711 2800
Web Site: https://www.shinpoly.co.in
Semiconductor Silicon Product Mfr
N.A.I.C.S.: 334413

Shin-Etsu Polymer Vietnam Co., Ltd. (1)
9 Floor VIT Building No 519 Kim Ma Street, Ngoc Khanh Ward Ba Dinh District, Hanoi, Vietnam
Tel.: (84) 2462741445
Semiconductor Silicon Product Mfr
N.A.I.C.S.: 334413

Shin-Etsu Quartz Products Co., Ltd. (1)
1-22-2 Nishi-Shinjuku, Shinjuku-ku, Tokyo, 160-0023, Japan
Tel.: (81) 33 348 1912
Web Site: https://www.sqp.co.jp
Quartz Glass Product Mfr
N.A.I.C.S.: 327212
Toshiyuki Kato *(Pres)*

Shin-Etsu Silicone (Nantong) Co., Ltd. (1)
Tongdalu 85 Economic and Technological Development Area, Nantong, 226017, Jiangsu, China
Tel.: (86) 51351088688
Silicone Products Mfr
N.A.I.C.S.: 334413

Shin-Etsu Silicone International Trading (Shanghai) Co., Ltd. (1)
29th Floor Juneyao International Plaza No 789 Zhaojiabang, Xuhui District, Shanghai, 200032, China
Tel.: (86) 216 443 5550
Web Site: https://www.shinetsu.com.cn
Emp.: 40
Silicone Products Distr
N.A.I.C.S.: 424690

Shin-Etsu Silicone Korea Co., Ltd. (1)
15th floor GT Tower 411 Seocho-daero, Seocho-Gu, Seoul, 06615, Korea (South)
Tel.: (82) 2 590 2500
Web Site: https://www.shinetsu.net
Sales Range: $25-49.9 Million
Emp.: 100
Silicone Products Mfr & Distr
N.A.I.C.S.: 325211
Takeda Kazumi *(Pres)*

Shin-Etsu Silicone Taiwan Co., Ltd (1)
Rm D 11F No 167 Dunhua N Rd, Songshan Dist, Taipei, 105406, Taiwan
Tel.: (886) 22 715 0055
Web Site: https://www.shinetsu.com.tw
Silicone Rubber Mfr
N.A.I.C.S.: 325212

Plant (Domestic):

Shin-Etsu Silicone Taiwan Co., Ltd - Hsin-Chu Factory (2)
No 25 Kuang Fu S Rd Hsin-Chu Ind Park, Hsin-chu, Taiwan
Tel.: (886) 3 5983111
Silicone Rubber Compound Mfr
N.A.I.C.S.: 325212

Shin-Etsu Silicones (Thailand) Ltd (1)
7th Floor Harindhorn Tower 54 North Sathorn Road, Bangkok, 10500, Thailand
Tel.: (66) 2 632 2941
Web Site: https://www.shinetsu.co.jp
Sales Range: $50-74.9 Million
Emp.: 10
Silicone Products Mfr & Distr
N.A.I.C.S.: 325998

Shin-Etsu Silicones Europe B.V (1)
Bolderweg 32, 1332 AV, Almere, Netherlands
Tel.: (31) 36 549 3170
Web Site: http://www.shinetsu.co.jp
Sales Range: $25-49.9 Million
Emp.: 45
Silicone Products Mfr & Distr

INTERNATIONAL PUBLIC

N.A.I.C.S.: 325211

Shin-Etsu Silicones India Pvt. Ltd. (1)
Unit No 403A Fourth Floor Eros Corporate Tower Nehru Place, New Delhi, 110019, India
Tel.: (91) 1143623081
Semiconductor Silicon Product Whslr
N.A.I.C.S.: 423840

Shin-Etsu Silicones of America, Inc. (1)
1150 Damar Dr, Akron, OH
44305-1201 (100%)
Tel.: (330) 630-9860
Web Site: https://www.shinetsusilicones.com
Sales Range: $75-99.9 Million
Emp.: 175
Producers & Sellers of Silicone
N.A.I.C.S.: 424690
Kazuhiro Kitani *(Pres & CEO)*

Shin-Etsu Singapore Pte. Ltd. (1)
4 Shenton Way 10-03/06 SGX Centre 2, Singapore, 068807, Singapore
Tel.: (65) 6 743 7277
Web Site: https://www.shinetsu.com.sg
Sales Range: $25-49.9 Million
Emp.: 20
Silicone Products Whslr
N.A.I.C.S.: 424610

Shin-Etsu Technology (Suzhou) Co., Ltd. (1)
Block 4 No 1 Qiming Road Suzhou Industrial Park, 215121, Suzhou, China
Tel.: (86) 512 6276 3270
Vinyl Chloride Monomer Mfr & Distr
N.A.I.C.S.: 325211

Shin-Etsu Unit Co., Ltd. (1)
1-406-1 Yoshino-cho, Kita-ku, Saitama, 331-8620, Japan
Tel.: (81) 48 654 4881
Web Site: http://www.shinetsu-unit.co.jp
Construction Engineering Services
N.A.I.C.S.: 541330

Shin-Etsu Yofc (Hubei) Optical Preform Co., Ltd. (1)
Extra No 1 Changfei Avenue, Jianghan Salt and Chemical Industrial Park, Qianjiang, Hubei, China
Tel.: (86) 7286709777
Optical Fiber Product Mfr
N.A.I.C.S.: 335921

Shin-Etsu do Brasil Representacao de Produtos Quimicos Ltda. (1)
Rua Coronel Oscar Porto 736-8 Andar-Sala 84, Sao Paulo, 04003-003, SP, Brazil
Tel.: (55) 113 939 0690
Web Site: http://www.shinetsu.com.br
Semiconductor Silicon Product Mfr
N.A.I.C.S.: 334413

Shinano Electric Refining Co., Ltd. (1)
5F Kanda Urban Building 4-2 Kanda-Tsukasamachi 2-chome, Chiyoda-ku, Tokyo, 101-0048, Japan
Tel.: (81) 35 298 1601
Web Site: https://www.shinano-sic.co.jp
Emp.: 70
Abrasive Products Mfr & Distr
N.A.I.C.S.: 327910
Masao Sakaki *(Pres)*

Plant (Domestic):

Shinano Electric Refining Co., Ltd. - Kashiwabara Plant (2)
2222 Oaza-Kashiwabara Shinano-machi, Kami-Minochi-gun, Nagano, 389-1305, Japan
Tel.: (81) 26 255 3010
Silicone Resin Mfr
N.A.I.C.S.: 325211

Shinano Polymer Co., Ltd. (1)
2146-5 Hirooka Kataishi, Shiojiri, 399-0705, Nagano, Japan
Tel.: (81) 263 54 1010
Polymer Resin Mfr
N.A.I.C.S.: 325211

Shinkoh Mold Co., Ltd. (1)
2-13-1 Isobe, Annaka, 379-0127, Gunma, Japan

AND PRIVATE COMPANIES

Tel.: (81) 273853877
Emp.: 70
Silicone & Resin Product Mfr
N.A.I.C.S.: 325211

Shintech Inc. (1)
3 Greenway Plz Ste 1150, Houston, TX 77046 (100%)
Tel.: (713) 965-0713
Web Site: https://www.shintech.com
Sales Range: $25-49.9 Million
Emp.: 16
Mfr of Plastic Resins
N.A.I.C.S.: 325211
Chihiro Kanagawa (Chm)

Subsidiary (Domestic):

Shintech Louisiana LLC (2)
9750 La Hwy 1 S, Addis, LA 70710-2821
Tel.: (225) 685-1199
Polyvinyl Chloride Resins Mfr
N.A.I.C.S.: 325211

Simcoa Operations Pty. Ltd. (1)
973 Marriott Road, Wellesley, 6233, WA, Australia (100%)
Tel.: (61) 89 780 6744
Web Site: https://www.simcoa.com.au
Emp.: 175
Silicon Production
N.A.I.C.S.: 325998

Skyward Information System Co., Ltd. (1)
3-7-1 Kanda Ogawamachi, Chiyoda-ku, Tokyo, Japan
Tel.: (81) 332190550
Semiconductor Silicon Product Mfr
N.A.I.C.S.: 334413

Skyward Information Systems Co., Ltd (1)
3-7-1 Kandaogawamachi Mitsuwa Ogawamachi Bldg 4f, Chiyoda-ku, 101-0052, Japan
Tel.: (81) 332190550
Information Technology Consulting Services
N.A.I.C.S.: 541512

Suzhou Shin-Etsu Polymer Co., Ltd. (1)
A-10 Fenfu Economic and Technical Development Zone, Wujiang, Jiangsu, China
Tel.: (86) 5123255640
Silicone Products Mfr
N.A.I.C.S.: 334413

Tatsuno Chemical Industries, Inc. (1)
1-21-9 Narihira, Sumida-ku, Tokyo, 130-0002, Japan
Tel.: (81) 35 637 2022
Web Site: https://www.tatsuno-chem.co.jp
Synthetic Resin Product Mfr
N.A.I.C.S.: 325211

Topco Quartz Product Co., Ltd. (1)
No 8 Wen-Hua Road Hsin-Chu Ind Park, Hsin-chu, 303, Taiwan
Tel.: (886) 35985668
Quartz Glass Products Mfr
N.A.I.C.S.: 327215

Yamagata Shin-Etsu Quartz Products Co., Ltd. (1)
2-4-1 Shogehigashi, Tendo, Yamagata, Japan
Tel.: (81) 23 655 3221
Web Site: https://www.sqp.co.jp
Emp.: 60
Quartz Glass Products Mfr & Distr
N.A.I.C.S.: 327215
Yamada Naoki (Pres)

Young Shin Quartz Co., Ltd. (1)
9-2 Yongso 1-gil Gwanghyewon-myeon, Jincheon, 27809, Chungbuk, Korea (South)
Tel.: (82) 43 535 2338
Web Site: https://www.ysq.co.kr
Quartz Glass Product Mfr
N.A.I.C.S.: 327212
Lee Chiwan (Pres)

Zhejiang Shin-Etsu High-Tech Chemical Co., Ltd. (1)
No 66 Lizheng Road Jiashan Economic Development Zone, Jiashan, 314116, Zhejiang Sheng, China
Tel.: (86) 57384755071
Silicone Products Mfr
N.A.I.C.S.: 334413

SHIN-NIHON TATEMONO CO., LTD.
4th floor Forecast Shinjuku South 4-3-17 Shinjuku, Shinjuku-ku, Tokyo, 160-0022, Japan
Tel.: (81) 359620775
Web Site: http://www.kksnt.co.jp
Year Founded: 1975
8893—(TKS)
Rev.: $163,659,760
Assets: $225,098,720
Liabilities: $164,134,080
Net Worth: $60,964,640
Earnings: $12,855,040
Emp.: 44
Fiscal Year-end: 03/31/20
Real Estate Agents & Brokers
N.A.I.C.S.: 531210
Tomohiko Ikeda (Pres & CEO)

SHINAGAWA REFRACTORIES CO., LTD.
8 Fl Shin-Otemachi Bldg 2-2-1 Otemachi, Chiyoda, Tokyo, 100-0004, Japan
Tel.: (81) 362651600 JP
Web Site: https://www.shinagawa.co.jp
Year Founded: 1903
5351—(TKS)
Rev.: $952,996,750
Assets: $1,025,455,570
Liabilities: $450,603,700
Net Worth: $574,851,870
Earnings: $101,000,800
Emp.: 3,340
Fiscal Year-end: 03/31/24
Refractories & Ceramics Mfr
N.A.I.C.S.: 327120
Toshihiko Kaneshige (Sr Mng Exec Officer)

Subsidiaries:

PT Shinagawa Refractories Indonesia (1)
Tiang Bendera III Number 52/10 RT 007 / RW 003, Roa Malaka Tambora West, Jakarta, 11230, Indonesia
Tel.: (62) 212 269 3011
Web Site: https://www.shinagawa.co.id
Nonmetallic Mineral Product Mfr
N.A.I.C.S.: 327999

Shenyang Shinagawa Metallurgy Materials Co., Ltd. (1)
Santai Laobianxiang, Yuhong, Shenyang, 110146, Liaoning, China
Tel.: (86) 248 926 0601
Clay Building Material Mfr
N.A.I.C.S.: 327120

Shinagawa Fine Ceramics Co., Ltd. (1)
707 Inbe, Bizen, 705-0001, Okayama, Japan
Tel.: (81) 869642221
Web Site: https://www.sifce.co.jp
Emp.: 70
Refractories Mfr
N.A.I.C.S.: 327120

Shinagawa Kaihatsu Co., Ltd. (1)
2638-2 Mitsuishi, Bizen, 705-0132, Okayama, Japan
Tel.: (81) 869620575
Refractories Mfr
N.A.I.C.S.: 327120

Shinagawa Kigyo Co., Ltd. (1)
1-1-4 Shinagawa, Minato, Nagoya, 455-0055, Japan
Tel.: (81) 526520245
Refractories Mfr
N.A.I.C.S.: 327120

Shinagawa Refractories Australasia New Zealand Ltd. (1)
24 Rayner Road, Huntly, 3740, New Zealand
Tel.: (64) 78287019
Web Site: http://www.shinagawa.co.nz
Refractories & Ceramics Mfr
N.A.I.C.S.: 327120

Shinagawa Refractories Australasia Pty. Ltd. (1)
23 Glastonbury Avenue, Unanderra, 2526, NSW, Australia (100%)
Tel.: (61) 242211700
Web Site: https://www.shinagawa.com.au
Sales Range: $50-74,9 Million
Emp.: 70
Refractory Mfr
N.A.I.C.S.: 327120

Shinagawa Refractories Co., Ltd. - Ako Works (1)
1576-2 Higashioki Nakahiro, Ako, 678-0232, Hyogo, Japan
Tel.: (81) 791433138
Refractories Mfr
N.A.I.C.S.: 327120

Shinagawa Refractories Co., Ltd. - Furnace Construction Division (1)
1 Kawasaki Chuo, Chuo, 260-0835, Chiba, Japan
Tel.: (81) 43 262 2095
Refractories Mfr
N.A.I.C.S.: 327120

Shinagawa Refractories Co., Ltd. - Okayama Works (1)
88 Higashi-katakami, Bizen, 705-8615, Okayama, Japan
Tel.: (81) 869643311
Refractories Mfr
N.A.I.C.S.: 327120

Shinagawa Refractories Co., Ltd. - Yumoto Works (1)
1-1 Iwasaki Iwagaoka Joban, Iwaki, 972-8313, Fukushima, Japan
Tel.: (81) 24 643 2121
Web Site: https://www.shinagawa.co.jp
Refractories Mfr
N.A.I.C.S.: 327120

Shinagawa Roko Co., Ltd. (1)
1 Kokan-cho, Fukuyama, 721-0931, Hiroshima, Japan
Tel.: (81) 849411504
Web Site: https://www.s-rokoh.com
Emp.: 590
Refractories Mfr
N.A.I.C.S.: 327120

Teikoku Yogyo Co., Ltd. (1)
1801 Kugui, Bizen, 705-0024, Okayama, Japan
Tel.: (81) 86 964 2841
Web Site: https://www.teikokuyogyo.co.jp
Adhesive Mfr
N.A.I.C.S.: 325520

SHINDAEYANG PAPER CO., LTD.
674 Seonggok-dong, Danwon-gu, Ansan, Gyeonggi-do, Korea (South)
Tel.: (82) 314990800
Year Founded: 1982
016590—(KRS)
Rev.: $518,800,506
Assets: $678,434,426
Liabilities: $174,285,393
Net Worth: $504,149,032
Earnings: $39,332,758
Emp.: 119
Fiscal Year-end: 12/31/22
Corrugated & Solid Fiber Box Mfr
N.A.I.C.S.: 322211

SHINDEN HIGHTEX CORPORATION
6F KDX Ginza East Building 3-7-2 Irifune, Chuo-ku, Tokyo, 104-0042, Japan
Tel.: (81) 335370101
Web Site: https://www.shinden.co.jp
3131—(TKS)
Rev.: $279,503,850
Assets: $122,807,190
Liabilities: $75,995,170
Net Worth: $46,812,020
Earnings: $1,930,120
Emp.: 131
Fiscal Year-end: 03/31/24
Liquid Crystal Displays, Semiconductor & Electronic Components Sales & Distr
N.A.I.C.S.: 423690
Tamotsu Shiroshita (Founder)

Subsidiaries:

SDT THAI CO., LTD. (1)
26/159 Richmond Palace 1F Soi Sukhumvit 43 Sukhumvit Rd Klongton-Nua, Wattana, Bangkok, Thailand
Tel.: (66) 22618795
Electronic Components Distr
N.A.I.C.S.: 423690

Shinden Hightex Korea Corporation (1)
502 Jungang B/D 275 Seocho-Daero, Seocho-Gu, Seoul, 6596, Korea (South)
Tel.: (82) 25239961
Web Site: http://www.shinden.co.jp
Emp.: 5
Electronic Components Distr
N.A.I.C.S.: 423690

Shinden Hong Kong Limited (1)
Unit 6 21/F Peninsula Tower 538 Castle Peak Road, Cheung Sha Wan, Kowloon, China (Hong Kong)
Tel.: (852) 26205162
Web Site: https://www.shinden.co.jp
Electronic Components Distr
N.A.I.C.S.: 423690

SHINDENGEN ELECTRIC MANUFACTURING CO., LTD.
New-Otemachi Bldg 2-2-1 Otemachi, Chiyoda-ku, Tokyo, 100-0004, Japan
Tel.: (81) 332794431
Web Site: https://www.shindengen.co.jp
Year Founded: 1949
6844—(TKS)
Rev.: $675,945,210
Assets: $956,262,090
Liabilities: $487,500,720
Net Worth: $468,761,370
Earnings: ($4,706,320)
Emp.: 5,276
Fiscal Year-end: 03/31/24
Semiconductors & Electronic Products Mfr
N.A.I.C.S.: 334413
Yoshinori Suzuki (Pres)

Subsidiaries:

Akita Shindengen Co., Ltd. (1)
114-2 Kamiyachi Oura, Yurihonjo, 015-8558, Akita, Japan
Tel.: (81) 184222327
Web Site: https://www.asd.shindengen.co.jp
Emp.: 742
Semiconductors
N.A.I.C.S.: 333242

Guangzhou Shindengen Electronic Co., Ltd. (1)
2 Heng Rd Yonghe Economic Zone Zhengcheng, Guangzhou Economic Technical Development Area, Guangzhou, Guangdong, China
Tel.: (86) 2082973472
Web Site: http://www.shindengen.co.jp
Electrical Equipment
N.A.I.C.S.: 335999

Hermes Systems Inc. (1)
1-18-6 Nishi-Shimbashi 7th Floor Cross Office Uchisaiwa, Minato-ku, Tokyo, 105-0003, Japan
Tel.: (81) 36 327 7767
Web Site: https://www.hermes.ne.jp
Software Development Services
N.A.I.C.S.: 541511

Higashine Shindengen Co., Ltd. (1)
5600-1 Higashineko, Higashine, 999-3701, Yamagata, Japan
Tel.: (81) 237435211
Web Site: https://www.hsd.shindengen.co.jp

SHINDENGEN ELECTRIC MANUFACTURING CO., LTD.

Shindengen Electric Manufacturing Co., Ltd.—(Continued)
Sales Range: $100-124.9 Million
Emp.: 362
Semiconductors
N.A.I.C.S.: 333242

Lumphun Shindengen Co., Ltd. (1)
105 Moo 4, Northern Region Industrial Estate I-EA-T Free Zone Banklang Muang, Lamphun, 51000, Thailand
Tel.: (66) 53581406
Web Site: http://www.shindengen.co.jp
Sales Range: $400-449.9 Million
Emp.: 1,800
Semiconductors
N.A.I.C.S.: 333242

Nippon Vender Net Co., Ltd. (1)
2nd Floor Preciza Building 4-8-3 Iidabashi, Chiyoda-ku, Tokyo, 102-0072, Japan
Tel.: (81) 332650978
Web Site: https://www.vendernet.jp
Emp.: 69
Vendor Net Systems Sales
N.A.I.C.S.: 561499

Okabe Shindengen Co., Ltd. (1)
342-1 Hongo, Fukaya, 369-0214, Saitama, Japan
Tel.: (81) 485855846
Web Site: https://osd.shindengen.co.jp
Electric Equipment & Power Supply
N.A.I.C.S.: 335999

PT Shindengen Indonesia (1)
Kawasan Greenland International Industrial Center GIIC Blok AD No 02, Kota Deltamas Desa Nagasari Kecamatan Serang Baru Kabupaten, Bekasi, 17330, Indonesia
Tel.: (62) 2122157080
Web Site: http://www.shindengen.co.jp
Sales Range: $50-74.9 Million
Emp.: 200
Electrical Equipment
N.A.I.C.S.: 335999

Shindengen (H.K.) Co., Ltd. (1)
Suite 2006B 20/F Exchange Tower 33 Wang Chiu Road, Kowloon Bay, Kowloon, China (Hong Kong)
Tel.: (852) 23171884
Sales Range: $25-49.9 Million
Emp.: 100
Electrical Equipment
N.A.I.C.S.: 335999

Shindengen (Shanghai) Electric Co., Ltd. (1)
Room1506 Sheng GaoInt'l Building 137 Xian Xia Road, Chang Ning, Shanghai, China
Tel.: (86) 2162708000
Power Supply Product Mfr
N.A.I.C.S.: 333613

Shindengen (Thailand) Co., Ltd. (1)
60/58 Moo 19 Soi Nava Nakorn 13 Klongnueng, Klongluang, Pathumthani, 12120, Thailand
Tel.: (66) 252915102
Web Site: http://www.shindengen.co.jp
Sales Range: $200-249.9 Million
Emp.: 625
Electrical Equipment
N.A.I.C.S.: 335999

Shindengen America Inc. (1)
2333 Waukegan Rd Ste 250, Bannockburn, IL 60015
Tel.: (847) 444-1363
Web Site: http://www.shindengen.com
Emp.: 10
Electrical Equipment
N.A.I.C.S.: 335999

Shindengen Device Commerce Co., Ltd. (1)
Sanpousakuma Bldg 1-11 Kandasakumacho, Chiyoda-ku, Tokyo, 101-0025, Japan
Tel.: (81) 3 3256 8881
Web Site: http://www.shindengen.co.jp
Electrical Equipment & Units Sales
N.A.I.C.S.: 423610

Shindengen Electric Manufacturing Co., Ltd.- Hanno Factory (1)
10-13 Minamicho, Hanno, 357-8585, Saitama, Japan
Tel.: (81) 42 973 3111

Web Site: http://www.shindengen.co.jp
Semiconductor Devices Mfr
N.A.I.C.S.: 334413

Shindengen Enterprise Co., Ltd. (1)
3-14-1 Saiwai-cho, Asaka, Saitama, 351-8503, Japan
Tel.: (81) 484869455
Health & Welfare Services
N.A.I.C.S.: 621399

Shindengen India Pvt. Ltd. (1)
Plot No 283/2 Bommasandra-Jigani Link Road, Jigani Industrial Area Jigani Hobli Anekal Taluk, Bengaluru, 560105, Karnataka, India
Tel.: (91) 806 715 6900
Electrical Equipment Mfr & Distr
N.A.I.C.S.: 335999

Shindengen Kumamoto Technoresearch Co., Ltd. (1)
1-17-3 Hikarinomori Kikuyo-cho, Kikuchigun, Kumamoto, 869-1108, Japan
Tel.: (81) 963375200
Web Site: https://www.sdkt.co.jp
Emp.: 42
Software Services
N.A.I.C.S.: 513210

Shindengen Mechatronics Co., Ltd. (1)
11-8 Inari-cho, Hanno, 357-0037, Saitama, Japan (47.5%)
Tel.: (81) 429716211
Web Site: http://www.smt.shindengen.co.jp
Sales Range: $50-74.9 Million
Emp.: 60
Solenoid Sales & Manufacturing
N.A.I.C.S.: 423610

Shindengen Philippines Corp. (1)
120 Excellence Avenue Cor Quality Drive, Carmelray Industrial Park I Canlubang, Calamba, 4028, Laguna, Philippines
Tel.: (63) 495493146
Web Site: http://www.shindengen.co.jp
Semiconductor Devices Mfr
N.A.I.C.S.: 334413

Shindengen Singapore Pte Ltd. (1)
4 Shenton Way 09-05/06 SGX Centre, Techpark at Chai Chee, Singapore, 068807, Singapore
Tel.: (65) 64450082
Sales Range: $25-49.9 Million
Emp.: 14
Electrical Equipment
N.A.I.C.S.: 335999

Shindengen Three E Co., Ltd. (1)
3-1 Ashikariba, Hanno, 357-0013, Saitama, Japan
Tel.: (81) 429742121
Web Site: https://www.ste-shindengen.co.jp
Sales Range: $50-74.9 Million
Emp.: 248
Power Supply Product Mfr
N.A.I.C.S.: 335999

Shindengen UK Ltd. (1)
6th Floor 2 Kingdom Street, London, W2 6BD, United Kingdom
Tel.: (44) 2081874997
Web Site: http://www.shindengen.co.uk
Sales Range: $25-49.9 Million
Emp.: 4
Electrical Equipment
N.A.I.C.S.: 335999

Shindengen Vietnam Co., Ltd. (1)
Plot No D-4 Thang Long, Industrial ParkII Lieu Xa commune, Yen My, Hung Yen, Vietnam
Tel.: (84) 221 397 4640
Electrical Equipment Mfr & Distr
N.A.I.C.S.: 335999

SHINDO ENG. LAB., LTD.
21 Mayu-Ro 238Beon-Gil, Jeongwang 1-Dong, Siheung, Korea (South)
Tel.: (82) 314345088
Web Site: https://www.lcd.co.kr
Year Founded: 1989
290520—(KRS)
Rev.: $16,732,342
Assets: $55,560,863

Liabilities: $8,331,444
Net Worth: $47,229,419
Earnings: ($307,484)
Emp.: 62
Fiscal Year-end: 12/31/22
Display Component Mfr
N.A.I.C.S.: 334419
Nam-Yeol Heo *(CFO & Exec Dir)*

SHINE BOX CAPITAL CORP.
1900 520-3rd Avenue SW, Calgary, T2P 0R3, AB, Canada
Tel.: (613) 898-4787
Year Founded: 2018
RENT.P—(TSXV)
Assets: $9,703
Liabilities: $44,658
Net Worth: ($34,955)
Earnings: ($31,967)
Fiscal Year-end: 06/30/24
Asset Management Services
N.A.I.C.S.: 523940
Dobrijevic Nebojsa *(CEO & CFO)*

SHINE DEVELOPMENT BANK LTD.
Siddhartha Road Rupandehi, Butwal, 32908, Nepal
Tel.: (977) 71 551500
Web Site:
  http://www.shinebank.com.np
Banking Services
N.A.I.C.S.: 522110
Sarjan Bhattarai *(CEO)*

SHINE FASHIONS (INDIA) LTD.
605 Marathon Chambers P K Road Panch Rasta Mulund West, Mumbai, 400080, India
Tel.: (91) 2225939522
Web Site: https://shinefashions.in
Year Founded: 2014
543244—(BOM)
Rev.: $2,541,071
Assets: $1,495,354
Liabilities: $729,501
Net Worth: $765,853
Earnings: $105,917
Fiscal Year-end: 03/31/23
Interlining Fabric Distr
N.A.I.C.S.: 424310
Anil Z. Mehta *(Founder)*

SHINE JUSTICE LTD.
PO Box 12011, George Street, Brisbane, 4003, QLD, Australia
Tel.: (61) 730066000
Web Site:
  https://www.shinejustice.com.au
SHJ—(ASX)
Rev.: $130,698,450
Assets: $395,683,759
Liabilities: $213,640,491
Net Worth: $182,043,268
Earnings: $4,143,964
Emp.: 995
Fiscal Year-end: 06/30/24
Lawyer
N.A.I.C.S.: 541110
Simon Morrison *(CEO & Mng Dir)*

Subsidiaries:

Best Wilson Buckley Family Law Pty. Ltd. (1)
135 Margaret Street, PO Box 3701, Toowoomba, 4350, QLD, Australia
Tel.: (61) 746390000
Web Site: http://www.bwbfamilylaw.com.au
Law Practice Services
N.A.I.C.S.: 541110
Jennnifer Ryder *(Gen Mgr)*

Carr & Co Divorce & Family Lawyers Pty. Ltd. (1)
Level 8 28 The Esplanade, Perth, 6000, WA, Australia
Tel.: (61) 893228000
Web Site: https://www.carrco.com.au

INTERNATIONAL PUBLIC

Law Practice Services
N.A.I.C.S.: 541110

My Insurance Claim Limited (1)
Level 1 242 Ferry Road, Waltham, Christchurch, 8141, New Zealand
Tel.: (64) 508555555
Web Site:
  http://www.myinsuranceclaim.co.nz
Insurance Services
N.A.I.C.S.: 524210

Nerve Solutions Group Pty. Ltd. (1)
Level 13 160 Ann Street, Brisbane, 4000, QLD, Australia
Tel.: (61) 1300463783
Web Site: http://www.nervesolutions.com.au
Information Technology Services
N.A.I.C.S.: 541511

Sciacca's Lawyers Pty. Ltd. (1)
Level 8 157 Ann Street, Brisbane, 4000, QLD, Australia
Tel.: (61) 738678888
Web Site: https://www.sciaccas.com.au
Law Practice Services
N.A.I.C.S.: 541110

SHINE MINERALS CORP.
700-1620 Dickson Avenue, Kelowna, V1Y 9Y2, BC, Canada
Tel.: (250) 979-7022 BC
Web Site: http://www.shineminerals.ca
SMR—(TSXV)
Assets: $176,996
Liabilities: $835,622
Net Worth: ($658,626)
Earnings: ($261,904)
Fiscal Year-end: 06/30/24
Gold & Copper Mining Services
N.A.I.C.S.: 212220
Devinder Randhawa *(Chm & CEO)*

SHINE RESUNGA DEVELOPMENT BANK LIMITED
KalikaNagar 11 Rupandehi, Butwal, Rupandehi, Nepal
Tel.: (977) 71415502
Web Site: https://www.srdb.com.np
SHINE—(NEP)
Rev.: $52,291,921
Assets: $475,250,576
Liabilities: $428,967,783
Net Worth: $46,282,793
Earnings: $5,680,544
Emp.: 683
Fiscal Year-end: 07/16/23
Commercial Banking Services
N.A.I.C.S.: 522110
Mohan Chapagain *(Dir-Pub)*

Subsidiaries:

Purnima Bikas Bank Limited (1)
Narayansthan, Narayansthan, Rupandehi, Nepal
Tel.: (977) 71 520856
Web Site: http://www.purnimabank.com
Sales Range: Less than $1 Million
Commercial Banking Services
N.A.I.C.S.: 522110
Suraj Upreti *(Chm)*

SHINE@SPRING PTE. LTD.
521 Bukit Batok Street 23 Level 3E, Singapore, 659544, Singapore
Tel.: (65) 67419555 SG
Web Site: http://www.shine-spring.com
Year Founded: 1972
Sales Range: $25-49.9 Million
Emp.: 75
Beauty & Personal Care Products & Services Retailer
N.A.I.C.S.: 456120
Koh Hoon Kiat *(Owner)*

SHINECHLEL INVEST JOINT STOCK COMPANY
11th Khoroo, Sukhbaatar District, Ulaanbaatar, Mongolia
Tel.: (976) 11 350821

AND PRIVATE COMPANIES

Building Construction Services
N.A.I.C.S.: 236220

SHINECO, INC.
No 20 Jinhe East Road Room 3310
North Tower Zhengda Center, Chaoyang District, Beijing, 100026, China
Tel.: (86) 1087227366   DE
Web Site: https://www.biosisi.com
SISI—(NASDAQ)
Rev.: $9,801,856
Assets: $84,179,379
Liabilities: $47,601,684
Net Worth: $36,577,695
Earnings: ($24,352,735)
Emp.: 119
Fiscal Year-end: 06/30/24
Holding Company; Plant-Based Product Mfr
N.A.I.C.S.: 551112
Sai Wang (CFO)

SHINELONG AUTOMOTIVE LIGHTWEIGHT APPLICATION LIMITED
2 Middle Yangguang Road, Zhangjia Town, Kunshan, Jiangsu, China
Tel.: (86) 51236832657   Ky
Web Site:
  https://www.shinlone.com.cn
Year Founded: 2002
1930—(HKG)
Rev.: $30,418,773
Assets: $86,839,275
Liabilities: $37,427,518
Net Worth: $49,411,757
Earnings: $2,698,028
Emp.: 383
Fiscal Year-end: 12/31/22
Software Development Services
N.A.I.C.S.: 541511
Ming-Chih Chen (CTO)

SHINEMORE TECHNOLOGY MATERIALS CORPORATION LTD.
No 208 Sec 2 Binhai Rd, Dayuan Township, Taoyuan, 337, Taiwan
Tel.: (886) 33864289
Web Site:
  https://www.shinemore.com.tw
Year Founded: 1997
8291—(TPE)
Rev.: $3,111,716
Assets: $11,782,509
Liabilities: $8,414,908
Net Worth: $3,367,602
Earnings: ($1,855,642)
Fiscal Year-end: 12/31/22
Circuit Board Mfr & Distr
N.A.I.C.S.: 334412
Sasaki Beji (Chm)

SHINEPUKUR CERAMICS LIMITED
Level 9 149-150 Tejgaon I/A, Dhaka, 1208, Bangladesh
Tel.: (880) 9609100300   BD
Web Site:
  https://www.shinepukur.com
Year Founded: 1997
SPCERAMICS—(DHA)
Rev.: $19,983,802
Assets: $73,827,781
Liabilities: $20,082,422
Net Worth: $53,745,359
Earnings: $672,567
Emp.: 2,992
Fiscal Year-end: 06/30/22
Ceramic Tableware Mfr
N.A.I.C.S.: 339999
Mohammad Faruque Ali (Exec Dir-Production)

SHINER INTERNATIONAL, INC.
No 18 North PV Road Shizlling Industrial Park, National High-tech Development Zone, Haikou, 570125, Hainan, China
Tel.: (86) 89865483846   NV
Web Site:
  http://www.en.shinerinc.com
Year Founded: 2003
Sales Range: $75-99.9 Million
Emp.: 393
Packaging Film Products Mfr
N.A.I.C.S.: 322220
Yuet Ying (Chm)

Subsidiaries:

Hainan Shiner Industrial Co., Ltd.   (1)
19/Floor Didu Bldg Pearl River Plz, No2 North Longkun Road, Haikou, 570125, China
Tel.: (86) 89868581565
Web Site: http://www.shinerinc.com
Sales Range: $125-149.9 Million
Emp.: 50
Plastics Packing Product Mfr
N.A.I.C.S.: 326199
Qingtao Xing (Pres)

SHINEROAD INTERNATIONAL HOLDINGS LIMITED
Unit 6 16/F K Wah Centre 191 Java Road, Hong Kong, China (Hong Kong)
Tel.: (852) 36125717   Ky
Web Site: http://www.shineroad.com
1587—(HKG)
Rev.: $102,254,443
Assets: $77,619,578
Liabilities: $14,239,789
Net Worth: $63,379,789
Earnings: $6,691,745
Emp.: 176
Fiscal Year-end: 12/31/22
Food Flavor Mfr & Distr
N.A.I.C.S.: 311999
Haixiao Huang (Founder & Chm)

Subsidiaries:

Shineroad Food Technology (Vietnam) Co., Ltd.   (1)
26 Le Van Mien street, Thao Dien Ward District 2, Ho Chi Minh City, Vietnam
Tel.: (84) 2836364220
Web Site: http://www.shineroad.com.vn
Food & Beverage Distr
N.A.I.C.S.: 424490

SHINGAKUKAI HOLDINGS CO., LTD.
1-15 1-chome Kita Hongo-dori, Shiroishi Ward, Sapporo, 003-0025, Hokkaido, Japan
Tel.: (81) 118635557
Web Site:
  https://www.shingakukai.co.jp
Year Founded: 1976
9760—(TKS)
Rev.: $31,225,640
Assets: $154,488,920
Liabilities: $88,382,310
Net Worth: $66,106,610
Earnings: ($11,018,870)
Emp.: 1,000
Fiscal Year-end: 03/31/24
Holding Company; Educational & Sport Club Services
N.A.I.C.S.: 551112

SHINHA, INC.
Hyundai Office Building 1202 9-4 Sunae Dong, Bundang Gu, Seongnam, 463-783, Gyungi Do, Korea (South)
Tel.: (82) 317111417
Web Site: http://www.shinha.co.kr
Year Founded: 1986
Semiconductor Equipment Mfr
N.A.I.C.S.: 333242
K. M. Suh (Pres)

SHINHAN 2ND SPECIAL PURPOSE ACQUISITION CO., LTD.
70 Yeoui-daero Yeongdeungpo-gu, Seoul, Korea (South)
Tel.: (82) 2 3772 4071
203650—(KRS)
Investment Services
N.A.I.C.S.: 523999
Won-Bae Lee (CEO)

SHINHAN 3RD SPECIAL PURPOSE ACQUISITION CO LTD
Shinhan Investment Tower 70 Yeoui-daero Yeongdeungpo-gu, Seoul, 07325, Korea (South)
Tel.: (82) 237723461
Investment Services
N.A.I.C.S.: 523999
Kim Chul-Sik (CEO)

SHINHAN 4TH SPECIAL PURPOSE ACQUISITION CO., LTD.
70 Yeoui-daero, Yeongdeungpo-gu, Seoul, Korea (South)
Tel.: (82) 237722365
Investment Advisory Services
N.A.I.C.S.: 523940
Won-Bae Lee (CEO)

SHINHAN ALPHA REIT
136 Sejong-daero, Jung-gu, Seoul, 03159, Korea (South)
Tel.: (82) 221587400
Web Site: http://www.shalphareit.com
Year Founded: 2017
293940—(KRS)
Real Estate Investment Services
N.A.I.C.S.: 531390
Nopil Park (Gen Mgr)

SHINHAN ENG. & CONST. CO., LTD.
Shinhan Bldg 12-3 Yeouido-dong, PO Box No 61, Youngdeungpo-gu, 150-010, Seoul, Korea (South)
Tel.: (82) 2 369 0035
Web Site: http://www.seco.co.kr
Year Founded: 1968
Rev.: $52,169,140
Assets: $145,504,649
Liabilities: $108,791,577
Net Worth: $36,713,072
Earnings: ($1,440,464)
Emp.: 30
Fiscal Year-end: 12/31/18
Construction Engineering Services
N.A.I.C.S.: 237990
Choon-Hwan Kim (Chm & CEO)

Subsidiaries:

Shinhan Eng. & Const. Co., Ltd.-Bugang Factory   (1)
1-3 Buyomg-ri Geumnam-myeon, Yeongigun, Sejong, Chungnam, Korea (South)
Tel.: (82) 43 279 5800
Construction Engineering Services
N.A.I.C.S.: 541330

SHINHAN FINANCIAL GROUP CO., LTD.
20 Sejong-daero 9-gil, Jung-gu, Seoul, 04513, Korea (South)
Tel.: (82) 263603000   KR
Web Site:
  https://www.shinhangroup.com
Year Founded: 1982
SHG—(NYSE)
Rev.: $20,470,592,907
Assets: $513,483,168,060
Liabilities: $471,678,419,904
Net Worth: $41,804,748,156
Earnings: $3,323,783,086
Emp.: 191
Fiscal Year-end: 12/31/23
Financial Investment Services
N.A.I.C.S.: 551111

SHINHAN FINANCIAL GROUP CO., LTD.

Cheul Park (Co-Chm)

Subsidiaries:

Asia Trust Co., Ltd.   (1)
13th Floor 416 Yeongdong-daero KT and G Tower, Gangnam-gu Daechi-dong, Seoul, 06176, Korea (South)
Tel.: (82) 22 055 0000
Web Site: https://www.asiatrust.co.kr
Real Estate Services
N.A.I.C.S.: 531390

Banco Shinhan de Mexico S.A.   (1)
Paseo De La Reforma Number 250 Torre B 17th Floor, Delegacion Cuauhtemoc Colonia Juarez, 06600, Mexico, Mexico
Tel.: (52) 556 722 8000
Web Site: https://www.shinhanmexico.com
Financial Investment Services
N.A.I.C.S.: 523999

Goodmorning Shinhan Securities Co., Ltd.   (1)
23 2 Yoido Dong, Youngdungpo Gu, Seoul, 150 712, Korea (South)   (100%)
Tel.: (82) 237721000
Web Site: http://www.shinhaninvest.com
Sales Range: $600-649.9 Million
Emp.: 1,707
Securities & Broker Services
N.A.I.C.S.: 523150
Jin Kook Lee (Mng Dir-Retail Bus Grp & VP)

Subsidiary (US):

Good Morning Securities USA Limited   (2)
1325 Avenue of the Americas Ste 702, New York, NY 10019   (100%)
Tel.: (212) 397-4000
Web Site: http://www.goodi.com
Sales Range: $50-74.9 Million
Emp.: 5
Investment Banking & Securities Dealing
N.A.I.C.S.: 523150
Richard Pak (Mng Dir)

Jeju Bank   (1)
90 Ohhyeongil Jeju-Si, Jeju, 690-829, Korea (South)
Tel.: (82) 647200200
Web Site: http://www.e-jejubank.com
Sales Range: $200-249.9 Million
Emp.: 500
Banking Services
N.A.I.C.S.: 522110

LLP MFO Shinhan Finance   (1)
St Auezov 48 2nd Floor office 2/3, 050000, Almaty, Kazakhstan
Tel.: (7) 727 355 2550
Web Site: https://www.shinhanfinance.kz
Financial Investment Services
N.A.I.C.S.: 523999

Macquarie Investment Management Korea Co., Limited   (1)
20th Fl One IFC Yeouido-Dong 10 Gukjegeumyung-ro Yeongdeungpo-gu, Seoul, 150 945, Korea (South)   (51%)
Tel.: (82) 2 3703 9800
Web Site: http://www.macquarie.kr
Sales Range: $50-74.9 Million
Emp.: 20
Investment & Financial Advisors
N.A.I.C.S.: 523940

Neoplux Co., Ltd.   (1)
18F Glass Tower Bldg 534 Teheran-ro, Gangnam-gu, Seoul, 100-730, Korea (South)   (96.8%)
Tel.: (82) 25609700
Web Site: http://www.neoplux.co.kr
Investment Management Service
N.A.I.C.S.: 523999
Sangha Lee (CEO)

Orange Life Insurance Co., Ltd.   (1)
37 Seongdong-ro 7-gil, Jung-gu, Seoul, 100-130, Korea (South)   (100%)
Tel.: (82) 1 588 5005
Web Site: http://www.orangelife.co.kr
Fire Insurance Services
N.A.I.C.S.: 524113
Andrew Barrett (CFO)

P.T. Shinhan Sekuritas Indonesia   (1)

SHINHAN FINANCIAL GROUP CO., LTD.

Shinhan Financial Group Co., Ltd.—(Continued)
Equity Tower Building 50th Floor Sudirman Central Business Area, Jl Jend Sudirman Kav 52-53 Senayan, Jakarta, Indonesia
Tel.: (62) 2180869900
Web Site: https://www.shinhansekuritas.co.id
Finance Services
N.A.I.C.S.: 921130

PT Bank Shinhan Indonesia (1)
International Financial Center 2 30th and 31st Floor, Jalan Jenderal Sudirman Kav 22-23, Jakarta Selatan, 12920, Indonesia
Tel.: (62) 212 975 1500
Web Site: https://www.shinhan.co.id
Financial Investment Services
N.A.I.C.S.: 523999

PT Shinhan Asset Management Indonesia (1)
Jl Kebon Sirih No 71 RT 3/RW 2 Kb Sirih, Kec Menteng, Jakarta Pusat, 10340, Jakarta, Indonesia
Tel.: (62) 21 310 0078
Web Site: https://www.shinhan-am.co.id
Asset Management Services
N.A.I.C.S.: 523999

PT Shinhan Indo Finance (1)
Wisma Indomobil 1 Lt 10 Jl MT Haryono Kav 8, Kampung Melayu Jatinegara, Jakarta, 13330, Indonesia
Tel.: (62) 150 0336
Web Site: https://corp.ptsif.co.id
Financial Investment Services
N.A.I.C.S.: 523999

SBJ DNX Co., Ltd. (1)
4F Sanda Berge Building 5-36-7 Shiba, Minato-ku, Tokyo, Japan
Tel.: (81) 345300755
Web Site: https://www.sbjdnx.co.jp
Emp.: 51
Banking System Development Services
N.A.I.C.S.: 541511

Shinhan Alternative Investment Management Inc. (1)
23rd Floor Shinhan Investment Tower 70 Yeoui-daero 23-2, Yeongdeungpo-gu Yeouido-dong, Seoul, 07325, Korea (South)
Tel.: (82) 23 775 4520
Web Site: https://www.shinhanaim.com
Asset Management Services
N.A.I.C.S.: 523999

Shinhan Asset Management (Hong Kong) Ltd. (1)
Unit 7702B Level 77 International Commerce Centre 1 Austin Road West, Kowloon, China (Hong Kong)
Tel.: (852) 2 525 9110
Financial Investment Services
N.A.I.C.S.: 523999

Shinhan Asset Trust Co., Ltd. (1)
13th Floor 416 Yeongdong-daero, Gangnam-gu, Seoul, Korea (South)
Tel.: (82) 220550000
Web Site: https://www.shinhantrust.kr
Real Estate Investment Services
N.A.I.C.S.: 531190

Shinhan BNP Paribas Asset Management Co., Ltd. (1)
GoodmorningShinhan-Tower 18th Floor 23-2 Yeouido-Dong, Yeongdeunpo-gu, Seoul, Korea (South) (65%)
Tel.: (82) 2 767 5777
Web Site: http://www.shbnppam.com
Asset Management & Commercial Banking Services
N.A.I.C.S.: 522110
Lee Chang-Goo (CEO)

Shinhan Bank (1)
100 Daekyung Bldg 120 Bungi, Taepyungro, Jung-gu, Seoul, 100-102, Korea (South) (100%)
Tel.: (82) 27560505
Web Site: http://www.shinhan.com
Sales Range: $1-4.9 Billion
Emp.: 15,000
International Banking Services
N.A.I.C.S.: 522299

Affiliate (Domestic):

Chohung Investment Trust and Management Co., Ltd. (2)

23 8 Yoido Dong, Youndeungpo Ku, Seoul, 150707, Korea (South) (100%)
Tel.: (82) 27611144
Sales Range: $50-74.9 Million
Emp.: 60
Investment Trust & Management Services
N.A.I.C.S.: 523991

Subsidiary (Domestic):

Shinhan Aitas Co., Ltd. (2)
Fl 2 Excon Venture Building 15-24 Yeouido-dong, Yeongdeungpo-gu, Seoul, 150-969, Korea (South)
Tel.: (82) 2 2180 0400
Web Site: http://www.shinhanaitas.com
Sales Range: $75-99.9 Million
Emp.: 150
Fund Administration Services
N.A.I.C.S.: 523940

Division (Non-US):

Shinhan Bank America (2) (100%)
Web Site: http://www.shbamerica.com
Sales Range: $25-49.9 Million
Emp.: 200
Retail Banking
N.A.I.C.S.: 522110
Ji Young Yook (Pres & CEO)

Subsidiary (Non-US):

Shinhan Bank Europe GmbH (2)
An der Welle 7, 60322, Frankfurt am Main, Germany (80%)
Tel.: (49) 699757110
Sales Range: $50-74.9 Million
Emp.: 18
International Banking Services
N.A.I.C.S.: 522299
Suk Ho Sohn (Mng Dir)

Shinhan Canada Bank (2)
5095 Yonge St Unit B2, Toronto, M2N 6Z4, ON, Canada
Tel.: (416) 250-3550
Web Site: http://www.shinhan.ca
Emp.: 70
Commercial Banking Services
N.A.I.C.S.: 522110
Jong Joo Ahn (Pres & CEO)

Shinhan China Limited (2)
Web Site: http://www.shinhanchina.com
Sales Range: $50-74.9 Million
Emp.: 80
Commercial Banking Services
N.A.I.C.S.: 522110

Shinhan Kazakhstan Bank (2)
123/7 Dostyk Av, 050020, Almaty, Kazakhstan
Tel.: (7) 7273859600
Web Site: http://wwwshinhan.kz
Sales Range: $25-49.9 Million
Emp.: 48
Commercial Banking Services
N.A.I.C.S.: 522110

Shinhan Khmer Bank (2)
Sales Range: $25-49.9 Million
Emp.: 100
Commercial Banking Services
N.A.I.C.S.: 522110

Shinhan Bank (Cambodia) Plc (1)
Vanda Tower N 79 Kampuchea Krom Blvd, Sangkat Monourom Khan Prampir Meakkakra, Phnom Penh, Cambodia
Tel.: (855) 2 395 5001
Web Site: https://www.shinhan.com.kh
Emp.: 200
Banking Services
N.A.I.C.S.: 522110
Kim Nam Soo (Pres & CEO)

Shinhan Bank China Ltd. (1)
12th Fl Zhongyu Plaza No 6 Workers Stadium Road N, Chaoyang District, Beijing, 100027, China
Tel.: (86) 108 529 0088
Banking Services
N.A.I.C.S.: 522110
Myeong Seok Lee (Pres & CEO)

Shinhan Bank Kazakhstan JSC (1)
Dostyk Ave 38, 050010, Almaty, Kazakhstan
Tel.: (7) 727 356 9600

Web Site: https://www.shinhan.kz
Financial Transaction Services
N.A.I.C.S.: 522320

Shinhan Bank Vietnam Ltd. (1)
Ground Floor SCS Building Lot T2-4 D1 Street High-Tech Park, Tan Phu Ward Thu Duc City, Ho Chi Minh City, Vietnam
Tel.: (84) 283 622 0747
Web Site: https://www.shinhan.com.vn
Banking Services
N.A.I.C.S.: 522110

Shinhan Capital Co., Ltd. (1)
3rd-6th Floor Shinhan Bank 1-14 Namdaemunno 1-ga, Jung-gu, Seoul, Korea (South)
Tel.: (82) 27733400
Web Site: http://www.shcap.co.kr
Financial Management Services
N.A.I.C.S.: 523999

Shinhan Card Co., Ltd. (1)
Web Site: https://www.shinhancard.com
Emp.: 2,400
Credit Card Services
N.A.I.C.S.: 522210

Shinhan Credit Information Co., Ltd. (1)
122 Mullaebuk-ro Munrae-dong 3-ga, Yeongdeungpo-gu, Seoul, Korea (South)
Tel.: (82) 22 164 7000
Web Site: https://www.shinhanci.co.kr
Credit Card Information Services
N.A.I.C.S.: 522320

Shinhan DS Vietnam Co., Ltd. (1)
Room 1905 19th Floor Centec Building 72-74 Nguyen Thi Minh Khai, Vo Thi Sau Ward District 3, Ho Chi Minh City, Vietnam
Tel.: (84) 283 823 7255
Web Site: https://www.shinhands.vn
Software Development & Maintenance Services
N.A.I.C.S.: 541511
Kwang Sik Lee (CEO)

Shinhan Data System Co., Ltd. (1)
Baeknyungowan Building 17th Floor 34-1, Samgak-dong, Seoul, Jung-gu, Korea (South)
Tel.: (82) 27560056
Sales Range: $150-199.9 Million
Emp.: 600
Information Technology Consulting Services
N.A.I.C.S.: 541512

Shinhan Investment Asia Ltd. (1)
Units 7705A Level 77 International Commerce Center ICC, 1 Austin Road West, Kowloon, China (Hong Kong)
Tel.: (852) 3 713 5301
Financial Investment Services
N.A.I.C.S.: 523999

Shinhan Investment Corp. America Inc. (1)
1325 Avenue of the Americas Ste 7, New York, NY 10019-6026
Tel.: (212) 397-4000
Emp.: 10
Investment Banking Services
N.A.I.C.S.: 522110

Shinhan Investment Corp. Asia Ltd. (1)
77058 Level 77 International Commerce Centre 1 Austin Road West, Kowloon, China (Hong Kong)
Tel.: (852) 37135321
Web Site: http://www.shinhaninvest.com
Sales Range: $50-74.9 Million
Emp.: 7
Investment Banking Services
N.A.I.C.S.: 523150

Shinhan Life Insurance Co., Ltd. (1)
358 Samil-daero, Jung-gu, Seoul, 04542, Korea (South)
Tel.: (82) 221313000
Web Site: https://www.shinhanlife.co.kr
Sales Range: $700-749.9 Million
Emp.: 1,500
Fire Insurance Services
N.A.I.C.S.: 524113

Shinhan Microfinance Co., Ltd. (1)
No 206 Thiri Mingalar Street, East Ywama Insein Township, Yangon, Myanmar
Tel.: (95) 945 296 7837

INTERNATIONAL PUBLIC

Financial Investment Services
N.A.I.C.S.: 523999

Shinhan Securities Vietnam Co., Ltd. (1)
R 2201 22 Floor and R 805 8 Floor Centec Tower, 72-74 Nguyen Thi Minh Khai Ward Vo Thi Sau District 3, Ho Chi Minh City, Vietnam
Tel.: (84) 286 299 8000
Web Site: https://www.shinhansec.com.vn
Brokerage Services
N.A.I.C.S.: 523150
Han Bokhee (Gen Dir)

Shinhan Vietnam Finance Company (1)
Floor 23rd Saigon Trade Center 37 Ton Duc Thang, Ben Nghe ward District 1, Ho Chi Minh City, Vietnam
Tel.: (84) 283 911 3666
Web Site: https://www.shinhanfinance.com.vn
Financial Investment Services
N.A.I.C.S.: 523999

The Bank of Cheju (1)
3351 1100-ro, Cheju, Jeju, Korea (South)
Tel.: (82) 647592002
Web Site: https://www.jejubank.co.kr
Rev: $201,426,300
Assets: $5,783,040,160
Liabilities: $5,370,775,500
Net Worth: $412,264,660
Earnings: $18,027,800
Fiscal Year-end: 12/31/2022
Banking Services
N.A.I.C.S.: 522110
Park Woo-Hyuk (CEO)

SHINHAN NO. 9 ACQUISITION PURPOSE CO., LTD

4th FloorShinhan Investment Corp 70 Yeoui-daero, Yeongdeungpo-gu, Seoul, Korea (South)
Tel.: (82) 0237723683
405640—(KRS)
Investment Services
N.A.I.C.S.: 523999

SHINHOKOKU STEEL CORPORATION

5 13 1 Arajuku-machi, Kawagoe, 350 1124, Saitama, Japan
Tel.: (81) 492421950
Web Site: https://www.shst.co.jp
Year Founded: 1949
5542—(TKS)
Sales Range: $25-49.9 Million
Fabricated Material Mfr
N.A.I.C.S.: 332999
Tadashi Naruse (Pres)

SHINHUNG CO., LTD.

450 Cheongpa-ro, Jung-gu, Seoul, 100858, Korea (South)
Tel.: (82) 263662041
Web Site: https://www.shinhung.com
Year Founded: 1955
004080—(KRS)
Rev.: $90,641,411
Assets: $107,857,496
Liabilities: $25,893,607
Net Worth: $81,963,889
Earnings: $6,491,551
Emp.: 218
Fiscal Year-end: 12/31/22
Dental Product Mfr & Whslr
N.A.I.C.S.: 339114
Yong Ik Yi (Pres & CEO)

Subsidiaries:

Shinwon Dental Co. Ltd. (1)
22 Teheran-ro 51-gil, Gangnamgu, Seoul, Korea (South)
Tel.: (82) 15770023
Web Site: https://www.shinwon-dental.com
Dental Equipment Distr
N.A.I.C.S.: 423450

SHINIH ENTERPRISE CO., LTD.

Tangshan, 301505, Hebei, China
Tel.: (86) 2269380388
Web Site: http://ts.shinih.com
Timber Product Mfr
N.A.I.C.S.: 313220

Taiwan Kureha Co., Ltd. (1)
2-23 Tuku, Shui Hsiu Village Yen Shui Township, T'ainan, 73743, Taiwan
Tel.: (886) 66529543
Web Site: http://www.kureha.com.tw
Automotive Interiors Mfr
N.A.I.C.S.: 336360

Taixin Fiber Products (Suzhou) Co., Ltd. (1)
57 Lo Yang Road, Taicang, 215400, Jiangsu, China
Tel.: (86) 51253564768
Web Site: http://sztaisin.shinih.com
Timber Product Mfr
N.A.I.C.S.: 325220

Vft, Inc. (1)
1040 S Vail Ave, Montebello, CA 90640-6020
Tel.: (323) 728-2280
Web Site: http://www.shinih.com
Nonwoven Fiber Products Distr
N.A.I.C.S.: 313230

SHINIL ELECTRONICS CO., LTD.
308 Yeongok-gil Ipjang-myeon, Seobuk-gu, Cheonan, 31026, Chungcheongnam-do, Korea (South)
Tel.: (82) 220813420
Year Founded: 1959
002700—(KRS)
Rev.: $155,493,136
Assets: $117,259,463
Liabilities: $54,449,186
Net Worth: $62,810,276
Earnings: $798,994
Emp.: 133
Fiscal Year-end: 12/31/22
Household Electronic Product Mfr & Whslr
N.A.I.C.S.: 335220
Yun-Seog Jeong (CEO)

SHINING BUILDING BUSINESS CO., LTD.
No 408 sec 2 Taiwan Blvd West Dist, Taichung, Taiwan
Tel.: (886) 423227777
Web Site:
    http://www.shininggroup.com
Year Founded: 1990
5531—(TAI)
Rev.: $123,574,376
Assets: $1,342,654,909
Liabilities: $998,489,808
Net Worth: $344,165,100
Earnings: ($12,625,952)
Emp.: 145
Fiscal Year-end: 12/31/23
Residential Building Leasing Services
N.A.I.C.S.: 531110
Fang Wei Min (Pres)

SHINKI BUS CO., LTD.
1 Nishiekimae-cho, Himeji, 670-0913, Hyogo, Japan
Tel.: (81) 792231241
Web Site: https://www.shinkibus.co.jp
Year Founded: 1927
9083—(TKS)
Rev.: $327,062,800
Assets: $416,892,700
Liabilities: $103,631,580
Net Worth: $313,261,120
Earnings: $14,879,110
Fiscal Year-end: 03/31/24
Automobile Transportation Services
N.A.I.C.S.: 485113
Makoto Nagao (Pres & CEO)

SHINKIN CENTRAL BANK
3-7 Yaesu 1-chome, Chuo-ku, Tokyo, 103-0028, Japan
Tel.: (81) 352027711
Web Site: https://www.shinkin-central-bank.jp
Year Founded: 1950
8421—(TKS)
Rev.: $2,825,345,350
Assets: $314,784,222,640
Liabilities: $304,485,393,160
Net Worth: $10,298,829,480
Earnings: $212,478,450
Emp.: 1,263
Fiscal Year-end: 03/31/24
Cooperative Financial Institution
N.A.I.C.S.: 523940
Hiroshi Sudo (Deputy Pres & Sr Mng Dir)

Subsidiaries:

Shinkin Asset Management Co., Ltd. (1)
3-8-1 Kyobashi, Chuo-ku, Tokyo, 104-0031, Japan
Tel.: (81) 12 078 1812
Web Site: https://www.skam.co.jp
Emp.: 71
Asset Management Services
N.A.I.C.S.: 523940

Shinkin Capital Co., Ltd (1)
2-14-1 Kyobashi Kanematsu Building 7th floor, Chuo-ku, Tokyo, 104-0031, Japan
Tel.: (81) 362287820
Web Site: http://www.shinkin-vc.co.jp
Financial Management Consulting Services
N.A.I.C.S.: 541611

Shinkin Central Bank - Business Promotion Division (1)
3-7 Yaesu 1-chome, Chuo-ku, Tokyo, 103-0028, Japan
Tel.: (81) 352027638
Financial Management Consulting Services
N.A.I.C.S.: 541611

Shinkin Central Bank - Corporate Business Promotion Division (1)
3-7 Yaesu 1 Chome, Chuo-ku, Tokyo, 103-0028, Japan
Tel.: (81) 352027665
Commercial Banking Services
N.A.I.C.S.: 522110

Shinkin Central Bank - Operations Division (1)
3-7 Yaesu 1-Chome, Chuo-ku, Tokyo, 103 0028, Japan
Tel.: (81) 352027655
Banking & Investment Services
N.A.I.C.S.: 523150

Division (Domestic):

Shinkin Central Bank International Operations Center (2)
9-1 Ichigaya Honmuracho, Shinjuku-ku, Tokyo, 162 0845, Japan (100%)
Tel.: (81) 332685350
Web Site: http://www.shinkin.co.jp
Sales Range: $50-74.9 Million
Emp.: 70
Banking & Investment Services
N.A.I.C.S.: 523150

Shinkin Central Bank - Shinkin Business Solution Division (1)
3-7 Yaesu 1 Chome, Chuo-ku, Tokyo, 103-0028, Japan
Tel.: (81) 352027633
Web Site: http://www.shinkin-central-bank.jp
Business Support Services
N.A.I.C.S.: 561499

Shinkin Central Bank - Strategic Planning Division (1)
3-7 Yaesu 1-chome, Chuo-ku, Tokyo, 103-0028, Japan
Tel.: (81) 352027624
Sales Range: $450-499.9 Million
Emp.: 1,000
Financial Services
N.A.I.C.S.: 523940
Hiroshi Sudo (Sr Mng Dir & Sr Mng Dir)

Shinkin Central Bank - Transfer & Clearing Division (1)
1-3-7 Yaesu, Chuo-ku, Tokyo, 103-0028, Japan (100%)
Tel.: (81) 35 202 7711
Web Site: https://www.shinkin-central-bank.jp
Sales Range: $350-399.9 Million
Emp.: 1,248
Financial Services
N.A.I.C.S.: 522320

Shinkin Central Bank - Treasury Business Division (1)
3-7 Yaesu 1-chome, Chuo-ku, Tokyo, 103-0028, Japan (100%)
Tel.: (81) 352027642
Sales Range: $50-74.9 Million
Emp.: 50
Investment Advice
N.A.I.C.S.: 523940

Shinkin Central Bank - Treasury Division (1)
3-7 Yaesu 1-chome Chuo-ku, Chuo-ku, Tokyo, 103 0028, Japan
Tel.: (81) 352027660
Web Site: http://www.shinkin-central-bank.jp
Sales Range: $50-74.9 Million
Emp.: 50
Banking & Investment Services
N.A.I.C.S.: 523150

Shinkin Central Bank - Treasury Operations Division (1)
1-3-7 Yaesu, Chuo-ku, Tokyo, 103-0028, Japan (100%)
Tel.: (81) 35 202 7700
Web Site:
    https://www.shinkin-central-bank.jp
Rev.: $82,390,000
Emp.: 42
Banking & Investment Services
N.A.I.C.S.: 523150
Tomoaki Nishimura (Gen Mgr)

Shinkin Guarantee Co., Ltd (1)
3-8-1 Kyobashi, Chuo-ku, Tokyo, 104-0031, Japan
Tel.: (81) 335380810
Web Site: http://www.skgt.co.jp
Credit Guarantee Services
N.A.I.C.S.: 541990

Shinkin International Ltd. (1)
1st Floor 85 London Wall, 7-11 Finsbury Circus, London, EC2M 7AD, United Kingdom
Tel.: (44) 2075620500
Web Site: http://www.sil-uk.net
Sales Range: $75-99.9 Million
Emp.: 10
Loan Transactions, Broking & Securities Underwriting Services
N.A.I.C.S.: 522310

Shinkin Partners Co., Ltd (1)
Kamishige Building 5f, Chuo-ku, Tokyo, 103-0022, Japan
Tel.: (81) 332816050
Web Site: http://www.sk-partners.co.jp
Banking Staff Recruitment Services
N.A.I.C.S.: 561311

Shinkin Trust Bank, Ltd (1)
8-1 Kyobashi 3-chome, Chuo-ku, Tokyo, 104-0031, Japan
Tel.: (81) 335648451
Web Site: http://www.shinkintrust.co.jp
Sales Range: $25-49.9 Million
Emp.: 32
Financial Management Consulting Services
N.A.I.C.S.: 541611

The Shinkin Banks Information System Center Co., Ltd. (1)
12th floor Yaesu First Financial Building 1-3-7 Yaesu, Chuo-ku, Tokyo, 103-0028, Japan
Tel.: (81) 332451211
Web Site: https://www.shinkin.co.jp
Commercial Banking Services
N.A.I.C.S.: 522110
Hiroshi Hiramatsu (Chm)

SHINKO DENKI CO., LTD.
4-3 Nihonbashikabutocho Chuo-ku, Kabutocho Building, Tokyo, 103-0026, Japan
Tel.: (81) 3 3662 5271

No 41 Lianhua St, Bade Dist, Taoyuan, 33452, Taiwan
Tel.: (886) 33659903
Web Site: https://www.shinih.com
9944—(TAI)
Rev.: $69,162,037
Assets: $194,906,105
Liabilities: $80,016,577
Net Worth: $114,889,528
Earnings: $5,770,823
Emp.: 467
Fiscal Year-end: 12/31/23
Fabrics Mfr
N.A.I.C.S.: 313230

Subsidiaries:

American Nonwovens Inc. (1)
9141 Arrow Rte, Rancho Cucamonga, CA 91730
Tel.: (909) 466-8897
Web Site:
    http://www.americannonwoven.com
Emp.: 70
Nonwoven Fiber Products Mfr
N.A.I.C.S.: 313230

Hangzhou Shinih Fiber Products Co., Ltd. (1)
No 99 Jianshe 3th Rd Economy and Technology Development Zone, Xiaoshan, Hangzhou, 311215, Zhejiang, China
Tel.: (86) 57182835201
Web Site: http://hz.shinih.com
Sales Range: $50-74.9 Million
Emp.: 200
Fabric Products & Automobile Carpets Mfr
N.A.I.C.S.: 313230

MS Nonwovens Inc. (1)
275 Industrial Dr, Pontotoc, MS 38863-1326
Tel.: (662) 489-4100
Web Site: http://www.shinih.com
Sales Range: $25-49.9 Million
Emp.: 15
Nonwoven Fiber Products Distr
N.A.I.C.S.: 424690

Shinih (Vietnam) Co., Ltd. (1)
B3-3 Cu Chi NorthWest Industrial Zone, Cu Chi District, Ho Chi Minh City, Vietnam
Tel.: (84) 838924820
Web Site: http://vietnam.shinih.com
Nonwoven Fabric Mfr
N.A.I.C.S.: 313230
Rock Yang (Mgr-Sls)

Shinih Enterprise Co., Ltd. - Kuei Shan Factory (1)
365 Tatung Rd, Kuei Shan Village, Taoyuan, 33352, Taiwan
Tel.: (886) 33505715
Web Site: http://www.shinih.co.th
Sales Range: $25-49.9 Million
Emp.: 60
Synthetics Fiber Products Mfr
N.A.I.C.S.: 313110

Shinih Enterprise Co., Ltd. - Put Zu Factory (1)
1 Heng 1th Rd Put Zu Ind Park, Pu-tzu, 61355, Chiayi Hsien, Taiwan
Tel.: (886) 5 3692900
Web Site: http://www.shinih.co.th
Synthetics Fiber Products Mfr
N.A.I.C.S.: 313110

Shinih Enterprise Co., Ltd. - Yilan Factory (1)
No 163 Sec 1 Yi 3rd Rd, Toucheng, Yilan, 26141, Taiwan
Tel.: (886) 39772399
Web Site: http://www.shinih.co.th
Nonwoven Fabric Mfr
N.A.I.C.S.: 313230

Shinih Fiber Products (Suzhou) Co., Ltd. (1)
No 16 Dongcang N Rd, Taicang, 215400, Jiangsu, China
Tel.: (86) 51253564716
Web Site: http://sz.shinih.com
Timber Product Mfr
N.A.I.C.S.: 313230

Shinih Fiber Products (Tangshan) Co., Ltd. (1)
Econnmic Development Zone Lu Tai Farm,

SHINKO DENKI CO., LTD.

Shinko Denki Co., Ltd.—(Continued)

Web Site: http://www.shinkou-denki.co.jp
Year Founded: 1928
Car Electrical Parts & Equipment Distributor
N.A.I.C.S.: 423690
Sakae Kanaya *(Chm & CEO)*

SHINKO IND. LTD.
5-7-21 Ohzu, Minami-ku, Hiroshima, 732-0802, Japan
Tel.: (81) 82 508 1000
Web Site: http://www.shinkohir.co.jp
Year Founded: 1938
Sales Range: Less than $1 Million
Emp.: 506
Pumps & Steam Turbine Mfr
N.A.I.C.S.: 423830
Kanji Tsutsui *(Pres)*

Subsidiaries:

Ozuki Steel Industries Co Ltd (1)
2316-1 Oaza Yoshida, Shimonoseki, 750-1101, Yamaguchi, Japan
Tel.: (81) 832821111
Hull & Machinery Steel Casting Mfr
N.A.I.C.S.: 331513

SHINKO MUSIC ENTERTAINMENT CO., LTD.
2-1 Ogawa-machi Kanda, Chiyoda-ku, Tokyo, 101 8475, Japan
Tel.: (81) 3 3292 2865
Web Site: http://www.shinko-music.co.jp
Year Founded: 1932
Music Publishing & Printed Music Distr
N.A.I.C.S.: 512230
Natsuya Kusano *(Pres & CEO)*

Subsidiaries:

Shinko Music Publishing Co., Ltd. (1)
2-1 Kanda Ogawa-machi, Chiyoda-ku, Tokyo, 101 8475, Japan **(100%)**
Tel.: (81) 3 3292 2862
Web Site: http://www.shinko-music.co.jp
Sales Range: $10-24.9 Million
Emp.: 90
Music Publishers
N.A.I.C.S.: 512230
Natsuya Kusano *(Pres & CEO)*

SHINKO SHOJI CO., LTD.
Art Village Osaki Central Tower 13F 1-2-2 Osaki, Shinagawa-ku, Tokyo, 141-8540, Japan
Tel.: (81) 363618111 JP
Web Site: https://www.shinko-sj.co.jp
Year Founded: 1953
SKSJF—(OTCIQ)
Rev.: $1,162,348,670
Assets: $659,763,930
Liabilities: $288,817,340
Net Worth: $370,946,590
Earnings: $21,112,340
Emp.: 656
Fiscal Year-end: 03/31/24
Electronic Component Sales
N.A.I.C.S.: 423690
Tatsuya Ogawa *(Pres, Pres, CEO & CEO)*

Subsidiaries:

NOVALUX JAPAN CO., LTD. (1)
1-2-2 Osaki Art Village Osaki Central Tower 13F, Shinagawa-ku, Tokyo, 141-8540, Osaki, Japan **(100%)**
Tel.: (81) 363618101
Web Site: https://www.novalux.jp
Electronic Parts & Components Whslr
N.A.I.C.S.: 423690

NT Sales CO., LTD. (1)
13F Art Village Osaki Central Tower 1-2-2, Osaki Shinagawa-ku, Tokyo, 141-0032, Japan

Tel.: (81) 354355253
Web Site: http://www.nt-sales.co.jp
Sales Range: $50-74.9 Million
Emp.: 78
Electronic Parts & Components Whslr
N.A.I.C.S.: 423620
Fumiaki Sato *(Pres)*

NT Sales Hong Kong Ltd. (1)
Flat B 6/F Kader Building 22 Kai Cheung Road, Kowloon Bay, Kowloon, China (Hong Kong)
Tel.: (852) 27350041
Web Site: http://www.nt-sales.co.jp
Sales Range: $50-74.9 Million
Emp.: 5
Electronic Parts Whslr
N.A.I.C.S.: 423690

Novalux America Inc. (1)
17197 N Laurel Park Dr Ste 135, Livonia, MI 48152
Tel.: (678) 218-0808
Web Site: http://www.shinko-sj.co.jp
Electronic Parts & Components Whslr
N.A.I.C.S.: 423690

Novalux Hong Kong Electronics Limited (1)
3F Flat A First Group Center 14 Wang Tai Road, Kowloon Bay, Kowloon, China (Hong Kong)
Tel.: (852) 27559018
Web Site: http://www.novalux.com.hk
Sales Range: $25-49.9 Million
Emp.: 40
Electric Component Whslr
N.A.I.C.S.: 423690
Takamichi Sasaki *(Mng Dir)*

Novalux Malaysia Sdn. Bhd. (1)
Suite C412 Central Tower 4th Floor Wisma Consplant No 2 Jaian SS16/4, Subang Jaya, 47500, Petaling Jaya, Selangor, Malaysia
Tel.: (60) 356313569
Web Site: http://www.shinko-sj.co.jp
Sales Range: $50-74.9 Million
Emp.: 1
Electronic Parts & Components Whslr
N.A.I.C.S.: 423690
Fuji Wara *(Mng Dir)*

Novalux Shanghai Electronics Limited (1)
6205-6207 118 Ruijin 2 Road, Shanghai, 200020, China
Tel.: (86) 2164660481
Web Site: http://www.novalux.com.cn
Sales Range: $25-49.9 Million
Emp.: 19
Electronic Parts & Components Whslr
N.A.I.C.S.: 423690
Ishido Masanori *(Pres)*

Novalux Taiwan Electronics Ltd. (1)
3rd Fl No 191 Fu Shing N Rd, Taipei, Taiwan
Tel.: (886) 227191445
Web Site: http://www.shinko-sj.co.jp
Sales Range: $25-49.9 Million
Emp.: 20
Electronic Parts & Components Whslr
N.A.I.C.S.: 423620

Novalux Thailand Co., Ltd. (1)
283/49 Home Place Office Building 10th Fl Soi Sukhumvit 55, Thong Lo Klongton-Nua Watthana, Bangkok, 10110, Thailand
Tel.: (66) 20675953
Web Site: http://www.novalux.co.th
Sales Range: $50-74.9 Million
Emp.: 16
Electronic Parts & Components Whslr
N.A.I.C.S.: 423690

P.T. Novalux Indonesia (1)
Gedung BRI 2nd Ste 1500A Jalan Jendral, Sudiraman No 44-46, Jakarta, 102010, Indonesia
Tel.: (62) 215744059
Web Site: http://www.shinko-sj.co.jp
Sales Range: $50-74.9 Million
Emp.: 9
Electronic Parts & Components Whslr
N.A.I.C.S.: 423690

Shinko (Pte) Ltd. (1)
2 Leng Kee Rd No 04-05 Thye Hong Ctr, Singapore, 153086, Singapore

Tel.: (65) 63325700
Sales Range: $50-74.9 Million
Emp.: 10
Electronic Parts & Components Whslr
N.A.I.C.S.: 423690
K. Inoue *(Mng Dir)*

Shinko Shoji LSI Design Center Co., Ltd. (1)
Marumasu Building No 18 2F 1-1-5 Kita 7 West, Kita-ku, Sapporo, 060-0807, Hokkaido, Japan
Tel.: (81) 115581125
Web Site: http://www.sld-shinko.co.jp
Sales Range: $50-74.9 Million
Emp.: 83
Electronic Parts & Components Whslr
N.A.I.C.S.: 423690

SHINKO, INC.
8th Floor CS Tower 5208 Asakusa-bashi, Taito-ku, Tokyo, 111-0053, Japan
Tel.: (81) 358227600
Web Site: https://www.kk-shinko.com
Year Founded: 1953
7120—(TKS)
Emp.: 805
Semiconductor Product Mfr
N.A.I.C.S.: 334413
Hideaki Ishida *(Sr Mng Dir)*

SHINKONG INSURANCE CO. LTD.
11F No 15 Sec 2 Jianguo N Rd, Zhongshan Dist, Taipei, 104, Taiwan
Tel.: (886) 225075335
Web Site:
https://www.skinsurance.com.tw
Year Founded: 1963
2850—(TAI)
Rev.: $810,030,644
Assets: $1,537,942,909
Liabilities: $965,039,010
Net Worth: $572,903,899
Earnings: $95,300,137
Emp.: 1,700
Fiscal Year-end: 12/31/23
Insurance Services
N.A.I.C.S.: 524210
Ying-Lan Ho *(Pres)*

Subsidiaries:

Shin Kong Chao Feng Co., Ltd. (1)
No 20 Yongfu Street, Fenglin Town, Hualien, Taiwan
Tel.: (886) 38772666
Web Site: https://www.skcf.com.tw
Animal Farming Services
N.A.I.C.S.: 813410

Shin Kong Shien Ya International Co., Ltd. (1)
B1-1 No 35 Lane 11 Guangfu North Road, Songshan District, Taipei, Taiwan
Tel.: (886) 800636636
Web Site: http://www.sksy.com.tw
Skin Care Products Distr
N.A.I.C.S.: 424210

Shin Kong Wu Ho-Su Memorial Hospital (1)
No 95 Wenchang Road, Shilin District, Taipei, 111, Taiwan
Tel.: (886) 228332211
Web Site: https://www.skh.org.tw
Healthcare Services
N.A.I.C.S.: 621498

SHINKONG TEXTILE CO., LTD.
15F No 44 Sec 2 Zhongshan North Road, Taipei, 104, Taiwan
Tel.: (886) 25071258
Web Site:
https://www.sktextile.com.tw
1419—(TAI)
Rev.: $103,377,804
Assets: $563,437,240
Liabilities: $133,499,684
Net Worth: $429,937,555
Earnings: $21,222,014

Emp.: 611
Fiscal Year-end: 12/31/23
Apparels Mfr
N.A.I.C.S.: 315210

SHINMAYWA INDUSTRIES, LTD.
1-1 Shinmeiwa-cho, Takarazuka, 665-0052, Hyogo, Japan
Tel.: (81) 798565000
Web Site:
https://www.shinmaywa.co.jp
Year Founded: 1949
7224—(TKS)
Rev.: $1,699,166,600
Assets: $1,719,274,220
Liabilities: $1,000,542,480
Net Worth: $718,731,740
Earnings: $48,114,190
Emp.: 6,453
Fiscal Year-end: 03/31/24
N.A.I.C.S.: 336411
Tatsuyuki Isogawa *(Pres & CEO)*

Subsidiaries:

Chongqing Endurance & ShinMaywa Industries, Ltd. (1)
No 8 Shifolu, Jieshi Banan District, Chongqing, 401346, China
Tel.: (86) 236 196 3700
Web Site: http://www.shinmaywa.co.jp
Special Purpose Trucks Mfr, Distr & Maintenance Services
N.A.I.C.S.: 333924

Daiwa Sogyo Co., Ltd. (1)
55-3 Nagasawa, Shimizu-cho Sunto-gun, Shizuoka, 411-0905, Japan
Tel.: (81) 559756790
Emp.: 15
Automobile Parts Distr
N.A.I.C.S.: 441330

Godo Solution Inc. (1)
471 Iida-cho, Minami-ku, Hamamatsu, 435-0028, Shizuoka, Japan
Tel.: (81) 534650711
Emp.: 30
Industrial Material Distr
N.A.I.C.S.: 423840

ITAC, Ltd. (1)
1-1 Shinmeiwa-cho, Takarazuka, 665-0052, Japan
Tel.: (81) 798541802
Web Site: http://www.itac-j.co.jp
Electrical Equipment Distr
N.A.I.C.S.: 423610
Takahiro Asano *(Pres)*

Iwafuji Industrial Co Ltd (1)
5-1 Sakurayashiki Nishi, Mizusawa, Oshu, 023-0872, Iwate, Japan
Tel.: (81) 197233111
Web Site: https://www.iwafuji.co.jp
Emp.: 306
Construction Equipment Mfr & Sales
N.A.I.C.S.: 333120
Masayuki Oikawa *(Pres)*

Korea Vacuum Limited (1)
80 Dalseong2chadong 3-ro Guji-myeon, Dalseong-gun, Daegu, Korea (South)
Tel.: (82) 535917720
Emp.: 87
Vacuum Equipment Mfr
N.A.I.C.S.: 335210
In Woo Lee *(CEO)*

Maywa Komuten, Ltd. (1)
7-4-3 Kojima Nakacho, Chuo-Ku, Kobe, 650-0046, Japan
Tel.: (81) 789401000
Web Site: https://www.meiwa-koumuten.co.jp
Emp.: 161
Construction Engineering Services
N.A.I.C.S.: 541330

Maywa Koumuten, Ltd. (1)
7-4-3 Minatojima Nakamachi, Chuo-ku, Kobe, 650-0046, Japan
Tel.: (81) 78 940 1000
Web Site: https://www.meiwa-koumuten.co.jp
Emp.: 151

Engineeering Services
N.A.I.C.S.: 541330
Minoru Goto *(Mng Dir)*

ShinMaywa (America), Ltd. (1)
10737 Gateway W Ste 240, El Paso, TX 79935
Tel.: (915) 594-9862
Web Site: https://www.shinmaywa.co.jp
Sales Range: $50-74.9 Million
Emp.: 200
Industrial Machinery Mfr
N.A.I.C.S.: 333248

ShinMaywa (Asia) Pte. Ltd. (1)
Sales Range: $25-49.9 Million
Emp.: 15
Industrial Machinery Mfr
N.A.I.C.S.: 333248

ShinMaywa (Bangkok) Co., Ltd. (1)
No 159/2 Serm-Mit Tower Ground Floor Unit G03/1 Sukhumvit 21 Road, North Klongtoey Wattana, Bangkok, 10110, Thailand
Tel.: (66) 22594473
Web Site: https://www.shinmaywa.co.jp
Sales Range: $50-74.9 Million
Emp.: 29
Wire Terminating Machine Sales & Maintenance Services
N.A.I.C.S.: 423440
Nakagawa Yoshiharu *(Mng Dir)*

ShinMaywa (California), Ltd. (1)
2355 Crenshaw Blvd Ste 160, Torrance, CA 90501
Tel.: (714) 252-0027
Sales Range: $25-49.9 Million
Emp.: 13
Aircraft Parts & Auxiliary Equipment Mfr
N.A.I.C.S.: 336413

ShinMaywa (Shanghai) High-Tech Machinery Co., Ltd (1)
Building 6 333 Lane Zhujian Road Minhang, Youlejia City Industrial Park, Shanghai, 201107, China
Tel.: (86) 2152962966
Automatic Wire Processor Mfr & Distr
N.A.I.C.S.: 334419

ShinMaywa (Shanghai) Trading Co., Ltd. (1)
Building 6 Youlejia City Industrial Park 333 Lane Zhujian Road, Minhang, Shanghai, 201107, China
Tel.: (86) 215 296 2966
Web Site: http://www.shinmaywa.co.jp
Emp.: 60
Industrial Machinery Mfr
N.A.I.C.S.: 333248

ShinMaywa Aqua Technology Services, Ltd. (1)
10th floor Higashinada Center Building 8-6-26 Motoyama Minamimachi, Higashinada-ku, Kobe, 658-0015, Hyogo, Japan
Tel.: (81) 78 436 0760
Web Site: https://www.shinmaywa-aqua.co.jp
Emp.: 116
Installation, Maintenance & Repair of Fluid & Related Equipment
N.A.I.C.S.: 333996
Shimasaka Tadahiro *(Mng Dir)*

ShinMaywa Auto Engineering, Ltd. (1)
3-2-43 Shitte, Tsurumi-ku, Yokohama, 230-0003, Japan
Tel.: (81) 45 582 1522
Web Site: https://www.shinmaywa-auto.co.jp
Sales Range: $50-74.9 Million
Emp.: 180
Light Truck & Utility Vehicle Mfr
N.A.I.C.S.: 327910

ShinMaywa Iwakuni Aircraft Maintenance, Ltd. (1)
1-8-21 Imazucho Asahi Building 3F, Iwakuni, 740-0017, Yamaguchi, Japan
Tel.: (81) 827221621
Sales Range: $25-49.9 Million
Emp.: 135
Aircraft Parts & Auxiliary Equipment Mfr
N.A.I.C.S.: 336413

ShinMaywa Shoji, Ltd. (1)
Prera Nishiniya 3rd floor 4-8 Takamatsucho, Nishinomiya, 663-8204, Hyogo, Japan
Tel.: (81) 798651115
Real Estate Manangement Services
N.A.I.C.S.: 531390

ShinMaywa Soft Technologies, Ltd. (1)
6-84 Takkinocho, Nishinomiya, 663-8001, Hyogo, Japan
Tel.: (81) 798515922
Web Site: https://www.stec.co.jp
Emp.: 172
Computer Software Consulting Services
N.A.I.C.S.: 541511

ShinMaywa Waste Technology, Ltd. (1)
1-1 Shinmeiwa-cho, Takarazuka, 665-8550, Hyogo, Japan
Tel.: (81) 79 856 5046
Web Site: https://www.s-wastec.co.jp
Emp.: 265
Waste Treatment & Disposal
N.A.I.C.S.: 562219

Shinmaywa Aerobridge Malaysia Sdn. Bhd. (1)
41 Jalan Molek 1/8, Taman Molek, 81100, Johor Bahru, Johor, Malaysia
Tel.: (60) 75980724
Steel Products Mfr
N.A.I.C.S.: 332312

Shinmaywa Aerobridge Singapore Pte. Ltd. (1)
39 Tuas Basin Link, Singapore, Singapore
Tel.: (65) 65158360
Steel Products Mfr
N.A.I.C.S.: 332312

Shinmaywa Aqua Technology Service, Ltd. (1)
10th floor Higashi Kobe Center Building 8-6-26 Motoyamaminami-cho, Higashinada-ku, Kobe, 658-0015, Hyogo, Japan
Tel.: (81) 784360760
Web Site: https://www.shinmaywa-aqua.co.jp
Emp.: 115
Electrical Equipment Distr
N.A.I.C.S.: 423610

Shinmaywa Auto Sales, Ltd. (1)
3-2-43 Shitte, Tsurumi-ku, Yokohama, 230-0003, Kanagawa, Japan
Tel.: (81) 455800150
Automobile Parts Distr
N.A.I.C.S.: 441330

Shinmaywa Heartful, Ltd. (1)
1-1-1 Aoki, Higashinada-ku, Kobe, 658-0027, Hyogo, Japan
Tel.: (81) 784360661
Digital Marketing Services
N.A.I.C.S.: 541613

Shinmaywa Industries India Private Limited (1)
A-192 Sarita Vihar, New Delhi, 110076, India
Tel.: (91) 1141062861
Industrial Material Distr
N.A.I.C.S.: 423840

Shinmaywa Mexico S.A. De C.V. (1)
Calle Rio Lerma 232 Col Cuauhtemoc Piso 23, Delegacion Cuauhtemoc, 06500, Mexico, Mexico
Tel.: (52) 5588527972
Electrical Equipment Distr
N.A.I.C.S.: 423610

Shinmaywa Parking Technologies, Ltd. (1)
5th and 6th floors of Tamachi Kiyota Building 4-3-4 Shibaura, Minato-ku, Tokyo, 108-0023, Japan
Tel.: (81) 354391095
Construction Equipment Mfr & Distr
N.A.I.C.S.: 333120

Taiwan ShinMaywa Industries Co., Ltd. (1)
3F-2 No 111 Songjiang Rd, Zhongshan Dist, Taipei, 10486, Taiwan
Tel.: (886) 2 6617 8822
Web Site: http://www.shinmaywa.com.tw
Parking Equipment Mfr & Distr
N.A.I.C.S.: 333310

Tenryu Aero Component Co., Ltd. (1)
1-1 Sohara-Koa, Kakamigahara, Gifu, 504-0814, Japan
Tel.: (81) 583826431
Web Site: https://www.tenryu-aero.co.jp
Aircraft Part Mfr
N.A.I.C.S.: 336413

Thai ShinMaywa Co., Ltd. (1)
No 199 Moo 12 Soi Daramitr Petchkasem 120 Petchkasem Road, Om-noi Krathum Baen, Samut Sakhon, 74130, Thailand
Tel.: (66) 24200089
Sales Range: $25-49.9 Million
Emp.: 85
Truck Spare Parts Mfr
N.A.I.C.S.: 336390
Montri Khienduangchan *(Mgr-Personnel & Gen Affairs Dept)*

Toho Car Corporation (1)
3-2-43 Shirite, Tsurumi-ku, Yokohama, 230-0003, Kanagawa, Japan
Tel.: (81) 455759901
Emp.: 382
Automotive Parts Mfr & Distr
N.A.I.C.S.: 336390

TurboMAX Co., Ltd. (1)
208 Osongsaengmyeong 9ro Osong-eup, Heungdeok-gu, Cheongju, Chungcheongbuk-do, Korea (South)
Tel.: (82) 432756002
Web Site: https://www.turbomax.co.kr
Turbo Blower Mfr & Distr
N.A.I.C.S.: 333111

TurboMAX India Private Limited (1)
The Ambience Court Hi-Tech Business Park 21st Floor, Sector-19D Plot No 2 Vashi Navi Mumbai, Thane, 40075, Maharashtra, India
Tel.: (91) 9082419149
Turbo Blower Mfr & Distr
N.A.I.C.S.: 333111

SHINMEI CO., LTD.
1-21 Sakaemachidori 6-chome, Chuo-ku, Kobe, 650-0023, Hyogo, Japan
Tel.: (81) 78 371 2131 JP
Web Site: http://www.akafuji.co.jp
Year Founded: 1950
Sales Range: $1-4.9 Billion
Trading of Rice & Food Product Mfr
N.A.I.C.S.: 311212
Mitsuo Fujio *(Pres)*

Subsidiaries:

Shinmei Agri Co., Ltd. (1)
1-21 Sakaemachidori 6-chome, Chuo-ku, Kobe, 650-0023, Hyogo, Japan
Tel.: (81) 783712131
Web Site: http://www.akafuji.co.jp
Production, Processing & Sales of Rice Grain & Food Products
N.A.I.C.S.: 111160

SHINNIHON CORPORATION
Shin-Nihon Building 1-4-3 Hibino, Mihama-ku, Chiba, 261-0021, Japan
Tel.: (81) 432131111
Web Site: https://www.shinnihon-c.co.jp
Year Founded: 1964
1879—(TKS)
Rev.: $882,547,370
Assets: $1,111,497,940
Liabilities: $363,939,990
Net Worth: $747,557,950
Earnings: $81,210,460
Emp.: 574
Fiscal Year-end: 03/31/24
Construction Engineering Services
N.A.I.C.S.: 541330
Katsushi Takami *(Chm, Pres & CEO)*

Subsidiaries:

Ken Ken Co., Ltd. (1)
Sugimura Building 3rd floor 1-4-8 Nihonbashi Horidomecho, Chuo-ku, Tokyo, 103-0012, Japan
Tel.: (81) 356518211
Emp.: 139
Engineeering Services
N.A.I.C.S.: 541330
Hiroshi Shishido *(CEO)*

SHINNIHONSEIYAKU CO., LTD.
1-4-7 Otemon, Chuo-ku, Fukuoka, 810-0074, Japan
Tel.: (81) 927205800
Web Site: https://www.shinnihonseiyaku.co.jp
Year Founded: 1992
4931—(TKS)
Rev.: $266,959,770
Assets: $180,802,090
Liabilities: $41,405,600
Net Worth: $139,396,490
Earnings: $16,973,460
Emp.: 437
Fiscal Year-end: 09/30/23
Cosmetic Product Distr
N.A.I.C.S.: 456120
Takahiro Goto *(Pres & CEO)*

SHINNING CENTURY LIMITED
Site No 9 Lioli Maseru Industrial Area, PO Box 15507, 14310, Maseru, Lesotho
Tel.: (266) 22321823
Sales Range: $200-249.9 Million
Emp.: 2,000
All Other Cut & Sew Apparel Mfr
N.A.I.C.S.: 315250
Jennifer Chen Mei-Chaun *(Mng Dir)*

SHINOBU FOODS PRODUCTS CO., LTD.
2-3-18 Takeshima, Nishiyodogawa-ku, Osaka, 555-0011, Japan
Tel.: (81) 664770113
Web Site: https://www.shinobufoods.co.jp
Year Founded: 1971
2903—(TKS)
Rev.: $362,393,250
Assets: $201,175,350
Liabilities: $102,296,360
Net Worth: $98,878,990
Earnings: $7,713,870
Emp.: 500
Fiscal Year-end: 03/31/24
Food Products Mfr
N.A.I.C.S.: 311991

SHINOKEN GROUP CO., LTD.
Across Fukuoka 1-1-1 Tenjin, Chuo-ku, Fukuoka, 810-0001, Japan
Tel.: (81) 92 714 0040
Web Site: http://www.shinoken.co.jp
Year Founded: 1990
8909—(JAS)
Rev.: $933,093,920
Assets: $958,416,800
Liabilities: $519,719,200
Net Worth: $438,697,600
Earnings: $58,186,480
Emp.: 1,088
Fiscal Year-end: 12/31/21
Real Estate Lending Services
N.A.I.C.S.: 531110
Hideaki Shinohara *(Pres)*

Subsidiaries:

Ogawa Construction Co., Ltd. (1)
1-4 Yotsuya, Shinjuku-ku, Tokyo, 160-0004, Japan
Tel.: (81) 33 359 4111
Web Site: https://www.yotsuya-ogawa.co.jp
Condominium Development Services
N.A.I.C.S.: 236116

Shinoken Asset Management Co., Ltd. (1)
Wisma 46 - Kota BNI 24th Floor Jl Jend Sudirman Kav 1, Jakarta, 10220, Indonesia
Tel.: (62) 215744583
Web Site: https://shinoken-am.co.id
Financial Services

SHINOKEN GROUP CO., LTD.

Shinoken Group Co., Ltd.—(Continued)
N.A.I.C.S.: 921130

Shinoken Office Service Co., Ltd. (1)
1-1-1 Tenjin Acros, Chuo-ku, Fukuoka, 810-0001, Japan
Tel.: (81) 927140040
Web Site: https://www.shinoken-os.co.jp
Office Administrative Services
N.A.I.C.S.: 561110

SHINOZAKIYA INC.
870-1 Akanuma, Kasukabe, 344-0015, Saitama, Japan
Tel.: (81) 489704949
Web Site: https://www.shinozakiya.com
Year Founded: 1987
2926—(TKS)
Sales Range: $25-49.9 Million
Food Products Mfr
N.A.I.C.S.: 311991
Shigeru Tarumi (Chm & Pres)

SHINPO CO., LTD.
Wakabadai 110, Meito Ward, Nagoya, 465-0015, Aichi, Japan
Tel.: (81) 527762231
Web Site: https://www.shinpo-en.com
Year Founded: 1971
5903—(TKS)
Rev.: $44,852,420
Assets: $51,594,900
Liabilities: $9,385,980
Net Worth: $42,208,920
Earnings: $4,111,420
Emp.: 88
Fiscal Year-end: 06/30/24
Household Appliance Mfr & Distr
N.A.I.C.S.: 335220
Toshiaki Tanaka (Pres & CEO)

Subsidiaries:

Shinpo Co., Ltd. - Nagoya Factory (1)
3-10 Yawatayama Miyoshi-cho, Miyoshi, 470-0214, Aichi, Japan
Tel.: (81) 561323221
Web Site: https://www.shinpo-en.com
Smokeless Grill Mfr
N.A.I.C.S.: 335220

Shinpo Trade Co., Ltd. (1)
Room 6 Floor 13 Build A Orient International Plaza 85, Lou Shan Guan Road Changning District, Shanghai, China
Tel.: (86) 216 278 9977
Web Site: http://www.shinpo.jp
Smokeless Grill Mfr
N.A.I.C.S.: 335220

SHINPOONG INC.
144-32 Godeok-ro, Godeok-myeon, Pyeongtaek, Gyeonggi-do, Korea (South)
Tel.: (82) 316698271
Web Site: http://www.shinpoongpaper.com
Year Founded: 1960
002870—(KRS)
Rev.: $14,405,611
Assets: $86,224,527
Liabilities: $23,063,886
Net Worth: $63,160,641
Earnings: ($5,779,725)
Emp.: 18
Fiscal Year-end: 12/31/22
Paper Product Mfr & Distr
N.A.I.C.S.: 322219
Il-hong Chung (Founder)

SHINRY TECHNOLOGIES CO., LTD.
35/F Buliding 3 Nanshan i-Park Chongwen No 3370 Liuxian Avenue, Nanshan District, Shenzhen, 518055, China
Tel.: (86) 75586159680
Web Site: https://www.shinry.com
Year Founded: 2005
300745—(CHIN)
Rev.: $199,634,804
Assets: $537,410,471
Liabilities: $191,316,794
Net Worth: $346,093,676
Earnings: ($23,877,005)
Fiscal Year-end: 12/31/23
Automotive Electrical Equipment Mfr & Distr
N.A.I.C.S.: 336320
Wu Renhua (Chm, Pres & Gen Mgr)

Subsidiaries:

Shinry Technologies Co., Ltd. - Shenzen Plant (1)
Tangtou Road No 1 Shiyan, Linoya Industrial Park Baoan, Shenzhen, 518108, China
Tel.: (86) 75581790981
Web Site: https://www.shinry.com
Board Charger & DC Convertor Distr
N.A.I.C.S.: 423690

SHINSEGAE FOOD CO., LTD.
Baekyoung Seongsu Center 56 Seongsu-il-ro, Seongdong-gu, Seoul, Korea (South)
Tel.: (82) 233976000
Web Site: https://www.shinsegaefood.com
031440—(KRS)
Rev.: $1,082,471,065
Assets: $693,312,193
Liabilities: $469,295,328
Net Worth: $224,016,865
Earnings: ($4,129,838)
Emp.: 3,893
Fiscal Year-end: 12/31/22
Catering Services
N.A.I.C.S.: 722310
Hyun-Seok Song (CEO)

Subsidiaries:

Serinfood Inc. (1)
Tel.: (82) 332636004
Web Site: http://www.serinfood.co.kr
Food Product Mfr & Distr
N.A.I.C.S.: 311999

Shinsegae Food Co., Ltd. - Cheonan Plant (1)
101 2 Gongdan 3-Ro, Seobuk-Gu, Cheonan, Chungcheongnam-Do, Korea (South)
Tel.: (82) 416299191
Food Product Mfr & Distr
N.A.I.C.S.: 311999

Shinsegae Food Co., Ltd. - Icheon Plant 1 (1)
840 Jungbu-Daero, Hobeop-Myeon, Icheon, Gyeonggi-do, Korea (South)
Tel.: (82) 316392500
Food Product Mfr & Distr
N.A.I.C.S.: 311999

Shinsegae Food Co., Ltd. - Icheon Plant 2 (1)
2330-91 Gyeongchung-Daero, Bubal-Eup, Icheon, Gyeonggi-do, Korea (South)
Tel.: (82) 316451200
Food Product Mfr & Distr
N.A.I.C.S.: 311999

Shinsegae Food Co., Ltd. - Osan Plant (1)
387 Dongbu-Daero, Osan, Gyeonggi-do, Korea (South)
Tel.: (82) 313716500
Food Product Mfr & Distr
N.A.I.C.S.: 311999

Shinsegae Food Co., Ltd. - Seongsu Plant (1)
7 Achasan-Ro 5-Gil, Seongdong-Gu, Seoul, Korea (South)
Tel.: (82) 269251097
Food Product Mfr & Distr
N.A.I.C.S.: 311999

SHINSEGAE INC.
63 Sogong-ro, Jung-gu, Seoul, Korea (South)
Tel.: (82) 15881234
Web Site: https://www.shinsegae.com
Year Founded: 1930
004170—(KRS)
Rev.: $5,992,383,238
Assets: $11,005,232,252
Liabilities: $6,210,117,473
Net Worth: $4,795,114,779
Earnings: $311,452,066
Emp.: 2,593
Fiscal Year-end: 12/31/22
Department Store, Food & Beverage & Online Retail Services
N.A.I.C.S.: 455110
Byung Hoon Heo (Exec VP)

Subsidiaries:

EMART Inc. (1)
37 Sejong-daero 7-gil, Jung-gu, Seoul, 04511, Korea (South)
Tel.: (82) 23805678
Web Site: https://company.emart.com
Rev.: $21,875,694,294
Assets: $24,823,616,515
Liabilities: $14,555,197,079
Net Worth: $10,268,419,437
Earnings: ($66,128,791)
Emp.: 22,744
Fiscal Year-end: 12/31/2023
Household Product Distr
N.A.I.C.S.: 423620

Subsidiary (Domestic):

Shinsegae Engineering & Construction Co., Ltd. (2)
21st floor Danam Tower 10 Sowol-ro, Jung-gu, Seoul, 100-391, Korea (South) (88.2%)
Tel.: (82) 234066620
Web Site: https://www.shinsegae-enc.com
Rev.: $1,098,639,255
Assets: $794,313,602
Liabilities: $576,700,995
Net Worth: $217,612,607
Earnings: ($10,906,265)
Emp.: 872
Fiscal Year-end: 12/31/2022
Civil Engineering Construction Services
N.A.I.C.S.: 541330
Myeong Gyu Yun (Pres & CEO)

Affiliate (Domestic):

Starbucks Coffee Korea Co., Ltd. (2)
112 Sogong-ro Jung-gu, Seoul, Korea (South) (67.5%)
Tel.: (82) 230151100
Web Site: http://www.istarbucks.co.kr
Emp.: 4,871
Cafeteria Operator
N.A.I.C.S.: 722515

Subsidiary (Domestic):

eBay Korea Co., Ltd. (2)
34 Floor Gangnam Finance Center 152 Teheran-ro, Seoul, 135-984, Korea (South) (80.1%)
Tel.: (82) 25898986
Web Site: http://www.gmarket.co.kr
Apparel Accessory Services
N.A.I.C.S.: 458110

Gwangju Shinsegae, Co., Ltd. (1)
Mujindaero 932 Gwangcheon-dong, Seo-gu, Gwangju, Korea (South) (62.5%)
Tel.: (82) 623601234
Web Site: https://www.gjshinsegae.co.kr
Rev.: $141,798,324
Assets: $700,619,257
Liabilities: $94,758,489
Net Worth: $605,860,768
Earnings: $43,678,054
Emp.: 170
Fiscal Year-end: 12/31/2022
Supermarket & Grocery Store Operator
N.A.I.C.S.: 445110
Lee Dong Hoon (CEO)

SHINSEGAE I&C Co., Ltd. (1)
21st floor Mesa Building 2 Namdaemun Market 10-gil, Jung-gu, Seoul, Korea (South)
Tel.: (82) 233971234
Web Site: https://www.shinsegae-inc.com
Rev.: $457,799,593
Assets: $370,410,439

Liabilities: $91,272,033
Net Worth: $279,138,406
Earnings: $64,472,027
Emp.: 1,350
Fiscal Year-end: 12/31/2022
Information Technology Services
N.A.I.C.S.: 541512
Jang-wook Kim (Pres & CEO)

SHINSEGAE INTERNATIONAL INC.
449 Dosan-daero, Gangnam-gu, Seoul, Korea (South)
Tel.: (82) 216444490
Web Site: https://www.sikorea.co.kr
Year Founded: 1996
031430—(KRS)
Rev.: $1,191,823,902
Assets: $980,748,952
Liabilities: $341,319,439
Net Worth: $639,429,513
Earnings: $90,717,584
Emp.: 1,289
Fiscal Year-end: 12/31/22
Apparel Store Operator
N.A.I.C.S.: 458110
William Kim (Chm)

SHINSUN HOLDING (GROUP) CO., LTD.
18th Floor No 58 Xintang Road, Shangcheng District, Hangzhou, 310000, Zhejiang, China
Tel.: (86) 2161187000   CN
Web Site: https://www.shinsunholdings.com
Year Founded: 2019
2599—(HKG)
Rev.: $2,727,769,163
Assets: $16,162,611,182
Liabilities: $15,159,095,868
Net Worth: $1,003,515,313
Earnings: ($543,666,510)
Emp.: 1,256
Fiscal Year-end: 12/31/22
Holding Company
N.A.I.C.S.: 551112
Guoxiang Chen (Chm)

SHINSUNG DELTA TECH CO., LTD.
39 Gongdan-ro 271beon-gil, Seongsan-gu, Changwon, Gyeongsangnam-do, Korea (South)
Tel.: (82) 552601000
Web Site: https://www.gshinsung.com
Year Founded: 1987
065350—(KRS)
Rev.: $608,556,223
Assets: $481,559,583
Liabilities: $317,045,709
Net Worth: $164,513,873
Earnings: $12,983,311
Emp.: 310
Fiscal Year-end: 12/31/22
Electronic Components Mfr
N.A.I.C.S.: 334419
Ja-Cheon Koo (CEO)

Subsidiaries:

Indonesia Corporation of Shinsung Deltatech Co., Ltd. (1)
Kampung Garudu Rukun Tetangga 001 Rukun Warga 01, Cirarab Legok Kabupaten, Tangerang, Indonesia
Tel.: (62) 215977267
Washing Machine Parts Mfr
N.A.I.C.S.: 333994

Masan Plant of Shinsung Automotive Co.,Ltd. (1)
6 Bongamgongdan 13-gil, Masanhoewon-gu, Changwon, Gyeongsangnam-do, Korea (South)
Tel.: (82) 557199122
Electronic Component Mfr & Distr
N.A.I.C.S.: 334416

AND PRIVATE COMPANIES

Mexico Corporation of Shinsung Automotive Co,Ltd. (1)
Ave Luis Donaldo Colosio 288 B Desarrollo Industrial El Sabinal, 66634, Nuevo Leon, Mexico
Tel.: (52) 18181434198
Electronic Component Mfr & Distr
N.A.I.C.S.: 334416

Mexico Marine Corporation of Shinsung Deltatech Co., Ltd. (1)
VX39 2F, Nuevo Leon, Mexico
Tel.: (52) 8112105320
Electronic Component Mfr & Distr
N.A.I.C.S.: 334416

Mexico Monterrey Corporation of Shinsung Deltatech Co., Ltd. (1)
Ave Luis Donaldo Colosio 288 B Desarrollo Industrial El Sabinal, 66634, Nuevo Leon, Mexico
Tel.: (52) 18181454198
Refrigerator Parts Mfr
N.A.I.C.S.: 333415

Nanjing Corporation of Shinheung Global Co., Ltd. (1)
1103 E6 Tianan shumacheng YouFeng Dadao No 36, Qinhuai District, Nanjing, China
Tel.: (86) 2585809991
Electronic Component Mfr & Distr
N.A.I.C.S.: 334416

Nanjing Corporation of Shinsung Delta Tech Co., Ltd. (1)
85 Meillin St Jiangning Development Zone, Nanjing, China
Tel.: (86) 2552728999
Electric Vehicle Parts Mfr & Distr
N.A.I.C.S.: 334515

Polnad Corporation of Shinsung Automotive Co,Ltd. (1)
ul Stalowa 1, Godzikowice, 55-200, Olawa, Poland
Tel.: (48) 713035344
Electronic Component Mfr & Distr
N.A.I.C.S.: 334416

Shinheung Co.,Ltd. (1)
57 Saengnim-daero, Gimhae, Gyeongsangnam-do, Korea (South)
Tel.: (82) 557129581
Web Site: https://www.shinhungwood.co.kr
Electronic Component Mfr & Distr
N.A.I.C.S.: 334416

Shinhung Global Co., Ltd. (1)
35 Seongju-ro 97-gil, Seongsan-gu, Changwon, Gyeongsangnam-do, Korea (South)
Tel.: (82) 553314100
Web Site: https://www.shinhungglobal.co.kr
Wood Products Mfr
N.A.I.C.S.: 321999

Shinsung Automotive Co., Ltd. (1)
9-26 Wanam-ro, Seongsan-gu, Changwon, Gyeongsangnam-do, Korea (South)
Tel.: (82) 552622111
Web Site: https://us.ssautomotive.co.kr
Automotive Interior & Exterior Material Mfr
N.A.I.C.S.: 336360

Shinsung Mold Tech Co.,Ltd. (1)
172 Bonsan-ro Jinyeong-eup, Gimhae, Gyeongsangnam-do, Korea (South)
Tel.: (82) 557126600
Web Site:
 https://www.shinsungmoldtech.co.kr
Electronic Mould Mfr & Distr
N.A.I.C.S.: 333511

Shinsung ST Co., Ltd. (1)
Daea Building 7F 711 3 15-daero, Masanhoewon-gu, Changwon, Gyeongsangnam-do, Korea (South)
Tel.: (82) 7088232979
Electronic Component Mfr & Distr
N.A.I.C.S.: 334416

US Corporation of Shinheung Global Co., Ltd. (1)
110 Life s Good Way, Clarksville, TN 37040
Tel.: (931) 802-3591
Electronic Component Mfr & Distr
N.A.I.C.S.: 334416

SHINSUNG E&G CO., LTD.
14-15th floor A Tower 20 Gwacheondaero 7-gil, Bundang-gu, Gwacheon, Gyeonggi-do, Korea (South)
Tel.: (82) 63121000
Web Site: http://www.shinsung.co.kr
Year Founded: 1977
011930—(KRS)
Rev.: $509,398,202
Assets: $442,984,873
Liabilities: $281,017,659
Net Worth: $161,967,214
Earnings: $26,175,026
Emp.: 498
Fiscal Year-end: 12/31/22
Solar Cell Mfr
N.A.I.C.S.: 334413
Relaxation Muscle (Chm)

Subsidiaries:

Shinsung ENG Co., Ltd. (1)
8 Daewangpangyo-ro 395 beon-gil, Bundang-gu, Seongnam, Gyeonggi-do, Korea (South)
Tel.: (82) 31 788 9000
Web Site: http://www.shinsung-eng.co.kr
Sales Range: $150-199.9 Million
Emp.: 263
Air Purification Equipment Mfr & Distr
N.A.I.C.S.: 333413
Yoon-Soo Ahn (CEO)

Shinsung FA Corporation (1)
404-1 Baekhyeon-dong, Bundang-gu, Seongnam, 463-420, Gyeonggi-do, Korea (South) (35.82%)
Tel.: (82) 31 7889 200
Web Site: http://www.shinsungfa.co.kr
Sales Range: $150-199.9 Million
Emp.: 240
Fabrication Automation System Mfr
N.A.I.C.S.: 333998

Shinsung Vietnam Co., Ltd (1)
International Plaza 16th Floor Rm No 16C 343 Pham Ngu Lao Ward, District 1, Ho Chi Minh City, 0084, Vietnam
Tel.: (84) 8 6291 5611
Emp.: 30
Solar Cell Distr
N.A.I.C.S.: 423690

Suzhou Shinsung co., Ltd. (1)
185 Changbang-Rd Wujiang Economic Development Zone, Suzhou, Jiangsu, China
Tel.: (86) 512 6343 3888
Solar Cell Mfr
N.A.I.C.S.: 423690

SHINSUNG TONGSANG CO., LTD.
SHINSUNG Bldg 444 Dunchon 2-dong, Gangdong-gu, Seoul, Korea (South)
Tel.: (82) 237099000
Web Site: https://www.ssts.co.kr
Year Founded: 1968
005390—(KRS)
Rev.: $1,187,784,359
Assets: $822,932,702
Liabilities: $497,277,518
Net Worth: $325,655,183
Earnings: $63,738,223
Emp.: 1,105
Fiscal Year-end: 06/30/23
Apparels Mfr
N.A.I.C.S.: 315250
Tae-Soon Yeom (CEO)

SHINTO COMPANY LIMITED
4-7-2 Ronchicho, Takahama, 444-1314, Aichi, Japan
Tel.: (81) 566532631
Web Site:
 https://www.shintokawara.co.jp
Year Founded: 1963
5380—(TKS)
Ceramic Tile Mfr
N.A.I.C.S.: 327120
Tatsuya Ishikawa (Pres)

SHINTO TSUSHIN CO., LTD.
3-16-29 Marunouchi, Naka-ku, Nagoya, 460-0002, Aichi, Japan
Tel.: (81) 52 951 3831 JP
Web Site: http://www.shinto-tsushin.co.jp
Year Founded: 1972
Sales Range: $150-199.9 Million
Emp.: 209
Advertising & Public Relations Agency
N.A.I.C.S.: 541810
Kikuro Tani (Chm)

SHINTOKYO GROUP CO., LTD.
3-21 Jinyamae Tokiwadaira, Matsudo, 270-2265, Chiba, Japan
Tel.: (81) 47 383 5353
Web Site: http://www.mr-shintokyo.co.jp
Year Founded: 2012
Rev.: $35,062,200
Assets: $28,475,580
Liabilities: $19,297,800
Net Worth: $9,177,780
Earnings: $806,340
Emp.: 102
Fiscal Year-end: 05/31/19
Holding Company
N.A.I.C.S.: 551112
Katsuhide Yoshino (Pres)

SHINVA MEDICAL INSTRUMENT COMPANY, LTD.
Xinhua Medical Scientific Zone, Zibo New & Hi-Tech Industrial Development Zone Zibo, Shangdong, 255086, China
Tel.: (86) 5333587720
Web Site: https://www.shinva.com
Year Founded: 1943
600587—(SHG)
Rev.: $1,303,160,325
Assets: $1,818,458,160
Liabilities: $1,005,640,398
Net Worth: $812,817,762
Earnings: $70,565,854
Fiscal Year-end: 12/31/22
Medical Equipment Mfr & Distr
N.A.I.C.S.: 334510
Wang Yuquan (Chm)

SHINVEST HOLDING LIMITED
No 3 Kian Teck Crescent, Singapore, 628881, Singapore
Tel.: (65) 62651555
Web Site: http://www.shinvest.com.sg
Year Founded: 1989
BJW—(SES)
Rev.: $10,425,404
Assets: $152,359,935
Liabilities: $22,128,414
Net Worth: $130,231,521
Earnings: $25,639,243
Emp.: 3
Fiscal Year-end: 12/31/21
Investment Services
N.A.I.C.S.: 523999

Subsidiaries:

MediaGate Pte Ltd. (1)
20 Tampines Street 92, Singapore, 528875, Singapore
Tel.: (65) 67863100
CD Disc Mfr
N.A.I.C.S.: 326199

PrimeDisc International Limited (1)
12th Floor Unison Industrial Centre 27-31 Au Pui Wan Street, Fo Tan Shatin, Hong Kong, NT, China (Hong Kong)
Tel.: (852) 26903656
Web Site: http://www.primedisc.com.hk
Sales Range: $75-99.9 Million
Blank CD & DVD Discs Mfr
N.A.I.C.S.: 326199
Joshua Ying Ming Chan (Mng Dir)

Sin Hong Hardware Pte Ltd (1)
No 3 Kian Teck Crescent, Singapore, 628881, Singapore
Tel.: (65) 62651555
Web Site: https://www.sinhong.com
Industrial Fasteners Distr
N.A.I.C.S.: 423710

StoreWell Media Manufacturing Ltd. (1)
No 11 Singhua Road, Taoyuan City, Taoyuan, 330, Taiwan
Tel.: (886) 33639288
Web Site: http://www.storewell.com.tw
CD & DVD Discs Mfr
N.A.I.C.S.: 334610

SHINWA CO., LTD.
2-9-3 Naeshiro, Moriyama-ku, Nagoya, 463-0046, Aichi, Japan
Tel.: (81) 527962533
Web Site: https://www.shinwa-jpn.co.jp
Year Founded: 1951
7607—(TKS)
Rev.: $484,195,900
Assets: $408,032,000
Liabilities: $149,105,840
Net Worth: $258,926,160
Earnings: $16,974,380
Emp.: 900
Fiscal Year-end: 08/31/24
Industrial Machinery Mfr
N.A.I.C.S.: 333248
Tetsuo Nemoto (Pres)

Subsidiaries:

PT. SANTAKU SHINWA INDONESIA (1)
Delta Silicon 5 Industrial ParkJl Kenari Timur Blok G1A-30, Lippo Cikarang, Bekasi, 17530, Indonesia
Tel.: (62) 2129093162
Industrial Machinery Distr
N.A.I.C.S.: 423830

SHINWA (INDIA) ENGINEERING & TRADING PRIVATE LIMITED (1)
NDRAKRUPA No 17 3rd floor 100 feet ring road, 3rd pahse 6th block Banashankari 3rd stage, Bengaluru, 560 085, India
Tel.: (91) 8042162072
Industrial Machinery Distr
N.A.I.C.S.: 423830
Rohit Jha (Acct Mgr & Mgr-Admin)

SHINWA (SHANGHAI) Co., Ltd. (1)
Rm 404 huiYinMingZun Business Center No 609 East yunling road, Putuo District, Shanghai, China
Tel.: (86) 2164287284
Industrial Machinery Distr
N.A.I.C.S.: 423830

SHINWA INTEC Co., Ltd. (1)
128/395-397 36th floor Payatai Plaza Building Phayathai Road, Kweng Thungphayathai Khet Ratchathewi, Bangkok, 10400, Thailand
Tel.: (66) 22161548
Emp.: 50
Industrial Machinery Distr
N.A.I.C.S.: 423830

SHINWA INTEC MALAYSIA SDN, BHD. (1)
D-7-7 Capital4 Oasis Square 2 Jalan PJU1A/7A, Oasis Damansara, 47301, Petaling Jaya, Selangor, Malaysia
Tel.: (60) 378321730
Industrial Machinery Distr
N.A.I.C.S.: 423830
Faizul Azlan Ayub (Mgr-Engrg)

Shinwa Representacao Comercial do Brasil Ltda. (1)
Rua Joao Antunes do Nascimenton 77, Santa Rosalia-Sorocaba, Sao Paulo, 18095-470, Brazil
Web Site: http://www.shinwa-br.com.br
Emp.: 8
Industrial Machinery Distr
N.A.I.C.S.: 423830

Shinwa USA Corp. (1)
3233 Mineola Pike, Erlanger, KY 41018
Tel.: (859) 746-6700
Web Site: https://www.shinwa-usa.com

SHINWA CO., LTD.

Shinwa Co., Ltd.—(Continued)
Emp.: 20
Industrial Machinery Distr
N.A.I.C.S.: 423830

Shinwatec Limited (1)
Unit 3 Barberry Court Parkway Centrum 100, Burton-on-Trent, DE14 2UE, Staffordshire, United Kingdom
Tel.: (44) 1283845848
Web Site: https://www.shinwatec.co.uk
Industrial Machinery Distr
N.A.I.C.S.: 423830

YANTAI FRONTIER SPIRITS SHINWA MAINTENANCE TECHNOLOGY Co., Ltd. (1)
No 46 Xingyuanxi Road, Fushan, Yantai, Shandong, China
Tel.: (86) 5353805109
Industrial Machinery Distr
N.A.I.C.S.: 423830

YANTAI SHINWA JOINT TECHNOLOGY Co., Ltd. (1)
1 Jinhe Street, Fushan Hi-tech Industrial Zone, Yantai, Shandong, China
Tel.: (86) 5356433939
Industrial Machinery Distr
N.A.I.C.S.: 423830

SHINWA INDUSTRIAL CO., LTD.
5-3-13 Tamondori, Chuo-ku, Kobe, 650-0015, Hyogo, Japan
Tel.: (81) 783822231 **JP**
Web Site: https://shinwa.co.jp
Year Founded: 1949
Marine Instruments & Equipment Distr
N.A.I.C.S.: 423860
Masanori Matsushima (Chm)

Subsidiaries:

Kaigai Gijyutsu K.K. (1)
Relax Bldg 7F 2-5-15 Ohgi-cho, Naka-ku, Yokohama, 231-0027, Japan
Tel.: (81) 456647318
Web Site: https://www.kgkjp.com
Ship Radio & Satellite Communication Equipment Whslr & Installation Services
N.A.I.C.S.: 423860

SHINWA WISE HOLDINGS CO., LTD.
2nd Floor Yusen Building 2-3-2 Marunouchi, Chiyoda-ku, Tokyo, 100-0005, Japan
Tel.: (81) 352248610
Web Site: https://www.shinwa-wise.com
Year Founded: 1989
2437—(TKS)
Rev.: $24,096,465
Assets: $33,392,798
Liabilities: $9,904,196
Net Worth: $23,488,603
Earnings: $2,464,486
Fiscal Year-end: 05/31/23
Art Auction Services
N.A.I.C.S.: 459920
Hajime Baba (Pres)

SHINWHA INTERTEK CORPORATION
308 Maebong-ro Byeongcheon-myeon, Dongnam-gu, Cheonan, Chungcheongnam-do, Korea (South)
Tel.: (82) 415903300
Web Site: http://www.shinwha.com
Year Founded: 1977
056700—(KRS)
Rev.: $154,355,710
Assets: $132,553,737
Liabilities: $61,705,241
Net Worth: $70,848,497
Earnings: ($6,446,950)
Emp.: 321
Fiscal Year-end: 12/31/22
Optical Film & Lens Mfr

N.A.I.C.S.: 333310
Cheolheung Ahn (CEO)

Subsidiaries:

Dongguan Shinwha Intertek Corp. (1)
Caotong Industrial Hadi Village, Nancheng District, Dongguan, Guangdong, China
Tel.: (86) 76922983601
Optical Instrument & Lens Mfr
N.A.I.C.S.: 333310

Shinwha Intertek (Suzhou) Co., Ltd. (1)
No 667 Ganguan West Road Wujiang Economy Development Zone, Suzhou, Jiangsu, China
Tel.: (86) 51263091701
Optical Instrument & Lens Mfr
N.A.I.C.S.: 333310

Shinwha Intertek Slovakia S.r.o (1)
Voderady 402, Trnava pri, 919 42, Voderady, Slovakia
Tel.: (421) 335933722
Optical Instrument & Lens Mfr
N.A.I.C.S.: 333310

SHINWON CONSTRUCTION CO.,LTD.
109 Wawooan-gil, Bongdam-Eup, Hwaseong, Gyeonggi-do, Korea (South)
Tel.: (82) 2309840
Web Site: http://www.swc.co.kr
Year Founded: 1983
017000—(KRS)
Rev.: $144,357,202
Assets: $174,214,014
Liabilities: $102,241,619
Net Worth: $71,972,395
Earnings: $3,405,674
Emp.: 187
Fiscal Year-end: 12/31/22
Civil Engineering Services
N.A.I.C.S.: 237990
Kim Sung-Min (CEO)

SHINWON CORPORATION
Shinwon Building 328 Dokmak-ro, Mapo-gu, Seoul, Korea (South)
Tel.: (82) 232745000
Web Site: https://www.shinwon.com
Year Founded: 1973
009270—(KRS)
Rev.: $763,502,100
Assets: $391,265,793
Liabilities: $218,300,887
Net Worth: $172,964,906
Earnings: $13,469,349
Emp.: 725
Fiscal Year-end: 12/31/22
Sweater Mfr
N.A.I.C.S.: 315120
Jung Joo Park (CEO)

Subsidiaries:

P.T. SHINWON EBENEZER (1)
Desa Purwasari Kec Cikampek Kad, Karawang, West Java, Indonesia
Tel.: (62) 264313358
Web Site: http://www.sw.co.kr
Sales Range: $350-399.9 Million
Garments Mfr & Suppliers
N.A.I.C.S.: 315210

Qingdao Shinwon Garment Co., Ltd. (1)
Shinwon Bldg 532 Dohwa-dong Mapo-gu, Seoul, Korea (South)
Tel.: (82) 2 3274 5000
Web Site: http://www.sw.co.kr
Sales Range: $150-199.9 Million
Garments Mfr & Supplier
N.A.I.C.S.: 315250

SHINWON EBENEZER VIETNAM Co., Ltd. (1)
CN 14 Khaiquang Sub-Industrial complex, Khaiquang Commune, Vinh Yen, Vinh Phuc, Vietnam
Tel.: (84) 211 842 830

Web Site: http://www.sw.co.kr
Garments Mfr & Supplier
N.A.I.C.S.: 315250

Shanghai Shinwon Ebenezer Co., Ltd. (1)
Rm 11 M N Hechuan Bldg No 2016 Yishan Rd, 201103, Shanghai, China
Tel.: (86) 2161253980
Sales Range: $25-49.9 Million
Emp.: 65
Garments Mfr & Sales
N.A.I.C.S.: 315210

Shinwon Corporation (Bangladesh) (1)
Plot No 33 A Rd 99 Gulshan, Dhaka, 1212, Bangladesh
Tel.: (880) 2 988 0824
Web Site: http://www.sw.co.kr
Garments Mfr & Whslr
N.A.I.C.S.: 315250

SHINY CHEMICAL INDUSTRIAL CO., LTD.
No 5 Yeong Gong 1st Road, Yeong An Dist, Kaohsiung, 82841, Hsien, Taiwan
Tel.: (886) 78619171
Web Site: https://www.shinychem.com.tw
1773—(TAI)
Rev.: $322,211,636
Assets: $473,836,962
Liabilities: $189,177,369
Net Worth: $284,659,592
Earnings: $51,619,116
Emp.: 620
Fiscal Year-end: 12/31/23
Chemicals Mfr
N.A.I.C.S.: 325998
Jan Yen Sun (Founder, Co-Chm & Pres)

SHINYEI KAISHA
77-1 Kyomachi, Chuo-ku, Kobe, 651-0178, Japan
Tel.: (81) 783926800
Web Site: https://www.shinyei.co.jp
Year Founded: 1887
3004—(TKS)
Rev.: $265,748,440
Assets: $175,654,140
Liabilities: $125,325,600
Net Worth: $50,328,540
Earnings: $10,939,550
Emp.: 467
Fiscal Year-end: 03/31/24
Textile & Food Product Distr
N.A.I.C.S.: 424310
Hideo Akazawa (Pres & CEO)

Subsidiaries:

MARUOKA Shoji Co., Ltd. (1)
Eterno Harajyuku 3-4-2 Sendagaya, Shibuya-ku, Tokyo, 151-0051, Japan
Tel.: (81) 3 3405 4717
Web Site: http://www.maruoka-shoji.com
Textile Products Distr
N.A.I.C.S.: 424490

Shinkyowa Co., Ltd. (1)
2-3-34 Nagata Nishi, Higashiosaka, 577-0016, Osaka, Japan
Tel.: (81) 667892321
Web Site: https://www.shinyei-shc.co.jp
Hardware Mfr
N.A.I.C.S.: 332510

Shinyei (Shanghai) Trading Co., Ltd. (1)
Shanghai International Trade Centre Unit 1808 No 2201 Yan An West Rd, Changning District, Shanghai, China
Tel.: (86) 21 6275 2308
Textile Products Distr
N.A.I.C.S.: 424490

Shinyei Agritech Co., Ltd. (1)
3-1 Ushiyama, Awara, 910-4111, Fukui, Japan
Tel.: (81) 776 23 2019
Fruit & Vegetable Distr

INTERNATIONAL PUBLIC

N.A.I.C.S.: 424480

Shinyei Capacitor Co., Ltd. (1)
Shinei Building 5F 77-1 Kyomachi, Chuo-ku, Kobe, 650-0034, Hyogo, Japan
Tel.: (81) 783926909
Web Site: https://www.shinyei.co.jp
Emp.: 50
Electronic Parts Mfr & Distr
N.A.I.C.S.: 334416

Plant (Domestic):

Shinyei Capacitor Co., Ltd. - Nagano Plant (2)
313 Tanaka, Tomi, 389-0516, Nagano, Japan
Tel.: (81) 268620181
Electric Equipment Mfr
N.A.I.C.S.: 334416

Subsidiary (Non-US):

Shinyei Kaisha Electronics (M) Sdn. Bhd. (2)
No 313 Lot2557 6 1/2 Miles Jalan Skudai, 81200, Johor Bahru, Johor, Malaysia
Tel.: (60) 7 2386017
Web Site: http://www.shinyeikaishaelectronics.com
Electronic Equipment Mfr & Distr
N.A.I.C.S.: 334416

Shinyei Corporation of America (1)
1120 Avenue of the Americas Fl 4, New York, NY 10036
Tel.: (917) 484-7884
Web Site: http://www.sca-shinyei.com
Electronic Equipment Distr
N.A.I.C.S.: 423690

Shinyei LifeTex Co., Ltd. (1)
Eterno Harajyuku 3-4-2 Sendagaya, Shibuya-ku, Tokyo, 151-0051, Japan
Tel.: (81) 334054717
Web Site: http://www.shinyei-lifetex.co.jp
Textile Products Distr
N.A.I.C.S.: 424310

Shinyei Living Industry Co., Ltd. (1)
Shinei Building 77-1 Kyomachi, Chuo-ku, Kobe, 650-0034, Japan
Tel.: (81) 783926934
Web Site: https://www.shinyei.co.jp
Emp.: 5
Real Estate Manangement Services
N.A.I.C.S.: 531390

Shinyei Shoji (Qingdao) Trading Co., Ltd. (1)
Room 1310 Qingdao Yizhong Crown Holiday Hotel No 76, Hong Kong Middle Road, Qingdao, 266071, China
Tel.: (86) 53285730891
Web Site: https://www.skqd.com.cn
Frozen Food Product Distr
N.A.I.C.S.: 424420

Shinyei Technology Co., Ltd. (1)
6-5-2 Minatojima-Minamimachi, Chuo-ku, Kobe, 650-0047, Japan (100%)
Tel.: (81) 783046790
Web Site: https://www.shinyei.co.jp
Emp.: 180
Sensor & Measurement Equipment Developer, Mfr & Whslr
N.A.I.C.S.: 334513
Masaru Kishimoto (Pres)

Plant (Domestic):

Shinyei Technology Co., Ltd. - Fukuoka Plant (2)
1082-6 Shimotobaru, Kouge-machi Chikujo-gun, Fukuoka, 871-0923, Japan
Tel.: (81) 979848011
Electric Equipment Mfr
N.A.I.C.S.: 334419

SHINYOUNG SECURITIES CO., LTD.
16 Gukjegeumyung-ro 8-gil, Yeongdeungpo-gu, Seoul, 07330, Korea (South)
Tel.: (82) 220049000
Web Site: http://www.shinyoung.com
Year Founded: 1956

AND PRIVATE COMPANIES

001720—(KRS)
Rev.: $1,788,678,476
Assets: $7,751,088,307
Liabilities: $6,584,316,582
Net Worth: $1,166,771,725
Earnings: $79,370,058
Emp.: 654
Fiscal Year-end: 03/31/23
Securities Brokerage Services
N.A.I.C.S.: 523150
Yoon Jong Soo *(Deputy Gen Mgr)*

Subsidiaries:

Doosan Engineering & Construction Co., Ltd. (1)
726 Eonju-ro, Gangnam-gu, Seoul, 135-714, Korea (South)
Tel.: (82) 25103114
Web Site: https://www.doosanenc.com
Rev.: $1,532,520,000
Assets: $2,003,800,000
Liabilities: $1,516,180,000
Net Worth: $487,620,000
Earnings: ($64,500,000)
Emp.: 1,328
Fiscal Year-end: 12/31/2019
Construction Industry
N.A.I.C.S.: 236116
Jeongwon Park *(Chm & CEO-Doosan Grp)*

Subsidiary (Non-US):

Doosan Cuvex Co., Ltd. (2)
Tel.: (82) 332601114
Golf Club & Resort Management Operator
N.A.I.C.S.: 721110

Plant (Non-US):

Doosan Engineering & Construction Co., Ltd. - Doosan Vina (CPE Plant) (2)
Dung Quat Econ Zone Binh Thuan, Binh Soon, Quang Ngai, Vietnam
Tel.: (84) 553618900
Chemical Process Equipment Mfr
N.A.I.C.S.: 333248

SHIONOGI & CO., LTD.

1-8 Doshomachi 3-chome, Chuo-ku, Osaka, 541-0045, Japan
Tel.: (81) 662022161 JP
Web Site: https://www.shionogi.com
Year Founded: 1878
4507—(TKS)
Rev.: $2,875,885,410
Assets: $9,365,827,980
Liabilities: $1,086,393,160
Net Worth: $8,279,434,820
Earnings: $1,071,018,300
Emp.: 4,959
Fiscal Year-end: 03/31/24
Pharmaceuticals Product Mfr
N.A.I.C.S.: 325412
Isao Teshirogi *(Pres & CEO)*

Subsidiaries:

Aburahi Agroresearch Co.,Ltd. (1)
1405 Gotanda Koka-cho, Koka Town, Koka, 520-3423, Shiga, Japan
Tel.: (81) 748883215
Web Site: https://www.shionogi.com
Sales Range: $25-49.9 Million
Emp.: 38
Pharmaceuticals Product Mfr
N.A.I.C.S.: 325412
Kou Ozawa *(Gen Mgr)*

Aburahi Laboratories (1)
1405 Gotanda, Koka-cho, Koka, 520 3423, Shiga, Japan (100%)
Tel.: (81) 748883281
Web Site: http://www.shionogi.co.jp
Sales Range: $25-49.9 Million
Emp.: 100
Mfr of Pharmaceuticals
N.A.I.C.S.: 325412

Beijing Shionogi Pharmaceutical Technology Limited (1)
Room 07 20th Floor Jinghui Building No 118 Jianguo Road, Chaoyang District, Beijing, 100022, China
Tel.: (86) 106 567 8002

Medical Device Product Mfr & Distr
N.A.I.C.S.: 339112

C & O Pharmaceutical Technology (Holdings) Limited (1)
Tel.: (852) 28060109
Web Site: https://english.changao.com
Pharmaceuticals Product Mfr
N.A.I.C.S.: 325412
Kian Chuan Lee *(Exec Dir)*

Discovery Research Laboratories (1)
12 4 Sagisu 5 Chome, Osaka, 5530002, Japan (100%)
Tel.: (81) 664585861
Provider of Research Services
N.A.I.C.S.: 541715

Ezose Sciences, Inc. (1)
25 Riverside Dr, Pine Brook, NJ 07058
Tel.: (862) 926-1950
Web Site: http://www.ezose.com
Emp.: 10
Laboratory Instrument Mfr
N.A.I.C.S.: 334516
Hidehisa Asada *(VP-R&D)*

Nichia Pharmaceutical Industries Ltd. (1)
224-20 Hiraishiino Kawauchi-cho, Tokushima, 771-0132, Japan
Tel.: (81) 886652312
Pharmaceutical Preparation Mfr
N.A.I.C.S.: 325412

Saishin Igaku Co., Ltd. (1)
Shionogi Doshomachi Building 7-6 Doshomachi 4 Chome, Chuo-ku, Osaka, 541-0045, Japan
Tel.: (81) 662222876
Web Site: http://www.saishin-igaku.co.jp
Pharmaceutical Products Mfr & Distr
N.A.I.C.S.: 325412

Shionogi & Co., Ltd. - Kanegasaki Plant (1)
7 Moriyama Nishine Kanegasaki-cho, Isawa-gun, Iwate, 029-4503, Japan
Tel.: (81) 197445121
Pharmaceuticals Product Mfr
N.A.I.C.S.: 325412

Shionogi & Co., Ltd. - Settsu Plant (1)
5-1 Mishima 2-chome, Settsu, 566-0022, Osaka, Japan
Tel.: (81) 66 381 7341
Web Site: http://www.shionogi.co.jp
Sales Range: $150-199.9 Million
Emp.: 500
Pharmaceutical Products Mfr & Distr
N.A.I.C.S.: 424210

Shionogi Administration Service Co., Ltd. (1)
Doshomachi 4-chome No 7 No 6 Shionogi Doshomachi Building, Chuo-ku, Osaka, 541-0045, Japan
Tel.: (81) 66 209 4301
Medicine Distr
N.A.I.C.S.: 424210

Shionogi Analysis Center Co., Ltd. (1)
5-1 Mishima 2-chome Settsu, Osaka, 566-0022, Japan
Tel.: (81) 663817271
Web Site: http://www.shionogi-ac.co.jp
Emp.: 159
Pharmaceutical Products Mfr & Distr
N.A.I.C.S.: 325412
Yushiyuki Takeuchi *(Pres)*

Shionogi Business Partner Co., Ltd. (1)
Doshomachi 4-chome No 7 No 6 Shionogi Doshomachi Building 6F, Chuo-ku, Osaka, 541-0045, Japan
Tel.: (81) 66 209 6620
Medicine Distr
N.A.I.C.S.: 424210

Shionogi Career Development Center Co., Ltd. (1)
829 Tonouchi, Amagasaki, 661-0961, Hyogo, Japan
Tel.: (81) 66 209 6759
Career Development Services
N.A.I.C.S.: 611430

Shionogi Developmental Research Laboratories (1)
1-1 Futaba-cho 3-chome, Toyonaka, 561-0825, Osaka, Japan (100%)
Tel.: (81) 66 331 8081
Web Site: http://www.shionogi.com
Sales Range: $75-99.9 Million
Emp.: 360
Provider of Research Services
N.A.I.C.S.: 541715

Shionogi Digital Science Co., Ltd. (1)
3-6-3 Awajimachi Midosuji MTR Building 4th Floor, Chuo-ku, Osaka, 541-0047, Japan
Tel.: (81) 66 209 8004
Global Information & Communications Technology Solution Services
N.A.I.C.S.: 518210

Shionogi Europe B.V. (1)
Locatellikade 1 Parnassustoren, 1076 AZ, Amsterdam, Netherlands
Holding Company
N.A.I.C.S.: 551112

Shionogi General Service Co.,Ltd. (1)
Shionogi Doshomachi Building Doshomachi 4-chome, Chuo-ku, Osaka, 541-0045, Japan
Tel.: (81) 662270815
Pharmaceutical Products Mfr & Distr
N.A.I.C.S.: 424210

Shionogi Healthcare Co., Ltd. (1)
2-6-18 Kitahama Yodoyabashi Square 7th Floor, Chuo-ku, Osaka, 541-0041, Japan
Tel.: (81) 66 202 2728
Web Site: https://www.shionogi-hc.co.jp
Healthcare Product Mfr & Distr
N.A.I.C.S.: 339112

Shionogi Inc. (1)
400 Campus Dr, Florham Park, NJ 07932 (100%)
Tel.: (973) 966-6900
Web Site: https://www.shionogi.com
Sales Range: $25-49.9 Million
Emp.: 30
Pharmaceuticals Mfr
N.A.I.C.S.: 325412
Joseph Spagnardi *(Exec VP-Legal & Compliance)*

Shionogi Institute for Medical Science (1)
5 1 Mishima 2 Chome, Settsu, Osaka, 566 0022, Japan (100%)
Tel.: (81) 663822612
Sales Range: $25-49.9 Million
Emp.: 30
Provider of Pharmaceutical Products
N.A.I.C.S.: 325412

Shionogi Marketing Solutions Co., Ltd. (1)
Nissei Yodoyabashi East 2nd Floor 3-3-13 Imabashi, Chuo-ku, Osaka, 541-0042, Japan
Tel.: (81) 66 209 6660
Pharmaceutical Products Distr
N.A.I.C.S.: 424210

Shionogi Pharma Chemicals Co., Ltd (1)
224-20 Ebisuno Hiraishi Kawauchi, Tokushima, 771-0132, Japan
Tel.: (81) 886652312
Web Site: http://www.nichia-yakuhin.com
Pharmaceuticals Product Mfr
N.A.I.C.S.: 325412

Shionogi Pharma Co., Ltd (1)
5-1 Mishima 2-chome, Settsu, Osaka, 566-0022, Japan (100%)
Tel.: (81) 663817341
Medicinal Drugs & Investigational Drugs Mfr
N.A.I.C.S.: 325412

Shionogi Pharma, Inc. (1)
5 Concourse Pkwy Ste 1800, Atlanta, GA 30328
Tel.: (770) 442-9707
Sales Range: $350-399.9 Million
Emp.: 920
Brand Name Prescription Drugs Marketer & Sales to High-Prescribing Primary Care & Specialty Physicians
N.A.I.C.S.: 325412

Shionogi Pharmacovigilance Center Co., Ltd. (1)
Doshomachi 4-chome No 7 No 6, Chuo-ku, Osaka, 541-0045, Japan
Tel.: (81) 66 209 6823
Medical Device Product Mfr & Distr
N.A.I.C.S.: 339112

Shionogi Qualicaps, S.A. (1)
Avenida Monte De Valdelatas 4, 28108, Alcobendas, Spain (100%)
Tel.: (34) 916630800
Web Site: http://www.qualicaps.com
Sales Range: $50-74.9 Million
Emp.: 240
Mfr & Sales of Capsules
N.A.I.C.S.: 325412
Ciro Ahumada *(CEO)*

Shionogi Smile Heart Co., Ltd. (1)
3-2-1 Futaba-cho, Toyonaka, 561-0825, Osaka, Japan
Tel.: (81) 66 331 7118
Cleaning Service
N.A.I.C.S.: 561720

Shionogi Techno Advance Research Co., Ltd. (1)
3-1-1 Futaba-cho, Toyonaka, 561-0825, Osaka, Japan
Tel.: (81) 663318605
Web Site: https://www.shionogi.com
Emp.: 220
Pharmaceutical Products Mfr & Distr
N.A.I.C.S.: 325412

Taiwan Shionogi & Co., Ltd. (1)
4F No 2 Sec 2 Nanking East Road, Taipei, 10457, Taiwan (100%)
Tel.: (886) 225516336
Sales Range: $50-74.9 Million
Emp.: 80
Pharmaceuticals Mfr & Whslr
N.A.I.C.S.: 325412

SHIP HEALTHCARE HOLDINGS, INC.

3-20-8 Kasuga, Suita, 565-0853, Osaka, Japan
Tel.: (81) 663690130
Web Site: https://www.shiphd.co.jp
Year Founded: 1992
3360—(TKS)
Rev.: $4,170,830,680
Assets: $2,556,873,590
Liabilities: $1,616,825,830
Net Worth: $940,047,760
Earnings: $91,145,290
Emp.: 8,046
Fiscal Year-end: 03/31/24
Holding Company
N.A.I.C.S.: 551112
Kunihisa Furukawa *(Chm & CEO)*

Subsidiaries:

Ainet Systems, Inc. (1)
2-9-8 Minamisenba, Chuo-ku, Osaka, 542-0081, Japan
Tel.: (81) 661214120
Web Site: https://www.ains.co.jp
Emp.: 107
Medical Consulting Services
N.A.I.C.S.: 541611

Aurum Medical Co., Ltd. (1)
2-1-32 Higashiisoyama, Suzuka, Mie, Japan
Tel.: (81) 593880339
Web Site: https://www.aurum-net.co.jp
Medical Equipment Distr
N.A.I.C.S.: 423450

Central Uni Co., Ltd. (1)
2-3-16 Nishi Kanda, Chiyoda-ku, Tokyo, 101-0065, Japan
Tel.: (81) 335561331
Web Site: http://www.central-uni.co.jp
Medical Equipment Distr
N.A.I.C.S.: 423450
Masayuki Kawamura *(Pres)*

Chain Management Co., Ltd. (1)
23rd Floor of Grand Park Tower 3-4-1, Shibaura Minato-ku, Tokyo, 108-0023, Japan
Tel.: (81) 354427665
Web Site: http://www.cm21.co.jp

SHIP HEALTHCARE HOLDINGS, INC.

Ship Healthcare Holdings, Inc.—(Continued)
Medical Equipment Distr
N.A.I.C.S.: 423450

Chuoh Co., Ltd. (1)
1835-1 Kawahigashishita, Kagawacho,
Takamatsu, 761-1705, Japan
Tel.: (81) 878798811
Web Site: https://www.kk-chuoh.co.jp
Emp.: 114
Corporate Catering Services
N.A.I.C.S.: 722320

Clean Pair Kyushu Co., Ltd. (1)
2217-1 Oyamacho, Higashi-ku, Kumamoto,
861-8030, Japan
Tel.: (81) 963895263
Web Site: https://www.clean-pair.com
Emp.: 200
Air Conditioner Cleaning Services
N.A.I.C.S.: 561790

Euro Meditech Co., Ltd. (1)
NMF Takanawa Bldg 8F 2-2-20-4 Higashig-
otanda, Shinagawa-ku, Tokyo, 141-0022,
Japan
Tel.: (81) 354497585
Web Site: https://www.euro-meditec.co.jp
Medical Equipment Mfr
N.A.I.C.S.: 339112

F & S UNI Co. Ltd. (1)
2-3-16 Nishi-Kanda, Chiyoda-ku, Tokyo,
101-0065, Japan
Tel.: (81) 335563030
Web Site: https://www.fs-uni.co.jp
Emp.: 140
Medical Equipment Distr
N.A.I.C.S.: 423450

F&S UNI Management Co., Ltd. (1)
23rd Floor Grand Park Tower 3-4-1,
Shibaura Minato-ku, Tokyo, 108-0023, Ja-
pan
Tel.: (81) 354427661
Web Site: https://www.fsm.co.jp
Emp.: 2,059
Pharmaceutical Products Distr
N.A.I.C.S.: 424210

Grand-gourmet Co., Ltd. (1)
1-10 Kandasuda-Cho, Chiyoda-ku, Tokyo,
Japan
Tel.: (81) 33897300
Web Site: https://grand-gourmet.co.jp
Emp.: 1,048
Food Catering Services
N.A.I.C.S.: 722310

Grandic Inc. (1)
1-10 Kandasuda-Cho, Chiyoda-ku, Tokyo,
101-0041, Japan
Tel.: (81) 484869115
Web Site: https://www.grandic.co.jp
Emp.: 670
Medical Catering Services
N.A.I.C.S.: 524114

Green Animal Company (1)
3-20-8 Kasuga, Suita, Osaka, Japan
Tel.: (81) 663690130
Web Site: https://www.hs-gac.jp
Animal Health Care Services
N.A.I.C.S.: 812910

Green Hospital Supply, Inc. (1)
3-20-8 Kasuga, Suita, 565-0853, Osaka,
Japan
Tel.: (81) 663690092
Web Site: https://www.ghs-inc.co.jp
Medical Equipment Distr
N.A.I.C.S.: 423450

Green Life Co., Ltd. (1)
3-20-8 Kasuga, Suita, 565-0853, Osaka,
Japan
Tel.: (81) 663690121
Web Site: http://www.greenlife-inc.co
Construction Services
N.A.I.C.S.: 532412
Koichi Okimoto (Pres & CEO)

Green Life East Co., Ltd. (1)
1-4-16 Yaesu 11th Floor Tokyo Tatemono
Yaesu Building, Chuo-ku, Tokyo, 103-0028,
Japan
Tel.: (81) 352553338
Insurance Services
N.A.I.C.S.: 524210

Green Pharmacy Co., Ltd. (1)
3-20-8 Kasuga, Suita, Osaka, Japan
Tel.: (81) 663690118
Web Site: https://www.gp-inc.co.jp
Emp.: 334
Pharmacy Products Distr
N.A.I.C.S.: 456110

Heart Life Corporation (1)
3-12-17 Miyasaka, Setagaya-ku, Tokyo,
156-0051, Japan
Tel.: (81) 334286399
Web Site: https://www.hlcg.jp
Medical Equipment Distr
N.A.I.C.S.: 423450

I & C Co., Ltd. (1)
2nd floor Nishihonmachi Daigo Building
2-4-23 Awaza, Nishi-ku, Osaka, Japan
Tel.: (81) 643948770
Web Site: https://www.iandc-inc.jp
Building Materials Mfr
N.A.I.C.S.: 321992

JOYUP Co., Ltd. (1)
Shiraki Daini Building 2-8-12 Higashihie,
Hakata-ku, Fukuoka, 812-0007, Japan
Tel.: (81) 5058068182
Web Site: https://www.joyup.jp
Medical Equipment Mfr & Distr
N.A.I.C.S.: 339112

Japan Pana-USE Co., Ltd. (1)
2nd floor Nishihonmachi Daigo Building
2-4-23 Awaza, Nishi-ku, Osaka, 550-0011,
Japan
Tel.: (81) 643948723
Web Site: https://www.jpu.co.jp
Medical Consulting Services
N.A.I.C.S.: 541611

K-on Systems, Inc. (1)
23F Grand Park Tower 3-4-1, Shibaura
Minato-ku, Tokyo, 108-0023, Japan
Tel.: (81) 354427670
Web Site: https://www.k-on.co.jp
Medical Equipment Distr
N.A.I.C.S.: 423450

Kingrun Co., Ltd. (1)
1-10 Kandasuda-cho, Chiyoda-ku, Tokyo,
101-0041, Japan
Tel.: (81) 352963031
Web Site: https://www.kingrun.co.jp
Emp.: 2,983
Welfare Vehicle Mfr & Distr
N.A.I.C.S.: 336211

Kingrun Hokkaido Co., Ltd. (1)
5-1-5-1Shinhassamu 5-jo, Teine-ku Hok-
kaido, Sapporo, 006-0805, Japan
Tel.: (81) 116694400
Web Site: https://kingrun-hokkaido.co.jp
Emp.: 60
Medical Equipment Distr
N.A.I.C.S.: 423450

Kingrun Hounest Co., Ltd. (1)
MetLife Kandasudacho Building 6F 1-10
Kandasudacho, Chiyoda-ku, Tokyo, 101-
0041, Japan
Tel.: (81) 352963060
Web Site: https://kingrun-hounest.com
Civil Engineering Construction Services
N.A.I.C.S.: 541330

Kingrun Kansai Co., Ltd. (1)
5-1-12 Minami, Suita, 564-0043, Japan
Tel.: (81) 663881481
Emp.: 127
Windows & Door Curtain Whslr
N.A.I.C.S.: 423220

Kingrun Kyushu Co., Ltd. (1)
920-8 Tojima-cho inside Cosmo Industrial
Park, Higashi-ku, Kumamoto, Japan
Tel.: (81) 963895211
Welfare Vehicle Mfr
N.A.I.C.S.: 336211

Kingrun Medicare Co., Ltd. (1)
1-10 Kandasuda-cho, Chiyoda-Ku, Tokyo,
101-0041, Japan
Tel.: (81) 352965505
Emp.: 393
Catering Services
N.A.I.C.S.: 722320

Kingrun Renewal Co., Ltd. (1)
Yamajin Building 2F 1-1 Kanda
Ogawamachi, Chiyoda-ku, Tokyo, 101-0052,
Japan
Tel.: (81) 363241328
Web Site: https://eight-renewal.com
Residential Renovation Services
N.A.I.C.S.: 623210

Konishi Medical Instruments Co., Ltd. (1)
2-1-5 Uchiawajicho, Chuo-ku, Osaka, 540-
0038, Japan
Tel.: (81) 669411363
Web Site: https://www.kns-md.co.jp
Emp.: 1,127
Medical Equipment Distr
N.A.I.C.S.: 423450

Medical Tourism Japan Co., Ltd. (1)
Hon-Toori 3 cho-me North 6 Number 18
SMC-Building 3F, Shiroishi-ku, Sapporo,
Hokkaido, Japan
Tel.: (81) 118658555
Web Site: https://www.en.medical-
hokkaido.com
Pharmaceutical Products Distr
N.A.I.C.S.: 424210
Sakagami Katsuyaya (Chm)

Nakajima Medical Supply Co., Ltd. (1)
1-17-19 Sukegawa-cho, Hitachi, 317-0065,
Ibaraki, Japan
Tel.: (81) 294210500
Web Site: http://www.nakajima-ms.co.jp
Medical Equipment Distr
N.A.I.C.S.: 423450

Nihon Network Service Co., Ltd. (1)
1-4-10 Minatojima Minamimachi, Chuo-ku,
Kobe, 650-0047, Japan
Tel.: (81) 783066600
Web Site: http://www.nihonet.co.jp
Construction Services
N.A.I.C.S.: 236220

Nishino Medical Instruments Co., Ltd. (1)
2-6-6 Yushima, Bunkyo-ku, Tokyo, Japan
Tel.: (81) 338161227
Web Site: https://www.nishino-ika.co.jp
Pharmaceutical Products Distr
N.A.I.C.S.: 424210

Okkar Thiri Co., Ltd. (1)
No 28 Pyay Road 6 1/2 Miles 11 Quarters,
Hlaing Township, Yangon, Myanmar
Tel.: (95) 17538023
Web Site: https://www.okkarthiri.com
Medical Equipment Distr
N.A.I.C.S.: 423450

Organ Medical Co., Ltd. (1)
2-27-30 Sakura, Akita, 010-0042, Japan
Tel.: (81) 188327140
Web Site: https://www.organ-m.co.jp
Emp.: 17
Medical Equipment Distr
N.A.I.C.S.: 423450

Osaka Advanced Medical Image Center, Inc. (1)
5-20-1 Momoyamadai, Suita, 565-0854,
Osaka, Japan
Tel.: (81) 663696677
Web Site: https://www.oamic.co.jp
Medical Equipment Distr
N.A.I.C.S.: 423450

Osaka Heavy Ion Administration Company (1)
3-1-10 Otemae, Chuo-ku, Osaka, 540-0008,
Japan
Tel.: (81) 647943215
Web Site: https://www.osaka-himak.or.jp
Medical Equipment Distr
N.A.I.C.S.: 423450

Seiko Medical, Inc. (1)
6-9-10 Chikko, Wakayama, 640-8287, Ja-
pan
Tel.: (81) 734352333
Web Site: https://www.skmnet.co.jp
Emp.: 202
Medical Equipment Distr
N.A.I.C.S.: 423450

Ship Healthcare Food, Inc. (1)
4-13-15 Kasuga, Fukida, Osaka, 565-0853,
Japan
Tel.: (81) 663690095

INTERNATIONAL PUBLIC

Web Site: http://www.ship-hf.co.jp
Hospital Food Services
N.A.I.C.S.: 722310

Ship Healthcare Research & Consulting, Inc. (1)
5-20-1 Momoyamadai, Suita, 565-0854,
Osaka, Japan
Tel.: (81) 663383378
Web Site: https://www.shiprc.jp
Health Care Srvices
N.A.I.C.S.: 621999

Snow Everest Co., Ltd. (1)
No 631/5E5 Pyay Road Near Inya Road,
Kamayut Township, Yangon, Myanmar
Tel.: (95) 95067749
Web Site: https://www.snoweverestmm.com
Medical Equipment Distr
N.A.I.C.S.: 423450

Tik, Inc. (1)
1-17-6 Ojihoncho Suzuki Building, Kita-ku,
Tokyo, 114-0022, Japan
Tel.: (81) 339072035
Web Site: http://www.tik-inc.com
Medical Equipment Distr
N.A.I.C.S.: 423450

Tom-Medic Inc. (1)
14-1 Shimogawara, Oaza Takizawa, Ao-
mori, 039-3524, Japan
Tel.: (81) 177370030
Web Site: https://www.tom-medic.com
Medical Equipment Distr
N.A.I.C.S.: 423450

Yamada Shadowless Lamp Co., Ltd. (1)
6th Floor 2-3-16 Nishikanda, Chiyoda-ku,
Tokyo, 101-0065, Japan
Tel.: (81) 352126021
Web Site: http://www.skylux.co.jp
Medical Lighting Device Mfr & Distr
N.A.I.C.S.: 434510
Jun Masuda (Pres)

SHIPMASTER CONTAINERS LTD.
380 Esna Park Drive, Markham, L3R
1G5, ON, Canada
Tel.: (416) 493-9193
Web Site:
https://www.shipmaster.com
Year Founded: 1959
Rev.: $10,417,645
Emp.: 65
Corrugated Packaging Product Mfr
N.A.I.C.S.: 322211
Neil Fyfe (Pres)

SHIPONS A.D.
Sentandrejski put 165, 21000, Novi
Sad, Serbia
Tel.: (381) 21 64 11 220
Web Site: http://www.shipons.co.rs
Year Founded: 1958
SPNS—(BEL)
Sales Range: $1-9.9 Million
Electrical Product Whslr
N.A.I.C.S.: 423620
Velibor Doric (Exec Dir)

SHIPPING CORPORATION OF INDIA LIMITED
245 Madame Cama Road, Shipping
House, Mumbai, 400 021, India
Tel.: (91) 2222026666
Web Site: https://www.shipindia.com
Year Founded: 1961
523598—(BOM)
Rev.: $522,638,025
Assets: $1,829,463,090
Liabilities: $714,595,245
Net Worth $1,114,867,845
Earnings: $95,016,285
Emp.: 596
Fiscal Year-end: 03/31/21
Liner Services & Bulk Container &
Tanker Services
N.A.I.C.S.: 488510
Dipankar Haldar (Officer-Compliance,
Sec & Exec Dir-Legal Affairs)

AND PRIVATE COMPANIES   SHISEIDO COMPANY, LIMITED

SHIPWAY STAIRS & RAILINGS
1820 Ironstone Drive, Burlington, L7L 5V3, ON, Canada
Tel.: (905) 336-1296
Web Site:
   https://www.shipwaystairs.com
Year Founded: 1980
Rev.: $14,576,683
Emp.: 100
Construction & Remodeling Services
N.A.I.C.S.: 236118
Larry Shipway *(Founder & Pres)*

SHIRA REAL ESTATE DEVELOPMENT & INVESTMENTS P.L.C
5th Floor Building No 269 Noor Commercial Complex, PO Box 2721, Al Madina El Monawara, Amman, 11821, Jordan
Tel.: (962) 65545555
Web Site: http://www.shira-inv.com
Year Founded: 2004
SHRA—(AMM)
Rev.: $135,402
Assets: $22,839,990
Liabilities: $9,769,517
Net Worth: $13,070,473
Earnings: ($562,247)
Emp.: 1
Fiscal Year-end: 12/31/20
Real Estate Investment Services
N.A.I.C.S.: 531390

SHIRAI ELECTRONICS INDUSTRIAL CO., LTD.
1477-8 Minamisakura, Ukyo-ku, Yasu, 520-2322, Japan
Tel.: (81) 5861333
Web Site:
   https://www.shiraidenshi.co.jp
Year Founded: 1966
6658—(TKS)
Rev.: $190,586,130
Assets: $130,190,560
Liabilities: $77,773,260
Net Worth: $52,417,300
Earnings: $9,829,070
Emp.: 1,234
Fiscal Year-end: 03/31/24
Printed Circuit Board Mfr
N.A.I.C.S.: 334418
Minezo Kotani *(Co-CEO)*

Subsidiaries:

Ohmi High-Tech Co., Ltd.   (1)
220-2 Kibe, Chuzu-cho, Yasu, 520-2431, Shiga, Japan
Tel.: (81) 775895515
Web Site: https://www.ohmi-ht.com
Emp.: 128
Electronic Components Mfr
N.A.I.C.S.: 334419

Shirai Electronics Industrial Co., Ltd. - Moriyama Factory   (1)
457 Kawahara Tachiiricho, Moriyama, 524-0031, Shiga, Japan
Tel.: (81) 775811421
Web Site: https://www.shiraidenshi.co.jp
Electronic Components Mfr
N.A.I.C.S.: 334419

Shirai Electronics Industrial Co., Ltd. - Tominami Factory   (1)
13-5 Tomibako, Yasu, 520-2351, Shiga, Japan
Tel.: (81) 775884848
Web Site: http://www.shiraidenshi.co.jp
Electronic Components Mfr
N.A.I.C.S.: 334419

Shirai Electronics Industrial Co., Ltd. - Uzumasa Factory   (1)
13-3 Nomoto-cho Uzumasa, Ukyo-ku, Kyoto, 616-8113, Japan
Tel.: (81) 75 871 6170
Electronic Components Mfr
N.A.I.C.S.: 334419

Shirai Electronics Technology (HK) Ltd.   (1)
Suite 1003 10/F AXA Tower Landmark East 100 How Ming Street, Kwun Tong, Kowloon, China (Hong Kong)
Tel.: (852) 21104828
Electronic Components Distr
N.A.I.C.S.: 423690

Subsidiary (Non-US):

Shirai Electronics Technology (Zhuhai) Ltd   (2)
No 2 Seventh Street San Zao, Jin Wan district, Zhuhai, 519040, Guangdong, China
Tel.: (86) 7567516601
Electronic Components Distr
N.A.I.C.S.: 423690

Shirai Electronics Trading (Shanghai) Co., Ltd.   (1)
Unit B3 C1 18F Jun Yao International Plaza 789 Zhao Jia Bang Rd, Xuhui, Shanghai, 20032, China
Tel.: (86) 2164177722
Electronic Components Distr
N.A.I.C.S.: 423690

Shirai Electronics Trading (Shenzhen) Co., Ltd.   (1)
12B 12C Tower 1 YangGuangHuaYi Bldg No 3003 Nanhai Ave NanGuang Area, Nanshan Road Nanshan District, Shenzhen, Guangdong, China
Tel.: (86) 75527207800
Electronic Components Distr
N.A.I.C.S.: 423690

Shirai Logistics Service Co., Ltd.   (1)
Tel.: (81) 775875659
Emp.: 23
Logistics Consulting Servies
N.A.I.C.S.: 541614
Junichi Murakami *(Auditor)*

SHIRAZ PETROCHEMICAL COMPANY
KM 5 Doroodzan Road, PO Box 71365-111, 73481 97515, Marvdasht, Fars, Iran
Tel.: (98) 7132330091
Year Founded: 1959
Emp.: 1,874
Petrochemical Mfr
N.A.I.C.S.: 325110

SHIRAZ VEGETABLE OIL CO.
77/75 Ghaem Magham Farahani Avenue, Tehran, Iran
Tel.: (98) 21 884 1652
Web Site:
   http://www.shirazvegoil.com
Year Founded: 1954
Sales Range: $100-124.9 Million
Emp.: 900
Edible Oil Mfr
N.A.I.C.S.: 311224
S. A. Sadrnejad *(Mng Dir)*

SHIRBLE DEPARTMENT STORE HOLDINGS (CHINA) LIMITED
30 Honglig South Road, Futian District, Shenzhen, 518046, China
Tel.: (86) 75582061108
Web Site: http://www.shirble.net
Sales Range: $150-199.9 Million
Emp.: 2,763
Department Store Owner & Operator
N.A.I.C.S.: 455110
Xiangbo Yang *(Chm)*

SHIRDI INDUSTRIES LIMITED
A Wing 2nd Floor Mhatre Pen Bldg, Senapati Bapat Marg Dadar W, Mumbai, 400 028, Maharashtra, India
Tel.: (91) 2224318550
Web Site: http://www.asisindia.com
Sales Range: $25-49.9 Million
Emp.: 566
MDF & Particle Boards Mfr
N.A.I.C.S.: 322130

Rakesh Kumar Agarwal *(Mng Dir)*

SHIRDI SAI ELECTRICALS LTD.
6-3-8-879/B 3rd Floor G Pulla Reddy Sweets Building Green Lands, Telangana, 500016, India
Tel.: (91) 4066255266
Web Site: http://ssel.in
Year Founded: 1994
Electrical Energy Distr
N.A.I.C.S.: 221118
Thatavarthy Satyanarayana *(CEO)*

Subsidiaries:

Indo Tech Transformers Ltd.   (1)
Survey No 153-210 Illuppapattu Village Near Rajakulam, Kanchipuram, 631561, Tamil Nadu, India   **(73.64%)**
Tel.: (91) 4427281873
Web Site: https://www.indo-tech.com
Rev.: $28,517,048
Assets: $25,470,381
Liabilities: $7,284,582
Net Worth: $18,185,799
Earnings: $858,012
Emp.: 293
Fiscal Year-end: 03/31/2021
Power & Distribution Transformers Mfr
N.A.I.C.S.: 335311
Sathyamoorthy A. *(Compliance Officer & Sec)*

Plant (Domestic):

Indo Tech Transformers Ltd - Palakkad Plant   (2)
No VII 223 Koyyamarakkadu1, Kanjikode, Palakkad, 678 621, India
Tel.: (91) 4912566252
Sales Range: $10-24.9 Million
Emp.: 8
Electrical Transformer Mfr
N.A.I.C.S.: 334416

SHIRES INCOME PLC
1 George Street, Edinburgh, EH2 2LL, United Kingdom
Tel.: (44) 8085000040
Web Site:
   https://www.shiresincome.co.uk
SHRS—(LSE)
Rev.: $8,115,375
Assets: $158,307,246
Liabilities: $24,556,930
Net Worth: $133,750,316
Earnings: ($1,858,117)
Fiscal Year-end: 03/31/24
Investment Management Service
N.A.I.C.S.: 525990

SHIROHATO CO., LTD.
505 Takeda Mukaishiro-cho, Fushimi-ku, Kyoto, 612-8418, Japan
Tel.: (81) 756934609
Web Site: https://www.shirohato.co.jp
3192—(TKS)
Sales Range: $25-49.9 Million
Emp.: 122
Women's Underwear & Lingerie Online Retailer
N.A.I.C.S.: 424350
Masaru Ikegami *(Pres & CEO)*

SHIRPUR GOLD REFINERY LTD.
Refinery Site, Shirpur, Dhule, 425 405, Maharashtra, India
Tel.: (91) 912249186000
Web Site:
   https://www.shirpurgold.com
Rev.: $612,972,764
Assets: $141,211,286
Liabilities: $89,529,065
Net Worth: $51,682,220
Earnings: $3,057,431
Emp.: 46
Fiscal Year-end: 03/31/19
Gold Refinery Services
N.A.I.C.S.: 213114

Shyamal Padhiar *(Compliance Officer & Sec)*

SHISEIDO COMPANY, LIMITED
5-5 Ginza 7-chome, Chuo-ku, Tokyo, 104-0061, Japan
Tel.: (81) 335725111   JP
Web Site: https://corp.shiseido.com
Year Founded: 1872
SSDOF—(OTCIQ)
Rev.: $6,898,839,420
Assets: $8,901,473,730
Liabilities: $4,361,094,450
Net Worth: $4,540,379,280
Earnings: $154,200,410
Emp.: 30,540
Fiscal Year-end: 12/31/23
Cosmetics & Toiletries Mfr & Distr
N.A.I.C.S.: 325620
Angelica Munson *(Chief Digital Officer)*

Subsidiaries:

Shiseido (Australia) Pty. Limited   (1)
6-10 Walker Street, Locked Bag 3277, Rhodes, 2138, NSW, Australia   **(100%)**
Tel.: (61) 297432288
Web Site: http://www.shiseido.com.au
Sales Range: $25-49.9 Million
Emp.: 30
Distr of Cosmetics
N.A.I.C.S.: 456120
Debbie Whitehouse *(Mgr-Trng Bus Dev)*

Shiseido Beauty Salon Co., Ltd.   (1)
Nippon Life Hamamatsucho Crea Tower 2-3-1 Hamamatsucho, Minato-ku, Tokyo, 105-8620, Japan
Tel.: (81) 362187935
Beauty Salon Supplies Distr
N.A.I.C.S.: 424210

Shiseido China Co., Ltd.   (1)
2F-8F Block 3 826 Century Avenue, Pu-Dong District, Shanghai, 200120, China
Tel.: (86) 2138127000
Web Site: https://www.shiseidochina.com
Cosmetics Mfr & Distr
N.A.I.C.S.: 325620
Kentaro Fujiwara *(Pres & CEO)*

Subsidiary (Domestic):

Shiseido China Research Center Co., Ltd.   (2)
31 BDA International Business Park No 2 Jing Yuan North Road, Beijing Economic Tech Dev Zone, Beijing, China
Tel.: (86) 10 6785 6655
Cosmetics & Perfumes Research & Development
N.A.I.C.S.: 541715

Shiseido Liyuan Cosmetics Co., Ltd.   (2)
No 2 Hong Da Bei Road, Beijing Economic Technological Development Zone, Beijing, 100176, China
Tel.: (86) 1067883330
Cosmetics Mfr & Whslr
N.A.I.C.S.: 325620

Shiseido Hong Kong Ltd.   (1)
17/F One Kowloon 1 Wang Yuen Street, Kowloon Bay, Kowloon, China (Hong Kong)
Tel.: (852) 22626966
Web Site: https://www.shiseido.com.hk
Cosmetics & Perfume Wholesale Distr
N.A.I.C.S.: 424210

Shiseido International Inc.   (1)
1-6-2 Higashi-shimbashi, Minato-ku, Tokyo, 105-8310, Japan
Tel.: (81) 335725111
Web Site: https://www.shiseidogroup.com
Sales Range: $450-499.9 Million
Holding Company; Cosmetics Mfr & Whslr
N.A.I.C.S.: 551112

Subsidiary (US):

Shiseido Americas Corporation   (2)
900 3rd Ave, New York, NY 10022-4795
Tel.: (212) 805-2300
Web Site: https://www.shiseido.com

SHISEIDO COMPANY, LIMITED

Shiseido Company, Limited—(Continued)
Holding Company; Regional Managing Office; Cosmetics Mfr & Distr
N.A.I.C.S.: 551112
Ron Gee *(CEO)*

Subsidiary (Domestic):

Davlyn Industries Inc. (3)
7 Fitzgerald Ave, Monroe, NJ 08831-3729
Tel.: (609) 655-5600
Sales Range: $125-149.9 Million
Emp.: 300
Cosmetic Preparations
N.A.I.C.S.: 325620
Yuichi Watanabe *(VP)*

Gurwitch Products, L.L.C. (3)
13259 N Promenade Blvd, Stafford, TX 77477
Tel.: (281) 275-7000
Web Site: http://www.lauramercier.com
Sales Range: $125-149.9 Million
Emp.: 220
Cosmetic Products Developer, Mfr & Marketer
N.A.I.C.S.: 325620

Shiseido America Inc. (3)
366 Princeton Hightstown Rd, East Windsor, NJ 08520-1411
Tel.: (609) 371-5800
Web Site: http://www.shiseido.com
Cosmetics Mfr & Distr
N.A.I.C.S.: 325620
Linda Ten Eyck *(Sr VP-Sls Ops)*

Unit (Domestic):

Shiseido America Inc. - Distribution Facility (4)
178 Bauer Dr, Oakland, NJ 07436-3105
Tel.: (201) 337-3750
Cosmetics Warehouse & Distribution Facility
N.A.I.C.S.: 493110

Shiseido Studio (4)
155 Spring St, New York, NY 10012-5208
Tel.: (212) 625-8821
Web Site: http://www.shiseidostudio.com
Rev.: $1,000,000
Emp.: 10
Mfr of Cosmetics
N.A.I.C.S.: 812112

Subsidiary (Non-US):

Shiseido Cosmetics (Canada) Inc. (3)
303 Allstate Pkwy, Markham, L3R 5P9, ON, Canada (100%)
Tel.: (905) 763-1250
Web Site: http://www.shiseido.com
Sales Range: $25-49.9 Million
Emp.: 75
Distr of Cosmetics
N.A.I.C.S.: 456120
Paul Ramos *(Dir-Fin & Ops)*

Subsidiary (Non-US):

Shiseido International Europe S.A. (2)
Shiseido Europe Techno Center 79 rue Marcel Dassault, Boulogne, 92100, France
Tel.: (33) 1 4694 1000
Web Site: http://www.shiseido-europe.com
Emp.: 140
Holding Company; Regional Managing Office
N.A.I.C.S.: 551112

Subsidiary (Domestic):

Shiseido Europe S.A.S. (3)
11 rue du Faubourg Saint Honore, 75008, Paris, France
Tel.: (33) 146941000
Holding Company; Cosmetics & Perfumes Whslr
N.A.I.C.S.: 551112

Subsidiary (Non-US):

Shiseido Cosmetici (Italia) S.p.A. (4)
Viale Abruzzi 94, 20131, Milan, MI, Italy
Tel.: (39) 0002295081

Sales Range: $25-49.9 Million
Emp.: 50
Cosmetics & Perfumes Wholesale Distr
N.A.I.C.S.: 424210

Shiseido Deutschland GmbH (4)
Kalstrasse 20, 40221, Dusseldorf, Germany (100%)
Tel.: (49) 21191760
Web Site: http://www.shiseido.de
Sales Range: $25-49.9 Million
Emp.: 40
Cosmetics & Perfumes Wholesale Distr
N.A.I.C.S.: 424210

Shiseido U.K. Co., Ltd. (4)
10th Floor The Adelphi 1-11 John Adam Street, London, WC2N 6HT, United Kingdom (100%)
Tel.: (44) 2038100770
Web Site: http://www.shiseido.co.uk
Sales Range: $25-49.9 Million
Emp.: 18
Cosmetics & Perfumes Wholesale Distr
N.A.I.C.S.: 424210
S. Tanaka *(Mng Dir)*

Subsidiary (Domestic):

Shiseido International France S.A.S. (3)
Shiseido Europe Techno Center 79 rue Marcel Dassault, Boulogne, 92100, France
Tel.: (33) 146941000
Web Site: https://www.shiseido.fr
Cosmetics & Perfumes Mfr & Distr
N.A.I.C.S.: 325620

Subsidiary (Domestic):

Beaute Prestige International S.A. (4)
28/32 Avenue Victor Hugo, 75016, Paris, France
Tel.: (33) 140678000
Web Site: https://www.bpi-sa.com
Sales Range: $125-149.9 Million
Emp.: 300
Cosmetics & Perfume Mfr
N.A.I.C.S.: 325620
Louis De Sazaras *(Gen Mgr)*

Shiseido N.Z. Ltd. (1)
114 Felton Mathew Ave Glenn Innes, PO Box 18242 Auckland NZ 1743, Auckland, 1072, New Zealand (50%)
Tel.: (64) 95280759
Web Site: http://www.shiseido.co.nz
Sales Range: $25-49.9 Million
Emp.: 50
Provider of Cosmetics
N.A.I.C.S.: 456120

Shiseido Pharmaceutical Co., Ltd. (1)
Nippon Life Hamamatsucho Crea Tower 2-3-1 Hamamatsucho, Tokyo, 105-8620, Japan
Tel.: (81) 362187975
Web Site: https://www.shisedogroup.com
Pharmaceuticals Product Mfr
N.A.I.C.S.: 325412

Shiseido Professional Co., Ltd. (1)
1-1-16 Higashi-shimbashi, Minato-ku, Tokyo, 105-0021, Japan
Tel.: (81) 3 6218 7977
Professional Beauty Supplies Distr
N.A.I.C.S.: 424210

Shiseido Sales Co., Ltd. (1)
1-6-2 Higashi-shimbashi, Minato-ku, Tokyo, 105-8310, Japan
Tel.: (81) 3 6218 7455
Cosmetics & Perfumes Whslr
N.A.I.C.S.: 424210
Ryuichi Yabuki *(Pres & CEO)*

Shiseido Vietnam Inc. (1)
Lot 231-237 Amata Road Amata Industrial Park, Long Binh Ward, Bien Hoa, Dong Nai, Vietnam
Tel.: (84) 61 393 6468
Cosmetics Products Mfr
N.A.I.C.S.: 325620
Kenichi Saito *(Mng Dir)*

Taiwan Shiseido Co., Ltd. (1)
148 His-Yuan Road, Tao-Yuan Hsien, Chung-li, 32057, Taiwan

Tel.: (886) 34526191
Web Site: http://www.shiseido.com.tw
Cosmetic Products Mfr & Distr
N.A.I.C.S.: 325620

SHISH INDUSTRIES LIMITED
TP No 4 RS No 11 Paiki 12-13 B Paiki Plot C 1st Floor of 11, 12 Suryapur Mill Compound Varachha Road, Surat, 395006, Gujarat, India
Tel.: (91) 9825190407
Web Site:
https://www.shishindustries.com
Year Founded: 2012
540693—(BOM)
Rev.: $8,431,809
Assets: $6,526,048
Liabilities: $2,347,929
Net Worth: $4,178,119
Earnings: $812,745
Emp.: 46
Fiscal Year-end: 03/31/23
Plastic Product Mfr & Distr
N.A.I.C.S.: 326199
Satishkumar Maniya *(Chm & Mng Dir)*

Subsidiaries:

Greenenergy International Inc. (1)
501 Congress Ave Ste 150, Austin, TX 78701
Tel.: (914) 885-7693
Web Site: https://www.greenenergyinc.us
Package Product Mfr & Distr
N.A.I.C.S.: 326112

SHIV AUM STEELS LIMITED
515 The Summit Business Bay Near Weh Metro Station, A K Road Andheri East, Mumbai, 400093, India
Tel.: (91) 2226827900
Web Site:
https://www.shivaumsteels.com
Year Founded: 1982
SHIVAUM—(NSE)
Rev.: $59,617,529
Assets: $19,544,044
Liabilities: $8,063,521
Net Worth: $11,480,523
Earnings: $1,716,720
Emp.: 32
Fiscal Year-end: 03/31/23
Steel Products Mfr
N.A.I.C.S.: 332999
Dhwani S. Vora *(Sec & Compliance Officer)*

SHIV KAMAL IMPEX LIMITED
Ground Floor P-7 Green Park Extn, New Delhi, 110 016, India
Tel.: (91) 1126192964
Web Site:
https://www.shivkamalimpex.com
Year Founded: 1985
539683—(BOM)
Rev.: $40,173
Assets: $788,224
Liabilities: $389
Net Worth: $787,835
Earnings: $12,143
Emp.: 3
Fiscal Year-end: 03/31/23
Financial Support Services
N.A.I.C.S.: 523999
Girish Kumar *(CFO)*

SHIVA CEMENT LIMITED
Telighana PO Birangatoli Tehsil-Kutra, Sundargarh, Rourkela, 770018, Odisha, India
Tel.: (91) 6612461300
Web Site:
https://www.shivacement.com
Year Founded: 1985
532323—(BOM)
Rev.: $416,498
Assets: $166,835,465

INTERNATIONAL PUBLIC

Liabilities: $176,226,497
Net Worth: ($9,391,032)
Earnings: ($9,648,139)
Emp.: 141
Fiscal Year-end: 03/31/23
Cement Mfr
N.A.I.C.S.: 327310
R. P. Gupta *(Founder)*

SHIVA GLOBAL AGRO INDUSTRIES LTD.
Shri Hanuman Nagar Osman Nagar Road Village Dhakni Tq Loha, Nanded, Maharashtra, India
Tel.: (91) 2462226955
Web Site: https://www.shivaagro.org
530433—(BOM)
Rev.: $64,919,010
Assets: $37,154,259
Liabilities: $19,090,162
Net Worth: $18,064,097
Earnings: $683,604
Emp.: 121
Fiscal Year-end: 03/31/23
Fertilizer Mfr
N.A.I.C.S.: 325312
Deepak S. Maliwal *(Dir-Fin & Ops)*

Subsidiaries:

Kartik Agro Chem. Pvt ltd (1)
Opposite to S P Ofc, Vazirabad, Nanded, 431602, Maharashtra, India
Tel.: (91) 2462255072
Web Site: http://www.shivafertilizers.com
Pesticide Mfr
N.A.I.C.S.: 325320

Kirtiman Agro Genetics Ltd (1)
Near State Bank of India New Mondha, Nanded, 431602, Maharashtra, India
Tel.: (91) 2462284036
Sales Range: $25-49.9 Million
Emp.: 30
Agro Products Mfr
N.A.I.C.S.: 325320
Narayanlal Kalantri *(Exec Dir)*

Shiva Global Biotech Pvt Ltd (1)
Near State Bank of India New Mondha, Nanded, 431602, Maharashtra, India
Tel.: (91) 2462284036
Sales Range: $25-49.9 Million
Emp.: 15
Bio Fertilizer Distr
N.A.I.C.S.: 424910

SHIVA GRANITO EXPORT LIMITED
8 Bhatt Ji Ki Baari, Udaipur, 313 001, Rajasthan, India
Tel.: (91) 2942418228
Web Site: https://www.shivaexport.in
540072—(BOM)
Rev.: $881,943
Assets: $3,218,593
Liabilities: $1,289,337
Net Worth: $1,929,256
Earnings: ($213)
Fiscal Year-end: 03/31/21
Building Material Mfr & Distr
N.A.I.C.S.: 337991
Suresh Upadhyay *(Mng Dir)*

SHIVA MEDICARE LIMITED
8-2-676/A/A/A/1&2 Road No 13 Banjara Hills, Hyderabad, 500034, Telangana, India
Tel.: (91) 40 6455 1556
Web Site:
http://www.shivamedicare.com
Assets: $208,504
Liabilities: $485,534
Net Worth: ($277,030)
Earnings: ($180,667)
Fiscal Year-end: 03/31/18
Medical Equipment Whslr
N.A.I.C.S.: 423450
Shivarama Babu Velchuri *(Exec Dir)*

SHIVA MILLS LTD.
249-A Bye-Pass Road Mettupalayam Road, Coimbatore, 641043, Tamil Nadu, India
Tel.: (91) 4222435555
Web Site: https://www.shivamills.com
Year Founded: 2015
SHIVAMILLS—(NSE)
Rev.: $19,228,967
Assets: $13,877,262
Liabilities: $1,904,382
Net Worth: $11,972,879
Earnings: ($858,234)
Emp.: 525
Fiscal Year-end: 03/31/23
Yarn & Fabric Product Mfr
N.A.I.C.S.: 314999
S. V. Alagappan *(Chm & Co-Mng Dir)*

SHIVA SUITINGS LIMITED
384 M Dabholkar Wadi Kalbadevi RD, Mumbai, 400 002, Maharashtra, India
Tel.: (91) 22004849
Web Site: https://www.shivasuitings.com
Year Founded: 1985
521003—(BOM)
Rev.: $580,092
Assets: $316,082
Liabilities: $78,752
Net Worth: $237,330
Earnings: $11,886
Emp.: 16
Fiscal Year-end: 03/31/23
Apparel & Luxury Goods Mfr & Distr
N.A.I.C.S.: 315990
Sharad Kumar Sureka *(Mng Dir)*

SHIVA TEXYARN LIMITED
52 East Bashyakaralu Road, R S Puram, Coimbatore, 641 002, Tamil Nadu, India
Tel.: (91) 4222544955
Web Site: https://www.shivatex.in
Year Founded: 1980
SHIVATEX—(NSE)
Rev.: $51,182,099
Assets: $36,961,573
Liabilities: $20,881,962
Net Worth: $16,079,612
Earnings: ($796,115)
Emp.: 1,721
Fiscal Year-end: 03/31/23
Cotton Yarn Mfr
N.A.I.C.S.: 313110
S. V. Alagappan *(Chm)*

SHIVAGRICO IMPLEMENTS LTD.
A-1 Ground Floor, Adinath Apartments 281 Tardeo Road, Mumbai, 400 007, India
Tel.: (91) 2223893022
Web Site: https://www.shivagrico.in
Year Founded: 1965
522237—(BOM)
Rev.: $5,225,248
Assets: $3,769,711
Liabilities: $2,922,569
Net Worth: $847,142
Earnings: $13,512
Emp.: 242
Fiscal Year-end: 03/31/21
Agricultural Hand Tool Mfr
N.A.I.C.S.: 332216
Hemant Ranawat *(CFO)*

SHIVALIK BIMETAL CONTROLS LTD.
16-18 New Electronics Complex, Chambaghat, Solan, 173213, Himachal Pradesh, India
Tel.: (91) 1792230578
Web Site:
    https://www.shivalikbimetals.com
513097—(NSE)
Rev.: $28,360,291
Assets: $30,149,601
Liabilities: $11,107,838
Net Worth: $19,041,764
Earnings: $3,479,289
Emp.: 306
Fiscal Year-end: 03/31/21
Thermostatic Bimetal Mfr
N.A.I.C.S.: 339999
S. S. Sandhu *(Chm)*

Subsidiaries:

Shivalik Engineered Products Private Limited (1)
H2 Suneja Chambers Alaknanda Commercial Complex, New Delhi, 110019, India
Tel.: (91) 9871655595
Web Site: https://www.sbcl.co.in
Electric Equipment Mfr & Distr
N.A.I.C.S.: 335999

SHIVALIK RASAYAN LIMITED
1506 Chiranjiv Tower 43 Nehru Place, New Delhi, 110 019, India
Tel.: (91) 1126221811
Web Site:
    https://www.shivalikrasayan.com
Year Founded: 1981
539148—(BOM)
Rev.: $27,124,464
Assets: $49,544,971
Liabilities: $14,124,221
Net Worth: $35,420,750
Earnings: $3,366,486
Emp.: 226
Fiscal Year-end: 03/31/21
Agricultural Product Mfr & Distr
N.A.I.C.S.: 325320
Rahul Bishnoi *(Chm)*

SHIVAM CEMENTS LIMITED
Siddhartha Insurance Bhawan 2nd Floor, Anamnagar, Kathmandu, Nepal
Tel.: (977) 5706804
Web Site:
    http://www.shivamcement.com.np
Year Founded: 2003
Construction Services
N.A.I.C.S.: 236210
Surendra Kumar Goel *(Chm)*

SHIVANSH FINSERVE LTD.
22 First Floor Harsidhh Complex Income Tax Ashram Road, Opp Kalupur commercial Bank, Ahmedabad, 380 014, India
Tel.: (91) 7927541073
Web Site:
    https://www.shivanshfinserve.com
Year Founded: 1984
539593—(BOM)
Rev.: $399,208
Assets: $1,455,786
Liabilities: $579,975
Net Worth: $875,811
Earnings: $10,893
Fiscal Year-end: 03/31/21
Financial Support Services
N.A.I.C.S.: 523999
Jignesh Sudhirbhai Shah *(CFO)*

SHIVOM INVESTMENT & CONSULTANCY LTD.
Shop No 10 MMRDA Market Thakur Complex, Kandivali East, Mumbai, 400101, Maharashtra, India
Tel.: (91) 8232038374
Year Founded: 1990
539833—(BOM)
Rev.: $1,012,410
Assets: $8,071,793
Liabilities: $32,731
Net Worth: $8,039,062
Earnings: ($320,671)
Fiscal Year-end: 03/31/20
Financial Consulting Services
N.A.I.C.S.: 541611
Hitesh Patel *(CFO)*

SHIYAN TAIXIANG INDUSTRY CO., LTD.
No 258 Jilin Road, Longmen ETDZ, Shiyan, 420013, Hubei, China
Tel.: (86) 7198306877
Web Site:
    https://www.taixiangshiye.com
Year Founded: 1997
301192—(CHIN)
Rev.: $43,137,074
Assets: $113,917,853
Liabilities: $34,824,823
Net Worth: $79,093,030
Earnings: $4,465,289
Emp.: 200
Fiscal Year-end: 12/31/23
Automobile Parts Mfr & Distr
N.A.I.C.S.: 336211
Shibin Wang *(Chm)*

SHIZUKI ELECTRIC COMPANY, INC.
10-45 Taisha-cho, Nishinomiya, 662 0867, Hyogo, Japan
Tel.: (81) 798745821
Web Site: https://www.shizuki.co.jp
Year Founded: 1939
6994—(TKS)
Rev.: $173,876,050
Assets: $241,126,190
Liabilities: $90,603,270
Net Worth: $150,522,920
Earnings: $1,203,020
Fiscal Year-end: 03/31/24
Electrical & Electronic Capacitors Mfr
N.A.I.C.S.: 334416
Nobuaki Adachi *(Chm, Pres & CEO)*

Subsidiaries:

Akita Shizuki Co., Inc. (1)
35-2 Minamida Ashida Ugo-cho, Ogatsugun, Akita, 012-1115, Japan (100%)
Tel.: (81) 183621116
Web Site: https://akitashizuki.jp
Sales Range: Less than $1 Million
Emp.: 300
N.A.I.C.S.: 334416

American Shizuki Corporation (1)
301 W O St, Ogallala, NE 69153 (100%)
Tel.: (308) 284-3611
Web Site: http://www.ascapacitor.com
Sales Range: $50-74.9 Million
Electronic Components Mfr
N.A.I.C.S.: 334416

Hikami Manufacturing Co., Inc. (1)
1767 Isou, Tanba, 669-3464, Hyogo, Japan
Tel.: (81) 795823431
Web Site: http://www.hikami.co.jp
Emp.: 161
Electronic Components Mfr
N.A.I.C.S.: 334416

Kyushu Shizuki Co., Inc. (1)
Yamano 1915, Kama, Fukuoka, 820-0202, Japan (100%)
Tel.: (81) 948420651
Sales Range: $100-124.9 Million
Mfr of High & Low Voltage Capacitors
N.A.I.C.S.: 334416

Okayama Shizuki Co., Inc. (1)
Minobe 1626 2 Soujya, Okayama, 719-1152, Japan (100%)
Tel.: (81) 866958211
Automotive Capacitors Mfr
N.A.I.C.S.: 334416

Shizuki Electric (Shanghai) Trading Co., Inc. (1)
14A Zhao Feng World Trade Building No 369 Jiang Su Road, Shanghai, 200050, China
Tel.: (86) 2152400067
Web Site: http://www.shizuki.com.cn
Sales Range: $50-74.9 Million
Emp.: 10
Capacitors Distr
N.A.I.C.S.: 423690

Shizuki Electric (Thailand) Co., Ltd. (1)
Bang Chan Industrial Estate No 111 Soi Serithai 54, T Kannayao A Kannayao, Bangkok, 10230, Thailand
Tel.: (66) 29199600
Web Site: http://www.thai-shizuki.com
Sales Range: $50-74.9 Million
Emp.: 109
Capacitors Mfr & Distr
N.A.I.C.S.: 335999

SHIZUOKA FINANCIAL GROUP, INC.
1-10 Gofukucho, Aoi-ku, Shizuoka, Shizuoka, Japan
Tel.: (81) 543455411
Web Site: https://www.shizuoka-fg.co.jp
Year Founded: 2022
5831—(TKS)
Rev.: $2,290,536,860
Assets: $106,695,903,290
Liabilities: $98,741,515,220
Net Worth: $7,954,388,070
Earnings: $145,420
Emp.: 2,791
Fiscal Year-end: 03/31/24
Commercial Banking Services
N.A.I.C.S.: 551111
Hisashi Shibata *(Pres & CEO)*

Subsidiaries:

Shizuoka Bank, Ltd. (1)
2-1 Kusanagi-Kita, Shimizu-ku Shizuoka-shi, Shizuoka, 424-8677, Japan
Tel.: (81) 543455411
Web Site: http://www.shizuokabank.co.jp
Rev.: $2,338,688,000
Assets: $144,408,437,360
Liabilities: $133,874,206,400
Net Worth: $10,534,230,960
Earnings: $403,026,800
Emp.: 2,776
Fiscal Year-end: 03/31/2022
Banking Services
N.A.I.C.S.: 522110
Yutaka Fukushima *(Sr Exec Officer)*

Subsidiary (Domestic):

SHIZUGIN DC CARD CO., LTD. (2)
10 Gofukucho 1-chome, Aoi-Ku, Shizuoka, 420-8761, Japan
Tel.: (81) 54 345 5411
Web Site: http://www.shizuokabank.co.jp
Credit Card Processing & Consumer Loan Services
N.A.I.C.S.: 522310

Shizugin Business Create Co., Ltd. (2)
2-1 Kusanagikita Shimizu-Ku, Shizuoka, Japan
Tel.: (81) 543488800
Data Processing Services
N.A.I.C.S.: 518210

Shizugin Heartful Co., Ltd. (2)
Kusanagikita No 2 No 1 Shizugin Headquarters Tower Third Floor, Shimizu-ku, Shizuoka, Japan
Tel.: (81) 543485810
Banking Services
N.A.I.C.S.: 522110

Shizugin IT Solution Co., Ltd. (2)
Kusanagikita No 1 No 10, Shimizu-ku, Shizuoka, 424-8602, Japan
Tel.: (81) 543471111
Web Site: http://www.shizuoka-cs.co.jp
Emp.: 245
Banking Services
N.A.I.C.S.: 522110

Shizugin Lease Co., Ltd. (2)
1-1-2 Gofukucho Square 7th floor, Aoi-ku, Shizuoka, 420-0031, Japan
Tel.: (81) 542557788
Web Site: http://www.shizugin-lease.com
Emp.: 96
Machinery & Equipment Rental & Leasing Office
N.A.I.C.S.: 532420

SHIZUOKA FINANCIAL GROUP, INC.

Shizuoka Financial Group, Inc.—(Continued)

Shizugin Management Consulting Co., Ltd. (2)
2-1 Kusanagikita, Shimizu-ku, Shizuoka, 424-0883, Japan
Tel.: (81) 543481491
Web Site: http://www.shizugin-smc.jp
Management Consulting Services
N.A.I.C.S.: 541618

Shizugin Saison Card Co., Ltd. (2)
11-1 Minami-cho, Suruga-ku, Shizuoka, Japan
Tel.: (81) 570064606
Web Site: http://www.sgsaison.co.jp
Credit Card Services
N.A.I.C.S.: 522210

Shizugin TM Securities Co., Ltd. (2)
1-113 Otemachi, Aoi-ku, Shizuoka, 420-0853, Japan
Tel.: (81) 542546111
Web Site: http://www.shizugintm.co.jp
Sales Range: $50-74.9 Million
Emp.: 348
Mortgage & Nonmortgage Loan Brokers
N.A.I.C.S.: 522310

Subsidiary (Non-US):

Shizuoka Bank (Europe) S.A. (2)
Rue Jules Cockx 8-10, Box 9, Auderghem, 1160, Brussels, Belgium (100%)
Tel.: (32) 26460470
Web Site: https://www.shizuoka.co.jp
Sales Range: $1-9.9 Million
Emp.: 11
Finance & Securities-Related Services
N.A.I.C.S.: 921130
Hironaka Tani (Gen Mgr)

Subsidiary (Domestic):

Shizuoka Capital Co., Ltd. (2)
2-1 Kusanagikita Shimizu-ku, Shizuoka, 4240883, Japan (100%)
Tel.: (81) 543472210
Emp.: 100
Investment Advice
N.A.I.C.S.: 523940

Shizuoka Computer Service Co., Ltd. (2)
1-10 Kusanagikita Shimizu-Ku, Shizuoka, 4248602, Japan
Tel.: (81) 543471111
Data Processing Services
N.A.I.C.S.: 518210

Shizuoka Mortgage Service Co., Ltd. (2)
2-1 Kusanagikita, Shimizu-ku, Shizuoka, 424-0883, Japan
Tel.: (81) 543486720
Web Site: http://www.siz-mortgage.co.jp
Sales Range: $50-74.9 Million
Emp.: 400
Real Estate Agents & Brokers Offices
N.A.I.C.S.: 531210

SHIZUOKA SEIKI CO., LTD.
4-1 Yamana, Fukuroi, 437-8601, Shizuoka, Japan
Tel.: (81) 538 42 3111   JP
Web Site: http://www.shizuoka-seiki.co.jp
Year Founded: 1941
Sales Range: $75-99.9 Million
Emp.: 300
Industrial Heating & Cooling Equipment Mfr
N.A.I.C.S.: 333415
Naojiro Suzuki (Pres)

Subsidiaries:

Dalian Shizuoka Seiki Co., Ltd. (1)
IA-26 FTZ, Dalian, 100036, Liaoning, China
Tel.: (86) 411 8730 8407
Web Site: http://www.shizuoka-china.com.cn
Emp.: 40
Duct & Mobile Heater Mfr
N.A.I.C.S.: 335999
Naojiro Suzuki (Pres)

Shizuoka Hansung Co., Ltd. (1)
29 Boseokro 4Gil, Iksan, Jeon-Buk, Korea (South)
Tel.: (82) 63 830 8227
Web Site: http://www.hansungdryer.koreasme.com
Electric Equipment Mfr
N.A.I.C.S.: 335999
Suzuki Naojiro (CEO)

SHIZUOKAGAS CO., LTD.
1-5-38 Yahata, Suruga-ku, Shizuoka, 422-8688, Shizuoka, Japan
Tel.: (81) 542852111
Web Site: https://www.shizuokagas.co.jp
Year Founded: 1910
9543—(TKS)
Rev.: $1,517,288,360
Assets: $1,096,886,810
Liabilities: $285,641,920
Net Worth: $811,244,890
Earnings: $100,018,630
Emp.: 1,475
Fiscal Year-end: 12/31/23
Gas Distr
N.A.I.C.S.: 221210
Hiroshi Tonoya (Bd of Dirs & Chm)

Subsidiaries:

Chuen Gas Co., Ltd. (1)
Center 1-18-1, Kakegawa, 436-0056, Japan
Tel.: (81) 537232211
Gas Distr
N.A.I.C.S.: 221210

Fukuroi Gas Co., Ltd. (1)
1940-1 Takao, Fukuroi, 437-0023, Shizuoka, Japan
Tel.: (81) 538428410
Web Site: https://www.fukuroigas.co.jp
Petroleum Gas & Gas Equipment Whslr
N.A.I.C.S.: 424720

Gotemba Gas Co., Ltd. (1)
600 Kawashimata, Gotemba, 412-0045, Shizuoka Prefecture, Japan
Tel.: (81) 550820876
Web Site: https://www.gotemba-gas.jp
Gas Equipment Mfr
N.A.I.C.S.: 333132

Sado Gas Co., Ltd. (1)
Kasuga 183, Sado, 952-0006, Niigata, Japan
Tel.: (81) 259273631
Gas Distr
N.A.I.C.S.: 221210

Shimada Gas Co., Ltd. (1)
4-16-32 Yokoi, Shimada, 427-0024, Shizuoka, Japan
Tel.: (81) 547363900
Web Site: https://www.shimadagas.co.jp
Liquefied Petroleum Gas Distr
N.A.I.C.S.: 424720

Shimizu LNG Co., Ltd. (1)
1900 Sodeshi-cho, Shimizu-ku, Shizuoka, 424-0037, Japan
Tel.: (81) 543673511
Liquefied Natural Gas Mfr & Whslr
N.A.I.C.S.: 325120
Shigeru Katsumata (Pres & CEO)

Shimoda Gas Co., Ltd. (1)
Shimoda 467, Shimoda, 415-0016, Japan
Tel.: (81) 558221321
Gas Distr
N.A.I.C.S.: 221210

Shinshu Gas Co., Ltd. (1)
3-2700 Minoze-cho, Iida, 395-0054, Nagano, Japan
Tel.: (81) 265223808
Gas Distr
N.A.I.C.S.: 221210

Shizuoka Gas & Power Co., Ltd. (1)
Tel.: (81) 545551333
Electric Power Distr
N.A.I.C.S.: 221122

Shizuoka Gas Credit Co., Ltd. (1)
Yahata 1-5-38, Suruga-ku, Shizuoka, 422-8076, Japan
Tel.: (81) 542873203
Gas Distr
N.A.I.C.S.: 221210

Shizuoka Gas Energy Co., Ltd. (1)
Ikeda 50-5, Suruga-ku, Shizuoka, 422-8005, Japan
Tel.: (81) 542852221
Gas Distr
N.A.I.C.S.: 221210

Shizuoka Gas Engineering Co., Ltd. (1)
Ikeda 28, Suruga-ku, Shizuoka, 422-8005, Japan
Tel.: (81) 542838031
Air Conditioner Equipment Mfr
N.A.I.C.S.: 333415

Shizuoka Gas Insurance Service Co., Ltd. (1)
1-5-38 Yahata, Suruga-ku, Shizuoka, 422-8076, Japan
Tel.: (81) 542825748
Insurance Services
N.A.I.C.S.: 524210

Shizuoka Gas Living Co., Ltd. (1)
1-5-38 Yahata, Suruga-ku, Shizuoka, 422-8076, Japan
Tel.: (81) 542850252
Housing Equipment Distr
N.A.I.C.S.: 423990

Shizuoka Gas Service Co., Ltd. (1)
50-5 Ikeda, Suruga-ku, Shizuoka, 422-8005, Japan
Tel.: (81) 542852220
Gas Distr
N.A.I.C.S.: 221210

Shizuoka Gas System Solution Co., Ltd. (1)
Yahata 1-5-38, Suruga-ku, Shizuoka, 422-8076, Japan
Tel.: (81) 542829411
Information Processing Services
N.A.I.C.S.: 518210

Yoshida Gas Co., Ltd. (1)
Shimoyoshida 6-5-1, Fujiyoshida, 403-0004, Yamanashi, Japan
Tel.: (81) 555222161
Gas Distr
N.A.I.C.S.: 221210

SHK HONG KONG INDUSTRIES LIMITED
Room 1801 18th Fl Allied Kajima Bldg 138 Gloucester Rd, Wanchai, China (Hong Kong)
Tel.: (852) 28772340
Web Site: http://www.shki.com.hk
0666—(HKG)
Rev.: $5,454,857
Assets: $143,538,367
Liabilities: $869,207
Net Worth: $142,669,160
Earnings: $1,858,350
Emp.: 6
Fiscal Year-end: 12/31/19
Investment Management Service
N.A.I.C.S.: 523940
Mark Tai Chun Wong (Exec Dir)

SHL
1 Atwell Place, Thames Ditton, Surrey, KT7, United Kingdom
Tel.: (44) 2083358000
Web Site: https://www.shl.com
Assessment Services
N.A.I.C.S.: 561990

Subsidiaries:

BestHire, LLC (1)
PO Box 842, Vernon Rockville, CT 06066-0842
Tel.: (800) 539-0055
Web Site: http://www.besthire.com
Management Consulting Services
N.A.I.C.S.: 541618
Carl Slicer (Pres)

SHL AUTOMATISIERUNGSTECHNIK AG

INTERNATIONAL PUBLIC

Spaichinger Weg 14, 78583, Tuttlingen, Germany
Tel.: (49) 742993040
Web Site: http://www.shl.ag
Year Founded: 1989
Rev.: $17,239,512
Emp.: 58
Automated Polishing, Grinding & Burring Services
N.A.I.C.S.: 541330
Thomas Koch (Mgr-Technical Sls)

Subsidiaries:

SHL Automation Inc. (1)
5126 S Royal Atlanta Dr, Tucker, GA 30084
Tel.: (770) 934-0526
Engineeering Services
N.A.I.C.S.: 541330
Michael Fischer (Engr-Svc & Support)

SHL CONSOLIDATED BHD.
16th Floor Wisma Sin Heap Lee 346 Jalan Tun Razak, 50400, Kuala Lumpur, Malaysia
Tel.: (60) 321637788
Web Site: https://www.shlcb.com.my
SHL—(KLS)
Rev.: $44,147,725
Assets: $214,180,952
Liabilities: $18,604,444
Net Worth: $195,576,508
Earnings: $11,967,407
Emp.: 224
Fiscal Year-end: 03/31/23
Granite Mfr
N.A.I.C.S.: 327991
Winnie Kwee Wah Chok (Co-Sec)

Subsidiaries:

Sin Heap Lee Construction Sdn. Bhd. (1)
5th Floor Wisma Sin Heap Lee 346 Jalan Tun Razak, 50400, Kuala Lumpur, Malaysia
Tel.: (60) 21619288
Clay Brick Mfr
N.A.I.C.S.: 327120

Sin Heap Lee Development Sdn. Bhd. (1)
Clay Brick Mfr
N.A.I.C.S.: 327120

Subsidiary (Domestic):

SHL-M Sdn. Bhd. (2)
15th Floor Wisma Sin Heap Lee 346 Jalan Tun Razak, 50400, Kuala Lumpur, Malaysia
Tel.: (60) 321637766
Property Development Services
N.A.I.C.S.: 531390

SHL FINANCE COMPANY
PO Box 27072, 11417, Riyadh, 11417, Saudi Arabia
Tel.: (966) 8001221228
Web Site: https://shlfinance.com
Year Founded: 2008
1183—(SAU)
Rev.: $79,758,222
Assets: $1,154,200,598
Liabilities: $698,603,188
Net Worth: $455,597,410
Earnings: $25,567,158
Emp.: 238
Fiscal Year-end: 12/31/22
Financial Investment Services
N.A.I.C.S.: 523999
Yousef Abdullah Al-Shelash (Chm)

SHL TELEMEDICINE LIMITED
Yigal Alon 90, Tel Aviv, 67891, Israel
Tel.: (972) 35612212   II
Web Site: https://www.shl-telemedicine.com
Year Founded: 1987
SHLT—(NASDAQ)
Rev.: $57,075,000
Assets: $113,049,000
Liabilities: $36,588,000
Net Worth: $76,461,000

Earnings: ($6,855,000)
Emp.: 583
Fiscal Year-end: 12/31/23
Developer & Sales of Personal Telemedicine Systems & Provider of Medical Call Center Services to Patients
N.A.I.C.S.: 456199
Yossi Vadnagra (CFO)

Subsidiaries:

Personal Healthcare Telemedicine Services B.V. (1)
Stadhouderskade 125hs, 1074 AV, Amsterdam, Netherlands (100%)
Tel.: (31) 207784141
Sales Range: $25-49.9 Million
Emp.: 1
Pharmacies & Drug Stores
N.A.I.C.S.: 456110

SHL Telemedizin GmbH (1)
Balanstrasse 69 b, 81541, Munich, Germany (100%)
Tel.: (49) 89480590
Web Site: https://www.shl-telemedicine.com
Home-Based Medical Support Services
N.A.I.C.S.: 621610
Linus Drop (Co-Mng Dir)

SHL-JAPAN LTD.
6F STN Bldg 5-38-16 Chuo, Nakano-Ku, Tokyo, 164-0011, Japan
Tel.: (81) 3 5385 8781
Web Site: http://www.shl.co.jp
Year Founded: 1961
43270—(JAS)
Sales Range: Less than $1 Million
Emp.: 94
Personnel Assessment Services
N.A.I.C.S.: 541612
Nakamura Naohiro (Mng Dir)

SHLOMO ELIAHU HOLDINGS LTD.
2 Ibn Gvirol St, Tel Aviv, 64077, Israel
Tel.: (972) 3 6920015
Web Site: http://www.eliahu.com
Year Founded: 1965
Sales Range: $50-74.9 Million
Emp.: 150
Holding Company; Insurance, Banking & Financial Services
N.A.I.C.S.: 551112
Shlomo Eliahu (Founder & Chm)

Subsidiaries:

Eliahu Insurance Company Ltd. (1)
2 Ibn Gvirol St, 64077, Tel Aviv, Israel
Tel.: (972) 3 6920911
Web Site: http://www.eliahu.com
Emp.: 10
Insurance Services
N.A.I.C.S.: 524113
Gad Nussbaum (Sec)

Subsidiary (Domestic):

Migdal Insurance and Financial Holdings Ltd. (2)
Ef-Al 4 Ta Do-a 3063 Kiriyat Ar, Petah Tiqwa, 49511, Israel (61.56%)
Tel.: (972) 35637637
Web Site: https://www.migdalholdings.co.il
Rev.: $7,868,509,616
Assets: $56,598,906,423
Liabilities: $54,223,276,677
Net Worth: $2,375,629,746
Earnings: $162,654,508
Emp.: 4,583
Fiscal Year-end: 12/31/2023
Holding Company
N.A.I.C.S.: 551112
Yossi Ben Baruch (CEO)

Subsidiary (Domestic):

Migdal Insurance Company Ltd. (3)
4 Efal St, Petah Tiqwa, Israel (100%)
Tel.: (972) 39276363
Web Site: https://www.migdal.co.il

Sales Range: Less than $1 Million
Insurance Products & Services
N.A.I.C.S.: 524128

Subsidiary (Domestic):

Ihud David Berman Insurance Agency Ltd. (4)
34 Ben Yehuda Migdal Hagir Tower 8th Fl, 91370, Jerusalem, Israel
Tel.: (972) 2 500 6000
Sales Range: $25-49.9 Million
Emp.: 25
Insurance Management Services
N.A.I.C.S.: 524298
Nir Saban (Gen Mgr)

Ihud Peltours Diamonds Insurance Agency (2002) Ltd. (4)
Noam Building 23 Tuval Street, Ramat Gan, 52522, Israel
Tel.: (972) 3 611 4700
General Insurance Services
N.A.I.C.S.: 524210

Shaham Insurance Agencies Ltd (4)
19 Shamai, Jerusalem, 91021, Israel
Tel.: (972) 2 6219665
Emp.: 70
General Insurance Services
N.A.I.C.S.: 524210
Yehuda Halali (Mgr)

Subsidiary (Domestic):

Migdal Investment Portfolio Management (1998) Ltd (3)
28 Ahad Haam, Tel Aviv, Israel
Tel.: (972) 3 5194103
Portfolio Management Services
N.A.I.C.S.: 523940

SHO-BOND HOLDINGS CO., LTD.
78 Hakozakicho Nihonbashi, Chuo-ku, Tokyo, 103-0015, Japan
Tel.: (81) 368927101
Web Site: https://www.sho-bondhd.jp
Year Founded: 2008
1414—(TKS)
Rev.: $531,306,180
Assets: $809,477,020
Liabilities: $159,953,520
Net Worth: $649,523,500
Earnings: $89,076,620
Emp.: 1,019
Fiscal Year-end: 06/30/24
Holding Company
N.A.I.C.S.: 551112
Tatsuya Kishimoto (Pres)

Subsidiaries:

Kansai Kako Corporation (1)
9-9 Hiroshibacho, Suita, 564-0052, Japan
Tel.: (81) 661925830
Web Site: http://www.kansaikoko.com
Emp.: 20
Reinforcement Material Distr
N.A.I.C.S.: 423510

SHO-BOND (Hong Kong) Ltd. (1)
Room 15 22/F Technology Park 18 On Lai Street Siu Lek Yuen, Sha Tin, New Territories, China (Hong Kong)
Tel.: (852) 26378302
Infrastructure Construction Services
N.A.I.C.S.: 237310

SHOAL POINT ENERGY LTD.
Suite 203 700 West Pender Street, Vancouver, V6C 1G8, BC, Canada
Tel.: (604) 681-2300
Web Site: https://www.shoalpointenergy.com
SHP—(CNSX)
Rev.: $23,144
Assets: $74,183
Liabilities: $552,735
Net Worth: ($478,552)
Earnings: ($453,334)
Fiscal Year-end: 01/31/24
Oil & Gas Exploration Services
N.A.I.C.S.: 211120
Mark Jarvis (Chm, Pres & CEO)

SHOBIDO CORPORATION
23rd floor Shinagawa Intercity Building A 15-1 Konan 2-chome, Minato-ku, Tokyo, 108-6023, Japan
Tel.: (81) 334727890
Web Site: https://www.shobido-corp.co.jp
Year Founded: 1949
7819—(TKS)
Rev.: $144,940,870
Assets: $107,746,730
Liabilities: $63,079,730
Net Worth: $44,667,000
Earnings: $3,367,750
Emp.: 232
Fiscal Year-end: 09/30/23
General Merchandise Retailer
N.A.I.C.S.: 455219
Masahide Terada (Pres & CEO)

SHOBUNSHA HOLDINGS INC.
3-1 Kojimachi, Chiyoda-ku, Tokyo, 102-8238, Japan
Tel.: (81) 335568171
Web Site: https://www.mapple.co.jp
Year Founded: 1960
9475—(TKS)
Rev.: $42,370,100
Assets: $124,790,190
Liabilities: $40,909,290
Net Worth: $83,880,900
Earnings: $11,706,310
Emp.: 447
Fiscal Year-end: 03/31/24
Magazine Publisher
N.A.I.C.S.: 513130
Shigeo Kuroda (Pres)

Subsidiaries:

Canvas Mapple Co., Ltd. (1)
7F Urbannet Kojimachi Bldg 1-6-2 Kojimachi Chiyodaku, Tokyo, Japan
Tel.: (81) 332648025
Web Site: http://www.canvasmapple.jp
Emp.: 60
Software Development Services
N.A.I.C.S.: 541511
Yukihiro Yamamoto (Pres & CEO)

Mapple, Inc. (1)
3-1 Kojimachi, Chiyoda-ku, Tokyo, 102-8238, Japan
Tel.: (81) 335568155
Web Site: https://www.mapple.com
Emp.: 94
Digital Mapping Services
N.A.I.C.S.: 541360

Shobunsha Creative Co., Ltd. (1)
Room 402 Komiya Building 2-8-33 Goi Chuonishi, Ichihara, 290-0081, Japan
Tel.: (81) 436230103
Web Site: https://sc-mapple.jp
Emp.: 65
Geographic Information Services
N.A.I.C.S.: 541370

Tripcon Co., Ltd. (1)
Ichigo Hanzomon Bldg 7F 2-19 Hayabusa-cho Chiyoda-Ku, Tokyo, Japan
Tel.: (81) 362656170
Web Site: http://www.tripcon.com
Travel Information Services
N.A.I.C.S.: 519290
Daisuke Imai (Pres & CEO)

SHOCHIKU CO., LTD.
4-1-1 Togeki Bldg Tsukiji, Chuo-Ku, Tokyo, 104-8422, Japan
Tel.: (81) 355501516
Web Site: https://www.shochiku.co.jp
Year Founded: 1895
9601—(TKS)
Rev.: $605,684,520
Assets: $1,496,982,600
Liabilities: $827,218,660
Net Worth: $669,763,940
Earnings: $21,383,440
Emp.: 597
Fiscal Year-end: 02/29/24

Motion Picture Producer & Distr; Cinema Owner & Operator; Home Video Sales; Stage Producer & Presenter; Real Estate Operations
N.A.I.C.S.: 512110
Junichi Sakomoto (Chm)

Subsidiaries:

Kabukiza Co., Ltd. (1)
No 12-15 Ginza 4-chome, Chuo-ku, Tokyo, 104-0061, Japan
Tel.: (81) 335441075
Web Site: https://www.kabuki-za.co.jp
Rev.: $21,638,680
Assets: $168,678,190
Liabilities: $93,928,320
Net Worth: $74,749,870
Earnings: $1,807,950
Emp.: 13
Fiscal Year-end: 02/29/2024
Real Estate Lessors & Restaurant Operator
N.A.I.C.S.: 531120
Tadashi Abiko (Pres & CEO)

SHOE ZONE PLC
Haramead Business Centre Humberstone Road, Leicester, LE1 2LH, United Kingdom
Tel.: (44) 1162223000
Web Site: https://www.shoezone.com
SHOE—(AIM)
Rev.: $212,026,986
Assets: $137,902,263
Liabilities: $87,336,697
Net Worth: $50,565,566
Earnings: $14,724,473
Emp.: 2,664
Fiscal Year-end: 10/01/22
Shoe Retailer
N.A.I.C.S.: 458210
Anthony E. P. Smith (CEO)

SHOEI CHEMICAL INC.
Shinjuku Mitsui Bldg 1-1 Nishi Shinjuku 2 chome, Shinjuku-ku, Tokyo, 163-0443, Japan
Tel.: (81) 333446662 JP
Web Site: https://www.shoeichem.co.jp
Year Founded: 1956
Electronic Materials Mfr & Sales
N.A.I.C.S.: 334419
Shuichiro Asada (Pres & CEO)

Subsidiaries:

Nanosys, Inc. (1)
233 S Hillview Dr, Milpitas, CA 95035
Tel.: (408) 240-6700
Web Site: http://www.nanosysinc.com
Sales Range: $1-9.9 Million
Emp.: 100
Nanotechnology Mfr
N.A.I.C.S.: 334413
Noland Granberry (CFO)

SHOEI CO., LTD.
1-31-7 Taito, Taito-ku, Tokyo, 110-001, Japan
Tel.: (81) 356885160 JP
Web Site: https://www.shoei.com
Year Founded: 1959
7839—(TKS)
Rev.: $238,337,440
Assets: $232,587,450
Liabilities: $40,129,400
Net Worth: $192,458,050
Earnings: $50,112,120
Emp.: 785
Fiscal Year-end: 09/30/23
Helmets Mfr
N.A.I.C.S.: 339920
Kenichiro Ishida (Pres)

Subsidiaries:

Nacar Comercial Importadora e Exportadora LTDA. (1)
Rua Clodomiro Amazonas 456 Vila Nova Conceicao, Sao Paulo, Brazil
Tel.: (55) 1138149288

SHOEI CO., LTD.

Shoei Co., Ltd.—(Continued)
Web Site: https://www.nacar.com.br
Motor Vehicle & Parts Distr
N.A.I.C.S.: 423140

SHOEI EUROPE Distribution S.A.R.L. (1)
21 rue Gambetta Za du Petit Rocher, Za du Petit Rocher, 77210, Vulaines-sur-Seine, France
Tel.: (33) 16 072 1718
Web Site: http://www.shoeieurope.com
Sales Range: $25-49.9 Million
Emp.: 20
Motorcycle Helmets Distr
N.A.I.C.S.: 336991

Shoei (Europa) GmbH (1)
Elisabeth-Selbert-Str 13, 40764, Langenfeld, Germany
Web Site: http://www.shoei-europe.com
Sales Range: $25-49.9 Million
Emp.: 14
Motorcycle Helmets Mfr
N.A.I.C.S.: 336390
Kenichiro Ishida (Mng Dir)

Shoei Distribution GmbH (1)
Elisabeth-Selbert-Str 13, 40764, Langenfeld, Germany
Tel.: (49) 217 339 9750
Web Site: http://www.shoei-europe.com
Sales Range: $25-49.9 Million
Emp.: 15
Motorcycle Helmets Distr
N.A.I.C.S.: 441227

United Commercial Agencies W.L.L. (1)
Building 646 Al Hamriya, Sitra, Bahrain
Tel.: (973) 17731691
Air Conditioning Services
N.A.I.C.S.: 221330

W. White (Wholesale) Ltd. (1)
14 Karewa Place Te Rapa, Hamilton, New Zealand
Tel.: (64) 78495493
Web Site: https://www.whitespowersports.com
Motorcycle Parts Distr
N.A.I.C.S.: 423120

Wheels of Arabia Motorcycles Trading LLC (1)
4th Street Al Quoz Industrial Area 3, 410545, Dubai, United Arab Emirates
Tel.: (971) 143218525
Web Site: http://www.wheelsofarabia.ae
Motor Vehicle & Parts Distr
N.A.I.C.S.: 423140

Yamaimport S.A. (1)
Las Condes 8326, 7560244, Santiago, Chile
Tel.: (56) 222991000
Web Site: https://www.yamahamotos.cl
Motor Vehicle & Parts Distr
N.A.I.C.S.: 423140

SHOEI CORPORATION
158 Tabehara Tajima, Minamiaizu-machi, Fukushima, 967-0004, Japan
Tel.: (81) 241620566
Web Site: https://www.shoei-r.co.jp
Year Founded: 1968
9385—(TKS)
Rev.: $128,538,060
Assets: $63,594,810
Liabilities: $38,470,200
Net Worth: $25,124,610
Earnings: $6,669,490
Fiscal Year-end: 03/31/24
Plastic Film Packaging & Other Packaging Products Mfr
N.A.I.C.S.: 322220
Katsuyoshi Hyodo (Mng Dir)

SHOEI FOODS CORPORATION
5-7 Akihabara, Taito-ku, Tokyo, 110-8723, Japan
Tel.: (81) 332531211
Web Site: https://www.shoeifoods.co.jp
Year Founded: 1947
8079—(TKS)
Rev.: $777,021,460
Assets: $620,034,680
Liabilities: $251,106,530
Net Worth: $368,928,150
Earnings: $19,915,810
Emp.: 1,516
Fiscal Year-end: 10/31/23
Confectionery Product Mfr & Distr
N.A.I.C.S.: 311351
Ichiro Honda (Pres)

Subsidiaries:

Shoei Foods (U.S.A.), Inc. (1)
1900 Feather River Blvd, Olivehurst, CA 95961
Tel.: (530) 237-1295
Web Site: https://www.shoeifoodsusa.com
Dry Fruit Mfr & Distr
N.A.I.C.S.: 311423

SHOEI PRINTING CO., LTD.
1-3-23 Momodani, Ikuno-ku, Osaka, 544-0034, Japan
Tel.: (81) 667171181
Web Site: http://www.shoei-printing.com
Year Founded: 1918
Sales Range: $50-74.9 Million
Emp.: 200
Smart Cards Printing Services
N.A.I.C.S.: 323111
Yusuke Inoue (Chm)

Subsidiaries:

Daifuku Card Co., Ltd. (1)
1-4-14 Fukumachi, Nishiyodogawa-ku, Osaka, 555-0034, Japan
Tel.: (81) 664762221
Web Site: http://www.tomoegawa.co.jp
Smart Cards Printing Services
N.A.I.C.S.: 323111

Shoei Printing (Hong Kong) Co., Ltd. (1)
Unit 2202 22F The Metropolis Tower 10 Metropolis Drive, Hunghom, Kowloon, China (Hong Kong)
Tel.: (852) 3162 6763
Emp.: 8
Credit Cards Printing Services
N.A.I.C.S.: 323111
Mitsuhito Komura (Gen Mgr)

Shoei Printing Co., Ltd. - Osaka Factory (1)
1-3-23 Momodani, Ikuno-Ku, Osaka, 544-8686, Japan
Tel.: (81) 667171181
Web Site: http://www.shoei-printing.com
Credit & Cash Cards Mfr
N.A.I.C.S.: 326199

Shoei Printing Co.,Ltd. - Kawasaki Factory (1)
2-17-1 Mizusawa, Miyamae-ku, Kawasaki, 210-8577, Kanagawa, Japan
Tel.: (81) 449774561
Smart Cards Processing Services
N.A.I.C.S.: 323111

SHOEI YAKUHIN CO., LTD.
Senba Shoei Bldg 5-1 Azuchimachi 1-Chome, Chuo-ku, Osaka, 541-0052, Japan
Tel.: (81) 662622707
Web Site: https://www.shoei-yakuhin.co.jp
3537—(TKS)
Rev.: $149,352,950
Assets: $111,147,150
Liabilities: $57,361,580
Net Worth: $53,785,570
Earnings: $3,245,510
Emp.: 76
Fiscal Year-end: 03/31/24
Chemicals Mfr
N.A.I.C.S.: 325411
Makio Tetsuno (Chm)

Subsidiaries:

Shoei Trading (Thailand) Co., Ltd. (1)
90 CW Tower A Unit A2604, Huaykhwang Sub-District Huaykhwang District, Bangkok, 10310, Thailand
Tel.: (66) 26452055
Resin Mfr
N.A.I.C.S.: 325211

SHOFU INC.
11 Kamitakamatsucho Fukuina, Higashiyama-ku, Kyoto, 605-0983, Japan
Tel.: (81) 755611112
Web Site: https://www.shofu.co.jp
Year Founded: 1922
7979—(TKS)
Rev.: $231,878,800
Assets: $331,114,730
Liabilities: $56,079,240
Net Worth: $275,035,490
Earnings: $24,159,550
Emp.: 1,369
Fiscal Year-end: 03/31/24
Dental Equipment Mfr & Whslr
N.A.I.C.S.: 339114
Noriyuki Negoro (Pres)

Subsidiaries:

SHOFU BIOFIX INC. (1)
Shofu EST Building 3-16-2 Yushima, Bunkyo-ku, Tokyo, 113-0034, Japan
Tel.: (81) 368802118
Web Site: https://www.shofubiofix.co.jp
Dental Equipment Distr
N.A.I.C.S.: 423450

SHOFU Dental Asia-Pacific Pte. Ltd. (1)
10 Science Park Road 03-12 The Alpha Science Park II, Singapore, 117684, Singapore
Tel.: (65) 63772722
Web Site: https://www.shofu.com.sg
Dental Equipment Distr
N.A.I.C.S.: 423450
Patrick Loke (Mng Dir)

SHOFU Dental Corporation (1)
1225 Stone Dr, San Marcos, CA 92078-4059
Tel.: (760) 736-3277
Web Site: http://www.shofu.com
Dental Equipment Distr
N.A.I.C.S.: 423450

SHOFU Dental GmbH (1)
Am Brull 17, 40878, Ratingen, Germany
Tel.: (49) 210286640
Web Site: http://www.shofu.de
Dental Equipment Distr
N.A.I.C.S.: 423450
Martin Hesselmann (Mng Dir)

SHOFU UK (1)
Riverside House River Lawn Road, Tonbridge, TN9 1EP, Kent, United Kingdom
Tel.: (44) 1732783580
Web Site: https://www.shofu.de
Dental Equipment Distr
N.A.I.C.S.: 423450

Shiga Shofu Inc. (1)
2296 Kinose Shigaraki-cho, Koka, 529-1802, Shiga, Japan
Tel.: (81) 748830016
Dental Equipment Mfr
N.A.I.C.S.: 339114
Masuhiro Yasui (Pres)

Shofu Dental Trading (Shanghai) Co., Ltd. (1)
No 645 Jiye Road Sheshan Industrial Park Songjiang, Shanghai, 201602, China
Tel.: (86) 2157796980
Web Site: http://www.shofu.com.cn
Dental Equipment Distr
N.A.I.C.S.: 423450

SHOKO CO., LTD.
4-1 Shibakoen 2-chome, Minato-ku, Tokyo, 105-8432, Japan
Tel.: (81) 33 459 5111

INTERNATIONAL PUBLIC

Web Site: http://www.shoko.co.jp
Year Founded: 1947
Rev.: $1,100,033,200
Assets: $533,152,970
Liabilities: $433,731,830
Net Worth: $99,421,140
Earnings: $16,634,380
Emp.: 519
Fiscal Year-end: 12/31/19
Chemical Product Whslr
N.A.I.C.S.: 424690
Yutaka Saito (Mng Corp Officer)

Subsidiaries:

Cosmo Kasei Kogyo Co., Ltd. (1)
398-3 Shinmeicho, Koshigaya, 343-0805, Saitama, Japan
Tel.: (81) 489715551
Web Site: http://www.kosumokasei.co.jp
Packing Material & Other Product Distr
N.A.I.C.S.: 424130

Kyosan Light Metal Co., Ltd. (1)
5-14-3 Hirono, Suruga-ku, Shizuoka, 421-0121, Japan
Tel.: (81) 542562147
Web Site: http://www.klmc.co.jp
Emp.: 20
Aluminum Spacer Double Glazed Glass Mfr
N.A.I.C.S.: 327215

NK Global Co., Ltd. (1)
4-1 Shibakoen 2-chome, Minato-ku, Tokyo, 105-0011, Japan
Tel.: (81) 334595126
Nitrogen Fertilizer Mfr
N.A.I.C.S.: 325311

SHO-A Corporation (1)
4-1 Shibakoen 2-chome, Minato-ku, Tokyo, 105-0011, Japan
Tel.: (81) 334595046
Import & Export Chemical Product Whslr
N.A.I.C.S.: 424690

Shoko (Taiwan) Global Corporation (1)
8F-1 No 139 SongJiang Rd, Taipei, 104, Taiwan
Tel.: (886) 225042839
Nitrogen Fertilizer Mfr
N.A.I.C.S.: 325311

Shoko (Thailand) Co., Ltd. (1)
12th Floor Unit 04 Chartered Square Building 152 North Sathon Road, Silom Bangrak, Bangkok, 10500, Thailand
Tel.: (66) 22663940
Nitrogen Fertilizer Mfr
N.A.I.C.S.: 325311

Shoko Agri Co., Ltd. (1)
Shiba-chome No 4 No 1, Minato-ku, Tokyo, 105-8432, Japan
Tel.: (81) 334595221
Web Site: http://www.shokoagri.com
Fertilizer Agricultural Material Mfr & Whslr
N.A.I.C.S.: 325314

Shoko Farm Net K. K. (1)
3741-1 Asahimura yoshimi, Higashichiku-magun, Nagano, 390-1104, Japan
Tel.: (81) 263878023
Nitrogen Fertilizer Mfr
N.A.I.C.S.: 325311

Shoko Highpolymer Co., Ltd. (1)
2-2-12 Kanda Tukasamachi Kanda Tukasa-machi Building 8F, Chiyoda-ku, Tokyo, 101-0048, Japan
Tel.: (81) 332587131
Web Site: http://www.shokohp.co.jp
Chemical & Petrochemical Product Mfr
N.A.I.C.S.: 325110

Shoko Insurance Service Co., Ltd. (1)
Shiba Park Building B Building 3F 2-4-1 Shiba Park, Minato-ku, Tokyo, 105-8432, Japan
Tel.: (81) 334595190
Web Site: http://www.shoko-hoken.co.jp
Non Life Insurance & Life Insurance Services
N.A.I.C.S.: 524128

Shoko Korea Co., Ltd. (1)
322 Chungjeong Rizion 27 Seosomun-ro,

Seodaemun-gu, Seoul, 03741, Korea (South)
Tel.: (82) 27845111
Web Site: http://www.shodex.com
Pesticide & Organic Acid Product Distr
N.A.I.C.S.: 424690

Shoko Science Co., Ltd. (1)
1-3-3 Azamino Minami, Aoba-ku, Yokohama, 225-0012, Japan
Tel.: (81) 459136688
Web Site: http://www.shoko-sc.co.jp
Chemical & Petrochemical Product Mfr
N.A.I.C.S.: 325110

Showa Baido Co., Ltd. (1)
40 Shinki Fushi Kami-cho, Kami-gun, Kami, Miyagi, Japan
Tel.: (81) 229634141
Web Site: http://www.s-baido.co.jp
Fertilizer Agricultural Material Mfr & Whslr
N.A.I.C.S.: 325314

SHOKUBUN CO., LTD.
1807 Mukoudai 3-chome, Moriyama-ku, Nagoya, 463-8536, Aichi, Japan
Tel.: (81) 527731011
Web Site:
   https://www.shokubun.co.jp
Year Founded: 1977
9969—(TKS)
Rev.: $42,257,730
Assets: $36,579,740
Liabilities: $19,413,570
Net Worth: $17,166,170
Earnings: ($99,150)
Fiscal Year-end: 03/31/24
Food Delivery Services
N.A.I.C.S.: 812990
Mitsuo Fujio (Chm)

SHOMAL CEMENT COMPANY
Modares Bridge not reaching Qaim Maqam intersection No 269, PO Box 15875/4571, Shahid Beheshti St after, 15146, Tehran, Iran
Tel.: (98) 2188731107
Web Site: https://shomalcem.com
Year Founded: 1954
SIMS1—(THE)
Sales Range: Less than $1 Million
Emp.: 589
Cement Mfr
N.A.I.C.S.: 327310
Simal Shamal (CEO)

SHOOTING STAR ACQUISITION CORP.
Tel.: (604) 602-0001   Ca
Year Founded: 2018
SSSS.P—(TSXV)
Assets: $3,932
Liabilities: $81,811
Net Worth: ($77,879)
Earnings: ($46,568)
Fiscal Year-end: 09/30/22
Business Consulting Services
N.A.I.C.S.: 522299
Geoff Balderson (CEO & CFO)

SHOP APOTHEKE EUROPE N.V.
Erik de Rodeweg 11-13, 5975 WD, Sevenum, Netherlands
Tel.: (31) 778505900   Nl
Web Site: https://www.shop-apotheke-europe.com
Year Founded: 2001
RDC—(DEU)
Rev.: $1,189,012,471
Assets: $659,453,110
Liabilities: $137,281,613
Net Worth: $522,171,497
Earnings: ($20,598,813)
Emp.: 1,220
Fiscal Year-end: 12/31/20
Pharmaceutical Product Retailer
N.A.I.C.S.: 424210

Bjorn Soder (Vice Chm-Supervisory Bd)
Subsidiaries:

Aurora Gesundheit GmbH (1)
Knaackstrasse 64, 10435, Berlin, Germany
Tel.: (49) 3083799869
Web Site: https://www.gopuls.de
Medicines & Care Product Distr
N.A.I.C.S.: 424210

MedApp Holding B.V. (1)
Kastanjelaan 400, 5616 LZ, Eindhoven, Netherlands
Tel.: (31) 407820817
Web Site: https://www.medapp.nl
Healthcare & Fitness Services
N.A.I.C.S.: 713940

MedApp Nederland B.V. (1)
Kastanjelaan 400, 5616 LZ, Eindhoven, Netherlands
Tel.: (31) 407820817
Web Site: https://www.medapp.nl
Online Pharmacy Services
N.A.I.C.S.: 524292

Redcare S.R.L. (1)
Via Per Cascina Conighetto 1, Milan, 20049, Settala, Italy
Tel.: (39) 0800168002
Web Site: https://www.redcare.it
Para Pharmacy Healthcare Services
N.A.I.C.S.: 524114

Smartpatient GmbH (1)
Neumarkter Str 87, 81673, Munich, Germany
Tel.: (49) 89122249300
Web Site: https://www.smartpatient.eu
Global Disease Management Services
N.A.I.C.S.: 813212

nu3 GmbH (1)
Brueckenstrasse 5, 10179, Berlin, Germany
Tel.: (49) 8000335510
Web Site: https://www.nu3.de
Fitness Food Whslr
N.A.I.C.S.: 456191

SHOP DIRECT HOME SHOPPING LIMITED
1st Floor Skyways House Speke Road, Liverpool, L70 1AB, United Kingdom
Tel.: (44) 8442921000
Web Site: http://www.shopdirect.com
Year Founded: 2003
Sales Range: $1-4.9 Billion
Emp.: 3,700
Online Shopping Services
N.A.I.C.S.: 455219
Gareth Jones (Deputy CEO & Dir-Retail & Strategy)
Subsidiaries:

Littlewoods Shop Direct Home Shopping Ltd. (1)
Skyways House, Estuary Commerce Park, Speke Road, Liverpool, L70 1AB, United Kingdom
Tel.: (44) 870 263 1000
Shop-At-Home Retail Services
N.A.I.C.S.: 425120
Steven Rowe (Head-Design Interiors)

Shop Direct Financial Services Ltd (1)
Aintree Innovation Centre Fortune House Park Lane, Netherton, Bootle, L30 1SL, United Kingdom
Tel.: (44) 844 292 5000
Online Shopping Retailer
N.A.I.C.S.: 425120

Shop Direct Ireland Limited (1)
Cape House Westend Office Park, Blanchardstown, Dublin, Ireland
Tel.: (353) 1 811 2222
Web Site: http://www.littlewoodsireland.ie
Online Shopping Retailer
N.A.I.C.S.: 425120

SHOPER S.A.
ul Pawia 9, 31-154, Krakow, Poland

Tel.: (48) 501509509
Web Site: https://www.shoper.pl
Year Founded: 2005
SHO—(WAR)
Rev.: $38,769,055
Assets: $32,147,612
Liabilities: $17,830,793
Net Worth: $14,316,819
Earnings: $6,618,140
Emp.: 218
Fiscal Year-end: 12/31/23
Custom Computer Programming Services
N.A.I.C.S.: 541511
Anna Misko (Chief People Officer)

SHOPIFY INC.
151 O'Connor Street Ground floor, Ottawa, K2P 2L8, ON, Canada
Tel.: (613) 241-2828   Ca
Web Site: https://www.shopify.com
Year Founded: 2006
SHOP—(NYSE)
Rev.: $7,060,000,000
Assets: $11,299,000,000
Liabilities: $2,233,000,000
Net Worth: $9,066,000,000
Earnings: $132,000,000
Emp.: 8,300
Fiscal Year-end: 12/31/23
E-Commerce Software Developer
N.A.I.C.S.: 513210
Amy Shih-Hua Feng (Head-IR)

SHOPINVEST SAS
49 avenue Kleber, 75016, Paris, France
Tel.: (33) 83622700
Web Site: http://www.shopinvest.fr
Year Founded: 2006
Online Shopping
N.A.I.C.S.: 423620

SHOPPER360 LIMITED
138 Robinson Road 26-03 Oxley Tower, Singapore, 068906, Singapore
Tel.: (65) 62369350   SG
Web Site:
   http://www.shopper360.com.my
Year Founded: 1986
1F0—(SES)
Rev.: $38,239,061
Assets: $20,297,442
Liabilities: $4,487,295
Net Worth: $15,810,147
Earnings: $420,250
Emp.: 356
Fiscal Year-end: 05/31/24
Electronic Marketing Services
N.A.I.C.S.: 541870
Chow Siew Bee (Controller-Fin)
Subsidiaries:

Shopper360 Sdn. Bhd. (1)
505 5th Floor Block A Phileo Damansara 2 15 Jalan 16/11, 46350, Petaling Jaya, Selangor, Malaysia
Tel.: (60) 379551100
Digital Marketing Services
N.A.I.C.S.: 541613

ShopperPlus Myanmar Co., Ltd. (1)
No 15 Dhammazedi Road Ground Floor Opp Happy Zone, SanChaung Township, Yangon, Myanmar
Tel.: (95) 9256653864
Digital Marketing Services
N.A.I.C.S.: 541613
Aye Thidar Khine (Mgr-HR)

ShopperPlus Singapore Pte. Ltd. (1)
60D Kallang Pudding Rd 03-01 Ingolstadt Centre, Singapore, 349321, Singapore
Tel.: (65) 68410118
Digital Marketing Services
N.A.I.C.S.: 541613
Marvin Didjaya (Mgr-Channels Ops)

SHOPPERS STOP LIMITED
Umang Tower 5th Floor Mindspace

Off Link Road, Malad West, Mumbai, 400064, Maharashtra, India
Tel.: (91) 2242497000
Web Site:
   https://corporate.shoppersstop.com
532638—(BOM)
Rev.: $524,251,959
Assets: $634,803,356
Liabilities: $598,663,098
Net Worth: $36,140,258
Earnings: $9,262,275
Emp.: 6,319
Fiscal Year-end: 03/31/24
Department Stores
N.A.I.C.S.: 455110
B. S. Nagesh (Chm)

SHOPPES MANILA, INC.
Style Bldg No 1 Rolling Lane, Filinvest Rd Batasan Hills, Quezon City, 1126, Philippines
Tel.: (63) 2 931 9459
Web Site: http://www.kamiseta.com
Year Founded: 1992
Sales Range: $75-99.9 Million
Emp.: 300
Young Women's Clothing Mfr & Retailer
N.A.I.C.S.: 458110
Irene R. Dimson (Mgr-Franchises)

SHOPPINGPARTNER FR
87 Rue Baudin, 92300, Levallois-Perret, France
Tel.: (33) 155465060
Rev.: $23,300,000
Emp.: 25
N.A.I.C.S.: 423430
Amina El Faoudani (Dir-Pur)

SHOPRITE HOLDINGS LIMITED
Cnr William Dabs Street and Old Paarl Road, Brackenfell, 7560, Western Cape, South Africa
Tel.: (27) 219804000
Web Site:
   http://www.shopriteholdings.co.za
Year Founded: 1979
SHP—(JSE)
Rev.: $11,593,383,961
Assets: $5,405,422,533
Liabilities: $4,017,680,795
Net Worth: $1,387,741,738
Earnings: $333,759,334
Emp.: 160,000
Fiscal Year-end: 07/02/23
Holding Company; Food, Furniture & Homegoods Retailer; Fast Food Franchise Owner
N.A.I.C.S.: 551112
Christo H. Wiese (Chm)
Subsidiaries:

Computicket (Pty) Ltd. (1)
Cnr William Dabbs and Old Paarl Roads, PO Box 215, Parklands, Brackenfell, 7561, South Africa
Tel.: (27) 839804000
Web Site: https://computicket.com
Ticket Booking Services
N.A.I.C.S.: 561599
Kurt Drennan (Gen Mgr)

Sentra Namibia Ltd (1)
6 Diehl St S Industrial Area 20 Adimbi Toivo Yi Toivi St, Windhoek, Namibia   (100%)
Tel.: (264) 61 22 3008
Web Site: http://www.shoprite.co.za
Emp.: 20
Supermarket Operator
N.A.I.C.S.: 445110
Paul Malan (Gen Mgr)

Shoprite Checkers (Pty) Ltd (1)
Cnr William Dabbs Street and Old Paarl Road, Brackenfell, 7560, Western Cape, South Africa
Tel.: (27) 219801593

SHOPRITE HOLDINGS LIMITED

Shoprite Holdings Limited—(Continued)
Web Site:
https://www.shopriteholdings.co.za
Emp.: 150
Supermarket Operator
N.A.I.C.S.: 445110

Subsidiary (Domestic):

Freshmark (Pty) Ltd (2)
PO Box 1456, Brackenfell, 7561, South Africa
Tel.: (27) 21 980 8800
Web Site: http://www.shopriteholdings.co.za
Fruit & Vegetable Procurement & Distribution Services
N.A.I.C.S.: 424490

Shoprite Checkers (Pty) Ltd. (1)
Cnr William Dabbs & Old Paarl Roads, Brackenfell, Cape Town, 7561, South Africa
Tel.: (27) 219804000
Web Site: http://www.shoprite.co.za
Grocery Operations
N.A.I.C.S.: 445110
Pieter Engelbrecht (COO)

Shoprite Checkers Properties Ltd (1)
Corner William Dabs & Old Paarl Road, Cape Town, 7561, South Africa
Tel.: (27) 219804400
Property Development Services
N.A.I.C.S.: 531190

Shoprite Checkers Uganda Ltd (1)
Plot 1 Ben Kiwanuka St, Kampala, Uganda
Tel.: (256) 31 2228100
Emp.: 300
Grocery Distr
N.A.I.C.S.: 445110
Peet Coetzee (Gen Mgr)

Shoprite Ghana (Pty) Ltd (1)
Accra Mall Tetteh Quarshie Round About
PMB CT20 Cantonments, Accra, Ghana
Tel.: (233) 30282301320
Web Site: http://www.shoprite.co.za
Emp.: 540
Supermarket Operator
N.A.I.C.S.: 445110
Brett Marshall (Gen Mgr)

Shoprite Supermercados Lda (1)
Estrada De Catete, Luanda, Angola
Tel.: (244) 923597043
Supermarket Operator
N.A.I.C.S.: 445110

Shoprite Trading Ltd (1)
PO Box 31481, Chichiri, Blantyre, Malawi
Tel.: (265) 1872244
Sales Range: $100-124.9 Million
Emp.: 300
Supermarket Operator
N.A.I.C.S.: 445110
Jaco Dellemijn (Gen Mgr)

SHOPSTER ECOMMERCE INC.

7710 5th Street SE Suite 110A, Calgary, T2H 2L9, AB, Canada
Web Site: http://www.shopster.com
Year Founded: 2004
Sales Range: $1-9.9 Million
Emp.: 10
E-Commerce Software & Solutions
N.A.I.C.S.: 513210
George Tai (Sec)

SHORE CAPITAL GROUP PLC

Cassini House 57 St James s Street, London, SW1A 1LD, United Kingdom
Tel.: (44) 2074084050
Web Site:
https://www.shorecap.co.uk
Rev.: $54,991,713
Assets: $128,570,761
Liabilities: $42,197,453
Net Worth: $86,373,308
Earnings: $4,546,899
Emp.: 178
Fiscal Year-end: 12/31/18
Investment Banking Services
N.A.I.C.S.: 523150
Howard P. Shore (Chm)

Subsidiaries:

Puma Nominees Limited (1)
Bond St House, 14 Clifford St, London, W1S 4JU, United Kingdom
Tel.: (44) 20 7408 4090
Web Site: http://www.shorecapital.co.uk
Business Management Services
N.A.I.C.S.: 561110

Puma Property Advisors Limited (1)
Regency Court Glategny Esplanade, PO Box 282, Saint Peter Port, GY1 3RH, Guernsey
Tel.: (44) 1481 723 450
Web Site: http://www.pumabrandenburg.gg
Sales Range: $50-74.9 Million
Emp.: 10
Property Advisory Services
N.A.I.C.S.: 523940

Shore Capital Finance Limited (1)
Bond St House 14 Clifford St, London, W1S 4JU, United Kingdom
Tel.: (44) 2074084080
Web Site: http://www.shorecapital.co.uk
Emp.: 80
Financial Services
N.A.I.C.S.: 522291

Shore Capital International Limited (1)
Unter den Linden 32/34, 10117, Berlin, Germany
Tel.: (49) 302045870
Web Site: http://www.shorecap.de
Sales Range: $50-74.9 Million
Emp.: 15
Investment Banking Services
N.A.I.C.S.: 523150
Thomas Marlinghaus (COO)

Shore Capital Investments Limited (1)
Bond St House 14 Clifford St, London, W1S 4JU, United Kingdom
Tel.: (44) 2074084090
Web Site: http://www.shorecapital.co.uk
Investment Banking Services
N.A.I.C.S.: 523150

Shore Capital Stockbrokers Limited (1)
Bond St House 14 Clifford St, London, W1S 4JU, United Kingdom
Tel.: (44) 2074084080
Web Site: http://www.shorecap.co.uk
Sales Range: $50-74.9 Million
Emp.: 80
Investment Banking Services
N.A.I.C.S.: 523150

Shore Capital Trading Limited (1)
14 Clifford St, London, W1S 4JU, United Kingdom
Tel.: (44) 2074084050
Emp.: 60
Investment Banking Services
N.A.I.C.S.: 523150

Shore Capital and Corporate Limited (1)
Bond St House 14 Clifford St, London, W1X S4JU, United Kingdom
Tel.: (44) 2074084090
Sales Range: $50-74.9 Million
Emp.: 50
Investment Banking Services
N.A.I.C.S.: 523150

SHORE TO SHORE (PVT) LTD.

66 Expo Victoria Towers Park Street, Colombo, 01, Sri Lanka
Tel.: (94) 11 22 61000
Web Site: http://www.shrtoshr.com
Paper Products Mfr
N.A.I.C.S.: 322299

SHORTCUT MEDIA AB

Hollandargatan 20, 111 60, Stockholm, Sweden
Tel.: (46) 705465329
Web Site:
https://www.shortcutmedia.se
Entertainment Services
N.A.I.C.S.: 711130

Subsidiaries:

Oddway Film & Television AB (1)
Stampgatan 20B, Gothenburg, 411 01, Sweden
Tel.: (46) 317880730
Film Production Company
N.A.I.C.S.: 516120
David Stenberg (CEO)

Subsidiary (Domestic):

STARK Film AB (2)
Gamlestadsvagen 2 4, 415 02, Gothenburg, Sweden
Tel.: (46) 317077400
Web Site: http://www.stark.se
Film Producer
N.A.I.C.S.: 711510
Ann-Charlotte Hanfelt (CEO)

SHOUCHENG HOLDINGS LIMITED

7/F Bank of East Asia Harbour View Centre 56 Gloucester Road, Wanchai, China (Hong Kong)
Tel.: (852) 28612832   HK
Web Site:
https://www.shouchengholdings.com
Year Founded: 2017
0697—(HKG)
Rev.: $203,975,648
Assets: $1,741,164,353
Liabilities: $463,096,830
Net Worth: $1,278,067,523
Earnings: $116,579,243
Emp.: 515
Fiscal Year-end: 12/31/22
Holding Company; Steel Products Mfr & Distr, Electricity Generation & Shipping Services
N.A.I.C.S.: 551112
Liang Xu (Exec Dir)

Subsidiaries:

Shougang Concord Shipping Holdings Limited (1)
7/F Bank Of East Asia Harbour View Ctr 56 Gloucester Rd, Wanchai, China (Hong Kong)
Tel.: (852) 28764888
Web Site: http://www.shougang-intl.com.hk
Emp.: 15
Investment Management Service
N.A.I.C.S.: 523999
Sidney Yeung (Mgr-HR & Admin)

Subsidiary (Domestic):

SCIT Trading Limited (2)
5/F Bank Of East Asia Harbour View Ctr 56 Gloucester Rd, Wanchai, China (Hong Kong)
Tel.: (852) 28764888
Steel Product Distr
N.A.I.C.S.: 423510

Shougang Concord Shipping Services Limited (1)
6/F Bank of East Asia Harbour View Centre 56 Gloucester Road, Wanchai, China (Hong Kong)
Tel.: (852) 28764888
Shipping Transportation Services
N.A.I.C.S.: 488330

Shougang Concord Steel International Trading Co. Ltd. (1)
7th Floor Bank of East Asia Harbour View Centre 56 Gloucester Road, Wanchai, China (Hong Kong)
Tel.: (852) 2520 0886
Web Site: http://www.shougang-intl.com.hk
Emp.: 15
Metal Steel Products Distr
N.A.I.C.S.: 423510
Shu Hong (Gen Mgr)

SHOUGANG CENTURY HOLDINGS LIMITED

Room 1215 12/F Honour Industrial Centre 6 Sun Yip Street, Chai Wan, China (Hong Kong)
Tel.: (852) 25272218   HK

INTERNATIONAL PUBLIC

Web Site:
https://www.shougangcentury.com.hk
Year Founded: 1992
0103—(HKG)
Rev.: $314,190,855
Assets: $424,247,325
Liabilities: $212,885,093
Net Worth: $211,362,233
Earnings: $6,101,895
Emp.: 2,363
Fiscal Year-end: 12/31/22
Steel Cords Mfr
N.A.I.C.S.: 331512
Comor Kwok Kau Tang (Deputy Mng Dir)

Subsidiaries:

Hing Cheong Metals (China & Hong Kong) Limited (1)
Unit 2-3 G/F TCL Tower 8 Tai Chung Road, Tsuen Wan, China (Hong Kong)
Tel.: (852) 24987800
Nonferrous Metal Distr
N.A.I.C.S.: 423510

Jiaxing Eastern Steel Cord Co., Ltd. (1)
East Road No 1 Economic Development zone, Jiaxing, 314003, Zhejiang, China
Tel.: (86) 57382213511
Web Site: http://www.jesc.com.cn
Steel Pole Mfr
N.A.I.C.S.: 314994

Shougang Century (Shanghai) Management Co., Ltd. (1)
Room 2505 Tower 1 Soho Tianshan Plaza No 421 Ziyun Road, Changning District, Shanghai, 200051, China
Tel.: (86) 2162918806
Hose Wire & Steel Management Services
N.A.I.C.S.: 238120

Tengzhou Eastern Steel Cord Co., Ltd. (1)
1 DongFang Road Economic Development Zone, Tengzhou, 277500, Shandong, China
Tel.: (86) 6325252100
Emp.: 1,000
Steel Pole Mfr
N.A.I.C.S.: 314994

SHOUGANG FUSHAN RESOURCES GROUP LIMITED

6/F Bank of East Asia Harbour View Centre 56 Gloucester Road, Wanchai, China (Hong Kong)
Tel.: (852) 27650839   HK
Web Site: https://www.shougang-resources.com.hk
Year Founded: 1990
0639—(HKG)
Rev.: $1,047,376,673
Assets: $2,991,594,210
Liabilities: $610,248,788
Net Worth: $2,381,345,423
Earnings: $421,789,763
Emp.: 4,446
Fiscal Year-end: 12/31/22
Holding Company; Coking Coal Mining, Processing & Distribution
N.A.I.C.S.: 551112
Qingshan Liu (Deputy Mng Dir)

SHOUGANG GENERACION ELECTRICA S.A.A.

Av Republica de Chile 262, Jesus Maria, 11, Lima, 11, Peru
Tel.: (51) 56525891
Web Site:
https://www.shougesa.com.pe
Year Founded: 1997
SHOUGEC1—(LIM)
Sales Range: Less than $1 Million
Thermal Electricity Power Generation Services
N.A.I.C.S.: 221118
Kong Aimin (Chm & Gen Mgr)

SHOUGANG GROUP CO., LTD.

AND PRIVATE COMPANIES

Beijing Shijingshan District, Beijing, 100041, China
Tel.: (86) 1088291114   CN
Web Site:
http://www.shougang.com.cn
Year Founded: 1919
Sales Range: $15-24.9 Billion
Emp.: 13,000
Holding Company; Steel Products Mfr & Distr, Electricity Generation & Shipping Services
N.A.I.C.S.: 551112
Zhong Cao (Asst Gen Mgr)

Subsidiaries:

Shougang NEC Electronics Co., Ltd. (1)
No 45 Badachu Street, Shijingshan District, Beijing, 100041, China
Tel.: (86) 1058980808
Web Site: http://www.bsmc.com
Sales Range: $1-4.9 Billion
Emp.: 500
Semiconductor Integrated Circuit Mfr & Distr; Owned 50.3% by NEC Corporation & 49.7% by Shougang Corporation
N.A.I.C.S.: 334413
Shqi Yang (Mgr)

SHOUHANG HIGH-TECH ENERGY CO., LTD.
Building 20 Block 3 108 South 4th Ring W Rd, Fengtai, Beijing, 100070, China
Tel.: (86) 1052255555
Web Site: https://www.sh-ihw.com
Year Founded: 2001
002665—(SSE)
Rev.: $91,569,652
Assets: $1,073,064,424
Liabilities: $338,353,975
Net Worth: $734,710,448
Earnings: ($35,823,453)
Fiscal Year-end: 12/31/22
Air Cooling Systems Mfr
N.A.I.C.S.: 333415

SHOWA CHEMICAL INDUSTRY CO., LTD.
2-14-32 Akasaka, Minato-ku, Tokyo, 107-0052, Japan
Tel.: (81) 355756300
Web Site: https://www.showa-chemical.co.jp
4990—(TKS)
Rev.: $60,785,560
Assets: $89,420,080
Liabilities: $39,197,300
Net Worth: $50,222,780
Earnings: $3,860,240
Fiscal Year-end: 03/31/24
Chemical Products Mfr
N.A.I.C.S.: 325998
Kenzo Ishibashi (Pres)

Subsidiaries:

Radiolite Trading Co., Ltd. (1)
RM2715 602 BLDG Wangjingyuan ULO Park, Chaoyang Dist, Beijing, 100102, China
Tel.: (86) 1064752538
Web Site: http://www.radiolite-trading.cn
Chemical Products Distr
N.A.I.C.S.: 424690

SHOWA GLOVE CO.
565 Tohori, Himeji, 670-0802, Hyo, Japan
Tel.: (81) 792641234
Web Site: http://www.soanet.co.jp
Year Founded: 1954
Sales Range: $10-24.9 Million
Emp.: 3,155
Household & Industrial Glove Mfr
N.A.I.C.S.: 315990
Tsutomu Shimoda (Pres)

Subsidiaries:

Showa Best Glove, Inc. (1)
579 Edison St, Menlo, GA 30731
Tel.: (706) 862-2302
Web Site: http://www.showagroup.com
Glove Mfr
N.A.I.C.S.: 315990
Tom Egleston (VP-Sls & Mktg)

Plant (Domestic):

Best Manufacturing-Fayette (2)
931 2nd Ave SE, Fayette, AL 35555
Tel.: (205) 932-3202
Glove Mfr
N.A.I.C.S.: 315990

SHOWA HOLDINGS CO., LTD.
348 Toyo-ni, Kashiwa, 277 8556, Japan
Tel.: (81) 471310181   JP
Web Site: https://www.showa-holdings.co.jp
5103—(TKS)
Rev.: $58,617,480
Assets: $45,166,130
Liabilities: $25,931,030
Net Worth: $19,235,100
Earnings: ($3,509,910)
Emp.: 2,717
Fiscal Year-end: 03/31/24
Holding Company
N.A.I.C.S.: 551112

Subsidiaries:

Asuka Foods Co., Ltd. (1)
7-85-1 Ohara, Yao, 581-0092, Osaka, Japan
Tel.: (81) 729928850
Web Site: https://www.asukafoods.co.jp
Emp.: 300
Confectionery & Chinese Food Mfr & Whslr
N.A.I.C.S.: 311340

Showa Rubber (Malaysia) Sdn. Bhd. (1)
Plo 557 Jalan Keluli 3 Kawasan Perindustrian Pasir Gudang, Pasir Gudang, 81700, Johor Darul Takzim, Malaysia
Tel.: (60) 7 2528000
Web Site: http://www.showarubber-my.com
Sales Range: $25-49.9 Million
Emp.: 35
Rubber Linings & Industrial Rubber Products Mfr
N.A.I.C.S.: 326299
Bala Krishnan Nair (Mng Dir)

Wedge Holdings Co., Ltd. (1)
Koyo Building 3F 2-36-10 Minamisuna, Koto-ku, Tokyo, 136-0076, Japan (50.19%)
Tel.: (81) 362252161
Web Site: https://www.wedge-hd.com
Rev.: $5,423,850
Assets: $28,629,420
Liabilities: $4,629,770
Net Worth: $23,999,650
Earnings: ($3,637,170)
Fiscal Year-end: 09/30/2023
Holding Company
N.A.I.C.S.: 551112
Tatsuya Konoshita (CEO & Mng Dir)

Holding (Non-US):

Group Lease Public Company Limited (2)
63 Soi 1 Thetsabannimitrtai Road, Ladyao Chatuchak, Bangkok, 10900, Thailand
Tel.: (66) 25807555
Web Site: https://www.grouplease.co.th
Rev.: $68,482,596
Assets: $384,421,870
Liabilities: $245,548,974
Net Worth: $138,872,895
Earnings: ($41,349,254)
Emp.: 792
Fiscal Year-end: 12/31/2020
Motorcycle Leasing
N.A.I.C.S.: 441227
Muneo Tashiro (COO)

SHOWA MARUTSUTSU COMPANY, LTD.
8-1 Sakura-machi, Higashi-osaka, 579-8047, Osaka, Japan
Tel.: (81) 729814066
Web Site:
http://www.marutsutsu.co.jp
Sales Range: $10-24.9 Million
Emp.: 87
Paper Tubes, Cores, Protective Packaging, Molded Plastics & Paper Sticks Mfr
N.A.I.C.S.: 322120
Jun Sato (Chm)

Subsidiaries:

Showa Marutsutsu Company, Ltd. - Hiroshima Plant (1)
3-12-18 Minamikata, Mihara, 729-0419, Hiroshima, Japan
Tel.: (81) 848 86 3129
Paper Products Mfr
N.A.I.C.S.: 322130

Showa Marutsutsu Company, Ltd. - Hokuriku Plant (1)
Nomi, Nomi, 923-1237, Ishikawa, Japan
Tel.: (81) 761 51 4300
Paper Products Mfr
N.A.I.C.S.: 322130

Showa Marutsutsu Company, Ltd. - Suzuka Plant (1)
1-1 Hiratanaka-machi, Suzuka, 513-0846, Mie, Japan
Tel.: (81) 59 378 2577
Paper Products Mfr
N.A.I.C.S.: 322130

Showa Plastics Molding Co., Ltd. (1)
297 Shin-machi, Katsuragi, 639-2127, Nara, Japan
Tel.: (81) 745 62 1391
Paper Products Mfr
N.A.I.C.S.: 322130

Showa Products Company, Ltd. (1)
8-1 Sakura-machi, Higashi-osaka, 579-8047, Osaka, Japan
Tel.: (81) 729814061
Web Site: http://www.marutsutsu.co.jp
Paper Products Mfr
N.A.I.C.S.: 322130

Subsidiary (Domestic):

Showa Products Company, Ltd. (2)
8-1 Sakura-machi Higashi-Osaka, Chuo-Ku, Osaka, 579-8047, Japan
Tel.: (81) 332422751
Web Site: http://www.marutsutsu.co.jp
Sales Range: $10-24.9 Million
Emp.: 50
Engineered Carriers Mfr
N.A.I.C.S.: 333993
Yasunori Iwamoto (Pres)

Showa Products Company, Ltd. (2)
2-100 Kajita Cho, Ohbu-Aichi, Nagoya, 474-0071, Japan
Tel.: (81) 562472371
Web Site: http://www.marutsutsu.co.jp
Emp.: 50
Engineered Carriers Mfr
N.A.I.C.S.: 322130
Jun Sato (Chm)

Showa Products Company, Ltd. (2)
6317-3 Ohaza-Minamikata, Hongo-Cho Toyota-Gun, Hiroshima, 729-0413, Japan
Tel.: (81) 848862127
Web Site: http://www.marutsutsu.co.jp
Engineered Tubes & Cores Mfr
N.A.I.C.S.: 333993

Showa Products Company, Ltd. (2)
1-1 Hirata-Naka-Machi, Suzuka, Mie, 513-0846, Japan
Tel.: (81) 593782577
Web Site: http://www.marutsutsu.co.jp
Engineered Carriers Mfr
N.A.I.C.S.: 322130

Showa Products Company, Ltd. (2)
2-5670 Nakanose-Cho, Nobeoka, Miyazaki, 882-0032, Japan
Tel.: (81) 982336446
Web Site: http://www.marutsutsu.co.jp
Engineered Carriers Mfr
N.A.I.C.S.: 322130

SHOWA SANGYO CO., LTD.

Showa Products Company, Ltd. (2)
448-1 Koaza-Seko Ohaza-Seko, Gifu, 501-0563, Japan (100%)
Tel.: (81) 585323455
Web Site: http://www.marutsutsu.co.jp
Sales Range: $10-24.9 Million
Emp.: 40
Multipurpose Plastic & Paper Product Mfr
N.A.I.C.S.: 325211
Kabushiro Yamasaki (Plant Mgr)

Showa Products Company, Ltd.
1950-2 Kabasaki-Cho, Ashikaga, 326-0004, Tochigi, Japan
Tel.: (81) 284421008
Web Site: http://www.marutsutsu.co.jp
Engineered Carriers Mfr
N.A.I.C.S.: 322130

SHOWA PAXXS CORPORATION
Pax Building 2-12 Honmuracho Ichigaya, Shinjuku-Ku, Tokyo, 162-0845, Japan
Tel.: (81) 332695111
Web Site: https://www.showa-paxxs.co.jp
Year Founded: 1935
3954—(TKS)
Rev.: $143,113,110
Assets: $220,218,760
Liabilities: $62,907,370
Net Worth: $157,311,390
Earnings: $6,358,820
Emp.: 467
Fiscal Year-end: 03/31/24
Packaging Container Mfr & Distr
N.A.I.C.S.: 322219
Koichi Onodera (Pres & CEO)

SHOWA SANGYO CO., LTD.
Kamakuragashi Bldg 2-2-1 Uchikanda, Chiyoda-ku, Tokyo, 101-8521, Japan
Tel.: (81) 332572011
Web Site: https://www.showa-sangyo.co.jp
Year Founded: 1936
2004—(TKS)
Rev.: $2,289,426,380
Assets: $1,733,393,180
Liabilities: $852,590,850
Net Worth: $880,802,330
Earnings: $81,686,380
Emp.: 2,858
Fiscal Year-end: 03/31/24
Food Mfr
N.A.I.C.S.: 311230
Kazuhiko Niitsuma (Pres, Pres, CEO & CEO)

Subsidiaries:

Boso Oil & Fat Co., Ltd. (1)
2-17-1 Hinode, Funabashi-shi, Chiba, 273-0015, Japan (87.74%)
Tel.: (81) 47 4335551
Web Site: http://www.boso.co.jp
Rev.: $107,560,320
Assets: $94,957,860
Liabilities: $56,905,860
Net Worth: $38,052,000
Earnings: ($4,539,060)
Emp.: 104
Fiscal Year-end: 03/31/2019
Vegetable Oil Mfr & Distr
N.A.I.C.S.: 311225
Kaoru Kawasaki (Pres)

Oban Co., Ltd. (1)
5-2 Aburagimachi, Nagasaki, 852-8035, Japan
Tel.: (81) 958447121
Fast Food Restaurants
N.A.I.C.S.: 722513

Shikishima Starch Co., Ltd. (1)
5-5-1 Nago Sakaemachi, Suzuka, 513-0043, Mie, Japan
Tel.: (81) 593850512
Web Site: http://www.shikishima-starch.co.jp
Sales Range: $25-49.9 Million
Emp.: 98
Corn Mfr

SHOWA SANGYO CO., LTD.

Showa Sangyo Co., Ltd.—(Continued)
N.A.I.C.S.: 311221
Toshiro Ogawa (Pres)

Shosan Engineering Co., Ltd. (1)
2-20-2 Hinode, Funabashi, 273-0015, Chiba, Japan
Tel.: (81) 474101371
Sales Range: $25-49.9 Million
Emp.: 19
Building Equipment Contractors
N.A.I.C.S.: 238290

Shosan Kaihatsu Co., Ltd. (1)
2-1-1 Yatsu, 362-8511, Ageo, Saitama, Japan **(100%)**
Tel.: (81) 332572011
Web Site: http://www.shosan-plaza.co.jp
Real Estate Agencies
N.A.I.C.S.: 531210
Tomoyuki Miyagawa (Pres)

Shosan Shoji Co., Ltd. (1)
1-9-3 Itabashi Shosan Shoji Building, Itabashi-ku, Tokyo, 173-8580, Japan
Tel.: (81) 335797272
Web Site: http://www.shosan.co.jp
Sales Range: $50-74.9 Million
Emp.: 198
Wine Merchants Whslr
N.A.I.C.S.: 445320
Osamu Minorikawa (Pres)

Swing Bakery Co., Ltd. (1)
1-1-11 Matsuzakidai, Inzai, 270-1338, Chiba, Japan
Tel.: (81) 476451600
Web Site: https://swb.co.jp
Emp.: 350
Bakery Products Whslr
N.A.I.C.S.: 311812

SHOWA SHINKU CO., LTD.
3062-10 Tana, Chuo-ku, Sagamihara, 252-0244, Kanagawa, Japan
Tel.: (81) 427640321
Web Site:
   https://www.showashinku.co.jp
Year Founded: 1953
6384—(TKS)
Rev.: $49,330,430
Assets: $94,747,740
Liabilities: $19,413,570
Net Worth: $75,334,170
Earnings: $1,084,040
Emp.: 197
Fiscal Year-end: 03/31/24
Electronic Components Mfr
N.A.I.C.S.: 334419
Eiichi Chiba (Auditor)

Subsidiaries:

Fec Corporation (1)
229-3 Kashiwabara, Sayama, 350-1335, Japan
Tel.: (81) 429546371
Vacuum Equipment Mfr
N.A.I.C.S.: 334515

Sansei - Showa Co., Ltd. (1)
31000 Bainbridge Rd, Solon, OH 44139
Tel.: (440) 248-4440
Sales Range: $1-9.9 Million
Emp.: 5
Monolithic Filter Mfr
N.A.I.C.S.: 334413
Paul S. Biddlestone (Pres)

Showa Shinku Machinery Trading (Shanghai) Co., Ltd. (1)
No 1188 Huijin Road Qingpu Industrial Zone, Shanghai, 201707, China
Tel.: (86) 2159702577
Vacuum Product Mfr
N.A.I.C.S.: 334512

SHOWA SYSTEM ENGINEERING CORPORATION
PMO Nihonbashi Edo-dori 1-5 Kodenmacho Nihonbashi, Chuo-Ku, Tokyo, 103-0001, Japan
Tel.: (81) 336399051
Web Site: https://www.showa-sys-eng.co.jp

Year Founded: 1966
47520—(TKS)
Sales Range: Less than $1 Million
Software Development Services
N.A.I.C.S.: 513210
Yuichi Ozaki (Pres & CEO)

SHOWBOX CORP.
310 Dosandaero, Gangnam-gu, Seoul, 06054, Korea (South)
Tel.: (82) 232185500
Web Site: http://www.showbox.co.kr
Year Founded: 2002
086980—(KRS)
Rev.: $43,476,864
Assets: $125,158,086
Liabilities: $21,486,688
Net Worth: $103,671,398
Earnings: ($1,629,785)
Emp.: 61
Fiscal Year-end: 12/31/22
Movie Production & Distribution Services
N.A.I.C.S.: 512110
Signal Light (CEO)

SHOWCASE INC.
14F Roppongi First Building 1-9-9 Roppongi, Minato-ku, Tokyo, 106-0032, Japan
Tel.: (81) 355755117   JP
Web Site: https://www.showcase-tv.com
Year Founded: 1996
3909—(TKS)
Rev.: $40,292,470
Assets: $24,538,490
Liabilities: $13,839,680
Net Worth: $10,698,810
Earnings: ($829,530)
Fiscal Year-end: 12/31/23
Software Publisher
N.A.I.C.S.: 513210
Masahiro Mori (Co-Founder & Chm)

SHOWCASE MINERALS INC.
7070E Farrell Road S E, Calgary, T2H 0T2, AB, Canada
Tel.: (825) 449-8044   BC
Web Site:
   https://showcaseminerals.com
Year Founded: 2020
SHOW—(CNSX)
Assets: $230,023
Liabilities: $15,268
Net Worth: $214,755
Earnings: ($126,103)
Fiscal Year-end: 10/31/22
Mineral Exploration Services
N.A.I.C.S.: 212390
Kirk Reed (Pres)

SHRADDHA PRIME PROJECTS LTD
A-309 Kanara Business Centre Premises CS Limited Link Road, Laxmi Nagar Ghatkopar E, Mumbai, 400075, India
Tel.: (91) 2231479024   In
Web Site:
   https://shraddhaprimeprojects.in
Year Founded: 1993
531771—(BOM)
Rev.: $14,106
Assets: $162,132
Liabilities: $3,049
Net Worth: $159,083
Earnings: ($34,280)
Emp.: 2
Fiscal Year-end: 03/31/21
Survey Instruments Mfr
N.A.I.C.S.: 334519
O. J. Bansal (Mng Dir)

SHRADHA INFRAPROJECTS LIMITED
Block No F/8 2nd Floor Shradha House Near Shri Mohini Complex, Kingsway, Nagpur, 440001, Maharashtra, India
Tel.: (91) 122530709
Web Site: https://www.shradhainfra.in
Year Founded: 1997
SHRADHA—(NSE)
Rev.: $884,148
Assets: $29,066,650
Liabilities: $20,413,560
Net Worth: $8,653,089
Earnings: $293,726
Emp.: 8
Fiscal Year-end: 03/31/20
Infrastructure Construction & Development Services
N.A.I.C.S.: 236220
Shreyas Sunil Raisoni (Mng Dir)

SHREE AJIT PULP AND PAPER LIMITED
Survey No 239 Near Morai Railway Crossing, Village Salvav Via-Vapi, Valsad, 396 191, Gujarat, India
Tel.: (91) 2602437059
Web Site: http://www.shreeajit.com
Year Founded: 1995
Rev.: $39,346,339
Assets: $29,070,624
Liabilities: $13,482,849
Net Worth: $15,587,775
Earnings: $1,193,639
Emp.: 266
Fiscal Year-end: 03/31/18
Paper Mfr
N.A.I.C.S.: 322299
Gautam D. Shah (Chm & Mng Dir)

SHREE ASHTAVINAYAK CINE VISION LTD
A - 204/205 VIP Plaza 2nd Floor B/7 Veera Industrial Estate, Off Andheri Malad Link Road Andheri W, Mumbai, 400053, Maharashtra, India
Tel.: (91) 2240497800
Web Site:
   http://www.ashtavinayakindia.com
Sales Range: $25-49.9 Million
Emp.: 19
Entertainment & Film Industry
N.A.I.C.S.: 512131
Hiren J. Gandhi (Exec Dir)

SHREE BHAVYA FABRICS LTD.
252 New Cloth Market Raipur, Ahmedabad, 380 002, Gujarat, India
Tel.: (91) 7922172949
Web Site:
   https://www.shreebhavyafabric.com
Year Founded: 1988
521131—(BOM)
Rev.: $23,358,905
Assets: $19,152,693
Liabilities: $15,427,076
Net Worth: $3,725,617
Earnings: $184,441
Emp.: 148
Fiscal Year-end: 03/31/23
Textile Product Mfr & Whslr
N.A.I.C.S.: 314999
Purshottam R. Agarwal (Chm & Mng Dir)

SHREE BHAWANI PAPER MILLS LIMITED
33 Daya Nand Marg, Allahabad, 211002, Uttar Pradesh, India
Tel.: (91) 5322548401
Web Site: http://www.shbhawani.com
Paper Mfr
N.A.I.C.S.: 322120
Girish Tandon (Mng Dir)

SHREE CEMENT LIMITED

INTERNATIONAL PUBLIC

Bangur Nagar, Beawar, Ajmer, 305 901, Rajasthan, India
Tel.: (91) 146222810106
Web Site:
   https://www.shreecement.com
SHREECEM—(BOM)
Rev.: $1,903,173,090
Assets: $2,936,547,705
Liabilities: $827,817,900
Net Worth: $2,108,729,805
Earnings: $312,529,035
Emp.: 6,259
Fiscal Year-end: 03/31/21
Cement Mfr
N.A.I.C.S.: 327310
H. M. Bangur (Chm & Mng Dir)

Subsidiaries:

Union Cement Company (1)
Alrams Road Khor Khuwair, Ras al Khaimah, United Arab Emirates
Tel.: (971) 72668166
Web Site: https://uccrak.com
Cement Mfr
N.A.I.C.S.: 327310
Hussain Hassan Mirza Modh Al Sayegh (Chm)

SHREE GANESH BIOTECH INDIA LTD.
126 3/2 75C Park Street 3rd Floor Kamdhenu Building, Kolkata, 700016, West Bengal, India
Tel.: (91) 3323988213
Web Site:
   https://www.shreeganeshbiotech.com
539470—(BOM)
Rev.: $2,349,689
Assets: $10,186,620
Liabilities: $2,297,995
Net Worth: $7,888,625
Earnings: $43,239
Emp.: 5
Fiscal Year-end: 03/31/21
Agricultural Chemical Product Mfr
N.A.I.C.S.: 325320
Komal Mani Shukla (Sec)

SHREE GANESH ELASTOPLAST LIMITED
119 Ground Floor Kamdhenu Complex Opp Sahajanand College, Polytechnic Road, Ahmedabad, 380 015, Gujarat, India
Tel.: (91) 7964503388
Web Site:
   https://www.shreeelastoplastltd.com
530797—(BOM)
Rev.: $1,702,454
Assets: $427,561
Liabilities: $39,087
Net Worth: $388,475
Earnings: $69,565
Emp.: 6
Fiscal Year-end: 03/31/21
Rubber Product Mfr & Distr
N.A.I.C.S.: 325998
Bharat V. Mashruwala (Compliance Officer)

SHREE GANESH FORGINGS LTD.
412 Emca House SBS Road, Fort, Mumbai, 400 001, India
Tel.: (91) 22 66311054   In
Web Site:
   http://www.shreeganeshforgings.com
Year Founded: 1972
Rev.: $67,759
Assets: $10,872,944
Liabilities: $23,413,558
Net Worth: ($12,540,614)
Earnings: ($867,933)
Fiscal Year-end: 03/31/18
Forged Steel Pipe Flanges, Fittings & Motor Vehicle Components Mfr
N.A.I.C.S.: 332111

AND PRIVATE COMPANIES

Deepak Balkrishan Sekhri *(Chm & Mng Dir)*

SHREE GANESH JEWELLERY HOUSE (I) LIMITED
Avani - Signature 4th Floor - 402 91A/1 Park Street, Kolkata, 700016, West Bengal, India
Tel.: (91) 3330259382
Web Site: http://www.sgjhl.com
Rev.: $316,949
Assets: $527,913,933
Liabilities: $608,445,985
Net Worth: ($80,532,051)
Earnings: ($111,766,761)
Emp.: 108
Fiscal Year-end: 03/31/16
Gold Jewelry Mfr & Exporter
N.A.I.C.S.: 339910

SHREE GANESH REMEDIES LIMITED
Plot No 6011 GIDC Industrial Estate, Ankleshwar, 393 002, Gujarat, India
Tel.: (91) 7574976076
Web Site:
https://www.ganeshremedies.com
540737—(BOM)
Rev.: $6,985,609
Assets: $8,271,633
Liabilities: $1,446,199
Net Worth: $6,825,434
Earnings: $1,331,448
Emp.: 79
Fiscal Year-end: 03/31/21
Pharmaceutical Preparation Mfr & Distr
N.A.I.C.S.: 325411
Chandulal Kothia *(Chm & Mng Dir)*

SHREE GLOBAL TRADEFIN LIMITED
A2 2nd Floor Madhu Estate Pandurang Budhkar Marg Lower Pare, Mumbai, 400013, India
Tel.: (91) 2262918111
Web Site: https://www.sgtl.in
Year Founded: 1986
512463—(BOM)
Rev.: $268,250
Assets: $45,790,044
Liabilities: $1,108,830
Net Worth: $44,681,214
Earnings: $165,479
Emp.: 9
Fiscal Year-end: 03/31/21
Investment Management Service
N.A.I.C.S.: 523940
Rajesh R. Gupta *(Chm & Mng Dir)*

Subsidiaries:

Indrajit Properties Private Limited (1)

Lloyds Realty Developers Limited (1)
A-2 Madhu Estate 2nd Floor Pandurang Budhkar Marg Lower Parel, Mumbai, 400 013, India
Tel.: (91) 2262918111
Web Site: https://lloydsrealty.com
Real Estate Development Services
N.A.I.C.S.: 531210

Lloyds Steels Industries Ltd. (1)
Plot No A-5/5 MIDC Industrial Area, Murbad Dist, Thane, 421401, Maharashtra, India (53.4%)
Tel.: (91) 2524222271
Web Site: https://www.lloydsengg.in
Rev.: $38,175,901
Assets: $44,463,749
Liabilities: $21,040,177
Net Worth: $23,423,572
Earnings: $4,414,975
Emp.: 163
Fiscal Year-end: 03/31/2023
Hardware Product Mfr
N.A.I.C.S.: 332510
Ashok Tandon *(Mng Dir)*

Simon Developers & Infrastructure Private Limited (1)

SHREE HANUMAN SUGAR & INDUSTRIES LIMITED
Premises No 9 Ground Floor Vasundhara Building 2/7 Sarat Bose Road, Kolkata, 700020, India
Tel.: (91) 3322821184
Web Site:
https://www.hanumansugar.com
Year Founded: 1932
Rev.: $119,439
Assets: $25,606,003
Liabilities: $12,040,484
Net Worth: $13,565,519
Earnings: $10,686,919
Fiscal Year-end: 06/30/17
Sugar Products Mfr
N.A.I.C.S.: 311314
Bimal Kumar Nopany *(Chm & Mng Dir)*

SHREE HARI CHEMICALS EXPORT LIMITED
401 402 A Wing Oberoi Chambers OPP SAB TV New Link Road Andheri West, Mumbai, 400053, India
Tel.: (91) 2249634834
Web Site:
https://www.shreeharichemicals.in
Year Founded: 1987
524336—(BOM)
Rev.: $12,412,385
Assets: $10,734,716
Liabilities: $8,583,131
Net Worth: $2,151,586
Earnings: ($2,374,222)
Emp.: 71
Fiscal Year-end: 03/31/23
Acid Dye Mfr
N.A.I.C.S.: 325130
Bankesh Chandra Agrawal *(Chm & Mng Dir)*

SHREE INVESTMENT & FINANCE COMPANY LIMITED
Dilli Bazar, PO Box 10717, Kathmandu, Nepal
Tel.: (977) 14422038
Web Site:
https://www.shreefinance.com.np
Year Founded: 1994
SIFC—(NEP)
Sales Range: Less than $1 Million
Financial Services
N.A.I.C.S.: 523999
Sashi Raj Pandey *(Chm)*

SHREE KARTHIK PAPERS LIMITED
No 25 50 Feet Road Krishnasamy Nagar, Ramanathapuram, Coimbatore, 641045, Tamil Nadu, India
Tel.: (91) 4224217174
Web Site:
http://www.shreekarthikpapers.in
Year Founded: 1991
516106—(BOM)
Rev.: $10,103,372
Assets: $5,006,467
Liabilities: $4,756,807
Net Worth: $249,660
Earnings: $50,014
Emp.: 42
Fiscal Year-end: 03/31/23
Paper Mfr
N.A.I.C.S.: 322120
M. S. Velu *(Chm, CEO & Mng Dir)*

SHREE KRISHNA INFRASTRUCTURE LTD.
101 1st Floor 36 Shri Rang Residency, Vadia Rajpipla, Gujarat, 393145, India
Tel.: (91) 8849865932

Web Site: https://www.skifl.com
Year Founded: 1990
542146—(BOM)
Rev.: $83,029
Assets: $1,375,925
Liabilities: $1,691
Net Worth: $1,374,234
Earnings: $2,997
Emp.: 4
Fiscal Year-end: 03/31/23
Real Estate Investment Services
N.A.I.C.S.: 531390
Amit Kotia *(CFO)*

SHREE KRISHNA PAPER MILLS & INDUSTRIES LIMITED
4830/2 Prahlad Street Ansari Road, Daryaganj, New Delhi, 110002, India
Tel.: (91) 1146263200
Web Site: https://www.skpmil.com
Year Founded: 1974
500388—(BOM)
Rev.: $9,532,996
Assets: $10,539,015
Liabilities: $7,658,824
Net Worth: $2,880,191
Earnings: ($446,956)
Emp.: 222
Fiscal Year-end: 03/31/21
Paper Mfr
N.A.I.C.S.: 322120
Narendra K. Pasari *(Mng Dir)*

SHREE MANUFACTURING COMPANY LIMITED
Suite 712 Prasad Chambers Opera House, Mumbai, 400004, Maharashtra, India
Tel.: (91) 2266631999
Web Site: https://www.smcl.co.in
Year Founded: 1976
503863—(BOM)
Rev.: $19,110
Assets: $25,551
Liabilities: $268,008
Net Worth: ($242,456)
Earnings: ($14,205)
Fiscal Year-end: 03/31/21
Textile Products Mfr
N.A.I.C.S.: 313110
Vishal Dedhia *(CFO & Exec Dir)*

SHREE METALLOYS LIMITED
103 Sun Square Nr Regenta Hotel Off CG Road, Ahmedabad, 380009, India
Tel.: (91) 7926300054
Web Site: https://shreemetalloys.com
531962—(BOM)
Rev.: $10,969,689
Assets: $1,003,571
Liabilities: $11,431
Net Worth: $992,140
Earnings: $74,347
Emp.: 10
Fiscal Year-end: 03/31/23
Precious Metal Whslr
N.A.I.C.S.: 423940
Pratik Radheshyam Kabra *(Chm & Mng Dir)*

SHREE NARMADA ALUMINIUM INDUSTRIES LIMITED
95 /1 Bharuch Palej Road Bholav, Bharuch, 392001, Gujarat, India
Tel.: (91) 2642260624
Web Site: https://www.snailbh.in
513127—(BOM)
Sales Range: $1-9.9 Million
Aluminium Products Mfr
N.A.I.C.S.: 331318
Krishna Swamy *(Compliance Officer)*

SHREE NIDHI TRADING COMPANY LIMITED
7 Lyons Range 3rd Floor Room No 9

SHREE PUSHKAR CHEMICALS & FERTILISERS LTD.

& 10, Kolkata, 700 001, India
Tel.: (91) 844 300 7953
Web Site:
http://www.shreenidhitrading.com
Year Founded: 1982
540253—(BOM)
Rev.: $34,275
Assets: $1,462,772
Liabilities: $34,435
Net Worth: $1,428,337
Earnings: ($10,502)
Emp.: 9
Fiscal Year-end: 03/31/21
Investment Management Service
N.A.I.C.S.: 523150
Tanumay Laha *(Mng Dir & Compliance Officer)*

SHREE OSFM E-MOBILITY LIMITED
104 Green Park Plot No 2&3 Sector 3 Opposite Ghansoli Railway Station, Ghansoli, Navi Mumbai, 400701, Maharashtra, India
Tel.: (91) 2227544431
Web Site:
https://www.shreeosfm.com
Year Founded: 2006
SHREEOSFM—(NSE)
Rev.: $10,012,344
Assets: $5,096,472
Liabilities: $2,616,235
Net Worth: $2,480,237
Earnings: $353,286
Emp.: 154
Fiscal Year-end: 03/31/23
Human Resource Consulting Services
N.A.I.C.S.: 541612

SHREE PACETRONIX LTD.
Plot No 15 Sector II Pithampur, Dhar, 454775, Madhya Pradesh, India
Tel.: (91) 7292411105
Web Site:
https://www.pacetronix.com
527005—(BOM)
Rev.: $2,439,542
Assets: $1,983,232
Liabilities: $823,333
Net Worth: $1,159,899
Earnings: $390,824
Emp.: 59
Fiscal Year-end: 03/31/23
Medical Equipment Mfr
N.A.I.C.S.: 339112
Atul Kumar Sethi *(Co-Mng Dir)*

SHREE PRECOATED STEELS LIMITED
1 Ground Floor Citi Mall New Link Road, Andheri W, Mumbai, 400 053, India
Tel.: (91) 7208182677
Web Site: https://www.spsl.com
Year Founded: 2007
533110—(BOM)
Assets: $649,745
Liabilities: $765,925
Net Worth: ($116,180)
Earnings: ($63,677)
Emp.: 3
Fiscal Year-end: 03/31/23
Coated Flat Steel Products Mfr
N.A.I.C.S.: 331110
Harsh L. Mehta *(Mng Dir)*

SHREE PUSHKAR CHEMICALS & FERTILISERS LTD.
301/302 3rd Floor Atlanta Centre Near Udyog Bhawan Sonawala Road, Goregaon East, Mumbai, 400 063, India
Tel.: (91) 2242702525
Web Site:
https://www.shreepushkar.com

Shree Pushkar Chemicals & Fertilisers Ltd.—(Continued)
Year Founded: 1994
539334—(BOM)
Rev.: $82,962,688
Assets: $78,768,827
Liabilities: $26,299,910
Net Worth: $52,468,917
Earnings: $4,464,133
Emp.: 334
Fiscal Year-end: 03/31/23
Chemical Products Mfr
N.A.I.C.S.: 325998
Punit Makharia *(Chm & Co-Mng Dir)*

SHREE RAJASTHAN SYNTEX LTD.
27-A First Floor Meera Nagar, Housing Board Colony, Udaipur, 313 001, Rajasthan, India
Tel.: (91) 2942440334
Web Site: https://www.srsl.in
Year Founded: 1981
503837—(BOM)
Rev.: $5,217,440
Assets: $17,832,510
Liabilities: $22,497,288
Net Worth: ($4,664,778)
Earnings: ($3,295,779)
Emp.: 274
Fiscal Year-end: 03/31/21
Textile Products Mfr
N.A.I.C.S.: 314999
Vikas Ladia *(CEO & Mng Dir)*

Subsidiaries:

Shree Rajasthan Syntex Ltd. - Polycot Division (1)
Simalwara Road, Dungarpur, 314 001, Rajasthan, India
Tel.: (91) 2964 302400
Web Site: http://www.srsl.in
Emp.: 300
Polypropylene Filament Yarn Mfr
N.A.I.C.S.: 313110
B. K. Mazumdar *(Pres)*

SHREE RAJESHWARANAND PAPER MILLS LIMITED
451-B Bharauch - Jhagadia Road Vilage - Govali, Taluka Jhagadia, Bharuch, 393 001, Gujarat, India
Tel.: (91) 2645227705
Web Site: http://shreerajeshwaranand.com
Year Founded: 1991
516086—(BOM)
Rev.: $10,528,648
Assets: $15,320,251
Liabilities: $13,098,692
Net Worth: $2,221,559
Earnings: ($1,980,891)
Emp.: 5
Fiscal Year-end: 03/31/20
Newsprint Paper Mfr
N.A.I.C.S.: 322120
Amrish R. Patel *(Chm)*

SHREE RAM PROTEINS LTD.
B-206 Second Floor The Imperial Heights Opp Big Bazaar 150 Feet, Ring Road, Rajkot, 360 005, Gujarat, India
Tel.: (91) 2812581152
Web Site: https://www.shreeramproteins.com
SRPL—(NSE)
Rev.: $19,511,384
Assets: $12,718,626
Liabilities: $5,995,660
Net Worth: $6,722,966
Earnings: $461,040
Emp.: 24
Fiscal Year-end: 03/31/23
Textile Products Mfr
N.A.I.C.S.: 314999
Lalitkumar Vasoya *(Mng Dir)*

SHREE RAMA MULTI-TECH LIMITED
1557 Motibhoyan Kalol-Khatraj Rd, Gandhinagar, 382 721, Gujarat, India
Tel.: (91) 7966747101
Web Site: https://www.srmtl.com
Year Founded: 1987
532310—(BOM)
Rev.: $21,473,934
Assets: $16,598,728
Liabilities: $4,282,708
Net Worth: $12,316,020
Earnings: $1,194,792
Emp.: 343
Fiscal Year-end: 03/31/24
Packaging Products Mfr
N.A.I.C.S.: 322220
Krunal Shah *(CFO)*

SHREE RANG MARK TRAVELS LIMITED
214 Anil Kunj Paldi Circle, Ahmedabad, 380006, Gujarat, India
Tel.: (91) 22 24143502
Web Site: http://www.srmtl.in
Sales Range: Less than $1 Million
Travel Agency Services
N.A.I.C.S.: 561510

SHREE RENUKA SUGARS LIMITED
7th Floor Devchand House Shiv Sagar Estate Dr Annie Besant Road, Worli, Mumbai, 400 018, India
Tel.: (91) 2224977744
Web Site: https://www.renukasugars.com
RENUKA—(NSE)
Rev.: $776,084,537
Assets: $942,748,307
Liabilities: $1,033,403,826
Net Worth: ($90,655,519)
Earnings: ($15,905,253)
Emp.: 1,979
Fiscal Year-end: 03/31/21
Sugar Mfr
N.A.I.C.S.: 311313
Narendra M. Murkumbi *(Founder)*

Subsidiaries:

KBK Chem-Engineering Private Limited (1)
Tel.: (91) 2066759900
Web Site: https://kbk-chem.com
Engineeering Services
N.A.I.C.S.: 541330

Unit (Domestic):

KBK Chem-Engineering Private Limited - Pune Unit (2)
Gat No-540 Urwade Road Kasar Amboli Tal Mulshi Pirangut, Pune, 412 111, Maharashtra, India
Tel.: (91) 2066765001
Engineeering Services
N.A.I.C.S.: 541330

Renuka Vale do IVAI S/A (1)
Estrada Mariza Km 03, Caixa Postal 91, Sao Pedro do Ivai, Parana, 86945-000, Brazil
Tel.: (55) 433 451 8000
Web Site: https://www.valedoivai.com.br
Sugar Mfr & Distr
N.A.I.C.S.: 111930

Unit (Domestic):

Renuka Vale Do IVAI S/A - Cambui Unit (2)
Rodovia PR 455 s/n Lote 336 Gleba Aquidaban Distrito de, Sao Miguel do Cambui Marialva, Parana, 86900-000, Brazil
Tel.: (55) 4432358550
Methanol Mfr
N.A.I.C.S.: 325199

Renuka do Brasil S/A (1)
Av Nove de Julho 5 519 5th floor, Sao Paulo, 01407-200, Brazil
Tel.: (55) 1130746900
Web Site: http://www.renukadobrasil.com.br
Sugar Mfr
N.A.I.C.S.: 325199
Paulo Adalberto Zanetti *(Pres & CEO)*

Revati S.A (1)
Estr Municipal CRD 339, Brejo Alegre, Sao Paulo, 16265-000, Brazil
Tel.: (55) 1836468700
Sugar Mfr
N.A.I.C.S.: 311314

SHREE SALASAR INVESTMENTS LTD.
404 Niranjan 99 Marine Drive Marine Lines, Mumbai, 400 002, Maharashtra, India
Tel.: (91) 2222816379
Web Site: http://www.shreesalasar.in
Year Founded: 1980
503635—(BOM)
Rev.: $430,921
Assets: $14,947,305
Liabilities: $10,998,621
Net Worth: $3,948,684
Earnings: $20,442
Fiscal Year-end: 03/31/23
Investment Management Service
N.A.I.C.S.: 523999
Dismas Gigool *(CFO & Officer-Compliance)*

SHREE SECURITIES LIMITED
3 Synagogue Street 3rd Floor Room No 18G, Kolkata, 700 001, West Bengal, India
Tel.: (91) 3322313366
Web Site: http://www.shreesecindia.com
538975—(BOM)
Rev.: $52,851
Assets: $2,886,805
Liabilities: $13,321
Net Worth: $2,873,485
Earnings: ($26,030)
Fiscal Year-end: 03/31/23
Financial Support Services
N.A.I.C.S.: 523999
Basant Kumar Sharma *(CEO & Mng Dir)*

SHREE STEEL WIRE ROPES LIMITED
Gat No 183-185 KIDC, Village Dheku Taluka Khalapur Dist Raigad, Khopoli, 410 202, Maharashtra, India
Tel.: (91) 2192263547
Web Site: https://www.sswrl.com
513488—(BOM)
Rev.: $2,251,164
Assets: $2,035,721
Liabilities: $301,639
Net Worth: $1,734,082
Earnings: $118,495
Fiscal Year-end: 03/31/21
Steel Wire Rope Mfr
N.A.I.C.S.: 314994
Manoj Bansidhar Jeswani *(Chm, Mng Dir & Compliance Officer)*

SHREE TIRUPATI BALAJEE FIBC LTD.
Plot No A P 14 Apparel Park Sez Phase-II, Industrial Area, Pithampur, 454774, Madhya Pradesh, India
Tel.: (91) 7314217400
Web Site: https://www.tirupatibalajee.com
Year Founded: 2009
TIRUPATI—(NSE)
Rev.: $21,136,706
Assets: $14,159,295
Liabilities: $6,476,194
Net Worth: $7,683,101
Earnings: $1,123,698
Emp.: 600
Fiscal Year-end: 03/31/23
Polyethylene Mfr

N.A.I.C.S.: 325211
Arunendra Jeet Singh *(Gen Mgr-Intl Mktg)*

SHREE TULSI ONLINE.COM LIMITED
4 Netaji Subhas Road 1st Floor, Kolkata, 700 001, India
Tel.: (91) 33 22624717
Web Site: http://www.shreetulsionline.com
Year Founded: 1982
Rev.: $9,908
Assets: $2,489,017
Liabilities: $28,774
Net Worth: $2,460,243
Earnings: ($861,439)
Fiscal Year-end: 03/31/19
Business Application Software Development Services
N.A.I.C.S.: 541511
Vinod Kumar Bothra *(Exec Dir)*

SHREE VASU LOGISTICS LIMITED
Logistics Park Opp Jaika Automobiles Ring Road No 1, Raipur, 492001, Chhattisgarh, India
Tel.: (91) 7716614848
Web Site: https://www.shreevasulogistics.com
Year Founded: 1987
SVLL—(NSE)
Rev.: $12,210,191
Assets: $16,622,217
Liabilities: $13,234,938
Net Worth: $3,387,279
Earnings: $245,465
Emp.: 590
Fiscal Year-end: 03/31/23
Logistic Services
N.A.I.C.S.: 541614
Atul Garg *(Mng Dir)*

SHREEJAL INFO HUBS LIMITED
912 Krushal Commercial Bldg M G Rd Chembur W Above Shopper Stop, Mumbai, 400049, Maharashtra, India
Tel.: (91) 22 2525 1934
Year Founded: 1962
Rev.: $7,104
Earnings: ($4,461)
Fiscal Year-end: 03/31/16
Information Support Services
N.A.I.C.S.: 518210
Priti Mukesh Vora *(Compliance Officer)*

SHREEJI TRANSLOGISTICS LIMITED
Shreeji House Sector 19C Plot No 107 Vashi, Navi Mumbai, 400 705, India
Tel.: (91) 2240746666
Web Site: https://www.shreejitranslogistics.com
Year Founded: 1976
540738—(BOM)
Rev.: $15,033,932
Assets: $11,217,287
Liabilities: $7,903,681
Net Worth: $3,313,606
Earnings: $140,129
Emp.: 281
Fiscal Year-end: 03/31/21
Logistics Management Services
N.A.I.C.S.: 541614
Bipin Shah *(Exec Dir)*

SHREENATH INVESTMENT COMPANY LIMITED
801-802 Dalamal Tower Nariman Point, Mumbai, 400021, India
Tel.: (91) 2266381800
Web Site: https://www.shreenathinvestment.in
503696—(BOM)
Rev.: $367,035
Assets: $8,441,419
Liabilities: $16,667
Net Worth: $8,424,753
Earnings: $297,215
Fiscal Year-end: 03/31/21
Financial Investment Services
N.A.I.C.S.: 523999
Vikas Mapara *(Mng Dir)*

SHREEOSWAL SEEDS & CHEMICALS LIMITED
Nasirabad Highway Opp Balkavi Bairagi College, Village- Kanawati Neemuch, Indore, 458441, Madhya Pradesh, India
Tel.: (91) 7423297511
Web Site: https://www.oswalseeds.com
Year Founded: 2002
OSWALSEEDS—(NSE)
Rev.: $32,666,327
Assets: $15,364,702
Liabilities: $10,045,453
Net Worth: $5,319,249
Earnings: $684,192
Emp.: 28
Fiscal Year-end: 03/31/23
Agriculture Seed Mfr
N.A.I.C.S.: 325320

Subsidiaries:
Shreeoswal Psyllium Exports India Limited (1)
Highway Opp Balkavi Bairagi College, Village-Kanawati, Neemuch, 458441, Madhya Pradesh, India
Tel.: (91) 7423297511
Web Site: https://www.oswalpsyllium.com
Psyllium Product Mfr
N.A.I.C.S.: 327999

SHREESHAY ENGINEERS LIMITED
Shop No F04 1st floor Eternity MallNaupada, Teen Haath Naka LBS Marg Wagle I E, Thane, 400604, Maharashtra, India
Tel.: (91) 2225082300
Web Site: https://www.shreeshay.com
541112—(BOM)
Real Estate Development Services
N.A.I.C.S.: 531390
Kishore D. Patel *(Mng Dir)*

SHREEVATSAA FINANCE & LEASING LIMITED
120/500 10 Lajpat Nagar, Kanpur, 208005, Uttar Pradesh, India
Tel.: (91) 5122530991
Web Site: http://www.svfl.in
Year Founded: 1986
532007—(BOM)
Rev.: $139,102
Assets: $2,924,136
Liabilities: $37,581
Net Worth: $2,886,555
Earnings: $82,795
Emp.: 4
Fiscal Year-end: 03/31/21
Financial Services
N.A.I.C.S.: 523999
Anil Kumar Sharma *(Chm & Mng Dir)*

SHRENIK LTD.
1009 10th Floor Shivalik Shilp Iscon Cross Road, Ahmedabad, 380015, Gujarat, India
Tel.: (91) 7926440303
Web Site: https://www.shrenikltd.com
SHRENIK—(NSE)
Rev.: $16,093,328
Assets: $31,604,244
Liabilities: $24,058,300
Net Worth: $7,545,945
Earnings: $27,506
Emp.: 4
Fiscal Year-end: 03/31/23
Stationery Product Distr
N.A.I.C.S.: 424120
Shrenik Sudhirbhai Vimawala *(Chm & Mng Dir)*

SHRENUJ & CO., LTD.
405 Dharam Palace 100-103 NS Patakar Marg, Mumbai, 400 007, India
Tel.: (91) 2266373500
Web Site: http://www.shrenuj.com
Year Founded: 1906
Diamond Jewelry Mfr
N.A.I.C.S.: 339910

Subsidiaries:
Simon Golub & Sons Inc. (1)
5506 6th Ave S, Seattle, WA 98108
Tel.: (206) 762-4800
Web Site: http://www.simongolub.com
Sales Range: $50-74.9 Million
Emp.: 100
Watch, Parts & Other Jewelry Distr
N.A.I.C.S.: 423940

SHREYANS INDUSTRIES LIMITED
PO Sahabana Chandigarh Road Village Bholapur, Ludhiana, 141123, Punjab, India
Tel.: (91) 1612685270
Web Site: https://www.shreyansgroup.com
516016—(BOM)
Rev.: $52,820,354
Assets: $54,369,069
Liabilities: $23,494,817
Net Worth: $30,874,253
Earnings: $1,197,965
Emp.: 1,301
Fiscal Year-end: 03/31/21
Paper Products Mfr
N.A.I.C.S.: 322299
Rajneesh Oswal *(Chm & Mng Dir)*

Subsidiaries:
Adinath Textiles Limited (1)
Village Bholapur P O Sahabana Chandigarh Road, Ludhiana, 141123, Punjab, India
Tel.: (91) 9876100948
Web Site: https://www.adinathtextiles.com
Rev.: $230,654
Assets: $464,918
Liabilities: $254,148
Net Worth: $210,770
Earnings: $43,069
Emp.: 23
Fiscal Year-end: 03/31/2021
Textile Products Mfr
N.A.I.C.S.: 314999
Rajneesh Oswal *(Chm & Mng Dir)*

Shreyans Industries Limited - Shreyans Papers Plant (1)
Malikpur, Sangrur, Ahmedgarh, 148021, Punjab, India
Tel.: (91) 1675 240347
Emp.: 500
Paper Products Mfr
N.A.I.C.S.: 322299
Anil Kumar *(CEO & Exec Dir)*

SHREYAS INTERMEDIATES LIMITED
Plots Nos D-21 D-22 and D-23 MIDC Industrial Area, Lote Parshuram, Ratnagiri, 415722, Maharashtra, India
Tel.: (91) 2242766500
Web Site: https://www.shreyasmediates.com
Year Founded: 1992
526335—(BOM)
Rev.: $70,552
Assets: $3,505,797
Liabilities: $1,160,566
Net Worth: $2,345,231
Earnings: ($187,885)
Emp.: 3
Fiscal Year-end: 03/31/23
Synthetic Dye & Pigment Mfr
N.A.I.C.S.: 325130

SHREYAS SHIPPING & LOGISTICS LIMITED
D 301-305 Level 3 Tower II Seawoods Grand Central Plot No R1 Sector 40, Nerul Node, Navi Mumbai, 400706, India
Tel.: (91) 2268110300
Web Site: https://www.transworld.com
520151—(BOM)
Rev.: $77,011,935
Assets: $95,610,060
Liabilities: $37,996,140
Net Worth: $57,613,920
Earnings: $6,042,855
Emp.: 41
Fiscal Year-end: 03/31/21
Logistic Services
N.A.I.C.S.: 541614
Ramesh S. Ramakrishnan *(Chm)*

Subsidiaries:
BSL Freight Solution Private Limited (1)
D 301-305 Level 3 Tower II Seawoods Grand Central Plot No R1 Sector 40, Nerul Node, Navi Mumbai, 400706, India
Tel.: (91) 2268110300
Logistic Services
N.A.I.C.S.: 488510

Transworld Feeders FZCO (1)
Plot No S 20119 Jebel Ali Free Zone South, PO Box 261844, Dubai, United Arab Emirates
Tel.: (971) 48035500
Logistic Services
N.A.I.C.S.: 488510

Transworld Shipping & Logistics LLC (1)
Office No 510 5th Floor Al Mana Building Above Ford Showroom Building, PO Box 37656, No 100 Al Matar St, Doha, Qatar
Tel.: (974) 44512980
Logistic Services
N.A.I.C.S.: 488510

SHRI BAJRANG ALLIANCE LIMITED
521/C Urla Industrial Complex Urla, Raipur, 493221, Chhattisgarh, India
Tel.: (91) 7714288000
Web Site: https://www.sbal.co.in
Year Founded: 1990
526981—(BOM)
Rev.: $29,224,200
Assets: $30,796,639
Liabilities: $9,877,181
Net Worth: $20,919,458
Earnings: $297,993
Emp.: 287
Fiscal Year-end: 03/31/21
Steel Products Mfr
N.A.I.C.S.: 331210
Narendra Goel *(Chm)*

Subsidiaries:
Shri Bajrang Agro Processing Limited (1)
Urla Growth Center, Village Borjhara, Raipur, 493221, Chhattisgarh, India
Tel.: (91) 7714288019
Web Site: http://www.sbafoods.com
Food Products Mfr
N.A.I.C.S.: 311999

SHRI BHOLANATH CARPETS LTD.
G T Road P O Thathra Kachhawan, Varanasi, 221 313, India
Tel.: (91) 9984600671
Web Site: https://www.bholanath.biz
530841—(BOM)
Rev.: $2,130,823
Assets: $3,820,566
Liabilities: $2,264,541
Net Worth: $1,556,026
Earnings: $10,484
Emp.: 18
Fiscal Year-end: 03/31/23
Carpet Mfr
N.A.I.C.S.: 314110
Bholanath Baranwal *(Chm)*

SHRI DINESH MILLS LTD.
Near Indiabulls Mega Mall Akota Road, PO Box No 2501, Vadodara, 390 020, Gujarat, India
Tel.: (91) 2652960061
Web Site: https://www.dineshmills.com
Year Founded: 1935
503804—(BOM)
Rev.: $12,581,644
Assets: $26,325,256
Liabilities: $6,125,028
Net Worth: $20,200,228
Earnings: $2,865,823
Emp.: 298
Fiscal Year-end: 03/31/23
Textile Products Mfr
N.A.I.C.S.: 314999
Bharatbai U. Patel *(Chm, CEO & Mng Dir)*

Subsidiaries:
Dinesh Remedies Ltd. (1)
Village Mahuwad Haranmad Road Padra - Jambusar Highway, Taluka Padra, Vadodara, 391 440, India
Tel.: (91) 9727723259
Web Site: https://www.dineshremedies.com
Emp.: 100
Gelatin Capsules Mfr
N.A.I.C.S.: 325412

SHRI GANG INDUSTRIES & ALLIED PRODUCTS LIMITED
F-32/3 Ground Floor Okhla Industrial Area Phase-II, New Delhi, 110020, India
Tel.: (91) 1142524454
Web Site: https://www.shrigangindustries.com
Year Founded: 1989
523309—(BOM)
Rev.: $16,695,882
Assets: $20,155,231
Liabilities: $14,788,286
Net Worth: $5,366,944
Earnings: $1,577,831
Emp.: 159
Fiscal Year-end: 03/31/23
Edible Oil Mfr & Whslr
N.A.I.C.S.: 311225
G. S. Khurana *(Sec & VP)*

SHRI JAGDAMBA POLYMERS LIMITED
802 Narnarayan Complex, Navrangpura, Ahmedabad, 380009, India
Tel.: (91) 7926565792
Web Site: https://www.shrijagdamba.com
Year Founded: 1985
512453—(BOM)
Rev.: $40,327,390
Assets: $30,040,034
Liabilities: $4,476,159
Net Worth: $25,563,875
Earnings: $3,604,412
Emp.: 1,409

SHRI JAGDAMBA POLYMERS LIMITED

Shri Jagdamba Polymers Limited—(Continued)
Fiscal Year-end: 03/31/23
Woven Polypropylene Mfr
N.A.I.C.S.: 313110
Ramakant Jhabarmal Bhojnagarwala *(Chm & Mng Dir)*

SHRI KALYAN HOLDINGS LIMITED
B-19 Lal Bahadur Nagar East, Behind Kesar Kothi JLN Marg, Jaipur, 302017, India
Tel.: (91) 1414034062
Web Site:
https://www.shrikalyan.co.in
Year Founded: 1993
532083—(BOM)
Rev.: $188,837
Assets: $1,467,384
Liabilities: $381,201
Net Worth: $1,086,183
Earnings: $35,105
Emp.: 8
Fiscal Year-end: 03/31/23
Holding Company
N.A.I.C.S.: 551112
Rajendra Kumar Jain *(Chm)*

SHRI KESHAV CEMENTS & INFRA LIMITED
215/2 Jyoti Tower 6th Cross Nazar Camp Karbhar Galli, M Vadgaon, Belgaum, 590 005, Karnataka, India
Tel.: (91) 9108009041
Web Site:
https://www.keshavcement.com
530977—(BOM)
Rev.: $11,021,351
Assets: $31,647,743
Liabilities: $29,921,865
Net Worth: $1,725,879
Earnings: ($1,151,732)
Emp.: 192
Fiscal Year-end: 03/31/21
Cement Mfr
N.A.I.C.S.: 327310
Venkatesh H. Katwa *(Chm)*

SHRI KRISHNA DEVCON LTD.
Sri Krishna 8th Floor 805/806 Opp Laxmi Industrial Estate, New Link Road Andheri West, Mumbai, 400053, India
Tel.: (91) 7314041485
Web Site:
https://www.shrikrishnadevcon.com
531080—(BOM)
Rev.: $3,859,733
Assets: $23,688,064
Liabilities: $14,430,370
Net Worth: $9,257,694
Earnings: $578,215
Emp.: 9
Fiscal Year-end: 03/31/23
Real Estate Services
N.A.I.C.S.: 531390
Sunil Kumar Jain *(Mng Dir)*

SHRI KRISHNA PRASADAM LIMITED
RO 27/5 Basement, East Patel Nagar, New Delhi, 110008, India
Tel.: (91) 1125812714
Web Site:
http://www.shrikrishnaprasad.com
Year Founded: 2009
Gems, Diamonds, Jewelry & Precious Stones Distr
N.A.I.C.S.: 423940

SHRI MAHALAXMI AGRICULTURAL DEVELOPMENT LTD.
57 58 59 Shree Krishna Centre 6th Floor Mithakhali Cross Road, Mithakhil, Ahmedabad, 380006, Gujarat, India
Tel.: (91) 7961344987
Crop Farming Services
N.A.I.C.S.: 111998
Kiran Bhogate *(Exec Dir)*

SHRI NIWAS LEASING & FINANCE LIMITED
47/18 Rajendra Place Metro Station, New Delhi, 110 060, India
Tel.: (91) 9891709895
Web Site:
https://www.shriniwasleasing.in
538897—(BOM)
Rev.: $47,600
Assets: $484,820
Liabilities: $3,010
Net Worth: $481,810
Earnings: ($105,112)
Fiscal Year-end: 03/31/20
Financial Support Services
N.A.I.C.S.: 523999
Rajni Tanwar *(Mng Dir)*

SHRI RAJIVLOCHAN OIL EXTRACTION LTD.
27/3 Jawahar Nagar, Raipur, 492001, CT, India
Tel.: (91) 7712225441
Web Site: https://sroel.com
Year Founded: 1994
Edible Oil Extraction & Mfr
N.A.I.C.S.: 311225

SHRI VASUPRADA PLANTATIONS LIMITED
21 Strand Road, Kolkata, 700 001, West Bengal, India
Tel.: (91) 3322309601
Web Site: https://www.svpl.in
538092—(BOM)
Rev.: $16,863,824
Assets: $31,199,436
Liabilities: $15,199,439
Net Worth: $15,999,998
Earnings: ($2,022,698)
Emp.: 3,021
Fiscal Year-end: 03/31/22
Tea Mfr
N.A.I.C.S.: 311920
K. M. Vineethakumar *(Gen Mgr-Comml-South)*

SHRI VENKATESH REFINERIES LTD.
Gat No 16, Umarde Erandol, Jalgaon, 425109, Maharashtra, India
Tel.: (91) 2588244452
Web Site: https://richsoya.in
Year Founded: 2003
543373—(BOM)
Refinery Services
N.A.I.C.S.: 237120
Dinesh Ganapati Kabre *(Chm & Mng Dir)*

SHRICON INDUSTRIES LIMITED
First Floor 112 B Shakti Nagar, Kota, 324009, Rajasthan, India
Tel.: (91) 7443559282
Web Site: https://shricon.in
Year Founded: 1984
508961—(BOM)
Rev.: $204,112
Assets: $538,241
Liabilities: $123,614
Net Worth: $414,627
Earnings: $145,015
Fiscal Year-end: 03/31/23
Civil Engineering Services
N.A.I.C.S.: 541330
Lokesh Tiwari *(CFO)*

SHRIJI POLYMERS (INDIA) LTD.
Plot No 8.9 & 15-D Industrial Area, Maksi Road, Ujjain, 456010, India
Tel.: (91) 734 2524071
Web Site:
http://www.shrijipolymers.com
Year Founded: 2003
Plastic Packaging Products Mfr
N.A.I.C.S.: 326160
Anand Bangur *(Co-Founder & Chm)*

Subsidiaries:
Four M Propack Pvt. Ltd. (1)
Mehra Industrial Complex Asha Usha Compound Vikhroli W, Mumbai, 400 083, India
Tel.: (91) 22 2571 8174
Web Site: http://www.fourmpropack.com
Medicinal Bottle Mfr
N.A.I.C.S.: 326160

SHRINKFLEX (THAILAND) PUBLIC COMPANY LIMITED
68/2-5 Moo 5, Bang Samak Bangpakong, Chachoengsao, 24130, Thailand
Tel.: (66) 38540000 TH
Web Site:
https://www.shrinkflexthailand.com
Year Founded: 2007
SFT—(THA)
Rev.: $27,024,758
Assets: $32,168,967
Liabilities: $10,095,167
Net Worth: $22,073,800
Earnings: $882,951
Fiscal Year-end: 12/31/23
Digital Printing Product Mfr & Distr
N.A.I.C.S.: 333248
Sung Cheong Tsoi *(CEO)*

SHRIRAM ASSET MANAGEMENT CO.LTD.
511 512 Meadows Sahar Plaza J B Nagar, Andheri East, Mumbai, 400059, India
Tel.: (91) 3323373012
Web Site: https://www.shriramamc.in
531359—(BOM)
Rev.: $699,730
Assets: $9,735,364
Liabilities: $446,988
Net Worth: $9,288,376
Earnings: ($483,280)
Emp.: 41
Fiscal Year-end: 03/31/23
Asset Management Services
N.A.I.C.S.: 523999
Prabhakar D. Karandikar *(Chm)*

SHRIRAM PROPERTIES LIMITED
Shriram House No 31 T Chowdaiah Road, Near Bhasyam Circle Sadashiva Nagar, Bengaluru, 560080, India
Tel.: (91) 8040229999
Web Site:
https://www.shriramproperties.com
Year Founded: 2000
543419—(BOM)
Real Estate Services
N.A.I.C.S.: 531210
M. Murali *(Chm & Mng Dir)*

SHRIRAM TRANSPORT FINANCE COMPANY LIMITED
Wockhardt Towers 3rd Floor West Wing G Block Bandra-Kurla Complex, Bandra East, Mumbai, 400051, Maharashtra, India
Tel.: (91) 2240959595
Web Site:
https://www.shriramfinance.in
Year Founded: 1979

INTERNATIONAL PUBLIC

511218—(BOM)
Rev.: $3,657,861,040
Assets: $25,250,302,740
Liabilities: $20,033,246,208
Net Worth: $5,217,056,531
Earnings: $721,782,867
Emp.: 64,052
Fiscal Year-end: 03/31/23
Commercial Vehicle Finance
N.A.I.C.S.: 522220
S. Lakshminarayanan *(Chm)*

SHRIRO PACIFIC LTD.
18 Westlands Road One Island East, Quarry Bay, China (Hong Kong)
Tel.: (852) 25245031 CN
Web Site: http://www.shriro.com
Year Founded: 1906
Sales Range: $350-399.9 Million
Emp.: 3,500
International Distr & Marketer of Photographic Equipment & Electronics
N.A.I.C.S.: 423410
Vasco Fung *(Grp CEO)*

Subsidiaries:
GELEC (HK) Ltd. (1)
9 Fl 905 B - 908 Tower A Manulife Financial Center Wai Yip St, Kowloon, China (Hong Kong)
Tel.: (852) 29198383
Web Site: http://www.gelec.com.hk
Sales Range: $75-99.9 Million
Emp.: 140
Electronics Parts & Equipment Whslr
N.A.I.C.S.: 423690
Ricky Cheung *(Mng Dir)*

Subsidiary (Non-US):
GELEC (Macau) Limitada (2)
Av da Praia Grande No 762-804 Ed China Plaza 18 and ar J1, Macau, China (Macau)
Tel.: (853) 2871 5686
Electronic Product Distr
N.A.I.C.S.: 423690
Brian Cheong *(Branch Mgr)*

GELEC (UK) Ltd (2)
Suite 101 Communications House 9 St Johns Street, Colchester, CO2 7NN, United Kingdom
Tel.: (44) 1206 533 049
Web Site: http://www.gelecuk.com
Industrial Equipment Distr
N.A.I.C.S.: 423830
Antony Potter *(Mng Dir)*

Monaco Corporation Ltd. (1)
231 Bush Road, Albany, 0632, Auckland, New Zealand
Tel.: (64) 94157444
Web Site: http://www.monacocorp.co.nz
Sales Range: $25-49.9 Million
Emp.: 95
Magnetic Recording Tapes & Electronic Materials & Component Mfr
N.A.I.C.S.: 334610
Tim Hargreaves *(CEO)*

Neil Pryde Ltd. (1)
20/F YKK Building Phase 2 No 2 San Lik Street, Tuen Mun, China (Hong Kong)
Tel.: (852) 2456 6566
Web Site: http://www.pryde-group.com
Emp.: 2,500
Sporting Goods Mfr & Distr
N.A.I.C.S.: 339920
Neil Pryde *(Chm)*

Subsidiary (US):
Cabrinhakites, Inc. (2)
400 Hana Hwy, Kahului, HI 96732
Tel.: (808) 893-0286
Web Site: http://www.cabrinhakites.com
Surfing Board Mfr & Distr
N.A.I.C.S.: 339920

Shriro (Guangzhou) Co. Ltd. (1)
Suite 2301 TaiKoo Hui Tower 1 385 Tianhe Road, Tianhe District, Guangzhou, 510620, China
Tel.: (86) 20 3868 2959
Web Site: http://www.shrirochina.cn
Golf Course Equipment Distr

Shriro (H.K.) Ltd. (1)
18 Westlands Road, One Island East,
Quarry Bay, China (Hong Kong)
Tel.: (852) 25245031
Web Site: http://www.shriro.com.hk
Sales Range: $25-49.9 Million
Emp.: 50
Photography & Instrumentation
N.A.I.C.S.: 423410
Egon Heldner (Mng Dir)

Shriro (Malaysia) Sdn Bhd. (1)
Lots 22 & 24 Jalan 225 Section 51A, Darul Ehsan, 46100, Petaling Jaya, Selangor, Malaysia
Tel.: (60) 3 7874 9842
Web Site: http://www.shriro.com.my
Emp.: 90
Sporting Goods Mfr & Distr
N.A.I.C.S.: 339920
Michael Teh (Mng Dir)

Shriro (Singapore) Pte Ltd. (1)
11 Chang Charn Road 06-01 Shriro House, Singapore, 159640, Singapore
Tel.: (65) 64727777
Web Site: http://www.shriro.com.sg
Sales Range: $50-74.9 Million
Emp.: 82
Photographic Equipment & Supplies Whslr
N.A.I.C.S.: 423410
Ben Ang (Mng Dir)

Shriro Equipment Ltd. (1)
18 Westlands Road, One Island East, Quarry Bay, China (Hong Kong)
Tel.: (852) 25245031
Web Site:
http://www.shriroequipment.com.hk
Sales Range: $25-49.9 Million
Emp.: 40
Construction & Mining Machinery
N.A.I.C.S.: 423810

Shriro Graphic Limited (1)
2/F Metropole Square, 2 On Yiu Street, Sha Tin, NT, China (Hong Kong)
Tel.: (852) 27129131
Web Site: http://www.shriro.com
Sales Range: $25-49.9 Million
Emp.: 35
Industrial Machinery & Equipment Whslr
N.A.I.C.S.: 423830

Shriro Holdings Limited (1)
Level 7 67 Albert Avenue, Chatswood, 2067, NSW, Australia
Tel.: (61) 294155000
Web Site: https://www.shriro.com.au
Rev.: $79,640,090
Assets: $52,612,847
Liabilities: $20,282,452
Net Worth: $32,330,395
Earnings: $4,858,440
Emp.: 153
Fiscal Year-end: 06/30/2024
Kitchen Appliances & Consumer Products Distr
N.A.I.C.S.: 423990
Shane Booth (CFO & Sec)

Shriro Machinery Limited (1)
18 Westlands Rd, One Island East, Quarry Bay, China (Hong Kong)
Tel.: (852) 28306990
Web Site: http://www.shriromachine.com.hk
Sales Range: $25-49.9 Million
Emp.: 30
Construction Equipment Whslr
N.A.I.C.S.: 423810
Albert Y. C. Yu (Mng Dir)

Shriro Marketing (Thailand) Ltd. (1)
Shriro House 89/169 Moo 3 Vibhavadee Rangsit Road Talad Bangkhen, Laksi, Bangkok, 10210, Thailand
Tel.: (66) 2 792 5000
Web Site: http://www.shriro.co.th
Photographic Equipment Distr
N.A.I.C.S.: 423410
Jaruwan Pongleerat (Asst Brand Mgr)

Shriro Shanghai Co. Ltd. (1)
Unit 8-12 15/F CIMIC Tower, 1090 Century Avenue Pudong, Shanghai, 200120, China
Tel.: (86) 2158352919
Web Site: http://www.shriro.com
Electronic Parts & Equipment Whslr
N.A.I.C.S.: 423690

Shriro Trading (Vietnam) Co. Ltd. (1)
Unit 505 5th F ABC Building10 Pho Quang Str Ward 2, Tan Binh Dist, Ho Chi Minh City, Vietnam
Tel.: (84) 8 39976814
Web Site: http://www.shriro.com.vn
Medical Equipment Distr
N.A.I.C.S.: 423450
Michael Teh (Gen Mgr)

Shriro Trading Co. Ltd. (1)
8/F The Itoyama Tower 3-7-18 Mita, Minato-ku, Tokyo, 108-0073, Japan
Tel.: (81) 3 5440 2610
Web Site: http://www.shriro.co.jp
Sports Product Distr
N.A.I.C.S.: 423910

Shriro Webb Ltd. (1)
8/F No 37 Lane 258 Ruiguang Road, Neihu Dist, Taipei, Taiwan
Tel.: (886) 2 2506 8832
Web Site: http://www.shriro.com.tw
Photographic Equipment Distr
N.A.I.C.S.: 423410
Bill Li (Mng Dir)

SHRISTI INFRASTRUCTURE DEVELOPMENT CORPORATION LTD.
Plot No X 1 2 3 Block EP Sector V Salt Lake City, Kolkata, 700091, India
Tel.: (91) 3340202020
Web Site:
https://www.shristicorp.com
Year Founded: 1999
511411—(KOL)
Rev.: $38,379,964
Assets: $215,778,163
Liabilities: $199,944,668
Net Worth: $15,833,495
Earnings: ($12,088,617)
Emp.: 43
Fiscal Year-end: 03/31/21
Civil Engineering & Infrastructure Development Services
N.A.I.C.S.: 541330
Badri Kumar Tulsyan (CFO)

Subsidiaries:

Haldia Water Services Pvt. Ltd. (1)
Unit No 130B 18th Floor Infinity Business Center Benchmark Building, Salt Lake Electronics Complex Plot C1 Block-GP Sector-V Salt Lake City, Kolkata, 700 091, India
Tel.: (91) 8252587401
Web Site: https://haldiawater.com
Water Utility Services
N.A.I.C.S.: 221310

SHRYDUS INDUSTRIES LIMITED
M/s Mangalam Housing Development Finance Ltd 24 26 Hemanta Basu Sarani, Kolkata, 700001, India
Tel.: (91) 9831100117
Web Site: https://shrydus.com
Year Founded: 1983
511493—(BOM)
Rev.: $1,116,576
Assets: $828,643
Liabilities: $599,520
Net Worth: $229,123
Earnings: $35,873
Emp.: 4
Fiscal Year-end: 03/31/23
Investment Banking Services
N.A.I.C.S.: 523150
Hemal Kampani (Mng Dir)

SHS ANTWERP AVIATION N.V.
International Airport Antwerp Luchthavenlei B69, Deurne, B 2100, Antwerp, Belgium
Tel.: (32) 3 304 82 09
Web Site: http://www.flyvlm.com
Oil Transportation Services
N.A.I.C.S.: 481111

SHS GROUP, LTD.
199 Airport Road West, Antrim, Belfast, BT3 9ED, United Kingdom
Tel.: (44) 28 9045 4647
Web Site: http://www.shs-group.co.uk
Year Founded: 1975
Sales Range: $10-24.9 Million
Emp.: 1,000
Artificially Carbonated Water Mfr & Distr
N.A.I.C.S.: 312111
Joseph Sloan (Chm)

Subsidiaries:

Beverage Brands (UK) Ltd (1)
Rockwood House Parkhill Road, Torquay, TQ1 2DU, Devon, United Kingdom
Tel.: (44) 1803 201020
Beverage Product Mfr
N.A.I.C.S.: 312111

Bottlegreen Drinks Ltd (1)
Frogmarsh Mills, Woodchester, GL5 5ET, Gloucestershire, United Kingdom
Tel.: (44) 1453 874000
Web Site: http://www.bottlegreendrinks.com
Beverage Product Mfr
N.A.I.C.S.: 312111

Caledonian Bottlers Plc (1)
Unit 1 Cumnock Business Park, Cumnock, KA18 3BY, Ayrshire, United Kingdom
Tel.: (44) 1290 422909
Web Site: http://www.caledonian-bottlers.co.uk
Emp.: 48
Glass Container Mfr
N.A.I.C.S.: 327213
Colin Noon (Gen Mgr)

SHS Sales & Marketing GB Limited (1)
Manderson House 5230 Valiant Court Delta Way, Brockworth, Gloucester, GL3 4FE, United Kingdom
Tel.: (44) 1452 378500
Web Site: http://www.shs-sales.co.uk
Emp.: 100
Marketing Consulting Services
N.A.I.C.S.: 541613
Marcus Freer (Mng Dir)

SHS Sales & Marketing Ltd (1)
Unit Q1 Aerodrome Business Park, Rathcoole, Dublin, Ireland
Tel.: (353) 1 4016200
Web Site: http://www.shs-sales.ie
Marketing Consulting Services
N.A.I.C.S.: 541613
David O'Neill (Mng Dir)

The British Pepper & Spice Company Ltd (1)
Rhosili Road, Brackmills, Northampton, NN4 7AN, United Kingdom
Tel.: (44) 1604 766461
Web Site: http://www.britishpepper.co.uk
Emp.: 400
Spice Product Mfr & Distr
N.A.I.C.S.: 311942

SHS HOLDINGS LTD.
19 Tuas Avenue 20, Singapore, 638830, Singapore
Tel.: (65) 65156116   SG
Web Site:
https://www.shsholdings.com.sg
Year Founded: 1971
566—(SES)
Rev.: $26,534,176
Assets: $200,636,297
Liabilities: $99,628,106
Net Worth: $101,008,191
Earnings: ($16,362,465)
Emp.: 375
Fiscal Year-end: 12/31/20
Holding Company; Corrosion Prevention, Structural Construction & Petroleum Refining Services
N.A.I.C.S.: 551112
Thomas Siok Kwee Lim (CEO-Corrosion Prevention Svcs)

Subsidiaries:

Hetat Holdings Pte. Ltd. (1)
19 Tuas Avenue 20, Singapore, 638830, Singapore
Tel.: (65) 65156116
Web Site: https://www.hetat.com
Steel Engineering & Construction Services
N.A.I.C.S.: 237990

Lesoon Equipment Pte. Ltd. (1)
81 Tuas South Street 5, Singapore, 637651, Singapore   (94.5%)
Tel.: (65) 67902900
Web Site: https://www.lesoon.com.sg
Sales Range: $25-49.9 Million
Surface Preparation & Finishing Equipments Distr
N.A.I.C.S.: 423830

Subsidiary (Non-US):

Speedlock Equipment Sdn. Bhd. (2)
40 Jalan Ros Merah 2/2 Taman Johor Jaya, 81100, Johor Bahru, Johor, Malaysia
Tel.: (60) 73520631
Web Site: https://my282-speedlock-equipment-sdn-bhd.contact.page
Sales Range: $25-49.9 Million
Emp.: 10
Blasting Equipments Distr
N.A.I.C.S.: 423830

SHS Offshore Pte. Ltd. (1)
81 Tuas South Street 5, Singapore, 637651, Singapore
Tel.: (65) 6863 6858
Web Site: http://www.shss.com
Offshore Engineering Services
N.A.I.C.S.: 237990

SHS System Pte. Ltd. (1)
81 Tuas South Street 5, Singapore, 637651, Singapore
Tel.: (65) 67902888
Web Site: http://www.seehupseng.com.sg
Sales Range: $10-24.9 Million
Grit Blasting & Painting Services
N.A.I.C.S.: 561990

See Hup Seng CP Pte Ltd (1)
81 Tuas South Street 5, Singapore, 637651, Singapore
Tel.: (65) 67902888
Construction & Engineering Services
N.A.I.C.S.: 541330

Sinenergy Pte. Ltd. (1)
19 Tuas Avenue 20, Singapore, 638830, Singapore
Tel.: (65) 63518557
Web Site: https://www.sinenergy.com.sg
Solar Energy Services
N.A.I.C.S.: 213112

TLC Modular Construction Joint Stock (1)
Hoa Lam Building 5th Floor 02 Thi Sach Street, District1, Ho Chi Minh City, Vietnam
Tel.: (84) 2873067779
Web Site: http://www.tlcmodular.com
Construction Engineering Services
N.A.I.C.S.: 541330

Xiang Tong (Shanghai) International Trading Pte Co., Ltd (1)
15H/I Sheng Quan Building No 28 TanJiaDu Road, Putuo District, Shanghai, 200063, China
Tel.: (86) 2132568071
Steel Engineering & Construction Services
N.A.I.C.S.: 237990

SHUAA CAPITAL PSC
The H Hotel Dubai Office Tower 15 Floor Office No 1502, PO Box 31045, Dubai, United Arab Emirates
Tel.: (971) 43303600   AE
Web Site: https://www.shuaa.com
Year Founded: 1979
SHUAA—(DFM)
Rev.: $43,949,576
Assets: $468,715,973
Liabilities: $373,499,515
Net Worth: $95,216,457
Earnings: ($314,391,749)
Emp.: 125
Fiscal Year-end: 12/31/23
Financial & Investment Services
N.A.I.C.S.: 523150

SHUAA CAPITAL PSC

SHUAA Capital psc—(Continued)

Fawad Tariq Khan (Head-Investment Banking)

Subsidiaries:

Abu Dhabi Financial Group, LLC (1)
Al Khatem Tower Floor 33 Abu Dhabi Global Market Al Maryah Island, PO Box 112230, Abu Dhabi, United Arab Emirates
Tel.: (971) 26390099
Web Site: http://www.adfg.ae
Investment Management, Venture Capital & Private Equity Firm
N.A.I.C.S.: 523999

Subsidiary (Domestic):

ADCM Altus Investment Management Limited (2)
ADGM Square - Al Khatem Tower Abu Dhabi Global Market Square, PO Box 112230, Abu Dhabi, United Arab Emirates
Tel.: (971) 2639 0099
Web Site: http://www.goldilocksfund.com
Asset Management & Custody Banking
N.A.I.C.S.: 523999

Holding (Non-US):

Northacre PLC (2)
3 Orchard Place, London, SW1H 0BF, United Kingdom (68.84%)
Tel.: (44) 2073498000
Web Site: https://www.northacre.com
Sales Range: $1-9.9 Million
Emp.: 24
Holding Company; Residential Property Development & Interior Design
N.A.I.C.S.: 551112
Niccolo Barattieri di San Pietro (CEO)

Subsidiary (Domestic):

Intarya Limited (3)
8 Albion Riverside 8 Hester Road, London, SW11 4AX, United Kingdom
Tel.: (44) 2073498020
Web Site: http://www.nstudio.com
Emp.: 10
Interior Design Services
N.A.I.C.S.: 541410
Nashmita Rajiah (Head-Interior Architecture)

Nilsson Architects Limited (3)
8 Albion Riverside 8 Hester Road, London, SW11 4AX, United Kingdom (100%)
Tel.: (44) 2073498030
Web Site: http://www.northacre.com
Emp.: 25
Architectural Services
N.A.I.C.S.: 541310
Klas Nilsson (Founder)

Waterloo Investments Limited (3)
8 Albion Riverside 8 Hester Rd, London, SW11 4AX, Battersea, United Kingdom (100%)
Tel.: (44) 2073498000
Web Site: http://www.northacre.com
Development Management Services
N.A.I.C.S.: 541611

Amwal International Investment Company KSCC (1)
Mazaya Tower 2 Fl 11 Khalid Bin Walid St Murqab Sharq, PO Box 4871, Safat, 13049, Kuwait, Kuwait (87.22%)
Tel.: (965) 2 228 1140
Web Site: http://www.amwal-invest.com
Rev.: $16,944,200
Assets: $60,859,256
Liabilities: $5,400,003
Net Worth: $55,459,253
Earnings: $3,613,381
Emp.: 20
Fiscal Year-end: 12/31/2019
Financial Investment Services
N.A.I.C.S.: 523999
Bader Fahad Abdullah AlRezaihan (Chm)

Subsidiary (Domestic):

Noor Capital Markets for Diversified Investments (2)
27th Floor Dar al Awadi, Ahmad al Jaber Street Sharq, Kuwait, Kuwait
Tel.: (965) 2225 3888

Emp.: 4
Real Estate Development Services
N.A.I.C.S.: 531390
Mohammad Fathi Al-Sagher (Gen Mgr)

Gulf Finance Corporation PJSC (1)
Tiffany Tower Level 29 Jumeirah Lakes Towers, PO Box 35356, Dubai, United Arab Emirates
Tel.: (971) 45010100
Web Site: http://www.gulffinance.com
Consumer Lending Services
N.A.I.C.S.: 522291
Saleh Alhashemi (Chm)

SHUAA Capital International Ltd. (1)
Level 18 Tower II Al Fattan Currency House, PO Box 31045, Dubai International Fin Ctr, Dubai, United Arab Emirates (100%)
Tel.: (971) 43303600
Web Site: http://www.shuaa.com
Sales Range: $50-74.9 Million
Emp.: 44
Financial Investment
N.A.I.C.S.: 523999

SHUAA Capital Saudi Arabia, pjsc (1)
Hamad Tower 27th Floor King Fahad Road, PO Box 8181, Riyadh, 11482, Saudi Arabia
Tel.: (966) 114666990
Investment Banking Services
N.A.I.C.S.: 523150

SHUAA Partners (1)
DIFC The Gate West Wing 2nd Level, PO Box 31045, Dubai, United Arab Emirates
Tel.: (971) 43199499
Web Site: http://www.shuaapartners.com
Private Equity Services
N.A.I.C.S.: 523150

SHUAA Partners Ltd. (1)
Level 15 Office No 1502, PO Box 31045, Dubai, United Arab Emirates
Tel.: (971) 43303600
Web Site: http://www.shuaa.com
Sales Range: $50-74.9 Million
Emp.: 35
Private Equity Investment Services
N.A.I.C.S.: 523999

SHUANG YUN HOLDINGS LIMITED

No 4 Sungei Kadut Street 2, Singapore, 729226, Singapore
Web Site: https://www.shuangyunholding.com
Year Founded: 2017
1706—(HKG)
Rev.: $74,373,602
Assets: $115,312,515
Liabilities: $71,795,227
Net Worth: $43,517,288
Earnings: $443,579
Emp.: 518
Fiscal Year-end: 12/31/22
Holding Company
N.A.I.C.S.: 551112
Chai Ling Tan (CEO)

SHUANG-BANG INDUSTRIAL. CORP.

No 3 Yongsing Rd, Nangang Industrial Dist, Nant'ou, 540, Taiwan
Tel.: (886) 492257450
Web Site: https://www.shuang-bang.com
Year Founded: 1989
6506—(TPE)
Rev.: $68,368,852
Assets: $77,176,625
Liabilities: $34,283,995
Net Worth: $42,892,630
Earnings: $8,027,483
Fiscal Year-end: 12/31/22
Chemical Products Mfr
N.A.I.C.S.: 325199
Chung-Tang Chang (Chm & Chief Strategy Officer)

SHUANGHUA HOLDINGS LIMITED

9/F Tongsheng Building 458 Fushan Road Pudong, Shanghai, 200122, China
Tel.: (86) 2150586337
Web Site: http://www.shshuanghua.com
1241—(HKG)
Rev.: $2,865,002
Assets: $42,615,893
Liabilities: $1,941,872
Net Worth: $40,674,020
Earnings: ($2,800,840)
Emp.: 64
Fiscal Year-end: 12/31/22
Automotive Heating, Ventilation & Cooling Components Mfr & Distr
N.A.I.C.S.: 336390
Ping Zheng (Founder, Chm & CEO)

Subsidiaries:

Shanghai Shuanghua Autoparts Co., Ltd (1)
9/f Tongsheng Mansion No 458 Fushan Rd, Pudong New Area, Shanghai, 200122, China
Tel.: (86) 2150586065
Sales Range: $25-49.9 Million
Emp.: 2
Automobile Parts Distr
N.A.I.C.S.: 423120
Shaowen Ding (Mgr-Sls)

Shanghai Youshen Industry Co., Ltd. (1)
F9 No 458 Fushan Road, Pudong, Shanghai, 200122, China
Tel.: (86) 21 58876888
Web Site: http://www.shyoushen.com
Sales Range: $200-249.9 Million
Emp.: 100
Automotive Air Conditioning Parts Mfr
N.A.I.C.S.: 336390
Carol Ting (Mgr)

SHUANGLIANG ECO-ENERGY SYSTEMS COMPANY LIMITED

Shuangliang Industry Park, Ligang, Jiangyin, 214444, Jiangsu, China
Tel.: (86) 51086638086
Web Site: https://www.sl-ecoenergy.com
Year Founded: 1982
600481—(SHG)
Rev.: $2,032,480,747
Assets: $3,080,852,658
Liabilities: $2,110,067,907
Net Worth: $970,784,751
Earnings: $134,225,868
Emp.: 2,000
Fiscal Year-end: 12/31/22
Absorption Chiller Mfr
N.A.I.C.S.: 335220
Miao Wenbin (Chm)

Subsidiaries:

Jiangsu Hengchuang Packing Material Co., Ltd. (1)
No 1 Shuangliang Road Shuangliang Industiral Park Ligang, Jiangyin, 214444, Jiangsu, China
Tel.: (86) 51086630169
Household & Commercial Appliance Mfr
N.A.I.C.S.: 334512

Jiangsu Leasty Chemical Co., Ltd. (1)
Shuangliang Binjiang Ind Park, Ligang Town, Jiangyin, 214444, China
Tel.: (86) 51086630265
Household & Commercial Appliance Mfr
N.A.I.C.S.: 334512

Shuangliang Clyde Bergemann GmbH (1)
Berliner Strasse 91, 40880, Ratingen, Germany
Tel.: (49) 210289419
Web Site: http://www.seescb.com
Air Cooler Condenser Mfr
N.A.I.C.S.: 333415

Shuangliang Royal Tech CSP Technology Co., Ltd. (1)

INTERNATIONAL PUBLIC

Office 1103b IFC Beijing No 8 Jianguomenwai Av, Chaoyang District, Beijing, 100022, China
Tel.: (86) 1085660380
Web Site: http://en.royalcsp.com
Heating Equipment Mfr
N.A.I.C.S.: 333414

SHUBARKOL KOMIR JSC

Asfaltnaya str 8, 100004, Karaganda, Kazakhstan
Tel.: (7) 7212930110
Year Founded: 1985
SHUK—(KAZ)
Rev.: $287,299,430
Assets: $507,086,141
Liabilities: $445,984,596
Net Worth: $61,101,545
Earnings: $59,075,502
Fiscal Year-end: 12/31/23
Coal Mining Services
N.A.I.C.S.: 213113
Kim Sergey Pavlovich (Pres & CEO)

SHUBARKOL PREMIUM JSC

Bukhar-Zhyrau avenue building 49/6, Kazybek bi district, 100000, Karaganda, Kazakhstan
Tel.: (7) 212996368
Web Site: https://shubarkolpremium.kz
Year Founded: 2017
SHUP—(KAZ)
Rev.: $87,805,700
Assets: $59,095,347
Liabilities: $40,049,336
Net Worth: $19,046,011
Earnings: $21,902,216
Fiscal Year-end: 12/31/21
Coal Product Mfr & Distr
N.A.I.C.S.: 324199
Omarov Nurbek Abilgazymovich (Gen Dir)

SHUBHAM POLYSPIN LTD.

Block No 748 Saket Industrial Estate Near Kaneriya Oil Mill, Jetpura Basantpura Road Borisana Taluka-Kadi, Mehsana, 382728, India
Tel.: (91) 9998556554
Web Site: https://shubhampolyspin.in
542019—(BOM)
Rev.: $5,342,137
Assets: $3,513,427
Liabilities: $1,667,457
Net Worth: $1,845,970
Earnings: $60,620
Emp.: 52
Fiscal Year-end: 03/31/21
Synthetic Fiber Mfr
N.A.I.C.S.: 325220
Ankit A. Somani (Mng Dir)

SHUBHLAXMI JEWEL ART LTD.

Shop No 1 Ground Floor D & I Excelus Waghawadi Road, Bhavnagar, 364002, India
Tel.: (91) 9537461111
Web Site: https://www.shubhlaxmiltd.in
SHUBHLAXMI—(NSE)
Rev.: $9,349,727
Assets: $4,110,965
Liabilities: $1,885,582
Net Worth: $2,225,382
Earnings: $121,875
Fiscal Year-end: 03/31/23
Jewel Art Services
N.A.I.C.S.: 458310
Narendrasinh J. Chauhan (Mng Dir)

SHUEI YOBIKO CO., LTD.

2-7-1 Takajo, Aoi-ku, Shizuoka, 420-0839, Japan
Tel.: (81) 542251150

Web Site: https://www.shuei-yobiko.co.jp
Year Founded: 1972
4678—(TKS)
Rev.: $68,373,840
Assets: $58,802,560
Liabilities: $30,366,340
Net Worth: $28,436,220
Earnings: ($2,809,250)
Fiscal Year-end: 03/31/24
Educational Support Services
N.A.I.C.S.: 611710

SHUFERSAL
30 Benjamin Smotkin Street, PO Box 15103, Rishon le Zion, Israel
Tel.: (972) 1800686868
Web Site: http://www.shufersal.co.il
Year Founded: 1958
Grocery Products Retailer
N.A.I.C.S.: 445110
Mauricio Wior (Chm)

SHUHUA SPORTS CO., LTD.
Shichun Industrial Zone, Chidian, Jinjiang, 362123, Fujian, China
Tel.: (86) 59585933668
Web Site: http://www.shuhua.cn
Year Founded: 1996
605299—(SHG)
Rev.: $189,765,426
Assets: $257,769,472
Liabilities: $76,923,798
Net Worth: $180,845,674
Earnings: $15,365,222
Fiscal Year-end: 12/31/22
Sporting Product Mfr & Distr
N.A.I.C.S.: 339920
Weijian Zhang (Chm & Pres)

SHUI ON COMPANY LIMITED
34/F Shui On Centre 6-8 Harbour Road, Wanchai, China (Hong Kong)
Tel.: (852) 28791888
Web Site: http://www.shuion.com
Year Founded: 1971
Sales Range: $150-199.9 Million
Emp.: 1,000
Holding Company; Property Development, Construction & Construction Materials
N.A.I.C.S.: 551112
Vincent Hong Sui Lo (Chm)

Subsidiaries:

SOCAM Development Limited (1)
12/F New Kowloon Plaza 38 Tai Kok Tsui Road, Kowloon, China (Hong Kong)
Tel.: (852) 23984888
Web Site: http://www.socam.com
Rev.: $804,142,500
Assets: $1,161,397,500
Liabilities: $787,440,000
Net Worth: $373,957,500
Earnings: ($15,555,000)
Emp.: 2,299
Fiscal Year-end: 12/31/2022
Holding Company; Cement & Construction Operations
N.A.I.C.S.: 551112

Subsidiary (Domestic):

Dynamic Mark Limited (2)
12th Floor New Kowloon Plaza, 38 Tai Kok Tsui Road, Kowloon, China (Hong Kong)
Tel.: (852) 23984888
Web Site: http://www.socam.com
Emp.: 200
Construction Materials Whslr
N.A.I.C.S.: 423390
Stephen Wing Kee Lee (Exec Dir-Construction)

Subsidiary (Non-US):

Guizhou Shui On Cement Development Management Co. Ltd (2)
13th-Fl Industrial & Commerical Bank of China Bldg, 1 Shengfu Rd, 550001, Guiyang, Guizhou, China
Tel.: (86) 8515800066
Management Consulting Services
N.A.I.C.S.: 541618

Subsidiary (Domestic):

Jade City International Limited (2)
12th-Floor New Kowloon Plz, Tai Kok Tsui, Kowloon, China (Hong Kong)
Tel.: (852) 23984888
Real Estate Agents & Brokers
N.A.I.C.S.: 531210

Affiliate (Non-US):

Lafarge Dujiangyan Cement Co. Ltd. (2)
PO Box 058, Dujiangyan, 611833, Sichuan, China
Tel.: (86) 2887196888
Web Site: http://www.lafarge.com.cn
Building Material Dealers
N.A.I.C.S.: 444180

Subsidiary (Domestic):

Pat Davie Limited (2)
Room 1205-06 12/F New Kowloon Plaza 38 Tai Kok Tsui Road, Kowloon, China (Hong Kong)
Tel.: (852) 2398 4999
Web Site: http://www.patdavie.com
Sales Range: $75-99.9 Million
Emp.: 110
Nonresidential Property Managers
N.A.I.C.S.: 531312
Gilbert Ng (Exec Dir)

Subsidiary (Domestic):

P.D. (Contractors) Limited (3)
12th-Floor New Kowloon Plaza, Tai Kok Tsui, Kowloon, China (Hong Kong)
Tel.: (852) 23984999
Web Site: http://www.patdavie.com
Sales Range: $50-74.9 Million
Emp.: 155
Residential Buildings & Dwellings Lessors
N.A.I.C.S.: 531110
Vincent Hong Sui Lo (Chm)

Subsidiary (Domestic):

Shui On Building Contractors Limited (2)
12th-Floor New Kowloon Plz, Tai Kok Tsui, Kowloon, China (Hong Kong)
Tel.: (852) 23984888
Web Site: http://www.shuion.com
Residential Buildings & Dwellings Lessors
N.A.I.C.S.: 531110
Stephen Wing Kee Lee (Exec Dir)

Shui On Building Materials Limited (2)
13th-Floor New Kowloon Plz, Tai Kok Tsui, Kowloon, China (Hong Kong)
Tel.: (852) 23984888
Web Site: http://www.shuion.co.hk
Emp.: 200
Lumber Plywood Millwork & Wood Panel Whslr
N.A.I.C.S.: 423310
David Ngai Shing Chen (Gen Mgr)

Shui On Construction Company Limited (2)
12th-Floor New Kowloon Plaza, Tai Kok Tsui, Kowloon, China (Hong Kong)
Tel.: (852) 23984888
Emp.: 200
Industrial Building Construction
N.A.I.C.S.: 236210
Stephen Wing Kee Lee (Exec Dir)

Shui On Rock Products Limited (2)
13th-Fl New Kowloon Plaza, Tai Kok Tsui, Kowloon, China (Hong Kong)
Tel.: (852) 23984061
Nonresidential Buildings Lessors
N.A.I.C.S.: 531120

Shui On Land Limited (1)
26/F Shui On Plaza 333 Huai Hai Zhong Road, Shanghai, 200021, China
Tel.: (86) 2163861818
Web Site: http://www.shuionland.com
Rev.: $704,306,370
Assets: $17,691,924,750
Liabilities: $10,531,961,820
Net Worth: $7,159,962,930
Earnings: ($35,697,930)
Emp.: 3,141
Fiscal Year-end: 12/31/2020
Property Development Services
N.A.I.C.S.: 531390
Vincent H. S. Lo (Chm)

Wuhan Shui On Tiandi Property Development Co., Ltd. (1)
1628 Zhongshan Road Room 3303 New World International Trade Centre, Wuhan, 430022, China
Tel.: (86) 2782711111
Real Estate Development Services
N.A.I.C.S.: 531390

SHUI-MU INTERNATIONAL CO., LTD.
6F No 168 Songjiang Rd, Zhongshan District, Taipei, Taiwan
Tel.: (886) 266189999
Web Site: https://www.asogroup.com.tw
Year Founded: 1952
8443—(TAI)
Rev.: $38,804,146
Assets: $54,650,283
Liabilities: $29,170,809
Net Worth: $25,479,473
Earnings: ($6,585,749)
Emp.: 408
Fiscal Year-end: 12/31/22
Footwear Mfr & Marketer
N.A.I.C.S.: 316210

SHUKRA JEWELLERY LIMITED
Panchdhara Complex 3rd Floor Near The Grand Bhagwati Hotel SG Highway, Bodakdev, Ahmedabad, 380 054, Gujarat, India
Tel.: (91) 7940024009
Web Site: https://www.shukrajewellery.com
Year Founded: 1991
523790—(BOM)
Rev.: $1,161,233
Assets: $6,575,564
Liabilities: $1,743,773
Net Worth: $4,831,790
Earnings: $22,062
Emp.: 6
Fiscal Year-end: 03/31/21
Diamond Jewelry Mfr
N.A.I.C.S.: 339910
Sudhir Kumar Prajapati (CFO)

SHUKRA PHARMACEUTICALS LIMITED
Veer House 3rd Floor Judges Bungalow Road, Ahmedabad, 380054, India
Tel.: (91) 79 66522247
Web Site: http://www.shukrapharma.com
Pharmaceutical Product Mfr & Distr
N.A.I.C.S.: 325412

SHUMBA COAL LIMITED
Plot 2780 Manong Close Extension 9, PO Box 70311, Gaborone, Botswana
Tel.: (267) 3186072
Web Site: https://shumbaenergy.com
Year Founded: 2011
SHCL—(BOT)
Rev.: $487,609,000
Assets: $17,788,203,000
Liabilities: $10,151,279,000
Net Worth: $7,636,924,000
Earnings: ($2,240,735,000)
Fiscal Year-end: 06/30/22
Coal Mining Support Services
N.A.I.C.S.: 213113
Mashale Phumaphi (Mng Dir)

SHUMEN-TABAC AD
Tel.: (359) 54830492
SHTB—(BUL)
Sales Range: Less than $1 Million
Tobacco Product Mfr
N.A.I.C.S.: 312230
Margarita Todorova (Dir-IR)

SHUN HO HOLDINGS LIMITED
3rd Floor Shun Ho Tower 24-30 Ice House Street, Central, China (Hong Kong)
Tel.: (852) 25253788   HK
Web Site: https://www.shunho.com.hk
0253—(HKG)
Rev.: $78,117,593
Assets: $1,263,147,855
Liabilities: $178,894,995
Net Worth: $1,084,252,860
Earnings: $82,520,168
Emp.: 387
Fiscal Year-end: 12/31/22
Hotel Management & Operations;Property Investment & Development
N.A.I.C.S.: 561110
Albert Wing Ho Hui (Exec Dir)

SHUN HO PROPERTY INVESTMENTS LTD
Tel.: (852) 25253788
Web Site: https://shunho.com.hk
0219—(HKG)
Rev.: $78,117,593
Assets: $1,271,533,148
Liabilities: $174,503,130
Net Worth: $1,097,030,018
Earnings: $83,045,085
Emp.: 387
Fiscal Year-end: 12/31/22
Property Management Services
N.A.I.C.S.: 531390
Albert Wing Ho Hui (Exec Dir)

SHUN ON ELECTRONIC CO., LTD.
2F No 19 Lane 146 xinhu 2nd Rd, Neihu District, Taipei, 11494, Taiwan
Tel.: (886) 227965628
Web Site: https://www.soe-ele.com
Year Founded: 1996
6283—(TAI)
Rev.: $42,151,475
Assets: $85,397,165
Liabilities: $27,153,503
Net Worth: $58,243,662
Earnings: ($6,496,452)
Emp.: 1,700
Fiscal Year-end: 12/31/23
Computer Keyboard Switches Mfr
N.A.I.C.S.: 334419
Chin Jong Hwa (Chm)

Subsidiaries:

DongGuan Shun On Electronic Co., Ltd. (1)
Jinlong Industrial Zone Sanzhong Administrative Zone, Qingxi Town, Dongguan, Guangdong, China
Tel.: (86) 76987317940
Keyboard Membrane Mfr
N.A.I.C.S.: 325212

JiaXing Shun On Electronic Technoloy Co.,Ltd. (1)
No 738 ZhengYuan Road Economic Development Zone, Jiaxing, 314000, ZheJiang, China
Tel.: (86) 57383912888
Web Site: http://www.soe-ele.com
Switch Mfr
N.A.I.C.S.: 334419

Polytech Electronics Technology (Dong Guan) Co.,Ltd (1)
Jin Xing Industrial Zone, QingXi Town, Dongguan, 523648, GuangDong, China
Tel.: (86) 76986814718
Phone & Automotive Keypads Mfr
N.A.I.C.S.: 334220

Singapore Polytech Component Pte. Ltd. (1)

Shun On Electronic Co, Ltd.—(Continued)

10 Ubi Crescent 04-68, Singapore, 408564, Singapore
Tel.: (65) 6749 8606
Web Site: http://www.polytech.com.sg
Sales Range: $25-49.9 Million
Emp.: 500
Keyboard Membrane Mfr
N.A.I.C.S.: 325212

SHUN TAK HOLDINGS LIMITED

Penthouse 39/F West Tower Shun Tak Centre 200 Connaught Road, Central, China (Hong Kong)
Tel.: (852) 28593111   HK
Web Site:
   https://www.shuntakgroup.com
Year Founded: 1972
XUN—(DEU)
Rev.: $468,640,076
Assets: $7,031,828,569
Liabilities: $2,459,278,183
Net Worth: $4,572,550,385
Earnings: ($60,881,567)
Emp.: 1,501
Fiscal Year-end: 12/31/22
Transportation & Property Development Services
N.A.I.C.S.: 488999
Pansy Catilina Chiu King Ho *(Chm & Mng Dir)*

Subsidiaries:

Destinations Network Tourism Marketing & PR Company Limited   (1)
Rua de Pequim No 202A-246 Macau Finance Centre 11 Andar H, Macau, China (Macau)
Tel.: (853) 28703080
Web Site: http://www.dnetwork.com.hk
Marketing Strategy & Consulting Services
N.A.I.C.S.: 541613

Macau Matters Company Limited   (1)
11 Floor Chun Wo Commercial Centre 25 Wing Wo Street, Sheung Wan, China (Hong Kong)
Tel.: (852) 21237888
Web Site: http://www.macaumatters.com
Retail Market Services
N.A.I.C.S.: 455219
Agnes Chan *(Asst Mgr-Mktg & Design)*

Nova Taipa - Urbanizacoes, Limitada   (1)
Avenida de Kwong Tung, Taipa, China (Macau)
Tel.: (853) 28833128
Real Estate Development Services
N.A.I.C.S.: 531190

Shun Tak Property Management Limited   (1)
Room 908-10 9/F West Tower Shun Tak Centre 200 Connaught Road Central, Hong Kong, China (Hong Kong)
Tel.: (852) 28593131
Property Management Services
N.A.I.C.S.: 531311

Shun Tak Real Estate Ltd.   (1)
Room G07 Shun Tak Centre 200 Connaught Road Central, Hong Kong, China (Hong Kong)
Tel.: (852) 28578998
Property Leasing & Real Estate Services
N.A.I.C.S.: 531311

Shun Tak Travel Services Limited   (1)
Room 1618 China Merchants Tower Shun Tak Centre, 200 Connaught Road, Central, China (Hong Kong)
Tel.: (852) 28593496
Web Site: http://www.shuntaktravel.com
Travel Agency Services
N.A.I.C.S.: 561510
Ivor Wong *(Gen Mgr)*

SHUN THAI RUBBER GLOVES INDUSTRY PUBLIC COMPANY LIMITED

9 Moo 4 Kached Muang, Rayong, 21100, Thailand
Tel.: (66) 386344825
Web Site:
   http://www.shunthaiglove.com
Year Founded: 1988
Rev.: $47,629,007
Assets: $54,846,319
Liabilities: $7,394,108
Net Worth: $47,452,212
Earnings: $5,484,639
Fiscal Year-end: 12/31/21
Natural Rubber Mfr
N.A.I.C.S.: 325212
Chakarn Saengraksawong *(Chm)*

SHUN WO GROUP HOLDINGS LIMITED

Tel.: (852) 25689611   Ky
Web Site: http://www.swgrph.com
1591—(HKG)
Rev.: $31,250,822
Assets: $18,339,408
Liabilities: $7,077,391
Net Worth: $11,262,018
Earnings: ($579,765)
Emp.: 72
Fiscal Year-end: 03/31/22
Foundation Contract Services
N.A.I.C.S.: 238910
Kwo Foo Shum *(Dir-Technical)*

SHUNFA HENGYE CORP.

No 777 Shixin North Road, Xiaoshan District, Hangzhou, 311215, Zhejiang, China
Tel.: (86) 57182860631
Web Site: http://www.sfhy.cn
Year Founded: 1993
000631—(SSE)
Rev.: $43,130,697
Assets: $1,290,405,224
Liabilities: $418,956,352
Net Worth: $871,448,872
Earnings: $22,736,250
Fiscal Year-end: 12/31/22
Real Estate Support Services
N.A.I.C.S.: 531390
Xu Xiaojian *(Chm)*

SHUNFENG INTERNATIONAL CLEAN ENERGY LTD.

Room C 30F Bank of china Tower, 1 Garden Road Central, Hong Kong, China (Hong Kong)
Tel.: (852) 23639138   Ky
Web Site: https://www.sfcegroup.com
SHUNF—(OTCIQ)
Rev.: $43,357,194
Assets: $700,431,712
Liabilities: $838,709,016
Net Worth: ($138,277,304)
Earnings: ($24,732,360)
Emp.: 91
Fiscal Year-end: 12/31/22
Solar Cell Products Mfr
N.A.I.C.S.: 334419
Yi Zhang *(Chm)*

Subsidiaries:

Jiangsu Shunfeng Photovoltaic Technology Co., Ltd.   (1)
No 99 Yanghu Road High and New Tech Industrial Development Zone, Wujin District, Changzhou, 213164, Jiangsu, China
Tel.: (86) 519 86163888
Web Site: http://www.sf-pv.com
Emp.: 1,000
Solar Cells Mfr & Whslr
N.A.I.C.S.: 334419

S.A.G. Solar GmbH & Co. KG   (1)
Sasbacher Str 5, 79111, Freiburg, Germany
Tel.: (49) 761 4770 0
Web Site: http://www.sagsolar.com
Solar Power Plant Systems Installation & Services
N.A.I.C.S.: 221114
David Hogg *(CEO)*

Subsidiary (Domestic):

meteocontrol GmbH   (2)
Spicherer Str 48, 86157, Augsburg, Bavaria, Germany
Tel.: (49) 821346660
Web Site: http://www.meteocontrol.de
Sales Range: $25-49.9 Million
Emp.: 140
Energy Management Services
N.A.I.C.S.: 541618
Martin Schneider *(Member-Mgmt Bd & Mng Dir)*

Suniva, Inc.   (1)
5775 Peachtree Industrial Blvd, Norcross, GA 30092
Tel.: (404) 477-2700
Web Site: https://www.suniva.com
Solar Cell Mfr
N.A.I.C.S.: 334419

SHUNLIBAN INFORMATION SERVICE CO., LTD.

Building 5 No 57 Wusi West Road, Chengxi District, Xining, 810008, Qinghai, China
Tel.: (86) 971 801 3495
Web Site: http://www.my0606.com.cn
000606—(SSE)
Rev.: $118,661,145
Assets: $230,227,135
Liabilities: $163,718,674
Net Worth: $66,508,461
Earnings: ($182,627,852)
Fiscal Year-end: 12/31/20
Pharmaceuticals Mfr
N.A.I.C.S.: 325412
Cong Peng *(Chm & Pres)*

SHUNSIN TECHNOLOGY HOLDINGS LIMITED

11F5 No 495 Guangfu south Road, Xinyi District, Taipei, 110, Taiwan
Tel.: (886) 222688368
Web Site:
   https://www.shunsintech.com
6451—(TAI)
Rev.: $170,541,215
Assets: $482,393,487
Liabilities: $245,569,892
Net Worth: $236,823,595
Earnings: $15,285,522
Fiscal Year-end: 12/31/23
Semiconductor Mfr
N.A.I.C.S.: 334413
Wen-Yi Hsu *(Chm & Gen Mgr)*

Subsidiaries:

ShunSin Technology (Zhongshan) Limited   (1)
No 9 Jianye East Road, Torch Hi-tech Development Zone, Zhongshan, China
Tel.: (86) 76023381357
Semiconductor Packaging & Testing Services
N.A.I.C.S.: 541420

SHUNTEN INTERNATIONAL (HOLDINGS) LIMITED

27/F The Galaxy 313 Castle Peak Road, New Territories, Kwai Chung, China (Hong Kong)
Tel.: (852) 3 700 7300   Ky
Web Site: http://www.shunten.com.hk
0932—(HKG)
Rev.: $21,022,837
Assets: $31,828,782
Liabilities: $18,588,340
Net Worth: $13,240,442
Earnings: ($5,724,777)
Emp.: 152
Fiscal Year-end: 03/31/22
Health & Beauty Supplements Mfr & Distr
N.A.I.C.S.: 325411
Xihua Wang *(Chm-Acting & CEO-Acting)*

Subsidiaries:

H365 Health Products Limited   (1)
27/F The Galaxy 313 Castle Peak Road, Kwai Chung, China (Hong Kong)
Tel.: (852) 24680365
Web Site: http://www.h365.com.hk
Pharmaceuticals Product Mfr
N.A.I.C.S.: 325412

Health Proof International Company Limited   (1)
27/F The Galaxy 313 Castle Peak Road, Kwai Chung, China (Hong Kong)
Tel.: (852) 22975563
Web Site: http://www.health-proof.com
Healthcare Supplement Product Distr
N.A.I.C.S.: 456191

IAHGames Hong Kong Limited   (1)
Unit 1109-1110 11/F The Wave 4 Hing Yip Street, Kwun Tong, Kowloon, China (Hong Kong)
Tel.: (852) 38997722
Web Site: http://www.iahgames.com
Game Publisher
N.A.I.C.S.: 459120

Royal Medic (Holdings) Limited   (1)
27/F The Galaxy 313 Castle Peak Road, Kwai Chung, China (Hong Kong)
Tel.: (852) 22970000
Web Site: http://www.royalmedic.com.hk
Pharmaceuticals Product Mfr
N.A.I.C.S.: 325412
Amy Au *(Sr Mgr-HR & Admin)*

SHUNYA INTERNATIONAL MARTECH BEIJING CO LTD

Room 101 Bungalow Building 41 Yard No 12 Shuangqiao Street, Chaoyang District, Beijing, 100024, China
Tel.: (86) 1085095771
Web Site:
   http://www.shunyagroup.com
Year Founded: 2007
300612—(CHIN)
Rev.: $147,740,720
Assets: $102,399,598
Liabilities: $69,552,124
Net Worth: $32,847,474
Earnings: ($11,061,035)
Fiscal Year-end: 12/31/23
Integrated Communication Services
N.A.I.C.S.: 541990
Ren Xiang *(Chm & CEO)*

SHURGARD SELF STORAGE

100 Jenkins Lane, East Ham, London, IG11 7ZL, United Kingdom
Tel.: (44) 1252521010
Web Site: https://www.shurgard.com
LOK—(LSE)
Rev.: $29,723,206
Assets: $380,612,363
Liabilities: $175,244,994
Net Worth: $205,367,369
Earnings: $4,457,395
Emp.: 171
Fiscal Year-end: 07/31/21
Self-Service Storage Facilities
N.A.I.C.S.: 531130
Andrew Jacobs *(CEO)*

Subsidiaries:

Lok'nStore Limited   (1)
One Fleet Place, Walker Rd, London, EC4M 7WS, United Kingdom
Tel.: (44) 8005873322
Web Site: https://www.loknstore.co.uk
Sales Range: $25-49.9 Million
Emp.: 5
Storage Services
N.A.I.C.S.: 493110

SHURWID INDUSTRIES LTD.

H-2 R-7 L-7 Rupayan Prime, Dhanmondi, Dhaka, 1205, Bangladesh
Tel.: (880) 29612213
Web Site: http://www.shurwid.org
Year Founded: 2004

AND PRIVATE COMPANIES

SHURWID—(DHA)
Rev.: $2,484,599
Assets: $10,443,321
Liabilities: $2,336,523
Net Worth: $8,106,798
Earnings: $916,878
Emp.: 99
Fiscal Year-end: 06/30/19
Steel Products Mfr
N.A.I.C.S.: 332618
Mahmudul Hasan *(Chm)*

SHUTTLE INC.
No 30 Lane 76 Ruiguang Road,
Neihu District, Taipei, 114, Taiwan
Tel.: (886) 287926168
Web Site: https://www.shuttle.eu
Year Founded: 1983
2405—(TAI)
Rev.: $56,629,646
Assets: $146,702,307
Liabilities: $21,627,554
Net Worth: $125,074,752
Earnings: $465,516
Fiscal Year-end: 12/31/23
Motherboards & Barebones Systems Mfr
N.A.I.C.S.: 334412
Yu Li Na *(Chm)*

Subsidiaries:

Japan Shuttle Co., Ltd. **(1)**
2nd floor Lead Sea Sumiyoshi Building
1-16-13 Sumiyoshi, Koto-ku, Tokyo, 135-0002, Japan
Tel.: (81) 356251670
Web Site: https://shuttle-japan.jp
Computer Mfr
N.A.I.C.S.: 334111

Shuttle Computer Group Inc. **(1)**
17068 Evergreen Pl, Industry, CA 91766
Tel.: (626) 820-9000
Web Site:
 https://www.shuttlecomputers.com
Computer Mfr
N.A.I.C.S.: 334111

Shuttle Computer Handels GmbH **(1)**
Fritz-Strassmann-Str 5, 25337, Elmshorn, Germany
Tel.: (49) 4121476860
Web Site: https://www.shuttle.eu
Computer Mfr
N.A.I.C.S.: 334111

SHUYU CIVILIAN PHARMACY CORPORATION LTD.
No 56 Shanda North Road, Licheng District, Jinan, 250100, Shandong, China
Tel.: (86) 4000106666
Web Site:
 https://www.shuyupingmin.com
Year Founded: 1999
301017—(CHIN)
Rev.: $1,294,509,067
Assets: $1,314,602,306
Liabilities: $981,330,124
Net Worth: $333,272,182
Earnings: $18,740,563
Fiscal Year-end: 12/31/23
Pharmaceutical Product Mfr & Distr
N.A.I.C.S.: 325412
Li Wenjie *(Chm)*

SHUZ TUNG MACHINERY INDUSTRIAL CO., LTD.
No 17-1 Houliao Road, Waipu Dist, Taichung, 43859, Taiwan
Tel.: (886) 426831886
Web Site: https://www.shuztung.com
Year Founded: 1978
4537—(TAI)
Automated Machinery Equipment Mfr
N.A.I.C.S.: 333998
Tien-Tsai Chuang *(Chm)*

SHV HOLDINGS N.V.
Rijnkade 1, 3511 LC, Utrecht, Netherlands
Tel.: (31) 302338833 NI
Web Site: http://www.shv.nl
Year Founded: 1896
Rev.: $22,953,577,720
Assets: $15,188,387,410
Liabilities: $8,030,549,590
Net Worth: $7,157,837,820
Earnings: $589,051,850
Emp.: 59,000
Fiscal Year-end: 12/31/18
Holding Company Consumer Goods & Raw Materials Trading Oil & Gas Exploration & Production Heavy Lifting & Transportation Services & Equity Investment Activities
N.A.I.C.S.: 551112
Annemiek Fentener van Vlissingen *(Chm-Supervisory Bd)*

Subsidiaries:

ERIKS Group nv **(1)**
Robonsbosweg 7 D, NL-1816 MK, Alkmaar, Netherlands **(100%)**
Tel.: (31) 725475888
Web Site: http://www.eriks.com
Sales Range: $1-4.9 Billion
Emp.: 7,000
Holding Company; Industrial Supplies Distr
N.A.I.C.S.: 551112

Subsidiary (US):

Diamond Gear Company, Ltd. **(2)**
13750 Hollister Dr, Houston, TX 77086
Tel.: (713) 590-0270
Web Site: http://www.diamond-gear.com
Sales Range: $25-49.9 Million
Emp.: 25
Gear Mfr
N.A.I.C.S.: 333612

Subsidiary (Non-US):

ERIKS UK Holdings Ltd. **(2)**
Amber Way, Halesowen, B62 8WG, W Midlands, United Kingdom **(100%)**
Tel.: (44) 1215086000
Web Site: http://www.eriks.co.uk
Emp.: 200
Holding Company; Industrial Supplies Distr
N.A.I.C.S.: 551112
M.T.A. Beckers *(CEO)*

Subsidiary (Domestic):

ERIKS Industrial Services Ltd. **(3)**
Amber Way, Halesowen, B62 8WG, W Midlands, United Kingdom
Tel.: (44) 1215086000
Web Site: http://www.eriks.co.uk
Sales Range: $25-49.9 Million
Emp.: 50
Industrial Supplies Distr
N.A.I.C.S.: 423840
M.T.A. Beckers *(CEO)*

Subsidiary (Domestic):

ERIKS bv **(2)**
Toermalijnstraat 5, Alkmaar, 1812, Netherlands
Tel.: (31) 725141514
Web Site: http://www.eriks.nl
Sales Range: $125-149.9 Million
Emp.: 500
Industrial Supplies Distr
N.A.I.C.S.: 423840
Paul Vos *(CEO & Mng Dir)*

Subsidiary (US):

Industrial Controls Distributors LLC **(2)**
17 Christopher Way, Eatontown, NJ 07724
Tel.: (732) 918-9000
Web Site:
 http://www.industrialcontrolsonline.com
Sales Range: $75-99.9 Million
Emp.: 42
Fiscal Year-end: 12/31/2012
Industrial Heating & Air Conditioning Process Equipment Distr
N.A.I.C.S.: 423720

Joe Eichelberger *(CEO)*

Branch (Domestic):

Industrial Controls Distributors **(3)**
11501 Goldcoast Dr, Cincinnati, OH 45249
Tel.: (513) 733-5200
Web Site:
 http://www.industrialcontrolsonline.com
Sales Range: $50-74.9 Million
Emp.: 30
Industrial Heating & Air Conditioning Process Equipment Distr
N.A.I.C.S.: 423830
Shiveoy Russ *(Mgr-Sls)*

Industrial Controls Distributors **(3)**
232 N Governor Printz Blvd, Lester, PA 19029
Tel.: (610) 521-7400
Web Site:
 http://www.industrialcontrolsonline.com
Sales Range: $1-9.9 Million
Emp.: 17
Hazardous Waste Treatment & Disposal
N.A.I.C.S.: 562211
George Poole *(Branch Mgr)*

Subsidiary (Non-US):

Maagtechnic AG **(2)**
Sonnentalstrasse 8, 8600, Dubendorf, Switzerland **(100%)**
Tel.: (41) 848111333
Web Site: http://www.maagtechnic.ch
Sales Range: $150-199.9 Million
Emp.: 580
Industrial Equipment Mfr & Distr
N.A.I.C.S.: 333248
Joel Souchon *(Mng Dir)*

Subsidiary (US):

Rawson, Inc. **(2)**
2010 McAllister Rd, Houston, TX 77092
Tel.: (713) 684-1400
Web Site: http://www.rawsonlp.com
Sales Range: $100-124.9 Million
Emp.: 80
Instruments & Control Equipment
N.A.I.C.S.: 423830
Dennis Betz *(VP-Mktg & Product Mgmt)*

The Newdell Company **(2)**
13750 Hollister Rd, Houston, TX 77086
Tel.: (713) 590-1312
Web Site: http://www.newdellco.com
Sales Range: $25-49.9 Million
Emp.: 80
Valves Mfr & Distr
N.A.I.C.S.: 332911
Curg Click *(Dir-Mktg)*

Makro N.V. **(1)**
Rijnkade 1, 3511 LC, Utrecht, Netherlands
Tel.: (31) 302338833
Web Site: http://www.shv.nl
Cash & Carry Distr
N.A.I.C.S.: 424490
P. J. Kennedy *(Pres)*

Subsidiary (Non-US):

Makro South America **(2)**
Rua Carlos Lisdegno Carlucci 519, 05536-900, Sao Paulo, Brazil
Tel.: (55) 1137452814
Web Site: http://www.makro.com.br
Sales Range: $25-49.9 Million
Emp.: 15
Cash & Carry Supermarkets
N.A.I.C.S.: 445110
Ricardo Kandelman *(CEO)*

Subsidiary (Domestic):

Makro Atacadista S.A. **(3)**
Rua Carlos L Carlucci 519, 05536-900, Sao Paulo, SP, Brazil **(62%)**
Tel.: (55) 1137452814
Web Site: http://www.makro.com.br
Self-Service Wholesale Stores
N.A.I.C.S.: 445110

Subsidiary (Non-US):

Makro Comercializadora S.A. **(3)**
Prolongacion Ave Romulo Gallegos Carretera Petare-Guarenas, La Urbina, 1061, Caracas, Venezuela **(75%)**
Tel.: (58) 2122421811

SHV HOLDINGS N.V.

Web Site: http://www.makro.com.ve
Self-Service Wholesale Stores
N.A.I.C.S.: 445110

Makro de Colombia S.A. **(3)**
Cra 39 193-63 Autopista Norte, Bogota, Colombia **(56.4%)**
Tel.: (57) 16781616
Web Site: http://www.makro.com.co
Cash & Carry Distr
N.A.I.C.S.: 424490
Nelson Davila *(Office Mgr)*

Mammoet Holding B.V. **(1)**
Haven 580 Karel Doormanweg 47, Schiedam, 3454, Netherlands **(100%)**
Tel.: (31) 102042424
Web Site: http://www.mammoet.com
Sales Range: $500-549.9 Million
Emp.: 2,000
Heavy Lifting & Freight Transportation Services
N.A.I.C.S.: 483111
Jan Kleijn *(CEO)*

Subsidiary (Non-US):

Mammoet Deutschland GmbH **(2)**
Am Haupttor/ Bau 3737, 06237, Leuna, Germany
Tel.: (49) 3461432681
Web Site: http://www.mammoet.com
Sales Range: $50-74.9 Million
Emp.: 140
Heavy Lifting & Freight Transportation Services
N.A.I.C.S.: 237990

Subsidiary (US):

Mammoet USA, Inc. **(2)**
20525 Farm 521 Rd, Rosharon, TX 77583-8127
Tel.: (281) 369-2200
Web Site: http://www.mammoet.com
Sales Range: $50-74.9 Million
Emp.: 115
Heavy Lifting & Freight Transportation Services
N.A.I.C.S.: 483211
Barbara Hensley *(Controller)*

NPM Capital N.V. **(1)**
Breitnerstraat 1, 1077 BL, Amsterdam, Netherlands
Tel.: (31) 205705555
Web Site: http://www.npm-capital.com
Emp.: 20
Privater Equity Firm
N.A.I.C.S.: 523999
Bart Coopmans *(Dir-Investments)*

Holding (Domestic):

Dieseko Group B.V. **(2)**
Lelystraat 49, 3364 AH, Sliedrecht, Netherlands **(65%)**
Tel.: (31) 184 410333
Web Site: http://www.diesekogroup.com
Sales Range: $75-99.9 Million
Emp.: 150
Hydraulic Vibratory Equipment Mfr & Distr
N.A.I.C.S.: 333120
Dirk Smulders *(CEO)*

Hak B.V. **(2)**
Jagerspad 7, Giessen, Netherlands
Tel.: (31) 0183446500
Web Site: http://www.hak.nl
Sales Range: $75-99.9 Million
Canned Vegetable Mfr
N.A.I.C.S.: 311421

Subsidiary (Domestic):

Infinitas Learning Netherlands B.V. **(2)**
Het Spoor 8-14, 3994 AK, Houten, Netherlands
Tel.: (31) 306383520
Web Site: http://www.infinitaslearning.com
Sales Range: $400-449.9 Million
Educational Books, CD-ROMs & Other Materials Publisher
N.A.I.C.S.: 513130

Subsidiary (Non-US):

Bildungsverlag EINS GmbH **(3)**
Ettore-Bugatti-Strasse 6-14, 51149, Cologne, Germany

SHV HOLDINGS N.V.

SHV Holdings N.V.—(Continued)
Tel.: (49) 22038982101
Web Site: http://www.westermanngruppe.de
Sales Range: $25-49.9 Million
Emp.: 150
Trade & Professional Book Publisher
N.A.I.C.S.: 513130

Liber AB (3)
Rasundavagen 12, 113 98, Solna, Sweden
Tel.: (46) 86909000
Web Site: http://www.liber.se
Sales Range: $10-24.9 Million
Emp.: 150
Educational Support Services
N.A.I.C.S.: 561499
Asa Norberg *(CEO)*

Subsidiary (Domestic):

Wolters-Noordhoff Groningen (3)
Winschoterdiep 70A, 9723 AB, Groningen, Netherlands
Tel.: (31) 505226922
Web Site: http://www.noordhoffuitgevers.nl
Sales Range: $75-99.9 Million
Emp.: 450
Education Services
N.A.I.C.S.: 513120
Erjan Holl *(Mng Dir)*

Holding (Domestic):

Kramp Groep BV (2)
Breukelaarweg 33, 7051DW, Varsseveld, Netherlands (32%)
Tel.: (31) 315 254 299
Web Site: http://www.kramp.com
Rev.: $976,682,539
Assets: $679,767,338
Liabilities: $463,345,435
Net Worth: $216,421,904
Earnings: $48,502,256
Emp.: 3,000
Fiscal Year-end: 12/31/2019
Farm Machinery Whslr
N.A.I.C.S.: 423820

Holding (Non-US):

Grene Kramp Holding A/S (3)
Kobbervej 6, 6900, Skjern, Denmark
Tel.: (45) 96808383
Web Site: http://www.grene.com
Industrial Machinery Distr
N.A.I.C.S.: 333111
Carsten Thygesen *(Mng Dir)*

Subsidiary (Non-US):

Grene AS (4)
Vestvollveien 34 E, 518, Skedsmokorset, Norway
Tel.: (47) 22 80 38 30
Web Site: http://www.Grene.no
Emp.: 2
Industrial Machinery Distr
N.A.I.C.S.: 423830
Tony Isler *(Mng Dir)*

Grene Ab OY (4)
Mestarintie 2, Kimitoen, 25700, Finland
Tel.: (358) 242064600
Web Site: http://www.grene.fi
Sales Range: $25-49.9 Million
Emp.: 15
Agricultural Machinery Equipment Whslr
N.A.I.C.S.: 423820

Subsidiary (Domestic):

Grene Danmark A/S (4)
Kobbervej 6, DK-6900, Skjern, Denmark
Tel.: (45) 96808500
Web Site: http://group.grene.com
Industrial Machinery Distr
N.A.I.C.S.: 423830
Allan Pedersen *(Sls Dir)*

Subsidiary (Non-US):

Grene Sp. z o.o. (4)
Modla Krolewska ul Skandynawska 1, 62-571, Stare Miasto, Poland
Tel.: (48) 63 240 91 00
Web Site: http://www.grene.pl
Emp.: 20
Agriculture & Forestry Equipment Distr
N.A.I.C.S.: 423830

Subsidiary (Domestic):

Grene Dustrybucja Sp. z o.o. (5)
Modla Krolewska Skandynawska 1, Stare Miasto, 62-571, Poland
Tel.: (48) 632409211
Agricultural Machinery Distr
N.A.I.C.S.: 423820
Marian Fedko *(Mng Dir)*

Holding (US):

Makerbot Industries, LLC (2)
One MetroTech Ctr, Brooklyn, NY 11201
Tel.: (347) 334-6800
Web Site: http://www.makerbot.com
Printing Machinery & Equipment Mfr
N.A.I.C.S.: 333248
Marty Markowitz *(Pres)*

Nutreco N.V. (1)
Prins Frederiklaan 4, 3818 KC, Amersfoort, Netherlands
Tel.: (31) 334226100
Web Site: http://www.nutreco.com
Rev.: $6,168,078,448
Earnings: $307,075,440
Emp.: 10,967
Fiscal Year-end: 12/31/2015
Animal Nutrition Products & Fish Feed Mfr
N.A.I.C.S.: 311119
Viggo Halseth *(Chief Innovation Officer)*

Subsidiary (Domestic):

Nutreco Nederland B.V. (2)
Veerstraat 38, Boxmeer, 5831 JN, Netherlands
Tel.: (31) 485589955
Web Site: http://www.nutreco.com
Animal & Fish Feed Mfr
N.A.I.C.S.: 311119
Harm de Wildt *(Mng Dir)*

Subsidiary (Non-US):

Skretting Canada (2)
1370 East Kent Avenue, V5X2Y2, Vancouver, BC, Canada
Tel.: (604) 325-0302
Web Site: http://www.skretting.ca
Aquaculture Feed Mfr
N.A.I.C.S.: 311119

Skretting Japan (2)
Abundant 95 12-1 3 Chome, Suite 701, 812-0013, Fukuoka, Japan
Tel.: (81) 924321301
Aquaculture Feed Distr
N.A.I.C.S.: 424910

Subsidiary (US):

Skretting USA (2)
712 E 2400 N, Tooele, UT 84074
Tel.: (435) 277-2100
Web Site: http://www.skrettingusa.com
Fish & Shrimp Feed Mfr
N.A.I.C.S.: 311119
James Knight *(Ops Mgr)*

Subsidiary (Domestic):

Trouw Nutrition International B.V. (2)
Stationsstraat 77, 3811 MH, Amersfoort, Netherlands
Tel.: (31) 334226100
Web Site: http://www.trouwnutrition.com
Holding Company; Animal Feed & Supplement Mfr
N.A.I.C.S.: 551112

Subsidiary (Non-US):

Frank Wright Limited (3)
Blenheim House Blenheim Rd, Ashbourne, DE6 1HA, Derbyshire, United Kingdom
Tel.: (44) 1335341100
Web Site: http://gb.trouwnutrition.co.uk
Animal Nutrition Products Mfr & Whslr & Research Services
N.A.I.C.S.: 311119
Roderick Prince *(Dir-Intl & Pet)*

Trouw Nutrition Belgium (3)
Akkerhage 4, Gent, Belgium
Tel.: (32) 92439120
Web Site: https://www.trouwnutrition-benelux.com
Animal Food Distr
N.A.I.C.S.: 424910

Trouw Nutrition China (3)
6/F Block C Wanlin Technology Building No 8 Malianwa North Road, Haidian District, Beijing, 100085, China
Tel.: (86) 1063706277
Web Site: https://www.trouwnutrition.com.cn
Animal Feed Mfr & Whslr
N.A.I.C.S.: 311119

Trouw Nutrition Denmark (3)
Park Alle 14, 6600, Vejen, Denmark
Tel.: (45) 7536133
Web Site: http://www.trouw.dk
Animal Food Distr
N.A.I.C.S.: 424910

Trouw Nutrition Deutschland GmbH (3)
Gempfinger Str 15, 86666, Burgheim, Germany
Tel.: (49) 8432890
Web Site: http://www.trouwnutrition.de
Animal Nutrition Product Mfr
N.A.I.C.S.: 311119
Anton Einberger *(Mng Dir)*

Trouw Nutrition France (3)
Bord Haut de Vigny, 95450, Vigny, France
Tel.: (33) 134678888
Web Site: https://www.trouwnutrition.fr
Animal Food Distr
N.A.I.C.S.: 424910

Trouw Nutrition Hungary (3)
Topart u 1, PO Box 33, 2851, Kornye, Hungary
Tel.: (36) 34573571
Animal Food Distr
N.A.I.C.S.: 424910

Trouw Nutrition Ireland (3)
36 Ship Street, Belfast, BT15 1JL, Co Antrim NI, United Kingdom
Tel.: (44) 2890748233
Web Site: http://trouw-nutrition.co.uk
Animal Food Distr
N.A.I.C.S.: 424910

Trouw Nutrition Italia S.p.A. (3)
Localita Vignetto 17, 37060, Mozzecane, VR, Italy
Tel.: (39) 0456764311
Web Site: https://www.trouwnutrition.it
Animal Food Distr
N.A.I.C.S.: 424910

Trouw Nutrition Mexico (3)
Av C No 1101 Fraccionamiento Central de Carga, San Nicolas de los Garza, Nuevo Leon, CP 66494, Mexico
Tel.: (52) 8181447400
Web Site: https://www.trouwnutrition.mx
Animal Food Distr
N.A.I.C.S.: 424910

Subsidiary (Domestic):

Trouw Nutrition Nederland B.V. (3)
Nijverheidsweg 2, 3881 LA, Putten, Netherlands
Tel.: (31) 341371611
Web Site: https://www.trouwnutrition-benelux.com
Animal Feed Mfr & Distr
N.A.I.C.S.: 311119

Subsidiary (Non-US):

Trouw Nutrition South Africa (3)
137 Terrace Road, Sebenza, 1610, South Africa
Tel.: (27) 115240440
Web Site: http://www.advit.co.za
Animal Health, Welfare Management Products
N.A.I.C.S.: 311119
Kobus Coetzee *(Area Mgr)*

Subsidiary (US):

Trouw Nutrition USA, LLC (3)
115 Executive Dr, Highland, IL 62249-0219
Tel.: (618) 654-2070
Web Site: http://www.trouwnutritionusa.com
Custom Animal Feed Premixe Mfr
N.A.I.C.S.: 311119
Mike Hooper *(Dir-Mktg)*

SHV Energy N.V. (1)
Taurus Avenue 19, 2132 LS, Hoofddorp, Netherlands

INTERNATIONAL PUBLIC

Tel.: (31) 235555700
Web Site: http://www.shvenergy.com
Sales Range: $1-4.9 Billion
Emp.: 14,000
Holding Company; Liquefied Petroleum Gas (Bottled Gas) Dealers
N.A.I.C.S.: 551112
Fulco van Lede *(Member-Mgmt Bd)*

Subsidiary (Non-US):

Butan Plin d.d. (2)
Verovskova 64A, SLO 1001, Ljubljana, Slovenia (70%)
Tel.: (386) 15889813
Web Site: http://www.butanplin.si
Sales Range: $25-49.9 Million
Emp.: 90
Liquefied Petroleum Gas (Bottled Gas) Dealers
N.A.I.C.S.: 457210
Tomaz Grm *(Mng Dir)*

Butan Plin d.o.o. (2)
Ulica Rijeke Dragonje 23, Novigrad, 52100, Croatia (70%)
Tel.: (385) 52211895
Web Site: http://www.butanplin.hr
Emp.: 50
Liquefied Petroleum Gas (Bottled Gas) Dealers
N.A.I.C.S.: 457210
Andrea Valleno *(Mng Dir)*

Calor Group (2)
Tachbrook Pk, Warwick, CV34 6RL, United Kingdom (100%)
Tel.: (44) 1926330088
Web Site: http://www.calor.co.uk
Sales Range: $100-124.9 Million
Emp.: 300
Liquefied Petroleum Gas Distr
N.A.I.C.S.: 457210

Subsidiary (Domestic):

Calor Gas Ltd. (3)
Athena House Athena Drive, Tachbrook Park, Warwick, CV34 6RL, United Kingdom (100%)
Tel.: (44) 3458508796
Web Site: http://www.calor.co.uk
Sales Range: $125-149.9 Million
Emp.: 300
Liquefied Petroleum Gas Distr
N.A.I.C.S.: 457210

Calor Gas Northern Ireland Ltd. (3)
Airport Rd W Sydenham, Belfast, BT3 9EE, United Kingdom (100%)
Tel.: (44) 2890458466
Web Site: http://www.calorgas.ie
Sales Range: $25-49.9 Million
Emp.: 40
Liquefied Petroleum Gas Distr
N.A.I.C.S.: 457210
Oliver Kenny *(Area Mgr-Sls)*

Subsidiary (Non-US):

Calor Teoranta (3)
Longmile Rd, Dublin, 12, Ireland (100%)
Tel.: (353) 14505000
Web Site: http://www.calorgas.ie
Sales Range: $25-49.9 Million
Emp.: 80
Liquefied Petroleum Gas
N.A.I.C.S.: 457210
Michael Kossack *(CEO)*

Subsidiary (Non-US):

Compagnie de Gaz de Petrole Primagaz S.A. (2)
4 Rue Herault de Sechelles, PO Box 97, 75829, Paris, Cedex 17, France (100%)
Tel.: (33) 0158615000
Web Site: http://www.primagaz.fr
Sales Range: $25-49.9 Million
Emp.: 45
Liquefied Petroleum Gas
N.A.I.C.S.: 457210

Subsidiary (Non-US):

Bizimgaz Sanayi ve Ticaret A.S. (3)
Ataturk Mah Ertugrul Gazi Sok Metropol Istanbul Sitesi C2 Blok No 2 A, 34758, Istanbul, Turkiye (99.07%)
Tel.: (90) 216 513 51 50
Web Site: http://www.bizimgaz.com

AND PRIVATE COMPANIES

Liquefied Petroleum Gas
N.A.I.C.S.: 457210

Gaspol S.A. (3)
Al Jana Pawla II 80, 00-175, Warsaw,
Poland **(79.65%)**
Tel.: (48) 225300000
Web Site: http://www.gaspol.pl
Sales Range: $125-149.9 Million
Liquefied Petroleum Gas Distr
N.A.I.C.S.: 457210
Sylwester Smigiel *(Pres)*

Liquigas SpA (3)
Via Tucidide 56, 20134, Milan,
Italy **(70%)**
Tel.: (39) 02701681
Web Site: http://www.liquigas.com
Liquified Bottled Gas Products
N.A.I.C.S.: 457210

Primagas GmbH (3)
Luisenstrasse 113, 47799, Krefeld,
Germany **(72.74%)**
Tel.: (49) 21518520
Web Site: http://www.primagas.de
Sales Range: $50-74.9 Million
Liquefied Petroleum Gas
N.A.I.C.S.: 457210
Gobst Deercks *(CEO)*

Primagaz Belgium N.V. (3)
Technology Ctr, Humaniteitslaan 235, 1620,
Drogenbos, Belgium **(100%)**
Tel.: (32) 25580404
Web Site: http://www.primagaz.be
Sales Range: $25-49.9 Million
Emp.: 40
Liquefied Petroleum Gas
N.A.I.C.S.: 457210

Primagaz Central Europe GmbH (3)
Salztorgasse 2 Apt 5, 1010, Vienna,
Austria **(100%)**
Tel.: (43) 15320546
Web Site: http://www.primagaz.com
Sales Range: $25-49.9 Million
Emp.: 11
Liquefied Petroleum Gas
N.A.I.C.S.: 457210
Brand Stratter *(Mng Dir)*

Primagaz Danmark A/S (3)
Sandvadsvej 11, 4600, Koge,
Denmark **(100%)**
Tel.: (45) 56631220
Web Site: http://www.primagaz.dk
Sales Range: $25-49.9 Million
Emp.: 45
Liquefied Petroleum Gas
N.A.I.C.S.: 457210

Primagaz Distribucion S.A. (3)
Calle Entenza 332 334 1a, 08029, Barcelona, Spain **(100%)**
Tel.: (34) 933633770
Web Site: http://www.primagaz.es
Sales Range: $25-49.9 Million
Emp.: 20
Liquefied Petroleum Gas
N.A.I.C.S.: 457210

Primagaz GmbH (3)
St Johanner Strasse 11, 6370, Kitzbuhel,
Austria **(100%)**
Tel.: (43) 53566992
Web Site: http://www.primagaz.at
Sales Range: $25-49.9 Million
Emp.: 20
Liquefied Petroleum Gas
N.A.I.C.S.: 457210

Primagaz Hungaria Rt. (3)
Irinyi Jozsex 420, 1117, Budapest,
Hungary **(100%)**
Tel.: (36) 0012099900
Web Site: http://www.primagaz.hu
Sales Range: $50-74.9 Million
Liquefied Petroleum Gas
N.A.I.C.S.: 457210

Primagaz Nederland B.V. (3)
PO Box 305, 7400 AH, Deventer,
Netherlands **(100%)**
Tel.: (31) 575582200
Web Site: http://www.primagaz.nl
Sales Range: $25-49.9 Million
Emp.: 75
Liquefied Petroleum Gas
N.A.I.C.S.: 457210
Thomas Mortcay *(Mng Dir)*

Primaplyn Spol. s.r.o. (3)
Na Pankraci 30, 140 00, Prague, 4, Czech
Republic **(100%)**
Tel.: (420) 261001565
Web Site: http://www.primagas.cz
Sales Range: $25-49.9 Million
Emp.: 15
Liquefied Petroleum Gas
N.A.I.C.S.: 457210

Probugas a.s. (3)
Nam 1 Maja 18, 811 06, Bratislava,
Slovakia **(50%)**
Tel.: (421) 240201307
Web Site: http://www.probugas.sk
Sales Range: $25-49.9 Million
Emp.: 30
Liquefied Petroleum Gas
N.A.I.C.S.: 457210

Subsidiary (Domestic):

SHV Gas Supply & Risk Management SAS (3)
22 Pl Des Vosges La Defense, 92979,
Paris, Cedex, France **(100%)**
Tel.: (33) 149039587
Web Site: http://wwwshvgas.com
Sales Range: $25-49.9 Million
Emp.: 30
Liquefied Petroleum Gas (Bottled Gas)
Dealers
N.A.I.C.S.: 457210
Ernst Brandstaetter *(Mng Dir & Gen Mgr)*

Subsidiary (Non-US):

iPRAGAZ A.S. (3)
19 Mayis Caddesi Nova Baran Plaza No 4
Kat 13 17, 34360, Istanbul, Turkiye
Tel.: (90) 2122320400
Web Site: http://www.ipragaz.com.tr
Liquefied Petroleum Gas
N.A.I.C.S.: 457210

Subsidiary (Non-US):

Foshan Shunran SHV Gas Co., Ltd. (2)
3/F Xinde Building 38 Xiandong Road, Daliang Shunde, Foshan, Guangdong,
China **(90%)**
Tel.: (86) 75722221793
Web Site: http://www.shv.nl
Liquefied Petroleum Gas Distr
N.A.I.C.S.: 457210

Liquivex d.o.o. (2)
Zabljak b b, 74230, Usora, Bosnia & Herzegovina
Tel.: (387) 987 32 891 220
Web Site: http://www.liquivex.com
Petroleum Product Distr
N.A.I.C.S.: 424720

Subsidiary (US):

Pinnacle Propane, LLC (2)
600 E Las Colinas Blvd Ste 2000, Irving,
TX 75039
Tel.: (972) 444-0300
Web Site: http://www.pinnpropane.com
Propane Distr
N.A.I.C.S.: 424720
Eric T. Kalamaras *(CFO & Sr VP)*

Subsidiary (Domestic):

Alliant Gas, LLC (3)
600 E Las Colinas Blvd Ste 2000, Irving,
TX 75039-5607
Tel.: (877) 532-5427
Web Site: http://www.alliantgas.com
Propane Distr
N.A.I.C.S.: 424720

Subsidiary (Non-US):

Primagaz Norge AS (2)
Svelvikveien 185, 3037, Drammen, Norway
Tel.: (47) 22 88 19 70
Web Site: http://www.primagaz.no
Petroleum Product Distr
N.A.I.C.S.: 424720
Richard W. Wright *(Country Mgr-Sls)*

Primagaz Sverige AB (2)
Kraftverksvagen, 444 32, Stenungsund,
Sweden
Tel.: (46) 303 72 71 00
Web Site: http://www.primagaz.se

Emp.: 25
Petroleum Product Distr
N.A.I.C.S.: 424720
Orjan Andersson *(Acct Mgr)*

SHV Energy Private Ltd. (2)
8-2-334 Serene Chambers 4th Floor Rd 7,
Banjara Hills, Hyderabad, 500034,
India **(51%)**
Tel.: (91) 4023540079
Web Site: http://www.supergas.com
Sales Range: $25-49.9 Million
Emp.: 50
Bottled or Bulk Liquified Petroleum
N.A.I.C.S.: 457210
Ajay Kumar *(CEO)*

SHV Gas Brasil Ltda. (2)
Edificio Palacio Austergesilo de Athayde-Centro, 20030 905, Rio de Janeiro,
Brazil **(100%)**
Tel.: (55) 2139745151
Web Site: http://www.supergasbras.com.br
Sales Range: $50-74.9 Million
Emp.: 150
Petroleum Product Whslr
N.A.I.C.S.: 457210

Subsidiary (Domestic):

Supergasbras Distribuidora de Gas S.A. (3)
Rua Sao Jose 90/16 Centro, 90 17
andar/RJ, 20013-900, Rio de Janeiro, RJ,
Brazil **(49%)**
Tel.: (55) 2125336555
Web Site: http://www.supergasbras.com.br
Liquefied Petroleum Gas
N.A.I.C.S.: 457210

SHYAM CENTURY FERROUS LTD.
Century House P 151, Tartala Main
Road, Kolkata, 700 027, India
Tel.: (91) 3324484169
Web Site:
 https://www.shyamcentury.com
SHYAMCENT—(NSE)
Rev.: $18,520,402
Assets: $18,391,833
Liabilities: $2,283,236
Net Worth: $16,108,597
Earnings: $382,473
Emp.: 112
Fiscal Year-end: 03/31/21
Ferro Alloy & Steel Product Mfr
N.A.I.C.S.: 331110
Ritu Agarwal *(Sec)*

SHYAM METALICS & ENERGY LTD.
Trinity Tower 7th Floor 83 Topsia
Road, Kolkata, 700046, West Bengal,
India
Tel.: (91) 3340164000
Web Site:
 https://www.shyammetalics.com
Year Founded: 1991
SHYAMMETL—(NSE)
Rev.: $1,525,350,998
Assets: $1,341,487,920
Liabilities: $482,732,450
Net Worth: $858,755,470
Earnings: $101,721,719
Emp.: 3,038
Fiscal Year-end: 03/31/23
Steel Mfrs
N.A.I.C.S.: 331110
Dev Kumar Tiwari *(Dir-Ops)*

Subsidiaries:

Mittal Corp. Limited (1)
315 Jolly Bhawan 1 10 New Marine Lines,
Mumbai, 400020, India
Tel.: (91) 2222007526
Web Site: http://www.mittalcorp.net
Stainless Steel Mfr
N.A.I.C.S.: 331513
Karan Mittal *(Mng Dir)*

SHYAM TELECOM LTD
Shyam House Plot No 3 Amrapali
Circle Vaishali Nagar, Jaipur, 302021,
Rajasthan, India
Tel.: (91) 1415100343
Web Site:
 http://www.shyamtelecom.com
SHYAMTEL—(NSE)
Rev.: $422,003
Assets: $3,740,209
Liabilities: $1,729,482
Net Worth: $2,010,727
Earnings: ($64,237)
Emp.: 23
Fiscal Year-end: 03/31/21
Mobile Communication Equipment
Mfr
N.A.I.C.S.: 334220
Ajay Khanna *(Mng Dir)*

Subsidiaries:

Shyam Telecom Inc. (1)
6 Kilmer Rd Ste D, Edison, NJ 08817-2432
Tel.: (732) 985-1324
Web Site: https://shyamtelecom.com
Mobile Communication Equipment Mfr
N.A.I.C.S.: 334220

SHYAMA INFOSYS LIMITED
3rd Floor Plot-395/397 Ruia Building
Kalbadevi Road Dabhol Karwadi, Kalbadevi, Mumbai, 400002, Maharashtra, India
Tel.: (91) 2222420751
531219—(BOM)
Rev.: $38,102
Assets: $1,175,050
Liabilities: $29,550
Net Worth: $1,145,500
Earnings: $4,663
Fiscal Year-end: 03/31/22
Software Development Services
N.A.I.C.S.: 541511
Swaraj Kumar Singh *(Exec Dir)*

SHYAMKAMAL INVESTMENTS LIMITED
Shop No 25 LG Target The Mall
Chandavarkar Road Opp BMC Ward
off, Borivali West, Mumbai, 400092,
Maharashtra, India
Tel.: (91) 7990733924
Web Site:
 https://www.shyamkamal.com
Year Founded: 1982
505515—(BOM)
Rev.: $36
Assets: $274,012
Liabilities: $39,698
Net Worth: $234,314
Earnings: ($31,881)
Fiscal Year-end: 03/31/23
Industrial Machinery Leasing Services
N.A.I.C.S.: 532490
Kailashchandra Subhkaran Kedia
(Chm)

SHYAMPUR SUGAR MILLS LTD.
Chini Shilpa Bhaban Share office 5th
floor 3 Dilkusha C/A, Dhaka, 1000,
Bangladesh
Tel.: (880) 9515668
SHYAMPSUG—(DHA)
Sales Range: Less than $1 Million
Sugar Cane Product Mfr
N.A.I.C.S.: 311314
Kayes Khan *(Sec)*

SHYMKENT MUNAI ONIMDERI JSC
7th km of Lengerskoe Road, 160050,
Shymkent, Kazakhstan
Tel.: (7) 7252 436038
Web Site: http://www.rb.kz
Sales Range: $25-49.9 Million
Petroleum & Oil Products Distr &
Storage Services
N.A.I.C.S.: 424720

SI CAPITAL PARTNERS LTD

— Shymkent Munai Onimderi JSC—(Continued)

SI CAPITAL PARTNERS LTD
7 Ulitsa Znamenka Building 3, Moscow, 119019, Russia
Tel.: (7) 4957109912
Web Site: http://www.si-cp.com
Privater Equity Firm
N.A.I.C.S.: 523999
Dmitry Razorenov *(Mng Partner)*

Subsidiaries:

Dodoni S.A. (1)
1 Tagmatarhi Kostaki Eleousa, 45110, Ioannina, Greece **(93.75%)**
Tel.: (30) 2651089700
Web Site: http://www.dodonidairy.com
Sales Range: $125-149.9 Million
Emp.: 400
Milk & Cheese Products Mfr
N.A.I.C.S.: 311511
Michael A. O'Neill *(CEO)*

SI RESOURCES CO., LTD.
9fl 68 Saemunan-ro, Jongno-gu, Seoul, Korea (South)
Tel.: (82) 27802388
Web Site: https://www.siresource.co.kr
Year Founded: 1987
065420—(KRS)
Rev.: $3,618,108
Assets: $15,378,280
Liabilities: $1,833,690
Net Worth: $13,544,591
Earnings: ($738,847)
Emp.: 13
Fiscal Year-end: 12/31/22
Coal Mining Services
N.A.I.C.S.: 423520
Sun Ok Ten *(CEO)*

SI-TECH INFORMATION TECHNOLOGY CO.,LTD.
14/F No 6 Zhongguancun South Avenue, Haidian Dist, Beijing, 100086, China
Tel.: (86) 1082193708
Web Site: http://www.si-tech.com.cn
Year Founded: 1995
300608—(CHIN)
Rev.: $122,609,038
Assets: $352,649,821
Liabilities: $126,654,221
Net Worth: $225,995,600
Earnings: $3,101,756
Fiscal Year-end: 12/31/23
Business Software Development Software Services
N.A.I.C.S.: 513210
Feizhou Wu *(Chm & Gen Mgr)*

SI6 METALS LIMITED
168 Stirling Highway, Nedlands, 6009, WA, Australia
Tel.: (61) 398551885 AU
Web Site: https://www.si6metals.com
SI6—(ASX)
Rev.: $8,519
Assets: $3,712,173
Liabilities: $294,877
Net Worth: $3,417,296
Earnings: ($2,212,413)
Fiscal Year-end: 06/30/21
Metal Mining Services
N.A.I.C.S.: 212290
Ian Kiers *(Chm)*

SIA KALNOZOLS CELTNIECIBA
Daugavgrivas iela 7, 1048, Riga, Latvia
Tel.: (371) 7607999
Web Site: http://www.kalnozols.eu
Year Founded: 1988
Sales Range: $75-99.9 Million
Emp.: 380

Industrial & Residential Construction Services
N.A.I.C.S.: 236210
Ojars Karklins *(Dir-HR)*

SIA PARTNERS & COMPANY
21 rue de Berri, Paris, 75008, France
Tel.: (33) 142777617
Web Site: http://www.sia-partners.com
Management & Consulting Firm
N.A.I.C.S.: 541618
Dan Connor *(CEO)*

Subsidiaries:

Caiman Consulting, Corp. (1)
15127 NE 24th St Ste 547, Redmond, WA 98052
Tel.: (213) 842-1332
Sales Range: $1-9.9 Million
Emp.: 40
Business Consultation & Project Management Services
N.A.I.C.S.: 541618
Shari Sparling *(Mgr-Talent)*

Sia Partners, Inc. (1)
1400 Post Oak Blvd, Houston, TX 77056
Tel.: (713) 621-9288
Lessors of Residential Buildings & Dwellings
N.A.I.C.S.: 531110

SIA RIGAS SATIKSME
Vestienas Street 35, 1035, Riga, Latvia
Tel.: (371) 6710 4800 LV
Web Site: http://www.rigassatiksme.lv
Year Founded: 2003
Public Transport Services
N.A.I.C.S.: 488999
Viktors Zakis *(Head-Customer Svc & Comm)*

Subsidiaries:

Sia Rigas Karte (1)
Cesu str 31/ 3 entrance 8 3 floor, Riga, 1012, Latvia **(51%)**
Tel.: (371) 67326300
Web Site: https://rigaskarte.lv
Smart Payment Services
N.A.I.C.S.: 522320
Pavels Tulovskis *(Dir-Technical)*

SIAB HOLDINGS BERHAD
82 Jalan BP 7/8 Bandar Bukit Puchong, 47120, Puchong, Malaysia
Tel.: (60) 380527117 MY
Web Site: https://www.siabmy.com
Year Founded: 1984
SIAB—(KLS)
Rev.: $29,998,095
Assets: $37,914,074
Liabilities: $26,392,593
Net Worth: $11,521,481
Earnings: $4,078,095
Fiscal Year-end: 12/31/22
Holding Company
N.A.I.C.S.: 551112
Wai Hoe Ng *(Mng Dir)*

SIAG SCHAAF INDUSTRIE AG
Kamenzer Strasse 3, 04347, Leipzig, Germany
Tel.: (49) 34123910
Web Site: http://www.siag.de
Construction & Engineering Services
N.A.I.C.S.: 236210
Rechtsanwalt Andrew Seidl *(CEO)*

Subsidiaries:

SIAG Industrie GmbH (1)
Kamenzer Strasse 3, 04347, Leipzig, Germany
Tel.: (49) 3412391316
Power Turbine Distr
N.A.I.C.S.: 423860

SIAM CITY CEMENT PUBLIC COMPANY LIMITED
Column Tower 3rd 10th - 12th Fl 199 Ratchadapisek Road, Klongtoey, Bangkok, 10110, Thailand
Tel.: (66) 27977000
Web Site: https://www.siamcitycement.com
Year Founded: 1969
SCCC—(THA)
Rev.: $1,249,337,031
Assets: $2,034,651,059
Liabilities: $1,046,562,075
Net Worth: $988,088,983
Earnings: $72,755,847
Emp.: 4,307
Fiscal Year-end: 12/31/23
Cement Aggregates, Concrete & Related Construction & Building Materials.
N.A.I.C.S.: 327310
Paul Heinz Hugentobler *(Chm)*

Subsidiaries:

Conwood Company Limited (1)
1448/14 Crystal Design Center CDC L1 Building RM 111 Soi Ladprao 87, Klongchan Bangkapi, Bangkok, 10240, Thailand
Tel.: (66) 27977444
Web Site: https://conwood.com
Floor & Wall Decoration Services
N.A.I.C.S.: 238330

Subsidiary (Non-US):

PT. Conwood Indonesia (1)
Menara Jamsostek North Tower 14th Floor Jl Jend Gatot Subroto No 38, South Jakarta, 12710, Indonesia
Tel.: (62) 215 296 2146
Web Site: https://www.conwood.co.id
Floor & Wall Decoration Services
N.A.I.C.S.: 238330
Sukit Ngamsangapong *(Pres)*

Globe Cement Company Limited (1)
Column Tower 3rd 10th 12th Floor 199 Ratchadapisek Road, Klongtoey, Bangkok, 10110, Thailand **(100%)**
Tel.: (66) 27977000
Web Site: http://www.globecement.com
Cement Mfr
N.A.I.C.S.: 327310
Olarn Chawang *(Dir-Comml & Logistics)*

Insee Digital Company Limited (1)
Column Tower 3rd 10th 12th Floor 199 Ratchadapisek Road, Klongtoey, Bangkok, 10110, Thailand
Tel.: (66) 27977000
Information Technology Management & Development Services
N.A.I.C.S.: 541511
Hans Keril Ante *(CTO)*

Insee Ecocycle Company Limited (1)
Column Tower 3rd 10th 12th fl 199 Ratchadapisek Rd, Klongtoey, Bangkok, 10110, Thailand
Tel.: (66) 1732773776
Web Site: https://www.inseeecocycle.com
Industrial Waste Management Services
N.A.I.C.S.: 562998

Insee Ecocycle Lanka (Private) Limited (1)
Tel.: (94) 117800800
Web Site: https://ecocycle.lk
Waste Management & Industrial Services
N.A.I.C.S.: 562998
Najila Ranganath *(Mgr-Comml)*

Khmer Cement Industry Company Limited (1)
N 9 St 80 Corner St 75, 12201, Phnom Penh, Cambodia **(75%)**
Tel.: (855) 234309023
Sales Range: $25-49.9 Million
Emp.: 47
Cement Mfr
N.A.I.C.S.: 327310

Siam City Cement (Bangladesh) Limited (1)
Tower 52 9th Floor Road-11 Block-C, Banani Model Town, Dhaka, 1213, Bangladesh
Tel.: (880) 9609011200
Cement Mfr
N.A.I.C.S.: 327310
Nasirul Alam *(Gen Sls Mgr)*

Siam City Cement (Lanka) Limited (1)
Level 25 Access Tower II No 278/4 Union Place, 2, Colombo, Sri Lanka **(98.95%)**
Tel.: (94) 117800800
Cement Mfr & Distr
N.A.I.C.S.: 327310
Paul Heinz Hugentobler *(Chm)*

Subsidiary (Domestic):

Mahaweli Marine Cement (Private) Limited (2)
Level 25 Access Tower II No 278/4 Union Place, Mawatha, 2, Colombo, Sri Lanka **(90%)**
Tel.: (94) 117800800
Web Site: https://www.siamcitycement.com
Cement Distr
N.A.I.C.S.: 423320

Siam City Cement (Vietnam) Limited (1)
11 Doan Van Bo, Ward 13 District 4, Ho Chi Minh City, Vietnam
Tel.: (84) 2873017018
Web Site: https://www.siamcitycement.com
Emp.: 700
Cement Mfr & Distr
N.A.I.C.S.: 327310

Siam City Cement Nhon Trach Limited (1)
Ong Keo Industrial zone Phuoc Khanh, Nhon Trach, Dong Nai, Vietnam
Tel.: (84) 3570017
Cement Mfr
N.A.I.C.S.: 327310

Siam City Cement Public Company Limited - Saraburi Factory (1)
99 Moo 9 and 219 Moo 5 Mitraparb Road Km 129-131Tambon Tabkwang, Kaeng Khoi, 18260, Saraburi, Thailand
Tel.: (66) 36240930
Cement Mfr
N.A.I.C.S.: 327310

Siam City Concrete Company Limited (1)
Column Tower 3rd 10th 12th Floor 199 Ratchadapisek Road, Klongtoey, Bangkok, 10110, Thailand
Tel.: (66) 27977555
Ready Mixed Concrete & Aggregate Mfr
N.A.I.C.S.: 327320

SIAM CITY FACTORING PUBLIC CO., LTD.
2922 205 206 Charn Issara Tower 2 11th Fl, New Petchburi Rd Huay Khwang, Bangkok, 10310, Thailand
Tel.: (66) 23082080
Web Site: http://www.siamfactor.co.th
Sales Range: $25-49.9 Million
Emp.: 30
Factoring Services
N.A.I.C.S.: 522299
Noppadol Nilrat *(VP)*

SIAM COMMERCIAL BANK PUBLIC COMPANY LIMITED
9 Ratchadapisek Road Jatujak, Bangkok, 10900, Thailand
Tel.: (66) 25441000 TH
SCB—(OTCIQ)
Rev.: $3,944,114,223
Assets: $109,235,738,853
Liabilities: $95,513,594,974
Net Worth: $13,722,143,879
Earnings: $899,429,817
Emp.: 23,977
Fiscal Year-end: 12/31/20
Banking, Securities & Other Financial Services
N.A.I.C.S.: 523999
Siribunchong Uthayophas *(Sec & Exec VP)*

AND PRIVATE COMPANIES

Subsidiaries:

Cambodian Commercial Bank Ltd. (1)
26 Monivong Blvd Sangkat Phsar Thmei II, Khan Daun Penh, Phnom Penh, Cambodia
Tel.: (855) 23213601
Web Site: http://www.scb.co.th
Commercial Banking Services
N.A.I.C.S.: 522110
Suriyah Termlertmanauswong (Branch Mgr)

Mahisorn Co., Ltd. (1)
SCB Park Plz Bldg 21th Floor, 18-19 Rutchadapisek Rd Jatuja, 10900, Bangkok, Thailand (100%)
Tel.: (66) 29375400
Commericial Banking
N.A.I.C.S.: 522110

Monix Co., Ltd. (1)
No 9 2nd Floor Learning Center Rutchadapisek Rd, Chatuchak, Bangkok, 10900, Thailand
Tel.: (66) 2 113 1113
Web Site: https://www.monix.co.th
Financial Services
N.A.I.C.S.: 522110
Qinbin Jimmy Fan (CEO)

SCB 10X Co., Ltd. (1)
No 2525 One Unit Number 1/301-1/305 3rd Floor Rama 4 Road, FYI Center Building Office Zone Klongtoei, Bangkok, 10110, Thailand
Tel.: (66) 27957828
Information Technology Services
N.A.I.C.S.: 541511
Arthid Nanthawithaya (Chm)

SCB Asset Management Co., Ltd. (1)
(100%)
Tel.: (66) 29491500
Open-End Investment Funds
N.A.I.C.S.: 525910
Narongsak Plodmechai (CEO)

SCB Protect Co., Ltd. (1)
G Tower Grand Rama 9 Building 20th Floor No 9 Rama 9 Road, Huaykwang, Bangkok, 10310, Thailand
Tel.: (66) 2 037 7899
Web Site: https://www.scbjuliusbaer.com
Banking Services
N.A.I.C.S.: 522110
Sarut Ruttanaporn (Chm)

SCB Securities Co., Ltd. (1)
19 Tower 3 2nd 20th-21st Fl SCB Park Plaza Ratchadapisek Rd, 19 Ratchadapisek Rd, 10900, Bangkok, Chatuchak, Thailand (100%)
Tel.: (66) 2 949 1999
Web Site: https://www.scbs.com
Sales Range: $200-249.9 Million
Emp.: 256
Securities & Commodity Exchanges
N.A.I.C.S.: 523210
Boontip Kritchaikul (Mng Dir & Head-Equities)

SCB Training Center Co., Ltd. (1)
SCB Head Ofc Bldg 8th Fl Zone C, 9 Rutchadapisek Rd Jatujak, Bangkok, 10090, Thailand (100%)
Tel.: (66) 25441702
Professional & Management Development Training
N.A.I.C.S.: 611430
Shunsaku Yahata (Gen Mgr)

SCB Training Centre Co., Ltd. (1)
9 Rutchadapisek Rd Jatujak, 10900, Thailand
Tel.: (66) 81 847 9297
Banking Services
N.A.I.C.S.: 522110

SCB-Julius Baer (Singapore) Pte. Ltd. (1)
7 Straits View Marina One East Tower 05-01, Singapore, 018936, Singapore
Tel.: (65) 69732020
Banking Services
N.A.I.C.S.: 522110

SCB-Julius Baer Securities Co., Ltd. (1)
No 801 Sukhumvit Road, Khlongtan Nuea Wattana, Bangkok, Thailand
Tel.: (66) 20989999
Web Site: https://www.scbjuliusbaer.com
Wealth Management Services
N.A.I.C.S.: 522180

Scb Abacus Co., Ltd. (1)
SCB Park Plaza 19 Tower 3 Ratchadapisek Rd, Chatuchak, Bangkok, 10900, Thailand
Tel.: (66) 2 544 6566
Web Site: https://www.scbabacus.com
Financial Services
N.A.I.C.S.: 522110
Phornnapas Chalermtiarana (COO)

Siam Commercial Leasing Public Company Limited (1)
3rd-6th 9th 22nd-23rd Sino-Thai Tower 32/24-27 Soi Sukhumvit Road, Klongtoeynua Wattana, Bangkok, 10110, Thailand
Tel.: (66) 22601200
Web Site: http://www.scbls.co.th
Rev.: $118,630,081
Emp.: 1,248
Leasing Services
N.A.I.C.S.: 532490

Siam Pitiwat Co., Ltd. (1)
Siam Piwat Tower 989 Rama 1 Road, Pathumwan, 10330, Bangkok, Thailand (100%)
Tel.: (66) 2 658 1000
Web Site: https://www.siampiwat.com
Sales Range: $50-74.9 Million
Emp.: 100
Commericial Banking
N.A.I.C.S.: 522110

SIAM EAST SOLUTIONS PCL
15/1 Highway-Rayong No 3191 Rd T Huey-Pong A, Huai Pong Subdistrict Mueang Rayong District, Rayong, 21150, Thailand
Tel.: (66) 38682540
Web Site:
  https://www.siameastsolutions.com
Year Founded: 1993
SE—(THA)
Rev.: $18,871,943
Assets: $16,531,593
Liabilities: $3,767,464
Net Worth: $12,764,130
Earnings: $1,858,349
Emp.: 105
Fiscal Year-end: 12/31/23
Industrial Equipment Distr
N.A.I.C.S.: 423830
Thanachart Numnonda (Chm)

SIAM GLOBAL HOUSE PUBLIC COMPANY LIMITED
232 Moo 19 Rob, Muang, Roi Et, 45000, Thailand
Tel.: (66) 4361985099
Web Site:
  http://www.globalhouse.co.th
Year Founded: 1995
GLOBAL—(THA)
Rev.: $963,736,462
Assets: $1,140,176,772
Liabilities: $452,787,429
Net Worth: $687,389,344
Earnings: $78,180,206
Emp.: 10,985
Fiscal Year-end: 12/31/23
Furniture Mfr
N.A.I.C.S.: 337122
Apisit Rujikeatkamjorn (Chm)

Subsidiaries:

Global House (Cambodia) Co., Ltd. (1)
5811 st 1992 Sangkat Phnom Penh Thmey, Bayap Village Khan Sen Sok, Phnom Penh, Cambodia
Tel.: (855) 23232232
Web Site:
  https://www.globalhousecambodia.com
Commercial Goods Distr
N.A.I.C.S.: 423110
Phath Sreymom (Mgr-Mdsg)

SIAM PAN GROUP PUBLIC COMPANY LIMITED
488 Nakornsawan Road Dusit, Bangkok, 10300, Thailand
Tel.: (66) 22800202
Web Site:
  http://www.siampangroup.com
Year Founded: 1959
SPG—(THA)
Rev.: $80,843,753
Assets: $176,444,691
Liabilities: $11,799,123
Net Worth: $164,645,568
Earnings: $10,560,994
Emp.: 730
Fiscal Year-end: 12/31/23
Lubricating Oil Distr & Whslr
N.A.I.C.S.: 811191
Muk Rotrakarn (Chm)

Subsidiaries:

Siam Battery Industry Company Limited - Pathumthani Factory (1)
28/8 Soi Jai Ua Krungthep-Pathumthani Road, T Bangkayang Muang District, Pathumthani, Thailand
Tel.: (66) 29752780
Lubrication Equipment Installation Services
N.A.I.C.S.: 811191

SIAM RAJATHANEE CO., LTD.
329 Moo 10 Kuson Song Samakkhi Soi 1 Old Railway Road, Samrong Phrapadaeng, Samut Prakan, 10130, Thailand
Tel.: (66) 23639300
Web Site:
  http://www.siamrajathanee.co.th
Year Founded: 1976
Sales Range: $25-49.9 Million
Emp.: 4,474
Industrial Equipment Distr
N.A.I.C.S.: 423830

Subsidiaries:

Kessel (Thailand) Pte., Ltd. (1)
289 9 Moo 10 Old Railway Road, Samrong Phrapradaeng, Samut Prakan, Thailand
Tel.: (66) 27435010
Sales Range: $25-49.9 Million
Emp.: 27
Mfr of Pipe Fittings; Joint Venture Between Siam Rajanthanee Co., Ltd. (51%) & Crane Co. (49%)
N.A.I.C.S.: 332919
Orasa Vimolchalao (Mng Dir)

SIAM SPORT SYNDICATE PUBLIC COMPANY LIMITED
66-26 - 29 Soi Ramindra 40Â Ramintra Road Nuanchan, Bungkum District, Bangkok, 10230, Thailand
Tel.: (66) 2508 8000
Web Site: http://www.siamsport.co.th
Year Founded: 1973
Rev.: $36,047,429
Assets: $49,254,824
Liabilities: $48,772,506
Net Worth: $482,318
Earnings: ($5,271,335)
Fiscal Year-end: 12/31/18
Newspaper Publishing Services
N.A.I.C.S.: 513110
Sarayuth Mahawaleerat (Mng Dir)

SIAM STEEL INTERNATIONAL PUBLIC COMPANY LIMITED
51 M00 2 Poochao Rd Bangyaprak, Phrapradaeng, Bangkok, 10130, Samutprakarn, Thailand
Tel.: (66) 23842876
Web Site: https://www.siamsteel.com
Year Founded: 1953
SIAM—(THA)
Rev.: $65,569,334
Assets: $106,561,410
Liabilities: $24,512,746
Net Worth: $82,048,663

SIAMESE ASSET PUBLIC COMPANY LIMITED

Earnings: $1,167,156
Emp.: 830
Fiscal Year-end: 12/31/23
Steel Products Mfr
N.A.I.C.S.: 331110
Surapol Kunanantakul (Pres)

Subsidiaries:

Siam Okamura Steel Co., Ltd. (1)
51/5 Moo 2 Poochao Rd Bangyaprak, Phra Pradaeng, 10130, Samutprakarn, Thailand
Tel.: (66) 23840075
Web Site:
  https://www.siamokamurasteel.com
Furniture Mfr & Distr
N.A.I.C.S.: 337121

SIAM STEEL SERVICE CENTER PUBLIC COMPANY LIMITED
51/3 Moo 2 Poochaosamingprai Road Bangyaprak, Samut Prakan, 10130, Thailand
Tel.: (66) 23859251
Web Site: https://www.ssscth.com
Year Founded: 1985
SSSC—(THA)
Rev.: $157,496,725
Assets: $113,553,912
Liabilities: $19,185,146
Net Worth: $94,368,766
Earnings: $7,740,960
Emp.: 457
Fiscal Year-end: 12/31/23
Steel Sheet Mfr
N.A.I.C.S.: 331110
Wanchai Kunanantakul (Chm)

Subsidiaries:

Siam Environmental Technology Co., Ltd. (1)
120/88 Moo 6 Theparak Road Bang Muang, A Muang Samutprakarn, Samut Prakan, 10270, Thailand
Tel.: (66) 2 385 1226
Web Site: https://www.siamentech.com
Environmental Resource Management Services
N.A.I.C.S.: 541620

Siam MTK Co., Ltd. (1)
60/6 Moo 3 Mabyangporn, Siam Eastern Industrial Estate Pluakdaeng, Rayong, 21140, Thailand
Tel.: (66) 388915204
Web Site: https://www.siammtk.co.th
Emp.: 96
Steel Products Mfr
N.A.I.C.S.: 331513

SIAM WELLNESS GROUP PUBLIC COMPANY LIMITED
565 567 B U Place Building 22nd Floor, Soi Suthiporn Prachasongkroh Dindaeng, Bangkok, 10400, Thailand
Tel.: (66) 2641661920
Web Site:
  https://www.siamwellnessgroup.com
SPA—(THA)
Rev.: $43,008,228
Assets: $57,596,283
Liabilities: $31,290,273
Net Worth: $26,306,010
Earnings: $9,695,786
Emp.: 602
Fiscal Year-end: 12/31/23
Spa Owner & Operator
N.A.I.C.S.: 812112
Pranee Suphawatanakiat (Chm)

SIAMESE ASSET PUBLIC COMPANY LIMITED
1077/48 Phahon Yothin Road, Phayathai, Bangkok, 10400, Thailand
Tel.: (66) 26171555 TH
Web Site:
  https://corp.siameseasset.co.th
Year Founded: 2010

SIAMESE ASSET PUBLIC COMPANY LIMITED

Siamese Asset Public Company Limited—(Continued)
SA—(THA)
Rev.: $58,246,942
Assets: $632,507,756
Liabilities: $457,637,522
Net Worth: $174,870,234
Earnings: $6,880,080
Fiscal Year-end: 12/31/23
Investment Management Service
N.A.I.C.S.: 523999

SIAMGAS AND PETROCHEMICALS PUBLIC COMPANY LIMITED
553 The Palladium Building A Floor 30 Ratchaprarop Road Makkasan, Ratchathewi, Bangkok, 10400, Thailand
Tel.: (66) 21209999
Web Site: https://www.siamgas.com
Year Founded: 2001
SGP—(THA)
Rev.: $2,644,761,596
Assets: $1,542,642,250
Liabilities: $1,078,071,750
Net Worth: $464,570,500
Earnings: $30,396,140
Fiscal Year-end: 12/31/23
Petrochemical Mfr
N.A.I.C.S.: 424710
Worawit Weeraborwompong *(Chm & Chm)*

Subsidiaries:

Siam Lucky Marine Company Limited (1)
553 Palladium Tower 33th Floor Ratchaprarop Road Makkasan, Ratchathewi, Bangkok, 10400, Thailand
Tel.: (66) 2 120 9899
Web Site: http://www.siamluckymarine.com
Oil & Gas Transportation Services
N.A.I.C.S.: 483211

SingGas (LPG) Private Limited (1)
31 Defu Lane 9, Singapore, 539271, Singapore
Tel.: (65) 6 555 9222
Web Site: https://www.singgas.com.sg
Liquefied Petroleum Gas Distr
N.A.I.C.S.: 221210

Super Gas Company Limited (1)
Cang Go Dau A xa Phuoc Thai, Long Thanh, Dong Nai, Vietnam
Tel.: (84) 61 2214668
Petroleum Product Distr
N.A.I.C.S.: 424720

SIANTAR TOP TBK
Jl Tambaksawah 21-23 Waru, Sidoarjo, 61256, Indonesia
Tel.: (62) 318667382
Web Site: https://www.siantartop.co.id
Year Founded: 1972
STTP—(INDO)
Rev.: $309,582,451
Assets: $356,016,317
Liabilities: $41,218,928
Net Worth: $314,797,389
Earnings: $59,601,544
Emp.: 1,453
Fiscal Year-end: 12/31/23
Snack Product Mfr
N.A.I.C.S.: 311919
Agus Suhartanto *(Chm)*

SIASUN ROBOT & AUTOMATION CO., LTD.
No 33 Quanyun Street, Hunnan New District, Shenyang, 110168, China
Tel.: (86) 2431167327
Web Site: https://www.siasun.com
Year Founded: 2000
300024—(CHIN)
Rev.: $558,694,892
Assets: $1,672,564,862
Liabilities: $1,042,949,953
Net Worth: $629,614,909
Earnings: $6,841,310
Fiscal Year-end: 12/31/23
Industrial Robot Mfr & Distr
N.A.I.C.S.: 333998
Hu Kunyuan *(Chm)*

SIAT BRAUN SA
46 Rue General De Gaulle, PO Box 46201, Molsheim, Urmatt, 67126, France
Tel.: (33) 388495900
Web Site: http://www.siatbraun.fr
Year Founded: 1818
Sales Range: $75-99.9 Million
Sawmill Operator
N.A.I.C.S.: 321113
Philippe Siat *(Chm & CEO)*

Subsidiaries:

Siat Braun SA (1)
46 Rue Du General De Gaulle, 67126, Molsheim, Cedex, France (100%)
Tel.: (33) 388495900
Web Site: http://www.siatbraun.fr
Sawmill Mfr
N.A.I.C.S.: 321113
Paul Siat *(CEO)*

SIAT SOCIETA' INTERNAZIONALE APPLICAZIONI TECNICHE SPA
Via Puecher 22, 22078, Turate, CO, Italy
Tel.: (39) 02964951
Web Site: https://www.siat.com
Year Founded: 1970
Industrial Machinery Mfr
N.A.I.C.S.: 423830

Subsidiaries:

Combi Packaging Systems, LLC (1)
5365 E Center Dr NE, Canton, OH 44721 (100%)
Tel.: (330) 456-9333
Web Site: http://www.combi.com
Sales Range: $1-9.9 Million
Emp.: 70
Packaging Machinery Mfr
N.A.I.C.S.: 333993
Sue Lewis *(Mgr-Mktg)*

SIAULIU BANKAS AB
Tilzes G 149, Siauliai, 76348, Lithuania
Tel.: (370) 841595607 LT
Web Site: https://www.sb.lt
Year Founded: 1992
SAB1L—(RSE)
Rev.: $112,870,343
Assets: $4,866,878,892
Liabilities: $4,367,688,993
Net Worth: $499,189,898
Earnings: $67,827,098
Emp.: 882
Fiscal Year-end: 12/31/21
Commercial Banking Services
N.A.I.C.S.: 522110
Algirdas Butkus *(Chm-Mgmt Bd)*

Subsidiaries:

Bonum Publicum GD UAB (1)
Laisves Ave 3, LT-04215, Vilnius, Lithuania
Tel.: (370) 852362723
Web Site: http://www.bonumpublicum.lt
Fire Insurance Services
N.A.I.C.S.: 524210

Minera UAB (1)
Seimyniskiu St 1A, LT-09312, Vilnius, Lithuania
Tel.: (370) 68856660
Web Site: http://www.minera.lt
Real Estate Manangement Services
N.A.I.C.S.: 531210

SB Lizingas UAB (1)
Karaliaus Mindaugo Ave 35, LT-44307, Kaunas, Lithuania
Tel.: (370) 37407200
Web Site: https://www.sblizingas.lt
Emp.: 50
Financial Lending Services
N.A.I.C.S.: 522220

Siauliu Banko Investiciju Valdymas UAB (1)
Seimyniskiu Str 1A, LT-09312, Vilnius, Lithuania
Tel.: (370) 852722477
Real Estate Services
N.A.I.C.S.: 531390

SIAV S.P.A.
via Rossi 5/n, 35030, Rubano, PD, Italy
Tel.: (39) 0498979797
Web Site: https://www.siav.com
Year Founded: 1990
SIAV—(ITA)
Information Technology Services
N.A.I.C.S.: 541512
Alfieri Voltan *(Pres)*

SIBANYE-STILLWATER LIMITED
Cnr 14th Avenue Hendrik Potgieter Road Bridgeview House Ground Floor, Weltevreden Park, Westonaria, 1709, South Africa
Tel.: (27) 112789600 ZA
Web Site: https://www.sibanyestillwater.com
Year Founded: 2013
SBSW—(NYSE)
Rev.: $6,003,654,453
Assets: $7,548,717,245
Liabilities: $4,823,350,479
Net Worth: $2,725,366,766
Earnings: ($1,976,679,095)
Emp.: 82,788
Fiscal Year-end: 12/31/23
Gold Ore Mining Services
N.A.I.C.S.: 212220
Charl Keyter *(CFO)*

Subsidiaries:

Lonmin Plc (1)
Connaught House 1-3 Mount Street, London, W1K 3NB, United Kingdom
Tel.: (44) 2039081070
Web Site: http://www.lonmin.com
Gold, Platinum Group Metals & Coal Mining Operations
N.A.I.C.S.: 212220

Subsidiary (Non-US):

Messina Platinum Mines Ltd. (2)
23 Elizabeth Street, 0699, Polokwane, Limpopo, South Africa
Tel.: (27) 156338206
Web Site: http://www.lonmin.com
Sales Range: $50-74.9 Million
Emp.: 54
Platinum Mining Services
N.A.I.C.S.: 212290

Western Platinum Ltd. (2)
1 Platinum Rd, Brakpan, 1540, South Africa (82%)
Tel.: (27) 113656500
Sales Range: $200-249.9 Million
Emp.: 350
Metal Mining Services
N.A.I.C.S.: 213114
Ricardo Diedericks *(Mgr-Process)*

SWC Trading Inc. (1)
1600 1st Ave S, Columbus, MT 59019
Tel.: (406) 322-8711
Web Site: http://www.stillwaterrecycling.com
Metal Smelting & Refining Services
N.A.I.C.S.: 213114

St Helena Hospital Proprietary Limited (1)
Hamlet Road Extension, Lejweleputswa District, Welkom, 9459, South Africa
Tel.: (27) 573914611
Medical Devices
N.A.I.C.S.: 622110

INTERNATIONAL PUBLIC

SIBAR
4 rue Bartisch, 67100, Strasbourg, Bas Rhin, France
Tel.: (33) 388658190
Web Site: http://www.sibar.fr
Year Founded: 1954
Sales Range: $10-24.9 Million
Emp.: 62
Real Estate Planning & Development
N.A.I.C.S.: 531110

SIBAR AUTO PARTS LIMITED
D4 D5 Industrial Estate Renigunta Road, Chittoor Dist, Tirupati, 517 506, Andhra Pradesh, India
Tel.: (91) 8772271355
Web Site: https://www.sibarauto.com
Year Founded: 1983
520141—(BOM)
Rev.: $1,614,156
Assets: $2,783,586
Liabilities: $1,293,882
Net Worth: $1,489,703
Earnings: ($292,672)
Emp.: 87
Fiscal Year-end: 03/31/21
Cylinder Blocks & Heads Mfr
N.A.I.C.S.: 336310
P. Veeranarayana *(Mng Dir)*

SIBELGA S.C.R.L.
Boulevard Emile Jacqmain 96, 1000, Brussels, Belgium
Tel.: (32) 25494100
Web Site: http://www.sibelga.be
Sales Range: $650-699.9 Million
Emp.: 1,020
Electricity & Natural Gas Distribution Services
N.A.I.C.S.: 221122

Subsidiaries:

Metrix (1)
Quai Des Usines 16, 1000, Brussels, Belgium
Tel.: (32) 2 549 42 00
Web Site: http://www.metrix.eu
Sales Range: $10-24.9 Million
Emp.: 50
Gas & Electricity Meter Reading Services
N.A.I.C.S.: 561990

SIBERIAN GOSTINEC PJSC
ul Universitetskaya 4, Surgut, 628406, Russia
Tel.: (7) 3462774059 RU
SIBG—(MOEX)
Sales Range: Less than $1 Million
Food Product Mfr & Distr
N.A.I.C.S.: 311421
Dmitriy A. Khodas *(Gen Dir)*

SIBERNAME.COM INC.
275 Slater Street Suite 900, Ottawa, K1P 5H9, ON, Canada
Tel.: (613) 482-2085
Web Site: http://www.sibername.com
Year Founded: 2000
Sales Range: $1-9.9 Million
Emp.: 11
Domain Name Registration, Website Hosting & Web Marketing
N.A.I.C.S.: 518210
Bulent Turkoglu *(Dir-Ops)*

SIBIRGASSERVICE
124 Frunze St, Novosibirsk, 630005, Russia
Tel.: (7) 3832110211
Web Site: https://www.gazsib.ru
Year Founded: 1965
SBGS—(MOEX)
Sales Range: Less than $1 Million
Building Construction Services
N.A.I.C.S.: 236210
Igor V. Domarenko *(Gen Dir)*

AND PRIVATE COMPANIES

SIBURAN RESOURCES LIMITED
Suite 8 18 Stirling Highway, Nedlands, 6009, WA, Australia
Tel.: (61) 8 9386 3600
Web Site: http://www.siburan.com.au
Year Founded: 2009
Rev.: $117,757
Assets: $260,556
Liabilities: $87,254
Net Worth: $173,302
Earnings: ($166,068)
Fiscal Year-end: 06/30/18
Gold & Uranium Exploration Services
N.A.I.C.S.: 212220
Neil Sheather (Mng Dir)

SIC INSURANCE COMPANY LIMITED
28/29 Ring Road East Osu, PO Box 2363, Accra, Ghana
Tel.: (233) 302780600
Web Site: https://www.sic-gh.com
Year Founded: 1962
SIC—(GHA)
Rev.: $37,008,629
Assets: $96,399,727
Liabilities: $52,074,539
Net Worth: $44,325,188
Earnings: $1,943,959
Fiscal Year-end: 12/31/19
Insurance Services
N.A.I.C.S.: 524298
Patience Opoku (Head-HR)

Subsidiaries:

SIC Financial Services Limited (1)
No 67 A and B Switchback Road, Cantonments, Accra, Ghana
Tel.: (233) 302767051
Web Site: https://www.sic-fsl.com
Financial Investment Services
N.A.I.C.S.: 523999
James Amo-Aboagye (Head-Compliance & Internal Audit)

SICA INVEST S.A.
Parc Scientifique Erasmus Bureau 19 bte 32 route de de Lennik 451, BE-1070, Brussels, Belgium
Tel.: (32) 15 63 88 81
Web Site: http://www.sicainvest.com
Investment Services
N.A.I.C.S.: 523999
Adolf Schroyens (Mng Dir)

SICA SPA
Via Stoppata 28, 48011, Alfonsine, RA, Italy
Tel.: (39) 054488711
Web Site: http://www.sica-italy.com
Year Founded: 1962
Sales Range: $25-49.9 Million
Emp.: 140
Plastic Pipe Processing Machinery
N.A.I.C.S.: 333248
Valeria Giacomoni (Mng Dir)

SICAAP SA
Route de Saint Jean d'Angely, BP 20, 17101, Saintes, France
Tel.: (33) 546938260
Rev.: $25,900,000
Emp.: 22
Nondurable Goods
N.A.I.C.S.: 424990
Nathalie Miallier (Mgr & Fin)

SICABLE COTE D'IVOIRE
ZI Vridi rue du Textile 15, BP 35, 15, Abidjan, 15, Cote d'Ivoire
Tel.: (225) 21213502
Web Site: https://www.sicable.ci
CABC—(BRVM)
Sales Range: Less than $1 Million
Electrical Cable Product Mfr
N.A.I.C.S.: 335929

Pascal Crousaud (Deputy CEO & CFO)

SICAE DE LA SOMME ET DU CAMBRAISIS
11 Rue de la Republique, BP 40058, 80208, Peronne, Cedex, France
Tel.: (33) 322864545
Web Site: http://www.sicaesomme.fr
Sales Range: $25-49.9 Million
Emp.: 70
Electric Power Services
N.A.I.C.S.: 221122
Eric Desrousseaux (VP)

SICAGEN INDIA LTD
4th Floor SPIC House 88 Mount Road, Guindy, Chennai, 600032, India
Tel.: (91) 4440754075
Web Site: https://www.sicagen.com
Year Founded: 2004
533014—(BOM)
Rev.: $108,325,640
Assets: $75,448,714
Liabilities: $22,746,838
Net Worth: $52,701,876
Earnings: $2,136,563
Emp.: 267
Fiscal Year-end: 03/31/23
Building Material Trading company
N.A.I.C.S.: 523160
Ashwin C. Muthiah (Chm)

Subsidiaries:

SDB Cisco (India) Ltd. (1)
No 4 7th Ave Harrington Rd, Chetpet, Chennai, 600 031, Tamil Nadu, India
Tel.: (91) 4428361831
Web Site: http://www.sdbcisco.com
Sales Range: $25-49.9 Million
Emp.: 100
Security Services
N.A.I.C.S.: 561612

Subsidiary (Domestic):

Modern Protection & Investigations Ltd. (2)
G 7 & 8 Nav Bharat Estate Zakharia Bundur Rd, Sewri W, Mumbai, 400015, Maharashtra, India
Tel.: (91) 2224187205
Web Site: http://www.modernprotection.com
Security Agencies
N.A.I.C.S.: 561612

SICAL LOGISTICS LIMITED
23/2 Coffee Day Square Vittal Mallya Road, Bengaluru, 560001, India
Tel.: (91) 8033402300
Web Site: https://www.sical.in
520086—(BOM)
Rev.: $141,266,580
Assets: $377,673,660
Liabilities: $286,508,040
Net Worth: $91,165,620
Earnings: ($16,631,160)
Emp.: 653
Fiscal Year-end: 03/31/20
Freight Transportation Services
N.A.I.C.S.: 488510
V. Radhakrishnan (Compliance Officer & Sec)

Subsidiaries:

Sical Iron Ore Terminals Limited (1)
73 Armenian St, Chennai, 600001, Tamil Nadu, India
Tel.: (91) 4466157071
Sales Range: $25-49.9 Million
Emp.: 1
Logistic Services
N.A.I.C.S.: 541614

SICARD HOLIDAY CAMPERS
7526 Hwy 20, Smithville, L0R 2A0, ON, Canada
Tel.: (905) 957-3344

Web Site: http://www.sicardrv.com
Rev.: $27,213,769
Emp.: 75
Recreational Vehicle Dealers
N.A.I.C.S.: 441210
Blair Sicard (Principal)

SICC S.P.A.
Via Toscana 32, 60030, Monsano, AN, Italy
Tel.: (39) 073121881
Year Founded: 1978
Sales Range: $50-74.9 Million
Emp.: 184
Modular Kitchens Mfr
N.A.I.C.S.: 337126
Alfiero Latini (Chm & CEO)

Subsidiaries:

Martival Technologie S.A. (1)
28 Rue de la Courbe, BP 44, 88160, Le Thillot, France
Tel.: (33) 329252004
Sales Range: $25-49.9 Million
Emp.: 30
Kitchen Cabinet Mfr
N.A.I.C.S.: 337110

SICC France S.a.s. (1)
BP 44, 88160, Le Thillot, France
Tel.: (33) 329252004
Sales Range: $25-49.9 Million
Emp.: 5
Metal Household Furniture Mfr
N.A.I.C.S.: 337126

SICC USA Inc. (1)
900 Park Centre Blvd Ste 476, Miami, FL 33169
Tel.: (305) 627-4277
Furniture Retailer
N.A.I.C.S.: 449110

SICCAR POINT ENERGY LIMITED
3rd Floor H1 Hill of Rubislaw Anderson Drive, Aberdeen, AB15 6BY, United Kingdom
Tel.: (44) 1224678008
Web Site: http://www.siccarpointenergy.co.uk
Oil & Gas Exploration & Production Services
N.A.I.C.S.: 211120
Jonathan Roger (CEO)

SICHER ELEVATOR CO., LTD.
No 1 Sicher Road, Lianshi Industrial Park, Huzhou, 313013, Zhejiang, China
Tel.: (86) 5723787198
Web Site: https://www.sicher-elevator.com
Year Founded: 2007
301056—(CHIN)
Rev.: $101,908,831
Assets: $205,233,267
Liabilities: $89,179,211
Net Worth: $116,054,056
Earnings: $12,742,127
Fiscal Year-end: 12/31/23
Elevator Product Mfr & Distr
N.A.I.C.S.: 333921
Dongliu Li (Chm & Gen Mgr)

SICHUAN ANNING IRON & TITANIUM CO., LTD.
No 80 Anning Road, Panlian Town, Panzhihua, 617200, Sichuan, China
Tel.: (86) 8128117310
Web Site: http://www.scantt.com
Year Founded: 1994
002978—(SSE)
Rev.: $280,229,793
Assets: $919,045,259
Liabilities: $152,983,420
Net Worth: $766,061,838
Earnings: $153,701,608
Fiscal Year-end: 12/31/22

Iron Ore Mining Services
N.A.I.C.S.: 212210
Yangyong Luo (Chm & Gen Mgr)

SICHUAN CHANGHONG ELECTRIC CO., LTD.
No 35 Mianxing East Road Hi-tech Zone, Mianyang, 621000, Sichuan, China
Tel.: (86) 8162418436   CN
Web Site: http://www.changhong.com
Year Founded: 1993
600839—(SHG)
Rev.: $12,984,424,980
Assets: $12,009,498,429
Liabilities: $8,803,197,543
Net Worth: $3,206,300,886
Earnings: $65,689,285
Emp.: 70,000
Fiscal Year-end: 12/31/22
Household Appliances Mfr
N.A.I.C.S.: 335220
Liu Jiang (Chm)

Subsidiaries:

Changhong (Hong Kong) Trading Limited (1)
3701 37 Floor West Tower Shun Tak Centre, Street No 168, Hong Kong, China (Hong Kong)
Tel.: (852) 36902186
Web Site: http://www.changhong.com.hk
Sales Range: $25-49.9 Million
Emp.: 40
Electronics Wholesale Trade Broker
N.A.I.C.S.: 425120

Changhong Electric (Australia) Pty Ltd. (1)
2/251 Ferntree Gully Rd, Mount Waverley, 3149, VIC, Australia
Tel.: (61) 385457388
Web Site: http://www.changhong.com.au
Sales Range: $25-49.9 Million
Emp.: 20
Electrical Appliance Television & Radio Set Whslr
N.A.I.C.S.: 423620

Changhong Europe Electric S.r.o. (1)
Argentinska 286/38, 17000, Prague, Czech Republic
Tel.: (420) 322321411
Web Site: http://www.changhong.cz
Semiconductor & Related Device Mfr
N.A.I.C.S.: 334413

Changhong Jiahua Holdings Limited (1)
Unit 1412 14/F West Tower Shun Tak Centre 168-200 Connaught Road, Central, China (Hong Kong) (52.53%)
Tel.: (852) 31522178
Web Site: http://www.changhongit.com
Rev.: $4,888,236,398
Assets: $2,033,722,410
Liabilities: $1,698,402,000
Net Worth: $335,320,410
Earnings: $46,641,540
Emp.: 1,357
Fiscal Year-end: 12/31/2022
Holding Company; Electronic Products Mfr
N.A.I.C.S.: 551112
Yong Zhao (Chm)

Guangdong Changhong Electronics Co., Ltd (1)
No 1 Xingye North Road Nantou Town, Zhongshan, 528427, Guangdong, China
Tel.: (86) 76023138293
Consumer Electronics Mfr & Distr
N.A.I.C.S.: 334310

Zhong Shan Changhong Electric Co., Ltd (1)
No 1 North Xingye Road, Nantou Town, Zhongshan, 528427, Guangdong, China
Tel.: (86) 53188926116
Web Site: http://changhonghvac.shilinzhongyou.com
Cconsumer Electronic Products Mfr & Distr
N.A.I.C.S.: 333415

SICHUAN CHENGFEI INTE-

SICHUAN CHENGFEI INTE

SICHUAN CHENGFEI INTE—(CONTINUED)

GRATION TECHNOLOGY CO., LTD.
No 666-1 Section 2 Riyue Avenue, Qingyang District, Chengdu, 610091, China
Tel.: (86) 2887455115
Web Site: https://www.cac-citc.com
Year Founded: 2000
002190—(SSE)
Rev.: $214,018,796
Assets: $669,210,001
Liabilities: $183,713,793
Net Worth: $485,496,208
Earnings: $8,201,634
Emp.: 2,500
Fiscal Year-end: 12/31/22
Automotive Cover Molds Mfr
N.A.I.C.S.: 336390
Shi Xiaoqing *(Chm & Gen Mgr)*

Subsidiaries:

China Aviation Lithium Battery (Luoyang) Co., Ltd. (1)
No 66 North Binhe Road High-tech Zone, Luoyang, 471003, Henan, China
Tel.: (86) 37960695350
Web Site: http://www.en.calb.cn
Storage Battery Mfr
N.A.I.C.S.: 335910
Jianbo Xu *(Deputy Gen Mgr)*

SICHUAN CHUANHUAN TECHNOLOGY CO., LTD
Dongliu Industrial Park Dazhu County, Dazhou, 635100, Sichuan, China
Web Site: http://www.chuanhuan.com
300547—(CHIN)
Rev.: $127,342,800
Assets: $176,495,436
Liabilities: $36,501,192
Net Worth: $139,994,244
Earnings: $17,187,768
Fiscal Year-end: 12/31/22
Rubber Hose Mfr & Distr
N.A.I.C.S.: 326220
Motong Wen *(Founder & Chm)*

SICHUAN CHUANTOU ENERGY CO., LTD.
Floor 6 No 1 Linjiang West Street, Wuhou District, Chengdu, 610041, Sichuan, China
Tel.: (86) 2886098649
Web Site: https://en.ctny.com.cn
Year Founded: 1988
600674—(SHG)
Rev.: $208,123,147
Assets: $8,473,609,694
Liabilities: $3,055,160,216
Net Worth: $5,418,449,478
Earnings: $617,779,207
Emp.: 7,000
Fiscal Year-end: 12/31/23
Electric Power Generation & Distribution Services
N.A.I.C.S.: 221111
Liu Tibin *(Chm)*

SICHUAN CRUN CO., LTD.
No 85 Gangbei 6th Road North Area Modern Industrial Port, Pixian County, Chengdu, 611743, Sichuan, China
Tel.: (86) 2861777787
Web Site: https://www.chuanrun.com
Year Founded: 1992
002272—(SSE)
Rev.: $238,487,961
Assets: $460,187,620
Liabilities: $251,771,865
Net Worth: $208,415,755
Earnings: $1,677,078
Fiscal Year-end: 12/31/22
Hydraulic Equipment Mfr

N.A.I.C.S.: 333998
Yongzhong Luo *(Chm & Gen Mgr)*

SICHUAN DANFU ENVIRONMENT TECHNOLOGY CO.,LTD
Heilong Town, Qingshen County, Meishan, 620461, Sichuan, China
Tel.: (86) 2838926033
Web Site: https://www.scdanfu.cn
Cold Compressors, Refrigerating Equipment, Air Conditioning & Temperature Control Products Mfr
N.A.I.C.S.: 333415

SICHUAN DAWN PRECISION TECHNOLOGY CO., LTD.
No 8 Zhuyi Avenue, Qingshen County, Meishan, 620460, Sichuan, China
Tel.: (86) 2838858588
Web Site: http://www.cpt-world.com
Year Founded: 2003
300780—(SSE)
Rev.: $97,816,526
Assets: $311,062,953
Liabilities: $139,929,239
Net Worth: $171,133,714
Earnings: $17,303,738
Fiscal Year-end: 12/31/22
Mechanical Transmission Parts Mfr & Distr
N.A.I.C.S.: 333613
Yongzhi Lei *(Chm & Gen Mgr)*

Subsidiaries:

Chengdu Dawn Precision M&E Sales Co., Ltd. (1)
No 123 West Section of Hupan Road Xinglong Street, Pilot Free Trade Zone Tianfu New District, Chengdu, Sichuan, China
Tel.: (86) 2838858833
Machine Tools Mfr
N.A.I.C.S.: 333517

Guangzhou CPT M&E Equipment Co., Ltd. (1)
207 Runyi Bussiness Center No 12 Daguannan Road, Tianhe District, Guangzhou, Guangdong, China
Tel.: (86) 2062817860
Machine Tools Mfr
N.A.I.C.S.: 333517
Huang Tao *(Gen Mgr)*

Powermach Imp & Exp Co., Ltd. (1)
2709-2710 Times Plaza No 2 Zongfu Road, Jinjiang District, Chengdu, Sichuan, China
Tel.: (86) 2886725563
Machine Tools Mfr
N.A.I.C.S.: 333517
Chelsea Zhou *(Mgr)*

Shanghai CPT Machinery Co., Ltd. (1)
No 168 Shenxu Road Jinduxi Road, Songjiang District, Shanghai, China
Tel.: (86) 2151693066
Machine Tools Mfr
N.A.I.C.S.: 333517
Qiu Guowei *(Gen Mgr)*

Tianjin CPT M&E Equipment Co., Ltd. (1)
20-2 315 Xiqing Avenue, Jinsheng Industry Park Xiqing District, Tianjin, China
Tel.: (86) 2227984126
Machine Tools Mfr
N.A.I.C.S.: 333517
Wang Qiuzhong *(Mgr)*

SICHUAN DEVELOPMENT LOMON CO., LTD.
No 42 Shuxi Road Hi-tech Industrial Park, Jinniu District, Chengdu, 610041, Sichuan, China
Tel.: (86) 2887579929
Web Site: http://www.isantai.com
Year Founded: 1997
002312—(SSE)
Rev.: $1,407,297,434

Assets: $2,153,295,692
Liabilities: $876,436,526
Net Worth: $1,276,859,165
Earnings: $149,396,102
Emp.: 670
Fiscal Year-end: 12/31/22
Electronic Receipt, Automatic Teller Machine (ATM) Monitoring & Digital Bank Network Security Monitoring Systems Mfr & Distr
N.A.I.C.S.: 334419
Zhu Quanfang *(Chm)*

SICHUAN DISCOVERY DREAM SCIENCE & TECHNOLOGY CO., LTD.
14th Floor Building B5 Zone D Jingrong Center, Tianfu New District, Chengdu, 610213, Sichuan, China
Tel.: (86) 2885590402
Web Site: https://www.gxwin.cn
Year Founded: 2009
301213—(CHIN)
Rev.: $14,421,888
Assets: $125,038,836
Liabilities: $11,342,916
Net Worth: $113,695,920
Earnings: $2,458,404
Fiscal Year-end: 12/31/22
Software Development Services
N.A.I.C.S.: 541511
Wei Qiang *(Chm & Gen Mgr)*

SICHUAN DOWELL SCIENCE&TECHNOLOGY INC
No 89 South 4th Road New Garden Singapore Industrial Park, High-tech Zone, Chengdu, 610041, Sichuan, China
Tel.: (86) 2885136056
Web Site: https://www.dowellchem.cn
Year Founded: 2003
300535—(CHIN)
Rev.: $102,059,811
Assets: $199,471,052
Liabilities: $60,766,873
Net Worth: $138,704,178
Earnings: $4,004,140
Emp.: 600
Fiscal Year-end: 12/31/23
Leather Chemical Mfr & Distr
N.A.I.C.S.: 325199
Jianlin Yan *(Chm & Gen Mgr)*

SICHUAN EM TECHNOLOGY CO., LTD.
188 Sanxing Road, Mianyang, 621000, Sichuan, China
Tel.: (86) 8162295680
Web Site: https://www.dongfang-insulation.com
Year Founded: 1966
601208—(SHG)
Rev.: $511,094,764
Assets: $1,271,273,562
Liabilities: $658,094,505
Net Worth: $613,179,057
Earnings: $58,266,477
Emp.: 1,800
Fiscal Year-end: 12/31/22
Insulating & Polymer Material Mfr
N.A.I.C.S.: 326113

Subsidiaries:

Sichuan Dongfang Insulating Material Co., Ltd. (1)
188 Sanxing Road, Mianyang, 621000, Sichuan, China
Tel.: (86) 8162295680
Insulating & Polymer Material Mfr
N.A.I.C.S.: 326113
Desheng Zhang *(Reg Mgr-Bus)*

SICHUAN ENERGY INVESTMENT DEVELOPMENT CO., LTD.

INTERNATIONAL PUBLIC

No 789 Renhe Road, Wenjiang District, Chengdu, 611130, Sichuan, China
Tel.: (86) 2886299666 CN
Web Site: https://en.scntgf.com
Year Founded: 2011
1713—(HKG)
Rev.: $465,181,172
Assets: $722,780,732
Liabilities: $275,576,090
Net Worth: $447,204,642
Earnings: $42,477,837
Emp.: 2,828
Fiscal Year-end: 12/31/22
Power Supplies Distr
N.A.I.C.S.: 423610
Huang Huiling *(Sec)*

Subsidiaries:

Sichuan Chemical Works Group Ltd. (1)
No 311 Tuanjie Road, Qingbaijiang District, Chengdu, China
Tel.: (86) 2889300000
Chemical Products Mfr
N.A.I.C.S.: 325998

Sichuan Chuanhua Yongxin Construction Engineering Co., Ltd. (1)
No 311 Tuanjie East Road, Qingbaijiang District, Chengdu, China
Tel.: (86) 2889300855
Web Site: http://www.scchyx.com
Construction Services
N.A.I.C.S.: 236220

Sichuan EII Coal Bed Methane Investment & Development Co., Ltd. (1)
F18 Block A Genesis Plaza No 468 Bisheng Road, Jinjiang District, Chengdu, China
Tel.: (86) 2880583552
Methane Gas Extraction Services
N.A.I.C.S.: 211130

Sichuan Energy Huaxi Biomass Energy Development Co., Ltd. (1)
No 66 Huangjia Mountain, Daan District, Zigong, 643010, China
Tel.: (86) 8134731111
Biomass Electric Power Generation Services
N.A.I.C.S.: 221117

Sichuan Energy Industry Investment Electric Power Development Co., Ltd. (1)
No 789 Renhe Road, Wenjiang District, Chengdu, 611130, China
Tel.: (86) 288299770
Electricity Power Generation Services
N.A.I.C.S.: 221118

Sichuan Energy Investment Distributed Energy Systems Co., Ltd. (1)
Block A Genesis Plaza No 468 Bisheng Road, Jinjiang District, Chengdu, 610063, China
Tel.: (86) 2880583535
Electricity Power Distr
N.A.I.C.S.: 221122

Sichuan Energy Investment Huicheng Training Management Co., Ltd. (1)
No 47 Dawan Rd W, Qingbaijiang District, Chengdu, 610300, Sichuan, China
Tel.: (86) 2889300032
Education Training Services
N.A.I.C.S.: 611430

Sichuan Energy Investment Panzhihua Hydropower Development Co., Ltd. (1)
No 88 Jianfu Lane Qingxiangping Street, West District, Panzhihua, Sichuan, China
Tel.: (86) 8125181100
Hydro Power Generation Services
N.A.I.C.S.: 221111

Sichuan Energy Investment Runjia Real Estate Co., Ltd. (1)
No 47 Dawan Rd W, Qingbaijiang District, Chengdu, 610300, Sichuan, China
Tel.: (86) 2889307088
Real Estate Services
N.A.I.C.S.: 531390

AND PRIVATE COMPANIES — SICHUAN HEZONG MEDICINE PHARMACEUTICAL CO.

Sichuan Energy New-type Urbanization Investment Co., Ltd. (1)
F19 Block A Genesis Plaza No 468 Bisheng Road, Jinjiang District, Chengdu, 610023, China
Tel.: (86) 2880582131
Construction Services
N.A.I.C.S.: 236220

Sichuan Energy Wind Power Co., Ltd. (1)
F15 Block A Genesis Plaza No 468 Bisheng Road, Jinjiang District, Chengdu, China
Tel.: (86) 2880583960
Wind Energy Services
N.A.I.C.S.: 221115

Sichuan Everbright Energy Conservation & Environmental Protection Investment Co., Ltd. (1)
F15 Block A Genesis Plaza No 468 Bisheng Road, Jinjiang District, Chengdu, 610063, China
Tel.: (86) 2868738583
Water Environmental Management Services
N.A.I.C.S.: 541620

Sichuan Hydropower Investment & Management Group., Ltd. (1)
No 789 Renhe Road, Wenjiang District, Chengdu, 611130, Sichuan, China
Tel.: (86) 2886299998
Electricity Power Generation Services
N.A.I.C.S.: 221118

Sichuan Jinding Industrial & Financial Holding Co., Ltd. (1)
Building A Fontaine International No 88 Jiaozi North 1st Road, High-tech Zone, Chengdu, 610041, China
Tel.: (86) 2861011000
Web Site: https://www.jdkg.com
Financial Banking Services
N.A.I.C.S.: 522110

Sichuan Natural Gas Investment Co., Ltd. (1)
F17 Block 1 Genesis Plaza No 468 Bisheng Road, Jinjiang District, Chengdu, 610000, China
Tel.: (86) 2884777777
Natural Gas Services
N.A.I.C.S.: 211130

Sichuan NengTou E&M Material Trade Co., Ltd. (1)
F16 Block A Genesis Plaza No 468 Bisheng Road, Jinjiang District, Chengdu, China
Tel.: (86) 2880583653
Electrical & Mechanical Equipment Distr
N.A.I.C.S.: 423610

Sichuan Sunfor Light Co., Ltd. (1)
No 2 Xinda Road Western Hi-Tech Zone, Chengdu, 610097, China
Tel.: (86) 2887827799
Led Lighting Product Mfr
N.A.I.C.S.: 335139
Adria Xh Wu (Mgr-Bus-Global)

Sichuan Western Sunny Electric Power Development Co., Ltd. (1)
F32 Times No 8 No 68 Zhiquan Section Dongdajie Street, Jinjiang District, 610000, China
Tel.: (86) 2886679935
Electricity Power Generation Services
N.A.I.C.S.: 221118

SICHUAN ETROL TECHNOLOGIES CO., LTD.
No 6 Building No 9 Dijin Road, Haidian District, Beijing, 100095, China
Tel.: (86) 1062971668
Web Site: https://www.etrol.com
Year Founded: 1998
300370—(SSE)
Rev.: $64,842,336
Assets: $270,208,224
Liabilities: $149,090,760
Net Worth: $121,117,464
Earnings: $(57,864,456)
Emp.: 878
Fiscal Year-end: 12/31/22
Industrial Automation Products Mfr
N.A.I.C.S.: 334513

Zhang Zhigang (Chm)

SICHUAN EXPRESSWAY COMPANY LIMITED
252 Wuhouci Da Jie, Chengdu, 610041, Sichuan, China
Tel.: (86) 2885527510 CN
Web Site: https://en.cygs.com
Year Founded: 1997
601107—(SHG)
Rev.: $1,391,013,126
Assets: $5,652,129,834
Liabilities: $3,023,755,348
Net Worth: $2,628,374,486
Earnings: $107,006,941
Emp.: 4,150
Fiscal Year-end: 12/31/22
Highway Construction & Management Services
N.A.I.C.S.: 237310
Renrong Guo (CFO)

SICHUAN FUHUA AGRICULTURAL SCIENCE INVESTMENT GROUP
Wutongqiao District Bridge Town, Sichuan, 614800, Leshan, China
Tel.: (86) 833 3359989
Web Site: http://www.fuhuagroup.com
Year Founded: 1999
Agricultural Products Development & Mfr
N.A.I.C.S.: 325320

Subsidiaries:

Sichuan Leshan Fuhua Crop Protection Technology Investment Co., Ltd. (1)
Gongyu Village Qiaogou Town, Wutongqiao District, Sichuan, 614800, Leshan, China
Tel.: (86) 833 3359989
Agricultural Products Development & Mfr
N.A.I.C.S.: 325320

SICHUAN FULIN TRANSPORTATION GROUP CO., LTD.
No 98 Mianzhou Avenue North Section, Mianyang, 610091, Sichuan, China
Tel.: (86) 2883262759
Web Site: http://www.scflyy.cn
Year Founded: 2002
002357—(SSE)
Rev.: $102,435,896
Assets: $381,816,270
Liabilities: $187,002,144
Net Worth: $194,814,126
Earnings: $8,304,997
Emp.: 3,000
Fiscal Year-end: 12/31/22
Food Transportation Services
N.A.I.C.S.: 488490
Cai Liangfa (Pres, Gen Mgr & Dir)

SICHUAN FURONG TECHNOLOGY CO., LTD.
No 518 Chongshuang Avenue 2nd Section, Chongzhou, Chengdu, 611230, Sichuan, China
Tel.: (86) 2882255381
Web Site: https://www.scfrkj.cn
Year Founded: 2011
603327—(SHG)
Rev.: $316,442,435
Assets: $341,764,151
Liabilities: $78,750,121
Net Worth: $263,014,030
Earnings: $54,931,963
Fiscal Year-end: 12/31/22
Aluminum Product Mfr & Distr
N.A.I.C.S.: 331313
Jingzhong Zhang (Chm)

SICHUAN GOLDEN SUMMIT (GRP) JOINT-STOCK CO., LTD.
No 55 Group 1 Xinnong, Ledu Town Emeishan, Sichuan, 614224, Sichuan, China
Tel.: (86) 8336179595
Web Site: http://www.scjd.cn
Year Founded: 1988
600678—(SHG)
Rev.: $50,242,294
Assets: $89,942,486
Liabilities: $51,582,497
Net Worth: $38,359,990
Earnings: $1,820,581
Fiscal Year-end: 12/31/22
Nonmetallic Ore Mining Services
N.A.I.C.S.: 212311
Liang Fei (Chm)

SICHUAN GOLDSTONE ASIA PHARMACEUTICAL INC.
8th Floor A1 Dadi New Guanghua Plaza, No 8 Jiayuan Road, Chengdu, 610072, Sichuan, China
Tel.: (86) 2887086807 CN
Web Site: https://www.goldstone-group.com
300434—(CHIN)
Rev.: $174,461,040
Assets: $429,611,364
Liabilities: $106,221,024
Net Worth: $323,390,340
Earnings: $30,718,116
Emp.: 160
Fiscal Year-end: 12/31/22
Pharmaceutical Developer & Mfr
N.A.I.C.S.: 325412
Ma Yiping (Chm & Gen Mgr)

SICHUAN GUANGAN AAA PUBLIC CO., LTD.
No 86 Qujiang North Road, Guangan District, Guang'an, 638000, Sichuan, China
Tel.: (86) 8262983049
Web Site: http://www.sc-aaa.com
Year Founded: 1999
600979—(SHG)
Rev.: $362,508,953
Assets: $1,450,478,297
Liabilities: $825,931,277
Net Worth: $624,547,020
Earnings: $23,718,895
Emp.: 2,500
Fiscal Year-end: 12/31/22
Electric Power Generation & Distribution Services
N.A.I.C.S.: 221111
Zhengjun Yu (Chm)

SICHUAN GUOGUANG AGRO-CHEMICAL CO., LTD.
No 899 Beijing Road Economy and Technology Development Zone, Chengdu, 610100, Sichuan, China
Tel.: (86) 2827015275
Web Site: https://www.scggic.com
Year Founded: 1984
002749—(SSE)
Rev.: $231,437,424
Assets: $317,128,739
Liabilities: $86,137,773
Net Worth: $230,990,966
Earnings: $15,948,724
Emp.: 920
Fiscal Year-end: 12/31/22
Agricultural Chemical Mfr
N.A.I.C.S.: 325320
He Jie (Chm & Pres)

SICHUAN HAITE HIGH-TECH CO., LTD.
No 1 Keyuan South Road High tech Zone, Chengdu, 610041, Sichuan, China
Tel.: (86) 2885921102
Web Site: https://www.schtgx.com
Year Founded: 1991
002023—(SSE)
Rev.: $127,715,267
Assets: $988,161,595
Liabilities: $397,466,236
Net Worth: $590,695,359
Earnings: $1,806,358
Fiscal Year-end: 12/31/22
Aviation Technical Services
N.A.I.C.S.: 488190
Wan Tao (Chm)

SICHUAN HAOWU ELECTRO-MECHANICAL CO., LTD.
No 1558 Hanyu Avenue, Shizhong District, Neijiang, 610093, Sichuan, China
Tel.: (86) 2863286976
Web Site: http://www.hwgf757.com
Year Founded: 1997
000757—(SSE)
Rev.: $488,685,071
Assets: $378,532,215
Liabilities: $136,581,120
Net Worth: $241,951,095
Earnings: $(9,225,263)
Fiscal Year-end: 12/31/22
Diesel Engine Mfr
N.A.I.C.S.: 336310
Caiyin Lu (Chm)

SICHUAN HEBANG BIOTECHNOLOGY CO., LTD.
C6 Building No 8 Guangfu Road, Qingyang District, Chengdu, 610073, Sichuan, China
Tel.: (86) 2862050230
Web Site: https://www.hebang.cn
Year Founded: 2002
603077—(SHG)
Rev.: $1,830,668,299
Assets: $3,384,008,859
Liabilities: $609,253,010
Net Worth: $2,774,755,849
Earnings: $534,475,970
Fiscal Year-end: 12/31/22
Chemical Products Mfr
N.A.I.C.S.: 325180
Xiaoping Zeng (Chm & Gen Mgr)

SICHUAN HEXIE SHUANGMA CO., LTD.
Room 2 26/F Office Building 1 Chengdu International Financial Center, No 1 Section 3 Hongxing Road Jinjiang District, Chengdu, 610000, Sichuan, China
Tel.: (86) 2863231548
Web Site: https://sc-shuangma.com
Year Founded: 1999
000935—(SSE)
Rev.: $171,230,253
Assets: $1,012,384,246
Liabilities: $97,443,244
Net Worth: $914,941,002
Earnings: $115,895,454
Fiscal Year-end: 12/31/22
Cement Product Mfr & Distr
N.A.I.C.S.: 327310
Canwen Huang (Gen Mgr)

SICHUAN HEZONG MEDICINE PHARMACEUTICAL CO.
13F No 18 Youlian First Street, Jinniu District, Chengdu, 610081, Sichuan, China
Tel.: (86) 2869569969
Web Site: http://www.hezongyy.com
Year Founded: 2007
300937—(SSE)
Rev.: $557,275,497
Assets: $223,463,167
Liabilities: $108,338,523
Net Worth: $115,124,644
Earnings: $5,898,934
Fiscal Year-end: 12/31/22
Medical Product Mfr & Distr

Sichuan Hezong Medicine Pharmaceutical Co.—(Continued)
N.A.I.C.S.: 339112
Yanfei Li *(Chm)*

SICHUAN HONGDA CO., LTD.
28F Hongda International Sqr No 2 Jnl Est Rd, Chengdu, 610041, China
Tel.: (86) 8388620489
Web Site: https://www.sichuanhongda.com
Year Founded: 1979
600331—(SHG)
Rev.: $412,811,634
Assets: $329,938,161
Liabilities: $271,877,075
Net Worth: $58,061,086
Earnings: $8,446,253
Fiscal Year-end: 12/31/22
Chemical Product Mfr & Distr
N.A.I.C.S.: 325180
Huang Jianjun *(Chm & Gen Mgr)*

SICHUAN HUATI LIGHTING TECHNOLOGY CO., LTD.
580 Shuanghua Rd 3rd Section, Southwest Airport Economic Development Zone, Chengdu, 610207, China
Tel.: (86) 2885871857
Web Site: https://www.huaticn.com
Year Founded: 2004
603679—(SHG)
Rev.: $60,804,249
Assets: $204,386,781
Liabilities: $84,066,185
Net Worth: $120,320,596
Earnings: ($10,702,397)
Emp.: 700
Fiscal Year-end: 12/31/22
Urban Lighting Services
N.A.I.C.S.: 541320

SICHUAN HUIYUAN OPTICAL COMMUNICATIONS CO., LTD.
Room 2605 Building C Maoye Center No 28 North Section of Tianfu Avenue, PO Box 611731, Wuhou District, Chengdu, Sichuan, China
Tel.: (86) 2885516606
Web Site: https://www.schy.com.cn
Year Founded: 1993
000586—(SSE)
Rev.: $62,661,756
Assets: $78,375,478
Liabilities: $33,396,372
Net Worth: $44,979,106
Earnings: $2,555,898
Emp.: 200
Fiscal Year-end: 12/31/22
Optical Fiber Mfr
N.A.I.C.S.: 335921
Li Hongxing *(Chm)*

SICHUAN INJET ELECTRIC CO., LTD.
No 686 Jinshajiang West Road, Deyang, 618000, Sichuan, China
Tel.: (86) 8386930000
Web Site: https://www.injet.cn
Year Founded: 1996
300820—(SSE)
Rev.: $180,073,151
Assets: $402,600,889
Liabilities: $190,579,845
Net Worth: $212,021,045
Earnings: $47,608,208
Emp.: 40,000
Fiscal Year-end: 12/31/22
Electrical Equipment Mfr & Distr
N.A.I.C.S.: 335999
Jun Wang *(Chm)*

SICHUAN JINSHI TECHNOLOGY CO., LTD.
186 meters E of the intersection of S Second Rd Checheng West Third Rd, Chengdu Economic & Technological Development Zone Longquanyi District, Chengdu, 610100, Sichuan, China
Tel.: (86) 2868618883
Web Site: https://www.jinshigp.com
Year Founded: 2008
002951—(SSE)
Rev.: $25,920,662
Assets: $283,683,381
Liabilities: $31,608,055
Net Worth: $252,075,325
Earnings: ($5,136,801)
Fiscal Year-end: 12/31/22
Packaging Product Mfr & Distr
N.A.I.C.S.: 333993
Haijian Li *(Chm & Gen Mgr)*

SICHUAN JIUYUAN YINHAI SOFTWARE CO., LTD.
Building 2 No 3 Keyuan 1st Road Hi-tech Zone, Chengdu, 610063, Sichuan, China
Tel.: (86) 2865516099
Web Site: http://www.yinhai.com
Year Founded: 2008
002777—(SSE)
Rev.: $180,072,182
Assets: $355,783,863
Liabilities: $119,506,542
Net Worth: $236,277,321
Earnings: $25,857,538
Fiscal Year-end: 12/31/22
Software Development Services
N.A.I.C.S.: 541511
Lian Chunhua *(Chm & Gen Mgr)*

SICHUAN JIUZHOU ELECTRIC CO., LTD.
No 259 Jiuzhou Avenue Kechuang Park, Mianyang, 621000, Sichuan, China
Tel.: (86) 8162312421
Web Site: http://www.jiuzhoutech.com
Year Founded: 1958
000801—(SSE)
Rev.: $545,397,545
Assets: $824,362,798
Liabilities: $385,377,108
Net Worth: $438,985,689
Earnings: $27,790,369
Emp.: 6,500
Fiscal Year-end: 12/31/22
Television Product Mfr
N.A.I.C.S.: 334220
Yang Baoping *(Chm)*

SICHUAN KELUN PHARMACEUTICAL CO., LTD.
No 36 West Baihua Road, Qingyang District, Chengdu, 610071, Sichuan, China
Tel.: (86) 2886127705
Web Site: https://www.kelun.com
Year Founded: 1996
002422—(SSE)
Rev.: $2,655,336,551
Assets: $4,790,220,524
Liabilities: $2,419,150,126
Net Worth: $2,371,070,398
Earnings: $239,901,831
Fiscal Year-end: 12/31/22
Pharmaceuticals Mfr
N.A.I.C.S.: 325412
Liu Gexin *(Chm)*

Subsidiaries:

Klus Pharma Inc. (1)
101 College Rd E 2F Princeton Forrestal Ctr, Princeton, NJ 08540
Tel.: (609) 662-1864
Web Site: http://www.kluspharma.com
Bio Therapeutic Mfr
N.A.I.C.S.: 325412

SICHUAN KEXIN MECHANICAL AND ELECTRICAL EQUIPMENT CO., LTD.
No 21 Tuojiang Road, Economic Development Zone Shifang, Sichuan, 618400, China
Tel.: (86) 8388265111
Web Site: http://www.sckxjd.com
Year Founded: 1997
300092—(CHIN)
Rev.: $210,827,942
Assets: $335,998,309
Liabilities: $121,490,477
Net Worth: $214,507,831
Earnings: $23,030,341
Emp.: 1,000
Fiscal Year-end: 12/31/23
Industrial Equipment Mfr
N.A.I.C.S.: 335312
Lin Zhenhua *(Chm)*

SICHUAN LANGSHA HOLDING LTD.
No 63 Wainan Street, Yibin, 644000, Sichuan, China
Tel.: (86) 8318216216
Web Site: http://www.langsha.com
Year Founded: 1996
600137—(SHG)
Rev.: $45,876,556
Assets: $93,221,402
Liabilities: $19,472,132
Net Worth: $73,749,270
Earnings: $2,425,635
Fiscal Year-end: 12/31/22
Holding Company
N.A.I.C.S.: 551112
Weng Rongdi *(Chm & Gen Mgr)*

SICHUAN LANGUANG DEVELOPMENT CO., LTD.
Hi-tech Zone West 9th Avenue core, Gaoxin District, Chengdu, 611731, Sichuan, China
Tel.: (86) 2887826466
600466—(SHG)
Rev.: $6,581,500,190
Assets: $39,568,647,357
Liabilities: $32,460,307,005
Net Worth: $7,108,340,353
Earnings: $505,953,044
Fiscal Year-end: 12/31/20
Pharmaceutical Product Mfr & Distr
N.A.I.C.S.: 325412

SICHUAN LUTIANHUA CO., LTD.
No 38 Lizilin Road, Naxi District, Luzhou, 646300, Sichuan, China
Tel.: (86) 8304125388
Web Site: http://www.sclth.com
Year Founded: 1959
000912—(SSE)
Rev.: $1,057,834,098
Assets: $1,462,740,285
Liabilities: $583,767,012
Net Worth: $878,973,273
Earnings: $51,564,975
Fiscal Year-end: 12/31/22
Fertilizer Mfr
N.A.I.C.S.: 212390
Yong Tu *(Chm-Supervisory Bd)*

Subsidiaries:

Jiuhe Company Limited (1)
5th Floor Kowloon Pearl Building No 33 Xijiao Road, Jiulongpo District, Chongqing, 400050, China
Tel.: (86) 4006366699
Web Site: https://www.jiuhe.net
Chemical Fertilizer Distr
N.A.I.C.S.: 424910
Zhao Yongqing *(Gen Mgr)*

SICHUAN MEIFENG CHEMICAL INDUSTRY CO., LTD.
No 10 Yinghua South Road 1st Section, Deyang, 618000, Sichuan, China
Tel.: (86) 8382232227
Web Site: https://www.scmeif.com
Year Founded: 1974
000731—(SSE)
Rev.: $689,322,470
Assets: $726,421,401
Liabilities: $123,345,907
Net Worth: $603,075,494
Earnings: $87,339,428
Fiscal Year-end: 12/31/22
Chemical Fertiliser Mfr
N.A.I.C.S.: 325311
Wang Yong *(Chm & Pres)*

SICHUAN MINGXING ELECTRIC POWER CO., LTD.
No 56 Mingyue Road Development Zone, Suining, 629000, Sichuan, China
Tel.: (86) 8252210076
Web Site: http://www.mxdl.com.cn
Year Founded: 1988
600101—(SHG)
Rev.: $333,746,342
Assets: $535,105,776
Liabilities: $160,796,175
Net Worth: $374,309,601
Earnings: $22,348,395
Fiscal Year-end: 12/31/22
Electric Power Generation & Supply
N.A.I.C.S.: 221111
Chen Feng *(Chm)*

SICHUAN NEW ENERGY POWER COMPANY LIMITED
16th Floor Building 2 No 716 Middle Section of Jiannan Avenue, High-tech Zone, Chengdu, 610301, Sichuan, China
Tel.: (86) 2862070817
Web Site: https://cndl.scnyw.com
Year Founded: 1997
000155—(SSE)
Rev.: $533,719,747
Assets: $2,716,482,619
Liabilities: $1,483,927,768
Net Worth: $1,232,554,850
Earnings: $99,653,126
Fiscal Year-end: 12/31/22
Chemical Fertiliser Mfr
N.A.I.C.S.: 325311

SICHUAN NEWSNET MEDIA (GROUP) CO., LTD.
16F Building 7 & 2 6F Building 5 Area D No 599 Shijicheng South Road, Chengdu Hi-Tech Industrial Development Zone, Chengdu, 610036, Sichuan, China
Tel.: (86) 2862616168
Web Site: http://www.newssc.org
Year Founded: 2009
300987—(SSE)
Rev.: $27,649,197
Assets: $128,900,608
Liabilities: $15,409,279
Net Worth: $113,491,329
Earnings: $3,915,363
Fiscal Year-end: 12/31/22
Media Advertising Services
N.A.I.C.S.: 541840
Zhiyue Zhang *(Chm)*

SICHUAN QIAOYUAN GAS CO., LTD.
No 1399 Guanwen Road, Dujiangyan, Chengdu, 611830, Sichuan, China
Tel.: (86) 4008016616
Web Site: https://www.qygas.com
Year Founded: 2002
301286—(CHIN)
Rev.: $141,460,138

Assets: $277,166,081
Liabilities: $38,712,381
Net Worth: $238,453,700
Earnings: $28,072,400
Fiscal Year-end: 12/31/23
Industrial Gas Mfr
N.A.I.C.S.: 325120
Zhiyong Qiao *(Chm)*

SICHUAN ROAD & BRIDGE GROUP CO., LTD.
No 12 Jiuxing Avenue High-tech Zone, Chengdu, Sichuan, China
Tel.: (86) 2885088879
Web Site: https://www.scrbc.com.cn
600039—(SHG)
Rev.: $18,975,223,313
Assets: $29,245,142,815
Liabilities: $22,786,590,214
Net Worth: $6,458,552,601
Earnings: $1,574,291,988
Fiscal Year-end: 12/31/22
Construction Engineering Services
N.A.I.C.S.: 541330

SICHUAN SHENGDA FORESTRY INDUSTRY CO., LTD.
No 42 Donghuazheng Street, Jinjing District, Chengdu, 610000, Sichuan, China
Tel.: (86) 2886619110
Web Site: http://www.shengdawood.com
Year Founded: 2005
002259—(SSE)
Rev.: $259,448,824
Assets: $136,169,902
Liabilities: $101,310,015
Net Worth: $34,859,888
Earnings: ($8,859,998)
Fiscal Year-end: 12/31/22
Wood Products Mfr
N.A.I.C.S.: 321999
Lai Xuri *(Chm)*

SICHUAN SHUDAO EQUIPMENT AND TECHNOLOGY CO., LTD.
No 569 tongshanqiao Road North Area of Modern Industrial Port, Pidu District, Chengdu, 611743, Sichuan, China
Tel.: (86) 2887893658
Web Site: https://www.shudaozb.com
Year Founded: 2001
300540—(CHIN)
Rev.: $94,137,619
Assets: $245,165,693
Liabilities: $101,526,905
Net Worth: $143,638,788
Earnings: $4,598,161
Fiscal Year-end: 12/31/23
Liquefied Natural Gas Device Mfr
N.A.I.C.S.: 333998
Hu Shengxia *(Chm)*

SICHUAN TEWAY FOOD GROUP CO., LTD.
No 333 Tengfei 1st Road, Xihanggang Street Shuangliu District, Chengdu, 610200, Sichuan, China
Tel.: (86) 2882808188
Web Site: https://www.teway.cn
Year Founded: 2007
603317—(SHG)
Rev.: $377,775,712
Assets: $676,970,639
Liabilities: $111,888,523
Net Worth: $565,082,117
Earnings: $47,975,340
Emp.: 2,740
Fiscal Year-end: 12/31/22
Spice Food Product Mfr
N.A.I.C.S.: 311942
Wen Deng *(Chm & Pres)*

SICHUAN TIANYI COMHEART TELECOM CO., LTD.
No 198 Section 1 Snow Mountain Avenue, Dayi County, Chengdu, 611330, Sichuan, China
Tel.: (86) 2888208089
Web Site: https://www.tianyisc.com
Year Founded: 2001
300504—(CHIN)
Rev.: $359,791,254
Assets: $429,201,078
Liabilities: $108,129,151
Net Worth: $321,071,927
Earnings: $14,182,919
Emp.: 4,000
Fiscal Year-end: 12/31/23
Communication Equipment Mfr & Distr
N.A.I.C.S.: 334210
Shihong Li *(Chm)*

SICHUAN WESTERN RESOURCES HOLDING CO., LTD.
No 168 Bisheng Road, Jinjiang District, Chengdu, China
Tel.: (86) 288 591 0202
Web Site: http://www.scxbzy.com
600139—(SHG)
Rev.: $21,927,415
Assets: $463,804,973
Liabilities: $357,893,964
Net Worth: $105,911,009
Earnings: ($30,746,183)
Fiscal Year-end: 12/31/20
Holding Company
N.A.I.C.S.: 551112
Yong Xia *(Chm)*

Subsidiaries:

Hengneng Car Co., Ltd. (1)
Room 2005 Yueda 889 Square Wanhangdu Road, Jingan District, Shanghai, 200040, China
Tel.: (86) 2162321999
Web Site: http://www.hneauto.com
Automotive Parts Mfr & Distr
N.A.I.C.S.: 336330

Long Power Systems (Suzhou) Co., Ltd. (1)
8 Dongwang Road Suzhou Industrial Park, Suzhou, 215002, China
Tel.: (86) 51262818888
Web Site: http://www.longpowers.com
Lithium Battery Mfr & Distr
N.A.I.C.S.: 335910
Bill Huang *(Founder, Pres & CEO)*

SICHUAN XICHANG ELECTRIC POWER CO., LTD.
No 66 Shengli Road, Xichang, 615000, Sichuan, China
Tel.: (86) 8343830505
Web Site: http://www.scxcdl.com
Year Founded: 1994
600505—(SHG)
Rev.: $180,153,151
Assets: $650,227,711
Liabilities: $445,100,011
Net Worth: $205,127,699
Earnings: $6,343,314
Fiscal Year-end: 12/31/22
Electric Power Generation & Distribution Services
N.A.I.C.S.: 221118
Lin Mingxing *(Chm)*

SICHUAN XINJINLU GROUP CO., LTD.
22F-23F Building 21 Yinxin Wuzhou Plaza 1st Phase No 733, Taishan South Road 2nd Section, Deyang, 618000, Sichuan, China
Tel.: (86) 8382207936
Web Site: http://www.xjinlu.cn
Year Founded: 1979
000510—(SSE)
Rev.: $364,703,539

Assets: $364,074,320
Liabilities: $177,186,821
Net Worth: $186,887,499
Earnings: ($24,880,181)
Fiscal Year-end: 12/31/23
Chemical Product, PVC Resins & Caustic Soda Mfr
N.A.I.C.S.: 325110
Zhang Zhenya *(Sec)*

SICHUAN XUNYOU NETWORK TECHNOLOGY CO., LTD.
Floor 6 and 7 Building 7 No 599 Shijicheng South Road, High-tech Zone Pilot Free Trade Zone, Chengdu, 610041, Sichuan, China
Tel.: (86) 2865598000
Web Site: http://www.xunyou.com
Year Founded: 2008
300467—(CHIN)
Rev.: $49,916,412
Assets: $130,963,716
Liabilities: $36,355,176
Net Worth: $94,608,540
Earnings: ($2,927,340)
Emp.: 170
Fiscal Year-end: 12/31/22
Network Gaming Accelerator
N.A.I.C.S.: 513210
Xu Yuan *(Pres & Dir)*

SICHUAN YAHUA INDUSTRIAL GROUP CO., LTD.
Building 1 Hangxing International Plaza No 66 Tianfu 4th Street, High-tech Zone, Chengdu, 610041, Sichuan, China
Tel.: (86) 2885325316
Web Site: http://www.scyahua.com
Year Founded: 2001
002497—(SSE)
Rev.: $2,029,740,041
Assets: $2,056,330,046
Liabilities: $465,817,253
Net Worth: $1,590,512,793
Earnings: $637,171,409
Emp.: 4,000
Fiscal Year-end: 12/31/22
Explosives Mfr
N.A.I.C.S.: 325920
Rong Zheng *(Chm)*

SICHUAN ZHONGGNG LIGHTG PRTCN TECH CO., LTD.
No 19 Tianyu Road Western Park, Hi-Tech Zone, Chengdu, 611731, Sichuan, China
Tel.: (86) 2886083899
Web Site: https://en.zhongguang.com
Year Founded: 1987
300414—(CHIN)
Rev.: $78,171,271
Assets: $165,445,058
Liabilities: $27,617,854
Net Worth: $137,827,204
Earnings: $3,606,887
Fiscal Year-end: 12/31/23
Lightning Protection Equipment Mfr
N.A.I.C.S.: 335931
Wang Xueying *(Chm & Gen Mgr)*

Subsidiaries:

Sichuan Accuracy Test & Accreditation Co., Ltd. (1)
No 839 Gaodianzi RD West Park Hi-tech Zone, Chengdu, Sichuan, China
Tel.: (86) 2864723795
Web Site: https://www.accuracytest.org
Testing Protection Product Mfr
N.A.I.C.S.: 334519

SICHUAN ZIGONG CONVEYING MACHINE GROUP CO., LTD.
No 3 Fuchuan Road Hi-Tech Industrial Zone, Zigong, 643000, Sichuan, China
Tel.: (86) 8138233588
Web Site: https://china-pipeconveyor.com
Year Founded: 2003
001288—(SSE)
Rev.: $144,958,366
Assets: $487,181,608
Liabilities: $201,679,653
Net Worth: $285,501,955
Earnings: $14,075,200
Emp.: 800
Fiscal Year-end: 12/31/23
Belt Product Mfr & Distr
N.A.I.C.S.: 326220

SICILY BY CAR S.P.A.
Galileo Galilei 10H, 39100, Bolzano, BZ, Italy
Tel.: (39) 0916390111
Web Site: https://www.sicilybycar.it
Year Founded: 1963
SBC—(EUR)
Vehicle Rental Services
N.A.I.C.S.: 532120
Tommaso Dragotto *(CEO)*

SICIT GROUP S.P.A.
Via Arzignano 80, Chiampo, 36072, Vicenza, Italy
Tel.: (39) 0444450946
Web Site: http://www.sicitgroup.com
Year Founded: 1960
SICT—(ITA)
Rev.: $77,580,551
Assets: $152,969,923
Liabilities: $45,029,735
Net Worth: $107,940,188
Earnings: $11,427,545
Emp.: 141
Fiscal Year-end: 12/31/20
Agrochemical Products Distr
N.A.I.C.S.: 424910
Valter Peretti *(Chm)*

SICON LTD.
Wilton Works Naas Road, Naas Rd, Clondalkin, Ireland
Tel.: (353) 14091600   IE
Web Site: http://www.sicon.ie
Year Founded: 1999
Sales Range: $1-4.9 Billion
Emp.: 2,858
Holding Company
N.A.I.C.S.: 551112
Liam Nagle *(Grp CEO)*

Subsidiaries:

Sisk Group (1)
Wilton Works Naas Rd, Naas Road, Dublin, 22, Ireland
Tel.: (353) 14091600
Web Site: http://www.siskgroup.com
Sales Range: $1-4.9 Billion
Emp.: 100
Holding Company; Construction, Stonework, Architectural Glazing & Healthcare Solutions
N.A.I.C.S.: 551112
Gerard Penny *(Dir-Grp Fin)*

Subsidiary (Domestic):

John Sisk and Son (Holdings) Limited (2)
Wilton Works, Naas Road, 22, Clondalkin, Ireland
Tel.: (353) 14091500
Web Site: http://www.siskgroup.ie
Sales Range: $125-149.9 Million
Emp.: 500
Holding Company
N.A.I.C.S.: 551112
Stephen Bowcott *(Mng Dir)*

Subsidiary (Domestic):

John Sisk & Son Limited-Ireland (3)
Wilton Works Clondalkin Naas Road, Dublin, Ireland

SICON LTD.

Sicon Ltd.—(Continued)
Tel.: (353) 14091500
Web Site: http://www.johnsiskandson.com
Emp.: 1,700
General Contracting Construction
N.A.I.C.S.: 238190
Garry Crabtree *(Mng Dir)*

Subsidiary (Non-US):

John Sisk & Son Limited-UK (3)
1 Curo Park, Frogmore, Saint Albans, AL22 2DD, Hertfordshire, United Kingdom
Tel.: (44) 1727875551
General Construction & Civil Engineering
N.A.I.C.S.: 236220
John Dennehy *(Dir-Comml)*

Subsidiary (Domestic):

Origo Distribution Limited (2)
Magna Drive Magna Business Park Cicywest, Magna Business Park, 24, Dublin, Ireland **(100%)**
Tel.: (353) 14666700
Web Site: http://www.origo.ie
Emp.: 60
Premium Branded Products Distr
N.A.I.C.S.: 449210
Joe Cunniam *(Mng Dir)*

Stone Developements Limited (2)
Old Leighlin, Carlow, Ireland **(100%)**
Tel.: (353) 599721227
Web Site: http://www.stonedevelopments.ie
Sales Range: $25-49.9 Million
Emp.: 100
Natural Stone Contractor & Distr
N.A.I.C.S.: 423320

Subsidiary (Non-US):

Erinstone N.V. (3)
Nijverheidsstraat 34, 2620, Hemiksem, Belgium **(100%)**
Tel.: (32) 38707120
Web Site: http://www.erinstone.com
Sales Range: $50-74.9 Million
Emp.: 10
Limestone Retailer & Stonework Contracting
N.A.I.C.S.: 423320

Joint Venture (Domestic):

Williaam Cox Ltd. (2)
Unit AF 40, Cloverhill Industrial Estate, Clondalkin, 22, Dublin, Ireland
Tel.: (353) 14605400
Web Site: https://williaamcox.com
Sales Range: $25-49.9 Million
Emp.: 50
Architectural Glazing, Coxdome Daylight Products, Smoke & Heat Ventilation & Plastic Distr
N.A.I.C.S.: 541310

SICPA HOLDING SA
Av de Florissant 41, 1008, Prilly, Switzerland
Tel.: (41) 21 627 55 55
Web Site: http://www.sicpa.com
Year Founded: 1927
Emp.: 3,000
Secured Identification, Traceability & Authentication Solutions
N.A.I.C.S.: 325910
Philippe Amon *(Chm & CEO)*

Subsidiaries:

Cabot Security Materials Inc. (1)
325 E Middlefield Rd, Mountain View, CA 94043-4003
Tel.: (650) 603-5918
Sales Range: $1-9.9 Million
Biological Product Mfr
N.A.I.C.S.: 325414

China Banknote SICPA Security Ink Co., Ltd (1)
No 5 Yuncheng Road Beijing Economic & Technological Development Area, 100176, Beijing, China
Tel.: (86) 1067871566
Print Ink Mfr
N.A.I.C.S.: 325910
Alex Sudan *(Gen Mgr)*

Meyercord Revenue Inc. (1)
475 Village Dr, Carol Stream, IL 60188-1830 **(100%)**
Tel.: (630) 682-6200
Web Site: http://www.meyercord.com
Sales Range: $25-49.9 Million
Emp.: 80
Tax Stamp Printing Solutions
N.A.I.C.S.: 323111

P.T. SICPA Peruri Securink (1)
Graha Iskandarsyah building 6th floor JI Iskandarsyah Raya 66 C, Kebayoran Baru, Jakarta, 12160, Indonesia
Tel.: (62) 217206508
Security System Installation Services
N.A.I.C.S.: 561621
Maruf Hidayah *(VP-HR & Corp Comm)*

SICPA ASSAN Urun Guvenligi Sanayi ve Ticaret A.S. (1)
Yayla Mahallesi Ruya Sokak No 2 Assan Tesisleri, Tuzla, 34940, Istanbul, Turkiye
Tel.: (90) 2165811050
Security System Installation Services
N.A.I.C.S.: 561621
Ozlem Biyan Tanriseven *(Mgr-Pur & Logistics)*

SICPA Argentina SA (1)
14 de Julio 642/8, C1427CJN, Buenos Aires, Argentina
Tel.: (54) 1145539600
Security System Installation Services
N.A.I.C.S.: 561621

SICPA Asia Development Pte. Ltd. (1)
629 Aljunied Road 06-11 CitiTech Industrial Building, Singapore, 389838, Singapore
Tel.: (65) 68487156
Security System Installation Services
N.A.I.C.S.: 561621
Nicolas Schindler *(Dir-Bus Dev)*

SICPA Australia Pty Ltd (1)
Unit 2 59 Lara Way, Campbellfield, 3061, VIC, Australia
Tel.: (61) 393576920
Security System Installation Services
N.A.I.C.S.: 561621
Howard Carter *(Mng Dir)*

SICPA Brasil Industria de Tintas e Sistemas Ltda. (1)
Rua Echapora 328 Distrito Industrial de Santa Cruz, Rio de Janeiro, 23565-150, Brazil
Tel.: (55) 2124181200
Security System Installation Services
N.A.I.C.S.: 561621

SICPA Ecuador GSS SA (1)
Luis Tamayo N24-33 y Alfredo Baquerizo Moreno, Edificio Torres del Castillo Torre 2 Piso 14, Quito, Ecuador
Tel.: (593) 2 297 9600
Security Ink Mfr
N.A.I.C.S.: 325910

SICPA France SAS (1)
7 rue du Lys, 24000, Perigueux, France
Tel.: (33) 156605045
Security System Installation Services
N.A.I.C.S.: 561621

SICPA Germany GmbH (1)
Gewerbepark Lindach D7, 84489, Burghausen, Germany
Tel.: (49) 867787560
Security System Installation Services
N.A.I.C.S.: 561621

SICPA Government Security Solutions LATAM SpA (1)
Avenida Alonso de Cordova 5670, Las Condes, 7560875, Santiago, Chile
Tel.: (56) 222109700
Security System Installation Services
N.A.I.C.S.: 561621

SICPA India Private Limited (1)
308-312 Mercantile House 15 Kasturba Gandhi Marg, New Delhi, 110001, India
Tel.: (91) 1123355243
Security System Installation Services
N.A.I.C.S.: 561621
Pankaj Saraswat *(Mgr-Technical Svcs)*

SICPA Inks Pakistan (Private) Limited (1)
Jinnah Avenue Malir Halt, Karachi, 75100, Pakistan
Tel.: (92) 2134507818
Print Ink Mfr
N.A.I.C.S.: 325910
Nusrat Ali *(Mgr-Procurement)*

SICPA Italia S.p.A. (1)
Localita Arnad Le Vieux 41, 11020, Arnad, Italy
Tel.: (39) 012 596 9011
Security Ink Mfr
N.A.I.C.S.: 325910

SICPA Kenya Limited (1)
145 Isaac Gathanju Road, PO Box 25494-00603, Lavington, Nairobi, Kenya
Tel.: (254) 709807000
Security System Installation Services
N.A.I.C.S.: 561621

SICPA Mexicana S.A. de C.V. (1)
Calle Atlacomulco No 505-A Colonia San Andres Atoto, 53500, Naucalpan, Mexico
Tel.: (52) 5553599719
Security System Installation Services
N.A.I.C.S.: 561621

SICPA Product Security (Beijing) Co., Ltd. (1)
Unit 706B 7/F Zhao Lin Plaza Tower B 19 Rong Hua Middle Road, Economic & Technological Development Area, 100176, Beijing, China
Tel.: (86) 1067870207
Print Ink Mfr
N.A.I.C.S.: 325910
Qin Xuan *(Mgr-Bus Dev)*

SICPA Product Security Sdn. Bhd (1)
C-01-01 iTech Tower Jalan Impact Cyber 6, 63000, Cyberjaya, Selangor, Malaysia
Tel.: (60) 386862525
Security System Installation Services
N.A.I.C.S.: 561621
Alain Augsburger *(Gen Mgr)*

SICPA Product Security, LLC (1)
8000 Research Way, Springfield, VA 22153
Tel.: (703) 455-8050
Print Ink Mfr
N.A.I.C.S.: 325910

SICPA Securink Corp. (1)
4049 Meacham Blvd, Fort Worth, TX 76117
Tel.: (817) 498-6768
Web Site: http://www.sicpa.com
Sales Range: $1-9.9 Million
Emp.: 12
Printing Ink Mfr
N.A.I.C.S.: 325910
Scott Stacy *(Mgr)*

SICPA Securink Corporation (1)
3256 F X Tessier Street, Vaudreuil-Dorion, J7V 5V5, QC, Canada
Tel.: (450) 510-2223
Print Ink Mfr
N.A.I.C.S.: 325910

SICPA Security Solutions Albania Sh.p.k. (1)
Highway Tirana Durres Km 4 behind Coca-Cola Building, 1051, Tirana, Albania
Tel.: (355) 44508711
Security System Installation Services
N.A.I.C.S.: 561621

SICPA Security Solutions Arabia Africa FZ-LLC (1)
Shatha Tower Office 3602 Dubai Media City, PO Box 502780, Dubai, United Arab Emirates
Tel.: (971) 44468900
Security System Installation Services
N.A.I.C.S.: 561621

SICPA Security Solutions CE, a.s. (1)
Michalska 14, 811 03, Bratislava, Slovakia
Tel.: (421) 259202220
Security System Installation Services
N.A.I.C.S.: 561621

SICPA Security Solutions Georgia LLC (1)
79 Chargali Street, Temka District, 0178, Tbilisi, Georgia
Tel.: (995) 322434580

INTERNATIONAL PUBLIC

Security System Installation Services
N.A.I.C.S.: 561621

SICPA Services Canada Ltd. (1)
Suite 300 - 1000 West 3rd Street, Vancouver, V7P 3J6, BCA , Canada
Tel.: (604) 988-4850
Security System Installation Services
N.A.I.C.S.: 561621
Vahid Pishvaei *(Mgr-Industrialization)*

SICPA South Africa (Pty) Limited (1)
1 Enterprise Close, Linbro Business Park, Sandton, 2065, South Africa
Tel.: (27) 11 201 4500
Security Ink Mfr
N.A.I.C.S.: 325910

SICPA Spain, S.L.U. (1)
Republica Dominicana 6 Poligono Industrial El Olivar, 28806, Alcala de Henares, Madrid, Spain
Tel.: (34) 918863561
Security System Installation Services
N.A.I.C.S.: 561621
Francisco de Yeregui *(Dir-Fin)*

SICPA Togo SAU (1)
Cite OUA LOME 2-opposite CICA RE Building 02, BP 20947, Lome, Togo
Tel.: (228) 2 253 5950
Security Ink Mfr
N.A.I.C.S.: 325910

SICPA Turkey Urun Guvenligi Sanayi ve Ticaret A.S. (1)
Yayla Mahallesi Ruya Sokak No 2 Assan Tesisleri, Tuzla, 34940, Istanbul, Turkiye
Tel.: (90) 216 581 1050
Security Ink Mfr
N.A.I.C.S.: 325910

SICPA UK Ltd (1)
29 Star Road Partridge Green, Horsham, RH13 8RA, West Sussex, United Kingdom
Tel.: (44) 1403712700
Security System Installation Services
N.A.I.C.S.: 561621

SICPAGSS Morocco SA (1)
Indusparc Module n 9 Chemin Tertiaire 1015, Sidi Moumen, 20400, Casablanca, Morocco
Tel.: (212) 522588900
Security System Installation Services
N.A.I.C.S.: 561621

STA Technologies Inc. (1)
5401 Venice Ave NE, Albuquerque, NM 87113
Tel.: (505) 563-4336
Security System Installation Services
N.A.I.C.S.: 561621
Richard Einhorn *(VP)*

Sicpa North America, Inc. (1)
5610 International Pkwy, Minneapolis, MN 55428
Tel.: (800) 728-8200
Web Site: http://www.sicpa.com
Sales Range: $1-9.9 Million
Emp.: 64
Miscellaneous Chemical Product & Preparation Mfr
N.A.I.C.S.: 325998
Peter Mulheran *(Sec)*

Tawada Limited (1)
Plot 140 Samuel Akintola Boulevard, Abuja, Nigeria
Tel.: (234) 9 234 4565
Security Ink Mfr
N.A.I.C.S.: 325910

SIDAMO
ZI de Gailletrous, 41260, La Chaussee-Saint-Victor, France
Tel.: (33) 2 54 74 09 82
Web Site: http://www.sidamo.fr
Sales Range: $10-24.9 Million
Emp.: 40
Abrasive Products, Diamond Blades & Shop Equipment Mfr & Distr
N.A.I.C.S.: 423830
Patrice Veneault *(Pres)*

SIDDARTH BUSINESSES LIMITED

A-31 Gali No 2 Madhu Vihar Hanuman Mandir, New Delhi, 110092, India
Tel.: (91) 7940063353
Year Founded: 1983
Sales Range: Less than $1 Million
Emp.: 7
Milk Production & Distr
N.A.I.C.S.: 112120

SIDDHARTH EDUCATION SERVICES LIMITED

101 Chirag Arcade 1st Floor, ER Road behind Nagrik Stor, Thane, 400 601, India
Tel.: (91) 2225334903
Web Site:
http://www.siddharthacademy.in
Education Training Services
N.A.I.C.S.: 611410
Kavita Mujumdar *(Chm & Mng Dir)*

SIDDHARTH SHRIRAM GROUP

Kirti Mahal 6th Floor Rajendra Place, New Delhi, 110008, India
Tel.: (91) 1125739103
Holding Company
N.A.I.C.S.: 551112
Siddharth Shriram *(Chm)*

Subsidiaries:

Honda India Power Products Limited (1)
Plot no 5 Sector 41 Kasna Greater Noida Industrial Development Area, Distt Gautam Budh Nagar, Noida, 201 310, UP, India
Tel.: (91) 1202590100
Web Site: http://www.hondasielpower.com
Rev.: $130,148,655
Assets: $107,967,405
Liabilities: $25,315,290
Net Worth: $82,652,115
Earnings: $6,643,455
Emp.: 782
Fiscal Year-end: 03/31/2021
Portable Generators & Water Pumping Equipment
N.A.I.C.S.: 335312
Vinay Mittal *(Exec Dir)*

Honda Siel Cars India Ltd. (1)
Plot No A-1 Sector 40/ 41 Surajpur-Kasna Road, Greater Noida Industrial Devel, Noida, 201 306, Gautam Budh Nagar UP, India
Tel.: (91) 1202341313
Web Site: http://www.hondacarindia.com
Automobile Mfr
N.A.I.C.S.: 336110

Usha International Limited (1)
Plot No 3 Sector 32 Institutional Area, Gurgaon, India
Tel.: (91) 124 4583100
Appliance Mfr
N.A.I.C.S.: 335210
Jayati Singh *(VP-Mktg-Cooking Appliances & Sewing Machines)*

Subsidiary (Domestic):

Mawana Sugars Limited (2)
Plot No 3 Institutional Area Sector - 32, Gurgaon, 122 001, Haryana, India (66.41%)
Tel.: (91) 1244298000
Web Site: https://www.mawanasugars.com
Rev.: $200,930,594
Assets: $188,414,772
Liabilities: $137,952,633
Net Worth: $50,462,139
Earnings: $9,996,305
Emp.: 1,519
Fiscal Year-end: 03/31/2021
Sugar, Chemical & Edible Oils Mfr
N.A.I.C.S.: 311314
Dharam Pal Sharma *(Exec Dir)*

SIDDHARTHA BANK LIMITED

130/23 Hattisar Kamaladi, PO Box 13806, Kathmandu, Nepal
Tel.: (977) 15970020

Web Site:
https://www.siddharthabank.com
Year Founded: 2002
SBL—(NEP)
Rev.: $125,982,947
Assets: $1,930,823,574
Liabilities: $1,755,796,806
Net Worth: $175,026,768
Earnings: $24,903,119
Emp.: 1,862
Fiscal Year-end: 07/15/21
Banking Services
N.A.I.C.S.: 522110
Manoj Kumar Kedia *(Chm)*

Subsidiaries:

Siddhartha Capital Limited (1)
Sama Marga Narayanchaur Naxal, Kathmandu, Nepal
Tel.: (977) 14421279
Web Site: https://www.siddharthacapital.com
Mutual Fund Operator
N.A.I.C.S.: 525910

SIDDHARTHA FINANCE LIMITED

Praharitole Rupandehi, Siddharthanagar, Nepal
Tel.: (977) 71 521478 NP
Year Founded: 1995
Financial Services
N.A.I.C.S.: 523999

SIDDHARTHA INSURANCE LIMITED

Siddhartha Insurance complex, 4th Floor, PO Box 24876, Babarmahal Hanumansthan, Kathmandu, Nepal
Tel.: (977) 14257766
Web Site:
http://www.siddharthainsurance.com
SIL—(NEP)
Rev.: $12,928,304
Assets: $51,309,449
Liabilities: $30,811,458
Net Worth: $20,497,991
Earnings: $2,925,211
Fiscal Year-end: 07/15/21
Insurance Services
N.A.I.C.S.: 524298
Deepak Kumar Dhoot *(Head-Claims & Deputy Gen Mgr)*

SIDDHARTHA TUBES LIMITED

Old IDA Building 3rd Floor 15-16, Jawahar Marg, Indore, 452 007, MP, India
Tel.: (91) 731 3912030 In
Web Site: http://www.siddhart.com
Year Founded: 1986
Rev.: $8,084,374
Assets: $36,673,895
Liabilities: $54,468,998
Net Worth: ($17,795,103)
Earnings: ($2,538,165)
Fiscal Year-end: 03/31/16
Tube & Pipe Mfr
N.A.I.C.S.: 326122
Nainesh J. Sanghvi *(Chm & Mng Dir)*

SIDDHESWARI GARMENTS LIMITED

9 India Exchange Place 3rd Floor, Kolkata, 700 001, India
Tel.: (91) 3322107112
Web Site:
https://www.siddheswari.co.in
Year Founded: 1994
526877—(BOM)
Rev.: $41,289
Assets: $2,694,643
Liabilities: $13,439
Net Worth: $2,681,203
Earnings: $6,637
Fiscal Year-end: 03/31/21
Hosiery Garment Mfr & Distr
N.A.I.C.S.: 315120

Sanjay Kumar Shah *(CFO)*

SIDDHIKA COATINGS LIMITED

L-9 LGF Kalkaji, New Delhi, 110019, India
Tel.: (91) 1141601441
Web Site: https://www.siddhika.com
Year Founded: 2010
SIDDHIKA—(NSE)
Rev.: $2,894,674
Assets: $3,871,759
Liabilities: $596,824
Net Worth: $3,274,935
Earnings: $238,115
Emp.: 82
Fiscal Year-end: 03/31/22
Construction Services
N.A.I.C.S.: 236210

Subsidiaries:

SCL Contracts Private Limited (1)
B-13 Hind Saurashtra Industrial Estate Near Marol Naka, Marol Andheri East, Mumbai, 400059, India
Tel.: (91) 2249749704
Web Site: https://www.sclcontracts.com
Painting Contractor Services
N.A.I.C.S.: 238320

SIDDIQSONS TINPLATE LIMITED

Ocean Tower 27 th Floor G-3 Block 9 Scheme 5, Main Clifton road, Karachi, Pakistan
Tel.: (92) 2135166571
Web Site:
http://www.siddiqsonstinplate.com
STPL—(PSX)
Rev.: $15,806,594
Assets: $21,967,757
Liabilities: $10,379,920
Net Worth: $11,587,836
Earnings: $11,091
Emp.: 198
Fiscal Year-end: 06/30/23
Tin Plate Mfr
N.A.I.C.S.: 332431
Muhammad Naeem-ul-Hasnain Mirza *(COO)*

SIDERURGICA DEL ORINOCO ALFREDO MANEIRO

Av La Estancia Edificio General de Seguros, 7th Floor Chuao, Caracas, Venezuela
Tel.: (58) 212 600 3901
Web Site: http://www.sidor.com
Steel Products Mfr
N.A.I.C.S.: 331110
Miguel Alvarez *(CEO)*

SIDERURGICA J.L. ALIPERTI S.A.

Rua Afonso Aliperti 180, Agua Funda, 04156-090, Sao Paulo, Brazil
Tel.: (55) 1121379800 BR
Web Site: http://www.aliperti.com.br
Year Founded: 1924
APTI4—(BRAZ)
Rev.: $6,169,178
Assets: $87,866,679
Liabilities: $48,033,284
Net Worth: $39,833,395
Earnings: $2,891,975
Fiscal Year-end: 12/31/23
Spring Mfr
N.A.I.C.S.: 332613
Caetano Aliperti *(Dir-IR)*

SIDERURGICA VENEZOLANA SIVENSA S.A.

Venezuela Avenue Torre America Building 11th Floor Sivensa, Urb Bello Monte, Caracas, Venezuela
Tel.: (58) 2127076200

Web Site:
https://www.sivensa.com.ve
Year Founded: 1948
SVS—(BVC)
Rev.: $6,481,626
Assets: $1,044,139,596
Liabilities: $166,599,139
Net Worth: $877,540,457
Earnings: ($1,096,529)
Emp.: 14
Fiscal Year-end: 09/30/23
Steel Products Mfr
N.A.I.C.S.: 331110
Oscar Augusto Machado Koeneke *(Pres)*

Subsidiaries:

Fundametal (1)
Av Venezuela Edf Torre America 11th floor Urb Bello Monte, Capital District, Caracas, Venezuela
Tel.: (58) 2127076135
Web Site: http://www.fundametal.edu.ve
Steel Producer
N.A.I.C.S.: 332111

International Briquettes Holding (1)
Avenida Venezuela Edificio Torre America Piso 11, Urbanizacion Bello Monte, Caracas, Venezuela (70%)
Tel.: (58) 2127076127
Web Site: http://www.ibh.com.ve
Sales Range: $100-124.9 Million
Hot Briquetted Iron Producer
N.A.I.C.S.: 332111

Siderurgica del Turbio S.A. (1)
Av Venezuela Edif Torre America Piso 11 Sivensa Urb Bello Monte, Caracas, Venezuela
Tel.: (58) 2127076200
Steel Mfrs
N.A.I.C.S.: 331110

SIDESHOW LTD.

4th Floor 54 St Johns Square, Farringdon, London, EC1V 4JL, United Kingdom
Tel.: (44) 20 7193 8768 UK
Web Site:
http://www.sideshowagency.com
Year Founded: 2010
Advetising Agency
N.A.I.C.S.: 541810
Tony Hill *(Founder)*

Subsidiaries:

Thinking Juice Ltd. (1)
26-32 Oxford Road, Bournemouth, BH8 8EZ, Dorset, United Kingdom
Tel.: (44) 1202 985 985
Web Site: http://www.thinkingjuice.co.uk
N.A.I.C.S.: 541810
Ashley Evans *(Acct Mgr)*

SIDETRADE S.A.

114 rue, 92100, Boulogne-Billancourt, France
Tel.: (33) 146841400
Web Site: https://www.sidetrade.com
Year Founded: 2000
ALBFR—(EUR)
Rev.: $48,282,653
Assets: $82,809,614
Liabilities: $48,251,830
Net Worth: $34,557,783
Earnings: $6,210,840
Emp.: 313
Fiscal Year-end: 12/31/23
Software Development Services
N.A.I.C.S.: 541511
Olivier Novasque *(Founder, Chm & CEO)*

Subsidiaries:

CreditPoint Software, Inc. (1)
100 S Cincinnati Ave Ste 510, Tulsa, OK 74103
Tel.: (918) 376-9440
Web Site:
http://www.creditpointsoftware.com

SIDETRADE S.A.

SIDETRADE S.A.—(Continued)
Software Publisher
N.A.I.C.S.: 513210
Chris Calvert *(Dir-Mktg & Sls)*

Shs Viveon AG (1)
Clarita-Bernhard-Strasse 27, 81249, Munich, Germany (87.85%)
Tel.: (49) 897472570
Web Site: https://www.shs-viveon.com
Information Technology Management Services
N.A.I.C.S.: 541512
Olivier Novasque *(CEO)*

Subsidiary (Non-US):

SHS Viveon Schweiz AG (2)
Industriestrasse 47, 6300, Zug, Switzerland
Tel.: (41) 417631304
Information & Technology Services
N.A.I.C.S.: 541519

SIDEXA
130 Avenue Du General Leclerc,
92340, Paris, France
Tel.: (33) 141879043
Web Site: http://www.sidexa.fr
Rev.: $21,800,000
Emp.: 56
Information Technology Services
N.A.I.C.S.: 518210
Jacques Leloup *(Chm)*

SIDH AUTOMOBILES LIMITED
R-13 S/F Greater Kailash-I, New Delhi, 110 048, Delhi, India
Tel.: (91) 1141053325
Web Site: https://sidhgroup.in
Year Founded: 1985
Rev.: $5,261
Assets: $545,846
Liabilities: $37,352
Net Worth: $508,494
Earnings: ($1,745)
Fiscal Year-end: 03/31/18
Finance Management Services
N.A.I.C.S.: 522291
Anil Sharma *(Board of Directors & Mng Dir)*

SIDI KERIR PETROCHEMICALS CO.
KM 36 Alexandria/Cairo Desert Road El-Amerya, El-Nahda Territory, Alexandria, Egypt
Tel.: (20) 34770131
Web Site: https://www.sidpec.com
Year Founded: 1997
SKPC.CA—(EGX)
Rev.: $426,805,348
Assets: $349,427,046
Liabilities: $147,209,928
Net Worth: $202,217,118
Earnings: $79,549,917
Emp.: 1,076
Fiscal Year-end: 12/31/23
Petrochemical Mfr
N.A.I.C.S.: 325110
Mohamed Ibrahim *(Chm & CEO)*

SIDIZ, INC.
9F 8-2 Garak-dong, 67-20 Seogyo-dong, Seoul, Korea (South)
Tel.: (82) 234006339
Web Site: http://www.sidiz.com
Year Founded: 1998
134790—(KRS)
Rev.: $192,223,320
Assets: $67,199,786
Liabilities: $17,092,182
Net Worth: $50,107,604
Earnings: $2,010,502
Fiscal Year-end: 12/31/22
Furniture Mfr
N.A.I.C.S.: 337122
Tae-Il Son *(CEO)*

SIDMA STEEL S.A.
188 Megaridos Avenue, 19300, Aspropyrgos, Greece
Tel.: (30) 2103498200 GR
Web Site: https://www.sidma.gr
Year Founded: 1931
SIDMA—(ATH)
Rev.: $278,085,279
Assets: $197,870,939
Liabilities: $182,093,236
Net Worth: $15,777,703
Earnings: $31,467,670
Emp.: 241
Fiscal Year-end: 12/31/21
Steel Products Processing Services
N.A.I.C.S.: 331513
Michael C. Samonas *(CFO)*

Subsidiaries:

PANELCO S.A. (1)
Lamia Industry OT4B, 35100, Lamia, Phthiotis, Greece
Tel.: (30) 22310661223
Web Site: http://www.panelco.gr
Sales Range: $25-49.9 Million
Emp.: 60
Insulation Sheets Mfr
N.A.I.C.S.: 326140

SIDMA BULGARIA S.A (1)
Tel.: (359) 28104421
Web Site: https://sidma.bg
Sales Range: $25-49.9 Million
Emp.: 30
Steel Product Distr
N.A.I.C.S.: 423510

SIDMA ROMANIA SRL (1)
Tel.: (40) 212090270
Web Site: https://www.sidma.ro
Sales Range: $25-49.9 Million
Emp.: 40
Steel Processing Services
N.A.I.C.S.: 331110

SIDMA S.A. STEEL PRODUCTS - Thessaloniki Steel Service and Distribution Center (1)
Palaiokastro, Oraiokastro, Thessaloniki, 541 10, Greece
Tel.: (30) 2310687111
Steel Processing Services
N.A.I.C.S.: 331110
Danny Benardout *(Gen Mgr)*

SIEBERTHEAD LIMITED
1st Fl 35-39 Old St, London, EC1V 9HX, United Kingdom
Tel.: (44) 2076899090
Web Site: http://www.sieberthead.com
Sales Range: $10-24.9 Million
Emp.: 25
Brand Development & Integration, Graphic Design, Logo & Package Design
N.A.I.C.S.: 541810
Satkar Gidda *(Owner)*

SIEGFRIED HOLDING AG
Untere Bruhlstrasse 4, CH-4800, Zofingen, Switzerland
Tel.: (41) 627461111
Web Site: https://www.siegfried.ch
SFZN—(SWX)
Rev.: $1,363,101,996
Assets: $1,988,026,608
Liabilities: $1,111,166,297
Net Worth: $876,860,310
Earnings: $173,492,239
Emp.: 3,411
Fiscal Year-end: 12/31/22
Active Pharmaceutical Ingredients Mfr
N.A.I.C.S.: 325412
Marianne Spaene *(Head-Bus Dev, Mktg & Sls-Global)*

Subsidiaries:

Hameln Pharmaceuticals GmbH (1)
Langes Feld 13, 31789, Hameln, Germany (100%)
Tel.: (49) 51515810
Web Site: http://www.hameln-pharma.de
Pharmaceuticals Product Mfr
N.A.I.C.S.: 325412
Christian Kanzelmeyer *(Co-CEO)*

Hameln RDS GmbH (1)
Langes Feld 13, 31789, Hameln, Germany (100%)
Tel.: (49) 5151 581 0
Web Site: http://www.hameln-pharma.de
Pharmaceutical Research, Development & Supply Chain Services
N.A.I.C.S.: 541715
Darrin Schellin *(Gen Mgr)*

SCI Pharmtech Inc. (1)
186-2 Hai-Hu-Tsun Lu-Chu-Hsiang, 33856, Taoyuan, Taiwan
Tel.: (886) 33541700
Web Site: http://www.sci-pharmtech.com.tw
Sales Range: $50-74.9 Million
Emp.: 170
Pharmaceutical Substances Mfr
N.A.I.C.S.: 325412
Michele Seah *(Sr VP)*

Siegfried (Nantong) Pharmaceuticals Co., Ltd. (1)
No 5 Tongshun Road NETDA, Nantong, 226017, Jiangsu, China
Tel.: (86) 51389183000
Emp.: 270
Pharmaceuticals Product Mfr
N.A.I.C.S.: 325412

Siegfried (USA) Inc. (1)
33 Industrial Park Rd, Pennsville, NJ 08070
Tel.: (856) 678-3601
Web Site: http://www.siegfried-usa.com
Emp.: 181
Pharmaceutical Substances Mfr
N.A.I.C.S.: 325412

Subsidiary (Domestic):

Alliance Medical Products, Inc. (2)
9342 Jeronimo Rd, Irvine, CA 92618
Tel.: (949) 768-4690
Web Site: http://www.amp-us.com
Sales Range: $10-24.9 Million
Emp.: 100
Surgical & Medical Instrument Mfr
N.A.I.C.S.: 339112

Siegfried AG (1)
Untere Bruhlstrasse 4, 4800, Zofingen, Switzerland
Tel.: (41) 627461111
Pharmaceutical Ingredient Mfr
N.A.I.C.S.: 325411

Siegfried Barbera S.L. (1)
Ronda de Santa Maria 158, Barbera del Valles, 08210, Barcelona, Spain
Tel.: (34) 937286100
Emp.: 490
Pharmaceutical Ingredient Mfr
N.A.I.C.S.: 325411

Siegfried El Masnou, S.A. (1)
Camil Fabra 58, El Masnou, 08320, Barcelona, Spain
Tel.: (34) 934977000
Emp.: 394
Pharmaceutical Ingredient Mfr
N.A.I.C.S.: 325411

Siegfried Generics (Malta) Ltd (1)
HHF070 Hal Far Industrial Estate, Hal Far, BBG3000, Malta
Tel.: (356) 22277711
Sales Range: $25-49.9 Million
Emp.: 50
Pharmaceutical Substances Mfr
N.A.I.C.S.: 325412
Vittorio Giromini *(Plant Mgr)*

Siegfried Hameln GmbH (1)
Langes Feld 13, 31789, Hameln, Germany
Tel.: (49) 51515810
Emp.: 503
Pharmaceuticals Product Mfr
N.A.I.C.S.: 325412

Siegfried Ltd (1)
Untere Bruehlstrasse 4, 4800, Zofingen, Switzerland
Tel.: (41) 627461111
Web Site: http://www.siegfried.ch
Sales Range: $200-249.9 Million
Emp.: 600
Pharmaceutical Substances Mfr

INTERNATIONAL PUBLIC

N.A.I.C.S.: 325412

Subsidiary (Domestic):

Siegfried Evionnaz SA (2)
Route Du Simplon 1 36, 1902, Evionnaz, Switzerland
Tel.: (41) 277661200
Emp.: 366
Pharmaceutical Product Mfr & Distr
N.A.I.C.S.: 325412

Siegfried Malta Ltd. (1)
HHF070 Hal Far Industrial Estate, Hal Far, BBG 3000, Malta
Tel.: (356) 22277786
Emp.: 151
Pharmaceuticals Product Mfr
N.A.I.C.S.: 325412

Siegfried PharmaChemikalien Minden GmbH (1)
Karlstrasse 15, 32423, Minden, Germany
Tel.: (49) 5713910
Emp.: 445
Pharmaceutical Chemicals Mfr
N.A.I.C.S.: 325199

Siegfried Shanghai (1)
31B Pu Fa Tower, 588 S Pudong Rd Pudong, Shanghai, 200120, China
Tel.: (86) 2158765019
Web Site: http://www.siegfried.ch
Sales Range: $25-49.9 Million
Emp.: 4
Pharmaceutical Substances Mfr
N.A.I.C.S.: 325412

Siegfried St. Vulbas SAS (1)
Parc Industriel de la Plaine de l'Ain 530 Allee de la Luye, 01150, Saint-Vulbas, France
Tel.: (33) 971169100
Emp.: 145
Pharmaceuticals Product Mfr
N.A.I.C.S.: 325412

Siegried PharmaChemikalien Minden GmbH (1)
Karlstrasse 15, 32423, Minden, Germany
Tel.: (49) 5713910
Pharmaceutical Product Mfr & Distr
N.A.I.C.S.: 325412

SIEGWERK DRUCKFARBEN AG & CO. KGAA
Alfred-Keller-Str 55, 53721, Siegburg, Germany
Tel.: (49) 22413040
Web Site: http://www.siegwerk.com
Year Founded: 1820
Sales Range: $1-4.9 Billion
Emp.: 4,400
Printing Supplies & Ink Mfr
N.A.I.C.S.: 325910
Herbert Forker *(Pres & CEO)*

Subsidiaries:

OOO Siegwerk (1)
2A 4th Street Gorelovo Villozy Settlement, Lomonosov Area Northern Part of Industrial Zone, 188508, Saint Petersburg, Russia
Tel.: (7) 8124494979
Printing Ink Mfr
N.A.I.C.S.: 325910
Alfia Kanukova *(Sls Mgr)*

PT. Siegwerk Indonesia (1)
Jl Pajajaran No 10 RT 001/03, Desa Gandasari Kec, Tangerang, 15134, Jatiuwung, Indonesia
Tel.: (62) 21 5917941
Emp.: 200
Printing Ink Mfr
N.A.I.C.S.: 325910
Soni Rusmayudhi *(Project Mgr & Production Mgr)*

Siegwerk (Thailand) Ltd. (1)
1/51 Moo 2 Rama 2 Road Ta-sai, Samutsakorn Industrial Estate Ampur Muang, Samut Sakhon, 74000, Thailand
Tel.: (66) 34490014
Printing Ink Mfr
N.A.I.C.S.: 325910
Jutarat Maneekit *(Mgr-HR)*

Siegwerk Argentina S.A. (1)
Descartes 3595 Parque Industrial Tortugui-

AND PRIVATE COMPANIES

tas, B1667AYC, Buenos Aires, Argentina
Tel.: (54) 11 5554 9200
Printing Ink Mfr
N.A.I.C.S.: 325910
Ruben Neri *(Dir-Comml)*

Siegwerk Backnang GmbH (1)
Wanne 6, 71522, Backnang, Germany
Tel.: (49) 7191 174 0
Web Site: http://www.siegwerk.com
Emp.: 50
Printing Ink Distr
N.A.I.C.S.: 423840

Siegwerk Baski Murekkepleri San. Ve Tic. A.S. (1)
Istanbul Deri Organize Sanayi Bolgesi, H6 Parsel 1 Yol Orhanli/Tuzla, 34957, Istanbul, Turkiye
Tel.: (90) 216 394 03 24
Printing Ink Mfr
N.A.I.C.S.: 423840

Siegwerk Benelux N.V. (1)
Winninglaan 3, 9140, Temse, Belgium
Tel.: (32) 3 8906220
Emp.: 15
Printing Ink Distr
N.A.I.C.S.: 423840
Herbert Forker *(Gen Mgr)*

Siegwerk Brasil Ind. Tintas Ltda. (1)
Rua Luiz Lawrie Reid 454/490, Campanario, Diadema, 09930-760, Brazil
Tel.: (55) 1135686500
Printing Ink Mfr
N.A.I.C.S.: 325910

Siegwerk Budingen GmbH (1)
Industriestrasse 36, 63654, Budingen, Germany
Tel.: (49) 604296190
Printing Ink Mfr
N.A.I.C.S.: 325910

Siegwerk Canada Inc. (1)
236 Wood Street, PO Box 1180, Prescott, K0E 1T0, ON, Canada
Tel.: (613) 925-5922
Web Site: http://www.siegwerk.com
Sales Range: $25-49.9 Million
Emp.: 50
Ink & Printing Supplies Mfr
N.A.I.C.S.: 325910

Siegwerk Centroamerica S.A. (1)
8a Calle 13-63 Granjas de San Cristobal, Zona 8 de Mixco, Guatemala, Guatemala
Tel.: (502) 24796330
Web Site: http://www.siegwerk.com
Sales Range: $25-49.9 Million
Emp.: 53
Ink & Printing Supplies Mfr
N.A.I.C.S.: 325910

Siegwerk Chile S. A. (1)
Pedro Jorquera 156 Parque Industrial, Puerto Pudahuel, Santiago, Chile
Tel.: (56) 2 2599 5100
Emp.: 30
Printing Ink Distr
N.A.I.C.S.: 423840
Jorge Fuentes *(Mng Dir)*

Siegwerk Colombia Ltda. (1)
Autopista Medellin KM 7 8 Via Siberia, Celta Trade Park Bodega 52-2, Bogota, Colombia
Tel.: (57) 15528920
Emp.: 40
Printing Ink Distr
N.A.I.C.S.: 423840
Camilo Arboleda *(Mng Dir)*

Siegwerk EIC LLC (1)
1 Quality Products Rd, Morganton, NC 28655
Tel.: (800) 368-4657
Printing Ink Mfr
N.A.I.C.S.: 325910
John Kilbo *(Reg Mgr-Technical)*

Branch (Domestic):

Siegwerk EIC LLC - Chicago Branch (2)
450 Wegner Dr, West Chicago, IL 60185
Printing Ink Mfr
N.A.I.C.S.: 325910

Siegwerk EIC LLC - Dallas Branch (2)
11910 Shiloh Rd Ste 118, Dallas, TX 75228
Printing Ink Mfr
N.A.I.C.S.: 325910

Siegwerk EIC LLC - Los Angeles Branch (2)
1920 S Quaker Ridge PL, Ontario, CA 91761
Printing Ink Mfr
N.A.I.C.S.: 325910

Siegwerk El Salvador S.A. de C.V. (1)
Final 27 Avenida Sur, Boulevard Venezuela, Colonia Cucumacayan No 10-28, San Salvador, El Salvador
Tel.: (503) 22574996
Ink & Printing Supplies Mfr
N.A.I.C.S.: 325910

Siegwerk Finland Oy (1)
Liekokatu 2, 37150, Nokia, Finland
Tel.: (358) 102 32 61
Printing Ink Distr
N.A.I.C.S.: 423840

Siegwerk France S.A.S (1)
13 Route de Taninges, Vetraz-Monthoux, 74100, Vetraz, France
Tel.: (33) 450877400
Printing Ink Mfr
N.A.I.C.S.: 325910
Kriemhilt Roppert *(Head-Tech Waterbased Inkjet)*

Siegwerk Hilversum BV (1)
2e Loswal 18, 1216 BC, Hilversum, Netherlands
Tel.: (31) 356260930
Printing Ink Mfr
N.A.I.C.S.: 325910

Siegwerk India Private Limited (1)
904A-904B Vijaya Building, 17 Barakhamba Road, New Delhi, 110001, India
Tel.: (91) 11 30489201
Web Site: http://www.siegwerk.com
Emp.: 50
Printing Ink Distr
N.A.I.C.S.: 423840

Siegwerk Italy SpA (1)
Via A De Gasperi 24, San Pietro Mosezzo, 28060, Novara, Italy
Tel.: (39) 0321 540 111
Printing Ink Distr
N.A.I.C.S.: 423840

Siegwerk Malaysia Sdn Bhd (1)
Lot 50 Jalan PBP 3 Taman Industri Pusat, Bandar Puchong Darul Ehsan, 47100, Puchong, Selangor, Malaysia
Tel.: (60) 3 8068 5521
Emp.: 60
Printing Ink Distr
N.A.I.C.S.: 423840
Janeti Loganadan *(Mgr-Ops)*

Siegwerk Mexico S.A. de C.V. (1)
Lote 1 Manzana 4, Parque Industrial Exportec 1, 50200, Toluca, Edo de Mexico, Mexico
Tel.: (52) 7222769080
Web Site: http://www.siegwerk.com
Ink & Printing Supplies Mfr
N.A.I.C.S.: 325910
Gabriel Jose Amado Rivera *(CFO)*

Siegwerk OOO (1)
Aeroportovskaya Street 5 Dubrovki Village, Solnechnogorsk Area Moscow region, 141580, Moscow, Russia
Tel.: (7) 495 787 11 37
Emp.: 50
Printing Ink Distr
N.A.I.C.S.: 423840
Nikolai Vinokurov *(Mgr-Application Tech & Flexible Packaging Dept)*

Siegwerk Peru S.A.C. (1)
No 653 Ulrb Santa Raquel Dist, Av Industrial Separator, Ate, Peru
Tel.: (51) 13482543
Printing Ink Mfr
N.A.I.C.S.: 325910
Rolando Chirinos Fernandez *(Mgr-Tech)*

Siegwerk Philippines Inc. (1)
70 Profit St Phase 4 Bulacan Metro Warehouse Center, Sta Rita Guiguinto, Bulacan, 3015, Philippines

SIEM INDUSTRIES INC.

Tel.: (63) 25194041
Web Site: http://www.siegwerk.com
Emp.: 30
Printing Ink Distr
N.A.I.C.S.: 423840
Dionisio Lucas *(Gen Mgr)*

Siegwerk Poland Marki Sp. z o.o. (1)
ul Pilsudskiego 121d, 05-270, Marki, Poland
Tel.: (48) 22 7716400
Printing Ink Distr
N.A.I.C.S.: 423840

Siegwerk Portugal, Unipessoal Lda. (1)
Quinta dos Estrangeiros Armazem 52 Rua C, Zona Norte, Venda do Pinheiro, 2665-601, Portugal
Tel.: (351) 219663883
Printing Ink Distr
N.A.I.C.S.: 423840

Siegwerk Scandinavia AB (1)
Limhamnsgardens Alle 15, 216 16, Limhamn, Sweden
Tel.: (46) 40 389 100
Printing Ink Distr
N.A.I.C.S.: 423840
Jesper Delfin *(Mgr-Fin & Admin)*

Siegwerk Shanghai Ltd. (1)
689 Shen Fu Road Xinzhuang Industrial Zone, Minhang District, Shanghai, 201108, China
Tel.: (86) 21 54423689
Printing Ink Distr
N.A.I.C.S.: 423840
Theresa Huang *(CFO)*

Siegwerk Singapore Pte. Ltd. (1)
71 Toh Guan Road East 04-06 TCH Tech Centre, Singapore, 608598, Singapore
Tel.: (65) 6261 8511
Printing Ink Distr
N.A.I.C.S.: 423840
Rajaguru Lingam *(Head-InHouse Svcs)*

Siegwerk South Africa (Proprietary) Limited (1)
33 Loper Avenue Spartan, Kempton Park, 1619, South Africa
Tel.: (27) 11 453 0582
Web Site: http://www.siegwerk.com
Emp.: 80
Printing Ink Distr
N.A.I.C.S.: 423840
Jonathan Johnston *(Mng Dir)*

Siegwerk Spain, S.A. (1)
C/Albert Amon n 1 Poligono Industrial El Corzo, Loeches, 28890, Madrid, Spain
Tel.: (34) 918862084
Printing Ink Distr
N.A.I.C.S.: 423840

Siegwerk Switzerland AG (1)
Neuenburgstr 48, 3282, Bargen, Switzerland
Tel.: (41) 32 391 7200
Web Site: http://www.siegwerk.com
Printing Ink Distr
N.A.I.C.S.: 423840

Siegwerk UK Ltd (1)
106 Golborne Enterprise Park Kid Glove Road, Golborne, Warrington, WA3 3GR, Cheshire, United Kingdom
Tel.: (44) 1942 402500
Web Site: http://www.siegwerk.com
Emp.: 5
Printing Ink Distr
N.A.I.C.S.: 423840
Oliver Wittman *(Mng Dir)*

Siegwerk USA Co. (1)
3535 SW 56th St, Des Moines, IA 50321
Tel.: (515) 471-2100
Web Site: http://www.siegwerk.com
Sales Range: $50-74.9 Million
Emp.: 225
Printing Ink & Supplies Mfr
N.A.I.C.S.: 325910
Becky Cornelius *(Coord-Mktg)*

Subsidiary (Domestic):

Siegwerk Environmental Inks (2)
1 Quality Products Rd, Morganton, NC 28655
Tel.: (828) 391-2312

Printing Ink Distr
N.A.I.C.S.: 423840

Branch (Domestic):

Siegwerk USA Inc. - Boiling Springs Branch (2)
150 Belcher Rd, Boiling Springs, SC 29316
Tel.: (864) 599-0525
Printing Ink Mfr
N.A.I.C.S.: 325910

Siegwerk USA Inc. - Drums Branch (2)
Can Do Flex Bldg B 80 Hillside Dr Ste 100, Drums, PA 18222
Tel.: (570) 708-0267
Printing Ink Mfr
N.A.I.C.S.: 325910

Siegwerk Vietnam Company Limited (1)
Block B Street No 2A Industrial park of Dong an, Thuan An, Binh Duong, Vietnam
Tel.: (84) 6503765618
Printing Ink Distr
N.A.I.C.S.: 423840

Siegwerk West Africa Ltd. (1)
Km9 Ibadan/Lagos Express Way, Antonia Village, Ibadan, Oyo, Nigeria
Tel.: (234) 27515004
Printing Ink Mfr
N.A.I.C.S.: 325910
Jayesh Bhavsar *(Mgr-Factory)*

SIEL FINANCIAL SERVICES LIMITED
Plot No 152 Sector-3 IMT Manesar, Gurgaon, 122050, India
Tel.: (91) 1244557700
Web Site:
  https://www.sielfinancial.com
Year Founded: 1990
532217—(BOM)
Rev.: $45,231
Assets: $28,908
Liabilities: $658,534
Net Worth: ($629,627)
Earnings: ($874)
Fiscal Year-end: 03/31/23
Financial Services
N.A.I.C.S.: 541611
Parmeet Singh Sood *(Mng Dir)*

SIEM INDUSTRIES INC.
Ugland House South Church Street, PO Box 309, Georgetown, KY1-1104, Grand Cayman, Cayman Islands
Tel.: (345) 9491030 Ky
Web Site:
  https://www.siemindustries.com
Year Founded: 1980
SEMUF—(OTCIQ)
Rev.: $647,160,000
Assets: $3,870,881,000
Liabilities: $2,126,405,000
Net Worth: $1,744,476,000
Earnings: ($299,547,000)
Emp.: 1,182
Fiscal Year-end: 12/31/19
Holding Company; Oil & Gas Operations; Renewable Energy; Ocean Transportation; Automobiles; Potash Mining; Ethanol Processing & Distillers' Grain Production; Financial Services
N.A.I.C.S.: 551112
Kristian Siem *(Founder & Chm)*

Subsidiaries:

Siem Capital AB (1)
Sveavagen 17 14th Floor, SE-111 57, Stockholm, Sweden
Tel.: (46) 8 145420
Investment Services
N.A.I.C.S.: 523999

Siem Capital UK Ltd. (1)
3rd Floor 30 Charles II Street, London, SW1Y 4AE, United Kingdom
Tel.: (44) 20 7747 0545

SIEM INDUSTRIES INC.

Siem Industries Inc.—(Continued)
Investment Services
N.A.I.C.S.: 523999

Siem Kapital AS (1)
Jerpefaret 12 Voksenlia, N-0788, Oslo, Norway
Tel.: (47) 2322 0500
Investment Services
N.A.I.C.S.: 523999

Joint Venture (Non-US):

GTL Resources PLC (2)
107 Cheapside, London, EC2V 6DN, United Kingdom
Tel.: (44) 1642794000
Web Site: http://www.gtlresources.com
Sales Range: $25-49.9 Million
Emp.: 73
Ethanol Producer
N.A.I.C.S.: 325193
Richard Ruebe (CEO)

Siem Shipping Inc.
30 Charles II Street, London, SW1Y 4AE, United Kingdom (73.5%)
Tel.: (44) 207 747 0500
Web Site: http://www.siemshipping.com
Sales Range: $200-249.9 Million
Emp.: 909
Reefer Transportation Services
N.A.I.C.S.: 488390

Subsidiary (Non-US):

STAR Reefers AS (2)
Jerpefaret 12, 0788, Oslo, Norway
Tel.: (47) 23220500
Web Site: http://www.star-reefers.com
Freight Transportation Services
N.A.I.C.S.: 488510

Subsidiary (Domestic):

STAR Reefers Ltd (2)
40 Brighton Road, Sutton, SM2 5BN, United Kingdom
Tel.: (44) 2077470500
Web Site: http://www.star-reefers.com
Sales Range: $25-49.9 Million
Freight Transportation Services
N.A.I.C.S.: 488510

SIEM OFFSHORE AS
Nodeviga 14, 4610, Kristiansand, Norway
Tel.: (47) 38600400
Web Site: https://www.sea1offshore.com
SIOFF—(OSL)
Rev.: $274,306,000
Assets: $1,019,891,000
Liabilities: $660,514,000
Net Worth: $359,377,000
Earnings: $30,897,000
Emp.: 1,179
Fiscal Year-end: 12/31/22
Oil & Gas Industry Support Vessel Operator
N.A.I.C.S.: 213112
Kristian Siem (Chm)

Subsidiaries:

Siem Offshore Australia Pty Ltd. (1)
Lvl 3-Subsea House 1008 Hay Street, Perth, 6000, WA, Australia
Tel.: (61) 863819650
Oil Services
N.A.I.C.S.: 213112

Siem Offshore Servicos Maritimos Ltda. (1)
Av Rodrigues Alves 261 - 4 Andar Saude, Rio de Janeiro, 20220-360, RJ, Brazil
Tel.: (55) 2135159700
Shipping Services
N.A.I.C.S.: 488210

Siem Offshore do Brasil SA (1)
Av Rodrigues Alves 261-4 Andar Saude, Rio de Janeiro, 20220-360, RJ, Brazil
Tel.: (55) 2135159700
Oil & Gas Industry Support
N.A.I.C.S.: 325412

SIEMENS AKTIENGESELL-SCHAFT
Werner-von-Siemens-Strasse 1, 80333, Munich, Germany
Tel.: (49) 8938035491   De
Web Site: https://www.siemens.com
Year Founded: 1847
SIE—(DEU)
Rev.: $70,180,405,360
Assets: $152,175,251,280
Liabilities: $103,263,049,760
Net Worth: $48,912,201,520
Earnings: $4,949,807,200
Emp.: 293,000
Fiscal Year-end: 09/30/20
Electric Equipment Mfr
N.A.I.C.S.: 335999
Christoph Zindel (Member-Mgmt Bd)

Subsidiaries:

AIT Applied Information Technologies GmbH & Co. KG (1)
Leitzstrasse 45, 70469, Stuttgart, Germany
Tel.: (49) 71149066430
Web Site: https://www.aitgmbh.de
Software Development Services
N.A.I.C.S.: 541511

ANF DATA spol. s r.o. (1)
Zeleny Pruh 1560/99, 140 00, Prague, Czech Republic
Tel.: (420) 244091111
Web Site: http://www.anfdata.cz
Sales Range: $50-74.9 Million
Emp.: 200
Software Development Services
N.A.I.C.S.: 513210
Max Ruzicka (Mgr-Sls)

AS AUDIO-SERVICE Gesellschaft mit beschrankter Haftung (1)
Alter Postweg 190, 32584, Lohne, Germany
Tel.: (49) 573268784800
Web Site: https://www.audioservice.com
Sales Range: $50-74.9 Million
Emp.: 18
Hearing Aid Mfr
N.A.I.C.S.: 334510

Acrorad Co., Ltd. (1)
13-23 Suzaki, Uruma, 904-2234, Okinawa, Japan
Tel.: (81) 989348960
Web Site: https://www.acrorad.co.jp
Sales Range: $25-49.9 Million
Emp.: 63
Radiation Detector Device Mfr & Distr
N.A.I.C.S.: 334511
Ryoichi Ohno (Pres & CEO)

Aimsun Limited (1)
Waterhouse Square 138, Holborn, London, EC1N 2ST, United Kingdom
Tel.: (44) 7401977191
Software Services
N.A.I.C.S.: 541511
Gavin Jackman (Mng Dir)

Aimsun Pte Ltd. (1)
36 Robinson Road 02-01, Singapore, 068877, Singapore
Tel.: (65) 81865589
Transportation Services
N.A.I.C.S.: 485999
Karen Cheung (Mng Dir)

Aimsun Pty Ltd. (1)
333 George Street Level 13, Sydney, 2000, NSW, Australia
Tel.: (61) 290088557
Transportation Services
N.A.I.C.S.: 485999

Aimsun S.L. (1)
Ronda Universitat 22 B, 08007, Barcelona, Spain
Tel.: (34) 933171693
Web Site: http://www.aimsun.com
Software Development Services
N.A.I.C.S.: 541511

Aimsun SARL (1)
54 Rue de Clichy, 75009, Paris, France
Tel.: (33) 186954152
Software Services
N.A.I.C.S.: 541511

Airport Munich Logistics and Services GmbH (1)
Sudallee 1 D, 85356, Munich, Germany
Tel.: (49) 899788030
Web Site: https://www.airportmunichls.com
Sales Range: $25-49.9 Million
Emp.: 5
Logistic Software Development Services
N.A.I.C.S.: 541511

Alpha Verteilertechnik GmbH (1)
Ringstrasse 60, Altenmarkt, 93413, Cham, Germany
Tel.: (49) 99713940
Web Site: https://www.verteiler.com
Sales Range: $75-99.9 Million
Emp.: 250
Electric Wiring Supplies Distr
N.A.I.C.S.: 423610

Audio SAT Sp. z o.o. (1)
ul Chlebowa 4/8, 61-003, Poznan, Poland
Tel.: (48) 616536822
Web Site: http://www.audioservice.pl
Sales Range: $25-49.9 Million
Emp.: 100
Hearing Aid Mfr
N.A.I.C.S.: 334510

Befund24 GmbH (1)
Henkestrasse 127, 91052, Erlangen, Germany
Tel.: (49) 91316258900
Web Site: https://www.befund24.de
Communication Service
N.A.I.C.S.: 541990

Beijing Siemens Cerberus Electronics Ltd. (1)
No18 Xinxi Rd Shangdi Information Industry Base 2/F Ruibao Dasha, Haidian, Beijing, 100085, China
Tel.: (86) 1062962255
Fire Protection System Mfr
N.A.I.C.S.: 334290

Berliner Vermogensverwaltung GmbH (1)
Otto-Hahn-Ring 6, 81739, Munich, Bavaria, Germany
Tel.: (49) 303860
Wealth Management Services
N.A.I.C.S.: 523940

Block Imaging Parts & Service, LLC (1)
1845 Cedar St, Holt, MI 48842
Tel.: (517) 668-8800
Health Care Srvices
N.A.I.C.S.: 541511

Brightly Software Australia Pty. Ltd. (1)
Lvl 9 257 Collins Street, Melbourne, 3000, VIC, Australia
Tel.: (61) 390260555
Software Development Services
N.A.I.C.S.: 541511

Broadcastle Ltd. (1)
Sefton Park Bells Hill Stoke Poges, Slough, SL2 4JS, Berkshire, United Kingdom
Tel.: (44) 1753 434 500
Investment Management Service
N.A.I.C.S.: 523999

Certas AG (1)
Schweizerisc Alarm- und Einsatzzentrale Kalkbreitestrasse 51, PO Box 8021, 8003, Zurich, Switzerland
Tel.: (41) 446373737
Web Site: https://www.certas.ch
Sales Range: $25-49.9 Million
Emp.: 170
Alarm Systems & Services; Joint Venture Between Siemans AG (50%) & Securitas AB (50%)
N.A.I.C.S.: 561621

Chemtech Servicos de Engenharia e Software Ltda. (1)
Rua Paulo Emidio Barbosa 485 Quadra V Lote 2, Rio de Janeiro, 21941-615, Brazil
Tel.: (55) 21 3503 9100
Web Site: http://www.chemtech.com.br
Sales Range: $350-399.9 Million
Emp.: 1,300
Software Development Services
N.A.I.C.S.: 541511

INTERNATIONAL PUBLIC

Chung Tak Lighting Control Systems (Guangzhou) Ltd. (1)
Second Light Industrial Estate Qiaoxing Road Dong Huan Street, Panyu, 511400, Guangzhou, China
Tel.: (86) 20 8487 6119
Lighting Equipment Mfr
N.A.I.C.S.: 335139

Crabtree South Africa Pty. Limited (1)
Corner Wadeville and Davidson Roads, Wadeville, Germiston, 1422, South Africa
Tel.: (27) 118747600
Web Site: https://www.crabtree.co.za
Electrical Component Mfr & Distr
N.A.I.C.S.: 334419
Adriaan Pretorius (Mgr-IT)

DPC Polska Sp. z o.o. w likwidacji (1)
ul Idzikowskiego 16, 00-710, Warsaw, Poland
Tel.: (48) 690410909
Web Site: https://dpcpolska.pl
Investment Management Service
N.A.I.C.S.: 523999

Demag Delaval Desoil Services (Sherkate Sahami Khass) (1)
Tola Industrial Park Qeshm Free Zone, Qeshm, Iran
Tel.: (98) 7635340515
Investment Management Service
N.A.I.C.S.: 523999
Behroez Khousravi (Gen Mgr)

ELIN EBG Traction GmbH (1)
Cumberlandstr 32-34, 1141, Vienna, Austria
Tel.: (43) 51707 30358
Traction Equipment Whslr
N.A.I.C.S.: 423690

ESTEL Rail Automation SPA (1)
15 rue Colonel Amerouche, BP 246, Rouiba, Algeria
Tel.: (213) 23862203
Web Site: https://www.estel-ra.dz
Sales Range: $50-74.9 Million
Emp.: 146
Railway Signalling Communication System Mfr
N.A.I.C.S.: 334290
Abdelmadjid Belouanas (Chm)

ETM professional control GmbH (1)
Marktstrasse 3, 7000, Eisenstadt, Austria
Tel.: (43) 26827410
Web Site: https://www.winccoa.com
Sales Range: $25-49.9 Million
Emp.: 10
Process Automation Software Development Services
N.A.I.C.S.: 541511

Electrium Sales Limited (1)
Commercial Centre Lakeside Plaza Walkmill Lane, Bridgtown, Cannock, WS11 0XE, United Kingdom
Tel.: (44) 1543455000
Web Site: https://www.electrium.co.uk
Sales Range: $200-249.9 Million
Emp.: 700
Electronic Components Mfr
N.A.I.C.S.: 335999

Enlighted Energy Systems Pvt Ltd. (1)
KG Pinnacle 6th Floor Block no 17 Gandhi Street 100 Feet Road, Adambakkam, Chennai, 600088, India
Tel.: (91) 4449595947
Information Technology Services
N.A.I.C.S.: 541511
Vinoth Kumar (Sr Engr-Design)

EthosEnergy Poland S.A. (1)
ul Powstancow Slaskich 85, 42-701, Lubliniec, Poland
Tel.: (48) 343572100
Web Site: https://ethosenergy.com
Turbine Generator Mfr
N.A.I.C.S.: 333611
Janusz Olowski (Dir-Production & Member-Mgmt Bd)

Fabrica Electrotecnica Josa, S.A. (1)
Av de la Llana 95-105, 08191, Barcelona, Spain
Tel.: (34) 935610500

AND PRIVATE COMPANIES | SIEMENS AKTIENGESELLSCHAFT

Web Site: https://www.bjc.es
Sales Range: $50-74.9 Million
Emp.: 17
Electrical Materials Mfr
N.A.I.C.S.: 335999

Fast Track Diagnostics Ltd. (1)
Seaview No 2 Qui-Si-Sana Seafront, Sliema, SLM 3110, Malta
Tel.: (356) 27654302
Health Care Srvices
N.A.I.C.S.: 621999

Fast Track Diagnostics Luxembourg S.a r.l. (1)
27 rue Henri Koch, 4354, Esch-sur-Alzette, Luxembourg
Tel.: (352) 281098252
Web Site: https://www.siemens-healthineers.com
Health Care Srvices
N.A.I.C.S.: 621999

Flender (Pty) Ltd. (1)
Private Bag X71, Midrand, 1685, South Africa
Tel.: (27) 115712103
Web Site: http://www.flender.com
Electrical & Electronic Product Mfr
N.A.I.C.S.: 335999

Flender Limited (1)
Unit 5 Off Lockside Road Stourton, Leeds, LS10 1EP, United Kingdom
Tel.: (44) 1134900410
Gear Box Mfr & Distr
N.A.I.C.S.: 333612
Simon Nadin *(CEO & Mng Dir)*

Flender S.p.A. (1)
Calle Nestor del Fierro Flores 401, 1240000, Antofagasta, Chile
Tel.: (56) 996450435
Mechanical Engineering Services
N.A.I.C.S.: 541330

Grupo Siemens S.A. de C.V. (1)
Ejercito Nacional No 350 Piso 3 Chapultepec Morales, Miguel Hidalgo, Mexico, 11570, Mexico
Tel.: (52) 5553282000
Investment Management Service
N.A.I.C.S.: 523999

HV-Turbo Italia S.r.l. (1)
Via Nino Bixio 3, 21020, Mornago, Italy
Tel.: (39) 0331903890
Web Site: http://www.hv-turbo.it
Sales Range: $50-74.9 Million
Emp.: 12
Air & Gas Compressor Whslr
N.A.I.C.S.: 532490

HaCon Ingenieurgesellschaft mbH (1)
Lister Strasse 15, 30163, Hannover, Germany
Tel.: (49) 511336990
Web Site: https://www.hacon.de
Software Development Services
N.A.I.C.S.: 513210

Huba Control AG (1)
Industriestrasse 17, 5436, Wurenlos, Switzerland
Tel.: (41) 564368200
Web Site: http://www.hubacontrol.com
Sales Range: $125-149.9 Million
Emp.: 30
Pressure Measuring Component Mfr & Distr
N.A.I.C.S.: 334519

ILLIT Grundstucksverwaltungs-Management GmbH (1)
Marktplatz 3, 82031, Grunwald, Germany
Tel.: (49) 89856380373
Investment Management Service
N.A.I.C.S.: 523999

ITH icoserve technology for healthcare GmbH (1)
Innrain 98, 6020, Innsbruck, Austria
Tel.: (43) 512890590
Web Site: https://www.ith-icoserve.com
Emp.: 100
Health Care Consulting Services
N.A.I.C.S.: 812199

Industrieschutz Assekuranz Vermittlung GmbH (1)
Solinger Strasse 10, 45481, Mulheim an der Ruhr, Germany **(100%)**
Tel.: (49) 208469300
Web Site: http://www.industrieschutz.info
Sales Range: $50-74.9 Million
Emp.: 6
Provider of Insurance Services
N.A.I.C.S.: 524298

Innomotics GmbH (1)
Vogelweiherstr 1 - 15, 90441, Nuremberg, Germany
Tel.: (49) 9119580
Motor Mfr & Distr
N.A.I.C.S.: 333996

Iriel Industria Comercio de Sistemas Electricos Ltda. (1)
Av Nazaire 2100, Canoas, 92035-000, Brazil
Tel.: (55) 51 3478 9000
Web Site: http://www.iriel.com.br
Emp.: 200
Electronic Component Mfr & Distr
N.A.I.C.S.: 334419
Luciano Gomes *(Plant Mgr)*

Jawa Power Holding GmbH (1)
Freyeslebenstr 1, 91052, Erlangen, Germany
Tel.: (49) 9131183203
Investment Management Service
N.A.I.C.S.: 523999

KACO new energy GmbH (1)
Werner-von-Siemens-Allee 1, 74172, Neckarsulm, Germany
Tel.: (49) 71328960
Web Site: https://www.kaco-newenergy.com
Renewable & Environment Services
N.A.I.C.S.: 221118

Subsidiary (Non-US):

KACO New Energy Italia S.r.l. (2)
Via Dei Lecci 113, 00062, Bracciano, Italy
Tel.: (39) 069962172
Renewable Energy Services
N.A.I.C.S.: 221118

Subsidiary (US):

KACO New Energy, Inc. (2)
4040 Binz-Engleman Rd, San Antonio, TX 78219
Tel.: (210) 446-4238
Web Site: http://www.kaco-newenergy.com
Solar PV Inverter Mfr
N.A.I.C.S.: 335999
Rob Allman *(Gen Mgr)*

Subsidiary (Non-US):

KACO new energy SARL (2)
2 Allee des Vendanges, 77183, Croissy-Beaubourg, France
Tel.: (33) 160930110
Renewable Energy Services
N.A.I.C.S.: 221118

KDAG Beteiligungen GmbH (1)
Siemensstrasse 92, Vienna, 1210, Austria
Tel.: (43) 517070
Investment Management Service
N.A.I.C.S.: 523999

Kintec S.A. (1)
78 Vouliagmenis Ave, Voula, 16673, Athens, Greece
Tel.: (30) 2106628891
Sales Range: $50-74.9 Million
Emp.: 70
Designs, Manufactures, Installs & Maintains Electrical & Electronic Systems for Security, Control, Measurement, Automation & Fire Safety/Extinguishing
N.A.I.C.S.: 334419

Koden Co., Ltd. (1)
Akiyoshi-Kyobashi Building 1-17-2 Kyobashi, Chuo-ku, Tokyo, 104-0031, Japan
Tel.: (81) 353916171
Web Site: https://www.hkd.co.jp
Emp.: 285
Investment Management Service
N.A.I.C.S.: 523999

Koncar-Energetski Transformatori, d.o.o. (1)
Josipa Mokrovica 12, 10090, Zagreb, Croatia
Tel.: (385) 13795504
Web Site: https://www.kpt.hr
Electrical & Electronic Product Mfr
N.A.I.C.S.: 336320
Boris Potocki *(Pres)*

Mechanik Center Erlangen GmbH (1)
Gunther-Scharowsky-Str 21, Postfach 3220, 91058, Erlangen, Germany
Tel.: (49) 9131732130
Web Site: http://www.mechanikcenter.de
Sales Range: $25-49.9 Million
Emp.: 20
Engineering Technical Services
N.A.I.C.S.: 541330
Gerd-Friedrich Witthus *(Gen Mgr)*

Mendix Technology B.V. (1)
Wilhelminakade 197, 3072 AP, Rotterdam, Netherlands
Tel.: (31) 102760434
Software Services
N.A.I.C.S.: 541511
Derckjan Kruit *(Founder & VP-Dev)*

Mochida Siemens Medical Systems Co. Ltd. (1)
Koujimachi KS Square 5-3-3 Koujimachi, Chiyoda-ku, Tokyo, 102-0083, Japan
Tel.: (81) 335 11 8100
Web Site: http://msm.mochida.co.jp
Medical Equipment Mfr & Whslr
N.A.I.C.S.: 339112

Nertus Mantenimiento Ferroviario y Servicios S.A. (1)
C/ Antonio de Cabezon s/n, 28034, Madrid, Spain
Tel.: (34) 913009899
Web Site: https://www.nertus.es
Emp.: 500
Railway Rolling Stock Maintenance Services
N.A.I.C.S.: 811310
D. Jose Ignacio Martin-Yague *(CEO, Dir-Bus Dev & Mgr-Ops)*

OEZ Slovakia, spol. s r.o. (1)
Pri majeri 10, 831 07, Bratislava, Slovakia
Tel.: (421) 249212511
Web Site: https://www.oez.sk
Electronic Components Mfr
N.A.I.C.S.: 335999

OEZ s.r.o. (1)
Sedivska 339, 561 51, Letohrad, Czech Republic
Tel.: (420) 465672111
Web Site: https://www.oez.com
Electrical Equipment Mfr & Distr
N.A.I.C.S.: 335999
Ivan Hanzl *(Head-Export)*

OOO Legion T2 (1)
40 Korp 4 Ul Bolshaya Ordynka, Moscow, 119017, Russia
Tel.: (7) 4954117711
Software Development Services
N.A.I.C.S.: 541511

OOO Siemens (1)
st Dubininskaya 96, 115093, Moscow, Russia
Tel.: (7) 4957371000
Web Site: http://new.siemens.com
Sales Range: $1-4.9 Billion
Emp.: 3,000
Computer & Engineering Services
N.A.I.C.S.: 541519
Moeller Gietrich *(Gen Mgr)*

Oktopus S.A./N.V. (1)
Avenue Louise 331, 1050, Brussels, Belgium
Tel.: (32) 25420542
Web Site: https://www.oktopus.be
Sales Range: $10-24.9 Million
Emp.: 50
Security System Services
N.A.I.C.S.: 561621

Omnetric GmbH (1)
Wittelsbacherplatz 1 Bayern, 80333, Munich, Germany
Tel.: (49) 8963600
Web Site: http://www.omnetric.com
Information Technology Services
N.A.I.C.S.: 541512
Daniel Rui Felicio *(CEO)*

P.T. Siemens Healthineers Indonesia (1)
Arkadia Office Park Tower F Level 18 Pasar Minggu, T B Simatupang Kav 88 Jakarta Raya, Jakarta, 12520, Indonesia
Tel.: (62) 81119562888
Diagnostic Healthcare Services
N.A.I.C.S.: 621610

P.T. Siemens Indonesia (1)
Jalan Jendral Ahmad Yani Kav 67-68 Pulomas, Jl TB Simatupang Kav 88, Jakarta, 13210, Indonesia **(94%)**
Tel.: (62) 8117797788
Web Site: https://www.siemens.com
Sales Range: $50-74.9 Million
Mfr & Sales of Electronic Equipment
N.A.I.C.S.: 449210

PT Siemens Mobility Indonesia (1)
Arkadia Office Park Tower F Level 18 Jl TB Simatupang Kav 88, Pasar Minggu, Jakarta, 12520, Indonesia
Tel.: (62) 8117797788
Transportation Services
N.A.I.C.S.: 485999
Praka Nugraha *(Head-Country)*

Parallel Graphics Ltd. (1)
Block B Unit 2 Broomfield Business Park Malahide Co, Dublin, Ireland
Tel.: (353) 12143380
Web Site: https://www.parallelgraphics.com
Engineeering Services
N.A.I.C.S.: 541330

Petnet Soluciones, S.L. (1)
Ronda De Europa 5 Tres Cantos, Madrid, Spain
Tel.: (34) 915148000
Pharmaceuticals Product Mfr
N.A.I.C.S.: 325412

Polarion AG (1)
St Gallerstrasse 57, 9200, Gossau, Switzerland
Tel.: (41) 716900477
Web Site: https://polarion.plm.automation.com
Computer Software Services
N.A.I.C.S.: 541511

Poseidon International Limited (1)
Unit D2 Abbotswell Road West Tullos, Aberdeen, AB12 3AD, Aberdeenshire, United Kingdom
Tel.: (44) 1224238820
Subsea Engineering Services
N.A.I.C.S.: 541330

Proyectos de Energia S.A. de C.V. (1)
Chapultepec No 304-A Regina, Monterrey, 64290, Nuevo Leon, Mexico
Tel.: (52) 8183513106
Electric & Gas Utility Services
N.A.I.C.S.: 926130

R & S Restaurant Services GmbH (1)
Siemensdamm 50, 13629, Berlin, Germany
Tel.: (49) 8963600
Restaurant Services
N.A.I.C.S.: 722511

REMECH Systemtechnik GmbH (1)
Werner-von-Siemens-Str 1, 07333, Unterwellenborn, Germany
Tel.: (49) 367157530
Web Site: https://www.remech.de
Industrial Machinery Mfr
N.A.I.C.S.: 333248

RISICOM Ruckversicherung AG (1)
Marktplatz 3, 82031, Grunwald, Germany **(100%)**
Tel.: (49) 8969388270
Reinsurance Services
N.A.I.C.S.: 524130

Radium Lampenwerk Gesellschaft mbH (1)
Dr-Eugen-Kersting-Strasse 6, 51688, Wipperfurth, Germany
Tel.: (49) 2267811
Web Site: https://www.radium.de
Sales Range: $100-124.9 Million
Emp.: 500
Lighting Equipment Mfr
N.A.I.C.S.: 335139

SIEMENS AKTIENGESELLSCHAFT / INTERNATIONAL PUBLIC

Siemens Aktiengesellschaft—(Continued)

SAT Systemy automatizacnej techniky spol. s.r.o. (1)
Lamacska Cesta 3/A, 841 04, Bratislava, Slovakia
Tel.: (421) 259685656
Web Site: https://www.siemens.sk
Sales Range: $25-49.9 Million
Emp.: 5
Energy Consulting Services
N.A.I.C.S.: 541690

SIELOG Systemlogik GmbH (1)
Siemensstrasse 90 / 22 151, 1210, Vienna, Austria
Tel.: (43) 1 90 87 012
Web Site: http://www.sielog.com
Software Development Services
N.A.I.C.S.: 541511
Daniel Achermann (Co-Mng Dir)

SIEMENS (AUSTRIA) PROIECT SPITAL COLTEA SRL (1)
Str Sfintilor 1, Bucharest, 21063, Romania
Tel.: (40) 213140990
Construction Engineering Services
N.A.I.C.S.: 541330

SIMAR Nordost Grundstucks-GmbH (1)
St-Martin-Str 76, 81541, Munich, Germany
Tel.: (49) 8963681973
Electric Equipment Mfr
N.A.I.C.S.: 335999

SIMEA SIBIU S.R.L. (1)
Florian Rieger Street No 4, 550018, Sibiu, Romania
Tel.: (40) 369130600
Web Site: https://www.siemens.com
Sales Range: $25-49.9 Million
Emp.: 90
Electrical Engineering Services
N.A.I.C.S.: 541330
Aurel Baloi (Gen Mgr)

SIPRIN s.r.o. (1)
Lamacska cesta 3/A, 831 01, Bratislava, Slovakia
Tel.: (421) 259683660
Web Site: https://www.siprin.sk
Sales Range: $25-49.9 Million
Emp.: 300
Electrical Engineering Services
N.A.I.C.S.: 541330

SWTS Pte Ltd (1)
10 Gul Avenue, Singapore, 629654, Singapore (100%)
Tel.: (65) 68614466
Web Site: https://swts.com
Engineering Services & Industrial Solutions
N.A.I.C.S.: 811210
CK Ong (Sls Mgr)

SYKATEC Systeme, Komponenten, Anwendungstechnologie GmbH & Co. KG
Frauenauracher Strasse 80, 91056, Erlangen, Germany
Tel.: (49) 9131982028
Web Site: http://www.sykatec.de
Sales Range: $125-149.9 Million
Emp.: 400
Industrial, Railway & Power Converter Metal Systems & Components Mfr
N.A.I.C.S.: 332999

Siemens (NZ) Limited (1)
Level 3 Building C Millennium Centre 600 Great South Road, Ellerslie, Auckland, New Zealand
Tel.: (64) 95805500
Web Site: https://www.siemens.com
Power Transmission & Distr Services
N.A.I.C.S.: 221118

Siemens - Libya (1)
Haii Al-Andulus Behind People's Hall, POB 91531, Tripoli, Libya
Tel.: (218) 214478733
Sales Range: $150-199.9 Million
Emp.: 130
Power Transmission & Distr Services
N.A.I.C.S.: 221121

Siemens A.E. (1)
Agisilaou 6 - 8, Marousi, 151 23, Athens, Greece (100%)

Tel.: (30) 2106864111
Web Site: https://www.siemens.com
Sales Range: $300-349.9 Million
Emp.: 1,000
Mfr & Sales of TV Sets & Switchgear
N.A.I.C.S.: 334310

Siemens A/S (1)
Ostre Aker Vei 88, PO Box 1, 0596, Oslo, Norway (100%)
Tel.: (47) 22633000
Web Site: https://www.siemens.com
Sales Range: $1-4.9 Billion
Emp.: 1,600
Industrial Solutions & Services
N.A.I.C.S.: 333310
Kjell Age Pettersen (CEO-Acting)

Siemens A/S (1)
Borupvang 9, 2750, Ballerup, Denmark (100%)
Tel.: (45) 44774477
Web Site: http://new.siemens.com
Emp.: 814
Sales Company
N.A.I.C.S.: 449210

Siemens AB (1)
Evenemangsgatan 21, 169 79, Solna, Sweden (100%)
Tel.: (46) 87281051
Web Site: https://www.siemens.se
Sales Range: $400-449.9 Million
Emp.: 600
Development, Manufacturing & Sales of Electric Lamps
N.A.I.C.S.: 335139

Siemens Advanced Engineering Pte Ltd. (1)
The Siemens Center 60 MacPherson Road, Singapore, 348615, Singapore (100%)
Tel.: (65) 64906000
Web Site: https://www.siemens.com.sg
Sales Range: $350-399.9 Million
Emp.: 1,834
Supplier of Products, Systems & Solutions in the Fields of Electrical Engineering & Electronics
N.A.I.C.S.: 541330

Siemens Aktiengesellschaft Osterreich (1)
Siemensstrasse 90, 1210, Vienna, Austria
Tel.: (43) 517070
Web Site: https://www.siemens.com
Emp.: 400
Energy Consulting Services
N.A.I.C.S.: 541690

Subsidiary (Non-US):

Siemens d.o.o. Sarajevo (2)
Hamdije Cemerlica 2, 71000, Sarajevo, Bosnia & Herzegovina
Tel.: (387) 38549591
Web Site: https://www.mobility.siemens.com
Rev.: $28,409,885
Emp.: 6
Medical Equipment Distr
N.A.I.C.S.: 423450

Siemens Audiologiai Technika Kereskedelmi es Szolgaltato Korlatolt Felelossegu Tarsasag (1)
Huvosvolgyi ut 33, Budapest, 1026, Hungary
Tel.: (36) 1 2 750 750
Web Site: http://w1.hearing.siemens.com
Hearing Instruments Mfr
N.A.I.C.S.: 334510

Siemens Audiologicka Technika s.r.o. (1)
Bieblova 1227/19, Prague, 150 00, Czech Republic
Tel.: (420) 257 328 161
Web Site: http://www.sluchadla.cz
Sales Range: $25-49.9 Million
Emp.: 10
Hearing Aids Mfr & Distr
N.A.I.C.S.: 334510
Petr Vanek (Gen Mgr)

Siemens Audiologie AG (1)
Soodstrasse 57, 8134, Adliswil, Switzerland
Tel.: (41) 44 711 74 74
Web Site: http://www.siemens.ch
Hearing Instruments Mfr
N.A.I.C.S.: 334510

Siemens Audiologie S.A.S. (1)
175 Bd Anatole, 93201, Saint Denis, France
Tel.: (33) 149331515
Hearing Aid Mfr
N.A.I.C.S.: 334510

Siemens Audiologie Techniek B.V. (1)
Werner Von Siemensstraat 13, Zoetermeer, 2712 PN, Netherlands
Tel.: (31) 70 333 3800
Sales Range: $25-49.9 Million
Emp.: 35
Hearing Aid Distr
N.A.I.C.S.: 423450

Siemens Automation & Drives Group (1)
Gleiwitzer Strasse 555, 90475, Nuremberg, Germany (100%)
Tel.: (49) 8002663287
Sales Range: $15-24.9 Billion
Emp.: 70,600
Mfr of Process Automation Equipment, Drives & Electrical Installation Technology
N.A.I.C.S.: 333248
Jurgen Brandes (CEO-Large Drives)

Siemens Bangladesh Ltd. (1)
ZN Tower Siemens House Plot-02 Road-08 Gulshan-1, Dhaka, 1212, Bangladesh
Tel.: (880) 29893536
Web Site: http://www.siemens.com.bd
Sales Range: $25-49.9 Million
Emp.: 215
Energy Consulting Services
N.A.I.C.S.: 541690
Bul Hassan (CFO)

Siemens Bank GmbH (1)
Otto-Hahn-Ring 6, 81739, Munich, Germany
Tel.: (49) 8963625311
Banking Services
N.A.I.C.S.: 522110

Siemens Beteiligungen Inland GmbH (1)
Wittelsbacherplatz 2, 80333, Munich, Germany
Tel.: (49) 8963600
Investment Management Service
N.A.I.C.S.: 523999

Siemens Beteiligungsverwaltung GmbH & Co. OHG (1)
Marktplatz 3, 82031, Grunwald, Bavaria, Germany
Tel.: (49) 8963600
Investment Management Service
N.A.I.C.S.: 523999

Siemens Building Technologies (Pty) Ltd. (1)
300 Janadel Avenue, Private Bag x 71, Halfway House, Midrand, 1685, Gauteng, South Africa
Tel.: (27) 116522000
Web Site: https://www.siemens.com
Building Construction Services
N.A.I.C.S.: 237990

Siemens Building Technologies Ltd. (1)
Sennweidstrasse 47, CH 6312, Steinhausen, Switzerland (100%)
Tel.: (41) 585579221
Web Site: http://www.siemens.com
Sales Range: $1-4.9 Billion
Emp.: 200
Building Control Systems: Safety, Comfort & Security
N.A.I.C.S.: 334512

Subsidiary (Domestic):

Alarmcom AG (2)
Asylstrasse 68, CH 8708, Mannedorf, Switzerland
Tel.: (41) 1 922 6155
Web Site: http://www.alarmcom.com
Fire & Intrusion Detection Systems & Video Surveillance Technology
N.A.I.C.S.: 561621

Subsidiary (Non-US):

Alarmcom AB (3)
Electrovanwagen 4, 141 87, Huddinge, Sweden
Tel.: (46) 8 447 4030

Web Site: http://www.alarmcom.se
Sales Range: $10-24.9 Million
Emp.: 16
Fire & Intrusion Detection Systems & Video Surveillance Technology Services
N.A.I.C.S.: 561621

Alarmcom GmbH (3)
Fabrikstrasse 17, 70794, Filderstadt, Germany (100%)
Tel.: (49) 711778970
Web Site: http://www.alarmcom.de
Sales Range: $10-24.9 Million
Emp.: 32
Fire & Intrusion Detection Systems & Video Surveillance Technology
N.A.I.C.S.: 561621

Alarmcom Leptonics Pty Ltd (3)
800 810 Parramatta Rd, Lewisham, Sydney, 2049, NSW, Australia (100%)
Tel.: (61) 295646363
Web Site: http://www.alarmcom.com.au
Sales Range: $10-24.9 Million
Emp.: 30
Provider of Fire & Intrusion Detection Systems & Video Surveillance Technology
N.A.I.C.S.: 561621

Siemens AS (3)
Ostre Aker Vei 88, 0596, Oslo, Norway
Tel.: (47) 22633000
Web Site: https://www.siemens.com
Sales Range: $100-124.9 Million
Emp.: 900
Fire & Intrusion Detection Systems & Video Surveillance Technology
N.A.I.C.S.: 561621

Siemens Fire & Securities Products (3)
Lainzerstrasse 54, 1130, Vienna, Austria (100%)
Tel.: (43) 18767050
Sales Range: $10-24.9 Million
Emp.: 4
Fire & Intrusion Detection Systems & Video Surveillance Technology
N.A.I.C.S.: 561621

Siemens S.p.A. (3)
Via Vipiteno 44, 20128, Milan, Italy
Tel.: (39) 0224365492
Web Site: https://www.siemens.com
Sales Range: $10-24.9 Million
Emp.: 15
Provider of Fire & Intrusion Detection Systems & Video Surveillance Technology
N.A.I.C.S.: 561621

Siemens SAS (3)
95 rue Alexandre Fourny, F 94507, Champigny-sur-Marne, Cedex, France
Tel.: (33) 148811177
Web Site: http://www.siemens.fr
Sales Range: $10-24.9 Million
Emp.: 100
Provider of Fire & Intrusion Detection Systems & Video Surveillance Technology; Sales Office
N.A.I.C.S.: 561621
Nicolas Petrovic (CEO)

Subsidiary (Domestic):

Cerbex AG (2)
Dornierstrasse, CH-9423, Altenrhein, Switzerland
Tel.: (41) 1718582323
Web Site: http://www.cerbex.ch
Private Communication Systems
N.A.I.C.S.: 334418

Subsidiary (Non-US):

Siemens Building Technologies A/S (2)
Borupvang 9, 2750, Ballerup, Denmark (100%)
Tel.: (45) 44774477
Web Site: http://new.siemens.com
Sales Range: $75-99.9 Million
Emp.: 450
Provider of Fire & Security Systems
N.A.I.C.S.: 561621

Siemens Building Technologies AB (2)
Johanneslundsvagen 12-14, SE 141 87, Upplands Vasby, Sweden

AND PRIVATE COMPANIES

SIEMENS AKTIENGESELLSCHAFT

Tel.: (46) 857841000
Web Site: http://www.siemens.se
Emp.: 1,200
Provider of Fire & Security Systems
N.A.I.C.S.: 561621

Siemens Building Technologies AG (2)
Siemens Allee 84, 76187, Karlsruhe, Germany **(100%)**
Tel.: (49) 7215950
Web Site: http://www.siemens.de
Provider of Security Systems & Services
N.A.I.C.S.: 561621
Axel Meier *(CFO)*

Plant (Domestic):

Siemens Building Technologies AG (2)
Industriestrasse 22, 8604, Volketswil, Switzerland **(100%)**
Tel.: (41) 585578700
Web Site: http://new.siemens.com
Sales Range: $75-99.9 Million
Emp.: 360
Provider of Fire & Security Systems
N.A.I.C.S.: 561621

Division (Domestic):

Siemens Building Technologies AG (2)
Tafernstrasse 5, CH 5405, Zurich, Dattwil, Switzerland **(100%)**
Tel.: (41) 585586670
Web Site: http://www.buildingtechnologies.com
Sales Range: $75-99.9 Million
Mfr & Distr of Fire Safety & Security Products
N.A.I.C.S.: 561621

Subsidiary (Non-US):

Siemens Building Technologies AS (2)
Ostre Aker vei 88, PO Box 1, Alnabru, 0613, Oslo, Norway **(100%)**
Tel.: (47) 22633000
Web Site: http://new.siemens.com
Sales Range: $25-49.9 Million
Emp.: 100
Provider of Fire & Security Systems
N.A.I.C.S.: 561621

Siemens Building Technologies Ltd. (2)
10/F Tower B Manulife Financial Centre 223-231 Wai Yip Street, Kwun Tong, Kowloon, China (Hong Kong) **(100%)**
Tel.: (852) 25833388
Web Site: http://new.siemens.com
Sales Range: $75-99.9 Million
Emp.: 400
Provider of Fire & Security Systems
N.A.I.C.S.: 561621

Siemens Building Technologies Ltd. (2)
Hawthorne Rd, Staines-upon-Thames, TW18 3AY, Middlesex, United Kingdom **(100%)**
Tel.: (44) 1784461616
Web Site: http://www.siemens.com
Sales Range: $75-99.9 Million
Emp.: 400
Fire Safety & Security Systems
N.A.I.C.S.: 561621
Andrew Robinson *(Mng Dir-UK & Ireland)*

Siemens Building Technologies Oy (2)
Italahdenkalu 18C, PO Box 146, FI 00211, Helsinki, Finland **(100%)**
Tel.: (358) 9681601
Sales Range: $25-49.9 Million
Emp.: 70
Provider of Fire & Security Systems
N.A.I.C.S.: 561621

Siemens Building Technologies S.p.A. (2)
Via Lealberto e Piero Pirelle 10, IT 20126, Milan, Italy
Tel.: (39) 022431
Web Site: http://www.cerberus.it
Sales Range: $25-49.9 Million
Emp.: 230
Provider of Fire & Security Systems

N.A.I.C.S.: 561621

Siemens Building Technologies SA
ZI-617 Rue Fourny, BP 20, 78531, Buc, France **(100%)**
Tel.: (33) 130846600
Web Site: http://www.sbt.siemens.com
Sales Range: $125-149.9 Million
Emp.: 350
Private Communication Systems & Public Communication Networks
N.A.I.C.S.: 334418

Siemens Building Technologies s.r.o (2)
Siemens Ova 1, Prague, 15500, Czech Republic **(100%)**
Tel.: (420) 233033303
Web Site: http://www.siemens.cz
Sales Range: $25-49.9 Million
Emp.: 60
Provider of Security Systems & Services
N.A.I.C.S.: 561621
Eduardo Palisek *(Gen Mgr)*

Siemens Cerberus Kft. (2)
Nimrod U 3, 1031 HU, Budapest, Hungary **(100%)**
Tel.: (36) 12508684
Web Site: http://www.cerberus.hu
Sales Range: $25-49.9 Million
Emp.: 32
Public Communication Networks
N.A.I.C.S.: 334418

Siemens Cerberus SA (2)
Lluis Muntadas 5 - 2 Pl, Cornella de Llobregat, ES-08940, Barcelona, Spain **(100%)**
Tel.: (34) 935076000
Sales Range: $25-49.9 Million
Emp.: 70
Provider of Fire & Security Systems
N.A.I.C.S.: 561621

Siemens Pte. Ltd. (2)
The Siemens Center 60 MacPherson Road, Singapore, 348615, Singapore **(100%)**
Tel.: (65) 64906000
Power Generation & Engineering Services
N.A.I.C.S.: 221118

Siemens S.A. (2)
Ave Ermano Marckaetti 1435 5 Andar, CEP 05038001, Sao Paulo, SP, Brazil
Tel.: (55) 38173278
Provider of Fire & Security Systems
N.A.I.C.S.: 561621

Siemens Sp. z o.o. - Building Technologies (2)
Ul Zupnicza 11, 03-821, Warsaw, Poland
Tel.: (48) 228708700
Web Site: http://new.siemens.com
Sales Range: $10-24.9 Million
Emp.: 50
Fire & Security Systems
N.A.I.C.S.: 561621

Siemens Canada Limited (1)
1577 North Service Road East, Oakville, L6H 0H6, ON, Canada **(100%)**
Tel.: (905) 465-8000
Web Site: https://new.siemens.com
Sales Range: $100-124.9 Million
Emp.: 400
Electrical & Electronic Products Mfr
N.A.I.C.S.: 334513
Faisal Kazi *(Pres & CEO)*

Subsidiary (Domestic):

Siemens Building Technologies Ltd. (2)
1577 North Service Road East, Oakville, L6H 0H6, ON, Canada **(100%)**
Tel.: (905) 465-8000
Sales Range: $25-49.9 Million
Emp.: 150
Distr of Fire Alarm Equipment
N.A.I.C.S.: 334290

Siemens Canada (2)
5005 Levy St, Saint Laurent, H4R 2N9, QC, Canada **(100%)**
Tel.: (514) 338-3000
Web Site: http://new.siemens.com
Sales Range: $25-49.9 Million
Emp.: 100
Electrical Repair Shops

N.A.I.C.S.: 811114

Siemens Canada Ltd. (2)
1425 Trans Canada Hwy Ste 400, Dorval, H9P 2W9, QC, Canada **(100%)**
Tel.: (514) 822-7300
Web Site: http://www.siemens.ca
Switchboard Mfr
N.A.I.C.S.: 335313

Siemens Circuit Protection Systems Ltd. (1)
90 Jin Zhang Zhi Road, Zhang Yan Jinshan, Shanghai, 201514, China
Tel.: (86) 2157214171
Electric Equipment Mfr
N.A.I.C.S.: 335313

Siemens Concentrated Solar Power Ltd. (1)
Industrial Zone West 3 HaHachshara Street, Beit Shemesh, 99107, Israel
Tel.: (972) 29950111
Power Generation Services
N.A.I.C.S.: 221118

Siemens Corporation (1)
200 Massachusetts Ave NW Ste 600, Washington, DC 20001 **(100%)**
Tel.: (212) 258-4000
Web Site: http://www.usa.siemens.com
Sales Range: $25-49.9 Million
Emp.: 30
Transformer Mfr
N.A.I.C.S.: 335311

Subsidiary (Domestic):

Aimsun Inc. (2)
500 7th Ave 8th Fl, New York, NY 10018
Tel.: (917) 267-8534
Software Development Services
N.A.I.C.S.: 513210

American Healthware Systems (2)
651 E 5th St, Brooklyn, NY 11218-2410
Tel.: (718) 435-6300
Sales Range: $10-24.9 Million
Computer Software Development
N.A.I.C.S.: 541511

Bytemark Inc. (2)
1 Pennsylvania Plz, New York, NY 10119
Tel.: (212) 206-8719
Web Site: https://www.bytemark.co
Information Technology Services
N.A.I.C.S.: 513210
Vishal Arora *(Sr VP-Delivery & Ops)*

Demag Delaval Turbomachinery Corp. (2)
840 Nottingham Way, Hamilton, NJ 08638
Tel.: (609) 890-5000
Turbine Products Mfr
N.A.I.C.S.: 333611
Joe Kaeser *(Pres)*

Foundation Enterprise Systems (2)
51 Valley Stream Pkwy, Malvern, PA 19355
Tel.: (610) 219-1600
Sales Range: $50-74.9 Million
Information Retrieval Services
N.A.I.C.S.: 517810

HearX West LLC (2)
771 Village Blvd Ste 206, West Palm Beach, FL 33409
Tel.: (561) 345-6622
Web Site: http://www.hearusa.com
Healthcare Products Retailer
N.A.I.C.S.: 456199

J2 Innovations, Inc. (2)
1550 Valley Vista Dr, Diamond Bar, CA 91765
Tel.: (909) 217-7040
Web Site: https://www.j2inn.com
Software Development Services
N.A.I.C.S.: 513210
David Packer *(CFO)*

Optisphere Networks Inc. (2)
1881 Campus Commons Dr, Reston, VA 20191-1519 **(100%)**
Tel.: (703) 262-2100
Sales Range: $25-49.9 Million
Emp.: 2
Communication Signal Enhancement Network Services
N.A.I.C.S.: 517810

PETNET Solutions Cleveland, LLC (2)
2035 E 86th St Rm Jb-122, Cleveland, OH 44106-2963
Tel.: (865) 218-2000
Web Site: http://www.petnetsolutions.com
Emp.: 635
Radioactive Diagnostic Substance Mfr
N.A.I.C.S.: 325413
Barry Scott *(CEO)*

Pace Global Energy Services, LLC (2)
4401 Fair Lkes Ct, Fairfax, VA 22033
Tel.: (703) 818-9100
Web Site: http://www.paceglobal.com
Sales Range: $1-9.9 Million
Other Scientific & Technical Consulting Services
N.A.I.C.S.: 541690

Rexton Inc. (2)
5010 Cheshire Ln N Ste 1A, Minneapolis, MN 55446
Tel.: (763) 553-0787
Web Site: http://www.rexton.com
Sales Range: $25-49.9 Million
Hearing Aids
N.A.I.C.S.: 334510

Russelectric Inc. (2)
S Shore Park, Hingham, MA 02043-4387
Tel.: (781) 749-6000
Web Site: http://www.russelectric.com
Sales Range: $50-74.9 Million
Emp.: 400
Switchgear & Switchboard Apparatus Mfr
N.A.I.C.S.: 335313
Dorian Alexandrescu *(Pres & CEO)*

Siemens Applied Automation (2)
500 Hwy 60, Bartlesville, OK 74003-1223
Tel.: (918) 662-7000
Sales Range: $50-74.9 Million
Mfr of Analysers
N.A.I.C.S.: 334513
Robert Delumyea *(Treas)*

Siemens Capital Company LLC (2)
200 Wood Ave S Ste 200, Iselin, NJ 08830-2726
Tel.: (732) 590-2500
Financial Management Services
N.A.I.C.S.: 523999

Siemens Corp. - Mountain View Branch (2)
685 E Middlefield Rd, Mountain View, CA 94039-7393
Tel.: (650) 969-9112
Emp.: 200
Mfr, Designer & Marketer of Medical Diagnostic Ultrasound Imaging Systems
N.A.I.C.S.: 334517
John Pavlidis *(CEO & Pres-Siemens Ultrasound Div)*

Siemens Corporate Research (2)
755 College Rd E, Princeton, NJ 08540-6632
Tel.: (609) 734-6500
Sales Range: $75-99.9 Million
System Software Development Services
N.A.I.C.S.: 541512
Sonny Xue *(Mgr-Res)*

Siemens Demag Delaval Turbomachinery, Inc. (2)
840 Nottingham Way, Trenton, NJ 08638-4448
Tel.: (609) 890-5000
Turbine Generator Mfr
N.A.I.C.S.: 333611
Jorge Sequeira *(Mgr-Procurement & Facilities)*

Siemens Diagnostics Finance Co. LLC (2)
1717 Deerfield Rd Ste 1, Deerfield, IL 60015-3909
Tel.: (847) 267-5300
Investment Management Service
N.A.I.C.S.: 523999

Siemens Financial Services, Inc. (2)
170 Wood Ave S, Iselin, NJ 08830
Tel.: (609) 954-2489
Investment Management Service
N.A.I.C.S.: 523999

SIEMENS AKTIENGESELLSCHAFT — INTERNATIONAL PUBLIC

Siemens Aktiengesellschaft—(Continued)

Siemens Financial, Inc. (2)
170 Wood Ave S, Iselin, NJ 08830
Tel.: (732) 590-6573
Financial Management Services
N.A.I.C.S.: 523999

Siemens Fossil Services, Inc. (2)
3504 Lake Lynda Dr Ste 390, Orlando, FL 32817-8462
Tel.: (407) 736-1311
Emp.: 8
Engineering Construction Services
N.A.I.C.S.: 237990

Siemens Government Technologies, Inc. (2)
2231 Crystal Dr Ste No 700, Arlington, VA 22202
Tel.: (703) 483-2000
Web Site: https://www.siemensgovt.com
Physical Security System Services
N.A.I.C.S.: 561621
Anne Altman *(Chm)*

Siemens Hearing Instruments Inc. (2)
Ten Constitution Ave, Piscataway, NJ 08855-1397
Tel.: (732) 562-6600
Web Site: http://www.usa.siemens.com
Sales Range: $75-99.9 Million
Orthopedic Appliances
N.A.I.C.S.: 334510

Subsidiary (Domestic):

HearUSA, Inc. (3)
11400 N Jog Rd, Palm Beach Gardens, FL 33418
Tel.: (561) 478-8770
Web Site: https://www.hearusa.com
Sales Range: $75-99.9 Million
Hearing Tests & Services
N.A.I.C.S.: 423450

Subsidiary (Domestic):

Siemens Logistics LLC (2)
2700 Esters Blvd Ste 200B, Dallas-Fort Worth Airport, TX 75261
Tel.: (972) 947-7100
Airport Logistics Services
N.A.I.C.S.: 488119
Andrew Savage *(Pres & CEO)*

Unit (Domestic):

Siemens PLM Software (2)
5800 Granite Pkwy Ste 600, Plano, TX 75024
Tel.: (972) 987-3000
Web Site: https://www.plm.automation.siemens.com
Sales Range: $1-4.9 Billion
Emp.: 150
Product Lifecycle Management (PLM) Software & Services
N.A.I.C.S.: 541512

Subsidiary (Domestic):

Mentor Graphics Corporation (3)
8005 SW Boeckman Rd, Wilsonville, OR 97070-7777
Tel.: (503) 685-7000
Web Site: http://www.mentor.com
Electronic Design Automation Software Mfr, Designer & Marketer
N.A.I.C.S.: 541511
Joseph Sawicki *(Exec VP-IC EDA)*

Branch (Domestic):

Mentor Graphics (4)
1811 Pike Rd, Longmont, CO 80501
Tel.: (720) 494-1000
Computer Programming Services
N.A.I.C.S.: 541511

Mentor Graphics (4)
300 Nickerson Rd Ste 200, Marlborough, MA 01752
Tel.: (508) 480-0881
Computer Software Design Services
N.A.I.C.S.: 541512

Mentor Graphics (4)
360E Quality Cir Ste 500, Huntsville, AL 35806
Tel.: (256) 864-3800
Electronic Design Automation Software Mfr, Designer & Marketer
N.A.I.C.S.: 541511

Subsidiary (Non-US):

Mentor Graphics (Canada) Limited (4)
411 Leggett Drive Suite 502, Kanata, K2K 3C9, ON, Canada
Tel.: (613) 963-1000
Software & Hardware Design Solutions Developer
N.A.I.C.S.: 541511

Mentor Graphics (Deutschland) GmbH (4)
Arnulfstrasse 201, 80634, Munich, Germany
Tel.: (49) 89 570 960
Electronic Design Automation Software Development Services
N.A.I.C.S.: 541512

Branch (Domestic):

Mentor Graphics (Deutschland) GmbH (5)
Peterzeller Strasse 8, 78048, Villingen-Schwenningen, Germany
Tel.: (49) 772140600
Software Development Services
N.A.I.C.S.: 541511

Subsidiary (Non-US):

Mentor Graphics (Espana) S.L. (4)
Ronda de Europa 5, Tres Cantos, 28760, Madrid, Spain
Tel.: (34) 914 199 692
Electronic Design Automation Software Development Services
N.A.I.C.S.: 541511

Mentor Graphics (Finland) Oy (4)
Tarvonsalmenkatu 19, 02600, Espoo, Finland
Tel.: (358) 207459859
Electronic Design Automation Software & Hardware Developer
N.A.I.C.S.: 541511

Mentor Graphics (France) SARL (4)
Le Pasteur Building 13/15 Rue Jeanne Braconnier, 92360, Meudon, France
Tel.: (33) 140947474
Electronic Design Automation Software Development Services
N.A.I.C.S.: 541512

Mentor Graphics (India) Private Limited (4)
LG UB Ground Mezzanine 1st-10th Floor & Terrace, Plot No-7A/2 Sector-142, Noida, 201304, Uttar Pradesh, India
Tel.: (91) 1204304500
Electronic Design Software Services
N.A.I.C.S.: 541511
Raghu Panicker *(Sls Dir-Country)*

Mentor Graphics (Ireland) Limited (4)
East Park Shannon Free Zone, V14 YD96, Shannon, Clare, Ireland
Tel.: (353) 61256200
Electronic Design Automation Software Development Services
N.A.I.C.S.: 541511
Martin Gennery *(Mgr-Site)*

Mentor Graphics (Korea) LLC (4)
Pangyo Mirae Asset Center 7F 12 Pangyoyeok-ro 192 beon-gil, Bundang-gu, Seongnam, 463-400, Gyeonggi, Korea (South)
Tel.: (82) 3180610790
Software Development Services
N.A.I.C.S.: 541511

Mentor Graphics (Netherlands) B.V. (4)
Eindhoven Bedrijvencentrum Mu High Tech Campus 10, 5656 AE, Eindhoven, Netherlands
Tel.: (31) 88 241 8500
Electronic Design Automation Software Developer
N.A.I.C.S.: 541512

Mentor Graphics (Sales and Services) Private Limited (4)
RMZ Eco World Unit No 701 to 704 Campus 8B 7th Floor, Sarjapur-Marathalli Outer Ring Road Devarabeesanahalli, Bengaluru, 560 103, Karnataka, India
Tel.: (91) 8067624000
Software Distr
N.A.I.C.S.: 423430
Raghu Panicker *(Dir-Sls-Country)*

Mentor Graphics (Scandinavia) AB (4)
Evenemangsgatan 21, Solna, 169 79, Kista, Sweden
Tel.: (46) 86329500
Electronic Design Automation Software Distr
N.A.I.C.S.: 423430

Mentor Graphics (Schweiz) AG (4)
Seestrasse 40, 8802, Kilchberg, Switzerland
Tel.: (41) 447151030
Electronic Design Automation Software Development Services
N.A.I.C.S.: 541512

Mentor Graphics (Shanghai) Electronic Technology Co., Ltd. (4)
5F Lujiazui Century Financial Plaza No 759 South Yanggao Road, Pudong District, Shanghai, 200127, China
Tel.: (86) 2161016300
Electronic Design Automation Tool Mfr
N.A.I.C.S.: 334413

Mentor Graphics (Taiwan) Limited (4)
8F No 3 Park St Nan Gang District, Taipei, 11503, Taiwan
Tel.: (886) 2 2652 8888
Electronic Design Automation Software Distr
N.A.I.C.S.: 541512

Mentor Graphics (UK) Limited (4)
Rivergate Newbury Business Park London Road, Newbury, RG14 2QB, Berks, United Kingdom
Tel.: (44) 1635 811 411
Electronic Design Automation Software Developer
N.A.I.C.S.: 541512

Mentor Graphics Asia Pte Ltd. (4)
The Siemens Center 60 Macpherson Road 11th Floor, Singapore, 348615, Singapore (100%)
Tel.: (65) 67790075
Electronic Design Automation Software Distr
N.A.I.C.S.: 423430
Brandon Tai *(Acct Mgr)*

Division (Domestic):

Mentor Graphics Corp. - Embedded Software Division (4)
46871 Bayside Pkwy, Fremont, CA 94538
Tel.: (408) 941-4600
Real-Time Software Engineering Tools Mfr
N.A.I.C.S.: 541512

Holding (Domestic):

Mentor Emulation Division (5)
1 Federal St 36th Fl, Boston, MA 02110-2012
Tel.: (781) 290-0960
Computer Software Design Services
N.A.I.C.S.: 541512

Subsidiary (Non-US):

Mentor Graphics Development (Shenzhen) (4)
Room 2401 24F No 3088 Jintian Road, Futian District, Shenzhen, 518026, China
Tel.: (86) 755 8282 2700
Electronic Design Automation Software Solutions Provider
N.A.I.C.S.: 541511

Mentor Graphics Egypt Company (4)
78 El Nozha Street, Heliopolis, 11361, Cairo, Egypt
Tel.: (20) 22441306
Software Publisher
N.A.I.C.S.: 513210

Mentor Graphics Germany GmbH (4)
Arnulfstrasse 201, 80634, Munich, Germany
Tel.: (49) 89570960

Electronic Design Automation Software Services
N.A.I.C.S.: 541512

Mentor Graphics Japan Co. Ltd. (4)
Gotenyama Trust Tower 4-7-35 Kitashinagawa, Shinagawa-ku, Tokyo, 140-0001, Japan (100%)
Tel.: (81) 354883030
Web Site: http://www.mentorg.co.jp
Emp.: 170
Electronic Design Automation Software Developer
N.A.I.C.S.: 541512
Yukio Tsuchida *(Pres)*

Branch (Domestic):

Mentor Graphics Japan Co., Ltd. - Nagoya Branch (5)
Nagoya Intercity 1-11-11 Nishiki, Naka-ku, Nagoya, 460-0003, Aichi, Japan
Tel.: (81) 52 204 2010
Software Development Services
N.A.I.C.S.: 541512

Mentor Graphics Japan Co., Ltd. - Osaka Branch (5)
SORA Shin-Osaka 21 2-1-3 Nishimiyahara, Yodogawa-ku, Osaka, 532-0004, Japan
Tel.: (81) 663999521
Electronic Design Automation Software Developer
N.A.I.C.S.: 541512

Subsidiary (Non-US):

Mentor Graphics Magyarorszag kft (4)
Montevideo u 2/C, Budapest, 1037, Hungary
Tel.: (36) 18887300
Electronic Software & Hardware Design Solutions Provider
N.A.I.C.S.: 541511

Mentor Graphics Pakistan Development (Private) Limited (4)
Floors No 5-6-7-8th Ali Tower 105 B2 MM Alam Road, Gulberg III, Lahore, 54660, Pakistan
Tel.: (92) 4236099100
Software Development Services
N.A.I.C.S.: 541511

Mentor Graphics SARL (4)
Piazza Montanelli 20, Sesto San Giovanni, 20099, Milan, Italy
Tel.: (39) 022498941
Electronic Design Automation Software Developer
N.A.I.C.S.: 541512

Division (Non-US):

Mentor Graphics-Mechanical Analysis Division (4)
81 Bridge Road Hampton Court, London, KT8 9HH, Surrey, United Kingdom
Tel.: (44) 2084873000
Simulation Software Development Services
N.A.I.C.S.: 541511

Subsidiary (Non-US):

Microelectronics Research & Development Ltd (5)
Infopark D Gabor Denes utca 2 fszt 1, 1117, Budapest, Hungary
Tel.: (36) 1 815 4200
Integrated Circuit Testing Services
N.A.I.C.S.: 334515

Branch (Domestic):

Siemens PLM Software (3)
2435 N Central Expy, Richardson, TX 75080-2759
Tel.: (972) 680-9700
Sales Range: $25-49.9 Million
Emp.: 35
Computer Softwares Mfr
N.A.I.C.S.: 541512

Siemens PLM Software (3)
360E Quality Cir, Huntsville, AL 35806-2814
Tel.: (256) 705-2500
Web Site: http://www.siemens.com
Sales Range: $25-49.9 Million
Emp.: 119

AND PRIVATE COMPANIES SIEMENS AKTIENGESELLSCHAFT

Internet-Based Product Life Cycle Collaboration Solutions Supplier
N.A.I.C.S.: 541511

Siemens PLM Software (3)
2321 N Loop Dr, Ames, IA 50010-8281
Tel.: (515) 296-9908
Web Site:
http://www.plm.automation.siemens.com
Sales Range: $25-49.9 Million
Emp.: 95
Web-Enabled Software Mfr For 3-D Design & Animation
N.A.I.C.S.: 513210

Subsidiary (Non-US):

Siemens Product Lifecycle Management Software (DE) GmbH (3)
Hohenstaufenring 48-54, Franz Geuer St 10 50823, 50674, Cologne, Germany
Tel.: (49) 221208020
Web Site:
http://www.plmautomation.siemen.com
Sales Range: $25-49.9 Million
Emp.: 160
Software Services
N.A.I.C.S.: 541511

Division (Domestic):

Siemens Product Lifecycle Management Software (DE) GmbH (4)
Nonnendammallee 101 5 OG Bauteil C, 13269, Berlin, Germany
Tel.: (49) 304677750
Web Site: http://www.plm-solutions.de
Sales Range: $75-99.9 Million
N.A.I.C.S.: 449210

Subsidiary (Non-US):

Siemens UGS Tecnomatix (3)
10 Abba Eban Ave Bldg C, 46725, Herzliyya, Israel
Tel.: (972) 99594777
Web Site: http://www.tecnomatix.com
Sales Range: $75-99.9 Million
Emp.: 140
Computer Software & Services
N.A.I.C.S.: 334610

Subsidiary (Domestic):

Siemens Product Lifecycle Management Software Inc. (2)
5800 Granite Pkwy Ste 600, Plano, TX 75024
Tel.: (972) 987-3000
Web Site:
http://www.plm.automation.siemens.com
Software Development Services
N.A.I.C.S.: 541511

Subsidiary (Non-US):

Computational Dynamics Ltd. (3)
200 Shepherds Bush Road, London, W6 7NL, United Kingdom
Tel.: (44) 2074716200
Web Site: http://www.cd-adapco.com
Emp.: 120
Computer System Design Services
N.A.I.C.S.: 541512

Subsidiary (Domestic):

Siemens Product Lifecycle Management Software II (US) Inc. (3)
5800 Granite Pkwy Ste 600, Plano, TX 75024
Tel.: (972) 987-3000
Emp.: 150
Software Development Services
N.A.I.C.S.: 541511

Subsidiary (Domestic):

Siemens Public, Inc. (2)
3411 Silverside Rd Ste 100 HB, Wilmington, DE 19810
Tel.: (302) 479-7150
Financial Investment Services
N.A.I.C.S.: 523999

Siemens Real Estate Corp. (2)
170 Wood Ave S, Iselin, NJ 08830-2725
Tel.: (732) 321-3189
Real Estate Consultant
N.A.I.C.S.: 541618

Siemens Technology to Business (2)
1995 University Ave, Berkeley, CA 94704-1074
Tel.: (510) 665-1330
Web Site: http://www.ttb.siemens.com
Sales Range: $25-49.9 Million
Emp.: 25
Computer Software Development
N.A.I.C.S.: 541511

Siemens Transportation Systems, Inc. (2) (100%)
7464 French Rd, Sacramento, CA 95828
Tel.: (916) 681-3000
Safety & Control Systems, Catenaries & Transmission Lines & Rolling Stock for Mass Transit & Main Lines
N.A.I.C.S.: 541611

Siemens USA Holdings, Inc. (2)
601 Lexington Ave Fl 56, New York, NY 10022-4611
Tel.: (212) 258-4000
Investment Management Service
N.A.I.C.S.: 523999
Barbara W. Humpton *(Pres & CEO)*

The Colorado Medical Cyclotron, LLC (2)
2525 S Downing St, Denver, CO 80210-5817
Tel.: (865) 218-2000
Pharmaceuticals Product Mfr
N.A.I.C.S.: 325412

Transport & Distribution Inc. (2)
1651 S Archibald Ave, Ontario, CA 91761
Tel.: (866) 664-8726
Logistics Consulting Servies
N.A.I.C.S.: 541614

TurboCare, Inc. (2)
2140 Westover Rd, Chicopee, MA 01022
Tel.: (413) 593-0500
Web Site: http://www.ethosenergygroup.com
Emp.: 100
Turbo Machinery Part & Equipment Mfr
N.A.I.C.S.: 333611
Mark Dobler *(Gen Mgr)*

VistaScape Security Systems Corp. (2)
5901B Peachtree-Dunwoody Rd Ste 550, Atlanta, GA 30328
Tel.: (678) 919-1130
Web Site: http://www.vistascape.com
Developer of Video Analytic Technologies & Integrated Security Systems
N.A.I.C.S.: 561621

Wheelabrator Air Pollution Control Inc. (2)
437 Grant St Ste 918 Frick Bldg, Pittsburgh, PA 15219-4429
Tel.: (412) 562-7300
Web Site: https://www.wheelabrator.us
Air Pollution Control Device Mfr
N.A.I.C.S.: 334512

Winergy Drive Systems Corp. (2)
1401 Madeline Ln, Elgin, IL 60124
Tel.: (847) 531-7400
Turbine Gear Unit Mfr
N.A.I.C.S.: 333611

Siemens Diagnostics Holding II B.V. (1)
Prinses Beatrixlaan 800, Hague, 2595 BN, South Holland, Netherlands
Tel.: (31) 703333333
Investment Management Service
N.A.I.C.S.: 523999

Siemens Digital Business Builder GmbH (1)
Otto-Hahn-Ring 6, 81739, Munich, Germany
Tel.: (49) 89780522910
Banking & Financial Services
N.A.I.C.S.: 522110

Siemens Digital Logistics GmbH (1)
Nachtweideweg 1-7, 67227, Frankenthal, Germany
Tel.: (49) 6233459430
Web Site: https://www.siemens-digital-logistics.com
Information Technology Services
N.A.I.C.S.: 541512
Uwe Schumacher *(VP-Bus Dev)*

Siemens Digital Logistics Sp. z o.o. (1)
Ul Swobodna 1, 50-088, Wrocław, Poland
Tel.: (48) 717992100
Information Technology Services
N.A.I.C.S.: 541519

Siemens EOOD (1)
2 Kukush Str, Sofia, 1309, Bulgaria
Tel.: (359) 28115650
Web Site: http://www.siemens.bg
Rev.: $95,536,497
Emp.: 260
Energy Consulting Services
N.A.I.C.S.: 541690
Boryana Manolova *(CEO)*

Siemens Electric Machines s.r.o. (1)
Drasov 126, 664 24, Drasov, Czech Republic
Tel.: (420) 549 426 103
Emp.: 800
Generator & Motor Engine Mfr
N.A.I.C.S.: 335312
Heinrich Jurtan *(Gen Mgr)*

Siemens Electrical Apparatus Ltd. (1)
455 Zhujiang Rd, Suzhou, 215129, China
Tel.: (86) 51266611188
Sales Range: $400-449.9 Million
Emp.: 1,500
Electronic Products Mfr
N.A.I.C.S.: 334419

Siemens Electrical Drives Ltd. (1)
No 1 Haitaichuangxin 5th Road Outside Outer Ring Road Huayuan Industry, Hi-Tech Industry Park, Tianjin, 300384, China
Tel.: (86) 2223901111
Automation Technology Services
N.A.I.C.S.: 811114

Siemens Eletroeletronica Ltda. (1)
Av Abiurana 1655 Distrito Industrial, Manaus, 69075-010, Brazil
Tel.: (55) 11 3908 2211
Electrical Products Mfr
N.A.I.C.S.: 335999

Siemens Factory Automation Engineering Ltd. (1)
No 1258 Boxue Road, Jiading District, Shanghai, 201801, China
Tel.: (86) 2125057600
Sales Range: $100-124.9 Million
Emp.: 500
Switchgear & Switchboard Apparatus Mfr
N.A.I.C.S.: 335313

Siemens Finance B.V. (1)
Prinses Beatrixlaan 800 PB 16068, 2595 BN, Hague, Netherlands
Tel.: (31) 703332522
Data Processing Services
N.A.I.C.S.: 541513

Siemens Finance Sp. z o.o. (1)
ul Zupnicza 11, 03-821, Warsaw, Poland
Tel.: (48) 223073103
Web Site: https://www.siemens.com
Equipment Financial Leasing Services
N.A.I.C.S.: 522220

Siemens Finance and Leasing Ltd. (1)
No 7 Wangjing Zhonghuan Nanlu, PO Box 8543, Chaoyang District, Beijing, 100102, China
Tel.: (86) 1064767997
Equipment Leasing Services
N.A.I.C.S.: 532490

Siemens Financial Services AB (1)
Evenemangsgatan 21, 169 79, Solna, Sweden
Tel.: (46) 2002000
Web Site: https://www.siemens.com
Financial Management Services
N.A.I.C.S.: 523999

Siemens Financial Services Holdings Ltd. (1)
Sefton Park Bells Hill, Stoke Poges, SL2 4JS, Buckinghamshire, United Kingdom
Tel.: (44) 1753434000
Web Site: http://new.siemens.com
Sales Range: $75-99.9 Million
Emp.: 200
Electrical Product Whslr
N.A.I.C.S.: 423690
Thomas Riesterer *(Mng Dir)*

Siemens Financial Services Ltd. (1)
7 Wangjing Zhonghuan Nanlu, Chaoyang District, Beijing, 100102, China
Tel.: (86) 1064768888
Investment Financing Services
N.A.I.C.S.: 523999

Siemens Financial Services Ltd. (1)
Sefton Park Bells Hill, Stoke Poges, SL2 4JS, Buckinghamshire, United Kingdom
Tel.: (44) 1753980078
Web Site: http://new.siemens.com
Sales Range: $100-124.9 Million
Emp.: 15
Financial Management Services
N.A.I.C.S.: 523999

Siemens Financial Services Private Limited (1)
130 Pandurang Budhkar Marg Worli, Mumbai, 400018, Maharashtra, India
Tel.: (91) 2239677000
Financial Management Services
N.A.I.C.S.: 523999

Siemens Financieringsmaatschappij N.V. (1)
Prinses Beatrixlaan 800, 2595 BN, Hague, Netherlands
Tel.: (31) 703332458
Web Site: http://www.siemens.com
Emp.: 2,500
Financial Management Services
N.A.I.C.S.: 523999
P. Rathgeb *(Chm-Supervisory Bd)*

Siemens Finansal Kiralama A.S. (1)
Esentepe Mah Yakacik Cad No 111/14, Sisli, 34870, Istanbul, Türkiye
Tel.: (90) 2164593030
Web Site: https://www.siemens.com
Investment Management Service
N.A.I.C.S.: 523999

Siemens Fire & Security Products, S.A. (1)
De Europa 5, 28760, Tres Cantos, Spain
Tel.: (34) 915 14 80 00
Security Device Mfr & Distr
N.A.I.C.S.: 334290

Siemens Fonds Invest GmbH (1)
Otto-Hahn-Ring 6, 81739, Munich, Germany
Tel.: (49) 8978051067
Fund Management Services
N.A.I.C.S.: 523940
Josef Mehl *(CFO)*

Siemens France Holding S.A.S. (1)
9 boulevard Finot, 93527, Saint Denis, France
Tel.: (33) 149223100
Web Site: http://www.siemens.fr
Emp.: 800
Power Transmission & Distr
N.A.I.C.S.: 221122

Subsidiary (Domestic):

Siemens Lease Services SAS (2)
9 Boulevard Finot, 93200, Saint Denis, France
Tel.: (33) 1 49 22 42 22
Web Site: http://www.siemens.fr
Sales Range: $50-74.9 Million
Emp.: 60
Financial Lending Services
N.A.I.C.S.: 522220

Siemens Fuel Gasification Technology GmbH & Co. KG (1)
Halsbruecker Strasse 34, Freiberg, 9599, Germany
Tel.: (49) 3731785351
Sales Range: $50-74.9 Million
Emp.: 95
Coal Gasification Testing Services
N.A.I.C.S.: 211130
Guido Schuld *(Mng Dir)*

Siemens Global Innovation Partners Management GmbH (1)
Wittelsbacherplatz 2, Munich, 80333, Bavaria, Germany
Tel.: (49) 8963600
Financial Investment Services
N.A.I.C.S.: 523999

SIEMENS AKTIENGESELLSCHAFT

Siemens Aktiengesellschaft—(Continued)

Siemens Healthcare (Private) Limited (1)
4th Floor State Life Building 15-A Sir Agha Khan Davis Road, Lahore, 54000, Pakistan
Tel.: (92) 4236365501
Web Site: https://www.siemens-healthineers.com
Health Care Srvices
N.A.I.C.S.: 621999
Shoaib Rashid *(Sls Mgr)*

Siemens Healthcare A/S (1)
Borupvang 9, 2750, Ballerup, Denmark
Tel.: (45) 44774477
Health Care Srvices
N.A.I.C.S.: 621999
Christian Etgen *(Mgr-Customer Svcs)*

Siemens Healthcare AB (1)
Box 3120, 169 03, Solna, Sweden
Tel.: (46) 20225022
Medical & Diagnostic Imaging Services
N.A.I.C.S.: 621512

Siemens Healthcare AG (1)
Freilagerstrasse 40, 8047, Zurich, Switzerland
Tel.: (41) 581991199
Web Site: http://www.siemens-healthineers.com
Medical & Diagnostic Imaging Services
N.A.I.C.S.: 621512

Siemens Healthcare AS (1)
Ostre Aker vei 88, 0596, Oslo, Norway
Tel.: (47) 22634400
Health Care Srvices
N.A.I.C.S.: 621999
Fredrik Altmeier *(Mng Dir)*

Siemens Healthcare Diagnostics Manufacturing Limited (1)
Chapel Lane, Swords, Dublin, K67 AT86, Ireland
Tel.: (353) 18132222
Health Care Srvices
N.A.I.C.S.: 621999

Siemens Healthcare Diagnostics, S. de R.L. de C.V. (1)
Av Ejercito Nacional No 350 Floor 3 Col Polanco V Section, Del Miguel Hidalgo, 11560, Mexico, Mexico
Tel.: (52) 5553282000
Healtcare Services
N.A.I.C.S.: 621511

Siemens Healthcare FZ LLC (1)
Building 40 Floor 2, PO Box 32349, Dubai Healthcare City, Dubai, United Arab Emirates
Tel.: (971) 43660700
Web Site: https://www.siemens-healthineers.com
Medical & Diagnostic Imaging Services
N.A.I.C.S.: 621512

Siemens Healthcare Inc. (1)
10th Floor M1 Tower 141 H V Dela Costa Street, Salcedo, Makati, 1227, Philippines
Tel.: (63) 288146765
Web Site: https://www.siemens-healthineers.com
Healtcare Services
N.A.I.C.S.: 621511
Michael Fisar *(Head-Customer Svcs)*

Siemens Healthcare K.K. (1)
Gate City Osaki West Tower 1-11-1 Osaki, Shinagawa-ku, Tokyo, 141-8644, Japan
Tel.: (81) 334937500
Healtcare Services
N.A.I.C.S.: 621511

Siemens Healthcare Kft. (1)
Gizella ut 51-57, 1143, Budapest, Hungary
Tel.: (36) 18488960
Web Site: https://www.siemens-healthineers.com
Health Care Srvices
N.A.I.C.S.: 621999
Imre Nagy *(Engr-Customer Svcs)*

Siemens Healthcare Limited (1)
Charn Issara Tower II 26th Floor 2922/292 New Petchburi Road, Bangkapi Huay Kwang, Bangkok, 10310, Thailand
Tel.: (66) 20791140

Web Site: https://www.siemens-healthineers.com
Healtcare Services
N.A.I.C.S.: 621511
Pawinee Ruangkachon *(Bus Mgr)*

Siemens Healthcare Limited (1)
Business Gate Building C1 Airport Road, Qurtubah District, Riyadh, 11423, Saudi Arabia
Tel.: (966) 8006090900
Web Site: https://www.siemens-healthineers.com
Health Care Srvices
N.A.I.C.S.: 621511
Majed Al Attas *(Mgr)*

Siemens Healthcare Limited (1)
Park View, Watchmoor Park, Camberley, GU15 3YL, Surrey, United Kingdom
Tel.: (44) 1276696000
Web Site: https://www.siemens-healthineers.com
Hospital & Healthcare Services
N.A.I.C.S.: 622110
Mark Pugh *(Mktg Mgr-Clinic)*

Siemens Healthcare Limited (1)
Millennium Centre Level 2 Building A 600 Great South Road, Ellerslie, Auckland, 1051, New Zealand
Tel.: (64) 800310300
Healtcare Services
N.A.I.C.S.: 621511
Jocelyn Cameron *(Acct Mgr)*

Siemens Healthcare Limited (1)
Deutsches Haus Floor 7th 33 Le Duan Str, Ben Nghe Ward District 1, Ho Chi Minh City, Vietnam
Tel.: (84) 2838282266
Web Site: https://www.siemens-healthineers.com
Healtcare Services
N.A.I.C.S.: 621511
Pedro Vilaca *(Gen Mgr)*

Siemens Healthcare Ltd. (1)
Laila Tower 6th Floor 8 Gulshan Avenue Gulshan-01, Dhaka, 1212, Bangladesh
Tel.: (880) 29893536
Healtcare Services
N.A.I.C.S.: 621511

Siemens Healthcare Ltd. (1)
Hamelacha Street 14, Industrial Park Afeq, Rosh Ha'Ayin, 48091, Israel
Tel.: (972) 39151597
Web Site: https://www.siemens-healthineers.com
Health Care Srvices
N.A.I.C.S.: 621999

Siemens Healthcare Medical Solutions Limited (1)
Chapel Lane, Swords, Dublin, K67 AT86, Ireland
Tel.: (353) 3002475
Web Site: https://www.siemens-healthineers.com
Health Care Srvices
N.A.I.C.S.: 621999

Siemens Healthcare Nederland B.V. (1)
Princess Beatrixlaan 800, 2595 BN, Hague, Netherlands
Tel.: (31) 882100500
Web Site: https://www.siemens-healthineers.com
Health Care Srvices
N.A.I.C.S.: 621999

Siemens Healthcare Oy (1)
Tarvonsalmenkatu 19, 02600, Espoo, Finland
Tel.: (358) 105112000
Web Site: https://www.siemens-healthineers.com
Health Care Srvices
N.A.I.C.S.: 621999

Siemens Healthcare Private Limited (1)
unit no 9A 9th Floor North Tower Godrej One Pirojshanagar, Eastern Express Highway Vikhroli East, Mumbai, 400079, India
Tel.: (91) 2233700600
Web Site: https://www.siemens-healthineers.com

Healtcare Services
N.A.I.C.S.: 621511
Sadhana Sheth *(Sr Gen Mgr & Head-Govt Affairs)*

Siemens Healthcare Pte. Ltd. (1)
The Siemens Center 60 MacPherson Road Level 13, Singapore, 348615, Singapore
Tel.: (65) 18006334225
Web Site: https://www.siemens-healthineers.com
Healtcare Services
N.A.I.C.S.: 621511
Sandy Ng *(Head-HR)*

Siemens Healthcare Pty. Ltd. (1)
Level 3 141 Camberwell Rd, Hawthorn East, 3123, VIC, Australia
Tel.: (61) 1800310300
Web Site: https://www.siemens-healthineers.com
Healtcare Services
N.A.I.C.S.: 621511

Siemens Healthcare S.A. (1)
Route 8 km 18 Calle 122, 4785, San Martin, Buenos Aires, Argentina
Tel.: (54) 1154326000
Web Site: https://www.siemens-healthineers.com
Hospital & Healthcare Services
N.A.I.C.S.: 622110

Siemens Healthcare S.A. (1)
Edificio Siemens Urbanizacion Los Ruices Piso 4, Avenida Don Diego Cisneros, Caracas, 1071, Venezuela
Tel.: (58) 2122038690
Healtcare Services
N.A.I.C.S.: 621511

Siemens Healthcare S.A.C. (1)
Av Domingo Orue 971, Surquillo, Lima, Peru
Tel.: (51) 12150030
Healtcare Services
N.A.I.C.S.: 621511

Siemens Healthcare S.A.E. (1)
Building MB4 Floor 1, PO Box 17631, Maadi Technology Park, Cairo, Egypt
Tel.: (20) 23240000
Web Site: https://www.siemens-healthineers.com
Health Care Srvices
N.A.I.C.S.: 621999
Ahmed Abdel Hady *(Mgr-Comml)*

Siemens Healthcare S.r.l. (1)
Via Vipiteno nr 4, 20128, Milan, Italy
Tel.: (39) 0224362373
Web Site: https://www.siemens-healthineers.com
Health Care Srvices
N.A.I.C.S.: 621999
Attilio Tulimiero *(Acct Mgr-Strategic)*

Siemens Healthcare S.r.l. (1)
Centrul pentru Sprijinirea Afacerilor West Gate Business Center, Corp H5 Etaj 4 Strada Preciziei Nr 24 Sector 6, 062204, Bucharest, Romania
Tel.: (40) 216550033
Web Site: https://www.siemens-healthineers.com
Health Care Srvices
N.A.I.C.S.: 621999
Cristi Dragomir *(Engr-Sls)*

Siemens Healthcare SARL (1)
Ivory Tower 3 5th floor Boulevard des Almohades, 20250, Casablanca, Morocco
Tel.: (212) 522493000
Web Site: https://www.siemens-healthineers.com
Health Care Srvices
N.A.I.C.S.: 621999
Tahar Amar *(Reg Sls Mgr)*

Siemens Healthcare SAS (1)
6 rue du General Audran, Saint-Denis, 92400, Courbevoie, Cedex, France
Tel.: (33) 811700716
Web Site: https://www.siemens-healthineers.com
Health Care Srvices
N.A.I.C.S.: 621999

Siemens Healthcare Saglik Anonim Sirketi (1)
Yakacik Cad No 111, Kartal, 34870, Istan-

INTERNATIONAL PUBLIC

bul, Turkiye
Tel.: (90) 2164440633
Web Site: https://www.siemens-healthineers.com
Medical & Diagnostic Imaging Services
N.A.I.C.S.: 621512

Siemens Healthcare Sdn. Bhd. (1)
Level 16 CP Tower No 11 Jalan 16/11 Pusat Dagang Seksyen 16, 46350, Petaling Jaya, Selangor, Malaysia
Tel.: (60) 379525555
Web Site: https://www.siemens-healthineers.com
Healtcare Services
N.A.I.C.S.: 621511
Norazilawati Abdullah *(Head-Bus Support)*

Siemens Healthcare d.o.o. (1)
Omladinskih brigada 90v, 11070, Belgrade, Serbia
Tel.: (381) 112096104
Health Care Srvices
N.A.I.C.S.: 621999
Marijana Djordjevic *(Head-Fin)*

Siemens Healthcare d.o.o. (1)
Letaliska cesta 29 C, 1000, Ljubljana, Slovenia
Tel.: (386) 14746187
Medical & Diagnostic Imaging Services
N.A.I.C.S.: 621512
Ana Pirc *(Fin Dir)*

Siemens Healthcare d.o.o. (1)
Heinzelova 70/A, 10000, Zagreb, Croatia
Tel.: (385) 16105258
Web Site: https://www.siemens-healthineers.com
Hospital & Health Care Services
N.A.I.C.S.: 622110
Daniel Bakic *(Head-Healthcare Diagnostics)*

Siemens Healthcare s.r.o. (1)
Lamacska cesta 3/B, 841 04, Bratislava, Slovakia
Tel.: (421) 903619061
Web Site: https://www.siemens-healthineers.com
Medical & Diagnostic Imaging Services
N.A.I.C.S.: 621512

Siemens Healthcare, Unipessoal, Lda. (1)
Rua Irmaos Siemens 1 - 1A, 2720-093, Lisbon, Portugal
Tel.: (351) 214204172
Web Site: https://www.siemens-healthineers.com
Health Care Srvices
N.A.I.C.S.: 621999

Siemens Healthcare, s.r.o. (1)
Budejovicka 779/3b, 140 00, Prague, 4, Czech Republic
Tel.: (420) 233032005
Web Site: https://www.siemens-healthineers.com
Health Care Srvices
N.A.I.C.S.: 621999
Pavel Lizec *(Head-Bus Relationship Mgmt)*

Siemens Healthineers AG (1)
Henkestrasse 127, 91052, Erlangen, Germany (75.01%)
Tel.: (49) 6966826602
Web Site: http://www.siemens-healthineers.com
Rev.: $23,932,001,328
Assets: $51,533,281,826
Liabilities: $31,516,723,705
Net Worth: $20,016,558,122
Earnings: $1,683,408,765
Emp.: 71,000
Fiscal Year-end: 09/30/2023
Diagnostic & Therapeutic Systems & Devices Mfr
N.A.I.C.S.: 339112
Bernd Montag *(CEO & Member-Mgmt Bd)*

Subsidiary (Domestic):

Siemens Healthcare GmbH (2)
Henkestr 127, 91052, Erlangen, Germany
Tel.: (49) 499131840
Web Site: http://www.siemens-healthineers.com
Diagnostic & Therapeutic Systems & Devices Mfr, Developer & Marketer
N.A.I.C.S.: 339112

AND PRIVATE COMPANIES — SIEMENS AKTIENGESELLSCHAFT

Darleen Caron *(Chief HR Officer-Healthineers & Dir-Labor)*

Subsidiary (Domestic):

Siemens Healthcare Diagnostics Holding GmbH (3)
Ludwig-Erhard-Strasse 12, 65760, Eschborn, Germany
Tel.: (49) 6196771311111
Investment Management Service
N.A.I.C.S.: 523999

Subsidiary (Non-US):

Dada Behring S.A. (4)
Rue Verheyden 39, B 1070, Brussels, Belgium
Tel.: (32) 25269189
Diagnostic Testing Instruments
N.A.I.C.S.: 334510

Siemens Diagnostics (Shanghai) Co. Ltd. (4)
Rm 1008 Ocean Twr No 550, Shanghai, 200001, China
Tel.: (86) 2163506018
Sales Range: $75-99.9 Million
Emp.: 70
Mfr of Diagnostic Testing Instruments
N.A.I.C.S.: 334510

Siemens Diagnostics Limited (4)
Shinkawa Sanko Bldg 1 3 17 Shinkawa, Chuo-ku, Tokyo, 104 0033, Japan
Tel.: (81) 335373900
Web Site: http://www.siemens.co.jp
Mfr of Diagnostic Testing Instruments
N.A.I.C.S.: 334510

Siemens Diagnostics Pty. Ltd. (4)
Level 5 18 20 Orion Rd, Lane Cove, 2066, NSW, Australia
Tel.: (61) 294296600
Sales Range: $50-74.9 Million
Emp.: 45
Mfr of Diagnostic Testing Instruments
N.A.I.C.S.: 334510

Siemens Healthcare Diagnostics (Pty.) Limited (4)
300 Janadel Avenue Halfway House, Private Bag x71, Midrand, Johannesburg, 1685, South Africa
Tel.: (27) 116522345
Web Site: http://www.diagnostics.siemens.com
Diagnostic Imaging Center Operator
N.A.I.C.S.: 621512
David Tshiporo *(Gen Mgr)*

Siemens Healthcare Diagnostics AB (4)
Evenemangsgatan 21, 169 04, Solna, Sweden
Tel.: (46) 87307000
Web Site: https://www.siemens-healthineers.com
Emp.: 20
Diagnostic Imaging Center Operating Services
N.A.I.C.S.: 621512

Siemens Healthcare Diagnostics AG (4)
Freilagerstrasse 40, 8047, Zurich, Switzerland
Tel.: (41) 581991199
Web Site: https://www.siemens-healthineers.com
Sales Range: $100-124.9 Million
Emp.: 65
Diagnostic Testing Instruments
N.A.I.C.S.: 334510

Siemens Healthcare Diagnostics AS (4)
Ostre Aker vei 88, 0596, Oslo, Norway
Tel.: (47) 22634400
Web Site: https://www.siemens-healthineers.com
Diagnostic Imaging Center Operator
N.A.I.C.S.: 621512

Siemens Healthcare Diagnostics ApS (4)
Borupvang 9, 2750, Ballerup, Denmark
Tel.: (45) 44774477
Diagnostic Center Operator
N.A.I.C.S.: 621512

Siemens Healthcare Diagnostics B.V. (4)
Prinses Beatrixlaan 800, 2595 BN, Hague, Netherlands
Tel.: (31) 703332752
Web Site: http://new.siemens.com
Emp.: 80
Diagnostic Imaging Center Operating Services
N.A.I.C.S.: 621512

Siemens Healthcare Diagnostics GmbH (4)
Siemensstrasse 90, 1210, Vienna, Austria
Tel.: (43) 3401170119
Web Site: https://www.siemens-healthineers.com
Sales Range: $10-24.9 Million
Emp.: 7
Diagnostic Imaging Center Operator
N.A.I.C.S.: 621512
Wolfgang Koeppl *(Gen Mgr)*

Subsidiary (US):

Siemens Healthcare Diagnostics Inc. (4)
511 Benedict Ave, Tarrytown, NY 10591-5097
Tel.: (914) 631-8000
Web Site: http://www.siemens-healthineers.com
Sales Range: $450-499.9 Million
Emp.: 250
Immuno-Diagnostic Systems & Immuno-chemistry Kits Mfr, Developer & Marketer
N.A.I.C.S.: 334516

Unit (Domestic):

Siemens Healthcare Diagnostics Inc. - Chicago (5)
1717 Deerfield Rd, Deerfield, IL 60015-0778
Tel.: (847) 267-5300
Sales Range: $1-4.9 Billion
Emp.: 6,400
Clinical Diagnostics
N.A.I.C.S.: 325412

Siemens Healthcare Diagnostics Inc. - Flanders (5)
62 Flanders Bartley Rd, Flanders, NJ 07836
Tel.: (973) 927-2828
Web Site: http://www.dpcweb.com
Sales Range: $100-124.9 Million
Emp.: 850
Immuno-Diagnostic Systems & Immuno-chemistry Kits Mfr
N.A.I.C.S.: 325412
David Stein *(Gen Mgr)*

Subsidiary (Non-US):

Siemens Healthcare Diagnostics K.K. (4)
Osaki West Tower 1-11-1 Osaki, Shinagawa-ku, Tokyo, 141-8673, Japan
Tel.: (81) 34937500
Health Care Diagnostic Services
N.A.I.C.S.: 621512

Siemens Healthcare Diagnostics Limited (4)
22/F Two Landmark East 100 How Ming St, Kwun Tong, China (Hong Kong)
Tel.: (852) 28707888
Health Care Diagnostic Services
N.A.I.C.S.: 621512

Siemens Healthcare Diagnostics Ltd (4)
Dr Fahrettin Kerim Gokay Cad No 45 Altunizade Uskudar, 34662, Istanbul, Turkiye
Tel.: (90) 2163258900
Diagnostic Testing Instruments
N.A.I.C.S.: 334510

Siemens Healthcare Diagnostics Ltda. (4)
Carrera 65 11-40, Bogota, Colombia
Tel.: (57) 1 425 31 24
Diagnostic Center Operating Services
N.A.I.C.S.: 621512

Siemens Healthcare Diagnostics Manufacturing Ltd (4)
Northern Rd Chilton Indstl Est, Sudbury, CO10 2XQ, United Kingdom
Tel.: (44) 1787880022
Sales Range: $50-74.9 Million
Emp.: 250
Diagnostic Instrument Mfr
N.A.I.C.S.: 334510

Siemens Healthcare Diagnostics OY (4)
Majurinkatu 1, Espoo, 02601, Finland
Tel.: (358) 10 511 2100
Diagnostic Center
N.A.I.C.S.: 621512

Subsidiary (Domestic):

Siemens Healthcare Diagnostics Products GmbH (4)
Emil-Von-Behring-Str 76, Marburg, 35041, Hesse, Germany
Tel.: (49) 64213913
Diagnostic Center Operating Services
N.A.I.C.S.: 621512

Subsidiary (Non-US):

Siemens Healthcare Diagnostics Products Ltd (4)
Glyn Rhonwy Caernarfon, Gwynedd, LL55 4EL, Wales, United Kingdom
Tel.: (44) 1286871871
Diagnostic Imaging Center Operator
N.A.I.C.S.: 621512

Siemens Healthcare Diagnostics S.A.S. (4)
9 Boulevard Finot, Saint Denis, 93527, France
Tel.: (33) 149229016
Diagnostic Center Operator
N.A.I.C.S.: 621512

Siemens Healthcare Diagnostics S.r.l (4)
Viale Piero e Alberto Pirelli 10, 20126, Milan, Italy
Tel.: (39) 0224362373
Web Site: http://diagnostics.siemens.com
Sales Range: $100-124.9 Million
Diagnostic Testing Instruments
N.A.I.C.S.: 334510

Siemens Healthcare Diagnostics SA (4)
Guido Gezellestraat 125, 1654, Huizingen, Belgium
Tel.: (32) 25364572
Web Site: http://www.healthcare.siemens.com
Emp.: 100
Healthcare Diagnostic Center Operator
N.A.I.C.S.: 621512

Siemens Healthcare Diagnostics Sp. z o.o. (4)
ul Zupnicza 11, 03-821, Warsaw, Poland
Tel.: (48) 228708059
Web Site: http://www.siemens.pl
Sales Range: $75-99.9 Million
Emp.: 30
Diagnostic Testing Instruments
N.A.I.C.S.: 334510

Siemens Healthcare Diagnostics, Unipessoal Lda. (4)
Rua Irmaos Siemens 1, Amadora, 2720-093, Portugal
Tel.: (351) 21 417 8481
Sales Range: $10-24.9 Million
Emp.: 70
Healthcare Diagnostic Center Operator
N.A.I.C.S.: 621512
Ivan Franca *(Gen Mgr)*

Subsidiary (US):

Siemens Molecular Imaging, Inc. (4)
2501 N Barrington Rd, Hoffman Estates, IL 60195-2061
Tel.: (847) 304-7700
Sales Range: $400-449.9 Million
Emp.: 963
Medical Analytical Equipment Mfr
N.A.I.C.S.: 334510
Mark S. Andreaco *(Sr VP)*

Subsidiary (Non-US):

Siemens Medical Solutions AS (3)
Gizella ut 51-57, 1143, Budapest, Hungary
Tel.: (36) 14711000
Web Site: http://new.siemens.com
Sales Range: $25-49.9 Million
Emp.: 15
Provider of Software for Medical Services
N.A.I.C.S.: 334610
Laszlo Emre *(Mng Dir)*

Siemens Medical Solutions Diagnostics (3)
No 4/5 Luis Muntadas, 8022, Barcelona, Spain
Tel.: (34) 932536800
Sales Range: $50-74.9 Million
Emp.: 100
Diagnostic Testing Instruments
N.A.I.C.S.: 334510

Siemens Medical Solutions Diagnostics (3)
Dade Behring House Corp Pk, PO Box 50726, Old Pretoria Rd, 1683, Midrand, Rendjesfontein, South Africa
Tel.: (27) 112373400
Sales Range: $1-9.9 Million
Emp.: 21
Diagnostic Testing Instruments
N.A.I.C.S.: 334510

Siemens Medical Solutions Diagnostics Ltd. (3)
22th Fl 2 Landmark E, 100 How Ming St Kwon Tong, Kowloon, China (Hong Kong)
Tel.: (852) 28707888
Sales Range: $25-49.9 Million
Emp.: 12
Diagnostic Testing Instruments
N.A.I.C.S.: 334510

Siemens Medical Solutions Diagnostics, Unipessoal (3)
Rua Irmaos Siemens 1 - 1A, 2720-093, Lisbon, Portugal
Tel.: (351) 214204172
Web Site: http://www.siemens.com.pg
Sales Range: $25-49.9 Million
Emp.: 79
Diagnostic Testing Instruments
N.A.I.C.S.: 334510
Antonio Gambus *(Mng Dir)*

Subsidiary (Domestic):

Siemens Medical Solutions Health Services GmbH (3)
Kolner Strasse 10B, 65760, Eschborn, Germany **(100%)**
Tel.: (49) 61969240
Web Site: http://www.siemens.de
Sales Range: $25-49.9 Million
Emp.: 50
Provider of Software Solutions for the Healthcare Industry
N.A.I.C.S.: 334610

Subsidiary (Non-US):

Siemens Medical Solutions Health Services Italia (3)
Piazza Sante Bargellini 21, 00157, Rome, Italy
Tel.: (39) 06596921
Web Site: http://www.siemensmedical.com
Sales Range: $25-49.9 Million
Emp.: 14
Provider of Software for the Health Services Field
N.A.I.C.S.: 334610

Siemens Medical Solutions Ltda. (3)
Avenida Mutinga 3800, Sao Paulo, 05110-901, SP, Brazil
Tel.: (55) 1139082211
Web Site: http://www.siemens.com.br
Diagnostic Products
N.A.I.C.S.: 339112
Jose Goncalves Pereira Neto *(Mgr-Press Rels)*

Subsidiary (US):

Siemens Medical Solutions USA, Inc. (3)
40 Liberty Blvd, Malvern, PA 19355-1406
Tel.: (610) 448-4500
Web Site: https://www.siemens-healthineers.com
Sales Range: $1-4.9 Billion
Emp.: 8,000

SIEMENS AKTIENGESELLSCHAFT — INTERNATIONAL PUBLIC

Siemens Aktiengesellschaft—(Continued)
Diagnostic & Therapeutic Systems & Devices Mfr, Developer & Marketer
N.A.I.C.S.: 339112

Subsidiary (Domestic):

Corindus Vascular Robotics, Inc. (4)
309 Waverley Oaks Rd Ste 105, Waltham, MA 02452
Tel.: (508) 653-3335
Web Site: http://www.corindus.com
Rev.: $10,781,000
Assets: $33,525,000
Liabilities: $42,731,000
Net Worth: ($9,206,000)
Earnings: ($34,989,000)
Emp.: 90
Fiscal Year-end: 12/31/2018
Precision Vascular Robotic-Assisted Systems Mfr
N.A.I.C.S.: 339112
David W. Long (CFO)

Branch (Domestic):

Siemens Medical Equipment-New York (4)
2 Penn Plz, New York, NY 10121-0101
Tel.: (212) 563-2380
Web Site: http://www.siemensmedical.com
Sales Range: $25-49.9 Million
Emp.: 100
Medical Equipment Sales
N.A.I.C.S.: 423450

Siemens Medical Solutions Ultrasound Division (4)
685 E Middlefield Rd Mountain, Mountain View, CA 94043
Tel.: (650) 969-9112
Web Site: http://www.ssiemens.com
Sales Range: $450-499.9 Million
Emp.: 200
Diagnostic Equipment Mfr & Distr
N.A.I.C.S.: 423450
Jeff Gundy (Pres)

Subsidiary (US):

Varian Medical Systems, Inc. (2)
3120 Hansen Way M/S G100, Palo Alto, CA 94304-1038
Tel.: (213) 337-4615
Web Site: https://www.varian.com
Rev.: $3,168,200,000
Assets: $4,462,200,000
Liabilities: $2,377,400,000
Net Worth: $2,084,800,000
Earnings: $269,200,000
Emp.: 10,613
Fiscal Year-end: 10/02/2020
Integrated Cancer Therapy Systems, X-Ray Tubes & Flat Panel Digital Subsystems
N.A.I.C.S.: 334510
Vy H. Tran (Sr VP-Compliance & Quality)

Subsidiary (Domestic):

Cancer Treatment Services International, Inc. (3)
887 Covenant Ave #316, Pittsburgh, PA 15237
Tel.: (412) 204-1260
Web Site: http://www.cancertreatmentservices.com
Sales Range: $1-9.9 Million
Emp.: 5
Outpatient Cancer Treatment
N.A.I.C.S.: 621498
Stanley M. Marks (Co-Founder & Chm)

CyberHeart, Inc. (3)
2490 Hospital Dr Ste 310, Mountain View, CA 94040
Tel.: (408) 701-5000
Web Site: http://www.cyberheartinc.com
Cardiac Treatment
N.A.I.C.S.: 621999

Mobius Medical Systems, LP (3)
4615 Southwest Fwy Ste 330, Houston, TX 77027
Tel.: (263) 854-1711
Web Site: http://www.mobiusmed.com
Electromedical Product Mfr
N.A.I.C.S.: 334510
Nathan Childress (Founder)

Subsidiary (Non-US):

Noona Healthcare Oy (3)
Alvar Aalton katu 5, 00100, Helsinki, Finland
Tel.: (358) 9430771
Web Site: http://www.noona.com
Emp.: 300
Healtcare Services
N.A.I.C.S.: 621610
Jani Ahonala (Co-Founder & CEO)

VMS Deutschland Holdings G.m.b.H. (3)
Alsfelder Strasse 6, 64289, Darmstadt, Germany
Tel.: (49) 61517313300
Medical Device Mfr
N.A.I.C.S.: 334510

Varian Medical France S.A.S. (3)
Batiment Astrale 9 Avenue Reaumur, 92350, Le Plessis-Robinson, Cedex, France (100%)
Tel.: (33) 146012222
Web Site: http://www.varian.com.fr
Sales Range: $25-49.9 Million
Emp.: 80
Mfr of Cancer Treatment Equipment
N.A.I.C.S.: 339112

Subsidiary (Domestic):

Varian Medical System Latin America, Ltd. (3)
5200 Blue Lagoon Dr Ste 890, Miami, FL 33126 (100%)
Tel.: (305) 929-1970
Web Site: http://www.varian.com
Sales Range: $100-124.9 Million
Cancer Treatment Equipment
N.A.I.C.S.: 339112

Subsidiary (Non-US):

Varian Medical Systems (China) Co. Ltd. (3)
No 8 Yuncheng St, Beijing Economic Technological Development Area, Beijing, 100176, China
Tel.: (86) 1087858785
Emp.: 200
Medical Equipment Mfr
N.A.I.C.S.: 339112
Zhang Xiao (Mng Dir)

Varian Medical Systems Australasia Holdings Pty. Ltd. (3)
Suite 3 13A Narabang Way, Belrose, Sydney, 2085, NSW, Australia
Tel.: (61) 294850100
Integrated Cancer Therapy System Mfr
N.A.I.C.S.: 334510
Diana Andruczyk (Acct Mgr)

Varian Medical Systems Australasia Pty Ltd. (3)
Suite 3 13A Narabang Way, Belrose, Sydney, 2085, NSW, Australia (100%)
Tel.: (61) 294850100
Web Site: http://www.varian.com
Sales Range: $100-124.9 Million
Mfr of Cancer Treatment Equipment
N.A.I.C.S.: 339112

Varian Medical Systems Belgium N.V. (3)
Park Hill E Mommaertslaan 16B, 1831, Diegem, Belgium
Tel.: (32) 27201008
Web Site: http://www.farian.com
Sales Range: $10-24.9 Million
Emp.: 23
Medical Equipment Mfr
N.A.I.C.S.: 339112

Varian Medical Systems Brasil Ltda. (3)
Avenida Beirute 870 Polo Industrial Multivias Jardim Ermida I, Jundiai, Sao Paulo, Brazil (100%)
Tel.: (55) 1134572655
Web Site: https://www.varian.com
Sales Range: $25-49.9 Million
Emp.: 100
Mfr of Cancer Treatment Equipment
N.A.I.C.S.: 339112

Varian Medical Systems Canada, Inc. (3)
Ste 705 - 386 Broadway, Winnipeg, R3C 3R6, MB, Canada
Tel.: (204) 987-8770
Web Site: http://www.varian.com
Emp.: 120
Medical Equipment Mfr
N.A.I.C.S.: 339112

Varian Medical Systems Deutschland GmbH (3)
Alsselderstrasse 6, 64289, Darmstadt, Germany (100%)
Tel.: (49) 615173130
Web Site: http://www.varian.com
Sales Range: $25-49.9 Million
Emp.: 130
Mfr of Cancer Treatment Equipment
N.A.I.C.S.: 339112
Holger Maar (Mng Dir)

Subsidiary (Domestic):

MeVis Medical Solutions AG (4)
Caroline-Herschel-Str 1, 28359, Bremen, Germany
Tel.: (49) 421224950
Web Site: https://www.mevis.de
Rev.: $19,143,338
Assets: $30,968,040
Liabilities: $7,559,924
Net Worth: $23,408,116
Earnings: $5,430,562
Emp.: 101
Fiscal Year-end: 09/30/2023
Medical Software Developer & Marketer
N.A.I.C.S.: 513210
Marcus Kirchhoff (Member-Exec Bd)

Subsidiary (Non-US):

Varian Medical Systems Finland OY (3)
Alvar Aallon katu 5, 00100, Helsinki, Finland (100%)
Tel.: (358) 9430771
Web Site: https://www.varian.com
Sales Range: $25-49.9 Million
Emp.: 300
Mfr of Cancer Treatment Equipment
N.A.I.C.S.: 339112

Varian Medical Systems France (3)
9 Avenue Reaumur, 92350, Le Plessis-Robinson, France
Tel.: (33) 146012222
Web Site: http://www.varian.com
Emp.: 193
Medical Equipment Mfr
N.A.I.C.S.: 339112

Varian Medical Systems Gesellschaft m.b.H. (3)
Liebermannstrasse A01 404, 2345, Brunn am Gebirge, Austria
Tel.: (43) 2236377196
Medical Equipment Distr
N.A.I.C.S.: 423450

Varian Medical Systems Haan G.m.b.H. (3)
Bergische Strasse 16, Haan, Haan, Germany
Tel.: (49) 21295510
Web Site: http://www.varian.com
Medical Equipment Distr
N.A.I.C.S.: 541380

Varian Medical Systems Hungary Kft (3)
MOM Park SAS Tower Csorsz utca 45, 1124, Budapest, Hungary
Tel.: (36) 15012600
Emp.: 29
Medical Equipment Mfr
N.A.I.C.S.: 339112

Varian Medical Systems Iberica S.L. (3)
Avenida de Europa 16 2, Alcobendas, 28108, Spain
Tel.: (34) 913344800
Web Site: http://www.varian.com
Mfr of Cancer Treatment Equipment
N.A.I.C.S.: 339112

Varian Medical Systems Imaging Laboratory Gmbh (3)
Tafernstrasse 7, 5405, Baden-Dattwil, Switzerland
Tel.: (41) 562030404

Sales Range: $25-49.9 Million
Emp.: 185
Medical Equipment Mfr
N.A.I.C.S.: 339112

Varian Medical Systems India Pvt Ltd. (3)
F1 2nd Fl Ali Twrs 55 Greams Rd, Chennai, 600006, India (100%)
Tel.: (91) 4428295970
Web Site: http://www.varian.com
Sales Range: $50-74.9 Million
Emp.: 250
Mfr of Cancer Treatment Equipment
N.A.I.C.S.: 339112

Varian Medical Systems International (India) Pvt. Ltd. (3)
Unit No 33 3rd Floor Kalpataru Square Off Andheri Kurla Road, Andheri East, Mumbai, 400 059, Maharashtra, India
Tel.: (91) 2267852210
Medical Equipment Mfr
N.A.I.C.S.: 339112
Suman Sil (Mgr-Sls-India & Bangladesh)

Varian Medical Systems International AG (3)
Hinterbergstrasse 14, Cham, 6330, Switzerland (100%)
Tel.: (41) 417498844
Web Site: http://www.varian.com
Sales Range: $25-49.9 Million
Emp.: 200
Mfr of Cancer Treatment Equipment
N.A.I.C.S.: 339112
Devlees Chauwer (Mng Dir)

Varian Medical Systems Italia SpA (3)
Via Brescia 28, Cornusco, 20063, Italy (100%)
Tel.: (39) 02921351
Web Site: http://www.varian.com
Sales Range: $100-124.9 Million
Emp.: 70
Mfr of Cancer Treatment Equipment
N.A.I.C.S.: 339112

Varian Medical Systems KK (3)
Kabutocho Daiichi Heiwa Bld, 5-1 Nihonbashi-Kabutocho, Tokyo, 103-0006, Chuo-ku, Japan (100%)
Tel.: (81) 344865010
Cancer Treatment Equipment Mfr
N.A.I.C.S.: 339112

Varian Medical Systems Nederland B.V. (3)
Kokemolen 2, 3994 DH, Houten, Netherlands (100%)
Tel.: (31) 306340506
Web Site: http://www.varian.com
Sales Range: $100-124.9 Million
Emp.: 20
Mfr of Cancer Treatment Equipment
N.A.I.C.S.: 339112

Varian Medical Systems Pacific, Inc. (3)
14/Floor Tower 1 The Gateway Harbour City 25 Canton Road, Tsimshatsui, Kowloon, China (Hong Kong) (100%)
Tel.: (852) 27242836
Sales Range: $10-24.9 Million
Emp.: 35
Mfr of Cancer Treatment Equipment
N.A.I.C.S.: 339112

Varian Medical Systems Poland Sp. z o.o. (3)
ul Osmanska 12, 02-823, Warsaw, Poland
Tel.: (48) 225489200
Medical Device Mfr
N.A.I.C.S.: 334510
Andrzej Broniek (Sr Mgr-Education Dept)

Varian Medical Systems Scandinavia AS (3)
Lyskaer 9, 2730, Herlev, Denmark (100%)
Tel.: (45) 44500100
Web Site: http://www.varian.com
Sales Range: $10-24.9 Million
Emp.: 40
Mfr of Cancer Treatment Equipment
N.A.I.C.S.: 339112

Varian Medical Systems Trading (Beijing) Co., Ltd. (3)

AND PRIVATE COMPANIES — SIEMENS AKTIENGESELLSCHAFT

No 8 Yun Cheng St Beijing Economic Technological Development Zone, Area BDA, Beijing, 100176, China **(100%)**
Tel.: (86) 1087858785
Sales Range: $100-124.9 Million
Cancer Treatment Equipment Mfr
N.A.I.C.S.: 339112

Varian Medical Systems UK Holdings Limited (3)
Gatwick Road, Crawley, RH10 9RG, West Sussex, United Kingdom
Tel.: (44) 1293601200
Web Site: http://www.varian.com
Emp.: 240
Holding Company
N.A.I.C.S.: 551112

Varian Medical Systems UK Ltd. (3)
Oncology House Gatwick Road, Crawley, RH10 9RG, West Sussex, United Kingdom
Tel.: (44) 1293601200
Web Site: http://www.varian.com
Mfr of Cancer Treatment Equipment
N.A.I.C.S.: 339112

Unit (Domestic):

Varian Medical Systems, Inc. - Oncology Systems (3)
3100 Hansen Way, Palo Alto, CA 94304-1028
Tel.: (650) 493-4000
Web Site: http://www.varian.com
Sales Range: $100-124.9 Million
Medical & Radiographic Linear Accelerators
N.A.I.C.S.: 334510
Christopher A. Toth (Pres)

Subsidiary (Non-US):

Varinak Bulgaria Ltd. (3)
85 Alexander Malinov Blvd 4th Floor Office 12, Sofia, 1715, Bulgaria
Tel.: (359) 24836081
Medical Equipment Mfr
N.A.I.C.S.: 339112

Varinak Europe SRL (3)
Intrarea Valului Nr 26 Sector 1, Bucharest, Romania
Tel.: (40) 212426600
Medical Equipment Mfr
N.A.I.C.S.: 339112

humediQ global GmbH (3)
St Martin Str 64, 81541, Munich, Germany
Tel.: (49) 8964956284
Web Site: http://www.humediq.com
Surgical & Medical Instrument Mfr
N.A.I.C.S.: 339112
Max Geier (CFO)

Siemens Healthineers International AG (1)
Freilagerstrasse 40, 8047, Zurich, Switzerland
Tel.: (41) 581991199
Healthcare Management Consulting Services
N.A.I.C.S.: 621498

Siemens Healthineers Ltd. (1)
PoongSan building 6th floor 23 ChungJoeng-ro, Seodaemun-gu, Seoul, 03737, Korea (South)
Tel.: (82) 234507200
Healthcare Services
N.A.I.C.S.: 621511
Sangbeom Jeong (Sr Mgr)

Siemens Healthineers Nederland B.V. (1)
Prinses Beatrixlaan 800, 2595 BN, Hague, Netherlands
Tel.: (31) 884244444
Healthcare Management Consulting Services
N.A.I.C.S.: 621498

Siemens Hearing Instruments (Suzhou) Co. Ltd. (1)
120 Su Tong Rd China Singapore Suzhou Industrial Park, Suzhou, 215021, Jiang-Su, China
Tel.: (86) 512 676 132 01
Sales Range: $100-124.9 Million
Emp.: 50
Hearing Instruments Mfr
N.A.I.C.S.: 334510

Fu Jian Tong (Mgr-Sls)

Siemens Hearing Instruments Inc. (1)
320 Pinebush Rd Unit 7, Cambridge, N3C 2V3, ON, Canada
Tel.: (519) 622-5200
Web Site: http://www.siemenscopenfivan.com
Emp.: 50
Hearing Aid Mfr
N.A.I.C.S.: 334510
Jeff Malpass (CEO)

Siemens Hearing Instruments K.K. (1)
5-29-15 Sagamiohno, Minami-ku, Sagamihara, 252-0303, Kanagawa, Japan
Tel.: (81) 42 765 7211
Hearing Aid Mfr & Distr
N.A.I.C.S.: 334510

Siemens Hearing Instruments Pty. Ltd. (1)
Level 4 11 Finchley St, PO Box 1950, Milton, 4064, QLD, Australia
Tel.: (61) 7 3858 7700
Web Site: http://www.hearing.siemens.com
Emp.: 100
Hearing Aid Mfr
N.A.I.C.S.: 334510
Paul Guthrie (Mng Dir)

Siemens Hearing Solution (Pty.) Ltd. (1)
5 Hunter St Fernridge Office Park Block 5, Ferndale, 2194, Randburg, South Africa
Tel.: (27) 11 399 5940
Web Site: http://w1.hearing.siemens.com
Sales Range: $25-49.9 Million
Emp.: 30
Hearing Aid Mfr
N.A.I.C.S.: 334510
Michelle Reyneke (Exec Dir)

Siemens High Voltage Circuit Breaker Co., Ltd. (1)
6th Road, Xisha, Hangzhou, 310018, China
Tel.: (86) 5716910380
Circuit Breaker Mfr
N.A.I.C.S.: 335312

Siemens Horeapparater A/S (1)
Borupvang 3, 2750, Ballerup, Denmark
Tel.: (45) 63 15 40 00
Web Site: http://www.siemens.dk
Hearing Aid Mfr
N.A.I.C.S.: 334510

Siemens Horeapparater AS (1)
Ostre Aker vei 88, 0596, Oslo, Norway
Tel.: (47) 22633000
Web Site: http://new.siemens.com
Emp.: 15
Hearing Equipment Mfr
N.A.I.C.S.: 334510

Siemens IT Services S.A. (1)
Coronel Manuel E Arias 3751, Buenos Aires, 1430, Argentina
Tel.: (54) 1163158800
Information Technology Consulting Services
N.A.I.C.S.: 541511

Siemens Immobilien Chemnitz-Voerde GmbH (1)
Marktplatz 3, Grunwald, 82031, Bavaria, Germany
Tel.: (49) 2871920
Administrative Management Consulting Services
N.A.I.C.S.: 541611

Siemens Industrial Automation Ltd. (1)
23-25/F Xuhuiyuan Bldg 1089 No 2 Zhongshan Nan Rd, Shanghai, 200030, China
Tel.: (86) 21 5410 8666
Emp.: 30
Automation & Drive System Installation Services
N.A.I.C.S.: 238210

Siemens Industrial LLC (1)
New Cairo-Fifth Settlement Bureau 175 Al-Horreya Axis - 90 South Road, PO Box 245, 11835, Cairo, Egypt
Tel.: (20) 226141190
Banking & Financial Services
N.A.I.C.S.: 522110

Siemens Industrial Solutions & Services Group (1)
Schuhstrasse 60, D-91052, Erlangen, Germany
Tel.: (49) 913170
Web Site: http://www.siemens.de
Sales Range: $25-49.9 Billion
Emp.: 83,500
Technical Services for Process & Manufacturing Companies
N.A.I.C.S.: 541330

Subsidiary (US):

Siemens Industry, Inc. (2)
200 Massachusetts Ave NW Ste 600, Washington, DC 20001 **(100%)**
Tel.: (770) 751-2000
Web Site: https://www.siemens.com
Sales Range: $1-4.9 Billion
Emp.: 9,400
Electrical Motors, Switchgear & Power Switching Equipment, Regulator & Control Systems & Industrial & Building Systems Marketer & Mfr
N.A.I.C.S.: 335313
Christopher Romeo (Dir-Sls & Traffic Svcs)

Subsidiary (Domestic):

Republic Intelligent Transportation Services, Inc. (3)
371 Bel Marin Keys Blvd No 200, Novato, CA 94949
Tel.: (415) 884-3000
Electrical Equipment Installation & Transportation Engineering Services
N.A.I.C.S.: 238210

Branch (Domestic):

Siemens Industry, Inc. - New York (3)
155 Plant Ave, Hauppauge, NY 11788-3801
Tel.: (631) 231-3600
Sales Range: $25-49.9 Million
Emp.: 42
Fluid Meter & Counting Device Services
N.A.I.C.S.: 334514

Unit (Domestic):

Siemens Industry, Inc. - Philadelphia (3)
1201 Sumneytown Pike, Spring House, PA 19477-1019
Tel.: (423) 262-5710
Web Site: http://www.sea.siemens.com
Sales Range: $100-124.9 Million
Emp.: 300
Mfr of Industrial Automated Systems & Dimensional Measuring Gages
N.A.I.C.S.: 334513

Subsidiary (Non-US):

Moore Products Co. B.V. (4)
Wagenmakerstraat 3, 2984 BD, Ridderkerk, Netherlands **(100%)**
Tel.: (31) 180 461111
Web Site: http://www.moore-solutions.com
Sales Range: $25-49.9 Million
Emp.: 3
Mfr of Industrial Instrumentation
N.A.I.C.S.: 334513

Unit (Domestic):

Siemens Intelligent Transportation Systems (3)
8004 Cameron Rd, Austin, TX 78754-3808
Tel.: (512) 837-8310
Sales Range: $50-74.9 Million
Emp.: 250
Traffic Systems Mfr
N.A.I.C.S.: 336999

Subsidiary (Domestic):

eMeter Corporation (3)
4000 E 3rd Ave 4th Fl, Foster City, CA 94404
Tel.: (650) 227-7770
Web Site: http://www.emeter.com
Sales Range: $10-24.9 Million
Emp.: 100
Electricity Metering & Grid Management Software Publisher
N.A.I.C.S.: 513210
Larsh Johnson (Co-Founder & CTO)

Subsidiary (Non-US):

Siemens VAI Metals Technologies GmbH & Co (2)
Turmstrasse 44, 4020, Linz, Austria
Tel.: (43) 7065925685
Web Site: http://www.siemens-vai.com
Sales Range: $400-449.9 Million
Emp.: 1,700
Engineering Services & Metal Mining & Processing Equipment Mfr
N.A.I.C.S.: 541330

Siemens Industriegetriebe GmbH (1)
Thierbacher Str 24, 9322, Penig, Sachsen, Germany
Tel.: (49) 3738161211
Financial Investment Services
N.A.I.C.S.: 523999

Siemens Industriepark Karlsruhe GmbH & Co. KG (1)
Siemensallee 84, 76187, Karlsruhe, Germany
Tel.: (49) 7215950
Real Estate Manangement Services
N.A.I.C.S.: 531390

Siemens Industry Software (India) Private Limited (1)
Tower D 16th Floor Global Business Park Mehrauli, Gurgaon, 122002, Haryana, India
Tel.: (91) 1244092200
Web Site: http://www.siemens.co.in
Emp.: 4
Software Development Services
N.A.I.C.S.: 541511
Peter Edwards (Mng Dir)

Siemens Industry Software (Shanghai) Co., Ltd. (1)
13/F Cloud-9 Office Tower 1018 Changning Road, Shanghai, 200042, China
Tel.: (86) 2122086861
Software Development Services
N.A.I.C.S.: 541511

Siemens Industry Software (TW) Co., Ltd. (1)
9/F No 63 Chou Tze St, Neihu, Taipei, Taiwan
Tel.: (886) 226570000
Engineering Services
N.A.I.C.S.: 541330
Tino Hildebrand (Chm)

Siemens Industry Software A/S (1)
Gydevang 39 - 41, 3450, Allerod, Denmark
Tel.: (45) 33244434
Web Site: http://www.automation.siemens.com
Software Development Services
N.A.I.C.S.: 541511

Siemens Industry Software AB (1)
Kronborgsgrand 7, 164 87, Kista, Sweden
Tel.: (46) 850699000
Sales Range: $25-49.9 Million
Emp.: 10
Software Development Services
N.A.I.C.S.: 541511
Ola Janson (Dir-Sls)

Siemens Industry Software AG (1)
Freilagerstrasse 40, 8047, Zurich, Switzerland
Tel.: (41) 447557272
Software Development Services
N.A.I.C.S.: 541511

Siemens Industry Software B.V. (1)
Akeleibaan 60, 2908 KA, Capelle aan den IJssel, Netherlands
Tel.: (31) 102642828
Web Site: http://www.automation.siemens.com
Software Development Services
N.A.I.C.S.: 541511

Siemens Industry Software GmbH (1)
Wolfgang-Pauli-Strasse 2, 4020, Linz, Austria
Tel.: (43) 732377550
Software Development Services
N.A.I.C.S.: 513210

Siemens Industry Software K.K. (1)
2-2-1 Yoyogi 9th Floor, Shibuya-ku, Tokyo, 151-8583, Japan

SIEMENS AKTIENGESELLSCHAFT

Siemens Aktiengesellschaft—(Continued)
Tel.: (81) 353546700
Software Development Services
N.A.I.C.S.: 541511

Siemens Industry Software Limited (1)
223-231 Wai Yip Street, Kwun Tong, Kowloon, China (Hong Kong)
Tel.: (852) 22303333
Software Development Services
N.A.I.C.S.: 541511

Siemens Industry Software Ltd. (1)
5005 Levy Street, Saint Laurent, H4R 2N9, QC, Canada
Tel.: (514) 338-3000
Sales Range: $25-49.9 Million
Emp.: 25
Software Development Services
N.A.I.C.S.: 541511

Siemens Industry Software Ltd. (1)
10 Abba Eban Blvd Building C 5th Floor, POB 2155, Herzliyya, 46120, Israel
Tel.: (972) 99552636
Software Development Services
N.A.I.C.S.: 541511

Siemens Industry Software Ltd. (1)
16th Fl SEI Tower 39 Eonju-ro 30-gil, Gangnam-gu, Seoul, 06292, Korea (South)
Tel.: (82) 230162000
Engineeering Services
N.A.I.C.S.: 541330
Jinbok Yoo (Mgr-Svc)

Siemens Industry Software Ltda. (1)
Rua Niteroi 400 - 8o tô walk, Sao Caetano do Sul, 09510-210, Sao Paulo, Brazil
Tel.: (55) 1142287600
Sales Range: $25-49.9 Million
Emp.: 10
Software Development Services
N.A.I.C.S.: 541511
Paulo Costa (Gen Mgr)

Siemens Industry Software Pte. Ltd, (1)
60 Macpherson Road 10th Floor, Singapore, 348615, Singapore
Tel.: (65) 63338998
Engineeering Services
N.A.I.C.S.: 541330

Siemens Industry Software S.L. (1)
Lluis Muntadas No 5, Cornella De Llobregat, 08940, Barcelona, Spain
Tel.: (34) 935102200
Web Site: http://www.plm.automation.siemens.com
Software Development Services
N.A.I.C.S.: 541511

Siemens Industry Software S.r.l (1)
Via Vipiteno 4, 20128, Milan, Italy
Tel.: (39) 02210571
Web Site: http://www.plm.automation.siemens.com
Software Development Services
N.A.I.C.S.: 541511

Siemens Industry Software SA (Pty.) Ltd, (1)
Tijgervallei Office Park Block 6 Silverlakes Road, Pretoria, 0081, Gauteng, South Africa
Tel.: (27) 128099500
Software Development Services
N.A.I.C.S.: 541511

Siemens Industry Software SAS (1)
13 Ave Morane Saulnier Espace Velizy, Immeuble Le Chavez, 78140, Velizy-Villacoublay, France
Tel.: (33) 130 670 100
Sales Range: $25-49.9 Million
Emp.: 8
Software Development Services
N.A.I.C.S.: 541511

Siemens Industry Software Sdn. Bhd. (1)
1B-3-18 One Precinct Lengkik Mayang Pasir, 11950, Bayan Lepas, Penang, Malaysia
Tel.: (60) 46384702
Engineeering Services
N.A.I.C.S.: 541330

Siemens Industry Software, s.r.o. (1)
Mezi Vodami 2035/31, 143 20, Prague, Czech Republic
Tel.: (420) 602129781
Sales Range: $25-49.9 Million
Emp.: 150
Software Development Services
N.A.I.C.S.: 541511
Mariusz Zabielski (CEO)

Siemens Inmobiliaria S.A. de C.V. (1)
Poniente No 116-590, Mexico, 2300, Mexico
Tel.: (52) 5553282000
Software Development Services
N.A.I.C.S.: 541511

Siemens Innovaciones S.A. de C.V. (1)
Guillermo Barroso No 20-4, Mexico, Mexico
Tel.: (52) 55 5328 2186
Conveying Equipment Mfr
N.A.I.C.S.: 333922

Siemens International Trading Ltd. (1)
Siemens Shanghai Ctr No 500 Dalian Rd, Shanghai, 200131, China
Tel.: (86) 2138893413
Medical Equipment Distr
N.A.I.C.S.: 423450

Siemens Israel Ltd. (1)
14 Hamelacha St Afeq Industrial Park, 48091, Rosh Ha'Ayin, Israel
Tel.: (972) 39151500
Web Site: http://www.siemens.co.il
Sales Range: $250-299.9 Million
Emp.: 600
Electric Power Distribution Services
N.A.I.C.S.: 221122

Siemens Japan Holding K.K. (1)
Takanawa Park Tower 20-14 Higashi-Gotanda 3-chome, Shinagawa-ku, Tokyo, 141-8641, Japan
Tel.: (81) 354238500
Investment Management Service
N.A.I.C.S.: 523999

Siemens Japan K.K. (1)
Gate City Osaki West Tower 1-11-1 Osaki, Shinagawa-Ku, Tokyo, 141-8641, Japan
Tel.: (81) 334934204
Web Site: http://new.siemens.com
Medical Device & Electronic Equipment Whslr
N.A.I.C.S.: 423450
Junichi Obata (Pres & CEO)

Siemens K.K. (1)
Takanawa Park Twr 20 14 Higashi Gotanda 2 Chome Shinagawa ku, Tokyo, 141, Japan (83%)
Tel.: (81) 354238489
Web Site: http://www.siemens.co.jp
Sales Range: $200-249.9 Million
Emp.: 301
Mfr & Sales of Electronic Equipment
N.A.I.C.S.: 334419

Siemens Kameda Healthcare IT Systems K. K. (1)
Park Tower Takanawa 3-20-14 Higashi Gotanda, Shinagawa-ku, Tokyo, 141-0022, Japan
Tel.: (81) 354236270
Web Site: http://www.kameda-hi.com
Sales Range: $25-49.9 Million
Emp.: 43
Medical Equipment Distr
N.A.I.C.S.: 423450

Siemens Kapitalanlagegesellschaft mbH (1)
Otto-Hahn-Ring 6, Bavaria, 81739, Munich, Germany
Tel.: (49) 8963635222
Web Site: https://www.swfinstitute.org
Sales Range: $50-74.9 Million
Emp.: 30
Financial Management Services
N.A.I.C.S.: 523999
Josef Mehl (CEO)

Siemens Kenya Ltd. (1)
Park Lift Bldg 2nd Ave, Park land, PO Box 5 08 67, City Square, 0200, Nairobi, Kenya
Tel.: (254) 202856000
Electrical Engineering Services

N.A.I.C.S.: 541330

Siemens LLC (1)
Corner of 9th and 10th Street, PO Box 47015, Masdar City opposite Presidential Flight, Abu Dhabi, United Arab Emirates
Tel.: (97) 26165100
Web Site: http://new.siemens.com
Engineeering Services
N.A.I.C.S.: 541330

Siemens Lease B.V. (1)
Werner von Siemensstraat 1, Zoetermeer, 2712 PN, Netherlands
Tel.: (31) 70 333 2276
Electrical Engineering Services
N.A.I.C.S.: 541330

Siemens Limitada (1)
Rua dos Deportes JAT V Building 9th Floor, Caixa Postal 4 84, Maputo, Mozambique
Tel.: (258) 13104160
Sales Range: $25-49.9 Million
Emp.: 30
Industrial Solutions & Services
N.A.I.C.S.: 541420

Siemens Limited (1)
2922/333 New Petchburi Road, HuayKwang Bangkapi, Bangkok, 10310, Thailand
Tel.: (66) 27154264
Web Site: http://new.siemens.com
Sales Range: $500-549.9 Million
Emp.: 1,100
Engineeering Services
N.A.I.C.S.: 541330

Siemens Limited (1)
Baladia/Binzager Street, PO Box 4621, Al Azizia, Jeddah, 21412, Saudi Arabia
Tel.: (966) 126618888
Web Site: http://www.siemens.com.sa
Sales Range: $1-4.9 Billion
Emp.: 1,500
Industrial Solution & Services
N.A.I.C.S.: 541330

Siemens Limited (1)
100 Ajose Adeogun Street, Lagos, 101241, Nigeria
Tel.: (234) 14480148
Web Site: http://new.siemens.com
Sales Range: $150-199.9 Million
Emp.: 140
Power Generation & Distr Services
N.A.I.C.S.: 221118

Siemens Limited (1)
8F No 3 Park St, Nangang District, Taipei, 11503, Taiwan (100%)
Tel.: (886) 226528888
Web Site: http://new.siemens.com
Sales Range: $500-549.9 Million
Emp.: 500
Mfr of Telecommunication Equipment & Systems
N.A.I.C.S.: 517111

Siemens Limited (1)
No 223-231 Wai Yip Street, Manulife Financial Centre Kwun Tong, Kowloon, China (Hong Kong)
Tel.: (852) 22303333
Engineeering Services
N.A.I.C.S.: 541330

Siemens Logistics AG (1)
Logistic Services
N.A.I.C.S.: 541614

Siemens Logistics Automation Systems (Beijing) Co., Ltd. (1)
No 7 Wangjing Zhonghuan Nanlu, Chaoyang District, Beijing, 100102, China
Tel.: (86) 1064764450
Logistic Services
N.A.I.C.S.: 541614

Siemens Logistics GmbH (1)
Lilienthalstrasse 16/18, 78467, Konstanz, Germany
Tel.: (49) 7531862500
Web Site: https://www.siemens-logistics.com
Airport Logistics Services
N.A.I.C.S.: 488119
Thomas Knobloch (CFO)

Siemens Logistics India Private Limited (1)
Logistic Services

INTERNATIONAL PUBLIC

N.A.I.C.S.: 541614
Arun Kanaujia (CEO)

Siemens Logistics Limited (1)
2 Chun Wan Road Room 1111-1113 11 F Commercial Building, Airport Freight Forwarding Centre Chek Lap Kok, Hong Kong, China (Hong Kong)
Tel.: (852) 31275307
Logistic Services
N.A.I.C.S.: 541614
James Lin (CEO)

Siemens Logistics Ltd. (1)
274 Mackenzie Avenue Suite 350, Ajax, L1S 2E9, ON, Canada
Tel.: (905) 683-8200
Logistic Services
N.A.I.C.S.: 541614

Siemens Logistics Pte. Ltd. (1)
Logistic Services
N.A.I.C.S.: 541614
Lars Heimlich (Sls Dir)

Siemens Logistics S.L. (1)
Unipersonal Ronda de Europa 5, 28760, Tres Cantos, Spain
Tel.: (34) 915148000
Logistic Services
N.A.I.C.S.: 541614

Siemens Logistics S.r.l. (1)
Via Vipiteno 4, 20128, Milan, Italy
Tel.: (39) 02210571
Logistic Services
N.A.I.C.S.: 484110

Siemens Logistics SAS (1)
40 avenue des Fruitiers, Saint-Denis, 93527, Paris, France
Tel.: (33) 185570000
Logistic Services
N.A.I.C.S.: 484110

Siemens Ltd. (1)
D Tower Gwanghwamun Jongno 3-gil, Jongno-gu, Seoul, 03155, Korea (South)
Tel.: (82) 234507000
Web Site: https://www.siemens.com
Electrical Equipment Mfr & Distr
N.A.I.C.S.: 335999
ChewKong Lum (Pres, CEO & CFO)

Siemens Ltd. (1)
9th Floor Ocean Park Building No 01 Dao Duy Anh, Dong Da Dist, Hanoi, Vietnam
Tel.: (84) 2435776688
Web Site: https://www.siemens.com
Sales Range: $25-49.9 Million
Emp.: 70
Engineeering Services
N.A.I.C.S.: 541330

Siemens Ltd. (1)
163 Hendrik Verwoerd Drive, Private Bag X71, Halfway House, Cape Town, 7500, South Africa (70%)
Tel.: (27) 116522000
Web Site: http://new.siemens.com
Sales Range: $1-4.9 Billion
Emp.: 2,000
Communication Equipment Mfr
N.A.I.C.S.: 334290

Siemens Ltd. (1)
East Park Shannon Free Zone, Leeson Close, Shannon, V14 YD96, Ireland (100%)
Tel.: (353) 61256200
Web Site: http://www.siemens.ie
Sales Range: $50-74.9 Million
Emp.: 133
Sales Company
N.A.I.C.S.: 449210
Gary O'Callaghan (CEO)

Siemens Ltd. (1)
885 Mountain Highway, Bayswater, 3153, VIC, Australia (100%)
Tel.: (61) 131773
Web Site: http://new.siemens.com
Sales Range: $300-349.9 Million
Emp.: 2,000
Mfr & Sales of Transmission Equipment, PBXs, Switchgear & Control Systems
N.A.I.C.S.: 335313

Siemens Ltd. (1)
Birla Aurora Level 21 Plot No 1080 Dr An-

AND PRIVATE COMPANIES — SIEMENS AKTIENGESELLSCHAFT

nie Besant Road, Worli, Mumbai, 400030, India
Tel.: (91) 2239677000 **(69%)**
Web Site: https://www.siemens.com
Sales Range: $450-499.9 Million
Emp.: 7,170
Mfr & Sales of Motors & Switchgear; Power Switching Installation & Railway Signaling Equipment; Medical Equipment
N.A.I.C.S.: 335312
Sunil Mathur *(CEO & Mng Dir)*

Subsidiary (Domestic):

C&S Electric Limited **(2)**
210 211 212 Second Floor Salcon Aurum Building Plot No 4, Jasola District Centre, New Delhi, 110025, India **(99.22%)**
Tel.: (91) 1169225600
Web Site: https://www.cselectric.co.in
Emp.: 5,000
Electric Equipment Mfr
N.A.I.C.S.: 423610

Plant (Domestic):

C&S Electric Limited C&S ACB, Switches & MCCB Plant **(3)**
A-7 & 8 Sector- VIII, Gautam Budh Nagar, Noida, 201 301, Uttar Pradesh, India
Tel.: (91) 120391430102
Electrical Equipment Distr
N.A.I.C.S.: 423610

C&S Electric Limited C&S Busduct Plant II **(3)**
Plot no 1C Sector-8C Integrated Industrial Estate, Ranipur, Haridwar, 249403, Uttarakhand, India
Tel.: (91) 1334239551
Electrical Equipment Distr
N.A.I.C.S.: 423610

C&S Electric Limited C&S Busduct Plant- I **(3)**
B-1 Site-IV Surajpur Ind Area Kasna Road, Gautam Budh Nagar, Noida, Uttar Pradesh, India
Tel.: (91) 120391450001
Electrical Equipment Distr
N.A.I.C.S.: 423610

C&S Electric Limited C&S Bustrunking Plant **(3)**
Plot No 1A Sector 8C Integrated Industrial Estate, Ranipur, Haridwar, 249403, Uttarakhand, India
Tel.: (91) 133423921213
Electrical Equipment Distr
N.A.I.C.S.: 423610

C&S Electric Limited C&S Export Division Plant **(3)**
Plot No 63 NSEZ, Noida, Uttar Pradesh, India
Tel.: (91) 1203074391
Electrical Equipment Distr
N.A.I.C.S.: 423610

C&S Electric Limited C&S Lighting & Wiring Accessories Plant **(3)**
Plot No 2 Sector 8C Integrated Industrial Estate, Ranipur, Haridwar, 249403, Uttarakhand, India
Tel.: (91) 1334308130144
Electrical Equipment Distr
N.A.I.C.S.: 423610

C&S Electric Limited C&S MCB Plant **(3)**
Plot No 1B Sector-8C Integrated Industrial Estate, Ranipur, Haridwar, 249403, Uttarakhand, India
Tel.: (91) 133430810102
Electrical Equipment Distr
N.A.I.C.S.: 423610

C&S Electric Limited C&S MV Plant **(3)**
Plot No- 26A Sector 31 Surajpur Industrial Area Kasna Road, Noida, 201305, Uttar Pradesh, India
Tel.: (91) 1204710000
Electrical Equipment Distr
N.A.I.C.S.: 423610

C&S Electric Limited C&S Switchboard Plant -I **(3)**
C-59 Phase-II, Gautam Budh Nagar, Noida, 201 305, Uttar Pradesh, India

Tel.: (91) 120304880001
Electrical Equipment Distr
N.A.I.C.S.: 423610

C&S Electric Limited C&S Switchboard Plant-II **(3)**
Plot No-10 Sector-11 Integrated Industrial Estate, Ranipur, Haridwar, 249403, Uttarakhand, India
Tel.: (91) 133430800001
Electrical Equipment Distr
N.A.I.C.S.: 423610

C&S Electric Limited C&S TC Contactor, Overload Relay & Motor Starter Plant **(3)**
C-58 Phase-I, Gautam Budh Nagar, Noida, 201 305, Uttar Pradesh, India
Tel.: (91) 1203048709
Electrical Equipment Distr
N.A.I.C.S.: 423610

C&S Electric Limited CSH Gensets Plant **(3)**
12-A Sector-9 Integrated Industrial Estate US Nagar, Pantnagar, 263 153, Uttarakhand, India
Tel.: (91) 5944250383
Electrical Equipment Distr
N.A.I.C.S.: 423610

C&S Electric Limited Protection & Measurement Devices Plant **(3)**
C-60 Wing -A Phase-II, Gautam Budh Nagar, Noida, 201 305, Uttar Pradesh, India
Tel.: (91) 1203057700
Electrical Equipment Distr
N.A.I.C.S.: 423610

Affiliate (Domestic):

RS Components & Controls (India) Ltd. **(3)**
1701/1 7th Floor Tower No-I Express Trade Tower-II Sector-132, Noida, 201 301, India
Tel.: (91) 8001035282
Web Site: https://www.in.rsdelivers.com
Sales Range: $1-9.9 Million
Emp.: 80
Distr of Electronic Components; Joint Venture of Electrocomponents plc (50%) & Controls & Switchgear Company Ltd. (50%)
N.A.I.C.S.: 334419

Siemens Ltd., China **(1)**
No 7 Wangjing Zhonghuan South Road, Chaoyang, Beijing, 100102, China **(100%)**
Tel.: (86) 4006162020
Web Site: https://www.siemens.com
Electronic Equipment Mfr & Distr
N.A.I.C.S.: 449210

Subsidiary (Domestic):

Siemens Electrical Drives (Shanghai) Ltd. **(2)**
No 460 Gaoxianghuan Road, Pudong, Shanghai, 200137, China
Tel.: (86) 2161687162
Voltage Converter Mfr
N.A.I.C.S.: 335311

Siemens X-Ray Vacuum Technology Ltd. **(2)**
No 7 Building Land Lot 93 Wuxi National Hi-Tech, Industrial Development Zone, Wuxi, 214028, Jiangsu, China
Tel.: (86) 51080103900
Web Site: http://www.medical.siemens.com
Medical Equipment Mfr
N.A.I.C.S.: 334510

Siemens Malaysia Sdn Bhd **(1)**
Level 15 CP Tower N0 11 Jalan 16/11 Pusat Dagang Seksyen 16, 46350, Petaling Jaya, Selangor, Malaysia **(100%)**
Tel.: (60) 379525555
Web Site: https://www.siemens.com
Sales Range: $350-399.9 Million
Emp.: 900
Industrial Solutions & Services
N.A.I.C.S.: 541420

Siemens Manufacturing S.A. **(1)**
Autopista Medellin Km 8 5 Costado Sur, Tenjo, Cundinamarca, Colombia
Tel.: (57) 2942400
Web Site: http://new.siemens.com
Electric Equipment Mfr
N.A.I.C.S.: 335999

Siemens Manufacturing and Engineering Centre Ltd. **(1)**
2128 Shitai Road, Baoshan, Shanghai, 201908, China
Tel.: (86) 2138891199
Web Site: http://www.smec-siemens.com
Electrical Engineering Services
N.A.I.C.S.: 541330
Teumner Heinz *(Gen Mgr)*

Siemens Medical Instruments Pte. Ltd. **(1)**
18 Tai Seng Street 08-08, Singapore, 539775, Singapore
Tel.: (65) 63709666
Web Site: https://www.sivantos.com
Sales Range: $200-249.9 Million
Emp.: 800
Hearing Instruments Mfr
N.A.I.C.S.: 334510
Chia Choonkit *(VP)*

Subsidiary (Non-US):

P.T. Siemens Hearing Instruments **(2)**
Jl Beringin Lat-12 2nd Floor Muka Kuning, Batam, 29433, Indonesia
Tel.: (62) 770 612777
Emp.: 600
Audiological Equipment Mfr
N.A.I.C.S.: 334510

Siemens Medical Solutions Diagnostics Europe Limited **(1)**
Chapel Lane Swords, Dublin, Ireland
Tel.: (353) 1 8132222
Surgical & Medical Instrument Mgr
N.A.I.C.S.: 339112

Siemens Medical Solutions Diagnostics Holding I B.V. **(1)**
Prinses Beatrixlaan 800, Hague, 2595 BN, Netherlands
Tel.: (31) 703 33 37 98
Emp.: 50
Investment Management Service
N.A.I.C.S.: 523999
Van Den Brink *(Mgr)*

Siemens Medicina d.o.o. **(1)**
Zmaja od Bosne 7, 71000, Sarajevo, Bosnia & Herzegovina
Tel.: (387) 33727658
Hospital & Health Care Services
N.A.I.C.S.: 622110
Muris Hebibovic *(Engr-Customer Svc)*

Siemens Mobility A/S **(1)**
Borupvang 9, 2750, Ballerup, Denmark
Tel.: (45) 44774477
Transportation Services
N.A.I.C.S.: 485999
Steen Norby Nielsen *(CEO)*

Siemens Mobility AB **(1)**
Evenemangsgatan 21, 169 04, Solna, Sweden
Tel.: (46) 87281000
Transportation Services
N.A.I.C.S.: 485999
Rikard Tegnevi *(Acct Mgr-Svc)*

Siemens Mobility AG **(1)**
Hammerweg 1, 8304, Wallisellen, Switzerland
Tel.: (41) 585580111
Transportation Services
N.A.I.C.S.: 485999
Markus Scheidegger *(Head-Sls Rail Infrastructure)*

Siemens Mobility AS **(1)**
Ostre Aker vei 88, 0596, Oslo, Norway
Tel.: (47) 22633000
Transportation Services
N.A.I.C.S.: 484110
Frode Oien *(Mgr-Document Control)*

Siemens Mobility Austria GmbH **(1)**
Siemensstrasse 90, 1210, Vienna, Austria
Tel.: (43) 517070
Railway Transportation Services
N.A.I.C.S.: 532411

Siemens Mobility B.V. **(1)**
Werner von Siemensstraat 5, 2712 PN, Zoetermeer, Netherlands
Tel.: (31) 703032695
Web Site: https://www.mobility.siemens.com

Transportation Services
N.A.I.C.S.: 484110
Fred Dissel *(Mgr-Bus Unit Rail Solution & Svcs)*

Siemens Mobility EOOD **(1)**
2 Kukush Str, Sofia, Bulgaria
Tel.: (359) 28115404
Web Site: https://www.mobility.siemens.com
Railroad Transportation Services
N.A.I.C.S.: 488210
Kalin Ivanov *(CEO)*

Siemens Mobility GmbH **(1)**
Otto-Hahn-Ring 6, 81739, Munich, Germany
Tel.: (49) 8938035491
Railroad Transportation Services
N.A.I.C.S.: 488210
Michael Peter *(CEO)*

Siemens Mobility Group **(1)**
Werner-Von-Siemens-Strasse 67, 91052, Erlangen, Germany
Tel.: (49) 913170
Web Site: http://www.mobility.siemens.com
Sales Range: $1-4.9 Billion
Emp.: 25,000
Rail, Road & Air Transportation Solutions
N.A.I.C.S.: 336510
Alexander Biron von Curland *(Sr Exec VP-Middle East)*

Subsidiary (Domestic):

Siemens Transportation Systems **(2)**
Krauss Maffei Str 2, 80997, Munich, Germany
Tel.: (49) 8988993300
Web Site: http://www.siemens.com
Sales Range: $1-4.9 Billion
Emp.: 18,400
Mfr of Railroad Vehicles, Signaling & Control Technologies, Automation Systems, Electrification & Telecommunication Systems
N.A.I.C.S.: 336510

Siemens Werk Uerdingen Transportation Systems **(2)**
Duisburger Str 145, 47829, Krefeld, Uerdingen, Germany **(100%)**
Tel.: (49) 21514501
Sales Range: $350-399.9 Million
Emp.: 1,200
Mfr & Distribution of Rail Vehicles, Components & Car-Spring Products
N.A.I.C.S.: 488210

Siemens Mobility Kft. **(1)**
Gizella ut 51-57, 1143, Budapest, Hungary
Tel.: (36) 14711303
Web Site: https://www.mobility.siemens.com
Transportation Services
N.A.I.C.S.: 484110
Zsolt Till *(Head-R&D)*

Siemens Mobility LLC **(1)**
St Bolshaya Tatrskaya 9, 115184, Moscow, Russia
Tel.: (7) 4957371948
Transportation Services
N.A.I.C.S.: 484110
Jochen Rosenzweig *(CEO)*

Siemens Mobility LLC **(1)**
The Galleries 2 Third Floor-Unit 303, PO Box 31916, Dubai, United Arab Emirates
Tel.: (971) 43660000
Web Site: https://www.mobility.siemens.com
Transportation Services
N.A.I.C.S.: 485999
Axel Eickhorn *(CFO)*

Siemens Mobility Limited **(1)**
7th Floor Euston House 24 Eversholt Street, London, NW1 1AD, United Kingdom
Tel.: (44) 2078746772
Travel Arrangement Services
N.A.I.C.S.: 561599
Sambit Banerjee *(Mng Dir)*

Siemens Mobility Limited **(1)**
Units 905 907 9 F Tower B 223 231 Wai Yip Street, Manulife Financial Centre, Kwun Tong, China (Hong Kong)
Tel.: (852) 25833388
Transportation Services
N.A.I.C.S.: 485999
Jens-Peter Brauner *(CEO)*

Siemens Mobility Limited **(1)**

SIEMENS AKTIENGESELLSCHAFT / INTERNATIONAL PUBLIC

Siemens Aktiengesellschaft—(Continued)

Charn Issara Tower II 28th Floor 2922/300-303 New Petchaburi Road, Bangkapi Huay Kwang, Bangkok, 10310, Thailand
Tel.: (66) 20795455
Transportation Services
N.A.I.C.S.: 485999
Kamphon Rattanakijkamol *(Mgr-Technical Bid)*

Siemens Mobility Ltd. (1)
14 Hamelacha str, Rosh Ha'Ayin, 4809133, Israel
Tel.: (972) 39151914
Transportation Services
N.A.I.C.S.: 484110
Ravit Yitzhaki *(Mgr-Contract)*

Siemens Mobility Ltd. (1)
D-Tower 10F 17 Jong-ro 3-gil, Jongro-gu, Seoul, 03155, Korea (South)
Tel.: (82) 234507000
Transportation Services
N.A.I.C.S.: 485999

Siemens Mobility Oy (1)
Tarvonsalmenkatu 19, 02600, Espoo, Finland
Tel.: (358) 105115151
Web Site: https://www.mobility.siemens.com
Transportation Services
N.A.I.C.S.: 485999
Antti Halonen *(CFO)*

Siemens Mobility Pte. Ltd. (1)
60 MacPherson Road, Singapore, 348615, Singapore
Tel.: (65) 64906000
Web Site: https://www.mobility.siemens.com
Transportation Services
N.A.I.C.S.: 485999
Kenneth Yeap *(Dir-Sls & Bids)*

Siemens Mobility Pty Ltd. (1)
Level 6 380 Docklands Drive, Docklands, 3008, VIC, Australia
Tel.: (61) 1300724518
Web Site: https://www.mobility.siemens.com
Transportation Services
N.A.I.C.S.: 485999

Siemens Mobility Rail & Road Transportation Solutions Single-Member Societe Anonyme (1)
Agisilaou 6 - 8, Maroussi, 151 23, Athens, Greece
Tel.: (30) 21330992990
Railway Transportation Services
N.A.I.C.S.: 532411

Siemens Mobility Rail & Road Transportation Solutions Societe Anonyme (1)
Str Agisilaou 6-8, Attica, Maroussi, Greece
Tel.: (30) 21330992990
Web Site: https://www.mobility.siemens.com
Transportation Services
N.A.I.C.S.: 485999

Siemens Mobility S. de R.L. de C.V. (1)
Av National Army 350, Mexico, Mexico
Tel.: (52) 573212957115
Web Site: https://www.mobility.siemens.com
Transportation Services
N.A.I.C.S.: 485999

Siemens Mobility S.A. (1)
Edificio Lumina Olivos Blas Parera 3551 - P 2, B1636CSE, Olivos, Buenos Aires, Argentina
Tel.: (54) 1154326340
Web Site: https://www.mobility.siemens.com
Travel Arrangement Services
N.A.I.C.S.: 561599
Miguel Cafiero *(CEO)*

Siemens Mobility S.A.C. (1)
Av Domingo Orue 971, Lima, Peru
Tel.: (51) 12150030
Web Site: https://www.mobility.siemens.com
Transportation Services
N.A.I.C.S.: 485999

Siemens Mobility S.R.L. (1)
24 Preciziei Str West Gate H5 Building 5th Floor, 062204, Bucharest, Romania
Tel.: (40) 216296686
Web Site: https://www.mobility.siemens.com

Transportation Services
N.A.I.C.S.: 484110
Adrian Stoica *(Mng Dir & CFO)*

Siemens Mobility S.r.l. (1)
Via Vipiteno 4, 20128, Milan, Italy
Tel.: (39) 0224322202
Web Site: https://www.mobility.siemens.com
Transportation Services
N.A.I.C.S.: 484110

Siemens Mobility SAS (1)
150 avenue of the Republic, 92320, Chatillon, France
Tel.: (33) 185570059
Web Site: https://www.mobility.siemens.com
Transportation Services
N.A.I.C.S.: 485999
Sophie Stambouli *(Gen Counsel)*

Siemens Mobility Saudi Ltd. (1)
Fluor Arabia Building 2nd Floor, PO Box 719, Al Khobar, 31952, Eastern Province, Saudi Arabia
Tel.: (966) 138659672
Web Site: https://www.mobility.siemens.com
Transportation Services
N.A.I.C.S.: 484110
Alexander Pollak-Bolck *(CFO)*

Siemens Mobility Sdn. Bhd. (1)
Level 1 Reception CP Tower No 11 Jalan 16/11 Pusat Dagang Seksyen 16, Petaling Jaya, Selangor, Malaysia
Tel.: (60) 379525555
Web Site: https://www.mobility.siemens.com
Transportation Services
N.A.I.C.S.: 485999
Chan Jeeleng *(Mgr-Reg Bid)*

Siemens Mobility Sp. z o.o. (1)
ul Zupnicza 11, 03-821, Warsaw, Mazowieckie, Poland
Tel.: (48) 228709761
Transportation Services
N.A.I.C.S.: 484110
Krzysztof Celinski *(CEO)*

Siemens Mobility SpA (1)
Alonso de Cordova 4580 Piso 3, Las Condes, 7550000, Santiago, Chile
Tel.: (56) 224771000
Railway Transportation Services
N.A.I.C.S.: 532411

Siemens Mobility Ulasim Sistemleri Anonim Sirketi (1)
Esentepe Mah Yakacik Cad No 111 16/2, Kartal, Istanbul, Turkiye
Tel.: (90) 2164592601
Transportation Services
N.A.I.C.S.: 485999
Kadir Caglar *(Project Mgr)*

Siemens Mobility d.o.o. (1)
Letaliska cesta 29 C, 1000, Ljubljana, Slovenia
Tel.: (386) 14746115
Web Site: https://www.mobility.siemens.com
Electrical & Electronic Product Mfr
N.A.I.C.S.: 335999
Ales Zalokar *(Project Mgr)*

Siemens Mobility d.o.o. Cerovac (1)
Sobovica bb, 34000, Kragujevac, Serbia
Tel.: (381) 346195426
Web Site: https://www.mobility.siemens.com
Transportation Services
N.A.I.C.S.: 484110
Bogdan Kravic *(CFO)*

Siemens Mobility, S.L.U. (1)
Ronda de Europa 5, 28760, Tres Cantos, Madrid, Spain
Tel.: (34) 915148000
Web Site: https://www.mobility.siemens.com
Mobility Transport Services
N.A.I.C.S.: 485991
Franck Pascual *(Mgr-Quality & EHS)*

Siemens Mobility, Unipessoal Lda. (1)
Rua Irmaos Siemens n 1-1A, 2720-093, Amadora, Portugal
Tel.: (351) 214178000
Web Site: https://www.mobility.siemens.com
Transportation Services
N.A.I.C.S.: 484110

Siemens Mobility, s.r.o. (1)

Siemensova 2715/1, 155 00, Prague, 5, Czech Republic
Tel.: (420) 233032251
Web Site: https://www.mobility.siemens.com
Transportation Services
N.A.I.C.S.: 485999
Petr Bezouska *(Mgr-Process)*

Siemens Mobility, s.r.o. (1)
Lamacska cesta 3/A, Karlova Ves, 841 04, Bratislava, Slovakia
Tel.: (421) 259682751
Web Site: https://www.mobility.siemens.com
Transportation Services
N.A.I.C.S.: 484110
Martina Kralikova *(Mgr-HR)*

Siemens Nederland N.V. (1)
Prinses Beatrixlaan 800, 2595 BN, Hague, Netherlands **(100%)**
Tel.: (31) 703333333
Web Site: https://www.siemens.com
Sales Range: $1-4.9 Billion
Emp.: 2,200
Power Generation, Infrastructure & Internet Connectivity Equipment Mfg & Services
N.A.I.C.S.: 221118

Siemens Oesterreich AG (1)
Siemensstrasse 90, Postfach 83, 1211, Vienna, Austria **(74%)**
Tel.: (43) 517070
Web Site: http://www.siemens.at
Sales Range: $1-4.9 Billion
Emp.: 11,800
Mfr & Distr of Telecommunication; Data Systems; Medical Engineering Products; Power Electronics; Control Equipment & Switchgear
N.A.I.C.S.: 334290

Subsidiary (Domestic):

Siemens Konzernbeteiligungen GmbH (2)
Siemensstrasse 90, 1210, Vienna, Austria
Tel.: (43) 5170723611
Investment Management Service
N.A.I.C.S.: 523999

Siemens Liegenschaftsverwaltung GmbH (2)
Siemensstrasse 92, Vienna, Austria
Tel.: (43) 517070
Investment Management Service
N.A.I.C.S.: 523999

Siemens Personaldienstleistungen GmbH (2)
Siemensstrasse 90, 1210, Vienna, Austria
Tel.: (43) 5170735189
Web Site: http://new.siemens.com
Sales Range: $300-349.9 Million
Emp.: 1,400
Recruitment Services
N.A.I.C.S.: 813920
Zummer Gerhard *(Mng Dir)*

Siemens Transformers Austria GmbH & Co KG (2)
Wolfgang-Pauli-Strasse 2, 4020, Linz, Austria
Tel.: (43) 517070
Sales Range: $100-124.9 Million
Emp.: 370
Power Transmission Equipment Mfr
N.A.I.C.S.: 333613

Siemens Osakeyhtio Oy (1)
Tarvonsalmenkatu 19, 02600, Espoo, Finland
Tel.: (358) 105115151
Banking & Financial Services
N.A.I.C.S.: 522110

Siemens Osakeyhtioe (1)
Tarvonsalmenkatu 19, 02600, Espoo, Finland **(100%)**
Tel.: (358) 105115151
Web Site: https://www.siemens.com
Sales Range: $200-249.9 Million
Emp.: 600
Technology & Related Services, Communications, Energy & Transportation Sectors
N.A.I.C.S.: 334290
Janne Ohman *(CEO)*

Branch (Non-US):

Siemens Medical Solutions Diagnostics SIA (2)

Lidosta Riga Teritorija, Marupes pag, 1053, Riga, Latvia
Tel.: (371) 67015531
Web Site: http://www.healthcare.siemens.com
Pharmaceutical Products Distr
N.A.I.C.S.: 424210

Siemens PETNET Korea Co. Ltd. (1)
470 Chungjeongno 3 Sam Ga, Seodaemun-Gu, Seoul, 120-013, Korea (South)
Tel.: (82) 27019318
Medical Equipment Mfr
N.A.I.C.S.: 334510

Siemens PLM Software Computational Dynamics K.K. (1)
Shin-Yokohama Square Building 16th Floor 2-3-12 Shin, Kohoku-ku, Yokohama, 222-0033, Kanagawa, Japan
Tel.: (81) 54753285
Information Technology Services
N.A.I.C.S.: 541511

Siemens Pakistan Engineering Co. Ltd. (1)
B-72 Estate Avenue SITE, Karachi, 75700, Pakistan **(74.65%)**
Tel.: (92) 212566213
Web Site: https://www.siemens.com
Sales Range: $400-449.9 Million
Emp.: 1,400
Power Generation Services
N.A.I.C.S.: 335312

Siemens Pensionskasse AG (1)
Siemensstrasse 90, Vienna, Austria
Tel.: (43) 5170735093
Pension Fund Services
N.A.I.C.S.: 525110

Siemens Plant Operations Tahaddart SARL (1)
Route National De Rabat, 90000, Tangiers, Morocco
Tel.: (212) 5 39 33 93 60
Electrical Engineering Services
N.A.I.C.S.: 541330

Siemens Postal, Parcel & Airport Logistics Limited (1)
Regus House Office G22 450 Bath Road, Longford, Heathrow, UB7 0EB, United Kingdom
Tel.: (44) 2087578708
Logistic Services
N.A.I.C.S.: 541614
Lee Ellis *(Mgr-Site)*

Siemens Power Automation Ltd. (1)
Building 4 Hua Rui Industry Park Cheng Xin Avenue Jiangning Economical, Technological Developing Zone, Nanjing, 211100, China
Tel.: (86) 2551170188
Web Site: http://cn.siemens.com
Electrical Engineering Services
N.A.I.C.S.: 541330

Siemens Private Finance Versicherungs- und Kapitalanlagenvermittlungs-GmbH (1)
Otto-Hahn-Ring 6, Munich, 81739, Germany
Tel.: (49) 8963631110
Web Site: http://privatefinance.siemens.com
Financial Management Services
N.A.I.C.S.: 523999

Siemens Process Automation & Drives (U.K.) Ltd. (1)
Sir William Siemens House Princess Road, Manchester, M20 2UR, North West England, United Kingdom **(100%)**
Tel.: (44) 1276696000
Web Site: http://www.siemens.co.uk
Sales Range: $50-74.9 Million
Emp.: 108
Mfr of Industrial Instrumentation
N.A.I.C.S.: 334513

Division (Domestic):

Siemens Automation & Drives (2)
2 Fountain Ct Victoria St, Saint Albans, AL1 2HA, United Kingdom
Tel.: (44) 727884670
Web Site: http://www.plm.automation.siemens.com

AND PRIVATE COMPANIES — SIEMENS AKTIENGESELLSCHAFT

Sales Range: $25-49.9 Million
Emp.: 2
Mfr & Retailer of Robotic Vision Systems
N.A.I.C.S.: 333310

Siemens Measurement Systems (2)
Wilbury Way, Hitchin, SG4 0TS, Herts, United Kingdom **(100%)**
Tel.: (44) 462424800
Web Site: http://www.siemens-industry.co.uk
Sales Range: $25-49.9 Million
Emp.: 56
Mfr of Dimensional Measurement Systems
N.A.I.C.S.: 334513

Siemens Product Lifecycle Management Software 2 (IL) Ltd. (1)
10 Abba Eban Blvd, Herzliyya, 46725, Israel
Tel.: (972) 99594777
Software Development Services
N.A.I.C.S.: 541511

Siemens Product Lifecycle Management Software II (BE) BVBA (1)
Het-Zuiderkruis 63, 's-Hertogenbosch, 5215 MV, Netherlands
Tel.: (31) 27095600
Sales Range: $25-49.9 Million
Emp.: 100
Software Development Services
N.A.I.C.S.: 541511

Siemens Program and System Engineering s.r.o. (1)
Dubravska Cesta 4, 845 37, Bratislava, Slovakia
Tel.: (421) 2 5968 4001
Web Site: http://www.siemens-pse.sk
Sales Range: $150-199.9 Million
Emp.: 600
Software Development Services
N.A.I.C.S.: 541511

Siemens Programm- und Systementwicklung GmbH&Co. KG (1)
Harburger Schlossstrasse 18, 21079, Hamburg, Germany
Tel.: (49) 4076780
Web Site: http://www.siemens-pse.de
Sales Range: $25-49.9 Million
Emp.: 248
Software Development Services
N.A.I.C.S.: 541511
Josef Aigner *(Gen Mgr)*

Siemens Protection Devices Limited (1)
North Farm Road, PO Box 8, Hebburn, NE31 1LX, United Kingdom
Tel.: (44) 1914015555
Emp.: 200
Electric Equipment Mfr
N.A.I.C.S.: 334419

Siemens Rail Automation Holdings Limited (1)
PO Box 79, Langley Park Pew Hill, Chippenham, SN15 1JD, Wiltshire, United Kingdom
Tel.: (44) 1249441441
Web Site: http://www.siemens.co.uk
Electronic Transport Equipment Mfr
N.A.I.C.S.: 334419
Paul Copeland *(Mng Dir)*

Siemens Real Estate GmbH & Co. OHG (1)
Otto-Hahn-Ring 6, 81739, Munich, Germany
Tel.: (49) 8963600
Web Site: http://www.realestate.siemens.com
Rev.: $2,907,058,000
Real Estate Manangement Services
N.A.I.C.S.: 531390
Zsolt Sluitner *(CEO)*

Siemens Real Estate Ltd. (1)
Siemens House Oldbury, RG12 8FZ, Bracknell, United Kingdom - England
Tel.: (44) 1344 646 768
Real Estate Investment Services
N.A.I.C.S.: 531390

Siemens Real Estate Management (Pty.) Ltd. (1)
300 Janadel Ave Halfway Gardens, Midrand, 1685, South Africa
Tel.: (27) 116522000
Web Site: https://www.siemens.com
Real Estate Manangement Services
N.A.I.C.S.: 531390

Siemens Renting S.A. (1)
Ronda De Europa 5, Tres Cantos, 28760, Madrid, Spain
Tel.: (34) 915148183
Web Site: https://www.siemens.com
Emp.: 45
Financial Lending Services
N.A.I.C.S.: 522220
Nick Muntz *(Gen Mgr)*

Siemens Rt. (1)
Gizella ut 51-57, 1143, Budapest, Hungary **(100%)**
Tel.: (36) 14711000
Web Site: http://new.siemens.com
Sales Range: $50-74.9 Million
Emp.: 2,000
Mfr of Medium & Low Voltage Switchgear & Systems
N.A.I.C.S.: 335313

Siemens S.A. (1)
Tour CB21 - 16 place de l'Iris, 92040, Paris, Cedex, France **(100%)**
Tel.: (33) 185570000
Web Site: https://www.siemens.com
Sales Range: $700-749.9 Million
Emp.: 1,400
Mfr & Sales of Measuring Instruments & Medical Equipment
N.A.I.C.S.: 334516

Siemens S.A. (1)
Ronda de Europa 5, Tres Canto, 28760, Madrid, Spain **(100%)**
Tel.: (34) 491514754
Web Site: https://assets.new.siemens.com
Sales Range: $1-4.9 Billion
Emp.: 3,342
Mfr & Sales of Motors Generators, Power Converters, High & Low Voltage Switchgear & Medical Equipment
N.A.I.C.S.: 335313

Siemens S.A. (1)
Avenida Don Diego Cisneros, Urbanizacion Los Ruices, Caracas, 1071, Venezuela **(100%)**
Tel.: (58) 2122038755
Sales & Assembly of Communication Equipment & Power Engineering
N.A.I.C.S.: 541330

Siemens S.A. (1)
Autopista Medellin Km 8 5 Costado Sur, Cundinamarca, 80150, Tenjo, Colombia **(94%)**
Tel.: (57) 6019157900
Web Site: https://www.siemens.com
Sales Range: $100-124.9 Million
Emp.: 1,300
Mfr of Motors, Transformers, Fans & Switchgear
N.A.I.C.S.: 335312

Siemens S.A. (1)
Rua Irmaos Siemens 1, 2720-093, Amadora, Portugal **(100%)**
Tel.: (351) 214178000
Web Site: https://www.siemens.com
Sales Range: $600-649.9 Million
Emp.: 1,150
Power Generation & Distr Services
N.A.I.C.S.: 221118
Joana Garoupa *(Dir-Mktg)*

Siemens S.A. (1)
Rue du Lac Neuchatel Les Berges du Lac, 1053, Tunis, Tunisia
Tel.: (216) 71166400
Web Site: http://www.siemens.com.tn
Sales Range: $25-49.9 Million
Emp.: 40
Information Technology, Communications, Transportation & Power Industry Support Services
N.A.I.C.S.: 561499

Siemens S.A. (1)
Casablanca Marina Ivory 3 tower 7th floor, Boulevard Sidi Mohammed Ben Abdellah, 20030, Casablanca, Morocco
Tel.: (212) 522669200
Web Site: https://www.siemens.com
Sales Range: $10-24.9 Million
Emp.: 300
Industry, Energy & Healthcare Services & Solutions
N.A.I.C.S.: 339999

Siemens S.A. (1)
Ciudad de Guayaquil 1306, 11400, Montevideo, Uruguay
Tel.: (598) 26045555
Web Site: http://www.siemens.com.uy
Electrical Engineering Services
N.A.I.C.S.: 541330

Siemens S.A. (1)
Cerro El Plomo 6000 10th floor, 7500498, Santiago, Chile
Tel.: (56) 224771000
Web Site: https://www.siemens.com
Emp.: 1,600
Electrical Engineering Services
N.A.I.C.S.: 541330

Siemens S.A. (1)
Calle Siemens No 43 Parque Industrial Santa Elena, 1137, Antiguo Cuscatlan, San Salvador, El Salvador
Tel.: (503) 22487333
Web Site: http://www.siemens-centram.com
Sales Range: $25-49.9 Million
Emp.: 150
Electrical Engineering Services
N.A.I.C.S.: 541330

Siemens S.A. (1)
Calle Manuel Zambrano Panamericana Norte KM2 5, Quito, Ecuador
Tel.: (593) 22943900
Rev.: $36,470,364
Emp.: 10
Electrical Engineering Services
N.A.I.C.S.: 541330

Siemens S.A. (1)
Colonia Quezada Calle La Salud Edificio Siemens Apartado, 10 98, Tegucigalpa, Honduras
Tel.: (504) 2 32 40 62
Electrical Engineering Services
N.A.I.C.S.: 541330

Siemens S.A. (1)
200 Este de la Plaza, PO Box 10022-1000, La Uruca, San Jose, 1000, Costa Rica
Tel.: (506) 2875120
Hospital & Healthcare Services
N.A.I.C.S.: 622110

Siemens S.A./N.V. (1)
Guido Gezellestraat 123, Huizingen, 1654, Beersel, Belgium **(100%)**
Tel.: (32) 25362111
Web Site: https://www.siemens.com
Sales Range: $1-4.9 Billion
Emp.: 1,000
Mfr & Sales of Switchgear & Long-Range Communications Equipment & Components; Refurbisher of Data Processing Equipment & Developer of Data Systems & Telecommunications Software
N.A.I.C.S.: 335313
Andre Bouffioux *(CEO)*

Siemens S.p.A. (1)
via Vipiteno 4, 20128, Milan, Italy **(100%)**
Tel.: (39) 022431
Web Site: http://new.siemens.com
Sales Range: $400-449.9 Million
Emp.: 2,000
Mfr of Drives & Standard Products for Automation Systems; X-ray Equipment & Actuator Components for the Automobile Industry
N.A.I.C.S.: 333612

Siemens SA (1)
Carretera Norte Km 6 Apartado 7, Managua, Nicaragua
Tel.: (505) 249 1111
Web Site: http://w1.siemens.com
Power Generation, Dist & IT Workflow Solution Services
N.A.I.C.S.: 221118

Siemens SA (1)
21 rue Edmond Reuter, Hamm, 5326, Contern, Luxembourg
Tel.: (352) 438431
Web Site: https://www.siemens.com
Sales Range: $25-49.9 Million
Emp.: 150
Industrial Solutions & Services
N.A.I.C.S.: 541420

Siemens SAC (1)
Av Domingo Orue 971, Surquillo, 34, Lima, Peru
Tel.: (51) 12150030
Web Site: https://www.siemens.com
Sales Range: $200-249.9 Million
Emp.: 174
Power Generation & Transmission Services
N.A.I.C.S.: 221118

Siemens SIA (1)
Airport Riga Territory Marupe Parish, 1053, Riga, Latvia
Tel.: (371) 7015500
Web Site: http://www.siemens.lv
Sales Range: $50-74.9 Million
Emp.: 96
Power Transmission & Distr Services
N.A.I.C.S.: 221121
Dzintra Rubule *(Mgr-Mktg)*

Siemens Sanayi Ve Ticaret A.S (1)
Yakacik Caddesi No 111, Kartal, 34870, Istanbul, Turkiye **(75%)**
Tel.: (90) 2164592000
Web Site: https://www.siemens.com
Sales Range: $900-999.9 Million
Emp.: 2,460
Mfr & Sales of Power Engineering, Electrical Installations, Communications Products & Automotive Systems
N.A.I.C.S.: 221122
Huseyin Gelis *(Chm & CEO)*

Siemens Schweiz AG (1)
Freilagerstrasse 40, 8047, Zurich, Switzerland
Tel.: (41) 848822844
Web Site: https://www.siemens.com
Sales Range: $1-4.9 Billion
Emp.: 5,700
Mfr, Developer & Distributor of Telecommunication & Security Systems Equipment
N.A.I.C.S.: 334290

Siemens Servicios S.A. de C.V. (1)
Poniente 122 Ste 579, 02300, Mexico, Mexico
Tel.: (52) 5553282199
Web Site: https://www.siemens.com
Financial Investment Services
N.A.I.C.S.: 523999

Siemens Shanghai Medical Equipment Ltd. (1)
No 278 Zhou Zhu Rd, Shanghai, 201318, China
Tel.: (86) 2138895000
Web Site: http://www.ssme.com.cn
Sales Range: $200-249.9 Million
Emp.: 800
Medical Equipment Mfr
N.A.I.C.S.: 334510

Siemens Shenzhen Magnetic Resonance Ltd. (1)
Floor B1 Building R1, South District Hightech Zone Shennan Avenue, Shenzhen, 518057, Guangdong, China
Tel.: (86) 75526525421
Web Site: https://www.med4598.yixie8.com
Electro Medical Magnetic Resonance Mfr
N.A.I.C.S.: 334510
Kun Zhu *(Sr Engi-Software)*

Siemens Signalling Co., Ltd. (1)
No 30 Fengcheng Second Road, Economic Technology Development Zone, Xi'an, 710016, Shaanxi, China
Tel.: (86) 2986522777
Railroad Equipment Mfr & Whslr
N.A.I.C.S.: 336510

Siemens Soluciones Tecnologicas S.A. (1)
Avenida San Martin No 1800 Edificio Tacuaral Piso 5to, Santa Cruz, Bolivia
Tel.: (591) 33110011
Electrical Engineering Services
N.A.I.C.S.: 541330

Siemens Sp. z o.o. (1)
ul Zupnicza 11, 03-821, Warsaw, Poland
Tel.: (48) 228709000
Web Site: http://www.siemens.pl
Sales Range: $800-899.9 Million
Emp.: 2,047
Power Transmission & Distr Services
N.A.I.C.S.: 221118

Siemens Spezial-Investmentaktiengesellschaft mit

SIEMENS AKTIENGESELLSCHAFT

INTERNATIONAL PUBLIC

Siemens Aktiengesellschaft—(Continued)

TGV (1)
Otto-Hahn-Ring 6, Munich, 81739, Bavaria, Germany
Tel.: (49) 8963600
Financial Investment Services
N.A.I.C.S.: 523999

Siemens Surge Arresters Ltd. (1)
No 6 Bldg J1 Plot Wuxi Export Processing Zone, Wuxi, 214028, Jiangsu, China
Tel.: (86) 510 8520 5588
Sales Range: $50-74.9 Million
Emp.: 20
Electric Equipment Mfr
N.A.I.C.S.: 334419
Shen Xiaowen *(Mgr)*

Siemens TOO (1)
Dostyk Ave 117/6, 050059, Almaty, Kazakhstan
Tel.: (7) 7272449929
Health Care Srvices
N.A.I.C.S.: 621999
Nataliya Shapovalova *(Dir-HR)*

Siemens Technology Accelerator GmbH (1)
Otto-Hahn-Ring 6, 81739, Munich, Germany
Tel.: (49) 8963635853
Web Site: http://www.siemens.com
Sales Range: $25-49.9 Million
Emp.: 10
Technology Development Services
N.A.I.C.S.: 541511

Siemens Technopark Berlin GmbH&Co. KG (1)
Wohlrabedamm 32, 13629, Berlin, Germany
Tel.: (49) 3038627821
Real Estate Investment Services
N.A.I.C.S.: 525990

Siemens Technopark Mulheim Verwaltungs-GmbH (1)
Mellinghofer Strasse 55, Mulheim an der Ruhr, 45473, Germany
Tel.: (49) 2084560
Medical Equipment Distr
N.A.I.C.S.: 423450

Siemens Technopark Nurnberg GmbH & Co. KG (1)
Landgrabenstrasse 59, Nuremberg, 90489, Germany
Tel.: (49) 9114338500
Web Site: http://www.realestate.siemens.com
Real Estate Manangement Services
N.A.I.C.S.: 531390

Siemens Technopark Nurnberg Verwaltungs GmbH (1)
Landgrabenstr 94, 90443, Nuremberg, Germany
Tel.: (49) 9112529624
Sales Range: $700-749.9 Million
Emp.: 2,000
Investment Management Service
N.A.I.C.S.: 523999

Siemens Transmission & Distribution SAS (1)
1 Rue De La Neva, Grenoble, 38000, France
Tel.: (33) 456586600
Electric Power Distribution Services
N.A.I.C.S.: 221122

Siemens Treasury GmbH (1)
Otto-Hahn-Ring 6, Bavaria, 81739, Munich, Germany
Tel.: (49) 8938035491
Financial Investment Services
N.A.I.C.S.: 523999

Siemens Ukraine (1)
St Yaroslavska 58, 04071, Kiev, Ukraine
Tel.: (380) 443922300
Web Site: https://www.siemens.com
Sales Range: $200-249.9 Million
Emp.: 300
Engineeering Services
N.A.I.C.S.: 541330

Siemens Uruguay S.A. (1)
Guayaquil City 1306, 11400, Montevideo, Uruguay
Tel.: (598) 26045555
Web Site: http://www.siemens.com.uy
Healtcare Services
N.A.I.C.S.: 621511

Siemens VAI Manufacturing (Taicang) Co., Ltd. (1)
18 Suzhou Rd, Taicang, 215400, China
Tel.: (86) 512 5318 6888
Sales Range: $25-49.9 Million
Emp.: 100
Industrial Machinery Mfr
N.A.I.C.S.: 333248

Siemens VAI Metals Technologies GmbH (1)
Reithallenstrasse 1, 77731, Willstatt, Germany
Tel.: (49) 78524100
Web Site: http://www.siemens.de
Emp.: 35
Electrical Engineering Equipment & Steel Mfr
N.A.I.C.S.: 335999
Martin Fleischer *(CEO)*

Siemens VAI Metals Technologies S.r.l. (1)
Via L Pomini n 92, Marnate, 21050, Varese, Italy
Tel.: (39) 0331 74 12 11
Industrial Machinery Mfr
N.A.I.C.S.: 333248

Siemens VAI Metals Technologies SAS (1)
41 route de Feurs, Savigneux, 42600, France
Tel.: (33) 477966300
Sales Range: $100-124.9 Million
Emp.: 400
Electric Equipment Mfr
N.A.I.C.S.: 335999

Siemens Venture Capital GmbH (1)
Otto-Hahn-Ring 6, 81739, Munich, Germany
Tel.: (49) 8963633585
Emp.: 5
Venture Capital Investment Services
N.A.I.C.S.: 523910
Ralf Schnell *(CEO & Co-Mng Dir)*

Siemens W.L.L. (1)
Building - 1029 Office No - 23 Road - 3621 Block Al Seef, PO Box 830, Manama, Bahrain
Tel.: (973) 17225501
Web Site: http://www.siemens.com.bh
Sales Range: $25-49.9 Million
Emp.: 53
Energy & Healthcare Services
N.A.I.C.S.: 541690

Siemens WLL (1)
5th Floor Jaidah Square Bldg Al Matar Street, PO Box 21757, Doha, 21757, Qatar
Tel.: (974) 44560222
Web Site: https://www.mobility.siemens.com
Sales Range: $100-124.9 Million
Emp.: 300
Power, Communication & Medical Solution Services
N.A.I.C.S.: 221122

Siemens Wind Power Blades (Shanghai) Co., Ltd. (1)
1333 Miao Xiang Rd, Shanghai, China
Tel.: (86) 21 3829 1104
Sales Range: $25-49.9 Million
Emp.: 5
Wind Power Blade Mfr
N.A.I.C.S.: 333611
Markus M. Tacke *(CEO)*

Siemens Wiring Accessories Shandong Ltd. (1)
No 126 Yumin Road High-Tech Development Zone, Zibo, 255100, China
Tel.: (86) 5333919686
Wiring Accessory Whslr
N.A.I.C.S.: 423390

Siemens d.d. (1)
Heinzelova 70a, 10000, Zagreb, Croatia
Tel.: (385) 16105222
Web Site: https://www.siemens.com
Sales Range: $250-299.9 Million
Emp.: 600
Medical Equipment Distr
N.A.I.C.S.: 423450

Siemens d.o.o. (1)
Letaliska cesta 29 C, 1000, Ljubljana, Slovenia
Tel.: (386) 14746100
Web Site: https://new.siemens.com
Sales Range: $200-249.9 Million
Emp.: 150
Power Generation & Distr Services
N.A.I.C.S.: 221118

Siemens d.o.o. (1)
Omladinskih Brigada 90V, 11070, Belgrade, Serbia
Tel.: (381) 112096001
Web Site: https://www.siemens.com
Sales Range: $75-99.9 Million
Emp.: 215
Power Transmission & Distr Services
N.A.I.C.S.: 221121

Siemens d.o.o. (1)
Bosmal City Centar Milana Preloga 12b, 71000, Sarajevo, Bosnia & Herzegovina
Tel.: (387) 33727600
Sales Range: $50-74.9 Million
Emp.: 55
Medical Equipment Distr
N.A.I.C.S.: 423450

Siemens d.o.o. Podgorica (1)
Svetlane Kane Radevic 3/I, 81000, Podgorica, Montenegro
Tel.: (382) 20205710
Rev.: $4,360,587
Emp.: 5
Medical Equipment Distr
N.A.I.C.S.: 423450

Siemens plc (1)
Sir William Siemens House Princess Road, Frimley, Manchester, M20 2UR, North West England, United Kingdom (100%)
Tel.: (44) 1276696000
Web Site: http://new.siemens.com
Sales Range: $5-14.9 Billion
Emp.: 16,500
Energy, Industrial, Infrastructure & Engineering Services
N.A.I.C.S.: 541330
Brian Holliday *(Mng Dir-Digital Factory)*

Siemens s.r.o. (1)
Lamacska cesta 3/A, PO Box 96, 841 04, Bratislava, Slovakia
Tel.: (421) 259681114
Web Site: http://www.siemens.com
Sales Range: $350-399.9 Million
Emp.: 4,000
Drive Control & Automation Equipment Mfr
N.A.I.C.S.: 335999

Siemens srl (1)
Preciziei Street No 24, 062204, Bucharest, Romania
Tel.: (40) 216296400
Web Site: http://www.siemens.ro
Sales Range: $400-449.9 Million
Emp.: 1,700
Power Transmission & Distr Services
N.A.I.C.S.: 221121

Siemens, Inc. (1)
15th Floor NEX Tower 6786 Ayala Avenue, Makati, 1229, Philippines
Tel.: (63) 272193355
Web Site: https://www.siemens.com
Sales Range: $150-199.9 Million
Emp.: 1,000
Transportation Systems & Services
N.A.I.C.S.: 488999

Siemens, S.A. de C.V. (1)
Ejercito Nacional No 590 3er Piso Col Polanco V Seccion, Deleg Miguel Hidalgo, 11560, Mexico, Mexico (100%)
Tel.: (52) 5553282000
Sales Range: $1-4.9 Billion
Emp.: 9,039
Power Transmission & Distr Services
N.A.I.C.S.: 221121

Siemens, s.r.o. (1)
Siemensova 1, Stodulky, 155 00, Prague, Czech Republic
Tel.: (420) 800909090
Web Site: http://new.siemens.com
Sales Range: $350-399.9 Million
Emp.: 2,000
Technology Development Services
N.A.I.C.S.: 541512

Eduard Palisek *(Gen Mgr)*

Siteco Aydinlatma Teknigi Tic. Ve San. Ltd. Sti. (1)
Fahrettin Kerim Gokay Cad No 31 B Blok, Altunizade, 34662, Istanbul, Turkiye
Tel.: (90) 216 327 45 45
Web Site: http://www.siteco.com.tr
Lighting Equipment Mfr
N.A.I.C.S.: 335139
Niyazi Avci *(Gen Mgr)*

Siteco Beleuchtungstechnik GmbH (1)
Georg-Simon-Ohm-Strasse 50, 83301, Traunreut, Germany
Tel.: (49) 8669330
Web Site: http://www.siteco.de
Lighting Equipment Mfr
N.A.I.C.S.: 335139

Siteco Belysning AS (1)
Tevlingveien 23, 1081, Oslo, Norway
Tel.: (47) 23 37 32 50
Web Site: http://www.siteco.no
Lighting Equipment Mfr
N.A.I.C.S.: 335139

Siteco Lighting Austria GmbH (1)
Leonard-Bernstein-Strasse 10, Vienna, 1220, Austria
Tel.: (43) 1 25024 0
Web Site: http://www.siteco.at
Sales Range: $50-74.9 Million
Emp.: 30
Lighting & Electrical Equipment Distr
N.A.I.C.S.: 423610

Siteco Lighting Poland Sp. z o.o. (1)
Migdalowa 4, 02-796, Warsaw, Poland
Tel.: (48) 22 645 11 83
Web Site: http://www.siteco.com.pl
Sales Range: $25-49.9 Million
Emp.: 18
Lighting Equipment Mfr
N.A.I.C.S.: 335139

Siteco Lighting Systems S.r.l. (1)
Via Libero Temolo 4, 20126, Milan, Italy
Tel.: (39) 03200692561
Web Site: http://www.sitecoitalia.it
Lighting Equipment Mfr & Distr
N.A.I.C.S.: 335139

Siteco Lighting, S.L.U. (1)
Av Leonardo da Vinci 15, 28906, Madrid, Spain
Tel.: (34) 910029095
Web Site: http://www.siteco.com
Sales Range: $25-49.9 Million
Emp.: 10
Lighting Equipment Mfr
N.A.I.C.S.: 335139

Siteco Lighting, spol. s r.o. (1)
U Nikolajky 1085/15, Prague, 150 00, Czech Republic
Tel.: (420) 251 013 800
Web Site: http://www.siteco.cz
Lighting Equipment Mfr
N.A.I.C.S.: 335139

Siteco Osterreich GmbH (1)
Leonard-Bernstein-Strasse 10, 1220, Vienna, Austria
Tel.: (43) 1250240
Web Site: http://www.siteco.de
Lighting Equipment Mfr & Distr
N.A.I.C.S.: 335139

Siteco Schweiz AG (1)
Zurcherstrasse 46, 8400, Winterthur, Switzerland
Tel.: (41) 525572222
Web Site: http://www.osram.ch
Sales Range: $25-49.9 Million
Emp.: 30
Lighting Equipment Mfr
N.A.I.C.S.: 335139

Siteco Sistemi d.o.o. (1)
Trzaska Cesta 23, 2000, Maribor, Slovenia
Tel.: (386) 2 300 42 77
Web Site: http://www.siteco.si
Sales Range: $25-49.9 Million
Emp.: 17
Lighting Equipment Mfr
N.A.I.C.S.: 335139

Sivantos Limited (1)
Platinum House Sussex Manor Business

Park, Gatwick Road, Crawley, RH10 9NH, West Sussex, United Kingdom
Tel.: (44) 1293423700
Web Site: http://www.sivantos.co.uk
Hearing Equipment Mfr
N.A.I.C.S.: 334510
David Smith *(Mng Dir)*

Steiermarkische Medizinarchiv GesmbH (1)
Stiftingtalstr 4-6, 8010, Graz, Austria
Tel.: (43) 13401170119
Web Site: https://www.marc.co.at
Medical Equipment Mfr & Distr
N.A.I.C.S.: 334510

Sunny World (Shaoxing) Green Lighting Co., Ltd. (1)
No 308 North Paozhong Road, Shaoxing, 312071, Zhejiang, China
Tel.: (86) 57588222167
Lighting Equipment Mfr
N.A.I.C.S.: 335139

TASS International B.V. (1)
Automotive Campus 10, 5708 JZ, Helmond, Netherlands
Tel.: (31) 888277100
Web Site: https://www.tass.plm.automation.com
Emp.: 200
Construction Services
N.A.I.C.S.: 236220
Bauke Ter Steeg *(Mgr-Domain Expert)*

TGB Technisches Gemeinschaftsburo GmbH (1)
Panoramaweg 1, 34131, Kassel, Germany
Tel.: (49) 561935670
Web Site: http://www.tgb-kassel.de
Sales Range: $25-49.9 Million
Emp.: 85
Mechanical Power Transmission Construction Services
N.A.I.C.S.: 237130
Dirk Kaemmerer *(CEO)*

Telecomunicacion, Electronica y Comunicacion S.A. (1)
Ronda de Europa 5, Tres Cantos, 28760, Madrid, Spain
Tel.: (34) 915147500
Web Site: https://www.tecosa.es
Security System Services
N.A.I.C.S.: 561621

Telecomunicacion, Electronica y Conmutacion S.A. (1)
Ronda de Europa 5, Tres Cantos, 28760, Madrid, Spain
Tel.: (34) 5147500
Web Site: https://www.tecosa.es
Technical Assistance Services
N.A.I.C.S.: 541618

TurboCare B.V. (1)
Industrieplein 3, Hengelo, 7553 LL, Netherlands
Tel.: (31) 742402610
Web Site: http://www.turbocare.com
Emp.: 14
Compressor & Turbine Generator Mfr
N.A.I.C.S.: 333912
Jos Derkink *(VP-Europe, Middle East & Africa)*

TurboCare C.A. (1)
Zona Industrial Calle 146 Esq Av 62 Edificio TurboCare, Diagonal al Cuerpo de Bomberos, Maracaibo, 4009, Venezuela
Tel.: (58) 261 7302500
Turbine Parts Distr
N.A.I.C.S.: 423830

TurboCare S.p.A. (1)
Corso Romania 661, Turin, 10156, Italy
Tel.: (39) 011 00 59 081
Web Site: http://www.turbocare.com
Sales Range: $75-99.9 Million
Emp.: 260
Steam & Gas Turbine Equipment Repair Services
N.A.I.C.S.: 811310
Franco Merlo *(CEO & Gen Mgr)*

TurboCare Sp. z.o.o. (1)
Paprotna 12a, 51-117, Wroclaw, Poland
Tel.: (48) 71 326 69 00
Web Site: http://www.turbocare.com.pl

Sales Range: $100-124.9 Million
Emp.: 290
Turbine Generator Mfr
N.A.I.C.S.: 333611

UAB Siemens (1)
J Jasinskio Str 16c, 01112, Vilnius, Lithuania
Tel.: (370) 52391500
Sales Range: $125-149.9 Million
Emp.: 30
Transporation System & Communication Services
N.A.I.C.S.: 237130
Janne Ohman *(CEO)*

UGS Israeli Holdings (Israel) Ltd. (1)
22 Rivlin Yosef, Jerusalem, Israel
Tel.: (972) 99594777
Investment Management Service
N.A.I.C.S.: 523999

VA TECH (UK) Ltd. (1)
Halesfield 9, Telford, TF7 4QW, United Kingdom
Tel.: (44) 1952585252
Web Site: https://www.vatech.co.uk
Engineeering Services
N.A.I.C.S.: 541330
Nick Smith *(Dir-Ops)*

VIB Verkehrsinformationsagentur Bayern GmbH (1)
Richard-Strauss-Str 76, Munich, 81679, Bavaria, Germany
Tel.: (49) 7219651333
Traffic Information Portal Services
N.A.I.C.S.: 519290

VMZ Berlin Betreibergesellschaft mbH (1)
Ullsteinstrasse 120, 12109, Berlin, Germany
Tel.: (49) 30814530
Web Site: http://www.vmzberlin.com
Traffic Management Services
N.A.I.C.S.: 488111
Reinhard Giehler *(Mng Dir)*

Vendigital Limited (1)
91 Wimpole Street, London, W1G 0EF, United Kingdom
Tel.: (44) 2045793558
Web Site: https://www.vendigital.com
Business Management Consulting Services
N.A.I.C.S.: 541611

Wattsense S.A.S. (1)
Immeuble Daytona 4 chemin du Tronchon, 69410, Champagne-au-Mont-d'Or, France
Tel.: (33) 428298349
Web Site: https://www.wattsense.com
Building & Construction Services
N.A.I.C.S.: 236220

Weiss Spindeltechnologie GmbH (1)
Birkenfelder Weg 14, Maroldsweisach, 96126, Schweinfurt, Germany
Tel.: (49) 953292290
Web Site: https://www.weissgmbh.com
Sales Range: $100-124.9 Million
Emp.: 32
Spindle Unit Mfr
N.A.I.C.S.: 333248
Thomas Winter *(Dir-Comml)*

Winergy AG (1)
Am Industriepark 2, Friedrichsfeld, 46562, Voerde, Germany
Tel.: (49) 2871924
Web Site: http://www.winergy-group.com
Wine Turbine Component Mfr
N.A.I.C.S.: 333611

Winergy Drive Systems (Tianjin) Co. Ltd. (1)
No 20 Shuangchen Middle Road Beichen Economic Development Area, Tianjin, 300400, China
Tel.: (86) 22 2697 2063
Electric Power Distribution Services
N.A.I.C.S.: 221122

eos.uptrade GmbH (1)
Schanzenstrasse 70, 20357, Hamburg, Germany
Tel.: (49) 408080700
Web Site: https://www.eos-uptrade.de
Emp.: 130
Software Development Services
N.A.I.C.S.: 513210

evosoft GmbH (1)
Marienbergstr 76-82, 90411, Nuremberg, Germany
Tel.: (49) 911539910
Web Site: https://www.evosoft.com
Software Development Services
N.A.I.C.S.: 541511

evosoft Hungary Szamitastechnikai Kft. (1)
Infopark Magyar Tudosok krt 11, 1117, Budapest, Hungary
Tel.: (36) 13816400
Software Development Services
N.A.I.C.S.: 541511

iMetrex Technologies Limited (1)
Clonshaugh Industrial Estate, 17, Dublin, Ireland
Tel.: (353) 12500500
Protection & Security Services
N.A.I.C.S.: 561612

sinius GmbH (1)
Hofmannstr 51, Munich, 81379, Bavaria, Germany
Tel.: (49) 8963600
Electrical Engineering Services
N.A.I.C.S.: 541330

SIEMENS ENERGY AG
Otto-Hahn-Ring 6, 81739, Munich, Germany
Tel.: (49) 8978050   De
Web Site: https://www.siemens-energy.com
ENR—(DEU)
Rev.: $33,584,070,796
Assets: $51,701,921,002
Liabilities: $42,218,864,667
Net Worth: $9,483,056,335
Earnings: ($4,951,435,355)
Emp.: 94,000
Fiscal Year-end: 09/30/23
Renewable Energy Services
N.A.I.C.S.: 221111
Joe Kaeser *(Chm-Supervisory Bd)*

Subsidiaries:

Dresser-Rand Group Inc. (1)
West8 Tower Ste 1000 10205 Westheimer Rd, Houston, TX 77042
Tel.: (713) 354-6100
Web Site: http://www.dresser-rand.com
Emp.: 7,900
Holding Company; Custom-Engineered Rotating Equipment Designer & Mfr
N.A.I.C.S.: 551112
Jesus M. Pacheco *(Exec VP-Tech & Innovation)*

Subsidiary (Domestic):

Dresser-Rand Company (2)
West8 Twr Ste 1000 10205 Westheimer Rd, Houston, TX 77042
Tel.: (713) 935-3400
Web Site: http://www.dresser-rand.com
Custom-Engineered Rotating Equipment Designer & Mfr
N.A.I.C.S.: 333611
Dan Simpson *(Exec VP-Global Solutions)*

Subsidiary (Non-US):

Dresser-Rand Canada, Inc. (3)
9330-45 Avenue, Edmonton, T6E 6S1, AB, Canada
Tel.: (780) 436-0604
Web Site: http://www.dresser-rand.com
Emp.: 50
Hydraulic Turbine Machinery Designer & Mfr
N.A.I.C.S.: 333611
Alan Grieves *(Gen Mgr)*

Plant (Domestic):

Dresser-Rand Co. - Burlington (3)
3800 W Ave, Burlington, IA 52601-4345
Tel.: (319) 753-5431
Web Site: http://www.dresser-rand.com
Custom-Engineered Rotating Equipment Mfr & Whslr
N.A.I.C.S.: 333611

Dresser-Rand Co. - Olean (3)
500 Paul Clark Dr, Olean, NY 14760
Tel.: (716) 375-3000
Web Site: http://www.dresser-rand.com
Turbine Mfr
N.A.I.C.S.: 333611

Dresser-Rand Co. - Painted Post (3)
100 E Chemung St, Painted Post, NY 14870
Tel.: (607) 937-2011
Web Site: http://www.dresser-rand.com
Emp.: 700
Compressors & Spare Parts Mfr
N.A.I.C.S.: 333912
Jeff Wood *(Gen Mgr)*

Dresser-Rand Co. - Wellsville (3)
37 Coats St, Wellsville, NY 14895-1003
Tel.: (585) 593-3100
Web Site: http://www.dresser-rand.com
Compressors & Spare Parts Mfr
N.A.I.C.S.: 333912

Subsidiary (Non-US):

Dresser-Rand S.A. (3)
31 Boulevard Winston Churchill, 76080, Le Havre, Cedex 7013, France
Tel.: (33) 235255225
Web Site: http://www.dresser-rand.com
Turbine & Compressor Designer & Mfr
N.A.I.C.S.: 811310
Walter Nye *(VP-Ops)*

Subsidiary (Non-US):

Dresser-Rand AS (4)
Kirkegardsveien 45, 3601Å, Kongsberg, Norway
Tel.: (47) 32287070
Web Site: http://www.dresser-rand.com
Hydraulic Turbine Machinery Designer & Mfr
N.A.I.C.S.: 333611

Dresser-Rand Company Ltd. (4)
Werrington Parkway, Peterborough, PE4 5HG, Cambridgeshire, United Kingdom
Tel.: (44) 1733292200
Web Site: http://www.dresser-rand.com
Hydraulic Turbine Machinery Designer & Mfr
N.A.I.C.S.: 333611

Subsidiary (Domestic):

Dresser-Rand (UK) Ltd. (5)
Hareness Circle Altebs Industrial Estate, Aberdeen, AB12 3LY, Scotland, United Kingdom
Tel.: (44) 1224241000
Web Site: http://www.dresser-rand.com
Gas Turbines, Generator & Compressor Sets Packager
N.A.I.C.S.: 333611

Subsidiary (Non-US):

Dresser-Rand GmbH (4)
Brinkstrasse 21, Oberhausen, D-46419, Nordrhein, Germany
Tel.: (49) 208656020
Web Site: http://www.dresser-rand.com
Diesel & Gas Turbines Generator Mfr
N.A.I.C.S.: 333611

Subsidiary (Domestic):

Dresser-Rand Services, LLC (3)
520 Kelly Ln, Louisiana, MO 63353
Tel.: (573) 754-4557
Web Site: http://www.dresser-rand.com
Emp.: 100
Industrial Machinery Repair Services
N.A.I.C.S.: 811310
Mike Smith *(Gen Mgr)*

Subsidiary (Non-US):

Dresser-Rand Trinidad & Tobago Limited (3)
Amazon Drive / Point Lisas Industrial Estate, Couva, Trinidad & Tobago
Tel.: (868) 6792662
Web Site: http://www.dresser-rand.com
Hydraulic Turbine Machinery Designer & Mfr
N.A.I.C.S.: 333611

Ethos Energy Group Limited (1)
Ethos House Craigshaw Business Park

SIEMENS ENERGY AG

Siemens Energy AG—(Continued)
Craigshaw Road, Aberdeen, AB12 3QH,
United Kingdom **(49%)**
Tel.: (44) 1224367200
Web Site: https://ethosenergy.co
Oil & Gas Rotating Equipment Services
N.A.I.C.S.: 811310
Ana B. Amicarella *(CEO)*

HSP Hochspannungsgerate GmbH (1)
Camp-Spich-Strasse 18, 53842, Troisdorf,
Germany
Tel.: (49) 224125260
Web Site: https://www.hspkoeln.de
Sales Range: $125-149.9 Million
Emp.: 330
Bush Mfr & Services
N.A.I.C.S.: 326199
Matthias Baca *(CEO)*

Limited Liability Company Siemens Energy (1)
St Nemiga 40 Office 701, Minsk, 220004,
Belarus
Tel.: (375) 172173484
Automation Equipment Mfr
N.A.I.C.S.: 334512

Materials Solutions Limited (1)
Unit 4 Coneybury Road Worcester Six Business Park, Worcester, WR4 0AD, United Kingdom
Tel.: (44) 1905732160
Web Site: https://www.materialssolutions.co.uk
Additive Mfr
N.A.I.C.S.: 339999
Alan Huggins *(Mgr-Pur & Inventory)*

Siemens Energy A/S (1)
Borupvang 9, 2750, Ballerup, Denmark
Tel.: (45) 44774477
Automation Equipment Mfr
N.A.I.C.S.: 334512

Siemens Energy B.V. (1)
Stadhouderslaan 900, 2382 BL, Zoeterwoude, Netherlands
Tel.: (31) 715792444
Web Site: http://www.siemens-energy.com
Developer, Mfr & Retailer Heat Recovery Steam Generators
N.A.I.C.S.: 333611

Branch (Non-US):

Siemens Energy B.V. - Germany Branch (2)
Sibylla-Merian-Str 3, 45665, Recklinghausen, Germany
Tel.: (49) 2361 98690
Heat Exchanger Distr
N.A.I.C.S.: 423720

Subsidiary (Domestic):

Siemens Heat Transfer Technology B.V. (2)
Industrieplein 1, 7553 LL, Hengelo,
Netherlands **(100%)**
Tel.: (31) 748515888
Web Site: http://www.siemens-energy.com
Engineering, Repair, Modification & Field Services for Boiler Installations
N.A.I.C.S.: 541330

Subsidiary (Non-US):

Siemens Heat Transfer Technology Free Zone LLC (2)
Alexandria Public Free Zone Street 2/6 Block number 310, Alexandria, Egypt
Tel.: (20) 16 552 3915
Web Site: http://www.siemens-energy.com
Heat Exchanger Distr
N.A.I.C.S.: 423720

Siemens Energy Canada Limited (1)
1577 North Service Road East, Oakville,
L6H 0H6, ON, Canada
Tel.: (905) 465-8000
Web Site: https://www.siemens-energy.com
Emp.: 1,500
Eletric Power Generation Services
N.A.I.C.S.: 221111
Arne Wohlschlegel *(Mng Dir)*

Siemens Energy Global GmbH & Co. KG (1)
Otto-Hahn-Ring 6, 81739, Munich, Germany
Tel.: (49) 8978050
Electrical & Electronic Product Mfr
N.A.I.C.S.: 336320
Andreas C. Hoffmann *(Chm)*

Siemens Energy K.K. (1)
4th Floor JR Tokyu Meguro Building 3-1-1,
Kami Osaki Shinagawa-ku, Tokyo, 141-0021, Japan
Tel.: (81) 367565300
Renewable Energy Power Generation Services
N.A.I.C.S.: 221114

Siemens Energy Limited (1)
2922/333 Charn Issara Tower II 35F New Petchburi Rd, Bangkok, Thailand
Tel.: (66) 20791191
Renewable Energy Power Generation Services
N.A.I.C.S.: 221114

Siemens Energy Pte. Ltd. (1)
60 MacPherson Road, Singapore, 348615,
Singapore
Tel.: (65) 64906000
Renewable Energy Power Generation Services
N.A.I.C.S.: 221114

Siemens Energy Pty. Ltd. (1)
885 Mountain Highway, Bayswater, 3153,
VIC, Australia
Tel.: (61) 1300477167
Renewable Energy Power Generation Services
N.A.I.C.S.: 221114

Siemens Energy Sdn. Bhd. (1)
Level 1 Reception CP Tower Pusat Perdagangan Seksyen, 16 No 11 Jalan 16/11,
46350, Petaling Jaya, Selangor, Malaysia
Tel.: (60) 379525555
Renewable Energy Power Generation Services
N.A.I.C.S.: 221114

Siemens Energy, Inc. (1)
4400 N Alafaya Trl, Orlando, FL 32826-2301 **(100%)**
Tel.: (407) 736-2000
Web Site: http://www.powergeneration.siemens.com
Sales Range: $900-999.9 Million
Emp.: 3,000
Planning, Construction & Upgrades of Power Plants; Manufacture, Sale & Service of Steam & Gas Turbine Generators, Components & Directly Associated Instrumentation & Controls
N.A.I.C.S.: 333611
Paul A. Camuti *(Founder)*

Subsidiary (Domestic):

Advanced Airfoil Components LLC (2)
13111 Bay Industrial Dr Ste 100, Gibsonton,
FL 33534
Tel.: (813) 437-8200
Web Site: https://www.advanced-airfoils.com
Gas Turbine Engine Mfr
N.A.I.C.S.: 333611
Kevin Updegrove *(CEO)*

Siemens Generation Services Company (2)
3501 Quadrangle Blvd Ste 175, Orlando,
FL 32817
Tel.: (407) 736-1400
Web Site: https://www.siemensgs.com
Power Generation Services
N.A.I.C.S.: 221118

Siemens Gamesa Renewable Energy 9REN, S.L. (2)
Calle Ramirez de Arellano 37, 28043, Madrid, Spain
Tel.: (34) 915031700
Wind Turbine Mfr & Distr
N.A.I.C.S.: 333611

Siemens Gamesa Renewable Energy, S.A. (1)
Parque Tecnologico de Bizkaia Edificio 222,
48170, Zamudio, Spain **(67.07%)**
Tel.: (34) 944037352
Web Site: http://www.siemensgamesa.com
Rev: $9,640,807,942
Assets: $17,337,582,838
Liabilities: $13,542,597,181
Net Worth: $3,794,985,658
Earnings: ($922,730,989)
Emp.: 25,869
Fiscal Year-end: 09/30/2022
Wind Turbine Mfr & Wind Farm Operator; Aeronautics
N.A.I.C.S.: 333611
Christoph Wollny *(COO)*

Subsidiary (Domestic):

Apoyos y Estructuras Metalicas S.A. (2)
Camino De Labiano 45, Mutilea alga Aranguren, 21192, Bilbao, Navarra,
Spain **(100%)**
Tel.: (34) 948292830
Structural Steel Erection Contractors
N.A.I.C.S.: 238120

Subsidiary (Non-US):

CG Hibbert Ltd (2)
No 8 Bond Channel View Road, Dover,
CT17 9TW, Kent, United Kingdom
Tel.: (44) 1304 207353
Warehousing & Storage Services
N.A.I.C.S.: 493110

Subsidiary (Domestic):

Cametor S.L. (2)
Calle Portal De Gamarra 40, Vitoria,
Spain **(100%)**
Tel.: (34) 944317614
Real Estate Property Lessors
N.A.I.C.S.: 531190

Cantarey Reinosa, S.A. (2)
P Alejandro Calonge n 3, 39200, Reinosa,
Cantabria, Spain
Tel.: (34) 942 774100
Motor & Generator Mfr
N.A.I.C.S.: 335312

Compass Transworld Logistics, S.A. (2)
Plaza Europa Cdad Del Transporte 12 - 1
Planta, Noain, 31119, Spain **(100%)**
Tel.: (34) 948167200
Logistics Consulting Servies
N.A.I.C.S.: 541614

Estructuras Metalicas Singulares S.A. (2)
Camino De Labiano 25, Aranguren, Bilbao,
Navarra, Spain **(100%)**
Tel.: (34) 948292830
Fabricated Structural Metal Mfr
N.A.I.C.S.: 332312

Subsidiary (Non-US):

Gamesa Blade Tianjin Co Ltd. (2)
No 10 Xiangzun Road Tianxiang Industrial Park Xiqing Economic, Tianjin, 300385,
China
Tel.: (86) 2223971800
Wind Turbine Mfr
N.A.I.C.S.: 333611

Subsidiary (Domestic):

Gamesa Electric, S.A. (2)
Parque tecnologico de Bizkaia Edificio 206,
48170, Zamudio, Vizcaya, Spain
Tel.: (34) 944317600
Web Site: https://www.gamesaelectric.com
Electrical & Electronic Equipment Mfr
N.A.I.C.S.: 335999
Juan Barandiaran *(Mng Dir)*

Subsidiary (Non-US):

Gamesa Energia Polska Sp. Z.o.o (2)
Krucza 16-22, Warsaw, 00-526, Poland
Tel.: (48) 224342644
Web Site: http://www.gamesacorp.com
Wind Electric Power Generation Services
N.A.I.C.S.: 221118

Gamesa Energiaki Hellas, A.E. (2)
Adrimeiou 9, 11525, Athens, Greece
Tel.: (30) 2106753300
Web Site: http://www.gamesacorp.com
Eletric Power Generation Services
N.A.I.C.S.: 221118

Gamesa Energie France, E.U.R.L. (2)
97 allee Alexandre Borodine, Saint Priest,
69800, Lyon, France
Tel.: (33) 472794705
Web Site: http://www.gamesacorp.com
Engineeering Services
N.A.I.C.S.: 541330
Delphine Henri *(Mgr)*

Gamesa Eolica Brasil, Ltd. (2)
Dos Polimeros S/N, Camacari, 42810-220,
Brazil
Tel.: (55) 7136321225
Eletric Power Generation Services
N.A.I.C.S.: 221118

Gamesa Eolica France SARL (2)
97 Allee Alexandre Borodine - Cedre 3,
69800, Saint Priest, France
Tel.: (33) 4 72 79 47 05
Web Site: http://www.gamesacorp.com
Wind Electric Power Generation Services
N.A.I.C.S.: 221118

Subsidiary (US):

Gamesa Wind PA LLC (2)
1801 Market St Ste 2700, Philadelphia, PA 19103 **(100%)**
Tel.: (215) 428-9750
Web Site: http://www.gamesacorp.com
Motor & Generator Mfr
N.A.I.C.S.: 335312

Subsidiary (Non-US):

Gamesa Wind Sweden AB (2)
Solma Strambvag 78, Solna, 171 54, Sweden
Tel.: (46) 703622702
Wind Electric Power Generation Services
N.A.I.C.S.: 221118

Subsidiary (US):

Gamesa Wind US LLC (2)
400 Gamesa Dr, Fairless Hills, PA 19030-5010 **(100%)**
Tel.: (215) 428-9750
Web Site: http://www.gamesacorp.com
Motor & Generator Mfr
N.A.I.C.S.: 335312

Subsidiary (Non-US):

Gamesa Wind, GmbH (2)
Wurzburger Strasse 152, Aschaffenburg,
63743, Germany **(100%)**
Tel.: (49) 602115090
Web Site: http://www.gamesacorp.com
Eletric Power Generation Services
N.A.I.C.S.: 221118

RSR Power Private Limited (2)
No 6 GPR Towers Park Road, Tusker Town Shivajinagar, Bengaluru, 560 051, Karnataka, India
Tel.: (91) 8022862070
Eletric Power Generation Services
N.A.I.C.S.: 221118

Subsidiary (Domestic):

S.E. Cabezo Negro, S.A. (2)
Calle Jose Luis Albareda 1 - A Y B, Zaragoza, 50004, Spain
Tel.: (34) 944317600
Wind Turbine Generator Mfr
N.A.I.C.S.: 333611

Subsidiary (Non-US):

Siemens Gamesa Renewable Energy (Beijing) Co., Ltd. (2)
Siemens Center Beijing 12 Floor No 7 South Wangjing Zhonghuan Road, Chaoyang District, Beijing, 100102, China
Tel.: (86) 1064719610
Renewable Energy Services
N.A.I.C.S.: 221111

Siemens Gamesa Renewable Energy (Pty) Ltd. (2)
Siemens Park Halfway House 300 Janadel Avenue, Midrand, Johannesburg, 1685,
South Africa
Tel.: (27) 116523617
Wind Renewable Energy Services
N.A.I.C.S.: 221115
Janek Winand *(Mng Dir)*

AND PRIVATE COMPANIES • SIEMENS ENERGY AG

Siemens Gamesa Renewable Energy B.V. (2)
Prinses Beatrixlaan 800, 2595 BN, Hague, Netherlands
Tel.: (31) 613405603
Renewable Energy Services
N.A.I.C.S.: 221118
David Molenaar *(CEO)*

Siemens Gamesa Renewable Energy Deutschland GmbH (2)
Am Lunedeich 151B, 27572, Bremerhaven, Germany
Tel.: (49) 47180040
Web Site: http://www.adwenoffshore.com
Wind Energy Converter Mfr
N.A.I.C.S.: 333611

Siemens Gamesa Renewable Energy Egypt LLC (2)
5th Floor Bureau 175 2nd Business Sector Al-Horreya Axis 90 South Road, 5th Settlement, 11431, Cairo, Egypt
Tel.: (20) 22511048
Renewable Energy Services
N.A.I.C.S.: 221118
Ayman Saad *(CEO)*

Siemens Gamesa Renewable Energy Italia S.r.l. (2)
Via Vipiteno 4, 20128, Milan, Italy
Tel.: (39) 022431
Renewable Energy Services
N.A.I.C.S.: 221118
Fabio Recalcati *(Mgr-Svcs)*

Siemens Gamesa Renewable Energy Italy, S.P.A. (2)
Centro Direzionale Argonauta Via Ostiense 131/L Corpo C1 9 piano, 00154, Rome, Italy
Tel.: (39) 065750531
Renewable Energy Services
N.A.I.C.S.: 221118
Corrado Labriola *(Sls Mgr)*

Siemens Gamesa Renewable Energy Japan K.K. (2)
14F Tokyo Shiodome building 1-9-1 Higashi Shimbashi, Minato-ku, Tokyo, 105-0021, Japan
Tel.: (81) 362591175
Renewable Energy Services
N.A.I.C.S.: 221111
Russell Cato *(Mng Dir)*

Siemens Gamesa Renewable Energy Kft. (2)
Gizella ut 51-57, 1143, Budapest, Hungary
Tel.: (36) 14711410
Renewable Energy Services
N.A.I.C.S.: 221118
David Papp *(CEO)*

Siemens Gamesa Renewable Energy LLC (2)
14th Floor Saigon Centre 65 Le Loi Street, Ben Nghe Ward District 1, Ho Chi Minh City, Vietnam
Tel.: (84) 2835207713
Renewable Energy Services
N.A.I.C.S.: 221111
Scott Powers *(Sls Dir)*

Siemens Gamesa Renewable Energy Lanka (Private) Limited (2)
51 Negombo-Colombo Main Road, Kurana, Negombo, Sri Lanka
Tel.: (94) 312235890
Renewable Energy Services
N.A.I.C.S.: 221111
Sampath Kariyawasam *(Gen Mgr)*

Siemens Gamesa Renewable Energy Limited (2)
Sir William Siemens Way Alexandra Dock, Hull, HU9 1TA, United Kingdom
Tel.: (44) 1914952244
Wind Electric Power Generation Services
N.A.I.C.S.: 221115
David Rooney *(VP-Sls)*

Siemens Gamesa Renewable Energy Limited (2)
Seoul Square 5th Floor 416 Hangangdaero, Jung-gu, Seoul, 04637, Korea (South)
Tel.: (82) 232874491
Renewable Energy Services
N.A.I.C.S.: 221111

Siemens Gamesa Renewable Energy SARL (2)
Anfa Place Blvd de la Corniche Centre d'Affaires Est, 20200, Casablanca, Morocco
Tel.: (212) 522669200
Renewable Energy Services
N.A.I.C.S.: 221118

Siemens Gamesa Renewable Energy Service GmbH (2)
Beim Strohhause 17-31, 20097, Hamburg, Germany
Tel.: (49) 40822118000
Wind Turbine Developer, Mfr, Distr, Installation & Maintenance Services
N.A.I.C.S.: 333611
Kai Frobose *(Mng Dir & Head-Project Mgmt & Svc)*

Subsidiary (Non-US):

Siemens Gamesa Renewable Energy Service Limited (3)
10 Waterloo Place, Edinburgh, EH1 3EG, United Kingdom
Tel.: (44) 1316239286
Web Site: http://www.senvion.com
Wind Turbine Product Mfr & Distr
N.A.I.C.S.: 333611
Raymond Gilfedder *(Mng Dir & Head-Northern Europe)*

Siemens Gamesa Renewable Energy Service S.A.S. (3)
10 Avenue de l'Arche Immeuble le Colisee, La Defense-Les Faubourgs de l'Arche, 92419, Courbevoie, Cedex, France
Tel.: (33) 1 41 38 93 93
Web Site: http://www.senvion.com
Wind Turbine Distribution, Installation & Maintenance Services
N.A.I.C.S.: 423830
Olivier Perot *(Dir Gen-Southwestern Europe)*

Siemens Gamesa Renewable Energy Service S.r.l. (3)
Via Vipiteno 4, 20128, Milan, Italy
Tel.: (39) 039022431
Web Site: http://www.senvion.com
Wind Turbine Distribution, Installation & Maintenance Services
N.A.I.C.S.: 423830
Carlo Schiapperelli *(Mng Dir)*

Subsidiary (Non-US):

Siemens Gamesa Renewable Energy Singapore Private Limited (2)
MacPherson Road 60, Singapore, 348615, Singapore
Tel.: (65) 64906004
Renewable Energy Services
N.A.I.C.S.: 221111

Siemens Gamesa Renewable Energy Technology (China) Co., Ltd. (2)
8 Chuangxin 4th Rd, Xiqing Qu, Tianjin, 300384, China (100%)
Tel.: (86) 2223780154
Motor & Generator Mfr
N.A.I.C.S.: 335312

Siemens Gamesa Renewable Energy d.o.o. (2)
Heinzelova 70 A, 10000, Zagreb, Croatia
Tel.: (385) 16105494
Renewable & Environment Services
N.A.I.C.S.: 221118
Ivan Cohan *(Mng Dir)*

Subsidiary (Domestic):

Sistemas Energeticos Cabanelas, S.A. (2)
Calle De Antonio Gomez Vilaso-bl 3 Ptl 2 Y 3, Santiago de Compostela, 15702, La Coruna, Spain
Tel.: (34) 944318500
Eletric Power Generation Services
N.A.I.C.S.: 221118

Sistemas Energeticos Cuntis, S.A. (2)
Poligono Del Tambre Via Pasteur 7, Santiago de Compostela, 15890, Spain
Tel.: (34) 944318500
Eletric Power Generation Services
N.A.I.C.S.: 221118

Sistemas Energeticos La Plana, S.A. (2)
Calle Jose Luis Albareda 1 - B 1, Zaragoza, 50004, Spain
Tel.: (34) 944317600
Eletric Power Generation Services
N.A.I.C.S.: 221118

Sistemas Energeticos Loma del Reposo, S.L. (2)
Cl Tecnologico de Bizkaia 222, Zamudio, 48170, Biscay, Spain
Tel.: (34) 944 318 500
Eletric Power Generation Services
N.A.I.C.S.: 221118

Sistemas Energeticos Sierra de Lourenza, S.A. (2)
Poligono Teknologi Elkartegia Edif 222, Zamudio, 48170, Spain
Tel.: (34) 944318500
Eletric Power Generation Services
N.A.I.C.S.: 221118

Sistemas Energeticos del Sur, S.A. (2)
Avenida Eduardo Dato 69 - Tercera Planta Modulo 5, Seville, 41005, Spain
Tel.: (34) 944317600
Eletric Power Generation Services
N.A.I.C.S.: 221118

Valencia Power Converters S.A. (2)
Camino Benisano Olocau Pq Empresarial Turianova S-N, Valencia, 46181, Spain (100%)
Tel.: (34) 962798228
Electronic Parts & Equipment Whslr
N.A.I.C.S.: 423690

Siemens Industrial Turbomachinery (Huludao) Co., Ltd. (1)
No 3 7th Street, Hi-tech Industrial Development Zone, Huludao, 125000, Liaoning, China
Tel.: (86) 4293056000
Web Site: http://en.sith.com.cn
Steam Turbine Mfr
N.A.I.C.S.: 333611

Siemens Industrial Turbomachinery AB (1)
Slottsvagen 2-6, 612 83, Finspang, Sweden
Tel.: (46) 87281000
Web Site: http://new.siemens.com
Emp.: 570
Turbine Generator Mfr
N.A.I.C.S.: 333611

Siemens Industrial Turbomachinery Ltd. (1)
Jopesh Ruston Building Waterside South, PO Box 1, Lincoln, LN5 7FD, United Kingdom
Tel.: (44) 1522584000
Emp.: 180
Industrial Gas Turbine Mfr
N.A.I.C.S.: 333611
Steve Bosch *(Mng Dir)*

Siemens Ltda (1) (100%)
Sales Range: $450-499.9 Million
Emp.: 5,370
Mfr, Sales & Distribution of Motors, Hydroelectric Power Generators, Switchgear, Power Switching Installations, Power Cables; Electromedical Instruments & Equipment; Lighting Systems
N.A.I.C.S.: 335312

Siemens Power Control GmbH (1)
Robert-Bosch-Str 25, 63225, Langen, Germany
Tel.: (49) 6103310300
Web Site: https://siemens-energy-power-control.de
Sales Range: $125-149.9 Million
Emp.: 18
Eletric Power Generation Services
N.A.I.C.S.: 221118
Ruediger Burkhardt *(CEO)*

Siemens Power Operations, Inc. (1)
Barangay Santa Rita, 4200, Batangas, 4200, Philippines
Tel.: (63) 437237826
Power Generation Services
N.A.I.C.S.: 221118

Siemens Power Plant Automation Ltd. (1)
7 Wangjing Zhonghuan Nanlu, ChaoYang District, 100102, Beijing, China
Tel.: (86) 1064768888
Web Site: http://www.w1.siemens.com.cn
Power Station Instrumentation & Control Services
N.A.I.C.S.: 541330

Siemens S.A. (1)
Lumina Olivos Building Blas Parera 3551 - P 2 Olive trees, Munro-Partido de Vicente Lopez, B1636CSE, Buenos Aires, Argentina (100%)
Tel.: (54) 91154326000
Web Site: https://www.siemens.com
Sales Range: $450-499.9 Million
Emp.: 2,590
Mfr & Sales of Power Engineering Products; Switchgear; Communications Systems
N.A.I.C.S.: 335312

Siemens Transformer (Jinan) Co., Ltd. (1)
No 10 Weihua West Road, Shizhong, Jinan, Shandong, China
Tel.: (86) 53187291500
Web Site: http://www.stcl.com.cn
Power Transformer Mfr
N.A.I.C.S.: 335311

Siemens Transformer (Wuhan) Company Ltd. (1)
12F Career Service Center Hanshi Avenue Yangluo, Economic Development Zone, Wuhan, 430415, Hubei, China
Tel.: (86) 2789620000
Web Site: http://cn.siemens.com
Power Transformer Mfr
N.A.I.C.S.: 333613

Siemens Transformers Canada Inc. (1)
3400 Bellefeuille, PO Box 1115, Trois Rivieres, G9H 5K4, QC, Canada
Tel.: (819) 374-4651
Web Site: http://new.siemens.com
Emp.: 100
Power Transmission Equipment Mfr
N.A.I.C.S.: 333613

Siemens Transformers S.r.l. (1)
Via di Spini 9, 38121, Trento, Italy
Tel.: (39) 0461 957111
Emp.: 10
Power Transformer Mfr
N.A.I.C.S.: 335311

Trench Austria GmbH (1)
Paschinger Strasse 49, 4060, Leonding, Austria
Tel.: (43) 73267930
Web Site: http://www.trench-group.com
Reactor Product Mfr
N.A.I.C.S.: 335311

Subsidiary (Non-US):

Trench France S.A. (2)
16 Rue du General Cassagnou, 68302, Saint Louis, Cedex, France
Tel.: (33) 389702323
Web Site: https://trench-group.com
Electric Equipment Mfr
N.A.I.C.S.: 335999

Trench Germany GmbH (2)
Nurnberger Strasse 199, 96050, Bamberg, Germany
Tel.: (49) 95118030
Web Site: https://trench-group.com
Power Transmission Equipment Mfr
N.A.I.C.S.: 333613

Trench High Voltage Products Ltd. (2)
No 2 Jingshenxisan Street Daoyi Economic Development Zone, Shenbei New District, Shenyang, 110136, China
Tel.: (86) 2488923999
Web Site: https://trench-group.com
Electric Equipment Mfr
N.A.I.C.S.: 335999

Trench Italia S.r.l. (2)
Strada Curagnata 37, 17014, Cairo Montenotte, Italy

SIEMENS ENERGY AG

Siemens Energy AG—(Continued)
Tel.: (39) 0195161111
Web Site: https://trench-group.com
Renewable Energy Generation Services
N.A.I.C.S.: 221111

Trench Limited (2)
71 Maybrook Drive, Scarborough, M1V
4B6, ON, Canada
Tel.: (416) 298-8108
Emp.: 500
High Voltage Products Mfr
N.A.I.C.S.: 335311
Selim Hostut *(CEO)*

SIENNA CANCER DIAGNOSTICS LIMITED
1 Dalmore Drive, Scoresby, 3179,
VIC, Australia
Tel.: (61) 3 8288 2141 AU
Web Site:
http://www.siennadiagnostics.com
Year Founded: 2002
SDX—(ASX)
Rev.: $456,306
Assets: $6,280,111
Liabilities: $276,186
Net Worth: $6,003,925
Earnings: ($1,888,063)
Fiscal Year-end: 06/30/19
Biotechnology Research & Development Services
N.A.I.C.S.: 541715
Geoffrey Cumming *(Chm)*

SIENNA RESOURCES INC.
2905 - 700 West Georgia Street, PO
Box 10112, Pacific Centre, Vancouver, V7Y 1C6, BC, Canada
Tel.: (604) 646-6900 BC
Web Site:
https://siennaresources.com
Year Founded: 1983
SIE—(TSXV)
Rev.: $4,093
Assets: $1,696,744
Liabilities: $701,245
Net Worth: $995,499
Earnings: ($317,380)
Fiscal Year-end: 12/31/19
Metal Mining Services
N.A.I.C.S.: 212290
Jason Gigliotti *(Pres)*

Subsidiaries:

Sienna Resources Sweden AB (1)

SIENNA SENIOR LIVING INC.
302 Town Centre Blvd Ste 300,
Markham, L3R 0E8, ON, Canada
Tel.: (905) 477-4006 BC
Web Site: https://www.siennaliving.ca
Year Founded: 1973
SIA—(TSX)
Rev.: $512,506,481
Assets: $1,295,245,224
Liabilities: $889,296,883
Net Worth: $405,948,341
Earnings: $5,775,266
Emp.: 12,263
Fiscal Year-end: 12/31/19
Assisted Living Communities for Seniors
N.A.I.C.S.: 623312
Dino Chiesa *(Chm)*

Subsidiaries:

Leisureworld Senior Care LP (1)
302 Town Center Blvd, Markham, L3R 0E8,
ON, Canada
Tel.: (905) 477-4006
Senior Citizen Homes Management Services
N.A.I.C.S.: 623312
Lois Cormack *(CEO)*

Sienna-RSH Niagara Falls LP (1)

SIERRA CABLES PLC
39/1A Galvarusa Road Korathota, PO
Box 06, Kaduwela, Sri Lanka
Tel.: (94) 114412000
Web Site:
https://www.sierracables.com
SIRA—(COL)
Rev.: $29,252,313
Assets: $35,377,973
Liabilities: $20,916,191
Net Worth: $14,461,781
Earnings: $1,702,193
Emp.: 276
Fiscal Year-end: 03/31/21
Cables & Wires Mfr
N.A.I.C.S.: 332618
Daya Shamendra Panditha *(CEO & Mng Dir)*

SIERRA CONSTRUCTION
1401 Dundas Street, PO Box 20053,
Woodstock, N4S 8X8, ON, Canada
Tel.: (519) 421-9689
Web Site:
http://www.sierraconstruction.ca
Year Founded: 1994
Rev.: $25,622,400
Emp.: 80
Building Construction Services
N.A.I.C.S.: 236210
Cliff Zaluski *(Owner & Pres)*

SIERRA GRANDE MINERALS INC.
9648-128th Street Suite 210, Surrey,
V3T 2X9, BC, Canada
Tel.: (604) 357-4731
Web Site: https://sierragrande.ca
Year Founded: 1994
SIERF—(NASDAQ)
Assets: $1,645,190
Liabilities: $91,126
Net Worth: $1,554,064
Earnings: ($300,333)
Fiscal Year-end: 12/31/22
Mineral Exploration Services
N.A.I.C.S.: 213114

Subsidiaries:

Minera Grenville S.A.C. (1)
Calle Tarata 220 Dpto 902, Miraflores,
Lima, Peru
Tel.: (51) 1 4467904
Mineral Mining Services
N.A.I.C.S.: 212390
Juan Carlos Chinga Cruz *(Gen Mgr)*

SIERRA METALS INC.
200 Bay St South Tower Suite 2800,
Toronto, M5J 2J3, ON, Canada
Tel.: (416) 366-7777 Ca
Web Site:
https://www.sierrametals.com
SMTS—(NYSEAMEX)
Rev.: $272,014,000
Assets: $396,824,000
Liabilities: $192,192,000
Net Worth: $204,632,000
Earnings: ($22,108,000)
Emp.: 1,460
Fiscal Year-end: 12/31/21
Precious & Base Metal Mining Services
N.A.I.C.S.: 212230
Gabriel Pinto *(VP-Sustainability & Corp Affairs)*

SIERRA ONCOLOGY, INC.
2150 885 West Georgia Street, Vancouver, V6C 3E8, BC, Canada
Tel.: (650) 376-8679 DE
Web Site:
http://www.sierraoncology.com
Year Founded: 2003
SRRA—(NASDAQ)
Rev.: $300,000
Assets: $109,367,000
Liabilities: $13,369,000
Net Worth: $95,998,000
Earnings: ($94,659,000)
Emp.: 109
Fiscal Year-end: 12/31/21
Pharmaceuticals Mfr
N.A.I.C.S.: 325412
Robert E. Pelzer *(Chm)*

Subsidiaries:

Sierra Oncology Canada ULC (1)
885 Georgia St W, Vancouver, V6C 3E8,
BC, Canada
Tel.: (604) 558-6536
Pharmaceutical Drug & Supplement Whslr
N.A.I.C.S.: 424210

SIERRA RUTILE HOLDINGS LIMITED
Level 8 225 St George Terrace,
Perth, WA, Australia
Tel.: (61) 862515555
Web Site: https://sierra-rutile.com
SRX—(ASX)
Rev.: $176,301,000
Assets: $209,770,000
Liabilities: $94,260,000
Net Worth: $115,510,000
Earnings: ($20,107,000)
Emp.: 2,048
Fiscal Year-end: 12/31/23
Sand Mining
N.A.I.C.S.: 212322
Maurice Cole *(CFO)*

SIERRA WIRELESS, INC.
13811 Wireless Way, Richmond, V6V
3A4, BC, Canada
Tel.: (604) 231-1100 Ca
Web Site:
http://www.sierrawireless.com
Year Founded: 1993
SW—(TSX)
Rev.: $473,209,000
Assets: $547,053,000
Liabilities: $269,399,000
Net Worth: $277,654,000
Earnings: ($89,017,000)
Emp.: 1,007
Fiscal Year-end: 12/31/21
Wireless Data Communication Equipment Mfr
N.A.I.C.S.: 517112
Marc Overton *(Chief Solutions Officer)*

Subsidiaries:

Genx Mobile, Inc. (1)
2030 Fortune Dr #100, San Jose, CA
95131 (100%)
Tel.: (408) 943-9882
Web Site: http://www.genxmobile.com
Sales Range: $1-9.9 Million
Emp.: 22
Designs & Manufactures Wireless Data
Equipment for Telematic, Security & Fleet
Service Companies
N.A.I.C.S.: 517112
Rodric Fan *(Pres & CEO)*

Sierra Wireless America, Inc. (1)
2738 Loker Ave W Ste A, Carlsbad, CA
92010
Tel.: (760) 444-5650
Web Site: http://www.sierrawireless.com
Emp.: 37
Communication Equipment Distr
N.A.I.C.S.: 423690

Sierra Wireless France (1)
5 Boulevard Gallieni, 92442, Issy-les-Moulineaux, Cedex, France
Tel.: (33) 146290800
Web Site: http://www.sierrawireless.com
Sales Range: $250-299.9 Million
Emp.: 250
Wireless Communications Software & Hardware Mfr
N.A.I.C.S.: 517112

INTERNATIONAL PUBLIC

Sierra Wireless Services America
Holdings Inc. (1)
400 Interstate North Pkwy Ste 1350, Atlanta, GA 30339-2119
Tel.: (770) 693-5950
Web Site: http://www.sierrawireless.com
Holding Company Comprised of Subsidiaries that Develop & Market Communication
& Information Products & Services
N.A.I.C.S.: 334290

Subsidiary (Domestic):

Airdesk, Inc. (2)
37 Bon Air Dr, Warminster, PA 18974
Tel.: (215) 734-7000
Wireless Mobile Services
N.A.I.C.S.: 517810

Broadband Networks Inc. (2)
2820 E College Ave Ste B, State College,
PA 16801-7548
Tel.: (888) 534-4973
Web Site: http://www.bnisolutions.com
Telecommunications Systems Solutions
N.A.I.C.S.: 517810

Uplink Security, Inc. (2)
1600 Parkwood Cir Ste 500, Atlanta, GA
30339
Tel.: (770) 693-3500
Web Site: http://www.uplink.com
Wireless Security Solutions Through Technology, Networks & Application Development
N.A.I.C.S.: 517112

Wireless Maingate AB (1)
Drottninggatan 16, PO Box 244, 371 24,
Karlskrona, Sweden
Tel.: (46) 455363700
Web Site: http://www.wirelessmaingate.com
Emp.: 30
Wireless Telecommunication Services
N.A.I.C.S.: 517810

SIETEL LIMITED
C/- Cook s Body Works Pty Ltd 140-144 Cochranes Road, Moorabbin,
3189, VIC, Australia
Tel.: (61) 395535740
Web Site: https://www.sietel.com.au
SSL—(ASX)
Rev.: $10,112,522
Assets: $59,360,035
Liabilities: $5,456,211
Net Worth: $53,903,823
Earnings: $446,633
Fiscal Year-end: 09/30/23
Industrial & Commercial Real Estate
Investment Services
N.A.I.C.S.: 523940
Geoffrey L. Rees *(Chm)*

Subsidiaries:

Alliance Appliances Australia P/L (1)
144 Cochranes Road, Moorabbin, 3189,
VIC, Australia
Tel.: (61) 438397143
Web Site: https://allianceappliances.com.au
Electronic & Home Appliance Distr
N.A.I.C.S.: 423620

Cooks Body Works Pty Ltd (1)
144 Cochranes Rd, Moorabbin, 3189, VIC,
Australia
Tel.: (61) 395554166
Web Site:
https://www.cooksbodyworks.com.au
Sales Range: $25-49.9 Million
Emp.: 20
Truck Bodies Mfr
N.A.I.C.S.: 336211
Con Theodoropoulos *(Mng Dir)*

SIEU THANH CORPORATION
A20 Tan Phong Nguyen Huu Tho St,
Tan Phong Ward Dist 7, Ho Chi Minh
City, Vietnam
Tel.: (84) 862628888
Web Site:
https://sieuthanhvietnam.vn
Year Founded: 1994
ST8—(HOSE)
Rev.: $544,211

Assets: $11,407,456
Liabilities: $188,284
Net Worth: $11,219,172
Earnings: $159,444
Emp.: 11
Fiscal Year-end: 12/31/23
Office Equipment Whslr
N.A.I.C.S.: 423420
David Cam Hao Ong *(Exec Dir)*

SIEVI CAPITAL OYJ
Pohjoisesplanadi 33, FI-00100, Helsinki, FI-00100, Finland
Tel.: (358) 405006898
Web Site: https://www.sievicapital.fi
Year Founded: 2012
KHG—(HEL)
Rev.: $298,680,870
Assets: $383,814,991
Liabilities: $296,315,267
Net Worth: $87,499,724
Earnings: ($21,061,927)
Emp.: 1,237
Fiscal Year-end: 12/31/23
Investment Services
N.A.I.C.S.: 523999
Asa-Matti Lyytinen *(Chm)*

Subsidiaries:

Indoor Group Oy (1)
Kuninkaalantie 19, 01300, Vantaa, Finland
Tel.: (358) 103855474
Web Site: https://www.indoorgroup.fi
Sales Range: $1-4.9 Billion
Emp.: 700
Household Furniture Mfr & Distr
N.A.I.C.S.: 337122
Pasi Kohmo *(CEO)*

SIEYUAN ELECTRIC CO., LTD.
No 3399 Huaning Road, Minhang District, Shanghai, 201108, China
Tel.: (86) 2161610471
Web Site: https://www.sieyuan.com
Year Founded: 1993
002028—(SSE)
Rev.: $1,479,408,503
Assets: $2,205,760,602
Liabilities: $880,948,603
Net Worth: $1,324,811,999
Earnings: $171,345,732
Emp.: 5,000
Fiscal Year-end: 12/31/22
Power Transmission Services
N.A.I.C.S.: 221122
Dong Zengping *(Chm & Gen Mgr)*

SIF BANAT-CRISANA S.A.
Calea Victoriei 35 A, 310158, Arad, Romania
Tel.: (40) 257304438 RO
Web Site: https://www.lion-capital.ro
Year Founded: 1996
LION—(BUC)
Rev.: $41,519,060
Assets: $931,631,904
Liabilities: $59,632,838
Net Worth: $871,999,066
Earnings: $93,198,914
Emp.: 32
Fiscal Year-end: 12/31/23
Financial & Investment Services
N.A.I.C.S.: 523940
Teodora Sferdian *(Member-Mgmt Bd & Deputy Gen Dir)*

Subsidiaries:

BIOFARM SA (1)
99 Logofatul Tautu St, Sector 3, 031212, Bucharest, Romania
Tel.: (40) 213010600
Web Site: https://www.biofarm.ro
Rev.: $60,878,081
Assets: $107,255,188
Liabilities: $12,902,084
Net Worth: $94,353,104
Earnings: $16,727,025
Emp.: 399
Fiscal Year-end: 12/31/2023

Pharmaceuticals Product Mfr
N.A.I.C.S.: 325412
Andrei Hrebencluc *(Chm)*

Calipso S.A (1)
Pta Independentei nr 53 bl A10, Oradea, 410067, Bihor, Romania
Tel.: (40) 259 475271
Web Site: http://www.calipso-oradea.ro
Sales Range: $10-24.9 Million
Emp.: 88
Food Catering Services
N.A.I.C.S.: 722320
Jecu Loan *(Dir Gen)*

Central SA (1)
Strada Regele Ferdinand nr 22-26, Cluj-Napoca, Romania
Web Site: https://www.magazincentral.ro
General Merchandise Product Distr
N.A.I.C.S.: 455219

Cora SA (1)
A1-2 P 9 B-Dul Dacia, Hunedoara, Romania
Tel.: (40) 254712244
Supermarkets Operation Services
N.A.I.C.S.: 445110

LEGUME FRUCTE S.A. (1)
29 Str Dambovitei, Oradea, 410546, Romania
Tel.: (40) 359802533
Web Site: http://www.lforadea.ro
Sales Range: $25-49.9 Million
Emp.: 14
Vegetables & Fruits Distr
N.A.I.C.S.: 424480

NAPOTEX S.A. (1)
str Traian Vuia nr 208, 400397, Cluj-Napoca, Romania
Tel.: (40) 264591044
Web Site: http://www.napotex.ro
Sales Range: $50-74.9 Million
Emp.: 10
Apparels & Shoes Distr
N.A.I.C.S.: 424310

Napomar S.A. (1)
14 B-dul Muncii, 400641, Cluj-Napoca, Romania
Tel.: (40) 264415006
Web Site: https://www.napomar.ro
Sales Range: $100-124.9 Million
Emp.: 342
Grinding Machine Mfr
N.A.I.C.S.: 333517

S.C. VRANCART S.A. (1)
Str Ecaterina Teodoroiu nr 17, 625100, Adjud, Vrancea, Romania
Tel.: (40) 237640800
Web Site: https://www.vrancart.ro
Rev.: $108,663,807
Assets: $168,330,824
Liabilities: $90,673,250
Net Worth: $77,657,574
Earnings: $1,177,730
Emp.: 1,221
Fiscal Year-end: 12/31/2023
Paperboard Mfr
N.A.I.C.S.: 322130

SAI Muntenia Invest SA (1)
Serghei Vasilievici Rahmaninov Street 46-48, 020199, Bucharest, Romania
Tel.: (40) 213873210
Web Site: https://www.munteniainvest.ro
Investment Management Service
N.A.I.C.S.: 523940

SIF Hoteluri SA (1)
Emanuil Gojdu Square No 53 bl A10, Oradea, Romania
Tel.: (40) 259475271
Web Site: https://www.sif-hoteluri.ro
Hotel Operator
N.A.I.C.S.: 721110

SIF Imobiliare PLC (1)
Karpenisiou 30, 1077, Nicosia, Cyprus   (99.99%)
Tel.: (357) 22843000
Web Site: https://www.sif-imobiliare.ro
Rev.: $5,220,244
Assets: $56,759,138
Liabilities: $57,544
Net Worth: $56,701,594
Earnings: $4,879,438
Fiscal Year-end: 12/31/2020

Real Estate Investment Trust
N.A.I.C.S.: 525990

Silvana S.A. (1)
2 Str Plopilor, 455100, Cehu Silvaniei, Salaj, Romania
Tel.: (40) 260650876
Web Site: http://www.skd.ro
Sales Range: $25-49.9 Million
Emp.: 190
Apparels Mfr
N.A.I.C.S.: 315210
Laura Coroian *(Gen Mgr)*

Soiza S.A. (1)
5 P-Ta Libertatii, Sighetu Marmatiei, 435500, Maramures, Romania
Tel.: (40) 262312847
Sales Range: $25-49.9 Million
Emp.: 12
Branded Apparels Retailer
N.A.I.C.S.: 458110

Somplast SA (1)
str George Cosbuc nr 147, 425200, Nasaud, Bistrita-Nasaud, Romania
Tel.: (40) 263360032
Web Site: https://www.somplast.ro
Sales Range: $50-74.9 Million
Plastics Product Mfr
N.A.I.C.S.: 326220

Trans Euro Hotel S.A. (1)
23 B-Dul Bucuresti, Baia Mare, 430275, Maramures, Romania
Tel.: (40) 262222405
Web Site: http://www.eurohotel-bm.eu
Sales Range: $10-24.9 Million
Emp.: 20
Home Management Services
N.A.I.C.S.: 721110
Luminita Ghilacs *(Mgr)*

Vrancart SA (1)
Str Ecaterina Teodoroiu nr 17, Vrancea, 625100, Adjud, Romania
Tel.: (40) 237640800
Web Site: https://www.vrancart.ro
Paper & Corrugated Cardboard Mfr
N.A.I.C.S.: 322130

SIF MUNTENIA S.A.
SV Rachmaninov street no 46-48 sect 2, 20199, Bucharest, Romania
Tel.: (40) 213873210
Web Site: https://longshield.ro
SIF4—(BUC)
Rev.: $19,183,889
Assets: $501,559,058
Liabilities: $20,603,164
Net Worth: $480,955,894
Earnings: $45,814,339
Emp.: 1
Fiscal Year-end: 12/31/23
Investment Management Service
N.A.I.C.S.: 523940
Florica Trandafir *(Chm)*

Subsidiaries:

Avicola S.A. (1)
Splaiul Unirii nr 16 et 3 cam 310 sector 4, Bucharest, Romania
Tel.: (40) 374600100
Web Site: http://www.avicolabucuresti.ro
Sales Range: $10-24.9 Million
Emp.: 166
Poultry Farming Services
N.A.I.C.S.: 112310
Mariana Teitler *(Dir-Comml)*

Firos S.A. (1)
Bdul Timisoara no 100 sector 6, Bucharest, Romania
Tel.: (40) 217770509
Web Site: https://www.firos.ro
Building Materials Distr
N.A.I.C.S.: 444180

Fondul Roman de Garantare a Creditelor Pentru Intreprinzatorii Privati - IFN S.A. (1)
46 Matasari Street sector 2, Bucharest, Romania
Tel.: (40) 21 252 3220
Web Site: https://www.frgc.ro
Financial Services
N.A.I.C.S.: 523940

ICPE S.A. (1)
Splaiul Unirii 313, 030138, Bucharest, Romania
Tel.: (40) 215893300
Web Site: https://www.icpe.ro
Electric & Metrology Product Mfr
N.A.I.C.S.: 334515

SIFAS
Bretelle de l'autoroute, 19 Chemin de font Graissan, 06250, Mougins, France
Tel.: (33) 493458800
Web Site: http://www.sifas.fr
Furniture Mfr & Whslr
N.A.I.C.S.: 449110

SIFCA SA
Abidjan boulevard de Havre 01, PO Box 1289, Abidjan, Cote d'Ivoire
Tel.: (225) 2175 7575   CI
Web Site: http://www.groupesifca.com
Year Founded: 1964
Sales Range: $700-749.9 Million
Emp.: 33,000
Holding Company; Sugar Cane, Vegetable Oil & Natural Rubber Production
N.A.I.C.S.: 551112
Pierre Billon *(CEO)*

Subsidiaries:

Societe Internationale de Plantations d'Heveas SA (1)
53 rue du Capitaine Guynemer, 92400, Courbevoie, France   (55.59%)
Tel.: (33) 1 41 16 28 00
Web Site: https://www.siph.com
Rev.: $244,985,222
Assets: $341,256,639
Liabilities: $169,756,094
Net Worth: $171,500,544
Earnings: ($4,104,139)
Emp.: 13,091
Fiscal Year-end: 12/31/2015
Natural Rubber Production
N.A.I.C.S.: 111421
Frederique Varennes *(Sec)*

SIFI CJ LOGISTIC SA
Rahmaninov nr 46 - 48 subsol Cam U11, Bucharest, Romania
Tel.: (40) 264416663
Web Site: https://www.comatcluj.ro
Year Founded: 1991
CACU—(BUC)
Rev.: $4,892,462
Assets: $8,418,458
Liabilities: $77,682
Net Worth: $8,340,776
Earnings: $967,626
Emp.: 1
Fiscal Year-end: 12/31/22
Industrial Space Rental Services
N.A.I.C.S.: 531120

SIFI CJ STORAGE S.A.
str Traian Vuia nr 208, 400397, Cluj-Napoca, Romania
Tel.: (40) 264416629
Web Site: https://www.napotex.ro
NTEX—(BUC)
Rev.: $4,748,169
Assets: $4,347,455
Liabilities: $65,549
Net Worth: $4,281,906
Earnings: $1,078,621
Fiscal Year-end: 12/31/22
Warehouse & Storage Services
N.A.I.C.S.: 493110

SIFI CLUJ RETAIL S.A.
Sector 2 Str Serghei Vasilievici Rahmaninov nr 46 48, Suibsol Cam U10, Bucharest, Romania
Tel.: (40) 264595532
Web Site: https://www.artaculinaracluj.ro

SIFI CLUJ RETAIL S.A.

Sifi Cluj Retail S.A.—(Continued)
Year Founded: 1991
ARCU—(BUC)
Rev.: $1,821,749
Assets: $14,977,835
Liabilities: $811,855
Net Worth: $14,165,980
Earnings: $1,031,845
Emp.: 4
Fiscal Year-end: 12/31/22
Restaurant Operating Services
N.A.I.C.S.: 722511

SIFTON PROPERTIES LTD.
PO Box 5099, London, N6A 4M8, ON, Canada
Tel.: (519) 434-1000
Web Site: http://www.sifton.com
Year Founded: 1923
Rev.: $34,790,151
Emp.: 800
Construction Services
N.A.I.C.S.: 236220
Glen Sifton *(Pres)*

SIFY TECHNOLOGIES LIMITED
Tidel Park 2nd Floor 4 Rajiv Gandhi Salai, Taramani, Chennai, 600 113, India
Tel.: (91) 4422540770
Web Site:
   https://www.sifytechnologies.com
Year Founded: 1995
SIFY—(NASDAQ)
Rev.: $368,900,464
Assets: $642,483,346
Liabilities: $444,883,175
Net Worth: $197,600,171
Earnings: $17,170,949
Emp.: 3,641
Fiscal Year-end: 03/31/22
IT Infrastructure Management, Communication & Internet Services
N.A.I.C.S.: 517111
Raju Vegesna *(Chm, Co-CEO & Mng Dir)*

SIG PLC
Adsetts House 16 Europa View, Sheffield, S9 1XH, United Kingdom
Tel.: (44) 1142856300   UK
Web Site: https://www.sigplc.com
Year Founded: 1956
SHI—(LSE)
Rev.: $2,545,046,140
Assets: $1,567,623,512
Liabilities: $1,151,753,876
Net Worth: $415,869,636
Earnings: ($188,994,624)
Emp.: 6,446
Fiscal Year-end: 12/31/20
Holding Company; Insulation, Interior & Exterior Building Materials Whslr
N.A.I.C.S.: 551112
Richard Monro *(Sec)*

Subsidiaries:

Air Trade Centre Belgium, N.V. (1)
Hoogstraat 180, Zaventem, 1930, Belgium
Tel.: (32) 2 725 31 80
Web Site: http://www.airtradecentre.com
Sales Range: $50-74.9 Million
Emp.: 75
Air Conditioning Equipment Whslr
N.A.I.C.S.: 423730

BEK Baustoffe Slovakia s.r.o. (1)
Odborarska 52, 831 30, Bratislava, Slovakia
Tel.: (421) 910877967
Web Site: http://www.bek.sk
Building Materials Whslr
N.A.I.C.S.: 423390

BLH Bauelemente fur Luftentechnik Hennen GmbH (1)
Johann-Philipp-Reis-Strasse 1, 54293, Trier, Germany
Tel.: (49) 65181090
Web Site: http://www.blh-trier.de

Emp.: 83
Air Outlet & Ventilation Duct Mfr
N.A.I.C.S.: 333415

Barcol-Air B.V. (1)
Cantekoogweg 10-12, 1442 LG, Purmerend, Netherlands
Tel.: (31) 299689300
Web Site: http://www.barcol-air.nl
Thermal Indoor Climate Design Services
N.A.I.C.S.: 541490

Flex-R Limited (1)
Sandswood House Hillbottom Road, Sands Industrial Estate, High Wycombe, HP12 4HJ, Bucks, United Kingdom
Tel.: (44) 1494448792
Web Site: http://www.flex-r.co.uk
Roofing System Services
N.A.I.C.S.: 238160

HCKP B.V. (1)
Tielenstraat 19, 5145 RC, Waalwijk, Netherlands
Tel.: (31) 41 665 0075
Web Site: https://www.hckp.nl
Climate Ceiling Design Services
N.A.I.C.S.: 541490

Interland Techniek B.V. (1)
Tielenstraat 17, 5145 RC, Waalwijk, Netherlands
Tel.: (31) 41 631 7830
Web Site: https://www.interlandtechniek.nl
Climate Control Design Services
N.A.I.C.S.: 541490

Isolatec b.v.b.a (1)
Scheepvaartkaai 5C, 3500, Hasselt, Belgium
Tel.: (32) 1 122 3999
Web Site: https://www.isolatec.be
Insulation Material Distr
N.A.I.C.S.: 423330

J S McCarthy Limited (1)
Turnpike Road, Ballymount, Dublin, D22 P5R7, Ireland
Tel.: (353) 18983777
Web Site: http://www.jsmccarthy.ie
Industrial Painting & Coating Services
N.A.I.C.S.: 238320

LITT Diffusion SAS (1)
Point Sud Building 40 Rue Gabriel Crie, BP 84010, 92240, Malakoff, France
Tel.: (33) 149653350
Web Site: http://www.litt.fr
Sales Range: $150-199.9 Million
Construction Materials Whslr
N.A.I.C.S.: 423390
Marc Thulliez *(Publr & Dir-Publication)*

Lariviere SAS (1)
36 bis rue Delaage, 49004, Angers, Cedex 01, France
Tel.: (33) 24 124 2000
Web Site: https://www.lariviere.fr
Roofing & Insulation Materials Mfr & Installer
N.A.I.C.S.: 327120

Leaderflush & Shapland Holdings Limited (1)
Magma House 16 Davy Court Castle Mound Way, Rugby, CV23 0UZ, Warwickshire, United Kingdom
Tel.: (44) 1623343111
Web Site:
   http://www.leaderflushshapland.co.uk
Integrated Doorset Mfr
N.A.I.C.S.: 321911

Maury S.A.S. (1)
Rte de Toulouse-81700 St Germain Des Pres, Paris, France
Tel.: (33) 563755457
Web Site: http://www.maury-sas.fr
Silo Mfr
N.A.I.C.S.: 327390

Mayplas Limited (1)
Chamberhall Street, Peel Industrial Estate, Bury, BL9 0LU, United Kingdom
Tel.: (44) 1614478320
Web Site: https://mayplas.co.uk
Thermal Insulation Product Mfr
N.A.I.C.S.: 326140

Meldertse Plafonneerartikelen N.V. (1)

Bosstraat 56-60, 3560, Lummen, Belgium
Tel.: (32) 13532600
Web Site: http://www.mpa-bouw.be
Finishing Material & Insulation Distr
N.A.I.C.S.: 423330

Melle Dachbaustoffe GmbH (1)
Hansemannstrasse 1-3, 41468, Neuss, Germany
Tel.: (49) 2131523390
Web Site: http://www.melle.de
Building Materials Whslr
N.A.I.C.S.: 423390

Parking Ventilation Equipment Limited (1)
Unit 5 Prince of Wales Mill Birds Royd Lane, Brighouse, HD6 1LQ, West Yorkshire, United Kingdom
Tel.: (44) 8452020234
Web Site: http://pveuk.com
Ventilation Parking Design Services
N.A.I.C.S.: 561790

Profant Lufttechnik Handels GmbH (1)
Stattegger Strasse 131, 8045, Graz, Austria
Tel.: (43) 316 691 1100
Web Site: https://www.profant.at
Ventilation & Fire Smoke Dilution Product Mfr
N.A.I.C.S.: 333413

SIG France S.A.S (1)
8-16 rue Paul Vaillant-Couturier, 92240, Malakoff, France
Tel.: (33) 149653365
Insulation & Interior Roofing Distr
N.A.I.C.S.: 423330

SIG Germany GmbH (1)
Maybachstrasse 14, Hanau, 63456, Steinheim, Germany
Tel.: (49) 618167110
Web Site: http://www.sig-germany.de
Roofing & Insulation Material Distr
N.A.I.C.S.: 423330

SIG International Trading Limited (1)
Trafford Point 1 Twining Road, Stretford, Manchester, M17 1SH, United Kingdom
Tel.: (44) 3301231760
Roofing & Insulation Material Product Distr
N.A.I.C.S.: 423330

SIG Sp z o.o. (1)
Ul Kamieniskiego 51, 30-644, Krakow, Poland
Tel.: (48) 12 298 4800
Web Site: https://www.sig.pl
Building Materials Whslr
N.A.I.C.S.: 423390

SIG Technische Isoolatiespecialist B.V. (1)
Zijlweg 2, 5145 NR, Waalwijk, Netherlands
Tel.: (31) 416565111
Web Site:
   http://www.technischeisolatiespecialist.nl
Roofing & Insulation Material Distr
N.A.I.C.S.: 423330

SIG Trading (Ireland) Ltd. (1)
42 Ocasey Ave Parkwest, Dublin, 12, Ireland (100%)
Tel.: (353) 14992400
Web Site: http://www.sig.ie
Sales Range: $25-49.9 Million
Emp.: 80
Insulation Materials Whslr
N.A.I.C.S.: 444180

Subsidiary (Domestic):

SIG Building Products Limited (2)
Sig House First Floor Ballymount Retail Centre Ballymount Road Lower, Dublin, Ireland
Tel.: (353) 1 645 4944
Web Site: http://www.sig.ie
Building Materials Distr
N.A.I.C.S.: 423390

Unit (Domestic):

SIG Insulation Dublin (2)
Turnpike Road Ballymount, Nangor Rd, Dublin, D22 P5R7, Ireland
Tel.: (353) 18951700
Web Site: http://www.siginsulation.ie
Insulation Material Distr

INTERNATIONAL PUBLIC

N.A.I.C.S.: 444180

SIG Trading Limited (1)
Signet House 17 Europa View, Sheffield Business Park, Sheffield, S9 1XH, United Kingdom (100%)
Tel.: (44) 114 285 6300
Web Site: http://www.sigplc.com
Insulation, Interior & Exterior Building Materials Whslr
N.A.I.C.S.: 423330

Unit (Domestic):

SIG Insulation Omagh (2)
Unit B2 Killybrack Business Park 3 Killybrack Road, Omagh, BT7 97DG, Co Tyrone, United Kingdom
Tel.: (44) 288 224 6220
Web Site: http://www.siginsulation.ie
Insulation Material Distr
N.A.I.C.S.: 444180

SIG Technical Insulation - Aberdeen (2)
Broadfold Road Bridge of Don, Aberdeen, AB23 8EE, United Kingdom
Tel.: (44) 1224771566
Web Site:
   http://www.sigtechnicalinsulation.co.uk
Sales Range: $25-49.9 Million
Emp.: 100
Insulation Products Distr
N.A.I.C.S.: 326140

SIG Technical Insulation - Glasgow (2)
95 Westburn Drive, Cambuslang, Glasgow, G72 7NA, United Kingdom
Tel.: (44) 141 643 3600
Web Site:
   http://www.sigtechnicalinsulation.co.uk
Sales Range: $25-49.9 Million
Emp.: 50
Insulation Products Distr
N.A.I.C.S.: 326140

SIG Technical Insulation - London East, Beckton (2)
19-21 Alpine Way London Industrial Park, Beckton, London, E6 6LA, United Kingdom
Tel.: (44) 2074739310
Web Site:
   http://www.sigtechnicalinsulation.co.uk
Insulation Products Distr
N.A.I.C.S.: 326140

SIG Technical Insulation - Newton-Le-Willows (2)
Sunbeam Street, Newton-le-Willows, WA12 8NG, Lancs, United Kingdom
Tel.: (44) 1925225252
Web Site:
   http://www.sigtechnicalinsulation.co.uk
Insulation Products Distr
N.A.I.C.S.: 423330

SIG Technical Insulation - Plymouth (2)
87 St Modwen Road, Parkway Industrial Estate, Plymouth, PL6 8LH, United Kingdom
Tel.: (44) 175 267 5414
Web Site:
   http://www.sigtechnicalinsulation.co.uk
Sales Range: $25-49.9 Million
Insulation Products Distr
N.A.I.C.S.: 326140

SIG Technical Insulation - Portsmouth (2)
Unit 2 Quadra Sharps Close, Portsmouth, PO3 5PS, Hants, United Kingdom
Tel.: (44) 2392696733
Web Site:
   http://www.sigtechnicalinsulation.co.uk
Emp.: 16
Thermal Insulation Product Distr
N.A.I.C.S.: 423330

SIG Technical Insulation - Swansea (2)
Princess House Princess Way, Fforestfach, Swansea, SA1 3LW, United Kingdom
Tel.: (44) 1792588461
Web Site:
   http://www.sigtechnicalinsulation.co.uk
Sales Range: $1-9.9 Million
Insulation Products Distr
N.A.I.C.S.: 326140

AND PRIVATE COMPANIES — SIGMA HEALTHCARE LTD.

SIG Technical Insulation - Tyneside (2)
Federation Business Park Saint Omers Road, Dunston, Gateshead, NE11 9EE, Tyne & Wear, United Kingdom
Tel.: (44) 1912263110
Web Site: http://www.sigtechnicalinsulation.co.uk
Insulation Products Distr
N.A.I.C.S.: 326140

Societe Industrielle de l'Ouest des Produits Isolants SAS (1)
ZI de la Rangle, 27460, Alizay, France (100%)
Tel.: (33) 23 298 3000
Web Site: https://www.ouestisol.fr
Sales Range: $50-74.9 Million
Industrial Insulation Products Mfr
N.A.I.C.S.: 326140

WeGo FloorTec GmbH (1)
Juri-Gagarin-Ring 11, 19370, Parchim, Germany
Tel.: (49) 387142010
Web Site: http://www.sml-parchim.de
Flooring System Services
N.A.I.C.S.: 238330

WeGo Systembaustoffe GmbH (1)
Maybachstrasse 14, Hanau-Steinheim, 63456, Hanau, Germany
Tel.: (49) 6181 6711 0
Web Site: http://www.wego-systembaustoffe.de
Building Materials Whslr
N.A.I.C.S.: 423390

SIGACHI INDUSTRIES LIMITED
229/1 & 90 4th Floor Kalyan Tulasiram Chambers, Madeenaguda, Hyderabad, 500049, India
Tel.: (91) 4040114874
Web Site: https://sigachi.com
Year Founded: 1989
543389—(BOM)
Rev.: $26,755,435
Assets: $18,210,101
Liabilities: $5,351,881
Net Worth: $12,858,220
Earnings: $4,130,530
Emp.: 900
Fiscal Year-end: 03/31/21
Pharmaceuticals Product Mfr
N.A.I.C.S.: 325412
Shreya Mitra (Compliance Officer & Sec)

SIGDO KOPPERS S.A.
Malaga 120 8th floor, Las Condes, Santiago, Chile
Tel.: (56) 28374333
Web Site: https://www.sigdokoppers.cl
Year Founded: 1960
SK—(SGO)
Rev.: $4,006,223,000
Assets: $4,994,485,000
Liabilities: $2,881,192,000
Net Worth: $2,113,293,000
Earnings: $193,740,000
Fiscal Year-end: 12/31/23
Holding Company
N.A.I.C.S.: 551112
Naoshi Matsumoto Takahashi (Deputy Chm-Bus Admin)

Subsidiaries:

Comercial Asiandina S.A. (1)
Calle Patricia Vinuela 50 Panamericana Norte Km 15 1/2 Lampa, Santiago, Chile
Tel.: (56) 2 837 3000
Sales Range: $50-74.9 Million
Emp.: 200
Industrial Machinery Mfr
N.A.I.C.S.: 333248

Compania de Hidrogeno del Bio-Bio S.A. (1)
Malaga 120 Piso 8, Las Condes, 7550133, Santiago, Chile
Tel.: (56) 2 837 1100
Refined Petroleum Mfr
N.A.I.C.S.: 324110
Juan Pablo Aboitiz Dominguez (CEO)

Empresa Nacional de Explosivos SA (1)
El Trovador No 4253, Las Condes, Santiago, Chile
Tel.: (56) 228377600
Web Site: https://www.enaex.com
Rev.: $1,848,440,000
Assets: $1,902,715,000
Liabilities: $1,020,275,000
Net Worth: $882,440,000
Earnings: $166,899,000
Emp.: 6,954
Fiscal Year-end: 12/31/2023
Metal Mining Services
N.A.I.C.S.: 213114
Juan Andres Errazuriz Dominguez (CEO)

Ferrocarril del Pacifico S.A. (1)
San Francisco de Borja 750 Estacion Central, Region Metropolitana, Santiago, Chile
Tel.: (56) 228378000
Web Site: https://www.fepasa.com
Railroad Freight Transportation Services
N.A.I.C.S.: 488210

Ingenieria Y Construccion Sigdo Koppers Group S.A. (1)
Malaga 120, Las Condes, 7550133, Santiago, Chile
Tel.: (56) 22 837 4333
Web Site: https://www.skic.com
Engineering & Construction Services
N.A.I.C.S.: 541330

Ingenieria y Construccion Sigdo Koppers S.A. (1)
Malaga 120, Las Condes, Santiago, Chile
Tel.: (56) 228374333
Web Site: http://www.skic.com
Sales Range: $900-999.9 Million
Industrial Construction & Erection Services
N.A.I.C.S.: 236210

Subsidiary (Domestic):

Constructora Logro S.A. (2)
Av Apoquindo N 4700 Piso 8, Las Condes, Santiago, Chile
Tel.: (56) 2 837 46 00
Industrial Engineering Services
N.A.I.C.S.: 541330
Enrique Ramos (Gen Mgr)

SK Industrial S.A. (2)
Asturias 149 - 2 Piso, Las Condes, Chile
Tel.: (56) 2 837 4700
Web Site: http://www.skindustrial.cl
Sales Range: $75-99.9 Million
Emp.: 500
Industrial Equipment Maintenance Services
N.A.I.C.S.: 811310
Jose Manuel Borgono Barros (Gen Mgr)

Sigdoscaf S.A. (2)
Villaseca 21 Office 902, Nunoa, Santiago, Chile
Tel.: (56) 2 225 93 63
Construction Engineering Services
N.A.I.C.S.: 541330

Magotteaux Group S.A. (1)
rue Adolphe Dumont, 4051, Vaux-sous-Chevremont, Belgium (95%)
Tel.: (32) 43617617
Web Site: https://www.magotteaux.com
Sales Range: $700-749.9 Million
Crushing & Grinding Equipment Mfr
N.A.I.C.S.: 333131

SKC Maquinarias S.A. (1)
Eduardo Frei Montalva Avenue Route 5 North N 15800, Lampa, 6761569, Santiago, Chile
Tel.: (56) 228373301
Web Site: http://www.skcmaquinarias.cl
Sales Range: $75-99.9 Million
Construction Machinery & Equipment Distr
N.A.I.C.S.: 423810

SKC Maquinarias S.A.C. (1)
Antigua Carretera Panamericana Sur KM 20 2, Villa El Salvador, Lima, Peru
Tel.: (51) 1 7194100
Sales Range: $50-74.9 Million
Emp.: 75

Agricultural Machinery & Equipment Rental Services
N.A.I.C.S.: 532490

SKC Rental Locacao de Equipamentos Ltda. (1)
Avenida Juscelino Kubitschek de Oliveira 520, Bairro Cidade Industrial, Curitiba, 81290-000, Brazil
Tel.: (55) 30030621
Web Site: http://www.skcrental.com
Sales Range: $50-74.9 Million
Construction Equipment Rental Services
N.A.I.C.S.: 532412

SKC Rental S.A. (1)
Panamericana Norte 15800, Lampa, Santiago, Chile
Tel.: (56) 228373600
Web Site: http://ww2.skrental.com
Mining Equipment & Machinery Rental Services
N.A.I.C.S.: 532490

SKC Servicios Automotrices S.A. (1)
Panamericana Norte KM 15 1/2, Lampa, 9380000, Santiago, Chile
Tel.: (56) 2 837 3321
Web Site: http://www.skc.cl
Sales Range: $25-49.9 Million
Emp.: 54
Automotive Repair & Maintenance Services
N.A.I.C.S.: 811198
Gonsalo Ladbe (Gen Mgr)

Sigdotek S.A (1)
Av Presidente Eduardo Frei Montalva 4230, Renca, Chile
Tel.: (56) 2 837 3700
Agricultural Machinery & Equipment Distr
N.A.I.C.S.: 423820

Sk Comercial S.A. (1)
Avda Eduardo Frei Montalva 16 180, Lampa, Santiago, Chile
Tel.: (56) 22 837 3300
Spare Parts Distr
N.A.I.C.S.: 423120

Sk Godelius S.A. (1)
El Trovador 4253 Office 101, Las Condes, Santiago, Chile
Tel.: (56) 228376700
Web Site: https://www.godelius.com
Automation Product Mfr
N.A.I.C.S.: 335314
Fernando Bracco (CEO & Founder)

Skberge S.A. (1)
Av Americo Vespucio 1561, Vitacura, Santiago, Chile
Tel.: (56) 22 837 1200
Web Site: https://www.skberge.cl
Automobile Parts Distr
N.A.I.C.S.: 441330

SIGETRONICS, INC.
497 TechnoValley-ro, Bongdong-eup Wanju-gun, Jeonbuk, Korea (South)
Tel.: (82) 632624650
Web Site: https://www.sigetronics.com
Year Founded: 2008
429270—(KRS)
Semiconductor Mfr
N.A.I.C.S.: 334413
Kyu-Hwan Shim (CEO)

SIGFOX SA
Batiment E-volution 425 rue Jean Rostand, 31670, Labege, France
Tel.: (33) 582080710
Web Site: http://www.sigfox.com
Year Founded: 2009
Emp.: 80
Wireless Network Technology Solutions
N.A.I.C.S.: 334220

SIGHTRON JAPAN INC.
3-9-19 Nishiochiai, Shinjuku-ku, Tokyo, 161-0031, Japan
Tel.: (81) 0369083327
Web Site: https://www.sightron.co.jp
Emp.: 100

Sports Optics Products Distr; Firearms Mfr, Import & Sales
N.A.I.C.S.: 423460

Subsidiaries:

Daicel Pyrotechnics Ltd. (1)
760 Hamagawacho, Takasaki, Japan
Tel.: (81) 274671077
Ammunition & Explosives Mfr, Distr & Sales
N.A.I.C.S.: 332993

SIGMA A.D.
Batajnicki put 23, Belgrade, Serbia
Tel.: (381) 24567400
Year Founded: 1998
SIGMA—(BEL)
Sales Range: Less than $1 Million
Emp.: 21
Control & Measuring Instrument Mfr
N.A.I.C.S.: 334519
Milan Beslac (Board of Directors & Dir)

SIGMA HEALTHCARE LTD.
Level 6 2125 Dandenong Road, Clayton, 3168, VIC, Australia
Tel.: (61) 392159215   AU
Web Site: https://sigmahealthcare.com.au
Year Founded: 1912
SIG—(ASX)
Rev.: $2,262,828,145
Assets: $938,568,217
Liabilities: $344,187,044
Net Worth: $594,381,173
Earnings: $3,617,601
Fiscal Year-end: 01/31/24
Pharmaceutical Mfr & Distr
N.A.I.C.S.: 325412
Mark Hooper (CEO & Mng Dir)

Subsidiaries:

Allied Master Chemists of Australia Limited (1)
1408 Centre Road, Clayton, 3168, VIC, Australia
Tel.: (61) 395429400
Web Site: http://www.amcal.com.au
Pharmacy Retailer
N.A.I.C.S.: 456110

Guardian Pharmacies Australia Pty. Ltd. (1)
3 Myer Place, Rowville, VIC, Australia
Tel.: (61) 392159596
Web Site: https://www.guardianpharmacies.com.au
Pharmacy & Health Care Services
N.A.I.C.S.: 524114

Health Haven Pty Ltd (1)
Gladstone Park Shopping Centre U 163, Tullamarine, 3043, VIC, Australia
Tel.: (61) 393388730
Pharmaceutical Products Distr
N.A.I.C.S.: 424210

Linton Street Pty. Ltd. (1)
PO Box 149, Cloverdale, WA, Australia
Tel.: (61) 894781166
Web Site: https://swaps.com.au
Emp.: 25
Drugs & Druggist Sundries Whslr
N.A.I.C.S.: 424210

Pharmacy Wholesalers (Wellington) Limited (1)
7-19 Fitzherbert Street Petone, Wellington, 6008, New Zealand
Tel.: (64) 45687436
Web Site: http://www.pwl.co.nz
Sales Range: $25-49.9 Million
Emp.: 20
Pharmaceuticals Product Mfr
N.A.I.C.S.: 325412
Brendan Whirehoka (Branch Mgr)

QDL Limited (1)
46 Dividend St, Mansfield, 4122, QLD, Australia
Tel.: (61) 732121621
Pharmaceuticals Product Mfr
N.A.I.C.S.: 325412

SIGMA HEALTHCARE LTD.

Sigma Healthcare Ltd.—(Continued)

Sigma (W.A.) Pty Ltd (1)
26 Wheeler St, Belmont, 6104, WA, Australia
Tel.: (61) 894789700
Sales Range: $75-99.9 Million
Emp.: 120
Pharmaceutical Products Mfr & Distr
N.A.I.C.S.: 325412
Mark Smith *(Gen Mgr)*

Sigma Company Limited Northern Territory (1)
3/2205 Coonawarra Rd, Winnellie, 0820, NT, Australia (100%)
Tel.: (61) 889844025
Web Site: http://www.sigma.com.au
Mfr & Distributor of Pharmaceuticals
N.A.I.C.S.: 325412
Mark Hooper *(CEO)*

Sigma Company Limited Queensland (1)
46 Dividend St, Mansfield, 4122, QLD, Australia (100%)
Tel.: (61) 732121621
Web Site: http://www.sigma.com.au
Sales Range: $50-74.9 Million
Emp.: 150
Mfr & Distributor of Pharmaceuticals
N.A.I.C.S.: 325412

Sigma Company Limited South Australia (1)
227 S Rd, Ridleyton, Adelaide, 5008, SA, Australia (100%)
Tel.: (61) 883469561
Web Site: http://www.sigma.com.au
Sales Range: $25-49.9 Million
Emp.: 70
Mfr & Distributor of Pharmaceuticals
N.A.I.C.S.: 325412

Sigma Company Limited Tasmania (1)
McKay Avenue, Grove Estate, Glenorchy, 7010, TAS, Australia (100%)
Tel.: (61) 362723211
Web Site:
http://www.sigmahealthcare.com.au
Sales Range: $25-49.9 Million
Emp.: 50
Mfr & Distributor of Pharmaceuticals
N.A.I.C.S.: 325412

Sigma Company Limited Western Australia (1)
10 Craft Street, Canning Vale, 6155, WA, Australia (100%)
Tel.: (61) 800500760
Web Site: http://www.sigma.com.au
Sales Range: $25-49.9 Million
Emp.: 60
Mfr & Distributor of Pharmaceuticals
N.A.I.C.S.: 325412

Sigma Health Care (1)
Level 6 2125 Dandenong Road, Clayton, 3168, VIC, Australia (100%)
Tel.: (61) 392159215
Web Site: https://sigmahealthcare.com.au
Sales Range: $200-249.9 Million
Emp.: 1,000
Mfr & Distributor of Pharmaceuticals
N.A.I.C.S.: 325412

Sigma NZ Limited (1)
110 Mt Eden Road, Mount Eden, Auckland, New Zealand
Tel.: (64) 96236111
Pharmaceuticals Product Mfr
N.A.I.C.S.: 325412

SIGMA KOKI CO., LTD.
5F Sigma Koki Tokyo Head office
1-19-9 Midori, Sumida-ku, Tokyo, 130-0021, Japan
Tel.: (81) 356388228 JP
Web Site: https://www.sigma-koki.com
Year Founded: 1977
7713—(TKS)
Rev.: $74,117,930
Assets: $138,446,450
Liabilities: $25,137,830
Net Worth: $113,308,620
Earnings: $4,541,070
Emp.: 371
Fiscal Year-end: 05/31/24
Optical Laser Equipment Mfr & Marketer
N.A.I.C.S.: 333310
Yosuke Kondo *(Pres & CEO)*

Subsidiaries:

Shanghai Sigma Koki Co.,Ltd. (1)
3355 Jin Du Road Xinzhuang Industrial Zone, Minhang, Shanghai, 201108, China
Tel.: (86) 2154424309
Web Site: http://www.shanghai-sigma.com
Optical Product Mfr
N.A.I.C.S.: 333310

Sigma Koki Co., Ltd. - Hidaka Plant (1)
17-2 Shimotakahagi Shinda, Hidaka, 350-1297, Saitama, Japan
Tel.: (81) 429856221
Web Site: http://www.sigma-koki.com
Sales Range: $100-124.9 Million
Optoelectronic Component Mfr
N.A.I.C.S.: 334419

Sigma Koki Co., Ltd. - Noto Plant (1)
61-2 Wakabadai Shika-machi, Hakui, 955-0375, Ishikawa, Japan
Tel.: (81) 767 38 1114
Web Site: http://www.sigma-koki.com
Optical Machinery Mfr
N.A.I.C.S.: 333248

TAC COAT CO.,LTD (1)
4144-5 Kiriishi Kanae, Iida, 395-0807, Nagono, Japan
Tel.: (81) 265212211
Web Site: http://www.sigma-koki.com
Optical Coating Products Mfr
N.A.I.C.S.: 339115

SIGMA LITHIUM CORPORATION
Suite 2200 HSBC Building 885 West Georgia St, Vancouver, V6C 3E8, BC, Canada Ca
Web Site:
https://www.sigmalithium.com
Year Founded: 2011
SGML—(NASDAQ)
Rev.: $5,410,248
Assets: $241,652,550
Liabilities: $98,412,389
Net Worth: $143,240,162
Earnings: ($99,513,839)
Emp.: 1,165
Fiscal Year-end: 12/31/22
Investment Services
N.A.I.C.S.: 523999
Ana Cabral Gardner *(Co-Chm & Co-CEO)*

SIGMA S.A. DE C.V.
Blvd del Ejercito Nacional Km 3.5 Soyapango, San Salvador, El Salvador
Tel.: (503) 25676000
Web Site: http://www.sigmaq.com
Display, Packaging & Labeling Product Mfr
N.A.I.C.S.: 326112
Henry Yarhi *(Pres)*

Subsidiaries:

Bufkor, Inc. (1)
13101 56th Ct N Ste 815, Clearwater, FL 33760-4021
Tel.: (727) 572-9991
Web Site: http://www.bufkor.com
Sales Range: $10-24.9 Million
Emp.: 9
Fiscal Year-end: 12/31/2013
Mfr & Distributor of Jewelry Boxes, Jewelry Displays & Packaging
N.A.I.C.S.: 424990
Henry Yarhi *(Chm)*

Cajas y Empaques de Guatemala, S.A. (1)
31 calle 25-83 Zona 12, Guatemala, Guatemala
Tel.: (502) 23019700
Packaging Products Mfr
N.A.I.C.S.: 326199

Cartonera Nacional, S. A. (1)
Boulevard al Sur Km 8, San Pedro Sula, Honduras
Tel.: (504) 5657500
Web Site: http://www.cartonera.com.co
Packaging Products Mfr
N.A.I.C.S.: 326199

Chippenhook Corporation (1)
1825 Lakeway Dr Ste 400, Lewisville, TX 75057
Tel.: (972) 906-1800
Web Site: http://www.chippenhook.com
Sales Range: $10-24.9 Million
Emp.: 100
Visual Displays & Packaging Mfr
N.A.I.C.S.: 561910
Sherrie Betham *(Sls Mgr-Key Acct)*

Kontein, una division de Sigma, S. A. de C.V. (1)
Parque Industrial y Comercial de Desarrollo, Soyapango, San Salvador, El Salvador
Tel.: (503) 25676300
Packaging Products Mfr
N.A.I.C.S.: 326199

Litografia Byron Zadik, S.A. (1)
3 Avenida 7-80 Zona 3 de Mixco, Colonia El Rosario, Guatemala, Guatemala
Tel.: (502) 23019800
Packaging Products Mfr
N.A.I.C.S.: 326199

Specialty Products, S. A. de C.V. (1)
Calle Cojutepeque Edif 13 Zona Franca San Bartolo Ilopango, San Salvador, El Salvador
Tel.: (503) 25676400
Packaging Products Mfr
N.A.I.C.S.: 326199

SIGMA SOLVE LIMITED
305-308 3Rd Floor Alpha Megacone House Opp Armieda Sindhu Bhavan Road, SG Highway, Ahmedabad, 380054, Gujarat, India
Tel.: (91) 7947431283
Web Site:
https://www.sigmasolve.com
Year Founded: 2010
543917—(BOM)
Rev.: $6,820,646
Assets: $7,567,904
Liabilities: $1,364,331
Net Worth: $6,203,573
Earnings: $1,831,485
Emp.: 252
Fiscal Year-end: 03/31/23
Software Development Services
N.A.I.C.S.: 541511
Prakash Ratilal Parikh *(Chm & Mng Dir)*

SIGMA-TAU INDUSTRIE FARMACEUTICHE RIUNITE S.P.A.
SS Pontina Km 30 400, Pomezia, 00044, Rome, Italy
Tel.: (39) 0691391
Web Site: http://www.sigma-tau.it
Year Founded: 1957
Sales Range: $300-349.9 Million
Emp.: 2,416
Mfr of Medicinal Chemicals, Pharmaceuticals & Botanical Products
N.A.I.C.S.: 325411
Montevecchi Andrea *(CEO)*

Subsidiaries:

Sigma Tau B.V. (1)
Groenewoudsedijk 55, Utrecht, 3528 BG, Netherlands (100%)
Tel.: (31) 306702020
Web Site: http://www.sigma-tau.nl
Sales Range: $25-49.9 Million
Emp.: 15

INTERNATIONAL PUBLIC

Mfr of Medicinal Chemicals, Pharmaceuticals & Botanical Products
N.A.I.C.S.: 325411
Sasoun Zarrilli *(Gen Mgr)*

Sigma-Tau Arzneimittel GmbH (1)
Schadow Str 44, D 40212, Dusseldorf, Germany (100%)
Tel.: (49) 2113694993
Web Site: http://www.sigma-tau.de
Sales Range: $25-49.9 Million
Emp.: 50
Mfr of Medicinal Chemicals, Pharmaceuticals & Botanical Products
N.A.I.C.S.: 325411

Sigma-Tau Espana S.A. (1)
Poligono Ind Azque, Tercera Avda 13 14 15, E 28806, Alcala de Henares, Spain (100%)
Tel.: (34) 918883600
Web Site: http://www.sigmatau.com
Sales Range: $25-49.9 Million
Emp.: 45
Mfr of Medicinal Chemicals, Pharmaceuticals & Botanical Products
N.A.I.C.S.: 325411

Sigma-Tau France S.A.R.L. (1)
5 Ave De Verdun, 94200, Ivry-sur-Seine, France (100%)
Tel.: (33) 145210269
Web Site: http://www.sigmatau.fr
Sales Range: $1-9.9 Million
Emp.: 26
Mfr of Medicinal Chemicals, Pharmaceuticals & Botanical Products
N.A.I.C.S.: 325411

Sigma-Tau Pharmaceuticals, Inc. (1)
9841 Washingtonian Blvd, Gaithersburg, MD 20878
Tel.: (301) 948-1041,
Web Site: http://www.sigmatau.com
Sales Range: $50-74.9 Million
Emp.: 100
Pharmaceuticals
N.A.I.C.S.: 424210
Antonio Amato *(VP-Res)*

SIGMARENOPRO, INC.
Aloni Noa kh St 1, Kiryat Motzkin, 26402, Israel
Tel.: (972) 3 6860331 NV
Year Founded: 2017
Assets: $6,404
Liabilities: $15,723
Net Worth: ($9,319)
Earnings: ($27,618)
Emp.: 1
Fiscal Year-end: 06/30/20
Business Management Services
N.A.I.C.S.: 561110
Omar Aamar *(Chm, Pres, CEO, CFO, Treas & Sec)*

SIGMAROC PLC
6 Heddon Street, London, W1B 4BT, United Kingdom
Tel.: (44) 2071297828 UK
Web Site: https://www.sigmaroc.com
Year Founded: 1999
SRC—(AIM)
Rev.: $679,112,598
Assets: $1,220,560,465
Liabilities: $627,465,287
Net Worth: $593,095,178
Earnings: $67,652,108
Emp.: 2,045
Fiscal Year-end: 12/31/22
Construction Material Investment Services
N.A.I.C.S.: 523999
David Barrett *(Co-Founder & Chm)*

Subsidiaries:

B-Mix Beton NV (1)
Kanaalweg 110, 3980, Tessenderlo, Belgium
Tel.: (32) 11239120
Web Site: https://www.b-mixbeton.b
Construction Services
N.A.I.C.S.: 236220

AND PRIVATE COMPANIES / SIGNA SPORTS UNITED N.V.

Canteras La Belonga S.A. (1)
Cellagu - Latores S/N, Asturias, 33193, Oviedo, Spain
Tel.: (34) 985256123
Web Site: https://canteraslabelonga.com
Construction Material Mfr & Distr
N.A.I.C.S.: 326299

Carrieres du Hainaut SCA (1)
Rue de Cognebeau 245, 7060, Soignies, Belgium
Tel.: (32) 67347800
Web Site: https://www.carrieresduhainaut.com
Building Material Mfr & Distr
N.A.I.C.S.: 327120

Clogrennane Lime Limited (1)
Clogrennane, Carlow, Ireland
Tel.: (353) 599131811
Emp.: 30
Lime Product Mfr
N.A.I.C.S.: 325180
Brendan Walsh (Mgr-Quality & Environmental)

Cuvelier Philippe SA (1)
Rue Sous Beaufays 1, 4570, Marchin, Belgium
Tel.: (32) 85311026
Web Site: https://www.cuveliersa.be
Crushed Product Mfr
N.A.I.C.S.: 327999

Draseikiu Karjeras UAB (1)
Draseikiu K Lapiu Sen, 54411, Kaunas, Lithuania
Tel.: (370) 69859989
Web Site: https://www.draseikiukarjeras.lt
Limestone Quarrying Services
N.A.I.C.S.: 212311

Fels Holding GmbH (1)
Geheimrat-Ebert-Str. 12, 38640, Goslar, Germany
Tel.: (49) 53217030
Holding Company
N.A.I.C.S.: 551112

Subsidiary (Domestic):

Fels Vertriebs und Service GmbH & Co. KG. (2)
Geheimrat-Ebert-Str 12, 38640, Goslar, Germany
Tel.: (49) 53217030
Web Site: https://www.fels.de
Construction Materials Whslr
N.A.I.C.S.: 423320

Fels-Werke GmbH (2)
Privy Councilor Ebert Str 12, 38640, Goslar, Germany
Tel.: (49) 53217030
Web Site: https://www.fels.de
Lime Products & Other Building Materials Mfr
N.A.I.C.S.: 327410
Bernd Rowert (Head-Strategic Mktg & Comm)

Foelfach Stone Limited (1)
Foelfach Quarry Cynwyl Road, Carmarthen, SA33 6AR, Carmarthenshire, United Kingdom
Tel.: (44) 7779873224
Web Site: https://www.foelfachstone.co.uk
Stone Product Mfr
N.A.I.C.S.: 327991

Goijens Recycling N.V. (1)
Industrieterrein Kanaal Noord 1150, Limburg, 3960, Bree, Belgium
Tel.: (32) 89461475
Web Site: https://www.goijens.be
Road Construction Services
N.A.I.C.S.: 237310

Guiting Quarry Limited (1)
Guiting Quarry Upper Coscombe Temple Guiting, Cheltenham, GL54 5SB, United Kingdom
Tel.: (44) 1451600670
Building Stone Mining Services
N.A.I.C.S.: 212311

Johnston Quarry Group Limited (1)
Westfield Lodge Great Tew, Chipping Norton, OX7 4BT, United Kingdom
Tel.: (44) 1608489900
Web Site: https://johnstonquarries.co.uk

Limestone Quarrying Services
N.A.I.C.S.: 212311

Juuan Dolomiittikalkki Oy (1)
Onninpolku 1, 83900, Juuka, Finland
Tel.: (358) 500809999
Web Site: https://dolomiittikalkki.fi
Limestone Quarrying Services
N.A.I.C.S.: 212311

Nordkalk Corporation (1)
Skrabbolevagen 18, 21600, Pargas, Finland
Tel.: (358) 207537000
Web Site: http://www.nordkalk.com
Sales Range: $450-499.9 Million
Emp.: 1,000
Limestone-Based Products Producer
N.A.I.C.S.: 212312
Marcel Gestranius (Deputy CEO & CFO)

Subsidiary (Non-US):

Nordkalk AB (2)
Sjogatan 17, SE-89160, Ornskoldsvik, Sweden (100%)
Tel.: (46) 104762500
Web Site: https://www.nordkalk.se
Sales Range: $50-74.9 Million
Emp.: 10
Limestone Products Sales
N.A.I.C.S.: 212313

Unit (Domestic):

Nordkalk AB (3)
Lisselhedsvagen 3, 79434, Orsa, Sweden (100%)
Tel.: (46) 250550200
Web Site: http://www.nordkalk.se
Carbonate Products Producer
N.A.I.C.S.: 325180

Subsidiary (Non-US):

Nordkalk AB (2)
Vasario 16 g-ve nr 46, LH-76291, Siauliai, Lithuania
Tel.: (370) 41521786
Sales Range: $25-49.9 Million
Emp.: 2
Limestone, Quicklime & Carbonated Products Whslr
N.A.I.C.S.: 327410
Arturas Kiudulas (Mgr)

Nordkalk AS (2)
Faehlmanni 11a, Laane-Viru County, EE-46301, Rakke, Estonia (100%)
Tel.: (372) 3260720
Web Site: https://www.nordkalk.ee
Sales Range: $25-49.9 Million
Emp.: 70
Quicklime, Limestone & Carbonate Products Sales
N.A.I.C.S.: 327410

Unit (Domestic):

Nordkalk AS (3)
Kurevere Hanila Vaid, EE-90102, Lihula, Laanema, Estonia
Tel.: (372) 4775155
Web Site: http://www.nordkalk.ee
Dolomite Producer
N.A.I.C.S.: 212312

Subsidiary (Non-US):

Nordkalk Sp. z o.o. (2)
Pl Na Groblach 21, 31-101, Krakow, Poland (100%)
Tel.: (48) 413060167
Web Site: https://www.nordkalk.pl
Sales Range: $25-49.9 Million
Emp.: 15
Limestone & Carbonated Products Sales
N.A.I.C.S.: 327410

Subsidiary (Domestic):

Suomen Karbonaatti Oy (2)
Sementtitie 29, FIN-53500, Lappeenranta, Finland
Tel.: (358) 207109826
Web Site: https://www.karbonaatti.com
Paper Pigments Producer
N.A.I.C.S.: 325130

Poundfield Precast Limited (1)
The Grove Creeting St Peter, Ipswich, IP6 8QG, Suffolk, United Kingdom

Tel.: (44) 1449723150
Web Site: https://www.poundfield.com
Concrete Products Mfr
N.A.I.C.S.: 327390

Retaining (UK) Limited (1)
Hughes House Cargo Fleet Road, Middlesbrough, TS3 6AG, United Kingdom
Tel.: (44) 1642233400
Web Site: https://www.retaininguk.com
Retaining Wall Construction Services
N.A.I.C.S.: 238110

Righcast Limited (1)
Unit W4 Junction 38 Business Park, Darton, Barnsley, S75 5QQ, United Kingdom
Tel.: (44) 1226399166
Web Site: https://rightcastltd.com
Precast Concrete Product Mfr & Distr
N.A.I.C.S.: 327390

Ronez Limited (1)
La Route Du Nord, Saint John, JE3 4AR, Jersey
Tel.: (44) 1534867200
Web Site: https://www.ronez.com
Construction Materials Mfr
N.A.I.C.S.: 327331
Paul M. Pinel (Sls Mgr)

The Bath Stone Company Limited (1)
Stoke Hill Mine Midford Lane, Limpley Stoke, Bath, BA2 7GP, Somerset, United Kingdom
Tel.: (44) 1225723792
Web Site: https://bathstone.com
Emp.: 17
Limestone & Bath Stone Services
N.A.I.C.S.: 212312

SIGMAXYZ HOLDINGS INC.
Toranomon Towers Office 9th Floor
4-1-28 Toranomon, Minato-ku, Tokyo, 105-0001, Japan
Tel.: (81) 364303400
Web Site: https://www.sigmaxyz.com
Year Founded: 2008
6088-----(TKS)
Rev.: $148,130,100
Assets: $120,929,950
Liabilities: $33,724,220
Net Worth: $87,205,730
Earnings: $21,363,520
Fiscal Year-end: 03/31/24
Business Management Consulting Services
N.A.I.C.S.: 541611
Hideki Kurashige (Founder & Co-Chm)

Subsidiaries:

SXF Inc. (1)
9F Toranomon Towers Office 4-1-28 Toranomon, Minato-ku, Tokyo, 105-0001, Japan
Tel.: (81) 368412910
Web Site: https://www.sigmaxyz.com
Financial Processing Services
N.A.I.C.S.: 522320

SIGN-UP TECHNOLOGIES LTD.
Lynton House Station Approach Woking, Fulham, Surrey, GU22 7PY, United Kingdom
Tel.: (44) 20 3355 2631
Web Site: http://www.sign-up.to.com
Sales Range: $10-24.9 Million
Emp.: 50
Email Marketing Software
N.A.I.C.S.: 513210
Matt McNeill (Founder & CEO)

SIGNA HOLDING GMBH
Freyung 3, A-1010, Vienna, Austria
Tel.: (43) 1 532 98 48 0
Web Site: http://www.signa.at
Year Founded: 1999
Holding Comapny; Real Estate Development & Investment Services
N.A.I.C.S.: 551112
Peter Kern (Sr Project Mgr)

Subsidiaries:

GALERIA Kaufhof GmbH (1)
Leonhard-Tietz-Strasse 1, 50676, Cologne, Germany (100%)
Tel.: (49) 2212230
Web Site: http://www.galeria-kaufhof.de
Departmental Stores Operating Services
N.A.I.C.S.: 455110
Olivier Van den Bossche (Chm-Mgmt Bd, CEO & Dir-Labor)

Subsidiary (Domestic):

Sportscheck GmbH (2)
Neuhauser Strasse 21, 80331, Munich, Germany
Tel.: (49) 8961101616
Web Site: http://www.sportscheck.com
Sales Range: $350-399.9 Million
Emp.: 910
Sporting Apparel & Accessory Store Retailer Distr
N.A.I.C.S.: 423910
Sebastian Klauke (Chm-Supervisory Bd)

Karstadt Warenhaus GmbH (1)
Theodor Althoff Strasse 2, D 45133, Essen, Germany
Tel.: (49) 2017271
Web Site: http://www.karstadt.de
Sales Range: $5-14.9 Billion
Emp.: 25,000
Departmental Store Operator
N.A.I.C.S.: 455110
Stephan Fanderl (Chm)

SIGNA Financial Services AG (1)
Ramistrasse 50, 8001, Zurich, Switzerland
Tel.: (41) 442515777
Financial Services
N.A.I.C.S.: 523940

SIGNA Prime Selection AG (1)
Maria-Theresien-Strabe 31, 6020, Innsbruck, Austria
Tel.: (43) 5125851190
Investment Holding Services
N.A.I.C.S.: 523940
Manuel Pirolt (CFO)

SIGNA Real Estate Capital Partners (1)
Maximiliansplatz 12, 80333, Munich, Germany
Tel.: (49) 89232372780
Real Estate Manangement Services
N.A.I.C.S.: 531210

Selfridges & Co. (1)
400 Oxford Street, London, W1A 1AB, United Kingdom (50%)
Tel.: (44) 1133698040
Web Site: http://www.selfridges.com
Departmental Store Operator
N.A.I.C.S.: 455110
Paul Kelly (CEO)

SIGNA SPORTS UNITED N.V.
Kantstrasse 164 Upper West, 10623, Berlin, Germany
Tel.: (49) 30700108900 NI
Web Site: http://www.signa-sportsunited.com
SSU---(NYSE)
Rev.: $1,305,373,472
Assets: $1,608,380,280
Liabilities: $850,187,728
Net Worth: $758,192,552
Earnings: ($694,815,368)
Emp.: 3,623
Fiscal Year-end: 09/30/22
Holding Company; Sports Equipment & Apparel Retailer
N.A.I.C.S.: 551112
Stephan Zoll (CEO)

Subsidiaries:

SIGNA Sports United GmbH (1)
Kantstrasse 164 Upper West, 10623, Berlin, Germany
Tel.: (49) 30700108900
Web Site: http://www.signa-sportsunited.com
Sports Equipment & Apparel Retailer
N.A.I.C.S.: 459110

SIGNA SPORTS UNITED N.V.

SIGNA Sports United N.V.—(Continued)

Subsidiary (US):

Tennis Express, LP (2)
10770 Westheimer Rd, Houston, TX 77042
Tel.: (713) 781-4848
Web Site: http://www.tennisexpress.com
Sporting Goods Retailer
N.A.I.C.S.: 459110
Todd White (Mgr)

Subsidiary (Non-US):

Wiggle Ltd. (2)
3 Optima Northarbour Spur, Portsmouth, PO6 3TU, United Kingdom
Tel.: (44) 2392314811
Web Site: http://www.wiggle.co.uk
Sales Range: $125-149.9 Million
Sporting Goods Retailer
N.A.I.C.S.: 459110
Brian McBride (Chm)

Subsidiary (Domestic):

Chain Reaction Cycles Ltd. (3)
1 Balmoral Plaza Boucher Road, County Antrim, Belfast, BT12 6HR, United Kingdom
Tel.: (44) 28 90 682703
Web Site:
http://www.chainreactioncycles.com
Cycling Goods Online Retailer
N.A.I.C.S.: 423910
Chris Watson (Mng Dir)

Subsidiary (US):

Yucaipa Acquisition Corporation (2)
9130 W Sunset Blvd, Los Angeles, CA 90069
Tel.: (310) 228-2894
Investment Services
N.A.I.C.S.: 523999
Ronald W. Burkle (Chm & Pres)

SIGNAL CAPITAL PARTNERS LIMITED

4th Floor 25 Golden Square, London, W1F 9LU, United Kingdom
Tel.: (44) 2037505600 UK
Web Site:
https://www.signalcapital.com
Year Founded: 2015
Private Equity & Asset Management Services
N.A.I.C.S.: 523999

Subsidiaries:

PrimeTel PLC (1)
The Maritime Centre 141 Omonoias Avenue, 3045, Limassol, Cyprus
Tel.: (357) 22102210
Web Site: http://www.primetel.com.cy
Telecommunication Services
N.A.I.C.S.: 517810
Hermes Stephanou (Mng Dir)

SIGNAL ENTERTAINMENT GROUP CORP.

2F 11 Citizen-daero 109beon-gil, Hoyang-dong, Anyang, Gyeonggi-do, Korea (South)
Tel.: (82) 2 224 3235
Web Site: http://www.sicis.co.kr
Year Founded: 1991
Computer-Related Communication System Integration & Consulting Services
N.A.I.C.S.: 334220
Jeong-Sang Kim (CEO)

SIGNAL GOLD INC.

20 Adelaide Street East Suite 401, Toronto, M5C 2T6, ON, Canada
Tel.: (416) 304-6622 ON
Web Site:
https://www.anacondamining.com
Year Founded: 1994
SGNL—(OTCIQ)
Rev.: $21,746,256
Assets: $74,747,639
Liabilities: $19,308,293
Net Worth: $55,439,347
Earnings: ($5,582,521)
Emp.: 100
Fiscal Year-end: 12/31/21
Gold Ore Exploration & Mining
N.A.I.C.S.: 213114
Dustin Angelo (Pres & CEO)

SIGNAL IDUNA GRUPPE

Joseph-Scherer-Str 3, 44139, Dortmund, Germany
Tel.: (49) 2311350
Web Site: http://www.signal-iduna.de
Year Founded: 1999
Sales Range: $5-14.9 Billion
Insurance, Banking & Miscellaneous Financial Services
N.A.I.C.S.: 524298
Karl-Joseph Bierth (Member-Mgmt Bd)

Subsidiaries:

SIGNAL IDUNA Gruppe (1)
Neue Rabenstrasse 15-19, 20354, Hamburg, Germany
Tel.: (49) 4041240
Web Site: http://www.signal-iduna.de
Assurance, Banking & Miscellaneous Financial Services
N.A.I.C.S.: 524298
Reinhold Schulte (Chm-Supervisory Bd)

Subsidiary (Domestic):

DEURAG Deutsche Rechtsschutz-Versicherung AG
Abraham-Lincoln-Str 3, 65189, Wiesbaden, Germany
Tel.: (49) 6 11 771 0
Web Site: http://www.deurag.de
General Insurance Services
N.A.I.C.S.: 524210

Deutscher Ring Krankenversicherungsverein a.G. (2)
Neue Rabenstrasse 15-19, 20354, Hamburg, Germany
Tel.: (49) 4041247969
Web Site: http://www.deutscherring-kranken.de
Emp.: 800
Health Insurance Services
N.A.I.C.S.: 524114
Ulrich Leitermann (Partner)

Subsidiary (Non-US):

SIGNAL Biztosito Zrt. (2)
Alkotas u 50, Budapest, 1123, Hungary
Tel.: (36) 40 405 405
Web Site: http://www.signal.hu
Fire Insurance Services
N.A.I.C.S.: 524113

SIGNAL IDUNA ASIGURARE REASIGURARE S.A. (2)
60 Calea Floreasca 8th floor, District 1, Bucharest, 014462, Romania
Tel.: (40) 031 730 71 00
Web Site: http://www.signal-iduna.ro
Fire Insurance Services
N.A.I.C.S.: 524113
Tiberiu Maier (Pres)

Subsidiary (Domestic):

SIGNAL IDUNA Pensionskasse AG (2)
Neue Rabenstrasse 15-19, 20354, Hamburg, Germany
Tel.: (49) 40 4124 0
Web Site: http://www.si-pk.de
General Insurance Services
N.A.I.C.S.: 524210

Subsidiary (Non-US):

SIGNAL IDUNA Polska Towarzystwo Ubezpieczen S.A. (2)
ul Przyokopowa 31, 01-208, Warsaw, Poland
Tel.: (48) 22 50 56 100
Web Site: http://www.signal-iduna.pl
Fire Insurance Services
N.A.I.C.S.: 524113

SIGNAL IDUNA Reinsurance Ltd (2)
Bundesplatz 1, PO Box 7737, 6302, Zug, Switzerland
Tel.: (41) 41 709 05 05
Web Site: http://www.sire.ch
Reinsurance Services
N.A.I.C.S.: 524130
Andreas Gadmer (Chief Risk Officer)

SIGNALHORN TRUSTED NETWORKS GMBH

Illerstrasse 15, 71522, Backnang, Germany
Tel.: (49) 71919710 De
Web Site: http://www.signalhorn.com
Sales Range: $25-49.9 Million
Emp.: 90
Satellite Communication Solutions
N.A.I.C.S.: 517111
Robert J. Kubbernus (Pres & CEO)

Subsidiaries:

Signalhorn AG (1)
Satellitenbodenstation Leuk Brentjong 2, Postfach 17, 3953, Leuk, Switzerland
Tel.: (41) 27 4749111
Web Site: http://www.signalhorn.com
Satellite Communication Services
N.A.I.C.S.: 517410
Robert Kubbermus (CEO)

SIGNALSERVIS A.D.

Svetozara Markovica 64, Leskovac, Serbia
Tel.: (381) 16 212 563
Year Founded: 1958
Sales Range: Less than $1 Million
Emp.: 6
Handicraft Product Mfr
N.A.I.C.S.: 315990
Dragan Mladenovic (CEO)

SIGNATURE AG

Emil Riedel Str 21, 80538, Munich, Germany
Tel.: (49) 1621777795
Web Site: http://www.signature-ag.de
BUY—(VIE)
Sales Range: Less than $1 Million
Holding Company
N.A.I.C.S.: 551112

SIGNATURE INTERNATIONAL BERHAD

Lot 24 Jalan Teknologi Taman Sains Selangor 1 Kota Damansara PJU 5, 47810, Petaling Jaya, Selangor, Malaysia
Tel.: (60) 1800880009
Web Site: https://signature.my
Year Founded: 1994
SIGN—(KLS)
Rev.: $134,444,929
Assets: $217,390,728
Liabilities: $127,312,365
Net Worth: $90,078,364
Earnings: $15,163,474
Emp.: 470
Fiscal Year-end: 12/31/23
Kitchen Appliances Mfr
N.A.I.C.S.: 321999
Yoey Sun Chooi (Exec Dir)

Subsidiaries:

Kubiq Sdn Bhd (1)
Lot 24 Jalan Teknologi Taman Sains Selangor 1 PJU 5, Kota Damansara, 47810, Petaling Jaya, Selangor, Malaysia
Tel.: (60) 126224028
Web Site: http://www.kubiq.com
Kitchen Cabinet Mfr
N.A.I.C.S.: 337110

Signature Academy Sdn Bhd (1)
Lot 24 Jalan Teknologi Taman Sains Selangor 1 PJU 5, Kota Damansara, 47810, Petaling Jaya, Selangor, Malaysia
Tel.: (60) 362867196

INTERNATIONAL PUBLIC

Kitchen Cabinet Installation Training Services
N.A.I.C.S.: 238350

Signature Aluminium Sdn Bhd (1)
No 23 Jalan Haji Abdul Manan 3/KU8, Kawasan Perindustrian Meru Barat, 42200, Klang, Selangor, Malaysia
Tel.: (60) 333931880
Web Site:
http://www.signaturealuminium.com
Aluminum Window & Door Mfr
N.A.I.C.S.: 332321

Signature Kitchen Sdn Bhd (1)
Lot 24 Jalan Teknologi Taman Sains Selangor 1 PJU 5, Kota Damansara, 47810, Petaling Jaya, Selangor, Malaysia
Tel.: (60) 362867070
Web Site: http://www.signaturekitchen.com
Kitchen Cabinet Mfr
N.A.I.C.S.: 337110

Signature Obicorp Sdn Bhd (1)
Lot 24 Jalan Teknologi Taman Sains Selangor 1 PJU 5, Kota Damansara, 47810, Petaling Jaya, Selangor, Malaysia
Tel.: (60) 1300889000
Web Site: http://www.signatureobicorp.com
Home Furnishings Products Whslr.
N.A.I.C.S.: 423620

SIGNATURE RESOURCES LTD.

401 Bay Street Suite 2704, Toronto, M5H 2Y4, ON, Canada
Tel.: (416) 840-6345 BC
Web Site:
https://www.signatureresources.ca
Year Founded: 2010
SGGTF—(OTCQB)
Rev.: $141,458
Assets: $1,023,404
Liabilities: $1,760,497
Net Worth: ($737,093)
Earnings: ($3,411,930)
Emp.: 5
Fiscal Year-end: 10/31/22
Gold Mining Services
N.A.I.C.S.: 212220
Donna Mclean (CFO)

SIGNATUREGLOBAL (INDIA) LIMITED

Unit No101 Ground Floor Tower-A Signature Tower South City-1, Gurgaon, 122001, Haryana, India
Tel.: (91) 1244398011
Web Site:
https://www.signatureglobal.in
Year Founded: 2000
543990—(BOM)
Real Estate Development Services
N.A.I.C.S.: 531190
Pradeep Kumar Aggarwal (Founder)

SIGNAUX GIROD S.A.

881 Route des Fontaines Bellefontaine, CS 30004, 39401, Morez, Cedex, France
Tel.: (33) 384346100 FR
Web Site: https://www.signaux-girod.fr
Year Founded: 1905
ALGIR—(EUR)
Sales Range: $100-124.9 Million
Sign Mfr
N.A.I.C.S.: 339950
Claude Girod (Chm & CEO)

Subsidiaries:

ACE Mobilier Urbain SA (1)
Rue de Trazegnies 500, Monceau-sur-Sambre, 6031, Charleroi, Belgium
Tel.: (32) 71 31 05 06
Web Site: http://www.ace-mu.com
Furniture Mfr
N.A.I.C.S.: 337122

Alfa-Girod Kft. (1)
Fehervari ut 75, 9028, Gyor, Hungary
Tel.: (36) 96 519229

AND PRIVATE COMPANIES

Web Site: http://www.alfa-girod.hu
Sign Board Mfr
N.A.I.C.S.: 339950

GS Plus (1)
Birchmere Business Centre Eastern Way,
Thamesmead, London, SE28 8BF, United
Kingdom
Tel.: (44) 20 8921 6872
Web Site: http://www.gsplus.org
Food Catering Services
N.A.I.C.S.: 722320
Peter Brooks (Chm)

Girod Maroc (1)
Lot 32 Zone Sapino, 27223, Casablanca,
Nouaceur, Morocco
Tel.: (212) 5 22 59 07 42
Web Site: http://www.signaux-girod.com
Emp.: 13
Sign Board Mfr
N.A.I.C.S.: 339950
Nadia Taouil (Gen Mgr)

Girod Semnalizare Rutiera RSL (1)
Calea Lugojului Nr 9A, Ghiroda, 300135,
Timis, Romania
Tel.: (40) 356 437 400
Web Site: http://www.girod-semnalizare.ro
Sign Mfr
N.A.I.C.S.: 339950

IRS Girod Ltd (1)
59 Turbine Way Ecotech business park,
Swaffham, Norfolk, PE37 7XD, United Kingdom
Tel.: (44) 1760 721 399
Web Site: http://www.irs-girod.co.uk
Sign Board Mfr
N.A.I.C.S.: 339950

Senales Girod SL (1)
Santa Coloma Pol Ind Puigtio 40, Gerona,
17412, Macanet de la Selva, Spain
Tel.: (34) 972875222
Web Site: http://www.sgirod.com
Sign Board Mfr
N.A.I.C.S.: 339950

SIGNET INDUSTRIES LIMITED
Plot No 99 Smart Industrial ParkNear
NATRI Pithampur, Dhar, 454775,
Madhya pradesh, India
Tel.: (91) 7314217800
Web Site:
  https://www.groupsignet.com
Year Founded: 1985
SIGIND—(NSE)
Rev.: $122,353,792
Assets: $87,353,432
Liabilities: $62,599,808
Net Worth: $24,753,624
Earnings: $1,565,194
Emp.: 400
Fiscal Year-end: 03/31/23
Plastic Tank Mfr
N.A.I.C.S.: 326122
Mukesh Sangla (Chm & Mng Dir)

SIGNET JEWELERS LIMITED
Clarendon House 2 Church Street,
Hamilton, HM11, Bermuda
Tel.: (441) 2965872   BM
Web Site:
  https://www.signetjewelers.com
Year Founded: 1950
SIG—(NYSE)
Rev.: $7,171,100,000
Assets: $6,813,200,000
Liabilities: $4,646,700,000
Net Worth: $2,166,500,000
Earnings: $775,900,000
Emp.: 14,297
Fiscal Year-end: 02/03/24
Holding Company; Fine Jewelry Retailer
N.A.I.C.S.: 551112
Joan M. Hilson (Chief Fin & Strategy Officer)

Subsidiaries:

Service Jewelry & Repair, Inc. (1)
1024 Glenbrook Way, Hendersonville, TN
37075-1230
Tel.: (615) 826-5339
Web Site:
  http://www.servicejewelryandrepair.com
Jewelry Stores
N.A.I.C.S.: 458310
Dana Bowman (Mgr)

Signet Group Limited (1)
110 Cannon Street, London, EC4N 6EU,
United Kingdom
Tel.: (44) 2076485200
Web Site: http://www.signetjewelers.com
Holding Company; Regional Managing Office; Jewelry Retailer
N.A.I.C.S.: 551112

Subsidiary (Domestic):

Signet Group Services Limited (2)
15 Golden Square, London, W1F 9JG,
United Kingdom
Tel.: (44) 2073179700
Office Administrative & IT Support Services
N.A.I.C.S.: 561110

Signet Holdings Limited (2)
110 Cannon Street, London, EC4N 6EU,
United Kingdom
Tel.: (44) 2076485200
Holding Company
N.A.I.C.S.: 551112

Subsidiary (Domestic):

Ernest Jones Limited (3)
Unit SU506 Middle Mall Bull Ring Centre,
Birmingham, B5 4BE, United Kingdom
Tel.: (44) 1216162611
Web Site: http://www.ernestjones.co.uk
Jewelry Retailer
N.A.I.C.S.: 458310

Leslie Davis Limited (3)
Hunters Road Hockley, Birmingham, B19
1DS, United Kingdom
Tel.: (44) 8456001141
Jewelry & Watch Retailer
N.A.I.C.S.: 458310

Subsidiary (Domestic):

Signet Trading Ltd. (2)
3 Imperial Place Maxwell Rd Hertfordshire,
Borehamwood, WD6 1JN, United
Kingdom   (100%)
Tel.: (44) 8709090301
Jewelry Store Operator
N.A.I.C.S.: 458310

Signet Group Treasury Services Inc. (1)
375 Ghent Rd, Fairlawn, OH 44333
Tel.: (330) 668-5931
Jewelry Retailer
N.A.I.C.S.: 458310

Signet UK Finance plc (1)
110 Cannon Street, London, EC4N 6EU,
United Kingdom
Tel.: (44) 2076485200
Jewelry Retailer
N.A.I.C.S.: 423940

Sterling Jewelers, Inc. (1)
375 Ghent Rd, Akron, OH
44333-4601   (100%)
Tel.: (330) 668-5000
Web Site: http://www.sterlingjewelers.com
Jewelry Store Operator
N.A.I.C.S.: 458310

Subsidiary (Domestic):

Osterman's Inc. (2)
803 E Washington St, Medina, OH
44256   (100%)
Tel.: (330) 723-3103
Web Site: http://www.signetgroupplc.com
Retail Jewelry
N.A.I.C.S.: 458310

Zale Corporation (1)
901 W Walnut Hill Ln MS 5B-12, Irving, TX
75038-1003
Tel.: (972) 580-4000
Web Site: http://www.zalecorp.com
Rev.: $1,888,016,000
Assets: $1,187,255,000
Liabilities: $1,001,926,000
Net Worth: $185,329,000
Earnings: $10,012,000
Emp.: 11,900
Fiscal Year-end: 07/31/2013
Holding Company; Jewelry Stores
N.A.I.C.S.: 551112

Subsidiary (Domestic):

Zale Delaware, Inc. (2)
901 W Walnut Hill Ln, Irving, TX
75038   (100%)
Tel.: (972) 580-4000
Web Site: http://www.zalecorp.com
Sales Range: $150-199.9 Million
Emp.: 2,247
Retail Jewelry
N.A.I.C.S.: 458310

Subsidiary (Domestic):

Jewel Re-Insurance Ltd. (3)
901 W Walnut Hill Ln, Irving, TX 75308
Tel.: (972) 580-4000
Web Site: http://www.zalecorp.com
Sales Range: $75-99.9 Million
Insurance Services
N.A.I.C.S.: 524210

Jeweler's Financial Service, Inc. (3)
901 West Walnut Hill Ln, Irving, TX
75038   (100%)
Tel.: (972) 580-4000
Web Site: http://www.zalecorp.com
Sales Range: $400-449.9 Million
Emp.: 428
Credit Card Servicing
N.A.I.C.S.: 522299

Jewelers Credit Corp. (3)
901 W Walnut Hill Ln, Irving, TX 75038
Tel.: (972) 580-4000
Lending & Credit Services
N.A.I.C.S.: 522299

Piercing Pagoda (3)
901 W Walnut Hill Ln, Irving, TX 75038
Tel.: (972) 580-4000
Web Site: http://www.pagoda.com
Gold Jewelry Sales
N.A.I.C.S.: 458310

TXDC, LP (3)
901 W Walnut Hill Ln, Irving, TX 75038
Tel.: (972) 580-4000
Sales Range: $100-124.9 Million
Credit Services
N.A.I.C.S.: 561499

Zale Employees Child Care Association, Inc. (3)
901 W Walnut Hill Ln, Irving, TX 75038
Tel.: (972) 580-4000
Sales Range: $75-99.9 Million
Employer Association
N.A.I.C.S.: 624410

Zale Indemnity Company (3)
901 West Walnut Hill Ln, Irving, TX 75038
Tel.: (972) 580-4000
Web Site: http://www.zalecorp.com
Sales Range: $100-124.9 Million
Emp.: 11,900
Insurance Services
N.A.I.C.S.: 524298

Zale Life Insurance Company (3)
901 W Walnut Hill Ln, Irving, TX 75038
Tel.: (972) 580-4039
Web Site: http://www.zalecorp.com
Sales Range: $150-199.9 Million
Insurance Services
N.A.I.C.S.: 524113

Zale Puerto Rico Inc. (3)
901 W Walnut Hill Ln, Irving, TX
75038   (100%)
Tel.: (972) 580-4000
Web Site: http://www.zalecorp.com
Sales Range: $650-699.9 Million
Emp.: 2,247
Jewelry Stores in Puerto Rico
N.A.I.C.S.: 458310

SIGNETICS CORPORATION
483 Beopheung-ri Tanhyeon-myeon,
P'aju, Gyeonggi-do, Korea (South)
Tel.: (82) 319407400
Web Site: http://www.signetics.com
Year Founded: 1966

SIGNIFY N.V.

033170—(KRS)
Rev.: $220,589,235
Assets: $148,191,916
Liabilities: $47,475,049
Net Worth: $100,716,867
Earnings: $5,776,951
Emp.: 137
Fiscal Year-end: 12/31/22
Semiconductor Mfr
N.A.I.C.S.: 334413
Song Young-Hee (CEO)

Subsidiaries:

Signetics High Technology, Inc. (1)
4677 Old Ironsides Dr Ste 380, Santa
Clara, CA 95054
Tel.: (408) 907-2692
Web Site: http://www.signetics.com
Sales Range: $25-49.9 Million
Semiconductor Assembly Mfr
N.A.I.C.S.: 334413

SIGNIFY N.V.
High Tech Campus 48, 5656 AE,
Eindhoven, Netherlands
Tel.: (31) 202455340   NI
Web Site: https://www.signify.com
Year Founded: 1891
LIGHT—(EUR)
Rev.: $8,109,216,490
Assets: $8,942,369,955
Liabilities: $5,634,578,027
Net Worth: $3,307,791,927
Earnings: $564,429,096
Emp.: 34,619
Fiscal Year-end: 12/31/22
Holding Company; Lighting Products
Designer, Mfr & Whslr
N.A.I.C.S.: 551112
Arthur P. M. van de Poel (Chm-Supervisory Bd)

Subsidiaries:

Signify Belgium N.V. (1)
High Tech Campus 48, 5656 AE, Eindhoven, Netherlands
Tel.: (31) 202455340
Web Site: https://www.signify.com
Lighting Product Mfr & Distr
N.A.I.C.S.: 335139

Signify France S.A.S. (1)
33 Rue de Verdun, CS 60019, 92156,
Suresnes, Cedex, France
Tel.: (33) 157328200
Electric Light Mfr & Distr
N.A.I.C.S.: 335131

Signify GmbH (1)
Rontgenstrasse 22, 22335, Hamburg, Germany
Tel.: (49) 80074454775
Information Technology Services
N.A.I.C.S.: 541519

Signify Holding B.V. (1)
High Tech Campus 48, 5656 AE, Eindhoven, Netherlands
Tel.: (31) 20 24 55340
Web Site: https://www.signify.com
Holding Company
N.A.I.C.S.: 551112

Subsidiary (US):

Cooper Lighting, LLC (2)
1121 Hwy 74 S, Peachtree City, GA 30269
Tel.: (770) 486-4800
Web Site: http://www.cooperlighting.com
Electrical Apparatus & Equipment Whslr
N.A.I.C.S.: 423610

Plant (Domestic):

Cooper Lighting, LLC - Eufaula (3)
4 Hummingbird Ln, Eufaula, AL 36027
Tel.: (334) 687-0095
Web Site: http://www.cooperlighting.com
Lighting Fixture Mfr
N.A.I.C.S.: 335132

Cooper Lighting, LLC - Vicksburg (3)
5035 Hwy 61 S, Vicksburg, MS 39180
Tel.: (601) 638-1522

SIGNIFY N.V.

Signify N.V.—(Continued)

Web Site: http://www.cooperlighting.com
Lighting Fixture Mfr
N.A.I.C.S.: 335132

Subsidiary (Non-US):

Iluminacion Cooper de las Californias S. de R.L. de C.V. (3)
Calle Orbita 3, Col Parque Industrial O Colonia II, Mexicali, 21600, Mexico (100%)
Tel.: (52) 165611916
Sales Range: $200-249.9 Million
Emp.: 750
Electrical Apparatus & Equipment Whslr
N.A.I.C.S.: 423610

Subsidiary (Non-US):

Framas Lightings Limited (2)
No 5-8 3/F Vigor Industrial Building block A14-20 Cheung Tat Road, Tsing Yi, New Territories, China (Hong Kong)
Tel.: (852) 24976113
Home Appliance Mfr
N.A.I.C.S.: 335220

Lightolier de Mexico, S.A. de C.V. (2)
Av Las Industrias No 1, Ciudad Camargo, 33750, Chihuahua, Mexico
Tel.: (52) 6484628800
Residential Lighting Fixture Mfr & Whslr
N.A.I.C.S.: 335131
Fernando Arriaga (Plant Mgr)

Luceplan S.p.A (2)
Via ET Moneta 40, 20161, Milan, Italy
Tel.: (39) 02 662421
Web Site: http://www.luceplan.com
Residential Lighting Fixture Mfr
N.A.I.C.S.: 335131
Paolo Rizzatto (Co-Founder)

Subsidiary (Non-US):

Luceplan GmbH (3)
Prenzlauer Allee 39, 10405, Berlin, Germany
Tel.: (49) 30 44 33 84 0
Web Site: http://www.luceplan.com
Lighting Equipment Whslr
N.A.I.C.S.: 423610

Luceplan Scandinavia A/S (3)
Klubiensvej 22 Pakhus 48, Copenhagen, 2100, Denmark
Tel.: (45) 36 13 21 00
Web Site: http://www.luceplan.dk
Lighting Equipment Whslr
N.A.I.C.S.: 423440
Lars Lokdam (Chm)

Subsidiary (US):

Luceplan USA, Inc (3)
600 Meadowlands Pkwy Ste 265, Secaucus, NJ 07094
Tel.: (201) 558-1800
Electronic Equipment Whslr
N.A.I.C.S.: 423690

Subsidiary (Non-US):

Luceplan s.a.r.l. (3)
225 r du Faubourg Saint Honore, 75008, Paris, France
Tel.: (33) 1 44 83 92 87
Web Site: http://www.luceplan.com
Lighting Equipment Mfr
N.A.I.C.S.: 335139

Subsidiary (Non-US):

Modular Lighting Instruments NV (2)
Armoedestraat 71, 8800, Roeselare, Belgium
Tel.: (32) 51265656
Web Site: https://www.supermodular.com
Architectural Lighting Fixture Mfr
N.A.I.C.S.: 335132
Paul Rommens (Mng Dir)

Modular Lighting Paris (2)
31 Rue Du Mail, 75002, Paris, France
Tel.: (33) 145422425
Web Site: https://www.supermodular.com
Lighting Equipment Mfr
N.A.I.C.S.: 335139

Subsidiary (US):

Once Innovations, Inc. (2)
3955 Annapolis Ln N, Plymouth, MN 55447
Tel.: (763) 381-5621
Web Site: https://www.once.lighting
Light Emitting Diode Product Mfr
N.A.I.C.S.: 334413

Subsidiary (Non-US):

Signify (China) Investment Co., Ltd. (2)
No 255 Hechuan Road,China Science & Technology Oasis Phase III Bldg 5, Minhang District, Shanghai, 200233, China
Tel.: (86) 2134147200
Web Site: http://www.signify.com
Lighting Equipment Mfr
N.A.I.C.S.: 335139

Subsidiary (Domestic):

Philips & Yaming Lighting Co., Ltd. (3)
1001 Jiaxin Road, Jiading District, Shanghai, 201801, China
Tel.: (86) 21 59101818
Web Site: http://cn.yaming-lighting.com
Lighting Fixture Mfr
N.A.I.C.S.: 335132

Subsidiary (Non-US):

Signify Netherlands B.V. (2)
(100%)
Tel.: (31) 402750000
Web Site: https://www.signify.com
Lighting Products Designer, Mfr & Whslr
N.A.I.C.S.: 335139

Division (US):

Bodine Group Holding Company Inc. (3)
236 Mt Pleasant Dr, Collierville, TN 38017-2752
Tel.: (901) 853-7211
Web Site: http://www.signify.com
Emergency Lighting Equipment/Holding Company
N.A.I.C.S.: 335139

Unit (US):

Hadco (3)
100 Craftway Dr, Littlestown, PA 17340-1651
Tel.: (717) 359-7131
Web Site: http://www.signify.com
Lighting Fixture Mfr
N.A.I.C.S.: 335131

Division (US):

Hanover Lantern Inc. (3)
425 E Middle St, Hanover, PA 17331
Tel.: (717) 632-6464
Web Site: http://www.hanoverlantern.com
Outdoor Lighting Fixture Mfr
N.A.I.C.S.: 335132
Tim Raubenstine (CEO & Pres)

Subsidiary (Domestic):

Modular Lighting Nederland B.V. (3)
Bouwerij 54, 1185 XX, Amstelveen, Netherlands
Tel.: (31) 20 347 3047
Web Site: https://www.modular.nl
Decoration Lighting Mfr
N.A.I.C.S.: 335139

Division (US):

Philips Consumer Luminaires Corporation (3)
1600 Fleetwood Dr, Elgin, IL 60123
Tel.: (800) 825-5844
Lighting Equipment Mfr
N.A.I.C.S.: 335139

Philips Lighting
200 Franklin Sq Dr, Somerset, NJ 08873-4186
Tel.: (732) 563-3000
Web Site: http://www.usa.lighting.philips.com
Lighting Producer Mfr & Marketer for Commercial & Industrial Use
N.A.I.C.S.: 335139

Philips Solid-State Lighting Solutions, Inc. (3)
3 Burlington Woods Dr 4th Fl, Burlington, MA 01803
Tel.: (617) 423-9999
Web Site: http://www.colorkinetics.com
Light Emitting Diode Mfr
N.A.I.C.S.: 334413
Jeffrey Cassis (CEO)

Strand Lighting, Inc. (3)
10911 Petal St, Dallas, TX 75238
Tel.: (214) 647-7880
Web Site: http://www.strandlighting.com
Lighting Equipment Mfr
N.A.I.C.S.: 335132
Philip O'Donnell (CEO)

Subsidiary (Non-US):

Signify Poland Sp. z o.o. (2)
Aleje Jerozolimskie 195B, 02 222, Warsaw, Poland (100%)
Tel.: (48) 80074454775
Web Site: https://www.signify.com
Lighting Equipment Mfr
N.A.I.C.S.: 335139

Signify Saudi Arabia (2)
Al Ahsa St Inara Plaza, Riyadh, 10113, Saudi Arabia (51%)
Tel.: (966) 11 510 2647
Web Site: https://www.signify.com
Lighting Fixture Mfr
N.A.I.C.S.: 335131
Fahad Al Hobayb (CEO)

SIGNPOST CORPORATION

6F PMO Nihonbashi Honcho 4-12-20 Nihonbashi Honcho, Chuo-ku, Tokyo, 103-0023, Japan
Tel.: (81) 356526031
Web Site: https://signpost.co.jp
Year Founded: 2007
3996—(TKS)
Rev.: $19,458,740
Assets: $19,064,430
Liabilities: $9,683,520
Net Worth: $9,380,910
Earnings: ($2,384,200)
Fiscal Year-end: 02/29/20
Information Technology Consulting Services
N.A.I.C.S.: 541512
Yasushi Kambara (Founder & Pres)

SIGNPOST INDIA LIMITED

202 Pressman House A Near 70 Nehru Rd Vile Parle East, Mumbai, 400099, India
Tel.: (91) 8291190000
Web Site:
https://www.signpostindia.com
Year Founded: 2008
SIGNPOST—(NSE)
Emp.: 239
Advertising Services
N.A.I.C.S.: 541810
Shripad Prahlad Ashtekar (Dir)

Subsidiaries:

Pressman Advertising Limited (1)
Pressman House 10A Lee Road, Kolkata, 700 020, India
Tel.: (91) 1800309400
Web Site:
https://www.pressmanadvertising.in
Rev.: $2,776,137
Assets: $6,489,524
Liabilities: $649,890
Net Worth: $5,839,634
Earnings: $774,132
Emp.: 56
Fiscal Year-end: 03/31/2021
Advertising Services
N.A.I.C.S.: 541810
Niren Suchanti (Chm & Mng Dir)

SIGNPOST NV

Wolfsakker 5a, 9160, Lokeren, Belgium
Tel.: (32) 746851005
Web Site: https://signpost.eu

INTERNATIONAL PUBLIC

Software Publisher
N.A.I.C.S.: 513210
Arne Vandendriessche (CEO)

Subsidiaries:

Academic Software bv (1)
Wolfsakker 5a, 9160, Lokeren, Belgium
Tel.: (32) 496649974
Web Site: https://academicsoftware.com
Emp.: 100
Software Publisher
N.A.I.C.S.: 513210
Frederik Meheus (CEO)

Subsidiary (Non-US):

asknet GmbH (2)
Vincenz-Priessnitz-Str 3, 76131, Karlsruhe, Germany (100%)
Tel.: (49) 721964580
Web Site: http://www.asknet-solutions.com
Rev.: $100,598,666
Assets: $39,000,292
Liabilities: $33,775,813
Net Worth: $5,224,480
Earnings: ($1,960,079)
Emp.: 66
Fiscal Year-end: 12/31/2020
Online Software Retailing Services
N.A.I.C.S.: 513210
Christian Herkel (CEO & Member-Exec Bd)

Subsidiary (Non-US):

asknet K.K. (3)
3F Metlife Kabutocho Bldg 5-1 Nihonbashi Kabutocho, Chue-Ku, Tokyo, 103-0026, Japan
Tel.: (81) 368684900
Web Site: http://www.asknet.com
Emp.: 2
Electronic Software Distr
N.A.I.C.S.: 541511

SIGONG TECH CO., LTD.

225-20 Pangyoyeok-ro, Bundang-gu, Seongnam, 13494, Gyeonggi-do, Korea (South)
Tel.: (82) 234380077
Web Site:
https://www.sigongtech.com
Year Founded: 1988
020710—(KRS)
Rev.: $76,859,153
Assets: $124,754,391
Liabilities: $29,564,017
Net Worth: $95,190,374
Earnings: $5,310,886
Emp.: 190
Fiscal Year-end: 12/31/22
Interior Design Services
N.A.I.C.S.: 541410
Park Ki-Seok (Chm)

Subsidiaries:

i-Scream Media Co., Ltd. (1)
225-20 Pangyoyeok-ro, Bundang-gu, Seongnam, Gyeonggi, Korea (South)
Tel.: (82) 234402300
Web Site: http://www.i-screammedia.com
Education Services
N.A.I.C.S.: 611710
Park Ki-seok (Dir)

SIGULDAS CMAS

Kalnabeites 8, Siguldas, Riga, 2150, Latvia
Tel.: (371) 767972040
Web Site: https://www.sigmas.lv
Year Founded: 1957
W2I—(STU)
Rev.: $1,697,236
Assets: $2,280,961
Liabilities: $258,733
Net Worth: $2,022,229
Earnings: $72,232
Emp.: 28
Fiscal Year-end: 12/31/23
Agricultural Services
N.A.I.C.S.: 115116
Sarmite Arcimovica (Mgr-Production & Tale Dept)

SIGURD MICROELECTRONICS CORP.
No 436 Sec 1 Pei-Shing Rd Chu-Tung, Hsin-chu, Taiwan
Tel.: (886) 35959213
Web Site: https://www.sigurd.com.tw
6257—(TAI)
Rev.: $506,213,428
Assets: $1,226,901,357
Liabilities: $579,411,731
Net Worth: $647,489,625
Earnings: $69,934,070
Emp.: 2,610
Fiscal Year-end: 12/31/23
Integrated Circuits Mfr
N.A.I.C.S.: 334413
Ching-Cheng Tien *(Head)*

Subsidiaries:

AMBERSAN Medical Technology Co., Ltd. (1)
3F-2 No 31 Xintai Road, Hsinchu, Zhubei, Taiwan
Tel.: (886) 36126688
Web Site: https://www.ambersan.com.tw
Medical Equipment Mfr & Distr
N.A.I.C.S.: 339112

Flatek, Inc. (1)
2F No 151 Xinhu 1st Rd, Neihu Dist, New Taipei City, 114, Taiwan
Tel.: (886) 277201881
Web Site: https://www.flatek.com
Integrated Circuit Testing Services
N.A.I.C.S.: 541380

OPS Electronic (ShenZhen) Limited (1)
1F Building 2 Peng Feng Fa Industeral Area No 175 Gong Ye Dong Road, Longhua Town Bao an District, Shenzhen, China
Tel.: (86) 75527707166
Electronic Component Mfr & Distr
N.A.I.C.S.: 334416

Sigurd Microelectronics Corp. - Chung-Shing Factory (1)
No 11 Lane 169 Section 2 Chung-Shing Road, Chu-Tung, Hsin-chu, 310, Taiwan
Tel.: (886) 3 5824502
Sales Range: $200-249.9 Million
Emp.: 700
Integrated Circuits Assembling & Testing Services
N.A.I.C.S.: 334418
Benjamin Lin *(Mgr-Sls)*

Sigurd Microelectronics Corp. - Hu-Kou Factory (1)
No 1 Siwei Road Hsinchu Industrial Park, Hukuo, Hsin-chu, 303, Taiwan
Tel.: (886) 35971698
Sales Range: $200-249.9 Million
Emp.: 540
Integrated Circuits Testing Services
N.A.I.C.S.: 334418
Gloria Lin *(Mgr-HR)*

Sigurd Microelectronics Corp. - Pei-Shing Factory (1)
No 436 Sec 1 Pei-Shing Rd, Chu-Tung, Hsin-chu, 310, Taiwan
Tel.: (886) 35959213
Web Site: http://www.sigurd.com.tw
Sales Range: $400-449.9 Million
Electronic Testing Equipment Mfr
N.A.I.C.S.: 334515

Sigurd UTC Corporation (1)
No 2 Li-Hsin 3rd Road Hsinchu Science Park, Hsinchu, Taiwan
Tel.: (886) 357887806610
Semiconductor Test Services
N.A.I.C.S.: 541380

TEST-SERV Inc. (1)
No 34 Guangfu South Road Hsinchu Industrial Zone, Hsinchu, Taiwan
Tel.: (886) 35970670
Web Site: https://www.testserv.com.tw
Automated Machinery Equipment Mfr & Distr
N.A.I.C.S.: 334290

TPfusion Corp. (1)
3 -13 -10 Nagara Naka, Kitaku, Osaka, Japan
Tel.: (81) 663532780
Web Site: http://www.tpfusion.com
Digital Information Services
N.A.I.C.S.: 518210

TST Co., Ltd. (1)
307/33 Nguyen Van Troi, Ward 1 Tan Binh District, Ho Chi Minh City, Vietnam
Tel.: (84) 937008739
Web Site: https://www.tst-vn.com
Emp.: 300
Semiconductor Equipment Mfr & Distr
N.A.I.C.S.: 333242

Tpfusion, Inc. (1)
1F No 411 Sec 2 Tiding Blvd, Neihu District, Taipei, Taiwan
Tel.: (886) 277201881
Web Site: http://www.tpfusion.com
Digital Information Services
N.A.I.C.S.: 519290

Winstek Semiconductor Co., Ltd. (1)
No 176-5 Luliaokeng 6th Ling, Qionglin Township, Hsinchu, 307410, Taiwan
Tel.: (886) 35936565
Web Site: https://www.winstek.com.tw
Rev.: $123,414,064
Assets: $233,057,405
Liabilities: $50,025,295
Net Worth: $183,032,111
Earnings: $28,686,083
Fiscal Year-end: 12/31/2022
Testing Laboratory Services
N.A.I.C.S.: 541380
Richard Weng *(Gen Mgr)*

SIGURNOST - VRACAR A.D.
Cerska 76a, Belgrade, Serbia
Tel.: (381) 11 2836 780
Web Site: http://www.sigurnostvracar.co.rs
Year Founded: 1982
SGRV—(BEL)
Sales Range: $1-9.9 Million
Emp.: 1,300
Private Security Services
N.A.I.C.S.: 561612
Mirko Durovic *(Gen Mgr)*

SIGURNOST AS A.D.
Cerska 76a, 11000, Belgrade, Serbia
Tel.: (381) 112836780
Web Site: https://www.sigurnostas.co.rs
Year Founded: 2002
SIAS—(BEL)
Rev.: $212,691
Assets: $34,487
Liabilities: $47,054
Net Worth: ($12,567)
Earnings: ($998)
Emp.: 16
Fiscal Year-end: 12/31/20
Private Security Services
N.A.I.C.S.: 561612
Slavisa Ristic *(Exec Dir)*

SIGVARIS HOLDING AG
Groblistrasse 8, 9014, Saint Gallen, Switzerland
Tel.: (41) 712724000
Web Site: http://www.sigvaris.com
Surgical & Medical Instrument Mfr
N.A.I.C.S.: 339112

Subsidiaries:

PANI TERESA MEDICA S.A. (1)
Ul Powidzka 50, Gutowo Male, 62-300, Warsaw, Poland
Tel.: (48) 61 200 43 88
Web Site: https://www.pani-teresa.com.pl
Orthopaedic Product Mfr
N.A.I.C.S.: 339113

SIHUI FUJI ELECTRONICS TECHNOLOGY CO., LTD.
No 2 Electronics Industrial Zone, Xiamao Town Sihui County, Zhaoqing, 526236, Guangdong, China
Tel.: (86) 7583527998
Web Site: https://www.fsqualitypcb.com
Year Founded: 2009
300852—(SSE)
Rev.: $171,141,156
Assets: $234,430,176
Liabilities: $61,472,076
Net Worth: $172,958,100
Earnings: $31,673,285
Emp.: 1,500
Fiscal Year-end: 12/31/22
Electronic Product Mfr & Distr
N.A.I.C.S.: 334419
Tianming Liu *(Chm)*

SII SP. Z O.O.
al Niepodleglosci 69, 02-626, Warsaw, Poland
Tel.: (48) 22 486 37 37
Web Site: http://www.pl.sii.eu
Year Founded: 1979
Sales Range: $50-74.9 Million
Emp.: 2,000
Information Technology Engineering Services
N.A.I.C.S.: 541512
Gregoire Nitot *(Founder & CEO)*

SIIC ENVIRONMENT HOLDINGS LTD.
One Temasek Avenue 3702, Millenia Tower, Singapore, 039192, Singapore
Tel.: (65) 65382598
Web Site: https://www.siicenv.com
0807—(HKG)
Rev.: $1,066,604,504
Assets: $6,001,118,292
Liabilities: $3,847,532,946
Net Worth: $2,153,585,346
Earnings: $143,613,521
Emp.: 6,372
Fiscal Year-end: 12/31/23
Water Purification & Wastewater Treatment Systems
N.A.I.C.S.: 924110
Hanguang Huang *(Gen Mgr)*

Subsidiaries:

Longjiang Environmental Protection Group Co., Ltd. (1)
No 1 Shunjiang Street, Daowai District, Harbin, 150050, China
Tel.: (86) 45186036638
Web Site: https://www.ljep.com.cn
Emp.: 3,000
Environmental Protection Services
N.A.I.C.S.: 924110

Nanfang Water Co., Ltd. (1)
Room 3001 Block C Galaxy World No 1 Yabao Road, Longgang District, Shenzhen, China
Tel.: (86) 7558 930 9866
Web Site: https://www.southwater.com.cn
Waste Management Services
N.A.I.C.S.: 221310

Tianmen Kaidi Water Services Co., Ltd. (1)
No 86 Renmin Avenue West Jingling, Tianmen, 431700, Hubei, China
Tel.: (86) 7285242018
Water Supply Services
N.A.I.C.S.: 221310

Wuhan Kaidi Water Management & Operation Co., Ltd. (1)
Building 1 International Enterprise Center Phase 2 Te 1 Guans, Wuhan, 430074, Hubei, China
Tel.: (86) 2767848927
Water Treatment Plant Management & Operation Services
N.A.I.C.S.: 221310

Wuhan Kaidi Water Project & Engineering Co., Ltd. (1)
Building 1 International Enterprise Center Phase 2 Te 1 Guans, Wuhan, 430074, Hubei, China
Tel.: (86) 2767848927
Water Treatment Plant Construction Services
N.A.I.C.S.: 237110

SIILI SOLUTIONS OYJ
Ruoholahdenkatu 21, 00180, Helsinki, Finland
Tel.: (358) 103205440
Web Site: https://www.siili.com
Year Founded: 2005
SIILI—(HEL)
Rev.: $127,703,432
Assets: $114,461,472
Liabilities: $70,947,550
Net Worth: $43,513,922
Earnings: $4,047,054
Emp.: 1,248
Fiscal Year-end: 12/31/22
Computer System Design Services
N.A.I.C.S.: 541512
Harry Brade *(Chm)*

SIIX CORPORATION
SIIX Bldg 1-4-9 Bingo-machi, Chuoku, Osaka, 541-0051, Japan
Tel.: (81) 662666400
Web Site: https://www.siix.co.jp
7613—(TKS)
Rev.: $2,196,255,120
Assets: $1,537,381,420
Liabilities: $902,507,370
Net Worth: $634,874,050
Earnings: $58,031,650
Emp.: 12,734
Fiscal Year-end: 12/31/23
Electronic Parts Whslr
N.A.I.C.S.: 423690
Shiro Murai *(Chm)*

Subsidiaries:

Guangdong Midea-SIIX Electronics Co., Ltd. (1)
A building Penglai Road, Midea Industrial Town Beijiao Shunde, Foshan, Guangdong, China
Tel.: (86) 75722605192
Electronic Products Mfr
N.A.I.C.S.: 334419

Hefei Midea-SIIX Electronics Co., Ltd. (1)
NO 88 Innovation road Hi-New Technology, Hefei, 230088, Anhui, China
Tel.: (86) 55162573702
Electronic Products Mfr
N.A.I.C.S.: 334419

PT SIIX Electronics Indonesia (1)
Jalan Beringin Lot 9 Batamindo Industrial Park Mukakuning, Batam, 29433, Indonesia
Tel.: (62) 770611486
Electronic Components Distr
N.A.I.C.S.: 423690
Tadanori Kawanishi *(Pres & Dir)*

PT. SIIX EMS Indonesia (1)
Jl Maligi VIII Lot S-4, Kawasan Industri KIIC, Karawang, 41361, West Java, Indonesia
Tel.: (62) 2189114685
Electronic Products Mfr
N.A.I.C.S.: 334419

PT. SIIX Trading Indonesia (1)
Jl Maligi VIII Lot S-4, Kawasan Industri KIIC, Karawang, 41361, West Java, Indonesia
Tel.: (62) 2129569378
Electronic Products Mfr
N.A.I.C.S.: 334419

Panyu Kyokuto Sakata Electronics Ltd. (1)
Luo Jia, Shi Ji Town Panyu, Guangzhou, Guangdong, China
Tel.: (86) 2084625382
Electronic Products Mfr
N.A.I.C.S.: 334419

SIIX (Shanghai) Co., Ltd. (1)
A 2509-11 NanFeng City No 100 ZunYi Road, Shanghai, 200051, China
Tel.: (86) 2152835870
Electronic Components Distr

SIIX CORPORATION

SIIX CORPORATION—(Continued)
N.A.I.C.S.: 423690

SIIX (Shanghai) Co., Ltd. Jading LC (1)
No 415 Xingping Road, Jiading, Shanghai, 201818, China
Tel.: (86) 21390041299
Electronic Products Mfr
N.A.I.C.S.: 334419

SIIX Bangkok Co., Ltd. (1)
172/9 Moo 8 Soi Suksawadi 74 Suksawadi Road, Bangkru, Phra Pradaeng, 10130, Samut Prakan, Thailand
Tel.: (66) 24630118
Web Site: http://www.siix.co.jp
Electronic Equipment Whslr
N.A.I.C.S.: 423690

SIIX Coxon Precision Phils., Inc. (1)
107 Competence Drive Carmelray Industrial Park 1 Sepz Canlubang, Calamba, 4028, Laguna, Philippines
Tel.: (63) 495022435
Electronic Components Distr
N.A.I.C.S.: 423690

SIIX EMS (DONG GUAN) Co., Ltd. (1)
Technical Industrial Area, Dalingshan Town, Dongguan, 523820, Guangdong, China
Tel.: (86) 76985601508
Web Site: http://www.siix.co.jp
Sales Range: $400-449.9 Million
Emp.: 1,600
Electronic Components & Devices Mfr
N.A.I.C.S.: 335999

SIIX EMS (Shanghai) Co., Ltd. (1)
No 415 Xingping Road, Jiading, Shanghai, 201818, China
Tel.: (86) 2139905910
Electronic Components Distr
N.A.I.C.S.: 423690
F. Nishisaki (Gen Mgr)

SIIX EMS (Thailand) Co., Ltd. (1)
172/7 Moo 8 Soi Suksawadi 74 Suksawadi Rd, Bangkru, Samut Prakan, 10130, Phra Pradaeng, Thailand
Tel.: (66) 24630118
Web Site: http://www.siix-ems.com
Electronic Equipment & Parts Whslr
N.A.I.C.S.: 423690

SIIX EMS Mexico, S. de R.L de C.V. (1)
Av Santiago Poniente No 108 Parque Industrial Colinas de San Luis, 78423, San Luis Potosi, Mexico
Tel.: (52) 4442989130
Electronic Components Distr
N.A.I.C.S.: 423690
Sho Kawaguchi (Sls Mgr)

SIIX EMS Philippines, Inc. (1)
108 Competence Drive Carmelray Industrial Park 1 Sepz Canlubang, Calamba, 4028, Laguna, Philippines
Tel.: (63) 495084011
Electronic Components Distr
N.A.I.C.S.: 423690
Cynthia Centeno (Asst Mgr-HRMD)

SIIX EMS Slovakia s.r.o. (1)
Kmetova 120, 949 01, Nitra, Slovakia
Tel.: (421) 372302032
Electronic Components Distr
N.A.I.C.S.: 423690
Jan Maluch (Mgr-Quality)

SIIX Electronics Co., Ltd. (1)
1-3-25 Machiya, Midori-ku, Sagamihara, 252-0101, Kanagawa, Japan
Tel.: (81) 427834300
Electronic Components Distr
N.A.I.C.S.: 423690

SIIX Europe GmbH (1)
Hans-bockler-str 18, 47877, Willich, Germany
Tel.: (49) 215494690
Web Site: http://www.siix.co.jp
Sales Range: $25-49.9 Million
Electronic Equipments & Parts Whslr
N.A.I.C.S.: 423690

SIIX H.K. Ltd. (1)
Room 2201-2 Shun Tak Centre West Tower 200 Connaught Road, Hong Kong, China (Hong Kong)
Tel.: (852) 25496111
Web Site: http://www.siix.co.jp
Sales Range: $25-49.9 Million
Electronic Product Whslr
N.A.I.C.S.: 423690

SIIX Hubei Co., Ltd. (1)
No 168 Huairen Road Xiaohan Avenue, Xiaogan, 432000, Hubei, China
Tel.: (86) 7122113336
Electronic Components Distr
N.A.I.C.S.: 423690

SIIX Hungary Kft. (1)
Teglagyari ut 9, Nagykoros, 2750, Budapest, Hungary
Tel.: (36) 53949900
Electronic Products Mfr
N.A.I.C.S.: 334419

SIIX Logistics Phils, Inc. (1)
108 Competence Drive Carmelray Industrial Park 1 Sepz Canlubang, Calamba, 4028, Laguna, Philippines
Tel.: (63) 495024993
Electronic Components Distr
N.A.I.C.S.: 423690
Laila Tan (Mgr-Fin)

SIIX Malaysia Sdn. Bhd. (1)
Level 32 Menara Allianz Sentral 203 Jalan Tun Sambanthan, Kuala Lumpur Sentral Wilayah Persekutuan, 50470, Kuala Lumpur, Malaysia
Tel.: (60) 327758022
Electronic Components Distr
N.A.I.C.S.: 423690

SIIX Phils., Inc. (1)
108 Competence Drive Canlubang, Carmelray Industrial Park 1 SEPZ, Calamba, 4028, Laguna, Philippines
Tel.: (63) 495024993
Electronic Products Mfr
N.A.I.C.S.: 334419

SIIX Singapore Pte., Ltd. (1)
No 8 Kim Chuan Drive 03-02 Siix Building, Singapore, 537083, Singapore
Tel.: (65) 62850330
Web Site: http://www.siix.co.jp
Sales Range: $25-49.9 Million
Electronic Equipments & Parts Mfr
N.A.I.C.S.: 423690

SIIX TWN Co., Ltd. (1)
5F No 3 Nanking East Road Section 5, Taipei, 105, Taiwan
Tel.: (886) 227685526
Electronic Components Distr
N.A.I.C.S.: 423690

SIIX U.S.A. Corp. (1)
651 Bonnie Ln, Elk Grove Village, IL 60007
Tel.: (847) 593-3211
Sales Range: $25-49.9 Million
Emp.: 20
Electronic Equipment Whslr
N.A.I.C.S.: 423610
Linda Loda (Office Mgr)

SIIX Vietnam Company Limited (1)
16th Fl Icon4 Tower 243A De La Thanh Street Lang Thuong Ward, Dong Da District, Hanoi, Vietnam
Tel.: (84) 437606635
Electronic Components Distr
N.A.I.C.S.: 423690

SIIX do Brasil Ltda. (1)
Rua Iguatemi 252 Cj 11 E 12, Itaim-Bibi, Sao Paulo, 01451-010, Brazil
Tel.: (55) 1130781766
Web Site: http://www.siix.co.jp
Sales Range: $50-74.9 Million
Electric Component Whslr
N.A.I.C.S.: 423690

SIIX-AGT Medtech Pte. Ltd. (1)
No 8 Kim Chuan Drive 02-07 SIIX Building, Singapore, 537083, Singapore
Tel.: (65) 69968129
Electronic Products Mfr
N.A.I.C.S.: 334419

Shanghai Kyokuto Precision Electronics Ltd. (1)
388 Jiuyuan Road, Qingpu Industrial Zone, Shanghai, China
Tel.: (86) 2169225866
Electronic Products Mfr
N.A.I.C.S.: 334419

Shinto - Welbest Manufacturing, Inc. (1)
048 A Rodriguez Avenue Santolan, Pasig, Philippines
Tel.: (63) 26451583
Electronic Products Mfr
N.A.I.C.S.: 334419

Takaya SIIX Electronics (Shanghai) Co., Ltd. (1)
No 555 Huocheng Road, Jiading Industrial Zone, Shanghai, 201821, China
Tel.: (86) 2139108384
Electronic Products Mfr
N.A.I.C.S.: 334419

SIJIN INTELLIGENT FORMING MACHINERY CO., LTD.
No 1832 Jiangnan Road, High technology zone, Ningbo, 315103, Zhejiang, China
Tel.: (86) 57488365336
Web Site: https://www.machinesijin.com
Year Founded: 1993
003025—(SSE)
Rev.: $71,354,762
Assets: $177,073,266
Liabilities: $36,132,010
Net Worth: $140,941,256
Earnings: $19,560,289
Fiscal Year-end: 12/31/22
Industrial Machinery Product Mfr & Distr
N.A.I.C.S.: 333248
Zhongming Li (Chm & Gen Mgr)

SIKA AG
Zugerstrasse 50, CH-6340, Baar, Switzerland
Tel.: (41) 584366800 CH
Web Site: https://www.sika.com
Year Founded: 1910
SIKA—(SWX)
Rev.: $12,459,645,233
Assets: $16,685,920,177
Liabilities: $10,108,093,126
Net Worth: $6,577,827,051
Earnings: $1,178,048,780
Emp.: 33,547
Fiscal Year-end: 12/31/23
Real Estate Manangement Services
N.A.I.C.S.: 551112
Christoph Ganz (Reg Mgr-Americas)

Subsidiaries:

ABC Kimya Sanayi ve Dis Ticaret Anonim Sirketi (1)
Ortakoy Sanayi Sitesi Ilter Bulvari No 16, Silivri, Istanbul, Turkiye
Tel.: (90) 212 422 1356
Web Site: https://www.abcsealants.com.tr
Polyurethane Foam Mfr & Distr
N.A.I.C.S.: 326150

Adeplast S.R.L. (1)
Str Adeplast no 164A, Corlatesti Prahova county, 107063, Ploiesti, Romania
Tel.: (40) 24 433 8000
Web Site: https://www.adeplast.ro
Construction Chemical Product Mfr & Distr
N.A.I.C.S.: 325998
Daniel Soare (Dir)

Apurva India Pvt. Ltd. (1)
New Udyog Mandir No 2 Office No 2 2nd Floor 7-C Pitambar Lane, Mahim West, Mumbai, 400 016, India
Tel.: (91) 222 447 5051
Web Site: https://www.apurvaindia.in
Acid Resistant Cement Mfr
N.A.I.C.S.: 327120

Belineco LLC (1)
Ag Mikhanovichi building of LLC Evrosklad 2nd Floor Office 3, Minsk, Belarus
Tel.: (375) 16 297 3022
Web Site: https://www.belineco.com
Polyurethane Foam Mfr
N.A.I.C.S.: 326150

Butterfield Color, Inc. (1)
625 W Illinois Ave, Aurora, IL 60506
Tel.: (630) 906-1980
Web Site: https://www.butterfieldcolor.com
Decorative Concrete Color Additives, Concrete Stamping Tools, Release Agents, Concrete Acid Stains, Sealers & Overlay Products Mfr
N.A.I.C.S.: 325998
Keith Boudart (Natl Sls Mgr)

Emseal Joint Systems, Ltd. (1)
25 Bridle Ln, Westborough, MA 01581-2603
Tel.: (508) 836-0280
Web Site: https://www.emseal.com
Prefabricated Metal Building & Component Mfr
N.A.I.C.S.: 332311

Enewall Ltd. (1)
4 Netherton Road, Wishaw, ML2 0EQ, United Kingdom
Tel.: (44) 169 837 3305
Web Site: https://www.enewall.co.uk
Ready-Mix Concrete Mfr & Distr
N.A.I.C.S.: 327320

Everbuild Building Products Limited (1)
Site 41 Knowsthorpe Way, Cross Green Industrial Estate, Leeds, LS9 0SW, United Kingdom
Tel.: (44) 113 240 3456
Web Site: https://www.everbuild.co.uk
Adhesive Product Mfr & Distr
N.A.I.C.S.: 325520
David Seymour (Founder)

FAIST ChemTec GmbH (1)
Weinsheimer Strasse 96, 67547, Worms, Germany
Tel.: (49) 62413010
Industrial Application Acoustic Reduction Products Developer, Mfr & Whslr
N.A.I.C.S.: 332999

Haberkorn Abdichtungssysteme GmbH (1)
Hohe Brucke, 6961, Wolfurt, Austria
Tel.: (43) 55746950
Web Site: http://www.haberkorn.com
Sales Range: $10-24.9 Million
Emp.: 300
Sealing System Distr
N.A.I.C.S.: 424610

Hago PU GmbH (1)
Bodenseestrasse 217, 81243, Munich, Germany
Tel.: (49) 89 897 7020
Polyurethane Foam Mfr
N.A.I.C.S.: 326150

Home of Heart (Shanghai) E-Commerce Co., Ltd. (1)
No 252 Jiangchang 3rd Road, Jing'an District, Shanghai, China
Tel.: (86) 218 017 1833
Adhesive Product Mfr & Distr
N.A.I.C.S.: 325520

Hydrotech Membrane Corporation (1)
10 951 Parkway Boulevard, Montreal, QC, Canada
Tel.: (514) 353-6000
Web Site: https://en.hydrotechmembrane.ca
Roofing Material Whslr
N.A.I.C.S.: 423330

Jiangsu Crevo Science & Technology Co., Ltd. (1)
Zhongtian Road E District, Chang Kun Industrial Park Sha Jia Town Changshou, Chongqing, Jiangsu, China
Tel.: (86) 5125 250 5858
Web Site: https://www.crevo.cn
Adhesive Product Mfr & Distr
N.A.I.C.S.: 325520

KPM Industries Ltd. (1)
555 Michigan Drive Suite 100, San Joaquin, Oakville, L6L 0G4, ON, Canada
Tel.: (905) 639-2993
Web Site: https://www.kpmindustries.com
Adhesive Product Mfr & Distr
N.A.I.C.S.: 325520
William Whitaker King (Founder)

AND PRIVATE COMPANIES — SIKA AG

KVK Parabit, A.S. (1)
Nadrazni 450, 542 24, Svoboda nad Upou, Czech Republic
Tel.: (420) 49 984 7511
Web Site: https://www.kvkparabit.com
Asphalt Strip Distr
N.A.I.C.S.: 424720

LLC Sika Ukraina (1)
Mykola Hrinchenko Street 4, 03038, Kiev, Ukraine
Tel.: (380) 44 492 9419
Web Site: https://ukr.sika.com
Construction Materials Mfr & Distr
N.A.I.C.S.: 325520

Mortero SpA (1)
Mortero Spa Arriere Port, 06000, Bejaia, Algeria
Tel.: (213) 55 561 3957
Web Site: https://www.mortero-dz.com
Construction Chemical Product Mfr & Distr
N.A.I.C.S.: 325998

Oy Sika Finland Ab (1)
Koskelontie 23 C, PL 49, 02921, Espoo, Finland
Tel.: (358) 951 1431
Web Site: https://fin.sika.com
Construction Materials Mfr & Distr
N.A.I.C.S.: 325520

P.T. Sika Indonesia (1)
JL Raya Cibinong Bekasi Km 20 Limusnunggal, Cileungsi, Bogor, 16820, West Java, Indonesia
Tel.: (62) 21 823 0025
Web Site: https://idn.sika.com
Emp.: 300
Construction Materials Mfr & Distr
N.A.I.C.S.: 325520

Parex Ltd. (1)
Holly Lane Industrial Estate, Atherstone, CV9 2QZ, Warwickshire, United Kingdom
Tel.: (44) 182 771 1755
Web Site: https://www.parex.co.uk
Highway Product Mfr
N.A.I.C.S.: 336999

ParexGroup SA (1)
19 Pl de la Resistance, F-92446, Issy-les-Moulineaux, Cedex, France
Tel.: (33) 141174545
Web Site: http://www.parex-group.com
Architectural Coating Decoration, Protection & Maintenance Materials Mfr & Whslr
N.A.I.C.S.: 327310
Caroline Geoffroy *(Mgr-Comm)*

Subsidiary (Non-US):

Davco Construction Materials Pty Limited (2)
67 Elizabeth Street, Wetherill Park, 2164, NSW, Australia
Tel.: (61) 296163000
Web Site: http://www.davco.com.au
Sales Range: $50-74.9 Million
Emp.: 200
Building Products & Ceramic Tile Adhesives Mfr
N.A.I.C.S.: 325520
Andrew Nunn *(Mng Dir)*

Subsidiary (US):

Parex USA, Inc. (2)
2150 Eastridge Ave, Riverside, CA 92507
Tel.: (714) 778-2266
Web Site: https://www.parexusa.com
Architectural Coating Decoration, Protection & Maintenance Materials Mfr & Whslr
N.A.I.C.S.: 327310
Rodrigo Lacerda *(Pres & CEO)*

Subsidiary (Domestic):

Parex, Inc. (3)
1870 Stone Mtn Lithonia Rd, Lithonia, GA 30058-5470
Tel.: (770) 482-7872
Web Site: http://www.parexusa.com
Sales Range: $25-49.9 Million
Emp.: 50
Architectural Coating Decoration, Protection & Maintenance Materials Mfr & Whslr
N.A.I.C.S.: 327310
Buck Buchanan *(Dir-Sls)*

Subsidiary (Domestic):

ParexLanko (2)
8 Rte De Lille, 59230, Saint-Amand-les-Eaux, France
Tel.: (33) 327223000
Web Site: http://www.parexlanko.com
Architectural Coating Decoration, Protection & Maintenance Materials Mfr & Whslr
N.A.I.C.S.: 327310

ParexKlaukol S.A. (1)
Dr Ignacio Arieta 3817, B1754AQQ, San Justo, Buenos Aires, Argentina
Tel.: (54) 5 167 9999
Web Site: https://www.klaukol.com.ar
Adhesive Product Mfr & Distr
N.A.I.C.S.: 325520

Polypag AG (1)
Tiefenackerstrasse 52, 9450, Altstatten, Switzerland
Tel.: (41) 71 757 6411
Web Site: https://www.polypag.ch
Polyurethane Foam Mfr & Distr
N.A.I.C.S.: 326150
Marlene Nestola *(Mgr)*

Propex Concrete Systems Corporation (1)
4019 Industry Dr, Chattanooga, TN 37416
Web Site: https://www.fibermesh.com
Concrete Reinforcement Fiber Mfr
N.A.I.C.S.: 325220

S I K A Bel LLC (1)
Zhdanovichsky s/s 109, 223035, Minsk, Belarus
Tel.: (375) 17 516 3971
Web Site: https://blr.sika.com
Concrete Admixture Mfr & Distr
N.A.I.C.S.: 327390

Sika (Cambodia) Ltd. (1)
Legacy Business Center Unit 12BC at 12th Floor Building 29 Street 245, Sangkat Toul Tumpung 2 Khan Chamkarmorn, 12311, Phnom Penh, Cambodia
Tel.: (855) 2 390 1450
Web Site: https://khm.sika.com
Emp.: 50
Ready-Mix Conorete Mfr & Distr
N.A.I.C.S.: 327320
Torsten Nowack *(Mng Dir)*

Sika (China) Ltd. (1)
No 28 Jingdong Road, Suzhou Industrial Park, Suzhou, 215121, Jiangsu, China
Tel.: (86) 5126 273 2888
Web Site: https://www.sika.cn
Construction Chemicals Mfr & Distr
N.A.I.C.S.: 325998

Subsidiary (Domestic):

Axson Technologies Shanghai Co., Ltd. (2)
N 53 Tai Gu Road Wai Gao Qiao Free Trade Zone, Shanghai, 200131, China
Tel.: (86) 2158683037
Web Site: http://www.axson-technologies.cn
Resin Material Whslr
N.A.I.C.S.: 424610

Sika Guangzhou Ltd (2)
No 96 JunDa Road Eastern Section GET, Guangzhou, 510530, Guangdong, China
Tel.: (86) 20 8226 6066
Web Site: http://www.sika.cn
Sales Range: $50-74.9 Million
Emp.: 100
Chemical Distr
N.A.I.C.S.: 424520

Subsidiary (Domestic):

Sika (Guangzhou) Trading Company Ltd (3)
Room 2 Level II No 96 JunDa Road Eastern Section GET, Guangzhou, 510530, Jiangsu, China
Tel.: (86) 20 8226 6066
Web Site: http://www.sika.com
Chemical Distr
N.A.I.C.S.: 424520

Subsidiary (Domestic):

Sika Sarnafil Waterproofing Systems (Shanghai) Ltd. (2)
No 4555 Huaning Road, Shanghai, 201108, China
Tel.: (86) 2134073788
Web Site: http://www.sarnafil.cn
Sales Range: $125-149.9 Million
Emp.: 255
Polymer Membranes Mfr
N.A.I.C.S.: 326299

Sika (Jiangsu) Building Material Ltd. (1)
Xinfeng Town Industrial Park, Dantu District, Zhenjiang, 212142, China
Tel.: (86) 5118 558 8866
Ready-Mix Concrete Mfr & Distr
N.A.I.C.S.: 327320

Sika (Jiangsu) Industrial Material Ltd. (1)
No 25 Zhongtian Road, Zone E Changkun Industrial Park Shajiabang Town, Changshu, Jiangsu, China
Tel.: (86) 51252505858
Construction Material Mfr & Distr
N.A.I.C.S.: 327120

Sika (NZ) Ltd (1)
Tel.: (64) 9 820 2900
Web Site: https://nzl.sika.com
Sales Range: $50-74.9 Million
Emp.: 100
Construction Materials Mfr & Distr
N.A.I.C.S.: 325520
Mike Edwards *(Gen Mgr)*

Sika (Sichuan) Building Material Ltd. (1)
No 89 Xinghua Road 2nd Road, Deng Shuangchuan-Zhejiang Cooperation Industrial Park, Xinjin, 611430, Sichuan, China
Tel.: (86) 288 259 2299
Ready-Mix Concrete Mfr & Distr
N.A.I.C.S.: 327320

Sika (Thailand) Ltd. (1)
700/37 Moo 5 Amata City Chonburi Industrial Estate, KM 57 Bangna-Trad Rd Tumbol Klong Tamhru, Amphur Muang, 20000, Chonburi, Thailand (100%)
Tel.: (66) 3 810 9500
Web Site: http://tha.sika.com
Emp.: 450
Construction Chemicals Mfr
N.A.I.C.S.: 325199
Suwatchai Phuwapattanachart *(Mgr-TM Concrete Bus)*

Sika Abyssinia Chemicals Manufacturing PLC (1)
Bole Woreda 3 House No New Tropical Mall, PO Box 1596-1110, Addis Ababa, Ethiopia
Tel.: (251) 11 650 5681
Web Site: https://eth.sika.com
Construction Chemical Product Mfr & Distr
N.A.I.C.S.: 325998

Sika Albania SH.P.K. (1)
Rruga e Rinasit Tirana Business Park Building no 7 4th Floor, Tirana, Albania
Tel.: (355) 4 454 0070
Web Site: https://alb.sika.com
Construction Chemical Product Distr
N.A.I.C.S.: 424690

Sika Angola (SU), Limitada (1)
Kikuxi Industrial Zone Travessa Mota and Company Apartment 135, Viana, Luanda, Angola
Tel.: (244) 935111049
Web Site: https://ago.sika.com
Chemicals Mfr
N.A.I.C.S.: 325199

Sika Argentina S.A.I.C. (1)
Juan B Alberdi 5250, Caseros, B1678CSI, Buenos Aires, Argentina
Tel.: (54) 114 734 3500
Web Site: https://arg.sika.com
Sales Range: $50-74.9 Million
Emp.: 200
Construction Chemicals Mfr
N.A.I.C.S.: 325998
Daniele Sedele *(Gen Mgr)*

Sika Asia Pacific Mgt. Pte. Ltd (1)
200 Pandan Loop 06-02 Pantech 21 Ind Complex, Singapore, 128388, Singapore
Tel.: (65) 67371292
Web Site: http://www.sika.com.sg
Emp.: 24
Chemicals Mfr & Distr
N.A.I.C.S.: 325520

Sika Australia Pty. Ltd (1)
55 Elizabeth Street, Wetherill Park, 2164, NSW, Australia
Tel.: (61) 29 725 1145
Web Site: https://aus.sika.com
Emp.: 100
Chemical Distr
N.A.I.C.S.: 424690

Sika Automotive (Tianjin) Co. Ltd. (1)
No 18 XEDA 3rd Branch Road, Tianjin Xiqing Economic-Technological Development Area, Tianjin, 300385, China
Tel.: (86) 225 938 2304
Polyurethane Foam Distr
N.A.I.C.S.: 424690

Sika Automotive AG (1)
Kreuzlingerstrasse 35, 8590, Romanshorn, Switzerland
Tel.: (41) 58 436 3777
Automotive Bonding Distr
N.A.I.C.S.: 423110

Sika Automotive Deutschland GmbH (1)
Flinschstrasse 10-16, 60388, Frankfurt am Main, Germany
Tel.: (49) 69941740
Automotive Spare Parts Distr
N.A.I.C.S.: 486210

Sika Automotive Gastonia Inc. (1)
1909 Kyle Ct, Gastonia, NC 28052
Tel.: (704) 810-0500
Polyurethane Foam Distr
N.A.I.C.S.: 424690

Sika Automotive Slovakia, s.r.o. (1)
Rybniona 38/e, 831 06, Bratislava, Slovakia
Tel.: (421) 24 920 0411
Web Site: https://svk.sika.com
Construction Chemical Product Mfr
N.A.I.C.S.: 325998

Sika Automotive Terrassa S.A. (1)
Ind Can Parellada/ Saturn 34, Terrassa, Spain
Tel.: (34) 93 705 0600
Automotive Bonding Distr
N.A.I.C.S.: 423110

Sika BH d.o.o. (1)
Dzemala Bijedica 299, Sarajevo, Bosnia & Herzegovina
Tel.: (387) 3 378 8390
Web Site: https://bih.sika.com
Boat Mfr
N.A.I.C.S.: 336612

Sika Baltic SIA (1)
Piedrujas Street 7 k-5, Riga, 1073, Latvia
Tel.: (371) 6 737 5547
Web Site: https://lva.sika.com
Sales Range: $50-74.9 Million
Emp.: 10
Construction Materials Mfr & Distr
N.A.I.C.S.: 325520
Bjorn Salmi *(Chm)*

Sika Bangladesh Limited (1)
SkylarkMAK84 8th Floor House No 84 Block D, Bir Uttam Khadamul Bashar Road No 11 Banani, 1213, Dhaka, Bangladesh
Tel.: (880) 131 309 5060
Web Site: https://bgd.sika.com
Emp.: 15
Ready-Mix Concrete Mfr & Distr
N.A.I.C.S.: 327320

Sika Belgium NV (1)
Venecoweg 37, 9810, Nazareth, Belgium (100%)
Tel.: (32) 9 381 6500
Web Site: https://bel.sika.com
Specialty Chemicals Mfr & Distr
N.A.I.C.S.: 325998
Bernard Van Sever *(Gen Mgr)*

Subsidiary (Domestic):

Sika Automotive Belgium SA (2)
Avenue de Landas 2 Zoning Industriel, Saintes, 1480, Saintes, Walloon Brabant, Belgium
Tel.: (32) 2 367 2120

SIKA AG

INTERNATIONAL PUBLIC

Sika AG—(Continued)
Web Site: http://www.sika.com
Sales Range: $25-49.9 Million
Emp.: 42
Automotive Part Whslr
N.A.I.C.S.: 423110

Sika Bolivia SA (1)
Carretera Cotoca km 11 Frente al cementerio Montesacro, Sopocachi, 13603, Santa Cruz, Bolivia
Tel.: (591) 3 346 4504
Web Site: https://bol.sika.com
Construction Materials Mfr & Distr
N.A.I.C.S.: 325520

Sika Bulgaria EOOD (1)
247 Botevgradsko Shosse Blvd p k 1517 zh k Levski V, 1517, Sofia, Bulgaria
Tel.: (359) 2 942 4590
Web Site: https://bgr.sika.com
Construction Chemical Product Mfr & Distr
N.A.I.C.S.: 325998

Sika CZ, s.r.o. (1)
Bystrcka 1132/36, 624 00, Brno, South Moravian, Czech Republic
Tel.: (420) 800116116
Web Site: https://cze.sika.com
Sales Range: $50-74.9 Million
Emp.: 350
Chemicals Mfr & Distr
N.A.I.C.S.: 325520
Zdenek Bilek *(Gen Mgr)*

Sika Cameroon SARL (1)
ZI Magzi-Bonaberi, BP 1049, Douala, Cameroon
Tel.: (237) 23 339 0384
Web Site: https://cmr.sika.com
Liquid & Powder Admixture Distr
N.A.I.C.S.: 424690

Sika Canada Inc. (1)
601 Avenue Delmar, Pointe-Claire, H9R 4A9, QC, Canada
Tel.: (514) 697-2610
Web Site: https://can.sika.com
Sales Range: $50-74.9 Million
Emp.: 230
Construction Materials Mfr & Distr
N.A.I.C.S.: 325520
George Ghazzawi *(Mgr-Sls-Central Reg)*

Sika Chemicals Ghana Ltd. (1)
Kpone Rd, Kpone Katamanso district, Accra, Ghana
Tel.: (233) 257959292
Web Site: https://gha.sika.com
Chemicals Mfr
N.A.I.C.S.: 325180

Sika Colombia S.A.S. (1)
Vereda Canavita Km 20 5 Autopista Norte, Tocancipa, Cundinamarca, 251010, Colombia
Tel.: (57) 1 878 6333
Web Site: https://col.sika.com
Ready-Mix Concrete Mfr & Distr
N.A.I.C.S.: 327320

Sika Company for General Trading LLC (1)
Qoreetan, 33-0884, Erbil, Iraq
Tel.: (964) 7730374451
Web Site: https://irq.sika.com
Construction Services
N.A.I.C.S.: 236210

Sika Corporation (1)
201 Polito Ave, Lyndhurst, NJ 07071-3601
Tel.: (201) 933-8800 (100%)
Web Site: http://www.sikausa.com
Emp.: 900
Specialty Chemicals, Sealants & Adhesives Developer, Mfr & Whslr
N.A.I.C.S.: 325998
Mark Daniels *(VP-Transportation A & C)*

Subsidiary (Domestic):

Axson Technologies US, Inc. (2)
1611 Hults Dr, Eaton Rapids, MI 48827 (100%)
Tel.: (517) 663-8191
Web Site: http://www.axson-technologies.com
Epoxy & Urethane Products Mfr & Sls
N.A.I.C.S.: 325998

Plant (Domestic):

Sika Corp. - Conyers Plant (2)
1930 Sarasota Business Pkwy, Conyers, GA 30013
Tel.: (770) 760-1300
Web Site: http://usa.sika.com
Specialty Chemicals Mfr
N.A.I.C.S.: 325998

Sika Corp. - Fairless Hills Plant (2)
150 Ben Fairless Dr, Fairless Hills, PA 19030
Tel.: (215) 295-6600
Web Site: https://usa.sika.com
Specialty Chemicals Mfr
N.A.I.C.S.: 325998

Sika Croatia d.o.o. (1)
Puskariceva 77a, Lucko, 10250, Zagreb, Croatia
Tel.: (385) 1 659 4240
Web Site: http://sika-croatia.hr
Chemicals Mfr & Distr
N.A.I.C.S.: 325520

Sika Danmark A / S (1)
Hirsemarken 5, 3520, Farum, Denmark
Tel.: (45) 4 818 8585
Web Site: https://dnk.sika.com
Construction Materials Mfr & Distr
N.A.I.C.S.: 325520
Per Eskildsen *(Mgr-Sls)*

Sika Djibouti FZE (1)
Warehouse No DWH30 East Africa Holdings FZ Route 19 PK-12, PO Box 4037, Djibouti, Djibouti
Tel.: (253) 7 785 4793
Construction Chemical Product Distr
N.A.I.C.S.: 423390

Sika Dominicana SA (1)
Calle D 5 Casi Esquina Isabel Aguiar Zona Industrial de Herrera, Santo Domingo, 11113, Dominican Republic
Tel.: (809) 530 7171
Web Site: https://dom.sika.com
Chemicals Mfr & Distr
N.A.I.C.S.: 325998

Sika Ecuatoriana SA (1)
Km 3 5 via Duran-Tambo, PO Box 10093, Duran, Guayaquil, Guayas, Ecuador
Tel.: (593) 4 281 2700
Web Site: https://ecu.sika.com
Chemical Products Mfr & Distr
N.A.I.C.S.: 325180

Sika Egypt for Construction Chemicals S.A.E. (1)
222 El-Hegaz St, Heliopolis, Cairo, 11361, Egypt
Tel.: (20) 22 180 6632
Web Site: https://egy.sika.com
Emp.: 150
Construction Materials Mfr & Distr
N.A.I.C.S.: 325520
Ahmed Medhat *(Mgr-Pur, Key Accounts & Major Projects)*

Subsidiary (Domestic):

Sika Manufacturing for Construction Products, S.A.E. (2)
1st Industrial Zone A Section 10 Block, El Obour City, Cairo, 13035, Egypt
Tel.: (20) 246100714
Web Site: http://www.sika.eg
Chemicals Mfr & Distr
N.A.I.C.S.: 325520

Sika El Djazair SPA (1)
08 Route de L Arbaa, Les Eucalyptus, Algiers, 16111, Algeria
Tel.: (213) 21 50 21 84
Web Site: http://www.sikaeldjazair.com
Construction Materials Mfr & Distr
N.A.I.C.S.: 325520

Sika Estonia Ou (1)
Valge tn 13, 11415, Tallinn, Estonia
Tel.: (372) 605 4000
Web Site: https://est.sika.com
Construction Chemical Product Mfr & Distr
N.A.I.C.S.: 325998

Sika Guatemala SA (1)
14 calle B 12-05 zone 10, 07007, Guatemala, Guatemala
Tel.: (502) 2 313 3300

Web Site: https://www.gtm.sika.com
Emp.: 60
Construction Materials Mfr & Distr
N.A.I.C.S.: 325520

Sika Gulf B.S.C. (1)
PO Box 15776, Adliya, Bahrain
Tel.: (973) 1 773 8188
Construction Chemical Product Mfr & Distr
N.A.I.C.S.: 325998
Amin Farag *(Gen Mgr)*

Sika Hellas ABEE (1)
May Day 15, Kryoneri, 145 68, Dhionisos, Attica, Greece
Tel.: (30) 210 816 0600
Web Site: https://grc.sika.com
Emp.: 100
Construction Engineering Services
N.A.I.C.S.: 541330
Spyros Hatzifotis *(CEO)*

Sika Holding CH AG & Co KG (1)
Kornwestheimer Strasse 103-107, 70439, Stuttgart, Germany
Tel.: (49) 7 118 0090
Web Site: https://deu.sika.com
Construction Chemical Product Mfr & Distr
N.A.I.C.S.: 325998

Sika Holding GmbH (1)
Kornwestheimer Strasse 103-107, 70439, Stuttgart, Baden-Wurttemberg, Germany
Tel.: (49) 71180090
Chemicals Mfr & Distr
N.A.I.C.S.: 325520

Subsidiary (Domestic):

Schonox GmbH (2)
Alfred-Nobel-Str 6, 48720, Rosendahl, Germany
Tel.: (49) 25479100
Web Site: http://www.schoenox.de
Emp.: 300
Flooring Adhesive Mfr
N.A.I.C.S.: 325520

Sika Automotive GmbH (2)
Reichsbahnstrasse 99, Postfach 540209, 22502, Hamburg, Germany
Tel.: (49) 40540020
Web Site: https://automotive.sika.com
Chemical Distr
N.A.I.C.S.: 424690

Sika Deutschland GmbH (2)
Kornwestheimerstrasse 103-107, 70439, Stuttgart, Germany
Tel.: (49) 71180090
Web Site: https://deu.sika.com
Chemicals Mfr & Distr
N.A.I.C.S.: 325520

Subsidiary (Domestic):

Sika Trocal GmbH (3)
Muelheimer Strasse 26, 53840, Troisdorf, Germany
Tel.: (49) 224114500
Web Site: http://www.sika.de
Emp.: 130
Chemicals Mfr
N.A.I.C.S.: 325520

Subsidiary (Domestic):

Tricosal GmbH & Co. KG (2)
Von Helmholtz St 1, 89257, Illertissen, Germany
Tel.: (49) 73031800
Web Site: http://www.tricosal.de
Sales Range: $25-49.9 Million
Emp.: 75
Cement Mfr
N.A.I.C.S.: 327310

Joint Venture (Domestic):

part GmbH (2)
Stuttgarter Str 139, 72574, Bad Urach, Germany
Tel.: (49) 71259696500
Web Site: http://www.part-info.com
Automotive Abrasive & Surface Treatment Mfr
N.A.I.C.S.: 327910
Jochen Gaukel *(Mng Dir)*

Sika Hong Kong Ltd. (1)
Rm 1507-12 15/F Block A New Trade Plaza 6 On Ping Street, Sha Tin, New Territories, China (Hong Kong)
Tel.: (852) 2 686 8108
Web Site: https://hkg.sika.com
Construction Chemicals Mfr & Distr
N.A.I.C.S.: 325998

Sika Huangaria Kft (1)
Prielle Kornelia u 6, 1117, Budapest, Hungary
Tel.: (36) 13712020
Web Site: https://hun.sika.com
Sales Range: $25-49.9 Million
Emp.: 40
Chemical Distr
N.A.I.C.S.: 424690
Gohanna Krchina *(Mgr)*

Sika Hungaria Kft. (1)
Rozalia Park 5-7, 2051, Budapest, Hungary
Tel.: (36) 1 371 2020
Web Site: https://hun.sika.com
Construction Chemical Product Mfr & Distr
N.A.I.C.S.: 325998

Sika India Private Ltd (1)
Plot No D 101/2, MIDC Industrial Area Shiravane Nerul, Navi Mumbai, 400706, Maharashtra, India
Tel.: (91) 226 270 4038
Web Site: https://ind.sika.com
Sales Range: $50-74.9 Million
Emp.: 60
Concrete Additives Mfr & Distr
N.A.I.C.S.: 325998
M. Mukhopadhyay *(Head-Concrete)*

Subsidiary (Domestic):

Axson India Pvt. Ltd. (2)
Office n 8 Building Symphony C - 2rd Floor Nos 5-6 Sr 201 A, Range Hills Road Bhosale Nagar, 411 020, Pune, India (100%)
Tel.: (91) 2025560710
Web Site: http://www.axson-technologies.com
Resin Material Whslr
N.A.I.C.S.: 424610

Sika Informationssysteme AG (1)
In der Luberzen 1, 8902, Urdorf, 8902, Aargau, Switzerland
Tel.: (41) 566485050
Web Site: http://www.sika.com
Sales Range: $75-99.9 Million
Emp.: 120
Construction Adhesives Mfr & Distr
N.A.I.C.S.: 325520

Sika Ireland Ltd (1)
Sika House, Ballymun Industrial Estate, Dublin, D11DA2V, Ireland
Tel.: (353) 1 862 0709
Web Site: https://irl.sika.com
Sales Range: $25-49.9 Million
Emp.: 30
Building Chemicals Mfr & Distr
N.A.I.C.S.: 325520
Declan Carroll *(Mng Dir)*

Sika Italia S.p.A. (1)
Via Luigi Einaudi 6, Peschiera Borromeo, 20068, Milan, Italy
Tel.: (39) 025 477 8111
Web Site: https://ita.sika.com
Chemicals Mfr & Distr
N.A.I.C.S.: 325998
Fritz Burkard *(Gen Mgr)*

Subsidiary (Domestic):

Axson Italia S.r.l. (2)
Via Morandi 13 15, 21047, Saronno, Italy (100%)
Tel.: (39) 0296702336
Web Site: http://www.axson-technologies.com
Distribution Center for Manufactured Chemicals
N.A.I.C.S.: 325998

Sika Kazakhstan LLP (1)
Tabachnozavodskaya No 20, Almaty, 050050, Kazakhstan
Tel.: (7) 7272980547
Sales Range: $25-49.9 Million
Emp.: 13
Chemical Distr
N.A.I.C.S.: 424690

Sika Kenya Limited (1)

AND PRIVATE COMPANIES

SIKA AG

Office Complex Mombasa Road, PO Box 38645, SEMCO Industrial Park, 00623, Nairobi, Kenya
Tel.: (254) 71 114 0234
Web Site: https://ken.sika.com
Construction Chemical Product Distr
N.A.I.C.S.: 423390

Sika Kimia Sdn. Bhd. (1)
Lot 689 Nilai Industrial Estate, 71800, Nilai, Negeri Sembilan, Malaysia
Tel.: (60) 6 799 1762
Web Site: https://mys.sika.com
Sales Range: $50-74.9 Million
Emp.: 150
Construction Materials Distr
N.A.I.C.S.: 423320

Sika Korea Ltd (1)
Marchim-daero Miyang-myeon, Anseong, Gyeonggi, Korea (South)
Tel.: (82) 26 912 1500
Web Site: https://kor.sika.com
Chemical Distr
N.A.I.C.S.: 424690

Sika LLC (1)
Boyuk Sor Qesebesi Dernegul Sosesi No 6023, 1029, Baku, Azerbaijan
Tel.: (994) 125119072
Sales Range: $25-49.9 Million
Emp.: 24
Construction Materials Mfr & Distr
N.A.I.C.S.: 325520
Adem Yayla *(Gen Mgr)*

Sika Lanka (Private) Limited (1)
58/12B Raja Mawatha, Ekala, Ja-Ela, 11350, Sri Lanka
Tel.: (94) 11 223 9977
Web Site: https://lka.sika.com
Emp.: 22
Ready-Mix Concrete Mfr & Distr
N.A.I.C.S.: 327320

Sika Limited (1)
Watchmead, Welwyn Garden City, AL7 1BQ, Hertfordshire, United Kingdom - England
Tel.: (44) 1707394444
Web Site: https://gbr.sika.com
Sales Range: $50-74.9 Million
Emp.: 100
Construction Materials Mfr & Distr
N.A.I.C.S.: 325520

Subsidiary (Non-US):

Axson UK Ltd. (2)
15 Studlands Park Ind Estate Newmarket, Suffolk, Newmarket, CB8 7AU, United Kingdom (100%)
Tel.: (44) 1638660062
Web Site: http://www.axson-technologies.com
Resin Material Whslr
N.A.I.C.S.: 424610
Colin Evans *(Mng Dir)*

Incorez Ltd. (2)
Miller Street, Preston, PR1 1EA, Lancashire, United Kingdom
Tel.: (44) 177 220 1964
Web Site: https://www.incorez.com
Sales Range: $25-49.9 Million
Emp.: 50
Chemicals Mfr
N.A.I.C.S.: 325211

Sarnafil Ltd. (2)
Robberds Way Bowthorpe Industrial Estate, Norwich, NR5 9JF, United Kingdom
Tel.: (44) 1603748985
Web Site: http://gbr.sarnafil.sika.com
Sales Range: $25-49.9 Million
Emp.: 60
Roofing Contractors
N.A.I.C.S.: 238160

Division (Non-US):

Sika Limited - Sika Liquid Plastics (2)
Sika House Miller Street, Preston, PR1 1EA, Lancashire, United Kingdom
Tel.: (44) 177 225 9781
Web Site: https://gbr.liquidplastics.sika.com
Emp.: 200
Mfr of Quality, Seamless, Cold Applied, Liquid Systems & Coatings for Waterproofing Flat Roofs, Associated Walls, Balconies & Walkways
N.A.I.C.S.: 326199

Sika Ltd. (1)
1-2-7 Motoakasaka Akasaka K Tower 7th floor, Minato-ku, Tokyo, 108-6110, Japan
Tel.: (81) 36 433 2101
Web Site: https://jpn.sika.com
Emp.: 206
Chemicals Mfr & Distr
N.A.I.C.S.: 325998
Julio Moura *(VP)*

Subsidiary (Domestic):

Axson Japan K.K. (2)
2-5-12 Onishi, Okazaki, 444-0871, Japan (100%)
Tel.: (81) 564262591
Web Site: http://www.axson.jp
Resin Material Whslr
N.A.I.C.S.: 424610

DCS Co., Ltd. (2)
Tosho Building B 3F 3-6-4 Nishi-Shinjuku, Shinjuku-ku, Tokyo, 160-0023, Japan
Tel.: (81) 353810330
Web Site: http://www.dyflex.co.jp
Waterproofing Materials Mfr & Sales
N.A.I.C.S.: 339999

Dyflex Co. Ltd (2)
Akasaka K Tower 7F 1-2-7 Motoakasaka, Minato-ku, Tokyo, 107-0051, Japan
Tel.: (81) 36 434 5085
Web Site: https://www.dyflex.co.jp
Emp.: 100
Polyurethane Membrane Mfr
N.A.I.C.S.: 325211

Hankyu Hanshin Building Management Co., Ltd. (2)
1-12-39 Umeda Shinhankyu Bldg, Kita-Ku, Osaka, 530-0001, Japan
Tel.: (81) 663439003
Web Site: http://www.d-money.net
Property Management Services
N.A.I.C.S.: 531311

Sika Manufacturing Nigeria Limited (1)
Isheri Riverview Estate Lagos-Ibadan Expressway, 10 Western Industrial Avenue, 102109, Lagos, Ogun, Nigeria
Tel.: (234) 809 044 2223
Web Site: https://nga.sika.com
Construction Chemical Product Mfr & Distr
N.A.I.C.S.: 325998

Sika Manufacturing for Construction S.A.E. (1)
222 El-Hegaz St Heliopolis 2943 El Horria, 11361, Cairo, Egypt
Tel.: (20) 22 180 6734
Construction Chemical Product Mfr & Distr
N.A.I.C.S.: 325998

Sika Maroc SA (1)
ZI Ouled Saleh Bouskoura, BP 191, Casablanca, 20180, Morocco
Tel.: (212) 2 233 4154
Web Site: http://www.marsika.com
Sales Range: $50-74.9 Million
Emp.: 78
Chemicals Mfr & Distr
N.A.I.C.S.: 325520
Claude Juallard *(Mgr)*

Sika Mauritius Ltd (1)
Zone Industrielle Plaine Lauzun, Port Louis, Mauritius
Tel.: (230) 212 8621
Web Site: https://mus.sika.com
Emp.: 46
Chemicals Mfr & Distr
N.A.I.C.S.: 325998

Sika Mexicana SA de CV (1)
Carretera Libre a Celaya Km 8 5, Fraccionamiento Lomas de Balvanera Corregidora, 76920, Queretaro, Mexico
Tel.: (52) 555 395 4333
Web Site: https://www.mex.sika.com
Sales Range: $50-74.9 Million
Emp.: 100
Chemical Products Mfr & Distr
N.A.I.C.S.: 325180
Rols Manser *(Gen Mgr)*

Subsidiary (Domestic):

Axson Mexico, S.A. de C.V. (2)
San Luis Potosi #211 Piso 7 Col Roma, 06700, Mexico, Mexico
Tel.: (52) 5552644922
Web Site: http://www.axson.com.mx
Resin Material Whslr
N.A.I.C.S.: 424610

Sika Mocambique Limitada (1)
Boane-Matola Rio-Parcela 3441, Maputo, Mozambique
Tel.: (258) 2 173 0367
Web Site: https://moz.sika.com
Sealing & Gluing Mfr
N.A.I.C.S.: 325520

Sika Mongolia LLC (1)
504 5th Floor Central Tower 8th Khoroo Sukhbaatar D Square-2, Sukhbaatar District, 14200, Ulaanbaatar, Mongolia
Tel.:
Web Site: https://mng.sika.com
Ready-Mix Concrete Mfr & Distr
N.A.I.C.S.: 327320
Baigalmaa Naidan *(Mgr)*

Sika Myanmar Limited (1)
No 12/B Parami Avenue Hninsi Street, Yankin Township, Yangon, Myanmar
Tel.: (95) 165 7970
Web Site: https://mmr.sika.com
Ready-Mix Concrete Mfr & Distr
N.A.I.C.S.: 327320

Sika Near East SAL (1)
Sector 5 Road 70, PO Box 55163, Sin El-Fil Jisr el-Bacha, Beirut, Lebanon
Tel.: (961) 151 0270
Web Site: https://lbn.sika.com
Sales Range: $25-49.9 Million
Emp.: 20
Construction Materials Mfr & Distr
N.A.I.C.S.: 325520
Elie Eid *(Gen Mgr)*

Sika Nederland BV (1)
Zonnebaan 56, PO Box 40390, 3542 EG, Utrecht, Netherlands
Tel.: (31) 30 241 0120
Web Site: https://nld.sika.com
Sales Range: $25-49.9 Million
Emp.: 145
Chemical Distr
N.A.I.C.S.: 424690
Piet Nieuwpoort *(Gen Mgr)*

Sika Nicaragua Sociedad Anonima (1)
Ofiplaza El Retiro Building 5 Second Floor Suite 524 B, Managua, Nicaragua
Tel.: (505) 2 254 7607
Web Site: https://nic.sika.com
Ready-Mix Concrete Mfr & Distr
N.A.I.C.S.: 327320

Sika Norge AS (1)
Tel.: (47) 6 706 7900
Web Site: https://nor.sika.com
Chemicals Mfr & Distr
N.A.I.C.S.: 325520

Sika Osterreich GmbH (1)
Bingser Dorfstrasse 23, 6700, Bludenz, Austria
Tel.: (43) 506100
Web Site: https://www.aut.sika.com
Construction Chemical Product Mfr & Distr
N.A.I.C.S.: 325998

Sika Pakistan Ltd (1)
First Floor 141 CCA Phase IV DHA, Lahore, Punjab, Pakistan
Tel.: (92) 35694266
Sales Range: $25-49.9 Million
Emp.: 15
Chemicals Mfr & Distr
N.A.I.C.S.: 325520

Sika Panama SA (1)
Calle 4ta Parque Industrial Costa del Este, 0899-11691, Panama, Panama
Tel.: (507) 2714727
Sales Range: $25-49.9 Million
Emp.: 15
Industrial Chemicals Mfr
N.A.I.C.S.: 325998

Sika Paraguay S.A. (1)
Avda Artigas 3533 Almost Sgto Martinez, Asuncion, Paraguay
Web Site: https://pry.sika.com
Ready-Mix Concrete Mfr & Distr
N.A.I.C.S.: 327320

Sika Peru SA (1)
Habilitacion Industrial El Lucumo Mz B Lote 6, Lurin, Lima, 16, Peru
Tel.: (51) 1 618 6060
Web Site: https://per.sika.com
Emp.: 200
Chemicals Mfr & Distr
N.A.I.C.S.: 325180
Otto Schroeder *(Gen Mgr)*

Sika Philippines Inc. (1)
888 Marcos Alvarez Ave, Talon V, Las Pinas, 1747, Philippines
Tel.: (63) 28 806 2875
Web Site: https://phl.sika.com
Ready-Mix Concrete Mfr & Distr
N.A.I.C.S.: 327320

Sika Poland Sp.z.o.o., (1)
ul Karczunkowska 89, 02-871, Warsaw, Masovian, Poland
Tel.: (48) 22 272 8700
Web Site: https://pl.sika.com
Sales Range: $50-74.9 Million
Emp.: 100
Building Chemicals Mfr & Distr
N.A.I.C.S.: 325998

Subsidiary (Domestic):

Euro - Agro Warszawa Sp. z o.o. (2)
ul Bellottiego 1, 01-022, Warsaw, Masovian, Poland
Tel.: (48) 228683798
Alcoholic Beverage Distr
N.A.I.C.S.: 424820

Sika Portugal - Productos Construcao Industria SA (1)
Rua de Santarem 113, 4400-292, Vila Nova de Gaia, Portugal
Tel.: (351) 22 377 6900
Web Site: https://prt.sika.com
Construction Chemical Product Mfr
N.A.I.C.S.: 325998

Sika Portugal - Productos Construcao e Industria SA (1)
Rua de Santarem 113, 4400-292, Vila Nova de Gaia, Portugal
Tel.: (351) 22 377 6900
Web Site: http://www.prt.sika.com
Emp.: 120
Construction Chemicals Mfr & Distr
N.A.I.C.S.: 325520
David Santos *(Mgr-Indus)*

Sika Productos Para La Construccion S.A. (1)
150mts West From the sports plaza Multi Comercial Baden Office 27, Heredia, Barreal, Costa Rica
Tel.: (506) 2 293 3870
Web Site: https://cri.sika.com
Ready-Mix Concrete Mfr & Distr
N.A.I.C.S.: 327320

Sika Qatar LLC (1)
Bldg 144 Street 2, PO Box 201847, New Industrial Area, Doha, Qatar
Tel.: (974) 4 016 3366
Construction Chemical Product Mfr & Distr
N.A.I.C.S.: 325998

Sika Romania S.R.L. (1)
Str Ioan Clopotel Nr 4, Judetul Brasov, 500 450, Brasov, Romania
Tel.: (40) 268406212
Web Site: https://rou.sika.com
Chmicals Mfr & Distr
N.A.I.C.S.: 325520

Sika SA Chile (1)
Avda Pdte Salvador Allende 85, 8941077, San Joaquin, Santiago, Chile
Tel.: (56) 22 510 6500
Web Site: https://chl.sika.com
Sales Range: $75-99.9 Million
Emp.: 180
Chemical Products Mfr & Distr
N.A.I.C.S.: 325998
Rodrigo Vernal *(Head-Civil Works)*

Sika Saudi Arabia Co., Ltd. (1)
PO Box 112356, 11583, Riyadh, Saudi Arabia
Tel.: (966) 12 692 7079
Web Site: https://gcc.sika.com
Construction Chemical Product Mfr & Distr
N.A.I.C.S.: 325998

SIKA AG

Sika AG—(Continued)

Sika Schweiz AG (1)
Tuffenwies 16, 8048, Zurich, Switzerland
Tel.: (41) 58 436 4040
Web Site: https://che.sika.com
Sales Range: $250-299.9 Million
Emp.: 800
Chemicals Mfr & Distr
N.A.I.C.S.: 325520
Roland Bischoff (Gen Mgr)

Subsidiary (Domestic):

Sika Manufacturing AG (2)
Industriestrasse 26, 6060, Sarnen, Switzerland
Tel.: (41) 584367966
Web Site: http://www.sika.com
Sales Range: $125-149.9 Million
Emp.: 350
Chemicals Mfr
N.A.I.C.S.: 325520

Sika Senegal S.U.A.R.L (1)
Route Sebi Ponty Bargny, Diamniadio, Dakar, Senegal
Tel.: (221) 76 600 9149
Web Site: https://sen.sika.com
Tile Adhesives Mfr
N.A.I.C.S.: 325520

Sika Singapore Pte. Ltd. (1)
28 Tuas South Ave 8, Singapore, 637648, Singapore
Tel.: (65) 6 861 0632
Web Site: https://sgp.sika.com
Sales Range: $25-49.9 Million
Emp.: 20
Chemical Distr
N.A.I.C.S.: 424690

Sika Slovenija d.o.o. (1)
Prevale 13, Trzin, 1236, Slovenia
Tel.: (386) 1580 95 34
Web Site: http://www.sika.si
Sales Range: $25-49.9 Million
Emp.: 21
Construction Materials Mfr & Distr
N.A.I.C.S.: 325520
Tomo Znidarsic (Mgr-Roofing)

Sika Slovensko spol. s.r.o. (1)
Rybnicna 38 E, 831 06, Bratislava, Slovakia
Tel.: (421) 249200411
Web Site: https://svk.sika.com
Sales Range: $25-49.9 Million
Emp.: 35
Construction Materials Mfr & Distr
N.A.I.C.S.: 325520
Marek Mikus (Mgr)

Subsidiary (Domestic):

Axson Central Europe s.r.o (2)
Tovarenska 49, Zlate Moravce, 953 01, Slovakia
Tel.: (421) 257272933
Resin Material Whslr
N.A.I.C.S.: 424610
Lubica Vanikova (Mgr-Sls)

Sika South Africa (Pty) Ltd (1)
9 Hocking Place, Westmead, Pinetown, 3608, KwaZulu-Natal, South Africa
Tel.: (27) 31 792 6500
Web Site: https://zaf.sika.com
Sales Range: $75-99.9 Million
Emp.: 132
Chemical Distr
N.A.I.C.S.: 424690
Mervyn Naidoo (Mgr-KwaZulu Natal Reg)

Sika Srbija d.o.o. (1)
Patriarch Paul no 1, 22310, Simanovci, Serbia
Tel.: (381) 22 215 5777
Web Site: https://srb.sika.com
Construction Chemical Product Mfr & Distr
N.A.I.C.S.: 325998

Sika Supply Center AG (1)
Industriestrasse 26, 6060, Sarnen, Obwalden, Switzerland
Tel.: (41) 416669966
Web Site: http://www.sikabau.ch
Sales Range: $50-74.9 Million
Emp.: 90
Chemicals Mfr & Distr
N.A.I.C.S.: 325520

Sika Sverige AB (1)
Domnarvsgatan 15, Box 8016, 16308, Spanga, Friesland, Sweden
Tel.: (46) 86218900
Web Site: https://swe.sika.com
Sales Range: $50-74.9 Million
Emp.: 100
Chemicals Mfr & Distr
N.A.I.C.S.: 325520
Kenneth Baggstrom (Mgr)

Sika Taiwan Ltd (1)
No 1380 Section 3 Fuguo Road, Luzhu District, Taoyuan, Taoyuan, Taiwan
Tel.: (886) 3 352 8622
Web Site: https://twn.sika.com
Sales Range: $25-49.9 Million
Emp.: 40
Construction Materials Mfr & Distr
N.A.I.C.S.: 327120
Steve Changb (Gen Mgr)

Sika Tanzania Construction Chemicals Limited (1)
Plot No 135 Salasala, PO Box 7079, Mbezi Industrial Area, Dar es Salaam, Tanzania
Tel.: (255) 73 494 4957
Web Site: https://www.tza.sika.com
Ready-Mix Concrete Mfr & Distr
N.A.I.C.S.: 327320

Sika Technology AG (1)
Zugerstrasse 50, 6341, Baar, Zug, Switzerland
Tel.: (41) 584366800
Chemicals Mfr & Distr
N.A.I.C.S.: 325520
Ernst Bartschi (CEO)

Sika Tunisienne Sarl (1)
Zone Industrielle, 2086, Douar Hicher, Manouba, Tunisia
Tel.: (216) 7 002 2700
Web Site: https://tun.sika.com
Emp.: 70
Construction Materials Mfr & Distr
N.A.I.C.S.: 327120

Sika Turkey Otomotiv Sanayi ve Tic. Ltd. Sti. (1)
Yenisehir Mh Reyhan Cd Enginsu Slt VL1 D 37/12, Pendik, 34912, Istanbul, Turkiye
Tel.: (90) 216 560 0801
Polyurethane Foam Distr
N.A.I.C.S.: 424690

Sika UAE LLC (1)
Saih Shuaib 4 Plot No 61 DM No 533-279, PO Box 126212, Dubai Industrial City, Dubai, United Arab Emirates
Tel.: (971) 4 439 8200
Web Site: https://gcc.sika.com
Sales Range: $50-74.9 Million
Emp.: 75
Construction Materials Mfr & Distr
N.A.I.C.S.: 325520

Sika Uruguay SA (1)
Av Jose Belloni 5514, Manga, 12200, Montevideo, Uruguay
Tel.: (598) 2 220 2227
Web Site: https://ury.sika.com
Construction Materials Mfr & Distr
N.A.I.C.S.: 325520

Sika Venezuela SA (1)
Avenida Iribarren Borges Parcela 8-1 61-901, Zona Industrial Municipal Sur, 2003, Valencia, Carabobo, Venezuela
Tel.: (58) 241 300 1111
Web Site: https://ven.sika.com
Ready-Mix Concrete Mfr & Distr
N.A.I.C.S.: 327320

Sika Yapi Kimyasallari A.S. (1)
J 7 Parcel Aydinli 2 Yol Orhanli Role, Tuzla, Istanbul, 34957, Turkiye
Tel.: (90) 216 581 06 00
Web Site: http://www.sika.com.tr
Chemicals Mfr & Distr
N.A.I.C.S.: 325520
Borayil Brrim (Gen Mgr)

Sika d.o.o. (1)
Autoput za Novi Sad 244b, Zemun, Belgrade, Serbia
Tel.: (381) 113774011
Web Site: http://www.sika.rs
Sales Range: $25-49.9 Million
Emp.: 40
Construction Materials Mfr & Distr

N.A.I.C.S.: 325520

Sika, S.A.U. (1)
Ctra de Fuencarral 72, 28108, Alcobendas, Madrid, Spain
Tel.: (34) 91 657 2375
Web Site: https://esp.sika.com
Emp.: 230
Specialty Chemicals Mfr & Distr
N.A.I.C.S.: 325998
Gonzalo Causin (Dir Gen)

Subsidiary (Domestic):

Axson Technologies Spain S.L. (2)
Ramon Turro 100 1, 08005, Barcelona, Spain (100%)
Tel.: (34) 932251620
Web Site: http://www.axson-technologies.com
Chemical Products Sales
N.A.I.C.S.: 424690

SikaBau AG (1)
Reitmensstrasse 7, 8952, Schlieren, Zurich, Switzerland
Tel.: (41) 58 436 4465
Web Site: http://www.sikabau.ch
Building Chemicals Mfr & Distr
N.A.I.C.S.: 325998

Supermassa do Brasil Ltda. (1)
Das Caravelas no 01 Bairro do Tirirical, Sao Luis, Maranhao, Brazil
Tel.: (55) 32452879
Web Site: https://www.supermassa.com.br
Construction Material Mfr & Distr
N.A.I.C.S.: 327120

United Gilsonite Laboratories (1)
1396 Jefferson Ave, Dunmore, PA 18509-2415
Tel.: (570) 344-1202
Web Site: http://www.ugl.com
Cement Paints, Glazing & Caulking Compounds, Wall Patching Materials, Paint Sundries, Clear Finishes, Drylok Masonry Waterproofing Products; Temproof Stove & Fireplace Maintenance Products
N.A.I.C.S.: 325510
Joseph M. McGraw (Dir-Mktg & Adv)

SIKARIN PUBLIC COMPANY LIMITED

976 Lasalle Road, Bangna, Bangkok, 10260, Thailand
Tel.: (66) 23669900
Web Site: https://www.sikarin.com
Year Founded: 1979
SKR—(THA)
Rev.: $170,829,360
Assets: $269,922,165
Liabilities: $52,572,456
Net Worth: $217,349,709
Earnings: $26,184,206
Emp.: 2,928
Fiscal Year-end: 12/31/23
Acute Care Hospital Services
N.A.I.C.S.: 622110
Surasak Suttamas (Chief Admin Officer)

SIKKO INDUSTRIES LTD.

508 Iskon Elegance Nr Jain Temple Nr Prahaladnagar Pick-up Stand, S G Highway Vejalpur, Ahmedabad, 380051, Gujarat, India
Tel.: (91) 7966168950
Web Site: https://www.sikkoindia.in
Year Founded: 1997
SIKKO—(NSE)
Rev.: $5,985,864
Assets: $5,454,721
Liabilities: $2,599,952
Net Worth: $2,854,769
Earnings: $346,802
Emp.: 64
Fiscal Year-end: 03/31/23
Nursery Product Distr
N.A.I.C.S.: 325520
C. S. Ankita Lunagariya (Chief Compliance Officer & Sec)

INTERNATIONAL PUBLIC

SIKO CORPORATION

2-3-27 Ono, Hatsukaichi, 739 0434, Japan
Tel.: (81) 829 55 0520
Web Site: http://www.siko.co.jp
Year Founded: 1931
Emp.: 100
Paper & Packaging Mfr
N.A.I.C.S.: 322219
Tadanobu Shiraishi (Pres)

Subsidiaries:

Western Paperbag Co., Ltd. (1)
15F Osaka Ekimae Building No 3 1-1-3-1500 Umeda, Kita-ku, Osaka, 530-0001, Japan
Tel.: (81) 663458456
Emp.: 1
Kraft Paper Bags Mfr & Sales
N.A.I.C.S.: 322220
Tadanobu Shiraishi (Pres)

SIKOZY REALTORS LIMITED

B-3 Trishul Apartment Village Mudre Khurd Taluka-Karjat, Raigad Dist, Mumbai, 410201, Maharashtra, India
Tel.: (91) 2148221745
Web Site:
https://www.sikozyrealtors.in
524642—(BOM)
Rev.: $43,748
Assets: $539,449
Liabilities: $64,438
Net Worth: $475,011
Earnings: $1,009
Emp.: 2
Fiscal Year-end: 03/31/21
Real Estate Development Services
N.A.I.C.S.: 531390
Pawan Kalantre (Compliance Officer)

SIL GROUP LLC

62 3rd Lane Tigran Mets Avenue, Yerevan, 375018, Armenia
Tel.: (374) 10529918
Web Site: http://www.sil.am
Sales Range: $1-4.9 Billion
Emp.: 6,500
Holding Company; Production, Trade, Construction, Services, Maintenance & Banking
N.A.I.C.S.: 551112

Subsidiaries:

Sil Insurance - Insurance Closed Joint Stock Company (1)
39 & 39-1/1 Tigran Mets Avenue, 0018, Yerevan, Armenia
Tel.: (374) 1052 63 88
Web Site: http://www.silinsurance.am
Sales Range: $100-124.9 Million
Emp.: 180
General Insurance Services
N.A.I.C.S.: 524210

SIL INVESTMENTS LTD

Pachpahar Road, Bhawani Mandi, 326502, Rajasthan, India
Tel.: (91) 7433222090
Web Site:
https://www.silinvestments.in
Year Founded: 1934
521194—(BOM)
Rev.: $5,954,331
Assets: $226,473,928
Liabilities: $22,827,420
Net Worth: $203,646,508
Earnings: $3,430,106
Emp.: 6
Fiscal Year-end: 03/31/23
Textile Mfr
N.A.I.C.S.: 313240
Shalini Nopany (Mng Dir)

SILA A.D.

Pacirski put 67, Stara Moravica, 24340, Backa Topola, Serbia
Tel.: (381) 24 741 030

AND PRIVATE COMPANIES

Web Site: http://www.sila.rs
Year Founded: 1960
Chains & Metal & Plastic Household Wares & Equipment Mfr
N.A.I.C.S.: 332999
Bela Mehes Jr. *(Dir Gen)*

SILBITZ GROUP GMBH
Dr-Maruschky-Str 2, 07613, Silbitz, Germany
Tel.: (49) 36693129689 De
Web Site: http://www.silbitz-group.com
Year Founded: 1938
Sales Range: $150-199.9 Million
Emp.: 860
Iron & Steel Foundry Mfr
N.A.I.C.S.: 331511
Torsten Tiefel *(Mng Dir)*

Subsidiaries:

Silbitz Guss GmbH (1)
Dr-Maruschky-Strasse 2, 07613, Silbitz, Germany
Tel.: (49) 3669 380 0
Web Site: http://www.silbitz-group.com
Sales Range: $125-149.9 Million
Emp.: 450
Iron & Steel Foundries Operator & Products Mfr
N.A.I.C.S.: 331513
Torsten Tiefel *(Member-Mgmt Bd)*

SILC SA
1 Bd Liedot, 16000, Angouleme, France
Tel.: (33) 545974160
Web Site: https://www.silc.fr
Year Founded: 1965
MLSIL—(EUR)
Tour Operator
N.A.I.C.S.: 561520
Jean Luc Maury *(CEO)*

SILENCE THERAPEUTICS PLC
72 Hammersmith Road, London, W14 8TH, United Kingdom
Tel.: (44) 2034576900 UK
Web Site: https://www.silence-therapeutics.com
Year Founded: 1994
SLN—(NASDAQ)
Rev.: $25,375,000
Assets: $93,822,000
Liabilities: $76,772,000
Net Worth: $17,050,000
Earnings: ($43,267,000)
Emp.: 109
Fiscal Year-end: 12/31/23
Holding Company; Systemic RNAi Biotherapeutics Research & Development
N.A.I.C.S.: 551112
Iain G. Ross *(Chm)*

SILENSEED LTD.
The Goldyne Savad Institute of Gene Therapy, Hadassah Hebrew University Medical Center, 9112001, Jerusalem, Israel
Tel.: (972) 2 6743430 II
Web Site: http://www.silenseed.com
Year Founded: 2008
Emp.: 6
Biopharmaceutical Mfr
N.A.I.C.S.: 325412
Amotz Shemi *(CEO)*

SILERGY CORP.
10F No 653 Bannan Rd Zhonghe Dist, Zhonge District, New Taipei City, 23557, Taiwan
Tel.: (886) 222215266
Web Site: https://www.silergy.com
6415—(TAI)
Rev.: $504,507,486
Assets: $1,125,674,832
Liabilities: $94,231,103
Net Worth: $1,031,443,730
Earnings: $20,832,924
Emp.: 1,690
Fiscal Year-end: 12/31/23
Analog Integrated Circuits Mfr
N.A.I.C.S.: 334412
Issac Wei Chen *(Chm)*

Subsidiaries:

NXP B.V., (1)
High Tech Campus 60, Eindhoven, 5656 AG, Netherlands
Tel.: (31) 402 729 999
Electronic Components Mfr
N.A.I.C.S.: 334515

Shanghai Silergy Microelectronics Technology Co., Ltd. (1)
Room A208 Shuzi Industries Park No 1018 Dongsanliqiao Road, Pudongxin District, Shanghai, China
Tel.: (86) 2161649398
Electronic Components Distr
N.A.I.C.S.: 423690

Silergy Semiconductor (Samoa) Limited (1)
Portcullis TrustNet Chambers, PO Box 1225, Apia, Samoa (Western)
Tel.: (685) 571 8775 9971
Electronic Components Mfr
N.A.I.C.S.: 334515

Silergy Semiconductor Technology (Hangzhou) Co. Ltd. (1)
Technology Mansion Eastern Software Park No 90 Wensan Road, Hangzhou, Zhejiang, China
Tel.: (86) 571 8775 9971
Electronic Components Mfr
N.A.I.C.S.: 334515

SILESIA GERHARD HANKE GMBH & CO.KG
Am Alten Bach 20-24, Neuss, 41470, Germany
Tel.: (49) 21377840
Web Site: http://www.silesia.com
Rev.: $164,145,841
Emp.: 500
Flavor Mfr
N.A.I.C.S.: 311930
Clemens Hanke *(Pres & CEO)*

Subsidiaries:

Silesia B.V. (1)
Gidemark 125, 1351 HL, Almere, Netherlands
Tel.: (31) 365468310
Web Site: http://www.silesiabv.nl
Flavoring Agent Distr
N.A.I.C.S.: 424490
Marcel Zijdenbos *(Mgr-Comml)*

Silesia Ceska republika spol s.r.o. (1)
Vyskocilova 3/741, 14 000, Prague, Czech Republic
Tel.: (420) 241485757
Flavoring Agent Distr
N.A.I.C.S.: 424490

Silesia Colombia Ltda. (1)
Autopista Medellin Km 7 costado Occidental Cell Trade Park, Via D No 41-04 Funza, Cundinamarca, Colombia
Tel.: (57) 17427833
Flavoring Agent Distr
N.A.I.C.S.: 424490

Silesia Flavours (Shanghai) Co. Ltd. (1)
Xin Zhuang Industrial Park Building D & F 1588 Zhuan Xing Road, Min Hang District, Shanghai, 201108, China
Tel.: (86) 2164421266
Flavoring Agent Mfr
N.A.I.C.S.: 311930
Pierre Jenniskens *(Dir-Technical)*

Silesia Flavours (Thailand) LTD (1)
32/41 Sino-Thai Tower 16th Sukhumvit 21 Road, Soi Asoke Wattana, Bangkok, 10110, Thailand
Tel.: (66) 26617350

Flavoring Agent Distr
N.A.I.C.S.: 424490

Silesia Flavours Austria GmbH (1)
Dr Hans Lechner Strasse 6, 5071, Wals, Austria
Tel.: (43) 6628564620
Flavoring Agent Distr
N.A.I.C.S.: 424490

Silesia Flavours Espaa S.L. (1)
Calle Virgen del Pilar 2-2 1a, Molins de Rei, 08750, Barcelona, Spain
Tel.: (34) 936803105
Flavoring Agent Distr
N.A.I.C.S.: 424490
Javier Soler *(Mgr-Sls)*

Silesia Flavours Gda Ticaret ve Servis Limited irketi (1)
Bolges 14 Cadde Gomen Konutlari, Yani M6 35 Baakehr, 34306, Istanbul, Turkiye
Tel.: (90) 2124855657
Flavoring Agent Distr
N.A.I.C.S.: 424490
Elif Aydemir *(Gen Mgr)*

Silesia Flavours Hungary Kft. (1)
Fti t 56, 1047, Budapest, Hungary
Tel.: (36) 12321445
Flavoring Agent Distr
N.A.I.C.S.: 424490

Silesia Flavours Inc. (1)
5250 Prairie Stone Pkwy, Hoffman Estates, IL 60192
Tel.: (847) 645-0270
Flavoring Agent Mfr & Distr
N.A.I.C.S.: 311930
Sydney Hunter *(Mgr-Customer Support Grp)*

Silesia Flavours Ltd. (1)
The Flavor House Stone Enterprise Centre Emerald Way, Stone Business Park, Stone, ST 15 OSR, Staffordshire, United Kingdom
Tel.: (44) 1785819222
Flavoring Agent Distr
N.A.I.C.S.: 424490

Silesia Flavours Polska Sp.z o.o. (1)
Ul Pilchowicka 27, 02-175, Warsaw, Poland
Tel.: (48) 228323568
Flavoring Agent Distr
N.A.I.C.S.: 424490
Jacek Koizol *(Dir-Comml)*

Silesia Flavours Scandinavia Aps (1)
Lyskaer 15 1, 2730, Herlev, Denmark
Tel.: (45) 44520444
Web Site: http://www.silesia.dk
Flavoring Agent Distr
N.A.I.C.S.: 424490
Maria Spang *(Mgr-Confectionery & Beverages Sls)*

Silesia Flavours South East Asia Pte. Ltd. (1)
41 Science Park Road 01 12 14 The Gemini Science Park II, Singapore, 117610, Singapore
Tel.: (65) 677326777
Flavoring Agent Mfr & Distr
N.A.I.C.S.: 311930
Jorgen Hejl *(Mng Dir)*

Silesia Flavours Switzerland GmbH (1)
Kasernenstrasse 10, 8180, Bulach, Switzerland
Tel.: (41) 434114131
Flavoring Agent Distr
N.A.I.C.S.: 424490
Rolf Schneider *(Mng Dir)*

Silesia Flavours Ukraine LLC (1)
Vul Zroshuvalna 7 Office 403, 2099, Kiev, Ukraine
Tel.: (380) 442840451
Flavoring Agent Distr
N.A.I.C.S.: 424490
Mikhail Igdalov *(Gen Mgr)*

Silesia France S.A. (1)
28 Avenue de Toutevoie, 60270, Gouvieux, France
Tel.: (33) 344580991
Flavoring Agent Distr
N.A.I.C.S.: 424490

Silesia Italia S.r.l. (1)

P le Damino Chiesa 11, 20149, Milan, Italy
Tel.: (39) 0236709400
Flavoring Agent Distr
N.A.I.C.S.: 424490
Arianna Scotti *(Dir-Comml)*

Silesia de Mexico S. DE R. L. de C.V. (1)
Hidalgo No 6, Colonia Felpie Angeles, 454681, El Salto, Jalsico, Mexico
Tel.: (52) 3336889300
Flavoring Agent Distr
N.A.I.C.S.: 424490

SILEX SYSTEMS LTD.
Lucas Heights Science and Technology Centre New Illawarra Road, Lucas Heights, 2234, NSW, Australia
Tel.: (61) 297048888
Web Site: https://www.silex.com.au
SILXF—(OTCIQ)
Rev.: $2,630,796
Assets: $18,420,607
Liabilities: $1,509,927
Net Worth: $16,910,680
Earnings: ($5,307,603)
Fiscal Year-end: 06/30/21
Research & Development in the Physical, Engineering & Life Sciences (except Nanotechnology & Biotechnology)
N.A.I.C.S.: 541715
Michael P. Goldsworthy *(Founder, CEO & Mng Dir)*

Subsidiaries:

Translucent Inc. (1)
952 Commercial St, Palo Alto, CA 94303
Tel.: (650) 213-9311
Web Site: http://www.translucentinc.com
Developer of Silicon-Based Electronic & Photonic Products
N.A.I.C.S.: 334413
Andrew Clark *(VP-Engrg)*

SILGO RETAIL LIMITED
B 11 Mahalaxmi Nagar Jln Marg, Jaipur, 302017, India
Tel.: (91) 7055570555
Web Site: https://www.silgo.in
Year Founded: 2016
SILGO—(NSE)
Rev.: $4,353,706
Assets: $6,164,324
Liabilities: $2,607,771
Net Worth: $3,556,553
Earnings: $300,084
Emp.: 45
Fiscal Year-end: 03/12/21
Jewellery Distr
N.A.I.C.S.: 423940
Nitin Jain *(Chm & Mng Dir)*

SILHOUETTE INTERNATIONAL SCHMIED AG
Ellbognerstrasse 24, Postfach 538, 4020, Linz, Austria
Tel.: (43) 73238480
Web Site: http://www.silhouette-international.com
Year Founded: 1964
Sales Range: $250-299.9 Million
Emp.: 1,600
Designer & Eyewear Mfr
N.A.I.C.S.: 339115
Torres Gunter *(Mgr-Mktg)*

Subsidiaries:

Silhouette Benelux (1)
Desguinlei 6, 2018, Antwerp, Belgium (100%)
Tel.: (32) 482450
Web Site: http://www.silhouette-international.com
Sales Range: $10-24.9 Million
Emp.: 19
Eyewear
N.A.I.C.S.: 339113

Silhouette France S.a.r.l. (1)

SILHOUETTE INTERNATIONAL SCHMIED AG

Silhouette International Schmied AG—(Continued)
16 Rue Jules Sulnier, 93200, Saint Denis, France
Tel.: (33) 142433048
Web Site: http://www.silhouette.com
Sales Range: $25-49.9 Million
Emp.: 10
Eyewear
N.A.I.C.S.: 339113

Silhouette Italia S.r.l. (1)
Via Del Lavoro 8, 22100, Como, Italy
Tel.: (39) 0318110900
Web Site: http://www.silhouette.com
Sales Range: $25-49.9 Million
Emp.: 30
Optical Eyewear Whslr
N.A.I.C.S.: 456130
Villotti Michele (Mgr)

Silhouette Norge AS (1)
Grenseveien 99, 0663, Oslo, Norway (100%)
Tel.: (47) 23379000
Web Site: http://www.silhouette.com
Sales Range: $25-49.9 Million
Emp.: 9
Eyewear
N.A.I.C.S.: 339113

Silhouette Optical Co. Ltd. (1)
988-18 Daechi-Dong, Kangnam-Ku, Seoul, 822-568, Korea (South)
Tel.: (82) 25681001
Sales Range: $25-49.9 Million
Emp.: 9
Eyewear
N.A.I.C.S.: 339113

Silhouette Optical Espana S.A. (1)
Ch Ausias Marc 74 Entlo, Barcelona, 8013, Spain
Tel.: (34) 932440980
Web Site: http://www.silhouette-international.com
Sales Range: $25-49.9 Million
Emp.: 14
Eyewear
N.A.I.C.S.: 339113
Ignacio Carretero (Mgr-Silhouette Spain & Gen Mgr)

Silhouette Optical Ltd. (1)
260 Cannon St, Green Island, NY 12183
Tel.: (518) 272-5500
Sales Range: $25-49.9 Million
Emp.: 100
Eyewear
N.A.I.C.S.: 339113
Jane Corry (Pres)

Silhouette Scandinavia A/S (1)
Zalocheschke Alley No 12, 4600, Koge, Denmark (100%)
Tel.: (45) 43206500
Web Site: http://www.silhouette.com
Sales Range: $25-49.9 Million
Emp.: 7
Eyewear
N.A.I.C.S.: 339113

Silhouette Schweiz GmbH (1)
Industriestrasse 47, 6300, Zug, Switzerland
Tel.: (41) 7672222
Sales Range: $25-49.9 Million
Emp.: 9
Eyewear
N.A.I.C.S.: 339113

Silhouette Sverige AB (1)
Karl XI vag 61, 302 32, Halmstad, Sweden
Tel.: (46) 35144891
Sales Range: $25-49.9 Million
Emp.: 13
Eyewear
N.A.I.C.S.: 339113

Silhouette UK Ltd. (1)
2 Bath Road, Chiswick, London, W4 1LW, United Kingdom (100%)
Tel.: (44) 2089878899
Web Site: http://www.silhouette.com
Sales Range: $25-49.9 Million
Emp.: 30
Eyewear
N.A.I.C.S.: 339113

Silhouette Vertriebs GmbH (1)
Schwieberdinger Strasse 56, D-71636, Ludwigsburg, Germany

Tel.: (49) 7141442010
Web Site: http://www.silhouette.com
Sales Range: $25-49.9 Million
Emp.: 40
Eyewear
N.A.I.C.S.: 339113

SILICON CRAFT TECHNOLOGY PUBLIC COMPANY LIMITED
40 3rd Fl La Unique Plaza Thetsabanrangsannua Rd, Ladyao Chatuchak, Bangkok, 10900, Thailand
Tel.: (66) 25899991 TH
Web Site: https://www.sic.co.th
Year Founded: 2002
SICT—(THA)
Rev.: $19,452,858
Assets: $33,865,986
Liabilities: $14,749,137
Net Worth: $19,116,850
Earnings: $4,097,342
Emp.: 159
Fiscal Year-end: 12/31/23
Semiconductor Device Distr
N.A.I.C.S.: 423690
Manop Dhamsirianunt (CEO)

SILICON INTEGRATED SYSTEMS CORP.
No 180 Sec 2 Gongdao 5th Rd, Hsinchu, 30046, Taiwan
Tel.: (886) 35166000 TW
Web Site: https://www.sis.com
Year Founded: 1987
2363—(TAI)
Rev.: $6,121,325
Assets: $627,129,902
Liabilities: $4,774,159
Net Worth: $622,355,744
Earnings: $18,275,319
Emp.: 195
Fiscal Year-end: 12/31/23
Silicon Chips, Wafers & Semiconductors Mfr
N.A.I.C.S.: 334413

Subsidiaries:

HuiTong Intelligence Co., Ltd. (1)
8F No 51 Ln 258 Ruiguang Rd, Neihu Dist, Taipei, 114, Taiwan
Tel.: (886) 227991695
Web Site: https://www.htitec.com
Wireless Product Mfr
N.A.I.C.S.: 334513

Linkvast Technologies Inc. (1)
4F No 180 Sec2 Gongdaowu Road, Hsinchu, Taiwan (100%)
Tel.: (886) 289131168
Web Site: http://www.linkvast.com
Semiconductor Research & Design
N.A.I.C.S.: 334413

Silicon Integrated Systems Ltd. (1)
518040 Rm Benyuan Bldg No 6015 Shennan Rd, Futian Dist, Shenzhen, 518040, China (Hong Kong)
Tel.: (852) 75585879818
Web Site: http://www.sis.com
Computer Equipment Mfr
N.A.I.C.S.: 334118

SILICON MITUS
Uspace-1 Tower A 8th Floor 660 Daewangpangyo Road, Bundang District, Seongnam, 13494, Gyeonggi, Korea (South)
Tel.: (82) 70 7882 9200
Web Site:
   http://www.siliconmitus.com
Year Founded: 2007
Sales Range: $100-124.9 Million
Emp.: 100
Semiconductor Chip Mfr & Distr
N.A.I.C.S.: 334413
Youm Huh (Founder, Chm & CEO)

Subsidiaries:

Silicon Mitus Technology Inc. (1)
20370 Town Center Ln Ste 211, Cupertino, CA 95014 (100%)
Tel.: (408) 446-3151
Web Site: http://www.siliconmitus.com
Fabless Specialists in Development & Design of Power Management Integrated Chips Solutions
N.A.I.C.S.: 541512
Hanseung Lee (Head-Design Center)

SILICON MOTION TECHNOLOGY CORPORATION
Flat C 19/F Wing Cheong Commercial Building Nos 19-25 Jervois Street, Cheung Sha Wan, Kowloon, China (Hong Kong)
Tel.: (852) 23074768 Ky
Web Site:
   https://www.siliconmotion.com
SIMO—(NASDAQ)
Rev.: $945,921,000
Assets: $961,250,000
Liabilities: $228,649,000
Net Worth: $732,601,000
Earnings: $172,510,000
Emp.: 1,643
Fiscal Year-end: 12/31/22
Semiconductors & Related Products Mfr & Marketer
N.A.I.C.S.: 334413
James Chow (Chm)

Subsidiaries:

Silicon Motion, Inc. (1)
8F-1 No 36 Taiyuan St, Jhubei City, Hsinchu, 302, Taiwan
Tel.: (886) 35526888
Web Site: http://www.siliconmotion.com.tw
Sales Range: $100-124.9 Million
Emp.: 341
Semiconductors & Related Products Mfr & Marketer
N.A.I.C.S.: 334413

Subsidiary (US):

Silicon Motion, Inc. (2)
690 N McCarthy Blvd Ste 200, Milpitas, CA 95035 (100%)
Tel.: (408) 519-7200
Web Site: http://www.siliconmotion.com.tw
Sales Range: $25-49.9 Million
Emp.: 26
Semiconductors & Related Products Mfr & Marketer
N.A.I.C.S.: 334413

SILICON OPTRONICS, INC.
4F 10-2 1st Rd Li Hsin, East District, Hsinchu, 300, Taiwan
Tel.: (886) 35678986
Web Site: https://www.soinc.com.tw
Year Founded: 2004
3530—(TAI)
Rev.: $54,400,044
Assets: $102,311,975
Liabilities: $24,433,499
Net Worth: $77,878,476
Earnings: ($9,376,238)
Fiscal Year-end: 12/31/23
Semiconductor Devices Mfr
N.A.I.C.S.: 334413
He Xinping (Chm)

SILICON POWER COMPUTER & COMMUNICATION, INC.
7F No 106 Zhouzi St, Neihu District, Taipei, 114, Taiwan
Tel.: (886) 287978833
Web Site: https://www.silicon-power.com
Year Founded: 2003
4973—(TPE)
Rev.: $135,838,977
Assets: $86,971,485
Liabilities: $26,577,057
Net Worth: $60,394,428

INTERNATIONAL PUBLIC

Earnings: $5,731,389
Fiscal Year-end: 12/31/22
Electronic Components Mfr
N.A.I.C.S.: 334419
Chi-Han Li (Exec VP)

SILICON RENTALS SOLUTIONS LIMITED
Ground Floor Mohini Heights Unit No 5 5th Rd, Khar West, Mumbai, 400052, Maharashtra, India
Tel.: (91) 9082560851
Web Site: https://silicongroup1.com
Year Founded: 1993
543615—(BOM)
Rev.: $4,358,144
Assets: $6,809,076
Liabilities: $701,900
Net Worth: $6,107,176
Earnings: $1,279,731
Emp.: 52
Fiscal Year-end: 03/31/23
Computer Rental Services
N.A.I.C.S.: 532420

SILICON STUDIO CORP.
1-21-3 Ebisu Shibuya-ku, Tokyo, 150-0013, Japan
Tel.: (81) 354887070
Web Site:
   http://www.siliconstudio.co.jp
3907—(TKS)
Rev.: $32,287,860
Assets: $22,397,310
Liabilities: $9,933,090
Net Worth: $12,464,220
Earnings: $1,418,000
Emp.: 261
Fiscal Year-end: 11/30/23
Game Development & Software
N.A.I.C.S.: 513210
Teruyasu Sekimoto (Chm)

Subsidiaries:

Ignis Imageworks Corp. (1)
1F F Nissei Bldg 3-16-3 Ebisu Shibuya-ku, Tokyo, 150-0011, Japan
Tel.: (81) 354687631
Web Site: http://www.ignisimageworks.co.jp
Image & Video Production Services
N.A.I.C.S.: 512110

SILICON TOUCH TECHNOLOGY, INC.
9-4F-3 Prosperity Road I, Science-Based Industrial Park, Hsinchu, 300, Taiwan
Tel.: (886) 35645656
Web Site: https://www.siti.com
Year Founded: 1996
3288—(TPE)
Rev.: $3,622,893
Assets: $6,905,325
Liabilities: $3,822,718
Net Worth: $3,082,606
Earnings: $88,047
Fiscal Year-end: 12/31/22
Electrical Motor Machine Mfr
N.A.I.C.S.: 335312
Chi-Yuan Chin (Pres)

Subsidiaries:

Xiamen Silicon Touch Technology Inc. (1)
Room 201D North Floor No 34 GuanRi Road Xiamen Software Park II, Siming District, Xiamen, 361005, Fujian, China
Tel.: (86) 5922529188
Digital Integrated Circuit Machine Mfr & Distr
N.A.I.C.S.: 334513

SILICON VALLEY INFOTECH LIMITED
10 Princep Street 2nd Floor, Kolkata, 700 072, India
Tel.: (91) 3322256851

Web Site:
http://www.siliconvalleyinfo.net
Rev.: $5,580
Assets: $702,803
Liabilities: $460,443
Net Worth: $242,360
Earnings: ($43,189)
Emp.: 9
Fiscal Year-end: 03/31/19
Financial Services
N.A.I.C.S.: 523999
Santosh Kumar Jain *(Mng Dir)*

SILICON2 CO., LTD.
904-911 H-square S-dong 231 Pangyo-ro, Bundang-Gu, Seongnam, 13494, Gyeonggi-do, Korea (South)
Tel.: (82) 317893850
Web Site: https://www.siliconii.com
Year Founded: 2002
257720—(KRS)
Online Shopping Operator
N.A.I.C.S.: 334413
Sung-Woon Kim *(CEO)*

SILICONE ENGINEERING LTD.
Blackwater Road Greenbank Business Park, Blackburn, BB1 3HJ, Lancashire, United Kingdom
Tel.: (44) 8454856861 UK
Web Site: http://www.silicone.co.uk
Year Founded: 1959
Sales Range: $25-49.9 Million
Emp.: 90
Silicone Rubber Molding Extrusion Cable & Electrical Harnesse for the Food & Transportation Industry Mfr
N.A.I.C.S.: 326291
Dennis Beadman *(Mng Dir)*

SILITECH TECHNOLOGY CORPORATION
No 73 Kuirou Shan Rd, Tamsui Dist, Taipei, 25144, Taiwan
Tel.: (886) 226232666
Web Site: https://www.silitech.com
3311—(TAI)
Rev.: $68,165,274
Assets: $109,820,101
Liabilities: $24,239,117
Net Worth: $85,580,984
Earnings: $3,902,286
Emp.: 1,279
Fiscal Year-end: 12/31/23
Keypad Mfr
N.A.I.C.S.: 334118
Warren Chen *(Vice Chm)*

Subsidiaries:
Silitech (Hong Kong) Holding Ltd. (1)
Rooms 1610-11 CC Wu Building 302-8 Hennessy Road, Wanchai, China (Hong Kong)
Tel.: (852) 25749068
Silicone Rubber Product & Plastic Mfr
N.A.I.C.S.: 326291

Silitech Electronic (SuZhou) Co., Ltd. (1)
No 269 Hsin Fong Road Xujang Industry Area, Xukou Town Wuzhong District, Suzhou, 215164, Jiangsu, China
Tel.: (86) 512 66380988
Web Site: http://www.silitech.com
Mobile Keypads Mfr
N.A.I.C.S.: 325212

Silitech Technology (Europe) Ltd. (1)
Unit 1 Eagle Industrial Estate, Witney, OX28 4YR, Oxfordshire, United Kingdom
Tel.: (44) 1993700213
Web Site: http://www.silitech.com
Sales Range: $25-49.9 Million
Emp.: 5
Electronic Components Mfr
N.A.I.C.S.: 334419

Silitech Technology Corporation Limited (1)
No 539 Nanhuan Road of Shajing, Baoan District, Shenzhen, 518104, Guangdong, China
Tel.: (86) 75527234188
Web Site: http://www.silitech.com
Keyboards Mfr & Distr
N.A.I.C.S.: 334118

Silitech Technology Corporation Limited (1)
Room 801C Tower 1 China Hong Kong City, 33 Canton Road, Kowloon, China (Hong Kong)
Tel.: (852) 2782 1043
Web Site: http://www.silitech.com.my
Rubber Keypads Mfr & Distr
N.A.I.C.S.: 325212

Xurong Electronic (Shenzhen) Co., Ltd. (1)
No 461 NanHuan Road of ShaJing, BaoAn District, Shenzhen, 518104, Guangdong, China
Tel.: (86) 75527234188
Silicone Rubber Product & Plastic Mfr
N.A.I.C.S.: 326291

SILK LOGISTICS HOLDINGS LIMITED
850 Lorimer Street, Port Melbourne, 3207, VIC, Australia
Tel.: (61) 392816900 AU
Web Site: https://www.silklogisticsholding.com
Year Founded: 2014
SLH—(ASX)
Rev.: $319,462,085
Assets: $236,270,457
Liabilities: $187,103,736
Net Worth: $49,166,721
Earnings: $10,694,399
Fiscal Year-end: 06/26/23
Holding Company
N.A.I.C.S.: 551112
Brendon Pentland *(CFO)*

Subsidiaries:
101Warehousing Pty. Ltd. (1)
Unit 1 8 Vulcan Drive, Truganina, Melbourne, 3029, VIC, Australia
Tel.: (61) 383532184
Web Site: https://101warehousing.com.au
Warehouse Software Development Services
N.A.I.C.S.: 541511

FMC West Pty. Ltd. (1)
1 Hines road, O'Connor, WA, Australia
Tel.: (61) 893142213
Web Site: https://fmcwest.com.au
Container Unpacking Services
N.A.I.C.S.: 811310

Fremantle Freight & Storage Pty. Ltd. (1)
2 Roper Street, O'Connor, 6163, WA, Australia
Tel.: (61) 893142213
Web Site: https://www.fremantlefreightstorage.com
Port & Shipping Storage Services
N.A.I.C.S.: 488310

Rocke Brothers Pty. Ltd. (1)
Lot 2 29 Alick Road, Brooklyn, 3012, VIC, Australia
Tel.: (61) 393146211
Web Site: https://rocke.com.au
Freight Forwarding & Transportation Services
N.A.I.C.S.: 561910

SILK ROAD CAPITAL LTD.
Suite 301 Regency Olympic Street 16, Ulaanbaatar, Mongolia
Tel.: (976) 77119799 CH
Web Site: http://www.silkroadc.com
Holding Company; Investment Banking, Corporate Finance & Advisory Services
N.A.I.C.S.: 551112
Sardor Koshnazarov *(Mng Dir)*

Subsidiaries:
Eurasia Capital (1)
Suite 301 Regency Olympic Street 16, Ulaanbaatar, Mongolia
Tel.: (976) 77119799
Web Site: http://www.eurasiac.com
Investment Banking & Advisory Services
N.A.I.C.S.: 523150

Mandalay Capital (1)
10/A Kanbawza Avenue Golden Valley 1 St, Bahan T/S, 11201, Yangon, Myanmar
Tel.: (95) 1 539590
Web Site: http://www.mandalayc.com
Investment Banking & Advisory Services
N.A.I.C.S.: 523150

Silk Road Bank AD Skopje (1)
Dame Gruev No 1, Skopje, 1000, North Macedonia
Tel.: (389) 2 3251 900
Web Site: http://silkroadbank.com.mk
Commericial Banking
N.A.I.C.S.: 522110
Milena P. Percinkova *(Gen Mgr)*

SILK ROAD ENERGY INC.
520 3rd Avenue SW Suite 1900, Calgary, T2P 0R3, AB, Canada AB
Web Site: http://www.silkroadenergy.com
Year Founded: 2010
Rev.: $42,705
Assets: $50,541
Liabilities: $307,614
Net Worth: ($257,074)
Earnings: ($242,861)
Fiscal Year-end: 09/30/17
Investment Services
N.A.I.C.S.: 523999
Richard Derrick Colling *(CFO)*

SILK ROAD ENERGY SERVICES GROUP LIMITED
Unit 3501 35th Floor West Tower, Shun Tak Centre 168-200 Connaught Road, Central, China (Hong Kong)
Tel.: (852) 2 559 2210 Ky
Web Site: http://www.silkroadenergy.com.hk
8250—(HKG)
Rev.: $16,888,254
Assets: $64,350,573
Liabilities: $17,165,690
Net Worth: $47,184,882
Earnings: ($3,867,465)
Emp.: 390
Fiscal Year-end: 06/30/21
Holding Company
N.A.I.C.S.: 551112
Wai Hung Li *(Exec Dir)*

SILK ROAD GROUP S.A.
49a Chavchavadze Ave, 0179, Tbilisi, Georgia
Tel.: (995) 32 225 35 81 GE
Web Site: http://silkroadgroup.net
Year Founded: 1997
Emp.: 5,000
Investment Management Service
N.A.I.C.S.: 523999
George Ramishvili *(Founder & Chm)*

Subsidiaries:
Silknet JSC (1)
95 Tsinamdzgvrishvili Street, 0112, Tbilisi, Georgia
Tel.: (995) 32 210 00 00
Web Site: http://www.silknet.com
Emp.: 1,600
Telecommunication Servicesb
N.A.I.C.S.: 517111
Ilia Enukashvili *(Strategy Officer)*

Subsidiary (Domestic):
Geocell LLC (2)
#3 Gotua Str, The right riverside, 0160, Tbilisi, Georgia
Tel.: (995) 32 277 0100
Web Site: http://www.geocell.com.ge
Telecommunication Servicesb
N.A.I.C.S.: 517121
Pavel Smolysky *(Gen Dir)*

SILK ROAD LOGISTICS HOLDINGS LIMITED
Unit 17-18 36th Floor China Merchants Tower Shun Tak Centre, Nos 168-200 Connaught Road, Central, China (Hong Kong)
Tel.: (852) 28956733
Web Site: http://www.silkroadlogistics.com.hk
0988—(HKG)
Rev.: $949,748
Assets: $46,157,550
Liabilities: $97,877,925
Net Worth: ($51,720,375)
Earnings: ($12,697,215)
Emp.: 30
Fiscal Year-end: 12/31/22
Coal Prodcuts Mfr
N.A.I.C.S.: 324199
Yuk Ching Chiu *(Sec)*

SILKAN
Immeuble le Sirius 9 route du Colonel Marcel Moraine, 92360, Meudon, France
Tel.: (33) 1 4601 0327
Web Site: http://www.silkan.com
Simulation Systems Developer
N.A.I.C.S.: 334515
Pierre Fiorini *(Pres & CEO)*

Subsidiaries:
SILKAN Solutions Inc. (1)
4700 Rue De La Savane Bureau 218, Montreal, H4P 1T7, QC, Canada
Tel.: (514) 585-7975
Software Development Services
N.A.I.C.S.: 541511

SILKBANK LIMITED
20th-22nd Floors Centrepoint, Off Shaheed-e-Millat Expressway Near KPT Interchange Korangi, Karachi, 74900, Pakistan
Tel.: (92) 21111007455
Web Site: http://www.silkbank.com.pk
SILK—(KAR)
Rev.: $31,249,398
Assets: $1,324,631,235
Liabilities: $1,255,260,283
Net Worth: $69,370,952
Earnings: ($25,457,339)
Emp.: 4,423
Fiscal Year-end: 12/31/19
Private Bank Services
N.A.I.C.S.: 522110
Goharulayn Afzal *(Dir-HR, Trng & Dev & Admin)*

SILKEBORG IF INVEST A/S
JYSK park Ansvej 104, 8600, Silkeborg, Denmark
Tel.: (45) 86804477
Web Site: https://silkeborgif.com
Year Founded: 1917
SIF—(CSE)
Rev.: $24,980,104
Assets: $102,124,119
Liabilities: $56,430,959
Net Worth: $45,693,160
Earnings: $11,996,643
Emp.: 93
Fiscal Year-end: 12/31/22
Professional Football Club Operator
N.A.I.C.S.: 711211
Claus Kjær Agerskov Christensen *(CFO & Fin Dir)*

SILKROAD NICKEL LTD.
50 Armenian Street 03-04 Wilmer Place, Singapore, 179938, Singapore
Tel.: (65) 63278971
Web Site: http://www.silkroadnickel.com
STP—(SES)
Rev.: $475,000
Assets: $24,870,000

SILKROAD NICKEL LTD.

Silkroad Nickel Ltd.—(Continued)
Liabilities: $16,089,000
Net Worth: $8,781,000
Earnings: ($3,641,000)
Fiscal Year-end: 12/31/20
Nickel Ore Exploration, Mining, Production & Sale
N.A.I.C.S.: 212230
Kah Ing Hong *(CEO)*

SILKROAD VISUAL TECHNOLOGY CO LTD
17F Culture & Sports Industry Headquarters Building No 3030 Fuqiang Rd, Futian District, Shenzhen, 518040, Guangdong, China
Tel.: (86) 75588321687
Web Site: http://www.silkroadcg.com
Year Founded: 2000
300556—(CHIN)
Rev.: $201,542,406
Assets: $308,773,412
Liabilities: $175,322,770
Net Worth: $133,450,642
Earnings: $3,241,987
Fiscal Year-end: 12/31/23
Computer Graphic Design Services
N.A.I.C.S.: 541430
Meng Di Li *(Chm & Gen Mgr)*

SILKWAVE INC.
Unit 1211 Level 12 Core F Cyberport 3 100 Cyberport Road, Hong Kong, China (Hong Kong)
Tel.: (852) 21593300
Web Site:
  http://www.cmmbvision.com
471—(HKG)
Sales Range: $1-9.9 Million
Emp.: 30
Holding Company
N.A.I.C.S.: 551112
Chau Chi Wong *(Chm & CEO)*

SILLA CO., LTD.
30 Godeokbizvalley-ro 6-gil, Gangdong-gu, Seoul, Korea (South)
Tel.: (82) 234349900
Web Site: https://www.sla.co.kr
Year Founded: 1967
004970—(KRS)
Rev.: $331,841,998
Assets: $549,479,949
Liabilities: $120,692,083
Net Worth: $428,787,866
Earnings: $10,887,403
Emp.: 496
Fiscal Year-end: 12/31/22
Deep Sea Fishing Services
N.A.I.C.S.: 114111
Kwangse Lee *(Co-CEO)*

Subsidiaries:

SILLA Engineering Co., Ltd (1)
271 Asanvalley-ro, Dunpo-myeon, Asan, Chungcheongnam-do, Korea (South)
Tel.: (82) 414222000
Web Site: https://www.sillaeng.co.kr
Industrial Mold Mfr
N.A.I.C.S.: 333511
Yong Mun Shin *(CEO)*

SILLA SG Co., Ltd (1)
Tel.: (82) 221427311
Sea Food Product Mfr & Distr
N.A.I.C.S.: 311710

Plant (Domestic):

SILLA SG Co., Ltd - Busan Factory (2)
1414 Nakdong-daero, Sasang-gu, Busan, Korea (South)
Tel.: (82) 51 302 3811
Seafood Product Mfr
N.A.I.C.S.: 311710

SILLA TEXTILE CO., LTD.
Ansim-ro 65-gil, Dong-gu, Daegu, Korea (South)
Tel.: (82) 539601117
Web Site: http://www.sla.co.kr
Year Founded: 1976
001000—(KRS)
Rev.: $3,397,522
Assets: $24,495,012
Liabilities: $12,689,099
Net Worth: $11,805,913
Earnings: ($27,489)
Emp.: 10
Fiscal Year-end: 12/31/22
Polyester Textile Mfr
N.A.I.C.S.: 313110
Kwangse Lee *(Co-CEO)*

SILLAJEN INC
9th floor 109 Sogong-ro, Seoul, 46508, Korea (South)
Tel.: (82) 3682600
Web Site: http://www.sillajen.com
Year Founded: 2006
215600—(KRS)
Rev.: $3,845,249
Assets: $79,343,129
Liabilities: $18,796,538
Net Worth: $60,546,591
Earnings: ($19,372,239)
Emp.: 56
Fiscal Year-end: 12/31/22
Cancer Treatment Services
N.A.I.C.S.: 622310
Kim Jae-Kyung *(CEO)*

Subsidiaries:

SillaJen Biotherapeutics, Inc. (1)
450 Sansome St 2nd Fl, San Francisco, CA 94111
Tel.: (415) 281-8886
Therapeutic Product Development Services
N.A.I.C.S.: 541714
Helena H. Chaye *(Chief Bus Officer)*

SILLENGER EXPLORATION CORP.
277 Lakeshore Rd East Suite 206, Oakville, L6J 1H9, ON, Canada
Tel.: (905) 582-2434
Web Site: http://www.sillenger.com
Year Founded: 2007
SLGX—(OTCBB)
Assets: $1
Liabilities: $27,000
Net Worth: ($26,999)
Earnings: ($38,000)
Fiscal Year-end: 02/29/20
Gold Exploration Services
N.A.I.C.S.: 212220

SILLY MONKS ENTERTAINMENT LTD.
Survey no 91 3rd floor Technical Block Sundarayya Vignana Kendram, Gachibowli, Hyderabad, 500032, India
Tel.: (91) 8008121236
Web Site:
  https://www.sillymonks.com
SILLYMONKS—(NSE)
Rev.: $2,347,006
Assets: $1,429,603
Liabilities: $561,861
Net Worth: $867,742
Earnings: ($550,495)
Emp.: 31
Fiscal Year-end: 03/31/23
Entertainment Services
N.A.I.C.S.: 711130
Sanjay Reddy *(Founder & Chm)*

SILMAASEMA OYJ
Radiokatu 3, 00240, Helsinki, Finland
Tel.: (358) 103016000
Web Site: http://www.silmaasema.fi
Medical Equipment Mfr & Distr
N.A.I.C.S.: 339112

Teppo Linden *(CEO)*

SILTRONIC AG
Einsteinstrasse 172, 81677, Munich, Germany
Tel.: (49) 8985643000
Web Site: http://www.siltronic.com
Year Founded: 1958
Emp.: 700
Silicon Wafers Mfr
N.A.I.C.S.: 325211
Tobias Ohler *(Chm-Supervisory Bd)*

SILTRONTECH ELECTRONICS CORPORATION
6F No 118 Singshan Rd, Neihu District, Taipei, 11469, Taiwan
Tel.: (886) 227909668
Web Site: http://www.siltron.com.tw
Year Founded: 1992
Sales Range: $125-149.9 Million
Emp.: 120
Electronic Parts Distr
N.A.I.C.S.: 423690
Wu Cheng *(Chm)*

SILVA PHARMACEUTICALS LTD.
House 65 Road 8/A New, Dhanmondi, Dhaka, 1209, Bangladesh
Tel.: (880) 28191336
Web Site:
  https://www.silvapharma.com
Year Founded: 2003
SILVAPHL—(CHT)
Rev.: $9,271,295
Assets: $28,386,999
Liabilities: $2,049,522
Net Worth: $26,337,477
Earnings: $1,390,304
Emp.: 945
Fiscal Year-end: 06/30/21
Pharmaceuticals Product Mfr
N.A.I.C.S.: 325412
Silvana Mirza *(Chm)*

SILVANO FASHION GROUP AS
Tulika 15/17, 10613, Tallinn, Estonia
Tel.: (372) 6845000
Web Site:
  https://www.silvanofashion.com
SFG—(WAR)
Rev.: $64,683,740
Assets: $79,757,148
Liabilities: $16,987,526
Net Worth: $62,769,621
Earnings: $12,260,735
Emp.: 1,626
Fiscal Year-end: 12/31/23
Cut & Sew Apparel Manufacturing (except Contractors)
N.A.I.C.S.: 315250
Toomas Tool *(Chm-Supervisory Bd)*

Subsidiaries:

Gimil OOO (1)
Novovilenskaja 28, 220053, Minsk, Belarus
Tel.: (375) 172880704
Women Innerwear Mfr
N.A.I.C.S.: 315250

Lauma Lingerie AS (1)
Ziemelu 19, Liepaja, LV-3405, Latvia
Tel.: (371) 63410222
Web Site: https://www.laumalingerie.com
Ladies Lingerie Whslr
N.A.I.C.S.: 424350
Alisa Besoka *(Mgr-Mktg & Sls)*

Milavitsa SP ZAO (1)
Novovilenskaya str 28, 220053, Minsk, Belarus
Tel.: (375) 172880770
Ladies Lingerie Whslr
N.A.I.C.S.: 424350

Silvano Fashion OOO (1)
Sholkovychnaya 30A lit A A1, Kiev, 01024, Ukraine
Tel.: (380) 445370636

INTERNATIONAL PUBLIC

Ladies Lingerie Whslr
N.A.I.C.S.: 424350

Silvano Fashion SIA (1)
Alberta iela 11-61, Riga, LV-1010, Latvia
Tel.: (371) 63410200
Ladies Lingerie Whslr
N.A.I.C.S.: 424350

Silvano Fashion ZAO (1)
Novodmitrovskaja 5A stroenie 4 3 etazh, 127015, Moscow, Russia
Tel.: (7) 4956401857
Ladies Lingerie Whslr
N.A.I.C.S.: 424350

Yunona OAO (1)
Vjaliki Gastinec 40, 220053, Minsk, Belarus
Tel.: (375) 176754621
Ladies Lingerie Whslr
N.A.I.C.S.: 424350

SILVER BASE GROUP HOLDINGS LIMITED
25th Floor One Hennessy 1 Hennessy Road, Hong Kong, China (Hong Kong)
Tel.: (852) 23687777
Web Site:
  http://www.silverbasegroup.com
0886—(HKG)
Rev.: $121,000,136
Assets: $298,346,476
Liabilities: $248,535,818
Net Worth: $49,810,657
Earnings: ($28,677,413)
Emp.: 172
Fiscal Year-end: 03/31/21
Liquor Distr
N.A.I.C.S.: 424820
Guoxing Liang *(Founder, Chm & CEO)*

Subsidiaries:

Silver Base International Development Co., Ltd. (1)
27 F The Sun, Wanchai, China (Hong Kong)
Tel.: (852) 28921602
Alcoholic Beverages Exporter
N.A.I.C.S.: 424820
Marco Tse *(Mgr-Sls)*

SILVER BEAR RESOURCES PLC
100 University Avenue 8th Floor, Toronto, M5J 2Y1, ON, Canada
Tel.: (416) 309-2131
Web Site:
  https://www.silverbearresources.com
Year Founded: 2004
SBR—(TSX)
Rev.: $40,590,236
Assets: $91,865,529
Liabilities: $139,869,489
Net Worth: ($48,003,960)
Earnings: ($36,776,255)
Emp.: 354
Fiscal Year-end: 12/31/20
Silver Mining & Extraction Services
N.A.I.C.S.: 212220
Judith Webster *(Sec & Mgr-IR)*

SILVER BULL RESOURCES INC.
Suite 1605 777 Dunsmuir Street, Vancouver, V7Y 1K4, BC, Canada
Tel.: (604) 687-5800
Web Site:
  https://www.silverbullresources.com
SVBL—(OTCQB)
Rev.: $272,682
Assets: $6,252,826
Liabilities: $386,151
Net Worth: $5,866,675
Earnings: ($3,168,199)
Emp.: 5
Fiscal Year-end: 10/31/22
Metal Mining Services
N.A.I.C.S.: 212290

Timothy T. Barry *(Pres & CEO)*

SILVER BULLET DATA SERVICES GROUP PLC
Spaces The Harley Building 77 New Cavendish St, London, W1W 6XB, United Kingdom
Tel.: (44) 2039346630   UK
Web Site:
   https://www.wearesilverbullet.com
Year Founded: 2013
SBDS—(AIM)
Rev.: $7,344,427
Assets: $13,624,431
Liabilities: $6,037,823
Net Worth: $7,586,608
Earnings: ($9,116,426)
Emp.: 69
Fiscal Year-end: 12/31/22
Management Consulting Services
N.A.I.C.S.: 541618

SILVER BULLET MINES CORP.
20 Holly Street Suite 300, Toronto, M4S 3B1, ON, Canada
Tel.: (416) 865-0123
Web Site:
   http://www.pinehurstcapital.net
SBMI—(TSXV)
Assets: $2,392,645
Liabilities: $2,517,194
Net Worth: ($124,550)
Earnings: ($1,659,593)
Fiscal Year-end: 06/30/24
Asset Management Services
N.A.I.C.S.: 523940

SILVER CITY MINERALS LIMITED
Suite 9-330 Churchill Avenue, Subiaco, 6008, WA, Australia
Tel.: (61) 8 6489 1600
Web Site:
   http://www.silvercityminerals.com
Rev.: $177,311
Assets: $4,521,629
Liabilities: $29,539
Net Worth: $4,492,091
Earnings: ($1,077,237)
Emp.: 4
Fiscal Year-end: 06/30/19
Silver, Lead & Zinc Mining Services
N.A.I.C.S.: 212220
Sonu Cheema *(Sec)*

SILVER DOLLAR RESOURCES, INC.
179-2945 Jacklin Road Suite 416, Victoria, V9B 6J9, BC, Canada
Tel.: (250) 474-7999
Web Site:
   https://www.silverdollars.com
Year Founded: 2018
4YW—(DEU)
Rev.: $51,325
Assets: $11,959,725
Liabilities: $102,986
Net Worth: $11,856,739
Earnings: ($1,371,192)
Emp.: 2
Fiscal Year-end: 08/31/23
Mineral Exploration Services
N.A.I.C.S.: 213115
Michael Romanik *(Pres & CEO)*

SILVER DRAGON RESOURCES INC.
200 Davenport Road, Toronto, M5R 1J2, ON, Canada
Tel.: (416) 223-8500   DE
Web Site:
   https://www.silverdragon.com
Year Founded: 1996
SDRG—(OTCBB)
Sales Range: Less than $1 Million
Silver Mining Services

N.A.I.C.S.: 212220
Marc M. Hazout *(Pres & CEO)*

SILVER EGG TECHNOLOGY CO., LTD.
Facade Esaka Bldg 10F 1-23-43 Esaka-cho, Suita, 564-0063, Osaka, Japan
Tel.: (81) 663861931   JP
Web Site: https://www.silveregg.co.jp
Year Founded: 1998
3961—(TKS)
Rev.: $8,897,970
Assets: $9,916,110
Liabilities: $1,039,650
Net Worth: $8,876,460
Earnings: $64,530
Fiscal Year-end: 12/31/22
Marketing Services
N.A.I.C.S.: 541613
Thomas Foley *(Co-Founder, Pres & CEO)*

SILVER ELEPHANT MINING CORP.
Suite 1610 409 Granville Street, Vancouver, V6C 1T2, BC, Canada
Tel.: (604) 569-3661   BC
Web Site: https://www.silverelef.com
ELEF—(OTCIQ)
Assets: $48,537,672
Liabilities: $8,883,789
Net Worth: $39,653,884
Earnings: ($5,342,749)
Emp.: 14
Fiscal Year-end: 12/31/21
Coal Mining
N.A.I.C.S.: 212115
John R. Lee *(Chm & CEO)*

Subsidiaries:

Red Hill Mongolia LLC   (1)
8/F Monnis Tower Chinggis Avenue 1st Khoroo, Sukhbaatar District, Ulaanbaatar, 14240, Mongolia
Tel.: (976) 11 331669
Web Site: http://www.prophecy.mn
Sales Range: $50-74.9 Million
Emp.: 50
Coal Mining Services
N.A.I.C.S.: 212115
Orgil Sukhee *(Exec Dir)*

SILVER FERN FARMS LIMITED
283 Princes Street, PO Box 941, Dunedin, 9054, New Zealand
Tel.: (64) 34773980   NZ
Web Site:
   http://www.silverfernfarms.com
Year Founded: 1948
Sales Range: $1-9.9 Million
Sheep, Lamb, Venison & Beef Processor
N.A.I.C.S.: 311611
Phil Buck *(Gen Mgr-Plant Ops)*

Subsidiaries:

B. Brooks (Norwich) Limited   (1)
Little Melton, Norwich, United Kingdom   (100%)
Tel.: (44) 1603819500
Web Site: http://www.ppcsbrooks.co.uk
Meat Processed from Carcasses
N.A.I.C.S.: 311612

PPCS USA Inc.   (1)
12 Galaxy Ct, Sewell, NJ 08080-2214   (100%)
Tel.: (856) 853-7400
Local Freight Trucking
N.A.I.C.S.: 484110

Silver Fern Farms (UK) Limited   (1)
The Stables Four Mile Stable Barns Cambridge Road, Newmarket, CB8 0TN, Suffolk, United Kingdom
Tel.: (44) 1223810800
Web Site: http://www.silverfernfarms.com

Sales Range: $50-74.9 Million
Emp.: 10
Processed Meats Distr
N.A.I.C.S.: 424470

Silver Fern Farms GmbH   (1)
Rondenberg 25, D-22525, Hamburg, Germany   (100%)
Tel.: (49) 40 890 6696
Web Site: http://www.silverfernfarms.com
Sales Range: $50-74.9 Million
Emp.: 10
Meat & Meat Products Whslr
N.A.I.C.S.: 424470

Silver Fern Farms GmbH   (1)
Rondenberg 25, 22525, Hamburg, Germany
Tel.: (49) 408906696
Processed Meats Distr
N.A.I.C.S.: 424470

Silver Fern Farms NV   (1)
Molendries 11A, 9300, Aalst, Belgium   (100%)
Tel.: (32) 53603150
Sales Range: $50-74.9 Million
Emp.: 3
Meat & Meat Product Whslr
N.A.I.C.S.: 424470

Venison Rotorua Limited   (1)
7 Pururu Street, Rotorua, 3201, New Zealand
Tel.: (64) 73481567
Sales Range: $25-49.9 Million
Emp.: 60
Game Processing & Sales
N.A.I.C.S.: 311611

SILVER FIELDS RESOURCES INC.
555 Burrard Street Suite 900, Vancouver, V7X 1M8, BC, Canada
Tel.: (604) 684-0454
Web Site:
   http://www.silverfieldsresources.com
Year Founded: 1987
SRFF—(OTCIQ)
Mineral Exploration Services
N.A.I.C.S.: 213114
Christopher D. England *(Pres & CEO)*

SILVER GRAIL RESOURCES LTD.
2130 Crescent Road, Victoria, V8S 2H3, BC, Canada
Tel.: (778) 430-5680
Web Site: https://www.silvergrail.com
Year Founded: 1979
SVGAF—(OTCIQ)
Assets: $684,040
Liabilities: $19,879
Net Worth: $664,161
Earnings: ($133,714)
Fiscal Year-end: 03/31/24
Mineral Exploration Services
N.A.I.C.S.: 213114

SILVER GRANT INTERNATIONAL HOLDINGS GROUP LTD.
Room 4013B 40th/F Office Building Convention & Exhibition Plaza, 1 Harbor Road, Wanchai, China (Hong Kong)
Tel.: (852) 28770030   HK
Web Site:
   https://www.silvergrant.com.cn
Year Founded: 1960
0171—(HKG)
Rev.: $12,352,710
Assets: $1,277,394,705
Liabilities: $704,344,298
Net Worth: $573,050,408
Earnings: $94,688,895
Emp.: 66
Fiscal Year-end: 12/31/22
Property & Investment Services
N.A.I.C.S.: 523999

Hing Tsung Chu *(Chm, Co-CEO & Exec Dir)*

Subsidiaries:

Beijing East Gate Development Co.,Ltd   (1)
No 9/19/29/39 Dongzhong St, Dongcheng Dist, Beijing, 100027, China
Tel.: (86) 1064158797
Web Site: http://www.bjeastgate.com
Apartment Leasing Services
N.A.I.C.S.: 531110

SILVER HAMMER MINING CORP.
206-595 Howe Street, Vancouver, V6C 2T5, BC, Canada
Tel.: (778) 344-4653   BC
Web Site:
   https://www.silverhammermining.com
Year Founded: 2017
HAMR—(CNSX)
Assets: $6,975,504
Liabilities: $263,131
Net Worth: $6,712,372
Earnings: ($1,521,565)
Fiscal Year-end: 09/30/22
Mineral Exploration Services
N.A.I.C.S.: 213115
Alnesh Mohan *(Sec)*

SILVER INVESTMENT PARTNERS GMBH & CO. KG
Am Neuenhainer Wald 2, 61462, Konigstein, Germany
Tel.: (49) 6174 913 80 0
Web Site: http://www.silver-ip.com
Privater Equity Firm
N.A.I.C.S.: 523999
Philipp Amereller *(Mng Partner)*

Subsidiaries:

COHEMI Group GmbH   (1)
Georg-Baumgarten-Strasse 3, 60549, Frankfurt am Main, Germany
Tel.: (49) 69697125990
Web Site: https://www.cohemi-group.com
Information Technology Consulting Services
N.A.I.C.S.: 541690

Subsidiary (Domestic):

IQ Solutions GmbH   (2)
Landsberger Strasse 110, Munich, Germany
Tel.: (49) 893077300
Web Site: https://www.iq-gmbh.de
Information Technology Services
N.A.I.C.S.: 541511
Erol Anil *(CEO)*

Crystal GmbH   (1)
Ostendstrasse 25, 12459, Berlin, Germany
Tel.: (49) 3053042500
Web Site: http://www.crystal-gmbh.com
Optical Instrument Mfr
N.A.I.C.S.: 333310
Andreas Wenzel *(CEO)*

SILVER LIFE CO., LTD.
4-32-4 Nishishinjuku Shinjuku-Ku, Tokyo, 160-0023, Japan
Tel.: (81) 363005622
Web Site: http://www.silver-life.co.jp
9262—(TKS)
Sales Range: Less than $1 Million
Emp.: 260
Food Product Mfr & Distr
N.A.I.C.S.: 311412
Takahisa Shimizu *(Pres & CEO)*

SILVER MINES LIMITED
Level 28 88 Phillip Street, GPO Box 225, Sydney, 2000, NSW, Australia
Tel.: (61) 283163997
Web Site:
   https://www.silvermines.com.au
SVL—(ASX)
Rev.: $130,619
Assets: $90,052,912
Liabilities: $3,717,857

SILVER MINES LIMITED

Silver Mines Limited—(Continued)
Net Worth: $86,335,055
Earnings: ($10,190,292)
Fiscal Year-end: 06/30/22
Silver Mining Services
N.A.I.C.S.: 212220
Keith Perrett *(Chm)*

Subsidiaries:

Bowdens Silver Pty. Limited (1)
68 Maloneys Road, Lue, Mudgee, 2850, NSW, Australia
Tel.: (61) 263736420
Web Site: https://www.bowdenssilver.com.au
Emp.: 23
Metal & Mining Services
N.A.I.C.S.: 213114
Blake Hjorth *(Officer-Community Liaison)*

SILVER MOUNTAIN MINES INC.
223 Riverview Circle SE, Calgary, T2C 4K6, AB, Canada
Tel.: (403) 229-9140 AB
Web Site: http://www.silvermountainmine.com
Year Founded: 2008
SMM—(TSXV)
Rev.: $391
Assets: $4,927,777
Liabilities: $275,180
Net Worth: $4,652,597
Earnings: ($46,916)
Fiscal Year-end: 12/31/20
Silver & Gold Mining Services
N.A.I.C.S.: 212220
Steve Konopelky *(Pres & CEO)*

SILVER NORTH RESOURCES LTD.
Suite 410-325 Howe Street, Vancouver, V6C 1Z7, BC, Canada
Tel.: (604) 687-3520 AB
Web Site: https://silvernorthres.com
Year Founded: 2005
TARSF—(OTCQB)
Rev.: $1,755
Assets: $5,291,416
Liabilities: $652,794
Net Worth: $4,638,622
Earnings: ($587,309)
Emp.: 1
Fiscal Year-end: 09/01/23
Metal Exploration Services
N.A.I.C.S.: 213114
Mark Thomas Brown *(Chm)*

Subsidiaries:

Alianza Holdings Ltd. (1)
Suite 410 325 Howe Street, Vancouver, V6C 1Z7, BC, Canada
Tel.: (604) 687-3520
Web Site: http://www.tarsis.ca
Sales Range: Less than $1 Million
Holding Company; Gold Mining & Exploration Services
N.A.I.C.S.: 551112

Subsidiary (Non-US):

Anderson Peru Mining and Exploration S.A.C. (2)
Av Malecon Cisneros 1270 Int 1402, Lima, Miraflores, Peru
Tel.: (51) 1 1243 32 57
Mineral Resource Exploration Services
N.A.I.C.S.: 213115

Compania Minera Canadian Shield Peru S.A.C. (2)
Calle Dos De Mayo No 472, Lima, Miraflores, Peru
Tel.: (51) 17196152
Mineral Resource Exploration Services
N.A.I.C.S.: 213115

SILVER OAK (INDIA) LIMITED
Plot No 110 Sector 1 Industrial Area Pithampur, Dhar, 454775, India
Tel.: (91) 792403170
Web Site: https://silveroakindia.co.in
Year Founded: 1984
531635—(BOM)
Rev.: $396,323
Assets: $4,281,761
Liabilities: $1,697,054
Net Worth: $2,584,707
Earnings: $68,122
Fiscal Year-end: 03/31/21
Liquor Mfr & Brewery Services
N.A.I.C.S.: 312120
Sunil Khandelwal *(CFO)*

SILVER ONE RESOURCES INC.
Guinness Tower Suite 1000 - 1055 W Hastings St, Vancouver, V6E 2E9, BC, Canada
Tel.: (604) 974-5274 BC
Web Site: https://www.silverone.com
Year Founded: 2007
SLVRF—(OTCQX)
Rev.: $63,222
Assets: $26,930,942
Liabilities: $986,775
Net Worth: $25,944,167
Earnings: ($1,618,594)
Fiscal Year-end: 12/31/20
Silver Mining Services
N.A.I.C.S.: 212220
Gregory Crowe *(Pres & CEO)*

SILVER PEARL HOSPITALITY & LUXURY SPACES LIMITED
Osiya Shambhu Lodge Sangla Chitkul Road, VPO Rakchham Sangla, Tehsils, 172106, Himachal Pradesh, India
Tel.: (91) 3340069937
Web Site: https://www.silverpearlhospital.com
Year Founded: 2011
543536—(BOM)
Rev.: $151,250
Assets: $1,629,375
Liabilities: $13,980
Net Worth: $1,615,395
Earnings: ($3,321)
Emp.: 34
Fiscal Year-end: 03/31/23
Hotel Operator
N.A.I.C.S.: 721110

SILVER PHOENIX RESOURCES INC.
566 Riverview Dr Unit 104, Chatham, N7M 0N2, ON, Canada
Tel.: (778) 331-8505 BC
Web Site: https://www.atlasglobalbrands.com
Year Founded: 2003
SP—(CNSX)
Assets: $21,716
Liabilities: $48,033
Net Worth: ($26,317)
Earnings: ($93,752)
Emp.: 2
Fiscal Year-end: 12/31/19
Gold & Silver Exploration & Mining Services
N.A.I.C.S.: 212220

SILVER RANGE RESOURCES LTD.
510-1100 Melville Street, Vancouver, V6E 4A6, BC, Canada
Tel.: (604) 687-2522 BC
Web Site: https://www.silverrange.com
Year Founded: 2010
SNG—(TSXV)
Rev.: $15,389
Assets: $7,418,302
Liabilities: $76,358
Net Worth: $7,341,944

Earnings: ($745,562)
Fiscal Year-end: 12/31/23
Silver Mining
N.A.I.C.S.: 212220
Glenn R. Yeadon *(Sec)*

SILVER RIDGE HOLDINGS BHD
No 1 Jalan 1/68F Off Jalan Tun Razak, Unit E-19-02 Level 19 Icon Tower East Wing, 55000, Kuala Lumpur, Wilayah Persekutuan, Malaysia
Tel.: (60) 21810985 MY
Web Site: https://www.silverridge.com.my
Year Founded: 1995
SRIDGE—(KLS)
Rev.: $2,464,813
Assets: $4,072,114
Liabilities: $2,278,412
Net Worth: $1,793,702
Earnings: ($942,606)
Emp.: 90
Fiscal Year-end: 06/30/23
Investment Holding Services
N.A.I.C.S.: 551112
Muhammad Suhaimi Abdullah *(Mng Dir)*

SILVER SANDS RESOURCES CORP.
830 - 1100 Melville, Vancouver, V6E 4A6, BC, Canada
Tel.: (604) 786-7774
Web Site: https://www.silversandscorp.com
Year Founded: 2018
SAND—(CNSX)
Assets: $104,325
Liabilities: $188,406
Net Worth: ($84,081)
Earnings: $805,145
Fiscal Year-end: 01/31/24
Mining Services
N.A.I.C.S.: 212290
Keith Anderson *(Pres & CEO)*

SILVER SPRUCE RESOURCES INC.
Suite 440 1600 Bedford Highway, Bedford, B4A 1E8, NS, Canada
Tel.: (902) 527-5700
Web Site: https://www.silverspruce.com
Year Founded: 1996
SSEBF—(OTCQB)
Assets: $301,350
Liabilities: $277,434
Net Worth: $23,916
Earnings: ($1,207,862)
Emp.: 3
Fiscal Year-end: 10/31/22
Mineral Exploration Services
N.A.I.C.S.: 213114
Brian K. Penney *(Chm & CEO)*

SILVER STAR INSURANCE COMPANY LIMITED
Silver Star House 5-Bank Square, PO Box 2533, Lahore, 54000, Pakistan
Tel.: (92) 42 37324488
Web Site: http://www.ssic.com.pk
Sales Range: $1-9.9 Million
Emp.: 53
Insurance Services
N.A.I.C.S.: 524298

SILVER TIDE HOLDINGS LIMITED
Room A & B 14th Floor Skyline Tower 18 Tong Mei Road, Mongkok, Kowloon, China (Hong Kong)
Tel.: (852) 2 129 0158 Ky
Web Site: http://www.silvertide.hk
Year Founded: 1990

INTERNATIONAL PUBLIC

1943—(HKG)
Rev.: $56,387,089
Assets: $38,296,613
Liabilities: $6,698,318
Net Worth: $31,598,294
Earnings: $1,822,100
Emp.: 45
Fiscal Year-end: 03/31/21
Holding Company
N.A.I.C.S.: 551112
Chi Ming Ip *(Chm & CEO)*

Subsidiaries:

Hop Fat Yuk Ying Engineering Limited (1)
Room A and B 14th Floor Skyline Tower 18 Tong Mei Road, Mongkok, Kowloon, China (Hong Kong)
Tel.: (852) 21290158
Web Site: https://www.hfyy.hk
Construction Services
N.A.I.C.S.: 236220

SILVER TIGER METALS INC.
Tel.: (902) 492-0298 Ca
Web Site: https://www.silvertigermetals.com
Year Founded: 2010
SLVTF—(OTCQX)
Assets: $64,872,423
Liabilities: $2,121,350
Net Worth: $62,751,072
Earnings: ($2,747,171)
Fiscal Year-end: 03/31/23
Precious Metals Exploration, Development & Mining
N.A.I.C.S.: 212220
Glenn Jessome *(Pres & CEO)*

Subsidiaries:

Pacemaker Silver Mining, S.A. de C.V. (1)
Avenida Doctor Aguilar 162 Prados del Centenario, Hermosillo, 83250, Sonora, Mexico
Tel.: (52) 662 2131554
Silver Ore Mining Services
N.A.I.C.S.: 212220
Jose Velazquez *(Country Mgr)*

SILVER TOUCH TECHNOLOGIES LIMITED
2nd Floor Saffron Tower Opp Central Mall Panchvati Cross Road, Ahmedabad, 380006, India
Tel.: (91) 7940022770
Web Site: https://www.silvertouch.com
Year Founded: 1995
543525—(BOM)
Rev.: $19,941,574
Assets: $17,721,539
Liabilities: $6,317,703
Net Worth: $11,403,837
Earnings: $1,164,558
Emp.: 715
Fiscal Year-end: 03/31/23
Information Technology Services
N.A.I.C.S.: 541512
Vipul Thakkar *(Chm & Mng Dir)*

Subsidiaries:

Silver Touch Technologies Canada Limited (1)
55 Albert St Ste 100, Markham, L3P 2T4, ON, Canada
Tel.: (647) 829-2482
Web Site: https://www.silvertouch.ca
Software Provider
N.A.I.C.S.: 423430

Silver Touch Technologies Inc. (1)
1149 Green St, Iselin, NJ 08830
Tel.: (201) 331-9818
Web Site: https://www.silvertouchinc.com
Software Provider
N.A.I.C.S.: 423430

AND PRIVATE COMPANIES — SILVERFLEET CAPITAL LIMITED

SILVER VIPER MINERALS CORP.
1055 W Hastings St Suite 300, Vancouver, V6E 2E9, BC, Canada
Tel.: (604) 687-8566
Web Site:
https://www.silverviperminerals.com
Year Founded: 2016
VIPRF—(OTCQB)
Rev.: $4,249
Assets: $3,098,128
Liabilities: $157,474
Net Worth: $2,940,654
Earnings: ($6,418,923)
Fiscal Year-end: 12/31/21
Metal Exploration Services
N.A.I.C.S.: 213114
Carla Hartzenberg (CFO)

SILVER WOLF EXPLORATION LTD.
900 570 Granville St, Vancouver, V6C 3P1, BC, Canada
Tel.: (604) 682-3701
Web Site:
https://silverwolfexploration.com
Year Founded: 1950
SWLFF—(OTCQB)
Assets: $1,057,467
Liabilities: $267,590
Net Worth: $789,877
Earnings: ($722,550)
Emp.: 4
Fiscal Year-end: 12/31/21
Mineral Exploration Services
N.A.I.C.S.: 213114
Nathan Harte (CFO)

Subsidiaries:

Compania Minera Mexicana de Gray Rock, S.A. de C.V. (1)

SILVER X MINING CORP
Suite 1012 - 1030 West Georgia St, Vancouver, V6E 2Y3, BC, Canada
Tel.: (647) 259-6901   BC
Web Site:
https://www.oroxmining.com
Year Founded: 2009
AGXPF—(OTCQB)
Rev.: $185
Assets: $49,476
Liabilities: $503,762
Net Worth: ($454,286)
Earnings: ($288,890)
Emp.: 8
Fiscal Year-end: 02/29/20
Gold Mining Services
N.A.I.C.S.: 212220
Matthew Roma (CFO)

SILVER-WEIBULL SWEDEN AB
Industrigatan 15, 281 43, Hassleholm, Sweden
Tel.: (46) 451384800   SE
Web Site: http://www.silver-weibull.se
Year Founded: 1922
Sales Range: $1-9.9 Million
Emp.: 43
Sugar Processing Equipment Mfr & Whslr
N.A.I.C.S.: 333998
Ann Pettersson (Coord-Admin)

Subsidiaries:

Silver Weibull Production AB (1)
Industrigatan 15, Hassleholm, 281 43, Sweden
Tel.: (46) 451 384800
Web Site: http://www.silver-weibull.se
Sugar Centrifugal Machinery Mfr
N.A.I.C.S.: 333241
Mats Olsson (Mgr-Tech)

Silver Weibull do Brasil (1)
Rua Italo Poli 200 Colina Verde, Jaboticabal, 14887-360, Sao Paulo, Brazil

Tel.: (55) 16 3202 8614
Sugar Centrifugal Machinery Mfr
N.A.I.C.S.: 333241

SILVERARROW CAPITAL HOLDING LTD.
Chart House Suite 302, 6 Burrells Wharf Square, London, E14 3TN, United Kingdom
Tel.: (44) 20 3637 2185
Web Site:
http://www.silverarrowcapital.com
Private Investment Firm
N.A.I.C.S.: 523999
Thomas P. Limberger (Co-Founder, Partner & CEO)

Subsidiaries:

PrivatAir SA (1)
Geneva Terminal C3 Chemin des Papillons 18, PO Box 572, 1215, Geneva, Switzerland   (51%)
Tel.: (41) 229296700
Web Site: http://www.privatair.com
Chartered Passenger Air Transportation Services
N.A.I.C.S.: 481211
Thomas Limberger (Chm)

Subsidiary (Non-US):

PrivatAir Gmbh (2)
Airport Gardens Peter-Muller-Strasse 26, 40468, Dusseldorf, Germany
Tel.: (49) 211 5423 0300
Web Site: http://www.privatair.com
Chartered Passenger Air Transportation Services
N.A.I.C.S.: 481211

PrivatAir Saudi Arabia (2)
106A Bin Homran Building Tahlia Street, Jeddah, 21533, Saudi Arabia
Tel.: (966) 2 665 9111
Web Site: http://www.privatair.com
Chartered Passenger Air Transportation Services
N.A.I.C.S.: 481211
Moaaz Khanani (Dir-Fin & Admin)

SILVERBRIDGE HOLDINGS LTD.
Unit D Castle Walk Corporate Park Cnr Nossob and Swakop streets, Erasmuskloof, Pretoria, 0048, South Africa
Tel.: (27) 123600100   ZA
Web Site:
http://www.silverbridge.co.za
Year Founded: 1995
SVB—(JSE)
Rev.: $7,227,536
Assets: $4,738,369
Liabilities: $1,256,251
Net Worth: $3,482,118
Earnings: $158,157
Emp.: 82
Fiscal Year-end: 06/30/22
Holding Company
N.A.I.C.S.: 551112
Robert Emslie (Chm)

SILVERCORP METALS INC.
Suite 1750-1066 W Hastings Street, Vancouver, V6E 3X1, BC, Canada
Tel.: (604) 669-9397   BC
Web Site:
https://silvercorpmetals.com
Year Founded: 1991
SVM—(NYSEAMEX)
Rev.: $217,923,000
Assets: $723,538,000
Liabilities: $103,424,000
Net Worth: $620,114,000
Earnings: $43,284,000
Emp.: 1,334
Fiscal Year-end: 03/31/22
Silver & Other Metal Mining Services
N.A.I.C.S.: 212220
Rui Feng (Founder, Chm & CEO)

Subsidiaries:

Adventus Mining Corporation (1)
220 Bay Street Suite 550, Toronto, M5J 2W4, ON, Canada
Tel.: (416) 306-8201
Web Site: https://www.adventusmining.com
Rev.: $40,000
Assets: $98,193,000
Liabilities: $95,678,000
Net Worth: $2,515,000
Earnings: $19,110,000
Emp.: 166
Fiscal Year-end: 12/31/2021
Mineral Exploration Services
N.A.I.C.S.: 213114
Brian Dalton (Chm)

Subsidiary (Domestic):

Luminex Resources Corp. (2)
410 - 625 Howe Street, Vancouver, V6C 2T6, BC, Canada
Tel.: (604) 646-1890
Web Site:
https://www.luminexresources.com
Rev.: $1,018,578
Assets: $39,663,761
Liabilities: $476,316
Net Worth: $39,187,445
Earnings: ($11,123,614)
Fiscal Year-end: 12/31/2020
Metal Exploration Services
N.A.I.C.S.: 213114
Diego Benalcazar (Pres)

SILVERCREST METALS, INC.
570 Granville Street Suite 501, Vancouver, V6C 3P1, BC, Canada
Tel.: (604) 694-1730
Web Site:
https://www.silvercrestmetals.com
SILV—(NYSEAMEX)
Rev.: $43,510,000
Assets: $355,349,000
Liabilities: $78,355,000
Net Worth: $276,994,000
Earnings: $31,301,000
Emp.: 375
Fiscal Year-end: 12/31/22
Metal Exploration Services
N.A.I.C.S.: 213114
Pierre Beaudoin (COO)

SILVERFISH RESOURCES INC.
9285-203B Street, Langley, V1M 2L9, BC, Canada
Tel.: (778) 919-8615   BC
Web Site:
https://www.silverfishresources.com
Year Founded: 2020
SFRIF—(OTCQB)
Assets: $268,511
Liabilities: $131,689
Net Worth: $136,822
Earnings: ($162,490)
Fiscal Year-end: 06/30/22
Mineral Mining Services
N.A.I.C.S.: 213115
Brandon Schwabe (CFO)

SILVERFLEET CAPITAL LIMITED
1 Carter Lane, London, EC4V 5ER, United Kingdom
Tel.: (44) 2078221000   UK
Web Site:
http://www.silverfleetcapital.com
Year Founded: 1984
Privater Equity Firm
N.A.I.C.S.: 523999
Neil MacDougall (Mng Partner)

Subsidiaries:

COVENTYA Holding SAS (1)
Parc d'Activites des Chanteraines, 7 Rue du Commandant d'Estienne d'Orves, 92396, Villeneuve-la-Garenne, France
Tel.: (33) 1 47 15 73 00
Web Site: http://www.coventya.com

Sales Range: $125-149.9 Million
Emp.: 570
Holding Company
N.A.I.C.S.: 551112
Thomas Costa (CEO)

Subsidiary (US):

COVENTYA Inc. (2)
132 Clear Rd, Oriskany, NY 13424
Tel.: (315) 768-6635
Web Site: http://www.coventya.com
Sales Range: $1-9.9 Million
Emp.: 23
Specialty Chemicals Mfr
N.A.I.C.S.: 325998
Thomas Costa (CEO)

Branch (Domestic):

COVENTYA Inc. (3)
4639 Van Epps Rd, Brooklyn Heights, OH 44131
Tel.: (216) 351-1500
Specialty Chemicals Mfr
N.A.I.C.S.: 325998
Greg Terrell (Mgr-Sls-Natl)

Subsidiary (Non-US):

COVENTYA India Pvt. Ltd. (2)
Gat no 520 B Shelkewadi Rihe Road At and Post Ghotawade, Taluka Mulashi, Pune, 411042, India
Tel.: (91) 20 67 90 19 00
Specialty Chemicals Mfr & Distr
N.A.I.C.S.: 325998
Chandrashekhar Marathe (Mng Dir)

Subsidiary (Domestic):

COVENTYA SAS (2)
Parc d'Activites des Chanteraines, 7 Rue du Commandant d'Estienne d'Orves, 92396, Villeneuve-la-Garenne, cedex, France
Tel.: (33) 1 47 15 73 00
Specialty Chemicals Mfr & Distr
N.A.I.C.S.: 325998
Laurent L. Theret (Dir Gen)

Subsidiary (Non-US):

COVENTYA South East Asia Pte. Ltd. (2)
1 Science Park Road #01-07 The Capricom, Singapore Science Park II, Singapore, 117528, Singapore
Tel.: (65) 6908 4870
Specialty Chemicals Mfr & Distr
N.A.I.C.S.: 325998
Didier Brouckaert (Mng Dir)

COVENTYA Surface Treatment Technology (Suzhou) Co. Ltd. (2)
1088 Yinzhong South Road, Wuzhong District, Suzhou, 215124, China
Tel.: (86) 512 6708 2628
Specialty Chemicals Mfr & Distr
N.A.I.C.S.: 325998
Joseph Chianale (Mng Dir)

Politeknik Metal Sanayi ve Ticaret A.S. (2)
Tuzla Kimyaclar Org San Bol Melek Aras Bulvar Kristal Caddesi, No B1/B4, Istanbul, Turkiye
Tel.: (90) 216 504 02
Web Site: http://www.pm.com.tr
Aluminum Surface Treatment Chemicals Mfr
N.A.I.C.S.: 325998

Paramount Holdings Ltd (1)
8-10 Grosvenor Gardens, London, SW1W 0BD, United Kingdom
Tel.: (44) 207 881 8870
Sales Range: $50-74.9 Million
Cafe & Restaurant Owner & Operator
N.A.I.C.S.: 722511

Schneider Versand GmbH (1)
Strandbaddamm, 22877, Wedel, Germany
Tel.: (49) 805040203
Web Site: http://www.schneider.de
Sales Range: $350-399.9 Million
Promotional Product Retailer
N.A.I.C.S.: 459410

Silverfleet Capital Partners LLP (1)
One Carter Lane, London, EC4V 5ER, United Kingdom

SILVERFLEET CAPITAL LIMITED

Silverfleet Capital Limited—(Continued)
Tel.: (44) 20 7822 1000
Web Site: http://www.silverfleetcapital.com
Private Equity invesment Management Firm
N.A.I.C.S.: 523940
Neil MacDougall (Chm)

TJ Hughes Limited (1)
Hughes house London Road, Liverpool, L3 8JA, Merseyside, United Kingdom
Tel.: (44) 1512072600
Web Site: http://www.tjhughes.co.uk
Sales Range: $125-149.9 Million
Department Stores
N.A.I.C.S.: 455110

SILVERHUB MEDIA UK LTD.
RSM Davidson House The Forbury, Reading, RG1 3EU, United Kingdom
Tel.: (44) 2076447656 UK
Web Site: http://www.silverhub.media
Year Founded: 2016
Celebrity News Syndicate
N.A.I.C.S.: 516210
Nick Evans-Lombe (Co-Founder & Mng Dir)

SILVERLAKE AXIS LTD.
Level 2A KPMG Tower First Avenue Bandar Utama, 47800, Petaling Jaya, Selangor Darul Ehsan, Malaysia
Tel.: (60) 377306100 BM
Web Site:
 https://www.silverlakeaxis.com
Year Founded: 1989
5CP—(SES)
Rev.: $567,554,817
Assets: $1,210,231,110
Liabilities: $358,066,628
Net Worth: $852,164,482
Earnings: $126,179,358
Emp.: 2,850
Fiscal Year-end: 06/30/23
Banking Software & Technology Solutions
N.A.I.C.S.: 513210
Peng Ooi Goh (Founder & Chm)

Subsidiaries:

Cyber Village Sdn Bhd (1)
Unit 901C Level 9 Tower C Uptown 5 No 5 Jalan SS 21/39, Damansara Utama, 47400, Petaling Jaya, Selangor Darul Ehsan, Malaysia
Tel.: (60) 377241377
Web Site: https://www.cyber-village.net
Sales Range: $1-9.9 Million
Emp.: 80
Web-based Technology Solutions & E-Commerce Consulting Services
N.A.I.C.S.: 541690
Shii Huey Sua (Mng Dir)

Merimen Online Sdn. Bhd. (1)
Block D Level 1 UPM-MTDC Technology Center 3 Universiti Putra Malaysia, 43400, Serdang, Malaysia
Tel.: (60) 389428281
Web Site: https://www.merimen.com
Electronic Insurance Claim Services
N.A.I.C.S.: 524298

Merimen Technologies (Singapore) Pte. Ltd. (1)
6 Raffles Quay 18-00, Singapore, 048580, Singapore
Tel.: (65) 62240010
Electronic Insurance Claim Services
N.A.I.C.S.: 524298

Merimen Technologies (Thailand) Co. Ltd. (1)
120 Kasemkij Building Room No 302 3rd floor Silom Road, Suriyawongse Bangrak, Bangkok, 10500, Thailand
Tel.: (66) 2406730
Electronic Insurance Claim Services
N.A.I.C.S.: 524298

Merimen Technologies - FZE (1)
DSO-THUB-G-059D DTEC Technohub 1 Building Silicon Oasis Authority, Dubai, United Arab Emirates
Tel.: (971) 585001036
Electronic Insurance Claim Services
N.A.I.C.S.: 524298

Merimen Technologies Hong Kong Limited (1)
13/F 68 Yee Wo Street, Causeway Bay, China (Hong Kong)
Tel.: (852) 37965633
Electronic Insurance Claim Services
N.A.I.C.S.: 524298

Merimen Technologies Japan K.K. (1)
Pacific Century Place Marunouchi 8F Marunouchi 1-11-1, Chiyoda-ku, Tokyo, 100-6208, Japan
Tel.: (81) 368608525
Electronic Insurance Claim Services
N.A.I.C.S.: 524298

Merimen Technologies Philippines Inc. (1)
Level 40 PBCOM Tower 6795 Ayala Ave, Bel-Air, Makati, 1209, Philippines
Tel.: (63) 283302126
Electronic Insurance Claim Services
N.A.I.C.S.: 524298

Motobiznes Online Sdn. Bhd. (1)
36th Floor Menara Maxis Kuala Lumpur City Centre, 50088, Kuala Lumpur, Malaysia
Tel.: (60) 389438088
Web Site: https://www.motobiz.net.my
Electronic Insurance Claim Services
N.A.I.C.S.: 524298

P.T. Merimen Technologies Indonesia (1)
Sampoerna Strategic Square South Tower, Level 18 JI Jend Sudirman Kav 45-46, Jakarta Selatan, 12930, Indonesia
Tel.: (62) 2129069405
Electronic Insurance Claim Services
N.A.I.C.S.: 524298

QR Agoracloud Sdn. Bhd. (1)
1-01 Bangunan Yin 1st Floor No 7 Section 16/11 Off Jalan Damansara, 46350, Petaling Jaya, Selangor, Malaysia
Tel.: (60) 379553188
Web Site: https://www.qragoracloud.com
Software Development Services
N.A.I.C.S.: 541511

Silverlake Digital Economy Sdn. Bhd. (1)
Level 2A KPMG Tower First Avenue, Bandar Utama, 47800, Petaling Jaya, Selangor Darul Ehsan, Malaysia
Tel.: (60) 377216000
Web Site: https://www.silverlake-digital-economy.com
Software Development Services
N.A.I.C.S.: 541511

Silverlake Symmetri (Malaysia) Sdn. Bhd. (1)
Lot 2 03 Level 2 1 First Avenue, Bandar Utama, 47800, Petaling Jaya, Selangor, Malaysia
Tel.: (60) 376138800
Web Site:
 https://www.silverlakesymmetri.com
Software Development Services
N.A.I.C.S.: 541511

Silverlake Symmetri (Philippines) Enterprises, Inc. (1)
3F Shops at Ayala North Exchange 6796 Ayala Avenue corner Salcedo St, Legaspi Village San Lorenzo, Makati, 1229, Philippines
Tel.: (63) 277984400
Software Development Services
N.A.I.C.S.: 541511

X-Infotech Africa Limited (1)
The Mirage Tower 2 4th Floor Suite 5 Waiyaki Way off Chiromo Rd, PO Box 28309-00100, Westlands, Nairobi, Kenya
Tel.: (254) 205100278
Web Site: https://www.x-infotech.com
Software Development Services
N.A.I.C.S.: 541511
Vadim Teresko (CEO)

SILVERLINE ENDUSTRI VE TICARET A.S.
Flatofis Istanbul Defterdar Mah Otakcilar St No 78 Floor, 2 Interior Door No 19 Eyup, 34050, Istanbul, Turkiye
Tel.: (90) 2124844800
Web Site: https://www.silverline.com
Year Founded: 1994
SILVR—(IST)
Emp.: 346
Kitchen Appliances Mfr
N.A.I.C.S.: 332215
Mustafa Lacin (Chm & Gen Mgr)

SILVERLINE TECHNOLOGIES LTD.
Unit-121 SDF IV Seepz, Andheri E, Mumbai, 400096, Maharashtra, India
Tel.: (91) 2228291950
Web Site:
 https://www.silverlinetech.com
Year Founded: 1992
500389—(BOM)
Sales Range: $1-9.9 Million
Emp.: 2
Software Development Services
N.A.I.C.S.: 541511
Kumar Subramanian (Vice Chm)

SILVEROAK COMMERCIALS LIMITED
11 Radhamandir Building 213 Sir Bhalchandra Road Behind Ruia College, Matunga E, Mumbai, 400 019, India
Tel.: (91) 2224143502
Web Site: http://www.silveroak.co.in
Year Founded: 1985
512197—(BOM)
Sales Range: Less than $1 Million
Emp.: 38
Stock Brokerage Services
N.A.I.C.S.: 523150
Kiran Sudhakar Patil (Compliance Officer)

SILVERPOINT INFRATECH LIMITED
85 Bentick Street 5th Floor Yashoda Chamber Room No 6 Lalbazar, Howrah, 711109, India
Tel.: (91) 8232062881
Web Site:
 https://www.silverpointinfratech.com
Year Founded: 1997
Rev.: $70,951
Assets: $6,706,632
Liabilities: $186,717
Net Worth: $6,519,915
Earnings: ($1,733)
Emp.: 4
Fiscal Year-end: 03/31/18
Construction Engineering Services
N.A.I.C.S.: 541330
Sanjay Kumar Drolia (Chm, Mng Dir & CFO)

SILVERSTRIPE LIMITED
Level 5 101 Courtenay Place, Wellington, 6011, New Zealand
Tel.: (64) 4 978 7330
Web Site: http://www.silverstripe.com
Year Founded: 2000
Sales Range: $10-24.9 Million
Content Management Software Development Services
N.A.I.C.S.: 513210
Sam Minnee (Co-Founder & CEO)

Subsidiaries:

SilverStripe Limited - Australia (1)
123/838 Collins St Docklands, Melbourne, 3008, VIC, Australia
Tel.: (61) 3 8352 4431
Web Site: http://www.silverstripe.com
Content Management Software
N.A.I.C.S.: 513210
Marcus Nyeholt (Mgr-Dev)

INTERNATIONAL PUBLIC

SILVERTON SPINNERS LIMITED
P-22 CIT Road Scheme - 55, Kolkata, 700014, India
Tel.: (91) 33 22658157
Cotton Yarn Mfr
N.A.I.C.S.: 313110
Chandra Prakash Mehra (Mng Dir)

SILVERY DRAGON PRE-STRESSED MATERIALS CO., LTD.
No 62 Shuangjiang Road, Beichen district, Tianjin, 300400, China
Tel.: (86) 2226983535
Web Site: https://www.yinlong.com
Year Founded: 1998
603969—(SHG)
Rev.: $345,879,879
Assets: $455,554,111
Liabilities: $157,439,056
Net Worth: $298,115,055
Earnings: $14,582,197
Fiscal Year-end: 12/31/22
Steel Product Mfr & Distr
N.A.I.C.S.: 331221
Xie Zhifeng (Chm & Gen Mgr)

SIM LEISURE GROUP LTD.
138 Robinson Road 26-03 Oxley Tower, Singapore, 68906, Singapore
Tel.: (65) 62369353 SG
Web Site: https://www.simleisure.com
Year Founded: 2018
URR—(SES)
Rev.: $29,491,511
Assets: $49,482,804
Liabilities: $25,554,201
Net Worth: $23,928,603
Earnings: $6,328,037
Emp.: 198
Fiscal Year-end: 12/31/23
Theme Park Operator
N.A.I.C.S.: 713110
Sim Choo Kheng (Founder & CEO)

Subsidiaries:

Sim Leisure Gulf Contracting LLC (1)
Unit S-10 Al Asayal Street 318th Road, Al Quoz Industrial Area 2, Dubai, United Arab Emirates
Tel.: (971) 43804241
Theme Park Operator
N.A.I.C.S.: 713110
Wesley Rae (COO)

SIM LIAN GROUP LIMITED
205 Upper Bukit Timah Road 02-01, Singapore, 588181, Singapore
Tel.: (65) 63036200
Web Site: http://www.simlian.com.sg
Year Founded: 1976
Sales Range: $800-899.9 Million
Property Development & Management Services
N.A.I.C.S.: 531311
Ah Han Kuik (Chm)

Subsidiaries:

Perumahan SLG Selatan Sdn. Bhd. (1)
No 765 & 8157 Off Jalan Senai Utama Taman Senai Utama, 81200, Senai, Johor, Malaysia
Tel.: (60) 75998008
Sales Range: $25-49.9 Million
Emp.: 4
Residential Property Development Services
N.A.I.C.S.: 236115

Porta Pumper Pte Ltd (1)
24 Woodlands Walk, Singapore, 738389, Singapore
Tel.: (65) 67754466
Web Site: http://www.portapumper.com.sg

Sales Range: $50-74.9 Million
Emp.: 10
Portable Toilet Leasing Services
N.A.I.C.S.: 532490
Krisztine Teo *(Mgr-Mktg)*

S&L City Builders Pte. Ltd. (1)
205 Upper Bukit Timah Road, Singapore, 588181, Singapore
Tel.: (65) 63036200
Web Site: http://www.simlian.com.sg
Emp.: 150
Residential Building Construction Services
N.A.I.C.S.: 236115

Sim Lian (Bishan) Pte. Ltd. (1)
205 Upper Bukit Timah Raod 02-01, Singapore, 588181, Singapore
Tel.: (65) 67676777
Real Estate Property Development Services
N.A.I.C.S.: 531210

Subsidiary (Domestic):

RCS Engineering Pte Ltd (2)
18 Boon Lay Way 05-121 Tradehub 21, Jurong E, Jurong, 609966, Singapore
Tel.: (65) 63161180
Sales Range: $10-24.9 Million
Emp.: 50
Construction Engineering Services
N.A.I.C.S.: 541330
Christopher Sia *(Exec Dir)*

Sim Lian-Koru Bena JV Pte. Ltd. (2)
205 Upper Bukit Timah Rd Unit 02-01, Singapore, 588181, Singapore
Tel.: (65) 63036200
Emp.: 75
Commercial Building Construction Services
N.A.I.C.S.: 236220
Hung Dong Sheng *(Gen Mgr)*

Weldanpower Enterprises & Engineering Services Pte Ltd (2)
205 Upper Bukit Timah Rd Unit 02-02, Singapore, 588181, Singapore
Tel.: (65) 68624055
Emp.: 18
Construction Materials Trading & Engineering Services
N.A.I.C.S.: 423320
Raymond Tan *(Mgr-Admin)*

Sim Lian (East Coast) Pte. Ltd. (1)
52 Hillview Terrace, Singapore, Singapore
Tel.: (65) 64433760
Residential Property Development Services
N.A.I.C.S.: 236115

Sim Lian (Mount Faber) Pte. Ltd. (1)
205 Upper Bukit Timah Road #02-01, Singapore, 588181, Singapore
Tel.: (65) 63036163
Web Site: http://www.simlian.com.sg
Residential Property Development Services
N.A.I.C.S.: 236115
Ah Han Kuik *(CEO)*

Sim Lian (Newton) Pte. Ltd. (1)
205 Upper Bukit Timah Rd #02-01, Singapore, 588181, Singapore (100%)
Tel.: (65) 6303 6200
Web Site: http://www.simlian.com.sg
Real Estate Property Development Services
N.A.I.C.S.: 531311

Sim Lian (Simei) Pte. Ltd. (1)
52 Hillview Terrace, Singapore, Singapore
Tel.: (65) 67866968
Residential Property Development Services
N.A.I.C.S.: 236115

Sim Lian (Tampines) Pte. Ltd. (1)
205 Upper Bukit Timah Road 02-01, Singapore, 588181, Singapore
Tel.: (65) 63036200
Residential Property Development Services
N.A.I.C.S.: 236115

Subsidiary (Domestic):

Sim Lian (Hougang) Pte. Ltd. (2)
205 Upper Bukit Timah Road Unit 02-01, Singapore, 588181, Singapore
Tel.: (65) 63036200
Web Site: http://www.simlian.com.sg
Emp.: 80
Residential Property Development Services
N.A.I.C.S.: 236115
Huang Dong Sheng *(Gen Mgr)*

Sim Lian (Tampines Central) Pte. Ltd. (2)
205 Upper Bukit Timah Road Unit 02-01, Singapore, 588181, Singapore
Tel.: (65) 63036200
Web Site: http://www.simlian.com.sg
Residential Property Development Services
N.A.I.C.S.: 236115

Sim Lian (Ubi) Pte. Ltd. (1)
205 Upper Bukit Rd Timah Rd unit 02-01, Singapore, 588181, Singapore
Tel.: (65) 63036200
Web Site: http://www.simliangroup.com.sg
Emp.: 80
Residential Property Development Services
N.A.I.C.S.: 236115
Dong Sheng Huang *(Gen Mgr)*

Sim Lian Construction Co. (Pte.) Ltd. (1)
205 Upper Bukit Timah Road 02-01 Sim Lian, Singapore, 588181, Singapore
Tel.: (65) 63036200
Web Site: http://www.simlian.com.sg
Sales Range: $50-74.9 Million
Emp.: 70
Residential Building Construction Services
N.A.I.C.S.: 236115
D. S. Huang *(Gen Mgr)*

Unigrade Trading Pte Ltd (1)
No 6 Tuas S St 2 01-01, Singapore, 638042, Singapore
Tel.: (65) 68624733
Web Site: http://www.unigrade.com.sg
Emp.: 20
Lubricant & Petroleum Products Distr
N.A.I.C.S.: 424720
Finian Fernandez *(Gen Mgr)*

SIM TECHNOLOGY GROUP LIMITED
Unit 1206 12/F Billion Trade Centre 31 Hung To Road, Kwun Tong, Kowloon, China (Hong Kong)
Tel.: (852) 23686824
Web Site: http://www.sim.com
2000—(OTCIQ)
Rev.: $81,538,845
Assets: $262,483,418
Liabilities: $95,277,519
Net Worth: $167,205,899
Earnings: ($64,899,868)
Emp.: 716
Fiscal Year-end: 12/31/22
Investment Holding Company
N.A.I.C.S.: 523940
Rongrong Tang *(VP-Bus Operation)*

Subsidiaries:

Shanghai SIM Technology Limited (1)
SIM Technology Building No 700 Yishan Road, Shanghai, 200233, China
Tel.: (86) 2132523392
Investment Holding Services
N.A.I.C.S.: 551112

Shanghai Suncom Logistics Limited (1)
B Area 4floor 16 Building No 69 Xiya Road Waigaoqiao Free Trade Zone, Shanghai, 200131, China
Tel.: (86) 2150461403
Communication Module Distr
N.A.I.C.S.: 423690

SIMAC TECHNIEK NV
De Run 1101, 5503 LB, Veldhoven, Netherlands
Tel.: (31) 40 258 29 44 Nl
Web Site: http://www.simac.com
Year Founded: 1971
Rev.: $309,477,790
Assets: $140,516,673
Liabilities: $80,721,749
Net Worth: $59,794,925
Earnings: $7,891,653
Emp.: 1,063
Fiscal Year-end: 12/31/19
Information & Communication Technology Services
N.A.I.C.S.: 519290
Nico I. M. Hermans *(Vice Chm-Supervisory Bd)*

Subsidiaries:

Simac 3Services BV (1)
De Hootkamp 4, 5321 JT, Hedel, Netherlands
Tel.: (31) 73 599 60 30
Emp.: 40
Information Technology Consulting Services
N.A.I.C.S.: 541512
Robert Decant *(Pres)*

Simac Business Solutions bv (1)
De Run 1101, 5503 LB, Veldhoven, Netherlands
Tel.: (31) 40 258 28 00
Healthcare & Retail Software Development Services
N.A.I.C.S.: 541511
Wim van der Velden *(Mng Dir)*

Simac Document Solutions bv (1)
Amperestraat 36, 6716 BN, Ede, Netherlands
Tel.: (31) 318649699
Web Site: http://www.simac.com
Data Processing Services
N.A.I.C.S.: 518210

Simac Electronics bv (1)
Eindstraat 53, 5151 AE, Drunen, Netherlands
Tel.: (31) 416 387 700
Sales Range: $25-49.9 Million
Emp.: 40
Electronic Components Distr
N.A.I.C.S.: 423690
Marcel Leenen *(Mng Dir)*

Simac ICT Netherlands B.V. (1)
De Run 1101, 5503 LB, Veldhoven, Netherlands
Tel.: (31) 40 258 29 11
Emp.: 35
Information Technology Consulting Services
N.A.I.C.S.: 541512
Eric van Schagen *(Gen Mgr)*

Simac Masic & TSS bv (1)
Jan Campertstraat 21, 6416 SG, Heerlen, Netherlands
Tel.: (31) 45 750 21 00
Web Site: http://www.simac.com
Sales Range: $25-49.9 Million
Semiconductor Equipment Distr
N.A.I.C.S.: 423690

Simac QuadCore bv (1)
De Run 1101, 5503 LB, Veldhoven, Netherlands
Tel.: (31) 40 258 21 00
Emp.: 30
Systems Integrator & Automated Operational Processor
N.A.I.C.S.: 518210
Har Heuberger *(Dir-Simac IDS)*

Simac Triangle B.V (1)
Schoutlaan 18, 6002 EA, Weert, Netherlands
Tel.: (31) 495 46 21 21
Sales Range: $25-49.9 Million
Emp.: 18
Information Technology Consulting Services
N.A.I.C.S.: 541512

SIMAT TECHNOLOGIES PUBLIC COMPANY LIMITED
No 123 Chalongkrung 31 Ladkrabang Industrial Estate Chalongkrung Rd, Lamplatiew Ladkrabang, Bangkok, 10520, Thailand
Tel.: (66) 23260999
Web Site: https://www.simat.co.th
Year Founded: 1999
SIMAT—(THA)
Rev.: $2,540,723
Assets: $52,295,517
Liabilities: $16,511,825
Net Worth: $35,783,692
Earnings: $714,824
Emp.: 344
Fiscal Year-end: 12/31/23
Information Technology Solutions Services
N.A.I.C.S.: 519290
Thongkam Manasilapapan *(Chm)*

Subsidiaries:

Simat Label Company Limited (1)
No 123 Soi Chalongkrung 31 Chalongkrung Road, Ladkrabang Industrial Estate Lamplatew Sub-District, Bangkok, 10520, Thailand
Tel.: (66) 23260999
Electric Equipment Mfr
N.A.I.C.S.: 334419

SIMAVITA LIMITED
Suite 2.02 Level 2 54 Miller Street, North Sydney, 2060, NSW, Australia
Tel.: (61) 2 8405 6300
Web Site: http://www.simavita.com
Medical Device Mfr
N.A.I.C.S.: 339112
Peta Jurd *(Chief Comml Officer & Sec)*

SIMBA ESSEL ENERGY INC.
210905 West Pender Street, Vancouver, V6C 1L6, BC, Canada
Tel.: (604) 641-4450 BC
Web Site: https://www.simbaenergy.ca
Year Founded: 1990
SMBZF—(OTCIQ)
Sales Range: Less than $1 Million
Oil & Gas Exploration
N.A.I.C.S.: 211120
Robert G. Dinning *(Pres)*

Subsidiaries:

International Resource Strategies Liberia Energy, Inc. (1)

SIMBA-DICKIE-GROUP GMBH
Werkstrasse 1, 90765, Furth, Germany
Tel.: (49) 911 9765 01 De
Web Site: http://www.simba-dickie-group.com
Year Founded: 1982
Toy Mfr
N.A.I.C.S.: 339930
Maximilian Stork *(Sr Mgr-Product)*

Subsidiaries:

Jada Toys, Inc. (1)
938 Hatcher Ave, City of Industry, CA 91748
Tel.: (626) 810-8382
Web Site: http://www.jadatoys.com
Die-Cast Automotive Toy & Remote Control Toy Mfr
N.A.I.C.S.: 339930
May Li *(Pres)*

Subsidiary (Non-US):

Jada Toys Co., Ltd (2)
Unit 308 3/F Tower B New Mandarin Plaza No 14 Science Museum Road, TST East, Kowloon, China (Hong Kong)
Tel.: (852) 21561968
Sales Range: $10-24.9 Million
Emp.: 40
Die-Cast Automotive Toy & Remote Control Toy Mfr
N.A.I.C.S.: 339930

SIMBETON SA
Str Uzinelor nr 12, Bihor, Oradea, Romania
Tel.: (40) 359315111
SIOB—(BUC)
Rev.: $1,375,073
Assets: $1,589,978
Liabilities: $562,894
Net Worth: $1,027,084
Earnings: $137,786
Emp.: 32
Fiscal Year-end: 12/31/19
Concrete Products Mfr

SIMBETON SA

Simbeton SA—(Continued)
N.A.I.C.S.: 327390

SIMBHAOLI SUGARS LIMITED
A-112 Sector 63, Noida, 201307, Uttar Pradesh, India
Tel.: (91) 5731226411 In
Web Site:
https://www.simbhaolisugars.com
Year Founded: 1933
539742—(BOM)
Rev.: $169,945,627
Assets: $250,486,098
Liabilities: $252,281,314
Net Worth: ($1,795,216)
Earnings: ($3,697,980)
Emp.: 1,450
Fiscal Year-end: 03/31/23
Sugar Refining Services
N.A.I.C.S.: 311314
Gurpal Singh *(Exec Dir)*

Subsidiaries:

Integrated Casetech Consultants Pvt
Ltd (1)
A-112 Sector 63, Noida, 201301, India
Tel.: (91) 1204806666
Web Site: https://www.intcasetech.com
Sales Range: $25-49.9 Million
Emp.: 25
Sugar Consultant Services
N.A.I.C.S.: 541690

Simbhaoli Power Private Limited (1)
Kothi No 1 Power Division Compound, Siddhapur, 245 207, Uttar Pradesh, India
Tel.: (91) 5731226411
Web Site: https://www.simbhaolipower.com
Power Generation Services
N.A.I.C.S.: 221118

Simbhaoli Sugars Limited - Brijnathpur Ethanol Division (1)
Brijnathpur, Ghaziabad, 245 101, Uttar Pradesh, India
Tel.: (91) 9927049979
Sales Range: $25-49.9 Million
Emp.: 10
Methanol Mfr
N.A.I.C.S.: 325193
N. K. Tyagi *(Gen Mgr)*

Simbhaoli Sugars Limited - Chilwaria Sugar Division (1)
Unit Chilwaria 13 km Bahraich To Gonda Rd, Chilwaria District, Bahraich, 271 801, India
Tel.: (91) 5252 244251
Web Site: http://www.simbhaolisugars.com
Sugar Mfr
N.A.I.C.S.: 311314

SIMBLE SOLUTIONS LTD.
Level 2 383 George Street, Sydney, 2000, NSW, Australia
Tel.: (61) 282083366
Web Site:
https://www.simblegroup.com
Year Founded: 2009
SIS—(ASX)
Rev.: $992,370
Assets: $826,495
Liabilities: $1,116,553
Net Worth: ($290,058)
Earnings: ($1,515,345)
Fiscal Year-end: 12/31/22
Custom Computer Programming Services
N.A.I.C.S.: 541511
Ben Loiterman *(Chm)*

SIMCERE PHARMACEUTICAL GROUP
No 699-18 Xuanwu Avenue, Nanjing, 210042, Jiangsu, China
Tel.: (86) 2585566666 Ky
Web Site: http://www.simcere.com
Year Founded: 1995
Pharmaceutical Mfr & Distr
N.A.I.C.S.: 325412

Jinsheng Ren *(Founder, Chm & CEO)*

Subsidiaries:

Jiangsu Simcere Vaxtec Bio-Pharmaceutical Co., Ltd. (1)
No 88 Kunlun Rd, Xinbei Dist, Changzhou, 213022, China
Tel.: (86) 51981668935
Pharmaceuticals Product Mfr
N.A.I.C.S.: 325412

Simcere Pharmaceutical Co., Ltd. (1)
No 699-18 Xuanwu Avenue Xuzhuang Software Park Qixia District, Nanjing, 210042, China
Tel.: (86) 2585566666
Web Site: http://www.simcere.com
Pharmaceuticals Product Mfr
N.A.I.C.S.: 325412

Subsidiary (Domestic):

Jiangsu Simcere Pharmaceutical R&D Co., Ltd. (2)
No 699-18 Xuanwu Avenue, Xuanwu District, Nanjing, 210042, China
Tel.: (86) 25 85566666
Web Site: http://www.simcere.com
Emp.: 400
Pharmaceutical Products Research & Development Services
N.A.I.C.S.: 541715

Jilin Boda Pharmaceutical Co., Ltd. (2)
No 188 Xinxing Road, Longshan District, Liaoyuan, 136200, Jilin, China
Tel.: (86) 4375082988
Pharmaceuticals Product Mfr
N.A.I.C.S.: 325412

Shandong Simcere Medgenn Bio-Pharmaceutical Co., Ltd. (2)
No 699-18 Xuan Wu Avenue, Xuan Wu District, 210042, Nanjing, China
Tel.: (86) 25 8556 6666
Pharmaceuticals Product Mfr
N.A.I.C.S.: 325412

Simcere of America Inc. (1)
502 Carnegie Ctr, Princeton, NJ 08540
Tel.: (650) 390-7528
Web Site: http://eng.simcere.com
Pharmaceuticals Product Mfr
N.A.I.C.S.: 325412
Jefferey Zhenhuan Zheng *(Mgr-Bus Dev)*

SIMCO SONG DA JOINT STOCK COMPANY
SIMCO Song Da Building Van Phuc New Urban Area Van Phuc Ward, Ha Dong, Hanoi, Vietnam
Tel.: (84) 2422232414
Web Site: https://www.simco.vn
Year Founded: 1997
SDA—(HNX)
Rev.: $1,865,305
Assets: $13,721,903
Liabilities: $3,161,277
Net Worth: $10,560,626
Earnings: $933,783
Fiscal Year-end: 12/31/21
Civil & Industrial Construction Services
N.A.I.C.S.: 237990
Vu Duc Quan *(Gen Mgr)*

SIMCONTROL SOLUTIONS LTD.
Izocolor Building 19 Dudesti Pantelimon Street Sector 3, 033091, Bucharest, Romania
Tel.: (40) 314252514 RO
Web Site: http://www.simcontrol-solutions.com
Electrical Equipment Distr
N.A.I.C.S.: 423610

SIME DARBY BERHAD
Level 9 Menara Sime Darby Oasis Corporate Park, Jalan PJU 1A/2 Ara Damansara, 47301, Petaling Jaya, 47301, Selangor, Malaysia
Tel.: (60) 376232000 MY
Web Site:
https://www.simedarby.com
Year Founded: 1979
SIME—(KLS)
Rev.: $10,519,245,000
Assets: $7,481,677,500
Liabilities: $3,429,855,000
Net Worth: $4,051,822,500
Earnings: $293,782,500
Emp.: 22,862
Fiscal Year-end: 06/30/22
Holding Company
N.A.I.C.S.: 551112
Samsudin Osman *(Chm)*

Subsidiaries:

Brisbane BMW Bodyshop Pty. Ltd. (1)
400 Nudgee Rd, Hendra, 4011, QLD, Australia
Tel.: (61) 736233000
Web Site: https://www.brisbanebmw.com.au
Car Dealing Services
N.A.I.C.S.: 441110

CICA Vietnam Company Limited (1)
569A Nguyen Tam Trinh, Hoang Mai District, Hanoi, Vietnam
Tel.: (84) 2439780857
Web Site: https://www.cica.com.vn
Industrial Equipment Distr
N.A.I.C.S.: 423830

Changsha Chuang Yue Motors Sales & Services Company Limited (1)
No 104-107 Building 2-A Mingfa Commercial Plaza, No 378 Moon Island Road Wangcheng District, Changsha, Huhan, China
Tel.: (86) 73182936666
Automobile Parts Distr
N.A.I.C.S.: 441330

Chengdu Bow Yue Used Cars Centre Co. Ltd. (1)
No 3 South Jinke Road, Jinniu District, Chengdu, Sichuan, China
Tel.: (86) 2865135300
Automobile Parts Distr
N.A.I.C.S.: 441330

Chongqing Bow Chuang Motor Sales & Services Co. Ltd. (1)
No 15Jinkai Main Road Gaoxin Zone, New North District, Chongqing, China
Tel.: (86) 63217088
Automobile Parts Distr
N.A.I.C.S.: 441330

Cognis Oleochemicals (Malaysia) Sdn. Bhd. (1)
Level 9 Building A Peremba Square, Saujana Resort Section U2, 40150, Shah Alam, Selangor, Malaysia
Tel.: (60) 3 7845 3000
Sales Range: $450-499.9 Million
Emp.: 1,100
Oleochemical Products Mfr; Owned 50% by Sime Darby Berhad & 50% by PTT Chemical Public Company Limited
N.A.I.C.S.: 325199

Corporate Travel Management (S) Pte. Ltd. (1)
10 Toh Guan Road 08-02, Singapore, 608838, Singapore (69.1%)
Travel Agency
N.A.I.C.S.: 561510

Foshan Sime Darby Elco Power Equipment Limited (1)
10-1 Weiye Rd, Beijiao Industrial Park Beijiao Shunde, Foshan, China
Tel.: (86) 4006806728
Web Site: https://en.sdelco.com
Generator Set & Spare Parts Distr
N.A.I.C.S.: 423120

Guangdong Deda Bow Ma Motor Service Co. Ltd. (1)
No 628 Yingbin Road, Panyu, Guangzhou, GuangDong, China
Tel.: (86) 208 479 3232

INTERNATIONAL PUBLIC

Automobile Parts Distr
N.A.I.C.S.: 441330

HMG Hardchrome Pty. Ltd. (1)
1 Mundin Street, Pinkenba, Murarrie, 4008, QLD, Australia
Tel.: (61) 1300509931
Web Site: https://www.hmg.net.au
Industrial Equipment Mfr
N.A.I.C.S.: 333248
Dean Mehmet *(Chm)*

Hangzhou Sime Darby Trading Co. Ltd. (1)
No 532 Shi Xiang Road, Gong Shu District, Hangzhou, China
Tel.: (86) 57186560199
Automobile Parts Distr
N.A.I.C.S.: 441330

Nanjing Sime Darby Motors Sales & Services Co. Ltd. (1)
No 16 Run Qi Road Dongshan Street, Jiangning District, Nanjing, China
Tel.: (86) 2551877599
Automobile Parts Distr
N.A.I.C.S.: 441330

Performance Munich Autos Pte. Ltd. (1)
315 Alexandra Road, Singapore, 159941, Singapore
Tel.: (65) 63333933
Web Site: https://www.pma-bmw.com.sg
Car Dealing Services
N.A.I.C.S.: 441110

Shanghai Sime Darby Motor Sales & Services Co. Ltd. (1)
No 208 Hubin Road, Huangpu District, Shanghai, China
Tel.: (86) 2163869599
Automobile Parts Distr
N.A.I.C.S.: 441330

Shantou Bow Yue Dehong Motors Services Co. Ltd. (1)
No 74 Tianshan Road, Shantou, Guangdong, China
Tel.: (86) 75488482626280
Automobile Parts Distr
N.A.I.C.S.: 441330

Shantou Bow Yue Vehicle Trading Co. Ltd. (1)
No 74 Tianshan Road, Shantou, Guangdong, China
Tel.: (86) 75488482323364
Automobile Parts Distr
N.A.I.C.S.: 441330

Shenzhen Bow Chuang Vehicle Trading Co. Ltd. (1)
Block1 Ma Que Ling Gong Ye Qu Shen Nan Da Dao, Nan Shan District, Shenzhen, China
Tel.: (86) 75526544888
Automobile Parts Distr
N.A.I.C.S.: 441330

Shenzhen Sime Darby Motor Enterprises Co. Ltd. (1)
Block2 Ma Que Ling Gong Ye Qu Shen Nan Da Dao, Nan Shan District, Shenzhen, China
Tel.: (86) 7552 654 4888
Automobile Parts Distr
N.A.I.C.S.: 441330

Sime Darby (China) Enterprise Management Co. Ltd. (1)
No 00001 Beihai Road, Binhai Economic and Technological Development Area, Weifang, 261108, Shandong, China
Tel.: (86) 5367570300
Web Site:
https://www.simedarbylogistics.com
Shipping Services
N.A.I.C.S.: 488510
Liew Thiam Huat *(Mng Dir)*

Sime Darby Auto Bavaria Sdn Bhd (1)
Level 6 Block 1 Sime Darby Motors City, Pusat Automotif Sime Darby No 6 Jalan PJU 1A/7 Ara Damansara, 47301, Petaling Jaya, Selangor, Malaysia
Tel.: (60) 1300133338
Web Site: https://www.bmw-autobavaria.com

AND PRIVATE COMPANIES — SIME DARBY BERHAD

Car Dealing Services
N.A.I.C.S.: 441110

Sime Darby Auto ConneXion Sdn Bhd (1)
Ford at Level 3 Block 2 Sime Darby Motors City, Pusat Automotif Sime Darby No 6 Jalan PJU 1A/7 Ara Damansara, 47301, Petaling Jaya, Selangor, Malaysia
Tel.: (60) 1300383181
Web Site: https://www.sdacford.com.my
Car Dealing Services
N.A.I.C.S.: 441110

Sime Darby Auto Hyundai Sdn Bhd (1)
No 1 Jalan Pelukis U1/46 Temasya Industrial Park Seksyen U1, No 6 Jalan PJU 1A/7 Ara Damansara, 40150, Shah Alam, Selangor Darul Ehsan, Malaysia
Tel.: (60) 376282500
Car Dealing Services
N.A.I.C.S.: 441110

Sime Darby Auto Performance Sdn Bhd (1)
6 Jalan PJU 1A/7, Ara Damansara, 47301, Petaling Jaya, Malaysia
Tel.: (60) 376239911
Web Site: https://dealer.porsche.com
Car Dealing Services
N.A.I.C.S.: 441110

Sime Darby Auto Selection Sdn Bhd (1)
Lot 33 Jalan Pelukis U1/46, Temasya Industrial Park, 40150, Shah Alam, Selangor, Malaysia
Tel.: (60) 327053792
Web Site: https://sdas.my
Car Dealing Services
N.A.I.C.S.: 441120

Sime Darby Elco Power Japan Limited (1)
3F Bldg B Makuhari Techno-Garden 1-3 Nakase, Mihama-ku, Chiba, 261-0023, Chiba, Japan
Tel.: (81) 434458550
Web Site: https://www.jp.sdelco.com
Generator Set & Spare Parts Distr
N.A.I.C.S.: 423120

Sime Darby Elco Power Korea Limited (1)
123 Samsong Techno Valley B-dong 140 Tongil-ro, Deogyang-gu, Goyang, Gyeonggi, Korea (South)
Tel.: (82) 269528380
Web Site: https://kr.sdelco.com
Engine Distr
N.A.I.C.S.: 423120

Sime Darby Energy & Utilities (1)
Persiaran Kewajipan USJ7, 47600, Subang Jaya, Selangor Darul Ehsan, Malaysia
Tel.: (60) 358918555
Web Site: http://www.simedarbyenergyutilities.com
Energy & Utility Engineering Services
N.A.I.C.S.: 541330
Jauhari Hamidi (Exec VP)

Subsidiary (Domestic):

Mecomb Malaysia Sdn. Bhd. (2)
1 Jalan Puchong Taman Perindustrian, Puchong Utama, 47100, Puchong, Selangor, Malaysia
Tel.: (60) 380688000
Web Site: https://www.mecomb.com
Sales Range: $25-49.9 Million
Emp.: 100
Energy & Utility Engineering Services
N.A.I.C.S.: 541330
Shankar Lingam (Gen Mgr)

Subsidiary (Non-US):

Mecomb Singapore Limited (3)
6 Jurong Pier Road, Singapore, 619158, Singapore (69%)
Tel.: (65) 65721200
Web Site: http://www.mecomb.com
Emp.: 100
Marketing & Sale of Industrial Products, Mechanical, Electrical & Electronic Equipment; Joint Venture of Sime Darby Berhad (69.1%) & Data I/O Corporation (30.9%)
N.A.I.C.S.: 423690

Tommy Chua (Mng Dir)

Sime Darby Energy Solutions Sdn Bhd (1)
Kompleks Kejuruteraan Tractors Workshop 3-1 Jalan Puchong, Taman Perindustrian Puchong Utama, 47100, Puchong, Selangor, Malaysia
Tel.: (60) 380688000
Web Site: https://www.simedarbyenergy.com
Gas Engine Maintenance Services
N.A.I.C.S.: 811310
Lim Daw Yuen (Gen Mgr)

Sime Darby Hong Kong Limited (1)
5/F Fantabi House 380 Castle peak Rd, Tsuen Wan, China (Hong Kong) (74.9%)
Tel.: (852) 28950777
Web Site: http://www.simedarby.com
Sales Range: $1-4.9 Billion
Emp.: 3,000
Distribution & Sales of Cars, Trucks & Construction Equipment; Rice Importers; Shipping Agents; Property Management; Printing of Packaging Materials & Leasing of Motor Vehicles
N.A.I.C.S.: 423120
Peter Goh (CEO)

Sime Darby Industrial (B) Sdn Bhd (1)
Lot 69 Gadong, Beribi Industrial II, BE1118, Bandar Seri Begawan, BE1118, Brunei Darussalam
Tel.: (673) 2453918
Engine Distr
N.A.I.C.S.: 423120

Sime Darby Industrial Power Sdn Bhd (1)
No 100 Jalan Subang Baru 2A Seksyen U3, 40150, Shah Alam, Selangor, Malaysia
Tel.: (60) 378320811
Web Site: https://www.sdip.com.my
Engine Distr
N.A.I.C.S.: 423120

Sime Darby Industrial Sdn Bhd (1)
No 1 Jalan Puchong, Taman Perindustrian Puchong Utama, 47100, Puchong, Selangor Darul Ehsan, Malaysia
Tel.: (60) 380688000
Web Site: https://www.tractors.com.my
Engine Distr
N.A.I.C.S.: 423120
C. K. Teoh (Mng Dir)

Sime Darby Lockton Insurance Brokers Sdn Bhd (1)
19th Floor Menara JKG No 282 Jalan Raja Laut, PO Box 12355, 50774, Kuala Lumpur, Malaysia
Tel.: (60) 327722000
Web Site: https://www.simedarbylockton.com
Insurance Services
N.A.I.C.S.: 524210
Jeffri Salim Davidson (Chm)

Sime Darby Managing Agency (Hong Kong) Limited (1)
Units 7-11 29/F CDW Building 388 Castle Peak Road, Tsuen Wan, China (Hong Kong)
Tel.: (852) 31939633
Web Site: https://www.sdma.com.hk
Motor Insurance Services
N.A.I.C.S.: 524210
Ronald Lam (Gen Mgr)

Sime Darby Material Handling Sdn Bhd (1)
Tractors Engineering Complex 1 Jalan Puchong, Taman Perindustrian Puchong Utama, 47100, Puchong, Selangor, Malaysia
Tel.: (60) 194518003
Web Site: https://www.sdmh.com.my
Lift Truck Distr
N.A.I.C.S.: 423830

Sime Darby Motor Group (NZ) Limited (1)
3 Mauranui Avenue, Epsom, Auckland, 1051, New Zealand
Tel.: (64) 95268920
Web Site: https://www.simedarby.co.nz
Car Dealing Services
N.A.I.C.S.: 441110

Sime Darby Motors Group (Australia) Pty Limited (1)
Locked Bag 206, Silverwater, 1811, NSW, Australia
Tel.: (61) 299338997
Web Site: https://simedarbymotors.com.au
Emp.: 780
Automobile Parts Distr
N.A.I.C.S.: 441330

Sime Darby Motors Sdn. Bhd. (1)
19th Floor Wisma Sime Darby, Jalan Raja Laut, 50350, Kuala Lumpur, Malaysia
Tel.: (60) 326914122
Motor Vehicle Distr & Retailer
N.A.I.C.S.: 441227

Subsidiary (Domestic):

Inokom Corporation Sdn. Bhd. (2)
Lot 38 Mukim Padang Meha, Padang Serai, 09400, Kulim, Kedah Darul Aman, Malaysia (51%)
Tel.: (60) 44031888
Web Site: https://www.inokom.my
Light Commercial Motor Vehicle Mfr
N.A.I.C.S.: 336110

Subsidiary (Non-US):

Regent Motors Limited (2)
305 Alexandra Road, Singapore, 159942, Singapore (69.1%)
Tel.: (65) 64777399
Web Site: https://www.regentmotors.com.sg
Sole Distributor for Ford, Land Rover & Leyland Daf Vehicles & Parts
N.A.I.C.S.: 423120

Sime Darby Plantation Sdn. Bhd. (1)
Main Block Level 3 Plantation Tower No 2 Jalan PJU 1A/7 Ara Damansara, 47301, Petaling Jaya, Selangor, Malaysia (100%)
Tel.: (60) 378484000
Web Site: http://www.simedarbyplantation.com
Sales Range: $200-249.9 Million
Emp.: 748
Rubber Mfr
N.A.I.C.S.: 325212
Renaka Ramachandran (CFO)

Subsidiary (Domestic):

Golden Hope Latex Sdn. Bhd. (2)
Gudang No 6A, Jln Dermaga, Port Klang, Malaysia
Tel.: (60) 3 3166 3400
Fats & Oils Refining & Blending
N.A.I.C.S.: 311225

Hoscote Rubber Estates Limited (2)
1841 Ladang Benut, Simpang Rengam, 86200, Johor, Malaysia
Tel.: (60) 77557977
Rubber Products Mfr
N.A.I.C.S.: 326299

Subsidiary (Non-US):

Hudson & Knight (Proprietary) Limited (2)
511 Commissioner Street, Boksburg, 1460, South Africa
Tel.: (27) 118969005
Web Site: http://hudsonandknight.co.za
Sales Range: $25-49.9 Million
Emp.: 200
Fats & Oils Refining & Blending
N.A.I.C.S.: 311225

New Britain Palm Oil Limited (2)
NBPOL Corporate Office, Mosa, Kimbe, West New Britain, Papua New Guinea (100%)
Tel.: (675) 9852177
Web Site: https://www.nbpol.com.pg
Sales Range: $550-599.9 Million
Oil Palm Tree Plantations & Palm Oil Processing Mills Owner & Operator
N.A.I.C.S.: 113210
Mohd Azlan Shah Mohd Zain (CEO)

Subsidiary (Non-US):

Sime Darby Oils Liverpool Refinery Ltd. (3)
45 Derby Road, Kirkdale, Liverpool, L20 8DY, United Kingdom
Tel.: (44) 1519224875
Web Site: https://simedarbyoils.co.uk
Palm Oil Whslr
N.A.I.C.S.: 423990

Subsidiary (Domestic):

Perkhidmatan Komputer Perladangan Sdn. Bhd. (2)
2nd Floor East Wing Wisne Chinselaz 1 201-A Jalan Tun Razak, 50400, Kuala Lumpur, Malaysia
Tel.: (60) 321606271
Management Consulting Services
N.A.I.C.S.: 541618

Sime Darby Beverages Sdn Bhd (2)
Locked Bag 29 KM3 Jalan Bruas, Sitiawan, Perak, Malaysia
Tel.: (60) 56931911
Web Site: http://www.simedarbyplantation.com
Sales Range: $10-24.9 Million
Emp.: 45
Food Mfr
N.A.I.C.S.: 311999

Sime Darby Bioganic Sdn. Bhd. (2)
Bt 9 Telok Panglima Garang Industrial Estate, Klang-Banting Road, 42500, Kuala Langat, Malaysia
Tel.: (60) 331226301
Web Site: http://www.gold-trie.com
Sales Range: $10-24.9 Million
Emp.: 30
Fats & Oils Refining & Blending
N.A.I.C.S.: 311225
Ahmad Jaril Asis (Gen Mgr)

Sime Darby Jomalina Sdn. Bhd. (2)
9th Mile Jalan Banting-Klang, Telok Panglima Garang Industrial Estate, Kuala Langat, 42500, Selangor Darul Ehsan, Malaysia
Tel.: (60) 331226301
Web Site: http://www.jomalina.com
Emp.: 25
Palm Oil & Palm Kernel Oil Products Producer
N.A.I.C.S.: 311225
Tenwee Teck (VP)

Subsidiary (Non-US):

Sime Darby Oils Zwijndrecht Refinery B.V. (2)
Lindtsedijk 8, 3336 LE, Zwijndrecht, Netherlands
Tel.: (31) 886464599
Web Site: https://simedarbyoils.nl
Sales Range: $25-49.9 Million
Emp.: 230
Oil-Based Food Ingredient Developer & Mfr
N.A.I.C.S.: 311225
Julius Augspurger (Mgr-Tech)

Subsidiary (Domestic):

Sime Darby Research Sdn. Bhd. (2)
Km 10 Jalan Banting Kelanang 207, Kuala Langat, 42700, Selangor Darul Ehsan, Malaysia
Tel.: (60) 331202311
Web Site: http://www.simedarby.com.my
Emp.: 500
Regulation of Agricultural Marketing & Commodities
N.A.I.C.S.: 926140
Hari Krishna (Mng Dir)

Sime Darby Property Berhad (1)
Block G 10th Floor No 2 Jalan PJU 1A/7A, Ara Damansara, 47301, Petaling Jaya, Selangor, Malaysia (51%)
Tel.: (60) 378495000
Web Site: https://simedarbyproperty.com
Sales Range: $200-249.9 Million
Emp.: 300
Property Investment & Development
N.A.I.C.S.: 524126
Gerard Yuen (Chief Mktg & Sls Officer)

Subsidiary (Domestic):

Impian Golf Resort Berhad (2)
14Th Mile Jalan Cheras, 43000, Kajang, Malaysia
Tel.: (60) 387344195
Web Site: http://www.igcc.com.my
Sales Range: $50-74.9 Million
Emp.: 52
Real Estate Property Lessors

SIME DARBY BERHAD

INTERNATIONAL PUBLIC

Sime Darby Berhad—(Continued)
N.A.I.C.S.: 531190
Syed Jan Al-Jeffri *(Gen Mgr)*

Kuala Lumpur Golf & Country Club Berhad (2)
10 Jalan 1 70, D Off Jalan Bukit Kiara, 60000, Kuala Lumpur, Malaysia **(100%)**
Tel.: (60) 320119188
Web Site: https://www.klgcc.com
Sales Range: $100-124.9 Million
Provide Golfing, Sporting & Other Recreational Activities & Services
N.A.I.C.S.: 459110
Steven Allan Thielke *(CEO)*

Melawati Development Sdn. Bhd. (2)
G floor Wisma LT Lorong Perak, Pusat Bandar Melawati, 53100, Kuala Lumpur, Malaysia
Tel.: (60) 341087777
Web Site: http://www.simedarbyproperty.com
Sales Range: $25-49.9 Million
Emp.: 50
Real Estate Property Lessors
N.A.I.C.S.: 531190
Mohamed Shahreza *(Head-Town Ship)*

Negara Properties (M) Berhad (2)
No 1 Lorong Perak, Pusat Bandar Melawati, 53100, Kuala Lumpur, Malaysia
Tel.: (60) 3 4108 7777
Sales Range: $75-99.9 Million
Emp.: 200
Real Estate Property Lessors
N.A.I.C.S.: 531190

Subsidiary (Domestic):

Negara Properties Builders Sdn. Bhd. (3)
No1 Lorong Perak, Pusat Bandar Melawati, 53100, Kuala Lumpur, Malaysia
Tel.: (60) 341072066
Real Estate Property Lessors
N.A.I.C.S.: 531190

Subsidiary (Non-US):

Sime Darby Australia Limited (2)
22 Bishop Street, Jolimont, Perth, 6053, WA, Australia **(80.9%)**
Web Site: http://www.simedarby.com.au
Sales Range: $25-49.9 Million
Emp.: 78
Distribution & Service of Suzuki Cars & Motorcycles; Assembly & Distribution of Bicycles; Travel & Tour Agency, Motel Operations & Management
N.A.I.C.S.: 423120

Sime Darby Rent-A-Car Sdn Bhd (1)
Mezzanine Floor Persada Johor International Convention Centre, Jalan Salim Off Jalan Abdullah Ibrahim, 80000, Johor Bahru, Malaysia
Tel.: (60) 72209490
Web Site: https://www.hertzmalaysia.com
Motor Vehicle Rental Services
N.A.I.C.S.: 532111

Sime Darby Services Private Limited (1)
305 Alexandra Road Vantage Automotive Centre Basement 1, Singapore, 159942, Singapore
Tel.: (65) 97478128
Web Site: https://www.simedarbyservices.sg
Motor Vehicle Rental Services
N.A.I.C.S.: 532111

Sime Darby Singapore Limited (1)
305 Alexandra Road 03-01 Vantage Automotive Centre, Singapore, 159942, Singapore
Tel.: (65) 65140557
General Insurance Agency Services
N.A.I.C.S.: 524210

Sime Darby Swedish Auto Sdn Bhd (1)
Block 6 Sime Darby Motors City No 6 Jalan PJU 1A/7, Ara Damansara, 47301, Petaling Jaya, Selangor, Malaysia
Tel.: (60) 376233200
Web Site: https://www.swedishauto.com.my
Car Dealing Services
N.A.I.C.S.: 441110

Sime Darby Vantage (Thailand) Limited (1)
298/8 Charoen Nakhon Road, Bukkhalo Sub-district Thonburi District, Bangkok, 10600, Thailand
Tel.: (66) 24765555
Web Site: https://www.simedarby.co.th
Emp.: 600
Automobile Parts Distr
N.A.I.C.S.: 441330

Site Technology Asia Pacific Sdn Bhd (1)
No 2 Jalan Tiara Sentral 1, Kawasan Perindustrian Nilai Utama, 71800, Nilai, Negeri Sembilan, Malaysia
Tel.: (60) 67997717
Engine Distr
N.A.I.C.S.: 423120

Tractors Malaysia 1982 Sdn. Bhd. (1)
No 63 & 64 JALAN IKS MJ4 Taman IKS, malim jaya, 75250, Melaka, Malaysia
Tel.: (60) 63362630
Web Site: http://www.tractors.com.my
Sales Range: $75-99.9 Million
Emp.: 500
Sells & Services New & Used Tractors, Heavy Equipment, Engines, Agricultural Tractors, Industrial Gas Turbines & Assembly, Marketing, Distribution & Servicing of Passenger & Commercial Vehicles
N.A.I.C.S.: 561499

Subsidiary (Non-US):

Hastings Deering (Australia) Limited (2)
98 Kerry Road, Archerfield, 4108, QLD, Australia **(100%)**
Tel.: (61) 737172271
Web Site: https://www.hastingsdeering.com.au
Marketing & Distribution of Caterpillar Heavy Equipment, Engines & Lift Trucks
N.A.I.C.S.: 532412
Mark Scott *(CEO, Mng Dir & COO)*

Subsidiary (Non-US):

Hastings Deering (PNG) Ltd. (3)
Spring Gdn Rd, PO Box 6308, Boroko, Port Moresby, Papua New Guinea **(100%)**
Tel.: (675) 9864105
Sales Range: $75-99.9 Million
Emp.: 250
Marketing & Distribution of Caterpillar Heavy Equipment & Trucks
N.A.I.C.S.: 532412

Hastings Deering (Solomon Islands) Limited (3)
Ranadi Industrial Area, Ranadi, Honiara, Guadalcanal, Solomon Islands **(100%)**
Tel.: (677) 30274
Sale & Distribution & Servicing of New & Used Caterpillar Tractors, Earthmoving Equipment, Lift Trucks, Engines & Replacement Parts
N.A.I.C.S.: 237990

Subsidiary (Non-US):

Tractors Singapore Limited (2)
26 Benoi Sector, Singapore, 629858, Singapore **(69.1%)**
Tel.: (65) 62612222
Web Site: https://www.tractors.com.sg
Sales Range: $75-99.9 Million
Emp.: 200
Sales & Service of New & Used Earthmoving & Other Heavy Equipment & Related Equipment & Parts
N.A.I.C.S.: 532412
Ngpock Yin *(Mng Dir)*

Tractors Petroleum Services Sdn Bhd (1)
Lot 3411 Phase 1 Kemaman Supply Base, 24007, Kemaman, Terengganu, Malaysia
Tel.: (60) 162992020
Engine Distr
N.A.I.C.S.: 423120

Tractors Singapore (Maldives) Private Limited (1)
Flat No R12-01 Lot No 11122 Hithigas 7 Hulhumale, Magu, 23000, Maldives
Tel.: (960) 3350028
Web Site: https://maldives.tractors.com.sg
Engine Distr
N.A.I.C.S.: 423120

Transport Engineering Solutions Pty Limited (1)
9/450 Princes Hwy, Noble Park, 3174, VIC, Australia
Tel.: (61) 387915400
Web Site: https://www.transporteng.com.au
Transportation Equipment Distr
N.A.I.C.S.: 423860

UMW Holdings Berhad (1)
Menara UMW Jalan Puncak Off Jalan P Ramlee, 50250, Kuala Lumpur, Malaysia **(100%)**
Tel.: (60) 320252025
Web Site: http://www.umw.com.my
Rev: $2,364,754,838
Assets: $2,833,155,270
Liabilities: $1,244,905,943
Net Worth: $1,588,249,328
Earnings: $79,923,443
Emp.: 7,053
Fiscal Year-end: 12/31/2020
Holding Company; Automotive Mfr; Heavy & Industrial Equipment Mfr; Engineering Services; Oil & Gas Services
N.A.I.C.S.: 551112
Azmin Che Yusoff *(COO-Corp)*

Subsidiary (Domestic):

Assembly Services Sdn Bhd (2)
Persiaran Selangor, 40000, Shah Alam, Selangor, Malaysia
Tel.: (60) 351232000
Automobile Part Equipment Mfr & Distr
N.A.I.C.S.: 336390
Azizul Khilmi Mohd Asarani *(Sr Engr)*

Automotive Industries Sendirian Berhad (2)
Lot 9 Jalan Puchong Section 22, Lion Industrial Park, 40300, Shah Alam, Selangor, Malaysia
Tel.: (60) 351918487
Web Site: https://www.aisb.com.my
Motor Vehicle Parts & Accessory Mfr
N.A.I.C.S.: 336390
Ismail Cob *(Gen Mgr)*

Joint Venture (Domestic):

KYB-UMW Malaysia Sdn Bhd (2)
Lot 8 Jalan Waja 16 Telok Panglima Garang, 42500, Kuala Langat, Selangor Darul Ehsan, Malaysia
Tel.: (60) 333220800
Web Site: https://www.kyb.com.my
Sales Range: $25-49.9 Million
Emp.: 750
Power Steering Pumps Mfr
N.A.I.C.S.: 336330
Makoto Kimura *(Mng Dir)*

Subsidiary (Domestic):

KYB-UMW Steering Malaysia Sdn Bhd (2)
Lot 8 Jalan Waja 16 Telok Panglima Garang, 42500, Kuala Langat, Selangor, Malaysia
Tel.: (60) 331226222
Industrial Machinery Equipment Mfr & Distr
N.A.I.C.S.: 333248

Subsidiary (Non-US):

Lubritech Limited (2)
Kai Chiu Road 169, Xinhui, Jiangmen, 529100, Guangdong, China
Tel.: (86) 7506396398
Web Site: https://www.lubritech-int.com
Lubricant Mfr
N.A.I.C.S.: 324191
Yee Yi Ong *(Asst Mgr-Sls & Mktg)*

Subsidiary (Domestic):

UMW Corporation Sdn Bhd (2)
Jalan Puncak off Jalan P Ramlee, 50250, Kuala Lumpur, Malaysia
Tel.: (60) 320252025
Industrial Machinery Equipment Mfr & Distr
N.A.I.C.S.: 333248

Subsidiary (Domestic):

Lubetech Sdn Bhd (3)
Lot 8 Jalan Utas 15/7 Seksyen 15, 40200, Shah Alam, Selangor Darul Ehsan, Malaysia
Tel.: (60) 351635316
Investment Holding Company Services
N.A.I.C.S.: 551112

U-Travelwide Sdn Bhd (3)
No 10 Jalan Utas 15/7, 40200, Shah Alam, Selangor, Malaysia
Tel.: (60) 351633500
Automobile Part Equipment Mfr & Distr
N.A.I.C.S.: 336390

UMW Advantech Sdn Bhd (3)
Jalan Utas 15/7, PO Box 7052, 40915, Shah Alam, Selangor, Malaysia
Tel.: (60) 351635000
Industrial Machinery Equipment Mfr & Distr
N.A.I.C.S.: 333248
Kamarul Shakirin Samsudin *(Asst Gen Mgr)*

UMW Aero Assets Sdn Bhd (3)
Lot 29138 Mukim Bandar Serendah, Hulu Selangor, 48200, Serendah, Selangor, Malaysia
Tel.: (60) 360287000
Aerospace Equipment & Tooling Mfr
N.A.I.C.S.: 336419

UMW Development Sdn Bhd (3)
No 16 Level 3 Jalan Utas 15/7 Seksyen 15, 40200, Shah Alam, Selangor, Malaysia
Tel.: (60) 19 669 3777
Web Site: https://www.umwhvmpark.com.my
Industrial Machinery Equipment Mfr & Distr
N.A.I.C.S.: 333248

Subsidiary (Non-US):

UMW Equipment & Engineering Pte. Ltd. (3)
108 International Road, Singapore, 629173, Singapore
Tel.: (65) 62653155
Web Site: https://www.umwequipment.com
Automobile Part Equipment Mfr & Distr
N.A.I.C.S.: 336390
Hamad Kama Piah Othman *(Chm)*

UMW Industrial Equipment (Shanghai) Co. Ltd. (3)
No 1332 Dongshi Beijie, Wucheng District, Jinhua, 321000, Zhejiang, China
Tel.: (86) 57982423980
Automobile Part Equipment Mfr & Distr
N.A.I.C.S.: 336390

UMW Industrial Trading (Shanghai) Co. Ltd. (3)
Room 118 Building A No 118 East Huguang Road, Minhang District, Shanghai, 201108, China
Tel.: (86) 2154300338
Web Site: https://www.umw.com.cn
Industrial Machinery Equipment Mfr & Distr
N.A.I.C.S.: 333248

Subsidiary (Domestic):

UMW Industries (1985) Sdn Bhd (3)
No 16 Jalan Utas 15/7, PO Box 7052, Selangor Darul Ehsan, 40200, Shah Alam, Selangor, Malaysia
Tel.: (60) 351633800
Web Site: https://mg.umw-industries.com.my
Automobile Part Equipment Mfr & Distr
N.A.I.C.S.: 336390

UMW Lubricant International Sdn Bhd (3)
Lot 8 Jalan Utas 15/7 Seksyen 15, Selangor Darul Ehsan, 40200, Shah Alam, Selangor, Malaysia
Tel.: (60) 351635316
Web Site: https://www.repsoloil.com.my
Lubricant Mfr
N.A.I.C.S.: 324191
Nurhanis Hanapi *(Mgr-Brand)*

UMW M&E Sdn Bhd (3)
Lot 8 Jalan Utas 15/7 Seksyen 15, Selangor Darul Ehsan, 40200, Shah Alam, Selangor, Malaysia
Tel.: (60) 351635000
Industrial Machinery Equipment Mfr & Distr
N.A.I.C.S.: 333248

Subsidiary (Domestic):

UMW Grantt International Sdn Bhd (4)

AND PRIVATE COMPANIES — SIMON GROUP PLC

Lot 8 Jalan Utas 15/7 Seksyen 15, 40200, Shah Alam, Selangor Darul Ehsan, Malaysia
Tel.: (60) 351635316
Lubricant Mfr
N.A.I.C.S.: 324191
Ahmad Asri Md Ramli (Mgr-Sls)

Subsidiary (Domestic):

UMW Pennzoil Distributors Sdn Bhd (3)
Lot 8 Jalan Utas 15/7 Seksyen 15, 40200, Shah Alam, Selangor Darul Ehsan, Malaysia
Tel.: (60) 351635316
Web Site: https://www.pennzoil.my
Pennzoil Product Distr
N.A.I.C.S.: 424720
Badiyatul Shima Baharuddin (Mgr-Brand)

UMW Training Centre Sdn Bhd (3)
No 10 Jalan Utas 15/7, PO Box 7052, 40915, Shah Alam, Selangor, Malaysia
Tel.: (60) 351633553
Training & Development Services
N.A.I.C.S.: 611430
Adly Azamin Azman (Gen Mgr)

Subsidiary (Non-US):

UMW Equipment Systems (Vietnam) Company Limited (2)
12A Doc Lap Avenue Vietnam - Industrial Park, Binh Hoa Ward, Thuan An, Binh Duong, Vietnam
Tel.: (84) 274374333
Automobile Part Equipment Mfr & Distr
N.A.I.C.S.: 336390

Subsidiary (Domestic):

UMW Industrial Power Services Sdn. Bhd. (2)
No 12 Jalan Utas 15/7 Seksyen 15, Selangor Darul Ehsan, 40200, Shah Alam, Selangor, Malaysia
Tel.: (60) 351633600
Web Site: https://www.sgeneration.com.my
Sales Range: $25-49.9 Million
Emp.: 169
Diesel & Gas Engine Generator Sets Mfr
N.A.I.C.S.: 336310

UMW Toyota Motor Sdn. Bhd. (2)
Level 31 & 32 Menara Southpoint Midvalley City, Medan Syed Putra Selatan, 59200, Kuala Lumpur, Selangor, Malaysia (51%)
Tel.: (60) 327081000
Web Site: https://www.toyota.com.my
Sales Range: $1-4.9 Billion
Emp.: 3,435
Automobile Mfr
N.A.I.C.S.: 336110
Akio Takeyama (Chief Motorsport Officer)

Vantage Automotive Limited (1)
305 Alexandra Road, Singapore, 159942, Singapore
Tel.: (65) 62728828
Web Site: https://www.vantageauto.com.sg
Emp.: 120
Automobile Parts Distr
N.A.I.C.S.: 423120

Weifang Sime Darby Port Co. Ltd. (1)
No 00001 Beihai Road, Binhai Economic and Technological Development Area, Weifang, 261108, Shandong, China
Tel.: (86) 5367577800
Shipping Services
N.A.I.C.S.: 488510
Zang Qian (Gen Mgr)

Yunnan Bow Yue Vehicle Trading Co. Ltd. (1)
Beside HongQiao Overpass East 3rd Ring Road, Kunming, China
Tel.: (86) 87163922999
Automobile Parts Distr
N.A.I.C.S.: 441330

SIMEC ATLANTIS ENERGY LTD

Level 4 21 Merchant Road 04-01, Singapore, 058267, Singapore
Tel.: (65) 69567576
Web Site: https://saerenewables.com
SAE—(AIM)
Rev.: $10,681,646
Assets: $106,878,314
Liabilities: $99,705,882
Net Worth: $7,172,431
Earnings: ($13,961,121)
Emp.: 22
Fiscal Year-end: 12/31/22
Power Generation Structures Mfr & Services
N.A.I.C.S.: 237130
Timothy James Cornelius (CEO)

Subsidiaries:

Marine Current Turbines Limited (1)
Bristol and Bath Science Park Dirac Crescent Emersons Green, Bristol, BS16 7FR, United Kingdom
Tel.: (44) 1179577600
Tidal Power Generation Services
N.A.I.C.S.: 221118
David Rust (Office Mgr-Drawing)

SIMEC Uskmouth Power Limited (1)
Uskmouth Power Station West Nash Road Nash, Newport, NP18 2BZ, United Kingdom
Tel.: (44) 1633292700
Power Generation Services
N.A.I.C.S.: 221118
Neal Darbyshire (Mgr-Engrg)

SIMEC SA

Str Dorobantilor 106B, Sibiu, Romania
Tel.: (40) 269 236468
Web Site: http://www.simec.ro
Sales Range: $1-9.9 Million
Emp.: 76
Freight Transportation Services
N.A.I.C.S.: 484220

SIMEI MEDIA CO. LTD.

No 59 Nanfu Road, Hangzhou, 310008, Zhejiang, China
Tel.: (86) 57186588028
Web Site: http://www.simei.cc
Year Founded: 2000
002712—(SSE)
Rev.: $587,669,655
Assets: $336,534,026
Liabilities: $111,495,375
Net Worth: $225,038,652
Earnings: ($57,442,217)
Emp.: 360
Fiscal Year-end: 12/31/22
Advertising Related Services
N.A.I.C.S.: 541890
JianHua Yu (VP & Deputy Gen Mgr)

Subsidiaries:

Hangzhou Zhangwei Technology Co., Ltd.
No 3 Building C Zhongheng Century Science Park, No 4028 South Ring Road Binjiang District, Hangzhou, Zhejiang, China
Tel.: (86) 57156680191
Advertising Media Services
N.A.I.C.S.: 541840

SIMFABRIC SA

Aleja Jana Pawla II 27, 00-867, Warsaw, Poland
Tel.: (48) 519486720
Web Site: https://www.simfabric.com
Year Founded: 2016
SIM—(WAR)
Emp.: 70
Software Development Services
N.A.I.C.S.: 541511
Julia Natalia Leszczynska (Chm & CEO)

SIMILARWEB LTD.

121 Menachem Begin Rd, Tel Aviv, 6701203, Israel
Tel.: (972) 35447782   II
Web Site: https://www.similarweb.com
Year Founded: 2009
SMWB—(NYSE)
Rev.: $218,019,000
Assets: $239,013,000
Liabilities: $223,466,000
Net Worth: $15,547,000
Earnings: ($29,373,000)
Emp.: 899
Fiscal Year-end: 12/31/23
Web Analytics Services
N.A.I.C.S.: 518210
Or Offer (Co-Founder & CEO)

Subsidiaries:

Embee Mobile, Inc. (1)
580 Market St Ste 250, San Francisco, CA 94104
Tel.: (415) 217-2785
Web Site: http://www.embeemobile.com
Software Publisher
N.A.I.C.S.: 513210
Russell Tillitt (CEO)

Similarweb SG Pte. Ltd. (1)
79 Robinson Road Floor 6, Singapore, Singapore
Tel.: (65) 60183845
Software Development Services
N.A.I.C.S.: 541511

SIMINN HF

Armuli 25, 108, Reykjavik, Iceland
Tel.: (354) 5506000
Web Site: https://www.siminn.is
Year Founded: 1906
SIMINN—(ICE)
Rev.: $171,901,479
Assets: $367,521,183
Liabilities: $114,318,541
Net Worth: $253,202,643
Earnings: $274,788,166
Emp.: 597
Fiscal Year-end: 12/31/22
Telecommunication Servicesb
N.A.I.C.S.: 517810

SIMMONDS MARSHALL LTD.

Mumbai - Pune Rd, Kasarwadi, Pune, 410501, India
Tel.: (91) 2135683939
Web Site: https://www.simmondsmarshall.com
507998—(BOM)
Rev.: $18,392,638
Assets: $24,209,558
Liabilities: $18,723,405
Net Worth: $5,486,153
Earnings: ($2,439,897)
Emp.: 308
Fiscal Year-end: 03/31/21
Metal Nuts & Products Mfr
N.A.I.C.S.: 332999

SIMMTECH HOLDINGS CO., LTD.

73 Sandan-ro, Heungdeok-gu, Cheongju, Chungcheongbuk-do, Korea (South)
Tel.: (82) 439098000   KR
Web Site: https://www.simmtechholdings.com
Year Founded: 1987
036710—(KRS)
Rev.: $1,311,889,970
Assets: $1,086,366,332
Liabilities: $600,833,029
Net Worth: $485,533,304
Earnings: $143,007,302
Emp.: 33
Fiscal Year-end: 12/31/22
Printed Circuit Board Mfr
N.A.I.C.S.: 334412
Chun Se-Ho (Chm)

Subsidiaries:

Simmtech (Xi'an) Co., Ltd. (1)
Zone B Guanzhong Comprehensive Bonded Zone No 28 Xinxi Avenue, Xi'an, Shaanxi, China
Tel.: (86) 2963351800
Circuit Board Distr
N.A.I.C.S.: 423690

Simmtech America Inc. (1)
1286 Kifer Rd Ste 103, Sunnyvale, CA 94086
Tel.: (408) 734-9909
Emp.: 4
Circuit Board Distr
N.A.I.C.S.: 423690

Simmtech Japan Inc. (1)
SJI Building 6F 2-22-6, Shinkawa, Chuo, Tokyo, Japan
Tel.: (81) 3 3523 9700
Circuit Board Distr
N.A.I.C.S.: 423690

Simmtech Niching (Suzhou) Co., Ltd. (1)
215-021 Block C 01-03/04 No 5 Xing Han Street, Suzhou Industrial Park, Suzhou, China
Tel.: (86) 51262897400
Circuit Board Distr
N.A.I.C.S.: 423690

SIMO INTERNATIONAL

54 Rue du 19 Janvier, 92380, Paris, France
Tel.: (33) 147927272
Web Site: https://simo-international.com
Year Founded: 1985
MLSIM—(EUR)
Sales Range: $1-9.9 Million
Sportswear Whslr
N.A.I.C.S.: 424350

SIMON BAILES LTD.

Tannery Lane, Northallerton, DL7 8DS, N Yorkshire, United Kingdom
Tel.: (44) 1609801468
Web Site: http://www.simonbailes.co.uk
Year Founded: 1979
Sales Range: $10-24.9 Million
Emp.: 80
Car Dealership Owner & Operator
N.A.I.C.S.: 441110

Subsidiaries:

Simon Bailes Stockton (1)
Church Rd, Stockton, TS18 1TH, United Kingdom (100%)
Tel.: (44) 642612621
Web Site: http://www.simonbailes.co.uk
Vehicle Motor Retailing
N.A.I.C.S.: 441110

SIMON GROUP PLC

Clough Lane, Killingholme, DN40 3LX, North Lincolnshire, United Kingdom
Tel.: (44) 1469540381   UK
Web Site: http://www.simonports.co.uk
Year Founded: 1897
Sales Range: $25-49.9 Million
Emp.: 205
Port Operation Services
N.A.I.C.S.: 488310
Gary Walker (Exec Dir)

Subsidiaries:

Humber Sea Terminal Ltd (1)
Clough Lane, Killingholme, DN40 3LX, North Lincolnshire, United Kingdom (100%)
Tel.: (44) 1469 540 381
Web Site: http://www.simonports.co.uk
Sales Range: $50-74.9 Million
Emp.: 200
Port & Cargo Operations
N.A.I.C.S.: 488310

Immingham Storage Co. Ltd. (1)
W Riverside Immingham Dock, Immingham, DN40 2QU, Lincs, United Kingdom (100%)
Tel.: (44) 1469572615
Web Site: http://www.simonstorage.com

SIMON GROUP PLC

Simon Group plc—(Continued)
Sales Range: $25-49.9 Million
Emp.: 100
Storage of Chemicals, Oils & Gases
N.A.I.C.S.: 424690
Keith Jackson (Sr Mgr-Terminal)

Irish Bulk Liquid Storage Ltd. (1)
Foynes Harbour, Foynes, Limerick,
Ireland **(50.01%)**
Tel.: (353) 6965506
Web Site: http://www.simonstorage.co.uk
Sales Range: $50-74.9 Million
Emp.: 8
Storage of Chemicals, Oils & Gases
N.A.I.C.S.: 424690

Port Sutton Bridge Ltd. (1)
W Bank, Bridge, Spalding, PE12 9QR, Lincolnshire, United Kingdom **(100%)**
Tel.: (44) 406351133
Web Site: http://www.simongrp.co.uk
Sales Range: $25-49.9 Million
Emp.: 50
Import/Export Dry Cargo Handling
N.A.I.C.S.: 488320

Seal Sands Storage Ltd. (1)
Seal Sands Rd, Middlesbrough, TS2 1UB,
United Kingdom **(100%)**
Tel.: (44) 1642546775
Web Site: http://www.simonstorage.com
Sales Range: $50-74.9 Million
Emp.: 60
Specialized Storage of Chemicals
N.A.I.C.S.: 424690
David Lyon (Mng Dir)

Simon Aerials Ltd. (1)
Courtstown Industrial Park, Little Island,
Cork, Ireland **(100%)**
Tel.: (353) 21383011
Self-Propelled Telescopic & Articulated Machines; Scissor Lifts Mfr
N.A.I.C.S.: 325520

Simon-Lift GmbH (1)
Weinheimer St 58-60, Morlenbach, 69509,
Hessen, Germany **(100%)**
Tel.: (49) 620972150
Web Site: http://www.simon-lift.de
Sales Range: $50-74.9 Million
Emp.: 4
Sales of Aerial Work Platforms
N.A.I.C.S.: 425120

Velva Liquids (North Shields) Ltd. (1)
Northumberland Dock, North Shields, NE29
6DY, United Kingdom **(100%)**
Tel.: (44) 912960999
Web Site: http://www.simonstorage.com
Sales Range: $25-49.9 Million
Emp.: 16
Storage of Chemicals, Oils & Gases
N.A.I.C.S.: 424690

SIMON MOKSTER SHIPPING A/S
Skogstostraen 37, Stavanger, 4029,
Norway
Tel.: (47) 51839000
Web Site: http://www.mokster.no
Year Founded: 1968
Sales Range: $75-99.9 Million
Emp.: 500
Shipping Company
N.A.I.C.S.: 488510
Atle Holgersen (Mgr-Mktg)

Subsidiaries:

NorSea Group AS (1)
Risavika Havnering 14, 4056, Tananger,
Norway
Tel.: (47) 40004321
Web Site: https://norseagroup.com
Holding Company; Support Activities for Oil
& Gas Operations
N.A.I.C.S.: 551112
May Britt Lilletvedt (CEO)

Subsidiary (Domestic):

NorSea AS (2)
Risavika Havnering 14, 4056, Tananger,
Norway
Tel.: (47) 4 000 4321

Web Site: https://www.norseagroup.com
Sales Range: $75-99.9 Million
Emp.: 200
Supply Base Logistic & Onshore & Offshore
Industry Support Service
N.A.I.C.S.: 213112

Vestbase AS (2)
Omagaten 110 C, N 6500, Kristiansund,
Norway
Tel.: (47) 71572200
Web Site: http://www.vestbase.com
Sales Range: $50-74.9 Million
Emp.: 220
Logistics Supplier for Offshore Related Activities
N.A.I.C.S.: 211120
Alf Dahl (Mng Dir)

SIMONA AG
Teichweg 16, 55606, Kirn, Germany
Tel.: (49) 6752140
Web Site: https://www.simona.de
Year Founded: 1857
SIM0—(BER)
Rev.: $768,473,991
Assets: $670,292,467
Liabilities: $264,070,796
Net Worth: $406,221,671
Earnings: $40,376,646
Emp.: 1,734
Fiscal Year-end: 12/31/22
Thermoplastic Product Mfr
N.A.I.C.S.: 325211
Rolf Goessler (Chm-Supervisory Bd)

Subsidiaries:

Dehoplast Polska Sp. z o.o. (1)
ul Lotnicza 4, 82-500, Kwidzyn, Poland
Web Site: https://dehoplast.com.pl
Plastics Product Mfr
N.A.I.C.S.: 326199

Industrial Drive Inc. (1)
1255 23rd St NW, Washington, DC 20005
Tel.: (202) 331-2480
Web Site: http://www.industrydive.com
Online Media Services
N.A.I.C.S.: 541890

OOO Simona Rus (1)
Projektiruemy Proezd No 4062 D 6 Str 16
BC Portplaza, 115432, Moscow, Russia
Tel.: (7) 4996830041
Web Site: http://www.simona-ru.com
Emp.: 7,000
Thermoplastic Product Distr
N.A.I.C.S.: 424610

SIMONA Boltaron Inc. (1)
1 General St, Newcomerstown, OH 43832
Web Site: http://www.boltaron.com
Emp.: 120
Thermoplastic Product Mfr
N.A.I.C.S.: 325211
Alicia Spence (Acct Mgr)

SIMONA INDIA PRIVATE LIMITED (1)
406 Signature 1 Nr Divyabhaskar SG Highway, Ahmedabad, 380051, Gujarat, India
Tel.: (91) 7940508899
Thermoplastic Product Mfr
N.A.I.C.S.: 325211
Tanish Dadhania (Exec Dir-Sls)

Simona America, Inc. (1)
101 Power Blvd, Archbald, PA
18403 **(100%)**
Web Site: http://www.simona-america.com
Thermoplastic Semi-Finished Parts Mfr & Distr
N.A.I.C.S.: 326199

Subsidiary (Domestic):

Laminations, Inc. (2)
101 Power Blvd PEI Industrial Park, Archbald, PA 18403
Tel.: (570) 348-7921
Web Site: http://www.laminations.com
Sales Range: $25-49.9 Million
Emp.: 110
Polyolefin & Fluoropolymer Sheet Products
Mfr & Supplier
N.A.I.C.S.: 326199

Simona Asia Ltd. (1)
Rm 501 5/F CCT Telecom Building 11 Wo
Shing Street, Fo Tan, Sha Tin, New Territories, China (Hong Kong)
Tel.: (852) 29470193
Thermoplastic Product Distr
N.A.I.C.S.: 424610

Subsidiary (Non-US):

Simona Engineering Plastics (Guangdong) Co. Ltd. (2)
No 368 Jinou Road High New Technology
Industrial Development Zone, Jiangmen,
529000, Guangdong, China
Tel.: (86) 7503870338
Web Site: http://www.simonade.com
Thermoplastic Product Distr
N.A.I.C.S.: 424610

Simona Far East Ltd. (1)
Room 501 5/F CCT Telecom Building 11
Wo Shing Street, Fo Tan, Hong Kong,
China (Hong Kong)
Tel.: (852) 29 47 01 93
Web Site: http://www.simona-cn.com
Thermoplastic Product Distr
N.A.I.C.S.: 424610

Subsidiary (Non-US):

Simona Engineering Plastics Trading Co. Ltd. (2)
Unit 1905 Tower B The Place No 100 Zunyi
Road, Changning District, Shanghai,
200051, China
Tel.: (86) 21 6267 0881
Web Site: http://www.simona-cn.com
Thermoplastic Product Distr
N.A.I.C.S.: 424610

Simona Iberica Semielaborados S.L. (1)
C/ Doctor Josep Castells 26-30, E - 08830,
Sant Boi de Llobregat, Spain
Tel.: (34) 936354103
Web Site: https://www.simona-es.com
Thermoplastic Product Distr
N.A.I.C.S.: 424610

Simona PMC, LLC (1)
2040 Industrial Dr, Findlay, OH 45840
Tel.: (419) 429-0042
Web Site: http://www.simona-pmc.com
Plastic Sheet Product Mfr
N.A.I.C.S.: 326112
Eric Short (VP & Gen Mgr)

Simona Plast-Technik s.r.o. (1)
At Autodilen no 23, CZ-43603, Litvinov,
Czech Republic
Tel.: (420) 476767312
Web Site: https://www.simona-cz.com
Plastics Product Mfr
N.A.I.C.S.: 326113

Simona Polska Sp. z o.o. (1)
Ul Rakietowa 35, Wojkowice, 54-615, Wroclaw, Poland
Tel.: (48) 713528020
Web Site: https://www.simona-pl.com
Thermoplastic Product Distr
N.A.I.C.S.: 424610

Simona S.A.S. (1)
43 avenue de l'Europe, 95330, Domont,
Cedex, France
Tel.: (33) 139354949
Web Site: https://www.simona-fr.com
Thermoplastic Product Distr
N.A.I.C.S.: 424610
Hubert Charles (Pres)

Simona S.r.l. (1)
Via Volontari del Sangue 54a, I - 20093,
Cologno Monzese, MI, Italy
Tel.: (39) 02250851
Web Site: https://www.simona-it.com
Emp.: 10
Thermoplastic Product Distr
N.A.I.C.S.: 424610
Giovanni Vesco (Mng Dir)

Simona UK Ltd. (1)
Telford Drive, Brookmead Industrial Park,
Stafford, ST16 3ST, Great Britain, United
Kingdom
Tel.: (44) 1785222444
Emp.: 15
Thermoplastic Product Distr

INTERNATIONAL PUBLIC

N.A.I.C.S.: 424610

Simona-Plastics CZ, s.r.o. (1)
Zdebradska ul 70, 25101, Ricany, Czech
Republic
Tel.: (420) 323 63 78 37
Web Site: http://www.simona-cz.com
Thermoplastic Product Distr
N.A.I.C.S.: 424610

SIMONDS FARSONS CISK PLC
The Brewery Mdina Road Zone 2,
Central Business District, Birkirkara,
CBD 2010, Malta
Tel.: (356) 23814114
Web Site: https://www.farsons.com
Year Founded: 1928
SFC—(MAL)
Rev.: $127,604,144
Assets: $232,121,735
Liabilities: $81,930,714
Net Worth: $150,191,021
Earnings: $16,697,604
Emp.: 910
Fiscal Year-end: 01/31/23
Beers & Beverages Brewer & Producer; Wine & Spirits Importer &
Sales; Franchised Food Retailer
N.A.I.C.S.: 445320
Marcantonio Stagno d'Alcontres (Vice Chm)

Subsidiaries:

Eco Pure Premium Water Company Limited (1)
San Gwakkin Buildings Centrija, Triq San
Gwakkin, Mriehel, BKR 3000, Malta
Tel.: (356) 23814411
Web Site: http://www.farsons.com
Sales Range: $25-49.9 Million
Emp.: 20
Water Bottler
N.A.I.C.S.: 312112

Farsons (Sales & Marketing) Limited (1)
The Brewery Mdina Road Zone 2, Central
Business District, Birkirkara, CBD 2010,
Malta
Tel.: (356) 23814226
Web Site: http://www.farsons.com
Sales Range: $150-199.9 Million
Emp.: 700
Alcoholic Beverages Mfr
N.A.I.C.S.: 312140

Farsons Beverage Imports Company Limited (1)
The Brewery Mdina Road Zone 2, Central
Business District, Birkirkara, CBD 2010,
Malta
Tel.: (356) 23814400
Web Site: https://www.farsons.com
Beverage Distr
N.A.I.C.S.: 424810

Farsonsdirect (1)
The Brewery Mdina Road Zone 2, Central
Business District, Birkirkara, CBD 2010,
Malta
Tel.: (356) 23814444
Web Site: https://www.farsonsdirect.com
Sales Range: $25-49.9 Million
Emp.: 5
Online Wine Retailer
N.A.I.C.S.: 312130

Food Chain (Holdings) Limited (1)
303 Trident House Qormi Road, Marsa,
MRS 9049, Malta
Tel.: (356) 23814111
Web Site: https://www.farsons.com
Sales Range: $10-24.9 Million
Emp.: 20
Fast Food Restaurants
N.A.I.C.S.: 722513

Quintano Foods Limited (1)
303 Qormi Road, Marsa, MRS 9049, Malta
Tel.: (356) 23814556
Web Site: http://www.quintanofoods.com
Sales Range: $25-49.9 Million
Emp.: 55
Food Distr

Trident Developments Limited (1)
No 4 Level 2 Mdina Road Zone 2, Trident Park Notabile Gardens Central Business District, Birkirkara, CBD 2010, Malta
Tel.: (356) 99428282
Web Site: https://tridentestatesplc.com
Real Estate Development & Management
N.A.I.C.S.: 531390
Christopher Ciantar *(COO)*

Wands Limited (1)
The Brewery Mdina Road Zone 2, Central Business District, Birkirkara, CBD 2010, Malta
Tel.: (356) 23814400
Web Site: http://www.farsonsdirect.com
Wine Import & Distribution
N.A.I.C.S.: 424820
Pierre Spafraace *(Gen Mgr)*

SIMONDS GROUP LIMITED
Level 1 570 St Kilda Road, Melbourne, 3004, VIC, Australia
Tel.: (61) 396820700   AU
Web Site:
  https://www.simondsgroup.com.au
Year Founded: 1949
SIO—(ASX)
Rev.: $443,028,844
Assets: $105,697,783
Liabilities: $93,340,010
Net Worth: $12,357,772
Earnings: $2,009,882
Emp.: 600
Fiscal Year-end: 06/30/24
Residential Dwelling Construction Services
N.A.I.C.S.: 531110
Mick Myers *(CFO)*

Subsidiaries:

City Wide Building & Training Services Pty Ltd (1)
16 / 25 Ourimbah Road, Tweed Heads, 2485, NSW, Australia
Tel.: (61) 130 042 9287
Web Site: https://cwbts.com.au
Professional Training Services
N.A.I.C.S.: 611430

House of Learning Pty Ltd (1)
Level 4 570 St Kilda Rd, Melbourne, 3004, VIC, Australia
Tel.: (61) 130 053 4363
Web Site: https://buildersacademy.com.au
Professional Training Services
N.A.I.C.S.: 611430

Simonds Homes NSW Pty Ltd (1)
5/58 Norwest Blvd, Baulkham Hills, 2153, NSW, Australia
Tel.: (61) 1300746663
Civil Construction Services
N.A.I.C.S.: 541330

Simonds Queensland Constructions Pty Ltd (1)
3894 Pacific Hwy, Loganholme, 4129, QLD, Australia
Tel.: (61) 1300 746 6637
Web Site: http://www.simonds.com.au
Civil Construction Services
N.A.I.C.S.: 541330

SIMONDS HOMES MELBOURNE PTY. LTD.
Level 2 28 Albert Road, Melbourne, 3205, VIC, Australia
Tel.: (61) 1300733133   AU
Web Site:
  http://www.simonds.com.au
Year Founded: 1953
Sales Range: $50-74.9 Million
Emp.: 300
New Single-Family Housing Design & Construction Services
N.A.I.C.S.: 236115
Scott Mahony *(Sec)*

SIMONE S.P.A.
Via Riviera di Chiaia 256, 80121, Naples, Italy
Tel.: (39) 0818043920
Web Site: https://edizioni.simone.it
Year Founded: 2011
SMN—(ITA)
Books Publishing Services
N.A.I.C.S.: 513130

SIMONSWERK GMBH
Bosfelder Weg 5, 33378, Rheda-Wiedenbruck, Germany
Tel.: (49) 52424130
Web Site:
  http://www.simonswerk.com
Year Founded: 1889
Hinge Systems
N.A.I.C.S.: 332510
Michael Meier *(Mng Dir)*

Subsidiaries:

Colcom Group S.p.A. (1)
Via degli Artigiani 56 Int 1, Nave, 25075, Brescia, Italy
Tel.: (39) 0302532008
Web Site: http://www.colcom.it
Glass Distr
N.A.I.C.S.: 423390
Angelo Biasotti *(Mgr-Technical & R&D)*

SIMPAC HOLDINGS CO., LTD
SIMPAC Bldg 13th Floor 52 Gukjegeumyung-ro, Yeongdeugpo-gu, Seoul, 07330, Korea (South)
Tel.: (82) 2 3780 4908
Web Site:
  http://www.simpacholdings.com
Year Founded: 2001
Emp.: 1,000
Holding Company
N.A.I.C.S.: 551112
Jin-Sik Choi *(Chm & CEO)*

Subsidiaries:

SIMPAC America Co. Ltd. (1)
141 Bupyeongbuk-ro, Bupyeong-gu, 403-858, Incheon, 403-858, Korea (South)
Tel.: (82) 325100114
Web Site: https://www.simpac.co.kr
Rev.: $515,599,423
Assets: $740,230,503
Liabilities: $280,273,828
Net Worth: $459,956,674
Earnings: $58,397,343
Emp.: 500
Fiscal Year-end: 12/31/2022
Presses Mfr
N.A.I.C.S.: 333998
Jin Shik Choi *(Chm)*

Subsidiary (Non-US):

Meise Machine Co., Ltd. (2)
14-33 3-Chome, Taiseicho, Fujieda, Shizuoka, Japan
Tel.: (81) 54 636 4477
Press Machinery Distr
N.A.I.C.S.: 423830

SIMPAC India Co., Ltd. (2)
No Q308 3rd Floor Mayur Trade Center, Chinchwad Station Chinchwad, Pune, India
Tel.: (91) 99 2336 9069
Press Machinery Distr
N.A.I.C.S.: 423830

Subsidiary (Domestic):

SIMPAC METAL Co., Ltd. (2)
438 Jeongmi-ro, Jeongmi-myeon, Dangjin, Chungcheongnam-do, Korea (South)
Tel.: (82) 41 360 0100
Web Site: http://www.simpacmetal.com
Emp.: 59
Ferro Alloy Mfr
N.A.I.C.S.: 331110
Hyo-seok Song *(CEO)*

Subsidiary (Non-US):

SIMPAC Machinery (M) Sdn. Bhd. (2)
Unit No Rd 0705 A-06-09 Endah Regal Condominium Taman Sri Endah, 57000, Kuala Lumpur, Malaysia
Tel.: (60) 19 257 7762
Press Machinery Distr
N.A.I.C.S.: 423830

SIMPAC Thailand Co., Ltd. (2)
688/27 Srinakarin Rd, Nhongbon Parawat, Bangkok, Thailand
Tel.: (66) 2 361 9563
Press Machinery Distr
N.A.I.C.S.: 423830

SIMPAC Tianjin Co., Ltd (2)
Shuangkon Village shuangkon Township, Belchen, Tianjin, China
Tel.: (86) 22 8683 7605
Press Machinery Distr
N.A.I.C.S.: 423830

SIMPAC INDUSTRIES Co., Ltd. (1)
64 Gajwa-Ro, Seo-Gu, Incheon, 228000, Korea (South)
Tel.: (82) 32 590 8800
Web Site: http://www.simpacindustry.co.kr
Emp.: 300
Industrial Machinery & Equipment Mfr
N.A.I.C.S.: 333998
Kin Wong Wan *(Mgr-Overseas Sls)*

Plant (Domestic):

SIMPAC INDUSTRIES Co., Ltd. - Kajwa 2 Plant (2)
124 Geonji-ro, Seo-gu, Incheon, Korea (South)
Tel.: (82) 32 575 1991
Industrial Machinery & Equipment Mfr
N.A.I.C.S.: 333612

SIMPAC INDUSTRIES Co., Ltd. - Namdong Plant (2)
418 Cheongneung-daero, Namdong-gu, Incheon, Korea (South)
Tel.: (82) 32 818 6661
Industrial Machinery & Equipment Mfr
N.A.I.C.S.: 333248

Simpac Metal Co., Ltd. (1)
153 Geudong-ro, Nam-gu, 37863, Pohang, Gyeongsangbuk-do, Korea (South)
Tel.: (82) 54 271 8700
Web Site: http://www.simpacmetal.com
Rev.: $215,490,659
Assets: $247,079,932
Liabilities: $65,382,537
Net Worth: $181,697,395
Earnings: $15,557,245
Emp.: 201
Fiscal Year-end: 12/31/2017
54 271 8778
N.A.I.C.S.: 331110

Plant (Domestic):

SIMPAC METALLOY Co., Ltd - Plant 2 (2)
22 Seowonjee-Ro, Nam-Gu, Pohang, Gyeongsangbuk-do, Korea (South)
Tel.: (82) 54 278 3991
Ferro Alloy Mfr
N.A.I.C.S.: 331110

SIMPLE S.A.
Ul Bronislawa Czecha 49/51, 04-555, Warsaw, Poland
Tel.: (48) 22 812 58 98
Web Site: http://www.simple.com.pl
SME—(WAR)
Sales Range: Less than $1 Million
Information Technology Consulting Services
N.A.I.C.S.: 541512

Subsidiaries:

Medinet Systemy Informatyczne Sp. z o.o. (1)
ul Oleska 121, 45-231, Opole, Poland
Tel.: (48) 774551050
Web Site: http://www.medinet.opole.pl
Information Technology Services
N.A.I.C.S.: 541511

SIMPLEX CASTINGS LTD.
601/602 A Fairlink Center Off Andheri Link Road, Andheri West, Mumbai, 400053, India
Tel.: (91) 2240034768
Web Site:
  https://www.simplexcastings.com
513472—(BOM)
Rev.: $14,136,023
Assets: $17,773,299
Liabilities: $14,117,703
Net Worth: $3,655,596
Earnings: ($2,036,868)
Emp.: 292
Fiscal Year-end: 03/31/23
Metal Casting & Engineering Services
N.A.I.C.S.: 331523
Om Prakash Patel *(Exec Dir)*

Subsidiaries:

Simplex Castings Ltd. - Bhilai Works (1)
5 Industrial Estate, Bhilai, 490 026, India
Tel.: (91) 788 2283031
Fabricated Metal Mfr
N.A.I.C.S.: 332312

Simplex Castings Ltd. - Urla Works (1)
Ural Industrial Estate, Raipur, 493 221, India
Tel.: (91) 771 2323805
Fabricated Metal Mfr
N.A.I.C.S.: 332312

SIMPLEX FINANCIAL HOLDINGS CO., LTD.
27th Floor Shin-Marunouchi Building 1-5-1 Marunouchi, Chiyoda-ku, Tokyo, 100-6527, Japan
Tel.: (81) 352085739
Web Site:
  http://www.simplexasset.com
Year Founded: 2006
7176—(TKS)
Rev.: $98,925,260
Assets: $124,968,660
Liabilities: $44,372,930
Net Worth: $80,595,730
Earnings: $43,685,490
Fiscal Year-end: 03/31/24
Holding Company
N.A.I.C.S.: 551112
Hiromasa Mizushima *(Pres & CEO)*

Subsidiaries:

Simplex Asset Management Co., Ltd. (1)
27th Floor Shin-Marunouchi Building 1-5-1, Marunouchi Chiyoda-ku, Tokyo, 100-6527, Japan
Tel.: (81) 352085211
Web Site: https://www.simplexasset.com
Investment Management Service
N.A.I.C.S.: 523940
Hiromasa Mizushima *(Pres & CEO)*

SIMPLEX INFRASTRUCTURES LIMITED
Simplex House 27 Shakespeare Sarani, Kolkata, 700 017, India
Tel.: (91) 3323011600
Web Site:
  https://www.simplexinfra.com
Year Founded: 1924
523838—(BOM)
Rev.: $235,220,910
Assets: $1,243,696,421
Liabilities: $1,207,477,969
Net Worth: $36,218,452
Earnings: ($56,469,037)
Emp.: 1,468
Fiscal Year-end: 03/31/23
Engineeering Services
N.A.I.C.S.: 541330
Sukumar Dutta *(CFO)*

Subsidiaries:

Simplex Infrastructures L.L.C (1)
Way No 2137 Bldg 9115, PO Box 1797, 114, Muscat, Oman
Tel.: (968) 24695368

SIMPLEX INFRASTRUCTURES LIMITED

Simplex Infrastructures Limited—(Continued)
Sales Range: $150-199.9 Million
Emp.: 100
Construction Engineering Services
N.A.I.C.S.: 541330
Badal Rudra *(Dir-Technical)*

SIMPLEX PAPERS LTD
30 Keshavrao Khadye Marg Sant
Gadge Maharaj Chowk, Mumbai,
400011, India
Tel.: (91) 2223082951
Web Site: https://www.simplex-group.com
533019—(BOM)
Rev.: $8,162
Assets: $198,031
Liabilities: $1,787,894
Net Worth: ($1,589,863)
Earnings: ($80,250)
Emp.: 1
Fiscal Year-end: 03/31/20
Paper Mfr
N.A.I.C.S.: 322120

SIMPLEX REALTY LTD
30 Keshavrao Khadye Marg Sant
Gadge Maharaj Chowk, Mumbai,
400011, India
Tel.: (91) 2223082951
Year Founded: 1912
503229—(BOM)
Rev.: $1,261,471
Assets: $15,199,011
Liabilities: $486,520
Net Worth: $14,712,491
Earnings: $75,531
Emp.: 28
Fiscal Year-end: 03/31/21
Residential & Commercial Real Estate Development
N.A.I.C.S.: 237210
Nandan Damani *(Chm & Mng Dir)*

Subsidiaries:

Simplex Renewable Resources Private Limited (1)
Presidency Building N 1/13 Ist Floor St Marks Road, Bengaluru, 560 001, Karnataka, India
Tel.: (91) 8041076803
Web Site: http://www.simplex-energy.com
Renewable Energy
N.A.I.C.S.: 221111

SIMPLICITY HOLDING LTD.
Unit 13 8/F Vanta Industrial Centre 21-33 Tai Lin Pai Road, Kwai Chung, New Territories, China (Hong Kong)
Tel.: (852) 2 377 3677   Ky
Web Site:
http://www.simplicityholding.com
Year Founded: 2003
8367—(HKG)
Rev.: $14,588,799
Assets: $12,918,250
Liabilities: $7,920,662
Net Worth: $4,997,588
Earnings: $1,128,704
Emp.: 170
Fiscal Year-end: 03/31/21
Restaurant Operators
N.A.I.C.S.: 722511
Suet Hing Wong *(Chm)*

Subsidiaries:

Foodies Group Limited (1)
8/F Remex Centre 42 Wong Chuk Hang Road, Wong Chuk Hang, Hong Kong, China (Hong Kong)
Tel.: (852) 37912564
Web Site: http://www.afoodieworld.com
Food Restaurant Services
N.A.I.C.S.: 722511
Lily Ng *(CEO)*

Wealthy Development (HK) Limited (1)
Unit 2 19/F Laurels Industrial Centre No 32 Tai Yau Street, San Po Kong, Kowloon, China (Hong Kong)
Tel.: (852) 37065428
Web Site: http://www.wealthgroupshk.com
Engineering Construction Services
N.A.I.C.S.: 541330

SIMPLICITY MARKETING LTD.
Marshall's Mill Marshall Street 5th Floor, East Wing, Leeds, LS11 9YJ, United Kingdom
Tel.: (44) 113886104
Web Site: http://www.flashtalking.com
Marketing Services
N.A.I.C.S.: 541613
John Nardone *(CEO)*

Subsidiaries:

Flashtalking, Inc. (1)
142 W 36th Str 10th Fl, New York, NY 10018
Tel.: (917) 580-6634
Web Site: http://www.flashtalking.com
Media Marketing & Advertising Agency Services
N.A.I.C.S.: 541810
Ben Kartzman *(Co-Founder & CEO)*

SIMPLILEARN SOLUTIONS PVT LTD
Manoj Arcade 53/1C 24th Main 2nd Sector, HSR Layout, Bengaluru, 560102, India
Tel.: (91) 80 6534 0329
Web Site: http://www.simplilearn.com
Year Founded: 2009
Online Education & Training Courses
N.A.I.C.S.: 513210

Subsidiaries:

Simplilearn Americas LLC (1)
10685-B Hazelhurst Dr Ste 11236, Houston, TX 77043-3238
Tel.: (281) 816-4305
Web Site: http://www.simplilearn.com
Professional & Management Online Education & Training Courses
N.A.I.C.S.: 513210
Krishna Kumar *(Co-Founder & CEO)*

Subsidiary (Domestic):

Market Motive, Inc. (2)
10 Victor Sq Ste 250, Scotts Valley, CA 95066-3518
Tel.: (831) 706-2369
Web Site: http://www.marketmotive.com
Digital Marketing Training Services
N.A.I.C.S.: 513210
Michael Stebbins *(CEO)*

SIMPLO TECHNOLOGY CO., LTD.
No 471 Sec 2 Bade Rd, Hukou Township, 30348, Hsinchu, Taiwan
Tel.: (886) 35695920
Web Site: http://www.simplo.com.tw
Year Founded: 1992
Electronic Components Mfr
N.A.I.C.S.: 334419
Fu-Hsiang Sung *(Chm & Gen Mgr)*

SIMPLY BETTER BRANDS CORP.
206 - 595 Howe Street, Vancouver, V6C 2T5, BC , Canada
Tel.: (855) 553-7441
Web Site:
https://www.simplybetterbrands.com
Year Founded: 2017
PKANF—(OTCIQ)
Software Publisher
N.A.I.C.S.: 513210
Brian Meadows *(CFO)*

SIMPLY GROUP
2225 Sheppard Ave E Suite 800, Toronto, ON, Canada
Tel.: (800) 764-5138
Web Site:
http://www.mysimplygroup.com
Year Founded: 2013
Holding Company: Home, Energy & Consumer Services
N.A.I.C.S.: 551112

Subsidiaries:

Simply Green Home Services Inc. (1)
2225 Sheppard Ave E Suite 800, Toronto, M2J 5C2, ON, Canada
Residential Heating & Cooling Products
N.A.I.C.S.: 333415

Subsidiary (Domestic):

DealNet Capital Corp. (2)
325 Milner Avenue Suite 300, Toronto, M1B 5N1, ON, Canada
Tel.: (416) 843-2881
Web Site: http://www.dealnetcapital.com
Rev.: $13,170,546
Assets: $177,961,153
Liabilities: $151,452,475
Net Worth: $26,508,679
Earnings: ($1,364,423)
Emp.: 288
Fiscal Year-end: 12/31/2019
Consumer Engagement & Consumer Finance Businesses Investment
N.A.I.C.S.: 523999
Barclay Morton *(Sr VP-Sls & Mktg)*

Subsidiary (Domestic):

EcoHome Financial Inc. (3)
130 King St West Suite 501, PO Box 158, Toronto, M5X 1C7, ON, Canada
Web Site: http://www.ecohomefinancial.com
Financial Services
N.A.I.C.S.: 522110

SIMPLY SOLVENTLESS CONCENTRATES LTD.
273209 Range Road 20 Rocky View County, Calgary, T4B 4P2, AB, Canada
Tel.: (403) 796-3640
Web Site:
https://www.simplysolventless.ca
HASH—(TSX)
Consumer Goods
N.A.I.C.S.: 532289

Subsidiaries:

CannMart Inc. (1)
5800 Ambler Drive Suite 210, Mississauga, L4W 4J4, ON, Canada
Web Site: http://www.cannmart.com
Cannabis Product Distr
N.A.I.C.S.: 459999

SIMPLYBIZ GROUP PLC
The John Smiths Stadium Stadium Way, Huddersfield, HD1 6PG, United Kingdom
Tel.: (44) 1484439100   UK
Web Site:
http://www.simplybizgroup.co.uk
Year Founded: 2002
Rev.: $64,321,548
Assets: $58,598,268
Liabilities: $24,880,406
Net Worth: $33,717,861
Earnings: $3,615,438
Emp.: 417
Fiscal Year-end: 12/31/18
Financial Investment Advisory Services
N.A.I.C.S.: 523940
Neil Stevens *(Co-CEO)*

Subsidiaries:

Comparison Creator Limited (1)
Springboard Business Innovation Centre Llantarnam Park, Cwmbran, NP44 3XF, United Kingdom
Tel.: (44) 1633647973
Web Site:
http://www.comparisoncreator.com

INTERNATIONAL PUBLIC

Information Technology Development Services
N.A.I.C.S.: 541511

Defaqto Ltd. (1)
Unit 12 Haddenham Business Park, Haddenham, HP17 8LJ, Buckinghamshire, United Kingdom
Tel.: (44) 1844295454
Web Site: http://www.defaqto.com
Emp.: 60
Financial Advising Service
N.A.I.C.S.: 523940
Zahid Bilgrami *(CEO)*

Defaqto Nordic AS (1)
Vassbonnveien 18, 1410, Kolbotn, Norway
Tel.: (47) 91249041
Web Site: http://www.defaqto.no
Insurance Services
N.A.I.C.S.: 524210

Gateway Surveying Services Limited (1)
Weston House Bradgate Park View, Chellaston, Derby, DE73 5UJ, United Kingdom
Tel.: (44) 1293820233
Web Site:
http://www.gatewaysurveyors.co.uk
Property Surveying Services
N.A.I.C.S.: 541370
Peter Hughes *(CEO)*

SIFA Limited (1)
Fintel House St Andrew's Road, Huddersfield, HD1 6NA, United Kingdom
Tel.: (44) 3300021102
Web Site: http://www.sifa.co.uk
Business Support Services
N.A.I.C.S.: 561499

Simply Biz Mortgages Limited (1)
St Andrew's House St Andrew's Road, Huddersfield, HD1 6NA, United Kingdom
Tel.: (44) 1484439160
Web Site:
http://www.simplybizmortgages.co.uk
Mortgage Services
N.A.I.C.S.: 522310
Martin Reynolds *(CEO)*

Simply Biz Services Limited (1)
St Andrew's House St Andrew's Road, Huddersfield, HD1 6NA, United Kingdom
Tel.: (44) 1484439100
Web Site: http://www.simplybiz.co.uk
Business Support Services
N.A.I.C.S.: 561499

Verbatim Asset Management Limited (1)
St Andrew's House St Andrew's Road, Huddersfield, HD1 6NA, United Kingdom
Tel.: (44) 8081240007
Web Site:
http://www.verbatimassetmanagement.com
Asset Management Services
N.A.I.C.S.: 523940
Peter Hugh Smith *(Deputy Chm)*

Zest Technology Limited (1)
Leatherhead House Station Road, Leatherhead, KT22 7FG, Surrey, United Kingdom
Tel.: (44) 8453726644
Web Site: http://www.zestbenefits.com
Software Development Services
N.A.I.C.S.: 513210
Ray Sieber *(Mng Dir)*

SIMPLYCAST.COM
73 Tacoma Dr Ste 400, Dartmouth, B2W 3Y6, NS, Canada
Tel.: (902) 835-8974
Web Site: http://www.simplycast.com
Sales Range: $1-9.9 Million
Interactive Marketing Software
N.A.I.C.S.: 513210
Saeed El-Darahali *(Pres & CEO)*

SIMPLYHEALTH GROUP LIMITED
Hambleden House, Waterloo Court, Andover, SP10 1LQ, Hampshire, United Kingdom
Tel.: (44) 1264353211   UK
Web Site:
http://www.simplyhealth.co.uk

AND PRIVATE COMPANIES

Year Founded: 1872
Rev.: $313,701,744
Assets: $471,314,028
Liabilities: $159,642,716
Net Worth: $311,671,312
Earnings: ($31,090,990)
Emp.: 1,226
Fiscal Year-end: 12/31/18
Health Insurance Products & Services
N.A.I.C.S.: 524114
Romana Abdin (CEO)

Subsidiaries:

Denplan Limited (1)
Denplan Court Victoria Road, Winchester, SO23 7RG, Hants, United Kingdom (100%)
Tel.: (44) 1962828000
Web Site: http://www.denplan.co.uk
Emp.: 350
Dental Care Payment Plan Services
N.A.I.C.S.: 524128
Sandy Brown (Dir-Dentists)

SIMPO A.D.
Workers 12, Vranje, Serbia
Tel.: (381) 17 422 911
Web Site: http://www.simpo.rs
Year Founded: 1963
Sales Range: $10-24.9 Million
Emp.: 4,317
Furniture Product Mfr
N.A.I.C.S.: 337121

Subsidiaries:

Simpo Line D.O.O. (1)
Stefana Prvovencanog 58, 17 500, Vranje, Serbia
Tel.: (381) 17414809
Web Site: http://www.simpoline.rs
Business Consulting Services
N.A.I.C.S.: 541611

Simpo SIK D.O.O. (1)
Kosovska 67, 18 430, Kursumlija, Serbia
Tel.: (381) 27381141
Web Site: http://www.simposik.rs
Emp.: 600
Wood Product Rental Services
N.A.I.C.S.: 423990

SIMPPLE LTD.
BLOCK71 Ayer Rajah Crescent, Singapore, 139951, Singapore
Tel.: (65) 68162194
Web Site: https://www.simpple.ai
Year Founded: 2016
SPPL—(NASDAQ)
Rev.: $3,473,083
Assets: $6,493,779
Liabilities: $3,865,652
Net Worth: $2,628,127
Earnings: ($5,610,132)
Emp.: 56
Fiscal Year-end: 12/31/23
Real Estate Development Services
N.A.I.C.S.: 531190
Jiexiang Aloysius Chong (Founder)

SIMPSON & COMPANY LIMITED
861/862 Anna Salai, Chennai, Tamilnadu, India
Tel.: (91) 4428584918
Web Site: http://www.simpsons.in
Year Founded: 1840
Emp.: 639
Motor Vehicles Mfr
N.A.I.C.S.: 336211

SIMRAN FARMS LIMITED
1-B Vikas Rekha Complex Near Tower Chouraha Khatiwala Tank, Indore, 452001, MP, India
Tel.: (91) 7314255900
Web Site: https://www.simranfarms.com
Year Founded: 1989

519566—(BOM)
Rev.: $44,012,541
Assets: $12,549,250
Liabilities: $10,217,202
Net Worth: $2,332,048
Earnings: $1,717,266
Emp.: 434
Fiscal Year-end: 03/31/21
Poultry Farming Services
N.A.I.C.S.: 112990
Harender Singh Bhatia (Chm & Mng Dir)

SIMRIS GROUP AB
Herrestadsvagen 24A, Hammenhog, 276 50, Skanes Fagerhult, Sweden
Tel.: (46) 414445050
Web Site: https://simrisgroup.com
Year Founded: 2011
SIMRIS.B—(OMX)
Rev.: $264,914
Assets: $6,967,106
Liabilities: $1,178,072
Net Worth: $5,789,034
Earnings: ($3,125,248)
Emp.: 13
Fiscal Year-end: 12/31/20
Natural Food Product Mfr
N.A.I.C.S.: 311999
Fredrika Gullfot (Founder)

Subsidiaries:

Simris Biologics GmbH (1)
Magnusstrasse 11, 12489, Berlin, Germany
Tel.: (49) 3063924481
Web Site: https://simrisbiologics.com
Pesticide Mfr
N.A.I.C.S.: 325320

SIMS CAB DEPOT CORP.
200 Moulinette Road, PO Box 340, Long Sault, K0C 1P0, ON, Canada
Tel.: (613) 534-2289
Web Site: https://www.cabdepot.com
Year Founded: 1954
Sales Range: $10-24.9 Million
Emp.: 40
Designer & Mfr of Cabs & Custom Metal Fabrications
N.A.I.C.S.: 332999
Chuck Crawford (CEO)

SIMTEX INDUSTRIES LIMITED
Khagan Birulia Ashulia Savar, Dhaka, 1341, Bangladesh
Tel.: (880) 1955577607
Web Site: https://www.simtexgroup.com
Year Founded: 2000
SIMTEX—(CHT)
Rev.: $13,812,121
Assets: $24,029,062
Liabilities: $7,514,674
Net Worth: $16,514,387
Earnings: $604,205
Emp.: 672
Fiscal Year-end: 06/30/23
Sewing Thread Mfr
N.A.I.C.S.: 313110
Md. Anisur Rahman (Chm)

SIMULA TECHNOLOGY INC.
14F No 1351, Zhongzheng Rd, Taoyuan, 33071, Taiwan
Tel.: (886) 33010008
Web Site: https://www.simulatechnology.com
Year Founded: 1990
3511—(TPE)
Rev.: $132,289,779
Assets: $110,951,036
Liabilities: $33,011,975
Net Worth: $77,939,061
Earnings: $11,297,158
Emp.: 550
Fiscal Year-end: 12/31/22
Electronic Parts Mfr & Distr

N.A.I.C.S.: 334419
Joe Huang (Chm)

Subsidiaries:

Simula Technology (ShenZhen) Co., Ltd. (1)
No 1 Laotaikeng Industrial Park Baolong 6th Rd, Longgang District, Shenzhen, Guangdong, China
Tel.: (86) 7553 390 1555
Electronic Components Mfr
N.A.I.C.S.: 334419

Simula Technology Corp. (1)
2445 Augustine Dr Ste 150, Santa Clara, CA 95054
Tel.: (408) 659-9122
Electronic Components Mfr
N.A.I.C.S.: 334419

SIN GHEE HUAT CORPORATION LTD.
32 Penhas Road 01-01, Singapore, 208191, Singapore
Tel.: (65) 63981118
Web Site: http://www.singheehuat.com.sg
Rev.: $36,461,687
Assets: $66,346,433
Liabilities: $3,667,670
Net Worth: $62,678,763
Earnings: $1,751,559
Fiscal Year-end: 06/30/19
Stainless Steel Products Mfr
N.A.I.C.S.: 331110
Hua Meng Chia (CFO)

Subsidiaries:

SG Metals Pte. Ltd. (1)
51 Benoi Road Block 2, Singapore, 629908, Singapore
Tel.: (65) 68302300
Web Site: http://www.singheehuat.com.sg
Stainless Steel Products Whslr
N.A.I.C.S.: 423510

SG Specialty Metals Pte. Ltd. (1)
32 Gul Crescent, Singapore, 629537, Singapore
Tel.: (65) 65119352
Iron & Steel Product Mfr
N.A.I.C.S.: 331110
Mah Wei Woon (Sls Mgr)

Subsidiary (Non-US):

SG Metals (Suzhou) Ltd. (2)
1207 Wangdun Road No 188, Suzhou Industrial Park, Jiangsu, 215028, China
Tel.: (86) 51262806028
Iron & Steel Product Mfr
N.A.I.C.S.: 331110

SIN HENG CHAN (MALAYA) BERHAD
Suite 2 02 Level 2 Wisma EC No 2 Lorong Dungun Kiri Damansara Heights, 50490, Kuala Lumpur, Malaysia
Tel.: (60) 320947992
Web Site: https://www.shcm.com.my
SHCHAN—(KLS)
Rev.: $11,509,829
Assets: $92,554,108
Liabilities: $37,243,367
Net Worth: $55,310,741
Earnings: $3,170,189
Emp.: 37
Fiscal Year-end: 12/31/22
Animal Feed Mfr
N.A.I.C.S.: 311111
Keng Weng Choo (Mng Dir)

SIN HENG HEAVY MACHINERY LIMITED
26 Gul Road, Singapore, 629346, Singapore
Tel.: (65) 68616111
Web Site: https://www.sinheng.com.sg

SINA CORPORATION

BKA—(SES)
Rev.: $50,162,842
Assets: $96,818,905
Liabilities: $16,380,368
Net Worth: $80,438,537
Earnings: $6,055,442
Emp.: 149
Fiscal Year-end: 12/31/23
Cranes, Aerial Lifts & Lifting Equipment Rentals & Trading
N.A.I.C.S.: 532490
Cheng Guan Tan (Exec Dir)

Subsidiaries:

P.T. SH Machinery Indonesia (1)
Komplek Ruko Graha Boulevard Blok A No 28 Gading Serpong, Desa Curug Sangereng Kecamatan Kelapa Dua, Tangerang, 15810, Indonesia
Tel.: (62) 2129009788
Crane & Aerial Lift Rental Services
N.A.I.C.S.: 532412

SH Equipment (HK) Limited (1)
5008 50th Floor Central Plaza 18 Harbour Road, Wanchai, China (Hong Kong)
Tel.: (852) 6568616111
Crane Equipment Part Distr
N.A.I.C.S.: 423830

SH Equipment (Myanmar) Company Limited (1)
Web Site: https://www.shmyanmar.com
Crane Equipment Part Distr
N.A.I.C.S.: 423830
Myo Kyaw Zin (Sr Mgr)

SH Heavy Machinery Sdn. Bhd. (1)
Lot 50622 Jalan Bukit Kemuning Seksyen 32, 40460, Shah Alam, Selangor, Malaysia
Tel.: (60) 355259688
Crane Equipment Part Distr
N.A.I.C.S.: 423830

Sin Heng Aerial Lifts Pte. Ltd. (1)
26 Gul Road, Singapore, 629346, Singapore
Tel.: (65) 6 861 2280
Web Site: https://www.shal.com.sg
Aerial Lift Part Distr
N.A.I.C.S.: 423840

Sin Heng Vina Co. Ltd. (1)
61 Road C My Thai, Tan Phu Ward District 7, Ho Chi Minh City, Vietnam
Tel.: (84) 2854173928
Web Site: http://www.sinheng.com.vn
Crane Equipment Part Distr
N.A.I.C.S.: 423830

SIN WEE SENG INDUSTRIES SDN. BHD.
Lot Ptd 4085 Kawasan Perindustrian Parit Jamil, Parit Jawa, 84150, Muar, Johor, Malaysia
Tel.: (60) 69875999
Web Site: http://www.swssofa.com
Year Founded: 1965
Sofa Mfr
N.A.I.C.S.: 337121
Mei Wan Ng (Sec)

SINA CORPORATION
No 8 SINA Plaza Courtyard 10 the West Xibeiwang E Road, Haidian District, Beijing, 100193, China
Tel.: (86) 1082628888
Web Site: http://www.sina.com.cn
Year Founded: 1995
SINA—(NASDAQ)
Rev.: $1,743,617,000
Assets: $7,468,828,000
Liabilities: $3,570,915,000
Net Worth: $3,897,913,000
Earnings: ($70,542,000)
Emp.: 8,300
Fiscal Year-end: 12/31/19
Internet Services
N.A.I.C.S.: 517810
Bonnie Yi Zhang (CFO)

Subsidiaries:

Beijing New Media Information Technology Co. Ltd. (1)

SINA CORPORATION

SINA Corporation—(Continued)
8/F Sohu International Plaza No 1 Park, Zhongguancun East Road, Beijing, 100084, China
Tel.: (86) 1062726627
Online Media Services
N.A.I.C.S.: 541511

SINA Corp. - Beijing (1)
20F Beijing Ideal International Plaza No 58 Northwest 4th Ring Rd, Beijing, 100080, Haidian, China
Tel.: (86) 10 82628888
Web Site: http://www.corp.sina.com.cn
Sales Range: $100-124.9 Million
Emp.: 500
Chinese Internet Media in North America & Abroad
N.A.I.C.S.: 516210

SINA Corp. - Redwood (1)
1731 Embarcadero Rd Ste 220, Palo Alto, CA 94303
Tel.: (650) 210-9888
Web Site: http://www.sina.com
Sales Range: $25-49.9 Million
Emp.: 45
Internet Media for the Chinese in North America & Abroad
N.A.I.C.S.: 517810

SINA Corp. - Shanghai (1)
1468 Nan Jing Rd W, United Plaza Ste 1802, Shanghai, 200040, China
Tel.: (86) 2162895678
Web Site: http://www.sina.com.cn
Sales Range: $200-249.9 Million
Emp.: 529
Internet Media for the Chinese in North America & Abroad
N.A.I.C.S.: 516210

SINA Corp. - Taipei (1)
6F-2 No 1 Guangfu S Rd, 105, Taipei, Taiwan
Tel.: (886) 2 2742 1989
Web Site: http://www.sina.com.tw
Internet Media for the Chinese in North America & Abroad
N.A.I.C.S.: 516210

SINA.com Technology (China) Co. Ltd. (1)
Rm 1802 Zhongxin Mansion Nanjing West Road, Jing'An District, Shanghai, China
Tel.: (86) 8552955237
Online Media Services
N.A.I.C.S.: 513199

Unit (US)

SINA.com Online (2)
883 N Shoreline Blvd Ste C 200, Mountain View, CA 94043
Tel.: (650) 210-9888
Web Site: http://www.home.sino.com
Emp.: 25
Online Media Services
N.A.I.C.S.: 513199

Weibo Corporation (1)
8/F Qihao Plaza No 8 Xinyuan S Road, Chaoyang District, Beijing, 100027, China (77.6%)
Tel.: (86) 1058983336
Web Site: http://www.weibo.com
Rev.: $1,836,332,000
Assets: $7,129,454,000
Liabilities: $3,784,709,000
Net Worth: $3,344,745,000
Earnings: $85,555,000
Emp.: 5,935
Fiscal Year-end: 12/31/2022
Social Media Platform
N.A.I.C.S.: 541810
Gaofei Wang (CEO)

SINA DAROU LABORATORIES COMPANY
52nd Blvd 15th Kilometer Karaj Makhsoos Road, 33561, Tehran, 33561, Iran
Tel.: (98) 21441945213
Web Site: https://www.sinadarou.com
Year Founded: 1962
DSIN1—(THE)
Sales Range: Less than $1 Million
Pharmaceuticals Product Mfr
N.A.I.C.S.: 325412

SINA TILE & CERAMIC CO.
No 21 Mirdamad Blvd, Tehran, Iran
Tel.: (98) 2122062614
Web Site: http://www.sinatile.ir
Year Founded: 1995
SINA1—(THE)
Sales Range: Less than $1 Million
Building Materials Mfr
N.A.I.C.S.: 327120

SINAD HOLDING COMPANY
CMC Tower King Fahd Road, PO Box 55756, Riyadh, 11544, Saudi Arabia
Tel.: (966) 0112353399
Web Site: https://sinadholding.com
Year Founded: 1977
4080—(SAU)
Rev.: $471,663,504
Assets: $783,680,868
Liabilities: $360,407,316
Net Worth: $423,273,552
Earnings: $3,213,584
Emp.: 22
Fiscal Year-end: 12/31/22
Investment Management Service
N.A.I.C.S.: 523999

SINANEN HOLDINGS CO., LTD.
1-39-20 Higashishinagawa, Shinagawa-ku, Tokyo, 140-0002, Japan
Tel.: (81) 364787800   JP
Web Site: https://www.sinanengroup.co.jp
Year Founded: 1927
8132—(TKS)
Rev.: $2,302,144,020
Assets: $717,052,800
Liabilities: $364,640,650
Net Worth: $352,412,150
Earnings: ($6,867,790)
Emp.: 1,764
Fiscal Year-end: 03/31/24
Holding Company; Gasoline & Petroleum Products Whslr, Retailer & Fuel Dealer
N.A.I.C.S.: 551112
Masaki Yamazaki (Pres & CEO)

Subsidiaries:

Hidaka Toshi Gas Co., Ltd. (1)
473 Shimokayama, Hidaka, 350-1233, Saitama, Japan
Tel.: (81) 429894041
Web Site: http://www.ht-gas.co.jp
Gas Distr
N.A.I.C.S.: 457210

Indess Co., Ltd. (1)
5-3-10 Haramachida, Machida-shi, Tokyo, 194-0013, Japan
Tel.: (81) 427394404
Web Site: https://www.indess.jp
Emp.: 61
Bicycle Mfr
N.A.I.C.S.: 336991

Melife Co., Ltd. (1)
6th floor West Building Sumitomo Fudosan Sanda Twin Building 5-27, Mita 3-chome Minato-ku, Tokyo, 108-6306, Japan
Tel.: (81) 120046370
Web Site: https://www.melife.co.jp
Fuel Oil Distr
N.A.I.C.S.: 424720

Melife-East Co., Ltd. (1)
12th floor Sendai Park Building 3-6-1 Kokubuncho, Aoba-ku, Sendai, 980-0803, Miyagi, Japan
Tel.: (81) 222129530
Web Site: http://www.melife-east.co.jp
Gas Distr
N.A.I.C.S.: 457210

Melife-West Co., Ltd. (1)
6th floor Higobashi Union Building 1-9-6 Edobori, Nishi-ku, Osaka, 550-0002, Japan
Tel.: (81) 671660500
Web Site: https://www.melife-west.co.jp
Emp.: 156
Gas Distr
N.A.I.C.S.: 457210

Sinanen Bike Co., Ltd. (1)
5-27 Mita 3-Chome, Minato-ku, Tokyo, 108-6306, Japan
Tel.: (81) 364787840
Bicycle Mfr
N.A.I.C.S.: 336991

Sinanen Co., Ltd. (1)
6th floor West Building Sumitomo Fudosan Sanda Twin Building, 3-5-27 Mita Minato-ku, Tokyo, 108-6306, Japan
Tel.: (81) 364787900
Web Site: https://www.sinanen.com
Emp.: 138
Gas Distr
N.A.I.C.S.: 457210

Sinanen Ecowork Co., Ltd. (1)
3-5-27 Mita Sumitomo Fudosan Mita Twin Building West Building 6F, Minato-ku, Tokyo, 108-6306, Japan
Tel.: (81) 364787830
Web Site: https://www.sinanenecowork.com
Bicycle Mfr
N.A.I.C.S.: 336991

Sinanen Facilities Co., Ltd. (1)
2-3-16 Kamogawa, Okegawa, Saitama, 363-0024, Japan
Tel.: (81) 487891551
Web Site: https://www.sinanen-f.com
Emp.: 33
Bicycle Mfr
N.A.I.C.S.: 336991

Sinanen Mobility Plus Co., Ltd. (1)
Sumitomo Fudosan Mita Twin Building West Building 6F 3-5-27 Mita, Minato-ku, Tokyo, 108-6306, Japan
Tel.: (81) 364787906
Web Site: https://www.sinanen-mplus.com
Bicycle Mfr
N.A.I.C.S.: 336991

Sinanen Zeomic Co., Ltd. (1)
1-1 Nakagawa-honmachi, Minato-ku, Nagoya, 455-0051, Aichi, Japan
Tel.: (81) 526532201
Web Site: https://www.zeomic.co.jp
Emp.: 46
Industrial Inorganic Chemical Mfr
N.A.I.C.S.: 325180
Mutsuaki Murao (Pres)

Takara Building Maintenance Co., Ltd. (1)
4-10-1 Nakanedai, Ibaraki, Ryugasaki, 301-0002, Japan
Tel.: (81) 97667111
Web Site: https://www.takara-gr.co.jp
Emp.: 1,000
Bicycle Mfr
N.A.I.C.S.: 336991

SINARMAS LAND LIMITED
108 Pasir Panjang Road 06-00 Golden Agri Plaza, Singapore, 118535, Singapore
Tel.: (65) 62207720   SG
Web Site: https://www.sinarmasland.com
Year Founded: 1988
A26—(SES)
Rev.: $1,015,916,837
Assets: $6,007,075,662
Liabilities: $2,208,751,798
Net Worth: $3,798,323,864
Earnings: $291,554,949
Fiscal Year-end: 12/31/23
Holding Company; Commercial, Residential, Industrial Properties, Hotels & Resorts Construction
N.A.I.C.S.: 551112
Muktar Widjaja (CEO)

Subsidiaries:

PT AFP Dwilestari (1)
Jalan Hang Lekiu Nongsa, Batam, Indonesia
Tel.: (62) 778761222
Real Estate Services
N.A.I.C.S.: 531390

SINATEX SA
Str Popa Nan 82 S2, Bucharest, Romania
Tel.: (40) 213216090   RO
Web Site: http://www.sinatex.ro
Year Founded: 1994
SINA—(BUC)
Rev.: $13,379,844
Assets: $1,558,795
Liabilities: $1,227,741
Net Worth: $331,053
Earnings: $6,154,284
Emp.: 1
Fiscal Year-end: 12/31/22
Fabric Mfr & Whslr
N.A.I.C.S.: 313210

SINBON ELECTRONICS CO., LTD.
4F-13 No 79 Sec 1 Xintai 5th Rd, Xizhi Dist, New Taipei City, 221, Taiwan
Tel.: (886) 226989999
Web Site: https://www.sinbon.com
3023—(TAI)
Rev.: $1,071,398,141
Assets: $1,000,132,602
Liabilities: $544,140,337
Net Worth: $455,992,265
Earnings: $101,111,609
Emp.: 5,137
Fiscal Year-end: 12/31/23
Electronic Components Mfr
N.A.I.C.S.: 335313
Joseph Wang (Chm & CEO)

Subsidiaries:

Beijing SINBON Electronics Co., Ltd. (1)
New Feida Electronics Science & Technology Industry Development Cente, Shahe Changping, Beijing, 102206, China
Tel.: (86) 10 69733330
Electrical Goods Mfr
N.A.I.C.S.: 334419

Hong Kong SINBON Electronics Co., Ltd. (1)
Unit 05 18/F Lemmi Centre 50 Hoi Yuen Road, Kowloon, Kwun Tong, China (Hong Kong)
Tel.: (852) 23772768
Electronic Equipment Mfr & Distr
N.A.I.C.S.: 334419

JAPAN SINBON ELECTRONICS CO.,LTD (1)
Chiyoda 4-1-7, Naka-Ku, Nagoya, 460 0012, Aichi, Japan
Tel.: (81) 523220168
Electronic Components Mfr & Distr
N.A.I.C.S.: 334417

Jiangyin SINBON Electronics Co., Ltd. (1)
No 288 Chengjiang Middle Rd, Jiangyin, 214434, Jiangsu, China
Tel.: (86) 51086404098
Web Site: http://www.sinbon.com
Connector Mfr
N.A.I.C.S.: 334417

Korea Sinbon Electronics Co., Ltd. (1)
Room No 301 DongA B D 632 Kojan-Dong, NamDong-Gu, Incheon, 405-817, Korea (South)
Tel.: (82) 328147730
Electronic Component Sales
N.A.I.C.S.: 423690

SINBON Electronics Co., Ltd - Miaoli Factory (1)
No 582 Kuo Hwa Road, Miao-li, 360, Taiwan
Tel.: (886) 37 330099
Web Site: http://www.sinbon.com

AND PRIVATE COMPANIES / SINCO PHARMACEUTICALS HOLDINGS LTD.

Electronic Components Mfr
N.A.I.C.S.: 334417

SINBON Hungary Kft. (1)
Buzavirag utca 8/D, 2800, Tatabanya, Hungary
Tel.: (36) 34513196
Electronic Equipment Mfr & Distr
N.A.I.C.S.: 334417

SINBON Ohio LLC (1)
815 S Brown School Rd, Vandalia, OH 45377
Tel.: (937) 415-2070
Electronic Equipment Mfr & Distr
N.A.I.C.S.: 334417

SINBON Technologies Tennessee LLC (1)
211 Industrial Park Dr, Cumberland City, TN 37050
Tel.: (931) 220-8988
Sales Range: $25-49.9 Million
Emp.: 3
Electronic Products Mfr
N.A.I.C.S.: 334417
Bryan Walker *(Office Mgr)*

Shanghai SINBON Electronics Co., Ltd. (1)
3F Building 60 No 461, Hong Cao Road, Shanghai, 200233, China
Tel.: (86) 21 54262200
Electronic Products Sales
N.A.I.C.S.: 423690

Shenzhen SINBON Electronics Co., Ltd. (1)
Room 1605-1608 Song De Office Building Xiameilin Second Street, Futian District, Shenzhen, 518040, Guangdong, China
Tel.: (86) 75583024009
Web Site: http://www.sinbon.com
Electronic Components Distr
N.A.I.C.S.: 423690

Sinbon USA L.L.C. (1)
6925 216th St SW Ste D, Lynnwood, WA 98036
Tel.: (425) 712-8500
Electrical Component Mfr
N.A.I.C.S.: 334417

T-CONN Precision Co., Ltd. (1)
4F-3 No 79 Sec 1 Xintai 5th Rd, Xizhi Dist, New Taipei City, 221, Taiwan
Tel.: (886) 226983890
Web Site: https://www.t-conn.com
Power Connector Mfr & Distr
N.A.I.C.S.: 334417

UK SINBON Electronics Co., Ltd. (1)
Office 8 Marcus House Park Hall Business Village, Longton, Stoke-on-Trent, ST3 5XA, United Kingdom
Tel.: (44) 1782 599313
Electronic Components Mfr
N.A.I.C.S.: 335999

SINCAP GROUP LIMITED
2 Shenton Way 02-02 SGX Centre 1, Singapore, 059817, Singapore
Tel.: (65) 62368888
Web Site:
  http://www.sincapgroup.com.sg
5UN—(CAT)
Rev.: $485,573
Assets: $131,397
Liabilities: $1,210,124
Net Worth: ($1,078,727)
Earnings: ($188,857)
Emp.: 500
Fiscal Year-end: 12/31/22
Gypsum Mining; Alumina & Coal Distr
N.A.I.C.S.: 212390
Hao Fu *(Chm & CEO)*

SINCERE CO., LTD.
6F Hongo MK Building 1-28-34 Hongo, Bunkyo-ku, Tokyo, 113-0033, Japan
Tel.: (81) 356159059
Web Site: https://www.sincere-vision.com
7782—(TKS)
Rev.: $42,263,490
Assets: $38,286,000
Liabilities: $20,681,530
Net Worth: $17,604,470
Earnings: $2,091,550
Fiscal Year-end: 12/31/23
Contact Lens Mfr & Distr
N.A.I.C.S.: 339115

Subsidiaries:

Sincere Taiwan Co., Ltd. (1)
6F No 263 Siwei 3rd Rd Lingya Dist, Kaohsiung, Taiwan
Tel.: (886) 73311088
Contact Lens Distr
N.A.I.C.S.: 423460

Sincere Vision Co., Ltd. (1)
Room 302 3/F Fu Fai Commercial Centre 27 Hillier Street, 27 Sheung Wan Hong Kong Sheung Wan Commercial Center 3, Sheung Wan, China (Hong Kong)
Tel.: (852) 2 323 3100
Web Site: http://www.sincere-vision.com
Contact Lens Distr
N.A.I.C.S.: 423460

SINCERE NAVIGATION CORPORATION
14F No 368 Sec 1 Fu Hsing S Road, Da'an Dist, Taipei, 10656, Taiwan
Tel.: (886) 227037055
Web Site: https://www.snc.com.tw
Year Founded: 1968
2605—(TAI)
Rev.: $138,326,134
Assets: $690,528,605
Liabilities: $171,026,417
Net Worth: $519,502,188
Earnings: $16,643,578
Emp.: 294
Fiscal Year-end: 12/31/23
Cargo Transportation Services
N.A.I.C.S.: 488320
Yih-Ren Lee *(VP)*

Subsidiaries:

Heywood Limited (1)
Web Site: http://www.heywood.co.uk
Holding Company
N.A.I.C.S.: 551112

Ocean Wise Limited (1)
Tel.: (44) 1420768262
Web Site: http://www.oceanwise.eu
Shipping Services
N.A.I.C.S.: 811310

Poseidon Marine Ltd. (1)
391 Stavanger Drive, Saint John, A1A 0A1, NL, Canada
Tel.: (709) 739-4321
Web Site: https://www.pmcl.ca
Shipping Services
N.A.I.C.S.: 811310

SINCERE WATCH (HONG KONG) LIMITED
Offices Nos 6101-6103 61/F The Center 99 Queens Road, Central, China (Hong Kong)
Tel.: (852) 2969 9900 Ky
Web Site:
  http://www.sincerewatch.com.hk
Year Founded: 1954
0444—(HKG)
Rev.: $17,587,197
Assets: $150,394,162
Liabilities: $56,800,470
Net Worth: $93,593,692
Earnings: ($27,124,494)
Emp.: 117
Fiscal Year-end: 03/31/21
Jewelry & Watch Mfr & Distr
N.A.I.C.S.: 339910
Yuet Wah Chu *(Chm)*

Subsidiaries:

Sincere Watch Co., Ltd. (1)
Room 305 3F Wouldwide House Building 131, Sec 3 Min Sheng E Rd, Taipei, 105, Taiwan
Tel.: (886) 227139966
Watch Distr
N.A.I.C.S.: 423940

SINCERITY APPLIED MATERIALS HOLDINGS CORP.
Level 2 627 Chapel Street, South Yarra, Melbourne, 3141, VIC, Australia
Tel.: (61) 421007277 NV
Web Site:
  https://sincerityplastics.com
Year Founded: 2011
SINC—(OTCIQ)
Sales Range: $1-9.9 Million
Crowdfunding Services
N.A.I.C.S.: 525990
Yiwen Zhang *(Chm, Pres & CEO)*

SINCERITY ENGINEERING COMPANY LIMITED
Floor 25 341 Lot A, Phuc Thinh Apartment Blk Cao Dat St. Ward 1Dist 5, Ho Chi Minh City, Vietnam
Tel.: (84) 8 54050721
Engineeering Services
N.A.I.C.S.: 541330

Subsidiaries:

CTCI Vietnam Company Limited (1)
6 Floor Charmvit Tower 117 Tran Duy Hung Road, Cau Giay District, Hanoi, Vietnam (17%)
Tel.: (84) 2438335513
Web Site: https://www.vietnam.ctci.com
Sales Range: $50-74.9 Million
Emp.: 200
Engineering & Construction Services
N.A.I.C.S.: 541330

SINCH AB
Lindhagensgatan 112, 112 51, Stockholm, Sweden
Tel.: (46) 856616600 SE
Web Site: https://www.sinch.com
SINCH—(OMX)
Holding Company; Cloud Telecommunications Services
N.A.I.C.S.: 551112
Johan Hedberg *(Co-Founder)*

Subsidiaries:

Sinch America, Inc. (1)
1 Alliance Ctr 3500 Lenox Rd NE Ste 1875, Atlanta, GA 30326
Tel.: (470) 300-8394
Web Site: http://www.sinch.com
Mobile Messaging Infrastructure Services
N.A.I.C.S.: 517810

Subsidiary (Domestic):

Inteliquent, Inc. (2)
550 W Adams St Ste 900, Chicago, IL 60661
Tel.: (312) 384-8000
Web Site: https://www.sinch.com
Emp.: 1,000
Telecommunication Servicesb
N.A.I.C.S.: 517121
David A. Lopez *(Sr VP-Strategic Relationship)*

Subsidiary (Domestic):

Broadvox LLC (3)
550 W Adams St Ste 900, Chicago, IL 60661-3636
Internet Protocol Telecommunications Services
N.A.I.C.S.: 517810

Voyant Communications, LLC (3)
2300 Berkshire Ln N Ste 4, Minneapolis, MN 55441
Tel.: (866) 629-8200
Web Site: http://www.voyant.com
Voice & Data Solution Services
N.A.I.C.S.: 517810
Scott Sawyer *(Gen Counsel)*

Sinch Mobile AB (1)
Lindhagensgatan 74, 112 18, Stockholm, Sweden
Tel.: (46) 844682803
Web Site: http://www.sinch.com
Cloud Telecommunications Services
N.A.I.C.S.: 517810

Sinch UK Ltd. (1)
Cap House 9-12 Long Lane, London, EC1A 9HA, United Kingdom
Tel.: (44) 2084321260
Mobile Messaging Infrastructure Services
N.A.I.C.S.: 517810

SINCLAIR DENTAL/DENTAIRE
900 Harbourside Drive, North Vancouver, V7P 3T8, BC, Canada
Tel.: (604) 986-1544
Web Site:
  https://www.sinclairdental.com
Year Founded: 1971
Rev.: $64,773,988
Emp.: 300
Dental Equipment Distr
N.A.I.C.S.: 339114
Rory Young *(Dir-Tech Svc)*

SINCLAIR GARAGES (PORT TALBOT) LTD.
Dan-y-Bryn Road, Port Talbot, SA13 1AL, United Kingdom
Tel.: (44) 281 296 7975
Web Site:
  http://www.sinclairgroup.co.uk
Year Founded: 1945
Sales Range: $350-399.9 Million
Emp.: 563
New & Used Car Dealer
N.A.I.C.S.: 441110
Gerald Sinclair *(Chm)*

SINCLAIR SUPPLY LTD.
10914 120th St, Edmonton, T5H 3P7, AB, Canada
Tel.: (780) 452-3110
Web Site:
  http://www.sinclairsupply.ca
Sales Range: $10-24.9 Million
Emp.: 32
Refrigeration, Hydronics & Solar Equipment
N.A.I.C.S.: 423740

SINCLAIRS HOTELS LIMITED
147 Block G New Alipore, Kolkata, 700053, India
Tel.: (91) 9830556333
Web Site:
  https://www.sinclairshotels.com
Year Founded: 1971
523023—(BOM)
Rev.: $4,686,072
Assets: $18,481,991
Liabilities: $3,122,356
Net Worth: $15,359,635
Earnings: $972,863
Emp.: 379
Fiscal Year-end: 03/31/22
Hotel & Resort Operator
N.A.I.C.S.: 721110
Navin Suchanti *(Chm)*

SINCO PHARMACEUTICALS HOLDINGS LTD.
E5-1805 New Century Global Center 1700 Tianfu Avenue North, Gaoxin District, Chengdu, China
Tel.: (86) 2862912988 Ky
Web Site: http://www.sinco-pharm.com
Year Founded: 2011
6833—(HKG)
Rev.: $318,919,302
Assets: $199,976,353
Liabilities: $115,201,148
Net Worth: $84,775,205
Earnings: $9,752,465

SINCO PHARMACEUTICALS HOLDINGS LTD.

Sinco Pharmaceuticals Holdings Ltd.—(Continued)
Emp.: 231
Fiscal Year-end: 12/31/22
Holding Company
N.A.I.C.S.: 551112

SINDH ABADGAR'S SUGAR MILLS LIMITED
209 2nd Floor Progressive Plaza Beaumont Road, Karachi, Pakistan
Tel.: (92) 2135638212
Web Site: https://www.sasmltd.com
Year Founded: 1984
SASML—(PSX)
Rev.: $19,910,982
Assets: $15,793,052
Liabilities: $6,652,596
Net Worth: $9,140,456
Earnings: $1,343,195
Emp.: 391
Fiscal Year-end: 09/30/23
Sugar Mfr
N.A.I.C.S.: 311314
Deoo Mal Essarani (Chm & CEO)

SINDH BANK LIMITED
3rd Floor Federation House Abdullah Shah Ghazi Road, Clifton, Karachi, Pakistan
Tel.: (92) 21 35829 394   PK
Web Site:
http://www.sindhbankltd.com
Year Founded: 2010
Commericial Banking
N.A.I.C.S.: 522110
Tariq Ahsan (Pres & CEO)

Subsidiaries:

Sindh Leasing Company Limited (1)
3rd Floor Imperial Court Dr Ziauddin Ahmed Road, Karachi, 75530, Pakistan
Tel.: (92) 2135640701
Financial Services
N.A.I.C.S.: 523999
Rehan Anjum (CEO)

SINDH MODARABA MANAGEMENT LIMITED
1st floor Imperial Court Dr Ziauddin Ahmed Road, Karachi, 75530, Pakistan
Tel.: (92) 2135640708
Web Site:
https://www.sindhmodarabaltd.com
SINDM—(PSX)
Rev.: $1,006,095
Assets: $6,397,202
Liabilities: $200,979
Net Worth: $6,196,223
Earnings: $469,154
Emp.: 14
Fiscal Year-end: 06/30/23
Insurance Management Services
N.A.I.C.S.: 524298
Muhammad Bila (Chm)

Subsidiaries:

Sindh Insurance Limited (1)
3rd Floor Imperial Court Dr Ziauddin Ahmed Road, Karachi, Pakistan
Tel.: (92) 2135640715
Web Site: http://www.sindhinsuranceltd.com
Trading Services
N.A.I.C.S.: 523160
Muhammad Bilal (Chm)

SINDHU BIKASH BANK LTD.
Barhabise Bazar, Bahrabise, Nepal
Tel.: (977) 11662340
Web Site:
https://www.sindhubank.com.np
SINDU—(NEP)
Rev.: $3,347,812
Assets: $41,721,112
Liabilities: $37,115,235
Net Worth: $4,605,877
Earnings: $346,965

Emp.: 136
Fiscal Year-end: 07/16/22
Commercial Banking Services
N.A.I.C.S.: 522110

SINDHU TRADE LINKS LIMITED
129 Transport Centre New Rothak Road Punjabi Bagh, New Delhi, 110035, India
Tel.: (91) 1128315036
Web Site:
https://www.sindhutrade.com
Year Founded: 1992
532029—(BOM)
Rev.: $99,086,783
Assets: $186,668,596
Liabilities: $93,855,107
Net Worth: $92,813,489
Earnings: $8,579,789
Emp.: 2,100
Fiscal Year-end: 03/31/21
Transportation & Financial Services
N.A.I.C.S.: 488999
Satya Pal Sindhu (Mng Dir)

Subsidiaries:

Hari Bhoomi Communications Private Limited (1)
Tel.: (91) 1140451115
Web Site: https://www.haribhoomi.com
Newspaper Publishers
N.A.I.C.S.: 513110

Indus Automotives Pvt Ltd (1)
Korba Road Garud Nagar Shopping Complex SECL Gevra Project Korba, Chittaurgarh, 495452, New Delhi, India
Tel.: (91) 7815 275608
Web Site: http://www.indusauto.in
Automotive Spare Parts Distr
N.A.I.C.S.: 423120
M. N. Ansari (Asst Mgr)

Pt. Param Mitra Coal Resources (1)
Suite 1705 17th Floor The East Building, JL Lingkar Megakuningan KAV E 3 2 No 1, Jakarta, Indonesia
Tel.: (62) 215 5793 8476
Web Site: http://www.paramresources.com
Coal Mining & Exploration Services
N.A.I.C.S.: 212115
Dev Sindhu (Co-Pres)

SINDOH CO., LTD.
277-22 2-Ga Seongsu-dong, Seongdong-gu, Seoul, 133-705, Korea (South)
Tel.: (82) 24601114
Web Site: https://www.sindoh.com
Year Founded: 1960
029530—(KRS)
Rev.: $290,069,297
Assets: $796,524,474
Liabilities: $65,032,140
Net Worth: $731,492,334
Earnings: $34,527,706
Emp.: 305
Fiscal Year-end: 12/31/22
Office Automation Products Mfr & Sales
N.A.I.C.S.: 334118
Suk-Hyung Woo (Chm)

SINDU VALLEY TECHNOLOGIES LTD.
No 3 2nd Floor Dr TCM Royan Road Opp Ayyappan Temple, Bengaluru, 560053, Karnataka, India
Tel.: (91) 26706176
Web Site: https://sinduvalley.com
Year Founded: 1976
505504—(BOM)
Assets: $324
Liabilities: $44,086
Net Worth: ($43,762)
Earnings: ($18,704)
Emp.: 1
Fiscal Year-end: 03/31/23

Information Technology Consulting Services
N.A.I.C.S.: 541512
Sandhya Deshpande (Sec)

SINENG ELECTRIC CO., LTD.
No 6 Hehui Road, Huishan, Wuxi, 214000, Jiangsu, China
Tel.: (86) 51088888118
Web Site: https://www.si-neng.com
Year Founded: 2012
300827—(SSE)
Rev.: $328,331,269
Assets: $647,948,317
Liabilities: $503,608,468
Net Worth: $144,339,849
Earnings: $11,451,712
Fiscal Year-end: 12/31/22
Power Electronic Equipment Mfr & Distr
N.A.I.C.S.: 335999
Qiang Wu (Chm)

SINERGIYA INVEST HOLDING AD
Bul Botevgradsko Shose 239 Ofis 1, 5300, Sofia, Bulgaria
Tel.: (359) 886505520
Web Site: https://sinergyinvest.com
Year Founded: 1997
SIMT—(BUL)
Sales Range: Less than $1 Million
Fiber Glass Mfr
N.A.I.C.S.: 327212
Milena Petkova (Exec Dir)

SINETECH
2 Samantha Street, Strijdom Park, Randburg, 2169, Gauteng, South Africa
Tel.: (27) 118867874
Web Site: http://www.sinetech.co.za
Year Founded: 1995
Eletric Power Generation Services
N.A.I.C.S.: 221118
Bert Mondello (Chm)

SINFONIA TECHNOLOGY CO., LTD.
Shiba NBF Tower 1-30 Shiba-daimon 1-chome, Minato-ku, Tokyo, 105-8564, Japan
Tel.: (81) 354731826   JP
Web Site: http://www.sinfo-t.jp
Year Founded: 1917
Sales Range: $750-799.9 Million
Emp.: 3,669
Multi-Platform Electrical Machinery Mfr
N.A.I.C.S.: 333998
Fuminori Saito (Pres)

Subsidiaries:

PT. SINFONIA TECHNOLOGY INDONESIA (1)
Graha Paramita 8th Floor Suite E JI Denpasar Raya Block D2 KAV 8, Kuningan, Jakarta, 12940, Indonesia
Tel.: (62) 212523606
Web Site: http://www.sinfo-t.jp
Electrical Machine Product Whslr
N.A.I.C.S.: 423610
Aldy Nurhasan (Acct Mgr)

SINFONIA MICROTEC (DONGGUAN) CO., LTD. (1)
Block 10 Xihu Industrial Area, Shilong, Dongguan, Guang Dong, China
Tel.: (86) 76986184431
Web Site: http://www.sinfo-mt.co.jp
Automobile Spare Parts Mfr
N.A.I.C.S.: 335314
Masayoshi Akashi (Pres)

SINFONIA MICROTEC (HONG KONG) CO.,LTD. (1)
Room2213A 22/F Asia Trade Centre Lei Muk Road, Kwai Chung, Hong Kong, New Territories, China (Hong Kong)

INTERNATIONAL PUBLIC

Tel.: (852) 24258072
Web Site: http://www.sinfo-mt.co.jp
Automobile Spare Parts Mfr
N.A.I.C.S.: 335314
Masayoshi Akashi (Pres)

SINFONIA TECHNOLOGY (SHANGHAI) CO., LTD. (1)
Room3006 Building B Far East International Plaza No 317 Xian Xia road, Changning, Shanghai, 200051, China
Tel.: (86) 2162750606
Web Site: http://www.sinfo-t.jp
Electrical Machine Product Whslr
N.A.I.C.S.: 423610

SINFONIA TECHNOLOGY (SINGAPORE) PTE. LTD. (1)
101 Cecil Street 13-12 Tong Eng Building, Singapore, 69533, Singapore
Tel.: (65) 62236122
Web Site: http://www.sinfo-t.jp
Electrical Machine Product Whslr
N.A.I.C.S.: 423610

SINFONIA TECHNOLOGY (THAILAND) CO., LTD. (1)
12th Floor Room 1205 319 Chamchuri Square Building Phayathai Road, Pathumwan, Bangkok, 10330, Thailand
Tel.: (66) 21605068
Web Site: http://www.sinfo-t.jp
Electrical Machine Product Whslr
N.A.I.C.S.: 423610
Yuki Marimoto (Mgr-Procurement)

SING HOLDINGS LIMITED
96 Robinson Road 10-01 SIF Building, Singapore, 068899, Singapore
Tel.: (65) 65366696
Web Site:
https://www.singholdings.com
5IC—(SES)
Rev.: $4,412,633
Assets: $583,355,298
Liabilities: $337,691,434
Net Worth: $245,663,864
Earnings: $7,622,510
Emp.: 70
Fiscal Year-end: 12/31/23
Building Investment Services
N.A.I.C.S.: 236116
Puay Kuan Tay (CFO)

Subsidiaries:

Meyer Development Pte. Ltd. (1)
3 Meyer Place Meyer Residence, Singapore, Singapore
Tel.: (65) 63448802
Residential Property Management Services
N.A.I.C.S.: 531311

Sing Holdings (Bellerive) Pte. Ltd. (1)
96 Robinson Road 10-01, Singapore, Singapore
Tel.: (65) 67343688
Residential Property Development Services
N.A.I.C.S.: 236116

Sing Holdings (Cairnhill) Pte. Ltd. (1)
96 Robinson Road 10-01 SIF Building, Singapore, 068899, Singapore
Tel.: (65) 6 536 6696
Web Site: https://www.singholdings.com
Emp.: 10
Residential Property Development Services
N.A.I.C.S.: 236116

SING LEE SOFTWARE (GROUP) LIMITED
16th Floor Buiding 9 West City Best Space No 158 Zixuan Road, Sandun Xihu District, Hangzhou, 310030, China
Tel.: (86) 57188480666   BM
Web Site: http://www.singlee.com.cn
Year Founded: 1993
8076—(HKG)
Rev.: $11,926,840
Assets: $13,451,724
Liabilities: $7,912,382

Net Worth: $5,539,342
Earnings: ($2,580,692)
Emp.: 767
Fiscal Year-end: 12/31/22
Software Support Services
N.A.I.C.S.: 541512
Yung Lai Hung (Co-Founder, Chm & Compliance Officer)

SING TAO NEWS CORPORATION LIMITED
Sing Tao News Corporation Building 7 Chun Cheong Street, Tseung Kwan O Industrial Estate, Tseung Kwan O, New Territories, China (Hong Kong)
Tel.: (852) 27982323
Web Site:
   http://www.singtaonewscorp.com
1105—(HKG)
Rev.: $1,039,135,200
Assets: $261,966,983
Liabilities: $41,674,268
Net Worth: $220,292,715
Earnings: ($17,694,960)
Emp.: 1,114
Fiscal Year-end: 12/31/22
Media & Property Holding
N.A.I.C.S.: 541840
Ronald Jeffery Yiu Chong Yang (Dir-Printing Ops)

Subsidiaries:

China Human Capital Management Company Limited (1)
Room 0707 No 113 Zhichun Road, Haidian District, Beijing, 100086, China
Tel.: (86) 1064496688
Media Related Operation & Newspaper Publishing Services
N.A.I.C.S.: 541840

GC Media Teamwork Limited (1)
18/F Sing Tao News Corporation Building 3 Tung Wong Road, Shau Kei Wan, China (Hong Kong)
Tel.: (852) 31813239
Newspaper Publishing Services
N.A.I.C.S.: 513110

Global China Circulation & Distribution Limited (1)
Sing Tao News Corporation Building 7 Chun Cheong Street, Tseung Kwan O Industrial Estate New Territories, Tseung Kwan O, China (Hong Kong)
Tel.: (852) 27982220
Media Related Operation & Newspaper Publishing Services
N.A.I.C.S.: 541840

Headline Daily Limited (1)
Sing Tao News Corporation Building 7 Chun Cheong Street, Tseung Kwan O Industrial Estate, Tseung Kwan O, New Territories, China (Hong Kong)
Tel.: (852) 2 798 2323
Web Site: http://hd.stheadline.com
Online News Publisher
N.A.I.C.S.: 513110
Ting Yiu Lai (CEO)

JJ Printing Limited (1)
7 Chun Cheong Street Tseung Kwan O Industrial Estate, Tseung Kwan O, China (Hong Kong)
Tel.: (852) 31813960
Media Related Operation & Newspaper Publishing Services
N.A.I.C.S.: 541840

Premier Printing Group Limited (1)
7 Chun Cheong Street Tseung Kwan O Industrial Estate, Tseung Kwan O, New Territory, China (Hong Kong)
Tel.: (852) 39260900
Printing Services
N.A.I.C.S.: 323117

Sing Tao (Canada) Limited (1)
221 WhiteHall Drive, Markham, L3R 9T1, ON, Canada
Tel.: (416) 596-8140
Investment Holding Services
N.A.I.C.S.: 551112

Sing Tao (U.K.) Ltd. (1)
Unit 12 Wing Yip Business Centre 395 Edgware Road Cricklewood, London, NW2 6LN, United Kingdom
Tel.: (44) 2087327628
Web Site: https://singtao.co.uk
Newspaper Publishing Services
N.A.I.C.S.: 513110

Sing Tao Newspaper Group Limited (1)
Sing Tao News Corporation Building 7 Chun Cheong Street, Tseung Kwan O Industrial Estate New Territories, Tseung Kwan O, China (Hong Kong)
Tel.: (852) 27982323
Web Site: https://www.singtaonewscorp.com
Media Related Operation & Newspaper Publishing Services
N.A.I.C.S.: 541840

Sing Tao Newspapers Los Angeles Ltd. (1)
17059 Green Dr, City of Industry, CA 91745
Tel.: (626) 956-8200
Newspaper Publishing Services
N.A.I.C.S.: 513110

Sing Tao Newspapers New York Ltd. (1)
188 Lafayette St, New York, NY 10013
Tel.: (212) 699-3800
Web Site: http://us.nysingtao.com
Sales Range: $1-9.9 Million
Newspaper Publishing Services
N.A.I.C.S.: 513110

Sing Tao Newspapers San Francisco Ltd. (1)
845 Cowan Rd, Burlingame, CA 94010
Tel.: (650) 239-9696
Newspaper Publishing Services
N.A.I.C.S.: 513110

Sing Tao Publishing Limited (1)
2/F 7 Chun Cheong Street, Industrial Estate, Tseung Kwan O, New Territories, China (Hong Kong)
Tel.: (852) 27982579
Books Publishing Services
N.A.I.C.S.: 513120

SING YANG (OVERSEAS) LIMITED
8 11th Floor Tungtex Bldg, 203 Wai Yip St Kwun Tong, Kowloon, China (Hong Kong)
Tel.: (852) 27977900
Clothing & Furnishings Whslr
N.A.I.C.S.: 424350
Lem Loi (Mgr)

SINGAMAS CONTAINER HOLDINGS LIMITED
15th Floor Allied Kajima Building No 138 Gloucester Road, Wanchai, China (Hong Kong)
Tel.: (852) 25987831   HK
Web Site: https://www.singamas.com
Year Founded: 1988
0716—(HKG)
Rev.: $98,937,833
Assets: $103,562,258
Liabilities: $19,555,440
Net Worth: $84,006,818
Earnings: $7,212,038
Emp.: 2,970
Fiscal Year-end: 12/31/22
Container Mfr & Logistic Services
N.A.I.C.S.: 541614
Siong Seng Teo (Chm, Chm, CEO & Exec Dir)

Subsidiaries:

DY Terminal Ltd. (1)
19th Fl Rykadan Capital Tower 135 Hoi Bun Road, Kowloon, China (Hong Kong)
Tel.: (852) 25987831
Sales Range: $25-49.9 Million
Emp.: 14
General Warehousing & Storage
N.A.I.C.S.: 493110
Chang Yun Chung (Chm)

Eng Kong Container Services Ltd. (1)
19/F Rykadan Capital Tower 135 Hoi Bun Road, Kowloon, China (Hong Kong) (73.3%)
Tel.: (852) 25987831
Web Site: http://www.singamas.com
Freight Transportation Arrangement
N.A.I.C.S.: 488510

Guangxi Singamas Container Co., Ltd. (1)
Room 613 Block A No 1 Eight Avenue Complex Building Guangxi, Qinzhou Bonded Port Area, Qinzhou, China
Tel.: (86) 7773881007
Container Mfr
N.A.I.C.S.: 332439

Huizhou Pacific Container Co., Ltd (1)
Dongfeng Vlg Xinxu Town, Huiyang Dist, 516223, Huizhou, Guangdong, China
Tel.: (86) 7523528555
Sales Range: $200-249.9 Million
Emp.: 900
Metal Container Mfr
N.A.I.C.S.: 332439

Huizhou Singamas Energy Equipment Co., Ltd. (1)
Dongfeng Village, Xinxu Huiyang, Huizhou, 516223, Guangdong, China
Tel.: (86) 7523528555
Container Mfr
N.A.I.C.S.: 332439

PT. Java Pacific (1)
Jl Raya Surabaya-Krian KM 24-25 Desa Keboharan, Krian, Sidoarjo, Jawa Timur, Indonesia
Tel.: (62) 31 898 1666
Web Site: https://www.javapacific.co.id
Specialized Container Mfr
N.A.I.C.S.: 423440

Qidong Singamas Offshore Equipment Co., Ltd. (1)
No 1 Taiping Road, Huiping, Qidong, 226262, Jiangsu, China
Tel.: (86) 51383689757
Container Mfr
N.A.I.C.S.: 332439

Shanghai Baoshan Pacific Container Co., Ltd. (1)
No 2020 Bao Yang Road, Baoshan District, Shanghai, 201900, China
Tel.: (86) 2133792588
Sales Range: $25-49.9 Million
Emp.: 50
Metal Container Mfr
N.A.I.C.S.: 332439

Shanghai Pacific International Container Co., Ltd. (1)
No 2667 Jia Zhu Road, Jia Ding, Shanghai, 201815, China
Tel.: (86) 2169021222
Container Mfr
N.A.I.C.S.: 332439

Shanghai Reeferco Container Co., Ltd. (1)
No 509 Jia An Road, Jiading District, Shanghai, 201821, China
Tel.: (86) 2139108055
Web Site:
   http://www.singamas.en.ec21.com
Air-Conditioning & Warm Air Heating Equipment Mfr
N.A.I.C.S.: 333415

Singamas Container Industry Co., Ltd. (1)
Xinjie Street, Yixing, 214204, Jiangsu, China
Tel.: (86) 51087131501
Container Mfr
N.A.I.C.S.: 332439

Singamas Logistics (Qingdao) Co., Ltd. (1)
No 308 Longgangshan Road Economic Technological Development Zone, Qingdao, 266555, Shandong, China
Tel.: (86) 53286058696
Container Mfr
N.A.I.C.S.: 332439

Singamas Logistics (Tianjin) Co., Ltd. (1)
No 197 Ji Yun Yi Dao Tianjin Port Container Logistics Center, Tianjin, 300461, China
Tel.: (86) 2225701386
Container Mfr
N.A.I.C.S.: 332439

Singamas Terminals (HK) Ltd. (1)
19th Fl Dah Sing Financial Ctr, Wanchai, China (Hong Kong)
Tel.: (852) 25987831
Web Site: http://www.singamas.com
Emp.: 40
Marine Cargo Handling
N.A.I.C.S.: 488320

Tianjin Singamas Container Co., Ltd. (1)
No 197 Ji Yun Yi Dao Tianjin Port Container Logistics Center, Tianjin, 300461, China
Tel.: (86) 2225701386
Sales Range: $10-24.9 Million
Emp.: 40
Warehousing & Storage
N.A.I.C.S.: 493110

Xiamen Pacific Container Manufacturing Co., Ltd. (1)
No 9 WuLv Road TongAn Industrial Concentration Zone, Xiamen, 361100, Fujian, China
Tel.: (86) 5923751997
Container Mfr
N.A.I.C.S.: 332439

SINGAPORE ASAHI CHEMICAL & SOLDER INDUSTRIES PTE. LTD.
47 Pandan Road, Singapore, 609288, Singapore
Tel.: (65) 6262 1616
Web Site:
   http://www.asahisolder.com
Year Founded: 1977
Emp.: 35
Soldering & Metal Product Mfr
N.A.I.C.S.: 333992
Vincent Kho (CEO)

Subsidiaries:

Asahi Metals (Hong Kong) Ltd. (1)
Unit 1 7/F Global Trade Centre 15 Wing Kin Road, Kwai Chung, New Territories, China (Hong Kong)
Tel.: (852) 24091028
Web Site: http://www.asahisolder.com
Sales Range: $25-49.9 Million
Soldering & Metal Product Distr
N.A.I.C.S.: 333992
Tenu Kho (Pres)

Asahi Metals (Shenzhen) Ltd. (1)
55 Que Shan Industrial Area Longhua Baoan Town, Shenzhen, 518109, Guangdong, China
Tel.: (86) 755 2811 1800
Web Site: http://www.asahisolder.com
Emp.: 30
Soldering & Metal Product Distr
N.A.I.C.S.: 333992
Yo Kho (Gen Mgr)

Asahi Solder Technology (Beijing) Co. Ltd. (1)
N Block Chuang Xin Yuan Badachu Gaokeji Yuan Qu, Shijingshan District, Beijing, 100041, China
Tel.: (86) 10 8879 9379
Soldering & Metal Product Distr
N.A.I.C.S.: 333992
C. S. Tan (Gen Mgr)

Asahi Solder Technology (Thailand) Co. Ltd (1)
294/85 RK Office Park Romklao Road Klongsampravet, Ladkrabang, Bangkok, 10520, Thailand
Tel.: (66) 2184 9667
Web Site: http://www.asahisolder.com
Emp.: 1
Soldering & Metal Product Mfr
N.A.I.C.S.: 333992
Apichet Kotvieng (Mgr-Product Dev)

Asahi Solder Technology (Wuxi) Co. Ltd. (1)

SINGAPORE ASAHI CHEMICAL & SOLDER INDUSTRIES PTE. LTD.

Singapore Asahi Chemical & Solder Industries Pte. Ltd.—(Continued)

No 6 Changjiang Road Wuxi National Hi-Tech Industrial Development Zone, Wuxi, 214028, Jiangsu, China
Tel.: (86) 510 8521 7080
Soldering & Metal Product Distr
N.A.I.C.S.: 333992
Yu Guoxin (Gen Mgr)

Global Advance Metals Technology (S) Pte. Ltd. (1)
47 Pandan Road, Singapore, 609288, Singapore
Tel.: (65) 6262 1616
Web Site: http://www.asahisolder.com
Soldering & Metal Product Mfr
N.A.I.C.S.: 333992
S. T. Ong (Dir-Dept)

PT Asahi Solder Technology Indonesia (1)
J1 Jababeka IV SFB Blok T No 2J Kawasan Industri-Cikarang, Bekasi, 17530, Indonesia
Tel.: (62) 21 893 4333
Soldering & Metal Product Mfr
N.A.I.C.S.: 333992
H. S. Tan (Gen Mgr)

Quantum Chemical Technologies (S) Pte. Ltd. (1)
47 Pandan Road, Singapore, 609288, Singapore
Tel.: (65) 6262 1616
Emp.: 30
Chemicals Mfr
N.A.I.C.S.: 325998
K. H. Chew (Dir-R&D)

Sinasahi Solder (M) Sdn. Bhd. (1)
62/64 Jalan Perdagangan 16 Taman Universiti Industrial Park, Sekudai, 81300, Johor Bahru, Malaysia
Tel.: (60) 7 520 6770
Web Site: http://www.asahisolder.com
Emp.: 20
Soldering & Metal Product Mfr
N.A.I.C.S.: 333992
Vincent Kho (Gen Mgr)

Singapore Asahi Pte. Ltd. (1)
923-378 9F Osaka-Ekimae 4th Building 1-11-4 Umeda, Kita-ku, Osaka, 530-001, Japan
Tel.: (81) 50 3577 5186
Soldering & Metal Product Distr
N.A.I.C.S.: 333992
Tomoko Yamakado (Dir)

SINGAPORE EXCHANGE LIMITED

2 Shenton Way 02-02 SGX Centre 1, Singapore, 068804, Singapore
Tel.: (65) 62368888 SG
Web Site: https://www.sgx.com
Year Founded: 1999
SPXCF—(OTCIQ)
Rev.: $885,074,472
Assets: $2,802,029,641
Liabilities: $1,539,629,492
Net Worth: $1,262,400,148
Earnings: $422,797,332
Emp.: 1,205
Fiscal Year-end: 06/30/23
Stock Exchange
N.A.I.C.S.: 523210
Boon Chye Loh (CEO)

Subsidiaries:

SGX Link Pte Ltd (1)
2 Shenton Way 02-02 SGX Centre 1, Singapore, 068804, Singapore (100%)
Tel.: (65) 6 236 8888
Web Site: http://www.sgx.com
Sales Range: $350-399.9 Million
Emp.: 600
Securities & Commodity Exchanges
N.A.I.C.S.: 523210

Singapore Exchange Derivatives Clearing Limited (1)
2 Shenton Way 02-02 SGX Centre 1, Singapore, 068804, Singapore
Tel.: (65) 62368888

Web Site: https://www.sgx.com
Emp.: 600
Commodities Trading Services
N.A.I.C.S.: 523210
Chew Choon Seng (Chm)

Singapore Exchange Derivatives Trading Limited (1)
5 Tampines Central 6 # 03-40, 529482, Singapore, Singapore (100%)
Tel.: (65) 67829705
Commodity Contracts Brokerage
N.A.I.C.S.: 523160

Singapore Exchange Securities Trading Limited (1)
2 Shenton Way 02-02, SGX Centre 1, Singapore, 068804, Singapore (100%)
Tel.: (65) 62368888
Web Site: https://www.sgx.com
Sales Range: $350-399.9 Million
Emp.: 600
Securities & Commodity Exchanges
N.A.I.C.S.: 523210
Magnus Bocker (CEO)

The Baltic Exchange Ltd. (1)
4th Floor 107 Leadenhall St, London, EC3A 4AF, United Kingdom (100%)
Tel.: (44) 2072839300
Web Site: https://www.balticexchange.com
Investment Holding Company; Maritime Shipping Contract Trading & Settlement Services
N.A.I.C.S.: 551112
Mark Jackson (CEO)

Subsidiary (Non-US):

The Baltic Exchange (Asia) Pte. Ltd. (2)
2 Shenton Way 02-02 SGX Centre 1, Singapore, 068804, Singapore
Tel.: (65) 31634918
Web Site: https://www.balticexchange.com
Maritime Shipping Contract Trading & Settlement Services
N.A.I.C.S.: 425120

The Central Depository (Pte) Limited (1)
4 Shenton Way 02-01 SGX Centre 2, Singapore, 068807, Singapore
Tel.: (65) 65357511
Stock Exchange Services
N.A.I.C.S.: 523210

SINGAPORE KITCHEN EQUIPMENT LIMITED

Blk 115A Commonwealth Drive 01-27/28, Singapore, 149596, Singapore
Tel.: (65) 64727337
Web Site: https://www.singaporekitchenequipmentltd.com
5WG—(CAT)
Rev.: $25,160,895
Assets: $28,365,356
Liabilities: $16,262,999
Net Worth: $12,102,357
Earnings: $625,192
Emp.: 145
Fiscal Year-end: 12/31/22
Kitchen Design & Consulting Services
N.A.I.C.S.: 541410
Sally Chwee Choo Chua (Co-Founder, CEO & Mng Dir)

SINGAPORE LAND GROUP LIMITED

24 Raffles Place, Singapore, 48621, Singapore
Tel.: (65) 60116000
Web Site: https://singaporeland.com
UILCF—(OTCIQ)
Rev.: $506,679,241
Assets: $6,754,522,563
Liabilities: $716,650,743
Net Worth: $6,037,871,820
Earnings: $59,882,710
Emp.: 6
Fiscal Year-end: 12/31/20

Holding Company for Property Investment & Development
N.A.I.C.S.: 551112
Hock San Lim (Pres & CEO)

Subsidiaries:

Alprop Pte Ltd (1)
02-19 1 Bt Batok Central Link, Singapore, 658713, Singapore
Tel.: (65) 67941480
Web Site: http://www.westmall.com.sg
Sales Range: $50-74.9 Million
Emp.: 9
Property Management Services
N.A.I.C.S.: 531390

Marina Centre Holdings Private Limited (1)
6 Raffles Boulevard, Singapore, 039594, Singapore
Tel.: (65) 63398787
Web Site: http://www.marinasquare.com.sg
Grocery Products Retailer
N.A.I.C.S.: 445110
Zhen Jun Tan (Sr Mgr-Fin)

Singapore Land Limited (1)
24 Raffles Place 22-01/06 Clifford Centre, Singapore, 048621, Singapore (99.77%)
Tel.: (65) 62229312
Web Site: http://www.uic.com.sg
Sales Range: $350-399.9 Million
Holding Company; Property Developer
N.A.I.C.S.: 551112
Hock San Lim (Pres & CEO)

Subsidiary (Domestic):

Interpex Services Private Limited (2)
5 Shenton Way #02-14, Podium Block, UIC Building, Singapore, 068808, Singapore (100%)
Tel.: (65) 6294 4591
Building Management & Maintenance Services
N.A.I.C.S.: 236220

S.L. Development Management Pte Limited (2)
5 Shenton Way #02-14, Podium Block, UIC Building, Singapore, 068808, Singapore (100%)
Investment Services
N.A.I.C.S.: 523999

S.L. Homes Pte. Ltd. (2)
5 Shenton Way #02-14 Podium Block UIC Building, Singapore, 068808, Singapore (100%)
Provider of Property Development Services
N.A.I.C.S.: 524126

Subsidiary (Non-US):

S.L. Realty Management Services (HK) Limited (2)
22nd Floor, Prince's Building, Central, China (Hong Kong) (100%)
Property Management Agents
N.A.I.C.S.: 531210

Subsidiary (Domestic):

Shing Kwan Realty (Pte) Limited (2)
24 Raffles Place UIC Building, Singapore, 048621, Singapore (100%)
Tel.: (65) 62229312
Web Site: http://www.singland.com.sg
Sales Range: $75-99.9 Million
Emp.: 180
Property Investment
N.A.I.C.S.: 523999
Lim Hocksen (Mng Dir)

UIC Asian Computer Services Pte Ltd (1)
750A Technopark Chai Chee 06-01 Chai Chee Road, Singapore, 469 001, Singapore
Tel.: (65) 62415388
Web Site: https://www.uicacs.com.sg
Sales Range: $25-49.9 Million
Emp.: 100
Information Technology Consulting Services
N.A.I.C.S.: 541512

UIC Development (Private) Limited (1)
5 Shenton Way 02-16 UIC Building, Singapore, 068808, Singapore

INTERNATIONAL PUBLIC

Tel.: (65) 62201311
Real Estate Management Services
N.A.I.C.S.: 531390

UIC Technologies Pte Ltd (1)
750A Viva Business Park 06-01 Chai Chee Road, Singapore, 469001, Singapore
Tel.: (65) 62415388
Web Site: https://www.uictech.com.sg
Emp.: 120
Information Technology Consulting Services
N.A.I.C.S.: 541512
Chang Sek Yew (Gen Mgr)

SINGAPORE LIFE PTE LTD

18 Robinson Road #04-03, Singapore, 048547, Singapore
Tel.: (65) 6911 1111 SG
Web Site: http://singlife.com
Insurance Services
N.A.I.C.S.: 524298
Ray Ferguson (Chm)

SINGAPORE MEDICAL GROUP LIMITED

1004 Toa Payoh North 06-03 to 07, Singapore, 318995, Singapore
Tel.: (65) 6 887 4232
Web Site: http://www.smg.sg
5OT—(CAT)
Rev.: $76,131,175
Assets: $152,380,880
Liabilities: $26,649,686
Net Worth: $125,731,194
Earnings: $11,865,109
Emp.: 296
Fiscal Year-end: 12/31/21
Holding Company; Medical Clinics Owner & Operator
N.A.I.C.S.: 551112
Sian Jing Wong (CFO)

Subsidiaries:

Astra Centre for Women & Fertility Pte. Ltd. (1)
38 Irrawaddy Road 05-40 Mt Elizabeth Novena Specialist Centre, Singapore, 329563, Singapore
Tel.: (65) 6 333 6636
Web Site: https://www.mygynae.com.sg
Obstetric & Gynaecology Healthcare Services
N.A.I.C.S.: 621111

Cancer Centre Pte. Ltd. (1)
290 Orchard Road 17-05/06 Paragon Medical, Singapore, 238859, Singapore
Tel.: (65) 68351000
Cancer Treatment Services
N.A.I.C.S.: 621111
Wong Seng Weng (Dir-Medical)

CardioScan Asia Pte. Ltd. (1)
1004 Toa Payoh North 06-03, Singapore, 318995, Singapore
Tel.: (65) 67359552
Hospital Care Services
N.A.I.C.S.: 622110
Harry Mond (Dir-Medical)

HiDoc Pte. Ltd. (1)
1004 Toa Payoh North 06-03/07, Singapore, 318995, Singapore
Tel.: (65) 6 887 5000
Web Site: https://www.hidoc.sg
Online Medical Consultation Services
N.A.I.C.S.: 621420
Carolyn Goh (Founder & CTO)

Kids Clinic @ Bishan Pte. Ltd. (1)
Blk 116 Bishan Street 12 01-28, Singapore, 570116, Singapore
Tel.: (65) 6 356 8909
Web Site: https://kidsclinic.sg
Paediatric Healthcare Services
N.A.I.C.S.: 621111

SMG Astra Women's Specialists Pte. Ltd. (1)
38 Irrawaddy Road 05-21/22 Mt Elizabeth Novena Specialist Centre, Singapore, 329563, Singapore
Tel.: (65) 6 353 3878
Web Site: https://www.astrawomenspecialists.com

AND PRIVATE COMPANIES

Obstetric & Gynaecology Healthcare Services
N.A.I.C.S.: 621111

SMG Orthopaedic Group Pte. Ltd. (1)
3 Mount Elizabeth 17-14 Mount Elizabeth Medical Centre, Singapore, 228510, Singapore
Tel.: (65) 68368000
Web Site: http://orthopaedic.smg.sg
Orthopaedic Healthcare Services
N.A.I.C.S.: 621111
Andrew Quoc Dutton (Dir-Medical)

SMG Specialist Centre Pte. Ltd. (1)
38 Irrawaddy Road Mount Elizabeth Novena 05-34/35, Singapore, 329563, Singapore
Tel.: (65) 67351000
Web Site: http://www.specialistcentre.sg
Medical Care Services
N.A.I.C.S.: 621610

TOGC @Gleneagles Pte. Ltd. (1)
6 Napier Road 08-19, Singapore, 258499, Singapore
Tel.: (65) 6 475 1158
Web Site: https://togc.sg
Obstetric & Gynaecology Healthcare Services
N.A.I.C.S.: 621111

The Breast Clinic Pte. Ltd. (1)
290 Orchard Road 16-12 Paragon Tower 1 via Lobby F, Singapore, 238859, Singapore
Tel.: (65) 6 362 8880
Web Site: https://www.thebreastclinic.sg
Clinic Care Services
N.A.I.C.S.: 621498
Anthony P. H. Tang (Dir-Medical)

The Dental Studio Pte. Ltd. (1)
Paragon via Lift Lobby E or F 09-09/10 290 Orchard Road, Singapore, 238859, Singapore
Tel.: (65) 6 836 0050
Web Site: https://www.dentalstudio.sg
Dental Healthcare Providing Services
N.A.I.C.S.: 621210
Lynette Ng (Dir-Clinical)

The Lasik Surgery Clinic Pte. Ltd. (1)
290 Orchard Road 16-01/02 Paragon Medical, Singapore, 238859, Singapore
Tel.: (65) 68361000
Lasik Surgery Services
N.A.I.C.S.: 621493

Wellness & Gynaecology Centre Pte. Ltd. (1)
290 Orchard Road 16-07/08 Paragon Tower 1 via Lift Lobby F, Singapore, 238859, Singapore
Tel.: (65) 6 235 2152
Web Site: https://www.agemanagement.com.sg
Health Care Srvices
N.A.I.C.S.: 621610

SINGAPORE O&G LTD.
229 Mountbatten Road 02-02 Mountbatten Square, Singapore, 398007, Singapore
Tel.: (65) 6 440 4123
Web Site: http://www.sog.com.sg
1D8—(SES)
Rev.: $30,114,998
Assets: $43,682,564
Liabilities: $11,187,145
Net Worth: $32,495,419
Earnings: $7,166,930
Emp.: 80
Fiscal Year-end: 12/31/20
Women's Medical & Surgical Services
N.A.I.C.S.: 621111
Keen Whye Lee (Co-Founder)

Subsidiaries:

Beh's Clinic for Women Pte. Ltd. (1)
339 Thomson Road 05-03 Thomson Medical Centre, Singapore, 307677, Singapore
Tel.: (65) 6 352 9227
Web Site: https://www.drbeh.com.sg

Gynaecology Healthcare Services
N.A.I.C.S.: 621111

Subsidiary (Domestic):

Choo Wan Ling Women's Clinic Pte. Ltd. (2)
38 Irrawaddy Road 10-30 Mt Elizabeth Novena Specialist Centre, Singapore, 329563, Singapore
Tel.: (65) 62623060
Web Site: http://www.drchoowl.com
Gynaecology Healthcare Services
N.A.I.C.S.: 621111

Subsidiary (Domestic):

Heng Clinic for Women Pte. Ltd. (3)
319 Joo Chiat Place 02-08 Parkway East Medical Centre, Singapore, 427989, Singapore
Tel.: (65) 6440 7266
Obstetric & Gynaecology Healthcare Services
N.A.I.C.S.: 621111

Subsidiary (Domestic):

K W Lee Clinic & Surgery for Women Pte. Ltd. (4)
Gleneagles Medical Centre 6 Napier Road 08-15/16, Singapore, 258499, Singapore
Tel.: (65) 6 471 1233
Web Site: http://drkwlee.com.sg
Obstetric & Gynaecology Healthcare Services
N.A.I.C.S.: 621111

Subsidiary (Domestic):

SOG-SC Hong Clinic for Women Pte. Ltd. (5)
820 Thomson Road 07-62 Mount Alvernia Medical Centre Block D, Singapore, 574623, Singapore
Tel.: (65) 6352 2220
Web Site: http://drhongsc.com.sg
Obstetric & Gynaecology Healthcare Services
N.A.I.C.S.: 621111

Subsidiary (Domestic):

SOG-Natalie Chua Clinic for Women Pte. Ltd. (6)
319 Joo Chiat Place 02-07 Parkway East Medical Centre, Singapore, 427989, Singapore
Tel.: (65) 64408328
Obstetric & Gynaecology Healthcare Services
N.A.I.C.S.: 621111

SOG-Andy Tan Clinic for Women Pte. Ltd. (1)
Gleneagles Medical Centre 6 Napier Road 08-03, Singapore, 258499, Singapore
Tel.: (65) 66906088
Obstetric & Gynaecology Services
N.A.I.C.S.: 621111

SOG-CC Tan Breast, Thyroid & General Surgery Pte. Ltd. (1)
Gleneagles Medical Centre 6 Napier Road 08-15/16, Singapore, 258499, Singapore
Tel.: (65) 66902477
Web Site: https://cctansurgery.com.sg
Breast & Thyroid General Surgeon Services
N.A.I.C.S.: 622110

SOG-Cindy Pang Clinic for Women Pte. Ltd. (1)
38 Irrawaddy Road 08-25 Mt Elizabeth Novena Specialist Centre, Singapore, 329563, Singapore
Tel.: (65) 6 694 2162
Web Site: https://gynonc.com.sg
Obstetric & Gynaecology Healthcare Services
N.A.I.C.S.: 621111
Genesis Kok (Mgr-Clinic)

Subsidiary (Domestic):

SOG-Radhika Breast & General Surgicare Pte. Ltd. (2)
6 Napier Road 06-01 Gleneagles Medical Centre, Singapore, 258499, Singapore
Tel.: (65) 6475 7281
Web Site: http://breastclinic.com.sg

Cancer Treatment Services
N.A.I.C.S.: 622310

Subsidiary (Domestic):

SOG-SK Lim Breast & General Surgicare Pte. Ltd. (3)
820 Thomson Road 07-62 Mount Alvernia Medical Centre, Singapore, 574623, Singapore
Tel.: (65) 62623202
Web Site: http://sklimsurgery.com.sg
Cancer Treatment Services
N.A.I.C.S.: 622310

SOG-Clara Ong Clinic for Women Pte. Ltd. (1)
Gleneagles Medical Centre 6A Napier Road 08-15/16, Singapore, 258500, Singapore
Tel.: (65) 62541741
Web Site: http://www.claraongclinic.com.sg
Obstetric & Gynecology Services
N.A.I.C.S.: 621111

SOG-HL Sim Colorectal, Endoscopy & General Surgery Pte. Ltd. (1)
38 Irrawaddy Road 06-53 Mount Elizabeth Novena Specialist Centre, Singapore, 329563, Singapore
Tel.: (65) 66904151
Web Site: https://hlsimsurgery.com.sg
Colorectal Surgery Services
N.A.I.C.S.: 622110

SINGAPORE PAINCARE HOLDINGS LIMITED
601 Macpherson Road 06-20/21 Grantral Mall, Singapore, 368242, Singapore
Tel.: (65) 69722257 SG
Web Site: https://sgpaincare.com
Year Founded: 2018
FRQ—(CAT)
Rev.: $16,362,356
Assets: $29,792,516
Liabilities: $13,456,095
Net Worth: $16,336,421
Earnings: $182,290
Emp.: 70
Fiscal Year-end: 06/30/23
Holding Company
N.A.I.C.S.: 551112
Bernard Lee Mun Kum (CEO)

Subsidiaries:

DR+ Medical & Paincare Marsiling (1)
18 Marsiling Lane 01-269, Singapore, 730018, Singapore
Tel.: (65) 62697435
Medical Devices
N.A.I.C.S.: 621999

Paincare Center Pte. Ltd. (1)
Mount Elizabeth Novena Specialist Centre 38 Irrawaddy Road 07-33, Singapore, 329563, Singapore
Tel.: (65) 67344500
Medical Devices
N.A.I.C.S.: 621999

Ready Fit Physiotherapy Private Limited (1)
23 Binjai Park, Singapore, Singapore
Tel.: (65) 88002351
Web Site: https://www.readyfitphysio.com
Physiotherapy Clinic Operator
N.A.I.C.S.: 621340

Singapore Paincare Center @ Novena Pte. Ltd. (1)
Mount Elizabeth Novena Specialist Centre 38 Irrawaddy Road 07-33, Singapore, 329563, Singapore
Tel.: (65) 67344500
Medical Devices
N.A.I.C.S.: 621999

Singapore Paincare TCM Wellness Pte. Ltd. (1)
6 Raffles Boulevard No 03-134-136 Marina Square, Singapore, Singapore
Tel.: (65) 62662168
Web Site: https://www.sgpaincaretcm.com
Poincare Clinic Operator
N.A.I.C.S.: 621340

SINGAPORE POST LIMITED

SINGAPORE POST LIMITED
10 Eunos Road 8 02-20 Singapore Post Centre, Singapore, 408600, Singapore
Tel.: (65) 68412000
Web Site: https://www.singpost.com
S08—(SES)
Rev.: $1,249,902,185
Assets: $2,323,770,283
Liabilities: $1,270,813,633
Net Worth: $1,052,956,649
Earnings: $60,374,954
Emp.: 3,981
Fiscal Year-end: 03/31/24
Postal Service
N.A.I.C.S.: 491110
Simon Claude Israel (Chm)

Subsidiaries:

Andromeda Nominees Pty. Ltd. (1)
1/58-82 Produce Drive, Dandenong South, 3175, VIC, Australia
Tel.: (61) 397013007
Web Site: https://www.formby.com.au
Logistics & Commercial Furniture Services
N.A.I.C.S.: 541614

BagTrans Group Pty. Ltd. (1)
8 Brabham Drive, Eastern Creek, 2766, NSW, Australia
Tel.: (61) 1300279182
Parcel Delivery Services
N.A.I.C.S.: 561431

BagTrans Pty. Limited (1)
8 Brabham Drive, Eastern Creek, 2766, NSW, Australia
Tel.: (61) 1300279182
Web Site: http://www.bagtrans.com.au
Parcel Delivery Services
N.A.I.C.S.: 561431

F.S. Mackenzie Limited (1)
2nd Floor Bowden House Luckyn Lan Essex, Basildon, SS14 3AX, United Kingdom
Tel.: (44) 1268275555
Web Site: http://www.fsmac.com
Logistics Transportation Services
N.A.I.C.S.: 541614

FPS Global Logistics Pte. Ltd. (1)
511 Kampong Bahru Road 05-03 Keppel Distripark, Singapore, 99447, Singapore
Tel.: (65) 62401900
Food Transportation Services
N.A.I.C.S.: 926120

FPS Logistics (USA) Inc. (1)
1472 W 178th St, Gardena, CA 90248
Tel.: (310) 808-1050
Web Site: http://www.fpslogistics.com
Logistics Management Services
N.A.I.C.S.: 541614
Anna Liu (Mgr)

Famous Holdings Pte. Ltd. (1)
511 Kampong Bahru Road 05-03 Keppel Distripark, Singapore, 99447, Singapore
Tel.: (65) 62401900
Food Transportation Services
N.A.I.C.S.: 926120

Famous Pacific Shipping (NZ) Limited (1)
Floor 19 Tower A United Building No 51 You-Yi-Bei Road, Hexi District, Tianjin, 300204, China
Tel.: (86) 2283281118
Transport & Logistic Services
N.A.I.C.S.: 541614

Famous Pacific Shipping (WA) Pty. Ltd. (1)
73 North Lake Road, Perth, Myaree, 6154, WA, Australia
Tel.: (61) 893300000
Web Site: https://www.famous.com.au
International Shipping Services
N.A.I.C.S.: 813910

Flemington Fields Pty. Ltd. (1)
80 Dowd Street, Welshpool, 6106, WA, Australia
Tel.: (61) 862582300
Web Site: https://www.gkrtransport.com.au
Transport & Logistics Services
N.A.I.C.S.: 541614

SINGAPORE POST LIMITED

Singapore Post Limited—(Continued)

Freight Management Holdings Pty. Ltd. (1)
Morris Moor Ground Floor 1 Cochranes Road, Moorabbin, 3189, VIC, Australia (100%)
Tel.: (61) 1300769605
Web Site: https://fmhgroup.com.au
Freight Transportation Services
N.A.I.C.S.: 541614

General Storage Company Pte. Ltd. (1)
502 Chai Chee Lane, Singapore, 469025, Singapore
Tel.: (65) 64218381
Web Site: https://www.lockandstore.com
Self-Storage Facilities Services
N.A.I.C.S.: 561210

Lock Store (Ayer Rajah) Pte. Ltd. (1)
6 Ayer Rajah Crescent, Singapore, 139962, Singapore
Tel.: (65) 64218388
Web Site: https://www.lockandstore.com
Self-Storage Facilities Services
N.A.I.C.S.: 561210

Lock Store (Chai Chee) Pte. Ltd. (1)
502 Chai Chee Lane, Singapore, 469025, Singapore
Tel.: (65) 18003703737
Self-Storage Facilities Services
N.A.I.C.S.: 561210

Lock Store (Tanjong Pagar) Pte. Ltd. (1)
37 Keppel Rd 01-03 Tanjong Pagar Distripark, Singapore, 089064, Singapore
Tel.: (65) 64218384
Self-Storage Facilities Services
N.A.I.C.S.: 561210

Lock and Store (Glenmarie) Sdn. Bhd. (1)
No.5 Jalan Penyair U1/44 Off Jalan Glenmarie Temasya Industrial Park, 40150, Shah Alam, Selangor, Malaysia
Tel.: (60) 355618000
Self-Storage Facilities Services
N.A.I.C.S.: 561210

Logistics Holdings Australia Pty. Ltd. (1)
Group General Counsel Morris Moor Ground Floor 1 Cochranes Road, Moorabbin, 3189, VIC, Australia
Tel.: (61) 1300769605
Web Site: https://logisticsholdings.com.au
Logistics Transportation Services
N.A.I.C.S.: 541614

Niche Logistics Pty. Ltd. (1)
54-66 Aylesbury Drive, Altona, 3018, VIC, Australia
Tel.: (61) 1300642439
Web Site: https://nichelogistics.com.au
Accounting Services
N.A.I.C.S.: 541219

Otway Logistics Pty. Ltd. (1)
51 Victoria Rd, Kenwick, 6107, WA, Australia
Tel.: (61) 431876087
Web Site: https://www.otalogistics.com.au
Logistics Transportation Services
N.A.I.C.S.: 541614

Quantium Solutions (Australia) Pty. Ltd. (1)
Lot 1 Keylink Industrial Estate - North 395 Pembroke Road, Minto, 2566, NSW, Australia
Tel.: (61) 297330700
International Shipping Services
N.A.I.C.S.: 813910

Quantium Solutions (Hong Kong) Limited (1)
Units 1201-03 12/F Port 33 33 Tseuk Luk Street, San Po Kong Kowloon, Hong Kong, China (Hong Kong)
Tel.: (852) 23181213
International Shipping Services
N.A.I.C.S.: 813910

Quantium Solutions (Singapore) Pte. Ltd. (1)
10 Eunos Road 8 Singapore Post Centre, Singapore, 408600, Singapore
Tel.: (65) 62295995
Web Site: https://www.quantiumsolutions.com
Cross Border Shipping Services
N.A.I.C.S.: 813910

The Store House Limited (1)
9/F Hong Kong Industrial Building 444-452 Des Voeux Road West, Western District, Hong Kong, China (Hong Kong)
Tel.: (852) 38959401
Web Site: https://www.thestorehouse.com.hk
Self-Storage Facilities Services
N.A.I.C.S.: 561210

efm Logistics Pty. Ltd. (1)
Morris Moor Ground Floor 1 Cochranes Road, Moorabbin, 3189, VIC, Australia
Tel.: (61) 1300577299
Web Site: https://www.efmlogistics.com.au
Logistics Transportation Services
N.A.I.C.S.: 541614

SINGAPORE PRESS HOLDINGS LTD.
1000 Toa Payoh North News Centre, Singapore, 318994, Singapore
Tel.: (65) 63196319
Web Site: http://www.sph.com.sg
Year Founded: 1984
T39—(SES)
Rev.: $720,731,356
Assets: $6,681,278,393
Liabilities: $2,942,707,722
Net Worth: $3,738,570,672
Earnings: ($84,935,635)
Emp.: 3,875
Fiscal Year-end: 08/31/20
Publisher of Newspapers & Magazines
N.A.I.C.S.: 513110
Ginney May Ling Lim (Gen Counsel, Co-Sec & Exec VP-Corp Comm & CSR)

Subsidiaries:

Beerfest Asia Pte. Ltd. (1)
1000 Toa Payoh North News Centre, Singapore, 318994, Singapore
Tel.: (65) 63194020
Web Site: http://www.beerfestasia.com
Organizing Event Concert Services
N.A.I.C.S.: 711310

Blu Inc Media Sdn. Bhd. (1)
Lot 7 Jalan Bersatu 13/4 section 13, 46200, Petaling Jaya, Selangor, Malaysia
Tel.: (60) 379527000
Web Site: http://www.bluinc.com.my
Magazine Publishing Services
N.A.I.C.S.: 513120

Blu Inc Media Singapore Pte Ltd (1)
82 Genting Lane Level 7 Media Centre, Singapore, 349567, Singapore
Tel.: (65) 63196319
Books Publishing Services
N.A.I.C.S.: 513130

Constellar Holdings Pte. Ltd. (1)
1 Expo Drive #02-01, Singapore, 486150, Singapore (40%)
Tel.: (65) 64032160
Web Site: https://www.constellar.co
Holding Company; Convention & Trade Show Organizer
N.A.I.C.S.: 551112
Robin Hu (Chm)

Subsidiary (Domestic):

Sphere Exhibits Pte Ltd (2)
1000 Toa Payoh North News Centre Annexe Block Level 6, Singapore, 318994, Singapore
Tel.: (65) 63194020
Web Site: http://www.sphereexhibits.com.sg
Consumer Segment Event Organizing Services
N.A.I.C.S.: 711310

Subsidiary (Domestic):

Exhibits Inc Pte Ltd (3)
1000 Toa Payoh North News Centre Podium Block Level 3 Mezzanine Floor, Singapore, 318994, Singapore
Tel.: (65) 63193373
Web Site: http://www.exhibitsinc.com.sg
Sales Range: $25-49.9 Million
Emp.: 8
Exhibition Organizing Services
N.A.I.C.S.: 561920

FastJobs Sdn. Bhd. (1)
Unit A-13-5 Northpoint Office Mid Valley City No 1 Jalan Medan, Syed Putra Utara, 59200, Kuala Lumpur, Malaysia
Tel.: (60) 39 776 7238
Web Site: http://www.fastjobs.my
Employment Placement Services
N.A.I.C.S.: 561311

Focus Publishing Ltd (1)
SPH News Centre 1000 Toa Payoh North, Singapore, 318994, Singapore
Tel.: (65) 63196319
Magazine Publishing Services
N.A.I.C.S.: 513120
Alan Chen (CEO)

Han Language Centre Pte. Ltd. (1)
130 Jurong Gateway Rd 04-225, Singapore, 600130, Singapore
Tel.: (65) 65695600
Web Site: http://www.hceg.com.sg
Language School Services
N.A.I.C.S.: 611630

Lianhe Investments Pte. Ltd. (1)
1000 Tao Payoh North, Singapore, Singapore (100%)
Tel.: (65) 67438800
Holding Company
N.A.I.C.S.: 551112

Lianhe Publishing Pte Ltd. (1)
1000 Toa Payoh North News Center, Singapore, 318994, Singapore (100%)
Tel.: (65) 63196319
Web Site: http://www.sph.com.sg
Sales Range: $800-899.9 Million
Emp.: 3,000
Newspaper Publishers
N.A.I.C.S.: 513110

Life-Medic Healthcare Supplies Pte. Ltd. (1)
2 Jurong Port Road, Singapore, 619088, Singapore
Tel.: (65) 6 754 2183
Web Site: https://www.lifemedic.sg
Medical Equipment Distr
N.A.I.C.S.: 423450

MI Publishing Sdn Bhd (1)
46 2nd Fl Jln 27-70A, Desa Sri Hartamas, 50480, Kuala Lumpur, Malaysia (100%)
Tel.: (60) 323004855
Periodical Publishers
N.A.I.C.S.: 513120

Magazines Incorporated Pte. Ltd. (1)
82 Genting Ln SPH Media Centre, Singapore, 349567, Singapore (100%)
Tel.: (65) 63196319
Web Site: http://www.sph.com.sg
Sales Range: $800-899.9 Million
Emp.: 3,000
Periodical Publishers
N.A.I.C.S.: 513120

Magazines World Sdn Bhd (1)
Lot 7 Jalan Bersatu 13-4, Section 13, 46200, Petaling Jaya, Selangor, Malaysia
Tel.: (60) 379572097
Book Periodical & Newspaper Whslr
N.A.I.C.S.: 424920

OctoRocket Pte. Ltd. (1)
1000 Toa Payoh North Digital Business, Level 1 Digital Division News Centre, Singapore, 318994, Singapore
Tel.: (65) 31381394
Web Site: http://www.octorocket.business.site
Food & Beverage Whslr
N.A.I.C.S.: 445298

Orange Valley Nursing Homes Pte. Ltd. (1)
2 International Business Park The Strategy Tower 1 10-11, Singapore, 609930, Singapore
Tel.: (65) 6 499 4699

INTERNATIONAL PUBLIC

Web Site: https://www.orangevalley.sg
Women Healthcare Services
N.A.I.C.S.: 621610

Orchard 290 Ltd. (1)
290 Orchard Road, 238859, Singapore, 238859, Singapore (100%)
Tel.: (65) 67331900
Web Site: http://www.paragon.sg
Sales Range: $25-49.9 Million
Emp.: 40
Holding Company
N.A.I.C.S.: 551112
Eugenie Yap (Gen Mgr)

PT MI Magazines (1)
Jl HR Rasuna Said Kav, C22 Ged Pasat Perilman 3rd Flo, 12940, Jakarta, Indonesia (70%)
Tel.: (62) 215278815
Periodical Publishers
N.A.I.C.S.: 513120

Quotz Pte. Ltd. (1)
61 Ubi Ave 2 Automobile Megamart 03-12/13, Singapore, 408898, Singapore
Tel.: (65) 6 744 7571
Web Site: https://www.quotz.com.sg
Car Distr
N.A.I.C.S.: 441110

SGCM Pte. Ltd. (1)
61 Ubi Ave 2 Automobile Megamart, Singapore, 408898, Singapore
Tel.: (65) 6 744 1514
Web Site: https://www.sgcarmart.com
Car Distr
N.A.I.C.S.: 441110

SI Portal.com Sdn Bhd (1)
DF2-07-03A Level 7 Persoft Tower 6B Persiaran Tropicana, 47410, Petaling Jaya, Selangor, Malaysia
Tel.: (60) 378031791
Web Site: http://www.shareinvestor.com.my
Sales Range: $25-49.9 Million
Emp.: 13
Financial Application Software Development Services
N.A.I.C.S.: 541511

SPH AlphaOne Pte Ltd (1)
SPH News Centre 1000 Toa Payoh North, Singapore, 318994, Singapore
Tel.: (65) 63196319
Newspaper Publishing Services
N.A.I.C.S.: 513110

SPH AsiaOne Ltd (1)
1000 Toa Payoh North News Centre, Singapore, 318994, Singapore
Tel.: (65) 63196319
Web Site: http://www.asiaone.com
Business Portal Services
N.A.I.C.S.: 561499
Karen Lim (Editor)

SPH Magazines Pte Ltd. (1)
1000 Toa Payoh North News Centre Annexe Block Level 6, Singapore, 318994, Singapore (100%)
Tel.: (65) 63196319
Web Site: http://www.sphmagazines.com.sg
Holding Company
N.A.I.C.S.: 551112
Caroline Ngui (Editor-in-Chief-Grp)

Subsidiary (Non-US):

ACP Magazines Pte. Ltd. (2)
Unit 801 804 Level 8 Uptown 2 No 2 Jalan SS21/37, Damansara Uptown, 47400, Petaling Jaya, Selangor Darul Ehsan, Malaysia (100%)
Tel.: (60) 377259998
Web Site: http://www.acpmagazines.com.my
Sales Range: $25-49.9 Million
Emp.: 60
Magazines Publisher & Distr
N.A.I.C.S.: 513120
Satvinder Kaur (Mgr-Production)

Blu Inc Media (China) Limited. (2)
No 20 Donghu Road Room 604, Xuhui District, Shanghai, China
Tel.: (86) 21 5404 6362
Web Site: http://www.china-boating.com
Yacht Operating Services
N.A.I.C.S.: 713930

Subsidiary (Domestic):

clickTRUE Pte. Ltd. (2)

998 Toa Payoh North 03-25, Singapore, 318993, Singapore (100%)
Tel.: (65) 6 950 3366
Web Site: https://www.clicktrue.biz
Sales Range: $25-49.9 Million
Emp.: 30
Online Marketing Specialists in Social Media & Search Engine Marketing
N.A.I.C.S.: 516210
Jackie Lee (CEO)

SPH MediaBoxOffice Pte Ltd. (1)
1000 Toa Payoh North, News Ctr, 318994, Singapore, Singapore (80%)
Tel.: (65) 63196319
Sales Range: $25-49.9 Million
Emp.: 20
Advertising Agencies
N.A.I.C.S.: 541810
Alan Chan (CEO)

SPH MultiMedia Private Limited (1)
SPH News Centre 1000, Toa Payoh North, Singapore, 318994, Singapore
Tel.: (65) 63196319
Web Site: http://www.sph.com.sg
Newspaper Publishing Services
N.A.I.C.S.: 513110

SPH REIT Management Pte. Ltd. (1)
1000 Toa Payoh North News Centre, Singapore, 318994, Singapore
Tel.: (65) 6 319 3380
Web Site: https://www.sphreit.com.sg
Real Estate Investment Services
N.A.I.C.S.: 531190
Leong Horn Kee (Co-Chm)

SPH Radio Private Limited (1)
1000 Toa Payoh North News Centre, Singapore, 318994, Singapore
Tel.: (65) 63191900
Web Site: http://www.sphradio.sg
Radio Station Services
N.A.I.C.S.: 516110

SPH UnionWorks Pte Ltd. (1)
1000 Toa Payoh North, News Centre, Singapore, 318994, Singapore (70%)
Tel.: (65) 63198555
Web Site: http://www.sph.com.sg
Sales Range: $25-49.9 Million
Emp.: 30
Radio & Television Broadcasting & Wireless Communications Equipment Mfr
N.A.I.C.S.: 334220

Singapore Press, Washington (1)
National Press Bldg Ste 916 529 14th St NW, Washington, DC 20045
Tel.: (202) 662-8726
Sales Range: $25-49.9 Million
Emp.: 3
Newspaper Publishing
N.A.I.C.S.: 813920

Sphere Exhibits Malaysia Sdn. Bhd. (1)
Lot 1008 Level 10 Tower 2 Faber Towers Jalan Desa Bahagia Taman Desa, 58100, Kuala Lumpur, Malaysia
Tel.: (60) 379891133
Web Site: http://www.sphereexhibits.com.my
Event & Exhibition Services
N.A.I.C.S.: 561920

Straits Times Press Pte Ltd (1)
1000 Toa Payoh North News Centre, Singapore, 318994, Singapore
Tel.: (65) 6319 6319
Web Site: http://www.stbooks.sg
Newspaper Publishing Services
N.A.I.C.S.: 513110
Sumiko Tan (Exec Editor)

Tamil Murasu Ltd (1)
1000 Toa Payoh North Annexe level 3, Singapore, 318994, Singapore
Tel.: (65) 63196319
Web Site: http://www.tamilmurasu.sg
Newspaper Publishing Services
N.A.I.C.S.: 513110

Times Development Pte Ltd (1)
1000 Toa Payoh North News Centre, Singapore, 318994, Singapore
Tel.: (65) 63196319
Properties Development Services
N.A.I.C.S.: 531390

Times Properties Private Limited (1)
1000 Toa Payoh North, Singapore, 318994, Singapore (100%)
Tel.: (65) 63196319
Real Estate Agents & Brokers Offices
N.A.I.C.S.: 531210

SINGAPORE SHIPPING CORPORATION LIMITED
200 Cantonment Road 09-01 Southpoint, Singapore, 089763, Singapore
Tel.: (65) 62204906
Web Site: https://www.singaporeshipping.com
S19—(SES)
Rev.: $47,366,000
Assets: $187,278,000
Liabilities: $69,467,000
Net Worth: $117,811,000
Earnings: $11,514,000
Emp.: 110
Fiscal Year-end: 03/31/23
Ship Management Services
N.A.I.C.S.: 488390
Chio Kiat Ao Ow (Chm)

Subsidiaries:

Ow Brothers Pte Ltd (1)
200 Cantonment Road Southpoint 09-01, Singapore, Singapore
Tel.: (65) 62204906
Marine Shipping Services
N.A.I.C.S.: 483111

SSC Ship Management Pte Ltd (1)
200 Cantonment Road 09-01 Southpoint, Singapore, 089763, Singapore
Tel.: (65) 62204906
Ship Management Services
N.A.I.C.S.: 541618

Seatrade Ship Management Pte Ltd (1)
200 Cantonment Road 09-01 Southpoint, Singapore, Singapore
Tel.: (65) 62204906
Ship Management Services
N.A.I.C.S.: 541618

SINGAPORE TOURISM BOARD
Tourism Ct, 1 Orchard Spring Ln, Singapore, 247729, Singapore
Tel.: (65) 67366622 SG
Web Site: http://www.stb.gov.sg
Year Founded: 1964
Sales Range: $50-74.9 Million
Emp.: 416
Tourism Bureau
N.A.I.C.S.: 561520
G. B. Srithar (Reg Dir-India, Middle East, South Asia, and Africa)

SINGAPURA FINANCE LTD.
150 Cecil Street 01-00, Singapore, 069543, Singapore
Tel.: (65) 68800633
Web Site: https://www.singapurafinance.com
Year Founded: 1969
S23—(SES)
Rev.: $36,468,984
Assets: $880,924,032
Liabilities: $689,091,873
Net Worth: $191,832,159
Earnings: $4,662,577
Emp.: 99
Fiscal Year-end: 12/31/23
Financial Planning Services
N.A.I.C.S.: 523999
Jamie Miang Yeow Teo (CEO)

Subsidiaries:

SBS Nominees Private Limited (1)
150 Cecil Street 01-00, Singapore, 069543, Singapore
Tel.: (65) 68800633
Sales Range: $10-24.9 Million
Emp.: 50
Nominee Services

N.A.I.C.S.: 561990
Teo Chiang Long (Mgr)

SBS Realty Services (Private) Limited (1)
150 Cecil Street 01-00, Singapore, 96543, Singapore
Tel.: (65) 68800633
Real Estate Manangement Services
N.A.I.C.S.: 531210

SINGASIA HOLDINGS LIMITED
211 New Bridge Road Suite 03-01 Lucky Chinatown, Singapore, 059432, Singapore
Tel.: (65) 64995757 Ky
Web Site: http://www.singasia.com.sg
8293—(HKG)
Rev.: $4,351,429
Assets: $4,309,252
Liabilities: $2,048,246
Net Worth: $2,261,006
Earnings: ($1,014,813)
Emp.: 95
Fiscal Year-end: 07/31/21
Human Resource Consulting Services
N.A.I.C.S.: 541612
Hak Chor Sim (Co-Founder, Chm & Officer-Compliance)

Subsidiaries:

Aegis Cleaning & Maintenance Services Pte. Ltd. (1)
27 New Bridge Road, Singapore, 059391, Singapore
Tel.: (65) 64991751
Web Site: http://www.aegis-cms.com.sg
Hotel & Resort Cleaning Services
N.A.I.C.S.: 561720
Desmond Quek (Dir-Ops)

Aegis Resource Management Pte. Ltd. (1)
211 New Bridge Road 03-22, Singapore, 059432, Singapore
Tel.: (65) 64995717
Web Site: http://www.aegis-rm.com.sg
Management Consulting Services
N.A.I.C.S.: 541618

SAE Agency Pte. Ltd. (1)
Bugis Village 239 Victoria Street Level 2, Singapore, 188028, Singapore
Tel.: (65) 69020960
Web Site: https://sae-agency.com.sg
Recruitment Services
N.A.I.C.S.: 541612

SingAsia Resources Pte. Ltd. (1)
239A Victoria Street, Bugis Village, Singapore, 188029, Singapore
Tel.: (65) 69020960
Web Site: https://www.sar.com.sg
Temporary Staffing Services
N.A.I.C.S.: 561320

TCC Korea Inc. (1)
4F 4F Sindorim Forceville 102 Saemal-ro, Guro-gu, Seoul, Korea (South)
Tel.: (82) 220390114
Web Site: http://www.tcckorea.com
Direct Employment & Placement Services
N.A.I.C.S.: 561311

SINGATRON ENTERPRISE CO., LTD.
No 209 Section 2 Chung-Chen Road, Hu-Kou, Hsinchu, 30343, Taiwan
Tel.: (886) 35992862
Web Site: https://singatron.com.tw
Year Founded: 1976
6126—(TPE)
Rev.: $121,706,532
Assets: $132,969,890
Liabilities: $68,902,667
Net Worth: $64,067,223
Earnings: $9,253,510
Fiscal Year-end: 12/31/22
Electronic Component Mfr & Distr
N.A.I.C.S.: 334419
Hsin-Nan Kan (Chm)

SINGER FINANCE LANKA PLC
Tel.: (94) 112400400
Web Site: https://www.singerfinance.com
Year Founded: 2004
SFIN—(COL)
Rev.: $25,141,974
Assets: $106,350,784
Liabilities: $89,789,260
Net Worth: $16,561,524
Earnings: $1,361,619
Emp.: 751
Fiscal Year-end: 03/31/23
Financial Lending Services
N.A.I.C.S.: 523999
Aravinda Perera (Chm)

SINGER THAILAND PUBLIC COMPANY LIMITED
72 NT Bangrak Building 17th Floor, Charoen Krung Rd Bangrak, Bangkok, 10500, Thailand
Tel.: (66) 23524777
Web Site: https://www.singerthai.co.th
Year Founded: 1969
SINGER—(THA)
Rev.: $88,703,787
Assets: $559,942,891
Liabilities: $152,677,107
Net Worth: $407,265,784
Earnings: ($110,353,296)
Emp.: 2,258
Fiscal Year-end: 12/31/23
Sewing machines Mfr
N.A.I.C.S.: 321999
Adisak Sukumvitaya (Chm)

Subsidiaries:

SG Capital Co. Ltd. (1)
CAT Telecom Building Bangrak 17th Floor 72 Charoenkrung Rd, Bangrak Subdistrict Bangrak District, Bangkok, 10500, Thailand
Tel.: (66) 22347171
Web Site: http://www.sgcapital.co.th
Insurance Brokerage Services
N.A.I.C.S.: 524210

SG Capital Public Company Limited (1)
72 NT Bangrak Tower Floor 20 Charoen Krung Road, Bangrak, Bangkok, 10500, Thailand
Tel.: (66) 20282828
Web Site: https://www.sgcapital.co.th
Financial Loan Services
N.A.I.C.S.: 522390

SG Service Plus Co. Ltd. (1)
8 Moo 4 Sam Kok-Sena Road, Bangnomkho Amphur Sena, Phra Nakhon Si Ayutthaya, 13110, Thailand
Tel.: (66) 23524777
Emp.: 156
Automotive Spare Parts Distr
N.A.I.C.S.: 423120

SINGHA ESTATE PCL
Suntowers Building B 40th Floor 123 Vibhavadi-Rangsit Road Chom Phon, Chatuchak, Bangkok, 10900, Thailand
Tel.: (66) 20505555
Web Site: https://www.singhaestate.co.th
Year Founded: 1995
S—(THA)
Rev.: $428,385,214
Assets: $2,177,662,921
Liabilities: $1,514,779,423
Net Worth: $662,883,498
Earnings: $7,009,422
Emp.: 3,174
Fiscal Year-end: 12/31/23
Real Estate Manangement Services
N.A.I.C.S.: 531390
Chutinant Bhirombhakdi (Chm)

Subsidiaries:

Jupiter Hotels Limited (1)

SINGHA ESTATE PCL

Singha Estate PCL—(Continued)
2nd Floor 90 St Vincent Street, Glasgow,
G2 5UB, United Kingdom
Tel.: (44) 1413330545
Web Site: https://www.jupiterhotels.co.uk
Hotel Operator
N.A.I.C.S.: 721110

KLAS Management Co., Ltd. (1)
123 Suntowers Building B 22nd Floor
Vibhavadi-Rangsit Road Chom Phon,
Chatuchak, Bangkok, Thailand
Tel.: (66) 20505555
Real Estate Investment Services
N.A.I.C.S.: 531190

Nirvana U Co., Ltd. (1)
The Enterprize Park 89/60-62 Moo 15
Bangna-Trad Rd km 5, Bangkaew Bang-
plee, Samut Prakan, 10540, Thailand
Tel.: (66) 2 170 9449
Web Site: https://www.nirvana.co.th
Ecommerce Services
N.A.I.C.S.: 513130
Natheethong Thongthai *(Gen Mgr)*

OHL US LLC (1)
26-15 Ulmer St, College Point, NY 11354-
1144
Tel.: (718) 554-2320
Web Site: http://www.ohlusa.com
Construction Services
N.A.I.C.S.: 236220
Ashok Patel *(CEO)*

**S Hotels & Resorts Public Company
Limited** (1)
123 Suntowers Building B 10th Floor
Vibhavadi-Rangsit Rd, Chom Phon
Chatuchak, Bangkok, 10900, Thailand
Tel.: (66) 20589888
Web Site: https://www.shotelsresorts.com
Rev.: $283,193,613
Assets: $1,101,200,029
Liabilities: $631,470,655
Net Worth: $469,729,374
Earnings: $2,522,387
Emp.: 2,695
Fiscal Year-end: 12/31/2023
Resort & Hotel Operator
N.A.I.C.S.: 721110
Dirk Andre L. De Cuyper *(CEO)*

**S Hotels and Resorts Management
Co., Ltd.** (1)
No 123 Suntowers Building B 10th floor
Vibhavadi-Rangsit Road, Chom Phon
Chatuchak, Bangkok, 10900, Thailand
Tel.: (66) 20589888
Real Estate Investment Services
N.A.I.C.S.: 531190

**S Hotels and Resorts PublicCo.,
Ltd.** (1)
123 Suntowers Building B 10th Floor
Vibhavadi-Rangsit Rd, Chatuchak, Bang-
kok, 10900, Thailand
Tel.: (66) 20589888
Web Site: https://www.shotelsresorts.com
Hotel & Resort Management Services
N.A.I.C.S.: 721110

S Industrial Estate Co., Ltd. (1)
No 123 Suntowers Building B 22nd floor
Vibhavadi-Rangsit Road, Chom Phon
Chatuchak, Bangkok, 10900, Thailand
Tel.: (66) 20505555
Real Estate Investment Services
N.A.I.C.S.: 531190

S.I.F. Co., Ltd. (1)
No 123 Suntowers Building B 22nd floor
Vibhavadi-rangsit Road, Chom Phon
Chatuchak, Bangkok, 10900, Thailand
Tel.: (66) 20505555
Real Estate Investment Services
N.A.I.C.S.: 531190

S.I.F.1Co., Ltd. (1)
123 Suntowers Building B 10th Floor Soi
Choei Phuang, Vibhavadi-Rangsit Road
Chom Phon Chatuchak, Bangkok, 10900,
Thailand
Tel.: (66) 20589888
Real Estate Investment Services
N.A.I.C.S.: 531190

SINGHA PARATECH PUBLIC COMPANY LIMITED

132 Mu-4 Tambol BanMoh Amphur
Promburi, Sing Buri, 16120, Thailand
Tel.: (66) 3659 9379 TH
Web Site:
http://www.singhaparatech.com
Year Founded: 1994
Wood Flooring Products Mfr & Distr
N.A.I.C.S.: 321918

SINGHE HOSPITALS PLC

362 Colombo Road, Ratnapura, Sri
Lanka
Tel.: (94) 457555555
Web Site:
https://www.singhehospital.com
SINH.N0000—(COL)
Rev.: $3,725,794
Assets: $5,064,817
Liabilities: $2,529,779
Net Worth: $2,535,038
Earnings: $12,231
Emp.: 474
Fiscal Year-end: 03/31/21
Health Care Srvices
N.A.I.C.S.: 621610
Navinda Weerasinghe *(Mng Dir)*

SINGLE WELL INDUSTRIAL CORP.

No 77 Zhongshan Rd, Tucheng Dist,
New Taipei City, 236, Taiwan
Tel.: (886) 222686191
Web Site:
https://www.singlewell.com.tw
Year Founded: 1989
3490—(TPE)
Rev.: $16,618,141
Assets: $51,131,883
Liabilities: $10,566,207
Net Worth: $40,565,676
Earnings: $3,729,919
Fiscal Year-end: 12/31/22
Industrial Compound Mold Mfr
N.A.I.C.S.: 333511
Hsiang-Heng Wang *(Pres)*

Subsidiaries:

**Single Well Meticulous Industry (Kun-
shan) Co., Ltd.** (1)
No 266 Changxing East Road, Suzhou City,
Kunshan, Jiangsu, China
Tel.: (86) 51257663780
Industrial Mold Mfr
N.A.I.C.S.: 333511

SINGLEPOINT GROUP INTER-NATIONAL, INC.

Suite 400 255 Consumer Road, To-
ronto, M2J 1R, ON, Canada
Tel.: (800) 530-3328
Web Site:
http://www.singlepointgi.com
Year Founded: 1947
Holding Company; Call Center Ser-
vices
N.A.I.C.S.: 551112
Jonathan Finley *(Pres & CEO)*

Subsidiaries:

General Revenue Corporation (1)
4660 Duke Dr Ste 300, Mason, OH 45040-
8466
Tel.: (513) 469-1472
Web Site: http://www.generalrevenue.com
Sales Range: $125-149.9 Million
Emp.: 500
Collection Agency
N.A.I.C.S.: 561440

SINGSONG HOLDINGS CO., LTD.

53-1 Yeouinaru-ro, Yeongdeungpo-
gu, Seoul, Korea (South)
Tel.: (82) 27801400
Web Site:
http://www.singsongholdings.com
Year Founded: 1970

006880—(KRS)
Rev.: $160,612,736
Assets: $185,883,003
Liabilities: $112,150,467
Net Worth: $73,732,536
Earnings: $1,149,606
Emp.: 14
Fiscal Year-end: 12/31/22
Holding Company; Real Estate; Grain
Trading; Food Storage
N.A.I.C.S.: 551112
Kap-Joo Cho *(Chm & CEO)*

SINGTEX INDUSTRIAL CO., LTD.

No 10 Wuquan 2nd Rd, Xinzhuang
District, New Taipei City, 24892, Tai-
wan
Tel.: (886) 285127888
Web Site: https://www.singtex.com
Year Founded: 1989
4433—(TPE)
Rev.: $100,610,043
Assets: $165,919,426
Liabilities: $95,416,690
Net Worth: $70,502,736
Earnings: $3,656,067
Fiscal Year-end: 12/31/22
Textile Products Mfr
N.A.I.C.S.: 313310
Sung-Yun Huang *(Pres)*

Subsidiaries:

GFUN Industrial Corp. (1)
No 3 Gongye 6th Rd, Guanyin Dist,
Taoyuan, Taiwan
Tel.: (886) 34389538
Web Site: https://www.gfun.com.tw
Emp.: 240
Waterproof Fabric Mfr
N.A.I.C.S.: 313320

SINGULAR HEALTH GROUP LTD.

2/41 Discovery Drive, Bibra Lake,
6163, WA, Australia
Tel.: (61) 1300167795
Web Site: https://www.singular.health
Year Founded: 2020
SHG—(ASX)
Rev.: $674,036
Assets: $1,955,126
Liabilities: $1,914,771
Net Worth: $40,355
Earnings: ($3,514,584)
Fiscal Year-end: 06/30/23
Software Development Services
N.A.I.C.S.: 541511
Steven Wood *(Sec)*

Subsidiaries:

Singular 3DP Pty. Ltd. (1)
Unit 2/41 Discovery Drive, Bibra Lake,
6163, WA, Australia
Tel.: (61) 894346050
Web Site: https://medicad.com.au
3D Printing Device Mfr & Distr
N.A.I.C.S.: 339113

SINGULARITY ACQUISITION CORP.

3F International Chamber of Com-
merce Building A Fuhua 1st Road,
Futian District, Shenzhen, Guang-
dong, China
Tel.: (86) 0755 8323 4020 Ky
Year Founded: 2021
Investment Services
N.A.I.C.S.: 523999
Erlu Lin *(CEO)*

SINGULUS TECHNOLOGIES AG

Hanauer Landstrasse 103, 63796,
Kahl, Germany
Tel.: (49) 61884400
Web Site: https://www.singulus.com

INTERNATIONAL PUBLIC

SNG—(MUN)
Rev.: $80,803,284
Assets: $79,257,866
Liabilities: $128,490,468
Net Worth: ($49,232,602)
Earnings: ($10,817,926)
Emp.: 296
Fiscal Year-end: 12/31/23
CD & DVD Replication Systems Mfr
N.A.I.C.S.: 334112
Wolfhard Leichnitz *(Chm-Supervisory Bd)*

Subsidiaries:

**SINGULUS Nano Deposition Tech-
nologies GmbH** (1)
Hanauer Landstr 103, Kahl, 63796, Ger-
many
Tel.: (49) 6188 4400
Web Site: http://www.singulus.de
Sales Range: $50-74.9 Million
Emp.: 25
Compact Disc System Mfr
N.A.I.C.S.: 334310

**SINGULUS STANGL Solar
GmbH** (1)
Fraunhoferstr 9, 82256, Fuerstenfeldbruck,
Germany
Tel.: (49) 8141 36 00 0
Web Site: http://www.stangl.de
Semiconductor Devices Mfr
N.A.I.C.S.: 334413
Armin Schalk *(Gen Mgr)*

**SINGULUS TECHNOLOGIES
IBERICA S.L.** (1)
Avda Francesc Macia 81-C, 8173, Sant Cu-
gat del Valles, Spain
Tel.: (34) 936750025
Sales Range: $50-74.9 Million
Emp.: 6
Industrial Machinery Distr
N.A.I.C.S.: 423830
Carlos Calleja *(Gen Mgr)*

**SINGULUS TECHNOLOGIES TAI-
WAN Limited** (1)
13F No 223 Sec 5 Nanjing East Road,
Songshau District, 10569, Taipei, Taiwan
Tel.: (886) 2 2748 3366
Emp.: 4
Compact Disc Replication Mfr
N.A.I.C.S.: 334310
Tony Nam *(Gen Mgr)*

**STEAG Electronic Systems spol
s.r.o** (1)
Rybarska 4, 91501, Trencin,
Slovakia (100%)
Tel.: (421) 327740211
Sales Range: $150-199.9 Million
Emp.: 260
Electronic Parts & Equipment Whslr
N.A.I.C.S.: 423690

**Singulus Manufacturing Guangzou
Ltd.** (1)
Unit 1 No 3 Development Rd Jiushuikeng
Industrial Area, Dalong Street, 511400,
Guangzhou, China
Tel.: (86) 2034885010
Web Site: http://www.singulus.de
Sales Range: $25-49.9 Million
Emp.: 40
Communication Equipment Mfr
N.A.I.C.S.: 334290
Frank Zheng *(Pres)*

Singulus Mastering B.V. (1)
Luchthavenweg 10, 5657, Eindhoven,
Netherlands (100%)
Tel.: (31) 407501400
Web Site: http://www.singulus.nl
Sales Range: $25-49.9 Million
Emp.: 40
Computer Related Services
N.A.I.C.S.: 541519
Guido Dalessi *(CEO)*

**Singulus Technologies Asia Pacific
Pte. Ltd.** (1)
03-54/55 Vertex 33 Ubi Avenue 3, Singa-
pore, 408868, Singapore
Tel.: (65) 67411912
Web Site: http://www.singlus.com.sg

Sales Range: $25-49.9 Million
Emp.: 30
Major Household Appliance Mfr
N.A.I.C.S.: 335220

Singulus Technologies France S.A.R.L. (1)
1 rue des Alpes, 68390, Sausheim, France
Tel.: (33) 389311129
Sales Range: $25-49.9 Million
Communication Equipment Mfr
N.A.I.C.S.: 334290

Singulus Technologies Italia Srl (1)
Via Piave 102, Senigallia, 60019, Italy (100%)
Tel.: (39) 0717930312
Web Site: http://www.singulus.it
Sales Range: $25-49.9 Million
Emp.: 2
Communication Equipment Mfr
N.A.I.C.S.: 334290

Singulus Technologies Latin America Ltda. (1)
Rua Joaquim Floriano 466-Conjunto 1610
Edif Brascan Office, Itaim Bibi, Sao Paulo, 04534-002, SP, Brazil
Tel.: (55) 1121652410
Machinery Equipment Mfr
N.A.I.C.S.: 333248

Singulus Technologies Shanghai Co., Ltd. (1)
Room B412-413 No 1400 Jiangchang Road, Jingan District, Shanghai, 200072, China
Tel.: (86) 2161073997
Machinery Equipment Mfr
N.A.I.C.S.: 333248

Singulus Technologies, Inc. (1)
429 D Hayden Station Rd, Windsor, CT 06095 (100%)
Tel.: (860) 683-8000
Sales Range: $25-49.9 Million
Emp.: 15
Communication Equipment Mfr
N.A.I.C.S.: 334290

Singulus Vika China Limited (1)
Qiao Xing Rd, 3rd Floor No 17-25, 51140, Foshan, Guangzhou, China
Tel.: (86) 2061926666
Sales Range: $25-49.9 Million
Emp.: 16
Communication Equipment Mfr
N.A.I.C.S.: 334290

SINHER TECHNOLOGY INC.
No 27-1 Lane 169 Kang Ning Street, Xizhi District, New Taipei City, 22180, Taiwan
Tel.: (886) 226926960
Web Site: https://www.sinher.com.tw
Year Founded: 2002
4999—(TAI)
Rev.: $62,413,255
Assets: $130,382,185
Liabilities: $19,562,084
Net Worth: $110,820,101
Earnings: $124,693
Emp.: 1,195
Fiscal Year-end: 12/31/23
Computer Parts & Components Mfr
N.A.I.C.S.: 334118
Ting Hung Su (Chm)

Subsidiaries:

Chongqing SNR Technology Co., Ltd. (1)
No 12 Geshan Road, Taiwanese Industrial Park Bishan District, Chongqing, China
Tel.: (86) 23643036368
Electrical Component Mfr
N.A.I.C.S.: 335999

Kunshan Wanhe Precision Electron Co., Ltd. (1)
No 89 Huguang Road, Zhangpu Town, Kunshan, Jiangsu, China
Tel.: (86) 51257374787
Electrical Component Mfr
N.A.I.C.S.: 335999

SINIL PHARMACEUTICAL CO., LTD.
28 Boksanggol-gil, Angseong-myeon, Chungju, Chungcheongbuk-do, Korea (South)
Tel.: (82) 7223300
Web Site: http://www.sinilpharm.com
Year Founded: 1971
012790—(KRS)
Rev.: $61,365,424
Assets: $109,551,883
Liabilities: $14,998,189
Net Worth: $94,553,694
Earnings: $9,324,483
Emp.: 388
Fiscal Year-end: 12/31/22
Pharmaceuticals Product Mfr
N.A.I.C.S.: 325412

SINIORA FOOD INDUSTRIES P.L.C.
King Abdullah II Bin AlHussein Industrial Estate, PO Box 191, Sahab, 11512, Amman, 11512, Jordan
Tel.: (962) 64023772
Web Site: https://www.siniorafood.com
Year Founded: 1920
SNRA—(AMM)
Rev.: $100,085,965
Assets: $96,720,827
Liabilities: $38,943,711
Net Worth: $57,777,116
Earnings: $9,976,241
Emp.: 1,035
Fiscal Year-end: 12/31/20
Food Products Mfr
N.A.I.C.S.: 311999
Khaled Al-Muhtaseb (Dir-Products Supply)

Subsidiaries:

Diamond Meat Processing L.L.C. (1)
PO Box 20754, Dubai, United Arab Emirates
Tel.: (971) 42860382
Web Site: https://www.almasadubai.com
Veal Product Mfr
N.A.I.C.S.: 311612

Saudi Siniora Trading Company L.L.C. (1)
PO Box 2256, Riyadh, 11451, Saudi Arabia
Tel.: (966) 12448424
Food Products Mfr
N.A.I.C.S.: 311999

Siniora Food Industries Company (1)
PO Box 132, Jerusalem, Israel
Tel.: (972) 22796804
Food Products Mfr
N.A.I.C.S.: 311999
Alaa I. Amad (Mgr-Pur)

Siniora Gulf General Trading Co., LLC (1)
Business Bay-Clover Bay Tower, PO Box 413025, Dubai, United Arab Emirates
Tel.: (971) 45538529
Food Products Mfr
N.A.I.C.S.: 311999

Trakya Et ve Sut Urunleri San. Tic. A.S. (1)
Icerenkoy Mah Askent Sk Kosifler Oto Blok No 3A Floor, 13 Interior Door No 18 Atasehir, Istanbul, Turkiye
Tel.: (90) 2122674848
Web Site: https://www.polonez.com.tr
Meat Product Mfr & Distr
N.A.I.C.S.: 311612

SINJIA LAND LIMITED
Block 16 Kallang Place 011618 Kallang Basin Industrial Estate, Singapore, 339156, Singapore
Tel.: (65) 62247320
Web Site: https://www.sinjl.com
5HH—(CAT)
Rev.: $512,005
Assets: $2,123,002
Liabilities: $749,072
Net Worth: $1,373,930
Earnings: ($1,134,591)
Emp.: 6
Fiscal Year-end: 12/31/23
Holding Company; Property Development; Integrated Mechanical Components Mfr
N.A.I.C.S.: 551112
Jeff Weixiong Cheong (CEO)

Subsidiaries:

G4 Station Pte Ltd (1)
11 Mackenzie Road Selegie, 228675, Singapore
Tel.: (65) 63345644
Web Site: http://www.g4station.com
Online Booking Services
N.A.I.C.S.: 561599

HLN Metal (Shenzhen) Co., Ltd. (1)
Block 9 Level 1 North Wing He Yi Yong Fa Northern Technology Park, Shenzhen, Shenzhen, 518104, Guangdong, China
Tel.: (86) 755 6151 5899
Extruded Aluminum Products Mfr
N.A.I.C.S.: 331314

HLN Metal (Suzhou) Co., Ltd (1)
No 199 Tongyuan Road Block 6, Suzhou Industrial Park, Suzhou, 215021, China
Tel.: (86) 512 6292 7075
Metal Products Mfr
N.A.I.C.S.: 332999

HLN Technologies Sdn Bhd (1)
19 A Jalan Badu Taruka Tampoi Industrial Estate, Johor, 80350, Malaysia
Tel.: (60) 7 238 6743
Web Site: http://www.hlntech.com
Electronic Components Mfr
N.A.I.C.S.: 334419

Process Innovation Technology Pte Ltd (1)
Unit 01-03 37 Kallang Pudding Road Block B, Tong Lee Building, Singapore, 349315, Singapore
Tel.: (65) 6226 1051
Sales Range: $25-49.9 Million
Emp.: 28
Plastic Foam Product Mfr
N.A.I.C.S.: 326150
Francis Ng (Mgr)

Subsidiary (Non-US):

Process Innovation Technology (Suzhou) Co., Ltd. (2)
No 30 Dongzhuang Road Luzhi Town, Wuzhong District, Suzhou, 215127, Jiangsu, China
Tel.: (86) 51266018928
Molded Rubber Goods Mfr
N.A.I.C.S.: 326299

Sinjia Properties Sdn. Bhd. (1)
56 Jalan Kempas Utama 2/2 Taman Kempas Utama, 81200, Johor Bahru, Malaysia
Tel.: (60) 62247320
Boarding House & Hostel Operator
N.A.I.C.S.: 721199

SINJIN SM CO., LTD.
352-73 Jangmu-ro Janggye-myeon, Jangsu gun, Cheongju, Jeollabuk-do, Korea (South)
Tel.: (82) 313697400
Year Founded: 1991
138070—(KRS)
Rev.: $50,871,393
Assets: $85,120,086
Liabilities: $26,126,864
Net Worth: $58,993,222
Earnings: $3,330,484
Emp.: 187
Fiscal Year-end: 12/31/22
Standard Plate Mfr
N.A.I.C.S.: 331315
Hong-Ki Kim (CEO)

Subsidiaries:

Shinjin ESCO Co., Ltd. (1)
449-1 Guirae-ri Jeongnam-myeon, Hwaseong, Gyeonggi-do, Korea (South)
Tel.: (82) 3180476911
Web Site: https://www.shinjin-esco.com
Steel Cutting Tool Mfr
N.A.I.C.S.: 333515

Shinjin-SM (Thailand) Co., Ltd. (1)
7/363 Moo 6 Amata City Industrial Estate, Mabyangporn Subdistrict, Rayong, Thailand
Tel.: (66) 386504056
Web Site: https://www.shinjin-sm.co.th
Steel Product Mfr & Distr
N.A.I.C.S.: 331210

SINKANG INDUSTRIES CO., LTD.
No 8 Da'an Road, Xinzhuang Dist, Taipei, 242, Taiwan
Tel.: (886) 222020152
Web Site: https://www.sinkang.com.tw
Year Founded: 1971
2032—(TAI)
Rev.: $93,602,665
Assets: $61,726,804
Liabilities: $7,563,851
Net Worth: $54,162,953
Earnings: ($680,532)
Emp.: 200
Fiscal Year-end: 12/31/23
Steel Products Mfr
N.A.I.C.S.: 331221

SINKO INDUSTRIES LTD.
1-4-5 Minamimorimachi, Kita-ku, Osaka, 530-0054, Japan
Tel.: (81) 663671811
Web Site: https://www.sinko.co.jp
Year Founded: 1950
6458—(TKS)
Rev.: $343,343,230
Assets: $581,931,180
Liabilities: $159,505,910
Net Worth: $422,425,270
Earnings: $43,493,800
Emp.: 1,616
Fiscal Year-end: 03/31/24
Air Conditioning Equipment Mfr & Distr
N.A.I.C.S.: 333415
Shozo Takeda (CEO)

Subsidiaries:

SINKO Air Conditioning (H.K.) Limited (1)
Unit A 12/Fl Loyong Court Comm Bldg Lockhart Road, Wanchai, 212-220, China (Hong Kong)
Tel.: (852) 28022239
Web Site: https://www.sinko.co.jp
Air Conditioning Equipment Distr
N.A.I.C.S.: 423730

SINKO Air Conditioning (Thailand) Co., Ltd. (1)
889/4-5 Moo 21 Soi Chongsiri Bangplee-Tamru RD Bangpleeyai, Bang Phli, 10540, Samutprakarn, Thailand
Tel.: (66) 21734546
Air Conditioning Equipment Mfr & Distr
N.A.I.C.S.: 333415

SINKO Air Conditioning Industries Ltd. (1)
1458-4 Kusakabe, Tsuyama, 708-1117, Okayama, Japan
Tel.: (81) 868293141
Air Conditioning Equipment Mfr
N.A.I.C.S.: 333415

Plant (Domestic):

SINKO Air Conditioning Industries Ltd. - Kanagawa Factory (2)
160-1 Bodai, Hadano, 259-1302, Kanagawa, Japan
Tel.: (81) 463752111
Air Conditioning Equipment Mfr
N.A.I.C.S.: 333415

SINKO Atmos Co., Ltd. (1)
1-11-4 ShinOhashi, Koto-ku, Tokyo, 135-0007, Japan
Tel.: (81) 356383800
Web Site: https://www.sinkoatmos.co.jp

SINKO INDUSTRIES LTD.

Sinko Industries Ltd.—(Continued)
Emp.: 168
Air Conditioner Repair & Maintenance Services
N.A.I.C.S.: 811412

SINKO Kucho Service Co., Ltd. (1)
1-11-4 Shinohashi, Koto-ku, Tokyo, 135-0007, Kanagawa, Japan
Tel.: (81) 356383800
Web Site: https://sinkoatmos.co.jp
Emp.: 168
Air Conditioner Repair & Maintenance Services
N.A.I.C.S.: 811412

Shanghai SINKO Air Conditioning & Equipment Co., Ltd. (1)
518 San Xiang Road, Si Jing Village Song Jiang, Shanghai, 201601, China
Tel.: (86) 216 761 9090
Web Site: http://www.sinko.cn
Air Conditioning Equipment Mfr & Distr
N.A.I.C.S.: 333415
Jack Lu (Mgr-Sls)

Shanghai Sinko Refrigeration Machine Co., Ltd. (1)
886 Dong Zha Road West Qi Xin Road Xin Zhuang Minhang District, Shanghai, 201100, China
Tel.: (86) 2154880982
Air Conditioning Equipment Mfr & Distr
N.A.I.C.S.: 333415

Taiwan SINKO Kogyo Co., Ltd. (1)
19-1 Ta Chiu Tien Tu Keng Tsun Kuei Shan Hsiang, Taoyuan, Hsien, Taiwan
Tel.: (886) 3 350 3004
Web Site: http://www.sinko.com.tw
Air Conditioning Equipment Mfr & Distr
N.A.I.C.S.: 333415

SINKO-BANK, LTD.
11 Bld 1 Posledny Lane, 107045, Moscow, Russia
Tel.: (7) 4957374140
Web Site: http://www.sinko-bank.ru
Year Founded: 1994
Sales Range: Less than $1 Million
Financial Investment Services
N.A.I.C.S.: 523940
Gennady Barsegov (CEO)

SINMAG EQUIPMENT CORP.
No 23 Wuquan 6th Road Wugu Industrial Zone, Wugu District, New Taipei City, Taiwan
Tel.: (886) 222981148
Web Site: https://sinmag.com.tw
Year Founded: 1983
1580—(TPE)
Rev.: $123,081,606
Assets: $116,290,060
Liabilities: $31,671,794
Net Worth: $84,618,266
Earnings: $11,089,829
Fiscal Year-end: 12/31/22
Kitchen Appliance Mfr & Distr
N.A.I.C.S.: 332215
Shun-Ho Hsieh (Chm)

SINMAH CAPITAL BERHAD
Tel.: (60) 63353329
Web Site: https://www.sinmah.com.my
Year Founded: 1994
SMCAP—(KLS)
Rev.: $28,231,583
Assets: $42,728,648
Liabilities: $22,047,053
Net Worth: $20,681,595
Earnings: ($5,612,062)
Emp.: 155
Fiscal Year-end: 12/31/20
Animal Feeds Mfr & Whslr
N.A.I.C.S.: 311119
Choon Kai Fong (Exec Dir)

Subsidiaries:

Sinmah Development Sdn. Bhd. (1)
No 88 Jalan KU 4 Taman Krubong Utama, 75260, Melaka, Malaysia
Tel.: (60) 63353329
Web Site: https://www.sinmah.com.my
Property Development Services
N.A.I.C.S.: 237210

SINNAR BIDI UDYOG LIMITED
Camel House Nasik Pune Road, Nasik, 422011, India
Tel.: (91) 2532594231
Web Site: https://www.sinnarbidi.com
509887—(BOM)
Rev.: $838,079
Assets: $1,135,471
Liabilities: $617,865
Net Worth: $517,607
Earnings: $52,982
Emp.: 40
Fiscal Year-end: 03/31/23
Tobacco Product Mfr & Distr
N.A.I.C.S.: 312230
Madhav Digamber Deshpande (CFO)

SINO AG
Ernst-Schneider-Platz 1, 40212, Dusseldorf, Germany
Tel.: (49) 21136110
Web Site: https://www.sino.de
Year Founded: 1998
XTP—(DEU)
Assets: $15,354,896
Liabilities: $2,792,803
Net Worth: $12,562,093
Earnings: ($1,103,875)
Emp.: 25
Fiscal Year-end: 12/31/23
Investment Management Service
N.A.I.C.S.: 523999

SINO AGRO FOOD, INC.
Room 3801 Block A China Shine Plaza, No 9 Lin He Xi Road Tianhe District, Guangzhou, 510610, China
Tel.: (86) 2022057860
Web Site: http://www.sinoagrofood.com
SIAF—(OTCIQ)
Rev.: $9,892,000
Assets: $517,821,000
Liabilities: $121,936,000
Net Worth: $395,885,000
Earnings: ($132,061,000)
Emp.: 173
Fiscal Year-end: 12/31/20
Agricultural Food Products Mfr
N.A.I.C.S.: 311999
Yip Kun Lee (Founder, Chm, Pres & CEO)

SINO ASSURANCE INC.
20th Floor 6009 Yitian Road New World Center, Futian District, Shenzhen, China
Tel.: (86) 75582520166
Year Founded: 1997
SNAS—(OTCIQ)
Sales Range: $1-9.9 Million
Emp.: 190
Insurance Services
N.A.I.C.S.: 524298
Guokang Tu (Chm & CEO)

SINO BIOENERGY CORP.
Rm 309 No 21 On Kui Street NT, Fanling Industrial Building On Lok Tsuen, Fanling, China (Hong Kong)
Tel.: (852) 62338867
Web Site: http://www.sfbe2016.com
SFBE—(OTCIQ)
Sales Range: Less than $1 Million
Building Material & Paving Material Mfr
N.A.I.C.S.: 327120

SINO BIOLOGICAL INC.
Building 9 Jing Dongbei Technology Park No18 Kechuang 10th St BDA, Beijing, 100176, China
Tel.: (86) 4008909989
Web Site: https://www.sinobiological.com
Year Founded: 2016
301047—(CHIN)
Rev.: $91,040,634
Assets: $929,673,011
Liabilities: $32,914,944
Net Worth: $896,758,068
Earnings: $36,638,267
Fiscal Year-end: 12/31/23
Biotechnology Research & Development Services
N.A.I.C.S.: 541714
Liangzhi Xie (Chm)

Subsidiaries:

Sino Biological Europe GmbH (1)
Dusseldorfer Str 40, 65760, Eschborn, Germany
Tel.: (49) 61969678656
Bio Technology Services
N.A.I.C.S.: 541714

Sino Biological Japan Inc. (1)
3-2-1 Sakado KSP West Building 2F Tech-Pot, Takatsu-ku, Kawasaki, 213-0012, Kanagawa, Japan
Tel.: (81) 444001330
Bio Technology Services
N.A.I.C.S.: 541714

Sino Biological US Inc. (1)
1400 Liberty Ridge Dr Ste 101, Wayne, PA 19087
Tel.: (215) 583-7898
Gene Therapy & Antibody Drug Development Services
N.A.I.C.S.: 621498

SINO BIOPHARMACEUTICAL LIMITED
Unit 09 41/F Office Tower Convention Plaza 1 Harbour Road, Wanchai, China (Hong Kong)
Tel.: (852) 28029886
Web Site: https://www.sinobiopharm.com
Year Founded: 2000
1177—(OTCIQ)
Rev.: $3,984,882,034
Assets: $8,870,220,979
Liabilities: $3,616,628,268
Net Worth: $5,253,592,712
Earnings: $692,653,135
Emp.: 26,272
Fiscal Year-end: 12/31/22
Research & Development Of Chemical Medicines
N.A.I.C.S.: 541715
Cheung Ling Cheng (Vice Chm)

Subsidiaries:

Chia Tai Tianqing Pharmaceutical Group Co., Ltd. (1)
No 369 South Youzhou Rd, Haizhou District, Lianyungang, 222062, Jiangsu, China
Tel.: (86) 51886095133
Web Site: https://www.cttq.com
Emp.: 14,000
Pharmaceutical Product Mfr & Distr
N.A.I.C.S.: 325412

Subsidiary (Domestic):

Lianyungang Runzhong Pharmaceutical Co., Ltd. (2)
No 16 Jinqiao Rd, Lianyungang Economic Development Zone, Lianyungang, 222069, Jiangsu, China
Tel.: (86) 51886075992
Web Site: http://rz.cttq.com
Pharmaceutical Product Mfr & Distr
N.A.I.C.S.: 325412
Zhaocheng Tang (Gen Mgr)

Jiangsu Chiatai Qingjiang Pharmaceutical Co., Ltd. (1)
2F Building 9 Xuzhuang Software Park No 699-8 Xuanwu Avenue, Nanjing, China

INTERNATIONAL PUBLIC

Tel.: (86) 25 68551657
Web Site: http://www.ctqjpharm.com
Pharmaceutical Product Mfr & Distr
N.A.I.C.S.: 325412
Yong Zhu (Gen Mgr)

Plant (Domestic):

Jiangsu Chiatai Qingjiang Pharmaceutical Co., Ltd. - Huaian Plant (2)
No 9 Hantai North Road, Huai'an, 223001, China
Tel.: (86) 51786283327
Pharmaceuticals Product Mfr
N.A.I.C.S.: 325412

Softhale NV (1)
Bioville Abis Building Agoralaan, 3590, Diepenbeek, Belgium
Tel.: (32) 11286992
Web Site: https://www.softhale.com
Pharmaceuticals Mfr
N.A.I.C.S.: 325412

invoX Pharma Limited (1)
5 Merchant Square Paddington, London, W21AY, United Kingdom
Tel.: (44) 203 786 5144
Web Site: https://invoxpharma.com
Biopharmaceutical Products Research & Development
N.A.I.C.S.: 541714
Ben Toogood (CEO)

Subsidiary (Domestic):

F-star Therapeutics, Inc. (2)
Eddeva B920 Babraham Research Campus, Cambridge, CB22 3AT, United Kingdom
Tel.: (44) 1223497400
Web Site: http://www.f-star.com
Rev.: $21,167,000
Assets: $123,021,000
Liabilities: $26,164,000
Net Worth: $96,857,000
Earnings: ($31,283,000)
Emp.: 84
Fiscal Year-end: 12/31/2021
Biopharmaceutical Company
N.A.I.C.S.: 325412
Eliot Forster (Pres & CEO)

SINO CLEAN ENERGY INC.
Room 1502 Bldg D Wangzuo International City Bldg, No 3 Tangyan Rd, Gaoxin District, Xi'an, Shaanxi, China
Tel.: (86) 29 82091099
Web Site: http://www.sinocei.net
Sales Range: $100-124.9 Million
Emp.: 176
Holding Company; Coal Water Slurry Fuel Producer & Distr
N.A.I.C.S.: 551112
Baowen Ren (Chm, Pres & CEO)

SINO DAREN CO. LTD.
Office 5B 5F China Harbour Building 370 King's Road, North Point, China (Hong Kong)
Tel.: (852) 28156986
Web Site: http://www.ittqc.com
Year Founded: 2010
Holding Company; Human Resource Web Portal
N.A.I.C.S.: 551112
Alex Pui Yin Wong (Pres, CFO & Treas)

SINO ENERGY INTERNATIONAL HOLDINGS GROUP LIMITED
District B Shoes Industry Parks Baogai Town, Shishi, Fujian, China
Tel.: (86) 59583099030
Web Site: http://www.activegroup-int.com
Sales Range: $75-99.9 Million
Emp.: 1,441
Investment Services
N.A.I.C.S.: 523999
Xiuman Cai (Co-Founder)

AND PRIVATE COMPANIES

SINO GAS HOLDINGS GROUP LIMITED
Room 3103 Block A1 Caifu Shiji Square 13 Haian Road, Tianhe District, Guangzhou, China Ky
Web Site: https://www.sinogasholdings.com
Year Founded: 2018
1759—(HKG)
Rev.: $194,687,638
Assets: $132,351,019
Liabilities: $75,994,129
Net Worth: $56,356,890
Earnings: $929,054
Emp.: 427
Fiscal Year-end: 12/31/23
Holding Company
N.A.I.C.S.: 551112
Guang Ji (Chm)

SINO GEOPHYSICAL CO., LTD.
Floor 22 Tower 2 Beichen New Era Building No 13 Beiyuan Road, Chaoyang District, Beijing, 100107, China
Tel.: (86) 1084922368
Web Site: https://www.sinogeo.com
Year Founded: 2003
300191—(CHIN)
Rev.: $67,563,288
Assets: $279,457,776
Liabilities: $101,679,084
Net Worth: $177,778,692
Earnings: $5,764,824
Emp.: 70
Fiscal Year-end: 12/31/22
Geological Data Analytical Services for Oil & Gas Industry
N.A.I.C.S.: 541360
Jinming Zhou (Chm & Gen Mgr)

SINO GOLF HOLDINGS LTD.
Room 4501 45/F One Midtown 11 Hoi Shing Road, Tsuen Wan, Hong Kong, NT, China (Hong Kong)
Tel.: (852) 39766928 BM
Web Site: http://www.sinogolf.com
Year Founded: 1988
0361—(HKG)
Rev.: $61,126,560
Assets: $62,298,030
Liabilities: $30,503,738
Net Worth: $31,794,293
Earnings: ($2,033,498)
Emp.: 910
Fiscal Year-end: 12/31/22
Holding Company; Assembled & Packaged Golf Clubs, Club Heads, Shafts, Golf Bags & Related Accessories Designer, Developer, Mfr & Seller
N.A.I.C.S.: 551112
Augustine Chun Man Chu (Founder)

Subsidiaries:

Sino Golf Manufacturing Co. Ltd. (1)
Unit K 20/F Kings Wing Plaza 2 1 On Kwan Street, Shek Mun, Sha Tin, NT, China (Hong Kong) (100%)
Tel.: (852) 2 375 5238
Web Site: http://www.sinogolf.com
Sales Range: $25-49.9 Million
Emp.: 20
Assembled & Packaged Golf Clubs, Club Heads, Shafts, Golf Bags & Related Accessories Designer, Developer & Mfr
N.A.I.C.S.: 339920

Subsidiary (Domestic):

CTB Golf (HK) Ltd. (2)
1901-13 Delta House, 3 On Yiu St, Sha Tin, China (Hong Kong) (100%)
Tel.: (852) 23755238
Web Site: http://www.sinogolf.com
Sales Range: $25-49.9 Million
Assembled & Packaged Golf Clubs, Club Heads, Shafts, Golf Bags & Related Accessories Designer, Developer & Mfr & Seller
N.A.I.C.S.: 339920

Sino Golf Leisure Company Ltd. (2)
1906 Delta House, 3 On Yiu Street, Sha Tin, China (Hong Kong) (100%)
Tel.: (852) 23755238
Web Site: http://www.sinogolf.com
Sales Range: $25-49.9 Million
Assembled & Packaged Golf Clubs, Club Heads, Shafts, Golf Bags & Related Accessories Designer, Developer, Mfr & Seller
N.A.I.C.S.: 339920
Augustine Chun Man Chu (Exec Dir)

SINO GRANDNESS FOOD INDUSTRY GROUP LIMITED
F 56 Block A Union Plaza No 5022 Bin He Road, Nanshan District, Shenzhen, 518033, China
Tel.: (86) 75582821186
Web Site: https://www.grandnessgroups.com
Rev.: $513,388,519
Assets: $670,964,673
Liabilities: $197,787,684
Net Worth: $473,176,989
Earnings: $22,355,457
Emp.: 10,000
Fiscal Year-end: 12/31/18
Canned Vegetables & Fruits Mfr
N.A.I.C.S.: 311421
Tuanbo Li (Chief Technical Officer)

SINO GREAT WALL CO., LTD.
Sino Great Wall Bldg #3 Jinxiu St Yizhuang EDZ, Beijing, 100176, China
Tel.: (86) 1067865229
Web Site: http://www.sgwde.com
Year Founded: 1984
Property Leasing Services
N.A.I.C.S.: 531190
Alex Chen (Chm)

SINO GREEN LAND CORPORATION
Suite 2711A 27F Exchange Tower 33 Wang Chiu Rd, Kowloon Bay, Kowloon, China (Hong Kong)
Tel.: (852) 31040598 NV
SGLA—(OTCIQ)
Liabilities: $222,658
Net Worth: ($222,658)
Earnings: ($35,659)
Emp.: 2
Fiscal Year-end: 12/31/22
Holding Company; Fruits & Vegetables Wholesale Distr, Marketer & Sales
N.A.I.C.S.: 551112
David Lazar (Chm, Pres, CEO, CFO & Sec)

SINO HARBOUR HOLDINGS GROUP LIMITED
Room 1215 Tower B Hunghom Commercial Centre 37-39 Ma Tau Wai Road, Hunghom, Kowloon, China (Hong Kong)
Tel.: (852) 2 363 1300 BM
Web Site: http://www.sinoharbour.com.hk
1663—(HKG)
Rev.: $266,406,604
Assets: $707,520,563
Liabilities: $398,943,979
Net Worth: $308,576,584
Earnings: $48,471,201
Emp.: 311
Fiscal Year-end: 03/31/22
Residential & Commercial Property Developer
N.A.I.C.S.: 236117
Feng Shi (Deputy Chm & Co-CEO)

Subsidiaries:

Zhejiang IPS Pharmaceutical Technology Company Limited (1)
No 18 Chaowang Road, Xiacheng District, Hangzhou, Zhejiang, China
Tel.: (86) 4008166169
Web Site: http://www.zhejiangips.com
Pharmaceutical Research Services
N.A.I.C.S.: 541714
Assad Kazeminy (Founder, Pres & CEO-Global)

SINO HORIZON HOLDINGS LIMITED
450 Ruijin 2 Road, Huangpu District, Shanghai, China
Tel.: (86) 2164332999
Web Site: http://www.sinohorizon.cn
2923—(TAI)
Rev.: $2,056,065,330
Assets: $17,849,489,285
Liabilities: $9,552,909,013
Net Worth: $8,296,580,272
Earnings: $180,382,560
Fiscal Year-end: 12/31/20
Property Development, Leasing & Management
N.A.I.C.S.: 237210

SINO ICT HOLDINGS LIMITED
Unit 02-03 69/F ICC-International Commerce Centre, 1 Austin Road West Tsishatsui, Kowloon, China (Hong Kong)
Tel.: (852) 23427788
Web Site: http://www.sino-ict.com
Year Founded: 1984
0365—(HKG)
Rev.: $29,531,040
Assets: $147,611,978
Liabilities: $102,538,560
Net Worth: $45,073,418
Earnings: ($4,219,230)
Emp.: 358
Fiscal Year-end: 12/31/22
Electronic Equipment Mfr & Whslr
N.A.I.C.S.: 334419
Yuan Xia (CEO)

SINO MEDICAL SCIENCES TECHNOLOGY, INC.
2nd Floor TEDA Biopharm Res Building B 5 4th St TEDA, Tianjin, 300457, China
Tel.: (86) 2259862900
Web Site: https://www.sinomed.com
Year Founded: 2007
688108—(SHG)
Rev.: $27,076,730
Assets: $149,892,963
Liabilities: $25,290,378
Net Worth: $124,602,585
Earnings: ($22,798,405)
Emp.: 500
Fiscal Year-end: 12/31/22
Medical Product Mfr & Distr
N.A.I.C.S.: 339112
Jianhua Sun (Chm & Gen Mgr)

Subsidiaries:

Beijing Sun Technology Inc. (1)
701-707 7/F Zhongkun Plaza No 59 Gaoliangqiaoxiejie, Haidian District, Beijing, China
Tel.: (86) 1080482240
Medical Equipment Mfr
N.A.I.C.S.: 339112

Sinomed B.V. (1)
Wilhelminakade 173, 3072AP, Rotterdam, Netherlands
Tel.: (31) 103076295
Medical Equipment Mfr
N.A.I.C.S.: 339112

Sinomed K.K. (1)
N-Flat 201 4-21-12 Takanawa, Minato-ku, Tokyo, 108-0074, Japan
Tel.: (81) 367216656
Medical Equipment Mfr
N.A.I.C.S.: 339112

SINO OIL AND GAS HOLDINGS LIMITED
44/F Office Tower Convention Plaza 1 Harbour Road, Wanchai, China (Hong Kong)
Tel.: (852) 28023623
Web Site: http://www.sino-oilgas.hk
0702—(HKG)
Rev.: $69,242,700
Assets: $591,732,600
Liabilities: $461,210,723
Net Worth: $130,521,878
Earnings: ($70,530,450)
Emp.: 300
Fiscal Year-end: 12/31/22
Oil & Gas Exploitation & Extraction Services
N.A.I.C.S.: 211120
Terence Tze Fan Wan (CFO)

SINO PROSPER GROUP HOLDINGS LTD.
Room 802 8/F Tower Two Lippo Centre, No 89 Queensway, Hong Kong, China (Hong Kong)
Tel.: (852) 31134414 Ky
Web Site: http://www.sinoprosper.com
Rev.: $4,465,447
Assets: $70,349,401
Liabilities: $10,542,853
Net Worth: $59,806,548
Earnings: ($8,387,701)
Emp.: 48
Fiscal Year-end: 03/31/19
Metal Exploration
N.A.I.C.S.: 212290
Ngai Man Leung (Chm)

SINO SPLENDID HOLDINGS LIMITED
8/F E168 166-168 Des Voeux Road Central, Sheung Wan, China (Hong Kong)
Tel.: (852) 22377288
Web Site: http://www.sinosplendid.com
8006—(HKG)
Rev.: $8,449,043
Assets: $14,078,933
Liabilities: $971,295
Net Worth: $13,107,638
Earnings: ($5,485,433)
Emp.: 42
Fiscal Year-end: 12/31/22
Investment Holding Company
N.A.I.C.S.: 523999
Chi Wa Chow (CEO, Compliance Officer & Sec)

Subsidiaries:

TTG Asia Media Pte. Ltd (1)
1 Science Park Road 04-07 The Capricorn Science Park II, Singapore, 117528, Singapore
Tel.: (65) 63957575
Web Site: http://www.ttgasiamedia.com
Travel Book Publisher
N.A.I.C.S.: 513130
Darren Hung Meng Ng (Mng Dir)

SINO STRATEGIC INTERNATIONAL LIMITED
Level 7 420 King William Street, Adelaide, 5000, SA, Australia
Tel.: (61) 873246000
Web Site: http://www.sino.com.au
Sales Range: $1-9.9 Million
Diversified Investment Services; Gaming, Internet & Mobile Media Services
N.A.I.C.S.: 523940
Leonora Yung (Chm)

Subsidiaries:

Sino Investment Services Pty. Ltd. (1)

SINO STRATEGIC INTERNATIONAL LIMITED

Sino Strategic International Limited—(Continued)
Level 2 419 Collins Street, Melbourne, 3000, VIC, Australia
Tel.: (61) 396296615
Web Site: http://www.sino.com.au
Financial Investment Advisory Services
N.A.I.C.S.: 523940

SINO TACTFUL CO., LTD.
8F-1 No 328 Changchun Rd, Zhongshan Dist, Taipei, 104010, Taiwan
Tel.: (886) 277033909
Web Site: https://sinotact.com
Year Founded: 1990
5481—(TPE)
Rev.: $3,144,903
Assets: $53,490,007
Liabilities: $12,475,195
Net Worth: $41,014,813
Earnings: ($911,737)
Fiscal Year-end: 12/31/23
Electronic Component Mfr & Distr
N.A.I.C.S.: 334419
Andy Lee *(Chm)*

SINO TECHFIBRE LIMITED
South Muhuang Road & West Railroad, Longkou Economic Development Zone, Longkou, 265716, Shandong, China
Tel.: (86) 5358889111
Sales Range: $10-24.9 Million
Polyurethane Synthetic Leather Products Mfr
N.A.I.C.S.: 326150
Wenheng Li *(Exec Dir)*

SINO VISION WORLDWIDE HOLDINGS LIMITED
Unit 2004-6 20/F Strand 50 50 Bonham Strand, Sheung Wan, Hong Kong, China (Hong Kong)
Tel.: (852) 38455500 Ky
Web Site:
  http://www.sinovisionworldwide.com
Year Founded: 2000
8086—(HKG)
Rev.: $5,672,798
Assets: $20,835,171
Liabilities: $20,627,127
Net Worth: $208,045
Earnings: ($6,253,853)
Emp.: 32
Fiscal Year-end: 06/30/21
Holding Company
N.A.I.C.S.: 551112
He Wang *(Exec Dir)*

SINO WEALTH ELECTRONIC LTD.
No 3 Lane 767 JinZhong Road, Shanghai, 200335, China
Tel.: (86) 2161219988
Web Site:
  https://www.sinowealth.com
Year Founded: 1994
300327—(CHIN)
Rev.: $224,905,356
Assets: $277,664,868
Liabilities: $69,253,704
Net Worth: $208,411,164
Earnings: $45,349,200
Emp.: 400
Fiscal Year-end: 12/31/22
Integrated Circuit Products Mfr
N.A.I.C.S.: 334413
Fu Qiming *(Chm)*

Subsidiaries:

Sino Wealth Electronic(Shanghai) Ltd. (1)
7B Zhongke Building, Hi-tech Industrial Area, Shenzhen, 518040, China
Tel.: (86) 75525181447
Web Site: https://en.sinowealth.com
Integrated Circuit Mfr & Distr
N.A.I.C.S.: 334413

SINO-AGRI LEADING BIOSCIENCES CO., LTD.
9/F Block C Global Finance & News Center No A1 Xuanwumenwai Street, Beijing, 100052, China
Tel.: (86) 1059337477
Web Site: https://www.sino-agri-sal.com
Year Founded: 2009
603970—(SHG)
Rev.: $1,642,507,940
Assets: $876,661,278
Liabilities: $668,233,926
Net Worth: $208,427,352
Earnings: $29,530,767
Fiscal Year-end: 12/31/22
Agrochemical Mfr & Distr
N.A.I.C.S.: 325320

SINO-AMERICAN SILICON PRODUCTS INC.
No 8 Industrial East Road 2 Hsinchu Science Park, Hsin-chu, Taiwan
Tel.: (886) 35772233 CN
Web Site: https://www.saswafer.com
Year Founded: 1981
5483—(TPE)
Rev.: $2,680,465,316
Assets: $7,374,185,437
Liabilities: $4,692,797,167
Net Worth: $2,681,388,270
Earnings: $581,409,180
Emp.: 10,663
Fiscal Year-end: 12/31/23
Silicon Wafers Mfr
N.A.I.C.S.: 334413
Hsiu-Lan Hsu *(Chm & CEO)*

Subsidiaries:

GlobalWafers Co., Ltd. (1)
4F No 8 Industrial East Road 2 Hsinchu Science Park, Hsin-chu, Taiwan
Tel.: (886) 35772233
Web Site: http://www.sas-globalwafers.com
Non Ferrous Metal Mfr
N.A.I.C.S.: 331523
Doris Hsu *(Chm)*

Subsidiary (Non-US):

GlobalWafers Japan Co., Ltd. (2)
6-861-5 Seiro-machi Higashiko, Kitakanbara-gun, Niigata, 957-0197, Japan
Tel.: (81) 252563200
Web Site: http://www.sas-globalwafers.co.jp
Emp.: 1,224
Nonferrous Metal Distr
N.A.I.C.S.: 424610
Doris Hsu *(Chm & CEO)*

SunEdison Semiconductor Limited (2)
9 Battery Road, Singapore, 049910, Singapore
Tel.: (65) 65898494
Web Site: http://www.gw-semi.com
Holding Company; Semiconductor Mfr
N.A.I.C.S.: 551112
Donna K. Martin *(Chief HR Officer & Sr VP)*

Subsidiary (Non-US):

MEMC Electronic Materials S.p.A. (3)
Viale Gherzi 31, 28100, Novara, Italy
Tel.: (39) 0321 334444
Web Site: http://www.gw-semi.com
Polished & Epitaxial Silicon Wafers Mfr
N.A.I.C.S.: 334413

MEMC Electronic Materials Sdn. Bhd. (3)
Jalan SS 8/2 Sungai Way Free Industrial Zone, 47300, Petaling Jaya, Selangor Darul Ehsan, Malaysia
Tel.: (60) 378773277
Web Site: http://www.sunedisonsemi.com
Polished Wafers Mfr
N.A.I.C.S.: 334413

MEMC Japan Ltd. (3)
11-2 Kiyohara Industrial Park, Utsunomiya, 321-3296, Tochigi, Japan
Tel.: (81) 286676333
Web Site: http://www.sunedisonsemi.com
Polished & Epitaxial Silicon Wafers Mfr
N.A.I.C.S.: 334413

MEMC Korea Company (3)
854 Manghyang-Ro Seonggeo-eup, Sebukgu, Cheonan, 331-831, Chungcheongnam-do, Korea (South)
Tel.: (82) 415504114
Web Site: http://www.sunedisonsemi.com
Polished Wafers Mfr
N.A.I.C.S.: 334413

SunEdison Semiconductor Technology (Shanghai) Ltd. (3)
Kirin Plaza Suite 406 No 666 Gubei Road, ChangNing District, Shanghai, 200336, China
Tel.: (86) 21 6070 7800
Web Site: http://www.sunedisonsemi.com
Semiconductor Whslr
N.A.I.C.S.: 423690

Subsidiary (US):

SunEdison Semiconductor, LLC (3)
501 Pearl Dr, Saint Peters, MO 63376
Tel.: (636) 474-5000
Web Site: http://www.gw-semi.com
Semiconductor Whslr
N.A.I.C.S.: 334413
Horacio Mendez *(Sr VP & Gen Mgr-Advanced Technologies Bus)*

Subsidiary (Non-US):

Taisil Electronic Materials Corp. (3)
2 Creation Road 1, Science Based Industrial Park, Hsin-chu, 30077, Taiwan
Tel.: (886) 35783131
Web Site: http://www.sunedisonsemi.com
Polished & Epitaxial Wafers Mfr
N.A.I.C.S.: 334413
Michael Shueh *(Pres)*

GlobitTech, Inc. (1)
200 FM 1417 W, Sherman, TX 75092
Tel.: (903) 957-1999
Web Site: http://www.globitech.com
Semiconductor Device Distr
N.A.I.C.S.: 423690
Mark England *(Pres)*

Kunshan Sino Silicon Technology Co., Ltd. (1)
No 303 Hanpu Rd, Chengbei, Kunshan, Jiangsu, China
Tel.: (86) 51257781260
Nonferrous Metal Distr
N.A.I.C.S.: 423510
Olive Ho *(Acct Mgr)*

SINO-ENTERTAINMENT TECHNOLOGY HOLDINGS LTD.
Suite No 2 3/F Sino Plaza 255 Gloucester Road, Causeway Bay, China (Hong Kong) Ky
Web Site: https://www.sinotecw.com
Year Founded: 2014
6933—(HKG)
Rev.: $1,884,789
Assets: $73,085,153
Liabilities: $42,661,937
Net Worth: $30,423,216
Earnings: ($15,161,508)
Emp.: 35
Fiscal Year-end: 12/31/22
Holding Company
N.A.I.C.S.: 551112
Chi Wai Yuen *(Sec)*

SINO-GERMAN UNITED AG
Maximilianstrasse 54, 80538, Munich, 80538, Germany
Tel.: (49) 8923886846
Web Site: https://www.sgu-ag.de
SGU—(DUS)
Rev.: $3,245,378
Assets: $2,538,901
Liabilities: $1,214,257
Net Worth: $1,324,644
Earnings: ($22,077)
Fiscal Year-end: 12/31/23
Financial Services

INTERNATIONAL PUBLIC

N.A.I.C.S.: 523940

SINO-HIGH (CHINA) CO., LTD.
No 51 Chongfu Road Nanjing Chemical Industrial Park, Liuhe District, Nanjing, 210047, Jiangsu, China
Tel.: (86) 2558392388
Web Site:
  https://www.sinohighchem.com
Year Founded: 2008
301076—(CHIN)
Rev.: $60,285,584
Assets: $168,145,090
Liabilities: $13,872,826
Net Worth: $154,272,264
Earnings: $12,923,834
Fiscal Year-end: 12/31/23
Chemical Product Mfr & Distr
N.A.I.C.S.: 327120
Liuxin Yan *(Chm)*

SINO-I TECHNOLOGY LIMITED
12/F The Octagon No 6 Sha Tsui Road Tsuen Wan New Territories, Hong Kong, China (Hong Kong)
Tel.: (852) 28913733
Web Site: http://www.sino-i.com
0250—(HKG)
Rev.: $125,386,488
Assets: $293,855,263
Liabilities: $93,086,414
Net Worth: $200,768,849
Earnings: $14,318,586
Emp.: 5,418
Fiscal Year-end: 12/31/20
Financial Information Services
N.A.I.C.S.: 522291
Rong Liu *(Chm)*

Subsidiaries:

Beijing Xinnet Cyber Information Company Limited (1)
Room 805 Jinwantong Plaza No 418 Huizhou Road, Hefei, 230001, China
Tel.: (86) 5512862208
Web Site: http://www.xinnet.com
Information Technology Consulting Services
N.A.I.C.S.: 541512

CE Dongli Technology Company Limited (1)
8F Xintiandi International Square Sui Xi Road Luyang District, Hefei, 230001, China
Tel.: (86) 5515450377
Information Technology Consulting Services
N.A.I.C.S.: 541512

SINO-LIFE GROUP LIMITED
Unit 601 6/F Ovest 77 Wing Lok Street Sheung Wan, Hong Kong, China (Hong Kong)
Tel.: (852) 23226225 Ky
Web Site:
  http://www.sinolifegroup.com
Year Founded: 2005
8296—(HKG)
Rev.: $10,946,848
Assets: $39,984,235
Liabilities: $21,617,528
Net Worth: $18,366,707
Earnings: $87,890
Emp.: 218
Fiscal Year-end: 12/31/22
Funeral Services
N.A.I.C.S.: 812220
Tien-Tsai Liu *(CEO & Compliance Officer)*

Subsidiaries:

Bau Shan Life Science Technology Co., Ltd. (1)
4F-14 292 Fu Kuo Rd, Kaohsiung, 81358, Taiwan
Tel.: (886) 79518383
Web Site: https://www.baushan.com.tw
Funeral Services
N.A.I.C.S.: 812210

AND PRIVATE COMPANIES — SINOCHEM CORPORATION

SINO-OCEAN GROUP HOLDINGS LIMITED
Suite 601 One Pacific Place 88 Queensway, Hong Kong, China (Hong Kong)
Tel.: (852) 28992880
Web Site: https://www.sinooceangroup.com
Year Founded: 1993
3377—(OTCIQ)
Rev.: $6,386,600,714
Assets: $34,070,715,136
Liabilities: $27,440,511,049
Net Worth: $6,630,204,087
Earnings: ($2,166,849,662)
Emp.: 13,428
Fiscal Year-end: 12/31/22
Investment Holding Company
N.A.I.C.S.: 523999
Honghui Wang (Exec Dir)

Subsidiaries:

Gemini Investment (Holding) Limited (1)
Suite 610 One Pacific Place 88 Queensway, No 89 Queensway, Hong Kong, China (Hong Kong)
Tel.: (852) 28663938
Web Site: https://www.geminiinvestments.com.hk
Rev.: $135,737,520
Assets: $1,697,453,145
Liabilities: $877,841,198
Net Worth: $819,611,948
Earnings: ($42,047,970)
Emp.: 71
Fiscal Year-end: 12/31/2022
Real Estate Development & Investment
N.A.I.C.S.: 531390
Adrian Puf Ying Sum (Chm & CEO)

Subsidiary (Domestic):

Charterway Developments Limited (2)
3-4 F Kee Shing Ctr 74-76 Kimberley Rd, Tsim Sha Tsui, Kowloon, China (Hong Kong)
Tel.: (852) 23661211
Web Site: http://www.hkgbusiness.com
Real Estate Property Investment Services
N.A.I.C.S.: 531110

SINO-PLATINUM METALS CO., LTD.
No 988 Keji Road The High and New Technology Industry Development Zone, Kunming, 650106, Yunnan, China
Tel.: (86) 87168328190
Web Site: https://www.sino-platinum.com.cn
Year Founded: 2000
600459—(SHG)
Rev.: $5,722,515,064
Assets: $1,835,788,659
Liabilities: $965,935,812
Net Worth: $869,852,847
Earnings: $57,141,213
Emp.: 330
Fiscal Year-end: 12/31/22
Precious Metal Product Mfr
N.A.I.C.S.: 332999
Junmei Guo (Chm, Vice Chm & Gen Mgr)

SINO-THAI ENGINEERING & CONSTRUCTION PUBLIC COMPANY LIMITED
32/59-60 29-30 Floor Sino-Thai Tower Sukhumvit Soi 21 Asoke Road, Klongtoey Nua Wattana, Bangkok, 10110, Thailand
Tel.: (66) 22601321   TH
Web Site: http://www.stecon.co.th
Year Founded: 1962
STEC—(THA)
Rev.: $871,132,144
Assets: $1,385,142,638
Liabilities: $857,581,791
Net Worth: $527,560,847
Earnings: $15,635,799
Emp.: 1,593
Fiscal Year-end: 12/31/23
Engineering & Construction Services
N.A.I.C.S.: 237990
Teeraphong Wichiranon (Sr VP-Admin Div)

Subsidiaries:

HTR Corporation Ltd (1)
32-46-12 Sukhumvit 21 Wattana, Bangkok, Thailand
Tel.: (66) 22598911
Emp.: 30
Real Estate Property Lessors
N.A.I.C.S.: 531190

SINOBANGLA INDUSTRIES LIMITED
Navana DH Tower Suite 901 & 902, 9th Floor 6 Panthapath, Dhaka, 1215, Bangladesh
Tel.: (880) 255013465
Web Site: https://www.sinobangla.com
Year Founded: 1996
SINOBANGLA—(CHT)
Rev.: $762,412
Assets: $5,938,021
Liabilities: $4,572,823
Net Worth: $1,365,198
Earnings: ($405,598)
Emp.: 1,507
Fiscal Year-end: 06/30/22
Plastics Bag Mfr
N.A.I.C.S.: 326111
Ma Jiang (Chm)

SINOBIOPHARMA, INC.
8 Zhong Tian Road, Nantong, Jiangsu, China
Tel.: (86) 51385328336   NV
Web Site: http://www.sinobp.com
Year Founded: 2006
Sales Range: $1-9.9 Million
Emp.: 110
Pharmaceuticals Mfr
N.A.I.C.S.: 325412
Lequn Lee Huang (Pres, CEO & CFO)

SINOCARE INC.
265 Guyuan Road High Tech Industrial Development Zone, Changsha, 410205, Hunan, China
Tel.: (86) 73189935529
Web Site: http://www.sinocare.com.cn
Year Founded: 2002
300298—(CHIN)
Rev.: $395,015,400
Assets: $648,243,648
Liabilities: $206,892,036
Net Worth: $441,351,612
Earnings: $60,495,552
Emp.: 1,170
Fiscal Year-end: 12/31/22
Medical Device Mfr
N.A.I.C.S.: 339112
Li Shaobo (Chm & Gen Mgr)

Subsidiaries:

Polymer Technology Systems, Inc. (1)
7736 Zionsville Rd, Indianapolis, IN 46268
Tel.: (317) 870-5610
Web Site: http://www.ptsdiagnostics.com
Medical Equipment Whslr
N.A.I.C.S.: 423450
Robert S. Huffstodt (Pres & CEO)

Trividia Health, Inc. (1)
2400 NW 55th Ct, Fort Lauderdale, FL 33309
Tel.: (954) 677-9201
Diabetes Management Products Mfr
N.A.I.C.S.: 339112
Scott Verner (Pres & CEO)

Subsidiary (Domestic):

Trividia Manufacturing Solutions, Inc. (2)
89 Bridge St, Lancaster, NH 03584
Web Site: http://www.trividiams.com
Pharmaceuticals & Personal Care Products Mfr
N.A.I.C.S.: 325412
Dennis Wogaman (Sr Dir-Ops)

SINOCELLTECH GROUP LTD.
Yard No 31 Kechuang Seventh Street, Beijing Economic and Technological Development Zone, Beijing, 100176, China
Tel.: (86) 1058628288
Web Site: http://www.sinocelltech.com
Year Founded: 2007
688520—(SHG)
Rev.: $143,654,009
Assets: $384,116,934
Liabilities: $418,120,537
Net Worth: ($34,003,602)
Earnings: ($72,867,010)
Emp.: —
Fiscal Year-end: 12/31/22
Pharmaceutical Product Mfr & Distr
N.A.I.C.S.: 325412
Liangzhi Xie (Chm & Gen Mgr)

SINOCHEM CORPORATION
11/F Central Tower Chemsunny World Trade Center 28 Fuxingmennei Street, Beijing, 100031, China
Tel.: (86) 1059568888
Web Site: http://www.sinochem.com
Sales Range: $5-14.9 Billion
Emp.: 60,000
Oil Extraction Services
N.A.I.C.S.: 211120
Bin Li (VP)

Subsidiaries:

Beijing Chemsunny Property Company Limited (1)
Room 1701 Jinyu Mansion A129 Xuanwumen Xidajie Street, Xicheng, Beijing, 100031, China
Tel.: (86) 1066412098
Web Site: http://www.chemsunny.com
Organic Product Distr
N.A.I.C.S.: 424690

Changzhou Sinochem Qinfeng Plastics Co. Ltd. (1)
880 Zhongwu Road, Changzhou, 213018, Jiangsu, China
Tel.: (86) 519 882 8729
Sales Range: $50-74.9 Million
Emp.: 125
Aluminum-Plastics Composite Panels Mfr
N.A.I.C.S.: 326199

Chemiforward Dyres Trading Co. (1)
Al Maktoum Hospital Rd, PO Box 3854, Dubai, United Arab Emirates (100%)
Tel.: (971) 44270517
Sales Range: $10-24.9 Million
Emp.: 12
N.A.I.C.S.: 211120

China Foreign Economy and Trade Trust Co., Ltd. (1)
Fuxingmen Inner St 28, Beijing, 100031, China
Tel.: (86) 1059568808
Web Site: http://www.fotic.com.cn
Real Estate Management Services
N.A.I.C.S.: 531210

China Jinmao Holdings Group Limited (1)
4702-03 Convention Plaza Office Building No 1 Harbour Road, Convention Plaza 1 Harbour Road, Wanchai, China (Hong Kong)
Tel.: (852) 28299668
Web Site: https://www.chinajinmao.cn
Rev.: $11,490,830,195
Assets: $58,414,881,341
Liabilities: $42,812,486,016
Net Worth: $15,602,395,326
Earnings: $722,875,222
Emp.: 11,534
Fiscal Year-end: 12/31/2022
Property Development Services
N.A.I.C.S.: 531390
Hui Zhang (Sr VP)

China Liaohua United Foreign Trade Co. Ltd. (1)
No 134 Hongwei Rd 7 F Jingmao Mansion, Hongwei District, Liaoyang, 111003, Liaoning, China (20%)
Tel.: (86) 195156202
Sales Range: $50-74.9 Million
Emp.: 30
N.A.I.C.S.: 211120

China National Seed Group Co., Ltd (1)
15/F Sinochem Tower A2 Fuxingmenwai Dajie, Beijing, 100045, China
Tel.: (86) 1088079999
Web Site: http://www.chinaseeds.com.cn
Real Estate Management Services
N.A.I.C.S.: 531210

China Yanshan United Foreign Trade Co. Ltd. (1)
No 2 Bldg Yingfeng Street, Fang Shan District, Beijing, 102500, China (20%)
Tel.: (86) 1069342481
Sales Range: $350-399.9 Million
Emp.: 1,000
N.A.I.C.S.: 211120

Dalian West Pacific Petrochemical Co. Ltd. (1)
Haiqing Dao Economic & Technical Development Zone, Dalian, 116600, Liaoning, China
Tel.: (86) 411 8750 6666
Web Site: http://www.sinochem.com
N.A.I.C.S.: 211120

Emerald Energy Plc (1)
17th Fl New Zealand House 80 Haymarket, London, SW1Y 4TE, United Kingdom
Tel.: (44) 2079252440
Web Site: http://www.emeraldenergy.com
Sales Range: $75-99.9 Million
Emp.: 5
Hydrocarbons Exploration Services
N.A.I.C.S.: 211120
Richard Konn (Sec)

Far East Horizon Limited (1)
Room 6708 Floor 67 International Commerce Center 1 Austin Road West, Kowloon, China (Hong Kong)
Tel.: (852) 25888688
Rev.: $3,110,753,074
Assets: $48,665,711,675
Liabilities: $40,694,732,499
Net Worth: $7,970,979,176
Earnings: $957,718,072
Emp.: 19,337
Fiscal Year-end: 12/31/2023
Financial Investment Services
N.A.I.C.S.: 523999
Mingzhe Wang (CFO)

Subsidiary (Non-US):

International Far Eastern Leasing Co., Ltd. (2)
Rm 3302 Jinmao Tower No 88 Shiji Dadao, Pudong New Area, Shanghai, 200121, China
Tel.: (86) 2150490099
Web Site: http://www.sinochem.com
Sales Range: $200-249.9 Million
Emp.: 725
Industrial Equipment Leasing & Financing Services
N.A.I.C.S.: 532490

Guangdong Chemicals Imp. & Exp. Corporation (Group) (1)
No 58 Zhan Qian Rd, Guangzhou, 510160, Guangdong, China (100%)
Tel.: (86) 2086672288
Web Site: http://www.sinochem-guangdong.com
Sales Range: $100-124.9 Million
Emp.: 150
N.A.I.C.S.: 211120

Jin Mao (Shanghai) Real Estate Co., Ltd. (1)

6949

SINOCHEM CORPORATION

Sinochem Corporation—(Continued)
88 Century Ave, Pudong, Shanghai, 202162, Chongming, China
Tel.: (86) 2159406822
Real Estate Manangement Services
N.A.I.C.S.: 531210

Jin Mao Investment (Chang Sha) Co., Ltd. (1)
3F Wuqiang Building No 2 Lutian Rd Changsha National Hi-Tech Pack, Changsha, 410205, Hunan, China
Tel.: (86) 73189806600
Real Estate Manangement Services
N.A.I.C.S.: 531210

Manulife-Sinochem Life Insurance Company Ltd.
21st Fl Jin Mao Bldg 88 Century Rd Pu Dong, Shanghai, 200121, China **(49%)**
Tel.: (86) 2150492288
Web Site: https://www.manulife-sinochem.com
Sales Range: $75-99.9 Million
Emp.: 200
Life Insurance Products & Services
N.A.I.C.S.: 524113

Rillfung Company Ltd. (1)
Room 4601 06 Office Tower Convention Plaza 1 Harbour Road, Wan Chai, Hong Kong, China (Hong Kong)
Tel.: (852) 28240202
Web Site: http://www.sinochem.com
Sales Range: $25-49.9 Million
Emp.: 24
Crude Oil Transportation
N.A.I.C.S.: 486990

Sinochem (U.S.A.) Inc. (1)
1330 Post Oak Blvd Ste 2500, Houston, TX 77056-3853
Tel.: (713) 686-0700
Web Site: http://www.sinochem-usa.com
Sales Range: $50-74.9 Million
Emp.: 4
N.A.I.C.S.: 211120

Sinochem (United Kingdom) Ltd. (1)
17th Fl New Zealand House 80 Haymarket, London, SW1Y 4TQ, United Kingdom **(100%)**
Tel.: (44) 2079307060
Web Site: http://www.sinochem-uk.com
Sales Range: $50-74.9 Million
Emp.: 25
N.A.I.C.S.: 211120
Leijia Zhao *(Mng Dir)*

Sinochem American Holdings Inc. (1)
1330 Post Oak Blvd Ste 2500, Houston, TX 77056
Tel.: (713) 263-8880
Web Site: http://www.sinochem.com
Sales Range: $50-74.9 Million
Emp.: 5
N.A.I.C.S.: 211120

Sinochem Asia Holdings Co., Ltd. (1)
9 Temasek Boulevard 18 01, Suntec Twr Two, Singapore, 38989, Singapore **(100%)**
Tel.: (65) 63370110
Sales Range: $200-249.9 Million
Emp.: 20
N.A.I.C.S.: 211120
Thomas Schulz *(Mgr-Fin)*

Sinochem Electronic Information Technology Co. (1)
No 16 Dong San Huan N Rd, Chao Yang District, Beijing, 100026, China **(100%)**
Tel.: (86) 1065075755
Sales Range: $50-74.9 Million
Emp.: 60
Petroleum & Natural Gas Extraction
N.A.I.C.S.: 211120

Sinochem Europe Holdings PLC (1)
17 Fl New Zealand House Haymarket, London, SW1Y 4TE, United Kingdom
Tel.: (44) 2079307060
Web Site: http://www.sinochem.com
Sales Range: $50-74.9 Million
Emp.: 5
N.A.I.C.S.: 211120
Lei Jiazhao *(Branch Mgr)*

Sinochem Fertilizer Macao Commercial Offshore Limited (1)
Ed Nam Kwong, Macau, China (Macau)
Tel.: (853) 28715858
Real Estate Manangement Services
N.A.I.C.S.: 531210

Sinochem Finance Co., Ltd. (1)
F3 Central Tower Chemsunny World Trade Center 28 FuxingmenneiStreet, Xicheng District, Beijing, 100031, China
Tel.: (86) 1059569332
Real Estate Manangement Services
N.A.I.C.S.: 531210

Sinochem Franshion Property (Beijing) Co., Ltd. (1)
22 Floor Block B Landgent Center No 20 East 3RD Ring Iddle Road, Beijing, 100022, China
Tel.: (86) 1057681515
Real Estate Manangement Services
N.A.I.C.S.: 531210

Sinochem Guangdong Import and Export Corporation (1)
No 58 Zhanquian Rd, Guangzhou, 510160, China **(100%)**
Tel.: (86) 2086672288
Web Site: http://www.sinochem-guangdong.com
Sales Range: $100-124.9 Million
Emp.: 150
N.A.I.C.S.: 211120

Sinochem Hebei Corporation (1)
707 Lianmeng Road Sinchem Building, Shijiazhuang, 050061, Hebei, China **(100%)**
Tel.: (86) 31185028888
Web Site: http://www.sinochemhebei.com
Petrochemicals Importer & Exporter
N.A.I.C.S.: 325110
Zhao Caijun *(Gen Mgr)*

Sinochem Hong Kong Investment Co., Ltd. (1)
47 Fl Ofc Tower Convention Plz, 1 Harbour Rd, Hong Kong, China (Hong Kong) **(50%)**
Tel.: (852) 28240100
Web Site: http://www.sinochem.com
Sales Range: $50-74.9 Million
Emp.: 60
N.A.I.C.S.: 211120

Sinochem International Advertising & Exhibition Co. Ltd. (1)
18Fl Sinochem Tower A2 Fu Xing Men Wai Dajie, Beijing, 100045, China
Tel.: (86) 88079813
N.A.I.C.S.: 541810

Sinochem International Chemicals (Hong Kong) Co. Ltd. (1)
47 Fl Ofc Tower Convention Plz, 1 Harbour Rd, Wanchai, China (Hong Kong) **(100%)**
Tel.: (852) 28240100
Web Site: http://www.sinochem.com
Sales Range: $50-74.9 Million
Emp.: 40
Petroleum & Natural Gas
N.A.I.C.S.: 211120

Sinochem International Corporation (1)
Sinochem International Plaza No 233 Changqing North Road, Pilot Free Trade Zone, Shanghai, 200125, China
Tel.: (86) 2131769818
Web Site: https://www.sinochem.com
Rev.: $12,827,843,208
Assets: $9,864,111,708
Liabilities: $6,137,482,581
Net Worth: $3,726,629,127
Earnings: $183,994,523
Emp.: 220,000
Fiscal Year-end: 12/31/2022
Chemical Products Distr
N.A.I.C.S.: 424690
Liu Hongsheng *(Gen Mgr)*

Subsidiary (Domestic):

Sinochem Xingzhong Oil Staging (Zhoushan) Co., Ltd.) (2)
No 1 Xingzhong Rd, Zhoushan, 316000, Zhejiang, China
Tel.: (86) 5802026251
Web Site: http://www.xz.sinochem.com

Petroleum Terminal Operator
N.A.I.C.S.: 424710

Sinochem International Hotel and Property Management Co., Ltd. (1)
No A2 Sinochem Tower Fuxingmenwaidaji, Beijing, 10 0045, China **(50%)**
Tel.: (86) 1088078298
Web Site: http://www.property.sinochem.com
Sales Range: $150-199.9 Million
Emp.: 114
Property Management Services; Joint Venture Between Sinochem & Forstera Co., Ltd.
N.A.I.C.S.: 531210

Sinochem International Industry Co. Ltd. (1)
F9 Central Tower Chemsunny World Trade Center 28 Fuxingmennei Street, Xicheng District, Beijing, 100031, China
Tel.: (86) 1059569538
N.A.I.C.S.: 211120

Sinochem International Oil (Hong Kong) Co., Ltd. (1)
47/F Office Tower Convention Plaza 1 Harbour Road, Wanchai, China (Hong Kong) **(100%)**
Tel.: (852) 2824 0100
Web Site: http://www.sinochem.com
Sales Range: $50-74.9 Million
Emp.: 50
Petroleum Development Services
N.A.I.C.S.: 211120

Sinochem International Oil (London) Co., Ltd. (1)
11 F Westminster Tower 3 Albert Embankment, London, SE1 7SP, United Kingdom **(100%)**
Tel.: (44) 2077357878
Web Site: http://www.sinochem.com
Sales Range: $50-74.9 Million
Emp.: 18
Crude Oil Trading & Risk Hedging
N.A.I.C.S.: 213112
Wendy Liu *(Mng Dir)*

Sinochem International Oil (Singapore) Pte. Ltd. (1)
9 Temasek Blvd 18 03 Suntec Twr Two, Singapore, 38989, Singapore
Tel.: (65) 63390110
Web Site: http://www.singnet.com
Sales Range: $50-74.9 Million
Emp.: 13
N.A.I.C.S.: 211120
Larry Lien *(Mng Dir)*

Sinochem International Oil (Tianjin) Co., Ltd. (1)
Room1502 Building A Youyi Tower No 50 Youyi Road, Hexi District, Tianjin, 300061, China
Tel.: (86) 2288376706
Real Estate Manangement Services
N.A.I.C.S.: 531210

Sinochem International Oil Co. (1)
F9 Central Tower Chemsunny World Trade Center 28 Fuxingmennei Street, Xicheng District, Beijing, 100031, China **(100%)**
Tel.: (86) 1059569575
Web Site: http://www.sinochem.com
Sales Range: $50-74.9 Million
Emp.: 80
Import & Export of Crude Oil & Oil Products
N.A.I.C.S.: 424720

Sinochem International Tendering Co., Ltd. (1)
21/F Sinochem Tower No A2, Fuxingmenwai Dajie, Beijing, 100045, China **(100%)**
Tel.: (86) 1088079249
Web Site: http://www.sinochemitc.com
Sales Range: $25-49.9 Million
Emp.: 100
Tendering, International Trading & Engineering Project Consulting; Legal & Financial Consulting, Financing, Procurement, Design & Construction Management to Technology & Equipment Importation
N.A.I.C.S.: 561499

Sinochem Investment (Singapore) Co., Ltd. (1)
9 Temasek Blvd 18 01 02 03 Suntec Tower 2, Singapore, 38989, Singapore **(100%)**
Tel.: (65) 63370110
Web Site: http://www.sinochem.com
Emp.: 20
oil trading
N.A.I.C.S.: 211120
Heng Xiaolei *(Mng Dir)*

Sinochem Japan Co. Ltd. (1)
6 F lmc Building Shin Bashi 5 5 1Shin Bashi, Minato-ku, Tokyo, 105 0004, Japan **(100%)**
Tel.: (81) 334347890
Web Site: http://www.sinochemjp.co.jp
Sales Range: $50-74.9 Million
Emp.: 15
N.A.I.C.S.: 211120

Sinochem Jiangsu Co., Ltd. (1)
Floors 21&22 Jin Cheng Tower No 216 Middle Longpan Road, Nanjing, 210002, China
Tel.: (86) 2551817888
Web Site: http://www.sinochemjiangsu.com
Sales Range: $75-99.9 Million
Emp.: 200
International Trade, Domestic Distribution, Research & Development, Manufacturing & Storage of Pharmaceutical Products
N.A.I.C.S.: 325412
Dong Jianhua *(Gen Mgr)*

Sinochem Korea Co., Ltd. (1)
Room 1103 Chang-Kyo B/D 1 Chang-Kyo Dong, Chung-gu, Seoul, Korea (South)
Tel.: (82) 27718883
N.A.I.C.S.: 211120

Sinochem Liaoning (1)
Rainbow Building No 23 Renmin Rd Building 32-33, Zhongshan District, Dalian, 116600, Liaoning, China **(100%)**
Tel.: (86) 41182820643
Web Site: http://www.sinochemliaoning.com
Sales Range: $50-74.9 Million
Emp.: 100
Mineral Resources, Petroleum Chemicals & Logistics Trading
N.A.I.C.S.: 238990
Guijie Hu *(Gen Mgr)*

Sinochem Ningbo Import & Export Co. (1)
21 Jiang Xia St, 315000, Ningbo, China **(100%)**
Tel.: (86) 57487348868
Web Site: http://www.ninhua.cn
Sales Range: $100-124.9 Million
Emp.: 200
N.A.I.C.S.: 211120
Liu Jian Ping *(Pres)*

Sinochem Oil Anhui Co., Ltd. (1)
Rm 1412-1421 Tower A Blue Business Port No 188 South Qianshan Road, Hefei, 230031, Anhui, China
Tel.: (86) 5513712555
Web Site: http://www.sinochem.com
Real Estate Manangement Services
N.A.I.C.S.: 531210

Sinochem Oil Fujian Co., Ltd. (1)
Room B 12/F International Plaza No 8 Lujiang Road, Xiamen, 361001, Fujian, China
Tel.: (86) 5928129068
Real Estate Manangement Services
N.A.I.C.S.: 531210

Sinochem Oil Guangdong Co., Ltd. (1)
Rm 7105 Office Building Zhongxin Plaza No 233 Tianhe North Road, Guangzhou, 510613, Guangdong, China
Tel.: (86) 2038772230
Real Estate Manangement Services
N.A.I.C.S.: 531210

Sinochem Oil Hunan Co., Ltd. (1)
2nd floor Tianxin venture building No 318 Xinshao East Road, Tianxin district, Changsha, 410004, Hunan, China
Tel.: (86) 73188738101
Real Estate Manangement Services
N.A.I.C.S.: 531210

Sinochem Oil Jiangsu Co., Ltd. (1)
32F Nanjing Sunny World Center No 188 Lushan Road, Jianye District, Nanjing, 210019, Jiansu, China
Tel.: (86) 2586308300
Real Estate Manangement Services

AND PRIVATE COMPANIES

Sinochem Oil Jiangxi Co., Ltd. (1)
26/F Unit C Dingfeng Business Center No 1368 Hongguzhong Rd, Nanchang, 330038, Jiangxi, China
Tel.: (86) 7916665683
Real Estate Manangement Services
N.A.I.C.S.: 531210

Sinochem Oil Liaoning Co., Ltd. (1)
Rm 3-1404 No 67 Huizhan Road, Shahekou District, Dalian, 116021, Liaoning, China
Tel.: (86) 41184990477
Real Estate Manangement Services
N.A.I.C.S.: 531210

Sinochem Oil Shandong Co., Ltd. (1)
Room 2006-2010 20/F Huaxin International Business Plaza, No 28 Changjiang Road Yantai Economy Technology Development Zone, 264006, Shandong, China
Tel.: (86) 5356109300
Real Estate Manangement Services
N.A.I.C.S.: 531210
Nianwen huang (Deputy Gen Mgr)

Sinochem Oil Shanxi Co., Ltd. (1)
F33 International Energy Center No 100 Yingze West Street, Taiyuan, 030024, Shanxi, China
Tel.: (86) 3516198750
Real Estate Manangement Services
N.A.I.C.S.: 531210

Sinochem Oil Zhejiang Co., Ltd. (1)
Rm 1018 San Rui Mansion No 36 Qing Chun Road, Hangzhou, 310003, Zhejiang, China
Tel.: (86) 57187221959
Real Estate Manangement Services
N.A.I.C.S.: 531210

Sinochem Petroleo Brazil Limited (1)
Praia de Botafogo 228 sala 1401, Rio de Janeiro, 22250-040, Brazil
Tel.: (55) 2135509250
Real Estate Manangement Services
N.A.I.C.S.: 531210

Sinochem Petroleum Exploration and Production Co., Ltd. (1)
F8 Central Tower Chemsunny World Trade Center 28 Fuxingmennei, Beijing, 100031, China
Tel.: (86) 10 59568800
Emp.: 100
Real Estate Manangement Services
N.A.I.C.S.: 531210
Leo Li (Project Mgr-Fin)

Sinochem Petroleum Netherlands Cooperatief U.A. (1)
Weena 723 Entrance C, Rotterdam, 3013 AM, Netherlands
Tel.: (31) 104022512
Real Estate Manangement Services
N.A.I.C.S.: 531210

Sinochem Plastics Co. Ltd. (1)
Room 701 Sinochem Tower A2 Fuxingmennei Street, Beijing, 100045, China
Tel.: (86) 1088078520
Web Site: http://www.sinochem.com
N.A.I.C.S.: 211120

Sinochem Pudong Trading Co., Ltd. (1)
2506 Rm No 88 Jinmao Tower, Shigi Dadao Pudo District, Shanghai, 200121, China **(100%)**
Tel.: (86) 2150475118
Web Site: http://www.sinochem-pudong.com
Sales Range: $50-74.9 Million
Emp.: 27
N.A.I.C.S.: 211120

Sinochem Qingdao Co., Ltd. (1)
The North Building Golden Plaza 20 Xiangging Zhong Road, Qingdao, China
Tel.: (86) 53255736222
Web Site: http://www.sinochemqingdao.com
Real Estate Manangement Services
N.A.I.C.S.: 531210
Ying Pan (Mgr-Sls)

Sinochem Quanzhou Petrochemical Co., Ltd. (1)

Huiquan Petrochemical Industrial Park, Quanzhou, Fujian, China
Tel.: (86) 59527570001
Web Site: http://www.qpcc.com.cn
Real Estate Manangement Services
N.A.I.C.S.: 531210

Sinochem Shanghai Import and Export Corp. (1)
17 19th Fl No 33 He Nan Rd, Shanghai, 200002, China **(100%)**
Tel.: (86) 2163289888
Sales Range: $100-124.9 Million
Emp.: 250
Petroleum & Natural Gas Production
N.A.I.C.S.: 211120

Sinochem Tianjin Co. Ltd. (1)
No 58 Nanjing Road, Tianjin, 300042, China **(100%)**
Tel.: (86) 2223146216
Web Site: http://www.sinochemtianjin.com
Sales Range: $100-124.9 Million
Emp.: 150
N.A.I.C.S.: 211120

Sinochem Trading (Singapore) Pte. Ltd. (1)
9 Temasek Blvd 18 01 02 03, Suntec Twr Two, Singapore, 038989, Singapore **(100%)**
Tel.: (65) 63380110
Web Site: http://www.sinochem.com
N.A.I.C.S.: 211120
Chan Hanson (Gen Mgr)

Sinochem Yantai Crop Nutrition Co., Ltd. (1)
Rm 906 Qili Building No 80 Chaoyang Street, Yantai, 264001, Shandong, China
Tel.: (86) 535 6633090
Real Estate Manangement Services
N.A.I.C.S.: 531210

Sinochem Yunlong Co., Ltd. (1)
Jinsuo Industrial Park, Kunming, 655204, Yunnan, China
Tel.: (86) 2865316525
Web Site: http://www.sinochemzhyl.com
Real Estate Manangement Services
N.A.I.C.S.: 531210

Sinofert Holdings Limited (1)
Units 4705 47th Floor Office Tower Convention Plaza1 Harbour Road, 1 Harbour Road, Wanchai, China (Hong Kong) **(51.65%)**
Tel.: (852) 36561588
Web Site: http://www.sinofert.com
Rev.: $3,184,910,971
Assets: $2,882,949,020
Liabilities: $1,535,523,510
Net Worth: $1,347,425,510
Earnings: $155,757,920
Emp.: 4,504
Fiscal Year-end: 12/31/2022
Fertilizer Mfr
N.A.I.C.S.: 325311
Harry Yang (Exec Dir)

Subsidiary (Non-US):

Sinochem Fertilizer Co., Ltd. (2)
10 th Fl Central Tower Chem Sunny World Trade Ctr, 28 Fuxingmennei Dajie, Beijing, 100031, China **(100%)**
Tel.: (86) 1088079601
Sales Range: $50-74.9 Million
Emp.: 150
Fertilizer Mfr
N.A.I.C.S.: 325311

Suzhou Everforutne Import & Export, Ltd. (1)
12/F International Trade Tower, 6 Xihuan Road, Suzhou, 215004, China **(100%)**
Tel.: (86) 51268621909
Web Site: http://www.szeverfortune.com
Sales Range: $200-249.9 Million
Emp.: 100
Chemicals
N.A.I.C.S.: 325998
Xinyuan Cheng (Mgr-Fin)

US Agri-Chemicals Corporation (1)
3225 State Rd 630 W, Fort Meade, FL 33841-9778
Tel.: (863) 285-8121
Sales Range: $125-149.9 Million
Emp.: 280
Phosphates

N.A.I.C.S.: 325312

Yu Hua Loong Trading Sdn. Bhd. (1)
Suite 1505 15 Floor Plaza See Hoy Chan, Jalan Raja Chulan, Kuala Lumpur, 50200, Malaysia **(100%)**
Tel.: (60) 320787966
Sales Range: $50-74.9 Million
Emp.: 2
N.A.I.C.S.: 211120

SINOCLOUD GROUP LIMITED

Unit 1403 14/F Kowloon Centre 33 Ashley Road, Tsim Sha Tsui, Hong Kong, China (Hong Kong)
Tel.: (852) 31012800 BM
Web Site:
   http://www.sinocloudgroup.com
Year Founded: 2001
5EK—(SES)
Rev.: $1,734,136
Assets: $11,317,350
Liabilities: $16,633,777
Net Worth: ($5,316,427)
Earnings: ($21,458,790)
Emp.: 109
Fiscal Year-end: 06/30/22
IT Consulting, Systems, Application Architecture & Project Management for Financial Industry
N.A.I.C.S.: 541690
Karen Yin Ling Chu (CFO & Sec)

Subsidiaries:

Brilliant Time Limited (1)
16 F Jardine House 1 Connaught Place, Central, China (Hong Kong)
Tel.: (852) 25070507
Information Technology Consulting Services
N.A.I.C.S.: 541512

SINOCOM PHARMACEUTICAL, INC.

Economic Technical Development Zone Second Road Nineth Road Junction, No 2, Anqing, Anhui, China
Tel.: (86) 21913863 NV
Web Site: http://www.sinocom-pharma.com
Sales Range: $100-124.9 Million
Emp.: 174
Pharmaceuticals Distr
N.A.I.C.S.: 424210
Chi Kwong Wan (Chm)

SINODATA CO., LTD.

9th Floor Block B Chuangye Building No 11 Anxiang North Road, Chaoyang District, Beijing, 100191, China
Tel.: (86) 1051663199
Web Site:
   https://www.sinodata.net.cn
Year Founded: 2003
002657—(SSE)
Rev.: $173,111,403
Assets: $381,401,991
Liabilities: $101,588,007
Net Worth: $279,813,985
Earnings: ($23,667,186)
Emp.: 570
Fiscal Year-end: 12/31/22
Software Applications
N.A.I.C.S.: 513210
Zhu Yedong (Chm & Gen Mgr)

SINOENERGY CORPORATION

1603-1604 Tower B Fortune Centre Ao City, Beiyuan Road Chaoyang District, Beijing, 100107, China
Tel.: (86) 1084928149 NV
Web Site:
   http://www.sinoenergycorp.com
Year Founded: 1999
Sales Range: $25-49.9 Million
Emp.: 857
Pressurized Containers For Compressed Natural Gas Designer, Mfr & Marketer

SINOHOPE TECHNOLOGY HOLDINGS LIMITED

N.A.I.C.S.: 332439
Bo Huang (CEO)

SINOFIBERS TECHNOLOGY CO., LTD.

No 569 Yulong North Road, Xinbei District, Changzhou, 213127, Jiangsu, China
Tel.: (86) 51989620691
Year Founded: 2008
300777—(SSE)
Rev.: $111,921,250
Assets: $635,248,421
Liabilities: $88,497,321
Net Worth: $546,751,099
Earnings: $83,608,944
Fiscal Year-end: 12/31/22
Carbon Products Mfr
N.A.I.C.S.: 335991

SINOFORTUNE FINANICIAL HOLDINGS LIMITED

16/F CMA Building 64-66 Connaught Road Central, Central, China (Hong Kong)
Tel.: (852) 22979900 Ky
Web Site: http://www.firstchina.hk
Year Founded: 2001
8123—(HKG)
Rev.: $23,053,913
Assets: $29,682,510
Liabilities: $12,162,863
Net Worth: $17,519,648
Earnings: ($3,910,680)
Emp.: 50
Fiscal Year-end: 12/31/22
Holding Company
N.A.I.C.S.: 551112
Jiawei Wang (Chm & CEO)

SINOGAS WEST INC.

308 901 Centre West NW, Calgary, T2E 2P6, AB, Canada
Tel.: (416) 820-0416
Year Founded: 2007
Investment Services
N.A.I.C.S.: 523999
Wise Wong (Pres & CEO)

SINOHEALTH HOLDINGS LIMITED

Room 1111 No 5 Wangjiang Second Street, Huangge Town Nansha District, Guangzhou, Guangdong, China
Web Site: https://ir.sinohealth.cn Ky
Year Founded: 2007
2361—(HKG)
Rev.: $54,856,280
Assets: $110,453,727
Liabilities: $13,470,176
Net Worth: $96,983,551
Earnings: $13,975,964
Emp.: 759
Fiscal Year-end: 12/31/23
Health Care Srvices
N.A.I.C.S.: 621610
Xuhui Yi (CFO)

SINOHOPE TECHNOLOGY HOLDINGS LIMITED

6/F & Unit 702-3 7/F 100 Queen's Road Central Central, Hong Kong, China (Hong Kong)
Tel.: (852) 36160815 VG
Web Site: https://www.sinohope.com
Year Founded: 1990
1611—(HKG)
Rev.: $1,219,230,399
Assets: $104,230,286
Liabilities: $85,259,133
Net Worth: $18,971,152
Earnings: ($26,634,499)
Emp.: 653
Fiscal Year-end: 09/30/22
Holding Company
N.A.I.C.S.: 551112

SINOHOPE TECHNOLOGY HOLDINGS LIMITED

Sinohope Technology Holdings Limited—(Continued)
Andrew Zhang *(CTO)*

Subsidiaries:

New Huo Asset Management (Hong Kong) Limited (1)
Unit 703A 7/F 100 Queens Road Central, Central, China (Hong Kong)
Tel.: (852) 36193393
Web Site: https://www.nhasset.com
Asset Management Services
N.A.I.C.S.: 531390

Pantene Industrial Co., Limited (1)
Suite 1603A Tower 2 Nina Tower 8 Yeung UK Road, Tsuen Wan, Hong Kong, China (Hong Kong)
Tel.: (852) 31668282
Web Site: http://www.pantene.com.hk
Electronic Product Mfr & Distr
N.A.I.C.S.: 334413

SINOHUB, INC.
6/F, Bldg 51, Rd 5, Qiongyu Blvd. Technology Park, Nanshan District, Shenzhen, 518057, China
Tel.: (86) 75526612106   DE
Year Founded: 2000
Sales Range: $150-199.9 Million
Emp.: 1,042
Electronic Component Supply Chain Management Services
N.A.I.C.S.: 423690
Henry T. Cochran *(Chm, CEO, Treas & Sec)*

Subsidiaries:

B2B CHIPS, LTD. (1)
Rm 12B A Block Hongsong Building Tairan 6th Rd Chegongmiao, Futian District, Shenzhen, 518040, China
Tel.: (86) 755 8273 6008
Web Site: http://www.b2bchips.com
Sales Range: $150-199.9 Million
Emp.: 1,000
Supply Chain Management Services
N.A.I.C.S.: 561499

SINOHUB ELECTRONICS SHENZHEN, LTD. (1)
6/F Building 1 No 5 Qiongyu Road Central Area Technology Pa, Shenzhen, 518057, Guangdong, China
Tel.: (86) 75526612106
Electronic Supply Chain Management Services
N.A.I.C.S.: 561499

SINOLIGHT CORPORATION
Sinolight Tower Qiyang Road, Chaoyang District, Beijing, 100102, China
Tel.: (86) 10 6477 8888
Web Site: http://www.sinolight.cn
Financial Services
N.A.I.C.S.: 522320
Xuezhong Chen *(Chm)*

Subsidiaries:

China Haisum Engineering Co., Ltd. (1)
No 21 Baoqing Road, Shanghai, 200031, China
Tel.: (86) 2164370093
Web Site: https://www.haisum.com
Rev.: $803,035,912
Assets: $850,953,070
Liabilities: $619,518,019
Net Worth: $231,435,051
Earnings: $29,075,647
Emp.: 1,059
Fiscal Year-end: 12/31/2022
Engineeering Services
N.A.I.C.S.: 541330
Zhao Guoang *(Chm)*

SINOLINK SECURITIES CO., LTD.
Sichuan Dongchenggen street No 95, Qingyang District, Chengdu, 610015, Sichuan, China
Tel.: (86) 2886690021
Web Site: http://www.gjzq.com.cn
Year Founded: 1988
600109—(SHG)
Rev.: $804,924,348
Assets: $14,346,139,266
Liabilities: $9,947,074,167
Net Worth: $4,399,065,099
Earnings: $168,240,478
Fiscal Year-end: 12/31/22
Security Brokerage Services
N.A.I.C.S.: 523150
Yun Ran *(Chm)*

SINOLINK WORLDWIDE HOLDINGS LIMITED
28th Floor Infinitus Plaza 199 Des Voeux Road, Central, China (Hong Kong)
Tel.: (852) 28518811
Web Site: http://www.sinolinkhk.com
1168—(HKG)
Rev.: $3,262,343
Assets: $1,428,586,755
Liabilities: $405,987,285
Net Worth: $1,022,599,470
Earnings: ($15,270,803)
Emp.: 628
Fiscal Year-end: 12/31/22
Real Estate Developer & Investor, LPG & Natural Gas Distr, Pipeline Constructor, Transportation, Storage, Whslr & Retail Business & Electricity Generator & Supplier
N.A.I.C.S.: 531390
Wei Chen *(Exec Dir)*

Subsidiaries:

Enerchina Holdings Limited (1)
28th Fl Infinitus Plz 199 desvoeux road, 199 Des Voeux Rd, Central, China (Hong Kong)
Tel.: (852) 25211181
Web Site: http://www.enerchina.com.hk
Sales Range: $50-74.9 Million
Emp.: 20
Investment Banking & Securities Dealing
N.A.I.C.S.: 523150

Leader Faith International (1)
C-o Offshore Incorporations Limited, Road Town, Virgin Islands (British) **(100%)**
Tel.: (284) 4948184
Web Site: http://www.harneys.com
Holding Company
N.A.I.C.S.: 551112

Ocean Diamond Limited (1)
C/O AMS Trustees Limited, PO Box 116C Sea Meadow House, Road Town, Virgin Islands (British) **(100%)**
Tel.: (284) 4943399
Holding Company
N.A.I.C.S.: 551112

Sinolink International Investment (Group) Limited (1)
c/o Offshore Incorporations Limited, Road Town, Virgin Islands (British) **(100%)**
Tel.: (284) 4948184
Web Site: http://www.sinolinkintl.co.uk
Holding Company
N.A.I.C.S.: 551112
Yaping Ou *(Chm)*

Sinolink Properties Agent Limited (1)
Rm 2501-02 28th Floor Vicwood Plz, Central District, Central, China (Hong Kong) **(100%)**
Tel.: (852) 31130606
Web Site: http://www.sinolinkhk.com
Land Subdivision
N.A.I.C.S.: 237210

Sinolink Worldwide Ltd (1)
28th Floor Infinitus Plaza, 199 Des Voeux Road, Central, China (Hong Kong) **(100%)**
Tel.: (852) 28518811
Web Site: https://www.sinolinkhk.com
Sales Range: $25-49.9 Million
Emp.: 10
Land Subdivision
N.A.I.C.S.: 237210

Smart Orient Investments Limited (1)
c/o Offshore Incorporations Limited, Road Town, Virgin Islands (British) **(100%)**
Tel.: (284) 4942233
Holding Company
N.A.I.C.S.: 551112

SINOMA INTERNATIONAL ENGINEERING CO., LTD.
No 16 Wangjing North Road, Chaoyang District, Beijing, 100102, China
Tel.: (86) 1064399057
Web Site: https://www.sinoma.com.cn
Year Founded: 2001
600970—(SHG)
Rev.: $5,450,223,219
Assets: $6,147,519,497
Liabilities: $3,974,734,895
Net Worth: $2,172,784,602
Earnings: $308,046,796
Emp.: 10,000
Fiscal Year-end: 12/31/22
Engineeering Services
N.A.I.C.S.: 541330
Yuan Wang *(CFO & VP)*

Subsidiaries:

CBMI Construction Co., Ltd. (1)
No 7 Longqing Road, Beijing Yizhuang Economic and Technological Development Zone, Beijing, 100176, China
Tel.: (86) 1067285000
Web Site: https://www.cbmi.com.cn
Sales Range: $200-249.9 Million
Emp.: 1,000
Cement Plant Construction Services
N.A.I.C.S.: 236210

Chengdu Design & Research Institute of Building Materials Industry Co., Ltd. (1)
69 Xinhong Road, Chenghua District, Chengdu, 610051, China
Tel.: (86) 2884333777
Web Site: https://www.sinoma-cdi.com
Integrated Equipment Mfr
N.A.I.C.S.: 335999
Chen Tao *(Deputy Gen Mgr)*

LNV Technology Pvt. Ltd. (1)
V Floor Sigapi Achi Building 18/3 Rukmani Lakshmipathy Road, Egmore, Chennai, 600 008, Tamil Nadu, India
Tel.: (91) 4443990000
Web Site: https://www.lnvtechnology.com
Industrial Machinery Equipment Mfr
N.A.I.C.S.: 333248
Song Shoushun *(Chm)*

Sinoma (Handan) Construction Co., Ltd. (1)
No 87 jianshe Street, Handan, 056003, Hebei, China
Tel.: (86) 3103142088
Web Site: http://www.sinoma-cbmhc.com
Construction Engineering Services
N.A.I.C.S.: 541330

Sinoma (Suzhou) Construction Co., Ltd. (1)
Qianjin East Road No 586, Kunshan, Jiangsu, China
Tel.: (86) 51255183801
Web Site: http://www.sinoma-suzhou.com
Construction Engineering Services
N.A.I.C.S.: 541330

Sinoma International Environmental Engineering Co., Ltd. (1)
Zhongcai International Building No 16 Wangjing North Road, Chaoyang District, Beijing, 100102, China
Tel.: (86) 1064399528
Web Site: http://www.sinoma-envir.com
Domestic Waste Disposal Services
N.A.I.C.S.: 562998

Sinoma Tangshan Heavy Machinery Co., Ltd. (1)
Gengyangxi Road, Fengrun District, Tangshan, Hebei, China
Tel.: (86) 3155152960
Web Site: http://www.en.sinomazczj.com

INTERNATIONAL PUBLIC

Integrated Equipment Mfr
N.A.I.C.S.: 335999

Tianjin Cement Industry Design & Research Institute Co., Ltd. (1)
No 1 Yinheli Rd N, Beichen District, Tianjin, 300400, China
Tel.: (86) 2226915565
Web Site: http://www.sinoma-tcdri.cn
Emp.: 4,617
Integrated Equipment Mfr
N.A.I.C.S.: 335999

Tianjin Tsubakimoto Conveyor Systems Co., Ltd. (1)
No 1 Yinheli Bei Road, Beichen District, Tianjin, 300400, China
Tel.: (86) 2286890212
Bulk Material Handling System Mfr
N.A.I.C.S.: 333922

SINOMAB BIOSCIENCE LIMITED
Units 303 & 305 to 307 No 15 Science Park West Avenue, Hong Kong Science Park Pak Shek Kok, Hong Kong, New Territories, China (Hong Kong)
Tel.: (852) 34269833   HK
Web Site: https://www.sinomab.com
Year Founded: 2001
3681—(HKG)
Assets: $196,746,920
Liabilities: $23,326,069
Net Worth: $173,420,850
Earnings: ($42,329,165)
Emp.: 112
Pharmaceutical Product Mfr & Distr
N.A.I.C.S.: 325412
Shui On Leung *(Founder, Chm & CEO)*

SINOMACH GENERAL MACHINERY SCIENCE & TECHNOLOGY CO., LTD.
No 616 Penglai Road, Economic and Technological Development Zone, Hefei, 230601, Anhui, China
Tel.: (86) 55165335534
Web Site: https://guotone.com
Year Founded: 1993
600044—(SHG)
Rev.: $110,613,143
Assets: $161,146,038
Liabilities: $68,455,811
Net Worth: $92,690,227
Earnings: $5,789,310
Fiscal Year-end: 12/31/22
Pipes Mfr
N.A.I.C.S.: 326122
Du Shiwu *(Sec)*

SINOMACH PRECISION INDUSTRY CO., LTD.
No 6 Fenghua Road, Luoyang, 471039, Henan, China
Tel.: (86) 37964884656
Web Site: https://www.zysbearing.com
Year Founded: 1958
002046—(SSE)
Rev.: $482,413,895
Assets: $737,341,811
Liabilities: $289,080,904
Net Worth: $448,260,907
Earnings: $32,752,919
Fiscal Year-end: 12/31/22
Bearing Products Mfr
N.A.I.C.S.: 332991

SINOMAG TECHNOLOGY CO., LTD.
23rd Floor Building No 1 No 3818 South Erhuan Road, Zhengwu District, Hefei, 230071, Anhui, China
Tel.: (86) 55162865265
Web Site: http://www.sinomagtech.com

AND PRIVATE COMPANIES

Year Founded: 1998
300835—(SSE)
Rev.: $130,267,290
Assets: $232,837,465
Liabilities: $93,162,504
Net Worth: $139,674,960
Earnings: $14,760,182
Fiscal Year-end: 12/31/22
Magnetic Material Mfr
N.A.I.C.S.: 334610
Yonghong Xiong (Chm)

SINOMAX GROUP LIMITED

Units 2005-2007 Level 20 Tower 1
MegaBox Enterprise Square Five No
38, Wang Chiu Road Kowloon Bay,
Kowloon, China (Hong Kong)
Tel.: (852) 27547798
Web Site: http://www.sinomax.com
1418—(HKG)
Rev.: $401,874,900
Assets: $285,337,605
Liabilities: $172,252,755
Net Worth: $113,084,850
Earnings: ($4,741,088)
Emp.: 2,477
Fiscal Year-end: 12/31/22
Visco-Elastic Products Including
Medical Products Mfr & Distr
N.A.I.C.S.: 326140
Chi Fan Lam (Founder & Chm)

Subsidiaries:

Chengdu Xingang Sponge Co.,
Ltd. (1)
5 Road of Garden Furniture Xinfan Town
Xindu District, Chengdu, 610500,
China (51%)
Tel.: (86) 2883091839
Web Site: http://www.cdxghm.com
Rev.: $19,369,589
Sponge Product Mfr & Distr
N.A.I.C.S.: 326299

Dormeo North American, LLC (1)
Dormeo Octaspring 1901 10th St Ste 500,
Plano, TX 75074
Tel.: (855) 436-7636
Web Site: http://www.dormeo.com
Mattress Mfr & Distr
N.A.I.C.S.: 337910
Zack Vinh (Mgr-Shipping)

Sinomax USA, Inc. (1)
295 5th Ave Ste 606, New York, NY 10016
Web Site: http://www.sinomax-usa.com
Mattress Mfr & Distr
N.A.I.C.S.: 337910
Frank Chen (Pres & CEO)

SINOMEDIA HOLDING LIMITED

F/7 The Place SinoMedia Tower 9
Guanghua Road, Chaoyang District,
Beijing, China
Tel.: (86) 1065896888   HK
Web Site:
http://www.sinomedia.com.hk
Year Founded: 1999
0623—(HKG)
Rev.: $101,016,396
Assets: $256,209,221
Liabilities: $30,274,171
Net Worth: $225,935,050
Earnings: $5,759,208
Emp.: 205
Fiscal Year-end: 12/31/22
Investment Management Service
N.A.I.C.S.: 523940
Xin Chen (Chm)

Subsidiaries:

CTV Golden Bridge International Media (Hong Kong) Company
Limited (1)
Unit 1301 13/F Tower One Lippo Centre 89
Queensway, Central, China (Hong Kong)
Tel.: (852) 39767300
Web Site: http://en.cctvgb.com.cn
Advertising Services
N.A.I.C.S.: 541810

Sinomedia (Asia Pacific) Company
Limited (1)
Unit 1301 13/F Tower One Lippo Centre 89
Queensway, Central, China (Hong Kong)
Tel.: (852) 39767300
Advertising Agency Services
N.A.I.C.S.: 541810
Debby Chan (Gen Mgr)

Sinomedia Global Pte. Ltd. (1)
9 Temasek Boulevard 07-01 Suntec Tower
Two, Singapore, 038989, Singapore
Tel.: (65) 6 255 1345
Web Site: https://www.sinomedia.com.sg
Advertising Services
N.A.I.C.S.: 541810

SINOMINE RESOURCE GROUP CO., LTD.

39th Floor Rayzone No 161 Jinze
Road, Fengtai Dist, Beijing, 100089,
China
Tel.: (86) 1088588188
Web Site: https://www.sinomine.cn
Year Founded: 1999
002738—(SSE)
Rev.: $1,128,987,836
Assets: $1,612,136,148
Liabilities: $554,301,769
Net Worth: $1,057,834,379
Earnings: $462,594,666
Emp.: 680
Fiscal Year-end: 12/31/22
Geological Engineering Services
N.A.I.C.S.: 213115
Wang Pingwei (Chm & CEO)

Subsidiaries:

Albania Sinomine Resource Co.
SHPK. (1)
NjesiaBashkiake Nr 5 Rruga Ilo-
MitkeQafezezi Vila Nr 12, Tirana, Albania
Tel.: (355) 699669426
Mineral Exploration Services
N.A.I.C.S.: 213114

Cabot Specialty Fluids Inc. (1)
10001 Woodloch Forest Dr Ste 275, The
Woodlands, TX 77380
Tel.: (281) 298-9955
Sales Range: $10-24.9 Million
All Other Miscellaneous Chemical Product
& Preparation Mfr
N.A.I.C.S.: 325998
Patrick M. Prevost (Pres & CEO)

Canada Sinomine Resources
INC. (1)
800-885 West Georgia Street, Vancouver,
BC, Canada
Tel.: (604) 891-7715
Mineral Exploration Services
N.A.I.C.S.: 213114

Dundee Precious Metals Tsumeb
(Pty) Ltd (1)
Heritage Square Building 100 Robert
Mugabe Avenue, Windhoek, Namibia
Tel.: (264) 613850000
Web Site: https://www.dundeeprecious.com
Metal Ore Exploration Services
N.A.I.C.S.: 212290

PT. Sinomine Resource Exploration
Indonesia (1)
JL pluitselatanraya No 1 kawasan CBD plui-
tmenaracemara, Jakarta Utara, Indonesia
Tel.: (62) 82220762811
Geophysical Surveying Services
N.A.I.C.S.: 541360

Sinomine DRC Resources Exploration SARL (1)
No 1320 Avenue Meteo II Quartier Golf
Commune, Lubumbashi, Congo, Democratic Republic of
Tel.: (243) 813078008
Geological Exploration Services
N.A.I.C.S.: 213112

Sinomine Overseas Geo-tech Services (Tianjin) Co., Ltd. (1)
No 36 of Fangwu Rd, Light & Textile Industrial Zone in New Seashore Area, Tianjin,
China
Tel.: (86) 2259795565
Web Site: http://www.sinomine.cn
Freight Forwarding Services
N.A.I.C.S.: 488510

Sinomine Resource (Malaysia) SDN.
BHD. (1)
Lot 7590E Ting Atas 2 Jln Jeli Kelewek Tanah Merah, 17500, Kelantan, Malaysia
Tel.: (60) 99581159
Gold Mining Services
N.A.I.C.S.: 212220

Sinomine Specialty Fluids
Limited (1)
Cabot House Hareness Circle Altens Industrial Estate, Aberdeen, AB12 3LY, United
Kingdom
Tel.: (44) 1224 897 229
Chemical Products Distr
N.A.I.C.S.: 325998

Sinononferrous Metals Resources
(Zimbabwe) (Private) Ltd. (1)
No 5 Howden Close Avondate, Harare, Zimbabwe
Tel.: (263) 737 222 228
Metal Mining Services
N.A.I.C.S.: 212290

Tantalum Mining Corporation of
Canada Limited (1)
Bernic Lk, PO Box 2000, Lac Du Bonnet,
R0E 1A0, MB, Canada (100%)
Tel.: (204) 884-2400
Mfr of Ferroalloy Ores, Except Vanadium
N.A.I.C.S.: 212290

Zambia Nonferrous Metals Exploration & Construction Company
Limited (1)
No 1 Sector of Chambishi Zone in ZC CZ,
Lusaka, Zambia
Tel.: (260) 97 531 6284
Metal Mining Services
N.A.I.C.S.: 213114

Subsidiary (Domestic):

Sinomine Zambia Trading Company
Limited (2)
PO Box 8066, Kitwe, Zambia
Tel.: (260) 965623939
Freight Forwarding Services
N.A.I.C.S.: 488510

Zhongkuang Zambia Services Company Limited (2)
Plot No 8 ZCCZ Chingola/Chambishi Road
Junction Chambishi, Kitwe, Zambia
Tel.: (260) 976389776
Emp.: 80
Vehicle Repair Services
N.A.I.C.S.: 811111

SINON CORPORATION

No 101 Nanrong Rd, Dadu District,
Taichung, 43245, Taiwan
Tel.: (886) 426933841
Web Site: https://www.sinon.com.tw
1712—(TAI)
Rev.: $625,030,553
Assets: $502,154,859
Liabilities: $222,289,144
Net Worth: $279,865,714
Earnings: $34,549,036
Emp.: 1,369
Fiscal Year-end: 12/31/23
Agricultural Chemical Mfr
N.A.I.C.S.: 325320
Tien-Fa Yang (Founder)

Subsidiaries:

Chong Shan Sinon Agriculture Service Co., Ltd. (1)
110 Jianghai 2nd Road, Jiangmen, 529020,
Guangdong, China
Tel.: (86) 750 3860987
Agricultural Pesticides Mfr
N.A.I.C.S.: 325320

Sinon (Thailand) Co., Ltd. (1)
26/56 TPI Tower Fl 20 Chantatmai Road
Thungmahamek Sathorn, Bangkok, 10120,
Thailand
Tel.: (66) 26786870
Emp.: 27
Agricultural Chemicals Whslr
N.A.I.C.S.: 424910

Sinon Australia Pty. Limited (1)
PO Box 456, Golden Square, 3555, VIC,
Australia
Tel.: (61) 354418907
Web Site: https://www.sinon.com.au
Food Product Mfr & Distr
N.A.I.C.S.: 311999

Sinon Chemical (China) Co., Ltd. (1)
No 28 Beicun Road Zhelin, Fengxian,
Shanghai, China
Tel.: (86) 2157493733
Food Product Mfr & Distr
N.A.I.C.S.: 311999

Sinon EU GmbH (1)
Im Alten Dorfe 37, 22359, Hamburg, Germany
Tel.: (49) 4065995039
Sales Range: $50-74.9 Million
Emp.: 3
Agricultural Chemicals Mfr & Distr
N.A.I.C.S.: 325320
Hans D. Brandt (Mng Dir)

Sinon Orchid Garden, Inc. (1)
No 97 Hui Chung Road, Taichung, 40747,
Taiwan
Tel.: (886) 423175505
Web Site: http://sinon.imb2b.com
Emp.: 40
Orchid Cultivation Services
N.A.I.C.S.: 115112

Sinon Professional Baseball Co.,
Ltd. (1)
403 West Road Meichuan West 6th Floor
No 23, Taichung, 40667, Taiwan
Tel.: (886) 4 23753371
Web Site: http://www.bulls.com.tw
Sales Range: $50-74.9 Million
Emp.: 10
Professional Baseball Teams Management
Services
N.A.I.C.S.: 711211

Sinon USA, Inc. (1)
1080 Carol Ln Ste 264, Lafayette, CA
94549
Tel.: (925) 299-1418
Food Product Mfr & Distr
N.A.I.C.S.: 311999

Sinon do Brasil LTDA (1)
Avenida Carlos Gomes 1340/1001, Bairro
Boa Vista, Porto Alegre, 90480-001, RS,
Brazil
Tel.: (55) 5130238181
Web Site: http://www.sinon.com.br
Sales Range: $50-74.9 Million
Emp.: 10
Agrochemical Mfr & Distr
N.A.I.C.S.: 325320

Weightstone Vineyard Estate & Winery Co., Ltd. (1)
No 60 Nanrong Road, Dadu District, Taichung, 43245, Taiwan
Tel.: (886) 426930788
Web Site: https://weightstone.tw
Wine Beverage Mfr & Distr
N.A.I.C.S.: 312130

Yumei Biotec Corporation (1)
No 50 Gongyequ 21st Rd, Nantun Dist, Taichung, 408, Taiwan
Tel.: (886) 423580051
Food Product Mfr & Distr
N.A.I.C.S.: 311999

SINOPAC FINANCIAL HOLDINGS COMPANY LTD.

3F 6F-13F 306 Sec 2 Bade Road,
Taipei, 104, Taiwan
Tel.: (886) 281618935
Web Site: http://www.sinopac.com
2890—(TAI)
Rev.: $2,361,591,939
Assets: $86,650,806,084
Liabilities: $80,762,179,126
Net Worth: $5,888,626,958

SINOPAC FINANCIAL HOLDINGS COMPANY LTD.

SinoPac Financial Holdings Company Ltd.—(Continued)
Earnings: $617,965,482
Emp.: 9,914
Fiscal Year-end: 12/31/23
Holding Company
N.A.I.C.S.: 551112
Jenny Huang (Sec)

Subsidiaries:

Bank SinoPac (China) Ltd. (1)
Room 3501 Room 3601 Building 4 Financial City No 248 Lushan Road, Jianye District, Nanjing, Jiangsu, China
Tel.: (86) 2588866000
Web Site: https://www.sinopac.com.cn
Financial Investment Services
N.A.I.C.S.: 523999

Pinnacle Investment Management Ltd. (1)
23rd Fl Two International Finance Ctr, Hong Kong, China (Hong Kong)
Tel.: (852) 29076686
Management Consulting Services
N.A.I.C.S.: 541618

RSP Information Service Company Ltd. (1)
23rd Fl Two International Finance Ctr, Hong Kong, China (Hong Kong)
Tel.: (852) 28012866
Computer Related Services
N.A.I.C.S.: 541519

Shanghai International Asset Management (Hong Kong) Co., Ltd. (1)
1501 15/F Shanghai Industrial Investment Building 48-62 Hennessy Road, Wanchai, China (Hong Kong)
Tel.: (852) 28401608
Web Site: http://www.siam.com.hk
Investment Banking & Securities Dealing
N.A.I.C.S.: 523150

SinoPac Asset Management (Asia) Ltd. (1)
Room 601 6/F Lee Garden Three 1 Sunning Road, Causeway Bay, China (Hong Kong)
Tel.: (852) 25868288
Web Site: https://www.sinopacam.com
Banking Security Services
N.A.I.C.S.: 523150
Gladys Lang (Dir)

SinoPac Asset Management Corporation (1)
6F No 306 Sec 2 Bade Rd, 104, Taipei, Taiwan
Tel.: (886) 2 816 8888
Web Site: http://www.sinopac.com
Financial Investment Activities
N.A.I.C.S.: 523999

SinoPac Call Center Co., Ltd. (1)
Bank 8th Floor No 441 Yucheng Road, Kaohsiung, 813, Taiwan
Tel.: (886) 75596288
Web Site: http://www.mma.com.tw
Business Support Services
N.A.I.C.S.: 561499

SinoPac Capital Ltd. (1)
Unit 3-6 128th Flr 1 Peking Rd Chim Sha Tsui, Kowloon, China (Hong Kong)
Tel.: (852) 28012828
Emp.: 4
Financial Investment Activities
N.A.I.C.S.: 523999

SinoPac Financial Consulting Co., Ltd. (1)
9th Fl No 306 Sec 2 Bade Rd, Taipei, Taiwan
Tel.: (886) 281618717
Investment Advice
N.A.I.C.S.: 523940

SinoPac Futures (Asia) Ltd. (1)
23/F Two Intl Finance Ctr 8 Finance St, Central District, Hong Kong, China (Hong Kong)
Tel.: (852) 25868288
Web Site: http://www.sinopacasia.com
Securities Brokerage Services
N.A.I.C.S.: 523150

SinoPac International Leasing Corp. (1)
Unit 3403-1 Building 7 No 492 Xinglinwan Road, Jimei District, Xiamen, 361000, Fujian, China
Tel.: (86) 5925289076
Web Site: https://www.spil.sinopac.com
Financial Lending Services
N.A.I.C.S.: 522220

SinoPac Leasing (Tianjin) Co., Ltd. (1)
21-Office 10 21-Office 11 Building 3 Zhongyu Plaza, No 86 Hongjin Avenue Longxi Street Yubei District, Chongqing, 401120, China
Tel.: (86) 236 767 8935
Web Site: https://www.splt.sinopac.com
Financial Lending Services
N.A.I.C.S.: 522220

SinoPac Leasing Corporation (1)
Sales Range: $50-74.9 Million
Emp.: 80
Truck Utility Trailer & RV (Recreational Vehicle) Rental & Leasing
N.A.I.C.S.: 532120
John Chung Yao (Gen Mgr)

SinoPac Life Insurance Agent Co., Ltd. (1)
12th Fl No 36, Nanking E Rd Sec 3, 104, Taipei, Taiwan
Tel.: (886) 225063333
Direct Life Insurance Carriers
N.A.I.C.S.: 524113
Sandy Shiau (Chm)

SinoPac Property Insurance Agent Co., Ltd. (1)
9th Fl No 36, Nanking E Rd Sec 3, 104, Taipei, Taiwan
Tel.: (886) 225063333
Direct Property & Casualty Insurance Carriers
N.A.I.C.S.: 524126

SinoPac Securities (Asia) Ltd. (1)
7th Floor Lee Garden Three 1 Sunning Road, Causeway Bay, China (Hong Kong)
Tel.: (852) 25868288
Web Site: https://www.sinopacasia.com
Securities Advisory & Asset Management Services
N.A.I.C.S.: 531390

SinoPac Securities (Asia) Nominees Ltd. (1)
21 F One Peking Road, Tsim Sha Tsui, Kowloon, China (Hong Kong)
Tel.: (852) 25868288
Web Site: http://www.sinopac.com.hk
Sales Range: $100-124.9 Million
Emp.: 200
Securities Brokerage Services
N.A.I.C.S.: 523150

SinoPac Securities (Europe) Ltd. (1)
6 Lloyd's Avenue, London, EC3N 3AX, United Kingdom
Tel.: (44) 2076149999
Web Site: http://www.sinopac.com
Emp.: 7
Securities Brokerage Services
N.A.I.C.S.: 523150

SinoPac Securities Co. Ltd. (1)
7F 18F 20F No 2 Sec 1 Chongqing S Rd, Zhongzheng Dist, Taipei, 100, Taiwan
Tel.: (886) 223114345
Web Site: https://securities.sinopac.com
Investment Banking & Securities Dealing
N.A.I.C.S.: 523150

Subsidiary (Domestic):

SinoPac Futures Corp. (2)
8th Floor No 2 Section 1 Chongqing South Road, Taipei, 10044, Taiwan
Tel.: (886) 223811799
Web Site: https://www.spf.com.tw
Emp.: 110
Investment Management Service
N.A.I.C.S.: 523999

SinoPac Securities Investment Services Corp. (2)
2 Chung Ching S Road Section 1 18th Floor, Taipei, 100, Taiwan
Tel.: (886) 2 2388 4583

Securities Brokerage Services
N.A.I.C.S.: 523150

SinoPac Securities Investment Trust Corporation (1)
7th Fl No 306 Sec 2 Bade Rd, 104, Taipei, Taiwan
Tel.: (886) 23123866
Web Site: http://www.sinopac.com
Open-End Investment Funds
N.A.I.C.S.: 525910

SinoPac Solutions & Services Ltd. (1)
7th Floor Lee Garden Three 1 Sunning Road, Causeway Bay, China (Hong Kong)
Tel.: (852) 25868956
Web Site: https://www.sinopacsolutions.com
Banking Security Services
N.A.I.C.S.: 523150

SinoPac Venture Capital Co., Ltd. (1)
6F No 306 Bader Rd Sec 2, Bade Rd, 104, Taipei, Taiwan
Tel.: (886) 281618888
Financial Investment Activities
N.A.I.C.S.: 523999

Sinopac Card Services Co., Ltd. (1)
12th Fl 760 Pa Te Rd Sec 4, Taipei, Taiwan
Tel.: (886) 225288999
Credit Union
N.A.I.C.S.: 522130

SINOPEC ASSETS MANAGEMENT CO LTD
12F, 22 Chaoyangmenbei Avenue, Chaoyang District, 100728, Beijing, China
Tel.: (86) 10 5996 0114
Chemicals Mfr
N.A.I.C.S.: 325999
Leng Tai Min (Dir & VP)

SINOPEC KANTONS HOLDINGS LIMITED
34/F CitiCorp Centre 18 Whitfield Rd, Causeway Bay, China (Hong Kong)
Tel.: (852) 25080228
Web Site: http://www.sinopec.com.hk
0934—(OTCIQ)
Rev.: $185,857,809
Assets: $2,015,620,566
Liabilities: $447,110,137
Net Worth: $1,568,510,429
Earnings: $164,930,318
Emp.: 235
Fiscal Year-end: 12/31/19
Logistics & Trading Company
N.A.I.C.S.: 523160
Zhi Jun Ye (Mng Dir)

SINOPEC SHANDONG TAISHAN PETROLEUM CO., LTD.
No 369 Dongyue Street, Tai'an, 271000, Shandong, China
Tel.: (86) 5386269600
000554—(SSE)
Rev.: $431,013,075
Assets: $274,947,988
Liabilities: $143,315,083
Net Worth: $131,632,905
Earnings: $1,315,955
Fiscal Year-end: 12/31/22
Petroleum Oil Product Mfr
N.A.I.C.S.: 324199

SINOPEP-ALLSINO BIOPHARMACEUTICAL CO., LTD.
Room 1201 Block E No 1378 Wenyi West Road, Hangzhou Normal University Science and Technology Park Yuhang District, Hangzhou, 311121, Zhejiang, China
Tel.: (86) 51885797889
Web Site: http://www.sinopep.com.cn
Year Founded: 2009

INTERNATIONAL PUBLIC

688076—(SHG)
Rev.: $91,441,355
Assets: $354,130,808
Liabilities: $83,876,715
Net Worth: $270,254,093
Earnings: $18,126,567
Emp.: 900
Fiscal Year-end: 12/31/22
Pharmaceutical Product Mfr & Distr
N.A.I.C.S.: 325412
Deyi Zhao (Chm & Dir)

SINOPHARM GROUP CO. LTD.
1001 Zhongshan Road West, Shanghai, 2000051, China
Tel.: (86) 2123052666   CN
Web Site: http://www.sinopharmgroup.com.cn
Year Founded: 2003
1099—(HKG)
Rev.: $69,927,282,551
Assets: $47,684,575,726
Liabilities: $33,903,746,676
Net Worth: $13,780,829,050
Earnings: $1,853,425,954
Emp.: 108,316
Fiscal Year-end: 12/31/20
Pharmaceutical Products Distr
N.A.I.C.S.: 551112
Qiyu Chen (Vice Chm)

Subsidiaries:

Guangdong Yuexing Pharmaceutical Co., Ltd. (1)
9 F Medicine Bldg, 22 Zhanqian Rd, Guangzhou, 510160, Guangdong, China
Tel.: (86) 2022299989
Pharmaceutical Products Distr
N.A.I.C.S.: 424210

Shanghai Sinopharm Waigaoqiao Co., Ltd. (1)
3F No 221 Fuzhou Rd, Shanghai, 200002, China
Tel.: (86) 2163392030
Web Site: http://www.sinopharmgroup.com
Sales Range: $25-49.9 Million
Emp.: 30
Pharmaceutical & Health Care Products Distr
N.A.I.C.S.: 424210

Sinopharm Bio-pharmaceutical Co., Ltd. (1)
6th Floor Building 3 No 3601 Dongfang Road, Pudong New Area, Shanghai, China
Tel.: (86) 2150184699
Web Site: http://www.sinopharm-bio.com
Pharmaceutical Products Distr
N.A.I.C.S.: 424210

Sinopharm Holding Guangdong Xinlong Co., Ltd. (1)
Yiyao Bldg No 22, Zhanqian Rd, Guangzhou, 510160, Guangdong, China
Tel.: (86) 2022299710
Pharmaceutical Products Distr
N.A.I.C.S.: 424210

Sinopharm Holding Liuzhou Co., Ltd. (1)
No 23 Bayi Rd, Liuzhou, Guangxi, China
Tel.: (86) 7722821537
Pharmaceutical Products Distr
N.A.I.C.S.: 424210

Sinopharm Holding Nanning Co., Ltd. (1)
No 7 Zhongyao Rd, Nanning, Guangxi, China
Tel.: (86) 7713183508
Pharmaceutical Products Distr
N.A.I.C.S.: 424210

Sinopharm Holding Ningxia Co., Ltd. (1)
Building No 20 Shangjing Qingyuan Zhiping Road, Xingqing District, Yinchuan, 750001, Ningxia, China
Tel.: (86) 951 672 3593
Web Site: https://www.sinopharm-nx.com
Pharmaceutical Products Distr
N.A.I.C.S.: 424210

Sinopharm Holding Shenyang Co., Ltd. (1)
No 158-1 Xuelian Street, Sujiatun District, Shenyang, 110102, China
Tel.: (86) 246 272 3333
Web Site: https://www.sy-yy.com
Emp.: 1,478
Pharmaceutical Products Distr
N.A.I.C.S.: 424210

SINOPHARM TECH HOLDINGS LIMITED
Units 307-313 3/F Wireless Centre Phase One Hong Kong Science Park, Pak Shek Kok, Hong Kong, New Territories, China (Hong Kong)
Tel.: (852) 2 411 5779   Ky
Web Site: http://www.cvg.com.hk
Year Founded: 1999
8156—(HKG)
Rev.: $10,036,321
Assets: $17,528,769
Liabilities: $35,657,682
Net Worth: ($18,128,913)
Earnings: ($14,253,064)
Emp.: 73
Fiscal Year-end: 06/30/21
Lottery Operator
N.A.I.C.S.: 713290
Kwai Lan Cheung (Founder & Chm)

SINOPOWER SEMICONDUCTOR, INC.
5F No 6 Dusing 1st Rd Hsinchu Science Park, Hsinchu, 300096, Taiwan
Tel.: (886) 35635818
Web Site: https://www.sinopowersemi.com
Year Founded: 2008
6435—(TPE)
Rev.: $93,948,035
Assets: $78,213,332
Liabilities: $30,753,963
Net Worth: $47,459,369
Earnings: $14,261,608
Emp.: 98
Fiscal Year-end: 12/31/22
Electronic Circuits Mfr
N.A.I.C.S.: 334419

SINOPS, INC.
5F Tokyo Tatemono Umeda Buildi 1-12-12 Umeda, Kita-Ku, Osaka, 530-0001, Japan
Tel.: (81) 663411225
Web Site: http://www.sinops.jp
Year Founded: 1987
4428—(TKS)
Software Development Services
N.A.I.C.S.: 541511
Hiroshi Minamitani (Founder, Chm & Pres)

SINOSAFE GENERAL INSURANCE CO., LTD.
Hua an Insurance Building No 117 Fuhua 1st Road, Futian District, Shenzhen, Guangdong, China
Tel.: (86) 755 8266 5888
Web Site: http://www.sinosafe.com.cn
Year Founded: 1996
Insurance Services
N.A.I.C.S.: 524210

SINOSEAL HOLDING CO., LTD.
No 8 Wuke West 4th Road, Wuhou District, Chengdu, 610045, Sichuan, China
Tel.: (86) 2885373902
Web Site: https://www.sns-china.com
Year Founded: 1993
300470—(CHIN)
Rev.: $192,874,328
Assets: $426,771,725
Liabilities: $66,721,462
Net Worth: $360,050,263
Earnings: $48,829,244
Fiscal Year-end: 12/31/23
Mechanical Seals Mfr
N.A.I.C.S.: 339991
Peng Wei (Chm)

SINOSOFT CO., LTD.
Jia No 6 Building, Xinkexiangyuan Zhongguancun Haidian District, Beijing, 100190, China
Tel.: (86) 1062570007
Web Site: https://www.sinosoft.com.cn
Year Founded: 1996
603927—(SHG)
Rev.: $941,340,989
Assets: $958,759,743
Liabilities: $571,425,571
Net Worth: $387,334,172
Earnings: $89,658,275
Fiscal Year-end: 12/31/22
Application Development Services
N.A.I.C.S.: 541511
Chun Zuo (Chm & Gen Mgr)

SINOSOFT TECHNOLOGY GROUP LIMITED
No 26 Tianpu Road, Pukou District, Nanjing, Jiangsu, China
Tel.: (86) 2584816867
Web Site: http://www.sinosoft-technology.com
Year Founded: 1998
1297—(HKG)
Rev.: $80,333,230
Assets: $297,532,170
Liabilities: $45,641,232
Net Worth: $251,890,938
Earnings: ($21,575,830)
Emp.: 418
Fiscal Year-end: 12/31/22
Application Software Products
N.A.I.C.S.: 513210
Yingmei Xin (Chm & CEO)

SINOSOFT TECHNOLOGY PLC
3rd Floor No 50 Building Jiangsu Software Park, No 168 Long Pan Zhong Road, Nanjing, 210002, China
Tel.: (86) 25 8481 5959
Web Site: http://www.sinosoft-technology.com
Sales Range: $10-24.9 Million
Emp.: 366
Software Products Development & Sales
N.A.I.C.S.: 449210
Yifa Yu (CFO)

SINOSTAR CABLE CO., LTD.
No 8 South Road, Huanke Park, Yixing, 214200, Jiangsu, China
Tel.: (86) 51080713366
Web Site: http://www.zcdl.com
Year Founded: 2003
300933—(SSE)
Rev.: $362,122,572
Assets: $481,373,559
Liabilities: $259,356,919
Net Worth: $222,016,640
Earnings: $10,710,723
Fiscal Year-end: 12/31/22
Wire & Cable Mfr
N.A.I.C.S.: 331491
Nanping Du (Chm)

SINOSTAR PEC HOLDINGS LIMITED
No 27 Huanghe Road, Dongming County, Heze, 274500, Shandong, China
Tel.: (86) 5307286138   SG
Web Site: https://www.sinostar-pec.com

C9Q—(SES)
Rev.: $487,566,005
Assets: $406,892,360
Liabilities: $219,264,040
Net Worth: $187,628,320
Earnings: $28,278,583
Emp.: 640
Fiscal Year-end: 12/31/20
Investment Holding Services
N.A.I.C.S.: 551112
Liu Cheng Zhang (CEO)

SINOSTEEL CORPORATION
Sinosteel Plz 8 Haidian St, Beijing, 100080, China
Tel.: (86) 1062686689
Web Site: http://www.sinosteel.com
Sales Range: $15-24.9 Billion
Emp.: 30,000
Metal Miner, Mfr & Distr
N.A.I.C.S.: 212290
Siwei Xu (Chm)

Subsidiaries:

Sinosheel Xingtai Machinery & Mill Roll Co., Ltd. (1)
No 1 Xinxing Street, Xingtai, Hebei, China
Tel.: (86) 3192116386
Web Site: http://www.xt-zhagun.com
Emp.: 3,800
Mining Machinery & Equipment Mfr
N.A.I.C.S.: 333131

Sinosteel Australia Pty. Ltd. (1)
Level 8 251 St Georges Terrace, Perth, 6000, WA, Australia
Tel.: (61) 893385555
Web Site: http://www.sinosteel.com.au
Mining Machinery & Equipment Mfr
N.A.I.C.S.: 333131
David Sun (Mng Dir)

Sinosteel Luoyang Institute of Refractories Research Co., Ltd. (1)
Xiyuan road 43, Luoyang, 471039, China
Tel.: (86) 37964205114
Web Site: http://en.lirrc.com
Iron & Steel Mfr
N.A.I.C.S.: 331110

Sinosteel Metals & Resources Co., Ltd. (1)
20F 8 Haidian St, Beijing, 100080, China
Tel.: (86) 1062686333
Web Site: http://www.sinomerco.com
Iron & Steel Product Whslr
N.A.I.C.S.: 423510
Liu Shengjun (Mng Dir)

Sinosteel Refractory Co., Ltd. (1)
N 36 Fengchan Road, Zhengzhou, 471039, Henan, China
Tel.: (86) 37163838936
Web Site: http://www.sinosteelrefractory.com
Emp.: 5,758
Refractory Brick Product Mfr
N.A.I.C.S.: 327120

Sinosteel Shenzhen Co., Ltd. (1)
22/F International Trade Centre, Shenzhen, 518014, Guangdong, China
Tel.: (86) 75582211227
Web Site: http://www.sinosteelsz.hzyjmx.com
Ratchet Tie Product Distr
N.A.I.C.S.: 423990

Sinosteel Xi'an Heavy Machinery Co., Ltd. (1)
No 1 Zhonggang Road Xi'an Economy and Technology Development Zone, Jingwei Industrial Park, Xi'an, Shaanxi, China
Tel.: (86) 2986969226
Web Site: http://en.xamm.com
Mining Machinery & Equipment Mfr
N.A.I.C.S.: 333131

Sinosteel Zhengzhou Research Institute of Steel Wire & Steel Wire Products Co., Ltd. (1)
No 70 Science Avenue High-Tech Zone, Zhengzhou, Henan, China
Tel.: (86) 37167852000
Web Site: http://www.zrw.cn
Mining Machinery & Equipment Mfr

N.A.I.C.S.: 333131
Qiu Wenpeng (Chm-Labour Union)

SINOSTEEL ENGINEERING & TECHNOLOGY CO., LTD.
No 8 Haidian Street, Beijing, 100080, China
Tel.: (86) 1062688188
Web Site: https://mecc.sinosteel.com
000928—(SSE)
Rev.: $2,627,985,241
Assets: $3,745,064,574
Liabilities: $2,790,588,729
Net Worth: $954,475,844
Earnings: $88,607,633
Fiscal Year-end: 12/31/22
Carbon Products Mfr
N.A.I.C.S.: 335991

Subsidiaries:

Bejing Bestpower Electrical Technology Co., Ltd. (1)
No 18 East Jiancaicheng Road Xisanqi, Haidian District, Beijing, 100096, China
Tel.: (86) 1082918866
Web Site: http://www.en.bestpower.cc
Electrical Automation System Services
N.A.I.C.S.: 238210

Sinosteel Equipment & Engineering (Bolivia) Ltda. (1)
Nro 710 - Edif Torre Empresarial Cainco - Piso 15, Cochabamba, Bolivia
Tel.: (591) 76544668
Engineeering Services
N.A.I.C.S.: 541330

Sinosteel Equipment & Engineering (Saudi Arabia) Company (1)
Ababtain Tower Dhahran St, Al Khobar, Saudi Arabia
Tel.: (966) 1386551111
Web Site: http://www.sinosteel.com.sa
Engineeering Services
N.A.I.C.S.: 541330
Khan Hassam (Mgr-Procurement)

Sinosteel Equipment & Engineering (Turkey) Co., Ltd. (1)
Room 365 11th Floorm B1 Egs Business Park, Ataturk Road Yesilkoy Street Bakirkoy District, 34149, Istanbul, Türkiye
Tel.: (90) 2124658196
Engineeering Services
N.A.I.C.S.: 541330

Sinosteel Project & Technology (Brazil) Ltda. (1)
Rua Dos Incofidentes 1190m 4th Floor Funcionarios, Belo Horizonte, 30140-907, Minas Gerais, Brazil
Tel.: (55) 3136154688
Engineeering Services
N.A.I.C.S.: 541330

SINOSTEEL NEW MATERIALS CO., LTD.
No 9 South Section Huolishan Avenue, Ma'anshan, 243000, Anhui, China
Tel.: (86) 5555200288
Web Site: https://www.sinosteelnmc.com
Year Founded: 2002
002057—(SSE)
Rev.: $387,837,071
Assets: $699,113,502
Liabilities: $229,754,786
Net Worth: $469,358,716
Earnings: $54,724,242
Emp.: 1,700
Fiscal Year-end: 12/31/22
Electronic Components Mfr
N.A.I.C.S.: 334419
Mao Haibo (Chm)

SINOSTONE (GUANGDONG) CO., LTD.
No 112 Minger Road, Mingcheng Town Gaoming District, Foshan, 528518, Guangdong, China

SINOSTONE (GUANGDONG) CO., LTD.

Sinostone (Guangdong) Co., Ltd.—(Continued)
Tel.: (86) 75788830998
Web Site: https://www.sinostone.cn
Year Founded: 2007
001212—(SSE)
Rev.: $92,174,734
Assets: $235,201,857
Liabilities: $36,152,902
Net Worth: $199,048,955
Earnings: $12,089,493
Fiscal Year-end: 12/31/22
Stone Material Mfr & Distr
N.A.I.C.S.: 327991
Zhou Jun *(Chm & Gen Mgr)*

SINOSUN TECHNOLOGY CO., LTD.
Floor 16 Block C Tairan Building Tairan 8th Road Chegongmiao, Futian District, Shenzhen, 518040, China
Tel.: (86) 75583415666
Web Site: https://www.sinosun.com
Year Founded: 2003
300333—(CHIN)
Rev.: $19,995,768
Assets: $102,251,916
Liabilities: $3,039,660
Net Worth: $99,212,256
Earnings: ($17,917,848)
Emp.: 110
Fiscal Year-end: 12/31/22
Electronic Payment Security Systems Mfr
N.A.I.C.S.: 334118
Kaiyan Wei *(Chm & Gen Mgr)*

SINOTECH ENERGY LIMITED
3/F 19 Ronghua South Road, Beijing Econ-Tech Dev Area, Beijing, 100176, China
Tel.: (86) 1087125555   Ky
Web Site:
　http://ir.sinotechenergy.com
Sales Range: $25-49.9 Million
Emp.: 60
Oil Drilling Services
N.A.I.C.S.: 213111
Qingzeng Liu *(Chm)*

SINOTRUK (HONG KONG) LIMITED
Sinotruk Tower No 777 Hua ao Road Innovation Zone, Jinan, 250101, Shandong, China
Tel.: (86) 53158061285   HK
Web Site: http://www.sinotruk.com
Year Founded: 1956
3808—(HKG)
Rev.: $15,044,913,282
Assets: $17,007,575,668
Liabilities: $11,541,133,721
Net Worth: $5,466,441,946
Earnings: $1,137,377,417
Emp.: 25,469
Fiscal Year-end: 12/31/20
Automobile Mfr
N.A.I.C.S.: 336120
Cai Dong *(Chm & Pres)*

Subsidiaries:

Sinotruk (Hong Kong) Hongye Limited
Sinotruk Tower No777 Huaao Road, Innovation Zone, Jinan, Shandong, China
Tel.: (86) 13964001581
Web Site:
　https://www.sinotruk10.en.ec21.com
Emp.: 1,000
Heavy Duty Truck Mfr
N.A.I.C.S.: 336120
Jack Zhu *(Mgr-Bus)*

Sinotruk (Hong Kong) International Investment Limited   (1)
Rm 2-3 21/F Shun Tak Ctr China Merchants Twr Sheung Wan, Hong Kong, China (Hong Kong)
Tel.: (852) 28108911

Automotive Engineering Consulting Services
N.A.I.C.S.: 541330

Sinotruk International Co., Ltd.   (1)
Zhongqi Road, Shizhong District, Jinan, 250116, China
Tel.: (86) 53185827672
Web Site: https://www.sinotruk-international.com
Heavy Duty Truck Mfr
N.A.I.C.S.: 336120
Aaron White *(Mgr-Sls)*

Sinotruk Ji'nan HOWO Bus Co., Ltd.   (1)
Zhangqiu Wang Pan Rd No 19777, Jinan, Shandong, China
Tel.: (86) 53185589034
Bus Mfr
N.A.I.C.S.: 336510

Sinotruk Liuzhou Yunli Special Vehicles Co., Ltd.   (1)
12 Leye Rd, Xinxing Industrial Park, Liuzhou, 545112, Guangxi, China
Tel.: (86) 7723269367
Web Site: https://en.yunli.com
Heavy Duty Truck Mfr & Distr
N.A.I.C.S.: 336120

SINOTRUK JINAN TRUCK CO., LTD.
South End of Dangjiazhuang, Shizhong District, Jinan, 250116, Shandong, China
Tel.: (86) 53158067588
Web Site: http://www.jntruck.com
Year Founded: 1998
000951—(SSE)
Rev.: $4,046,670,899
Assets: $4,825,760,692
Liabilities: $2,777,161,884
Net Worth: $2,048,598,808
Earnings: $30,005,628
Emp.: 8,168
Fiscal Year-end: 12/31/22
Heavy Truck Mfr
N.A.I.C.S.: 423110
Wang Chen *(Chm)*

SINOVAC BIOTECH LTD.
No 39 SHANGDI West Road, Haidian District, Beijing, 100085, China
Tel.: (86) 1056931800   AG
Web Site: https://www.sinovac.com
Year Founded: 1999
SVA—(NASDAQ)
Rev.: $1,492,761,000
Assets: $14,114,568,000
Liabilities: $1,401,907,000
Net Worth: $12,712,661,000
Earnings: $107,884,000
Emp.: 3,558
Fiscal Year-end: 12/31/22
Vaccine Developer & Marketer
N.A.I.C.S.: 325412
Weidong Yin *(Chm, Pres, CEO, Mng Dir & Sec)*

Subsidiaries:

Sinovac Biotech Co.,Ltd.   (1)
No 39 Shangdi West Road, Haidian District, Beijing, 100085, China
Tel.: (86) 1082799800
Vaccines Mfr & Sales
N.A.I.C.S.: 325414

Tangshan Yian Biological Engineering Co., Ltd.   (1)
No 120 Huoju Road Hi-tech Development Area, Tangshan, 063000, China
Tel.: (86) 3153178866
Vaccines Mfr
N.A.I.C.S.: 325414

SINOVATION VENTURES CO., LTD
Dinghao Tower Block B No 3 Haidian Street, Haidian District, Beijing, China
Tel.: (86) 010 57525200

Web Site:
　http://www.sinovationventures.com
Year Founded: 2009
Venture Capital Firm
N.A.I.C.S.: 523940
Kai-Fu Lee *(Chm & Co-CEO)*

SINOVEL WIND GROUP CO., LTD.
Culture Building 59 Zhongguancun Street, Haidian District, 100872, Beijing, China
Tel.: (86) 1062515566
Web Site:
　http://www.sinovelwind.com
Rev.: $82,859,273
Assets: $909,725,890
Liabilities: $708,952,041
Net Worth: $200,773,849
Earnings: $26,832,771
Emp.: 1,700
Fiscal Year-end: 12/31/18
Wind Turbine Mfr
N.A.I.C.S.: 333611
Zhong Ma *(Chm & Pres)*

SINPAS GAYRIMENKUL YATIRIM ORTAKLIGI AS
Sinpas Plaza Barboros Bulvari Yenidogan Sok No 36, Besiktas, 34349, Istanbul, Darphane, Turkiye
Tel.: (90) 2123102700
Web Site: https://www.sinpas.com.tr
Year Founded: 2007
SNGYO—(IST)
Rev.: $57,617,209
Assets: $1,368,247,180
Liabilities: $418,498,930
Net Worth: $949,748,249
Earnings: $25,077,572
Emp.: 1,826
Fiscal Year-end: 12/31/23
Real Estate Investment Services
N.A.I.C.S.: 531390
Avni Celik *(Chm)*

SINPHAR PHARMACEUTICAL CO., LTD.
No 84 Zhongshan Rd Zhongshan Village, Yilan, 110, Taiwan
Tel.: (886) 227603688
Web Site: https://www.sinphar.com.tw
1734—(TAI)
Rev.: $96,894,401
Assets: $204,423,976
Liabilities: $93,306,089
Net Worth: $111,117,887
Earnings: $11,667,353
Fiscal Year-end: 12/31/23
Pharmaceuticals Mfr
N.A.I.C.S.: 325412
Yu-Liang Pai *(Gen Mgr)*

Subsidiaries:

CANCAP PHARMACEUTICAL LTD.   (1)
240-13071 Vanier Place, Richmond, V6V 2J1, BC, Canada
Tel.: (604) 278-2188
Web Site: http://www.cancappharma.com
Sales Range: $25-49.9 Million
Emp.: 60
Nutraceutical Capsules Mfr
N.A.I.C.S.: 325412

Tian-Li Pharmaceutical Development   (1)
No 599 Yuhang Economic Development Zone, Hangzhou, Zhejiang, China
Tel.: (86) 57186168980
Web Site: http://www.tlpharm.com.cn
Pharmaceuticals Mfr
N.A.I.C.S.: 325412

SINSIN PHARM.CO.,LTD.,
9 Sojeongsandandong-ro, Sojeongmyeon, Sejong, Korea (South)
Tel.: (82) 317761141
Web Site: http://www.sinsin.com

INTERNATIONAL PUBLIC

Year Founded: 1959
002800—(KRS)
Rev.: $70,507,106
Assets: $92,970,433
Liabilities: $47,310,014
Net Worth: $45,660,419
Earnings: $3,340,464
Emp.: 321
Fiscal Year-end: 12/31/22
Drug Product Mfr & Distr
N.A.I.C.S.: 325411

Subsidiaries:

Sinsin Pharm.Co., Ltd. - Ansan Plant   (1)
90 Beomjigi-ro 141beon-gil Danwon-gu, Ansan, Gyeonggi-do, Korea (South)
Tel.: (82) 317761141
Medicinal Plaster Product Mfr
N.A.I.C.S.: 339113

Trinet Industries Inc.   (1)
335 N Puente St Unit D, Brea, CA 92821
Tel.: (714) 599-8280
Web Site: https://trinetinds.com
Emp.: 5
Medicinal Plaster Product Distr
N.A.I.C.S.: 424210

SINSIN PHARMACEUTICAL CO., LTD.
9 Sojeongsandan-dong-ro Sojeongmyeon, Sejong Special Self-Governing City 1st floor, Sejong, 13488, Gyeonggi, Korea (South)
Tel.: (82) 442702700
Web Site: https://www.sinsin.com
Year Founded: 1959
002800—(KRS)
Rev.: $68,086,972
Assets: $105,162,641
Liabilities: $54,746,434
Net Worth: $50,416,207
Earnings: ($1,333,494)
Emp.: 311
Fiscal Year-end: 12/31/21
Pharmaceuticals Product Mfr
N.A.I.C.S.: 325412
Hanki Kim *(CEO & VP)*

SINTAL AGRICULTURE PLC
54 Klaptsova st, 61093, Kharkiv, Ukraine
Tel.: (380) 57 717 79 95
Web Site:
　http://www.sintalagriculture.com
Sales Range: $25-49.9 Million
Grain Farming & Distr
N.A.I.C.S.: 111191
Vadim Mogyla *(CEO)*

SINTANA ENERGY, INC.
82 Richard Street East, Toronto, M5C 1P1, ON, Canada
Tel.: (416) 361-0737
Web Site: https://sintanaenergy.com
SEUSF—(OTCQB)
Petroleum Product Mfr & Distr
N.A.I.C.S.: 324199
Douglas G. Manner *(CEO)*

SINTEF
Strindveien 4, Trondheim, Norway
Tel.: (47) 40005100
Web Site: http://www.sintef.no
Year Founded: 1950
Rev.: $395,530,872
Assets: $523,241,466
Liabilities: $220,440,406
Net Worth: $302,801,060
Earnings: $18,336,054
Emp.: 2,003
Fiscal Year-end: 12/31/19
Research Services
N.A.I.C.S.: 541715
Reidar Bye *(Deputy CEO & Exec VP)*

AND PRIVATE COMPANIES

Subsidiaries:

MARINTEK (1)
Marine Technology Centre Otto Nielsens veg 10, 7052, Trondheim, Norway
Tel.: (47) 73 59 5500
Web Site: http://www.sintef.no
Sales Range: $25-49.9 Million
Emp.: 205
Marine Technology & Research
N.A.I.C.S.: 541715

Subsidiary (US):

MARINTEK (USA), Inc. (2)
2603 Augusta #200, Houston, TX 77057 (100%)
Tel.: (713) 452-2767
Web Site: http://www.marintekusa.com
Sales Range: $25-49.9 Million
Emp.: 6
Marine Hydrodynamics, Construction Engineering & Technical Operations
N.A.I.C.S.: 541715
Yusong Cao (Mgr-Res & Tech)

Subsidiary (Non-US):

MARINTEK do Brasil Ltda. (2)
Rua Lauro Muller 116 Ste 2201, Botafogo, Rio de Janeiro, CEP 22290-160, RJ, Brazil (100%)
Tel.: (55) 2120251811
Web Site: http://www.marintek.com.br
Sales Range: $25-49.9 Million
Emp.: 4
R&D & Advanced Technical Consultancy Services in Marine & Materials Technologies
N.A.I.C.S.: 541620

Molab AS (1)
Halvor Heyeredals, Mo i Rana, 8626, Norway (60%)
Tel.: (47) 75136350
Web Site: http://www.molab.no
Sales Range: $25-49.9 Million
Emp.: 71
Business Services
N.A.I.C.S.: 561499

SINTEF Building and Infrastructure AS (1)
PO Box 12, 0314, Oslo, Norway (100%)
Tel.: (47) 22965555
Web Site: http://www.byggforsk.no
Sales Range: $100-124.9 Million
Emp.: 300
Commercial & Institutional Building Construction
N.A.I.C.S.: 236220

SINTEF Holding AS (1)
Strindvegen 4, 7035, Trondheim, Norway
Tel.: (47) 73593000
Sales Range: $75-99.9 Million
Emp.: 200
Space Research & Technology
N.A.I.C.S.: 927110
Unni M. Steanmo (Pres & CEO)

SINTEF NBL (Norwegian Fire Research Laboratory) AS (1)
Tillerbruveien 202, Trondheim, 7092, Norway (100%)
Tel.: (47) 73591078
Web Site: http://www.spsf.no
Sales Range: $25-49.9 Million
Emp.: 29
Space Research & Technology
N.A.I.C.S.: 927110
Paul Pedersen (Gen Mgr)

SINTEF Petroleum Research AS (1)
SP Andersens Vei 15 B, 7465, Trondheim, Norway (100%)
Tel.: (47) 73591261
Web Site: http://www.sintef.no
Sales Range: $50-74.9 Million
Emp.: 120
Petroleum Refineries
N.A.I.C.S.: 324110

SINTEF Raufoss Manufacturing AS (1)
Bygning 100 Raufoss Industripark, PO Box 163, 2831, Raufoss, Norway
Tel.: (47) 4000 1011
Emp.: 85
Laboratory Equipment Mfr
N.A.I.C.S.: 334516

Sintef TTO AS (1)
Strindveien 4, 7034, Trondheim, Norway (100%)
Tel.: (47) 73593000
Web Site: http://www.sintef.no
Sales Range: $50-74.9 Million
Research & Technological Invention Services
N.A.I.C.S.: 541713
Anders Lian (Pres & CEO)

Sinvent Venture II AS (1)
S P Andersens Veg 5, Trondheim, Norway (100%)
Tel.: (47) 73593000
Web Site: http://www.sintef.no
Space Research & Technology
N.A.I.C.S.: 523150

Unimed Innovation AS (1)
Olav Kyrres Gate 9 MTFS, Trondheim, 7034, Norway (100%)
Tel.: (47) 73593000
Web Site: http://www.sintef.no
Clinical Research Trials
N.A.I.C.S.: 541380

SINTEPLAST S.A.
Av Jujuy 2001 Carlos Spegazzini Pdo de Ezeiza, Buenos Aires, Argentina
Tel.: (54) 11 6333 7400   Ar
Web Site: http://www.sinteplast.com
Year Founded: 1958
Architectural, Industrial & Automotive Paints & Coatings Mfr & Distr
N.A.I.C.S.: 325510
Gabriel Rodriguez (Chm & Comml Dir-Retail Market)

SINTER REF SA
Str Independentei 59, Prahova, Azuga, Romania
Tel.: (40) 244326451
SIEP—(BUC)
Rev.: $24,205
Assets: $6,858,063
Liabilities: $284,960
Net Worth: $6,573,102
Earnings: ($374,981)
Emp.: 2
Fiscal Year-end: 12/31/22
Refractory Products Mfr
N.A.I.C.S.: 327120

SINTERCAST AB
Kungsgatan 2, 641 30, Katrineholm, Sweden
Tel.: (46) 15079440
Web Site: https://www.sintercast.com
Year Founded: 1983
SINT—(OMX)
Rev.: $11,117,667
Assets: $12,222,878
Liabilities: $1,742,111
Net Worth: $10,480,767
Earnings: $3,100,209
Emp.: 32
Fiscal Year-end: 12/31/22
On-Line Process Control & Compacted Graphite Iron Supplier
N.A.I.C.S.: 336110
Steve Dawson (Pres & CEO)

Subsidiaries:

SinterCast Inc. (1)
1755 Park St Ste 200, Naperville, IL 60563
Tel.: (262) 501-3794
Web Site: http://www.sintercast.com
Compacted Graphite Iron Mfr
N.A.I.C.S.: 335991

SinterCast Ltd. (1)
30 Anyards Rd, KT11 2LA, Cobham, Surrey, United Kingdom - England
Tel.: (44) 1932862100
Sales Range: $50-74.9 Million
Emp.: 1
Industry Machinery Mfr & Whslr
N.A.I.C.S.: 423830

SINTERCOM INDIA LTD.
Gat No 127 At Post Mangrul Tal-Maval, Talegaon Dabhade, Pune, 410 507, India
Tel.: (91) 2048522679
Web Site: https://www.sintercom.co.in
Year Founded: 2007
SINTERCOM—(NSE)
Rev.: $6,507,581
Assets: $20,731,240
Liabilities: $6,573,146
Net Worth: $14,158,094
Earnings: ($642,176)
Emp.: 87
Fiscal Year-end: 03/31/21
Automobile Parts Mfr
N.A.I.C.S.: 336390
Hari N. Nair (Chm)

SINTESI S.P.A
Via Irpinia 64, Saonara, 35020, Padua, Italy
Tel.: (39) 0498790666
Web Site: http://www.sintesi.eu
Year Founded: 1997
MLSNT—(EUR)
Sales Range: Less than $1 Million
Machine Tools Mfr
N.A.I.C.S.: 333517
Francesco Bottene (Chm)

SINTEX INDUSTRIES, LTD.
Sintex Industries BVM, Kalol, 382 721, Gujarat, India
Tel.: (91) 2764 253000
Web Site: http://www.sintex.in
502742—(BOM)
Rev.: $243,782,000
Assets: $1,476,402,200
Liabilities: $1,036,800,800
Net Worth: $439,601,400
Earnings: ($175,897,400)
Emp.: 5,702
Fiscal Year-end: 03/31/20
Broadwoven Fabric Mills
N.A.I.C.S.: 314120
Rahul A. Patel (Mng Dir)

Subsidiaries:

AIP SAS (1)
6 Rue Jean Perrin, 69680, Chassieu, France
Tel.: (33) 472477430
Web Site: http://www.nief-plastic.com
Sales Range: $25-49.9 Million
Plastics Product Mfr
N.A.I.C.S.: 326130
Laurent Maes (Dir)

Bright AutoPlast Pvt. Ltd. (1)
502 Pressman House 70 A Nehru Road Vile Parle East, Mumbai, 400099, Maharashtra, India
Tel.: (91) 2226124920
Web Site: http://www.brightautoplast.com
Sales Range: $125-149.9 Million
Emp.: 300
Plastics Product Mfr
N.A.I.C.S.: 326199

NP Hungaria Kft (1)
Ipari park 07/54, 5440, Kunszentmarton, Jasz-Nagykun-Szolnok, Hungary
Tel.: (36) 56 56 11 00
Web Site: http://www.nief-plastic.com
Plastics Product Mfr
N.A.I.C.S.: 326199

NP Nord SAS (1)
1 & 3 Rue Gustave Delory, Caudry, 59540, Nord, France
Tel.: (33) 3 27 85 11 25
Web Site: http://www.nief-plastic.com
Sales Range: $25-49.9 Million
Emp.: 60
Plastics Product Mfr
N.A.I.C.S.: 326199

NP Savoie SAS (1)
Parc d'Activites Val Guiers 520 Route de Tramonet, 73330, Belmont-Tramonet, France
Tel.: (33) 4 76 37 38 80
Web Site: http://www.nief-plastic.com
Sales Range: $25-49.9 Million
Plastics Product Mfr
N.A.I.C.S.: 326199

NP Slovakia SRO (1)
Bojnicka 3, 831 04, Bratislava, Slovakia
Tel.: (421) 244632494
Web Site: http://www.np-slovakia.com
Sales Range: $25-49.9 Million
Plastics Product Mfr
N.A.I.C.S.: 326130

NP Tunisia SARL (1)
ZI Mghira 3 Lot N 3 Route De Fouchana, 2082, Ben Arous, Tunisia
Tel.: (216) 79408318
Plastics Product Mfr
N.A.I.C.S.: 326199

NP Vosges SAS (1)
Zone Artisanale Hellieule No 1 10 rue Jean Prouve, BP 202, 88100, Saint-Die-des-Vosges, Cedex, France
Tel.: (33) 329516320
Web Site: http://www.nief-plastic.com
Sales Range: $50-74.9 Million
Plastics Product Mfr
N.A.I.C.S.: 326199

Nief Plastic SAS (1)
10 Rue Jean Rostand, BP 315, 69740, Genas, France
Tel.: (33) 478401152
Web Site: http://www.nief-plastic.com
Sales Range: $200-249.9 Million
Plastics Product Mfr
N.A.I.C.S.: 326130

SICMO SAS (1)
42 Grande Rue, 39100, Villette-les-Dole, Jura, France
Tel.: (33) 384820072
Plastics Product Mfr
N.A.I.C.S.: 326199

SIMOP SAS (1)
P A de la Maison Neuve 7 rue Clement Ader, 44980, Sainte-Luce-sur-Loire, France
Tel.: (33) 240256054
Web Site: http://www.simop.eu
Sales Range: $25-49.9 Million
Plastics Product Mfr
N.A.I.C.S.: 326199

Segaplast Maroc SA (1)
Parc d activite Oukacha II Bat C6 C8 Boulevard Moulay Slimane, Ain Sebaa, 20250, Casablanca, Morocco
Tel.: (212) 522666744
Web Site: http://www.nief-plastic.com
Emp.: 80
Plastics Product Mfr
N.A.I.C.S.: 326130
Stephane Giles (Mgr)

Sintex Holdings USA, Inc. (1)
837 Cedar St, Wausaukee, WI 54177-9617
Tel.: (715) 856-6321
Sales Range: $25-49.9 Million
Emp.: 100
Plastic Water Tanks Mfr
N.A.I.C.S.: 332420

Siroco SAS (1)
10 rue Jean Rostand - ZI, BP 315, 69745, Genas, Cedex, France
Tel.: (33) 478909696
Web Site: http://www.siroco-hvac.com
Sales Range: $25-49.9 Million
Heat Exchanger Mfr
N.A.I.C.S.: 332410
Julien Brochier (Mgr-Sls)

Thermodole SAS (1)
20 Rue De Crissey, 39100, Dole, Jura, France
Tel.: (33) 384721628
Web Site: http://www.nief-plastic.com
Sales Range: $25-49.9 Million
Emp.: 80
Plastics Product Mfr
N.A.I.C.S.: 326199

Wausaukee Composites Inc. (1)
837 Cedar St, Wausaukee, WI 54177
Tel.: (715) 856-6321
Web Site: http://www.wauscomp.com

SINTEX INDUSTRIES, LTD.

Sintex Industries, Ltd.—(Continued)
Sales Range: $150-199.9 Million
Emp.: 300
Plastics Processing
N.A.I.C.S.: 326199
Jack Verdegan *(Mgr-Mfg Svcs)*

Subsidiary (Domestic):

Wasaukee Composites Owosso, Inc. (2)
401 S Delaney Rd, Owosso, MI 48867
Tel.: (989) 725-2900
Sales Range: $50-74.9 Million
Emp.: 130
Plastic Product Distr
N.A.I.C.S.: 424610
Brandon Craven *(Plant Mgr)*

Zeppelin Mobile systems India limited (1)
B 193 A Phase II, Noida, 201 305, Uttar Pradesh, India
Tel.: (91) 120 2563480
Web Site: http://www.zeppelinindia.com
Emp.: 100
Shelters & Insulated Bodies Mfr
N.A.I.C.S.: 336211
Dinesh Khera *(VP)*

SINTEX PLASTICS TECHNOLOGY LIMITED
Near Seven Garnala, Kalol, 382 721, Gujarat, India
Tel.: (91) 2764253000
Web Site: http://www.sintexplastics.com
Year Founded: 1931
540653—(BOM)
Rev.: $113,484,803
Assets: $459,066,003
Liabilities: $452,711,468
Net Worth: $6,354,535
Earnings: ($51,299,083)
Emp.: 2,027
Fiscal Year-end: 03/31/22
Plastic Product Mfr & Distr
N.A.I.C.S.: 326199
Amit D. Patel *(Chm & Mng Dir)*

SINTEZA S.A.
Sos Borsului nr 35, 410605, Oradea, Romania
Tel.: (40) 259456116
Web Site: https://www.sinteza.ro
STZ—(BUC)
Rev.: $4,026,361
Assets: $9,455,590
Liabilities: $3,673,569
Net Worth: $5,782,021
Earnings: $2,329,419
Emp.: 67
Fiscal Year-end: 12/31/23
Organic Chemical Product Mfr
N.A.I.C.S.: 325199

SINTOKOGIO LTD.
24th floor Dai Nagoya Building
3-28-12 Meieki, Nakamura-Ku, Nagoya, 450-6424, Aichi, Japan
Tel.: (81) 525829211
Web Site: https://www.sinto.co.jp
6339—(TKS)
Rev.: $763,421,950
Assets: $1,242,435,430
Liabilities: $402,040,030
Net Worth: $840,395,400
Earnings: $57,546,660
Emp.: 1,683
Fiscal Year-end: 03/31/24
Industrial Machines & Tools Mfr
N.A.I.C.S.: 333248
Atsushi Nagai *(Pres)*

Subsidiaries:

CFS Co., Ltd. (1)
3399-16 Shimami-cho inside, Niigata East Port Industrial Park Kita-ku, Niigata, 950-3102, Japan
Tel.: (81) 252554333

Emp.: 23
Industrial Machinery Equipment Mfr
N.A.I.C.S.: 333248

Chemisch Thermische Prozesstechnik GmbH (1)
Schmiedlstrasse 10, 8042, Graz, Austria
Tel.: (43) 31641010
Emp.: 7
Air Pollution Control Machinery Mfr & Distr
N.A.I.C.S.: 333248

Subsidiary (Non-US):

CTP France (2)
Immeuble Danica B 21 Avenue Georges Pompidou, 69486, Lyon, France
Tel.: (33) 472913023
Sales Range: $25-49.9 Million
Emp.: 3
Air Pollution Control Equipment Mfr
N.A.I.C.S.: 333248
Robert Kobierski *(Gen Mgr)*

Subsidiary (US):

CTP Sinto America Inc. (2)
4630 Delaware St, Delaware, OH 43015-8654
Tel.: (614) 763-6543
Web Site: http://www.ctp-airpollutioncontrol.com
Business Management Consulting Services
N.A.I.C.S.: 541618

Subsidiary (Domestic):

CTP-DUMAG GmbH (2)
Am Kanal 8-10, 2352, Gumpoldskirchen, Austria
Tel.: (43) 720 595404
Web Site: http://www.ctp-dumag.com
Sales Range: $25-49.9 Million
Emp.: 5
Combustion Equipment Mfr
N.A.I.C.S.: 333248
Robert Schroeger *(Gen Mgr)*

Daito Kihan Co., Ltd. (1)
5-2-13 Mizuhai, Higashi-osaka, 578-0921, Osaka, Japan
Tel.: (81) 729656662
Industrial Machinery & Equipment Whslr
N.A.I.C.S.: 423830

Endeco Omega Sinto (Pty) Ltd. (1)
192 Lamp Road, Wadeville, Gauteng, South Africa
Tel.: (27) 11 907 1785
Die Casting Machine Mfr
N.A.I.C.S.: 333517

FROHN GmbH (1)
Nettestr 83-87, 58762, Altena, Germany
Tel.: (49) 23 529 2810
Web Site: https://www.frohn.com
Shot Peening Accessory Mfr
N.A.I.C.S.: 332811
Peter Beckmerhagen *(Mng Dir)*

Finishing Associates, Inc. (1)
1119 Mearns Rd, Warminster, PA 18974
Tel.: (267) 803-2851
Mass Finishing Equipment Mfr & Distr
N.A.I.C.S.: 333248

Fujiwa Denki Co., Ltd. (1)
71-2 Tsukeda Nishijo, Oharucho, Ama, 490-1144, Aichi, Japan
Tel.: (81) 524854161
Emp.: 37
Automatic Pouring Machine Mfr
N.A.I.C.S.: 333248
Katsutoshi Suzuki *(Pres)*

Fujiwa Denki Co., Ltd. - Toyokawa Factory (1)
71-2 Tsukeda Nishijo, Ama, 442-8505, Aichi, Japan
Tel.: (81) 533850078
Automatic Pouring Machine Mfr
N.A.I.C.S.: 333248

Guangzhou Sinto Zhongtong Machinery Co., Ltd. (1)
No 3 Jinsha Road in Ankai Property Building, Nansha District, Guangzhou, 511457, Guangdong, China
Tel.: (86) 203 905 1865
Web Site: https://www.sinto-gx.com
Casting Equipment Whslr

N.A.I.C.S.: 423830

Heinrich Wagner Sinto Maschinenfabrik GmbH (1)
Tel.: (49) 27529070
Sales Range: $100-124.9 Million
Emp.: 300
Molding Machinery Equipment Mfr
N.A.I.C.S.: 333248
Klaus Wilbert *(Mng Dir)*

Jiangsu Taisintong Machinery Technology Co., Ltd. (1)
No 215 Fang Da Road, Xishan Economic Technological Development Area, Wuxi, 214000, Jiangsu, China
Tel.: (86) 5108 562 6650
Die Casting Machine Mfr
N.A.I.C.S.: 333517

Korea Sinto Co., Ltd. (1)
13 91 Road Nongong-ro, Nongong-eup Dalseonggun, Daegu, 711-855, Korea (South)
Tel.: (82) 536154901
Web Site: https://www.koreasinto.com
Metal Steel Products Distr
N.A.I.C.S.: 423510
Tae Yong Lee *(CEO)*

Laempe Mossner Sinto GmbH (1)
Hintern Hecken 3, 39179, Barleben, Germany
Tel.: (49) 39 202 6920
Web Site: https://www.laempe.com
Emp.: 300
Automotive Engine Mfr
N.A.I.C.S.: 332119
Andreas Mossner *(Mng Dir)*

MEIKIKOU Co., Ltd. (1)
Higashi 180 Okute-cho, Toyoake, 470-1111, Aichi, Japan
Tel.: (81) 562928113
Sales Range: $50-74.9 Million
Emp.: 230
Material Handling Equipment Mfr
N.A.I.C.S.: 333511
Masayuki Hirayama *(Chm)*

Omega Sane Foundry Machinery Pvt. Ltd. (1)
21 Gananjay Society Unit 4, Kothrud, Pune, 411038, India
Tel.: (91) 202 539 9005
Die Casting Machine Mfr
N.A.I.C.S.: 333517

Omega Sinto (Italy) S.R.L. (1)
Omega Tecnostudio Via F lli Rosselli 17/22, 31020, Villorba, TV, Italy
Tel.: (39) 042 260 9557
Chemical Equipment Mfr
N.A.I.C.S.: 325998

Omega Sinto Foundry Machinery (Malaysia) Sdn. Bhd. (1)
Plot 151538 Lorong Kledang Utara 15, Kawasan Perindustrian Menglembu, 31450, Ipoh, Perak, Malaysia
Tel.: (60) 5 281 6507
Die Casting Machine Mfr
N.A.I.C.S.: 333517

Omega Sinto Foundry Machinery Limited (1)
Morley Way Woodston, Peterborough, PE2 7BW, United Kingdom
Tel.: (44) 173 323 2231
Web Site: https://www.ofml.net
Chemical Equipment Mfr
N.A.I.C.S.: 325998

PT. Sinto Indonesia (1)
Kawasan Industri Greenland Jl Greenland Boulevard Blok AF No 11, Kota Deltamas, Bekasi, 17530, Indonesia
Tel.: (62) 218 997 3252
Web Site: https://www.sintoindonesia.com
Welding Machine Distr
N.A.I.C.S.: 423830
Masahito Murakoshi *(Pres)*

Pressenge Maquinas Ltda. (1)
Rua Clodoaldo Gomes 440, Distrito Industrial, Joinville, 89219-550, Santa Catarina, Brazil
Tel.: (55) 473 027 9565
Web Site: https://www.rotojato.com.br
Plating Machine Distr

INTERNATIONAL PUBLIC

N.A.I.C.S.: 423830

Qingdao Sinto Machinery Co., Ltd. (1)
No 55 Xindong Road Jiulong Street Office, Jiaozhou, 266319, Shandong, China
Tel.: (86) 5328 182 7811
Web Site: https://www.sinto.cn
Machine Tools Mfr
N.A.I.C.S.: 333517

Roberts Sinto De Mexico, S. De R. L. De C. V. (1)
Calle del Comercio 212 Parque Industrial Marfer, 66367, Santa Catarina, Nuevo Leon, Mexico
Tel.: (52) 8181901818
Web Site: https://www.robertssinto.com
Metalworking Machines Mfr
N.A.I.C.S.: 333519

S.A.S 3DCeram-Sinto (1)
27 Rue Du Petit Theil, 87280, Limoges, France
Tel.: (33) 55 504 1090
Web Site: https://www.3dceram.com
Ceramic Products Mfr
N.A.I.C.S.: 327110

SINTO S-PRECISION, LTD. (1)
260-63 Hase, Atsugi, 243-0036, Kanagawa, Japan (100%)
Tel.: (81) 464000001
Emp.: 70
Precision Instrument Mfr, Distr & Maintenance Services
N.A.I.C.S.: 332721
Katsumi Kouno *(Vice Chm)*

SINTO V-CERAX, LTD. (1)
3-1 Honohara, Toyokawa, 442-8505, Aichi, Japan (100%)
Tel.: (81) 533859190
Web Site: https://vcerax.sinto.co.jp
Emp.: 70
Ceramic Processing Services
N.A.I.C.S.: 212323

SandMold Systems, Inc. (1)
313 W State St, Newaygo, MI 49337
Tel.: (231) 652-1623
Web Site: http://www.smssandmold.com
Emp.: 50
Laundry Equipment Mfr
N.A.I.C.S.: 333248
Rich Witte *(VP-Foundry Sls)*

Shinwa Kikou Co., Ltd. (1)
29-15 Narikawa Aza-Nishiyaji, Fukushima, 960-1108, Japan
Tel.: (81) 245452070
Web Site: http://www.sinto.co.jp
Packaging Machinery Mfr
N.A.I.C.S.: 333993

Siambrator Co., Ltd. (1)
27/9 Moo 5 Paholyothin Road, Klong Nueng, Khlong Luang, 12120, Phatumthani, Thailand
Tel.: (66) 25163925
Emp.: 6
Steel Shot & Grit Mfr
N.A.I.C.S.: 332311

Sinto America, Inc. (1)
3001 W Main St, Lansing, MI 48917
Tel.: (517) 371-2460
Web Site: http://www.sinto.co.jp
Industrial Equipment Mfr & Whslr
N.A.I.C.S.: 333248

Subsidiary (Domestic):

National Peening, Inc. (2)
1902 Weinig St, Statesville, NC 28677
Tel.: (704) 872-0113
Web Site: https://www.sintoamerica.com
Sales Range: $1-9.9 Million
Emp.: 70
Shot Peening
N.A.I.C.S.: 332710

Sinto Bharat Manufacturing Private Limited (1)
204 G S T Road NH-45, Kolambakkam Village Madurantagam Taluk, Kanchipuram, 603308, Tamil Nadu, India
Tel.: (91) 442 756 5125
Web Site: https://www.sintobharat.com
Automatic Mold Handling Machine Mfr
N.A.I.C.S.: 333511

AND PRIVATE COMPANIES — SIOEN INDUSTRIES NV

Sinto Brasil Produtos Limitada (1)
Rua Costa Barros 3021 - Jardim Guairaca,
Sao Paulo, 03210-001, SP, Brazil
Tel.: (55) 1133219500
Foundry Equipment Supplier
N.A.I.C.S.: 423510

Sinto Engineering, LTD. (1)
3-1 Honohara, Toyokawa, 442-8505, Aichi, Japan
Tel.: (81) 533890818
Web Site: https://se.sinto.co.jp
Emp.: 60
Engineeering Services
N.A.I.C.S.: 541330

Sinto Frohn Metal Abrasive (Qingdao) Co., Ltd. (1)
55 Xindong Road Qingdao, Jiulong Subdistrict, Jiaozhou, Shandong, China
Tel.: (86) 5328 182 7867
Web Site: https://www.frohn.cn
Stainless Steel Mfr
N.A.I.C.S.: 331210

Sinto Information Systems LTD. (1)
3-1 Honohara, Toyokawa, 442-8505, Aichi, Japan
Tel.: (81) 533853114
Emp.: 23
Telecommunication Servicesb
N.A.I.C.S.: 517810

Sinto Turkey Makina Sanayi ve Ticaret A.S.
Kobi Organize Sanayi Bolgesi 107 Cadde No 4, Odunpazari, 26110, Eskisehir, Turkiye
Tel.: (90) 222 236 9068
Web Site: https://www.sintoturkey.com.tr
Machine Tools Mfr
N.A.I.C.S.: 333517

Sintokogio (Kunshan) Co., Ltd. (1)
88 Baifu Road Economic Development Zone Baifu Office Park B-F2, Kunshan, 215314, China
Tel.: (86) 51255000696
Web Site: https://www.sinto-csk.cn
Emp.: 45
Industrial Machinery Equipment Mfr
N.A.I.C.S.: 333248

Sintokogio Ltd. - Ichinomiya Works (1)
180-1 Komaki Oki-cho, Toyokawa, 441-1205, Aichi, Japan
Tel.: (81) 533936148
Emp.: 300
Laundry Equipment Mfr
N.A.I.C.S.: 333248

Sintokogio Ltd. - Koda Works (1)
1 Nishinagane Sakazaki Kota-cho, Nukata, 444-0104, Aichi, Japan
Tel.: (81) 564623411
Industrial Machinery Equipment Mfr
N.A.I.C.S.: 333248

Sintokogio Ltd. - Nishiharu Works (1)
51 Shinmei Ufukuji, Kita-ku, Nagoya, 481-8678, Aichi, Japan
Tel.: (81) 568 22 1141
Industrial Equipment Mfr
N.A.I.C.S.: 333248

Sintokogio Ltd. - Oharu Works (1)
71-2 Aza-Tukeda Oaza-Nishijo Oharu-Cho, Ama, 490-1144, Aichi, Japan
Tel.: (81) 524418551
Industrial Machinery Equipment Mfr
N.A.I.C.S.: 333248

Sintokogio Ltd. - Osaki Works (1)
1-1 Kado Osaki-cho, Toyokawa, 442-8515, Aichi, Japan
Tel.: (81) 53 386 3111
Web Site: http://www.sinto.co.jp
Industrial Machinery & Equipment Mfr
N.A.I.C.S.: 333248

Sintokogio Ltd. - Shinshiro Works (1)
3-35 Minami-Gaitsu, Omiya-ji, Shinshiro, 441-1304, Aichi, Japan
Tel.: (81) 53 623 6001
Web Site: https://www.sinto.co.jp
Industrial Machinery & Equipment Mfr
N.A.I.C.S.: 333248

Sintokogio Ltd. - Toyokawa Works (1)
3-1 Honohara, Toyokawa, 442-8505, Aichi, Japan
Tel.: (81) 53 385 3111
Web Site: https://www.sinto.co.jp
Sales Range: $200-249.9 Million
Emp.: 60
Laundry Equipment Mfr
N.A.I.C.S.: 333248

Sintokogio Ltd. - Toyota Division (1)
4-22 Midorigaoka, Toyota, 471-0838, Aichi, Japan
Tel.: (81) 565 28 0360
Web Site: http://www.sinto.co.jp
Industrial Machinery Mfr
N.A.I.C.S.: 333248

TOUJYUKOUSAN Co., Ltd. (1)
3-1 Honohara, Toyokawa, 442-8505, Aichi, Japan
Tel.: (81) 53 389 0488
Web Site: http://www.sinto.co.jp
Industrial Machinery Mfr
N.A.I.C.S.: 333248

Taiwan Sintong Machinery Co., Ltd. (50.9%)
No 9 Gongye 5th Rd, Guanyin Dist, Taoyuan, 32853, Taiwan
Tel.: (886) 3 483 9966
Web Site: https://www.twsinto.com.tw
Emp.: 70
Surface Treatment & Milling Equipment Mfr
N.A.I.C.S.: 423440
Masuo Lee *(Pres)*

Taiwanabrator Co., Ltd. (55.9%)
No 586 Sec 2 Zhong Shan S Rd, Da Yuan, Taoyuan, 337, Taiwan
Tel.: (886) 33813812
Web Site: https://www.tbshot.com.tw
Steel Shot & Grit Mfr
N.A.I.C.S.: 332312

Thai Sintokogio Co., Ltd. (1)
44 Moo 4, Banchang U-Thai Rojana Industrial Park 2, Ayutthaya, 13210, Thailand
Tel.: (66) 35 200 7108
Web Site: https://www.thaisinto.co.th
Emp.: 104
Casting Equipment Mfr
N.A.I.C.S.: 333248
Kampol Srethbhakdi *(Chm)*

Tinker Omega Sinto LLC (1)
2424 Columbus Ave, Springfield, OH 45503
Tel.: (937) 322-2272
Web Site: https://www.tinkeromega.com
Machine Tools Mfr
N.A.I.C.S.: 333517
Wil Tinker *(Pres)*

Toju Kosan, Ltd. (1)
3-1 Honohara, Toyokawa, 442-8505, Aichi, Japan
Tel.: (81) 53 389 0488
Die Casting Machine Mfr
N.A.I.C.S.: 333517

WES Omega Sinto Foundry Machinery Pty. Ltd. (1)
16 Lanyon Street, Dandenong, 3175, VIC, Australia
Tel.: (61) 39 794 8400
Web Site: https://www.wesomega.com.au
Machine Tools Mfr
N.A.I.C.S.: 333517
Les Craig *(Mng Dir-Sales)*

Wuxi Tai Sintong Machinery Co., Ltd. (1)
69 Hongxiang Road, Hongshang Subdistrict Wuxi Xinqu, Wuxi, Jiangsu, China
Tel.: (86) 510 8562 6650
Web Site: http://www.sinto.co.jp
Industrial Machinery Mfr
N.A.I.C.S.: 333248

Zhejiang Sinto Abrasive Co., Ltd. (1)
No 2511 Xinkai Road, Pinghu Economic Development Zone, Pinghu, 314200, Zhejiang, China
Tel.: (86) 57389170123
Web Site: https://www.sinto-zb.com
Steel Balls, Sand Casting Mfr
N.A.I.C.S.: 332992

SINTROL OY
Ruosilantie 15, 00390, Helsinki, Finland
Tel.: (358) 95617360
Web Site: http://www.sintrol.com
Year Founded: 1993
Sales Range: $10-24.9 Million
Emp.: 60
Monitoring Solutions
N.A.I.C.S.: 334513
Karl Ehrstrom *(CEO)*

SINTRONES TECHNOLOGY CORP.
2F -3 No 738 Zhongzheng Rd, Zhonghe Dist, New Taipei City, 235, Taiwan
Tel.: (886) 282280101
Web Site: https://www.sintrones.com
Year Founded: 2009
6680—(TPE)
Electrical Products Distr
N.A.I.C.S.: 423690
Hsu Yu-Jui *(Chm & Pres)*

SINTRONIC TECHNOLOGY INC.
3F NO 46 Ln 66 Ruiguang Rd, Neihu Dist, Taipei, 11491, Taiwan
Tel.: (886) 227936889
Web Site: http://www.sintronic.com.tw
Year Founded: 2000
3536—(TAI)
Rev.: $21,610,767
Assets: $46,867,352
Liabilities: $42,280,636
Net Worth: $4,586,716
Earnings: ($3,579,125)
Emp.: 1,245
Fiscal Year-end: 12/31/21
Cold Cathode Fluorescent Lamps (CCFLs) & Other Electronic Components Mfr & Sales
N.A.I.C.S.: 335139

Subsidiaries:

Gulf Semiconductor (Shan Dong) Co., Ltd. (1)
No 1659 Keyuan Road Suncun Area Hi-NEW Tech Development Zone, Jinan, 250104, China
Tel.: (86) 53183130300
Precision Ceramic Product Mfr
N.A.I.C.S.: 327110

Gulf Semiconductor Ltd. (1)
Rm 212 2/F Wing On Plaza 62 Mody Road TST East, Kowloon, China (Hong Kong)
Tel.: (852) 27227163
Precision Ceramic Product Mfr
N.A.I.C.S.: 327110

SINWA LIMITED
28 Joo Koon Circle, Singapore, 629057, Singapore
Tel.: (65) 68626300   SG
Web Site: http://www.sinwaglobal.com
Year Founded: 1965
5CN—(SES)
Sales Range: Less than $1 Million
Logistics Management Services
N.A.I.C.S.: 541614
Sim Yong Teng *(Chm)*

Subsidiaries:

Sinwa Ship Supply (HK) Pte. Ltd. (1)
Unit D 25F Gold King Industrial Building 34-41 Tai Lin Pai Road, Hong Kong, New Territories, China (Hong Kong)
Tel.: (852) 29758663
Logistic Services
N.A.I.C.S.: 541614

Sinwa Thailand Ltd. (1)
68 Moo 6, Thamnop Sub District Amphoe Singhanakhon, Songkhla, 90280, Thailand
Tel.: (66) 915678332
Marine Logistic Services
N.A.I.C.S.: 488510

SINWA SINGAPORE PTE LTD
28 Joo Koon Cir, 629057, Singapore, Singapore
Tel.: (65) 68626300
Web Site: http://www.sinwaglobal.com
Sales Range: $75-99.9 Million
Marine Logistics & Offshore Management Services
N.A.I.C.S.: 541614
Kok Liang Chew *(Sec)*

Subsidiaries:

Francois Marine Services Pte Ltd (1)
30 Pandan Road, Singapore, 609277, Singapore
Tel.: (65) 67272200
Web Site: http://www.francoismarine.com
Marine Support Services
N.A.I.C.S.: 488510

SINYI REALTY INC.
No 100 Section 5 Xinyi Road, Xinyi District, Taipei, 110, Taiwan
Tel.: (886) 227557666
Web Site: https://www.sinyi.com.tw
Year Founded: 1987
9940—(TAI)
Rev.: $464,531,785
Assets: $1,019,689,160
Liabilities: $609,857,624
Net Worth: $409,831,536
Earnings: $57,927,137
Emp.: 5,319
Fiscal Year-end: 12/31/23
Real Estate Brokerage Services
N.A.I.C.S.: 531390
Chou Ken Yu *(Chm)*

SIOEN INDUSTRIES NV
Fabriekstraat 23, B-8850, Ardooie, Belgium
Tel.: (32) 51740900
Web Site: http://www.sioen.com
SIOE—(EUR)
Rev.: $570,703,053
Assets: $561,828,163
Liabilities: $291,452,524
Net Worth: $270,375,639
Earnings: $30,731,198
Emp.: 4,834
Fiscal Year-end: 12/31/19
Fine Chemicals, Coated Technical Textiles & Vinyl Coated Fabrics Mfr
N.A.I.C.S.: 325998
Pascale Sioen *(Exec Dir)*

Subsidiaries:

Coatex NV (1)
Industriezone Sappenleen Sappenleenstraat 3-4, 8970, Poperinge, Belgium
Tel.: (32) 5 734 6160
Web Site: https://www.coatex.be
Textile Products Mfr
N.A.I.C.S.: 313310

Confection Tunisienne De Securite Sarl - C.T.S. Sarl (1)
5 Impasse 2 Rue de l'Energie Solaire-Z I, La Charguia, 2035, Tunis, Tunisia
Tel.: (216) 7 177 3477
Die Casting Machine Mfr
N.A.I.C.S.: 333517

Dimension-Polyant (UK) Ltd. (1)
Unit 8 Kingdom Close Kingdom Business Park Segensworth East, Fareham, PO15 5TJ, Hampshire, United Kingdom
Tel.: (44) 148 957 0551
Sailing Cloth Mfr
N.A.I.C.S.: 314999

Dimension-Polyant GmbH (100%)
Speefeld 7, 47906, Kempen, Germany
Tel.: (49) 21528910
Web Site: http://www.dimension-polyant.com

SIOEN INDUSTRIES NV

Sioen Industries NV—(Continued)
Sailcloth Mfr
N.A.I.C.S.: 313210
Uwe Stein *(Mng Dir)*

Dimension-Polyant Inc. (1)
78 Highland Dr, Putnam, CT 06260
Tel.: (860) 928-8300
Sailing Cloth Mfr
N.A.I.C.S.: 314999

Dimension-Polyant SAS (1)
4 Place Du Petit Hunier ZA, Les Minimes, 17000, La Rochelle, France
Tel.: (33) 54 628 2201
Sailing Cloth Mfr
N.A.I.C.S.: 314999

Dimension-Polyant Sailcloth Pty. Ltd. (1)
Unit 7/9 Powells Rd, Brookvale, 2100, NSW, Australia
Tel.: (61) 29 905 9565
Sailing Cloth Mfr
N.A.I.C.S.: 314999

Dynatex NV (1)
Fabriekstraat 23, 8850, Ardooie, Belgium
Tel.: (32) 5 174 0900
Web Site: https://www.dynatex.be
Curtain Mfr
N.A.I.C.S.: 314120

European Master Batch NV (1)
Rijksweg 15, 2880, Bornem, Belgium
Tel.: (32) 3 890 6400
Textile Machinery Mfr
N.A.I.C.S.: 333248

Fontana International GmbH (1)
Stefan-Fechter-Weg 8, 4020, Linz, Austria
Tel.: (43) 73 290 8001
Web Site: https://www.fontana-international.com
Geosynthetic Distr
N.A.I.C.S.: 424690

Gairmeidi Caomhnaithe Dhun Na Ngall Teoranta Ltd. (1)
Industrial Estate Bunbeg Co, Donegal, Ireland
Tel.: (353) 74 953 1169
Textile Products Mfr
N.A.I.C.S.: 313310

James Dewhurst Ltd. (1)
Altham Lane, Accrington, BB5 5YA, Lancashire, United Kingdom **(100%)**
Tel.: (44) 1282775311
Web Site: http://www.jamesdewhurst.com
Industrial Woven & Non-Woven Textiles Mfr
N.A.I.C.S.: 314999
Malcolm Blackwell *(CEO)*

P.T. Sioen Semarang Asia (1)
No 2A Kel Randu Garut KecTugu Kota, Kawasan Industri Wijayakusuma KIW JI Tugu Industri Raya, Semarang, 50153, Jawa Tengah, Indonesia
Tel.: (62) 2 486 6089
Textile Products Mfr
N.A.I.C.S.: 313310

PT. Sioen Indonesia (1)
Kawasan Berikat Nusantara KBN Marunda JI Pontianak Blok C2-03, Cilincing, Jakarta Utara, 14120, Indonesia
Tel.: (62) 214 485 3222
Clothes Mfr
N.A.I.C.S.: 315990

PT. Sungin Tex (1)
Jalan Raya Narogong Km 12 5 Pangkalan IV Desa Cikiwul, Kec Bantar Gebang, Bekasi, 17152, Barat, Indonesia
Tel.: (62) 21 825 2222
Clothes Mfr
N.A.I.C.S.: 315990

Richard SAS (1)
Rue Lavoisier - Zac Novo, 59160, Lomme, France
Tel.: (33) 32 000 1888
Textile Products Mfr
N.A.I.C.S.: 313310

Roland Real Estate Sp. z o.o. (1)
Ul Nadbrezezna 1 PL, 62500, Konin, Poland
Tel.: (48) 63 244 3925

Real Estate Services
N.A.I.C.S.: 531390

Roltrans Tegelen BV (1)
Kasteellaan 33, 5932 AE, Tegelen, Netherlands
Tel.: (31) 77 376 9292
Textile Products Mfr
N.A.I.C.S.: 313310

Saint Clair Textiles SAS (1)
415 Avenue De Savoie, 38110, Saint-Clair-de-la-Tour, France
Tel.: (33) 47 483 5100
Web Site: https://www.saintclairtextiles.com
Textile Products Mfr
N.A.I.C.S.: 313310
Xavier Christophe *(Dir)*

Saint Freres Confection SAS (1)
2 Route De Ville, BP 37, 80420, Flixecourt, France
Tel.: (33) 32 251 5170
Textile Products Mfr
N.A.I.C.S.: 313310

Saint Freres SAS (1)
4 Rue De Ville Le Marclet, 80420, Flixecourt, France
Tel.: (33) 32 251 5145
Clothes Mfr
N.A.I.C.S.: 315990

Sioen Ballistics Oy (1)
Valuraudantie 20, 00700, Helsinki, Finland
Tel.: (358) 9825501
Web Site: http://www.sioenballistics.com
Protective Armour Products Mfr
N.A.I.C.S.: 315990

Sioen Coated Fabrics (Shanghai) Trading Co. Ltd. (1)
Wai Gao Qiao Free Trading Zone 168 Mei Sheng Road Guo Lian Mansion, 1st Floor Pudong, Shanghai, 200131, China
Tel.: (86) 216 384 2521
Textile Products Mfr
N.A.I.C.S.: 313310

Sioen Fabrics SA (1)
Urbino 6, Zoning Industriel du Blanc Ballot Avenue, 7700, Mouscron, Belgium
Tel.: (32) 5 685 6880
Clothes Mfr
N.A.I.C.S.: 315990

Sioen France SAS (1)
Pavillon Hermes 110 Avenue Gustave Eiffel ZI La Coupe, 11100, Narbonne, France
Tel.: (33) 46 842 3515
Textile Products Mfr
N.A.I.C.S.: 313310

Sioen NV (1)
Fabriekstraat 23 B, 8850, Ardooie, Belgium
Tel.: (32) 5 174 0800
Clothes Mfr
N.A.I.C.S.: 315990

Sioen Nederland BV (1)
Kasteellaan 33, 5932 AE, Tegelen, Netherlands
Tel.: (31) 76 541 6888
Clothes Mfr
N.A.I.C.S.: 315990

Sioen Technical Felts SA (1)
181 Rue Ernest Solvay, 4000, Liege, Belgium
Tel.: (32) 4 229 9447
Web Site: https://www.sioentechnicalfelts.com
Textile Products Mfr
N.A.I.C.S.: 313310

Sioen Tunisie SARL (1)
7 Impasse 2 Rue de l'Energie Solaire Z I, La Charguia, 2035, Tunis, Tunisia
Tel.: (216) 7 180 7547
Clothes Mfr
N.A.I.C.S.: 315990

Sioen Zaghouan SA (1)
Rue Ismail Sabri, Zone Industrielle, 1100, Zaghouan, Tunisia
Tel.: (216) 7 268 0660
Clothes Mfr
N.A.I.C.S.: 315990

Ursuit AB (1)
Flottiligatan 85, 72131, Vasteras, Sweden
Tel.: (46) 705 594 2474

Dry Suit Product Distr
N.A.I.C.S.: 458110

Ursuit Baltics AS (1)
Kooli 7, Torva, 68604, Valga, Estonia
Tel.: (372) 766 8350
Web Site: https://www.ursuit.ee
Sporting Goods Mfr
N.A.I.C.S.: 339920
Sami Eskonaho *(CEO & Mng Dir)*

Ursuit Oy (1)
Teijonkatu 3, 20750, Turku, Finland
Tel.: (358) 20 779 8850
Web Site: https://www.ursuit.com
Dry Suit Product Distr
N.A.I.C.S.: 458110

SIOS CORP.

SIOS building 2-12-3 Minami Azabu, Minato-ku, Tokyo, 106-0047, Japan
Tel.: (81) 364015111   JP
Web Site: http://www.sios.com
Year Founded: 1997
Holding Company
N.A.I.C.S.: 551112

Subsidiaries:

SIOS Corporation (1)
2-12-3 Minami Azabu CYOS Building, Minato-ku, Tokyo, 106-0047, Japan
Tel.: (81) 364015111
Web Site: https://www.sios.jp
Rev.: $112,653,010
Assets: $47,545,540
Liabilities: $39,129,710
Net Worth: $8,415,830
Earnings: ($127,620)
Fiscal Year-end: 12/31/2023
Software & Hardware Products Sales
N.A.I.C.S.: 541715
Nobuo Kita *(Chm, Pres & CEO)*

Subsidiary (Domestic):

Gluegent, Inc. (2)
4-1-28 Toranomon Towers Toranomon, Minato-ku, Tokyo, 105-0001, Japan
Tel.: (81) 364024650
Web Site: http://www.gluegent.com
Sales Range: $25-49.9 Million
Emp.: 60
Software Development Solutions
N.A.I.C.S.: 541511

Keyport Solutions, Inc. (2)
Tokyo Dia Bldg No 2 7th Floor 1-28-38 Shinkawa, Chuo-ku, Tokyo, 104 0033, Japan **(90.51%)**
Tel.: (81) 3 3523 8601
Web Site: http://www.keyportsolutions.com
Sales Range: $10-24.9 Million
Systems Design & Consulting & Finance Application Solutions
N.A.I.C.S.: 541512
Noboru Morita *(Pres)*

SIP INDUSTRIES LIMITED

Module 28 II Floor Block 1 SIDCO Electronic Complex, Thiru Vi Ka Industrial Estate Guindy, Chennai, 600032, India
Tel.: (91) 4428193521
Web Site: https://sip-industries.com
Year Founded: 1986
523164—(BOM)
Sales Range: Less than $1 Million
Chemical & Resin Mfr
N.A.I.C.S.: 325998
K. C. Raghunathan *(Chm, Mng Dir & Compliance Officer)*

SIPA RESOURCES LIMITED

Unit 5 1st Floor Subiaco Court 12-20 Railway Road, Subiaco, 6008, WA, Australia
Tel.: (61) 893881551
Web Site: https://www.sipa.com.au
SRI—(ASX)
Rev.: $1,003,233
Assets: $1,651,416
Liabilities: $288,659
Net Worth: $1,362,758
Earnings: ($67,401)

INTERNATIONAL PUBLIC

Emp.: 11
Fiscal Year-end: 06/30/24
Mineral Mining & Exploration
N.A.I.C.S.: 333131
Burkhard N. Eisenlohr *(Mgr-Uganda)*

Subsidiaries:

Sipa Exploration NL (1)
Unit 8 Subiaco Court 12-20 Railway Road, Subiaco, 6008, Australia
Tel.: (61) 894816259
Web Site: http://www.sipa.com.au
Sales Range: $50-74.9 Million
Emp.: 6
Gold Ore Mining Services
N.A.I.C.S.: 212220

SIPAD KOMERC D.D.

Ul Trampina br 12/IV, 71000, Sarajevo, Bosnia & Herzegovina
Tel.: (387) 33202330061
SPKMR—(SARE)
Rev.: $41,254
Assets: $17,759,274
Liabilities: $1,850,153
Net Worth: $15,909,121
Earnings: ($114,284)
Emp.: 1
Fiscal Year-end: 12/31/21
Construction Engineering Services
N.A.I.C.S.: 237990

SIPAD SRBOBRAN A.D.

Turijski put 20, Srbobran, Serbia
Tel.: (381) 21 731 155
Web Site: http://www.sipad.co.rs
Year Founded: 1950
Sales Range: $1-9.9 Million
Emp.: 74
Furniture Mfr
N.A.I.C.S.: 337122

SIPAD-KRAJINA A.D.

Paje Jovanovica Bb, 78000, Banja Luka, Bosnia & Herzegovina
Tel.: (387) 51388635
SKBL-R-A—(BANJ)
Sales Range: Less than $1 Million
Emp.: 2
Construction Materials Whslr
N.A.I.C.S.: 423390
Velimir Balaban *(Chm)*

SIPAI HEALTH TECHNOLOGY CO., LTD.

7/F Building 3 Xingguangyao Plaza No 1888 Caoyang Road, Putuo District, Shanghai, China   Ky
Web Site:
https://www.medbankshealthtech.com
Year Founded: 2014
0314—(HKG)
Rev.: $631,145,224
Assets: $448,836,968
Liabilities: $167,829,605
Net Worth: $281,007,364
Earnings: ($210,167,962)
Emp.: 3,200
Fiscal Year-end: 12/31/22
Health Care Srvices
N.A.I.C.S.: 621610
Xuguang Ma *(Chm)*

SIPEF NV

Kasteel Calesberg Calesbergdreef 5, B-2900, Schoten, Belgium
Tel.: (32) 36419700
Web Site: https://www.sipef.com
SISAF—(OTCIQ)
Rev.: $443,886,000
Assets: $1,080,242,000
Liabilities: $191,423,000
Net Worth: $888,819,000
Earnings: $77,689,000
Emp.: 23,057
Fiscal Year-end: 12/31/23
Agro Industrial Business

N.A.I.C.S.: 111120
Francois Van Hoydonck (Mng Dir)

Subsidiaries:

Galley Reach Holdings Ltd. (1)
PO Box 2, Port Moresby, Papua New Guinea
Tel.: (675) 3230512
Rubber Mfr
N.A.I.C.S.: 326299

PT Tolan Tiga (1)
Gedung Bank Sumut Jalan Imam Bonjol No 18, Medan, North Sumatra, Indonesia
Tel.: (62) 614152043
Web Site: http://www.tolantiga.co.id
Farm Management Services
N.A.I.C.S.: 115116
Adam James (Chm)

SIPOREX D.D. TUZLA
Ul Nikole Tesle br 3, 75000, Tuzla, Bosnia & Herzegovina
Tel.: (387) 35308212
SPRXRK1—(SARE)
Rev.: $574,700
Assets: $10,938,355
Liabilities: $10,938,355
Earnings: ($8,928)
Fiscal Year-end: 12/31/21
Real Estate Lending Services
N.A.I.C.S.: 531190

SIPSA SA
El Bosque Norte 0440 Piso 09, Santiago, Chile
Tel.: (56) 3623300
Year Founded: 1987
SIPSA—(SGO)
Sales Range: Less than $1 Million
Marine Transportation Services
N.A.I.C.S.: 488510
Alexander Paul Tachi Scott (CEO)

SIPUP CORPORATION
2 Mitzpe, Shoham, 6082102, Israel
Tel.: (972) 545774447   NV
Year Founded: 2012
SPUP—(OTCIQ)
Yogurt Mfr
N.A.I.C.S.: 311514
Yochai Ozeri (CFO)

SIQ MOUNTAIN INDUSTRIES, INC.
1-841 McCurdy Place, Kelowna, V1X 8C8, BC, Canada
Web Site: http://www.siqmountain.com
SIQ—(TSXV)
Assets: $3,739
Liabilities: $67,882
Net Worth: ($64,144)
Earnings: ($23,355)
Fiscal Year-end: 08/31/22
Asset Management Services
N.A.I.C.S.: 523940
Richard Lee (CFO)

SIQUAR HARDWARE INDUSTRY CO., LTD.
No 220 An Pei Rd, Kaohsiung, 824, Taiwan
Tel.: (886) 76162621
Web Site: http://www.siquar.com
Year Founded: 1980
Sales Range: $125-149.9 Million
Emp.: 100
Stamping Technology in Furniture Fittings, Building Hardware & Various Stamping OEM & ODM Parts
N.A.I.C.S.: 332119
Pan C. F. Frank (Founder)

Subsidiaries:

Siquar USA Inc. (1)
14020 Bolsa Ln, Cerritos, CA 90703-7026
Tel.: (562) 926-9999

Web Site: http://www.siquar.com
Rev.: $10,336,985
Emp.: 20
Specializes in the Stamping Technology of Various Metal
N.A.I.C.S.: 423310

SIR CORP.
5360 South Service Road Suite 200, Burlington, L7L 5L1, ON, Canada
Tel.: (905) 681-2997
Web Site: https://www.sircorp.com
Year Founded: 1992
Rev.: $229,336,306
Assets: $67,985,452
Liabilities: $203,915,033
Net Worth: ($135,929,581)
Earnings: $18,938,160
Emp.: 5,500
Fiscal Year-end: 08/31/19
Restaurant
N.A.I.C.S.: 722511
Peter Fowler (CEO)

Subsidiaries:

Jack Astor's (Boisbriand) Realty Inc. (1)
3395 Av Des Grandes Tourelles, Boisbriand, J7H 0A7, QC, Canada
Tel.: (450) 419-9785
Food Delivery Services
N.A.I.C.S.: 492210
Mason Rahal (Gen Mgr)

Jack Astor's (Dorval) Realty Inc. (1)
3051 boul des Sources, Dorval, H9B 1Z6, QC, Canada
Tel.: (514) 685-5225
Food Delivery Services
N.A.I.C.S.: 492210
David Bird (Gen Mgr)

Jack Astor's (Greenfield) Realty Inc. (1)
3500 boul Taschereau, Greenfield Park, J4V 2H7, QC, Canada
Tel.: (450) 671-4444
Food Delivery Services
N.A.I.C.S.: 492210
Bryan Bird (Gen Mgr)

Jack Astor's (Laval) Realty Inc. (1)
1820 Pierre-Peladeau Ave, Laval, H7T 2Z1, QC, Canada
Tel.: (450) 681-6683
Food Delivery Services
N.A.I.C.S.: 492210
Johanne Godin (Gen Mgr)

SIR ROYALTY INCOME FUND
5360 South Service Road Suite 200, Burlington, L7L 5L1, ON, Canada
Tel.: (905) 681-2997
SIRZF—(OTCIQ)
Rev.: $5,573,047
Assets: $38,707,750
Liabilities: $5,393,864
Net Worth: $33,313,886
Earnings: $3,841,244
Fiscal Year-end: 12/31/21
Investment Management Service
N.A.I.C.S.: 525990

SIR SHADI LAL ENTERPRISES LTD
Upper Doab Sugar Mills, Shamli, 247776, UP, India
Tel.: (91) 1398250082
Web Site: https://www.sirshadilal.com
Year Founded: 1993
532879—(BOM)
Rev.: $75,266,878
Assets: $113,752,589
Liabilities: $67,870,639
Net Worth: $45,881,950
Earnings: ($1,950,926)
Emp.: 722
Fiscal Year-end: 03/31/21
Sugar Alcohol & Ethanol Mfr
N.A.I.C.S.: 325193
Vivek Viswanathan (Co-Mng Dir)

SIRAKORN PUBLIC COMPANY LIMITED
53/35 Village No 8, Bangkrang Sub-District Muang, Nonthaburi, 11000, Thailand
Tel.: (66) 203571003   TH
Web Site: https://www.sirakorn.co.th
Year Founded: 1989
SK—(THA)
Rev.: $19,883,694
Assets: $19,192,932
Liabilities: $7,624,195
Net Worth: $11,568,737
Earnings: $1,251,149
Emp.: 125
Fiscal Year-end: 12/31/23
Concrete Product Mfr & Distr
N.A.I.C.S.: 327390
Kovit Hunhirun (Mng Dir)

SIRCA PAINTS INDIA LTD.
G-82 Kirti Nagar, Badli Industrial Area Phase 2 Samaypur, Delhi, 110015, India
Tel.: (91) 1142083083
Web Site: https://www.sircapaints.com
Year Founded: 2006
543686—(BOM)
Rev.: $32,683,101
Assets: $37,409,028
Liabilities: $5,576,908
Net Worth: $31,832,120
Earnings: $5,528,050
Emp.: 239
Fiscal Year-end: 03/31/23
Painting Product Mfr & Distr
N.A.I.C.S.: 325510
Sanjay Aggarwal (Chm & Mng Dir)

SIRCONIC GROUP GMBH
Muenchner Strasse 3, 83395, Freilassing, Germany
Tel.: (49) 8654 778851 0   De
Web Site: http://www.sirconic-group.de
Year Founded: 2002
Sales Range: $1-9.9 Million
Customized Commercial Content Management & eBusiness Software Publisher
N.A.I.C.S.: 541511
Michael Grassmann (Co-Founder & Mng Partner)

SIREINE AUTO BOURG LA REINE
12 B Avenue Du General Leclerc, 92340, Bourg-la-Reine, France
Tel.: (33) 146111515
Web Site: http://www.sireine-auto.com
Rev.: $23,900,000
Emp.: 50
Automobile Dealership
N.A.I.C.S.: 441110
Nathalie Ponthieux (Gen Mgr)

SIREN GOLD LIMITED
Level 2 41-43 Ord Street, West Perth, 6005, WA, Australia
Tel.: (61) 864584200   AU
Web Site: https://www.sirengold.com.au
Year Founded: 2017
SNG—(ASX)
Rev.: $17,439
Assets: $13,121,360
Liabilities: $335,150
Net Worth: $12,786,210
Earnings: ($1,346,861)
Fiscal Year-end: 12/31/23
Gold Ore & Silver Ore Mining
N.A.I.C.S.: 212220
Sebastian Andre (Sec)

SIRETUL PASCANI SA
Strada Moldovei 19 Pascani, 705200, Iasi, Romania
Tel.: (40) 232 719 151
Web Site: http://www.siretul.ro
Sales Range: $1-9.9 Million
Emp.: 282
Textile & Apparel Mfr
N.A.I.C.S.: 314999
Constantin Zamcanu (Gen Dir)

SIRIM BERHAD
1 Persiaran Dato Menteri Section 2, PO Box 7035, Shah Alam, 40700, Selangor, Malaysia
Tel.: (60) 3 5544 6000   MY
Web Site: http://www.sirim.my
Technology & Industrial Research Services
N.A.I.C.S.: 541715
Ahmad Fadzil Mohamad Hani (Pres & CEO)

Subsidiaries:

SIRIM Tech Venture Sdn. Bhd. (1)
Lot 13 Jalan Pahat 16/8A Section 16, Shah Alam, 40 200, Selangor Darul Ehsan, Malaysia   (100%)
Tel.: (60) 3 5510 0433
Web Site: http://www.sirimtechventure.my
Research & Development Services
N.A.I.C.S.: 541715
Ajmain Kassim (CEO)

SIRIO PHARMA CO., LTD.
No 83 Taishan Rd, Shantou, 515057, Guangdong, China
Tel.: (86) 75486888688
Web Site: https://www.siriopharma.com
Year Founded: 1993
300791—(SSE)
Rev.: $352,019,557
Assets: $587,688,721
Liabilities: $208,394,751
Net Worth: $379,293,970
Earnings: $29,804,898
Fiscal Year-end: 12/31/22
Pharmaceutical Product Mfr & Distr
N.A.I.C.S.: 325412
Peiqing Lin (Chm & Gen Mgr)

Subsidiaries:

Ayanda GmbH (1)
Am Hunengrab 20, 16928, Pritzwalk, Germany
Tel.: (49) 339866360
Web Site: http://www.sirio-europe.com
Pharmaceuticals Product Mfr
N.A.I.C.S.: 325412
Peiqing Lin (Mng Dir)

SIRIO SPA
Via Filippo Re 43-45, Fornace Zarattini, 48124, Ravenna, Italy
Tel.: (39) 0544502414
Web Site: http://www.siriospa.it
Year Founded: 1993
Catering Services
N.A.I.C.S.: 721110
Luciano Giuseppe Lomonaco (Founder & Chm)

SIRIOS RESOURCES INC.
1400 Marie-Victorin 210, Montreal, J3V 6B9, QC, Canada
Tel.: (450) 482-0603
Web Site: https://www.sirios.com
SOI—(TSXV)
Rev.: $169,973
Assets: $27,941,178
Liabilities: $1,592,123
Net Worth: $26,349,055
Earnings: ($726,967)
Emp.: 7
Fiscal Year-end: 06/30/24
Natural Resources Exploration & Production

SIRIOS RESOURCES INC.

Sirios Resources Inc.—(Continued)
N.A.I.C.S.: 212220
Dominique Doucet (Pres & CEO)

SIRIUS PETROLEUM PLC
1st Floor 25 Bury Street, London,
SW1Y 6AL, United Kingdom
Tel.: (44) 2037407460
Web Site:
  http://www.siriuspetroleum.com
Rev.: $59,000
Assets: $18,594,000
Liabilities: $6,573,000
Net Worth: $12,021,000
Earnings: ($2,269,000)
Emp.: 10
Fiscal Year-end: 12/31/17
Petroleum Exploration Services
N.A.I.C.S.: 211120
Olukayode Kuti (CEO)

SIRIUS REAL ESTATE LIMITED
Plaza House Fifth Floor Admiral Park,
Saint Peter Port, GY1 2HU, Channel
Islands, Guernsey
Tel.: (44) 1481746024
Web Site: https://www.sirius-real-
  estate.com
SRE—(LSE)
Rev.: $291,495,791
Assets: $2,577,919,275
Liabilities: $1,285,452,191
Net Worth: $1,292,467,084
Earnings: $86,013,382
Emp.: 421
Fiscal Year-end: 03/31/24
Real Estate Company
N.A.I.C.S.: 237210
Andrew Coombs (CEO)

Subsidiaries:

Bizspace Ltd. (1)
Kinnaird House 1 Pall Mall East, London,
SW1Y 5AU, United Kingdom
Tel.: (44) 2083717180
Web Site: https://www.bizspace.co.uk
Emp.: 213
Commercial Real Estate Services
N.A.I.C.S.: 531312
Emma Long (Dir-Sls & Mktg)

Sirius Facilities GmbH (1)
Eichhornstrasse 3, 10785, Berlin, Germany
Tel.: (49) 8004040880
Web Site: https://www.siriusfacilities.com
Emp.: 302
Real Estate Development Services
N.A.I.C.S.: 531390

SIRIUS XM CANADA HOLDINGS INC.
135 Liberty Street 4th Floor, Toronto,
M6K 1A7, ON, Canada
Tel.: (416) 408-6000
Web Site: http://www.siriusxm.ca
Year Founded: 2002
Satellite Radio Entertainment Services
N.A.I.C.S.: 516210
Mark Redmond (Pres & CEO)

Subsidiaries:

Sirius XM Canada Inc. (1)
135 Liberty Street 4th Floor, Toronto, M6K
1A7, ON, Canada
Tel.: (416) 513-7470
Web Site: http://www.sirius.ca
Satellite Radio Broadcasting Services
N.A.I.C.S.: 516110

SIRIUSPOINT LTD.
3 Waterloo Lane, Pembroke, HM 08,
Bermuda
Tel.: (441) 5423300   BM
Web Site: https://www.siriuspt.com
Year Founded: 2011
SPNT—(NYSE)
Rev.: $2,737,300,000

Assets: $12,871,500,000
Liabilities: $10,340,900,000
Net Worth: $2,530,600,000
Earnings: $363,700,000
Emp.: 999
Fiscal Year-end: 12/31/23
Holding Company; Property & Casualty Reinsurance Services
N.A.I.C.S.: 551112
Thomas Leonardo (Head-Accident & Health-Global)

SIRIUSVISION CO., LTD.
1189-4 Nippa-cho, Kohoku-ku, Yokohama, 223-0057, Kanagawa, Japan
Tel.: (81) 455959288
Web Site: https://www.siriusvision.jp
Year Founded: 1966
6276—(TKS)
Rev.: $16,214,830
Assets: $23,794,040
Liabilities: $4,339,080
Net Worth: $19,454,960
Earnings: $638,100
Emp.: 112
Fiscal Year-end: 12/31/23
Printing Machinery Mfr
N.A.I.C.S.: 333248
Junichi Tsujitani (Pres)

Subsidiaries:

NAVITAS (Shanghai) Co., Ltd. (1)
407room King Tower 28 Xin Jin Qiao Road,
Pudong District, Shanghai, China
Tel.: (86) 21 38726010
Printing Machine Mfr & Distr
N.A.I.C.S.: 333248

NAVITAS (Suzhou) Co., Ltd. (1)
5-4A Chunhui Road Weiting Zhen, Suzhou
Industrial Park, Suzhou, 215122, Jiangsu
Province, China
Tel.: (86) 512 62753008
Web Site: http://www.navitas.com.cn
Printing Machine Mfr & Distr
N.A.I.C.S.: 333248

Navitas Inmolding Solutions Co.,
Ltd. (1)
1-5-15 Hamaderaishizu-cho, Higashi Nishi-
ku, Sakai, 592-8335, Osaka, Japan
Tel.: (81) 72 241 1166
Web Site: http://www.nis-corp.co.jp
Plastic Product Mfr & Distr
N.A.I.C.S.: 326199
Yasuyuki Sekiguchi (Exec Dir)

SIRMA AD
Yanko Komitov 9 Et 2 Ap 9, Burgas,
8000, Bulgaria
Tel.: (359) 82907024
Web Site: http://www.sirmaad.eu
SGH—(BUL)
Rev.: $45,444,696
Assets: $53,905,192
Liabilities: $8,969,526
Net Worth: $44,935,666
Earnings: ($825,056)
Fiscal Year-end: 12/31/23
Ginned Cotton Mfr
N.A.I.C.S.: 115111

SIRMA GROUP HOLDING JSC
135 Tsarigradsko Shosse Blvd, 1784,
Sofia, Bulgaria
Tel.: (359) 29768310   BG
Web Site: https://www.sirma.com
Year Founded: 1992
SGH—(BUL)
Rev.: $43,329,103
Assets: $67,508,001
Liabilities: $17,633,815
Net Worth: $49,874,186
Earnings: ($5,971,747)
Emp.: 498
Fiscal Year-end: 12/31/22
Software Development Services
N.A.I.C.S.: 541511
Chavdar Dimitrov (Co-Founder & Deputy Chm)

Subsidiaries:

EngView Systems Corp. (1)
203-5890 Monkland Ave, Montreal, H4A
1G2, QC, Canada
Tel.: (514) 343-0290
Web Site: http://www.engview.com
Software Distribution Services
N.A.I.C.S.: 541512

Subsidiary (Non-US):

EngView Latin America Ltda (2)
Rua Joao Azevedo Marques 215 sl 13,
09750-030, Sao Bernardo do Campo, Brazil
Tel.: (55) 11 2564 7325
Software Distribution Services
N.A.I.C.S.: 541512
Thais Bardal (Mgr-Sls)

Ontotext AD (1)
Twins Centre fl 3 79 Nikola Gabrovski str,
Sofia, 1700, Bulgaria
Tel.: (359) 2 974 61 60
Web Site: http://www.ontotext.com
Emp.: 55
Computer System Design Services
N.A.I.C.S.: 541512

Panaton Inc. (1)
202 N 9th St Ste 201, Boise, ID 83702
Tel.: (415) 999-4450
Web Site: http://www.panaton.com
Software Consulting Services
N.A.I.C.S.: 541512
Dejan Nenov (CEO)

Sirma ITT Corp. (1)
135 Tsarigradsko shose blvd, Sofia, 1784,
Bulgaria
Tel.: (359) 2 976 8316
Web Site: http://www.sirmaitt.com
Emp.: 40
Software Management Services
N.A.I.C.S.: 541512
Yavor Djonev (CEO)

SIRNAOMICS LTD.
46/F Hopewell Centre 183 Queens
Road East, Wanchai, China (Hong
Kong)
Tel.: (852) 37696260   Ky
Web Site:
  https://www.sirnaomics.com
Year Founded: 2007
2257—(HKG)
Rev.: $2,114,000
Assets: $163,931,000
Liabilities: $52,371,000
Net Worth: $111,560,000
Earnings: ($97,378,000)
Emp.: 222
Fiscal Year-end: 12/31/22
Biotechnology Research & Development Services
N.A.I.C.S.: 541714
Francois J. Lebel (Chief Medical Officer)

Subsidiaries:

Sirnaomics Biopharmaceuticals
(Guangzhou) Co., Ltd. (1)
12 Luoxuan 3 Road STE 4-306 Guangzhou
International Bio-island, Guangzhou, China
Tel.: (86) 2084229842
Pharmaceutical Product Mfr & Distr
N.A.I.C.S.: 325412

Sirnaomics Biopharmaceuticals (Suzhou) Co., Ltd. (1)
218 Xinghu Street STE A4-415 BioBay, Suzhou, China
Tel.: (86) 51262956283
Pharmaceutical Product Mfr & Distr
N.A.I.C.S.: 325412

US Sirnaomics Inc. (1)
20511 Seneca Meadows Pkwy Ste 200,
Germantown, MD 20876
Tel.: (301) 740-1730
Biopharmaceutical Product Research & Development Services
N.A.I.C.S.: 541714

SIROHIA & SONS LTD

INTERNATIONAL PUBLIC

6 Bishop Lefroy Road 4th Floor Suite
No 19, Kolkata, 700 020, India
Tel.: (91) 3340170700
Web Site: https://www.sirohia.com
538667—(BOM)
Rev.: $46,006
Assets: $3,372,550
Liabilities: $5,011
Net Worth: $3,367,539
Earnings: ($17,737)
Emp.: 2
Fiscal Year-end: 03/31/23
Agricultural Chemical Mfr
N.A.I.C.S.: 325320
Rakesh Sirohia (Chm & Mng Dir)

SIRONA BIOCHEM CORP.
c/o WeWork 595 Burrard St, Vancouver, V7X 1L3, BC, Canada
Tel.: (604) 641-4466   BC
Web Site:
  https://www.sironabiochem.com
Year Founded: 2006
ZSB—(DEU)
Rev.: $26,262
Assets: $779,335
Liabilities: $2,675,706
Net Worth: ($1,896,372)
Earnings: ($1,920,403)
Emp.: 7
Fiscal Year-end: 10/31/23
Pharmaceuticals Mfr
N.A.I.C.S.: 325412
Howard Verrico (Founder, Chm, CEO & Sec)

Subsidiaries:

TFChem S.A.S (1)
Voie de l'innovation Pharma Parc II,
Chaussee du Vexin, 27100, Val-de-Reuil,
France
Tel.: (33) 232090116
Web Site: http://www.tfchemistry.com
Sales Range: $50-74.9 Million
Pharmaceutical Products Mfr & Distr
N.A.I.C.S.: 325412
Geraldine Deliencourt-Godefroy (Founder & Chief Scientific Officer)

SIRPUR PAPER MILLS LTD
5-9-22/1/1 1st Floor Adarshnagar,
Hyderabad, 500 063, Andhra
Pradesh, India
Tel.: (91) 40 2323 6301
Web Site: http://www.sirpurpaper.com
Year Founded: 1938
Sales Range: $50-74.9 Million
Paper Mfr
N.A.I.C.S.: 322120

Subsidiaries:

Sirpur Paper Mills Ltd. - Plant (1)
Sirpur-Kaghaznagar, Kagaznagar, 504296,
Andhra Pradesh, India
Tel.: (91) 8738238044
Variety & Colour Paper Mfr
N.A.I.C.S.: 322299

SIRTEC INTERNATIONAL COMPANY LTD.
3F No 49 Guanqian Rd, Zhongzheng
Dist, Taipei, 100, Taiwan
Tel.: (886) 277255356
Web Site: https://www.sirtec.com.tw
Year Founded: 1968
5356—(TPE)
Rev.: $108,595,470
Assets: $199,746,289
Liabilities: $48,011,869
Net Worth: $151,734,420
Earnings: $18,274,894
Fiscal Year-end: 12/31/23
Computer & Peripheral Equipment Mfr
N.A.I.C.S.: 334118
Wang Tze-Chun (Chm, CEO & Gen Mgr)

SIS DISTRIBUTION (THAILAND) PUBLIC COMPANY LIMITED
No 9 Pakin Building 9th Floor Room No 901 Ratchadaphisek Road, Din Daeng, Bangkok, 10400, Thailand
Tel.: (66) 20203000
Web Site: https://www.sisthai.com
Year Founded: 1992
SIS—(THA)
Rev.: $808,913,809
Assets: $297,854,924
Liabilities: $187,813,662
Net Worth: $110,041,262
Earnings: $18,845,898
Emp.: 784
Fiscal Year-end: 12/31/23
IT Products Wholesale Distr
N.A.I.C.S.: 423430

Subsidiaries:

SiS International Holdings Limited (1)
803 Nine Queens Road, Central, China (Hong Kong)
Tel.: (852) 21383938
Web Site: http://www.sisinternational.com.hk
Rev.: $1,176,535,448
Assets: $1,127,157,503
Liabilities: $626,741,168
Net Worth: $500,416,335
Earnings: $14,134,013
Emp.: 1,022
Fiscal Year-end: 12/31/2022
Computer Equipment & Software Whslr
N.A.I.C.S.: 423430
Hwee Noi Lim (Exec Dir)

Subsidiary (Domestic):

SiS International Ltd (2)
3101 No 1 Hung To Road, Kwun Tong, Kowloon, China (Hong Kong)
Tel.: (852) 3 626 8638
Web Site: https://www.sisdistribution.com.hk
Computer Equipment & Software Whslr
N.A.I.C.S.: 423430

SiS Mobile Holdings Limited (2)
3118 No 1 Hung To Road, Kwun Tong, Kowloon, China (Hong Kong)
Tel.: (852) 21383938
Web Site: http://www.sismobile.com.hk
Rev.: $234,266,715
Assets: $26,261,813
Liabilities: $6,045,030
Net Worth: $20,216,783
Earnings: $2,735,130
Emp.: 48
Fiscal Year-end: 12/31/2022
Mobile Phone Distr
N.A.I.C.S.: 423690
Kiah Meng Lim (Mng Dir)

SISB PCL
498/12 Soi Ramkhamhaeng 39 Tepleela 1 Wangthonglang, Bangkok, 10310, Thailand
Web Site: http://www.sisb.ac.th
SISB—(THA)
Rev.: $56,356,995
Assets: $135,334,699
Liabilities: $53,954,001
Net Worth: $81,380,698
Earnings: $19,077,767
Emp.: 1,049
Fiscal Year-end: 12/31/23
Education Services
N.A.I.C.S.: 611710
Yew Hock Koh (Founder & CEO)

SISLEYHONDA.COM.
88 Steeles Avenue West, Thornhill, L4J 1A1, ON, Canada
Tel.: (905) 709-8531
Web Site: http://sisleyhonda.com
Rev.: $53,133,025
Emp.: 105
New & Used Car Dealers
N.A.I.C.S.: 441110
Doug Sanguine (Mgr-Parts)

SISRAM MEDICAL LTD.
OFEK 15 Building 18 HaHarash Street Industrial Park, Caesarea, 38900, Israel
Tel.: (972) 46275357
Web Site: https://www.sisram-medical.com
Year Founded: 2013
1696—(HKG)
Rev.: $359,292,000
Assets: $613,502,000
Liabilities: $143,977,000
Net Worth: $469,525,000
Earnings: $32,898,000
Emp.: 722
Fiscal Year-end: 12/31/23
Medical Equipment Mfr
N.A.I.C.S.: 339112
Liu Yi (Chm)

Subsidiaries:

Shanghai Foshion Medical System Co., Ltd. (1)
No9 9B Lane 449 North Nujiang Road, Shanghai, 200333, China
Tel.: (86) 4008330556
Web Site: https://foshion.net
Pharmaceutical Mfr & Distr
N.A.I.C.S.: 325412

SISTEM FTO 011 A.D.
Autoput za Zagreb 18, Zemun, Belgrade, Serbia
Tel.: (381) 112284050
Year Founded: 1988
SFTO—(BEL)
Assets: $133,896
Liabilities: $727
Net Worth: $133,168
Earnings: $3,700
Emp.: 114
Fiscal Year-end: 12/31/22
Security System Services
N.A.I.C.S.: 561621
Aleksandar Hajdukovic (Exec Dir)

SISTEMA PJSFC
13/1 Mokhovaya St, Moscow, 125009, Russia
Tel.: (7) 4957370101   RU
Web Site: https://www.sistema.com
Year Founded: 1993
AKFS—(MOEX)
Rev.: $10,808,301,060
Assets: $23,637,910,320
Liabilities: $21,935,868,060
Net Worth: $1,702,042,260
Earnings: $718,530,210
Emp.: 150,000
Fiscal Year-end: 12/31/21
Diversified Holding Company
N.A.I.C.S.: 551112
Ali Musayevich Uzdenov (Mng Partner & Member-Mgmt Bd)

Subsidiaries:

Agroholding Steppe JSC (1)
Soborny Pereulok 19, 344002, Rostov-na-Donu, Russia
Tel.: (7) 8633090710
Web Site: http://www.ahstep.ru
Agricultural Services
N.A.I.C.S.: 115116
Uzdenov Ali (Co-Chm)

JSC Sistema Mass media (1)
Shchepkina 51/4 1, 129110, Moscow, Russia
Tel.: (7) 4952296363
Web Site: http://sistema.vc
Video Production & Distribution Services
N.A.I.C.S.: 512110

NVision Group JSC (1)
29/2 Novoslobodskaya Str, 127055, Moscow, Russia
Tel.: (7) 495 641 12 12
Web Site: http://www.nvg.ru
IT Services
N.A.I.C.S.: 541512

Subsidiary (Non-US):

NVision Czech Republic a.s. (2)
Ohradni 1369/8 Michle, 140 00, Prague, Czech Republic
Tel.: (420) 211 029 115
Web Site: http://www.nvisioncz.com
Emp.: 200
Communications Equipment & Information Transmittal Systems Mfr
N.A.I.C.S.: 334290

NVision Ukraine, AO (2)
1 Severo Syretskaya Uilitsa, Kiev, 04136, Ukraine
Tel.: (380) 44 239 99 99
Emp.: 1,000
Information Technology Products & Services
N.A.I.C.S.: 541512
Anatoliy Mysnyk (Head-Network Infrastructure)

OJSC ANK Bashneft (1)
30 Karl Marks St, Ufa, 450077, Russia
Tel.: (7) 495 228 1596
Oil & Gas Exploration Services
N.A.I.C.S.: 213112

RTI JSC (1)
st Elektrozavodskaya 27/9, 107023, Moscow, Russia   (84.7%)
Tel.: (7) 4957880007
Web Site: http://www.aorti.ru
Holding Company
N.A.I.C.S.: 551112

Subsidiary (Domestic):

JSC RTI Systems Concern (2)
8th March 10 P 1, Moscow, 127 083, Russia
Tel.: (7) 495 614 16 72
Web Site: http://www.rtisystems.ru
Radio & Defense System Research Services
N.A.I.C.S.: 541715

Mikron JSC (2)
Akademika Valieva street 6/1 Zelenograd, 124460, Moscow, Russia
Tel.: (7) 9166064994
Web Site: http://en.mikron.ru
Microelectronics Mfr
N.A.I.C.S.: 335999
Gennady Krasnikov (Gen Dir)

Segezha Group (1)
10 Presnenskaya emb Block C, 123112, Moscow, Russia
Tel.: (7) 4999628200
Web Site: http://www.segezha-group.com
Holding Company; Pulp, Paper & Sawmills Operator; Timber Tract Operations
N.A.I.C.S.: 551112
Evgeniy Batalov (Member-Mgmt Bd, VP & Head-Woodwork & Forest Resources Div)

Subsidiary (Domestic):

JSC Segezha Pulp & Paper Mill (2)
Zavodskaya Street 1, 186420, Segezha, Karelia, Russia
Tel.: (7) 81431 4 3311
Web Site: http://www.scbk.ru
Emp.: 2,000
Pulp & Paper Mill Operator
N.A.I.C.S.: 322120
Alexander Uvarov (Head-Mktg Res)

Subsidiary (Non-US):

Segezha Packaging Limited (2)
Unit 1 Block 4 Ashbourne Business Park, Ashbourne, Ireland
Tel.: (353) 1 835 8866
Web Site: http://www.segezha-packaging.com
Emp.: 1,000
Packing Paper Mfr
N.A.I.C.S.: 322299

Subsidiary (Non-US):

OOO Segezha Packaging (3)
28 Petrovsko-Razumovskiy Passage, 127287, Moscow, Russia
Tel.: (7) 499 962 8200
Web Site: http://www.segezha-packaging.ru
Paper Packaging Products Whslr
N.A.I.C.S.: 424130
Roman Borisov (Sls Dir)

Sacchificio Tordera S.p.A. (3)
Via S Michele Del Carso 163, IT-21100, Varese, Italy
Tel.: (39) 0332261549
Web Site: http://www.segezha-packaging.com
Packing Paper Mfr
N.A.I.C.S.: 322220

Segezha Packaging A/S (3)
Stigsborgvej 36, DK 9400, Norresundby, Denmark
Tel.: (45) 96323232
Web Site: http://www.segezha-packaging.com
Sales Range: $50-74.9 Million
Paper Sack Mfr & Sales
N.A.I.C.S.: 322299
Rob Franken (Officer-Reg Sls)

Segezha Packaging GmbH (3)
Fautenbacher Str 24, DE-77855, Achern, Germany
Tel.: (49) 7841 64 60
Web Site: http://www.segezha-packaging.com
Paper Sack Mfr
N.A.I.C.S.: 322299

Segezha Packaging S.A.S. (3)
Immeuble Acmo 10 Avenue Reaumur, FR-92140, Clamart, France
Tel.: (33) 171 54 7111
Web Site: http://www.segezha-packaging.com
Paper Mfr
N.A.I.C.S.: 322299

Segezha Packaging, s.r.o. (3)
Uvalno 343, CZ-79391, Uvalno, Czech Republic
Tel.: (420) 554699111
Web Site: http://www.segezha-packaging.com
Paper Sack Mfr
N.A.I.C.S.: 322220

Sistema-Hals Development Company (1)
5/4 B Tatarskaya Street, Moscow, 115184, Russia   (71.1%)
Tel.: (7) 957857742
Web Site: http://www.sistema-hals.ru
Real Estate Owner, Developer & Manager
N.A.I.C.S.: 531390

VAO Intourist (1)
Shabolovka street 31G, Moscow, Russia
Tel.: (7) 4957301950
Web Site: http://www.intourist.com
Tourism
N.A.I.C.S.: 561520

SITA ENTERPRISES LIMITED
Tardeo Road, Mumbai, 400034, India
Tel.: (91) 2266627383   In
Web Site: https://www.sitaenterprises.com
Year Founded: 1982
512589—(BOM)
Rev.: $81,227
Assets: $1,457,567
Liabilities: $21,933
Net Worth: $1,435,634
Earnings: $38,224
Emp.: 3
Fiscal Year-end: 03/31/21
Financial Investment Services
N.A.I.C.S.: 523999
Vasant Kumar Vora (CFO)

SITA INC. N.V.
26 Chemin De Joinville 1216 Cointrin, BP 31, Geneva, 1216, Switzerland
Tel.: (41) 227476000
Web Site: http://www.sita.aero
Year Founded: 1949
Sales Range: $700-749.9 Million
Emp.: 3,500
Air transport Communications & Information Technology Solutions
N.A.I.C.S.: 517112
Ian Riddell (Sr VP-Corp & Tech Svcs)

SITA INC. N.V.

SITA Inc. N.V.—(Continued)

Subsidiaries:

CHAMP Cargosystems S.A (1)
Lux Tech Center building 2 rue Edmond Reuter Zone d'Activites, Weiergewan, 5326, Contern, Luxembourg
Tel.: (352) 26 81 62 02
Web Site: http://www.champ.aero
Information Technology Consulting Services
N.A.I.C.S.: 541512
Arnaud Lambert (CEO)

Subsidiary (Non-US):

CHAMP Cargosystems (Germany) GmbH (2)
Saonestrasse 3a, 60528, Frankfurt, Germany
Tel.: (49) 6966906200
Information Technology Consulting Services
N.A.I.C.S.: 541512
Markus Flacke (Mng Dir)

CHAMP Cargosystems (Switzerland) AG (2)
Werdstrasse 21, 8004, Zurich, Switzerland
Tel.: (41) 442458140
Information Technology Consulting Services
N.A.I.C.S.: 541512
Walter Mittelholzer (Product Mgr)

CHAMP Cargosystems (UK) Ltd (2)
The Old Vinyl Factory 252-254 Blyth Road, Hayes, UB3 1HA, Middlesex, United Kingdom
Tel.: (44) 2085878098
Information Technology Consulting Services
N.A.I.C.S.: 541512

CHAMP Cargosystems Philippines, Inc. (2)
7F Robinsons Summit Center 6783 Ayala Avenue, Makati, 1226, Philippines
Tel.: (63) 29765830
Information Technology Consulting Services
N.A.I.C.S.: 541512
L. C. Angeles (Mng Dir)

SITA Inc. (1)
11 Loyang Way, Singapore, 508723, Singapore
Tel.: (65) 6545 3711
Web Site: http://www.sita.aero
Communications & IT Services
N.A.I.C.S.: 517810
Sumesh Patel (Pres-Asia Pacific)

Subsidiary (Non-US):

SITA Inc. (2)
Levell 6 100 Arthur St, North Sydney, 2060, NSW, Australia
Tel.: (61) 292401530
Web Site: http://www.sita.com
Sales Range: $25-49.9 Million
Emp.: 50
Communications & IT Services
N.A.I.C.S.: 517810

SITA SC (1)
26 Chemin De Joinville, BP 131, 1216, Geneva, Switzerland
Tel.: (41) 227476111
Web Site: http://www.sita.aero
Sales Range: $100-124.9 Million
Emp.: 300
Shared Communications Services
N.A.I.C.S.: 517810
Paul Coby (Chm)

Signature Technologies Inc. (1)
3728 Benner Rd, Miamisburg, OH 45342
Tel.: (937) 859-6323
Sales Range: $10-24.9 Million
Emp.: 50
Transportation Signaling Devices
N.A.I.C.S.: 334290
Daniel Morton (Mgr-HR)

SITARA CHEMICAL INDUSTRIES LTD.

32 KM Sheikhupura Road, Faisalabad, Pakistan
Tel.: (92) 414689141
Web Site: https://www.sitara.com.pk
SITC—(KAR)
Rev.: $91,172,408
Assets: $192,621,387
Liabilities: $87,652,491
Net Worth: $104,968,897
Earnings: $6,357,591
Emp.: 2,172
Fiscal Year-end: 06/30/19
Caustic Soda Mfr
N.A.I.C.S.: 325998
Muhammad Adrees (CEO)

Subsidiaries:

Aziz Fatimah Medical and Dental College (1)
West Canal Road, Faisal Town, Faisalabad, Pakistan
Tel.: (92) 4187529315
Web Site: https://www.afmdc.edu.pk
Healtcare Services
N.A.I.C.S.: 621999

Sitara Developers (pvt.) Ltd (1)
434 D McDonald, Faisalabad, 38000, Pakistan
Tel.: (92) 414689141
Web Site: http://www.sitaramall.pk
Property Management Services
N.A.I.C.S.: 531312
Ijaz Ahmed Qaiser (Mgr-Ops)

SITARA ENERGY LTD.

4th Floor Sitara Tower Sitara Chowk New Civil Lines, PO Box No 256, Faisalabad, Pakistan
Tel.: (92) 412644069   PK
Web Site: https://www.sitara.pk
Year Founded: 1991
SEL—(PSX)
Rev.: $3,841,004
Assets: $12,620,031
Liabilities: $8,508,508
Net Worth: $4,111,523
Earnings: ($372,446)
Emp.: 75
Fiscal Year-end: 06/30/23
Electric Power Generation & Distribution Services
N.A.I.C.S.: 221111
Mian Javed Iqbal (CEO)

SITARA PEROXIDE LTD.

26-KM Sheikhupura Road, Faisalabad, Pakistan
Tel.: (92) 412400900
Web Site: http://www.sitaraperoxide.com
Year Founded: 1981
SPL—(PSX)
Rev.: $6,269,468
Assets: $14,052,018
Liabilities: $6,368,136
Net Worth: $7,683,882
Earnings: ($1,227,510)
Emp.: 292
Fiscal Year-end: 06/30/22
Chemical Products Mfr
N.A.I.C.S.: 325199
Sharmeen Imran (Chm)

SITASHREE FOOD PRODUCTS LTD.

332/4/2 RD Udyog Nagar, Palda Nemavar Road, Indore, 452001, MP, India
Tel.: (91) 8120881208
Web Site: http://www.sitashri.com
Rev.: $20,180
Assets: $25,204,401
Liabilities: $42,962,898
Net Worth: ($17,758,497)
Earnings: ($5,067,831)
Emp.: 3
Fiscal Year-end: 03/31/18
Wheat & Pulse Product Processor
N.A.I.C.S.: 111140
Dinesh Agrawal (Founder, Chm & CFO)

SITC INTERNATIONAL HOLDINGS COMPANY LIMITED

21/F World Trade Centre 280 Gloucester Road, Causeway Bay, China (Hong Kong)
Tel.: (852) 28243748   Ky
Web Site: http://www.sitc.com
1308—(HKG)
Rev.: $2,428,959,000
Assets: $2,652,463,000
Liabilities: $721,405,000
Net Worth: $1,931,058,000
Earnings: $536,174,000
Emp.: 2,142
Fiscal Year-end: 12/31/23
Marine Transportation Services
N.A.I.C.S.: 488320
Shaopeng Yang (Chm)

Subsidiaries:

PT. SITC Indonesia (1)
Menara Bidakara 1 Level 2 Jl Jend Gatot Subroto Kav 71-73, Jakarta, 12870, Indonesia
Web Site: http://www.sitc.co.id
Freight Transportation Services
N.A.I.C.S.: 488510

SITC Container Lines (Sarawak) Sdn. Bhd. (1)
Shoplot 4376 Lot 3804 Ground Floor Jalan Diwarta Parkcity COMM, Square Phase 7 Bintulu Town District, 97000, Bintulu, Sarawak, Malaysia
Tel.: (60) 86351811
Logistic Services
N.A.I.C.S.: 488510
Marco Xu (Branch Mgr)

SITC Japan Co., Ltd. (1)
Freight Transportation Services
N.A.I.C.S.: 488510

SITC Logistics (Japan) Co., Ltd. (1)
Tel.: (81) 783338228
Freight Forwarding Services
N.A.I.C.S.: 488510

SITC Shipping Asia Pte. Limited (1)
15 Hoe Chiang Road 13-04Tower Fifteen, Singapore, 89316, Singapore
Tel.: (65) 63335819
Web Site: http://www.sitc.com
Freight Transportation Services
N.A.I.C.S.: 488510

SITC Steamship Co., Ltd. (1)
9F No 69 Sec 3 Minsheng E Rd, Taipei, Taiwan
Tel.: (886) 225048598
Freight Transportation Services
N.A.I.C.S.: 488510

SITC Vietnam Co., Ltd. (1)
R419 420 421 TD Business Center Lot 20A Le Hong Phong Dang Giang, Ngo Quyen, Haiphong, Vietnam
Tel.: (84) 2253757800
Web Site: https://sitc.vn
Freight Transportation Services
N.A.I.C.S.: 488510

SITE GROUP INTERNATIONAL LTD

Tel.: (61) 731145188
Web Site: http://www.site.edu.au
SIT—(ASX)
Rev.: $6,053,607
Assets: $6,631,562
Liabilities: $4,561,379
Net Worth: $2,070,183
Earnings: ($2,681,581)
Emp.: 49
Fiscal Year-end: 06/30/24
Vocational Education Services
N.A.I.C.S.: 611710
Vernon Alan Wills (CEO, Mng Dir & Dir-Intl Ops)

Subsidiaries:

Site Education Australia Pty Ltd (1)
1 Holden St, 5007, Hindmarsh, SA, Australia
Tel.: (61) 883462788
Web Site: http://www.site.edu.au

Educational Support Services
N.A.I.C.S.: 611710

Site Group Holdings Pty Ltd (1)
L 3 Hindmarsh Stadium Holden St, Hindmarsh, 5007, SA, Australia
Tel.: (61) 883462788
Investment Management Service
N.A.I.C.S.: 523940

SITE INTEGRATION PLUS INC.

1356 rue Newton, Boucherville, J4B 5H2, QC, Canada
Tel.: (450) 449-0094   QC
Web Site: http://www.groupe-sip.com
Year Founded: 2001
Electrical & Telecommunications Contractor
N.A.I.C.S.: 238210
David Lefrancois (Dir-Major Accts-Security)

SITEC INDUSTRIETECHNOLOGIE GMBH

Bornaer Str 192, 9114, Chemnitz, Germany
Tel.: (49) 3714708241
Web Site: http://www.sitec-technology.de
Year Founded: 1991
Sales Range: $25-49.9 Million
Industrial Machinery Mfr
N.A.I.C.S.: 333248
Jorg Lassig (Co-Mng Dir)

SITECH ATLANTIC LTD.

81 Ilsley Avenue Unit 7, Dartmouth, B3B 1L5, NS, Canada
Tel.: (902) 468-4181
Web Site: http://www.sitech-atlantic.ca
Year Founded: 2010
Construction Equipment Distr
N.A.I.C.S.: 423810

SITEMAKER SOFTWARE LIMITED

50 Eastcastle Street Suite 360, London, W1W 8EA, United Kingdom
Tel.: (44) 207 580 4155
Web Site: http://www.moonfruit.com
Sales Range: $1-9.9 Million
Emp.: 20
Software Publisher & Website Developer
N.A.I.C.S.: 513210
Wendy Tan White (Co-Founder & CEO)

SITESERV INVESTMENTS LIMITED

The Grange Newcastle Road, Lucan Co, Dublin, Ireland
Tel.: (353) 16011500   IE
Web Site: http://www.siteserv.com
Year Founded: 2012
Sales Range: $200-249.9 Million
Emp.: 2,300
Holding Company; Contract Construction Support Services
N.A.I.C.S.: 551112
Denis O'Brien (Owner & CEO)

Subsidiaries:

Deborah Services Limited (1)
Unit C Cedar Court Office Park Denby Dale Road, Thornes Moor Road, Wakefield, WF4 3QZ, Calder Grove, United Kingdom
Tel.: (44) 1924378222
Web Site: http://www.deborahservices.co.uk
Contract Scaffolding & Industrial Services
N.A.I.C.S.: 238990
Steve Flounders (Mng Dir)

RoanKabin Manufacturing Limited (1)
Old Milltown, Kill, Kildare, Ireland
Tel.: (353) 45886100
Web Site: http://www.roankabin.ie

AND PRIVATE COMPANIES — SIVA VENTURES LIMITED

Emp.: 30
Modular, Off-Site & Portable Building Mfr & Sales
N.A.I.C.S.: 236117
Tom Mcdormitt (Mgr-Ops)

Subsidiary (Domestic):

RoanKabin Sales & Marketing Limited (2)
Old Milltown, Kill, Kildare, Ireland
Tel.: (353) 45886100
Web Site: http://www.roankabin.ie
Sales Range: $25-49.9 Million
Emp.: 27
Modular, Off-Site & Portable Building Sales
N.A.I.C.S.: 423990
Declan Duignan (Mgr-Sls)

Sierra Communications Limited (1)
Knockmitten Lane North, New Nangor Road, Dublin, 12, Ireland
Tel.: (353) 14190900
Web Site: http://www.sierra.ie
Sales Range: $250-299.9 Million
Emp.: 850
Utilities Contractor
N.A.I.C.S.: 238990
T. J. Malone (Mng Dir)

Subsidiary (Domestic):

Holgate Infrastructure & Motorway Services Limited (2)
Westland House, New Nagor Road, Dublin, 12, Ireland
Tel.: (353) 1 419 0900
Web Site: http://www.holgate.ie
Contract Vehicle Containment & Environmental Noise Barrier Erection Services
N.A.I.C.S.: 238990
Patrick O'Reilly (Dir-Accoustic Solutions)

Siteserv Access & Formwork (1)
The Grange Newcastle Road, Lucan Co, Dublin, Ireland
Tel.: (353) 16011500
Web Site: http://www.siteservaccess.ie
Emp.: 30
Peri Formwork, Scaffolding & Temporary Fencing Contractor Services
N.A.I.C.S.: 238990
Keith English (Controller-Fin)

SITEX PROPERTIES AG
Alpenblickstrasse 20, 8853, Lachen, Switzerland
Tel.: (41) 415458510
Web Site: http://www.sitex.ch
Year Founded: 2010
Rev.: $328,461,000
Real Estate Investment Services
N.A.I.C.S.: 523999
Adriana Ospel (Chm)

SITHEGA HOLDINGS (PTY) LTD.
Suite 7 1st Floor Katherine & West 114 West Street Message, Sandton, 2196, South Africa
Tel.: (27) 110442600
Web Site: http://www.sithega.co.za
Year Founded: 2018
Holding Company
N.A.I.C.S.: 551112
Thabo Dloti (Mng Dir)

Subsidiaries:

Prescient Limited (1)
Prescient House Westlake Business Park Otto Close Westlake, Cape Town, 7945, South Africa
Tel.: (27) 217003600
Web Site: http://www.prescient.co.za
Investment Management, Fund Services & Administration, Stockbroking, Wealth Management, Retail & Institutional Retirement & Insurance Products
N.A.I.C.S.: 523999
Herman Steyn (Exec Dir)

SITI B&T GROUP S.P.A.
Via Prampolini 18, 41043, Formigine, MO, Italy
Tel.: (39) 059446111
Web Site: http://www.sitibt.com
Year Founded: 1961
SITI—(ITA)
Sales Range: Less than $1 Million
Industrial Machinery Mfr
N.A.I.C.S.: 333248
Fabio Tarozzi (Chm & CEO)

SITKA GOLD CORP.
1500-409 Granville Street, Vancouver, V6C 1T2, BC, Canada
Tel.: (604) 979-0509
Web Site: https://www.sitkagoldcorp.com
SIG—(TSXV)
Rev.: $32,660
Assets: $15,385,645
Liabilities: $2,188,406
Net Worth: $13,197,239
Earnings: ($1,302,283)
Fiscal Year-end: 12/31/22
Metal Exploration Services
N.A.I.C.S.: 213114
Mike Burke (VP)

SITOBIOTECH CO.,LTD.
Renxin industrial park, Dingtao district, Heze, 274100, Shandong, China
Tel.: (86) 5302264997
Web Site: https://www.sitobiotech.com
Year Founded: 2010
300583—(CHIN)
Rev.: $180,257,450
Assets: $456,388,142
Liabilities: $165,469,988
Net Worth: $290,918,154
Earnings: $6,423,323
Fiscal Year-end: 12/31/23
Biological Drug Product Mfr & Distr
N.A.I.C.S.: 325412
Mi Qi (Chm)

SITOY GROUP HOLDINGS LTD.
9/F Sitoy Tower No 164 Wai Yip Street KwunTong, Kowloon, China (Hong Kong)
Tel.: (852) 23450295
Web Site: https://www.sitoy.com
1023—(HKG)
Rev.: $183,780,893
Assets: $299,011,367
Liabilities: $73,459,527
Net Worth: $225,551,840
Earnings: ($19,818,938)
Emp.: 4,000
Fiscal Year-end: 06/30/21
Handbags & Leather Goods Mfr
N.A.I.C.S.: 316990
Michael Wah keung Yeung (Chm)

Subsidiaries:

Sitoy (Hong Kong) Handbag Factory Limited (1)
4-5/F The Genplas Building 56 Hoi Yuen Road, Kwun Tong, Kowloon, China (Hong Kong)
Tel.: (852) 23450295
Handbag Mfr
N.A.I.C.S.: 316990

Sitoy (Yingde) Luggage Co., Ltd. (1)
Huaqiao Industrial Zone, Yingde, Donghuang, Guangdong, China
Tel.: (86) 763 263 0698
Travel Goods Mfr & Distr
N.A.I.C.S.: 316990

SITRA HOLDINGS INTERNATIONAL LIMITED
15 Hillview Terrace, Singapore, 669226, Singapore
Tel.: (65) 67423223
Web Site: https://www.sitraholdings.com
Year Founded: 1979
5LE—(CAT)
Rev.: $10,989,016
Assets: $9,470,832
Liabilities: $2,708,896
Net Worth: $6,761,936
Earnings: ($1,664,763)
Emp.: 31
Fiscal Year-end: 12/31/23
Wood Product Distr
N.A.I.C.S.: 321999
Teresa Tan (Founder)

Subsidiaries:

Sitra Agencies Pte Ltd (1)
37 Tannery Ln, Singapore, 347790, Singapore
Tel.: (65) 6841 4339
Furniture Distr
N.A.I.C.S.: 423210

Sitra Dove Construction & Logistic Pte. Ltd. (1)
18 Sungei Kadut Street 2, Singapore, Singapore
Tel.: (65) 67422133
Logistics Consulting Servies
N.A.I.C.S.: 541614

Suncoast Sitra Pte Ltd (1)
15 Hillview Ter, Singapore, 669226, Singapore
Tel.: (65) 6742 3223
Web Site: http://www.sitraglobal.com
Furniture Distr
N.A.I.C.S.: 423210

SITRONIX TECHNOLOGY CORPORATION
11F-1 No 5 Taiyuan 1st St, Zhubei, 302, Hsinchu, Taiwan
Tel.: (886) 35526500
Web Site: https://www.sitronix.com.tw
Year Founded: 1998
8016—(TAI)
Rev.: $546,874,992
Assets: $640,402,311
Liabilities: $163,113,601
Net Worth: $477,288,710
Earnings: $79,026,257
Emp.: 1,212
Fiscal Year-end: 12/31/23
Integrated Circuits Mfr & Distr
N.A.I.C.S.: 334413
Vincent Mao (Chm, CEO & Gen Mgr)

Subsidiaries:

Forcelead Technology Corp. (1)
6F-9 No 5 Taiyuan 1st St, Hsinchu, Jhubei, 302, Taiwan
Tel.: (886) 35601180
Web Site: https://www.forcelead.com.tw
IC Chip Mfr
N.A.I.C.S.: 334413

INFSitronix Technology Corp. (1)
6F-3 No 5 Taiyuan 1st St, Hsinchu County, Zhubei, 302, Taiwan
Tel.: (886) 35601828
Web Site: http://www.infsitronix.com.tw
Integrated Circuit Design Services
N.A.I.C.S.: 541380

Sensortek Technology Corp. (1)
11F No 5 Taiyuan 2nd St, Hsinchu, Jhubei, 302, Taiwan
Tel.: (886) 35601000
Web Site: https://www.sensortek.com.tw
Sensor Product Mfr
N.A.I.C.S.: 334513
Jacky Chou (Officer-IR)

Sitronix Technology (Shenzhen) Co., Ltd. (1)
26F Building A Sunhope e-Metro No 7018 Caitian Road, Futian District, Shenzhen, China
Tel.: (86) 75583439077
Computer Software Consulting Services
N.A.I.C.S.: 541512

mCore Technology Corp. (1)
6F-2 No 5 Taiyuan 1st St, Hsinchu, Jhubei, 302, Taiwan
Tel.: (886) 35601999
Web Site: https://www.mcore.com.tw
Microcontroller Product Mfr
N.A.I.C.S.: 334413

SIV CAPITAL LIMITED
13 Kurilpa Street, West End, 4101, QLD, Australia
Tel.: (61) 1300934497
Web Site: https://www.sivcapital.com.au
SIV—(ASX)
Rev.: $794,239
Assets: $5,622,549
Liabilities: $80,861
Net Worth: $5,541,688
Earnings: $239,484
Emp.: 120
Fiscal Year-end: 06/30/24
Rental Operations & Rental Finance Services
N.A.I.C.S.: 522291
Allan English (Founder)

SIVA SF
Pirsenteret, Trondheim, N-7462, Norway
Tel.: (47) 48039000
Web Site: http://www.siva.no
Year Founded: 1968
Sales Range: $25-49.9 Million
Emp.: 8,000
Real Estate Services
N.A.I.C.S.: 531210
Espen Susegg (Pres)

Subsidiaries:

SIVA Eiendom Holding (1)
Pirsenteret, Trondheim, 7462, Norway
Tel.: (47) 48039000
Property Management Services
N.A.I.C.S.: 531312

SIVA International Management AS (1)
Havnegata 9, 7010, Trondheim, Norway
Tel.: (47) 913 83 161
Web Site: http://www.sivaim.no
Sales Range: $25-49.9 Million
Emp.: 3
Business Management Consulting Services
N.A.I.C.S.: 541611
Inga Visnevska (Mgr-Intl Project)

Subsidiary (Non-US):

CRONOMAR d.o.o (2)
Velimira Skorpika 6, Sibenik, 22000, Croatia
Tel.: (385) 22 340 480
Web Site: http://www.cronomar.hr
Sales Range: $25-49.9 Million
Emp.: 3
Business Management Consulting Services
N.A.I.C.S.: 541611
Malvin Villabo (CEO)

SIVA VENTURES LIMITED
Sterling Towers 327 Anna Salai, Teynampet, Chennai, 600 006, India
Tel.: (91) 4424313001
Web Site: http://www.svl.co.in
Year Founded: 1986
Sales Range: $50-74.9 Million
Emp.: 200
Investment Holding Company
N.A.I.C.S.: 551112
C. Sivasankaran (Founder & Chm)

Subsidiaries:

Siva Shipping AS (1)
Stortingsgaten 2, N 0158, Oslo, Norway
Tel.: (47) 22030000
Web Site: http://www.sivashipping.com
Sales Range: $25-49.9 Million
Emp.: 10
Shipping Services
N.A.I.C.S.: 483111

Subsidiary (Non-US):

JB Ugland Shipping Singapore Pte. Ltd. (2)
8 Temasek Blvd 22-02 Suntec Tower 3, Sin-

SIVA VENTURES LIMITED

Siva Ventures Limited—(Continued)
gapore, 038988, Singapore
Tel.: (65) 68359008
Web Site: http://www.sivashipping.com
Sales Range: $25-49.9 Million
Shipping Services
N.A.I.C.S.: 483111
Deepak Bhandari (CFO)

WinWinD Oy (1)
Keilaranta 13, FI-02150, Espoo, Finland
Tel.: (358) 207410160
Web Site: http://www.winwind.com
Sales Range: $50-74.9 Million
Emp.: 800
Wind Turbine Mfr
N.A.I.C.S.: 333611
Guru Vijendran (Mng Dir, COO & CFO)

SIVAROM REAL ESTATE PUBLIC COMPANY LIMITED
662/45 Rama 3 Road, Bang Phong Phang Subdistrict Ya Nawa District, Bangkok, 10120, Thailand
Tel.: (66) 22953361
Web Site: https://www.sivarom.co.th
Year Founded: 2017
SVR—(THA)
Rev.: $26,992,647
Assets: $60,192,966
Liabilities: $38,798,172
Net Worth: $21,394,795
Earnings: $2,247,782
Fiscal Year-end: 12/31/23
Real Estate Development Services
N.A.I.C.S.: 531390
Pawin Chamniprasart (Chm)

SIVENT D.D. LJUBLJANA
Tehnoloski park 19, 1000, Ljubljana, Slovenia
Tel.: (386) 1 6208250
Web Site: http://www.sivent.si
Sales Range: $1-9.9 Million
Emp.: 2
Investment Services
N.A.I.C.S.: 523999
Bojana Vinkovic (CEO)

SIVERS SEMINCONDUCTORS AB
Torshamnsgatan 48, 164 40, Kista, Sweden
Tel.: (46) 87036800
Web Site: https://www.sivers-semiconductors.com
Year Founded: 1951
SIVE—(OMX)
Rev.: $12,420,223
Assets: $147,152,210
Liabilities: $31,004,056
Net Worth: $116,148,154
Earnings: ($8,090,890)
Emp.: 130
Fiscal Year-end: 12/31/22
Electronic Components Mfr
N.A.I.C.S.: 334419
Tomas Duffy (Chm)

SIVOTA PLC
New London House 172 Drury Lane, London, WC2B 5QR,
United Kingdom UK
Web Site: https://www.sivotacapital.com
Year Founded: 2011
SIV—(LSE)
Rev.: $5,918,000
Assets: $21,289,000
Liabilities: $4,897,000
Net Worth: $16,392,000
Earnings: ($5,114,000)
Emp.: 30
Fiscal Year-end: 12/31/22
Asset Management Services
N.A.I.C.S.: 523999
Tim Weller (Chm)

SIWANI MAKMUR TBK
Mayapada Tower 1 Lantai 21 Jl Jend Sudirman Kav 28, Jakarta, 12920, Indonesia
Tel.: (62) 215213555
Web Site: http://www.siwani.co.id
Plastic Packaging Products Mfr
N.A.I.C.S.: 326112
Yudhi Surjadjaja (Sec)

SIWARD CRYSTAL TECHNOLOGY CO., LTD.
No 1-1 Ln 111 Sec 3 Zhongshan Rd, Tanzi Dist, Taichung, 427018, Taiwan
Tel.: (886) 425347909
Web Site: https://www.siward.com.tw
Year Founded: 1988
2484—(TAI)
Rev.: $77,026,519
Assets: $172,493,698
Liabilities: $38,743,810
Net Worth: $133,749,889
Earnings: $8,526,832
Emp.: 752
Fiscal Year-end: 12/31/23
Quartz Crystals Mfr & Distr
N.A.I.C.S.: 334419
Chang Yu An (VP)

Subsidiaries:

SCT USA.Inc. (1)
220 W Los Angeles Ave, Simi Valley, CA 93065
Tel.: (805) 584-9495
Web Site: https://www.sct-usa.com
Premium Carbide Cutting Tool Mfr
N.A.I.C.S.: 333515

SE JAPAN Co. (1)
Regus Azabu Green Terrace 5F N 504, Minamiazabu 3-20-1 Minato-ku, Tokyo, 106-0047, Japan
Tel.: (81) 368598580
Web Site: https://www.se-japan.jp
Optical Material Mfr & Distr
N.A.I.C.S.: 333310

SIWARD Electronic Technology (Shenzhen) Inc. (1)
Room 2315 Block A Tian an Digital Times Chegongmiao, Futian District, Shenzhen, 518040, China
Tel.: (86) 75582723201
Electric Component Whslr
N.A.I.C.S.: 423610

Siward Crystal Technology Co., Ltd. - Wuxi Factory (1)
No 10 Hanjiang Road, Wuxi New District, Wuxi, 214028, Jiangsu, China
Tel.: (86) 510 85226747
Web Site: http://www.siward.com.tw
Quartz Crystal Mfr
N.A.I.C.S.: 334419

Siward Crystal Technology Co., Ltd. - Yamagata Factory (1)
3 2 74 Tohrimachi, Yonezawa, 992-0025, Yamagata, Japan
Tel.: (81) 238244318
Sales Range: $25-49.9 Million
Emp.: 30
Crystal Oscillators Mfr
N.A.I.C.S.: 334515

Siward Technology Co., Ltd. (1)
6F-3 No 716 Chung Cheng Road, Chungoo, Taipei, 235, Taiwan
Tel.: (886) 282273839
Sales Range: $100-124.9 Million
Emp.: 500
Quartz Crystal Mfr
N.A.I.C.S.: 339999

SIX GROUP AG
Pfingstweidstrasse 110, CH 8005, Zurich, Switzerland
Tel.: (41) 58 399 2111 CH
Web Site: http://www.six-group.com
Year Founded: 2008
Rev.: $1,163,319,872
Assets: $13,033,157,470
Liabilities: $8,057,974,976
Net Worth: $4,975,182,464
Earnings: $124,086,080
Emp.: 2,710
Fiscal Year-end: 12/31/19
Holding Company; Securities Trading, Securities Services, Financial Information & Payment Transaction Services
N.A.I.C.S.: 551112
Thomas Zeeb (Head-Markets)

Subsidiaries:

BME Clearing SAU (1)
Plaza de la Lealtad 1, 28014, Madrid, Spain
Tel.: (34) 91 709 5000
Web Site: https://www.bmeclearing.es
Clearing Services
N.A.I.C.S.: 522320
Santiago Carrillo Menendez (Chm)

Bolsas y Mercados Espanoles, Sociedad Holding de Mercados Sistemas Financieros, S.A. (1)
Plaza de la Lealtad 1, 28014, Madrid, Spain (93.16%)
Tel.: (34) 915891102
Web Site: http://www.bolsasymercados.es
Rev.: $351,554,151
Assets: $16,482,389,063
Liabilities: $16,025,296,265
Net Worth: $457,092,798
Earnings: $155,884,852
Emp.: 752
Fiscal Year-end: 12/31/2018
Stock Exchange Services
N.A.I.C.S.: 523210
Marta Bartolome (CFO)

Bolsa de Barcelona (2)
Passeig de Gracia 19, 08007, Barcelona, Spain
Tel.: (34) 934013555
Web Site: http://www.borsabcn.es
Sales Range: $50-74.9 Million
Emp.: 63
Stock Exchange Services
N.A.I.C.S.: 523210
Joan Hortala i Arau (Chm)

Bolsa de Bilbao (2)
C Jose Maria Olabarri 1, 48001, Bilbao, Spain
Tel.: (34) 944034400
Web Site: http://www.bolsabilbao.es
Sales Range: $50-74.9 Million
Emp.: 50
Stock Exchange Services
N.A.I.C.S.: 523210

Infobolsa, S.A. (2)
Plaza de la Lealtad 1, 28014, Madrid, Spain
Tel.: (34) 917095610
Web Site: http://www.infobolsa.es
Holding Company
N.A.I.C.S.: 551112

Sociedad Rectora de la Bolsa de Valores de Barcelona, S.A. (2)
Paseo Gracia 19, 08007, Barcelona, Spain (100%)
Tel.: (34) 934013555
Web Site: http://www.borsabcn.es
Sales Range: $50-74.9 Million
Emp.: 41
Securities & Commodity Exchanges
N.A.I.C.S.: 523210
Jose Antuneza (Gen Mgr)

Sociedad Rectora de la Bolsa de Valores de Valencia, S.A. (2)
Calle Libreros 2, Valencia, 46002, Spain (100%)
Tel.: (34) 963870100
Securities & Commodity Exchanges
N.A.I.C.S.: 523210
Vicente Olmos (Pres)

CETREL SA (1)
10 rue Gabriel Lippmann, 05365, Munsbach, Luxembourg
Tel.: (352) 3 55 66 1
Web Site: http://www.cetrel.lu
Credit Card Issuing Services
N.A.I.C.S.: 522210
Roland Ludwig (CEO)

INTERNATIONAL PUBLIC

Europerformance SIX Telekurs (1)
89 avenue Francois-Arago, 92017, Nanterre, Cedex, France
Tel.: (33) 1 7072 4400
Web Site: http://www.europerformance.fr
Financial Investment Services
N.A.I.C.S.: 523940

LATAM Exchanges Data Inc. (1)
1001 Brickell Bay Dr Ste 2734, Miami, FL 33131
Tel.: (786) 671-3311
Web Site: http://www.led-inc.com
Financial Services
N.A.I.C.S.: 523999

Open Finance SL (1)
Calle del Pintor Sorolla 23, 46002, Valencia, Spain
Tel.: (34) 96 045 4600
Web Site: https://www.openfinance.es
Financial Consulting Services
N.A.I.C.S.: 541611

Oslo Clearing ASA (1)
Tollbugt 2, PO Box 4, 51, Oslo, Norway
Tel.: (47) 23 17 96 00
Web Site: http://www.osloclearing.no
Securities Dealing Services
N.A.I.C.S.: 523150
Cato Waehle (CIO)

PayLife Bank GmbH (1)
Marxergasse 1B, Vienna, 1030, Austria
Tel.: (43) 1 717 01 0
Web Site: http://www.paylife.at
Sales Range: $75-99.9 Million
Emp.: 300
Credit Card Products & Services
N.A.I.C.S.: 522210
Robert Komatz (Sr VP-Acquiring Austria)

Subsidiary (Domestic):

PayLife Service GmbH (2)
Marxergasse 1B, 1030, Vienna, Austria
Tel.: (43) 1 717 01 0
Electronic Financial Payment Services
N.A.I.C.S.: 522320

SECB Swiss Euro Clearing Bank GmbH (1)
Solmsstrasse 83, Frankfurt am Main, 60486, Germany
Tel.: (49) 699798980
Web Site: http://www.secb.de
Sales Range: $15-24.9 Billion
Emp.: 23
Credit Institution
N.A.I.C.S.: 522299
Ayse Kun (Mng Dir)

SIX Card Solutions Ltd (1)
Hardturmstrasse 201, 8021, Zurich, Switzerland
Tel.: (41) 848661111
Web Site: http://www.six-group.com
Sales Range: $200-249.9 Million
Emp.: 340
Credit, Debit & Customer Card Processing Services
N.A.I.C.S.: 522320

SIX Digital Exchange Ltd. (1)
Lerchenstrasse 16, 8045, Zurich, Switzerland
Tel.: (41) 58 508 3000
Web Site: https://www.sdx.com
Financial Services
N.A.I.C.S.: 523999
Mathias Studach (Head-Finance-Risk)

SIX Exchange Regulation Ltd. (1)
Hardturmstrasse 201, 8021, Zurich, Switzerland
Tel.: (41) 58 399 3030
Web Site: https://www.ser-ag.com
Exchange Regulation Services
N.A.I.C.S.: 522320
Andreas Von Planta (Chm)

SIX Financial Information (1)
Pfingstweidstrasse 110, 8005, Zurich, Switzerland
Tel.: (41) 583995111
Web Site: http://www.six-group.com
Sales Range: $1-4.9 Billion
Emp.: 3,500
International Financial Investment Information
N.A.I.C.S.: 523999
Thomas Gross (CEO)

AND PRIVATE COMPANIES — SIXT SE

Subsidiary (Domestic):

Rolotec AG (2)
Albrecht-Haller-Strasse 9, 2501, Biel/Bienne, Switzerland
Tel.: (41) 323448600
Web Site: http://www.rolotec.ch
Sales Range: $25-49.9 Million
Emp.: 70
Stock Exchange Information Software
N.A.I.C.S.: 513210
Jorg Buser *(CEO)*

Subsidiary (Non-US):

SIX AB (2)
Olof Palmes gata 11, Stockholm, 11362, Sweden
Tel.: (46) 858616300
Web Site: http://www.six.se
Sales Range: $10-24.9 Million
Emp.: 110
Financial Information Services
N.A.I.C.S.: 519290
Fredrik Koch *(Head-Product Dev & Mktg)*

Subsidiary (Non-US):

SIX Norge AS (3)
Holbergsgate 1, N 0166, Oslo, Norway
Tel.: (47) 23326620
Web Site: http://www.six-telekurs.nl
Financial Information Services
N.A.I.C.S.: 519290

SIX Telekurs Finland Oy (3)
Aleksanterinkatu 17, 00130, Helsinki, Finland
Tel.: (358) 207 33 40 43
Web Site: http://www.six-telekurs.fi
Emp.: 3
Financial Information Services
N.A.I.C.S.: 519290
Bo Nordlander *(Gen Mgr)*

Subsidiary (Non-US):

SIX Financial Information Luxembourg S.A. (2)
15 rue Leon Laval, BP 2135, 3372, Leudelange, Luxembourg
Tel.: (352) 261161
Web Site: http://www.six-financial-information.com
Sales Range: $25-49.9 Million
Emp.: 23
Financial Information Services
N.A.I.C.S.: 519290

SIX Financial Information Monaco SAM (2)
Les Acanthes 6 avenue des Citronniers, 98000, Monaco, Monaco
Tel.: (377) 97977161
Web Site: http://www.six-financial-information.com
Sales Range: Less than $1 Million
Emp.: 4
Financial Information Services
N.A.I.C.S.: 519290

SIX Telekurs (Deutschland) GmbH (2)
Le Palais Herrengasse 1-3 2nd Floor, 1010, Vienna, Austria
Tel.: (43) 153245710
Web Site: http://www.six-financial-information.com
Emp.: 5
Financial Information Services
N.A.I.C.S.: 519290

SIX Telekurs (U.K.) Ltd. (2)
6 Devonshire Square, London, EC2M 4YE, United Kingdom
Tel.: (44) 2075505000
Web Site: http://www.telekurs.co.uk
Sales Range: $25-49.9 Million
Emp.: 60
Financial Information Services
N.A.I.C.S.: 519290
Martin Cole *(Mng Dir)*

SIX Telekurs Espana SA (2)
Paseo de la Castellana 40 bis, Madrid, 28047, Spain
Tel.: (34) 915775500
Web Site: http://www.six-telekurs.es
Sales Range: $25-49.9 Million
Emp.: 15
Financial Information Services
N.A.I.C.S.: 519290
Eric Nadal *(Gen Mgr)*

SIX Telekurs France SAS (2)
5 boulevard Montmartre, 75002, Paris, France
Tel.: (33) 153000100
Web Site: http://www.sixgroup.com
Sales Range: $150-199.9 Million
Emp.: 378
Multi-Platform Financial Data Services
N.A.I.C.S.: 518210
Karl Landolt *(CEO)*

Subsidiary (Domestic):

EuroPerformance (3)
89 avenue Francois Arago, 92017, Nanterre, France
Tel.: (33) 170724400
Web Site: http://www.europerformance.fr
Sales Range: $25-49.9 Million
Emp.: 50
Financial Information Services
N.A.I.C.S.: 519290

Subsidiary (Non-US):

SIX Telekurs Hong Kong Ltd. (2)
19th Fl One International Finance Centre, 1 Harbour View Street, Central, China (Hong Kong)
Tel.: (852) 29710388
Web Site: http://www.sixgroup.com
Sales Range: $25-49.9 Million
Emp.: 35
Financial Information Services
N.A.I.C.S.: 519290

SIX Telekurs Italia S.r.l. (2)
Via del Vecchio Politecnico 3, 20121, Milan, Italy
Tel.: (39) 027645631
Web Site: http://www.telekurs-financial.com
Financial Information Services
N.A.I.C.S.: 519290

SIX Telekurs Japan Ltd. (2)
Hulic Kakigaracho Bldg 5F 1-28-5 Nihonbashi, Chuo ku, Tokyo, 103-0014, Japan
Tel.: (81) 338082271
Web Site: http://www.six-financial-information.com
Sales Range: $25-49.9 Million
Emp.: 22
Financial Information Services
N.A.I.C.S.: 519290

Subsidiary (US):

SIX Telekurs USA Inc. (2)
9 W Broad St Ste 806, Stamford, CT 06907
Tel.: (203) 353-8100
Web Site: http://www.tkusa.com
Sales Range: $50-74.9 Million
Emp.: 110
Financial Information Services
N.A.I.C.S.: 519290

SIX Financial Information Belgium SA (1)
29 Boulevard Louis Schmidt, 1040, Brussels, Belgium
Tel.: (32) 2 790 0500
Financial Services
N.A.I.C.S.: 541513

SIX Financial Information Denmark A/S (1)
Nikolaj Plads 2 5, 1067, Copenhagen, Denmark
Tel.: (45) 33 41 1111
Financial Data Processing Services
N.A.I.C.S.: 522320
Martin Blomqvist *(Acct Mgr)*

SIX Financial Information Deutschland GmbH (1)
Franklinstrasse 61-63, 60486, Frankfurt am Main, Germany
Tel.: (49) 69 717 00 0
Web Site: http://www.six-financial.com
Emp.: 40
Financial Data Processing Services
N.A.I.C.S.: 522320

SIX Financial Information Espana SA (1)
Paseo de la Castellana 40bis, 28046, Madrid, Spain
Tel.: (34) 91 577 5500
Emp.: 8
Financial Data Processing Services
N.A.I.C.S.: 522320
Andres Iguaz *(Mgr-Sls)*

SIX Financial Information Finland Oy (1)
Aleksanterinkatu 17, 00100, Helsinki, Finland
Tel.: (358) 403 52 46 87
Web Site: http://www.sixgroup.fi
Financial Data Processing Services
N.A.I.C.S.: 522320

SIX Financial Information France SAS (1)
4 rue de la Bourse, 75002, Paris, France
Tel.: (33) 1 5300 0100
Financial Data Processing Services
N.A.I.C.S.: 522320
Laurence Lagniel *(Head-IT Dev)*

SIX Financial Information Hong Kong Limited (1)
20/F One International Finance Center 1 Harbour View Street, Central, China (Hong Kong)
Tel.: (852) 852 2971 0388
Financial Data Processing Services
N.A.I.C.S.: 522320

SIX Financial Information Italia Srl (1)
Via del Vecchio Politecnico 3, 20121, Milan, Italy
Tel.: (39) 02 76 45 631
Financial Data Processing Services
N.A.I.C.S.: 522320

SIX Financial Information Japan Ltd (1)
Hulic Kakigaracho Bldg. 5F 1-28-5 Nihonbashi, Kakigaracho Chuo-KuKakigaracho Chuo-Ku, Tokyo, 103-0014, Japan
Tel.: (81) 3 3808 2271
Financial Data Processing Services
N.A.I.C.S.: 522320
Alain Delfosse *(Mng Dir)*

SIX Financial Information Nederland BV (1)
Parnassusweg 819, 1082 LZ, Amsterdam, Netherlands
Tel.: (31) 20 3012 888
Financial Data Processing Services
N.A.I.C.S.: 522320

SIX Financial Information Nordic AB (1)
Olof Palmes Gata 11, 111 37, Stockholm, Sweden
Tel.: (46) 85 861 6300
Financial Services
N.A.I.C.S.: 523999

SIX Financial Information Norway AS (1)
Pilestredet Park 31, 0176, Oslo, Norway
Tel.: (47) 23 32 6620
Web Site: http://www.six-financial-information.com
Emp.: 1
Financial Data Processing Services
N.A.I.C.S.: 522320
Jonas Kullgren *(Head-Sls)*

SIX Financial Information Singapore Pte Ltd (1)
5 Temasek Boulevard, 16-01 Suntex Tower Five, Singapore, 038985, Singapore
Tel.: (65) 6338 3808
Financial Data Processing Services
N.A.I.C.S.: 522320
Bhavesh Shah *(Sr Mgr-Sls)*

SIX Financial Information UK Ltd (1)
6 Devonshire Square, London, EC2M 4YE, United Kingdom
Tel.: (44) 20 7550 5000
Web Site: http://www.six-financial-information.com
Emp.: 80
Financial Data Processing Services
N.A.I.C.S.: 522320

SIX Financial Information USA Inc (1)
48 Wall St 31st Fl, New York, NY 10005
Tel.: (212) 635-5500
Financial Data Processing Services
N.A.I.C.S.: 522320

SIX Interbank Clearing Ltd. (1)
Hardturmstrasse 201, 8021, Zurich, Switzerland
Tel.: (41) 583994200
Web Site: http://www.six-interbank-clearing.com
Sales Range: $50-74.9 Million
Emp.: 70
Interbank Payment System Operator
N.A.I.C.S.: 522320
Andreas Galle *(Head-Bus Mgmt)*

SIX Payment Services (USA) Corp (1)
PO Box 4554, Oak Brook, IL 60522-4554
Tel.: (888) 727-0220
Electronic Financial Payment Services
N.A.I.C.S.: 522320

SIX Paynet Ltd. (1)
Hardturmstrasse 201, CH 8021, Zurich, Switzerland
Tel.: (41) 448329511
Web Site: http://www.paynet.ch
Sales Range: $50-74.9 Million
Emp.: 25
Electronic Payment Transaction, Invoicing & Archiving Services
N.A.I.C.S.: 522320
Ulrike Eckardt *(Dir-Mktg)*

SIX SIS AG (1)
Pfingstweidstrasse 110, 8021, Zurich, Switzerland
Tel.: (41) 58 399 3111
Web Site: http://www.six-securities-services.com
Sales Range: $350-399.9 Million
Emp.: 550
Central Securities Depository Services
N.A.I.C.S.: 522320
Fabrizio Pescosolido *(Head-Relationship Mgmt & Sls)*

SIX Securities Services Ltd (1)
Brandschenkestrasse 47, 8001, Zurich, Switzerland
Tel.: (41) 58 399 3111
Financial Investment Services
N.A.I.C.S.: 523940
Avi Ghosh *(Head-Mktg & Comm)*

SIX Swiss Exchange Ltd. (1)
Pfingstweidstrasse 110, 8005, Zurich, Switzerland
Tel.: (41) 583992878
Web Site: http://www.six-swiss-exchange.com
Sales Range: $200-249.9 Million
Emp.: 400
Stock Exchange
N.A.I.C.S.: 523210

SIX Trade Repository Ltd. (1)
Pfingstweidstrasse 110, 8021, Zurich, Switzerland
Tel.: (41) 58 399 6650
Trade Repository Services
N.A.I.C.S.: 425120

SIXT SE
Zugspitzstrasse 1, 82049, Pullach, Germany
Tel.: (49) 89744440
Web Site: https://www.sixt.de
Year Founded: 1912
SIX2—(DEU)
Rev.: $3,996,572,374
Assets: $7,119,553,068
Liabilities: $4,909,340,399
Net Worth: $2,210,212,669
Earnings: $369,950,992
Emp.: 8,735
Fiscal Year-end: 12/31/23
Car Rental Services
N.A.I.C.S.: 532111
Erich Sixt *(Chm-Mgmt Bd)*

Subsidiaries:

Sixt AG (1)
Pfingstweidstrasse 3, Zurich, 0822, Switzerland (100%)
Tel.: (41) 14459090

SIXT SE

Sixt SE—(Continued)
Sales Range: $25-49.9 Million
Emp.: 40
Passenger Car Rental Services
N.A.I.C.S.: 532111

Sixt B.V. (1)
Kruisweg 791, 2132 NG, Hoofddorp, Netherlands (100%)
Tel.: (31) 235698656
Web Site: https://www.sixt.nl
Sales Range: $25-49.9 Million
Passenger Car Rental Services
N.A.I.C.S.: 532111

Sixt Beteiligungen GmbH & Co. Holding KG (1)
Zugspitzstrasse 1, D-82049, Pullach, Germany
Tel.: (49) 89744440
Web Site: http://ag.sixt.de
Holding Company
N.A.I.C.S.: 551112

Sixt Car Sales GmbH (1)
Gutenbergstrasse 4, Munchen, 85748, Garching, Germany
Tel.: (49) 8932198321
Web Site: https://www.sixtcarsales.de
New & Used Car Distr
N.A.I.C.S.: 441120

Sixt Finance B.V. (1)
Smaragdlaan 3, 2132 VX, Hoofddorp, Netherlands (100%)
Tel.: (31) 2356 98650
Credit Services
N.A.I.C.S.: 522390

Sixt GmbH & Co. Autovermietung KG (1)
Zugspitzstr 1, 82049, Pullach, Germany
Tel.: (49) 89744440
Web Site: https://www.sixt.com
Auto Rentals Services
N.A.I.C.S.: 532111

Sixt Leasing (Schweiz) AG (1)
Grossmattstrasse 9, 8902, Urdorf, Switzerland (100%)
Tel.: (41) 848555500
Web Site: http://www.sixt-leasing.ch
Sales Range: $50-74.9 Million
Car Lending Services
N.A.I.C.S.: 532112

Sixt Leasing G.m.b.H. (1)
Liesinger Flur Gasse 2B, Vienna, 1230, Austria (100%)
Tel.: (43) 15036920
Car Lending Services
N.A.I.C.S.: 532112

Sixt Location Longue Duree SARL (1)
42 avenue de Saxe, Paris, 75007, France (100%)
Tel.: (33) 0140650100
Sales Range: $50-74.9 Million
Emp.: 6
Car Rental Services
N.A.I.C.S.: 532111

Sixt Plc (1)
Durrant House 47 Holywell St, Chesterfield, S41 7SJ, United Kingdom (100%)
Tel.: (44) 1246220111
Web Site: http://www.sixt.co.uk
Sales Range: $75-99.9 Million
Emp.: 150
Car Rental Services
N.A.I.C.S.: 532111

Sixt R&D Private Limited (1)
Building 9 6th Floor Cessna Business Park Kaverappa Layout, Kadubeesanahalli Bellandur, Bengaluru, 560103, India
Tel.: (91) 8049205555
Web Site: https://www.sixtindia.co.in
Car Rental Services
N.A.I.C.S.: 532111

Sixt Ride GmbH & Co. (1)
Zugspitzstrasse 1, 82049, Pullach, Germany
Tel.: (49) 30340440440
Web Site: https://www.sixt.de
Car Rental Services
N.A.I.C.S.: 532111

Sixt SAS (1)
42 avenue de Saxe, 75007, Paris, France (100%)
Tel.: (33) 140650100
Web Site: http://www.sixt.fr.com
Car Rental Services
N.A.I.C.S.: 532111

Sixt VIP Services GmbH (1)
Zugspitzstr 1, Pullach, 80538, Germany (100%)
Tel.: (49) 6252525
Web Site: http://www.sixt.com
Car Rental Services
N.A.I.C.S.: 532111

United Kenning Rental Group Ltd. (1)
Durrant House 47 Holywell St, Chesterfield, S41 7SJ, United Kingdom (100%)
Tel.: (44) 1246220111
Web Site: http://www.sixt.co.uk
Sales Range: $75-99.9 Million
Emp.: 200
Car Rental Services
N.A.I.C.S.: 532111

Subsidiary (Domestic):

Europa Service Car Ltd. (2)
Durrant House Holywell Street, Chesterfield, S41 7SJ, United Kingdom (100%)
Tel.: (44) 1246246112
Sales Range: $50-74.9 Million
Emp.: 6
Car Rental Services
N.A.I.C.S.: 532111

Sixt Kenning Ltd. (2)
Durrant House 47 Holywell Street, Chesterfield, S41 7SJ, United Kingdom (100%)
Tel.: (44) 1246220111
Web Site: http://www.sixt.co.uk
Sales Range: $75-99.9 Million
Emp.: 150
Car Rental Services
N.A.I.C.S.: 532111

United Rental Group Ltd. (2)
Durrant House 47 Holywell Street, Chesterfield, S41 7SJ, United Kingdom (100%)
Tel.: (44) 1246282000
Web Site: https://www.unitedrentalsystems.co.uk
Sales Range: $25-49.9 Million
Emp.: 18
Car Rental Services
N.A.I.C.S.: 532111

e-Sixt GmbH & Co. KG (1)
Schaumburgstrasse 14-16, 45657, Recklinghausen, Germany (97%)
Tel.: (49) 8974444
Web Site: http://se.sixt.com
Car Rental Services
N.A.I.C.S.: 532111

SIXTH OF OCTOBER FOR DEVELOPMENT & INVESTMENT CO.
Km 38 Cairo-Alexandria Desert Road, Sheikh Zayed City, Giza, Egypt
Tel.: (20) 238270398
Web Site: https://www.sodic.com
Year Founded: 1996
OCDI.CA—(EGX)
Rev.: $217,850,495
Assets: $816,471,016
Liabilities: $633,339,376
Net Worth: $183,131,640
Earnings: $29,078,053
Fiscal Year-end: 12/31/23
Real Estate Investment Services
N.A.I.C.S.: 531390
Shehab ElOrabi (COO)

SIXTH WAVE INNOVATIONS INC.
210 Waterfront Drive Suite 110, Halifax, B4A 0H3, NS, Canada
Tel.: (902) 835-0403   BC
Web Site: https://sixthwave.com
Year Founded: 2007
SIXWF—(OTCEM)
Assets: $1,617,612
Liabilities: $3,764,320
Net Worth: ($2,146,708)
Earnings: ($6,975,600)
Fiscal Year-end: 08/31/22
Uranium Mining Services
N.A.I.C.S.: 212290
John Veltheer (CFO)

Subsidiaries:

6th Wave Innovations Corp. (1)
615 Arapeen Dr Ste 303, Salt Lake City, UT 84108
Tel.: (410) 279-1529
Web Site: http://sixthwave.com
Research & Development in Nanotechnology
N.A.I.C.S.: 541713

SIXTY NORTH GOLD MINING LTD.
3200 650 West Georgia Street, Vancouver, V6B 4P7, BC, Canada
Tel.: (604) 818-1400
Web Site: https://www.sixtynorthgold.com
Year Founded: 2016
SXNTF—(OTCIQ)
Rev.: $79
Assets: $6,818,721
Liabilities: $415,668
Net Worth: $6,403,053
Earnings: ($521,519)
Fiscal Year-end: 10/31/22
Gold Mining Services
N.A.I.C.S.: 212220
John Campbell (CFO)

SIXTY S.P.A.
Via Erasmo Piaggio 35, Abruzzi, Chieti, 66013, Italy
Tel.: (39) 08715891   IT
Web Site: http://www.sixty.net
Year Founded: 1989
Sales Range: $50-74.9 Million
Emp.: 300
Denim Clothing Mfr
N.A.I.C.S.: 315250
Vittorio Hassan (Chm)

Subsidiaries:

SIXTY CANADA (1)
225 Chabanel St West Suite 620, Montreal, H2N 2C9, QC, Canada
Tel.: (514) 906-4430
Fashion Apparels Retailer
N.A.I.C.S.: 458110

SIXTY GROUP RUSSIA (1)
45A Volgogradsky pr-t, 109316, Moscow, Russia
Tel.: (7) 495 6579107
Web Site: http://www.misssixty.com
Sales Range: $25-49.9 Million
Emp.: 50
Fashion Apparels Retailer
N.A.I.C.S.: 458110

SIXTY PORTUGAL (1)
rua do Cavaco 26 Santa Marinha, 4400-408, Vila Nova de Gaia, Portugal
Tel.: (351) 22 3770230 9
Fashion Apparels Retailer
N.A.I.C.S.: 458110

SIXTY UK Ltd (1)
2 King's Ex Change18 Tileyard Road, London, N7 9AH, United Kingdom
Tel.: (44) 8707516040
Fashion Apparels Retailer
N.A.I.C.S.: 458110

SIXXON TECH. CO., LTD.
110-2 4th Floor No 189 Section 2 Keelung Road, Xinyi District, Taipei, Taiwan
Tel.: (886) 227321635
Web Site: https://www.sixxontech.com
Year Founded: 2020
4569—(TAI)
Rev.: $39,772,653

INTERNATIONAL PUBLIC

Assets: $92,168,217
Liabilities: $6,640,407
Net Worth: $85,527,810
Earnings: $3,094,280
Fiscal Year-end: 12/31/23
Medical Equipment Mfr
N.A.I.C.S.: 339112
Alex Wang (Fin Dir)

SIYARAM SILK MILLS LIMITED
H 3/2 MIDC A Road Tarapur, Boisar, Thane, 401506, Maharashtra, India
Tel.: (91) 2230400500
Web Site: https://www.siyaram.com
SIYSIL—(NSE)
Rev.: $264,730,229
Assets: $206,511,205
Liabilities: $79,022,539
Net Worth: $127,488,666
Earnings: $29,516,460
Emp.: 3,254
Fiscal Year-end: 03/31/22
Textile Products Mfr
N.A.I.C.S.: 313310
Ramesh D. Poddar (Chm & Co-Mng Dir)

Subsidiaries:

Cadini S.R.L. (1)
Via di Compiobbi 2H, Bagno a Ripoli, Firenze, Italy
Tel.: (39) 0550944846
Web Site: https://www.cadini.com
Men Clothing Distr
N.A.I.C.S.: 458110

SIYATA MOBILE, INC.
100 - 736 Granville St, Vancouver, V6Z 1G3, BC, Canada
Tel.: (514) 500-1181   BC
Web Site: https://siyata.net
Year Founded: 1986
SYTA—(NASDAQ)
Rev.: $7,545,488
Assets: $12,050,589
Liabilities: $9,563,941
Net Worth: $2,486,648
Earnings: ($23,625,542)
Emp.: 27
Fiscal Year-end: 12/31/21
Communication Equipment Mfr
N.A.I.C.S.: 334290
Marc Seelenfreund (Founder & CEO)

SIZEMASTERS TECHNOLOGY LIMITED
Plot No 123 Ramtekdi Industrial Area Hadapsar, Pune, 411013, India
Tel.: (91) 8180955600
Web Site: https://www.sizemasters.in
Year Founded: 1991
513496—(BOM)
Rev.: $95,798
Assets: $1,305,521
Liabilities: $135,196
Net Worth: $1,170,326
Earnings: $14,496
Fiscal Year-end: 03/31/23
Metal Product Mfr & Distr
N.A.I.C.S.: 331410
J. P. Gupta (Chm & Mng Dir)

SJ CHEM CO., LTD.
40 Tancheon Saneopdanji-gil, Tancheon-myeon, Gongju, Chungcheongnam-do, Korea (South)
Tel.: (82) 638369454
Web Site: https://sj-chem.com
Year Founded: 1992
217910—(KRS)
Chemical Product Mfr & Distr
N.A.I.C.S.: 325312
Bae Dong-Soo (CEO)

SJ CORPORATION LIMITED
311 3rd Floor Laxmi Enclave Gajera

School Road, Katargam, Surat, 395 004, Gujarat, India
Tel.: (91) 2228449521
Web Site: https://www.sjcorp.in
504398—(BOM)
Rev: $2,614,088
Assets: $1,689,455
Liabilities: $651,064
Net Worth: $1,038,391
Earnings: $42,384
Emp.: 5
Fiscal Year-end: 03/31/23
Diamond Jewelry Mfr
N.A.I.C.S.: 339910
Deepak Bhikhalal Upadhyay *(Mng Dir)*

SJ GROUP CO., LTD.
156 Dogok-ro, Gangnam-Gu, Seoul, Korea (South)
Tel.: (82) 234336518
Web Site: http://www.sj-group.co.kr
Year Founded: 2008
306040—(KRS)
Rev: $137,752,280
Assets: $147,679,278
Liabilities: $51,408,545
Net Worth: $96,270,733
Earnings: $21,302,861
Emp.: 174
Fiscal Year-end: 12/31/21
Luggage & Other Protective Case Mfr
N.A.I.C.S.: 316990
Oheum Yeon *(VP)*

SJEC CORPORATION
28 Weixin Road Zhongxin Ecological Hub, Suzhou, 215122, China
Tel.: (86) 512 62746790
Web Site: http://www.sjec.com.cn
Year Founded: 1992
601313—(SHG)
Elevators, Escalators, Passenger Conveyors & Car Parking Systems Mfr & Whslr
N.A.I.C.S.: 333921
Xiaosheng Tan *(Deputy Gen Mgr)*

Subsidiaries:

Qihoo 360 Security Technology Co., Ltd. (1)
Building No 2 6 Jiuxianqiao Road, Chaoyang District, Beijing, 100015, China
Tel.: (86) 1089180702
Web Site: http://www.360.cn
Software Publisher
N.A.I.C.S.: 513210
Zhou Hongyi *(CEO)*

SJG SEJONG CO., LTD.
82 Hyoja-ro, Buk-gu, Ulsan, Korea (South)
Tel.: (82) 522191699
Web Site: https://www.sjg-sejong.com
Year Founded: 1976
033530—(KRS)
Rev: $1,425,743,168
Assets: $881,610,753
Liabilities: $573,735,802
Net Worth: $307,874,950
Earnings: $1,318,555
Emp.: 698
Fiscal Year-end: 12/31/22
Motor Vehicle Parts Mfr & Distr
N.A.I.C.S.: 336390
Suh Hae-Sook *(Chm)*

Subsidiaries:

Asentec Co., Ltd. (1)
190-23 Sandong-ro, Eumbong-myeon, Asan, Chungcheongnam, Korea (South)
Tel.: (82) 415473810
Web Site: https://www.asentec.co.kr
Emp.: 300
Automotive Equipment Distr
N.A.I.C.S.: 423120

Beijing Sejong Auto Parts Co., Ltd. (1)
Fuqian st 22 Beixiaoying, Shunyi District, Beijing, China
Tel.: (86) 1060487755
Automotive Equipment Distr
N.A.I.C.S.: 423120

Chongqing Sejong Auto Parts Co., Ltd. (1)
No 388 Shuanghe Street, Longxing Town Yubei District, Chongqing, 401135, China
Tel.: (86) 2388566004
Automotive Equipment Distr
N.A.I.C.S.: 423120

Jiangsu Asentec Sensor Parts Co., Ltd. (1)
No 46 South LaoShan Road Economic and Technological Development Zone, Yancheng, Jiangsu, China
Tel.: (86) 51583309301
Automotive Equipment Distr
N.A.I.C.S.: 423120

Qinchuan Sejong Auto Parts.,Ltd. (1)
No 2 Cuiqing Road Jinkai Park New Northern Zone, Chongqing, China
Tel.: (86) 2367196352
Automotive Equipment Distr
N.A.I.C.S.: 423120

Sejong Alabama LLC (1)
450 Old Fort Rd E, Fort Deposit, AL 36032
Tel.: (334) 227-0821
Automotive Equipment Distr
N.A.I.C.S.: 423120

Sejong Czech S.R.O (1)
Na Novem poli 385/1a, Stare Mesto, 733 01, Karvina, Czech Republic
Tel.: (420) 552305811
Web Site: https://www.sjcz.c
Automotive Equipment Distr
N.A.I.C.S.: 423120

Sejong Ev Co., Ltd. (1)
137 Cheomdansaneop 1-Ro Daesowon-Myeon, Chungju, Chungcheongbuk-do, Korea (South)
Tel.: (82) 438410319
Automobile Parts Mfr
N.A.I.C.S.: 336390

Sejong Georgia LLC (1)
1641 Lukken Industrial Dr, LaGrange, GA 30240
Tel.: (706) 845-7091
Automotive Equipment Distr
N.A.I.C.S.: 423120

Sejong Slovakia S.R.O (1)
Zilinska cesta 469/82, Lietavska Lucka, 013 11, Zilina, Slovakia
Tel.: (421) 415628022
Automotive Equipment Distr
N.A.I.C.S.: 423120

Sejung Co., Ltd. (1)
65-20 Asanho-ro 840 beon-gil, Dunpo-myeon, Asan, Chungcheongnam, Korea (South)
Tel.: (82) 415399899
Automotive Equipment Distr
N.A.I.C.S.: 423120

Sewoom Co., Ltd. (1)
22-19 Jeongsin-ro, Jeongeup, Jeollabuk, Korea (South)
Tel.: (82) 7078290070
Automotive Equipment Distr
N.A.I.C.S.: 423120

Taicang Sejong Industrial Co., Ltd. (1)
Lu Jia Beilu Road Taicang Economy Development Area, Taicang, Jiangsu, China
Tel.: (86) 51253202000
Automotive Equipment Distr
N.A.I.C.S.: 423120

Yancheng Sejong Auto Parts Co., Ltd. (1)
Sejong Road No 1 Yanlong Sub-district Office, Yandu District, Yancheng, Jiangsu, China
Tel.: (86) 7075965876
Automotive Equipment Distr
N.A.I.C.S.: 423120

SJK CO., LTD.
4F SJ TechnoVill Gasan-dong 278 Beokkok-ro, Geumcheon-gu, Seoul, Korea (South)
Tel.: (82) 28663333
Web Site: http://www.sejin.com
Year Founded: 1972
080440—(KRS)
Rev: $3,794,860
Assets: $50,915,348
Liabilities: $38,698,026
Net Worth: $12,217,322
Earnings: ($10,049,281)
Fiscal Year-end: 12/31/20
Automobile Parts Mfr
N.A.I.C.S.: 336110
Do-Yoon Kim *(CEO)*

Subsidiaries:

SEJIN America, Inc. (1)
2144 Zanker Rd, San Jose, CA 95131
Tel.: (408) 487-9000
Web Site: http://www.sejin.com
Electronic Components Mfr
N.A.I.C.S.: 334419

Sejin Electron Inc. - Osan Factory (1)
157-1 Gajang-dong, 447-210, Osan, Gyeonggi-do, Korea (South)
Tel.: (82) 31 371 0312
Web Site: http://www.sejin.com
Automotive Electronic Parts Mfr
N.A.I.C.S.: 336320

SJL PARTNERS LLC
26F Seoul Finance Center 136 Sejong-daero, Jung-gu, Seoul, 04520, Korea (South)
Tel.: (82) 269119701
Web Site: http://www.sjlpartners.com
Privater Equity Firm
N.A.I.C.S.: 523999
Steve Suk Jung Lim *(Mng Partner)*

Subsidiaries:

MPM Holdings Inc. (1)
260 Hudson River Rd, Waterford, NY 12188 (50%)
Tel.: (518) 237-3330
Web Site: http://www.momentive.com
Rev: $2,705,000,000
Assets: $2,830,000,000
Liabilities: $2,234,000,000
Net Worth: $596,000,000
Earnings: $69,000,000
Emp.: 5,200
Fiscal Year-end: 12/31/2018
Holding Company
N.A.I.C.S.: 551112
Suraj Kunchala *(Controller)*

Subsidiary (Domestic):

Momentive Performance Materials Inc. (2)
260 Hudson River Rd, Waterford, NY 12188
Tel.: (518) 233-3330
Web Site: https://www.momentive.com
Sales Range: $1-4.9 Billion
Emp.: 5,199
Thermoplastics, Silicon-Based Products & Fused Quartz & Specialty Ceramics Mfr
N.A.I.C.S.: 325211
Suraj Kunchala *(Controller)*

SJM CO., LTD.
20 Byeolmang-ro 459 beon-gi, Danwon-gu, Ansan, Gyeonggi-do, Korea (South)
Tel.: (82) 314903838
Web Site: https://www.sjmflex.com
Year Founded: 1975
123700—(KRS)
Rev: $138,242,320
Assets: $186,592,207
Liabilities: $43,019,854
Net Worth: $143,572,353
Earnings: $3,776,964
Emp.: 302
Fiscal Year-end: 12/31/22
Automobile Parts Mfr
N.A.I.C.S.: 336390

Subsidiaries:

SJM FLEX (pty) LTD (1)
Nicoll St, PO Box 14131, Sidwell, Port Elizabeth, 6061, Eastern Cape, South Africa
Tel.: (27) 414025600
Emp.: 300
Automotive Spare Parts Distr
N.A.I.C.S.: 423120
Deon Joubert *(Mng Dir)*

SJM GmbH (1)
Mundenheimer Strasse 100, 67061, Ludwigshafen, Germany
Emp.: 9
Automobile Spare Parts Mfr
N.A.I.C.S.: 336390

SJM NORTH AMERICA INC. (1)
305 E Eisenhower Pkwy Ste 110, Ann Arbor, MI 48108
Tel.: (734) 384-7075
Emp.: 5
Automotive Spare Parts Distr
N.A.I.C.S.: 423120

YANTAI SJM Co., LTD. (1)
No 15 Guangzhou Road, Yantai, 264006, China
Tel.: (86) 5356115912
Automotive Spare Parts Distr
N.A.I.C.S.: 423120

SJM HOLDINGS CO., LTD.
401-5 Moknae-dong, Danwon-gu, Ansan, Kyungki-do, Korea (South)
Tel.: (82) 314914151
Web Site: https://www.sjmholdings.co.kr
Year Founded: 1975
025530—(KRS)
Rev: $141,299,570
Assets: $251,703,373
Liabilities: $49,869,376
Net Worth: $201,833,997
Earnings: $1,322,880
Emp.: 8
Fiscal Year-end: 12/31/22
Holding Company
N.A.I.C.S.: 551112

Subsidiaries:

Changha SJM Co., Ltd. (1)
No 1389 Leifeng Road, Changsha, Hunan, China
Tel.: (86) 73188358063
Flex Tube Mfr
N.A.I.C.S.: 332996

SJM HOLDINGS LIMITED
18th Floor China Merchants Tower Shun Tak Centre, Nos 168 200 Connaught Road, Central, China (Hong Kong)
Tel.: (852) 39608000
Web Site: https://www.sjmholdings.com
SJMHF—(OTCIQ)
Rev: $853,527,931
Assets: $6,728,398,533
Liabilities: $4,681,879,177
Net Worth: $2,046,519,355
Earnings: ($1,003,054,430)
Emp.: 18,600
Fiscal Year-end: 12/31/22
Hotel & Gaming Operations
N.A.I.C.S.: 721120
David Hong Kuen Shum *(Exec Dir)*

SJOSTRAND COFFEE INT AB
PO Box 559 89, 102 16, Stockholm, Sweden
Tel.: (46) 87411244
Web Site: https://sjostrandcoffee.com
Year Founded: 2013
Dessert & Beverage Bar Operator
N.A.I.C.S.: 722515
Jenny Svensson *(CEO)*

SJOVA-ALMENNAR TRYGGINGAR HF

Sjostrand Coffee Int AB—(Continued)

SJOVA-ALMENNAR TRYGGINGAR HF
Kringlan 5, 103, Reykjavik, Iceland
Tel.: (354) 4402000
Web Site: https://www.sjova.is
SJOVA—(ICE)
Rev.: $246,193,810
Assets: $497,665,087
Liabilities: $330,199,196
Net Worth: $167,465,891
Earnings: $33,215,209
Emp.: 183
Fiscal Year-end: 12/31/23
Insurance Services
N.A.I.C.S.: 524113

SJS ENTERPRISES LIMITED
Sy Nos-28/P16 Agra Village & 85/P6, Bm Kaval Village Kengeri Hobli, Bengaluru, 560060, Karnataka, India
Tel.: (91) 8028425055
Web Site: https://www.sjsindia.com
Year Founded: 1996
543387—(BOM)
Rev.: $34,828,521
Assets: $52,353,756
Liabilities: $9,326,772
Net Worth: $43,026,984
Earnings: $6,519,923
Fiscal Year-end: 03/31/21
Motor Vehicle Parts Mfr
N.A.I.C.S.: 336390
Ramesh C. Jain *(Chm)*

SJVN LTD.
Shakti Sadan Corporate Office Complex Shanan, Shimla, 171006, Himachal Pradesh, India
Tel.: (91) 1772660075
Web Site: https://sjvn.nic.in
Year Founded: 1988
533206—(BOM)
Rev.: $344,947,504
Assets: $4,699,030,875
Liabilities: $3,011,935,960
Net Worth: $1,687,094,915
Earnings: $109,281,656
Emp.: 1,061
Fiscal Year-end: 03/31/24
Hydroelectric Power Operator & Distr
N.A.I.C.S.: 221111
Nand Lal Sharma *(Chm & Mng Dir)*

Subsidiaries:

SJVN Arun-3 Power Development Company Pvt. Ltd. (1)
Arun Sadan SAPDC Complex Ward No 9, Khandbari Municipality Sakhuwasabaha, Tumlingtar, Nepal
Tel.: (977) 29575141
Web Site: https://www.sapdc.com.np
Power Generation Services
N.A.I.C.S.: 221111

SK BIOSCIENCE CO., LTD.
310 Pangyo-ro, Bundang-Gu, Seongnam, Gyeonggi-do, Korea (South)
Tel.: (82) 220082200
Web Site: https://www.skbioscience.com
Year Founded: 2018
302440—(KRS)
Rev.: $350,308,743
Assets: $1,642,861,371
Liabilities: $306,975,940
Net Worth: $1,335,885,431
Earnings: $93,920,646
Emp.: 1,072
Fiscal Year-end: 12/31/22
Biological Product Mfr
N.A.I.C.S.: 325414
Jae-Yong Ahn *(CEO)*

SK D&D CO., LTD.
ECO Hub 332 Pangyo-ro, Bundang-gu, Seongnam, Gyeonggi-do, Korea (South)
Tel.: (82) 23984700
Web Site: https://www.skdnd.com
Year Founded: 2004
210980—(KRS)
Rev.: $432,155,846
Assets: $1,680,938,956
Liabilities: $1,146,289,136
Net Worth: $534,649,821
Earnings: $58,455,511
Emp.: 269
Fiscal Year-end: 12/31/22
Real Estate Developers
N.A.I.C.S.: 237210
Yoonsong Ham *(Pres & CEO)*

SK DISCOVERY CO.,LTD.
ECO Hub 332 Pangyo-ro, Bundang-gu, Seongnam, 13493, Gyeonggi-do, Korea (South)
Tel.: (82) 220087399
Web Site: https://www.skdiscovery.com
Year Founded: 1969
006120—(KRS)
Sales Range: $5-14.9 Billion
Basic Chemicals Mfr
N.A.I.C.S.: 325199
Jae-yong Ahn *(CEO-SK Bioscience)*

Subsidiaries:

SK Chemicals America, Inc. (1)
2 Park Plz Ste 1250, Irvine, CA 92614
Tel.: (949) 336-8088
Web Site: http://www.skchemicals.com
Emp.: 8
Plastic Material Whslr
N.A.I.C.S.: 424610
Michael Tae *(Gen Counsel & Exec VP)*

SK Chemicals Co., Ltd. - Osan Plant
12 430-11 Nambu-daero, 447-310, Osan, Gyeonggi, Korea (South)
Tel.: (82) 316684185
Pharmaceuticals Product Mfr
N.A.I.C.S.: 325411

SK Chemicals GmbH (1)
TOPAS 1 Mergenthalerallee 77, 65760, Eschborn, Germany
Tel.: (49) 61969020611
Pharmaceutical Products Distr
N.A.I.C.S.: 424210

SK Chemicals Qingdao Ltd. (1)
12 Jiangshan Middle Road Qingdao Economic & Technical Development Zone, Shandong, 266000, China
Tel.: (86) 53286763281
Prepreg Material Mfr
N.A.I.C.S.: 314994

SK Chemicals Suzhou Co., Ltd. (1)
188 Jiangxingdonglu Wujiang Economic Development Zone, Jiangsu, 215217, China
Tel.: (86) 51285162002
Polyester Mfr
N.A.I.C.S.: 325211

SK Gas Co., Ltd. (1)
ECO Hub SK Discovery Complex 332 Pangyo-ro, Bundang-gu, Seongnam, 13493, Gyeonggi-do, Korea (South) **(72.2%)**
Tel.: (82) 262008114
Web Site: https://www.skgas.co.kr
Rev.: $6,186,751,714
Assets: $4,472,972,876
Liabilities: $2,677,506,299
Net Worth: $1,795,466,577
Earnings: $197,178,633
Emp.: 510
Fiscal Year-end: 12/31/2022
Liquefied Petroleum Gas Distribution Services
N.A.I.C.S.: 221210
Byung Suk Yoon *(CEO)*

SK Petrochemical Co., Ltd (1)
310 Pangyo-ro, Bundang-gu, Seongnam, 463-400, Gyeonggi-do, Korea (South)
Tel.: (82) 2 2008 2032
Web Site: http://www.skpetrochemical.com
Chemical Mfr & Distr

N.A.I.C.S.: 325199

Plant (Domestic):

SK Petrochemical Co., Ltd - Ulsan Plant
718 Cheoyong-ro, Nam-gu, Ulsan, 680-160, Korea (South)
Tel.: (82) 522790121
Chemicals Mfr
N.A.I.C.S.: 325199

SK Pharma Beijing Co., Ltd. (1)
23F SK Tower No 6 Jia Jianguomenwai Avenue, Chaoyang District, Beijing, 100022, China
Tel.: (86) 1059240909
Pharmaceutical Products Distr
N.A.I.C.S.: 424210

SK U.S.A, Inc (1)
55E 59St 11th Fl, New York, NY 10022
Tel.: (212) 583-2430
Web Site: http://www.skusa.com
Rev.: $2,664,000
Emp.: 8
Business Support Services
N.A.I.C.S.: 541611
Aden Chung *(Mgr-Investment)*

SK ENGINEERING & CONSTRUCTION CO., LTD.
SKEC 32 Insadong 7-gil, Jongno-gu, Seoul, 3149, Korea (South)
Tel.: (82) 2 3700 7114
Web Site: http://www.skec.com
Year Founded: 1977
Engineering & Construction Services
N.A.I.C.S.: 237990
Casey Choi *(CEO)*

Subsidiaries:

N-Compass Development Co., (1)
1401 Enclave Pkwy Ste 100, Houston, TX 77077
Tel.: (281) 496-8505
Web Site: http://www.ncompassdev.com
Project Management Services
N.A.I.C.S.: 561110
Jim Dudley *(Pres & CEO)*

Nanjing Co., Ltd. (1)
No F G H 16F International Financial Center Hanzhong Road No 1, Nanjing, 210005, China
Tel.: (86) 25 8470 1223
Construction Engineering Services
N.A.I.C.S.: 541330

SBC General Trading & Contracting Co., Ltd. (1)
Office No C5 3rd Floor Ajial Mall, PO Box 46069, Fahaheel, 64011, Kuwait
Tel.: (965) 2392 5934
Web Site: http://www.sbckw.com
Construction Engineering Services
N.A.I.C.S.: 541330
Heung hee Lee *(COO)*

SK E&C Anadolu LLC. (1)
718 Sokak 13/5 Yildizevler Mah Yildiz, Cankaya, Ankara, Turkiye
Tel.: (90) 12 442 3307
Construction Engineering Services
N.A.I.C.S.: 541330

SK E&C BETEK corp. (1)
2 Park Plz Ste 1250, Irvine, CA 92614
Tel.: (949) 336-5100
Construction Engineering Services
N.A.I.C.S.: 541330
Thomas Y. Yoo *(Gen Mgr)*

SK E&C Consultores (1)
Av Naciones Unidas 1014 y Av Amazonas Edificio La Previsora, Torre A Piso 11 Oficina 1102, Guayaquil, Ecuador
Tel.: (593) 2 226 0500
Construction Engineering Services
N.A.I.C.S.: 541330

SK E&C Jurong Investment Pte. Ltd. (1)
50 Raffles place 22-03A Singapore Land Tower, Singapore, 048623, Singapore
Tel.: (65) 6532 6085
Construction Engineering Services
N.A.I.C.S.: 541330

INTERNATIONAL PUBLIC

SK E&C-SCADO Company (1)
5th Fl Sadat Tower Golden Belt Area Khobar Dammam Highway, PO Box 2017, Al Khobar, 31952, Saudi Arabia
Tel.: (966) 3 887 2333
Construction Engineering Services
N.A.I.C.S.: 541330

SKEC India Pvt. Ltd. (1)
6th Floor Tower A Building No 6 DLF Cyber City Phase 3 Sector 24& 25A, Gurgaon, 122002, Haryana, India
Tel.: (91) 124 423 9000
Web Site: http://www.skec.com
Emp.: 300
Construction Engineering Services
N.A.I.C.S.: 541330
Samul Verma *(Deputy Gen Mgr)*

SKEC Thai Limited (1)
Unit 2702 27th Floor Two Pacific Place 142 Sukhumvit Road, Klongtoey, Bangkok, 10110, Thailand
Tel.: (66) 2 254 7211
Construction Engineering Services
N.A.I.C.S.: 541330

Shanxi SK Guolin Hi-Tech Road Material Co. Ltd. (1)
Dongfu 1 Baqiaozhenzheng Rd, Baqiao District, Xi'an, Shanxi, China
Tel.: (86) 29 8361 0790
Construction Engineering Services
N.A.I.C.S.: 541330

Sunlake Co., Ltd. (1)
5 Richard Way SW, Calgary, T3E 7M8, AB, Canada
Tel.: (587) 779-2688
Construction Engineering Services
N.A.I.C.S.: 541330
Brian Jin Jun *(CEO)*

Thai Woo Ree Engineering CO., Ltd. (1)
23/3 Nongha Road Tambon Huaypong Amphur Muang, Rayong, 21150, Thailand
Tel.: (66) 38 606 234
Construction Engineering Services
N.A.I.C.S.: 541330
Withaya Jaiyen *(Mgr-Tank Construction)*

SK HYNIX INC.
2091 Gyeongchung-daero Bubal-eub, Icheon, 17336, Gyeonggi-do, Korea (South)
Tel.: (82) 3151854114 KR
Web Site: https://www.skhynix.com
Year Founded: 1983
000660—(KRS)
Rev.: $39,558
Assets: $88,676
Liabilities: $31,460
Net Worth: $57,216
Earnings: $8,847
Emp.: 22,157
Fiscal Year-end: 12/31/21
Semiconductor Product Mfr
N.A.I.C.S.: 334413
Jung-Ho Park *(Chm)*

Subsidiaries:

Gauss Labs Inc. (1)
230 Homer Ave, Palo Alto, CA 94301
Tel.: (408) 547-3730
Web Site: https://www.gausslabs.ai
Telecommunication Services
N.A.I.C.S.: 517810

HappyNarae America LLC (1)
Premiere Pkwy 2915 Ste 305, Duluth, GA 30097
Tel.: (770) 878-8898
Web Site: https://www.happynarae.co.kr
Industrial Material Distr
N.A.I.C.S.: 423840

Hynix Semiconductor (Wuxi) Ltd. (1)
Lot K7 Wuxi Export Processing Zone, Wuxi New District, Wuxi, Jiangsu, China
Tel.: (86) 51085208888
Semiconductor Equipment Mfr
N.A.I.C.S.: 334413

Hynix Semiconductor Europe Holding Ltd (1)

AND PRIVATE COMPANIES

SK INC.

Unit 4 Horizon Business Village 1 Brooklands Road, Weybridge, KT13 0TJ, Surrey, United Kingdom
Tel.: (44) 1932827700
Semiconductor Equipment Mfr
N.A.I.C.S.: 334413

Hyundai Display Technology Inc. (1)
San 136-1 Ami-Ri Bubal-Eub, Icheon, 467-866, Gyeonggi-Do, Korea (South)
Tel.: (82) 316396419
Web Site: http://www.hydis.com
Sales Range: $200-249.9 Million
Emp.: 1,000
Semiconductor Equipment Mfr
N.A.I.C.S.: 334413
Jason Lin *(CEO)*

Key Foundry Ltd. (1)
5F No 69 Zhou-Zi Street, Nei Hu, Taipei, 11493, Taiwan
Tel.: (886) 226577898
Semiconductor Mfr
N.A.I.C.S.: 333242

Key Foundry Shanghai Co., Ltd. (1)
Room 321 Bridge Ascendas Plaza 333 Tian Yao Qiao Road, Xuhui District, Shanghai, China
Tel.: (86) 2161516647
Web Site: https://www.key-foundry.com
Semiconductor Distr
N.A.I.C.S.: 423690

Key Foundry, Inc. (1)
100 Century Ctr Ct Ste 200, San Jose, CA 95112
Tel.: (408) 625-5999
Semiconductor Mfr
N.A.I.C.S.: 333242

SK Hynix Semiconductor (China) Ltd. (1)
Lot K7 Wuxi High-tech Zone Comprehensive Bonded Zone, New District, Wuxi, 214028, Jiangsu, China
Tel.: (86) 51085208888
Semiconductor Mfr
N.A.I.C.S.: 334413

SK hyeng Inc. (1)
2091 Gyeongchung-daero Bubal-eup, Icheon, 17336, Gyeonggi-do, Korea (South)
Tel.: (82) 80947678
Web Site: https://www.skhyeng.com
Semiconductor Mfr & Distr
N.A.I.C.S.: 334413

SK hynix (China) Ltd. (1)
Lot K7 Wuxi Export Processing Zone, Wuxi New District, Wuxi, Jiangsu, China
Tel.: (86) 51085208888
Semiconductor Equipment Mfr
N.A.I.C.S.: 334413

SK hynix America Inc. (1)
3101 N 1st St, San Jose, CA 95134
Tel.: (408) 232-8000
Web Site: http://www.skhynix.com
Sales Range: $25-49.9 Million
Semiconductor Mfr & Distr
N.A.I.C.S.: 334413

SK hynix Asia Pte. Ltd. (1)
9 Straits View 12-07/12 Marina One West Tower, Singapore, 018937, Singapore
Tel.: (65) 67239351
Sales Range: $25-49.9 Million
Emp.: 20
Semiconductor Mfr
N.A.I.C.S.: 334413

SK hynix Deutschland GmbH (1)
Am Prime-Parc 13 Kelsterbacher Str 16, 65479, Raunheim, Germany
Tel.: (49) 6142921100
Web Site: http://www.hynix.co.kr
Sales Range: $25-49.9 Million
Emp.: 30
Semiconductor Mfr
N.A.I.C.S.: 334413

SK hynix Inc. (1)
1 Hyangjeong-dong, Hungduk-gu, Chongju, Chungbuk, Korea (South)
Tel.: (82) 43 270 3114
Web Site: http://www.hynix.co.kr
Semiconductor Mfr
N.A.I.C.S.: 333242

SK hynix Japan Inc. (1)
23F Shiroyama Trust Tower 4-3-1 Toranomon, Minatoku, Tokyo, 105-6023, Japan
Tel.: (81) 364035500
Sales Range: $25-49.9 Million
Emp.: 45
Semiconductor Mfr
N.A.I.C.S.: 334413
Yoon Young Jun *(Pres)*

SK hynix Memory Solutions America Inc. (1)
3103 N 1st St, San Jose, CA 95134
Tel.: (408) 514-3500
Web Site: https://www.skhms.com
Emp.: 70,000
Computer Related Services
N.A.I.C.S.: 541519

SK hynix Memory Solutions Eastern Europe, LLC (1)
st Nemiga 5 office 75 4th floor, 220030, Minsk, Belarus
Tel.: (375) 17 308 3800
Web Site: https://www.skhms.by
Semiconductor Mfr
N.A.I.C.S.: 334413
Natalia Ryzhenkova *(CEO)*

SK hynix Memory Solutions Inc. (1)
3103 N First St, San Jose, CA 95134
Tel.: (408) 987-2400
Web Site: http://www.skhms.com
Sales Range: $25-49.9 Million
Emp.: 56
Semiconductor Mfr
N.A.I.C.S.: 334413
Hemant K. Thapar *(CEO)*

SK hynix Semiconductor (Shanghai) Co., Ltd. (1)
19F Arch Shanghai Tower 2 No 533 Lou Shan Guan Road, Shanghai, 200051, China
Tel.: (86) 2152080505
Web Site: http://hsa.hynix.com
Semiconductor Mfr
N.A.I.C.S.: 334413

SK hynix Semiconductor Hong Kong Ltd. (1)
Suite 4401-02 44/F One Island East 18 Westlands Road, Taikoo Place, Hong Kong, China (Hong Kong)
Tel.: (852) 29711660
Semiconductor Mfr
N.A.I.C.S.: 334413

SK hynix Semiconductor India Pvt. Ltd. (1)
Unit 10 Level 8 Innovator Building, ITPB International Technology Park Bangalore White Field Road, Bengaluru, 560 066, India
Tel.: (91) 8041265271
Web Site: http://www.skhynix.com
Sales Range: $25-49.9 Million
Emp.: 5
Semiconductor Mfr
N.A.I.C.S.: 334413

SK hynix Semiconductor Taiwan Inc. (1)
10F No 308 Zhifu Rd, Zhongshan Dist, Taipei, 10466, Taiwan
Tel.: (886) 235182300
Sales Range: $25-49.9 Million
Emp.: 100
Semiconductor Mfr
N.A.I.C.S.: 334413

SK hynix UK Ltd. (1)
Unit 4 1 Brooklands Road, Horizon Business Village, Weybridge, KT13 0TJ, Surrey, United Kingdom
Tel.: (44) 1932827700
Sales Range: $25-49.9 Million
Semiconductor Mfr
N.A.I.C.S.: 334413

SK hynix Wuxi Semiconductor Sales Ltd. (1)
Lot K7 Wuxi High-tech Zone Comprehensive Bonded Zone, New District, Wuxi, 214028, China
Tel.: (86) 51085208779
Semiconductor Equipment Mfr
N.A.I.C.S.: 334413

SK hynix system ic Inc. (1)
215 Daesin-ro, Heungdeok-gu, Cheongju, 28429, Chungcheongbuk-do, Korea (South)
Tel.: (82) 9075114
Web Site: https://www.skhynixsystemic.com
Semiconductor Mfr & Distr
N.A.I.C.S.: 334413

SK hystec Inc. (1)
2091 Gyeongchung-daero Bubal-eup, Icheon, 17336, Gyeonggi-do, Korea (South)
Tel.: (82) 80947673
Web Site: https://www.skhystec.com
Logistic Services
N.A.I.C.S.: 541614

SiliconFile Technologies Inc. (1)
19F 20F Bundang Square 263 Seohyendong Bundang-gu, Seongnam, 463-050, Korea (South)
Tel.: (82) 31 8093 5700
Web Site: http://www.siliconfile.com
Semiconductor Products
N.A.I.C.S.: 334413
Sung Kyu Han *(CEO)*

SkyHigh Memory China Limited (1)
4401-02 44/F One Island East 18 Westlands Road, Hong Kong, China (Hong Kong)
Tel.: (852) 82316067026
Web Site: https://skyhighmemory.com
Semiconductor Mfr
N.A.I.C.S.: 334413

SkyHigh Memory Limited (1)
Suite 4401-02 44/F One Island East 18 Westlands Road, Hong Kong, China (Hong Kong)
Tel.: (852) 316067026
Web Site: https://skyhighmemory.com
Technology Services
N.A.I.C.S.: 541512

Suzhou Happynarae Co., Ltd. (1)
Room1171 Building2 No 88 Huachi Street SIP, SuZhou, Jiangsu, China
Tel.: (86) 18115678778
Industrial Material Mfr
N.A.I.C.S.: 333248

SK IE TECHNOLOGY CO., LTD.

26 Jongno, Jongno-Gu, Seoul, Korea (South)
Tel.: (82) 221215114
Web Site: https://skietechnology.com
Year Founded: 2019
361610—(KRS)
Emp.: 252
Primary Battery Mfr
N.A.I.C.S.: 335910
Jae-Sok Rho *(Pres & CEO)*

SK INC.

26 Jong-ro, Jongno-gu, Seoul, 03188, Korea (South)
Tel.: (82) 221215114 KR
Web Site: https://eng.sk.com
Year Founded: 1991
034730—(KRS)
Rev.: $75,274,527,880
Assets: $126,627,306,840
Liabilities: $78,916,182,280
Net Worth: $47,711,124,560
Earnings: $174,218,560
Emp.: 1
Fiscal Year-end: 12/31/20
Software Development Services
N.A.I.C.S.: 551112
Yong-ho Jang *(CEO)*

Subsidiaries:

AMPAC Fine Chemicals LLC (1)
Hwy 50 & Hazel Ave, Rancho Cordova, CA 95741 **(100%)**
Tel.: (916) 357-6880
Web Site:
  http://www.ampacfinechemicals.com
Fine Chemicals Mfr
N.A.I.C.S.: 325998
William Dubay *(VP-Tech)*

Subsidiary (Domestic):

AMPAC Fine Chemicals Texas, LLC (2)
914 S 16th St, La Porte, TX 77571 **(100%)**
Tel.: (916) 357-6880
Web Site:
  http://www.ampacfinechemicals.com
Fine Chemicals Mfr
N.A.I.C.S.: 325998

Atom Power, Inc. (1)
13245 Reese Blvd W Ste 130, Huntersville, NC 28078
Web Site: https://www.atompower.com
Electric Power Distr
N.A.I.C.S.: 221122

Busan Jungkwan Energy Co., Ltd. (1)
83 Sandan 1-ro, Jeonggwan-eup Gijanggun, Busan, Korea (South)
Tel.: (82) 517227900
Integrated Energy Services
N.A.I.C.S.: 541690

Chungcheong Energy Service Co., Ltd. (1)
244 Sandan-Ro Songjeong-Dong, Heungdeok-gu, Cheongju, Chungcheongbuk-do, Korea (South)
Tel.: (82) 432614114
Solar Power Generation Services
N.A.I.C.S.: 332912

Custom Controllers UK Limited (1)
Kingswood Lakeside, Cannock, WS11 8JD, United Kingdom
Tel.: (44) 3331211008
Web Site:
  https://www.customcontrollers.com
Electric & Electronic Appliances Mfr
N.A.I.C.S.: 335220

Envirofone Limited (1)
Rapida 102 Blakeney Way Kingswood Lakeside, Cannock, WS11 8JD, United Kingdom
Tel.: (44) 3339990951
Web Site: https://www.envirofone.com
Computer & Laptop Distr
N.A.I.C.S.: 423430

Environment Management Corporation Co., Ltd. (1)
K-Tower 88 Iljik-ro, Manan-gu, Anyang, 13901, Gyeonggi-do, Korea (South)
Tel.: (82) 3180912000
Web Site: https://www.emc-env.com
Sewage Treatment Services
N.A.I.C.S.: 562219

EverCharge, Inc. (1)
548 Market St 31647, San Francisco, CA 94104-5401
Web Site: https://evercharge.com
Electric Vehicle Charging Services
N.A.I.C.S.: 561990

Green Technology Management Pty. Ltd. (1)
38 Ridgehaven Pl, Bella Vista, 2153, NSW, Australia
Tel.: (61) 292232319
Web Site:
  https://www.greentechmanagement.com.au
Solar Electric Power Distr
N.A.I.C.S.: 221114

Hweechan Co., Ltd. (1)
786 Sanroknam-ro Andeok-Myeon, Seogwipo, Jeju-do, Korea (South)
Tel.: (82) 648050114
Web Site: https://www.luceville.com
Hotel & Restaurant Management Services
N.A.I.C.S.: 721110

IGE Co., Ltd. (1)
415 Bongsu-Daero, Seo-gu, Incheon, Korea (South)
Tel.: (82) 263293500
Solar Power Generation Services
N.A.I.C.S.: 332912

Iberian Lube Base Oils Company, S.A. (1)
C/Retama 7 planta 14, 28045, Madrid, Spain
Tel.: (34) 914674400
Web Site: https://www.ilboc.com
Lubricant Oil Mfr
N.A.I.C.S.: 324191

Id Quantique S.A. (1)

6971

SK INC.

SK Inc.—(Continued)
Rue Eugene-Marziano 25, 1227, Geneva, Switzerland
Tel.: (41) 223018371
Web Site: https://www.idquantique.com
Quantum Information & Communication Services
N.A.I.C.S.: 541715

Jeonbuk Energy Service Co., Ltd. (1)
80 Seokam-Ro 3-gil, Iksan, Jeollabuk-do, Korea (South)
Tel.: (82) 638308500
Solar Power Generation Services
N.A.I.C.S.: 332912

Key Capture Energy, LLC (1)
25 Monroe St Ste 300, Albany, NY 12210
Tel.: (516) 279-2955
Web Site: https://www.keycaptureenergy.com
Energy Storage System Services
N.A.I.C.S.: 541690
Brian Hayes *(CEO)*

Martis Capital, LLC (1)
101 California St 3260, San Francisco, CA 94111
Tel.: (415) 592-5908
Web Site: https://www.martiscapital.com
Investment Services
N.A.I.C.S.: 523940

Narae Energy Service Co., Ltd. (1)
29 Wirye-Daero 4-gil, Hanam, Korea (South)
Tel.: (82) 264777799
Web Site: https://www.skens.com
Power Plant Energy Services
N.A.I.C.S.: 541990

POSK (Pinghu) Steel Processing Center Co., Ltd. (1)
2222 Xingming Road, Economic Development Zone, Pinghu, 314200, Zhejiang, China
Tel.: (86) 57385223333
Information Technology Services
N.A.I.C.S.: 541512

Passkey, Inc. (1)
50 Hudson Yards 68 Fl, New York, NY 10001
Tel.: (646) 490-8032
Web Site: https://www.passkeyinvest.com
Energy Storage System Services
N.A.I.C.S.: 541690
Kyungyeol Song *(COO)*

Pusan City Gas Co., Ltd. (1)
513 Hwangryeongdaero Namcheondong, Suyeong-gu, Busan, 48313, Korea (South)
Tel.: (82) 15440009
Solar Power Generation Services
N.A.I.C.S.: 332912

SK Bio-Pharma Tech (Shanghai) Co., Ltd. (1)
Room 309 866 Halei Road Zhangjiang High Tech Park, Shanghai, China
Tel.: (86) 2150804990
Pharmaceutical Mfr & Distr
N.A.I.C.S.: 325412

SK Biopharmaceuticals Co., Ltd. (1)
99 Seorin-dong, Jongro-gu, Seoul, Korea (South) (100%)
Tel.: (82) 2 2121 0110
Web Site: http://www.skbp.com
Biopharmaceutical Research & Development Services
N.A.I.C.S.: 325412

Subsidiary (US):

SK Life Science, Inc. (2)
22-10 Route 208 S, Fair Lawn, NJ 07410
Tel.: (201) 421-3851
Web Site: http://www.sklifescienceinc.com
Medical Research & Development Services
N.A.I.C.S.: 541715
Jaeyon Yoon *(VP-CMS Bus)*

SK E&S Americas, Inc. (1)
1980 Post Oak Blvd Ste 2000, Houston, TX 77056
Tel.: (281) 833-4206
Solar Power Generation Services

SK Earthon Co., Ltd. (1)
SK Building 26 Jong-ro, Jongno-gu, Seoul, Korea (South)
Tel.: (82) 221215114
Web Site: https://www.skearthon.com
Crude Oil Product Mfr
N.A.I.C.S.: 324110

SK Enmove Co., Ltd. (1)
SK Bldg 26 Jongno, Jongno-gu, Seoul, Korea (South)
Tel.: (82) 221216114
Web Site: https://www.skenmove.com
Emp.: 289
Lubricant Oil Mfr & Distr
N.A.I.C.S.: 324191

SK Enpulse Co., Ltd. (1)
1043 Gyeonggi-daero, Pyeongtaek, Gyeonggi-do, Korea (South)
Tel.: (82) 316608400
Web Site: https://www.skenpulse.com
Emp.: 631
Semiconductor Parts Mfr & Distr
N.A.I.C.S.: 334413

SK Forest Co., Ltd. (1)
51 Jong-ro, Jongno-gu, Seoul, 03161, Korea (South) (100%)
Tel.: (82) 237002800
Reforestation Services
N.A.I.C.S.: 113210

SK GC Americas, Inc. (1)
11700 Katy Fwy Ste 900, Houston, TX 77079
Tel.: (713) 850-0005
Petrochemical Product Mfr & Distr
N.A.I.C.S.: 325110

SK Geo Centric (Beijing) Holding Co., Ltd. (1)
Room 2606 SK Building No Jia 6 Jianguomenwai Street, Chaoyang, Beijing, China
Tel.: (86) 1059205612
Petrochemical Product Mfr & Distr
N.A.I.C.S.: 325110

SK Geo Centric Co., Ltd. (1)
51 Jong-ro, Jongno-gu, Seoul, Korea (South)
Tel.: (82) 221215114
Web Site: https://www.skgeocentric.com
Emp.: 1,069
Petrochemical Mfr & Distr
N.A.I.C.S.: 325110

SK Geo Centric International Trading (Guangzhou) Co., Ltd. (1)
Room 206 No 74 Baoguang Street Bonded Area, Guangzhou, Guangdong, China
Tel.: (86) 2085100312
Petrochemical Product Mfr & Distr
N.A.I.C.S.: 325110

SK Geo Centric International Trading (Shanghai) Co., Ltd. (1)
Unit 1204A No 1438 Hongqiao Road, Changning, Shanghai, China
Tel.: (86) 2161970100
Petrochemical Product Mfr & Distr
N.A.I.C.S.: 325110

SK Geo Centric Japan Co., Ltd. (1)
Tokyo Midtown Hibiya Hibiya Mitsui Tower 32F 1-1-2 Yurakucho, Chiyoda-ku, Tokyo, 100-0006, Japan
Tel.: (81) 335913041
Petrochemical Product Mfr & Distr
N.A.I.C.S.: 325110

SK Geo Centric Singapore Pte. Ltd. (1)
9 Straits View 12-07/12 Marina One West Tower, Singapore, 18937, Singapore
Tel.: (65) 66711570
Petrochemical Product Mfr & Distr
N.A.I.C.S.: 325110

SK Nexilis Co., Ltd. (1)
2 3sandan 2-gil Buk-Myeon, Jeongeup, Jeollabuk-do, Korea (South)
Tel.: (82) 635304114
Web Site: https://www.sknexilis.com
Battery Copper Foil Mfr
N.A.I.C.S.: 335910

SK On Co., Ltd. (1)

51 Jong-ro, Jongno-gu, Seoul, Korea (South)
Tel.: (82) 221215114
Web Site: https://eng.sk-on.com
Emp.: 2,889
Electric Vehicle Battery Mfr & Distr
N.A.I.C.S.: 335910

SK PIC Global Co., Ltd. (1)
SKC 6F Block-B the K Twin Towers 50 Jongro-1 gil, Jongro-gu, Seoul, Korea (South)
Tel.: (82) 237871234
Web Site: https://www.skpicglobal.com
Petrochemical Product Mfr & Distr
N.A.I.C.S.: 325110

SK Pharmteco Inc. (1)
12460 Akron St Ste 100, Rancho Cordova, CA 95742
Tel.: (678) 342-1611
Web Site: https://www.skpharmteco.com
Pharmaceutical Mfr & Distr
N.A.I.C.S.: 325412
Audrey E. Greenberg *(Co-Founder & Chief Bus Officer)*

SK Pucore Co., Ltd. (1)
50 Jong-ro 1-gil The Twin Towers K Bldg B 10th Floor, Jongno-gu, Seoul, 3142, Korea (South)
Tel.: (82) 237871234
Web Site: https://www.skpucore.com
Information & Communication Technology Services
N.A.I.C.S.: 541512

SK Pucore USA Inc. (1)
1 SKC Dr, Covington, GA 30014
Tel.: (678) 342-1611
Web Site: https://skpucore.us
Polyurethane Chemical Mfr & Distr
N.A.I.C.S.: 325211

SK Shieldus America, Inc. (1)
970 Peachtree Industrial Blvd 203, Suwanee, GA 30024
Tel.: (678) 975-8118
Cyber Security Services
N.A.I.C.S.: 541690

SK Shipping Co., Ltd. (1)
21st Fl 416 Hangang-daero, Jung-gu, Seoul, 04637, Korea (South) (83.1%)
Tel.: (82) 237888400
Web Site: https://www.skshipping.com
Shipping Services
N.A.I.C.S.: 483111

Subsidiary (Non-US):

SK Shipping Europe PLC (2)
6th fl Capital Tower 91 Waterloo Road, London, SE1 8RT, United Kingdom
Tel.: (44) 2031700910
Sales Range: $25-49.9 Million
Emp.: 10
Shipping Freight Transportation Services
N.A.I.C.S.: 483111

SK Shipping Japan Co., Ltd. (2)
Sales Range: $25-49.9 Million
Emp.: 3
Marine Transportation Services
N.A.I.C.S.: 488390

SK Shipping Singapore Pte Ltd. (2)
9 Straits View 12-07/12 Marina One West Tower, Singapore, 18937, Singapore
Tel.: (65) 62495919
Sales Range: $25-49.9 Million
Emp.: 20
Petroleum Product Whslr
N.A.I.C.S.: 424720

SK Siltron CSS, LLC (1)
1317 Straits Dr, Bay City, MI 48706
Tel.: (989) 321-9000
Web Site: https://sksiltroncss.com
Silicon Wafer Mfr & Distr
N.A.I.C.S.: 334413

SK Siltron Inc. (1)
132-11 3gondan 3-ro, Gumi, Gyeongsangbuk-do, Korea (South)
Tel.: (82) 544708499
Web Site: https://www.sksiltron.com
Production of Expitaxial Wafers, Administration, Recruiting & Business Planning
N.A.I.C.S.: 334413

SK Specialty (Xian) Co., Ltd. (1)

1211 Baoba Road Xian Gaoxin Comprehensive Bonded Zone, Xian, Shaanxi, China
Tel.: (86) 2968039592
Warehouse Services
N.A.I.C.S.: 561720

SK Specialty Co., Ltd. (1)
59-33 Gaheunggongdan-ro, Gyeongju, 36059, Gyeongsangbuk-do, Korea (South)
Tel.: (82) 546308114
Web Site: https://www.skspecialty.com
Emp.: 770
Special Gas Mfr & Distr
N.A.I.C.S.: 325120

SK Specialty Japan Co., Ltd. (1)
1077-24 Mizohigashi Kawaradacho, Yokkaichi, 510-0874, Mie, Japan
Tel.: (81) 593495800
Web Site: https://skst-jp.com
Emp.: 8
Special Gas Distr
N.A.I.C.S.: 424690

SK Specialty Jiangsu Co., Ltd. (1)
No 68 Longxi Road New Area Zhenjiang, Jiangsu, China
Tel.: (86) 51180869800
Special Gas Mfr & Distr
N.A.I.C.S.: 325120

SK Specialty Taiwan Co., Ltd. (1)
No 12 Nanhuan Road, Wuqi, Taichung, Taiwan
Tel.: (886) 426595511
Special Gas Distr
N.A.I.C.S.: 424690

SK Specialty(Shanghai) Co., Ltd. (1)
Room 602 THE SUMMIT 118 Suzhou Avenue West Industrial Park, Suzhou, China
Tel.: (86) 51267302842
Special Gas Distr
N.A.I.C.S.: 424690

SK Stoa Co., Ltd. (1)
402 World Cup Buk-Ro, Mapo-gu, Seoul, 3925, Korea (South)
Tel.: (82) 15660106
Web Site: https://corp.skstoa.com
Electronic Shopping Services
N.A.I.C.S.: 541380

SK Telecom China Holding Co., Ltd. (1)
25th Floor SK Tower No 6 Jia Jianguomenwai Avenue, Chaoyang District, Beijing, 100022, China
Tel.: (86) 1059207777
Mobile Telecommunications Services
N.A.I.C.S.: 517121

SK Telecom Japan Inc. (1)
Tokyo Midtown Hibiya 32F 1-1-2, Yurakucho Chiyoda-ku, Tokyo, 100-0006, Japan
Tel.: (81) 335913800
Mobile Telecommunications Services
N.A.I.C.S.: 517121

SK biotek Co., Ltd. (1)
323 Expo-ro, Yuseong-gu, Daejeon, Korea (South)
Tel.: (82) 428667521
Web Site: http://www.skbiotek.com
Custom Chemical Development, Advanced Intermediates & Active Pharmaceutical Ingredient Mfr
N.A.I.C.S.: 325414
Dongkeun Lee *(Mgr-Strategy Grp)*

Subsidiary (Non-US):

SK biotek Ireland Limited (2)
Swords Campus Watery Lane, Swords, K67 AY91, Co Dublin, Ireland
Tel.: (353) 18139000
Custom Chemical Development, Advanced Intermediates & Active Pharmaceutical Ingredient Mfr
N.A.I.C.S.: 325414
Joyce FitzHarris *(Dir-Strategy)*

Sapeon Inc. (1)
4151 Burton Dr, Santa Clara, CA 95054
Tel.: (408) 818-9115
Web Site: https://www.sapeon.org
Artificial Intelligence Semiconductor Mfr
N.A.I.C.S.: 334511

Stock Must Go Limited (1)
Blakeney Way Kingswood Lakeside, Can-

AND PRIVATE COMPANIES

nock, WS11 8JD, United Kingdom
Tel.: (44) 3301201541
Web Site: https://www.stockmustgo.co.uk
Computer & Electronic Product Mfr
N.A.I.C.S.: 334111

Sustainable Product Stewards Pty. Ltd. (1)
1 Marple Avenue, Villawood, 2613, NSW, Australia
Tel.: (61) 481832152
Web Site: https://www.spsaust.com.au
Waste Processing Services
N.A.I.C.S.: 562920

Teraon Co., Ltd. (1)
Room 618 Bangbae Leadersville 2201 Nambusunhwan-ro, Seocho-gu, Seoul, Korea (South)
Tel.: (82) 7082447266
Web Site: www.teraon.com
Electronic Component Mfr & Distr
N.A.I.C.S.: 334416

Tes Consumer Solutions Ltd. (1)
Blakeney Way Kingswood Lakeside, Cannock, WS11 8JD, United Kingdom
Tel.: (44) 1543223444
Web Site:
 https://www.tesconsumersolutions.com
Computer Hardware Mfr
N.A.I.C.S.: 332510

Tes-Amm (Singapore) Pte. Ltd. (1)
No 9 Benoi Sector, Singapore, 629844, Singapore
Tel.: (65) 64088600
Web Site: https://www.tes-amm.com
Electronic Equipment Recycling Services
N.A.I.C.S.: 562119

Tes-Amm Japan K.K. (1)
1 Chome-2-31 Miyashimo, Chuo-ku, Sagamihara, 252-0212, Kanagawa, Japan
Tel.: (81) 427036211
Web Site: https://www.tes-amm-jp.com
Asset Management Services
N.A.I.C.S.: 531390

Woori Fine Chem Co., Ltd. (1)
809 Technology Development Center Gyeonggi Techno Park 705 Haean-ro, Ansan, Gyeonggi-do, Korea (South)
Tel.: (82) 315004777
Web Site: https://www.woorifinechem.com
Petrochemical Mfr
N.A.I.C.S.: 325110

Yeoju Energy Service Co., Ltd. (1)
26 Jong-Ro, Jongno-gu, Seoul, Korea (South)
Tel.: (82) 221213028
Solar Power Generation Services
N.A.I.C.S.: 332912

SK INNOVATION CO., LTD.
SK Bldg 26 Jongno, Jongno-gu, Seoul, Korea (South)
Tel.: (82) 221215114 KR
Web Site:
 https://www.skinnovation.com
096770—(KRS)
Rev.: $31,431,367
Assets: $35,418,294
Liabilities: $21,196,507
Net Worth: $14,221,788
Earnings: ($1,998,947)
Emp.: 2,424
Fiscal Year-end: 12/31/21
Natural Gas Extraction Services
N.A.I.C.S.: 211130
Myoung Lee Young (CFO & Sr Exec VP-Fin)

Subsidiaries:

Boryeong LNG Terminal Co., Ltd. (1)
450 Ocheonhaean-ro, Boryeong, Chungcheongnam, Korea (South) (50%)
Tel.: (82) 262639990
Electric Power Distribution Services
N.A.I.C.S.: 221122
SinDuk Kang (CEO)

FSK L&S Co., Ltd. (1)
6th Floor SK U-Tower 9 Seongnam-daero 343beon-gil, Bundang-gu, Seongnam, 13558, Gyeonggi-do, Korea (South)
Tel.: (82) 316204612
Web Site: https://www.fskins.com
Logistic Services
N.A.I.C.S.: 541614
Jae H. Chung (Chm)

Guangdong SK Advanced Polymer Co., Ltd (1)
Guangdong Zhaoqing High Technology, Industry Development Zone, 526238, Zhaoqing, Guangdong, China
Tel.: (86) 758 362 5003
Web Site: http://eng.skenergy.com
Natural Gas Exploration Service
N.A.I.C.S.: 211130

Netruck Co., Ltd. (1)
Room 1306 Janggyo Building 363 Samildaero, Jung-gu, Seoul, Korea (South)
Tel.: 1 588 0782
Web Site: https://www.netruck.co.kr
Transportation Support Services
N.A.I.C.S.: 488490

Ningbo SK Performance Rubber Co., Ltd. (1)
No 187 Haihe Road, Ningbo Petrochemical Economic Technological Development Zone Zhenhai, Ningbo, Zhejiang, China
Tel.: (86) 57486657863
Petrochemical Products Mfr
N.A.I.C.S.: 325998

SK (Beijing) Road Science & Technology Co., Ltd (1)
A1018 South Gate 1 No 14 Jiuxianqiao Road, Chaoyang District, Beijing, 100015, China
Tel.: (86) 10 5867 1616
Oil Exploration Services
N.A.I.C.S.: 211130

SK Asphalt (Shanghai) Co., Ltd. (1)
Natural Gas Exploration Service
N.A.I.C.S.: 211130

SK E&S Co., Ltd. (1)
SK Seorin Building 26 Jongno, Jongno-gu, Seoul, 03188, Korea (South)
Tel.: (82) 221213114
Web Site: https://www.skens.com
Emp.: 2,507
Holding Company; Gas & Electric Power Distr
N.A.I.C.S.: 551112

Subsidiary (Domestic):

Busan City Gas Co., Ltd. (2)
513 Hwangryeongdaero Namcheondong, Suyeong-Gu, Busan, 48313, Korea (South) (67.32%)
Tel.: (82) 516071178
Web Site: http://www.skens.com
Rev.: $729,020,739
Assets: $926,482,271
Liabilities: $336,576,107
Net Worth: $589,906,164
Earnings: $15,550,373
Emp.: 324
Fiscal Year-end: 12/31/2021
Liquefied Natural Gas Distr
N.A.I.C.S.: 221210
Jeong Joon Yu (CEO)

Chonnam City Gas Co., Ltd. (2)
1603-9 Chorye-Dong, Suncheon, Chollanam-Do, Korea (South)
Tel.: (82) 617209000
Gas Production & Distribution Services
N.A.I.C.S.: 211120

Wirye Energy Service Co., Ltd. (2)
35 Cheonggyecheonro, Jongnogu, Seoul, Korea (South) (100%)
Tel.: (82) 2 2121 3691
Web Site: http://www.skens.com
Gas Production & Distribution Services
N.A.I.C.S.: 211120

Yeongnam Energy Service Co., Ltd. (2)
586 Changpo-dong Buk-gu Pohang-si, Gyeongsan, Gyeongsangbuk, Korea (South)
Tel.: (82) 54 280 5114
Gas Production & Distribution Services
N.A.I.C.S.: 211120

SK Energy Americas, Inc. (1)
11700 Katy Fwy Ste 900, Houston, TX 77079
Tel.: (713) 871-1184
Petroleum Product Distr
N.A.I.C.S.: 424720

SK Energy Europe Limited (1)
3F 175-179 Oxford street, London, W1D 2JS, United Kingdom
Tel.: (44) 2074370211
Web Site: http://www.chn.skenergy.com
Oil & Gas Exploration Services
N.A.I.C.S.: 213112

SK Energy Hong Kong Limited (1)
Unit 5 39/F Far East Finance Centre No 16 Harcourt Road, Admiralty, Central, China (Hong Kong)
Tel.: (852) 28650114
Oil Refining Services
N.A.I.C.S.: 324110

SK Global Chemical (China) Holding Co., Ltd. (1)
Room 2606 SK Building No Jia 6 Jianguomenwai Street, Chaoyang, Beijing, China
Tel.: (86) 1059205612
Chemical Product Mfr & Distr
N.A.I.C.S.: 325998

SK Global Chemical Co., Ltd. (1)
Tel.: (82) 221215114
Emp.: 1,022
Petrochemical Mfr & Distr
N.A.I.C.S.: 325110
Kyung-Soo Na (Pres & CEO)

Plant (Domestic):

SK Global Chemical Co., Ltd. - Ulsan Plant (2)
110 Gosa-dong, Nam-gu, Ulsan, 680-130, Korea (South)
Tel.: (82) 52 208 2114
Chemical Products Mfr
N.A.I.C.S.: 325998

SK Global Chemical International Trading (Guangzhou) Co., Ltd. (1)
Room 2001 Tower 1 Taikoo Hui No 385 Tianhe Road, Tianhe District, Guangzhou, China
Tel.: (86) 2085100312
Petrochemical Product Distr
N.A.I.C.S.: 424690

SK Global Chemical International Trading (Shanghai) Co., Ltd. (1)
Gubei International Fortune Center II 15F No No 1438 Hongqiao Road, Changning, Shanghai, China
Tel.: (86) 2161970100
Petrochemical Product Distr
N.A.I.C.S.: 424690

SK Global Chemical Japan Co., Ltd. (1)
Tokyo Midtown Hibiya Hibiya Mitsui Tower 32F 1-1-2 Yurakucho, Chiyoda-ku, Tokyo, 100-0006, Japan
Tel.: (81) 335913041
Petrochemical Product Distr
N.A.I.C.S.: 424690

SK Global Chemical Singapore Pte. Ltd. (1)
9 Straits View 12-07/12 Marina One West Tower, Singapore, 018937, Singapore
Tel.: (65) 66711570
Petrochemical Product Distr
N.A.I.C.S.: 424690

SK Incheon Petrochem Co., Ltd. (1)
415 Bongsu-daero, Seo-gu, Incheon, 22771, Korea (South)
Tel.: (82) 325705151
Petroleum Product Mfr & Distr
N.A.I.C.S.: 324199
Yun Seok Choi (Pres & CEO)

SK Lubricants Co., Ltd. (1)
26 Jongno, Jongno-gu, 110-110, Seoul, Korea (South)
Tel.: (82) 221216114
Web Site: https://www.sklubricants.com
Emp.: 289
Petroleum Lubricant Mfr & Distr
N.A.I.C.S.: 324191
DongSeob Jee (Pres & CEO)

Subsidiary (US):

SK Lubricants Americas Inc. (2)
1300 Post Oak Blvd Ste 450, Houston, TX 77056
Tel.: (713) 622-5729
Web Site: http://www.sklubricants.com
Lubricant Oil Mfr & Distr
N.A.I.C.S.: 324191

Subsidiary (Non-US):

SK Lubricants Japan Co., Ltd. (2)
Tokyo Midtown Hibiya Hibiya Mitsui Tower 32F 1-1-2 Yurakucho, Chiyoda-Ku, Tokyo, 100-0006, Japan
Tel.: (81) 369102680
Oil & Gas Exploration Services
N.A.I.C.S.: 213112

SK Materials Renewtech Co., Ltd. (1)
72 Cheoyong-ro, Nam-gu, Ulsan, Korea (South)
Tel.: (82) 52 256 1641
Carbon Dioxide Mfr & Distr
N.A.I.C.S.: 325998

SK Permian, LLC (1)
11700 Katy Fwy Ste 900, Houston, TX 77079
Tel.: (713) 341-5820
Petrochemical Product Mfr & Distr
N.A.I.C.S.: 325998

SK Primacor Americas LLC (1)
2301 N Brazosport B-7701, Freeport, TX 77541
Tel.: (713) 341-5853
Petrochemical Product Distr
N.A.I.C.S.: 424690

SK Primacor Europe, S.L.U. (1)
Calle Velazquez 123 - 3rd Floor, 28006, Madrid, Spain
Tel.: (34) 919917873
Petrochemical Product Distr
N.A.I.C.S.: 424690

SK Saran Americas LLC (1)
564 Bldg Saran, Midland, MI 48667
Tel.: (989) 202-1575
Petrochemical Product Distr
N.A.I.C.S.: 424690

SK Trading International Co., Ltd. (1)
SK Bldg 26 Jongno, Jongno-gu, Seoul, Korea (South)
Tel.: (82) 221215218
Web Site:
 https://www.sktradinginternational.com
Petroleum Product Distr
N.A.I.C.S.: 424720
Sok Won Suh (Pres & CEO)

Shandong SK Hightech Oil Co., Ltd. (1)
No 15211 Shijidadao Road, Gaoxin District, Jinan, China
Tel.: (86) 13470060008
Petrochemical Product Mfr & Distr
N.A.I.C.S.: 325998

SK INTERNATIONAL EXPORT LIMITED
A-2 Unit No 78 Shah & Nahar Industrial Estate S J Road, Lower Parel, Mumbai, 400013, India
Tel.: (91) 2267477630
Web Site:
 https://www.skinternational.in
Year Founded: 1987
542728—(BOM)
Rev.: $886,961
Assets: $919,225
Liabilities: $162,472
Net Worth: $756,753
Earnings: ($36,940)
Fiscal Year-end: 03/31/23
Exports Apparel Mfr
N.A.I.C.S.: 315990
Hitesh Shrawankumar Sadh (Mng Dir)

SK JAPAN CO., LTD.

SK JAPAN CO., LTD.

SK Japan Co., Ltd.—(Continued)
6F NS21 Building 3-1-18 Tanimachi,
Chuo-ku, Osaka, 540-0012, Japan
Tel.: (81) 667651300
Web Site: https://www.sk-japan.co.jp
Year Founded: 1965
7608—(TKS)
Rev.: $75,239,080
Assets: $42,412,380
Liabilities: $8,663,980
Net Worth: $33,748,400
Earnings: $5,352,950
Emp.: 128
Fiscal Year-end: 02/29/24
Household Store Operator
N.A.I.C.S.: 449210
Hironori Yao (Pres)

SK JEWELLERY GROUP LIMITED

7 Changi Business Park Vista 01-01,
Singapore, 486042, Singapore
Tel.: (65) 68122833   SG
Web Site:
  http://www.sookeegroup.com
Year Founded: 1991
Rev.: $102,850,962
Assets: $107,620,198
Liabilities: $60,205,767
Net Worth: $47,414,432
Earnings: $4,443,875
Emp.: 500
Fiscal Year-end: 12/31/19
Investment Holding Services
N.A.I.C.S.: 551112
Yong Guan Lim (Co-Founder)

Subsidiaries:

Love & Co. Pte. Ltd.   (1)
Ion Orchard B2-64, Singapore, 238801,
Singapore
Tel.: (65) 65098633
Web Site: http://www.love-and-co.com
Jewellery Distr
N.A.I.C.S.: 423940

Love & Co. Sdn. Bhd.   (1)
The Gardens Midvalley City Lot F-239A,
59200, Kuala Lumpur, Malaysia
Tel.: (60) 322825633
Jewellery Distr
N.A.I.C.S.: 423940

SOO KEE Jewellery Pte Ltd   (1)
7 Changi Business Park Vista 01-01, Singapore, 486042, Singapore
Tel.: (65) 68122818
Web Site: http://www.skjewellery.com
Jewelry Retailer
N.A.I.C.S.: 611519

Sk Bullion Pte. Ltd.   (1)
24 Raffles Place 01-04 Clifford Centre, Singapore, 048621, Singapore
Tel.: (65) 65359633
Web Site: http://skbullion.com
Jewellery Distr
N.A.I.C.S.: 423940

SK KAKEN CO.,LTD.

3-5-25 Nakahozumi, Ibaraki, Osaka,
567-0034, Japan
Tel.: (81) 726217727
Web Site: https://www.sk-kaken.co.jp
Year Founded: 1955
4628—(TKS)
Rev.: $666,836,630
Assets: $1,210,132,360
Liabilities: $201,380,260
Net Worth: $1,008,752,100
Earnings: $78,163,250
Emp.: 2,299
Fiscal Year-end: 03/31/24
Coating Product Mfr
N.A.I.C.S.: 325510
Minoru Fujii (Chm)

Subsidiaries:

SK Kaken (M) Sdn. Bhd.   (1)
Suite 13 01 Level 13 Centrepoint South The Boulevard Mid Valley City, Lingkaran Syed Putra, 59200, Kuala Lumpur, Malaysia
Tel.: (60) 322829800
Wall Coating Mfr
N.A.I.C.S.: 325510
Bryan Chee Seng *(Asst Mgr-Sls)*

SK Kaken (Thailand) Co., Ltd.   (1)
518/5 Maneeya Center Building 6th floor Pleonchit Rd Lumpini, Pathumwan, Bangkok, 10330, Thailand
Tel.: (66) 26520600
Architectural Painting Services
N.A.I.C.S.: 541310

SKK (HK) Co., Ltd.   (1)
38/F Lee and Man Commercial Center 169 Electric Road North Point, Hong Kong, China (Hong Kong)
Tel.: (852) 25293968
Painting Material Mfr
N.A.I.C.S.: 325510

SKK (S) Pte. Ltd.   (1)
14 Pandan Road, Singapore, 609262, Singapore
Tel.: (65) 62740020
Web Site: https://skk.com.sg
Emp.: 110
Painting Material Mfr
N.A.I.C.S.: 325510
Ren Ong *(Mgr-Sls)*

SK MATERIALS CO., LTD.

59-33 Gaheunggongdan-ro, 36059,
Yeongi, Gyeongsangbuk-do, Korea
(South)
Tel.: (82) 546308114
Web Site: http://www.sk-materials.com
Year Founded: 1982
036490—(KRS)
Rev.: $878,582,256
Assets: $1,875,541,583
Liabilities: $1,411,226,621
Net Worth: $464,314,962
Earnings: $139,883,186
Emp.: 794
Fiscal Year-end: 12/31/20
Semiconductor Mfr
N.A.I.C.S.: 334413
Yong Hwan Kim (Auditor)

Subsidiaries:

Liaoning East Shine Chemical Technology Co., Ltd.   (1)
Fluorination Yimatu Town, Fuxin Mongolian Autonomous, Fuxin, Liaoning, China
Tel.: (86) 418 293 8817
Web Site: http://www.ocim.co.kr
Specialty Chemicals Mfr
N.A.I.C.S.: 325998

OCI Materials Japan Co., Ltd.   (1)
1077-24 Mizohigashi Kawarada-cho, Yokkaichi, Mie, Japan
Tel.: (81) 59 349 5800
Chemical Products Mfr
N.A.I.C.S.: 325998

OCI Materials Taiwan Co., Ltd.   (1)
No 12 Nanhuan Road Wuqi Dist, Wuci Dist, Taichung, 43541, Taiwan
Tel.: (886) 4 2659 5511
Web Site: http://www.ocim.co.kr
Emp.: 12
Semiconductor Device Distr
N.A.I.C.S.: 423690

SK Airgas Co., Ltd.   (1)
San142-1 Yongjam-Dong, Nam-Gu, Ulsan, 680-070, Korea (South)
Tel.: (82) 70 7437 1500
Web Site: http://www.skairgas.co.kr
Emp.: 40
Chemical Products Distr
N.A.I.C.S.: 424690
Shin Yoo *(Gen Mgr)*

SK NETWORKS CO., LTD.

19 Gyeongsu-daero 976beon-gil,
Jangan-gu, Seoul, 4534, Korea
(South)
Tel.: (82) 7078002114   KR
Web Site:
  https://www.sknetworks.co.kr
Year Founded: 1956
001740—(KRS)
Rev.: $7,414,164,082
Assets: $7,285,931,653
Liabilities: $5,406,235,549
Net Worth: $1,879,696,104
Earnings: $66,299,480
Emp.: 3,601
Fiscal Year-end: 12/31/22
Holding Company; Energy Production, Telecommunications, Engineering, Construction, International Trade & Finance
N.A.I.C.S.: 551112
Dae-Sik Cho (Exec Dir)

Subsidiaries:

Beijing Xinjincheng Co., Ltd.   (1)
SK Bldg 26F No 6 Jia Jianguomenwai Avenue, Chaoyang District, Beijing, 100022, China
Tel.: (86) 10 5929 7988
Web Site: http://www.sk.com
Emp.: 100
Steel Products Whslr
N.A.I.C.S.: 423510
Maggie Wang *(Gen Mgr)*

Dandong SK Networks Building Materials Co., Ltd.   (1)
No 8 Riverside Backstreet, Zhen'an District, Dandong, China
Tel.: (86) 415 398 1111
Construction Materials Whslr
N.A.I.C.S.: 423390

Kiwi Steel N.Z. Limited   (100%)
12 Hautu Drive, Wiri, Auckland, 2104, New Zealand
Tel.: (64) 92772700
Web Site: https://www.kiwisteel.co.nz
Sales Range: $25-49.9 Million
Emp.: 45
N.A.I.C.S.: 331513

MRO Korea Co., Ltd.
Sales Range: $25-49.9 Million
Emp.: 100
Facilities Maintenance Product Mfr & Distr
N.A.I.C.S.: 423840

Northern Copper Industrial Co., Ltd.   (1)
Dongfengshan, Xincheng, Shanxi, China
Tel.: (86) 359 603 1978
Web Site: http://northern.sknetworks.com
Copper Mining Services
N.A.I.C.S.: 212230

Obzee N.Y Inc.   (1)
632 W 28 St, New York, NY 10001-3952
Tel.: (212) 477-7778
Fashion Design Services
N.A.I.C.S.: 541490

P.T. SK Networks Indonesia   (1)
Treasury Tower 25th Floor Suite 25A District 8, Sudiman Central Business District Lot 28 JL Jendral Sudiman Kav 52-53, Jakarta, 12190, Indonesia
Tel.: (62) 2150300011
Petroleum Product Distr
N.A.I.C.S.: 424720
John Liang *(Mgr-Steel Mktg)*

PT. SK Networks   (1)
Equity Tower Building 26th Fl General Sudirman St Lot 9, Jakarta, 12190, Indonesia
Tel.: (62) 21 515 5688
Sales Range: $50-74.9 Million
Emp.: 25
Coal Mining Services
N.A.I.C.S.: 213113
Hyung Soon Park *(Pres)*

Subsidiary (Domestic):

PT. Karya Bumi Baratama   (2)
UOB Plaza 38th Floor Jl M H Thamrin Kav 8-10, Jakarta, 10230, Indonesia
Tel.: (62) 21 23566877
Web Site: http://www.kbb.co.id
Coal Mining Services
N.A.I.C.S.: 213113

PT. Rimba Sunkyong   (2)
24 Jin W R Mongonsidi, Padang, West Sumatra, Indonesia
Tel.: (62) 75137940
N.A.I.C.S.: 541360

PT. SK Networks Inni Joa Plantation   (2)
Tower l26th Suite 2603A Sudirman Sudirman Central Business District, Jl Jend Sudirman Kav, Jakarta, 12190, Indonesia
Tel.: (62) 21 515 5688
Investment Management Service
N.A.I.C.S.: 523999

SK (Guangzhou) Metal Co., Ltd.   (1)
Dongle Road the Eastern of Guangzhou Development District, Lezhu New Village, Guangzhou, 510663, China
Tel.: (86) 2032363688
Petroleum Product Distr
N.A.I.C.S.: 424720

SK Networks (China) Holdings Co., Ltd.   (1)
9F SK Building No 61 Shengli South Street, Heping District, Shenyang, 110001, Liaoning, China
Tel.: (86) 2431370777
Petroleum Product Distr
N.A.I.C.S.: 424720

SK Networks (Guangzhou) Auto Service   (1)
Room 2501 HNA No 8 Linhezhong Road, Tianhe, Guangzhou, 510610, Tianhe District, China
Tel.: (86) 20 8550 1045
Web Site: http://www.sknetworks.co.kr
Emp.: 5
Automobile Inspection & Maintenance Services
N.A.I.C.S.: 811198

SK Networks (Liaoning) Logistics Co., Ltd.   (1)
No 31 Aihe Street, Zhenxing District, Dandong, 118009, Liaoning, China
Tel.: (86) 4153851199
Petroleum Product Distr
N.A.I.C.S.: 424720

SK Networks (Qingdao) Auto Service   (1)
No 298 Chongqing South Road, Sifang District, Qingdao, 266000, China
Tel.: (86) 532 8496 7577
Automobile Inspection & Maintenance Services
N.A.I.C.S.: 811198

SK Networks (Shanghai) Co., Ltd.   (1)
Room No 1012A MT1 the Mixc Office Building No 3999 Hongxin Road, Minhang, Shanghai, 201103b, China
Tel.: (86) 2162950088
Emp.: 50
Industrial Chemicals & Steel Products Whslr
N.A.I.C.S.: 424690

SK Networks (Shanghai) Marketing Co., Ltd.   (1)
A-903 500 Ruby Road E, Shanghai, China
Tel.: (86) 21 32093338
Web Site:
  http://chinafashion.sknetworks.com
Fashion Design Services
N.A.I.C.S.: 541490

SK Networks (Shenyang) Auto Service   (1)
No 187 Daxi Road, Shenhe District, Shenyang, China
Tel.: (86) 24 2297 5000
Automobile Inspection & Maintenance Services
N.A.I.C.S.: 811198

SK Networks (Xiamen) Steel Processing Center Co., Ltd.   (1)
8-14 Hongxi Road Torch Hi-tech Industal Development Zone, Xiangan, Xiamen, 361100, Fujian, China
Tel.: (86) 5927769672
Petroleum Product Distr
N.A.I.C.S.: 424720

SK Networks (Zhangjiagang) Metal Products Co., Ltd.   (1)

AND PRIVATE COMPANIES

Room 1038 Guo Tai Times Plaza No 65
Renmin M Road, Zhangjiagang, China
Tel.: (86) 512 5671 9131
Sales Range: $25-49.9 Million
Emp.: 9
Metal Product Whslr
N.A.I.C.S.: 423510
Dong Hoon Lee *(Gen Mgr)*

SK Networks America Inc. (1)
17785 Center Court Dr Ste 375, Cerritos, CA 90703
Tel.: (562) 207-1182
Petroleum Product Distr
N.A.I.C.S.: 424720

SK Networks Australia Pty. Ltd. (1)
15 Wonderland Dr, Eastern Creek, 2766, NSW, Australia **(100%)**
Tel.: (61) 288821012
Web Site: http://www.sknetworks.com
Sales Range: $50-74.9 Million
Emp.: 8
Provider of Energy Production, Telecommunications, Engineering, Construction, International Trade & Finance
N.A.I.C.S.: 522299

SK Networks Auto Service H.K (1)
Unit 6311 63/f Center 99 Queen's Road, Central, Hong Kong, China (Hong Kong)
Tel.: (852) 2154 7600
Emp.: 5
Automotive Repair & Maintenance Services
N.A.I.C.S.: 811198
Patrick Yeung *(Mgr-Fin)*

SK Networks Brazil Co., Ltd. (1)
Av Roque Petroni Junior 850 Torre A-Bacaetava CJ 122, Jardim Das Acacias, Sao Paulo, Brazil
Tel.: (55) 11998051414
Petroleum Product Distr
N.A.I.C.S.: 424720

SK Networks Co., Ltd. - Mumbai Office (1)
404 5F 36 Turner Road, Bandra W, Mumbai, 400 050, India
Tel.: (91) 22 2645 4343
N.A.I.C.S.: 541360

SK Networks Co., Ltd. - Qingdao Office (1)
Room 1902 Huayin Tower 5 Donghai Xi Road, Qingdao, 266071, China
Tel.: (86) 532 8387 4333
Sales Range: $25-49.9 Million
Emp.: 10
N.A.I.C.S.: 541360

SK Networks Co., Ltd. - Taiwan Office (1)
Nankng East Road Sec 3 287 5th Floor Room A-1, Taipei, 105, Taiwan
Tel.: (886) 227183949
N.A.I.C.S.: 541360

SK Networks Co., Ltd. - Wuhan Office (1)
1817 Tower 1 New World Intl Trade Center No 568 Jianshe Ave, Wuhan, China
Tel.: (86) 2785775840
Sales Range: $25-49.9 Million
Emp.: 8
N.A.I.C.S.: 541360
Seung Pang *(Gen Mgr)*

SK Networks Co., Ltd.-Shanghai (1)
Room No 801 Building A Dawning Center 500 Hong Bao Shi Rd, Shanghai, China **(40%)**
Tel.: (86) 21 6295 0088
Web Site: http://www.sknetworks.co.kr
Sales Range: $10-24.9 Million
Emp.: 50
Integrated Marketing & Trading Solutions
N.A.I.C.S.: 541613
Kim Eun-seon *(Head-Trading)*

SK Networks Deutschland GmbH (1)
Lyoner Strasse 34, 60528, Frankfurt, Germany **(100%)**
Tel.: (49) 6966900124
Web Site: http://www.sk.com
Sales Range: $25-49.9 Million
N.A.I.C.S.: 541360

SK Networks HONG KONG LIMITED (1)
Unit 6311 63/F The Center 99 Queen's Road, Central, Hong Kong, China (Hong Kong)
Tel.: (852) 21547600
Sales Range: $25-49.9 Million
Emp.: 7
Wine Products Whslr
N.A.I.C.S.: 424820
Hyong Ju Yo *(Mng Dir)*

SK Networks Japan Co., Ltd. (1)
Orix Bldg 10F 5-8-11 Shimbashi, Minato-Ku, Tokyo, 105-0004, Japan
Tel.: (81) 354037791
Sales Range: $25-49.9 Million
Emp.: 8
Steel Products Mfr
N.A.I.C.S.: 331110

SK Networks METAL (Xiamen) Co., Ltd. (1)
Room No 318 3rd Fl Xiang-An Bei Road No 3699 Huoju, Xiamen, 361101, Fujian, China
Tel.: (86) 592 776 9672
Metal Products Mfr
N.A.I.C.S.: 332999

SK Networks PS (Shantou) Co., Ltd. (1)
Huangjin Wei Zhuchi, Shantou, 515041, Guangdong, China **(100%)**
Tel.: (86) 754 881 7218
N.A.I.C.S.: 541360

SK Networks Resources Canada Ltd. (1)
1200 Waterfront Ctr 200 Burrard St, Vancouver, V7X 1TQ, BC, Canada
Tel.: (604) 687-5744
Sales Range: $200-249.9 Million
Emp.: 600
Petroleum Product Mfr
N.A.I.C.S.: 324199

SK Networks Service Co., Ltd. (1)
Rm 202 2/F Charmant Officetel 1119 Ingye-Dong, Paldal-Gu, Suwon, 442070, Kyonggi-Do, Korea (South)
Tel.: (82) 7078052003
Communication Equipment Repair & Maintenance Services
N.A.I.C.S.: 811210

SK Networks Trading (Malaysia) Sdn Bhd (1)
Suite 1409 Kenanga International Jalan Sultan Ismail, Kuala Lumpur, 50250, Malaysia
Tel.: (60) 321610911
Web Site: http://www.sknetworks.co.kr
Sales Range: $25-49.9 Million
Emp.: 5
Coal, Chemicals & Steel Wholesale Trade Brokers
N.A.I.C.S.: 425120
Seung Hyoung *(Pres)*

SK Networks do Brasil, Ltda. (1)
Av das Nacoes Unidas 12 399 10th Floor 105-A Brooklin Paulista, Sao Paulo, 04578-000, Brazil
Tel.: (55) 11 7455 7375
Web Site: http://brasil.sknetworks.com
Sales Range: $25-49.9 Million
Emp.: 10
Steel Product Distr
N.A.I.C.S.: 423510

SK Pinx Co., Ltd. (1)
863 Sanroknam-ro, Andeok-myeon, Seogwipo, 63525, Jeju-do, Korea (South)
Tel.: (82) 647925200
Real Estate Management Services
N.A.I.C.S.: 531390

SK Steel Australia Pty. Ltd. (1)
15 Wonderland Dr, Eastern Creek, Sydney, 2766, NSW, Australia
Tel.: (61) 2 8882 1000
Web Site: http://www.sknetworks.co.kr
Steel Products Whslr
N.A.I.C.S.: 331513
Brad Wilbers *(Mgr-Key Accts)*

SL International Limited (1)
No 10 St 242 Vithei Okhna Peich Sangkat Chaktomuk, Khan Daun Penh, Phnom Penh, Cambodia
Tel.: (855) 23213099
N.A.I.C.S.: 541360

Shanghai Launch-SK Automobile Service Co., Ltd. (1)
3 Floor 77Jinan Rd, Pudong, Shanghai, China
Tel.: (86) 21 5169 6099
Web Site: http://www.speedmate.cn
Automobile Inspection & Maintenance Services
N.A.I.C.S.: 811198

Zhangjiagang Dongbu High Technology Metal Products Co., Ltd. (1)
Qigan Central Road Economic Development Zone, Zhangjiagang, Jiangsu, China
Tel.: (86) 512 5695 1051
Metal Product Whslr
N.A.I.C.S.: 423510

SK OCEANPLANT CO.,LTD.
51-1 Naesan 3-gil, Goseong-gun, Donghae, Gyeongnam, Korea (South)
Tel.: (82) 556737014
Web Site: https://skoceanplant.com
Year Founded: 1999
100090—(KRS)
Rev.: $530,633,717
Assets: $935,743,017
Liabilities: $532,333,616
Net Worth: $403,409,402
Earnings: $21,486,661
Emp.: 523
Fiscal Year-end: 12/31/22
Steel Pole Mfr
N.A.I.C.S.: 331210

Subsidiaries:

SAMKANG M&T CO., LTD - Korea Factory (1)
2029 Joseonteukgu-ro, Donghae, 638-842, Gyeongsangnam-do, Korea (South)
Tel.: (82) 70 8640 2196
Steel Pole Mfr
N.A.I.C.S.: 331110

SAMKANG M&T CO., LTD - Miryang Factory (1)
40 Yangdongnonggongdanji-gil, Hanam-eup, Miryang, 627-895, Gyeongsangnam-do, Korea (South)
Tel.: (82) 55 391 7020
Emp.: 90
Steel Pole Mfr
N.A.I.C.S.: 331110
Park Yaongon *(Mgr)*

SK REIT(REAL ESTATE INVESTMENT TRUST) CO., LTD
15F 136 Sejong-Daero, Jung-Gu, Seoul, Korea (South)
Tel.: (82) 263537070
Web Site: https://www.skreit.co.kr
Year Founded: 2021
395400—(KRS)
Real Estate Investment Management Services
N.A.I.C.S.: 531390
Yeoun-Suk Yoon *(Gen Mgr)*

SK SECURITIES ACPC NO. 7 COMPANY ACQUISITION PURPOSE CO., LTD
31 Gukjegeumyung-ro 8-gil Yeongdeungpo-gu, Seoul , 07332, Korea (South)
Tel.: (82) 2 3773 9933
Year Founded: 2021
Emp.: 100
Investment Services
N.A.I.C.S.: 523999
Kwon Chi-wan *(CEO)*

SK SECURITIES CO., LTD.
31 Gukjegeumyung-Ro 8-Gil, Yeongdeungpo-gu, Seoul, 07332, Korea (South)
Tel.: (82) 237738245
Web Site: https://www.sks.co.kr
Year Founded: 1955
001510—(KRS)
Financial Investment Services

N.A.I.C.S.: 523999
Dan Lim *(Asst Mgr-ESG Fin)*

SK SIGNET INC.
42F 108 Yeoui-daero, Yeongdeungpo-gu, Seoul, Korea (South)
Tel.: (82) 319946115
Web Site: https://sksignet.us
Year Founded: 2016
260870—(KRS)
Charger Mfr
N.A.I.C.S.: 335999
Jung-ho Shin *(CEO & Mng Dir)*

SK SQUARE CO., LTD.
SK Square SK T-Tower 65 Eulji-ro, Jung-gu, 04539, Seoul, 4539, Korea (South)
Web Site: https://www.sksquare.com
402340—(KRS)
Semiconductor Device Mfr & Distr
N.A.I.C.S.: 334413

Subsidiaries:

SK Planet, Inc. (1)
264 Pangyo-ro, Bundang-gu, Seongnam, 463-400, Gyeonggi-do, Korea (South)
Tel.: (82) 261190114
Web Site: https://www.skplanet.com
Software Development Services
N.A.I.C.S.: 541511

SK TARGET GROUP LIMITED
No 18 Jalan LP 2A/2 Taman Lestari Perdana, Seri Kembangan, 43300, Selangor, Malaysia
Tel.: (60) 389441388   Ky
Web Site: http://www.targetprecast.com
Year Founded: 1993
8427—(HKG)
Rev.: $6,493,333
Assets: $10,710,476
Liabilities: $3,028,360
Net Worth: $7,682,116
Earnings: $22,857
Emp.: 69
Fiscal Year-end: 05/31/24
Electrical Conduit Product Mfr & Distr
N.A.I.C.S.: 335932
Swee Keong Loh *(Founder, Chm & CEO)*

Subsidiaries:

Target Precast Industries Sdn. Bhd. (1)
No 18 Jalan LP 2A/2 Taman Lestari Perdana, 43300, Seri Kembangan, Selangor, Malaysia
Tel.: (60) 389441388
Precast Concrete Junction Box Mfr & Whslr
N.A.I.C.S.: 327390

SK TELECOM CO., LTD.
SK T-Tower 65 Eulji-ro, Jung-gu, Seoul, 04539, Korea (South)
Tel.: (82) 261002114   KR
Web Site: https://www.sktelecom.com
Year Founded: 1984
SKM—(NYSE)
Rev.: $13,069,868,474
Assets: $22,355,912,741
Liabilities: $13,279,417,484
Net Worth: $9,076,495,257
Earnings: $850,568,561
Emp.: 939
Fiscal Year-end: 12/31/23
Telecommunication Servicesb
N.A.I.C.S.: 517112
Young Sang Ryu *(Pres & CEO)*

Subsidiaries:

11Street Co., Ltd. (1)
Seoul Square 416 Hangang-daero, Jung-gu, Seoul, 04637, Korea (South)
Tel.: (82) 21 599 0110
Web Site: https://global.11st.co.kr

SK TELECOM CO., LTD.

SK Telecom Co., Ltd.—(Continued)
Shopping Portal Services
N.A.I.C.S.: 423690
Sangho Lee (CEO)

SK Broadband Co., Ltd. (1) (100%)
Tel.: (82) 262665500
Sales Range: $1-4.9 Billion
Emp.: 1,358
Internet Website Services & Telecommunications Services
N.A.I.C.S.: 517810

Subsidiary (Domestic):

Broadband CS Co., Ltd. (2)
6F SK Broadband Bldg 3-1 Dongseon-dong, Seongbuk-gu, Seoul, Korea (South)
Tel.: (82) 23201221
Web Site: http://www.broadbandcs.com
Service Center Specializing in Subscriber Acquisition & Customer Support
N.A.I.C.S.: 517810

Broadband Media Co., Ltd. (2)
7F Severance Bldg 84-11 Namdaemunro 5-ga, Chung-gu, Seoul, Korea (South)
Tel.: (82) 23133123
Web Site: http://www.broadbandmedia.kr
TV-Portal Services
N.A.I.C.S.: 516120

SK Communications Co., Ltd. (1)
T Tower 30 Sowol-ro 2-gil, Jung-gu, Seoul, 04637, Korea (South) (64.65%)
Tel.: (82) 221060912
Web Site: https://www.skcomms.co.kr
Sales Range: $50-74.9 Million
Emp.: 297
Website & Search Engine Operator
N.A.I.C.S.: 519290

Subsidiary (Domestic):

Cyworld Co., Ltd (2)
29-1 Nonhyeon-ro 158-gil, Gangnam-gu Sinsa-dong, Seoul, 04925, Korea (South)
Tel.: (82) 16704242
Web Site: https://www.cyworld.com
Social Networking Website Operator
N.A.I.C.S.: 516210

SK Planet Co., Ltd. (1)
Jung-gu Euljiro 65 (Euljiro 2-ga) SK T-tower, Seoul, Korea (South)
Tel.: (82) 1599 0011
Web Site: http://www.skplanet.com
Advertising & Marketing Communications Services
N.A.I.C.S.: 541890

SK Shieldus Co., Ltd. (1)
Shinko Building 4F627 Bongeunsa-ro, Gangnam-gu, Seoul, 06083, Korea (South) (55%)
Tel.: (82) 218006400
Web Site: https://www.skshieldus.com
Electronic Article Surveillance System Distr
N.A.I.C.S.: 423690

SK Telink Co., Ltd. (1) (83.46%)
Web Site: http://www.sktelink.com
Telecommunication Servicesb
N.A.I.C.S.: 517111

SK shieldus Co (1)
4th&5th fl. 23, 227-gil, Bundang-gu, Seongnam-si, Gyeonggido, Pangyo-ro, 13486, Korea (South) (55%)
Tel.: (82) 3151805000
Web Site: https://www.skshieldus.com
Security Services & Electronic Security Systems Mfr
N.A.I.C.S.: 561621

SK-ELECTRONICS CO., LTD.
436-2 Tatetomita-cho Ichijo-agaru Higashi Horikawa-dori, Kamigyo-ku, Kyoto, 602 0955, Japan
Tel.: (81) 754412333
Web Site: https://www.sk-el.co.jp
Year Founded: 2001
6677—(TKS)
Rev.: $199,321,170
Assets: $296,454,170
Liabilities: $72,268,370
Net Worth: $224,185,800
Earnings: $23,992,560
Emp.: 385
Fiscal Year-end: 09/30/23
Photomasks Mfr
N.A.I.C.S.: 339999
Masanori Ishida (Pres)

Subsidiaries:

Finex Co., LTD. (1)
No 45 Section 2 Huandong Road, Tainan Science Park Shanhua District, T'ainan, 741014, Taiwan (93.05%)
Tel.: (886) 65053228
Web Site: https://finex-tech.com.tw
Photomasks Mfr & Distr
N.A.I.C.S.: 325992
Kensaku Hirai (Chm)

SK-Electronics Co., Ltd. - Kyoto Plant (1)
62-1 Tominoshiro Shimotsuya, Kumiyama-cho Kuse-gun, Kyoto, 613-0035, Japan
Tel.: (81) 77 444 2921
Web Site: http://www.sk-el.co.jp
Photomasks Mfr
N.A.I.C.S.: 325992

SK-Electronics Co., Ltd. - Shiga Plant (1)
Omi Minakuchi No 2 Technopark Hinoki-gaoka, Minakchi-cho, Koka, 528-0068, Shiga, Japan
Tel.: (81) 748651390
Web Site: https://www.sk-el.co.jp
Photomasks Mfr
N.A.I.C.S.: 325992

SK-Electronics Shanghai Co., Ltd. (1)
Rm1901A Kirin Plaza 666 Gubei Road, Changning District, Shanghai, 200336, China
Tel.: (86) 2161250108
Photomask & Electronic Device Distr
N.A.I.C.S.: 424690

SKE Korea Co., Ltd. (1)
5F-505 129-12 Dongseo Road, Seobuk-gu, Cheonan, ChungNam, Korea (South)
Tel.: (82) 415220818
Photomask Mfr & Distr
N.A.I.C.S.: 325992

SKA INVEST AS
Fannestrandsveien 55, 6415, Molde, Norway
Year Founded: 2005
Privater Equity Firm
N.A.I.C.S.: 523999
Stale Karlsen (Owner, Chm & CEO)

Subsidiaries:

Hydal Transportsystemer AS (1)
Hydroveien 160, 4265, Havik, 4265, Norway (100%)
Tel.: (47) 52845400
Web Site: http://www.hytrans.no
Motor Vehicle Aluminum Extrusions
N.A.I.C.S.: 331318
Kjell Magne Thorshaug (CEO)

SKAHA FORD INC.
198 Parkway Place, Penticton, V2A 8G8, BC, Canada
Tel.: (250) 492-3800
Web Site: https://www.skahaford.com
Year Founded: 1984
Rev.: $26,926,027
Emp.: 55
New & Used Car Dealers
N.A.I.C.S.: 441110
Jack Muise (Owner)

SKAKO A/S
Bygmestervej 2, 5600, Faborg, Denmark
Tel.: (45) 63113860
Web Site: https://www.skako.com
SKAKO—(CSE)
Rev.: $63,364,732
Assets: $55,571,038
Liabilities: $34,421,438
Net Worth: $21,149,600
Earnings: $3,628,077
Emp.: 205
Fiscal Year-end: 12/31/22
Industrial Equipment Distr
N.A.I.C.S.: 423810
Christian Herskind Jorgensen (Deputy Chm)

Subsidiaries:

Skako Concrete A/S (1)
Bygmestervej 2, Faaborg, 5600, Middelfart, Denmark
Tel.: (45) 63616100
Construction Equipment Mfr
N.A.I.C.S.: 333120
Falke Tieldal (Sls Mgr)

Skako Concrete S.A. (1)
Parc du Melantois 102 rue des Sequoias, CS 60438, 59814, Lesquin, Cedex, France
Tel.: (33) 320244413
Construction Equipment Mfr
N.A.I.C.S.: 333120
Herve Delmotte (Sls Mgr)

Skako Concrete, Inc. (1)
7985 Dunbrook Rd Ste F, San Diego, CA 92126
Tel.: (858) 271-7341
Construction Equipment Mfr
N.A.I.C.S.: 333120
Preben Rasmussen (Pres & Mgr-US)

Skako GmbH (1)
An der Ziegelei 32b, Haltern Am See, 45721, Recklinghausen, Germany
Tel.: (49) 2364106023
Construction Equipment Mfr
N.A.I.C.S.: 333120
Dirk Ehrenheim (Reg Mgr)

Skako Vibration A/S (1)
Bygmestervej 2, Faaborg, 5600, Middelfart, Denmark
Tel.: (45) 63616340
Web Site: https://skako.com
Construction Equipment Mfr
N.A.I.C.S.: 333120
Lionel Girieud (Mng Dir)

Skako Vibration Ltd. (1)
Station Road, Industrial Estate, Tadcaster, LS24 9SG, North Yorkshire, United Kingdom
Tel.: (44) 1937838010
Construction Equipment Mfr
N.A.I.C.S.: 333120

Skako Vibration S.A. (1)
83 rue du Rhin Napoleon, B P 70, 67100, Strasbourg, Cedex, France
Tel.: (33) 388401200
Construction Equipment Mfr
N.A.I.C.S.: 333120
Antonio Henriques (Acct Mgr)

SKANDIA GREENPOWER AS
Henrik Wergelands gate 29, 4612, Kristiansand, Norway
Tel.: (47) 38701616
Web Site: https://www.skandiaenergi.no
Year Founded: 2015
SKAND—(EUR)
Electricity Distribution Services
N.A.I.C.S.: 237990
Lars Erik Dypvik (VP)

SKANDINAVISK HOLDING A/S
Sydmarken 42, DK-2860, Soborg, Denmark
Tel.: (45) 39 5562 00   DK
Holding Company
N.A.I.C.S.: 551112
Jorgen Tandrup (Chm)

Subsidiaries:

Scandinavian Tobacco Group A/S (1)
Sandtoften 9, 2820, Gentofte, Denmark (51%)
Tel.: (45) 39556200

INTERNATIONAL PUBLIC

Web Site: https://www.st-group.com
Rev.: $60,270,792,700
Assets: $104,017,364,850
Liabilities: $39,761,169,250
Net Worth: $64,256,195,600
Earnings: $10,154,729,550
Emp.: 10,000
Fiscal Year-end: 12/31/2022
Cigarettes, Smoking Tobacco, Cigars, Chewing Tobacco & Snuff Mfr
N.A.I.C.S.: 312230
Nigel Northridge (Chm)

Subsidiary (US):

Cigars International, Inc. (2)
1911 Spillman Dr, Bethlehem, PA 18015
Tel.: (484) 285-0400
Web Site:
  http://www.cigarsinternational.com
Sales Range: $75-99.9 Million
Emp.: 300
Cigars & Accessories Retailer
N.A.I.C.S.: 424940
Craig Reynolds (Pres)

General Cigar Co. Inc. (2)
10900 Nuckols Rd Ste 100, Glen Allen, VA 23060
Tel.: (804) 935-2800
Web Site: http://www.st-group.com
Sales Range: $100-124.9 Million
Emp.: 40
Handmade Cigars Mfr & Distr
N.A.I.C.S.: 312230
Regis Broersma (Pres)

Subsidiary (Non-US):

General Cigar Dominicana S.A. (2)
Zona Franca Industrial Etapa I Calle La Paloma Esq Villa Gonzalez, Santiago, Dominican Republic
Tel.: (809) 226 2500
Web Site: http://www.st-group.com
Sales Range: $300-349.9 Million
Emp.: 2,206
Tobacco Processing & Cigar Mfr
N.A.I.C.S.: 312230
Jhonys Diaz (VP-Ops)

Honduras American Tabaco, S.A. de C.V. (2)
Barrio el Quiquisque Carretera a El Paraiso, Contiguo a la Escuela Normal Espana y frente al Instituto Pedro Nufio, Danli, El Paraiso, Honduras
Tel.: (504) 27636674
Web Site: http://www.st-group.com
Sales Range: $300-349.9 Million
Emp.: 1,059
Tobacco Processing & Cigar Mfr
N.A.I.C.S.: 312230
Edwin Ariel Guevara (Gen Mgr-Premium)

Subsidiary (US):

Lane Limited (2)
2280 Mountain Industrial Blvd, Tucker, GA 30084
Tel.: (770) 934-8540
Web Site: http://www.st-group.com
Sales Range: $25-49.9 Million
Emp.: 110
Specialty Tobacco Products Mfr & Marketer
N.A.I.C.S.: 312230
Joe Hettinger (VP-Trade Mktg)

Subsidiary (Domestic):

Mac Baren Tobacco Company A/S (2)
Porthusvej 100, 5700, Svendborg, Denmark
Tel.: (45) 63 225 200
Web Site: http://www.mac-baren.com
Emp.: 140
Tobacco Products Mfr & Whslr
N.A.I.C.S.: 312230
Simon Sophus Nielsen (CEO)

Subsidiary (US):

Sutliff Tobacco Company, LLC (3)
600 Perdue Ave, Richmond, VA 23224
Tel.: (804) 233-7668
Web Site: http://www.sutliff-tobacco.com
Tobacco Products Mfr & Whslr
N.A.I.C.S.: 312230
Phill Green (Pres)

AND PRIVATE COMPANIES — SKANDINAVISKA ENSKILDA BANKEN AB

Subsidiary (Non-US):

Maga T.E.A.M. S.r.L (2)
Via G Puccini 103, 52100, Arezzo, Italy
Tel.: (39) 0575984094
Web Site: http://www.st-group.com
Sales Range: $50-74.9 Million
Emp.: 5
Cigars & Lighters Retailer
N.A.I.C.S.: 424990

P.G.C. Hajenius BV (2)
Rokin 96, 1012 KZ, Amsterdam, Netherlands
Tel.: (31) 206237494
Web Site: http://www.hajenius.com
Sales Range: $25-49.9 Million
Emp.: 10
Cigar Retailer
N.A.I.C.S.: 459991
Tom Bodde (Mng Dir)

SM Benelux Sales BV (2)
Nieuwstraat 75-77, CB 5521, Eersel, Netherlands
Tel.: (31) 402085600
Web Site: http://www.st-group.com
Sales Range: $50-74.9 Million
Emp.: 71
Cigars & Matches Retailer
N.A.I.C.S.: 424940
Tom Bodde (Mng Dir)

SM d.o.o. Zagreb (2)
Josipa Loncara 3, 10090, Zagreb, Croatia
Tel.: (385) 1 3463777
Cigars & Matches Whslr
N.A.I.C.S.: 424940

Subsidiary (Domestic):

Scandinavian Tobacco Group Assens (2)
Tobaksvej 1, DK-5610, Assens, Denmark
Tel.: (45) 64 71 10 32
Web Site: http://www.st-group.com
Sales Range: $25-49.9 Million
Emp.: 142
Fine Cut & Pipe Tobacco Mfr
N.A.I.C.S.: 312230
Jacob Bjerre (Gen Mgr)

Subsidiary (Non-US):

Scandinavian Tobacco Group Australia Pty Ltd. (2)
718 Princes Highway, Springvale, 3171, VIC, Australia
Tel.: (61) 385589999
Sales Range: $25-49.9 Million
Emp.: 59
Tobacco Product Mfr
N.A.I.C.S.: 312230
Tony Garcia (Mng Dir)

Scandinavian Tobacco Group Houthalen N.V. (2)
Houthalen Factory Europark 1030, 3530, Houthalen, Limburg, Belgium
Tel.: (32) 11520910
Web Site: http://www.st-group.com
Sales Range: $75-99.9 Million
Emp.: 460
Cigar Mfr
N.A.I.C.S.: 312230

Scandinavian Tobacco Group New Zealand Ltd. (2)
Level 1/18-26 Amelia Earhart Avenue Airport Oaks, PO Box 201230, Auckland Airport, Auckland, 2151, New Zealand
Tel.: (64) 800 442 866
Web Site: http://www.st-group.com
Sales Range: $25-49.9 Million
Emp.: 7
Hand-Made & Machine-Made Cigars, Pipe Tobacco, Tobacco Accessories & Distr of Swedish Match Lighters & Fire Products
N.A.I.C.S.: 424940
Tony Garcia (Mng Dir)

Scandinavian Tobacco Group Polska Sp z o.o. (2)
Algierska 17, Warsaw, 03-977, Poland
Tel.: (48) 228142278
Web Site: http://www.st-group.com
Sales Range: $25-49.9 Million
Emp.: 14
Cigars & Lighters Retailer
N.A.I.C.S.: 424940

Scandinavian Tobacco Group Spain S.A. (2)
C/Cronos 63 4a planta, 28037, Madrid, Spain
Tel.: (34) 913816400
Sales Range: $50-74.9 Million
Emp.: 60
Cigars & Matches Distr
N.A.I.C.S.: 424990

Scandinavian Tobacco Group Tobacco Service B.V. (2)
Nobelstraat 33, Tubbergen, 7651 DD, Overijssel, Netherlands
Tel.: (31) 546624622
Web Site: http://www.tobaccoservice.nl
Sales Range: $10-24.9 Million
Emp.: 40
Cigar Mfr
N.A.I.C.S.: 312230
Karin Brink (Mgr-Export)

Subsidiary (US):

Thompson & Company of Tampa, Inc. (2)
5401 Hangar Ct, Tampa, FL 33634-5341
Tel.: (813) 884-6955
Web Site: http://www.thompsoncigar.com
Designer Linens & Tobacco Products Retailer, Catalog & Mail Order Services
N.A.I.C.S.: 459991

Unit (Domestic):

Thompson Cigar (3)
1911 Spillman Dr Dept #32, Bethlehem, PA 18015
Tel.: (813) 884-6344
Web Site: http://www.thompsoncigar.com
Tobacco Products Retailer
N.A.I.C.S.: 459991

SKANDINAVISK LOGISTIK AS
Smedeland 22, 2600, Glostrup, Denmark
Tel.: (45) 4371 14 14
Web Site: http://www.skanlog.com
Third Party Logistics Services
N.A.I.C.S.: 541614
Benny Winther (Founder & Owner)

Subsidiaries:

Skanlog AB (1)
Bolindervagen 10, 635 10, Eskilstuna, Sweden **(100%)**
Tel.: (46) 16155700
Web Site: http://www.skanlog.com
Process Physical Distribution & Logistics Consulting Services
N.A.I.C.S.: 541614
Cecilia Carlstrom (Mgr-Warehouse)

SKANDINAVISKA ENSKILDA BANKEN AB
Kungstradgardsg 8, SE-106 40, Stockholm, Sweden
Tel.: (46) 771625353 SE
Web Site: https://www.seb.se
Year Founded: 1972
SEBA—(OTCIQ)
Rev.: $6,069,451,360
Assets: $371,175,938,560
Liabilities: $350,185,137,120
Net Worth: $20,990,801,440
Earnings: $1,922,271,680
Emp.: 15,500
Fiscal Year-end: 12/31/20
Commercial Banking Services
N.A.I.C.S.: 551111
Jesper Ovesen (Vice Chm)

Subsidiaries:

DSK Hyp AG (1)
Stephanstrasse 14-16, 60313, Frankfurt am Main, Germany
Tel.: (49) 696681960
Web Site: http://www.dskhyp.de
Investment Banking Services
N.A.I.C.S.: 522110

Enskilda Kapitalforvaltning SEB AB (1)
Kungstradgardsgatan 8, Stockholm, 10640, Sweden
Tel.: (46) 86769000
Web Site: http://www.seb.se
Asset Management Services
N.A.I.C.S.: 523940
Annika Falkengren (Exec Mgr)

Eurocard AB (1)
Magnus Ladulasgatan 2, 103 83, Stockholm, Sweden
Tel.: (46) 8146700
Web Site: http://www.eurocard.se
Sales Range: $200-249.9 Million
Emp.: 500
Credit Card Services
N.A.I.C.S.: 522210
Ulrica Baathe (Mgr-Brand)

Key Asset Management (UK) Limited (1)
2-6 Cannon Street, London, EC4M 6XX, United Kingdom
Tel.: (44) 20 7246 5700
Web Site: http://www.keyhedge.com
Sales Range: $50-74.9 Million
Emp.: 20
Asset Management Services
N.A.I.C.S.: 523940

L.W.M. SA (1)
4 rue Peternelchen, 2370, Howald, Luxembourg
Tel.: (352) 26 23 24 73
Web Site: http://www.lwm.lu
Emp.: 9
Financial Management Services
N.A.I.C.S.: 523999
Eric Leclerc (Founder & Partner)

SEB AG (1)
Stephenstrasse 14-16, 60313, Frankfurt am Main, Germany
Tel.: (49) 692580
Web Site: http://www.seb.de
Emp.: 800
Investment Banking & Wealth Management Services
N.A.I.C.S.: 523150
Magnus Carlsson (Chm-Supervisory Bd)

SEB Asset Management Norge AS (1)
Filipstad Brygge 1, 123, Oslo, Norway
Tel.: (47) 22827000
Asset Management Services
N.A.I.C.S.: 523940

SEB Asset Management S.A. (1)
4 Rue Pnelchen, Howald, 2370, Luxembourg
Tel.: (352) 26231
Sales Range: $50-74.9 Million
Emp.: 20
Asset Management Services
N.A.I.C.S.: 523940

SEB Elu- ja Pensionikindlustus AS (1)
Tornimae 2, 15010, Tallinn, Estonia
Tel.: (372) 665 8020
Fire Insurance Services
N.A.I.C.S.: 524113
Intrek Holst (Gen Mgr)

SEB Enskilda Corporate Finance Oy Ab (1)
Unioninkatu 30, PO Box 599, 00101, Helsinki, Finland
Tel.: (358) 9 616 289 00
Web Site: http://www.seb.fi
Sales Range: $200-249.9 Million
Emp.: 400
Investment Banking Services
N.A.I.C.S.: 523150

SEB Finans AB (1)
Gustavslundsvagen 42, 167 81, Bromma, Sweden
Tel.: (46) 86347600
Web Site: http://www.sebfinans.seb.se
Sales Range: $200-249.9 Million
Emp.: 300
Leasing, Factoring & Other Special Financial Services
N.A.I.C.S.: 522299

SEB Fonder AB (1)
Sergelstorg 2, S 106 40, Stockholm, Sweden **(100%)**
Tel.: (46) 86769000
Sales Range: $100-124.9 Million
Emp.: 150
N.A.I.C.S.: 522299

SEB Foretagsinvest (1)
Kuntstradgardsgatan 8, Stockholm, 10640, Sweden **(100%)**
Tel.: (46) 87638000
Web Site: http://www.foretagsinvest.se
Sales Range: $200-249.9 Million
Emp.: 300
N.A.I.C.S.: 523940

SEB Gyllenberg Fondbolag Ab (1)
Unioninkatu 30, Helsinki, 100, Finland
Tel.: (358) 9131551
Sales Range: $200-249.9 Million
Emp.: 30
Portfolio Management Services
N.A.I.C.S.: 523940
Petteri Karttunen (Gen Mgr)

SEB Hong Kong Trade Services Ltd (1)
17 Floor Jardine House 1 Connaught Place, Central, China (Hong Kong)
Tel.: (852) 31592888
Sales Range: $50-74.9 Million
Emp.: 3
Trade Financing Services
N.A.I.C.S.: 522299
Carl Christensson (Country Mgr)

SEB Internal Supplier AB (1)
Sergels Torg 2, Stockholm, 106 40, Sweden
Tel.: (46) 87635000
Insurance Agency & Brokerage Services
N.A.I.C.S.: 524210

SEB Investment Management AB (1)
Sergels Torg 2, 10540, Stockholm, Sweden **(100%)**
Tel.: (46) 87635000
Web Site: http://www.sebgroup.se
Sales Range: $800-899.9 Million
Emp.: 2,000
Investment Management Service
N.A.I.C.S.: 523940

SEB Kort AB (1)
Magnus Ladulasgatan 2, Stockholm, 103 83, Sweden
Tel.: (46) 8 14 68 55
Web Site: http://www.seb.se
Financial Credit Intermediation Services
N.A.I.C.S.: 522299

SEB Leasing Oy (1)
Etelaesplanadi 18, PO Box 630, 00101, Helsinki, Finland
Tel.: (358) 9 616 280 00
Web Site: http://www.seb.fi
Sales Range: $50-74.9 Million
Emp.: 1
Financial Lending Services
N.A.I.C.S.: 522220
Timo Ahonen (Head-Project & Asset Fin)

SEB Leasing, CJSC (1)
11 Mikhailova Street, 195009, Saint Petersburg, Russia
Tel.: (7) 812 334 0360
Web Site: http://www.seb.com.ru
Financial Lending Services
N.A.I.C.S.: 522220

SEB Merchant Banking (1)
Kungstradgardsgatan 8, Stockholm, 106 40, Sweden **(100%)**
Tel.: (46) 87638000
Web Site: http://www.sebgroup.com
Sales Range: $50-74.9 Million
Emp.: 30
N.A.I.C.S.: 522299
Magnus Carlsson (CEO)

SEB Pank, AS (1)
Tornimae 2, 15010, Tallinn, Estonia
Tel.: (372) 665 5100
Web Site: http://www.seb.ee
Financial Management Services
N.A.I.C.S.: 523999
Allan Parik (Chm-Mgmt Bd)

SEB Private Bank (1)
4 rue Peternelchen, 2370, Howald, Luxembourg
Tel.: (352) 26231
Web Site: http://www.sebgroup.lu

SKANDINAVISKA ENSKILDA BANKEN AB

Skandinaviska Enskilda Banken AB—(Continued)
Sales Range: $100-124.9 Million
Emp.: 250
Banking Services
N.A.I.C.S.: 522299
Alan Henneberry (CFO)

SEB Securities Service (1)
Liffmeleden 110, SE 106 40, Stockholm,
Sweden (100%)
Tel.: (46) 87635770
Web Site: http://www.seb.se
Sales Range: $100-124.9 Million
Emp.: 250
N.A.I.C.S.: 523940

SEB Securities, Inc. (1)
245 Park Ave 42nd Fl, New York, NY 10167
Tel.: (212) 692-4760
Web Site: http://www.enskilda.com
Sales Range: $50-74.9 Million
Emp.: 50
Securities Broker
N.A.I.C.S.: 523150

Skandinaviska Enskilda Banken (1)
25 Rue Balzac, PO Box 125, F 75363,
Paris, France (100%)
Tel.: (33) 153831950
Web Site: http://taz.vv.sebank.se
Sales Range: $50-74.9 Million
Emp.: 20
Banking Services
N.A.I.C.S.: 522299

**Skandinaviska Enskilda Banken
A/S** (1)
Bernstorffsgade 50, 1577, Copenhagen,
Denmark
Tel.: (45) 33282828
Sales Range: $350-399.9 Million
Emp.: 60
Commercial Banking Services
N.A.I.C.S.: 522110

**Skandinaviska Enskilda Banken
S.A.** (1)
4 rue Peternelchen, 2370, Howald, Luxembourg
Tel.: (352) 26 23 1
Web Site: http://www.sebgroup.lu
Emp.: 23
Commercial Banking Services
N.A.I.C.S.: 522110
Peter Kubicki (Mng Dir)

**Skandinaviska Enskilda Banken
South East Asia Limited** (1)
50 Collyer Quay Suite 12-03 OUE Bayfront,
Singapore, 49321, Singapore (100%)
Tel.: (65) 62235644
Web Site: http://www.mb.seb.se
Sales Range: $1-9.9 Million
Emp.: 100
Banking
N.A.I.C.S.: 522299
Jan Stjernstrom (Gen Mgr)

Skandinaviska Enskilda Banken Ltd (1)
One Carter Lane, London, EC4V 5AM,
United Kingdom
Tel.: (44) 20 72464000
Web Site: http://www.sebbank.se
Sales Range: $100-124.9 Million
Emp.: 20
Commercial Banking Services
N.A.I.C.S.: 522110

SKANE-MOLLAN AB
Silosgatan 5, Tagarp, 268 75, Svalov,
Sweden
Tel.: (46) 41850102
Web Site: https://www.skane-mollan.se
Year Founded: 1971
SKMO—(OMX)
Rev.: $25,472,290
Assets: $18,161,042
Liabilities: $2,910,075
Net Worth: $15,250,967
Earnings: $1,946,294
Emp.: 29
Fiscal Year-end: 12/31/22
Grain Foodstuff Product Mfr
N.A.I.C.S.: 311211
Anders Persson (Mng Dir)

SKANEM AS
Hesbygaten 5, PO Box 1529, 4093,
Stavanger, Norway
Tel.: (47) 51 85 97 80 NO
Web Site: http://www.skanem.com
Year Founded: 1905
Sales Range: $150-199.9 Million
Emp.: 1,000
Self Adhesive Labels Mfr
N.A.I.C.S.: 561910
Ole Rugland (Chm)

Subsidiaries:

Skanem Bangkok Co., Ltd. (1)
Amata Nakorn Industrial Estate 700/247
Moo 1, Bankao, Chon Buri, 20160, Thailand
Tel.: (66) 384653159
Label Printing Services
N.A.I.C.S.: 323111
Chairat Teekhasaenee (Mng Dir)

**Skanem Interlabels Industries (P)
Ltd.** (1)
110 Ravi Industrial Estate Off Mahakali
Caves Road, Andheri, 400 093, Mumbai,
India
Tel.: (91) 226581433
Web Site: http://www.interlabels.com
Emp.: 200
Label Printing Services
N.A.I.C.S.: 323111
Ole Rugland (CEO)

Skanem Interlabels Nairobi Ltd. (1)
Maasai Road Off Mombasa Road, PO Box
65, Viwandani, 00507, Nairobi, Kenya
Tel.: (254) 202471001
Web Site: http://www.interlabelsafrica.com
Label Printing Services
N.A.I.C.S.: 323111
Sachen Gudka (Mng Dir)

Skanem Poznan Sp. z o. o. (1)
Poznanska 34B, Tarnowo Podgorne,
Swadzim, 62-080, Poland
Tel.: (48) 618962000
Label Printing Services
N.A.I.C.S.: 323111
Sawomir Lis (Mng Dir)

SKANRAY TECHNOLOGIES PRIVATE LIMITED
Plot No 15-17 Hebbal Industrial Area,
Mysore, 570 016, India
Tel.: (91) 8212415559 In
Web Site: https://www.skanray.com
Year Founded: 2007
Electronic Medical Devices Mfr &
Distr
N.A.I.C.S.: 334510
Vishwaprasad Alva (Mng Dir)

SKANSEN BRANDS PTY. LTD.
126 Woodlands Drive, Braeside,
3195, VIC, Australia
Tel.: (61) 3 9587 8283 AU
Web Site:
http://www.skansen.com.au
Plush Toy Designer, Licensor, Mfr &
Distr
N.A.I.C.S.: 533110
Adam Schoff (Mng Dir)

SKANSKA AB
Warfvinges vag 25, SE-112 74,
Stockholm, Sweden
Tel.: (46) 104480000 SE
Web Site: https://www.skanska.se
Year Founded: 1887
SKAB—(OTCIQ)
Rev.: $15,283,186,752
Assets: $14,198,488,297
Liabilities: $9,023,200,052
Net Worth: $5,175,288,244
Earnings: $775,895,174
Emp.: 27,666
Fiscal Year-end: 12/31/22
Holding Company; Commercial, Residential & Civil Real Estate Development, Engineering & Construction Services

N.A.I.C.S.: 551112
Anders Danielsson (Pres & CEO)

Subsidiaries:

**Elizabeth River Crossings Opco,
LLC** (1)
99 Canal Ctr Plz Ste 125, Alexandria, VA
22314-1559 (50%)
Tel.: (757) 334-0404
Web Site: http://www.driveert.com
Highway, Street & Bridge Construction
N.A.I.C.S.: 237310
Leila Rice (Mgr-Pub Affairs)

Heinz Essmann GmbH (1)
Im Weingarten 2, 32107, Bad Salzuflen,
Germany (100%)
Tel.: (49) 52227910
Web Site: http://www.essmann.de
Sales Range: $100-124.9 Million
Emp.: 300
Roofing for Construction Related Industries
N.A.I.C.S.: 238160
Ralf Dahmer (CEO)

Orkdalsvegen AS (1)
Bardshaug Vest, Orkanger, N-7300, Norway
Tel.: (47) 72480207
Web Site: http://www.orkdalsvegen.no
Sales Range: $25-49.9 Million
Emp.: 10
Public Roads Administration & Construction
N.A.I.C.S.: 237310

Skanska Danmark A/S (1)
Havneholmen 25, 1561, Copenhagen, Denmark
Tel.: (45) 44680565
Web Site: http://www.skanska.dk
Real Estate Development, Property Management & Asphalt Paving Services
N.A.I.C.S.: 237210

Skanska EMV AS (1)
Madara 25, 10612, Tallinn, Estonia
Tel.: (372) 6 403 300
Web Site: http://www.skanska.ee
Sales Range: $50-74.9 Million
Emp.: 20
Commercial Building Construction Services
N.A.I.C.S.: 236220
Andres Aavik (Gen Mgr)

Skanska Financial Services AB (1)
Rasundavagen 2, Solna, 169 83, Sweden
Tel.: (46) 104480000
Web Site: http://www.skanska.se
Sales Range: $150-199.9 Million
Emp.: 50
Financial Services
N.A.I.C.S.: 561499
Cecilia Hamberg (Mgr-HR)

Skanska Latin America SA (1)
Reconquista 134 5 piso, 1035, Buenos Aires, Argentina
Tel.: (54) 11 4341 7000
Web Site: http://www.la.skanska.com
Construction & Mining Services
N.A.I.C.S.: 237990

Subsidiary (Non-US):

Skanska Brasil Ltda (2)
Rua Verbo Divino 1207 Bloco B, Chacara
Santo Antonio, Sao Paulo, 04719-002, Brazil
Tel.: (55) 11 3583 4400
Web Site: http://www.la.skanska.com
Emp.: 13
Construction Engineering Services
N.A.I.C.S.: 541330
Sebastio Alves (Mgr-Bus Dev)

Subsidiary (Domestic):

Breitener Energetica S/A (3)
Principal S-No, Maracanau, Brazil
Tel.: (55) 9221238484
Web Site: http://www.breitener.com.br
Electric Power Distribution
N.A.I.C.S.: 221122

Subsidiary (Non-US):

Skanska Chile S.A. (2)
Av Apoquindo 4001 of 604, Las Condes,
Santiago, 7550162, Chile
Tel.: (56) 2 820 5600
Web Site: http://www.la.skanska.com

Power Transmission Construction Services
N.A.I.C.S.: 237130

Skanska Colombia S.A.S (2)
Calle 99 7A -77 Edificio Advance Piso 5 Ofc
501, Bogota, Colombia
Tel.: (57) 1 616 1177
Civil Engineering Construction Services
N.A.I.C.S.: 237990

**Skanska Magyarorszag Ingatlan
Kft.** (1)
Green House Kassak Lajos utca 19-25, Budapest, 1134, Hungary
Tel.: (36) 1382 9100
Web Site: http://www.skanska.hu
Sales Range: $25-49.9 Million
Emp.: 13
Commercial Property Development
N.A.I.C.S.: 237210
Marcin Lapinski (Mng Dir)

Skanska Norway A/S (1)
Lakkegata 53, 0187, Oslo, Norway
Tel.: (47) 40006400
Web Site: http://www.skanska.no
Sales Range: $100-124.9 Million
Emp.: 4,300
House Building, Heavy Construction & Civil
Engineering
N.A.I.C.S.: 236118

Skanska Oy (1)
Nauvontie 18, 00280, Helsinki,
Finland (100%)
Tel.: (358) 20719211
Web Site: https://www.skanska.fi
Sales Range: $800-899.9 Million
Emp.: 3,400
House Building, Heavy Construction & Civil
Engineering
N.A.I.C.S.: 236118

**Skanska Property Czech Republic,
s.r.o.** (1)
Krizikova 682 / 34a, 186 00, Prague, Czech
Republic
Tel.: (420) 267095111
Web Site: http://www.skanska.cz
Sales Range: $25-49.9 Million
Real Estate Development Services
N.A.I.C.S.: 531390

Skanska S.A. (1)
Aleja Solidarnosci 173, 00-877, Warsaw,
Poland
Tel.: (48) 225613000
Web Site: http://www.skanska.pl
Property Management Services
N.A.I.C.S.: 531312

Subsidiary (Domestic):

**Skanska Property Poland Sp.
z.o.o.** (2)
Aleja Solidarnosci 173, 00-877, Warsaw,
Poland
Tel.: (48) 22 653 8400
Web Site: https://www.skanska.pl
Property Management Services
N.A.I.C.S.: 531311
Katarzyna Zawodna (Pres & CEO)

Skanska Sverige AB (1)
Warfvinges vag 25, 112 74, Stockholm,
Sweden
Tel.: (46) 104480000
Web Site: https://www.skanska.se
Sales Range: $150-199.9 Million
Emp.: 250
Commercial, Residential & Civil Real Estate
Development, Engineering & Construction
Services
N.A.I.C.S.: 531390

Subsidiary (Domestic):

**Skanska Bostadsutveckling Norden
AB** (2)
Warsvinges-Vag 25, 169 83, Solna, Sweden
Tel.: (46) 104480000
Web Site: http://www.skanska.com
Sales Range: $150-199.9 Million
Emp.: 30
Property Development Services
N.A.I.C.S.: 531390
Jan Odelstam (Pres-Bus Unit)

Skanska Byggsystem AB (2)

Rasundavagen 2, 169 83, Solna, Sweden
Tel.: (46) 104480000 **(100%)**
Web Site: http://www.skanska.se
Sales Range: $25-49.9 Million
Emp.: 40
Engineering Services
N.A.I.C.S.: 236220

Skanska Fastigheter Goteborg AB **(2)**
Kils Gatan 4, 405 18, Gothenburg, Sweden
Tel.: (46) 104485620 **(100%)**
Web Site: http://www.skanska.se
Sales Range: $75-99.9 Million
Emp.: 200
Real Estate
N.A.I.C.S.: 531210

Skanska Fastigheter Stockholm AB **(2)**
Rasundavagen 2, SE 169 83, Solna, Sweden
Tel.: (46) 0850435000 **(100%)**
Web Site: http://www.skanska.se
Sales Range: $50-74.9 Million
Emp.: 100
Real Estate
N.A.I.C.S.: 531210

Skanska Kommersiell Utveckling Norden AB **(2)**
Warfvinges vag 25, 112 51, Stockholm, Sweden
Tel.: (46) 104480000
Web Site: http://www.skanska.se
Commercial Property Development Services
N.A.I.C.S.: 237210
Andreas Joons *(Officer-Press)*

Branch (Domestic):

Skanska Sverige AB **(2)**
Drottningtorget 14, Malmo, 20533, Sweden
Tel.: (46) 104480000
Web Site: http://www.skanska.se.com
Sales Range: $50-74.9 Million
N.A.I.C.S.: 236118
Johan Karlstrom *(Gen Mgr)*

Skanska UK PLC **(1)**
Maple Cross House Denham Way Maple Cross, Rickmansworth, WD3 9SW, Herts, United Kingdom **(100%)**
Tel.: (44) 1923776666
Web Site: http://www.skanska.co.uk
Sales Range: $900-999.9 Million
Emp.: 500
Construction Services
N.A.I.C.S.: 236220
Meliha Duymaz *(CFO & Exec VP)*

Subsidiary (Domestic):

Cementation Foundations Skanska Ltd. **(2)**
Maple Cross House Denham Way Maple Cross, Rickmansworth, WD3 9SW, Hertfordshire, United Kingdom **(100%)**
Tel.: (44) 1923923100
Web Site: http://www.skanska.co.uk
Sales Range: $25-49.9 Million
Emp.: 100
N.A.I.C.S.: 541330

Skanska Technology Limited **(2)**
Denham Way, Maple Cross, Rickmansworth, WD3 9SW, Hertfordshire, United Kingdom **(100%)**
Tel.: (44) 1923776666
Web Site: http://www.skanska.co.uk
Emp.: 300
Building & Civil Engineering
N.A.I.C.S.: 237310

Skanska Technology Limited **(2)**
Kenfig Industrial Est Margam, Port Talbot, SA13 2PR, W Glam, United Kingdom **(100%)**
Tel.: (44) 656742000
Web Site: http://www.skanska.co.uk
Sales Range: $25-49.9 Million
Emp.: 30
Construction Services
N.A.I.C.S.: 237310

Skanska USA Inc. **(1)**
350 5th Ave 32nd Fl, New York, NY 10118
Tel.: (917) 438-4500
Web Site: http://usa.skanska.com
Sales Range: $1-4.9 Billion
Emp.: 7,400
Holding Company; Regional Managing Office
N.A.I.C.S.: 551112
Bryan Northrop *(Exec VP & Gen Mgr)*

Subsidiary (Domestic):

Skanska Commercial Development USA Inc **(2)**
Empire State Bldg 350 5th Ave 32nd Fl, New York, NY 10118-3290
Tel.: (917) 438-4500
Web Site: http://www.usa.skanska.com
Sales Range: $25-49.9 Million
Emp.: 40
Commercial Building Construction Services
N.A.I.C.S.: 236220
Rob Ward *(Pres)*

Skanska USA Building Inc. **(2)**
389 Interpace Pkwy 5th Fl, Parsippany, NJ 07054 **(100%)**
Tel.: (973) 753-3500
Web Site: http://usa.skanska.com
General Contractors for Construction Management
N.A.I.C.S.: 236220
Paul Hewins *(Pres & CEO)*

Branch (Domestic):

Skanska USA Building Inc. **(3)**
4309 Impor Blvd Ste 200, Durham, NC 27703
Tel.: (336) 759-7800
Sales Range: $25-49.9 Million
Emp.: 50
Nonresidential Construction
N.A.I.C.S.: 236220
Sal Taddeo *(COO-East)*

Skanska USA Building Inc. **(3)**
2555 SW 153rd Dr, Beaverton, OR 97006-5144
Tel.: (503) 641-2500
Sales Range: $125-149.9 Million
Emp.: 400
General Construction Contractor
N.A.I.C.S.: 236220
Jeff Fisher *(VP-Bus Dev)*

Skanska USA Building Inc. **(3)**
30 Burton Hills Blvd Ste 400, Nashville, TN 37215-6403
Tel.: (615) 665-5500
Sales Range: $25-49.9 Million
Emp.: 33
General Contractors for Commercial Buildings
N.A.I.C.S.: 236220
Marsh Ragland *(VP)*

Skanska USA Building Inc. **(3)**
221 Yale Ave N Ste 400, Seattle, WA 98109
Tel.: (206) 726-8000
Web Site: http://www.usa.skanska.com
Sales Range: $25-49.9 Million
Emp.: 100
Commercial & Industrial Construction Contracting Services
N.A.I.C.S.: 236115

Skanska USA Building Inc. - Michigan **(3)**
26100 American Dr Ste 200, Southfield, MI 48034
Tel.: (248) 351-8300
Sales Range: $25-49.9 Million
Emp.: 30
General Contractors, Construction Management, Interiors
N.A.I.C.S.: 236220
Bob Skinner *(VP)*

Subsidiary (Domestic):

Skanska USA Civil Inc. **(2)**
1616 Whitestone Expy, Whitestone, NY 11357-3055 **(100%)**
Tel.: (718) 767-2600
Web Site: http://usa.skanska.com
Sales Range: $900-999.9 Million
Emp.: 3,500
Group Holding Company; Property Development & Management; Underground & Above-Ground Heavy Construction & Management

N.A.I.C.S.: 236220

Subsidiary (Domestic):

Industrial Contractors, Inc. **(3)**
401 Northwest 1st St, Evansville, IN 47708
Tel.: (812) 423-7832
Web Site: http://www.industrialcontractors.com
Sales Range: $500-549.9 Million
Emp.: 2,400
Industrial Construction Services
N.A.I.C.S.: 236210
Dan Hoefling *(VP)*

Skanska Koch **(3)**
400 Roosevelt Ave, Carteret, NJ 07008-3511
Tel.: (732) 969-1700
Web Site: http://usa.skanska.com
Sales Range: $25-49.9 Million
Bridge Repair; Structural Steel Erection & Fabrication
N.A.I.C.S.: 237310

Skanska USA Civil Northeast Inc. **(3)**
1616 Whitestone Expy, Whitestone, NY 11357-3055
Tel.: (718) 767-2600
Web Site: http://www.usa.skanska.com
Mfr of Small Rubber Parts for Building, Machine Tools
N.A.I.C.S.: 238210

Underpinning & Foundation Constructors, Inc. **(3)**
4636 54th Rd, Maspeth, NY 11378-1020
Tel.: (718) 786-6557
Sales Range: $25-49.9 Million
Emp.: 50
Foundation for Highways & Buildings
N.A.I.C.S.: 236210
Craig Meltzer *(Project Mgr)*

Skanskar Financial Services AB **(1)**
Warfvinges vag 25, 112 74, Stockholm, Sweden
Tel.: (46) 10 448 0000
Web Site: https://www.skanska.se
Construction Services
N.A.I.C.S.: 236220

Voigt & Co. Baugesellschaft GmbH **(1)**
Kitzingstrasse 7 9, PO Box 480344, 12253, Berlin, Germany **(100%)**
Tel.: (49) 3076189189
Mfr of Small Rubber Parts for Building, Machine Tools
N.A.I.C.S.: 236118

SKANSKA ENERGI AB
Skattebergavagen 7 Box 83, 247 22, Sodra Sandby, Sweden
Tel.: (46) 4650700
Web Site: http://www.skanska-energi.se
Rev.: $31,682,650
Assets: $37,925,742
Liabilities: $15,418,256
Net Worth: $22,507,486
Earnings: ($2,828,000)
Emp.: 59
Fiscal Year-end: 12/31/16
Power Distr
N.A.I.C.S.: 221122
Anders Moller *(CEO)*

SKARBIEC HOLDING S.A.
al Armii Ludowej 26, 00-609, Warsaw, Poland
Tel.: (48) 225213000
Web Site: https://www.skarbiecholding.pl
Year Founded: 1997
SKH—(WAR)
Sales Range: Less than $1 Million
Investment Management
N.A.I.C.S.: 523999
Piotr Szulec *(Pres)*

Subsidiaries:

SKARBIEC Towarzystwo Funduszy Inwestycyjnych S.A. **(1)**
Al Armii Ludowej 26, 00-609, Warsaw, Poland
Tel.: (48) 225213199
Web Site: http://www.skarbiec.pl
Fund Management Services
N.A.I.C.S.: 523940

SKARDIN INDUSTRIAL CORP.
8F No 123-1 Hsing De Road, Sanchung District, New Taipei City, Taiwan
Tel.: (886) 285123068
Web Site: https://www.skardin.com
Year Founded: 1982
3466—(TPE)
Rev.: $36,469,218
Assets: $57,139,824
Liabilities: $24,731,045
Net Worth: $32,408,780
Earnings: $131,976
Emp.: 272
Fiscal Year-end: 12/31/22
Electric Equipment Mfr
N.A.I.C.S.: 334419

SKB SHUTTERS CORPORATION BERHAD
Lot 22 Jln Teknologi Tmn Sains Selangor 1 Kota Damansara, 47810, Petaling Jaya, Selangor, Malaysia
Tel.: (60) 361572277
Web Site: https://www.skb-shutters.com
SKBSHUT—(KLS)
Rev.: $18,436,765
Assets: $44,415,872
Liabilities: $19,506,955
Net Worth: $24,908,917
Earnings: $2,374,855
Fiscal Year-end: 06/30/22
Shutters Mfr
N.A.I.C.S.: 321918
Siew Huey Sin *(Exec Dir)*

SKB-BANK PAO
Ulitsa Kuybisheva 75, Ekaterinburg, 620026, Russia
Tel.: (7) 3432228193
Web Site: http://www.skbbank.ru
Sales Range: Less than $1 Million
Commercial Banking Services
N.A.I.C.S.: 522110
Denis P. Repnikov *(Chm-Mgmt Bd)*

SKC CO., LTD.
Kyobo Tower 1303-22 Seocho 4-dong, Seocho-gu, Seoul, 137-070, Korea (South)
Tel.: (82) 2 3787 1234   KR
Web Site: http://www.skc.kr
Coated Film Mfr
N.A.I.C.S.: 322220
Shin-won Chey *(Chm)*

Subsidiaries:

SKC (Beijing) Polyurethane Co., Ltd. **(1)**
Room No 2313 International Trade Center 2201 West Yan'an Road, Shanghai, 200336, China
Tel.: (86) 21 6270 2866
Web Site: http://www.skc.kr
Sales Range: $25-49.9 Million
Emp.: 20
Chemical Product Whslr
N.A.I.C.S.: 424690

SKC Co., Ltd. - Jincheon Factory **(1)**
#27 Godeung 1gil Iwol-myeon, Jincheon, 365-822, Chungcheongbuk-do, Korea (South)
Tel.: (82) 43 539 4545
Coated Film Mfr
N.A.I.C.S.: 322220

SKC Co., Ltd. - Suwon Factory **(1)**
633 Jeongja-dong, Jangan-gu, Suwon, 440-840, Gyeonggi-do, Korea (South)
Tel.: (82) 31 250 7114
Chemical Products Mfr
N.A.I.C.S.: 325998

SKC CO., LTD.

SKC Co., Ltd.—(Continued)

SKC Co., Ltd. - Ulsan Factory (1)
55 Gosa-dong, Nam-gu, Ulsan, 680-130, Korea (South)
Tel.: (82) 52 278 5151
Web Site: http://www.skcfilms.com
Coated Film Mfr
N.A.I.C.S.: 322220

SKC Europe GmbH (1)
Arabella Center Lyoner Str 44-48, 60528, Frankfurt am Main, Germany
Tel.: (49) 69 669 013 0
Web Site: http://www.skc-europe.com
Sales Range: $25-49.9 Million
Emp.: 8
Polyethylene Terephthalate Film Mfr
N.A.I.C.S.: 326113
K. S. Song (Mgr)

SKC Europe pu Sp. z o.o. (1)
Strefowa 16, Dzierzoniow, 58-200, Lower Silesia, Poland
Tel.: (48) 71 734 53 96
Web Site: http://www.skceuropepu.com
Sales Range: $25-49.9 Million
Emp.: 15
Chemical Product Whslr
N.A.I.C.S.: 424690

SKC Inc. (1)
1000 SKC Dr, Covington, GA 30014
Tel.: (678) 342-1000
Web Site: http://www.skcfilms.com
Emp.: 278
Plastics Films Mfr
N.A.I.C.S.: 326112
Hojin Kim (CEO)

SKC Solmics Co., Ltd. (1)
1043 Gyeonggidaero, Pyeongtaek, 17784, Gyeonggi-do, Korea (South) (100%)
Tel.: (82) 316608400
Web Site: http://www.skcsolmics.com
Rev.: $119,408,445
Assets: $197,855,490
Liabilities: $115,422,073
Net Worth: $82,433,417
Earnings: $342,678
Emp.: 544
Fiscal Year-end: 12/31/2019
Electronic Components Mfr
N.A.I.C.S.: 334419
Rok Jun Oh (CEO)

Subsidiary (Domestic):

SK Telesys Co., Ltd. (2)
Naewae Bldg Euljiro 2-ga, Jung-gu, Seoul, 100844, Korea (South)
Tel.: (82) 7074032063
Web Site: http://www.sktelesys.co.kr
Emp.: 216
Communication Equipment Mfr
N.A.I.C.S.: 334290

Plant (Domestic):

SKC Solmics Co., Ltd. - Anseong Plant (2)
205-53 Samjuk-ro Samjuk-myeon, Anseong, 17512, Gyeonggi-do, Korea (South)
Tel.: (82) 3180027100
Electronic Components Mfr
N.A.I.C.S.: 334419

SKC Solmics Co., Ltd. - Pyeongtaek Plant (2)
24 Chupalsandan-2-gil Paengseong-eup, Pyeongtaek, 17998, Gyeonggi-do, Korea (South)
Tel.: (82) 316158220
Electronic Components Mfr
N.A.I.C.S.: 334419

SKEENA RESOURCES LIMITED
Suite 650 1021 W Hastings St, Vancouver, V6E 0C3, BC, Canada
Tel.: (604) 684-8725 BC
Web Site:
https://www.skeenaresources.com
Year Founded: 1979
SKE—(NYSE)
Assets: $144,040,038
Liabilities: $52,044,027
Net Worth: $91,996,011

Earnings: ($80,505,282)
Emp.: 83
Fiscal Year-end: 12/31/23
Mineral Exploration Services
N.A.I.C.S.: 213114
Walter Coles Jr. (Exec Chm)

Subsidiaries:

QuestEx Gold & Copper Ltd. (1)
666 Burrard St Suite 500, Vancouver, V6C 3P6, BC, Canada
Tel.: (250) 768-1511
Web Site: http://www.questex.ca
Assets: $7,094,571
Liabilities: $467,871
Net Worth: $6,626,700
Earnings: ($1,342,282)
Emp.: 5
Fiscal Year-end: 03/31/2021
Metal Mining & Exploration Services
N.A.I.C.S.: 212290
Joseph Mullin (CEO)

SKEGGS GROUP LIMITED
69 Buckingham Street, PO Box 15, Arrowtown, Dunedin, 9302, New Zealand
Tel.: (64) 34420441
Web Site: http://www.skeggs.co.nz
Year Founded: 1952
Sales Range: $200-249.9 Million
Emp.: 3
Holding Company
N.A.I.C.S.: 551112
David Skeggs (Mng Dir)

Subsidiaries:

Akarua Limited (1)
Cromwell Cairnmuir Roa, PO Box 120, Cromwell, New Zealand
Tel.: (64) 34450897
Wine Mfr
N.A.I.C.S.: 312130
Matt Connell (Gen Mgr)

Akarua Winery (1)
Rapid Number 210 Cairnmuir Road, PO Box 120, Central Otago, Seaview, 9384, New Zealand
Tel.: (64) 450897
Web Site: http://www.akarua.com
Sales Range: $25-49.9 Million
Winery
N.A.I.C.S.: 312130

Marlborough Mussel Co Limited (1)
Nolans Road, Blenheim, Grovetown, New Zealand
Tel.: (64) 35789123
Web Site: http://www.skeggs.co.nz
Fresh & Frozen Seafood Processing
N.A.I.C.S.: 311710

Pacifica Shipping Limited (1)
Level 2 Windsor Court 128 Parnell Road, Parnell, Auckland, New Zealand
Tel.: (64) 9 304 0022
Web Site: http://www.pacship.co.nz
Sales Range: $50-74.9 Million
Shipping Transportation Services
N.A.I.C.S.: 488390
Leigh Cooper (Mgr-Sls & Mktg)

Port Denarau Marina Limited (1)
Denarau Island, PO Box 023, Port Denarau, Nadi, Fiji
Tel.: (679) 6750600
Web Site: http://www.denaraumarina.com
Sales Range: $50-74.9 Million
Marine Cargo Handling & Fishing
N.A.I.C.S.: 713930
Cynthia Rasch (Gen Mgr)

Southern Discoveries Limited (1)
PO Box 814, Queenstown, New Zealand
Tel.: (64) 34411137
Travel Tour Operator
N.A.I.C.S.: 561520
John Robson (Gen Mgr)

SKELJUNGUR HF
Borgartun 26, 105, Reykjavik, Iceland
Tel.: (354) 444 3000
Web Site: http://www.skeljungur.is
Rev.: $421,220

Assets: $201,314
Liabilities: $120,471
Net Worth: $80,843
Earnings: $11,596
Fiscal Year-end: 03/31/20
Petroleum Product Distr
N.A.I.C.S.: 424720
Arni Petur Jonsson (CEO)

Subsidiaries:

P/F Demich (1)
Stiojagota 2, 100, Torshavn, Faroe Islands
Tel.: (298) 350300
Web Site: http://www.demich.fo
Heat Pump Installation Services
N.A.I.C.S.: 238220

SKELLERUP HOLDINGS LIMITED
Level 3 205 Great South Road, Greenlane, Auckland, 1051, New Zealand
Tel.: (64) 95238240 NZ
Web Site:
http://www.skellerupholdings.co.nz
SKL—(NZX)
Rev.: $199,483,852
Assets: $205,129,785
Liabilities: $70,299,641
Net Worth: $134,830,144
Earnings: $30,467,105
Emp.: 800
Fiscal Year-end: 06/30/23
Holding Company; Rubber & Foam Products, Footwear & Vacuum Pumps Mfr, Marketer & Distr
N.A.I.C.S.: 551112
Elizabeth M. Coutts (Chm)

Subsidiaries:

Ambic Equipment Limited (1)
1 Parkside Avenue Two Station Lane, Witney, OX28 4YF, Oxfordshire, United Kingdom
Tel.: (44) 1993776555
Web Site: https://www.ambic.co.uk
Sales Range: $50-74.9 Million
Emp.: 25
Livestock Health Products Mfr & Distr
N.A.I.C.S.: 424910
Mark Cinderey (Mgr-Sls)

Conewango Products Corp (1)
1890 Lyndon Blvd, Falconer, NY 14733
Tel.: (716) 664-6712
Web Site: http://www.conewango.com
Rubber Products Mfr & Distr
N.A.I.C.S.: 326299
Jeffrey Perkins (Gen Mgr)

Deks Industries Pty Limited (1)
841 Mtn Hwy, PO Box 569, Bayswater, 3153, VIC, Australia
Tel.: (61) 387278800
Web Site: http://www.deks.com.au
Sales Range: $25-49.9 Million
Emp.: 20
Plumbing Products Mfr & Distr
N.A.I.C.S.: 332913
Andrew Neese (Gen Mgr)

Gulf Rubber Australia Pty Limited (1)
12 Green Street, Revesby, Sydney, 2212, NSW, Australia
Tel.: (61) 287236100
Web Site: http://www.gulfrubber.com
Sales Range: $25-49.9 Million
Emp.: 50
Moulded Rubber Components Mfr & Distr
N.A.I.C.S.: 326299

Masport Inc (1)
6801 Cornhusker Hwy, Lincoln, NE 68507
Tel.: (402) 466-8428
Web Site: http://www.masportpump.com
Sales Range: $25-49.9 Million
Emp.: 18
Vacuum Pumps Equipments Mfr & Whslr
N.A.I.C.S.: 333248
John Gilbert (Mgr-Sls)

Skellerup Industries Limited (100%)

INTERNATIONAL PUBLIC

Tel.: (64) 33899189
Web Site: https://www.skellerup.co.nz
Sales Range: $75-99.9 Million
Emp.: 200
Dairy & Industrial Rubber Products Mfr & Distr
N.A.I.C.S.: 326291
David Mair (CEO)

Skellerup Rubber Products Jiangsu Limited (1)
Baochang Town, Haimen, Nantong, 226151, Jiangsu, China
Tel.: (86) 51382771999
Rubber Footwear Mfr
N.A.I.C.S.: 316210

Skellerup Rubber Services Limited (1)
3 Monier Place, PO Box 11265, Mount Wellington, Auckland, 1060, New Zealand
Tel.: (64) 95820412
Web Site:
https://www.skelleruprubberservices.co.nz
Sales Range: $25-49.9 Million
Emp.: 50
Industrial Rubber Mfr
N.A.I.C.S.: 326299

Stevens Filterite Limited (1)
22-30 Birdwood Street, Featherston, 5710, New Zealand
Tel.: (64) 63086048
Sales Range: $25-49.9 Million
Emp.: 6
Milk Filters Mfr
N.A.I.C.S.: 339999

Talbot Advanced Technologies Limited (1)
78 Wigram Road, Christchurch, New Zealand
Tel.: (64) 33389084
Web Site:
https://www.talbottechnologies.co.nz
Industrial Equipment Mfr
N.A.I.C.S.: 333415

Thorndon Rubber Co Limited (1)
3 Monier Pl, Wellington, 1060, New Zealand
Tel.: (64) 45673135
Web Site: http://www.thorndonrubber.com
Sales Range: $25-49.9 Million
Emp.: 45
Rubber Products Mfr
N.A.I.C.S.: 326299
Mark Ho (Mgr-Bus Unit)

Tumedei S.p.A. (1)
via Bolzano 12, Ala, 38061, Trento, Italy
Tel.: (39) 0464671452
Web Site: https://www.tumedei.it
Precision Rubber & Plastic Component Mfr
N.A.I.C.S.: 326299

Tumidei SpA (1)
Via Bolzano 12 Ala, Trento, 38061, Italy
Tel.: (39) 0464671452
Web Site: http://www.tumedei.it
Emp.: 70
Furniture Mfr & Distr
N.A.I.C.S.: 337126
Olivier Marin (Gen Mgr)

Ultralon Products (NZ) Limited (1)
11 Jipcho Rd, PO Box 19 639, Wigram, Christchurch, 8042, New Zealand
Tel.: (64) 33894325
Web Site: http://www.ultralon.co.nz
Sales Range: $25-49.9 Million
Emp.: 50
Polystyrene Foam Product Mfr
N.A.I.C.S.: 326140
Paul Goddard (Gen Mgr)

SKET VERSEILMASCHINENBAU GMBH
Schonebecker Str 82-84, 39104, Magdeburg, Germany
Tel.: (49) 391405580
Web Site: http://www.sketvmb.de
Sales Range: $10-24.9 Million
Emp.: 100
Cable & Wire Production Machinery Mfr
N.A.I.C.S.: 333248
Johann Erich Wilms (Mng Dir)

AND PRIVATE COMPANIES — SKF AB

Subsidiaries:

Spirka Schnellflechter GmbH (1)
Wilhelminenhofstrasse 76 77, 12459, Berlin, Germany
Tel.: (49) 305499180
Web Site: http://www.spirka-schnellflechter.com
Emp.: 50
Braiding Machinery Mfr
N.A.I.C.S.: 333248
Harald Baumbach (Mng Dir & Mgr-Sls)

Subsidiary (Domestic):

Spirka Schnellflechter GmbH (2)
PO Box 1712, 31046, Alfeld, Germany
Tel.: (49) 66217871480
Braiding Machinery Mfr
N.A.I.C.S.: 333248

Wardwell Braiding Machine Co. (1)
1211 High St, Central Falls, RI 02863
Tel.: (401) 724-8800
Web Site: http://www.wardwell.com
Braiding Machinery Mfr
N.A.I.C.S.: 333248
John Tomaz (VP)

SKF AB
Sven Wingqvists gata 2, 415 26, Gothenburg, Sweden
Tel.: (46) 313371000   SE
Web Site: http://www.skf.com
Year Founded: 1907
SKFRY—(OTCIQ)
Rev.: $9,536,275,800
Assets: $10,272,695,400
Liabilities: $5,227,734,600
Net Worth: $5,044,960,800
Earnings: $622,128,600
Emp.: 39,514
Fiscal Year-end: 12/31/23
Roller Bearings, Seals & Washers, Spindles & Linear Motion Products Mfr
N.A.I.C.S.: 332991
Carina Bergfelt (Gen Counsel & Sr VP-Grp People, Comm, Legal & Sustainability)

Subsidiaries:

CR Seals India Pvt Ltd. (1)
13 5 Singasandra 13th Km Hosur Rd, Bengaluru, 560 068, India (100%)
Tel.: (91) 8025730207
Web Site: http://www.products.skf.com
Sales Range: $100-124.9 Million
Emp.: 340
Ball & Roller Bearing Mfr
N.A.I.C.S.: 332991

Fairskf (Taiwan) Co., Ltd. (1)
No 137 Chung Hsing N St, Taipei, 241, Taiwan (40%)
Tel.: (886) 222783060
Web Site: http://www.fairskf.com
Sales Range: $25-49.9 Million
Emp.: 15
Bearings & Units, Seals, Mechatronics, Services & Lubrication Systems
N.A.I.C.S.: 332991

General Bearing International Trading Ltd. (1)
9/F Tower B Central Towers No 567 Langao Road, Putuo District, Shanghai, China
Tel.: (86) 2161484819
Bearing Component Mfr
N.A.I.C.S.: 332991

Lincoln Helios (India) Ltd. (1)
249 and 250 Bommasandra Industrial Area Phase 3 Hosur Road, Bengaluru, 560 099, India
Tel.: (91) 8061301000
Web Site: http://www.lincolnindustrial.com
Lubrication Equipment & Component Mfr
N.A.I.C.S.: 333914
Anand Desai (Mgr-Fin)

Lincoln Lubrication (SA) Pty. Ltd. (1)
17 Indianapolis Boulevard, Germiston, Gauteng, South Africa
Tel.: (27) 119071192
Web Site: http://www.lincolnsa.com

Lubrication Equipment Mfr
N.A.I.C.S.: 333914
Harry Schmitz (Mng Dir)

Lutsk Bearing Plant (1)
34 Bozhenko Str, 43017, Lutsk, Ukraine
Tel.: (380) 0332746302
Web Site: http://www.lbp.com.ua
Sales Range: $400-449.9 Million
Emp.: 1,200
N.A.I.C.S.: 332991

Monitoring Control Center MCC AB (1)
Kaserngatan 14, Kiruna, 981 37, Norrbotten, Sweden
Tel.: (46) 98082880
Web Site: http://www.mccab.com
Sales Range: $25-49.9 Million
Emp.: 15
Industrial Engineering Services
N.A.I.C.S.: 541330
Magnus Backe (CEO)

Oy SKF AB (1)
Saterinkatu 6, PO Box 286, 02600, Espoo, Finland (100%)
Tel.: (358) 207400700
Web Site: http://www.skf.com
Sales Range: $25-49.9 Million
Emp.: 50
Sales of Ball & Roller Bearings
N.A.I.C.S.: 423840

P.T. SKF Indonesia (1)
Jl Tipar-Inspeksi Cakung Drain, Jakarta, 13910, Timur, Indonesia (60%)
Tel.: (62) 21 460 5925
Web Site: https://www.skf.com
Sales Range: $200-249.9 Million
Emp.: 500
N.A.I.C.S.: 332991

P.T. Skefindo Primatama (1)
BRI II Building 8th floor Suite 801, Jl Jend Sudirman Kav 44-46, Jakarta, 10210, Indonesia (100%)
Tel.: (62) 2157932244
Web Site: http://www.skfindonesia.com
Sales Range: $25-49.9 Million
Emp.: 80
N.A.I.C.S.: 332991

PT. SKF Industrial Indonesia (1)
Talavera Office Park 9th Floor, Jakarta, 12430, Indonesia
Tel.: (62) 2139507300
Web Site: https://www.skf.com
Gasket & Sealing Device Mfr
N.A.I.C.S.: 339991

Peer Bearing GmbH (1)
Kokkolastrasse 2, 40882, Ratingen, Germany
Tel.: (49) 210 259 7950
Web Site: https://www.peerbearing.com
Emp.: 1,600
Roller & Ball Bearing Mfr
N.A.I.C.S.: 332991

Pilgrim International Ltd. (1)
Earl Business Centre Dowry Street, Oldham, OL8-2PF, United Kingdom (100%)
Tel.: (44) 1617857700
Web Site: https://www.pilgrim-international.co.uk
Sales Range: $1-9.9 Million
Emp.: 30
Power & Marine Bolt Mfr
N.A.I.C.S.: 332722

RFT S.p.A. (1)
Strada Per Poirino 41, 14019, Villanova d'Asti, Italy
Tel.: (39) 0141949611
Bearing Seals Mfr
N.A.I.C.S.: 339991

SKF (Schweiz) AG (1)
Eschenstrasse 5, PO Box 236, 8603, Schwerzenbach, Switzerland (100%)
Tel.: (41) 448258181
Web Site: https://www.skf.com
Sales Range: $25-49.9 Million
Emp.: 40
Sales of Ball & Roller Bearings
N.A.I.C.S.: 423840

SKF (Shanghai) Bearings Ltd. (1)
No 999 Xin Jin Qiao Road, Pudong, Shanghai, China

Tel.: (86) 2150325655
Gasket & Sealing Device Mfr
N.A.I.C.S.: 339991

SKF (Thailand) Ltd. (1)
72/70 Rama III Road, Bangkok, 10120, Thailand (100%)
Tel.: (66) 22969300
Web Site: https://www.skf.com
Sales Range: $50-74.9 Million
Sales of Ball & Roller Bearings
N.A.I.C.S.: 423840

SKF (U.K.) Ltd. (1)
Sundon Park Road, Luton, LU3 3BL, Bedfordshire, United Kingdom (100%)
Tel.: (44) 1582490049
Web Site: https://www.skf.com
Sales Range: $100-124.9 Million
Emp.: 450
Mfr of Ball & Roller Bearing
N.A.I.C.S.: 332991

Division (Domestic):

SKF (U.K.) Ltd. - Aeroengine & Super Precision Division (2)
Oldends Lane, Stonehouse, GL10 3RH, Gloucestershire, United Kingdom
Tel.: (44) 1453 852 570
Web Site: http://www.skf.com
Sales Range: $25-49.9 Million
Emp.: 220
Aircraft Part Mfr
N.A.I.C.S.: 336413
Derwyn Roberts (Gen Mgr)

SKF (U.K.) Ltd. - Aerospace Division (2)
Strode Road, Clevedon, BS21 6QQ, North Somerset, United Kingdom
Tel.: (44) 1275876021
Web Site: http://www.skf.com
Sales Range: $75-99.9 Million
Aircraft Part Mfr
N.A.I.C.S.: 336413

Unit (Domestic):

SKF (U.K.) Ltd. - Railway Sales Unit (2)
Sundon Park Road, Luton, LU3 3BL, Bedfordshire, United Kingdom
Tel.: (44) 1582 490049
Sales Range: $25-49.9 Million
Emp.: 18
Bearing Mfr
N.A.I.C.S.: 332991

Subsidiary (Domestic):

SKF Engineering Products Limited (2)
Sundon Pk Rd, Luton, LU3 3BL, United Kingdom (100%)
Tel.: (44) 582496740
Web Site: http://www.skf.co.uk
Sales Range: $75-99.9 Million
Emp.: 600
General Engineers
N.A.I.C.S.: 541330

SKF AB - Rail Business Unit (1)
40 Albemarle Street, Williamstown, 3016, VIC, Australia
Tel.: (61) 3 93974440
Web Site: http://www.skf.com
Roller Bearing Mfr
N.A.I.C.S.: 332991

SKF Actuation System (Liestal) AG (1)
Oristalstrasse 97, 4410, Liestal, Switzerland
Tel.: (41) 61 925 41 11
Web Site: http://www.skf.com
Emp.: 150
Bearing Mfr
N.A.I.C.S.: 333613

SKF Actuation System (Taipei) Co., Ltd. (1)
No 6 Pao Kao Road, Hsin Tien, Taipei, 231, Taiwan
Tel.: (886) 2 291 334 22
Electronic Equipment Distr
N.A.I.C.S.: 423690

SKF Actuators AB (1)
Hornsgatan 1, SE 415 50, Gothenburg, Sweden (100%)

Tel.: (46) 313371000
Sales Range: $25-49.9 Million
Emp.: 100
Mfr & Retailer of Ball & Roller Bearings
N.A.I.C.S.: 332991
Robert Wiktor (Mng Dir)

SKF Argentina S.A. (1)
Pan-American Highway Km 36 Tortuguitas, C1068 AAA, Buenos Aires, Argentina (100%)
Tel.: (54) 3327458000
Sales Range: $50-74.9 Million
Emp.: 120
Mfr of Bearings
N.A.I.C.S.: 332991

SKF Asia & Pacific Pte. Ltd. (1)
20 Toh Guan Road 01-01, Singapore, 608839, Singapore (100%)
Tel.: (65) 68767777
Web Site: https://www.skf.com
Sales Range: $50-74.9 Million
Emp.: 150
Ball & Roller Bearing Manufacturing
N.A.I.C.S.: 332991

Subsidiary (Domestic):

SKF Treasury Centre Asia Pacific Pte Ltd. (2)
1 Changi South Lane 2nd Floor Accord Famous Distri Centre, Singapore, 486070, Singapore
Tel.: (65) 68767777
Web Site: http://www.skf.com
Financial Management Services
N.A.I.C.S.: 523999

SKF Vehicle Parts Asia (Pte) Ltd. (2)
No 1 Changi South Lane, Singapore, 486070, Singapore (100%)
Tel.: (65) 68767777
Web Site: http://www.skf.com
Sales Range: $25-49.9 Million
Emp.: 100
Bearings & Units, Seals, Mechatronics, Services & Lubrication Systems
N.A.I.C.S.: 332991
Lim Wee Beng (Gen Mgr)

SKF Australia (Manufacturing) Pty. Ltd. (1)
17-21 Stamford Road, Oakleigh, 3166, VIC, Australia
Tel.: (61) 3 92690800
Web Site: http://www.skf.com.au
Sales Range: $50-74.9 Million
Emp.: 200
Bearing Equipment Mfr
N.A.I.C.S.: 333613

SKF AutoBalance Systems AB (1)
Hornsgatan 1, 415 50, Gothenburg, Sweden
Tel.: (46) 31 337 10 00
Roller Bearing Mfr
N.A.I.C.S.: 332991
Magnus Granffelt (Mgr)

SKF Automotive Components Corp. (1)
1171 Jisa-Dong, Gangseo-gu, Busan, 618 230, Korea (South)
Tel.: (82) 519702400
Web Site: http://www.skf.com
Emp.: 120
Ball & Roller Bearing Manufacturing
N.A.I.C.S.: 332991

SKF B.V. (1)
Meidoornkade 14, PO Box 2350, 3992 AE, Houten, Netherlands
Tel.: (31) 306075957
Web Site: https://www.skf.com
Gasket & Sealing Device Mfr
N.A.I.C.S.: 339991

SKF BSS S.p.A. (1)
Corso Giulio Cesare 424/29, 10156, Turin, Italy
Tel.: (39) 011 222 1111
Industrial Bearing Mfr
N.A.I.C.S.: 332991

SKF Bearing Ind. (Malaysia) Sdn. Bhd. (1)
Lot 7910 Nilai Industrial Estate, PO Box 26, 71807, Nilai, Malaysia (100%)
Tel.: (60) 67992200

SKF AB

SKF AB—(Continued)
Web Site: http://www.skf.com.my
Sales Range: $100-124.9 Million
Emp.: 500
Bearings & Units, Seals, Mechatronics, Services & Lubrication Systems
N.A.I.C.S.: 332991

SKF Bearing Services Taiwan Ltd.
Rm 605 Fl 6 No 131 Min Sheng E Rd Section 3, Taipei, 105, Taiwan (100%)
Tel.: (886) 227187800
Web Site: http://www.skf.tw
Sales Range: $50-74.9 Million
Emp.: 62
Sale of Ball & Roller Bearings
N.A.I.C.S.: 423840

SKF Bearings India Ltd. (1)
Mahatma Gandhi Memorial Bldg, Mumbai, 400 002, Maharashtra, India (51%)
Tel.: (91) 226 633 7777
Web Site: https://www.skf.com
Sales Range: $25-49.9 Million
Emp.: 100
Mfr of Ball & Roller Bearings; Plants Located in Poona & Bangalore
N.A.I.C.S.: 332991

SKF Belgium S.A. (1)
Berkenlaan 8C, Diegem, 1831, Brussels, Belgium (100%)
Tel.: (32) 27296611
Web Site: https://www.skf.com
Sales Range: $75-99.9 Million
Emp.: 130
Sales of Ball & Roller Bearings
N.A.I.C.S.: 423840

SKF Bosnia and Herzegovina (1)
Fra Andela Zvizdovica 1, 71000, Sarajevo, Bosnia & Herzegovina (100%)
Tel.: (387) 33201793
Web Site: https://www.skf.com
Sales Range: $25-49.9 Million
Emp.: 3
Ball & Roller Bearing Manufacturing
N.A.I.C.S.: 332991

SKF Bulgaria (1)
51 6 September st, Sofia, 1000, Bulgaria (100%)
Tel.: (359) 29804891
Web Site: http://www.skf.bg
Sales Range: $50-74.9 Million
Emp.: 10
Sales of Bearings
N.A.I.C.S.: 423840

SKF CZ, a.s. (1)
Delnicka 1628/9, Holesovice, 170 00, Prague, Czech Republic
Tel.: (420) 234642111
Web Site: https://www.skf.com
Gasket & Sealing Device Mfr
N.A.I.C.S.: 339991
Antonin Vlcek *(Acct Mgr)*

SKF Canada Limited (1)
40 Executive Court, Toronto, M1S 4N4, ON, Canada (100%)
Tel.: (416) 299-1220
Web Site: https://www.skf.com
Sales Range: $25-49.9 Million
Emp.: 100
Mfr & Sales of Ball & Roller Bearings
N.A.I.C.S.: 332991

SKF Centrala Handlowo-Techniczna Sp.z.o.o. (1)
ul Pulawska 303, 02-785, Warsaw, Poland
Tel.: (48) 225494700
Web Site: http://www.skf.pl
Sales Range: $25-49.9 Million
Emp.: 50
Ball & Roller Bearing Manufacturing
N.A.I.C.S.: 332991

SKF Chilena S.A.I.C.
Av Parque 1307 Parque 3 Modulo 10, Pudahuel, 9020000, Santiago, Chile (100%)
Tel.: (56) 24372000
Web Site: https://www.skf.com
Sales Range: $50-74.9 Million
Emp.: 150
Ball & Roller Bearings
N.A.I.C.S.: 423840

SKF China Limited (1)
Unit 2210-11 22/F China United Centre No 28 Marble Road, North Point, China (Hong Kong) (100%)
Tel.: (852) 25108111
Sales Range: $25-49.9 Million
Sales of Ball & Roller Bearings
N.A.I.C.S.: 423840

Subsidiary (Non-US):

SKF (China) Co., Ltd. (2)
377 Bansongyuan Road, Shanghai, 200011, China
Tel.: (86) 21 53068866
Web Site: http://www.skf.com
Business Management Consulting Services
N.A.I.C.S.: 541611
Jiming Zhu *(Pres)*

Subsidiary (Domestic):

ABBA Hitech (Shanghai) Co., Ltd. (3)
A4 Factory 5399 Waiqingsong Road, Qing Pu, Shanghai, China
Tel.: (86) 21 69212233
Industrial Machinery Mfr
N.A.I.C.S.: 333248

Beijing Nankou SKF Railway Bearing Co. Ltd. (3)
Nankou Town, Changping, Beijing, 102202, China (50%)
Tel.: (86) 1069776751
Sales Range: $100-124.9 Million
Emp.: 500
Provider of Ball Bearings
N.A.I.C.S.: 332991

Branch (Domestic):

SKF (China) Co., Ltd. - Beijing Office (3)
Room 1017 Unit 2 Bright China Chang An Bldg 7 Jian Guo Men Nei Ave, Beijing, 100005, China
Tel.: (86) 1065102381
Web Site: http://www.skf.com.cn
Sales Range: $25-49.9 Million
Emp.: 12
Bolt Mfr & Distr
N.A.I.C.S.: 332722

SKF (China) Co., Ltd. - Chengdu Office (3)
Unit E 27/F City Tower No 86 1st Section Renmin Nan Road, Chengdu, 610016, Sichuan, China
Tel.: (86) 400 175 3699
Web Site: http://www.skf.com.cn
Provider of Ball Bearings
N.A.I.C.S.: 332991

SKF (China) Co., Ltd. - Dalian Office (3)
21st Fl Rm 2102 Senmao Building, 147 Zhongshan Lu, Dalian, 116011, China
Tel.: (86) 41139608855
Web Site: http://www.skf.com.cn
Provider of Ball Bearings
N.A.I.C.S.: 332991

SKF (China) Co., Ltd. - Guangzhou Office (3)
Room 4414-4416 Metro Plaza No 183 Tian He Bei Road, Guangzhou, 510075, China
Tel.: (86) 2087789308
Web Site: http://www.skf.com.cn
Provider of Ball Bearings
N.A.I.C.S.: 332991

SKF (China) Co., Ltd. - Nanjing Office (3)
Room A8 23/F Shang Mao Century Plaza No 49 Zhong Shan Road South, Nanjing, 210005, Jiangsu, China
Tel.: (86) 400 175 3699
Web Site: http://www.skf.com.cn
Provider of Ball Bearings
N.A.I.C.S.: 332991

SKF (China) Co., Ltd. - Xi'an Office (3)
Rm 602 6/F NIFC Fengcheng 8 Road, Economic and Technological Development Zone, Xi'an, 710002, Shaanxi, China
Tel.: (86) 87535318
Web Site: http://www.skf.com.cn
Provider of Ball Bearings
N.A.I.C.S.: 332991

Subsidiary (Domestic):

SKF (China) Investment Co. Ltd. (3)
689 Bejing Rd E, 200001, Shanghai, China (100%)
Tel.: (86) 2163501166
Web Site: http://www.skf.com
Sales Range: $75-99.9 Million
Emp.: 200
Provider of Investment Services
N.A.I.C.S.: 523940

SKF (China) Sales Co., Ltd. (3)
No 1189 Yuanqi Road, Anting Town Jiading District, Shanghai, 201814, China
Tel.: (86) 4001753699
Sales Range: $25-49.9 Million
Emp.: 50
Provider of Ball Bearings
N.A.I.C.S.: 332991

SKF (Dalian) Bearings and Precision Technologies Co. Ltd. (3)
No 87 Huai He Zhong Road, Dalian Economic & Technological Development Area, Dalian, 116600, Liaoning, China
Tel.: (86) 41139219000
Web Site: https://www.skf.com
Roller Bearing Distr
N.A.I.C.S.: 423840

SKF (Shanghai) Automotive Technology Co. Ltd. (3)
No 328 Yuanguo Road, Anting Town Jiading District, Shanghai, 201814, China
Tel.: (86) 2169574300
Sales Range: $100-124.9 Million
Emp.: 450
Industrial Bearing Mfr
N.A.I.C.S.: 332991

SKF (Shanghai) Investment Consultancy Co. Ltd. (3)
28 Eastern Tower No 689 Beijing Road E, Shanghai, 200011, China
Tel.: (86) 21 5306 8866
Web Site: http://www.skf.com
Investment Management Service
N.A.I.C.S.: 523999

SKF Actuation System (Pinghu) Co., Ltd. (3)
Economic Development Zone prosperity Road 888, Pinghu, 314200, Zhejiang, China
Tel.: (86) 57385621111
Web Site: http://www.skf.com
Sales Range: $100-124.9 Million
Emp.: 300
Actuator Mfr
N.A.I.C.S.: 333995

SKF Automotive Bearings Company Limited (3)
No 5291 Hu Yi Hwy Jia Ding Dist, Shanghai, 201806, China (70%)
Tel.: (86) 2159580188
Web Site: http://www.skf.com
Rev.: $60,000,000
Emp.: 130
Provider of Ball Bearings
N.A.I.C.S.: 332991

SKF Precision Machinery (Shanghai) Co Ltd. (3)
No 999 Xin Jin Qiao Road, Pudong, Shanghai, 201206, China
Tel.: (86) 2150325655
Web Site: http://www.skf.com.cn
Industrial Machinery Mfr
N.A.I.C.S.: 333248

SKF Sealing Solutions (Wuhu) Co. Ltd. (3)
No 208 Hua Shan Road, Wuhu Area The China Pilot Free Trade Zone, Wuhu, 241009, Anhui, China
Tel.: (86) 5532391666
Web Site: https://www.skf.com
Sealing Device Mfr
N.A.I.C.S.: 339991

SKF Commerce d.o.o. (1)
Bulevar Mihajla Pupina 10 Z/1, Belgrade, 11070, Serbia
Tel.: (381) 3 1116181
Web Site: http://www.skf.com
Sales Range: $25-49.9 Million
Roller Bearing Mfr
N.A.I.C.S.: 332991

SKF Coupling Systems AB (1)
Ovako Industriomrade, Hofors, 81332, Sweden
Tel.: (46) 290 284 00
Web Site: http://www.couplings.skf.com
Sales Range: $25-49.9 Million
Emp.: 75
Coupling System Mfr & Distr
N.A.I.C.S.: 332913

SKF Croatia d.o.o. (1)
Samoborska 255, Zagreb, 10090, Croatia
Tel.: (385) 13496874
Web Site: http://www.skf.com
Sales Range: $25-49.9 Million
Roller Bearing Mfr
N.A.I.C.S.: 332991

SKF Danmark A/S (1)
Stamholmen 151 7, 2650, Hvidovre, Denmark (100%)
Tel.: (45) 43436633
Web Site: http://www.skf.dk
Sales Range: $25-49.9 Million
Emp.: 30
Sales of Ball & Roller Bearings
N.A.I.C.S.: 423840

SKF Dataservice AB (1)
Hornsgatan 1, 415 50, Gothenburg, Sweden (100%)
Tel.: (46) 313371000
Web Site: http://www.skf.se
Sales Range: $400-449.9 Million
Emp.: 2,000
Computer Services
N.A.I.C.S.: 518210

SKF Distribution (Shanghai) Co. Ltd. (1)
No 291 Meiyue Road, Pudong New District Free Trade Zone, Shanghai, 200131, China
Tel.: (86) 4001753699
Gasket & Sealing Device Mfr
N.A.I.C.S.: 339991

SKF Economos GmbH (1)
Gabelhoferstrasse 25, Judenburg, A 8750, Austria
Tel.: (43) 3572825550
Web Site: http://www.skf.com
Sales Range: $75-99.9 Million
Emp.: 200
Hydraulic & Pneumatic Seal Mfr
N.A.I.C.S.: 339991

Subsidiary (Non-US):

SKF Economos Canada Inc. (2)
40 ex ct microsa, Mississauga, L4Z 1R9, ON, Canada
Tel.: (905) 712-1600
Sealing Device Mfr
N.A.I.C.S.: 339991

SKF Economos China Co. Ltd. (2)
No 120 Zhuzhou Road, Qingdao, 266101, China
Tel.: (86) 53288701660
Web Site: http://www.skf.com.cn
Sealing Device Mfr
N.A.I.C.S.: 339991

SKF Economos Denmark A/S (2)
Falstervej 10A, 5800, Nyborg, Denmark
Tel.: (45) 6531 1127
Sales Range: $25-49.9 Million
Emp.: 7
Sealing Device Mfr
N.A.I.C.S.: 339991
Jesper Marcher *(Head-Sls)*

SKF Economos Deutschland GmbH (2)
Robert-Bosch-Strasse 11, 74321, Bietigheim-Bissingen, Germany
Tel.: (49) 71425930
Web Site: https://www.skf.com
Sales Range: $25-49.9 Million
Sealing Device Mfr
N.A.I.C.S.: 339991

SKF Economos NL B.V. (2)
Twekkeler-es 28, 7547 SM, Enschede, Netherlands
Tel.: (31) 53 432 1962
Web Site: http://www.skf.com
Sales Range: $25-49.9 Million
Emp.: 14
Sealing Device Mfr

AND PRIVATE COMPANIES — SKF AB

N.A.I.C.S.: 339991

SKF Economos Schweiz GmbH (2)
Hungerbuelstrasse 17, 8500, Frauenfeld, Switzerland
Tel.: (41) 52 7212021
Web Site: http://www.skf.com
Sealing Device Mfr
N.A.I.C.S.: 339991

SKF Economos Sealing Solutions (Thailand) Ltd. (2)
797 Rama 9 Road, Bangkapi Huaykwang, Bangkok, 10310, Thailand
Tel.: (66) 2 769 9000
Web Site: http://www.economosthai.com
Sealing Device Mfr
N.A.I.C.S.: 339991

SKF Economos Sverige AB (2)
Ryssviksvagen 2, 13136, Nacka, Sweden
Tel.: (46) 8 4620180
Sealing Device Mfr
N.A.I.C.S.: 339991

Subsidiary (US):

SKF Economos USA Inc. (2)
26820 Fargo Ave, Cleveland, OH 44136
Tel.: (216) 378-2600
Sales Range: $25-49.9 Million
Emp.: 20
Hydraulic & Pneumatic Seal Mfr
N.A.I.C.S.: 339991

Subsidiary (Non-US):

SKF Economos Ukraine Ltd. (2)
Ul O Teligi 15A, 04112, Kiev, Ukraine
Tel.: (380) 444 401 181
Sealing Device Mfr
N.A.I.C.S.: 339991

SKF Economos do Brasil Ltda. (2)
Rodovia Anhanguera km 30, Cajamar, 07770-000, Sao Paulo, Brazil
Tel.: (55) 800141152
Web Site: http://www.skf.com.br
Sealing Device Mfr
N.A.I.C.S.: 339991

SKF Espanola S.A. (1)
Avenida de la Vega 21, 28108, Madrid, Alcobendas, Spain (100%)
Tel.: (34) 917684200
Web Site: https://www.skf.com
Sales Range: $25-49.9 Million
Emp.: 80
Mfr of Ball & Roller Bearings; Plant Located in Tudela
N.A.I.C.S.: 332991
Josemaria Estebe (Mng Dir)

SKF Estonia OU (1)
Saratee 7, Harjumaa, EE-75312, Estonia
Tel.: (372) 6997 900
Web Site: http://www.skf.com
Industrial Machinery Mfr
N.A.I.C.S.: 333248

SKF Eurotrade AB (1)
Hornsgatan 1, 415 50, Gothenburg, Sweden (100%)
Tel.: (46) 313371000
Web Site: http://www.skf.com
Sales Range: $550-599.9 Million
Emp.: 2,000
Sales of Bearings, Special Steels, Elastomeric Seals & Products Related to Rolling Bearing Technology
N.A.I.C.S.: 423840

SKF France S.A. (1)
34 avenue des Trois Peuples, 78180, Montigny-le-Bretonneux, France (99.9%)
Tel.: (33) 13 012 7300
Web Site: https://www.skf.com
Sales Range: $800-899.9 Million
Emp.: 2,700
Mfr & Sales of Ball & Roller Bearings
N.A.I.C.S.: 332991

Subsidiary (Domestic):

RKS S.A.-SKF Slewing Bearings (2)
89 - Yonne, PO Box 137, 89204, Avallon, France (99%)
Tel.: (33) 386314100
Web Site: http://www.skf.com
Sales Range: $25-49.9 Million
Emp.: 300
Mfr & Sales of Slewing Bearings

N.A.I.C.S.: 332991

SKF Aeroengine France S.A.S.U. (2)
Zone Industrielle No 2 59 - Nord, 59309, Valenciennes, France
Tel.: (33) 327235212
Web Site: https://www.skf.com
Aircraft Part Mfr
N.A.I.C.S.: 336413

SKF Lubrication Systems France SAS (2)
Rue Robert Amy, BP 130, 49404, Saumur, France
Tel.: (33) 2 41 40 42 00
Web Site: http://www.skf.com
Sales Range: $25-49.9 Million
Emp.: 50
Lubricant Mfr
N.A.I.C.S.: 333914

Transrol S.A.S. (2)
148 Rue Felix Esclangon, 73024, Chambery, France
Tel.: (33) 479686868
Web Site: http://www.skf.fr
Sales Range: $25-49.9 Million
Emp.: 230
Mfr of Ball & Roller Screws
N.A.I.C.S.: 332991

SKF GmbH (1)
Gunnar-Wester-Strasse 12, PO Box 1440, 97421, Schweinfurt, Germany (100%)
Tel.: (49) 9721560
Web Site: https://www.skf.com
Sales Range: $10-24.9 Million
Emp.: 4,000
Mfr of Ball & Roller Bearings; Plants Located in Bad-Cannstatt, Muhlheim, Luchow, Schweinfurt
N.A.I.C.S.: 332991

Branch (Domestic):

SKF GmbH (2)
Mueclen Strasse, PO Box 3020, 66340, Puttlingen, Germany (100%)
Tel.: (49) 68064980
Sales Range: $10-24.9 Million
Emp.: 4,000
Mfr of Slide & Plain Bearings
N.A.I.C.S.: 333613

Subsidiary (Domestic):

SKF Linearsysteme GmbH (2)
Parisstrasse 1, 97424, Schweinfurt, Germany (100%)
Tel.: (49) 9721298340
Sales Range: $25-49.9 Million
Emp.: 175
Mfr of Linear Ball Bearings & Rail Guides
N.A.I.C.S.: 332991

SKF Lubrication Systems Germany AG (2)
Motzener Strasse 35/37, PO Box 97 04 44, 12277, Berlin, Germany
Tel.: (49) 30 720 02 0
Web Site: http://www.skf.com
Lubricant Mfr
N.A.I.C.S.: 324191

SKF Marine GmbH (2)
Hermann-Blohm-Strasse 5, 20457, Hamburg, Germany
Tel.: (49) 4030110
Web Site: http://www.bv-industries.com
Sales Range: $75-99.9 Million
Emp.: 350
Ship Components Mfr
N.A.I.C.S.: 336999

Branch (Domestic):

SKF Sealing Solution GmbH (2)
Dusseldorfer Str 121, 51379, Leverkusen, Germany (100%)
Tel.: (49) 2 171 7130
Web Site: https://www.skf.com
Sales Range: $50-74.9 Million
Emp.: 400
Sealing Solutions
N.A.I.C.S.: 339991

SKF Hellas S.A. (1)
Syngrou Avenue 128, 17671, Kallithea, Greece (100%)
Tel.: (30) 2106897500

Web Site: https://www.skf.com
Sales Range: $25-49.9 Million
Emp.: 12
Sales of Ball & Roller Bearing
N.A.I.C.S.: 423840

SKF Holding Mexicana, S.A. de C.V. (1)
Km 125 Autopista Mex-Puebla No 1103, Zona Industrial Norte, 72014, Puebla, Mexico
Tel.: (52) 2222294900
Web Site: http://www.skf.com.mx
Investment Management Service
N.A.I.C.S.: 523940

SKF Industrial Service Shanghai Co., Ltd. (1)
SBIZ Industrial Zone Building A-12 No 199 Changjian Road, Baoshan District, Shanghai, China
Tel.: (86) 2133850108
Gasket & Sealing Device Mfr
N.A.I.C.S.: 339991

SKF Industrie S.p.A (1)
Via Pinerolo 44/A, Airasca, 10060, Turin, Italy
Tel.: (39) 01198521
Web Site: https://www.skf.com
Gasket & Sealing Device Mfr
N.A.I.C.S.: 339991

SKF International AB (1)
SKF Treasury Ctr Hornsgatan 1, Gothenburg, 41550, Sweden (100%)
Tel.: (46) 313371000
Web Site: http://www.skf.com
Sales Range: $50-74.9 Million
Emp.: 25
Financial Clearing
N.A.I.C.S.: 522320

SKF Iran (1)
8th Floor No 114 Kaj Abadi St, Mellat Park District Valiasr Ave, Tehran, 1966913200, Iran
Tel.: (98) 2122666515
Web Site: http://www.skf.com
Sales Range: $50-74.9 Million
Sale of Ball & Roller Bearings
N.A.I.C.S.: 423840

SKF Israel LTD (1)
Caesarea Business & Industrial Park, PO Box 3592, Caesarea, 38900, Israel
Tel.: (972) 4 627 62 12
Sales Range: $25-49.9 Million
Emp.: 7
Roller Bearing Mfr
N.A.I.C.S.: 332991
Benjamin Danan (Mng Dir)

SKF Japan Ltd. (1)
Innotek Building 4F, Kohoku Ward Shin-Yokohama 3-17-6, Yokohama, 222-0033, Japan (100%)
Tel.: (81) 454782600
Web Site: https://www.skf.com
Sales Range: $50-74.9 Million
Sale of Ball & Roller Bearings
N.A.I.C.S.: 423840

Unit (Domestic):

SKF (Japan) Product Service Center (2)
11400-1102 Aza-Harayama Tamagawa Chino, Nagano, 391-0011, Japan (100%)
Tel.: (81) 266796064
Web Site: http://www.skf.com
Sales Range: $25-49.9 Million
Emp.: 30
Sales of Ball & Roller Bearings
N.A.I.C.S.: 332991

Subsidiary (Domestic):

SKF Lubrication Systems Japan Ltd. (2)
1-15-22 Imagome Higashi-Osaka, Osaka, 578-0903, Japan
Tel.: (81) 72 964 5055
Automotive Lubricant Distr
N.A.I.C.S.: 424720

SKF Kazakhstan (1)
Samal-2 build 104 floor 5, 050051, Almaty, Kazakhstan
Tel.: (7) 727 334 0064

Web Site: http://products.skf.com
Ball Bearing Mfr
N.A.I.C.S.: 332991

SKF Kenya Limited (1)
PO Box 18880-00500, Industrial Area, 254, Nairobi, Kenya
Tel.: (254) 710799799
Web Site: https://www.skf.com
Sales of Ball & Roller Bearings
N.A.I.C.S.: 423840

SKF Korea Ltd. (1)
60 Centum buk-daero, Haeundae-gu, Busan, 612-050, Korea (South)
Tel.: (82) 519465300
Web Site: https://www.skf.com
Sales Range: $25-49.9 Million
Emp.: 50
Ball & Roller Bearings
N.A.I.C.S.: 332991

Plant (Domestic):

SKF Korea LTD - AD Factory (2)
99 Gwahaksandan 2 19 beon, Gangseo, Busan, 618-230, Korea (South)
Tel.: (82) 519702400
Web Site: http://www.skf.com
Roller Bearing Mfr
N.A.I.C.S.: 332991

SKF Lietuva UAB (1)
Savanoriu pr 151, Vilnius, 03150, Lithuania
Tel.: (370) 52132713
Web Site: http://www.skf.com
Sales Range: $25-49.9 Million
Roller Bearing Mfr
N.A.I.C.S.: 332991

SKF Logistics Services AB (1)
Hornsgatan 1, Gothenburg, 41550, Sweden
Tel.: (46) 31 337 10 00
Emp.: 2,000
Logistics Consulting Servies
N.A.I.C.S.: 541614
Jorgen Tholin (Gen Mgr)

SKF Logistics Services Belgium NV/SA (1)
Heerstervelweg 16, 3700, Tongeren, Limburg, Belgium
Tel.: (32) 1 239 0320
Web Site: https://www.skf.com
Logistics Consulting Servies
N.A.I.C.S.: 541614

SKF Loziska a.s. (1)
U Mestanskeho pivovaru 7, 17004, Prague, Czech Republic (100%)
Tel.: (420) 23 464 2111
Web Site: https://www.skf.com
Sales Range: $50-74.9 Million
Emp.: 55
Sales of Ball & Roller Bearings
N.A.I.C.S.: 423840

SKF Lubrication Competence Center AB (1)
Sattunagatan 7, 582 73, Linkoping, Sweden
Tel.: (46) 13 15 80 30
Web Site: http://www.skf.com
Sales Range: $25-49.9 Million
Industrial Machinery Mfr
N.A.I.C.S.: 333248

SKF Lubrication Systems CZ s.r.o (1)
Vintirovska 1084, 35635, Chodova Plana, Czech Republic
Tel.: (420) 352355999
Gasket & Sealing Device Mfr
N.A.I.C.S.: 339991
Jaroslav Rejcha (Mgr-Fin, HR, and IT)

SKF Magnetic Bearings (1)
928 72nd Ave NE, Calgary, T2E 8V9, AB, Canada (100%)
Tel.: (403) 232-9290
Web Site: http://www.skf.com
Sales Range: $25-49.9 Million
Emp.: 35
Mfr of Magnetic Bearings
N.A.I.C.S.: 332991

SKF Magnetic Mechatronics S.A.S. (1)
2 Rue des Champs, Vernon 27 - Eure, 27950, Saint Marcel, France
Tel.: (33) 232643300

SKF AB

SKF AB—(Continued)

Gasket & Sealing Device Mfr
N.A.I.C.S.: 339991

SKF Maktrade d.o.o. (1)
Vasil Gjorgov 16 Centar Zebra, 1000, Skopje, North Macedonia (100%)
Tel.: (389) 23118265
Web Site: https://www.skf.com
Sales Range: $25-49.9 Million
Emp.: 2
Ball Bearing Mfr
N.A.I.C.S.: 332991

SKF Malaysia Sdn. Bhd. (1)
Lot 7910 Kawasan Perindustrian Nilai, 71807, Nilai, Negeri Sembilan, Malaysia
Tel.: (60) 67992121
Web Site: https://www.skf.com
Ball & Roller Bearings Mfr
N.A.I.C.S.: 332991

SKF Marine GmbH (1)
Hermann-Blohm-Strasse 5, 20457, Hamburg, Germany
Tel.: (49) 4030110
Marine Machinery Mfr
N.A.I.C.S.: 336611
Mathias Rusch (Chm)

SKF Marine Singapore Pte. Ltd. (1)
20 Toh Guan Road 01-01, Singapore, 608839, Singapore
Tel.: (65) 66863373
Marine Machinery Mfr
N.A.I.C.S.: 336611
C. J. Ng (Mng Dir)

SKF Mekan AB (1)
Fredsgatan 3, PO Box 89, SE 641 21, Katrineholm, Sweden
Tel.: (46) 015074000
Web Site: http://www.skfmekan.se
Sales Range: $200-249.9 Million
Emp.: 700
Mfr of Housings
N.A.I.C.S.: 332991

SKF Middle East & North Africa (1)
Av De Bale 3, 1140, Brussels, Belgium (100%)
Tel.: (32) 27296611
Web Site: http://www.intertrade.skf.com
Sales Range: $25-49.9 Million
Emp.: 120
Provider of Administrative Services for Sales to the Middle East & Africa
N.A.I.C.S.: 561110

SKF Moscow (1)
Presnenskaya nab Building 10 block C floor 52 BC, Tower on the Embankment, 123112, Moscow, Russia (100%)
Tel.: (7) 4955101820
Web Site: http://www.skf.ru
Sales Range: $25-49.9 Million
Emp.: 25
Ball Bearing Mfr
N.A.I.C.S.: 332991

SKF Multitec AB (1)
Bjorngatan 16, SE 254 67, Landskrona, Sweden (100%)
Tel.: (46) 42253500
Web Site: http://www.multitec.skf.com
Sales Range: $25-49.9 Million
Emp.: 36
Ball Bearing Mfr
N.A.I.C.S.: 332991
Patrick Hultman (Mng Dir)

SKF Nederland B.V. (1)
Meidoornkade 14, Houten, 3992 AE, Utrecht, Netherlands
Tel.: (31) 306075957
Web Site: http://www.skf.com
Sales Range: $150-199.9 Million
Ball & Roller Bearings Sales
N.A.I.C.S.: 423840

Subsidiary (Domestic):

SKF Engineering & Research Centre B.V. (2)
Kelvinbaan 16, PO Box 2350, NL 3430 DT, Nieuwegein, Netherlands (100%)
Tel.: (31) 306075957
Web Site: http://www.skf.com
Sales Range: $1-9.9 Million
Emp.: 200

Bearings & Units, Seals, Mechatronics, Services & Lubrication Systems
N.A.I.C.S.: 332991

SKF Lubrication Systems The Netherlands B.V. (2)
Meidoornkade 14, 3992 AE, Houten, Netherlands
Tel.: (31) 534765165
Web Site: http://www.skf.com
Sales Range: $25-49.9 Million
Lubricant Mfr
N.A.I.C.S.: 333914

SKF Maintenance Products B.V. (2)
Meidoornkade 14, Houten, 3992 AE, Utrecht, Netherlands (100%)
Tel.: (31) 306307200
Web Site: http://www.skf.com
Sales Range: $25-49.9 Million
Sales of Mounting & Maintenance Products
N.A.I.C.S.: 444140

SKF Research & Development Co. (2)
Meidoornkade 14, 3992 AE, Houten, Netherlands
Tel.: (31) 306075957
Web Site: http://www.skf.com
Roller Bearing Research & Development Services
N.A.I.C.S.: 541715

SKF New Zealand Limited (1)
67 Lady Ruby Dr E Tamaki, PO Box 58549, Auckland, 1730, Greenmount, New Zealand (100%)
Tel.: (64) 92740056
Web Site: http://www.skf.co.nz
Sales Range: $10-24.9 Million
Emp.: 20
Sales of Ball & Roller Bearings
N.A.I.C.S.: 423840

SKF Nigeria Limited (1)
3rd Floor Elephant Cement House Assbifi Road opposite Shoprite, PMB 21140, Alausa, Ikeja, Nigeria
Tel.: (234) 1 7742546
Web Site: http://www.skf.com
Roller Bearing Distr
N.A.I.C.S.: 423830

SKF Norge A/S (1)
Gjerdrums vei 8, PO Box 44, 0484, Oslo, Norway (100%)
Tel.: (47) 23182990
Web Site: https://www.skf.com
Sales Range: $25-49.9 Million
Emp.: 27
Sales of Ball & Roller Bearings
N.A.I.C.S.: 423840
Asbjorn Kjekshus (Mng Dir)

SKF Osterreich AG (1)
Seitenstettner Strasse 15, PO Box 205, 4400, Steyr, Upper Austria, Austria (100%)
Tel.: (43) 72527970
Web Site: https://www.skf.com
Sales Range: $200-249.9 Million
Emp.: 900
Mfr of Ball & Roller Bearings
N.A.I.C.S.: 332991

SKF Pakistan Pvt. Ltd. (1)
11 Bangalore Town Cooperative Housing Society, Karachi, 75350, Sindh, Pakistan (100%)
Tel.: (92) 21 430 0059
Web Site: http://www.skf.com.pk
Sales Range: $25-49.9 Million
Emp.: 10
Bearing Marketing & Sales
N.A.I.C.S.: 332991

SKF Philippines, Inc. (1)
Ground Floor Alegria Building, Makati, 1231, Luzon, Philippines (100%)
Tel.: (63) 28104058
Web Site: https://www.skf.com
Sales Range: $1-9.9 Million
Emp.: 30
Sales of Ball & Roller Bearings
N.A.I.C.S.: 423840
Mario Pilones (Mng Dir)

SKF Polska S.A. (1)
ul Pulawska 303, 02-785, Warsaw, Poland
Tel.: (48) 225494700
Web Site: https://www.skf.com

Gasket & Sealing Device Mfr
N.A.I.C.S.: 339991

SKF Portugal Rolamentos, Lda. (1)
Casal De Alfragide Lote 1, 2720-413, Amadora, Portugal (100%)
Tel.: (351) 214247000
Web Site: https://www.skf.com
Sales Range: $50-74.9 Million
Emp.: 37
Sales of Ball & Roller Bearings
N.A.I.C.S.: 423840

SKF Poznan S.A. (1)
ul Nieszawska 15, 61-022, Poznan, Poland
Tel.: (48) 618743000
Web Site: http://www.skf.com
Sales Range: $200-249.9 Million
Emp.: 700
Ball Bearing Mfr
N.A.I.C.S.: 332991

SKF Reinsurance Co. Ltd. (1)
Hornsgatan 1, 415 50, Gothenburg, Sweden (100%)
Tel.: (46) 313371000
Web Site: http://www.skf.com
Sales Range: $50-74.9 Million
Emp.: 6
Reinsurance
N.A.I.C.S.: 524130
Klas Iloson (Mng Dir)

SKF Romania S.R.L. (1)
319G Splaiul Independentei Str Atrium Building Groundfloor, 060044, Bucharest, Romania (100%)
Tel.: (40) 216671370
Web Site: http://www.skf.com
Sales Range: $25-49.9 Million
Emp.: 15
Ball Bearing Mfr
N.A.I.C.S.: 332991

SKF Sealing Solutions (Qingdao) Co. (1)
Rm 608 Unit B Fullhope Plaza 12 Hong Kong Central Road, Qingdao, China
Tel.: (86) 53285028667
Gasket & Sealing Device Mfr
N.A.I.C.S.: 339991

SKF Sealing Solutions AB (1)
Bjorngatan 16, PO Box 35, 261 22, Landskrona, Sweden
Tel.: (46) 418 578 00
Web Site: http://www.skf.com
Sales Range: $25-49.9 Million
Sealing Device Mfr
N.A.I.C.S.: 339991

SKF Sealing Solutions Austria GmbH (1)
Gabelhofer Strasse 25, 8750, Judenburg, Steiermark, Austria
Tel.: (43) 357282555
Gasket & Sealing Device Mfr
N.A.I.C.S.: 339991
Andrea Huebler (Mgr-Logistics)

SKF Sealing Solutions Korea Co., Ltd. (1)
40 Nongongjungang-ro 45-gil, Nongong-eup Dalseong-gun, Daegu, 711-857, Korea (South)
Tel.: (82) 536151001
Web Site: https://www.skfkorea.co.kr
Emp.: 509
Sealing Device Mfr
N.A.I.C.S.: 339991

SKF Sealing Solutions S.A. de C.V. (1)
Governor Curiel 2690, 44940, Guadalajara, Jalisco, Mexico
Tel.: (52) 3335407500
Sales Range: $150-199.9 Million
Emp.: 400
Bearing & Seal Distr
N.A.I.C.S.: 423840

SKF Services d.o.o. (1)
Samoborska 255, 10090, Zagreb, Croatia (100%)
Tel.: (385) 1 349 6874
Web Site: https://www.skf.com
Sales Range: $25-49.9 Million
Emp.: 11
Bearing Whslr
N.A.I.C.S.: 423840

SKF Slovenija d.o.o. (1)
Ukmarjeva ulica 6, 1000, Ljubljana, Slovenia (100%)
Tel.: (386) 1 600 8880
Web Site: https://www.skf.com
Sales Range: $25-49.9 Million
Emp.: 5
Ball Bearing Mfr
N.A.I.C.S.: 332991

SKF Slovensko s.r.o. (1)
Plynarenska 7/B, 821 09, Bratislava, Slovakia
Tel.: (421) 255563600
Web Site: http://www.skf.sk
Sales Range: $25-49.9 Million
Emp.: 9
Ball Bearing Mfr
N.A.I.C.S.: 332991

SKF South Africa (Pty) Limited (1)
6 Marlin Road, Jet Park, Boksburg, 1467, Gauteng, South Africa
Tel.: (27) 118213500
Web Site: https://www.skf.com
Sales Range: $50-74.9 Million
Emp.: 140
Mfr of Ball & Roller Bearings
N.A.I.C.S.: 332991

SKF Sved Golyoscsapagy Reszvenytarsasag (1)
Csata utca 25, PO Box 52, 2040, Budaors, Hungary (100%)
Tel.: (36) 23445200
Web Site: http://www.skf.hu
Sales Range: $25-49.9 Million
Emp.: 42
Sales of Ball & Roller Bearings
N.A.I.C.S.: 423840

SKF Sved Golyoscsapagy Zrt (1)
Csata utca 25, 2040, Budaors, Hungary
Tel.: (36) 23445200
Web Site: https://www.skf.com
Gasket & Sealing Device Mfr
N.A.I.C.S.: 339991

SKF Sverige AB (1)
von Utfallsgatan 2, 415 50, Gothenburg, Sweden (100%)
Tel.: (46) 313371000
Web Site: https://www.skf.se
Sales Range: $400-449.9 Million
Emp.: 2,000
Mfr & Retailer of Ball & Roller Bearings
N.A.I.C.S.: 332991

SKF Taiwan Co., Ltd. (1)
No 1 9th Floor No 10 Lane 609 Section 5 Zhongzhong Road, Sanchong District, New Taipei City, 241405, Taiwan
Tel.: (886) 229990696
Web Site: https://www.skf.com
Sales Range: $25-49.9 Million
Emp.: 15
Roller Bearing Mfr
N.A.I.C.S.: 332991
Gavin Garland (CEO)

SKF Technologies (India) Private Limited (1)
3 Milestone No-39 Ahmedabad-Rajkote Highway 8A, Kerala Village Bavla Taluka, Ahmedabad, 382 220, India
Tel.: (91) 271 4619 100
Sealing Device Mfr
N.A.I.C.S.: 339991

SKF Turk Sanayi ve Ticaret (1)
Aydinevler Mah Ismet Inonu Cad Kucukyali Office Park A, Block No 20/1 Maltepe, 34394, Istanbul, Turkiye (100%)
Tel.: (90) 8503930777
Web Site: https://www.skf.com
Sales Range: $25-49.9 Million
Sales of Ball & Roller Bearings
N.A.I.C.S.: 423840

SKF Tver Ltd. (1)
Kalininskiy Raion Burashevo 40 U, Тver, 170540, Russia
Tel.: (7) 4822620011
Web Site: http://www.skf.com
Sales Range: $25-49.9 Million
Emp.: 70
Roller Bearing Mfr
N.A.I.C.S.: 332991

SKF USA Inc. (1)

890 Forty Foot Rd, Lansdale, PA
19446 **(100%)**
Tel.: (267) 436-6780
Sales Range: $1-4.9 Billion
Roller Bearings, Seals & Washers, Spindles
& Linear Motion Products Mfr
N.A.I.C.S.: 332991

Subsidiary (Domestic):

General Bearing Corporation **(2)**
44 High St, West Nyack, NY 10994-2702
Tel.: (845) 358-6000
Web Site: https://www.generalbearing.com
Sales Range: $200-249.9 Million
Emp.: 100
Bearing Mfr
N.A.I.C.S.: 332991

Subsidiary (Domestic):

WMW Machinery Company, Inc. **(3)**
44 High St, West Nyack, NY
10994-2702 **(100%)**
Tel.: (845) 358-3330
Web Site: http://www.generalbearing.com
Sales Range: $100-124.9 Million
Distr of Machine Tools
N.A.I.C.S.: 423830

Subsidiary (Domestic):

Kaydon Corporation **(2)**
2860 McCracken St, Muskegon, MI
49441 **(100%)**
Tel.: (231) 755-3741
Web Site: https://www.kaydonbearings.com
Bearing Systems, Components & Metal Alloy Products Designer & Mfr
N.A.I.C.S.: 332991
John Saber *(Dir-Aerospace & Defense)*

Subsidiary (Non-US):

Cooper Roller Bearings Company
Limited **(3)**
Wisbech Road Kings Lynn, Norfolk, PE30
5JX, United Kingdom **(100%)**
Tel.: (44) 1553763447
Web Site: https://www.cooperbearings.com
Roller Bearing Mfr
N.A.I.C.S.: 332991

Subsidiary (US):

The Cooper Split Roller Bearing
Corp. **(4)**
2115 Aluminum Ave, Hampton, VA
23661 **(100%)**
Tel.: (757) 460-0925
Web Site: http://www.cooperbearings.com
Bearing Mfr
N.A.I.C.S.: 332991

Subsidiary (Domestic):

Industrial Tectonics Inc. **(3)**
7222 W Huron River Dr, Dexter, MI 48130
Tel.: (734) 426-4681
Web Site: http://www.itiball.com
Industrial Ball Mfr
N.A.I.C.S.: 332991

Kaydon Ring & Seal, Inc. **(3)**
1600 Wicomico St, Baltimore, MD
21230 **(100%)**
Tel.: (410) 547-7700
Sealing Rings & Dynamic Seals Mfr
N.A.I.C.S.: 336310

Subsidiary (Domestic):

Lincoln Holdings Enterprises,
Inc. **(2)**
1 Lincoln Way, Saint Louis, MO 63120-1508
Tel.: (314) 679-4200
Web Site: http://www.lincolnindustrial.com
Sales Range: $400-449.9 Million
Emp.: 450
Holding Company; Lubricating Equipment
Mfr
N.A.I.C.S.: 551112

Subsidiary (Domestic):

Alemite LLC **(3)**
5148 N Hanley Rd, Saint Louis, MO 63134
Tel.: (803) 802-0001
Web Site: http://www.alemite.com

Sales Range: $25-49.9 Million
Emp.: 28
Mfr of Lubricating Systems
N.A.I.C.S.: 333914

Division (Non-US):

Stewart Warner Corporation of
Canada **(4)**
349 MacDonald Ave, Belleville, K8N 5B8,
ON, Canada
Tel.: (613) 968-6761
Web Site:
http://www.stewartwarnercanada.com
Sales Range: $25-49.9 Million
Emp.: 15
Mfr of Lubrication System Components
N.A.I.C.S.: 332912
Chad Carter *(Mgr-Warehouse)*

Subsidiary (Non-US):

SKF Lubrication Systems Germany
GmbH **(3)**
Heinrich-Hertz-Strasse 2-8, 69190, Walldorf,
Germany **(100%)**
Tel.: (49) 6227330
Web Site: http://www.lincolnindustrial.de
Sales Range: $100-124.9 Million
Emp.: 300
Automated Lubrication Systems, Lubrication
Tools & Equipment Mfr
N.A.I.C.S.: 811191
Volker Pieschel *(CEO)*

Subsidiary (Domestic):

Peer Bearing Company **(2)**
2200 Norman Dr, Waukegan, IL 60085
Tel.: (847) 578-1000
Web Site: https://www.peerbearing.com
Sales Range: $100-124.9 Million
Emp.: 200
Ball & Roller Bearings Mfr
N.A.I.C.S.: 332991
Patrick Tong *(Pres)*

SKF Actuation & Motion Control **(2)**
800 Forty Foot Rd, Lansdale, PA
19446 **(100%)**
Tel.: (267) 436-6000
Sales Range: $25-49.9 Million
Emp.: 50
Roller Bearings & Seals Related Services
Distr
N.A.I.C.S.: 332991

SKF Aeroengine **(2)**
1 Maroco Rd, Falconer, NY 14733
Tel.: (716) 661-2600
Web Site: http://www.skf.com
Sales Range: $150-199.9 Million
Ball & Roller Bearings for Aerospace Applications Mfr
N.A.I.C.S.: 332991

SKF Asset Management Services,
Inc. **(2)**
2001 N Main St Ste 510, Walnut Creek, CA
94596
Tel.: (925) 943-7077
Asset Management Services
N.A.I.C.S.: 523940
Katy Dubnoff *(Gen Mgr)*

SKF Automotive Division **(2)**
46815 Port St, Plymouth, MI 48170-6060
Tel.: (734) 414-6800
Web Site: http://www.skf.com
Sales Range: $25-49.9 Million
Emp.: 90
Mfr & Sales of Ball Bearings
N.A.I.C.S.: 332991

SKF Condition Monitoring Inc. **(2)**
9444 Balboa Ave, San Diego, CA
92123-1819 **(99.8%)**
Tel.: (858) 496-3400
Web Site: http://www.skfcm.com
Sales Range: $50-74.9 Million
Emp.: 120
Mfr & Sales of Monitoring Systems
N.A.I.C.S.: 334519

SKF Coupling Systems, Inc. **(2)**
145 Colebrook River Rd, Winsted, CT
06098
Tel.: (860) 489-1817
Web Site: http://www.skf.com
Coupling System Mfr

N.A.I.C.S.: 332913

SKF Industrial & Service Division **(2)**
890 Forty Foot Rd, Lansdale, PA
19446 **(99.8%)**
Tel.: (267) 436-6000
Web Site: http://www.skf.com
Sales Range: $100-124.9 Million
Ball Bearing Mfr
N.A.I.C.S.: 332991

SKF Machine Support Inc. **(2)**
3443 N Sam Houston Pkwy W, Houston,
TX 77086
Tel.: (281) 925-2849
Industrial Machinery Mfr
N.A.I.C.S.: 333248

SKF Reliability Systems Inc. **(2)**
4141 Ruffin Rd, San Diego, CA 92123
Tel.: (800) 959-1366
Business Management Consulting Services
N.A.I.C.S.: 541611

SKF Sealing Solutions **(2)**
900 N State St, Elgin, IL 60123 **(100%)**
Tel.: (847) 742-7840
Web Site: https://www.skf.com
Sales Range: $150-199.9 Million
Dynamic Fluid Sealing Devices Mfr
N.A.I.C.S.: 339991
Dan Duffy *(Dir-Sls & Mktg)*

Subsidiary (Domestic):

SKF Polyseal, Inc. **(3)**
1754 W 500 S, Salt Lake City, UT 84104
Tel.: (801) 973-9171
Sales Range: $25-49.9 Million
Mfr of Mobile Hydraulic Seals
N.A.I.C.S.: 339991

Unit (Domestic):

SKF USA Inc. - North American Technical Center **(2)**
46815 Port St, Plymouth, MI 48170-6060
Tel.: (734) 414-6800
Web Site: http://www.skf.com
Mfr & Sales of Ball Bearings
N.A.I.C.S.: 332991

SKF Ukraine **(1)**
Bozhenko Str 34, 263017, Lutsk,
Ukraine **(100%)**
Tel.: (380) 33 278 3302
Web Site: https://www.skf.com
Ball Bearing Mfr
N.A.I.C.S.: 332991

SKF Uruguay S.A. **(1)**
La Paz 1678, 11200, Montevideo, Uruguay
Tel.: (598) 24000000
Sales Range: $25-49.9 Million
Emp.: 50
Roller Bearing Mfr
N.A.I.C.S.: 332991

SKF Venezolana S.A. **(1)**
Av Trinidad con calle Caracas Centro Profesional Viscaya, Nivel PH Colinas de Tamanaco, Caracas, Venezuela
Tel.: (58) 212 4178416
Industrial Bearing Mfr
N.A.I.C.S.: 332991

SKF Vietnam **(1)**
105 Ton Dat Tien Crescent Plaza Ward 2 L
4, Room 04 Tan Phu Rd District 7, Ho Chi
Minh City, Vietnam **(100%)**
Tel.: (84) 18002282
Web Site: https://www.skf.com
Sales Range: Less than $1 Million
Emp.: 16
Bearing Whslr
N.A.I.C.S.: 423840

SKF Zambia Ltd. **(1)**
5th Floor Sunshare Tower Katima Mulilo
Road, Lusaka, 10101, Copperbelt,
Zambia **(100%)**
Tel.: (260) 212223333
Web Site: https://www.skf.com
Sales Range: $50-74.9 Million
Emp.: 69
Sales of Ball & Roller Bearings
N.A.I.C.S.: 423840

SKF Zimbabwe (Pvt.) Ltd, **(1)**
Harare Sorting Central Office, PO Box 199,

Corner Airport & Deep Rd, Harare,
Zimbabwe **(100%)**
Tel.: (263) 4743118
Web Site: http://www.intertrade.skf.com
Sales Range: Less than $1 Million
Emp.: 40
Sales of Ball & Roller Bearings
N.A.I.C.S.: 423840

SKF de Mexico, S.A. de C.V. **(1)**
Km 125 Mex- Pue Highway 1103, 72014,
Puebla, Mexico **(100%)**
Tel.: (52) 2222294900
Sales Range: $50-74.9 Million
Emp.: 200
Mfr of Ball & Roller Bearings; Plants in
Puebla & Celaya
N.A.I.C.S.: 332991

SKF del Peru S.A. **(1)**
Av Jorge Basadre 349 piso 6 edificio We-Work, PO Box 27, San Isidro, 15073, Lima,
Peru **(100%)**
Tel.: (51) 4415222
Sales Range: $75-99.9 Million
Emp.: 150
Sales of Ball & Roller Bearings
N.A.I.C.S.: 423840

SKF do Brasil Ltda. **(1)**
Rod Anhanguera Km 30, Jardim Nova Jordanesia, Cajamar, 07750-000,
Brazil **(100%)**
Tel.: (55) 8000141152
Sales Range: $200-249.9 Million
Emp.: 900
Mfr of Ball & Roller Bearings
N.A.I.C.S.: 332991

Shanghai Peer Bearing Co. Ltd. **(1)**
9/F Tower B Central Towers 567 Langao
Road, Putuo District, Shanghai, 200333,
China
Tel.: (86) 2161484816
Roller & Ball Bearing Mfr
N.A.I.C.S.: 332991

Venture Aerobearings LLC **(1)**
8701 Palmetto Commerce Pkwy Ste 100,
Ladson, SC 29456
Tel.: (843) 695-2800
Web Site: https://ventureaerobearings.com
Jet Engine Bearing Mfr
N.A.I.C.S.: 333613

SKF INDIA LIMITED
Mahatma Gandhi Memorial Building
Netaji Subhash Road Charni Road
W, Mumbai, 400 002, India
Tel.: (91) 226 633 7777
Web Site: http://www.skfindia.com
Year Founded: 1907
500472—(NSE)
Rev.: $505,089,585
Assets: $358,782,060
Liabilities: $101,385,375
Net Worth: $257,396,685
Earnings: $53,912,040
Emp.: 1,681
Fiscal Year-end: 03/31/22
Automobile Service Equipment Mfr &
Distr
N.A.I.C.S.: 334519
Manish Bhatnagar *(Mng Dir)*

SKI CLUB OF GREAT BRITAIN LIMITED
Connect House 133-137 Alexandra
Road, Wimbledon, London, SW19
7JY, United Kingdom
Tel.: (44) 2084102000
Web Site: http://www.skiclub.co.uk
Not-for-Profit Snowsports Club
N.A.I.C.S.: 713940
Tim Whelan *(Head-Fin)*

SKIDMORE GROUP HOLDINGS INC.
1200 Lougheed Highway, Coquitlam,
V3K 6S4, BC, Canada
Tel.: (604) 438-1000
Web Site:
https://www.skidmoregroup.com
Year Founded: 2017

SKIDMORE GROUP HOLDINGS INC.

Skidmore Group Holdings Inc.—(Continued)
Investment Holding Company
N.A.I.C.S.: 551112
Garry Skidmore *(Pres)*

SKIL INFRASTRUCTURE LIMITED
SKIL House 209 Bank Street Cross Lane, Off Shahid Bhagat Singh Rd, Mumbai, 400 023, India
Tel.: (91) 2266199000
Web Site: http://www.skilgroup.co.in
Year Founded: 1990
Sales Range: $150-199.9 Million
Emp.: 850
Infrastructure Construction Services
N.A.I.C.S.: 237310
Nikhil Gandhi *(Chm)*

SKILL HIRE WA
3/271 Berkshire Road, Forrestfield, 6058, WA, Australia
Tel.: (61) 861519200   AU
Web Site: https://skillhire.com.au
Year Founded: 2016
GO2—(ASX)
Rev.: $22,742,818
Assets: $23,289,877
Liabilities: $19,970,742
Net Worth: $3,319,135
Earnings: ($2,060,285)
Fiscal Year-end: 06/30/21
Recruitment Services
N.A.I.C.S.: 561320
Billy Ferreira *(Founder & Mng Dir)*

Subsidiaries:

NARA Training and Assessing Pty. Ltd.   (1)
3/271 Berkshire Road, Forrestfield, 6058, WA, Australia
Tel.: (61) 1800487246
Web Site: https://www.naratraining.com.au
Forklift Training Services
N.A.I.C.S.: 611699

Skill Hire Indigenous Contracting Pty. Ltd.   (1)
3/271 Berkshire Road, Forrestfield, 6058, WA, Australia
Tel.: (61) 893762800
Web Site: https://skillhire.com.au
Employment Training & Staffing Services
N.A.I.C.S.: 561311

Skill Hire WA Pty. Ltd.   (1)
3/271 Berkshire Road, Forrestfield, 6058, WA, Australia
Tel.: (61) 893762800
Web Site: https://www.skillhire.com.au
Training & Skills Development Services
N.A.I.C.S.: 611430

SKILLCAST GROUP PLC
80 Leadenhall St, London, EC3A 3DH, United Kingdom
Tel.: (44) 2079295000   UK
Web Site: https://www.skillcast.com
Year Founded: 2001
SKL—(AIM)
Rev.: $11,415,786
Assets: $16,997,172
Liabilities: $7,192,575
Net Worth: $9,804,597
Earnings: $512,716
Emp.: 86
Fiscal Year-end: 12/31/21
Software Development Services
N.A.I.C.S.: 541511

SKILLFINDER INTERNATIONAL LIMITED
6th Floor 50 Mark Lane, London, EC3R 7QR, United Kingdom
Tel.: (44) 203 763 9500   UK
Web Site: http://www.skillfindergroup.com
Year Founded: 2014

Temporary Employment Agency Services
N.A.I.C.S.: 561311

Subsidiaries:

I.T. Skillfinder Ltd   (1)
20 St Dunstan's Hill, London, EC3R 8HY, United Kingdom
Tel.: (44) 20 7256 3550
Web Site: http://www.it-skillfinder.co.uk
Sales Range: $10-24.9 Million
Emp.: 20
IT Recruitment Services
N.A.I.C.S.: 561311
Darren Hall *(Co-Founder & Mng Dir)*

SKILLFUL CRAFTSMAN EDUCATION TECHNOLOGY LIMITED
Floor 4 Building 1 No 311 Yanxin Road, Huishan District, Wuxi, 214000, Jiangsu, China
Tel.: (86) 51081805788   Ky
Web Site: https://kingwayup.com
Year Founded: 2019
EDTK—(NASDAQ)
Rev.: $11,323,744
Assets: $43,642,638
Liabilities: $16,688,396
Net Worth: $26,954,242
Earnings: ($20,906,985)
Emp.: 71
Fiscal Year-end: 03/31/23
Holding Company
N.A.I.C.S.: 551112
Xiaofeng Gao *(Co-Founder, Chm & Co-CEO)*

SKILLPAGES HOLDINGS LIMITED
Block 1 Blackrock Business Park, Blackrock, Dublin, Ireland
Tel.: (353) 1 2000 210
Web Site: http://www.skillpages.com
Year Founded: 2010
Emp.: 49
Skill-Oriented Social Media Website
N.A.I.C.S.: 551112
Carlos Garcia *(Product Mgr)*

SKIN ELEMENTS LIMITED
Office 7 36 Ord St, West Perth, 6005, WA, Australia
Tel.: (61) 894864792
Web Site: http://www.soleoorganics.com
Skin Care Product Provider
N.A.I.C.S.: 812112
Peter Malone *(Chm)*

SKIN N SKIN CO., LTD.
14-1 Donyu 2-ro, Munsan-eup, Paju, Gyeonggi-do, Korea (South)
Tel.: (82) 7050734910
Web Site: https://www.skinnskin.co.kr
Year Founded: 2006
159910—(KRS)
Rev.: $16,418,662
Assets: $27,097,645
Liabilities: $6,035,277
Net Worth: $21,062,368
Earnings: ($7,704,174)
Emp.: 90
Fiscal Year-end: 12/31/22
Chemical Product Mfr & Distr
N.A.I.C.S.: 325312
Se-hwan Seo *(Mng Dir)*

SKINBIOTHERAPEUTICS PLC
The Core Newcastle Helix, Newcastle upon Tyne, NE4 5TF, United Kingdom
Tel.: (44) 1914957325   UK
Web Site: https://www.skinbiotherapeutics.com
SBTX—(AIM)
Rev.: $101,505

Assets: $4,188,521
Liabilities: $827,674
Net Worth: $3,360,847
Earnings: ($3,791,570)
Emp.: 12
Fiscal Year-end: 06/30/22
Skin Care Services
N.A.I.C.S.: 611511
Stuart Ashman *(CEO)*

Subsidiaries:

AxisBiotix Limited   (1)
The Core Bath Lane Newcastle Helix, Newcastle upon Tyne, NE4 5TF, United Kingdom
Tel.: (44) 1914957325
Web Site: https://axisbiotix.com
Biotechnology Research & Experimental Development Services
N.A.I.C.S.: 541714

SKION GMBH
Gunther-Quandt-Haus Seedammweg 55, 61352, Bad Homburg, Germany
Tel.: (49) 6172404531   De
Web Site: http://www.skion.de
Year Founded: 2006
Investment Holding Company
N.A.I.C.S.: 551112
Frank Richter *(Mng Dir)*

Subsidiaries:

ALTANA AG   (1)
Abelstrasse 43, Wesel, 46385, Germany   (100%)
Tel.: (49) 2816708
Web Site: http://www.altana.com
Rev.: $2,518,501,308
Assets: $3,744,033,537
Liabilities: $967,445,934
Net Worth: $2,776,587,603
Earnings: $189,311,213
Emp.: 6,458
Fiscal Year-end: 12/31/2019
Holding Company; Specialty Chemical Developer, Mfr & Marketer
N.A.I.C.S.: 551112
Matthias L. Wolfgruber *(Chm-Supervisory Bd)*

Subsidiary (Domestic):

ALTANA Chemie AG   (2)
Abelstrasse 45, 46483, Wesel, Germany
Tel.: (49) 281670200
Web Site: http://www.altana.com
Sales Range: $1-4.9 Billion
Emp.: 600
Additives, Pharmaceuticals & Chemicals Researcher, Developer, Mfr & Marketer
N.A.I.C.S.: 325998

Subsidiary (Domestic):

ACTEGA Coatings-Sealants GmbH   (3)
Abelstrasse 45, 46483, Wesel, Germany
Tel.: (49) 281670732
Web Site: http://www.altana.com
Sales Range: $25-49.9 Million
Emp.: 5
Chemical Products Mfr
N.A.I.C.S.: 325998

Subsidiary (Domestic):

ACTEGA DS GmbH   (4)
Straubinger Strasse 12, Bremen, 28219, Germany   (100%)
Tel.: (49) 421390020
Web Site: http://www.actega.com
Sales Range: $25-49.9 Million
Sealants Mfr
N.A.I.C.S.: 325520

ACTEGA Rhenania Coatings GmbH   (4)
Rhenaniastrasse 29-37, Grevenbroich, 41516, Germany   (100%)
Tel.: (49) 21812940
Web Site: http://www.actega.com
Sales Range: $50-74.9 Million
Chemical Coatings Mfr
N.A.I.C.S.: 325998

INTERNATIONAL PUBLIC

Subsidiary (Non-US):

ACTEGA Foshan Co., Ltd.   (5)
No 22 Xing Ye Road Bejiao Industrial Estate, Shunde Region, Foshan, 528311, Guangdong, China   (100%)
Tel.: (86) 75726655372
Web Site: http://www.actega.com
Sales Range: $75-99.9 Million
Emp.: 100
Can & Coil Coatings Mfr
N.A.I.C.S.: 325510

ACTEGA Rhenacoat S.A.   (5)
1 Avenue Francois Sommer Zl de Glaire, PO Box 30324, 08202, Sedan, Cedex, France   (100%)
Tel.: (33) 476236672
Web Site: http://www.actega.com
Sales Range: $50-74.9 Million
Emp.: 50
Coating Mfr
N.A.I.C.S.: 325510
Thierry Tabeaud *(Mng Dir)*

Salchi-Rhenacoat s.r.l.   (5)
Viale dell' Industria 3A-3B, 20040, Milan, Italy   (51%)
N.A.I.C.S.: 311230

Subsidiary (Domestic):

ACTEGA Terra GmbH   (4)
Industriestrasse 12, 31275, Lehrte, Germany   (100%)
Tel.: (49) 513250090
Web Site: http://www.actega.com
Sales Range: $25-49.9 Million
Emp.: 150
Coating Mfr
N.A.I.C.S.: 325510
Joerg Eck *(Gen Mgr)*

Subsidiary (Non-US):

ACTEGA WIT Inc.   (4)
125 Technology Dr, Lincolnton, NC 28092
Tel.: (704) 735-8282
Coating & Sealant Mfr
N.A.I.C.S.: 325510
Mark Westwell *(Pres & CEO)*

Subsidiary (Domestic):

BYK-Chemie GmbH   (3)
Abelstrasse 45, 46483, Wesel, Germany   (100%)
Tel.: (49) 2816700
Web Site: https://www.byk.com
Sales Range: $150-199.9 Million
Emp.: 600
Coatings, Inks & Plastics Additives Mfr
N.A.I.C.S.: 311230
Alison Avery *(Mng Dir & CFO)*

Subsidiary (Non-US):

BYK Japan KK   (4)
1-4-4 Dojimahama, Kita-ku, Osaka, 530-0004, Japan   (100%)
Tel.: (81) 647971470
Web Site: http://www.byk.com
Sales Range: $25-49.9 Million
Emp.: 30
Coatings, Inks & Plastics Additives Mfr
N.A.I.C.S.: 325510

BYK-Cera B.V.   (4)
Danzigweg 23, PO Box 535, Deventer, 7400 AM, Netherlands   (100%)
Tel.: (31) 570678200
Web Site: http://www.byk.com
Sales Range: $25-49.9 Million
Emp.: 120
Paints Mfr
N.A.I.C.S.: 325510
Wim Blok *(Mng Dir)*

BYK-Chemie Japan KK   (4)
3-29 Ichigaya-Honmuracho, Shinjuku-ku, Tokyo, 162-0845, Japan   (100%)
Tel.: (81) 364575501
Web Site: http://www.byk.com
Sales Range: $25-49.9 Million
Emp.: 20
Coatings, Inks & Plastics Additives Mfr
N.A.I.C.S.: 325510
Masaru Fukuda *(Mng Dir)*

Subsidiary (US):

BYK-Chemie USA, Inc.   (4)

524 S Cherry St, Wallingford, CT 06492
Tel.: (203) 265-2086
Web Site: http://www.byk.com
Sales Range: $25-49.9 Million
Emp.: 90
Coatings, Inks & Plastics Additives Mfr
N.A.I.C.S.: 325510

Subsidiary (Domestic):

BYK-Gardner GmbH (3)
Lausitzer Str 8, 82538, Geretsried, Germany (100%)
Tel.: (49) 817134930
Web Site: http://www.bykgardner.com
Sales Range: $50-74.9 Million
Emp.: 120
Coating Mfr
N.A.I.C.S.: 332812
George Schrodir *(Mng Dir)*

Subsidiary (US):

BKY-Gardner USA (4)
Rivers Park II 9104 Guilford Rd, Columbia, MD 21046-2729
Tel.: (301) 483-6500
Web Site: http://www.byk.com
Sales Range: $25-49.9 Million
Emp.: 35
Additives for Coatings & Plastics
N.A.I.C.S.: 325510
Mike Gogoel *(Pres)*

Subsidiary (Domestic):

ELANTAS GmbH (3)
Abelstrasse 43, 46483, Wesel, Germany
Tel.: (49) 2816708
Web Site: http://www.elantas.com
Sales Range: $350-399.9 Million
Electrical Insulation Materials Mfr
N.A.I.C.S.: 325211
Wolfgang Schutt *(Chm-Mgmt Bd)*

Subsidiary (Non-US):

ELANTAS (Tongling) Co. Ltd. (4)
Tongling Economic & Technology Development Zone, Tongling, 244000, Anhui, China
Tel.: (86) 5622819390
Electrical Insulation Materials Mfr
N.A.I.C.S.: 325211

ELANTAS (Zhuhai) Co. Ltd. (4)
Fine Chemical Area Gaolan Port Economic Zone, Zhuhai, 519050, Guangdong, China (100%)
Tel.: (86) 756 7710 415
Web Site: http://www.elantas.com
Sales Range: $25-49.9 Million
Emp.: 30
Electrical Insulation Materials Mfr
N.A.I.C.S.: 325211
Matthias L. Wolfgruber *(Chm-Mgmt Bd & CEO)*

Subsidiary (Domestic):

ELANTAS Beck GmbH (4)
Grossmannstr 105, Hamburg, 20539, Germany
Tel.: (49) 40789460
Web Site: http://www.elantas.com
Sales Range: $700-749.9 Million
Emp.: 130
Electrical Insulation Materials Mfr
N.A.I.C.S.: 325211
Ulrich Haring *(Mgr-Key Acct Mgmt)*

Subsidiary (Non-US):

ELANTAS Beck India Ltd. (5)
147 Mumbai-Pune Road, Pimpri, Pune, 411018, India
Tel.: (91) 206 719 0600
Web Site: http://www.elantas.com
Rev.: $73,500,309
Assets: $84,425,059
Liabilities: $15,537,222
Net Worth: $68,887,837
Earnings: $9,129,352
Emp.: 181
Fiscal Year-end: 12/31/2021
Electrical Insulation Materials Mfr
N.A.I.C.S.: 325211
Ravindra Kumar *(Pres & CEO-Elantas PDG)*

Subsidiary (Non-US):

ELANTAS Deatech s.r.l. (4)
Zona Industriale Campolungo 35, 63100, Ascoli Piceno, Italy (100%)
Tel.: (39) 07363081
Web Site: http://www.elantas.com
Sales Range: Less than $1 Million
Emp.: 80
Electrical Insulation Materials Mfr
N.A.I.C.S.: 325211

ELANTAS Isolantes Eletricos do Brasil Ltda. (4)
Rua Venezia 10 - Bairro Estiva, Cerquilho, Sao Paulo, 18520-000, Brazil
Tel.: (55) 1533848390
Web Site: http://www.elantas.com
Sales Range: $25-49.9 Million
Emp.: 35
Electrical Insulation Materials Mfr
N.A.I.C.S.: 325211
Gabriel Birenbaum *(Gen Mgr)*

ELANTAS Italia S.r.l. (4)
Strada Antolini 1, 43044, Collecchio, PR, Italy
Tel.: (39) 0736 3081
Web Site: http://www.elantas.com
Electrical Insulation Materials Mfr
N.A.I.C.S.: 325211
Antonio Nastasi *(Mng Dir)*

Subsidiary (US):

ELANTAS PDG, Inc. (4)
5200 N Second St, Saint Louis, MO 63147 (100%)
Tel.: (314) 621-5700
Web Site: http://www.elantas.com
Sales Range: $100-124.9 Million
Emp.: 228
Electrical Insulation Materials Mfr
N.A.I.C.S.: 325211
Susan W. Graham *(Pres & CEO)*

Subsidiary (Non-US):

Von Roll Holding AG (4)
Passwangstrasse 20, 4226, Breitenbach, Switzerland (100%)
Tel.: (41) 617855111
Web Site: http://www.vonroll.com
Rev.: $261,079,444
Assets: $282,451,550
Liabilities: $59,802,565
Net Worth: $222,648,985
Earnings: $10,395,372
Emp.: 912
Fiscal Year-end: 12/31/2022
Plastics Material & Resin Manufacturing
N.A.I.C.S.: 325211
Ravindra Kumar *(Chm)*

Subsidiary (Non-US):

IBIC (5)
Ab 8080 L Suite 81, 1800, Vilvoorde, Belgium (100%)
Tel.: (32) 22550100
Web Site: http://wwwabicbelgium.be
Sales Range: $50-74.9 Million
Emp.: 3
Sales Company
N.A.I.C.S.: 423610

Isola S.p.A. (5)
Via Villa Fontana snc, Cap 20, 55014, Marlia, LU, Italy (100%)
Tel.: (39) 058 393 6929
Web Site: https://www.isolaspa.it
Sales Range: $25-49.9 Million
Emp.: 10
Waste & Scrap Paper Collection & Processing
N.A.I.C.S.: 562998

OOO Von Roll (5)
Ulitsa Sokolnicheskiy Val 1A, 107113, Moscow, Russia
Tel.: (7) 4997077071
Web Site: http://www.vonroll.com
Emp.: 15
Insulation Material Distr
N.A.I.C.S.: 423330

Pearl Insulations Private Ltd (5)
Plot No 505 506 Phase IV Peenya Industrial Area II Stage, Bengaluru, 560 058, India (51%)
Tel.: (91) 8028361069
Sales Range: $10-24.9 Million
Emp.: 280
Covered Specialty Conductors (CSC)
N.A.I.C.S.: 335931

Pearl Metal Products (Bangalore) Pvt. Ltd. (5)
Plot No 507 IV Phase II Stage Peenya Industrial Area, Bengaluru, 560 058, India (51%)
Tel.: (91) 80 283 61069
Sales Range: $50-74.9 Million
Emp.: 230
Covered Specialty Conductors (CSC)
N.A.I.C.S.: 335931

Shenzhen Shengbida Electrical Material Co., Ltd. (5)
5G Jinyun Bldg No 6033 Shen Nan Road Futian Area, Shenzhen, 518040, China
Tel.: (86) 755 2553 5258
Web Site: http://www.vonroll.com
Sales Range: $25-49.9 Million
Emp.: 30
Electric Composite Material Mfr
N.A.I.C.S.: 335999

Subsidiary (Domestic):

Swiss Insulating Works Ltd. (5)
Passwang Strasse 20, Breitenbach, 4226, Switzerland (100%)
Tel.: (41) 617855111
Sales Range: $100-124.9 Million
Emp.: 400
Electrical Insulating Materials
N.A.I.C.S.: 335932
Stesan Sinckh *(Mgr-Site)*

Subsidiary (Non-US):

Transalpina GmbH (5)
Gloriettegasse 12, PO Box 73, A 1131, Vienna, Austria (100%)
Tel.: (43) 0187769160
Web Site: http://www.transalpina-industrialsolutions.com
Sales Range: $25-49.9 Million
Emp.: 20
N.A.I.C.S.: 331511

Valdoie Mica SAS (5)
5 avenue Charpentier, 90300, Valdoie, France
Tel.: (33) 38 490 1010
Industrial Equipment Mfr & Distr
N.A.I.C.S.: 333248

Von Roll (India) Pvt. Ltd. (5)
15/1/2 20/1B Kempalinganahalli Kunigal Road, Nelamangala, Bengaluru, 562 123, India
Tel.: (91) 802 308 7700
Industrial Equipment Mfr & Distr
N.A.I.C.S.: 333248

Von Roll Asia Pte. Ltd. (5)
6 Serangoon North Avenue 5 03-01, Singapore, 554910, Singapore (75%)
Tel.: (65) 65564788
Sales Range: $50-74.9 Million
Emp.: 13
Sales Company
N.A.I.C.S.: 423610
Daniel Chow *(Gen Mgr)*

Von Roll Automotive GmbH (5)
Theodor-Sachs-Strasse 1, 86199, Augsburg, Germany
Tel.: (49) 821 9020
Industrial Equipment Mfr
N.A.I.C.S.: 333248

Von Roll BHU Umwelttechnik GmbH (5)
Stuttgarter Strasse 57, 74321, Bietigheim-Bissingen, Germany
Tel.: (49) 7142 788350
Web Site: http://www.bhu-tech.de
Sales Range: $25-49.9 Million
Emp.: 25
Environmental Engineering Services
N.A.I.C.S.: 541330
Reinhold Brenner *(Gen Mgr)*

Von Roll Composite S.A.S. (5)
Departement Usinage Ave Des 3 Chenes, F 90000, Belfort, France (100%)
Tel.: (33) 384557730
Web Site: http://www.vonroll.com
Sales Range: $25-49.9 Million
Emp.: 61
N.A.I.C.S.: 331511

Von Roll Deutschland GmbH (5)
Theodor-Sachs-Strasse 1, 86199, Augsburg, Germany (100%)
Tel.: (49) 8219020
Web Site: http://www.vonroll-isola.com
Sales Range: $50-74.9 Million
Emp.: 170
N.A.I.C.S.: 331511
Christoph Rascyk *(Gen Mgr)*

Von Roll Deutschland GmbH (5)
Theodor-Sachs-Strasse 1, 86199, Augsburg, Germany
Tel.: (49) 821 9020
Web Site: http://www.vonroll.com
Sales Range: $125-149.9 Million
Emp.: 120
Eletric Power Generation Services
N.A.I.C.S.: 221118

Von Roll Deutschland Holding GmbH (5)
Theodor-Sachs-Strasse 1, 86199, Augsburg, Germany
Tel.: (49) 821 9020
Web Site: https://www.vonroll.com
Sales Range: $100-124.9 Million
Emp.: 150
Investment Management Service
N.A.I.C.S.: 523999
Michael Kuss *(Gen Mgr)*

Von Roll France S.A. (5)
27 Faubourg de Belfort, PO Box 49, 90100, Delle, France
Tel.: (33) 384 36 84 36
Web Site: http://www.vonroll.com
Sales Range: $125-149.9 Million
Emp.: 130
Electric Power Distribution Services
N.A.I.C.S.: 221122

Subsidiary (Domestic):

Von Roll Infratec Holding AG (5)
Bahnhofstrasse 23, 6300, Zug, Switzerland (100%)
Tel.: (41) 417200105
Web Site: http://www.vonroll-infratec.ch
Sales Range: $25-49.9 Million
Emp.: 20
Iron Foundries
N.A.I.C.S.: 331511

Subsidiary (Domestic):

Industrial Berearbeitungscenter AG (6)
Passwang Strasse 20, 4226, Breitenbach, Switzerland (100%)
Tel.: (41) 617855111
Web Site: http://www.vonroll.com
Sales Range: $75-99.9 Million
N.A.I.C.S.: 331511

Matra (6)
Industriering 19, CH 3250, Lyss, Switzerland
Tel.: (41) 323872828
Web Site: http://www.robert-aebi.com
Sales Range: $25-49.9 Million
Machine Trading
N.A.I.C.S.: 541330

Rieter Machine Works Ltd. (6)
Klosterstrasse 32, 8406, Winterthur, Switzerland (100%)
Tel.: (41) 52 208 8622
Web Site: https://www.rieter.com
Industry Castings (Ferrous Metals)
N.A.I.C.S.: 331511

Robert Aebi AG (6)
Riedthofstrasse 100, 8105, Regensdorf, Switzerland (100%)
Tel.: (41) 44 842 5111
Web Site: https://www.robert-aebi.ch
Sales Range: $25-49.9 Million
Emp.: 650
Machine Trading
N.A.I.C.S.: 541330
Marcel Zahner *(CEO & Member-Exec Bd)*

Savre SA (6)
via Cantonale 46, Mezzovico, 6805, Mezzovico-Vira, Ticino, Switzerland (100%)
Tel.: (41) 91 946 3424
Web Site: https://www.savre.ch

SKION GMBH

SKion GmbH—(Continued)
Sales Range: $25-49.9 Million
Emp.: 13
Insulation Products & Services
N.A.I.C.S.: 331511

Subsidiary (Non-US):

Strack GmbH (6)
Mottmann St 5 C, D 53842, Troisdorf,
Germany (100%)
Tel.: (49) 241492100
Web Site: http://www.strack-yalye.de
Sales Range: $25-49.9 Million
Emp.: 3
Infrastructure Systems
N.A.I.C.S.: 541330

Subsidiary (Domestic):

Von Roll Casting (Emmenbrucke)
AG (6)
Rueggisingerstrasse 2, CH-6020, Emmenbrucke, Switzerland (100%)
Tel.: (41) 412693131
Web Site: http://www.vonroll-infratec.ch
Sales Range: $50-74.9 Million
Emp.: 210
Industry Castings (Ferrous Metals)
N.A.I.C.S.: 423510
Danileo Feato (Gen Mgr)

Von Roll Eisen & Stahlgiesserei
AG (6)
Johan Renfer strasse 51-55, CH-2500,
Biel/Bienne, Switzerland (99.83%)
Tel.: (41) 323417444
Metal Castings
N.A.I.C.S.: 331523

Subsidiary (Non-US):

Von Roll Hydro Tech GmbH (6)
Armaturen Strasse B NR 4, Prenzlau,
17291, Germany (100%)
Tel.: (49) 3984730
Web Site: http://www.awp-gwa.de
Sales Range: $10-24.9 Million
Infrastructure Systems
N.A.I.C.S.: 541330
Iyad Titi (Mgr-Sls)

Subsidiary (Domestic):

Von Roll Hydrotec S.A. (6)
Von Roll Strasse 24, CH 4702, Oensingen,
Switzerland (100%)
Tel.: (41) 324361111
Web Site: http://www.vonroll-infratec.ch
Sales Range: $25-49.9 Million
N.A.I.C.S.: 331511

Von Roll Schweiz AG (6)
Passwangstrasse 20, 4226, Breitenbach,
Switzerland (100%)
Tel.: (41) 61 785 5111
Web Site: http://www.vonrollgroup.com
Sales Range: $75-99.9 Million
Emp.: 400
Iron & Metal Foundries
N.A.I.C.S.: 331511

VonRoll Hydroservices AG (6)
VonRoll Strasse 24, 4702, Oensingen,
Switzerland (100%)
Tel.: (41) 623881111
Web Site: http://www.vonroll-hydro.ch
Infrastructure Systems
N.A.I.C.S.: 541330

Subsidiary (Domestic):

Von Roll Insulation & Composites
Holding AG (5)
Passwangstrasse 20, 4226, Breitenbach,
Switzerland
Tel.: (41) 617855111
Web Site: https://www.vonroll.com
Investment Management Service
N.A.I.C.S.: 523999

Subsidiary (Non-US):

Von Roll Isola Czech Republic (5)
Taborska 31, 14016, Prague, Czech
Republic (100%)
Tel.: (420) 261215212
Web Site: http://www.vonroll.com

Sales Range: Less than $1 Million
Emp.: 2
Insulation Products & Services
N.A.I.C.S.: 331511

Von Roll Isola GmbH (5)
Isola Strasse 2, D 52348, Duren,
Germany (100%)
Tel.: (49) 4218085000
Web Site: http://www.vonrollisola.com
Sales Range: $100-124.9 Million
Emp.: 260
N.A.I.C.S.: 331511

Subsidiary (Domestic):

Von Roll Isola Mtec Ltd. (5)
Passwangstrasse 20, CH 4226, Breitenbach, Switzerland (100%)
Tel.: (41) 617855111
Web Site: http://www.vonroll.com.br
Sales Range: $100-124.9 Million
Emp.: 400
Electrical Insulating Materials
N.A.I.C.S.: 335932
Rols Spindelen (Mgr-Products)

Subsidiary (Non-US):

Von Roll Isola Poland (5)
ul Fabryczna 14D, 53609, Wroclaw,
Poland (100%)
Tel.: (48) 713590941
Web Site: http://www.vonroll.com
Insulation Products & Services
N.A.I.C.S.: 331511

Von Roll Isola S.A. (5)
27 Faubourg De Belfort, PO Box 49, 90100,
Delle, France (100%)
Tel.: (33) 384368436
Web Site: http://www.vonroll.com
Sales Range: $1-9.9 Million
Emp.: 213
Insulation Products & Services
N.A.I.C.S.: 331511

Division (Domestic):

Von Roll Isola France S.A. (6)
48 Faubourg De Belfort, 90100, Delle,
France (100%)
Tel.: (33) 384368383
Web Site: http://www.vonroll.com
Sales Range: $25-49.9 Million
Emp.: 100
Wire Mfr & Distr
N.A.I.C.S.: 331222

Von Roll Isola France S.A., Resins &
Varnish Division (6)
145 Rue De La Republique, PO Box 128,
69883, Meyzieu, Cedex, France (100%)
Tel.: (33) 478045904
Web Site: http://www.vonroll.com
Insulation Products & Services
N.A.I.C.S.: 331511

Von Roll Isola France S.A., Samica
Division (6)
5 avenue Charpentier, 90300, Valdoie,
France (100%)
Tel.: (33) 384901010
Web Site: http://www.vonroll.com
Sales Range: $25-49.9 Million
Emp.: 30
Insulating Systems for Wind Turbine Generators Mfr
N.A.I.C.S.: 325211

Subsidiary (Non-US):

Von Roll Isola, Winding Systems
GmbH (5)
Oswald Greiner Strasse 3, Dobeln, 4720,
Germany (60%)
Tel.: (49) 3431716690
Web Site: http://www.poetzsch.de
Sales Range: Less than $1 Million
Emp.: 400
N.A.I.C.S.: 331511
Thomas Poetzsch (Gen Mgr)

Von Roll Italia S.p.A. (5)
Via XXV Aprile 12, I-24050, Bergamo,
Ghisalbe, Italy (100%)
Tel.: (39) 03639403101
Web Site: http://www.vonroll.com
Sales Range: $25-49.9 Million
Emp.: 40
Insulation Products & Systems

N.A.I.C.S.: 335999

Subsidiary (Domestic):

Von Roll Management AG (5)
Passwangstrasse 20, 4226, Breitenbach,
Switzerland
Tel.: (41) 617855111
Web Site: https://www.vonroll.com
Eletric Power Generation Services
N.A.I.C.S.: 221118
Achim Klotz (CEO)

Subsidiary (Non-US):

Von Roll REACH GmbH (5)
Theodor-Sachs-Strasse 1, 86199, Augsburg, Germany
Tel.: (49) 821 9020
Web Site: http://www.vonroll.com
Emp.: 32
Electronic Materials Mfr
N.A.I.C.S.: 334419
Peter Daas (Gen Mgr)

Von Roll Shanghai Co., Ltd (5)
Unit C No 1235 Minqiang Road, Songiang
Industrial Zone, Shanghai, 201612, China
Tel.: (86) 216768 702 0821
Web Site: http://www.vonroll.com
Insulation Products & Systems Sales
N.A.I.C.S.: 423610

Subsidiary (Domestic):

Von Roll Solar AG (5)
Steinacherstrasse 101, 8804, Wadenswil,
Switzerland
Tel.: (41) 44 204 3005
Sales Range: $75-99.9 Million
Emp.: 10
Eletric Power Generation Services
N.A.I.C.S.: 221118

Von Roll Switzerland AG (5)
Passwangstrasse 20, Breitenbach, 4226,
Switzerland
Tel.: (41) 61 785 51 11
Emp.: 400
Eletric Power Generation Services
N.A.I.C.S.: 221118
Stefan Finckh (Gen Mgr)

Subsidiary (Non-US):

Von Roll Trading (Shanghai) Co.,
Ltd. (5)
Unit C No 1235 Minqiang Road, Shanghai,
China
Tel.: (86) 216768 702 0821
Industrial Equipment Mfr & Distr
N.A.I.C.S.: 333248

Von Roll UK Ltd (5)
Wharfedale Road Euroway Estate, Bradford, BD4 6SG, West Yorkshire, United
Kingdom
Tel.: (44) 1274 68 77 77
Electrical Insulation Products Distr
N.A.I.C.S.: 423610

Subsidiary (US):

Von Roll USA Holding, Inc. (5)
1 W Campbell Rd, Schenectady, NY 12306
Tel.: (518) 344-7200
Investment Management Service
N.A.I.C.S.: 523999

Subsidiary (Domestic):

Von Roll USA, Inc. (6)
200 Von Roll Dr, Schenectady, NY
12306-2442 (100%)
Tel.: (518) 344-7100
Web Site: http://www.vonroll.com
Sales Range: $10-24.9 Million
Electrical Insulators & Insulating Materials
N.A.I.C.S.: 335932

Subsidiary (Domestic):

John C. Dolph Company (7)
20 New Rd, Monmouth Junction, NJ 08852
Tel.: (732) 329-2333
Web Site: http://www.dolphs.com
Custom Compounding Materials Mfr
N.A.I.C.S.: 325510

Von Roll Austral, Inc. (7)
1055 Shadix Industrial Way, Douglasville,
GA 30134-3975 (50%)

INTERNATIONAL PUBLIC

Tel.: (770) 920-2222
Web Site: http://www.vonroll.com
Sales Range: $25-49.9 Million
Emp.: 60
Electrical Insulation Materials Mfr
N.A.I.C.S.: 335999
Bill Murton (Gen Mgr)

Unit (Domestic):

Von Roll Isola, EL Paso (7)
PO Box 1414, New Haven, CT 06506-1414
N.A.I.C.S.: 331511

Von Roll Isola-Midwest (7)
4853 W 130th St, Cleveland, OH 44135-5137
Tel.: (216) 433-7474
Web Site: http://www.vonroll.com
Sales Range: $25-49.9 Million
Emp.: 30
Extraction & Processing of Mica
N.A.I.C.S.: 335932
Larry Schwender (Gen Mgr)

Subsidiary (Domestic):

Von Roll Water Holding AG (5)
Passwangstrasse 20, Breitenbach, 4226,
Switzerland
Tel.: (41) 617855111
Web Site: http://www.vonroll.com
Emp.: 350
Investment Management Service
N.A.I.C.S.: 523999

Subsidiary (Non-US):

Von Roll do Brasil Ltda. (5)
Avenida Parque Central s/n Distrito Industrial, Maracanau, 61939-140, Ceara, Brazil
Tel.: (55) 854 008 4884
Industrial Equipment Mfr & Distr
N.A.I.C.S.: 333248

Plant (Non-US):

Von Roll do Brasil Ltda. - Production
Plant (5)
Av Parque Central S/N 1o Distrito Industrial,
Maracanau, 61939-140, Ceara, Brazil
Tel.: (55) 85 4008 4884
Electrical Insulation Materials Mfr
N.A.I.C.S.: 335999
Gilberto Gusmao (Mgr-Sls)

Subsidiary (Domestic):

Eckart GmbH & Co. KG (3)
Guntersthal 4, 91235, Hartenstein, Germany
Tel.: (49) 9152770
Web Site: http://www.eckart.net
Sales Range: $450-499.9 Million
Metallic Pigments Mfr
N.A.I.C.S.: 325130
Wolfgag Schuett (Mng Dir)

Subsidiary (US):

Eckart America Corporation (4)
830 E Erie St, Painesville, OH 44077
Tel.: (440) 954-7600
Web Site: http://www.eckartamerica.com
Rev: $13,100,000
Emp.: 132
Metallic Pigments & Powders
N.A.I.C.S.: 325130
Joe Perdue (Mgr-Mktg)

Subsidiary (Non-US):

Eckart Asia Ltd. (4)
12/F Asia Orient Tower, 33 Lockhart Road,
Wanchai, China (Hong Kong)
Tel.: (852) 29262932
Web Site: http://www.eckart.net
Sales Range: $25-49.9 Million
Emp.: 21
Metallic Pigments & Powders Mfr
N.A.I.C.S.: 325130

Subsidiary (Non-US):

Eckart Shanghai Co. Ltd. (5)
Unit C Floor 13 E Ocean Centre Phase II,
588-618 Yan An Dong Road, Shanghai,
200001, China
Tel.: (86) 2153855300
Web Site: http://www.eckart.com
Metallic Pigments & Powders Mfr

AND PRIVATE COMPANIES

N.A.I.C.S.: 325130

Subsidiary (Non-US):

Eckart Benelux B.V. (4)
Verlengde Velmolen 42, Uden, 5406 NT, Netherlands
Tel.: (31) 413214000
Web Site: http://www.eckart.net
Sales Range: $25-49.9 Million
Emp.: 5
Metallic Pigments Whslr
N.A.I.C.S.: 424690
G. Reehuis *(Mng Dir)*

Eckart France S.A. (4)
31 rue Amilcar Cipriani, Cedex, 93402, Saint-Ouen, France
Tel.: (33) 149181949
Web Site: http://www.eckart.net
Sales Range: $25-49.9 Million
Emp.: 7
Metallic Pigments Whslr
N.A.I.C.S.: 424690

Eckart Italia S.r.l. (4)
Strada Caifango 3, 27055, Rivanazzano, Pavia, Italy
Tel.: (39) 0383945011
Web Site: http://www.eckart.net
Sales Range: $25-49.9 Million
Emp.: 69
Metallic Pigments Mfr
N.A.I.C.S.: 325130

Eckart Pigments Ky (4)
Titaanitie, Pori, 28840, Finland
Tel.: (358) 26281900
Web Site: http://www.eckart.net
Sales Range: $25-49.9 Million
Emp.: 15
Metallic Pigments & Powders Mfr
N.A.I.C.S.: 325130
Pekka Eskelinen *(Mgr-Quality & Res)*

Eckart Switzerland SA (4)
Rue du Camping 2, Vetroz, 1963, Valais, Switzerland
Tel.: (41) 273454800
Web Site: http://www.eckart.net
Sales Range: $25-49.9 Million
Emp.: 45
Metallic Pigments Mfr
N.A.I.C.S.: 325130
Dominique Pfannatter *(Mng Dir)*

Eckart UK Ltd. (4)
Unit C The Sidings, Station Road, Ampthill, MK45 2QY, Bedfordshire, United Kingdom
Tel.: (44) 1525409520
Web Site: http://www.eckart.net
Sales Range: $25-49.9 Million
Emp.: 9
Metallic Pigments Distr
N.A.I.C.S.: 424690
Allison Butler *(Sec)*

Eckart de Mexico Industries, S.R.L. de C.V. (4)
Av De las Granjas 1121, Col San Pablo Xalpo, Tlalnepantla, CP 54090, Mexico
Tel.: (52) 5553941240
Web Site: http://www.eckart.net
Sales Range: $25-49.9 Million
Emp.: 7
Metallic Pigments Mfr
N.A.I.C.S.: 325130

Subsidiary (Non-US):

Actega Artistica S.A. (2)
Parque Empresarial A Granxa Rua F, 36475, Porrino, Pontevedra, Spain
Tel.: (34) 986231606
Chemical & Allied Product Whslr
N.A.I.C.S.: 424690
Eduardo Alonso *(Mgr-ERP IT)*

Actega Do Brasil Tintas E Vernizes Ltda. (2)
Rua Nossa Senhora da Penha No 800 - 850, Aracariguama, 18147-000, SP, Brazil
Tel.: (55) 1130421506
Adhesive & Sealing Compound Mfr
N.A.I.C.S.: 325520
Luis Felipe Amaral *(Controller)*

Subsidiary (Domestic):

Actega GmbH (2)
Abelstrasse 43, 46483, Wesel, Germany
Tel.: (49) 2816708
Web Site: http://www.actega.com
Adhesive & Sealing Compound Mfr
N.A.I.C.S.: 325520

Actega Metal Print GmbH (2)
Mielestr 13, 31275, Lehrte, Germany
Tel.: (49) 51325009500
Web Site: http://www.actega-metal-print.com
Metal Printing Services
N.A.I.C.S.: 323120
Jan Franz Allerkamp *(CEO)*

Actega Rhenania GmbH (2)
Rhenaniastrasse 29-37, 41516, Grevenbroich, Germany
Tel.: (49) 21812940
Coating & Laminated Adhesive Mfr
N.A.I.C.S.: 325520

Subsidiary (Non-US):

BYK (Tongling) Co., Ltd. (2)
Sixth Cuihu Road, Tongling Economic and Technological Development Zone, Tongling, 244000, Anhui, China
Tel.: (86) 5622830637
Chemical & Allied Product Whslr
N.A.I.C.S.: 424690
Zefa Ni *(Mgr-EHS)*

BYK Additives (Shanghai) Co., Ltd. (2)
Pugong Road 25, Shanghai Chemical Industry Park Fengxian District, Shanghai, 201507, China
Tel.: (86) 2137498888
Chemical & Allied Product Whslr
N.A.I.C.S.: 424690
Yingfeng Xie *(Head-Mktg Svcs)*

BYK Additives Ltd. (2)
Moorfield Road, Widnes, WA8 3AA, Cheshire, United Kingdom
Tel.: (44) 151 495 2222
Web Site: http://www.byk.com
Sales Range: $25-49.9 Million
Emp.: 100
Inorganic Chemicals Mfr & Distr
N.A.I.C.S.: 325180
Frank Wright *(Mng Dir)*

Subsidiary (US):

BYK Additives Inc. (3)
1212 Church St, Gonzales, TX 78629
Tel.: (830) 672-2891
Web Site: http://www.byk.com
Sales Range: $75-99.9 Million
Inorganic Chemicals Mfr & Distr
N.A.I.C.S.: 325180
John Du *(Mgr-Tech Products)*

Subsidiary (Non-US):

BYK Additives GmbH (4)
Stadtwaldstrasse 44, 85368, Moosburg, Germany
Tel.: (49) 8761 72150 0
Web Site: http://www.byk.com
Inorganic Chemical Products Developer & Mfr
N.A.I.C.S.: 325180
Georg Schroeder *(Mng Dir)*

Plant (Domestic):

BYK Additives Inc. (4)
1600 W Hill St, Louisville, KY 40210
Tel.: (502) 772-4403
Web Site: http://www.byk.com
Inorganic Chemicals Mfr & Distr
N.A.I.C.S.: 325180
Jerry Amy *(Plant Mgr)*

Subsidiary (Non-US):

BYK Asia Pacific Pte. Ltd. (2)
89 Science Park Drive Lobby A 03-04 The Rutherford Science Park 1, Singapore, 118261, Singapore
Tel.: (65) 68747673
Chemical & Allied Product Whslr
N.A.I.C.S.: 424690
Puay Hoon Tan *(Mgr-Mktg Svcs)*

BYK Korea LLC (2)
Seoul Office 901 904 102 IPark-1 239 Jeongjail-ro, Bundang-gu, Seongnam, 13556, Gyeonggi, Korea (South)
Tel.: (82) 317243500

Paint & Coating Mfr
N.A.I.C.S.: 325510

Colormix Industria e Comercio de Pigmentos Ltda. (2)
Av Aruana 280 Galpao 6, Barueri, SP, Brazil
Tel.: (55) 1155456644
Chemical & Allied Product Whslr
N.A.I.C.S.: 424690

ECKART Asia Limited (2)
4/F YOCO Building 41 Nguyen Thi Minh Khai St, Dist 1, Ho Chi Minh City, Vietnam
Tel.: (84) 2838243371
Chemical & Allied Product Whslr
N.A.I.C.S.: 325998

ECKART Asia Limited (2)
No 74 Yan Ping South Road, Zhong Zheng District, Taipei, 10042, Taiwan
Tel.: (886) 930016236
Paint & Coating Mfr
N.A.I.C.S.: 325510

ECKART Zhuhai Co. Ltd. (2)
Gaolan Port Economic Zone, Zhuhai, 519050, China
Tel.: (86) 7567228600
Chemical & Allied Product Whslr
N.A.I.C.S.: 424690

Subsidiary (Domestic):

Elantas Europe GmbH (2)
Grossmannstr 105, 20539, Hamburg, Germany
Tel.: (49) 40789460
Emp.: 140
Paint & Coating Mfr
N.A.I.C.S.: 325510

Subsidiary (Non-US):

Elantas Europe Srl. (2)
Zona Industriale Campolungo 35, 63100, Ascoli Piceno, Italy
Tel.: (39) 07363081
Emp.: 110
Paint & Coating Mfr
N.A.I.C.S.: 325510
Alessandro Borio *(Sls Mgr-Technical)*

Elantas Malaysia Sdn. Bhd. (2)
Lot 550 Jalan Keretapi Lama Batu 7 1/2 Jalan Kapar/KU15, 42200, Kapar, Selangor, Malaysia
Tel.: (60) 332918878
Chemical & Allied Product Whslr
N.A.I.C.S.: 424690
Felice Chong *(Office Mgr)*

Subsidiary (US):

Paul N. Gardner Company, Inc. (2)
316 NE 1st St, Pompano Beach, FL 33060-6608
Tel.: (954) 946-9454
Web Site: http://www.gardco.com
Measuring & Testing Instrument Mfr & Distr
N.A.I.C.S.: 334519

PolyAd Services LLC (2)
4170 Shoreline Dr, Earth City, MO 63045
Tel.: (314) 506-3136
Web Site: http://www.polyadservices.com
Plastic Additive Mfr
N.A.I.C.S.: 325998

Subsidiary (Non-US):

Schmid Rhyner AG (2)
Soodring 29, 8134, Adliswil, Switzerland (100%)
Tel.: (41) 447126400
Web Site: http://www.schmid-rhyner.ch
Sales Range: $25-49.9 Million
Emp.: 50
Printing Ink Mfr
N.A.I.C.S.: 325910
Jakob Rohner *(CEO)*

ELIQUO WATER GROUP GmbH (1)
Seedammweg 55, 61352, Bad Homburg, Germany
Tel.: (49) 6172 404 0
Web Site: http://www.eliquowater.com
Emp.: 350
Water Treatment Equipment Mfr
N.A.I.C.S.: 333310
Reinhard Hubner *(Mng Dir)*

SKION GMBH

EnviroChemie GmbH (1)
In den Leppsteinswiesen 9, 64380, Rossdorf, Germany
Tel.: (49) 6154 6998 0
Web Site: http://www.envirochemie.com
Water Treatment Machinery Mfr
N.A.I.C.S.: 333310
Peter Leyendecker *(Member-Mgmt Bd)*

Subsidiary (Non-US):

EnviroChemie (2)
Skeppsgatan 19, 211 11, Malmo, Sweden
Tel.: (46) 40 627 03 00
Water Treatment Machinery Distr
N.A.I.C.S.: 423830

EnviroChemie AG (2)
Twirrenstr 6, 8733, Eschenbach, Switzerland
Tel.: (41) 55 286 18 18
Web Site: http://www.envirofalk.ch
Water Treatment Machinery Distr
N.A.I.C.S.: 423830

EnviroChemie Abwasserreinigungs Ges.m.b.H. (2)
Europastrasse 8/4, 9500, Villach, Austria
Tel.: (43) 732 370332
Water Treatment Machinery Distr
N.A.I.C.S.: 423830

EnviroChemie BV (2)
Waarderweg 52 c, 2031 BP, Haarlem, Netherlands
Tel.: (31) 23 53 45 405
Web Site: http://www.envirochemie.de
Water Treatment Machinery Distr
N.A.I.C.S.: 423830

EnviroChemie Bulgaria EOOD (2)
Evlogi Georgiev Blvd 100 St 4 app 7, 1505, Sofia, Bulgaria
Tel.: (359) 2 8463065
Web Site: http://www.envirochemie.bg
Emp.: 3
Water Treatment Machinery Distr
N.A.I.C.S.: 423830

EnviroChemie FZE (2)
Building No 7W - A Office No 3059, Dubai Airport Free Zone Area, Dubai, United Arab Emirates
Tel.: (971) 504826842
Web Site: http://www.envirochemie.com
Emp.: 3
Water Treatment Machinery Distr
N.A.I.C.S.: 423830
Visakh John Thomas *(Project Engr-Sls)*

EnviroChemie Polska Sp.z o.o. (2)
ul Rownolegla 9A, 02-235, Warsaw, Poland
Tel.: (48) 22 8463841
Web Site: http://www.envirochemia.pl
Water Treatment Machinery Distr
N.A.I.C.S.: 423830
Lech Iwaniuk *(Mgr-Sls)*

EnviroChemie Romania SRL (2)
Str Visarion Nr 13, 010422, Bucharest, Romania
Tel.: (40) 21 3112870
Web Site: http://www.envirochemie.ro
Water Treatment Machinery Distr
N.A.I.C.S.: 423830
Pintea Ana *(Mgr-Mktg & Svc)*

EnviroChemie Tratamentos Especializados Ltda. (2)
Estrada da Curicica 1280, Curicica Jacarepagua, 22710-552, Rio de Janeiro, Brazil
Tel.: (55) 21 24414393
Web Site: http://www.envirochemie-br.com
Emp.: 45
Water Treatment Machinery Distr
N.A.I.C.S.: 423830
Cleibson Moreira Da Silva *(Gen Mgr)*

Subsidiary (Domestic):

EnviroFALK GmbH (2)
Gutenbergstrasse 7, 56457, Westerburg, Germany
Tel.: (49) 2663 9908 0
Web Site: http://www.envirofalk.com
Emp.: 65
Water Treatment Machinery Mfr
N.A.I.C.S.: 333310
Erhard Burggraf *(Co-Chm)*

SKION GMBH

SKion GmbH—(Continued)

Subsidiary (Non-US):

ENVIRO FALK AG (3)
Gewerbestrasse 5, 6330, Cham, Switzerland
Tel.: (41) 41 7404414
Water Treatment Machinery Distr
N.A.I.C.S.: 423830

Subsidiary (Non-US):

OOO Enviro-Chemie GmbH (2)
86 Belinskogo str sector 7 floor 8, 620026, Yekaterinburg, Russia
Tel.: (7) 343 278 2780
Web Site: http://www.envirochemie.ru
Emp.: 35
Water Treatment Machinery Distr
N.A.I.C.S.: 423830
Marina Chebotaeva (Mng Dir)

Skion Water GmbH (1)
Seedammweg 55, Bad Homburg v.d. Hohe, 61352, Frankfurt, Germany
Tel.: (49) 6172 404 534
Water & Wastewater Technology Solutions
N.A.I.C.S.: 562998
Reinhard Hubner (CEO)

Subsidiary (Non-US):

Doosan Enpure Ltd. (2)
Doosan House Parklands Business Park, Rubery, Birmingham, B45 9PZ, United Kingdom
Tel.: (44) 1216832800
Web Site: http://www.doosanenpure.com
Construction & Engineering Services
N.A.I.C.S.: 541330

Ovivo Inc. (2)
1010 Sherbrooke Street West Suite 1700, Montreal, H3A 2R7, QC, Canada (100%)
Tel.: (514) 284-2224
Web Site: http://www.ovivowater.com
Water Treatment Products & Solutions
N.A.I.C.S.: 221310
Malek Salamor (Sr VP-Electronics)

Subsidiary (Non-US):

Ovivo Aqua Austria GmbH (3)
Paracelsusweg 1, 8144, Tobelbad, Steiermark, Austria
Tel.: (43) 3136 62188 0
Web Site: http://www.ovivowater.at
Water & Industrial Ultra Pure Water Production & Wastewater Treatment Technologies & Services
N.A.I.C.S.: 221310

Ovivo China Co., Ltd. (3)
SOHO Bld 8 No 115 Lane 572 Bibo Road, Zhangjiang Hi-Tech Park Pudong, 201203, Shanghai, China
Tel.: (86) 2150804558
Web Site: http://www.ovivowater.cn
Water Treatment & Management Engineering
N.A.I.C.S.: 541330

Ovivo Deutschland GmbH (3)
Max-Planckstr 9-11, 71254, Ditzingen, Germany
Tel.: (49) 7152 3138600
Web Site: http://www.ovivowater.de
Water & Wastewater Treatment Equipment Mfr, Facilities Construction & Maintenance Services
N.A.I.C.S.: 221310

Ovivo Holland B.V. (3)
Energieweg 1, 2382 NA, Zoeterwoude, Netherlands
Tel.: (31) 715899218
Web Site: http://www.ovivowater.nl
Water & Wastewater Treatment Equipment Mfr, Facilities Construction & Maintenance Services
N.A.I.C.S.: 221310

Ovivo Middle East L.L.C. (3)
PO Box 119876, Dubai, United Arab Emirates
Tel.: (971) 4 223 0746
Web Site: http://www.ovivowater.ae
Water & Wastewater Services
N.A.I.C.S.: 221310

Ovivo Singapore Pte. Ltd. (3)
10 Ang Mo Kio Street 65 #01-05 Techpoint, Singapore, 569059, Singapore
Tel.: (65) 6743 0338
Web Site: http://www.ovivowater.sg
Water & Wastewater Treatment Equipment Mfr, Facilities Construction & Maintenance Services
N.A.I.C.S.: 221310

Ovivo UK Limited (3)
760 The Crescent, Colchester, CO4 9YQ, Essex, United Kingdom
Tel.: (44) 1206 756 600
Web Site: http://www.ovivowater.co.uk
Water & Wastewater Treatment Equipment Mfr, Facilities Construction & Maintenance Services
N.A.I.C.S.: 221310

Unit (Domestic):

Ovivo UK Limited - Industrial Division, Colchester (4)
760 The Crescent, Colchester, CO4 9YQ, Essex, United Kingdom
Tel.: (44) 1206 756 600
Web Site: http://www.ovivowater.co.uk
Water Treatment Systems Engineering, Construction & Maintenance Services
N.A.I.C.S.: 237110

Ovivo UK Limited - Industrial Division, Wolverhampton (4)
1 10 Second Floor Railway Drive, Wolverhampton, WV1 1LH, United Kingdom
Tel.: (44) 1902721212
Web Site: http://www.ovivowater.co.uk
Water Treatment & Systems Engineering, Construction & Maintenance Services
N.A.I.C.S.: 237110

Subsidiary (US):

Ovivo USA, LLC (3)
4246 River Boat Rd Ste 300, Salt Lake City, UT 84123
Tel.: (801) 931-3111
Web Site: http://www.ovivowater.us
Water & Wastewater Treatment Equipment Mfr, Facilities Construction & Maintenance Services
N.A.I.C.S.: 221310

Subsidiary (Domestic):

ALAR Engineering Corporation (4)
9651 196th St, Mokena, IL 60448
Tel.: (708) 479-6100
Web Site: http://www.alarcorp.com
Rev.: $2,400,000
Emp.: 30
Consumer Electronics & Appliances Rental
N.A.I.C.S.: 532210
Vickey Hansen (Pres)

Unit (Domestic):

Ovivo USA, LLC - Houston (4)
1322 Space Park Dr, Houston, TX 77058
Tel.: (281) 480-7955
Web Site: http://www.ovivowater.us
Water & Wastewater Treatment Equipment Mfr, Facilities Construction & Maintenance Services
N.A.I.C.S.: 221310

Subsidiary (Non-US):

Ramivo Manufacturing Hungary Kft. (3)
Szabadsag utca 91, Tamasi, 7090, Hungary
Tel.: (36) 74 573 961
Web Site: http://www.ramivo.hu
Service Industry Machinery Mfr
N.A.I.C.S.: 333310
Janos Szabadkai (Gen Mgr)

Subsidiary (US):

Wastech Controls & Engineering, Inc. (3)
21201 Itasca St, Chatsworth, CA 91311
Tel.: (818) 998-3500
Web Site: http://www.wastechengineering.com
Sales Range: $1-9.9 Million
Emp.: 22
Engineering Services Whol Professional Equipment

N.A.I.C.S.: 541330

SKIPPER LIMITED
3A Loudon Street 1st Floor, Kolkata, 700017, India
Tel.: (91) 33 2289 2327
Web Site: http://www.skipperlimited.com
Year Founded: 1981
Metal & PVC Pipe, Tube & Related Products Mfr & Distr
N.A.I.C.S.: 331210
Sajan Kumar Bansal (Mng Dir)

SKISTAR AB
Box 7322, SE-103 90, Stockholm, Sweden
Tel.: (46) 28088050
Web Site: http://www.skistar.com
SKIS:B—(OMX)
Rev.: $403,082,319
Assets: $820,571,150
Liabilities: $494,258,994
Net Worth: $326,312,156
Earnings: $37,631,572
Emp.: 1,402
Fiscal Year-end: 08/31/23
Alpine Ski Resorts Owner & Operator
N.A.I.C.S.: 713920
Eivor Andersson (Chm)

Subsidiaries:

Fjallinvest AB (1)
Salfjallsgarden, 780 67, Salen, Dalarna, Sweden
Tel.: (46) 28088060
Sales Range: $300-349.9 Million
Emp.: 700
Recreational Services
N.A.I.C.S.: 713990

Fjallmedia AB (1)
Salfjallsgarden, 780 67, Salen, Dalarna, Sweden
Tel.: (46) 28084144
Web Site: http://www.skistar.com
Sales Range: $25-49.9 Million
Emp.: 35
Resort Advertising Services
N.A.I.C.S.: 541850

Hemsedal Skisenter A/S (1)
Skiheisvegen 1, 3560, Hemsedal, Norway
Tel.: (47) 32055030
Web Site: http://www.skistar.com
Ski Resort
N.A.I.C.S.: 713920

Subsidiary (Domestic):

Hemsedal Booking AS (2)
Skiheisveien 1, 3560, Hemsedal, Buskerud, Norway
Tel.: (47) 32055300
Web Site: http://www.skistar.com
Sales Range: $25-49.9 Million
Emp.: 50
Skiing Facilities & Support Services
N.A.I.C.S.: 713920

Knettsetra AS (1)
In the middle of Trysilfjellet, 2420, Trysil, Norway
Tel.: (47) 62451550
Web Site: https://www.knettsetra.no
Restaurant Services
N.A.I.C.S.: 722511

Salens Hogfjallshotell AB (1)
Cluvers vag 35, 780 67, Salen, Sweden
Tel.: (46) 28087000
Web Site: https://www.en.hogis.se
Hotel & Resort Services
N.A.I.C.S.: 721110
Thommy Backner (CEO)

SkiStar Norge AS (1)
Skiheisveien 1 Hemsedal, 3560, Hemsedal, Buskerud, Norway
Tel.: (47) 32055060
Sales Range: $75-99.9 Million
Emp.: 300
Recreational Services
N.A.I.C.S.: 561990

Subsidiary (Domestic):

Trysilfjellet Alpin AS (2)
Trysil Turistsenter, 2420, Trysil, Hedmark, Norway
Tel.: (47) 62452000
Web Site: http://www.skistar.com
Sales Range: $25-49.9 Million
Emp.: 35
Skiing Facilities & Support Services
N.A.I.C.S.: 713920
Gry Hammer Odden (Mgr)

Subsidiary (Domestic):

Trysilfjellet Golf AS (3)
Golfvegen 1, 2420, Trysil, Hedmark, Norway
Web Site: http://www.trysilgolf.no
Sales Range: $50-74.9 Million
Emp.: 10
Golf Course Operation Services
N.A.I.C.S.: 713910

Vemdalens Sportsaffarer & Skiduthyrning AB (1)
Vemdalsskalet, 840 92, Vemdalen, Harjedalen, Sweden
Tel.: (46) 684 151 00
Sports & Skiing Supplies
N.A.I.C.S.: 423910

SKJERN BANK AS
Banktorvet 3, 6900, Skjern, Denmark
Tel.: (45) 96821333
Web Site: https://www.skjernbank.dk
Year Founded: 1906
SKJE—(CSE)
Rev.: $36,799,352
Assets: $1,624,704,172
Liabilities: $1,427,432,970
Net Worth: $197,271,201
Earnings: $21,738,797
Emp.: 195
Fiscal Year-end: 12/31/22
Banking Services
N.A.I.C.S.: 522110
Hans Ladekjaer Jeppesen (Chm)

SKLADOVA TEHNIKA AD-GORNA ORYAHOVITSA
25 Sveti Knyaz Boris I Str, 5100, Gorna Oryahovitsa, Bulgaria
Tel.: (359) 618 60576
Web Site: http://www.st-bg.com
Year Founded: 1916
Material Handling Equipment Mfr
N.A.I.C.S.: 339999

SKLAVENITIS J&S S.A.
80 Kifissou Ave 12132, Peristeri, Greece
Tel.: (30) 210 512 4990
Supermarket Operator
N.A.I.C.S.: 445110
Maria S. Sklavenitou (Chm)

SKM EGG PRODUCTS EXPORTS (INDIA) LIMITED
185 Chennimalai Rd, Erode, 638001, Tamil Nadu, India
Tel.: (91) 4242262963
Web Site: http://www.skmegg.com
Year Founded: 1996
Bakery Products Mfr
N.A.I.C.S.: 311813
SKM Shree Shivkumar (CEO)

Subsidiaries:

SKM Europe BV (1)
Ridderplantsoen 7, 3523 HV, Utrecht, Netherlands
Tel.: (31) 30 232 58 42
Web Site: http://www.skmeurope.nl
Emp.: 5
Egg Product Mfr & Whslr
N.A.I.C.S.: 311999
Branko Klawer (Dir-Sls & New Product Dev)

SKM Japan Co., Ltd (1)
2-42-7 Matsubara YS Building 5F, Setagaya, Tokyo, 156-0043, Japan

Tel.: (81) 3 6304 7313
Web Site: http://www.skmjapan.jp
Emp.: 8
Egg Product Whslr
N.A.I.C.S.: 424420
Mac Ohi *(Pres)*

SKO-ENERGO S.R.O.
Tr Vaclava Klementa 869, 293 60, Mlada Boleslav, Czech Republic
Tel.: (420) 326817477
Web Site: http://www.sko-energo.cz
Sales Range: $75-99.9 Million
Emp.: 300
Utility Construction & Energy Solution Services
N.A.I.C.S.: 237120
Uorel Jaromir *(CEO)*

SKODA TRANSPORTATION A.S.
Emila Skody 2922/1, 301 00, Plzen, Czech Republic
Tel.: (420) 378186666   CZ
Web Site: http://www.skoda.cz
Commercial Transportation Engineering Services
N.A.I.C.S.: 541330
Tomas Krsek *(Chm)*

Subsidiaries:

Transtech Oy   (1)
Elektroniikkatie 2, FI-90590, Oulu, Finland
Tel.: (358) 8 870 6900
Web Site: http://www.transtech.fi
Train Mfr
N.A.I.C.S.: 336510
Lasse Orre *(CEO)*

SKODA VENTURES, INC.
Posada Del Rey Via Italia, Panama, Panama
Tel.: (507) 6725 8263   NV
Year Founded: 2012
Apparel & Accessories Retailer
N.A.I.C.S.: 424350
Ronald Guillermo *(Pres, CEO, CFO, Principal Acctg Officer & Treas)*

SKONEC ENTERTAINMENT CO., LTD.
7-9F Chosun-naehwa B/D 577 Seolleung-ro, Gangnam-gu, Seoul, Korea (South)
Tel.: (82) 24583742
Web Site: https://www.skonec.com
Year Founded: 2002
276040—(KRS)
Rev.: $367,081
Assets: $22,798,165
Liabilities: $3,254,043
Net Worth: $19,544,122
Earnings: ($3,411,960)
Emp.: 65
Fiscal Year-end: 12/31/22
Software Development Services
N.A.I.C.S.: 541511
Dae Shil Hwang *(CEO)*

SKOPSKI PAZAR A.D. SKOPJE
no 7 st Gjorche Petrov, 1000, Skopje, North Macedonia
Tel.: (389) 22404300
Web Site:
  https://www.skopskipazar.com.mk
Year Founded: 1952
SPAZ—(MAC)
Rev.: $5,176,285
Assets: $54,193,997
Liabilities: $18,226,622
Net Worth: $35,967,375
Earnings: $444,005
Fiscal Year-end: 12/31/19
Supermarket Services
N.A.I.C.S.: 445110

SKOVIN AD
15th Korpus nb 3, 1000, Skopje, North Macedonia
Tel.: (389) 23145701
Web Site: http://www.skovin.com.mk
Year Founded: 1979
SKOV—(MAC)
Rev.: $2,363,639
Assets: $2,992,199
Liabilities: $9,170,182
Net Worth: ($6,177,983)
Earnings: ($2,202,598)
Fiscal Year-end: 12/31/19
Wine Mfr
N.A.I.C.S.: 312130

Subsidiaries:

Skovin AG   (1)
Oberbilker Allee 9, 40215, Dusseldorf, Germany
Tel.: (49) 21194219262
Winery Product Retailer
N.A.I.C.S.: 445320

Skovin S.R.O.   (1)
28 Regiment 44, 100 00, Prague, Czech Republic
Tel.: (420) 775106156
Web Site: http://www.skovin.cz
Winery Product Retailer
N.A.I.C.S.: 445320
Milan Beronja *(Mgr-IT)*

SKP RESOURCES BHD
Level 7 Menara Milenium Jalan Damanlela, Pusat Bandar Damansara Damansara Heights, 50490, Kuala Lumpur, Malaysia
Tel.: (60) 320849000
Web Site: https://www.skpres.com
Year Founded: 1974
SKPRES—(KLS)
Rev.: $532,283,175
Assets: $273,765,503
Liabilities: $89,993,862
Net Worth: $183,771,640
Earnings: $29,739,259
Emp.: 7,983
Fiscal Year-end: 03/31/23
Television Mfr
N.A.I.C.S.: 334220
Poh San Gan *(Exec Dir)*

Subsidiaries:

Bangi Plastics Sdn. Bhd.   (1)
Lot 1804 Jalan Lengkok Emas Kawasan Perindustrian, 71800, Nilai, Negeri Sembilan, Malaysia
Tel.: (60) 67990010
Plastic Mfr
N.A.I.C.S.: 325211

Plastictecnic (M) Sdn. Berhad   (1)
Lot 1 Jalan P/2A Kawasan Perusahaan PKT 1, 43650, Bandar Baru Bangi, Selangor, Malaysia
Tel.: (60) 389256950
Web Site: https://www.plastictecnic.com
Plastic Mfr
N.A.I.C.S.: 325211

Sun Tong Seng Mould-Tech Sdn. Bhd.   (1)
16 Jalan P/8, MIEL Industrial Area Bangi New Town, 43650, Bangi, Selangor Darul Ehsan, Malaysia
Tel.: (60) 389258132
Web Site: https://www.suntongseng.com
Plastic & Pheonolic Material Mfr
N.A.I.C.S.: 325211
Gan Poh San *(Mng Dir)*

Syarikat Sin Kwang Plastic Industries Sdn. Bhd.   (1)
421 4th Miles Jalan Kluang, 83000, Batu Pahat, Johor Darul Takzim, Malaysia
Tel.: (60) 74325707
Plastic Contract Mfr
N.A.I.C.S.: 326199

SKP SECURITIES LIMITED
1702-03 BioWonder 789 Anandapur EM Bypass, Jawaharlal Nehru Road, Kolkata, 700107, India
Tel.: (91) 3366777000
Web Site:
  https://www.skpsecurities.com
531169—(BOM)
Rev.: $2,240,165
Assets: $7,593,609
Liabilities: $3,548,816
Net Worth: $4,044,793
Earnings: $371,956
Emp.: 45
Fiscal Year-end: 03/31/23
Securities Brokerage Services
N.A.I.C.S.: 523150
Naresh Pachisia *(Founder & Mng Dir)*

SKRR EXPLORATION INC.
228 - 1122 Mainland Street, Vancouver, V6B 5L1, BC, Canada
Tel.: (250) 558-8340   BC
Web Site: https://www.skrr.ca
Year Founded: 2006
B041—(DEU)
Assets: $4,221,121
Liabilities: $159,628
Net Worth: $4,061,494
Earnings: ($706,607)
Fiscal Year-end: 04/30/24
Investment Services
N.A.I.C.S.: 523999
Sherman Dahl *(Pres)*

SKS TECHNOLOGIES GROUP LIMITED
700 Spencer St, Melbourne, 3003, VIC, Australia
Tel.: (61) 392895000
Web Site: https://www.sks.com.au
Year Founded: 1856
SKS—(ASX)
Rev.: $91,157,574
Assets: $39,893,660
Liabilities: $31,783,598
Net Worth: $8,110,063
Earnings: $4,423,483
Emp.: 739
Fiscal Year-end: 06/30/24
Electric & Industrial Products Mfr & Distr
N.A.I.C.S.: 335132
Peter Jinks *(Chm & Mng Dir)*

Subsidiaries:

Stokes Appliance Parts   (1)
Unit 2 170 Rooks Road, Nunawading, 3131, VIC, Australia
Tel.: (61) 398727474
Web Site: https://www.stokesap.com.au
Sales Range: $50-74.9 Million
Emp.: 100
Appliance Spare Parts Distr
N.A.I.C.S.: 423690

Stokes Appliance Parts   (1)
Unit 2 170 Rooks Rd, Nunawading, 3131, VIC, Australia
Tel.: (61) 398727474
Web Site: https://www.stokesap.com.au
Sales Range: $50-74.9 Million
Emp.: 12
Heating Equipment Mfr
N.A.I.C.S.: 333414
David Marinucci *(Gen Mgr)*

SKSHU PAINT CO., LTD
No 518 Liyuan North Avenue, Licheng District, Putian, 351100, Fujian, China
Tel.: (86) 5942886205
Web Site: http://www.3treespaint.com
Year Founded: 2002
603737—(SHG)
Rev.: $1,591,906,516
Assets: $1,930,347,034
Liabilities: $1,583,120,453
Net Worth: $347,226,582
Earnings: $46,263,625
Emp.: 100

Fiscal Year-end: 12/31/22
Coating Product Mfr & Distr
N.A.I.C.S.: 325510
Jie Hong *(Chm & Gen Mgr)*

SKUE SPAREBANK
Jordeshagen 5, Nesbyen, 3540, Oslo, Norway
Tel.: (47) 35028400
Web Site:
  https://www.skuesparebank.no
Year Founded: 1842
SKUE—(EUR)
Commercial Banking Services
N.A.I.C.S.: 522110
Hans Kristian Glesne *(CEO)*

SKW EAST ASIA LIMITED
Sanbancho KS Building 6f Sanbancho 2, Chiyoda Ku, Tokyo, 102 0075, Japan
Tel.: (81) 332887351
Web Site: http://www.skwea.co.jp
Year Founded: 1986
Sales Range: $1-9.9 Million
Emp.: 11
Metallurgical Products & Natural Food Products Mfr
N.A.I.C.S.: 332111
Walter Bolzer *(Chm)*

SKW STAHL-METALLURGIE HOLDING AG
Prinzregentenstr 68, 81675, Munich, Germany
Tel.: (49) 89 5998923 0
Web Site: http://www.skw-steel.com
Rev.: $284,618,723
Assets: $168,155,587
Liabilities: $175,339,153
Net Worth: ($7,183,566)
Earnings: $1,213,432
Emp.: 591
Fiscal Year-end: 12/31/17
Desulphurization & Secondary Metallurgy Solutions
N.A.I.C.S.: 325998

Subsidiaries:

Affimex Cored Wire S. de R.L. de C.V.   (1)
Carretera a Minatitlan Kilometro 2 Tapeyxtles, 28239, Manzanillo, Colima, Mexico
Tel.: (52) 314 334 1708
Web Site: http://www.affimex.net
Cored Wire Mfr
N.A.I.C.S.: 333992

Affival KK   (1)
Tamaki Building 7F 2-15-17 Shinbashi, Minato-ku, Tokyo, 105-0004, Japan
Tel.: (81) 33 508 86 82
Steel Product Distr
N.A.I.C.S.: 423510

Affival Korea Co. Ltd.   (1)
4th Floor Dongyang Building 200-6, Nonhyeon-dong Gangnam, Seoul, 135-826, Korea (South)
Tel.: (82) 2 34 52 58 11
Web Site: http://www.affival.com
Liquid Steel Treatment Services
N.A.I.C.S.: 331513

Affival S.A.   (1)
70 Rue Del Abbaye, PO Box 22, F59730, Solesmes, France
Tel.: (33) 327736060
Web Site: http://www.affivalinc.com
Sales Range: $50-74.9 Million
Emp.: 130
Mfr of Industrial Wire
N.A.I.C.S.: 331222

Subsidiary (US):

Affival Inc.   (2)
6400 Sheridan Dr Ste 138, Williamsville, NY 14221-4842
Tel.: (716) 558-0222
Web Site: http://www.affival.com

SKW STAHL-METALLURGIE HOLDING AG

SKW Stahl-Metallurgie Holding AG—(Continued)
Sales Range: $25-49.9 Million
Emp.: 70
Mfr of Industrial Wire
N.A.I.C.S.: 331222

ESM Group, Inc. (1)
300 Corporate Pkwy 118 N, Amherst, NY 14226-1212
Tel.: (716) 446-8914
Web Site: http://www.esmgroupinc.com
Sales Range: $25-49.9 Million
Emp.: 22
Desulfurization & Secondary Metallurgy Services, Caster Segment Maintenance & Equipment Design Services; Supplier of Specialty Magnesium
N.A.I.C.S.: 333519

Division (Domestic):

ESM Group, Inc. - Ashland Caster Division (2)
100 Armco Rd, Ashland, KY 41101
Tel.: (606) 326-9255
Desulfurizing Reagent Mfr
N.A.I.C.S.: 325998

Subsidiary (Non-US):

ESM Tianjin Co. Ltd. (2)
28-H Yun Xiang Building 72-74 XI Kang Road, He Ping District, Tianjin, 300074, China
Tel.: (86) 10 84983735
Fabricated Metal Product Mfr & Distr
N.A.I.C.S.: 332312

SKW Metallurgy Sweden AB (1)
Stockviksvagen 20, 854 67, Sundsvall, Sweden
Tel.: (46) 60134200
Web Site: http://www.skw-metallurgie.eu
Metal Products Mfr
N.A.I.C.S.: 332999

SKW Quab Chemicals Inc. (1)
Park 80 W 250 Pehle Ave Ste 308, Saddle Brook, NJ 07663
Tel.: (201) 556-0300
Web Site: http://www.quab.com
Chemical Products Mfr
N.A.I.C.S.: 325998
Karen O'Neill (Dir-Mktg & Logistics)

Tecnosulfur Sistema de Tratamento de Metais Liquidos S/A (1)
Avenida Luis Paulo Franco 603, Belo Horizonte, 30320-570, Brazil
Tel.: (55) 31 3286 8004
Chemical Products Mfr
N.A.I.C.S.: 325998
Michael Ulegh (Gen Mgr)

SKY & SPACE GLOBAL LTD.
1202 Hay Street, West Perth, 6005, WA, Australia
Tel.: (61) 865562400
Web Site: http://www.skyandspace.global
Telecommunication Services
N.A.I.C.S.: 517112
Meir Moalem (CEO & Mng Dir)

SKY CHINAFORTUNE HOLDINGS GROUP LIMITED
Room 1512 15/F New World Tower 1 16-18 Queens Road, Central, China (Hong Kong)
Tel.: (852) 21673333   HK
Web Site: http://www.skychinafortune.com
Rev.: $3,087,490
Assets: $89,815,090
Liabilities: $14,590,715
Net Worth: $75,224,376
Earnings: ($663,880)
Emp.: 31
Fiscal Year-end: 12/31/19
Holding Company; Animal Feed Wholesale Trade Distr; Real Estate Investment, Property Management & Brokerage Services
N.A.I.C.S.: 551112

SKY DIGITAL STORES CORP.
8/F South Block Yuan Xing Technology Building, 1 Song Ping Shan Road High-tech Park, Nanshan District, Shenzhen, China
Tel.: (86) 755 82718088   NV
Web Site: http://www.skyc.cc
Year Founded: 2006
Sales Range: $50-74.9 Million
Emp.: 388
Mobile Phones & Electronic Products Retailer
N.A.I.C.S.: 449210

SKY E&M CO., LTD.
2423-16 Geumsan-ro Chubu-myeon, Geumsan-gun, Daejeon, 306-230, Chungcheong, Korea (South)
Tel.: (82) 428258630
Web Site: http://www.leechem.net
131100—(KRS)
Rev.: $56,806,848
Assets: $112,803,531
Liabilities: $51,989,712
Net Worth: $60,813,819
Earnings: ($1,879,227)
Fiscal Year-end: 12/31/22
Chemical Products Mfr
N.A.I.C.S.: 325998

SKY GOLD CORP.
1240-789 W Pender St, Vancouver, V6C 1H2, BC, Canada
Tel.: (604) 683-3995   BC
Web Site: https://www.skygoldcorp.com
Year Founded: 1994
SKYG—(OTCIQ)
Rev.: $14,865
Assets: $4,489,070
Liabilities: $55,178
Net Worth: $4,433,892
Earnings: ($993,549)
Fiscal Year-end: 06/30/21
Investment Services
N.A.I.C.S.: 523999
John Parker Masters (CFO & Sec)

SKY GREENLAND APS
Ny Lufthavnsvej 100, Norresundby, Aalborg, 9400, Denmark
Tel.: (45) 38 30 66 40
Airline Operator
N.A.I.C.S.: 488119

SKY ICT PUBLIC COMPANY LIMITED
55 A A Capital Ratchada Building 5th-7th Floor, Ratchadapisek Road Dindaeng, Bangkok, 10400, Thailand
Tel.: (66) 20297888
Web Site: https://skyict.co.th
Year Founded: 1997
SKY—(THA)
Rev.: $120,242,514
Assets: $335,391,474
Liabilities: $197,605,871
Net Worth: $137,785,603
Earnings: $15,932,683
Fiscal Year-end: 12/31/23
Computer Systems Integration & IT Services
N.A.I.C.S.: 541512
Siriwat Tovachirakul (Chm)

SKY INDUSTRIES LTD.
1101 Universal Majestic, Ghatkopar Mankhurd Link Road Chembur West, Mumbai, 400 043, India
Tel.: (91) 2267137900
Web Site: https://www.skycorp.in
526479—(BOM)
Rev.: $9,020,538
Assets: $7,110,137
Liabilities: $2,753,024
Net Worth: $4,357,113

Earnings: $212,002
Emp.: 70
Fiscal Year-end: 03/31/23
Woven Fabrics Mfr
N.A.I.C.S.: 313210
Shailesh S. Shah (Mng Dir)

SKY ISRAEL PRIVATE EQUITY FUND
20 Lincoln St 28th Floor, Tel Aviv, 6713412, Israel
Tel.: (972) 35652219   IL
Web Site: http://www.skyfund.co.il
Year Founded: 2005
Private Equity
N.A.I.C.S.: 523999
Nir Digan (Founder & Mng Partner)

Subsidiaries:

Aztek Technologies (1984) Ltd. (1)
Hama ayan 1, Modi'in-Maccabim-Re'ut, 7171002, Israel
Tel.: (972) 9181111
Web Site: http://www.aztek.co.il
Software Publisher
N.A.I.C.S.: 513210
Mark Blank (CEO)

Subsidiary (Domestic):

NGSoft Corporation (2)
HaHarash St 4 Building B 1st Floor, Hod Hasharon, 45240, Israel
Tel.: (972) 72 2754500
Web Site: http://www.ngsoft.com
Emp.: 150
Software Development Services
N.A.I.C.S.: 541511
Ronel Mor (Chief Creative Officer)

SKY LIGHT HOLDINGS LTD.
Rm 1910-12 19/F Kwong Sang Hong Centre 151-153 Hoi Bun Road Kwun Tong, Kowloon, China (Hong Kong)
Tel.: (852) 27908343   Ky
Web Site: http://www.sky-light.com.hk
Year Founded: 2000
3882—(HKG)
Rev.: $53,177,318
Assets: $69,060,630
Liabilities: $32,107,305
Net Worth: $36,953,325
Earnings: ($3,980,168)
Emp.: 860
Fiscal Year-end: 12/31/22
Holding Company
N.A.I.C.S.: 551112
Terry Wing Fong Tang (Founder, Chm & CEO)

Subsidiaries:

Sky Light Electronics (Shenzhen) Limited (1)
No 8 9 Building Antuoshan Xinsha Road Shajing Bao'An, High-tech Industrial Park, Shenzhen, 518104, Guangdong, China
Tel.: (86) 75527511234
Camera Equipment Mfr & Distr
N.A.I.C.S.: 333310

Sky Light Technology (Heyuan) Limited (1)
XinYongyi Building XinYongyi Hi-Tech Ind Park Hi-Tech 3 Rd, Hi-Tech Zone, Heyuan, 517000, Guangdong, China
Tel.: (86) 7622859666
Camera Equipment Mfr & Distr
N.A.I.C.S.: 333310
Yongmou Wu (Gen Mgr)

SKY METALS LIMITED
2 Hawthorn Place, PO Box 8620, Orange, 2800, NSW, Australia
Tel.: (61) 263601587
Web Site: https://skymetals.com.au
SKY—(ASX)
Rev.: $14,022
Assets: $12,298,178
Liabilities: $851,690
Net Worth: $11,446,488
Earnings: ($1,354,052)

INTERNATIONAL PUBLIC

Fiscal Year-end: 06/30/24
Crude Petroleum Extraction Services
N.A.I.C.S.: 211120
Norman Alfred Seckold (Chm)

SKY NETWORK TELEVISION LIMITED
10 Panorama Road Mt Wellington, Auckland, 1060, New Zealand
Tel.: (64) 95799999
Web Site: https://www.skytv.co.nz
Year Founded: 1990
SKT—(ASX)
Rev.: $521,098,126
Assets: $504,484,912
Liabilities: $199,992,726
Net Worth: $304,492,186
Earnings: $34,185,574
Emp.: 900
Fiscal Year-end: 06/30/21
Television Broadcasting
N.A.I.C.S.: 516120
Chris Major (Dir-External Affairs)

Subsidiaries:

Non Trading PS Limited (1)
10 Niall Burgess Rd Mt Wellington, PO Box 22897, Otahuhu, Auckland, 1640, New Zealand
Tel.: (64) 95257310
Web Site: http://www.osb.co.nz
Emp.: 26
Television Broadcasting Services
N.A.I.C.S.: 516120
Mick Tindill (Gen Mgr)

Screen Enterprises Limited (1)
Symonds St, PO Box 8434, Auckland, 1150, New Zealand
Tel.: (64) 800232876
Web Site: http://www.fatso.co.nz
Online Movie Rental Services
N.A.I.C.S.: 516210
Brent Elston (Mgr-Customer Svc)

Sky Network Services Limited (1)
10 Panorama Road, PO Box 68700, Mount Wellington, Auckland, 1060, New Zealand
Tel.: (64) 800244566
Web Site: http://www.igloo.co.nz
Television Broadcasting Services
N.A.I.C.S.: 516120

SKY ONE NETWORK (HOLDING) LTD.
Sky One Logistics Centre 7A Ho Tung Garden Ho Tung Bridge, Kwu Tung, Sheung Shui, New Territories, China (Hong Kong)
Tel.: (852) 35118120   HK
Web Site: http://www.skyone-china.com
Year Founded: 1999
Sales Range: $10-24.9 Million
Emp.: 200
Logistic Services
N.A.I.C.S.: 541614
Dicky Yiu Chung Suen (Co-Founder)

Subsidiaries:

Sky One Express (HK) Limited (1)
Hope Sea Ind Centre, Kowloon, China (Hong Kong) (100%)
Tel.: (852) 2244 5542
Web Site: http://www.skyone-china.com
Logistics Consulting Servies
N.A.I.C.S.: 541614

Sky One International Freight Limited (1)
Unit 2 8/F Yip Bldg 53-57 Kwai Fung Crescent, Kwai Chung, Hong Kong, China (Hong Kong) (51%)
Tel.: (852) 29056000
Web Site: http://www.skyonessi.com
Freight Forwarding & Logistics Consulting Services
N.A.I.C.S.: 541614

Subsidiary (Non-US):

Sky One SSI Logistics Limited (2)

AND PRIVATE COMPANIES

Room 1604 Block A Yingte Apartment 28
Xibahe Xili, Chaoyang District, Beijing,
100028, China
Tel.: (86) 10 64475070
Web Site: http://www.skyonessi.com
Freight Forwarding & Logistics Consulting
Services
N.A.I.C.S.: 541614

Sky One Logistics (HK) Limited (1)
7a Ho Tung Garden Ho Tung Bridge Kwu
Tung Sheung Shui, Hong Kong, China
(Hong Kong) (100%)
Tel.: (852) 3511 8120
Web Site: http://www.skyone-china.com
Emp.: 14
Logistics Consulting Servies
N.A.I.C.S.: 541614
Terry Lam (Office Mgr)

SKY PERFECT JSAT HOLDINGS INC.
Akasaka Intercity 8-1 Akasaka
1-chome, Minato-ku, Tokyo, 107-0052, Japan
Tel.: (81) 355711500
Web Site:
http://www.skyperfectjsat.space
Year Founded: 2007
9412—(TKS)
Rev.: $805,573,920
Assets: $2,679,766,710
Liabilities: $881,965,690
Net Worth: $1,797,801,020
Earnings: $117,254,790
Fiscal Year-end: 03/31/24
Holding Company
N.A.I.C.S.: 551112
Shinji Takada (Chm)

Subsidiaries:

JSAT International Inc. (1)
1401 H St NW Ste 220, Washington, DC 20005
Tel.: (202) 379-4400
Web Site: http://www.jsati.com
Satellite Telecommunication Services
N.A.I.C.S.: 517410

JSAT Mobile Communications Inc. (1)
Holland Hills Mori Tower 19F 5-11-2 Toranomon, Minato-ku, Tokyo, 105-0001, Japan
Tel.: (81) 364591170
Web Site: https://www.jsatmobile.com
Emp.: 22
Satellite Telecommunication Services
N.A.I.C.S.: 517410

SKY Perfect Broadcasting Corporation (1)
Akasaka Intercity AIR 1-8-1, Akasaka Minato-ku, Tokyo, 107-0052, Japan
Tel.: (81) 355717009
Web Site: http://www.sptvbroadcast.com
Television Broadcasting Services
N.A.I.C.S.: 334220

SKY Perfect Entertainment Corporation (1)
1-8-1 Akasaka, Minato-ku, Tokyo, 107-0052, Japan
Tel.: (81) 355717800
Web Site: https://www.skyperfectv.co.jp
Television Broadcasting Services
N.A.I.C.S.: 516120

SKY Perfect JSAT Corporation (1)
AKASAKA INTERCITY AIR 8-1 Akasaka 1-chome, Minato-ku, Tokyo, 107-0052, Japan
Tel.: (81) 355717800
Web Site: https://www.skyperfectjsat.space
Television Broadcasting
N.A.I.C.S.: 516120
Eiichi Yonekura (Pres)

Subsidiary (Domestic):

Wakuwaku Japan Corporation (2)
1-7-1 Akasaka, Minato-ku, Tokyo, 107-0052, Japan (100%)
Tel.: (81) 355716900
Web Site: http://www.wakuwakujapan.tv
Television Broadcasting Services
N.A.I.C.S.: 516120

Masafumi Kawanishi (Pres & CEO)

SKY RESORT INTERNATIONAL LIMITED
Lot 23 DBKK No 2 Industri E33 Mile 2 5 Jalan Tuaran Likas 8820, Kota Kinabalu, Sabah, Malaysia
Tel.: (60) 88 277484   DE
Year Founded: 2000
Investment Services
N.A.I.C.S.: 523999

SKY SILK AO
Dom Svyazi 2 Microdistrict, 130000, Aktau, Kazakhstan
Tel.: (7) 7292500000
Web Site: http://www.skytelecom.kz
Sales Range: $25-49.9 Million
Emp.: 110
Wireless & Satellite Telecommunications Services
N.A.I.C.S.: 517112

SKY SOLAR HOLDINGS, LTD.
Unit 417 4th Floor Tower Two Lippo Centre 89 Queensway Admiralty, Hong Kong Special Administrative Region, Hong Kong, China (Hong Kong)
Tel.: (852) 3960 6548   Ky
Web Site:
http://www.skysolarholdings.com
Year Founded: 2009
SKYS—(NASDAQ)
Rev.: $48,948,000
Assets: $405,354,000
Liabilities: $368,291,000
Net Worth: $37,063,000
Earnings: ($42,012,000)
Emp.: 135
Fiscal Year-end: 12/31/19
Holding Company;Solar Parks Owner & Operator; Electricity Distr
N.A.I.C.S.: 551112
Weili Su (Founder)

Subsidiaries:

Sky Capital America Inc. (1)
30 Morris Turnpike Ste 204, Short Hills, NJ 07078
Tel.: (973) 788-5050
Solar Electric Power Services
N.A.I.C.S.: 221114

Sky Solar Bulgaria Co., EOOD (1)
Of 1 fl 6 89 Al Malinov bul, 1715, Sofia, Bulgaria
Tel.: (359) 29756526
Solar Electric Power Services
N.A.I.C.S.: 221114

Sky Solar Japan K.K. (1)
TUG-I Bldg 9F Misakicho 2-4-1, Chiyodaku, Tokyo, 101-0061, Japan
Tel.: (81) 352753470
Solar Electric Power Services
N.A.I.C.S.: 221114

Sky Solar Renewable Energy (Wuxi) Co., Ltd. (1)
Suite 2503 Tower 1 Soho Tianshan Plaza 1717 Tianshan Road, Changning District, Shanghai, 200336, China
Tel.: (86) 2161638808
Solar Electric Power Services
N.A.I.C.S.: 221114

SKY-MOBI LIMITED
10th Floor Block B Union Building No 2 Zijinghua Road, Xihu District, Hangzhou, 310013, Zhejiang, China
Tel.: (86) 571 8777 0978   Ky
Web Site: http://www.sky-mobi.com
Year Founded: 2005
Mobile Application Platform & Game Publisher
N.A.I.C.S.: 513210

Subsidiaries:

Hangzhou Taiku Technologies Co., Ltd. (1)
1-520 No 1500 Wenyi West Road, Hangzhou, 310000, Zhejiang, China
Tel.: (86) 13588064084
Mobile Video Production Services
N.A.I.C.S.: 512110

SKYALP FINANSAL TEKNOLOJILER VE DANISMANLIK AS
Inkilap Mh Dr Adnan Buyukdeniz Cad No 4/2 Cessas Plaza Kat 3 D 7, Umraniye, 34676, Istanbul, Turkiye
Tel.: (90) 2169705757
Web Site: https://www.skyalp.com.tr
Year Founded: 1992
IDEAS—(IST)
Rev.: $1,244,512
Assets: $2,259,110
Liabilities: $728,411
Net Worth: $1,530,699
Earnings: $566,005
Fiscal Year-end: 12/31/22
Business Consulting Services
N.A.I.C.S.: 541611
Namik Kemal Gokalp (Chm)

SKYCHAIN TECHNOLOGIES INC.
1112 West Pender Street Unit 407, Vancouver, V6E 2S1, BC, Canada
Tel.: (604) 688-5464   BC
Web Site:
https://skychaintechnologiesinc.com
Year Founded: 1977
SKTCF—(OTCEM)
Assets: $1,214,769
Liabilities: $4,780,452
Net Worth: ($3,565,682)
Earnings: ($3,947,034)
Fiscal Year-end: 03/31/23
Mineral Exploration Services
N.A.I.C.S.: 212290
Bill Zhang (Pres & CEO)

SKYCITY ENTERTAINMENT GROUP LIMITED
Level 13 99 Albert Street, PO Box 6443, Wellesley Street, Auckland, New Zealand
Tel.: (64) 93636000
Web Site: http://www.skycity.co.nz
Year Founded: 1993
SKC—(ASX)
Rev.: $561,648,288
Assets: $2,017,388,894
Liabilities: $830,306,952
Net Worth: $1,187,081,942
Earnings: $112,254,594
Emp.: 3,784
Fiscal Year-end: 06/30/21
Entertainment Services
N.A.I.C.S.: 611620
Rob Hamilton (CFO)

Subsidiaries:

Horizon Tourism (New Zealand) Limited (1)
1 Tanglin Rd, Singapore, 247905, Singapore
Tel.: (65) 67388188
Casino Operator
N.A.I.C.S.: 713210
Angela Ong (Gen Mgr)

SKYCITY Adelaide Pty Limited (1)
North Terrace, Adelaide, 5000, SA, Australia
Tel.: (61) 882122811
Web Site: http://www.adelaidecasino.com.au
Sales Range: $600-649.9 Million
Emp.: 1,200
Casino Operator
N.A.I.C.S.: 713290
Richard Krawczyk (Mgr-Security & Surveillance)

SKYCITY ENTERTAINMENT GROUP LIMITED

SKYCITY Auckland Holdings Limited (1)
Level 6 Federal House 86 Federal Street Auckland Central, Auckland, 1010, New Zealand
Tel.: (64) 93636141
Web Site: http://www.skycityauckland.co.nz
Casino Operator
N.A.I.C.S.: 713210
Nigel Morrison (CEO)

SKYCITY Casino Management Limited (1)
Level 6 Federal House 86, Federal Street, Auckland, New Zealand
Tel.: (64) 93636141
Web Site:
http://www.skycityentertainmentgroup.com
Sales Range: $1-4.9 Billion
Emp.: 3,500
Casino Operator
N.A.I.C.S.: 713210
Nigel Morrison (CEO)

SKYCITY Darwin Pty Limited (1)
Gilruth Avenue Mindil Beach, Darwin, 0820, NT, Australia
Tel.: (61) 889438888
Web Site: http://www.skycitydarwin.com.au
Sales Range: $300-349.9 Million
Emp.: 700
Casino Operator
N.A.I.C.S.: 713290
Brandon Tan (VP-Intl Bus-Melbourne)

SKYCITY Investments Queenstown Limited (1)
Second Fl 16-24 Beach St, 9348, Queenstown, New Zealand
Tel.: (64) 34410400
Casino Operator
N.A.I.C.S.: 713210

SKYCITY Management Limited (1)
Victoria St, Auckland, 1010, New Zealand
Tel.: (64) 93636000
Web Site: http://www.skycityauckland.co.nz
Sales Range: $200-249.9 Million
Emp.: 2,000
Casino Operator
N.A.I.C.S.: 721120
Nigel Morrison (CEO)

Sky Tower Limited (1)
86 Federal Street, Level 6 Federal House, Auckland, New Zealand (100%)
Tel.: (64) 93636000
Web Site: http://www.skycityauckland.co.nz
Sales Range: $50-74.9 Million
Emp.: 25
Amusement & Recreation Industries
N.A.I.C.S.: 713990

Skycity Auckland Limited (1)
Cnr Victoria & Federal St, PO Box 90643, Auckland, 1010, New Zealand (100%)
Tel.: (64) 93636000
Web Site: http://www.skycityauckland.co.nz
Sales Range: $500-549.9 Million
Emp.: 3,000
Hotels & Motels
N.A.I.C.S.: 721110
Ejaaz Dean (Gen Mgr-Casino Ops)

Skycity Darwin Holdings Pty Limited (1)
L 3 3 Mgm Grand Darwin Gilruth Ave, Mindl Beach, Darwin, 0800, NT, Australia (100%)
Tel.: (61) 889438888
Web Site: http://www.skycitydarwin.com.au
Holding Company
N.A.I.C.S.: 551112
Callum Mallett (Gen Mgr)

Skycity Hamilton Limited (1)
346 Victoria St, PO Box 954, Hamilton, New Zealand (100%)
Tel.: (64) 78344900
Web Site: http://www.skycityhamilton.co.nz
Sales Range: $50-74.9 Million
Emp.: 100
Artists Athletes Entertainers & Public Figures Agents & Managers
N.A.I.C.S.: 711410
Michelle Baillie (Gen Mgr)

Skycity Investments Australia Limited (1)

SKYCITY ENTERTAINMENT GROUP LIMITED

Skycity Entertainment Group Limited—(Continued)
North Terrace, GPO Box 1918, Adelaide, 5001, SA, Australia
Tel.: (61) 882122811
Web Site: http://www.adelaidecasino.com.au
Emp.: 1,300
Investment Services
N.A.I.C.S.: 523999
David Christian *(Gen Mgr)*

Skycity Queenstown Casinos Limited (1)
Level 2 Stratton House 16-24 Beach Street, Queenstown, 9300, New Zealand **(60%)**
Tel.: (64) 34410400
Web Site: http://skycityqueenstown.co.nz
Amusement & Recreation Industries
N.A.I.C.S.: 713990

SKYFAME REALTY (HOLDINGS) LIMITED
Unit 1401 14/F Capital Centre, 151 Gloucester Road, Wanchai, China (Hong Kong)
Tel.: (852) 21112259
Web Site: http://www.tianyudc.com
0059—(HKG)
Rev.: $290,626,456
Assets: $3,431,372,069
Liabilities: $3,191,693,684
Net Worth: $239,678,384
Earnings: ($504,694,336)
Emp.: 839
Fiscal Year-end: 12/31/22
Hotel Services
N.A.I.C.S.: 561110
Pan Yu *(Chm & CEO)*

SKYFII LIMITED
Level 2 100 William Street, Woolloomooloo, Sydney, 2011, NSW, Australia
Tel.: (61) 281881188 AU
Web Site: http://www.skyfii.io
BEO—(ASX)
Rev.: $16,110,742
Assets: $13,737,705
Liabilities: $13,269,002
Net Worth: $468,703
Earnings: ($4,953,211)
Fiscal Year-end: 06/30/24
Data Analytic Services
N.A.I.C.S.: 518210
Wayne Arthur *(Founder & CEO)*

Subsidiaries:

CrowdVision Limited (1)
Mercury House 117 Waterloo Road, London, SE1 8UL, United Kingdom
Tel.: (44) 2890918200
Web Site: https://www.crowdvision.com
Video Production Services
N.A.I.C.S.: 512120

CrowdVision, Inc. (1)
2301 W Anderson Ln Ste 104, Austin, TX 78757
Web Site: https://www.crowdvision.com
Automated Pedestrian Analytic Services
N.A.I.C.S.: 518210

SKYHARBOUR RESOURCES LTD.
777 Dunsmuir Street - Suite 1610, Vancouver, V7Y 1K4, BC, Canada
Tel.: (604) 558-5847 BC
Web Site: https://www.skyharbourltd.com
Year Founded: 1981
SYHBF—(OTCQX)
Rev.: $7,408
Assets: $18,001,097
Liabilities: $363,691
Net Worth: $17,637,407
Earnings: ($2,174,247)
Fiscal Year-end: 03/31/22
Mineral Exploration Services
N.A.I.C.S.: 213114
James G. Pettit *(Chm)*

SKYLAND GROUP S.R.L.
Via Vincenzo Capelli 2, 20124, Milan, Italy
Tel.: (39) 0236646245 IT
Holding Company
N.A.I.C.S.: 551112

Subsidiaries:

Skyland Energy S.r.l. (1)
Via Vincenzo Capelli 2, 20124, Milan, Italy
Tel.: (39) 0236646245
Web Site: https://www.skyland.energy
Solar Electric Power Generation Services
N.A.I.C.S.: 221114

SKYLAND PETROLEUM PTY LIMITED
Level 5 56 Pitt Street, Sydney, 2000, NSW, Australia
Tel.: (61) 2 8823 3179
Year Founded: 2005
Petroleum Exploration Services
N.A.I.C.S.: 211120
Maruf R. *(Officer-Project Comm)*

SKYLIGHT HEALTH GROUP INC.
5045 Orbitor Dr, Mississauga, L4W 4Y4, ON, Canada
Web Site: https://www.skylighthealthgroup.com
Year Founded: 2014
SLHG—(NASDAQ)
Rev.: $10,280,119
Assets: $24,619,976
Liabilities: $2,999,350
Net Worth: $21,620,626
Earnings: ($7,417,076)
Emp.: 80
Fiscal Year-end: 12/31/20
Healthcare Services
N.A.I.C.S.: 621610
Prad Sekar *(Founder & CEO)*

Subsidiaries:

APEX Family Medicine LLC (1)
300 S Jackson St Ste 100, Denver, CO 80209
Tel.: (303) 321-6683
Web Site: http://www.apexfamilymedicine.com
Freestanding Ambulatory Surgical & Emergency Centers
N.A.I.C.S.: 621493
Renee Salazar *(Mgr-HR)*

SKYLINE INTERNATIONAL DEVELOPMENT INC.
90 Eglinton Avenue East Suite 800-150 Kingstreet Left Suite 2108, Toronto, M58 1G9, ON, Canada
Tel.: (416) 368-2565 ON
Web Site: http://www.skylineinvestments.com
Year Founded: 1998
Emp.: 35
Hospitality Real Estate Investment Trust
N.A.I.C.S.: 525990
Blake D. Lyon *(CEO)*

Subsidiaries:

2029861 Ontario Ltd. (1)
200 Victoria St, Toronto, M5B 1V8, ON, Canada
Tel.: (416) 368-2565
Investment Management Service
N.A.I.C.S.: 523940

SKYLINE INVESTMENT S.A.
Plac Unii 2 Pulawska Street, 02-566, Warsaw, Poland
Tel.: (48) 228591780
Web Site: https://www.skyline.com.pl
Year Founded: 1997
SKL—(WAR)
Rev.: $406,504
Assets: $19,329,776
Liabilities: $3,466,209
Net Worth: $15,863,567
Earnings: ($405,488)
Fiscal Year-end: 12/31/23
Financial Consulting Services
N.A.I.C.S.: 523940
Marek Wierzbowski *(Deputy Chm-Supervisory Bd)*

Subsidiaries:

Skyline Bio Sp. z.o.o. (1)
Al KEN 18 lok 3b, 02-797, Warsaw, Poland
Tel.: (48) 228591780
Fund Management Services
N.A.I.C.S.: 523150

Skyline Venture Sp. z o.o. (1)
Komisji Edukacji Narodowej 18, Warsaw, 02-797, Masovian, Poland
Tel.: (48) 228591780
Web Site: http://www.skyline.com.pl
Sales Range: $50-74.9 Million
Emp.: 11
Investment Management Service
N.A.I.C.S.: 523940
Jerzy Rey *(CEO)*

SKYLINE MILLARS LIMITED
4th floor Churchgate House 32-34 Veer Nariman Road Fort, Mumbai, 400 001, India
Tel.: (91) 2222047471
Web Site: https://www.skylinemillarsltd.com
505650—(BOM)
Rev.: $69,876
Assets: $3,244,758
Liabilities: $155,518
Net Worth: $3,089,239
Earnings: ($221,030)
Emp.: 6
Fiscal Year-end: 03/31/23
Construction Machinery Mfr
N.A.I.C.S.: 333120
Vinod N. Joshi *(Chm)*

SKYLINE VENTURES INDIA LIMITED
2nd Floor 35 Navodaya Colony Road 2 Banjara Hills, Hyderabad, 500034, Telangana, India
Tel.: (91) 4023555808
Web Site: http://www.svil.in
Year Founded: 1988
538919—(BOM)
Sales Range: Less than $1 Million
Real Estate Support Services
N.A.I.C.S.: 531390
Madhu Avalur *(Mng Dir)*

SKYMARK AIRLINES INC.
1-5-5 Haneda Airport, Ota-ku, Tokyo, 144-0041, Japan
Tel.: (81) 357088280
Web Site: http://www.skymark.co.jp
Airline Transportation Services
N.A.I.C.S.: 481111
Kimiyoshi Sakaki *(Auditor)*

SKYMASTS ANTENNAS LTD.
Equilibrium House Mansion Close, Moulton Park Industrial Estate, Northampton, NN3 6RU, United Kingdom
Tel.: (44) 1604494132
Web Site: http://www.skymasts.com
Sales Range: $10-24.9 Million
Emp.: 20
Antenna Mfr
N.A.I.C.S.: 334220
Danny Merrills *(Dir-Tech)*

SKYMISSION GROUP HOLDINGS LIMITED
RM 1101 Yuen Long Centre 55 Sau Fu St, Yuen Long, Hong Kong, New Territories, China (Hong Kong)
Tel.: (852) 24780198 Ky

INTERNATIONAL PUBLIC

Web Site: http://www.skymission.group
Year Founded: 1998
1429—(HKG)
Holding Company
N.A.I.C.S.: 551112
Yam Cheung Leung *(Chm)*

SKYMOONS TECHNOLOGY, INC.
41-13 Burim-ro 170beon-gil, Dongan-gu, Anyang, Gyeonggi-do, Korea (South)
Tel.: (82) 313455100
Web Site: https://skymoonstech.com
Year Founded: 1990
033790—(KRS)
Rev.: $8,748,448
Assets: $19,396,066
Liabilities: $1,348,042
Net Worth: $18,048,024
Earnings: $1,324,038
Emp.: 22
Fiscal Year-end: 12/31/22
Communication Equipment Mfr
N.A.I.C.S.: 334210
Pu Zhang *(CEO)*

SKYPAK SERVICE SPECIALIST LIMITED
1A J K Industrial Estate Off Mahakali Caves Road, Andheri E, Mumbai, 400093, Maharashtra, India
Tel.: (91) 22 67890303
Web Site: http://www.skypak.co.in
Rev.: $83,659
Assets: $861,750
Liabilities: $1,999,118
Net Worth: ($1,137,368)
Earnings: $66,846
Fiscal Year-end: 03/31/17
Transportation Services
N.A.I.C.S.: 488999

SKYSCAPE CAPITAL, INC.
320 Bay Street Suite 1600, Toronto, M5H 4A6, ON, Canada
Tel.: (416) 368-6200
SKY.P—(TSX)
Assets: $186,176
Liabilities: $101,658
Net Worth: $84,518
Earnings: ($124,641)
Fiscal Year-end: 12/31/20
Asset Management Services
N.A.I.C.S.: 523940
Roger Daher *(CEO, CFO & Sec)*

SKYSTAR BIO-PHARMACEUTICAL COMPANY
4/F Building B Chuangye Square No 48 Keji Road, Gaoxin District, Xi'an, Shaanxi, China
Tel.: (86) 2988193188 NV
Web Site: http://www.skystarbio-pharmaceutical.com
Year Founded: 1998
Sales Range: $25-49.9 Million
Emp.: 318
Veterinary Healthcare & Medical Care Products Mfr & Distr
N.A.I.C.S.: 325412

SKYTEL CO. LTD.
Skytel Plaza Building, Chinggiskhan Ave-9, Ulaanbaatar, 210603, Mongolia
Tel.: (976) 11318488
Web Site: http://www.skytel.mn
Year Founded: 1999
Mobile Phone Services
N.A.I.C.S.: 517112
Jung Nam Cho *(VP)*

Subsidiaries:

SkyNetworks Co. Ltd. (1)

AND PRIVATE COMPANIES — SLATE ASSET MANAGEMENT LP

4th Floor, Skytel Plaza Bldg, PO Box 2033, Chinggis Avenue-9, Ulaanbaatar, 211213, Mongolia
Tel.: (976) 11318840
Web Site: http://www.skynetworks.mn
Broadband Network Services
N.A.I.C.S.: 517810

SKYWAYS EXPRESS AB
PO Box 168, 190 46, Arlandastad, Sweden
Tel.: (46) 859513500
Web Site: http://www.skyways.se
Sales Range: $200-249.9 Million
Emp.: 450
Oil Transportation Services
N.A.I.C.S.: 481111

SKYWORLD DEVELOPMENT BERHAD
G Floor Block B Wisma NTP World Excella Business Park, Jalan Ampang Putra Ampang, 55100, Kuala Lumpur, Malaysia
Tel.: (60) 342709968 MY
Web Site:
https://www.skyworldgroup.com.my
Year Founded: 2006
SKYWLD—(KLS)
Rev.: $145,616,531
Assets: $329,872,558
Liabilities: $151,495,235
Net Worth: $178,377,323
Earnings: $22,541,934
Emp.: 242
Fiscal Year-end: 03/31/24
Real Estate Development Services
N.A.I.C.S.: 531190
Datuk Seri Ng Thien Phing (Founder)

SKYWORTH GROUP LIMITED
Room 1601-04 Westlands Centre 20 Westlands Road, Quarry Bay, China (Hong Kong)
Tel.: (852) 22904700
Web Site: https://www.skyworth.com
Year Founded: 1988
KYW0—(DEU)
Rev.: $7,406,263,846
Assets: $8,918,088,170
Liabilities: $5,886,685,866
Net Worth: $3,031,402,304
Earnings: $194,810,589
Emp.: 31,400
Fiscal Year-end: 12/31/22
Holding Company; Consumer Electronics & Appliances Mfr & Distr
N.A.I.C.S.: 551112
Wei Ping Lin (Exec Dir)

Subsidiaries:

PT. Skyworth Industry Indonesia (1)
East Jakarta Industrial Park Plot 5G Cikarang, Selatan, Bekasi, 17750, Jawa Barat, Indonesia (100%)
Tel.: (62) 218970462
Television & Washing Machine Mfr
N.A.I.C.S.: 335220

Shenzhen Chuangwei-RGB Electronics Co., Ltd.
22-24F East District Skyworth Semiconductor Design Bldg 18 High-Tech S, 4th Road Nanshan District, Shenzhen, China (100%)
Tel.: (86) 755 2601 0666
Web Site: http://www.skyworth.com
Television & Other Consumer Electronic Products Mfr
N.A.I.C.S.: 334310

Skyworth Electrical Appliances (Shenzhen) Co., Ltd. (1)
9/F South District Technology Bldg Skyworth Science Park, Tangtou Industrial Zone Shiyan, Baoan District, Shenzhen, 518108, China (100%)
Tel.: (86) 755 2601 0666
Web Site: http://www.skyworth.com
Consumer Electric Appliance Mfr & Whslr
N.A.I.C.S.: 335220

SL CORPORATION
32 Geomdan Industrial Complex-ro, Buk-gu, Daegu, Geomdan-dong, Korea (South)
Tel.: (82) 538568511
Web Site: https://www.slworld.com
Year Founded: 1954
005850—(KRS)
Rev.: $3,201,870,596
Assets: $2,248,565,533
Liabilities: $940,056,516
Net Worth: $1,308,509,017
Earnings: $118,677,459
Emp.: 4,600
Fiscal Year-end: 12/31/22
Automobile Part & Accessories Mfr
N.A.I.C.S.: 336110
Choong Kon Lee (Chm & CEO)

Subsidiaries:

HSL Electronics Corp. (1)
1033 Daecheon-dong, Dalseo-gu, Daegu, Korea (South)
Tel.: (82) 535848511
Automobile Mfr
N.A.I.C.S.: 336110

SL Alabama LLC (1)
2481 Airport Blvd, Alexander City, AL 35010
Tel.: (256) 397-8511
Emp.: 650
Automotive Spare Parts Distr
N.A.I.C.S.: 423120
Jack Coltrain (Plant Mgr)

SL Corporation - Ansan Plant (1)
1061 Singil-dong, Ansan, Gyunggido, Korea (South)
Tel.: (82) 3149885116
Automobile Mfr
N.A.I.C.S.: 336110

SL Corporation - Cheonan Plant (1)
50-9 Omok-li, SungGeo-eup, Cheonan, Chungnam, Korea (South)
Tel.: (82) 415558511
Automobile Mfr
N.A.I.C.S.: 336110

SL Corporation - Dague Plant (1)
887-4 Gumdan-dong, Buk-gu, Daegu, Korea (South)
Tel.: (82) 533828511
Automobile Mfr
N.A.I.C.S.: 336110

SL Corporation - Hwasung Plant (1)
549 Namyangman-ro, Ujeong-eup, Hwaseong, Gyeonggi, Korea (South)
Tel.: (82) 313518522
Automobile Mfr
N.A.I.C.S.: 336110

SL Corporation - Jillyang Plant (1)
77 Gongdan 6-ro, Jillyang-eup, Gyeongsan, Gyeongsangbuk, Korea (South)
Tel.: (82) 538568511
Automobile Mfr
N.A.I.C.S.: 336110

SL Corporation - Seosan Plant (1)
93 Suseoksaneop-ro, Seosan, Chungcheongnam, Korea (South)
Tel.: (82) 416678530
Automobile Mfr
N.A.I.C.S.: 336110

SL Corporation - Sungsan Plant (1)
28 Seongseo-ro 67-gil, Dalseo-gu, Daegu, Korea (South)
Tel.: (82) 535818511
Automobile Mfr
N.A.I.C.S.: 336110

SL Corporation - Ulsan Plant (1)
272-1 Yeompo-ro, Ulsan, Korea (South)
Tel.: (82) 522898522
Automobile Mfr
N.A.I.C.S.: 336110

SL Lightech Corporation (1)
1061 Singil-dong, Ansan, Gyunggido, Korea (South)
Tel.: (82) 31 489 8511
Automobile Spare Parts Mfr
N.A.I.C.S.: 336110

SL Lighting Co., Ltd. (1)
887-4 Gumdan-dong, Bukgu, Daegu, Korea (South)
Tel.: (82) 53 382 8511
Web Site: http://www.slworld.com
Automobile Spare Parts Mfr
N.A.I.C.S.: 336110

SL Seobong Co., Ltd (1)
50-8 Omok-li, SungGeo-eup, Cheonan, Chungnam, Korea (South)
Tel.: (82) 41 555 8511
Automotive Spare Parts Distr
N.A.I.C.S.: 423120

SL Sungsan Corporation (1)
100-18 Galsan-dong, Dalseogu, Daegu, Korea (South)
Tel.: (82) 53 581 8511
Automobile Spare Parts Mfr
N.A.I.C.S.: 336110

SL Tennessee, LLC. (1)
312 Frank L Diggs Dr, Clinton, TN 37716
Tel.: (865) 457-8511
Automotive Spare Parts Distr
N.A.I.C.S.: 423120

SL ENERGY CO., LTD.
49 Wongomae-ro 2beon-gil Giheung-gu, Giheung-gu, Yongin, Gyeonggi-do, Korea (South)
Tel.: (82) 312826425
Web Site:
http://www.semiconlight.com
Year Founded: 2007
214310—(KRS)
Rev.: $24,506,953
Assets: $87,201,612
Liabilities: $32,349,133
Net Worth: $54,852,478
Earnings: ($12,722,197)
Emp.: 77
Fiscal Year-end: 12/31/22
LED Lighting Mfr
N.A.I.C.S.: 334413
E. H. Park (Pres-LED Bus Dept)

SLA CREATION SA
18 rue Mado Robin, BP 148, 26905, Valence, Cedex, France
Tel.: (33) 4 75 82 10 20
Web Site: http://www.sla-paris.com
Sales Range: $1-9.9 Million
Cosmetics Mfr
N.A.I.C.S.: 325620
Serge Louis Alvarez (Chm & CEO)

SLACAN INDUSTRIES INC.
145 Roy Blvd, Brantford, N3R 7K1, ON, Canada
Tel.: (519) 758-8888
Web Site: http://www.slacan.com
Sales Range: $25-49.9 Million
Emp.: 200
Pole Line Hardware Designer & Mfr
N.A.I.C.S.: 335931
John McGraw (CFO)

SLAM EXPLORATION LTD.
295 Hutchinson Dr, Miramichi, E1V 6C7, NB, Canada
Tel.: (506) 623-8960 Ca
Web Site:
https://www.slamexploration.com
Year Founded: 1996
SXL—(TSXV)
Rev.: $186,764
Assets: $1,103,248
Liabilities: $419,869
Net Worth: $683,379
Earnings: ($474,684)
Fiscal Year-end: 01/31/24
Base Metals & Gold Exploration & Mining Services
N.A.I.C.S.: 212230
Michael R. Taylor (Pres & CEO)

SLANCHEV BRYAG AD
Tel.: (359) 55422510
SLB—(BUL)

887-4 Gumdan-dong, Bukgu, Daegu, Korea (South)
Tel.: (82) 53 382 8511
Web Site: http://www.slworld.com
Automobile Spare Parts Mfr
N.A.I.C.S.: 336110

Sales Range: Less than $1 Million
Resort Operator
N.A.I.C.S.: 721110
Margarita Pologova (Dir-Investor Relations)

SLANCHEV BRYAG HOLDING AD
Tel.: (359) 56820085
HSLB—(BUL)
Sales Range: Less than $1 Million
Asset Management Services
N.A.I.C.S.: 523940
Steliana Dolchinkova (Dir-Investor Relations)

SLANG WORLDWIDE, INC.
50 Carroll Street, Toronto, M4M 3G3, ON, Canada
Web Site: http://www.slangww.com
SLNG—(CNSX)
Rev.: $20,980,419
Assets: $84,181,665
Liabilities: $31,964,307
Net Worth: $52,217,358
Earnings: ($10,999,898)
Emp.: 99
Fiscal Year-end: 12/31/20
Cannabis Product Distr
N.A.I.C.S.: 424590
Peter Miller (Founder & Co-CEO)

SLANTCHO JSC
16 Dunav Str, 5250, Svishtov, Bulgaria
Tel.: (359) 63160165
Web Site: https://www.slantcho.com
Year Founded: 1979
SLR—(BUL)
Sales Range: Less than $1 Million
Instant Infant Food Mfr
N.A.I.C.S.: 311999
Stefka Nedelcheva (Dir-IR)

SLANTSE STARA ZAGORA TABAC JSC
1 Stamo Pulev Str, 6000, Stara Zagora, Bulgaria
Tel.: (359) 42230117
Web Site:
https://www.slancetabac.bg
Year Founded: 1875
SUN—(BUL)
Sales Range: Less than $1 Million
Tobacco Product Mfr
N.A.I.C.S.: 312230

SLATE ASSET MANAGEMENT LP
121 King Street W Suite 200, Toronto, M5h 3T9, ON, Canada
Tel.: (416) 644-4264 ON
Web Site: http://www.slateteam.com
Real Estate Investment & Trust Management Services
N.A.I.C.S.: 531390
Blair Welch (Co-Founder & Partner)

Subsidiaries:

Slate Capital Corp. (1)
200 Front Street West Suite 2400, Toronto, M5V 3K2, ON, Canada
Tel.: (416) 644-4264
Real Estate Investment Trust
N.A.I.C.S.: 525990
Blair Welch (CEO)

Slate Grocery REIT (1)
121 King St W Suite 200, Toronto, M5H 3T9, ON, Canada
Tel.: (416) 644-4264
Web Site: http://www.slateam.com
Rev.: $126,130,000
Assets: $1,323,554,000
Liabilities: $870,836,000
Net Worth: $452,718,000
Earnings: $41,605,000
Fiscal Year-end: 12/31/2020
Real Estate Investment Trust

SLATE ASSET MANAGEMENT LP

Slate Asset Management LP—(Continued)
N.A.I.C.S.: 525990
Joe Pleckaitis (CFO)

SLATE OFFICE REIT
121 King Street West Suite 200, Toronto, M5H 3T9, ON, Canada
Tel.: (416) 644-4264
Web Site: https://www.slateam.com
Year Founded: 2012
SOT.UN—(TSX)
Rev.: $164,924,525
Assets: $1,308,532,851
Liabilities: $828,493,973
Net Worth: $480,038,878
Earnings: $47,782,351
Fiscal Year-end: 12/31/19
Real Estate Investment Services
N.A.I.C.S.: 523999
Blair Welch (Founder)

Subsidiaries:

Yew Grove REIT plc (1)
1st Floor 57 Fitzwilliam Square, Dublin, 2 D02 CP02, Ireland
Tel.: (353) 14853950
Web Site: http://www.ygreit.com
Rev.: $14,682,499
Assets: $190,081,520
Liabilities: $53,006,156
Net Worth: $137,075,363
Earnings: $8,607,597
Emp.: 12
Fiscal Year-end: 12/31/2020
Real Estate Investment Trust Services
N.A.I.C.S.: 531190
Jonathan Laredo (CEO)

SLATINSKA BANKA D.D.
Vladimira Nazora 2, 33520, Virovitica, Croatia
Tel.: (385) 33637000
Web Site: https://www.slatinska-banka.hr
Year Founded: 1992
SNBA—(ZAG)
Rev.: $10,758,362
Assets: $259,268,131
Liabilities: $231,501,269
Net Worth: $27,766,862
Earnings: $993,487
Emp.: 179
Fiscal Year-end: 12/31/23
Banking Services
N.A.I.C.S.: 522110
Angelina Horvat (Chm-Mgmt Bd)

SLAVE LAKE ZINC CORP.
207 St Patricks Ave, North Vancouver, V7L 3N3, BC, Canada
Tel.: (604) 396-5762
Web Site: https://www.zinccorp.ca
SLZNF—(OTCIQ)
Rev.: $4,220
Assets: $617,523
Liabilities: $168,452
Net Worth: $449,071
Earnings: ($631,780)
Fiscal Year-end: 09/30/23
Financial Consulting Services
N.A.I.C.S.: 541611
Ritch Wigham (CEO)

SLAVEJ AD SKOPJE
Ul Vasil Gjorgov no 45, Skopje, North Macedonia
Tel.: (389) 23217633
Web Site: https://slavej.mk
SLAV—(MAC)
Rev.: $2,992,584
Assets: $2,988,790
Liabilities: $470,994
Net Worth: $2,517,796
Earnings: ($28,774)
Fiscal Year-end: 12/31/23
Medical Device Mfr
N.A.I.C.S.: 339112

SLAVIA CAPITAL GROUP, A.S.
Mostova 2, 811 02, Bratislava, Slovakia
Tel.: (421) 259317110
Web Site: http://www.slaviacapital.com
Year Founded: 1995
Sales Range: $10-24.9 Million
Emp.: 200
Holding Company
N.A.I.C.S.: 551112
Peter Gabalec (Chm & CEO)

Subsidiaries:

PALMA a.s. (1)
Racianska 76, 83604, Bratislava, Slovakia
Tel.: (421) 249245111
Web Site: http://www.palma.sk
Fats, Oils, Fruit Syrups, Household Chemicals, Hygiene Products, Soaps & Feed Additives Mfr
N.A.I.C.S.: 311225

SLAVIA CAPITAL Praha, a.s. (1)
Betlemske nam 251/2, 110 00, Prague, Czech Republic
Tel.: (420) 255 788 105
Investment Management Service
N.A.I.C.S.: 523940

SLAVIA JSCB
5A Kedrova Str, Moscow, 117292, Russia
Tel.: (7) 4959692415
Web Site: http://www.slaviabank.ru
Sales Range: Less than $1 Million
Commercial Banking Services
N.A.I.C.S.: 522110
Belyaeva Tatiana Borisovna (Chm-Exec Bd)

SLAVICA PARAFARM A.D.
Somborski put 58, Subotica, Serbia
Tel.: (381) 24 561 135
Year Founded: 1997
SPRFS—(BEL)
Sales Range: Less than $1 Million
Emp.: 9
Detergent & Soap Cleanser Mfr
N.A.I.C.S.: 325611
Horvat Sedzida (Exec Dir)

SLAVNEFT-MEGIONNEFTEGAZ OAO
4 4th Lesnoy lane, 125047, Moscow, 125047, Russia
Tel.: (7) 4957878206
Web Site: https://www.slavneft.ru
Year Founded: 1964
MFGS—(MOEX)
Rev.: $5,098,434,920
Assets: $8,540,254,320
Liabilities: $4,259,142,630
Net Worth: $4,281,111,690
Earnings: $398,927,160
Fiscal Year-end: 12/31/19
Oil & Natural Gas Drilling, Extraction & Production
N.A.I.C.S.: 211120
Vadim V. Yakovlev (Chm)

SLAVUTYCH, PJSC
7 Kirov St vil Katerinovka, Pokrovske, 53607, Ukraine
Tel.: (380) 5638 2 19 45
Oil & Grain Flour Mfr
N.A.I.C.S.: 111199

SLAVYANSK HIGH VOLTAGE INSULATORS WORKS, PJSC
79 Kramatorskaya str, Slavyansk, 84105, Ukraine
Tel.: (380) 6262 79 2 87
Web Site: http://www.szvi.com.ua
Year Founded: 1957
Electronic Insulator Mfr
N.A.I.C.S.: 334419

SLAWINSKI & CO. GMBH
Industriestrasse 11, 57076, Siegen, Germany
Tel.: (49) 27170040
Web Site: http://www.slawinski.de
Year Founded: 1914
Sales Range: $25-49.9 Million
Emp.: 122
Mfr of Torispherical Heads, Ellipsodial Heads & Tank Bottoms
N.A.I.C.S.: 339999
Konstantin Slawinski (Mng Dir)

SLB DEVELOPMENT LTD.
29 Harrison Road 07-00 Lian Beng Building, Singapore, 369648, Singapore
Tel.: (65) 65010306
Web Site: https://www.slbdevelopment.com.sg
Year Founded: 2017
1J0—(CAT)
Rev.: $7,536,865
Assets: $278,000,000
Liabilities: $140,255,650
Net Worth: $137,744,350
Earnings: ($16,378,659)
Emp.: 12
Fiscal Year-end: 05/31/24
Commercial Property Development Services
N.A.I.C.S.: 531210

SLC AGRICOLA S.A.
Av Nilo Pecanha 2900 Room 301, Boa Vista District, Porto Alegre, 91330002, RS, Brazil
Tel.: (55) 5132307799
Web Site: https://www.slcagricola.com.br
SLCJY—(OTCIQ)
Rev.: $1,441,934,989
Assets: $3,162,093,529
Liabilities: $2,116,751,820
Net Worth: $1,045,341,709
Earnings: $187,053,545
Emp.: 5,757
Fiscal Year-end: 12/31/23
Cotton, Soybean & Corn
N.A.I.C.S.: 111920
Eduardo Silva Logemann (Chm)

Subsidiaries:

Terra Santa Agro S.A. (1)
Praca General Gentil Falcao 108 8th Floor Apt 81, Brooklin Novo, Sao Paulo, 04571-150, Brazil
Tel.: (55) 1155059811
Web Site: https://www.terrasantapa.com.br
Soybean, Corn & Cotton & Land Appreciation
N.A.I.C.S.: 311224
Silvio Tini de Araujo (Chm)

SLD ENTERTAINMENT, INC.
1-20-2 Sakuragaokacho Shibuya-ku, Tokyo, 150-0041, Japan
Tel.: (81) 362775031
Web Site: http://www.sld-inc.com
3223—(TKS)
Sales Range: $25-49.9 Million
Emp.: 247
Restaurant Operators
N.A.I.C.S.: 722511
Naoki Ban (Pres)

SLEEP CYCLE AB
Drakegatan 10, 412 50, Gothenburg, Sweden
Tel.: (46) 709395327
Web Site: https://www.sleepcycle.com
Year Founded: 2009
SLEEP—(OMX)
Rev.: $22,117,883
Assets: $21,593,283
Liabilities: $15,880,094

INTERNATIONAL PUBLIC

Net Worth: $5,713,189
Earnings: $4,321,747
Emp.: 45
Fiscal Year-end: 12/31/23
Software Development Services
N.A.I.C.S.: 541511
Anne Broeng (Chm)

SLEEPAID HOLDING CO.
Room 10 1/F Wellborne Commercial Centre, 8 Java Road, North Point, China (Hong Kong)
Tel.: (852) 28062312
Web Site: http://www.sleepaidco.com
Year Founded: 2014
Rev.: $1,719,168
Assets: $1,162,358
Liabilities: $2,222,208
Net Worth: ($1,059,850)
Earnings: ($423,042)
Emp.: 27
Fiscal Year-end: 12/31/18
Bedding Products Mfr & Distri
N.A.I.C.S.: 337910
Huihe Zheng (Pres, Treas & Sec)

SLEEPZ AG
Schluterstrasse 38, 10629, Berlin, Germany
Tel.: (49) 30203050
Web Site: http://www.sleepz.com
Year Founded: 1997
BTBB—(DEU)
Sales Range: $1-9.9 Million
Emp.: 57
Holding Company
N.A.I.C.S.: 551112
Oliver Borrmann (Member-Exec Bd)

SLEIMAN AGRICULTURAL ESTABLISHMENT
Sharazad Tower Baghdad Str, PO Box 270, Lattakia, 270, Syria
Tel.: (963) 41461861
Web Site: http://www.sleiman-agri.com
Year Founded: 1966
Sales Range: $100-124.9 Million
Emp.: 100
Seeds, Fertilizers, Pesticides, Organic Products, Soil Correctors & Complete Drip Irrigation Systems
N.A.I.C.S.: 221310
Assem S. Suleiman (Gen Mgr)

Subsidiaries:

Arab Drip Irrigation Technology Company Ltd. (1)
PO Box 270, Lattakia, Syria
Tel.: (963) 41461861
Web Site: http://www.sleiman-agri.com
Sales Range: $75-99.9 Million
Emp.: 70
Irrigation Systems; 50% Owned by Adritec Group International, E.C. & 50% Owned by Sleiman Agricultural Establishment
N.A.I.C.S.: 221310

SLF REALISATION FUND LIMITED
124 Bridge Road, Chertsey, KT16 8LH, Surrey, United Kingdom
Tel.: (44) 1932575888
SLFX—(LSE)
Rev.: $2,323,667
Assets: $29,142,031
Liabilities: $2,879,637
Net Worth: $26,262,394
Earnings: ($3,870,412)
Emp.: 1
Fiscal Year-end: 06/30/24
Investment Management Service
N.A.I.C.S.: 525990

SLICKER RECYCLING LIMITED
Lombard House Worcester Road,

Stourport-On-Severn, London, DY13 9BZ, Worcs, United Kingdom
Tel.: (44) 330 159 8325 UK
Web Site: http://www.slickerrecycling.com
Year Founded: 2000
Water Oil Recycling Services
N.A.I.C.S.: 562998

SLIGRO FOOD GROUP N.V.
Corridor 11, 5466 RB, Veghel, Netherlands
Tel.: (31) 413343500
Web Site: http://www.sligrofoodgroup.nl
Year Founded: 1935
SLIGR—(EUR)
Rev.: $2,679,689,186
Assets: $1,533,563,566
Liabilities: $1,016,619,901
Net Worth: $516,943,665
Earnings: $42,089,359
Emp.: 4,113
Fiscal Year-end: 12/31/22
Food Sales & Service
N.A.I.C.S.: 445110
K. M. Slippens *(CEO & Chm-Exec Bd)*

Subsidiaries:

Bouter B.V. (1)
Edisonstraat 64, 2723 RR, Zoetermeer, Netherlands
Tel.: (31) 79 345 1515
Web Site: https://www.bouter.nl
Kitchen Equipment Repair Services
N.A.I.C.S.: 811412

Gebroeders Kramer B.V. (1)
Jan van Galenstraat 4, 1051 KM, Amsterdam, North Holland, Netherlands
Tel.: (31) 20 680 0260
Web Site: http://www.gebr-kramer.nl
Vegetables & Fruits Distr
N.A.I.C.S.: 424480

Sligro BS Breda B.V. (1)
Kapittelweg 10, 4827 HG, Breda, Netherlands
Tel.: (31) 88 754 5771
Food Products Distr
N.A.I.C.S.: 445110

Sligro BS Deventer B.V. (1)
Nering Bogelweg 40, 7418 HJ, Deventer, Netherlands
Tel.: (31) 53 480 0500
Food Products Distr
N.A.I.C.S.: 445110

Sligro BS Maastricht B.V. (1)
Habitat Girth 59, 6229 RC, Maastricht, Netherlands
Tel.: (31) 47 851 7170
Food Products Distr
N.A.I.C.S.: 445110

Sligro Food Group Nederland B.V. (1)
Corridor 11, 5466 RB, Veghel, Netherlands
Tel.: (31) 413343500
Web Site: http://www.sligrofoodgroup.nl
Sales Range: $150-199.9 Million
Food Products Distr
N.A.I.C.S.: 424490

Subsidiary (Domestic):

Retail Service Groep B.V. (2)
Corridor 11, Veghel, 5466 RB, Noord-Brabant, Netherlands
Tel.: (31) 413343500
Web Site: http://www.sligro.nl
Emp.: 750
Food Products Distr
N.A.I.C.S.: 424490
Koen Slippens *(CEO)*

Sligro B.V. (2)
Kennedylaan 3, 5466 AA, Veghel, Netherlands
Tel.: (31) 413341075
Web Site: https://www.sligro.nl
Sales Range: $125-149.9 Million
Food Products Distr
N.A.I.C.S.: 424490

A. Aalbers *(Mgr-Controlling)*

Sligro-ISPC Belgium N.V. (1)
Straatsburgdok-Zuidkaai 8, 2030, Antwerp, Belgium
Tel.: (32) 3 231 1101
Web Site: https://www.sligro-ispc.be
Food Product Whslr
N.A.I.C.S.: 445110

Tintelingen B.V (1)
Oranje Nassaulaan 27, 5211 AT, 's-Hertogenbosch, Netherlands
Tel.: (31) 736904051
Web Site: https://www.tintelingen.nl
Sales Range: $25-49.9 Million
Gift Shop Operating Services
N.A.I.C.S.: 459420

Van Hoeckel B.V. (1)
Corridor 11, 5466 RB, Veghel, Netherlands
Tel.: (31) 736312690
Web Site: https://www.vanhoeckel.nl
Sales Range: $10-24.9 Million
Emp.: 100
Food Service for Institutional Market (Hospitals & Nursing Homes)
N.A.I.C.S.: 624210
Paul Vanberkel *(Mng Dir)*

SLING GROUP HOLDINGS LIMITED
Unit 1 21st Floor Yen Sheng Centre 64 Hoi Yuen Road, Kwun Tong, Kowloon, China (Hong Kong)
Tel.: (852) 37097275 Ky
Web Site: http://www.sling-inc.com.hk
Year Founded: 1999
8285—(HKG)
Rev.: $13,488,228
Assets: $6,927,898
Liabilities: $6,588,832
Net Worth: $339,066
Earnings: ($2,405,473)
Emp.: 55
Fiscal Year-end: 12/31/22
Leather Product-Mfr & Distr
N.A.I.C.S.: 316990
Frederick Heng Chung Yau *(Chm & Compliance Officer)*

SLJUNKARA A.D.
Jezerska bb, Bela Crkva, Serbia
Tel.: (381) 113699044
Year Founded: 2003
SLJU—(BEL)
Rev.: $13,912
Assets: $121,338
Liabilities: $359,309
Net Worth: ($237,971)
Earnings: $46
Fiscal Year-end: 12/31/22
Construction Sand Mining Services
N.A.I.C.S.: 212321

SLOBODA GP A.D.
Save Kovacevica bb, Obrenovac, Serbia
Tel.: (381) 118721498
Year Founded: 1947
SLBG—(BEL)
Sales Range: $1-9.9 Million
Emp.: 20
Pipeline Construction Services
N.A.I.C.S.: 237990
Radoje Dinovic *(Gen Mgr)*

SLOGA A.D.
Svetosavska 118, Kac, Serbia
Tel.: (381) 216211315
Year Founded: 1991
SLPP—(BEL)
Rev.: $2,700,275
Assets: $10,768,323
Liabilities: $968,958
Net Worth: $9,799,365
Earnings: ($1,035,496)
Fiscal Year-end: 12/31/22
Grain Farming Services
N.A.I.C.S.: 111191
Miro Nedovic *(Gen Mgr)*

SLOGA A.D.
Zarka Zrenjanina 13, Titel, Serbia
Tel.: (381) 21 860 079
Year Founded: 2001
SLTL—(BEL)
Sales Range: Less than $1 Million
Emp.: 25
Heavy Construction Services
N.A.I.C.S.: 237990
Jovan Bratic *(Exec Dir)*

SLOGA A.D.
Devojacki bunar bb, Perlez, Banatski Karlovac, Serbia
Tel.: (381) 233813002
Year Founded: 2002
SLPZE—(BEL)
Sales Range: $1-9.9 Million
Cereal Crop Farming Services
N.A.I.C.S.: 111998
Miroslav Dobrosavljevic *(Exec Dir)*

SLOGA A.D.
Milentija Popovica 1, Zrenjanin, Serbia
Tel.: (381) 230 458 625
Year Founded: 1974
Sales Range: Less than $1 Million
Cereal Crop Farming Services
N.A.I.C.S.: 111998
Dusan Marjanovic *(CEO)*

SLOGA A.D.
Dimitrija Tucovica 149, Uzice, Serbia
Tel.: (381) 31516188
Web Site: https://www.hotel-zlatibor.com
Year Founded: 1962
SLGU—(BEL)
Sales Range: Less than $1 Million
Emp.: 25
Home Management Services
N.A.I.C.S.: 721110
Slobodan Milovanovic *(Exec Dir)*

SLOGA A.D.
Vuka Karadzica 13, Valjevo, Serbia
Tel.: (381) 14 221 378
Year Founded: 1947
SLVA—(BEL)
Sales Range: $1-9.9 Million
Emp.: 111
Home Management Services
N.A.I.C.S.: 721110
Milos Filipovic *(Exec Dir)*

SLOGA A.D.
Magistralni put 019, Nova Varos, Serbia
Tel.: (381) 33 63 850
Year Founded: 1960
Sales Range: Less than $1 Million
Emp.: 70
Automobile Parts Mfr
N.A.I.C.S.: 336390
Dusan Mandic *(Gen Dir)*

SLOGA A.D.
Pobrdje bb, 36300, Novi Pazar, Serbia
Tel.: (381) 20 361 668
Web Site: http://www.slogaigm.rs
Year Founded: 1963
Sales Range: $1-9.9 Million
Brick & Roofing Tile Mfr
N.A.I.C.S.: 327331
Asim Besnicanin *(Dir)*

SLOGA A.D.
Jase Petrovica 20, Aleksandrovac, Serbia
Tel.: (381) 37 552 335
Year Founded: 1998
Sales Range: Less than $1 Million
Emp.: 3
Retail Store Operator
N.A.I.C.S.: 445298
Dragan Cocic *(Exec Dir)*

SLOGAN INC.
Dai-ichi Hoki Honsha Building 3rd floor 2-11-7 Minami-aoyama, Minato-ku, Tokyo, 107-0062, Japan
Tel.: (81) 364349754
Web Site: https://www.slogan.jp
Year Founded: 2005
9253—(TKS)
Rev.: $10,053,620
Assets: $13,953,120
Liabilities: $3,757,700
Net Worth: $10,195,420
Earnings: $645,190
Emp.: 110
Fiscal Year-end: 02/29/24
Human Resource Consulting Services
N.A.I.C.S.: 541612

Subsidiaries:

TeamUp, Inc. (1)
3rd Floor Daiichi Hoki Head Office Building 2-11-17 Minami-Aoyama, Minato-ku, 107-0062, Japan
Tel.: (81) 364345220
Web Site: https://www.teamup.jp
Human Resource Software Development Services
N.A.I.C.S.: 541511

SLOMAN NEPTUN SCHIFFAHRTS-AKTIENGESELLSCHAFT
Langenstr 44, 28195, Bremen, Germany
Tel.: (49) 42117630
Web Site: https://www.sloman-neptun.com
Year Founded: 1873
Marine Transportation Services
N.A.I.C.S.: 483111
Christian Reincke *(Mng Dir-Liner Svc)*

SLOTTSVIKEN FASTIGHET-SAKTIEBOLAG
Kyrkogatan 24, 411 15, Gothenburg, Sweden
Tel.: (46) 18194950 SE
Web Site: http://www.slottsviken.se
Year Founded: 1983
Real Estate Manangement Services
N.A.I.C.S.: 531210
Jakob Osterberg *(CEO)*

SLOVENSKE ENERGETICKE STROJARNE AS
Tovarenska 210, Tlmace, 935 28, Levice, Slovakia
Tel.: (421) 366381111
Web Site: http://www.ses.sk
Year Founded: 1992
1SES01AE—(BRA)
Sales Range: Less than $1 Million
Industrial Boiler Distr
N.A.I.C.S.: 423720
Martin Pastika *(Gen Mgr)*

SLOVENSKE ZELEZNICE, D.O.O.
Kolodvorska 11, 1506, Ljubljana, Slovenia
Tel.: (386) 12914203
Web Site: http://www.slo-zeleznice.si
Year Founded: 1991
Sales Range: $600-649.9 Million
Passenger & Freight Railroad Operator
N.A.I.C.S.: 482111
Dusan Mes *(Dir Gen)*

Subsidiaries:

Prometni institut Ljubljana d. o. o. (1)

SLOVENSKE ZELEZNICE, D.O.O.

Slovenske zeleznice, d.o.o.—(Continued)
Kolodvorska Ulica 11, 1000, Ljubljana, Slovenia
Tel.: (386) 1 291 46 26
Web Site: http://www.prometni-institut.si
Sales Range: $25-49.9 Million
Emp.: 31
Transport Technology Research & Development Services
N.A.I.C.S.: 541715

SZ - Infrastruktura, d. o. o. (1)
Kolodvorska 11, 1000, Ljubljana, Slovenia
Tel.: (386) 1 29 14 021
Railway Track Construction Services
N.A.I.C.S.: 237990
Matjaz Kranjc (CEO)

SZ - Tovorni promet, d. o. o. (1)
Kolodvorska 11, 1000, Ljubljana, Slovenia
Tel.: (386) 1 29 14 280
Rail Freight Transportation Services
N.A.I.C.S.: 482111

SZ-ZIP, storitve, d. o. o. (1)
Kolodvorska 11, 1000, Ljubljana, Slovenia
Tel.: (386) 1 434 04 86
Facility Management & Janitorial Services
N.A.I.C.S.: 561210

SZ-Zelezniski zdravstveni dom Ljubljana (1)
Celovska cesta 4, 1000, Ljubljana, Slovenia
Tel.: (386) 1 231 02 42
General Medical Services
N.A.I.C.S.: 621491

SLOVMAG, A.S.
Lubenik 236, 049 18, Lubenik, Slovakia
Tel.: (421) 584814301
Web Site: http://www.slovmag.sk
Year Founded: 1994
Sales Range: $150-199.9 Million
Emp.: 600
Clay Refractories
N.A.I.C.S.: 327120
Jan Galoviz (Mgr)

SLP RESOURCES BERHAD
PT 1 Lot 57A Lorong Perusahaan 5, Kulim Industrial Estate, 09000, Kulim, Kedah, Malaysia
Tel.: (60) 44891858
Web Site: https://www.sinliplas.com.my
SLP—(KLS)
Rev.: $39,310,523
Assets: $48,522,699
Liabilities: $7,664,913
Net Worth: $40,857,786
Earnings: $4,355,559
Emp.: 274
Fiscal Year-end: 12/31/22
Holding Company; Polymer & Plastic Packaging Mfr & Sales
N.A.I.C.S.: 551112
Khoon Tee Khaw (Founder & Chm)

Subsidiaries:

Sinliplas Holding Sdn. Bhd. (1)
PT 1 Lot 57-A Lorong Perusahaan 5 Kulim Industrial Estate, 09000, Kulim, Kedah, Malaysia
Tel.: (60) 44891858
Web Site: https://www.sinliplas.com.my
Investment Management Service
N.A.I.C.S.: 523999

Sinliplas Sdn. Bhd. (1)
Pt 1 Lot 57a Lorong Perusahaan 5 Kulim Industrail Estate, 09000, Kulim, Kedah, Malaysia
Tel.: (60) 44891858
Web Site: http://www.sinliplas.com.my
Sales Range: $150-199.9 Million
Plastic Products Mfr & Distr
N.A.I.C.S.: 326199

SLS BIO CO., LTD.
7th floor Gwanggyo Central Biz Tower 260 Changryong-daero, Yeongtong-Gu, Suwon, 16229, Gyeonggi-do, Korea (South)
Tel.: (82) 3180667270
Web Site: https://www.slabs.co.kr
Year Founded: 2007
246250—(KRS)
Pharmaceutical Preparation Mfr
N.A.I.C.S.: 325412
Young-Tae Lee (CEO)

SLS CO LTD
107 Gwanggyo-ro Yeongtong-gu, Suwon, 16229, Gyeonggi-do, Korea (South)
Tel.: (82) 7088577903
Pharmaceutical Product Mfr & Distr
N.A.I.C.S.: 325412

SLS GROUP INDUSTRIES INC.
Suite 201 - 4599 Tillicum St, Burnaby, V5J 3J9, BC, Canada
Tel.: (604) 874-2226
Web Site: https://www.sls-lighting.com
Year Founded: 1985
Rev.: $10,868,119
Emp.: 50
Electrical Products Distr
N.A.I.C.S.: 423610

SLS REALTY REIT
Bul Hristofor Kolumb 43, 1592, Sofia, Bulgaria
Tel.: (359) 29809440
SLSP—(BUL)
Sales Range: Less than $1 Million
Real Estate Investment Services
N.A.I.C.S.: 531210
Tsvetelina Nikolova (Dir-Investor Relations)

SLTN B.V.
Colosseum 9, Hilversum, 1213 NN, Netherlands
Tel.: (31) 356888400 NI
Web Site: http://www.sltn.nl
Year Founded: 1997
Sales Range: $100-124.9 Million
Emp.: 400
Information Technology Management, Equipment Distr & Consulting Services
N.A.I.C.S.: 541519
Eugene Tuijnman (Founder & CEO)

Subsidiaries:

SLTN Zuid Nederland B.V. (1)
Hogeweg 11, NL-5301 LB, Zaltbommel, Netherlands (100%)
Tel.: (31) 418574700
Web Site: http://www.sltn.nl
Sales Range: $25-49.9 Million
Emp.: 35
Information Technology Management, Equipment Distr & Consulting Services
N.A.I.C.S.: 541519

SM AUTO STAMPING LIMITED
C-13 Midc Ambad, Nashik, 422010, Maharashtra, India
Tel.: (91) 2536621103
Web Site: https://www.smautostamping.com
Year Founded: 1998
543065—(BOM)
Fabricated Metal Products Mfr
N.A.I.C.S.: 332312
Mukund Narayan Kulkarni (Mng Dir)

SM BEXEL CO., LTD.
48-15 Dogomyeon-ro, Dogo-myeon, Asan, Chungcheongnam-do, Korea (South)
Tel.: (82) 415297731
Web Site: https://smbexel.com
Year Founded: 1975
010580—(KRS)
Rev.: $108,062,539
Assets: $118,169,224
Liabilities: $65,257,991
Net Worth: $52,911,233
Earnings: $7,283,956
Emp.: 275
Fiscal Year-end: 12/31/22
Automobile Parts Mfr
N.A.I.C.S.: 336350
Yoo Byung Sun (CEO)

SM ENERGY TEKNIK & ELECTRONICS LIMITED
SM Bhavan Plot No- B7 & B10 Road No 8 & 15, Wagle Ind Estate, Thane, 400 604, India
Tel.: (91) 2225820145 In
Web Site: http://www.smenergy.com
Year Founded: 1982
Assets: $15,638
Liabilities: $966,276
Net Worth: ($950,638)
Earnings: $12,884
Fiscal Year-end: 03/31/17
Textile Products Mfr
N.A.I.C.S.: 313310

SM INVESTMENTS CORPORATION
10th Floor OneE-Com Center Ocean Drive Mall of Asia Complex, Pasay, 1300, Philippines
Tel.: (63) 28570100 PH
Web Site: https://www.sminvestments.com
Year Founded: 1958
SM—(OTCIQ)
Rev.: $9,853,403,231
Assets: $26,367,583,602
Liabilities: $14,051,254,515
Net Worth: $12,316,329,087
Earnings: $1,500,780,644
Emp.: 140,029
Fiscal Year-end: 12/31/22
Financial Investment Services
N.A.I.C.S.: 551112
Teresita T. Sy-Coson (Vice Chm)

Subsidiaries:

2GO Group Inc. (1)
8th Floor Tower 1 Double Dragon Plaza Macapagal Boulevard corner, EDSA Extension, Pasay, 1302, Philippines (52.85%)
Tel.: (63) 2 528 7000
Web Site: http://www.2go.com.ph
Rev.: $320,488,397
Assets: $268,709,397
Liabilities: $255,419,154
Net Worth: $13,290,243
Earnings: ($23,773,277)
Emp.: 2,105
Fiscal Year-end: 12/31/2021
Freight & Passenger Ship Transportation Services
N.A.I.C.S.: 483112
Francis C. Chua (Vice Chm)

Subsidiary (Domestic):

2GO Express, Inc. (2)
General Aviation Area, Manila Domestic Airport, Pasay, Philippines
Tel.: (63) 2 855 1776
Oil Transportation Services
N.A.I.C.S.: 488190

2GO Travel, Inc. (2)
Pier 4 Corporate Ticketing Zaragoza Gate North Harbour Port Area Tondo, Manila, Philippines
Tel.: (63) 5287250
Web Site: http://www.travel.2go.com.ph
Passenger Transportation Services
N.A.I.C.S.: 483112

MCC Transport Philippines, Inc. (2)
9th Floor One E-com Center Harbor Drive, corner Sun SM Bay City, 1300, Pasay, Metro Manila, Philippines
Tel.: (63) 2 859 3401
Freight Transportation Arrangement

INTERNATIONAL PUBLIC

N.A.I.C.S.: 488510

Negros Navigation Co., Inc. (2)
15 Times Plaza Building United Nations Ave corner Taft Ave, Ermita, Manila, 1000, Philippines
Tel.: (63) 2 554 8777
Shipping Services
N.A.I.C.S.: 488510

North Harbor Tugs Corporation (2)
Rm 105-A The Mercantile Insurance Building General Luna Cor, Beaterio Street Intramuros, Manila, Philippines
Tel.: (63) 25266764
Web Site: http://www.northharbortugs.com
Freight Transportation & Cargo Services
N.A.I.C.S.: 488510
Zander Asnawi (Gen Mgr)

ScanAsia Overseas, Inc. (2)
9th Floor Tower 1 Double Dragon Plaza DD Meridian Park corner, Macapagal Ave and EDSA Extension Bay Area, Pasay, 1300, Philippines
Tel.: (63) 25287171
Web Site: http://scanasia.ph
Food Products Distr
N.A.I.C.S.: 311991

The Supercat Fast Ferry Corporation (2)
Pier 4 North Reclamation Area, Cebu, Philippines
Tel.: (63) 322337000
Web Site: http://www.supercat.com.ph
Freight Transportation & Cargo Services
N.A.I.C.S.: 488510
Ramon Tuburan (Asst VP)

Multi-Realty Development Corporation
10 Floor Lockin Building, 1226, Makati, Philippines
Tel.: (63) 28101111
Real Estate Development Services
N.A.I.C.S.: 531390

Philippines Urban Living Solutions, Inc. (1)
6F Mytown Sydney 3376 Harvard Street Metro Manila, Makati, Philippines
Tel.: (63) 27388640
Web Site: https://www.urbanlivingsolutions.ph
Rental Housing Services
N.A.I.C.S.: 624229

Primebridge Holdings, Inc (1)
10th Floor One E Com Center Harbor Dr, Mall of Asia Complex Cbp-1a, Pasay, 1300, Philippines
Tel.: (63) 28311000
Real Estate Development Services
N.A.I.C.S.: 531390

SM Prime Holdings, Inc. (1)
7/F MOA Square Seashell Lane corner Coral Way Mall of Asia Complex, Brgy 76 Zone 10 CBP 1-A, Pasay, 1300, Philippines (49.7%)
Tel.: (63) 28311000
Web Site: https://www.smprime.com
Rev.: $1,712,162,067
Assets: $16,731,588,224
Liabilities: $9,776,884,146
Net Worth: $6,954,704,078
Earnings: $453,159,533
Emp.: 13,489
Fiscal Year-end: 12/31/2021
Shopping Mall Operator
N.A.I.C.S.: 531190
Henry T. Sy Jr. (Chm)

Subsidiary (Domestic):

Costa del Hamilo, Inc. (2)
10/F One E-Com Center Harbor Drive Mall of Asia Complex CBP 1-A, Pasay, 1300, Philippines (100%)
Tel.: (63) 8570100
Web Site: http://www.hamilocoast.com
Real Estate Services
N.A.I.C.S.: 531390
Niko Dinglasan (Mgr-Customer Svcs)

SM Development Corporation (2)
15/F Two E-Com Center Harbor Drive MOA complex, Pasay, 1300, Philippines (100%)
Tel.: (63) 288570100

Web Site: http://www.smdc.com
Fiscal Year-end: 12/31/2012
Real Estate Development Services
N.A.I.C.S.: 531210
Henry T. Sy Jr. *(Chm)*

SM Hotels & Conventions Corp. (2)
10/F OneE-com Center Sunset Drive Mall
of Asia Complex, Pasay, 1300,
Philippines (100%)
Tel.: (63) 288570100
Web Site: http://www.smhotels.com.ph
Hotel Services
N.A.I.C.S.: 721110
Dhang Bonoan *(Mgr-HR)*

SM Retail Inc. (1)
Bldg F SM Corporate Offices J W Diokno
Boulevard, Mall of Asia Complex, Pasay,
Philippines
Tel.: (63) 2 831 8000
Web Site: https://smretailcareers.com
Home Products Retailer
N.A.I.C.S.: 449129
Michael Briones *(Mgr-Character Mdse)*

**SM LIFE DESIGN GROUP CO.,
LTD.**
376 Jikji-gil, P'aju, 10881, Gyeonggi-
do, Korea (South)
Tel.: (82) 319557171
Web Site: https://smlifedesign.com
Year Founded: 1962
063440—(KRS)
Rev.: $38,585,751
Assets: $51,904,164
Liabilities: $11,814,027
Net Worth: $40,090,137
Earnings: $1,908,090
Emp.: 24
Fiscal Year-end: 12/31/22
Media & Publishing Services
N.A.I.C.S.: 513199

SM ROBOTICS INC
40 Imi-ro, Uiwang, Korea (South)
Tel.: (82) 314221519
Web Site:
 http://www.smrobotics.co.kr
Horse Racing Game Development
Services
N.A.I.C.S.: 513210
Jeon Joo-Sik *(CEO)*

SM VINA CO., LTD.
601 Ilsin Building 38 Mapo-daero,
Mapo-gu, Seoul, Korea (South)
Tel.: (82) 269537020
Web Site: https://www.smvina.co.kr
Year Founded: 1991
299670—(KRS)
Apparel Retailer
N.A.I.C.S.: 424350
Yoon Dong-Ryul *(CEO)*

**SM WIRTSCHAFTSBERA-
TUNGS AG**
Fronackerstrasse 34, 71063, Sindelf-
ingen, Germany
Tel.: (49) 70314690960
Web Site: https://www.smw-ag.de
SMWN—(DUS)
Rev.: $408,434
Assets: $18,523,016
Liabilities: $2,240,865
Net Worth: $16,282,150
Earnings: ($673,364)
Emp.: 7
Fiscal Year-end: 12/30/23
Asset Management Services
N.A.I.C.S.: 523940
Martin Schmitt *(Chm-Mgmt Bd &
CEO)*

**SMA SOLAR TECHNOLOGY
AG**
Sonnenallee 1, 34266, Niestetal, Ger-
many
Tel.: (49) 56195220 De

Web Site: https://www.sma.de
SMTGF—(OTCIQ)
Rev.: $2,101,834,712
Assets: $1,790,388,830
Liabilities: $1,032,935,314
Net Worth: $757,453,517
Earnings: $249,110,343
Emp.: 4,377
Fiscal Year-end: 12/31/23
Inverters Mfr & Sales
N.A.I.C.S.: 335312
Jurgen Reinert *(CEO & Member-
Mgmt Bd)*

Subsidiaries:

SMA Altenso GmbH
Sonnenallee 1, Fritzlar, 34266, Niestetal,
Germany
Tel.: (49) 56195220
Web Site: https://www.sma-altenso.com
Solar Photovoltaic Device Mfr
N.A.I.C.S.: 334413

SMA Australia Pty Ltd. (1)
Level 1 213 Miller Street, North Sydney,
2060, NSW, Australia
Tel.: (61) 294914200
Web Site: https://www.sma-australia.com.au
Sales Range: $25-49.9 Million
Emp.: 9
Solar Inverter Mfr
N.A.I.C.S.: 335312

**SMA Beijing Commercial Company
Ltd.**
716 Bldg A Beijing Agr Sci Mansion No11
Mid Shuguang Rd, W Suburb Banjing Haid-
ian, Beijing, China
Tel.: (86) 1051501685
Web Site: http://www.sma-china.com.cn
Sales Range: $50-74.9 Million
Emp.: 10
Photovoltaic Inverters Whslr
N.A.I.C.S.: 423720

SMA Benelux SPRL. (1)
Generaal de Wittelaan 19B, 2800,
Mechelen, Antwerp, Belgium
Tel.: (32) 15286739
Web Site: https://www.sma-benelux.com
Sales Range: $25-49.9 Million
Emp.: 17
Solar Power Inverters Mfr
N.A.I.C.S.: 335312
Jan Van Laethem *(Mng Dir)*

SMA Canada, Inc. (1)
2425 Matheson Blvd East 7th Floor, Mississauga, L4W 5K4, ON, Canada
Solar Energy Supply Services
N.A.I.C.S.: 221114

SMA Czech Republic s.r.o. (1)
Avenir Bus Park Budova C Radlicka 740
113D, 15800, Prague, Czech Republic
Tel.: (420) 235510111
Web Site: http://www.sma-czech.com
Sales Range: $25-49.9 Million
Emp.: 14
Solar Inverter Mfr
N.A.I.C.S.: 335311
David Rehacek *(Mng Dir)*

SMA France S.A.S. (1)
Le Parc Technologique de Lyon 240 Allee
Jacques Monod - Bat M2, 69791, Saint
Priest, France
Tel.: (33) 472229700
Web Site: https://www.sma-france.com
Sales Range: $25-49.9 Million
Emp.: 35
Solar Inverter Mfr
N.A.I.C.S.: 335312

SMA Hellas AE. (1)
102 Plifglifaba Visilitfipsani, Alimos, Athens,
16675, Greece
Tel.: (30) 2109856660
Web Site: http://www.sma-hellas.com
Sales Range: $25-49.9 Million
Emp.: 11
Solar Inverter Mfr
N.A.I.C.S.: 327910
Haris Christidis *(Gen Mgr)*

**SMA Iberica Tecnologia Solar,
S.L.** (1)
Avda Corts Catalanes 9 Plta 3 Of 17-18,

Sant Cugat del Valles, 08173, Barcelona,
Spain
Tel.: (34) 935635000
Web Site: https://www.sma-iberica.com
Solar Energy Supply Services
N.A.I.C.S.: 221114
Ivan Moreno Perez *(Sr Project Mgr & Engr-
Application)*

SMA Italia S.r.l. (1)
Via dei Missaglia 97, 20142, Milan, Italy
Tel.: (39) 0289347200
Web Site: https://www.sma-italia.com
Solar Energy Supply Services
N.A.I.C.S.: 221114
Laura Volpi *(Fin Mgr)*

SMA Japan Kabushiki Kaisha (1)
Celestine Shiba Mitsui Building 8F 3-23-1
Shiba, Minato-ku, Tokyo, 105-0014, Japan
Tel.: (81) 334519532
Web Site: https://www.sma-japan.com
Solar Power Generation Services
N.A.I.C.S.: 221114

SMA Magnetics Sp. z o.o. (1)
ul Komandosow 3/1, 32-085, Modlnica,
Poland
Tel.: (48) 122830950
Web Site: https://www.sma-magnetics.com
Magnetic Core Mfr
N.A.I.C.S.: 332999

SMA Middle East Limited (1)
Masdar City Incubator Building-Level 1 Of-
fice 121, PO Box 133193, Abu Dhabi,
United Arab Emirates
Tel.: (971) 22346177
Solar Energy Supply Services
N.A.I.C.S.: 221114
Thorsten Ronge *(Mng Dir)*

SMA Solar India Private Limited (1)
1101 Sigma Building Technology Street Hi-
ranandani Business Park, Powai, Mumbai,
400076, India
Tel.: (91) 2261713829
Web Site: https://www.sma-india.com
Solar Energy Supply Services
N.A.I.C.S.: 221114
Anita Virnave *(Office Mgr-HR)*

**SMA Solar Technology (Shanghai)
Co., Ltd.** (1)
Room 1707 17th Floor Century Plaza 1198
Century Avenue, Pudong New Area, Shang-
hai, 200122, China
Tel.: (86) 2150858806
Web Site: https://www.sma-china.com
Solar Energy Supply Services
N.A.I.C.S.: 221114
Charles Wang *(Sr Acct Mgr)*

**SMA Solar Technology America,
LLC.** (1)
3925 Atherton Rd, Rocklin, CA 95765
Tel.: (916) 625-0870
Web Site: https://www.sma-america.com
Sales Range: $50-74.9 Million
Emp.: 160
Solar Inverter Mfr
N.A.I.C.S.: 335312

**SMA Solar Technology Portugal, Uni-
pessoal Lda**
Centro de Empresas Maquijig-Armazem 4
Parque Indus das Carrascas, Estrada Na-
cional 252 Km 11 5, 2950-402, Palmela,
Portugal
Tel.: (351) 212387860
Web Site: http://www.sma-portugal.com
Sales Range: $25-49.9 Million
Emp.: 4
Solar Inverter Mfr
N.A.I.C.S.: 335313

**SMA Solar Technology South Africa
(Pty.) Ltd.** (1)
The Boulevard Office Park Block F Ground
Floor, Searle Street off Nelson Mandela
Blvd Woodstock, Cape Town, 7925, South
Africa
Tel.: (27) 218260600
Solar Energy Supply Services
N.A.I.C.S.: 221114

SMA Solar UK Ltd. (1)
Unit G1 307 Upper Fourth Street Witan Stu-
dios, Milton Keynes, MK9 1EH, United
Kingdom

Tel.: (44) 1908304899
Web Site: https://www.sma-uk.com
Solar Energy Supply Services
N.A.I.C.S.: 221114

SMA South America SpA (1)
Cerro el Plomo 5630 Piso 18 Of 1804, Las
Condes, Santiago, Chile
Tel.: (56) 228202100
Web Site: https://www.sma-south-
 america.com
Solar Energy Supply Services
N.A.I.C.S.: 221114
Christian Knaack *(Mgr-Svc)*

**SMA Technology Australia Pty.
Ltd.** (1)
67 Epping Road, North Ryde, 2113, NSW,
Australia
Tel.: (61) 296692889
Web Site: http://www.sma-australia.com.au
Sales Range: $25-49.9 Million
Emp.: 8
Solar Inverter Mfr
N.A.I.C.S.: 335312

SMA Technology Korea Co., Ltd. (1)
8Fl 3M Tower 735-32 Yeoksam Dong,
Gangnam-gu, Seoul, 135-923, Korea
(South)
Tel.: (82) 25088887
Web Site: http://www.sma-korea.com
Sales Range: $25-49.9 Million
Emp.: 15
Photovoltaic Inverter Mfr
N.A.I.C.S.: 334413
Myung Paevree *(Mng Dir)*

Zeversolar GmbH (1)
Sonnenallee 1, 34266, Niestetal, Germany
Tel.: (49) 22180051550
Web Site: https://www.zeversolar.com
Solar Inverter Mfr
N.A.I.C.S.: 335999

emerce Africa (Pty.) Ltd. (1)
The Boulevard Office Park Block F Ground
Floor Searle Street, Woodstock, Cape
Town, 7925, South Africa
Tel.: (27) 218260600
Web Site: http://www.emerce-africa.co.za
Online Shopping Services
N.A.I.C.S.: 423620
Thorsten Ronge *(Mng Dir)*

emerce GmbH (1)
Sonnenallee 1, 34266, Niestetal, Germany
Tel.: (49) 5619522422
Web Site: http://www.emerce-energy.com
Solar System Installation Services
N.A.I.C.S.: 238210
Stefanie Hegener *(Mng Dir)*

**SMALANDSSTENARS ME-
KANISKA VERKSTAD - SMV
INDUSTRIER AB**
Parkgatan 6, Smalandsstenar, 333
31, Sweden SE
Tel.: (46) 371 343 40
Web Site: http://www.smv.se
Sales Range: $10-24.9 Million
Emp.: 65
Holding Company; Mechanical Power
Press Mfr & Distr
N.A.I.C.S.: 551112
Magnus Torell *(Deputy Mng Dir)*

Subsidiaries:

Presservice Ljungby AB (1)
PO Box 10, Ljungby, Sweden
Tel.: (46) 372 694 90
Web Site: http://www.presservice.se
Industrial Machinery Mfr
N.A.I.C.S.: 333248
Christian Nothin *(Engr-Svc)*

SMV Presses (UK) Ltd (1)
240-244 Stratford Road, Shirley, Solihull,
B90 3AE, West Midlands, United Kingdom
Tel.: (44) 121 744 2003
Industrial Machinery Distr
N.A.I.C.S.: 333248

SMV Presses A/S (1)
Lovenornsgade 17, 8700, Horsens, Den-
mark
Tel.: (45) 79 253 000

SMALANDSSTENARS MEKANISKA VERKSTAD - SMV INDUSTRIER AB

Smalandsstenars Mekaniska Verkstad - SMV Industrier AB—(Continued)
Industrial Machinery Distr
N.A.I.C.S.: 333998

SVEA Maskiner AS (1)
Graaterudveien 20, Drammen, 3036, Norway
Tel.: (47) 3227 7750
Web Site: http://www.svea.no
Emp.: 15
Industrial Equipment Distr
N.A.I.C.S.: 423830
Per Martin Bakken *(Mgr-Space)*

Smalandsstenars Mekaniska Verkstad SMV AB (1)
Parkgatan 6, Smalandsstenar, 13331, Sweden
Tel.: (46) 371 343 40
Web Site: http://www.smv.se
Emp.: 50
Mechanical Power Press Mfr & Distr
N.A.I.C.S.: 333248
Lars-Olof Andersson *(Mgr-Fin)*

SMALL INDUSTRY CREDIT GUARANTEE CORPORATION
Charn Issara Tower II 18th Fl 2922 243, New Petchburi Rd, Bangkok, 10310, Thailand
Tel.: (66) 23082741
Web Site: http://www.sbcg.or.th
Year Founded: 1992
Sales Range: $100-124.9 Million
Emp.: 141
Credit Guarantee Services
N.A.I.C.S.: 522210

SMALTO SA
44 Rue Francois 1er, 75008, Paris, France
Tel.: (33) 147209604
Web Site: https://www.smalto.com
MLSML—(EUR)
Sales Range: $1-9.9 Million
Holding Company
N.A.I.C.S.: 551112
Thierry Le Guenic *(CEO)*

SMAREGI, INC.
3F 4-2-12 Hommachi, Chuo-ku, Osaka, 541-0053, Japan
Tel.: (81) 677772211
Web Site: https://www.corp.smaregi.jp
Year Founded: 2005
4431—(TKS)
Sales Range: Less than $1 Million
Information Technology Services
N.A.I.C.S.: 541511
Makoto Tokuda *(Founder)*

SMART AGRO LTD.
49 Rothschild Avenue, Tel Aviv, Israel
Tel.: (972) 35665005
Web Site: http://www.smartagrofund.com
SMAG—(TAE)
Assets: $11,309,020
Liabilities: $613,621
Net Worth: $10,695,400
Earnings: ($5,079,154)
Fiscal Year-end: 12/31/23
Agricultural Services
N.A.I.C.S.: 531190
Erez Meltzer *(Chm)*

SMART CLOSET, INC.
70 Primrose Dr, Cornwall, C0A 1H4, PE, Canada   NV
ZSYC—(OTCIQ)
Digital Marketing Services
N.A.I.C.S.: 541613
Lirong Huang *(CEO)*

SMART CONCRETE PUBLIC COMPANY LIMITED
11 Moo 9 Banbung-Klang Rd Tumbon Nhong-Irun, Amphur Banbung, Chon Buri, 20220, Thailand
Tel.: (66) 38442500
Web Site: http://www.smartblock.co.th
Year Founded: 2004
SMART—(THA)
Rev.: $20,838,104
Assets: $23,978,284
Liabilities: $4,367,994
Net Worth: $19,610,290
Earnings: $3,111,280
Fiscal Year-end: 12/31/23
Concrete Block Mfr
N.A.I.C.S.: 327331
Pratheep Theepakornsukkasem *(Chm)*

Subsidiaries:
Smart Concrete Public Company Limited - Bangkok Factory (1)
947/144 Moo 12 Bangna Complex Building Bangna-Trad Rd Bangna, Bangkok, 10260, Thailand
Tel.: (66) 23992105
Concrete Brick & Block Mfr
N.A.I.C.S.: 327331

SMART EYE AB
Masthamnsgatan 3, 413 27, Gothenburg, Sweden
Tel.: (46) 31606160
Web Site: https://www.smarteye.se
Year Founded: 1999
SEYE—(OMX)
Rev.: $20,153,680
Assets: $154,323,328
Liabilities: $34,728,858
Net Worth: $119,594,470
Earnings: ($31,238,163)
Emp.: 274
Fiscal Year-end: 12/31/22
Software Development Services
N.A.I.C.S.: 541511
Gabi Zijderveld *(CMO)*

Subsidiaries:
Smart Eye Japan Co., Ltd. (1)
Daiwa Kandabashi Bldg 3F 1-17-5, Kanda-Nishiki-cho Chiyoda-ku, Tokyo, 101-0054, Japan
Tel.: (81) 362737725
Software Development Services
N.A.I.C.S.: 518210

iMotions A/S (1)
Kristen Bernikows Gade 6 4th Floor, 1105, Copenhagen, Denmark
Tel.: (45) 71998098
Web Site: https://www.imotions.com
Software Development Services
N.A.I.C.S.: 541511

SMART FINSEC LTD.
F88 2nd Floor Industrial Pocket District Centre, West Delhi, New Delhi, 110 027, India
Tel.: (91) 1125167071
Web Site: https://www.smartfinsec.com
539494—(BOM)
Rev.: $3,687,399
Assets: $1,630,537
Liabilities: $174,425
Net Worth: $1,456,113
Earnings: $169,350
Emp.: 3
Fiscal Year-end: 03/31/23
Financial Support Services
N.A.I.C.S.: 523999
Arun Khera *(Chm & Mng Dir)*

SMART GLOBE HOLDINGS LIMITED
Flat 08 17/F Kodak House II No 39 Healthy Street East, North Point, China (Hong Kong)
Tel.: (852) 21544242   Ky
Web Site: http://www.smartglobehk.com
Year Founded: 2012
1481—(HKG)
Rev.: $16,975,032
Assets: $18,331,426
Liabilities: $3,009,288
Net Worth: $15,322,138
Earnings: $2,971,664
Emp.: 333
Fiscal Year-end: 12/31/19
Printing Product Mfr & Distr
N.A.I.C.S.: 323111
Derek Tak Ling Lam *(Chm)*

Subsidiaries:
CP Printing Limited (1)
Flat 08 17/F Kodak House II No 39 Healthy Street East North Point, Hong Kong, China (Hong Kong)
Tel.: (852) 21544242
Web Site: https://www.cpprinting.com.hk
Commercial Printing Product Mfr
N.A.I.C.S.: 323111

SMART GOOD THINGS HOLDING S.A.
59 avenue Marceau, la-Defense, 75016, Paris, France
Tel.: (33) 493439542
Web Site: https://www.smartgoodthings.com
MLSGT—(EUR)
Holding Company
N.A.I.C.S.: 551112

SMART METERING SYSTEMS PLC
2nd Floor 48 St Vincent Street, Glasgow, G2 5TS, United Kingdom
Tel.: (44) 1412493850   UK
Web Site: http://www.sms-plc.com
Year Founded: 1995
SMS—(AIM)
Rev.: $149,890,960
Assets: $731,053,050
Liabilities: $437,809,457
Net Worth: $293,243,593
Earnings: $5,242,465
Emp.: 1,225
Fiscal Year-end: 12/31/19
Gas Meter Reading Services
N.A.I.C.S.: 561990
Alan H. Foy *(CEO)*

Subsidiaries:
Utility Partnership Limited (1)
Prennau House Copse Walk Cardiff Gate Business Park, Cardiff, CF23 8XH, United Kingdom
Tel.: (44) 2920739500
Web Site: http://www.up-ltd.co.uk
Sales Range: $10-24.9 Million
Emp.: 138
Energy Management & Metering Solutions
N.A.I.C.S.: 541690

SMART PARKING LTD.
85 Dundas Place, Albert Park, 3206, VIC, Australia
Tel.: (61) 386444021
Web Site: https://www.smartparking.com
SPZ—(ASX)
Rev.: $36,527,149
Assets: $38,432,208
Liabilities: $19,772,362
Net Worth: $18,659,846
Earnings: $2,463,050
Fiscal Year-end: 06/30/24
Parking Management & Technology Solutions
N.A.I.C.S.: 812930
Richard Ludbrook *(CFO & Sec)*

Subsidiaries:
Enterprise Parking Solutions Ltd. (1)

INTERNATIONAL PUBLIC

71-75 Shelton Street, London, United Kingdom
Tel.: (44) 8455270522
Web Site: https://www.enterpriseparking.co.uk
Car Park Management Services
N.A.I.C.S.: 561612

NE Parking Ltd. (1)
Unit 43 Elmdon Trading Estate Bickenhill Lane, Marston Green, Birmingham, United Kingdom
Tel.: (44) 3330230051
Web Site: https://www.ne-parking.com
Car Park Management Services
N.A.I.C.S.: 561612

Smart Parking Technology (1)
Unit 43 Elmdon Trading Estate Bickenhill Lane, Marston Green, Birmingham, B37 7HE, United Kingdom
Tel.: (44) 845 230 3081
Web Site: http://www.smartparking.com
Design, Development & Management of Parking Technology
N.A.I.C.S.: 812930
Susan Taylor *(Gen Mgr)*

SMART POWER CORP.
Suite 909 Tower B Chang An International Building, Xi'an, 710068, Shanxi, China
Tel.: (86) 2987651097
Web Site: http://www.creg-cn.com   NV
CREG—(NASDAQ)
Assets: $136,469,546
Liabilities: $27,223,879
Net Worth: $109,245,667
Earnings: ($746,786)
Emp.: 14
Fiscal Year-end: 12/31/23
Recovered Energy Power Plants Development, Construction & Operation
N.A.I.C.S.: 221118
Guohua Ku *(Chm & CEO)*

SMART PRODUCTS NIGERIA PLC
373 Agege Motor Road Challenge, Mushin, Lagos, Nigeria
Tel.: (234) 18131247
Web Site: https://smartproductsplc.com
Year Founded: 1966
SMURFIT—(NIGE)
Rev.: $33,467
Assets: $145,392
Liabilities: $73,468
Net Worth: $71,924
Earnings: $4,503
Emp.: 2
Fiscal Year-end: 12/31/22
Palm Oil Mfr
N.A.I.C.S.: 311224

SMART RADAR SYSTEM INC.
Fine Digital 3F 41 Seongnam-daero 925beon-gil, Bundang-gu, Seongnam, 13496, Gyeonggi-do, Korea (South)
Tel.: (82) 15330217
Web Site: https://www.smartradarsystem.com
Year Founded: 2017
424960—(KRS)
Automobile Parts Mfr & Distr
N.A.I.C.S.: 334511

SMART SCORE CO., LTD.
8F Cosmo Daechi Tower 8 Teheran-ro 98-gil, Seoul, 06181, Gangnam-gu, Korea (South)
Tel.: (82) 18777281   KR
Web Site: https://www.smartscore.kr
Golf Score-keeping Software, Golf-related IT solutions & Customized Services
N.A.I.C.S.: 513210
Seong-hoon Jeong *(CEO)*

AND PRIVATE COMPANIES

Subsidiaries:

MAJESTY GOLF KOREA Co., Ltd. (1)
Trade Tower No 3404 511, Yeongdong-Daero Gangnam-Gu, Seoul, Korea (South)
Tel.: (82) 25806910
Web Site: http://www.majesty-golf.co.kr
Golf Mfr
N.A.I.C.S.: 459110
Jae-wook Kim *(Co-CEO)*

Subsidiary (Non-US):

MAJESTY GOLF & Co., Ltd. (2)
7FL Meijiseimeikan 2-1-1 Marunouchi, Chiyoda-ku, Tokyo, 100-0005, Japan (85.6%)
Tel.: (81) 3 6275 6300
Web Site: http://www.maruman.co.jp
Golf Product Mfr
N.A.I.C.S.: 339920

Subsidiary (US):

MARUMAN AMERICA, INC. (3)
15375 Barranca Pkwy Ste A-108, Irvine, CA 92618
Tel.: (949) 453-8800
Web Site: http://www.marumanamerica.com
Golf Equipment Distr
N.A.I.C.S.: 423910
Bosuk Jang *(CEO)*

Subsidiary (Non-US):

Maruman (Beijing) Commerce & Trade Co., Ltd. (3)
608 Colorful Plaza No 16 North Street Guangshun Chaoyang District, Beijing, China
Tel.: (86) 1059780570
Golf Equipment Distr
N.A.I.C.S.: 423910

Maruman (Hong Kong) Holding Ltd. (3)
Rm 809 New City Centre No 2 Lei Yue Mun Road Kwun Tong, Kowloon, China (Hong Kong)
Tel.: (852) 21510871
Golf Equipment Distr
N.A.I.C.S.: 423910

Maruman Golf Corporation (3)
5F No345 Xinhu 2nd Rd Neuhu District, Taipei, Taiwan
Tel.: (886) 277215885
Web Site: http://www.maruman.com.tw
Golf Equipment Distr
N.A.I.C.S.: 423910

Maruman Shanghai Sports Goods Trading CO (3)
3D-E Shanghai New Goldenbridge Plaza 23 West Beijing Road, Huang Pu District, Shanghai, China
Tel.: (86) 2153079018
Golf Equipment Distr
N.A.I.C.S.: 423910

Marumankorea Co., Ltd. (3)
Daebong Bldg 13F 238 Teheran-Ro Gangnam-Gu, Seoul, Korea (South)
Tel.: (82) 25806900
Web Site: http://www.marumankorea.com
Golf Equipment Distr
N.A.I.C.S.: 423910

SMART SHARE GLOBAL LIMITED
6th Floor 799 Tianshan W Road, Changning District, Shanghai, 200335, China
Tel.: (86) 2160503535 Ky
Web Site: https://enmonster.com
Year Founded: 2017
EM—(NASDAQ)
Rev.: $434,839,090
Assets: $656,909,478
Liabilities: $252,235,139
Net Worth: $404,674,339
Earnings: ($108,969,080)
Emp.: 3,656
Fiscal Year-end: 12/31/22
Holding Company
N.A.I.C.S.: 551112

Mars Guangyuan Cai *(Co-Founder, Chm, CEO & Partner)*

SMART SOLUTIONS CO., LTD.
942 Gosaek Dong, Gweonseon Gu, Suwon, 441-813, Gyunggi Do, Korea (South)
Tel.: (82) 312373425
Web Site: http://www.semisysco.com
Year Founded: 2000
136510—(KRS)
Rev.: $8,974,121
Assets: $21,689,126
Liabilities: $39,180,528
Net Worth: ($17,491,402)
Earnings: ($58,327,745)
Emp.: 43
Fiscal Year-end: 12/31/22
Detector Equipment Mfr
N.A.I.C.S.: 334519

SMART SOLUTIONS MARKETING PANAMA, S.A.
City of Knowledge Clayton Building 239 3rd Floor, PO Box 0834-1924, Panama, Panama
Tel.: (507) 317 1636
Emp.: 87
Information Technology Consulting Services
N.A.I.C.S.: 541512

SMART TRAFFIC LTD.
Broad Quay House Prince Street, Bristol, BS1 4DJ, United Kingdom
Tel.: (44) 845 331 3512
Web Site: http://www.smart-traffic.co.uk
Year Founded: 2006
Sales Range: $10-24.9 Million
Emp.: 180
Search Engine Optimization Services
N.A.I.C.S.: 541890
Andy Birt *(CEO)*

Subsidiaries:

Smart Traffic Pty Ltd (1)
Studio 1 37-45 Myrtle Street, Chippendale, Sydney, 2008, NSW, Australia
Tel.: (61) 282053133
Web Site: http://www.smart-traffic.com.au
Search Engine Optimization Services
N.A.I.C.S.: 519290

SMART WOOD SAS
130 rue de la Liberte, Saint-Sauveur, 60320, France
Tel.: (33) 3 44 85 51 00 FR
Web Site: http://www.smartwood.world
Year Founded: 1928
Emp.: 900
Wooden Sticks Mfr
N.A.I.C.S.: 321999

Subsidiaries:

smart wood Germany GmbH & Co. KG (1)
Albert-Einstein-Strasse 4, 23617, Stockelsdorf, Germany
Tel.: (49) 451499010
Ice Cream Stick Mfr
N.A.I.C.S.: 321999

SMART-CORE HOLDINGS LIMITED
15/F Tower B Regent Centre 70 Ta Chuen Ping Street, Kwai Chung, New Territories, China (Hong Kong)
Tel.: (852) 27551101 Ky
Web Site: http://www.smart-core.com.hk
Year Founded: 2005
2166—(HKG)
Rev.: $1,275,774,945
Assets: $364,760,160
Liabilities: $211,642,478

Net Worth: $153,117,683
Earnings: $48,417,488
Emp.: 579
Fiscal Year-end: 12/31/22
Electronic Components Distr
N.A.I.C.S.: 423690

Subsidiaries:

Quiksol International HK Pte Limited (1)
4F-A Jia Cheng Plaza No 128 West of Zhongxin Avenue, Suzhou Industrial Park, Suzhou, China
Tel.: (86) 51262806402
Electric Equipment Mfr
N.A.I.C.S.: 334419

Shenzhen Smart-Core Technology Co., Ltd. (1)
Unit ABCD 16th Floor Tower A Financial Technology Building, No 11 Keyuan Road Yuehai Street Nanshan District, Shenzhen, 518057, Guangdong, China
Tel.: (86) 75526037700
Electronic Components Distr
N.A.I.C.S.: 423690

SMARTAC INTERNATIONAL HOLDINGS LIMITED.
Room 2101 21st Floor COFCO Tower 262 Gloucester Road, Causeway Bay, China (Hong Kong)
Tel.: (852) 2123 9985 Ky
Web Site: http://www.smartacgroup.com
Year Founded: 1977
Rev.: $3,691,551
Assets: $46,140,162
Liabilities: $7,729,833
Net Worth: $38,410,330
Earnings: ($7,498,440)
Emp.: 97
Fiscal Year-end: 12/31/19
Zirconium chemicals, New Energy Materials & Rechargeable Batteries Mfr & Exporter
N.A.I.C.S.: 325998
Xin Min Yang *(Chm)*

Subsidiaries:

Century Dragon Investment Limited (1)
Ste 2611 26 F Tower 2 Times Sq 1 Matheson, Causeway Bay, China (Hong Kong)
Tel.: (852) 21239986
Web Site: http://www.chinazirconium.com.hk
Sales Range: $25-49.9 Million
Emp.: 3
Industrial Chemicals Mfr
N.A.I.C.S.: 325180
Pony Ma *(Mgr)*

Lucky Creation Enterprise (Shanghai) Limited (1)
2nd Floor Haibo Building No 3615 GongHeXin Road, Jing An District, Shanghai, 200435, China
Tel.: (86) 2136120168
Web Site: http://www.luckyce.com
Marketing Services
N.A.I.C.S.: 541613

SMARTBROKER HOLDING AG
Seydelstrasse 18, 10117, Berlin, Germany
Tel.: (49) 3020456382
Web Site: https://smartbroker-holding.de
Year Founded: 1998
SB1—(MUN)
Rev.: $51,374,110
Assets: $70,471,061
Liabilities: $22,927,380
Net Worth: $47,543,681
Earnings: ($6,479,717)
Emp.: 261
Fiscal Year-end: 12/31/23
Financial Support Services
N.A.I.C.S.: 523940

Stefan Zmojda *(Chief Revenue Officer & Member-Exec Bd)*

SMARTCENTRES REAL ESTATE INVESTMENT TRUST
3200 Highway 7, Vaughan, L4K 5Z5, ON, Canada
Tel.: (905) 326-6400 AB
Web Site: https://www.smartcentres.com
Year Founded: 2001
SRU.UN—(TSX)
Rev.: $389,687,306
Assets: $8,834,482,045
Liabilities: $4,264,938,147
Net Worth: $4,569,543,898
Earnings: $772,639,181
Emp.: 378
Fiscal Year-end: 12/31/21
Real Estate Investment Trust
N.A.I.C.S.: 525990
Peter Forde *(Pres & COO)*

SMARTCHASE CORP.
380 Wellington St Tower B, London, N6A 5B5, ON, Canada
Tel.: (226) 223-1566 NV
Web Site: https://www.smartchase.ca
Year Founded: 2006
Investment Holding Company; Oil & Gas Exploration Services
N.A.I.C.S.: 551112
Thomas Jones *(CEO, CFO, Treas & Sec)*

SMARTCOOL SYSTEMS INC.
Suite 1502 - 5955 Balsam Street, Vancouver, V6M 0A1, BC, Canada
Tel.: (604) 669-1388 Ca
Web Site: http://www.smartcool.net
Year Founded: 2000
SSCFF—(OTCEM)
Energy Saving Technology Services
N.A.I.C.S.: 561990
Steven Martin *(Exec VP)*

Subsidiaries:

Smartcool Systems (EMEA) Ltd. (1)
6-7 Delta Park Wilson Road, Alton, GU34 2RQ, Hampshire, United Kingdom
Tel.: (44) 1420 544 868
Sales Range: $25-49.9 Million
Emp.: 16
Air Conditioning & Refrigeration Equipment Distr
N.A.I.C.S.: 423730
George Burnes *(CEO)*

Subsidiary (Domestic):

Smartcool Systems UK Ltd. (2)
West Gate 104 High Street, Alton, GU34 1EN, Hampshire, United Kingdom
Tel.: (44) 1420 540 460
Web Site: http://www.smartcool.co.uk
Energy Saving Module Distr
N.A.I.C.S.: 423690

Smartcool Systems (USA) Inc. (1)
4923 W 34th St, Houston, TX 77092
Tel.: (713) 263-7888
Energy Consulting Services
N.A.I.C.S.: 541690

Subsidiary (Domestic):

Total Energy Concepts Inc. (2)
7676 Design Rd Ste 400, Baxter, MN 56425
Tel.: (218) 844-5848
Web Site: http://totalenergyconcepts.com
Electrical & HVAC Contractor
N.A.I.C.S.: 238210

SMARTCRAFT ASA
Hvervenmoveien 45, 3511, Honefoss, Norway
Tel.: (47) 70178400
Web Site: https://www.smartcraft.com
Year Founded: 1987

SMARTCRAFT ASA

SmartCraft ASA—(Continued)
SMCRT—(OSL)
Rev.: $37,100,868
Assets: $101,613,061
Liabilities: $23,682,616
Net Worth: $77,930,445
Earnings: $9,941,622
Emp.: 206
Fiscal Year-end: 12/31/23
Software Development Services
N.A.I.C.S.: 541511
Gunnar Haglund (Chm)

Subsidiaries:

Bygglet AB (1)
von Utfallsgatan 1, 415 05, Gothenburg, Sweden
Tel.: (46) 770339788
Web Site: https://bygglet.com
Emp.: 41
Construction Services
N.A.I.C.S.: 541310

Congrid Oy (1)
Urho Kekkosen katu 3B, 00100, Helsinki, Finland
Tel.: (358) 706673603
Web Site: https://congrid.com
Construction Services
N.A.I.C.S.: 541310

Cordel Norge AS (1)
Borgundfjordvegen 80, 6017, Alesund, Norway
Tel.: (47) 70178410
Web Site: https://cordel.no
Software Products Distr
N.A.I.C.S.: 423430

El-Info i Vaxjo AB (1)
Lineborgsplan 3, 352 33, Vaxjo, Sweden
Tel.: (46) 470724030
Web Site: https://el-vis.com
Electrical Information Services
N.A.I.C.S.: 238210

Elverdi Norge AS (1)
H Chr Stormers gate 22, 8300, Svolvaer, Norway
Tel.: (47) 90066363
Web Site: https://elverdi.no
Information Technology Services
N.A.I.C.S.: 541519

Homerunbynet OY (1)
Kauppakatu 13, 74100, Iisalmi, Finland
Tel.: (358) 201980020
Web Site: https://homerun.net
Apartment Construction Services
N.A.I.C.S.: 236210

Inprog AS (1)
Neptunvegen 6, 7652, Verdal, Norway
Tel.: (47) 40122000
Web Site: https://www.inprog.no
Information Technology Services
N.A.I.C.S.: 541519

Kvalitetskontroll AS (1)
Torsvikhogda 2, 5337, Rong, Norway
Tel.: (47) 56382750
Web Site: https://www.kvalitetskontroll.no
Emp.: 28
Building & Construction Services
N.A.I.C.S.: 532412

SMARTDISPLAYER TECHNOLOGY CO., LTD.
No 2-1 Gongjian Rd, Qidu Dist, Keelung, 20647, Taiwan
Tel.: (886) 224525100
Web Site:
http://www.smartdisplayer.com
Year Founded: 2002
6717—(TPE)
Rev.: $8,927,793
Assets: $17,745,478
Liabilities: $6,393,669
Net Worth: $11,351,810
Earnings: $602,211
Emp.: 120
Fiscal Year-end: 12/31/23
Digital Card Mfr
N.A.I.C.S.: 334111

SMARTER BUSINESS LIMITED
John De Mierre House, Bridge Road, Haywards Heath, RH16 1UA, W Sussex, United Kingdom
Tel.: (44) 1444 220060 UK
Web Site:
http://www.smarterbusiness.co.uk
Procurement & Negotiation Services
N.A.I.C.S.: 541618
Bradley Wingrave (CEO)

Subsidiaries:

Business Advisory Service Limited (1)
John De Mierre House, Bridge Road, Haywards Heath, RH16 1UA, W Sussex, United Kingdom
Tel.: (44) 845 1800 700
Web Site: http://www.bas-energy.co.uk
Business Electricity Consultancy & Advisory Services
N.A.I.C.S.: 523940

SMARTERWORK.COM LTD.
80 London St, Reading, RG1 4SJ, Berks, United Kingdom
Tel.: (44) 1189888850 UK
Web Site:
http://www.smarterwork.com
Year Founded: 1999
Outsourcing Services for Internet, Marketing & Creative, Research, Writing, Legal & Translation; Web Design, Personal Assistance, Software Development & Business Consulting
N.A.I.C.S.: 541512
Francois de Borchgrave (Co-Founder)

SMARTGEN (ZHENGZHOU) TECHNOLOGY CO., LTD.
No 28 Xuemei Street, Zhengzhou, 450001, Henan, China
Tel.: (86) 37167988888
Web Site:
https://www.smartgen.com.cn
Year Founded: 1998
301361—(CHIN)
Rev.: $30,469,318
Assets: $156,341,770
Liabilities: $6,411,428
Net Worth: $149,930,342
Earnings: $10,130,815
Emp.: 300
Fiscal Year-end: 12/31/23
Generator Product Mfr & Distr
N.A.I.C.S.: 335312
Xinzheng Yang (Chm)

SMARTGROUP CORPORATION LTD.
Level 8 133 Castlereagh Street, Sydney, 2000, NSW, Australia
Tel.: (61) 300476278
Web Site:
https://www.smartgroup.com.au
SIQ—(ASX)
Rev.: $171,384,102
Assets: $284,399,564
Liabilities: $118,319,597
Net Worth: $166,079,967
Earnings: $42,176,282
Emp.: 835
Fiscal Year-end: 12/31/23
Salary Packaging, Novated Leasing, Fleet Management & Vehicle Buying Services
N.A.I.C.S.: 525990
Michael Carapiet (Chm)

Subsidiaries:

Salary Packaging Solutions Pty. Ltd. (1)
Level 8 550 Bourke Street, Melbourne, 3000, VIC, Australia
Tel.: (61) 800555582

Financial Services
N.A.I.C.S.: 523999

Selectus Pty. Ltd. (1)
Level 8 550 Bourke Street, Melbourne, 3000, VIC, Australia
Tel.: (61) 1300010203
Web Site: http://www1.selectus.com.au
Financial Services
N.A.I.C.S.: 523999

Smartfleet Management Pty. Ltd. (1)
Level 12 550 Bourke Street, Melbourne, 3000, VIC, Australia
Tel.: (61) 1300555665
Web Site:
https://www.smartfleetaustralia.com.au
Fleet Management Services
N.A.I.C.S.: 561110

Smartsalary Pty. Limited (1)
GPO Box 4244, Sydney, 2001, NSW, Australia
Tel.: (61) 1300476278
Web Site: https://www.smartsalary.com.au
Financial Services
N.A.I.C.S.: 523999

Smartsalary Software Solutions Pty. Ltd. (1)
Level 9 30 Currie Street, Adelaide, 5000, SA, Australia
Tel.: (61) 800680180
Financial Services
N.A.I.C.S.: 523999

SMARTIKS YAZILIM A.S.
Yildiz Teknik Universitesi Davutpasa Kampusu Teknopark D2 Blok No Z06, Esenler, 34220, Istanbul, Turkiye
Tel.: (90) 2124837430
Web Site:
https://www.smartiks.com.tr
Year Founded: 2006
SMART—(IST)
Rev.: $1,822,967
Assets: $3,568,203
Liabilities: $1,239,962
Net Worth: $2,328,241
Earnings: $211,918
Fiscal Year-end: 12/31/22
Software Development Services
N.A.I.C.S.: 541511
Serkan Karahanoglu (Chm)

Subsidiaries:

Compello Bilgi Teknolojisi Hizmetleri ve Ticaret A.S. (1)
Sahrayicedit Mh Halk Sk Kayalar Is Merkezi No 39/A Kadikoy, Istanbul, Turkiye
Tel.: (90) 2164690597
Web Site: https://www.compello.com.tr
Software Development Services
N.A.I.C.S.: 541511

SMARTKEM, INC.
Manchester Technology Center Hexagon Tower Delaunays Road, Blackley, Manchester, M9 8GQ, United Kingdom
Tel.: (44) 1617211514 DE
Web Site: https://www.smartkem.com
Year Founded: 2009
SMTK—(OTCQB)
Rev.: $40,000
Assets: $7,525,000
Liabilities: $1,642,000
Net Worth: $5,883,000
Earnings: ($11,495,000)
Emp.: 50
Fiscal Year-end: 12/31/22
Semiconductor Product Mfr & Distr
N.A.I.C.S.: 334413
Barbra C. Keck (CFO)

SMARTLINK HOLDINGS LIMITED
CITIPOINT - Unit No B-701, B-702 & B-703 Andheri-Kurla Road, J B Nagar Andheri East, Mumbai, 400 059, India
Tel.: (91) 2249386666

INTERNATIONAL PUBLIC

Web Site:
https://www.smartlinkholdings.com
Year Founded: 1993
532419—(BOM)
Rev.: $9,948,798
Assets: $31,364,661
Liabilities: $4,964,672
Net Worth: $26,399,989
Earnings: $1,396,243
Emp.: 28
Fiscal Year-end: 03/31/21
Networking Equipment Mfr
N.A.I.C.S.: 334210
K. R. Naik (Founder & Chm)

Subsidiaries:

Synegra EMS Limited (1)
Plot No L-5A Verna Salcette, Verna Industrial Estate South Goa, Goa, 403722, India
Tel.: (91) 8322885433
Web Site: https://www.synegra.com
Electronic Products Mfr
N.A.I.C.S.: 334111

SMARTLOGIC UK
200 Aldersgate, London, EC1A 4HD, United Kingdom
Tel.: (44) 2031764500
Web Site: http://www.smartlogic.com
Year Founded: 1996
Sales Range: $1-9.9 Million
Emp.: 40
Software Development Services
N.A.I.C.S.: 541511
Jeremy Bentley (CEO & Co-Founder)

Subsidiaries:

Smartlogic US (1)
560 S Winchester Blvd Ste 500, San Jose, CA 95128
Tel.: (408) 213-9500
Data Processing Services
N.A.I.C.S.: 518210
Toby Conrad (Co-Founder & Sr VP)

SMARTPAY HOLDINGS LIMITED
205-209 Wairau Road, Wairau Valley, Auckland, 0627, New Zealand
Tel.: (64) 94422700
Web Site:
https://www.smartpay.co.nz
SPY—(NZX)
Rev.: $34,572,396
Assets: $50,745,582
Liabilities: $24,809,814
Net Worth: $25,935,768
Earnings: $2,231,776
Emp.: 23
Fiscal Year-end: 03/31/22
Technology Services for Merchants & Retailers
N.A.I.C.S.: 517810
Gregor John Barclay (Chm)

Subsidiaries:

Cadmus Payment Solutions Pty Limited (1)
Level 2 3 Carlingford Rd, Epping, 2121, NSW, Australia
Tel.: (61) 288762300
Web Site: http://www.smartpayltd.com
Sales Range: $25-49.9 Million
Emp.: 1
Electronic Payment Device Mfr
N.A.I.C.S.: 334511

SmartPay Cadmus Limited (1)
182-190 Wairau Road, Glenfield, 0627, New Zealand
Tel.: (64) 94422700
Web Site: http://www.smartpay.co.nz
Sales Range: $25-49.9 Million
Emp.: 100
Telecommunication Services[b]
N.A.I.C.S.: 517112
Ian Bailey (Mng Dir)

SmartPay New Zealand Limited (1)
205-209 Wairau Road, Wairau Valley, Auckland, 0627, New Zealand

AND PRIVATE COMPANIES

Tel.: (64) 800476278
Web Site: http://www.smartpay.co.nz
Sales Range: $50-74.9 Million
Emp.: 70
Electronic Payment Services
N.A.I.C.S.: 522320

SMARTPHOTO GROUP N.V.
Kwatrechtsteenweg 160, B 9230, Wetteren, Belgium
Tel.: (32) 93659810
Web Site:
  https://www.smartphotogroup.com
SMAR—(EUR)
Rev.: $82,338,657
Assets: $89,451,759
Liabilities: $36,972,804
Net Worth: $52,478,955
Earnings: $5,924,887
Emp.: 229
Fiscal Year-end: 12/31/22
Photographic Services
N.A.I.C.S.: 812921

Subsidiaries:

Smartphoto AG (1)
Hauptstr 70, 4132, Muttenz, Switzerland
Tel.: (41) 844808404
Web Site: http://www.smartphoto.ch
Digital Online Photography Services
N.A.I.C.S.: 541921

Smartphoto Nederland BV (1)
Beursstraat 1A, 7551 HP, Hengelo, Netherlands
Tel.: (31) 541200700
Web Site: http://www.smartphoto.nl
Digital Online Photography Services
N.A.I.C.S.: 541921

Smartphoto Nordic AB (1)
Kalendegatan 10F, 211 35, Malmo, Sweden
Tel.: (46) 52517000
Web Site: https://www.smartphoto.se
Digital Online Photography Services
N.A.I.C.S.: 541921

SMARTQUANTUM GROUP SA
4 rue de Broglie, 22300, Lannion, France
Tel.: (33) 2 96 48 59 35
High-Speed Network Security Products Mfr
N.A.I.C.S.: 541512
Frederic Fabre (Chm & Pres)

Subsidiaries:

SmartQuantum S.A. (1)
4 rue Ampere, 22300, Lannion, France
Tel.: (33) 2 96 48 59 35
Security System Designer
N.A.I.C.S.: 561621

SMARTREE ROMANIA SRL
Baneasa Business Technology Park Sos Bucuresti-Ploiesti, No 42-44 Building A Wing A2 et 4 Sector 1, Bucharest, Romania
Tel.: (40) 213 01 90 90 RO
Web Site: http://www.smartree.com
Year Founded: 2000
Payroll Services
N.A.I.C.S.: 541214
Alexandra Peligrad (CEO)

SMARTSET SERVICES, INC.
26 2365 Abbeyglen Way, Kamloops, V1S 1Y3, BC, Canada
Tel.: (778) 362-3037
Year Founded: 2018
SMAR.P—(TSXV)
Rev.: $118,803
Assets: $200,119
Net Worth: $200,119
Earnings: $42,813
Fiscal Year-end: 03/31/24
Asset Management Services
N.A.I.C.S.: 523940
Randy Clifford (CEO, CFO & Sec)

SMARTSPACE SOFTWARE PLC
Norderstedt House James Carter Road, Mildenhall, IP28 7RQ, United Kingdom
Tel.: (44) 1638510900 UK
Web Site:
  http://www.smartspaceplc.com
SMRT—(AIM)
Rev.: $6,864,632
Assets: $22,519,144
Liabilities: $6,713,925
Net Worth: $15,805,219
Earnings: ($3,717,437)
Emp.: 54
Fiscal Year-end: 01/31/23
Internet Telephone Services
N.A.I.C.S.: 517121
Frank Beechinor (CEO)

Subsidiaries:

Space Connect Pty Limited (1)
2-6 Glenferrie Road, PO Box 2368, Caulfield Junction, Malvern, 3144, VIC, Australia
Tel.: (61) 399334644
Web Site: https://www.spaceconnect.com.au
Computer Software Development Services
N.A.I.C.S.: 541511

SwipedOn Limited (1)
1/115 The Strand, Tauranga, 3110, New Zealand
Tel.: (64) 7886136
Web Site: https://www.swipedon.com
Computer Software Development Services
N.A.I.C.S.: 541511
Hadleigh Ford (Founder & CEO)

SMARTTECH247 GROUP PLC
165 Fleet Street, London, EC4 A2DY, United Kingdom
Tel.: (44) 2890726019 UK
Web Site:
  https://www.smarttech247.com
Year Founded: 2022
S247—(AIM)
Management Consulting Services
N.A.I.C.S.: 541618
Ronan Murphy (Chm)

SMARTVALUE CO., LTD.
2-3-2 Utsubohonmachi Nishi-ku, Osaka, 550-0004, Japan
Tel.: (81) 664481711
Web Site:
  http://www.smartvalue.ad.jp
9417—(TKS)
Rev.: $23,723,080
Assets: $25,110,140
Liabilities: $11,687,380
Net Worth: $13,422,760
Earnings: ($2,164,560)
Emp.: 280
Fiscal Year-end: 06/30/24
Cloud Services
N.A.I.C.S.: 513210
Jun Shibuya (Pres)

Subsidiaries:

North Detail Co., Ltd. (1)
Sosei Square 13F 1-6 Kita 1 West, Chuo-ku, Sapporo, 060-0001, Japan
Tel.: (81) 112047007
Web Site: https://www.northdetail.co.jp
Cloud Development Services
N.A.I.C.S.: 518210

SMARTWATER TECHNOLOGY LIMITED
27 Queen Ann's Gate, London, SW1H 9BU, United Kingdom
Tel.: (44) 800 521 669
Web Site: http://www.smartwater.com
Liquid Theft Protection Product Mfr; Security & Forensic Services
N.A.I.C.S.: 325998
Phil Cleary (Co-Founder & CEO)

Subsidiaries:

SmartWater CSI, LLC (1)
500 W Cypress Creek Rd Ste 560, Fort Lauderdale, FL 33309
Tel.: (954) 320-7290
Web Site: https://www.smartwatercsi.com
Sales Range: $1-9.9 Million
Emp.: 7
Liquid Theft Protection Product Mfr
N.A.I.C.S.: 325998
Antonio Arserio (Gen Mgr)

SMB KENZAI CO., LTD.
2-2-1 Toranomon, Minato-ku, Tokyo, 105-0001, Japan
Tel.: (81) 355735101
Web Site: http://www.smb-kenzai.com
Year Founded: 1966
Plywood, Wood Products, Wooden Building Materials, Housing Apparatus, Ceramic, Metal & Resin Building Materials Purchasing & Selling
N.A.I.C.S.: 423310
Tomoharu Kurokawa (Pres)

SMB-MEHANIZACIJA I TRANSPORT A.D.
Cantavirski put 14, 24000, Subotica, Serbia
Tel.: (381) 24 566 076
Web Site:
  http://www.smb.backabanat.com
Year Founded: 2002
Sales Range: Less than $1 Million
Construction Support Services
N.A.I.C.S.: 238290

SMC CORPORATION
Akihabara UDX15F 4-14-1 Sotokanda, Chiyoda-ku, Tokyo, 101-0021, Japan
Tel.: (81) 352078271
Web Site: https://www.smcworld.com
Year Founded: 1959
SMCAY—(OTCIQ)
Rev.: $5,913,615,240
Assets: $13,823,329,800
Liabilities: $1,617,659,550
Net Worth: $12,205,670,250
Earnings: $1,610,446,530
Emp.: 22,988
Fiscal Year-end: 03/31/23
Automatic Control Device & Filtration Element Mfr
N.A.I.C.S.: 334519
Yoshiyuki Takada (Chm)

Subsidiaries:

A.M. Pneumatik d.o.o. (1)
Krecanska 15A pp 1, 75000, Tuzla, Bosnia & Herzegovina
Tel.: (387) 3 536 4430
Web Site: https://www.ampneumatik.com
Compressed Air Equipment Mfr
N.A.I.C.S.: 333912

Advanced Pressure Technology, Inc. (1)
687 Technology Way, Napa, CA 94558
Tel.: (707) 259-0102
Web Site: https://aptech-online.com
Sales Range: $50-74.9 Million
Emp.: 140
Semiconductor Devices Mfr
N.A.I.C.S.: 334413
Rene Zakhour (Founder)

Alsaggaf Trading Co. (1)
PO Box 3385, Jeddah, 21471, Saudi Arabia
Tel.: (966) 2 673 1857
Automatic Control Equipment Mfr & Distr
N.A.I.C.S.: 334512

Assistech Cia. Ltda. (1)
De las Malvas E7-15 y Julio Arellano, Quito, Ecuador
Tel.: (593) 2 243 1803
Web Site: https://www.assistech.com.ec
Engineering Product Distr
N.A.I.C.S.: 423490

Codex Negoce SARL (1)
40 Avenue Jean Jaures, Dakar, Senegal
Tel.: (221) 77 333 7548
Automatic Control Equipment Mfr & Distr
N.A.I.C.S.: 334512
Luca Giolivo (Mng Dir)

Commitment Engineering Supplies (W.L.L.) (1)
Building No 136 Al Wakkalat Street, Doha, Qatar
Tel.: (974) 4 435 7497
Web Site: https://www.cewqatar.com
Plumbing Contract Services
N.A.I.C.S.: 238220

Electric Center Eurl (1)
8 Bis Rue Ain Soltan Les Oliviers, Kouba, Algiers, Alger, Algeria
Tel.: (213) 2 144 9514
Web Site: https://www.eck-dz.com
Automatic Control Equipment Mfr & Distr
N.A.I.C.S.: 334512

Electro-Serv (Pvt.) Ltd. (1)
No 247 2/1 Standley Thilakarathne Mawatha, Nugegoda, Colombo, Sri Lanka
Tel.: (94) 11 532 4110
Web Site: https://www.electro-serv.lk
Automatic Control Equipment Mfr & Distr
N.A.I.C.S.: 334512

Faraday Engineering Company Limited (1)
19 Ogunshefunmi Street Off Akinremi Street Anifowose, Ikeja, Lagos, Nigeria
Tel.: (234) 803 302 9427
Automatic Control Equipment Mfr & Distr
N.A.I.C.S.: 334512
Ishola Adebayo Akinola (Mng Dir)

Flow Controls Ltd. (1)
Pemba Street Off Lusaka Road, PO Box 26131-00504, Industrial Area, Nairobi, Kenya
Tel.: (254) 72 675 5888
Web Site: https://www.flow.co.ke
Industrial Spare Parts Distr
N.A.I.C.S.: 423840

High Tower Engineering LLC (1)
PO Box 4010, 112, Ruwi, Oman
Tel.: (968) 2 423 1990
Automatic Control Equipment Mfr & Distr
N.A.I.C.S.: 334512
Ahmad Hassouneh (Sls Mgr)

Hydrotek Engineering Co. (1)
Al Rai Area-At the junction of Ghazally Street and Street 22, PO Box 2295, Opposite to Centerpoint Safat, 13023, Kuwait, Kuwait
Tel.: (965) 180 8555
Web Site: https://www.hydrotek.com
Plumbing Related Product Mfr & Distr
N.A.I.C.S.: 332913
Abdulaziz Al Hajeri (Gen Mgr)

Interstab Engineering d.o.o.e.l. (1)
3rd Macedonian Brigade 54a, 1000, Skopje, North Macedonia
Web Site: https://www.interstab.mk
Industrial Equipment Mfr & Distr
N.A.I.C.S.: 333248

Jubilee Corporation (1)
First Floor Fakhri Trade Center Shahrah-e-Liaquat, PO Box 677, Karachi, 74200, Pakistan
Tel.: (92) 213 260 2200
Web Site:
  https://www.jubileecorporation.com
Automatic Control Equipment Mfr & Distr
N.A.I.C.S.: 334512

LLP SMC Kazakhstan (1)
Office 509 4 Tsiolkovskiy Str, Nur-Sultan, Kazakhstan
Tel.: (7) 717 254 1407
Automatic Control Equipment Mfr & Distr
N.A.I.C.S.: 334512
Vitaly Suhostavskij (Mng Dir)

PNEUMOTEC Corp. (1)
St Electrotechnical 44-b, 02222, Kiev, Ukraine
Tel.: (380) 44 468 8924
Web Site: https://www.pneumotec.com.ua
Automatic Control Equipment Mfr & Distr
N.A.I.C.S.: 334512

SMC CORPORATION — INTERNATIONAL PUBLIC

SMC Corporation—(Continued)

PT SMC Automation Indonesia (1)
EJIP Industrial Park Plot 6J-1, Bekasi, 17857, Cikarang Selatan, Indonesia
Tel.: (62) 21 897 1123
Automatic Control Equipment Mfr & Distr
N.A.I.C.S.: 334512
David Wong *(Pres)*

PT SMC Pneumatics Indonesia (1)
Ejip Industrial Park Plot 6J-1, Cikarang Selatan, 17550, Bekasi, Indonesia
Tel.: (62) 218971123
Fluid Power Cylinder & Actuator Mfr
N.A.I.C.S.: 333995

SC SMC Romania S.r.l. (1)
Str Frunzei 29 Sector 2, Bucharest, Romania
Tel.: (40) 21 320 5111
Emp.: 100
Automatic Control Equipment Mfr & Distr
N.A.I.C.S.: 334512
Victor Dahnovici *(Comml Dir)*

SMC (Beijing) Manufacturing Co. Ltd. (1)
Jia No 1 Tianzhu Rd Part A of Beijing Tianzhu Airport Industrial Zone, Beijing Tianzhu Export Process, 101312, Beijing, China
Tel.: (86) 1080480101
Web Site: http://www.smcworld.co.cn
Fluid Power Cylinder & Actuator Mfr
N.A.I.C.S.: 333995

Plant (Domestic):

SMC (Beijing) Manufacturing Co., Ltd - 3rd Plant of Beijing (2)
No 3 TianZhu East Road Area A Beijing TianZhu Airport Industrial Zone, Beijing, 10312, China
Tel.: (86) 10 80480101
Web Site: http://www.smcworld.com
Automatic Control Equipment Mfr
N.A.I.C.S.: 333248

SMC (China) Co. Ltd. (1)
A2 Xingsheng St, 100176, Beijing, China
Tel.: (86) 1067882111
Web Site: http://www.smc.com.cn
Sales Range: $800-899.9 Million
Emp.: 4,000
Fluid Power Cylinder & Actuator Mfr
N.A.I.C.S.: 333995

Plant (Domestic):

SMC (China) Co., Ltd. - 1st Plant of Beijing (2)
No 7 Wan Yuan St Beijing Economic & Technological Development Zone, Beijing, 100176, China
Tel.: (86) 10 67882111
Web Site: http://www.smcworld.com
Electronic Components Mfr
N.A.I.C.S.: 334419
Zhao Tong *(Mng Dir)*

SMC (Myanmar) Co., Ltd. (1)
No-74 Lann Thit Road Nant Thar Kone Rd, Insein Township, Yangon, Myanmar
Tel.: (95) 995 425 6566
Automatic Control Equipment Mfr & Distr
N.A.I.C.S.: 334512
Tada Pradip Na Talang *(Mng Dir)*

SMC Argentina S.A. (1)
Austria Norte 1831 Troncos del Talar, Parque Industrial Tigre, C 1427 ECH, Buenos Aires, Argentina
Tel.: (54) 1147150233
Web Site: http://www.smc.eu
Sales Range: $25-49.9 Million
Emp.: 50
Fluid Power Cylinder & Actuator Mfr
N.A.I.C.S.: 333995
Ernesto Gesualdi *(Gen Mgr)*

SMC Austria GmbH (1)
Girakstrasse 2-8, 2100, Korneuburg, Austria
Tel.: (43) 226 262 2800
Emp.: 200
Industrial Automation Product Distr
N.A.I.C.S.: 423830
Robert Angel *(Mng Dir)*

SMC Automacao do Brasil Ltda. (1)
Av Piraporinha 777 - Jd Planalto, Sao Bernardo do Campo, 09891-001, Brazil
Tel.: (55) 114 082 0600
Web Site: https://smcbr.com.br
Industrial Valve Mfr & Distr
N.A.I.C.S.: 332911

SMC Automation (Taiwan) Co., Ltd. (1)
No 16 Lane 205 Nanshan Rd Sec 2, Luzhu-Dist, Taoyuan, 338, Taiwan
Tel.: (886) 3 322 3443
Web Site: https://www.smc.com.tw
Automatic Control Equipment Mfr & Distr
N.A.I.C.S.: 334512

SMC Automation AB (1)
Ekhagsvagen 29-31, Segeltorp, 141 71, Huddinge, Sweden
Tel.: (46) 8 603 1200
Emp.: 80
Automatic Control Equipment Mfr & Distr
N.A.I.C.S.: 334512
Torbjorn Lundberg *(Mng Dir)*

SMC Automation AS (1)
Vollsveien 13 B Granfoss Naeringspark, 1366, Lysaker, Norway
Tel.: (47) 6 712 9020
Emp.: 10
Automatic Control Equipment Mfr & Distr
N.A.I.C.S.: 334512
Stig Grani *(Country Mgr)*

SMC Automation Bolivia SRL (1)
Avenida Canal Cotoca 2635 Between 2nd and 3rd Ring, Santa Cruz, Bolivia
Tel.: (591) 364 9957
Web Site: https://www.smcbolivia.com.bo
Automatic Control Equipment Mfr
N.A.I.C.S.: 334512

SMC Automation China Co., Ltd. (1)
A2 XingSheng Street BDA, Beijing, 100176, China
Tel.: (86) 106 788 5566
Emp.: 6,127
Automatic Control Equipment Mfr & Distr
N.A.I.C.S.: 334512
Ma Qing Hai *(Mng Dir)*

SMC Automation Israel Ltd. (1)
Sderot HaMiktsoot 11, Modi'in-Maccabim-Re'ut, Israel
Tel.: (972) 8 635 5577
Automatic Control Equipment Mfr & Distr
N.A.I.C.S.: 334512

SMC Automation OU (1)
Laki 12, 10621, Tallinn, Estonia
Tel.: (372) 651 0370
Industrial Automation Product Distr
N.A.I.C.S.: 423830
Eduard Sauks *(Sls Mgr)*

SMC Automation Oy (1)
PB72, 02231, Espoo, Finland
Tel.: (358) 20 751 3513
Emp.: 40
Industrial Automation Product Distr
N.A.I.C.S.: 423830
Johan Grasbeck *(Mng Dir)*

SMC Automation SIA (1)
Dzelzavas iela 117, Riga, LV-1021, Latvia
Tel.: (371) 6 781 7700
Automatic Control Equipment Mfr & Distr
N.A.I.C.S.: 334512
Egils Lieknins *(Country Mgr)*

SMC Automation UAB (1)
Zalgirio g 96, LT-09300, Vilnius, Lithuania
Tel.: (370) 5 230 8118
Automatic Control Equipment Mfr & Distr
N.A.I.C.S.: 334512
Marius Lipnickas *(Sls Mgr)*

SMC Belgium N.V. (1)
Temesselei 232, 2160, Wommelgem, Belgium
Tel.: (32) 3 355 1464
Emp.: 25
Pneumatic Equipment Distr
N.A.I.C.S.: 423830
Hugues Maes *(Gen Mgr)*

SMC Colombia S.A.S. (1)
Parque Industrial Gran Sabana Lote 34, Tocancipa, Colombia
Tel.: (57) 1 745 5002
Web Site: https://smc.com.co
Industrial Automation Products Mfr
N.A.I.C.S.: 335314

SMC Colombia Sucursal de SMC Chile S.A. (1)
Parque Industrial Gran Sabana Vereda Tibito lote M Bodega 34, Bogota, Tocancipa, Colombia
Tel.: (57) 1 745 5002
Web Site: https://www.smcworld.com
Automatic Control Equipment Mfr
N.A.I.C.S.: 334512

SMC Corporation (Australia) Pty. Ltd. (1)
14-18 Hudson Avenue Castle Hill, Sydney, 2154, NSW, Australia
Tel.: (61) 29 354 8222
Emp.: 222
Automatic Control Equipment Mfr & Distr
N.A.I.C.S.: 334512

SMC Corporation (Chile), S.A. (1)
Av La Montana 1115 P Norte Km 16, 5 Parque Industrial Valle Grande, Lampa, Santiago, Chile
Emp.: 50
Automation Pneumatic Component Distr
N.A.I.C.S.: 423830
Teruo Watase *(Gen Dir)*

SMC Corporation (India) Pvt. Ltd. (1)
A-4 Sector-88 Gautam Budh Nagar, Noida, 201 305, Uttar Pradesh, India
Tel.: (91) 120 478 0222
Web Site: https://www.smcin.com
Industrial Spare Parts Distr
N.A.I.C.S.: 423840

SMC Corporation (Mexico) S.A.de.C.V. (1)
Carr Silao-Trejo KM 2 5 S/N, Predio San Jose del Durazno, 36100, Silao, Gto, Mexico
Tel.: (52) 4727225500
Web Site: http://www.smc.com.mx
Sales Range: $50-74.9 Million
Emp.: 175
Industrial Machinery Mfr
N.A.I.C.S.: 333248

SMC Corporation (NZ) Limited (1)
5 Pacific Rise Mt, Auckland, 1060, Wellington, New Zealand
Tel.: (64) 9 573 7000
Emp.: 46
Automatic Control Equipment Mfr & Distr
N.A.I.C.S.: 334512

SMC Corporation (Singapore) Pte. Ltd. (1)
33 Tuas Avenue 8, Singapore, 639251, Singapore
Tel.: (65) 6 861 0888
Web Site: https://www.smcsing.com.sg
Automatic Control Equipment Mfr & Distr
N.A.I.C.S.: 334512
David Wong *(Mng Dir)*

SMC Corporation (Vietnam) Co., Ltd. (1)
No 63 Lo Lu Street, Truong Thanh Ward Thu Duc, Ho Chi Minh City, Vietnam
Tel.: (84) 286 281 1110
Web Site: https://www.smc-vietnam.com.vn
Automatic Control Equipment Mfr & Distr
N.A.I.C.S.: 334512
Gerald Ho *(Gen Dir)*

SMC Corporation (ZA) (Pty) Ltd. (1)
Unit 4 Midrand Central Business Park 1019 Morkels Close, Midrand, Johannesburg, 1682, South Africa
Tel.: (27) 10 900 1233
Automatic Control Equipment Mfr & Distr
N.A.I.C.S.: 334512
Kevin O'carroll *(Mng Dir)*

SMC Corporation Middle East FZE (1)
Office FZJOA1406 Tower A Jafza One Building, PO Box 261035, Jebel Ali Free Zone, Dubai, United Arab Emirates
Tel.: (971) 4 252 3034
Automatic Control Equipment Mfr & Distr
N.A.I.C.S.: 334512
Eddie Tee Choon Chin *(Country Mgr)*

SMC Corporation Peru S.A.C. (1)
Av Argentina 2078, Lima, Peru
Tel.: (51) 425 3399
Web Site: https://www.smcperu.com
Industrial Automation Product Distr
N.A.I.C.S.: 423830

SMC Corporation of America (1)
10100 SMC Blvd, Noblesville, IN 46060
Tel.: (317) 899-4440
Web Site: https://www.smcusa.com
Sales Range: $100-124.9 Million
Emp.: 1,160
Industrial Valve Mfr
N.A.I.C.S.: 332911

SMC Danmark A/S (1)
Egeskovvej 1, 8700, Horsens, Denmark
Tel.: (45) 7 025 2900
Emp.: 30
Industrial Automation Product Distr
N.A.I.C.S.: 423830
Steen Herbild *(Mng Dir)*

SMC Deutschland GmbH (1)
Boschring 13-15, 63329, Egelsbach, Germany
Tel.: (49) 6 103 4020
Emp.: 650
Industrial Automation Product Distr
N.A.I.C.S.: 423830
Ralf Laber *(Mng Dir)*

SMC Espana S.A. (1)
Zuazobidea 14, 01015, Vitoria-Gasteiz, Spain
Tel.: (34) 945184100
Web Site: http://www.smc.eu
Sales Range: $50-74.9 Million
Emp.: 250
Fluid Power Cylinder & Actuator Mfr
N.A.I.C.S.: 333995
German Berakoetxea *(Mng Dir)*

SMC France S.A. (1)
1 Boulevard de Strasbourg Parc Gustave Eiffel Bussy Saint Georges, 77607, Marne-la-Vallee, Cedex, France
Tel.: (33) 16 476 1000
Emp.: 250
Industrial Automation Product Distr
N.A.I.C.S.: 423830
Olivier Chevalier *(Mng Dir)*

SMC Hellas EPE (1)
Anagenniseos 7-9 - P C, 14342 N Philadelphia, Athens, 14342, Greece
Tel.: (30) 2102717265
Web Site: http://www.smc.eu
Sales Range: $25-49.9 Million
Emp.: 3
Industrial Valve Mfr
N.A.I.C.S.: 332911
Dimitris Paparvanitis *(Gen Mgr)*

SMC Hungary Ipari Automatizalasi Kft (1)
Torbagy u 15-19, 2045, Torokbalint, Hungary
Tel.: (36) 23513000
Web Site: http://www.smc.eu
Sales Range: $25-49.9 Million
Emp.: 37
Industrial Supplies Merchant Whslr
N.A.I.C.S.: 423840
Andras Fenyo *(Mng Dir)*

SMC Industrial Automation (Ireland) Limited (1)
2002 Citywest Road Citywest Business Campus Citywest, Dublin, Ireland
Tel.: (353) 1 403 9000
Emp.: 50
Industrial Automation Product Distr
N.A.I.C.S.: 423830
Shaun Buchanan *(Mng Dir)*

SMC Industrial Automation Bulgaria EOOD (1)
Mladost 4 Business Park Sofia building 8 building C floor 6, Sofia, 1766, Bulgaria
Tel.: (359) 2807670
Web Site: https://www.smc.eu
Sales Range: $50-74.9 Million
Emp.: 10
Industrial Supplies Whslr
N.A.I.C.S.: 423840
Plamen Turkedjiev *(Mng Dir)*

SMC Industrial Automation CZ s.r.o. (1)
Hudcova 78a, 612 00, Brno, Czech Republic

Tel.: (420) 541424611
Web Site: https://www.smc.eu
Sales Range: $25-49.9 Million
Emp.: 40
Industrial Machinery & Equipment Merchant Whslr
N.A.I.C.S.: 423830
Robert Angel *(Mng Dir)*

SMC Industrial Automation Polska Sp.z.o.o. (1)
ul Stefana Batorego 10A, Pass, 05-870, Blonie, Poland
Tel.: (48) 223444000
Web Site: http://www.smc.eu
Emp.: 80
Industrial Supplies Whslr
N.A.I.C.S.: 423840

SMC Industrial Automation d.o.o. (1)
Toplice Milana 14A, 11050, Belgrade, Serbia
Tel.: (381) 11 414 6520
Automatic Control Equipment Mfr & Distr
N.A.I.C.S.: 334512
Marjan Matoh *(Mng Dir)*

SMC Industrijska Automatika d.o.o. (1)
Zagrebacka avenija 106, 10000, Zagreb, Croatia
Tel.: (385) 1 370 7288
Web Site: https://www.smc.eu
Sales Range: $50-74.9 Million
Emp.: 7
Industrial Equipment Whsr
N.A.I.C.S.: 423830
Marjan Matoh *(Dir)*

SMC Industrijska Avtomatika d.o.o. (1)
Mirnska cesta 7, 8210, Trebnje, Slovenia
Tel.: (386) 73885412
Web Site: http://www.smc.eu
Pneumatic Equipment Mfr
N.A.I.C.S.: 335999

SMC Italia S.p.A (1)
Via Garibaldi 62, 20061, Carugate, Italy
Tel.: (39) 02 92 711
Pneumatic Automation Valves Mfr
N.A.I.C.S.: 332912

SMC Italia S.p.A. - Carsoli Factory (1)
Localita Recocce, 67061, Carsoli, Italy
Tel.: (39) 0863 9041
Pneumatic Automation Valves Mfr
N.A.I.C.S.: 332911

SMC Korea Co., Ltd. (1)
Scout B/D 8F 14 Gukhoe-daero 62-gil, Yeouido-dong Yeongdeungpo-gu, Seoul, 07235, Korea (South)
Tel.: (82) 23 219 0700
Emp.: 740
Automatic Control Equipment Mfr & Distr
N.A.I.C.S.: 334512
Nagata Shuji *(Mng Dir)*

SMC Manufacturing (Australia) Pty. Ltd. (1)
14-18 Hudson Avenue, Castle Hill, 2154, NSW, Australia
Tel.: (61) 293548222
Web Site: http://www.smcaus.com.au
Sales Range: $25-49.9 Million
Emp.: 250
Engineeering Services
N.A.I.C.S.: 541330
Wayne Driver *(Mng Dir)*

SMC Manufacturing (Singapore) Pte. Ltd. (1)
91 Tuas Ave 1, 639521, Jurong, 639521, Singapore
Tel.: (65) 68611868
Sales Range: $150-199.9 Million
Emp.: 640
Industrial Machinery & Equipment Whslr
N.A.I.C.S.: 423830
C. S. Loh *(Mng Dir)*

SMC Nederland B.V. (1)
De Ruyterkade 120, 1011 AB, Amsterdam, Netherlands
Tel.: (31) 20 531 8888
Emp.: 65
Automatic Control Equipment Mfr & Distr
N.A.I.C.S.: 334512

Bart Tuijnman *(Mng Dir)*

SMC Neumatica Venezuela S.A. (1)
Ave Michelena Zona Industrial Edificio Canaima Local 4, Valencia, Carabobo, Venezuela
Tel.: (58) 2418345617
Web Site: http://www.smc.eu
Emp.: 10
Industrial Machinery & Equipment Whslr
N.A.I.C.S.: 423830

SMC Pneumaticos Do Brasil Ltda (1)
Av Piraporinha 777 Barro Planalto, Sao Bernardo do Campo, 09891-001, Sao Paulo, Brazil
Tel.: (55) 1140820600
Web Site: http://www.smcpneumaticos.com.br
Sales Range: $50-74.9 Million
Emp.: 150
Industrial Valve Mfr
N.A.I.C.S.: 332911

SMC Pneumatics (Australia) Pty.Ltd. (1)
14-18 Hudson Avenue, PO Box 581, Castle Hill, 2154, NSW, Australia
Tel.: (61) 293548222
Web Site: http://www.smcaus.com.au
Sales Range: $25-49.9 Million
Emp.: 250
Engineeering Services
N.A.I.C.S.: 541330
Wayne Driver *(Mng Dir)*

SMC Pneumatics (Canada) Ltd. (1)
2715 Digital Circle Suite 2, Oakville, L6H 5A5, ON, Canada
Tel.: (905) 812-0400
Web Site: https://www.smcautomation.ca
Business Support Services
N.A.I.C.S.: 332911

SMC Pneumatics (Chile) S.A. (1)
Av La Montana 1115 Valle, Parque Industrial Valle Grande - Lampa, Santiago, Chile
Tel.: (56) 22708600
Web Site: http://www.smc.eu
Sales Range: $50-74.9 Million
Emp.: 60
Industrial Machinery & Equipment Whslr
N.A.I.C.S.: 423830

SMC Pneumatics (Guangzhou) Limited (1)
2 Dongming Road 3 Science Park Hi-Tech Industrial Development Zone, Guangzhou, 510660, China
Tel.: (86) 2028397668
Web Site: http://www.smcgz.com.cn
Sales Range: $50-74.9 Million
Emp.: 150
Fluid Power Cylinder & Actuator Mfr
N.A.I.C.S.: 333995

SMC Pneumatics (Hong Kong) Ltd. (1)
29th Fl Clifford Ctr 778-784 Cheung, Sha Wan Road Lai Chi Kok, Kowloon, China (Hong Kong)
Tel.: (852) 27440121
Web Site: http://www.smchk.com.hk
Industrial Machinery & Equipment Whslr
N.A.I.C.S.: 423830

Subsidiary (Non-US):

XIAMEN SMART CONCEPT PNEUMATICS CO. (2)
Section X Y Z Floor 5th Rihua Mansion No 8 Xinfeng 2 Road, HuoJu High-tech Zone, Xiamen, 361006, Fujian, China
Tel.: (86) 592 550 7348
Web Site: http://www.smchk.com.hk
Pneumatic Equipment Mfr
N.A.I.C.S.: 336320

SMC Pneumatics (India) Pvt. Ltd. (1)
D-107 to 112 Phase II Extn, Gautam Budh Nagar, Noida, 201 305, U.P, India
Tel.: (91) 120 478 0222
Web Site: https://www.smcpneumaticsproducts.in
Sales Range: $100-124.9 Million
Emp.: 400
Pneumatic Vacuum Components Mfr
N.A.I.C.S.: 335999

SMC Pneumatics (Ireland) Ltd. (1)
Citywest Business Campus Naas Road Co 2002, Saggart, Dublin, 4, Ireland
Tel.: (353) 14039000
Web Site: http://www.smcpneumatics.ie
Sales Range: $25-49.9 Million
Emp.: 20
Industrial Supplies Whslr
N.A.I.C.S.: 423840
Shaun Buchanan *(Mng Dir)*

SMC Pneumatics (New Zealand) Ltd. (1)
5 Pacific Rise, PO Box 62-226, Mount Wellington, Auckland, 1060, New Zealand
Tel.: (64) 95737007
Web Site: http://www.smc.co.nz
Sales Range: $25-49.9 Million
Emp.: 50
Pump & Pumping Equipment Mfr
N.A.I.C.S.: 333914
Wayne Driver *(Mng Dir)*

SMC Pneumatics (S.E.A) Sdn.Bhd. (1)
Lot 36 Jalan Delima 1/1, Subang Hi-Tech Industrial Park, Subang Jaya, 47500, Selangor, Malaysia
Tel.: (60) 356350590
Web Site: http://www.smcmy.com.my
Sales Range: $50-74.9 Million
Emp.: 100
Transportation Equipment & Supplies Whslr
N.A.I.C.S.: 423860

SMC Pneumatics (S.E.A.) Pte. Ltd. (1)
33 Tuas Ave 8, Jurong, 639251, Singapore
Tel.: (65) 68610888
Web Site: http://www.smcsing.com.sg
Emp.: 75
Industrial Machinery & Equipment Whslr
N.A.I.C.S.: 423830
David Wong *(Mng Dir)*

SMC Pneumatics (Taiwan) Co. Ltd. (1)
No 16 Lane 205 Section 2 Nanshan Road, Luzhu District, Taoyuan, 838333, Taiwan
Tel.: (886) 33223443
Web Site: http://www.smc.com.tw
Motor Vehicle Supplies & New Parts Whslr
N.A.I.C.S.: 423120

Plant (Domestic):

SMC Pneumatics (Taiwan) Co., Ltd. - Touliu Factory (2)
No 148 Tou-Kon 10 Rd, Douliu, Yunlin-Hsien, Taiwan
Tel.: (886) 5 557 5888
Pneumatic Cylinders & Valves Mfr
N.A.I.C.S.: 333995

SMC Pneumatics (U.K.) Ltd. (1)
Vincent Avenue Crownhill, Milton Keynes, MK8 0AN, Buckinghamshire, United Kingdom
Tel.: (44) 1908563888
Web Site: http://www.smcpneumatics.co.uk
Sales Range: $150-199.9 Million
Emp.: 300
Industrial Supplies Whslr
N.A.I.C.S.: 423840
Kevin O'Carroll *(Mng Dir)*

SMC Pneumatics Bolivia S.R.L. (1)
Avenida Canal Cotoca 2635, Santa Cruz, Bolivia
Tel.: (591) 3649959
Web Site: http://www.smcbolivia.com.bo
Industrial Supplies Whslr
N.A.I.C.S.: 423840
Ernesto Peralta *(Gen Mgr)*

SMC Pneumatics Colombia. (1)
Gran Sabana Industrial Park Lot 34, Tocancipa, Colombia
Tel.: (57) 1 745 5002
Web Site: https://smc.com.co
Pneumatic Equipment Mfr
N.A.I.C.S.: 332912

SMC Pneumatics Finland Oy (1)
Tiistinniityntie 4, PL 72, 02231, Espoo, Finland
Tel.: (358) 207 513 513
Web Site: http://www.smc.fi
Sales Range: $25-49.9 Million
Emp.: 40
Pneumatic Equipment Mfr

N.A.I.C.S.: 335999

SMC Pneumatics Korea Co. Ltd. (1)
Scout B/D 8F 14 Gukhoe-daero 62-gil Yeouido-dong, Yeongdeungpo-gu, 07235, Seoul, Korea (South)
Tel.: (82) 232190700
Web Site: http://www.smckorea.co.kr
Sales Range: $25-49.9 Million
Emp.: 50
Fluid Power Pump & Motor Mfr
N.A.I.C.S.: 333996

Subsidiary (Domestic):

SMC Pneumatics Korea Co.,Ltd. - Daejon Factory (2)
Air B/D 3F 653-25 Deungchon-Dong Gangseo-gu, Seoul, Korea (South)
Tel.: (82) 42 605 2000
Industrial Equipment Mfr
N.A.I.C.S.: 333248

SMC Pneumatics Latvia SIA (1)
Smerla 1-705, 1006, Riga, Latvia
Tel.: (371) 7817700
Web Site: http://www.smclv.lv
Industrial Machinery & Equipment Whslr
N.A.I.C.S.: 423830

SMC Pneumatics N.V./S.A. (1)
Nijverheidsstraat 20, Antwerp, 2160, Wommelgem, Belgium
Tel.: (32) 33551464
Web Site: http://www.smcpneumatics.be
Sales Range: $25-49.9 Million
Emp.: 20
Pneumatic Automation Products Mfr
N.A.I.C.S.: 334416
H. Maes *(Gen Mgr)*

SMC Pneumatics Norway AS (1)
Vollsveien 13b Granfos Naringspark, Lysaker, 1366, Norway
Tel.: (47) 67129020
Web Site: http://www.smc-norge.no
Sales Range: $25-49.9 Million
Emp.: 5
Oil & Gas Field Machinery & Equipment Mfr
N.A.I.C.S.: 333132
Anton Tgernlund *(Gen Mgr)*

SMC Pneumatics Sweden AB (1)
Ekhagsvagen 29-31, PO Box 5017, Segeltorp, 14171, Stockholm, Sweden
Tel.: (46) 86031200
Web Site: http://www.smc.nu
Sales Range: $25-49.9 Million
Emp.: 50
Fluid Power Cylinder & Actuator Mfr
N.A.I.C.S.: 333995
Ulf Petersen *(Dir-Tech)*

SMC Pneumatik A/S (1)
Egeskovvej 1, 8700, Horsens, Denmark
Tel.: (45) 70252900
Web Site: https://www.smc-pneumatik.dk
Sales Range: $25-49.9 Million
Emp.: 28
Industrial Machinery & Equipment Whslr
N.A.I.C.S.: 423830
Steen Herbild *(Gen Mgr)*

SMC Pneumatik AG (1)
Dorfstrasse 7, PO Box 117, Weisslingen, 8484, Zurich, Switzerland
Tel.: (41) 523963131
Web Site: http://www.smc.ch
Sales Range: $25-49.9 Million
Emp.: 120
Industrial Machinery Mfr
N.A.I.C.S.: 333248
D. Langmeier *(Gen Mgr)*

SMC Pneumatik GmbH (1)
Girakstrasse 8, 2100, Korneuburg, Austria
Tel.: (43) 226262280
Web Site: http://www.smc.at
Sales Range: $50-74.9 Million
Emp.: 220
Metal Valve & Pipe Fitting Mfr
N.A.I.C.S.: 332919
Robert Angel *(Mng Dir)*

SMC Pneumatik LLC (1)
Business center building 3 15 Kondratjevskij prospect, 195197, Saint Petersburg, Russia
Tel.: (7) 8123036600
Web Site: http://www.smc.eu
Pneumatic Automation Equipment Mfr
N.A.I.C.S.: 334512

SMC CORPORATION

SMC Corporation—(Continued)

Alexej Kourychev *(Mng Dir)*

SMC Pneumatique S.A. (1)
1 Boulevard de Strasbourg, Parc Gustave Eiffel Bussy Saint Georges, 77607, Marne-la-Vallee, France
Tel.: (33) 164761000
Web Site: http://www.smc.com
Sales Range: $50-74.9 Million
Emp.: 250
Fluid Power Cylinder & Actuator Mfr
N.A.I.C.S.: 333995
Olivier Chevalier *(Mng Dir)*

SMC Pnomatik Sanayi Ticaret ve Servis A.S. (1)
Gulbahar Caddesi Aydin Plaza No 9/4, Gunesli, 34212, Istanbul, Turkiye
Tel.: (90) 212 489 0 440
Web Site: http://www.smcworld.com
Pneumatic Component Mfr
N.A.I.C.S.: 335999

SMC Priemyselna Aumtomatizacia spol s.r.o. (1)
Fantranska 1223, 01301, Teplicka nad Vahom, Slovakia
Tel.: (421) 413213211
Web Site: http://www.smc.eu
Sales Range: $25-49.9 Million
Emp.: 12
Fluid Power Cylinder & Actuator Mfr
N.A.I.C.S.: 333995
Robert Angel *(Mng Dir)*

SMC Priemyselna Automatizacia Spol.s.r.o. (1)
Fantranska 1223, 01301, Teplicka nad Vahom, Slovakia
Tel.: (421) 41 321 3211
Automatic Control Equipment Mfr & Distr
N.A.I.C.S.: 334512
Robert Angel *(Mng Dir)*

SMC Romania S.r.l. (1)
Str Frunzei 29 Sector 2, Bucharest, 21531, Romania
Tel.: (40) 213205111
Web Site: http://www.smc.eu
Sales Range: $25-49.9 Million
Emp.: 41
Fluid Power Cylinder & Actuator Mfr
N.A.I.C.S.: 333995

SMC Schweiz AG (1)
Dorfstrasse 7, Weisslingen, 8484, Pfaffikon, Switzerland
Tel.: (41) 52 396 3131
Emp.: 100
Automatic Control Equipment Mfr & Distr
N.A.I.C.S.: 334512
Daniel Langmeier *(Mng Dir)*

SMC Sucursal Portugal S.A. (1)
Alameda dos Moinhos 9G, Alfragide, 2720-381, Lisbon, Portugal
Tel.: (351) 214724500
Web Site: http://www.sms.eu
Industrial Supplies Whslr
N.A.I.C.S.: 423840

SMC Thailand Ltd. (1)
134/6 Moo 5 Tiwanon Road, Bangkadi Amphur Muang, 12000, Pathumthani, Thailand
Tel.: (66) 20195656
Web Site: http://www.smcthai.co.th
Emp.: 242
Fluid Power Cylinder & Actuator Mfr
N.A.I.C.S.: 333995
Panyaphol Supannavong *(Mng Dir)*

SMC Turkey Otomasyon A.S. (1)
Halkali Merkez Mah Basin Ekspres Cad Capital Tower No 9 Kat 11, Kucukcekmece, 34301, Istanbul, Turkiye
Tel.: (90) 212 489 0440
Emp.: 135
Automatic Control Equipment Mfr & Distr
N.A.I.C.S.: 334512
Turgay Ucar *(Gen Mgr)*

Saadani Trading & Industrial Services S.A.E. (1)
94 Ismail El Fangry Str, Nasr, Egypt
Tel.: (20) 22 402 9662
Web Site: https://www.saadanigroup.com.eg
Engineering Product Distr
N.A.I.C.S.: 423840

Shoketsu-SMC Corporation (1)
Lot 9-E Main St First Philippine Industrial Park II FPIP II Sta, Anastacia, Santo Tomas, 4234, Batangas, Philippines
Tel.: (63) 288090565
Web Site: http://www.shoketsu-smc.oom.ph
Sales Range: $25-49.9 Million
Emp.: 60
Industrial Valve Mfr
N.A.I.C.S.: 332911

UAB SMC Pneumatics (1)
Laisves pr 55-202, 07190, Vilnius, Lithuania
Tel.: (370) 5 2308118
Web Site: http://www.smclt.lt
Sales Range: $50-74.9 Million
Emp.: 3
Industrial Machinery & Equipment Whslr
N.A.I.C.S.: 423830

SMC CREDITS LIMITED
24 Ashoka Chambers Rajendra Place Pusa Road, New Delhi, 110060, India
Tel.: (91) 1145012880
Web Site: https://www.smccredits.com
Year Founded: 1992
532138—(BOM)
Rev.: $704,795
Assets: $69,933,335
Liabilities: $2,919,876
Net Worth: $67,013,459
Earnings: $613,805
Fiscal Year-end: 03/31/21
Financial Services
N.A.I.C.S.: 522390
Rajesh Goenka *(Chm & CFO)*

SMC ELECTRIC LIMITED
1/F Shell Industrial Building 12 Lee Chung Street, Chai Wan, China (Hong Kong)
Web Site: https://www.smcelectric.com.hk
Year Founded: 2018
2381—(HKG)
Rev.: $32,823,991
Assets: $23,519,761
Liabilities: $5,627,655
Net Worth: $17,892,106
Earnings: $2,885,283
Emp.: 106
Fiscal Year-end: 12/31/22
Electric Product Mfr & Distr
N.A.I.C.S.: 335999
Chun Wah Leung *(CEO)*

Subsidiaries:

Speed Power Limited (1)
1/F Shell Ind Bldg 12 Lee Chung Street, Chai Wan Industrial District, Hong Kong, China (Hong Kong)
Tel.: (852) 25580181
Electrical Appliance Mfr & Distr
N.A.I.C.S.: 335210

SMC GLOBAL SECURITIES LIMITED
11/6B Shanti Chamber Pusa Road, New Delhi, 110005, India
Tel.: (91) 1166075200
Web Site: https://www.smctradeonline.com
Year Founded: 1990
543263—(BOM)
Rev.: $123,066,926
Assets: $325,875,691
Liabilities: $220,179,346
Net Worth: $105,696,345
Earnings: $13,660,156
Emp.: 2,027
Fiscal Year-end: 03/31/21
Financial Services
N.A.I.C.S.: 522390
Subhash C. Aggarwal *(Chm & Mng Dir)*

Subsidiaries:

SMC Comex International DMCC (1)
2404 One Lake Plaza Tower Cluster T Jumeirah Lake Towers, PO Box 117210, Dubai, United Arab Emirates
Tel.: (971) 45139780
Web Site: https://smccomex.com
General Insurance Services
N.A.I.C.S.: 524210

SMC Global IFSC Private Limited (1)
Unit No 222 2nd Floor Signature Building Block No 13B Road 1C Zone-I, Gift-SEZ Gift City, Gandhinagar, 382355, Gujarat, India
Tel.: (91) 7486041438
Web Site: https://www.smcglobalifsc.com
Stock Broking & Clearing Services
N.A.I.C.S.: 523210

SMC Insurance Brokers Private Limited (1)
Parsvnath Metro Mall Near Pratap Nagar Metro Station Pratap Nagar, New Delhi, 110007, India
Tel.: (91) 1166222266
Web Site: https://www.smcinsurance.com
General Insurance Services
N.A.I.C.S.: 524210

SMC Real Estate Advisors Private Limited (1)
11/5B 3rd Floor Pusa Road, New Delhi, 110005, India
Tel.: (91) 9250005154
Web Site: https://www.smcrealty.com
Real Estate Development Services
N.A.I.C.S.: 531390

SMC INVESTMENT TRADING JOINT STOCK COMPANY
396 Ung Van Khiem Phuong 25, Quan Binh Thanh, Ho Chi Minh City, Vietnam
Tel.: (84) 838992299
Web Site: http://www.smc.vn
SMC—(HOSE)
Rev.: $564,504,931
Assets: $254,562,069
Liabilities: $221,693,945
Net Worth: $32,868,124
Earnings: $(38,122,319)
Emp.: 1,399
Fiscal Year-end: 12/31/23
Metal Product Whslr
N.A.I.C.S.: 423510
Nguyen Ngoc Anh *(Chm, CEO & Gen Dir)*

SMCORE INC.
Seoul City Tower 20F 110 Huam-ro, Jung-gu, Seoul, 4175, Korea (South)
Tel.: (82) 220909200
Web Site: https://www.smck.com
Year Founded: 1940
007820—(KRS)
Rev.: $88,216,858
Assets: $84,257,763
Liabilities: $30,384,897
Net Worth: $53,872,866
Earnings: $1,894,306
Emp.: 273
Fiscal Year-end: 12/31/22
Industrial Automation Machinery Mfr
N.A.I.C.S.: 333248

Subsidiaries:

HPCL-Mittal Energy Limited (1)
INOX Toweers Sector 16 A Plot No 17, Noida, 201 301, UP, India
Tel.: (91) 1204634500
Web Site: https://www.hmel.in
Petrochemical Mfr
N.A.I.C.S.: 325110
Aditya Mittal *(Chm)*

SAFE-RUN INc (1)
No 111 Heng Chang Jing Road, Kunshan, 215337, Jiangsu, China
Tel.: (86) 51286181888
Web Site: https://en.safe-run.cn
Tiles Mfr
N.A.I.C.S.: 326211

INTERNATIONAL PUBLIC

Shin-Heung Machine Co., Ltd. - Chungju Factory 1 (1)
24-11 Gaheoung-li Kakum-myun, Chungju, North Chungcheong, Korea (South)
Tel.: (82) 43 855 8551
Web Site: http://www.smck.com
Structural Steel Mfr
N.A.I.C.S.: 331110

Shin-Heung Machine Co., Ltd. - Jeonju Factory (1)
803 Bongdong-Eup 3rd Industrial Complex, Wanju-kun, Jeonju, 565-904, Korea (South)
Tel.: (82) 63 261 4011
Web Site: http://www.smck.com
Emp.: 6
Stacker Crane & Conveyor Mfr
N.A.I.C.S.: 333922

SMCP S.A.
49 Rue Etienne Marcel, 75001, Paris, France
Tel.: (33) 55805100
Web Site: https://www.smcp.com
SMCP—(EUR)
Rev.: $1,358,317,695
Assets: $2,594,988,410
Liabilities: $1,292,305,994
Net Worth: $1,302,682,415
Earnings: $12,363,396
Emp.: 6,820
Fiscal Year-end: 12/31/23
Clothing Accessory Mfr & Distr
N.A.I.C.S.: 315120
Daniel Lalonde *(CEO)*

Subsidiaries:

De Fursac SA (1)
112 rue de Richelieu, 75002, Paris, France
Tel.: (33) 140079797
Web Site: http://www.defursac.fr
Emp.: 252
Men's Clothing Retailer
N.A.I.C.S.: 458110
Camille Weibel *(Dir-Publication)*

SMCP Asia Limited (1)
Suite 3203A-5A 32/F The Centrium 60 Wyndham Street, Central, China (Hong Kong)
Tel.: (852) 39994100
Women & Men Clothing Retailer
N.A.I.C.S.: 458110
Stephane Ledru *(CEO)*

SMCP USA Inc. (1)
44 Wall St, New York, NY 10005
Tel.: (212) 510-8390
Women & Men Clothing Retailer
N.A.I.C.S.: 458110
Paul Griffin *(CEO)*

Sandro Andy S.A.S. (1)
150 Boulevard Haussmann, 75008, Paris, France
Tel.: (33) 140699700
Web Site: http://fr.sandro-paris.com
Emp.: 903
Apparel Product Mfr
N.A.I.C.S.: 315990
Evelyne Chetrite *(Founder, Chm, Pres & Dir-Artistic)*

SME LEASING LTD.
Office 304 3rd Floor Business Arcade Shahrah-e-Faisal, Karachi, Pakistan
Tel.: (92) 21343221289
Web Site: https://www.smelease.com
Year Founded: 2002
SLL—(PSX)
Rev.: $75,540
Assets: $1,204,590
Liabilities: $1,176,339
Net Worth: $28,250
Earnings: $4,425
Fiscal Year-end: 12/31/22
Financial Lending Services
N.A.I.C.S.: 523999
Bilal Mustafa *(Chm)*

SME SECURITIES CORPORATION

39 Ngo Quyen, Hoan Kiem, Hanoi, Vietnam
Tel.: (84) 4 2220 5678
Web Site: http://www.smes.vn
Emp.: 130
Investment Banking & Securities Brokerage Services
N.A.I.C.S.: 523150
Chi Huy Phan *(CEO)*

SMEC CO., LTD.
157-10 Golden root-ro, Juchon-myeon, Gimhae, 50969, Gyeongsangnam-do, Korea (South)
Tel.: (82) 553404800 KR
Web Site: https://www.esmec.com
Year Founded: 2011
099440—(KRS)
Rev.: $122,315,948
Assets: $148,474,962
Liabilities: $91,092,186
Net Worth: $57,382,776
Earnings: $7,426,178
Emp.: 160
Fiscal Year-end: 12/31/22
Communication Equipment & Industrial Machinery Mfr
N.A.I.C.S.: 334290
Young-sup Choi *(CEO)*

Subsidiaries:

SMEC America Corp. (1)
14 W Forest Ave, Englewood, NJ 07631
Tel.: (201) 816-7632
Web Site: https://www.esmecamerica.com
Telecommunications Equipment Mfr
N.A.I.C.S.: 334210
Peter Jung *(Chief Sls Officer)*

SMEC Co., Ltd. - Hyeonpung Factory (1)
43 Techno-daero 6-gil Yuga-myeon, Dalseong-gun, Daegu, Korea (South)
Tel.: (82) 536159411
Telecommunications Equipment Mfr
N.A.I.C.S.: 334210

SMEC Vina Co., Ltd. (1)
Floor 4 B5/D6 New Urban Area Cau Giay District, Dich Vong Ward Cau Giay District, Hanoi, Vietnam
Tel.: (84) 2471028688
Web Site: https://www.smecvina.com
Mechanical Machinery Mfr
N.A.I.C.S.: 333618

SMEDIO INC.
8F Central Square 2-3-1 Shinkawa, Chuo-ku, Tokyo, 104-0033, Japan
Tel.: (81) 352999300
Web Site: https://www.smedio.co.jp
3913—(TKS)
Rev.: $5,764,170
Assets: $8,430,010
Liabilities: $886,250
Net Worth: $7,543,760
Earnings: ($1,155,670)
Emp.: 49
Fiscal Year-end: 12/31/23
Software Publisher
N.A.I.C.S.: 513210
Sadanori Iwamoto *(Pres & CEO)*

Subsidiaries:

Johospace Co., Ltd. (1)
1186-6 Shinbou, Minami-ku, Okayama, Okayama, Japan
Tel.: (81) 862350277
Web Site: http://www.johospace.co.jp
Software Development Services
N.A.I.C.S.: 541511

Taosoftware Co., Ltd. (1)
Central Square 8F 2-3-1 Shinkawa, Chuo-ku, Tokyo, 104-0033, Japan
Tel.: (81) 368028247
Web Site: https://www.taosoftware.co.jp
Emp.: 14
Software Development Services
N.A.I.C.S.: 541511
Takeshi Takeshi *(CEO)*

SMETEX GMBH
Durmersheimer Strasse 28, 76185, Karlsruhe, Germany
Tel.: (49) 721 986148 0
Web Site: http://www.smetex.de
Energy, Water & Real Estate Industries Measurement & Control Technology Maintenance & Services
N.A.I.C.S.: 334513

SMI CULTURE & TRAVEL GROUP HOLDINGS LIMITED
Unit 2610 26th Floor Office Tower Convention Plaza, No 1 Harbour Road, Hong Kong, China (Hong Kong)
Tel.: (852) 3521 6800 Ky
2366—(HKG)
Sales Range: $1-9.9 Million
Investment Holding Company
N.A.I.C.S.: 551112
Chien-Chiang Wu *(Chm)*

SMI HOLDINGS GROUP LIMITED
Suite 6701-2 & 13 67/F The Center, 99 Queen's Road, Central, China (Hong Kong)
Tel.: (852) 3915 5800 BM
Web Site: http://www.smi198.com
Year Founded: 2004
Theater Operator
N.A.I.C.S.: 512131
Chi Chung Cheng *(Exec Dir)*

SMI TELECOMS LLC
80-83 Long Lane, London, EC1A 9ET, United Kingdom
Tel.: (44) 20 3239 4517
Web Site: http://www.smi-t.com
Telecommunication Software
N.A.I.C.S.: 513210
Phil Brooks *(CEO)*

SMI VANTAGE LIMITED
300 Beach Road 31 03 The Concourse, Singapore, 199555, Singapore
Tel.: (65) 67186678
Web Site: https://www.sin-mi.com
Year Founded: 1986
Y45—(SES)
Rev.: $1,333,086
Assets: $18,631,345
Liabilities: $10,984,068
Net Worth: $7,647,277
Earnings: ($2,436,458)
Emp.: 300
Fiscal Year-end: 03/31/23
Infrastrcuture Management Services
N.A.I.C.S.: 561499
Mark Francis Bedingham *(Pres & CEO)*

SMIFFY'S UK
Peckett Plaza Caldicott Drive, Gainsborough, DN21 1FJ, Lincolnshire, United Kingdom
Tel.: (44) 1427 619 799
Web Site: http://www.smiffys.com
Year Founded: 1894
Sales Range: $50-74.9 Million
Emp.: 232
Costume & Cosmetic Product Whslr
N.A.I.C.S.: 424350
Ian Brookes *(Controller-Natl Acct)*

SMIFS CAPITAL MARKETS LTD.
Vaibhav 4F 4 Lee Road, Kolkata, 700020, India
Tel.: (91) 3322900544
Web Site: https://www.smifscap.com
508905—(BOM)
Rev.: $6,903,159
Assets: $14,375,565

Liabilities: $335,723
Net Worth: $14,039,842
Earnings: $61,195
Emp.: 21
Fiscal Year-end: 03/31/23
Financial Services
N.A.I.C.S.: 523999
Kishor Shah *(Mng Dir)*

SMILES INCLUSIVE LIMITED
Unit 3/38-40 Township Drive, West Burleigh, Burleigh Heads, 4219, QLD, Australia
Tel.: (61) 755687645 AU
Web Site: http://www.smilesinc.com.au
Rev.: $5,628,113
Assets: $57,117,819
Liabilities: $31,285,161
Net Worth: $25,832,658
Earnings: ($3,892,304)
Fiscal Year-end: 06/30/18
Health Care Srvices
N.A.I.C.S.: 541715
David Usasz *(Chm)*

SMIS CORPORATION BERHAD
Lot 3 Jalan Pemaju U115 Seksyen U1 Hicom Glenmarie Industrial Park, 55200, Kuala Lumpur, Malaysia
Tel.: (60) 392219898
Web Site: https://www.smis.com.my
SMISCOR—(KLS)
Rev.: $32,677,037
Assets: $25,390,476
Liabilities: $6,841,905
Net Worth: $18,548,571
Earnings: $4,158,307
Emp.: 386
Fiscal Year-end: 12/31/22
Machine Part Mfr
N.A.I.C.S.: 333248
Siew Foong Yap *(Exec Dir)*

Subsidiaries:

Grand Carpet Industries Sdn. Bhd. (1)
Lot 3 Jalan Sultan Hishamuddin 2, North Port Industrial Area, 42000, Port Klang, Selangor, Malaysia
Web Site: https://www.gcisb.com
Automobile Parts Mfr
N.A.I.C.S.: 336390

Machinery & Industrial Supplies Sdn. Bhd. (1)
19 Jalan Dua Off Jalan Chan Sow Lin, 55200, Kuala Lumpur, Malaysia
Tel.: (60) 39 221 9898
Web Site: https://www.missb.my
Industrial Product Distr
N.A.I.C.S.: 423840

Sanyco Grand Industries Sdn. Bhd. (1)
Lot 3 Jalan Pemaju U1/15 Seksyen U1, Hicom Glenmarie Industrial Park, 40150, Shah Alam, Selangor, Malaysia
Web Site: https://www.sgisb.com
Automobile Parts Mfr
N.A.I.C.S.: 336390
Moo Cy *(Mgr-Technical)*

SMIT HOLDINGS LIMITED
1/F Harbour View 2 16 Science Park East Avenue Hong Kong Science, Park Shatin, Hong Kong, New Territories, China (Hong Kong)
Tel.: (852) 22016300 Ky
Web Site: http://www.smit.com.cn
Year Founded: 2002
2239—(HKG)
Rev.: $29,410,713
Assets: $247,235,256
Liabilities: $59,650,536
Net Worth: $187,584,720
Earnings: $57,112,673
Emp.: 171
Fiscal Year-end: 12/31/22

Security Device Distr
N.A.I.C.S.: 423610
Xueliang Huang *(Founder, Chm & CEO)*

Subsidiaries:

S2C Shanghai Co., Ltd. (1)
Bldg E1 No 2555 Xiupu Road Pudong, Shanghai, 201315, China
Tel.: (86) 4008888427
Prototyping Solution Services
N.A.I.C.S.: 541714

S2C Taiwan Inc. (1)
5F-5 No 65 Gaotie 7th Rd, Hsinchu, Zhubei, Taiwan
Tel.: (886) 36675782
Prototyping Solution Services
N.A.I.C.S.: 541714
Peter Liu *(Mgr-IT)*

SMIT Group Limited (1)
22A Guoshi Building No 1801 Shahe West Road Yuehai Street, Gaoxin District Nanshan District, Shenzhen, China
Tel.: (86) 75561363366
Electronic Equipment Mfr & Distr
N.A.I.C.S.: 335999

Shenzhen SMiTSense Technology Co, Ltd. (1)
23F Building 3 Chongwen Park Nanshan Zhiyuan No 3370 Liuxian Avenue, Nanshan District, Shenzhen, China
Tel.: (86) 75561363399
Semiconductor Product Mfr & Distr
N.A.I.C.S.: 334413

SMITH & NEPHEW PLC
Building 5 Croxley Park Hatters Lane, Hertfordshire, Watford, WD18 8YE, United Kingdom
Tel.: (44) 1923477100 UK
Web Site: http://www.smith-nephew.com
Year Founded: 1896
SNN—(NYSE)
Rev.: $5,215,000,000
Assets: $9,966,000,000
Liabilities: $4,707,000,000
Net Worth: $5,259,000,000
Earnings: $223,000,000
Emp.: 19,012
Fiscal Year-end: 12/31/22
Holding Company; Medical Devices Developer & Marketer
N.A.I.C.S.: 551112
Deepak Nath *(CEO)*

Subsidiaries:

Adler Mediequip Private Limited (1)
Podium Floor Tower 4 World Trade Center S No 1, Kharadi, Pune, 411 014, Maharashtra, India
Tel.: (91) 206 712 6850
Web Site: https://www.adlermediequip.com
Medical Equipment Mfr & Distr
N.A.I.C.S.: 339112

Atracsys Sarl (1)
Route du Verney 20B, 1070, Puidoux, Switzerland
Tel.: (41) 21 533 0900
Web Site: https://www.atracsys-measurement.com
Medical Equipment Mfr & Distr
N.A.I.C.S.: 339112

Osiris Therapeutics, Inc. (1)
7015 Albert Einstein Dr, Columbia, MD 21046-1707
Tel.: (443) 545-1800
Web Site: http://www.osiris.com
Rev.: $142,824,000
Assets: $101,502,000
Liabilities: $22,974,000
Net Worth: $78,528,000
Earnings: $36,901,000
Emp.: 342
Fiscal Year-end: 12/31/2018
Stem Cell Therapeutic Research
N.A.I.C.S.: 325414
Laine Dyess *(VP-Sls)*

Smith & Nephew (Alberta) Inc. (1)

SMITH & NEPHEW PLC

Smith & Nephew plc—(Continued)

10102 114 St, Fort Saskatchewan, T8L 3W4, AB, Canada
Tel.: (780) 992-5500
Wound Care Product Mfr
N.A.I.C.S.: 339113

Smith & Nephew (Malaysia) Sdn Bhd (1)
Menara AmFirst 9th Fl No 1 Jalan 19/3, Petaling Jaya, 46300, Selangor, Malaysia
Tel.: (60) 3 7958 7103
Emp.: 45
Medical Device Mfr & Distr
N.A.I.C.S.: 334510

Smith & Nephew (Overseas) Limited (1)
15 Adam Street, London, WC2N 6LA, United Kingdom
Tel.: (44) 20 7401 7646
Sales Range: $25-49.9 Million
Emp.: 60
Medical Device Mfr & Distr
N.A.I.C.S.: 334510

Smith & Nephew (Pty) Limited (1)
30 The Boulevard Westend Office Park, PO Box 92, Westville, 3600, Durban, South Africa
Tel.: (27) 312428111
Web Site: https://www.smith-nephew.com
Sales Range: $50-74.9 Million
Emp.: 200
Medical Device Mfr
N.A.I.C.S.: 334510

Smith & Nephew A/S (1)
Snaroyveien 36, Fornebu, 1364, Norway
Tel.: (47) 66842020
Web Site: http://www.smith-nephew.com
Sales Range: $25-49.9 Million
Emp.: 30
Medical Device Mfr & Distr
N.A.I.C.S.: 334510

Smith & Nephew A/S (1)
Kay Fiskers Plads 9 1, 2300, Copenhagen, Denmark
Tel.: (45) 45806100
Web Site: http://www.smith-nephew.com
Emp.: 40
Medical Device Mfr & Distr
N.A.I.C.S.: 334510

Smith & Nephew AB (1)
Krokslatts fabrikker 39, 431 37, Molndal, Sweden
Tel.: (46) 317465800
Web Site: http://www.smith-nephew.com
Medical Device Mfr & Distr
N.A.I.C.S.: 334510

Smith & Nephew Colombia S.A.S. (1)
Calle 100 7-33 Torre 1 Piso 3, Bogota, Colombia
Tel.: (57) 1 605 7373
Medical Equipment Mfr & Distr
N.A.I.C.S.: 339112

Smith & Nephew FZE (1)
Building No 52 1st Floor, PO Box 9715, Dubai Health Care City, Dubai, United Arab Emirates
Tel.: (971) 44299111
Web Site: http://www.smith-nephew.com
Medical Device Mfr & Distr
N.A.I.C.S.: 334510

Smith & Nephew France SAS (1)
40-52 Boulevard Du Parc, 92200, Neuilly-sur-Seine, France
Tel.: (33) 24 383 2323
Medical Equipment Mfr & Distr
N.A.I.C.S.: 339112

Smith & Nephew GmbH (1)
Concorde Business Park 1/C/3, 2320, Schwechat, Austria
Tel.: (43) 17079102
Web Site: http://www.smith-nephew.com
Sales Range: $25-49.9 Million
Emp.: 50
Medical Device Mfr & Distr
N.A.I.C.S.: 334510

Smith & Nephew GmbH (1)
Mainstrasse 2, 45768, Marl, Germany
Tel.: (49) 236591810

Web Site: http://www.smith-nephew.de
Medical Device Mfr & Distr
N.A.I.C.S.: 334510

Smith & Nephew Group Research Centre (1)
York Science Park Heslington, York, YO1 5DF, North Yorkshire, United Kingdom (100%)
Tel.: (44) 1904824000
Sales Range: $25-49.9 Million
Emp.: 100
Research Services
N.A.I.C.S.: 541715

Smith & Nephew Healthcare Limited (1)
Healthcare House 101 Hessle Road, Hull, HU3 2BN, East Yorkshire, United Kingdom
Tel.: (44) 1482 222200
Web Site: http://www.smith-nephew.com
Emp.: 800
Medical Device Mfr & Distr
N.A.I.C.S.: 334510

Smith & Nephew Healthcare Private Limited (1)
B-501 Dynasty Business Park J B Nagar Andheri Kurla Road, Andheri East, Mumbai, 400 059, India
Tel.: (91) 2240055090
Web Site: http://www.smith-nephew.com
Sales Range: $25-49.9 Million
Emp.: 70
Medical Device Mfr & Distr
N.A.I.C.S.: 334510

Smith & Nephew Healthcare Sdn Berhad (1)
Menara AmFirst 9th Floor No 1 Jalan 19/3, 46300, Petaling Jaya, Selangor, Malaysia
Tel.: (60) 3 7958 7103
Web Site: http://www.smith-nephew.com
Medical Device Mfr & Distr
N.A.I.C.S.: 334510

Smith & Nephew KK (1)
14th floor South building wood trade center building 2-4-1 hamamsucho, Minato-ku, Tokyo, 105-5114, Japan (100%)
Tel.: (81) 354038800
Web Site: https://www.smith-nephew.com
Medical Device Mfr & Distr
N.A.I.C.S.: 334510

Subsidiary (Domestic):

Smith & Nephew Endoscopy KK (2)
2-4-1 Shiba Park Building A Hall Third Floor, Minato-ku, Tokyo, Japan (100%)
Tel.: (81) 3 5403 8825
Emp.: 134
Medical Device Distr
N.A.I.C.S.: 423450
Shinya Tsuchihashi (Pres & CEO)

Smith & Nephew Orthopaedics KK (2)
2-4-1 Shiba Park Building A Hall 3rd Floor, Minato-ku, Tokyo, 105-0011, Japan (100%)
Tel.: (81) 3 5403 8001
Emp.: 214
Medical Device Distr
N.A.I.C.S.: 423450
Shinya Tsuchihashi (Pres & CEO)

Smith & Nephew Wound Management KK (2)
2-4-1 Shiba Park Building A Hall 3rd Floor, Minato-ku, Tokyo, 105-0011, Japan (100%)
Tel.: (81) 3 5403 8830
Medical Device Distr
N.A.I.C.S.: 423450
Shinya Tsuchihashi (Pres & CEO)

Smith & Nephew Korea (1)
13th Fl ASEM Tower 159-1 Samsung-Dong, Kangnam-gu, 135798, Seoul, Korea (South)
Tel.: (82) 2 60017570
Web Site: http://www.smith-nephew.com
Sales Range: $25-49.9 Million
Emp.: 68
Medical Device Mfr & Distr
N.A.I.C.S.: 334510

Smith & Nephew Lda. (1)
Rua do Parque Tejo N 7 7 A e 7 B, Forte da Casa, 2625-437, Vila Franca de Xira, Portugal
Tel.: (351) 214460650
Web Site: http://www.ortopedia.smith-nephew.pt
Medical Device Mfr & Distr
N.A.I.C.S.: 334510

Smith & Nephew Limited (1)
Unit 813-816 8th Floor Delta House 3 On Yiu Street, Sha Tin, New Territories, China (Hong Kong)
Tel.: (852) 26487700
Web Site: http://www.smith-nephew.com
Sales Range: $25-49.9 Million
Emp.: 19
Medical Device Mfr & Distr
N.A.I.C.S.: 334510

Smith & Nephew Manufacturing AG (1)
Schachenallee 29, 5000, Aarau, Switzerland
Tel.: (41) 62 832 0606
Medical Equipment Mfr & Distr
N.A.I.C.S.: 339112

Smith & Nephew Medical (Shanghai) Limited (1)
15F One Museum Place No 669 Xinzha Road, Jingan District, Shanghai, 200041, China
Tel.: (86) 2123303000
Medical Device Mfr & Distr
N.A.I.C.S.: 334510

Smith & Nephew Medical (Suzhou) Limited (1)
No 12 Wuxiang Rd Area A Export Processing Zone No 200, Suzhou, 215121, China
Tel.: (86) 51267333100
Surgical Appliance Mfr
N.A.I.C.S.: 339113

Smith & Nephew Medical Ltd. (1)
Hessle Rd, PO Box 81, Kingston upon Hull, HU3 2BN, United Kingdom (100%)
Tel.: (44) 1482222200
Web Site: http://www.smith-nephew.com
Sales Range: $200-249.9 Million
Emp.: 1,000
Surgical Dressing Mfr
N.A.I.C.S.: 339113

Smith & Nephew Nederland CV (1)
Kruisweg 637, Hoofddorp, 2132 NB, Netherlands
Tel.: (31) 20 654 39 99
Web Site: http://www.smithnephew.nl
Sales Range: $50-74.9 Million
Emp.: 110
Medical Device Mfr & Distr
N.A.I.C.S.: 334510

Smith & Nephew Operations B.V. (1)
Bloemlaan 2, 2132 NP, Hoofddorp, Netherlands
Tel.: (31) 20 654 3999
Medical Equipment Mfr & Distr
N.A.I.C.S.: 339112

Smith & Nephew Orthopedics GmbH (1)
Alemannenstrasse 14, 78532, Tuttlingen, Germany
Tel.: (49) 74622080
Web Site: http://www.smith-nephew.de
Medical Device Mfr & Distr
N.A.I.C.S.: 334510

Smith & Nephew Orthopedics Hellas SA (1)
8 Kleanthous Street, Ilioupoli, 16346, Athens, Greece
Tel.: (30) 2109913190
Sales Range: $25-49.9 Million
Emp.: 20
Medical Device Distr
N.A.I.C.S.: 423450

Smith & Nephew Oy (1)
Lentajantie 1 3rd floor, 01530, Vantaa, Finland
Tel.: (358) 207866300
Web Site: http://www.smith-nephew.com
Emp.: 25
Medical Device Mfr & Distr
N.A.I.C.S.: 334510

INTERNATIONAL PUBLIC

Smith & Nephew Pte Limited (1)
29 Media Circle 06 05, Singapore, 138565, Singapore
Tel.: (65) 62700552
Sales Range: $25-49.9 Million
Emp.: 50
Medical Device Mfr & Distr
N.A.I.C.S.: 334510
Phyllis Tang (Dir-HR)

Smith & Nephew Pty Limited (1)
Pinnacle Office Park Suite 1 01 Level 1 Building B 4 Drake Ave, Macquarie Park, 2113, NSW, Australia
Tel.: (61) 298573999
Web Site: https://www.smith-nephew.com
Sales Range: $25-49.9 Million
Emp.: 100
Medical Device Mfr & Distr
N.A.I.C.S.: 334510

Smith & Nephew S.A. de C.V. (1)
Av Insurgentes Sur No 1602 Col Credito Constructor Deleg Benito Juarez, 03940, Mexico, Mexico
Tel.: (52) 5 340 2260
Medical Equipment Mfr & Distr
N.A.I.C.S.: 339112

Smith & Nephew SA-NV (1)
Ikaroslaan 45, 1930, Zaventem, Belgium
Tel.: (32) 27022911
Sales Range: $25-49.9 Million
Emp.: 100
Medical Device Mfr & Distr
N.A.I.C.S.: 334510
Antoine Vidts (Mng Dir)

Smith & Nephew SAS (1)
40 - 52 boulevard du Parc, 92200, Neuilly-sur-Seine, France
Tel.: (33) 800111220
Web Site: https://www.smith-nephew.com
Medical Device Mfr
N.A.I.C.S.: 334510
Bertrand Lhuillier (Pres)

Smith & Nephew SAU (1)
Fructuos Gelabert 2 y 4 Edificio Conata 1, 08970, Sant Joan Despi, Barcelona, Spain
Tel.: (34) 933737301
Web Site: http://www.smith-nephew.com
Emp.: 120
Medical Device Mfr
N.A.I.C.S.: 334510

Smith & Nephew Schweiz AG (1)
Theilerstrasse 1A, 6300, Zug, Switzerland
Tel.: (41) 41 766 2222
Medical Equipment Mfr & Distr
N.A.I.C.S.: 339112

Smith & Nephew Sp. Z o. o. (1)
Ul Osmanska 12, 02-823, Warsaw, Poland
Tel.: (48) 223604120
Web Site: http://www.smith-nephew.com
Sales Range: $25-49.9 Million
Emp.: 20
Medical Device Mfr
N.A.I.C.S.: 334510

Smith & Nephew Srl (1)
Via Archimede 42, 20864, Agrate Brianza, MB, Italy
Tel.: (39) 0800176894
Web Site: https://www.smith-nephew.com
Medical Device Mfr & Distr
N.A.I.C.S.: 334510

Smith & Nephew UK Limited (1)
15 Adam Street, London, WC2N 6LA, United Kingdom
Tel.: (44) 20 7401 7646
Medical Device Mfr
N.A.I.C.S.: 334510

Smith & Nephew, Inc. (1)
1450 Brooks Rd, Memphis, TN 38116-1804 (100%)
Tel.: (901) 396-2121
Web Site: http://www.smith-nephew.com
Emp.: 1,215
Surgical Equipment Mfr & Whslr
N.A.I.C.S.: 339113

Subsidiary (Domestic):

ArthroCare Corporation (2)
7000 W William Cannon, Austin, TX 78735
Tel.: (512) 391-3900

AND PRIVATE COMPANIES

SMITHS GROUP PLC

Web Site: http://www.arthrocare.com
Rev.: $377,989,000
Assets: $594,141,000
Liabilities: $191,046,000
Net Worth: $403,095,000
Earnings: $26,056,000
Emp.: 1,840
Fiscal Year-end: 12/31/2013
Soft Tissue Treatment Technology Mfr, Designer, Developer & Marketer
N.A.I.C.S.: 334510

Subsidiary (Domestic):

ArthroCare Medical Corporation (3)
7500 Rialto Blvd Ste 100, Austin, TX 78735
Tel.: (512) 391-3900
Surgical & Medical Equipment Mfr
N.A.I.C.S.: 334510

Subsidiary (Non-US):

ArthroCare Singapore Pte. Ltd. (3)
Lower Delta Road 120, Cendex Centre 12-11, Singapore, 169208, Singapore
Tel.: (65) 62769022
Medical & Surgical Instruments Mfr
N.A.I.C.S.: 334510

Subsidiary (Domestic):

Healthpoint, Ltd. (2)
3909 Hulen St, Fort Worth, TX 76107-7253
Tel.: (817) 900-4000
Pharmaceutical & Medical Products Mfr & Marketer
N.A.I.C.S.: 325412
Robert E. Bancroft (Exec VP-Strategic & Comml Dev)

Lifemodeler, Inc. (2)
2730 Cmino Cpstrano, San Clemente, CA 92672
Tel.: (949) 366-6829
Web Site: http://www.lifemodeler.com
Sales Range: $10-24.9 Million
Emp.: 20
Research & Development in Biotechnology
N.A.I.C.S.: 541714

Rotation Medical, Inc. (2)
15350 25th Ave N Ste 100, Plymouth, MN 55447-2082
Tel.: (763) 335-8042
Web Site: https://www.rotationmedical.com
Dental Equipment & Supplies Mfr
N.A.I.C.S.: 339114
Tom Westling (Chm & COO)

Division (Domestic):

Smith & Nephew, Inc. - Advanced Wound Management (2)
5600 Clearfork Main St, Fort Worth, TX 76109
Tel.: (727) 392-1261
Web Site: http://www.snwmd.com
Sales Range: $50-74.9 Million
Emp.: 200
Mfr of Specialty Wound Care, I.V. Dressings, Skin Care
N.A.I.C.S.: 339113

Smith & Nephew, Inc. - Endoscopy Division (2)
150 Minuteman Rd, Andover, MA 01810-5885
Tel.: (978) 749-1000
Web Site: http://www.endo.smith-nephew.com
Sales Range: $100-124.9 Million
Emp.: 500
Surgical & Medical Instrument Mfr
N.A.I.C.S.: 339112

Smith and Nephew Hellas S.A. (1)
8 Kleanthous Streeet, Ilioupoli, 16346, Athens, Greece
Tel.: (30) 2109913190
Web Site: http://www.smith-nephew.com
Emp.: 5
Medical Device Mfr & Distr
N.A.I.C.S.: 334510

Smith ve Nephew Medikal Cihazlar Ticaret Limited Sirketi (1)
Mahmutbey Mahallesi 2538 Sokak 6/Z1 Kisik Plaza Apt, Bagcilar, 34218, Istanbul, Turkiye
Tel.: (90) 212 226 2255
Medical Equipment Mfr & Distr

N.A.I.C.S.: 339112

T. J. Smith & Nephew, Limited (1)
101 Hessle Road, Hull, HU3 2BN, United Kingdom
Tel.: (44) 1482 225181
Web Site: http://www.smith-nephew.com
Medical Device Mfr & Distr
N.A.I.C.S.: 334510

Tenet Medical Engineering Inc. (1)
203-11979 40 Street SE Suite 203, Calgary, T2Z 4M3, AB, Canada
Tel.: (403) 571-0750
Orthopedic Product Mfr & Distr
N.A.I.C.S.: 334510

SMITH BROS. & WILSON (BC) LTD.
9788 186th Street, Surrey, V4N 3N7, BC, Canada
Tel.: (604) 324-1155
Web Site: https://www.sbw.ca
Year Founded: 1897
General Contractors & Building Construction
N.A.I.C.S.: 238190

SMITH FINANCIAL CORPORATION
16 York Street Suite 2000, Toronto, M5J 0E6, ON, Canada
Tel.: (905) 483-5331
Investment Services
N.A.I.C.S.: 523999
Stephen Smith (Owner)

Subsidiaries:

Home Capital Group Inc. (1)
145 King St West Suite 2300, Toronto, M5H 1J8, ON, Canada (100%)
Tel.: (416) 360-4663
Web Site: https://www.homecapital.com
Rev.: $429,741,607
Assets: $15,760,559,175
Liabilities: $14,531,408,766
Net Worth: $1,229,150,409
Earnings: $191,450,514
Emp.: 778
Fiscal Year-end: 12/31/2021
Holding Company; Deposit, Mortgage Lending, Retail Credit & Credit Card Issuing Services
N.A.I.C.S.: 551112
John Hong (Chief Compliance Officer & Sr VP)

Subsidiary (Domestic):

Home Trust Company (2)
145 King Street West Suite 2300, Toronto, M5H 1J8, ON, Canada
Tel.: (416) 775-5000
Web Site: https://www.hometrust.ca
Sales Range: $200-249.9 Million
Emp.: 500
Mortgage & Nonmortgage Loan Brokers
N.A.I.C.S.: 522310
John Hong (Chief Compliance Officer & Sr VP)

SMITHS & FOUNDERS INDIA LIMITED
505 5th Floor Brigade Rubix No 20 HMT Main Road, Bengaluru, 560013, Karnataka, India
Tel.: (91) 8029724155
Web Site: https://www.smithsandfounders.com
Year Founded: 1982
513418—(BOM)
Rev.: $1,263,789
Assets: $1,326,779
Liabilities: $842,807
Net Worth: $483,972
Earnings: $96,082
Emp.: 65
Fiscal Year-end: 03/31/21
Automobile Parts Mfr
N.A.I.C.S.: 336110
Suresh Shastry (Chm & Mng Dir)

SMITHS CITY GROUP LIMITED
261 Opawa Road Hillsborough, Christchurch, 8022, New Zealand
Tel.: (64) 3 9833000
Web Site: http://www.smithscitygroup.co.nz
Year Founded: 1918
SCY—(NZX)
Rev.: $138,277,680
Assets: $87,093,500
Liabilities: $58,553,630
Net Worth: $28,539,870
Earnings: $(1,138,915)
Emp.: 463
Fiscal Year-end: 04/30/19
General Merchandise Retailer
N.A.I.C.S.: 455211
Roy James Campbell (CEO)

Subsidiaries:

Alectra Limited (1)
18 Watts Rd, Christchurch, New Zealand (100%)
Tel.: (64) 39833199
Emp.: 300
Plastics Product Mfr
N.A.I.C.S.: 326199

L V Martin & Son Limited (1)
11 Ngauranga Gorge Rd, PO Box 13349, Johnsonville, Wellington, 6037, New Zealand (80%)
Tel.: (64) 44969899
Web Site: http://www.lvmartin.co.nz
Sales Range: $25-49.9 Million
Emp.: 30
Marketing Consulting Services
N.A.I.C.S.: 541613
Stephen Salmon (Gen Mgr)

Powerstore Limited (1)
Moorhouse Ave, PO Box 2343, Christchurch, 8011, New Zealand (100%)
Tel.: (64) 39833444
Web Site: http://www.powerstore.co.nz
Emp.: 9
Store Retailers
N.A.I.C.S.: 459999
Rick Anderson (Mgr-Smiths City Grp)

Smithcorp Finance Limited (1)
550 Colombo St, Christchurch, 8011, New Zealand (100%)
Tel.: (64) 39833000
Web Site: http://www.smithcorp.co.nz
Sales Range: $50-74.9 Million
Emp.: 50
Credit Card Issuing
N.A.I.C.S.: 522210
Martin Simcock (Gen Mgr)

Smiths City (Christchurch) Limited (1)
Bush Inn Centre Cnr Waimari & Riccarton Road, Christchurch, 8042, New Zealand (100%)
Tel.: (64) 33431300
Web Site: http://www.smithscity.com
Sales Range: $25-49.9 Million
Emp.: 17
Household Cooking Appliance Mfr
N.A.I.C.S.: 335220
Brian Limb (Mgr-Store)

Smiths City (Nelson) Limited (1)
197 Queen St, Richmond, 7020, New Zealand (100%)
Tel.: (64) 35439080
Web Site: http://www.smithcity.co.nz
Emp.: 9
Household Cooking Appliance Mfr
N.A.I.C.S.: 335220
Richard Hellings (Mng Dir)

Smiths City (Southern) Limited (1)
28 Irwell St Gore, Christchurch, 9710, New Zealand (100%)
Tel.: (64) 32039024
Web Site: http://www.smithscity.co.nz
Household Cooking Appliance Mfr
N.A.I.C.S.: 335220
Roy Campbell (CEO)

Smiths City Properties Limited (1)
550 Colombo St, Christchurch, New Zealand (100%)
Tel.: (64) 39 8 33000

Web Site: http://smithscitygroup.co.nz
Household Appliances Mfr
N.A.I.C.S.: 335220

SMITHS GROUP PLC
4th Floor 11-12 Saint James s Square, London, SW1Y 4LB, United Kingdom
Tel.: (44) 2070041600   UK
Web Site: http://www.smiths.com
Year Founded: 1851
SMIN—(LSE)
Rev.: $3,771,346,600
Assets: $5,408,039,000
Liabilities: $2,420,268,200
Net Worth: $2,987,770,800
Earnings: $280,646,800
Fiscal Year-end: 07/31/23
Holding Company; Threat Detection Systems, Medical Devices, Energy Components & Communications Components Mfr
N.A.I.C.S.: 551112
William C. Seeger (Executives, Bd of Dirs)

Subsidiaries:

Flex-Tek Group (US) LLC (1)
1473 Gould Dr, Cookeville, TN 38506
Tel.: (931) 432-7212
Web Site: https://www.flextekgroup.com
Construction Product Mfr & Distr
N.A.I.C.S.: 333120
Pat McCaffrey (Pres)

Flexible Ducting, Limited (1)
29 Dunsinane Avenue, Milngavie, Dundee, DD2 3QF, United Kingdom (100%)
Tel.: (44) 1419564551
Web Site: http://www.flexibleducting.co.uk
Emp.: 100
Flexible Ducting, Hose & Tubing Products Mfr
N.A.I.C.S.: 326220

Flexschlauch Produktions GmbH (1)
Reepschlagerstrasse 10b, PO Box 3220, 23556, Lubeck, Germany (100%)
Tel.: (49) 4518999401
Web Site: https://www.flexschlauch-luebeck.de
Sales Range: $25-49.9 Million
Emp.: 16
Hose Mfr
N.A.I.C.S.: 326220
Patrick Henry (Co-Mng Dir)

Gastite Systems Deutschland GmbH (1)
Gewerbestrasse 12, 86836, Graben, Germany
Tel.: (49) 82329963344
Web Site: https://www.gastite.de
Pipe Fitting Product Mfr & Distr
N.A.I.C.S.: 332996

Gastite Systems Limited (1)
Brooklyn House 44 Brook Street, Shepshed, LE12 9RG, Leicestershire, United Kingdom
Tel.: (44) 1509508939
Web Site: https://www.gastite.co.uk
Pipe Fitting Product Mfr & Distr
N.A.I.C.S.: 332996

Hi-Tech Duravent, Inc. (1)
528 Carwellyn Rd, Abbeville, SC 29620
Web Site: http://www.hitechduravent.com
Industrial Airhose Mfr
N.A.I.C.S.: 326220

Huafeng Smiths Interconnect (Sichuan) Co., Ltd. (1)
No 120 Sanjiang Avenue, Economic Development Zone, Mianyang, 621000, Sichuan, China
Tel.: (86) 8162315566
Web Site: https://www.hf-smiths.cn
Microwave Component Mfr & Distr
N.A.I.C.S.: 334419

Hypertac SpA (1)
Via Da Bissone 7 A, Sestri Ponente, 16153, Genoa, Italy
Tel.: (39) 01060361
Electronic Components Mfr

SMITHS GROUP PLC

Smiths Group plc—(Continued)
N.A.I.C.S.: 334419

Hypertronics Corporation (1)
16 Brent Dr, Hudson, MA
01749-2904 **(100%)**
Tel.: (978) 568-0451
Web Site: http://www.hypertronics.com
Sales Range: $50-74.9 Million
Emp.: 150
Electric & Electronic Connectors Mfr
N.A.I.C.S.: 334417

Industrias John Crane Mexico S.A. de C.V. (1)
679 Poniente 152, Vallejo Delegacion Azcapotzalco, 2300, Mexico, Mexico
Tel.: (52) 15553850568
Mechanical Sealing Mfr & Distr
N.A.I.C.S.: 339991

JC Production Solutions, Inc (1)
6308 W I-20, Midland, TX 79706
Tel.: (432) 685-3334
Web Site: http://www.productionsolutions.net
Emp.: 30
Industrial Pump Mfr
N.A.I.C.S.: 333914

John Crane (Ireland) Limited (1)
Bay 53/54, Shannon Industrial Estate, Shannon, Y14 YC90, Clare, Ireland
Tel.: (353) 61470773
Mechanical Sealing Mfr & Distr
N.A.I.C.S.: 339991

John Crane A.S. (1)
Jana Sigmunda 78, 78349, Lutin, Czech Republic
Tel.: (420) 585721111
Mechanical Sealing Mfr & Distr
N.A.I.C.S.: 339991

John Crane Baku LLC (1)
Dostluq Street No 32 Salyan Highway 10th km, PO Box AZ1023, Sabail district, Az1023, Baku, Azerbaijan
Tel.: (994) 125815591
Mechanical Sealing Mfr & Distr
N.A.I.C.S.: 339991

John Crane Belgium N.V. (1)
Glasstraat 37, Merksem, 2170, Antwerp, Belgium
Tel.: (32) 32397157
Web Site: https://www.johncrane.com
Emp.: 5,000
Mechanical Seal Product Mfr
N.A.I.C.S.: 339991

John Crane Egypt Sealing Systems LLC (1)
139 Mogamma El Massanee St, PO Box 151, El Amerya, Cairo, Egypt
Tel.: (20) 224285010
Mechanical Sealing Mfr & Distr
N.A.I.C.S.: 339991

John Crane Endustriyel Sizdirmazlik Sistemleri Ltd. (1)
Ferhat Pasa Mah 25 Sokak No 41-43, Atasehir, 34888, Istanbul, Turkiye
Tel.: (90) 2123209200
Mechanical Sealing Mfr & Distr
N.A.I.C.S.: 339991

John Crane France S.A.S. (1)
114 Rue Jules Ferry, BP 35, Deville les Rouen, 76250, Rouen, France
Tel.: (33) 232823940
Mechanical Sealing Mfr & Distr
N.A.I.C.S.: 339991

John Crane Group Limited (1)
361-366 Buckingham Avenue, Slough, SL1 4LU, United Kingdom **(100%)**
Tel.: (44) 1753224000
Sales Range: $75-99.9 Million
Emp.: 350
Holding Company; Mechanical Seals Mfr
N.A.I.C.S.: 551112

Subsidiary (Non-US):

JOHN CRANE PACKING (PTY) LTD. (2)
No 2 No 1 Carel Lotter Road, Nuffield, Springs, 1560, South Africa
Tel.: (27) 11 363 2621

Web Site: http://www.johncrane.co.uk
Sales Range: $50-74.9 Million
Emp.: 168
Industrial Sealing Device Mfr
N.A.I.C.S.: 339991

John Crane (Japan) Inc. (2)
1-27-16 Hamamatsu-Cho 4Th Floor Hamamatsu-Cho Ds Bldg, Minato-Ku, Tokyo, 105-0013, Japan **(51%)**
Tel.: (81) 335789255
Sales Range: $25-49.9 Million
Emp.: 100
Mechanical Seals
N.A.I.C.S.: 339991

John Crane (Korea) Co. Ltd (2)
15F Westgate Tower 70 Chungjungro, Seodaemun-gu, Seoul, 03738, Korea (South)
Tel.: (82) 23617022
Web Site: https://www.johncrane.com
Mechanical Seals
N.A.I.C.S.: 339991

John Crane (Pty) Ltd. (2)
2 Jansen Road Nuffield, PO Box 890, Springs, Johannesburg, 1559, Gauteng, South Africa **(100%)**
Tel.: (27) 118126300
Sales Range: $50-74.9 Million
Emp.: 150
Mechanical Seals
N.A.I.C.S.: 339991

John Crane (Switzerland) AG (2)
Hohenrainstrasse 10, Birsfelden, 4133, Pratteln, Switzerland
Tel.: (41) 614269292
Mechanical Seals
N.A.I.C.S.: 339991

John Crane (Thailand) Ltd (2)
Um Tower Floor 31 No 9/311 9/317 Ramkhamhaeng Road, Suanluang, Bangkok, 10250, Thailand
Tel.: (66) 27174507
Web Site: http://www.johncrane.co.th
Industrial Machinery Mfr
N.A.I.C.S.: 333248

John Crane - Kuwait (2)
C/O Al Julaiah Petroleum Services Block 4 Street 85, Intersection MA10 & MA8 South Shuaiba Industrial Area Mina Abdulla, Kuwait, Kuwait
Tel.: (965) 2 326 3820
Web Site: https://www.johncrane.com
Mechanical Seals Mfr
N.A.I.C.S.: 339991

John Crane Argentina SA (2)
Almafuerte 922, 8000, Bahia Blanca, Buenos Aires, Argentina **(100%)**
Tel.: (54) 2914556011
Sales Range: $25-49.9 Million
Emp.: 70
Mechanical Seals
N.A.I.C.S.: 339991

John Crane Australia Pty Ltd. (2)
549-551 Somerville Road, Sunshine, 3020, VIC, Australia **(100%)**
Tel.: (61) 392894777
Sales Range: $25-49.9 Million
Emp.: 45
Mechanical Seals
N.A.I.C.S.: 339991

John Crane Benelux (2)
Rue De La Jonction 7, Ignace Motte, 7390, Quaregnon, Belgium **(100%)**
Tel.: (32) 65793840
Web Site: http://www.johncrane.com
Sales Range: $25-49.9 Million
Emp.: 21
Mechanical Seals
N.A.I.C.S.: 339991

John Crane Canada (2)
3545 Thimens Ville, Saint Laurent, H4R 1V5, QC, Canada
Tel.: (514) 332-9391
Web Site: http://www.johncrane.com
Sales Range: $25-49.9 Million
Emp.: 35
Mechanical Seals Mfr
N.A.I.C.S.: 332913

Subsidiary (US):

John Crane Caribe Ltd. (2)

654 Mount Rivera Ave Ste 933, San Juan, PR 00918 **(100%)**
Tel.: (787) 760-4650
Web Site: http://www.johncrane.com
Sales Range: $50-74.9 Million
Emp.: 9
Mechanical Seals
N.A.I.C.S.: 423840

Subsidiary (Non-US):

John Crane China Ltd. (2)
No 9 1st Haitaihuake Road, Huayuan Science Park Binhai Hi-Tech Industrial Area, Tianjin, 300384, China **(100%)**
Tel.: (86) 2258398588
Web Site: http://www.johncrane.com.cn
Sales Range: $1-9.9 Million
Emp.: 180
Mechanical Seals
N.A.I.C.S.: 339991

John Crane Columbia (2)
Calle 46A No 82-54 Int 13-14, San Cayetano Cundinamarca, Bogota, 111011, Colombia **(100%)**
Tel.: (57) 601 410 1747
Web Site: http://www.johncrane.com
Mechanical Seals
N.A.I.C.S.: 339991

John Crane Czech Republic (2)
Jana Sigmunda 78, 783 49, Lutin, Czech Republic **(100%)**
Tel.: (420) 58 572 1211
Web Site: https://www.johncrane.com
Sales Range: $100-124.9 Million
Emp.: 320
Mechanical Seals
N.A.I.C.S.: 339991

John Crane Ges.m.b.H (2)
Industriestrasse 39-45, 4050, Traun, Austria **(100%)**
Tel.: (43) 722976706
Sales Range: $25-49.9 Million
Emp.: 7
Mechanical Seals Mfr
N.A.I.C.S.: 339991

John Crane GmbH (2)
Werner-von-Siemens-Strasse 6, 36041, Fulda, Germany **(100%)**
Tel.: (49) 6612810
Web Site: http://www.johncrane.de
Sales Range: $50-74.9 Million
Emp.: 150
Mechanical Seals
N.A.I.C.S.: 339991

John Crane Holland, B.V. (2)
Bergen 9-17, 2993 LR, Barendrecht, Netherlands **(100%)**
Tel.: (31) 180656500
Web Site: http://www.johncrane.nl
Sales Range: $25-49.9 Million
Emp.: 44
Mechanical Seals
N.A.I.C.S.: 339991
Celine Boland (CFO & VP)

John Crane Iberica (2)
Cement No 1 Torrejon de Ardoz, 28850, Madrid, Spain **(100%)**
Tel.: (34) 916559640
Sales Range: $25-49.9 Million
Emp.: 80
Mechanical Seals
N.A.I.C.S.: 339991

John Crane Mexico SA de CV (2)
Poniente 152 No 667 Industrial Vallejo, Azcapotzalco Distrito Federal, 2300, Mexico, Mexico **(100%)**
Tel.: (52) 1555 385 0568
Web Site: https://www.johncrane.com
Mechanical Seals
N.A.I.C.S.: 339991

John Crane Middle East-Central Region (2)
Jebel Ali Free Zone, PO Box 61040, Jebel Ali, Dubai, United Arab Emirates **(100%)**
Tel.: (971) 4 812 7800
Web Site: http://www.johncrane.com
Sales Range: $25-49.9 Million
Emp.: 75
Mechanical Seals
N.A.I.C.S.: 339991

John Crane Norge (2)

INTERNATIONAL PUBLIC

Skvadronveien 27, Sola, Stavanger, 4050, Norway **(100%)**
Tel.: (47) 5 194 4260
Web Site: https://www.johncrane.com
Sales Range: $25-49.9 Million
Emp.: 10
Mechanical Seals
N.A.I.C.S.: 339991

John Crane Rus LLC (2)
B savvinsky Per D 11, 119435, Moscow, 119435, Russia **(100%)**
Tel.: (7) 4959701275
Sales Range: $25-49.9 Million
Emp.: 7
Mechanical Engineered Sealing Systems
N.A.I.C.S.: 339991

John Crane Safematic Oy (2)
Punasillantie 15, PO Box 10, 40950, Muurame, Finland **(100%)**
Tel.: (358) 108525611
Web Site: http://www.johncrane.fi
Sales Range: $50-74.9 Million
Emp.: 100
Mechanical Seals Mfr
N.A.I.C.S.: 339991

John Crane Saudi Arabia Co. Ltd (2)
PO Box 48598, Jeddah, 21582, Saudi Arabia **(966)** 3 3407490
Industrial Machinery Mfr
N.A.I.C.S.: 333248

John Crane Sealing Systems India Pvt. Ltd. (2)
No 11 1st Phase Peenya Industrial Area, Opp To Ravi Kirloskar Hospital, Bengaluru, 560058, India
Tel.: (91) 8022186220
Web Site: http://www.johncrane.co.uk
Mechanical Seals Mfr
N.A.I.C.S.: 339991

John Crane Sigma a.s. (2)
46 B-dul Republicii floor 4, Prahova District, Ploiesti, 031042, Romania **(100%)**
Tel.: (40) 74 465 1751
Web Site: https://www.johncrane.com
Mechanical Seals
N.A.I.C.S.: 339991

John Crane Singapore Pte. Ltd. (2)
15 Tuas View Place, Singapore, 637432, Singapore **(100%)**
Tel.: (65) 65181800
Web Site: http://www.johncrane.com.sg
Sales Range: $25-49.9 Million
Emp.: 100
Mechanical Seals
N.A.I.C.S.: 339991

John Crane SpA (2)
Via Giotto 3, Muggeo, 20835, Milan, Lombardia, Italy **(100%)**
Tel.: (39) 03927141
Web Site: https://www.johncrane.com
Sales Range: Less than $1 Million
Mechanical Seals
N.A.I.C.S.: 339991

John Crane Sverige AB (2)
Victor Hasselblads gata 9, 421 31, Vastra Frolunda, Gothenburg, Sweden **(100%)**
Tel.: (46) 317644400
Sales Range: $25-49.9 Million
Emp.: 20
Mechanical Seals
N.A.I.C.S.: 339991

John Crane Taiwan (2)
No 324-4 Fengren Road, Renwu District, Kaohsiung, 81465, Taiwan **(100%)**
Tel.: (886) 73719141
Sales Range: $1-9.9 Million
Emp.: 31
Mechanical Seals
N.A.I.C.S.: 339991

John Crane Turkey (2)
Huzur Mah Ahmet Bayman Cad No 17, Seyrantepe, Istanbul, 34485, Turkiye **(100%)**
Tel.: (90) 2123209200
Web Site: http://www.johncrane.co.uk
Sales Range: $25-49.9 Million
Emp.: 6
Mechanical Seals
N.A.I.C.S.: 339991

AND PRIVATE COMPANIES SMITHS GROUP PLC

Subsidiary (Domestic):

John Crane UK Ltd. (2)
361-366 Buckingham Avenue, Slough, SL1 4LU, United Kingdom (100%)
Tel.: (44) 75 322 4000
Web Site: http://www.johncrane.co.uk
Sales Range: $100-124.9 Million
Mechanical Seals
N.A.I.C.S.: 339991

Branch (Domestic):

John Crane UK Ltd. (3)
31 Nash Road Trafford Park, Manchester, M17 1SS, United Kingdom (100%)
Tel.: (44) 1618722484
Web Site: http://www.johncrane.com
Sales Range: $50-74.9 Million
Emp.: 116
Mechanical Seals
N.A.I.C.S.: 339991

Subsidiary (Non-US):

John Crane Venezuela (2)
Carretera Via a Perija, Km 8 1/2 Avenida 50 Local No 185-72 Zona Industrial El Silencio, Maracaibo, 4001, Zulia, Venezuela
Tel.: (58) 2613000000
Mechanical Seals
N.A.I.C.S.: 339991
Marisol Shoda *(Asst Gen Mgr)*

Subsidiary (US):

John Crane, Inc. (2)
6400 W Oakton St, Morton Grove, IL 60053
Tel.: (847) 967-2400
Web Site: http://www.johncrane.com
Sealing Device Mfr
N.A.I.C.S.: 339991

Subsidiary (Domestic):

John Crane Production Solutions Inc. (3)
11182 US Hwy 69 N, Tyler, TX 75706
Tel.: (903) 881-9083
Web Site: http://www.johncrane.com
Sales Range: $50-74.9 Million
Emp.: 23
Petroleum Industry Machinery Distr
N.A.I.C.S.: 423830

John Crane Sealol (3)
75 Commerce Dr Suite 101, Warwick, RI 02886 (100%)
Tel.: (401) 463-8700
Web Site: http://www.johncrane.com
Sales Range: $50-74.9 Million
Emp.: 150
Mechanical Seals
N.A.I.C.S.: 339991

Subsidiary (Non-US):

PT John Crane Indonesia (2)
Komplek Balikpapan Baru Ruko Sentra Eropa Ii Blok Ab-4 No 01, West Java, Balikpapan, 76114, East Kalimantan, Indonesia (70%)
Tel.: (62) 542875126
Mechanical Seals Mfr
N.A.I.C.S.: 339991

John Crane Hellas - Engineered Sealing Systems Monoprosopi Epe (1)
Building O-1 and O-2 NATO Avenue, Aspropyrgos of Attica, 19300, Athens, Greece
Tel.: (30) 2105584123
Mechanical Sealing Mfr & Distr
N.A.I.C.S.: 339991

John Crane Hungary Kft (1)
Gyar Street 2, Pest, 2040, Budaors, Hungary
Tel.: (36) 23886935
Mechanical Sealing Mfr & Distr
N.A.I.C.S.: 339991

John Crane International Inc. (1)
175 E Crossroads Pkwy Unit E, Chicago, IL 60440
Tel.: (630) 410-4444
Mechanical Sealing Mfr & Distr
N.A.I.C.S.: 339991

John Crane Italia SpA (1)
Via Giovanni Verga 22, 57014, Livorno, Puglia, Italy
Tel.: (39) 0586961568
Mechanical Sealing Mfr & Distr
N.A.I.C.S.: 339991

John Crane Kazakhstan TOO (1)
Ozkenova Street 16 A Md, 060010, Atyrau, Kazakhstan
Tel.: (7) 7122304125
Mechanical Sealing Mfr & Distr
N.A.I.C.S.: 339991

John Crane Malaysia Sdn Bhd (1)
Menara IMC 8 Jalan Sultan Ismail Suite 14 3 Level 14, 50250, Kuala Lumpur, Wilayah Persekutuan, Malaysia
Tel.: (60) 320201090
Mechanical Sealing Mfr & Distr
N.A.I.C.S.: 339991

John Crane Middle East FZE (1)
PO Box 61040, Jebel Ali Free Zone, Dubai, United Arab Emirates
Tel.: (971) 48127800
Mechanical Sealing Mfr & Distr
N.A.I.C.S.: 339991

John Crane Peru SAC (1)
Av Guillermo Dansey 2124, Distrito De Cercado De Lima, 15081, Lima, Peru
Tel.: (51) 14223020
Mechanical Sealing Mfr & Distr
N.A.I.C.S.: 339991

John Crane Poland Sp. z o.o. (1)
Ul Piastowska 39, 82-500, Kwidzyn, Poland
Tel.: (48) 600987011
Mechanical Sealing Mfr & Distr
N.A.I.C.S.: 339991

John Crane Slovakia SRO (1)
Laurinska 18, 81101, Bratislava, Slovakia
Tel.: (421) 903414365
Mechanical Sealing Mfr & Distr
N.A.I.C.S.: 339991

PolyPhaser Corporation (1)
10701 Airport Rd Hayden, Hayden, ID 83835 (100%)
Tel.: (208) 635-6400
Web Site: https://www.polyphaser.com
Sales Range: $50-74.9 Million
Emp.: 130
Mfr of Lightning Protection Systems
N.A.I.C.S.: 335999

Seebach Filter Solutions India Pvt. Ltd. (1)
Gat No 362 Milkat No 728/1 728/2 Bangalore-Pune Highway, Village Shindewadi Tal Khandala District, Satara, 412 801, Maharashtra, India
Tel.: (91) 2169244750
Engineered Filtration Equipment Mfr
N.A.I.C.S.: 333413

Seebach Filtration USA, Inc. (1)
1219 Stewart Plz, Dunbar, WV 25064
Tel.: (304) 720-3746
Engineered Filtration Equipment Mfr
N.A.I.C.S.: 333413

Seebach GmbH (1)
Neckarweg 3, Vellmar, 34246, Kassel, Germany
Tel.: (49) 561982970
Web Site: https://www.seebach.com
Engineered Filtration Equipment Mfr
N.A.I.C.S.: 333413

Smiths Connectors Asia Pte. Ltd. (1)
450 Alexandra Road 05-02 UE Bizhub West, Singapore, 119960, Singapore
Tel.: (65) 68461655
Electronic Components Mfr
N.A.I.C.S.: 334419

Smiths Detection Benelux BV (1)
Bergen 9, 2993 LR, Barendrecht, Netherlands
Tel.: (31) 850685250
Threat Detection & Security Screening Product Mfr
N.A.I.C.S.: 334290

Smiths Detection GmbH (1)
Im Herzen 4, Wiesbaden, Germany
Tel.: (49) 61194120
Thread Detection & Security Screening Product Mfr
N.A.I.C.S.: 334290

Smiths Detection Group Limited (1)
Century House Maylands Avenue, Hemel Hempstead, London, HP2 7DE, United Kingdom
Tel.: (44) 1923658000
Sales Range: $25-49.9 Million
Emp.: 40
Holding Company; Threat Detection Equipment Mfr
N.A.I.C.S.: 551112
Alain McInnes *(CFO)*

Subsidiary (US):

PathSensors, Inc. (2)
701 E Pratt St, Baltimore, MD 21202
Tel.: (443) 557-6150
Web Site: http://www.pathsensors.com
Chemicals Mfr
N.A.I.C.S.: 325414
Jeanette Simpson *(VP-Tech Dev)*

Subsidiary (Non-US):

Smiths Detection (Asia Pacific) Pte Ltd (2)
UE BizHub West 05-02/03/04 450 Alexandra Road, Singapore, 119960, Singapore
Tel.: (65) 64661700
Web Site: https://www.smithsdetection.com
Xray Scanner Distr
N.A.I.C.S.: 423450

Smiths Detection (Australia) Pte Ltd (2)
Unit 5 Botany Grove Estate 14A Baker St, Botany, 2019, NSW, Australia
Tel.: (61) 283389722
Web Site: https://www.smithsdetection.com
Threat Detection Services
N.A.I.C.S.: 561611

Smiths Detection (Thailand) Ltd (2)
99/3 Moo 5 Kingkaew Road, Tambon Rachatheva, Bang Phli, 10540, Samutprakarn, Thailand
Tel.: (66) 217821915
Web Site: https://www.smithsdetection.com
Threat Detection Services
N.A.I.C.S.: 561611

Group (Non-US):

Smiths Detection Europe, Africa, Middle East Headquarters (2)
Im Herzen 4, 65205, Wiesbaden, Germany
Tel.: (49) 6 119 4120
Web Site: https://www.smithsdetection.com
Sales Range: $125-149.9 Million
X-Ray Inspection Units Mfr for Luggage, Mail & Freight Scanning
N.A.I.C.S.: 561621

Subsidiary (Non-US):

Smiths Detection - France (3)
36 rue Charles Heller, 94405, Vitry-sur-Seine, France
Tel.: (33) 155535555
Web Site: https://www.smithsdetection.com
Sales Range: $25-49.9 Million
Emp.: 50
Trace Detection & X-Ray Imaging Equipment Mfr
N.A.I.C.S.: 334517

Smiths Detection Italia S.R.L. (3)
Via Giotto 3, 20835, Muggio, MB, Italy
Tel.: (39) 039611671
Web Site: https://www.smithsdetection.com
Threat Detection Equipment Distr
N.A.I.C.S.: 423830

Subsidiary (Domestic):

Smiths Heimann GmbH (3)
Im Herzen 4, 65205, Wiesbaden, Germany
Tel.: (49) 61194120
Web Site: https://www.smithsdetection.com
Sales Range: $75-99.9 Million
Xray Scanner Mfr & Distr
N.A.I.C.S.: 334510

Subsidiary (Non-US):

Smiths Heimann S.A.S. (3)
36 rue Charles Heller, 94405, Vitry-sur-Seine, France
Tel.: (33) 15 553 5555
Web Site: https://www.smithsdetection.com
Emp.: 200

Threat Detection Equipment Distr
N.A.I.C.S.: 423830

Division (US):

Smiths Detection Inc. (2)
2202 Lakeside Blvd, Edgewood, MD 21040
Tel.: (410) 612-4000
Electronic Parts & Communications Equipment Wholesale Distr
N.A.I.C.S.: 423690

Unit (Domestic):

Smiths Detection Livewave (3)
88 Silva Ln Ste 250 Tech Plaza 4, Middletown, RI 02842
Tel.: (401) 848-7678
Web Site: http://www.smithsdetection.com
Sales Range: $25-49.9 Million
Emp.: 23
Software for Security
N.A.I.C.S.: 561621

Subsidiary (Non-US):

Smiths Detection New Zealand Ltd (2)
1/180 Montgomerie Rd, Airport Oaks, Auckland, 2022, New Zealand
Tel.: (64) 99180540
Web Site: https://www.smithsdetection.com
Threat Detection Services
N.A.I.C.S.: 561611

Subsidiary (Domestic):

Smiths Detection UK Ltd (2)
459 Pk Ave, Bushey, Watford, WD23 2BW, Herts, United Kingdom
Tel.: (44) 23658000
Web Site: http://www.smithsdetection.com
Sales Range: $25-49.9 Million
Emp.: 300
Trace Detection & X-Ray Imaging Equipment Mfr
N.A.I.C.S.: 334517

Subsidiary (Domestic):

Smiths Detection Watford Ltd. (3)
Century House Maylands Avenue, Hemel Hempstead, HP2 7DE, Hertfordshire, United Kingdom
Tel.: (44) 1923658000
Sales Range: Less than $1 Million
Emp.: 300
Trace Detection & X-Ray Imaging Equipment Mfr
N.A.I.C.S.: 334517

Subsidiary (Non-US):

Smiths Detection Veecon Systems Private Ltd (2)
B-58 Shivalik Malviya Nagar, New Delhi, 110 017, India
Tel.: (91) 11 2669 2462
Web Site: http://www.smithsdetection.com
Sales Range: $10-24.9 Million
Emp.: 25
Security System Services
N.A.I.C.S.: 561621

Smiths Heimann Rus LLC (2)
Oktyabrskaya Emb 104 Build 5, 193079, Saint Petersburg, Russia
Tel.: (7) 8124495944
Web Site: https://www.smithsdetection.com
Sales Range: $10-24.9 Million
Emp.: 31
Threat Detection Services
N.A.I.C.S.: 561611

Smiths Detection Japan GK (1)
Spaces Otemachi Otemachi Building 1-6-1 Otemachi, Chiyoda-ku, Tokyo, 100-0004, Japan
Tel.: (81) 368413891
Threat Detection & Security Screening Product Mfr
N.A.I.C.S.: 334290

Smiths Detection Limited (1)
Century House Maylands Avenue, Hemel Hempstead, HP2 7DE, United Kingdom
Tel.: (44) 1923658000
Thread Detection & Security Screening Product Mfr
N.A.I.C.S.: 334290
Roland Carter *(Pres)*

SMITHS GROUP PLC

Smiths Group plc—(Continued)

Smiths Detection Malaysia Sdn Bhd (1)
Lot 8 Jalan SiLC 1, Kawasan Perindustrian SiLC Iskandar Puteri, 79200, Johor Bahru, Johor, Malaysia
Tel.: (60) 75600888
Threat Detection & Security Screening Product Mfr
N.A.I.C.S.: 334290

Smiths Detection Middle East FZE (1)
DAFZA Building 8W Block A 4th Floor, PO Box 48225, Dubai, United Arab Emirates
Tel.: (971) 47029555
Threat Detection & Security Screening Product Mfr
N.A.I.C.S.: 334290
Jerome de Chassey *(VP-Commercial)*

Smiths Detection Montreal Inc. (1)
6865 Century Avenue Suite 3002, Mississauga, L5N 7K2, ON, Canada
Tel.: (905) 817-5990
Thread Detection & Security Screening Product Mfr
N.A.I.C.S.: 334290

Smiths Detection Rus LLC (1)
Oktyabrskaya Emb 104 Build 5, 193079, Saint Petersburg, 193079, Russia
Tel.: (7) 8124495944
Threat Detection & Security Screening Product Mfr
N.A.I.C.S.: 334290

Smiths Detection Systems Private Limited (1)
10th Floor 9B Building DLF Cyber City DLF Phase -III, Gurgaon, 122 002, Haryana, India
Tel.: (91) 1244702670
Threat Detection & Security Screening Product Mfr
N.A.I.C.S.: 334290

Smiths Group Americas LLC (1)
101 Lindenwood Dr Ste 125, Malvern, PA 19355-1755 **(100%)**
Tel.: (610) 578-9600
Web Site: http://www.smiths-group.com
Sales Range: $25-49.9 Million
Emp.: 30
Holding Company
N.A.I.C.S.: 334511

Smiths Group International Holdings Limited (1)
Level 10 255 Blackfriars Road, London, SE1 9AX, United Kingdom
Tel.: (44) 2078085569
Holding Company
N.A.I.C.S.: 551112

Smiths Interconnect Group Limited (1)
Level 10 255 Blackfriars Road, London, SE1 9AX, United Kingdom
Tel.: (44) 2070041600
Emp.: 3,400
Holding Company; Signal, Power & Microwave Electronic Components & Sub-Systems Mfr
N.A.I.C.S.: 551112

Subsidiary (Non-US):

Hypertac GmbH (2)
Ulrichsbergerstrasse 17, 94469, Deggendorf, Germany **(100%)**
Tel.: (49) 991250120
Sales Range: $25-49.9 Million
Emp.: 75
Mfr of Connectors for Signal & Power Applications
N.A.I.C.S.: 334417

Subsidiary (Domestic):

Hypertac Limited (2)
Level 10 255 Blackfriars Road, London, SE1 9AX, United Kingdom **(100%)**
Tel.: (44) 2084508033
Sales Range: $25-49.9 Million
Emp.: 100
Mfr of Electrical Connectors
N.A.I.C.S.: 334417

Subsidiary (US):

Plastronics Socket Partners, Ltd. (2)
2601 Texas Dr, Irving, TX 75062
Tel.: (972) 258-2580
Sales Range: $1-9.9 Million
Emp.: 12
Electronic Parts & Equipment Merchant Whslr
N.A.I.C.S.: 423690
Anne Pfaff *(Principal)*

Smiths Interconnect, Inc. (2)
4726 Eisenhower Blvd, Tampa, FL 33634
Tel.: (813) 901-7200
Holding Company; Regional Managing Office; Electronic Components Mfr
N.A.I.C.S.: 551112

Smiths Interconnect India Private Limited (1)
Vaswani Centropolis Ground Floor Vaswani Centropolis Langford Rd, Bheemanna Garden Shanti nagar Near Jayanagar, Bengaluru, 560027, India
Tel.: (91) 8042410529
Electronic Components Mfr
N.A.I.C.S.: 334419

Smiths Medical Danmark ApS (1)
Winghouse Orestads Boulevard 73, 2300, Copenhagen, Denmark
Tel.: (45) 7 027 2090
Medical Equipment Mfr & Distr
N.A.I.C.S.: 339112

Smiths Medical Do Brasil Produtos Hospitalares Ltda. (1)
Rua George Ohm 206/230-Conj 51/52 Torre B, Sao Paulo, 04576-020, Brazil
Tel.: (55) 113 372 5959
Medical Equipment Mfr & Distr
N.A.I.C.S.: 339112

Smiths Medical India Private Limited (1)
Western Edge - II Western Express Highway, Borivali-East, Mumbai, 400 066, India
Tel.: (91) 222 870 5210
Medical Device Mfr & Distr
N.A.I.C.S.: 339112

Smiths Medical Osterreich GmbH (1)
Europaring A03 5 02, 2345, Brunn am Gebirge, Austria
Tel.: (43) 18 906 4440
Medical Equipment Mfr & Distr
N.A.I.C.S.: 339112

Smiths Medical Schweiz AG (1)
Zurichstrasse 33, 8134, Adliswil, Switzerland
Tel.: (41) 43 388 6200
Medical Device Mfr & Distr
N.A.I.C.S.: 339112

Smiths Pensions Limited (1)
Level 10 255 Blackfriars Road, London, SE1 9AX, United Kingdom
Tel.: (44) 1214523748
Pension Services
N.A.I.C.S.: 525110

Smiths Specialty Engineering (1)
Tel.: (44) 2078085500
Sales Range: $1-4.9 Billion
Emp.: 11,000
Flexible Hose, Mechanical Housing & Specialty Electro-Mechanical Component Mfr
N.A.I.C.S.: 423830

Subsidiary (Non-US):

FIBERCOMposite Company, Inc. (2)
Tel.: (432) 267-9800
Web Site: http://www.productionsolutions.net
Sales Range: $25-49.9 Million
Emp.: 100
Fiberglass Rod Mfr
N.A.I.C.S.: 423830

Flexible Technologies Inc. (2) **(100%)**
Tel.: (864) 366-5441
Web Site: https://www.flexibletechnologies.com
Sales Range: $200-249.9 Million
Emp.: 400
Non Metallic Flexible Ducting & Hose Mfr

N.A.I.C.S.: 326199

Smiths Tubular Systems-Laconia, Inc. (1)
9 Capitol St, Concord, NH 03301
Tel.: (603) 528-1871
Web Site: http://www.lewisandsaunders.com
Sales Range: $125-149.9 Million
Emp.: 300
Mfr of Rigid Tubular Assemblies & Metal Hose Assemblies
N.A.I.C.S.: 332996
Fred Edgington *(Gen Mgr)*

Subsidiary (Domestic):

Smiths Tubular Systems (2)
603 Hendee St, Springfield, MA 01104-3003
Tel.: (413) 739-5631
Web Site: http://www.titeflex.com
Sales Range: $50-74.9 Million
Emp.: 200
Mfr of Rigid Tubular Assemblies & Metal Hose Assemblies
N.A.I.C.S.: 332996
Dennis LeClerc *(Acct Mgr-Customer Svc)*

TRAK Microwave Corporation (1)
4726 Eisenhower Blvd, Tampa, FL 33634
Tel.: (813) 901-7200
Web Site: http://www.trak.com
Advanced Radar, Electronic Warfare Systems, Satellite Communications, Data Links & Public Safety Radio Networks Systems
N.A.I.C.S.: 334511

Subsidiary (Domestic):

TECOM Industries, Inc. (2)
375 Conejo Rdg Ave, Thousand Oaks, CA 91361
Tel.: (805) 267-0100
Web Site: http://tecom-ind.info
Sales Range: $25-49.9 Million
Emp.: 100
Antenna Systems Mfr for the Wireless Communications, SATCOM, Aerospace & Military Markets
N.A.I.C.S.: 334220

Subsidiary (Non-US):

TRAK Microwave Ltd. (2)
Block 29 Dunsinane Avenue, Dundee, DD2 3QF, United Kingdom **(100%)**
Tel.: (44) 1382427200
Web Site: http://www.trakeurope.com
Sales Range: $25-49.9 Million
Emp.: 100
High Reliability Microwave, RF Components & Sub Systems Mfr
N.A.I.C.S.: 334220
Alan McNeill *(Officer-Export Compliance)*

Titeflex Europe S.A.S. (1)
22 Avenue Maurice Chevalier, PO Box 73, Ozoir-la-Ferriere, 77833, Paris, France
Tel.: (33) 160185200
Web Site: http://www.titeflex.com
Sales Range: $25-49.9 Million
Emp.: 70
Mfr of Metal Hose Assemblies & Fittings
N.A.I.C.S.: 332996

Transtector Systems, Inc. (1)
10701 Airport Rd, Hayden, ID 83835
Tel.: (208) 635-6400
Web Site: https://www.transtector.com
Communication Equipment Mfr
N.A.I.C.S.: 334290

Tutco Inc (1)
500 Gould Dr, Cookeville, TN 38506-4100 **(100%)**
Tel.: (931) 432-4141
Web Site: https://www.tutco.com
Sales Range: $100-124.9 Million
Emp.: 350
Electrical Heating Elements Mfr
N.A.I.C.S.: 335210

U.S. Hose Corp. (1)
815 Forestwood Dr, Romeoville, IL 60446
Tel.: (815) 886-1140
Flexible Hose Mfr
N.A.I.C.S.: 326220
John Devine *(CEO)*

Subsidiary (Non-US):

AmniTec B.V. (2)

INTERNATIONAL PUBLIC

Abraham van Stolkweg 118, 3041 JA, Rotterdam, 3041 JA, Netherlands **(100%)**
Tel.: (31) 102982121
Sales Range: $1-9.9 Million
Emp.: 24
Flexible Hose Mfr
N.A.I.C.S.: 332999
Hans Pijnacker *(Mng Dir)*

AmniTec Limited (2)
Abercanaid, Merthyr Tydfil, CF48 1UX, United Kingdom
Tel.: (44) 1685385641
Web Site: https://amnitec.co.uk
Emp.: 100
Flexible Hose Mfr
N.A.I.C.S.: 326220
David Puddy *(Mgr-Sls)*

Subsidiary (Domestic):

Fulton Bellows, LLC (2)
2801 Red Dog Ln, Knoxville, TN 37914-7914
Tel.: (865) 546-0550
Web Site: https://fultonbellows.com
Precision Metal Bellow, Bellow Assembly & Thermal Actuator Mfr
N.A.I.C.S.: 333998
Linda Pearson *(Mgr-Sls)*

Kreisler Manufacturing Corporation (2)
180 Van Riper Ave, Elmwood Park, NJ 07407
Tel.: (201) 791-0700
Web Site: http://www.kreislermfg.com
Sales Range: $25-49.9 Million
Emp.: 234
Aerospace & Industrial Precision Metal Components & Assemblies Mfr
N.A.I.C.S.: 336412
Michael D. Stern *(Pres)*

Subsidiary (Domestic):

Kreisler Industrial Corporation (3)
180 Van Riper Ave, Elmwood Park, NJ 07407-2610 **(100%)**
Tel.: (201) 791-0700
Industrial Precision Metal Components & Assemblies Mfr
N.A.I.C.S.: 332999
Harry Mueller *(Plant Mgr)*

Subsidiary (Domestic):

Lakes Region Tubular Products, Inc. (2)
51 Growtth Rd, Laconia, NH 03246
Tel.: (603) 528-2838
Sales Range: $1-9.9 Million
Emp.: 45
Aircraft Parts & Auxiliary Equipment Mfr
N.A.I.C.S.: 336413
Chuck Tenander *(Dir)*

Plant (Domestic):

U.S. Hose Corp. - Houston (2)
2020 Greens Rd Ste 400, Houston, TX 77032
Tel.: (281) 458-0400
Web Site: http://www.ushosecorp.com
Sales Range: $10-24.9 Million
Emp.: 24
Flexible Hose Mfr
N.A.I.C.S.: 326220

SMITHS METAL CENTRES LTD.

Stratton Business Pk, London Rd, Biggleswade, SG18 8QB, Bedfordshire, United Kingdom
Tel.: (44) 1767604500 UK
Web Site: http://www.smithmetal.com
Year Founded: 1780
Sales Range: $125-149.9 Million
Emp.: 200
Non-Ferrous Metals, Stainless Steel & Engineering Metals Distr
N.A.I.C.S.: 425120
Hugh Dye *(Chm & CEO)*

SMITHS NEWS PLC

AND PRIVATE COMPANIES

Rowan House, Kembrey Park, Swindon, SN2 8UH, Wilts, United Kingdom
Tel.: (44) 3451288888
Web Site:
https://www.smithsnews.co.uk
SMWPY—(OTCIQ)
Rev.: $1,359,664,260
Assets: $236,409,080
Liabilities: $276,351,480
Net Worth: ($39,942,400)
Earnings: $29,207,880
Fiscal Year-end: 08/27/22
Book, Periodical & Newspaper Merchant Wholesalers
N.A.I.C.S.: 424920
Jonathan Bunting (CEO)

Subsidiaries:

Dawson Holdings Limited (1)
Blenheim House 1 Blenheim Road, Epsom, KT19 9AP, United Kingdom
Tel.: (44) 2031674128
Web Site: http://www.dawson.co.uk
Sales Range: $125-149.9 Million
Emp.: 408
Magazine & Newspaper Distr
N.A.I.C.S.: 424920

Subsidiary (Domestic):

Dawson Books Ltd (2)
Foxhills House, Brindley Close, Rushden, NN10 6DB, Northamptonshire, United Kingdom
Tel.: (44) 1933417500
Web Site: http://www.dawsonbooks.co.uk
Sales Range: $50-74.9 Million
Emp.: 180
Book Distr
N.A.I.C.S.: 424920
Sally Barber (Sr Mgr-Technical Sls)

Division (Domestic):

Dawson Media Direct (2)
464-465 Berkshire Avenue, Slough Trading Estate, Slough, SL1 4PL, Berkshire, United Kingdom
Tel.: (44) 1753967410
Sales Range: $25-49.9 Million
Emp.: 50
Supplier of Magazines & Newspapers to Airline Industry
N.A.I.C.S.: 424920

Martin-Lavell Limited (1)
464-465 Berkshire Avenue, Slough Trading Estate, Slough, SL1 4PL, United Kingdom
Tel.: (44) 8451238433
Web Site: https://www.martinlavell.co.uk
Newspaper & Magazine Distr
N.A.I.C.S.: 424920

Smiths News Instore Limited (1)
Blockhouse Close, Worcester, WR1 2BT, United Kingdom
Tel.: (44) 1905677234
Web Site: http://www.instore.co.uk
Newspaper & Magazine Distr
N.A.I.C.S.: 424920
Mike Frost (Mng Dir)

Smiths News Trading Limited (1)
Rowan House Kembrey Park, Swindon, SN2 8UH, Wiltshire, United Kingdom
Tel.: (44) 3451255222
Web Site: https://www.smithsnews.co.uk
Sales Range: $75-99.9 Million
Emp.: 250
Newspaper & Magazine Distr
N.A.I.C.S.: 424920

SMITHSON INVESTMENT TRUST PLC

6th Floor 125 London Wall, London, EC2Y 5AS, United Kingdom
Tel.: (44) 2035516337 UK
Web Site: https://www.smithson.co.uk
SSON—(LSE)
Assets: $3,172,198,732
Liabilities: $6,063,578
Net Worth: $3,166,135,154
Earnings: $674,102,549
Fiscal Year-end: 12/31/20

Portfolio Management & Investment Advice
N.A.I.C.S.: 523940
Mark Pacitti (Chm)

SMITHSTOWN LIGHT ENGINEERING LTD.

Bay H1A Smithstown Industrial Estate, County Clare, Shannon, Ireland
Tel.: (353) 61362111 IE
Web Site: http://www.sle.ie
Year Founded: 1974
Sales Range: $10-24.9 Million
Emp.: 55
Injection Mold Press Tool & Precision Component Mfr
N.A.I.C.S.: 333514
Gerard King (Mng Dir)

SMK CORPORATION

5-5 Togoshi 6-chome, Shinagawa-ku, Tokyo, 142-8511, Japan
Tel.: (81) 337851111
Web Site: https://www.smk.co.jp
Year Founded: 1925
6798—(TKS)
Rev.: $307,510,420
Assets: $386,314,840
Liabilities: $173,849,610
Net Worth: $212,465,230
Earnings: ($3,232,290)
Emp.: 4,104
Fiscal Year-end: 03/31/24
Electronic Components Mfr
N.A.I.C.S.: 334419
Yoshiyuki Kaku (Deputy Pres & CTO)

Subsidiaries:

SMK Career Service Corporation (1)
17-14 Togoshi 5-chome, Shinagawa-ku, Tokyo, 142-0041, Japan
Tel.: (81) 36 852 8176
Electronic Connector Mfr & Distr
N.A.I.C.S.: 334417
Takemi Ishibashi (Pres)

SMK Corporation - Hitachi Works (1)
20-9 Ishi Juo-cho, Hitachi, 319-1301, Ibaraki, Japan
Tel.: (81) 294202111
Electronic Components Mfr
N.A.I.C.S.: 334419

SMK Corporation - Toyama Works (1)
1-1 Yasuuchi Yatsuo-machi, Yatsuo, Toyama, 939-2366, Japan
Tel.: (81) 76 455 1212
Web Site: https://www.smk.co.jp
Electronic Components Mfr
N.A.I.C.S.: 334419

SMK Electronica S.A. de C.V. (1)
Calle Aguila Azteca No 19308 Col Baja Maq El Aguila Nave No B Planta 2, Tijuana, 22215, Baja California, Mexico
Tel.: (52) 664 625 9680
Web Site: http://www.smk.com
Emp.: 1,200
Electronic Components Mfr
N.A.I.C.S.: 334419
Morikawa Fusahiro (Pres)

SMK Electronics (Dongguan) Co., Ltd. (1)
Second East Turning Zhenxing Road, Gaobu, Dongguan, 523289, Guangdong, China
Tel.: (86) 76988873451
Electronic Components Mfr
N.A.I.C.S.: 334419
Nitchu Hajime (Pres)

SMK Electronics (Europe) Limited (1)
203 Digital Office Centre Balheary Demesne Balheary Road, Swords, Dublin, K67 E5A0, Ireland
Tel.: (353) 1 253 0530
Web Site: https://www.smkeurope.com
Electromechanical Product Mfr & Distr
N.A.I.C.S.: 334419

SMK Electronics (H.K.) Ltd. (1)
Unit E 9/F No 15 Wang Chiu Road, Kowloon Bay, Kowloon, China (Hong Kong)
Tel.: (852) 27954451
Web Site: http://www.smkhkg.com
Electronic Components Mfr
N.A.I.C.S.: 334419

SMK Electronics (M) Sdn Bhd (1)
Lot 15 Jalan Perusahaan 1 Kawasan Perindustrian Beranang, 43700, Beranang, Selangor Darul Ehsan, Malaysia
Tel.: (60) 387660166
Emp.: 507
Electronic Components Mfr
N.A.I.C.S.: 334419
Masahiro Shishido (Mng Dir)

SMK Electronics (Phils.) Corporation (1)
Lot C-4 Clark Premiere Industrial Park M A Roxas Highway, Clark Freeport Zone Clark Field, Angeles, Pampanga, Philippines
Tel.: (63) 455995780
Web Site: https://www.smk.co.jp
Electronic Components Mfr
N.A.I.C.S.: 334419
Mikio Otsubo (Pres)

SMK Electronics (Shenzhen) Co., Ltd. (1)
Section 5 Bldg 23 Baiwangxin Industrial Area Songbai Road Xili Street, Nanshan District, Shenzhen, 518108, Guangdong, China
Tel.: (86) 75586000999
Electrical Component Mfr
N.A.I.C.S.: 334419
Ebisu Yasu (Mng Dir)

SMK Electronics Corporation (1)
1055 Tierra Del Rey Ste F, Chula Vista, CA 91910
Tel.: (619) 216-6400
Web Site: https://www.smkusa.com
Sales Range: $25-49.9 Million
Emp.: 100
Electronic Components Mfr & Marketer
N.A.I.C.S.: 334419
Paul Evans (Pres)

Subsidiary (Domestic):

SMK-Link Electronics Corporation (2)
399 Knollwood Rd Ste 103, White Plains, NY 10603-1900
Tel.: (941) 461-9386
Sales Range: $25-49.9 Million
Emp.: 30
Computer Peripheral Equipment Mfr & Marketer
N.A.I.C.S.: 334118

SMK Electronics INT'L Trading (Shanghai) Co., Ltd. (1)
Room C707A Orient International Plaza No 85 Lou Shan Guan Road, Shanghai, 200336, China
Tel.: (86) 2162785600
Electronic Components Mfr
N.A.I.C.S.: 334419
Hata Fumikazu (Pres)

SMK Electronics Singapore Pte. Ltd. (1)
12 Tannery Road 04-02, Singapore, 347722, Singapore
Tel.: (65) 67450951
Web Site: https://www.smk.co.jp
Electronic Components Mfr
N.A.I.C.S.: 334419

SMK Electronics Technology Development (Shenzhen) Co., Ltd. (1)
New Jianxing Block A 901 Jianxing Science Technology Building, ShaHe West Road Nanshan District, Shenzhen, 518055, Guangdong, China
Tel.: (86) 75586007997
Electronic Components Mfr
N.A.I.C.S.: 334419
Sekii Akitoshi (Pres)

SMK Electronics Trading (Shanghai) Co., Ltd. (1)
Room C706A Orient International Plaza No 85 Lou Shan Guan Road, Shanghai, 200336, China

Tel.: (86) 216 278 5600
Electronic Connector Mfr & Distr
N.A.I.C.S.: 334417

SMK Electronics Trading (Shenzhen) Co., Ltd. (1)
ROOM14-1 Unit 1 building 10 Guobin Town hilltop Road, No 18 xingai Avenue Yubei District, Chongqing, 401147, Shaanxi, China
Tel.: (86) 18623640714
Electronic Components Mfr
N.A.I.C.S.: 334419

SMK Europe N.V. (1)
Web Site: http://www.smkeurope.com
Electronic Components Mfr
N.A.I.C.S.: 334419
Paul Evans (Pres)

SMK High-Tech Taiwan Trading Co., Ltd. (1)
12F-2 No 87 Sung Chiang Road, Taipei, 104-86, Taiwan
Tel.: (886) 225183650
Web Site: https://www.smk.co.jp
Electronic Components Mfr
N.A.I.C.S.: 334419

SMK Hungary Kft. (1)
Almaskerti Ipari Park 1, 5600, Bekescsaba, Hungary
Tel.: (36) 66 524 300
Web Site: http://www.smk.com
Emp.: 140
Electronic Components Mfr
N.A.I.C.S.: 334419
Michael Walsh (Mng Dir)

SMK Korea Co., Ltd. (1)
Room 2003 2nd floor 529 Seolleung-ro, Gangnam-gu, Seoul, 06149, Korea (South)
Electronic Components Mfr
N.A.I.C.S.: 334419

SMK Manufacturing, Inc. (1)
1055 Tierra Del Rey, Chula Vista, CA 91910
Tel.: (619) 216-6400
Electronic Connector Mfr
N.A.I.C.S.: 335313

SMK Mexicana S de RL de CV (1)
Alfonso Napoles Gandara 50 4th Floor, Colonia Pena Blanca Santa Fe, 01210, Mexico, Mexico
Tel.: (52) 5591711830
Electronic Components Mfr
N.A.I.C.S.: 334419

SMK Trading (H.K.) Ltd. (1)
Unit E 9/F No 15 Wang Chiu Road Kowloon Bay, Kowloon, China (Hong Kong)
Tel.: (852) 2 795 4451
Electronic Connector Mfr & Distr
N.A.I.C.S.: 334417

Showa Denshi Co., Ltd. (1)
1-2 Yasuuchi Yatsuo-machi, Toyama, 939-2366, Japan
Tel.: (81) 76 455 0030
Electronic Connector Mfr & Distr
N.A.I.C.S.: 334417
Atsushi Obinata (Pres)

Showa Enterprise Corporation (1)
17-14 Togoshi 5-chome, Shinagawa-ku, Tokyo, 142-0041, Japan
Tel.: (81) 33 781 6927
Electronic Connector Mfr & Distr
N.A.I.C.S.: 334417
Terutaka Ikeda (Pres)

Toyama Showa Co., Ltd. (1)
1-2 Yasuuchi Yatsuo-machi, Toyama, 939-2366, Japan
Tel.: (81) 76 455 2360
Electronic Connector Mfr & Distr
N.A.I.C.S.: 334417
Masanobu Ikeo (Pres)

SML GROUP LTD.

8th Floor SML Tower 165 Hoi Bun Road, Siu Lek Yuen, Kwun Tong, Kowloon, China (Hong Kong)
Tel.: (852) 2699 8082
Web Site: http://www.sml.com
Year Founded: 1985
Sales Range: $100-124.9 Million
Emp.: 1,000

SML GROUP LTD.

SML Group Ltd.—(Continued)
Apparel Branding & Packaging Services
N.A.I.C.S.: 561910
Simon Suen *(Founder & Chm)*

Subsidiaries:

Xterprise, Inc. (1)
2304 Tarpley Rd Ste 114, Carrollton, TX 75006
Tel.: (972) 690-9460
Web Site: http://www.xterprise.com
Sales Range: $1-9.9 Million
Emp.: 50
Supply Chain Management Services & RFID Technology
N.A.I.C.S.: 513210
Dean Frew *(Founder, Pres & CEO)*

SML ISUZU LIMITED
SCO 204-205 Sector 34-A, Chandigarh, 160135, India
Tel.: (91) 1722647700
Web Site: https://www.smlisuzu.com
SMLISUZU—(NSE)
Rev.: $81,349,687
Assets: $108,686,241
Liabilities: $73,801,182
Net Worth: $34,885,059
Earnings: ($18,221,412)
Emp.: 959
Fiscal Year-end: 03/31/21
Motor Vehicles Mfr
N.A.I.C.S.: 336110
S. K. Tuteja *(Chm)*

SMN POWER HOLDING SAOG
Jawharat A'Shatti, PO Box 121, E Y Building No 1023 First Floor Office 16 Way No 1013, 134, Muscat, Oman
Tel.: (968) 24935800   OM
Web Site:
   https://www.smnpower.com
Year Founded: 2011
SMNP—(MUS)
Rev.: $214,229,446
Assets: $584,346,455
Liabilities: $444,847,790
Net Worth: $139,498,666
Earnings: $26,737,870
Emp.: 19
Fiscal Year-end: 12/31/20
Holding Company
N.A.I.C.S.: 551112
Abdullah Al Yahya'ey *(Chm)*

SMO CLINPLUS CO., LTD.
Floor 23 Shanghai World Trade Tower No 500 Guangdong Road, Huangpu District, Shanghai, 200001, China
Tel.: (86) 2160755800
Web Site: https://www.smo-clinplus.com
Year Founded: 2009
301257—(SSE)
Rev.: $82,306,945
Assets: $162,964,976
Liabilities: $29,308,697
Net Worth: $133,656,279
Earnings: $10,166,561
Emp.: 4,061
Fiscal Year-end: 12/31/22
Pharmaceutical Product Mfr & Distr
N.A.I.C.S.: 325412

SMOLTEK NANOTECH HOLDING AB
Otterhallegatan 1, 411 18, Gothenburg, Sweden
Tel.: (46) 317010305
Web Site: https://www.smoltek.com
Application Development Services
N.A.I.C.S.: 541511
Anders Johansson *(CEO)*

SMOORE INTERNATIONAL HOLDINGS LIMITED
Internal Control and Internal Audit Center SMOORE, No 16 Dongcai Industrial Zone Baoan District, Shenzhen, Guangdong, China
Tel.: (86) 18925236359   Ky
Web Site:
   https://en.smooreholdings.com
Year Founded: 2009
6969—(HKG)
Rev.: $1,546,358,828
Assets: $3,531,829,309
Liabilities: $567,494,877
Net Worth: $2,964,334,432
Earnings: $227,776,086
Emp.: 11,556
Fiscal Year-end: 12/31/23
Holding Company
N.A.I.C.S.: 551112
Guisheng Wang *(CFO)*

Subsidiaries:

Transpire Bio Inc. (1)
2945 W Corporate Lakes Blvd Ste A, Weston, FL 33331
Tel.: (954) 908-2233
Web Site: https://www.transpirebio.com
Pharmaceutical Inhalation Therapy Services
N.A.I.C.S.: 621399

SMOOTH ROCK VENTURES CORP.
Suite 820-1130 West Pender St, Vancouver, V6E 4A4, BC, Canada
Web Site:
   https://www.smoothrockventure.com
SMRVF—(OTCIQ)
Assets: $1,804,294
Liabilities: $117,807
Net Worth: $1,686,488
Earnings: ($528,667)
Fiscal Year-end: 12/31/20
Metal Exploration Services
N.A.I.C.S.: 213114

SMOOTHWATER CAPITAL CORPORATION
Suite 4610 First Canadian Place, Toronto, M5X 1E5, ON, Canada
Tel.: (416) 644-6582
Web Site:
   http://www.smoothwatercapital.ca
Private Equity Firm
N.A.I.C.S.: 523999
Stephen J. Griggs *(CEO)*

Subsidiaries:

Haventree Bank (1)
100 King Street West Suite 4610, PO Box 1160, Stn TD, Toronto, M5K 1P2, ON, Canada   (100%)
Tel.: (647) 277-0051
Web Site: https://www.haventreebank.com
Trust, Mortgage & Deposit Services
N.A.I.C.S.: 523991
Michael Jones *(Pres & CEO)*

SMP BANK JSC
71/11 Sadovnicheskaya Street, Moscow, 115035, Russia
Tel.: (7) 495 981 81 81
Web Site: http://www.smpbank.com
Year Founded: 2001
SMPB—(SPBE)
Commercial Banking Services
N.A.I.C.S.: 522110
Artem Obolenskiy *(Chm)*

SMRT HOLDINGS BERHAD
Level 8 Tower Block CUCMS Campus Persiaran Bestari Cyber 11, 63000, Cyberjaya, Selangor Darul Ehsan, Malaysia
Tel.: (60) 327709199   MY
Web Site: https://www.smrt.holdings
SMRT—(KLS)
Rev.: $18,564,656
Assets: $13,005,079
Liabilities: $4,648,466
Net Worth: $8,356,614
Earnings: ($47,196)
Fiscal Year-end: 06/30/23
Education, Training & Human Resources Services
N.A.I.C.S.: 611430
R. Palaniappan *(Chm)*

Subsidiaries:

ASIAMET Education Group Berhad (1)
G-8 Jalan Kemacahaya 11, Taman Kemacahaya Batu 9, 43200, Cheras, Selangor Darul Ehsan, Malaysia   (23%)
Tel.: (60) 390805888
Web Site: http://www.aegb.com.my
Sales Range: $1-9.9 Million
Education Services
N.A.I.C.S.: 611710

N'osairis Technologies Solutions Sdn Bhd (1)
Unit 27-06 Q Sentral Jalan Stesen Sentral 2, 50470, Kuala Lumpur, Malaysia
Tel.: (60) 32 713 9760
Web Site: https://www.nosairis.com
Information Technology Services
N.A.I.C.S.: 541511
Ramani Kumar *(CEO)*

Talentoz Sdn Bhd (1)
A-07-07 Capital 1 Oasis Square No 2 Jalan PJU 1A/7A Oasis Damansara, 47301, Petaling Jaya, Selangor, Malaysia
Tel.: (60) 125344081
Web Site: https://www.talentoz.com
Information Technology Services
N.A.I.C.S.: 541511

SMRUTHI ORGANICS LIMITED
165-A Balaji Bhavan, Railway Lines, Solapur, 413 001, Maharashtra, India
Tel.: (91) 2172310267   In
Web Site:
   https://www.smruthiorganics.com
Year Founded: 1989
540686—(BOM)
Rev.: $16,923,242
Assets: $12,665,991
Liabilities: $4,494,191
Net Worth: $8,171,800
Earnings: $495,282
Emp.: 308
Fiscal Year-end: 03/31/23
Pharmaceutical Drug Mfr
N.A.I.C.S.: 325412
Purushotham Malaiah Eaga *(Chm & Mng Dir)*

SMS CO., LTD.
Sumitomo Real Estate Shibakoen Tower 2-11-1 Shibakoen Minato, Tokyo, 105-0011, Japan
Tel.: (81) 357301066
Web Site: https://www.bm-sms.co.jp
Year Founded: 2003
2175—(TKS)
Rev.: $356,761,530
Assets: $479,059,750
Liabilities: $186,342,510
Net Worth: $292,717,240
Earnings: $47,770,470
Emp.: 4,188
Fiscal Year-end: 03/31/24
Temporary Staffing Services
N.A.I.C.S.: 561320
Natsuki Goto *(CEO)*

Subsidiaries:

M3 Career, Inc. (1)
4-1-28 Toranomon Toranomon, Minato-ku, Tokyo, 105-0001, Japan
Tel.: (81) 368951751
Web Site: https://www.m3career.com
Career Services
N.A.I.C.S.: 561311

MIMS Japan Co., Ltd. (1)
Sumitomo Fudosan Shibakoen Tower 2-11-1 Shibakoen, Minato-ku, Tokyo, 105-0011, Japan
Tel.: (81) 366748385
Pharmaceutical Mfr & Distr
N.A.I.C.S.: 325412

MIMS Pte. Ltd. (1)
438A Alexandra Rd Alexandra Technopark 04-01/02, Singapore, 119967, Singapore
Tel.: (65) 62907400
Web Site: https://corporate.mims.com
Emp.: 1,000
Pharmaceutical Mfr & Distr
N.A.I.C.S.: 325412

SMS Philippines Healthcare Solutions Inc. (1)
10C Chatham House Condominiums 116 Valero Corner V A Rufino Streets, Salcedo Village, Makati, Philippines
Tel.: (63) 2834941617
Web Site: https://www.sms-philippines.com
Medical Consultancy Services
N.A.I.C.S.: 541611
Sheila Marie Rivero *(Acct Mgr)*

SMS ELECTRIC CO., LTD ZHENGZHOU
SMS Industrial Park at NO 85 Fifth Avenue, Economic and Technical Development Zone, Zhengzhou, 450016, China
Tel.: (86) 37167391344
Web Site: https://www.cnsms.com
Year Founded: 1996
002857—(SSE)
Rev.: $27,408,565
Assets: $92,102,667
Liabilities: $18,066,560
Net Worth: $74,036,107
Earnings: $1,817,436
Emp.: 419
Fiscal Year-end: 12/31/22
Electricity Metering Instrument Mfr & Distr
N.A.I.C.S.: 334513
Hu Kun *(Chm & Gen Mgr)*

SMS FINANCE SA
5 Allee Scheffer, Luxembourg, 2520, Luxembourg
Tel.: (352) 22626292545
Private Investment Firm
N.A.I.C.S.: 523999
Silvio Scaglia *(Owner)*

SMS GROUP LIMITED
65 Birkikara Hill, Saint Julian's, STJ 1143, Malta
Tel.: (356) 2577 0000
Web Site: http://www.sms.com.mt
Emp.: 500
Holding Company & Financial services
N.A.I.C.S.: 551112
Neville Mifsud *(Chm)*

Subsidiaries:

Holiday Malta Co. Ltd. (1)
Air Malta House, 314-316 Upper Richmond Road, Putney, SW15 6TU, London, United Kingdom
Tel.: (44) 2087853222
Web Site: http://www.holidaymalta.com
Sales Range: $25-49.9 Million
Emp.: 25
Tour Operator
N.A.I.C.S.: 561520

Subsidiary (Non-US):

Belleair Holidays Ltd. (2)
Air Malta House 314 Upper Richmond Rd, SW15 6TU, Putney, London, United Kingdom - England
Tel.: (44) 2087853266
Web Site: http://www.belleair.co.uk
Tour Operator
N.A.I.C.S.: 561520

Subsidiary (Domestic):

Malta Direct Travel Inc. (2)

SMS HOLDING GMBH

Air Malta House 314 Upper Richmond Rd, Putney, London, SW15 6TU, United Kingdom
Tel.: (44) 2085619079
Web Site: http://www.maltadirect.com
Sales Range: $25-49.9 Million
Emp.: 5
Travel Agency
N.A.I.C.S.: 561510

S. Mifsud & Sons Ltd. (1)
65 Birkirkara Hill, San Giljan, STJ 1143, Malta
Tel.: (356) 2577 0000
Web Site: http://www.sms.com.mt
Shipping, Tourism, Travel, Insurance, Cargo Handling, Legal & Financial Services
N.A.I.C.S.: 483111
Neville Mifsud (Chm & Mng Dir)

SMS INSURANCE AGENCY LTD (1)
Casa Roma Sir Augustus Bartolo Street, Valletta, XBX 1099, Malta
Tel.: (356) 2577 5000
Insurance Consulting Services
N.A.I.C.S.: 524298

SMS INTERNATIONAL SHORE OPERATIONS US Inc (1)
1007 N America Way Ste 505, Miami, FL 33132
Tel.: (305) 290-3000
Tour Operator
N.A.I.C.S.: 561520

SMS TRAVEL & TOURISM UK (1)
40/42 Kenway Road, London, SW5 0RA, United Kingdom
Tel.: (44) 20 7370 6293
Tour Operator
N.A.I.C.S.: 561520

smsmondial (1)
311 Republic Street, Valletta, VLT110, Malta
Tel.: (356) 2277 6010
Web Site: http://www.smsmondial.com.mt
Tour Operator
N.A.I.C.S.: 561520

SMS HOLDING GMBH
Wiesenstrasse 30, 57271, Hilchenbach, Germany
Tel.: (49) 2733 29 0   De
Web Site: http://www.sms-group.com
Year Founded: 1871
Rev.: $3,208,114,774
Assets: $4,808,822,572
Liabilities: $3,821,962,847
Net Worth: $986,859,724
Earnings: $20,520,736
Emp.: 13,872
Fiscal Year-end: 12/31/18
Holding Company; Plant Construction & Mechanical Engineering Services
N.A.I.C.S.: 551112
Burkhard Dahmen (Chm-Mgmt Bd & CEO)

Subsidiaries:

ARES Industrial Furnace (Tianjin) Co., Ltd. (1)
K1 5 301 No 6 of Rd 6th Hi Tech Development, Hi Tech Green Industrial Base Huayuan Industrial Park, Tianjin, 300384, China
Tel.: (86) 2223783878
Industrial Engineering Services
N.A.I.C.S.: 541330

Amova GmbH (1)
Obere Industriestrasse 8, 57250, Netphen, Germany
Tel.: (49) 2738210
Web Site: http://www.amova.eu
Logistic Services
N.A.I.C.S.: 488510
Bernd Klein (CEO)

BST Eltromat International GmbH (1)
Heidsieker Heide 53, 33739, Bielefeld, Germany
Tel.: (49) 52069990
Web Site: http://www.bst-eltromat.com
Electronic Components Mfr
N.A.I.C.S.: 334419
Jurgen Dillmann (Mng Dir)

DREVER International S.A. (1)
Allee des Noistiers 15, Angleur, 4031, Liege, Belgium
Tel.: (32) 43666262
Industrial Engineering Services
N.A.I.C.S.: 541330
Henin Eric (Mgr-Procurement)

Duma-Bandzink GmbH (1)
Blumenberger Strasse 143 145, 41061, Monchengladbach, Germany
Tel.: (49) 216157920
Industrial Engineering Services
N.A.I.C.S.: 541330
Daniel Plaetzer (Mng Dir)

Esmech Equipment Pvt. Ltd. (1)
Plot No A 254 259 and A 283 Road No 30A, Wagle Industrial Estate, Thane, 400 604, India
Tel.: (91) 2225821295
Industrial Engineering Services
N.A.I.C.S.: 541330
Ganesh Dake (Gen Mgr)

Fontaine Engineering und Maschinen GmbH (1)
Industriestr 28, 40764, Langenfeld, Germany
Tel.: (49) 2713270031
Industrial Engineering Services
N.A.I.C.S.: 541330
Jerome Gobel (Sls Mgr)

IAS GmbH (1)
Am Groben Teich 16 27, 58640, Iserlohn, Germany
Tel.: (49) 237143460
Industrial Engineering Services
N.A.I.C.S.: 541330
Torsten Schaefer (Gen Sls Mgr)

LUX Automation GmbH (1)
Am Trippelsberg 45, 40589, Dusseldorf, Germany
Tel.: (49) 21171080
Industrial Engineering Services
N.A.I.C.S.: 541330
Andrew Wolensky (Mgr)

MET/Con Metallurgical Plant & Process Consulting GmbH (1)
Ivo Beucker Strasse 43, 40237, Dusseldorf, Germany
Tel.: (49) 2118810
Industrial Engineering Services
N.A.I.C.S.: 541330
Ingo Schuster (Mng Dir)

Metix (Pty) Ltd. (1)
Head Offfice Block A 1st Floor 204 Rivonia Road Morningside, Sandton, Gauteng, South Africa
Tel.: (27) 116762300
Industrial Engineering Services
N.A.I.C.S.: 541330

PT SMS Siemag Metallurgical Services (1)
Jalan Raya Anyer KAV A0 1 Kawasan Industri Krakatau, Cilegon, 42443, Banten, Indonesia
Tel.: (62) 254315699
Industrial Engineering Services
N.A.I.C.S.: 541330

Paul Wurth S.A. (1)
32 rue d'Alsace, PO Box 2233, Luxembourg, 1122, Luxembourg   (100%)
Tel.: (352) 49701
Web Site: http://www.paulwurth.com
Sales Range: $800-899.9 Million
Emp.: 1,500
Steel Mfr & Engineering Services
N.A.I.C.S.: 541330
Heinrich Weiss (Vice Chm)

Subsidiary (US):

Paul Wurth Inc. (2)
135 Technology Dr Ste 500, Canonsburg, PA 15317
Tel.: (724) 873-7200
Sales Range: $25-49.9 Million
Emp.: 40
Steel Mfr & Engineering Services
N.A.I.C.S.: 541330
Jerry Peconi (VP-Fin)

Subsidiary (Non-US):

Paul Wurth do Brasil Ltda. (2)
Rua Andaluzita 110 - 7 ao 12 Andar, Belo Horizonte, 30310-030, MG, Brazil
Tel.: (55) 3132282800
Emp.: 90
Industrial Machinery Mfr
N.A.I.C.S.: 333248
Giovanni Monai (CEO)

SMS Digital GmbH (1)
Eduard Schloemann Strasse 4, 40237, Dusseldorf, Germany
Tel.: (49) 2118815332
Web Site: http://www.sms-digital.com
Consulting Services
N.A.I.C.S.: 541611
Bernhard Steenken (CEO)

SMS ELEX AG (1)
Eschenstrasse 6, 8603, Schwerzenbach, Switzerland
Tel.: (41) 448061646
Industrial Engineering Services
N.A.I.C.S.: 541330

SMS ELOTHERM GMBH (1)
In der Fleute 2, 42897, Remscheid, Germany
Tel.: (49) 2191 8910
Web Site: http://www.sms-elotherm.com
Industrial Equipment Mfr
N.A.I.C.S.: 334513
Dirk M. Schibisch (Mgr-Sls)

Subsidiary (Non-US):

SMS Elotherm India Pvt. Ltd. (2)
408/409 Excellencia - Lodha Supremus Road No 22 MIDC Wagle Estate, Thane, 400604, Maharashtra, India
Tel.: (91) 2225806179
Industrial Equipment Mfr
N.A.I.C.S.: 334513

SMS Elotherm Induction Tech. Co. Ltd. (2)
No 2200 South Lianhua Road, MinHang District, Shanghai, 201108, China
Tel.: (86) 2124086468
Industrial Equipment Mfr
N.A.I.C.S.: 334513
Chen Jialiang (Gen Mgr)

Subsidiary (US):

SMS Elotherm North America LLC (2)
13129 23 Mile Rd, Shelby, MI 48315
Tel.: (586) 469-8324
Industrial Equipment Mfr
N.A.I.C.S.: 334513
Torsten Schaefer (VP-Sls & Svc)

Subsidiary (Non-US):

SMS Elotherm S.A.S. (2)
Zone Industrielle Gare 5 Rue Saint Georges, 68130, Altkirch, France
Tel.: (33) 389891565
Industrial Equipment Mfr
N.A.I.C.S.: 334513

SMS Engineering (China) Ltd. (1)
No 2200 South Lianhua Road, Minhang, Shanghai, 201108, China
Tel.: (86) 2124086500
Industrial Engineering Services
N.A.I.C.S.: 541330

SMS GROUP K.K. (1)
Sapia Tower 25F 1-7-12 Marunouchi, Chiyoda-ku, Tokyo, 100-0005, Japan
Tel.: (81) 352930201
Web Site: http://www.sms-group.jp
Industrial Equipment Mfr
N.A.I.C.S.: 334513

SMS GULF FZE (1)
Dubai Airport Free Zone Building 4E Block A Office G16, PO Box 54795, Dubai, United Arab Emirates
Tel.: (971) 42045010
Web Site: http://www.sms-gulf.ae
Industrial Equipment Mfr
N.A.I.C.S.: 334513
Mahesh Kondaveeti (Engr-Electrical & Automation)

SMS Group Metalurgia do Brasil Ltda. (1)
Avenida Dois 230 Distrido, Industrial Parque Norte, 33200-000, Vespasiano, Brazil
Tel.: (55) 3121251160
Industrial Engineering Services
N.A.I.C.S.: 541330
Marcellus Piedade (CEO)

SMS Group Metalurji Servis San. Tic. Ltd. Sti. (1)
Nida Kule Kozyatagi Mah Degirmen Sok No 18 K 10 Kadikoy, 34742, Istanbul, Turkiye
Tel.: (90) 2162506550
Industrial Engineering Services
N.A.I.C.S.: 541330

SMS Group Process Technologies GmbH (1)
Daffingerstrasse 4, 1030, Vienna, Austria
Tel.: (43) 169857380
Industrial Engineering Services
N.A.I.C.S.: 541330
Herbert Weissenbaeck (Mng Dir)

SMS Group S.p.A. (1)
Via Udine 103, 33017, Tarcento, Italy
Tel.: (39) 0432799111
Industrial Engineering Services
N.A.I.C.S.: 541330
Carlo Treu (Project Mgr)

SMS Group Technical Services (UK) Ltd. (1)
Units 40 41 The Bridge Business Centre Beresford Way off Dunston Road, Derbyshire, Chesterfield, S41 9FG, United Kingdom
Tel.: (44) 1246266250
Industrial Engineering Services
N.A.I.C.S.: 541330
Christian Amos (Mgr-Procurement)

SMS Group Technical Services LLC (1)
Prospekt Karpova 58, Mariupol, 87515, Ukraine
Tel.: (380) 503330377
Industrial Engineering Services
N.A.I.C.S.: 541330
Sergey Zakolyukin (Mng Dir)

SMS Meer GmbH (1)
Ohlerkirchweg 66, 41069, Monchengladbach, Germany
Tel.: (49) 2161 350 0
Sales Range: $1-4.9 Billion
Emp.: 3,000
Industrial Machinery Mfr
N.A.I.C.S.: 333248

Subsidiary (Non-US):

Concast Technologies S.r.l (2)
Via Cividina 101 101, I-33100, Udine, Italy
Tel.: (39) 0432549411
Sales Range: $25-49.9 Million
Emp.: 65
Mfr of Machinery & Equipment
N.A.I.C.S.: 333120

Concast UK Limited (2)
Varsity House Unit 2 Falcon Ct, Preston Farm Industrial Estate, Stockton-on-Tees, TS18 3TS, United Kingdom
Tel.: (44) 642702340
Web Site: http://www.concast.net
Sales of Machinery & Equipment.
N.A.I.C.S.: 423830

Hertwich Engineering GmbH (2)
Weinbergerstrasse 6, Braunau, 5280, Austria   (100%)
Tel.: (43) 77228060
Web Site: http://www.hertwich.com
Sales Range: $25-49.9 Million
Emp.: 90
Aluminum Casthouse Equipment Mfr
N.A.I.C.S.: 333519
Franz Niedermair (Mng Dir)

SMS Concast AG (2)
Toedistrasse 9, Zurich, 8027, Switzerland
Tel.: (41) 442046511
Web Site: http://www.sms-concast.ch
Sales Range: $25-49.9 Million
Emp.: 100
Sales of Construction Machinery
N.A.I.C.S.: 423810

SMS HOLDING GMBH

SMS Holding GmbH—(Continued)
Luis Hernandez (CEO)

Subsidiary (US):

SMS Concast America Inc. (2)
100 Sandusky St, Pittsburgh, PA 15212-5822
Tel.: (412) 237-8950
Web Site: http://www.sms-concast.ch
Sales Range: $25-49.9 Million
Emp.: 7
Engineeering Services
N.A.I.C.S.: 541330
Nicholas Klipa (Pres & CEO)

Subsidiary (Non-US):

SMS Concast Iberica S.A. (2)
C Bailen 20 5A Planta, 8010, Barcelona, Spain
Tel.: (34) 932013333
Sales Range: $25-49.9 Million
Emp.: 20
Sales of Machinery & Equipment.
N.A.I.C.S.: 423830

Subsidiary (Domestic):

SMS Eumuco GmbH-Wagner Banning Ringwalzen Division (2)
Stockumer Strasse 28, 58435, Witten, Germany
Tel.: (49) 2302661404
Web Site: http://www.sms-meer.com
Sales Range: $25-49.9 Million
Emp.: 100
Ring & Wheel Rolling Machines
N.A.I.C.S.: 333519

Subsidiary (Non-US):

SMS Meer S.p.A. (2)
Via Udine 103, 33017, Tarcento, Udine, Italy
Tel.: (39) 0432799111
Web Site: http://www.sms-meer.it
Sales Range: $25-49.9 Million
Emp.: 160
Rolling Mill Technology: Wire-Rod Mills; Combined Bar & Wire-Rod Mills; Reinforcing-Bar Mills; Light Section Rolling Mills & Finishing Lines
N.A.I.C.S.: 333519

Subsidiary (US):

SMS Meer Service Inc. (2)
234 S Potter St, Bellefonte, PA 16823-1313
Tel.: (814) 355-4774
Web Site: http://www.sms-meer.us
Sales Range: $25-49.9 Million
Emp.: 6
Machine Tools
N.A.I.C.S.: 333517
James Gates (Gen Mgr)

SMS Metallurgical Service LLC (1)
Kirova str 159 office 710, 454091, Chelyabinsk, Russia
Tel.: (7) 3517793016
Industrial Engineering Services
N.A.I.C.S.: 541330
David Jeffrey (CEO)

SMS Metallurgical Service LLC (1)
12th Microrayon Business Center Dastan Building 21 Block B Floor 1, Aktobe, 03000, Kazakhstan
Tel.: (7) 7717319746
Industrial Engineering Services
N.A.I.C.S.: 541330
David Jeffrey (CEO)

SMS Metallurgy Polska Sp. z o.o. (1)
ul Kosciuszki 171, 40524, Katowice, Poland
Tel.: (48) 327463400
Industrial Engineering Services
N.A.I.C.S.: 541330
Krzysztof Warzecha (Chm & Mng Dir)

SMS Metallurgy Romania S.R.L. (1)
Strada Dumbrava Rosie Nr 3, 020461, Bucharest, Romania
Tel.: (40) 212100045
Industrial Engineering Services
N.A.I.C.S.: 541330
Bogdan Dumitrache (Engr-Automation)

SMS Mevac GmbH (1)
Eduard Schloemann Str 4, 40237, Dusseldorf, Germany
Tel.: (49) 2118818102
Industrial Engineering Services
N.A.I.C.S.: 541330
Rudiger Eggert (Sr Project Mgr)

SMS SAUDI ARABIA LLC. (1)
Taba Center 1st Floor Suite 4 Prince Sultan Road, PO Box 4822, Al Khobar, 31952, Saudi Arabia
Tel.: (966) 38875830
Industrial Equipment Mfr
N.A.I.C.S.: 334513
Tesmin Sunny (Mgr-Comml)

SMS SIEMAG TECHNOLOGY (BEIJING) CO., LTD. (1)
18th Floor Juanshitiandi Tower A Jia No 501 Wangjing Xilu, Chaoyang District, Beijing, 100102, China
Tel.: (86) 1059077100
Web Site: http://www.sms-siemag.cn
Industrial Equipment Mfr
N.A.I.C.S.: 334513
Xuelian Zheng (Mgr-HR)

SMS Siemag AG (1)
Eduard Schloemann Strasse 4, 40237, Dusseldorf, Germany
Tel.: (49) 2118810
Web Site: http://www.sms-group.com
Sales Range: $1-4.9 Billion
Emp.: 800
Casting & Rolling Mill Plastic Processing Machinery & Pressing & Forging Mfr.
N.A.I.C.S.: 333519

Subsidiary (Domestic):

GFA-Anlagenbau GmbH (2)
Eduard Schloemann Strasse 4, 40549, Dusseldorf, Germany
Tel.: (49) 2118810
Web Site: http://www.sms-siemag.com
Sales Range: $350-399.9 Million
Mfr Machinery & Equipment.
N.A.I.C.S.: 333120
Burkhard Dahmen (Gen Mgr)

Subsidiary (US):

Millcraft-SMS Services LLC (2)
750 Manifold Rd, Washington, PA 15301-9606
Tel.: (724) 222-5000
Sales Range: $75-99.9 Million
Emp.: 500
General Repair Services
N.A.I.C.S.: 811210

Subsidiary (Non-US):

SMS INNSE S.p.A. (2)
Via Milano 4, Donato Milanese, 20097, Milan, Italy
Tel.: (39) 0221241
Web Site: http://www.sms-innse.com
Sales Range: $25-49.9 Million
Emp.: 165
Engineering Company Specializing in Metallurgy
N.A.I.C.S.: 541330
Alberto Bregante (CEO)

SMS India Pvt. Ltd. (2)
286 Udyog Vihar Phase II, Gurgaon, 122016, India
Tel.: (91) 124 4351500
Sales Range: $25-49.9 Million
Emp.: 120
Engineering Specialists in Metallurgy
N.A.I.C.S.: 541330
Christine Klein (Mng Dir)

SMS Mevac UK Ltd. (2)
Road 4, Winsford, CW7 3RS, Cheshire, United Kingdom
Tel.: (44) 1606551421
Web Site: http://www.sms-mevac.co.uk
Sales Range: $25-49.9 Million
Emp.: 20
Design, Installation, Commissioning & Servicing of Capital Plant to Treat Liquid Iron & Liquid Steel
N.A.I.C.S.: 331110

Subsidiary (Domestic):

SMS Siemag AG (2)

Wiesenstrasse 30, 57271, Hilchenbach, Dahlbruch, Germany
Tel.: (49) 2733290
Web Site: http://www.sms-siemag.com
Sales Range: $700-749.9 Million
Metallurgical & Rolling Mill Technology Mfr
N.A.I.C.S.: 333519
Dieter Rosenthal (Mng Dir)

Subsidiary (Non-US):

SMS Siemag Equipamentos e Servicos Ltda. (2)
Rua Bernardo Guimaraes Nr 245 10th to 17th Fl Funcionarios, 30140 080, Belo Horizonte, Minas Gerais, Brazil
Tel.: (55) 3121251160
Sales Range: $10-24.9 Million
Emp.: 40
Engineering Company Specializing in Metallurgy
N.A.I.C.S.: 541330

Subsidiary (US):

SMS Siemag LLC (2)
100 Sandusky St, Pittsburgh, PA 15212-5822
Tel.: (412) 231-1200
Web Site: http://www.sms-siemag.us
Metalworking Machines Mfr
N.A.I.C.S.: 333519
Pete Fernie (CFO & VP)

Subsidiary (Non-US):

SMS Siemag South Africa (Pty) Ltd. (2)
Milner Place 4 Carse O'Gowerie Street, Sunny Side Office Park, Parktown, 2193, South Africa
Tel.: (27) 114801800
Web Site: http://www.sms-siemagsa.com
Sales Range: $25-49.9 Million
Emp.: 20
Engineering Company Specializing in Metallurgy
N.A.I.C.S.: 541330
Pieter Bezuidenhout (Mng Dir)

SMS Siemag Technology (Tianjin) Co., Ltd. (1)
No 12 SaiDa Bei Yi Dao, XiQing Economic Development Area, Tianjin, 300385, China
Tel.: (86) 102258062500
Industrial Engineering Services
N.A.I.C.S.: 541330
Tracy Li (Mgr-HR & Admin)

SMS TECHNICAL SERVICES LLC (1)
210 W Kensinger Dr Ste 300, Cranberry Township, PA 16066
Tel.: (724) 553-3420
Web Site: http://www.sms-technicalservices.us
Industrial Equipment Mfr
N.A.I.C.S.: 334513
Christine Salera (Gen Mgr-HR)

SMS Technical Services Gulf S.P.C. (1)
Jeera Tower Office 101 Block 428 Road 2811 Building 683 Seef, PO Box 82341, Manama, Bahrain
Tel.: (973) 17551364
Industrial Engineering Services
N.A.I.C.S.: 541330
Manjunath Mathpati (Mgr-Technical)

SMS group Technical Services South Africa (Pty.) Ltd. (1)
204 Rivonia Road Morningside, Sandton, 2196, South Africa
Tel.: (27) 114801800
Industrial Engineering Services
N.A.I.C.S.: 541330
Pieter Bezuidenhout (Mng Dir)

Sidernaval Equipos Siderurgicos S.A. (1)
Henao 7 1st Floor Apartado de Correos 559, 48009, Bilbao, Spain
Tel.: (34) 944239000
Web Site: http://www.sidernaval.es
Iron & Steel Industry Product Mfr.
N.A.I.C.S.: 331110

TBK Automatisierung und Messtechnik GmbH (1)

INTERNATIONAL PUBLIC

Schmiedlstrasse 8, 8042, Graz, Austria
Tel.: (43) 3164055740
Industrial Engineering Services
N.A.I.C.S.: 541330
Gernot Scheiflinger (Sr Engr-Sls)

elexis AG (1)
Industriestr 1, 57482, Wenden, Germany (88.95%)
Tel.: (49) 2762612130
Web Site: http://www.elexis.de
Sales Range: $200-249.9 Million
Emp.: 897
Industrial Automation System Mfr
N.A.I.C.S.: 333248
Eckhard Schulte (Chm-Supervisory Bd)

Subsidiary (Domestic):

EMG Automation GmbH (2)
Industriestrasse 1, Wenden, 57482, Germany
Tel.: (49) 2762 612 0
Web Site: http://www.emg-automation.com
Emp.: 350
Industrial Machinery Mfr
N.A.I.C.S.: 333248
Siegfried Koepp (CEO)

Subsidiary (Domestic):

BST International GmbH (3)
Heidsieker Heide 53, Bielefeld, 33739, Germany
Tel.: (49) 5206 999 0
Web Site: http://www.bst-international.com
Sales Range: $100-124.9 Million
Emp.: 350
Industrial Machinery Mfr
N.A.I.C.S.: 333248
Kristian Junke (Mng Dir)

Subsidiary (US):

BST North America, Inc. (4)
655 W Grand Ave Ste #220, Elmhurst, IL 60126
Tel.: (630) 833-9900
Web Site: http://www.bst-northamerica.com
Web Guiding & Inspection Systems Mfr & Sales
N.A.I.C.S.: 333248
Kim Hocking (Reg Mgr-Sls)

Subsidiary (Domestic):

Accuweb, Inc. (5)
4249 Argosy Ct, Madison, WI 53714
Tel.: (608) 223-0625
Web Site: http://www.accuweb.com
Sales Range: $10-24.9 Million
Emp.: 34
Industrial Machinery Mfr.
N.A.I.C.S.: 333248
Brian Buisker (VP & Gen Mgr)

Subsidiary (Domestic):

HEKUMA GmbH (2)
Dornierstr 14, 85399, Hallbergmoos, Germany
Tel.: (49) 811999770
Web Site: https://www.hekuma.com
Sales Range: $25-49.9 Million
Emp.: 200
Industrial Automation System Mfr.
N.A.I.C.S.: 333248
Bernhard Rupke (Mng Dir)

SMS LIFESCIENCES INDIA LTD.

Plot No 19-III Road No 71 Opp Bharatiya Vidya Bhavan Public School, Jubilee Hills, Hyderabad, 500096, Telangana, India
Tel.: (91) 4066288888
Web Site: https://www.smslife.in
Year Founded: 1990
540679—(BOM)
Rev.: $38,203,069
Assets: $47,346,154
Liabilities: $24,779,558
Net Worth: $22,566,597
Earnings: $1,364,115
Emp.: 567
Fiscal Year-end: 03/31/23
Chemical Products Mfr

AND PRIVATE COMPANIES

N.A.I.C.S.: 325199
Tvvsn Murthy (Mng Dir)

SMS PHARMACEUTICALS LTD
Plot No 72 H No 823343 4 Road No 5 Opp, SBI Executive Enclave Banjara Hills, Hyderabad, 500034, Telangana, India
Tel.: (91) 4025259999
Web Site:
https://www.smspharma.com
SMSPHARMA—(NSE)
Rev.: $77,345,050
Assets: $110,867,047
Liabilities: $54,829,975
Net Worth: $56,037,072
Earnings: $8,321,668
Emp.: 1,080
Fiscal Year-end: 03/31/21
Pharmaceutical Industry
N.A.I.C.S.: 424210
Ramesh Babu Potluri (Chm & Mng Dir)

Subsidiaries:

VKT Pharma Private Limited (1)
72 H No 8-2-334/ 3 & 4 4th Floor Road, No 05 Opp SBI Executive Enclave Banjara hills, Hyderabad, 500 034, India
Tel.: (91) 7032807337
Web Site: https://vktpharma.com
Medical Equipment Whslr
N.A.I.C.S.: 423450

SMSA TREEMONT ACQUISITION CORP.
Ruixing Industry Park, Dongping County, Tai'an, 271509, Shandong, China
Tel.: (86) 538 241 7858
Sales Range: $75-99.9 Million
Investment Services; Pharmaceutical Mfr
N.A.I.C.S.: 523999

SMT BELGIUM NV
Woluwelaan 9, 1800, Vilvoorde, Belgium
Tel.: (32) 22541411
Web Site: https://www.smt.network
Construction & Industrial Machinery Merchant Whslr
N.A.I.C.S.: 423830

Subsidiaries:

ROMCO Equipment Co. (1)
1519 W Belt Line Rd, Carrollton, TX 75006
Tel.: (214) 819-4100
Web Site: http://www.romco.com
Sales Range: $25-49.9 Million
Emp.: 200
Construction Machinery
N.A.I.C.S.: 423810
Bruce Monroe (Coord-Sls)

Subsidiary (Domestic):

Bee Equipment Sales, Ltd. (2)
2506 E Slaton Rd, Lubbock, TX 79404
Tel.: (806) 745-1511
Web Site: http://www.beeequip.com
Rev.: $3,600,000
Emp.: 17
Construction & Mining, except Oil Well, Machinery & Equipment Merchant Whslr
N.A.I.C.S.: 423810
Everett Monroe (Gen Partner)

Sierra Machinery, Inc. (2)
939 Hawkins Blvd, El Paso, TX 79915
Tel.: (575) 746-6592
Web Site: http://www.sierraelpaso.com
Sales Range: $1-9.9 Million
Emp.: 45
Industrial Machinery & Equipment Merchant Whslr
N.A.I.C.S.: 423830
Maria Teran (Pres & CEO)

SMT HOLDING
Woluwelaan 9, 1800, Vilvoorde, Belgium
Tel.: (32) 22541411
Web Site: https://www.smt.network
Holding Company
N.A.I.C.S.: 551112

SMT S.A.
ul Jutrzenki 183, 02-231, Warsaw, Poland
Tel.: (48) 22 380 4750
Web Site: http://www.smtsa.pl
Year Founded: 2000
Advertising Services
N.A.I.C.S.: 541810

SMTRACK BERHAD
Unit 29-7 7th Floor The Boulevard, Mid Valley City Lingkaran Syed Putra, 59200, Kuala Lumpur, Malaysia
Tel.: (60) 322013211 MY
Web Site:
https://www.smtrackberhad.my
Year Founded: 2004
0169—(KLS)
Rev.: $3,383,649
Assets: $23,714,269
Liabilities: $6,891,550
Net Worth: $16,822,719
Earnings: ($3,373,280)
Fiscal Year-end: 06/30/23
Radio Frequency Identification Equipment Mfr
N.A.I.C.S.: 334220
Osman Azmi (Deputy Chm)

SMU S.A.
5680 Cerro El Plomo Street 11th Floor, Las Condes, Santiago, Chile
Tel.: (56) 228188000
Web Site: https://www.smu.cl
SMU—(SGO)
Rev.: $3,242,884,483
Assets: $3,054,729,405
Liabilities: $2,040,399,498
Net Worth: $1,014,329,907
Earnings: $41,758,732
Emp.: 28,343
Fiscal Year-end: 12/31/20
Supermarket Operator
N.A.I.C.S.: 445110
Pilar Danobeitia Estades (Chm)

Subsidiaries:

Abu Gosch y Compania Limitada (1)
Cerro El Plomo N 5680 piso 10, Las Condes, Santiago, Chile
Tel.: (56) 228188000
Web Site: http://www.abu-goschiquique.cl
Warehouse Product Distr
N.A.I.C.S.: 493110

Inversiones Pacucha S.A. (1)
Avenida El Polo 670 interior 801 Centro Empresarial El Polo II, Distrito de Santiago de Surco Provincia Y Departamento de, Lima, Peru
Tel.: (51) 17006700
Convenience Food Retailer
N.A.I.C.S.: 445110

Inversiones del Sur S.A. (1)
Boston 6217, 11500, Montevideo, Uruguay
Tel.: (598) 94463355
Web Site:
https://www.inversionesdelsur.com
Real Estate Services
N.A.I.C.S.: 531390

Super 10 S.A. (1)
Cerro El Plomo N 5680 piso 10, Santiago, Las Condes, Chile
Tel.: (56) 228188000
Food Retailer
N.A.I.C.S.: 445298

SMURFIT KAPPA GROUP PLC
Beech Hill Clonskeagh, Dublin, 4, Ireland
Tel.: (353) 12027127 IE

SMURFIT KAPPA GROUP PLC

Web Site:
https://www.smurfitkappa.com
Year Founded: 1934
SK3—(ISE)
Rev.: $13,890,093,215
Assets: $13,529,156,731
Liabilities: $8,068,502,059
Net Worth: $5,460,654,672
Earnings: $1,024,279,211
Emp.: 48,624
Fiscal Year-end: 12/31/22
Holding Company; Containerboard & Corrugated Container Mfr
N.A.I.C.S.: 551112
Brian Marshall (Gen Counsel)

Subsidiaries:

Carton de Colombia, S.A. (1)
Calle 15 18-109 Puerto Isaacs, Valle del Cauca, Yumbo, Cali, Colombia
Tel.: (57) 24414000
Paperboard Paper Sack Mfr & Distr
N.A.I.C.S.: 322220

Grupo Smurfit Mexico, S.A. de C.V. (1)
Terret Torre Norte-Piso 8 and 9 Miguel de Cervantes Saavedra 301, Col Granada World Plaza, 11520, Mexico, Mexico
Tel.: (52) 555 729 2300
Paperboard Product Mfr & Distr
N.A.I.C.S.: 322220

Kappa Holding (Nederland) B.V. (1)
Warandelaan 2, Oosterhout, 4904 PC, Netherlands
Tel.: (31) 162480000
Web Site: http://www.smurfitkappa.com
Emp.: 70
Financial Management Services
N.A.I.C.S.: 523999
Erik Bunge (CEO)

Subsidiary (Domestic):

Kappa Quama International B.V. (2)
Ravelstraat 28, 4614 XD, Bergen-op-Zoom, Netherlands
Tel.: (31) 164 213141
Sales Range: $25-49.9 Million
Cardboard Mfr
N.A.I.C.S.: 322130

Plant (Domestic):

Nettingsdorfer Papierfabrik AG & Co KG - Benelux Plant (2)
Warandelaan 2, 4904 PC, Oosterhout, Netherlands
Tel.: (31) 162 48 00 00
Packaging Products Mfr
N.A.I.C.S.: 322220

Nettingsdorfer Papierfabrik AG & Co KG - Development Centre Plant (2)
Franklinstraat 1b, Hoogeveen, Netherlands
Tel.: (31) 528231302
Sales Range: $25-49.9 Million
Packaging Products Mfr
N.A.I.C.S.: 322220
Carola Vogel (VP)

Nettingsdorfer Papierfabrik AG & Co KG - Eindhoven Recycling Depot Plant (2)
Kanaaldijk Noord 25a, Eindhoven, 5613 DH, Netherlands
Tel.: (31) 402433830
Sales Range: $25-49.9 Million
Packaging Paper Products Mfr
N.A.I.C.S.: 322220

Nettingsdorfer Papierfabrik AG & Co KG - European Paper Sourcing BV Plant (2)
Mijnheerkensweg 31B, Roermond, 6041 TA, Netherlands
Tel.: (31) 475 47 41 70
Sales Range: $25-49.9 Million
Emp.: 1
Packaging Paper Products Mfr
N.A.I.C.S.: 322220

Nettingsdorfer Papierfabrik AG & Co KG - MNL Golfkarton De Zeeuw Plant (2)
Coldenhovenseweg 122, Eerbeek, Netherlands
Tel.: (31) 313678911
Packaging Paper Products Mfr
N.A.I.C.S.: 322220

Nettingsdorfer Papierfabrik AG & Co KG - Orko-Pak Plant (2)
Curieweg 15, 8013 RA, Zwolle, Netherlands
Tel.: (31) 384224923
Emp.: 22
Packaging Products Mfr
N.A.I.C.S.: 322220

Nettingsdorfer Papierfabrik AG & Co KG - Paper Production Technology Plant (2)
Groeneweg 10, Roermond, 6040 KE, Netherlands
Tel.: (31) 475334044
Sales Range: $25-49.9 Million
Packaging Paper Products Mfr
N.A.I.C.S.: 322220
Henk Hoevers (VP)

Plant (Non-US):

Nettingsdorfer Papierfabrik AG & Co KG - Paper Sales Benelux Plant (2)
Nettingsdorferstaarsse ln 28 4053, Vienna, 4053, Austria
Tel.: (43) 475474131
Sales Range: $25-49.9 Million
Packaging Paper Products Mfr
N.A.I.C.S.: 322220
Reeiter Reinhard (Mng Dir)

Plant (Domestic):

Nettingsdorfer Papierfabrik AG & Co KG - RapidCorr Eindhoven Plant (2)
Zwaanstraat 1, Eindhoven, NI5651 CA, Netherlands
Tel.: (31) 402564100
Sales Range: $25-49.9 Million
Packaging Products Mfr
N.A.I.C.S.: 322220
John Budderman (Plant Mgr)

Nettingsdorfer Papierfabrik AG & Co KG - Recycling Netherlands & Central Fibre Management Plant (2)
Zwaanstraat 1, Eindhoven, Netherlands
Tel.: (31) 40 2380570
Sales Range: $25-49.9 Million
Emp.: 2
Packaging Products Mfr
N.A.I.C.S.: 322220

Nettingsdorfer Papierfabrik AG & Co KG - Roermond Papier Plant (2)
Mijnheerkensweg 18, Roermond, 6041TA, Netherlands
Tel.: (31) 475384444
Sales Range: $50-74.9 Million
Emp.: 25
Packaging Products Mfr
N.A.I.C.S.: 322220
Tom Munten (Mgr-Sls)

Nettingsdorfer Papierfabrik AG & Co KG - TWINCORR Plant (2)
Doorsneeweg 42, Nieuwe Pekela, Netherlands
Tel.: (31) 597662200
Sales Range: $50-74.9 Million
Packaging Paper Products Mfr
N.A.I.C.S.: 322220

Nettingsdorfer Papierfabrik AG & Co KG - Trobox Kartonnages Plant (2)
Nijverheidsweg 6, Oosterhout, Netherlands
Tel.: (31) 162478147
Packaging Paper Products Mfr
N.A.I.C.S.: 322220

Nettingsdorfer Papierfabrik AG & Co KG - Trobox Verpakking Plant (2)
Biezenbeemd 1, Oosterhout, Netherlands
Tel.: (31) 162478147
Packaging Products Mfr
N.A.I.C.S.: 322220

Nettingsdorfer Papierfabrik AG & Co KG - Van Dam Golfkarton Plant (2)
Sojadijk 1 Industrienummer 9640, Helmond, Netherlands
Tel.: (31) 492585911
Packaging Paper Products Mfr

SMURFIT KAPPA GROUP PLC

Smurfit Kappa Group plc—(Continued)
N.A.I.C.S.: 322220

Nettingsdorfer Papierfabrik AG & Co KG - Zedek Plant (2)
Maagdenburgstraat 9, Deventer, 7421 ZA, Netherlands
Tel.: (31) 570698911
Web Site: http://www.smurfitkappa-zedek.nl
Sales Range: $50-74.9 Million
Packaging Paper Products Mfr
N.A.I.C.S.: 322220
Jack Pieterson (Gen Mgr)

Smurfit Kappa - ELCORR Plant (2)
Vossendaal 16, 4877 AB, Etten-Leur, Netherlands
Tel.: (31) 76 508 1500
Web Site: http://www.smurfitkappa.com
Packaging Paper Products Mfr
N.A.I.C.S.: 322220
Yoost Simons (Mng Dir)

Subsidiary (Domestic):

Smurfit Kappa Corrugated Benelux (2)
Warandelaan 2, 4904 PC, Oosterhout, Netherlands
Tel.: (31) 162480000
Web Site: http://www.smurfitkappa.com
Sales Range: $50-74.9 Million
Emp.: 60
Financial Management Services
N.A.I.C.S.: 523999
Elly Van Rooij (Mgr-Sls)

Smurfit Kappa Development Centre B.V. (2)
Franklinstraat 1b, 7903 AC, Hoogeveen, Netherlands
Tel.: (31) 528231302
Web Site: http://www.smurfit.com
Paper Products Research & Development Services
N.A.I.C.S.: 541715

Smurfit Kappa ELCORR B.V. (2)
Vossendaal 16, 4877 AB, Etten-Leur, Netherlands
Tel.: (31) 765081500
Sales Range: $50-74.9 Million
Corrugated Board Mfr
N.A.I.C.S.: 322211
Henk Verschuren (Controller)

Smurfit Kappa GSF B.V. (2)
Industrieweg West 3, 9665 PX, Oude Pekela, Netherlands
Tel.: (31) 597 67 06 70
Web Site: http://www.smurfitkappa.com
Solid Board Mfr
N.A.I.C.S.: 322211

Smurfit Kappa Group IS Nederland B.V. (2)
Hoevenseweg 37, 4847 LA, Etten-Leur, Netherlands
Tel.: (31) 765047230
Sales Range: $25-49.9 Million
Emp.: 5
Packaging Paper Products Mfr
N.A.I.C.S.: 322220

Smurfit Kappa MNL Golfkarton B.V. (2)
Coldenhovenseweg 122, 6961 EH, Eerbeek, Netherlands
Tel.: (31) 313678911
Web Site: http://www.smurfitkappa-mnl.com
Corrugated Board Packaging Services
N.A.I.C.S.: 322220
Caspar Jan van Schaardenburg (Mng Dir)

Smurfit Kappa Orko-Pak B.V. (2)
Curieweg 15, 8013 RA, Zwolle, Netherlands
Tel.: (31) 38 422 4923
Web Site: http://www.smurfitkappa-orko-pak.com
Sales Range: $25-49.9 Million
Packaging Products Mfr
N.A.I.C.S.: 322220
Peter Mathijsen (Mgr-Plant)

Smurfit Kappa Paper Sales Benelux B.V. (2)
Mijnheerensweg 18, 6041 TA, Roermond, Netherlands
Tel.: (31) 475352670

Sales Range: $25-49.9 Million
Paper Products Mfr
N.A.I.C.S.: 322120
Peter Fleurkens (Mgr-Fin)

Smurfit Kappa Paper Services B.V. (2)
Mijnheerenskwg 31B, 6041 TA, Roermond, Netherlands
Tel.: (31) 475474102
Web Site: http://www.smurfitkappapaperservice.com
Sales Range: $25-49.9 Million
Paper Products Mfr
N.A.I.C.S.: 322120
Peter Fleurkens (Gen Mgr)

Smurfit Kappa RapidCorr Eindhoven B.V. (2)
Zwaanstraat 1gebouw Tk, Eindhoven, 5651 CA, Netherlands
Tel.: (31) 402564100
Sales Range: $25-49.9 Million
Packaging Materials Mfr
N.A.I.C.S.: 322220

Smurfit Kappa Recycling B.V. (2)
Zwaanstraat 1, Eindhoven, 5651 CA, Netherlands
Tel.: (31) 402380570
Web Site: http://www.smurfitkappa-recycling.nl
Paper Materials Recycling Services
N.A.I.C.S.: 562920

Smurfit Kappa Roermond Papier B.V. (2)
Mijnheerenskwg 18, 6041 TA, Roermond, Netherlands
Tel.: (31) 475384444
Web Site: http://www.smurfitkappa-roermondpapier.com
Paperboard Mfr
N.A.I.C.S.: 322130
Go Cox (CEO)

Smurfit Kappa Trimbach B.V. (2)
Ravelstraat 28, 4614 XD, Bergen-op-Zoom, Netherlands
Tel.: (31) 164 213 141
Web Site: http://www.smurfitkappa-solidboardsolutions.com
Sales Range: $50-74.9 Million
Paper & Cardboard Mfr
N.A.I.C.S.: 322120

Smurfit Kappa Trobox Kartonnages B.V. (2)
Nijverheidsweg 6, Oosterhout, 4906CL, Netherlands
Tel.: (31) 162 47 81 47
Sales Range: $50-74.9 Million
Packaging Paper Products Mfr
N.A.I.C.S.: 322220
Dennis Codrington (Mng Dir)

Smurfit Kappa Twincorr (2)
Industrieweg 17, 7903 AH, Hoogeveen, Netherlands
Tel.: (31) 528293911
Web Site: http://www.smurfitkappa.com
Sales Range: $50-74.9 Million
Emp.: 161
Corrugated Packaging Board Mfr
N.A.I.C.S.: 322130
Klaas-Jan Bijker (Mgr-Sls)

Smurfit Kappa Van Dam Golfkarton B.V. (2)
Sojadijk 1, 5704 RL, Helmond, Netherlands
Tel.: (31) 492585911
Web Site: http://www.smurfitkappa-vandam.com
Sales Range: $50-74.9 Million
Emp.: 120
Packaging Paper Products Mfr
N.A.I.C.S.: 322220
Wim Peeters (Mng Dir)

Smurfit Kappa Vandra B.V. (2)
Wilhelminakanaal Zuid 106, 4903 RA, Oosterhout, Netherlands
Tel.: (31) 16 247 5100
Web Site: http://www.smurfitkappa-vandra.com
Sales Range: $50-74.9 Million
Packaging Paper Products Mfr
N.A.I.C.S.: 322220
C. J. Kees Koelewijn (Mng Dir)

Smurfit Kappa Zedek B.V. (2)
Maagdenburgstraat 9, 7421 ZA, Deventer, Netherlands
Tel.: (31) 570698911
Web Site: http://www.smurfitkappa-zedek.com
Sales Range: $50-74.9 Million
Corrugated Board Mfr
N.A.I.C.S.: 322211
Jack Pieterson (Mng Dir)

Smurfit Nederland Holding B.V. (2)
Voorsterweg 94, Loenen, 7371 EL, Netherlands
Tel.: (31) 55 5058111
Emp.: 70
Investment Management Service
N.A.I.C.S.: 523999
Rob Stalenhoes (Mgr-Sls)

Solidus Solutions (2)
Hoofdstraat 34, 9693 AH, Bad Nieuweschans, Netherlands
Tel.: (31) 503033000
Web Site: http://www.solidussolutions.com
Emp.: 65
Solid Board Mfr
N.A.I.C.S.: 322211

Plant (Domestic):

Smurfit Kappa Solid Board B.V. - Nieuweschans Plant (3)
Hoofdstraat 34, 9693 AH, Bad Nieuweschans, Netherlands
Tel.: (31) 50 3033000
Web Site: http://www.smurfitkappa.com
Emp.: 50
Solid Board Sheet Mfr
N.A.I.C.S.: 322130
Silke Zschweigert (Gen Mgr)

Subsidiary (Domestic):

Steijn Vastgoed B.V. (2)
Harmantsplantsoen 7, 1693 KA, Wervershoof, Netherlands
Tel.: (31) 228 583681
Real Estate Manangement Services
N.A.I.C.S.: 531390

Nettingsdorfer Papierfabrik AG & Co KG (1)
Nettingsdorfer Strabe 40, 4053, Haid, Austria
Tel.: (43) 72298630
Web Site: http://www.smurfitkappa-nettingsdorfer.com
Sales Range: $125-149.9 Million
Emp.: 35
Packaging Paper Products Mfr
N.A.I.C.S.: 322220
Ferdinand Fuhrmann (CEO)

Subsidiary (Non-US):

C.D. Haupt Papier-und Pappenfabrik GmbH & Co. KG (2)
Orpethaler Str 50, 34474, Diemelstadt, Germany
Tel.: (49) 5642 790
Packaging Paper Products Mfr
N.A.I.C.S.: 322220

Diekra Speditionsgesellschaft Mbh (2)
Orpethaler Strasse 50, Diemelstadt, 34474, Germany
Tel.: (49) 564279136
Paper Products Mfr
N.A.I.C.S.: 322299

Plant (Non-US):

Nettingsdorfer Papierfabrik AG & Co KG - Abercarn Plant (2)
Prince of Wales Industrial Estate Abercarn, Abercarn, NP115AR, United Kingdom
Tel.: (44) 1495241350
Sales Range: $25-49.9 Million
Emp.: 6
Packaging Paper Products Mfr
N.A.I.C.S.: 322220
Graham Wallis (Gen Mgr)

Nettingsdorfer Papierfabrik AG & Co KG - Agripack Plant (2)
Zone Industrielle La Moneda, Verquieres, France
Tel.: (33) 490902101

Packaging Paper Products Mfr
N.A.I.C.S.: 322220

Nettingsdorfer Papierfabrik AG & Co KG - Alcala Plant (2)
Avda de Camarmilla s/n, Alcala de Henares, Madrid, Spain
Tel.: (34) 918796091
Web Site: http://www.smurfitkappa.com
Packaging Products Mfr
N.A.I.C.S.: 322220

Nettingsdorfer Papierfabrik AG & Co KG - Alicante Plant (2)
Partida de Canastell B-393, San Vicente del Raspeig, Alicante, Spain
Tel.: (34) 965660200
Packaging Paper Products Mfr
N.A.I.C.S.: 322220

Nettingsdorfer Papierfabrik AG & Co KG - Ania Paper (2)
Via del Mulino, Ponte all'Ania, Barga, Italy
Tel.: (39) 058370031
Packaging Paper Products Mfr
N.A.I.C.S.: 322220

Nettingsdorfer Papierfabrik AG & Co KG - Asti Plant (2)
Strada Aniotto 3, Asti, 14100, Italy
Tel.: (39) 0141444777
Sales Range: $50-74.9 Million
Packaging Paper Products Mfr
N.A.I.C.S.: 322220

Nettingsdorfer Papierfabrik AG & Co KG - Baden Karton Plant (2)
Fabrikstrasse 1, Gernsbach, 76593, Germany
Tel.: (49) 7224630
Web Site: http://www.smurfitkappa.de
Packaging Paperboard Mfr
N.A.I.C.S.: 322130
Stesan Poell (Mgr-HR)

Nettingsdorfer Papierfabrik AG & Co KG - Bag In Box Plant (2)
7 Gogolya Str Leningrad, Vsevolozhsk, 188640, Russia
Tel.: (7) 812 329 03 76
Sales Range: $25-49.9 Million
Emp.: 15
Packaging Paper Products Mfr
N.A.I.C.S.: 322220
Evgenia Malianou (Gen Mgr)

Nettingsdorfer Papierfabrik AG & Co KG - Bag-in-Box Italy Plant (2)
Via Enzo Ferrari 39 Zona Industriale D3, Alessandria, Italy
Tel.: (39) 0131 241601
Corrugated Box Mfr
N.A.I.C.S.: 322211

Nettingsdorfer Papierfabrik AG & Co KG - Bernal Plant (2)
Espora 200 Bernal, Bernal, Buenos Aires, 1876, Argentina
Tel.: (54) 1152537000
Web Site: http://www.smurfitkappa.com.ar
Emp.: 700
Packaging Products Mfr
N.A.I.C.S.: 322220
Jorge Angel (Gen Mgr)

Nettingsdorfer Papierfabrik AG & Co KG - Birmingham Recycling Depot Plant (2)
Duddeston Mill Road, Saltley, Birmingham, B8 1AB, United Kingdom
Tel.: (44) 1213285033
Web Site: http://www.smurfitkappa.com
Paper Recycling Services
N.A.I.C.S.: 562920

Nettingsdorfer Papierfabrik AG & Co KG - Bizet Plant (2)
2 rue Goethe Paris, 75116, Paris, France
Tel.: (33) 1 49 52 32 00
Packaging Paper Products Mfr
N.A.I.C.S.: 322220

Nettingsdorfer Papierfabrik AG & Co KG - Brannogard Plant (2)
Brannogard, Torup, 314 97, Hylte, Sweden
Tel.: (46) 34548200
Packaging Paper Products Mfr
N.A.I.C.S.: 322220
Ulf Landen (Mgr)

AND PRIVATE COMPANIES — SMURFIT KAPPA GROUP PLC

Nettingsdorfer Papierfabrik AG & Co KG - Burgos I and Burgos II Plant (2)
Poligono Villayuda C/Alcalde Martin Cobos s/n, Burgos, 9007, Spain
Tel.: (34) 947474330
Packaging Products Products Mfr
N.A.I.C.S.: 322220
Angel Gomez (Gen Mgr)

Nettingsdorfer Papierfabrik AG & Co KG - CARTONNAGES DE LORRAINE Plant (2)
255 Rue Lavoisier Zone Industrielle, Ludres, 54710, France
Tel.: (33) 383261911
Sales Range: $25-49.9 Million
Emp.: 30
Packaging Paper Products Mfr
N.A.I.C.S.: 322220

Nettingsdorfer Papierfabrik AG & Co KG - Cartomills Arlon Plant (2)
Zone Artisanale de Weyler 17, Arlon, Belgium
Tel.: (32) 63245000
Packaging Paper Products Mfr
N.A.I.C.S.: 322220

Nettingsdorfer Papierfabrik AG & Co KG - Cartomills Ghlin Plant (2)
Rue de Douvrain 19, Ghlin, 7011, Belgium
Tel.: (32) 65321211
Sales Range: $50-74.9 Million
Emp.: 17
Packaging Paper Products Mfr
N.A.I.C.S.: 322220
Patrick van Orshaengen (Gen Mgr)

Nettingsdorfer Papierfabrik AG & Co KG - Cartomills Groot-Bijgaarden Plant (2)
Bosstraat 81, Groot-Bijgaarden, 1702, Belgium
Tel.: (32) 24810610
Sales Range: $50-74.9 Million
Emp.: 14
Packaging Paper Products Mfr
N.A.I.C.S.: 322220

Nettingsdorfer Papierfabrik AG & Co KG - Carton France Plant (2)
8 rue Charles Pathe, Vincennes, France
Tel.: (33) 143422854
Packaging Paper Products Mfr
N.A.I.C.S.: 322220

Nettingsdorfer Papierfabrik AG & Co KG - Cartonnerie Nouvelle de Champagne Plant (2)
Rue de Courcelles 114, Reims, 51053, France
Tel.: (33) 326504949
Sales Range: $25-49.9 Million
Emp.: 60
Industrial Packaging & Labeling Services
N.A.I.C.S.: 561910
Frederic Bovin (Mng Dir)

Nettingsdorfer Papierfabrik AG & Co KG - Cartonnerie d (2)
Route de Brieres, BP 67, 91152, Etampes, France
Tel.: (33) 169925600
Web Site: http://www.smurfitkappa.com
Packaging Paper Products Mfr
N.A.I.C.S.: 322220
David Bouchy (Mng Dir)

Nettingsdorfer Papierfabrik AG & Co KG - Cartonnerie d (2)
Quai de l'Ile Belon, 51318, Epernay, France
Tel.: (33) 326549494
Sales Range: $50-74.9 Million
Emp.: 20
Packaging Paper Products Mfr
N.A.I.C.S.: 322220
Bertrand Arnault (Gen Mgr)

Nettingsdorfer Papierfabrik AG & Co KG - Cartonnerie d'Aquitaine Plant (2)
Route de Prechac, 33730, Villandraut, France
Tel.: (33) 556650404
Sales Range: $25-49.9 Million
Emp.: 3
Packaging Paper Products Mfr
N.A.I.C.S.: 322220
Xavier Mone (Mng Dir)

Nettingsdorfer Papierfabrik AG & Co KG - Cartonnerie de Bigny Plant (2)
Route des Forges 5, Bigny, Vallenay, 18190, France
Tel.: (33) 248632000
Sales Range: $50-74.9 Million
Packaging Paper Products Mfr
N.A.I.C.S.: 322220

Nettingsdorfer Papierfabrik AG & Co KG - Cartonnerie de Dijon Plant (2)
ZI de Dijon Sud, Longvic, France
Tel.: (33) 380632400
Sales Range: $50-74.9 Million
Packaging Paper Products Mfr
N.A.I.C.S.: 322220

Nettingsdorfer Papierfabrik AG & Co KG - Cartonnerie de Gallargues Plant (2)
441 Avenue des Marchandises, 30660, Gallargues-le-Montueux, France
Tel.: (33) 466359090
Emp.: 20
Packaging Paper Products Mfr
N.A.I.C.S.: 322220
Jean-Luc Vallee (Plant Mgr)

Nettingsdorfer Papierfabrik AG & Co KG - Cartonnerie de Mortagne Plant (2)
Rte de la Louisiere, Mortagne-sur-Sevre, France
Tel.: (33) 251643100
Packaging Paper Products Mfr
N.A.I.C.S.: 322220

Nettingsdorfer Papierfabrik AG & Co KG - Cartonnerie de Roubaix Plant (2)
Z I Roubaix-Est, Lys-Lez-Lannoy, France
Tel.: (33) 3 20 89 51 00
Packaging Paper Products Mfr
N.A.I.C.S.: 322220

Nettingsdorfer Papierfabrik AG & Co KG - Cellulose du Pin Plant (2)
Allee des Fougeres, Biganos, 3380, France
Tel.: (33) 5 56 03 88 00
Web Site: http://www.smurfitkappa.fr
Emp.: 450
Packaging Paper Products Mfr
N.A.I.C.S.: 322220
Beatrice Martin (Gen Mgr)

Nettingsdorfer Papierfabrik AG & Co KG - Central Forestal Plant (2)
B Arriandi Iurreta, Iurreta, 48215, Spain
Tel.: (34) 946205192
Packaging Paper Products Mfr
N.A.I.C.S.: 322220

Nettingsdorfer Papierfabrik AG & Co KG - Ciudad Juarez Corrugated Plant (2)
Fulton 925 Parque Industrial A J Bermudez, 32470, Ciudad Juarez, Chihuahua, Mexico
Tel.: (52) 6566250976
Sales Range: $25-49.9 Million
Cardboard Packaging Products Mfr
N.A.I.C.S.: 322220

Nettingsdorfer Papierfabrik AG & Co KG - Cordoba Plant (2)
Avenida de la Torrecilla s/no Poligono Industrial La Torrecilla, Cordoba, Spain
Tel.: (34) 957291122
Solid Box Mfr
N.A.I.C.S.: 322211

Nettingsdorfer Papierfabrik AG & Co KG - CorrPrint Plant (2)
Kaermindevej 4, Vamdrup, Denmark
Tel.: (45) 75583255
Printing Paper Mfr
N.A.I.C.S.: 322120

Nettingsdorfer Papierfabrik AG & Co KG - Corrugated Equipment Plant (2)
Verkstadsvagen 18, PO Box 1104, Eslov, Sweden
Tel.: (46) 41368192
Packaging Machinery Mfr
N.A.I.C.S.: 333993

Nettingsdorfer Papierfabrik AG & Co KG - Culiacan Corrugated Plant (2)
Km 9 9 Carretera Culiacan - El Dorado, 80300, Culiacan, Sinaloa, Mexico
Tel.: (52) 6677605060
Web Site: http://www.smurfitkappa.com.mx
Sales Range: $50-74.9 Million
Emp.: 25
Cardboard Packaging Products Mfr
N.A.I.C.S.: 322220

Nettingsdorfer Papierfabrik AG & Co KG - Cusinati di Rosa Plant (2)
Via Roane 19, Rosa, 36027, Italy
Tel.: (39) 0424 868411
Packaging Paper Products Mfr
N.A.I.C.S.: 322220

Nettingsdorfer Papierfabrik AG & Co KG - DISTRIBUTION Plant (2)
5 rue du Petit Conseiller, Beychac-et-Caillau, France
Tel.: (33) 557804040
Emp.: 25
Packaging Paper Products Mfr
N.A.I.C.S.: 322220
Syras Herze (Gen Mgr)

Nettingsdorfer Papierfabrik AG & Co KG - Display Plant (2)
IDA Tallaght Business Park Whitestown, Tallaght, Dublin, Ireland
Tel.: (353) 14524333
Web Site: http://www.smurfitkappa.com
Emp.: 30
Counter & Hanging Display Whslr
N.A.I.C.S.: 423440
Jonathan Arthur (Gen Mgr)

Nettingsdorfer Papierfabrik AG & Co KG - Diss Plant (2)
Pulham St Mary, Diss, IP21 4QH, Suffolkshire, United Kingdom
Tel.: (44) 1379 676 531
Web Site: http://www.smurfitkappa.com
Sales Range: $50-74.9 Million
Emp.: 80
Packaging Paper Products Mfr
N.A.I.C.S.: 322220
Melvyn Mallott (Mng Dir)

Nettingsdorfer Papierfabrik AG & Co KG - Dore Emballage Plant (2)
Dousson-La-Riviere, La Chapelle-Agnon, France
Tel.: (33) 473952047
Packaging Paper Products Mfr
N.A.I.C.S.: 322220

Nettingsdorfer Papierfabrik AG & Co KG - Dublin Plant (2)
Ballymount Road, Walkinstown, Dublin, Ireland
Tel.: (353) 14090000
Web Site: http://www.smurfitkappa.com
Packaging Products Mfr
N.A.I.C.S.: 322220

Nettingsdorfer Papierfabrik AG & Co KG - Eslov Plant (2)
Verkstadsvagen 18, Box 1104, Eslov, Sweden
Tel.: (46) 41368000
Packaging Paper Products Mfr
N.A.I.C.S.: 322220

Nettingsdorfer Papierfabrik AG & Co KG - Espac Plant (2)
Partida de Canastell B-393, San Vicente del Raspeig, Alicante, Spain
Tel.: (34) 965660200
Packaging Paper Products Mfr
N.A.I.C.S.: 322220

Nettingsdorfer Papierfabrik AG & Co KG - Espana y Portugal Plant (2)
Avenida de Camarra, Alcala de Henares, Madrid, Spain
Tel.: (34) 918871980
Packaging Paper Products Mfr
N.A.I.C.S.: 322220

Nettingsdorfer Papierfabrik AG & Co KG - Fibers Plant (2)
Ave 16 de Septiembre 25 Col El Prieto Edo de Mexico, Mexico, Mexico
Tel.: (52) 5530675220
Packaging Paper Products Mfr
N.A.I.C.S.: 322220

Nettingsdorfer Papierfabrik AG & Co KG - FlexoLine Plant (2)
Madesjovagen 21, PO Box 826, Nybro, Sweden
Tel.: (46) 481 46 500
Packaging Paper Products Mfr
N.A.I.C.S.: 322220

Nettingsdorfer Papierfabrik AG & Co KG - Forli Plant (2)
Via Meucci 25, Forli, 47122, Italy
Tel.: (39) 0543720339
Sales Range: $25-49.9 Million
Emp.: 22
Corrugated Box Mfr
N.A.I.C.S.: 322211

Nettingsdorfer Papierfabrik AG & Co KG - France SAS Plant (2)
5 Avenue du General de Gaulle, Saint-Mande, 94165, France
Tel.: (33) 149574200
Packaging Paper Products Mfr
N.A.I.C.S.: 322220

Nettingsdorfer Papierfabrik AG & Co KG - Fustelpack Plant (2)
Via Emilia 705, Bertinoro, 47032, Italy
Tel.: (39) 0543462511
Sales Range: $25-49.9 Million
Packaging Paper Products Mfr
N.A.I.C.S.: 322220
Brusamarello Stefano (Mng Dir)

Nettingsdorfer Papierfabrik AG & Co KG - Galsgow Recycling Depot Plant (2)
37 - 49 Vermont Street, Glasgow, G41 1LT, United Kingdom
Tel.: (44) 141 4295426
Paper Materials Recycling Services
N.A.I.C.S.: 562920

Nettingsdorfer Papierfabrik AG & Co KG - Gosport Plant (2)
Wingate Road Fort Brockhurst Industrial Estate Elson Gosport, Gosport, PO124DR, United Kingdom
Tel.: (44) 2392584511
Web Site: http://www.smurfitkappa.com
Emp.: 40
Packaging Products Mfr
N.A.I.C.S.: 322220
Brian Fipzpatrick (Gen Mgr)

Nettingsdorfer Papierfabrik AG & Co KG - Grantorto Plant (2)
Via Carlo Alberto 26, Grantorto, Italy
Tel.: (39) 0499490099
Packaging Paper Products Mfr
N.A.I.C.S.: 322220

Nettingsdorfer Papierfabrik AG & Co KG - Guanajuato Corrugated Plant (2)
Km 56 2 Carretera Constitucion Queretaro - San Luis Potosi, San Jose Iturbide, Guanajuato, Mexico
Tel.: (52) 4191983400
Sales Range: $100-124.9 Million
Packaging Products Mfr
N.A.I.C.S.: 322220

Nettingsdorfer Papierfabrik AG & Co KG - Hamburg Recycling Depot Plant (2)
Bredowstrasse 8, 22113, Hamburg, Germany
Tel.: (49) 40 73 35 020
Packaging Paper Products Mfr
N.A.I.C.S.: 322220

Nettingsdorfer Papierfabrik AG & Co KG - Herzberger Papierfabrik - Board Mill Plant (2)
Andreasberger Strasse 1, Herzberg am Harz, 37412, Germany
Tel.: (49) 5521820
Paperboard Mfr
N.A.I.C.S.: 322220

Nettingsdorfer Papierfabrik AG & Co KG - Herzberger Papierfabrik - Converting Plant (2)
Andreasberger Strasse 1, Herzberg am Harz, Germany
Tel.: (49) 5521820
Packaging Paper Products Mfr

SMURFIT KAPPA GROUP PLC

Smurfit Kappa Group plc—(Continued)
N.A.I.C.S.: 322220

Nettingsdorfer Papierfabrik AG & Co KG - Herzberger Papierfabrik - Machine Systems Plant
Andreasberger Strasse 1, Herzberg am Harz, 37412, Germany
Tel.: (49) 5521820
Packaging Machinery Mfr
N.A.I.C.S.: 333993

Nettingsdorfer Papierfabrik AG & Co KG - Herzberger Wellpappe Plant (2)
Andreasbergerstrasse 6, 37412, Herzberg am Harz, Germany
Tel.: (49) 55218620
Packaging Paper Products Mfr
N.A.I.C.S.: 322220

Nettingsdorfer Papierfabrik AG & Co KG - Hoya Karton Plant (2)
Von-Bussche-St No 2, Hoya, 27318, Germany
Tel.: (49) 4251 814 0
Sales Range: $100-124.9 Million
Packaging Paper Products Mfr
N.A.I.C.S.: 322220

Nettingsdorfer Papierfabrik AG & Co KG - Huelva Plant (2)
Ctra Comercal A-493 Sector 1-3 1-4 Plan Parcial No 1, La Palma, Huelva, Spain
Tel.: (34) 959402853
Packaging Paper Products Mfr
N.A.I.C.S.: 322220

Plant (Domestic):

Nettingsdorfer Papierfabrik AG & Co KG - Interwell Plant (2)
Schellingstrasse 40, Haid, 4053, Austria
Tel.: (43) 7229 844 0
Packaging Paper Products Mfr
N.A.I.C.S.: 322220

Plant (Non-US):

Nettingsdorfer Papierfabrik AG & Co KG - Kawell Plant (2)
Romereschstrasse 33, Osnabruck, Germany
Tel.: (49) 541 6919 0
Packaging Paper Products Mfr
N.A.I.C.S.: 322220

Nettingsdorfer Papierfabrik AG & Co KG - Kolding Plant (2)
Jens Holms Vej 51, 6000, Kolding, Denmark
Tel.: (45) 79337933
Packaging Paper Products Mfr
N.A.I.C.S.: 322220

Nettingsdorfer Papierfabrik AG & Co KG - Kraftliner Pitea Plant (2)
Kolugnsvagen 30, 94186, Pitea, Sweden
Tel.: (46) 91197000
Web Site: http://www.smurfitkappa.com
Emp.: 520
Packaging Paper Products Mfr
N.A.I.C.S.: 322220
Per Seward (CEO)

Nettingsdorfer Papierfabrik AG & Co KG - La Francaise Plant (2)
Le Saula, La Francaise, France
Tel.: (33) 5 63 65 82 74
Packaging Paper Products Mfr
N.A.I.C.S.: 322220

Nettingsdorfer Papierfabrik AG & Co KG - Liquiwell Plant (2)
Wilhelmstrasse 19, Wulfrath, 42489, Germany
Tel.: (49) 2058 78310 0
Sales Range: $25-49.9 Million
Emp.: 2
Packaging Paper Products Mfr
N.A.I.C.S.: 322211
Thomas Mueller (Gen Mgr)

Nettingsdorfer Papierfabrik AG & Co KG - Lokfast Plant (2)
Gateway 25 Weston Avenue, West Thurrock, RM20 3ZD, Essex, United Kingdom
Tel.: (44) 1708861776
Solid Fiber Board Mfr

N.A.I.C.S.: 322211

Nettingsdorfer Papierfabrik AG & Co KG - Los Reyes Mill Plant (2)
Av Presidente Juarez 2030 Col Los Reyes Iztacala, Tlalnepantla, 54090, Mexico
Tel.: (52) 5557292300
Container & Box Board Mfr
N.A.I.C.S.: 322212

Nettingsdorfer Papierfabrik AG & Co KG - Lunata Plant (2)
Via Pesciatina 147, Lunata, 55100, Capannori, Italy
Tel.: (39) 05839391
Sales Range: $50-74.9 Million
Emp.: 20
Packaging Paper Products Mfr
N.A.I.C.S.: 322220

Nettingsdorfer Papierfabrik AG & Co KG - Lurgan Plant (2)
35 Annesborough Road Lurgan Craigavon, Armagh, United Kingdom
Tel.: (44) 28 38 323611
Packaging Paper Products Mfr
N.A.I.C.S.: 322220

Nettingsdorfer Papierfabrik AG & Co KG - MNL Golfkarton Soest Plant (2)
Koningsweg 26, PO Box 10, 3760 AA, Soest, Netherlands
Tel.: (31) 356095300
Sales Range: $50-74.9 Million
Emp.: 20
Packaging Paper Products Mfr
N.A.I.C.S.: 322220

Nettingsdorfer Papierfabrik AG & Co KG - Maine Emballages Plant (2)
Industrial Zone Beaufeu, Roeze-sur-Sarthe, France
Tel.: (33) 243773505
Packaging Paper Products Mfr
N.A.I.C.S.: 322220

Nettingsdorfer Papierfabrik AG & Co KG - Mantova Plant (2)
Via Panizza 2, Mantua, 46100, Italy
Tel.: (39) 0376276411
Sales Range: $25-49.9 Million
Emp.: 5
Packaging Paper Products Mfr
N.A.I.C.S.: 322220

Nettingsdorfer Papierfabrik AG & Co KG - Massa Lombards Plant (2)
Via Maestri del Lavoro 15, Massa Lombarda, 48024, Italy
Tel.: (39) 0545 982011
Web Site: http://www.smurfitkappa.it
Packaging Paper Products Mfr
N.A.I.C.S.: 322220

Nettingsdorfer Papierfabrik AG & Co KG - Mengibar Paper Plant (2)
Carretera Bailen Motril, 23620, Mengibar, Jaen, Spain
Tel.: (34) 953 37 07 75
Sales Range: $50-74.9 Million
Emp.: 12
Packaging Products Mfr
N.A.I.C.S.: 322220
Ramon Callejo (Gen Mgr)

Nettingsdorfer Papierfabrik AG & Co KG - Mexico Headquarters Plant (2)
Av Santa Fe No 481 Piso 15 Col Cruz Manca, Cuajimalpa, 05349, Mexico, Mexico
Tel.: (52) 5557292300
Sales Range: $25-49.9 Million
Emp.: 20
Packaging Paper Products Mfr
N.A.I.C.S.: 322220

Nettingsdorfer Papierfabrik AG & Co KG - Monterrey Corrugated Guadalupe Plant (2)
Av Dia Del Empresario 951 Col Jardines De Guadalupe, Guadalupe, 67116, Mexico
Tel.: (52) 8110015140
Web Site: http://www.smurfitkappa.com
Emp.: 30
Packaging Products Mfr
N.A.I.C.S.: 322220
Aslam Kumar (Gen Mgr)

Nettingsdorfer Papierfabrik AG & Co KG - Morava Paper Plant (2)

Zimrovice c p 223, Zimrovice, 74741, Czech Republic
Tel.: (420) 553 753 111
Web Site: http://www.smurfitkappa.cz
Emp.: 50
Packaging Paper Products Mfr
N.A.I.C.S.: 322220
Josef Vrtiska (CEO)

Nettingsdorfer Papierfabrik AG & Co KG - Nervion Plant (2)
B Arriandi s/n, 48015, Iurreta, Spain
Tel.: (34) 94 620 5105
Sales Range: $50-74.9 Million
Packaging Paper Products Mfr
N.A.I.C.S.: 322220

Plant (Domestic):

Nettingsdorfer Papierfabrik AG & Co KG - Nettingsdorfer Plant (2)
Nettingsdorfer Str 40, Haid, 4053, Austria
Tel.: (43) 72 29 86 30
Web Site: http://www.smurfitkappa.at
Emp.: 36
Packaging Paper Products Mfr
N.A.I.C.S.: 322220
Isabel Vaz (CEO)

Nettingsdorfer Papierfabrik AG & Co KG - Nettingsdorfer Service Center Plant (2)
Nettingsdorfer Str 40, Ansfelden, 4053, Austria
Tel.: (43) 72 29 86 328
Packaging Paper Products Mfr
N.A.I.C.S.: 322220

Plant (Non-US):

Nettingsdorfer Papierfabrik AG & Co KG - Nordwell Plant (2)
Wittenburger Weg 23, 24941, Flensburg, Germany
Tel.: (49) 461587181
Sales Range: $25-49.9 Million
Emp.: 7
Packaging Paper Products Mfr
N.A.I.C.S.: 322220

Nettingsdorfer Papierfabrik AG & Co KG - Northampton Plant (2)
Moulton Way, Northampton, NN36XJ, United Kingdom
Tel.: (44) 1604499211
Web Site: http://www.smurfitkappa.com
Sales Range: $50-74.9 Million
Emp.: 15
Packaging Paper Products Mfr
N.A.I.C.S.: 322220
Paul Gavin (Reg Dir)

Nettingsdorfer Papierfabrik AG & Co KG - Onwell Plant (2)
Florettgatan 9, Box 22102, Helsingborg, Sweden
Tel.: (46) 42 383660
Packaging Paper Products Mfr
N.A.I.C.S.: 322220

Nettingsdorfer Papierfabrik AG & Co KG - Orsenigo Cans Plant (2)
Via Verdi 14, Orsenigo, Italy
Tel.: (39) 031 635 211
Packaging Plastic Materials Mfr
N.A.I.C.S.: 322220

Nettingsdorfer Papierfabrik AG & Co KG - Orsenigo Plant (2)
Via Don Gnocchi 27, Orsenigo, 22030, Italy
Tel.: (39) 031 635200
Sales Range: $50-74.9 Million
Packaging Paper Products Mfr
N.A.I.C.S.: 322220

Nettingsdorfer Papierfabrik AG & Co KG - PLV France Emballages Plant (2)
37 Avenue de la Commune de Paris, Bretigny-sur-Orge, France
Tel.: (33) 169883730
Web Site: http://www.smurfitkappa.com
Emp.: 80
Packaging Paper Products Mfr
N.A.I.C.S.: 322220
Tiealeygel Stoabiele (Mng Dir)

Nettingsdorfer Papierfabrik AG & Co KG - PLV Lyon Plant

INTERNATIONAL PUBLIC

Route de Strasbourg 305, 01700, Miribel, France
Tel.: (33) 472262080
Web Site: http://www.smurfitkappa.fr
Emp.: 19
Packaging Paper Products Mfr
N.A.I.C.S.: 322220
Gacques Marlherbe (Gen Mgr)

Nettingsdorfer Papierfabrik AG & Co KG - Packaging Solutions Czech Plant (2)
Ovcary 276, Kolin, 28000, Czech Republic
Tel.: (420) 725470252
Web Site: http://www.smurfitkappa.co.cz
Sales Range: $25-49.9 Million
Emp.: 3
Packaging Paper Products Mfr
N.A.I.C.S.: 322220
Jan Kozelek (Bus Mgr)

Nettingsdorfer Papierfabrik AG & Co KG - Packaging Solutions Dublin Plant (2)
Ballymount Road, Walkinstown, Dublin, Ireland
Tel.: (353) 14291700
Packaging Paper Products Mfr
N.A.I.C.S.: 322220

Nettingsdorfer Papierfabrik AG & Co KG - Packaging Solutions Waterford Plant (2)
Store-All Commercial Centre Kilcohan, Waterford, Ireland
Tel.: (353) 51351628
Packaging Paper Products Mfr
N.A.I.C.S.: 322220

Nettingsdorfer Papierfabrik AG & Co KG - Paper Sales Germany Plant (2)
Am Fuchsberg 8, Neuss, 41468, Germany
Tel.: (49) 21313860100
Sales Range: $25-49.9 Million
Emp.: 2
Corrugated Paperboard Mfr
N.A.I.C.S.: 322211
Frank Cwielong (CEO)

Nettingsdorfer Papierfabrik AG & Co KG - Paper Sales Italy Plant (2)
Via del Mulino, Ponte all'Ania, Barga, 55051, Italy
Tel.: (39) 0583 700270
Sales Range: $50-74.9 Million
Packaging Paper Products Mfr
N.A.I.C.S.: 322220
Massimiliano Listi (Mgr-Mill)

Nettingsdorfer Papierfabrik AG & Co KG - Paper Sales UK & Ireland Plant (2)
Mill Street, Snodland, ME6 5AX, Kent, United Kingdom
Tel.: (44) 845 602 6574
Web Site: http://www.smurfitkappa.co.uk
Sales Range: $25-49.9 Million
Emp.: 13
Packaging Paper Products Mfr
N.A.I.C.S.: 322220
Martin Ferrari (Dir-Sls)

Nettingsdorfer Papierfabrik AG & Co KG - Parnalland Plant (2)
Avenue du Jura, 21700, Nuits-St-Georges, France
Tel.: (33) 380611236
Web Site: http://www.smurfitkappa.fr
Emp.: 7
Packaging Paper Products Mfr
N.A.I.C.S.: 322220
Tero Luoma (Gen Mgr)

Nettingsdorfer Papierfabrik AG & Co KG - Pastrengo Plant (2)
Loc Bagnol 14, Pastrengo, 37010, Italy
Tel.: (39) 0456759444
Packaging Paper Products Mfr
N.A.I.C.S.: 322220

Nettingsdorfer Papierfabrik AG & Co KG - Pegewell Plant (2)
Brobygatan, Landsbro, Vetlanda, 57012, Sweden
Tel.: (46) 38364700
Packaging Paper Products Mfr
N.A.I.C.S.: 322220

AND PRIVATE COMPANIES — SMURFIT KAPPA GROUP PLC

Nettingsdorfer Papierfabrik AG & Co KG - Poitou cartons Plant (2)
15 Rue De La Croix Chauvin, BP 10, 79390, Thenezay, France
Tel.: (33) 549630098
Packaging Paper Products Mfr
N.A.I.C.S.: 322220

Nettingsdorfer Papierfabrik AG & Co KG - Print Vision Chelmsford (2)
Robjohns Road Widford Industrial Estate, Chelmsford, CM1 3BB, Essex, United Kingdom
Tel.: (44) 1245493777
Sales Range: $25-49.9 Million
Emp.: 6
Packaging Products Mfr
N.A.I.C.S.: 322220
John McIlistar (Gen Mgr)

Nettingsdorfer Papierfabrik AG & Co KG - Print Vision Plant (2)
Mariner, Tamworth, Staffordshire, United Kingdom
Tel.: (44) 1827306400
Packaging Paper Products Mfr
N.A.I.C.S.: 322220

Nettingsdorfer Papierfabrik AG & Co KG - Print Vision Tannochside Plant (2)
Old Edinburgh Rd Uddingston, Tannochside, Glasgow, G716PQ, United Kingdom
Tel.: (44) 1698812901
Web Site: http://www.smurfitkappa.co.uk
Sales Range: $25-49.9 Million
Emp.: 70
Packaging Paper Products Mfr
N.A.I.C.S.: 322220
Ray Black (Gen Mgr)

Nettingsdorfer Papierfabrik AG & Co KG - Quart Plant (2)
Avenida Comarques Pais Valencia 131 131, Quart de Poblet, 46930, Valencia, Spain
Tel.: (34) 961597550
Web Site: http://www.smurfitkappa.com
Packaging Products Mfr
N.A.I.C.S.: 322220
Antonio Ferrando (Plant Mgr)

Nettingsdorfer Papierfabrik AG & Co KG - RapidCorr Euskirchen Plant (2)
Kolumbusstrasse 33, Euskirchen, 53881, Germany
Tel.: (49) 225194490
Sales Range: $25-49.9 Million
Emp.: 80
Packaging Paper Products Mfr
N.A.I.C.S.: 322220
Norbert Scherdin (Gen Mgr)

Nettingsdorfer Papierfabrik AG & Co KG - Recycling Germany & Central Fibre Management Plant (2)
Am Fuchsberg 8, Neuss, Germany
Tel.: (49) 2131 401 8820
Packaging Paper Products Mfr
N.A.I.C.S.: 322220

Nettingsdorfer Papierfabrik AG & Co KG - Rheinwelle Plant (2)
Durenerstrasse 10-12, Kreuzau, 52372, Germany
Tel.: (49) 24225080
Web Site: http://www.smurfitkappa.com
Emp.: 200
Packaging Paper Products Mfr
N.A.I.C.S.: 322220
Ralph Rogge (Gen Mgr)

Nettingsdorfer Papierfabrik AG & Co KG - Rol Pin - Mourenx Plant (2)
1964 Route de la Grande Lande, Mourenx, 40210, France
Tel.: (33) 5 58 04 42 42
Web Site: http://www.rolpin.com
Plywood Mfr
N.A.I.C.S.: 321212
Desme Christian (Dir)

Nettingsdorfer Papierfabrik AG & Co KG - Rovigo Plant (2)
Via Ca Dona 960, San Martino di Venezze, Italy
Tel.: (39) 042546781
Packaging Paper Products Mfr
N.A.I.C.S.: 322220

Nettingsdorfer Papierfabrik AG & Co KG - SSK Plant (2)
Mount Street, Nechells, Birmingham, B7 5RE, West Midlands, United Kingdom
Tel.: (44) 1213271381
Web Site: http://www.smurfitkappa.co.uk
Packaging Products Mfr
N.A.I.C.S.: 322220

Nettingsdorfer Papierfabrik AG & Co KG - San Felipe Mill Plant (2)
Carretera Panamericana Zona Industrial Carbonero Edo Yaracuy, San Felipe, 3201, Yaracuy, Venezuela
Tel.: (58) 2546007216
Web Site: http://www.smurfitkappa.com
Sales Range: $100-124.9 Million
Paperboard Mfr
N.A.I.C.S.: 322130
Rafael Concepcion (Gen Mgr)

Nettingsdorfer Papierfabrik AG & Co KG - Santiago Plant (2)
Calle El Roble N 430 Valle Grande Comuna Lampa, Santiago, Chile
Tel.: (56) 26568700
Packaging Paper Products Mfr
N.A.I.C.S.: 322220

Nettingsdorfer Papierfabrik AG & Co KG - Seviac Plant (2)
Rue des Vallieres-Nord ZI De Thise, 25220, Chalezeule, France
Tel.: (33) 381476860
Sales Range: $25-49.9 Million
Emp.: 25
Packaging Paper Products Mfr
N.A.I.C.S.: 322220
Jean-Philippe Guilbert (Mng Dir)

Nettingsdorfer Papierfabrik AG & Co KG - Sheetfeeding Windrush Plant (2)
Windrush Park Industrial Estate, Witney, OX29 7EX, United Kingdom
Tel.: (44) 1993771188
Web Site: http://www.smurfitkappa.com
Packaging Products Mfr
N.A.I.C.S.: 322220
Murray Disbrey (Gen Mgr)

Nettingsdorfer Papierfabrik AG & Co KG - Siemco Plant (2)
Zone Industrielle de la Gare, 44475, Carquefou, France
Tel.: (33) 240682515
Web Site: http://www.smurfitkappa.fr
Sales Range: $125-149.9 Million
Emp.: 260
Packaging Paper Products Mfr
N.A.I.C.S.: 322220
Emmanuel Rucker (Mng Dir)

Nettingsdorfer Papierfabrik AG & Co KG - Smurfit Kappa Packaging Solutions Plant (2)
South Quay Arklow, Wicklow, Ireland
Tel.: (353) 40232011
Sales Range: $25-49.9 Million
Emp.: 40
Packaging Paper Products Mfr
N.A.I.C.S.: 322220
Alan Moody (Plant Mgr)

Nettingsdorfer Papierfabrik AG & Co KG - Smurfit Kappa Treasury Plant (2)
Beech Hill Clonskeagh, Dublin, 4, Ireland
Tel.: (353) 1 26 00 900
Web Site: http://www.smurfitkappa.com
Packaging Paper Products Mfr
N.A.I.C.S.: 322220
Luis Martinez (Controller-Fin)

Nettingsdorfer Papierfabrik AG & Co KG - Snodland Recycling Depot Plant (2)
The Mill, Snodland, ME6 5AX, Kent, United Kingdom
Tel.: (44) 1634 241899
Web Site: http://www.smurfitkappa.com
Sales Range: $10-24.9 Million
Emp.: 17
Paper Products Recycling Services
N.A.I.C.S.: 562920

Nettingsdorfer Papierfabrik AG & Co KG - Sp. z o.o. Oddzial w Drezdenku Plant (2)
Ul Niepodleglosci 4, Drezdenko, 66-530, Poland
Tel.: (48) 957620222
Sales Range: $50-74.9 Million
Packaging Paper Products Mfr
N.A.I.C.S.: 322220

Nettingsdorfer Papierfabrik AG & Co KG - Sp. z o.o. Oddzial w Koninie Plant (2)
Moda Krolewska 17A, Stare Miasto, 62-571, Poland
Tel.: (48) 632402700
Packaging Paper Products Mfr
N.A.I.C.S.: 322220

Nettingsdorfer Papierfabrik AG & Co KG - Sp. z o.o. Oddzial w Warszawie Plant (2)
Ul Klasykow 36, Warsaw, 03163, Poland
Tel.: (48) 223308200
Web Site: http://www.smurfitkappa.pl
Sales Range: $50-74.9 Million
Emp.: 15
Packaging Paper Products Mfr
N.A.I.C.S.: 322220
Jacek Niewegllowski (Gen Mgr)

Nettingsdorfer Papierfabrik AG & Co KG - Stalybridge Plant (2)
Knowl Street, Stalybridge, FK15 3AR, United Kingdom
Tel.: (44) 1613383711
Web Site: http://www.smurfitkappa.co.uk
Sales Range: $50-74.9 Million
Emp.: 13
Packaging Paper Products Mfr
N.A.I.C.S.: 322220
Lynne Case (Gen Mgr)

Nettingsdorfer Papierfabrik AG & Co KG - Susegana Plant (2)
Via 4 Novembre 52, Susegana, 31058, Italy
Tel.: (39) 04387571
Sales Range: $50-74.9 Million
Corrugated Packaging Paper Board Mfr
N.A.I.C.S.: 322130

Nettingsdorfer Papierfabrik AG & Co KG - Tezze / Carmignano Plant (2)
Via Ghisa 36, Arzignano, 36071, Italy
Tel.: (39) 0444 473 000
Sales Range: $25-49.9 Million
Emp.: 20
Packaging Paper Products Mfr
N.A.I.C.S.: 322220
Luca Favero (Plant Mgr)

Nettingsdorfer Papierfabrik AG & Co KG - Totana Plant (2)
Pol Ind El Saladar C/Granado no 2, Totana, 30850, Murcia, Spain
Tel.: (34) 968418390
Sales Range: $25-49.9 Million
Emp.: 20
Packaging Products Mfr
N.A.I.C.S.: 322220
Antonio Fellando (Gen Mgr)

Nettingsdorfer Papierfabrik AG & Co KG - Turnhout Plant (2)
Bremheidelaan 1 - Industriezone 4, Turnhout, Belgium
Tel.: (32) 14405700
Packaging Paper Products Mfr
N.A.I.C.S.: 322220

Nettingsdorfer Papierfabrik AG & Co KG - Van Mierlo Plant (2)
Steenweg Op Mol 60, Turnhout, 2300, Belgium
Tel.: (32) 14402811
Web Site: http://www.smurfitkappa.com
Sales Range: $50-74.9 Million
Packaging Paper Products Mfr
N.A.I.C.S.: 322220
Jan Engelen (Mng Dir)

Nettingsdorfer Papierfabrik AG & Co KG - Varde Plant (2)
Malervej 15, Varde, Denmark
Tel.: (45) 76950150
Web Site: http://www.smurfitkappa.dk
Emp.: 3
Packaging Paper Products Mfr
N.A.I.C.S.: 322220

Nettingsdorfer Papierfabrik AG & Co KG - Vercelli Plant (2)
Via Walter Manzone 200, Vercelli, 13100, Italy
Tel.: (39) 0161227111
Sales Range: $25-49.9 Million
Packaging Paper Products Mfr
N.A.I.C.S.: 322220

Nettingsdorfer Papierfabrik AG & Co KG - Vignate Plant (2)
Via G Galilei 34, Vignate, Italy
Tel.: (39) 02953621
Packaging Paper Products Mfr
N.A.I.C.S.: 322220

Nettingsdorfer Papierfabrik AG & Co KG - Vigo Plant (2)
Ctra Coruna-Portugal Km 160, Porrino, 36400, Pontevedra, Spain
Tel.: (34) 986331350
Packaging Paper Products Mfr
N.A.I.C.S.: 322220

Nettingsdorfer Papierfabrik AG & Co KG - Vitop Moulding Plant (2)
Via Enzo Ferrari 39 Zona Industriale D3, Alessandria, 15121, Italy
Tel.: (39) 0131 241601
Sales Range: $25-49.9 Million
Emp.: 6
Packaging Paper Products Mfr
N.A.I.C.S.: 322220

Nettingsdorfer Papierfabrik AG & Co KG - Waren Recycling Depot Plant (2)
Warendorfer Strasse 5, Waren, Germany
Tel.: (49) 39 91 12 11 01
Packaging Paper Products Mfr
N.A.I.C.S.: 322220

Nettingsdorfer Papierfabrik AG & Co KG - Wellit Wellpappenwerk Plant (2)
Industriestr 2, Delbruck, 33129, Germany
Tel.: (49) 52505130
Web Site: http://www.smurfitkappa.de
Sales Range: $25-49.9 Million
Emp.: 10
Packaging Paper Products Mfr
N.A.I.C.S.: 322220
Joerg Hartmann (Gen Mgr)

Plant (Domestic):

Nettingsdorfer Papierfabrik AG & Co KG - Wellkart Plant (2)
Am Kirchenholz 2, Horsching, 4063, Austria
Tel.: (43) 7221 72600
Sales Range: $25-49.9 Million
Emp.: 18
Packaging Paper Products Mfr
N.A.I.C.S.: 322220
Friedrich Schopf (Gen Mgr)

Plant (Non-US):

Nettingsdorfer Papierfabrik AG & Co KG - Wellpack Plant (2)
Verkstadsvagen 18, Box 1104, Eslov, Sweden
Tel.: (46) 41368000
Packaging Machinery Mfr
N.A.I.C.S.: 333993

Nettingsdorfer Papierfabrik AG & Co KG - Wellpappe Bruhl Plant (2)
Fischenicherstrasse 21, Bruhl, Germany
Tel.: (49) 223270710
Packaging Paper Products Mfr
N.A.I.C.S.: 322220

Nettingsdorfer Papierfabrik AG & Co KG - Wellpappe Hanau Plant (2)
Ruhrstrasse 5-9, Hanau, Germany
Tel.: (49) 61811091 0
Web Site: http://www.smurfitkappa.de
Emp.: 160
Packaging Paper Products Mfr
N.A.I.C.S.: 322220
George Seldes (Mng Dir)

Nettingsdorfer Papierfabrik AG & Co KG - Wellpappe St.Leon Plant (2)
An der Autobahn 1, Sankt Leon-Rot, 68789, Germany
Tel.: (49) 62275290
Web Site: http://www.smurfitkappa.de
Packaging Paper Products Mfr
N.A.I.C.S.: 322220

SMURFIT KAPPA GROUP PLC

Smurfit Kappa Group plc—(Continued)
Andreas Schrader *(Gen Mgr)*

Nettingsdorfer Papierfabrik AG & Co KG - Wellpappenwerk Delitzsch Plant (2)
Carl-Friedrich-Benz-Str 36-38, 4509, Delitzsch, Germany
Tel.: (49) 342026660
Web Site: http://www.smurfitkappa.de
Packaging Paper Products Mfr
N.A.I.C.S.: 322220

Nettingsdorfer Papierfabrik AG & Co KG - Wellpappenwerk Dusseldorf Plant (2)
Am Hochofen 102, 40549, Dusseldorf, Germany
Tel.: (49) 21150830
Web Site: http://www.smurfitkappa.de
Sales Range: $50-74.9 Million
Emp.: 20
Packaging Paper Products Mfr
N.A.I.C.S.: 322220
Ingo Gruetters *(Mng Dir)*

Nettingsdorfer Papierfabrik AG & Co KG - Wellpappenwerk Germersheim Plant (2)
Hamburger Str 3, 76726, Germersheim, Germany
Tel.: (49) 72745030
Packaging Paper Products Mfr
N.A.I.C.S.: 322220

Nettingsdorfer Papierfabrik AG & Co KG - Wellpappenwerk Julich Plant (2)
Durener Str 16, 52428, Julich, Germany
Tel.: (49) 24616280
Sales Range: $50-74.9 Million
Emp.: 16
Packaging Paper Products Mfr
N.A.I.C.S.: 322220
Ingo Gruetters *(Gen Mgr)*

Nettingsdorfer Papierfabrik AG & Co KG - Wellpappenwerk Lubbecke Plant (2)
Berliner Str 100, Lubbecke, Germany
Tel.: (49) 5741600 0
Packaging Paper Products Mfr
N.A.I.C.S.: 322220

Nettingsdorfer Papierfabrik AG & Co KG - Wellpappenwerk Neuburg Plant (2)
Sehensander Weg 17, 86633, Neuburg an der Donau, Germany
Tel.: (49) 8431510
Packaging Paper Products Mfr
N.A.I.C.S.: 322220

Nettingsdorfer Papierfabrik AG & Co KG - Wellpappenwerk Plattling Plant (2)
Gottlieb-Daimler-Str 8, Plattling, Germany
Tel.: (49) 99315040
Packaging Paper Products Mfr
N.A.I.C.S.: 322220

Nettingsdorfer Papierfabrik AG & Co KG - Wellpappenwerk Waren Plant (2)
Warendorfer Str 7, Waren, 17192, Germany
Tel.: (49) 39917440
Sales Range: $50-74.9 Million
Packaging Paper Products Mfr
N.A.I.C.S.: 322220

Nettingsdorfer Papierfabrik AG & Co KG - Welltillverkaren Plant (2)
Hammarvagen 14, Arlov, Sweden
Tel.: (46) 40437350
Sales Range: $25-49.9 Million
Emp.: 1
Packaging Paper Products Mfr
N.A.I.C.S.: 322220

Nettingsdorfer Papierfabrik AG & Co KG - Zedek Plant (2)
Grevener Str 67, 48149, Munster, Germany
Tel.: (49) 251214080
Sales Range: $25-49.9 Million
Emp.: 15
Packaging Paper Products Mfr
N.A.I.C.S.: 322220

Jack Pieterson *(Gen Mgr)*

Nettingsdorfer Papierfabrik AG & Co KG - Zimrovice Plant (2)
Zimrovice c p 222, Zimrovice, 74741, Czech Republic
Tel.: (420) 553 753 111
Packaging Paper Products Mfr
N.A.I.C.S.: 322220

Nettingsdorfer Papierfabrik AG & Co KG - Zulpich Papier Plant (2)
Bessenicher Weg, Zulpich, 53909, Germany
Tel.: (49) 22523060
Web Site: http://www.smurfitkappa.com
Sales Range: $50-74.9 Million
Paper Products Mfr
N.A.I.C.S.: 322299
Peter Kramp *(Gen Mgr)*

Nettingsdorfer Papierfabrik AG & Co KG - Zwiesel Plant (2)
Am Talubergang 8, Zwiesel, 99227, Germany
Tel.: (49) 99225080
Web Site: http://www.smurfitkappa.de
Sales Range: $25-49.9 Million
Packaging Paper Products Mfr
N.A.I.C.S.: 322220
Martin Scheinert *(Gen Mgr)*

Subsidiary (Non-US):

Polska Smurfit Kappa Polska Sp. z.o.o. (2)
Ul Lukasiewicza 6, 83-000, Pruszcz Gdanski, Poland
Tel.: (48) 587739100
Web Site: http://www.smurfitkappa.com
Packaging Paper Products Mfr
N.A.I.C.S.: 322220
Slawomir Antoniuk *(Gen Mgr)*

Provence Alpes Cote d (2)
Quartier du Gheit, Contes, France
Tel.: (33) 493794949
Packaging Paper Products Mfr
N.A.I.C.S.: 322220

Plant (Non-US):

Smurfit Kappa Bag-in-Box (2)
Quai de l'Ile Belon, BP 21064, 51200, Epernay, France
Tel.: (33) 32 655 7010
Web Site: http://www.smurfitkappa.com
Emp.: 200
Paperboard Mfr
N.A.I.C.S.: 322130
Dominiqui Jissag *(Gen Mgr)*

Smurfit Kappa Cartonnage de Colmar (2)
Rue de l'Etang 6, 68126, Bennwihr Gare, France
Tel.: (33) 389214250
Web Site: http://www.smurfitkappa.com
Packaging Paper Products Mfr
N.A.I.C.S.: 322211

Smurfit Kappa Cartonnerie de Rennes (2)
ZI de la Bourdonnais, F-35520, La Meziere, France
Tel.: (33) 299131600
Web Site: http://www.smurfitkappa.com
Packaging Paper Products Mfr
N.A.I.C.S.: 322220

Smurfit Kappa Cerro Gordo Mill (2)
Km 15.5 Carretera Mexico-Laredo, Santa Clara, 55540, Mexico
Tel.: (52) 5557292300
Web Site: http://www.smurfitkappa.com
Paper Mills
N.A.I.C.S.: 322120

Smurfit Kappa Danmark - Herfolge (2)
Islandsvej 2, Herfolge, Koge, Denmark
Tel.: (45) 7933 7933
Web Site: http://www.smurfitkappa.com
Packaging Paper Products Mfr
N.A.I.C.S.: 322220

Smurfit Kappa Drogenbos (2)
Avenue Paul Gilson 439, 1620, Drogenbos, Belgium
Tel.: (32) 23710110
Web Site: http://www.smurfitkappa.com
Packaging Paper Products Mfr
N.A.I.C.S.: 322220

Smurfit Kappa Guadalajara Corrugated (2)
Km 1 2 Carretera Tala San Isidro Mazatepec, 45300, Tala, Jalisco, Mexico
Tel.: (52) 384 733 2390
Web Site: http://www.smurfitkappa.com
Packaging Paper Products Mfr
N.A.I.C.S.: 322220

Smurfit Kappa Hoya Paper (2)
Von-dem-Bussche-Strasse 1, 27318, Hoya, Germany
Tel.: (49) 42518140
Web Site: http://www.smurfitkappa.com
Packaging Paper Products Mfr
N.A.I.C.S.: 322220

Smurfit Kappa Interbox Plant (2)
Industrieweg 17, 2320, Hoogstraten, Belgium
Tel.: (32) 33147120
Web Site: http://www.solidus-solutions.com
Sales Range: $25-49.9 Million
Emp.: 10
Packaging Paper Products Mfr
N.A.I.C.S.: 322220
Richard Houden *(Gen Mgr)*

Smurfit Kappa Liquid Packaging (2)
Verkstadsvagen 18, Box 1104, 241 26, Eslov, Sweden
Tel.: (46) 41368000
Web Site: http://www.smurfitkappa.com
Sales Range: $50-74.9 Million
Emp.: 220
Packaging Paper Products Mfr
N.A.I.C.S.: 322220
Claes Bjareholt *(Gen Mgr)*

Smurfit Kappa News Press Ltd (2)
Kells Industrial Estate Virginia Road Kells, Meath, Ireland
Tel.: (353) 469280900
Web Site: http://www.smurfitkappa.com
Newspaper Printing Services
N.A.I.C.S.: 513110

Smurfit Kappa Nord Emballages (2)
41 rue de Lorraine, 02500, Hirson, France
Tel.: (33) 323993666
Web Site: http://www.smurfitkappa.com
Cardboard & Other Corrugated Products Mfr
N.A.I.C.S.: 322220

Smurfit Kappa Olen (2)
Lammerdries 57 - Industriezone De Heze, Olen, 2250, Belgium
Tel.: (32) 14259450
Web Site: http://www.smurfitkappa.com
Cardboard Mfr
N.A.I.C.S.: 322211
Van Herck *(Gen Mgr)*

Subsidiary (Non-US):

Smurfit Kappa OnWell AB (2)
Atlasgatan 8, 802 86, Gavle, Sweden
Tel.: (46) 26662570
Sales Range: $25-49.9 Million
Emp.: 2
Commercial Screen Printing Services
N.A.I.C.S.: 323113

Plant (Non-US):

Smurfit Kappa Participations SAS - Cartonnerie de Rethel (2)
Rue Hippolyte Noiret 1, Rethel, France
Tel.: (33) 324396161
Web Site: http://www.smurfitkappa.com
Corrugated Packaging Product Mfr
N.A.I.C.S.: 322212

Smurfit Kappa Polska Sp. z o.o. Oddzial w Pruszkowie (2)
Ul Groblowa 10, Pruskow, Poland
Tel.: (48) 227586700
Packaging Paper Products Mfr
N.A.I.C.S.: 322220

Smurfit Kappa Provence Mediterranee (2)
58 Boulevard Capitaine Geze, 13014, Marseille, France
Tel.: (33) 4 91 11 64 54
Web Site: http://www.smurfitkappa.com
Packaging Paper Products Mfr
N.A.I.C.S.: 322220

Smurfit Kappa Rena AS (2)
Storgata 1b, 8006, Bodo, Norway
Tel.: (47) 755 500 15
Web Site: http://www.smurfitkappa.com
Packaging Paper Products
N.A.I.C.S.: 424130

Smurfit Kappa Service (2)
Tilsiter Str 144, 22047, Hamburg, Germany
Tel.: (49) 4069443331
Web Site: http://www.smurfitkappa.com
Commercial Packaging Services
N.A.I.C.S.: 561910

Smurfit Kappa South (2)
Pottington Business Park Barnstaple, EX31 1LX, Devon, United Kingdom - England
Tel.: (44) 1271345011
Web Site: http://www.smurfitkappa.com
Packaging Paper Products Mfr
N.A.I.C.S.: 322220

Smurfit Kappa South West (2)
Oldmixon Estate Winterstoke Road Weston Super Mare, Weston-super-Mare, BS24 9BH, North Somerset, United Kingdom
Tel.: (44) 1934628251
Web Site: http://www.smurfitkappa.com
Packaging Products Mfr
N.A.I.C.S.: 322220

Smurfit Kappa Sud - Werk Feucht (2)
Industriestrasse 91, 90537, Feucht, Germany
Tel.: (49) 91284060
Web Site: http://www.smurfitkappa.com
Packaging Paper Products Mfr
N.A.I.C.S.: 322211

Smurfit Kappa Sverige AB (2)
Verkstadsvagen 18, 241 26, Eslov, Sweden
Tel.: (46) 41368000
Web Site: http://www.smurfitkappa.com
Corrugated Board Paper & Packaging Product Mfr
N.A.I.C.S.: 322220

Smurfit Kappa Swisswell (2)
Industriestrasse 1, Postfach 172, 4313, Mohlin, Switzerland
Tel.: (41) 61 855 6161
Web Site: http://www.smurfitkappa.com
Sales Range: $50-74.9 Million
Emp.: 15
Corrugated Packaging Product Mfr
N.A.I.C.S.: 322211
Christian Boettger *(Mgr-Sls)*

Subsidiary (Non-US):

Smurfit Kappa Wellpappenwerk Schneverdingen GmbH (2)
Moorweg 55, 29640, Schneverdingen, Germany
Tel.: (49) 5193890
Web Site: http://www.smurfitkappa.de
Sales Range: $50-74.9 Million
Packaging Paper Products Mfr
N.A.I.C.S.: 322220
Uwe Geistlinger *(Gen Mgr)*

Plant (Non-US):

Smurfit Kappa Zebrak (2)
Skandinavska 1000, 267 53, Zebrak, Czech Republic
Tel.: (420) 311544111
Sales Range: $50-74.9 Million
Packaging Paper Products Mfr
N.A.I.C.S.: 322220
Zdenek Suchitra *(Gen Mgr)*

Subsidiary (Non-US):

Smurfitkappa Wellpappe Nord GmbH (2)
Tilsiter Str 144, Hamburg, 22047, Germany
Tel.: (49) 5193 89 0
Packaging Paper Products Mfr
N.A.I.C.S.: 322220
Siegfried Jacobi *(Mng Dir)*

Smurfit Carton de Colombia, S.A. (1)
Puerto Isaacs Carrera Yumbo Km 15, Dumbo Balla, Cali, Colombia
Tel.: (57) 26914000
Web Site: http://www.smurfit.com.co

AND PRIVATE COMPANIES **SMURFIT KAPPA GROUP PLC**

Sales Range: $450-499.9 Million
Emp.: 2,500
Paperboard & Packaging Mfr
N.A.I.C.S.: 322212

Smurfit Carton de Venezuela, S.A. (1)
Avenida la Estancia Edificio Centro Banaven Torre C Piso 2, Chuao, 1010 A, Caracas, Venezuela
Tel.: (58) 2129596196
Web Site: http://www.smurfitkappa.com.ve
Sales Range: $25-49.9 Million
Emp.: 4
Paperboard & Packaging Mfr
N.A.I.C.S.: 322130

Smurfit Carton y Papel de Mexico S.A. de C.V. (1)
Tel.: (52) 5557292300
Web Site: http://www.smurfitkappa.com.mx
Sales Range: $125-149.9 Million
Emp.: 350
Paperboard & Packaging Products Mfr
N.A.I.C.S.: 322130

Smurfit Corrugated Cases (Cork) Limited (1)
Pouladuff Ind Est Togher, Cork, Ireland
Tel.: (353) 214962033
Web Site: http://www.smurfitkappa.com
Packaging Paper Materials Mfr
N.A.I.C.S.: 322220
Simon Slattery (Gen Mgr)

Smurfit Corrugated Ireland Ltd. (1)
Ballymount Rd, Walkinstown, Dublin, Ireland
Tel.: (353) 1409 00 00
Web Site: http://www.smurfitkappa.ie
Sales Range: $25-49.9 Million
Emp.: 18
Paper Materials Recycling Services
N.A.I.C.S.: 562920
John O'Loughlin (CEO)

Smurfit International B.V. (1)
Warandelaan 2, 4904 PC, Oosterhout, Netherlands
Tel.: (31) 162480000
Packaging Paper Product Mfr & Distr
N.A.I.C.S.: 322220

Smurfit Interwell GmbH & Co. KG (1)
Schellingstrasse 40, Haid, 4053, bei Ansfelden, Austria
Tel.: (43) 72298440
Web Site: http://www.smurfitkappa.at
Sales Range: $75-99.9 Million
Emp.: 160
Containerboard Mfr
N.A.I.C.S.: 322211
Johann Gruenwald (Dir-Tech)

Smurfit Kappa Cartonnerie de Getigne (SCAO) (1)
Z I Le Fief du Parc, 44190, Getigne, France
Tel.: (33) 240540521
Web Site: http://www.smurfitkappa.com
Corrugated Packaging Services
N.A.I.C.S.: 561910

Smurfit Kappa Cognac (1)
14 rue Burgaud des Marets, 16200, Jarnac, France
Tel.: (33) 545361800
Web Site: http://www.smurfitkappa.com
Corrugated Packaging Services
N.A.I.C.S.: 561910

Smurfit Kappa Connaught Packaging (1)
Merlin Park Ind Estate, Galway, Ireland
Tel.: (353) 9 175 5032
Web Site: http://www.smurfitkappa.ie
Sales Range: $25-49.9 Million
Emp.: 30
Packaging Paper Products Mfr
N.A.I.C.S.: 322220
Winston Depinna (Gen Mgr)

Smurfit Kappa Deutschland GmbH (1)
Tel.: (49) 40309010
Emp.: 100
Packaging Paper Products Mfr & Distr
N.A.I.C.S.: 322220

Subsidiary (Domestic):

Smurfit Kappa Baden Packaging GmbH (2)
An der Murg 1, 76599, Weisenbach, Germany
Tel.: (49) 72249950
Web Site: http://www.smurfitkappa.com
Folding Carton Packaging Products Mfr
N.A.I.C.S.: 322212
Thomas Rugh (Gen Mgr)

Plant (Domestic):

Smurfit Kappa C.D. Haupt Papier (2)
Orpethaler Strasse 50, 34474, Diemelstadt, Wrexen, Germany
Tel.: (49) 5642790
Web Site: http://www.smurfitkappa.de
Sales Range: $75-99.9 Million
Graphic Board
N.A.I.C.S.: 551112

Subsidiary (Domestic):

Smurfit Kappa Herzberger Papierfabrik (2)
Andreasberger Strasse 1, PO Box 1169, 37412, Herzberg, Germany
Tel.: (49) 5521820
Web Site: http://www.smurfitkappa-herzberger-papier.com
Sales Range: $200-249.9 Million
Paper & Paperboard Mfr
N.A.I.C.S.: 322130

Smurfit Kappa Neuss GmbH (2)
Am Fuchsberg 8, 41468, Neuss, Germany
Tel.: (49) 21 313 8030
Web Site: http://www.smurfitkappa.com
Sales Range: $50-74.9 Million
Solid Board Packaging Products Mfr
N.A.I.C.S.: 322211
Tom Wetzel (Gen Mgr)

Plant (Domestic):

Smurfit Kappa euro-lok-Werk Heppenheim (2)
Am Erbauwiesenweg 19, 64646, Heppenheim, Germany
Tel.: (49) 62 529 9110
Web Site: http://www.smurfitkappa.com
Packaging Paper Products Mfr
N.A.I.C.S.: 322220
Iris Steinhagen (Gen Mgr)

Smurfit Kappa Display (1)
Unit 17 Whitestown Industrial Estate, Tallaght, Dublin, Ireland
Tel.: (353) 1 452 4333
Web Site: https://www.smurfitkappadisplay.com
Sales Range: $25-49.9 Million
Emp.: 3
Display Advertising Services
N.A.I.C.S.: 541850
Jonathan Arthur (Gen Mgr)

Smurfit Kappa Espana, S.A (1)
Poligono Industrial Las Arenas, Alameda, Madrid, 28320, Pinto, Spain
Tel.: (34) 916910051
Web Site: http://www.smurfitkappa.com
Mfr of Paperboard & Packaging Products
N.A.I.C.S.: 322212

Plant (Domestic):

Smurfit Kappa Almeria (2)
Ctra de Iryda Sector IV La Canal-Paraje el Vizconde, Vicar, 04738, Almeria, Spain
Tel.: (34) 95 034 1550
Web Site: http://www.smurfitkappa.com
Sales Range: $25-49.9 Million
Emp.: 100
Packaging Products Mfr
N.A.I.C.S.: 322220
Antonio Lopez (Mgr-Comml)

Smurfit Kappa Bag-in-Box Mediterranean Plasticos Vicent (2)
Avila 12 Poligono Industrial L'Alfac III, Ibi, 03440, Alicante, Spain
Tel.: (34) 96 655 03 92
Web Site: http://www.smurfitkappa.com
Sales Range: $25-49.9 Million
Emp.: 100
Packaging Products Mfr
N.A.I.C.S.: 322220

Subsidiary (Non-US):

Smurfit Kappa Nervion, S.A. (2)
Tel.: (34) 946205115
Sales Range: $50-74.9 Million
Emp.: 220
Sack Paper Mfr
N.A.I.C.S.: 322130

Plant (Domestic):

Smurfit Kappa Sanguesa (2)
Avda Raimundo Lumbier s/n, Navarra, 31400, Sanguesa, Spain
Tel.: (34) 94 887 0000
Web Site: http://www.smurfitkappa.com
Sales Range: $50-74.9 Million
Emp.: 230
Paper Mills
N.A.I.C.S.: 322120
Eloy Nogal (Mgr-Export)

Smurfit Kappa Europe B.V. (1)
The Base Evert van de Beekstraat 104, 1118 CN, Schiphol, Netherlands
Tel.: (31) 207951500
Packaging Paper Product Mfr & Distr
N.A.I.C.S.: 322220

Smurfit Kappa Funding plc (1)
Beech Hill, Clonskeagh, Dublin, Ireland
Tel.: (353) 1 202 7000
Web Site: http://www.smurfitkappa.com
Sales Range: $50-74.9 Million
Emp.: 65
Paperboard & Packaging Product Mfr
N.A.I.C.S.: 322130
Gary McGann (CEO)

Smurfit Kappa Holdings Italia, S.p.A. (1)
Strada Di Serravalle 30, 15067, Novi Ligure, Italy
Tel.: (39) 0143330311
Investment Management Service
N.A.I.C.S.: 523999

Subsidiary (Domestic):

Smurfit SISA S.p.A. (2)
Strada Serravalle 30, 15067, Novi Ligure, AL, Italy
Tel.: (39) 01437731
Web Site: http://www.smurfit.it
Sales Range: $50-74.9 Million
Emp.: 120
Cardboard & Corrugated Paper Mfr
N.A.I.C.S.: 322211

Smurfit Kappa International France SAS (1)
2 Rue Goethe, F 75116, Paris, France
Tel.: (33) 49523200
Web Site: http://www.smurfitgroup.com
Sales Range: $25-49.9 Million
Emp.: 40
Packaging Products Mfr
N.A.I.C.S.: 322211

Smurfit Kappa Ireland Limited (1)
Ballymount Road, Walkinstown, Dublin, 4, Ireland (100%)
Tel.: (353) 12027000
Web Site: https://www.smurfitkappa.ie
Paperboard & Packaging Services
N.A.I.C.S.: 322211

Smurfit Kappa Italia S.p.A. - San Marzano (1)
Regione Leiso 100, San Marzano Oliveto, Italy
Tel.: (39) 0141856556
Web Site: http://www.smurfitkappa.com
Corrugated Carboard Packaging Mfr
N.A.I.C.S.: 322211

Smurfit Kappa Italia, S.p.A. (1)
Strada Serravalle 65, 15067, Novi Ligure, AL, Italy
Tel.: (39) 014377334
Packaging Paper Product Mfr & Distr
N.A.I.C.S.: 322220

Smurfit Kappa Kraftliner Pitea AB (1)
Kolugsvagen 30, 941 86, Pitea, Sweden
Tel.: (46) 91197000
Emp.: 520
Corrugated Packaging Paper Board Mfr
N.A.I.C.S.: 322130

Smurfit Kappa Nettingsdorfer AG & Co. KG (1)
Nettingsdorfer Strasse 40, Haid, 4053, Ansfelden, Austria
Tel.: (43) 72298630
Corrugated Board Mfr & Distr
N.A.I.C.S.: 322211

Smurfit Kappa Packaging LLC (1)
1301 International Pkwy Ste 550, Sunrise, FL 33323-2874
Tel.: (954) 514-2600
Holding Company
N.A.I.C.S.: 551112
Juan G. Castaneda (Pres)

Plant (Domestic):

Smurfit Kappa Fort Worth (2)
6433 Davis Blvd, North Richland Hills, TX 76180-4717
Tel.: (817) 498-3200
Sales Range: $50-74.9 Million
Emp.: 320
Corrugated Box Mfr
N.A.I.C.S.: 322211
Daryle Sheely (VP-Mfg)

Subsidiary (Domestic):

Smurfit Kappa Orange County LLC (2)
240 W Fletcher Ave, Orange, CA 92865 (100%)
Tel.: (714) 998-4411
Web Site: http://www.smurfitkappa.com
Corrugated/Solid Fiber Boxes Mfr
N.A.I.C.S.: 322211

Smurfit Kappa Packaging UK Limited (1)
Tel.: (44) 8702400361
Paperboard Product Mfr & Distr
N.A.I.C.S.: 322220

Smurfit Kappa Participations SAS (1)
5 Avenue Du General De Gaulle 6th Floor, 94160, Saint-Mande, France
Tel.: (33) 149574200
Paperboard Product Mfr & Distr
N.A.I.C.S.: 322220

Smurfit Kappa Specialties (1)
Luchthavenweg 13, NL-5667 EA, Eindhoven, Netherlands
Tel.: (31) 402140777
Specialty Solid, Graphic & Packaging Board Mfr
N.A.I.C.S.: 322130

Smurfit Kappa Treasury Funding Ltd. (1)
Beech Hill Clonskeagh, Dublin, 4, Ireland
Tel.: (353) 12600900
Web Site: http://www.smurfitkappa.com
Sales Range: $50-74.9 Million
Emp.: 65
Finance Company
N.A.I.C.S.: 522209
Gary McGann (CEO)

Smurfit Kappa Treasury Unlimited Company (1)
Beech Hill, Clonskeagh, Dublin, D04 N2R2, Ireland
Tel.: (353) 12027000
Financial Services
N.A.I.C.S.: 523999

Smurfit Kappa UK (1)
Darlington Road, West Auckland, Bishop Auckland, DL14 9PE, Durham, United Kingdom
Tel.: (44) 138 883 2531
Web Site: http://www.smurfitkappa.com
Sales Range: $50-74.9 Million
Emp.: 150
Corrugated Containers Mfr
N.A.I.C.S.: 322211
Clive Bowers (CEO)

Plant (Domestic):

Smurfit Kappa Central Resources (2)
3rd Floor Cunard Buildings Water Street, Liverpool, L3 1SF, United Kingdom
Tel.: (44) 870 240 0361
Sales Range: $25-49.9 Million
Emp.: 20
Packaging Paper Materials Mfr

SMURFIT KAPPA GROUP PLC

Smurfit Kappa Group plc—(Continued)
N.A.I.C.S.: 322220
Patrick Mcneill (CFO)

Smurfit Kappa Composites (2)
Richmond Works, Hensingham, Whitehaven, CA28 8TS, Cumbria, United Kingdom
Tel.: (44) 19 466 1671
Web Site: http://www.smurfitkappa.com
Composite Container Mfr
N.A.I.C.S.: 322219
Keith Nicole (Gen Mgr)

Smurfit Kappa Corby (2)
Arnsley Road Weldon Industrial Estate, Corby, NN17 5QW, Northants, United Kingdom
Tel.: (44) 1536406784
Web Site: http://www.smurfitkappa.com
Emp.: 9
Solid Board Packaging Products Mfr
N.A.I.C.S.: 322211

Smurfit Kappa Mold (2)
Mold Business Park, Maes Gwern, Mold, CH7 1XZ, Flintshire, United Kingdom
Tel.: (44) 1352750655
Web Site: http://www.smurfitkappa.com
Packaging Products Mfr
N.A.I.C.S.: 322220

Smurfit Kappa Peterborough (2)
Benwick Road, Whittlesey, Peterborough, PE7 2JA, Cambridgeshire, United Kingdom
Tel.: (44) 1733206050
Web Site: http://www.smurfitkappa.com
Packaging Paper Products Mfr
N.A.I.C.S.: 322220

Smurfit Kappa Recycling UK (2)
The Mill, Snodland, ME6 5AX, Kent, United Kingdom
Tel.: (44) 1634241899
Web Site: http://www.smurfitkappa.com
Sales Range: $25-49.9 Million
Emp.: 10
Paper Recycling Services
N.A.I.C.S.: 562920

Smurfit Kappa Recycling UK - Blackburn Plant (2)
Premier Business Park Crofthead Road Whitebirk Industrial Park, Blackburn, VV15SW, United Kingdom
Tel.: (44) 1254 664269
Web Site: http://www.smurfitkappa.com
Waste Material Recycling Services
N.A.I.C.S.: 562920

Smurfit Kappa Townsend Hook (2)
Mill St, Snodland, ME6 5AX, Kent, United Kingdom
Tel.: (44) 1634240205
Web Site: http://www.smurfitkappa-paperuk.com
Sales Range: $50-74.9 Million
Emp.: 160
Paper Mills
N.A.I.C.S.: 322120

Smurfit Kappa Yate (2)
Woodward Avenue, Yate, Bristol, BS37 5AP, United Kingdom
Tel.: (44) 145 432 7777
Web Site: http://www.smurfitkappa.com
Packaging Paper Products Mfr
N.A.I.C.S.: 322220
John Wroot (Dir-Ops)

Smurfit Kappa Wellpappenwerk Lubeck GmbH (1)
Glashuttenweg 11-15, 23568, Lubeck, Germany
Tel.: (49) 451 3102 0
Web Site: http://www.smurfitkappa.com
Packaging Paper Products Mfr
N.A.I.C.S.: 322220
Matthias Waller (Gen Mgr)

Smurfit Kappa do Brasil Industria de Embalagens S.A. (1)
Rua Castilho 392 Cj 162 Brooklin, Sao Paulo, CEP 04568-010, Brazil
Tel.: (55) 1121059000
Paperboard Product Mfr & Distr
N.A.I.C.S.: 322220

Smurfit Publications Limited (1)
Clanwilliam House Clanwilliam Place, Dublin, Ireland
Tel.: (353) 12405300
Commercial Publishing Services
N.A.I.C.S.: 513199

Smurfit S.A. (1)
Espora 200, Bernal, Buenos Aires, 1876, Argentina
Tel.: (54) 1152537000
Web Site: http://www.smurfit.com.ar
Rev.: $125,000,000
Emp.: 1,000
Paperboard & Packaging Mfr
N.A.I.C.S.: 322211
Angel Jorgealperto (CEO)

Subsidiary (Non-US):

Smurfit Kappa de Argentina, S.A. (2)
Tel.: (54) 1152537000
Packaging Products Mfr
N.A.I.C.S.: 322220

Waterford Castle Golf & Country Club Limited (1)
The Island, Waterford, Ireland
Tel.: (353) 51 878 203
Web Site: http://www.waterfordcastle.com
Emp.: 10
Home Management Services
N.A.I.C.S.: 721110
Jos Donvil (Gen Mgr)

SMVD POLY PACK LTD.
16 Strand Road Diamond Heritage 8th Floor Suite No-804B, Kolkata, 700001, West Bengal, India
Tel.: (91) 9330866856
Web Site: https://www.smvdpolypack.com
Year Founded: 2010
SMVD—(NSE)
Rev.: $9,332,350
Assets: $8,839,743
Liabilities: $5,836,187
Net Worth: $3,003,556
Earnings: $66,233
Emp.: 136
Fiscal Year-end: 03/31/21
Plastic Packaging Products Mfr
N.A.I.C.S.: 326112
Nirmal Parakh (CFO)

SMX (SECURITY MATTERS) PUBLIC LIMITED COMPANY
Mespil Business Ctr Mespil House Sussex Rd, D04 T4A6, Dublin, D04 T4A6, Ireland
Tel.: (353) 19201000 IE
Web Site: https://www.smx.tech
Year Founded: 2022
SMX—(NASDAQ)
Emp.: 20
Software Development Services
N.A.I.C.S.: 541511
Limor Moshe Lotker (CFO)

SMYL CHEVROLET PONTIAC BUICK GMC
3520 Kepler St, Whitecourt, T7S 0B5, AB, Canada
Tel.: (780) 778-2202
Web Site: https://www.smylchev.com
Year Founded: 1957
Rev.: $15,600,000
Emp.: 30
New & Used Car Dealers
N.A.I.C.S.: 441110
Joe Smyl (Owner)

SMYTHS TOYS HOLDING UNLIMITED COMPANY
Lyrr 1 Mervue Business Park, Galway, Ireland
Tel.: (353) 91 336 890 IE
Web Site: http://www.smythstoys.com
Year Founded: 2007
Holding Company; Toy Retailer
N.A.I.C.S.: 551112
Tony Smyth (Co-Mng Dir)

Subsidiaries:

Smyths Toys Unlimited Company (1)
Lyrr 1 Mervue Business Park, Galway, Ireland
Tel.: (353) 91 336 890
Web Site: http://www.smythstoys.com
Toy Retailer
N.A.I.C.S.: 459120
Padraig Smyth (Co-Mng Dir)

Toys "R" Us GmbH (1)
Kohlstrasse 8, 40827, Cologne, Germany
Tel.: (49) 22159720
Web Site: http://www.toysrus.de
Toy Retailer
N.A.I.C.S.: 459120
Lord Smith (CEO)

Subsidiary (Non-US):

Toys "R" Us AG (2)
Industriestrasse 29, 8305, Dietikon, Switzerland
Tel.: (41) 44 835 2635
Web Site: http://www.toysrus.ch
Toy Retailer
N.A.I.C.S.: 459120
Monika Merz (Pres)

Toys "R" Us Handelsgesellschaft m.b.H. (2)
Ikeaplatz 4, 4053, Haid, Austria
Tel.: (43) 722978712
Web Site: http://www.toysrus.at
Emp.: 10
Toy Retailer
N.A.I.C.S.: 459120
Franz Schweighofer (Mng Dir)

SN AIRHOLDING II NV
Corporate Village, Da Vincilaan 9, 1935, Zaventem, Belgium
Tel.: (32) 27232345
Holding Company
N.A.I.C.S.: 551112

Subsidiaries:

SN Brussels Airlines NV (1)
The Corporate Village, Da Vincilaan 9, 1935, Zaventem, Belgium (92%)
Tel.: (32) 27232345
Web Site: http://www.snbrusselsairlines.com
Sales Range: $750-799.9 Million
Emp.: 2,152
International Airline
N.A.I.C.S.: 481111

SNACK EMPIRE HOLDINGS LIMITED
57th Floor The Center 99 Queen's Road Central, Hong Kong, China (Hong Kong)
Tel.: (852) 25987500 Ky
Web Site: https://www.snackemp.com
Year Founded: 2003
1843—(HKG)
Rev.: $19,566,506
Assets: $24,382,364
Liabilities: $6,231,938
Net Worth: $18,150,426
Earnings: $1,365,691
Emp.: 122
Fiscal Year-end: 03/31/23
Holding Company
N.A.I.C.S.: 551112
Winnie Wing Yee Tung (Sec)

SNACKTIME PLC
Unit 17 Rufus Business Centre, Ravensbury Terrace, London, SW18 4RL, United Kingdom
Tel.: (44) 208 879 8300
Web Site: http://www.snacktimeuk.com
Sales Range: $25-49.9 Million
Emp.: 260
Snack & Chilled Drink Vending Machine Operator
N.A.I.C.S.: 311919
Timothy Henry Thorpe James (CFO)

SNAGA D.D. VARES
ul Put mira 13, 71330, Vares, Bosnia & Herzegovina
Tel.: (387) 32843006
SNGARK2—(SARE)
Rev.: $37,514
Assets: $1,110,264
Liabilities: $60,220
Net Worth: $1,050,043
Earnings: ($4,972)
Emp.: 1
Fiscal Year-end: 12/31/20
Food & Beverage Distr
N.A.I.C.S.: 424820

SNANDONG HONGCHUANG ALUMINUM INDUSTRY HOLDING COMPANY LIMITED
North of No 3 Canal Bridge east of Xinbo Road, Boxing County, Binzhou, 256500, Shandong, China
Tel.: (86) 5437026999
Web Site: https://www.hongchuangholding.com
Year Founded: 2000
002379—(SSE)
Rev.: $495,509,494
Assets: $364,383,504
Liabilities: $169,533,856
Net Worth: $194,849,647
Earnings: $3,207,115
Fiscal Year-end: 12/31/22
Aluminium Products Mfr
N.A.I.C.S.: 331315

SNAPPY COMMUNICATIONS CO. LTD.
2-1-3 Kanda Surugadai Plaza Ochanomizu Building 4F, Chiyoda-ku, Tokyo, 101-0062, Japan
Tel.: (81) 352819833
Web Site: http://www.snappy.ne.jp
Year Founded: 1998
Web Hosting Services & Music Publishers
N.A.I.C.S.: 518210
Yoshikazu Kobayashi (Pres)

SNAX 24 LTD.
3rd Meridien House 69-71 Clarendon Road, Watford, WD17 1DS, Hertfordshire, United Kingdom
Tel.: (44) 1442 861000
Web Site: http://www.snax24.co.uk
Year Founded: 1993
Sales Range: $350-399.9 Million
Emp.: 228
Fuel Forecourt Operator
N.A.I.C.S.: 424710
G. M. Ronson (Chm)

SNC HOLDING COMPANY LIMITED
103/25-34 Moo 17 Taparuk Rd, Sub Amphur, Bangsaotong District, Samut Prakan, 10540, Thailand
Tel.: (66) 27050820
Web Site: http://www.sncformer.com
Sales Range: $150-199.9 Million
Emp.: 1,000
Holding Company
N.A.I.C.S.: 551112

Subsidiaries:

SNC Former Public Company Limited (1)
No 333/3 Village No 6, Bang Phreang Subdistrict Bang Bo District, Samut Prakan, 10560, Thailand (50.15%)
Tel.: (66) 21080360
Web Site: https://www.sncformer.com
Rev.: $272,437,217
Assets: $341,503,425
Liabilities: $196,444,807
Net Worth: $145,058,617
Earnings: ($150,082)
Emp.: 2,056

Fiscal Year-end: 12/31/2023
Automotive & Home Air-Conditioning Products Mfr
N.A.I.C.S.: 333415
Rattapoom Nuntapatawee *(Mng Dir-Acctg & Fin Dept)*

Subsidiary (Domestic):

Immortal Part Company Limited (2)
333/2 333/4 Moo 6, Bangpreang District Amphur Bangbo, Samut Prakan, 10560, Thailand
Tel.: (66) 2 108 0370
Air Conditioner Equipment Mfr
N.A.I.C.S.: 333415

Paradise Plastic Company Limited (2)
128/888 Moo 1 Tambon Bangsaotong, Amphur Bangsaotong, Samut Prakan, 10540, Thailand
Tel.: (66) 2 763 8961 3
Plastics Product Mfr
N.A.I.C.S.: 326199

SAS Innovation Company Limited (2)
103/25 34 Moo 17 Taparuk Road, Bangsaotong District, Sub Amphur Bangsaotong, Samut Prakan, 10540, Thailand
Tel.: (66) 27050820
Web Site: http://www.sncformer.com
Real Estate Development Services
N.A.I.C.S.: 531390

SNC Atlantic Heat Pump Company Limited (2)
88/21-22 Moo2, Makhamku District Amphur Nikom Pattana, Rayong, 21180, Thailand
Tel.: (66) 38 893620 7
Pumps Mfr
N.A.I.C.S.: 333415

SNC Comp Parts Company Limited (2)
103/25 34 Moo 17 Taparuk Road, Bangsaotong District, Sub Amphur Bangsaotong, Samut Prakan, 10540, Thailand
Tel.: (66) 27050820
Sales Range: $25-49.9 Million
Emp.: 200
Compressor Metal Parts Mfr
N.A.I.C.S.: 332312

SNC Cooling Supply Company Limited (2)
103 25 34 Moo 17 Taparuk Road Bangsaotong District, Sub Amphur Bangsaotong, Samut Prakan, 10540, Thailand
Tel.: (66) 27050820
Web Site: http://www.sncsor.com
Sales Range: $150-199.9 Million
Emp.: 750
Air-Conditioner Parts Mfr
N.A.I.C.S.: 333415

SNC Fukui Holy Insulation Company Limited (2)
333/5 Bangpreang District Amphur Bangbo, Samut Prakan, 10560, Thailand
Tel.: (66) 2 108 03670 76
Pipes Mfr
N.A.I.C.S.: 331420

SNC Pyongsan Evolution Company Limited (2)
88/18 Moo 2 Ma-Kham-Koo Amphur, Nikom Pattana, Rayong, 21180, Thailand
Tel.: (66) 38893620
Web Site: http://www.sncformer.com
Sales Range: $50-74.9 Million
Emp.: 500
Metal Sheet Press Parts Mfr
N.A.I.C.S.: 332322
Somboon Gurdlin *(Mng Dir)*

Subsidiary (Domestic):

Infinity Part Company Limited (3)
88 / 18 Moo 2 Tambon Ma-Kham-Koo, Amphur Nikom Pattana, Rayong, 21180, Thailand
Tel.: (66) 3889 3619
Heat Exchanger Mfr
N.A.I.C.S.: 332410

Subsidiary (Domestic):

Toptech Diamond Tool Company Limited (2)
56 Moo3, Bangpra District Amphur Bangplee, Samut Prakan, 10540, Thailand
Tel.: (66) 2 182 1275 82
Web Site: http://www.toptechdiamond.com
Diamond Tool Mfr
N.A.I.C.S.: 333514

SNCF
2 place aux Etoiles, 93200, La Plaine Saint-Denis, France
Tel.: (33) 185078001   **FR**
Web Site: http://www.sncf.com
Rev.: $38,100,788,690
Earnings: $161,274,390
Emp.: 201,816
Fiscal Year-end: 12/31/18
Rail Transortation & Mobility Solutions Organization
N.A.I.C.S.: 813910
Jean-Pierre Farandou *(Chm & CEO)*

Subsidiaries:

Akiem (1)
Cap-West 15 Allees de l Europe, 92615, Clichy, France
Tel.: (33) 156 767430
Web Site: http://www.akiem.com
Locomotive Leasing Services
N.A.I.C.S.: 532411
Fabien Rochefort *(CEO)*

Compagnie de Transports de Cereales (1)
5 A Impasse Chalabre, 75829, Paris, France   **(100%)**
Tel.: (33) 1448587
Sales Range: $25-49.9 Million
Emp.: 21
Freight Transportation of Cereals
N.A.I.C.S.: 488510

Effia S.A. (1)
20 rue Le Peletier, 75009, Paris, France   **(100%)**
Tel.: (33) 806000115
Web Site: http://www.effia.com
Sales Range: $50-74.9 Million
Transport Solutions Consultant
N.A.I.C.S.: 487990

France Wagons S.A. (1)
Budapest 12 St, 75009, Paris, France   **(100%)**
Tel.: (33) 42812588
Sales Range: $25-49.9 Million
Emp.: 17
Freight Wagon Management
N.A.I.C.S.: 488510

Geodis SA (1)
26 Quai Charles Pasqua, 92300, Levallois-Perret, France
Tel.: (33) 156762600
Web Site: https://www.geodis.com
Sales Range: $1-4.9 Billion
Emp.: 23,800
Global Transportation
N.A.I.C.S.: 488510
Marie-Christine Lombard *(Chm-Mgmt Bd & CEO)*

Subsidiary (Non-US):

GW Freight Management Brazil (2)
Avenida Francisco Matarazzo 1350 5th floor, Sao Paulo, 05001-900, Brazil
Tel.: (55) 1126432000
Web Site: http://www.geodis.com
Sales Range: $25-49.9 Million
Emp.: 600
Freight Forwarding & Transportation Logistics Services
N.A.I.C.S.: 488510
Nicola Paparounis *(Mgr-Sls & Mktg)*

Subsidiary (Domestic):

Geodis Logistics SAS (2)
26 Quai Charles Pasqua, 92300, Levallois-Perret, France
Tel.: (33) 1 5676 2600
Web Site: http://www.geodis.com
Logistics, Warehousing & Transportation Linked to Logistics
N.A.I.C.S.: 485999

Subsidiary (Domestic):

Bourgey Montreuil (3)
ZA Du Rebauchet, PO Box 22, 73420, Mery-sur-Seine, France   **(99%)**
Tel.: (33) 479885400
Sales Range: $75-99.9 Million
Emp.: 400
Transportation
N.A.I.C.S.: 488510

Calberson SAS (3)
183 Ave De Clichy, 75017, Paris, France
Tel.: (33) 144851313
Sales Range: $1-4.9 Billion
Emp.: 11,000
Transportation Services Including Warehousing Management, Packaging, Order Preparation, Distribution, Computerized Tracking & Express Delivery
N.A.I.C.S.: 488510

Subsidiary (Domestic):

Bernis (4)
Euro Atlantic, Saint Yrieix, 16710, France   **(100%)**
Tel.: (33) 545691314
Web Site: http://www.bernis.net
Sales Range: $75-99.9 Million
Emp.: 80
Transportation
N.A.I.C.S.: 488510
Dominic Sellaudeau *(Gen Mgr)*

Bernis Transport (4)
Ave Ambroise Croizat, 24750, Boulazac, France   **(100%)**
Tel.: (33) 553355353
Sales Range: $75-99.9 Million
Emp.: 80
Transportation Services
N.A.I.C.S.: 488510

Calberson (4)
431 Rue De Clement Ader, PO Box 51, 42153, Riorges, France   **(100%)**
Tel.: (33) 477711984
Transportation
N.A.I.C.S.: 488510

Calberson (SNTR) Sud Ouest-Agen (4)
Zn Ind Jean Maleze Rue Denis Papin, 47240, Bon Encontre, France
Tel.: (33) 553960145
Sales Range: $50-74.9 Million
Emp.: 30
Transportation
N.A.I.C.S.: 488510

Calberson Mediterranee-Nice (4)
Gare Saint Roche Ave Denis Semeria, Nice, 06359, France   **(100%)**
Tel.: (33) 492004606
Web Site: http://www.zeodis.com
Sales Range: $50-74.9 Million
Emp.: 50
Transportation
N.A.I.C.S.: 488510

Calberson Montpellier (4)
Rue Du Traite De Rome, BP 248, ZAC Les Peyrieres, 34434, Saint-Jean-de-Vedas, France
Tel.: (33) 467071407
Sales Range: $50-74.9 Million
Emp.: 50
Transportation
N.A.I.C.S.: 488510

Calberson Normandie Agence Devreux (4)
Rue Jean Monnet ZAC Du Bois Des Communes, PO Box 1809, Evreux, 27018, France   **(100%)**
Tel.: (33) 232622162
Web Site: http://www.calberson.fr
Sales Range: $1-9.9 Million
Emp.: 100
Transportation
N.A.I.C.S.: 488510
Crevon Gulme *(Mng Dir)*

Calberson Rhone Alpes (4)
7 Rue Seinand Forest, 38120, Saint Egreve, France
Tel.: (33) 476560101
Sales Range: $75-99.9 Million
Emp.: 100
Transportation

N.A.I.C.S.: 488510
Eric Bardy *(Mng Dir)*

Calberson Roussillon (4)
ZI Lannoliea st 80, Carcassonne, 11000, France   **(100%)**
Tel.: (33) 468259044
Web Site: http://www.calbersonfranceexpress.com
Sales Range: $75-99.9 Million
Emp.: 13
Transportation
N.A.I.C.S.: 488510
Frederick Noreille *(Mgr)*

Calberson Sud Ouest-Toulouse (4)
80 Rte De Toulouse, 31150, Bruguieres, France   **(100%)**
Tel.: (33) 534276500
Web Site: http://www.geodis.com
Sales Range: $50-74.9 Million
Emp.: 50
Transportation
N.A.I.C.S.: 488510
Emmanuel Mercy *(Mng Dir)*

Dupont Bedu Transports (4)
14 Avenue Arsene d'Arsonval, 01000, Bourg-en-Bresse, France   **(100%)**
Tel.: (33) 4 74 45 57 00
Web Site: http://www.dupontbedu.fr
Sales Range: $75-99.9 Million
Emp.: 120
Logistics & Transportation Services
N.A.I.C.S.: 488510
Alain Derennes *(Chm)*

France Express 44-Nantes (4)
D2A Nantes Atlantique Rue Santos Dumont, PO Box 26, 44860, Saint-Aignan-Grandlieu, France
Tel.: (33) 892052828
Web Site: http://www.france-express.com
Sales Range: $250-299.9 Million
Emp.: 300
Transportation
N.A.I.C.S.: 488510

Geodis Bernis (4)
Zone Industrialle Allee Des Maisons Rouges, BP 385, Chateauroux, 36008, France   **(100%)**
Tel.: (33) 254081616
Web Site: http://www.bernis.net
Sales Range: $75-99.9 Million
Emp.: 60
Transportation & Freight Services
N.A.I.C.S.: 488510

Geodis Calberson (4)
Zn Ind Euro Val De Loire, PO Box 3, 41330, Fosse, France   **(100%)**
Tel.: (33) 254504463
Sales Range: $75-99.9 Million
Emp.: 60
Transportation
N.A.I.C.S.: 488510

Geodis Dusolier Calberson (4)
Zone Industrialle Des Souers Est, Rochefort, 17300, France
Tel.: (33) 546821200
Sales Range: $75-99.9 Million
Emp.: 100
Transportation
N.A.I.C.S.: 488510
Thierry Vie *(Mng Dir)*

SNT Noyon (4)
ZA De La Valle Barrey, BP 86, 14126, Mondeville, France   **(100%)**
Tel.: (33) 2 31 707070
Web Site: http://www.noyon.eu
Transportation & Logistics
N.A.I.C.S.: 488510

Societe Vellave de Transports (4)
7/9 Allees de l'Europe, 92615, Clichy, France
Tel.: (33) 1 56 76 2600
Web Site: http://www.geodis.com
Sales Range: $50-74.9 Million
Emp.: 30
Transportation & Logistics Services
N.A.I.C.S.: 488510

Ste. des Transports Rapides Bretons (4)
7 Rue De Niepce, Saint-Brieuc, 22000, France   **(100%)**

SNCF—(Continued)

Tel.: (33) 296622000
Web Site: http://www.morygroup.com
Sales Range: $75-99.9 Million
Emp.: 90
Transportation
N.A.I.C.S.: 488510

Transports Bernis (4)
ZI D Asnieres 29 Ave De La Prospective,
PO Box 1011, Bourges, 18000, France
Tel.: (33) 248688080
Web Site: http://www.bernis.net
Sales Range: $50-74.9 Million
Emp.: 50
Transportation
N.A.I.C.S.: 488510

Transports Dusolier (4)
310 Rue Morane Saulnier, 37210, Parcay-Meslay, France
Tel.: (33) 247405050
Web Site: http://www.geodis.com
Sales Range: $250-299.9 Million
Emp.: 200
Transportation
N.A.I.C.S.: 488510

Transports Lacassagne (4)
Parc d'Activites de Tronqueires, 15000, Aurillac, France (100%)
Tel.: (33) 329 022 008
Web Site: http://www.lacassagne33.com
Transportation & Delivery Services
N.A.I.C.S.: 488510
Jean Louis Lacassagne (Founder & Pres)

Transports Moulinois (4)
13 Rue Jacques Coeur, 03400, Yzuere, France (100%)
Tel.: (33) 470351150
Web Site: http://www.transportsmoulinois.fr
Sales Range: $75-99.9 Million
Emp.: 100
Transportation
N.A.I.C.S.: 488510

Transports Rapides Lozeriens (4)
Zone Artisanale 10, Marvejols, 48100, France (100%)
Tel.: (33) 466321147
Sales Range: $75-99.9 Million
Emp.: 15
Transportation
N.A.I.C.S.: 488510

Transquercy (4)
Parc D Activites Du Sycala, 46230, Fontanes, France (100%)
Tel.: (33) 565215050
Web Site: http://www.transquercy.fr
Sales Range: $50-74.9 Million
Emp.: 30
Transportation
N.A.I.C.S.: 488510

Subsidiary (Domestic):

Extand (3)
56 boulevard de l'Embouchure, 31085, Toulouse, Cedex, France
Tel.: (33) 562729494
Web Site: http://www.extand-relais.com
Domestic (French) Distribution-Express Distribution
N.A.I.C.S.: 488210

Subsidiary (US):

Geodis USA, Inc. (2)
7101 Executive Ctr Dr Ste 333, Brentwood, TN 37027
Tel.: (615) 401-6400
Web Site: http://www.geodis.us
Emp.: 10,141
Freight Transportation Arrangement Services
N.A.I.C.S.: 488510
Patrick Moebel (VP-Americas)

Subsidiary (Domestic):

Geodis Global Solutions USA, Inc. (3)
485 Woodbridge Plz Rte 1 S Bldg C Ste 410, Iselin, NJ 08830
Tel.: (732) 362-0600
Web Site: http://www.geodis.com
Trucking & Freight Forwarding Services
N.A.I.C.S.: 488510

Idalina Lopes (Coord-Payroll)

Geodis Logistics LLC (3)
7101 Executive Ctr Dr Ste 333, Brentwood, TN 37027-3283
Tel.: (615) 401-6400
Web Site: http://www.geodis.com
Supply Chain Management Services
N.A.I.C.S.: 493190
Fred Loeffel (Exec VP-Sls & Mktg)

Subsidiary (Non-US):

Geodis Wilson Belgium NV (2)
Bldg 765, Brussels, 1830, Belgium
Tel.: (32) 27535670
Web Site: http://www.geodiswilson.com
Rev.: $7,863,154
Emp.: 14
Freight Forwarding & Transportation Logistics Services
N.A.I.C.S.: 488510
Alain Beheldt (Mng Dir)

Geodis Wilson Canada Ltd (2)
3061 Orlando Dr, Mississauga, L4V 1R4, ON, Canada
Tel.: (905) 677-5266
Web Site: http://www.geodiswilson.com
Sales Range: $50-74.9 Million
Emp.: 25
Ground, Air & Water Freight Transportation
N.A.I.C.S.: 488510
Christopher Johnston (Mng Dir)

Geodis Wilson Chile SA (2)
Heuchuraba Calle Nueva N 1853, Santiago, 860-0094, Chile
Tel.: (56) 24277000
Web Site: http://www.geodiswilson.com
Freight Forwarding & Transportation Logistics Services
N.A.I.C.S.: 488510

Geodis Wilson Denmark A/S (2)
Oliefabriksvej 29 43, Kastrup, 2770, Denmark
Tel.: (45) 36998000
Web Site: http://www.geodiswilson.com
Sales Range: $10-24.9 Million
Emp.: 120
Freight Forwarding & Transportation Logistics Services
N.A.I.C.S.: 488510
Allan Geerg Nielsen (Mng Dir)

Geodis Wilson Finland Oy (2)
Juvan teollisuuskatu 25 Bldg 3, PO Box 41, FIN 02921, Espoo, Finland
Tel.: (358) 01084931
Web Site: http://www.geodiswilson.com
Sales Range: $50-74.9 Million
Emp.: 150
Freight Forwarding & Transportation Logistics Services
N.A.I.C.S.: 488510

Geodis Wilson Germany GmbH (2)
Flughafen Dus Air Cargo Ctr Rm 4621 24, 40474, Dusseldorf, Germany
Tel.: (49) 2114179950
Web Site: http://www.geodiswilson.com
Sales Range: $25-49.9 Million
Emp.: 15
Freight Forwarding & Transportation Logistics Services
N.A.I.C.S.: 488510
Rolf de Schrevel (Mng Dir)

Geodis Wilson Hong Kong Ltd (2)
Unit 1110 11th Floor Trayswer No 81, cheng sha wan rue 80, Kowloon, 42, China (Hong Kong)
Tel.: (852) 26213688
Web Site: http://www.geodiswilson.com
Sales Range: $25-49.9 Million
Emp.: 100
Logistic Services
N.A.I.C.S.: 561499
Simon Yam (Mng Dir)

Geodis Wilson Industrial Projects K.S.A. (2)
PO Box 3870, Al Khobar, 31952, Saudi Arabia
Tel.: (966) 38599000
Web Site: http://www.geodiswilson.com
Freight Transportation Services
N.A.I.C.S.: 488510

Geodis Wilson Korea Ltd. (2)
10th Floor Korea Association of Machinery Industry Bldg, 13-6 Yeouido-dong, Seoul, 150 729, Korea (South)
Tel.: (82) 237806200
Web Site: http://www.geodiswilson.com
Sales Range: $25-49.9 Million
Emp.: 70
Freight Forwarding & Transportation Logistics
N.A.I.C.S.: 488510
Ju Youn Kim (Mgr-HR)

Geodis Wilson Malaysia Sdn Bhd (2)
C 6 Aircargo Complex, Jalan Garuda Bayan Lepas, 11900, Penang, Malaysia
Tel.: (60) 46439348
Web Site: http://www.geodiswilson.com
Sales Range: $25-49.9 Million
Emp.: 24
Freight Forwarding & Transportation Logistics
N.A.I.C.S.: 488510
Sayhock Lim (Gen Mgr)

Geodis Wilson New Zealand Ltd. (2)
Manu Tapu Dr Percival Gull Pl, PO Box 73128, Auckland, 2022, New Zealand
Tel.: (64) 92550222
Web Site: http://www.geodiswilson.com
Sales Range: $25-49.9 Million
Emp.: 30
Freight Forwarding & Transportation Logistics
N.A.I.C.S.: 488510
Hujh Mackay (Mng Dir)

Geodis Wilson Norway AS (2)
Ulvenveien 90 B, PO Box 249, Okern, N 0510, Oslo, Norway
Tel.: (47) 23194800
Web Site: http://www.geodiswilson.com
Sales Range: $25-49.9 Million
Emp.: 45
Freight Forwarding & Transportation Logistics
N.A.I.C.S.: 488510

Geodis Wilson Singapore Ltd. (2)
7 Airline Rd Unit 07-11 Cargo Agents Bldg E, PO Box 531, Changi Airfreight, Singapore, 819834, Singapore
Tel.: (65) 65425454
Web Site: http://www.geodiswilson.com
Sales Range: $25-49.9 Million
Emp.: 90
Freight Forwarding & Transportation Logistics Services
N.A.I.C.S.: 488510

Geodis Wilson Sweden AB (2)
Masthuggstorget 3A, PO Box 7091, SE-402 32, Gothenburg, Sweden
Tel.: (46) 31429600
Web Site: http://www.geodiswilson.com
Sales Range: $125-149.9 Million
Emp.: 340
Transportation Logistics & Freight Forwarding Services
N.A.I.C.S.: 488510
Arne Hanson (Dir-Ops)

Geodis Wilson Taiwan Ltd. (2)
8F No 778 Sec 4 Bade Rd, Taipei, 11577, Taiwan
Tel.: (886) 226549138
Web Site: http://www.geodiswilson.com
Emp.: 50
Freight Forwarding & Transportation Logistics
N.A.I.C.S.: 488510
Philip Ger (Mng Dir)

Geodis Wilson Thailand Ltd. (2)
207 Soi Saeng Uthai Sukhumvit 50 Rd, Prakanong Klongtoey, Bangkok, 10260, Thailand
Tel.: (66) 2 741 4080
Web Site: http://www.geodiswilson.com
Freight Forwarding & Transportation Logistics
N.A.I.C.S.: 488510

Geodis Wilson UK Ltd. (2)
Cranford Ln Units 5 & 6, Parkway Trading Estate, Hounslow, TW5 9QA, Mddx, United Kingdom
Tel.: (44) 2088147000
Web Site: http://www.geodiswilson.com
Sales Range: $50-74.9 Million
Emp.: 130

Freight Forwarding & Transportation Logistics
N.A.I.C.S.: 488510

PEKAES Sp. z o.o. (2)
ul Spedycyjna 1, 05-870, Blonie, Poland (100%)
Tel.: (48) 224602626
Web Site: http://www.pekaes.pl
Transport & Provisional Services
N.A.I.C.S.: 541614
Maciej Bachman (CEO)

Grandes Lignes International (1)
Tour Mattei, 207 rue de Bercy, F - 75012, Paris, France
International Sales Development
N.A.I.C.S.: 482111

Subsidiary (Domestic):

EFFIA (2)
20 Blvd Poniatowski, 75012, Paris, France (100%)
Tel.: (33) 144754800
Web Site: http://www.sceta-parc.com
Automobile Parking Services
N.A.I.C.S.: 812930

Subsidiary (Non-US):

Rail Europe Espana (2)
Placa Espana 18, Torre De Madrid Planta 14, 28008, Madrid, Spain (100%)
Tel.: (34) 915478442
Web Site: http://www.raileurope.es
Sales Range: $25-49.9 Million
Emp.: 15
Railroad
N.A.I.C.S.: 482111

Keolis S.A. (1)
20 rue Le Peletier, 75320, Paris, Cedex 9, France (70%)
Tel.: (33) 171329000
Web Site: http://www.keolis.com
Rev.: $5,445,190,548
Assets: $4,430,863,080
Liabilities: $3,401,579,577
Net Worth: $1,029,283,503
Earnings: $48,138,300
Emp.: 55,472
Fiscal Year-end: 12/31/2016
Passenger Transportation System Operator
N.A.I.C.S.: 485112
Frederic Baverez (CEO-France)

Subsidiary (US):

Keolis Transit America, Inc. (2)
6053 W Century Blvd 9th Fl, Los Angeles, CA 90045
Tel.: (310) 981-9500
Web Site: http://www.tectrans.com
Sales Range: $75-99.9 Million
Emp.: 1,300
Transportation Management & Contracting Services
N.A.I.C.S.: 488999
Ryan Adams (Sr VP-Strategic Dev)

Logistra S.A. (1)
49 Rue De Ponthieu, 75008, Paris, France (100%)
Tel.: (33) 156696100
Web Site: http://www.logistra.fr
Sales Range: $25-49.9 Million
Emp.: 22
Freight Forwarding Services
N.A.I.C.S.: 488510

Naviland Cargo (1)
8 Ave des Minimes, 94302, Vincennes, France (100%)
Tel.: (33) 143984000
Web Site: http://www.naviland-cargo.com
Sales Range: $100-124.9 Million
Emp.: 300
Intermodal Freight Transportation
N.A.I.C.S.: 488510

Rail Europe Inc. (1)
44 S Broadway Fl 11, White Plains, NY 10601-4411
Tel.: (914) 682-2999
Web Site: http://www.raileurope.com
Rev.: $300,000,000
Emp.: 120
Distr of Travel Products Including Train Passes & Transatlantic Air, Hotel & Car Rental in Europe

AND PRIVATE COMPANIES

N.A.I.C.S.: 561510
Duncan Still *(Chief Comml Officer)*

SYSTRA (1)
72 rue Henry Farman, 75015, Paris, France
Tel.: (33) 140166100
Web Site: http://www.systra.com
Sales Range: $500-549.9 Million
Emp.: 3,400
Transport Infrastructure Consulting Services
N.A.I.C.S.: 541614
Philippe Naudi *(Exec VP-Bus Dev)*

SeaFrance S.A. (1)
1 Ave De Flandre, 75019, Paris, France
Tel.: (33) 153351100
Web Site: http://www.seafrance.com
Sales Range: $200-249.9 Million
Emp.: 1,000
Passenger & Freight Ferry Operator
N.A.I.C.S.: 483114

Societe Francaise de Construction Immobilere (1)
70 rue de L'Aqueduc, 75010, Paris, France
Tel.: (33) 155261600
Real Estate Management
N.A.I.C.S.: 531210

Societe de Transports de Vehicules Automobiles (1)
26 Quai Michelet, 92300, Levallois-Perret, France **(100%)**
Tel.: (33) 144855678
Web Site: http://www.stva.com
Rail Freight Transportation of Vehicles
N.A.I.C.S.: 488210
Jean-Michel Floret *(Chm-Exec Bd)*

VFLI (1)
6 Rue D Amsterdam, Paris, 75009, France **(100%)**
Tel.: (33) 155078100
Web Site: http://www.vfli.fr
Rail Freight Transportation
N.A.I.C.S.: 488210
Alain Ribat *(CEO)*

SNDL INC.
300 919 - 11 Avenue SW, Calgary, T2R 1P3, AB, Canada
Tel.: (403) 948-5227 **AB**
Web Site: https://sndl.com
Year Founded: 2006
SNDL—(NASDAQ)
Rev.: $570,825,022
Assets: $1,219,848,318
Liabilities: $181,250,365
Net Worth: $1,038,597,953
Earnings: ($291,342,976)
Emp.: 1,346
Fiscal Year-end: 12/31/22
Drug Mfr
N.A.I.C.S.: 325412
James Keough *(CFO)*

Subsidiaries:

Alcanna Inc. (1)
101 17220 Stony Plain Road, Edmonton, T5S1K6, AB, Canada
Tel.: (780) 944-9994
Web Site: http://www.alcanna.com
Rev.: $532,178,043
Assets: $381,217,560
Liabilities: $279,744,110
Net Worth: $101,473,450
Earnings: $53,305,341
Emp.: 1,767
Fiscal Year-end: 12/31/2020
Liquor Store Operator
N.A.I.C.S.: 445320
John Barnett *(Chm)*

Subsidiary (US):

Birchfield Ventures, LLC (2)
3375 US Hwy 1 S, Lawrenceville, NJ 08648 **(51%)**
Tel.: (609) 520-0008
Web Site: http://www.joecanals.com
Sales Range: $25-49.9 Million
Beer, Wine & Liquor Stores Operator
N.A.I.C.S.: 445320

Subsidiary (Non-US):

Liquor Stores GP, Inc. (2)

Tel.: (780) 944-9994
Web Site: http://www.liquorstoresgp.ca
Emp.: 120
Liquor Store Operator
N.A.I.C.S.: 445320

Subsidiary (Non-US):

Liquor Barn Inc. (3)
Tel.: (502) 426-4222
Web Site: http://www.liquorbarn.com
Sales Range: $10-24.9 Million
Alcohol Retail Stores Operator
N.A.I.C.S.: 445320

INDIVA Limited (1)
333 Preston Street Suite 710, Ottawa, K1S 5N4, ON, Canada
Tel.: (613) 883-8541
Web Site: https://www.indiva.com
Sales Range: Less than $1 Million
Investment Services
N.A.I.C.S.: 523999
Niel Marotta *(Founder, Pres & CEO)*

Inner Spirit Holdings Ltd. (1)
102 5740 2nd Street SW, Calgary, T2H 1Y6, AB, Canada
Tel.: (403) 930-9300
Web Site: http://www.innerspiritholdings.com
Rev.: $6,209,362
Assets: $17,408,987
Liabilities: $16,092,381
Net Worth: $1,316,605
Earnings: ($8,819,520)
Fiscal Year-end: 12/31/2019
Cannabis Medicine Mfr
N.A.I.C.S.: 325411
Darren Bondar *(Founder & CEO)*

Zenabis Global Inc. (1)
Suite 3100 666 Burrard Street, Vancouver, V6C 2X8, BC, Canada
Web Site: http://www.zenabis.com
Rev.: $55,480,047
Assets: $230,410,332
Liabilities: $164,887,094
Net Worth: $65,523,238
Earnings: ($97,223,584)
Emp.: 740
Fiscal Year-end: 12/31/2019
Holding Company
N.A.I.C.S.: 551112
Olen Vanderleeden *(Sr VP)*

Subsidiary (Domestic):

Bevo Farms Ltd (2)
22350 - Hwy 10, PO Box 73, STN Milner, Langley, V2Y 2R1, BC, Canada
Tel.: (604) 888-0420
Web Site: https://www.bevofarms.com
Sales Range: $25-49.9 Million
Emp.: 60
Farming Services
N.A.I.C.S.: 111998
John Hoekstra *(CFO & Exec VP)*

SNEF SA
87 Avenue des Aygalades, 13015, Marseille, France
Tel.: (33) 491615800
Web Site: https://www.snef.fr
Year Founded: 1905
Emp.: 12,000
Industrial Machinery Mfr
N.A.I.C.S.: 333248

SNELLING PAPER LIMITED
1410 Triole St, Ottawa, K1B 3M5, ON, Canada
Tel.: (613) 745-7184
Web Site:
http://www.snellingpaper.com
Year Founded: 1922
Rev.: $10,346,449
Emp.: 40
Food Service & Industrial Packaging Distr
N.A.I.C.S.: 424130
Randy Graham *(Pres & CEO)*

SNET SYSTEMS INC.
10F Sungwon Bldg 514 Seolleung-ro, Gangnam-gu, Seoul, 06162, Korea (South)

Tel.: (82) 234692939
Web Site:
https://www.snetsystems.com
Year Founded: 1999
038680—(KRS)
Rev.: $298,741,840
Assets: $207,838,918
Liabilities: $150,580,259
Net Worth: $57,258,658
Earnings: ($2,694,783)
Emp.: 244
Fiscal Year-end: 12/31/22
Information Technology Consultancy Services
N.A.I.C.S.: 519290
Park Hyo-Dae *(Chm)*

Subsidiaries:

Goodus, Inc. (1)
14 15th Floor Seongwon Building 514 Seolleung-Ro, Gangnam-gu, Seoul, Korea (South)
Tel.: (82) 7070174100
Web Site: https://www.goodus.com
Information Technology Services
N.A.I.C.S.: 541512

PT. S net Indonesia (1)
Menara Batavia 12th Floor Jl KH Mas Mansyur Kav 126, Jakarta, 10220, Indonesia
Tel.: (62) 2157939022
Web Site: https://www.s-net.co.id
Information Technology Consulting Services
N.A.I.C.S.: 541512
Sangwon Jang *(Chm)*

SNF SAS
ZAC de Milieux Rue Adrienne Bolland, 42163, Andrezieux-Boutheon, France
Tel.: (33) 477368600 **FR**
Web Site: http://www.snf-group.com
Year Founded: 1978
Sales Range: $700-749.9 Million
Emp.: 25
Water Soluble Polymer Mfr
N.A.I.C.S.: 325998
Rene Pich *(Pres)*

Subsidiaries:

BEIJING ZHIJIE FLOCCULANT (1)
Room 1209 Floor12 Baoneng Center Office Bldg Fu Tong Dongdaji, Wangjing Chaoyang District, Beijing, 100102, China
Tel.: (86) 10 84 53 62 01 5
Industrial Chemical & Polymer Whslr
N.A.I.C.S.: 424690

Biomontan GmbH (1)
Regensburger Strasse 5, 4470, Enns, Austria
Tel.: (43) 7223861310
Web Site: http://www.biomontan.com
Industrial Chemical & Polymer Distr
N.A.I.C.S.: 424690

FLOERGER NEDERLAND BV (1)
PO Box 54, 1250 AB, Laren, Netherlands
Tel.: (31) 35 531 1205
Industrial Chemical & Polymer Whslr
N.A.I.C.S.: 424690

Flonex AG (1)
Netzenstrasse 4, CH-4450, Sissach, Switzerland
Tel.: (41) 619758000
Web Site: http://www.flonex.ch
Sales Range: $25-49.9 Million
Emp.: 5
Water Treatment Chemicals
N.A.I.C.S.: 325998
Etienne Bolley *(Mng Dir)*

KF-SNF Co. Ltd. (1)
4th Floor nr 41 section 2 Roosevelt road, Taipei, Taiwan
Tel.: (886) 223 943 656
Industrial Chemical & Polymer Whslr
N.A.I.C.S.: 424690

KORONA JV SP ZOO (1)
Ul Przy Bazantarni 11, 02-793, Warsaw, Poland
Tel.: (48) 226 497 150
Web Site: http://www.koronajv.pl

SNF SAS

Industrial Chemical & Polymer Whslr
N.A.I.C.S.: 424690

OCI-SNF Co. Ltd. (1)
9th Floor OCI Building 94 Sogong-ro, Jung-gu, Seoul, 04532, Korea (South) **(100%)**
Tel.: (82) 2 3455 6100
Web Site: http://www.snfkorea.kr
Emp.: 30
Industrial Chemical & Polymer Whslr
N.A.I.C.S.: 424690
Han Young Bae *(Mgr)*

POLYCHEMIE GmbH (1)
Buhler Str 113 b, 66130, Saarbrucken, Germany
Tel.: (49) 681 588 226 0
Web Site: http://www.poly-chemie.de
Industrial Chemical & Polymer Distr
N.A.I.C.S.: 424690

PPC LLC (1)
PO Box 1296, Al Athaibah, 130, Muscat, Oman
Tel.: (968) 24595071
Industrial Chemical & Polymer Whslr
N.A.I.C.S.: 424690

PT SNF Florindo (1)
Karawaci Office Park B-37, Lippo Karawaci, Tangerang, 15811, Indonesia
Tel.: (62) 2155776221
Sales Range: $25-49.9 Million
Emp.: 30
Water Treatment Chemicals
N.A.I.C.S.: 325998
David Chand *(Gen Mgr)*

SNF (Australia) Pty Ltd. (1)
298 Broderick Rd, Lara, 3212, VIC, Australia
Tel.: (61) 352759200
Web Site: http://www.snf.com.au
Sales Range: $25-49.9 Million
Emp.: 50
Water Treatment Chemicals
N.A.I.C.S.: 325998

SNF (China) Flocculant Co. Ltd. (1)
Taixing Economic Development Zone West of Tongjiang Road, Taixing, 225442, Jiangsu, China
Tel.: (86) 5237676300
Web Site: http://www.snf-group.com
Sales Range: $50-74.9 Million
Emp.: 200
Water Treatment Chemicals
N.A.I.C.S.: 325998

SNF (INDIA) Pvt. Ltd. (1)
Plot No19 Jawahrlal Nehru Pharma City, Parawada, Visakhapatnam, 531019, Andhra Pradesh, India
Tel.: (91) 891 3058888
Web Site: http://www.snf-india.com
Polymer Compound Mfr & Distr
N.A.I.C.S.: 325998
M. Venkata Jagannath *(Deputy Gen Mgr-Customer Svc)*

SNF (UK) Ltd. (1)
Solutions House Ripley Close Normanton Industrial Estate, West Yorkshire, Normanton, WF6 1TB, United Kingdom
Tel.: (44) 1924311000
Web Site: http://www.snf.co.uk
Sales Range: $25-49.9 Million
Emp.: 15
Water Treatment Chemicals
N.A.I.C.S.: 325998
Ken Lowther *(Sec)*

SNF ARGENTINA srl (1)
La Pampa 1517 Piso 9 Oficina B, C1428DZE, Buenos Aires, Argentina
Tel.: (54) 11 4784 2849
Industrial Chemical & Polymer Whslr
N.A.I.C.S.: 424690

SNF Ambientagua (1)
Rua do Convento 144 a 160 A Zona Industrial de Fontiscos, 4780-427, Santo Tirso, Portugal
Tel.: (351) 252852713
Web Site: http://www.snf-group.com
Sales Range: $25-49.9 Million
Emp.: 12
Water Treatment Chemical Mfr
N.A.I.C.S.: 325998

SNF Canada Ltd. (1)

SNF SAS

SNF SAS—(Continued)
4 Director Court Suite 101, Vaughan, L4L 3Z5, ON, Canada
Tel.: (819) 378-1331
Web Site: http://www.snf-canada.com
Sales Range: $25-49.9 Million
Emp.: 12
Water Treatment Chemicals
N.A.I.C.S.: 325998
Line Jolin *(Gen Mgr)*

SNF Chile S.A (1)
Calle Nueva 1661-d Condominio el Parronal, Huechuraba, Santiago, Chile
Tel.: (56) 2 726 9800
Industrial Chemical & Polymer Whslr
N.A.I.C.S.: 424690

SNF FINLAND OY (1)
Mannerheimintie 40 A 36, 00100, Helsinki, Finland
Tel.: (358) 9 436 5 33 70
Web Site: http://www.snf-finland.fi
Industrial Chemical & Polymer Whslr
N.A.I.C.S.: 424690

SNF FLOERGER DE MEXICO sa de cv (1)
Av. de los Insurgentes Sur 863 Piso 14-01, Ciudad Juarez, 03810, Mexico
Tel.: (52) 5590000882
Web Site: http://www.snfmex.mx
Industrial Chemical & Polymer Whslr
N.A.I.C.S.: 424690
Julio Rubio Padilla *(Dir-Gen)*

SNF FLOERGER IBERICA slu (1)
C/ Andorra 54, Sant Boi del Llobregat, 08830, Barcelona, Spain
Tel.: (34) 93 480 14 51
Web Site: http://www.snfiberica.es
Industrial Chemical & Polymer Whslr
N.A.I.C.S.: 424690

SNF FLOERGER TURKEY (1)
Ikiteli OSB Aykosan Sitesi 2 Kisim 5 Ada C Blok, 34490, Istanbul, Turkiye
Tel.: (90) 212 549 9640
Web Site: http://www.snfturk.com
Emp.: 8
Industrial Chemical & Polymer Whslr
N.A.I.C.S.: 424690
Haluk Ajinci *(Gen Mgr)*

SNF Floerger Philippines Inc (1)
Unit 1608 Richville Corporate Tower 1107 Alabang-Zapote road, Alabang, Muntinlupa, 1780, Philippines
Tel.: (63) 2 772 58 51
Web Site: http://www.snf.com.ph
Industrial Chemical & Polymer Whslr
N.A.I.C.S.: 424690

SNF Hongrie Kft. (1)
3336 4 HRSZ, 2045, Torokbalint, Hungary
Tel.: (36) 34512460
Web Site: http://www.snf-group.com
Water Treatment Chemicals
N.A.I.C.S.: 325998

SNF Italia S.p.A. (1)
Via Vittorio Emanuele Orlando 32, 20814, Varedo, MB, Italy
Tel.: (39) 036236151
Web Site: http://www.snfitalia.it
Sales Range: $25-49.9 Million
Emp.: 16
Water Treatment Chemicals
N.A.I.C.S.: 325998

SNF JAPAN Co. Ltd. (1)
Nihonbashi Nikko Building 4F 2-10-8 Nihonbashi, Chuo-Ku, Tokyo, 103-0027, Japan
Tel.: (81) 335 161 611
Web Site: http://www.snf-jp.com
Industrial Chemical & Polymer Whslr
N.A.I.C.S.: 424690

SNF RSA Pty. Ltd. (1)
2 Rich Fond Circle Ridge Side Office Park, Umhlanga, 4619, South Africa
Tel.: (27) 31 536 8119
Industrial Chemical & Polymer Whslr
N.A.I.C.S.: 424690
Rob Daly *(Gen Mgr)*

SNF VOSTOK (1)
Most Tatar st 42, 115184, Moscow, Russia
Tel.: 7 (4956475010
Web Site: http://www.snf-group.ru

Industrial Chemical & Polymer Whslr
N.A.I.C.S.: 424690

SNF do Brasil Ltda. (1)
Estrada Bonsucesso Itaquaquecetuba 80, V Maria de Lourdes, Guarulhos, 07251-280, Sao Paulo, Brazil
Tel.: (55) 1123034290
Web Site: http://www.snf-group.com
Sales Range: $25-49.9 Million
Emp.: 15
Water Treatment Chemicals
N.A.I.C.S.: 325998

SOKOFLOK s.r.o. (1)
Tovarni 1362, PO Box 36, 356 05, Sokolov, Czech Republic
Tel.: (420) 35 235 0712
Web Site: http://www.sokoflok.cz
Industrial Chemical & Polymer Whslr
N.A.I.C.S.: 424690

Sokoflok Slovakia s.r.o. (1)
Bardejovska 10, 8006, Presov, Slovakia
Tel.: (421) 517765057
Web Site: http://www.sokoflok.sk
Sales Range: $25-49.9 Million
Emp.: 8
Water Treatment Chemical Mfr
N.A.I.C.S.: 325998

SNIACE S.A.
Avda de Burgos 12 4 Planta 28036, 28036, Madrid, Spain
Tel.: (34) 91 768 40 70
Web Site: http://www.sniace.com
Year Founded: 1939
Emp.: 500
Chemical Products Mfr & Whslr
N.A.I.C.S.: 325180

SNIPER RESOURCES LTD.
3374 West 19th Avenue, Vancouver, V6S 1C2, BC, Canada
Tel.: (604) 263-5614 BC
Web Site: http://www.sniperresources.com
Year Founded: 2006
Gold Mining Services
N.A.I.C.S.: 212220
Michael Lerner *(CEO & CFO)*

SNIPP INTERACTIVE INC.
Suite 1700 666 Burrard Street, Vancouver, V6C 2X8, BC, Canada
Tel.: (888) 997-6477 BC
Web Site: https://www.snipp.com
Year Founded: 2010
SNIPF—(OTCIQ)
Rev.: $15,276,212
Assets: $7,452,945
Liabilities: $3,890,387
Net Worth: $3,562,558
Earnings: $2,132,886
Emp.: 80
Fiscal Year-end: 12/31/21
Loyalty & Promotions Technology Company; Marketing Engagement Platforms Developer
N.A.I.C.S.: 541613
Jaisun Garcha *(CFO)*

Subsidiaries:

HIP Digital Media, Inc. (1)
883 Santa Cruz Ave, Menlo Park, CA 94025
Tel.: (650) 353-3585
Web Site: http://www.hipdigitalmedia.com
Promotional Marketing Technolog Services
N.A.I.C.S.: 512110
Baris Karadogan *(CEO)*

SNORRASON HOLDINGS EHF
Postholf 76, 620, Dalvik, Iceland
Tel.: (354) 4661940
Web Site: http://www.snorrason.com
Private Equity
N.A.I.C.S.: 523999
Bjorn Snorrason *(CEO)*

Subsidiaries:

CCNow, Inc. (1)
333 Washington Ave N Ste 300, Minnetonka, MN 55401
Tel.: (952) 646-5139
Web Site: http://www.ccnow.com
Online Retail & Electronic Payment Processing Services
N.A.I.C.S.: 425120

Subsidiary (Domestic):

Academic Superstore, LP (2)
2101 E Saint Elmo Rd Ste 360, Austin, TX 78744
Tel.: (512) 450-1199
Web Site: http://www.academicsuperstore.com
Educational Software Retailer
N.A.I.C.S.: 423430

Journey Publishing, Inc (2)
13755 Hutton Dr Ste 500, Dallas, TX 75234
Tel.: (972) 245-7511
Web Site: http://www.journeyed.com
Educational Software Distr
N.A.I.C.S.: 423430

Subsidiary (Non-US):

JourneyEd Canada Corp. (2)
6975 Meadowvale Town Centre Circle Unit 9, Mississauga, L5N 2R2, ON, Canada
Tel.: (972) 481-2000
Web Site: http://www.journeyed.ca
Educational Software Distr
N.A.I.C.S.: 513210

SNOW CITY CYCLE MARINE
1255 Kennedy Road, Toronto, M1P 2L4, ON, Canada
Tel.: (416) 752-1560
Web Site: http://www.snowcity.com
Year Founded: 1971
Rev: $10,344,100
Emp.: 17
Powersports Dealers
N.A.I.C.S.: 441227

SNOWBIRD AG
Ferdinandstrasse 25, 20095, Hamburg, Germany
Tel.: (49) 4022821580
Web Site: http://www.snowbird-ag.com
8S9—(DEU)
Sales Range: $200-249.9 Million
Emp.: 2,172
Textile Mfr
N.A.I.C.S.: 314999
Douxiang Qiu *(COO & Member-Mgmt Bd)*

SNOWFIT GROUP BERHAD
Lot 33842-A Jalan Balakong, 43300, Balakong, Selangor, Malaysia
Tel.: (60) 194336570
Web Site: https://www.snowfit.my
Year Founded: 2016
SNOWFIT—(KLS)
Rev.: $6,120,331
Assets: $4,533,026
Liabilities: $3,773,867
Net Worth: $759,159
Earnings: ($94,981)
Fiscal Year-end: 05/31/24
Fitness Equipment Distr
N.A.I.C.S.: 423910
Louis Low *(CEO & Founder)*

SNOWHOUSE SOLUTIONS INC.
66 Montee du Bois-Franc, Lac-Beauport, G3B 1Y5, QC, Canada
Web Site: http://www.snowhouse.ca
Camera Mfr
N.A.I.C.S.: 333310

SNOWLINE GOLD CORP.
1012 - 1030 West Georgia Street, Vancouver, V6E 2Y3, BC, Canada
Tel.: (778) 650-5485
Web Site: https://snowlinegold.com

SNWGF—(OTCQB)
Rev: $5,470,261
Assets: $37,230,449
Liabilities: $7,218,250
Net Worth: $30,012,198
Earnings: ($18,081,947)
Emp.: 14
Fiscal Year-end: 12/31/23
Investment Services
N.A.I.C.S.: 523999
Thomas Branson *(VP)*

SNOWSKY SALT INDUSTRY GROUP CO., LTD.
No 388 Times Sunshine Avenue West, Yuhua District, Changsha, 410004, Hunan, China
Tel.: (86) 73185661172
Web Site: https://www.snowskysalt.com.cn
Year Founded: 2011
600929—(SHG)
Rev.: $904,278,969
Assets: $1,312,153,198
Liabilities: $383,958,156
Net Worth: $928,195,042
Earnings: $107,993,335
Fiscal Year-end: 12/31/22
Chemical Products Mfr
N.A.I.C.S.: 325199
Ma Tianyi *(Chm)*

SNOWY HYDRO LIMITED
Monaro Highway, Cooma, 2630, NSW, Australia
Tel.: (61) 264532888 AU
Web Site: http://www.snowyhydro.com.au
Year Founded: 2001
Rev.: $2,028,493,510
Assets: $2,724,378,394
Liabilities: $1,120,237,297
Net Worth: $1,604,141,097
Earnings: $164,058,998
Emp.: 650
Fiscal Year-end: 06/30/18
Holding Company; Electricity Financial Hedge & Insurance Products; Electricity Generation & Distribution
N.A.I.C.S.: 551112
Paul Anthony Broad *(CEO & Mng Dir)*

Subsidiaries:

Direct Connect Australia Pty. Ltd. (1)
15 Shierlaw Avenue, Canterbury, 3126, VIC, Australia
Tel.: (61) 1300739751
Web Site: http://www.directconnect.com.au
Moving Services
N.A.I.C.S.: 484210

Latrobe Valley BV
Rokin 55, 1012 KK, Amsterdam, Netherlands
Tel.: (31) 20 305 3112
Electricity Generation & Distr
N.A.I.C.S.: 221111

Red Energy Pty. Limited (1)
2 William St, PO Box 4136, Richmond, 3121, VIC, Australia **(100%)**
Tel.: (61) 131 806
Web Site: http://www.redenergy.com.au
Electricity Distr
N.A.I.C.S.: 221122

Snowy Hydro Trading Pty. Ltd. (1)
Level 37 AMP Centre 50 Bridge Street, Sydney, 2000, NSW, Australia **(100%)**
Tel.: (61) 2 9278 1888
Electricity Derivative Trading Services
N.A.I.C.S.: 523160
Roger Whitby *(Mng Dir)*

SNP SCHNEIDER-NEUREITHER & PARTNER AG
Dossenheimer Landstrasse 100, 69121, Heidelberg, Germany
Tel.: (49) 622164250
Web Site: http://www.snpgroup.com

Year Founded: 1994
Rev.: $36,615,824
Emp.: 1,350
Software Development & Consulting Services
N.A.I.C.S.: 513210
Andreas Schneider-Neureither *(CEO & Member-Mgmt Bd)*

Subsidiaries:

SNP (Schweiz) AG (1)
Baarerstrasse 14, Zug, Switzerland
Tel.: (41) 415613250
Software Development & Consulting Services
N.A.I.C.S.: 541511
Andreas Schneider Neureither *(Mng Dir)*

SNP AUSTRIA GmbH (1)
Lassallestrasse 7b, Vienna, Austria
Tel.: (43) 7327711110
Software Development & Consulting Services
N.A.I.C.S.: 541511

SNP America, Inc. (1)
1400 Shepard Dr Ste 200, Sterling, VA 20164
Tel.: (703) 883-9340
Software Development & Consulting Services
N.A.I.C.S.: 541511

SNP Applications GmbH (1)
Speyerer Str 4, Heidelberg, Germany
Tel.: (49) 622164250
Software Development & Consulting Services
N.A.I.C.S.: 541511

SNP Consulting GmbH (1)
Wolfsburgstrasse 31, 06502, Thale, Germany
Tel.: (49) 39476100
Software Development & Consulting Services
N.A.I.C.S.: 541511
Andreas Schneider Neureither *(Mng Dir)*

SNP GL Associates (1)
Harborside Financial Ctr Plz 3 Ste 1000, Jersey City, NJ 07311
Tel.: (201) 451-9121
Emp.: 35
Software Consulting Services
N.A.I.C.S.: 541690
Roger Elwell *(Partner-Mgmt & VP-Sls)*

SNP Schneider-Neureither & Partner ZA (Pty) Limited (1)
Suite 7 Palazzo Towers West Montecasino William Nicol Drive, Fourways, South Africa
Tel.: (27) 115100510
Software Development & Consulting Services
N.A.I.C.S.: 541511

SNS BANK N.V.
Croeselaan 1, 3521 BJ, Utrecht, Netherlands
Tel.: (31) 302997481 NI
Web Site: http://www.snsbank.nl
Year Founded: 1817
Sales Range: $1-4.9 Billion
Emp.: 3,000
Commercial Banking Services
N.A.I.C.S.: 522110
M. W. J. Hinssen *(Chm-Mgmt Bd)*

Subsidiaries:

Algemene Spaarbank voor Nederland ASN N.V. (1)
Dezuydenhoutse rd weg 53, 2514 JM, Hague, Netherlands (100%)
Tel.: (31) 8000380
Web Site: http://www.asnbank.nl
Emp.: 160
Banking Services
N.A.I.C.S.: 522110

BLG Hypotheekbank N.V. (1)
Jos Klijnenlaan 288, 6164 AZ, Geleen, Netherlands
Tel.: (31) 800 24 24 24
Web Site: http://www.blg.nl
Mortgage Solutions

N.A.I.C.S.: 522310

SNS Assuradeuren B.V. (1)
Markt 17-18, 6211CJ, Maastricht, Netherlands
Tel.: (31) 433503855
Web Site: http://www.vacaturekrant.nl
Insurance Agencies & Brokerages
N.A.I.C.S.: 524210

SNS Assurantien B.V. (1)
Markt 17-18, 6211CJ, Maastricht, Netherlands
Tel.: (31) 433517777
Real Estate Property Lessors
N.A.I.C.S.: 531190

SNS Property Finance (1)
Westerdorpsstraat 66, 3871 AZ, Hoevelaken, Netherlands
Tel.: (31) 334644000
Web Site: http://www.snspropertyfinance.com
Sales Range: $75-99.9 Million
Emp.: 200
Property & Investment Financing Services
N.A.I.C.S.: 523999

SNS Regio Bank N.V. (1)
Croeselaan 1, 3521 BJ, Utrecht, Netherlands (100%)
Tel.: (31) 900 202 8888
Web Site: http://www.snsregiobank.nl
Commercial Banking, Financial Advisory & Intermediation Services
N.A.I.C.S.: 522110

SNS NETWORK TECHNOLOGY BERHAD
No 61 Jalan Sultan Nazrin Shah, 30250, Ipoh, Perak, Malaysia
Tel.: (60) 52424616
Web Site: https://www.sns.com.my
Year Founded: 1998
SNS—(KLS)
Rev.: $277,778,608
Assets: $116,846,736
Liabilities: $63,809,674
Net Worth: $53,037,062
Earnings: $6,957,452
Emp.: 340
Fiscal Year-end: 01/31/24
Software Development Services
N.A.I.C.S.: 541511
Yun Hung Ko *(Mng Dir)*

SNT CORPORATION
1-13-1 Kaizuka, Kawasaki-ku, Kawasaki, 210-0014, Kanagawa, Japan
Tel.: (81) 442007821
Web Site: https://www.snt.co.jp
Year Founded: 1948
6319—(TKS)
Rev.: $142,690,070
Assets: $256,937,310
Liabilities: $79,154,750
Net Worth: $177,782,560
Earnings: $6,365,430
Fiscal Year-end: 03/31/24
Forging Product Mfr
N.A.I.C.S.: 332111
Yasuyuki Hirayama *(Pres)*

Subsidiaries:

NKK Co., Ltd. (1)
Kamiyamakawa 4020-1, Yuki, 304-0006, Ibaraki, Japan
Tel.: (81) 296325137
Scaffolding Part Mfr
N.A.I.C.S.: 332323

Tsukuba Koki Co., Ltd. (1)
3333-3 Kamitezuna, Takahagi, 318-0004, Ibaraki, Japan
Tel.: (81) 293243481
Forging Product Mfr
N.A.I.C.S.: 333517

SNT HOLDINGS CO., LTD.
24 Teheran-ro, Gangnam-gu, Seoul, 153803, Korea (South)
Tel.: (82) 232795010

Web Site: https://www.hisntholdings.com
Year Founded: 1982
036530—(KRS)
Rev.: $1,249,842,549
Assets: $1,962,313,499
Liabilities: $569,214,765
Net Worth: $1,393,098,734
Earnings: $39,433,075
Emp.: 10
Fiscal Year-end: 12/31/22
Heat Machinery Industries
N.A.I.C.S.: 541330
Do Whan Kim *(Chm, Pres & CEO)*

Subsidiaries:

S&T Corporation (1)
12 Wanam-ro, Seongsan-gu, Changwon, Gyeongsangnam-do, Korea (South) (55.6%)
Tel.: (82) 552126500
Sales Range: $50-74.9 Million
Emp.: 252
Heat Exchanger Mfr
N.A.I.C.S.: 332410
Won Hwe Chung *(CEO)*

S&T Gulf Co., Ltd. (1)
PO Box 41033, Dammam, 31521, Saudi Arabia
Web Site: http://www.sntgulf.com
Emp.: 50
Petrochemical Refining Equipment Mfr
N.A.I.C.S.: 333248

S&T Mutual Savings Bank (1)
96-4 Rieses Tower 101 Gyungnam Jungang-dong, Changwon, Gyeongsangnam-do, Korea (South)
Tel.: (82) 552228100
Web Site: http://www.hisntm.com
Sales Range: $50-74.9 Million
Emp.: 3
Mutual Savings & Private Banking Services
N.A.I.C.S.: 522180

S&T Solution Co., Ltd. (1)
599 Nammyeon-ro, Seongsan-gu, Changwon, Gyeongsangnam-do, Korea (South)
Tel.: (82) 552805494
Web Site: https://www.hisnts.com
Sales Range: $25-49.9 Million
Emp.: 3
Software Development Services
N.A.I.C.S.: 541511

SNT Dynamics Co., Ltd. (1)
599 Nammyeon-ro, Seongsan-gu, Changwon, Gyeongnam, Korea (South)
Tel.: (82) 552805000
Web Site: https://www.hisntd.com
Rev.: $312,954,944
Assets: $714,072,632
Liabilities: $208,577,224
Net Worth: $505,495,408
Earnings: $17,645,946
Emp.: 546
Fiscal Year-end: 12/31/2022
Transportation Equipment & Machine Tool Mfr
N.A.I.C.S.: 336999
Kwon Jeong Won *(CEO)*

SNT Motiv Co., Ltd. (1)
363 Yeoraksongjeong-ro Cheolma-myeon, Gijang-gun, Busan, Korea (South)
Tel.: (82) 515092114
Web Site: http://www.sntmotiv.com
Rev.: $801,408,089
Assets: $939,948,291
Liabilities: $265,734,831
Net Worth: $674,213,460
Earnings: $67,118,969
Emp.: 770
Fiscal Year-end: 12/31/2022
Automobile Components Mfr & Whslr
N.A.I.C.S.: 336390
Hyung Chul Kim *(CEO)*

Sing Tec Development Pte. Ltd. (1)
16 Kian Teck Way, Singapore, 628749, Singapore
Tel.: (65) 63162108
Web Site: https://www.singtec.com.sg
Property Investment & Construction Services
N.A.I.C.S.: 236210

SO-YOUNG INTERNATIONAL INC.
2 F East Tower Poly Plaza No 66 Xiangbin Road, Chaoyang District, Beijing, China
Tel.: (86) 1052699283 Ky
Web Site: https://ir.soyoung.com
Year Founded: 2014
SY—(NASDAQ)
Rev.: $192,718,876
Assets: $489,946,122
Liabilities: $90,394,666
Net Worth: $399,551,456
Earnings: ($10,043,528)
Emp.: 1,573
Fiscal Year-end: 12/31/22
Holding Company
N.A.I.C.S.: 551112
Xing Jin *(Co-Founder, Chm & CEO)*

SOALTEE HOTEL LTD.
Tahachal, Post Box 3800, Kathmandu, Nepal
Tel.: (977) 4273999
Web Site: https://www.soalteehotel.com
Year Founded: 1965
SHL—(NEP)
Rev.: $16,911,361
Assets: $21,211,446
Liabilities: $5,408,765
Net Worth: $15,802,681
Earnings: $4,170,223
Fiscal Year-end: 07/16/23
Hotel & Restaurant Operator
N.A.I.C.S.: 721110
Dinesh Bahadur Bista *(Chm)*

SOANAR PTY. LTD.
320 Victoria Rd, Rydalmere, Sydney, 2116, NSW, Australia
Tel.: (61) 288323000 AU
Web Site: http://www.soanar.com
Year Founded: 1963
Sales Range: $25-49.9 Million
Emp.: 150
Electronic Components Mfr
N.A.I.C.S.: 334419
Neil Walker *(CEO)*

Subsidiaries:

Soanar Plus (1)
320 Victoria Rd, Rydalmere, 2116, NSW, Australia
Tel.: (61) 397240889
Web Site: http://www.soanarplus.com
Sales Range: $25-49.9 Million
Emp.: 100
Catalog Supplier
N.A.I.C.S.: 541614

SOARES DA COSTA CONSTRUCAO, SGPS, S.A.
Rua Daciano Baptista Marques 245 Lake Towers-Ed D-Piso 3, 4400-617, Vila Nova de Gaia, Portugal
Tel.: (351) 228342200
Web Site: http://www.soaresdacosta.com
Year Founded: 2002
Sales Range: $650-699.9 Million
Emp.: 3,785
Civil Construction Services
N.A.I.C.S.: 237990

Subsidiaries:

Soares da Costa America Inc (1)
6205 Blue Lagoon Dr Ste 310, Miami, FL 33126
Tel.: (305) 592-9399
Civil Engineering Services
N.A.I.C.S.: 541330
Antonio Miranda Esteves *(CEO)*

SOBAL CORPORATION
Osaki MT Building 5-9-11 Kitashina-

SOBAL CORPORATION

Sobal Corporation—(Continued)
gawa, Shinagawa-ku, Tokyo, 141-0001, Japan
Tel.: (81) 364096131
Web Site: https://www.sobal.co.jp
Year Founded: 1983
2186—(TKS)
Rev.: $79,017,840
Assets: $45,002,320
Liabilities: $11,770,880
Net Worth: $33,231,440
Earnings: $4,326,960
Emp.: 963
Fiscal Year-end: 02/28/22
Computer Equipment Developer & Sales
N.A.I.C.S.: 334118
Junichi Shiizu *(Founder)*

Subsidiaries:

Andor System Support Co., Ltd. (1)
2-15-8 Minamishinagawa, Shinagawa-ku, Tokyo, 140-0004, Japan
Tel.: (81) 334508101
Web Site: https://www.andor.jp
Embedded System Development Mfr
N.A.I.C.S.: 333923

CORERD Co. Ltd. (1)
AQUACITY Shibaura 7F 4-16-23 Shibaura, Minato-ku, Tokyo, 108-0023, Japan (100%)
Tel.: (81) 364350570
Web Site: http://www.corerd.co.jp
Computer Software Development Services
N.A.I.C.S.: 541511
Masao Higashitani *(Pres, CEO & Mng Dir)*

SOBHA LIMITED
SarjapurMarthahalli Outer Ring Road ORR Devarabisanahalli, Bellandur Post, Bengaluru, 560 103, Karnataka, India
Tel.: (91) 8046464500
Web Site: https://www.sobha.com
SOBHA—(NSE)
Rev.: $298,989,600
Assets: $1,530,185,748
Liabilities: $1,198,799,921
Net Worth: $331,385,828
Earnings: $8,500,674
Emp.: 3,061
Fiscal Year-end: 03/31/21
Diversified Construction, Manufacturing & Information Technology Services
N.A.I.C.S.: 236220
P. N. C. Menon *(Founder)*

Subsidiaries:

Sobha Concrete Products (1)
Plot No 329 Bommasandra Jigani link Road Industrial Area Jigani, Anekal Taluk, Bengaluru, 560 105, Karnataka, India
Tel.: (91) 8027825177
Web Site: http://www.sobhadevelopers.com
Sales Range: $25-49.9 Million
Emp.: 30
Concrete Block, Paver & Slab Mfr
N.A.I.C.S.: 327331
Rajkumar Pillai *(Exec Dir)*

Sobha Developers (Pune) Limited (1)
5th Floor Parakh House S No 1 Plot No 255 Boat Club Road, Pune, 411001, India
Tel.: (91) 2066251111
Web Site: http://www.sobha.com
Real Estate Development Services
N.A.I.C.S.: 531390
Manish Verma *(Head-Reg)*

Sobha Developers LLC. (1)
13 Floor Sobha Sapphire Business Bay, PO Box 52687, Dubai, United Arab Emirates
Tel.: (971) 4 423 8064
Real Estate Development Services
N.A.I.C.S.: 531390
Pankaj Malik *(VP-Sls)*

Sobha Developers Ltd. - RESTOPLUS SPRING MATTRESS DIVISION (1)
Plot no9 Jigini Link Road Industrial Area Hennagara Post, Bommasandra, Bengaluru, Karnataka, India
Tel.: (91) 80 22631710
Mattress Mfr
N.A.I.C.S.: 337910

Sobha Glazing & Metal Works (1)
Plot No 10 Jigani Bommasandra Link road Opposite to Biocon, KIADB Industrial Area Anekal Taluk, Bengaluru, 560105, India
Tel.: (91) 80 22631702
Web Site: http://www.sobha.com
Emp.: 280
Commercial Metal Building Construction
N.A.I.C.S.: 236210

Sobha Interiors (1)
Plot No 9 KIADB Industrial Area Jigani Bommasandra Link Road, Hennagara Post Anekal Taluk, Bengaluru, 560 105, India
Tel.: (91) 9880034774
Web Site: https://www.sobhainteriors.com
Residential & Commercial Interior Design Services
N.A.I.C.S.: 541410

Sobha Projects & Trade Pvt Ltd. (1)
23/1 Sonnenhalli Village Brookfield, Mahadevpura Post, Bengaluru, 560 048, Karnataka, India
Tel.: (91) 8067192555
Web Site: http://www.sptl.in
Sales Range: $25-49.9 Million
Emp.: 35
Residential & Commercial Building Interior Products Distr
N.A.I.C.S.: 423220
Pradeep Sukumaran *(Sr Gen Mgr)*

Subsidiary (Non-US):

Services & Trade Company LLC (2)
PO Box 823, 112, Ruwi, Oman
Tel.: (968) 22083000
Web Site: http://www.stcgroups.com
Residential & Commercial Building Interior Design Services
N.A.I.C.S.: 541410

Subsidiary (Domestic):

Industrial Management Technology & Contracting LLC (3)
Mina Al Fahal, PO Box 196, Mina Al Fahal, Muscat, 116, Oman
Tel.: (968) 2 470 7727
Web Site: https://www.imtac.com
Sales Range: $50-74.9 Million
Emp.: 150
Management Software Developer & Publisher
N.A.I.C.S.: 513210
Ashok Sardiwal *(CEO)*

Subsidiary (Non-US):

IMTAC Technologies LLC (4)
1201-1203 12th Fl Sobha Ivory 1 Business Bay, PO Box 9076, Tareq Bin Ziyad Street, Dubai, 9076, United Arab Emirates
Tel.: (971) 4 3373830
Web Site: http://www.icthealth.com
Emp.: 25
Management Software Developer & Publisher
N.A.I.C.S.: 513210
Gautham Dey *(CEO)*

IMTAC Yemen Ltd. (4)
Building No 7 Apt No 1 First Floor Yemeni Kuwati Building, Hadda Madeena Hadda, Sana'a, Yemen
Tel.: (967) 1420571
Web Site: http://www.imtac.com
Sales Range: $25-49.9 Million
Emp.: 17
Management Software Developer & Publisher
N.A.I.C.S.: 513210

Sobha Real Estate LLC (1)
Technopark Jebel Ali, PO Box 52687, Dubai, United Arab Emirates
Tel.: (971) 48867500
Web Site: http://www.sobha-me.com
Sales Range: $200-249.9 Million
Emp.: 1,000

Residential & Commercial Building Construction & Design Services
N.A.I.C.S.: 236210

SOBHA RENAISSANCE INFORMATION TECHNOLOGIES PVT LTD
SRIT House 113/1B ITPL Main Road, Kundalahalli, Bengaluru, 560 037, India
Tel.: (91) 8041951999
Web Site: http://www.renaissance-it.com
Year Founded: 1999
Management Software Developer & Publisher
N.A.I.C.S.: 513210
Madhu Nambiar *(Co-Founder)*

Subsidiaries:

Billing Components GmbH (1)
Leonrodstrasse 68, 80636, Munich, Germany
Tel.: (49) 89324610
Web Site: http://www.billing-components.com
Sales Range: $25-49.9 Million
Emp.: 10
Accounts Receivable & Billing Software Developer & Publisher
N.A.I.C.S.: 513210

Sobha CTG Solutions Australia Pty Ltd. (1)
6 O'Connell Street Level 13, Sydney, 2000, NSW, Australia
Tel.: (61) 292933800
Management Software Developer & Publisher
N.A.I.C.S.: 513210

SOBHAGYA MERCANTILE LTD.
61B Wing 6th Flr Mittal Towe 210 Nariman Point, Mumbai, 400 021, India
Tel.: (91) 2256301060
Financial Consulting Services
N.A.I.C.S.: 541611
Pradeep Soni *(Chief Compliance Officer)*

SOBHAN PHARMACEUTICAL COMPANY
No 295 West Dr Fatemi St, Post Box 14185565, 1411853695, Tehran, Iran
Tel.: (98) 21 6656 8181
Web Site: http://sobhandarou.com
Year Founded: 1976
Pharmaceuticals Product Mfr
N.A.I.C.S.: 325412
Keyvan Farahnak *(Mgr-Responsible)*

Subsidiaries:

Iran Daru Pharmaceutical Company (1)
Sh Yadegar Ave Saveh Road 3 Rah-e Azari, PO Box 13185 - 753, Tehran, Iran
Tel.: (98) 21 66628848
Web Site: http://www.irandaru.com
Emp.: 257
Pharmaceutical Preparation Mfr
N.A.I.C.S.: 325412

SOBINBANK JSB
15/56 Rochdelskaya Strasse, Moscow, 123022, Russia
Tel.: (7) 957252525
Web Site: http://www.sobinbank.ru
Sales Range: Less than $1 Million
Securities Brokerage Services
N.A.I.C.S.: 523150

SOBOTEC LTD.
67 Burford Road, Hamilton, L8E 3C6, ON, Canada
Tel.: (905) 578-1278
Web Site: http://www.sobotec.com
Year Founded: 1988
Rev.: $22,272,551

INTERNATIONAL PUBLIC

Emp.: 205
Aluminum Composite Panel System Mfr
N.A.I.C.S.: 423310
Chedo Sobot *(VP)*

SOBUTE NEW MATERIALS CO., LTD.
No 118 Liquan Road, Jiangning District, Nanjing, 211103, Jiangsu, China
Tel.: (86) 2583278608
Web Site: https://www.sobute.com
603916—(SHG)
Rev.: $521,576,748
Assets: $1,087,604,037
Liabilities: $442,601,060
Net Worth: $645,002,977
Earnings: $40,427,281
Fiscal Year-end: 12/31/22
Concrete Admixture Mfr & Distr
N.A.I.C.S.: 327320
Changwen Miao *(Chm)*

Subsidiaries:

PT Sobute Global Indonesia (1)
Springhill Office Tower Lt 11 unit A Jl Benyamin sueb Ruas D7 Blok D6, Kel Pademangan Timur Kec Pademangan, Jakarta Utara, Jakarta, Indonesia
Tel.: (62) 2122608586
Construction Materials Distr
N.A.I.C.S.: 423390

Sobute (BD) Co., Ltd. (1)
A5&B5 5thfloor Lake Breeze Apartment Plot No KA-10/3 Road No 13, North Baridhara, Dhaka, 1212, Bangladesh
Tel.: (880) 1704304167
Construction Materials Distr
N.A.I.C.S.: 423390

SOC CENTRALE BOIS SCIERIES MANCHE SA
12 rue Godot de Mauroy, 75009, Paris, France
Tel.: (33) 158361450
Web Site: https://www.scbsm.fr
CBSM—(EUR)
Sales Range: $10-24.9 Million
Real Estate Support Services
N.A.I.C.S.: 531390
Jacques Lacroix *(Chm & CEO)*

SOC.CANALISTAS LA FORESTA DE APOQUINDO S
Atalaya Nro 11281, Las Condes, Santiago, Chile
Tel.: (56) 2016566
CANALISTAS—(SGO)
Sales Range: Less than $1 Million
Water Distribution Services
N.A.I.C.S.: 488390
Pedraza Perez Pablo *(CEO & Gen Mgr)*

SOCEP S.A.
Constantza Port Berth 34, 900900, Constanta, Romania
Tel.: (40) 758034787
Web Site: https://www.socep.ro
SOCP—(BUC)
Rev.: $44,254,673
Assets: $143,937,473
Liabilities: $61,823,860
Net Worth: $82,113,614
Earnings: $21,545,438
Emp.: 442
Fiscal Year-end: 12/31/23
Port Operation Services
N.A.I.C.S.: 488320
Dorinel Cazacu *(Mng Dir)*

SOCFINAF SA
Societe Financiere des Caoutchoucs 4 Avenue Guillaume, 1650, Luxembourg, Luxembourg
Tel.: (352) 442877
Web Site: https://socfin.com

Year Founded: 1909
SOFAF—(LUX)
Rev.: $687,828,550
Assets: $975,174,649
Liabilities: $425,599,575
Net Worth: $549,575,074
Earnings: $81,571,927
Emp.: 25,453
Fiscal Year-end: 12/31/22
Architectural Design & Engineering Services
N.A.I.C.S.: 541310
Hubert Fabri *(Chm)*

Subsidiaries:

P.T. Socfin (1)
Jl K L Yos Sudarso No 106, Medan, 20115, North Sumatera, Indonesia
Tel.: (62) 616616066
Web Site: https://www.socfindo.co.id
Emp.: 10,000
Palm Oil & Rubber Product Mfr
N.A.I.C.S.: 311225

Socapalm S.A. (1)
BP 691, Douala, Cameroon
Tel.: (237) 695355911
Web Site: http://www.socapalm.com
Agricultural Services
N.A.I.C.S.: 115116

SOCFINASIA S.A.
Avenue Guillaume 4, 1650, Luxembourg, Luxembourg
Tel.: (352) 442877
Web Site: https://socfin.com
SCFNS—(LUX)
Rev.: $952,139,387
Assets: $1,214,849,927
Liabilities: $367,732,657
Net Worth: $847,117,270
Earnings: $107,296,297
Emp.: 7,857
Fiscal Year-end: 12/31/23
Portfolio Management Services
N.A.I.C.S.: 327910
Hubert Fabri *(Chm)*

Subsidiaries:

Coviphama Co., Ltd. (1)
23 Street 594 Sangkat Boeung Kak 2, Khan Toul Kork, Phnom Penh, Cambodia
Tel.: (855) 713334437
Rubber Products Mfr
N.A.I.C.S.: 326291

Induservices Fr S.A. (1)
Square des Places 3, 1700, Fribourg, Switzerland
Tel.: (41) 264255820
Information Technology Services
N.A.I.C.S.: 541511

PT Socfin Indonesia (1)
Jl K L Yos Sudarso No 106, Medan, 20115, Indonesia
Tel.: (62) 616616066
Web Site: https://www.socfindo.co.id
Rubber Products Mfr
N.A.I.C.S.: 326299

Socfin KCD Co., Ltd. (1)
3 Street 594 Sangkat Boeung Kak 2, Khan Toul Kork, Phnom Penh, Cambodia
Tel.: (855) 713334437
Rubber Products Mfr
N.A.I.C.S.: 326299

Socfinco Fr S.A. (1)
Square des Places 3, 1700, Fribourg, Switzerland
Tel.: (41) 264255820
Agricultural Financial Services
N.A.I.C.S.: 522299

Societe Camerounaise De Palmeraies S.A. (1)
Rue de la Motte Piquet Bonanjo, BP 691, Douala, Cameroon
Tel.: (237) 69 535 5911
Web Site: https://www.socapalm.com
Palm Plantation Services
N.A.I.C.S.: 115112

Sodimex Fr S.A. (1)
Square des Places 3, 1700, Fribourg, Switzerland
Tel.: (41) 264255840
Agricultural Equipment Distr
N.A.I.C.S.: 423820

Sogb S.A. (1)
01 BP 365, San Pedro, Cote d'Ivoire
Tel.: (225) 2734712316
Web Site: https://www.sogbci.com
Rubber Products Mfr
N.A.I.C.S.: 326291

SOCIAL ISLAMI BANK LIMITED
City Center Level 1923 28 and 29 901 Motijheel Commercial Area, Dhaka, 1000, Bangladesh
Tel.: (880) 9612001122
Web Site: https://www.siblbd.com
SIBL—(CHT)
Rev.: $198,494,051
Assets: $4,016,753,954
Liabilities: $3,826,229,358
Net Worth: $190,524,596
Earnings: $22,452,718
Emp.: 4,039
Fiscal Year-end: 12/31/22
Banking Services
N.A.I.C.S.: 522110
Walid Mahmud Sobhani *(CFO & Sr Exec VP)*

SOCIAL SECURITY & NATIONAL INSURANCE TRUST
Pension House, PO Box M. 149, Accra, Ghana
Tel.: (233) 667731   GH
Web Site: http://www.ssnit.com
Year Founded: 1972
Sales Range: $500-549.9 Million
National Pension Fund Administrator
N.A.I.C.S.: 525110
Darius Osei *(Gen Mgr-Medical Svcs)*

Subsidiaries:

The Trust Bank Ltd. (1)
Reinsurance House, 68 Kwame Nkrumah Avenue, Adabraka, Accra, Ghana (61.14%)
Tel.: (233) 21 240049
Sales Range: $25-49.9 Million
Emp.: 300
Savings, Commercial & Corporate Banking Services
N.A.I.C.S.: 522110

SOCIALLITE US AB
Box 55935, 102 16, Stockholm, Sweden
Tel.: (46) 841001092
Web Site: https://www.sociallite.us
Year Founded: 2016
845—(DEU)
Media Advertising Services
N.A.I.C.S.: 541840
Patrik Axelsson *(CEO)*

Subsidiaries:

Gravel Sweden AB (1)
Birger Jarlsgatan 20, 114 34, Stockholm, Sweden
Tel.: (46) 103350202
Web Site: https://gravel.se
Internet Marketing Services
N.A.I.C.S.: 541613

SOCIALWIRE CO., LTD.
Urbannet Uchisaiwaicho Building 3F 1-1-13 Shinbashi, Minato-ku, Tokyo, 105-0004, Japan
Tel.: (81) 353634878   JP
Web Site: https://www.socialwire.net
Year Founded: 2006
3929—(TKS)
Rev.: $24,252,090
Assets: $8,830,960
Liabilities: $8,269,110
Net Worth: $561,850
Earnings: ($965,060)
Emp.: 283
Fiscal Year-end: 03/31/24
News Wire & Incubation Office Services
N.A.I.C.S.: 519290
Mineyuki Yada *(Pres & CEO)*

Subsidiaries:

CROSSCOOP INDIA PVT LTD (1)
3rd Floor DLF Building No 9-A DLF Cyber City Phase-III, Gurgaon, 122002, Haryana, India
Tel.: (91) 1244545000
Web Site: http://www.crosscoop.com
Emp.: 250
Business Support Services
N.A.I.C.S.: 541611

CROSSCOOP PHILIPPINES INC (1)
GT Tower International 6813 Ayala Avenue Corner, HV Dela Costa Makati City, 1227, Manila, Philippines
Tel.: (63) 2 464 7100
Web Site: http://www.crosscoop.com
Emp.: 3
Business Support Services
N.A.I.C.S.: 541611
Kento Tsukamoto *(Gen Mgr)*

CROSSCOOP SINGAPORE PTE LTD (1)
80 Robinson Road, Singapore, 068898, Singapore
Tel.: (65) 64206370
Business Support Services
N.A.I.C.S.: 541611
Steffi Wiratman *(Mgr-Admin)*

CROSSCOOP VIETNAM CO LTD (1)
72 Le Thanh Ton Street District 1, Ho Chi Minh City, Vietnam
Tel.: (84) 8 3528 5400
Business Support Services
N.A.I.C.S.: 541611
Tong Anh Van *(Mgr)*

PT SOCIALWIRE INDONESIA (1)
Thamrin Road, UOB PLAZA 22nd Floor JL MH Thamrin No 10, Jakarta, 10230, Indonesia
Tel.: (62) 21 3192 0040
Business Support Services
N.A.I.C.S.: 541611

SOCIEDAD AGRICOLA LA ROSA SOFRUCO S.A.
Coyancura 2283 Office 603, Providencia, Santiago, Chile
Tel.: (56) 6386199
Web Site: http://www.sofruco.cl
Year Founded: 1939
SOFRUCO—(SGO)
Sales Range: Less than $1 Million
Fruit Farming Services
N.A.I.C.S.: 111336

SOCIEDAD COMERCIAL DEL PLATA S.A.
Lumina Thames Tower B Panamericana Collector 1804, C1003ABV, Buenos Aires, Argentina
Tel.: (54) 21526000   Ar
Web Site: https://www.scp.com.ar
Year Founded: 1927
CVVIF—(OTCIQ)
Sales Range: $150-199.9 Million
Holding Company; Energy, Telecommunications, Entertainment, Transportation & Real Estate Products & Services
N.A.I.C.S.: 551112
Santiago Nicholson *(Mgr-Comm & IR)*

SOCIEDAD DE INVERSIONES CAMPOS CHILENOS SA
Rosario Norte 615 piso 23 Las Condes, Santiago, Chile
Tel.: (56) 25715408
Web Site: https://camposchilenos.cl
Investment Management Service
N.A.I.C.S.: 525910
Joaquin Noguera Wilson *(Pres)*

SOCIEDAD DE INVERSIONES ORO BLANCO S.A.
Paulino Alfonso 331, Santiago, 810, Chile
Tel.: (56) 26335007
Investment Management Service
N.A.I.C.S.: 525910
Rafael Guilisasti Gana Morande *(Chm)*

SOCIEDAD DE INVERSIONES PAMPA CALICHERA SA
Paulino Alfonso 331, Santiago, 810, Chile
Tel.: (56) 26335007
CALICHERAA—(SGO)
Sales Range: Less than $1 Million
Investment Management Service
N.A.I.C.S.: 525990

SOCIEDAD ESTATAL DE PARTICIPACIONES INDUSTRIALES
C/Velazquez 134, 28006, Madrid, Spain
Tel.: (34) 913961000
Web Site: http://www.sepi.es
Sales Range: $50-74.9 Million
Emp.: 250
Holding Company
N.A.I.C.S.: 551112

Subsidiaries:

Compania Espanola de Tabaco en Rama, S.A. (1)
Avda de las Angustias N 20, Navalmoral de la Mata, 10300, Caceres, Spain
Tel.: (34) 927 533161
Web Site: http://www.cetarsa.es
Holding Company
N.A.I.C.S.: 551112
Jose Carlos Hidalgo Giraldo *(Assoc Dir-Admin & Fin)*

Corporacion de Radio y Television Espanola, S.A (1)
Avenida de Radio Television 4 Edificio Prado, 28223, Madrid, Spain
Tel.: (34) 913 461685
Radio & Television Broadcasting Services
N.A.I.C.S.: 516120

Subsidiary (Domestic):

Radio Nacional de Espana, S.A. (2)
Plaza Colon 4, 37001, Salamanca, Spain
Tel.: (34) 923281758
Web Site: http://www.rtve.es
Radio Broadcasting Services
N.A.I.C.S.: 516210

Correos Telecom, S.A. (1)
C/ Conde de Penalver 19B-6, 28006, Madrid, Spain
Tel.: (34) 913 531750
Web Site: http://www.correostelecom.es
Emp.: 55
Holding Company
N.A.I.C.S.: 551112
Fernando Arthilna *(Gen Mgr)*

Defex, S.A. (1)
Avda General Peron 38, Madrid, 28020, Spain
Tel.: (34) 915 557861
Holding Company
N.A.I.C.S.: 551112

ENUSA Industrias Avanzadas S.A. (1)
Santiago Rusinol 12, 28040, Madrid, Spain (60%)
Tel.: (34) 913474200
Web Site: http://www.enusa.es
Holding Company
N.A.I.C.S.: 327992
Jose Luis Gonzalez *(Pres)*

Subsidiary (Domestic):

EMPRESA PARA LA GESTION DE RESIDUOS INDUSTRIALES.

SOCIEDAD ESTATAL DE PARTICIPACIONES INDUSTRIALES
INTERNATIONAL PUBLIC

Sociedad Estatal de Participaciones Industriales—(Continued)
S.A. (2)
Condeade Penalver No 38 de, Madrid, 28006, Spain
Tel.: (34) 914 119 215
Web Site: http://www.empresa.es
Holding Company
N.A.I.C.S.: 551112
Guan Perez (Dir-Technical)

Equipos Nucleares, S.A. (ENSA) (1)
Avenida Juan Carlos I 8 39600, 28020, Cantabria, Maliano, Spain (100%)
Tel.: (34) 915553617
Web Site: http://www.ensa.es
Steam Generator Mfr for Nuclear Power Applications
N.A.I.C.S.: 221113

Subsidiary (Domestic):

ENWESA Operaciones, S.A. (2)
Poligono Industrial de Heras 136, 39792, Heras, Spain
Tel.: (34) 942 253815
Web Site: http://www.enwesa.es
Holding Company
N.A.I.C.S.: 551112

Equipos Termo-Metalicos, S.A. (1)
El Escudo 8 Poligono Industrial de Villalonquejar, 09001, Burgos, Spain
Tel.: (34) 947 298017
Web Site: http://www.etm.es
Mechanical Equipment Mfr
N.A.I.C.S.: 811310

Hipodromo de La Zarzuela, S.A. (1)
Avenida Padre Huidobro s/n, 28023, Madrid, Spain
Tel.: (34) 917 400540
Web Site: http://www.hipodromodelazarzuela.es
Holding Company
N.A.I.C.S.: 551112

Navantia, S.A. (1)
C/Velazquez 132, 28006, Madrid, Spain
Tel.: (34) 913 358400
Holding Company
N.A.I.C.S.: 551112

Sociedad Anonima Estatal de Caucion Agraria (1)
C/ Jorge Juan 19 - 4, 28001, Madrid, Spain
Tel.: (34) 912 093700
Web Site: http://www.saeca.es
Holding Company
N.A.I.C.S.: 551112

SOCIEDAD HIPODROMO CHILE S.A.
Av Hipodromo Chile N 1715, PO Box 9371, Independencia Commune, Santiago, Chile
Tel.: (56) 222709200
Web Site: https://www.hipodromo.cl
Year Founded: 1904
HIPODROMOA—(SGO)
Sales Range: Less than $1 Million
Horse Racetrack Operator
N.A.I.C.S.: 711212

SOCIEDAD HIPOTECARIA FEDERAL SNC
Ejercito Nacional Mexicano 180, Miguel Hidalgo, Mexico, 11590, Mexico
Tel.: (52) 5552634500
Web Site: http://www.shf.gob.mx
Year Founded: 2001
Sales Range: $50-74.9 Million
Financial Institution
N.A.I.C.S.: 522110
Edith Castro Bedolla (Dir-Market Dev)

SOCIEDAD INMOBILIARIA VINA DEL MAR S.A
Plaza Sucre S/N, Vina del Mar, Chile
Tel.: (56) 680017
INMOBVINA—(SGO)
Sales Range: Less than $1 Million
Real Estate Development Services
N.A.I.C.S.: 531390
Lucas Molina Achondo (Pres)

SOCIEDAD MATRIZ BANCO DE CHILE
Agustinas 975 Of 541 Piso 5, Santiago, Chile
Tel.: (56) 6533239
Web Site: http://www.sm-chile.cl
Banking Services
N.A.I.C.S.: 522110
Andronico Mariano Luksic Craig (Chm)

SOCIEDAD PESQUERA COLOSO S.A.
Av El Bosque Norte 0440 Piso 9 Oficina 902, Las Condes, Santiago, Chile
Tel.: (56) 2 371 2600
Web Site: http://www.coloso.cl
COLOSO—(SGO)
Sales Range: Less than $1 Million
Fishing Services
N.A.I.C.S.: 114111
Rafael Sepulveda Ruiz (CEO)

SOCIEDAD QUIMICA Y MINERA DE CHILE S.A.
El Trovador 4285 6th Floor, Santiago, Chile
Tel.: (56) 224252000
Web Site: http://www.sqm.com
Year Founded: 1983
SQM—(NYSE)
Rev.: $7,467,490,000
Assets: $10,778,837,000
Liabilities: $6,301,408,000
Net Worth: $4,477,429,000
Earnings: $930,267,000
Emp.: 7,682
Fiscal Year-end: 12/31/23
Producer of Iodine, Lithium, Nitrates, Industrial Chemicals, Specialty Fertilizers & Other Mined Products
N.A.I.C.S.: 325180
Carlos Cesar Diaz Ortiz (Sr VP-Ops-Potassium & Lithium)

Subsidiaries:

Ajay - Sqm Chile S.A. (1)
Avda Presidente Eduardo Frei M 4900, Renca, Santiago, Chile (51%)
Tel.: (56) 224437110
Sales Range: $25-49.9 Million
Emp.: 50
Chemical & Allied Products Whslr
N.A.I.C.S.: 424690

Azure Minerals Limited (1)
Level 1 34 Colin Street, West Perth, 6005, WA, Australia
Tel.: (61) 894812555
Web Site: http://www.azureminerals.com.au
Rev.: $1,261
Assets: $21,660,083
Liabilities: $1,871,557
Net Worth: $19,788,526
Earnings: ($15,341,107)
Emp.: 10
Fiscal Year-end: 06/30/2022
Minerals Exploration
N.A.I.C.S.: 213115

Subsidiary (Non-US):

Minera Piedra Azul, S.A. de C.V. (2)
Ave Javier De Leon 707 Col Pitic, Hermosillo, Sonora, Mexico
Tel.: (52) 6622855350
Web Site: http://www.azureminerals.com
Mineral Exploration Services
N.A.I.C.S.: 213115

Charlee SQM (Thailand) Co Ltd (1)
31 Soi 138 Ladpraw Rd, Klongjan Bangkapi, Bangkok, 10240, Thailand
Tel.: (66) 23778668
Web Site: http://www.sqm.com
Sales Range: $50-74.9 Million
Emp.: 100
Chemical & Allied Products Whslr
N.A.I.C.S.: 424690

Comercial Hydro S.A. (1)
El Trovador 4285, Santiago, Chile (60.64%)
Tel.: (56) 24252525
Chemical & Fertilizer Mineral Mining
N.A.I.C.S.: 212390

Exploraciones Mineras S.A. (1)
Los Militares 4290 Las Condes, Santiago, Chile (100%)
Tel.: (56) 24252000
Chemical & Allied Products Whslr
N.A.I.C.S.: 424690

Fertilizantes Naturales S.A. (1)
Provenza 251 Principal 1, 08008, Barcelona, Spain (66.67%)
Tel.: (34) 934877806
Web Site: http://www.sqm.com
Sales Range: $50-74.9 Million
Emp.: 4
Chemical & Fertilizer Mineral Mining
N.A.I.C.S.: 212390

Isapre Norte Grande Ltda. (1)
Hannibal Pinto 3228, Antofagasta, Chile
Tel.: (56) 55 241 2627
Web Site: https://www.isaprecruzdelnorte.cl
Health Care Srvices
N.A.I.C.S.: 621999

Minera Nueva Victoria S.A. (1)
Ex oficina Salitrera Iris S-N, Pozo al Monte, Iquique, Chile (100%)
Tel.: (56) 24252000
Web Site: http://www.sqm.com
Chemical & Fertilizer Mineral Mining
N.A.I.C.S.: 212390

North American Food Distributing Co., Inc. (1)
3969 Industrial Blvd, West Sacramento, CA 95691-5000
Tel.: (916) 373-1111
Web Site: https://www.nafdc.com
Sales Range: $25-49.9 Million
Emp.: 46
Food & Beverages Whslr
N.A.I.C.S.: 424820

Proinsa Ltda. (1)
El Trovador 4285, Santiago, Chile (60.58%)
Tel.: (56) 24252525
Chemical & Fertilizer Mineral Mining
N.A.I.C.S.: 212390

S.Q.I. Corporation NV (1)
Pietermaai 123, PO Box 897, Willemstad, Curacao (100%)
Tel.: (599) 94612544
Residential Property Managers
N.A.I.C.S.: 531311

SQM (Shanghai) Chemicals Co. Ltd. (1)
Room 4703-33 47F No 300 Middle Huaihai Road, Huangpu District, Shanghai, 200021, China
Tel.: (86) 215 116 2840
Chemical Products Distr
N.A.I.C.S.: 424690

SQM Beijing Commercial Co. Ltd. (1)
Room 1502c Cbd International Mansion No 16 Yong An Dong Li, Jian Wai Ave Chaoyang District, Beijing, 100022, China
Tel.: (86) 1064618950
Sales Range: $25-49.9 Million
Emp.: 2
Plant Nutrition & Fertilizer Distr
N.A.I.C.S.: 424910

SQM Brasil Ltda. (1)
Calcada das Margaridas 163-sala 2, Alphaville, Barueri, Sao Paulo, Brazil
Tel.: (55) 114 195 6315
Marketing Advisory Services
N.A.I.C.S.: 541613

SQM Comercial de Mexico S.A. de C.V. (1)
Moctezuma 144 piso 4 Ciudad del Sol, 45050, Zapopan, Jalisco, Mexico (100%)
Tel.: (52) 3335401100
Chemical & Allied Products Merchant Whslr
N.A.I.C.S.: 424690

SQM Corporation NV (1)
Pietermaai 123, PO Box 897, Willemstad, Curacao (100%)
Tel.: (599) 94612544
Residential Property Managers
N.A.I.C.S.: 531311

SQM Dubai - FZCO (1)
Jebel Ali Free Zone, PO Box 18222, Dubai, 18222, United Arab Emirates (100%)
Tel.: (971) 48838506
Web Site: http://www.sqm-vitas.com
Sales Range: $50-74.9 Million
Emp.: 6
Phosphate Rock Mining
N.A.I.C.S.: 212390

SQM Ecuador S.A. (1)
Ave Jose Orrantia y Ave Juan Tanca Marengo Edificio Executive Center, Guayaquil, Ecuador (100%)
Tel.: (593) 42158639
Sales Range: $25-49.9 Million
Emp.: 50
Farm Supplies Whslr
N.A.I.C.S.: 424910

SQM Europe NV (1)
Houtdok-Noordkaai 25a, Amberes, 2030, Antwerp, Belgium (100%)
Tel.: (32) 39700
Sales Range: $25-49.9 Million
Emp.: 35
Chemical & Allied Products Merchant Whslr
N.A.I.C.S.: 424690

SQM Iberian S.A. (1)
Calle Provenza 251 Pral 1a, 08008, Barcelona, Spain
Tel.: (34) 93 487 7806
Chemical Products Distr
N.A.I.C.S.: 424690

SQM Industrial S.A. (1)
El Trovador 4285, Santiago, Chile (100%)
Tel.: (56) 24252525
Chemical & Fertilizer Mineral Mining
N.A.I.C.S.: 212390
Contesse Patricio (CEO)

Subsidiary (Domestic):

Soquimich Comercial S.A. (2)
Los Militares 4290 Las Condes, Santiago, Chile
Tel.: (56) 4252525
Web Site: https://www.sqmc.cl
Sales Range: Less than $1 Million
Fertilizer Mfr
N.A.I.C.S.: 325311

SQM International N.V. (1)
Houtdok-Noordkaai 25a, 2030, Antwerp, Belgium
Tel.: (32) 3 203 9700
Chemical Products Distr
N.A.I.C.S.: 424690

SQM Investment Corporation NV (1)
Pietermaai 123, PO Box 897, Willemstad, Curacao (100%)
Tel.: (599) 94612544
Residential Property Managers
N.A.I.C.S.: 531311

SQM Italia SRL (1)
Via Antonio Meucci 5, Bagno a Ripoli, 50012, Italy
Tel.: (39) 055644418
Web Site: http://www.sqm.com
Sales Range: $50-74.9 Million
Emp.: 3
Agricultural Chemical Products Supplier
N.A.I.C.S.: 424910

SQM Japan Co. Ltd. (1)
207 5-3-10 Minami-Aoyama, Minato-ku, Tokyo, 107-0062, Japan
Tel.: (81) 35 778 3311
Chemical Products Distr
N.A.I.C.S.: 424690

SQM Japon Co. Ltda (1)
207 5-3-10 Minami-Aoyama, Minato-ku, Tokyo, 107-0062, Japan (100%)
Tel.: (81) 357783311
Sales Range: $50-74.9 Million
Emp.: 4
Chemical & Allied Products Merchant Whslr
N.A.I.C.S.: 424690

SQM Korea LLC (1)

Suite 22 Kyobo Building 15th Floor 1,
Jongno Jongno-gu, Seoul, 03154, Korea
(South)
Tel.: (82) 22 010 8803
Metal Mining Services
N.A.I.C.S.: 213114

**SQM Nitratos Mexico S.A. de
C.V.** (1)
Calle Industria Electrica S-N Lote 30, Manzana A Parque Industrial Bu, 45645,
Jalisco, Mexico (51%)
Tel.: (52) 3335401100
Web Site: http://www.sqm.com
Sales Range: $50-74.9 Million
Emp.: 37
Chemical & Fertilizer Mineral Mining
N.A.I.C.S.: 212390

SQM Nitratos S.A. (1)
Los Militares 4290, Santiago, Chile (99.99%)
Tel.: (56) 24252000
Web Site: http://www.sqm.com
Chemical & Allied Products Whslr
N.A.I.C.S.: 424690

SQM North America Corp (1)
2727 Pacef Ferry Rd Bldg 2 Ste 1425, Atlanta, GA 30339 (100%)
Tel.: (770) 916-9400
Sales Range: $25-49.9 Million
Emp.: 25
Nitrogenous Fertilizer Mfr
N.A.I.C.S.: 325311

SQM Peru S.A. (1)
Avda Camino Real N 348 Off 701 San
Isidro, Lima, Peru (100%)
Tel.: (51) 16112121
Web Site: http://www.sqm.com
Farm Supplies Whslr
N.A.I.C.S.: 424910

SQM Potasio S.A. (1)
Los Militares 4290, Santiago, Chile (100%)
Tel.: (56) 24252000
Alkalies & Chlorine Mfr
N.A.I.C.S.: 325180

SQM Salar S.A. (1)
El Trovador 4285, Santiago, 7550081,
Chile (100%)
Tel.: (56) 24252000
Sales Range: $1-4.9 Billion
Emp.: 3,000
Nonmetallic Mineral Product Mfr
N.A.I.C.S.: 327999

SQM Thailand Limited (1)
Unit 2962 Level 29 No 388 Exchange
Tower Sukhumvit Road, Bangkok, 10110,
Thailand
Tel.: (66) 2 104 9136
Fertilizer & Chemical Product Distr
N.A.I.C.S.: 424910

SQM Venezuela S.A. (1)
Calle Guaicaipuro Torre Forum Piso 6, UBR
El Rosal Apartado 63159, 1010, Caracas,
Venezuela
Tel.: (58) 2129513333
Web Site: http://www.palaciosortega.com
Pesticide & Agricultural Chemical Mfr
N.A.I.C.S.: 325320

SQMC International Limitada (1)
Los Militares 4290 Las Condes, Santiago,
Chile (60.64%)
Tel.: (56) 24252525
Chemical & Fertilizer Mineral Mining
N.A.I.C.S.: 325311

**Servicios Integrales de Transitos y
Transferencias S.A.** (1)
Arturo Prat N 1060, Tocopilla, Antofagasta,
Chile (100%)
Tel.: (56) 55414452
Chemical & Fertilizer Mineral Mining
N.A.I.C.S.: 212390

**Sociedad Servicios de Salud
Ltda**
Sec La Negra Lotes 1 Y 2 Antofagasta, El
Trovador 4285, Santiago, Chile
Tel.: (56) 24252428
Sales Range: $1-4.9 Billion
Emp.: 3,000
Chemical & Allied Products Whslr
N.A.I.C.S.: 424690

SOCIEDADE COMERCIAL

OREY ANTUNES, S.A.
Rua Maria Luisa Holstein 20, PT-
1070-313, Lisbon, Portugal
Tel.: (351) 213407046
Web Site: http://www.orey.com
Year Founded: 1886
ORE—(EUR)
Sales Range: $1-9.9 Million
Emp.: 251
Real Estate Investment Services
N.A.I.C.S.: 531390
Duarte Maia de Albuquerque d'Orey
(Chm & CEO)

**SOCIEDADE DAS AGUAS DA
CURIA SA**
PT-3780-541, 3780-541, Tamengos,
Anadia, Portugal
Tel.: (351) 231519800
Web Site:
  http://www.termasdacuria.com
CUR—(EUR)
Sales Range: Less than $1 Million
Hotel Operator
N.A.I.C.S.: 721110
Jose Kendall da Costa Basto (CEO &
CFO)

**SOCIEDADE NACIONAL DE
COMBUSTIVEIS DE ANGOLA,
E.P.**
Rua Rainha Ginga n 29 31, Luanda,
1316, Angola
Tel.: (244) 226643343 AO
Web Site: http://www.sonangol.co.ao
Year Founded: 1976
Rev.: $15,448,894,875
Assets: $44,624,807,501
Liabilities: $26,548,035,224
Net Worth: $18,076,772,277
Earnings: $257,525,172
Emp.: 13,000
Fiscal Year-end: 12/31/18
Oil & Gas Production & Exploration
N.A.I.C.S.: 211120
Sebastiao Gaspar Martins (Chm)

Subsidiaries:

Banco Economico S.A. (1)
Rua do 1 Congresso no 27, Bairro Ingombotas, Luanda, Angola
Tel.: (244) 222693600
Web Site: http://www.bancoeconomico.ao
Sales Range: $300-349.9 Million
Emp.: 500
Retail, Commercial & Investment Banking
N.A.I.C.S.: 522110
Marcos Erwin Mariscal Sachse (Deputy
Mgr-Micro & Small Bus Banking-Natl)

Puma Energy Holdings B.V. (1)
20th Floor Ito Tower, Gustav Mahlerplein
102, 1082 MA, Amsterdam, Netherlands
Tel.: (31) 205041800
Holding Company
N.A.I.C.S.: 551112

Subsidiary (Non-US):

Puma Energy International B.V. (2)
45 rue du Stand, CH 1204, Geneva, Switzerland
Tel.: (41) 22 594 69 00
Web Site: http://www.pumaenergy.net
Sales Range: $600-649.9 Million
Emp.: 1,800
Supply, Storage & Transportation of Petroleum Products
N.A.I.C.S.: 424710

Joint Venture (Non-US):

BP Malawi Limited (1)
8 Independence Drive, PO Box 469, Blantyre, Malawi (50%)
Tel.: (265) 1 824244
Web Site: http://www.bp.com
Petroleum Products Marketing
N.A.I.C.S.: 424720

BP Tanzania Limited (3)
Bandari Road, PO BOX 9043, Kurasini, Dar

es Salaam, Tanzania (50%)
Tel.: (255) 222112725
Sales Range: $100-124.9 Million
Emp.: 225
Petroleum & Petroleum Products Whslr;
Gasoline Service Stations; Owned 50% by
BP plc & 50% by Tanzanian Government
N.A.I.C.S.: 424720

Subsidiary (Non-US):

Puma Dominicana, S.A. (3)
Carretera San Pedro La Romana Km 3 El
Penon, Santo Domingo, Dominican Republic
Tel.: (809) 893 5200
Web Site: http://www.pumaenergy.net
Petroleum Storage & Distr
N.A.I.C.S.: 424710

**Puma Energy Botswana (Pty)
Ltd.** (3)
Plot 682 3 Botswana Road Main Mall, PO
Box 183, Gaborone, Botswana
Tel.: (267) 3951077
Web Site: http://www.bp.com
Sales Range: $250-299.9 Million
Emp.: 68
Petroleum & Fuels Distr
N.A.I.C.S.: 424720
Mahube Mpugwa (Mng Dir)

Puma Energy Cote d'Ivoire SA (3)
Rue de Canal de Vridi, BP 15, 522 Abidjan
15, Abidjan, Cote d'Ivoire
Tel.: (225) 21 27 00 72
Web Site: http://www.pumaenergy.com
Sales Range: $50-74.9 Million
Emp.: 50
Petroleum Storage, Transport & Distr
N.A.I.C.S.: 424710

Puma Energy Guatemala S.A. (3)
5 Ave 5-55 Zona 14 Europlaza Torre II Oficina 903, 01014, Guatemala, Guatemala
Tel.: (502) 23389000
Petroleum Storage & Distr
N.A.I.C.S.: 424710

**Puma Energy Namibia (Pty)
Limited** (3)
Mutual Tower Independence Ave 4th Fl,
Windhoek, Namibia
Tel.: (264) 612808111
Web Site: http://www.puma-energy.com
Sales Range: $50-74.9 Million
Emp.: 7
Petroleum & Petroleum Products Production
& Marketing; Gasoline Service Stations
N.A.I.C.S.: 424720
Angela Katjimune (Mgr-HR)

Puma Energy Paraguay SA (3)
tsgto Nicasio Vilaba No 650c Delfin
Chamorro, Fernando de la Mora Zona
Norte, Asuncion, Paraguay
Tel.: (595) 21672456
Emp.: 105
Petroleum Storage & Distr
N.A.I.C.S.: 424710
Rodrigo Zavala (Gen Mgr)

Subsidiary (US):

Puma Energy Puerto Rico, Inc. (3)
Carr 28 km 0 .2 Zona Portuaria, Guaynabo,
PR 00965
Tel.: (787) 679-7350
Petroleum Storage & Distr
N.A.I.C.S.: 424710

Subsidiary (Non-US):

**Puma Energy Services South Africa
Pty Ltd** (3)
32 Jellicoe Ave 8th Fl, Rosebank, Johannesburg, 2196, South Africa
Tel.: (27) 117506800
Web Site: http://www.trafigura.com
Emp.: 300
Petroleum Storage & Distr
N.A.I.C.S.: 424710
Jean-Pierre Valentini (Gen Mgr)

Puma Energy Zambia plc (3)
Mukuba Pension House, Dedani Kamathi
Road, 10101, Lusaka, Zambia
Tel.: (260) 122868498
Sales Range: $100-124.9 Million
Emp.: 135
Oil & Gas Refining, Storage & Marketing

N.A.I.C.S.: 213112
Sidy Bane (CEO)

Puma International Congo S.A. (3)
Immeuble SVP Construction 50 Avenue Felix Eboue Zone Portuaire, BP 1180, Pointe
Noire, Congo, Republic of
Tel.: (242) 660 84 10
Web Site: http://www.pumaenergy.net
Petroleum, Storage, Transport & Distr
N.A.I.C.S.: 424710

Pumangol Lda (3)
Edificio Caravela 1 Andar Rua Dr Agostinho
Neto, Lote 1 Bairro Praia do Bispo, Ingombota, Luanda, Angola
Tel.: (244) 934 764 587
Petroleum Distr
N.A.I.C.S.: 457120

Sonangol Distribuidora S.A. (1)
Rua Amilcar Cabral n 110-5 A, Luanda,
Angola
Tel.: (244) 2 392190
Oil & Gas Exploration Services
N.A.I.C.S.: 211120

Sonangol Gas Natural Limitada (1)
Edificio Cif One Luanda Av 1 Congresso
Mpla, Caixa Postal 2055, Luanda, Angola
Tel.: (244) 226 692 094
Oil & Gas Exploration Services
N.A.I.C.S.: 211120

**SOCIETA AZIONARIA PER LA
CONDOTTA DI ACQUA POTABILI S.P.A.**
Corso Re Umberto 9 bis, 10121, Turin, Italy
Tel.: (39) 011 55 941 IT
Web Site:
  http://www.acquepotabili.it
Sales Range: $75-99.9 Million
Water Distribution & Services
N.A.I.C.S.: 221310

**SOCIETA CATTOLICA DI
ASSICURAZIONE-SOCIETA
COOPERATIVA**
Lungadige Cangrande 16, 37126,
Verona, Italy
Tel.: (39) 0800572572 IT
Web Site: https://www.cattolica.it
Year Founded: 1896
Rev.: $5,398,975,641
Assets: $25,922,566,548
Liabilities: $23,661,429,297
Net Worth: $2,261,137,251
Earnings: $99,879,485
Emp.: 1,508
Fiscal Year-end: 12/31/16
Holding Company; Insurance Products & Services
N.A.I.C.S.: 551112
Paolo Bedoni (Chm)

Subsidiaries:

ABC Assicura S.p.A. (1)
Via Carlo Ederle 45, 37126, Verona,
Italy (100%)
Tel.: (39) 045 839 1111
Web Site: http://www.abcassicura.it
Property & Casualty Insurance Products &
Services
N.A.I.C.S.: 524126

BCC Assicurazioni S.p.A. (1)
Maciachini Business Park - MAC 1 Via Benigno Crespi 19, 20159, Milan,
Italy (49%)
Tel.: (39) 02466275
Web Site: https://www.bccassicurazioni.com
General Insurance Products & Services
N.A.I.C.S.: 524126

BCC Vita S.p.A. (1)
(70%)
Tel.: (39) 02466275
Web Site: http://www.bccvita.it
Life Insurance Products & Services
N.A.I.C.S.: 524113

FATA Assicurazioni Danni S.p.A. (1)
Via Urbana 169/A, 00184, Rome, Italy

SOCIETA CATTOLICA DI ASSICURAZIONE-SOCIETA COOPERATIVA

Societa Cattolica di Assicurazione-Societa Cooperativa—(Continued)

Tel.: (39) 06 47 65 1
Web Site: http://www.fata-assicurazioni.it
Rev.: $448,643,946
Assets: $868,391,411
Liabilities: $262,949,872
Net Worth: $605,441,539
Earnings: $7,524,208
Fiscal Year-end: 12/31/2014
Property & Casualty Insurance Products & Services
N.A.I.C.S.: 524126

SOCIETA EDITORIALE IL FATTO S.P.A.
Via Sant Erasmo 2, 00184, Rome, Italy
Tel.: (39) 06328181
Web Site: https://www.seif-spa.it
Year Founded: 2009
Newspaper Publishers
N.A.I.C.S.: 513110
Cinzia Monteverdi (Pres & CEO)

SOCIETA ESERCIZI COMMERCIALI INDUSTRIALI
Via degli Agresti 6, 40123, Bologna, Italy
Tel.: (39) 0512917711
Web Site: http://www.maccaferri.it
Sales Range: $25-49.9 Million
Emp.: 25
Holding Company
N.A.I.C.S.: 551112
Alessandro Maccaferri (VP)

Subsidiaries:

Arenaria S.r.l. (1)
Piazza Galileo Galilei n6, 40123, Bologna, Italy
Tel.: (39) 051 272002
Web Site: http://www.arenariasabbie.com
Real Estate Manangement Services
N.A.I.C.S.: 531390
Paolo Zedda (Pres)

Felsinea Factor s.p.a. (1)
PzzaGalileo 6, 40123, Bologna, Italy
Tel.: (39) 051 223262
Web Site: http://www.felsineafactor.it
Engineering Consulting Services
N.A.I.C.S.: 541330

Gnosis S.p.A. (1)
Via Lavoratori Autobianchi 1, 20832, Desio, Italy
Tel.: (39) 03621670001
Web Site: http://www.gnosis-bio.com
Biotechnology Research & Development Services
N.A.I.C.S.: 541714
Paolo Malesani (Dir-Comml)

Subsidiary (Non-US):

Gnosis Bioresearch S.A. (2)
Via Lischedi 4, 6592, Saint Antonino, Switzerland
Tel.: (41) 91 851 91 91
Biotechnology Research & Development Services
N.A.I.C.S.: 541714

Subsidiary (Domestic):

Gnosis Bioresearch S.r.l. (2)
Via Pomarico Pisticci Scalo, 75010, Pisticci, Italy
Tel.: (39) 0835 46 18 01
Biotechnology Research & Development Services
N.A.I.C.S.: 541714

Subsidiary (US):

Gnosis USA Inc. (2)
t 4259 W swamp RD Ste 305, Doylestown, PA 18902
Tel.: (215) 340-7960
Web Site: http://www.gnosisbio.com
Emp.: 4
Biotechnology Research & Development Services
N.A.I.C.S.: 541714

Nicole Foster (Gen Mgr)

Gruppo Industriale Maccaferri (1)
Via Agresti 6, Bologna, 40123, Italy
Tel.: (39) 0512917711
Web Site: http://www.maccaferri.it
Holding Company; Environmental Engineering, Real Estate & Mechanical Engineering
N.A.I.C.S.: 551112
Geetenog Maccaferri (Pres)

Subsidiary (Domestic):

Eridania Sadam SpA (2)
Via Degli Agresti 4-6, Bologna, 40100, Italy
Tel.: (39) 051 65 64 411
Web Site: http://www.eridaniasadam.it
Sugar Refineries
N.A.I.C.S.: 311314
Andrea Galloni (Dir-Bus Dev)

Hydrogeo Srl (2)
Via G Rossa 76, Casalecchio di Reno, 40033, Bologna, Italy
Tel.: (39) 0516130116
Web Site: http://www.hydrogeo.net
Iron & Stainless Steel Wire, Galvanized Wire, Netting & Gabions Mfr
N.A.I.C.S.: 331110
Fabrizio Ghiacci (Co-Pres, Gen Mgr & Mgr-Fences Product & Military Concertina)

Subsidiary (US):

Maccaferri, Inc. (2)
10303 Governor Ln Blvd, Williamsport, MD 21795
Tel.: (301) 223-6910
Web Site: http://www.maccaferri-usa.com
Sales Range: $25-49.9 Million
Emp.: 50
Mfr Environmental Control Products
N.A.I.C.S.: 332618

Manifatture Sigaro Toscano S.r.l. (1)
Largo G Toniolo 6, 00186, Rome, Italy
Tel.: (39) 06 684011
Web Site: http://www.toscanoitalia.it
Tobacco Product Distr
N.A.I.C.S.: 424940

Officine Maccaferri S.p.a. (1)
Via Kennedy 10, 40069, Zola Predosa, Italy
Tel.: (39) 05 16 43 60 00
Web Site: http://www.officinemaccaferri.com
Emp.: 3,000
Construction Materials Distr
N.A.I.C.S.: 423320

Subsidiary (Non-US):

A. Bianchini Ingeniero S.A. (2)
Gran Vial 8, Barcelona, 08170, Montornes del Valles, Spain
Tel.: (34) 93 568 65 10
Web Site: http://www.abianchini.es
Construction Materials Distr
N.A.I.C.S.: 423320
Xavier Hellin (Mgr-Fin)

Subsidiary (Domestic):

ELAS Geotecnica Srl (2)
Centro Commerciale Iotto 3 21, 20090, Segrate, Italy
Tel.: (39) 02 753 3252
Web Site: http://www.elasgeotecnica.it
Civil Engineering Services
N.A.I.C.S.: 541330

Italdreni Srl (2)
Via JF Kennedy 10, Zola Predosa, 40069, Bologna, Italy
Tel.: (39) 0516436000
Web Site: http://www.italdreni.it
Environmental Engineering Services
N.A.I.C.S.: 541330

Subsidiary (Non-US):

Linear Composites Limited (2)
Vale Mills Oakworth, Keighley, BD22 0EB, West Yorkshire, United Kingdom
Tel.: (44) 1535 643363
Web Site: http://www.linearcomposites.net
Construction Materials Distr
N.A.I.C.S.: 423320

Sebigas S.p.A. (1)
Via Santa Rita, 21057, Olgiate Olona, Italy
Tel.: (39) 03311817711
Web Site: http://www.sebigas.it

Gas Plant Construction Services
N.A.I.C.S.: 237120

SOCIETA REALE MUTUA DI ASSICURAZIONI
Via Corte d'Appello 11, 10122, Turin, TO, Italy
Tel.: (39) 011 4311111
Web Site: http://www.realegroup.eu
Year Founded: 1828
Insurance, Real Estate & Financial Products & Services Organization
N.A.I.C.S.: 813920
Luca Filippone (Co-Gen Mgr)

Subsidiaries:

Italiana Assicurazioni S.p.A. (1)
Via Marco Ulpio Traiano 18, 20149, Milan, Italy
Tel.: (39) 02 397161
Web Site: http://www.italiana.it
Life & General Insurance Products & Services
N.A.I.C.S.: 524298

Reale Seguros Generales, S.A. (1)
Calle Principe de Vergana 125, 28002, Madrid, Spain
Tel.: (34) 914 547 400
Web Site: http://www.reale.es
General Insurance Products & Services; Life Insurance & Pension Products & Services
N.A.I.C.S.: 524126

UNIQA Assicurazioni S.p.A. (1)
Via Carnia 26, 20132, Milan, Italy
Tel.: (39) 022685831
Web Site: http://www.uniqagroup.it
Health Insurance Carrier
N.A.I.C.S.: 524113
Michele Meneghetti (Pres)

Subsidiary (Domestic):

UNIQA Life S.p.A. (2)
Via Carnia 26, 20132, Milan, Italy
Tel.: (39) 02 281891
Web Site: http://www.uniqagroup.it
Life Insurance Products & Services
N.A.I.C.S.: 524113
Michele Meneghetti (CEO)

UNIQA Previdenza S.p.A. (2)
Via Carnia 26, 20132, Milan, Italy
Tel.: (39) 0281891
Web Site: http://www.unicagroup.it
Life Insurance Carrier
N.A.I.C.S.: 524113
Michele Meneghetti (CEO)

SOCIETATEA COMERCIALA DE TRATAMENT BALNEAR BUZIAS-S.A.
str Avram Iancu No 12 Floor P Ap Approx 1, Jud Timis, 305100, Buzias, Romania
Tel.: (40) 256321060
Web Site: https://www.buzias.ro
Year Founded: 1956
BALN—(BUC)
Rev.: $2,000,196
Assets: $5,499,154
Liabilities: $2,056,003
Net Worth: $3,443,151
Earnings: ($624,680)
Emp.: 53
Fiscal Year-end: 12/31/23
Accommodation Services
N.A.I.C.S.: 721110

SOCIETATEA COMERCIALA STICLA TURDA SA
str Fabricii nr 71, Turda, 401135, Cluj, Romania
Tel.: (40) 264317075
Web Site: http://www.sticla-turda.ro
Year Founded: 1921
Glassware Mfr
N.A.I.C.S.: 327215

SOCIETATEA DE ASIGURARI-

INTERNATIONAL PUBLIC

REASIGURARI MOLDCARGO S.A.
No 97 Vasile Alecsandri Street, MD-2012, Chisinau, Moldova
Tel.: (373) 79441105
Web Site: http://www.moldcargo.md
Financial Investment Services
N.A.I.C.S.: 523999
Stirbu Vladimir (Gen Dir)

Subsidiaries:

Auto Space S.R.L. (1)
18a Bucuriei Street, Chisinau, Moldova
Tel.: (373) 22123100
Web Site: http://www.autospace.md
Automotive Distr
N.A.I.C.S.: 423110

Continent S.R.L. (1)
17/1 Arborilor Street Center-Botanica Viaduct, Chisinau, 2025, Moldova
Tel.: (373) 22791477
Web Site: http://www.toyota.md
Automotive Distr
N.A.I.C.S.: 423110

SOCIETATEA DE INVESTITII FINANCIARE OLTENIA S.A.
1 Tufanele St, 200767, Craiova, Dolj, Romania
Tel.: (40) 251419335
Web Site: https://www.sifolt.ro
SIF5—(BUC)
Rev.: $87,600,586
Assets: $579,539,361
Liabilities: $78,884,361
Net Worth: $500,655,000
Earnings: $42,337,543
Emp.: 470
Fiscal Year-end: 12/31/22
Financial Services
N.A.I.C.S.: 523999
Cristian Busu (Vice Chm)

Subsidiaries:

Lactate Natura S.A. (1)
Bulevardul Independentei 23, 137395, Targoviste, Romania
Tel.: (40) 245216445
Web Site: https://lactatenatura.ro
Milk Product Mfr & Distr
N.A.I.C.S.: 311511

SOCIETATEA ENERGETICA ELECTRICA S.A.
Grigore Alexandrescu Street No 9, District 1, Bucharest, 010621, Romania
Tel.: (40) 212085999
Web Site: http://www.electrica.ro
Year Founded: 1998
EL—(BUC)
Rev.: $18,314,493
Assets: $966,912,703
Liabilities: $98,908,861
Net Worth: $868,003,842
Earnings: $5,278,965
Emp.: 72
Fiscal Year-end: 12/31/22
Electric Power Distribution Services
N.A.I.C.S.: 221122
Georgeta Corina Popescu (CEO)

Subsidiaries:

Distributie Energie Electrica Romania S.A. (1)
Str Ilie Macelaru nr 28A, Cluj-Napoca, 400380, Romania
Tel.: (40) 264929
Web Site: https://www.distributie-energie.ro
Electric Power Distribution Services
N.A.I.C.S.: 221122

Electrica Furnizare SA (1)
Sos Stefan cel Mare no 1A sector 1, 11736, Bucharest, Romania
Tel.: (40) 372442192
Web Site: http://www.electricafurnizare.ro
Electric Power Distr
N.A.I.C.S.: 221122

AND PRIVATE COMPANIES

Andrei Mirea *(Head-Legal Dept)*

Electrica Serv SA (1)
Sos Stefan cel Mare nr 1A District 1, 011736, Bucharest, Romania
Tel.: (40) 213065002
Web Site: https://www.electricaserv.ro
Electric Power Distr
N.A.I.C.S.: 221122
Cristian Andruhovici *(Dir-HR)*

Servicii Energetice Muntenia SA (1)
Str Costin Nenitescu no 5-9, Sector 6, Bucharest, Romania
Tel.: (40) 372140302
Web Site: http://www.electricasem.itp-sem.ro
Electric Power Distr
N.A.I.C.S.: 221122

Societatea de Distributie a Energiei Electrice Muntenia Nord SA (1)
Str Marasesti nr 44, Prahova, Ploiesti, Romania
Tel.: (40) 244405001
Web Site: http://www.edmn.ro
Electric Power Distr
N.A.I.C.S.: 221122
Eusebiu Rotaru *(Mgr-ITC Dept)*

Societatea de Distributie a Energiei Electrice Transilvania Nord SA (1)
Str Taberei nr 20, Cluj-Napoca, Romania
Tel.: (40) 264205702
Web Site: http://www.edtn.ro
Electric Power Distr
N.A.I.C.S.: 221122
Diana Schiau *(Head-Performance Mgmt)*

Societatea de Distributie a Energiei Electrice Transilvania Sud SA (1)
Str Pictor Luchian no 25, 500193, Brasov, Romania
Tel.: (40) 268305999
Web Site: http://www.sdeets.ro
Electric Power Distr
N.A.I.C.S.: 221122
Sinan Mustafa *(CEO)*

SOCIETE ANONYME BELGE DE CONSTRUCTIONS AERO-NAUTIQUES
Chaussee de Haecht 1470 Haachtsesteenweg, B-1130, Brussels, Belgium
Tel.: (32) 27295511
Web Site: https://www.sabca.be
Year Founded: 1920
SAB—(EUR)
Sales Range: $200-249.9 Million
Aircraft Mfr
N.A.I.C.S.: 336411

Subsidiaries:

SABCA Brussels NV (1)
Chaussee de Haecht 1470, 1130, Brussels, Belgium
Tel.: (32) 27295511
Aircraft Parts Mfr & Distr
N.A.I.C.S.: 336413

SABCA Casablanca NV (1)
Pole Industrielle Aeronautique, Nouasseur, Casablanca, 20000, Morocco
Tel.: (212) 522539491
Aircraft Parts Mfr & Distr
N.A.I.C.S.: 336413

SABCA Limburg N.V. (1)
Dellestraat 32, 3560, Lummen, Belgium
Tel.: (32) 13 53 01 11
Aircraft Mfr
N.A.I.C.S.: 336411
P. Reynaert *(Gen Mgr)*

SOCIETE ANONYME D'EXPLOSIFS ET DE PRODUITS CHIMIQUES
1 Terrasse Bellini, CS 70222, Paris, France
Tel.: (33) 1 40 69 80 00 FR
Web Site: http://www.epc-groupe.com
Year Founded: 1893
Explosive Mfr & Distr
N.A.I.C.S.: 325920

Subsidiaries:

AREX (1)
PO Box 998, Ras al Khaimah, United Arab Emirates
Tel.: (971) 723 621 26
Explosive Material Distr
N.A.I.C.S.: 424690

ATD JSC (1)
Rue du Manoir Queval, BP 151, 76143, Le Petit-Quevilly, Cedex, France
Tel.: (33) 235621988
Web Site: http://www.atd-demolition.fr
Coal Mining Explosive & Drilling Services
N.A.I.C.S.: 213113

Corse Expansif JSC (1)
Rue Nicolas Peraldi, 20090, Ajaccio, France
Tel.: (33) 495222685
Coal Mining Explosive & Drilling Services
N.A.I.C.S.: 213113

Diogen SA (1)
4 rue Racine, 44000, Nantes, France
Tel.: (33) 240739481
Coal Mining Explosive & Drilling Services
N.A.I.C.S.: 213113

EPC Cameroun (1)
5 rue Castelnau Prolongee, BP 15432, Douala, Cameroon
Tel.: (237) 33 43 16 83
Explosive Material Distr
N.A.I.C.S.: 424690

EPC Cote d'Ivoire (1)
Abidjan-Cocody Cite des cadres - Villa 78, Abidjan, Cote d'Ivoire
Tel.: (225) 22 48 81 41
Explosive Material Distr
N.A.I.C.S.: 424690

EPC Espana (1)
Avenida de la Constitucion n 39, Villatobas, 45310, Toledo, Spain
Tel.: (34) 925 152 080
Explosive Material Distr
N.A.I.C.S.: 424690

EPC France (1)
4 rue de Saint-Martin, 13310, Saint-Martin-de-Crau, France
Tel.: (33) 4 90 47 17 25
Web Site: http://www.epc-france.com
Explosive Material Distr
N.A.I.C.S.: 424690

EPC Gabon (1)
BP 4072, Libreville, Gabon
Tel.: (241) 76 98 99
Explosive Material Distr
N.A.I.C.S.: 424690
Noeline Gotoa *(Acct Mgr-Technical)*

EPC Guinee (1)
Boulevard Telly Diallo Immeuble Cherif Diallo Koulewondy, BP 4044, Conakry, Guinea
Tel.: (224) 30 47 70 31
Explosive Material Distr
N.A.I.C.S.: 424690

EPC Maroc (1)
RP 3011 Bouskoura Centre, 20180, Bouskoura, Morocco
Tel.: (212) 522 32 02 52
Explosive Material Distr
N.A.I.C.S.: 424690

EPC Norge AS (1)
Prestegarsalleen 71, 3070, Sande, Norway
Tel.: (47) 33 78 53 30
Explosive Material Distr
N.A.I.C.S.: 424690
Knut Tanbergmoen *(Mgr-Ops & Technical)*

EPC Senegal SA (1)
Lot 82 Route de l Aeroport - Ngor Almadies, BP 17776, Dakar, Senegal
Tel.: (221) 33 869 13 44
Web Site: http://www.epc-senegal.sn
Explosive Material Distr
N.A.I.C.S.: 424690
Ndiack Lakh *(Mgr-Technical)*

EPC Sverige AB (1)
Hugelsta, 635 02, Eskilstuna, Sweden
Tel.: (46) 16 13 90 77
Web Site: http://www.epc-groupe.se

Explosive Material Distr
N.A.I.C.S.: 424690
Ferdinand Bodenan *(Controller-Fin)*

EPC United Kingdom plc (1)
Venture Crescent, Alfreton, DE55 7RA, Derbyshire, United Kingdom
Tel.: (44) 1773 832 253
Web Site: http://www.epc-groupe.co.uk
Blasting & Drilling Service
N.A.I.C.S.: 238910
Ben Williams *(Mng Dir)*

Subsidiary (Domestic):

EPC-UK Additives (2)
Bramble Island Works Great Oakley Nr, Harwich, CO12 5JW, Essex, United Kingdom
Tel.: (44) 12 55 88 78 00
Additive Product Distr
N.A.I.C.S.: 424690

EPC-Belgique s.a (1)
Rue du Bois de Huy 5D, 4540, Amay, Belgium
Tel.: (32) 85 27 47 90
Web Site: http://www.epc-belgique.com
Explosive Material Distr
N.A.I.C.S.: 424690

Epc Andina S.A.C (1)
Av Los Insurgentes 1075, La Perla, Callao, Peru
Tel.: (51) 16142121
Commercial Explosive Mfr
N.A.I.C.S.: 325920

Epc Canada Inc. (1)
590 Rue Sainte-Anne, Yamachiche, Quebec, G0X 3L0, QC, Canada
Tel.: (819) 412-2100
Web Site: http://www.epc-groupe.ca
Commercial Explosive Mfr
N.A.I.C.S.: 325920
Olivier Vandenabelle *(Pres & CEO)*

Epc Japan Corporation (1)
Immeuble Nogizaka 513 9-6-30, Minato-ku Akasaka, Tokyo, 107-0052, Japan
Tel.: (81) 357977417
Commercial Explosive Mfr
N.A.I.C.S.: 325920

Irish Industrial Explosives Limited (1)
Clonagh, Enfield, Meath, A83 DY62, Ireland
Tel.: (353) 469541086
Web Site: http://www.iie-online.com
Commercial Explosive Mfr
N.A.I.C.S.: 325920
John Delaney *(Engr-Graduate Technical Svcs)*

Kemek LLC (1)
1001 Paxton St, Harrisburg, PA 17104
Tel.: (610) 984-7687
Commercial Explosive Mfr
N.A.I.C.S.: 325920
Shawn Sullivan *(Ops Mgr)*

Kemek Ltd. (1)
H11 Maynooth Business Campus, Maynooth, Kildar, Ireland
Tel.: (353) 16 549 900
Explosive Material Distr
N.A.I.C.S.: 424690

Maroc Dynamite (1)
625 Ave Mohammed 5 Avenue, 20000, Casablanca, Morocco
Tel.: (212) 522 59 22 49
Web Site: http://www.epc.com
Emp.: 100
Drilling & Blasting Services
N.A.I.C.S.: 238910
Frank Maueoux *(Mng Dir)*

Mineex SA (1)
Point E Residence Soukane Rue de Louga X Avenue Birago Diop RP, BP 6489, Dakar, Senegal
Tel.: (221) 338644007
Web Site: http://www.mineex.sn
Metal Mining Services
N.A.I.C.S.: 213114
Rokhaya Sall Mbaye *(Mng Dir)*

Modern Chemicals & Services Company Ltd. (1)
Olaya Street Akariya 2 Gate 10 Office 414,

PO Box 300834, Riyadh, 11372, Saudi Arabia
Tel.: (966) 114600608
Web Site: http://www.mcs-ksa.com
Commercial Explosive Mfr & Distr
N.A.I.C.S.: 325920
Ian Bradley *(Gen Mgr)*

Nitrokemine Guinee SA (1)
BP 4044, Conakry, Guinea
Tel.: (224) 623694711
Commercial Explosive Mfr
N.A.I.C.S.: 325920
Mamadou Saliou Barry *(Engr-Internship)*

Occamat SAS (1)
Misengrain, Noyant-la-Gravoyere Segre-en-Anjou-Bleu, 49520, Segre, France
Tel.: (33) 241616232
Web Site: http://www.occamat-demolition.fr
Waste Management Services
N.A.I.C.S.: 562998

Prodemo SASU (1)
137-139 avenue de Lattre-de-Tassigny, 93800, Epinay-sur-Seine, France
Tel.: (33) 148413575
Web Site: http://www.prodemo.fr
Wrecking & Demolition Services
N.A.I.C.S.: 238910

SEI EPC Italia S.p.A. (1)
Via Cefalonia 70, 25124, Brescia, Italy
Tel.: (39) 030 90411
Web Site: http://www.epc-groupe.it
Explosive Material Distr
N.A.I.C.S.: 424690

Serafina SA (1)
Barranco de los Juarez 69, 04867, Almeria, Spain
Tel.: (34) 950128095
Coal Mining Explosive & Drilling Services
N.A.I.C.S.: 213113

Sigenci SAS (1)
21B rue des Peupliers, 92752, Nanterre, Cedex, France
Tel.: (33) 155660735
Web Site: http://www.sigenci.com
Waste Management Services
N.A.I.C.S.: 562998

Silex Seguridad SL (1)
Camino de los Murcianos s / n, Villatobas, 45310, Toledo, Spain
Tel.: (34) 925595154
Web Site: http://www.silex-seguridad.com
Private Security Services
N.A.I.C.S.: 561612

Societe Congolaise des Explosifs (1)
Immeuble CNSS - 5eme etage - Appt 310 Entree C, BP 5974, Pointe Noire, Congo, Republic of
Tel.: (242) 529 09 64
Explosive Material Distr
N.A.I.C.S.: 424690

Ulster Industrial Explosives Ltd. (1)
PO Box 100, Carrickfergus, BT38 0BN, Antrim, United Kingdom
Tel.: (44) 2893351444
Web Site: http://www.uielimited.com
Commercial Explosive Mfr
N.A.I.C.S.: 325920
Ciaran McCann *(Supvr-Explosives & Engr-Technical Svcs)*

SOCIETE ARABE INTERNA-TIONALE DE BANQUE
56 Gameat El Dowal El Arabia Street Mohandessin, PO Box 54, Giza, Egypt
Tel.: (20) 233325000
Web Site: https://www.saib.com
Year Founded: 1976
SAIB.CA—(EGX)
Rev.: $404,038,689
Assets: $3,484,628,313
Liabilities: $3,085,071,368
Net Worth: $399,556,945
Earnings: $31,155,961
Emp.: 1,780
Fiscal Year-end: 12/31/23
Commercial Banking Services
N.A.I.C.S.: 522110

Societe Arabe Internationale de Banque—(Continued)

Mohamed Naguib Ibrahim *(Chm & Mng Dir)*

SOCIETE BIC S.A.
12 boulevard Victor Hugo, 92110, Clichy, France
Tel.: (33) 145195200   FR
Web Site: https://www.bicworld.com
Year Founded: 1953
BB—(EUR)
Rev: $2,498,445,745
Assets: $2,922,328,072
Liabilities: $883,917,651
Net Worth: $2,038,410,421
Earnings: $250,044,155
Emp.: 10,322
Fiscal Year-end: 12/31/23
Stationery Products, Disposable Lighters & Shavers Mfr
N.A.I.C.S.: 339940
Pierre Vareille *(Chm)*

Subsidiaries:

Advanced Magnetic Interaction, AMI S.A.S.U. (1)
2B Ave Pierre de Coubertin, 38170, Seyssinet-Pariset, France
Tel.: (33) 982493164
Web Site: http://ami.technology
Aerospace Technology Services
N.A.I.C.S.: 541715

BIC (Austria) Vertriebsgesellschaft mbH (1)
Campus 21 Liebermannstrasse F02, Brunn am Gebirge, 2345, Austria
Tel.: (43) 2236312090
Consumer Products Distr
N.A.I.C.S.: 424990

BIC (Ireland) Ltd. (1)
Regus Dublain Airport Blk-B The Cresent Building Nothwood Santry, Dublin, Ireland
Tel.: (353) 18102800
Web Site: http://ie.bicworld.com
Emp.: 3
Consumer Products Distr
N.A.I.C.S.: 424990

BIC (NZ) Ltd. (1)
GST 10-020-328 of 25 Normanby Road, Mt Eden, Auckland, 1150, New Zealand
Tel.: (64) 9 630 5970
Web Site: http://www.bicworld.com
Sales Range: $50-74.9 Million
Emp.: 80
Consumer Products Distr
N.A.I.C.S.: 424990

BIC (Romania) Marketing & Distribution SRL (1)
Victoria Park Sos Bucuresti Ploiesti nr 73-81, Cladirea 2 Etaj 3 Sector 1, Bucharest, 013685, Romania
Tel.: (40) 213126150
Consumer Products Distr
N.A.I.C.S.: 424990

BIC (Shanghai) Stationery Manufacturing Co. Ltd. (1)
Bldg T6 South Area Jinqiao Export Processing Zone No 5001 Hu, Shanghai, 201201, China
Tel.: (86) 2161464999
Emp.: 100
Stationery Products Mfr & Distr
N.A.I.C.S.: 322230

BIC (South Africa) Pty. Ltd. (1)
2234 Albertina Sisulu Road Industria West, Johannesburg, 2042, Gauteng, South Africa
Tel.: (27) 114740181
Web Site: http://www.za.bicworld.com
Consumer Products Distr
N.A.I.C.S.: 424990
Brett Griffith *(Mng Dir)*

BIC Amazonia SA (1)
Rua Ica 400, Manaus, 69075-090, Brazil
Tel.: (55) 92 3616 1500
Consumer Products Distr
N.A.I.C.S.: 424990

BIC Argentina SA (1)
Ruta Panamericana Colectora Este 2121, Boulogne Sur Mer, B1609JVC, Buenos Aires, Argentina
Tel.: (54) 1147086800
Web Site: http://www.bicworld.com
Consumer Products Distr
N.A.I.C.S.: 424990

BIC Australia Pty. Ltd. (1)
Level 4 574 St Kilda Road, Melbourne, 3004, VIC, Australia
Tel.: (61) 397982000
Web Site: http://www.au.bicworld.com
Consumer Products Distr
N.A.I.C.S.: 424990

BIC Belgium SPRL (1)
Rue du Commerce 31, Brussels, 1000, Belgium
Tel.: (32) 22193150
Web Site: http://www.bicworld.com
Emp.: 15
Office Equipment Distr
N.A.I.C.S.: 424120
Peggy Derop *(Gen Mgr)*

BIC Benelux S.A.
R du Commerce 31, 1090, Brussels, Belgium (98%)
Tel.: (32) 22193150
Web Site: http://www.bicworld.com
Sales Range: $25-49.9 Million
Emp.: 30
Marketing & Distribution of Writing Instruments
N.A.I.C.S.: 459410
Jean Codari *(Mgr)*

BIC Clichy SAS (1)
14 Rue Jeanne D Asnieres, 92110, Clichy, France
Tel.: (33) 145195200
Consumer Products Distr
N.A.I.C.S.: 424990

BIC Consumer Products Manufacturing Co. Inc.
500 Bic Dr, Milford, CT 06461-1734
Tel.: (203) 783-2000
Emp.: 50
Stationery Product Mfr
N.A.I.C.S.: 339940

BIC Corporation (1)
1 BIC Way Ste 1, Shelton, CT 06484 (89%)
Tel.: (203) 783-2000
Web Site: http://www.bicworldusa.com
Sales Range: $125-149.9 Million
Emp.: 300
Stationery Products, Lighters & Shavers Mfr
N.A.I.C.S.: 339940
John Augenstein *(Project Mgr-IT Quality & Svcs)*

Division (Domestic):

BIC Sport North America, Inc. (2)
2380 Cranberry Hwy, West Wareham, MA 02576
Tel.: (508) 291-2770
Web Site: http://www.bicsportna.com
Sales Range: $25-49.9 Million
Emp.: 10
Water Sports Equipment
N.A.I.C.S.: 423910
Chris Debereo *(Gen Mgr)*

Subsidiary (Non-US):

BIC de Guatemala (2)
33 Calle 26-38 Zona 12, Guatemala, CA, Guatemala (61%)
Tel.: (502) 24158787
Web Site: http://www.bic.com.mx
Sales Range: $25-49.9 Million
Emp.: 40
Distr of Pens & Pencils
N.A.I.C.S.: 424120

Division (Domestic):

Koozie Group (2)
14421 Myerlake Cir, Clearwater, FL 33760-2840 (100%)
Tel.: (727) 536-7895
Web Site: https://www.kooziegroup.com
Emp.: 700
Custom Imprinted Products Mfr
N.A.I.C.S.: 339940
Edgar Hernandez *(Pres)*

Subsidiary (Domestic):

Norwood Promotional Products, LLC (3)
14421 Myerlake Cir, Clearwater, FL 33760-2840
Tel.: (317) 275-2500
Web Site: http://www.norwood.com
Sales Range: $300-349.9 Million
Emp.: 650
Holding Company; Promotional Products Mfr & Imprinting Services
N.A.I.C.S.: 551112
Nicolas Paillot *(CEO)*

Subsidiary (Domestic):

Janesville Group Limited (4)
1309 Plainfield Ave, Janesville, WI 53545
Tel.: (608) 756-6900
Sales Range: $25-49.9 Million
Emp.: 85
Glassware, Art & Decorative Products Mfr
N.A.I.C.S.: 327110

Subsidiary (Non-US):

No Sabe Fallar, S.A. de C.V. (2)
Km. 41.5 Autopista Mexico-Queretaro, Parque Industrial la Luz, 54830, Cuautitlan Izcalli, Estado de Mexico, Mexico (80%)
Tel.: (52) 5550896000
Web Site: http://www.bic.com.mx
Mfr & Sales of Pens & Shavers
N.A.I.C.S.: 339940
Alejandro Goncales *(Mng Dir)*

BIC Deutschland GmbH & Co. (1)
Ginnheimer Str 4, 65760, Eschborn, 65760, Germany
Tel.: (49) 619650605
Emp.: 28
Consumer Products Distr
N.A.I.C.S.: 424990
Guido Schlegelmilch *(Gen Mgr)*

BIC GmbH (1)
Business Information & Controlling Munchner Strasse 66a, D-85221, Dachau, Germany
Tel.: (49) 8131272060
Web Site: https://www.bic-controlling.de
Financial Management Services
N.A.I.C.S.: 523999
Ute Felser *(Mng Dir)*

BIC Graphic Brasil Ltda. (1)
Rua Osasco 1744, Cajamar, 07753-040, Sao Paulo, Brazil
Tel.: (55) 1121588000
Web Site: http://www.bicgraphic.com.br
Consumer Products Distr
N.A.I.C.S.: 424990

BIC Graphic Europe SA (1)
Pol Ind Entrevias S/n, 43006, Tarragona, Spain
Tel.: (34) 977556044
Web Site: https://www.bicgraphic.com
Consumer Goods Mfr & Distr
N.A.I.C.S.: 322230

BIC Graphic France SASU (1)
14 rue Jeanne d Asnieres, 92611, Clichy, France
Tel.: (33) 145195200
Web Site: https://www.bicgraphic.com
Consumer Goods Distr
N.A.I.C.S.: 424990

BIC Iberia SA (1)
Poligono Industrial Entrevies Complejo Bic, Tarragona, 43006, Spain
Tel.: (34) 977553431
Pens & Mechanical Pencils Distr
N.A.I.C.S.: 424120
Mark Rugi *(Gen Mgr)*

BIC Italia Spa (1)
Via Tortona 33, Milan, 2144, Italy
Tel.: (39) 02 48981 1
Web Site: http://www.it.bicworld.com
Consumer Products Distr
N.A.I.C.S.: 424120

BIC Japan KK (1)
Ichigo Hatchobori Bldg 7F 1-14-1 Shintomi Chuo-ku, Chuo-Ku, Tokyo, 104-0041, Japan
Tel.: (81) 3 5542 3050
Web Site: http://www.bic-japan.co.jp
Emp.: 30

INTERNATIONAL PUBLIC

Consumer Products Distr
N.A.I.C.S.: 424990

BIC Maroc SARL (1)
92 Boulevard d Anfa 4eme etage, 20000, Casablanca, Morocco
Tel.: (212) 522642642
Stationery Product Distr
N.A.I.C.S.: 424120

BIC Netherlands BV (1)
HogaMoftan 6, Postbus 3180, Breda, 4822 MH, Netherlands
Tel.: (31) 165 59 59 00
Office Supplies Distr
N.A.I.C.S.: 424120

BIC Nordic AB (1)
F O Petersons Gata 32, Vastra Frolunda, 421 31, Sweden
Tel.: (46) 31696000
Sales Range: $25-49.9 Million
Emp.: 25
Consumer Products Distr
N.A.I.C.S.: 424990

BIC Pazarlama Ltd. (1)
Kasap ismail sok Sadikoglu is Mkz 6 No 7 D 8, Hasanpasa-Kadikoey, Istanbul, Turkiye
Tel.: (90) 216 337 89 04
Web Site: http://www.tr.bicworld.com
Emp.: 10
Consumer Products Distr
N.A.I.C.S.: 424990
Aykut Arat *(Mgr)*

BIC Polska SP ZOO (1)
ul Al Niepodleglosci 69, 02-626, Warsaw, Poland
Tel.: (48) 223326900
Web Site: https://bicmen.pl
Sales Range: $25-49.9 Million
Emp.: 45
Consumer Products Distr
N.A.I.C.S.: 424990
Zbigniew Werner *(Gen Mgr)*

BIC Portugal SA (1)
Gilza Figueiredo Avenida da Republica 59 -9, 1050-189, Lisbon, Portugal
Tel.: (351) 210308000
Office Supplies Distr
N.A.I.C.S.: 424120

BIC Product (Asia) Pte. Ltd. (1)
60 Alexandra Terrace 05-05, Singapore, 150060, Singapore
Tel.: (65) 62241488
Consumer Products Distr
N.A.I.C.S.: 424990

BIC Product (Korea) Ltd. (1)
2F Taesuk Bldg 275-5 Yangjae-Dong, Seocho-Gu, Seoul, 137863, Korea (South)
Tel.: (82) 2 5734102
Consumer Products Distr
N.A.I.C.S.: 424990

BIC Product (Singapore) Pte. Ltd. (1)
60 Alexandra Terrace 05-05 The Comtech, Singapore, 118502, Singapore
Tel.: (65) 62273066
Consumer Products Distr
N.A.I.C.S.: 424990

BIC Product (Thailand) Ltd. (1)
Unit No 900/3 IT Professional Tower 6th Floor, Yannawa, Bangkok, 10120, Thailand
Tel.: (66) 26827200
Consumer Products Distr
N.A.I.C.S.: 424990

BIC Stationery (Shanghai) Co. Ltd. (1)
Room 1802 Hongyi International Plaza No 288 Jiujiang Road Hu, Shanghai, 200001, China
Tel.: (86) 2163604963
Consumer Stationery Goods Mfr & Distr
N.A.I.C.S.: 322230

BIC Technologies SA (1)
11 rue Jeanne d'Asnieres, 92110, Clichy, France
Tel.: (33) 145195200
Consumer Products Distr
N.A.I.C.S.: 424990
Janice Chung *(CEO)*

BIC UK Ltd. (1)

AND PRIVATE COMPANIES

Chaplin House Wide Water Place, Harefield, UB9 6NS, Middlesex, United Kingdom **(100%)**
Tel.: (44) 1895827100
Web Site: http://www.bicuk.com
Sales Range: $10-24.9 Million
Emp.: 40
Support & Administrative Services
N.A.I.C.S.: 561110

BIC USA Inc. (1)
1 Bic Way Ste 1, Shelton, CT 06484-6223
Tel.: (203) 783-2000
Consumer Products Distr
N.A.I.C.S.: 424990

BIC Verwaltungs GmbH (1)
Ginnheimer Str 4, 65760, Eschborn, 65760, Germany
Tel.: (49) 61965060755
Sales Range: $25-49.9 Million
Emp.: 30
Stationery Products Mfr & Whslr
N.A.I.C.S.: 322230
Christian Kockmann *(Gen Mgr)*

BIC Violex SA (1)
58 Agiou Athanasiou street, Agios Stefanos, 14565, Greece
Tel.: (30) 2106299000
Consumer Goods Distr
N.A.I.C.S.: 423990

BIMA 83 SASU (1)
9 Rue de L'Industrie, BP 7, 68701, Cernay, France
Tel.: (33) 389757605
Web Site: http://www.bima83.fr
Solvent Dye Products Mfr & Distr
N.A.I.C.S.: 325130
Jean-Pierre Chapelle *(Chm)*

Conte SASU (1)
6 Rue Gerhard Hansen, 62200, Boulogne-sur-Mer, France
Tel.: (33) 145195200
Web Site: http://www.bicworld.com
Consumer Products Mfr
N.A.I.C.S.: 339999

DAPE 74 Distribution SASU (1)
30 Rue Pierre Beregovoy, Clichy, 92110, France
Tel.: (33) 145194800
Glassware & Plastic Products Whslr
N.A.I.C.S.: 424610

Electro-Centre SAS (1)
La Verrerie 3 Impasse De La Fontaine, 21370, Velars-sur-Ouche, France
Tel.: (33) 380760606
Consumer Products Distr
N.A.I.C.S.: 424990

Guy Laroche SA (1)
35 rue Francois, Paris, 75008, France **(73%)**
Tel.: (33) 140696800
Web Site: http://www.guylaroche.com
Emp.: 100
Men's & Women's Clothing & Fragrances
N.A.I.C.S.: 315210
Richard Rene *(Dir-Artistic)*

Industrial de Cuautitlan SA de CV (1)
Autopista Mexico Queretaro Km 41 5, Cuautitlan, 54716, Mexico
Tel.: (52) 5550896000
Web Site: http://www.bicworld.com
Emp.: 100
Consumer Products Distr
N.A.I.C.S.: 424990
Hiroaki Arai *(Office Mgr)*

Inkbox Ink Incorporated (1)
393 King Street West 2nd Floor, Toronto, ON, Canada
Web Site: https://inkbox.com
Emp.: 100
Permanent Tattoo Ink Mfr & Distr
N.A.I.C.S.: 325620

Norwood Promotional Products Europe S.L.U
Poligono Ind Entre Vias Complejo BIC, Tarragona, E-43046, Spain
Tel.: (34) 93 3965 900
Web Site: http://www.bicgraphic.eu
Emp.: 500
Consumer Products Distr

N.A.I.C.S.: 424990
Marc Rugi *(Gen Mgr)*

Norwood Promotional Products Italia S.P.A. (1)
Via Aosta 1, 24040, Ciserano-Zingonia, Italy
Tel.: (39) 035 809811
Web Site: http://www.norwoodeurope.it
Consumer Products Distr
N.A.I.C.S.: 424990

Rocket Innovations, Inc. (1)
239 Causeway St Ste 100, Boston, MA 02114
Web Site: https://www.getrocketbookpromo.com
Software Development & Design Services
N.A.I.C.S.: 541511

Societe BIC (Suisse) SA (1)
Via al Mulino 22A, 6814, Cadempino, 6814, Switzerland
Tel.: (41) 919851111
Web Site: http://www.ch.bicworld.com
Emp.: 12
Consumer Products Distr
N.A.I.C.S.: 424120
Sansossio Antonio *(Gen Mgr)*

Societe du Briquet Jetable 75 SASU (1)
Rue De Hauterive, Redon, 35600, France
Tel.: (33) 299712160
Consumer Goods Mfr
N.A.I.C.S.: 339999

Xenia Insurance Co. Ltd. (1)
C/o Conyers Dill Pearman Clarendon House 2 Church St, Hamilton, Bermuda
Tel.: (441) 295 1422
Insurance Management Services
N.A.I.C.S.: 524298

SOCIETE BSB HLM LES FOYERS
1 Rue Du Houx, 35700, Rennes, Ille Et Vilaine, France
Tel.: (33) 299845555
Web Site: http://www.sahlm-lesfoyers.com
Apartment Building Operator
N.A.I.C.S.: 531110
Benedict Berger *(Dir-Promotion)*

SOCIETE BURKINABE DES FIBRES TEXTILES
2744 Avenue William Ponty, BP 147, Sore, Bobo-Dioulasso, 01, Burkina Faso
Tel.: (226) 20970024
Web Site: http://www.sofitex.bf
Sales Range: $200-249.9 Million
Emp.: 1,200
Cotton Broadwoven Mill
N.A.I.C.S.: 313210
Celestin T. Tiendrebeogo *(Dir Gen)*

SOCIETE COMMERCIALE DE BRASSERIE SA
Provinciesteenweg 28, 3190, Boortmeerbeek, Belgium
Tel.: (32) 16601501
COBH—(EUR)
Sales Range: $100-124.9 Million
Beer Bottling Services
N.A.I.C.S.: 312120
Lien Meeus *(Chief Communication Officer)*

SOCIETE COMMERCIALE ET INDUSTRIELLE DES PRODUITS EN PLASTIQUE
Zone Industrielle Ksar Said, Manouba, 2086, Cambs, Tunisia
Tel.: (216) 71546404
Web Site: http://www.ipalpex.com
Sales Range: $25-49.9 Million
Emp.: 150
Plastic Tank Mfr
N.A.I.C.S.: 326122
Adnan Farhat *(Gen Mgr)*

Subsidiaries:

Adritec Tunis (1)
ZI Ksar Said 2086, Douar Hicher, Tunis, Tunisia
Tel.: (216) 71546404
Web Site: http://www.adritec.com
Irrigation Components & Accessories Mfr & Distr; 50% Owned by Adritec Group International, E.C. & 50% Owned by Societe Commerciale et Industrielle des Produits en Plastique
N.A.I.C.S.: 221310

SOCIETE COOPERATIVE AGRICOLE L'ENVOL DE RETZ
1 Les Petits Chardonnerets, Machecoul, 44270, Loire Atlantique, France
Tel.: (33) 240262845
Web Site: http://www.envol-de-retz.com
Rev.: $10,800,000
Emp.: 20
Game Bird Breeding, Production & Marketing
N.A.I.C.S.: 112990
Olivier de Chevigne *(Dir-Sls & Logistics)*

SOCIETE D'APPLICATION DES METHODES MODERNES D'ECLAIRAGE SA
24 rue des Amandiers, F-75020, Paris, France
Tel.: (33) 1 43 14 84 99 FR
Web Site: http://www.sammode.com
Year Founded: 1927
Electric Lighting Fixture Mfr
N.A.I.C.S.: 335132
Guillaume Cohade *(Dir-Product Offer & Innovation)*

Subsidiaries:

Hoffmeister-Leuchten GmbH (1)
Gewerbering 28-30, 58579, Schalksmuhle, Germany
Tel.: (49) 235550410
Web Site: http://www.hoffmeister.de
Electric Lamp Mfr
N.A.I.C.S.: 335139
Olaf Kleine Horstkamp *(Mng Dir)*

Subsidiary (Domestic):

SILL Leuchten GmbH (2)
Gewerbepark Central Haus 17, Sickingenstrasse 20-28, D-10553, Berlin, Germany
Tel.: (49) 306100050
Web Site: http://www.sill-lighting.com
Sales Range: $10-24.9 Million
Emp.: 125
Electric Lamp Mfr
N.A.I.C.S.: 335139
Stephan Warsow *(Mng Dir)*

SOCIETE D'ASSURANCE-DEPOTS DU CANADA
50 O'Connor St 17th Fl, PO Box 2340, Station D, Ottawa, K1P 5W5, ON, Canada
Tel.: (613) 992-7124
Web Site: http://www.cdic.ca
Year Founded: 1967
Sales Range: $100-124.9 Million
Emp.: 90
Depository Insurance Services
N.A.I.C.S.: 522180

SOCIETE D'EXPLOITATION DU PARC DES EXPOSITIONS DE LYON
Boulevard de l Europe, 69680, Chassieu, France
Tel.: (33) 472223344 FR
Web Site: http://www.eurexpo.com
Year Founded: 1984
Sales Range: $25-49.9 Million
Emp.: 40
Exposition & Trade Show Organizer & Facility Operator

N.A.I.C.S.: 561920
Bbaezner Anne Marie *(Chm)*

SOCIETE DE CONSTRUCTION GERATEK LTEE
535 Rue Pepin, Sherbrooke, J1L 1X3, QC, Canada
Tel.: (819) 564-2933
Web Site: http://www.constructiongeratek.com
Year Founded: 1980
Sales Range: $10-24.9 Million
Emp.: 40
Construction Services
N.A.I.C.S.: 236220
David Gosselin *(Pres & Gen Mgr)*

SOCIETE DE LA BOURSE DE LUXEMBOURG S.A.
35 A Blvd Joseph 2, 2227, Luxembourg, Luxembourg
Tel.: (352) 4779361
Web Site: http://www.bourse.lu
Sales Range: $25-49.9 Million
Emp.: 180
Stock Exchange Services
N.A.I.C.S.: 523210
Robert Scharfe *(Pres & CEO)*

SOCIETE DE LA CITE S.A.
Plz August De Pierre Pont, Carcassonne, 11000, France
Tel.: (33) 468719871 FR
Web Site: http://www.hoteldelacite.com
Sales Range: $10-24.9 Million
Emp.: 40
Hotel Operator
N.A.I.C.S.: 721110
Christine Pujol *(Owner)*

SOCIETE DE PARTICIPATION ET DE FINANCEMENT DANS LA COMM SA
89/91 rue du Faubourg Saint Honore, Ile-de-France, 75008, France
Tel.: (33) 144718019
Web Site: http://www.sofiouest.com
Year Founded: 1985
Investment Banking
N.A.I.C.S.: 523150
Patrice Hutin *(COO)*

Subsidiaries:

Spir Communication SA (1)
Europarc de Pichaury Batiment D5 89 Rue du Faubourg St Honore, BP 30460, 75008, Paris, France **(77.88%)**
Tel.: (33) 144718020
Web Site: http://www.spir.com
Sales Range: $1-9.9 Million
Media Advertising Services
N.A.I.C.S.: 541890
Thierry Vallenet *(CEO)*

SOCIETE DES BAINS DE MER ET DU CERCLE DES ETRANGERS A MONACO
Place du Casino, 98000, Monaco, Monaco
Tel.: (377) 98062000
Web Site: https://www.montecarlosbm.com
Year Founded: 1863
BAIN—(EUR)
Sales Range: $600-649.9 Million
Emp.: 2,986
Hotel & Casino Operator
N.A.I.C.S.: 721120
Jean-Luc Biamonti *(Chm & CEO)*

SOCIETE DES CARRIERES DE VIGNATS ET DE NORMANDIE
Les Carrieres, 61160, Necy, France
Tel.: (33) 2 33 67 88 00

SOCIETE DES CARRIERES DE VIGNATS ET DE NORMANDIE

Societe Des Carrieres De Vignats et de Normandie—(Continued)

Web Site: http://www.carrieres-vignats.fr
Year Founded: 1920
Mining & Excavation
N.A.I.C.S.: 212321

SOCIETE DES CHEMINS DE FER ET TRAMWAYS DU VAR ET DU GARD SA

31-32 quai de Dion Bouton, 92811, Puteaux, Cedex, France
Tel.: (33) 146964433
Web Site: https://var-et-gard.fr
MLCVG—(EUR)
Sales Range: Less than $1 Million
Holding Company
N.A.I.C.S.: 551112
Pierre Lebleu *(CEO)*

SOCIETE DES EAUX MINERALES D'OGEU SAS

Quartier les Fontaines, PO Box 4, 64680, Ogeu-les-Bains, France
Tel.: (33) 5 59 34 91 33
Web Site:
  http://www.ogeugroupe.com
Bottled Water Mfr
N.A.I.C.S.: 312112
Sebastien Carpentier *(Dir)*

Subsidiaries:

Eau Minerale Naturelle de Plancoet Source Sassay S.A.S.   (1)
Avenue de Sassay, BP 13, 22130, Plancoet, France
Tel.: (33) 2 96 84 39 10
Web Site: http://www.eau-plancoet.com
Sales Range: $10-24.9 Million
Mineral Water Mfr
N.A.I.C.S.: 312112
Nicolas Cherdronnet *(Pres)*

SOCIETE DES LECTEURS DU MONDE SA

80 boulevard Auguste Blanqui, 75013, Paris, France
Tel.: (33) 142172501
Web Site: http://www.sdllemonde.fr
Newspaper Publishing Services
N.A.I.C.S.: 513110
Julia Cage *(Pres & CEO)*

SOCIETE DMT SAS

Port 2961 Quai Cerealier, 59140, Dunkerque, Nord, France
Tel.: (33) 28 25 41 31
Web Site: http://www.dmtterminal.com
Sales Range: $25-49.9 Million
Emp.: 10
General Warehousing & Distribution Services
N.A.I.C.S.: 493110
Francisco Guedes *(Chm & Mng Dir)*

SOCIETE DU JOURNAL L'EST REPUBLICAIN SA

1 rue Theophraste Renaudot, 54180, Paris, France
Tel.: (33) 383598054
Web Site: http://www.estrepublicain.fr
Newspaper Publishing Services
N.A.I.C.S.: 513110
Gerard Lignac *(CHM)*

SOCIETE FERMIERE DU CASINO MUNICIPAL DE CANNES

1 Espace Lucien Barriere, FR-06400, Cannes, France
Tel.: (33) 492987800   FR
Web Site:
  https://www.groupesfcmc.com
Year Founded: 1919
FCMC—(EUR)
Sales Range: $50-74.9 Million

Emp.: 742
Casino Hotel Operator
N.A.I.C.S.: 721120
Alain Fabre *(Gen Mgr)*

SOCIETE FINANCIERE DES CAOUTCHOUCS SA

4 Avenue Guillaume, 1650, Luxembourg, Luxembourg
Tel.: (352) 442877
SOFIN—(LUX)
Rev.: $1,070,053,321
Assets: $1,285,561,716
Liabilities: $412,429,800
Net Worth: $873,131,916
Earnings: $81,574,547
Emp.: 35,226
Fiscal Year-end: 12/31/22
Holding Company
N.A.I.C.S.: 551112
Hubert Fabri *(Chm)*

Subsidiaries:

Societe Camerounaise De Palmeraies Socapalm S.A.   (1)
PO Box 691, Douala, Cameroon
Tel.: (237) 695355911
Web Site: https://socapalm.com
Palm Oilseed Mfr
N.A.I.C.S.: 311224

Sud Comoe Caoutchouc Scc S.A.   (1)
Adaou a 10 km d'Aboisso en venant d'Abidjan - Route A100, 1034, Aboisso, Cote d'Ivoire
Tel.: (225) 2721309001
Web Site: https://www.sogbci.com
Palm Oilseed Mfr
N.A.I.C.S.: 311224

SOCIETE FONCIERE, FINANCIERE ET DE PARTICIPATIONS S.A.

75 Avenue de la Grande Armee, Paris, 75116, France
Tel.: (33) 140664211
Web Site: http://www.societe-ffp.fr
Sales Range: $25-49.9 Million
Investor
N.A.I.C.S.: 523160
Jean-Philippe Peugeot *(Vice Chm)*

SOCIETE FRANCAISE DE CASINOS SA

16 Court Albert, 75008, Paris, France
Tel.: (33) 233500079
Web Site: https://www.casinos-sfc.com
SFCA—(EUR)
Sales Range: $10-24.9 Million
Emp.: 250
Casinos & Virtual Gaming Centers Owner & Operator
N.A.I.C.S.: 713210
Pascal Pessiot *(Chm)*

SOCIETE GENERALE DE BANQUE AU LIBAN S.A.L.

Saloumeh-Dekwaneh Saloumeh Roundabout, PO Box 112955, Beirut, Lebanon
Tel.: (961) 1 499 813   LB
Web Site: http://www.sgbl.com.lb
Year Founded: 1953
Sales Range: $1-4.9 Billion
Commercial & Investment Banking
N.A.I.C.S.: 522110
Antoun N. Sehnaoui *(Chm & CEO)*

Subsidiaries:

Banque Richelieu France   (1)
1-3-5 rue Paul Cezanne, 75008, Paris, France
Tel.: (33) 142890000
Web Site: http://www.banquerichelieu.com
Private Banking & Asset Management Services

N.A.I.C.S.: 523150
Subsidiary (Domestic):

Richelieu Gestion   (2)
1-3-5 rue Paul Cezanne, 75008, Paris, France
Tel.: (33) 1 42890000
Web Site: http://www.banquerichelieu.com
Banking Services
N.A.I.C.S.: 522110

Banque Richelieu Monaco   (1)
8 avenue de Grande-Bretagne, MC-98005, Monaco, Monaco
Tel.: (377) 92 16 5555
Web Site: http://www.banquerichelieu.com
Banking Services
N.A.I.C.S.: 523150

Societe Generale de Banque - Jordanie   (1)
Al-Abdali Building num 1, PO Box 560, Amman, 11118, Jordan   (87.67%)
Tel.: (962) 65600300
Web Site: http://www.sgbj.com.jo
Rev.: $122,791,166
Assets: $2,225,837,653
Liabilities: $1,988,460,357
Net Worth: $237,377,296
Earnings: $8,911,410
Emp.: 313
Fiscal Year-end: 12/31/2020
Banking Services
N.A.I.C.S.: 522110
Antoun Nabil Nicolas Sehnaoui *(Deputy Chm)*

SOCIETE GENERALE S.A.

29 Boulevard Haussmann, 75009, Paris, France
Tel.: (33) 142142000   FR
Web Site:
  https://www.societegenerale.com
Year Founded: 1864
GLE—(OTCIQ)
Rev.: $57,292,251,241
Assets: $1,677,147,636,521
Liabilities: $1,594,860,781,351
Net Worth: $82,286,855,169
Earnings: $2,690,481,330
Emp.: 126,000
Fiscal Year-end: 12/31/23
Financial Investment Services
N.A.I.C.S.: 523999
Frederic Oudea *(CEO)*

Subsidiaries:

ALD AUTOLEASING D GMBH   (1)
Nedderfeld 95, Hamburg, 22529, Germany
Tel.: (49) 40471040
Automobile Leasing Services
N.A.I.C.S.: 522220

ALD AUTOMOTIVE A/S   (1)
Helgeshoj Alle 34, 2630, Taastrup, Denmark
Tel.: (45) 33 55 80 00
Web Site: http://www.aldautomotive.dk
Sales Range: $75-99.9 Million
Emp.: 150
Fleet Management Services
N.A.I.C.S.: 532112
Hadrien Boisseau *(CEO)*

ALD AUTOMOTIVE AB   (1)
Eldarvagen 6, 187 75, Taby, Sweden
Tel.: (46) 8 501 122 00
Web Site: http://www.aldautomotive.se
Sales Range: $50-74.9 Million
Emp.: 70
Fleet Management Services
N.A.I.C.S.: 532112
Gunnar Kjellman *(Mng Dir)*

ALD AUTOMOTIVE AS   (1)
Holtet 45, 1368, Stabekk, Norway
Tel.: (47) 67 10 87 00
Web Site: http://www.aldautomotive.no
Sales Range: $25-49.9 Million
Emp.: 40
Passenger Car Leasing Services
N.A.I.C.S.: 532112

ALD AUTOMOTIVE GROUP PLC   (1)
Oakwood Park Lodge Causeway, Bristol, BS16 3JA, United Kingdom

INTERNATIONAL PUBLIC

Tel.: (44) 1179 082000
Fleet Management Services
N.A.I.C.S.: 532112
Mel Dawson *(Mng Dir)*

ALD AUTOMOTIVE SRO   (1)
U Stavoservisu 527/1, 108 00, Prague, Czech Republic
Tel.: (420) 955 525 000
Web Site: http://www.aldautomotive.cz
Emp.: 80
Fleet Management Services
N.A.I.C.S.: 532112

ALD Automotive Limited   (1)
Oakwood Drive Emersons Green, Bristol, BS16 7LB, United Kingdom
Tel.: (44) 3700011181
Web Site: http://www.aldautomotive.co.uk
Automotive Financial Leasing Services
N.A.I.C.S.: 522220
Tim Laver *(Mng Dir)*

ALD INTERNATIONAL SAS & CO. KG   (1)
Nedderfeld 95, 22529, Hamburg, Germany
Tel.: (49) 40 47104 0
Automotive Financial Leasing Services
N.A.I.C.S.: 522220

ALD LEASE FINANZ GMBH   (1)
Nedderfeld 95, 22529, Hamburg, Germany
Tel.: (49) 40 48091 0
Sales Range: $200-249.9 Million
Emp.: 350
Automotive Financial Leasing Services
N.A.I.C.S.: 522220

ALD S.A.   (1)
1 rue Eugene et Armand Peugeot, Rueil Malmaison, 92508, Paris, Cedex, France
Tel.: (33) 156761800
Web Site: http://www.aldautomotive.com
Sales Range: $50-74.9 Million
Emp.: 60
Auto Leasing & Fleet-Management Services
N.A.I.C.S.: 532112
Tim Albertsen *(CEO)*

Subsidiary (Non-US):

MKB-Euroleasing Autopark Zrt.   (2)
Ady Endre u 19, 1024, Budapest, Hungary
Tel.: (36) 14889922
Web Site: http://autoparkaukcio.hu
Automobile Leasing Services
N.A.I.C.S.: 532112

AXUS FINLAND OY   (1)
Ohtolankatu 4, Vantaa, 1510, Finland
Tel.: (358) 10 404 2501
Web Site: http://www.aldautomotive.fi
Sales Range: $50-74.9 Million
Emp.: 100
Fleet Management Services
N.A.I.C.S.: 532112
Pekka Kivinen *(Gen Mgr)*

AXUS ITALIANA SRL   (1)
Via Alexandre Gustave Eiffel, 00148, Rome, Italy
Tel.: (39) 06656851
Web Site: http://www.aldautomotive.it
Sales Range: $150-199.9 Million
Emp.: 450
Fleet Management Services
N.A.I.C.S.: 532112

AXUS NEDERLAND BV   (1)
Hoeksteen 60, 2132 MS, Hoofddorp, Netherlands
Tel.: (31) 20 658 7000
Web Site: http://www.aldautomotive.nl
Fleet Management Services
N.A.I.C.S.: 532112

AXUS SA/NV   (1)
Rue Colonel Bourgstraat 120, Brussels, 1140, Belgium
Tel.: (32) 2 706 41 11
Emp.: 220
Financial Management Services
N.A.I.C.S.: 523999

Altura Markets Sociedad de Valores SA   (1)
Parque Empresarial Cristalia Edificio 2-Planta 1 Via de los Poblados 3, 28033, Madrid, Spain
Tel.: (34) 917486100
Web Site: http://www.alturamarkets.com

AND PRIVATE COMPANIES

Brokerage Firm Services
N.A.I.C.S.: 523150
Sverre Hasvold (CEO)

BANQUE DE POLYNESIE SA (1)
355 Boulevard Pomare, BP 530, 98713, Papeete, French Polynesia
Tel.: (689) 46 66 99
Sales Range: $50-74.9 Million
Emp.: 10
Banking Services
N.A.I.C.S.: 522110
Rauch Olivier (Gen Mgr)

BRD - Groupe Societe Generale S.A. (1)
BRD Tower 1-7 Ion Mihalache Boulevard Sector 1, 011171, Bucharest, Romania (60.17%)
Tel.: (40) 213026161
Web Site: https://www.brd.ro
Rev.: $916,536,131
Assets: $18,211,802,741
Liabilities: $16,286,995,287
Net Worth: $1,924,807,454
Earnings: $359,642,275
Emp.: 6,030
Fiscal Year-end: 12/31/2023
Banking & Financial Services
N.A.I.C.S.: 523150
Traian Traicu (Head-Media Rels & Comm Dept)

BRD Asset Management Sai SA (1)
Str Dr Nicolae Staicovici nr 2 Opera Center II etaj 5 Sector 5, 050558, Bucharest, Romania
Tel.: (40) 213272228
Web Site: http://www.brdam.ro
Asset Management Services
N.A.I.C.S.: 523940
Mihai Purcarea (Chm & Gen Mgr)

BRD Finance IFN S.A. (1)
Cladirea City Offices Sos Oltenitei nr 2 etaj 4 sector 4, 041312, Bucharest, Romania
Tel.: (40) 213014830
Web Site: http://www.brdfinance.ro
Financial Services
N.A.I.C.S.: 541611
Idalina Nita (Mgr-IT)

Banco Societe Generale Brasil S.A. (1)
Avenida Paulista 2300-9 andar, Sao Paulo, 01310-300, Brazil
Tel.: (55) 1132178000
Financial Banking Services
N.A.I.C.S.: 522110
Daniela Bovi (Mgr)

Bank Deutsches Kraftfahrzeuggewerbe GmbH (1)
Nedderfeld 95, 22529, Hamburg, Germany
Tel.: (49) 40480910
Web Site: http://www.bdk-bank.de
Emp.: 790
Automotive Financing & Leasing Services
N.A.I.C.S.: 522220
Maike Klein (Mgr-Learning & Dev)

Banky Fampandrosoana Varotra SG (1)
14 Ialana Jeneraly Rabehevitra, BP 196, Antaninarenina, Antananarivo, 101, Madagascar
Tel.: (261) 202220691
Web Site: http://www.societegenerale.mg
Commercial Banking Services
N.A.I.C.S.: 522110
Gina Ralaimihoatra (Comm Mgr)

Boursorama S.A. (1)
18 Quai du Point du Jour, 92659, Boulogne-Billancourt, Cedex, France (100%)
Tel.: (33) 146095000
Web Site: http://www.groupe.boursorama.fr
Sales Range: $250-299.9 Million
Emp.: 810
Commercial Banking Services
N.A.I.C.S.: 522110
Patrick Sommelet (Deputy CEO)

COMPAGNIE GENERALE DE LOCATION D EQUIPEMENTS SA (1)
69 Avenue de Flandre, Marcq-en-Baroeul, 59708, France
Tel.: (33) 3 20 45 67 69
Industrial Equipment Rental Services

N.A.I.C.S.: 532490

Car Professional Fuhrparkmanagement und Beratungsgesellschaft mbH & Co. KG. (1)
Flughafenstrasse 54 house A, 22335, Hamburg, Germany
Tel.: (49) 40531050
Web Site: http://www.carprofessional.de
Emp.: 170
Automotive Fleet Management Services
N.A.I.C.S.: 532112

Credit du Nord S.A. (1)
28 place Rihour, 59800, Lille, France (80%)
Tel.: (33) 140224022
Web Site: http://www.credit-du-nord.fr
Sales Range: $1-4.9 Billion
Emp.: 7,613
Retail & Corporate Banking Services
N.A.I.C.S.: 522110

Branch (Domestic):

Credit du Nord (2)
50 rue d'Anjou, 75008, Paris, France
Tel.: (33) 140224438
Web Site: http://www.credit-du-nord.fr
Branches & Agencies of Foreign Banks
N.A.I.C.S.: 522299

DC MORTGAGE FINANCE NETHERLAND BV (1)
Prins Bernhardplein 200, Amsterdam, 1097 JB, Netherlands
Tel.: (31) 205214777
Financial Management Services
N.A.I.C.S.: 523999

Essox Finance S.R.O (1)
Karadzicova 16, 821 08, Bratislava, Slovakia
Tel.: (421) 249229650
Web Site: http://www.essoxfin.sk
Commercial Banking Services
N.A.I.C.S.: 522110

FENWICK LEASE (1)
59 Avenue de Chatou, 92500, Rueil-Malmaison, France
Tel.: (33) 141395900
Forklift Truck Whslr
N.A.I.C.S.: 423830

FRANFINANCE LOCATION (1)
57 Avenue De Chatou, Rueil-Malmaison, 92500, France
Tel.: (33) 141295556
Financial Management Services
N.A.I.C.S.: 523999

Fiditalia S.p.A. (1)
Via G Silva 34, 20149, Milan, Italy
Tel.: (39) 0243018799
Web Site: http://www.fiditalia.it
Emp.: 350
Retail Credit, Leasing, Credit Cards
N.A.I.C.S.: 522210

Franfinance S.A. (1)
53 rue du Port, 92724, Nanterre, Cedex, France (100%)
Tel.: (33) 826826555
Web Site: http://www.franfinance.fr
Vendor Financing
N.A.I.C.S.: 522310

Subsidiary (Non-US):

Adria Leasing SpA (2)
Viale Dei Mille 1D, 31100, Treviso, Italy (100%)
Tel.: (39) 0422545946
Vendor Financing
N.A.I.C.S.: 522310

Fraer Leasing SpA (2)
Piazza della Liberta 15, I-47023, Cesena, Italy
Tel.: (39) 0547368434
Web Site: http://www.franfinance.com
Vendor Financing
N.A.I.C.S.: 522310

Franfinance Italy SpA (2)
Piazza della Repubblica 32, 20124, Milan, Italy
Tel.: (39) 026784141
Web Site: http://www.franfinance.com
Vendor Financing

N.A.I.C.S.: 522310

Franfinance Spain (2)
6 Fl Caleruega St 81, 28033, Madrid, Spain (100%)
Tel.: (34) 913834340
Web Site: http://www.sgfinance.es
Sales Range: $25-49.9 Million
Emp.: 31
Vendor Financing
N.A.I.C.S.: 522310
Jose Luis Carande (Gen Mgr)

Franfinance UK Ltd. (2)
Partshot House 5 Key Rd, TW9 2PR, Richmond, Surrey, United Kingdom - England (100%)
Tel.: (44) 2089409888
Web Site: http://www.sgef.co.uk
Sales Range: $25-49.9 Million
Emp.: 30
Vendor Financing
N.A.I.C.S.: 522310
Giles Turner (Mng Dir)

GEFA Leasing GmbH (2)
Robert Daum Platz 1, Wuppertal, 42117, Germany (100%)
Tel.: (49) 2023820
Web Site: http://www.gefa.de
Sales Range: $800-899.9 Million
Emp.: 600
Vendor Financing
N.A.I.C.S.: 522310
Jochen Jehmlich (Chm & Mng Dir)

SG Equipment Finance (2)
nam Junkovych 2772/1, 155 00, Prague, Czech Republic (100%)
Tel.: (420) 955526700
Web Site: http://www.sgef.cz
Sales Range: $75-99.9 Million
Emp.: 120
Vendor Financing
N.A.I.C.S.: 522310
Reinhold Knodl (CEO & Mng Dir)

SG Equipment Finance (2)
Gladbachstrasse 105, 8044, Zurich, Switzerland (100%)
Tel.: (41) 3253900
Web Site: http://www.sgequipmentfinance.ch
Sales Range: $50-74.9 Million
Emp.: 20
Vendor Financing
N.A.I.C.S.: 522310
Adrian Troller (CEO)

SG Equipment Finance Austria GmbH (2)
Mariahilferstrasse 123/1/2 Top 122, 1060, Vienna, Austria (100%)
Tel.: (43) 15223410
Web Site: http://www.sgef.at
Sales Range: $50-74.9 Million
Emp.: 13
Vendor Financing
N.A.I.C.S.: 522310

SG Equipment Finance Hungary (2)
Vaci ut 1-3 B/4, 1062, Budapest, Hungary (100%)
Tel.: (36) 12118840
Web Site: http://www.sgef.hu
Sales Range: $50-74.9 Million
Emp.: 22
Vendor Financing
N.A.I.C.S.: 522310

SG Equipment Leasing Polska (2)
Marszalkowska 111, 00-102, Warsaw, Poland (100%)
Tel.: (48) 225284600
Web Site: http://www.sgef.pl
Sales Range: $50-74.9 Million
Emp.: 85
Vendor Financing
N.A.I.C.S.: 522310
Lech Zeyer (CEO)

SG Leasing (2)
Via Trivulzio 5, 20146, Milan, Italy (100%)
Tel.: (39) 02480811
Web Site: http://www.sgequipmentfinance.it
Sales Range: $25-49.9 Million
Emp.: 50
Vendor Financing
N.A.I.C.S.: 522310

Societe Generale Corporate & Investment Banking Australia (2)

SOCIETE GENERALE S.A.

Level 25 1 Bligh Street, Sydney, 2000, NSW, Australia
Tel.: (61) 292108000
Sales Range: $150-199.9 Million
Emp.: 270
Vendor Financing
N.A.I.C.S.: 522310

GEFA GESELLSCHAFT FUR ABSATZFINANZIERUNG MBH (1)
Robert-Daum-Platz 1, Wuppertal, 42117, Germany
Tel.: (49) 202 382 0
Web Site: http://www.gefa.de
Sales Range: $200-249.9 Million
Emp.: 50
Financial Lending Services
N.A.I.C.S.: 522220
Jochen Jemlich (Gen Mgr)

GENEFIM S.A. (1)
29 Boulevard Haussmann, Paris, 75009, France
Tel.: (33) 1 42 14 38 80
Real Estate Investment Services
N.A.I.C.S.: 531390

GENEGIS II (1)
30 Place Ronde Immeuble Espace 21, 92800, Puteaux, France
Tel.: (33) 1 42 14 55 17
Real Estate Development Services
N.A.I.C.S.: 531390

GENEGIS I SAS (1)
29 Boulevard Haussmann, 75009, Paris, France
Tel.: (33) 1 42 14 20 00
Commercial Banking Services
N.A.I.C.S.: 522110

Gefa Bank GmbH (1)
Robert-Daum-Platz 1, 42117, Wuppertal, Germany
Tel.: (49) 2023821000
Web Site: http://www.gefa-bank.de
Emp.: 620
Automotive Financing & Leasing Services
N.A.I.C.S.: 522220
Jurgen Jaquemotte (Head-IT Ops)

HANSEATIC BANK GMBH & CO KG (1)
Bramfelder Chaussee 101, Hamburg, 22177, Germany
Tel.: (49) 40 6 46 03 0
Commercial Banking Services
N.A.I.C.S.: 522110

Hanseatic Bank GmbH & Co. (1)
Bramfelder Chaussee 101, 22177, Hamburg, Germany (75%)
Tel.: (49) 40646030
Web Site: http://www.hanseaticbank.de
Sales Range: $1-4.9 Billion
Emp.: 331
International Bank
N.A.I.C.S.: 522320

KB Penzijni Spolecnost. A.S. (1)
Nam Junkovych 2772/1, Metro Stodulky Trasa B, 155 00, Prague, Czech Republic
Tel.: (420) 955525999
Web Site: http://www.kbps.cz
Commercial Banking Services
N.A.I.C.S.: 522110
Ondrej Horak (Mgr-Risk)

Kleinwort Benson Bank Limited (1)
14 St George St, London, W1S 1FE, United Kingdom (100%)
Tel.: (44) 2032077000
Web Site: http://www.kleinwortbenson.com
Private Banking Services
N.A.I.C.S.: 523150
Eric Barnett (CEO)

Subsidiary (Non-US):

Kleinwort Benson (Channel Islands) Limited (2)
Dorey Court Admiral Park, Saint Peter Port, GY1 3BG, Guernsey
Tel.: (44) 1481727111
Web Site: http://www.kleinwortbenson.com
Private Banking Servivces
N.A.I.C.S.: 523150
Michelle Norman (Mgr-Data)

Komercni Banka, A.S. (1)
Na Prikope 33, PO Box 839, 114 07,

SOCIETE GENERALE S.A.

Societe Generale S.A.—(Continued)
Prague, 1, Czech Republic (60.4%)
Tel.: (420) 955559550
Web Site: https://www.kb.cz
Rev.: $1,665,536,720
Assets: $58,285,494,520
Liabilities: $52,347,025,640
Net Worth: $5,938,468,880
Earnings: $608,545,280
Emp.: 7,687
Fiscal Year-end: 12/31/2021
Commercial Banking Services
N.A.I.C.S.: 522110
Jan Juchelka *(Chm & CEO)*

Subsidiary (Domestic):

ESSOX SRO
F A Gerstnera 52, 370 01, Ceske Budejovice, Czech Republic
Tel.: (420) 389010422
Web Site: http://www.essox.cz
Mortgage Loan Brokerage Services
N.A.I.C.S.: 522310

Factoring KB, a.s. (2)
namesti Junkovych 2772/1, 155 00, Prague, Czech Republic (100%)
Tel.: (420) 955 526 904
Web Site: http://www.factoringkb.cz
Sales Range: $25-49.9 Million
Emp.: 45
Factoring & Brokerage Services
N.A.I.C.S.: 523160
Adam Fiedler *(Chm & CEO)*

Investicni Kapitalova Spolecnost (2)
Dlouha 34, 110 15, Prague, Czech Republic (100%)
Tel.: (420) 224008888
Web Site: http://www.iks-kb.cz
Sales Range: $25-49.9 Million
Emp.: 45
Provider of Investment Services
N.A.I.C.S.: 523940

Subsidiary (Non-US):

Jugobanka A.D. Beograd (2)
Kralja Petra 19-21, 11000, Belgrade, Serbia, Serbia
Tel.: (381) 11 63 00 22
Web Site: http://www.jugobanka.com
Provider of Banking Services
N.A.I.C.S.: 522320

Komercni Banka Bratislava, a.s. (2)
Hodzovo namestie 1A, PO Box 137, 810 00, Bratislava, Slovakia (100%)
Tel.: (421) 59277328
Web Site: http://www.koba.sk
Sales Range: $1-4.9 Billion
Emp.: 9,238
Provider of Commercial Banking Services
N.A.I.C.S.: 522110

Subsidiary (Domestic):

Komercni Pojhtovna (2)
Karolinska 1/650, PO Box 39, 186 00, Prague, Czech Republic (51%)
Tel.: (420) 222095999
Web Site: http://www.kbpojistovna.cz
Sales Range: $75-99.9 Million
Emp.: 90
Provider of Insurance Services
N.A.I.C.S.: 524298
Sarka Sindlerova *(Head-of Client Svc & Ops Section)*

LA MAROCAINE VIE S.A (1)
37 Boulevard Moulay Youssef, Casablanca, 20000, Morocco
Tel.: (212) 522 43 11 00
General Insurance Services
N.A.I.C.S.: 524210

LLC PROSTOFINANCE (1)
9 Moskovsky Avenue 5-th Building 4-th Floor Office 5-401, Forum Park Plaza, Kiev, 04073, Ukraine
Tel.: (380) 44 498 21 66
Web Site: http://www.prostofinance.ua
Sales Range: $350-399.9 Million
Emp.: 550
Consumer Loan Financing Services
N.A.I.C.S.: 522291

LeasePlan Corporation N.V. (1)
Gustav Mahlerlaan 360, 1082 ME, Amsterdam, Netherlands
Tel.: (31) 207093000
Web Site: http://www.leaseplan.com
Rev.: $11,331,095,116
Assets: $35,038,461,885
Liabilities: $30,491,114,694
Net Worth: $4,547,347,191
Earnings: $451,282,303
Emp.: 7,736
Fiscal Year-end: 12/31/2019
Holding Company; Motor Vehicle Leasing & Fleet Management Services
N.A.I.C.S.: 551112
Tex Gunning *(Chm-Mgmt Bd & CEO)*

Subsidiary (Non-US):

LeasePlan Italia S.p.A. (2)
Viale Alessandro Marchetti 105, 00148, Rome, Italy
Tel.: (39) 06967071
Web Site: http://www.leaseplan.it
Passenger Car Leasing & Fleet Management Services
N.A.I.C.S.: 532112

Subsidiary (Domestic):

LeasePlan Nederland N.V. (2)
PJ Oudweg 41, 1314 CH, Almere, Netherlands
Tel.: (31) 365272700
Web Site: http://www.leaseplan.nl
Motor Vehicle Leasing & Fleet Management Services
N.A.I.C.S.: 532112

Subsidiary (Non-US):

LeasePlan Potugal (2)
Largoas Park Edificio 6, 2740-244, Lisbon, Portugal
Tel.: (351) 214 400 990
Web Site: http://www.leaseplan.pt
Car Rental Services
N.A.I.C.S.: 532111

MONTALIS INVESTMENT BV (1)
Amstelplein 1 Rembrandt Tr, 1096 HA, Amsterdam, Netherlands
Tel.: (31) 20 4622822
Investment Management Service
N.A.I.C.S.: 523999

Modra Pyramida Stavebni Sporitelna AS (1)
Belehradska 128 cp 222, 120 21, Prague, Czech Republic
Tel.: (420) 210220230
Web Site: http://www.modrapyramida.cz
Emp.: 700
Insurance Services
N.A.I.C.S.: 524210
Ludek Kohout *(CIO)*

Newedge Group SA (1)
52/60 Avenue des Champs Elysees, 75008, Paris, France (100%)
Tel.: (33) 155072020
Web Site: http://www.newedgegroup.com
Sales Range: $300-349.9 Million
Emp.: 2,438
Security Brokerage Services
N.A.I.C.S.: 523150

Subsidiary (Non-US):

Newedge Canada, Inc. (2)
1501 Av McGill College Bureau 1800, Montreal, H3A 3M8, QC, Canada
Tel.: (514) 841-6000
Web Site: http://www.newedge.com
Sales Range: $50-74.9 Million
Emp.: 25
Securities Broker
N.A.I.C.S.: 523150

Subsidiary (US):

Newedge USA, LLC (2)
550 W Jackson Blvd Ste 500, Chicago, IL 60661
Tel.: (312) 762-1000
Web Site: http://www.needge.com
Sales Range: $50-74.9 Million
Emp.: 400
Brokerage Services
N.A.I.C.S.: 523150
Edward Kevelson *(Head-OTC Energy)*

ORADEA VIE SA (1)
Tour D2 17 Bis Place des Reflets, La Defense, 92919, Paris, Cedex, France
Tel.: (33) 238796700
Web Site: http://www.oradeavie.fr
Sales Range: $50-74.9 Million
Emp.: 15
Insurance Management Services
N.A.I.C.S.: 524298

PODGORICKA BANKA SG GROUP (1)
Bulevar Revolucije Br 17, 81000, Podgorica, Montenegro
Tel.: (382) 20 415 500
Web Site: http://www.societegenerale.me
Sales Range: $100-124.9 Million
Emp.: 115
Commercial Banking Services
N.A.I.C.S.: 522110

RB Factoring LLC (1)
st Masha Poryvaeva 34 Building III Room 3 Floor 6, 107078, Moscow, Russia
Tel.: (7) 4956265101
Web Site: http://www.rosbank.ru
Emp.: 30
Commercial Banking Services
N.A.I.C.S.: 522110
Oleg Vindman *(Gen Mgr)*

RB Leasing LLC (1)
st Masha Poryvaeva 34 Room III room 80 floor 4, 107078, Moscow, Russia
Tel.: (7) 4955807334
Web Site: http://www.rosbank-leasing.ru
Financial Lending Services
N.A.I.C.S.: 532490

RB Specialized Depositary LLC (1)
Masha Poryvaeva st 34, 107078, Moscow, Russia
Tel.: (7) 84957255655
Web Site: http://www.depository.ru
Commercial Banking Services
N.A.I.C.S.: 522110

ROSBANK Group (1)
34 Mashi Poryvaevoy Street, 107078, Moscow, 107078, Russia (99.49%)
Tel.: (7) 4957898877
Web Site: https://www.rosbank.ru
Rev.: $1,473,733,580
Assets: $19,658,711,710
Liabilities: $16,884,367,840
Net Worth: $2,774,343,870
Earnings: $176,575,110
Fiscal Year-end: 12/31/2019
Commercial Banking Services
N.A.I.C.S.: 522110
Ilya Andreevich Polyakov *(Chm-Mgmt Bd)*

S.C. BRD Sogelease IFN S.A. (1)
Sediul Central - Turn BRD et 12 B-dul Ion Mihalache nr 1-7, District 1, Bucharest, Romania
Tel.: (40) 213014188
Web Site: http://www.brdleasing.ro
Commercial Banking Services
N.A.I.C.S.: 522110
Gabriela Mihailescu *(CFO & Exec Officer)*

SAS Normandie Habitat (1)
19 rue Jean Richard Bloch, 76300, Sotteville-les-Rouen, France
Tel.: (33) 23 573 2107
Web Site: https://www.normandie-habitat.com
Apartment & Property Selling Services
N.A.I.C.S.: 531110

SG ALD AUTOMOTIVE PORTUGAL SOCIEDADE GERAL DE COMERCIO E ALUGUER DE BENZ SA (1)
Sintra Business Park Zona Industrial de Abrunheira, Edificio 2 Escritorio 0C, Sintra, 2710-089, Portugal
Tel.: (351) 21 092 0300
Web Site: http://www.aldautomotive.pt
Sales Range: $50-74.9 Million
Emp.: 100
Car Lending Services
N.A.I.C.S.: 532112
Guillaumede de Leobardy *(Gen Mgr)*

SG Americas, Inc. (1)
220 N Park Rd Bldg 6, Wyomissing, PA 19610
Tel.: (484) 709-2093
Web Site: http://www.sgamerica.com
Heat Exchanger Mfr

INTERNATIONAL PUBLIC

N.A.I.C.S.: 332410

SG CAPITAL DEVELOPPEMENT (1)
Tour Societe Generale 17 Cours Valmy, 92972, Paris, France
Tel.: (33) 142142095
Financial Services
N.A.I.C.S.: 523999

SG DE BANQUES AU BURKINA (1)
248 Rue De I Hotel De Ville 01, BP 585, Ouagadougou, Burkina Faso
Tel.: (226) 50 32 32 32
Financial Management Services
N.A.I.C.S.: 523999

SG EQUIPMENT FINANCE BENELUX BV (1)
Astronaut 22 K, 3824 MJ, Amersfoort, Netherlands
Tel.: (31) 334508320
Web Site: http://www.sgef.nl
Sales Range: $50-74.9 Million
Emp.: 18
Automotive Financial Leasing Services
N.A.I.C.S.: 522220
Coert Noordkamp *(Mng Dir)*

SG EQUIPMENT FINANCE INTERNATIONAL GMBH (1)
Robert-Daum-Platz 5, Wuppertal, 42117, Germany
Tel.: (49) 202382572
Web Site: http://www.gefa.de
Sales Range: $350-399.9 Million
Emp.: 750
Equipment Financial Leasing Services
N.A.I.C.S.: 522220

SG EQUIPMENT FINANCE LIMITED (1)
Parkshot House 5 Kew Road, Richmond, TW9 2PR, Surrey, United Kingdom
Tel.: (44) 2086298400
Web Site: http://www.equipmentfinance.co.uk
Financial Management Services
N.A.I.C.S.: 523999
Mohcine Busta *(Sec)*

SG EQUIPMENT FINANCE SA & CO KG (1)
Robert-Daum-Platz 5, Wuppertal, 42117, Germany
Tel.: (49) 202479390
Web Site: http://www.gefa.de
Industrial Equipment Financial Leasing Services
N.A.I.C.S.: 522220

SG EQUIPMENT FINANCE USA CORP. (1)
480 Washington Blvd, Jersey City, NJ 07310-1900
Tel.: (201) 839-1100
Web Site: http://www.sgef.us
Emp.: 40
Investment Management Service
N.A.I.C.S.: 523999
Danny Lam *(COO)*

SG Equipment Finance Czech Republic S.R.O. (1)
Nam Junkovych 2772/1, 155 00, Prague, Czech Republic
Tel.: (420) 955526700
Web Site: http://www.equipmentfinance.cz
Insurance Services
N.A.I.C.S.: 524210
Reinhold Knoedl *(CEO & Mng Dir)*

SG Equipment Finance Iberia. E.F.C. S.A. (1)
Parque Norte Serrano Galvache 56 Edificio Abedul 3a Planta, 28033, Madrid, Spain
Tel.: (34) 913834340
Equipment Financing Services
N.A.I.C.S.: 522220

SG Equipment Finance Italy S.P.A. (1)
Via Antonio Tolomeo Trivulzio 7, 20146, Milan, MI, Italy
Tel.: (39) 024654681
Financial Lending Services
N.A.I.C.S.: 522220
Carlo Mescieri *(CEO)*

SG Equipment Finance S.A. (1)
Alameda Rio Negro 500-Torre B-20th Floor CJ 2014/2015, Barueri, 06454-000, Sao Paulo, Brazil
Tel.: (55) 1126662259
Equipment Financing Services
N.A.I.C.S.: 522220

SG FACTORING SPA (1)
Via Antonio Tolomeo Trivulzio 7, 20146, Milan, Italy
Tel.: (39) 0246775316
Web Site: http://www.factoring.societegenerale.it
Factoring Consulting Services
N.A.I.C.S.: 522299

SG FINANCIAL SERVICES HOLDING SA (1)
29 Boulevard Haussmann, 75009, Paris, France
Tel.: (33) 1 42 14 20 00
Investment Management Service
N.A.I.C.S.: 523999

SG FINANS AS (1)
Strandveien 18, PO Box 105, 1325, Lysaker, Oslo, Norway
Tel.: (47) 21 63 20 00
Web Site: http://www.sgfinans.no
Rev.: $71,017,416
Emp.: 30
Equipment Finance Leasing & Factoring Services
N.A.I.C.S.: 522299
Carsten Thorne *(CEO)*

SG HAMBROS LIMITED (1)
Exchange House 12 Primrose Street, London, EC2A 2EG, United Kingdom
Tel.: (44) 20 7597 3000
Web Site: http://www.privatebanking.co.uk
Sales Range: $50-74.9 Million
Emp.: 10
Commercial Banking Services
N.A.I.C.S.: 522110
Warwick Newbury *(Chm)*

SG Hambros Bank & Trust Limited (1)
SG House 41 Tower Hill, London, EC3N 4SG, United Kingdom
Tel.: (44) 2075973000
Web Site: http://www.sghambros.com
Sales Range: $100-124.9 Million
Emp.: 200
Research, Trading & Sales for Cross-Border Transactions in Continental European Equities
N.A.I.C.S.: 523910

SG Kleinwort Hambros Bank (CI) Limited (1)
18 Esplanade, PO Box 78, Saint Helier, JE4 8PR, Jersey
Tel.: (44) 1534815555
Emp.: 200
Commercial Banking Services
N.A.I.C.S.: 522110
Matt Falla *(Head-Private Banking)*

SG Kleinwort Hambros Bank (Gibraltar) Limited (1)
Hambro House 32 Line Wall Road, PO Box 375, Gibraltar, Gibraltar
Tel.: (350) 20002000
Asset Management Services
N.A.I.C.S.: 523940
Emma Perez *(CEO)*

SG Kleinwort Hambros Bank Limited (1)
5th Floor 8 St James's Square, London, SW1Y 4JU, United Kingdom
Tel.: (44) 2075973290
Web Site: http://www.kleinworthambros.com
Financial Asset Services
N.A.I.C.S.: 541611
Mouhammed Choukeir *(Co-CEO)*

SG OPTION EUROPE SA (1)
17 Cours Valmy, 92800, Puteaux, France
Tel.: (33) 1 42 13 66 40
Investment Management Service
N.A.I.C.S.: 523999

SG PRIVATE BANKING (JAPAN) LTD (1)
16th Floor Ark Mori Building 12-32 Akasaka 1-Chrome, Minato Ku, Tokyo, 107-6016, Japan
Tel.: (81) 3 6229 4300
Web Site: http://www.smbctb.co.jp
Sales Range: $200-249.9 Million
Emp.: 400
Commercial Banking Services
N.A.I.C.S.: 522110

SG PRIVATE BANKING BELGIQUE (1)
Kortrijksesteenweg 302, Gent, 9000, Belgium
Tel.: (32) 9 242 22 36
Sales Range: $100-124.9 Million
Emp.: 15
Commercial Banking Services
N.A.I.C.S.: 522110
Jan de Coninck *(Gen Mgr)*

SG PRIVATE BANKING MONACO (1)
13-15 Bd Des Moulins, Monaco, 98000, Monaco
Tel.: (377) 97 97 58 59
Web Site: http://www.societegenerale.com
Emp.: 20
Property Management & Banking Services
N.A.I.C.S.: 523940

SG Private Banking (Suisse) SA (1)
8 rue du Rhone, 1204, Geneva, Switzerland **(77.62%)**
Tel.: (41) 228190202
Web Site: http://www.sgprivatebanking.ch
Sales Range: $100-124.9 Million
Emp.: 200
Provider of Banking Services
N.A.I.C.S.: 522110

SG SECURITIES (PARIS) SAS (1)
Tour Societe Generale 17 Cours Valmy, Puteaux, 92800, France
Tel.: (33) 1 421 34 545
Securities Brokerage Services
N.A.I.C.S.: 523150

SG SERVICES SA (1)
17 Cours Valmy, 92800, Puteaux, France
Tel.: (33) 1 42 13 45 45
Sales Range: $350-399.9 Million
Emp.: 100
Financial Services
N.A.I.C.S.: 523999

SG Securities (Hong Kong) Limited (1)
38F No 68 Sec 5 Zhongxiao E Rd, Xinyi Dist, Taipei, 110, Taiwan
Tel.: (886) 221750800
Commercial Banking Services
N.A.I.C.S.: 522110

SG Securities Korea Co., Ltd. (1)
24F D1 D-Tower 17 Jongno 3-Gil, Jongno-gu, Seoul, 03155, Korea (South)
Tel.: (82) 221957777
Financial Banking Services
N.A.I.C.S.: 522110

SGB Finance S.A. (1)
1 Rue Celestin Freinet, BP 50102, 44201, Nantes, Cedex, France
Tel.: (33) 251727350
Loan Financing Services
N.A.I.C.S.: 522220
Raphael Kuredjian *(Deputy Mng Dir)*

SGSS DEUTSCHLAND KAPITALANLAGEGESELLSCHAFT MBH (1)
Apianstr 5, 85774, Unterfohring, Germany
Tel.: (49) 89330330
Asset Management Services
N.A.I.C.S.: 523940

SI DU 29 BOULEVARD HAUSSMANN (1)
29 Boulevard Haussmann, 75009, Paris, France
Tel.: (33) 1 53 43 57 00
Financial Management Services
N.A.I.C.S.: 523999

SOCIETE DES TERRAINS ET IMMEUBLES PARISIENS (1)
29 Bd Haussmann, 75009, Paris, France
Tel.: (33) 142142000
Web Site: http://www.societegenerale.com
Real Estate Development Services
N.A.I.C.S.: 531390

SOCIETE GENERALE (CHINA) LIMITED (1)
Taikang International Tower 18th Floor 2 Wudinghou Street, Xicheng District, Beijing, 100033, China
Tel.: (86) 10 5851 3888
Web Site: http://www.societegenerale.cn
Commercial Banking Services
N.A.I.C.S.: 522110

SOCIETE GENERALE BANK AND TRUST LUXEMBOURG (1)
11 Avenue Emile Reuter, Luxembourg, 2420, Luxembourg
Tel.: (352) 47 93 11 1
Web Site: http://www.privatebanking.lu
Commercial Banking Services
N.A.I.C.S.: 522110
Patrick Follea *(Vice Chm)*

SOCIETE GENERALE BANK NEDERLAND N.V. (1)
Amstelplein 1, 1096 HA, Amsterdam, Netherlands
Tel.: (31) 204622822
Sales Range: $50-74.9 Million
Emp.: 27
Commercial Banking Services
N.A.I.C.S.: 522110
Henk van Rooijen *(Country Mgr)*

SOCIETE GENERALE ENERGIE SA (1)
Tour Soc Generale 17 Cours Valmy, Puteaux, 92800, France
Tel.: (33) 142142000
Portfolio Management Services
N.A.I.C.S.: 523940

SOCIETE GENERALE INVESTMENTS (U.K.) LIMITED (1)
One Bank Street Canary Wharf, London, E14 4SG, United Kingdom
Tel.: (44) 2076766000
Web Site: http://www.sgib.com
Emp.: 3,600
Investment Management Service
N.A.I.C.S.: 523999
Ian James Fisher *(Mgr)*

SOCIETE GENERALE SCF (1)
17 Cours Valmy, 92800, Puteaux, France
Tel.: (33) 1 42 14 37 27
Commercial Banking Services
N.A.I.C.S.: 522110

SOCIETE GENERALE SECURITIES (NORTH PACIFIC) LTD (1)
Ark Mori Building 1-12-32 Akasaka, Minato-ku, Tokyo, 107-6015, Japan
Tel.: (81) 3 5549 5120
Web Site: http://www.sgcib.co.jp
Sales Range: $100-124.9 Million
Emp.: 25
Securities Brokerage Services
N.A.I.C.S.: 523150
Marcelo Marmas *(Pres)*

SOCIETE GENERALE SECURITIES SERVICES HOLDING SA (1)
170 Place Henri Regnaultgssfin, Paris, France
Tel.: (33) 142134545
Investment Management Service
N.A.I.C.S.: 523999
Christophe Baurand *(Head-Coverage Mktg & Solutions)*

SOCIETE GENERALE SPLITSKA BANKA D.D (1)
Rudera Boskovica 16, 21000, Split, Croatia
Tel.: (385) 21 304 304
Web Site: http://www.splitskabanka.hr
Sales Range: $200-249.9 Million
Emp.: 500
Commercial Banking Services
N.A.I.C.S.: 522110
Andre-Marc Prudent *(Chm-Mgmt Bd)*

SOFRAFI SA (1)
57 Av De Chatou, 92500, Rueil-Malmaison, France
Tel.: (33) 141395890
Financial Credit Management Services
N.A.I.C.S.: 522390

SOGECAP S.A (1)
50 Avenue Du General de Gaulle, La Defense, Paris, 92093, Cedex, France
Tel.: (33) 1 46 93 55 70
Web Site: http://www.societegenerale-insurance.com
Insurance Management Services
N.A.I.C.S.: 524298

SOGEFINANCEMENT SAS (1)
59 Avenue Chatou, 92358, Rueil-Malmaison, France
Tel.: (33) 1 41 29 60 00
Financial Management Services
N.A.I.C.S.: 523999

SOGELEASE FRANCE SA (1)
59 Avenue De Chatou, 92500, Rueil-Malmaison, France
Tel.: (33) 141296505
Financial Lending Services
N.A.I.C.S.: 522220

SOGELIFE SA (1)
11 Avenue Emile Reuter, 2420, Luxembourg, Luxembourg
Tel.: (352) 24 13 73 1
Web Site: http://www.sogelife.com
Emp.: 139
Fire Insurance Services
N.A.I.C.S.: 524113

SOGEPROM SA (1)
Immeuble Ile de France 3/4 Place de la Pyramide, La Defense, 92067, Paris, France
Tel.: (33) 1 46 35 60 00
Web Site: http://www.sogeprom.fr
Emp.: 10
Real Estate Development Services
N.A.I.C.S.: 531390
Henri du Boucher *(Pres & Mng Dir)*

SOGESSUR SA (1)
2 Rue Jacques Daguerre, Rueil-Malmaison, 92500, France
Tel.: (33) 1 41 39 55 09
Web Site: http://www.sogessur.fr
General Insurance Services
N.A.I.C.S.: 524210
Frederic Jacob-Peron *(Gen Mgr)*

SOGINFO SOCIETE DE GESTION ET D'INVESTISSEMENTS FONCIERS (1)
29 Bd Haussmann, 75009, Paris, France
Tel.: (33) 1 42 14 20 00
Investment Management Service
N.A.I.C.S.: 523999

Socecap SA (1)
Via Tiziano n 32, 20145, Milan, Italy
Tel.: (39) 0294321400
Web Site: http://www.societegenerale-insurance.it
General Insurance Services
N.A.I.C.S.: 524113

Societe Europeenne de Financement et d'Investissement SA (1)
15 Boulevard du Prince Henri, 1724, Luxembourg, Luxembourg
Tel.: (352) 26 73 91 60
Investment Management Service
N.A.I.C.S.: 523999

Societe Generale (Canada) (1)
1501 Av McGill College Bureau 1800, Montreal, H3A 3M8, QC, Canada **(100%)**
Tel.: (514) 841-6000
Web Site: http://www.socgen.com
Sales Range: $100-124.9 Million
Emp.: 125
Foreign Commercial Bank
N.A.I.C.S.: 522110

Societe Generale - Tokyo (1)
Palace Building 1-1-1 Marunouchi, Chiyoda-Ku, Tokyo, 100-8206, Japan **(100%)**
Tel.: (81) 367776800
Web Site: http://www.sgcib.co.jp
Sales Range: $100-124.9 Million
Emp.: 250
Commercial Bank
N.A.I.C.S.: 522110
Ramir Cimafranca *(Head-Prime Svcs)*

Societe Generale Bank & Trust (Middle East) FZE (1)
DIFC 4/F Gate Village 6, 29600, Dubai, United Arab Emirates
Tel.: (971) 4425 7500

SOCIETE GENERALE S.A.

Societe Generale S.A.—(Continued)
Private Banking & Wealth Management Services
N.A.I.C.S.: 523150
Richad Soundardjee *(Grp Chief Reg Officer-Middle East)*

Societe Generale Capital Partenaires SAS (1)
29 boulevard Haussmann, 75009, Paris, France
Tel.: (33) 1 4214 2000
Web Site: http://capitalpartenaires.com
Private Equity Investment Firm
N.A.I.C.S.: 523999
Marc Diamant *(Deputy Dir-Private Equity)*

Subsidiary (Domestic):

Gris Decoupage (2)
Zone Industrielle, Lesmenils, 54700, Pont-a-Mousson, France
Tel.: (33) 383808000
Web Site: http://www.gris-decoupage.com
Sales Range: $25-49.9 Million
Emp.: 150
Bolts, Nuts, Rivets & Washers
N.A.I.C.S.: 332722
Francis Gris *(Founder)*

Subsidiary (Non-US):

GRIS Umformtechnik GmbH (3)
Reidemeisterstrasse 9, 58849, Herscheid, Germany
Tel.: (49) 23576090   (100%)
Sales Range: $10-24.9 Million
Emp.: 50
Metal Stamping
N.A.I.C.S.: 332119
Frederic Bello *(CEO)*

Societe Generale Corporate & Investment Banking (1)
17 cours Valmy, 92897, Paris, France
Tel.: (33) 142142000
Web Site: http://www.sgcib.com
Sales Range: $700-749.9 Million
Emp.: 2,000
Corporate & Investment Banking Services
N.A.I.C.S.: 523150
Raj Malhotra *(Head-Debt Capital Markets-Asia Pacific)*

Societe Generale Energie U.S.A. (1)
1221 Ave of the Americas, New York, NY 10020-1001   (100%)
Tel.: (212) 278-5600
Sales Range: $450-499.9 Million
Emp.: 4
Oil Trading
N.A.I.C.S.: 424720
Lisette Lieberman *(Chief Compliance Officer-Americas)*

Societe Generale European Business Services S.A. (1)
West Gate Park Strada Preciziei nr 24 cladirea H4 etaj 5 Sector 6, 013981, Bucharest, Romania
Tel.: (40) 712345678
Web Site: http://www.sgebs.com
Financial Services
N.A.I.C.S.: 541611
Mihai Vladescu *(CFO)*

Societe Generale Financial (1)
245 Park Ave, New York, NY 10167   (100%)
Tel.: (212) 278-6000
Web Site: http://www.sgcib.com
Sales Range: $700-749.9 Million
Emp.: 2,000
Banking Services
N.A.I.C.S.: 523150
David Getzler *(Head-Equity Capital Markets-Americas)*

Societe Generale Ghana Limited (1)
2nd Crescent Royalt Castle Road Ring Road Central, PO Box 13119, Accra, Ghana   (51%)
Tel.: (233) 302214314
Web Site: https://societegenerale.com.gh
Rev.: $91,120,937
Assets: $713,793,031
Liabilities: $587,181,909
Net Worth: $126,611,122
Earnings: $35,548,367
Emp.: 535
Fiscal Year-end: 12/31/2023
Banking Services
N.A.I.C.S.: 522110
Kofi Ampim *(Chm)*

Societe Generale Global Solution Centre Private Limited (1)
Ascendas ITPB SEZ Voyager Building 10th Floor Whitefield Road, International Tech Park, Bengaluru, 560 066, India
Tel.: (91) 8067315000
Web Site: http://www.globalsolutioncenter.in
Emp.: 8,500
Information Technology Services
N.A.I.C.S.: 541511

Societe Generale MAROCAINE DE BANQUES SA (1)
55 Boulevard Abdelmoumen, Casablanca, 13090, Morocco
Tel.: (212) 22 43 88 88
Commercial Banking Services
N.A.I.C.S.: 522110

Societe Generale Private Banking (Suisse) S.A. (1)
Rue du Rhone 8, Case Postale 5022, 1204, Geneva, Switzerland
Tel.: (41) 228190202
Web Site: http://www.privatebanking.ch
Commercial Banking Services
N.A.I.C.S.: 522110
Anne Marion-Bouchacourt *(Chm)*

Societe Generale Private Wealth Management S.A. (1)
11 Avenue Emile Reuter, 2420, Luxembourg, Luxembourg
Tel.: (352) 4793111
Web Site: http://www.sgpwm.societegenerale.com
Emp.: 30
Asset Management Services
N.A.I.C.S.: 523940
Monsieur Alexandre Cegarra *(CEO)*

Societe Generale S.A. (1)
Ul Marszalkowska 111, 00-102, Warsaw, Poland
Tel.: (48) 225284000
Web Site: http://www.cib.societegenerale.pl
Investment Banking Services
N.A.I.C.S.: 523150

Societe Generale Securities (Thailand) Ltd. (1)
98 Sathorn Square Office Tower Unit 27-01 27th Floor, North Sathorn Road Silom Bangrak, Bangkok, 10500, Thailand
Tel.: (66) 23533400
Commercial Banking Services
N.A.I.C.S.: 522110

Societe Generale Securities Services (Ireland) Ltd. (1)
3rd Floor IFSC House Custom House Quay, Dublin, D01 R2P9, Ireland
Tel.: (353) 16750300
Asset Management Services
N.A.I.C.S.: 523940
Ian Duffy *(Mng Dir)*

Societe Generale Securities Services GmbH (1)
Humboldtstrasse 8, Aschheim, 85609, Munich, Germany
Tel.: (49) 89330330
Emp.: 255
Financial Security Services
N.A.I.C.S.: 523999

Societe Generale Securities Services S.P.A. (1)
Maciachini Center-MAC 2 Via Benigno Crespi 19/A, 20159, Milan, Italy
Tel.: (39) 0291781
Emp.: 600
Asset Management Services
N.A.I.C.S.: 523940
Oscar Maffioletti *(Mgr-Bus Process)*

Societe Generale Senegal SA (1)
19 Avenue Pdt L S Senghor, BP 323, Dakar, Senegal
Tel.: (221) 338394242
Web Site: http://www.societegenerale.sn
Commercial Banking Services
N.A.I.C.S.: 522110
Abdoul Aziz Niang *(COO)*

Societe Generale Strakhovanie LLC (1)
Zemlyanoy Val Str Bld 9 6th Floor 1 Section 1-6 Room, 105064, Moscow, Russia
Tel.: (7) 4957969556
Commercial Banking Services
N.A.I.C.S.: 522110
Mikhail Efimov *(Gen Dir & Dir-Technical)*

Societe Generale Strakhovanie Zhizni LLC (1)
Zemlyanoy Val Str Bld 9 6th Floor, 105064, Moscow, Russia
Tel.: (7) 4957969556
Commercial Banking Services
N.A.I.C.S.: 522110
Frederic Salaun *(Gen Dir)*

Societe Generale Zweigniederlassung Wien (1)
Prinz Eugen Strasse 8 - 10/5/Top 11, Vienna, Austria   (100%)
Tel.: (43) 1506950
Web Site: http://www.sgcib.com
Sales Range: $50-74.9 Million
Emp.: 25
Commercial Bank
N.A.I.C.S.: 522110
Andre Tissot *(Gen Mgr)*

Societe Generale de Banques au Senegal (1)
19 Avenue Leopold Sedar Senghor, Dakar, Senegal   (100%)
Tel.: (221) 33 839 5500
Web Site: http://societegenerale.sn
Sales Range: $200-249.9 Million
Banking Services
N.A.I.C.S.: 522110
Yann De Nanteuil *(CEO)*

Societe Generale de Banques en Cote d'Ivoire (1)
5 & 7 av Joseph Anoma 01, BP 1355, Abidjan, Cote d'Ivoire
Tel.: (225) 20201557
Web Site: http://www.sgbci.ci
Sales Range: $350-399.9 Million
Emp.: 1,000
Provider of Banking Services
N.A.I.C.S.: 522110
Coulibaly Tiemoko *(Chm)*

Societe Generale de Banques en Guinee Equatoriale S.A. (1)
Malabo II Rotonda Arab Contractors, Malabo, Equatorial Guinea
Tel.: (240) 240093357
Commercial Banking Services
N.A.I.C.S.: 522110

Societe Generale de Banques en Guinee-SGBG (1)
Cite Chemin de Fer Immeuble BOFFA, BP 1514, Conakry, Guinea   (53%)
Tel.: (224) 30 45 60 00
Web Site: http://www.sgbg.net
Sales Range: $100-124.9 Million
Emp.: 170
Banking Services
N.A.I.C.S.: 522110

Societe Generale de Leasing au Maroc SA (1)
55 Bd Abdelmoumen 5 Et 6 Et, 20360, Casablanca, Morocco
Tel.: (212) 5 22 43 88 70
Financial Lending Services
N.A.I.C.S.: 522220

Societe Generale-Frankfurt am Main (1)
Neue Mainzer Strasse 46-50, 60311, Frankfurt am Main, Germany   (100%)
Tel.: (49) 6971740
Web Site: http://www.societegenerale.de
Sales Range: $200-249.9 Million
Emp.: 3,250
Commercial Bank
N.A.I.C.S.: 522110

Societe Generale-London (1)
One Bank Street Canary Wharf, London, E14 4SG, United Kingdom
Tel.: (44) 2076766000
Web Site: http://www.societegenerale.co.uk
Sales Range: $50-74.9 Million
Emp.: 3,600
Commercial Bank

INTERNATIONAL PUBLIC

N.A.I.C.S.: 522110
Dominique Beretti *(Sr Mgr-Natural Resources & Infrastructure)*

Societe Marseillaise de Credit SA (1)
75 rue Paradis, 13006, Marseille, France
Tel.: (33) 491133400
Web Site: http://www.smc.fr
Banking Services
N.A.I.C.S.: 522110

Societe de Bourse Gilbert Dupont SNC (1)
50 Rue d'Anjou, 75008, Paris, France
Tel.: (33) 140224600
Web Site: http://www.gilbertdupont.fr
Intermediation Services
N.A.I.C.S.: 522180

TEMSYS SA (1)
Immeuble Cap West 15 Allee De L Europe, 92110, Clichy, France
Tel.: (33) 156761800
Sales Range: $150-199.9 Million
Emp.: 40
Office Machinery Rental & Leasing Services
N.A.I.C.S.: 532420
Jean-Francois Chanal *(Gen Dir)*

Ukrnafta PJSC (1)
Nesterovsky Str 3-5, Kiev, 04053, Ukraine   (56.8%)
Tel.: (380) 442263422
Web Site: http://www.ukrnafta.com
Sales Range: $1-4.9 Billion
Oil & Gas Exploration Services
N.A.I.C.S.: 211120

Joint Venture (Domestic):

Kashtan Petroleum Ltd. (2)
Geroiv Stalingrada Ave 24 Apt 141, Kiev, 04210, Ukraine
Tel.: (380) 444673115
Petroleum Services
N.A.I.C.S.: 211120

VALMINVEST (1)
29 boulevard Haussmann, Paris, 75009, France   (100%)
Tel.: (33) 1 42 14 20 00
Real Estate Development Services
N.A.I.C.S.: 531390

SOCIETE HOSPITALIERE D'ASSURANCE MUTUELLE
18 rue Edouard Rochet, 69372, Lyon, France
Tel.: (33) 4 7275 5025   FR
Web Site: http://www.sham.fr
Year Founded: 1927
Sales Range: $400-449.9 Million
Emp.: 952
Medical Insurance Products & Services
N.A.I.C.S.: 524114
Dominique Godet *(Dir Gen)*

Subsidiaries:

Sofaxis (1)
Route de Creton, 18110, Vasselay, France
Tel.: (33) 2 48 48 10 10
Web Site: http://www.sofaxis.com
Sales Range: $50-74.9 Million
Medical Insurance Brokerage Services
N.A.I.C.S.: 524210
Marc Jeannin *(Mng Dir & Dir-Publ)*

SOCIETE HOTELIERE ET IMMOBILIERE DE NICE SA
50 boulevard Victor Hugo, 06000, Nice, France
Tel.: (33) 493164146
Web Site: http://www.shin-hotels.com
Hotel Operator
N.A.I.C.S.: 721110
Henri Tshann *(CEO)*

SOCIETE IMMOBILIERE BALIMA
2 rue Tihama, 10000, Rabat, Morocco
Tel.: (212) 537708750
Web Site: https://balima.com
Year Founded: 1928
BAL—(CAS)
Sales Range: $1-9.9 Million
Real Estate Development Services
N.A.I.C.S.: 531390

SOCIETE INDUSTRIELLE ET FINANCIERE DE L'ARTOIS SA
31-32 quai de Dion Bouton, 92811, Puteaux, Cedex, France
Tel.: (33) 146964433
Web Site: https://sif-artois.fr
ARTO—(EUR)
Sales Range: $150-199.9 Million
Financial Banking Services
N.A.I.C.S.: 522110
Cedric De Bailliencourt *(Chm, CEO & CFO)*

SOCIETE IVOIRIENNE DE MANUTENTION ET DE TRANSIT SA
15 Abidjan Zone Industrielle de Vridi Rue des Petroliers, BP 648, 15, Abidjan, Cote d'Ivoire
Tel.: (225) 2721754101
Web Site: https://www.simat.ci
MLMAT—(EUR)
Sales Range: Less than $1 Million
Emp.: 150
Marine & Air Transportation Services
N.A.I.C.S.: 488390
Stephane Eholie *(Chm, CEO & Gen Mgr)*

SOCIETE LA BIOCHIMIE APPLIQUEE SAS
41 rue Delizy, 93692, Pantin, Cedex, France
Tel.: (33) 148101940
Web Site: http://www.solabia.com
Molecules & Active Ingredients for the Cosmetic, Pharmaceutical & Nutraceutical Industries Developer & Mfr
N.A.I.C.S.: 325412
Jean-Baptiste Dellon *(CEO)*

Subsidiaries:

Algatechnologies Ltd. (1)
Kibbutz Ketura, Eilot, 8884000, Israel
Tel.: (972) 86356425
Web Site: http://www.algatech.com
Biotechnology Research & Development Services
N.A.I.C.S.: 541714

Applechem Inc. (1)
2 Cranberry Rd Unit A4, Parsippany, NJ 07054
Tel.: (862) 210-8344
Web Site: https://www.applechem.com
Cosmetic, Beauty & Personal Care Products Supplier
N.A.I.C.S.: 456120
Samuel Lin *(Founder, CEO & Mng Dir)*

SOCIETE LORRAINE D'AGREGATS
59 Route De Metz, 57103, Thionville, Moselle, France
Tel.: (33) 382882100
Web Site: http://www.slag.fr
Rev.: $23,300,000
Emp.: 64
Sand & Gravel Construction Services
N.A.I.C.S.: 212321
Annette Conrad *(Sec)*

SOCIETE LUXEMBOURGEOISE DE NAVIGATION AERIENNE, S.A.
25 rue Gabriel Lippmann, Luxembourg, L-2987, Luxembourg
Tel.: (352) 24561   LU
Web Site: http://www.luxairgroup.lu
Year Founded: 1961
Rev.: $688,468,373
Assets: $875,642,486
Liabilities: $336,053,065
Net Worth: $539,589,421
Earnings: ($4,972,519)
Emp.: 2,726
Fiscal Year-end: 12/31/19
Holding Company; Air Transportation & Support Services
N.A.I.C.S.: 551112
Alberto O. Kunkel *(Exec VP-Tour Operating)*

Subsidiaries:

Luxair Commuter S.A. (1)
Aeroport de Luxembourg, L-2987, Luxembourg, Luxembourg
Tel.: (352) 24564242
Web Site: http://www.luxair.lu
Passenger Air Transportation Services
N.A.I.C.S.: 481111

LuxairCARGO (1)
Aeroport de Luxembourg, 2987, Luxembourg, Luxembourg   (100%)
Tel.: (352) 2456 6001
Web Site: http://www.luxaircargo.lu
Sales Range: $200-249.9 Million
Emp.: 1,100
Air Freight & Cargo Services
N.A.I.C.S.: 481112
Adrien Ney *(Pres & CEO)*

SOCIETE MAGHREBINE DE MONETIQUE - S2M
Casa Nearshore Park 2C-306-1100 Bd El Qods, Quartier Sidi Maarouf, 20270, Casablanca, Morocco
Tel.: (212) 522878300
Web Site: https://s2mworldwide.com
Year Founded: 1983
S2M—(CAS)
Sales Range: $10-24.9 Million
Software Development Services
N.A.I.C.S.: 541511

SOCIETE MAROCAINE DE COOPERATION PHARMACEUTIQUE
41 Rue Mohammed Diouri, Casablanca, Morocco
Tel.: (212) 522453200
Web Site: https://cooperpharma.ma
BLEG—(OTC)
Emp.: 100
Pharmaceuticals Product Mfr
N.A.I.C.S.: 325412

Subsidiaries:

Cipla Maroc SA (1)
1st Floor Building B Residence Ben Mahyou, ibnou Toufail street and Abdelhak Ben Mahyou street corner, Casablanca, Morocco   (24.9%)
Tel.: (212) 522454610
Web Site: https://www.cipla.com
Emp.: 66
Pharmaceutical Products Distr
N.A.I.C.S.: 424210

SOCIETE MARSEILLAISE DU TUNNEL PRADO CARENAGE SA
3 avenue Arthur Scott, 13395, Marseille, Cedex 10, France
Tel.: (33) 491808880
Web Site: https://www.tunnelsprado.com
Year Founded: 1989
SMTPC—(EUR)
Sales Range: $25-49.9 Million
Tunnel Operator
N.A.I.C.S.: 488490
Gilbert Saby *(Chm)*

SOCIETE MULTINATIONALE DE BITUMES, LTD
Boulevard de Petit Bassam, 12 BP 622, 12, Abidjan, 12, Cote d'Ivoire
Tel.: (225) 21237070   CI
Web Site: https://smb.ci
Year Founded: 1978
SMBC—(BRVM)
Sales Range: $300-349.9 Million
Crude Oil Refining Services
N.A.I.C.S.: 211120
Aminata Traore *(Chm)*

SOCIETE MUTUELLE D'ASSURANCE DU BATIMENT ET DES TRAVAUX PUBLICS
114 avenue Emile Zola, 75739, Paris, Cedex, France
Tel.: (33) 1 4059 7000   FR
Web Site: http://www.smabtp.fr
Sales Range: $1-4.9 Billion
Mutual Holding Company; Insurance Products & Services
N.A.I.C.S.: 551112
Christian Baffy *(Chm)*

Subsidiaries:

Societe de la Tour Eiffel SA (1)
11-13 avenue Friedland, 75008, Paris, France
Tel.: (33) 153430706
Web Site: https://www.societetoureiffel.com
Rev.: $91,731,979
Assets: $1,895,463,076
Liabilities: $158,626,780
Net Worth: $1,736,836,296
Earnings: ($52,102,881)
Fiscal Year-end: 12/31/2023
Holding Company; Real Estate & Asset Management Services
N.A.I.C.S.: 551112
Philippe Lemoine *(Dir Gen)*

Subsidiary (Domestic):

Tour Eiffel Asset Management (2)
20-22 rue de la Ville l'Eveque, 75008, Paris, France   (100%)
Tel.: (33) 1 44515500
Web Site: http://www.team-conseil.fr
Emp.: 22
Asset Management Services
N.A.I.C.S.: 523940

SOCIETE NATIONALE D'ELECTROLYSE ET DE PETROCHIMIE EST
Coastal Route N 111, Mohammedia, Morocco
Tel.: (212) 523324328
Web Site: https://www.snep.ma
SNP—(CAS)
Sales Range: Less than $1 Million
Electrolysis Product Mfr
N.A.I.C.S.: 335991
Rachid Mohammadi *(Gen Mgr)*

SOCIETE NATIONALE DE CREDIT ET D'INVESTISSEMENT
7 rue du Saint-Esprit, 1475, Luxembourg, Luxembourg
Tel.: (352) 46 19 711   LU
Web Site: http://www.snci.lu
Year Founded: 1977
Corporate Lending & Financing Services
N.A.I.C.S.: 522180
Patrick Nickels *(Chm)*

SOCIETE NATIONALE DE PROPRIETE D'IMMEUBLES SCA
2 Rue Guynemer, 69002, Lyon, France
Tel.: (33) 472569519
Web Site: https://sca-snpi.fr
MLPRI—(EUR)

Sales Range: Less than $1 Million
Real Estate Support Services
N.A.I.C.S.: 531390
Jean Douvre *(Gen Mgr & Mgr)*

SOCIETE POLYGONE S.A.
Route d'Irigny Zone Industriale Nord, BP 40, Brignais, 69530, Lyon, France
Tel.: (33) 472315454   FR
Web Site: http://www.jlevents.com
Sales Range: $1-4.9 Billion
Emp.: 3,000
Holding Company
N.A.I.C.S.: 551112
Olivier Ginon *(CEO)*

Subsidiaries:

GL Events S.A. (1)
59 Quai Rambaud, 69002, Lyon, France   (55.07%)
Tel.: (33) 478176176
Web Site: https://www.gl-events.com
Rev.: $1,313,455,798
Assets: $2,384,529,097
Liabilities: $1,746,978,240
Net Worth: $637,550,856
Earnings: $61,679,649
Emp.: 4,635
Fiscal Year-end: 12/31/2019
Fairs Conventions & Trade Shows Designer & Organizer
N.A.I.C.S.: 561920
Olivier Ginon *(Chm & CEO)*

SOCIETE POUR L'INFORMATIQUE INDUSTRIELLE
65 rue de Bercy, 75012, Paris, France
Tel.: (33) 142848222   FR
Web Site: http://www.sii-group.com
Year Founded: 1979
SII—(EUR)
Rev.: $1,114,064,956
Assets: $733,284,706
Liabilities: $442,897,003
Net Worth: $290,387,704
Earnings: $87,668,796
Emp.: 11,000
Fiscal Year-end: 03/31/23
Engineering Consulting Services
N.A.I.C.S.: 541330
Eric Matteucci *(Chm-Mgmt Bd)*

Subsidiaries:

CONCATEL S.L. (1)
Ciutat de la Justicia de Barcelona Av Carrilet 3 - Edificio D Pl 10, 08902, L'Hospitalet de Llobregat, Barcelona, Spain
Tel.: (34) 93 567 97 10
Web Site: http://sii-concatel.com
Sales Range: $25-49.9 Million
Emp.: 5
Information Technology Consulting Services
N.A.I.C.S.: 541512
Miquel Nogue *(Dir-IT Sys, Security & Product)*

CVT Argentina (1)
Av Colon 531 - Piso 3 oficina 2, 5500, Mendoza, Argentina
Tel.: (54) 2614291083
Web Site: http://www.groupe.sii.com
Emp.: 25
Information Technology Consulting Services
N.A.I.C.S.: 541512
Elio Saltalamacchia *(Gen Mgr)*

CVT Romania (1)
Blvd Unirii No 45 Bl E3 - Sc 5 Et 8 Ap 141, Sector 3, Bucharest, Romania
Tel.: (40) 21 320 23 10
Web Site: http://www.cvteam.ro
Sales Range: $25-49.9 Million
Emp.: 3
Information Technology Consulting Services
N.A.I.C.S.: 541512
Alexandra Nedelcu *(Office Mgr)*

SII Aix-en-Provence (1)
Parc de l'Escapade Batiment B - RN7, 13100, Le Tholonet, France
Tel.: (33) 442912850

SOCIETE POUR L'INFORMATIQUE INDUSTRIELLE

Societe Pour L'Informatique Industrielle—(Continued)
Information Technology Consulting Services
N.A.I.C.S.: 541512

SII Belgium (1)
Lenneke Marelaan 12/1, Sint-Stevens-Woluwe, 1932, Brussels, Belgium
Tel.: (32) 27136500
Web Site: https://sii-group.com
Sales Range: $25-49.9 Million
Emp.: 47
Information Technology Consulting Services
N.A.I.C.S.: 541512

SII Brest (1)
14 rue Amiral Romain Desfosses, 29200, Brest, France
Tel.: (33) 298466222
Information Technology Consulting Services
N.A.I.C.S.: 541512

SII Czech Republic (1)
Michelska 1552/58, 141 00, Prague, Czech Republic
Tel.: (420) 230233870
Web Site: http://www.sii.cz
Sales Range: $25-49.9 Million
Emp.: 5
Information Technology Consulting Services
N.A.I.C.S.: 541512
Arnaud Duval *(Mng Dir-Country)*

SII Deutschland GmbH (1)
Karl-Kurz-Strasse 36, 74523, Schwabisch Hall, Germany
Tel.: (49) 791931100
Web Site: https://sii-group.de
Information Technology Consulting & Engineering Services
N.A.I.C.S.: 541512

SII Ile-de-France (1)
104 av du President Kennedy, 75016, Paris, France
Tel.: (33) 153 92 37 00
Emp.: 6
Information Technology Consulting Services
N.A.I.C.S.: 541512
Gerard Lary *(Mgr)*

SII Le Mans (1)
83 boulevard Alexandre Oyon, 72100, Le Mans, France
Tel.: (33) 243 85 35 62
Web Site: http://www.groupe-sii.com
Information Technology Consulting Services
N.A.I.C.S.: 541512

SII Luxembourg SA (1)
21 rue Glesener, L-1631, Luxembourg, Luxembourg
Tel.: (352) 691242816
Web Site: https://sii-group.com
Information Technology & Engineering Services
N.A.I.C.S.: 541512

SII Lyon (1)
96 bd Vivier Merle - Immeuble Le Fontenoy, 69423, Lyon, France
Tel.: (33) 472 84 69 99
Web Site: http://www.groupe-sii.com
Sales Range: $25-49.9 Million
Emp.: 80
Information Technology Consulting Services
N.A.I.C.S.: 541512

SII Nantes (1)
1 rue Charles Lindbergh - Immeuble Concorde, 44346, Bouguenais, France
Tel.: (33) 240052828
Sales Range: $25-49.9 Million
Emp.: 20
Information Technology Consulting Services
N.A.I.C.S.: 541512

SII Poland Warsaw (1)
Biurowiec Metron 1 2 3 6 i 7 pietro al Niepodleglosci 69, 02-626, Warsaw, Poland
Tel.: (48) 224 86 37 37
Web Site: http://sii.pl
Sales Range: $10-24.9 Million
Emp.: 900
Information Technology Consulting Services
N.A.I.C.S.: 541512
Gregoire Nitot *(Founder)*

SII Rennes (1)
Le Newton - 3 bis avenue Belle Fontaine, 35510, Cesson Sevigne, France
Tel.: (33) 299 12 57 10
Sales Range: $75-99.9 Million
Emp.: 50
Information Technology Consulting Services
N.A.I.C.S.: 541512
Xavier Michard *(Mgr)*

SII Services Limited (1)
Cody Technology Park Ively Road, Farnborough, GU14 0LX, United Kingdom
Tel.: (44) 7538470405
Information Technology & Engineering Services
N.A.I.C.S.: 541512

SII Services Morocco (1)
2 angle du bd Anfa et rue Clos de Provence, 20200, Casablanca, Morocco
Tel.: (212) 5 22 43 83 90
Information Technology Consulting Services
N.A.I.C.S.: 541512

SII Sophia-Antipolis (1)
291 Rue Albert Caquot, 06560, Valbonne, France
Tel.: (33) 492 96 88 99
Web Site: http://www.groupe-sii.com
Information Technology Consulting Services
N.A.I.C.S.: 541512

SII Strasbourg (1)
4 rue de Sarrelouis, 67000, Strasbourg, France
Tel.: (33) 390 23 62 62
Information Technology Consulting Services
N.A.I.C.S.: 541512

SII Switzerland (1)
38bis Avenue Eugene-Lance, 1212, Geneva, Switzerland
Tel.: (41) 228270270
Information Technology Consulting Services
N.A.I.C.S.: 541512
Renaud Terlaud *(CIO)*

SII Toulouse (1)
7 rue Paulin Talabot - Immeuble New Horizon, 31100, Toulouse, France
Tel.: (33) 534 61 59 59
Sales Range: $75-99.9 Million
Emp.: 50
Information Technology Consulting Services
N.A.I.C.S.: 541512
Antoine Leclercq *(Mgr)*

SII Tours (1)
39 rue des Granges Galland, 37754, Saint-Avertin, France
Tel.: (33) 247 80 48 95
Web Site: http://www.groupe-sii.com
Information Technology Consulting Services
N.A.I.C.S.: 541512

SII Vitrolles (1)
20 route de l'aeroport, 13127, Vitrolles, France
Tel.: (33) 442 46 14 90
Web Site: http://www.groupe-sii.com
Sales Range: $25-49.9 Million
Emp.: 55
Information Technology Consulting Services
N.A.I.C.S.: 541512
Philippe Rampal *(Branch Mgr)*

Sii India IT & Engineering Services PVT Ltd. (1)
Leela Landmark 07 1st Cross 3rd Main Road Ashwini Layout Ejipura, Bengaluru, 560 047, India
Tel.: (91) 8067651111
Engineeering Services
N.A.I.C.S.: 541330

Sii Sweden AB (1)
The Works The slaughterhouse Livdjursgatan 4, 121 62, Johanneshov, Sweden
Tel.: (46) 760210870
Web Site: https://siisweden.se
Technology & Consulting Services
N.A.I.C.S.: 541512

UNIWAY (1)
Lenneke Marelaan 12/1, 1932, Saint-Stevens-Woluwe, Belgium
Tel.: (32) 27136500
Web Site: http://www.uniway.be
Sales Range: $25-49.9 Million
Emp.: 40
Web Designing Services
N.A.I.C.S.: 541511

Claude Leonard *(Mgr)*

SOCIETE TUNISIENNE DE VERRERIES S.A.
Zone Industrielle Djebel El Oust route de, Bir Mcherga, 1111, Zaghouan, Tunisia
Tel.: (216) 72640650
Web Site: https://www.sotuver.com.tn
Year Founded: 1963
SOTUV—(BVT)
Sales Range: Less than $1 Million
Glass Mfr
N.A.I.C.S.: 327211
Kaisar Medeb *(Deputy Gen Mgr)*

SOCIETY DEVELOPMENT BANK LIMITED
Mahendrapul-9, Pokhara, Nepal
Tel.: (977) 61551800
SODBL—(NEP)
Sales Range: Less than $1 Million
Banking Services
N.A.I.C.S.: 522110

SOCIONEXT INC.
Nomura Shin Yokohama Bld 2-10-23, Shin-Yokohama Kohoku-ku, Yokohama, 222-0033, Kanagawa, Japan
Tel.: (81) 45 568 1000
Web Site: http://www.socionext.com
Year Founded: 2015
Emp.: 2,800
Computer Softwares Mfr
N.A.I.C.S.: 513210
Masahiro Koezuka *(Chm & CEO)*

Subsidiaries:

Socionext America, Inc (1)
1250 East Arques Avenue, Sunnyvale, CA 94085
Tel.: (408) 737-5400
Computer Softwares Mfr
N.A.I.C.S.: 513210
Anthony Wong *(Dir-Mktg)*

Subsidiary (Domestic):

Bayside Design, Inc. (2)
846 N Hillview Dr, Milpitas, CA 95035
Tel.: (408) 934-0546
Web Site: http://www.baysidedesign.com
Semiconductor & Related Device Mfr
N.A.I.C.S.: 334413
Ravi Chekuri *(Dir-IC Packaging)*

SOCKETS, INC.
3F JPR Sendagaya Bldg 4-23-5 Sendagaya, Shibuya-ku, Tokyo, 151-0051, Japan
Tel.: (81) 357855518
Web Site: https://www.sockets.co.jp
Year Founded: 2000
3634—(TKS)
Sales Range: $10-24.9 Million
Emp.: 68
Business Services
N.A.I.C.S.: 561499
Koji Urabe *(Pres)*

SOCOMORE S.A.
Avenue Paul Dupleix, Vannes, France
Tel.: (33) 29743769
Web Site: https://www.socomore.com
Emp.: 100
Aerospace Component Mfr
N.A.I.C.S.: 336412

Subsidiaries:

The Flamemaster Corporation (1)
13576 Desmond St, Pacoima, CA 91331-2315 (100%)
Tel.: (818) 890-1401
Web Site: https://flamemaster.com
Sales Range: $1-9.9 Million
Adhesive Manufacturing
N.A.I.C.S.: 325520
Joseph Mazin *(Pres & CEO)*

INTERNATIONAL PUBLIC

SOCOPLAN
105 Route De Parthenay, 79100, Saint-Jean-de-Thouars, Deux Sevres, France
Tel.: (33) 549673232
Rev.: $37,000,000
Emp.: 198
Printing Services
N.A.I.C.S.: 322212
Eric Leval *(Mgr-Pur)*

SOCOVESA S.A.
Av Eliodoro Yanez 2962, Providencia, Santiago, Chile
Tel.: (56) 5204100
Web Site: https://www.socovesa.cl
Year Founded: 1965
SOCOVESA—(SGO)
Sales Range: Less than $1 Million
Real Estate Development Services
N.A.I.C.S.: 531311
Valeria Gori *(CEO)*

SOCRATES PRIVATSTIFTUNG
Moosstr 60, A-5020, Salzburg, Austria
Tel.: (43) 662 83 06 81 21
Holding Company; Project Development
N.A.I.C.S.: 551112

Subsidiaries:

ACM Projektentwicklung GmbH (1)
Gaisbergstrasse 6, Salzburg, 5020, Austria (100%)
Tel.: (43) 6626422330
Web Site: http://www.acm-projekt.at
Sales Range: $50-74.9 Million
Emp.: 6
Holding Company; Financial Investments
N.A.I.C.S.: 551112
Andreas Kaufmann *(Mng Dir)*

Joint Venture (Non-US):

Leica Camera AG (2)
Am Leitz-Park 5, 35578, Wetzlar, Germany (55%)
Tel.: (49) 644120800
Web Site: https://leica-camera.com
Sales Range: $350-399.9 Million
Photography Equipment Hunting Lense Projector Laser Rangefinder Binocular & Telescope Mfr
N.A.I.C.S.: 333310
Andreas Kaufmann *(Chm-Supervisory Bd)*

Subsidiary (US):

Leica Camera, Inc. (3)
1 Pearl Ct Unit A, Allendale, NJ 07401-1610
Tel.: (201) 995-0051
Web Site: http://www.leica-camera.com
Sales Range: $25-49.9 Million
Emp.: 30
Distr of Cameras, Binoculars & Accessories
N.A.I.C.S.: 333310
Matthias Harsch *(Chm-Exec Bd)*

SOCRESOURCES, INC.
4th Floor ENZO Building 399 Sen Gil Puyat Avenue, Makati, 1200, Philippines
Tel.: (63) 88041978 PH
Web Site: https://socres.com.ph
Year Founded: 1992
SOC—(PHI)
Rev.: $5,043,932
Assets: $36,376,683
Liabilities: $5,042,836
Net Worth: $31,333,847
Earnings: $941,540
Emp.: 38
Fiscal Year-end: 12/31/23
Holding Company; Oil Exploration
N.A.I.C.S.: 551112
David R. Baladad *(VP-Ops)*

Subsidiaries:

SOC Land Development Corporation (1)
2F 399 Enzo Bldg Jupiter St Sen Gil Puyat

Ave, Makati, 1209, Philippines
Tel.: (63) 288170762
Web Site: https://socland.com.ph
Residential Property Development
N.A.I.C.S.: 236117

SODA NIKKA CO., LTD.
Nihonbashi Front 5F 3-6-2 Nihonbashi, Chuo-ku, Tokyo, 103-8322, Japan
Tel.: (81) 332451802   JP
Web Site:
 https://www.sodanikka.co.jp
Year Founded: 1947
8158—(TKS)
Rev.: $423,925,740
Assets: $525,475,170
Liabilities: $330,764,400
Net Worth: $194,710,770
Earnings: $12,228,500
Emp.: 409
Fiscal Year-end: 03/31/24
Chemicals Mfr
N.A.I.C.S.: 325998
Takahiko Nagasu *(Pres)*

Subsidiaries:

PT. Soda Nikka Indonesia   (1)
Plaza Sentral Kav 47 No 3rd Floor JIGeneral Sudirman Karet Semanggi, Jakarta, 12930, Indonesia
Tel.: (62) 215201464
Web Site: https://sodanikka-indonesia.co.id
Chemical Products Mfr
N.A.I.C.S.: 325998

Soda Nikka Trading (Shanghai) Co., Ltd.   (1)
Room 1903 19th Floor 2201 Yan An Xi Road, Shanghai International Trade Center, Shanghai, China
Tel.: (86) 2162351084
Inorganic Chemical & Organic Chemical Mfr
N.A.I.C.S.: 325199

Soda Nikka Vietnam Co., Ltd.   (1)
835/9 Tran Hung Dao St, Ward 1 District 5, Ho Chi Minh City, Vietnam
Tel.: (84) 2838363287
Chemical Products Mfr
N.A.I.C.S.: 325998

SODA SANAYII A.S.
Icmeler Mahallesi D-100 Karayolu Caddesi No 44B Tuzla, 34947, Istanbul, Turkiye
Tel.: (90) 8502063635
Web Site:
 http://www.sisecamkimyasallar.com
SODA—(IST)
Rev.: $4,346,086,114
Assets: $12,021,332,316
Liabilities: $5,329,094,423
Net Worth: $6,692,237,894
Earnings: $1,250,548,654
Emp.: 22,698
Fiscal Year-end: 12/31/21
Soda Ash & Chromium Products Mfr
N.A.I.C.S.: 325180
Tahsin Burhan Ergene *(Pres-Chemicals Grp)*

Subsidiaries:

Oxyvit Kimya Sanayii ve Tic. A.S.   (1)
Mersin-Tarsus Organize Sanayi Bolgesi 1 Cad No 6, Akdeniz, 33400, Mersin, Turkiye
Tel.: (90) 3246764325
Web Site: https://www.oxyvit.com
Chromium Chemical Product Mfr
N.A.I.C.S.: 325998

Sisecam Elyaf Sanayii A.C.   (1)
Gaziosmanpasa OSB Mahallesi 12 Cadde No 6, Altieylul, 10100, Balikesir, Turkiye
Tel.: (90) 8502061583
Fiber Glass Products Mfr
N.A.I.C.S.: 327215
Altug Sener *(Mgr-Plant)*

Sisecam Trading Co.   (1)
RM 2105 Lippo Plaza 222 Huaihai Zhong Road, Shanghai, 200021, China
Tel.: (86) 2163910352
Fiber Glass Products Mfr
N.A.I.C.S.: 327215

SODALI LIMITED
103 Wigmore St, Marylebone, London, W1U 1QS, United Kingdom
Tel.: (44) 2071006451
Web Site: http://www.sodali.com
Management Consulting Services
N.A.I.C.S.: 541611
John Wilcox *(Chm)*

SODAPEM
Route De Galargues, Sommieres, 30250, Gard, France
Tel.: (33) 466800575
Sales Range: $25-49.9 Million
Emp.: 130
Aerospace Equipment Mfr
N.A.I.C.S.: 333517
Cedric Astier *(Mgr-Comml)*

SODAS SODYUM SANAYII A.S.
1476 Sokak No 2 Aksoy Residence Kat 13/A D 42, Alsancak, 35220, Izmir, Turkiye
Tel.: (90) 2324635933
Web Site: https://www.sodas.com.tr
Year Founded: 1974
SODSN—(IST)
Emp.: 122
Chemical Mfr & Whslr
N.A.I.C.S.: 325199
Umut Samaraz *(Mgr-Accounting & Fiscal)*

SODECIA A.A.
Rua do Espido 164-F, Edificio Via Norte, Maia, 4470 177, Portugal
Tel.: (351) 220 101 900
Web Site: http://www.sodecia.com
Sales Range: $600-649.9 Million
Emp.: 4,000
Automotive Components Mfr
N.A.I.C.S.: 336330
Rui Monteiro *(CEO)*

Subsidiaries:

SODECIA DA BAHIA, LTDA   (1)
Av Henry Ford 2000 - Predio Sodecia Caixa, PO Box 4440, 42810-900, Camacari, Brazil
Tel.: (55) 71 3649 10 00
Automobile Parts Distr
N.A.I.C.S.: 336390
Ualter Lopes *(Plant Mgr)*

Sodecia Argentina S.R.L   (1)
Parque Industrial La Plata Ruta 2Km 55 y Av 520, Abasto, B1933 CPB, Buenos Aires, Argentina
Tel.: (54) 221 491 50 38
Automobile Parts Distr
N.A.I.C.S.: 336390

Sodecia FSG (Dalian) Co., Ltd.   (1)
No 17 Tieshan East Road, Dalian Development Area, Dalian, 116600, China
Tel.: (86) 41139264801
Automobile Parts Distr
N.A.I.C.S.: 423120

Sodecia Global Tech & Automation Center Inc.   (1)
425 Sovereign Rd, London, N6M 1A3, ON, Canada
Tel.: (519) 453-9027
Automobile Parts Distr
N.A.I.C.S.: 336390
Jon Bysma *(Engr-Control)*

Sodecia India Pvt Ltd   (1)
Tapalmedu Pukkathurai, Kanchipuram, 603308, Tamilnadu, India
Tel.: (91) 44 2756 5331
Automobile Parts Distr
N.A.I.C.S.: 336390
P. Jayapandian *(Sr Engr-Quality)*

Sodecia India Pvt Ltd - III Unit (Domestic):

Sodecia India Pvt Ltd - III Unit   (2)
No 286 Mettukuppam Road, Vanagaram, Chennai, 600 095, Tamil Nadu, India
Tel.: (91) 44 2476 4956
Automobile Parts Distr
N.A.I.C.S.: 336390

Sodecia Minas Gerais   (1)
Av Prefeito Alberto Moura 900 Distrito Industrial, Sete Lagoas, Minas Gerais, Brazil
Tel.: (55) 31 2107 41 14
Automobile Parts Distr
N.A.I.C.S.: 336390
Rodrigo Alves *(Plant Mgr)*

Sodecia North America   (1)
24333 Sherwood Ave, Center Line, MI 48015-1060
Tel.: (586) 759-2200
Web Site: http://www.sodecia.com
Sales Range: $100-124.9 Million
Emp.: 200
Specialty Metal-Formed Automotive Components & Mechanical Assemblies Mfr; Owned by American International Group, Inc. & Orix Corporation
N.A.I.C.S.: 336370
Dan Pierce *(VP-HR)*

Sodecia South Africa (PTY) Ltd   (1)
Weavind Forum - 573 Fehrsen Street New Muckleneuk, 0181, Pretoria, South Africa
Tel.: (27) 127623004
Automobile Parts Distr
N.A.I.C.S.: 423120

Sodecia da Amazonia, Ltda.   (1)
Av Cosme Ferreira, 69083-000, Manaus, Amazonia, Brazil
Tel.: (55) 92 3616 48 20
Automobile Parts Distr
N.A.I.C.S.: 336390

Sodecia da Guarda - Soc.Ind.de Metalurgia da Guarda, SA   (1)
Parque Industrial da Guarda, 6300-625, Guarda, Portugal
Tel.: (351) 271 220 830
Automobile Parts Distr
N.A.I.C.S.: 336390

SODEVA
10 Rue Charles Montreuil, 73420, Mery, France
Tel.: (33) 479343974
Web Site: http://www.sodeva.com
Sales Range: $150-199.9 Million
Emp.: 35
Food Product Machinery Maker
N.A.I.C.S.: 333241
Francois Vulcain *(Mng Dir)*

Subsidiaries:

Les industries Sodevamerica Inc   (1)
3925 Grande Allee, Saint-Hubert, J4B 3V8, QC, Canada
Tel.: (514) 892-1986
Web Site: https://www.sodevamerica.com
Food Product Machinery Mfr
N.A.I.C.S.: 333241

SODEXO S.A.
255 quai de la Bataille de Stalingrad, 92130, Issy-les-Moulineaux, France
Tel.: (33) 130857500   FR
Web Site: https://www.sodexo.com
Year Founded: 1966
SW—(EUR)
Rev.: $21,405,766,720
Assets: $23,325,505,840
Liabilities: $19,425,843,840
Net Worth: $3,899,662,000
Earnings: $170,725,360
Emp.: 412,088
Fiscal Year-end: 08/31/21
Holding Company; Contract Food, Facility & Business Support Services
N.A.I.C.S.: 551112
Nathalie Bellon-Szabo *(CEO-Sports-Leisure Worldwide & CEO-Sports-Leisure Worldwide)*

Subsidiaries:

Bateaux Parisiens   (1)
Port de la Bourdonnais, 75007, Paris, France   **(100%)**
Tel.: (33) 825050101
Web Site: http://www.bateauxparisiens.com
Sales Range: $125-149.9 Million
Emp.: 270
Tourist Boat Operator
N.A.I.C.S.: 487210

Catamaran Cruisers Ltd./Bateaux London   (1)
Embankment Pier, Victoria Embankment, London, WC2N 6NU, United Kingdom   **(100%)**
Tel.: (44) 3301239044
Web Site: http://www.bateauxlondon.com
Sales Range: $25-49.9 Million
Emp.: 50
Tourist Boat Operator
N.A.I.C.S.: 487210

Centerplate, Inc.   (1)
1 Landmark Sq Fl 18, Stamford, CT 06901
Tel.: (203) 975-5900
Web Site: http://www.centerplate.com
Food Service, Catering & Merchandising Services Contractor
N.A.I.C.S.: 722310

Inspirus, LLC   (1)
100 N Rupert St, Fort Worth, TX 76107
Tel.: (817) 332-6765
Web Site: https://www.inspirus.com
Human Resource Consulting Services
N.A.I.C.S.: 541612

Lenotre SA   (1)
40 rue Pierre Curie, 78370, Plaisir, France
Tel.: (33) 130814634
Web Site: http://www.lenotre.fr
Sales Range: $100-124.9 Million
Emp.: 1,000
Luxury Catering Services
N.A.I.C.S.: 722320

Luncheon Tickets S.A.   (1)
Av Belgrano 456, Capital Federal, C1092AAR, Buenos Aires, Argentina   **(60%)**
Tel.: (54) 11 5129 2500
Web Site: http://www.ar.sodexho.com
Rev.: $12,000,000
Emp.: 200
Catering Services
N.A.I.C.S.: 722320

Motivcom Ltd   (1)
Avalon House Breckland Linford Wood, Milton Keynes, MK14 6LD, United Kingdom
Tel.: (44) 8450535529
Web Site: http://www.motivcom.com
Benefits & Rewards Services
N.A.I.C.S.: 541611

National Company for Mangement & Services Ltd   (1)
Al Hasa Road, PO Box 41491, Riyadh, 11521, Saudi Arabia   **(50%)**
Tel.: (966) 14785280
Sales Range: $100-124.9 Million
Emp.: 700
Catering Services
N.A.I.C.S.: 722320

Saba   (1)
Bldg El Amen 2nd Fl, Les Berges Du Lac, Tunis, Tunisia   **(99.75%)**
Tel.: (216) 71862777
Sales Range: $10-24.9 Million
Emp.: 12
Catering Services
N.A.I.C.S.: 722320

Siges   (1)
3 Ave Newton, PO Box 140, 78883, Saint-Quentin-en-Yvelines, Cedex, France   **(100%)**
Tel.: (33) 130857358
Web Site: http://www.sodexho.com
Sales Range: $50-74.9 Million
Emp.: 270
N.A.I.C.S.: 722511

Socat LLC   (1)
Medinat Qaboos, PO Box 232, 111, Muscat, Oman   **(50%)**
Tel.: (968) 24400700

SODEXO S.A.

Sodexo S.A.—(Continued)
Web Site: http://www.socat.com
Sales Range: $500-549.9 Million
Emp.: 2,600
Catering Services
N.A.I.C.S.: 722320

Sodexo (Angola) Limitada (1)
Rua da Boavista n 118, Complexo Testang 1, Luanda, Angola **(100%)**
Tel.: (244) 222 395 803
Catering Services
N.A.I.C.S.: 722320

Sodexo A/S (1)
Oldenburg Alle 1 1 sal, 2630, Taastrup, Denmark **(100%)**
Tel.: (45) 70263332
Web Site: http://dk.sodexo.com
Sales Range: $10-24.9 Million
Emp.: 12
Catering Services
N.A.I.C.S.: 722320

Sodexo AO (1)
18 bld 22 3-d Rybinskaya st BC Burevestnik, 107113, Moscow, Russia **(100%)**
Tel.: (7) 4952460110
Web Site: http://ru.sodexo.com
N.A.I.C.S.: 722511

Sodexo AS (1)
Lilleakerveien 10, 0283, Oslo, Norway **(100%)**
Tel.: (47) 22089100
Web Site: http://no.sodexo.com
Sales Range: $50-74.9 Million
Emp.: 700
Catering Services
N.A.I.C.S.: 722320
Thomas Havnegjerde (Pres)

Sodexo Argentina S.A. (1)
Av Libertador 110 - Pisos 5 y 6, 1087, Vicente Lopez, Buenos Aires, Argentina **(100%)**
Tel.: (54) 1152462500
Web Site: http://ar.sodexo.com
Sales Range: $200-249.9 Million
Emp.: 1,200
Catering Services
N.A.I.C.S.: 722320

Sodexo Australia Pty Limited (1)
Level 8 607 St Kilda Road, Melbourne, 3004, VIC, Australia **(100%)**
Tel.: (61) 417661469
Web Site: http://au.sodexo.com
Sales Range: $10-24.9 Million
Emp.: 70
Catering Services
N.A.I.C.S.: 722320

Division (Domestic):

Sodexo Australia Pty Limited (2)
Level 8 607 St Kilda Road, Melbourne, 3004, VIC, Australia **(100%)**
Tel.: (61) 398806300
Web Site: http://au.sodexo.com
Sales Range: $10-24.9 Million
Catering Services
N.A.I.C.S.: 722320

Sodexo Belgique (1)
Boulevard de la Plaine 15, 1050, Brussels, Belgium **(100%)**
Tel.: (32) 26791211
Web Site: http://www.sodexo.be
Sales Range: $50-74.9 Million
Emp.: 300
Catering Services
N.A.I.C.S.: 722320

Sodexo Belgium S.A. (1)
Boulevard de La Plaine 15, 1050, Brussels, Belgium
Tel.: (32) 26791211
Web Site: https://be.sodexo.com
Emp.: 3,500
Catering & Facilities Management Services
N.A.I.C.S.: 541513

Sodexo Benefits & Rewards Services Austria GmbH (1)
Iglaseegasse 21-23, 1190, Vienna, Austria **(100%)**
Tel.: (43) 1 3286060 0
Web Site: http://www.sodexo.at

Sales Range: $10-24.9 Million
Emp.: 18
Catering Services
N.A.I.C.S.: 722320
Antonio Stieha (Mng Dir)

Sodexo Cameroun (1)
Rue Castelnau, BP 992, Douala, Cameroon **(69.55%)**
Tel.: (237) 428280
Sales Range: $10-24.9 Million
Emp.: 15
Catering Services
N.A.I.C.S.: 722320

Sodexo Canada Inc. (1)
5420 North Service Road Suite 501, Burlington, L7L 6C7, ON, Canada **(100%)**
Tel.: (514) 866-7070
Web Site: https://ca.sodexo.com
Sales Range: $10-24.9 Million
Emp.: 40
Providers of Food & Facility Management Services
N.A.I.C.S.: 722511
Nancy Zuccarelli (Sr VP-Sls)

Sodexo Chile (1)
Perez Valenzuela 1635, Providencia, Santiago, Chile **(100%)**
Tel.: (56) 228100100
Web Site: http://cl.sodexo.com
Sales Range: $50-74.9 Million
Emp.: 300
Catering Services
N.A.I.C.S.: 722320

Sodexo Colombia S.A. (1)
Carrera 7a 116-50 Piso 2 Oficina 02-146 WeWork Edificio Flormorado, Bogota, Colombia **(80%)**
Tel.: (57) 16414100
Web Site: http://www.sodexo.com
Sales Range: $25-49.9 Million
Emp.: 150
Personal, Benefits & Rewards Services
N.A.I.C.S.: 561210

Sodexo Delinjeniere S.A. (1)
Newton Ave, PO Box 141, 78883, Saint-Quentin-en-Yvelines, Cedex, France **(99.99%)**
Tel.: (33) 130852755
Sales Range: $10-24.9 Million
Emp.: 50
Catering Services
N.A.I.C.S.: 722320

Sodexo Espagne (1)
Viladecans Business Park Calle de la Tecnologia 19 3 Planta, Viladecans, 08840, Barcelona, Spain **(100%)**
Tel.: (34) 936352200
Web Site: http://es.sodexo.com
Emp.: 7,000
Restaurants & Facilities Management
N.A.I.C.S.: 722511

Sodexo France Business & Industry (1)
255 quai de la bataille, de stalingrad, 92866, Paris, France
Tel.: (33) 130857500
Web Site: http://www.sodexhoalliance.com
Sales Range: $50-74.9 Million
Emp.: 400
Catering Services
N.A.I.C.S.: 722320

Sodexo Hong Kong Ltd (1)
Unit 801 8/F Skyway House 3 Sham Mong Road Tai Kok Tsui, Kowloon, China (Hong Kong) **(55.62%)**
Tel.: (852) 23888682
Web Site: http://www.sodexo.com
Sales Range: $10-24.9 Million
Emp.: 30
Catering Services
N.A.I.C.S.: 722320

Sodexo Ireland Ltd. (1)
Temple House 57 Temple Road Blackrock, Dublin, A95 Y5W5, Co Dublin, Ireland **(100%)**
Tel.: (353) 12833654
Web Site: http://ie.sodexo.com
Sales Range: $10-24.9 Million
Emp.: 800
Catering Services
N.A.I.C.S.: 722320

Sodexo Italia Spa (1)
via F lli Gracchi 36, 20092, Cinisello Balsamo, Italy **(98%)**
Tel.: (39) 02696841
Web Site: http://it.sodexo.com
Sales Range: $25-49.9 Million
Emp.: 200
Catering Services
N.A.I.C.S.: 722320

Sodexo Korea (1)
101-102 Unit 15 Mijin Lamer Palace Okpo Seongan-ro, Geoje, Gyeongsangnam-do, Korea (South) **(100%)**
Tel.: (82) 556885125
Web Site: http://kr.sodexo.com
Sales Range: $50-74.9 Million
Emp.: 410
Catering Services
N.A.I.C.S.: 722320

Sodexo Ltd. (1)
Solar House Kings Way, Stevenage, SG1 2UA, United Kingdom **(100%)**
Tel.: (44) 1438341400
Web Site: http://uk.sodexo.com
Sales Range: $25-49.9 Million
Emp.: 125
Catering Services
N.A.I.C.S.: 722320

Sodexo Ltd. (1)
1 Southampton Row, London, WC1B 5HA, United Kingdom **(100%)**
Tel.: (44) 2074040110
Web Site: http://uk.sodexo.com
Sales Range: $25-49.9 Million
Emp.: 120
Catering Services
N.A.I.C.S.: 722320

Sodexo Luxembourg S.A. (1)
39 rue du Puits Romain ZA Bourmicht -L-, 8070, Bertrange, Luxembourg
Tel.: (352) 26109200
Web Site: https://lu.sodexo.com
Catering & Facilities Management Services
N.A.I.C.S.: 541513

Sodexo MS Canada Ltd. (1)
3350 S Service Rd, Burlington, L7N 3M6, ON, Canada **(100%)**
Tel.: (905) 632-8592
Sales Range: $10-24.9 Million
Emp.: 90
Health Care Services & Supplier of Food Services
N.A.I.C.S.: 722511
Jerome Vos (VP-Fin)

Sodexo Magyarorszag Kft (1)
Hermina ut 63, 1146, Budapest, Hungary **(100%)**
Tel.: (36) 17803892
Web Site: http://hu.sodexo.com
Catering Services
N.A.I.C.S.: 722320

Sodexo Malaysia (1)
Unit 1101 Level 11 PJ Tower Amcorp Trade Centre, 18 Jalan Persiaran Barat, 46050, Petaling Jaya, Selangor Darul Ehsan, Malaysia **(80%)**
Tel.: (60) 379541024
Web Site: http://my.sodexo.com
Sales Range: $25-49.9 Million
Emp.: 500
Catering Services
N.A.I.C.S.: 722320

Sodexo Mexico Sa De CV (1)
Calle 56 N 780 Col Miami Cd Del Carmen, 24120, Campeche, Mexico **(100%)**
Tel.: (52) 19383824111
Web Site: http://mx.sodexo.com
Catering & On-Site Service Solutions
N.A.I.C.S.: 722320

Sodexo Namibia (1)
Transnamib Diesel Depot Ooievaar St, Windhoek, Namibia **(100%)**
Tel.: (264) 61257252
Sales Range: $10-24.9 Million
Emp.: 1
N.A.I.C.S.: 722511
Joe Hoarau (Mng Dir)

Sodexo Nederland B.V. (1)
Watermanweg 30, 3067 GG, Rotterdam, Netherlands **(100%)**

Tel.: (31) 884962000
Web Site: http://nl.sodexo.com
Sales Range: $50-74.9 Million
Emp.: 300
Catering Services
N.A.I.C.S.: 722320

Sodexo Nouvelle-Caledonie Restauration Francaise (1)
44 bis Rue de L'Alma, BP 4221, 98801, Noumea, Cedex, New Caledonia **(100%)**
Tel.: (687) 787640
Web Site: http://www.sodexo.com
N.A.I.C.S.: 722511

Sodexo Oy (1)
Atomitie 5, 00370, Helsinki, Finland **(100%)**
Tel.: (358) 105407000
Web Site: http://www.sodexo.fi
Sales Range: $150-199.9 Million
Emp.: 100
Catering Services
N.A.I.C.S.: 722320
Lar Finer (Mng Dir)

Sodexo Pass (1)
Boulevard de la Plaine 15, 1050, Brussels, Belgium **(99.6%)**
Tel.: (32) 25475588
Web Site: http://www.sodexho-pass.be
Sales Range: $25-49.9 Million
Emp.: 150
Restaurant Management
N.A.I.C.S.: 722511

Sodexo Pass (1)
Gulbahar Mah, Avni Dilligil Sok N24 A 6, 80300, Istanbul, Turkiye **(80%)**
Tel.: (90) 2122169170
Web Site: http://www.sodexho.com.tr
Sales Range: $25-49.9 Million
Emp.: 150
Catering Services
N.A.I.C.S.: 722320

Sodexo Pass (1)
5th Floor 509 Topiwala Centre Off S V Road, Near BMC Market Goregaon West, Mumbai, 400062, MH, India **(100%)**
Tel.: (91) 2240666888
Web Site: http://in.sodexo.com
Catering Services
N.A.I.C.S.: 722320
Sunil Nayak (CEO)

Sodexo Pass (1)
Bea delos Poblados 3 Crystalia, 28003, Madrid, Spain **(100%)**
Tel.: (34) 914452866
Web Site: http://www.sodexo.es
Sales Range: $10-24.9 Million
Emp.: 100
Catering Services
N.A.I.C.S.: 722320

Sodexo Pass Chile S.A (1)
Ave Santa Maria 0824, Providencia, Santiago, 26870200, Chile **(100%)**
Tel.: (56) 26870200
Web Site: http://www.sodexobeneficios.com
Sales Range: $10-24.9 Million
Emp.: 140
Catering Services
N.A.I.C.S.: 722320
Thierry Guihard (Gen Mgr)

Sodexo Pass GmbH (1)
Lyoner Strasse 9, 60528, Frankfurt am Main, Germany **(100%)**
Tel.: (49) 69739960
Web Site: http://www.sodexo.de
Sales Range: $10-24.9 Million
Emp.: 50
Catering Services
N.A.I.C.S.: 722320

Sodexo Pass Hungaria Kft. (1)
Hermina ut 63, PF 601, 1146, Budapest, Hungary **(100%)**
Tel.: (36) 17803892
Web Site: http://hu.sodexo.com
Sales Range: $10-24.9 Million
Emp.: 53
Catering Services
N.A.I.C.S.: 722320

Sodexo Pass Luxembourg (1)
39 rue du Puits Romain ZA Bourmicht, 8070, Luxembourg, Luxembourg **(100%)**

AND PRIVATE COMPANIES

Tel.: (352) 26109200
Web Site: http://lu.sodexo.com
Sales Range: $10-24.9 Million
Emp.: 9
N.A.I.C.S.: 722511

Sodexo Pass S.r.l. (1)
Via Gallarate 200, 20151, Milan,
Italy **(100%)**
Tel.: (39) 02380571
Web Site: http://www.sodexhopass.it
Sales Range: $10-24.9 Million
Emp.: 70
Catering Services
N.A.I.C.S.: 722320

Sodexo Pass SR sro (1)
Tomasikova 64, 83104, Bratislava,
Slovakia **(100%)**
Tel.: (421) 232660272
Web Site: http://sk.sodexo.com
Sales Range: $10-24.9 Million
Emp.: 15
Catering Services
N.A.I.C.S.: 722320

Sodexo Pass Venezuela CA (1)
Ave Blandin con Ave Los Chaguaramos
Torre Corp Banca Piso 16, La Castellana,
Caracas, 1060, Venezuela **(64%)**
Tel.: (58) 212 206 5622
Web Site: http://ve.beneficios-incentivos.sodexo.com
Sales Range: $25-49.9 Million
Emp.: 200
Catering Services
N.A.I.C.S.: 722320
Jose Paz *(Dir-Mktg)*

Sodexo Pass Venezuela CA (1)
Ave Principal De Lecherias Municipio Diego
Bautista Urbaneja, Centro Comercial Coconut Modul, Barcelona, Anzoategui,
Venezuela **(70%)**
Tel.: (58) 2812814923
Sales Range: $10-24.9 Million
Emp.: 5
Catering Services
N.A.I.C.S.: 722320

Sodexo Pass de Colombia SA (1)
Cr 7 No 127 - 48 floor 5 48 Ed Centro Empresarial, Torre A Piso 7-8, Bogota,
Colombia **(51%)**
Tel.: (57) 17421460
Web Site: http://co.sodexo.com
Sales Range: $10-24.9 Million
Emp.: 100
N.A.I.C.S.: 722511

Sodexo Polska Sp zoo (1)
ul Jutrzenki 137, 02-231, Warsaw,
Poland **(100%)**
Tel.: (48) 223389600
Web Site: http://pl.sodexo.com
Sales Range: $25-49.9 Million
Emp.: 150
Catering Services
N.A.I.C.S.: 722320

Sodexo Polska Spolka. z o.o. (1)
ul Jutrzenki 137, 02-231, Warsaw,
Poland **(100%)**
Tel.: (48) 22 338 9600
Web Site: http://pl.sodexo.com
Sales Range: $25-49.9 Million
Emp.: 108
Catering Services
N.A.I.C.S.: 722320
Robert Lech *(Pres)*

Sodexo Prestige (1)
Sodexo Prestige Surrey Hills Plain Tree
Cresent, Feltham, TW1 37HF, Mddx, United
Kingdom **(100%)**
Tel.: (44) 2085669222
Web Site: http://www.sodexho.co.uk
Sales Range: $10-24.9 Million
Emp.: 100
N.A.I.C.S.: 722511

**Sodexo Remote Sites Scotland
Ltd.** (1)
5th Floor The Exchange No 2 62 Market
Street, Aberdeen, AB11 5PJ, United Kingdom
Tel.: (44) 1224324388
Web Site:
https://www.sodexoremotesites.com
Catering & Facilities Management Services

N.A.I.C.S.: 541513

Sodexo Scandinavia (1)
Vastberga Alle 36 A, 117 94, Stockholm,
Sweden **(99.23%)**
Tel.: (46) 87755800
Web Site: http://www.sodexo-se.com
Sales Range: $1-4.9 Billion
Emp.: 8,000
Catering Services
N.A.I.C.S.: 722320

Branch (Domestic):

Sodexo (2)
Dalvagen 22, 169 79, Solna,
Sweden **(100%)**
Tel.: (46) 857884000
Web Site: http://se.sodexo.com
Sales Range: $25-49.9 Million
Emp.: 150
Catering Services
N.A.I.C.S.: 722320

Sodexo (2)
August Barks Gata 6A, SE 421 32, Vastra
Frolunda, Sweden **(100%)**
Tel.: (46) 031850550
Web Site: http://www.sodexho-se.com
Sales Range: $25-49.9 Million
Emp.: 150
Catering Services
N.A.I.C.S.: 722320

**Sodexo Service Solutions Austria
GmbH** (1)
Heiligenstadter Lande 27c, 1190, Vienna,
Austria
Tel.: (43) 1 328 60 57 0
Web Site: http://at.sodexo.com
Sales Range: $50-74.9 Million
Emp.: 300
Catering Services
N.A.I.C.S.: 722320

Sodexo Services Co., Ltd. (1)
Bldg 11 Block 28 Danba Rd, Putuo District,
200062, Shanghai, China **(100%)**
Tel.: (86) 2123256008
Web Site: http://www.sodexho-cn.com
Sales Range: $200-249.9 Million
Emp.: 1,500
Catering Services
N.A.I.C.S.: 722320

Sodexo Singapore Pte. Ltd. (1)
223 Mountbatten Road 02-18 223 Mountbatten, Singapore, 398008,
Singapore **(100%)**
Tel.: (65) 67438998
Web Site: http://www.sg.sodexo.com
Sales Range: $50-74.9 Million
Emp.: 700
N.A.I.C.S.: 722511

Sodexo Southern Africa Pty. Ltd. (1)
Pines Building The Avenue Office Park 45
Homestead Road, Rivonia, 2128, Johannesburg, South Africa **(100%)**
Tel.: (27) 118036600
Web Site: http://za.sodexo.com
Sales Range: $10-24.9 Million
Emp.: 35
Catering Services
N.A.I.C.S.: 722320

**Sodexo Spoleene Stravovani a
Sluzby Sro** (1)
Radlicka 2, 15000, Prague, Czech
Republic **(100%)**
Tel.: (420) 233113435
Web Site: http://cz.sodexo.com
Catering Services
N.A.I.C.S.: 722320

**Sodexo Toplu Yemek Ve Servis
A.S.** (1)
No 32 Kadikoy Kosuyolu Mah Mahmut Yesari Sok, 34718, Istanbul, Turkiye **(100%)**
Tel.: (90) 216 340 4500
Web Site: http://www.sodexo.com.tr
Sales Range: $200-249.9 Million
Emp.: 2,300
Catering & On-Site Services
N.A.I.C.S.: 722320

Sodexo Tunisia (1)
9 rue Med Ali Annabi, 1002, Tunis, Belvedere, Tunisia **(48.88%)**
Tel.: (216) 22200212

Catering Services
N.A.I.C.S.: 722320

Sodexo Tunisie (1)
09 Rue Med Ali Annabi, 1002, Tunis, Tunisia
Tel.: (216) 71186650
Web Site: http://www.sodexo.tn
Catering Services
N.A.I.C.S.: 722320

Sodexo do Brasil Comercial Ltda (1)
Av Ibirapuera 1196, Indianopolis, Sao
Paulo, 04028-000, SP, Brazil **(100%)**
Tel.: (55) 30035083
Web Site: http://www.br.sodexo.com
Sales Range: $25-49.9 Million
Emp.: 180
Catering & On-Site Service Solutions
N.A.I.C.S.: 722320

Sodexo do Brasil Sales & Commercial Ltda. (1)
Av Joao Dias 24, Santo Amaro, CEP 04724 000, Sao Paulo, SP, Brazil **(100%)**
Tel.: (55) 11 5693 5000
Web Site: http://www.sodexho.com.br
Sales Range: $50-74.9 Million
Emp.: 300
Catering Services
N.A.I.C.S.: 722320

Sodexo prehrana in storitve doo (1)
Tehnoloski Park 22a, Ljubljana, 1000,
Slovenia **(99.68%)**
Tel.: (386) 14205800
Web Site: http://si.sodexo.com
Sales Range: $10-24.9 Million
Emp.: 27
Catering Services
N.A.I.C.S.: 722320
Cveta Franko *(Mng Dir)*

Sodexo, Inc (1)
9801 Washingtonian Blvd, Gaithersburg,
MD 20878
Tel.: (301) 987-4000
Web Site: http://us.sodexo.com
Sales Range: $1-4.9 Billion
Emp.: 150,000
Manage & Operate Food Service Programs
& Other General Services in Health Care,
Educational, Business & Industrial Facilities
N.A.I.C.S.: 722310

Subsidiary (Domestic):

CK Franchising, Inc. (2)
1 Park Plz Ste 300, Irvine, CA 92614
Tel.: (888) 653-0915
Web Site: https://www.comfortkeepers.com
In-Home Senior Care Services
N.A.I.C.S.: 621610

Capitol Vending & Coffee (2)
4711 E 5th St, Austin, TX 78702-5033
Tel.: (512) 472-7462
Web Site:
http://www.capitolvendingandcoffee.com
Vending Machine Operators
N.A.I.C.S.: 445132

Doyon Universal Services, LLC (2)
701 W 8th Ave Ste 500, Anchorage, AK
99501-3408
Tel.: (907) 522-1300
Web Site: http://www.doyonuniversal.com
Sales Range: $50-74.9 Million
Emp.: 200
Manage & Operate Food Service Programs
& Other General Services in Health Care,
Educational, Business & Industrial Facilities
N.A.I.C.S.: 713990
Thomas Robert Kean *(Pres)*

Sodexo Remote Sites USA Inc. (2)
5749 Susitna Dr, Harahan, LA 70123
Tel.: (504) 733-5761
Web Site: http://www.sodexusa.com
Rev: $238,500,000
Emp.: 1,000
Caterers
N.A.I.C.S.: 722320

Tariq Al Ghanim (1)
Block 1 Building 100 Behind Ardiya Fire
Station, PO Box 64285, Ardiya Industrial
Area Al Shuwaikh, 70453, Kuwait,
Kuwait **(100%)**
Tel.: (965) 24319701
Web Site: http://www.tagholding.com

SODIAAL INTERNATIONAL SAS

Sales Range: $200-249.9 Million
Emp.: 1,600
Catering Services
N.A.I.C.S.: 722320

Teyseer Services Company (1)
1st Floor Building 39 Al Amir Street Freej Al
Nasr Midmac Roundabout, PO Box 2431,
Doha, Qatar **(100%)**
Tel.: (974) 44253000
Web Site: http://www.teyseer-services.com
Sales Range: $10-24.9 Million
Emp.: 30
Catering Services
N.A.I.C.S.: 722320

Universal Sodexho Congo (1)
BP 1624, Pointe Noire, Congo, Republic
of **(100%)**
Tel.: (242) 941970
Sales Range: $10-24.9 Million
Emp.: 25
Catering Services
N.A.I.C.S.: 722320

Universal Sodexho Gabon (1)
BP 608, Port-Gentil, Gabon **(89.69%)**
Tel.: (241) 55 2277
Catering Services
N.A.I.C.S.: 722320

Universal Sodexho Nigeria Ltd (1)
Plot 470 Transamadi industrial Lay out,
TMB 50006, Port Harcourt, Nigeria **(95%)**
Tel.: (234) 84232219
Sales Range: $10-24.9 Million
Emp.: 35
Catering Services
N.A.I.C.S.: 722320

Universal Sodexho Peru (1)
Los Libertadores 171 San Isidro Torre Real
San Isidro, 33, Lima, Peru **(99.99%)**
Tel.: (51) 14415111
Web Site: http://www.be.sodexo.com
Sales Range: $25-49.9 Million
Emp.: 133
N.A.I.C.S.: 722511
Alfredo Garcia *(Gen Mgr)*

SODIAAL INTERNATIONAL SAS

170 bis boulevard du Montparnasse,
75680, Paris, Cedex 14, France
Tel.: (33) 144109010 FR
Web Site: http://www.sodiaal.fr
Year Founded: 1990
Sales Range: $1-4.9 Billion
Emp.: 7,700
Cooperative Dairy Group
N.A.I.C.S.: 311514
Jorge Boucas *(CEO)*

Subsidiaries:

Candia (1)
78 rue de la Villette, 69425, Lyon, Cedex
03, France **(81%)**
Tel.: (33) 472405252
Web Site: http://www.candia.fr
Sales Range: $1-4.9 Billion
Emp.: 1,676
Dairy Products
N.A.I.C.S.: 311514
Yves Legros *(CEO)*

Yoplait S.A.S. (1)
150 Rue Gallieni, 92657, Boulogne, Cedex,
France **(49%)**
Tel.: (33) 800022121
Web Site: http://www.yoplait.fr
Sales Range: $5-14.9 Billion
Dairy Product Produce Mfr
N.A.I.C.S.: 311514

Subsidiary (Non-US):

YOPLAIT CANADA CO. (2)
1875 Buckhorn Gate Suite 201, Mississauga, L4W 5N9, ON, Canada
Web Site: https://www.yoplait.ca
Food Products Mfr
N.A.I.C.S.: 311412

Subsidiary (Domestic):

YOPLAIT FRANCE SAS (2)
150 rue Gallieni, 92641, Boulogne, Cedex,
France

SODIAAL INTERNATIONAL SAS

SODIAAL International SAS—(Continued)
Tel.: (33) 800022121
Web Site: http://www.yoplait.fr
Dairy Product Whslr
N.A.I.C.S.: 424430

Subsidiary (Non-US):

YOPLAIT IRELAND LIMITED (2)
Unit 16A Fonthill Industrial Park, Clondalkin,
Dublin, 22, Ireland
Tel.: (353) 818818988
Web Site: https://www.yoplait.ie
Dairy Product Whslr
N.A.I.C.S.: 424430

YOPLAIT SVERIGE AB (2)
Hollandargatan 20, 111 60, Stockholm,
Sweden
Tel.: (46) 200434345
Web Site: http://www.yoplait.se
Dairy Product Whslr
N.A.I.C.S.: 424430

Subsidiary (US):

YOPLAIT USA, INC. (2)
128 E Slosson Ave, Reed City, MI 49677
Tel.: (231) 832-3285
Web Site: http://www.yoplait.com
Fluid Milk Mfr
N.A.I.C.S.: 311511

Subsidiary (Non-US):

Yoplait UK Ltd. (2)
Harman House 1 George Street, Portsmith
Rd, Uxbridge, UB8 1QQ, Surrey, United
Kingdom
Tel.: (44) 8003580401
Web Site: https://www.yoplait.co.uk
Dairy Product Merchant Whslr
N.A.I.C.S.: 424430
Nick Wishman (Mng Dir)

SODICK CO., LTD.

3-12-1 Nakamachidai, Tsuzuki-ku,
Yokohama, 224-8522, Kanagawa,
Japan
Tel.: (81) 459423111 JP
Web Site: https://www.sodick.co.jp
Year Founded: 1976
6143—(TKS)
Rev: $476,263,660
Assets: $950,527,940
Liabilities: $403,683,330
Net Worth: $546,844,610
Earnings: ($32,642,360)
Emp.: 3,562
Fiscal Year-end: 12/31/23
Electrical Discharge Machines Mfr
N.A.I.C.S.: 333517
Kenichi Furukawa (Pres)

Subsidiaries:

Nano Techno Research
Corporation (1)
16500-2 Higashikaminaka, Miyazaki, Japan
Tel.: (81) 985743498
Web Site: http://www.ntr-corp.co.jp
Sales Range: $25-49.9 Million
Emp.: 33
Precision Machining Services
N.A.I.C.S.: 811210

Neo Plus Asia Co., Ltd. (1)
33 75 15th Fl Wall St Tower Surawong Rd,
Suriyawong Bangrak, Bangkok, 10500,
Thailand
Tel.: (66) 2632 7404
Industrial Machinery Whslr
N.A.I.C.S.: 423830

PT Sodick Technology Indonesia (1)
JI MH Thamrin - Lippo Cikarang Ruko Robson Blok B No 05 Cibatu, Cikarang Selatan,
Bekasi, 17530, Jawa Barat, Indonesia
Tel.: (62) 218 991 3325
Machine Tool Mfr & Distr
N.A.I.C.S.: 333517

Plustech Singapore Pte., Ltd. (1)
401 MacPherson Rd, Hotel Windsor No 02-35, Singapore, Singapore
Tel.: (65) 62858619
Sales Range: $50-74.9 Million
Emp.: 4
Industrial Machinery Whslr
N.A.I.C.S.: 423830

Shanghai Sodick Software Co.,
Ltd. (1)
No 471 Guiping Road, Xuhui District,
Shanghai, 200233, China
Tel.: (86) 216 485 1533
Web Site: https://www.3s.com.cn
Sales Range: $25-49.9 Million
Emp.: 100
Software Development Services
N.A.I.C.S.: 541511

Sodick (H.K.) Co., Ltd. (1)
5/F Edward Wong Tower 910 Cheung Sha
Wan Road, Tsim Sha Tsui, Kowloon, China
(Hong Kong)
Tel.: (852) 27210200
Electronic Parts Whslr
N.A.I.C.S.: 423690
Lawerance Lo (Mgr-Mktg)

Sodick (Taiwan) Co., Ltd. (1)
No 26 Keji 1st Rd 19 Neighbor, Wunhua
Vlg Gueishan, Taoyuan, Taiwan
Tel.: (886) 33289885
Sales Range: $50-74.9 Million
Emp.: 90
Electronic Parts Whslr & Services
N.A.I.C.S.: 423690

Sodick (Thailand) Co., Ltd. (1)
6084 Moo 19 Soi 19 Navanakorn Indus Estate Zone 3 Phaholyothin Rd, Klongnueng,
Khlong Luang, 12120, Pathum Thani, Thailand
Sales Range: $200-249.9 Million
Emp.: 600
Industrial Machinery Mfr
N.A.I.C.S.: 333519

Sodick Amoy Co., Ltd. (1)
No 376 W Yangguang Rd, Haicang Dist,
Xiamen, 361022, Fujian, China
Tel.: (86) 5926516000
Electric Discharge Machinery Development
& Mfr
N.A.I.C.S.: 336320

Sodick Co. Ltd. - Fukui Plant (1)
78 Nagaya Sakai-cho, Sakai, 919-0598,
Fukui, Japan
Tel.: (81) 776668877
Web Site: http://www.sodick.jp
Sales Range: $50-74.9 Million
Emp.: 250
Electrical Discharge Machines Mfr
N.A.I.C.S.: 335999
Ken Takahashi (Mng Dir)

Sodick DAC Co., Ltd. (1)
78 Tenement Sakai-cho, Sakai, 919-0598,
Fukui, Japan
Tel.: (81) 776668167
Web Site: http://www.sodick-dac.co.jp
Printing & Website Design Services
N.A.I.C.S.: 541512

Sodick Electromechanical (Shanghai)
Co., Ltd. (1)
No 436 Zhuguang Rd Xujing Town, Qingpu
Dist, Shanghai, 201702, China
Tel.: (86) 2151512828
Web Site: http://www.sodick.com.cn
Electric Discharge Machinery Sales & Services
N.A.I.C.S.: 811114

Sodick Enterprise (SZ) Co., Ltd. (1)
02 1F Jiazhou Bldg Dept Store 9013 Bing
He St, Fu Tian Dist, Shenzhen, Guangdong, China
Tel.: (86) 75583877688
Sales Range: $25-49.9 Million
Emp.: 60
Electric Discharge Machinery Sales & Services
N.A.I.C.S.: 811114
Gapy Wong (Gen Mgr)

Sodick Europe Ltd. (1)
Rowley Dr, Baginton, Coventry, CV3 4FG,
West Midlands, United Kingdom
Tel.: (44) 2476214314
Web Site: http://www.sodick.org
Sales Range: $25-49.9 Million
Emp.: 3
Electrical Discharge Machines Mfr

N.A.I.C.S.: 335999
Melanie Capp (Office Mgr)

Subsidiary (Non-US):

Sodick Deutschland GmbH (2)
Mundelheimer Weg 57, Lichtenbroich,
40472, Dusseldorf, Germany
Tel.: (49) 211 422 6080
Web Site: https://www.sodick.de
Sales Range: $25-49.9 Million
Emp.: 15
Electronic Parts Mfr
N.A.I.C.S.: 334419
Norbert Kempf (Gen Mgr)

Division (Domestic):

Sodick Deutschland GmbH (3)
Im Bresselsholze 5, 07819, Triptis, Germany
Tel.: (49) 3648285860
Operations Support Services
N.A.I.C.S.: 561210

Subsidiary (Non-US):

Sodick Hightech Germany
GmbH (2)
Mundelheimer Weg 57, Dusseldorf, 40472,
Germany
Tel.: (49) 2114226080
Web Site: http://www.shcgermany.de
Sales Range: $25-49.9 Million
Electrical Parts Supplier
N.A.I.C.S.: 423610

Sodick F.T Co., Ltd. (1)
Nisso 13th Building 2-5-1 Shin-Yokohama,
Kohoku-ku, Yokohama, 222-0033, Japan
Tel.: (81) 45 478 0571
Web Site: https://www.sodick-ft.co.jp
Machine Tool Mfr & Distr
N.A.I.C.S.: 333517

Sodick FA Co., Ltd. (1)
228 Haoka, Takaoka, 933-0958, Toyama,
Japan
Tel.: (81) 766254203
Web Site: http://www.sodick.jp
Power Supplies Mfr
N.A.I.C.S.: 335999

Sodick Inc. (1)
1605 N Penny Ln, Schaumburg, IL 60173-4555
Tel.: (847) 310-9000
Web Site: http://www.sodick.com
Linear Motor Wire Machinery & Parts Distr
& Maintenance Services
N.A.I.C.S.: 811310
Dave Thomas (Pres)

Sodick International Trading (Shanghai) Co., Ltd. (1)
Rm 1301 E Qiushi Ctr Zhuzilin, Shennan
Ave Futian, Shenzhen, Guangdong, China
Tel.: (86) 75588316967
Industrial Machinery Whslr
N.A.I.C.S.: 423830

Sodick International Trading (Shenzhen) Co., Ltd. (1)
Rm 1301 East Qiushi Center ZhuZiLin Shen
Nan Avenue, Futian, Shenzhen, 518000,
Guangdong, China
Tel.: (86) 7558 831 6967
Electric Discharge Machinery Sales & Services
N.A.I.C.S.: 811310

Sodick Japan Trading Co., Ltd. (1)
2-5-1 Shin-Yokohama, Kohoku-ku, Yokohama, 222-0033, Japan
Tel.: (81) 45 942 3111
Web Site: https://www.sodick-jt.co.jp
Machine Tool Distr
N.A.I.C.S.: 423830

Sodick Korea Co., Ltd. (1)
Okto Bldg 4F 1000-1 Doksan-Dong,
Gumchon-Gu, Seoul, 153-010, Korea
(South)
Tel.: (82) 2 807 4745
Web Site: http://www.sodickkorea.com
Sales Range: $25-49.9 Million
Emp.: 14
Metal Casting Machine Mfr
N.A.I.C.S.: 333248
Ogino Ryuwooseuke (CEO)

INTERNATIONAL PUBLIC

Sodick Philippines Inc. (1)
M201 Unit GRM Ecozone Storage Inc
Building 124 East Science Avenue, Laguna
Technopark, Binan, Laguna, Philippines
Tel.: (63) 49 544 0936
Machine Tool Mfr & Distr
N.A.I.C.S.: 333517

Sodick Singapore Pte., Ltd. (1)
Blk 50 Ubi Crescent Suite 01-04, Ubi Techpark, Singapore, 408568, Singapore
Tel.: (65) 67469089
Sales Range: $25-49.9 Million
Emp.: 30
Heavy Machine Whslr
N.A.I.C.S.: 333248
Jocelyn Wang (Mgr-Sls & Mktg)

Sodick Technologies India Private
Limited (1)
Tel.: (91) 8041146861
Web Site: http://www.sodick.co.in
Sales Range: $25-49.9 Million
Emp.: 5
Computer Numerical Control Machinery Mfr
N.A.I.C.S.: 333248
Ken Takahashi (Mng Dir)

Sodick Technology (M) Sdn.
Bhd. (1)
No C-G-22 Block C Jalan PJU 1A 3K Taipan 1 Damansara, Ara Damansara, Petaling Jaya, 47500, Selangor, Malaysia
Tel.: (60) 378426888
Web Site: http://www.sodick.jp
Sales Range: $50-74.9 Million
Emp.: 9
Machine Tool Whslr
N.A.I.C.S.: 423830
Steven Tan (Mng Dir)

Sodick Tom (Shanghai) Co., Ltd. (1)
No 28 Lane 229, Xiewei Road Xujing Town
Qingpu District, Shanghai, 201702, China
Tel.: (86) 215 988 9181
Machine Tool Mfr & Distr
N.A.I.C.S.: 333517

Sodick Vietnam Co., Ltd. (1)
14B Song Da Street, Ward 02 Tan Binh District, Ho Chi Minh City, Vietnam
Tel.: (84) 283 547 0457
Web Site: http://www.sodick.com.vn
Machine Tool Mfr & Distr
N.A.I.C.S.: 333517

Sozhou Sodick Special Equipment
Co., Ltd. (1)
No 18 Zhuyuan Rd, New District, Suzhou,
215011, China
Tel.: (86) 51268253533
Web Site: http://www.sodick.jp
Industrial Machinery Whslr
N.A.I.C.S.: 423830

Suzhou Sodick Hightech Co.,
Ltd. (1)
Ruidai St Beiqiao Town Xiangcheng Zone,
Suzhou, 215144, Jiangsu, China
Tel.: (86) 512 6599 8418
Sales Range: $100-124.9 Million
Emp.: 450
Plastic Injection Products Development &
Mfr
N.A.I.C.S.: 333511

Suzhou Sodick Special Equipment
Co., Ltd. (1)
No 18 Zhuyuan Rd, New Dist, Suzhou,
215011, Jiangsu, China
Tel.: (86) 512 6825 3533
Web Site: http://www.sodick.jp
Emp.: 300
Heavy Machines Mfr & Whslr
N.A.I.C.S.: 333517

SODIM, SGPS, SA

Av. Fontes Pereira de Melo 14 Piso
9, Lisbon, 1050-121, Portugal
Tel.: (351) 213184800
Web Site: http://sodim.pt
Holding Company
N.A.I.C.S.: 551112
Heinz-Peter Elstrodt (Chm)

Subsidiaries:

Semapa - Sociedade de Investimento
e Gastao SGPS, S.A. (1)

AND PRIVATE COMPANIES

Av Fontes Pereira de Melo 14-10, 1050-121, Lisbon, Portugal **(81.32%)**
Tel.: (351) 213184700
Web Site: https://www.semapa.pt
Rev.: $3,369,328,210
Assets: $4,919,499,074
Liabilities: $3,156,466,527
Net Worth: $1,763,032,547
Earnings: $331,415,750
Emp.: 5,986
Fiscal Year-end: 12/31/2022
Holding Company
N.A.I.C.S.: 551112
Rui Tiago Trindade Ramos Gouveia *(Sec)*

Subsidiary (Domestic):

ABAPOR - Comercio e Industria de Carnes, S.A. **(2)**
Herdade da Palmeira Olheiros do Meio, Lamarosa, 2100-406, Portugal
Tel.: (351) 243720025
Web Site: http://www.etsa.pt
Sales Range: $25-49.9 Million
Emp.: 200
Pet Food Mfr
N.A.I.C.S.: 311111
Eofeua Fantos *(Mng Dir)*

Argibetao - Sociedade de Novos Produtos de Argila e Betao, S.A. **(2)**
Padim da Graca - Apartado 222, 4711-911, Braga, Portugal
Tel.: (351) 253607900
Web Site: http://www.argibetao.pt
Cement Tiles Mfr
N.A.I.C.S.: 327120

Subsidiary (Non-US):

Argibetao SA **(2)**
Cl Enrique Ii 10 Enrique Ii 10, 33000, Asturias, Spain **(90.9%)**
Tel.: (34) 985723201
Data Processing Services
N.A.I.C.S.: 518210

Subsidiary (Domestic):

BIOLOGICAL - Gestao de Residuos Industriais, Lda. **(2)**
Rua Padre Adriano Olivais do Machio, 2660-119, Loures, Santo Antao do Tojal, Portugal
Tel.: (351) 219730044
Web Site: http://www.etsa.pt
Used Oil Refining Services
N.A.I.C.S.: 311225

CMP - Cimentos Maceira e Pataias, S.A. **(2)**
Lugar Fabrica Maceira, Maceira Liz, Leiria, 2405-019, Portugal
Tel.: (351) 244779700
Web Site: http://www.secil.pt
Sales Range: $50-74.9 Million
Emp.: 100
Cement Mfr
N.A.I.C.S.: 327310
Luis Costa *(Mng Dir)*

Cimentos Madeira, Lda. **(2)**
Estrada Monumental 433, 9000-236, Funchal, Madeira, Portugal
Tel.: (351) 291703300
Web Site: http://www.cimentosmadeira.com
Sales Range: $25-49.9 Million
Emp.: 20
Cement Mfr
N.A.I.C.S.: 327310
Jose Franco *(Exec Dir)*

Condind - Conservacao e Desenvolvimento Industrial, Lda. **(2)**
Sede Outao, 2901-901, Setubal, Portugal
Tel.: (351) 265534766
Web Site: http://www.secil.pt
Emp.: 100
Cement Mfr
N.A.I.C.S.: 327310

Subsidiary (Domestic):

Ciminpart - Investimentos e Participacoes, SGPS, S.A. **(3)**
Avenida Forcas Armadas 125 6, 1600-079, Lisbon, Portugal
Tel.: (351) 217927100
Web Site: http://www.secil.pt

Sales Range: $75-99.9 Million
Investment Management Service
N.A.I.C.S.: 523940

Subsidiary (Non-US):

Grasa Y Transportes Carvajal S.L. **(2)**
Pl Constitucion 5, 21290, Huelva, Spain
Tel.: (34) 959121036
General Freight Trucking Services
N.A.I.C.S.: 484230

Subsidiary (Domestic):

IRP - Industria de Rebocos de Portugal, S.A. **(2)**
Zona Industrial de Rio Maior Lote 358-363 Apartado 33, 2040-998, Rio Maior, Portugal
Tel.: (351) 243909800
Web Site: http://www.irp.pt
Cement Mortars Mfr
N.A.I.C.S.: 327310

ITS - Industria Transformadora de Subprodutos Animais, S.A. **(2)**
Herdade da Palmeira Olheiros do Meio, 2100-406, Lamarosa, Portugal
Tel.: (351) 243720020
Web Site: http://www.etsa.pt
Sales Range: $25-49.9 Million
Emp.: 72
Animal Byproducts Processing Services
N.A.I.C.S.: 311613
Luisa Mestre *(Asst Gen Mgr)*

Prescor Producao de Escorias Moidas, Lda. **(2)**
Aldeia P Pires, 2840-075, Seixal, Lisbon, Portugal
Tel.: (351) 212210436
Prescor Mfr
N.A.I.C.S.: 334513

SEBOL - Comercio e Industria de Sebo, S.A. **(2)**
Rua Padre Adriano Olivais do Macho, Loures, 2660-119, Santo Antao do Tojal, Portugal
Tel.: (351) 219828190
Sales Range: $25-49.9 Million
Emp.: 50
Pet Food Mfr
N.A.I.C.S.: 311111
Carlos Marcues *(Chm)*

Secil - Companhia Geral de Cal e Cimento, S.A. **(2)**
Av Eng Duarte Pacheco 19 7, 1070-100, Lisbon, Portugal
Tel.: (351) 217927100
Web Site: http://www.secil-group.com
Sales Range: $125-149.9 Million
Emp.: 300
Cement Mfr
N.A.I.C.S.: 327310

Subsidiary (Non-US):

Secil - Companhia de Cimento do Lobito, S.A. **(2)**
Morro De Quileva, Lobito, Benguela, Angola
Tel.: (244) 272222428
Cement Mfr & Whslr
N.A.I.C.S.: 327310

Subsidiary (Domestic):

Secil, Betoes e Inertes, S.G.P.S., S.A. **(2)**
Avenida Avenida Forcas Armadas 125 7th Fl, 1069-128, Lisbon, Portugal
Tel.: (351) 213172420
Readymix Concrete Mfr
N.A.I.C.S.: 327320

Subsidiary (Domestic):

Colegra - Exploracao de Pedreiras, S.A. **(3)**
Avenida Antonio Augusto de Aguiar 21 4, 1050-012, Lisbon, Portugal
Tel.: (351) 252301120
Stone Quarrying Services
N.A.I.C.S.: 212319

Quimipedra - Secil Britas, Calcarios e Deriados, Lda. **(3)**
R Fonte do Covao, 2970-000, Sesimbra, Portugal

Tel.: (351) 212 681 316
Cement Mfr
N.A.I.C.S.: 327310

Secil Britas, S.A. **(3)**
Travessa do Esporao n 582 Cabeca Santa, 4575-142, Porto, Portugal
Tel.: (351) 255617110
Web Site: http://www.secil-britas.pt
Sales Range: $25-49.9 Million
Emp.: 40
Sand & Gravel Quarrying Services
N.A.I.C.S.: 212321

Unibetao - Industrias de Betao Preparado, S.A. **(3)**
Avenida Antonio Augusto de Aguiar 21 3 Dto, 1050-012, Lisbon, Portugal
Tel.: (351) 213172420
Readymix Concrete Mfr
N.A.I.C.S.: 327320

Subsidiary (Non-US):

Secilpar, S.L. **(2)**
Calle Pez Volador 40 Plt Baja Pta D, 28007, Madrid, Spain
Tel.: (34) 914008870
Construction Materials Whslr
N.A.I.C.S.: 423320

Subsidiary (Non-US):

Secil Cabo Verde Comercio e Servicos, Lda. **(3)**
Avenida Macaronesias S/n Achada Grande Frente, Praia, 622, Cape Verde
Tel.: (238) 2633704
Construction Materials Whslr
N.A.I.C.S.: 423320
Pedro Viegas Galvao *(Gen Mgr)*

Subsidiary (Domestic):

ICV - Inertes de Cabo Verde, Lda. **(4)**
Zona Di Purga Nova Joao Varela, Praia, Cape Verde
Tel.: (238) 2671155
Construction Materials Whslr
N.A.I.C.S.: 423320

Subsidiary (Domestic):

Seminv, SGPS, S.A. **(2)**
Avenida Fontes Pereira de Melo 14 10, Lisbon, 1050121, Portugal
Tel.: (351) 213184700
Web Site: http://www.semapa.pt
Sales Range: $50-74.9 Million
Emp.: 40
Investment Management Service
N.A.I.C.S.: 523999

Subsidiary (Non-US):

Societe des Ciments de Gabes, S.A. **(2)**
75 Avenue Kheireddine Pacha, 1002, Tunis, Tunisia
Tel.: (216) 71 950 952
Cement Mfr & Whslr
N.A.I.C.S.: 327310

Subsidiary (Domestic):

Sud - Beton - Societe de Fabrication de Beton du Sud **(3)**
Rte de gabes KM 9, 3083, Sfax, Tunisia
Tel.: (216) 74289885
Sales Range: $25-49.9 Million
Emp.: 83
Readymix Concrete Mfr
N.A.I.C.S.: 327320
Jamal Mohamed *(Mgr-Admin)*

Zarzis Beton **(3)**
ZI Rte de Ben Guerdane, 4170, Jarjis, Medinine, Tunisia
Tel.: (216) 75748900
Cement Distr
N.A.I.C.S.: 423320

Subsidiary (Domestic):

The Navigator Company, S.A. **(2)**
Apartado 55, 2901-861, Setubal, Portugal **(69.4%)**
Tel.: (351) 265709000

Web Site: https://en.thenavigatorcompany.com
Rev.: $2,659,858,289
Assets: $3,142,702,455
Liabilities: $1,783,208,052
Net Worth: $1,359,494,403
Earnings: $423,631,632
Emp.: 3,246
Fiscal Year-end: 12/31/2022
Pulp & Paper Mfr
N.A.I.C.S.: 322120
Antonio Pedro Gomes Paula Neto Alves *(Sec)*

Subsidiary (Non-US):

Navigator Paper UK Limited **(3)**
5 The Courtyard London Road, Newbury, London, RG14 1AX, Berks, United Kingdom
Tel.: (44) 137272828
Web Site: https://navigator-paper.com
Paper & Paperboard Mfr
N.A.I.C.S.: 322219

Subsidiary (Domestic):

Accrol Group Holdings plc **(4)**
Roman Road, Blackburn, BB1 2LD, Lancashire, United Kingdom
Tel.: (44) 1254278844
Web Site: http://www.accrol.co.uk
Rev.: $185,456,406
Assets: $255,353,189
Liabilities: $137,995,945
Net Worth: $117,357,244
Earnings: ($3,584,381)
Emp.: 416
Fiscal Year-end: 04/30/2021
Sanitary Paper Product Mfr & Distr
N.A.I.C.S.: 322291

Subsidiary (Domestic):

Soporcel - Sociedade Portuguesa de Papel, SA. **(3)**
Peninsula Da Mitrena, PO Box 55, Freguesia Do Sado, 2901 861, Setubal, Portugal
Tel.: (351) 233900100
Web Site: http://www.portucelsoporcel.com
Sales Range: $200-249.9 Million
Emp.: 903
Pulp & Paper Mfr
N.A.I.C.S.: 322120

SODIPORC SA
Z I Grelet Rue Louis Pergaud, 16000, Angouleme, Charente, France
Tel.: (33) 545914193
Web Site: http://www.maitrecochon.fr
Year Founded: 1973
Pork Product Mfr & Distr
N.A.I.C.S.: 311611

SODITECH SA
1 Bis allee des Gabians, 06150, Cannes, France
Tel.: (33) 492194800
Web Site: https://www.soditech.com
SEC—(EUR)
Sales Range: $1-9.9 Million
Mechanical & Electronic Engineering Services
N.A.I.C.S.: 541330
Maurice Caille *(CEO)*

SODRA SKOGSAGARNA
Skogsudden, 351 89, Vaxjo, Sweden
Tel.: (46) 47089000   SE
Web Site: http://www.sodra.com
Year Founded: 1938
Rev.: $2,484,522,110
Assets: $3,144,046,290
Liabilities: $1,281,217,350
Net Worth: $1,862,828,940
Earnings: $232,773,240
Emp.: 3,150
Fiscal Year-end: 12/31/19
Holding Company; Paper, Pulp & Wood Products Mfr
N.A.I.C.S.: 551112
Lars Idermark *(Pres & CEO)*

Subsidiaries:

Monsteras Hamn AB **(1)**

SODRA SKOGSAGARNA

Sodra Skogsagarna—(Continued)

Monsteras Bruk, 383 25, Monsteras, Sweden
Tel.: (46) 499 155 32
Web Site: http://www.sodra.se
Logging Services
N.A.I.C.S.: 113310

Sodra Cell AB (1)
Skogsudden, 351 89, Vaxjo, Sweden
Tel.: (46) 47089000
Web Site: http://www.sodra.com
Sales Range: $1-4.9 Billion
Emp.: 350
Pulp Mill
N.A.I.C.S.: 322110
Gunilla Saltin (Pres)

Subsidiary (Non-US):

Sodra Cell Tofte (2)
ostre straandvei 52, Tofte, 3482, Norway
Tel.: (47) 32799000
Web Site: http://www.sodra.com
Sales Range: $100-124.9 Million
Emp.: 30
Mfr of Specialty Paper
N.A.I.C.S.: 322220
Christen Gronvold-Hansen (CEO)

Sodra Latvia SIA (1)
Skultes 1 Zvejniekciems, 2161, Riga, Latvia
Tel.: (371) 9217830
Web Site: http://www.sodra-latvia-sia.wood-me.com
Logging Services
N.A.I.C.S.: 113310
Maire Kurm (CFO)

Sodra Metsad OU (1)
Merivalja tee 1, 11911, Tallinn, Harjumaa, Estonia
Tel.: (372) 5163569
Logging Services
N.A.I.C.S.: 113310

Sodra Skog (1)
Skogsudden, Vaxjo, 35189, Sweden
Tel.: (46) 47089000
Web Site: http://www.sodra.com
Sales Range: $1-4.9 Billion
Emp.: 250
Forestry Services & Forest Raw Materials Supplier
N.A.I.C.S.: 115310

Sodra Skogsenergi (1)
Skogsudden, Vaxjo, 351 89, Sweden
Tel.: (46) 47089000
Web Site: http://www.sodra.com
Sales Range: $50-74.9 Million
Emp.: 220
Bio-fuel Mfr
N.A.I.C.S.: 457210

Sodra Timber AB (1)
Skogsudden, 35101, Vaxjo, Sweden
Tel.: (46) 47089000
Web Site: http://www.sodra.com
Sawmills & Timber Products Mfr
N.A.I.C.S.: 321113

SOFALINE
12 Rue Du General Ingold, 88230, Fraize, Vosges, France
Tel.: (33) 329504130
Rev.: $11,200,000
Emp.: 37
N.A.I.C.S.: 445110

SOFAME TECHNOLOGIES INC.
500 Alphonse D Roy, Montreal, H1W 3Y8, QC, Canada
Tel.: (514) 523-6545
Web Site: http://www.sofame.com
Year Founded: 1984
Sales Range: $1-9.9 Million
Emp.: 12
Fuel-Efficient Direct-Contact Water & Space Heater Mfr
N.A.I.C.S.: 333415
Luc Mandeville (Interim CFO, CTO & VP)

Subsidiaries:

Sofame Europe S.A.S. (1)
11 Rue de Louvain, 92400, Courbevoie, France
Tel.: (33) 145743405
Web Site: http://www.sofame.com
Water Heating System Mfr
N.A.I.C.S.: 333414

SOFCOM SYSTEMS LTD.
D-36 Flat No 802 Sheel Mohar Apartment C-Scheme, Subhash Marg, Jaipur, 302001, Rajasthan, India
Tel.: (91) 1412340221
Web Site: http://www.sofcomsystems.com
538923—(BOM)
Assets: $889,420
Liabilities: $433,237
Net Worth: $456,183
Earnings: ($35,449)
Fiscal Year-end: 03/31/21
Information Technology Services
N.A.I.C.S.: 541512
Kishore Mehta (Mng Dir)

SOFEMA
Route Nationale 19, Levallois-Perret, 77720, Seine-et-Marne, France
Tel.: (33) 164068207
Web Site: http://www.sofema-international.com
Rev.: $18,800,000
Emp.: 43
N.A.I.C.S.: 445110
Marie Schrarter (Mgr)

SOFIA COMMERCE-PAWN BROKERAGE AD
ul Ralevitsa 74 et 3 Ofis 3, Sofia, Bulgaria
Tel.: (359) 29629690
Web Site: http://www.sofiacommerce.net
SCOM—(BUL)
Sales Range: Less than $1 Million
Mortgage Banking Services
N.A.I.C.S.: 522310
Todor Angelov Vachev (Chm)

SOFIA HOTEL BALKAN AD
5 Sveta Nedelya Square, 1000, Sofia, 1000, Bulgaria
Tel.: (359) 29816541
Web Site: https://www.sofiabalkan.net
SHB—(BUL)
Sales Range: Less than $1 Million
Hotel Operator
N.A.I.C.S.: 721110
Desislava Yalamova (Dir-IR)

SOFIBOR
Gare Saint Louis, 33300, Bordeaux, Gironde, France
Tel.: (33) 556399866
Rev.: $14,400,000
Emp.: 98
N.A.I.C.S.: 444180
Jacques Vallois (Pres)

SOFIDEL S.P.A
Via Giuseppe Lazzareschi 23, 55016, Porcari, Lucca, Italy
Tel.: (39) 05832681
Web Site: http://www.sofidel.com
Year Founded: 1966
Specialty Paper Mfr
N.A.I.C.S.: 322291
Luigi Lazzareschi (CEO)

Subsidiaries:

ST Paper - Duluth Mill (1)
100 N Central Ave, Duluth, MN 55807
Tel.: (218) 628-5100
Emp.: 290
Paper Mfr
N.A.I.C.S.: 322120

Sofidel America Corporation (1)
1006 Marley Dr, Haines City, FL 33844
Tel.: (863) 547-1100
Web Site: http://www.cellynne.com
Sales Range: $25-49.9 Million
Emp.: 400
Specialty Paper Mfr
N.A.I.C.S.: 322299
Marc Allegre (VP)

SOFINA FOODS INC.
100 Commerce Valley Drive West, Markham, L3T 0A1, ON, Canada
Tel.: (905) 747-3333   Ca
Web Site: https://www.sofinafoods.com
Year Founded: 1995
Meat Product Mfr & Distr
N.A.I.C.S.: 311612
Michael Latifi (Founder, Chm & CEO)

Subsidiaries:

Janes Family Foods Ltd. (1)
3340 Orlando Drive, Mississauga, L4V 1C7, ON, Canada
Tel.: (905) 673-7145
Web Site: http://www.janesfamilyfoods.com
Emp.: 220
Frozen Poultry & Fish Products Mfr & Distr
N.A.I.C.S.: 311412
Steve Parkhill (Grp VP-Ops & Sr Dir-Mfg)

Quality Meat Group Ltd. (1)
145 East Drive, Brampton, L6T 1B9, ON, Canada
Tel.: (905) 790-3737
Emp.: 600
Deli Meat Products Mfr & Distr
N.A.I.C.S.: 327910

Santa Maria Foods ULC (1)
10 Armthorpe Road, Brampton, L6T 5M4, ON, Canada
Tel.: (905) 790-1991
Web Site: http://www.sharemastro.com
Emp.: 400
Deli Meat Products Mfr & Distr
N.A.I.C.S.: 311612
Frederick Jaques (CEO)

SOFINA S.A.
Rue de l'Industrie 31, B-1040, Brussels, Belgium
Tel.: (32) 25510611   BE
Web Site: https://sofinagroup.com
SOF—(EUR)
Rev.: $407,357,004
Assets: $10,622,634,362
Liabilities: $819,665,444
Net Worth: $9,802,968,919
Earnings: ($112,526,441)
Emp.: 87
Fiscal Year-end: 12/31/23
Investment Management Service
N.A.I.C.S.: 551112
David J. Verey (Chm)

SOFINE FOODS BV
Sperwerweg 11, 6374 AG, Landgraaf, Netherlands
Tel.: (31) 455697940   NI
Web Site: http://www.sofinefoods.com
Year Founded: 1963
Emp.: 50
Soy Alternative Foods Mfr
N.A.I.C.S.: 311999
Bart Merkus (Gen Mgr)

SOFIPRIM S.A.S.
45 Rue d Avignon, 94150, Rungis, France
Tel.: (33) 141802727
Web Site: http://www.sofiprim.com
Year Founded: 1982
Fresh Fruit & Vegetable Whslr
N.A.I.C.S.: 424480

INTERNATIONAL PUBLIC

Subsidiaries:

VINAS SAS (1)
45 rue d'Avignon - Bat C2, 94574, Rungis, France
Tel.: (33) 1 41 80 27 27
Web Site: http://www.vinas.fr
Fruit & Vegetable Whslr
N.A.I.C.S.: 424480

SOFIVA GENOMICS CO., LTD.
No 27 Baoqing Rd, Zhongzheng Dist, Taipei, 100, Taiwan
Tel.: (886) 223826615
Web Site: https://www.sofivagenomics.com.tw
Year Founded: 2012
6615—(TPE)
Rev.: $15,501,204
Assets: $25,240,190
Liabilities: $5,625,989
Net Worth: $19,614,201
Earnings: $1,349,248
Fiscal Year-end: 12/31/22
Health Care Srvices
N.A.I.C.S.: 621610
Yi-Ning Su (CEO & Mng Dir)

SOFT-WORLD INTERNATIONAL CORPORATION
13F No 1-16 Kuojian Rd, Qianzhen Dist, Kaohsiung, 806, Taiwan
Tel.: (886) 227889188
Web Site: https://www.soft-world.com
Year Founded: 1983
5478—(TPE)
Software Development Services
N.A.I.C.S.: 541511
Chin-Po Wang (Chm & Gen Mgr)

Subsidiaries:

CELAD Game Corporation (1)
7F-6 No 32 Sec 1 Chenggong Rd, Nangang, Taipei, 11570, Taiwan
Tel.: (886) 227662256
Web Site: https://www.celadgame.com
Online Game Development Services
N.A.I.C.S.: 339930

Game Topia Co., Ltd. (1)
7190 W Sunset Blvd 70E, Los Angeles, CA 90046
Tel.: (310) 853-2520
Web Site: https://www.topia.io
Software Development Services
N.A.I.C.S.: 541511

SOFT99 CORPORATION
2-6-5 Tanimachi, Chuo-ku, Osaka, 540-0012, Japan
Tel.: (81) 669422853
Web Site: https://www.soft99.co.jp
Year Founded: 1954
4464—(TKS)
Rev.: $197,467,140
Assets: $413,402,620
Liabilities: $52,318,150
Net Worth: $361,084,470
Earnings: $17,390,910
Emp.: 811
Fiscal Year-end: 03/31/24
Chemical Product Mfr & Distr
N.A.I.C.S.: 325998
Hideaki Tanaka (Pres & CEO)

Subsidiaries:

AION Co., Ltd. (1)
6-4 Tanimachi 2-chome Tanimachi Bldg 3F, Chuo-ku, Osaka, 540-0012, Japan
Tel.: (81) 6 4790 7855
Web Site: http://www.aion-kk.co.jp
Emp.: 260
Chemical Products Mfr
N.A.I.C.S.: 325998
Norio Kobayashi (Pres)

Plant (Domestic):

AION Co., Ltd. - Kanto Plant (2)
12 Kitatone Koga-shi, Ibaraki, 306-0213, Japan

Tel.: (81) 280920721
Chemical Products Mfr
N.A.I.C.S.: 325998

ANTERIA Co., Ltd. (1)
2-6-5 Tanimachi, Chuo-ku, Osaka, 540-0012, Japan
Tel.: (81) 669429901
Web Site: https://www.anteria.co.jp
Automobile Parts Distr
N.A.I.C.S.: 423140

HANERON Co., Ltd. (1)
2-22 Ota, Yao, 581-0037, Osaka, Japan
Tel.: (81) 729481117
Web Site: https://haneron.com
Electric Equipment Mfr
N.A.I.C.S.: 334419

Soft99 Corporation - Sanda Factory (1)
14-1 Sanda Technopark, Sanda, 669-1339, Japan
Tel.: (81) 795682599
Chemical Products Mfr
N.A.I.C.S.: 325998

SOFTBANK GROUP CORP.
1-7-1 Kaigan, Minato-ku, Tokyo, 105-7537, Japan
Tel.: (81) 368892000 JP
Web Site: https://group.softbank
Year Founded: 1981
SFBQF—(OTCIQ)
Rev.: $47,110,047,630
Assets: $315,023,758,560
Liabilities: $238,668,887,010
Net Worth: $76,354,871,550
Earnings: ($5,662,873,170)
Emp.: 63,339
Fiscal Year-end: 03/31/23
Holding Company; Telecommunications, Internet Publishing, Broadband Infrastructure, e-Commerce & Other Technology, Media & Marketing Services
N.A.I.C.S.: 551112
Masayoshi Son *(Chm & CEO)*

Subsidiaries:

Alibaba.com Japan Co., Ltd. (1)
2-2-1 Kyobashi Kyobashi Edgran 27F, Chuo-Ku, Tokyo, 104-0031, Japan
Tel.: (81) 345703194
Web Site: http://www.alibaba.co.jp
Sales Range: $25-49.9 Million
Emp.: 6
Online Marketing Services
N.A.I.C.S.: 541613
Makoto Kayama *(Pres & CEO)*

Arm Holdings Limited (1)
110 Fulbourn Road, Cambridge, CB1 9NJ, United Kingdom
Tel.: (44) 1223400400
Holding Company
N.A.I.C.S.: 551112

Subsidiary (Non-US):

ARM France SAS (2)
738 Avenue de Roumanille, Biot, 06410, Sophia-Antipolis, France
Tel.: (33) 497235100
Web Site: https://www.arm.com
Microprocessor Solutions Mfr
N.A.I.C.S.: 334413
Christophe Frey *(Gen Dir & VP-Ops)*

Branch (Domestic):

ARM France (3)
6 Avenue Gustave Eiffel, 78180, Montigny-le-Bretonneux, France (100%)
Tel.: (33) 139304789
Web Site: http://www.arm.com
Microprocessor Solutions Mfr
N.A.I.C.S.: 334413

Subsidiary (Non-US):

ARM KK (2)
Shinyokohama Square Bldg 17F 2-3-12 Shin-yokohama, Kohoku-ku, Yokohama, 222-0033, Kanagawa, Japan
Tel.: (81) 454775260
Web Site: https://www.arm.com
Microprocessor Solutions Mfr
N.A.I.C.S.: 334413

ARM Korea Limited (2)
8th Floor Kyungdong B/D 4-4 Sucae, Dong Bundang-Gu, Seongnam, 463-020, Gyeonggi-Do, Korea (South)
Tel.: (82) 317128234
Microprocessor Solutions Mfr.
N.A.I.C.S.: 334413

Subsidiary (Domestic):

ARM Ltd. (2)
110 Fulbourne Rd, Cambridge, CB1 9NJ, United Kingdom
Tel.: (44) 223400400
Web Site: http://www.arm.com
Microprocessor Solutions Mfr
N.A.I.C.S.: 334413
Simon Segars *(CEO)*

Branch (Domestic):

ARM Ltd. - Maidenhead (3)
Liberty House Moorbridge Rd, Maidenhead, SL6 8LT, Berkshire, United Kingdom
Tel.: (44) 1628427700
Web Site: http://www.arm.com
Microprocessor Solutions Mfr
N.A.I.C.S.: 334413

ARM Ltd. - Sheffield (3)
City Gate 8 St Mary's Gate, Sheffield, S1 4LW, United Kingdom
Tel.: (44) 114 282 8000
Web Site: https://www.arm.com
Microprocessor Solutions
N.A.I.C.S.: 334413

Subsidiary (Domestic):

Geomerics Limited (3)
110 Fulborn Rd, Cambridge, CB1 9NJ, United Kingdom (100%)
Tel.: (41) 1223 405701
Web Site: http://www.geomerics.com
Game Development Software Services
N.A.I.C.S.: 513210
Chris Doran *(Dir-Research Collaborations & EiR)*

Subsidiary (US):

ARM, Ltd. (2)
150 Rose Orchard Way, San Jose, CA 95134-1358
Tel.: (408) 576-1500
Web Site: https://www.arm.com
Semiconductor Mfr
N.A.I.C.S.: 334413
Simon Segars *(CEO)*

Branch (Domestic):

ARM, Ltd. - Texas (3)
Encino Trace 5707 SW Pkwy Bld 1 Ste 100, Austin, TX 78735
Tel.: (512) 327-9249
Web Site: https://www.arm.com
Microprocessor Solutions
N.A.I.C.S.: 518210

Berkshire Grey, Inc. (1)
Tel.: (202) 776-1400
Web Site: https://www.berkshiregrey.com
Rev.: $65,850,000
Assets: $113,841,000
Liabilities: $43,514,000
Net Worth: $70,327,000
Earnings: ($102,794,000)
Emp.: 280
Fiscal Year-end: 12/31/2022
Investment Services
N.A.I.C.S.: 523999
Mark Fidler *(CFO)*

DeeCorp Limited (1)
18-2 Nomura Real Estate Ginza Building 7th floor, Chuo-ku, Tokyo, 104-0061, Japan (100%)
Tel.: (81) 368599426
Web Site: http://www.deecorp.jp
Emp.: 150
Consulting & Outsourcing Services
N.A.I.C.S.: 541618
Kentaro Taniguchi *(Pres)*

Fukuoka SoftBank Hawks Corp. (1)
Fukuoka Dome 6F 2 2 2 Jigyohama, Chuo-ku, Fukuoka, 810-8650, Japan
Tel.: (81) 928441189
Web Site: http://www.hawkstown.com
Sales Range: $75-99.9 Million
Emp.: 230
Professional Baseball Club
N.A.I.C.S.: 711211
Masayoshi Son *(Chm)*

Subsidiary (Domestic):

Fukuoka SOFTBANK HAWKS Marketing Corp. (2)
2-2-2 Jigyohama, Chuo-Ku, Fukuoka, 810-0065, Japan
Tel.: (81) 928471953
Payment Processing Services
N.A.I.C.S.: 522320

HR Solutions Corp. (1)
10th floor Onward Park Building 3-10-5 Nihonbashi, Chuo-ku, Tokyo, 103-0027, Japan (69%)
Tel.: (81) 33 548 8711
Web Site: https://www.hr-s.co.jp
Recruitment Outsourcing & Consulting Services
N.A.I.C.S.: 561311
Shigeru Takei *(Pres)*

IDC Frontier Inc. (1)
4-29 Yotsuya, Shinjuku-ku, Tokyo, 160-0004, Japan
Tel.: (81) 343540000
Web Site: http://www.idcf.jp
Sales Range: $150-199.9 Million
Emp.: 800
Data Center Services
N.A.I.C.S.: 518210
Ichiro Nakayana *(Pres & CEO)*

Millennium Services Group Limited (1)
Level 1 205-211 Forster Road, Mount Waverley, 3149, VIC, Australia
Tel.: (61) 392962095
Web Site: http://www.millenniumsg.com
Rev.: $199,661,452
Assets: $36,293,654
Liabilities: $35,975,685
Net Worth: $317,969
Earnings: $1,701,708
Emp.: 4,300
Fiscal Year-end: 06/30/2022
Commercial Services & Supplies
N.A.I.C.S.: 561499
Royce Galea *(Exec Dir)*

Subsidiary (Domestic):

Millennium Cleaning (NSW) Pty Limited (2)
Suite B15 Level 1 Parkview Business Centre 1 Maitland Place, Baulkham Hills, 2153, NSW, Australia
Tel.: (61) 1300240132
Frontline Cleaning Services
N.A.I.C.S.: 561720

Millennium Cleaning (Qld) Pty Limited (2)
Unit 1 20 Smallwood Place, Murarrie, 4172, QLD, Australia
Tel.: (61) 1300240132
Frontline Cleaning Services
N.A.I.C.S.: 561720

Millennium Hi-Tech (SA) Pty Limited (2)
Unit 1 2-20 Magill Road, Norwood, 5067, SA, Australia
Tel.: (61) 1300240132
Frontline Cleaning Services
N.A.I.C.S.: 561720

SB China Holdings Pte. Ltd. (1)
15A-C HuaMin Empire Plaza, 728 YanAn Road, Shanghai, 200050, China (100%)
Tel.: (86) 2152534888
Web Site: http://www.sbcvc.com
Emp.: 50
Investment Holding Company
N.A.I.C.S.: 551112
Chauncey Shey *(Pres & Exec Mng Partner-SB China Venture Capital)*

SB Media Holdings Corp. (1)
2-4-5 Roppongi, Minato-ku, Tokyo, 106-0032, Japan (100%)
Tel.: (81) 355491300
Web Site: https://www.sbmm-holdings.co.jp
Sales Range: $50-74.9 Million
Emp.: 10
Holding Company
N.A.I.C.S.: 551112
Kosei Tsuchihashi *(Pres)*

Subsidiary (Domestic):

ITmedia Inc. (2)
3-12 Kioicho Reception on the 13th floor, Chiyoda-ku, Tokyo, 102-0094, Japan (59.8%)
Tel.: (81) 352105011
Web Site: https://corp.itmedia.co.jp
Rev.: $52,886,610
Assets: $75,208,580
Liabilities: $10,410,750
Net Worth: $64,797,830
Earnings: $9,921,610
Emp.: 339
Fiscal Year-end: 03/31/2024
Media Business Information Website
N.A.I.C.S.: 519290
Toshiki Otsuki *(Pres & CEO)*

Realize Mobile Communications Corp. (2)
2-4-5 Roppongi Minato-ku, Minato-Ku, Tokyo, 106- 0032, Japan (100%)
Tel.: (81) 355491350
Web Site: http://www.realize-mobile.co.jp
Sales Range: $25-49.9 Million
Mobile Internet Products & Services
N.A.I.C.S.: 517810
Masato Sakatani *(CEO)*

SoftBank Creative Corp. (2)
2-4-5 Roppongi D Square, Roppongi Minato-Ku, Tokyo, 106-0032, Japan (100%)
Tel.: (81) 35 549 1100
Web Site: https://www.softbankcr.co.jp
Sales Range: $50-74.9 Million
Online Book & Magazine Publisher
N.A.I.C.S.: 513210
Tsu Thihachi Kosai *(Gen Mgr)*

SoftBank Human Capital Corp. (2)
4-13-13 Akasaka, Minato-ku, Tokyo, 107-0052, Japan
Tel.: (81) 355491300
Web Site: http://www.softbankhc.co.jp
Sales Range: $10-24.9 Million
Emp.: 70
Job Search Website Development & Management Services
N.A.I.C.S.: 541612

Subsidiary (Domestic):

Ability Design, Ltd. (3)
3-21-1 Nihonbashi Hamacho, Chuo-ku, Tokyo, 103-0007, Japan
Tel.: (81) 356428497
Web Site: http://www.ability-design.com
Temporary & Permanent Employment Services
N.A.I.C.S.: 561311

SB Technology Corp. (1)
6-27-30 17F Shinjuku Eastside Square, Shinjuku-ku, Tokyo, 160-0022, Japan (89.8%)
Tel.: (81) 368923050
Web Site: https://www.softbanktech.co.jp
Rev.: $434,303,440
Assets: $341,697,340
Liabilities: $126,085,750
Net Worth: $215,611,590
Earnings: $56,740,240
Emp.: 1,447
Fiscal Year-end: 03/31/2024
E-Commerce & Website Technology Products & Support Services
N.A.I.C.S.: 541519
Mitsuhiro Sato *(Sr Exec VP)*

Subsidiary (Domestic):

Miracle Linux Corporation (2)
East Side Square 7th Floor 6-27-30 Shinjuku, Shinjuku-ku, Tokyo, 160-0022, Japan
Tel.: (81) 3 6205 9500
Software Developer
N.A.I.C.S.: 513210
Tatsuo Ito *(Pres)*

SOFTBANK PAYMENT SERVICE CORP. (1)
1-9-2 Higashishimbashi Shiodomesumitomo

SOFTBANK GROUP CORP.

SoftBank Group Corp.—(Continued)
Bldg 25f, Minato-Ku, Tokyo, 105-0021, Japan
Tel.: (81) 3 6889 2130
Financial Transaction Processing Services
N.A.I.C.S.: 522320

SOFTBANK Players Corp. (1)
1-9-1 Higashishimbashi Tokyoshiodome
Bldg 12kai, Minato-Ku, Tokyo, 105-0021, Japan
Tel.: (81) 368891620
Web Site: http://www.softbankplayers.co.jp
Sales Range: $25-49.9 Million
Emp.: 62
Tourism Software Development Services
N.A.I.C.S.: 541511
Hiroaki Fujii (CEO)

SVF HoldCo (UK) Limited (1)
110 Fulbourn Road, Cambridge, CB1 9NJ, United Kingdom
Tel.: (44) 1223400400
Web Site: http://www.arm.com
Sales Range: $1-4.9 Billion
Holding Company; Semiconductors & Other Electronic Components Designer & Mfr
N.A.I.C.S.: 551112
Simon Segars (Executives)

SoftBank AtWork Corporation (1)
Tokyo Port City Takeshiba Office Tower
1-7-1 Kaigan, Minato-ku, Tokyo, 105-7529, Japan (100%)
Tel.: (81) 36 889 2700
Web Site: https://www.softbankatwork.co.jp
Sales Range: $25-49.9 Million
Emp.: 219
Provider of Software Development & Management Products, Consulting & Services
N.A.I.C.S.: 541512
Eiji Shimagami (Gen Mgr)

SoftBank Corp. (1)
1-9-1 Higashi-Shimbashi, Minato-ku, Tokyo, 105-7317, Japan (100%)
Tel.: (81) 356428000
Web Site: http://www.softbank.jp
Sales Range: $15-24.9 Billion
Emp.: 5,600
Mobile Telecommunications Services
N.A.I.C.S.: 517112
Ken Miyauchi (COO & Sr Exec VP)

Subsidiary (Domestic):

BB Backbone Corporation (2)
1-7-1 Kaigan, Minato-ku, Tokyo, 105-7509, Japan (100%)
Tel.: (81) 35 907 3803
Web Site: https://www.bbbackbone.co.jp
Backbone Network Services
N.A.I.C.S.: 541519
Hidetoshi Tosaka (Pres)

BB Cable Corporation (2)
Tokyo Shiodome Building, 1-9-1 Higashi-Shimbashi, Minato-ku, Tokyo, 105-7303, Japan (100%)
Tel.: (81) 356428000
Sales Range: $25-49.9 Million
Emp.: 65
Cable Television Broadcasting Services
N.A.I.C.S.: 516210

BB Softservice Corp. (2)
1-18-12 Shibakohen, Minato-ku, Tokyo, 105-0011, Japan (100%)
Tel.: (81) 3 6889 1185
Web Site: http://www.bbss.co.jp
Broadband Infrastructure Software Services
N.A.I.C.S.: 518210
Shintaro Taki (Pres & CEO)

BBIX, Inc. (2)
Tokyo Shiodome Building, 1-9-1 Higashi-Shimbashi, Minato-ku, Tokyo, 105-7303, Japan (100%)
Tel.: (81) 356428000
Web Site: http://www.bbix.net
Internet Exchange Services
N.A.I.C.S.: 517810

CreativeBank Inc. (2)
8F New Otani Garden Court 4-1 Kioicho, Chiyoda-ku, Tokyo, 102-0094, Japan (56%)
Tel.: (81) 36 893 2300
Web Site: https://www.creativebank.co.jp

Internet Sales Promoter & Advertising Agency
N.A.I.C.S.: 541810
Tatsuya Okumura (CEO)

Cybertrust Japan Co., Ltd. (2)
ARK Hills Sengokuyama Mori Tower 35F
1-9-10, Roppongi Minato-ku, Tokyo, 106-0032, Japan
Tel.: (81) 362343800
Web Site: http://www.cybertrust.co.jp
Emp.: 100
Authentication & Security Software Development Services
N.A.I.C.S.: 541511
Yasutoshi Magara (Pres & CEO)

Subsidiary (US):

Japan Telecom America, Inc. (2)
100 Wall St Ste 1803, New York, NY 10005 (100%)
Tel.: (212) 442-4650
Web Site: http://www.jt-america.com
Network Support Services
N.A.I.C.S.: 541519

Subsidiary (Non-US):

Japan Telecom China Co., Ltd. (2)
1915 International Trade Center No 2201 Yan An West Road, Shanghai, 200336, China (100%)
Tel.: (86) 2162709066
Web Site: http://www.japan-telecom.co.jp
Network Support Services
N.A.I.C.S.: 541519

Subsidiary (Domestic):

LY Corporation (2)
Kioi Tower 1-3 Kioicho, Chiyoda-ku, Tokyo, 102-8282, Japan (53.73%)
Tel.: (81) 368968200
Web Site: https://www.lycorp.co
Rev.: $11,994,922,430
Assets: $59,780,635,090
Liabilities: $36,996,064,240
Net Worth: $22,784,570,850
Earnings: $748,245,390
Fiscal Year-end: 03/31/2024
Web Search Portal, Internet Advertising & e-Commerce Services
N.A.I.C.S.: 425120
Kentaro Kawabe (Pres & Co-CEO)

Subsidiary (Domestic):

Carview Corporation (3)
Tokyo Garden Terrace Kioicho Kioi Tower 22nd Floor 1-3 Kioicho, Chiyoda-ku, Tokyo, 102-8622, Japan
Tel.: (81) 36 893 7687
Web Site: https://www.carview.co.jp
Emp.: 146
Online Automobile Information & Used Vehicle Classified Services
N.A.I.C.S.: 517810

Firstserver, Inc. (3)
Nomura Fudosan Osaka Bldg 3F 1-8-15 Azuchimachi, Chuo-ku, Osaka, 541-0052, Japan
Tel.: (81) 662614638
Web Site: http://www.firstserver.co.jp
Sales Range: $100-124.9 Million
Emp.: 150
Internet Data Processing, Domain Registration & Other Services
N.A.I.C.S.: 518210
Masato Isobe (CEO)

Affiliate (Domestic):

GyaO Corporation (3)
1-3 Kioicho Choyoda Ward, Chiyoda-ku, Tokyo, 102-8021, Japan (66.7%)
Tel.: (81) 368237012
Web Site: http://www.gyao.co.jp
Emp.: 298
Internet Video Content Delivery & Advertising Services
N.A.I.C.S.: 518210
Kentaro Kawabe (Pres & CEO)

Subsidiary (Domestic):

Ikyu Corporation (3)
8F Sumitomo Seimei Akasaka Bldg 3-3-3 Akasaka, Minato-ku, Tokyo, 107-0052, Japan

Tel.: (81) 3 66850019
Web Site: http://www.ikyu.co.jp
Sales Range: $25-49.9 Million
Travel Booking Services
N.A.I.C.S.: 561599
Jun Sakaki (Chm, Pres & CEO)

Synergy Marketing, Inc. (3)
Dojima-Avanza 21F 1-6-20 Dojima, Kita-ku, Osaka, 530-0003, Japan
Tel.: (81) 6 4797 2300
Web Site: http://www.synergy-marketing.co.jp
Sales Range: $1-9.9 Million
Emp.: 230
CRM Software & Services
N.A.I.C.S.: 513210
Tashiro Masao (Pres & CEO)

ValueCommerce Co., Ltd. (3)
21F Kioi Tower Tokyo Garden Terrace Kioicho 1-3 Kioicho, Chiyoda-ku, Tokyo, 102-8282, Japan
Tel.: (81) 352106688
Web Site: https://www.valuecommerce.co.jp
Rev.: $208,417,640
Assets: $201,008,590
Liabilities: $41,745,920
Net Worth: $159,262,670
Earnings: $24,106,000
Emp.: 246
Fiscal Year-end: 12/31/2023
Online Advertising Services
N.A.I.C.S.: 541810
Jin Kagawa (Pres & CEO)

Yahoo! Japan Corporation (3)
Kioi Tower 1-3 Kioicho, Chiyoda-ku, Tokyo, 102-8282, Japan
Tel.: (81) 3 6896 8200
Web Site: http://www.yahoo.co.jp
Search Engine Publisher
N.A.I.C.S.: 519290
Kentaro Kawabe (Pres)

ZOZO, Inc. (3)
Midori-Cho 1-15-16, Inage district, Chiba, 263-0023, Chiba, Japan (51%)
Tel.: (81) 432135171
Web Site: http://www.corp.zozo.com
Rev.: $1,315,142,910
Assets: $1,116,670,140
Liabilities: $566,781,330
Net Worth: $549,888,810
Earnings: $283,401,420
Emp.: 1,331
Fiscal Year-end: 03/31/2023
Online Shopping Websites, Customer Support Center Operations & Logistics
N.A.I.C.S.: 458110
Koiji Yanagisawa (CFO & Exec VP)

Subsidiary (Domestic):

SOFTBANK TELECOM PARTNERS Corp. (2)
1-9-1 Higashishimbashi Tokyoshiodome
Bldg 18f, Minato-Ku, Tokyo, 105-0021, Japan
Tel.: (81) 368892500
Web Site: http://www.softbanktelecompartners.co.jp
Telecommunication Servicesb
N.A.I.C.S.: 517810
Yasuyuki Imai (Chm & CEO)

SoftBank Frameworks Corp. (2)
3419 Aomi Koto-ku, Tokyo, 135-0064, Japan (100%)
Tel.: (81) 335705720
Web Site: http://www.sbfw.co.jp
Sales Range: $75-99.9 Million
Emp.: 70
IT Logistics Outsourcing & Consulting Services
N.A.I.C.S.: 541614
Kou Nakamoto (Pres)

Subsidiary (Non-US):

Softbank Telecom Europe Ltd. (2)
85 Tottenham Court Road, London, W1T 4TQ, United Kingdom (100%)
Tel.: (44) 2072683391
Sales Range: $25-49.9 Million
Emp.: 2
Network Support Services
N.A.I.C.S.: 541519
Akihiro Oshima (Mng Dir)

INTERNATIONAL PUBLIC

Subsidiary (Domestic):

Vector Inc. (2)
Akasaka Garden City 18th Floor 4-15-1 Akasaka, Minato-ku, Tokyo, 107-0052, Japan (33.4%)
Tel.: (81) 355726080
Web Site: https://www.vector.co.jp
Rev.: $8,396,432
Assets: $13,143,272
Liabilities: $10,059,679
Net Worth: $3,083,593
Earnings: ($578,128)
Emp.: 27
Fiscal Year-end: 03/31/2021
Online Retail Software Download Website
N.A.I.C.S.: 518210
Nobuhiro Kajinami (Pres)

SoftBank Holdings, Inc. (1)
38 Glen Ave, Newton Center, MA 02459
Tel.: (617) 928-9300
Web Site: http://www.softbank.com
Holding Company; Venture Capital Investment Services
N.A.I.C.S.: 551112

Holding (Domestic):

Fortress Investment Group LLC (2)
1345 Ave of the Americas 46th Fl, New York, NY 10105
Tel.: (212) 798-6100
Web Site: https://www.fortress.com
Investment & Asset Management Services
N.A.I.C.S.: 523940
Peter Lionel Briger Jr. (Co-CEO & Principal)

Affiliate (Domestic):

ATI Physical Therapy, Inc. (3)
790 Remington Blvd, Bolingbrook, IL 60440
Tel.: (630) 296-2223
Web Site: https://www.atipt.com
Rev.: $635,671,000
Assets: $1,078,985,000
Liabilities: $1,030,538,000
Net Worth: $48,447,000
Earnings: ($492,379,000)
Emp.: 5,700
Fiscal Year-end: 12/31/2022
Physical Therapy Services
N.A.I.C.S.: 621340
Sharon Vitti (CEO)

Holding (Domestic):

CW Financial Services LLC (3)
900 19th St NW - 8th Fl, Washington, DC 20006
Tel.: (202) 715-9500
Web Site: http://www.cwcapital.com
Holding Company; Real Estate Finance & Investment Management Services
N.A.I.C.S.: 551112

Subsidiary (Domestic):

CWCapital Asset Management LLC (4)
7501 Wisconsin Ave Ste 500W, Bethesda, MD 20814
Tel.: (202) 715-9500
Web Site: http://www.cwcapital.com
Real Estate Asset Management Services
N.A.I.C.S.: 531390

Holding (Domestic):

DivX, LLC (3)
4350 La Jolla Village Dr Ste 950, San Diego, CA 92122
Tel.: (858) 882-0700
Web Site: http://www.divx.com
Media & Entertainment Software & Data Management Services
N.A.I.C.S.: 541511
Noel Egnatios (Gen Counsel)

Subsidiary (Domestic):

Drawbridge Global Macro Advisors LLC (3)
1345 Avenue Of The Americas 1, New York, NY 10105
Tel.: (212) 798-6100
Management Consulting Services
N.A.I.C.S.: 541618

Subsidiary (Non-US):

FPM Deutschland GmbH (3)

An der Welle 4, Frankfurt am Main, 60322, Germany
Tel.: (49) 6 25496700
Web Site: http://www.fortress.com
Investment & Asset Management Services
N.A.I.C.S.: 523940

Holding (Domestic):

FTAI Aviation Ltd. (3)
1345 Ave of the Americas 45th Fl, New York, NY 10105
Tel.: (212) 798-6100
Web Site: http://www.ftandi.com
Rev.: $455,802,000
Assets: $4,863,854,000
Liabilities: $3,739,754,000
Net Worth: $1,124,100,000
Earnings: ($128,992,000)
Emp.: 600
Fiscal Year-end: 12/31/2021
Transportation & Transportation-Related Infrastructure Investment Services
N.A.I.C.S.: 523999
Joseph P. Adams Jr. *(CEO)*

Subsidiary (Domestic):

Transtar, LLC (4)
900 Thompson Run Rd, Monroeville, PA 15146
Tel.: (412) 433-7570
Web Site: https://transtarrail.com
Operator of Railroads & Water Shipping Systems
N.A.I.C.S.: 483113

Subsidiary (Domestic):

Gary Railway Company (5)
1 N Buchanan St, Gary, IN 46402
Tel.: (219) 888-7910
Web Site: http://www.tstarinc.com
Sales Range: $75-99.9 Million
Emp.: 300
Rail Transportation Services
N.A.I.C.S.: 488210

Warrior & Gulf Navigation Company (5)
50 Viaduct Rd, Mobile, AL 36611-2540
Tel.: (251) 452-6000
Sales Range: $50-74.9 Million
Emp.: 150
Canal & Intracoastal Freight Transportation
N.A.I.C.S.: 483211

Holding (Domestic):

Finjan Holdings, Inc. (3)
2000 University Ave Ste 600, East Palo Alto, CA 94303
Tel.: (650) 282-3228
Web Site: https://www.finjan.com
Rev.: $13,150,000
Assets: $50,093,000
Liabilities: $10,936,000
Net Worth: $39,157,000
Earnings: ($16,490,000)
Emp.: 9
Fiscal Year-end: 12/31/2019
Internet Security Software
N.A.I.C.S.: 513210
Philip Hartstein *(Pres & CEO)*

Florida East Coast Industries, Inc. (3)
700 NW 1st Ave Ste 1620, Miami, FL 33136
Tel.: (305) 520-2300
Web Site: https://www.feci.com
Holding Company; Railroad Freight Transportation & Real Estate Development
N.A.I.C.S.: 551112
Husein A. Cumber *(Chief Strategy Officer)*

Subsidiary (Domestic):

Flagler Development Group LLC (4)
2855 Le Jeune Rd 4th Fl, Coral Gables, FL 33134
Tel.: (305) 520-2300
Web Site: http://www.flaglerdev.com
Holding Company; Commercial Real Estate Owner, Developer, Property Manager & Lessor
N.A.I.C.S.: 551112

Subsidiary (Domestic):

Codina Construction Corporation (5)
2020 Salzedo St 5th Fl, Coral Gables, FL 33134
Tel.: (305) 529-1300
Web Site: http://www.codina.com
Commercial Building Construction Services
N.A.I.C.S.: 236220

Flagler Development Company, LLC (5)
2855 Le Jeune Rd 4th Fl, Coral Gables, FL 33134
Tel.: (305) 520-2300
Web Site: http://www.flaglerdev.com
Commercial Real Estate Development Services
N.A.I.C.S.: 237210

Subsidiary (Domestic):

Fortress Credit Corp. (3)
1345 Avenue of the Americas Fl 46, New York, NY 10105
Tel.: (212) 798-6103
Investment & Asset Management Services
N.A.I.C.S.: 523940
Peter Lionel Briger Jr. *(Co-Chm & Pres)*

Subsidiary (Non-US):

Fortress Germany Asset Management GmbH (3)
An der Welle 4, Frankfurt am Main, 60322, Germany
Tel.: (49) 69 2549 6700
Web Site: http://www.fortress.com
Investment & Asset Management Services
N.A.I.C.S.: 523940

Fortress Investment Group (Australia) Pty. Ltd. (3)
Level 19 Gateway 1 Macquarie Place, Sydney, 2000, NSW, Australia
Tel.: (61) 282391900
Web Site: http://www.fortress.com
Investment & Asset Management Services
N.A.I.C.S.: 523940

Branch (Domestic):

Fortress Investment Group LLC - Dallas (3)
5221 N O'Connor Blvd Ste 700, Irving, TX 75039
Tel.: (972) 532-4300
Web Site: https://www.fortress.com
Investment & Asset Management Services
N.A.I.C.S.: 523940

Fortress Investment Group LLC - Menlo Park (3)
2494 Sand Hill Rd, Menlo Park, CA 94025
Tel.: (415) 284-7400
Web Site: http://www.fortress.com
Investment & Asset Management Services
N.A.I.C.S.: 523940
Peter Lionel Briger Jr. *(CEO & Principal)*

Holding (Domestic):

Holiday Retirement Corp. (3)
631 West Morse Ave, Winter Park, FL 32789
Tel.: (855) 223-2730
Web Site: http://www.holidayseniorliving.com
Retirement Community Property Management
N.A.I.C.S.: 623311
Karen Sheean *(Chief People Officer)*

Interpool, Inc. (3)
750 College Rd E, Princeton, NJ 08540
Tel.: (609) 452-8900
Web Site: https://www.tracintermodal.com
Intermodal Transportation Equipment Leasing Services
N.A.I.C.S.: 532411
Gregg Carpene *(Chief Legal Officer & Exec VP)*

Holding (Non-US):

Les Celliers De Calais S.A.S. (3)
Z I Marcel Doret Rue De Judee, 62100, Calais, France
Tel.: (33) 321976300
Rev.: $23,200,000
Emp.: 31
Liquor Stores
N.A.I.C.S.: 445320

John Colley *(Pres)*

Holding (Domestic):

MP Materials Corp. (3)
1700 S Pavilion Ctr Dr 8th Fl, Las Vegas, NV 89135
Tel.: (702) 844-6111
Web Site: http://www.mpmaterials.com
Rev.: $253,445,000
Assets: $2,336,452,000
Liabilities: $970,673,000
Net Worth: $1,365,779,000
Earnings: $24,307,000
Emp.: 681
Fiscal Year-end: 12/31/2023
Mining & Processing Facilities
N.A.I.C.S.: 212390
James H. Litinsky *(Chm & CEO)*

MicroFinancial Incorporated (3)
1600 District Ave Ste 200, Burlington, MA 01803
Tel.: (781) 994-4800
Holding Company; Equipment Leasing & Financing Services
N.A.I.C.S.: 551112
Richard F. Latour *(Pres & CEO)*

Subsidiary (Domestic):

TimePayment Corporation (4)
200 Summit Dr Ste 100, Burlington, MA 01803-5222
Tel.: (781) 994-4800
Web Site: https://timepayment.com
Equipment Financing & Leasing Services
N.A.I.C.S.: 522220
Jay Haverty *(Pres & CEO)*

Subsidiary (Domestic):

KLI Consulting Group, LLC (5)
16 Pierce St, Dover, NH 03820
Tel.: (603) 569-8980
Web Site: http://www.kingswoodleasing.com
Sales Financing Services
N.A.I.C.S.: 522220
Linda Tambeau *(Acct Mgr-Natl)*

LeaseQ, Inc. (5)
200 Summit Dr Ste 100, Burlington, MA 01803
Tel.: (888) 688-4519
Web Site: http://www.leaseq.com
Equipment Leasing & Financing Services
N.A.I.C.S.: 522299

Subsidiary (Domestic):

Noesis Energy, Inc. (6)
609 Castle Rdg Rd Ste 445, Austin, TX 78746
Tel.: (781) 352-0820
Web Site: http://www.noesis.com
Software Publisher
N.A.I.C.S.: 513210

Subsidiary (Domestic):

Wheaten Financial Inc. (5)
20331 Irvine Ave Ste 1, Newport Beach, CA 92660-0223
Tel.: (949) 722-6830
Web Site: http://www.wheatenfinancial.com
Investment Advice
N.A.I.C.S.: 523940
Aimee McChurch *(Pres)*

Holding (Domestic):

OneMain Holdings, Inc. (3)
601 NW 2nd St, Evansville, IN 47708-1013 (54.52%)
Tel.: (812) 424-8031
Web Site: https://www.onemainfinancial.com
Rev.: $4,564,000,000
Assets: $24,294,000,000
Liabilities: $21,108,000,000
Net Worth: $3,186,000,000
Earnings: $641,000,000
Emp.: 9,100
Fiscal Year-end: 12/31/2023
Holding Company; Consumer Financial Services
N.A.I.C.S.: 551112
Michael A. Hedlund *(Chief Acctg Officer, Sr VP & Controller)*

Subsidiary (Domestic):

Foursight Capital LLC (4)
2783 South Leadership Ct Ste 400, West Valley City, UT 84120
Tel.: (888) 960-8063
Web Site: https://www.foursight.com
Specialty Finance Services
N.A.I.C.S.: 525990
Mark Miller *(Founder, Pres & CEO)*

OneMain Assurance Services, Inc. (4)
3001 Meacham Blvd Ste 10, Fort Worth, TX 76137
Tel.: (817) 348-7500
Web Site: http://www.onemainfinancial.com
Insurance Services
N.A.I.C.S.: 524210

Joint Venture (Domestic):

Pester Marketing Company (3)
4643 S Ulster St Ste 350, Denver, CO 80237
Tel.: (303) 693-9331
Web Site: http://www.pestermarketing.com
Petroleum Merchant Whslr
N.A.I.C.S.: 424720
Rich Spresser *(Pres & CEO)*

Holding (Domestic):

SPB Hospitality LLC (3)
19219 Katy Fwy, Houston, TX 77094
Tel.: (346) 440-0772
Web Site: http://www.spbhospitality.com
Restaurants & Breweries Operators
N.A.I.C.S.: 722511
Morgan McClure *(Pres)*

Subsidiary (Domestic):

J. Alexander's Holdings, Inc. (4)
3401 West End Ave Ste 260, Nashville, TN 37202
Tel.: (615) 269-1900
Web Site: http://www.jalexanders.com
Rev.: $183,373,000
Assets: $237,119,000
Liabilities: $127,014,000
Net Worth: $110,105,000
Earnings: ($22,471,000)
Emp.: 3,200
Fiscal Year-end: 01/03/2021
Holding Company; Restaurants
N.A.I.C.S.: 551112
Lonnie J. Stout II *(Chm)*

Subsidiary (Domestic):

J. Alexander's Corporation (5)
3401 W End Ave Ste 260, Nashville, TN 37203-6862 (87%)
Tel.: (615) 269-1900
Web Site: http://www.jalexanders.com
Sales Range: $300-349.9 Million
Emp.: 2,720
Restaurant Operators
N.A.I.C.S.: 722310

Unit (Domestic):

J. Alexander's Restaurants of Kansas, Inc. (6)
11471 Metcalf Ave, Overland Park, KS 66210
Tel.: (913) 469-1995
Web Site: http://www.jalexanders.com
Sales Range: $1-9.9 Million
Emp.: 75
Restaurant Operators
N.A.I.C.S.: 722511

J. Alexander's Restaurants, Inc. - Ohio (6)
2629 Edmonson Rd, Cincinnati, OH 45209-1910
Tel.: (513) 531-7495
Web Site: http://www.jalexanders.com
Sales Range: $1-9.9 Million
Emp.: 105
Restaurant Operators
N.A.I.C.S.: 722511
Greg Spyrou *(Gen Mgr)*

J. Alexander's of Texas, Inc. (6)
255 E Basse Rd Ste 1300, San Antonio, TX 78209
Tel.: (210) 824-0275
Web Site: http://www.jalexanders.com
Sales Range: $25-49.9 Million
Emp.: 80
Restaurant Operators

SOFTBANK GROUP CORP.

SoftBank Group Corp.—(Continued)
N.A.I.C.S.: 722511

J. Alexanders Restaurants, Inc. (6)
1721 Galleria Blvd, Franklin, TN 37067
Tel.: (615) 771-7779
Web Site: http://www.jalexanders.com
Sales Range: $1-9.9 Million
Emp.: 100
Restaurant Operators
N.A.I.C.S.: 722511
Lonnie J. Stout II *(Pres)*

JAX (J.Alexander) Real Estate (6)
4325 Southpoint Blvd, Jacksonville, FL 32216
Tel.: (904) 279-0157
Sales Range: Less than $1 Million
Emp.: 2
Real Estate Agents & Brokers
N.A.I.C.S.: 531210
Lonnie J. Stout II *(Chm, Pres & CEO)*

Subsidiary (Domestic):

Stoney River, LLC (6)
3038 Sidco Dr, Nashville, TN 37204
Tel.: (615) 256-8500
Web Site: http://www.stoneyriver.com
Sales Range: $10-24.9 Million
Emp.: 250
Restaurant Operators
N.A.I.C.S.: 722511

Subsidiary (Domestic):

Krystal Restaurants LLC (4)
1455 Lincoln Pkwy E Ste 1600, Dunwoody, GA 30346
Tel.: (727) 709-3039
Web Site: https://www.krystal.com
Fast Food Restaurants Operator & Franchisor
N.A.I.C.S.: 722513
Casey Terrell *(CMO)*

Subsidiary (Non-US):

Sogo & Seibu Co., Ltd. (3)
1-1-2 Marunouchi, Chiyoda-ku, Tokyo, 100-0005, Japan
Tel.: (81) 362137152
Web Site: http://www.sogo-seibu.co.jp
Department Stores
N.A.I.C.S.: 455110
Yukio Horiuchi *(Chm)*

Subsidiary (Domestic):

The Seibu Department Stores, Ltd. (4)
1-28-1 Minami-ikebukuro, Toshima-ku, Tokyo, 171-8569, Japan
Tel.: (81) 339890111
Sales Range: $800-899.9 Million
Emp.: 4,620
Departmental Store Operator
N.A.I.C.S.: 455110

Joint Venture (Domestic):

Vice Media LLC (3)
90 N 11th St, Brooklyn, NY 11211
Tel.: (718) 599-3101
Web Site: http://www.vice.com
Sales Range: $150-199.9 Million
Emp.: 750
Magazine & Internet Publishing
N.A.I.C.S.: 513120
Shane Smith *(Co-Founder)*

Subsidiary (Domestic):

Carrot Creative LLC (4)
55 Washington St Ste 900, Brooklyn, NY 11201
Tel.: (718) 395-7934
Web Site: http://www.carrot.is
Emp.: 70
Advetising Agency
N.A.I.C.S.: 541810
Mike Germano *(Co-Founder & CEO)*

Subsidiary (Non-US):

Pulse Films Limited (4)
17 Hanbury Street, London, E1 6QR, United Kingdom
Tel.: (44) 20 7426 5700
Web Site: http://www.pulsefilms.co.uk

Motion Picture Production Services
N.A.I.C.S.: 512110
Thomas Benski *(Co-Founder & CEO)*

Subsidiary (Domestic):

Refinery 29, Inc. (4)
225 Broadway 23rd Fl, New York, NY 10007
Tel.: (212) 966-3112
Web Site: http://www.refinery29.com
Sales Range: $1-9.9 Million
Emp.: 59
Fashion, Beauty & Entertainment Website
N.A.I.C.S.: 519290
George Mitchell *(VP-Bus Affairs & Ops)*

Subsidiary (Domestic):

SoftBank Capital L.P. (2)
38 Glen Ave, Newton Center, MA 02459-1972   (99.7%)
Tel.: (617) 928-9300
Web Site: http://www.softbank.com
Sales Range: $50-74.9 Million
Capital Equity Investment Services
N.A.I.C.S.: 523999
Ronald D. Fisher *(Pres)*

SoftBank Korea Co., Ltd. (1)
13F A Wing Kyobo Tower 1303-22 Seocho-dong, Seocho-gu, Seoul, 137-920, Korea (South)   (100%)
Tel.: (82) 234849000
Web Site: http://www.softbank.co.kr
Sales Range: $50-74.9 Million
Emp.: 20
Investment Holding Company
N.A.I.C.S.: 551112
Greg Moon *(Pres & CEO)*

SoftBank Ventures Korea Inc. (1)
8th Floor Shinyeong Building 68-5 Cheongdam-dong, Gangnam-gu, Seoul, 135-798, Korea (South)
Tel.: (82) 2 3484 9000
Web Site: http://www.ventures.softbank.co.kr
Venture Capital Management Services
N.A.I.C.S.: 523910
Greg Moon *(Pres & CEO-Investment Div)*

Supercell Oy (1)
Itamerenkatu 11-13, 00180, Helsinki, Finland   (73.2%)
Tel.: (358) 400228080
Web Site: http://www.supercell.net
Sales Range: $700-749.9 Million
Emp.: 100
Online Video Game Developer
N.A.I.C.S.: 513210
Mikko Kodisoja *(Co-Founder & Dir-Creative)*

Tavigator, Inc. (1)
Midtown Tower 9-7-1 Akasaka, Minato-Ku, Tokyo, 107-6220, Japan
Tel.: (81) 364406803
Sales Range: $10-24.9 Million
Emp.: 5
Travel Agencies
N.A.I.C.S.: 561510

Telecom Express Co., Ltd. (1)
8-18-11 Ginza Ginza Sc Bldg 6f, Chuo-Ku, Tokyo, 104-0061, Japan
Tel.: (81) 351485580
Mobile Telecommunications Services
N.A.I.C.S.: 517112

SOFTBRAIN CO., LTD.
Nihonbashi 1-chome Mitsui Building 19F 1-4-1 Nihonbashi, Chuo-ku, Tokyo, Japan
Tel.: (81) 368809500
Web Site: http://www.softbrain.co.jp
Year Founded: 1992
Rev.: $90,732,299
Assets: $66,741,534
Liabilities: $18,839,710
Net Worth: $47,901,824
Earnings: $7,307,720
Fiscal Year-end: 12/31/19
Software Development Services
N.A.I.C.S.: 541511
Hirofumi Toyoda *(Pres & CEO)*

Subsidiaries:

Softbrain Integration Co., Ltd. (1)

8th Floor Kinoshita Building 2-3-5 Horidome-cho, Nihonbashi Chuo-ku, Tokyo, 103-0012, Japan
Tel.: (81) 368921180
Web Site: https://www.sbi.co.jp
Software Development Services
N.A.I.C.S.: 541511

mitoriz Co., Ltd. (1)
Sanyo Akasaka Building 5F 3-5-2, Akasaka Minato-ku, Tokyo, 107-0052, Japan
Tel.: (81) 363283630
Web Site: https://www.mitoriz.co.jp
Business Consulting Services
N.A.I.C.S.: 541618

SOFTCAMP CO., LTD.
4F 6 Seongnam-daero 779beon-gil, Bundang-gu, Seongnam, Gyeonggi-do, Korea (South)
Tel.: (82) 316974553
Web Site: https://www.softcamp.co.kr
258790—(KRS)
Rev.: $14,586,338
Assets: $25,037,698
Liabilities: $12,137,174
Net Worth: $12,900,524
Earnings: $497,978
Emp.: 137
Fiscal Year-end: 12/31/22
Computer & Information Security & Management Solutions
N.A.I.C.S.: 513210
Hwan-Kuk Bae *(CEO)*

SOFTCAT LTD.
Thames Industrial Estate, Fieldhouse Lane, Marlow, SL7 1LW, Bucks, United Kingdom
Tel.: (44) 1628 403 403
Web Site: http://www.softcat.com
Year Founded: 1993
Sales Range: $350-399.9 Million
Emp.: 400
Software Licensing & IT Services
N.A.I.C.S.: 423430
Graham Charlton *(CFO)*

SOFTCEN CO., LTD.
Banpo-daero 13 Seocho-gu, Seoul, Korea (South)
Tel.: (82) 220273800   KR
Web Site: https://www.btc.co.kr
Year Founded: 1988
032680—(KRS)
Rev.: $46,852,230
Assets: $78,669,644
Liabilities: $28,510,591
Net Worth: $50,159,053
Earnings: ($7,646,128)
Emp.: 25
Fiscal Year-end: 12/31/23
Computer Peripheral Equipment Mfr
N.A.I.C.S.: 334118
Jae-hong Kim *(Exec Dir)*

SOFTCREATE HOLDINGS CORP.
Shibuya Cross Tower Building 2-15-1 Shibuya, Shibuya-ku, Tokyo, 150-0002, Japan
Tel.: (81) 334861520
Web Site: https://www.softcreate.co.jp
Year Founded: 1969
3371—(TKS)
Rev.: $184,498,320
Assets: $206,879,780
Liabilities: $63,766,670
Net Worth: $143,113,110
Earnings: $21,528,770
Emp.: 963
Fiscal Year-end: 03/31/24
System Integration Services
N.A.I.C.S.: 541512
Masaru Hayashi *(Chm)*

INTERNATIONAL PUBLIC

Subsidiaries:

ATLED Co., Ltd. (1)
2-22-3 Shibuya Shibuyahigashiguchi Bldg, Shibuya-Ku, Tokyo, 150-0002, Japan
Tel.: (81) 334862812
Web Site: http://www.atledgroup.jp
Emp.: 3,000
Business Support Services
N.A.I.C.S.: 561499
Hashiguchi Kichi *(Gen Mgr)*

AtoJ, Inc. (1)
Minami Aoyama DF Building 8F 2-2-8 Minami Aoyama, Minato-ku, Tokyo, 107-0062, Japan
Tel.: (81) 357722581
Web Site: https://www.atoj.co.jp
Construction Services
N.A.I.C.S.: 541330

Ecbeing Corp. (1)
Shibuya Cross Tower 2-15-1 Shibuya, Shibuya-ku, Tokyo, 150-0002, Japan
Tel.: (81) 334865259
Web Site: https://www.ecbeing.net
Construction Design Services
N.A.I.C.S.: 541330

Softcreate Corporation (1)
Shibuya Cross Tower 2-15-1 Shibuya, Shibuya-ku, Tokyo, 150-0002, Japan
Tel.: (81) 334861520
Web Site: https://www.softcreate.co.jp
Information Technology Services
N.A.I.C.S.: 541511

Visumo Inc. (1)
Harajuku Sophia Building 6-10-11, Jingumae Shibuya-ku, Tokyo, 150-0001, Japan
Tel.: (81) 368224888
Web Site: https://visumo.asia
Marketing Services
N.A.I.C.S.: 541613

SOFTFRONT HOLDINGS CO., LTD.
Akasaka Shasta East 3F 4-2-19 Akasaka, Minato-ku, Tokyo, 107-0052, Japan
Tel.: (81) 335687007
Web Site: http://www.softfront.co.jp
Year Founded: 1997
2321—(TKS)
Rev.: $5,873,801
Assets: $3,402,708
Liabilities: $2,272,877
Net Worth: $1,129,831
Earnings: ($2,094,482)
Fiscal Year-end: 03/31/24
Software Development Services
N.A.I.C.S.: 541511
Kazunori Sato *(CTO & VP)*

Subsidiaries:

SOFTFRONT VIETNAM CO., LTD. (1)
Unit1101 HMC Tower 193 Dinh Tien Hoang Street, District 1, Ho Chi Minh City, Vietnam
Tel.: (84) 8 3820 7111
Software Development Services
N.A.I.C.S.: 541511

SOFTIMAT SA
Chaussee de Louvain 435, 1380, Lasne, Belgium
Tel.: (32) 23528381
Web Site: https://www.softimat.com
Year Founded: 1984
SOFT—(EUR)
Sales Range: $1-9.9 Million
Computer Products & Services
N.A.I.C.S.: 541512
Jean-Claude Loge *(Chm)*

Subsidiaries:

Allo Supplies (1)
Chaussee de Louvain 431, 1380, Lasne, Belgium
Tel.: (32) 23528400
Web Site: http://www.allosupplies.com
Computer Consumables & Small Peripherals Mfr

AND PRIVATE COMPANIES — SOFTLOGIC HOLDINGS PLC

N.A.I.C.S.: 518210

Popsy (1)
Chaussee de Louvain 431E, Lasne, Belgium
Tel.: (32) 23528311
Business Services
N.A.I.C.S.: 561439

Syremat SA (1)
Chaussee de Louvain 431E, B-1380, Lasne, Belgium
Tel.: (32) 23528311
Web Site: http://www.systemat.com
Emp.: 10
IT Solutions
N.A.I.C.S.: 519290
Vincent Schaller (Dir)

Systemat Belgium NV (1)
Spoorweglaan 25, 2610, Wilrijk, Belgium
Tel.: (32) 38205611
Web Site: http://www.systemat.com
IT Support & Managed Services
N.A.I.C.S.: 541511

Systemat Belgium sa - Charleroi (1)
ZI Jumet - Allee Centrale, Jumet, 6040, Charleroi, Belgium
Tel.: (32) 71255811
Web Site: http://www.systemat.com
Information Technology Services
N.A.I.C.S.: 561499

Systemat Luxembourg S.A. (1)
Parc D, 8308, Capellen, Luxembourg
Tel.: (352) 3171321
Business Services
N.A.I.C.S.: 561439
Manu Roche (Gen Mgr)

SOFTING AG
Richard-Reitzner-Allee 6, 85540, Haar, Germany
Tel.: (49) 89456560 De
Web Site: https://company.softing.com
Year Founded: 1979
SYT—(BER)
Rev.: $124,295,762
Assets: $113,764,842
Liabilities: $54,586,371
Net Worth: $59,178,471
Earnings: ($6,435,562)
Emp.: 432
Fiscal Year-end: 12/31/23
Software Service Provider
N.A.I.C.S.: 541511
Horst Schiessl (Chm-Supervisory Bd)

Subsidiaries:

Buxbaum Automation GmbH (1)
Thomas A Edison Str 1, A-7000, Eisenstadt, Austria
Tel.: (43) 720704560
Web Site: https://www.myautomation.at
Automation Product Mfr
N.A.I.C.S.: 334512

Softing Automotive Electronics (Kirchentellinsfurt) GmbH (1)
Einhornstrasse 10, 72138, Kirchentellinsfurt, Germany
Tel.: (49) 712199370
Automation Product Mfr
N.A.I.C.S.: 334512

Softing Automotive Electronics GmbH (1)
Richard-Reitzner-Allee 6, D-85540, Haar, Germany
Tel.: (49) 89456560
Web Site: https://www.automotive.softing.com
Automation Product Mfr
N.A.I.C.S.: 334512

Softing IT Networks GmbH (1)
Richard-Reitzner-Allee 6, 85540, Haar, Germany
Tel.: (49) 8945656660
Web Site: https://www.itnetworks.softing.com
Electric Equipment Mfr
N.A.I.C.S.: 334419

Softing Inc. (1)
2332 News Sentinel Dr Ste 120, Knoxville, TN 37921
Tel.: (865) 251-5252
Web Site: https://industrial.softing.com
Communication Product & Technology Mfr
N.A.I.C.S.: 334290

Softing Industrial Automation GmbH (1)
Richard-Reitzner-Allee 6, 85540, Haar, Germany
Tel.: (49) 89456560
Web Site: https://www.industrial.softing.com
Communication Product & Technology Mfr
N.A.I.C.S.: 334290

Subsidiary (Non-US):

Softing Italia s.r.l. (2)
Via M Kolbe 6, 20090, Cesano Boscone, MI, Italy
Tel.: (39) 024505171
Web Site: https://www.softingitalia.it
Communication Product & Technology Mfr
N.A.I.C.S.: 334290

Softing Singapore Pte. Ltd. (1)
73 Science Park Drive 02-12/13 Cintech I, Singapore Science Park 1, Singapore, 118254, Singapore
Tel.: (65) 65696019
Web Site: https://itnetworks.softing.com
Electric Equipment Mfr
N.A.I.C.S.: 334419

SOFTIP, A.S.
Business Center Aruba Galvaniho 7/D, 851 01, Bratislava, Slovakia
Tel.: (421) 484340111 Sk
Web Site: http://www.softip.sk
Year Founded: 1991
Sales Range: $10-24.9 Million
Information Technology Products & Services
N.A.I.C.S.: 541512
Martin Vlcko (Fin Dir)

SOFTJIN TECHNOLOGIES PRIVATE LIMITED
Unit 102 Mobius Tower I Fl SJR I Park EPIP White Field, Bengaluru, 560066, India
Tel.: (91) 08041779999
Web Site: http://www.softjin.com
Year Founded: 2000
Sales Range: $25-49.9 Million
Emp.: 100
Electronic Design Automation Software Services
N.A.I.C.S.: 513210
Ravi Pai (Chm & Mng Dir)

SOFTLAB S.P.A.
Piazzale K Adenauer 3, 00144, Rome, Italy
Tel.: (39) 06510391 IT
Web Site: https://www.soft.it
Year Founded: 2000
SOF—(ITA)
Sales Range: $1-9.9 Million
Wireless Applications, Security Equipment & Network Infrastructure Services
N.A.I.C.S.: 541512

Subsidiaries:

Emirates for Information Technology Co. (1)
Urwa Bin Uthayna Street Tla Al-Ali Area, 11194, Amman, Jordan
Tel.: (962) 65531140
Application Service Provider
N.A.I.C.S.: 518210

Flycell, Inc. (1)
120 Broadway 15th Fl, New York, NY 10271 (100%)
Tel.: (212) 400-1212
Web Site: http://www.flycell.com
Sales Range: $25-49.9 Million
Mobile & Online Media & Entertainment Services
N.A.I.C.S.: 517112

Millennium Software SAL (1)
1st Floor Antoine Samra Center Main Road, Fanar, Lebanon
Tel.: (961) 1900818
Emp.: 78
Business Planning Software Development Services
N.A.I.C.S.: 541511

SOFTLAB S.P.A.
Via Valentino Mazzola 66, 142, Rome, Italy
Tel.: (39) 06510391
Web Site: http://www.softlab-italia.it
Sales Range: $150-199.9 Million
Emp.: 580
IT Services
N.A.I.C.S.: 541519
Raffaele Rubinacci (Mng Dir)

SOFTLAB9 TECHNOLOGIES, INC.
Suite 605 815 Hornby Street, Vancouver, V6Z 2E6, BC, Canada
Tel.: (403) 605-9429
Web Site: http://www.softlab9.com
SOFT—(CNSX)
Assets: $132,192
Liabilities: $660,470
Net Worth: ($528,278)
Earnings: ($1,646,627)
Fiscal Year-end: 12/31/19
Information Technology Services
N.A.I.C.S.: 541512
Rahim Mohamed (CEO)

SOFTLINE AG
Gutenbergplatz 1, 04103, Leipzig, Germany
Tel.: (49) 341240510
Web Site: http://www.softline-group.com
Year Founded: 1983
SFD1—(DEU)
Sales Range: Less than $1 Million
Emp.: 205
Information Technology Services
N.A.I.C.S.: 541512
Martin Schaletzky (CEO)

Subsidiaries:

Insight Technology Solutions GmbH (1)
Am Prime-Parc 9, 65479, Raunheim, Germany
Tel.: (49) 6134288288
Web Site: http://www.insight.de
Computer Network Design & Management Products & Services
N.A.I.C.S.: 541512
Stefan Sennebogen (Country Mgr)

Softline Services GmbH (1)
Otto-Hahn-Strasse 20, 85609, Aschheim, Germany
Tel.: (49) 894518750
Web Site: http://www.softline-services.de
Software Development Services
N.A.I.C.S.: 513210
Sascha Snajder (Project Mgr)

Softline Solutions GmbH (1)
Gutenbergplatz 1, 04103, Leipzig, Germany
Tel.: (49) 341240510
Web Site: http://www.softline-solutions.de
Software Development Services
N.A.I.C.S.: 513210
Martin Schaletzky (Gen Mgr)

Softline Solutions Ltd. (1)
Kemp House/152 City Road, London, EC1V 2NX, United Kingdom
Tel.: (44) 2038211294
Software Development Services
N.A.I.C.S.: 513210

Softline Solutions N.V. (1)
Brusselstraat 51, 2018, Antwerp, Belgium
Tel.: (32) 28974695
Software Development Services
N.A.I.C.S.: 513210

Softline Solutions Netherlands B.V. (1)
Coltbaan 33, 3439 NG, Nieuwegein, Netherlands
Tel.: (31) 305500300
Web Site: http://www.softline-solutions.nl
Software Development Services
N.A.I.C.S.: 513210
Dennis Montanje (Mng Dir)

Xpertlink GmbH (1)
Otto-Hahn-Strasse 20, 85609, Aschheim, Germany
Tel.: (49) 8945187572
Software Development Services
N.A.I.C.S.: 513210

SOFTLOGIC HOLDINGS PLC
No 14 De Fonseka Place, 05, Colombo, 05, Sri Lanka
Tel.: (94) 115575000 LK
Web Site: https://www.softlogic.lk
Year Founded: 1991
SHL—(COL)
Rev.: $370,256,233
Assets: $628,157,458
Liabilities: $609,524,710
Net Worth: $18,632,749
Earnings: ($17,568,610)
Emp.: 11,453
Fiscal Year-end: 03/31/22
Investment Holding Company
N.A.I.C.S.: 551112
Ashok K. Pathirage (Chm, Chm, Mng Dir & Mng Dir)

Subsidiaries:

Asiri Hospital Holdings PLC (1)
No 181 Kirula Road, Narahenpita, 05, Colombo, 05, Sri Lanka (52.39%)
Tel.: (94) 114523300
Web Site: https://www.asirihealth.com
Rev.: $83,973,661
Assets: $170,619,207
Liabilities: $110,517,794
Net Worth: $60,101,413
Earnings: $9,281,367
Emp.: 11,000
Fiscal Year-end: 03/31/2021
Holding Company; Hospitals Owner & Operator
N.A.I.C.S.: 551112
Ashok K. Pathirage (Chm & Mng Dir)

Subsidiary (Domestic):

Asiri Central Hospitals PLC (2)
No. 181, Kirula Road, Narahenpita, Colombo, 5, Sri Lanka (70.92%)
Tel.: (94) 11 452 3300
Web Site: http://www.asirihospitals.com
Holding Company; Hospitals
N.A.I.C.S.: 551112

Asiri Diagnostics Services (Pvt) Ltd. (2)
No 21/1 Keppetipola Mawatha, Kandy, Sri Lanka (66.54%)
Tel.: (94) 812236786
General Medical Services
N.A.I.C.S.: 622110

Asiri Hospitals Matara (Pvt) Ltd (2)
No 191 Anagarika Dhamapala Mw, Matara, Sri Lanka
Tel.: (94) 41 439 0900
Hospital Management Services
N.A.I.C.S.: 622110

Affiliate (Domestic):

Asiri Surgical Hospital PLC (2)
No 21 Kirimandala Mawatha, Narahenpita, Colombo, 05, Sri Lanka (46.91%)
Tel.: (94) 11 4524400
Web Site: http://www.asirihealth.com
Rev.: $22,502,068
Assets: $45,984,437
Liabilities: $21,155,589
Net Worth: $24,828,848
Earnings: $4,573,428
Emp.: 11,000
Fiscal Year-end: 03/31/2021
Holding Company; Hospitals
N.A.I.C.S.: 551112
Ashok K. Pathirage (Chm & Mng Dir)

SOFTLOGIC HOLDINGS PLC

Softlogic Holdings PLC—(Continued)

Ceysand Resorts Ltd (1)
Aluthgama, Bentota, 80500, Sri Lanka
Tel.: (94) 34 2275073
Web Site: http://www.centarahotelsresorts.com
Emp.: 290
Hotel & Resort Management Services
N.A.I.C.S.: 721110
Sisira Senaratna *(Gen Mgr)*

Digital Health (Pvt) Ltd. (1)
Ground Floor Dialog Broadband Networks No 57, Srimath Anagarika Dharmapala Mawatha, Colombo, Sri Lanka
Tel.: (94) 11 799 0990
Web Site: https://www.doc.lk
Healtcare Services
N.A.I.C.S.: 621610
Navoda Rathnayake *(Mgr-Business Development)*

Softlogic Asset Management (Pvt) Ltd. (1)
Level 16 One Galle Face Tower, Colombo, Sri Lanka
Tel.: (94) 11 210 4304
Web Site: https://softlogicinvest.lk
Investment Management Service
N.A.I.C.S.: 523940
Iftikar Ahamed *(Mng Dir)*

Softlogic Australia (Pty) Ltd. (1)
Unit 4 15 Ricketts Rd, Mount Waverley, 3149, VIC, Australia
Tel.: (61) 39 543 7566
Web Site: https://softlogic.com.au
Software Solutions Services
N.A.I.C.S.: 541511

Softlogic Capital PLC (1)
No 14 De Fonseka Place, 05, Colombo, 05, Sri Lanka (54.15%)
Tel.: (94) 115575425
Web Site: https://www.softlogiccapital.lk
Rev.: $111,385,592
Assets: $310,801,713
Liabilities: $249,761,038
Net Worth: $61,040,675
Earnings: $1,939,858
Emp.: 11,000
Fiscal Year-end: 03/31/2021
Holding Company; Financial Services
N.A.I.C.S.: 551112
Ashok K. Pathirage *(Chm)*

Holding (Domestic):

Softlogic Finance PLC (2)
No 13 De Fonseka Place, 4, Colombo, Sri Lanka (62.17%)
Tel.: (94) 112359600
Web Site: https://www.softlogicfinance.lk
Rev.: $12,998,841
Assets: $111,028,443
Liabilities: $94,920,069
Net Worth: $16,108,374
Earnings: ($4,803,168)
Emp.: 463
Fiscal Year-end: 03/31/2021
Specialty Financing, Leasing & Lending Services
N.A.I.C.S.: 522220
Ashok K. Pathirage *(Chm)*

Softlogic Life Insurance PLC (2)
283 R A De Mel Mawatha, Colombo, 03, Sri Lanka (76.06%)
Tel.: (94) 2315555
Web Site: http://www.softlogiclife.lk
Sales Range: $25-49.9 Million
Emp.: 782
Insurance Services
N.A.I.C.S.: 524113
Ashok K. Pathirage *(Chm)*

Division (Domestic):

Asian Alliance Insurance PLC - ICT Division (3)
482 Galle Rd, Rawathawatta, Moratuwa, 10400, Western Province, Sri Lanka
Tel.: (94) 112641387
Web Site: http://www.asianalliance.lk
Emp.: 25
Online Insurance Services
N.A.I.C.S.: 524113

Softlogic Computers (Pvt) Ltd. (1)
2nd Floor 402 Galle Rd, Colombo, Sri Lanka
Tel.: (94) 11 539 1100
Web Site: https://www.printersl.lk
Printing Equipment Distr
N.A.I.C.S.: 424110

Softlogic Information Technologies (Pvt) Limited (1)
4th Floor 402 Galle Road, Colombo, 300, Sri Lanka (100%)
Tel.: (94) 11 539 1100
Sales Range: $50-74.9 Million
Emp.: 75
Computer Software & Information Technology Product Sales & Technical Support Services
N.A.I.C.S.: 423430
Hemantha U. Gunawardena *(CEO-Software Div)*

Softlogic Stockbrokers (Pvt) Ltd. (1)
Level 16 One Galle Face Tower, Colombo, Sri Lanka
Tel.: (94) 11 727 7000
Web Site: https://softlogicstockbrokers.lk
Financial Services
N.A.I.C.S.: 541611
Dihan Dedigama *(CEO)*

SOFTMAX CO., LTD.
12-11 Kajiyacho, Kagoshima, 892-0846, Japan
Tel.: (81) 992261222
Web Site: https://www.s-max.co.jp
Year Founded: 1974
3671—(TKS)
Sales Range: $25-49.9 Million
Emp.: 160
Medical Software
N.A.I.C.S.: 513210
Yoshio Nagasato *(Pres)*

SOFTOX SOLUTIONS AS
Martin Linges vei 25, 1364, Fornebu, Norway
Tel.: (47) 94859599
Web Site: https://www.soft-ox.com
Year Founded: 2012
6FV—(DEU)
Health Care Srvices
N.A.I.C.S.: 621610
Geir Hermod Almas *(CEO)*

SOFTRAK VENTURE INVESTMENT LTD.
201 Moon Light Shopping Centre Nr Maruti Towers Drive in Road, Memnagar, Ahmedabad, 380052, Gujarat, India
Tel.: (91) 8320825503
Web Site: https://softrakventure.in
Year Founded: 1993
531529—(BOM)
Information Technology Consulting Services
N.A.I.C.S.: 541512
Vipulbhai Sunilbhai Jana *(CFO)*

SOFTROCK MINERALS LTD
Year Founded: 1993
SFT—(TSXV)
Rev.: $112,241
Assets: $100,497
Liabilities: $72,462
Net Worth: $28,035
Earnings: ($12,211)
Emp.: 1
Fiscal Year-end: 12/31/20
Oil, Gas & Mineral Exploration
N.A.I.C.S.: 211120
E. Denis Gagnon *(Sec)*

SOFTRONIC AB
Hammarby kaj 10A, 12032, Stockholm, Sweden
Tel.: (46) 851909000
Web Site: https://www.softronic.se
Year Founded: 1984
SF7—(DEU)
Rev.: $88,936,135
Assets: $62,944,936
Liabilities: $21,317,732
Net Worth: $41,627,205
Earnings: $8,161,292
Emp.: 424
Fiscal Year-end: 12/31/20
Management Consulting Services
N.A.I.C.S.: 541611
Per Adolfsson *(CEO)*

Subsidiaries:

Consultus AB (1)
Hammarby Kaj 10A, 120 32, Stockholm, Sweden
Tel.: (46) 851909500
Web Site: https://consultus.se
Business Management Consulting Services
N.A.I.C.S.: 541611

Softronic Baltic AS (1)
Masina 9, 10144, Tallinn, Estonia
Tel.: (372) 606 48 70
Information Technology Consulting Services
N.A.I.C.S.: 541512

Softronic Danmark A/S (1)
Fruebergvej 3 Boks 18, 2100, Copenhagen, Denmark
Tel.: (45) 51 24 24 09
Information Technology Consulting Services
N.A.I.C.S.: 541512

SOFTSHIP AG
Notkestr 9, 22607, Hamburg, Germany
Tel.: (49) 40 89 06 8 0
Web Site: http://www.softship.com
Year Founded: 1989
Rev.: $7,622,440
Assets: $5,662,384
Liabilities: $1,742,272
Net Worth: $3,920,112
Earnings: $653,352
Emp.: 68
Fiscal Year-end: 12/31/15
Liner Shipping Software Developer
N.A.I.C.S.: 513210
Detlef Muller *(Mng Dir)*

Subsidiaries:

Softship America, Inc. (1)
36 Maple Pl Ste 203, Manhasset, NY 11030-1976
Tel.: (516) 441-5801
Software Development Services
N.A.I.C.S.: 541511

Softship Data Processing Pte Ltd (1)
WiseTech Global The Great Room One George Street, Singapore, 049145, Singapore
Tel.: (65) 62272497
Software Development Services
N.A.I.C.S.: 541511

Softship Inc. (1)
15th Floor Jollibee Plaza F Ortigas Jr Road corner Garnet Road, Ortigas Centre;, Pasig, 1605, Philippines
Tel.: (63) 25030285
Software Development Services
N.A.I.C.S.: 541511

SOFTSOL INDIA LIMITED
Development Center 4 Software Units Layout, Madhapur, Hyderabad, 500 081, Telangana, India
Tel.: (91) 4042568500
Web Site: https://www.softsolindia.com
Year Founded: 1993
532344—(BOM)
Rev.: $9,649,649
Assets: $21,946,238
Liabilities: $4,286,865
Net Worth: $17,659,373
Earnings: $9,568
Emp.: 168
Fiscal Year-end: 03/31/23
Information Technology Services

INTERNATIONAL PUBLIC

N.A.I.C.S.: 519290
Srinivasa Rao Madala *(Chm)*

SOFTSTAR ENTERTAINMENT, INC.
22F 1 No 77 Sec 2 Dunhua S Rd, Da an Dist, Taipei, 106, Taiwan
Tel.: (886) 227226266
Web Site: http://www.softstar.com.tw
Year Founded: 1988
6111—(TPE)
Rev.: $106,680,430
Assets: $233,247,318
Liabilities: $135,448,832
Net Worth: $97,798,485
Earnings: ($12,426,665)
Fiscal Year-end: 12/31/19
Software Development Services
N.A.I.C.S.: 541511
Tu Chun-Kuang *(Chm)*

SOFTTECH ENGINEERS LIMITED
SoftTech Towers S NO 1/1A/7 8 15 16 17 Plot No B C D 1-Baner, Opp Royal Enfield Showroom Baner Road, Pune, 411045, India
Tel.: (91) 2067183711
Web Site: https://www.softtech-engr.com
543470—(BOM)
Rev.: $8,013,249
Assets: $19,523,506
Liabilities: $7,182,855
Net Worth: $12,340,651
Earnings: $433,451
Emp.: 333
Fiscal Year-end: 03/31/23
Software Development Services
N.A.I.C.S.: 541511
Vijay Gupta *(Chm & Mng Dir)*

Subsidiaries:

AmpliNxt Private Limited (1)
6th Floor SoftTech Towers S NO1/1A/7 8 15 16 17 Plot No B C D 1-Baner, Opp Royal Enfield Showroom Baner Road, Pune, 411045, India
Tel.: (91) 2067183711
Web Site: https://amplinxt.com
Business Startup Consulting Services
N.A.I.C.S.: 541611

SoftTech Digital Pte. Ltd. (1)
30 Cecil Street 19-08 Prudential Tower, Singapore, 049712, Singapore
Tel.: (65) 4084718404
Software Provider
N.A.I.C.S.: 423430

SoftTech Government Solutions, Inc. (1)
Tel.: (408) 471-8404
Software Services
N.A.I.C.S.: 541519

SOFTWARE CIRCLE PLC.
Third Avenue The Village, Trafford Park, Manchester, M17 1FG, United Kingdom
Tel.: (44) 1618485700 UK
Web Site: https://www.softwarecircle.com
SFT—(AIM)
Rev.: $15,838,172
Assets: $29,815,703
Liabilities: $28,644,282
Net Worth: $1,171,421
Earnings: ($1,736,935)
Emp.: 92
Fiscal Year-end: 03/31/23
Office Supplies & Stationery Retailers
N.A.I.C.S.: 459410
Peter R. Gunning *(CEO)*

Subsidiaries:

Care Management Systems Limited (1)
Unit 6 Apex Court Almondsbury Business

Park, Bradley Stoke, Bristol, BS32 4JT, United Kingdom
Tel.: (44) 3300563333
Web Site: https://www.caredocs.co.uk
Healthcare Software Development Services
N.A.I.C.S.: 541511

Printing.com (UK Franchise) Limited (1)
Unit E Orchard Business Ctr 20 20, Maidstone, ME16 0JZ, Kent, United Kingdom
Tel.: (44) 1622764477
Web Site: http://www.maidstoneprinting.com
Printing Services
N.A.I.C.S.: 323111

Printing.com Europe Limited (1)
40 Great George St, Leeds, LS1 3DL, West Yorkshire, United Kingdom
Tel.: (44) 1132467374
Web Site: http://www.leeds-printing.com
Sales Range: $25-49.9 Million
Emp.: 3
Printing Services
N.A.I.C.S.: 323111

Topfloor Systems Limited (1)
Maple House South County Business Park, Leopardstown, Dublin, D18 F863, Ireland
Tel.: (353) 17918870
Web Site: https://www.topfloor.ie
Property Management & Development Services
N.A.I.C.S.: 531312

Vertical Plus Limited (1)
The Apex Derriford Business Park Brest Road, Plymouth, PL6 5FL, Devon, United Kingdom
Tel.: (44) 1752764400
Web Site: https://www.verticalplus.co.uk
Emp.: 25
Web Development Services
N.A.I.C.S.: 541512

Watermark Technologies Limited (1)
Unit 5 Quayside House Salts Mill Road, Shipley, BD18 3ST, United Kingdom
Tel.: (44) 1274926300
Web Site: https://www.watermarktech.co.uk
Document Management Software Development Services
N.A.I.C.S.: 541511

SOFTWARE EFFECTIVE SOLUTIONS CORP.
Executive tower 1 Unit 220 De La Rosa Street, Makati, 70520, Philippines
Tel.: (63) 9228991538 LA
SFWJ—(OTCIQ)
Assets: $2,332,000
Liabilities: $550,000
Net Worth: $1,782,000
Earnings: ($242,000)
Emp.: 10
Fiscal Year-end: 12/31/21
Electronic Product Distr
N.A.I.C.S.: 425120

SOFTWARE SERVICE, INC.
2-6-1 Nishi-Miyahara, Yodogawa-Ku, Osaka, 532-0004, Japan
Tel.: (81) 663507222
Web Site: https://www.softs.co.jp
Year Founded: 1969
3733—(TKS)
Rev.: $239,074,800
Assets: $283,004,440
Liabilities: $58,662,660
Net Worth: $224,341,780
Earnings: $34,485,760
Emp.: 1,715
Fiscal Year-end: 10/31/23
Software Development Services
N.A.I.C.S.: 541511
Akihiro Ootani (Pres)

SOFTWAREONE HOLDING AG
Riedenmatt 4, 6370, Stans, Switzerland
Tel.: (41) 844445544
Web Site:
  https://www.softwareone.com
SWON—(SWX)
Rev.: $1,201,912,294
Assets: $4,497,136,934
Liabilities: $3,736,366,786
Net Worth: $760,770,148
Earnings: $25,484,906
Emp.: 9,300
Fiscal Year-end: 12/31/23
Computer System Design Services
N.A.I.C.S.: 541512
Hans Grueter (CFO & Member-Exec Bd)

Subsidiaries:

Centiq Limited (1)
Phoenix Business Park 2 Millennium Way West, Nottingham, NG8 6AS, United Kingdom
Tel.: (44) 1159519666
Web Site: https://www.centiq.co.uk
Information Technology Services
N.A.I.C.S.: 541618

Comparex Brasil SA (1)
Rua Arizona 1366-cj 32, Brooklin, Sao Paulo, 04567-003, Brazil
Tel.: (55) 1134680500
Software Development Services
N.A.I.C.S.: 541511

Comparex Hrvatska doo (1)
Strojarska Cesta 20, 10000, Zagreb, Croatia
Tel.: (385) 99 427 6607
Software Development Services
N.A.I.C.S.: 541511

Comparex India Pvt. Ltd. (1)
A-34 2nd Floor Naraina Industrial Area Phase-II, New Delhi, 110 028, India
Tel.: (91) 114 747 4848
Software Development Services
N.A.I.C.S.: 541511

Comparex Indonesia PT (1)
Sona Topas Tower 6th Floor Jalan Jenderal Sudirman Kav 26, 12920, Jakarta, Indonesia
Tel.: (62) 21 250 6336
Software Development Services
N.A.I.C.S.: 541511

ISP D International Software Partners GmbH (1)
Friedensstrasse 9, 85586, Poing, Germany
Tel.: (49) 812 198 2180
Web Site: https://www.ispd.de
Software Development Services
N.A.I.C.S.: 541511
Christian Laube (Mng Dir)

Intelligence Partner U.K. Limited (1)
Finsgate 5-7 Cranwood St, London, EC1V 9LH, United Kingdom
Tel.: (44) 208 123 1626
Software Development Services
N.A.I.C.S.: 541511

Intelligence Partners SL (1)
Calle Gobelas 15, 28023, Madrid, Spain
Tel.: (34) 91 151 7102
Web Site:
  https://www.intelligencepartner.com
Information Technology Services
N.A.I.C.S.: 541519
Ignacio Bano (CEO)

OOO COMPAREX (1)
St Barclay 6 Building 3 7th Floor, 121087, Moscow, Russia
Tel.: (7) 495 982 3911
Software Development Services
N.A.I.C.S.: 541511

PT SoftwareONE Indonesia (1)
Menara Rajawali 18th Floor Jl Dr Ide anak Agung Gde Agung Lot 5 1, Kawasan Mega Kuningan, Jakarta, 12950, Indonesia
Tel.: (62) 215761515
Software Development Services
N.A.I.C.S.: 541511

Predica BMC Sp. z o.o (1)
Ul Altowa 2, 02-386, Warsaw, Poland
Tel.: (48) 884774451
Consulting Services
N.A.I.C.S.: 541618

Predica Bulgaria EOOD (1)
66 Vitosha Blvd 4th Floor, Sofia, Bulgaria
Tel.: (359) 885702327
Consulting Services
N.A.I.C.S.: 541618

Predica FZ LLC (1)
The Iridium Building Ste 17 Umm Suqeim Road, PO Box 391186, Al Barsha, Dubai, United Arab Emirates
Tel.: (971) 504708089
Consulting Services
N.A.I.C.S.: 541618

Predica Middle East LLC (1)
Commercial Bank Plaza Office No 18 Level 14, PO Box 27111, West Bay, Doha, Qatar
Tel.: (974) 66208340
Consulting Services
N.A.I.C.S.: 541618

Predica Sp z o.o. (1)
Altowa 2, 02-386, Warsaw, Poland
Tel.: (48) 883020055
Web Site: https://www.predicagroup.com
Emp.: 440
Information Technology Services
N.A.I.C.S.: 541511

Software Pipeline Ireland Ltd. (1)
Core House Pouladuff Road, Cork, Ireland
Tel.: (353) 216019980
Software Development Services
N.A.I.C.S.: 541511

SoftwareONE (Shanghai) Trading Co. Ltd. (1)
L903 Building 3 IM Shanghai No 1398 Kai Xuan Rd, Shanghai, 200050, China
Tel.: (86) 2180509288
Software Development Services
N.A.I.C.S.: 541511

SoftwareONE AB (1)
Farogatan 33, 164 51, Kista, Sweden
Tel.: (46) 84 650 1880
Software Development Services
N.A.I.C.S.: 541511

SoftwareONE Argentina SRL (1)
Olazabal 1515 Oficina 501 A, C1428, Buenos Aires, Argentina
Tel.: (54) 1153686606
Software Development Services
N.A.I.C.S.: 541511

SoftwareONE Australia Pty. Ltd. (1)
Level 11 80 Clarence Street, Sydney, 2000, NSW, Australia
Tel.: (61) 282290000
Software Development Services
N.A.I.C.S.: 541511

SoftwareONE BE BV (1)
Buro and Design Center-Esplanade 1 Suite 315, Box 3, 1020, Brussels, Belgium
Tel.: (32) 23731400
Software Development Services
N.A.I.C.S.: 541511

SoftwareONE Bolivia SRL (1)
Av Sanchez Bustamante N 487 calle 16 de Calacoto, Edif Business Center II piso 3 of 4, La Paz, Bolivia
Tel.: (591) 2124421
Software Development Services
N.A.I.C.S.: 541511

SoftwareONE Brazil CSI Ltda. (1)
Rua George Ohm 230-16 andar Torre B, Brooklin, Sao Paulo, 04576-020, Brazil
Tel.: (55) 113 796 5020
Software Development Services
N.A.I.C.S.: 541511

SoftwareONE Bulgaria OOD (1)
141 Tsarigradsko Shose Blvd VIP Security Building Floor 2, 1784, Sofia, Bulgaria
Tel.: (359) 24927040
Software Development Services
N.A.I.C.S.: 541511

SoftwareONE Canada Inc. (1)
2680 Skymark Ave Suite 510, Mississauga, L4W 5L6, ON, Canada
Software Development Services
N.A.I.C.S.: 541511

SoftwareONE Chile SpA (1)
Apoquindo 4001 of 302, Las Condes, Santiago, Chile
Tel.: (56) 233224359
Software Development Services
N.A.I.C.S.: 541511

SoftwareONE Colombia SAS (1)
Avenida Carrera 45 No 97-50 Ed Porto 100 Of 901-904, 110111, Bogota, Colombia
Tel.: (57) 1 756 1788
Software Development Services
N.A.I.C.S.: 541511

SoftwareONE Comercio e Servicos de Informatica Ltda. (1)
Andromeda Avenue 885 - 16th floor room 5, Sao Paulo, Brazil
Tel.: (55) 1137965020
Web Site: https://www.softwareone.com
Information Technology Services
N.A.I.C.S.: 541511

SoftwareONE Czech Republic sro (1)
Vyskocilova 1410/1, 140 00, Prague, 4, Czech Republic
Tel.: (420) 241405297
Web Site: https://www.softwareone.com
Software Development Services
N.A.I.C.S.: 541511

SoftwareONE Denmark ApS (1)
Bregnerodvej 144A, 3460, Birkerod, Denmark
Tel.: (45) 44889900
Web Site: https://www.softwareone.com
Software Development Services
N.A.I.C.S.: 541511

SoftwareONE Deutschland GmbH (1)
Konrad-Zuse-Platz 2, 81829, Munich, Germany
Tel.: (49) 8941 324 1400
Software Development Services
N.A.I.C.S.: 541511

SoftwareONE Dominican Republic Srl (1)
Av Sarasota 39 Edificio Sarasota Center 4to Piso Suite 408, Bella Vista, 10111, Santo Domingo, Dominican Republic
Tel.: (809) 542 2473
Software Development Services
N.A.I.C.S.: 541511

SoftwareONE Ecuador Soluciones SA (1)
Calle Japon E54 y alfonso perira edificio zaigen piso 11 oficina 1107, Quito, Ecuador
Tel.: (593) 990988987
Web Site: https://www.softwareone.com
Software Development Services
N.A.I.C.S.: 541511

SoftwareONE Espana S.A. (1)
EDIFICIO CRISTALIA PLAY - Parque Empresarial Cristalia, C/ Via de los Poblados 3 Edif 4b 1st floor, 28033, Madrid, Spain
Tel.: (34) 915981406
Web Site: https://www.softwareone.com
Information Technology Services
N.A.I.C.S.: 541511

SoftwareONE Experts Sdn Bhd (1)
Unit A-13-17, Level 13 Menara UOA Bangsar No 5 Jalan Bangsar Utama 1, 59000, Kuala Lumpur, Malaysia
Tel.: (60) 322897728
Web Site: https://www.softwareone.com
Software Development Services
N.A.I.C.S.: 541511

SoftwareONE France SAS (1)
120 Rue Jean Jaures, 92300, Levallois-Perret, France
Tel.: (33) 14 106 6800
Software Development Services
N.A.I.C.S.: 541511

SoftwareONE Hong Kong Ltd. (1)
Unit 1203 12/F NEO 123 Hoi Bun Road, Kwun Tong, Kowloon, China (Hong Kong)
Tel.: (852) 27512800
Web Site: https://www.softwareone.com
Software Development Services
N.A.I.C.S.: 541511

SoftwareONE Hungary Ltd. (1)
Montevideo utca 2/B, 1037, Budapest, Hungary

SOFTWAREONE HOLDING AG

SoftwareONE Holding AG—(Continued)
Tel.: (36) 204877515
Web Site: https://www.softwareone.com
Software Development Services
N.A.I.C.S.: 541511

SoftwareONE India Private Ltd. (1)
7th Floor International Tech Park Phase-I/Block-I, Village Behrampur Road Near Sector-59, Gurgaon, 122101, India
Tel.: (91) 1245024999
Web Site: https://www.softwareone.com
Software Development Services
N.A.I.C.S.: 541511

SoftwareONE Italia Srl (1)
Centro direzionale Milanofiori Strada 4 Palazzo Q8, 20089, Rozzano, MI, Italy
Tel.: (39) 028 945 5326
Software Development Services
N.A.I.C.S.: 541511

SoftwareONE Japan KK (1)
2-5-8 Akasaka Tokyo Hulic JP Akasaka Building 8th Floor, Minato-ku, Tokyo, 162-0067, Japan
Tel.: (81) 350052801
Web Site: https://www.softwareone.com
Software Development Services
N.A.I.C.S.: 541511

SoftwareONE Korea Ltd. (1)
201 2nd floor Lotte Castle Classe 9 Teheran-ro 63-gi, Gangnam-gu, Seoul, 06162, Korea (South)
Tel.: (82) 262032876
Web Site: https://www.softwareone.com
Software Development Services
N.A.I.C.S.: 541511

SoftwareONE Licensing Experts SRL (1)
Unirii View building 6-8 Corneliu Coposu Boulevard 6th Floor, District 3, 30606, Bucharest, Romania
Tel.: (40) 372735175
Web Site: https://www.softwareone.com
Software Development Services
N.A.I.C.S.: 541511

SoftwareONE Luxembourg SARL (1)
20 Rue Eugene Ruppert Centre d'Affaires NCI Batiment Laccolith, 2453, Luxembourg, Luxembourg
Tel.: (352) 26493500
Web Site: https://www.softwareone.com
Software Development Services
N.A.I.C.S.: 541511

SoftwareONE Netherlands B.V. (1)
Naritaweg 177, 1043 BW, Amsterdam, Netherlands
Tel.: (31) 202586800
Web Site: https://www.softwareone.com
Information Technology Services
N.A.I.C.S.: 541511

SoftwareONE Norway AS (1)
Brynsveien 18 E, 0667, Oslo, Norway
Tel.: (47) 23055500
Web Site: https://www.softwareone.com
Software Development Services
N.A.I.C.S.: 541511

SoftwareONE Osterreich GmbH (1)
Obere Donaustrasse 95, 1020, Vienna, Austria
Tel.: (43) 1878100
Web Site: https://www.softwareone.com
Software Development Services
N.A.I.C.S.: 541511

SoftwareONE Peru SAC (1)
Av Victor Andres Belaunde N 147 Via Principal 103, Centro Empresarial Real Torre Real 10 piso 2 Oficina 202, San Isidro, Lima, Peru
Tel.: (51) 922440190
Web Site: https://www.softwareone.com
Software Development Services
N.A.I.C.S.: 541511

SoftwareONE Philippines Corporation (1)
10th Floor One Ayala South Tower EDSA cor Ayala Avenue, San Lorenzo, Makati, 1223, Philippines
Tel.: (63) 288733131
Web Site: https://www.softwareone.com

Software Development Services
N.A.I.C.S.: 541511

SoftwareONE Polska Sp z o.o. (1)
Ul Siedmiogrodzka 9, 01-204, Warsaw, Poland
Tel.: (48) 22 487 9924
Software Development Services
N.A.I.C.S.: 541511

SoftwareONE Projects (Private) Limited (1)
37th Floor West Tower World Trade Center Echelon Square, 01, Colombo, Sri Lanka
Tel.: (94) 117450721
Information Technology Services
N.A.I.C.S.: 541618

SoftwareONE Pte. Ltd. (1)
150 Beach Road 31-00 Gateway West, Singapore, 189720, Singapore
Tel.: (65) 69220900
Web Site: https://www.softwareone.com
Software Development Services
N.A.I.C.S.: 541511

SoftwareONE SW1 Dominican Republic Srl (1)
Tel.: (809) 5422473
Web Site: https://www.softwareone.com
Information Technology Services
N.A.I.C.S.: 541511

SoftwareONE Slovakia sro (1)
Dunajska 7114/15, 811 08, Bratislava, Slovakia
Tel.: (421) 905110868
Web Site: https://www.softwareone.com
Software Development Services
N.A.I.C.S.: 541511

SoftwareONE Spain SL (1)
Edificio Cristralia Play-Parque Empresarial Cristalia-C/Via de los, Poblados 3 Edif 4b 1 Plant, 28033, Madrid, Spain
Tel.: (34) 915981406
Web Site: https://www.softwareone.com
Software Development Services
N.A.I.C.S.: 541511

SoftwareONE Taiwan Ltd. (1)
110 Floor 21-5 No 171 Songde Road, Xinyi District, Taipei, 11085, Taiwan
Tel.: (886) 221765186
Web Site: https://www.softwareone.com
Software Development Services
N.A.I.C.S.: 541511

SoftwareONE Thailand Co., Ltd. (1)
Tel.: (66) 21050410
Web Site: https://www.softwareone.com
Software Development Services
N.A.I.C.S.: 541511

SoftwareONE Turkey Bilisim Teknolojileri Ticaret Anonim Sirketi (1)
Ataturk Mah Ertugrul Gazi Sok A Blok Sk No 2E D 7, Atasehir, 34750, Istanbul, Turkiye
Tel.: (90) 2163321525
Web Site: https://www.softwareone.com
Software Development Services
N.A.I.C.S.: 541511

SoftwareONE UK Ltd. (1)
41-47 Hartfield Road, Wimbledon, London, SW19 3RQ, United Kingdom
Tel.: (44) 2035300270
Web Site: https://www.softwareone.com
Software Development Services
N.A.I.C.S.: 541511

SoftwareONE Ukraine Limited Liability Company (1)
St Mykola Hrinchenko 4-B Horizon Park Business Center, 03038, Kiev, 03038, Ukraine
Tel.: (380) 444995989
Web Site: https://www.softwareone.com
Software Development Services
N.A.I.C.S.: 541511

SoftwareONE Uruguay SpA (1)
Colonia 922, 11000, Montevideo, Uruguay
Tel.: (598) 94092140
Web Site: https://www.softwareone.com
Software Development Services
N.A.I.C.S.: 541511

SoftwareONE Vietnam Co. Limited (1)

Level 5 TTC Building 253 Hoang Van Thu Street, Tan Binh District, Ho Chi Minh City, Vietnam
Tel.: (84) 909548631
Web Site: https://www.softwareone.com
Software Development Services
N.A.I.C.S.: 541511

SoftwareONE, Informacijski Sistemi, doo (1)
Letaliska cesta 1, 1000, Ljubljana, Slovenia
Tel.: (386) 59250300
Web Site: https://www.softwareone.com
Software Development Services
N.A.I.C.S.: 541511

Softwareone Experts South Africa (Pty) Ltd. (1)
7th Floor Rosebank Mall Offices Cnr Baker and Cradock Streets, Rosebank, 2196, South Africa
Tel.: (27) 11 712 1300
Software Development Services
N.A.I.C.S.: 541511

Systematica Distribution Srl (1)
Via Luigi Sampietro 110, 21047, Saronno, VA, Italy
Tel.: (39) 029 641 0282
Web Site: https://www.systematika.it
Software Development Services
N.A.I.C.S.: 541511

TCL Digi Trade sro (1)
Polanecka 847/49a, Svinov, 721 00, Ostrava, Czech Republic
Tel.: (420) 55 860 1767
Web Site: https://www.tcl-digitrade.com
Software Development Services
N.A.I.C.S.: 541511

SOGAZ JSC

10 Akademika Sakharova av, 107078, Moscow, Russia
Tel.: (7) 4957392140
Web Site: http://www.sogaz.ru
Year Founded: 1993
Insurance Agents
N.A.I.C.S.: 524210
Anton Ustinov *(Chm)*

Subsidiaries:

VTB Insurance, Ltd. (1)
8 bld 1 Chistoprudniy boulevard, 101000, Moscow, Russia
Tel.: (7) 4955807333
Web Site: http://www.vtbins.ru
General Insurance Services
N.A.I.C.S.: 524210
Gennady A. Galperin *(Chm-Mgmt Bd & CEO)*

Subsidiary (Domestic):

Rosno MS (2)
Ozerkovskaya D 30, 115184, Moscow, Russia
Tel.: (7) 495 956 21 05
Medical Insurance Services
N.A.I.C.S.: 524114

SOGECLAIR

7 Avenue Albert Durand, PO Box 20069, 31703, Blagnac, France
Tel.: (33) 561717171
Web Site: http://www.sogeclair.com
Rev.: $87,293,010
Industrial Engineering & Design
N.A.I.C.S.: 541420
Philippe Robardey *(Pres & CEO)*

Subsidiaries:

A.V. Simulation SAS (1)
1 Cours de l'Ille Seguin, 92100, Boulogne-Billancourt, France
Tel.: (33) 146949780
Web Site: http://www.avsimulation.com
Engineeering Services
N.A.I.C.S.: 541330
Emmanuel Chevrier *(CEO)*

Aviacomp SAS (1)
7 Rue de Caulet, 31300, Toulouse, Cedex, France
Tel.: (33) 567042900
Aircraft Engine Parts Mfr

INTERNATIONAL PUBLIC

N.A.I.C.S.: 336412
Benoit Ferrane *(Dir-Technical & Innovation)*

Checkaero BV (1)
Wibautstraat 129, 1091 GL, Amsterdam, Netherlands
Tel.: (31) 205628200
Engineering Services
N.A.I.C.S.: 541330

Checkaero SARL (1)
16 avenue Pasterur L, 2310, Luxembourg, Luxembourg
Tel.: (352) 274048503189
Web Site: http://www.checkaero.com
Engineering Services
N.A.I.C.S.: 541330

MSB Design Inc. (1)
333-i Chemin du Tremblay, Boucherville, J4B 7M1, QC, Canada
Tel.: (514) 667-9399
Web Site: http://www.msbexpertise.com
Automobile Spare Parts Mfr
N.A.I.C.S.: 336390

Oktal SAS (1)
Immeuble Aurelien II 2 impasse Boudeville, 31100, Toulouse, France
Tel.: (33) 5 62 11 50 10
Web Site: http://www.oktal.fr
Industrial Machinery Distr
N.A.I.C.S.: 423830

Subsidiary (Domestic):

Oktal Synthetic Environment SAS (2)
11 avenue du Lac, 31 320, Vigoulet-Auzil, France
Tel.: (33) 567700200
Web Site: http://www.oktal-se.fr
Software Development Services
N.A.I.C.S.: 541511

Subsidiary (Non-US):

Sydac Ltd. (2)
Derwent Business Centre Clarke St, Derby, DE1 2BU, Derbyshire, United Kingdom
Tel.: (44) 1332299600
Mechanical Engineering Services
N.A.I.C.S.: 541330

Sera Ingenierie SAS (1)
12 av du Quebec Bat Hibiscus CS40357, 91978, Villebon-sur-Yvette, Cedex, France
Tel.: (33) 169298989
Web Site: http://www.sera-ingenierie.fr
Industrial Machinery Mfr
N.A.I.C.S.: 333248

Sogeclair Aerospace GmbH (1)
Georg Heyken Strasse 4, 21147, Hamburg, Germany
Tel.: (49) 404600470
Engineeering Services
N.A.I.C.S.: 541330

Sogeclair Aerospace Ltd (1)
Unit 18 Apex Court Woodlands Bradley Stoke, Bristol, BS324JT, United Kingdom
Tel.: (44) 1454275200
Engineeering Services
N.A.I.C.S.: 541330

Sogeclair Aerospace SA (1)
Calle Francisco Gasco Santillan N 2-B 2a planta Pologono Industrial, San Marcos Edificiio Mezquitas, 28906, Madrid, Spain
Tel.: (34) 916826574
Engineeering Services
N.A.I.C.S.: 541330

Sogeclair Aerospace Sarl (1)
Pole Elgazala des technologies de la communication, Toute de Raoud km 3 5 Cite Elgazala, Aryanah, Tunisia
Tel.: (216) 71857601
Engineeering Services
N.A.I.C.S.: 541330

SOGEMAR

208 Avenue De Champagne, Frignicourt, 51300, Vitry-le-Francois, France
Tel.: (33) 490591011
Sales Range: $25-49.9 Million
Emp.: 48
Grocery Stores

N.A.I.C.S.: 445110
Corinne Ferrier (Gen Mgr)

SOGIREST
Z.I. Blanzat, 22 Rue Eugene Sue, 03100, Montlucon, France
Tel.: (33) 470056991
Web Site: http://www.sogirest.fr
Rev.: $13,700,000
Emp.: 31
Restaurants & Restaurant Management Services
N.A.I.C.S.: 722511
Christine Benoit (Pres)

SOGN SPAREBANK
Minister of State Evensensveg 8, 6885, Ardalstangen, Norway
Tel.: (47) 57648510
Web Site: https://www.sognbank.no
0EW2—(LSE)
Sales Range: Less than $1 Million
Business Management Consulting Services
N.A.I.C.S.: 541611
Egon M. Moen (CEO)

SOHAR INTERNATIONAL BANK SAOG
Hai Al Mina, PO Box 44, 114, Muscat, 114, Oman
Tel.: (968) 24730000
Web Site:
  https://www.soharinternational.com
BKSB—(MUS)
Rev.: $384,033,968
Assets: $10,711,692,553
Liabilities: $9,165,881,400
Net Worth: $1,545,811,153
Earnings: $73,427,442
Emp.: 888
Fiscal Year-end: 12/31/21
Banking Services
N.A.I.C.S.: 522110
Kamran Haider (Head-Internal Audit)

Subsidiaries:

HSBC Bank Oman S.A.O.G. (1)
Al Khuwair, PO Box 1727, Seeb, 111, Oman
Tel.: (968) 24947798
Web Site: http://www.hsbc.co.om
Rev.: $202,251,742
Assets: $5,818,145,474
Liabilities: $4,885,538,200
Net Worth: $932,607,274
Earnings: $69,323,210
Fiscal Year-end: 12/31/2022
Banking Services
N.A.I.C.S.: 522110
Waleed Omar Abdul Monem Al Zawawi (Deputy Chm)

SOHAR POULTRY S.A.O.G
Ruwi 112, PO Box 2808, Muscat, Oman
Tel.: (968) 26886042
Web Site:
  http://www.soharpoultry.com
Year Founded: 1983
Poultry Operation Services
N.A.I.C.S.: 311615

SOHGO SECURITY SERVICES CO., LTD.
1-6-6 Motoakasaka, Minato-ku, Tokyo, 107-8511, Japan
Tel.: (81) 334707870 JP
Web Site: https://www.alsok.co.jp
2331—(TKS)
Rev.: $3,446,454,000
Assets: $3,751,578,210
Liabilities: $1,196,277,800
Net Worth: $2,555,300,410
Earnings: $180,631,470
Emp.: 38,192
Fiscal Year-end: 03/31/24
Security Services
N.A.I.C.S.: 561612
Atsushi Murai (Chm & CEO)

Subsidiaries:

ALSOK Asahi Harima Co., Ltd. (1)
17-3 Tonomachi Nipponkoa Insurance Hamada Building 2F, Hamada, Shimane, Japan
Tel.: (81) 855234887
Web Site:
  http://www.asahiharima.alsok.co.jp
Sales Range: $25-49.9 Million
Emp.: 150
Security Guard Services
N.A.I.C.S.: 561612

ALSOK Care & Support Co., Ltd. (1)
NTT Data Omori Sanno Building 1-3-5 Sanno, Ota-ku, Tokyo, 143-0023, Japan (100%)
Tel.: (81) 357189226
Web Site: https://acs.alsok.co.jp
Emp.: 190
Homage & Health Care Services
N.A.I.C.S.: 621610

ALSOK India Private Limited (1)
Unit No 110-112 1st Floor Eros Corporate Park Sector-2 Plot K, IMT Manesar, Gurgaon, 122 050, Haryana, India
Tel.: (91) 124 229 0612
Web Site: https://www.alsok.co.in
Security Services
N.A.I.C.S.: 561612

ALSOK Myanmar Security Services Co., Ltd. (1)
Rose Villa162 B Dhammazedi Road, Bahan Township, Yangon, Myanmar
Tel.: (95) 925 339 7024
Security Services
N.A.I.C.S.: 561612

ALSOK Thai Security Services Co., Ltd. (1)
15th Floor Ramaland Building 952 Rama IV Road, Suriyawongse Bangrak, Bangkok, 10500, Thailand
Tel.: (66) 26 329 1404
Web Site: https://www.alsok.co.th
Security Services
N.A.I.C.S.: 561612

ALSOK Trading Co., Ltd. (1)
E303 Sun Plaza No 88 Xianxia Rd, Changning Dist, Shanghai, China
Tel.: (86) 216 208 5553
Security Services
N.A.I.C.S.: 561612

ALSOK Vietnam Security Services Joint Stock Company (1)
Km92 New Highway No 5, Hung Vuong Ward Hong Bang District, Haiphong, Vietnam
Tel.: (84) 225 379 8966
Web Site: https://www.alsok.com.vn
Security Services
N.A.I.C.S.: 561612

Kita-Kanto Sohgo Security Services Co., Ltd. (1)
1-3-14 Fudomae, Utsunomiya, 320-0833, Tochigi, Japan
Tel.: (81) 286390308
Detective & Security Services
N.A.I.C.S.: 561611

PT. ALSOK BASS Indonesia Security Services (1)
Sentral Senayan II 22nd Floor Jl Asia Afrika No 8 Gelora Bung Karno, Senayan, Jakarta Pusat, 10270, Indonesia
Tel.: (62) 215 795 4005
Web Site: https://www.alsokbass.com
Security Services
N.A.I.C.S.: 561612

Security Operations Engineering (1)
1-6-6 Akasaka Minato-Yuan, Tokyo, 107-8511, Japan
Tel.: (81) 3 3423 2331
Web Site: http://www.alsok.co.jp
Electrical Construction
N.A.I.C.S.: 238210
Yasuo Ishiwata (Gen Mgr-IR)

Sokei Building Service Co., Ltd. (1)
118 Chiyoda Fuzimi Bldg 1 Fl, Chioda-ku, Tokyo, Japan
Tel.: (81) 3 3264 2923
Web Site: http://www.alsokbs.co.jp
Security Guard Services
N.A.I.C.S.: 561612
Imai Makoto (Pres)

SOHO CHINA LIMITED
11F Building A Chaowai SOHO 6B Chaowai Street, Chaoyang District, Beijing, 100020, China
Tel.: (86) 4008159888
Web Site: http://www.sohochina.com
0410—(HKG)
Sales Range: $300-349.9 Million
Emp.: 1,985
Real Estate Investment Services
N.A.I.C.S.: 531390
Shiyi Pan (Chm)

SOHO DEVELOPMENT S.A.
ul Smocza 27, 01-048, Warsaw, Poland
Tel.: (48) 882040320
Web Site:
  https://www.sohodevelopment.pl
Year Founded: 1997
SHD—(WAR)
Rev.: $4,827
Assets: $3,496,697
Liabilities: $222,053
Net Worth: $3,274,644
Earnings: ($339,685)
Fiscal Year-end: 12/31/23
Investment Services
N.A.I.C.S.: 523940
Maciej Wandzel (Chm-Mgmt Bd)

SOHO FLORDIS INTERNATIONAL PTY LTD.
Level 2 170 Pacific Highway, Saint Leonards, 2065, NSW, Australia
Tel.: (61) 2 9431 7299
Web Site: http://www.sfihealth.com
Nutraceutical Mfr
N.A.I.C.S.: 325411
Eng Liang Tan (Founder & Chm)

Subsidiaries:

Ginsana SA (1)
Via Mulini, 6934, Bioggio, Switzerland
Tel.: (41) 916103111
Web Site: http://www.ginsana-sa.com
Biological Product Mfr
N.A.I.C.S.: 325411

ProThera, Inc. (1)
10439 Double R Blvd, Reno, NV 89521
Tel.: (775) 850-8800
Web Site: http://www.protherainc.com
Sales Range: $1-9.9 Million
Emp.: 18
Nutraceutical Product Mfr
N.A.I.C.S.: 325411
Stephen Olmstead (Chief Science Officer)

SOHO GROUP
JL Rawa Sumur II Kav BB No 3 Kawasan Industri Pulogadung, Kel Jatinegara Kec Cakung, Jakarta, 13930, Indonesia
Tel.: (62) 2146832588
Web Site:
  https://www.sohogroup.com
Sales Range: $150-199.9 Million
Emp.: 3,300
Medicinal & Botanical Product Mfr
N.A.I.C.S.: 325411
Eng Liang Tan (Pres)

Subsidiaries:

PT. SOHO Global Medika (1)
Mayapada 2 Building 11th Floor Jl Jend Sudirman Kav 27, Jakarta, 12920, Indonesia
Tel.: (62) 2129858888
Pharmaceutical Product Mfr & Distr
N.A.I.C.S.: 325412

PT. SOHO Industri Pharmasi (1)
Jl Pulo Gadung No 6, Jakarta, 13920, Indonesia
Tel.: (62) 214605550
Emp.: 1,500
Pharmaceuticals Product Mfr
N.A.I.C.S.: 325412

PT. Universal Health Network (1)
Jl Tabib II No 6, Jakarta, Indonesia
Tel.: (62) 2160306677
Web Site: http://www.unihealth.biz
Pharmaceuticals Product Mfr
N.A.I.C.S.: 325412

Soho Flordis International Pty Ltd (1)
Level 4 156 Pacific Highway, Saint Leonards, 2065, NSW, Australia
Tel.: (61) 294317299
Web Site: http://www.sfihealth.com
Pharmaceutical Products Distr
N.A.I.C.S.: 424210
Eng Liang Tan (Chm)

SOHO HOLLY CORPORATION
Holly Bldg 50 Zhonghua Rd, Nanjing, 210001, China
Tel.: (86) 2552278888
Web Site: https://www.artall.com
Year Founded: 1979
600128—(SHG)
Rev.: $946,412,758
Assets: $834,702,814
Liabilities: $453,241,985
Net Worth: $381,460,830
Earnings: $4,596,563
Emp.: 5,000
Fiscal Year-end: 12/31/23
Apparel & Hobby Goods Mfr
N.A.I.C.S.: 315990
Tingchang Wu (Chm)

Subsidiaries:

Jiangsu Chemical Fertilizer Co., Ltd. (1)
6th Floor Textile Building No 482 Zhongshan East Road, Jiangsu, Nanjing, China
Tel.: (86) 2586635021
Web Site: https://www.jscf.com.cn
Fertilizer Mfr
N.A.I.C.S.: 325311

Jiangsu Holly Creations Co., Ltd. (1)
16F Holly Building 50 Zhonghua Road, Nanjing, 210001, China
Tel.: (86) 2552278905
Sock Mill Mfr
N.A.I.C.S.: 315120

Jiangsu Holly Environmental Technology Industirial Co., Ltd. (1)
Hongye Building No 50 Zhonghua Road, Nanjing, 210001, Jiangsu, China
Tel.: (86) 2552278021
Web Site: https://www.hollyeti.com
Air Purification Device Mfr
N.A.I.C.S.: 333413

Jiangsu Holly Ever-Prime International Co., Ltd. (1)
Hongye Building No 50 Zhonghua Road, Nanjing, 210001, China
Tel.: (86) 2552278307
Web Site: http://www.hollyever-prime.com
Apparel Product Mfr & Distr
N.A.I.C.S.: 315120

Jiangsu Holly Everlasting Inc. (1)
17F Holly Building 50 Zhonghua Road, Nanjing, 210001, China
Tel.: (86) 2552304581
Toy Mfr
N.A.I.C.S.: 339930

Jiangsu Holly International Technical Engineering Co., Ltd. (1)
Tel.: (86) 2552278737
Hardware Product Mfr
N.A.I.C.S.: 315990

Jiangsu Holly Shine Co., Ltd. (1)
11F Holly Building 50 Zhonghua Road, Nanjing, 210001, China
Tel.: (86) 2552278060
Hardware Product Mfr
N.A.I.C.S.: 315990

SOHO HOLLY CORPORATION

SOHO Holly Corporation—(Continued)

Jiangsu Holly Uwill Int'L Co., Ltd. (1)
Wood Products Mfr
N.A.I.C.S.: 321999

SOHO HOUSE & CO INC.
180 Strand, London, WC2R 1EA,
United Kingdom
Tel.: (44) 2078512300 DE
Web Site:
    https://www.sohouseco.com
Year Founded: 2021
SHCO—(NYSE)
Rev.: $972,214,000
Assets: $2,467,896,000
Liabilities: $2,483,272,000
Net Worth: ($15,376,000)
Earnings: ($220,580,000)
Emp.: 7,714
Fiscal Year-end: 01/01/23
Digital Marketing Services
N.A.I.C.S.: 541870
Nick Jones *(Founder)*

SOHONET LIMITED
5 Soho Street London, Greater London, W1D 3DG, United Kingdom
Tel.: (44) 2072926900
Web Site: https://www.sohonet.com
Year Founded: 1995
Information Technology & Services
N.A.I.C.S.: 513210
Chuck Parker *(Chm & CEO)*

Subsidiaries:

5th Kind, Inc (1)
5681 W Jefferson Blvd, Los Angeles, CA 90016
Tel.: (310) 405-0895
Web Site: http://www.5thkind.com
Computer System Design Services
N.A.I.C.S.: 541512
Steve Cronan *(Founder & CEO)*

SOHU.COM LTD.
Sohu Media Building Building 3 No 2
Kexueyuan South Road, Haidian District, Beijing, 100190, China
Tel.: (86) 1062726666 DE
Web Site: https://www.sohu.com
Year Founded: 1998
SOHU—(NASDAQ)
Rev.: $733,872,000
Assets: $1,977,776,000
Liabilities: $867,066,000
Net Worth: $1,110,710,000
Earnings: ($17,343,000)
Emp.: 4,900
Fiscal Year-end: 12/31/22
Internet Communication Services
N.A.I.C.S.: 513210
Charles Zhang *(Founder, Chm & CEO)*

Subsidiaries:

7Road.com Limited (1)
Room 2701 Xiangjiang Financial Building No 3046 Xinghai Avenue, Nanshan Street Qianhai Shenzhen-Hong Kong Cooperation Zone, Shenzhen, 518000, China
Tel.: (86) 75589799777
Web Site: https://www.7road.com
Game Software Development Services
N.A.I.C.S.: 513210

Beijing Sogou Technology Development Co., Ltd. (1)
9/F Souhu Network Mansion No 1 Yard Zhongguancun E Rd Haidi, Beijing, 100084, China
Tel.: (86) 1062726666
Online Gambling Services
N.A.I.C.S.: 541511

Beijing Sohu New Era Information Technology Co., Ltd. (1)
15/F Souhu Network Mansion No 1 Zhongguancun East Road Haidi, Beijing, 100000, China
Tel.: (86) 1062726666

Information Technology Consulting Services
N.A.I.C.S.: 541512

Changyou.com limited (1)
Changyou Building Raycom Creative Industrial Park, No 65 Bajiao East Road Shijingshan District, Beijing, 100043, China (100%)
Tel.: (86) 1061920800
Rev.: $485,763,000
Assets: $1,965,484,000
Liabilities: $1,133,840,000
Net Worth: $831,644,000
Earnings: $84,332,000
Emp.: 2,131
Fiscal Year-end: 12/31/2018
Online Game Developer
N.A.I.C.S.: 541511
Yaobin Wang *(CFO)*

Subsidiary (Non-US):

Changyou My Sdn. Bhd (2)
10 06 10th Floor The Gardens North Office Tower Lkr Syed Putra, Mid Valley City, 59200, Kuala Lumpur, Malaysia
Tel.: (60) 322870477
Web Site: http://my.changyou.com
Sales Range: $25-49.9 Million
Emp.: 25
Online Gambling Services
N.A.I.C.S.: 541511

Changyou.com India Private Limited (2)
Lm road Shivaji Nagar Borivali W, Mumbai, Maharashtra, India
Tel.: (91) 9920834810
Online Gambling Services
N.A.I.C.S.: 541511

Sohu.com (Hong Kong) Ltd. (1)
Room 2010-2011 20/F Millennium City 2 378 Kwun Tong Road, Kwun Tong, Hong Kong, China (Hong Kong)
Tel.: (852) 2899 2278
Sales Range: $25-49.9 Million
Emp.: 1
Online Gambling Services
N.A.I.C.S.: 541511

SOIKEN HOLDINGS INC.
13th floor Senri Life Science Center
1-4-2 Shinsenri Higashimachi, Toyonaka, 560-0082, Osaka, Japan
Tel.: (81) 668718888
Web Site: https://www.soiken.com
Year Founded: 1994
2385—(TKS)
Rev.: $32,082,760
Assets: $43,204,120
Liabilities: $4,335,340
Net Worth: $38,868,780
Earnings: ($4,117,640)
Fiscal Year-end: 06/30/24
Holding Company
N.A.I.C.S.: 551112
Kentaro Ishigami *(Pres)*

Subsidiaries:

Japan Preventive Medicine Inc. (1)
Senri Life Science Center 14F 1-4-2 Shinsenri Higashimachi, Toyonaka, 560-0082, Osaka, Japan
Tel.: (81) 120189139
Web Site: http://www.japanpm.com
Dietary Supplement Retailer
N.A.I.C.S.: 456191

NRL Pharma Inc. (1)
East Block 203 Kanagawa Science Park 3-2-1 Sakado, Takatsu-Ku, Kawasaki, 213-0012, Kanagawa, Japan
Tel.: (81) 44 850 9761
Web Site: https://www.nrl-pharma.co.jp
Health Supplement Mfr & Retailer
N.A.I.C.S.: 325411

SOIL MACHINE DYNAMICS LTD.
Turbinia Works Davy Bank, Wallsend, NE28 6UZ, Newcastle upon Tyne, United Kingdom
Tel.: (44) 19 1234 2222
Web Site: http://www.smd.co.uk

Year Founded: 1971
Sales Range: $150-199.9 Million
Emp.: 495
Remotely Operated Vehicle Mfr
N.A.I.C.S.: 336612
Paul Atkinson *(Dir-Engrg-Remote & Autonomous Solutions)*

Subsidiaries:

Soil Machine Dynamics Singapore Pte Ltd (1)
33 Ubi Avenue 3 01-59 Vertex, Singapore, 408868, Singapore
Tel.: (65) 65769160
Marine Equipment Distr
N.A.I.C.S.: 423860
Stephen Brand *(Engr-Technical Support)*

SOILBUILD BUSINESS SPACE REIT
23 Defu South Street 1 Level 3, Singapore, 533847, Singapore
Tel.: (65) 64154587 SG
Web Site: http://www.soilbuildreit.com
Rev.: $66,012,599
Assets: $1,043,063,390
Liabilities: $440,889,363
Net Worth: $602,174,027
Earnings: $25,068,319
Fiscal Year-end: 12/31/19
Real Estate Investment Management Services
N.A.I.C.S.: 531120
Roy Seng Wah Teo *(CEO)*

SOILBUILD CONSTRUCTION GROUP LTD.
23 Defu South Street 1, Singapore, 533847, Singapore
Tel.: (65) 65422882
Web Site:
    https://www.soilbuildconstruct.com
Year Founded: 1976
S7P—(SES)
Rev.: $187,374,082
Assets: $191,280,769
Liabilities: $157,081,724
Net Worth: $34,199,046
Earnings: $5,541,165
Emp.: 902
Fiscal Year-end: 12/31/23
General Construction Services
N.A.I.C.S.: 236220
Chap Huat Lim *(Founder, Chm & Co-CEO)*

Subsidiaries:

Soilbuild (Myanmar) Company Limited (1)
No 13A Mya Yadanar Street Bauk Htaw, Yankin Township, Yangon, Myanmar
Tel.: (95) 1401178
Building Construction Services
N.A.I.C.S.: 236220

Soilbuild Construction (Myanmar) Co., Ltd. (1)
Unit 1-2 Building-F3 Padonmar Street, Ward 24 Thuwana Thingangyun Township, Yangon, Myanmar
Tel.: (95) 12334611
Construction Services
N.A.I.C.S.: 236220

SOILBUILD GROUP HOLDINGS LTD.
25 Changi S St 1, 486059, Singapore, Singapore
Tel.: (65) 65422882
Web Site: http://www.soilbuild.com
Sales Range: $200-249.9 Million
Property Development Services
N.A.I.C.S.: 531311
Chap Huat Lim *(Founder & Chm)*

SOILTECH AS
Koppholen 25,, 4313, Sandnes, Norway

INTERNATIONAL PUBLIC

Tel.: (47) 48020555
Web Site: https://soiltech.no
STECH—(EUR)
Cleantech Service Provider
N.A.I.C.S.: 562211

Subsidiaries:

Oceanteam ASA (1)
Strandveien 15, 1366, Lysaker, Norway
Tel.: (47) 55108240
Web Site: https://www.oceanteam.nl
Rev.: $60,000
Assets: $2,877,000
Liabilities: $410,000
Net Worth: $2,467,000
Earnings: ($802,000)
Emp.: 3
Fiscal Year-end: 12/31/2023
Shipping & Offshore Construction Services
N.A.I.C.S.: 483111

Subsidiary (Non-US):

Oceanteam Mexico, S.A. de C.V. (2)
Calle 57 No 61 Entre 38 y 40 Col Miami, CP 24120, Ciudad del Carmen, Camp, Mexico
Tel.: (52) 1 938 3829246
Shipping & Offshore Construction Services
N.A.I.C.S.: 213112

SOITEC S.A.
Parc Technologique des Fontaines, Chemin des Franques, 38190, Bernin, France
Tel.: (33) 476927500
Web Site: https://www.soitec.com
SOI—(EUR)
Rev.: $733,933,584
Assets: $1,229,738,453
Liabilities: $552,086,511
Net Worth: $677,651,942
Earnings: $134,714,591
Emp.: 1,484
Fiscal Year-end: 03/31/20
Silicon-On-Insulator Wafer Mfr
N.A.I.C.S.: 334413
Paul Boudre *(CEO)*

Subsidiaries:

Dolphin Design SAS (1)
1bisA et 2A Chemin du Pre Carre, 38240, Meylan, France (80%)
Tel.: (33) 476411096
Web Site: https://www.dolphin-design.fr
Emp.: 160
Microelectronics Technology Product Engineering & Services
N.A.I.C.S.: 334413
Frederic Renoux *(Exec VP-Sls)*

Subsidiary (Non-US):

Dolphin Integration Inc. (2)
3080 boulevard Le Carrefour bureau 200, Laval, H7T 2R5, QC, Canada
Tel.: (450) 978-8885
Data Processing Services
N.A.I.C.S.: 518210

EpiGaN NV (1)
Kempische Steenweg 293, 3500, Hasselt, Belgium
Tel.: (32) 11566620
Web Site: https://www.epigan.com
Semiconductor Material Mfr
N.A.I.C.S.: 334413
Daniel Cuypers *(Mgr-Metrology)*

Frecnsys SAS (1)
18 rue Alain Savary, 25000, Besancon, France
Tel.: (33) 38 125 5363
Web Site: https://www.frecnsys.fr
Electrical & Electronic Product Mfr
N.A.I.C.S.: 334419
Sylvain Ballandras *(CEO)*

Soitec Japan Inc. (1)
9F Shin-Nisseki Building 3-4-2 Marunouchi, Chiyoda-ku, Tokyo, 100-0005, Japan
Tel.: (81) 5031522837
Semiconductor Mfr
N.A.I.C.S.: 334413

Soitec USA Inc. (1)

2 Centennial Dr, Peabody, MA 01960
Tel.: (978) 531-2222
Web Site: http://www.soitec.com
Sales Range: $25-49.9 Million
Emp.: 15
Mfr of Silicon-On-Insulator Wafers
N.A.I.C.S.: 334413

SOJITZ CORPORATION
1-1 Uchisaiwaicho 2-chome, Chiyoda-ku, Tokyo, 100-8691, Japan
Tel.: (81) 368715000   JP
Web Site: https://www.sojitz.com
Year Founded: 2003
2768—(TKS)
Rev.: $15,960,829,890
Assets: $19,082,230,530
Liabilities: $12,765,536,060
Net Worth: $6,316,694,470
Earnings: $666,056,650
Emp.: 23,296
Fiscal Year-end: 03/31/24
Trading & Business Development Services
N.A.I.C.S.: 423390
Shigeru Nishihara *(Chief Compliance Officer, Sr Mng Exec Officer & COO-Corp Plng)*

Subsidiaries:

Akita New Urban-Center Building Co., Ltd. (1)
4-1 Higashidori-Nakamachi, Akita, 010-8506, Japan
Tel.: (81) 188364290
Web Site: http://www.e-alve.com
Sales Range: $50-74.9 Million
Emp.: 6
Real Estate Management Services
N.A.I.C.S.: 531390
Hideya Moriyama *(CEO)*

American Biaxis Inc. (1)
100 Saulteaux Crescent, Winnipeg, R3J 3T3, MB, Canada
Tel.: (204) 837-0650
Plastic Materials Mfr
N.A.I.C.S.: 325211

Asia Cable Engineering Co., Pte. Ltd. (1)
623 Aljunied Rd 03 09, Aljunied Industrial Complex, Singapore, 389835, Singapore
Tel.: (65) 67413303
Web Site: http://www.sojitz-br.com
Sales Range: $700-749.9 Million
Emp.: 23
General Contractors
N.A.I.C.S.: 236220

Atlas Fertilizer Corporation (1)
2nd Floor Builders Center Building 170 Salcedo Street, Legaspi Village, Makati, 1229, Philippines
Tel.: (63) 28127881
Sales Range: $150-199.9 Million
Emp.: 400
Chemical Fertilizer Mfr & Distr
N.A.I.C.S.: 325314
Takashi Sumi *(Pres)*

Autrans (Thailand) Co., Ltd. (1)
75/31 Ocean Tower 2 Building 19 th Floor Soi Sukhumvit 19, Sukhumvit Road Klongtoeynua Wattana, Bangkok, 10110, Thailand
Tel.: (66) 2 661 7204
Web Site: https://www.autrans.biz
Emp.: 155
Logistic Services
N.A.I.C.S.: 541614

Autrans Corporation - Ingersoll Plant (1)
17 Underwood Rd, PO Box 1003, Ingersoll, N5C 3V6, ON, Canada
Tel.: (519) 425-0999
Automotive Assembling & Logistics Services
N.A.I.C.S.: 336110

Autrans De Venezuela, S.A. (1)
Av 1 Parcela 118 Zona Industrial Los Montones, Barcelona, Edo Anzoategui, Venezuela
Tel.: (58) 281 276 2288
Automotive Component Import & Distr
N.A.I.C.S.: 423120

Autrans India Private Limited (1)
Kubota Mini Excavator India Kubota Mini Excavator India, Chennai, 600032, Tamil Nadu, India
Tel.: (91) 8045388480
Web Site: http://www.kubotaminiexcavator.com
Two-Wheeled Vehicle Mfr
N.A.I.C.S.: 336211
V. R. Raj Kumar *(Head-Natl Sls)*

Biaxis Oy, Ltd. (1)
Teknikonkatu 2, 15520, Lahti, Finland
Tel.: (358) 2 051 0312
Web Site: https://www.biaxis.com
Plastic Materials Mfr
N.A.I.C.S.: 325211

Caltrax Inc. (1)
1805 - 30 Avenue SE, Calgary, T2G 4X8, AB, Canada
Tel.: (403) 234-0585
Web Site: https://www.caltrax.ca
Railcar Repair Services
N.A.I.C.S.: 488210

CoalinQ Corporation (1)
New Akasaka International Building West 4F 1-20 Akasaka 6-chome, Minato-ku, Tokyo, 107-8655, Japan
Tel.: (81) 335864122
Web Site: https://www.coalinq.com
Sales Range: $25-49.9 Million
Emp.: 10
Coal Trading & Information Retrieval Services
N.A.I.C.S.: 519290
Toshio Hosokawa *(Pres)*

Daiichibo Co., Ltd. (1)
1850 Masunaga, Arao, 864-0032, Kumamoto, Japan
Tel.: (81) 96 862 3520
Web Site: https://www.ichibo.co.jp
Emp.: 191
Textile Products Mfr
N.A.I.C.S.: 314999

Dalian Global Food Corporation (1)
IC-54 Free Trade Zone, Dalian, 116600, Liaoning, China   (90%)
Tel.: (86) 4118 730 0222
Web Site: https://www.xxmaguro.com
Sales Range: $25-49.9 Million
Emp.: 70
Tuna Fish Processing Services
N.A.I.C.S.: 114111
Toshiaki Miyabe *(Gen Mgr)*

Edotco Myanmar Limited (1)
Kanthayar Center - Office Tower 17th Floor - Unit 17-01-08, Corner of Kan Yeik Thar Road U Aung Myat Road Mingalar Taung Nyunt, Yangon, Myanmar
Tel.: (95) 9254376696
Telecommunication Tower Business Services
N.A.I.C.S.: 237130

FB Food Service (2017) Co., Ltd. (1)
37 Moo 1 Suksawad 43 Suksawad Rd Bangkru, Phrapradaeng, Samut Prakan, 10130, Thailand
Tel.: (66) 28193111
Web Site: https://www.fbfoodservice.com
Ready-To-Cook Product Mfr & Distr
N.A.I.C.S.: 311412

Filteren Co., Ltd. (1)
7-8 Sasamekitacho, Toda, 335-0033, Saitama, Japan
Tel.: (81) 48 449 8471
Web Site: https://www.filteren.co.jp
Sintered Plastic Filter Mfr & Distr
N.A.I.C.S.: 326199

Fuji Machine Asia Pte. Ltd. (1)
51 Ubi Avenue 1 01-24, Paya Ubi Industrial Park, Singapore, 408933, Singapore
Tel.: (65) 6 746 4966
Web Site: https://www.fma-smt.com
Emp.: 176
Machine & Peripheral Equipment Mfr
N.A.I.C.S.: 334118
Jun Sasaki *(Gen Mgr)*

Fuji Machine Mfg. (Singapore) Pte. Ltd. (1)
Blk 2/51 Ubi Ave 1 01-24 Paya Ubi Industrial Park, Singapore, 408933, Singapore
Tel.: (65) 67464966
Web Site: http://www.fujiamerica.com
Sales Range: $25-49.9 Million
Emp.: 20
Industrial Electronic Machinery Distr
N.A.I.C.S.: 423830
Tatsuyuki Shimizu *(Mng Dir)*

Fuji Nihon Seito Co., Ltd. (1)
1-4-10 Seikai, Shimizu-ku, Shizuoka, 424-0924, Japan   (100%)
Tel.: (81) 54 334 5353
Web Site: https://www.fnsugar.co.jp
Sales Range: $1-9.9 Million
Emp.: 100
Mfr of Refined Sugar, Liquid Sugar, Food Additives, Syrup, Inulin & Various Food Materials
N.A.I.C.S.: 311314

Hanshin Silo Co., Ltd. (1)
14-7 Uozakihamamachi, Higashinada-ku, Kobe, 658-0024, Hyogo, Japan
Tel.: (81) 78 451 1671
Web Site: https://www.hanshin-silo.co.jp
Grain Warehousing Services
N.A.I.C.S.: 493130

Hokko Chemical Co., Ltd. (1)
2-181 Umemachi, Konohana-ku, Osaka, 554-0032, Japan
Tel.: (81) 66 468 8453
Web Site: https://www.hokkou-kagaku.com
Emp.: 57
Manufacture, Processing & Sales of Paint & Ink Thinners
N.A.I.C.S.: 325510

Howa Machinery Singapore Pte. Ltd. (1)
37 Lorong 23 Geylang 01-01A Yu Li Industrial Building, Singapore, 388371, Singapore
Tel.: (65) 68424550
Web Site: http://www.howa-singapore.com
Industrial Machinery Repair Service & Distr
N.A.I.C.S.: 811310

Hyundai Motor (Thailand) Co., Ltd. (1)
92 Vibhavadi Rangsit Road, Talat Bang Khen Subdistrict Lak Si District, Bangkok, 10210, Thailand
Tel.: (66) 2 089 1888
Web Site: https://www.hyundai.co.th
New Car Dealers
N.A.I.C.S.: 441110

Hyundai Motor Argentina S.A. (1)
Panamericana 3611 1636, Olivos, Buenos Aires, Argentina
Tel.: (54) 113 220 3220
Web Site: https://www.hyundai.com.ar
New Car Dealers
N.A.I.C.S.: 441110

Hyundai Nishat Motor (Private) Limited (1)
1-B Aziz Avenue Canal Bank Road, Gulberg-V, Lahore, Pakistan
Tel.: (92) 4211 111 1466
Web Site: https://www.hyundai-nishat.com
New Car Dealers
N.A.I.C.S.: 441110

Hyundai de Puerto Rico (1)
101 Ave Conquistadores, Catano, PR 00962
Tel.: (787) 625-1010
Web Site: http://www.hyundaipr.com
Emp.: 60
Automotive Distr
N.A.I.C.S.: 423110

Import Motors II, Inc. (1)
1300 Concord Ave, Concord, CA 94520
Web Site: https://www.audiconcord.com
New Car Dealers
N.A.I.C.S.: 441110
Eddie Martz *(Gen Sls Mgr)*

Interflour Vietnam Ltd. (1)
11th Floor SFC Building 9 Dinh Tien Hoang, Da Kao District 1, Ho Chi Minh City, Vietnam
Tel.: (84) 2838205525
Flour Product Distr
N.A.I.C.S.: 424490

JACCS Finance Philippines Corporation (1)
38th Floor Robinsons Equitable Tower ADB Avenue corner Poveda Street, Ortigas Center, Pasig, Philippines
Tel.: (63) 286881253
Web Site: https://www.jaccs.com.ph
Financial Services
N.A.I.C.S.: 522220

JALUX Inc. (1)
Shinagawa Season Terrace 1-2-70 Konan, Minato-ku, Tokyo, 108-8209, Japan
Tel.: (81) 354607200
Web Site: http://www.jalux.com
Rev.: $327,274,234
Assets: $374,957,939
Liabilities: $200,681,467
Net Worth: $174,276,472
Earnings: ($4,116,519)
Emp.: 1,905
Fiscal Year-end: 03/31/2022
Holding Company; Aviation Industry Support, Insurance, Real Estate, Facility Support, Retail Store Operation, Food & Beverage Distribution Services
N.A.I.C.S.: 551112
Shigeki Yamazaki *(Exec Officer & Pres-Food & Beverage Unit)*

Subsidiary (Non-US):

J Value Co., Ltd. (2)
87 Soi Akapat Thonglor 13 Sukhumvit 55 Road, Klongtan-Nua Wattana, Bangkok, 10110, Thailand
Tel.: (66) 20592616
Web Site: https://www.jvalue.co.th
Emp.: 25
Food Product Whslr
N.A.I.C.S.: 424490
Haruo Endo *(Pres)*

Subsidiary (Domestic):

JAL-DFS Co., Ltd. (2)
Morita Bldg 5F 959 Hanazakicho, Chiba, 286-0033, Japan
Tel.: (81) 476228571
Web Site: http://www.jaldfs.co.jp
Sales Range: $50-74.9 Million
Emp.: 153
Duty Free Sales Services
N.A.I.C.S.: 455219
Seiji Nakamura *(CEO)*

Subsidiary (Non-US):

JALUX ASIA Ltd. (2)
159/14 Serm-Mit Tower 9th Floor Room 915 Sukhumvit 21 Asoke Road, North Klongtoey Wattana, Bangkok, 10110, Thailand
Tel.: (66) 225865313
Web Site: http://www.as.jalux.com
Sales Range: $25-49.9 Million
Emp.: 50
Processed Foodstuffs Distr
N.A.I.C.S.: 424420
Taichi Saito *(Pres)*

Subsidiary (Domestic):

JALUX Airport Inc. (2)
3 3 2 Haneda Airport, Terminal 5F Ota-Ku, Tokyo, Japan
Tel.: (81) 357569110
Web Site: http://www.jalux.com
Sales Range: $250-299.9 Million
Emp.: 1,000
Airport Shop Management Services
N.A.I.C.S.: 459420

Subsidiary (US):

JALUX Americas, Inc. (2)
390 Sepulveda Blvd Ste 3000, El Segundo, CA 90245
Tel.: (310) 524-1000
Sales Range: $50-74.9 Million
Emp.: 75
Aircraft Parts, Food, Wine & General Merchandise Distribution Services
N.A.I.C.S.: 423990

Subsidiary (Non-US):

JALUX Europe Ltd. (2)
Mimosa House, 12 Princes St, London, W1B 2LL, United Kingdom
Tel.: (44) 2074081020
Sales Range: $25-49.9 Million
Emp.: 10
Airport Shop Management Services

SOJITZ CORPORATION

Sojitz Corporation—(Continued)
N.A.I.C.S.: 488119

Subsidiary (Domestic):

JALUX Fresh Foods, Inc. (2)
2-3-1 Higashigotanda Sompo Japan Gotanda Joint Building, Shinagawa-ku, Tokyo, 141-0022, Japan
Tel.: (81) 363678837
Web Site: http://www.jaluxff.com
Emp.: 25
Fruit & Vegetable Distr
N.A.I.C.S.: 445230

Subsidiary (Non-US):

JALUX HONG KONG Co., Ltd. (2)
1908 19/F Miramar Tower 132 Nathan Road, Harbour City, Tsim Tsa Tsui, Kowloon, China (Hong Kong)
Tel.: (852) 2827 0163
Web Site: http://www.hk.jalux.com
Airline Cabin Service Items & Meals Supplier
N.A.I.C.S.: 722310

JALUX Inc.
Davidson House Forbury Square, Reading, RG1 3EU, Berkshire, United Kingdom
Tel.: (44) 1189000983
Airport Business Development Services
N.A.I.C.S.: 488119

Subsidiary (Domestic):

JALUX Insurance & Service Inc. (2)
2-5-5 Higashi-Shinagawa Harbor One Building 6F, Shinagawa-ku, Tokyo, Japan
Tel.: (81) 120258400
Web Site: http://www.jaluxhs.com
Life Insurance Agency Services
N.A.I.C.S.: 524210

Subsidiary (Non-US):

JALUX SHANGHAI Co., Ltd. (2)
Room 702 Huaihai Plaza No 1045 Huaihai Zhong Rd, Shanghai, 200031, China
Tel.: (86) 2134060663
Web Site: http://www.sh.jalux.com
Sales Range: $25-49.9 Million
Emp.: 30
Food & Beverage Whslr
N.A.I.C.S.: 424490
Hidekazu Nagai (CEO)

Subsidiary (Domestic):

JALUX Style Inc. (2)
Next Site Kamata Building 4F 1-2-5 Kamatahoncho, Ota-ku, Tokyo, 144-0053, Japan
Tel.: (81) 337305661
Web Site: http://www.jaluxstyle.com
Leather Goods Mfr & Distr
N.A.I.C.S.: 316990
Naoto Yokoyama (Mgr-Product Dev)

Subsidiary (Non-US):

JRE Development Co., Ltd. (2)
159 Serm-Mit Tower 9th Floor Room 915 Sukhumvit 21 Road, North Klongtoey Wattana, Bangkok, 10110, Thailand
Tel.: (66) 22586530
Web Site: http://jre.jalux.com
Apartment Development Services
N.A.I.C.S.: 531110

Jalux Singapore Pte. Ltd. (2)
1 Fullerton Road 02-01 One Fullerton, Singapore, 049213, Singapore
Tel.: (65) 68325102
Web Site: https://www.sg.jalux.com
Asset Management Services
N.A.I.C.S.: 523940
Hidebumi Mori (Pres)

Subsidiary (Domestic):

Japan Airport Delica Inc. (2)
1-8-2 Haneda Airport, Ota-ku, Tokyo, 144-0041, Japan
Tel.: (81) 357087790
Web Site: http://www.airdeli.co.jp
Food Products Mfr
N.A.I.C.S.: 311999

JAMPT Corporation (1)
3-8 Ipponyanagi, Yawata, Tagajo, 985-0874, Miyagi, Japan
Tel.: (81) 22 290 0630
Web Site: https://www.jampt.jp
3D Printed Metal Services
N.A.I.C.S.: 323111
Ryota Kusaka (Pres & CEO)

Japan Alumina Associates (Australia) Pty. Ltd. (1)
Level 16 37 St George Tr, PO Box 3085, Perth, 6000, WA, Australia (50%)
Tel.: (61) 892213877
Sales Range: $150-199.9 Million
Emp.: 4
Miner of Bauxite & Alumina
N.A.I.C.S.: 331313

Japan Best Foods Co., Ltd. (1)
Long Duc, Dong Nai, Vietnam
Tel.: (84) 251 368 1298
Web Site: https://www.japanbestfoods.com
Food Products Mfr
N.A.I.C.S.: 311991

Japan Facility Solutions, Inc. (1)
17th floor Shin-Osaki Kogyo Building 1-6-4 Osaki, Shinagawa-ku, Tokyo, 141-0032, Japan
Tel.: (81) 363712500
Web Site: http://www.j-facility.com
Sales Range: $25-49.9 Million
Emp.: 200
Facilities Environmental Management Consulting Services
N.A.I.C.S.: 541620

Japan Vietnam Fertilizer Company (1)
9th floor Zen Plaza Building 54-56 Nguyen Trai Street, District 1, Ho Chi Minh City, Vietnam
Tel.: (84) 286 290 5069
Web Site: https://www.jvf.com.vn
Fertilizer Mfr & Distr
N.A.I.C.S.: 325314

Plant (Domestic):

Japan Vietnam Fertilizer Company - Dong Nai Factory (2)
Go Dau Industrial Park, Dist Long Thanh, Ho Chi Minh City, Dong Nai, Vietnam
Tel.: (84) 613 841149
Fertilizer Mfr
N.A.I.C.S.: 325314

Japcon Inc. (1)
673 Urayasuminamimachi, Minami-ku, Okayama, 702-8024, Japan
Tel.: (81) 862655111
Web Site: https://www.japcon.co.jp
Aircraft Management Services
N.A.I.C.S.: 488190

Kyodo Sojitz Feed Company Limited (1)
Lot F5-F6-F7-F8,Thinh Phat Industrial Park, Luong Binh Commune, Ben Luc, Long An, Vietnam
Tel.: (84) 272 363 8383
Web Site: https://www.ksf.com.vn
Animal Feed Mfr
N.A.I.C.S.: 311119

Kyowa Synchro Technology Europe S.A.S. (1)
23 Rue de la Paix, 75002, Paris, France
Tel.: (33) 1 58 5617 15
Emp.: 3
Transmission Synchronizers Distr
N.A.I.C.S.: 423830
Koji Okumura (Pres)

Marin Sunwise Motors, Inc. (1)
595 Francisco Blvd E, San Rafael, CA 94901
Tel.: (628) 600-0579
Web Site: https://www.marinsubaru.net
Automotive Distr
N.A.I.C.S.: 423110

Meat One Corporation (1)
16F Roppongi T-Cube 3-1-1, Roppongi Minato-ku, Tokyo, 106-0032, Japan
Tel.: (81) 355743600
Meat Product Whslr
N.A.I.C.S.: 424520

Metal One Corporation (1)
(40%)
Web Site: http://www.mtlo.co.jp
Sales Range: $200-249.9 Million
Emp.: 103
Iron & Steel Products Mfr & Whslr
N.A.I.C.S.: 331110
Daiju Mita (Exec Officer)

Subsidiary (US):

Alloy Tool Steel, Inc. (2)
13525 E Freeway Dr, Santa Fe Springs, CA 90670-5686
Tel.: (562) 921-8605
Web Site: https://www.alloytoolsteel.com
Sales Range: $25-49.9 Million
Emp.: 20
Mfr of Ferroalloy Tools
N.A.I.C.S.: 423510
Tetsu Watanabe (Pres & CEO)

Subsidiary (Domestic):

M.O.TEC Corporation (1)
Mita Kokusai Building 1-4-28 Mita, Minato-ku, Tokyo, 104-0032, Japan
Tel.: (81) 354457800
Web Site: http://www.motec-co.jp
Sales Range: $350-399.9 Million
Emp.: 290
Sale, Leasing, Processing, Construction & Transportation of Construction Scaffolding Materials
N.A.I.C.S.: 423390

Subsidiary (US):

Maruichi American Corp. (2)
11529 Greenstone Ave, Santa Fe Springs, CA 90670
Tel.: (562) 903-8600
Sales Range: $25-49.9 Million
Emp.: 85
Mfr of Steel Pipe
N.A.I.C.S.: 331210
Shelly Morita (Pres)

Plateplus, Inc. (1)
21 Waterway Ave Ste 525, The Woodlands, TX 77380-3129 (100%)
Tel.: (281) 298-0320
Web Site: https://www.plateplus.com
Hot-Rolled Coil, Sheet & Plate Steel Products Mfr & Whslr
N.A.I.C.S.: 332999
James Ralston (Pres & CEO)

Plant (Domestic):

Plateplus, Inc. - Houston (3)
8807 Liberty Rd, Houston, TX 77028-5730
Tel.: (713) 672-4200
Web Site: https://www.plateplus.com
Emp.: 50
Hot-Rolled Coil, Sheet & Plate Steel Products Mfr & Whslr
N.A.I.C.S.: 423510

Subsidiary (Domestic):

Stainless One Corporation (2)
9F NMF Kanda Iwamotocho Building 3-8-16 Iwamotocho, Chiyoda-ku, Tokyo, 101-0032, Japan
Tel.: (81) 3 5833 9671
Web Site: http://www.stnls1.co.jp
Emp.: 58
Stainless Steel Products Distr
N.A.I.C.S.: 423510
Jyun Takao (Pres)

Metalart Corporation (1)
3-2-18 Noji, Kusatsu, 525-0059, Shiga, Japan (100%)
Tel.: (81) 77 563 2111
Web Site: https://www.metalart.co.jp
Sales Range: $50-74.9 Million
Emp.: 1,041
Mfr of Iron & Steel Forging
N.A.I.C.S.: 332111

Mill Valley Motors, Inc. (1)
1599 East Francisco Blvd, San Rafael, CA 94901
Tel.: (415) 549-9147
Web Site: https://www.bmwofsanrafael.com
New Car Dealers
N.A.I.C.S.: 441110

Ministop Vietnam Company Limited (1)
215 Dien Bien Phu, Ward 15 Binh Thanh, Ho Chi Minh City, Vietnam
Tel.: (84) 2835106870
Web Site: https://www.ministop.vn
Convenience Store Retailer
N.A.I.C.S.: 423210

My Vegetable Corporation (1)
1296-6 Toke-cho, Midori-ku, Chiba, 267-0061, Japan
Tel.: (81) 43 310 6937
Web Site: https://www.my-vegetable.com
Fresh Vegetable & Fruit Distr
N.A.I.C.S.: 445230

NI Chemical Corporation (1)
231 Shinminato, Mihama-ku, Chiba, 261-0002, Japan (100%)
Tel.: (81) 43 242 6471
Web Site: https://www.ni-chemical.co.jp
Chemical Tank Warehousing & Import/Export Shipping Services
N.A.I.C.S.: 493190

NMTronics India Pvt. Ltd. (1)
SDF NO E-17 and C-2 Noida Dadri Road Phase-II, Noida Special Economic Zone, Noida, 201 305, Uttar Pradesh, India
Tel.: (91) 120 460 3500
Web Site: https://www.nmtronics.com
Sales Range: $50-74.9 Million
Emp.: 100
Industrial Electronic Machinery Mfr
N.A.I.C.S.: 333248
Ravinder Bhardwa (Head-Bus & Gen Mgr)

Newland Vietnam Japan Joint Stock Company (1)
Lot A2 A3 Road No 1 Road No 6, Binh An Textiles Industrial Park Binh Thang Ward Di An Hamlet, Binh Dong, Vietnam
Tel.: (84) 274 373 9500
Web Site: https://www.newlandvj.com
Emp.: 256
Logistic Services
N.A.I.C.S.: 541614

Nichipac Co., Ltd. (1)
10 Ogawa, Machida, 194-0003, Tokyo, Japan
Tel.: (81) 427952511
Web Site: https://www.nichipac.com
Plastic Products Mfr & Distr
N.A.I.C.S.: 326199

Nihon Seiko Co. Ltd. (1)
3-2 Shimomiyabi-cho, Shinjuku-ku, Tokyo, 162-0822, Japan (13%)
Tel.: (81) 332350021
Web Site: http://www.nihonseiko.co.jp
Rev.: $103,043,290
Assets: $104,927,140
Liabilities: $40,803,530
Net Worth: $64,123,610
Earnings: $3,318,220
Fiscal Year-end: 03/31/2024
Mfr of Antimony Products
N.A.I.C.S.: 331410
Tamio Okada (Auditor)

Nippon Premium Bakery Inc. (1)
Unit 304 - 307 La Fuerza Plaza 2 2241 Chino Roces Avenue, Makati, Philippines
Tel.: (63) 28 403 4447
Web Site: https://www.fuwafuwa.com.ph
Bread Mfr
N.A.I.C.S.: 311811

Nissho Electronics Corporation (1)
3-5 Nibancho, Chiyoda-ku, Tokyo, 102-0084, Japan
Tel.: (81) 362725011
Web Site: https://www.nissho-ele.co.jp
Rev.: $351,470,400
Assets: $420,707,760
Liabilities: $162,060,000
Net Worth: $258,647,760
Earnings: $3,454,320
Emp.: 1,059
Fiscal Year-end: 03/31/2018
Information Technology Solutions & Services
N.A.I.C.S.: 541512
Toshiaki Kibe (Mng Exec Officer)

Subsidiary (Domestic):

AXISSOFT Corporation (2)
Davinci Higashi-Ikebukuro Bldg 3-23-5 Higashi-Ikebukuro, Toshima-ku, Tokyo, 170-0013, Japan
Tel.: (81) 359503521
Web Site: http://www.axissoft.co.jp

AND PRIVATE COMPANIES   SOJITZ CORPORATION

Sales Range: $25-49.9 Million
Emp.: 73
Database & Website Product Development & Support Services
N.A.I.C.S.: 541519

IPCity Corporation (2)
1-7-12 Shinonome, Koto-ku, Tokyo, 135-0062, Japan (100%)
Tel.: (81) 363662222
Web Site: http://www.ipcity.co.jp
Business Process Management Outsourcing Services
N.A.I.C.S.: 561499

NGC Corporation (2)
1-7-12 Shinonome KDX Toyosu Grand Square 8th floor, Koto-ku, Tokyo, 135-0062, Japan
Tel.: (81) 36 380 8141
Web Site: https://www.ngc.co.jp
Sales Range: $10-24.9 Million
Emp.: 58
Broadcast Computer Visualization & Digital Imaging Services
N.A.I.C.S.: 541519

Subsidiary (Non-US):

Nissho Electronics (Asia) Co., Ltd. (2)
16F Harbour Centre 25 Harbour Road, Wanchai, China (Hong Kong)
Tel.: (852) 28792701
Web Site: http://www.nelco-asia.com
Information Technology Support & Data Processing Outsourcing Services
N.A.I.C.S.: 541519

Nissho Iwai Cement Corporation (1)
Tam Bldg 2F 4-9 Nishi-shinbashi 1-chome, Minato-ku, Tokyo, 105-0003, Japan
Tel.: (81) 3 5532 0781
Web Site: http://www.nicement.com
Rev: $229,463,280
Emp.: 31
Ready Mix Concrete Distr
N.A.I.C.S.: 423320

Nissho Iwai Paper & Pulp Corporation (1)
1-11-30 Akasaka 11F Akasaka 1-chome Center Building, Minato-ku, Tokyo, 107-0052, Japan
Tel.: (81) 36 234 6350
Web Site: https://www.nipap.co.jp
Emp.: 98
Printing & Writing Paper Whslr
N.A.I.C.S.: 424110
Shinichi Matsuo *(CEO)*

Nissho Propane Sekiyu Corp. (1)
Sapporo Tokeida Building 5th Floor 1 Kita Nijo Nishi 2 Chome, Chuo Ku, Sapporo, 060 302, Hokkaido, Japan (100%)
Tel.: (81) 112815261
Web Site: http://www.nipg.co.jp
Rev: $120,000,000
Emp.: 150
LPG & Petroleum Products Sales
N.A.I.C.S.: 424720

Okayama Air Service Co., Ltd. (1)
673 Urayasuminamimachi, Minami-ku, Okayama, 702-8024, Japan
Tel.: (81) 862611111
Web Site: https://www.air-oas.co.jp
Emp.: 76
Aircraft Maintenance Services
N.A.I.C.S.: 488190

PT. Kaltim Methanol Industri (1)
Wisma KIE 1st Floor Jl Paku Aji, Kawasan Industri Pupuk Kaltim, Bontang, 75313, Kalimantan Timur, Indonesia
Tel.: (62) 5 484 1394
Web Site: https://www.kaltimmethanol.com
Chemical & Allied Product Mfr & Distr
N.A.I.C.S.: 325194

PT. Sojitz Indonesia (1)
Treasury Tower 35th Floor SCBD Lot 28 Jl Jend Sudirman Kav 52-53, District 8, Jakarta, 12190, Indonesia (72%)
Tel.: (62) 215 086 1000
Web Site: https://www.sojitz.com
Sales Range: $50-74.9 Million
Emp.: 100
Weaving, Knitting, Dyeing of Synthetic Fiber
N.A.I.C.S.: 313210

Phenix Jet Hong Kong, Ltd. (1)
Room 701-702 The Phoenix 23 Luard Road, Wanchai, China (Hong Kong)
Tel.: (852) 81924538
Aviation Services
N.A.I.C.S.: 488190

Phenix Jet International, LLC (1)
222 E Chalan Santo Papa Ste 201, Hagatna, GU 96910
Tel.: (671) 989-4534
Web Site: https://www.phenixjet.com
Aviation Services
N.A.I.C.S.: 488190

SOFCO Seafoods Inc. (1)
3F Akasaka 2 14 Plaza Bldg 2-14-32 Akasaka, Minato-ku, Tokyo, 107-0052, Japan
Tel.: (81) 355752271
Processed Sea Food Mfr & Distr
N.A.I.C.S.: 311710

Saigon Paper Corporation (1)
My Xuan A Industrial Zone, My Xuan Ward, Phu My, Ba Ria - Vung Tau, Vietnam
Tel.: (84) 25 489 9338
Web Site: https://www.saigonpaper.com
Household Paper Products Mfr
N.A.I.C.S.: 322299
Hiroto Murai *(Chm)*

Sendzimir Japan, Ltd. (1)
Sendzimir Japan Bldg 2-10-14, Higashi Kanda Chiyoda Ward, Tokyo, 101-0031, Japan
Tel.: (81) 33 861 1541
Web Site: https://www.sendzimir.co.jp
Emp.: 20
Industrial Machinery & Equipment Services
N.A.I.C.S.: 811310
Thaddeus M. Sendzimir *(Chm)*

Shaoxing Asahi Bearing Co., Ltd. (1)
77 Pingjiang Lu, Economic Development Zone, Shaoxing, Zhejiang, China
Tel.: (86) 57588651172
Emp.: 345
Lathing Ring Mfr
N.A.I.C.S.: 339910
Qinggui Huang *(Gen Mgr)*

Socafi, S.A. de C.V (1)
Calle 2 de Abril Num 60, Col Actipan Alc Benito Juarez, 03230, Mexico, Mexico
Tel.: (52) 555 200 2639
Web Site: https://www.afasa.com.mx
Automobile Self-Financing Services
N.A.I.C.S.: 522220

Sojitz (China) Co., Ltd. (1)
8th Floor Office Building Tower H Phoenix Landmark Plaza, No 5 Shuguang Xilijia Chaoyang District, Beijing, 100028, China
Tel.: (86) 105 732 2500
Web Site: https://www.sojitz.cn
International Trade & Development Services
N.A.I.C.S.: 522299

Sojitz (Dalian) Co., Ltd. (1)
7th Floor Senmao Building No 147 Zhongshan Road, Xigang District, Dalian, 116011, Liaoning, China
Tel.: (86) 41183601177
International Trade & Development Services
N.A.I.C.S.: 522299

Sojitz (Guangzhou) Co., Ltd. (1)
Room 1807A Goldlion Digital Network Building No 138 Tiyu East Road, Tianhe District, Guangzhou, 116011, Guangdong, China
Tel.: (86) 2038781206
International Trade & Development Services
N.A.I.C.S.: 522299

Sojitz (Hong Kong) Limited (1)
16F Canadia Centre 25 Harbour Road, Wanchai, China (Hong Kong) (100%)
Tel.: (852) 2 844 1811
Web Site: http://www.sojitz.co.jp
Sales Range: $50-74.9 Million
Emp.: 40
General Trading Company
N.A.I.C.S.: 523160

Sojitz (Malaysia) Sdn. Bhd. (1)
Level 23 Menara IMC No 8 Jalan Sultan Ismail, 50250, Kuala Lumpur, Malaysia
Tel.: (60) 320319989
International Trade & Development Services
N.A.I.C.S.: 522299

Sojitz (Shanghai) Co., Ltd. (1)
7th Floor Tower 1 Kerry Enterprise Centre No 128 West Tianmu Road, Jing An District, Shanghai, 200070, China
Tel.: (86) 2152034111
Web Site: http://www.sojitz.com
Sales Range: $75-99.9 Million
Emp.: 130
Provider of Wholesale Chemicals
N.A.I.C.S.: 424690

Sojitz (Thailand) Co., Ltd. (1)
19th Floor Q House Lumpini Building 1 South Sathorn Road Tungmahamek, Sathorn, Bangkok, 10120, Thailand
Tel.: (66) 22279200
International Trade & Development Services
N.A.I.C.S.: 522299

Sojitz Aerospace Corporation (1)
4th Floor Marunouchi Trust Tower Main 8-3 Marunouchi 1-chome, Chiyoda-ku, Tokyo, 100-0005, Japan
Tel.: (81) 36 870 7000
Web Site: https://www.sojitz-aero.com
Military Aerospace, Marine & Land Equipment Wholesale Trade Distr
N.A.I.C.S.: 425120
Mikio Takeuchi *(Chm)*

Subsidiary (US):

Sojitz Aerospace America Corporation (2)
1120 Avenue of the Americas 7th Fl, New York, NY 10036-8880
Tel.: (212) 704-6915
Web Site: https://www.sojitz-aero.com
Military Aerospace, Marine & Land Equipment Wholesale Trade Distr
N.A.I.C.S.: 425120

Sojitz Agro Corporation (1)
Room 2011 A-Nam Tower Bldg 702-10 Yoksam-1-Dong, Kangnam-Ku, Seoul, 135-513, Korea (South)
Tel.: (82) 2 2009 2071
Agricultural Chemical Products Distr
N.A.I.C.S.: 424690

Sojitz Aircraft Leasing B.V. (1)
World Trace Center Tower C Strawinskylaan 1241, 1077 XX, Amsterdam, Netherlands
Tel.: (31) 20 575 2360
Sales Range: $50-74.9 Million
Emp.: 4
Aircraft Leasing Services
N.A.I.C.S.: 532411
Haruyasu Fukuda *(Mng Dir)*

Sojitz Argentina S.A (1)
Av Corrientes 345 Piso 5, C1043AAD, Buenos Aires, Argentina
Tel.: (54) 1143132479
International Trade & Development Services
N.A.I.C.S.: 522299

Sojitz Asia Pte. Ltd. (1)
1 Wallich Street 24-01/02 Guoco Tower, Singapore, 078881, Singapore
Tel.: (65) 6 438 2566
Web Site: https://www.sojitz.com
Sales Range: $25-49.9 Million
Emp.: 80
Mfr of Steel Pipe
N.A.I.C.S.: 331210

Sojitz Asia Pte. Ltd. (1)
7th Floor I-K Tower Plot Cen A-2 North Avenue Gulshan-2, Dhaka, 1212, Bangladesh
Tel.: (880) 29851225
International Trade & Development Services
N.A.I.C.S.: 522299

Sojitz Asia Pte. Ltd. (1)
22F Canadia Tower 315 Monivong Street, Phnom Penh, Cambodia
Tel.: (855) 23991747
International Trade & Development Services
N.A.I.C.S.: 522299

Sojitz Australia Limited (1)
Level 11 115 Pitt Street, Sydney, 2000, NSW, Australia
Tel.: (61) 29 234 0811
Web Site: https://www.sojitz.com
Sales Range: $25-49.9 Million
Emp.: 20
Trading Office for Metals, Machinery & General Goods

N.A.I.C.S.: 423510
Hidetoshi Soga *(Mng Dir)*

Sojitz Australia Ltd. (1)
Level 4 PwC Haus Harbour City Section 44, Allotment 34 Granville Konedobu NCD, Port Moresby, Papua New Guinea
Tel.: (675) 3201091
International Trade & Development Services
N.A.I.C.S.: 522299

Sojitz Auto Group Osaka Co., Ltd. (1)
7-20-1 Fukushima KM Nishi Umeda Building 13th floor, Fukushima-ku, Osaka, 553-0003, Japan
Tel.: (81) 66 451 5888
Web Site: https://www.osaka.bmw.jp
New Car Dealers
N.A.I.C.S.: 441110

Sojitz Auto Group Tokyo Co., Ltd. (1)
2-12-10 Nihonbashi Kayabacho, Chuo-ku, Tokyo, 103-0025, Japan
Tel.: (81) 120269437
Web Site: https://sojitz-tokyo.bmw.jp
Emp.: 103
Automotive Distr
N.A.I.C.S.: 423110

Sojitz Automotive & Engineering, Inc. (1)
Kokusai Shin-Akasaka Bldg East Wing 6Fl 14-27 Akasaka 2-Chome, Minato-ku, Tokyo, 107-8655, Japan
Tel.: (81) 3 5520 3105
Web Site: http://www.sojitz-auto.com
Sales Range: $50-74.9 Million
Emp.: 60
Automotive Part Whslr
N.A.I.C.S.: 423120
Hiroaki Koike *(Pres & CEO)*

Sojitz Autrans Corporation (1)
1-1 Uchisaiwaicho 2-chome, Chiyoda-ku, Tokyo, 100-8691, Japan
Tel.: (81) 368713105
Web Site: http://www.sojitz-autrans.com
Emp.: 120
Automotive Part Whslr
N.A.I.C.S.: 423110
Masazumi Konishi *(Pres & CEO)*

Sojitz Beralt Tin & Wolfram (Portugal) S.A. (1)
Aldeia de S Francisco de Assis, Barroca Grande, Covilha, 6225-051, Portugal
Tel.: (351) 275 659 101
Emp.: 324
Tungsten Mining Services
N.A.I.C.S.: 213114
Manuel Pacheco *(Dir-Tech)*

Sojitz Building Materials Corporation (1)
Tokyo Sankei Building21F 1-7-2 Otemachi, Chiyoda-ku, Tokyo, 100-0004, Japan
Tel.: (81) 36 870 7800
Web Site: https://www.sojitz-bm.com
Sales Range: $150-199.9 Million
Emp.: 325
Building Materials Distr
N.A.I.C.S.: 423320
Tetsuya Onishi *(Pres)*

Sojitz Canada Corporation (1)
Suite 1610 1066 West Hastings Street, Vancouver, V6E 3X2, BC, Canada (100%)
Tel.: (604) 684-8351
Sales Range: $25-49.9 Million
Emp.: 15
Provider of Wholesale Goods
N.A.I.C.S.: 424990
Mitsuru Ishikawa *(Gen Mgr)*

Sojitz Coal Resources Pty. Ltd. (1)
L 34 345 Queen St, Brisbane, 4000, QLD, Australia
Tel.: (61) 732295577
Coal Mining Services
N.A.I.C.S.: 213113

Sojitz Commerce Development Corporation (1)
7th Floor of Daiwa Ginza Building 6-2-1 Ginza, Chuo-ku, Tokyo, 104-0061, Japan
Tel.: (81) 34 213 7330
Web Site: https://www.sojitz-sc.com
Emp.: 91

SOJITZ CORPORATION

INTERNATIONAL PUBLIC

Sojitz Corporation—(Continued)
Shopping Center Leasing & Management Services
N.A.I.C.S.: 531120

Sojitz Corporation Iran Ltd. (1)
5th Floor No 82 Shahid Soltani St Valiasr Ave, Tehran, 19677 13961, Iran
Tel.: (98) 212 620 1764
Web Site: https://www.sojitz.com
Sales Range: $25-49.9 Million
Emp.: 8
General Trading Company
N.A.I.C.S.: 425120

Sojitz Corporation of America (1)
1120 Avenue of the Americas 7FL, New York, NY 10036 **(100%)**
Tel.: (212) 704-6500
Web Site: https://sojitzamericas.com
Sales Range: $75-99.9 Million
Emp.: 18,000
Trading Company in Industrial Machinery, Metals, Grain, Frozen Foods, Electronics, Textiles, Petroleum, Chemicals, Automotives
N.A.I.C.S.: 423690
Shinchi Teranishi (CEO)

Subsidiary (Non-US):

Cymetech Corporation (2)
Tel.: (270) 395-3823
Web Site: https://www.cymetech.com
Chemical Products Mfr & Distr
N.A.I.C.S.: 325998
B. J. Melvin (Mgr-Customer Svc)

Subsidiary (Domestic):

Metton America, Inc. (2)
2727 Miller Cut-Off Rd, La Porte, TX 77571
Tel.: (281) 479-8078
Web Site: https://www.metton.com
Plastic Resin Mfr & Distr
N.A.I.C.S.: 325211

NIFAST Corporation (2)
815 Carol Ct, Carol Stream, IL 60188
Tel.: (630) 539-0097
Sales Range: $50-74.9 Million
Emp.: 25
Provider of Fasteners & Cold Heading Quality Wire for the Fastener Industry
N.A.I.C.S.: 423840
Bob Meifert (Controller)

Sojitz Energy Venture, Inc. (2)
2000 W Sam Houston Pkwy S Ste 1450, Houston, TX 77042
Tel.: (713) 963-9101
Web Site: http://www.sojitz-ev.com
Sales Range: $50-74.9 Million
Emp.: 9
Oil & Gas Exploration Services
N.A.I.C.S.: 213112

Sojitz Plastics America Inc. (2)
1051 Perimeter Dr Ste 460, Schaumburg, IL 60173
Tel.: (847) 956-7320
Web Site: http://www.sojitz-plastics.com
Emp.: 6
Packaging Plastic Products Mfr & Distr
N.A.I.C.S.: 322220

Stratosphere Quality, LLC (2)
12024 Exit 5 Pkwy, Fishers, IN 46037 **(65%)**
Tel.: (317) 578-1455
Web Site: http://www.stratospherequality.com
Management Consulting Services
N.A.I.C.S.: 541611
Charlie Ungetheim (VP-Ops)

Weatherford Motors, Inc. (2)
750 Potter St, Berkeley, CA 94710-2723
Tel.: (510) 654-8280
Automobile Dealers
N.A.I.C.S.: 441227

Sojitz Corporation of America (1)
Calle Esquilache 371 Oficina 901-A, San Isidro, Lima, Peru
Tel.: (51) 12025800
International Trade & Development Services
N.A.I.C.S.: 522299

Sojitz Cosmetics Corporation (1)
Akashi-cho 8-1, Chuo-ku, Tokyo, 104-0044, Japan
Tel.: (81) 3 3524 3201
Web Site: http://www.sojitz-cosmetics.com
Cosmetic Products Mfr & Distr
N.A.I.C.S.: 325620

Sojitz Energy Australia Pty. Ltd. (1)
Level 13 MLC Centre 19-29 Martin Place, Sydney, NSW, Australia
Tel.: (61) 2 9234 0811
Oil & Gas Exploration Services
N.A.I.C.S.: 213112

Sojitz Etame Ltd. (1)
7th Floor The Northern Shell Building 10 Lower Thames Street, London, EC3R 6EQ, United Kingdom
Tel.: (44) 20 7337 7930
Web Site: https://www.sojitz.com
Oil Fields Investment Services
N.A.I.C.S.: 523999

Sojitz Europe plc (1)
7th Floor 8 Finsbury Circus, London, EC2M 7EA, United Kingdom
Tel.: (44) 207 496 8700
Web Site: https://www.europe.sojitz.com
Sales Range: $700-749.9 Million
Emp.: 2,500
Commodities Trading House for Oil & Chemicals
N.A.I.C.S.: 523160

Sojitz Fashion (Shanghai) Trading Co., Ltd. (1)
Room 903 Jiaqi Building 666 Gubei Road, Changning District, Shanghai, China
Tel.: (86) 216 882 3808
Web Site: https://www.sh-vancet.com
Fabric Material & Clothing Whslr
N.A.I.C.S.: 424310

Sojitz Fashion Co., Ltd. (1)
9F Sawa-no-tsuru Bldg 2-1-2 Hiranomachi, Chuo-ku, Osaka, 541-0046, Japan
Tel.: (81) 66 231 9131
Web Site: https://www.vancet.net
Emp.: 64
Fabric Products Mfr & Distr
N.A.I.C.S.: 313310

Sojitz Foods Corporation (1)
3-1-1 Roppongi Tea Cube 16F, Minato-ku, Tokyo, 106-0032, Japan
Tel.: (81) 35 574 3300
Web Site: https://www.sojitz-foods.com
Emp.: 287
Food Product Whslr
N.A.I.C.S.: 424420

Sojitz Forest Products (EM) Sdn. Bhd. (1)
Suite 1-7-W2 7th Floor CPS Tower Centre Point Sabah No 1, Jalan Centre Point, 88000, Kota Kinabalu, 88000, Malaysia
Tel.: (60) 88256081
Web Site: http://www.sojitz.com
Sales Range: $50-74.9 Million
Emp.: 6
Timber Products & Plywood Whslr
N.A.I.C.S.: 423310
Hiroshi Tsukajama (Mng Dir)

Sojitz Fuso Philippines Corporation (1)
1016 EDSA Corner Corregidor Street, Bago Bantay Ramon Magsaysay I, Quezon City, Philippines
Tel.: (63) 28 234 2484
Web Site: https://www.fuso.com.ph
New Car Dealers
N.A.I.C.S.: 441110

Sojitz General Merchandise Corporation (1)
8-1-2-22 NMF Aoyama 1-chome Building 4F, Minato-ku Akasaka, Tokyo, 107-0052, Japan
Tel.: (81) 368945001
Web Site: http://www.sojitz-gmc.com
Emp.: 46
Footwear & Apparels Distr
N.A.I.C.S.: 424340
Haruo Hayashiya (Pres & CEO)

Sojitz General Property Management Corporation (1)
3-1 Daiba 2-chome, Minato-ku, Tokyo, 135-0091, Japan **(100%)**
Tel.: (81) 3 3570 9120
Web Site: http://www.sojitz-sogokanri.com
Condominium Management Services
N.A.I.C.S.: 531312

Sojitz Global Trading Nigeria Ltd. (1)
NIPOST TOWERS Block A 9th Floor 1/3 Ologun Agbaje Street, Victoria Island, Lagos, Nigeria **(100%)**
Tel.: (234) 1 462 7908
Web Site: https://www.sojitz.com
Sales Range: Less than $1 Million
Emp.: 11
General Trading Company
N.A.I.C.S.: 551112

Sojitz India Private Ltd. (1)
7th Floor Eros Corporate Tower Nehru Place, New Delhi, 110 019, India
Tel.: (91) 1166426400
International Trade & Development Services
N.A.I.C.S.: 522299

Sojitz Infinity Inc. (1)
1-6-1 Roppongi Izumi Garden Tower 9th floor, Minato-ku, Tokyo, 106-6009, Japan
Tel.: (81) 36 867 1540
Web Site: https://www.sojitz-infinity.com
Sales Range: $100-124.9 Million
Emp.: 540
Apparel Mfr & Distr
N.A.I.C.S.: 315990
Kohei Ono (Pres & CEO)

Sojitz Institute of Innovative Technologies, Ltd. (1)
2-1-1 Uchisaiwaicho Iino Building 17th floor, Chiyoda-ku, Tokyo, 100-8691, Japan
Tel.: (81) 36 871 4260
Web Site: https://www.sojitz-iit.com
New Technology Development Services
N.A.I.C.S.: 541511
Masashi Oki (Pres)

Sojitz Insurance Agency Corporation (1)
2-1-1 Uchisaiwaicho Iino Building 7th floor, Chiyoda-ku, Tokyo, 100-8691, Japan
Tel.: (81) 36 871 4205
Web Site: https://www.sojitz-ins.com
General Insurance Services
N.A.I.C.S.: 524210

Sojitz Insurance Brokers (HK) Ltd. (1)
16/F Harbour Centre 25 Harbour Rd, Wanchai, China (Hong Kong)
Tel.: (852) 28441876
Sales Range: $50-74.9 Million
Emp.: 80
Insurance Brokerage Services
N.A.I.C.S.: 524210
Toshiho Takenaka (Deputy Gen Mgr)

Sojitz Ject Corporation (1)
7th Floor 8-6 Nishi-Shimbashi 2-Chome, Minato-ku, Tokyo, 105-0003, Japan
Tel.: (81) 35 511 2121
Web Site: https://www.jectcorp.com
Emp.: 84
Carbon Products Mfr & Distr
N.A.I.C.S.: 335991
Toshihide Watanabe (Dir-Mktg)

Sojitz Kelanitissa (Private) Limited (1)
No 28 New Kelani Bridge Road, Wellampitiya, Sri Lanka
Tel.: (94) 11 465 7400
Web Site: https://www.skpl.lk
Power Generation
N.A.I.C.S.: 221112

Sojitz Korea Corporation (1)
Ferrum Tower 13F Suha-dong Eulji-ro 5Gil-19, Jung-gu, Seoul, 04539, Korea (South) **(100%)**
Tel.: (82) 2 772 8900
Web Site: https://www.sojitz.com
Sales Range: $50-74.9 Million
Emp.: 30
General Trading Company
N.A.I.C.S.: 523160
Nakadoi Makoto (Pres & CEO)

Sojitz Kyushu Corporation (1)
Elgala 5F 1-4-2 Tenjin, Chuo-ku, Fukuoka, 810-0001, Japan
Tel.: (81) 92 751 3308
Web Site: https://www.sojitz-kyushu.com

Emp.: 88
General Trading Services
N.A.I.C.S.: 523160
Atsushi Koda (Pres & CEO)

Sojitz Logistics Corporation (1)
2-1-1 Uchisaiwaicho Iino Building 7F, Chiyoda-ku, Tokyo, 100-8691, Japan
Tel.: (81) 36 871 5080
Web Site: https://www.sojitz-logistics.com
Emp.: 225
Logistics Consulting Servies
N.A.I.C.S.: 541614
Fumihiko Sato (Pres)

Sojitz Logistics Vietnam Co., Ltd. (1)
8th Floor Estar Building 147-149 Vo Van Tan, Ward 6 District 3, Ho Chi Minh City, Vietnam
Tel.: (84) 2839307892
Logistic Services
N.A.I.C.S.: 541614

Sojitz Logitech Co., Ltd. (1)
1 Kitaoyobi Kasamatsu-cho, Hashima-gun, Gifu, 501-6064, Japan
Tel.: (81) 58 388 3975
Web Site: https://www.sojitz-logitech.com
Emp.: 115
Cargo Handling Services
N.A.I.C.S.: 488320

Sojitz Machinery (Shanghai) Corporation (1)
705/A No 358 North Fute Road Waigaoqiao Free Trade Area, Shanghai, 200131, China **(100%)**
Tel.: (86) 21 5878 3263
Industrial Machinery Distr
N.A.I.C.S.: 423830

Sojitz Machinery Corporation (1)
1-6-1 Marunouch Marunouchi Center Building 2nd floor, Chiyoda-ku, Tokyo, 100-0005, Japan **(100%)**
Tel.: (81) 36 259 5600
Web Site: https://www.sojitz-mac.com
Emp.: 399
General Machinery Import/Export & Sales
N.A.I.C.S.: 423830
Tatsunobu Sako (Chm)

Sojitz Marine & Engineering Corporation (1)
3F 2-3-1 Nishi-shimbashi, Minato-ku, Tokyo, 105-0003, Japan
Tel.: (81) 335960888
Web Site: http://www.somec.co.jp
Sales Range: $300-349.9 Million
Ship Building & Repairing Services
N.A.I.C.S.: 336611
Hiroyuki Osone (Pres)

Sojitz Mexicana S.A. de C.V. (1)
Av Presidente Masaryk 101-802 Col Polanco V Seccion, Miguel Hidalgo, 11560, Mexico, DF, Mexico
Tel.: (52) 555 202 7468
Web Site: http://www.sojitz.com
Sales Range: $50-74.9 Million
Emp.: 17
General Trading Company
N.A.I.C.S.: 523160

Sojitz Middle East FZE (1)
JAFZA One Building Tower A Floor-6 Office No 605, PO Box 17178, Jebel Ali Free Zone North, Dubai, United Arab Emirates
Tel.: (971) 48848556
International Trade & Development Services
N.A.I.C.S.: 522299

Sojitz Mirai Power Corporation (1)
2-1-1 Uchisaiwaicho, Chiyoda-ku, Tokyo, 100-8691, Japan
Tel.: (81) 36 871 3333
Web Site: https://www.sojitz-miraipower.com
Solar Power Services
N.A.I.C.S.: 221114

Sojitz Mobility Corporation (1)
5-17-1 Tokaicho, Kagoshima, 891-0115, Japan
Tel.: (81) 992688082
Web Site: https://www.aa-k.com
Camper Mfr & Distr
N.A.I.C.S.: 336214

Sojitz New Urban Development Corporation (1)

AND PRIVATE COMPANIES

SOJITZ CORPORATION

1-2-9 Nishi-Shimbashi 17th Floor Hibiya Central Building, Minato-ku, Tokyo, 105-0003, Japan
Tel.: (81) 35 510 3600
Web Site: https://www.sojitz-nud.com
Emp.: 102
Shopping Center Leasing & Management Services
N.A.I.C.S.: 531120

Sojitz New Zealand Limited (1)
Level 15 Crombie Lockwood Tower 191 Queen St, PO Box 4073, Auckland, 1010, New Zealand
Tel.: (64) 99142970
Web Site: http://www.sojitz.com
Sales Range: $25-49.9 Million
Emp.: 4
General Trading Company
N.A.I.C.S.: 551112

Sojitz Now Apparel Ltd. (1)
16F Harbour Centre 25 Harbour Road, Wanchai, China (Hong Kong)
Tel.: (852) 2737 8181
Textile Garment Whslr
N.A.I.C.S.: 424350

Sojitz Offshore Project Pte. Ltd. (1)
77 Robinson Road 32-00 SIA Building, Singapore, 068896, Singapore
Tel.: (65) 64289292
Web Site: http://www.sojitz.com
Emp.: 1
Oil & Gas Equipment Handling Services
N.A.I.C.S.: 213112

Sojitz Oil & Gas (Egypt) Ltd. (1)
7th Floor The Northern Shell Building 10 Lower Thames Street, London, EC3R 6EQ, United Kingdom
Tel.: (44) 20 7337 7930
Web Site: http://www.sojitz.com
Oil & Gas Exploration Services
N.A.I.C.S.: 213112

Sojitz Petroleum Co., (Singapore) Pte. Ltd. (1)
77 Robinson Road 31-00, Singapore, 068896, Singapore
Tel.: (65) 64289260
Sales Range: $50-74.9 Million
Emp.: 8
Oil & Petroleum Products Distr
N.A.I.C.S.: 424720
Shigo Miyauchi (Mng Dir)

Sojitz Philippines Corporation (1)
23rd Floor NAC Tower 32nd Street, Fort Bonifacio Global City, Taguig, Philippines
Tel.: (63) 28 892 3076
Web Site: http://ph.sojitz.com
International Trade & Development Services
N.A.I.C.S.: 522299
Daisuke Ojima (Pres)

Sojitz Pla-Net Corporation (1)
Iino Building 1-1 Uchisaiwaicho 2-chome, Chiyoda-ku, Tokyo, 100-8691, Japan
Tel.: (81) 36 871 3000
Web Site: https://www.sojitz-planet.com
Emp.: 267
Plastic Product Whslr
N.A.I.C.S.: 424610
Norio Satake (Pres)

Subsidiary (Domestic):

Pla Matels Corporation (2)
Gotenyama Trust Tower 5F 4-7-35 Kitashinagawa, Shinagawa-ku, Tokyo, 140-0001, Japan   (90.64%)
Tel.: (81) 357899700
Web Site: http://www.plamatels.co.jp
Rev.: $589,769,760
Assets: $254,586,000
Liabilities: $160,923,720
Net Worth: $93,662,280
Earnings: $6,604,740
Emp.: 171
Fiscal Year-end: 03/31/2019
Plastics Product Mfr
N.A.I.C.S.: 326199
Kyota Kishimoto (Pres)

Subsidiary (Domestic):

Fujimatsu Co., Ltd. (3)
1-20-19 Shoji, Ikuno-ku, Osaka, 544-0002, Japan
Tel.: (81) 66 751 1212
Web Site: https://www.fujimatsu.co.jp
Plastic Product Distr
N.A.I.C.S.: 424610

Subsidiary (Non-US):

Pla Matels (Dalian) Co., Ltd. (3)
Room 403 No 3 Haitian Rd Free Trade Zone, Dalian, 116600, China
Tel.: (86) 41162778799
Plastic Product Distr
N.A.I.C.S.: 424610

Pla Matels (Hong Kong) Co., Ltd. (3)
Room 1401 14th Floor Harcourt House 39 Gloucester Road, Wanchai, China (Hong Kong)
Tel.: (852) 2992 0090
Emp.: 6
Plastic Product Distr
N.A.I.C.S.: 424610

Subsidiary (Non-US):

Pla Matels (Shenzhen) Co., Ltd. (4)
RM 906-908 Shenzhen Kerry Centre 2008 Renminnan Road Luohu, Shenzhen, 518001, Guangdong, China
Tel.: (86) 75588827623
Plastic Product Distr
N.A.I.C.S.: 424610

Subsidiary (Non-US):

Pla Matels (India) Pvt. Ltd. (3)
607 Regus Bund Garden Level 6 Kumar Business Complex Bund Garden Rd, Pune, 411001, Maharashtra, India
Tel.: (91) 2066894010
Plastic Product Distr
N.A.I.C.S.: 424610

Pla Matels (Philippines) Corporation (3)
5F Unit A Kingston Tower 8 L1 Acacia Ave Madrigal Business Park, Alabang, Muntinlupa, 1780, Philippines
Tel.: (63) 28075884
Plastic Product Distr
N.A.I.C.S.: 424610

Pla Matels (Shanghai) Co., Ltd. (3)
Room 517 Union Development Building of China 728 Xinhua Road, Shanghai, 200052, China
Tel.: (86) 2152588606
Plastic Product Distr
N.A.I.C.S.: 424610

Pla Matels (Thailand) Co., Ltd. (3)
159/39 Serm-Mit Tower Unit 2502/3 2502/4 25th Floor, Sukhumvit 21 Asoke Road Klongtoey-Nua Wattana, Bangkok, 10110, Thailand
Tel.: (66) 22581985
Plastic Product Distr
N.A.I.C.S.: 424610

Taiwan Pla Matels Corporation (3)
Room 1 28F No 758 Zhongming S Road South District, Taichung, 40255, Taiwan
Tel.: (886) 422606041
Plastic Product Distr
N.A.I.C.S.: 424610

Sojitz Pla-Net Holdings, Inc. (1)
Kokusai Shin Akasaka Bldg East 14-27 Akasaka 2-Chome, Minato-Ku, Tokyo, 107-8655, Japan
Tel.: (81) 3 5520 3001
Web Site: http://www.sojitz.com
Plastic Products Mfr & Distr
N.A.I.C.S.: 326199

Sojitz Plastics (China) Ltd. (1)
Rm 1603 Harbour Centre 25 Harbour, Wanchai, China (Hong Kong)
Tel.: (852) 28792831
Emp.: 30
Plastic Resin Material & Molding Machinery Distr
N.A.I.C.S.: 424610

Sojitz Private Equity, Inc. (1)
4F Jitsugetsukan Kojimachi Bldg 1-3-7 Kojimachi, Chiyoda-ku, Tokyo, 102-0083, Japan
Tel.: (81) 352103601
Web Site: http://www.sojitz.com
Investment Management & Advisory Services
N.A.I.C.S.: 523940

Sojitz Promotion Co., Ltd. (1)
1-20 Akasaka 6-chome, Minato-ku, Tokyo, 107-8655, Japan
Tel.: (81) 3 5520 4126
Tobacco Products Whslr
N.A.I.C.S.: 424940

Sojitz REIT Advisors K.K. (1)
1-18-1 Shinbashi Air Hall 3rd floor, Minato-ku, Tokyo, Japan
Tel.: (81) 35 501 0080
Web Site: https://www.sojitz-sra.com
Investment Management Service
N.A.I.C.S.: 523940
Toshio Sugita (Pres & CEO)

Sojitz Realnet Corporation (1)
12F Akasaka Twin Tower Main Tower 2-17-22 Akasaka, Minato-ku, Tokyo, 107-0052, Japan
Tel.: (81) 335882855
Web Site: http://www.sojitz-realnet.com
Real Estate Manangement Services
N.A.I.C.S.: 531390

Sojitz Research Institute, Ltd. (1)
2-1-1 Uchisaiwaicho Iino Building, Chiyoda-ku, Tokyo, 100-8691, Japan
Tel.: (81) 36 871 2802
Web Site: https://www.sojitz-soken.com
Sales Range: $25-49.9 Million
Emp.: 20
Business Consulting Services
N.A.I.C.S.: 541611

Sojitz Resources (Australia) Pty. Ltd. (1)
Level 21 221 St Georges Terrace, Perth, 6000, WA, Australia
Tel.: (61) 893212835
Investment Management Service
N.A.I.C.S.: 523999

Sojitz Sawada Power Co., Ltd. (1)
1942-11 Yahata, Sado, 952-1311, Niigata, Japan
Tel.: (81) 259511830
Sales Range: $75-99.9 Million
Emp.: 11
Thermal Power Generation Services
N.A.I.C.S.: 221118

Sojitz Shared Service Corporation (1)
18th floor Iino Building 2-1-1 Uchisaiwaicho, Chiyoda-ku, Tokyo, 100-8691, Japan
Tel.: (81) 36 871 3953
Web Site: https://www.sojitz-ss.com
Human Resource Consulting Services
N.A.I.C.S.: 541612

Sojitz Solar Betzweiler GmbH (1)
Schirmerstrasse 76, Dusseldorf, 40211, Nordrhein-Westfalen, Germany
Tel.: (49) 211 35510
Web Site: http://www.sojitz.com
Emp.: 10
Solar Power Generation Services
N.A.I.C.S.: 221118
Izumi Konno (Gen Mgr)

Sojitz Systems Corporation (1)
Minami-Shinagawa N Bldg Minami-Shinagawa 2-2-10, Shinagawa-ku, Tokyo, Japan
Tel.: (81) 334719451
Web Site: http://www.sojitz-sys.com
Rev.: $12,717
Emp.: 246
Software Development Services
N.A.I.C.S.: 541511

Sojitz Technoplas Corporation (1)
512-1 Manaka, Sakuragawa, 309-1342, Ibaraki, Japan
Tel.: (81) 296755980
Web Site: http://www.sojitz.com
Sales Range: $25-49.9 Million
Emp.: 15
Plastic Resin Mfr
N.A.I.C.S.: 325211
Yasuyuki Ishita (Pres)

Sojitz Textile (Shanghai) Co., Ltd. (1)
901 Kirin Plaza 666 Gu Bei Road, Chang Ning District, Shanghai, China
Tel.: (86) 2162781001
Web Site: http://www.sojitz.com

Sewn Products Mfr & Distr
N.A.I.C.S.: 315250
Nishimine Kozo (Gen Mgr)

Sojitz Tourist Corporation (1)
7th floor Iino Building 2-1-1 Uchisaiwaicho, Chiyoda-ku, Tokyo, 100-8691, Japan
Tel.: (81) 36 871 4260
Web Site: https://www.sojitz-tourist.com
Emp.: 50
Travel Agency Services
N.A.I.C.S.: 561510

Sojitz Tuna Farm Takashima Co., Ltd. (1)
801-4 Mukae Aouuramen-aza Takashima-cho, Matsuura, 859-4301, Nagasaki, Japan
Tel.: (81) 955 41 6038
Tuna Fishing Services
N.A.I.C.S.: 114111

Sojitz Tungsten Resources, Inc. (1)
Ste 255 555 Burrard Street, Vancouver, V7X 1M7, BC, Canada
Tel.: (604) 684-8351
Emp.: 1
Tungsten Mining Services
N.A.I.C.S.: 212290
Toru Sano (Mgr)

Sojitz Venezuela C.A. (1)
Av Francisco De Miranda Edf Parque Cristal, Ala Este Piso 3 Oficina 37 A, Caracas, 1060, Venezuela
Tel.: (58) 2122836055
Web Site: http://www.sojitz.com
Sales Range: $50-74.9 Million
Emp.: 6
General Trading Company
N.A.I.C.S.: 551112

Sojitz Vietnam Company Ltd. (1)
L 30 Floor Vietcombank Tower 5 Me Linh Square, Ben Nghe Ward District 1, Ho Chi Minh City, Vietnam
Tel.: (84) 2839318100
International Trade & Development Services
N.A.I.C.S.: 522299

Sojitz Yoshimoto Ringyo Corporation. (1)
173-2 Higashi Makoto, Ozora-cho Abashiri-gun, Tokyo, 099-3244, Japan
Tel.: (81) 152635650
Web Site: http://www.sojitz-yoshimoto-r.com
Emp.: 127
Lumber & Plywood Distr
N.A.I.C.S.: 423310

Sojitz do Brasil S.A. (1)
Av Paulista 1842 Torre Norte 21o andar, Sao Paulo, 01310-200, Brazil
Tel.: (55) 112 175 6000
Web Site: http://www.sojitz-br.com
Sales Range: $25-49.9 Million
Emp.: 50
Cotton Yarn Mfr
N.A.I.C.S.: 313110

Solvadis Deutschland Gmbh (1)
Konigsberger Strasse 1, 60487, Frankfurt am Main, Germany
Tel.: (49) 6957007100
Web Site: https://www.solvadis.com
Chemical Marketing & Distr
N.A.I.C.S.: 424690

Southwest Rail Industries Inc. (1)
501 S E St, Weimar, TX 78962
Tel.: (979) 725-9545
Web Site: https://www.southwestrail.com
Railcar Leasing Services
N.A.I.C.S.: 532120

Stettin Bay Lumber Co. Ltd. (1)
Lot 179 Megici Buluma, Kimbe, West New Britain, Papua New Guinea
Tel.: (675) 9835266
Sales Range: $300-349.9 Million
Emp.: 1,100
Provider of Logging & Timber Sawing
N.A.I.C.S.: 113310

Subaru Motor LLC (1)
5/7 Shchipok St Bldg 2 3, Moscow, 115054, Russia
Tel.: (7) 4959264646
Web Site: http://www.subaru.ru
Sales Range: $50-74.9 Million
Emp.: 100
Automotive Distr

SOJITZ CORPORATION

Sojitz Corporation—(Continued)
N.A.I.C.S.: 423110
Kishimoto Yoshiki *(Mng Dir)*

Supreme Development Co., Ltd. (1)
Unit E and F 14/F Block 2 49-53 Ta Chuen Ping Street, Vigor Industrial Building, Kwai Chung, China (Hong Kong)
Tel.: (852) 2 428 4428
Web Site: https://www.supremebags.com
Plastic Materials Mfr
N.A.I.C.S.: 325211

Taiyo Chemical Industry Co., Ltd. (1)
3 4 28 Imazuminami, Osaka, 538 0043, Tsurumi Ku, Japan (100%)
Tel.: (81) 669610855
Web Site: http://www.taiyo-kagaku.co.jp
Sales Range: $25-49.9 Million
Emp.: 50
Mfr of Vinyl Chloride Sheets
N.A.I.C.S.: 325211
Kimura Masahito *(Pres)*

Takahata Co., Ltd.
1-7 Wakayanagi Aza Kawakita Aramachi-mae, Kurihara, 989-5501, Miyagi, Japan
Tel.: (81) 228 32 2147
Web Site: http://www.sojitz.com
Emp.: 121
Sewn Products Mfr
N.A.I.C.S.: 315990
Ogura Honger *(Dir)*

Tayo Rolls Ltd. (1)
XLRI Campus Circuit House Area E, Jamshedpur, 831001, Jharkhand, India (100%)
Tel.: (91) 6572225643
Web Site: http://www.tayorolls.com
Sales Range: $200-249.9 Million
Emp.: 650
Mfr of Steel Ingot & Roll; Joint Venture of Sojitz Corporation & The Tata Group
N.A.I.C.S.: 331110
Suresh Padmanabhan *(Deputy CFO)*

The Long Binh Industrial Zone Development LLC (1)
Long Binh Industrial Zone, Bien Hoa, Dong Nai, Vietnam
Tel.: (84) 61 389 1105
Web Site: https://www.loteco.com.vn
Construction & Development Infrastructure Services
N.A.I.C.S.: 236220

Tokyo Yuso Co., Ltd. (1)
4-1 Chidoricho, Kawasaki-ku, Kawasaki, 210-0865, Kanagawa, Japan
Tel.: (81) 44 276 3801
Web Site: https://www.tokyoyuso.co.jp
Emp.: 80
Petroleum & Chemical Products Storage Services
N.A.I.C.S.: 493190

Vermitech Corporation (1)
1445 Shinmachi, Takasaki, 370-1301, Gunma, Japan
Tel.: (81) 27 442 3876
Web Site: https://www.vermitech.jp
Vermiculite Processing & Distr
N.A.I.C.S.: 327992

Vroom Co., Ltd. (1)
2418-2420 Ladproa Road, Phlabphla Wang Thonglang, Bangkok, 10310, Thailand
Tel.: (66) 35350880
New Car Dealers
N.A.I.C.S.: 441110
Hideki Yanagisawa *(Pres)*

Yahata Ready Mixed Concrete Co., Ltd. (1)
46-80 Nakahara, Tobata-ku, Kitakyushu, 804-0002, Fukuoka, Japan (58%)
Tel.: (81) 93 872 5822
Ready Mix Concrete Mfr & Distr
N.A.I.C.S.: 327320

Yamagata Newcity Development Co., Ltd (1)
1-1-1 Jyonan-machi, Yamagata, 990-8580, Japan
Tel.: (81) 236477211
Building Leasing & Management Services
N.A.I.C.S.: 531120

Yantai Sandie Plastic Products Co., Ltd. (1)
No 3 Yingbin Road Taocun Township, Qixia, Yantai, Shandong, China
Tel.: (86) 5355484737
Web Site: http://www.sojitz.com
Polyethylene Household Bag Mfr
N.A.I.C.S.: 326111

Zhejiang Asahi Bearing Co., Ltd. (1)
Caojiang Lu, Economic Development Zone, Shaoxing, Zhejiang, China
Tel.: (86) 57588600222
Emp.: 410
Lathing Ring Mfr
N.A.I.C.S.: 339910
Motoki Maeda *(Gen Mgr)*

Zhejiang Jinshuang Bearing Co., Ltd. (1)
No 808 Yuexiu Mid Road Cao'e street, Shangyu, Shaoxing, 312300, Zhejiang, China
Tel.: (86) 5758 212 6538
Web Site: https://www.sqjh.com
Emp.: 300
Lathing Ring Mfr
N.A.I.C.S.: 339910

e-Energy Corporation (1)
1-6-11 Nishishimbashi, Minato-ku, Tokyo, 105-0003, Japan
Tel.: (81) 368584830
Web Site: http://www.e-energy.co.jp
Nuclear Fuel & Equipment Distr
N.A.I.C.S.: 457210

SOK MARKETLER TICARET AS
Kisikli Mahallesi Hanimseti Sokak No 35 B/1 Uskudar, Istanbul, Türkiye
Tel.: (90) 8508080000
Web Site: https://kurumsal.sokmarket.com
Year Founded: 1995
SOKM—(IST)
Rev.: $1,831,395,556
Assets: $579,975,544
Liabilities: $491,469,234
Net Worth: $88,506,309
Earnings: $73,507,245
Fiscal Year-end: 12/31/22
Fruit & Vegetable Product Distr
N.A.I.C.S.: 445230
Ugur Demirel *(CEO)*

SOKEN CHEMICAL & ENGINEERING CO.,LTD.
3-29-5 Takada, Toshima-ku, Tokyo, 171-8531, Japan
Tel.: (81) 339833171
Web Site: https://www.sokenchem.com
Year Founded: 1948
4972—(TKS)
Rev.: $273,111,980
Assets: $334,347,020
Liabilities: $117,968,670
Net Worth: $216,378,350
Earnings: $17,377,690
Emp.: 1,119
Fiscal Year-end: 03/31/24
Coating Material Mfr
N.A.I.C.S.: 325510
Noriyuki Osaka *(Pres)*

Subsidiaries:

CHANG ZHOU SOKEN HEATING BOILER CO., LTD. (1)
No 12 Henguo Road, Henglin Town, Changzhou, Jiangsu, China
Tel.: (86) 51988783136
Web Site: https://www.zyheatingboiler.com
Boiler Mfr & Distr
N.A.I.C.S.: 332410

Hamaoka Soken Co., Ltd. (1)
8665-1 Ikeshinden, Omaezaki, 437-1612, Shizuoka, Japan
Tel.: (81) 537853331
Chemical Product Mfr & Distr
N.A.I.C.S.: 325998

Llaohe Soken Chemical Co., Ltd. (1)
Industrial Developing Zone, Xinlong tai Dis, Panjin, 124013, Liaoning, China
Tel.: (86) 427 7804564
Web Site: http://www.liaohe-soken.com
Chemical Products Mfr
N.A.I.C.S.: 325998

Sayama Soken Co., Ltd. (1)
1-13-1 Hirose-higashi, Sayama, 350-1320, Saitama, Japan
Tel.: (81) 429543261
Adhesive Mfr
N.A.I.C.S.: 325520

Soken Chemical Asia Co., Ltd. (1)
700/699 Moo 1, T Phanthong, Chon Buri, 20160, A Phanthong, Thailand
Tel.: (66) 38079900
Web Site: https://www.soken-asia.com
Adhesive Mfr
N.A.I.C.S.: 325520

Soken High-tech Material (NanJing) Co., Ltd. (1)
No 300 Chongfu Road Nanjing Chemical Industrial Park, Liuhe District, Nanjing, 210047, Jiangsu, China
Tel.: (86) 2558991131
Web Site: https://www.soken-nj.com
Adhesive Mfr & Distr
N.A.I.C.S.: 325520

Suzhou Soken Chemical Co., Ltd. (1)
Xinglong Street, Industrial Park, Suzhou, 215021, Jiangsu, China
Tel.: (86) 51262832891
Emp.: 160
Chemical Product Mfr & Distr
N.A.I.C.S.: 325998
Ying Cui *(Gen Mgr)*

SOKENSHA CO LTD
2-37-11 Katakura, Kanagawa-ku, Yokohama, 221-8741, Japan
Tel.: (81) 454911441
Web Site: https://www.sokensha.co.jp
Year Founded: 1966
7413—(TKS)
Rev.: $32,262,958
Assets: $19,973,566
Liabilities: $12,632,966
Net Worth: $7,340,599
Earnings: $46,250
Fiscal Year-end: 03/31/24
Natural Foods & Healthy Foods Whslr
N.A.I.C.S.: 456191
Yasushi Nakamura *(Pres & CEO)*

SOKO AIR D.D.
Rodoc bb, 88 000, Mostar, Bosnia & Herzegovina
Tel.: (387) 36350080
SAIRRK2—(SARE)
Assets: $2,104,244
Liabilities: $2,104,244
Earnings: ($137,397)
Fiscal Year-end: 12/31/21
Aircraft Equipment Mfr
N.A.I.C.S.: 336413

SOKO BRAVARSKO LIMARSKO D.D.
Rodoc bb, 88 000, Mostar, Bosnia & Herzegovina
Tel.: (387) 36350210
SBLMR—(SARE)
Rev.: $19
Assets: $705,588
Liabilities: $1,162
Net Worth: $704,426
Earnings: ($198,504)
Fiscal Year-end: 12/31/20
Fabricated Metal Products Mfr
N.A.I.C.S.: 332999

SOKO HELIKOPTERI D.D.
Rodoc bb, 88 000, Mostar, Bosnia & Herzegovina
Tel.: (387) 36350221
SHKMR—(SARE)
Rev.: $3,744

INTERNATIONAL PUBLIC

Assets: $1,430,248
Liabilities: $69,832
Net Worth: $1,360,416
Earnings: ($209,321)
Fiscal Year-end: 12/31/20
Fabricated Metal Products Mfr
N.A.I.C.S.: 332999

SOKO ZRAKOPLOVSTVO D.D.
Rodoc b b, 88000, Mostar, Bosnia & Herzegovina
Tel.: (387) 36 352 692
Emp.: 10
Aluminium Products Mfr
N.A.I.C.S.: 331313

SOKOCNICA A.D.
Rade Marijanca Bb, 78264, Sipovo, Bosnia & Herzegovina
Tel.: (387) 66289105
SKCN-R-A—(BANJ)
Sales Range: Less than $1 Million
Emp.: 1
Hotel Operator
N.A.I.C.S.: 721110
Slobodan Medic *(Chm)*

SOKOLICA A.D.
Rudnicka 44, Despotovac, Serbia
Tel.: (381) 35 611 190
Year Founded: 1948
SKLC—(BEL)
Sales Range: Less than $1 Million
Heavy Construction Services
N.A.I.C.S.: 237990
Bojan Markovic *(Exec Dir)*

SOKOMAN MINERALS CORP.
82 Richmond Street East, Toronto, M5C 1P1, ON, Canada
Tel.: (416) 361-3557
Web Site: https://www.sokomanminerals.com
Year Founded: 2006
SIC—(TSXV)
Rev.: $53,269
Assets: $5,891,043
Liabilities: $193,208
Net Worth: $5,697,834
Earnings: ($762,261)
Fiscal Year-end: 06/30/24
Iron Ore Mining Services
N.A.I.C.S.: 212210
Timothy P. Froude *(Pres & CEO)*

SOKOPREVOZ A.D.
Miladina Zivanovica bb, Sokobanja, Serbia
Tel.: (381) 18 830 115
Year Founded: 2002
Sales Range: $1-9.9 Million
Emp.: 29
Passenger Transportation Services
N.A.I.C.S.: 485999

SOKOUK HOLDING COMPANY K.S.C.C.
3rd Floor ITS Tower Bldg No 33 Mubarak Al Kabeer Street, Sharq, Kuwait, 26729, Kuwait
Tel.: (965) 1834000
Web Site: https://www.sokouk.com
Year Founded: 1998
SOKOUK—(KUW)
Rev.: $9,899,012
Assets: $165,051,181
Liabilities: $81,826,059
Net Worth: $83,225,123
Earnings: $1,622,422
Emp.: 17
Fiscal Year-end: 12/31/22
Real Estate Investment Services
N.A.I.C.S.: 523999
Ravindra Ninganagouda Shantagiri *(CFO)*

SOKRATHERM GMBH
Milchstr 12, 32120, Hiddenhausen, Germany
Tel.: (49) 522196210
Web Site: http://www.sokratherm.de
Year Founded: 1977
Sales Range: $10-24.9 Million
Electrical Component Mfr
N.A.I.C.S.: 335999
Hermann Meinhold *(Mng Dir)*

SOKTAS TEKSTIL SANAYI VE TICARET A.S.
Sehit Nevres Bulvari Deren Plaza No 10 K 1, Alsancak, 35170, Izmir, Turkiye
Tel.: (90) 2565182255
Web Site: https://www.soktas.com.tr
Year Founded: 1971
SKTAS—(IST)
Rev.: $53,320,906
Assets: $113,844,817
Liabilities: $58,331,670
Net Worth: $55,513,146
Earnings: ($867,759)
Emp.: 694
Fiscal Year-end: 12/31/23
Cotton Fabric Mfr
N.A.I.C.S.: 313220

SOL GLOBAL INVESTMENTS CORP.
Suite 5600 100 King Street West, Toronto, M5X 1C9, ON, Canada
Tel.: (212) 729-9208   ON
Web Site: https://www.solglobal.com
Year Founded: 2017
9SB—(DEU)
Rev.: $1,388,635
Assets: $114,231,096
Liabilities: $83,025,308
Net Worth: $31,205,788
Earnings: ($221,576,958)
Fiscal Year-end: 11/30/22
Research & Development Company
N.A.I.C.S.: 541715
Paul Kania *(Interim CEO)*

SOL S.P.A.
Via Borgazzi 27, 20900, Monza, Italy
Tel.: (39) 03923961   IT
Web Site: https://www.sol.it
Year Founded: 1927
SOL—(ITA)
Rev.: $1,223,567,775
Assets: $1,737,071,582
Liabilities: $922,935,155
Net Worth: $814,136,428
Earnings: $132,937,328
Emp.: 4,183
Fiscal Year-end: 12/31/20
Technical Gases, Home Care Services & Welding
N.A.I.C.S.: 221210
Aldo Fumagalli Romario *(Chm & Mng Dir)*

Subsidiaries:

Airsol B.V.   (1)
Swaardvenstraat 11, 5048AV, Tilburg, Netherlands
Tel.: (31) 134625784
Sales Range: $50-74.9 Million
Emp.: 50
Financial Transactions Processing Reserve & Clearinghouse Activities
N.A.I.C.S.: 522320

Allershausen Care GmbH   (1)
Werner v Siemens-Str 1, 85375, Neufahrn, Germany
Tel.: (49) 81666339
Web Site: https://ssz-allershausen.com
Medical Development Services
N.A.I.C.S.: 541715

B.T.G. Belgische Technische Gassen Bvba/sprl   (1)
Zoning Ouest 13 - 15, 7660, Lessines, Belgium   (100%)
Tel.: (32) 68270333
Web Site: http://btg.solgroup.com
Sales Range: $25-49.9 Million
Emp.: 20
Regulation & Administration of Communications Electric Gas & Other Utilities
N.A.I.C.S.: 926130

Behringer France S.A.R.L.
Zae Cap Nord 13 Rue de la Brot, BP 57523, 21075, Dijon, France
Tel.: (33) 380787262
Web Site: https://www.behringerfrance.fr
Metal Saw Mfr & Distr
N.A.I.C.S.: 332216

Behringer Srl   (1)
Via Gualco 4, 16165, Genoa, Italy   (51%)
Tel.: (39) 0108309103
Web Site: https://www.behringer.it
Commercial & Service Industry Machinery Mfr
N.A.I.C.S.: 333310

Bhoruka Specialty Gases Private Ltd.   (1)
Plot No 5A & 6 Whitefield Road, Doddanekundi Industrial Area Mahadevapura, Bengaluru, 560 048, Karnataka, India
Tel.: (91) 8041818200
Web Site: https://bhurukagases.com
Liquid Gas Product Mfr & Distr
N.A.I.C.S.: 324199

Biotechsol SRL   (1)
via Borgazzi 27, 20900, Monza, Italy
Tel.: (39) 0392396274
Web Site: https://www.biotechsol.com
Bio Technology Services
N.A.I.C.S.: 541714

Cryolab SRL   (1)
Via Montpellier 1, 00133, Rome, Italy
Tel.: (39) 0392109770
Web Site: https://cryolab.it
Biotechnological Development Services
N.A.I.C.S.: 541714

Cryos SRL   (1)
Via Alta Furia 51, Peveragno, 12016, Cuneo, CN, Italy
Tel.: (39) 0171348132
Web Site: https://www.ghiacciosecco-cryos.it
Logistic Services
N.A.I.C.S.: 484110

Diatheva SRL   (1)
Via Sant'Anna 131/135, Cartoceto, 61030, Pesaro, Italy
Tel.: (39) 0721830605
Web Site: https://www.diatheva.com
Research & Development Services
N.A.I.C.S.: 541714
Stefania Mariani *(CEO)*

Direct Medical Ltd Company   (1)
Suite 2 Gateway Center, Monksland Co Roscommon, Athlone, N37 CD77, Ireland
Tel.: (353) 906490190
Web Site: https://www.directmedical.ie
Medical Devices
N.A.I.C.S.: 621610

Dn Global Home Care Ltda   (1)
Alexander von Humboldt Street 153, Pituba, Salvador, Bahia, Brazil
Tel.: (55) 713 033 2999
Web Site: https://www.dnglobal.com.br
Healthcare Services
N.A.I.C.S.: 621610

Dolby Medical Home Respiratory Care Ltd.   (1)
North Suite Lomond Court Castle Business Park, Stirling, FK9 4TU, United Kingdom
Tel.: (44) 3301230305
Web Site: https://www.vivisol.co.uk
Healthcare Services
N.A.I.C.S.: 621610

Energetika Z.J. D.O.O.   (1)
Cesta Zelezarjev 8, 4270, Jesenice, Slovenia   (100%)
Tel.: (386) 45841802
Electric Power Distribution
N.A.I.C.S.: 221122

Flosit SAS   (1)
Aeropole Nouasseur, 20240, Casablanca, Morocco
Tel.: (212) 522539367
Research & Development Services
N.A.I.C.S.: 541714

France Oxygene SARL   (1)
15 Place Gutenberg, 59175, Templemars, France
Tel.: (33) 328559659
Web Site: https://www.franceoxygene.fr
Research & Development Services
N.A.I.C.S.: 541714

G.T.S. Sh.P.K.   (1)
Kombinat, Vaqarr, Tirana, Albania   (100%)
Tel.: (355) 42350981
Web Site: http://www.gts.al
Mental Health Practitioners Offices
N.A.I.C.S.: 621330

Gebze Gaz AS   (1)
Baris Mahallesi 1802 Sk No 17, 41400, Gebze, Kocaeli, Turkiye
Tel.: (90) 2626464220
Web Site: https://www.gebzegaz.com
Gas Distribution Services
N.A.I.C.S.: 221210

I.C.O.A. Srl   (1)
Via Emanuele Gianturco 11, 00196, Rome, Italy   (97.6%)
Tel.: (39) 0694443456
Web Site: http://www.icoa.it
Sales Range: $25-49.9 Million
Emp.: 15
Industrial Gas Mfr
N.A.I.C.S.: 325120

IL Point Srl   (1)
Viale dell Industria 13, 37135, Verona, Italy   (65%)
Tel.: (39) 045580892
Web Site: https://www.ilpoint.it
Medical Dental & Hospital Equipment & Supplies Whslr
N.A.I.C.S.: 423450

IMG d.o.o.   (1)
Bulevar Nikole Tesle Br, 11 070, Belgrade, Serbia   (99.55%)
Tel.: (381) 11603143
Industrial Gas Mfr
N.A.I.C.S.: 325120

Intensivpflegedienst Kompass GmbH   (1)
Planegger Str 41, 81241, Munich, Germany
Tel.: (49) 898 208 6775
Web Site: https://intensivpflege-kompass.de
Medical Devices
N.A.I.C.S.: 621610

Intensivservice Wanninger GmbH   (1)
Kronacher Strasse 1, 93057, Regensburg, Germany
Tel.: (49) 94 164 0840
Web Site: https://intensivservice.de
Medical Devices
N.A.I.C.S.: 621610

Irish Oxygen Company Ltd.   (1)
Waterfall Road, Cork, T12 PP40, Ireland
Tel.: (353) 214541821
Web Site: https://www.irishoxygen.com
Oxygen Gas Distribution Services
N.A.I.C.S.: 221210

Kisikana d.o.o   (1)
Brace Kavuric 12, 44000, Sisak, Croatia   (62.79%)
Tel.: (385) 44534852
Web Site: http://utp.solgroup.com
Sales Range: $25-49.9 Million
Emp.: 33
Industrial Gas Mfr
N.A.I.C.S.: 325120

Medtek Medizintechnik GmbH   (1)
Dieselstrasse 5, 67269, Grunstadt, Germany
Tel.: (49) 6359801790
Web Site: https://www.medtek-gmbh.de
Emp.: 6
Medical Devices
N.A.I.C.S.: 621610

Orthohub S.R.L.   (1)
Via di Tor Vergata 99/103A, 00133, Rome, Italy
Tel.: (39) 0686216628
Web Site: https://www.orthohub.it
Magneto Therapy & Press Therapy Device Mfr
N.A.I.C.S.: 339112

Pielmeier Medizintechnik GmbH   (1)
Wallbergstrasse 7, 82024, Taufkirchen, Germany
Tel.: (49) 89678055890
Web Site: https://www.pmt-med.de
Medical Development Services
N.A.I.C.S.: 541715

Profi Gesundheits - Service GmbH   (1)
Duhlwiesen 1, 55413, Eschweiler, Germany
Tel.: (49) 6721988330
Web Site: https://www.profi-gesundheits-service.de
Rehabilitation Clinic Services
N.A.I.C.S.: 623220

Respitek AS   (1)
Altunizade Mah Kisikli Cad No 35-1 Aksel Is Merkezi A Blok Kat 1, Uskudar, 34662, Istanbul, Turkiye
Tel.: (90) 2165458080
Web Site: https://respitek.com.tr
Medical Devices
N.A.I.C.S.: 621610

SOL See d.o.o.   (1)
    (99.88%)
Tel.: (389) 912031411
Emp.: 10
Industrial Gas Mfr
N.A.I.C.S.: 325120

SOL T.G. GmbH   (1)
Marie Curie Strasse 1, 2700, Wiener Neustadt, Austria   (100%)
Tel.: (43) 262289189
Web Site: http://www.sol-tg.at
Emp.: 30
Industrial Gas Mfr
N.A.I.C.S.: 325120

SOL Welding Srl   (1)
Via Meucci 26, Costabissara, Vicenza, Italy   (99.17%)
Tel.: (39) 0444290411
Web Site: http://www.tecnosol.com
Relay & Industrial Control Mfr
N.A.I.C.S.: 335314

SPG - Sol Plin Gorenjska d.o.o.   (1)
8 Cesta Zelezarjev, 4270, Jesenice, Slovenia   (100%)
Tel.: (386) 45833325
Industrial Gas Mfr
N.A.I.C.S.: 325120

Sicgilsol Gases Private Ltd.   (1)
No S2 Phase III Sipcot Industrial Complex, Ranipet, India
Tel.: (91) 442 852 1644
Natural Gas Distribution Services
N.A.I.C.S.: 221210

Sitex SA   (1)
Chemin des Aulx 12, 1228, Plan-les-Ouates, Switzerland
Tel.: (41) 848110000
Web Site: https://www.sitexsa.ch
Home Care Services
N.A.I.C.S.: 621610

Sol France SAS   (1)
8 Rue du Compas Z I Bethunes, 95060, Saint Ouen L'Aumone, France   (100%)
Tel.: (33) 134308660
Web Site: http://www.solfrance.com
Industrial Gas Mfr
N.A.I.C.S.: 325120

Sol Hydropower DOO   (1)
Aco Sopov 80, 1060, Skopje, North Macedonia
Tel.: (389) 22032411
Research & Development Services
N.A.I.C.S.: 541714

Sol India Private Ltd.   (1)
No 3 Tarapore Towers No 826 Anna Salai, Chennai, 600002, Tamilnadu, India
Tel.: (91) 4446350707
Web Site: https://www.sol-india.com
Medical Gas Pipeline Mfr & Distr
N.A.I.C.S.: 331210

SOL S.P.A.

SOL S.p.A.—(Continued)

Spitex Perspecta AG (1)
Tel.: (41) 612289828
Web Site: https://www.perspecta.ch
Health Care Srvices
N.A.I.C.S.: 621610

Sterimed SRL (1)
Tel.: (39) 0832366636
Web Site: https://www.sterimed.it
Medical Care Services
N.A.I.C.S.: 621610

T.G.K. Sofia AD (1)
Vladaiska Reka 12, 1510, Sofia,
Bulgaria **(78.46%)**
Tel.: (359) 29366449
Web Site: http://www.sofia.com
Industrial Gas Mfr
N.A.I.C.S.: 325120

T.G.S. AD (1)
16 Makedonska Brigada 18, 1000, Skopje,
North Macedonia **(96.16%)**
Tel.: (389) 23174026
Medical Dental & Hospital Equipment &
Supplies Whslr
N.A.I.C.S.: 423450

T.M.G. GmbH (1)
Warendorfer Strasse 10, 48361, Beelen,
Germany **(100%)**
Tel.: (49) 25861555
Web Site: http://www.tmg-beelen.de
Sales Range: $25-49.9 Million
Light Fixtures & Garden Furniture
N.A.I.C.S.: 337126

T.P.J. d.o.o. (1)
Trzaska c 23, 2000, Maribor,
Slovenia **(100%)**
Tel.: (386) 23324666
Web Site: http://www.tpj.com
Sales Range: $25-49.9 Million
Emp.: 2
Welding & Soldering Equipment Mfr
N.A.I.C.S.: 333992

TGK a.d. (1)
Lugovi Bb Kakmuz, 74317, Petrovo, Bosnia
& Herzegovina **(60.96%)**
Tel.: (387) 53252040
Sales Range: $1-9.9 Million
Emp.: 13
Industrial Gas Mfr
N.A.I.C.S.: 325120
Marco Annoni (Chm-Mgmt Bd & Pres)

TGT a.d. (1)
Street Nikole Pasica 28, 78250, Laktasi,
Bosnia & Herzegovina **(75.18%)**
Tel.: (387) 51784258
Sales Range: $1-9.9 Million
Emp.: 20
Petroleum Product Whslr
N.A.I.C.S.: 424720
Ivano Romanello (Member-Mgmt Bd)

Tesi Srl Tecnologia & Sicurezza (1)
Tel.: (39) 038264476
Web Site: https://www.tesisicurezza.com
Research & Development Services
N.A.I.C.S.: 541714

U.T.P. d.o.o (1)
Svetog Polikarpa 4, 52100, Pula,
Croatia **(61.53%)**
Tel.: (385) 52214886
Web Site: http://utp.solgroup.com
Sales Range: $25-49.9 Million
Emp.: 28
Medical Dental & Hospital Equipment &
Supplies Whslr
N.A.I.C.S.: 423450

VIVISOL B S.P.R.L. (1)
Zoning Ouest 14, 7860, Lessines,
Belgium **(100%)**
Tel.: (32) 68270640
Web Site: https://www.vivisol.be
Sales Range: $25-49.9 Million
Emp.: 30
Drugs & Druggists Whslr
N.A.I.C.S.: 424210

VIVISOL Calabria Srl (1)
Zona industriale, Porto Salvo Di VV Marina,
89811, Calabria, VV, Italy **(98.32%)**
Tel.: (39) 0963567484
Web Site: http://www.vivisol.miller.it

Pharmacies & Drug Stores
N.A.I.C.S.: 456110

Subsidiary (Domestic):

Vivisol Dello Stretto Srl (2)
Strada Zona Industriale, Vibo Valentia,
89900, Calabria, Italy **(98.32%)**
Tel.: (39) 0963567770
Industrial Gas Mfr
N.A.I.C.S.: 325120

VIVISOL Deutschland GmbH (1)
Hauptgeschaftsstelle Werner-von-Siemens-
Strasse 1, 85375, Neufahrn bei Freising,
Germany **(100%)**
Tel.: (49) 362892110
Web Site: https://www.vivisol.de
Sales Range: $50-74.9 Million
Retailers Stores
N.A.I.C.S.: 459999
Matteo Fumagalli Romario (Mng Dir)

VIVISOL France Sarl (1)
(100%)
Tel.: (33) 164391112
Web Site: https://www.vivisol.fr
Sales Range: $25-49.9 Million
Emp.: 50
Machinery & Equipment Rental & Leasing
Office
N.A.I.C.S.: 532420

VIVISOL Napoli Srl (1)
Via Giovanni Francesco Maggio, 81025,
Marcianise, CE, Italy **(70%)**
Tel.: (39) 0823821465
Web Site: http://www.vivisol.it
Sales Range: $25-49.9 Million
Emp.: 12
Medical Dental & Hospital Equipment &
Supplies Whslr
N.A.I.C.S.: 423450

VIVISOL Silarus S.R.L. (1)
Via Brodolini - zona industriale, 84091, Bat-
tipaglia, SA, Italy
Tel.: (39) 0828301849
Web Site: https://www.vivisolsilarus.com
Sales Range: $10-24.9 Million
Emp.: 12
Residential Care Facilities
N.A.I.C.S.: 623990

VIVISOL Umbria S.R.L. (1)
Via Mario Angeloni 8b, 06124, Perugia,
Italy **(70%)**
Tel.: (39) 0755001311
Web Site: http://www.vivisol.com
Industrial Gas Mfr
N.A.I.C.S.: 325120

VIVISOL srl (1)
(100%)
Tel.: (39) 0392396359
Web Site: https://www.vivisol.it
Sales Range: $10-24.9 Million
Emp.: 100
Home Care Services
N.A.I.C.S.: 621610

Vivicare GmbH (1)
Werner von Siemens Strasse 1, 85375,
Neufahrn bei Freising, Germany
Tel.: (49) 81656094566
Web Site: https://www.vivicare.de
Health Care Srvices
N.A.I.C.S.: 621610

Vivisol Adria DOO (1)
Tel.: (386) 82058812
Web Site: https://www.vivisol.si
Home Care Services
N.A.I.C.S.: 621610

Vivisol Brasil Ltda. (1)
Tel.: (55) 1148580338
Web Site: https://vivisol.com.br
Medical Equipment Distr
N.A.I.C.S.: 423450

Vivisol Czechia s.r.o. (1)
Na Ladech 125/6, 250 92, Prague, Czech
Republic
Tel.: (420) 286584553
Web Site: https://www.vivisol.cz
Home Care Services
N.A.I.C.S.: 621610

**Vivisol Heimbehandlungsgerate
GmbH** (1)

Richard Strauss Strasse 10, 1230, Vienna,
Austria
Tel.: (43) 15246283
Web Site: https://www.vivisol.at
Medical Care Services
N.A.I.C.S.: 621610

Vivisol Hellas SA (1)
Tel.: (30) 2106720400
Web Site: https://www.vivisol.gr
Home Care Services
N.A.I.C.S.: 621610

Vivisol Intensivservice GmbH (1)
Kronacher Strasse 1, 93057, Regensburg,
Germany
Tel.: (49) 941640840
Web Site: https://intensivservice.vivisol.de
Emp.: 6,000
Medical Development Services
N.A.I.C.S.: 541715

**Wip Weiterbildung In Der Pflege
GmbH** (1)
Werner-von-Siemens-Strasse 1, 85375,
Neufahrn bei Freising, Germany
Tel.: (49) 8982070742
Web Site: https://www.wip-fortbildung.de
Nursing Training Services
N.A.I.C.S.: 623110

ZDS Jesenice DOO (1)
Cesta Zelezarjev 8, 4270, Jesenice, Slove-
nia
Tel.: (386) 4 581 0240
Web Site: https://zds-jesenice.si
Electric Power Distribution Services
N.A.I.C.S.: 221122

SOL-GEL TECHNOLOGIES LTD.

Golda Meir 7, Ness Ziona, 7403650,
Israel
Tel.: (972) 89313433
Web Site: https://www.sol-gel.com
Year Founded: 1997
SLGL—(NASDAQ)
Rev.: $3,883,000
Assets: $46,628,000
Liabilities: $4,415,000
Net Worth: $42,213,000
Earnings: ($14,923,000)
Emp.: 55
Fiscal Year-end: 12/31/22
Biotechnology Research & Develop-
ment Services
N.A.I.C.S.: 541714
Alon Seri-Levy (Co-Founder & CEO)

SOLABIOS SA

33 boulevard de General Leclerc,
06240, Nice, France
Tel.: (33) 4 92 07 06 47
Web Site: http://www.solabios.com
Sales Range: $10-24.9 Million
Emp.: 40
Solar Power Producer
N.A.I.C.S.: 221118
Frederic Errera (Chm & CEO)

SOLAGRAN LIMITED

Level 11 492 St Kilda Road, Mel-
bourne, 3004, VIC, Australia
Tel.: (61) 398202699
Web Site: http://www.solagran.com
Sales Range: $1-9.9 Million
Biological Products Research & Com-
mercial Development Services
N.A.I.C.S.: 325414
Vagif Soultanov (Chm)

Subsidiaries:

SibEx Limited (1)
1a Kolkhoznaya St, Vlg Semiluzhki, Tomsk,
634530, Russia
Tel.: (7) 3822 545 060
Web Site: http://www.sibexzavod.ru
Biotechnology Products Mfr
N.A.I.C.S.: 541714

SOLANA D.D. TUZLA

INTERNATIONAL PUBLIC

Ul Soli 3, 75000, Tuzla, Bosnia &
Herzegovina
Tel.: (387) 35281260 BA
Web Site:
http://www.solanatuzla.com
Year Founded: 1885
SOLTRK3—(SARE)
Rev.: $17,213,206
Assets: $48,983,849
Liabilities: $14,479,861
Net Worth: $34,503,989
Earnings: $3,226,666
Emp.: 278
Fiscal Year-end: 12/31/21
Salt Mfr
N.A.I.C.S.: 311942
Ragib Babovic (Exec Dir-Production
& Maintenance)

SOLAR A/S

Industrivej Vest 43, 6600, Vejen, Den-
mark
Tel.: (45) 79300000
Web Site: https://www.solar.eu
Year Founded: 1919
SOLAR.B—(OMX)
Rev.: $666,882,800
Assets: $627,761,210
Liabilities: $305,544,570
Net Worth: $322,216,640
Earnings: $87,652,170
Emp.: 2,936
Fiscal Year-end: 12/31/21
Industrial Component Distr
N.A.I.C.S.: 423720
Jens Borum (Chm)

Subsidiaries:

Solar Nederland B.V. (1)
Toermalijnstraat 7, 1812 RL, Alkmaar, Neth-
erlands
Tel.: (31) 887652700
Web Site: https://www.solar.nl
Electrical Apparatus & Equipment Distr
N.A.I.C.S.: 423610
Andre Lankhorst (Mgr-Supply Chain Dev)

SOLAR ALLIANCE ENERGY INC.

620 1111 Melville Street, Vancouver,
V6E 4L4, BC, Canada
Tel.: (604) 288-9051 BC
Web Site:
http://www.solaralliance.com
Year Founded: 2003
SAN—(TSXV)
Rev.: $5,643,719
Assets: $1,361,253
Liabilities: $3,101,772
Net Worth: ($1,740,520)
Earnings: ($1,368,172)
Fiscal Year-end: 12/31/23
Solar Power Generation Services
N.A.I.C.S.: 221114
Jason Bak (Founder)

Subsidiaries:

Wildmare Wind Energy Corp. (1)

Wildmare Wind Energy Limited (1)

SOLAR APPLIED MATERIALS TECHNOLOGY CORPORATION

No 1 Gongye 3rd Road, Tainan Tech-
nology and Industrial Park Annan Dis-
trict, Tainan City, 70955, Taiwan
Tel.: (886) 65110123
Web Site:
https://www.solartech.com.tw
Year Founded: 1978
1785—(TPE)
Rev.: $806,384,454
Assets: $831,711,472
Liabilities: $418,883,438
Net Worth: $412,828,034
Earnings: $44,680,643
Emp.: 747

Fiscal Year-end: 12/31/22
Precious Metal Mfr & Distr
N.A.I.C.S.: 332215
Chien-Yung Ma (Chm)

Subsidiaries:

Forcera Materials Co., Ltd. (1)
No 56 Changchun Rd, Chang-An Village
Hukou Township, Hsinchu, 30347, Taiwan
Tel.: (886) 35696800
Web Site: https://www.forcera.com.tw
Metal Material Mfr & Distr
N.A.I.C.S.: 334413

Precision Packaging Materials
Corp. (1)
No 1 Sec 2 Huanyuan E Rd, Liuying Dist,
Tainan City, 73659, Taiwan
Tel.: (886) 6 623 1010
Web Site: https://www.ppmtech.com.tw
Metal Line Product Mfr
N.A.I.C.S.: 332312

Solar Applied Materials Technology
(Singapore) Pte. Ltd. (1)
Tel.: (65) 67563174
Metal Product Mfr & Distr
N.A.I.C.S.: 332312

Solar Applied Materials USA,
Inc. (1)
45311 Onondaga Dr, Fremont, CA 94539
Tel.: (510) 252-9548
Metal Product Mfr & Distr
N.A.I.C.S.: 332312

Solar Chemical Applied Material
Technology (KunShan) Co., Ltd. (1)
No 168 Wusongjiang South Road E T D Z,
Kunshan, 215300, China
Tel.: (86) 5125 763 8858
Metal Product Mfr & Distr
N.A.I.C.S.: 332312

Solar Green Materials Technology
Co., Ltd. (1)
No 135 East Road Chen Feng, Wusongjiang Economic Development Zone, Kunshan, 215300, Jiangsu, China
Tel.: (86) 5125 763 8858
Metal Product Mfr & Distr
N.A.I.C.S.: 332312

Universal Inspection & Certification
Technology Co., Ltd. (1)
Tel.: (886) 66231010
Metal Product Mfr & Distr
N.A.I.C.S.: 334413
C. F. Huang (CEO)

SOLAR CENTURY HOLDINGS LIMITED
50-52 Great Sutton St, Waterloo,
London, EC1V 0DF, United Kingdom
Tel.: (44) 20 7803 0100
Web Site:
  http://www.solarcentury.com
Year Founded: 1998
Sales Range: $75-99.9 Million
Emp.: 120
Solar Energy System Design & Installation Services
N.A.I.C.S.: 238290
Jeremy Leggett (Founder)

SOLAR COMPANY S.A.
ul Torowa 11, 61-315, Poznan, Poland
Tel.: (48) 61 871 30 20
Web Site: http://www.solar.com.pl
Year Founded: 1989
SOL—(WAR)
Sales Range: Less than $1 Million
Women's Clothing Mfr & Retailer
N.A.I.C.S.: 315250
Stanislaw Antoni Bogacki (Chm-Mgmt Bd)

SOLAR INDUSTRIES INDIA LIMITED
Solar House 14 Kachimet Amravati
Road, Nagpur, 440023, India
Tel.: (91) 7126634555
Web Site:
  https://www.solargroup.com
532725—(NSE)
Rev.: $346,307,325
Assets: $413,555,415
Liabilities: $189,408,765
Net Worth: $224,146,650
Earnings: $39,321,555
Emp.: 1,629
Fiscal Year-end: 03/31/21
Explosives Mfr; Ammonium Nitrate
Trading Services
N.A.I.C.S.: 325920
Khushboo Pasari (Officer-Compliance & Sec)

Subsidiaries:

Nigachem Nigeria Limited (1)
20 Sule Abuka Crescent Off Opebi Road,
Ikeja, Lagos, Nigeria
Tel.: (234) 8033222215
Web Site: https://www.nigachem.com.ng
Explosives Mfr
N.A.I.C.S.: 325920

Solar Mining Services Pty.
Limited (1)
Ground Floor Bates House Tybalt Place
Waterfall Office Park, Howick Close, Midrand, 1685, Gauteng, South Africa
Tel.: (27) 118831110
Web Site:
  https://www.solarminingservices.com
Explosives Mfr
N.A.I.C.S.: 325920

Solar Nitro chemicals Limited (1)
2nd Floor Oyster Pearl Galleria Chole
Road, PO Box 14431, Dar es Salaam, Tanzania
Tel.: (255) 763522662
Web Site: https://solarnitrochem.co.tz
Explosives Mfr
N.A.I.C.S.: 325920

Solar Patlayici Maddeler Sanayi Ve
Ticaret Anonim Sirketi (1)
Eskisehir Road 9th km Dumlupinar Bulvari
No 266 Tepe Prime B Blok No79, Cankaya,
06800, Ankara, Turkiye
Tel.: (90) 3122862425
Web Site: https://www.solarpatlayici.com
Explosives Mfr
N.A.I.C.S.: 325920

SOLAR MILLENNIUM AG
Nagelsbachstrasse 33, D-91052, Erlangen, Germany
Tel.: (49) 913194090
Web Site:
  http://www.solarmillennium.de
Year Founded: 1998
Renewable Energy Developer; Solar
Power Plant Engineering & Investment
N.A.I.C.S.: 221118
Oliver Blamberger (Member-Exec Bd)

Subsidiaries:

Solar Millennium MENA GmbH (1)
Nagelsbachstr 33, Erlangen, Germany
Tel.: (49) 913194090
Sales Range: $25-49.9 Million
Emp.: 45
Power Plant Construction Services
N.A.I.C.S.: 237130

Solar Trust of America, LLC (1)
3201 Enterprise Pkwy Ste 490, Cleveland,
OH 44122 (70%)
Tel.: (216) 763-8050
Web Site: http://solartrustofamerica.com
Holding Company; Solar Power Plant Development & Construction Services
N.A.I.C.S.: 551112

Subsidiary (Domestic):

STA Contracting, LLC (2)
363 N Sam Houston Pkwy E Ste 1710,
Houston, TX 77060
Tel.: (281) 741-6750
Web Site: http://solartrustofamerica.com
Solar Power Plant Construction Contractor
N.A.I.C.S.: 238990

STA Development, LLC (2)
1111 Broadway 5th Fl, Oakland, CA
94607 (100%)
Tel.: (510) 524-4517
Web Site: http://solartrustofamerica.com
Solar Power Plant Development Services
N.A.I.C.S.: 237210

SOLARA ACTIVE PHARMA SCIENCES LIMITED
2nd Floor Admin Block 27 Vandaloor
kelambakkam Road, Keelakottaiyur
Village, Chennai, 600032, Tamil
Nadu, India
Tel.: (91) 4443446700
Web Site: https://www.solara.co.in
Year Founded: 2017
541540—(BOM)
Rev.: $224,631,225
Assets: $356,753,670
Liabilities: $139,341,930
Net Worth: $217,411,740
Earnings: $30,221,100
Emp.: 2,575
Fiscal Year-end: 03/31/21
Pharmaceuticals Mfr
N.A.I.C.S.: 325412
Bharath R. Sesha (CEO & Mng Dir)

SOLAREAST HOLDINGS CO., LTD.
No 199 Yingzhou South Road, Haining Industry and Trade Park, Lianyungang, 222243, Jiangsu, China
Tel.: (86) 51885959992
Web Site: http://www.solareast.com
Year Founded: 1999
603366—(SHG)
Rev.: $547,206,866
Assets: $911,456,203
Liabilities: $373,394,151
Net Worth: $538,062,052
Earnings: $36,383,691
Fiscal Year-end: 12/31/22
Solar Heating Equipment Mfr & Distr
N.A.I.C.S.: 333414
Xinjian Xu (Chm)

SOLAREDGE TECHNOLOGIES, INC.
1 HaMada St, PO Box 12001, Herzliya Pituach, 4673335, Israel
Tel.: (972) 99576620 DE
Web Site: https://www.solaredge.com
Year Founded: 2006
SEDG—(NASDAQ)
Rev.: $3,110,279,000
Assets: $4,265,949,000
Liabilities: $2,089,583,000
Net Worth: $2,176,366,000
Earnings: $93,779,000
Emp.: 4,926
Fiscal Year-end: 12/31/22
Solar Photovoltaic Systems Mfr
N.A.I.C.S.: 334413
Yoav Galin (Co-Founder)

Subsidiaries:

Min Hagoren Development Ltd. (1)
Industrial Park 17 Hartom St, POB 45029,
Jerusalem, 9777517, Israel
Tel.: (972) 25888222
Web Site: http://criticalpower.solaredge.com
Rev.: $1,801,630
Assets: $56,006,077
Liabilities: $16,298,936
Net Worth: $39,707,141
Earnings: ($1,248,239)
Emp.: 187
Fiscal Year-end: 12/31/2023
Other Electronic Component Manufacturing
N.A.I.C.S.: 334419
Joseph Goren (Pres & CEO)

SOLAREDGE TECHNOLOGIES (INDIA) PRIVATE LIMITED (1)
14 2nd Floor B Wing Sankey Road Lower
Palace Orchards, Sadashivnagar, Bengaluru, 560 080, India
Tel.: (91) 9742077110
Solar Photovoltaic Device Mfr & Distr
N.A.I.C.S.: 334413

SOLAREDGE TEKNOLOJi. A.S. (1)
Ayazaga Mah Mimar Sinan Sok No 21
SEBA Office D Blok D 45, Istanbul, Turkiye
Tel.: (90) 2167061929
Solar Photovoltaic Device Mfr & Distr
N.A.I.C.S.: 334413

SolarEdge Technologies (Australia)
PTY LTD (1)
222 Exhibition St, Melbourne, 3000, VIC,
Australia
Tel.: (61) 1800465567
Semiconductor Equipment Mfr
N.A.I.C.S.: 333242
Gary Jubb (Mgr-Sls-Natl)

SolarEdge Technologies (Bulgaria)
Ltd. (1)
Ulitsa Prof D-r Ivan Stranski 19 Sofia-grad -
Yugozapaden, 1164, Sofia, Bulgaria
Tel.: (359) 24950485
Solar Electric Module Distr
N.A.I.C.S.: 423610

SolarEdge Technologies (Japan) Co.,
Ltd. (1)
Chigasaki Higashi 4-5-24 Building A,
Tsuzuki-ku, Yokohama, 103-0023, Japan
Tel.: (81) 5031989430
Semiconductor Equipment Mfr
N.A.I.C.S.: 333242

SolarEdge Technologies (Korea) Co.
Ltd. (1)
7F Pangyo Tech1 Tower2 131
Bungdangnaegok-ro, Bundang-gu, Seongnam, Gyeonggi-do, Korea (South)
Tel.: (82) 12710456810126517
Lithium Ion Batteries Mfr
N.A.I.C.S.: 325180

SolarEdge Technologies (Poland) Sp.
z o.o. (1)
Ul Opolska 22, 40-084, Katowice, Poland
Tel.: (48) 122005538
Web Site: https://www.solaredge.com
Solar Product Mfr
N.A.I.C.S.: 334413

SolarEdge Technologies (UK)
Ltd. (1)
15 Chester Road Colmworth Business Park,
Eaton Socon, PE19 8YT, Cambridgeshire,
United Kingdom
Tel.: (44) 8000281183
Solar Photovoltaic Device Mfr & Distr
N.A.I.C.S.: 334413

SolarEdge Technologies China (1)
Shanghai Cross Tower No 318 Fuzhou Rd
Unit 1409, Shanghai, 200001, China
Tel.: (86) 2162125536
Semiconductor Equipment Mfr
N.A.I.C.S.: 333242
James Higgins (Gen Mgr)

SolarEdge Technologies GmbH (1)
Werner-Eckert-Str 6, 81829, Munich, Germany
Tel.: (49) 894545970
Semiconductor Equipment Mfr
N.A.I.C.S.: 333242
Christoph Schon (Mgr-Sls-Central Europe)

SolarEdge Technologies Ltd. (1)
1 Hamada St, POB 12001, Herzliyya,
4673335, Israel
Tel.: (972) 99576620
Semiconductor Equipment Mfr
N.A.I.C.S.: 333242
Yaron Binder (VP-Product Mgmt)

Solaredge Technologies Italy
S.R.L. (1)
Via Enrico Reginato 85/H, 31100, Treviso,
Italy
Tel.: (39) 04221500205
Solar Photovoltaic Device Mfr & Distr
N.A.I.C.S.: 334413

SOLARGIGA ENERGY HOLDINGS LIMITED
Room 1402 Harbour Centre 25 Har-

SOLARGIGA ENERGY HOLDINGS LIMITED

Solargiga Energy Holdings Limited—(Continued)
bour Road, Wanchai, China (Hong Kong)
Tel.: (852) 34162000
Web Site: http://www.solargiga.com
0757—(HKG)
Rev.: $964,458,425
Assets: $1,086,278,170
Liabilities: $917,035,236
Net Worth: $169,242,934
Earnings: $156,126,625
Emp.: 3,029
Fiscal Year-end: 12/31/22
Polysilicon & Monocrystalline Silicon Ingots & Wafers Processor & Mfr
N.A.I.C.S.: 334413
Wenhua Tan *(Chm)*

Subsidiaries:

Jinzhou Jinmao Photovoltaic Technology Co., Ltd. (1)
No 1-5 Chifeng Street Xihai Industry Park, Jinzhou, 121007, Liaoning, China
Tel.: (86) 416 3595507
Photovoltaic Device Mfr
N.A.I.C.S.: 334413

Jinzhou Yangguang Energy Co., Ltd. (1)
No 1-5 Section 3 Chifeng Street, Economic and Technical Development Zone, Jinzhou, Liaoning, China
Tel.: (86) 4165081597
Solar Product Mfr
N.A.I.C.S.: 334413

Jinzhou Youhua Silicon Materials Co., Ltd. (1)
No 102 Jiefang West Rd, Jinzhou, Liaoning, China
Tel.: (86) 4167988123
Solar Product Mfr
N.A.I.C.S.: 334413

Solargiga Energy Holdings Limited - Jinzhou Plant (1)
No 1-5 Section 3 Chifeng Street, Economic and Technical Development Zone, Jinzhou, Liaoning, China
Tel.: (86) 4165081597
Web Site: http://www.solargiga.com
Monocrystalline Silicon Solar Ingots & Wafers Mfr
N.A.I.C.S.: 327999
Xin Tan *(CEO)*

Wealthy Rise International Limited (1)
Room 1402 Harbour Center 25 Harbour Road, Wanchai, China (Hong Kong)
Tel.: (852) 34162000
Web Site: http://www.solargiga.com
Monocrystalline Silicon Distr
N.A.I.C.S.: 423690

SOLARHYBRID AG

Keffelker Strasse 14, 59929, Brilon, Germany
Tel.: (49) 2961 96646 0   De
Year Founded: 2007
Sales Range: $10-24.9 Million
Emp.: 60
Solar Power Plants Mfr
N.A.I.C.S.: 237990
Tom Schroder *(CEO)*

SOLARIA ENERGIA Y MEDIO AMBIENTE, S.A.

C/ Princesa 2 - 4 Planta, 28008, Madrid, Spain
Tel.: (34) 915644272
Web Site: https://www.solariaenergia.com
Year Founded: 2002
SLR—(BIL)
Rev.: $150,314,051
Assets: $1,539,993,525
Liabilities: $1,167,958,126
Net Worth: $372,035,398
Earnings: $97,181,092
Emp.: 191

Fiscal Year-end: 12/31/22
Photovoltaic Modules & Cells Mfr
N.A.I.C.S.: 334413
Enrique Díaz-Tejeiro Gutierrez *(Chm)*

SOLARIS RESOURCES, INC.

Suite 555 999 Canada Place, Vancouver, V6C 3E1, BC, Canada
Tel.: (604) 687-1717
Web Site: http://www.solarisresources.com
SLS—(TSXV)
Rev.: $383,601
Assets: $46,681,518
Liabilities: $27,481,837
Net Worth: $19,199,681
Earnings: ($31,022,595)
Fiscal Year-end: 12/31/23
Mineral Exploration Services
N.A.I.C.S.: 213115
Richard Warke *(Chm)*

SOLARPARC GMBH

Karl-Legien-Strasse 188, 53117, Bonn, Germany
Tel.: (49) 22855920600   De
Web Site: http://www.solarparc.de
Solar & Wind Power Equipment Mfr
N.A.I.C.S.: 334419
Frank H. Asbeck *(Mng Dir)*

SOLARTECH INTERNATIONAL HOLDINGS LIMITED

Unit 15 18/F Concordia Plaza 1 Science Museum Road, Tsim Sha Tsui, Kowloon, China (Hong Kong)
Tel.: (852) 27961628
Web Site: http://www.1166hk.com
1166—(HKG)
Rev.: $37,181,194
Assets: $178,006,459
Liabilities: $47,882,922
Net Worth: $130,123,537
Earnings: ($18,536,877)
Emp.: 500
Fiscal Year-end: 06/30/20
Cables & Wires Mfr
N.A.I.C.S.: 333248
Kam Yee Chan *(Sec)*

Subsidiaries:

Brascabos Componentes Eletricos e Eletronicos Limitada (1)
Av Brasil 3464 Distrito Industrial, Rio Claro, 13505-600, SP, Brazil
Tel.: (55) 1935225122
Web Site: https://www.brascabos.com.br
Wires & Power Cords Mfr
N.A.I.C.S.: 331420
Glauber Marcal Rizzi *(Gen Mgr)*

Chaus Electrical Company Limited (1)
Unit 15 18/F Concordia Plaza 1 Science Museum Road, Tsim Sha Tsui, Kowloon, China (Hong Kong)
Tel.: (852) 2 796 1628
Web Site: https://www.chaus.com
Emp.: 1,000
Wire & Cable Mfr & Distr
N.A.I.C.S.: 335929

Dongguan Hua Yi Brass Products Co., Ltd. (1)
Huan Chang Bei Lu, Huayi Industrial Zone Changping, Dongguan, Guangdong, China
Tel.: (86) 7698 391 8628
Copper Rod Mfr & Distr
N.A.I.C.S.: 331420

Hua Yi Copper Products Company Limited (1)
Unit 15 18/F Concordia Plaza 1 Science Museum Road, Tsim Sha Tsui, Kowloon, China (Hong Kong)
Tel.: (852) 27589003
Web Site: https://www.1166hk.com
Copper Products Mfr & Sales
N.A.I.C.S.: 331420
Chau Lai Him *(Mng Dir)*

SIT Electronics Company Limited (1)
Pinthong Industrial Estate 789/71 Moo 1 Tambol, Nongkham A, Si Racha, 20230, Chon Buri, Thailand
Tel.: (66) 38296850
Sales Range: $50-74.9 Million
Emp.: 200
Wires & Connectors Mfr
N.A.I.C.S.: 331420

TEM Electronics (M) Sdn. Bhd. (1)
Lot A101 A102 Jalan 2A Kawasan Perusahaan MIEL Sungai Lalang, 08000, Sungai Petani, Kedah, Malaysia
Tel.: (60) 4 441 7802
Web Site: http://www.tem-group.com
Sales Range: $75-99.9 Million
Emp.: 250
Wires & Connectors Whslr
N.A.I.C.S.: 423510
Bee Ling *(Mgr-Matls & Customer Svc)*

SOLARTRON PUBLIC COMPANY LIMITED

77/31 32 33 Soi Chaeng Watthana 15 Intersection 2 Thung Song Hong, Lak Si, Bangkok, 10210, Thailand
Tel.: (66) 23920224   TH
Web Site: https://www.solartron.co.th
Year Founded: 1986
SOLAR—(THA)
Rev.: $7,881,626
Assets: $52,048,920
Liabilities: $34,624,092
Net Worth: $17,424,828
Earnings: ($4,841,688)
Fiscal Year-end: 12/31/22
Solar Cell Systems Mfr
N.A.I.C.S.: 339999
Patama Wongtoythong *(Deputy Chm, Sec & Exec Dir)*

SOLARVEST BIOENERGY INC.

439 Helmcken Street, Vancouver, V6B 2E6, BC, Canada
Tel.: (647) 204-4095
Web Site: https://www.solarvest.ca
Year Founded: 2005
0ZJ—(DEU)
Rev.: $52,126
Assets: $972,791
Liabilities: $5,080,960
Net Worth: ($4,108,168)
Earnings: ($585,715)
Fiscal Year-end: 07/31/24
Hydrogen Mfr
N.A.I.C.S.: 325120
Gerri J. Greenham *(CEO)*

Subsidiaries:

Solarvest (P.E.I.) Inc. (1)
64 Watts Ave, Charlottetown, C1E 2B8, PE, Canada
Tel.: (902) 892-7170
Biological Product Mfr
N.A.I.C.S.: 325414

SOLARVEST HOLDINGS BERHAD

L1-01 Pacific 63 PJ Centre No 5 Jalan 13/6 Seksyen 13, 46200, Petaling Jaya, Selangor, Malaysia
Tel.: (60) 376253211   MY
Web Site: https://solarvest.com
Year Founded: 2012
SLVEST—(KLS)
Rev.: $55,511,017
Assets: $55,968,302
Liabilities: $23,208,708
Net Worth: $32,759,595
Earnings: $4,067,908
Emp.: 168
Fiscal Year-end: 03/31/21
Holding Company
N.A.I.C.S.: 551112
Chong Chun Shiong *(CEO)*

SOLASIA PHARMA, K.K.

4F Sumitomo Fudosan ShibaKoen Tower 2111 Shibakoen Minato, Tokyo, 105-0011, Japan
Tel.: (81) 358438045   JP
Web Site: https://www.solasia.co.jp
Year Founded: 2006
4597—(TKS)
Rev.: $4,374,530
Assets: $15,803,610
Liabilities: $2,509,860
Net Worth: $13,293,750
Earnings: ($7,884,080)
Emp.: 27
Fiscal Year-end: 12/31/23
Pharmaceutical Products Distr
N.A.I.C.S.: 424210
Yoshihiro Arai *(Pres & CEO)*

Subsidiaries:

Solasia Medical Information Consulting (Shanghai) Co. Ltd. (1)
Unit03 18F Lujiazui Finance Plaza No 826 Century Avenue, Pudong, Shanghai, 200120, China
Tel.: (86) 2151167129
Web Site: https://www.solasia.com.cn
Pharmaceutical Products Distr
N.A.I.C.S.: 424210

SOLASTO CORPORATION

2-15-3 Konan Shinagawa Intercity C Building 12th floor, Minato-ku, Tokyo, 108-8210, Japan
Tel.: (81) 334502610
Web Site: https://www.solasto.co.jp
Year Founded: 1968
6197—(TKS)
Rev.: $893,268,790
Assets: $497,065,390
Liabilities: $361,659,540
Net Worth: $135,405,850
Earnings: $14,918,770
Emp.: 33,884
Fiscal Year-end: 03/31/24
Medical Outsourcing Services
N.A.I.C.S.: 621111
Yoshikazu Fujikawa *(Pres & CEO)*

Subsidiaries:

Nagoyaka CareLink Co., Ltd. (1)
6F A-Place Shinagawa East 1-7-18, Konan Minato-ku, Tokyo, 108-8210, Japan
Tel.: (81) 355772256
Web Site: https://www.nagoyaka-link.co.jp
Home Nursing Care Services
N.A.I.C.S.: 621610

SOLBORN, INC.

51 Hakdong-ro 95-gil, Gangnam-gu, Seoul, Korea (South)
Tel.: (82) 25197141
Web Site: http://www.solborn.co.kr
Year Founded: 1994
035610—(KRS)
Rev.: $71,956,939
Assets: $169,255,214
Liabilities: $29,335,703
Net Worth: $139,919,511
Earnings: ($31,992,910)
Emp.: 11
Fiscal Year-end: 12/31/22
Real Estate Manangement Services
N.A.I.C.S.: 531390
Ki-Tae Hong *(Chm & CEO)*

SOLCO BIOMEDICAL CO., LTD.

154 Seotan-ro, Seotan-myeon, Pyeongtaek, 17704, Gyeonggi-do, Korea (South)
Tel.: (82) 316104000
Web Site: http://www.solco.co.kr
043100—(KRS)
Rev.: $17,945,014
Assets: $41,334,327
Liabilities: $18,729,845
Net Worth: $22,604,482
Earnings: ($5,662,798)

Emp.: 104
Fiscal Year-end: 12/31/22
Medical Instrument Mfr
N.A.I.C.S.: 339112
Kim Jae Wook *(CEO)*

Subsidiaries:

RM Life Science Co., Ltd. (1)
1001 648 Seobusaet-gil, Geumcheon-gu,
Seoul, Korea (South)
Tel.: (82) 28389511
Web Site: http://www.rmlife.co.kr
Medical Device Mfr
N.A.I.C.S.: 339112

Solco Pyroelec UK Ltd. (1)
Unit 11 Kenyon Business Park Pilkington
Street, Bolton, BL3 6HL, United Kingdom
Tel.: (44) 1204869449
Web Site: https://www.solcopyroelec.co.uk
Heat Tracing & Leak Detection Product Mfr
N.A.I.C.S.: 334519
Bo Hwan Lee *(CEO)*

SOLDERA MINING CORP.
5 Hazelton Avenue Suite 400, Toronto, M5R 2E1, ON, Canada
Tel.: (248) 662-5565
Web Site: https://ammpower.com
AMMP—(CNSX)
Rev.: $146,526
Assets: $1,964,099
Liabilities: $5,226,304
Net Worth: ($3,262,205)
Earnings: ($2,606,088)
Fiscal Year-end: 05/31/24
Mineral Exploration Services
N.A.I.C.S.: 213115
Rene Bharti *(Pres)*

SOLE ELITE GROUP LIMITED
Wuli Industrial Park, Jinjiang, 362200, Futian, China
Tel.: (86) 595 88169779   Ky
Year Founded: 2006
Sales Range: $100-124.9 Million
Emp.: 1,876
Sport Shoe Sole Products Mfr
N.A.I.C.S.: 316210
Sixing Ding *(Chm & CEO)*

SOLEGREEN LTD.
Rothschild avenue 107, Jaffa, Tel Aviv, 6527107, Israel
Tel.: (972) 88634300
PQSA—(TAE)
Rev.: $38,364,691
Assets: $414,022,096
Liabilities: $318,255,279
Net Worth: $95,766,817
Earnings: ($86,369,110)
Fiscal Year-end: 12/31/23
Research & Development in Biotechnology (except Nanobiotechnology)
N.A.I.C.S.: 541714
Tom Shafran *(CEO)*

SOLEIL LEVANT AUTOMOBILES SARL
La Croix des Landes, 53940, Saint Berthevin, Mayenne, France
Tel.: (33) 243682154
Web Site: http://www.sla-bourdais.com
Sales Range: $10-24.9 Million
Emp.: 13
Automobile Dealership
N.A.I.C.S.: 441110
Gina Bourdais *(Mng Partner)*

SOLEKIA LIMITED
8-16-6 Nishikamata, Ota-ku, Tokyo, 144-8626, Japan
Tel.: (81) 337321131
Web Site: https://www.solekia.com
Year Founded: 1958
9867—(TKS)
Rev.: $166,426,580

Assets: $131,889,330
Liabilities: $65,432,390
Net Worth: $66,456,940
Earnings: $6,907,450
Emp.: 750
Fiscal Year-end: 03/31/24
System Consulting & Planning Services
N.A.I.C.S.: 541512
Yoshikazu Kobayashi *(Pres & CEO)*

Subsidiaries:

Solekia Hong Kong Limited (1)
Unit 10-18 32/F Tower 1 Millennium City 1 Room 3238 388 Kwun Tong Road, Kwun Tong, Kowloon, China (Hong Kong)
Tel.: (852) 3972 2519
Sales & Support of Electronic Device, Information Communication Equipment & Solution Services
N.A.I.C.S.: 423430

Solekia Platz Corp. (1)
8-16-6 Nishikamata, Ota-ku, Tokyo, 144-0051, Japan   (100%)
Tel.: (81) 337396118
System Consulting & Planning Services
N.A.I.C.S.: 541512
Yoshikazu Kobayashi *(Chm)*

Solekia Singapore Pte. Ltd. (1)
190 Middle Road 12-07 Fortune Centre, Singapore, 188979, Singapore
Tel.: (65) 8133732
Web Site: https://sg.solekia.com
System Consulting, Design & Maintenance Services; Import & Export of Electronic Devices, Components & Semiconductors
N.A.I.C.S.: 541512
Miura Takashi *(Mng Dir)*

Solekia Vietnam Limited (1)
Unit 04 17th Floor Keangnam hanoi Landmark Tower Lot E6 New Urban Area, Cau Giay Me Tri Ward, Tu Lien District, Hanoi, Vietnam
Tel.: (84) 4 6282 3098
System Consulting, Design & Maintenance Services; Import & Export of Electronic Devices, Components & Semiconductors
N.A.I.C.S.: 541512

SOLEX ENERGY LIMITED
Plot No 131/A Phase-1 H M Road G I D C Vitthal Udyognagar, Anand, 388121, Gujarat, India
Tel.: (91) 2692230317
Web Site: http://www.solex.in
Year Founded: 1998
SOLEX—(NSE)
Rev.: $19,709,646
Assets: $16,879,228
Liabilities: $12,367,880
Net Worth: $4,511,348
Earnings: $325,004
Emp.: 368
Fiscal Year-end: 03/31/23
Renewable Energy Solutions
N.A.I.C.S.: 221114
Anil Rathi *(Exec Dir)*

SOLGENIA S.P.A.
Loc Madonna di Lugo, Spoleto, 6049, Italy
Tel.: (39) 0743221820
Web Site: http://www.solgenia.com
Sales Range: $50-74.9 Million
Emp.: 300
Business Software & Solutions
N.A.I.C.S.: 513210
Ermanno Bonifazi *(Pres)*

Subsidiaries:

Gruppo PRO S.p.A. (1)
Via 2 Agosto 1980 19, 40056, Crespellano, Italy
Tel.: (39) 051969248
Business Intelligence Solutions
N.A.I.C.S.: 513210

SOLGOLD PLC
PO Box 7059, Cloisters Square PO, Perth, 6850, WA, Australia
Tel.: (61) 2038076996   UK
Web Site: https://www.solgold.com.au
SOLG—(LSE)
Assets: $309,731,199
Liabilities: $139,717,918
Net Worth: $170,013,281
Earnings: ($40,264,722)
Emp.: 254
Fiscal Year-end: 06/30/24
Gold Ore Mining Services
N.A.I.C.S.: 212220
Nicholas Mather *(CEO & Mng Dir)*

Subsidiaries:

Cornerstone Capital Resources Inc. (1)
1730 St. Laurent Blvd. Suite 800, Ottawa, K1G 3Y7, ON, Canada
Tel.: (709) 745-8377
Web Site: http://www.cornerstoneresources.com
Rev.: $229,708
Assets: $102,529,106
Liabilities: $16,163,535
Net Worth: $86,365,570
Earnings: ($54,897,425)
Fiscal Year-end: 12/31/2019
Mineral Exploration Services
N.A.I.C.S.: 213114
David Loveys *(CFO)*

Subsidiary (Non-US):

Cornerstone Ecuador S.A. (2)
Av 12 de Octubre N24-528 y Cordero, Edif Word Trade Center Torreb Ofc 205, Quito, Pichincha, Ecuador
Tel.: (593) 22232084
Web Site: http://www.cornerstoneecuador.com
Metal Mining Services
N.A.I.C.S.: 213114

SOLIA SA
18 Avenue du Romani, 66600, Rivesaltes, France
Tel.: (33) 468642222
Web Site: http://www.solia.fr
Year Founded: 1995
Sales Range: $25-49.9 Million
Emp.: 42
Plastic Container Mfr
N.A.I.C.S.: 326199

SOLID AUTOMOTIVE BERHAD
No 5 Jalan Dataran 5, Taman Kempas, 81200, Johor Bahru, Malaysia
Tel.: (60) 72386363
Web Site: https://www.solidautomotive.com
Year Founded: 1982
SOLID—(KLS)
Rev.: $73,392,335
Assets: $62,068,049
Liabilities: $20,580,611
Net Worth: $41,487,438
Earnings: $2,051,005
Emp.: 508
Fiscal Year-end: 04/30/23
Engine, Electrical & Other Motor Vehicle Parts Distr
N.A.I.C.S.: 423120
Min Choo Ker *(Mng Dir)*

Subsidiaries:

Borneo Technical Co. (M) Sdn. Bhd. (1)
Lot DC01 Lot 2 Persiaran Sukan Seksyen 13, 40100, Shah Alam, Selangor, Malaysia
Tel.: (60) 356247888
Web Site: https://borneogroup.com.my
Automobile Parts Distr
N.A.I.C.S.: 423120

JBS Auto-Tech Sdn Bhd - Johor Bahru Plant (1)
17 Jalan Kukuh Off Jalan Tampoi, Kawasan Perindustrian Tampoi, 81200, Johor Bahru, Johor, Malaysia
Tel.: (60) 72375075
Automobile Parts Mfr
N.A.I.C.S.: 336320

Solid Corporation Sdn Bhd (1)
No 7 Jalan Dataran 5 Taman Kempas, 81200, Johor Bahru, Johor, Malaysia
Tel.: (60) 7 238 5108
Automobile Parts Distr
N.A.I.C.S.: 423120

Subsidiary (Domestic):

Uni Point Marketing (M) Sdn Bhd (2)
No 6 Jalan Firma 2/2 Kawasan Perindustrian Tebrau I, Johor Bahru, 81100, Johar, Malaysia
Tel.: (60) 9 513 3928
Automobile Parts Distr
N.A.I.C.S.: 423120

Win Soon Auto Suppliers (JB) Sdn. Bhd. (1)
No 6Jalan Ipoh Batu 5 Kampung Batu, 51200, Kuala Lumpur, Wilayah Persekutuan, Malaysia
Tel.: (60) 362578494
Web Site: https://my521283-win-soon-auto-suppliers-sdn-bhd.contact.page
Automobile Parts Distr
N.A.I.C.S.: 423120

SOLID BANK JSC
Aleutkskaya st 33, Primorskii Krai, 690091, Vladivostok, Russia
Tel.: (7) 4232265722
Web Site: http://www.solidbank.ru
Year Founded: 1991
Sales Range: Less than $1 Million
Commercial Banking Services
N.A.I.C.S.: 522110
Vozisov Igor Vyacheslavovich *(Chm-Mgmt Bd)*

SOLID CARBIDE TOOLS LIMITED
A 735 TTC Industrial Area Khairne MIDC, Thane Belapur Road, Navi Mumbai, 400705, Maharashtra, India
Tel.: (91) 2227697041
Web Site: http://www.solidcarbide.in
Rev.: $7,920
Assets: $42,545
Liabilities: $206,664
Net Worth: ($164,119)
Earnings: ($45,950)
Fiscal Year-end: 03/31/18
Industrial Cutting Tool Mfr
N.A.I.C.S.: 333515
Dilip S. Shah *(CFO)*

SOLID CONTAINERS LTD.
2006 Fossberry Road Near ICI Ltd Reay Road East, Mumbai, 400033, India
Tel.: (91) 2224920212
Web Site: http://www.solidcontainers.net
Year Founded: 1964
502460—(BOM)
Rev.: $46,301
Assets: $637,400
Liabilities: $8,522,145
Net Worth: ($7,884,745)
Earnings: ($308,394)
Emp.: 3
Fiscal Year-end: 03/31/21
Paper Bag Mfr
N.A.I.C.S.: 322219
Francis Miranda *(CFO)*

SOLID GROUP, INC.
Green Sun formerly Solid House 2285 Don Chino Roces Avenue Extension, Makati, 1231, Philippines
Tel.: (63) 288431511
Web Site: https://www.solidgroup.com.ph

SOLID GROUP, INC.

Solid Group, Inc.—(Continued)
SGI—(PHI)
Rev.: $44,539,597
Assets: $258,433,921
Liabilities: $35,387,352
Net Worth: $223,046,569
Earnings: $9,601,248
Emp.: 435
Fiscal Year-end: 12/31/23
Real Estate Services
N.A.I.C.S.: 531311
Ana Maria A. Katigbak-Lim *(Asst Sec)*

Subsidiaries:

Casa Bocobo Hotel Inc. (1)
Jorge Bocobo St, Ermita, Manila, Philippines
Tel.: (63) 9178148927
Web Site: https://www.casabocobo.com
Hotel Operator
N.A.I.C.S.: 721110

Casba Bocobo Hotel Inc. (1)
Jorge Bocobo Street, Ermita, Manila, 1000, Philippines
Tel.: (63) 28 526 3783
Web Site: https://casa-bocobo-hotel.business.site
Hotel Operator
N.A.I.C.S.: 721110

Green Sun Hotel Management Inc. (1)
2285 Chino Roces Avenue Extension, Magallanes, Makati, 1200, Philippines
Tel.: (63) 28 548 4200
Web Site: https://www.greensun.com.ph
Hotel Operator
N.A.I.C.S.: 721110

My Solid Technologies & Devices Corp (1)
3rd Floor Green Sun 2285 Chino Roces Ave Extension, Makati, Philippines
Tel.: (63) 28 937 1111
Web Site: https://www.myphone.com.ph
Mobile Phone Distr
N.A.I.C.S.: 423690
Israel Cruz *(Sls Mgr)*

Omni Solid Services Inc. (1)
17 A Fernando St, Marulas, Valenzuela, 1440, Philippines
Tel.: (63) 28 277 9109
Web Site: https://www.omni.com.ph
Warehousing & Distribution Services
N.A.I.C.S.: 493110

Solid Laguna Corporation (1)
2000 East Service Road South Luzon Expressway, Bicutan, Paranaque, 1700, Philippines
Tel.: (63) 28370195
Web Site: http://www.omni.com.ph
Emp.: 100
Injection Molded Plastic Products Mfr
N.A.I.C.S.: 326199
Johnny A. Quinto *(Mgr-Testing Laboratory)*

Solid Video Corporation (1)
Green Sun 2285 Don Chino Roces Ave Ext, Makati, 1231, Philippines
Tel.: (63) 2 893 7994
Web Site: https://www.solidvideo.com
Sales Range: $25-49.9 Million
Emp.: 22
Video Equipment Distr
N.A.I.C.S.: 423410

Solid Video Corporation Solid Electronics Corporation (1)
Green Sun 2285 Don Chino Roces Ave Ext, Makati, 1231, Philippines
Tel.: (63) 2 893 7994
Web Site: https://www.solidvideo.com
Broadcasting Equipment Distr
N.A.I.C.S.: 423690

Solidservice Electronics Corporation (1)
4F Solvida Bldg G Araneta Ave Brgy, Tatalon, Quezon City, Philippines
Tel.: (63) 289201111
Web Site: https://www.solidservice.com.ph
Television & Audio Product Mfr & Distr
N.A.I.C.S.: 334220

SOLID INC.
10th Fl SOLiD Space 220 Pangyoyeok-ro, Bundang-gu, Seongnam, 463-400, Korea (South)
Tel.: (82) 316276000
Web Site: https://www.solid.co.kr
050890—(KRS)
Rev.: $214,595,516
Assets: $333,135,075
Liabilities: $157,587,939
Net Worth: $175,547,136
Earnings: $22,888,291
Emp.: 199
Fiscal Year-end: 12/31/22
Telecommunication Servicesb
N.A.I.C.S.: 517111
Seung Hui Lee *(CEO)*

Subsidiaries:

Solidsystems Inc. (1)
Solid Space 8F Pangyoyeok-ro 220 Bundang-gu Seongnam-si, Gyeonggi-do, Seoul, 463-400, Korea (South)
Tel.: (82) 31 627 6300
Web Site: http://www.solidsystems.co.kr
Networking Services
N.A.I.C.S.: 517111
Myong-woon Kim *(CEO)*

SOLID STATE PLC
Ravensbank Business Park Hedera Road, Redditch, B98 9EY, Worcestershire, United Kingdom
Tel.: (44) 1527830666
Web Site: https://www.solidstateplc.com
SOLI—(AIM)
Rev.: $156,999,150
Assets: $141,224,769
Liabilities: $69,303,024
Net Worth: $71,921,745
Earnings: $8,302,959
Fiscal Year-end: 03/31/23
Electronic Components Distr
N.A.I.C.S.: 423690
Gary Stephen Marsh *(CEO)*

Subsidiaries:

Solid State Supplies Limited (1)
Unit 2 Magazine B Ordnance Yard Upnor Road, Lower Upnor, Worcester, ME2 4UY, Kent, United Kingdom
Tel.: (44) 1634298900
Web Site: https://www.sssltd.com
Sales Range: $25-49.9 Million
Electronic Components Distr
N.A.I.C.S.: 423620
John MacMichael *(Mng Dir)*

Steatite Limited (1)
Ravensbank Business Park Acanthus Road, Redditch, B98 9EX, Worcestershire, United Kingdom
Tel.: (44) 1527512400
Web Site: https://www.steatite.co.uk
Sales Range: $25-49.9 Million
Electronic Components Mfr & Distr
N.A.I.C.S.: 423620
Matthew Thomas Richards *(Mng Dir)*

Division (Domestic):

Steatite Ltd - Embedded Division (2)
Ravensbank Business Park Acanthus Road, Redditch, B98 9EX, Worcestershire, United Kingdom
Tel.: (44) 1527512400
Web Site: https://www.steatite-embedded.co.uk
Sales Range: $25-49.9 Million
Embedded Boards & Computer Sales
N.A.I.C.S.: 423430

Steatite Ltd - Rugged Division (2)
Ravensbank Business Park Acanthus Road, Redditch, B98 9EX, Worcestershire, United Kingdom
Tel.: (44) 1527512400
Web Site: http://www.steatite-rugged.co.uk
Sales Range: $25-49.9 Million
Hand Held Computers Mfr
N.A.I.C.S.: 334111

SOLID STATE SYSTEM CO., LTD.
5F 1 No 22 Taiyuan St, Tai Yuen Hi-Tech Industrial Park Hsinchu, Zhubei, 30288, Taiwan
Tel.: (886) 35526568
Web Site: https://www.3system.com.tw
Year Founded: 1998
3259—(TPE)
Rev.: $12,588,094
Assets: $19,691,399
Liabilities: $4,131,288
Net Worth: $15,560,110
Earnings: ($4,895,069)
Emp.: 117
Fiscal Year-end: 12/31/22
Semiconductor Product Mfr
N.A.I.C.S.: 334413
Jeffrey Lin *(Chm)*

SOLID STONE COMPANY LIMITED
1501 Maker Chambers V, Nariman Point, Mumbai, 400 021, India
Tel.: (91) 2266115800
Web Site: https://www.solid-stone.com
513699—(BOM)
Rev.: $2,358,098
Assets: $6,223,667
Liabilities: $3,365,477
Net Worth: $2,858,190
Earnings: ($105,582)
Emp.: 32
Fiscal Year-end: 03/31/21
Stone Product Mfr
N.A.I.C.S.: 327991
Milan B. Khakhar *(Chm & Co-Mng Dir)*

SOLID WORLD S.P.A.
Via E Reginato 87, 31100, Treviso, Italy
Tel.: (39) 04221990911
Web Site: https://www.solidworld.it
Year Founded: 2003
S3D—(ITA)
Rev.: $68,418,458
Assets: $72,825,076
Liabilities: $59,600,061
Net Worth: $13,225,015
Earnings: ($2,071,098)
Emp.: 223
Fiscal Year-end: 12/31/23
Software Development Services
N.A.I.C.S.: 541511
Roberto Rizzo *(CEO & Chm)*

Subsidiaries:

Bio3DModel S.r.l. (1)
Via Signorelli 6/8-Loc Sambuca, 50028, Barberino Tavarnelle, Fl, Italy
Tel.: (39) 0550354533
Web Site: https://bio3dmodel.it
3D Printing Services
N.A.I.C.S.: 541990

SolidCam Italia S.r.l. (1)
Via Monari Sarde 2, 40010, Bentivoglio, BO, Italy
Tel.: (39) 0293997311
Web Site: https://solidcam.it
Software Development Services
N.A.I.C.S.: 541511

SolidWorld Middle East DMCC (1)
2704-39 Sangsbeel Business Centre AA1 Mazaya Business Avenue, Jumeirah Lake Towers, Dubai, United Arab Emirates
Tel.: (971) 42088000
Web Site: https://www.solidworld.ae
3D Printing Services
N.A.I.C.S.: 541990

Solidfactory S.r.l. (1)
via Roma 220, 31020, Villorba, TV, Italy
Tel.: (39) 0422722970
Web Site: https://solidfactory.it
Digital Transformation Services

INTERNATIONAL PUBLIC

N.A.I.C.S.: 518210

Tecnologia & Design S.c.a.r.l. (1)
Via delle Industrie 18/20, 31050, Ponzano Veneto, TV, Italy
Tel.: (39) 0422967863
Web Site: https://www.tecnologiaedesign.it
3D Printing Services
N.A.I.C.S.: 541990

Valore BF 3D S.r.l. (1)

SOLIDA-WERK WERKZEUGTECHNIK GMBH & CO.
Auf dem Knapp 10, DE-42855, Remscheid, Germany
Tel.: (49) 219137150
Web Site: http://www.solida-werk.de
Rev.: $17,932,200
Emp.: 75
Electric Hammer & Hydraulic Tools Mfr
N.A.I.C.S.: 332216
Thomas Schäfer *(Mng Dir)*

SOLIDARITY ALLIANCE INSURANCE COMPANY
Nazem Basha St, Damascus, Syria
Tel.: (963) 11 3016
Web Site: http://www.solidarity-sy.com
Year Founded: 2008
SAIC—(DSE)
Sales Range: Less than $1 Million
Insurance Management Services
N.A.I.C.S.: 524298
Azmi AliDib *(Gen Mgr)*

SOLIDARITY GROUP HOLDING BSC
Seef Tower - 9th Floor, PO Box 18668, Seef District, Manama, Bahrain
Tel.: (973) 17585222
Web Site: http://www.solidaritygroup.com
Sales Range: $75-99.9 Million
Emp.: 150
Insurance, Investment & Asset Management Services
N.A.I.C.S.: 524298
Ashraf Bseisu *(CEO)*

Subsidiaries:

Solidarity Takafol S.A. (1)
3 r Alexandre Fleming, 1525, Luxembourg, Luxembourg
Tel.: (352) 441067
General Insurance Services
N.A.I.C.S.: 524298

SOLIDCORE RESOURCES PLC
Narodnogo Opolcheniya str 2, 198216, Saint Petersburg, Russia
Tel.: (7) 8123343666
Web Site: http://www.polymetalnational.com
Year Founded: 2010
POLY—(MOEX)
Rev.: $30,293,690
Assets: $65,757,099
Liabilities: $41,509,169
Net Worth: $24,247,930
Earnings: ($3,114,810)
Emp.: 14,495
Fiscal Year-end: 12/31/22
Holding Company; Gold & Silver Ore Mining Services
N.A.I.C.S.: 551112
Maxim Nazimok *(CFO)*

Subsidiaries:

JSC Polymetal (1)
Narodnogo Opolcheniya str 2, 198216, Saint Petersburg, Russia
Tel.: (7) 8123343666

Web Site:
http://www.polymetalinternational.com
Metal Mining Services
N.A.I.C.S.: 212290
Maxim Nazimok *(CFO)*

Subsidiary (Domestic):

Albazino Resources Ltd (2)
2 Shosse Mashinostroitelei, Amursk, Russia
Tel.: (7) 8123208325
Gold & Silver Ore Mining Services
N.A.I.C.S.: 212220

Polymetal Eurasia LLC (1)
D Kunaeva str 10, Nur-Sultan, 010000, Kazakhstan
Tel.: (7) 7172610222
Gold Ore Mining Services
N.A.I.C.S.: 212220
Kazybek Toluspayev *(Dir-HR)*

SOLIDIUM OY
Unioninkatu 32 B, 00100, Helsinki, Finland
Tel.: (358) 10 830 8900 FI
Web Site: http://www.solidium.fi
Emp.: 12
Investment Holding Company
N.A.I.C.S.: 551112
Annareetta Lumme-Timonen *(Dir-Investment)*

SOLIDNOST A.D.
Veljka Vlahovica 55, Kraljevo, Serbia
Tel.: (381) 36 321 622
Year Founded: 1956
SLDS—(BEL)
Sales Range: Less than $1 Million
Emp.: 3
Beauty Salon Operator
N.A.I.C.S.: 812112
Tanja Ivanovic *(Exec Dir)*

SOLIDUS SECURITIES S.A.
Louise Riancourt 64 Apollon Tower 17th fl 1st wing, Athens, Greece
Tel.: (30) 2106900600
Web Site: https://www.solidus.gr
Securities Brokerage Services
N.A.I.C.S.: 523150
Panagiotis Goulas *(CEO & VP)*

SOLIDUSGOLD INC.
10th Floor 595 Howe Street, Vancouver, V6C 2T5, BC, Canada
Tel.: (604) 628-1162 BC
Web Site: http://www.solidusau.com
Year Founded: 2011
SDC—(TSXV)
Assets: $57,782
Liabilities: $176,965
Net Worth: ($119,183)
Earnings: ($128,188)
Fiscal Year-end: 03/31/20
Investment Services
N.A.I.C.S.: 523999
Kara Norman *(CFO)*

SOLIDWIZARD TECHNOLOGY CO., LTD.
No 28 Ln 78 Xing'ai Rd, Neihu District, Taipei, 114, Taiwan
Tel.: (886) 227951618
Web Site: https://swtc.com
Year Founded: 1997
8416—(TPE)
Rev.: $43,597,067
Assets: $53,572,898
Liabilities: $10,927,805
Net Worth: $42,645,093
Earnings: $9,570,522
Fiscal Year-end: 12/31/22
Information Technology Services
N.A.I.C.S.: 541512
Chien Hsing Lee *(Chm)*

SOLIDX AB
Sodergatan 13, 211 34, Malmo, Sweden
Tel.: (46) 706215327
Web Site: https://www.solidx.se
Year Founded: 2001
6OK—(DEU)
Software Development Services
N.A.I.C.S.: 541511
Gabriel Paulison *(Chm)*

SOLIKAMSKIY MAGNIYEVYI ZAVOD OAO
Pravda st 9, Solikamsk, 618541, Russia
Tel.: (7) 3425351171
Web Site: https://eng.smw.ru
MGNZ—(MOEX)
Sales Range: Less than $1 Million
Emp.: 3,109
Non Ferrous Metal Mfr
N.A.I.C.S.: 331110
Dimukhamedov Ruslan Rafkatovich *(Gen Dir)*

SOLIS HOLDINGS LIMITED
85 Tagore Lane, Singapore, 787527, Singapore
Tel.: (65) 67552292 Ky
Web Site:
https://www.thesolisgrp.com
Year Founded: 1983
2227—(HKG)
Rev.: $14,246,005
Assets: $53,094,751
Liabilities: $15,854,730
Net Worth: $37,240,021
Earnings: ($5,302)
Emp.: 141
Fiscal Year-end: 12/31/23
Building Maintenance Services
N.A.I.C.S.: 561790
Yong Hua Tay *(Founder & Chm)*

SOLIS MARKETING LIMITED
House No 4346 Ground Floor Gali No 4C Ansari Road, Darya Ganj, New Delhi, 110 002, India
Tel.: (91) 11 65912021 In
Year Founded: 1985
Rev.: $175,530
Assets: $1,786,755
Liabilities: $957,553
Net Worth: $829,202
Earnings: $2,235
Emp.: 2
Fiscal Year-end: 03/31/18
Durable Import & Export Services
N.A.I.C.S.: 522299
Arun Kumar Dey *(CFO)*

SOLIS MINERALS LTD.
550 Burrard Street Suite 2501, Vancouver, V6C 2B5, BC, Canada
Tel.: (604) 209-1658 BC
Web Site: https://solisminerals.com
Year Founded: 2005
SLM—(ASX)
Assets: $8,592,165
Liabilities: $330,269
Net Worth: $8,261,896
Earnings: ($8,841,924)
Fiscal Year-end: 05/31/24
Metal Mining Services
N.A.I.C.S.: 212290
Jason Cubitt *(Pres & CEO)*

SOLITAIRE GROUP LTD
Lynwood House 10 Victors Way, Barnet, EN5 5TZ, Herts, United Kingdom
Tel.: (44) 2084496125
Web Site:
http://www.solitairegroup.com
Sales Range: $10-24.9 Million
Emp.: 125
Residential & Commercial Real Estate Management Services

N.A.I.C.S.: 531390
George Brutton *(Chm)*

SOLITAIRE MACHINES TOOLS LIMITED
Shop 3-A Floor-Bas Plot 731 Part 3 Arun Chambers, Pandit Madan Mohan Malviya Marg Tardeo, Mumbai, 400 034, Maharashtra, India
Tel.: (91) 2266602156
Web Site:
http://www.smtgrinders.com
522152—(BOM)
Rev.: $1,894,238
Assets: $2,729,973
Liabilities: $558,189
Net Worth: $2,171,783
Earnings: $144,089
Emp.: 82
Fiscal Year-end: 03/31/22
Precision Centerless Grinder Mfr
N.A.I.C.S.: 333991
Ashok J. Sheth *(Chm & Mng Dir)*

Subsidiaries:

JBS Machinery Corporation (1)
2080 N 15th Ave, Melrose Park, IL 60160
Tel.: (708) 681-5577
Industrial Machinery Whslr
N.A.I.C.S.: 423830

Solitaire Machines Tools Limited - Plant I (1)
292 Dharamsinh Desai Marg Channi Road, Vadodara, 390 002, India
Tel.: (91) 265 277 2415
Sales Range: $25-49.9 Million
Emp.: 50
Industrial Machinery Mfr
N.A.I.C.S.: 333248
Ashok Sheth *(Mng Dir)*

Solitaire Machines Tools Limited - Plant II (1)
A-24/25 Krishna Industrial Estate, Gorwa, Vadodara, 390 016, India
Tel.: (91) 265 6580010
Grinding Machine Mfr
N.A.I.C.S.: 333248

SOLITON SYSTEMS, K.K.
2-4-3 Shinjuku, Shinjuku-ku, Tokyo, 160-0022, Japan
Tel.: (81) 53603811 JP
Web Site: https://www.soliton.co.jp
Year Founded: 1979
3040—(TKS)
Rev.: $135,121,220
Assets: $160,404,160
Liabilities: $81,485,370
Net Worth: $78,918,790
Earnings: $13,726,240
Emp.: 659
Fiscal Year-end: 12/31/23
Semiconductor Software Mfr
N.A.I.C.S.: 513210
Nobuo Kamada *(Pres)*

Subsidiaries:

Ji2, Inc. (1)
3900 Kilroy Airport Way Ste 280, Long Beach, CA 90806
Tel.: (714) 243-6121
Web Site: http://www.ji2.com
Emp.: 8
Electronic Data Processing, Software Support & Distribution
N.A.I.C.S.: 541511
Tetsuo Fujisawa *(Pres)*

SOLIX GROUP AB
Skeppsbron 2, 211 20, Malmo, Sweden
Tel.: (46) 406 688 310 SE
Web Site: http://www.solixgroup.com
Emp.: 1,100
Privater Equity Firm
N.A.I.C.S.: 523999
Denis Viet-Jacobsen *(CEO)*

Subsidiaries:

Geveko Markings Denmark A/S (1)
Longelsevej 34, 5900, Rudkobing, Denmark
Tel.: (45) 63517171
Web Site: http://www.geveko-markings.com
Highway Street & Bridge Construction
N.A.I.C.S.: 237310
Christian Schou Jensen *(Mgr-Mktg)*

Subsidiary (Non-US):

Geveko Markings France Sarl. (2)
46 Avenue des Freres Lumiere, F-78190, Trappes, France
Tel.: (33) 130 131 572
Web Site: http://www.geveko-markings.com
Traffic Road Signal Mfr
N.A.I.C.S.: 334290
Frederic Chatry *(Country Mgr)*

Geveko Markings Italy Srl. (2)
Via F Ili Cervi Pal Canova 1, Milan, 20090, Italy
Tel.: (39) 02 87233067
Web Site: http://www.geveko-markings.com
Road Safety & Traffic Signal Mfr
N.A.I.C.S.: 334290
Corrado Michaelides *(Country Mgr)*

Geveko Markings Netherlands BV (2)
Peppelenbos 17, 6662 WB, Elst, Netherlands
Tel.: (31) 481351166
Web Site: http://www.kerstenmarkeer.nl
Miscellaneous Durable Goods Whslr
N.A.I.C.S.: 423990

Geveko Markings Sweden AB (2)
Industrigatan 33, SE-291 22, Kristianstad, Sweden
Tel.: (46) 44203900
Web Site: http://www.geveko-markings.com
Road Safety & Traffic Signal Mfr
N.A.I.C.S.: 334290
Anders Wahlqvist *(Sls Mgr)*

Subsidiary (Non-US):

Geveko Markings Norway A/S (3)
Solgaard Skog 116, NO-1599, Moss, Norway
Tel.: (47) 94842445
Web Site: http://www.geveko-markings.com
Road Safety & Traffic Signal Mfr
N.A.I.C.S.: 334290
Anders Wahlqvist *(Sls Mgr)*

Subsidiary (Non-US):

Geveko Markings Switzerland AG (2)
Poststrasse 14, Postfach 1339, CH-6301, Zug, Switzerland
Tel.: (41) 41710 89 12
Web Site: http://www.geveko-markings.com
Road Safety & Traffic Signal Mfr
N.A.I.C.S.: 334290
Marcello Stuker *(Sls Mgr)*

Subsidiary (Non-US):

Geveko Markings Germany GmbH (3)
Renkenrunsstrasse 16, 79371, Mullheim, Germany
Tel.: (49) 763136870
Web Site: http://www.plastiroute.de
Highway & Street Construction
N.A.I.C.S.: 237310
Ralf Steinbach *(Gen Mgr & Sls Mgr)*

Subsidiary (Domestic):

LED-Mark ITS A/S (2)
Bygaden 76, 5953, Tranekaer, Denmark
Tel.: (45) 24295699
Web Site: http://www.ledmarkits.dk
Road Safety System Distr
N.A.I.C.S.: 423610
Bruno Hansen *(Gen Mgr)*

Subsidiary (Non-US):

Magyar Plastiroute Forgalomtechnikai Kft. (2)
Gat u 4-10 Lakihegy, H-2310, Szigetszentmiklos, Hungary
Tel.: (36) 24 475 275
Web Site: http://www.magyarplastiroute.hu

SOLIX GROUP AB

Solix Group AB—(Continued)
Highways Traffic Signal Installation Services & Mfr
N.A.I.C.S.: 238210
Sandor Pal *(Exec Dir)*

Subsidiary (Domestic):

Plastiroute Forgalomtechnikai Kft. (3)
Kulso Radi Ut 25, 2600, Vac, Hungary
Tel.: (36) 27 304 894
Web Site: http://www.plastiroute-vac.hu
Road Traffic Signal Mfr
N.A.I.C.S.: 334290
Jenovai Zoltan *(Mgr)*

Subsidiary (Non-US):

Preformed Markings Ltd (2)
Unit 6 Oyster Park, 109 Chertsey Road, Byfleet, KT14 7AX, Surrey, United Kingdom
Tel.: (44) 1932359270
Web Site: http://www.preformedmarkings.co.uk
Stationery & Office Supplies Whslr
N.A.I.C.S.: 424120
Jerry Peachment *(Reg Sls Mgr-South East & Central)*

SOLLIO COOPERATIVE GROUP

9001 Boulevard de l Acadie Suite 200, Montreal, H4N 3H7, QC, Canada
Tel.: (514) 384-6450   QC
Web Site: http://www.sollio.coop
Year Founded: 1922
Rev.: $5,572,522,064
Assets: $2,969,252,873
Liabilities: $1,477,382,292
Net Worth: $1,491,870,581
Earnings: $37,193,725
Emp.: 15,360
Fiscal Year-end: 10/26/19
Agricultural Services
N.A.I.C.S.: 111998
Mathieu Couture *(Second VP-Dairy Producer)*

Subsidiaries:

Interprovincial Cooperative Limited (1)
945 Marion Street, Winnipeg, R2J 0K7, MB, Canada
Tel.: (204) 233-3461
Web Site: https://www.ipco.ca
Agricultural Chemicals Mfr & Whslr
N.A.I.C.S.: 325320

Olymel Societe en Commandite (1)
2200 Pratte Ave Suite 400, Saint-Hyacinthe, J2S 4B6, QC, Canada
Tel.: (450) 771-0400
Web Site: https://www.olymel.com
Emp.: 15,000
Processor & Exporter of Fresh & Frozen Pork, Chicken & Turkey Meat
N.A.I.C.S.: 311615

Division (Domestic):

Olymel S.E.C. - Boucherville (2)
1580 Rue Eiffel, Boucherville, J4B 5Y1, QC, Canada
Tel.: (514) 858-9000
Web Site: http://www.olymel.com
Agrifood Distr
N.A.I.C.S.: 445298

SOLMAX INTERNATIONAL, INC.

2801 Marie-Victorin Boulevard, Varennes, J3X 1P7, QC, Canada
Tel.: (450) 929-1234
Web Site: http://www.solmax.com
Year Founded: 1981
Polyethylene Geomembranes Mfr
N.A.I.C.S.: 326199
Jean-Louis Vangeluwe *(Pres)*

Subsidiaries:

GSE Environmental, LLC (1)
19103 Gundle Rd, Houston, TX 77073
Tel.: (281) 443-8564
Web Site: http://www.gseworld.com
Geosynthetic Lining Products Mfr & Distr
N.A.I.C.S.: 326113

Subsidiary (Non-US):

GSE Australia Pty. Ltd. (2)
24 Regent Crescent, Moorebank, 2170, NSW, Australia
Tel.: (61) 2 9821 2977
Geosynthetic Lining Products Distr
N.A.I.C.S.: 424610

Plant (Domestic):

GSE Environmental, LLC - Spearfish Plant (2)
3150 1st Ave, Spearfish, SD 57783
Tel.: (605) 642-8531
Geosynthetic Lining Products Mfr
N.A.I.C.S.: 326113

Subsidiary (Non-US):

GSE Lining Technology Chile, S.A. (2)
Bucarest 150 of 402, Providencia, Santiago, Chile
Tel.: (56) 229428365
Geosynthetic Lining Products Mfr & Distr
N.A.I.C.S.: 326113

GSE Lining Technology Co. - Egypt S.A.E. (2)
Street No 28 The 4th Industrial Zone, The 6th of October City, Cairo, Egypt
Tel.: (20) 23 828 8888
Geosynthetic Lining Products Mfr & Distr
N.A.I.C.S.: 326113

GSE Lining Technology Co., Ltd. (2)
555 RASA Tower 26th Floor Phaholythin Road, Soi 19 Chatuchuk, Bangkok, 10900, Thailand
Tel.: (66) 2937 0091
Geosynthetic Lining Products Mfr & Distr
N.A.I.C.S.: 326113

GSE Lining Technology GmbH (2)
Normannenweg 28, 20537, Hamburg, Germany
Tel.: (49) 40 76742 0
Geosynthetic Lining Products Mfr & Distr
N.A.I.C.S.: 326113

Subsidiary (Domestic):

SynTec, LLC (2)
4800 Pulaski Hwy, Baltimore, MD 21224
Tel.: (410) 327-1070
Web Site: http://www.synteccorp.com
Geosynthetic Lining Products Mfr
N.A.I.C.S.: 326113

Ten Cate Geosynthetics North America Inc. (1)
365 S Holland Dr, Pendergrass, GA 30567
Tel.: (706) 693-2226
Web Site: http://www.tencategeo.us
Synthetic Fabrics & Non-Wovens Mfr
N.A.I.C.S.: 325220
Larry Nichols *(Reg Sls Mgr-Southeast)*

SOLNABERG PROPERTY AB

Stora Badhusgatan 18, 411 21, Gothenburg, Sweden
Tel.: (46) 31171300
Web Site:
   https://www.solnabergproperty.se
SOLNA—(OMX)
Rev.: $6,020,587
Assets: $74,409,696
Liabilities: $57,924,265
Net Worth: $16,485,431
Earnings: ($186,387)
Emp.: 1
Fiscal Year-end: 12/31/22
Real Estate Development Services
N.A.I.C.S.: 531110
Jorgen Lundgren *(CEO)*

SOLO GROWTH CORP.

1100 634-6th Ave SW, Calgary, T2P 0S4, AB, Canada
Tel.: (403) 455-7656   BC
Web Site:
   http://www.aldershotresources.com
Year Founded: 1987
Rev.: $29
Assets: $137,952
Liabilities: $141,495
Net Worth: ($3,543)
Earnings: ($314,371)
Fiscal Year-end: 01/31/18
Mineral Exploration Services
N.A.I.C.S.: 213114

SOLO OIL PLC

Princes House 38 Jermyn Street, London, SW1Y 6DN, United Kingdom
Tel.: (44) 207 440 0642
Web Site: http://www.solooil.co.uk
Rev.: $3,123,058
Assets: $29,763,595
Liabilities: $928,923
Net Worth: $28,834,672
Earnings: ($2,115,456)
Emp.: 1
Fiscal Year-end: 12/31/18
Audio Equipment Mfr
N.A.I.C.S.: 423620
Tom Reynolds *(CEO)*

SOLOCAL GROUP

204 rond-Point de Sevres, 92100, Boulogne-Billancourt, France
Tel.: (33) 46233750   FR
Web Site:
   https://www.solocalgroup.com
QS3—(DEU)
Rev.: $397,017,331
Assets: $347,638,812
Liabilities: $654,562,314
Net Worth: ($306,923,502)
Earnings: ($50,614,858)
Emp.: 2,426
Fiscal Year-end: 12/31/23
Holding Company; Online Media & Directory Publisher; Commercial Website Development & Advertising Services
N.A.I.C.S.: 551112
Eric Boustouller *(Deputy CEO)*

Subsidiaries:

Chronoresto SA (1)
23 Boulevard Jean Jaures, 93400, Saint-Ouen, France
Tel.: (33) 177458168
Web Site: http://www.chronoresto.fr
Online Meal Ordering Service
N.A.I.C.S.: 513199
William Robert *(Mng Dir)*

ClicRDV SARL (1)
204 Rond Point Du Pont De Sevres, 92 100, Boulogne-Billancourt, France
Tel.: (33) 183620404
Web Site: http://www.clicrdv.com
Software Development Services
N.A.I.C.S.: 541511
Anais Faure *(Acct Mgr)*

Effilab S.A.S (1)
204 Rond Point du Pont de Sevres, 92100, Boulogne-Billancourt, France
Tel.: (33) 146093131
Web Site: https://www.effilab.com
Digital Marketing Services
N.A.I.C.S.: 541613
Nikolas Jenan *(Head-Ops)*

LeadFormance S.A.S (1)
19 rue du Lac Saint-Andre, 73375, Le Bourget du Lac, France
Tel.: (33) 479252222
Web Site: http://www.leadformance.com
Online & Offline Marketing Services
N.A.I.C.S.: 541613
Marion Houchard *(Mktg Dir)*

Mappy S.A. (1)
47 rue de Charonne, 75011, Paris, France
Tel.: (33) 1 48 07 58 58
Web Site: http://fr.mappy.com
Application Software Development Services
N.A.I.C.S.: 541511

INTERNATIONAL PUBLIC

OptimizaClick, S.L. (1)
Paseo de la Castellana 81 15th Floor, 28046, Madrid, Spain
Tel.: (34) 918373990
Web Site: http://www.optimizaclick.com
Internet Marketing Services
N.A.I.C.S.: 541810

PJMS (1)
25 quai Gallieni, 92150, Suresnes, France
Tel.: (33) 810518518
Web Site: http://www.pjms.fr
Marketing Consulting Services
N.A.I.C.S.: 541613
Pascal Garcia *(Chm)*

PagesJaunes (1)
54 Grande Rue, 92310, Sevres, France (100%)
Tel.: (33) 141141010
Web Site: http://www.pagesjaunes.fr
Online Advertising & Information Services
N.A.I.C.S.: 541890

Sotravo SAS (1)
2 Boulevard Vauban, 78180, Montigny-le-Bretonneux, France
Tel.: (33) 1 72 82 30 00
Web Site: http://www.sotravo.fr
Internet Marketing Services
N.A.I.C.S.: 541810
Christine Bridelle *(Chm)*

Yelster Digital Gmbh (1)
Linke Wienzeile 8/29, 1060, Vienna, Austria
Tel.: (43) 14060005
Web Site: https://www.yelsterdigital.com
Emp.: 35
Internet Service Provider
N.A.I.C.S.: 517121

SOLOMAT LOCATION SAS

2 rue des Drubes, Etigny, 89510, Sens, France
Tel.: (33) 386974999
Web Site:
   http://www.solomatlocation.fr
Year Founded: 1960
Sales Range: $25-49.9 Million
Emp.: 200
Equipment Rental & Leasing
N.A.I.C.S.: 532490

SOLOMON DATA INTERNATIONAL CORPORATION

6F No 42 Shing Jung Rd, Nei-Hu Dist, Taipei, Taiwan
Tel.: (886) 277210240
5432—(TPE)
Rev.: $6,513,054
Assets: $13,272,676
Liabilities: $1,464,278
Net Worth: $11,808,398
Earnings: $1,239,940
Fiscal Year-end: 12/31/22
Electronic Components Mfr
N.A.I.C.S.: 334419
Johnny Chen *(Chm & CEO)*

SOLOMON SYSTECH (INTERNATIONAL) LIMITED

6/F No 3 Science Park East Avenue Hong Kong Science Park, Sha Tin, NT, China (Hong Kong)
Tel.: (852) 22071111
Web Site: http://www.solomon-systech.com
2878—(HKG)
Rev.: $190,843,000
Assets: $158,263,000
Liabilities: $49,079,000
Net Worth: $109,184,000
Earnings: $27,824,000
Emp.: 294
Fiscal Year-end: 12/31/22
Integrated Circuit Mfr for Mobile Phone Displays, Handheld Devices & Liquid-Crystal Display TVs
N.A.I.C.S.: 334513
Wai Ming Lo *(VP & Head-Large Display Bus)*

AND PRIVATE COMPANIES / SOLTEC POWER HOLDINGS S.A.

Subsidiaries:

Solomon Europe Limited (1)
Am Pfingstborn 40, 61479, Glashutten, Germany
Tel.: (49) 6174619892
Sales Range: $25-49.9 Million
Emp.: 300
Semiconductor & Related Device Mfr
N.A.I.C.S.: 334413

Solomon Systech (Shenzhen) Limited (1)
Bldg 6 Shenzhen Hi Tech Industrial Park 2nd Fl, Keji Central 2nd Rd Shenzhen H, Shenzhen, 516800, China
Tel.: (86) 75586169900
Emp.: 90
Semiconductor & Related Device Mfr
N.A.I.C.S.: 334413
Humphrey Leung *(CEO)*

Solomon Systech (UK) Limited (1)
1560 Parkway Solent Business Park, Fareham, Whiteley, PO15 7AG, Hampshire, United Kingdom
Tel.: (44) 3305880300
Semiconductor Product Mfr
N.A.I.C.S.: 334413

Solomon Systech Inc. (1)
405 S Camellia Dr, Chandler, AZ 85225
Tel.: (480) 633-2888
Semiconductor & Related Device Mfr
N.A.I.C.S.: 334413

Solomon Systech Japan Co., Ltd. (1)
Towa Hamamatsucho Bldg 8th Floor 6-2 Hamamatsucho 2-chome, Minato-ku, Tokyo, 105-0013, Japan
Tel.: (81) 57330726
Semiconductor & Related Device Mfr
N.A.I.C.S.: 334413

Solomon Systech Korea Limited (1)
1F SolomonKorea Inwoo Building 109-1 Samsung-Dong, Kangnam-Gu, Seoul, 135-090, Korea (South)
Tel.: (82) 234458011
Semiconductor Product Mfr
N.A.I.C.S.: 334111

Solomon Systech Limited (1)
Unit 607-613 6/F Wireless Centre 3 Science Park East Avenue, Hong Kong Science Park, Sha Tin, New Territories, China (Hong Kong)
Tel.: (852) 22071111
Sales Range: $100-124.9 Million
Emp.: 190
Semiconductor & Related Device Mfr
N.A.I.C.S.: 334413

Solomon Systech Pte. Ltd. (1)
180 Ang Mo Kio Ave 8 Block N 07-05, Singapore, 569830, Singapore
Tel.: (65) 67555665
Web Site: http://www.solomon-systech.com
Sales Range: $25-49.9 Million
Emp.: 26
Semiconductor & Related Device Mfr
N.A.I.C.S.: 334413

Solomon Systech Taiwan Limited (1)
7th Fl No 176 Gong Dao Wu Rd, Section 2 Hsin Chu 300, Hsin-chu, Taiwan
Tel.: (886) 35720660
Sales Range: $50-74.9 Million
Emp.: 120
Semiconductor & Related Device Mfr
N.A.I.C.S.: 334413

Solomon Technology, Corp. (1)
Sales Range: $1-9.9 Million
Emp.: 20
Computer & Software Stores
N.A.I.C.S.: 449210

WE3 Technology Company Limited (1)
3 F Wireless Centre No 3 Science Park East Avenue, Pak Shek Kok, Hong Kong, China (Hong Kong)
Tel.: (852) 2207 1147
Web Site: http://www.we3technology.com
Sales Range: $25-49.9 Million
Emp.: 30
Wireless Technologies Development Services

N.A.I.C.S.: 517112
Kenny Cheung *(CEO)*

SOLOMON TECHNOLOGY CORPORATION
6F No 42 Shing Zhong Rd, Nei Hu Dist, Taipei, Taiwan
Tel.: (886) 287918989
Web Site: https://www.solomon.com.tw
Year Founded: 1973
2359—(TAI)
Rev.: $138,000,027
Assets: $292,622,115
Liabilities: $107,579,969
Net Worth: $185,042,146
Earnings: $18,240,851
Emp.: 787
Fiscal Year-end: 12/31/23
Analog Switches Mfr
N.A.I.C.S.: 335931

Subsidiaries:

Futek Trading Co.Ltd (1)
C/O Newhaven Corporate Services BVI Limited 3rd Floor, Omar Hodge Building, Road Town, Tortola, Virgin Islands (British)
Tel.: (284) 494 5108
Electronic Components Mfr
N.A.I.C.S.: 334419

Solomon Goldentek Display (Dong-Guan) Ltd. (1)
No 168 Fu Xiang Boulevard Di Yong Industrial Zone, Gao-Bu District, Dongguan, 523273, Guangdong, China
Tel.: (86) 76988737888
Liquid Crystal Display Mfr
N.A.I.C.S.: 334419

Solomon Goldentek Display Corp. (1)
Sing Zhong Rd 42 7th floor, Neihu District, Taipei, 114, Taiwan
Tel.: (886) 287919821
Web Site: https://www.goldentek.com.tw
Sales Range: $25-49.9 Million
Emp.: 15
Liquid Crystal Displays & Modules Mfr
N.A.I.C.S.: 334419

SOLOMON WORLDWIDE HOLDINGS LIMITED
8/F Wui Tat Centre No 55 Connaught Road West, Sheung Wan, China (Hong Kong)
Tel.: (852) 25150081
8133—(HKG)
Rev.: $9,549,240
Assets: $6,396,930
Liabilities: $5,668,395
Net Worth: $728,535
Earnings: ($1,798,515)
Emp.: 133
Fiscal Year-end: 12/31/22
Metal Casting Parts & Components Mfr
N.A.I.C.S.: 332999
Jimmy Chiu Ming Choi *(Chm & Compliance Officer)*

SOLON EIENDOM ASA
Olav Vs Gate 5 7 Etg, 0161, Oslo, Norway
Tel.: (47) 22 29 66 90
Web Site: http://www.soloneiendom.no
SOLON—(OSL)
Sales Range: Less than $1 Million
Real Estate Development Services
N.A.I.C.S.: 531390
Simen Thorsen *(Chm)*

SOLOSAR
3 Rue Guillaume Schoettke, Sarreguemines, 557200, Moselle, France
Tel.: (33) 387985604
Web Site: http://www.solosar.fr
Rev.: $20,500,000
Emp.: 12

N.A.I.C.S.: 423720
Barbara Von Linsingen *(Mng Partner)*

SOLOWIN HOLDINGS, LTD.
Room 1910-1912A Tower 3 33 Canton Road, Tsim Sha Tsui, Kowloon, China (Hong Kong)
Tel.: (852) 34283893 Ky
Web Site: https://www.solomonwin.com.hk
Year Founded: 2021
SWIN—(NASDAQ)
Rev.: $4,291,000
Assets: $15,401,000
Liabilities: $6,477,000
Net Worth: $8,924,000
Earnings: ($4,556,000)
Emp.: 25
Fiscal Year-end: 03/31/24
Holding Company
N.A.I.C.S.: 551112

SOLSTAD OFFSHORE ASA
Nesavegen 39, PO Box 13, 4280, Skudeneshavn, Norway
Tel.: (47) 52856500 NO
Web Site: https://www.solstad.com
Year Founded: 1964
0G2Z—(LSE)
Rev.: $600,418,529
Assets: $2,403,392,758
Liabilities: $2,241,456,217
Net Worth: $161,936,542
Earnings: ($103,251,709)
Emp.: 3,400
Fiscal Year-end: 12/31/22
Offshore Services
N.A.I.C.S.: 488390
Lars Peder Solstad *(CEO)*

Subsidiaries:

Farstad Shipping ASA (1)
Skansekaia 4A, 6002, Alesund, Norway
Tel.: (47) 52856500
Rev.: $562,500,483
Assets: $3,621,768,461
Liabilities: $3,719,221,446
Net Worth: ($97,452,984)
Earnings: ($674,498,349)
Emp.: 3,620
Fiscal Year-end: 12/31/2018
Freight Vessel Management Services
N.A.I.C.S.: 483111
Karl-Johan Bakken *(CEO)*

Subsidiary (Non-US):

Farstad Shipping (Indian Pacific) Pty. Ltd. (2)
16 St Georges Terrace Level 9, Perth, 6000, WA, Australia
Tel.: (61) 894219300
Web Site: http://www.solstadfarstad.com
Marine Shipping Services
N.A.I.C.S.: 488320
Brett Silich *(Mng Dir)*

Farstad Shipping Ltd. (2)
Farstad House Badentoy Ave Badentoy Park, Portlethen, Aberdeen, AB12 4 YB, Scotland, United Kingdom
Tel.: (44) 1224784000
Web Site: http://www.farstad.com
Sales Range: $25-49.9 Million
Emp.: 22
Marine Shipping Services
N.A.I.C.S.: 488330

Farstad Shipping Singapore Pte Ltd (2)
78 Shenton Way #19-02 Lippo Centre, Singapore, 079120, Singapore
Tel.: (65) 62404500
Web Site: http://www.farstad.com
Shipping Services
N.A.I.C.S.: 483111
Andrew Coccoli *(Gen Mgr)*

Solstad Offshore (UK) Ltd. (1)
NEO House Riverside Drive, Aberdeen, AB11 7LH, Aberdeenshire, United Kingdom
Tel.: (44) 1224502929

Sales Range: $25-49.9 Million
Emp.: 10
Marine Engineering Services
N.A.I.C.S.: 541330

Solstad Shipping AS (1)
Nesavegen 39, 4280, Skudeneshavn, Norway
Tel.: (47) 52856500
Sales Range: $25-49.9 Million
Emp.: 80
Marine Engineering Services
N.A.I.C.S.: 541330

SOLSTICE GOLD CORPORATION
Suite 550 - 800 West Pender Street, Vancouver, V6C 2V6, BC, Canada
Tel.: (604) 283-7234
Web Site: https://www.solsticegold.com
SGCPF—(OTCIQ)
Rev.: $73,978
Assets: $406,938
Liabilities: $142,904
Net Worth: $264,033
Earnings: ($648,062)
Fiscal Year-end: 06/30/24
Gold Mining Services
N.A.I.C.S.: 212220
Pablo McDonald *(CEO)*

SOLSTICE MINERALS LIMITED
Principal Place of Business Unit 2 454 Roberts Road, Subiaco, 6008, WA, Australia
Tel.: (61) 892001838 AU
Web Site: https://www.solsticeminerals.com.au
Year Founded: 2011
SLS—(ASX)
Rev.: $211,026
Assets: $10,686,855
Liabilities: $482,278
Net Worth: $10,204,577
Earnings: ($4,507,396)
Emp.: 15
Fiscal Year-end: 06/30/23
Mineral Exploration Services
N.A.I.C.S.: 212390

SOLSTISS
45 Rue Pasteur, 59540, Caudry, France
Tel.: (33) 327851025
Web Site: http://www.solstiss.com
Year Founded: 1974
Rev.: $28,300,000
Emp.: 30
Piece Goods & Notions Whslr
N.A.I.C.S.: 424310
Herve Protais *(Dir)*

Subsidiaries:

Solstiss Inc. (1)
110 E 9th St b703, Los Angeles, CA 90079
Tel.: (213) 688-9797
Web Site: http://www.solstiss.com
Textile Products Distr
N.A.I.C.S.: 424310

SOLSTRA CAPITAL PARTNERS LLP
47 Park Lane, London, W1K 1PR, United Kingdom
Tel.: (44) 20 7647 6640 UK
Web Site: http://www.solstracapital.com
Year Founded: 2011
Real Estate & Private Equity Investment Firm
N.A.I.C.S.: 523999
Oscar Crohn *(Mng Partner)*

SOLTEC POWER HOLDINGS S.A.
Calle Gabriel Campillo s/n Pol Ind La

SOLTEC POWER HOLDINGS S.A.

Soltec Power Holdings S.A.—(Continued)
Serreta, Molina de Segura, 30500, Murcia, Spain
Tel.: (34) 968603153
Web Site: https://soltec.com
Year Founded: 2004
5PZ—(DEU)
Rev.: $3,385,149
Assets: $280,094,685
Liabilities: $26,147,304
Net Worth: $253,947,381
Earnings: $552,186
Emp.: 1,300
Fiscal Year-end: 12/31/22
Holding Company
N.A.I.C.S.: 551112
Raul Morales (CEO)

Subsidiaries:

Enviroscale, S.L. (1)
C/Gabriel Campillo Contreras POL IND, Molina de Segura, 30500, Murcia, Spain
Tel.: (34) 968968968
Web Site: https://enviroscale.com
Eletric Power Generation Services
N.A.I.C.S.: 221118

Seguidores Solares Soltec S.A. de C.V. (1)
Plaza Polanco B-6, 11510, Miguel Hidalgo, Mexico
Tel.: (52) 5555573144
Renewable Energy Equipment Mfr & Distr
N.A.I.C.S.: 333414

Soltec America LLC (1)
6100 Waterford Dr Ste 370, Miami, FL 33126
Tel.: (561) 690-1624
Renewable Energy Equipment Mfr & Distr
N.A.I.C.S.: 333414

Soltec Argentina, S.R.L. (1)
Vera Mujica 1080, Rosario, S2002QTF, Santa Fe, Argentina
Tel.: (54) 3414307574
Web Site: https://sol-tec.com.ar
Lacquer Mfr & Distr
N.A.I.C.S.: 325510

Soltec Australia, Pty. Ltd. (1)
Level 33 Australia Square 264 George Street, Sydney, 2000, NSW, Australia
Tel.: (61) 292581340
Renewable Energy Management Services
N.A.I.C.S.: 541690

Soltec Chile S.p.A. (1)
Rosario Norte 615 Oficina 1503, Las Condes, 7561211, Santiago, Chile
Tel.: (56) 225738559
Renewable Energy Equipment Mfr & Distr
N.A.I.C.S.: 333414

SOLTECH ENERGY SWEDEN AB
Birger Jarlsgatan 41A, 111 45, Stockholm, Sweden
Tel.: (46) 84418840
Web Site: https://www.soltechenergy.com
SOLT—(OMX)
Rev.: $288,324,205
Assets: $248,205,278
Liabilities: $147,089,664
Net Worth: $101,115,613
Earnings: ($16,472,492)
Emp.: 976
Fiscal Year-end: 12/31/23
Solar Energy Solutions
N.A.I.C.S.: 238220
Stefan Olander (CEO)

Subsidiaries:

Swede Energy Power Solutions AB (1)
Datorgatan 1, 561 33, Huskvarna, Sweden (60%)
Tel.: (46) 36 13 06 00
Web Site: http://www.swedeenergy.se
Emp.: 14
Energy Solutions & Consulting Services
N.A.I.C.S.: 541690

Christoffer Caesar (CEO)

SOLTEQ OYJ
Hatanpaan valtatie 24 4th floor, FI 33210, Tampere, Finland
Tel.: (358) 2014444
Web Site: https://www.solteq.com
Year Founded: 1982
SOLTEQ—(HEL)
Rev.: $73,846,320
Assets: $80,224,477
Liabilities: $55,900,065
Net Worth: $24,324,412
Earnings: ($5,832,074)
Emp.: 662
Fiscal Year-end: 12/31/22
Information Technology Services
N.A.I.C.S.: 519290
Kirsi Jalasaho (VP-People & Culture)

Subsidiaries:

Aponsa AB (1)
Arenavagen 41 floor 12, Johanneshov, SE-121 77, Stockholm, Sweden
Tel.: (46) 101308800
Information Technology Services
N.A.I.C.S.: 541511

Solteq Denmark A/S (1)
Havneholmen 25 9th Floor, 1561, Copenhagen, Denmark
Tel.: (45) 33448555
Information Technology Services
N.A.I.C.S.: 541511

SOLTWORKS CO., LTD.
4th floor 652 Seolleung-ro, Gangnam-gu, Seoul, 08380, Korea (South)
Tel.: (82) 69491256
Web Site: https://www.aiitone.com
Year Founded: 2008
Smart Electronic Technical Manual Software Developer
N.A.I.C.S.: 513210

SOLUCION EMPRESA ADMINISTRADORA HIPOTECARIA SA
Calle Centenario 156 Urb Santa Patricia, La Molina, Lima, Peru
Tel.: (51) 3119898
Web Site: https://seah.com.pe
Year Founded: 1979
SOLUCIC1—(LIM)
Rev.: $4,460,349,767
Assets: $51,779,428,900
Liabilities: $45,254,711,607
Net Worth: $6,524,717,294
Earnings: $1,259,296,143
Fiscal Year-end: 12/31/23
Mortgage Brokerage Services
N.A.I.C.S.: 522292
Cesar Gonzalo Rios Briceno (Chm)

SOLUCIONES CUATROOCHENTA, S.A.
Edificio Espaitec 2 Universitat Jaume I Avda Sos Baynat s/n, 12071, Castellon de la Plana, Spain
Tel.: (34) 964102835
Web Site: https://www.cuatroochenta.com
Year Founded: 2011
5XW—(DEU)
Rev.: $20,601,474
Assets: $33,685,959
Liabilities: $22,717,713
Net Worth: $10,968,246
Earnings: ($1,124,902)
Emp.: 280
Fiscal Year-end: 12/31/22
Software Development Services
N.A.I.C.S.: 541511
Celia Pallares (Chief HR Officer)

SOLUFEED LIMITED
The Depot Chichester Road Sidlesham Common, Chichester, PO20 7PY, West Sussex, United Kingdom
Tel.: (44) 1243554090
Web Site: http://www.uk.solufeed.com
Year Founded: 1990
Sales Range: $25-49.9 Million
Emp.: 6
Fertilizer Mfr
N.A.I.C.S.: 325314
Lorraine Holden (Fin Dir)

SOLUM CO., LTD.
357 Guseong-ro, Giheung-gu, Yongin, 16914, Gyeonggi-do, Korea (South)
Tel.: (82) 15880502
Web Site: https://www.solum-group.com
Year Founded: 2015
248070—(KRS)
Rev.: $1,299,715,177
Assets: $793,309,665
Liabilities: $570,884,308
Net Worth: $222,425,357
Earnings: $34,855,612
Emp.: 455
Fiscal Year-end: 12/31/22
Electronic Component Mfr & Distr
N.A.I.C.S.: 334419
Jeon Seong-Ho (CEO)

SOLUS ADVANCED MATERIALS CO., LTD.
1 3F 20 Tancheonsang-ro 151beongil, Bundang-gu, Seongnam, 13636, Gyeonggi-do, Korea (South)
Tel.: (82) 3180396301
Web Site: https://www.solusmaterials.com
Year Founded: 2019
336370—(KRS)
Rev.: $353,755,186
Assets: $1,120,617,992
Liabilities: $416,433,013
Net Worth: $704,184,979
Earnings: ($8,700,657)
Emp.: 282
Fiscal Year-end: 12/31/22
Electron Tube Mfr
N.A.I.C.S.: 334419
Kwangpyuk Suh (Co-CEO)

SOLUTIANCE AG
Grosbeerenstrase 179, 14482, Potsdam, Germany
Tel.: (49) 331867193
Web Site: https://www.solutiance.com
Year Founded: 1992
SLSA—(DEU)
Software Development Services
N.A.I.C.S.: 541511
Uwe Brodtmann (Chm & CEO)

SOLUTION DYNAMICS LIMITED
18 Canaveral Drive, Albany, 0632, New Zealand
Tel.: (64) 99707700
Web Site: https://www.solutiondynamics.com
SDL—(NZX)
Rev.: $24,188,397
Assets: $9,402,512
Liabilities: $5,005,981
Net Worth: $4,396,531
Earnings: $2,048,445
Emp.: 86
Fiscal Year-end: 06/30/23
Data Management, Electronic Digital Printing & Document Distr
N.A.I.C.S.: 518210
Indrajit Nelson Sivasubramaniam (CEO)

SOLUTION FINANCIAL, INC.
Suite 138 8600 Cambie Road, Richmond, V6X 4K1, BC, Canada
Tel.: (604) 233-1937

INTERNATIONAL PUBLIC

Web Site: https://www.solution.financial
Year Founded: 2004
SFI—(TSX)
Rev.: $15,917,768
Assets: $23,340,392
Liabilities: $12,784,777
Net Worth: $10,555,615
Earnings: $655,194
Emp.: 15
Fiscal Year-end: 10/31/22
Financial Investment Services
N.A.I.C.S.: 523999
Vincent Lau (VP-Ops)

Subsidiaries:

Solution Financial (Alberta) Inc. (1)

SOLUTION GROUP BERHAD
PT 13796 Jalan Tekno Usahawan 2, Technology Park, 57000, Kuala Lumpur, Malaysia
Tel.: (60) 327803890 MY
Web Site: https://www.solutionholdings.com.my
Year Founded: 2004
SOLUTN—(KLS)
Rev.: $7,026,934
Assets: $18,679,406
Liabilities: $3,094,753
Net Worth: $15,584,653
Earnings: ($8,329,077)
Emp.: 42
Fiscal Year-end: 12/31/22
Investment Holding Services
N.A.I.C.S.: 551112
Yong Hew Lim (Mng Dir-Grp)

SOLUTIONINC TECHNOLOGIES LIMITED
5692 Bloomfield Street, Halifax, B3K 1T2, NS, Canada
Tel.: (902) 420-0077
Web Site: https://www.solutioninc.com
Year Founded: 1997
STL.H—(TSXV)
Sales Range: Less than $1 Million
Computer Software & Services
N.A.I.C.S.: 517810
Glen Lavigne (Pres & CEO)

SOLUTIONS 30 SE
21 Rue du Puits Romain, L-8070, Luxembourg, Luxembourg
Tel.: (352) 28371389
Web Site: https://www.solutions30.com
Year Founded: 2003
S30—(EUR)
Rev.: $1,166,795,452
Assets: $798,984,435
Liabilities: $661,441,660
Net Worth: $137,542,775
Earnings: ($19,317,806)
Emp.: 6,916
Fiscal Year-end: 12/31/23
IT Services
N.A.I.C.S.: 541519
Gianbeppi Fortis (Co-Founder, CEO & Member-Mgmt Bd)

Subsidiaries:

Algor SRL (1)
Via Maestri del Lavoro 62, Villa del Conte, 35010, Padua, Italy
Tel.: (39) 0499325738
Web Site: https://www.algorgroup.com
Stainless Steel Tank Mfr
N.A.I.C.S.: 332420

Brabamij Infra BV (1)
Nail 69, 2910, Essen, Belgium
Tel.: (32) 36700280
Web Site: https://www.brabamij.be
Utility Contractor Services
N.A.I.C.S.: 237130

AND PRIVATE COMPANIES — SOLVAY S.A.

CFC Italia SRL (1)
Via E Fermi 9, 20090, Settala, MI, Italy
Tel.: (39) 029524001
Web Site: https://www.cfcitalia.it
Software Development Services
N.A.I.C.S.: 541511

I-Projects B.V. (1)
Kraanmeester 5, 6004 RR, Weert, Netherlands
Tel.: (31) 495820231
Web Site: https://www.i-projectsbv.nl
Industrial Machinery Retailer
N.A.I.C.S.: 423830

Janssens Field Services BV (1)
Slachthuislaan 78, 2060, Antwerp, Belgium
Tel.: (32) 3 235 6990
Web Site: https://www.jfs.be
Telecommunication Servicesb
N.A.I.C.S.: 517810
Christophe Vervroegen (CEO & Founder)

SFM30 SARL (1)
39-53 Boulevard d'Ornano, 93210, Saint Denis, France
Tel.: (33) 14 488 1624
Web Site: https://www.sfm30.com
Information Technology Services
N.A.I.C.S.: 541511

Sarl Sotranasa-Televideocom (1)
14 Du Pas De La Palla 128 Che Vc, 66000, Perpignan, Pyrenees Orientales, France (100%)
Tel.: (33) 468850481
Sales Range: $10-24.9 Million
Telecom Operator
N.A.I.C.S.: 517810
Benedicte Navarro (Dir-Admin)

Solutions 30 Operations GmbH (1)
Niederlassung Ludwigsburg Teinacher Strasse 49, 71634, Ludwigsburg, Germany
Tel.: (49) 714 113 3400
Web Site: https://solutions-30.de
Emp.: 450
Telecommunication Servicesb
N.A.I.C.S.: 517810

Unit-T BV (1)
Schalienhoevedreef 20T, 2800, Mechelen, Belgium
Tel.: (32) 15687777
Web Site: https://unit-t.eu
Emp.: 500
Telecommunication Servicesb
N.A.I.C.S.: 517810

SOLUTIONS CAPITAL MANAGEMENT SIM S.P.A.
Via Gonzaga 3, 20123, Milan, Italy
Tel.: (39) 0200633300
Web Site: https://www.scmsim.it
Year Founded: 2010
SCM—(ITA)
Rev.: $8,577,217
Assets: $6,409,141
Liabilities: $3,344,137
Net Worth: $3,065,004
Earnings: ($288,025)
Emp.: 12
Fiscal Year-end: 12/31/23
Portfolio Management Services
N.A.I.C.S.: 523940
Maria Leddi (Chm)

SOLUX CO., LTD.
32-22 Jeongannonggongdanji-Gil, Jeongan-Myeon, Gongju, 32511, Chungcheongnam-do, Korea (South)
Tel.: (82) 418556847
Web Site: https://www.solux.co.kr
Year Founded: 1995
290690—(KRS)
Rev.: $64,409,893
Assets: $67,970,649
Liabilities: $23,868,482
Net Worth: $44,102,167
Earnings: $3,824,118
Emp.: 204
Fiscal Year-end: 12/31/21
Light Mfr & Distr
N.A.I.C.S.: 335139

Bok-Duk Kim (CEO)

SOLVAC S.A.
Rue des Champs Elysees 43, 1050, Brussels, Belgium
Tel.: (32) 26396630
Web Site: https://www.solvac.be
SOLV—(EUR)
Sales Range: $350-399.9 Million
Pharmaceutical Product Mfr & Distr
N.A.I.C.S.: 325412
Bernard Laguiche (CEO)

SOLVANG ASA
Naringslivets hus Haakons VIIs gate 8, 4005, Stavanger, Norway
Tel.: (47) 51848400
Web Site: http://www.solvangship.no
SOLV—(OSL)
Rev.: $263,062,000
Assets: $1,071,575,000
Liabilities: $525,591,000
Net Worth: $545,984,000
Earnings: $75,264,000
Emp.: 43
Fiscal Year-end: 12/31/23
Petrochemical Gas Transport Services
N.A.I.C.S.: 324110
Egil Fjogstad (CFO)

Subsidiaries:

Solvang Maritime AS (1)
Haakon Viis Gate 8, Stavanger, 4005, Norway
Tel.: (47) 51848400
Web Site: http://www.solvangship.no
Marine Shipping Services
N.A.I.C.S.: 483111

SOLVAR LIMITED
40 Graduate Road, Bundoora, Melbourne, 3083, VIC, Australia
Tel.: (61) 390938255
Web Site: https://www.money3.com.au
SVR—(ASX)
Rev.: $144,225,427
Assets: $683,079,591
Liabilities: $438,860,842
Net Worth: $244,218,749
Earnings: $11,378,205
Emp.: 350
Fiscal Year-end: 06/30/24
Instant Cash Loan Lender
N.A.I.C.S.: 522390
Scott Joseph Baldwin (CEO & Mng Dir)

Subsidiaries:

Automotive Financial Services Pty Ltd (1)
Mezzanine Level 310 Ann Street, Brisbane, 4000, QLD, Australia
Tel.: (61) 73 387 1600
Web Site: https://www.afs.com.au
Automobile Financing Services
N.A.I.C.S.: 522220
Brian Anderson (Mng Dir & Gen Mgr)

Go Car Finance 2 Ltd. (1)
PO Box 9034, Newmarket, Auckland, New Zealand
Tel.: (64) 800462277
Web Site: https://www.gocar.co.nz
Car Lending Services
N.A.I.C.S.: 522220

Money3 Ballarat Pty Ltd. (1)
Shop 4 Coliseum Wlk, Ballarat, 3350, VIC, Australia
Tel.: (61) 353323600
Financial Support Services
N.A.I.C.S.: 522291

Money3 Dandenong Pty Ltd. (1)
1 20A Langhorne St, Dandenong, 3175, VIC, Australia
Tel.: (61) 397069288
Financial Services
N.A.I.C.S.: 522291

Money3 Reservoir Pty Ltd. (1)
261/263 Broadway, Reservoir, 3073, VIC, Australia
Tel.: (61) 394603330
Web Site: http://www.money3.com.au
Financial Services
N.A.I.C.S.: 522291

Money3 Wodonga Pty Ltd. (1)
Sesamie St Arcade 142 High St, Wodonga, 3690, VIC, Australia
Tel.: (61) 260563566
Web Site: http://www.money3.com.au
Sales Range: $50-74.9 Million
Emp.: 3
Financial Services
N.A.I.C.S.: 522291

SOLVAY S.A.
Rue de Ransbeek 310, 1120, Brussels, Belgium
Tel.: (32) 22642111 BE
Web Site: https://www.solvay.com
Year Founded: 1863
SOL—(MUN)
Rev.: $6,024,000,000
Assets: $7,022,000,000
Liabilities: $5,759,000,000
Net Worth: $1,263,000,000
Earnings: $1,417,000,000
Emp.: 9,000
Fiscal Year-end: 12/31/23
Biotechnology Research & Development Services
N.A.I.C.S.: 325412
Nicolas Boel (Chm)

Subsidiaries:

3S Solvay Shared Services-Sociedade de Servicos Partilhados Unipessoal Lda (1)
Avenida Tomas Ribeiro 43 2oc, Carnaxide, 2790-221, Portugal
Tel.: (351) 218319200
Web Site: http://www.solvay.com
Emp.: 300
Business Support Services
N.A.I.C.S.: 561499

Advanced Biochemical (Thailand) Company Ltd (1)
Map Ta Phut Industrial Estate 2/1 I-3 Road Map Ta Phut, Amphur Muang, 21150, Rayong, Thailand
Tel.: (66) 38 925000
Web Site: http://www.vinythai.co.th
Emp.: 500
Chemical Products Mfr
N.A.I.C.S.: 325998

Arili Plastik Sanayii AS (1)
Ramazanoglu Mahallesi Sanayi cad No 7 Kurtkoy, Pendik, 34906, Istanbul, Turkiye (44%)
Tel.: (90) 2163783620
Web Site: https://www.pipelife.com.tr
Sales Range: $50-74.9 Million
Provider of Plastic Pipe Products
N.A.I.C.S.: 326122

Barytine de Chaillac S.A. (1)
BP 1, Lefont A Bauge, F-36310, Chaillac, France
Tel.: (33) 254257481
Sales Range: $50-74.9 Million
Emp.: 47
Barite Mine
N.A.I.C.S.: 212390

Beijing Rhodia Eastern Chemical Co., Ltd (1)
No 143 Binhe Road Tong He District, Beijing, China
Tel.: (86) 1 061561321
Surface Active Agent Mfr
N.A.I.C.S.: 325613

Caleppiovinil S.p.A. (1)
Zona Industriale, Fucine, I-38026, Trento, Italy (100%)
Tel.: (39) 0463760411
Plastics
N.A.I.C.S.: 326199

Carrieres les Petons S.P.R.L. (1)
Rue Du Beau Sejour 52 Lieu Dit Les Petons, 5650, Walcourt, Belgium
Tel.: (32) 71655428
Web Site: http://www.solvay.com
Sales Range: $50-74.9 Million
Dimension Stone Mining Services
N.A.I.C.S.: 212311

Cavity GmbH (1)
Hans-Bockler-Allee 20, 30173, Hannover, Germany
Tel.: (49) 2843733777
Web Site: http://www.cavity-gmbh.de
Chemical & Plastic Product Mfr
N.A.I.C.S.: 325998

Chengdu Chuanlu Plastic Packaging & Service Co. Ltd. (1)
2 Fl Chuanlu Plastic Bldg 115 Fuquin West Road, Yangshijie Xiyanxian Str, 610031, Chengdu, China (25.5%)
Tel.: (86) 28 8484 8248
Plastics
N.A.I.C.S.: 326199

Cytec Asia Pacific Holdings Pty. Ltd. (1)
Suite 1 Level 1 Norwest Quay 21 Solent Circuit N-w Business Park, Baulkham Hills, 2153, NSW, Australia
Tel.: (61) 298466200
Petrochemical Mfr & Distr
N.A.I.C.S.: 325110

Cytec Engineered Materials GmbH (1)
Industriestrasse 3, 76684, Ostringen, Germany
Tel.: (49) 7253934000
Chemical Products Mfr
N.A.I.C.S.: 325998

Cytec Industrial Materials (OK) Inc. (1)
5350 S 129th E Ave, Tulsa, OK 74134
Tel.: (918) 252-3922
Chemical Products Mfr
N.A.I.C.S.: 325199

Cytec Industries, Inc. (1)
504 Carnegie Ctr, Princeton, NJ 08540
Tel.: (609) 860-4000
Web Site: http://www.solvay.com
Sales Range: $1-4.9 Billion
Specialty Chemicals Mfr
N.A.I.C.S.: 325998

Subsidiary (Non-US):

Cytec Australia Holdings Pty. Ltd. (2)
Suite 1 Level 1 Norwest Quay 21 Solent Circuit Northwest Business Park, Baulkham Hills, 2153, NSW, Australia
Tel.: (61) 298466200
Web Site: http://www.solvay.com
Specialty Chemicals Mfr
N.A.I.C.S.: 325998

Cytec Canada Inc. (2)
9061 Garner Road, Niagara Falls, L2H 0Y2, ON, Canada
Tel.: (905) 356-9000
Specialty Chemicals & Materials Mfr
N.A.I.C.S.: 325998
Melodie Allen (Mgr-HR)

Subsidiary (Domestic):

Cytec Carbon Fibers LLC (2)
800 Cel River Rd, Rock Hill, SC 29730
Tel.: (803) 328-3390
Web Site: http://www.solvay.com
Specialty Chemicals Mfr
N.A.I.C.S.: 325998
Dan Martins (Gen Mgr)

Subsidiary (Non-US):

Cytec Chile Limitada (2)
Avenida Las Dalias 2718 Parque Industrial, Macul, 7810653, Santiago, Chile
Tel.: (56) 225607900
Web Site: http://www.solvay.com
Specialty Chemicals Mfr
N.A.I.C.S.: 325998

Subsidiary (Domestic):

Cytec Engineered Materials Inc. (2)
2085 E Technology Cir Ste 102, Tempe, AZ 85284

SOLVAY S.A.

Solvay S.A.—(Continued)
Tel.: (480) 730-2000
Web Site: http://www.solvay.com
Specialty Chemicals Mfr
N.A.I.C.S.: 325998

Subsidiary (Domestic):

Cytec Engineered Materials Inc. (3)
1440 N Kraemer Blvd, Anaheim, CA 92806
Tel.: (714) 630-9400
Web Site: http://www.solvay.com
Specialty Chemicals Mfr
N.A.I.C.S.: 325998

Plant (Domestic):

Cytec Engineered Materials Inc. (3)
4300 Jackson St, Greenville, TX 75402-5721
Tel.: (903) 457-8500
Web Site: http://www.solvay.com
Specialty Chemicals Mfr
N.A.I.C.S.: 325998

Cytec Engineered Materials Inc. (3)
1300 Revolution St, Havre De Grace, MD 21078
Tel.: (410) 939-1910
Web Site: http://www.solvay.com
Specialty Chemicals Mfr
N.A.I.C.S.: 325998

Cytec Engineered Materials Inc. (3)
645 N Cypress St, Orange, CA 92867
Tel.: (714) 744-5660
Web Site: http://www.solvay.com
Specialty Chemicals Mfr
N.A.I.C.S.: 325998

Cytec Engineered Materials Inc. (3)
501 W 3rd St, Winona, MN 55987
Tel.: (507) 454-3611
Web Site: http://www.solvay.com
Specialty Chemicals Mfr
N.A.I.C.S.: 325998

Subsidiary (Domestic):

Cytec Engineered Materials Inc. (2)
1191 Hawk Cir, Anaheim, CA 92807
Tel.: (714) 632-8444
Web Site: http://www.solvay.com
Plastic Materials Mfr
N.A.I.C.S.: 325520

Subsidiary (Non-US):

Cytec Engineered Materials Ltd. (2)
Wrexham Industrial Estate Abenbury Way, Wrexham, LL13 9UZ, Clwyd, United Kingdom
Tel.: (44) 1978665200
Web Site: http://www.solvay.com
Specialty Chemicals Mfr
N.A.I.C.S.: 325998

Cytec Industrial Materials (Derby) Limited (2)
Composite House Sinclair Close, Heanor Gate Industrial Estate, Heanor, DE75 7SP, Derbyshire, United Kingdom
Tel.: (44) 1773766200
Web Site: http://www.solvay.com
Advanced Composite & Process Materials Mfr & Distr
N.A.I.C.S.: 325998

Subsidiary (Domestic):

Cytec - Med-Lab Ltd (3)
Copeland Street, Derby, DE1 2PU, United Kingdom
Tel.: (44) 1332349094
Web Site: http://www.med-lab.co.uk
Overhaul & Maintenance Materials for Aircraft Engines
N.A.I.C.S.: 336413
Mark Knight (Mng Dir)

Subsidiary (Non-US):

Cytec Industries (Shanghai) Co., Ltd (2)
No 3966 Jindu Road Xinzhuang Industry Zone, Minhang District, Shanghai, 201108, China
Tel.: (86) 2123501000
Web Site: http://www.solvay.com
Specialty Chemicals Mfr

N.A.I.C.S.: 325998

Plant (Domestic):

Cytec Industries Inc. (2)
7910 Mount Joy Rd, Mount Pleasant, TN 38474-0152
Tel.: (931) 379-3257
Web Site: http://www.solvay.com
Specialty Chemicals Mfr
N.A.I.C.S.: 325998

Subsidiary (Non-US):

Cytec Industries Pte. Ltd. (2)
1 Biopolis Dr 05-01 06 Aminos, Singapore, 138622, Singapore
Tel.: (65) 62911921
Web Site: http://www.solvay.com
Specialty Chemicals Mfr
N.A.I.C.S.: 325998

Cytec Korea Inc. (2)
4th Floor Pungrim Building 124 Teheran-Ro, Gangnam-gu, Seoul, 06234, Korea (South)
Tel.: (82) 269161200
Web Site: http://www.solvay.com
Specialty Chemicals Mfr
N.A.I.C.S.: 325998

Cytec Netherlands Holding B.V. (2)
Burgemeester Van Lierplien 75, Vlaardingen, 3134 ZB, Netherlands
Tel.: (31) 107137000
Web Site: http://www.solvay.com
Holding Company; Chemical Product Mfr
N.A.I.C.S.: 325998

Subsidiary (Domestic):

Cytec Industries B.V. (3)
Weena 505, 3013 AL, Rotterdam, Netherlands
Tel.: (31) 107137000
Web Site: http://www.solvay.com
Specialty Chemicals Mfr
N.A.I.C.S.: 325998

Subsidiary (Non-US):

Cytec de Mexico S.A. de C.V. (2)
Km 40 Carretera Guadalajara La Barca, Atequiza, 45860, Jalisco, Mexico
Tel.: (52) 3767374100
Web Site: http://www.solvay.com
Chemical Products Mfr
N.A.I.C.S.: 325998

Solvay Rayong Huay Pong
Hemaraj Eastern Industrial Estate 2/1 Soi G-2 Pakornsongkrohratch Road, Huay Pong, 21150, Amphur Muang, Rayong, Thailand
Tel.: (66) 38918101
Web Site: http://www.solvay.com
Chemical Products Mfr
N.A.I.C.S.: 325998

Cytec Process Materials (CA) Inc. (1)
12801 Ann St, Santa Fe Springs, CA 90670
Tel.: (562) 906-3300
Chemical Products Mfr
N.A.I.C.S.: 325199

Cytec Process Materials (Keighley) Ltd. (1)
500 Bradford Road Sandbeds, Keighley, BD20 5NG, United Kingdom
Tel.: (44) 1274550500
Chemical Products Mfr
N.A.I.C.S.: 325199

Cytec Process Materials S.r.l. (1)
Via Vigevano 1, 12084, Mondovi, CN, Italy
Tel.: (39) 0174566200
Chemical & Plastic Product Mfr
N.A.I.C.S.: 325998

Cytec Process Materials Sarl (1)
1 Rue De La Sausse, Saint Jean, 31240, Toulouse, France
Tel.: (33) 561378989
Chemical & Plastic Product Mfr
N.A.I.C.S.: 325998

Daehan Solvay Special Chemicals Company, Ltd. (1)
383 Daejung-Ril Onsan-Eup Ulju-Gun, 689-890, Seoul, Ulsan City, Korea (South)
Tel.: (82) 522310610

Web Site: http://www.solvayasiapacific.com
Sales Range: $50-74.9 Million
Emp.: 110
Barium & Strontium Carbonates Mfr
N.A.I.C.S.: 325998

Deven AD (1)
Industrial Zone, 9160, Devnya, Bulgaria
Tel.: (359) 519 95000
Web Site: http://www.solvay.bg
Sales Range: $75-99.9 Million
Emp.: 60
Thermal Electric Power Generation Services
N.A.I.C.S.: 221118
Piros Nomikos (Mgr)

European Carbon Fiber GmbH (1)
Regensburger Strasse 109, 93309, Kelheim, Germany
Tel.: (49) 9441990
Chemical & Plastic Product Mfr
N.A.I.C.S.: 325998

GOR Applicazioni Speciali S.p.A. (1)
Via Pinerolo 7, Buriasco, 10060, Turin, TO, Italy (100%)
Tel.: (39) 0121569111
Sales Range: $25-49.9 Million
Emp.: 100
Wood Stock Sheets Mfr
N.A.I.C.S.: 321219
Sabrizio Carrell (Dir)

Holmes Chapel Trading Ltd (1)
Oak House Reeds Crescent, Watford, WD24 4QP, Hertfordshire, United Kingdom
Tel.: (44) 1923 485 868
Financial Management Services
N.A.I.C.S.: 523999

Horizon Immobilien AG (1)
Hans-Bockler-Allee 20, Hannover, 30173, Germany
Tel.: (49) 5118570
Investment Advisory Services
N.A.I.C.S.: 523940

Liyang Rhodia Rare Earth New Material Co., Ltd (1)
No 9 Geqi Rd, East Suburb, Liyang, 213300, China
Tel.: (86) 51987318713
Chemical Products Mfr
N.A.I.C.S.: 325998

Nippon Solvay K.K. (1)
7th Fl Atago Green Hills Mori Tower Atago 2-5-1, Minato-Ku, Tokyo, 105-6207, Japan (100%)
Tel.: (81) 3 54254310
Web Site: http://www.solvayasiapacific.com
Sales Range: $25-49.9 Million
Emp.: 13
Mfr of Plastics & Chemicals
N.A.I.C.S.: 325211

Okorusu Fluorspar (Pty) Ltd (1)
60km North West of Orjiwarongo, PO Box 1236, Otjiwarongo, Namibia
Tel.: (264) 67305404
Web Site: http://www.solvay.com
Chemical Products Mfr
N.A.I.C.S.: 325180

Orbeo Climate Care S.A.S. (1)
Immeuble Pacific - 11/13 Cours, Valmy, 92800, France
Tel.: (33) 153565000
Chemical Products Mfr
N.A.I.C.S.: 325998

Oy Finnish Peroxides AB (1)
PO Box 1, FIN 45911, Voikkaa, Finland (100%)
Tel.: (358) 20415151
Web Site: http://www.sovay.com
Sales Range: $25-49.9 Million
Emp.: 70
Mfr of Peroxides
N.A.I.C.S.: 325998

PT. Cytec Indonesia (1)
Sampoerna Square South Tower 30th Fl Jl Jend Sudirman Kav 45-46, 12930, Jakarta, Indonesia
Tel.: (62) 2129927892
Chemical & Plastic Product Mfr
N.A.I.C.S.: 325998

Padanaplast S.p.A. (1)

INTERNATIONAL PUBLIC

Via Paganina 3, Roccabianca, Parma, 43010, Italy (72%)
Tel.: (39) 05215291
Web Site: http://www.padanplast.com
Sales Range: $25-49.9 Million
Emp.: 80
Chemical Products
N.A.I.C.S.: 325998

Peroxidos do Brazil Ltda (1)
Rua Joao Lunardelli 1301 CIC, Curitiba, 81460-100, PR, Brazil (70%)
Tel.: (55) 4133165200
Web Site: http://www.peroxidos.com.br
Sales Range: $50-74.9 Million
Emp.: 100
Persulphates, Peracetic Acid
N.A.I.C.S.: 325180

SIS Italia S.p.A. (1)
Viale Lombardia 20, Bollate, 20021, Milan, Italy
Tel.: (39) 0238351
Business Management Consulting Services
N.A.I.C.S.: 541611

SOLVAY VIENNA GmbH (1)
Stattermayergasse 28-30, Vienna, 1150, Austria
Tel.: (43) 1 716880
Web Site: http://www.solvay.at
Plastic Material Mfr & Distr
N.A.I.C.S.: 325211
Sylvia Prudky (Office Mgr)

SOLVAY-SPECIALITES-FRANCE S.A.S. (1)
25 Rue De Clichy, Paris, 75009, France
Tel.: (33) 140758000
Industrial Chemicals Mfr
N.A.I.C.S.: 325998

Sertow OOO (1)
1 Khimikov Street, 142204, Ivanovskoye, Russia
Tel.: (7) 4967 35 90 89
Sales Range: $50-74.9 Million
Emp.: 160
Chemical Products Mfr
N.A.I.C.S.: 325998
Anna Shatalova (Head-Sls)

Sichuan Chuanxi Plastic Co. Ltd. (1)
No. 1 Group Wuliang Village, 611730, Chengdu, Xipu, China (25.5%)
Mfr of Plastic Products
N.A.I.C.S.: 326199

Societa Bario e Derivati S.P.A. (1)
Via Degli Olivetti 84, 54100, Massa, Italy
Tel.: (39) 05858901
Web Site: http://www.solvay.com
Sales Range: $50-74.9 Million
Emp.: 145
Barium & Sodium Compounds
N.A.I.C.S.: 325180

Societa Elettrochimica Solfuri e Cloroderivati (ELESO) S.p.A. (1)
V Turati 12, 20121, Milan, Italy
Tel.: (39) 02290921
Industry Chemical Mfr
N.A.I.C.S.: 325180

Societa Gernerale per l'Industria della Magnesia (SGIM) S.p.A. (1)
Angera, Varese, Italy (100%)
Tel.: (39) 0331939111
Web Site: http://www.solvay.it
Chemical Products
N.A.I.C.S.: 325998

Sodufa B.V. (1)
, Weesp, Netherlands (100%)
Mfr of Chemicals, Plastics, Pharmaceuticals & Biochemicals
N.A.I.C.S.: 325412

SolVin SA (1)
rue de Ransbeek 310, 1120, Brussels, Belgium (75%)
Tel.: (32) 22642111
Web Site: http://www.solvinpvc.com
Sales Range: $450-499.9 Million
Emp.: 2,300
Plastics Mfr; Management of PVC Sales & Supply
N.A.I.C.S.: 325211

Subsidiary (Non-US):

Hispavic Iberica S.L. (2)

AND PRIVATE COMPANIES — SOLVAY S.A.

Marie Curie 1-3-5, Martorell, E 08760, Barcelona, Martorell, Spain **(100%)**
Tel.: (34) 937734900
Web Site: http://www.solvinpvc.com
Sales Range: $100-124.9 Million
Emp.: 400
Plastics Material & Resins Mfr & Distr
N.A.I.C.S.: 325211

SolVin France S.A. (2)
Avenue de la Republique, Tavaux, 39500, France
Tel.: (33) 384712000
Web Site: http://www.solvinpvc.com
Sales Range: $25-49.9 Million
Emp.: 100
Plastics Material & Resins Mfr
N.A.I.C.S.: 325211

SolVin GmbH & Co. KG (2)
Ludwigstrasse 12, 47495, Rheinberg, Germany **(75%)**
Tel.: (49) 2843732721
Sales Range: $50-74.9 Million
Emp.: 200
Plastics Materials & Resins Mfr & Distr
N.A.I.C.S.: 325211

SolVin Holding Nederland B.V. (2)
Schepersweg 1, Herten, 6049 CV, Netherlands
Tel.: (31) 475384888
Web Site: http://www.solvay.com
Emp.: 65
Holding Company
N.A.I.C.S.: 551112

SolVin Italia S.p.A. (2)
Via G Marconi 73, 44122, Ferrara, FE, Italy **(75%)**
Tel.: (39) 0532789411
Web Site: http://www.solvayplastics.com
Sales Range: $25-49.9 Million
Emp.: 10
Mfr & Distr of PVC Resins
N.A.I.C.S.: 325211

SolVin Spain S.L. (2)
Marie Curie 1-3-5, 08760, Martorell, Barcelona, Spain
Tel.: (34) 93 7734900
Web Site: http://www.solvay.com
Plastic Material & Resin Mfr
N.A.I.C.S.: 325211

Solvay & CPC Barium Strontium Monterrey S. de R.L. de C.V. (1)
Carretera A Garcia Km 8 5, 66000, Villa de Garcia, Nuevo Leon, Mexico
Tel.: (52) 81 81502900
Industrial Inorganic Chemical Mfr
N.A.I.C.S.: 325180

Solvay (Bangpoo) Specialty Chemicals Ltd. (1)
342 Bangpoo Industrial Estate Moo 4 Soi 6B Sukhumvit Road, Mueang District, 10280, Praeksa, Samut Prakan, Thailand
Tel.: (66) 27094112
Chemical Products Mfr
N.A.I.C.S.: 325199

Solvay (Beijing) Energy Technology Co., Ltd. (1)
No 74 Inside Ditan Park, Dongcheng District, Beijing, 100011, China
Tel.: (86) 1064266008
Chemical & Plastic Product Mfr
N.A.I.C.S.: 325998

Solvay (Schweiz) AG (1)
Zurcherstrasse 42, 5330, Bad Zurzach, Switzerland **(100%)**
Tel.: (41) 562696161
Web Site: http://www.solvay.com
Sales Range: $25-49.9 Million
Emp.: 30
Mfr of Soda Ash, Caustic Soda, Sodium Bicarbonate, Calcium Chloride, Chlorine Products & Hydrogen
N.A.I.C.S.: 325180

Solvay (Shanghai) International Trading Co., Ltd. (1)
No 3966 Jindu Road, Xinzhuang Industry Zone Minhang District, Shanghai, 201108, China
Tel.: (86) 2124089100
Chemical & Plastic Product Mfr
N.A.I.C.S.: 325998

Solvay (Shanghai) Ltd (1)
Building 7 No 899 Zu Chong Zhi Rd Zhang Jiang High-Tech Park, 201203, Shanghai, China
Tel.: (86) 21 50805080
Chemical Product Whslr
N.A.I.C.S.: 424690

Solvay (Thailand) Ltd. (1)
11 & 16th Fl Wave Place 55 Wireless Rd, 10330, Bangkok, Thailand
Tel.: (66) 26106400
Chemical Products Mfr
N.A.I.C.S.: 325199

Solvay (Zhenjiang) Chemicals Co., Ltd. (1)
No 66 Song Lin Shan Road, Zhenjiang New Area, Zhenjiang, 212006, Jiangsu, China
Tel.: (86) 51185305200
Chemical & Plastic Product Mfr
N.A.I.C.S.: 325998

Solvay - Organics - France S.A.S. (1)
25 Rue de Clichy, 75009, Paris, France
Tel.: (33) 140758000
Web Site: http://www.solvayorganics.com
Emp.: 300
Industrial Organic Chemicals Mfr
N.A.I.C.S.: 325199

Solvay Advanced Polymers France S.A. (1)
, Paris, France **(100%)**
Mfr of Chemicals, Plastics, Pharmaceuticals & Biochemicals
N.A.I.C.S.: 325412

Solvay Alexandria Trading LLC (1)
39 Medhat Al Meligi 1st Floor Kamarayet Roushdy Stanley Corniche Road, 21529, Alexandria, Egypt
Tel.: (20) 35419121
Chemical & Plastic Product Mfr
N.A.I.C.S.: 325998

Solvay Alkor Folie Spol sr.o. (1)
Areal Banskych Staveb, 435 61, Litomerice, Most-Cepirohy, Czech Republic **(100%)**
Tel.: (420) 35 346824
Mfr of Chemicals, Plastics, Pharmaceuticals & Biochemicals
N.A.I.C.S.: 325412

Solvay America, Inc. (1)
3737 Buffalo Speedway Ste 800, Houston, TX 77098-3701 **(100%)**
Tel.: (713) 525-6000
Web Site: http://www.solvay.com
Sales Range: $150-199.9 Million
Peroxygens & Derivatives; Hydrogen Peroxide; Sodium Carbonate Peroxyhydrate
N.A.I.C.S.: 325211

Subsidiary (Domestic):

Ausimont Industries, Inc. (2)
10 Leonards Ln, Thorofare, NJ 08086
Tel.: (856) 853-8119
Emp.: 130
Chemical Products Mfr
N.A.I.C.S.: 325998
Charles Jones *(Mgr)*

Chemlogics Group, LLC (2)
2915 Union Rd Ste D, Paso Robles, CA 93446-7312
Tel.: (805) 591-3314
Sales Range: $500-549.9 Million
Emp.: 277
Specialty Chemicals Mfr
N.A.I.C.S.: 325998
Janice Odell *(CFO)*

Solvay Advanced Polymers, L.L.C. (2)
175005 State Route 7, Marietta, OH 45750
Tel.: (740) 373-9242
Web Site: http://www.solvayamerica.com
Sales Range: $10-24.9 Million
Plastics Processing Services
N.A.I.C.S.: 611710

Solvay Chemicals, Inc. (2)
3737 Buffalo Speedway Ste 800, Houston, TX 77098-3701 **(100%)**
Tel.: (713) 525-6800
Web Site: http://www.solvay.us
Emp.: 100
Chemicals Mfr
N.A.I.C.S.: 325211

Solvay Finance (America) LLC (2)
3333 Richmond Ave, Houston, TX 77098
Tel.: (713) 525-6000
Financial Management Services
N.A.I.C.S.: 523999

Solvay Information Services NAFTA, LLC (2)
3333 Richmond Ave, Houston, TX 77098
Tel.: (713) 525-6000
Web Site: http://www.solvaychemicals.us
Sales Range: $50-74.9 Million
Plastic Materials Mfr
N.A.I.C.S.: 325211

Solvay Pharmaceuticals, Inc. (2)
901 Sawyer Rd, Marietta, GA 30062-2224 **(100%)**
Tel.: (770) 578-9000
Sales Range: $200-249.9 Million
Pharmaceuticals Mfr
N.A.I.C.S.: 325412

Solvay Solexis, Inc. (2)
800 Greenbank Rd, Wilmington, DE 19808
Tel.: (302) 999-8060
Web Site: http://www.solvay.com
Chemical Product Whslr
N.A.I.C.S.: 424690

Solvay Argentina S.A. (1)
Avenida Alicia Moreau De Justo 1930 4 Piso, C1107AFN, Buenos Aires, Puerto Madero, Argentina **(100%)**
Mfr of Chemicals, Plastics, Pharmaceuticals & Biochemicals
N.A.I.C.S.: 325412

Solvay Asia Pacific Pte. Ltd. (1)
1 Biopolis Dr Unit No 0501, Singapore, 138622, Singapore **(100%)**
Tel.: (65) 64388886
Web Site: http://www.solvay.com
Sales Range: $25-49.9 Million
Emp.: 11
Mfr of Chemicals & Pharmaceuticals
N.A.I.C.S.: 325412
Roger L. Kearns *(Chm)*

Solvay Bario e Derivati (SABED) S.p.A. (1)
Via Degli Oliveti 84, 54100, Massa, MS, Italy **(100%)**
Tel.: (39) 05858901
Web Site: http://www.solvay-bareumstrontum.com
Sales Range: $25-49.9 Million
Emp.: 100
Chemical Products
N.A.I.C.S.: 325998
Giolsee Savlo *(Mng Dir)*

Solvay Benvic & Cie Belgium S.N.C. (1)
Rue de Ransdeek 310, 1050, Brussels, Belgium **(100%)**
Tel.: (32) 25096111
Sales Range: $250-299.9 Million
Emp.: 600
Chemical, Plastic, Pharmaceutical & Biochemical Mfr
N.A.I.C.S.: 325412

Solvay Benvic Europe France S.A.S. (1)
57 Avenue de Tavaux, Chevigny Saint Sauveur, 21800, Chevigny-Saint-Sauveur, France **(100%)**
Tel.: (33) 380467300
Web Site: http://www.solvay.fr
Sales Range: $50-74.9 Million
Emp.: 120
Chemical Products
N.A.I.C.S.: 325998

Solvay Bulgaria AD (1)
8th Fl Rm 803 Administrative Bldg, Devnya, 9160, Varna, Bulgaria **(100%)**
Tel.: (359) 52685895
Chemicals Mfr
N.A.I.C.S.: 325998

Solvay Business Services Latvia SIA (1)
Gustava Zemgala Gatve 76 Block A 5th Floor, LV-1039, Riga, Latvia
Tel.: (371) 67118801

Chemicals Mfr
N.A.I.C.S.: 325211

Solvay Business Services Portugal Unipessoal Lda. (1)
Edificio Neopark Avenida Tomas Ribeiro 43-2C, 2790-211, Carnaxide, Portugal
Tel.: (351) 218319200
Chemical & Plastic Product Mfr
N.A.I.C.S.: 325998

Solvay Canada Inc. (1)
181 Bay Street Suite 4400, Toronto, M5J 2T3, ON, Canada
Tel.: (609) 860-4000
Chemical & Plastic Product Mfr
N.A.I.C.S.: 325998

Solvay Chemicals (Shanghai) Co. Ltd. (1)
No 3966 Jindu Road, Xinzhuang Industry Zone Minhang District, Shanghai, 201108, China
Tel.: (86) 2123501000
Chemical & Plastic Product Mfr
N.A.I.C.S.: 325998

Solvay Chemicals Finland Oy (1)
Yrjonojantie 2, 45910, Voikkaa, Finland
Tel.: (358) 207459400
Web Site: http://www.solvay.com
Industrial Inorganic Chemical Mfr
N.A.I.C.S.: 325180

Solvay Chemicals International SA (1)
Rue De Ransbeek 310, 1120, Brussels, Belgium
Tel.: (32) 22642111
Web Site: http://www.solvay.com
Industrial Chemicals Mfr
N.A.I.C.S.: 325180

Solvay Chemicals Ltd. (1)
Baronet Works, Warrington, WA4 6HA, United Kingdom **(100%)**
Tel.: (44) 1925651277
Web Site: http://www.solvay.com
Sales Range: $50-74.9 Million
Emp.: 200
Provider of Chemicals
N.A.I.C.S.: 325998

Solvay Chemie B.V. (1)
Schepersweg 1, 6049 CV, Herten, Netherlands **(100%)**
Tel.: (31) 475384888
Web Site: http://www.solvay.com
Sales Range: $1-9.9 Million
Caustic Soda, Chlorine Products, Sodium Chlorate, Hydrogen
N.A.I.C.S.: 325180

Solvay Chimica Italia S.p.A. (1)
Via Piave 6, 57013, Rosignano Solvay, LI, Italy
Tel.: (39) 0586721111
Web Site: http://www.solvay.it
Sales Range: $25-49.9 Million
Chemical Products
N.A.I.C.S.: 325998

Subsidiary (Domestic):

Solvay Chimica Bussi S.p.A. (2)
Piazzale Elettrochimica 1, 65022, Bussi sul Tirino, Pescara, Italy
Tel.: (39) 085 98001
Sales Range: $25-49.9 Million
Industrial Inorganic Chemical Mfr
N.A.I.C.S.: 325180

Solvay Coordination Internationale des Credits Commerciaux (CICC) S.A. (1)
Rue Du Prince Albert 33, B 1050, Brussels, Belgium **(100%)**
Tel.: (32) 25096111
Sales Range: $250-299.9 Million
Emp.: 700
Chemical, Plastic, Pharmaceutical & Biochemical Mfr
N.A.I.C.S.: 325412

Solvay Energie France S.A.S. (1)
25 Rue De Clichy, Paris, 75009, France
Tel.: (33) 140758302
Web Site: http://www.solvay.com
Electric Power Distribution Services
N.A.I.C.S.: 221122

SOLVAY S.A.

Solvay S.A.—(Continued)

Solvay Energy Services Italia S.r.l. (1)
Viale Lombardia 20, 20021, Bollate, MI, Italy
Tel.: (39) 02290921
Chemical & Plastic Product Mfr
N.A.I.C.S.: 325998

Solvay Energy Services S.A.S. (1)
25 Rue de Clichy, 75009, Paris, France
Tel.: (33) 140758302
Chemical & Plastic Product Mfr
N.A.I.C.S.: 325998

Solvay Engineered Polymers (Canada), Inc. (1)
625 Millway Ave, Concord, L4K 3T9, ON, Canada (100%)
Tel.: (905) 738-6433
Web Site: http://www.solvayengineeredpolymers.com
Sales Range: $25-49.9 Million
Emp.: 8
Chemical Products
N.A.I.C.S.: 325998

Solvay Farma Lda. (1)
Lagoas Pk 5C 6th Fl, 2740, Lisbon, Portugal (100%)
Tel.: (351) 218315800
Sales Range: $25-49.9 Million
Emp.: 80
Mfr of Pharmaceuticals
N.A.I.C.S.: 325412

Solvay Finance (Luxembourg) S.A. (1)
Rue Aldringen 14, L 1118, Luxembourg, Luxembourg (100%)
Tel.: (352) 26449800
Chemical Products
N.A.I.C.S.: 325998

Solvay Finance B.V. (1)
C J Van Houtenlaan 36, 1381 CP, Weesp, Netherlands (100%)
Tel.: (31) 294479000
Web Site: http://www.solvay.com.nl
Sales Range: $450-499.9 Million
Emp.: 1,500
Chemical Products
N.A.I.C.S.: 325998

Solvay Finance France S.A. (1)
25 Rue de Clichy, Paris, 75442, France
Tel.: (33) 140758000
Web Site: http://www.solvay.com
Financial Management Services
N.A.I.C.S.: 523999

Solvay Finance Ireland Unlimited (1)
Aib International Centre, Dublin, Ireland
Tel.: (353) 18291561
Financial Services
N.A.I.C.S.: 523999

Solvay Finance S.A. (1)
25 Rue De Clichy, Paris, France
Tel.: (33) 140758000
Financial Management Services
N.A.I.C.S.: 523999

Solvay Finanziaria S.p.A. (1)
Via Marostica 1, Milan, 20146, Italy
Tel.: (39) 02290921
Investment Management Service
N.A.I.C.S.: 523999

Solvay Fine Chemical Additives (Qingdao) Co., Ltd. (1)
No 788 Huaguan Road, Qingdao High-Tech Industry Dev Zone, Qingdao, 266111, Shandong, China
Tel.: (86) 53268011300
Chemical & Plastic Product Mfr
N.A.I.C.S.: 325998

Solvay Fluor GmbH (1)
Hans-Boeckler-Allee 20, 30173, Hannover, Germany
Tel.: (49) 5118570
Chemical & Plastic Product Mfr
N.A.I.C.S.: 325998

Solvay Fluor Italia S.p.A. (1)
Via Della Chimica 5, Porto Marghera, Venice, 30175, Italy
Tel.: (39) 041 5096998
Web Site: http://www.solvay.com

Flourine Compound Distr
N.A.I.C.S.: 424690

Solvay Fluor Mexico S.A. de C.V. (1)
Carretera Panamericana KM 23 5, col Granjas, 32690, Ciudad Juarez, Chihuahua, Mexico (100%)
Tel.: (52) 6566375700
Web Site: http://www.solvaychemicals.com
Sales Range: $50-74.9 Million
Mfr of Chemicals
N.A.I.C.S.: 325998

Solvay Flux GmbH (1)
Dieselstrasse 26, 30827, Garbsen, Germany
Tel.: (49) 5131462290
Chemical & Plastic Product Mfr
N.A.I.C.S.: 325998

Solvay GmbH (1)
Hans-Bockler-Allee 20, 30173, Hannover, Germany (100%)
Tel.: (49) 5118570
Web Site: http://www.solvay.de
Sales Range: $200-249.9 Million
Pharmaceuticals & Medicinal Products Mfr
N.A.I.C.S.: 325412

Subsidiary (Domestic):

Artus Mineralquellen GmbH & Co. KG (2)
Im Strand 40, PO Box 0341, 53553, Bad Honningen, Germany (100%)
Tel.: (49) 26359660
Web Site: http://www.artus-mineralquellen.ge
Sales Range: $25-49.9 Million
Emp.: 60
Alkaline Salts & Earth Compounds; Mineral Waters & Soft Drinks; Joint Venture of Artus Mineralquellen GmbH & Co. KG & Hubertus Sprudel GmbH
N.A.I.C.S.: 312112

Kandelium Barium Strontium GmbH & Co. KG (2)
Am Guterbahnhof, Bad Honningen, 53557, Hannover, Germany (100%)
Tel.: (49) 2635730
Web Site: https://www.kandelium.com
Sales Range: $25-49.9 Million
Emp.: 40
Chemicals Mfr
N.A.I.C.S.: 325998

Subsidiary (Domestic):

Solvay & CPC Barium Strontium International GmbH (3)
Hans-Bockler- Allee 20, Hannover, 30173, Germany
Tel.: (49) 51185700
Web Site: http://www.solvay.com
Sales Range: $125-149.9 Million
Emp.: 15
Industrial Inorganic Chemical Mfr
N.A.I.C.S.: 325180
Stephan Ahrens (CEO)

Subsidiary (Domestic):

Salzgewinnungsgesellschaft Westfalen mbH (2)
Graeser Brook 9, 48683, Ahaus, Germany (65%)
Tel.: (49) 2565600
Web Site: http://www.solvay.com
Sales Range: $25-49.9 Million
Salt
N.A.I.C.S.: 325998

Solvay Elektrolysespezialitaten (2)
Xantener Strasse 237, 47495, Rheinberg, Germany (100%)
Tel.: (49) 2843730
Sales Range: $200-249.9 Million
Emp.: 800
Mfr of Chemical Preparations
N.A.I.C.S.: 325998

Solvay Enzymes GmbH & Co. (2)
Hans Bockler Allee 20, Hannover, 30173, Germany (50%)
Tel.: (49) 5118570
Web Site: http://www.solvay.com
Sales Range: $400-499.9 Million
Enzymes; Joint Venture of Solvay Enzymes Gmbh & Co. & Miles (Lausanne) S.A.

N.A.I.C.S.: 325199

Solvay Infra Bad Hoenningen GmbH (2)
Am Guterbahnhof, 53557, Bad Honningen, Germany
Tel.: (49) 2635 73 0
Chemical Product Research & Development Services
N.A.I.C.S.: 541715

Solvay Interox GmbH (2)
Hans-Bockler-Allee 20, 30173, Hannover, Germany (100%)
Tel.: (49) 5118570
Web Site: http://www.solvay.de
Sales Range: $100-124.9 Million
Chemical Products
N.A.I.C.S.: 325998

Solvay Organics GmbH (2)
Hans-Bockler-Allee 20, 30173, Hannover, Germany
Tel.: (49) 5118570
Web Site: http://www.solvay.com
Chemical Products Mfr
N.A.I.C.S.: 325998

Solvay Soda Deutschland GmbH (2)
Xantener Strasse 237, D 47495, Rheinberg, Germany (100%)
Tel.: (49) 2843730
Sales Range: $200-249.9 Million
Emp.: 800
Chemicals Mfr
N.A.I.C.S.: 325998

Solvay Specialty Polymers Germany GmbH (2)
Rossstrasse 96, 40476, Dusseldorf, Germany (100%)
Tel.: (49) 2115135900
Web Site: http://www.solvayadvancedpolymers.com
Sales Range: $25-49.9 Million
Emp.: 15
Mfr of Chemicals, Plastics, Pharmaceuticals & Biochemicals
N.A.I.C.S.: 325412

Solvay Specialty Polymers Germany GmbH (2)
Hans-Bockler-Allee 20, 30173, Hannover, Germany
Tel.: (49) 511 8570
Plastic Materials Mfr
N.A.I.C.S.: 325211

Solvay Verwaltungs-und Vermittlungs GmbH (2)
Hans-Bockler-Allee 20, 30173, Hannover, Germany
Tel.: (49) 511 8570
Investment Management Service
N.A.I.C.S.: 523940

Solvay Healthcare Ltd. (1)
Hamilton House Mansbridge Rd, Southampton, SO18 3JD, United Kingdom (100%)
Tel.: (44) 2380467000
Web Site: http://www.solvayhealthcare.co.uk
Sales Range: $50-74.9 Million
Emp.: 120
Provider of Pharmaceuticals
N.A.I.C.S.: 325412

Solvay Hengchang (Zhangjiagang) Specialty Chemical Co., Ltd. (1)
Chemical Industry City East of Zhangyang Road, Yangshe Town, Zhangjiagang, 215617, Jiangsu, China
Tel.: (86) 51256769200
Chemical & Plastic Product Mfr
N.A.I.C.S.: 325998

Solvay Interox - Produtos Peroxidados Lda (1)
Av Marechal Gomes Da Costa 33, P 1800, Lisbon, Portugal
Tel.: (351) 218316100
Web Site: http://www.solvay.com
Hydrogen Peroxide, Sodium Perborate
N.A.I.C.S.: 325180

Solvay Interox Ltd. (1)
Solvay House Baronet Road, Warrington, WA4 6HA, United Kingdom (100%)
Tel.: (44) 1925651277
Web Site: http://www.solvay.co.uk
Chemical Products

N.A.I.C.S.: 325998

Solvay Interox Pty. Ltd. (1)
20-22 McPherson Street, Banksmeadow, 2019, NSW, Australia (100%)
Tel.: (61) 293168000
Web Site: http://www.solvay.com.au
Sales Range: $25-49.9 Million
Emp.: 50
Peroxygen & Derivatives: Hydrogen Peroxide, Sodium Perborate
N.A.I.C.S.: 325998

Solvay Interox S.A. (1)
Calle Mallorca 269, 08008, Barcelona, Spain (100%)
Tel.: (34) 934847400
Chemical Products
N.A.I.C.S.: 325998

Solvay Japan K.K. (1)
7th Fl Atago Green Hills MORI Tower Atago 2-5-1, Minato-ku, Tokyo, 105-6207, Japan
Tel.: (81) 354254790
Chemical & Plastic Product Mfr
N.A.I.C.S.: 325998

Solvay Lantian (Quzhou) Chemicals Co., Ltd. (1)
No 39 Huayang Road, Hi-Tech Industrial Park, Quzhou, 324012, Zhejiang, China
Tel.: (86) 5708598116
Chemical & Plastic Product Mfr
N.A.I.C.S.: 325998

Solvay Mexicana S. de R.L. de C.V. (1)
Carretera Garcia Km 8 5 Centro, Villa de Garcia, 66000, Nuevo León, Mexico
Tel.: (52) 8181502900
Investment Management Service
N.A.I.C.S.: 523940

Subsidiary (Domestic):

Solvay Quimica Y Minera Servicios SA de CV (2)
Carretera A Garcia Km 8 5, Villa de Garcia, 66350, Nuevo Leon, Mexico
Tel.: (52) 8181502900
Management Consulting Services
N.A.I.C.S.: 541611

Solvay Quimica Y Minera Ventas SA de CV (2)
Carretera A Garcia Km 8 5, Villa de Garcia, 66350, Nuevo Leon, Mexico
Tel.: (52) 8181502900
Management Consulting Services
N.A.I.C.S.: 541611

Solvay Minerales S.A. (1)
Carretera De Inca S N, 18130, Granada, Spain (100%)
Tel.: (34) 958583123
Sales Range: $1-9.9 Million
Emp.: 25
Chemical Products Mfr
N.A.I.C.S.: 325998
Ignacio Aguilar (Mng Dir)

Solvay NOH (1)
Rue de Ransbeek 310, 1120, Brussels, Belgium (100%)
Tel.: (32) 22642111
Web Site: http://www.solvay.com
Sales Range: $250-299.9 Million
Chemical, Plastic, Pharmaceutical & Biochemical Mfr
N.A.I.C.S.: 325412

Solvay New Zealand Ltd. (1)
1 Bush Street, Horowhenua, Levin, 5510, New Zealand
Tel.: (64) 63689372
Chemical & Plastic Product Mfr
N.A.I.C.S.: 325998

Solvay Osterreich GmbH (1)
Bahnhofstrasse 22, 4802, Ebensee, Austria (100%)
Tel.: (43) 613380680
Web Site: http://www.solvay.com
Sales Range: $50-74.9 Million
Mfr of Soda Ash, Sodium Bicarbonate, Quicklime, Precipitated Calcium Carbonate, Paints & Special Cements
N.A.I.C.S.: 325180

Solvay P&S GmbH (1)

AND PRIVATE COMPANIES — SOLVAY S.A.

Fritz Henkel Strasse 8, 39307, Genthin, Germany
Tel.: (49) 39338240222
Chemical & Plastic Product Mfr
N.A.I.C.S.: 325998

Solvay Paris (1)
25 Rue De Clichy, 75009, Paris, France
Tel.: (33) 1 40 75 80 00
Web Site: http://www.solvay.fr
Specialty Chemicals Mfr
N.A.I.C.S.: 325998

Subsidiary (Non-US):

Rhodia Argentia SA (2)
Avenida Alicia Moreau De Justo 1930 4 Floor - Puerto Madero, C1107AFN, Buenos Aires, Argentina
Tel.: (54) 1143162310
Web Site: http://www.rhodia-quimica.com.ar
Sales Range: $25-49.9 Million
Emp.: 15
Chemical Products Sales & Distr
N.A.I.C.S.: 424690
Marcos A. De Marchi (Pres)

Rhodia Asia Pacific Pte Ltd (2)
438B Alexandra Road 02-09/12 Alexandra Technopark, Singapore, 119968, Singapore
Tel.: (65) 62 91 19 21
Chemical Products Mfr
N.A.I.C.S.: 325998

Rhodia Belgium SA (2)
Rue Du Trone 98 Internal Postal, Box 14, 1050, Brussels, Belgium
Tel.: (32) 25 02 51 20
Industrial Chemical Products Mfr
N.A.I.C.S.: 325180

Rhodia Brazil Ltda (2)
Av Maria Coelho Aguiar 215 Bloco B 1 Andar Centro Empresarial, Sao Paulo, 05804-902, Brazil
Tel.: (55) 11 3741 7505
Web Site: http://www.rhodia.com.br
Chemical Products Mfr
N.A.I.C.S.: 325998

Rhodia Chile Ltda (2)
Av El Bosque Norte No 0440 Officina 304, Las Condes, Santiago, Chile
Tel.: (56) 22 03 51 00
Web Site: http://www.rhodia.com
Sales Range: $25-49.9 Million
Emp.: 5
Chemical Products Sales
N.A.I.C.S.: 424690

Rhodia China Co., Ltd (2)
3966 Jin Du Road Xin Zhuang Industry Zone, Min Hang District, Shanghai, 201108, China
Tel.: (86) 2124089100
Emp.: 600
Polyamide Plastic Products Mfr
N.A.I.C.S.: 325211

Rhodia Energy Asia Pacific Co. Ltd (2)
4 Fl Poonglim Bldg 823 Yeoksam-dong, Gangnam-Ku, Seoul, 135-784, Korea (South)
Tel.: (82) 2 3472 2707
Specialty Chemicals Mfr
N.A.I.C.S.: 325998

Rhodia Energy Brazil Ltda (2)
4 - Esq Com Rua C S/No, Paulinia, 13140-000, Sao Paulo, Brazil
Tel.: (55) 1938748000
Chemical Products Mfr
N.A.I.C.S.: 325998

Subsidiary (Domestic):

Rhodia Energy GHG S.A.S. (2)
Tour Pacific - 18 Eme Etage 11 Cours, Valmy, 92800, Puteaux, France
Tel.: (33) 1 53 56 61 10
Energy Management Services
N.A.I.C.S.: 926130

Rhodia Energy S.A.S. (2)
25 Rue De Clichy, Puteaux, Paris, 75009, France
Tel.: (33) 1 53 56 61 02
Energy Management Services
N.A.I.C.S.: 926130

Subsidiary (Non-US):

Rhodia Especialidades SA de CV (2)
Insurgenes 1971 Torre 3 Piso 6 Guadalupe Inn Alvaro Obregon, Mexico, 01060, Mexico
Tel.: (52) 5552832800
Chemical Products Mfr
N.A.I.C.S.: 325998

Rhodia Feixiang Specialty Chemicals Co., Ltd (2)
Fenghuang Town, Zhangjiagang, 215613, Jiangsu, China
Tel.: (86) 512 58490384
Web Site: http://www.feixiangchem.com
Chemical Products Mfr
N.A.I.C.S.: 325998

Rhodia GmbH (2)
Engesserstrasse 8, 79108, Freiburg, Germany
Tel.: (49) 761 511 0
Cellulose Acetate Mfr
N.A.I.C.S.: 325199

Subsidiary (US):

Rhodia Holding Inc (2)
8 Cedarbrook Dr, Cranbury, NJ 08540
Tel.: (609) 860-4000
Web Site: http://www.solvay.com
Sales Range: $150-199.9 Million
Emp.: 300
Investment Management Service
N.A.I.C.S.: 523940
Katia Haddad Francisco Braga (Dir-Market-Coatings Bus-Latin America Reg)

Subsidiary (Non-US):

Rhodia Holdings Ltd (2)
Oak House Reeds Crescent, Watford, WD24 4QP, Hertfordshire, United Kingdom
Tel.: (44) 1923 485 868
Investment Management Service
N.A.I.C.S.: 523940

Rhodia Iberia S.L. (2)
Capitan Haya 1, 28020, Madrid, Spain
Tel.: (34) 913958200
Web Site: http://www.rhodia.com
Industrial Chemicals Sales
N.A.I.C.S.: 424690

Rhodia Italia SpA (2)
Via Milano 78-80, 20021, Bollate, Milan, Italy
Tel.: (39) 02383341
Industrial Chemical Products Mfr
N.A.I.C.S.: 325998

Rhodia Japan K.K. (2)
Roppongi First Bldg 1-9-9 Roppongi, Minato-ku, Tokyo, 106-0032, Japan
Tel.: (81) 335 85 46 91
Web Site: http://www.rhodia.com
Chemical Products Mfr
N.A.I.C.S.: 325998

Rhodia Korea Co. Ltd (2)
4Fl Poonglim Bldg 823 Yeoksam-dong, Gangnam-Ku, Seoul, 135784, Korea (South)
Tel.: (82) 2 2186 2500
Web Site: http://www.solvay.com
Emp.: 270
Plastic Materials Mfr
N.A.I.C.S.: 325211

Subsidiary (Domestic):

Rhodia Laboratoire du Futur S.A.S. (2)
178 Avenue du Docteur Schweitzer, 33608, Pessac, France
Tel.: (33) 5 56 46 47 21
Sales Range: $25-49.9 Million
Emp.: 70
Chemical Product Research & Development Services
N.A.I.C.S.: 541715
Piul Dischrijer (Pres)

Subsidiary (Non-US):

Rhodia Limited (2)
Trinity St, PO Box 80, Oldbury, B69 4LN, West Midlands, United Kingdom
Tel.: (44) 121 552 3333
Sales Range: $50-74.9 Million
Emp.: 200
Chemical Products Mfr
N.A.I.C.S.: 325998

Rhodia Nicca Ltd (2)
Roppongi First Bldg 1-9-9 Roppongi, Minato-ku, Tokyo, 106-8540, Japan
Tel.: (81) 335 85 85 72
Web Site: http://www.rhodia.com
Chemical Products Distr
N.A.I.C.S.: 424690

Subsidiary (Domestic):

Rhodia Operations S.A.S. (2)
52 Rue de la haie coq, 93308, Aubervilliers, Cedex, France
Tel.: (33) 149376262
Web Site: http://www.solvay.com
Industrial Chemicals Mfr
N.A.I.C.S.: 325998

Subsidiary (Non-US):

Rhodia Poliamida Brasil Ltda (2)
Maria Coelho De Aguiar 215, Sao Paulo, 05804-902, Brazil
Tel.: (55) 1137477888
Organic Fiber Mfr
N.A.I.C.S.: 335220

Rhodia Poliamida e Especialidades Ltda (2)
Centro Empresarial Av Maria Coelho Aguiar 215 Bloco B 1 Andar, 05804-902, Sao Paulo, Brazil
Tel.: (55) 1137417505
Organic Fiber Mfr
N.A.I.C.S.: 325220

Rhodia Polymers & Specialties India Private Limited (2)
Phoenix House A Wing 4th Floor 462 Senapati Bapat Marg, Lower Parel West, Mumbai, 40013, India
Tel.: (91) 2266637100
Engineering Polymer Mfr
N.A.I.C.S.: 325998

Rhodia Reorganisation Ltd. (2)
Oak House Reeds Crescent, Watford, WD24 4QP, Hertfordshire, United Kingdom
Tel.: (44) 1923 485 868
Web Site: http://www.solvay.com
Sales Range: $25-49.9 Million
Emp.: 13
Industrial Inorganic Chemical Mfr
N.A.I.C.S.: 325180

Subsidiary (Domestic):

Rhodia SAS (2)
Rue Lavoisier, PO Box 21, 38800, La Rochelle, Cedex, France (100%)
Tel.: (33) 476695712
Sales Range: $75-99.9 Million
Emp.: 200
Producer of Chlorine & Caustic Soda
N.A.I.C.S.: 325998

Subsidiary (Non-US):

Rhodia Silica Korea Co. Ltd (2)
587-37 Hakik-dong, Nam-ku, Incheon, 402 040, Korea (South)
Tel.: (82) 3 2870 6114
Web Site: http://www.rhodia.com
Industrial Inorganic Chemical Mfr
N.A.I.C.S.: 325180

Rhodia Silica Qingdao Co., Ltd (2)
8 No 2 Xing Guo Road, Li Chang District, Qingdao, Shandong, China
Tel.: (86) 532 84 63 88 77
Inorganic Chemical Mfr
N.A.I.C.S.: 325180

Rhodia de Mexico SA de CV (2)
Blvd Adolfo Lopez Mateos No 261 Piso 3 Oficina 1 Col Los Alpes Deleg, Alvaro Obregon, 1010, Mexico, Mexico
Tel.: (52) 55 30 03 26 60
Web Site: http://www.solvay.com
Sales Range: $25-49.9 Million
Emp.: 25
Chemical Products Mfr
N.A.I.C.S.: 325998

Solvay Engineering Plastics Poland Sp. z o.o. (2)
Ul Walczaka 25, Gorzow, 66-407, Poland
Tel.: (48) 95 733 32 07
Web Site: http://www.solvay.com
Sales Range: $50-74.9 Million
Emp.: 250
Polyamide Mfr
N.A.I.C.S.: 325998

Solvay Solutions UK Limited (2)
34 Clarendon Road, Watford, WD17 1JJ, Hertfordshire, United Kingdom
Tel.: (44) 1215523333
Web Site: http://www.rhodia.co.uk
Sales Range: $25-49.9 Million
Emp.: 16
Chemical Products Mfr
N.A.I.C.S.: 325180

Subsidiary (US):

Solvay USA Inc. (2)
504 Carnegie Ctr, Princeton, NJ 08540
Tel.: (609) 860-4000
Web Site: http://www.solvay.us
Emp.: 350
Herbicides, Insecticides, Fungicides, Animal Health Products & Feed Additives, Organic Intermediates, Aroma Chemicals, Silicones, Rare Earths, Aluminas, Plastics, Packaging Film Mfr
N.A.I.C.S.: 325180

Division (Domestic):

Solvay University Park (3)
24601 Governors Hwy, University Park, IL 60484-4127
Tel.: (708) 534-6200
Web Site: http://www.solvay.com
Specialty Cleaning Surfactants Mfr
N.A.I.C.S.: 325613

Plant (Non-US):

Rhodia Halifax (4)
Burrwood Way, Holywell Green, Halifax, HX4 9BH, United Kingdom (100%)
Tel.: (44) 1422 312200
Web Site: http://www.rhodia.com
Sales Range: $25-49.9 Million
Emp.: 32
Specialty Surfactants & Chemicals Mfr
N.A.I.C.S.: 325613

Solvay Participations France S.A. (1)
25 Rue de Clichy Cedex 09, Paris, 75009, France
Tel.: (33) 140758000
Web Site: http://www.solvay.com
Emp.: 200
Industrial Inorganic Chemical Mfr
N.A.I.C.S.: 325180

Solvay Peroxidos Portugal Unipessoal LDA. (1)
Rua Eng Clement Dumoulin, 2625-106, Povoa de Santa Iria, Portugal
Tel.: (351) 219534000
Industrial Chemical Mfr & Distr
N.A.I.C.S.: 325199

Solvay Peroxythai Ltd (1)
11 & 16th Fl Wave Place 55 Wireless Rd, 10330, Bangkok, Thailand
Tel.: (66) 2 6106470
Web Site: http://www.solvay.com
Sales Range: $25-49.9 Million
Industrial Inorganic Chemical Mfr
N.A.I.C.S.: 325180

Solvay Polyolefins Europe S.A. (1)
Rue Du Prince Albert 33, B 1050, Brussels, Belgium (100%)
Tel.: (32) 25096111
Web Site: http://www.solvaypress.com
Sales Range: $200-249.9 Million
Emp.: 700
Chemical Products
N.A.I.C.S.: 325998

Solvay Quimica S.A. (1)
Avenida Alicia Moreau De Justo 1930 4 Piso - Puerto Madero, C1107AFN, Buenos Aires, Argentina (100%)
Tel.: (54) 1143162300
Web Site: http://www.solvayindupa.com
Chemical Products
N.A.I.C.S.: 325998

Solvay Quimica S.L. (1)

SOLVAY S.A.

Solvay S.A.—(Continued)

Marie Curie 1-3-5, 08760, Barcelona, Martorell, Spain **(100%)**
Tel.: (34) 937734900
Sales Range: $50-74.9 Million
Emp.: 200
Mfr of Chemicals
N.A.I.C.S.: 325998

Solvay S.A. - France (1)
25 Rue De Clichy, 75009, Paris, Cedex 09, France **(100%)**
Tel.: (33) 140758000
Web Site: http://www.solvay.fr
Sales Range: $50-74.9 Million
Emp.: 230
Mfr of Chemicals & Pharmaceuticals
N.A.I.C.S.: 325412

Solvay Sisecam Holding AG (1)
Stattermayergasse 28-30, 1150, Vienna, Austria
Tel.: (43) 1716880
Glass Products Mfr
N.A.I.C.S.: 327212

Solvay Sodi AD (1)
Industrial Zone, 9161, Devnya, Bulgaria **(79.3%)**
Tel.: (359) 5 199 5000
Web Site: https://www.solvay.bg
Emp.: 570
Chemical Products
N.A.I.C.S.: 325998
Violeta Targova *(Mgr-PR)*

Solvay Solexis S.p.A. (1)
Viale Lombardia 20, 20021, Bollate, MI, Italy
Tel.: (39) 0238351
Web Site: http://www.solvaysolexis.com
Sales Range: $125-149.9 Million
Emp.: 400
Specialty Chemicals & High Performance Materials Mfr
N.A.I.C.S.: 325998

Solvay Solutions Italia S.p.A. (1)
Via Leonardo Da Vinci 3/7, 57123, Livorno, Italy
Tel.: (39) 058 641 7111
Web Site: https://www.solvay.it
Mfr of Chemicals
N.A.I.C.S.: 325998
Marco Martinelli *(Gen Mgr)*

Solvay Solutions UK Ltd. (1)
Burrwood Way Holywell Green, Halifax, HX4 9BH, United Kingdom
Tel.: (44) 1422898300
Chemical Products Mfr
N.A.I.C.S.: 325199

Solvay Special Chem Japan Ltd. (1)
210-51 Ogata-cho, Tokushima-ken, Anan, 774-0022, Japan **(100%)**
Tel.: (81) 884273211
Chemical & Plastic Product Mfr
N.A.I.C.S.: 325998

Solvay Specialities India Private Limited (1)
Equinox Business Park Tower - 4 9th Floor, Unit N 903 Lbs Marg Kurla West, Mumbai, 400 070, India
Tel.: (91) 2266637139
Web Site: http://www.solvay.com
Chemical Products Mfr
N.A.I.C.S.: 325998

Solvay Speciality Polymers (Changshu) Co. Ltd (1)
Jiangsu Hi-Tech Fluorochemical Industrial Park, Hai Yu Town, Changshu, 215522, Jiangsu, China
Tel.: (86) 51252327710
Web Site: http://www.solvay.com
Plastic Materials Mfr
N.A.I.C.S.: 325211

Solvay Speciality Polymers France S.A.S. (1)
25 Rue De Clichy, 75009, Paris, France
Tel.: (33) 140758000
Polymers Mfr
N.A.I.C.S.: 325211

Solvay Specialty Chemicals Asia Pacific Pte Ltd (1)
1 Biopolis Drive 05-01/06 Amnios, Singapore, 138622, Singapore **(100%)**
Tel.: (65) 62911921
Web Site: http://www.solvay.sg
Plastics Product Mfr
N.A.I.C.S.: 325211

Solvay Specialty Chemicals Ltd. (1)
Solvay House North West Lostock Works, Norwich, CW9 7ZR, Cheshire, United Kingdom **(100%)**
Tel.: (44) 1606723331
Web Site: http://www.solvay.com
Sales Range: $25-49.9 Million
Emp.: 42
Chemical Products
N.A.I.C.S.: 325998

Solvay Specialty Polymers (Changshu) Co. Ltd. (1)
Jiangsu Hi-Tech Fluorochemical Industrial Park, Hai Yu, Changshu, 215522, China
Tel.: (86) 51252327710
Industrial Chemical Mfr & Distr
N.A.I.C.S.: 325199

Solvay Specialty Polymers Korea Company Ltd. (1)
Solvay Research & Innovation Center Seoul 150, Bukahyun-Ro Seodaemun-Gu, 03759, Seoul, Korea (South)
Tel.: (82) 221255400
Chemical Products Mfr
N.A.I.C.S.: 325199

Solvay Specialty Polymers Management s.r.l. (1)
Via Piave 6, Rosignano Marittimo, 57016, Livorno, Italy
Tel.: (39) 0586721111
Plastic Materials Mfr
N.A.I.C.S.: 325211

Solvay UK Holding Company Ltd (1)
Solvay House Baronet Road, Warrington, WA4 6HA, Cheshire, United Kingdom
Tel.: (44) 1925 651 277
Investment Management Service
N.A.I.C.S.: 523940

Solvay Vostok OOO (1)
Room 11-14 Bld 1 7 Gasheka St Floor 3, Vn Ter G Municipal District Presnensky, 123056, Moscow, Russia
Tel.: (7) 4956265706
Web Site: http://www.solvay.ru
Chemical & Plastic Product Mfr
N.A.I.C.S.: 325998

Solvay do Brasil Ltda (1)
Rua Urussui 300 5 Andar, 04542 903, Sao Paulo, Brazil **(100%)**
Tel.: (55) 1137085100
Web Site: http://www.solvay.com
Sales Range: $50-74.9 Million
Emp.: 120
Chemicals & Plastics Manufacturing
N.A.I.C.S.: 325211

Solvay-Carbonate-France S.A.S. (1)
Rue Gabriel Peri, Dombasle-sur-Meurthe, 54110, France **(100%)**
Tel.: (33) 383185454
Web Site: http://www.solvaychemicals.com
Sales Range: $1-4.9 Billion
Emp.: 5,000
Chemical Products
N.A.I.C.S.: 325998

Solvay-Electrolyse-France S.A. (1)
25 Rue De Lichy, 75442, Paris, Cedex, France **(100%)**
Tel.: (33) 140758000
Web Site: http://www.solvay.fr
Sales Range: $75-99.9 Million
Emp.: 160
Distr of Chemical Products
N.A.I.C.S.: 424690

Solvay-Fluores-France S.A.S. (1)
12 Cours Albert 1ER, 75008, Paris, France **(100%)**
Chemical Products
N.A.I.C.S.: 325998

Solvay-Olefines-Fines S.A. (1)
12 Cours Albert 1ER, 75008, Paris, France **(100%)**
Tel.: (33) 40758000
Sales Range: $50-74.9 Million
Emp.: 200
Chemical Products

Solvayfarma Lda. (1)
Lagoas Park Abisicio 5 C 6, 1800 255, Lisbon, Portugal **(100%)**
Tel.: (351) 218315800
Sales Range: $25-49.9 Million
Emp.: 80
Mfr & Distributor of Pharmaceuticals
N.A.I.C.S.: 325412

Solvic S.A. (1)
Rue Du Prince Albert 33, 1050, Brussels, Belgium **(100%)**
Tel.: (32) 25096111
Web Site: http://www.solvay.com
Sales Range: $200-249.9 Million
Emp.: 1,000
Polyvinyl Chloride (PVC)
N.A.I.C.S.: 325211

Vanilia S.R.L. (1)
Via Segrino 10, I 20098, San Giuliano Milanese, MI, Italy **(100%)**
Tel.: (39) 029883961
Sales Range: $25-49.9 Million
Emp.: 20
Provider of Industrial Products
N.A.I.C.S.: 334513

Zhuhai Solvay Specialty Chemicals Co. Ltd. (1)
No 3 Lianhua Road, Nanshui Town Jinwan District, Zhuhai, 519050, Guangdong, China
Tel.: (86) 7567685555
Chemical & Plastic Product Mfr
N.A.I.C.S.: 325998

SOLVENTIS A.V. SA

Diagonal 682 5 Plant, Barcelona, Spain
Tel.: (34) 932009578
Web Site: http://www.solventis.es
Year Founded: 2015
Financial & Consulting Services
N.A.I.C.S.: 523940
Alberto Moro *(CEO)*

Subsidiaries:

Qubitia Solutions S.L. (1)
Avda Bugallal 61D 2 A, 36004, Pontevedra, Spain
Tel.: (34) 886213038
Web Site: http://www.qubitia.com
Software Development Services
N.A.I.C.S.: 541511
Luis Taboada *(CEO)*

SOLVERDE - SOCIEDADE DE INVESTIMENTOS TURISTICOS DA COSTA VERDE, S.A.

Rua 19 N 85, 4500-254, Espinho, Portugal
Tel.: (351) 227335500
Web Site: http://www.solverde.pt
Year Founded: 1972
Sales Range: $100-124.9 Million
Emp.: 1,000
Hotels & Casinos
N.A.I.C.S.: 721110
Manuel Violas *(Chm & CEO)*

SOLVI S.A.

Rua Bela Cintra 967 10th andar, Bela Vista, CEP 01415-000, Sao Paulo, SP, Brazil
Tel.: (55) 11 3124 3500 BR
Web Site: http://www.solvi.com
Year Founded: 2006
Sales Range: $600-649.9 Million
Emp.: 13,142
Holding Company; Waste Management, Sanitation, Energy Recovery & Civil Engineering Services
N.A.I.C.S.: 551112
Carlos Leal Villa *(Pres & CEO)*

Subsidiaries:

Manaus Ambiental S.A. (1)
Rua do Bombeamento 01 Compensa, CEP 69029-160, Manaus, AM, Brazil **(100%)**
Tel.: (55) 08000 920 195

INTERNATIONAL PUBLIC

Web Site: http://www.manausambiental.com.br
Sales Range: $650-699.9 Million
Emp.: 654
Water Supply, Sewage Irrigation & Treatment Services
N.A.I.C.S.: 221310

Solvi Valorizacao Energetica S.A. (1)
Rua Bela Cintra 967 10 andar Bela Vista, CEP 01415-000, Sao Paulo, SP, Brazil
Tel.: (55) 1131243500
Web Site: http://www.solvi.com
Bio-Fuel Thermoelectric Plant Operator & Energy Recovery Services
N.A.I.C.S.: 221118

Vega Engenharia Ambiental S.A. (1)
249 Rua Clodomiro Amazonas 1andar, Itaim Bibi, CEP 04537-010, Sao Paulo, SP, Brazil **(100%)**
Tel.: (55) 1134915133
Web Site: http://www.vega.com.br
Sales Range: $75-99.9 Million
Emp.: 200
Integrated Waste Management & Recycling Services
N.A.I.C.S.: 562998

SOLVIAS AG

Romerpark 2, 4303, Kaiseraugst, Switzerland
Tel.: (41) 618456000
Web Site: http://www.solvias.com
Year Founded: 1999
Analytical Testing, Contract Research, Development & Manufacturing Company
N.A.I.C.S.: 541380
Karen Huebscher *(CEO)*

Subsidiaries:

Chemic Laboratories, Inc. (1)
480 Neponset St, Canton, MA 02021
Tel.: (781) 821-5600
Web Site: http://www.chemiclabs.com
Testing Laboratories
N.A.I.C.S.: 541380
Joseph St. Laurent *(Co-Founder, Pres & Chief Scientific Officer)*

SOLVVY INC.

7F 4-33-4 Nishi-Shinjuku, Shibuya-Ku, Tokyo, 160-0023, Japan
Tel.: (81) 362760401
Web Site: https://solvvy.co.jp
Year Founded: 2009
7320—(TKS)
Rev.: $33,332,980
Assets: $152,968,460
Liabilities: $134,277,360
Net Worth: $18,691,100
Earnings: $6,052,060
Emp.: 370
Fiscal Year-end: 06/30/24
Building Maintenance Services
N.A.I.C.S.: 561790
Takuya Arakawa *(Chm)*

Subsidiaries:

MEDIASEEK, Inc. (1)
1-27-6 Shirokane, Minato-ku, Tokyo, 108-0072, Japan
Tel.: (81) 354236600
Web Site: https://www.mediaseek.co.jp
Rev.: $8,586,160
Assets: $36,512,960
Liabilities: $6,466,240
Net Worth: $30,046,720
Earnings: $532,400
Emp.: 74
Fiscal Year-end: 07/31/2022
Software Development Services
N.A.I.C.S.: 541511
Mineyuki Fukuda *(Auditor)*

SOLWAY INVESTMENT GROUP LIMITED

Nikou Demetriou 20 A, Coral Court, 6031, Larnaca, Cyprus
Tel.: (357) 24 623095

Web Site: http://www.solway.ru
Privater Equity Firm
N.A.I.C.S.: 523999

Subsidiaries:

Compania Guatemalteca de Niquel, S.A. (1)
Ave Reforma 9-55 Zona 10 Edificio Reforma 10, 6to nivel oficina 603, Guatemala, 1010, Guatemala **(98.2%)**
Tel.: (502) 24190200
Web Site: http://www.cgn.com.gt
Emp.: 1,300
Nickel Mining
N.A.I.C.S.: 212230
Dimitri Kaudryakoz *(CEO)*

SOLXYZ CO., LTD.
3121 Shibaura msb Tamachi Tamachi Station Tower S 13F, Minato-ku, Tokyo, 108 0023, Japan
Tel.: (81) 367225011 JP
Web Site: https://www.solxyz.co.jp
Year Founded: 1981
4284—(TKS)
Rev.: $112,610,470
Assets: $84,576,610
Liabilities: $26,147,920
Net Worth: $58,428,690
Earnings: $5,338,770
Emp.: 827
Fiscal Year-end: 12/31/23
Software Development
N.A.I.C.S.: 513210
Akira Nagao *(Pres)*

Subsidiaries:

ASWARE Co., Ltd. (1)
LOOP-X 5F 3-9-15 Kaigan, Minato-ku, Tokyo, 108-0022, Japan
Tel.: (81) 367225720
Web Site: https://www.asware.jp
Information & Communication Technology Services
N.A.I.C.S.: 541519

Core Next Co., Ltd. (1)
5th Floor Loop-X Building 3-9-15, Kaigan Minato-ku, Tokyo, 108-0022, Japan
Tel.: (81) 367225058
Web Site: https://www.corenext.jp
Emp.: 34
System Development & Consulting Services
N.A.I.C.S.: 541512

E.I.SOL Co., Ltd. (1)
LOOP-X building 5F 3-9-15 Kaigan, Minato-ku, Tokyo, 108-0022, Japan
Tel.: (81) 367225040
Web Site: https://www.ei-sol.co.jp
Measurement Control Equipment Mfr & Distr
N.A.I.C.S.: 334519

Eek Co., Ltd. (1)
2nd floor DRIVE Doshin Building 3-6 Odori Nishi, Chuo-ku, Sapporo, 060-0042, Japan
Tel.: (81) 115229215
Web Site: https://eek.co.jp
E-Sports Consulting Services
N.A.I.C.S.: 541613

FFSOL Co., Ltd. (1)
Loop-X 5th Floor 3-9-15, Kaigan Minato-ku, Tokyo, 108-0022, Japan
Tel.: (81) 367225030
Web Site: https://www.ffsol.co.jp
Emp.: 45
Software Development Services
N.A.I.C.S.: 541512

Fleekdrive Co., Ltd. (1)
6F Loop-X 3-9-15, Kaigan Minato-ku, Tokyo, 108-0022, Japan
Tel.: (81) 367225015
Web Site: https://www.fleekdrive.co.jp
Cloud Storage Services
N.A.I.C.S.: 518210

Infinite Consulting Co., Ltd. (1)
LOOP-X Building 5F 3-9-15 Kaigan, Minato-ku, Tokyo, 108-0022, Japan
Tel.: (81) 367225055
Web Site: https://www.infinite-cs.co.jp
Information Technology Consulting Services
N.A.I.C.S.: 541690

Neumann Co., Ltd. (1)
3rd Floor Mita Suzuki Building 20-14 Shiba 5-chome, Minato-ku, Tokyo, 108-0014, Japan
Tel.: (81) 367225061
Web Site: https://www.neumann.jp
Driving School Services
N.A.I.C.S.: 611692

SOLYTECH ENTERPRISE CORPORATION
3F No 18 Wuquan 7th Road, Wugu District, Taipei, 248, Taiwan
Tel.: (886) 222991907
Web Site: https://www.soly-tech.com
1471—(TAI)
Rev.: $8,392,753
Assets: $54,141,369
Liabilities: $4,999,444
Net Worth: $49,141,926
Earnings: ($1,411,851)
Fiscal Year-end: 12/31/23
Power Supplies & Computer Products Mfr
N.A.I.C.S.: 335999

Subsidiaries:

Deer Electronics (Dong Guan) Co., LTD. (1)
Chang Shan Tou Qingxi Communalize, Dongguan, Guangdong, China
Tel.: (86) 76987733511
Web Site: http://www.soly-tech.com
Power Supplies Mfr
N.A.I.C.S.: 335999

SOLYTECH JAPAN CO., LTD. (1)
7F Hakata Gion Building 4-2 Gion-Machi, Hakata-ku, Fukuoka, 812-0038, Japan
Tel.: (81) 922637255
Sales Range: $50-74.9 Million
Emp.: 5
Electronic Components Distr
N.A.I.C.S.: 423690

SuperCase International Corporation (1)
2nd Shuncheng Road Golden Phenix Industrial District, Fenggang Town, Dongguan, Guangdong, China
Tel.: (86) 76986801188
Web Site: http://www.supercase.com
Engineered Precisition Plastic Products Mfr
N.A.I.C.S.: 332216

SOM DATT FINANCE CORPORATION LIMITED
8-2-502/1/A Ground Floor, JIVI Towers Road No 7 Banjara Hills, Hyderabad, 500034, Telangana, India
Tel.: (91) 1244396900
Web Site: https://somdattfin.com
Year Founded: 1993
511571—(BOM)
Rev.: $161,237
Assets: $2,823,572
Liabilities: $23,140
Net Worth: $2,800,432
Earnings: $86,410
Emp.: 2
Fiscal Year-end: 03/31/23
Financial Services
N.A.I.C.S.: 523999
Sandip Kumar Chaubey *(Compliance Officer & Sec)*

SOM DISTILLERIES & BREWERIES LTD
SOM House 23 Zone II Maharana Pratap Nagar, Bhopal, 462011, Madhya Pradesh, India
Tel.: (91) 7554271271
Web Site: https://www.somindia.com
507514—(BOM)
Rev.: $179,770,625
Assets: $109,326,959
Liabilities: $64,321,336
Net Worth: $45,005,623
Earnings: $7,230,058
Emp.: 476

Fiscal Year-end: 03/31/23
Distilleries & Breweries
N.A.I.C.S.: 312140
B. K. Goel *(VP-Comml)*

SOMA GOLD CORP.
1050 West Pender Street Suite 970, Vancouver, V6E 3S7, BC, Canada
Tel.: (604) 259-0302 BC
Web Site: https://www.somagoldcorp.com
Year Founded: 2010
SMAGF—(OTCQB)
Rev.: $18,031,553
Assets: $25,340,856
Liabilities: $25,398,900
Net Worth: ($58,044)
Earnings: $5,117,006
Fiscal Year-end: 12/31/20
Mining Exploration of Gold Properties
N.A.I.C.S.: 212220
Javier Cordova Unda *(Pres & CEO)*

SOMA PAPERS & INDUSTRIES LIMITED
Indian Mercantile Chambers 3rd Floor 14 R Kamani Marg, Ballard Estate, Mumbai, 400001, India
Tel.: (91) 2266314222
Web Site: https://www.somapapers.in
Rev.: $8,788
Earnings: ($1,625)
Fiscal Year-end: 03/31/16
Coated Paper Mfr
N.A.I.C.S.: 322120
Vikram Somani *(CFO)*

SOMA TEXTILES & INDUSTRIES LIMITED
2 Red Cross Place, Kolkata, 700 001, India
Tel.: (91) 3322487406
Web Site: https://www.somatextiles.com
SOMATEX—(NSE)
Rev.: $1,931,448
Assets: $20,962,619
Liabilities: $30,428,007
Net Worth: ($9,465,388)
Earnings: ($2,939,323)
Emp.: 26
Fiscal Year-end: 03/31/21
Textile Products Marketing & Mfr
N.A.I.C.S.: 313310
Arvind Kumar Somany *(Mng Dir)*

SOMAI PHARMACEUTICALS LTD
Lugar de Casal Pinheiro Urbanizacao Pinheiros Park II Block B R de Maio 52, 2580-507, Carregado, Portugal
Tel.: (351) 263244000
Web Site: https://somaipharma.eu
Year Founded: 2019
Pharmaceutical Manufacturing
N.A.I.C.S.: 325412
Michael Sassano *(Founder, Chm & CEO)*

SOMANY CERAMICS LIMITED
F-34 Sector-6, Noida, 201301, Uttar Pradesh, India
Tel.: (91) 1204627900
Web Site: https://www.somanyceramics.com
Year Founded: 1968
531548—(BOM)
Rev.: $227,031,291
Assets: $213,573,374
Liabilities: $110,510,100
Net Worth: $103,063,274
Earnings: $8,363,328
Emp.: 1,934
Fiscal Year-end: 03/31/21
Ceramic Tile Mfr
N.A.I.C.S.: 327120

Shreekant Somany *(Chm & Mng Dir)*

Subsidiaries:

Amora Ceramics Private Limited (1)
Sr No 147/1p2 Sartanpar Road, Near New Sartanpar Village Wankaner Dist, Morbi, 363622, Gujarat, India
Tel.; (91) 748 602 7752
Web Site: https://www.amoraceramics.com
Ceramic Mfr
N.A.I.C.S.: 327110

Schablona India Ltd. (1)
82/19 Bhakerwara Road Mundka, Delhi, 110041, India **(61.84%)**
Tel.; (91) 11 28341085
Web Site: http://www.schablona.in
Rev.: $78,064
Assets: $642,287
Liabilities: $3,595,246
Net Worth: ($2,952,959)
Earnings: ($123,969)
Emp.: 4
Fiscal Year-end: 03/31/2021
Kitchen Product Mfr
N.A.I.C.S.: 332215
N. Goenka *(Chm)*

Somany Ceramics Limited - KADI WORKS (1)
F 34 Sector 6, Distt Mehsana, Noida, 201 301, Uttar Pradesh, India
Tel.: (91) 1204627900
Web Site: http://www.somanyceramics.com
Ceramic Wall & Floor Tile Mfr
N.A.I.C.S.: 327120

Somany Global Ltd. (1)
777 - B 2nd Stage 100 Feet Road Opp New Horizon School, Indira Nagar, Bengaluru, 560008, Karnataka, India
Tel.: (91) 80 2520 3226
Web Site: http://www.somanyglobal.com
Ceramic Wall & Floor Tile Mfr
N.A.I.C.S.: 327120

SOMAPA INFORMATION TECHNOLOGY PUBLIC COMPANY LIMITED
12 Soi Phraya Suren Road Prayasuren 35, Bang Chan Road Khlong Sam Wa, Bangkok, 10510, Thailand
Tel.: (66) 27918888
Web Site: http://www.somapait.com
Sales Range: $1-9.9 Million
Emp.: 100
Computer Programming & Consulting Services
N.A.I.C.S.: 541511
Namchoke Somapa *(Mng Dir)*

SOMAR CORPORATION
11-2 Ginza 4-Chome, Chuo-Ku, Tokyo, 104-0061, Japan
Tel.: (81) 335422151
Web Site: https://www.somar.co.jp
Year Founded: 1948
8152—(TKS)
Rev.: $176,149,890
Assets: $177,537,990
Liabilities: $63,489,050
Net Worth: $114,048,940
Earnings: $9,062,310
Emp.: 464
Fiscal Year-end: 03/31/24
Chemical Product Mfr & Distr
N.A.I.C.S.: 325998
Futoshi Sotani *(Pres & Dir-Rep)*

Subsidiaries:

Siam Somar Co., Ltd. (1)
399 Interchange Building 26th Fl Unit 2 Sukhumvit Rd Klongtoey-Nua, Wattana, Bangkok, 101001, Thailand
Tel.: (66) 26112884
Chemical Products Distr
N.A.I.C.S.: 424690
George Chee *(Mgr-Sls)*

Plant (Domestic):

Siam Somar Co., Ltd. - Chonburi Factory (2)

SOMAR CORPORATION

Somar Corporation—(Continued)

700/832 Moo 6 Amata City Industrial Estate Chonburi, Nongtamlung, Phan Thong, 20160, Chonburi, Thailand
Tel.: (66) 38185388
Chemical Products Distr
N.A.I.C.S.: 424690

Somar Corporation (H.K.) Ltd. (1)
Suite No 5 on 15/F Tower 1 China Hong Kong City 33 Canton Road, Tsim Sha Tsui, Kowloon, China (Hong Kong)
Tel.: (852) 23753122
Chemical Products Distr
N.A.I.C.S.: 424690

Somar Corporation (Taiwan) Ltd. (1)
11F No 99 Sec 1 Xintai 5th Rd, Xizhi Dist, Taipei, 00221, Taiwan
Tel.: (886) 226976767
Chemical Products Distr
N.A.I.C.S.: 424690

Somar Corporation - Soka Factory (1)
19-1 Inari 5-Chome, Soka, 340-0003, Saitama, Japan
Tel.: (81) 489311511
Chemical Products Mfr
N.A.I.C.S.: 325998

Somar Corporation India Pvt. Ltd. (1)
Room No 412 Golden Square Prime Hosur Main Road, Davanam Sarovar Portico Suites, Bengaluru, 560 068, Karnataka, India
Tel.: (91) 8049116662
Chemical Products Distr
N.A.I.C.S.: 424690
Takayuki Kawano *(Mng Dir)*

Somar Europe B.V. (1)
Arlandaweg 92, 1043 EX, Amsterdam, Netherlands
Tel.: (31) 251336004
Web Site: https://www.somar-europe.com
Epoxy Liquid Coating Mfr & Distr
N.A.I.C.S.: 325510

Somar Fine Chemicals (Zhuhai) Co., Ltd. (1)
No 1 Nanhua 2nd Road, Nanshui town Jinwan District, Zhuhai, 519050, Guangdong, China
Tel.: (86) 7565120080
Chemical Products Distr
N.A.I.C.S.: 424690

Somar Vietnam Corporation (1)
Unit 1720 Prime Centre Building 53 Quang Trung, Nguyen Du Ward Hai Ba Trung District, Hanoi, Vietnam
Tel.: (84) 2473000961
Management Consulting Services
N.A.I.C.S.: 541611

SOMATHERM S.A.S.

13 Place Francheville, 24000, Perigueux, Dordogne, France
Tel.: (33) 553026970
Web Site: http://www.somatherm.fr
Rev.: $24,800,000
Emp.: 360
Industrial Contractor
N.A.I.C.S.: 332911
Steve Aubry *(Dir)*

SOMBOON ADVANCE TECHNOLOGY PUBLIC COMPANY LIMITED

No 215 Moo 2 Debaratna Road Tambol Bangclalong, Bangplee, Samut Prakan, 10540, Thailand
Tel.: (66) 20808123
Web Site: https://www.satpcl.co.th
SAT—(THA)
Rev.: $268,604,320
Assets: $303,639,666
Liabilities: $61,548,497
Net Worth: $242,091,169
Earnings: $28,207,223
Emp.: 2,081
Fiscal Year-end: 12/31/23
Automotive Parts & Accessories Mfr
N.A.I.C.S.: 336390
Yongkiat Kitaphanich *(Vice Chm-Exec Bd)*

Subsidiaries:

Bangkok Spring Industrial Company Limited (1)
No 112 Moo 2 KM 15 th Bangna-Trad Rd, Bangchalong Bangplee, Samut Prakan, 10540, Thailand (99.99%)
Tel.: (66) 20808123
Web Site: http://www.satpcl.co.th
Automotive Parts & Accessories Stores
N.A.I.C.S.: 441330

Somboon Malleable Iron Industrial Company Limited (1)
No 112 Moo 2 KM 15 th Bangna-Trad Rd, Bangchalong Bangplee, Samut Prakan, 10540, Thailand (99.99%)
Tel.: (66) 20808123
Automotive Parts & Accessories Stores
N.A.I.C.S.: 441330

SOMBORSKE NOVINE A.D.

Trg slobode 1/1, Sombor, Serbia
Tel.: (381) 25421469
Web Site: https://www.somborskenovine.co.rs
Year Founded: 2000
SMBR—(BEL)
Rev.: $333,736
Assets: $700,632
Liabilities: $541,540
Net Worth: $159,093
Earnings: $13,317
Emp.: 13
Fiscal Year-end: 12/31/20
Newspaper Publishing Services
N.A.I.C.S.: 513110
Srdan Vucurevic *(CEO)*

SOMEC S.P.A.

Via Palu 30, 31020, San Vendemiano, TV, Italy
Tel.: (39) 04384717
Web Site: https://www.somecgruppo.com
Year Founded: 1978
SOM—(ITA)
Rev.: $409,586,047
Assets: $363,003,643
Liabilities: $339,865,327
Net Worth: $23,138,315
Earnings: $11,451,595
Emp.: 1,031
Fiscal Year-end: 12/31/23
Fabrication Product Mfr
N.A.I.C.S.: 332999
Oscar Marchetto *(Chm)*

SOMERLEY CAPITAL HOLDINGS LIMITED

20/F China Building 29 Queen's Road, Central, China (Hong Kong)
Tel.: (852) 2 869 9090 Ky
Web Site: http://www.somerleycapital.com
Year Founded: 2016
8439—(HKG)
Rev.: $9,000,611
Assets: $14,983,865
Liabilities: $2,677,367
Net Worth: $12,306,498
Earnings: ($497,347)
Emp.: 48
Fiscal Year-end: 03/31/22
Financial Advisory Services
N.A.I.C.S.: 523940
Martin Nevil Sabine *(Founder, Chm & Compliance Officer)*

Subsidiaries:

Environmental Investment Services Asia Limited (1)
20/F China Building 29 Queens Road Central, Hong Kong, China (Hong Kong)
Tel.: (852) 28770088
Web Site: https://eisal.com

Asset Management Services
N.A.I.C.S.: 531390

SOMERSET MINERALS LIMITED

Level 2 22 Mount Street, Perth, 6000, WA, Australia
Tel.: (61) 861888181 AU
Web Site: https://somersetminerals.com.au
Year Founded: 2018
SMM—(ASX)
Rev.: $21,343
Assets: $2,675,172
Liabilities: $3,675,381
Net Worth: $1,000,210
Earnings: ($13,349,855)
Fiscal Year-end: 06/30/24
Mineral Exploration Services
N.A.I.C.S.: 213114
Alexander Molyneux *(Chm)*

SOMETA

2 Rue Des Jardins, 67260, Sarre-Union, Bas Rhin, France
Tel.: (33) 388016600
Web Site: http://www.matforsometa.fr
Rev.: $22,500,000
Emp.: 120
Movable Partition Contractor
N.A.I.C.S.: 238130
Jean-Marc Winstein *(Mgr-DP)*

SOMFY SA

50 avenue du Nouveau Monde, BP 152, FR-74307, Cluses, Cedex, France
Tel.: (33) 450967000 FR
Web Site: https://www.somfy-group.com
Year Founded: 1960
SO—(EUR)
Rev.: $1,653,299,158
Assets: $2,207,286,855
Liabilities: $604,469,027
Net Worth: $1,602,817,829
Earnings: $255,777,034
Emp.: 6,736
Fiscal Year-end: 12/31/22
Mfr, Designer & Marketer of Automatic Controls for Awnings, Roller Shutters & Interior Blinds
N.A.I.C.S.: 335311
Victor Despature *(Vice Chm-Supervisory Bd)*

Subsidiaries:

Automatismos Pujol SL (1)
C-16C km 4 Aptdo 1, 08272, Sant Fruitos de Bages, Spain
Tel.: (34) 938761950
Web Site: http://www.automatismospujol.es
Roll Up & Swing Door Mfr
N.A.I.C.S.: 332321

BFT Antriebssysteme GmbH (1)
Faber-Castell-Strasse 29, 90522, Oberasbach, Germany
Tel.: (49) 9117660090
Web Site: http://bft-antriebssysteme.de
Automatic Barrier & Door Mfr
N.A.I.C.S.: 334512

BFT Auto Gate & Door (Shanghai) Co. Ltd. (1)
Room 1303 No 2993 Gonghexin Road, Shanghai, 200072, China
Tel.: (86) 2161400501
Automatic Barrier & Door Mfr
N.A.I.C.S.: 334512

BFT Automation (South) Ltd. (1)
Enterprise House Murdock Road, Dorcan, Swindon, SN3 5HY, United Kingdom
Tel.: (44) 1488674750
Automatic Barrier & Door Mfr
N.A.I.C.S.: 334512

BFT Automation Ltd. (1)
Unit D3 Citylink Business Park Old Naas Road, Dublin, D12 YHY4, Ireland
Tel.: (353) 14564711
Automatic Barrier & Door Mfr
N.A.I.C.S.: 334512

BFT Automation New Zealand Ltd. (1)
224/a Bush Road, Albany, Auckland, 0632, New Zealand
Tel.: (64) 94445434
Automatic Barrier & Door Mfr
N.A.I.C.S.: 334512
Jesse Gao *(Mgr-Reg Sls)*

BFT Automation Systems PTL (1)
Plot no 6 Shed no 1 IDA Bollaram Near Miyapur, Hyderabad, 502325, Telangana, India
Tel.: (91) 4031929232
Automatic Barrier & Door Mfr
N.A.I.C.S.: 334512

BFT CZ Sro (1)
Ustecka 533/9, 184 00, Prague, Czech Republic
Tel.: (420) 226807136
Automatic Barrier & Door Mfr
N.A.I.C.S.: 334512

BFT Languedoc S.A.S. (1)
2000 Avenue du Marechal Juin, Nimes, 30900, Gard, France
Tel.: (33) 466219724
Automatic Doors & Gates Mfr
N.A.I.C.S.: 334419

BFT Middle East FZO (1)
AA-01 Ground Floor South Zone-2 Jebel Ali Free Zone, Dubai, United Arab Emirates
Tel.: (971) 48863553
Automatic Barrier & Door Mfr
N.A.I.C.S.: 334512
Paolo Nicosia *(Mng Dir)*

BFT Piemonte S.r.l. (1)
Via Valle Po 92, 12100, Cuneo, Piedmont, Italy
Tel.: (39) 0171904017
Building Automation System Installation Services
N.A.I.C.S.: 561790

BFT S.p.a. (1)
Via Lago di Vico 44, Schio, 36015, Vicenza, Italy
Tel.: (39) 0445696511
Web Site: http://www.bft.it
Emp.: 100
Building Automation System Installation Services
N.A.I.C.S.: 561790

Subsidiary (Non-US):

Automatismes BFT France S.A.S. (2)
Multiparc de Parilly 50 Rue Jean Zay Bat C, 69800, Saint Priest, Rhone, France
Tel.: (33) 478760988
Web Site: http://www.bft-france.com
Building Automation Control Systems Mfr
N.A.I.C.S.: 334512

BFT Adria D.O.O. (2)
Obrovac 39, Drazice, Rijeka, Croatia
Tel.: (385) 51502640
Web Site: http://www.bft.hr
Sales Range: $25-49.9 Million
Emp.: 13
Home Automation System Installation Services
N.A.I.C.S.: 238210
Sergeo Sestan *(Mng Dir)*

BFT Automation Australia PTY. Ltd. (2)
29 Bentley Street, Wetherill Park, 2164, NSW, Australia
Tel.: (61) 297570677
Web Site: http://www.bftaustralia.com.au
Sales Range: $25-49.9 Million
Emp.: 6
Automatic Doors & Gates Mfr & Distr
N.A.I.C.S.: 334512
Daniele Dal Cengio *(Mng Dir)*

BFT Automation UK Limited (2)
Unit 8E Newby Road Industrial Estate, Hazel Grove, Stockport, SK7 5DA, Cheshire, United Kingdom
Tel.: (44) 1614560456

SOMFY SA

Web Site: http://www.bft.co.uk
Sales Range: $25-49.9 Million
Emp.: 13
Automatic Doors & Gates Distr
N.A.I.C.S.: 423710

BFT Benelux S.A. (2)
Rue du commerce 12, 1400, Nivelles, Walloon Brabant, Belgium
Tel.: (32) 67550200
Web Site: http://www.bftbenelux.be
Home Automation System Installation Services
N.A.I.C.S.: 561790

BFT Group Italiberica de Automatismos S.L. (2)
Pol Palou Nord Sector F-C/Cami Can Basa n 6, 08401, Barcelona, Spain
Tel.: (34) 938614828
Web Site: http://www.bftautomatismos.com
Building Automation Control Systems Mfr
N.A.I.C.S.: 334512

BFT Polska Sp. z.o.o. (2)
ul Lipowa 21, 05-091, Zabki, Masovian, Poland
Tel.: (48) 228141222
Web Site: http://www.bft.pl
Sales Range: $25-49.9 Million
Emp.: 12
Automated Doors & Gates Whslr
N.A.I.C.S.: 423310

BFT Portugal S.A. (2)
ZI Pedrulha Lote 9 - Apto 8123, 3020-305, Coimbra, Portugal
Tel.: (351) 239082790
Web Site: http://www.bftportugal.com
Sales Range: $25-49.9 Million
Emp.: 7
Automatic Doors & Gates Mfr
N.A.I.C.S.: 332321

BFT Torantriebssysteme GmbH (2)
Faber-Castell-Str 29, 90522, Oberasbach, Bavaria, Germany
Tel.: (49) 9117660090
Web Site: http://www.bft-torantriebe.de
Automatic Door System Mfr
N.A.I.C.S.: 332321

Subsidiary (US):

BFT U.S. Inc. (2)
6100 Broken Sound Pkwy NW Ste 14, Boca Raton, FL 33487
Tel.: (561) 995-8155
Web Site: http://www.bft-usa.com
Sales Range: $25-49.9 Million
Emp.: 10
Automatic Doors & Gates Mfr
N.A.I.C.S.: 334512
Fabio Billo *(CEO)*

Subsidiary (Domestic):

O&O S.r.l. (2)
Via Arrigo Boito 300, 41019, Soliera, Italy
Tel.: (39) 0597878577
Web Site: http://www.oeo.it
Sales Range: $25-49.9 Million
Building Automation Control Systems Mfr
N.A.I.C.S.: 334512

SACS S.r.l. (2)
Via Armentera 8, 38051, Borgo Valsugana, Trento, Italy
Tel.: (39) 0461757471
Web Site: http://www.sacs.info
Sales Range: $25-49.9 Million
Emp.: 12
Automatic Car Parking Systems Mfr
N.A.I.C.S.: 541420

CMC S.A.R.L. (1)
2 Rue Sourde, Chevilly, 45520, Loiret, France
Tel.: (33) 238801582
Framework Contract Services
N.A.I.C.S.: 238130

Domis S.A. (1)
10 rue Jean Moulin, 74150, Rumilly, Haute Savoie, France
Tel.: (33) 450885300
Web Site: http://www.somfy.fr
Sales Range: $25-49.9 Million
Emp.: 25
Building Automation System Installation Services

N.A.I.C.S.: 561790

Energy Eye, Inc. (1)
13367 Kirkham Way Ste 110, Poway, CA 92064
Tel.: (858) 391-2751
Web Site: http://www.energy-eye.com
Energy Management Solutions
N.A.I.C.S.: 541618

NV Somfy S.A. (1)
Mercuriusstraat 19, 1930, Zaventem, Flemish Brabant, Belgium
Tel.: (32) 27120770
Web Site: http://www.somfy.be
Sales Range: $25-49.9 Million
Emp.: 35
Home Automation System Installation Services
N.A.I.C.S.: 238210

Ningbo Dooya Mechanic & Electronic Technology Co. Ltd. (1)
No 168 ShengGuang Road, Luotuo Industrial Zone Zhenghai District, Ningbo, Zhejiang, China
Tel.: (86) 57426291888
Smart Home Control Product Mfr
N.A.I.C.S.: 334512

PD Technology Ltd. (1)
5 Guy Street, Bradford, BD4 7BB, West Yorkshire, United Kingdom
Tel.: (44) 1274394000
Automated Doors & Windows Mfr
N.A.I.C.S.: 321911

Pujol LDA. (1)
Travessa Alexandre Sa Pinto 28-Armazem B, Esmoriz, 3885-631, Portugal
Tel.: (351) 256780020
Alarm Systems & Equipments Mfr
N.A.I.C.S.: 334419

SC Somfy S.R.L. (1)
Str Zizinului nr 18, 507220, Brasov, Romania
Tel.: (40) 374490355
Web Site: http://www.somfy.ro
Sales Range: $50-74.9 Million
Emp.: 7
Building Automation Control Distr
N.A.I.C.S.: 423440

SIMU GmbH (1)
Hombrucher Weg 12, 58638, Iserlohn, Germany
Tel.: (49) 237193830
Web Site: http://www.simu-antriebe.de
Sales Range: $25-49.9 Million
Emp.: 16
Motor & Shutter Controls Distr
N.A.I.C.S.: 423610
Michaela Ortmann *(Sec)*

SOMFY Brasil Ltda. (1)
Av Leonil Cre Bortolosso 88 Galpao 4, Vila Quitauna, Osasco, 06186-260, Sao Paulo, Brazil
Tel.: (55) 1136078160
Web Site: http://www.somfy.com.br
Sales Range: $25-49.9 Million
Emp.: 22
Home Automation System Installation Services
N.A.I.C.S.: 561790

Simu S.A.S. (1)
France et Export, BP 71, 70103, Gray, Haute-Saone, France
Tel.: (33) 384647500
Sales Range: $150-199.9 Million
Emp.: 300
Motor Distr
N.A.I.C.S.: 423610
Sarter Jean Luc *(Gen Mgr)*

Subsidiary (US):

Simu USA Inc. (2)
6100 Broken Sound Pkwy NW Ste 14, Boca Raton, FL 33487
Tel.: (561) 995-0335
Web Site: http://www.simu-us.com
Sales Range: $25-49.9 Million
Emp.: 15
Shutter Motors & Automated Systems Mfr
N.A.I.C.S.: 334512
Frank Watts *(Mng Dir)*

Sirem S.A.S. (1)
Chemin du Pilon Saint Maurice de Beynost, 01708, Miribel, France
Tel.: (33) 478558320
Web Site: http://www.sirem.fr
Rev.: $28,276,290
Emp.: 170
Gear Motors & Filtration Pumps Mfr
N.A.I.C.S.: 333612

Sisa Home Automatisation LTD. (1)
26 Hahagana St, PO Box 5230, Rishon le Zion, 75151, Israel
Tel.: (972) 733266756
Web Site: http://www.somfy-group.com
Sales Range: $25-49.9 Million
Home Automation System Installation Services
N.A.I.C.S.: 238390

Somfy (Thailand) Co., Ltd. (1)
3rd Floor 158/3 Sukhumit 55 Klongton Nua, Wattana, Bangkok, 10110, Thailand
Tel.: (66) 947865995
Web Site: http://www.somfy.co.th
Automatic Home & Building Control System Mfr
N.A.I.C.S.: 334512

Somfy AG (1)
Vorbuchenstrasse 17, 8303, Bassersdorf, Zurich, Switzerland
Tel.: (41) 448384030
Web Site: http://www.somfy.ch
Sales Range: $25-49.9 Million
Emp.: 25
Home Automation System Installation Services
N.A.I.C.S.: 561790

Somfy Activites SA (1)
50 avenue du Nouveau Monde, 74300, Cluses, France
Tel.: (33) 820055055
Web Site: https://www.somfy.fr
Automatic Home & Building Control System Mfr
N.A.I.C.S.: 334512
Charlotte Roure *(Mgr-Grp Talent)*

Somfy Argentina SRL (1)
Alvear 838, San Fernando, Buenos Aires, Argentina
Tel.: (54) 1147443474
Web Site: http://www.somfy.com.ar
Automatic Home & Building Control System Mfr
N.A.I.C.S.: 334512

Somfy Bulgaria AD (1)
258 Botevgradsko shose blvd Vrazhdebna quarter, Kremikovtsi District, Sofia, 1839, Bulgaria
Tel.: (359) 28407878
Web Site: https://www.somfy.bg
Automatic Home & Building Control System Mfr
N.A.I.C.S.: 334512
Dobromir Botev *(Sls Mgr-Professional Channels)*

Somfy China Co. Ltd. (1)
2nd Floor No 121 Lane 1520 Hua Shan Road, 200052, Shanghai, China
Tel.: (86) 21 62809660
Web Site: http://www.somfy.com.cn
Sales Range: $25-49.9 Million
Emp.: 50
Automatic Doors & Gates Mfr
N.A.I.C.S.: 334512
Richard Wang *(Gen Mgr)*

Somfy Co. Ltd. (1)
Rm 907 9/F Marina House 68 Hing Man St, Shau Kei Wan, China (Hong Kong)
Tel.: (852) 25236339
Web Site: http://www.somfy.com.hk
Home Automation System Installation Services
N.A.I.C.S.: 561790

Somfy Espana S.A. (1)
Paseo Ferrocarriles Catalanes 290-292, 08940, Cornella de Llobregat, Barcelona, Spain
Tel.: (34) 900206868
Web Site: http://www.somfy.es
Sales Range: $10-24.9 Million
Home Automation System Installation Services
N.A.I.C.S.: 561790

Somfy Ev Otomasyon Sistemleri Ticalet Ltd Sti (1)
Inkilap Mah Kucuksu Cad No 145, Umraniye, 34768, Istanbul, Turkiye
Tel.: (90) 2166513015
Web Site: http://www.somfy.com.tr
Home Automation System Installation Services
N.A.I.C.S.: 238390

Somfy GmbH (1)
Felix-Wankel-Strasse 50, 72108, Rottenburg am Neckar, Germany
Tel.: (49) 74729300
Web Site: http://www.somfy.de
Sales Range: $50-74.9 Million
Emp.: 250
Home Automation System Installation Services
N.A.I.C.S.: 238390
Jean-Luc Sarter *(Mng Dir)*

Somfy GmbH (1)
Johann-Herbst-Strasse 23, 5061, Elsbethen, Austria
Tel.: (43) 6626253080
Web Site: https://www.somfy.at
Home Automation System Installation Services
N.A.I.C.S.: 238210
Michael Hubner *(Mng Dir)*

Somfy Hellas S.A. (1)
Karamanlis 181 Ave, 13677, Acharnes, Greece
Tel.: (30) 2116000200
Web Site: http://www.somfy-group.com
Sales Range: $25-49,9 Million
Home Automation System Installation Services
N.A.I.C.S.: 238290

Somfy India Pvt. Ltd. (1)
S4 2nd Floor Genesis Complex A-32, Mohan Cooperative Industrial Estate Mathura Road, New Delhi, 110 044, India
Tel.: (91) 1146111555
Web Site: http://www.somfy.co.in
Building Automation Control System Distr
N.A.I.C.S.: 423440

Somfy Italia S.R.L. (1)
Via Copernico 38-40, 20090, Trezzano sul Naviglio, Italy
Tel.: (39) 024455583
Web Site: http://www.somfy.it
Sales Range: $10-24.9 Million
Home Automatic Controls Systems Mfr
N.A.I.C.S.: 561790

Somfy Joo Co. Ltd. (1)
1003 Pangyo Seven Venture Valley Building No 1 633 Sampyeong-dong, Bundang-gu, Seongnam, 463-400, Gyeonggi-do, Korea (South)
Tel.: (82) 316005250
Web Site: http://www.somfy.com
Sales Range: $10-24.9 Million
Emp.: 28
Home Automation Services
N.A.I.C.S.: 561990

Somfy K.F.T. (1)
Gyomroi ut 105, 1103, Budapest, Hungary
Tel.: (36) 18145120
Web Site: http://www.somfy.hu
Sales Range: $25-49.9 Million
Emp.: 13
Home Automation System Installation Services
N.A.I.C.S.: 238390

Somfy LLC (1)
ul Storozhevaya 26 Building 1, 111020, Moscow, Russia
Tel.: (7) 4957814772
Web Site: http://www.somfy.ru
Building Automation Control System Distr
N.A.I.C.S.: 423440

Somfy Latvia SIA (1)
Brivibas gatve 401C, 1024, Riga, Latvia
Tel.: (371) 120040555
Web Site: http://www.somfy.lv
Home Automation System Installation Services
N.A.I.C.S.: 238390

Somfy Ltd. (1)
Unit 7 Lancaster Way Airport West, Yeadon,

SOMFY SA

Somfy SA—(Continued)
Leeds, LS19 7ZA, West Yorkshire, United Kingdom
Tel.: (44) 1133913030
Web Site: http://www.somfy.co.uk
Sales Range: $25-49.9 Million
Home Automation Controls Retailer
N.A.I.C.S.: 423610

Somfy Maroc S.a.r.l.
29 rue Ibnou Majid El Bahar, 20100, Casablanca, Morocco
Tel.: (212) 522443500
Web Site: http://www.somfy.ma
Automatic Home & Building Control System Mfr
N.A.I.C.S.: 334512

Somfy Mexico SA DE CV (1)
Temazcal 19-B Colonia La Loma, Tlalnepantla, 54060, State of Mexico, Mexico
Tel.: (52) 5547777770
Web Site: http://www.somfy.mx
Automatic Home & Building Control System Mfr
N.A.I.C.S.: 334512

Somfy Middle East Co. Ltd. (1)
131 Agias Fylaxeos Ave & Eratous street, PO Box 56150, 3038, Limassol, Cyprus
Tel.: (357) 25345540
Web Site: http://www.somfy-group.com
Sales Range: $10-24.9 Million
Emp.: 40
Home Automation System Installation Services
N.A.I.C.S.: 561790

Somfy Nederland B.V.
Jacobus Ahrendlaan 1, 2132 LP, Hoofddorp, Netherlands
Tel.: (31) 235544900
Web Site: http://www.somfy.nl
Sales Range: $25-49.9 Million
Emp.: 50
Home Automation System Installation Services
N.A.I.C.S.: 238390
Sven Van Witzenburg (Mng Dir)

Somfy Nordic AB (1)
Limstensgatan 6, PO Box 60038, 216 10, Limhamn, Skane, Sweden
Tel.: (46) 40165900
Web Site: http://www.somfy.com
Sales Range: $25-49.9 Million
Emp.: 20
Home Automation System Installation Services
N.A.I.C.S.: 238390

Somfy Norway AS (1)
Industriveien 27D, 2020, Skedsmokorset, Norway
Tel.: (47) 41576639
Web Site: http://www.somfy.no
Automatic Home & Building Control System Mfr
N.A.I.C.S.: 334512

Somfy PTE. Ltd. (1)
50 Ubi Ave 3 02-16/17 Frontier, Singapore, 408866, Singapore
Tel.: (65) 63833855
Web Site: http://www.somfy.com.sg
Sales Range: $25-49.9 Million
Emp.: 13
Building Automation Control System Distr
N.A.I.C.S.: 423830

Somfy PTY. Ltd. (1)
Unit 20 Rydalmere Metro Centre 38-46 South Street, Rydalmere, 2116, NSW, Australia
Tel.: (61) 288457200
Web Site: http://www.somfy.com.au
Sales Range: $25-49.9 Million
Emp.: 25
Building Automation Control System Distr
N.A.I.C.S.: 423610

Somfy S.A.S. (1)
ZI Mecatronique de da Gare 50 Avenue du Nouveau Monde, Cluses, France
Tel.: (33) 450967000
Web Site: http://www.somfy.com
Sales Range: $550-599.9 Million
Emp.: 1,400
Electric Motors & Parts Distr
N.A.I.C.S.: 423610

Jean-Philippe Andre Demael (CEO)

Somfy South Africa Pty. Limited (1)
4 Falcon Crescent Airport City, Cape Town, South Africa
Tel.: (27) 213800344
Web Site: http://www.somfy.co.za
Automatic Home & Building Control System Mfr
N.A.I.C.S.: 334512

Somfy Sp. z.o.o.
UI Marywilska 34, 03-228, Warsaw, Masovia, Poland
Tel.: (48) 225095300
Web Site: http://www.somfy.pl
Sales Range: $25-49.9 Million
Emp.: 40
Home Automation System Installation Services
N.A.I.C.S.: 238390

Somfy Spol s.r.o. (1)
Bavorska 2780/2, Zlicin, 155 00, Prague, Czech Republic
Tel.: (420) 267910007
Web Site: http://ww.somfy-group.com
Sales Range: $25-49.9 Million
Emp.: 20
Home Automation System Installation Services
N.A.I.C.S.: 238210

Somfy Systems Inc. (1)
121 Herrod Blvd, Dayton, NJ 08810
Tel.: (609) 395-1300
Web Site: http://www.somfysystems.com
Sales Range: $25-49.9 Million
Emp.: 100
Tubular Motors Electric Controls & Mechanical Safety Brakes Mfr
N.A.I.C.S.: 335999

Somfy Taiwan Co. Ltd.
Room 1103 11F No 142 Sec 3 Minquan East Road, Songshan District, Taipei, 105, Taiwan
Tel.: (886) 2271660010
Automatic Home & Building Control System Mfr
N.A.I.C.S.: 334512

Somfy ULC (1)
6315 Shawson Dr Unit 1, L5T 1J2, Mississauga, ON, Canada
Tel.: (905) 564-6446
Web Site: http://www.somfy.com
Sales Range: $50-74.9 Million
Emp.: 10
Electrical Equipment Whslr
N.A.I.C.S.: 423610
Michael Lee (Pres)

Sopem spolka z ograniczona odpowiedzialnoscia (1)
ul Doktora Rudolfa Diesla 9 Sektor G, 32-005, Niepolomice, Poland
Tel.: (48) 124176800
Web Site: http://www.sopem.pl
Industrial Controller & Drive Product Mfr
N.A.I.C.S.: 335314

Spirel S.A.S.
ZI Francois Horteur, 73660, Saint-Remy-de-Maurienne, Savoie, France
Tel.: (33) 479831032
Motors & Automatic Controls Mfr
N.A.I.C.S.: 334519

Window Automation Industry SRL (1)
Via C Bassi 7/A, Galliera, 40015, Bologna, Italy
Tel.: (39) 0516672711
Web Site: https://www.way-srl.com
Automation Shutter & Window Mfr
N.A.I.C.S.: 337920
Riccardo Gardellini (Ops Mgr)

Zurfluh Feller S.A.S. (1)
11 rue des Herbiers, Noirefontaine, 25190, Autechaux-Roide, France
Tel.: (33) 381993300
Web Site: http://www.zurfluh-feller.fr
Sales Range: $100-124.9 Million
Emp.: 400
Roller Shutters Mfr
N.A.I.C.S.: 332999

SOMI CONVEYOR BELTINGS LIMITED

4F-15 Oliver House New Power House Road, Jodhpur, 342001, India
Tel.: (91) 7726866661
Web Site: https://www.somiconveyor.com
Year Founded: 2000
SOMICONVEY—(NSE)
Rev.: $6,419,404
Assets: $13,690,336
Liabilities: $5,158,458
Net Worth: $8,531,878
Earnings: $240,404
Emp.: 109
Fiscal Year-end: 03/31/21
Rubber Conveyor Belts Mfr
N.A.I.C.S.: 326220

SOMMER GMBH

Rembrandtstrasse 123, 33649, Bielefeld, Germany
Tel.: (49) 52145980
Web Site: http://www.sommer-online.de
Year Founded: 1935
Sales Range: $75-99.9 Million
Emp.: 250
Truck & Trailer Mfr
N.A.I.C.S.: 336211
Alexander Tietje (CEO & Mng Dir)

SOMNOMED LIMITED

Level 3 20 Clarke St, Crows Nest, 2065, NSW, Australia
Tel.: (61) 294670400   AU
Web Site: https://somnomed.com
Year Founded: 2004
SOMNF—(OTCIQ)
Rev.: $61,199,085
Assets: $46,611,382
Liabilities: $16,546,926
Net Worth: $30,064,456
Earnings: ($8,174,290)
Fiscal Year-end: 06/30/24
Dental Device Mfr & Sales
N.A.I.C.S.: 339114
Terence A. Flitcroft (Sec)

Subsidiaries:

SomnoMed AG (1)
Steinhauserstrasse 74, CH-6300, Zug, Switzerland
Tel.: (41) 415014640
Oral Devices Mfr & Distr
N.A.I.C.S.: 339114

SomnoMed Finland OY (1)
Aleksis Kiventie 30, Suomi, FI-65300, Vaasa, Finland
Tel.: (358) 80076666633
Oral Devices Mfr & Distr
N.A.I.C.S.: 339114

SomnoMed Inc. (1)
7460 Warren Pkwy Ste 190, Frisco, TX 75034
Tel.: (972) 377-3400
Web Site: http://www.somnomed.com
Sales Range: $25-49.9 Million
Emp.: 20
Dental Instruments Mfr
N.A.I.C.S.: 339114
Kien T. Nguyen (Pres)

SOMPO HOLDINGS, INC.

26-1 Nishi-Shinjuku 1-Chome, Shinjuku-ku, Tokyo, 160-8338, Japan
Tel.: (81) 333493000   JP
Web Site: https://www.sompo-hd.com
Year Founded: 2010
8630—(TKS)
Rev.: $32,611,400,060
Assets: $98,044,662,580
Liabilities: $79,085,477,200
Net Worth: $18,959,185,380
Earnings: $991,500
Emp.: 506
Fiscal Year-end: 03/31/24
Holding Company
N.A.I.C.S.: 551112

Kengo Sakurada (Pres, CEO-Grp & Exec Officer)

Subsidiaries:

Berjaya Sompo Insurance Berhad (1)
Level 36 Menara Bangkok Bank 105 Jalan Ampang, Jalan Imbi, 50450, Kuala Lumpur, Malaysia
Tel.: (60) 321707300
Web Site: https://www.berjayasompo.com.my
Property & Casualty Insurance
N.A.I.C.S.: 524126

Maritima Seguros S.A. (1)
Rua Coronel Xavier de Toledo No 114 9th andar, Sao Paulo, CEP 01048-902, SP, Brazil
Tel.: (55) 1133352990
Web Site: http://www.maritima.com.br
Emp.: 1,553
Holding Company; Insurance Products & Services
N.A.I.C.S.: 551112
Francisco Caiuby Vidigal Filho (CEO)

Subsidiary (Domestic):

Yasuda Seguros, S.A. (2)
Rua Cubatao 320 15th andar, Paraiso, Sao Paulo, CEP 04013-001, SP, Brazil
Tel.: (55) 1138861300
Web Site: http://www.yasuda.com.br
Sales Range: $150-199.9 Million
Emp.: 400
Fire, Marine & Casualty Insurance
N.A.I.C.S.: 524126

PT Sompo Insurance Indonesia (1)
Mayapada Tower II 19th Floor-JI Jendral Sudirman Kav 27, Jakarta, 12920, Indonesia
Tel.: (62) 811 131 4051
Web Site: https://www.sompo.co.id
Emp.: 600
Insurance Services
N.A.I.C.S.: 524210
Eric Nemitz (Pres)

Prime Assistance Inc. (1)
Harmony Tower 32-2 Honcho 1-chome, Nakano-ku, Tokyo, 164-0012, Japan
Tel.: (81) 35 365 1890
Web Site: https://prime-as.co.jp
Insurance Services
N.A.I.C.S.: 524210
Masato Oki (Pres & CEO)

SI Insurance (Europe), SA (1)
40 Avenue Monterey, 2163, Luxembourg, Luxembourg
Tel.: (352) 2 787 2606
Insurance Services
N.A.I.C.S.: 524210

Sompo Care Inc. (1)
12-8 higashishinagawa 4-chome Shinagawa Seaside East Tower, Shinagawa-ku, Tokyo, 140-0002, Japan   (100%)
Tel.: (81) 364558560
Web Site: https://www.sompocare.com
Emp.: 23,614
Nursing Care Facilities Operator
N.A.I.C.S.: 623110
Aoi Satoshi (Co-Pres & CEO)

Sompo Care Next Inc. (1)
12th Floor Shinagawa Seaside East Tower 12-8 Higashi Shinagawa 4-chome, Shinagawa-ku, Tokyo, 140-0002, Japan
Tel.: (81) 3 5783 4165
Web Site: http://www.sompocare-next.jp
Emp.: 7,198
Nursing Services
N.A.I.C.S.: 623110
Takeshi Endo (Pres & CEO)

Sompo Insurance (Hong Kong) Company Limited (1)
19/F Lincoln House Taikoo Place 979 King's Road, Quarry Bay, China (Hong Kong)
Tel.: (852) 2 573 2072
Web Site: https://www.sompo.com.hk
Insurance Services
N.A.I.C.S.: 524210
S. K. Li (CEO)

Sompo Insurance (Thailand) Public Company Limted (1)

AND PRIVATE COMPANIES

990 Abdulrahim Place 12th 14th Floor
Rama IV Road, Silom, Bangkok, 10500,
Thailand
Tel.: (66) 21193000
Web Site: https://www.sompo.co.th
Insurance Services
N.A.I.C.S.: 524210
Daniel Neo *(CEO)*

Sompo International Holdings Ltd. (1)
Waterloo House 100 Pitts Bay Road, Pembroke, HM 08, Bermuda
Tel.: (441) 2780400
Web Site: https://www.sompo-intl.com
Commercial Insurance & Reinsurance Services
N.A.I.C.S.: 524126
John V. Del Col *(Gen Counsel)*

Subsidiary (Non-US):

Endurance Worldwide Insurance Limited (2)
1st Floor 2 Minster Court Mincing Lane, London, EC3R 7BB, United Kingdom
Tel.: (44) 2073372800
Web Site: http://www.sompo-intl.com
Direct Health & Medical Insurance Carriers
N.A.I.C.S.: 524114

Subsidiary (US):

W. Brown & Associates Insurance Services, Inc. (2)
19000 MacArthur Blvd, Irvine, CA 92612
Tel.: (949) 851-2060
Web Site: http://www.wbais.com
Insurance Agencies & Brokerages
N.A.I.C.S.: 524210
Mark Pennington *(Sr VP)*

Sompo Japan Nipponkoa Asset Management Co., Ltd. (1)
Kyoritsu Nihonbashi Building 2-16 Nihonbashi 2-chome, Chuo-ku, Tokyo, 103-0027, Japan
Tel.: (81) 352903585
Web Site: https://sompo-am.com
Sales Range: $100-124.9 Million
Emp.: 15
Asset Management Services
N.A.I.C.S.: 523940

Sompo Japan Nipponkoa Insurance Inc.
26-1 Nishi-Shinjuku 1-chome, Shinjuku-ku, Tokyo, 160-8338, Japan
Tel.: (81) 120238381
Web Site: https://www.sompo-japan.co.jp
Sales Range: $5-14.9 Billion
Emp.: 21,705
General Insurance Products & Services
N.A.I.C.S.: 524126

Subsidiary (Non-US):

Nipponkoa Insurance Company (China) Limited (2)
9/F Tower 2 Kerry Plaza No 1 Zhongxin 4th Road, Futian, Shenzhen, 518048, China
Tel.: (86) 75582560055
Web Site: http://www.nipponkoa-cn.com
Insurance Management Services
N.A.I.C.S.: 524298

Joint Venture (Non-US):

PGA Sompo Insurance Corporation (2)
5th Floor Corinthian Plaza 121 Paseo de Roxas, Legaspi Village, Makati, 1229, Manila, Philippines
Tel.: (63) 28113417
Web Site: https://www.pgasompo.com.ph
Property & Casualty Insurance Products & Services
N.A.I.C.S.: 524126
Yuichiro Funabashi *(Pres & COO)*

Subsidiary (Non-US):

PT. Asuransi Sompo Japan Nipponkoa Indonesia (2)
Mayapada Tower II 19th Floor Jl Jendral Sudirman Kav 27, Jakarta, 12920, Indonesia
Tel.: (62) 21 2500 890
Web Site: http://www.sjnk.co.id
Fire, Marine & Casualty Insurance

N.A.I.C.S.: 524126
Kenji Tada *(Chm)*

Subsidiary (Domestic):

Saison Automobile and Fire Insurance Company, Limited
Sunshine 60 40th floor 3-1-1 Higashiikebukuro, Toshima-ku, Tokyo, 170-6068, Japan
Tel.: (81) 339882711
Web Site: https://www.ins-saison.co.jp
Emp.: 679
Casualty Insurance Services
N.A.I.C.S.: 524126

Subsidiary (Non-US):

Sompo Insurance (Thailand) Public Company Limited (2)
990 Abdulrahim Place 12th Floor 14 Rama IV Road, Silom Bangrak, Bangkok, 10500, Thailand
Tel.: (66) 02 119 3000
Web Site: http://www.sompo.co.th
Property & Casualty Insurance Products & Services
N.A.I.C.S.: 524126
Takanori Ono *(Chm & CEO)*

Subsidiary (Domestic):

Sompo Japan Nipponkoa Insurance Brokers (Thailand) Co., Ltd. (3)
90/53 Sathorn Thanil Bldg 18th Flr North Sathorn Rd Silom, Bangrak, 10500, Thailand
Tel.: (66) 2636 7288
Web Site: http://www.sompo.co.th
Insurance Brokerage Services
N.A.I.C.S.: 524210

Subsidiary (Domestic):

Sompo Japan Healthcare Services Inc.
1-26-2 Nishishinjuku Shinjukunomura Bldg 10f, Shinjuku-Ku, Tokyo, 160-0023, Japan
Tel.: (81) 3 3349 4923
Web Site: http://www.sj-healthcare.com
Health Care Srvices
N.A.I.C.S.: 621999

Subsidiary (Non-US):

Sompo Japan Nipponkoa Consulting (Korea) Inc. (2)
7th Floor Seoul Finance Center 84 Taepyungno 1-ga, Jung-gu, Seoul, 100-768, Korea (South)
Tel.: (82) 57756810
Business Consulting Services
N.A.I.C.S.: 541611

Subsidiary (Domestic):

Sompo Japan Nipponkoa Himawari Life Insurance, Inc. (2)
Shinjuku Central Park Bldg 13-1 Nishi-Shinjuku 6-chome, Shinjuku-ku, Tokyo, 163-8626, Japan
Tel.: (81) 3 6742 3111
Web Site: http://www.himawari-life.co.jp
Sales Range: $25-49.9 Billion
Emp.: 2,694
Life Insurance Products & Services
N.A.I.C.S.: 524113
Atsushi Kumanomido *(Pres)*

Subsidiary (US):

Sompo Japan Nipponkoa Holdings (Americas) Inc. (2)
777 3rd Ave 24th Fl, New York, NY 10017-1414
Tel.: (212) 416-1200
Holding Company; Regional Managing Office; Property & Casualty Insurance Products & Services
N.A.I.C.S.: 551112
Masato Fujikura *(Chm & CEO)*

Subsidiary (Domestic):

Sompo Japan Insurance Company of America (3)
777 3rd Ave 21st Fl, New York, NY 10017
Tel.: (212) 416-1200
Web Site: http://www.sompo-japan-us.com
Property & Casualty Insurance Services
N.A.I.C.S.: 524126
Hiroyuki Yamaguchi *(CEO)*

Subsidiary (Domestic):

Sompo Japan Claim Services (America), Inc. (4)
2 World Financial Ctr 43rd Fl 225 Liberty St, New York, NY 10281-1058
Tel.: (212) 416-1200
General Insurance Claims Adjusting Services
N.A.I.C.S.: 524291

Sompo Japan Fire & Marine Insurance Company of America (4)
777 3rd Ave 28th Fl, New York, NY 10017
Tel.: (212) 416-1200
Web Site: http://www.sompojapan.com
Sales Range: $50-74.9 Million
Emp.: 10
Fire & Marine Insurance Services
N.A.I.C.S.: 524126
Chikara Sakoda *(Dir-Mktg)*

Subsidiary (Non-US):

Sompo Japan Nipponkoa Insurance (China) Co., Ltd. (2)
10F Dalian Senmao Building 147 Zhongshan Road, Xigang District, Dalian, Liaoning, China
Tel.: (86) 41183603093
Web Site: http://www.sjnk.com.cn
General Insurance Services
N.A.I.C.S.: 524210

Sompo Japan Nipponkoa Insurance (Hong Kong) Co., Ltd. (2)
Room 1901 Lincoln House Taikoo Place 979 King's Road, Island East, Hong Kong, China (Hong Kong) (97.75%)
Tel.: (852) 28319980
Web Site: http://www.sompojapan.com.hk
Sales Range: $50-74.9 Million
Emp.: 66
Fire, Marine & Casualty Insurance
N.A.I.C.S.: 524126

Subsidiary (Domestic):

Sompo Japan Nipponkoa Management (HK) Co., Ltd. (3)
19th Floor Tai Tung Building, 8 Fleming Road, Wanchai, China (Hong Kong)
Tel.: (852) 2868 4413
Web Site: http://www.sompo.com.hk
Sales Range: $50-74.9 Million
Emp.: 30
Insurance Services
N.A.I.C.S.: 524128

Sompo Japan Nipponkoa Reinsurance Company Limited (3)
Room 1901 Lincoln House Taikoo Place 979 King's Road, Island East, Hong Kong, China (Hong Kong)
Tel.: (852) 28271268
Reinsurance Products & Services
N.A.I.C.S.: 524130

Subsidiary (Non-US):

Sompo Japan Nipponkoa Insurance (Taiwan) Brokers Co., Ltd. (2)
Room C 10th Floor Shen Hsiang Tang Sung Chiang Building No 146, Sung Chiang Road, Taipei, Taiwan
Tel.: (886) 2 2541 3768
Sales Range: $50-74.9 Million
Emp.: 10
Insurance Brokerage Services
N.A.I.C.S.: 524210
Keisuke Yamada *(Gen Mgr)*

Sompo Japan Nipponkoa Insurance Company of Europe Limited (2)
1st Floor 6 Devonshire Square, London, EC2M 4YE, United Kingdom
Tel.: (44) 2076289599
Sales Range: $50-74.9 Million
Emp.: 60
Fire, Marine & Casualty Insurance
N.A.I.C.S.: 524126

Subsidiary (Domestic):

Sompo Japan Nipponkoa Corporate Member Limited (3)
1st Floor 6 Devonshire Square, London, EC2M 4YE, United Kingdom
Tel.: (44) 2076289599

Web Site: http://www.sompo.co.uk
Insurance Agency Services
N.A.I.C.S.: 524210

Subsidiary (Non-US):

Sompo Japan Nipponkoa Insurance de Mexico, S.A. de C.V. (2)
Av Insurgentes Sur 1196 Piso 12 Desp 1201, Col Tlacoquemecatl del Valle, CP 03200, Mexico, DF, Mexico
Tel.: (52) 5555593717
Web Site: http://www.sjnk.mx
Sales Range: $25-49.9 Million
Emp.: 33
Fire, Marine & Casualty Insurance
N.A.I.C.S.: 524126
Satoshi Yokoyama *(Mng Dir)*

Subsidiary (Domestic):

Sonpo 24 Insurance Company Limited (2)
Sunshine 60 1-1 Higashi Ikebukuro 3 chome, Toshima-ku, Tokyo, Japan
Tel.: (81) 3 5957 0111
Web Site: http://www.sonpo24.co.jp
General Insurance Services
N.A.I.C.S.: 524210

Subsidiary (Non-US):

Tenet Sompo Insurance Pte. Ltd. (2)
50 Raffles Place 03-03, Singapore Land Tower, Singapore, 048623, Singapore (100%)
Tel.: (65) 64616555
Web Site: https://www.sompo.com.sg
Sales Range: $50-74.9 Million
Emp.: 247
General Insurance Products & Services
N.A.I.C.S.: 524126
Takanori Ono *(Mng Dir)*

United Insurance Company of Vietnam (2)
9th Floor Hanoi Tung Shing Square Building No 2 Ngo Quyen, Hoan Kiem District, Hanoi, Vietnam
Tel.: (84) 438262686
Web Site: https://uic.vn
Sales Range: $1-9.9 Million
Emp.: 40
Fire, Marine & Casualty Insurance
N.A.I.C.S.: 524126

Sompo Japan Nipponkoa Risk Management Inc. (1)
24-1 Nishi-shinjuku 1-chome, Shinjuku-ku, Tokyo, 160-0023, Japan
Tel.: (81) 3 3349 4330
Web Site: http://www.sjnk-rm.co.jp
Emp.: 300
Risk Management Consulting Services
N.A.I.C.S.: 541618
Hidehiro Sumi *(Pres)*

Sompo Taiwan Brokers Co., Ltd. (1)
9F No 28 Qingcheng Street, Taipei, 105403, Taiwan
Tel.: (886) 701 011 3768
Web Site: https://www.sompo.com.tw
Insurance Services
N.A.I.C.S.: 524298
Chin Yi Chen *(Pres & Chm)*

SON HA INTERNATIONAL JOINT STOCK COMPANY
Lot CN1 Tu Liem Industrial Zone Minh Khai, Bac Tu Liem District, Hanoi, Vietnam
Tel.: (84) 462656566
Web Site: http://www.sonha.com.vn
Year Founded: 1998
SHI—(HOSE)
Sales Range: $50-74.9 Million
Holding company; Fluid Tank Mfr
N.A.I.C.S.: 551112
Van Thuan Nguyen *(Deputy Gen Dir)*

SON HA SAI GON JSC
Tam Dong 2 Town Thoi Tam Thon Ward, Hoc Mon District, Ho Chi Minh City, Vietnam
Tel.: (84) 837100101

SON HA SAI GON JSC

Son Ha Sai Gon JSC—(Continued)
Web Site:
http://www.sonhasg.com.vn
SHA—(HOSE)
Sales Range: Less than $1 Million
Stainless Steel Products Mfr
N.A.I.C.S.: 332999
Le Hoang Ha *(Chm)*

SON LA SUGAR JOINT STOCK COMPANY
Hat Lot, Mai Son, Hanoi, Son La, Vietnam
Tel.: (84) 2123843274
Web Site:
https://www.miaduongsonla.vn
Year Founded: 1997
SLS—(HNX)
Rev.: $171,593,900
Assets: $134,195,400
Liabilities: $16,130,600
Net Worth: $118,064,800
Earnings: $52,311,500
Fiscal Year-end: 06/30/23
Sugar Mfr
N.A.I.C.S.: 311314
Viet Anh Dang *(Chm)*

SONA BLW PRECISION FORGINGS LTD.
Unit I Unit II & Unit III Sona Enclave Sector 35, Village Begumpur Khatola, Gurgaon, 122004, Haryana, India
Tel.: (91) 1244768200
Web Site:
https://www.sonacomstar.com
SONACOMS—(NSE)
Rev.: $322,184,881
Assets: $366,863,497
Liabilities: $92,275,643
Net Worth: $274,587,854
Earnings: $47,394,880
Emp.: 1,315
Fiscal Year-end: 03/31/23
Automotive Product Mfr & Distr
N.A.I.C.S.: 336390
Sunjay Kapur *(Chm)*

SONA NANOTECH INC.
Purdy's Wharf Tower II Suite 2001 - 1969 Upper Water Street, Halifax, B3J 3R7, NS, Canada
Tel.: (902) 442-0653
Web Site: https://www.sonanano.com
Year Founded: 2004
SNANF—(OTCQB)
Assets: $2,075,259
Liabilities: $1,197,834
Net Worth: $877,425
Earnings: $(1,887,555)
Emp.: 9
Fiscal Year-end: 10/31/23
Gold Nanorod & Nanoparticles Production
N.A.I.C.S.: 212220
Len Pagliaro *(Chief Scientific Officer)*

Subsidiaries:

Siva Therapeutics Inc. (1)
5401 E Dakota Ave Ste 21, Denver, CO 80246
Tel.: (720) 541-7941
Web Site: http://www.sivatherapeutics.com
Chemicals Mfr
N.A.I.C.S.: 325412
Len Pagliaro *(Pres & CEO)*

Sona Nanotech Ltd. (1)
1969 Upper Water Street Suite 2001, Halifax, B3J 3R7, NS, Canada
Tel.: (902) 880-9925
Web Site: http://sonanano.com
CTAB Free Gold Nanorod Production & Gold Nanoparticle Development
N.A.I.C.S.: 212220

SONACA S.A
Route nationale 5, 6041, Gosselies, Belgium
Tel.: (32) 71 25 51 11
Web Site: http://www.sonaca.com
Aircraft Part Mfr
N.A.I.C.S.: 336413
Bernard Delvaux *(CEO)*

Subsidiaries:

Belairbus sa (1)
Dreve Richelle 161/45, 1410, Waterloo, Belgium
Tel.: (32) 22481440
Web Site: http://www.belairbus.be
Aircraft Equipment Distr
N.A.I.C.S.: 423860

LMI Aerospace, Inc. (1)
411 Fountain Lakes Blvd, Saint Charles, MO 63301
Tel.: (636) 946-6525
Web Site: http://www.lmiaerospace.com
Sales Range: $300-349.9 Million
Alloy & Sheet Metal Products for Use by the Aerospace, Technology & Commercial Sheet Metal Industries Mfr
N.A.I.C.S.: 336413
Jay P. Inman *(Pres-Engrg Svcs)*

Subsidiary (Non-US):

L.M.I. Asia Pacific (Private) Limited (2)
229 2nd Floor St Joseph St, Negombo, 11500, Sri Lanka
Tel.: (94) 312225540
Web Site: http://www.lmiaerospace.com
Aircraft Equipment Mfr
N.A.I.C.S.: 334511
Ashoka Rangodagama *(Mgr-Site Ops)*

Subsidiary (Domestic):

LMI Everett - Merrill Creek (2)
1910 Merrill Creek Pkwy, Everett, WA 98203
Tel.: (425) 293-0340
Web Site: http://www.lmiaerospace.com
Aircraft Parts & Auxiliary Equipment Mfr
N.A.I.C.S.: 336413
Don McEwen *(Gen Mgr)*

LMI Finishing Inc. (2)
2104 N 170th East Ave, Tulsa, OK 74116-4919
Tel.: (918) 438-2122
Web Site: http://www.lmiaerospace.com
Aircraft Parts & Equipment
N.A.I.C.S.: 336413
David Filmore *(Gen Mgr)*

LMI San Diego (2)
4838 Ronson Ct, San Diego, CA 92111-1810
Tel.: (858) 571-1685
Web Site: http://www.lmiaerospace.com
Engineeering Services
N.A.I.C.S.: 541330
Jay P. Inman *(Pres)*

LMI Sun Valley (2)
8866 Laurel Canyon Blvd, Sun Valley, CA 91352-2920
Tel.: (818) 767-2326
Web Site: http://www.lmiaerospace.com
Aircraft Part Mfr
N.A.I.C.S.: 336413
Pablo Ontiveros *(Gen Mgr)*

Ozark Mountain Technologies, LLC (2)
106 Midland Dr, Cuba, MO 65453
Tel.: (573) 885-3018
Web Site: http://www.lmiaerospace.com
Metal Finishing & Anodizing Services
N.A.I.C.S.: 332813
Robert Will *(Gen Mgr)*

Valent Aerostructures - Lenexa, LLC (2)
11064 Strang Line Rd, Lenexa, KS 66215
Tel.: (913) 469-6400
Web Site: http://www.lmiaerospace.com
Steel Pole Mfr
N.A.I.C.S.: 331222
Butch Morris *(Mgr-Ops)*

Valent Aerostructures - Washington, LLC (2)
6325 Avantha Dr, Washington, MO 63090-1074
Tel.: (636) 231-4200
Web Site: http://www.lmiaerospace.com
Aircraft Equipment Mfr
N.A.I.C.S.: 334511
Mike Koirtyohann *(Production Mgr)*

Valent Aerostructures - Wichita, LLC (2)
2853 S Hillside, Wichita, KS 67216-2546
Tel.: (316) 682-4551
Web Site: http://www.lmiaerospace.com
Aircraft Equipment Mfr
N.A.I.C.S.: 334511
Dan Green *(Gen Mgr)*

Versaform Corporation (2)
1377 Specialty Dr, Vista, CA 92081
Tel.: (760) 599-4477
Web Site: http://www.lmiaerospace.com
Forming Machine Work & Sheet Metal Mfr
N.A.I.C.S.: 332322

Sonaca Montreal (1)
13075 Brault Saint-Janvier, Mirabel, J7J 1P3, QC, Canada
Tel.: (450) 434-6114
Web Site: http://www.sonacamontreal.com
Aircraft Equipment Distr
N.A.I.C.S.: 423860

SONADEZI CHAU DUC SHAREHOLDING COMPANY
Floor 9 Sonadezi Building No 01 Street 1, Bien Hoa 1 Industrial Park An Binh Ward, Bien Hoa, Dong Nai, Vietnam
Tel.: (84) 2518860788
Web Site:
https://www.sonadezichauduc.com
Year Founded: 2007
Industrial Park Services
N.A.I.C.S.: 712190
Dinh Ngoc Thuan *(Chm)*

SONADEZI LONG THANH
Long Thanh Industrial Zone Tam An, Long Thanh District, Long Thanh, Dong Nai, Vietnam
Tel.: (84) 2513514494
Web Site: https://www.szl.com.vn
Year Founded: 2003
Sales Range: $1-9.9 Million
Real Estate Development Services
N.A.I.C.S.: 531390
Pham Anh Tuan *(CEO)*

SONAECOM SGPS SA
Lugar do Espido via Norte, 4470-177, Maia, Portugal
Tel.: (351) 220132349
Web Site: https://sonaecom.pt
SNC—(EUR)
Rev.: $20,090,518
Assets: $1,525,002,760
Liabilities: $62,258,527
Net Worth: $1,462,744,232
Earnings: $46,473,121
Fiscal Year-end: 12/31/23
Newspaper Publishers
N.A.I.C.S.: 513110
Angelo Gabriel Dos Santos Pauperio *(Chm)*

Subsidiaries:

Excellium Services Belgium, S.A. (1)
Orion Bldg Belgicastraat 13, B-1930, Zaventem, Belgium
Tel.: (32) 28996161
Software Development Services
N.A.I.C.S.: 541511

Excellium Services, S.A. (1)
5 rue Goell, L-5326, Contern, Luxembourg
Tel.: (352) 26203964
Web Site: https://www.excellium-services.com
Emp.: 160
Software Development Services
N.A.I.C.S.: 541511

Inovretail, S.A. (1)

INTERNATIONAL PUBLIC

Edificio 4 A Lugar do Espido Via Norte, 4470-177, Maia, Portugal
Tel.: (351) 220301509
Web Site: https://www.inovretail.com
Software Development Services
N.A.I.C.S.: 541511

Publico - Comunicacao Social, S.A. (1)
Edificio Diogo Cao Doca de Alcantara Norte, 1350-352, Lisbon, Portugal
Tel.: (351) 210111000
Web Site: https://www.publico.pt
Real Estate Services
N.A.I.C.S.: 531390

SONAGI SGPS SA
Avenida Fontes Pereira de Melo 14-9, 1050-121, Lisbon, Portugal
Tel.: (351) 213184800
Web Site: http://www.sonagi.pt
Year Founded: 1868
SNG—(EUR)
Sales Range: $1-9.9 Million
Real Estate Asset Management Services
N.A.I.C.S.: 531390
Jose Manuel Galvao Teles *(Chm)*

SONAL ADHESIVES LIMITED
Plot no 28-1A Village Dheku Takai Adoshi Road Off Khopoli-Pen Road, Taluka - Khalapur Dist Raigad, Khopoli, 410 203, India
Tel.: (91) 2192262622
Web Site: https://www.sonal.co.in
Year Founded: 1992
526901—(BOM)
Rev.: $10,086,745
Assets: $3,528,529
Liabilities: $2,886,590
Net Worth: $641,940
Earnings: $271,662
Emp.: 22
Fiscal Year-end: 03/31/23
Adhesive Tape Mfr
N.A.I.C.S.: 322220
Sandeep Mohanlal Arora *(Mng Dir)*

SONAL MERCANTILE LIMITED
365 Vardhman Plaza 3rd Floor Sector-3, Rohini, New Delhi, 110085, India
Tel.: (91) 1149091417
Web Site:
https://www.sonalmercantile.in
Year Founded: 1985
538943—(BOM)
Rev.: $3,173,350
Assets: $72,939,263
Liabilities: $38,209,475
Net Worth: $34,729,789
Earnings: $2,157,813
Emp.: 8
Fiscal Year-end: 03/31/23
Financial Support Services
N.A.I.C.S.: 523999
Rohit Saraogi *(CFO)*

SONALIS CONSUMER PRODUCTS LIMITED
Shop No 1 Rameshwar CHS Ltd Near Union Bank Dahisar-East, Mumbai, 400068, Maharashtra, India
Tel.: (91) 9868611444
Web Site: https://www.appetitefood.in
Year Founded: 2020
543924—(BOM)
Rev.: $791,824
Assets: $757,524
Liabilities: $416,880
Net Worth: $340,645
Earnings: $364
Fiscal Year-end: 03/31/23
Food Product Mfr & Distr
N.A.I.C.S.: 311412
Shivang Shashikant Shah *(CFO)*

SONAM LTD.
Survey No 337/P Morbi-Rajkot Highway At Lajai Tal Tankara, Morbi, 363 641, Gujarat, India
Tel.: (91) 2822285987
Web Site: https://www.sonamquartz.com
Year Founded: 1996
SONAMCLOCK—(NSE)
Rev.: $9,981,356
Assets: $10,282,861
Liabilities: $4,018,212
Net Worth: $6,264,648
Earnings: $479,779
Emp.: 105
Fiscal Year-end: 03/31/23
Watch Mfr
N.A.I.C.S.: 334519
Jayesh Shah *(CEO)*

SONAR BANGLA INSURANCE LIMITED
Paramount Heights 14th Floor 65/2/1 Box Culvert Road, Paltan, Dhaka, Bangladesh
Tel.: (880) 1717356168
Web Site: https://www.sonarbanglains.com
Year Founded: 2000
SONARBAINS—(CHT)
Rev.: $290,929
Assets: $12,284,991
Liabilities: $1,679,841
Net Worth: $10,605,151
Earnings: $1,204,981
Emp.: 563
Fiscal Year-end: 12/31/22
Insurance Agency Services
N.A.I.C.S.: 524210
Kabir Hossain *(Chm)*

Subsidiaries:

Sonar Bangla Capital Management Ltd. (1)
Paramount Heights 8th Floor 65/2/1 Box Culvert Road, Purana Paltan, Dhaka, 1000, Bangladesh
Tel.: (880) 29511799
Web Site: http://www.sbcmlbd.com
Capital Management Services
N.A.I.C.S.: 523940
Emam Hossain *(CEO & Mng Dir)*

SONARDYNE INTERNATIONAL LTD.
Blackbushe Business Park, Yateley, GU46 6GD, Hants, United Kingdom
Tel.: (44) 1252872288
Web Site: http://www.sonardyne.com
Year Founded: 1971
Underwater Acoustic, Inertia, Optical & Sonar Technology
N.A.I.C.S.: 541715
John Ramsden *(Mng Dir)*

Subsidiaries:

Eiva a/s (1)
Niels Bohrs Vej 17, 8660, Skanderborg, Denmark
Tel.: (45) 86282011
Web Site: http://www.eiva.com
Software Publisher
N.A.I.C.S.: 513210
Jeppe Nielsen *(CEO)*

SONATA SOFTWARE LIMITED
TowerA Sonata Towers Global Village Sattva Global City RVCE Post, Kengeri Hobli Mysore Road, Bengaluru, 560059, Karnataka, India
Tel.: (91) 8067781999
Web Site: https://www.sonata-software.com
Year Founded: 1986
532221—(BOM)
Rev.: $771,955,275
Assets: $348,783,435
Liabilities: $198,742,635
Net Worth: $150,040,800
Earnings: $51,382,695
Emp.: 3,383
Fiscal Year-end: 03/31/22
Custom Computer Programming Services
N.A.I.C.S.: 541511
P. V. S. N. Raju *(Chief Delivery Officer)*

Subsidiaries:

Sonata Europe Limited (1)
11th Floor West The Mille 1000 Great West Road, Brentford, TW8 9HH, United Kingdom
Tel.: (44) 2088638833
Web Site: https://www.sonata-software.com
Software Development Services
N.A.I.C.S.: 541511

Sonata Software (Qatar) LLC (1)
Regus GATH Building 5th floor Fereej Bin Mahmoud South, PO Box 47095, Near Ramada Junction, Doha, Qatar
Tel.: (974) 40071700
Information Technology Services
N.A.I.C.S.: 541511

Sonata Software FZ-LLC (1)
Office 2117 21 st Floor Shatha Tower No 1, PO Box 502818, Dubai, United Arab Emirates
Tel.: (971) 4 375 4355
Information Technology Consulting Services
N.A.I.C.S.: 541512

Sonata Software GmbH (1)
Beethovernstrasse 8-10, 60325, Frankfurt, Germany
Tel.: (49) 6997554537
Software Development Services
N.A.I.C.S.: 541511

Sonata Software North America. Inc. (1)
39300 Civic Center Dr Ste 270, Fremont, CA 94538
Tel.: (510) 791-7220
Web Site: https://www.sonata-software.com
Software Development Services
N.A.I.C.S.: 541511

Subsidiary (Domestic):

Interactive Business Information Systems, Inc. (2)
420 Technology Pkwy Ste 100, Peachtree Corners, GA 30092 **(100%)**
Tel.: (770) 368-4000
Web Site: https://www.ibisinc.com
Computer Related Services
N.A.I.C.S.: 541519
Ranga Puranik *(Pres)*

Rezopia, Inc. (2)
39300 Civic Ctr Dr Ste 370, Redwood City, CA 94538 **(100%)**
Tel.: (510) 742-7206
Web Site: http://www.rezopia.com
Software Publisher
N.A.I.C.S.: 513210
Bernaad R. Chetty *(Mng Dir)*

Sonata Software Solutions Limited (1)
Tel.: (91) 2224943055
Information Technology Services
N.A.I.C.S.: 541511

TUI InfoTec GmbH (1)
Karl-Wiechert-Allee 23, 30625, Hannover, Germany
Tel.: (49) 5115679000
Web Site: http://www.tui-tech.com
Sales Range: $150-199.9 Million
Emp.: 420
Information Technology Services
N.A.I.C.S.: 518210

SONATRACH INTERNATIONAL HOLDING CORPORATION
Djenane El Malik, Hydra, 160335, Algiers, Algeria
Tel.: (213) 21548011
Web Site: http://www.sonatrach-dz.com
Sales Range: $25-49.9 Billion
Emp.: 49,602
Oil & Gas Exploration & Production Services
N.A.I.C.S.: 211120
Nordine Cherouati *(Pres)*

Subsidiaries:

BAOSEM (1)
125 Bois Des Cars, Algiers, Algeria
Tel.: (213) 21 36 92 22
Web Site: http://www.baosem.com
Advertising Services
N.A.I.C.S.: 541810

BASF SONATRACH PropanChem S.A. (1)
Carretera N-340 km 1 156, Apartado de Correos 520, 43080, Tarragona, Spain
Tel.: (34) 977256703
Web Site: http://www.basfsonatrachpropanchem.com
Propylene & Gasoline Producer; Owned 51% by BASF Aktiengesellschaft & 49% by SONATRACH International Holding Corporation
N.A.I.C.S.: 213112

GCB Spa. (1)
Prolongement du boulevard de l'ALN, 35000, Boumerdes, Algeria
Tel.: (213) 24 81 41 50
Web Site: http://www.gcb.dz
Construction Engineering Services
N.A.I.C.S.: 541330

Hyproc SC (1)
Zhun USTO, PO Box 7200, Es-Seddikia, Oran, 31025, Algeria
Tel.: (213) 41 42 62 62
Web Site: http://www.hyproc.dz
Marine Shipping Services
N.A.I.C.S.: 488510

Subsidiary (Domestic):

NAJDA MAGHREB SPA (2)
BP 24, Arzew, Oran, 31200, Algeria
Tel.: (213) 41 47 29 41
Emp.: 79
Marine Shipping Services
N.A.I.C.S.: 488510

SONDA S.A.
Teatinos 500, Santiago, Chile
Tel.: (56) 6575000
Web Site: http://www.sonda.cl
Year Founded: 1974
SONDA—(SGO)
Rev.: $1,256,077,799
Assets: $1,479,739,337
Liabilities: $777,267,767
Net Worth: $702,471,570
Earnings: $50,879,588
Emp.: 13,522
Fiscal Year-end: 12/31/21
Consultancy Services
N.A.I.C.S.: 541511
Patricio Garreton Kref *(Officer-IR & Head-Fin Analysis & M&A)*

Subsidiaries:

Microgeo S.A. (1)
Camino del Cerro 5154, Huechuraba, Chile
Tel.: (56) 226580801
Web Site: http://www.microgeo.cl
Information Technology Services
N.A.I.C.S.: 541511

Novis S.A. (1)
Teatinos 500, Santiago, Chile
Tel.: (56) 226575130
Web Site: http://www.novis.cl
Information Technology Services
N.A.I.C.S.: 541511

Pars Produtos Proces. De Datos Ltda. (1)
Av das Americas 700 - Block 01 - Room 229 to 239, Barra da Tijuca, Rio de Janeiro, 22640-100, RJ, Brazil
Tel.: (55) 2121220800
Web Site: http://www.pars.com.br
Software Development Services
N.A.I.C.S.: 541511

Servibanca S.A. (1)
Catedral 1888, Santiago, Chile
Tel.: (56) 225609600
Web Site: http://portal.servibanca.cl
BPO Services
N.A.I.C.S.: 561990

Soluciones Expertas S.A. (1)
Enrique Foster Norte 203, Las Condes, 7550068, Santiago, Chile
Tel.: (56) 229232900
Web Site: http://www.solex.biz
Information Technology Services
N.A.I.C.S.: 541511

Sonda Argentina S.A. (1)
Alsina 772, Buenos Aires, Argentina
Tel.: (54) 1152967500
Information Technology Services
N.A.I.C.S.: 541511

Sonda Mexico S.A. de C.V. (1)
Boulevard Adolfo Lopez Mateos 2259 Col Atlamaya CP, 01760, Mexico, Mexico
Tel.: (52) 5550107000
Information Technology Services
N.A.I.C.S.: 541511

Sonda Tecnol De Costa Rica S.A. (1)
Ofiplaza del Este Edificio A Piso 3 Barrio Dent, San Jose, Costa Rica
Tel.: (506) 22249596
Information Technology Services
N.A.I.C.S.: 541511

Sonda Uruguay S.A. (1)
Plaza Independencia 831 Piso 11, Montevideo, Uruguay
Tel.: (598) 29083000
Information Technology Services
N.A.I.C.S.: 541511

Sonda de Colombia S.A. (1)
Av Cra 45 Autopista Norte N118-68, Bogota, Colombia
Tel.: (57) 16466565
Information Technology Services
N.A.I.C.S.: 541511

Sonda del Peru S.A. (1)
Avenida Javier Prado Este 444 Piso 16, San Isidro, Lima, Peru
Tel.: (51) 16167000
Information Technology Services
N.A.I.C.S.: 541511

Sonda do Brasil S.A. (1)
Alameda Europa 1206 Condominio Polo Tambore, Santana de Parnaiba, SP, Brazil
Tel.: (55) 1131266000
Information Technology Services
N.A.I.C.S.: 541511

Tecnoglobal SA (1)
The Conqueror of Mount 4848, Huechuraba, Santiago, Chile
Tel.: (56) 226858500
Web Site: http://www.tecnoglobal.cl
Information Technology Services
N.A.I.C.S.: 541511

SONDEX A/S
Jernet 9, Kolding, 6000, Denmark
Tel.: (45) 76306100
Web Site: http://www.sondex.dk
Year Founded: 1984
Sales Range: $300-349.9 Million
Emp.: 1,000
Air-Conditioning & Warm Air Heating Equipment & Commercial & Industrial Refrigeration Equipment Mfr
N.A.I.C.S.: 333415
Nielsen Sontergaart *(Mng Dir)*

Subsidiaries:

Sondex Inc. (1)
7040 International Dr, Louisville, KY 40258
Tel.: (502) 933-9991
Web Site: http://www.sondex-usa.com
Sales Range: $25-49.9 Million
Emp.: 40
Oil & Gas Field Machinery & Equipment Mfr
N.A.I.C.S.: 333132
Snehal Pola *(Gen Mgr)*

SONDOTECNICA ENGENHARIA DE SOLOS S.A.

SONDOTECNICA ENGENHARIA DE SOLOS S.A.

Sondotecnica Engenharia de Solos
S.A.—(Continued)

Rua Voluntarios da Patria 45, Salas
501 a 504 7 ao 9 andar e Salas 1001
a 1003 Botafogo, Rio de Janeiro,
22270-900, RJ, Brazil
Tel.: (55) 2121027100
Web Site:
https://www.sondotecnica.com.br
Year Founded: 1954
SOND5—(BRAZ)
Rev.: $29,135,875
Assets: $17,601,937
Liabilities: $6,840,957
Net Worth: $10,760,980
Earnings: $2,123,130
Emp.: 400
Fiscal Year-end: 12/31/23
Engineeering Services
N.A.I.C.S.: 541330
Jaime Rotstein *(Founder)*

SONEC CORPORATION
2257-1 Sonemachi, Takasago, 676-0082, Hyogo, Japan
Tel.: (81) 794471551
Web Site: https://www.sonec-const.co.jp
Year Founded: 1944
1768—(TKS)
Rev.: $106,943,190
Assets: $76,788,370
Liabilities: $19,221,880
Net Worth: $57,566,490
Earnings: $951,840
Fiscal Year-end: 03/31/24
Construction Engineering Services
N.A.I.C.S.: 541330
Koichi Fukushima *(Pres)*

SONEL S.A.
Wokulskiego 11, 58-100, Swidnica, Poland
Tel.: (48) 748583800   PL
Web Site: https://www.sonel.pl
Year Founded: 1994
SON—(WAR)
Rev.: $54,495,427
Assets: $41,869,156
Liabilities: $12,719,512
Net Worth: $29,149,644
Earnings: $4,953,760
Fiscal Year-end: 12/31/23
Electrical Test & Measurement Equipment Mfr
N.A.I.C.S.: 334515
Katarzyna Lukaszczyk *(Vice Mgr-Export)*

Subsidiaries:

Sonel Instruments India Private Limited (1)
New No 4/255 Plot No 191 10th Street Maxworth Nagar Sunambukolathur, Kovilambakkam Keelkattalai, Chennai, 600117, India
Tel.: (91) 8047643704
Web Site: https://www.sonelinstrumentsindia.com
Emp.: 10
Electric Equipment Mfr
N.A.I.C.S.: 335999
Shyam Ravindran *(Mng Dir)*

SONEPAR S.A.
43-47 avenue de la Grande-Armee, F 75782, Paris, Cedex 16, France
Tel.: (33) 158441313   FR
Web Site: http://www.sonepar.com
Year Founded: 1998
Sales Range: $15-24.9 Billion
Emp.: 33,000
Electrical Equipment Distribution
N.A.I.C.S.: 423610
Francois Poncet *(CFO)*

Subsidiaries:

3C Toulouse SAS (1)
32 rue Edmond Rostand, 31200, Toulouse, France
Tel.: (33) 534251380
Web Site: http://www.3cclim.com
Electrical Equipment Distr
N.A.I.C.S.: 423610

AME Material Electrico, S.A.U. (1)
P l Catarroja Calle 31 32, Catarroja, 46470, Valencia, Spain
Tel.: (34) 961223300
Web Site: http://www.amelectrico.com
Emp.: 239
Electrical Equipment Distr
N.A.I.C.S.: 423610

Approvisionnement Electrique (1)
Sonepar Sud-Est Mediterannee 354 boulevard Charles Barnier, 83000, Toulon, France
Tel.: (33) 494933200
Web Site: http://www.approelec-sonepar.fr
Electrical Equipment Distr
N.A.I.C.S.: 423610

BALTZINGER SA (1)
Sonepar Nord-Est -Technoparc les Pres 33 avenue Lavoisier, 59650, Villeneuve d'Ascq, France
Tel.: (33) 3 20 33 66 99
Web Site: http://baltzinger.sonepar.fr
Hazardous Waste Disposal Service
N.A.I.C.S.: 562213

Bianchi (1)
Rn 193, 20600, Furiani, France
Tel.: (33) 495592000
Web Site: http://www.bianchi-elec.fr
Electrical Equipment Distr
N.A.I.C.S.: 423610

CECCI (1)
Sonepar Sud-Est Mediterranee 7 rue Francois Pellos, 06046, Nice, France
Tel.: (33) 493133600
Web Site: http://www.cecci-sonepar.fr
Electrical Equipment Distr
N.A.I.C.S.: 423610

CEFB (1)
5-7 avenue Jules-Ferry, 92245, Malakoff, France
Tel.: (33) 141173434
Web Site: http://www.francobelge.sonepar.fr
Electrical Equipment Distr
N.A.I.C.S.: 423610

CGE Distribution - S.A.S. (1)
15-17 boulevard du General de Gaulle, 92120, Montrouge, France
Tel.: (33) 140925858
Electrical Component Mfr
N.A.I.C.S.: 423610

Cable Solutions & Electrical (Sea) Pte Ltd. (1)
No 6 Changi South Street 2 01-01 Xilin Districentre Building D, Singapore, 486349, Singapore
Tel.: (65) 62927727
Web Site: http://www.cablesolutions.com.sg
Cable & Wire Mfr
N.A.I.C.S.: 335929

Cable Solutions (Thailand) Co. Ltd. (1)
64/12 Moo 12 Kingkaew Rd T Rachatewa, Bang Phli, Samut Prakan, 10540, Thailand
Tel.: (66) 27637652
Cable & Wire Mfr
N.A.I.C.S.: 335929

Cabus & Raulot SA (1)
310 chemin de l Armee d Afrique, BP 74, 13395, Marseille, Cedex, France
Tel.: (33) 491434240
Web Site: http://www.cabus.sonepar.fr
Heat Pumps Renovation Services
N.A.I.C.S.: 541330

Cardi AB (1)
Valhallavagen 8, 114 22, Stockholm, Sweden
Tel.: (46) 84429400
Web Site: http://www.cardi.se
Electric Lighting Equipment Mfr
N.A.I.C.S.: 335131

Centelha Equipamentos Eletricos Ltda. (1)
Av-Guilherme Maxwell 353, Bonsucesso, Rio de Janeiro, 21040-211, Brazil
Tel.: (55) 2121959200
Web Site: http://www.centelhario.com.br
Electrical Equipment Distr
N.A.I.C.S.: 423610

Comptoir Central d'Electricite - DEL (1)
ZAC Garosud 194 rue Patrice Lumumba, 34070, Montpellier, France
Tel.: (33) 499525150
Web Site: http://www.cce-sonepar.fr
Electrical Equipment Distr
N.A.I.C.S.: 423610

Comptoir Des Courants Faibles Sa (1)
73 rue Noel Pons, 92737, Nanterre, Cedex, France
Tel.: (33) 1 41 91 60 60
Web Site: http://www.ccf.sonepar.fr
Electronic Security Device Distr
N.A.I.C.S.: 423610

Comptoir Elbeuvien D'Electricite SA (1)
ZI Sud 60 boulevard Pierre Lefaucheux, 72100, Le Mans, France
Tel.: (33) 243614839
Web Site: http://www.cee.sonepar.fr
Electrical Equipment Distr
N.A.I.C.S.: 423610

Comptoir du Sud-Ouest SAS (1)
Zac de Madere - Immeuble Central Park 2 rue Pablo Neruda, 33140, Villenave-d'Ornon, France
Tel.: (33) 557815151
Web Site: http://www.le-cso.com
Logistics Consulting Servies
N.A.I.C.S.: 541614

Coredime (1)
5 rue Charles Darwin - ZAC 2000, PO Box 80140, 97824, Le Port, Cedex, France
Tel.: (33) 2 62 22 11 22
Web Site: http://www.coredime.com
Electrical Equipment Distr
N.A.I.C.S.: 423610

Crane Distribution NZ Limited (1)
Level 1 61 Normanby Road, Mt Eden, Auckland, 1024, New Zealand   (100%)
Tel.: (64) 9 623 6010
Web Site: http://www.corys.co.nz
Sales Range: $350-399.9 Million
Emp.: 33
Plumbing, Pipelines, Electrical & Safety Products Supplier
N.A.I.C.S.: 423720
Peter Garden *(Reg Mgr)*

Subsidiary (Domestic):

MasterTrade Ltd. (2)
58 Hazeldean Road, Addington, Christchurch, 8024, New Zealand
Tel.: (64) 33381009
Web Site: http://www.mastertrade.co.nz
Sales Range: $50-74.9 Million
Emp.: 30
Plumbing & Electrical Supplies
N.A.I.C.S.: 423610
Bryn Harrison *(CEO)*

DEP Engineering Co., Ltd. (1)
107/3 3rd Floor Chalermprakiat Rama 9 Road, Prawet, Bangkok, 10250, Thailand
Tel.: (66) 27267575
Web Site: http://www.depdis.com
Electrical Equipment Distr
N.A.I.C.S.: 423610

Daem (1)
3 rue des Violettes, 98000, Monaco, Monaco
Tel.: (377) 99 99 68 10
Web Site: http://www.daem-sonepar.fr
Electrical Equipment Distr
N.A.I.C.S.: 423610

Delec (1)
3-5 rue Ferdinand Lassalle, PO Box 92431, 31085, Toulouse, Cedex, France
Tel.: (33) 562727300
Electrical Equipment Distr
N.A.I.C.S.: 423610

Direction Des Filiales Outre-Mer (1)
31 Boulevard Yves Farge, 69007, Lyon, France

INTERNATIONAL PUBLIC

Tel.: (33) 472733606
Electrical Equipment Distr
N.A.I.C.S.: 423610

ELTRA DIYeuronet BV (1)
Frontstraat 14, 5405 AK, Uden, Netherlands
Tel.: (31) 413333999
Electrical Equipment Distr
N.A.I.C.S.: 423610

ESK India Commerce & Trade PVT. Ltd. (1)
Plot No-229/239 Rectangle No-51 Khasra No-02 National Highway -8, Kherki Daula Near Haldirams and Groz Tools Factory, Gurgaon, 122004, India
Tel.: (91) 1244370867
Web Site: http://www.eskindia.com
Electrical Equipment Distr
N.A.I.C.S.: 423610
Bharat Nagpal *(Dir-Fin & Control)*

Electrical Wholesale Services Pty Ltd (1)
Level 10 189 Kent St, Sydney, 2000, NSW, Australia
Tel.: (61) 92992700
Web Site: http://www.ewsco.com.au
Electrical Equipment Distr
N.A.I.C.S.: 423610

ElectroLAN SA (1)
Rue des Tunnels 67-69, 2000, Neuchatel, Switzerland
Tel.: (41) 327378888
Web Site: http://www.electrolan.ch
Electrical Equipment Distr
N.A.I.C.S.: 423610

Elektram spol. s r.o. (1)
Vazni 1125, 500 03, Hradec Kralove, Czech Republic
Tel.: (420) 495500011
Web Site: http://www.sonepar.cz
Electrical Equipment Distr
N.A.I.C.S.: 423610

Elektroskandia AB (1)
Norrvikenleden 97, Sollentuna, 19183, Sweden, Sweden
Tel.: (46) 8923500
Web Site: http://www.elektroskandia.se
Sales Range: $600-649.9 Million
Emp.: 200
Electrical Components
N.A.I.C.S.: 423610
Karen Kruger *(Dir-IT)*

Ets Szymanski SAS (1)
220 rue A Ohlen - Portes de Fer, BP 544, 98845, Noumea, New Caledonia
Tel.: (687) 25 38 33
Web Site: http://www.szymanski.nc
Electrical Equipment Distr
N.A.I.C.S.: 423610

GMT Tabur Electricite SA (1)
ZI Sud - B 07 60 boulevard Pierre Lefaucheux, 72029, Le Mans, France
Tel.: (33) 243612646
Web Site: http://tabur-electricite.sonepar.fr
Electrical Equipment Distr
N.A.I.C.S.: 423610

Hagemeyer Austria (1)
Prager Strasse 243, 1210, Vienna, Austria
Tel.: (43) 1291260
Web Site: http://www.hagemeyer.at
Sales Range: $50-74.9 Million
Emp.: 120
Electronic Components
N.A.I.C.S.: 334419
Martin Haiderer *(Mgr-IT)*

Hagemeyer Commerce & Trade (Shanghai) Co., Ltd. (1)
Floor 9 New Development Tower No 169 Gonghe Road, Shanghai, China
Tel.: (86) 2122302500
Web Site: http://www.hagemeyercn.com
Electrical Equipment Distr
N.A.I.C.S.: 423610

Hagemeyer Singapore PPS Pte Ltd. (1)
158 Kallang Way 08-00, Singapore, 349245, Singapore
Tel.: (65) 65565183
Web Site: http://www.hagemeyerasia.com
Electrical Equipment Distr

AND PRIVATE COMPANIES — SONEPAR S.A.

N.A.I.C.S.: 423610

Hagemeyer-PPS (Thailand) Ltd. (1)
19/145-146 UM Tower 14th Floor Ramkhamhaeng Road, Suanluang, 10250, Bangkok, Thailand
Tel.: (66) 27173921
Electrical Equipment Distr
N.A.I.C.S.: 423610

HoST Pte Ltd (1)
120 Eunos Avenue 7 01-04 Richfield Industrial Centre, Singapore, 409574, Singapore
Tel.: (65) 67412778
Web Site: http://www.host.sg
Automotive Accessory Distr
N.A.I.C.S.: 441330
T. V. Rajasekhar *(Dir-Mktg & Bus Dev)*

IESA (1)
2 San Pedro 11801, San Jose, Costa Rica
Tel.: (506) 22578500
Web Site: http://www.iesacr.com
Electrical Equipment Distr
N.A.I.C.S.: 423610

Industyl SAS (1)
20 boulevard du Colonel Fabien, 94200, Ivry-sur-Seine, France
Tel.: (33) 146715700
Web Site: http://www.industyl.com
Electrical Equipment Distr
N.A.I.C.S.: 423610

KVC Industrial Supplies (Thailand) Co. Ltd. (1)
49/17 Moo 7 Tambol Klong Song, Amphure Klong Luang, 12120, Bangkok, Pathum Thani, Thailand
Tel.: (66) 215347278
Electrical Equipment Distr
N.A.I.C.S.: 423610

L&H Group (1)
456 Lower Heidelberg Rd, Heidelberg, Heidelberg, 3084, VIC, Australia
Tel.: (61) 392433555
Web Site: http://www.landhgroup.com.au
Sales Range: $75-99.9 Million
Emp.: 200
Electrical Products & Services
N.A.I.C.S.: 423610
Robin Norris *(CEO)*

LUMINAIRE METAL UNION SAS (1)
120-122 rue Ambroise Croizat, 94500, Champigny-sur-Marne, France
Tel.: (33) 145168383
Web Site: http://www.lmu.sonepar.fr
Electrical Equipment Distr
N.A.I.C.S.: 423610

Le MAT' ELECTRIQUE (1)
120 avenue Jean Jaures, 69007, Lyon, France
Tel.: (33) 472735858
Web Site: http://www.lematelectrique.com
Electrical Equipment Distr
N.A.I.C.S.: 423610

MGIE - CEV (1)
36 avenue du Marechal de Lattre de Tassigny, 94410, Saint-Maur, France
Tel.: (33) 143963193
Web Site: http://www.mgie.sonepar.fr
Electrical Equipment Distr
N.A.I.C.S.: 423610

MGM Electric Limited (1)
724 Macdonell St, Thunder Bay, P7B 4A6, ON, Canada
Tel.: (807) 345-7767
Web Site: https://www.mgm-electric.com
Electrical Equipment Distr
N.A.I.C.S.: 423610
Malcolm Hope *(Mgr-Warehouse)*

Maclary (1)
Sonepar Sud-Est Mediterranee 8 rue Dominique Paez, 06200, Nice, France
Tel.: (33) 492297171
Electrical Equipment Distr
N.A.I.C.S.: 423610

Melexa S.A.S. (1)
Calle 18 No 69F-26, Bogota, Colombia
Tel.: (57) 15874400
Web Site: http://www.melexa.com
Electrical Equipment Distr
N.A.I.C.S.: 423610

Novilux (1)
35 rue des Favorites, 75015, Paris, France
Tel.: (33) 1 53 68 12 50
Web Site: http://www.novilux.sonepar.fr
Electric Lighting Equipment Distr
N.A.I.C.S.: 423610

PETROCAM (1)
Rua Bonsucesso 6, bonsucesso, Rio de Janeiro, 21040-320, Brazil
Tel.: (55) 2121957676
Web Site: http://www.petrocam.com.br
Electrical Equipment Distr
N.A.I.C.S.: 423610

PT Fanah Jaya Maindo (1)
Kawasan Industri Delta Silicon 3 JL Pinang Blok F-16 No 11, Lippo Cikarang, 17550, Bekasi, Indonesia
Tel.: (62) 2189908556
Electrical Equipment Distr
N.A.I.C.S.: 423610

Routeco Limited (1)
Davy Avenue Knowlhill, Milton Keynes, MK5 8HJ, United Kingdom
Tel.: (44) 908666777
Web Site: http://www.routeco.com
Electrical Equipment Distr
N.A.I.C.S.: 423610
Michael McGuinness *(Dir-IT)*

SLO Latvia Ltd. (1)
Maleju street 1a, Riga, 1057, Latvia
Tel.: (371) 67114444
Web Site: http://www.slo.lv
Electrical Equipment Distr
N.A.I.C.S.: 423610
Johan Verbeek *(Pres)*

Saint-Martin Electro Clim (1)
Lot N 2 - Galisbay, PO Box 3171, 97080, Marigot, Cedex, Saint-Martin, France
Tel.: (33) 590877314
Electrical Equipment Distr
N.A.I.C.S.: 423610

Sandler Com. Elect. Ltda. (1)
Rua Marques de Oliveira 352, Ramos, 21031-710, Rio de Janeiro, Brazil
Tel.: (55) 2122092329
Electrical Equipment Distr
N.A.I.C.S.: 423610

Shunmoon (Shanghai) Lighting Limited (1)
Room 1201 Jiahe International Mansion Bld 1 Lane 66 Huayuan Road, Hongkou, Shanghai, China
Tel.: (86) 2131757556
Web Site: http://www.supermoon.hk
Electrical Equipment Distr
N.A.I.C.S.: 423610

Sigmadis S.A. (1)
8 Chemin du Bois des Cotes, PO Box 9, 69530, Brignais, France
Tel.: (33) 4 72 31 99 31
Web Site: http://www.sigmadis.fr
Electric Equipment Mfr
N.A.I.C.S.: 423610

Slo Oy (1)
Ritakuja 2, PO Box 88, 01740, Vantaa, Finland
Tel.: (358) 1028311
Web Site: http://www.slo.fi
Electrical Material Distr
N.A.I.C.S.: 423610
Allan Sothmann *(Sls Dir-Power Distr & Industry)*

Socame SAS (1)
Zone de Gros - La Jambette, Martinique, 97232, Lamentin, France
Tel.: (33) 596501945
Electrical Equipment Distr
N.A.I.C.S.: 423610

Socolec SA (1)
ZI Sud - 58 boulevard Pierre Lefaucheux, 72027, Le Mans, Cedex, France
Tel.: (33) 243612666
Web Site: http://www.socolec.com
Electrical Equipment Distr
N.A.I.C.S.: 423610

Sonepar Belgium (1)
Noordlaan 15, 8520, Temse, Belgium
Tel.: (32) 56 36 47 00
Web Site: http://www.sonepar.com

Electrical Equipment
N.A.I.C.S.: 423610

Subsidiary (Domestic):

Cebeo (2)
Zwingelaarsstraat 7, 8500, Kortrijk, Belgium
Tel.: (32) 56365711
Web Site: http://www.cebeo.be
Sales Range: $200-249.9 Million
Emp.: 650
Electrical Material Distribution
N.A.I.C.S.: 423610

Subsidiary (Non-US):

Sonepar Canada, Inc. - Sesco Division (2)
205 Mackenzie Avenue Unit 3, Ajax, L1S 2G1, ON, Canada
Tel.: (905) 428-2446
Web Site: https://www.sesco.ca
Electrical Equipment Distr
N.A.I.C.S.: 423610

Sonepar Canada, Inc. - TEXCAN ONTARIO Division (2)
250 Chrysler Dr Unit 5, Brampton, L6S 6B6, ON, Canada
Tel.: (905) 595-3451
Web Site: http://www.texcan.com
Electrical Equipment Distr
N.A.I.C.S.: 423610
Chris Golf *(VP & Gen Mgr)*

Subsidiary (Domestic):

Sonepar Eltra (2)
Pachtgoedstraat 2, 9140, Temse, Belgium
Tel.: (32) 37806730
Web Site: http://www.eltra.be
Sales Range: $25-49.9 Million
Emp.: 100
Electrical Material Distribution
N.A.I.C.S.: 423610
Dirk Baum *(CEO & Mgr)*

Sonepar Canada (1)
989 Derry Rd E Ste 303, Mississauga, L5T 2J8, ON, Canada
Tel.: (905) 696-2838
Web Site: http://www.soneparcanada.com
Sales Range: $50-74.9 Million
Emp.: 2
Electrical Equipment
N.A.I.C.S.: 423610
Dave Syer *(VP-Vendor Rels & Bus Dev)*

Subsidiary (Domestic):

Dixon Electric Ltd. (2)
1158 Lorne Street, Sudbury, P3C 4S9, ON, Canada
Tel.: (705) 674-1981
Web Site: https://www.dixonelectric.ca
Emp.: 20
Electrical Contractor
N.A.I.C.S.: 238210
Serge Losier *(Mgr-Sls-North Bay)*

Gescan BC (2)
2441 United Blvd, Coquitlam, V3K 6A8, BC, Canada
Tel.: (604) 472-7130
Web Site: http://www.gescan.com
Sales Range: $25-49.9 Million
Electrical Material Distribution
N.A.I.C.S.: 423610
Jeff Derkuch *(Pres)*

Gescan Ontario (2)
2800 High Point Drive Unit 207, Milton, L9T 6P4, ON, Canada
Tel.: (905) 693-6311
Web Site: https://www.gescanautomation.com
Sales Range: $25-49.9 Million
Emp.: 6
Electrical Material Distr
N.A.I.C.S.: 423610
Ivan Romanov *(Dir-Sls & Mktg-Ontario)*

Gescan Prairies (2)
5005 12A St S E, Calgary, T2G5L5, AB, Canada
Tel.: (403) 253-7171
Web Site: http://www.gescan.com
Sales Range: $25-49.9 Million
Electrical Material Distribution
N.A.I.C.S.: 423610
Steve Dunne *(Mgr-Sls)*

Lumen (2)
4655 Autoroute 440 O, Laval, H7P 5P9, QC, Canada
Tel.: (450) 688-9249
Web Site: http://www.lumen.ca
Sales Range: $25-49.9 Million
Electrical Material Distribution
N.A.I.C.S.: 423610

SESCO (2)
361 Marwood Drive, Oshawa, L1H 7P8, ON, Canada
Tel.: (905) 576-4166
Web Site: http://www.sesco.ca
Electrical Products Distr
N.A.I.C.S.: 423610
Fabio Mazzotta *(Branch Mgr)*

Sonecable (2)
4655 Autoroute 440 O, Laval, H7P 5P9, QC, Canada
Tel.: (450) 688-9249
Web Site: https://www.lumen.ca
Sales Range: $50-74.9 Million
Electrical Material Distribution
N.A.I.C.S.: 423610
Claude Joannette *(VP)*

Texcan Division (2)
10449 120th Street, Surrey, V3V 4G4, BC, Canada
Tel.: (604) 528-3600
Web Site: https://www.texcan.com
Sales Range: $25-49.9 Million
Emp.: 90
Electrical Material Distribution
N.A.I.C.S.: 423610
Chris Golf *(Pres)*

Sonepar China (1)
355 Qinqiao Road, Jinqiao Export Processing Zone, 201206, Shanghai, China
Tel.: (86) 2161650300
Web Site: http://www.sonepar.com.cn
Sales Range: $1-4.9 Billion
Emp.: 150
Electrical Products Distr
N.A.I.C.S.: 423610

Subsidiary (Non-US):

Electric Fever Company (Hong Kong) (2)
Units 703-704 Yan Hing Centre, 9-13 Wong Chuk Yeung Street, Hong Kong, China (Hong Kong)
Tel.: (852) 28512027
Web Site: http://www.supermoon.hk
Sales Range: $25-49.9 Million
Emp.: 50
Electrical Material Distribution
N.A.I.C.S.: 423610
Michelle Chan *(Mng Dir)*

Subsidiary (Domestic):

Foshan Shunching Supermoon Trading Co., Ltd. (2)
F2 No 3-1 Tong Fu Dong Yi Jie, Chan Cheng District, 528 000, Foshan, China
Tel.: (86) 75783366363
Electrical Products
N.A.I.C.S.: 423610

Hite Electric Technology Co., Ltd. (2)
2F Block 1 777 Xin Jun Huan Road, Minhang District, 201114, Shanghai, PRC, China
Tel.: (86) 21 6057 2888
Web Site: http://www.hite-electric.com
Electrical Products
N.A.I.C.S.: 423610

Subsidiary (Non-US):

Supermoon Ltd (2)
9-13 Wong Chuk Yeung St, 9-13 Wong Chuk Yeung Street, Hong Kong, China (Hong Kong)
Tel.: (852) 26919166
Web Site: http://www.supermoon.hk
Sales Range: $25-49.9 Million
Emp.: 70
Electrical Material Distribution
N.A.I.C.S.: 423610
Alvin Mok *(CEO)*

Wing Kwong Electrical Co., Ltd (2)
Units 703-704 Yan Hing Centre, 9-13 Wong

SONEPAR S.A.
INTERNATIONAL PUBLIC

Sonepar S.A.—(Continued)
Chuk Yeung Street, Hong Kong, Fotan Shatin, China (Hong Kong)
Tel.: (852) 27812855
Web Site: http://www.sonepar.com
Sales Range: $25-49.9 Million
Emp.: 20
Electrical Material Distribution
N.A.I.C.S.: 423610
G. Hui *(Gen Mgr)*

Sonepar Deutschland Cable Services GmbH (1)
Landsberger Str 287 A, 80687, Munich, Germany
Tel.: (49) 89 58 999 0
Web Site: http://www.sonepar.de
Electrical Equipment Distr
N.A.I.C.S.: 423610

Sonepar Deutschland Erneuerbare Energien GmbH (1)
Peter-Muller-Str 18, 40468, Dusseldorf, Germany
Tel.: (49) 211994100
Electrical Equipment Distr
N.A.I.C.S.: 423610

Sonepar Deutschland GmbH (1)
Peter-Muller-Strasse 3, 40468, Dusseldorf, Germany
Tel.: (49) 211994100
Web Site: http://www.sonepar.de
Emp.: 100
Electrical Products Distribution
N.A.I.C.S.: 423610
Franciscus H. Lakerveld *(Chm-Mgmt Bd)*

Subsidiary (Domestic):

Industrie Elektro Handelsgesellschaft (2)
Am Lichtbogen 53, 45141, Essen, Germany
Tel.: (49) 20181400
Web Site: http://www.sonepar.com
Sales Range: $25-49.9 Million
Emp.: 80
Electrical Material Distribution
N.A.I.C.S.: 423610

Otto Kuhmann (2)
Furstenwall 183-185, D-40215, Dusseldorf, Germany
Tel.: (49) 21138991
Web Site:
http://www.okuhmann.sonepar.com
Sales Range: $25-49.9 Million
Emp.: 100
Electrical Material Distribution
N.A.I.C.S.: 423610

Subsidiary (Non-US):

Sonepar Ceska republika spol. s. r.o. (2)
Vazni 1125, 50003, Hradec Kralove, Czech Republic
Tel.: (420) 495500011
Web Site: http://www.sonepar.cz
Sales Range: $50-74.9 Million
Emp.: 200
Electrical Material Distr
N.A.I.C.S.: 423610
Jiri Louda *(CEO)*

Sonepar Hungary Kft (2)
Mechwart Andras St 4, 2330, Dunaharaszti, Hungary
Tel.: (36) 24814600
Web Site: http://www.sonepar.hu
Sales Range: $50-74.9 Million
Emp.: 120
Electrical Material Distribution
N.A.I.C.S.: 423610

Sonepar Osterreich GmbH (2)
Grossmarktstrasse 7b, Wien, A-1230, Vienna, Austria
Tel.: (43) 517060
Web Site: http://www.sonepar.at
Sales Range: $50-74.9 Million
Emp.: 250
Electrical Material Distr
N.A.I.C.S.: 423610

Sonepar France (1)
1/3 rue Eugene Varlin, BP 35, 92242, Malakoff, France
Tel.: (33) 146739530

Web Site: http://www.soneoar.com
Sales Range: $50-74.9 Million
Emp.: 60
Electrical Products Distribution

Sonepar France Region Ile-de-France (1)
5-7 avenue Jules Ferry, 92245, Malakoff, France
Tel.: (33) 141173434
Electrical Equipment Distr
N.A.I.C.S.: 423610

Sonepar France Region Mediterranee (1)
34 boulevard de l Europe, 13127, Vitrolles, France
Tel.: (33) 442794400
Electrical Equipment Distr
N.A.I.C.S.: 423610

Sonepar Iberica S.A. (1)
Poligono Industrial Na Sa de Butarque
Calle Ramon y Cajal n 24, 28914, Leganes, Madrid, Spain
Tel.: (34) 915572207
Web Site: http://www.sonepar.es
Sales Range: $550-599.9 Million
Emp.: 1,009
Electrical Material Distribution
N.A.I.C.S.: 423610
Luis Arconada *(Dir Gen)*

Subsidiary (Domestic):

Comercial Hispanofil, S.A. (2)
Pl Gamonal-Villimar, C/ Fuero del Trabajo s/n, 09007, Burgos, Spain
Tel.: (34) 947474242
Web Site: http://www.hispanofil.com
Sales Range: $125-149.9 Million
Emp.: 314
Electrical Material Distribution
N.A.I.C.S.: 423610

Dielectro Balear S.A. (2)
Gremio Carpinteros 43, Poligono son Castello, Palma de Mallorca, 7009, Spain (100%)
Tel.: (34) 971430486
Web Site: http://www.dielectrobalear.es
Emp.: 60
Electrical Material Distribution
N.A.I.C.S.: 423610
Antonio Fiol Serra *(Controller-Fin)*

Dielectro Canarias La Palma (2)
C/Blas Perez Gonzalez 3, 38760, Santa Cruz de la Palma, Santa Cruz de Teneri, Spain
Tel.: (34) 922 49 72 28
Web Site: http://dielectrocanarias.es
Electrical Material Distribution
N.A.I.C.S.: 423610
Jose Enrique Magdalena *(Dir-Provincial)*

Dimel Castilla, S.A. (2)
14 Pol Ind Gamonal-Villimar, 9007, Burgos, Spain
Tel.: (34) 94 747 4242
Web Site: http://www.dimel.com
Sales Range: $25-49.9 Million
Emp.: 81
Electrical Material Distribution
N.A.I.C.S.: 423610
Carlos Gonzales Fuentes *(Dir Gen)*

Guerin S.A. (2)
Ronda San Pedro 52 7, 08010, Barcelona, Spain
Tel.: (34) 932681912
Web Site: http://www.guerin.es
Sales Range: $150-199.9 Million
Emp.: 379
Electrical Material Distribution
N.A.I.C.S.: 423610

Sonibetica (2)
C/O Fuero del Trabajo s/n 2a planta, Pol Ind Gamonal-Villimar, 09007, Burgos, Spain
Tel.: (34) 947281154
Web Site: http://www.sonepar.com
Electrical Material Distribution
N.A.I.C.S.: 423610

Sonepar Italia S.p.A. (1)
Riviera Maestri del Lavoro 24, 35127, Padua, Italy
Tel.: (39) 0498292111

Web Site: http://www.sonepar.it
Sales Range: $50-74.9 Million
Emp.: 100
Electrical Material Distribution
N.A.I.C.S.: 423610

Subsidiary (Domestic):

Brollo Sonepar (2)
Via Piave 41, Caerano di San Marco, 31031, Treviso, Italy
Tel.: (39) 04236588
Electrical Material Distribution
N.A.I.C.S.: 423610

Cangiano Sonepar SpA (2)
Via Flli Bandiera snc, 80026, Casoria, Italy
Tel.: (39) 0815503111
Sales Range: $50-74.9 Million
Electrical Material Distribution
N.A.I.C.S.: 423610

Elettroingross S.p.A. (2)
Riviera Maestri del Lavoro 24, 35127, Padua, Italy
Tel.: (39) 0498946611
Web Site: http://www.elettroingrossweb.it
Electrical Material Distribution
N.A.I.C.S.: 423610
M. Bicknell *(Mng Dir)*

Femi Rinaldi S.p.a. (2)
Via C Correnti 33, 24124, Bergamo, Italy
Tel.: (39) 0354282800
Web Site: http://www.femirinaldi.it
Sales Range: $50-74.9 Million
Electrical Material Distribution
N.A.I.C.S.: 423610

Forel Sonepar S.p.A. (2)
Via Robino 129/131, 20025, Legnano, Italy
Tel.: (39) 0331427711
Web Site: http://www.sonepar.it
Sales Range: $25-49.9 Million
Emp.: 85
Electrical Material Distribution
N.A.I.C.S.: 423610

Mazzi Sonepar S.p.A. (2)
Via San Quirico 220, 50010, Campi Bisenzio, Italy
Tel.: (39) 055897741
Web Site: http://www.mazzisonepar.it
Electrical Material Distribution
N.A.I.C.S.: 423610

Migliore Sonepar S.p.A. (2)
Via Umberto Giordano 172, 90144, Palermo, Italy
Tel.: (39) 0916836211
Web Site: http://www.miglioresonepar.it
Electrical Material Distribution
N.A.I.C.S.: 423610

R.E.R Radio Elettrica Romana (2)
Via Idrovore della Magliana 75-a, I-00148, Rome, Italy
Tel.: (39) 06655181
Web Site: http://www.rer.it
Electrical Material Distribution
N.A.I.C.S.: 423610

Sonepar Immobiliare E Di Servizi (2)
Via Fratelli Bandiera SNC, 80026, Casoria, Italy
Tel.: (39) 0812508326
Electrical Material Distribution
N.A.I.C.S.: 423610

Sonepar Puglia S.p.A. (2)
Via Bitritto km 7+800, I-70026, Modugno, Italy
Tel.: (39) 0802010100
Web Site: http://www.soneparpuglia.it
Sales Range: $25-49.9 Million
Emp.: 91
Electrical Material Distribution
N.A.I.C.S.: 423610

Sonepar Sardegna S.p.A. (2)
Viale Marconi 165, 09131, Cagliari, Italy
Tel.: (39) 070485151
Web Site: http://www.soneparsardegna.it
Electrical Material Distribution
N.A.I.C.S.: 423610

Sonepar Mexico (2)
Av Belisario Dominguez 100 Col Lomas de la Selva, 62270, Cuernavaca, Mexico
Tel.: (52) 7771011118
Web Site: http://www.sonepar.com.mx

Sales Range: $150-199.9 Million
Emp.: 700
Electrical Material Distribution
N.A.I.C.S.: 423610
Urcesino Roberto Palacios Barro *(Mng Dir)*

Subsidiary (Domestic):

Distribuidora Santiago (2)
Muritz No 5 - Colonia Anahuac, 11320, Mexico, Mexico
Tel.: (52) 5552799898
Web Site: http://www.santiago.com.mx
Electrical Material Distribution
N.A.I.C.S.: 423610

Grupo Alcione (2)
Av Domingo Diez 910, Col Lomas de la Selva, Cuernavaca, Morelos, Mexico
Tel.: (52) 77 71 01 11 00
Web Site: http://www.alcione.mx
Electrical Material Distribution Services
N.A.I.C.S.: 423610

Sonepar Nederland (1)
Bovenkerkerweg 10-12, Amstelveen, 1185, Netherlands
Tel.: (31) 205450345
Sales Range: $75-99.9 Million
Emp.: 204
Electrical Material Distribution
N.A.I.C.S.: 423610
Jan Janse *(Mng Dir)*

Subsidiary (Domestic):

Otra Nv (2)
Bovenkerkerweg 10-12, 1185XE, Amstelveen, Netherlands
Tel.: (31) 205450850
Web Site: http://www.technischeunie.com
Sales Range: $50-74.9 Million
Electrical Material Distribution
N.A.I.C.S.: 423610

Otra Vastgoed (2)
Bovenkerkerweg 10-12, 1185XE, Amstelveen, Netherlands
Tel.: (31) 205450850
Sales Range: $25-49.9 Million
Emp.: 80
Electrical Material Distribution
N.A.I.C.S.: 423610

Sonepar Elar (2)
Frontstraat 8, 5400, Uden, Netherlands
Tel.: (31) 413333999
Web Site: http://www.sonepar.com
Electrical Material Distribution
N.A.I.C.S.: 423610

Sonepar Nederland Information Services B.V. (2)
Bovenkerkerweg 10-12, Amstelveen, 1185 XE, Netherlands
Tel.: (31) 205450850
Web Site: http://www.sonepar.com
Sales Range: $25-49.9 Million
Emp.: 65
Programming & Software
N.A.I.C.S.: 541511
W. Korving *(Mng Dir)*

Technische Unie (2)
Bovenkerkerweg 10-12, 1185XE, Amstelveen, Netherlands
Tel.: (31) 205450345
Web Site: http://www.technischeunie.com
Sales Range: $50-74.9 Million
Emp.: 250
Electrical Material Distribution
N.A.I.C.S.: 423610
Jan Janse *(Mng Dir)*

Sonepar South America Participacoes Ltda. (1)
Rua Joaquim Floriano 466 Conj 2008, Itaim Bibi, 04534-002, Sao Paulo, Brazil
Tel.: (55) 1121658244
Web Site: http://www.sonepar.com.br
Sales Range: $50-74.9 Million
Emp.: 13
Electrical Material Distr
N.A.I.C.S.: 423610

Subsidiary (Domestic):

Comercial Electrica DW S/A-Filial Blumenau (2)
Rua Tapajos 33-Salto Norte, 89065-450, Blumenau, SC, Brazil

AND PRIVATE COMPANIES — SONEPAR S.A.

Tel.: (55) 47 3321 7500
Web Site: http://www.eletricadw.com.br
Electrical Material Distribution
N.A.I.C.S.: 423610

Comercial Eletrica DW Ltda (2)
Rua Joao Bettega 2281 Portao, Curitiba, 81070-001, PR, Brazil
Tel.: (55) 4133165000
Web Site: http://www.eletricadw.com.br
Sales Range: $50-74.9 Million
Electrical Material Distribution
N.A.I.C.S.: 423610
Leonardo Dissenhe *(Dir-Comml)*

Dimensional Equipamentos Eletricos Ltda. (2)
Rua Leandro Castelar 404/418, Jardim Piratininga, 13484-322, Limeira, Brazil
Tel.: (55) 1934467400
Web Site: http://www.dimensional.com.br
Sales Range: $50-74.9 Million
Electrical Material Distribution & Industrial Automation Mfr
N.A.I.C.S.: 423610

Eletronor Distribuidora De Materiais Eletricos Ltda (2)
Rua Buarque de Macedo 85- Sao Geraldo, 90230-250, Porto Alegre, Brazil
Tel.: (55) 5133148000
Web Site: http://www.eletronor.com.br
Electrical Material Distribution
N.A.I.C.S.: 423610

Emel Materiais Eletricos SA (2)
Ave Sao Pedro 1312 Sao Geraldo, 90230124, Porto Alegre, Brazil
Tel.: (55) 5133264000
Web Site: http://www.emel.com.br
Sales Range: $25-49.9 Million
Electrical Material Distribution
N.A.I.C.S.: 423610

Proelt Engenharia Eletrica Ltda. (2)
R Dona Francisca 5725 Zona Industrial, 89219-000, Joinville, Brazil
Tel.: (55) 47 3177 2200
Web Site: http://www.proelt.com.br
Sales Range: $125-149.9 Million
Electrical Material Distr
N.A.I.C.S.: 423610
A. Lopes *(Gen Mgr)*

Sonepar Switzerland (1)
Geneva Business Center Avenue Des Morgines 12, 1213, Petit-Lancy, Switzerland
Tel.: (41) 228791140
Sales Range: $25-49.9 Million
Emp.: 15
Holding Company
N.A.I.C.S.: 551112
Herbert Willmy *(Mng Dir)*

Subsidiary (Domestic):

Dineo SA (2)
Chemin du Petit-Flon, 27, 1052, Lausanne, Switzerland
Tel.: (41) 216512550
Web Site: http://www.dineo.ch
Electrical Products
N.A.I.C.S.: 423610

Dysbox SA (2)
Rue de la piscine 10 Batiment 2B, 1950, Sion, Switzerland
Tel.: (41) 274518000
Web Site: http://www.dysbox.ch
Lighting & Electrical Equipment Mfr
N.A.I.C.S.: 335132
Georges Alvarez *(CEO)*

Electroplast SA (2)
Route des Jeunes 105, CH-1227, Carouge, Switzerland
Tel.: (41) 22 342 01 60
Web Site: http://www.sonepar.ch
Electrical Material Distribution
N.A.I.C.S.: 423610
Daniel Tavernier *(Mng Dir)*

Fabbri (2)
Via Boschina 21a, CH-6963, Lugano, Switzerland
Tel.: (41) 919732155
Web Site: http://www.fabbri.ch
Sales Range: $25-49.9 Million
Emp.: 50
Electrical Material Distribution
N.A.I.C.S.: 423610
Giancarlo Fabbri *(Founder)*

Winterhalter & Fenner AG (2)
Birgistrasse 10, 8304, Wallisellen, Switzerland
Tel.: (41) 448395811
Web Site: http://www.w-f.ch
Sales Range: $50-74.9 Million
Emp.: 300
Electronic Components
N.A.I.C.S.: 423690
Marcel Fehr *(Head-Computer Science)*

Sonepar USA, Inc. (1)
510 Walnut St Ste 400, Philadelphia, PA 19106
Tel.: (215) 399-5900
Web Site: http://www.sonepar-usa.com
Rev.: $1,400,000,000
Emp.: 4,000
Electrical Apparatus & Equipment Distr
N.A.I.C.S.: 423610
Doug Lauer *(CIO)*

Subsidiary (Domestic):

Brook Electrical Supply Company (2)
880 S Rohlwing Rd, Addison, IL 60101
Tel.: (847) 353-6300
Web Site: http://www.brookelectrical.com
Sales Range: $25-49.9 Million
Emp.: 100
Electrical Material Distribution
N.A.I.C.S.: 423610
John Finerty *(Acting Pres)*

Capital Tristate Co. (2)
8511 Pepco Pl, Upper Marlboro, MD 20772
Tel.: (301) 909-6500
Web Site: http://www.capitaltristate.com
Rev.: $28,669,576
Emp.: 105
Electrical Apparatus & Equipment Distr
N.A.I.C.S.: 423610
Brian Chavis *(Branch Mgr)*

Division (Domestic):

Capital Tristate (3)
12101 Insurance Way, Hagerstown, MD 21740-5176
Tel.: (301) 665-3799
Web Site: http://www.capitaltristate.com
Sales Range: $25-49.9 Million
Emp.: 65
Electrical Products
N.A.I.C.S.: 423610
Bill Bowers *(Acct Mgr)*

Subsidiary (Domestic):

Codale Electric Supply, Inc. (2)
5225 W 2400 S, Salt Lake City, UT 84120
Tel.: (801) 975-7300
Web Site: http://www.codale.com
Sales Range: $200-249.9 Million
Emp.: 200
Fiscal Year-end: 12/25/2010
Electrical Apparatus & Equipment Distr
N.A.I.C.S.: 423610
Jay R. Holt *(VP)*

Division (Domestic):

Grove Madsen Industries, a Division of Codale (3)
390 E 6th St, Reno, NV 89512
Tel.: (775) 322-3400
Web Site: http://www.g-m-i.com
Sales Range: $10-24.9 Million
Emp.: 20
Electrical Supplies Whslr
N.A.I.C.S.: 423610
Mike Madsen *(Pres)*

Subsidiary (Domestic):

Cooper Electric Supply Co. (2)
1 Matrix Dr, Monroe, NJ 08831
Tel.: (732) 747-2233
Web Site: http://www.cooper-electric.com
Sales Range: $25-49.9 Million
Emp.: 45
Electrical Apparatus Distribution
N.A.I.C.S.: 423610
Mike Dudas *(Pres)*

Subsidiary (Domestic):

Billows Electric Supply Co. (3)
9100 State Rd, Philadelphia, PA 19136
Tel.: (215) 332-9700
Web Site: http://www.billows.com
Sales Range: $25-49.9 Million
Emp.: 230
Electrical Supplies Distr
N.A.I.C.S.: 423610
Jeff Billow *(Pres)*

Subsidiary (Domestic):

Crawford Electric Supply Company (2)
1950 Gateway Dr, Irvine, TX 75038
Tel.: (972) 869-3633
Web Site: http://www.cescoltd.com
Sales Range: $25-49.9 Million
Emp.: 82
Electrical Supplies
N.A.I.C.S.: 423610
John Hardy *(Acting Pres)*

Subsidiary (Non-US):

ECM Limited (2)
36-38 Dunload Street, PO Box 931, Port of Spain, Trinidad & Tobago
Tel.: (868) 6252580
Electrical Equipment Distr
N.A.I.C.S.: 423610

Subsidiary (Domestic):

EOFF Electric Company (2)
3241 NW Industrial St, Portland, OR 97210
Tel.: (503) 222-9411
Web Site: http://www.eoff.com
Sales Range: $75-99.9 Million
Emp.: 185
Electrical Apparate & Equipment Distr
N.A.I.C.S.: 423610
Jeff Lee *(Branch Mgr)*

Subsidiary (Domestic):

Eck Supply Company (2)
1405 W Main St, Richmond, VA 23220
Tel.: (804) 359-5781
Web Site: http://www.ecksupply.com
Electrical Supplies Distr
N.A.I.C.S.: 423610
Ed C. Eck Jr. *(Chm)*

Friedman Electric Supply Co (2)
1321 Wyoming Ave, Exeter, PA 18643
Tel.: (570) 654-3371
Web Site: http://www.friedmanelectric.com
Sales Range: $10-24.9 Million
Emp.: 200
Electrical Supplies
N.A.I.C.S.: 423610
Robert C. Friedman *(Pres)*

Division (Domestic):

Friedman Electric, Industrial Automation Division (3)
1321 Wyoming Ave, Exeter, PA 18643
Tel.: (570) 654-3371
Web Site: http://www.friedmanelectric.com
Electrical Supplies
N.A.I.C.S.: 423610
Rich Potero *(Pres)*

Friedman Telecom (3)
1321 Wyoming Ave, Exeter, PA 18643
Tel.: (570) 654-3371
Web Site: http://www.friedmanelectric.com
Electrical Supplies
N.A.I.C.S.: 423610

Subsidiary (Domestic):

North Coast Electric Company (2)
2424 8th Ave S, Seattle, WA 98134
Tel.: (206) 436-4444
Web Site: http://www.ncelec.com
Sales Range: $200-249.9 Million
Emp.: 400
Providers of Electrical Services
N.A.I.C.S.: 423610
Peter R. Lemman *(CEO)*

Subsidiary (Domestic):

North Coast Lighting (3)
1038 116th Ave NE Ste 350, Bellevue, WA 98004
Tel.: (425) 454-2122
Web Site: http://www.northcoastlighting.com
Emp.: 20
Lighting Fixtures Whslr
N.A.I.C.S.: 423220

Jodi Akhlaghi *(Project Mgr)*

Subsidiary (Domestic):

NorthEast Electrical, Inc. (2)
560 Oak St, Brockton, MA 02301
Tel.: (800) 897-1769
Web Site: https://www.needco.com
Electrical Products Distr
N.A.I.C.S.: 423610
Frank Marandino *(Pres)*

One Source Distributors Inc. (2)
3951 Oceanic Dr, Oceanside, CA 92056
Tel.: (760) 966-4500
Web Site: http://www.1sourcedist.com
Sales Range: $125-149.9 Million
Emp.: 300
Electrical Apparatus & Equipment Distr
N.A.I.C.S.: 423610
Paul Judge *(Sr VP)*

QED, Inc. (2)
1661 W 3rd Ave, Denver, CO 80223-1438
Tel.: (303) 825-5011
Web Site: http://www.qedelectric.com
Electrical Supplies Distr
N.A.I.C.S.: 423610
Jason Green *(Acct Mgr)*

Stuart C. Irby Company (2)
815 S President St, Jackson, MS 39201-5908
Tel.: (601) 960-7304
Web Site: http://www.irby.com
Sales Range: $400-449.9 Million
Emp.: 745
Electrical Products Distr
N.A.I.C.S.: 423610
Mike Wigton *(Pres)*

Vallen (2)
2100 The Oaks Pkwy, Belmont, NC 28012
Tel.: (800) 932-3746
Web Site: http://www.vallen.com
Supplier of Procurement Solutions for Manufacturers
N.A.I.C.S.: 541614
Carol Marks *(VP-Bus Mgmt Sys)*

Branch (Domestic):

Industrial Distribution Group, Inc. - Cincinnati (3)
9407 Meridian Way, West Chester, OH 45069
Tel.: (513) 942-9100
Web Site: http://www.idg-corp.com
Sales Range: $75-99.9 Million
Industrial Supplies Distr
N.A.I.C.S.: 423840

Industrial Distribution Group, Inc. - Connecticut (3)
30 N Plains Industrial Rd, Wallingford, CT 06492
Tel.: (203) 284-5341
Web Site: http://www.idg-corp.com
Industrial Supply Distr
N.A.I.C.S.: 423830

Industrial Distribution Group, Inc. - Kingsford (3)
1021 Pyle Dr, Kingsford, MI 49802
Tel.: (906) 774-3991
Web Site: http://www.idg-corp.com
Sales Range: $50-74.9 Million
Emp.: 8
Industrial Supplies Distr
N.A.I.C.S.: 423840
Kelly Geib *(Mgr)*

Industrial Distribution Group, Inc. - Manitowoc (3)
4466 Custer St, Manitowoc, WI 54220
Tel.: (920) 684-3313
Web Site: http://www.idg-corp.com
Sales Range: $25-49.9 Million
Emp.: 40
Industrial Supplies Distr
N.A.I.C.S.: 423840

Industrial Distribution Group, Inc. - Nashua (3)
400 Amherst St Ste 302, Nashua, NH 03063
Tel.: (603) 324-1440
Web Site: http://www.idg-corp.com
Sales Range: $25-49.9 Million
Emp.: 20
Industrial Supplies Distr

SONEPAR S.A.

Sonepar S.A.—(Continued)
N.A.I.C.S.: 423840

Industrial Distribution Group, Inc. - Nashville (3)
3287 Franklin Limestone Rd Ste 301, Antioch, TN 37013
Tel.: (615) 515-1490
Web Site: http://www.idg-corp.com
Sales Range: $50-74.9 Million
Emp.: 10
Industrial Supplies Distr
N.A.I.C.S.: 423840
Russ Smith (Mgr-Sls)

Industrial Distribution Group, Inc. - Wichita (3)
4200 Esthner, Wichita, KS 67209
Tel.: (316) 942-8374
Web Site: http://www.idg-corp.com
Sales Range: $25-49.9 Million
Emp.: 31
Industrial Supplies Distr
N.A.I.C.S.: 423840
Lisa Mitchell (CEO)

Industrial Distribution Group, Inc. - York (3)
3100 Farmtrail Rd, York, PA 17406
Tel.: (717) 767-7575
Web Site: http://www.idg-corp.com
Sales Range: $25-49.9 Million
Industrial Supplies Distr
N.A.I.C.S.: 423840
Lynne Mellott (Coord-FPS)

Industrial Distribution Group, Inc.- St. Louis (3)
10435 Baur Blvd, Saint Louis, MO 63132-1904
Tel.: (314) 997-0600
Web Site: http://www.idg-corp.com
Industrial Supplies Distr
N.A.I.C.S.: 423840
Mike Quinn (Sls Mgr)

Subsidiary (Domestic):

Viking Electric Supply, Inc. (2)
451 Industrial Blvd, Minneapolis, MN 55413
Tel.: (612) 627-1300
Web Site: http://www.vikingelectric.com
Emp.: 200
Wholesale Electrical Distr
N.A.I.C.S.: 335999
Greg Hames (Pres)

WDC Puerto Rico Inc. (2)
Rd 1 KM 33.3 Bairoa, Caguas, PR 00725
Tel.: (787) 757-8600
Web Site: http://www.warrendelcaribe.com
Sales Range: $25-49.9 Million
Emp.: 50
Electrical Supplies
N.A.I.C.S.: 423610
Camille Roman (Asst Mgr-Ops)

Subsidiary (Domestic):

WDC Miami Inc. (3)
13130 NW 113th Ct, Medley, FL 33178
Tel.: (305) 884-2800
Sales Range: $25-49.9 Million
Emp.: 15
Electrical Supplies
N.A.I.C.S.: 423610
Juan Rivera (Gen Mgr)

Subsidiary (Domestic):

World Electric Supply (2)
4680 LB McCleod Rd, Orlando, FL 32811
Tel.: (407) 447-2000
Web Site: http://www.worldelectricsupply.com
Sales Range: $25-49.9 Million
Emp.: 20
Electrical Material Distribution
N.A.I.C.S.: 423610
Rusty Spradley (Mgr)

Sonic Automation Ltd. (1)
99/9 Central Chaengwattana 20th Fl Unit 2003 & 2005 Moo 2, Chaengwattana Road Bangtarad Pakkred, Nonthaburi, 11120, Thailand
Tel.: (66) 28353933
Web Site: http://www.sonicautomation.co.th
Industrial Automation Product Distr

N.A.I.C.S.: 423830
Eakgawee Singprasert (Asst Mgr-Sls)

Soninfo (1)
Perovskaya Oul 1, 111524, Moscow, Russia
Tel.: (7) 4957304017
Web Site: http://www.soninfo.ru
Sales Range: $25-49.9 Million
Emp.: 20
Electrical Material Distribution
N.A.I.C.S.: 423610

Spot (1)
14 rue Fernand Forest, PO Box 27864, 98863, Noumea, New Caledonia
Tel.: (687) 270800
Electrical Equipment Distr
N.A.I.C.S.: 423610

Supermoon Holdings Ltd. (1)
11/F Yan Hing Centre 9-13 Wong Chuk Yeung Street, Fo Tan New Territories, Hong Kong, China (Hong Kong)
Tel.: (852) 26919166
Web Site: http://www.supermoon.hk
Electrical Equipment Distr
N.A.I.C.S.: 423610

UAB SLO Lithuania (1)
Vilkpedes str 4, 3151, Vilnius, Lithuania
Tel.: (370) 5 215 00 70
Web Site: http://www.slo.lt
Emp.: 30
Electrical Equipment Distr
N.A.I.C.S.: 423610
Alfredas Babkovskis (Gen Mgr)

UBEL BV (1)
Welbergweg 70 Westermaat Zuidoost, 7556 PE, Hengelo, Netherlands
Tel.: (31) 742435334
Web Site: http://www.ubel.nl
Electrical Equipment Distr
N.A.I.C.S.: 423610

VDS (1)
9 R Fulgence Bienvenue, 92230, Gennevilliers, France
Tel.: (33) 1 46 13 02 02
Web Site: http://www.vds.sonepar.fr
Electrical Equipment Distr
N.A.I.C.S.: 423610

Vallen, Inc. (1)
4810-92 Avenue, Edmonton, T6B 2X4, AB, Canada
Tel.: (780) 468-3366
Web Site: http://www.vallen.ca
Industrial Equipment Distr
N.A.I.C.S.: 423840
Tom Taylor (Dir-Major Projects)

WARREN INC.
Paseo de Los Aviadores 6 Ensanche Miaraflores, Santo Domingo, Dominican Republic
Tel.: (809) 5676086
Web Site: http://www.warrendelcaribe.com
Electrical Equipment Distr
N.A.I.C.S.: 423610

Warren Panama S.A (1)
Via Tocumen Parque Industrial Las Olas Ofic 5-8 A, Paitilla, Panama
Tel.: (507) 2200201
Web Site: http://www.warren-pa.com
Electrical Equipment Distr
N.A.I.C.S.: 423610
Juan Riera (Mgr-Panama)

SONERI BANK LIMITED

2nd Floor 307 Upper Mall Scheme, Lahore, 54000, Pakistan
Tel.: (92) 4235713101
Web Site: http://www.soneribank.com
Year Founded: 1991
SNBL—(PSX)
Rev.: $103,769,050
Assets: $2,338,953,774
Liabilities: $2,237,330,987
Net Worth: $101,622,787
Earnings: $21,577,660
Emp.: 4,170
Fiscal Year-end: 12/31/23
Banking Services
N.A.I.C.S.: 522110
Muhammad Altaf Butt (Sec)

Subsidiaries:

Deposit Protection Corporation (1)

Evelyn House 26 Fife Ave/Cnr Blakiston, Harare, Zimbabwe
Tel.: (263) 24 225 2336
Web Site: https://www.dpcorp.co.zw
Deposit Protection Services
N.A.I.C.S.: 524128
Vusi Vuma (CEO)

SONETEL AB

PO Box 647, 114 11, Stockholm, Sweden
Tel.: (46) 852506000
Web Site: https://www.sonetel.com
Year Founded: 1994
SONE—(OMX)
Rev.: $2,188,879
Assets: $3,770,828
Liabilities: $1,716,823
Net Worth: $2,054,005
Earnings: ($72,120)
Emp.: 33
Fiscal Year-end: 06/30/23
Telecommunication Servicesb
N.A.I.C.S.: 517112
Henrik Thome (Founder & CEO)

SONG BA JOINT STOCK COMPANY

573 Nui Thanh Street Hoa Cuong Nam Ward, Hai Chau District, Da Nang, Vietnam
Web Site: http://www.songba.vn
SBA—(HOSE)
Rev.: $15,490,992
Assets: $50,801,912
Liabilities: $9,318,289
Net Worth: $41,483,622
Earnings: $7,223,621
Fiscal Year-end: 12/31/23
Investment Management Service
N.A.I.C.S.: 523999
Dinh Chau Hieu Thien (CEO)

SONG DA - THANH HOA JSC

25 Le Loi Avenue-Lam Son Ward, Thanh Hoa, Vietnam
Tel.: (84) 373852230
Web Site: https://www.thanhhoasongda.com
Year Founded: 2004
THS—(HNX)
Rev.: $22,678,100
Assets: $7,573,500
Liabilities: $3,534,800
Net Worth: $4,038,700
Earnings: $236,600
Emp.: 143
Fiscal Year-end: 12/31/23
Household Product Whslr
N.A.I.C.S.: 423210
Le Van Tuong (Member-Mgmt Bd & Deputy Gen Dir)

SONG DA 1.01 JSC

4th Floor CT1 Building Van Khe La Khe, Ha Dong, Hanoi, Vietnam
Tel.: (84) 437339959
Web Site: https://www.songda101.com.vn
SJC—(HNX)
Rev.: $61,297
Assets: $64,704,644
Liabilities: $60,732,660
Net Worth: $3,971,984
Earnings: ($9,271)
Fiscal Year-end: 12/31/21
Hydro Power Plant Construction Services
N.A.I.C.S.: 237990
Ta van Trung (Chm-Mgmt Bd)

SONG DA 10 JOINT STOCK COMPANY

10th and 11th Floor Song Da Building Pham Hung Street My Dinh 1 Ward, Nam Tu Liem District, Hanoi, Vietnam
Tel.: (84) 437683998

INTERNATIONAL PUBLIC

Web Site: https://www.songda10.com.vn
Year Founded: 1963
SDT—(HNX)
Rev.: $43,013,365
Assets: $110,218,853
Liabilities: $76,580,477
Net Worth: $33,638,377
Earnings: ($570,618)
Emp.: 2,739
Fiscal Year-end: 12/31/21
Industrial Works, Civil Works & Buildings Construction Services
N.A.I.C.S.: 236210

SONG DA 11 THANG LONG COMPANY LIMITED

BT03 24 Xa La Urban Phuc La Ward, Ha Dong District, Hanoi, Vietnam
Tel.: (84) 422463212
Emp.: 500
Construction & Engineering Services
N.A.I.C.S.: 237990
Vu Thanh Un (Deputy Gen Mgr)

SONG DA 12 JSC

8th floor Tower B Song Da Building Pham Hung street, My Dinh ward Nam Tu Liem district, Hanoi, Vietnam
Tel.: (84) 435573681
S12—(HNX)
Rev.: $76,302
Assets: $4,711,014
Liabilities: $11,598,418
Net Worth: ($6,887,404)
Earnings: ($142,634)
Emp.: 15
Fiscal Year-end: 12/31/23
Building Construction Services
N.A.I.C.S.: 236210

SONG DA 5 JOINT STOCK COMPANY

5th Floor Tower B HH4 Building Song Da My Dinh Urban Zone, My Dinh 1 ward Nam Tu Liem district, Hanoi, Vietnam
Tel.: (84) 2422255586
Web Site: https://songda5.com.vn
Year Founded: 1990
SD5—(HNX)
Rev.: $226,214,600
Assets: $149,514,800
Liabilities: $101,731,000
Net Worth: $47,783,800
Earnings: $2,105,200
Emp.: 1,228
Fiscal Year-end: 12/31/23
Civil & Industrial Construction Services
N.A.I.C.S.: 237990
Nguyen Manh Toan (Member-Mgmt Bd & Deputy Gen Dir)

Subsidiaries:

Song Da 505 Joint Stock Company (1)
Tower CTB - Sun Square Building - 21 Le Duc Tho Street, Nam Tu Liem, Hanoi, Vietnam
Tel.: (84) 462659505
Web Site: https://www.songda505.com.vn
Rev.: $62,720,100
Assets: $223,209,800
Liabilities: $139,277,800
Net Worth: $83,932,000
Earnings: $5,843,900
Fiscal Year-end: 12/31/2023
Industrial Building Construction Services
N.A.I.C.S.: 236210

SONG DA 9 JOINT STOCK COMPANY

Song Da 9 Building - Nguyen Hoang Street My Dinh 2 Ward, Nam Tu Liem District, Hanoi, Vietnam
Tel.: (84) 437683746
Web Site: https://songda9.com

AND PRIVATE COMPANIES

SD9—(HNX)
Rev.: $57,415,700
Assets: $210,875,800
Liabilities: $127,267,100
Net Worth: $83,608,700
Earnings: $1,582,900
Emp.: 1,388
Fiscal Year-end: 12/31/22
Civil Construction Services
N.A.I.C.S.: 237990
Tran The Quang *(Dir Gen)*

Subsidiaries:

ARTEX SECURITIES
CORPORATION (1)
33B Pham Ngu Lao, Hoan Kiem, Hanoi, Vietnam
Tel.: (84) 4 62959059
Web Site: http://www.artex.com.vn
Securities Brokerage Services
N.A.I.C.S.: 523150
Nguyen Van Binh *(Chm)*

NAM MU HYDROELECTRICITY
JSC (1)
Tan Thanh village, Ha Giang, Ha Giang, Vietnam
Tel.: (84) 19 3827 276
Web Site:
http://www.thuydiennammu.com.vn
Hydroelectric Power Generation Services
N.A.I.C.S.: 221111

Nam Mu Hydropower JSC (1)
Tan Thanh commune, Bac Quang district, Ha Giang, Vietnam
Tel.: (84) 219827276
Web Site:
https://www.thuydiennammu.com.vn
Rev.: $15,862,500
Assets: $36,384,000
Liabilities: $3,859,700
Net Worth: $32,524,300
Earnings: $5,374,100
Fiscal Year-end: 12/31/2023
Eletric Power Generation Services
N.A.I.C.S.: 221111
Tran Du *(Chief Acctg Officer)*

SONG DA N 9 MACHINERY AND
REPAIRING Co. Ltd (1)
Phu Nghia village, Chuong My district, Hanoi, Vietnam
Tel.: (84) 4 3868 234
Building Machinery Repair & Maintenance Services
N.A.I.C.S.: 811310

SONG DA-HOANG LIEN JSC (1)
No 63 Muong Hoa Road Sapa, Sa Pa, Lao Cai, Vietnam
Tel.: (84) 20 3871 727
Civil Construction Services
N.A.I.C.S.: 237990
Nguyen Thanh Kim *(Dir-Gen)*

SONG DA 9.06 JOINT STOCK COMPANY
Floor 1 CT5 Building My Dinh Urban Me Tri, Tu Liem, Hanoi, Vietnam
Tel.: (84) 4 3 75 57 141
Web Site:
http://www.songda906.com.vn
Building Materials & Concrete Structures Mfr
N.A.I.C.S.: 238120
Ngoc Anh Dinh *(Gen Dir)*

SONG DA ASSEMBLY CONSTRUCTION & INVESTMENT JSC
Lot 60 and 61 Zone 4B Van Phu Urban Phu La Ward, Ha Dong, Hanoi, Vietnam
Tel.: (84) 4 22112918
Web Site:
http://www.songdaic.com.vn
Rev.: $1,550,525
Assets: $17,513,635
Liabilities: $11,320,667
Net Worth: $6,192,968
Earnings: ($249,711)
Fiscal Year-end: 12/31/17
Civil Engineering Construction Services
N.A.I.C.S.: 237990

SONG DA CAO CUONG JSC
Km 28 100m Highway 18 Pha Lai Ward, Chi Linh town, Hai Duong, Vietnam
Tel.: (84) 2203580414
Web Site: https://songdacaocuong.vn
Year Founded: 2007
SCL—(HNX)
Rev.: $33,873,500
Assets: $34,126,800
Liabilities: $13,237,900
Net Worth: $20,888,900
Earnings: $1,596,800
Emp.: 1,635
Fiscal Year-end: 12/31/22
Construction Material Mfr & Whslr
N.A.I.C.S.: 327120

SONG DA CONSULTING JOINT - STOCK COMPANY
495 Nguyen Trai Thanh Xuan Nam, Thanh Xuan, Hanoi, Vietnam
Tel.: (84) 38542209
Web Site: https://www.sdcc.com.vn
SDC—(HNX)
Rev.: $5,254,700
Assets: $9,023,900
Liabilities: $3,737,800
Net Worth: $5,286,100
Earnings: $182,000
Emp.: 500
Fiscal Year-end: 12/31/23
Construction Services
N.A.I.C.S.: 237990
Manh Van Pham *(Chm-Mgmt Bd)*

SONG DA HOLDINGS
Pham Hung Street My Dinh, Thanh Xuan, Hanoi, Vietnam
Tel.: (84) 438541164
Web Site: http://www.songda.vn
Holding Company; Construction Services
N.A.I.C.S.: 551112
Hung Pham *(Vice Chm)*

Subsidiaries:

Song Da 207 Joint Stock
Company (1)
1st Floor, Song Da Building 162A Nguyen Tuan Rd, Thanh Xuan District, Hanoi, Vietnam
Tel.: (84) 435585985
Web Site: http://www.songda207.vn
Emp.: 200
Construction Services
N.A.I.C.S.: 236220

Song Da Mechanical-Assembling
Joint Stock Co. (1)
Lot A38 Dong Dua service area Ha Cau ward, My Dinh Nam Tu Liem District, Hanoi, Vietnam
Tel.: (84) 437832398
Web Site: https://www.someco.com.vn
Rev.: $6,110,200
Assets: $54,472,900
Liabilities: $63,340,600
Net Worth: ($8,867,700)
Earnings: $2,088,300)
Fiscal Year-end: 12/31/2023
Building Construction Services
N.A.I.C.S.: 236220

Song Da No 6 Joint Stock
Company (1)
Commercial House Van Khe Urban Area La Khe Ward, Ha Dong District, Hanoi, Vietnam
Tel.: (84) 2422253666
Web Site: https://songda6.com.vn
Rev.: $19,406,000
Assets: $128,549,500
Liabilities: $85,261,900
Net Worth: $43,287,600
Earnings: $7,800
Fiscal Year-end: 12/31/2022

Hydroelectric Plant Construction Services
N.A.I.C.S.: 221111
Ho Sy Hung *(Member-Mgmt Bd)*

SONG DA INDUSTRY TRADE JOINT STOCK COMPANY
41 Quyet Thang Street Yen Nghia Ward, Ha Dong District, Hanoi, Vietnam
Tel.: (84) 2433521290
Web Site: https://www.stp.com
Year Founded: 1996
STP—(HNX)
Rev.: $25,705,600
Assets: $18,759,700
Liabilities: $4,780,000
Net Worth: $13,979,700
Earnings: $450,000
Emp.: 350
Fiscal Year-end: 12/31/22
Hydroelectric Construction Services
N.A.I.C.S.: 221111

SONG DA NO. 11 JSC
7th floor Song Da - Ha Dong mixed-use building 131 Tran Phu street, Van Quan ward Ha Dong district, Hanoi, Vietnam
Tel.: (84) 2433544735
Web Site: https://songda11.vn
Year Founded: 1961
SJE—(HNX)
Rev.: $69,615,200
Assets: $191,789,700
Liabilities: $116,660,000
Net Worth: $75,129,700
Earnings: $7,670,100
Emp.: 1,200
Fiscal Year-end: 12/31/23
Civil Engineering Construction Services
N.A.I.C.S.: 237990

SONG DA TRANSPORTATION CONSTRUCTION JSC
8D Zone Song Da - Ha Dong Building Km 10 Nguyen Trai Street, Van Quan Ha Dong, Hanoi, Vietnam
Tel.: (84) 4 63280815
Web Site:
http://www.songdatc.com.vn
Sales Range: $1-9.9 Million
Stone Product Mfr
N.A.I.C.S.: 327991
Vu Khac Tiep *(Chm)*

SONG DA URBAN & INDUSTRIAL ZONE INVESTMENT & DEVELOPMENT JOINT STOCK COMPANY
Land lot TT2 Nam An Khanh new urban area An Khanh commune, Hoai Duc district, Hanoi, Vietnam
Tel.: (84) 437685592
Web Site:
https://www.sudicosd.com.vn
SJS—(HOSE)
Rev.: $17,140,189
Assets: $307,927,935
Liabilities: $194,150,550
Net Worth: $113,777,384
Earnings: $7,571,159
Emp.: 305
Fiscal Year-end: 12/31/23
Real Estate Development Services
N.A.I.C.S.: 531390

SONG DA-THANG LONG JOINT STOCK COMPANY
Van Khe New Urban Area - Ward La Khe, Ha Dong, Hanoi, Vietnam
Tel.: (84) 4 3355 4646
Web Site:
http://www.songdathanglong.com.vn
Year Founded: 2006
Real Estate & Construction Services

N.A.I.C.S.: 531390
Tri Dung Nguyen *(Gen Dir)*

SONG HO INDUSTRIAL CO., LTD.
No 61 Nan-Kong 3rd Road, Hsien, Nant'ou, Taiwan
Tel.: (886) 492252746
Web Site: https://www.songho.com
Year Founded: 1972
5016—(TPE)
Rev.: $78,981,209
Assets: $87,998,968
Liabilities: $41,816,997
Net Worth: $46,181,972
Earnings: $3,142,576
Emp.: 300
Fiscal Year-end: 12/31/22
Steel Wire Products Mfr
N.A.I.C.S.: 331222
Ting-Fang Lin *(Chm)*

SONG HONG CONSTRUCTION JOINT STOCK COMPANY
164 Lo Duc, Hai Ba Trung, Hanoi, Vietnam
Tel.: (84) 439727296
Web Site: https://incomex.com.vn
ICG—(HNX)
Rev.: $171,992
Assets: $12,004,193
Liabilities: $638,665
Net Worth: $11,365,528
Earnings: $53,532
Fiscal Year-end: 12/31/21
Construction Engineering Services
N.A.I.C.S.: 237990
Hung Pham *(Chm-Mgmt Bd & Gen Dir)*

SONG SHANG ELECTRONICS CO., LTD.
4F No 117 Zhongcheng Rd, Tucheng Dist, New Taipei City, 23674, Taiwan
Tel.: (886) 222686867
Web Site: https://www.song-shang.com.tw
Year Founded: 1988
6156—(TPE)
Rev.: $130,962,793
Assets: $134,120,752
Liabilities: $75,164,556
Net Worth: $58,956,195
Earnings: $7,143,013
Fiscal Year-end: 12/31/22
Electronic Component Mfr & Distr
N.A.I.C.S.: 334419
Ren-Jhih Bao *(Chm)*

Subsidiaries:

Zhong Tai Electronics (Hubei) Co.,
Ltd. (1)
No 19 Industrial Park Road, Rongcheng Town Jianli County, Jingzhou, Hubei, China
Tel.: (86) 7163083800
Power Supply Wire Mfr
N.A.I.C.S.: 335999

SONGCHENG PERFORMANCE DEVELOPMENT CO., LTD.
No 148 Zhijiang Road, Hangzhou, 310008, Zhejiang, China
Tel.: (86) 57187091255
Web Site: http://www.songcn.com
Year Founded: 1994
300144—(CHIN)
Rev.: $271,321,778
Assets: $1,276,859,083
Liabilities: $215,279,689
Net Worth: $1,061,579,393
Earnings: $15,481,105)
Fiscal Year-end: 12/31/23
Theme Park & Cultural Show Operator
N.A.I.C.S.: 713110
Qiaoling Huang *(Chm)*

SONGDA 7 JSC

Songcheng Performance Development Co., Ltd.—(Continued)

SONGDA 7 JSC
Sub-area 5 Au Ong Town, Muong/La District, Hanoi, Son La, Vietnam
Tel.: (84) 2466680228
Web Site:
 https://www.songda7.com.vn
SD7—(HNX)
Rev.: $265,000
Assets: $21,131,300
Liabilities: $7,536,200
Net Worth: $13,595,100
Earnings: $1,518,200
Fiscal Year-end: 12/31/22
Civil Engineering Construction Services
N.A.I.C.S.: 237990
Nguyen Huu Doanh *(Chm)*

SONGWON INDUSTRIAL CO., LTD.
83 Jangsaengpo-ro, Nam-Gu, 44781, Ulsan, 44781, Korea (South)
Tel.: (82) 522739841
Web Site: https://www.songwon.com
Year Founded: 1965
004430—(KRS)
Rev.: $1,019,733,403
Assets: $933,677,537
Liabilities: $410,106,463
Net Worth: $523,571,074
Earnings: $101,191,844
Emp.: 629
Fiscal Year-end: 12/31/22
Basic Chemical Mfr & Distr
N.A.I.C.S.: 325998
Jongho Park *(Chm, Chm & CEO)*

Subsidiaries:

Songwon International - India Pvt. Ltd. (1)
701 - Purva Plaza Shimpoli Road, Borivali West, Mumbai, 400 092, India
Tel.: (91) 22 28997419
Chemical Products Distr
N.A.I.C.S.: 424690

Songwon International - Japan K.K. (1)
1-5-8 Nishi Shinbashi, Minato-Ku, Tokyo, 105-0003, Japan
Tel.: (81) 362688721
Chemical Products Distr
N.A.I.C.S.: 424690

Songwon International AG (1)
Walzmuhlestrasse 48, 8500, Frauenfeld, Switzerland
Tel.: (41) 526350000
Emp.: 40
Chemical Products Distr
N.A.I.C.S.: 424690

Subsidiary (US):

Songwon International Americas, Inc. (2)
1311 W Parkwood Ave, Friendswood, TX 77456
Tel.: (281) 648-1585
Chemical Products Distr
N.A.I.C.S.: 424690

Subsidiary (Non-US):

Songwon Specialty Chemicals India Pvt. Ltd. (2)
GIDC Industrial Estate Panoli Plot No 26 - 28-B, Bharuch, Ankleshwar, 394 116, Gujarat, India
Tel.: (91) 8980047411
Web Site: http://www.songwon.com
Chemical Products Mfr
N.A.I.C.S.: 325998

Songwon Trading Co. Ltd. (1)
3rd Floor Unit 2 159 Tianzhou Road, Shanghai, 200233, China
Tel.: (86) 2154452218
Chemical Products Distr
N.A.I.C.S.: 424690

SONGZHI KALLANG AUTOMOTIVE AIR CONDITIONING CO., LTD.
No 4999 Huaning Road, Shanghai, 201108, China
Tel.: (86) 2154428913
Web Site: https://songzac.com
Year Founded: 1998
002454—(SSE)
Rev.: $593,191,825
Assets: $989,324,556
Liabilities: $401,185,769
Net Worth: $588,138,787
Earnings: $13,168,762
Emp.: 2,000
Fiscal Year-end: 12/31/22
Automotive Air Conditioner Mfr
N.A.I.C.S.: 336390
Chen Huanxiong *(Chm)*

Subsidiaries:

Beijin Songz Automobile Air Conditioning Co., Ltd. (1)
No 1 Middle Xiuzhong Road Yongfeng Base, Haidian District, Beijing, 100094, China
Tel.: (86) 1058711969
Motor Vehicle Parts Mfr
N.A.I.C.S.: 336390

Jianghuai (Anhui) Songz Automobile Air Conditioning Co., Ltd. (1)
No 62 Shixin Road, Jianghuai Industry Area Economic Development Zone, Hefei, 230601, Anhui, China
Tel.: (86) 5517116275
Motor Vehicle Parts Mfr
N.A.I.C.S.: 336390

Xiamen Songz Automobile Air Conditioning Co., Ltd. (1)
No 17-29 Lianshang Road Guannan Industrial Zone, Jimei District, Xiamen, 361023, Fujian, China
Tel.: (86) 5927559261
Motor Vehicle Parts Mfr
N.A.I.C.S.: 336390

SONI MEDICARE LIMITED
38 Kanota Bagh Jawaharlal Nehru Marg, Jaipur, 302 004, India
Tel.: (91) 1415163700
Web Site:
 https://www.sonihospitals.com
Year Founded: 1988
539378—(BOM)
Rev.: $3,416,574
Assets: $2,408,796
Liabilities: $2,492,996
Net Worth: ($84,201)
Earnings: ($80,721)
Fiscal Year-end: 03/31/23
Health Care Srvices
N.A.I.C.S.: 622110
Bimal Roy Soni *(Chm & Mng Dir)*

SONI SOYA PRODUCTS LTD.
CS-1 P Square Building 350 Goyal Nagar, Indore, 452016, Madhya Pradesh, India
Tel.: (91) 7314288552
Web Site: http://www.sonisoya.com
Year Founded: 1997
SONISOYA—(NSE)
Rev.: $24,547,098
Assets: $8,106,893
Liabilities: $7,651,085
Net Worth: $455,808
Earnings: $27,165
Emp.: 20
Fiscal Year-end: 03/31/20
Crop Farming Services
N.A.I.C.S.: 111998
Dilip Kumar Soni *(Mng Dir)*

Subsidiaries:

Soni Soya Products LLC (1)
1629 W 35th St, Gardena, CA 90249
Tel.: (963) 008-9998

Agriculture Product Farming Services
N.A.I.C.S.: 111998

SONIC HEALTHCARE LIMITED
Level 22 225 George Street, Sydney, 2000, NSW, Australia
Tel.: (61) 298555444
Web Site:
 https://www.sonichealthcare.com
Year Founded: 1987
SHL—(OTCIQ)
Rev.: $5,326,301,102
Assets: $8,485,772,315
Liabilities: $3,320,575,732
Net Worth: $5,165,196,583
Earnings: $461,583,752
Emp.: 40,500
Fiscal Year-end: 06/30/23
Medical Laboratories Services
N.A.I.C.S.: 621512
Christopher D. Wilks *(CFO & Dir-Fin)*

Subsidiaries:

ALTEHA ESV (1)
Route de Lennik 808, 1070, Brussels, Belgium
Tel.: (32) 25554007
Web Site: http://www.althea.com
Laboratory Testing Services
N.A.I.C.S.: 621512
Luc Jacob *(Mgr)*

Auburn Road Family Medical Centre Pty Limited (1)
22 24/1 Civic Road, Auburn, 2144, NSW, Australia
Tel.: (61) 297492444
Sales Range: $10-24.9 Million
Emp.: 7
Medical Diagnostic Services
N.A.I.C.S.: 621512

Aurigen SA (1)
Avenue de Sevelin 18, 1004, Lausanne, Switzerland
Tel.: (41) 21 623 4400
Web Site: https://www.aurigen.ch
Medical Laboratories Services
N.A.I.C.S.: 621511

Aurora Diagnostics, LLC (1)
11025 RCA Ctr Dr Ste 300, Palm Beach Gardens, FL 33410
Tel.: (561) 626-5512
Web Site: https://www.auroradx.com
Diagnostic Imaging Services
N.A.I.C.S.: 621512
James C. New *(Founder & Chm)*

Aurora Research Institute, LLC (1)
750 W Virginia St, Milwaukee, WI 53204
Tel.: (414) 979-4590
Web Site: https://www.aurorahealthcare.org
Research Services
N.A.I.C.S.: 541715

BPath Pty Limited (1)
205 Spencer St, Bunbury, 6231, WA, Australia
Tel.: (61) 897800300
Pathology & Diagnostic Imaging Services
N.A.I.C.S.: 621511

Bioanalytica AG (1)
Maihofstrasse 95a, 6006, Lucerne, Switzerland
Tel.: (41) 41 429 3131
Web Site: https://www.bioanalytica.ch
Medical & Diagnostic Laboratory Services
N.A.I.C.S.: 621511

Bioexam AG (1)
Maihofstrasse 95a, PO Box 6858, 6000, Lucerne, Switzerland
Tel.: (41) 41 429 3133
Web Site: https://www.bioexam.ch
Medical & Diagnostic Laboratory Services
N.A.I.C.S.: 621511

Bioscientia Healthcare GmbH (1)
Konrad-Adenauer-Strasse 17, 55218, Ingelheim, Germany
Tel.: (49) 6 132 7810
Web Site: http://www.bioscientia.de
Medical Diagnostic Services
N.A.I.C.S.: 621512
Johannes Brill *(Co-Mng Dir)*

INTERNATIONAL PUBLIC

Bioscientia Institut fur Medizinische Diagnostik GmbH Labor Jena (1)
Orlaweg 2, 07743, Jena, Germany
Tel.: (49) 36 414 0130
Web Site: http://www.bioscientia.de
Medical Diagnostic Services
N.A.I.C.S.: 621512
Jeanette Kruger *(Mgr-Laboratory)*

Bioscientia Institut fur medizinische Diagnostik GmbH (1)
Konrad Adenauer Str 17, 55218, Ingelheim, Germany
Tel.: (49) 6132781240
Web Site: http://www.bioscientia.com
Sales Range: $100-124.9 Million
Emp.: 700
Medical Diagnostic Services
N.A.I.C.S.: 621512

Bioscientia MVZ Saarbrucken GmbH (1)
Winterberg 1, 66119, Saarbrucken, Germany
Tel.: (49) 6818 837 9133
Web Site: http://www.bioscientia.de
Sales Range: $25-49.9 Million
Emp.: 40
Laboratory Testing Services
N.A.I.C.S.: 541380

Biotech Laboratories Pty Limited (1)
Lobby 2 Newdegate Street, Greenslopes, Brisbane, 4012, QLD, Australia
Tel.: (61) 738479488
Web Site: http://www.biotechlab.com.au
Emp.: 25
Microbiological Testing Services
N.A.I.C.S.: 541380
Glen Pinna *(Gen Mgr)*

Biovis Diagnostik MVZ GmbH (1)
Justus-Staudt-Str 2, Offheim, 65555, Limburg, Germany
Tel.: (49) 643 121 2480
Web Site: https://www.biovis.eu
Health Care Srvices
N.A.I.C.S.: 622110

Canterbury Medical Imaging Limited (1)
32 Oxford Terrace, Christchurch, 8011, Canterbury, New Zealand
Tel.: (64) 33644106
Web Site: http://www.cdhb.health.nz
Sales Range: $10-24.9 Million
Emp.: 20
Diagnostic Imaging Services
N.A.I.C.S.: 621512

Capital Pathology Pty Limited (1)
Equinox 4 Ground Floor 70 Kent St, Deakin, Canberra, 2600, ACT, Australia
Tel.: (61) 26 285 9800
Web Site: https://www.capitalpath.com.au
Medical & Diagnostic Laboratory Services
N.A.I.C.S.: 621512
Jason Gluch *(CEO)*

Clinilabo B.V.B.A. (1)
Henri Jasparlaan 101, 1060, Brussels, Belgium
Tel.: (32) 24253515
Web Site: http://www.clinilabo.be
Sales Range: $10-24.9 Million
Emp.: 30
Laboratory Testing Services
N.A.I.C.S.: 621511
Alain Derom *(Mgr-IT)*

Clinipath Pathology Pty Limited (1)
310 Selby St North, Osborne Park, 6017, WA, Australia
Tel.: (61) 89 371 4200
Web Site:
 https://www.clinipathpathology.com.au
Medical Equipment Distr
N.A.I.C.S.: 423450
Narelle Hadlow *(CEO)*

Clinpath Laboratories Pty Limited (1)
21 James Congdon Drive, Mile End, 5031, SA, Australia
Tel.: (61) 883662000
Web Site: https://www.clinpath.com.au
Sales Range: $50-74.9 Million
Emp.: 370
Laboratory Services
N.A.I.C.S.: 621511
Gideon Sinclair *(COO)*

DNA Labs (1)
14 Giffnock Avenue, Macquarie Park, 2113, NSW, Australia
Tel.: (61) 1300663244
DNA Testing Services
N.A.I.C.S.: 621511
Karl Baumgart *(Dir-Medical & Molecular Genetics)*

Diagnostic Medlab (1)
10 Harrison Road, Ellerslie, 1060, Auckland, New Zealand
Tel.: (64) 9 571 4001
Web Site: http://www.dml.co.nz
Emp.: 80
Pathology Laboratory Services
N.A.I.C.S.: 621511
Mee Ling Yeong *(Dir-Clinical-Cytopathology & Histopathology)*

Dianalabs SA (1)
Rue de la Colline 6, 1205, Geneva, Switzerland
Tel.: (41) 22 807 1468
Web Site: https://www.dianalabs.ch
Medical Laboratories Services
N.A.I.C.S.: 621511

DoctorDoctor Pty Limited (1)
Suite 2 Level 41 600 Bourke Street, Melbourne, 3000, VIC, Australia
Tel.: (61) 38 341 1200
Web Site: https://www.doctordoctor.com.au
Medical Devices
N.A.I.C.S.: 622110
Nic Richardson *(Gen Mgr)*

Douglass Hanly Moir Pathology Pty Limited (1)
14 Giffnock Avenue, Macquarie Park, 2113, NSW, Australia
Tel.: (61) 298555222
Web Site: https://www.dhm.com.au
Sales Range: $100-124.9 Million
Emp.: 1,000
Pathology Services
N.A.I.C.S.: 621511
Colin Goldschmidt *(CEO)*

Dr. Von Froreich - Bioscientia GmbH (1)
Grossmoorbogen 25, 21079, Hamburg, Germany
Tel.: (49) 40766960
Web Site: http://froreich-bioscientia.de
Sales Range: $25-49.9 Million
Emp.: 200
Medical Diagnostic Services
N.A.I.C.S.: 621511

Epworth Medical Imaging Pty Limited (1)
Level 2 89 Bridge Road, Richmond, 3121, VIC, Australia
Tel.: (61) 39 516 2244
Web Site: https://www.epworthmedicalimaging.com.au
Medical & Diagnostic Laboratory Services
N.A.I.C.S.: 621511
Pramit Phal *(CEO)*

GLP Medical GmbH (1)
Grossmoorring 4, 21079, Hamburg, Germany
Tel.: (49) 4033319333
Web Site: http://www.glp-shop.de
Sales Range: $25-49.9 Million
Emp.: 30
Medical Equipment Whslr
N.A.I.C.S.: 423450
Tammo V. Schrenck *(Mng Dir)*

HSL Pathology LLP (1)
1 Mabledon Place, London, WC1H 9AX, United Kingdom
Tel.: (44) 207 307 9400
Web Site: https://www.hslpathology.com
Medical Laboratories Services
N.A.I.C.S.: 621511
Annelize Matthee *(Head-Finance)*

Hanly Moir Pathology Pty Limited (1)
14 Giffnock Avenue, Macquarie Park, 2113, NSW, Australia
Tel.: (61) 29 855 5100
Web Site: https://www.dhm.com.au
Medical & Diagnostic Laboratory Services
N.A.I.C.S.: 621511
Andrew Cullen *(Chief Laboratory Officer)*

Hunter Imaging Group Pty Limited (1)
Newcastle Private Hospital 14 Lookout Road, PO Box 192, Ground Floor Kingston Building New Lambton Heights, Newcastle, 2305, NSW, Australia
Tel.: (61) 132336
Web Site: http://www.hunterimaging.com.au
Diagnostic Imaging Services
N.A.I.C.S.: 621512
Todd Forbes *(COO)*

IPN Learning Pty Limited (1)
Level 32 60 Margaret Street, Sydney, 2000, NSW, Australia
Tel.: (61) 282888932
Healthcare Training Services
N.A.I.C.S.: 611430

IPN Medical Centres (Qld) Pty Limited (1)
Level 1 147 George Street, Kedron, Beenleigh, 4207, QLD, Australia
Tel.: (61) 734511230
Web Site: http://www.ipn.com.au
Emp.: 20
Hospital Management Services
N.A.I.C.S.: 622110
Tenille Bell *(Mgr)*

IPN Services Pty Limited (1)
Level 21 225 George Street, Sydney, 2000, NSW, Australia
Tel.: (61) 282888988
Web Site: https://www.ipn.com.au
Sales Range: $25-49.9 Million
Emp.: 100
Web Hosting Services
N.A.I.C.S.: 518210
Ged Foley *(CEO)*

Illawarra X-Ray Pty Limited (1)
Suite 1 21-23 Denison Street, Wollongong, 2500, NSW, Australia
Tel.: (61) 242546900
Web Site: http://www.irg.com.au
Sales Range: $25-49.9 Million
Emp.: 20
Laboratory Testing Services
N.A.I.C.S.: 541380

Imagerie du Flon S.A. (1)
Rue de La Vigie 5, 1003, Lausanne, Switzerland
Tel.: (41) 213514242
Web Site: https://imagerieduflon.ch
Diagnostic Laboratory Services
N.A.I.C.S.: 621511

Independent Practitioner Network Limited (1)
Level 21 225 George Street, Sydney, 2000, NSW, Australia
Tel.: (61) 28 288 8988
Web Site: https://www.ipn.com.au
Sales Range: $10-24.9 Million
Emp.: 60
General Practice Management Services
N.A.I.C.S.: 621491
Connie Zollo *(Office Mgr)*

Klinisch Labo Rigo BV B.V.B.A. (1)
Bosdel 89, 3600, Genk, Limburg, Belgium
Tel.: (32) 89351500
Web Site: http://www.laborigo.be
Sales Range: $10-24.9 Million
Emp.: 49
Biological Testing Services
N.A.I.C.S.: 621511
Debeut Patrick *(Gen Mgr)*

L & A Services Pty Limited (1)
68 High Street, Taringa, Brisbane, 4068, QLD, Australia
Tel.: (61) 733778569
Health Care Srvices
N.A.I.C.S.: 621491

LabConsult GmbH. (1)
Mulhauser Strasse 9, 79110, Freiburg, Baden-Wurttemberg, Germany
Tel.: (49) 761400060
Web Site: http://www.labconsult.de
Laboratory Management Services
N.A.I.C.S.: 621512

Labo-Lokeren B.V.B.A. (1)
Zelestraat 84, 9160, Lokeren, East Flanders, Belgium
Tel.: (32) 93423030
Web Site: http://www.labolokeren.be
Sales Range: $25-49.9 Million
Emp.: 30
Biological Testing Services
N.A.I.C.S.: 541380
Annie J. Vereecken *(Gen Mgr)*

Labor 28 AG (1)
Mecklenburgische Strasse 28, 14197, Berlin, Germany
Tel.: (49) 30820930
Web Site: https://web.labor28.de
Sales Range: $25-49.9 Million
Emp.: 200
Medical Diagnostic Services
N.A.I.C.S.: 621511
Peter Peters *(Gen Mgr)*

Labor 28 Management GmbH (1)
Mecklenburgische Strasse 28, 14197, Berlin, Germany
Tel.: (49) 3 082 0930
Web Site: https://www.labor28.de
Emp.: 300
Investment Management Service
N.A.I.C.S.: 523940

Labor Hamburg - Luebeck MVZ GmbH (1)
Borsteler Chaussee 43, 22453, Hamburg, Germany
Tel.: (49) 4051440250
Sales Range: $25-49.9 Million
Emp.: 40
Laboratory Testing Services
N.A.I.C.S.: 541380
G. Schottdorf *(Head-Clinical Chemistry)*

Labor Hannover MVZ GmbH (1)
Nikolaistr 14-16, 30159, Hannover, Niedersachsen, Germany
Tel.: (49) 5118562570
Laboratory Testing Services
N.A.I.C.S.: 541380

Labor Lademannbogen MVZ GmbH (1)
Lademannbogen 61, 22339, Hamburg, Germany
Tel.: (49) 40538050
Sales Range: $25-49.9 Million
Emp.: 250
Medical Diagnostic Services
N.A.I.C.S.: 621512
Evangelos Kotsopoulos *(Co-Mng Dir)*

Labor Schottdorf Administration GmbH (1)
August-Wessels-Str 5, 86154, Augsburg, Germany
Tel.: (49) 82142010
Laboratory Testing Services
N.A.I.C.S.: 541380

Lifescreen Australia Pty Limited (1)
14 Giffnock Avenue, Macquarie Park, Macquarie Park, 2113, NSW, Australia
Tel.: (61) 180 067 3123
Web Site: https://www.lifescreen.com.au
Sales Range: $10-24.9 Million
Emp.: 20
Health Evaluation Services
N.A.I.C.S.: 621491
Christopher David Wilks *(Sec)*

MVZ Labor Bochum MLB GmbH (1)
Universitatsstr 140, 44799, Bochum, Germany
Tel.: (49) 234970670
Sales Range: $150-199.9 Million
Emp.: 1,000
Laboratory Testing Services
N.A.I.C.S.: 541380

MVZ Medizinisches Labor Celle GmbH (1)
Neumarkt 1, 29221, Celle, Germany
Tel.: (49) 51 419 2560
Web Site: https://www.ml-celle.de
Medical & Diagnostic Laboratory Services
N.A.I.C.S.: 621511

MVZ Pathologie Berlin Berger Fietze Linke Nadjari GmbH (1)
Scharnhorststrasse 13, 10115, Berlin, Germany
Tel.: (49) 308 200 7870
Web Site: https://www.mvz-pathologie-berlin.de
Medical & Diagnostic Laboratory Services
N.A.I.C.S.: 621511

MVZ fur Histologie, Zytologie und molekulare Diagnostik Trier GmbH (1)
Max-Planck-Str 5, 54296, Trier, Germany
Tel.: (49) 6519 925 8320
Web Site: https://www.patho-trier.de
Pathologist Services
N.A.I.C.S.: 621340

Maga Pty Limited (1)
Level 2 30 Ord St, West Perth, 6005, WA, Australia
Tel.: (61) 893201200
Web Site: http://www.skg.com.au
Laboratory Testing Services
N.A.I.C.S.: 541380

Med-Lab GmbH (1)
Helmholtzstrasse 1a, Stutensee, 76297, Karlsruhe, Germany
Tel.: (49) 7244741100
Web Site: https://www.medlab-gmbh.de
Pulse Oximeter Mfr
N.A.I.C.S.: 335999

Medica Arztebedarf AG (1)
Hottingerstrasse 5, 8024, Zurich, Switzerland
Tel.: (41) 43 411 1111
Web Site: https://medica-aerztebedarf.ch
Sales Range: $25-49.9 Million
Emp.: 205
Laboratory Testing Services
N.A.I.C.S.: 541380

Medica Medizinische Laboratorien Dr. F. Kappeli AG (1)
Wolfbachstrasse 17, 8024, Zurich, Switzerland
Tel.: (41) 442699999
Web Site: https://www.medica.ch
Health Screening Services
N.A.I.C.S.: 541380

Medisch labo Van Waes D. B.V. C.V.B.A. (1)
Legeweg 176, 8200, Brugge, West Flanders, Belgium
Tel.: (32) 50380440
Web Site: http://www.labovanwaes.be
Sales Range: $10-24.9 Million
Emp.: 22
Medical Laboratory Testing Services
N.A.I.C.S.: 621511
Dirk Van Wales *(Gen Mgr-Sls)*

Medisupport SA (1)
Alpenquai 28a, 6005, Lucerne, Switzerland
Tel.: (41) 41 417 1080
Web Site: https://www.medisupport.ch
Medical & Diagnostic Laboratory Services
N.A.I.C.S.: 621511
Willi Conrad *(VP)*

Medizinische Laboratorien Dr. Toggweiler AG (1)
Hertistrasse 1, 8304, Wallisellen, Switzerland
Tel.: (41) 44 877 3939
Web Site: https://www.labortoggweiler.ch
Health Care Srvices
N.A.I.C.S.: 622110

Medlab Central Limited (1)
Tel.: (64) 6 952 3180
Web Site: https://www.medlabcentral.co.nz
Sales Range: $50-74.9 Million
Emp.: 350
Laboratory Testing Services
N.A.I.C.S.: 621511
Cynric Temple-Camp *(CEO)*

Medlab Pathology Limited (1)
Unit 3 Sandyford Business Centre Sandyford Business Park, 18, Dublin, Ireland
Tel.: (353) 12933690
Web Site: https://www.sonichealthcare.ie
Sales Range: $10-24.9 Million
Emp.: 80
Medical Pathology Services
N.A.I.C.S.: 621511
Eamonn Madden *(Chm)*

Medlab South Limited (1)
137 Kilmore St, Christchurch, 8013, Canterbury, New Zealand
Tel.: (64) 95747399
Web Site: http://www.medlabsouth.co.nz

SONIC HEALTHCARE LIMITED

Sonic Healthcare Limited—(Continued)
Sales Range: $50-74.9 Million
Emp.: 300
Laboratory Testing Services
N.A.I.C.S.: 621511

Medvet BV (1)
Emiel Vloorsstraat 9, 2020, Antwerp, Belgium
Tel.: (32) 3 303 0800
Web Site: https://medvet.be
Veterinary Services
N.A.I.C.S.: 541940

Melbourne Pathology Pty Limited (1)
Tel.: (61) 39 287 7700
Web Site: https://www.mps.com.au
Pathology Services
N.A.I.C.S.: 621511
Barry Klibansky *(Head-Fin)*

Melbourne Pathology Services Pty Limited (1)
103 Victoria Parade, Collingwood, 3066, VIC, Australia
Tel.: (61) 39 287 7700
Web Site: https://www.mps.com.au
Medical & Diagnostic Laboratory Services
N.A.I.C.S.: 621511
David Pinkus *(CEO)*

New England Tissue Issue, PLLC (1)
1822 N Main St Ste 302, Fall River, MA 02720
Tel.: (508) 235-1118
Web Site: https://www.netissueissue.com
Laboratory Diagnostic Services
N.A.I.C.S.: 621511

New Zealand Radiology Group Limited (1)
15 Gilgit Road, Epsom, Auckland, 1003, New Zealand
Tel.: (64) 96303324
Web Site: http://www.radiology.co.nz
Sales Range: $25-49.9 Million
Emp.: 120
Radiology Services
N.A.I.C.S.: 621512

Orthopadietechnik Mayer & Behnsen GmbH (1)
Am Niederen Anger 11, 08297, Zwonitz, Germany
Tel.: (49) 37 754 5060
Web Site: https://www.mayer-behnsen.de
Emp.: 35
Orthopedic Footwear Mfr
N.A.I.C.S.: 316210

Penrith Medical Centre No. 2 Pty Limited (1)
61-79 Henry St penrose, Penrith, 2750, NSW, Australia
Tel.: (61) 247218755
General Medical Services
N.A.I.C.S.: 621498

Polyanalytic S.A. (1)
Avenue de Sevelin 18, 1004, Lausanne, Switzerland
Tel.: (41) 21 804 9202
Web Site: https://www.polyanalytic.ch
Medical Laboratories Services
N.A.I.C.S.: 621511

ProPath Services, LLC (1)
1355 River Bend Dr, Dallas, TX 75247
Tel.: (214) 638-2000
Web Site: https://www.propath.com
Anatomic Pathology Services
N.A.I.C.S.: 621511

Queensland X-Ray Pty Limited (1)
164 Grey Street, Queensland X-Ray Administration, Brisbane, 4101, QLD, Australia
Tel.: (61) 734228800
Web Site: https://www.qldxray.com.au
Sales Range: $100-124.9 Million
Emp.: 800
Diagnostic Imaging Services
N.A.I.C.S.: 621512
Kathy Lack *(Mgr-Fin)*

Radiology Victoria Pty Limited (1)
675 Boronia Road, Wantirna, 3152, VIC, Australia
Tel.: (61) 392978300
Web Site: https://www.radiologyvictoria.com.au
Health Care Srvices
N.A.I.C.S.: 621111

Redcliffe Peninsula Medical Services Pty Limited (1)
Anzac Avenue Corner Boardman Road, Redcliffe, 4021, QLD, Australia
Tel.: (61) 732848155
Web Site: http://www.itn.com.au
Health Care Services
N.A.I.C.S.: 621491
Shane Dann *(Mng Dir)*

SKG Radiology Pty Limited (1)
Level 3 1 Hood Street, Subiaco, 6008, WA, Australia
Tel.: (61) 89 320 1200
Web Site: https://www.skg.com.au
Emp.: 600
Radiological Laboratory Services
N.A.I.C.S.: 621511
Sonia DelDosso *(Mgr-Ops-Subaico)*

Seacoast Pathology, Inc. (1)
1 Hampton Rd Ste 307, Exeter, NH 03833
Tel.: (603) 778-8522
Web Site: https://www.seacoastpathology.com
Medical & Diagnostic Laboratory Services
N.A.I.C.S.: 621512

Sonic Clinical Services Pty Limited (1)
Level 21 225 George Street, Sydney, 2000, NSW, Australia
Tel.: (61) 28 288 8988
Web Site: https://www.scs.com.au
Health Care Srvices
N.A.I.C.S.: 622110
Gerard Foley *(CEO)*

Sonic Clinical Trials Pty Limited (1)
14 Giffnock Avenue, Macquarie Park, Macquarie Park, 2113, NSW, Australia
Tel.: (61) 29 855 6000
Web Site: https://www.sonicclinicaltrials.com.au
Medical Diagnostic Services
N.A.I.C.S.: 621512
Paulette Azar-Tannous *(CEO)*

Sonic HealthPlus - Naval Base (1)
9 Brown Avenue, Naval Base, Perth, 6165, WA, Australia
Tel.: (61) 89 437 1665
Web Site: http://www.sonichealthplus.com.au
Emp.: 20
Health Care Srvices
N.A.I.C.S.: 621491

Sonic HealthPlus Pty Limited (1)
Level 28 QV1 250 St George's Terrace, Perth, 6000, WA, Australia
Tel.: (61) 130 079 3004
Web Site: https://www.sonichealthplus.com.au
Emp.: 1,000
Healtcare Services
N.A.I.C.S.: 621498
Marcus Adonis *(Officer-Natl Medical)*

Sonic Healthcare Australia Pathology Pty Limited (1)
Level 17 Grosvenor Place 225 George Street, Sydney, 2000, NSW, Australia
Tel.: (61) 298551555
Web Site: https://www.sonicpathology.com.au
Diagnostic Laboratory Services
N.A.I.C.S.: 621511

Sonic Healthcare Australia Radiology Pty Limited (1)
Level 22 Grosvenor Place 225 George Street, Sydney, 2000, NSW, Australia
Tel.: (61) 298555444
Web Site: https://www.sonicradiology.com.au
Medical Laboratory Services
N.A.I.C.S.: 621511

Sonic Healthcare Services Pty Limited (1)
14 Giffnock Ave, Macquarie Park, Sydney, 2113, NSW, Australia
Tel.: (61) 298555222
Sales Range: $200-249.9 Million
Emp.: 2,000
Healtcare Services
N.A.I.C.S.: 621491

Sonic Healthcare USA, Inc. (1)
12357-A Riata Trace Pkwy Ste 210, Austin, TX 78727
Tel.: (512) 439-1600
Pathology Services
N.A.I.C.S.: 621511
Steve Shumpert *(CEO)*

Subsidiary (Domestic):

Clinical Pathology Laboratories, Inc. (2)
1111 W 34th St Ste 100, Austin, TX 78705
Tel.: (512) 467-0559
Web Site: https://www.cpllabs.com
Emp.: 1,900
Pathology Services
N.A.I.C.S.: 621511
Debbie Klein *(VP-HR)*

Division (Domestic):

American Esoteric Laboratories, Inc. (3)
1701 Century Center Cv, Memphis, TN 38134
Tel.: (901) 405-8200
Laboratory Testing Services
N.A.I.C.S.: 621511
Pamela Obrien *(VP-Sls & Mktg)*

Unit (Domestic):

American Esoteric Laboratories, Inc. - Central Region Laboratory (4)
2521 Perimeter Pl Dr, Nashville, TN 37214
Tel.: (615) 208-1950
Laboratory Testing Services
N.A.I.C.S.: 621511
Ed Colvin *(Mgr-Sls-Central Tennessee & South Central Kentucky Reg)*

American Esoteric Laboratories, Inc. - East (4)
1907 W Morris Blvd Ste F, Morristown, TN 37814
Tel.: (423) 586-3240
Esoteric & Clinical Laboratory Services
N.A.I.C.S.: 621511

Subsidiary (Domestic):

Clinical Laboratories of Hawaii, LLP (3)
91-1401 Fort Weaver Rd Ste A101, Ewa Beach, HI 96706-1940
Tel.: (808) 683-0024
Web Site: http://www.clinicallabs.com
Emp.: 180
Medical Testing Services
N.A.I.C.S.: 621512

Division (Domestic):

Clinical Pathology Laboratories Southeast, Inc. (3)
6490 Hazeltine National Dr Ste 170, Orlando, FL 32822
Tel.: (321) 445-6600
Web Site: http://www.cplse.com
Sales Range: $10-24.9 Million
Emp.: 100
Laboratory Testing Services
N.A.I.C.S.: 621511
Stephen Maxwell *(Mgr-Georgia & South Carolina)*

Subsidiary (Domestic):

Clinical Pathology Laboratories, Inc. - Bryan (3)
3201 University Dr E Ste 115, Bryan, TX 77802
Tel.: (979) 776-7302
Emp.: 1,900
Medical Laboratories
N.A.I.C.S.: 621511
Jim Gebhart *(VP)*

Division (Domestic):

Clinical Pathology Laboratories, Inc. - Lima Pathology Laboratories (3)
415 W Market St, Lima, OH 45801
Tel.: (419) 226-9595

INTERNATIONAL PUBLIC

Web Site: https://www.pathlabs.org
Anatomical Laboratory Testing Services
N.A.I.C.S.: 334516
Bob Schroeder *(Reg Mgr)*

East Side Clinical Laboratory, Inc. (3)
10 Risho Ave, East Providence, RI 02914
Tel.: (401) 455-8400
Emp.: 320
Laboratory Testing Services
N.A.I.C.S.: 541380
James Feeney *(VP-IT)*

Subsidiary (Domestic):

Sunrise Medical Laboratories, Inc. (3)
250 Miller Pl, Hicksville, NY 11801
Tel.: (516) 396-5800
Diagnostic Testing Services
N.A.I.C.S.: 621511
Joe Himplemann *(Dir-Mktg)*

Division (Domestic):

Sunrise Medical Laboratories (4)
4200-B Pleasant Valley Rd, Chantilly, VA 20151-1211
Tel.: (703) 222-2313
Laboratory Testing Services
N.A.I.C.S.: 621512
Robert Fedrick *(Office Mgr)*

Subsidiary (Domestic):

Pathology Laboratories, Inc. (2)
1946 N 13th St Ste 301, Toledo, OH 43604
Tel.: (419) 255-4600
Web Site: https://www.pathlabs.org
Laboratory Testing Services
N.A.I.C.S.: 541380
Vicki L. Hite *(VP-Sls)*

Sonic Nurse Connect Pty. Limited (1)
Suite 2 01A Building 3 35-41 Waterloo Road, Macquarie Park, 2113, NSW, Australia
Tel.: (61) 29 855 5250
Web Site: https://www.snc.com.au
Hospital & Health Care Services
N.A.I.C.S.: 622110
Leanne Matthews *(Mgr-Business Development)*

Sonic Pathology Australia Pty Limited (1)
Level 17 Grosvenor Place 225 George Street, Sydney, 2000, NSW, Australia
Tel.: (61) 29 855 1555
Web Site: https://www.sonicpathology.com.au
Medical & Diagnostic Laboratory Services
N.A.I.C.S.: 621511
Ian Clark *(CEO)*

Southcare Physiotherapy Pty Limited (1)
Suite 4 Medical Clinic St John of God Medical Centre 100 Murdoch Drive, Murdoch, 6150, WA, Australia
Tel.: (61) 86 332 6666
Web Site: http://www.southcare.com.au
Physiotherapy Services
N.A.I.C.S.: 621340

Southern IML Pathology Services Pty Limited (1)
Tel.: (61) 24 224 7474
Web Site: https://www.southernpath.com.au
Emp.: 350
Pathology Services
N.A.I.C.S.: 621511
Lawrie Bott *(CEO)*

Sullivan Nicolaides Pathology (1)
24 Hurworth Street, Townsville, Bowen Hills, 4006, QLD, Australia
Tel.: (61) 733778666
Web Site: https://www.snp.com.au
Sales Range: $50-74.9 Million
Emp.: 300
Pathology & Radiology Services
N.A.I.C.S.: 621511
Michael Harrison *(CEO, Mng Partner & Dir-Medical)*

Sullivan Nicolaides Pty Limited (1)
24 Hurworth Street, Taringa, Bowen Hills,

AND PRIVATE COMPANIES ... SONORA RESOURCES CORP.

4006, QLD, Australia
Tel.: (61) 733778666
Web Site: https://www.snp.com.au
Sales Range: $100-124.9 Million
Emp.: 1,000
Pathology Services
N.A.I.C.S.: 621511
Michael Harrison *(CEO, Mng Partner & Dir-Medical)*

Syscomp Biochemische Dienstleistungen GmbH (1)
August-Wessels-Str 5, 86154, Augsburg, Germany
Tel.: (49) 82142010
Web Site: https://labor-augsburg-mvz.de
Sales Range: $50-74.9 Million
Emp.: 500
Medical Diagnostic Services
N.A.I.C.S.: 621512

Taringa 24 Hour Medical Centre Pty Limited (1)
15 Morrow Street, Taringa, Brisbane, 4068, QLD, Australia
Tel.: (61) 73 870 7239
Web Site: http://www.ipnec.com.au
Emp.: 30
General Medical Services
N.A.I.C.S.: 621498
Penny Musumaci *(Gen Mgr)*

The Doctors Laboratory (Manchester) Limited (1)
Regents Place 4 Windsor Street, Salford Quays, Salford, M5 4HB, United Kingdom
Tel.: (44) 161 332 7181
Web Site: https://www.sonichealthcare.co.uk
Sales Range: $10-24.9 Million
Emp.: 25
Clinical Laboratory Diagnostic Services
N.A.I.C.S.: 621511
Andy Leeson *(Mgr-Sys)*

The Doctors Laboratory Limited (1)
The Halo Building 1 Mabledon Place, London, WC1H 9AX, United Kingdom
Tel.: (44) 207 307 7373
Web Site: https://www.sonichealthcare.co.uk
Clinical Laboratory Diagnostic Services
N.A.I.C.S.: 621511
David Byrne *(CEO)*

Ultrarad Holdings Pty Limited (1)
164 Grey Street, Brisbane, 4101, QLD, Australia
Tel.: (61) 733439466
Emp.: 50
Mortgage Investment Services
N.A.I.C.S.: 523999
John Scott *(Officer-Pur)*

Virion Labordiagnostik GmbH (1)
Wolfbachstrasse 17, 8024, Zurich, Switzerland
Tel.: (41) 442699944
Laboratory Testing Services
N.A.I.C.S.: 541380

WestPac Labs, Inc. (1)
10200 Pioneer Blvd Ste 500, Santa Fe Springs, CA 90670
Tel.: (562) 906-5227
Web Site: https://www.westpaclab.com
Medical & Diagnostic Laboratory Services
N.A.I.C.S.: 621511
Arlayn Ladson-Castle *(Dir-Compliance)*

SONIC INTERFREIGHT PUBLIC CO., LTD.
79/349 350 1st 2nd Floor Sathupradit Rd Chongnonsee, Yannawa, Bangkok, 10120, Thailand
Tel.: (66) 22132999
Web Site: http://www.sonic.co.th
SONIC—(THA)
Rev.: $46,294,846
Assets: $51,218,549
Liabilities: $9,047,398
Net Worth: $42,171,150
Earnings: $3,825,286
Emp.: 391
Fiscal Year-end: 12/31/23
Transportation Services
N.A.I.C.S.: 485999

Subsidiaries:

Grandlink Logistics CO., Ltd. (1)
79/345-350 Sathupradit Road Chongnonsee, Yannawa, Bangkok, 10120, Thailand
Tel.: (66) 22132666
Freight Forwarding Services
N.A.I.C.S.: 488510

SONID INC
50 2nd Industrial Complex 7-gil, Seobuk-gu, Cheonan, Chungcheongnam-d, Korea (South)
Tel.: (82) 414107777
Web Site: http://www.exax.co.kr
Year Founded: 1976
060230—(KRS)
Rev.: $58,982,421
Assets: $112,765,305
Liabilities: $53,802,269
Net Worth: $58,963,036
Earnings: ($8,989,855)
Emp.: 81
Fiscal Year-end: 12/31/22
Chemical Products Mfr
N.A.I.C.S.: 325998
Oh Joong-Geon *(CEO)*

SONIQUE LTD
35-39 Old Street First Fl, London, EC1V 9HX, United Kingdom
Tel.: (44) 20 7490 3889
Web Site: http://www.soniqueltd.com
Year Founded: 2005
Sales Range: $10-24.9 Million
Emp.: 5
Advertising, Audio/Visual, Digital/Interactive, Internet/Web Design, Multimedia, Podcasting, Production, Production (Ad, Film, Broadcast), Radio, T.V., Viral/Buzz/Word of Mouth
N.A.I.C.S.: 541810
Chris Ryan *(Owner)*

SONIX TECHNOLOGY CO., LTD.
10F-1 No 36 Taiyuan Street, Zhubei, 302, Hsinchu, Taiwan
Tel.: (886) 35600888
Web Site: https://www.sonix.com.tw
Year Founded: 1996
5471—(TAI)
Rev.: $85,350,630
Assets: $134,332,903
Liabilities: $17,860,328
Net Worth: $116,472,575
Earnings: $6,078,747
Emp.: 476
Fiscal Year-end: 12/31/23
Integrated Circuits Mfr & Distr
N.A.I.C.S.: 334413
Daniel Pan *(Chief Sls Officer)*

Subsidiaries:

Sonix Technology (Chengdu) Co., Ltd. (1)
Tian Fu Software Park, Chengdu, 610041, China
Tel.: (86) 2885331818
Computer System Design Services
N.A.I.C.S.: 541512

Sonix Technology (Shenzhen) Co., Ltd (1)
High Tech Industrial Park, Shenzhen, Guangdong, China
Tel.: (86) 75526719666
Integrated Circuits Mfr
N.A.I.C.S.: 334413

Sonix Technology KK (1)
Kobayashi bldg 2F 4-8-27, Kudanminami Chiyodaku, Tokyo, 102-0074, Japan
Tel.: (81) 362726070
Integrated Circuit Product Mfr & Distr
N.A.I.C.S.: 334413

SONMEZ FILAMENT SENTETIK IPLIK VE ELYAF SANAYI AS
Organize Sanayi Bolgesi Ali Osman Sonmez Bulvari No 1, Nilufer, Bursa, Turkiye
Tel.: (90) 2242431130
SONME—(IST)
Sales Range: Less than $1 Million
Polyester Fiber & Yarn Mfr
N.A.I.C.S.: 325220
Celal Sonmez *(Chm)*

SONMEZ PAMUKLU SANAYII AS
Demirtas Dumlupinarosb Mah Istanbul Street No 570 499, Osmangazi, 16250, Bursa, Turkiye
Tel.: (90) 2242610440
Web Site: http://www.sonmezholding.com.tr
Year Founded: 1975
SNPAM—(IST)
Sales Range: Less than $1 Million
Textile Products Mfr
N.A.I.C.S.: 314999
Celal Sonmez *(Chm, CEO & Exec Dir)*

Subsidiaries:

Sonmez Airlines Inc. (1)
Yeni Yalova Yolu 9 km, Bursa, Turkiye
Tel.: (90) 2242610440
Airline Transportation Vehicle & Spare Part Whslr
N.A.I.C.S.: 423860

Sonmez Cement Building & Mining Industry & Trade Inc. (1)
Adana Yumurtalik Serbest Bolgesi Sarimazi SB Mh 2 Bulvar 5, Cadde No 5/01, Ceyhan, Adana, Turkiye
Tel.: (90) 3226342170
Web Site: http://www.sonmezcimento.com.tr
Emp.: 230
Cement Mfr
N.A.I.C.S.: 327310

Sonmez Construction Inc. (1)
Yeni Yalova Yolu 9 km, Bursa, Turkiye
Tel.: (90) 2242610440
Recreation Facility Services
N.A.I.C.S.: 713990

Sonmez Energy Electricity Wholesale Trade Inc. (1)
Organize Sanayi Bolgesi Pembe Cadde No 8, Nilufer, Bursa, Turkiye
Tel.: (90) 2242420757
Electricity Power Distribution Services
N.A.I.C.S.: 221122

Sonmez Filament Synthetic Thread Industry Inc. (1)
Organize Sanayi Bolgesi Ali Osman Sonmez Bulvari No 1, Nilufer, Bursa, Turkiye
Tel.: (90) 2242431130
Polyester Thread Mfr
N.A.I.C.S.: 313110

Sonmez Food Tourism & Trade Inc. (1)
Yeni Yalova Yolu Sonmez Plaza Tesisleri Asmerkez, Bursa, Turkiye
Tel.: (90) 2242807400
General Merchandise Product Retailer
N.A.I.C.S.: 455219

Sonmez Petrol Industry & Trade Ltd. (1)
Yeni Yalova Yolu 9 km, Bursa, Turkiye
Tel.: (90) 2242610440
Petrol Retailer
N.A.I.C.S.: 457210

Sonmez-Koc Automotive Trade Inc. (1)
New Yalova Road 9 km, Bursa, Turkiye
Tel.: (90) 2242612244
Automobile Parts Mfr
N.A.I.C.S.: 336360

SONO GROUP N.V.
Waldmeisterstrasse 76, 80935, Munich, Germany
Tel.: (49) 8945205818
Web Site: https://www.sonomotors.com
Year Founded: 2020
SEVCQ—(OTCIQ)
Rev.: $2,456
Assets: $65,518,006
Liabilities: $71,691,141
Net Worth: ($6,173,134)
Earnings: ($68,820,744)
Emp.: 97
Fiscal Year-end: 12/31/20
Automotive Products Mfr
N.A.I.C.S.: 336390
Dmitry Lisitsyn *(Head-Investor Relations)*

SONOCAS S.A.S.
Route de la Selve, 02150, Saint-Quentin, France
Tel.: (33) 323800000
Web Site: http://www.cablisys.com
Year Founded: 1986
Rev.: $27,500,000
Emp.: 170
Nonferrous Wiredrawing & Insulating
N.A.I.C.S.: 332618

SONOCOM CO., LTD.
2-15-10 Meguro Hontyou, Meguro-Ku, Tokyo, 152-0002, Japan
Tel.: (81) 337164101
Web Site: https://www.sonocom.co.jp
Year Founded: 1962
79020—(TKS)
Sales Range: Less than $1 Million
Screen Mask Mfr
N.A.I.C.S.: 323113
Kiyohiro Takagi *(Pres & CEO)*

SONOKONG CO., LTD.
266 Angok-ro, Bucheon, Gyeonggi-do, Korea (South)
Tel.: (82) 226108750
Web Site: https://www.sonokong.co.kr
Year Founded: 1974
066910—(KRS)
Rev.: $51,146,241
Assets: $40,202,755
Liabilities: $25,759,213
Net Worth: $14,443,542
Earnings: ($5,864,470)
Emp.: 88
Fiscal Year-end: 12/31/22
Toy Mfr & Game Software Development Services
N.A.I.C.S.: 339930
Beomjin Lim *(CEO)*

SONOL ISRAEL, LTD.
Hagashish 6, Netanya, Israel
Tel.: (972) 98637777
Web Site: http://www.sonol.co.il
Year Founded: 1917
Gas Station & Convenience Store Operator
N.A.I.C.S.: 457110
Nir Galili *(CEO)*

SONOR INVESTMENTS LIMITED
Suite 2120 130 Adelaide Street West, Toronto, M5H 3P5, ON, Canada
Tel.: (416) 369-1499
Year Founded: 1960
SNI.PR.A—(TSXV)
Rev.: $4,018,749
Assets: $53,124,202
Liabilities: $1,089,638
Net Worth: $52,034,564
Earnings: $3,467,511
Fiscal Year-end: 12/31/23
Investment Services
N.A.I.C.S.: 523940
Michael R. Gardiner *(Chm & CEO)*

SONORA RESOURCES CORP.
Cerro del Padre 11, Guadalupe, 98619, Zacatecas, Mexico

SONORA RESOURCES CORP.

Sonora Resources Corp.—(Continued)
Tel.: (52) 8775137873
Year Founded: 2007
Mining Exploration Services
N.A.I.C.S.: 213114
Juan Miguel Rios Gutierrez *(Pres, CEO & Sec)*

SONORO ENERGY LTD.
Suite 600 520 5 Ave S W, Calgary, T2P 3R7, AB, Canada
Tel.: (403) 262-3252 BC
Web Site:
https://www.sonoroenergy.com
FDZN—(DEU)
Assets: $2,985,732
Liabilities: $1,957,353
Net Worth: $1,028,380
Earnings: $2,963,299
Fiscal Year-end: 12/31/23
Oil-Related Industrial Scale Sonic Reactor Mfr
N.A.I.C.S.: 333248
Christopher Atkinson *(Chm & CEO-Interim)*

Subsidiaries:

Oil Sands Sonoprocess Solutions Inc. (1)
2100-1066 West Hastings Street, Vancouver, BC, Canada
Tel.: (604) 736-2552
Web Site: http://www.sonictsi.com
Application & Development Services for Soil Remediation Solutions
N.A.I.C.S.: 562211

SONORO GOLD CORP.
300 - 2489 Bellevue Ave, West Vancouver, V7V 1E1, BC, Canada
Tel.: (604) 632-1764 BC
Web Site:
https://www.sonorogold.com
Year Founded: 1944
SMOFF—(OTCQB)
Rev.: $654,341
Assets: $2,113,768
Liabilities: $1,275,096
Net Worth: $838,672
Earnings: ($1,344,075)
Fiscal Year-end: 12/31/19
Mineral Exploration Services
N.A.I.C.S.: 212290
Melvin Herdrick *(VP-Exploration)*

Subsidiaries:

Oronos Gold Corp. (1)

SONOSCAPE MEDICAL CORP.
Sonoscape Medical Building No 368 Guangdian North Road, Guangming District, Shenzhen, 518057, Guangdong, China
Tel.: (86) 75526722890
Web Site:
https://www.sonoscape.com
Year Founded: 2002
300633—(CHIN)
Rev.: $298,637,438
Assets: $531,204,099
Liabilities: $88,096,520
Net Worth: $443,107,579
Earnings: $64,007,522
Emp.: 2,000
Fiscal Year-end: 12/31/23
Electro Medical Equipment Mfr & Distr
N.A.I.C.S.: 334510
Chen Zhiqiang *(Chm)*

SONOVA HOLDING AG
Laubisrutistrasse 28, 8712, Stafa, Switzerland
Tel.: (41) 589280101
Web Site: https://www.sonova.com
Year Founded: 1985

SOON—(SWX)
Rev.: $4,119,716,800
Assets: $6,118,855,000
Liabilities: $3,659,852,200
Net Worth: $2,459,002,800
Earnings: $725,446,600
Emp.: 17,608
Fiscal Year-end: 03/31/23
Wireless & Hearing Systems Designer, Developer, Producer & Distr
N.A.I.C.S.: 334510
Beat Hess *(Vice Chm)*

Subsidiaries:

Advanced Bionics LLC (1)
28515 Westinghouse Pl, Valencia, CA 91355
Tel.: (661) 362-1400
Web Site: http://www.advancedbionics.com
Sales Range: $100-124.9 Million
Emp.: 600
Developer of Implantable Neurostimulation Devices
N.A.I.C.S.: 339112

Subsidiary (Non-US):

Advanced Bionics Asia Pacific Ltd. (2)
Room 4103 41/F Hopewell Centre 183 Queen's Road East, Wanchai, China (Hong Kong)
Tel.: (852) 25267668
Web Site: http://www.advancedbionics.com
Hearing Aid Distr
N.A.I.C.S.: 423450

Advanced Bionics European Research Center GmbH (2)
Karl Wiechert Allee 3, 30625, Hannover, Lower Saxony, Germany
Tel.: (49) 5115700882
Cochlear Implant Systems Mfr
N.A.I.C.S.: 339113

Advanced Bionics SARL (2)
9 rue Maryse Bastie, CS 90606, 69675, Bron, Cedex, France
Tel.: (33) 472145460
Web Site: http://www.bionicear-europe.com
Sales Range: $25-49.9 Million
Emp.: 40
Developer of Implantable Neurostimulation Devices
N.A.I.C.S.: 339112

Advanced Bionics Spain, S.R.L. (2)
C/ Artesanos 14 Poligono Industrial de Canastell, San Vicente del Raspeig, 03690, Alicante, Spain
Tel.: (34) 965200210
Web Site: http://www.bionicear.eu
Hearing Implants Mfr
N.A.I.C.S.: 339113

Advanced Bionics UK Ltd. (2)
2 Breaks House Mill Court, Great Shelfort, Cambridge, CB22 5LD, United Kingdom
Tel.: (44) 1223847888
Web Site: http://www.advancedbionics.com
Emp.: 6
Cochlear Implants Mfr
N.A.I.C.S.: 339113

AudioNova International B.V. (2)
Aert Van Nesstraat 45, 3012 CA, Rotterdam, Netherlands (100%)
Tel.: (31) 104443535
Web Site: http://www.sonova.com
Hearing Aid Retailer
N.A.I.C.S.: 456199
Miranda Van Der Burg *(Office Mgr)*

Comfort Audio AB (1)
Olofsdalsvagen 40, 302 41, Halmstad, Sweden
Tel.: (46) 35 260 16 00
Web Site: http://www.comfortaudio.com
Sales Range: $10-24.9 Million
Emp.: 90
Hearing Aid Mfr
N.A.I.C.S.: 339112
Stefan Persson *(Mgr-Bus Dev-Work Life)*

Subsidiary (US):

Comfort Audio Inc. (2)
4520 Weaver Pkwy, Warrenville, IL 60555

Web Site: http://www.comfortaudio.com
Hearing Aid Mfr
N.A.I.C.S.: 339112

Connect Hearing (1)
301 - 1007 Langley Street, Victoria, V8W 1V7, BC, Canada
Tel.: (250) 413-2100
Web Site: https://www.connecthearing.ca
Hearing Testing Services
N.A.I.C.S.: 621340

Connect Hearing Hearing Retail Group Pty. Ltd. (1)
2 101 Union Street, Sydney, 2060, NSW, Australia
Tel.: (61) 293948410
Web Site:
http://www.connecthearing.com.au
Sales Range: $10-24.9 Million
Emp.: 25
Hearing Center Operator
N.A.I.C.S.: 621340

Hearing Retail Group Pty. Ltd. (1)
2/101 Union Street, North Sydney, Sydney, 2060, NSW, Australia
Tel.: (61) 293948400
Web Site:
http://www.connecthearing.com.au
Hearing Care Services
N.A.I.C.S.: 621610

Lukatit Investments 14 (Pty) Ltd. (1)
First Floor Selborne House Fourways Golf Park Roos Street, Fourways, Johannesburg, 2191, Gauteng, South Africa
Tel.: (27) 114677662
Web Site: http://www.unitron.com
Sales Range: $25-49.9 Million
Emp.: 20
Hearing Aid Distr
N.A.I.C.S.: 423450
Dion Watson *(Gen Mgr)*

Newport Health Network, Inc. (1)
5990 Greenwood Plz Blvd Ste 120, Greenwood Village, CO 80111
Tel.: (720) 385-3700
Web Site: http://www.newportaudiology.com
Hearing Testing & Hearing Aids Retailer
N.A.I.C.S.: 423450
Selonda Chambers *(Dir-Affiliate Rels)*

Phonak AG (1)
Laubisrutistrasse 28, 8712, Stafa, Zurich, Switzerland
Tel.: (41) 589280101
Web Site: http://www.phonak.com
Sales Range: $550-599.9 Million
Emp.: 1,200
Hearing Aid Distr
N.A.I.C.S.: 423450
Franz Petermann *(Dir-Mktg)*

Subsidiary (Non-US):

Hansaton Akustische Gerate Ges.m.b.H. (2)
Josef Lindner Strasse 4/4, 5073, Wals, Salzburg, Austria
Tel.: (43) 6624512620
Web Site: http://www.hansaton.at
Sales Range: $50-74.9 Million
Emp.: 200
Hearing Aid Distr
N.A.I.C.S.: 423450
Manfred Laaber *(Mng Dir)*

Lapperre Bhac N.V. (2)
Stationsstraat 22, 1702, Groot-Bijgaarden, Flemish Brabant, Belgium
Tel.: (32) 27007777
Web Site: http://www.lapperre.be
Sales Range: $50-74.9 Million
Emp.: 250
Hearing Aids Retailer
N.A.I.C.S.: 423450
Marc Heymans *(Gen Mgr)*

Phonak (Shanghai) Co. Ltd. (2)
4F Building 16 No 99 Tianzhou Road, Xuhui District, Shanghai, 200235, China
Tel.: (86) 21 6120 5533
Web Site: http://www.phonak.com.cn
Emp.: 200
Hearing Aid Distr
N.A.I.C.S.: 423450

Phonak AB (2)

INTERNATIONAL PUBLIC

Box 1039, Solna, 171 21, Stockholm, Sweden
Tel.: (46) 854620900
Web Site: http://www.phonak.com
Sales Range: $25-49.9 Million
Emp.: 22
Hearing Aid Distr
N.A.I.C.S.: 423450

Phonak AS (2)
Ovre Vollgate 6 5 etg, PO Box 525, Sentrum, 0105, Oslo, Norway
Tel.: (47) 96098600
Web Site: http://www.phonak.com
Emp.: 18
Hearing Aid Distr
N.A.I.C.S.: 423450

Subsidiary (Domestic):

Phonak Acoustic Implants SA (2)
Route de Denges 28 E, CH 1027, Lausanne, Switzerland (100%)
Tel.: (41) 216126126
Web Site: http://www.acousticimplants.com
Sales Range: $25-49.9 Million
Emp.: 40
Partially Implantable Hearing Instrument Designer & Mfr
N.A.I.C.S.: 339112

Subsidiary (Non-US):

Phonak B.V. (2)
Laanakkerweg 4, 4131 PA, Vianen, Netherlands
Tel.: (31) 886008850
Web Site: http://www.phonak.com
Sales Range: $25-49.9 Million
Emp.: 40
Hearing Aid Distr
N.A.I.C.S.: 423450

Phonak Belgium S.A./N.V. (2)
Doornveld 122, 1700, Zellik, Belgium
Tel.: (32) 24681981
Sales Range: $25-49.9 Million
Emp.: 6
Hearing Aids Retailer
N.A.I.C.S.: 423450
Marc Heymans *(CEO)*

Phonak CIS Ltd. (2)
st Tverskaya bld 12 p 9 office 103, 125009, Moscow, Russia
Tel.: (7) 4957880201
Web Site: http://www.phonak.com
Hearing Aids Retailer
N.A.I.C.S.: 423450

Phonak Canada Limited (2)
80 Courtneypark Drive Unit 1, Mississauga, L5W 0B3, ON, Canada
Tel.: (905) 677-1167
Web Site: https://www.phonak.com
Sales Range: $50-74.9 Million
Emp.: 110
Hearing Aids Mfr & Distr
N.A.I.C.S.: 334510

Subsidiary (Domestic):

Phonak Communications AG (2)
Laenggasse 17, 3280, Murten, Fribourg, Switzerland
Tel.: (41) 266729672
Web Site: http://www.phonak-communications.com
Sales Range: $50-74.9 Million
Emp.: 140
Hearing Aids Mfr & Distr
N.A.I.C.S.: 334510

Subsidiary (Non-US):

Phonak Danmark A/S (2)
Ostre Hougvej 42-44, 5500, Middelfart, Syddanmark, Denmark
Tel.: (45) 64417887
Web Site: http://www.phonak.dk
Sales Range: $25-49.9 Million
Emp.: 35
Hearing Aid Mfr & Distr
N.A.I.C.S.: 334510
Bjorn Wallentin *(Mng Dir)*

Phonak Duyu Sistemleri Ithalat Ihracat Ticaret Pazarlama Limited Sirketi (2)
Cumhuriyet Cad No 54 D 14 Kervansaray Apt B Blok, Elmadag Harbiye, 34367, Istan-

AND PRIVATE COMPANIES — SONY GROUP CORPORATION

bul, Turkiye
Tel.: (90) 2122326722
Web Site: http://www.phonak.com.tr
Sales Range: $50-74.9 Million
Emp.: 8
Hearing Aid Distr
N.A.I.C.S.: 423450

Phonak Finland OY (2)
Tullikatu 6 Tullintori 2nd floor, 33100, Tampere, Pirkanmaa, Finland
Tel.: (358) 102814477
Web Site: http://www.phonak.com
Sales Range: $25-49.9 Million
Emp.: 9
Hearing Aids Mfr & Distr
N.A.I.C.S.: 423450

Phonak GmbH (2)
Max-Eyth-Strasse 20, 70736, Fellbach, Germany
Tel.: (49) 711510700
Web Site: http://www.phonakpro.com
Emp.: 150
Hearing Aids Mfr & Distr
N.A.I.C.S.: 423450
Joachim Schoenhofen (Mng Dir)

Phonak Group Ltd. (2)
Lakeside Drive Centre Park, Warrington, WA1 1RX, Cheshire, United Kingdom
Tel.: (44) 1925623600
Web Site: http://www.phonakpro.com
Sales Range: $75-99.9 Million
Emp.: 170
Hearing Aid Distr
N.A.I.C.S.: 423450

Subsidiary (Domestic):

Phonak Hearing Systems AG (2)
Laubisrutistrasse 28, 8712, Stafa, Zurich, Switzerland
Tel.: (41) 589280101
Web Site: http://www.phonak.com
Sales Range: $250-299.9 Million
Emp.: 1,000
Hearing Aid Distr
N.A.I.C.S.: 423450
Lukas Braunschweiler (CEO)

Subsidiary (Non-US):

Phonak India Pvt. Ltd. (2)
503 - 506 B Wing Kanakia Zillion LBS Marg, Kurla W, Mumbai, 400 070, Maharashtra, India
Tel.: (91) 2267820600
Web Site: http://www.phonakpro.com
Sales Range: $25-49.9 Million
Emp.: 50
Hearing Aid Distr
N.A.I.C.S.: 423450
Andrea Geisinger (Mng Dir)

Phonak Italia S.R.L. (2)
Via Montecuccoli 30, 20147, Milan, Italy
Tel.: (39) 0800629007
Web Site: http://www.phonak.com
Emp.: 40
Hearing Aid Distr
N.A.I.C.S.: 423450
Marco Caron (Dir Gen)

Phonak Japan Co., Ltd. (2)
Lexington Plaza Nishi-gotanda 10th Fl 5-2-4, Nishi-gotanda Shinagawa-ku, Tokyo, 141-0031, Japan
Tel.: (81) 3 5436 4079
Web Site: http://www.phonak.com
Hearing Aid Distr
N.A.I.C.S.: 423450

Phonak Korea Ltd. (2)
Suite 1204 JEI Platz 186 Gasan Digital-1-ro, Geumcheon-Gu, Seoul, 153-792, Korea (South)
Tel.: (82) 218990089
Web Site: http://www.phonak.kr
Hearing Aid Distr
N.A.I.C.S.: 423450

Subsidiary (US):

Phonak LLC (2)
4520 Weaver Pkwy, Warrenville, IL 60555-3927
Tel.: (630) 821-5000
Web Site: http://www.phonak-us.com

Sales Range: $50-74.9 Million
Emp.: 200
Hearing Instruments Mfr
N.A.I.C.S.: 334510

Subsidiary (Non-US):

Phonak Mexicana S.A. de C.V. (2)
Av Insurgentes Sur 619 Piso 6 Col Insurgentes, Mixcoac Del Benito Juarez, 03920, Mexico, Mexico
Tel.: (52) 55 5611 0565
Emp.: 60
Hearing Aids Mfr & Distr
N.A.I.C.S.: 334510
Fernando Cardoso (Office Mgr)

Phonak New Zealand Ltd. (2)
Level 2 28 The Warehouse Way, Northcote, Auckland, 0627, New Zealand
Tel.: (64) 94861849
Web Site: http://www.phonak.com
Emp.: 45
Hearing Aid Distr
N.A.I.C.S.: 423450
Mike Sharp (Mng Dir)

Phonak Operation Center Vietnam Co., Ltd. (2)
Unit G01 Ground Floor CityView Building 12 Mac Dinh Chi street, district 1, Ho Chi Minh City, Binh Duong, Vietnam
Tel.: (84) 838274373
Web Site: http://www.phonak.com
Sales Range: $250-299.9 Million
Emp.: 600
Hearing Aid Distr
N.A.I.C.S.: 423450

Phonak Polska Sp. Z o.o. (2)
Plac Bankowy 1, 00-139, Warsaw, Poland
Tel.: (48) 227491900
Web Site: http://www.phonakpro.com
Sales Range: $25-49.9 Million
Emp.: 17
Hearing Aids Retailer
N.A.I.C.S.: 423450

Phonak Pty. Ltd. (2)
12 Inglewood Place, Norwest Business Park, Baulkham Hills, 2153, NSW, Australia
Tel.: (61) 288581800
Web Site: http://www.phonak.com
Sales Range: $25-49.9 Million
Emp.: 70
Hearing Aid Distr
N.A.I.C.S.: 423450
Launied Marshall (Pres)

Phonak Singapore Pte. Ltd. (2)
8 Kallang Avenue 13-08 Aperia Tower 1, Singapore, 339509, Singapore
Tel.: (65) 68952666
Web Site: http://www.phonak.com
Sales Range: $25-49.9 Million
Emp.: 12
Hearing Aids Mfr & Distr
N.A.I.C.S.: 334510
Urs Eller (Mng Dir)

Phonak Taiwan Pte. Ltd. (2)
4F No 661 Bannan Rd, Zhonghe Dist, New Taipei City, 235, Taiwan
Tel.: (886) 222216722
Web Site: http://www.phonak.com.tw
Sales Range: $25-49.9 Million
Emp.: 8
Hearing Aid Distr
N.A.I.C.S.: 423450

Phonak do Brasil Sistemas Audiologicos Ltda. (2)
Av Maria Coelho Aguiar 215 Block A - 4th Walking - Cj 02 and 03, Jd Sao Luis, Sao Paulo, 05804-900, Brazil
Tel.: (55) 800 701 8105
Web Site: http://www.phonak.com
Hearing Aids Mfr & Distr
N.A.I.C.S.: 334510

Sichuan i-hear Co., Ltd. (1)
25 Hua Li Bldg 105 Second Part of First Ring Rd W, Chengdu, 610071, Sichuan, China
Tel.: (86) 2161205533
Web Site: http://www.i-hear.cn
Hearing Aid Distr
N.A.I.C.S.: 423450

Sonova (Shanghai) Co., Ltd. (1)

4/F Building 16 No 99 Tianzhou Road, Xuhui District, Shanghai, 200233, China
Tel.: (86) 216 120 5533
Web Site: https://www.phonak.com
Electro Medical & Electrotherapeutic Mfr
N.A.I.C.S.: 334510

Sonova AG (1)
Laubisrutistrasse 28, 8712, Stafa, Switzerland
Tel.: (41) 589280101
Web Site: https://www.sonova.com
Emp.: 17,500
Software Development Services
N.A.I.C.S.: 541511

Sonova Canada Inc. (1)
80 Courtneypark Drive West Unit 1, Mississauga, L5W 0B3, ON, Canada
Tel.: (905) 677-1167
Web Site: https://www.phonakpro.ca
Electro Medical & Electrotherapeutic Mfr
N.A.I.C.S.: 334510

Sonova Communications AG (1)
Herrenschwandweg 4, CH-3280, Murten, Switzerland
Tel.: (41) 589289100
Web Site: https://www.sonova-communications.com
Energy Research & Development Services
N.A.I.C.S.: 926110

Sonova Denmark A/S (1)
Ostre Hougvej 42-44, 5500, Middelfart, Denmark
Tel.: (45) 6 441 7887
Web Site: https://www.phonak.com
Electro Medical & Electrotherapeutic Mfr
N.A.I.C.S.: 334510

Sonova Iberica S.A.U. (1)
Avenida de la Industria n 13-15 Poligono de Canastell, San Vicente del Raspeig, 03690, Alicante, Spain
Tel.: (34) 902331122
Web Site: https://www.phonak.es
Electro Medical & Electrotherapeutic Mfr
N.A.I.C.S.: 334510

Sonova Korea Ltd. (1)
Suite 1204 JEI Platz 186 Gasan Digital-1-ro, Geumcheon-gu, Seoul, 153-792, Korea (South)
Tel.: (82) 218990089
Electro Medical & Electrotherapeutic Mfr
N.A.I.C.S.: 334510

Sonova Nordic AB (1)
Box 1039, 171 21, Solna, Sweden
Tel.: (46) 854620900
Web Site: https://www.phonakpro.se
Electro Medical & Electrotherapeutic Mfr
N.A.I.C.S.: 334510

Sonova Operation Center Vietnam Co., Ltd. (1)
Unit G01 Ground Floor CityView Building 12 Mac Dinh Chi street, district 1, Ho Chi Minh City, Vietnam
Tel.: (84) 838274373
Web Site: https://www.phonakvietnam.com
Electro Medical & Electrotherapeutic Mfr
N.A.I.C.S.: 334510

Sonova RUS LLC (1)
St Tverskaya 12/9 office 103, 125009, Moscow, Russia
Tel.: (7) 4957880201
Web Site: https://www.phonak.com
Electro Medical & Electrotherapeutic Mfr
N.A.I.C.S.: 334510

Sonova Taiwan Pte. Ltd. (1)
4F No 661 Bannan Rd, Zhonghe Dist, New Taipei City, 235, Taiwan
Tel.: (886) 22 221 6722
Web Site: https://www.phonak.com.tw
Electro Medical & Electrotherapeutic Mfr
N.A.I.C.S.: 334510

Unitron Hearing Ltd. (1)
20 Beasley Drive, PO Box 9017, Kitchener, N2E 1Y6, ON, Canada
Tel.: (519) 895-0100
Web Site: https://www.unitron.com
Sales Range: $50-74.9 Million
Emp.: 200
Hearing Aid Mfr
N.A.I.C.S.: 334510

Subsidiary (Non-US):

Unitron Hearing (Suzhou) Co., Ltd. (2)
No 78 Qi Ming Road Export Processing Zone B, Suzhou Industrial Park, Suzhou, 215126, Jiangsu, China
Tel.: (86) 51262582258
Web Site: http://www.unitronhearing.com.cn
Sales Range: $200-249.9 Million
Emp.: 600
Hearing Aid Mfr
N.A.I.C.S.: 334510

Unitron Hearing AB (2)
Svetsarvagen 7, 17274, Solna, Sweden
Tel.: (46) 854620960
Web Site: http://www.unitron.com
Sales Range: $25-49.9 Million
Emp.: 20
Hearing Aid Distr
N.A.I.C.S.: 423450

Unitron Hearing AS (2)
PO Box 301 Sentrum, 0105, Oslo, Norway
Tel.: (47) 22 47 76 30
Sales Range: $25-49.9 Million
Emp.: 4
Hearing Aid Mfr
N.A.I.C.S.: 334510

Unitron Hearing B.V. (2)
Ir D S Tuijnmanweg 10, 4131 PN, Vianen, Utrecht, Netherlands
Tel.: (31) 886008810
Web Site: http://www.unitron.com
Sales Range: $25-49.9 Million
Emp.: 30
Hearing Aid Mfr
N.A.I.C.S.: 334510
Casparus A. M. van Opsta (Mgr)

Unitron Hearing Colombia Ltd. (2)
Avenida 15 No 124 29 Off No 703, Bogota, Colombia
Tel.: (57) 12149847
Web Site: http://www.unitron.com
Sales Range: $25-49.9 Million
Emp.: 12
Hearing Aid Mfr
N.A.I.C.S.: 334510

Unitron Hearing GmbH (2)
Max-Eyth-Strasse 20, Oeffingen, Fellbach, 70736, Germany
Tel.: (49) 7116585380
Web Site: http://www.unitron.com
Sales Range: $25-49.9 Million
Emp.: 10
Hearing Aid Distr
N.A.I.C.S.: 423450
Jochen Meuser (Mgr)

Subsidiary (US):

Unitron Hearing, Inc. (2)
14755 27 Ave N, Plymouth, MN 55447
Tel.: (763) 744-3300
Web Site: http://www.unitron.com
Sales Range: $25-49.9 Million
Emp.: 100
Hearing Aid Mfr
N.A.I.C.S.: 334510
Dennis Munter (Office Mgr)

SONOVIA LTD.
14 Izhak Sade St, 3 Menachem Begin St, Nahariyya, 2230507, Israel
Tel.: (972) 50 652 1727   II
Web Site: http://www.nano-textile.com
Year Founded: 2013
Assets: $76,783
Liabilities: $860,209
Net Worth: ($783,426)
Earnings: ($299,325)
Emp.: 1
Fiscal Year-end: 12/31/17
Anti-Bacterial Textile Product Mfr
N.A.I.C.S.: 314999
Joshua Herchcovici (Chm & CEO)

SONY GROUP CORPORATION
1-7-1 Konan, Minato-ku, Tokyo, 108-0075, Japan
Tel.: (81) 367482111   JP

SONY GROUP CORPORATION

Sony Group Corporation—(Continued)

Web Site: https://www.sony.com
Year Founded: 1946
SONY—(NYSE)
Rev.: $81,000,114,405
Assets: $212,177,238,092
Liabilities: $163,927,749,863
Net Worth: $48,249,488,228
Earnings: $6,099,496,295
Emp.: 113,000
Fiscal Year-end: 03/31/24
Consumer Electronics, Telecommunications & Information Products
N.A.I.C.S.: 334310
Kenichiro Yoshida *(Chm)*

Subsidiaries:

Altair Semiconductor Ltd. (1)
6 Haharash Street, PO Box 7158, Hod Hasharon, 4524079, Israel
Tel.: (972) 747800800
Web Site: https://altair.sony-semicon.com
Semiconductor Mfr
N.A.I.C.S.: 334413
Oded Melamed *(Co-Founder)*

FeliCa Networks, Inc (1)
Gate City Osaki 1-11-1 West Tower 16F Osaki, Shinagawa-ku, Tokyo, 141-0032, Japan
Tel.: (81) 354353131
Web Site: https://www.felicanetworks.co.jp
Sales Range: $50-74.9 Million
Emp.: 12
Mobile Phone Chip Mfr
N.A.I.C.S.: 334419
Tomoharu Hikita *(Pres & CEO)*

InterTrust Technologies Corporation (1)
400 N McCarthy Blvd Ste 220, Milpitas, CA 95035
Tel.: (408) 616-1600
Web Site: https://www.intertrust.com
Sales Range: $25-49.9 Million
Emp.: 60
Develops Digital Rights Management (DRM) Solutions for Providers of Music, Movies, Information & other Digital Content
N.A.I.C.S.: 541511
David Lockwood *(Pres & CEO)*

M3, Inc. (1)
Akasaka Intercity 10th floor 1-11-44 Akasaka, Minato-ku, Tokyo, 107-0052, Japan (49.8%)
Tel.: (81) 362298900
Web Site: https://corporate.m3.com
Rev.: $1,654,965,060
Assets: $2,872,624,650
Liabilities: $653,380,590
Net Worth: $2,219,244,060
Earnings: $351,530,760
Emp.: 10,533
Fiscal Year-end: 03/31/2023
Online Medical Marketing & Information Services
N.A.I.C.S.: 519290

Subsidiary (Domestic):

Clinical Porter Inc. (2)
1-11-44 Akasaka, Minato-ku, Tokyo, 107-0052, Japan
Tel.: (81) 366742523
Web Site: https://www.clipo.co.jp
Clinical Research Services
N.A.I.C.S.: 621111

Cosmotec Corporation (2)
Twin View Ochanomizu Building 2-3-9 Hongo, Bunkyo Ward, Tokyo, 113-0033, Japan (100%)
Tel.: (81) 368216960
Web Site: https://cosmotec.com
Emp.: 60
Photographic Printing Plates Mfr & Whslr
N.A.I.C.S.: 325992

Subsidiary (Non-US):

Doctors.net.uk Limited (2)
101 Park Drive Milton Park, Abingdon, OX14 4RY, Oxfordshire, United Kingdom
Tel.: (44) 1235828400
Web Site: https://www.doctors.net.uk

Sales Range: $25-49.9 Million
Emp.: 70
Online Health Care Services
N.A.I.C.S.: 513199

Subsidiary (Domestic):

ELAN Corporation (2)
15-12 Degawacho Matsumoto City, Nagano, 390-0826, Japan (55%)
Tel.: (81) 263292680
Web Site: https://www.kkelan.com
Rev.: $260,012,880
Assets: $115,236,240
Liabilities: $50,785,110
Net Worth: $64,451,130
Earnings: $14,927,940
Emp.: 555
Fiscal Year-end: 12/31/2022
Clothes, Towels Rental & Other Laundry Services
N.A.I.C.S.: 532289
Hideharu Sakurai *(Pres)*

Fuji CRS, K. K. (2)
1-7-4 Higashikawasakicho Harbor Land Daiya Nissei Bldg, Chuo-Ku, Kobe, 650-0044, Japan
Tel.: (81) 783601655
Clinical Support Services
N.A.I.C.S.: 621111

M PLUS Corporation (2)
Shibuya Mark City West 16th floor 1-12-1 Dogenzaka, Shibuya-ku, Tokyo, 150-0043, Japan
Tel.: (81) 343612653
Web Site: https://www.allm.plus
Medical Software Development Services
N.A.I.C.S.: 541511

Subsidiary (US):

M3 USA Corporation (2)
501 Office Center Dr Ste 410, Fort Washington, PA 19034
Tel.: (202) 293-2288
Web Site: https://usa.m3.com
Emp.: 10
Online Medical Marketing & Information Services
N.A.I.C.S.: 519290
Aki Tomaru *(CEO)*

Subsidiary (Domestic):

Michael Allen Company, LLC (3)
9 Old Kings Hwy S, Darien, CT 06820
Tel.: (203) 221-7900
Web Site: http://www.mac-island.com
Rev.: $2,720,000
Emp.: 16
Administrative Management & General Management Consulting Service
N.A.I.C.S.: 541611
Gary Peterson *(Sr Partner)*

NAS Recruitment Communications, LLC (3)
One Infinity Corporate Dr, Cleveland, OH 44125
Tel.: (216) 478-0300
Web Site: https://www.nasrecruitment.com
Advetising Agency
N.A.I.C.S.: 541810

Branch (Domestic):

NAS Recruitment Communications (4)
1 Infinity Corporate Ctr Ste 100, Cleveland, OH 44125-5370
Tel.: (210) 490-1662
Web Site: http://www.nasrecruitment.com
Sales Range: $10-24.9 Million
Emp.: 3
Recruitment
N.A.I.C.S.: 541810

NAS Recruitment Communications (4)
6133 Rockside Rd Ste 302, Independence, OH 44131
Tel.: (216) 478-0300
Web Site: http://www.nasrecruitment.com
Sales Range: $25-49.9 Million
Emp.: 12
Recruitment
N.A.I.C.S.: 541810

NAS Recruitment Communications (4)
1 Infinity Corporate Ctr Dr, Cleveland, OH 44125
Tel.: (216) 478-0300
Web Site: http://www.nasrecruitment.com
Sales Range: $25-49.9 Million
Emp.: 5
N.A.I.C.S.: 541810

NAS Recruitment Communications (4)
6160 S Syracuse Way Ste 100, Greenwood Village, CO 80111
Tel.: (303) 694-3600
Web Site: http://www.nasrecruitment.com
Sales Range: $25-49.9 Million
Emp.: 4
Recruitment
N.A.I.C.S.: 541810

NAS Recruitment Communications (4)
11011 King St 240, Overland Park, KS 66210
Tel.: (913) 663-2244
Web Site: http://www.nasrecruitment.com
Sales Range: $25-49.9 Million
Emp.: 5
Advetising Agency
N.A.I.C.S.: 541810

NAS Recruitment Communications (4)
8000 Norman Ctr Dr Ste 400, Minneapolis, MN 55437
Tel.: (952) 346-6540
Web Site: http://www.nasrecruitment.com
Sales Range: $25-49.9 Million
Emp.: 12
N.A.I.C.S.: 541810

NAS Recruitment Communications (4)
3 Gateway Ctr 1740, Pittsburgh, PA 15222
Tel.: (412) 391-3915
Web Site: http://www.nasrecruitment.com
Sales Range: $25-49.9 Million
Emp.: 6
Advetising Agency
N.A.I.C.S.: 541810

NAS Recruitment Communications (4)
4747 Executive Dr Ste 1080, San Diego, CA 92121-3114
Tel.: (866) 627-7327
Web Site: http://www.nasrecruitment.com
Sales Range: $25-49.9 Million
Emp.: 3
N.A.I.C.S.: 541810

NAS Recruitment Communications (4)
3000 Highwoods Blvd Ste 301, Raleigh, NC 27604
Tel.: (919) 872-6800
Web Site: http://www.nasrecruitment.com
Sales Range: $25-49.9 Million
Emp.: 7
N.A.I.C.S.: 541810

NAS Recruitment Communications (4)
4747 Executive Dr Ste 1080, San Diego, CA 92121
Tel.: (858) 677-2744
Web Site: http://www.nasrecruitment.com
Sales Range: $25-49.9 Million
Emp.: 3
Recruitment
N.A.I.C.S.: 541810

NAS Recruitment Communications (4)
430 Pacific Ave, San Francisco, CA 94133
Tel.: (415) 274-7940
Web Site: http://www.nasrecruitment.com
Sales Range: $25-49.9 Million
Emp.: 4
Recruitment
N.A.I.C.S.: 541810

Subsidiary (Domestic):

The Medicus Firm LLC (3)
16479 N Dallas Pkwy Ste 200, Addison, TX 75001 (100%)
Tel.: (972) 759-0331

INTERNATIONAL PUBLIC

Web Site: https://www.themedicusfirm.com
Sales Range: $1-9.9 Million
Emp.: 200
Physician Staffing Solutions
N.A.I.C.S.: 561311
Jim Stone *(Founder)*

Subsidiary (Domestic):

MIC Medical Corporation (2)
Akasaka Intercity 1-11-44 Akasaka, Minato-ku, Tokyo, 113-0034, Japan (75%)
Tel.: (81) 365856900
Web Site: http://www.micjp.co.jp
Sales Range: $25-49.9 Million
Emp.: 377
Medical Devices & Pharmaceuticals Mfr
N.A.I.C.S.: 339112
Masanobu Mitsuhashi *(Pres & CEO)*

Mebix, Inc. (2)
1-11-44 Akasaka, Minato-ku, Tokyo, 107-0052, Japan
Tel.: (81) 354726610
Web Site: https://www2.mebix.co.jp
Sales Range: $25-49.9 Million
Emp.: 100
Clinical Testing Software Development Services
N.A.I.C.S.: 541511
Minoru Tonogai *(Pres)*

Medical Pilot inc. (2)
Ninth Kowa Bldg 2F 1-8-10 Akasaka, Minato-ku, 107-0052, Tokyo, Japan
Tel.: (81) 3 6277 7181
Pharmaceuticals Product Mfr
N.A.I.C.S.: 325412

Mediscience Planning Inc. (2)
Tokyo Sumitomo Twin Building East Building 2-27-1 Shinkawa, Chuo-ku, Tokyo, 104-0033, Japan
Tel.: (81) 355448111
Web Site: https://www.mpi-cro.co.jp
Sales Range: $75-99.9 Million
Emp.: 1,431
Pharmaceutical Researcher, Developer & Mfr
N.A.I.C.S.: 325412
Akinori Urae *(Chm & CEO)*

Subsidiary (Domestic):

RINSYOIYAKU INC. (3)
1-3-1 Ginza, Chuo-ku, Tokyo, 104-0061, Japan
Tel.: (81) 3 3538 8231
Pharmaceutical Products Research Services
N.A.I.C.S.: 541715

Subsidiary (Domestic):

QLife, Inc. (2)
10th floor Toranomon 33 Mori Building 10F 3-8-21 Toranomon, Minato-ku, Tokyo, 105-0001, Japan
Tel.: (81) 368605020
Web Site: https://www.qlife.co.jp
Health Care Information Services
N.A.I.C.S.: 519290

Sony (China) Ltd. (1)
Room 301 3rd Floor Commercial Building, Dong Changan Jie, Ping An International Financial Center No 1 South Xinyuan Rd Chaoyang, Beijing, 100027, China
Tel.: (86) 1084586000
Web Site: https://www.sony.com.cn
Audio & Video Products Distr
N.A.I.C.S.: 449210

Sony (U.K.) Ltd. (1)
The Hts Brooklands, KT13 0XW, Waybridge, Surrey, United Kingdom - England (100%)
Tel.: (44) 932816000
Web Site: http://www.sony.co.uk
Sales Range: $100-124.9 Million
Emp.: 450
Home Audio & Video Equipment Mfr & Distr
N.A.I.C.S.: 334310

Subsidiary (Non-US):

Sony Nordic A/S (2)
Industriparken 29, 2750, Ballerup, Denmark
Tel.: (45) 43557000
Web Site: https://www.sony.dk
Emp.: 52

AND PRIVATE COMPANIES — SONY GROUP CORPORATION

Consumer Electronics Distr
N.A.I.C.S.: 423620

Sony Australia Limited (1)
165 Walker Street, North Sydney, 2060, NSW, Australia
Tel.: (61) 298876666
Web Site: http://www.sony.com.au
Sales Range: $50-74.9 Million
Emp.: 250
Household Audio & Video Electronic Products Distr & Sales
N.A.I.C.S.: 449210

Sony Austria GmbH (1)
Wienerbergstrasse 41, 1120, Vienna, Austria
Tel.: (43) 01610500
Web Site: https://www.sony.at
Sales Range: $25-49.9 Million
Emp.: 80
Electronic Household Video & Audio Products Sales & Service
N.A.I.C.S.: 449210

Subsidiary (Domestic):

Sony Pictures Filmverleih GmbH (2)
Apostelgasse 23, 1030, Vienna, Austria
Tel.: (43) 15971515
Web Site: https://www.sonypictures.at
Motion Picture Distr
N.A.I.C.S.: 512120

Sony Benelux B.V. (1)
Schipholweg 275, 1171 AA, Badhoevedorp, Netherlands
Tel.: (31) 206581911
Consumer Electronics Distr
N.A.I.C.S.: 423620

Sony Broadcast & Professional Europe (1)
Jays Close Viables, Basingstoke, RG22 4SB, Hants, United Kingdom
Tel.: (44) 1256355011
Web Site: http://www.sonybiz.net
Sales Range: $200-249.9 Million
Emp.: 850
Professional Broadcast-Use Video & Audio Equipment Distr
N.A.I.C.S.: 449210

Sony Business Solutions Corporation (1)
1-7-1 Konan, Minato-ku, Tokyo, 108-0075, Japan
Tel.: (81) 367482111
Web Site: https://www.sony.com
Sales Range: $150-199.9 Million
Emp.: 700
Software Development Services
N.A.I.C.S.: 541511

Sony Capital Corporation (1)
25 Madison Ave Ste 3360, New York, NY 10022-3211
Tel.: (212) 833-6800
Financial Services
N.A.I.C.S.: 523999

Sony Computer Science Laboratories, Inc., (1)
3-14-13 Higashigotanda Takanawa Muse Bldg, Shinagawa-Ku, Tokyo, 141-0022, Japan
Tel.: (81) 354484380
Web Site: http://www.sonycsl.co.jp
Sales Range: $25-49.9 Million
Emp.: 3
Computer Technology Research Services
N.A.I.C.S.: 541715
Mario Tokoro (Founder)

Sony Corporate Services (Japan) Corporation (1)
2-15-2 Konan Shinagawa Inter City B 11f, Minato-Ku, Tokyo, 108-0075, Japan
Tel.: (81) 357696600
Human Resource Consulting Services
N.A.I.C.S.: 541612

Sony Corporation of America (1)
25 Madison Ave 26th Fl, New York, NY 10010-8601
Tel.: (212) 833-6722
Web Site: http://www.sony.com
Sales Range: $15-24.9 Billion
Holding Company
N.A.I.C.S.: 512110

Karen E. Kelso (VP)

Subsidiary (Domestic):

Crackle (2)
37 Spencer Ave, Sausalito, CA 94965
Tel.: (415) 877-4800
Web Site: http://www.crackle.com
Online Video Sharing
N.A.I.C.S.: 513199

Crispin Corporation (2)
600 Wade Ave, Raleigh, NC 27605
Tel.: (919) 845-7744
Web Site: https://www.crispincorp.com
Media Asset Management Solutions
N.A.I.C.S.: 541511
David Jones (VP-IMS & Head-Bus Unit)

Joint Venture (Domestic):

Music Choice (2)
650 Dresher Rd, Horsham, PA 19044
Tel.: (215) 784-5840
Web Site: http://www.musicchoice.com
Emp.: 60
Music Video Cable Television Programming, Online & Mobile Publishing Services
N.A.I.C.S.: 516210
David Del Beccaro (Founder, Co-Pres & CEO)

Subsidiary (Domestic):

Sony Electronics, Inc. (2)
16450 W Bernardo Dr, San Diego, CA 92177
Tel.: (858) 942-2400
Holding Company; Household Audio & Video Equipment
N.A.I.C.S.: 334310
Stuart Redsun (Sr VP-Mktg)

Branch (Domestic):

Sony Business Solutions & Systems (3)
123 W Tryon Ave, Teaneck, NJ 07666
Tel.: (201) 833-5300
Web Site: http://www.sony.com
Sales Range: $50-74.9 Million
Emp.: 100
Electronic Equipment for Businesses
N.A.I.C.S.: 423690

Division (Domestic):

Sony Electronics Broadcast and Professional Co. (3)
3300 Zanker Rd, San Jose, CA 95134
Tel.: (408) 955-6565
Web Site: http://www.sony.com
Sales Range: $150-199.9 Million
Emp.: 800
Audio & Video Equipment Mfr
N.A.I.C.S.: 334310

Sony Electronics Inc (3)
1730 N 1st St, San Jose, CA 95112
Tel.: (408) 352-4000
Web Site: http://www.sony.com
Sales Range: $100-124.9 Million
Emp.: 300
Semiconductor Integrated Components Mfr
N.A.I.C.S.: 334413

Branch (Domestic):

Sony Electronics Inc. (3)
123 Tice Blvd, Woodcliff Lake, NJ 07675
Tel.: (201) 930-1000
Web Site: http://www.sony.com
Sales Range: $250-299.9 Million
Emp.: 700
Consumer Electronics Mfr
N.A.I.C.S.: 423620

Division (Domestic):

Sony Electronics Inc. Medical Systems Division (3)
1 Sony Dr, Park Ridge, NJ 07656
Tel.: (201) 930-1000
Sales Range: $50-74.9 Million
Emp.: 170
Medical Electronics Mfr
N.A.I.C.S.: 334419

Branch (Domestic):

Sony Electronics Inc.-Distribution Center (3)
5201 Blue Lagoon Dr Ste 400, Miami, FL 33126-2074 (100%)
Tel.: (305) 260-4000
Web Site: http://www.sony-latin.com
Sales Range: $75-99.9 Million
Emp.: 200
Consumer Electronics Distr
N.A.I.C.S.: 423620

Division (Domestic):

Sony Magnetic Products Inc. (3)
4275 W Main St, Dothan, AL 36305-1065
Tel.: (334) 793-7655
Sales Range: $125-149.9 Million
Emp.: 500
Magnetic & Optical Recording Tape Mfr
N.A.I.C.S.: 334610

Branch (Domestic):

Sony Magnetic Products Inc. (4)
5819 Riverside Dr Ste 100, Laredo, TX 78041-2529
Tel.: (956) 795-4500
Web Site: http://www.sony.com
Sales Range: $25-49.9 Million
Emp.: 150
Magnetic & Optical Recording Media Mfr
N.A.I.C.S.: 334610

Subsidiary (Domestic):

Sony Interactive Entertainment LLC (2)
2207 Bridgepointe Pkwy, San Mateo, CA 94404
Tel.: (855) 999-7669
Web Site: http://www.sie.com
Research, Development & Sales of Interactive & Digital Entertainment Products & Services
N.A.I.C.S.: 334118
Kazuo Miura (Deputy Pres)

Subsidiary (Domestic):

Sony Interactive Entertainment America LLC (3)
2207 Bridgepointe Pkwy, San Mateo, CA 94404
Tel.: (650) 655-8000
Web Site: https://www.playstation.com
Sales Range: $250-299.9 Million
Emp.: 1,000
Electronic Games & Accessories Mfr
N.A.I.C.S.: 423920

Subsidiary (Domestic):

Gaikai, Inc. (4)
65 Enterprise Ste 460, Aliso Viejo, CA 92656
Tel.: (949) 330-6850
Web Site: http://www.gaikai.com
Emp.: 165
Cloud-Based Gaming Services
N.A.I.C.S.: 513210
Ueli Gallizzi (CIO)

Subsidiary (Non-US):

Sony Interactive Entertainment Europe Ltd. (3)
10 Great Marlborough Street, London, W1F 7LP, United Kingdom
Tel.: (44) 2078595000
Emp.: 100
Gaming Console & Software Distr
N.A.I.C.S.: 423620

Sony Interactive Entertainment Inc. (3)
1-7-1 Konan, Minato-ku, Tokyo, 108-0075, Japan (100%)
Tel.: (81) 364388000
Web Site: http://www.sie.com
Sales Range: $800-899.9 Million
Emp.: 3,000
Research, Development & Sales of Interactive & Digital Hardware, Software, Content & Network Services
N.A.I.C.S.: 334118
Hermen Hulst (Head-Worldwide Studios)

Subsidiary (Domestic):

Sony Music Entertainment (2)
25 Madison Ave, New York, NY 10010
Tel.: (212) 833-8000
Web Site: https://www.sonymusic.com
Sales Range: $5-14.9 Billion
Recorded Music Production, Record Mfr & Distr
N.A.I.C.S.: 512250
Kevin Kelleher (COO)

Group (Domestic):

Columbia Records Group (3)
25 Madison Ave, New York, NY 10010
Tel.: (212) 833-8000
Web Site: http://www.columbiarecords.com
Music Publishing
N.A.I.C.S.: 512220
Shawn Holiday (Co-Head-Urban Music)

Epic Records Group (3)
550 Madison Ave, New York, NY 10022-3211
Tel.: (212) 833-8000
Web Site: http://www.epicrecords.com
Sales Range: $25-49.9 Million
Emp.: 50
Music Publishing
N.A.I.C.S.: 512230
David Bell (Exec VP & Head-Mktg)

RCA Music Group (3)
550 Madison Ave 6th Fl, New York, NY 10022
Tel.: (212) 930-8000
Web Site: http://www.rcarecords.com
Sales Range: $350-399.9 Million
Emp.: 3,000
Recorded Music & Entertainment Producer & Mfr
N.A.I.C.S.: 334610

Subsidiary (Domestic):

Provident Music Group (4)
741 Cool Springs Blvd E, Franklin, TN 37067
Tel.: (615) 261-6500
Sales Range: $25-49.9 Million
Emp.: 100
Recorded Music & Entertainment Producer & Mfr
N.A.I.C.S.: 512230
Terry Hemmings (Pres & CEO)

Subsidiary (Domestic):

Brentwood-Benson Music Publishing, Inc. (5)
2555 Meridian Blvd Ste 100, Franklin, TN 37067
Tel.: (615) 261-3300
Web Site: http://www.brentwoodbenson.com
Sales Range: $75-99.9 Million
Emp.: 60
Recorded Music & Entertainment Producer & Mfr
N.A.I.C.S.: 512230

Reunion Records (5)
741 Cool Springs Blvd E, Franklin, TN 37067
Tel.: (615) 261-6500
Web Site: http://www.reunionrecords.com
Sales Range: $50-74.9 Million
Emp.: 100
Recorded Music & Entertainment Producer & Mfr
N.A.I.C.S.: 561499

Unit (Domestic):

RED Distribution (3)
79 5th Ave 15 Fl, New York, NY 10003
Tel.: (212) 404-0600
Web Site: http://www.redmusic.com
Sales Range: $25-49.9 Million
Emp.: 80
Independent Record Distr
N.A.I.C.S.: 512250

Subsidiary (Non-US):

SONY MUSIC ENTERTAINMENT BV (3)
Sumatralaan 45, 1217 GP, Hilversum, Netherlands
Tel.: (31) 356298298

SONY GROUP CORPORATION

Sony Group Corporation—(Continued)

Web Site: http://www.sonymusic.nl
Emp.: 30
Recorded Optical Media Distr
N.A.I.C.S.: 512250

Sony DADC Canada Inc. (3)
1121 Leslie Street, Toronto, M3C 2J9, ON, Canada
Tel.: (416) 391-7970
Web Site: http://www.sonydadc.com
Sales Range: $100-124.9 Million
Emp.: 300
Recorded Music & Entertainment Producer & Mfr
N.A.I.C.S.: 334112

Sony Music Entertainment (Philippines), Inc. (3)
Suite 8C The Valero Tower 122 Valero Street Salcedo Village, Ortigas Center, Makati, 1227, Philippines
Tel.: (63) 26363721
Web Site: https://www.sonymusic.com.ph
Sales Range: $25-49.9 Million
Emp.: 60
Music Production & Distribution
N.A.I.C.S.: 512230

Sony Music Entertainment A/S (3)
Vognmagergade 7, 1120, Copenhagen, Denmark
Tel.: (45) 33760300
Web Site: https://www.sonymusic.dk
Sales Range: $25-49.9 Million
Emp.: 40
Music Production & Distribution
N.A.I.C.S.: 512230

Sony Music Entertainment AB (3)
Hollandargatan 13, 10363, Stockholm, Sweden
Tel.: (46) 84121700
Web Site: http://www.sonymusic.se
Sales Range: $25-49.9 Million
Emp.: 45
Music Production & Distribution
N.A.I.C.S.: 512230
Daniel Hoglund *(Head-Intl)*

Sony Music Entertainment Australia Pty. Ltd. (3)
33-39 Talavera Road, North Ryde, 2113, NSW, Australia
Tel.: (61) 298876666
Web Site: http://www.sonymusic.com.au
Music Production & Distribution
N.A.I.C.S.: 512230

Sony Music Entertainment Czech Republic s.r.o. (3)
Palackeho 1, 110 00, Prague, 1, Czech Republic
Tel.: (420) 246086150
Web Site: http://www.sonymusic.cz
Sales Range: $25-49.9 Million
Emp.: 10
Music Production & Distribution
N.A.I.C.S.: 512230

Sony Music Entertainment Germany GmbH (3)
Balanstr 73 Building 31, 81541, Munich, Germany
Tel.: (49) 8941360
Web Site: https://www.sonymusic.de
Music Entertainment Producer & Distr
N.A.I.C.S.: 512230
Patrick Mushatsi-Kareba *(CEO & Mng Dir)*

Division (Domestic):

Sony Music Classical (4)
Edison Hofe Schlegelstrasse 26 B, 10115, Berlin, Germany
Tel.: (49) 30138880
Web Site: http://www.sonymusicclassical.de
Music Production & Distribution
N.A.I.C.S.: 512230

Subsidiary (Non-US):

Sony Music Entertainment Austria GmbH (4)
Mariahilfer Strasse 77 - 79, 1060, Vienna, Austria
Tel.: (43) 160154109
Web Site: https://www.sonymusic.at
Sales Range: $25-49.9 Million
Emp.: 35
Music Production & Distribution
N.A.I.C.S.: 512230

Sony Music Entertainment Switzerland GmbH (4)
Limmatstrasse 264, 8005, Zurich, Switzerland
Tel.: (41) 444043232
Web Site: https://www.sonymusic.ch
Sales Range: $25-49.9 Million
Emp.: 30
Music Production & Distribution
N.A.I.C.S.: 512230
Julie Born *(Mng Dir)*

Division (Domestic):

Spassgesellschaft (4)
Neumarkter Str 28, 81673, Munich, Germany
Tel.: (49) 8941369407
Web Site: http://www.spassgesellschaft.de
Sales Range: $25-49.9 Million
Emp.: 25
Audio Visual & Digital Services
N.A.I.C.S.: 334310

Subsidiary (Non-US):

Sony Music Entertainment Hong Kong Limited (3)
Room 1001 10th Floor China Life Centre 18 Hung Luen Road Hung Hom, 979 King's Road Hunghom, Kowloon, China (Hong Kong)
Tel.: (852) 28631700
Web Site: https://www.sonymusic.com.hk
Sales Range: $25-49.9 Million
Emp.: 25
Music Production & Distribution
N.A.I.C.S.: 512230
Arieo Sung *(Mng Dir)*

Sony Music Entertainment Magyarorszag Kft. (3)
Levil u 4, 1023, Budapest, Hungary
Tel.: (36) 013160316
Web Site: http://www.sonymusic.hu
Sales Range: $25-49.9 Million
Emp.: 25
Music Distr
N.A.I.C.S.: 512230

Sony Music Entertainment Norway A/S (3)
Gjerdrums vei 10A, PO Box 4334, Torshov, 0412, Oslo, Norway
Tel.: (47) 22880000
Web Site: https://www.sonymusic.no
Sales Range: $50-74.9 Million
Emp.: 30
Music Production & Distribution
N.A.I.C.S.: 711130
Lena Midtveit *(Mng Dir)*

Sony Music Entertainment Operating (Thailand) Co., Ltd. (3)
319 Phayathai Road the 17th Floor Chamchuri Square R1706 R1707, Klongtuey, Bangkok, 10330, Thailand
Tel.: (66) 28539933
Web Site: https://www.sonymusic.co.th
Sales Range: $25-49.9 Million
Emp.: 80
Music Production & Distribution
N.A.I.C.S.: 512230

Sony Music Entertainment Poland Sp. z o.o. (3)
Ul Zajecza 2b, 00-351, Warsaw, Poland
Tel.: (48) 223366000
Web Site: https://www.sonymusic.pl
Sales Range: $25-49.9 Million
Emp.: 40
Music Production & Distribution
N.A.I.C.S.: 512230
Kazimierz Pulaski *(Mng Dir)*

Sony Music Entertainment UK Ltd. (3)
2 Canal Reach, London, N1C 4DB, United Kingdom
Tel.: (44) 2073618000
Web Site: https://www.sonymusic.co.uk
Music Mfr
N.A.I.C.S.: 512250
Jessica Carsen *(Sr VP-Comm)*

Subsidiary (Domestic):

Raymond Gubbay Ltd (4)
2 Canal Reach, London, N1C 4DB, United Kingdom
Tel.: (44) 2070253750
Web Site: https://www.raymondgubbay.co.uk
Opera & Ballet Music Entertainment Services
N.A.I.C.S.: 711310
Andrew Claye *(Head-Mktg)*

Unit (Domestic):

Sony Music Nashville (3)
1400 18th Ave S, Nashville, TN 37212
Tel.: (615) 558-1330
Web Site: http://www.sonynashville.com
Country Music Producer
N.A.I.C.S.: 512250
Taylor Lindsey *(Sr VP-A&R)*

Affiliate (Domestic):

Sony/ATV Music Publishing LLC (3)
10635 Santa Monica Blvd Ste 300, Los Angeles, CA 90025 **(100%)**
Tel.: (310) 441-1300
Web Site: http://www.sonyatv.com
Sales Range: $25-49.9 Million
Emp.: 45
Music Publishers
N.A.I.C.S.: 512230
Danny Strick *(Head-Creative)*

Joint Venture (Domestic):

EMI Music Publishing (4)
75 9th Ave, New York, NY 10011
Tel.: (212) 492-1200
Music Publisher & Distr
N.A.I.C.S.: 512230

Subsidiary (Non-US):

EMI Music Publishing (Belgium) SA NV (5)
E Plaskylaan 179, 1030, Brussels, Belgium
Tel.: (32) 22450320
Sales Range: $10-24.9 Million
Emp.: 4
Music Publisher & Distr
N.A.I.C.S.: 512250

EMI Music Publishing (Greece) LLC (5)
259 Messoghion Avenue, N Psychiko, 154 51, Athens, Greece
Tel.: (30) 2106714626
Sales Range: $10-24.9 Million
Emp.: 2
Music Publisher & Distr
N.A.I.C.S.: 512230

EMI Music Publishing (Holland) B.V. (5)
Groest 91 93, 1211 EB, Hilversum, Netherlands
Tel.: (31) 356462000
Sales Range: $25-49.9 Million
Emp.: 15
Music Publisher & Distr
N.A.I.C.S.: 512250

EMI Music Publishing Canada (5)
109 Atlantic Ave Ste 301, Toronto, M6K 1X4, ON, Canada
Tel.: (416) 583-5481
Web Site: http://www.emimusicpub.com
Music Publisher & Distr
N.A.I.C.S.: 512230

EMI Music Publishing Ceska Republika, a.s. (5)
Kovarova 39, Stodulky, 155 00, Prague, Czech Republic
Tel.: (420) 296397115
Web Site: http://www.emi.com
Sales Range: $10-24.9 Million
Emp.: 2
Music Publisher & Distr
N.A.I.C.S.: 512230

EMI Music Publishing Chile (5)
Alfredo Barros Errazuriz, Providencia, 1954, Santiago, Chile
Tel.: (56) 22091009
Sales Range: $10-24.9 Million
Emp.: 5
Music Publisher & Distr

N.A.I.C.S.: 512250

EMI Music Publishing Denmark A/S (5)
Bjorns Tradgardsgrand 1, SE 116-21, Stockholm, Sweden
Tel.: (46) 8 441 19 60
Web Site: http://www.sonyatv.com
Emp.: 19
Music Publisher & Distr
N.A.I.C.S.: 512230
Patrik Sventelius *(Mng Dir)*

EMI Music Publishing Hong Kong (5)
Unit 207 Prosterhui Millenni Plz, 6-8 Harbour Road, North Point, China (Hong Kong)
Tel.: (852) 29565400
Web Site: http://www.sonyatv.com
Sales Range: $25-49.9 Million
Emp.: 13
Music Publisher & Distr
N.A.I.C.S.: 512250

EMI Music Publishing Italia SRL (5)
Via Moremendo 2 27, 20149, Milan, Italy
Tel.: (39) 0248010216
Sales Range: $25-49.9 Million
Emp.: 23
Music Publisher & Distr
N.A.I.C.S.: 512250

EMI Music Publishing Ltd. (5)
30 Golden Sq, London, W1F 9LD, United Kingdom
Tel.: (44) 2030593059
Music Publisher & Distr
N.A.I.C.S.: 512230

EMI Music Publishing Malaysia SDN BHD (5)
Suite 21 7 The Boulevard Lingakaran Syed Putra, Mid Valley City, 59200, Kuala Lumpur, Malaysia
Tel.: (60) 22016888
Music Publishing & Distr
N.A.I.C.S.: 512250

EMI Music Publishing Mexico (5)
Blvd Manuel Avila Camacho 76 Piso 5, Col Lomas de Chapultepec Miguel Hidalgo, Mexico, 11000, Mexico
Tel.: (52) 5555407930
Sales Range: $10-24.9 Million
Emp.: 25
Music Publishing & Distr
N.A.I.C.S.: 512230

EMI Music Publishing Portugal (5)
Praca Nuno Rodriguez dos Santos, Urban Das Laranjeiras 7, 1600 171, Lisbon, Portugal
Tel.: (351) 217217400
Sales Range: $10-24.9 Million
Emp.: 5
Music Publisher & Distributor
N.A.I.C.S.: 512250

EMI Music Publishing Scandinavia AB (5)
Sveavagen 24 26, 103 63, Stockholm, Sweden
Tel.: (46) 858795500
Sales Range: $10-24.9 Million
Emp.: 14
Music Publisher & Distr
N.A.I.C.S.: 512250
Johnny Tennander *(Mng Dir)*

EMI Music Publishing Spain (5)
Calle Gran Via 39 7a Planta, Madrid, 28013, Spain
Tel.: (34) 915239940
Sales Range: $10-24.9 Million
Emp.: 20
Music Publisher & Distr
N.A.I.C.S.: 512250
Juan Ignacio *(Mng Dir)*

Subsidiary (Domestic):

Sony/ATV TREE Music Publishing Nashville (4)
8 Music Sq W, Nashville, TN 37203-3204
Tel.: (615) 726-8300
Web Site: http://www.sonyatv.com
Sales Range: $25-49.9 Million
Emp.: 170
Music Books & Sheet Music Copyright Publisher

AND PRIVATE COMPANIES — SONY GROUP CORPORATION

N.A.I.C.S.: 512230

Subsidiary (Domestic):

Acuff-Rose Music Publishing (5)
8 Music Sq W, Nashville, TN 37203-3207
Tel.: (615) 726-8300
Web Site: http://www.sonyatv.com
Sales Range: $75-99.9 Million
Emp.: 100
Music Publishing Services
N.A.I.C.S.: 512230

Joint Venture (Domestic):

VEVO LLC (3)
825 8th Ave 23rd Fl, New York, NY 10019
Tel.: (212) 331-1357
Web Site: http://www.vevo.com
Music Video Website Operator
N.A.I.C.S.: 516210
Alan Price *(CEO)*

Subsidiary (Domestic):

Sony Music Holding Inc. (2)
25 Madison Ave, New York, NY 10010
Tel.: (212) 833-8000
Music Publishers
N.A.I.C.S.: 334610
Steven E. Kober *(CEO)*

Sony Pictures Entertainment Inc. (2)
10202 Washington Blvd, Culver City, CA 90232-3119 **(100%)**
Tel.: (310) 244-4000
Web Site: https://www.sonypicturesstudios.com
Sales Range: $5-14.9 Billion
Emp.: 3,000
Diversified Motion Picture, Television & Communications Services
N.A.I.C.S.: 512110
Anthony J. Vinciquerra *(Chm & CEO)*

Subsidiary (Non-US):

2waytraffic N.V. (3)
Middenweg 1, 1217 HS, Hilversum, Netherlands
Tel.: (31) 0357508000
Web Site: http://www.2waytraffic.com
Sales Range: $25-49.9 Million
Emp.: 150
Interactive Entertainment Services
N.A.I.C.S.: 516120

Unit (Domestic):

2waytraffic Mobile (4)
Middenweg 1, 1217 HS, Hilversum, Netherlands
Tel.: (31) 357508000
Web Site: http://www.2waytraffic.com
Sales Range: $25-49.9 Million
Emp.: 60
Mobile Marketing, Entertainment, Internet & Customized Solutions
N.A.I.C.S.: 513210

Subsidiary (Domestic):

Alamo Drafthouse Cinemas, Ltd. (3)
13729 Research Blvd Ste 735, Austin, TX 78750
Tel.: (512) 219-5408
Web Site: http://www.drafthouse.com
Emp.: 100
Motion Picture Theaters (except Drive-Ins)
N.A.I.C.S.: 512131
Michael Kustermann *(CEO)*

CPE Holdings, Inc. (3)
10202 Washington Blvd Ste 1132, Culver City, CA 90232
Tel.: (310) 244-4000
Sales Range: $1-9.9 Million
Emp.: 51
Investment Management Service
N.A.I.C.S.: 523940

Califon Productions, Inc. (3)
10202 Washington Blvd, Culver City, CA 90232-3119
Tel.: (310) 244-8687
Motion Picture Production Services
N.A.I.C.S.: 512110

Group (Domestic):

Columbia TriStar Motion Picture Group (3)
10202 W Washington Blvd, Culver City, CA 90232-3119
Tel.: (310) 244-4000
Web Site: http://www.sonypicture.com
Sales Range: $800-899.9 Million
Emp.: 3,000
Motion Pictures Producer & Distr
N.A.I.C.S.: 512120

Subsidiary (Domestic):

Columbia Pictures (4)
10202 W Washington Blvd, Culver City, CA 90232
Tel.: (310) 244-4000
Web Site: http://www.sonypictures.com
Sales Range: $650-699.9 Million
Emp.: 3,000
Movie Production Services
N.A.I.C.S.: 512110
Sanford Panitch *(Pres)*

Subsidiary (Non-US):

Columbia TriStar Films (UK) (4)
25 Golden Sq, London, W1F 9LU, United Kingdom
Tel.: (44) 2075331000
Sales Range: $25-49.9 Million
Emp.: 200
Motion Picture Distr
N.A.I.C.S.: 512110

Subsidiary (Domestic):

Screen Gems Inc. (4)
10202 W Washington Blvd, Culver City, CA 90232
Tel.: (310) 244-4000
Web Site: http://www.sonypictures.com
Motion Picture Distr
N.A.I.C.S.: 512120

Subsidiary (Domestic):

Game Show Network, LLC (3)
2150 Colorada Ave Ste 100, Santa Monica, CA 90404 **(100%)**
Tel.: (310) 255-6800
Web Site: https://www.gameshownetwork.com
Sales Range: $200-249.9 Million
Emp.: 130
Cable Television Network
N.A.I.C.S.: 516210
John Zaccario *(Pres)*

Unit (Domestic):

GSN Games (4)
100 Summer St, Boston, MA 02110
Tel.: (857) 202-6669
Web Site: http://www.gsngames.com
Video Game Developer
N.A.I.C.S.: 513210
Susan Marciano *(Sr VP-Tech Ops & Facility Mgmt)*

Subsidiary (Non-US):

SPE Networks - Asia Pte. Ltd. (3)
3 Tampines Central 1 0201 05 Abacus Plaza, Singapore, 529540, Singapore **(100%)**
Tel.: (65) 62606060
Web Site: http://www.axn-asia.com
24-Hour Cable & Satellite Television Channel
N.A.I.C.S.: 516210

Subsidiary (Domestic):

Sony Pictures Animation Inc. (3)
9050 W Washington Blvd, Culver City, CA 90232
Tel.: (310) 840-8000
Web Site: https://www.sonypicturesanimation.com
Animation Picture Production Services
N.A.I.C.S.: 512110
Pam Marsden *(Head-Production)*

Unit (Domestic):

Sony Pictures Classics (3)
25 Madison Ave Fl 24, New York, NY 10010
Tel.: (212) 833-8333
Web Site: http://www.sonyclassics.com
Sales Range: $25-49.9 Million
Emp.: 27
Upscale Independent Art Film Producer, Acquirer & Distr
N.A.I.C.S.: 512120
Michael Barker *(Pres)*

Group (Domestic):

Sony Pictures Digital (3)
1202 W Washington Blvd, Culver City, CA 90232
Tel.: (310) 840-8676
Digital Content Producer for Movies, Games & Websites
N.A.I.C.S.: 512110

Subsidiary (Domestic):

Sony Online Entertainment, Inc. (4)
8928 Terman Ct, San Diego, CA 92121
Tel.: (858) 577-3100
Web Site: http://www.sonyonline.com
Sales Range: $200-249.9 Million
Emp.: 600
Online Gaming Products
N.A.I.C.S.: 713990

Sony Pictures Imageworks Inc. (4)
9050 W Washington Blvd, Culver City, CA 90232
Tel.: (310) 840-8000
Web Site: https://www.imageworks.com
Sales Range: $300-349.9 Million
Emp.: 2,000
Special Effects Creator for Motion Pictures
N.A.I.C.S.: 512110
Michelle Grady *(Exec VP)*

Unit (Domestic):

Sony Pictures Entertainment Worldwide Product Fulfillment (3)
150 Roger Ave, Inwood, NY 11096-1622 **(100%)**
Tel.: (718) 868-5800
Sales Range: $25-49.9 Million
Emp.: 100
Motion Picture & Video Services
N.A.I.C.S.: 512110

Sony Pictures Home Entertainment (3)
10202 W Washington Blvd, Culver City, CA 90232-3119
Tel.: (310) 244-4000
Sales Range: $800-899.9 Million
Video & DVD Distr
N.A.I.C.S.: 512120
Don Eklund *(Exec VP-Advanced Technologies)*

Subsidiary (Non-US):

Sony Pictures Networks India Private Limited (3)
4th Floor Interface Building No 7, Off Malad Link Road Malad West, Mumbai, 400 064, India
Tel.: (91) 2267081230
Web Site: http://www.sonypicturesnetworks.com
Television Channels Operator
N.A.I.C.S.: 515210
N.P. Singh *(CEO & Mng Dir)*

Subsidiary (Domestic):

Sony Pictures Releasing Corporation (3)
10202 W Washington Blvd, Culver City, CA 90232-3119
Tel.: (310) 244-4000
Sales Range: $800-899.9 Million
Motion Picture Distr
N.A.I.C.S.: 512120

Subsidiary (Non-US):

Sony Pictures Releasing GmbH (3)
Kemperplatz 1, 10785, Berlin, Germany
Tel.: (49) 3025755800
Web Site: https://www.sonypictures.de
Emp.: 30
Motion Picture Distr & Marketer
N.A.I.C.S.: 512120
Martin Bachmann *(Mng Dir)*

Sony Pictures Releasing of India Limited (3)
503 Alpha Main Street, Hiranandani Gardens Powai, Hiranandani Gardens Powai, Mumbai, 400 076, India
Tel.: (91) 2256975163
Web Site: http://www.sony.co.in
Motion Picture Distr & Marketer
N.A.I.C.S.: 512120

Subsidiary (Domestic):

Sony Pictures Television Inc. (3)
10202 W Washington Blvd, Culver City, CA 90232 **(100%)**
Tel.: (310) 244-4000
Web Site: https://www.sonypicturestelevision.com
Sales Range: $25-49.9 Million
Emp.: 35
Television Show Producer
N.A.I.C.S.: 516120
Mark Young *(Exec VP-Western Europe)*

Subsidiary (Domestic):

Jeopardy Productions, Inc. (4)
10202 Washington Blvd, Culver City, CA 90232
Tel.: (310) 244-8855
Web Site: https://www.jeopardy.com
Emp.: 100
Television Producer
N.A.I.C.S.: 512110

Sony Corporation of Hong Kong Ltd. (1)
Suite 3301 33/F Tower 1 The Gateway Harbour City, Kowloon, China (Hong Kong) **(100%)**
Tel.: (852) 29091111
Web Site: https://www.sony.com.hk
Electronic Components Mfr
N.A.I.C.S.: 334419

Sony DADC Corporation (1)
5-1-12 Kita-shinagawa, Shinagawa-ku, Tokyo, 141-0001, Japan
Tel.: (81) 3 5448 2220
Web Site: http://www.sonydad.com
Optical Recording Media Mfr & Distr
N.A.I.C.S.: 334610

Subsidiary (Non-US):

Entertainment Network Scandinavia AB (2)
Viaredsvagen 24, Boras, 504 94, Sweden
Tel.: (46) 33206100
Audio & Video Equipment Mfr
N.A.I.C.S.: 334310

OOO Sony DADC (2)
Office A100 4 Stasovoy Ul, 119 071, Moscow, Russia
Tel.: (7) 495 935 7218
Sales Range: $25-49.9 Million
Emp.: 15
Optical Recording Media Mfr
N.A.I.C.S.: 334610
Johannes Stegfellner *(Mng Dir)*

Subsidiary (US):

Sony DADC (2)
1800 N Fruitridge Ave, Terre Haute, IN 47804-1780 **(100%)**
Tel.: (812) 462-8100
Web Site: https://www.sonydadc.com
Sales Range: $350-399.9 Million
Emp.: 150
DVD, CD-ROM & Audio Recording Compact Discs Mfr
N.A.I.C.S.: 334610

Subsidiary (Non-US):

Sony DADC Austria AG (2)
Sonystrasse 20, Anif, Salzburg, 50821, Austria
Tel.: (43) 6246 880 555
Optical Storage Media Mfr & Distr
N.A.I.C.S.: 334610

Subsidiary (Non-US):

Sony DADC China Co., Ltd. (3)
2nd Floor No 99 Jiang Tian East Road Song-Jiang, Industrial Development Zone, 201600, Shanghai, China
Tel.: (86) 21 3760 3999
Emp.: 30
Optical Media Mfr
N.A.I.C.S.: 334610
Xiao Wu *(Gen Mgr)*

SONY GROUP CORPORATION — INTERNATIONAL PUBLIC

Sony Group Corporation—(Continued)

Subsidiary (Non-US):

Sony DADC Costa Rica Limitada (2)
Paseo Colon De La Pizza Hut 200 Norte Y 25 Oeste, San Jose, Costa Rica
Tel.: (506) 22484550
Web Site: www.sonydadc.com
Consumer Electronics Distr
N.A.I.C.S.: 423620

Sony DADC Czech Republic s.r.o (2)
Dobranska 545, 332 09, Stenovice, Czech Republic
Tel.: (420) 377159600
Sales Range: $75-99.9 Million
Emp.: 130
Compact Disc Mfr
N.A.I.C.S.: 334310
Werner Gangl *(Gen Mgr)*

Sony DADC France S.A.S. (2)
117th Ave Victorheto, 92100, Boulogne-Billancourt, France
Tel.: (33) 1 6413 8260
Electronic Component Mfr & Distr
N.A.I.C.S.: 334419

Sony DADC Germany GmbH (2)
Waldstr 37, Dietzenbach, 63128, Germany
Tel.: (49) 60744980
Optical Media Warehousing & Distr
N.A.I.C.S.: 493190

Sony DADC Hong Kong Ltd. (2)
5/F Ykk Bldg Ph Iii 7 San Ping Circuit, Tuen Mun, New Territories, China (Hong Kong)
Tel.: (852) 31271888
Sales Range: $25-49.9 Million
Emp.: 12
Optical Recording Media Mfr
N.A.I.C.S.: 334610

Sony DADC Iberia S.L. (2)
Avda Olimpico Francisco Fernandez Ochoa n 16, Poligono Industrial Urtinsa, 28923, Alcorcon, Madrid, Spain
Tel.: (34) 91 596 83 96
Sales Range: $25-49.9 Million
Emp.: 7
Optical Recording Media Distr
N.A.I.C.S.: 423990
Toshio Kohara *(Gen Mgr)*

Sony DADC Italia S.r.l. (2)
Via Cascina Nuova, 26814, Livraga, Italy
Tel.: (39) 0377 986450
Sales Range: $25-49.9 Million
Emp.: 6
Optical Recording Media Mfr
N.A.I.C.S.: 334610

Subsidiary (Domestic):

Sony DADC Japan Inc. (2)
Sumitomo-fudousan Nishi-Gotanda Bldg 6F 3-6-21 Nishi-Gotanda, Shinagawa-Ku, Tokyo, 141-0031, Japan
Tel.: (81) 3 3492 9667
Web Site: http://www.sonydadc.co.jp
Video & Audio Disc Mfr
N.A.I.C.S.: 334310

Plant (Domestic):

Sony DADC Japan Inc. - Ibaraki Facility (DADJ-I) (3)
6700-1 To Naka-shi, Ibaraki, 311-0122, Japan
Tel.: (81) 29 270 6700
Web Site: http://www.sonydadc.co.jp
Optical Recording Media Mfr
N.A.I.C.S.: 334610

Sony DADC Japan Inc. - Shizuoka Facility (DADJ-O) Oigawa (3)
200-3 Aikawa Yaidu-shi, Yaizu, 421-0216, Shizuoka, Japan
Tel.: (81) 54 622 1321
Web Site: http://www.sonydadc.co.jp
Optical Recording Media Mfr
N.A.I.C.S.: 334610

Sony DADC Japan Inc. - Shizuoka Facility (DADJ-Y) Yoshida (3)
1300-1 Ohata Yoshida-cho, Haibara-gun, Shizuoka, 421-0305, Japan
Tel.: (81) 548 33 1291
Web Site: http://www.sonydadc.co.jp
Sales Range: $100-124.9 Million
Emp.: 500
Optical Recording Media Mfr
N.A.I.C.S.: 334610

Subsidiary (Non-US):

Sony DADC Manufacturing India Private Limited (2)
Plot No C-106 TTC Industrial Area Pawne MIDC, Pawane Village, 400 705, Navi Mumbai, India
Tel.: (91) 22 6145 6800
Emp.: 10
Optical Recording Media Mfr
N.A.I.C.S.: 334610
Rajat Kakar *(Head-Home Entertainment Svcs Bus)*

Sony DADC UK Ltd. (2)
Kent House 14/17 Market Place 5th Floor, London, W1W 8AJ, United Kingdom
Tel.: (44) 2073079771
Web Site: http://www.sonydadc.com
Entertainment Software Development Services
N.A.I.C.S.: 541511

Sony Music Entertainment Mexico, S.A. de C.V. (2)
Boulevard Manuel Avila Camacho No 191, 11510, Mexico, Mexico
Tel.: (52) 5552493200
Web Site: https://www.sonymusic.com.mx
Audio Recording Services
N.A.I.C.S.: 512240

Sony Nuevo Laredo, S.A. de C.V. (2)
Blvrd Luis Donaldo Colosio Km 0 200 Sur, Nuevo Laredo, 88295, Mexico
Tel.: (52) 8677113000
Optical Recording Media Mfr
N.A.I.C.S.: 334610

Sony Deutschland GmbH (1)
Hugo Eckener Strasse 20, D 50829, Cologne, Germany
Tel.: (49) 221 537794
Web Site: http://www.sony.de
Sales Range: $200-249.9 Million
Emp.: 800
Televisions, Videotape Recorders & Players, Laser Disc Players & Closed-Circuit Television Equipment Mfr
N.A.I.C.S.: 334310

Sony Digital Network Applications Inc. (1)
2-21-28 Higashigotanda, Shinagawa-ku, Tokyo, 141-0022, Japan
Tel.: (81) 3 5448 3232
Web Site: http://www.sonydna.com
Rev.: $77,658,800
Emp.: 285
Software Development Services
N.A.I.C.S.: 541511

Sony Digital Products (Wuxi) Co., Ltd. (1)
No 64 Changjiang Road High-Tech Industry Development Zone, Wuxi, 214028, Jiangsu, China
Tel.: (86) 51085288888
Digital Camera Mfr
N.A.I.C.S.: 339999

Sony EMCS Corporation (1)
5-1-12 Kitashinagawa Gotenyama Technology Center, Shinagawa-Ku, Tokyo, 141-0001, Japan
Tel.: (81) 354484411
Electronic Component Mfr & Distr
N.A.I.C.S.: 334419

Sony Electronics (Singapore) Pte. Ltd. (1)
2 International Business Park 01 10 Tower 1, The Strategy, The Strategy, Singapore, 609930, Singapore
Tel.: (65) 65448000
Web Site: http://www.sony.com.sg
Sales Range: $25-49.9 Million
Emp.: 35
Cathode Ray Tubes Mfr
N.A.I.C.S.: 334419

Sony Electronics Vietnam Company Ltd. (1)
Level 7 President Place Building 93 Nguyen Du St Dist 1, Binh Thanh Dist, Ho Chi Minh City, Vietnam
Tel.: (84) 838222227
Consumer Electronics Distr
N.A.I.C.S.: 423620

Sony Engineering Corporation (1)
3-3-1 Tsujidoshinmachi Sony Shonan Technology, Fujisawa, 251-0042, Kanagawa, Japan (100%)
Tel.: (81) 466383411
Web Site: http://www.sonyengineering.co.jp
Sales Range: $550-599.9 Million
Emp.: 510
Electronic Components Mfr
N.A.I.C.S.: 334419

Sony Enterprise Co., Ltd. (1)
4-2-11 Ginza Hulic Ginza Sukiyabashi Bldg 7f, Chuo-Ku, Tokyo, 104-0061, Japan
Tel.: (81) 351592211
Property Management Services
N.A.I.C.S.: 531311

Sony Espana, S.A. (1)
Calle Sabino Arana 52, Barcelona, 8028, Spain
Tel.: (34) 93 402 64 00
Web Site: http://www.sony.es
Emp.: 10
Household Appliances Mfr
N.A.I.C.S.: 335220

Sony Europe Finance Plc (1)
Saint Helens 1 Undershaft, London, EC3A 8NP, United Kingdom (100%)
Tel.: (44) 2074268600
Web Site: http://www.sony.co.uk
Sales Range: $25-49.9 Million
Emp.: 70
Financial Services
N.A.I.C.S.: 561499

Sony Europe Limited (1)
The Heights Brooklands, Weybridge, KT13 0XW, Surrey, United Kingdom
Tel.: (44) 1932816000
Web Site: https://www.sony.co.uk
Emp.: 40
Consumer Electronics Distr
N.A.I.C.S.: 423620

Sony Finance International, Inc. (1)
1-1-1 Minamiaoyama, Minato-ku, Tokyo, 107-0062, Japan
Tel.: (81) 3 3475 8711
Sales Range: $50-74.9 Million
Emp.: 100
Credit Card Issuing Services
N.A.I.C.S.: 522210

Sony Financial Holdings Inc. (1)
1-9-2 Otemachi, Chiyoda-ku, Tokyo, 100-0004, Japan (100%)
Tel.: (81) 352906500
Web Site: https://www.sonyfg.co.jp
Rev.: $14,760,388,920
Assets: $122,022,027,900
Liabilities: $116,070,994,080
Net Worth: $5,951,033,820
Earnings: $562,390,440
Emp.: 11,055
Fiscal Year-end: 03/31/2019
Financial Services
N.A.I.C.S.: 525990
Atsuo Niwa *(Pres-Sony Assurance Inc)*

Subsidiary (Domestic):

Sony Assurance Inc. (2)
5-37-1 Kamata, Ota-ku, Tokyo, 144-0052, Japan
Tel.: (81) 357440300
Web Site: https://www.sonysonpo.co.jp
Sales Range: $800-899.9 Million
Emp.: 1,080
Property & Casualty Insurance Services
N.A.I.C.S.: 524126

Sony Bank Inc. (2)
2-1-6 Uchisaiwaicho, Chiyoda, Tokyo, 107-0062, Japan
Tel.: (81) 357851070
Web Site: https://www.sonybank.net
Financial Services
N.A.I.C.S.: 522110
Masaaki Tanaka *(Exec Officer)*

Subsidiary (Domestic):

SmartLink Network, Inc. (3)
1-1 Minami Aoyama 1-chome, Minato-ku, Tokyo, 107-0062, Japan
Tel.: (81) 3 3475 6021
Credit Card & Business Settlement Services
N.A.I.C.S.: 522180

Sony Bank Securities Inc. (3)
3-26 Kandanishikicho, Chiyoda-Ku, Tokyo, 101-0054, Japan
Tel.: (81) 358055221
Securities Brokerage Services
N.A.I.C.S.: 523150

Subsidiary (Domestic):

Sony Life Insurance Co., Ltd. (2)
1-9-2 Otemachi, Chiyoda-ku, Tokyo, 100-8179, Japan (100%)
Tel.: (81) 333779483
Web Site: http://www.sonyfh.co.jp
Emp.: 7,289
Fire Insurance Services
N.A.I.C.S.: 524113

Subsidiary (Domestic):

LIPLA Co., Ltd. (3)
5-1 Chigasakichuo Kohoku Tokyu S C Semmontengai 4f, Tsuzuki-Ku, Yokohama, 224-0032, Kanagawa, Japan
Tel.: (81) 459445151
Insurance Management Services
N.A.I.C.S.: 524298

Sony Global Treasury Services Plc (1)
15th Floor Aviva Tower St Helens 1 Undershaft, London, EC3A 8NP, United Kingdom
Tel.: (44) 2074268696
Emp.: 7
Treasury Services
N.A.I.C.S.: 921130
Bruno Dugandzic *(Gen Mgr)*

Sony Gulf FZE Limited (1)
Jebel Ali, PO Box 16871, Dubai, United Arab Emirates (100%)
Tel.: (971) 48815488
Web Site: http://www.sony-mea.com
Sales Range: $150-199.9 Million
Emp.: 300
Home Appliances & Electronics Products Distr
N.A.I.C.S.: 423620

Sony Holding (Asia) B.V. (1)
Schipholweg 275, Badhoevedorp, 1171 PK, Netherlands
Tel.: (31) 206581911
Investment Management Service
N.A.I.C.S.: 523940

Sony Honda Mobility Inc. (1)
c/o Honda Motor Company No 1-1 Minami-Aoyama 2-chome, Minato-ku, Tokyo, 107-8556, Japan (50%)
Tel.: (81) 334231111
Web Site: https://www.shm-afeela.com
Electric Motor Vehicle Designer, Developer & Mfr
N.A.I.C.S.: 336110
Izumi Kawanishi *(Pres & COO)*

Sony Hungaria kft (1)
Arpad Fejedelem Utja 26-28, 1023, Budapest, Hungary
Tel.: (36) 1 235 5349
Web Site: http://www.sony.hu
Electronic Components Mfr
N.A.I.C.S.: 327910

Sony India Pvt. Ltd. (1)
A-18 Mohan Cooperative Industrial Estate Mathura Road, New Delhi, 110044, India
Tel.: (91) 1166006600
Web Site: https://www.sony.co.in
Sales Range: $300-349.9 Million
Emp.: 900
Consumer Electronics Sales & Maintenance Services
N.A.I.C.S.: 423620

Sony International (Hong Kong) Ltd. (1)
25/F Tower I The Gateway 25 Canton Road, Tsimshatsui, Kowloon, China (Hong Kong)
Tel.: (852) 2 956 2255
Optical Recording Media Mfr & Distr
N.A.I.C.S.: 334610

Sony Ireland Ltd. (1)
4-6 Riverwalk Citywest Business Campus,
Tallaght, 24, Dublin, Ireland (100%)
Tel.: (353) 14131700
Web Site: http://www.sony.ie
Sales Range: $25-49.9 Million
Emp.: 40
Electronic Home Audio & Video Products Mfr
N.A.I.C.S.: 334310

Sony Italia S.p.A. (1)
Via Gulileo Galilei 40, 20092, Cinisello Balsamo, Milan, Italy
Tel.: (39) 02 618 381
Consumer Electronics Mfr & Distr
N.A.I.C.S.: 334419

Sony Korea Corporation (1)
24 Fl One IFC Gukjegeumr Yung-ro Yeouido-dong, Yeongdeungpo-gu, Seoul, 150-868, Korea (South)
Tel.: (82) 2 6001 4000
Sales Range: $150-199.9 Million
Emp.: 278
Consumer Electronics Distr
N.A.I.C.S.: 423620
Seonmi Kim *(Pres & CEO)*

Sony LSI Design Inc. (1)
134 Gohdo-cho, Hodogaya-ku, Yokohama, 240-0005, Kanagawa, Japan
Tel.: (81) 45 338 5250
Web Site: http://www.sony-lsi.co.jp
Rev.: $243,661,000
Emp.: 6,000
Electronic Circuits Mfr
N.A.I.C.S.: 334419

Sony Latin America Inc. (1)
5201 Blue Lagoon Dr Ste 400, Miami, FL 33126
Tel.: (305) 260-4000
Web Site: https://www.sony-asia.com
Sales Range: $50-74.9 Million
Emp.: 180
Audio Recording Services
N.A.I.C.S.: 512240

Subsidiary (Domestic):

AXN Latin America Inc. (2)
1688 Meridian Ave, Miami, FL 33139-2710
Tel.: (305) 532-4177
Sales Range: $25-49.9 Million
Emp.: 28
Motion Picture & Video Production Services
N.A.I.C.S.: 512110

Subsidiary (Non-US):

Sony Corporation of Panama, S.A. (2)
Via Simon Bolivar, Panama, 4317, Panama
Tel.: (507) 2789800
Web Site: http://www.sony.com.pa
Sales Range: $75-99.9 Million
Electronic Components & Related Products Mfr
N.A.I.C.S.: 334419
Consuelo de Cambra *(Corp Travel Planner)*

Sony Malaysia Sdn. Bhd. (1)
11th Centrepoint South The Boulevard Mid Valley City, Lingkaran Syed Putra, 59200, Kuala Lumpur, Malaysia
Tel.: (60) 322950200
Web Site: https://www.sony.com.my
Sales Range: $75-99.9 Million
Emp.: 240
Consumer Electronics Distr
N.A.I.C.S.: 423620

Subsidiary (Domestic):

Sony EMCS (Malaysia) Sdn. Bhd. (2)
Lot 5 Jalan Kemajuan Bangi Industrial Estate Section 13, 43650, Bandar Baru Bangi, Malaysia
Tel.: (60) 389257887
Consumer Electronics Mfr
N.A.I.C.S.: 334220

Sony Supply Chain Solutions (Malaysia) Sdn. Bhd. (2)
Lot 524 Jalan P10/10, 43650, Bandar Baru Bangi, Selangor Darul Ehsan, Malaysia
Tel.: (60) 3 8925 2102
Web Site: http://www.sscsm.sony.com.my

Emp.: 10
Supply Chain Management Services
N.A.I.C.S.: 541614
Francis Hiew *(Mng Dir)*

Sony Marketing (Japan) Inc. (1)
1-7-1 Konan, Minato-ku, Tokyo, 108-0075, Japan
Tel.: (81) 3 5792 1000
Electronic Appliance Distr
N.A.I.C.S.: 423620

Sony Mobile Communications AB (1)
Mobilvsgen 4, 221 88, Lund, Sweden (100%)
Tel.: (46) 108000000
Web Site: http://www.sonymobile.com
Sales Range: $5-14.9 Billion
Emp.: 3,000
Mobile Device Mfr
N.A.I.C.S.: 334220

Subsidiary (Domestic):

Sony Mobile Communications AB - Kista (2)
2 Torshamnsgatan 20, PO Box 64, 164 94, Kista, Sweden
Tel.: (46) 108000000
Web Site: http://www.sonymobile.com
Emp.: 4
Communication Equipment Mfr
N.A.I.C.S.: 334290

Subsidiary (Non-US):

Sony Mobile Communications Co., Ltd. (2)
Sony Ericsson Bldg No 16 Guangshun South St, Chaoyang Dist, Beijing, 100102, China
Tel.: (86) 1058656888
Telecommunications Equipment Mfr
N.A.I.C.S.: 334290

Subsidiary (US):

Sony Mobile Communications USA Inc. (2)
601 Brickell Key Dr, Miami, FL 33131
Tel.: (305) 755-6600
Web Site: http://www.sonymobile.com
Sales Range: $25-49.9 Million
Emp.: 43
Mobile Communications Services
N.A.I.C.S.: 517112

Sony Music Communications Inc. (1)
1-4 Ichigayatamachi Sme Ichigaya Bldg 2f, Shinjuku-Ku, Tokyo, 162-0843, Japan
Tel.: (81) 332667811
Communication Software Development Services
N.A.I.C.S.: 541511

Sony Music Distribution (Japan) Inc. (1)
4-5 Rokubancho, Chiyoda-Ku, Tokyo, 102-8353, Japan
Tel.: (81) 335155483
Entertainment Software Distr
N.A.I.C.S.: 423430

Sony Music Entertainment (Japan) Inc. (1)
4-5 Rokubancho, Chiyoda-ku, Tokyo, 102-8353, Japan
Tel.: (81) 335155050
Web Site: https://www.sme.co.jp
Optical Recording Media Mfr
N.A.I.C.S.: 334610
Alex Sancaya *(Mng Dir-Indonesia)*

Sony Network Communications Inc. (1)
1-7-1 Konan, Minato-ku, Tokyo, 108-0075, Japan
Tel.: (81) 357451500
Web Site: https://www.sonynetwork.co.jp
Sales Range: $1-4.9 Billion
Emp.: 828
Internet Connection & Entertainment Services
N.A.I.C.S.: 517810
Hirokazu Takagaki *(Pres)*

Subsidiary (Domestic):

Enigmo, Inc. (2)

6th floor NMF Aoyama 1-chome Building 8-1-22 Akasaka, Minato-ku, Tokyo, 107-0052, Japan
Tel.: (81) 357754760
Web Site: https://www.enigmo.co.jp
Rev.: $66,482,240
Assets: $122,781,120
Liabilities: $24,577,520
Net Worth: $98,203,600
Earnings: $6,892,160
Emp.: 134
Fiscal Year-end: 01/31/2023
Shopping Websites Development Services
N.A.I.C.S.: 541511
Shokei Suda *(Founder & CEO)*

SMN Corporation (2)
12th floor Osaki With Tower 2-11-1 Osaki, Shinagawa-ku, Tokyo, 141-0032, Japan (100%)
Tel.: (81) 354357931
Web Site: https://www.so-netmedia.jp
Rev.: $61,710,960
Assets: $44,115,140
Liabilities: $19,658,140
Net Worth: $24,457,000
Earnings: ($6,795,080)
Emp.: 80
Fiscal Year-end: 03/31/2024
Online Marketing Services
N.A.I.C.S.: 541613
Noriyoshi Nakagawa *(Exec VP)*

Subsidiary (Domestic):

Ruby Groupe Inc. (3)
2-43-10 Tomigaya, Shibuya-ku, Tokyo, 151-0063, Japan
Tel.: (81) 364514007
Web Site: https://www.rubygroupe.jp
Emp.: 86
E-commerce Operation & Marketing Services
N.A.I.C.S.: 541613

Subsidiary (Non-US):

So-net Entertainment Taiwan Limited (2)
2F Building E, 19-13 San Chung Road, Taipei, Taiwan (64%)
Tel.: (886) 226553551
Sales Range: $50-74.9 Million
Emp.: 200
Internet Service Provider
N.A.I.C.S.: 517810

Sony Network Taiwan Ltd. (2)
2F Building E No 19-13 Sanchong Rd, Nangang Dist, Taipei, 115, Taiwan
Tel.: (886) 2 2655 3551
Web Site: http://www.so-net.com.tw
Sales Range: $50-74.9 Million
Emp.: 20
Internet Service Provider
N.A.I.C.S.: 517810
Hirotake Nagata *(CEO)*

Sony New Zealand Ltd. (1)
North Shore Mail Centre, Akoranga Business Park Akoranga Drive Northcote, Auckland, 2022, New Zealand
Tel.: (64) 94886188
Web Site: https://www.sony.co.nz
Sales Range: $25-49.9 Million
Emp.: 9
Consumer Electronics Mfr & Distr
N.A.I.C.S.: 423620

Sony Optiarc Inc. (1)
4-16-1 Okata, Atsugi, 243-0021, Kanagawa, Japan
Tel.: (81) 462262200
Web Site: http://www.sony-optiarc.com
Sales Range: $50-74.9 Million
Emp.: 201
Optical Recording Media Mfr & Distr
N.A.I.C.S.: 334610

Sony PCL Inc. (1)
1-7-18 Konan, Minato-ku, Tokyo, 108-0075, Japan
Tel.: (81) 357929300
Web Site: https://www.sonypcl.jp
Video Production Services
N.A.I.C.S.: 512110

Sony Philippines, Inc. (1)
11th Floor Marajo Tower 312 26th Street West Cor 4th Avenue, Bonifacio Global City, Taguig, 1634, Philippines
Tel.: (63) 28603333
Web Site: https://www.sony.com.ph
Sales Range: $75-99.9 Million
Emp.: 12
Consumer Electronics Distr
N.A.I.C.S.: 423620

Sony Precision Devices (Huizhou) Co., Ltd. (1)
No 18 Sanheng Road Huitai Industrial Park, Huizhou, 516003, Guangdong, China
Tel.: (86) 7522606333
Electronic Components Mfr
N.A.I.C.S.: 334419

Sony Precision Engineering Center (Singapore) Pte. Ltd. (1)
52 Tuas Ave 9, Singapore, 639193, Singapore (100%)
Tel.: (65) 68615858
Web Site: http://www.sony.com.sg
Sales Range: $400-449.9 Million
Emp.: 2,000
Electronic Parts & Components Mfr & Distr
N.A.I.C.S.: 334419

Sony South Africa (Pty) Limited (1)
Sony South Africa Business Park 179 - 15th Road, Randjespark, Johannesburg, 1685, South Africa
Tel.: (27) 11 690 3200
Web Site: http://www.sony.co.za
Sales Range: $50-74.9 Million
Emp.: 100
Consumer Electronics Sales & Maintenance Services
N.A.I.C.S.: 423620

Sony Technology (Malaysia) Sdn. Bhd. (1)
North Plant Lot 4 Jalan P/1 Kawasan Perindustrian Bangi, Bandar Baru Bangi, Kajang, Selangor, Malaysia
Tel.: (60) 603 89258889
Audio Equipment Mfr
N.A.I.C.S.: 334310

Sony Thai Co. Ltd. (1)
4F Kromadit Bldg 2126 New Petchburi Rd Bangkapi Huay Kwang, 10310, Bangkok, Thailand
Tel.: (66) 27156000
Web Site: http://www.sony.co.th
Sales Range: $75-99.9 Million
Emp.: 150
Electronics Sales
N.A.I.C.S.: 423690

Sony of Canada Ltd. (1)
2235 Shepard Avenue East Suite 700, Toronto, M2J 5B5, ON, Canada (100%)
Tel.: (416) 499-1414
Web Site: https://fr.corporate.sony.ca
Sales Range: $150-199.9 Million
Emp.: 350
Radio & Television Broadcasting & Electronic Equipment
N.A.I.C.S.: 423620

Sony/Taiyo Corporation (1)
1402-14 Kansui Ogami Hijimachi, Hayamigun, Oita, 879-1504, Japan
Tel.: (81) 977729131
Web Site: https://www.sony-taiyo.co.jp
Sales Range: $50-74.9 Million
Emp.: 180
Microphone Mfr & Distr
N.A.I.C.S.: 334310

SOOCHOW SECURITIES CO., LTD.
No 5 Xingyang Street SIP, Suzhou, 215021, Jiangsu, China
Tel.: (86) 95330
Web Site: https://www.dwzq.com.cn
Year Founded: 1993
601555—(SHG)
Rev.: $1,472,192,097
Assets: $19,088,370,662
Liabilities: $13,672,047,121
Net Worth: $5,416,323,541
Earnings: $243,627,317
Fiscal Year-end: 12/31/22
Security Brokerage & Investment Management Services
N.A.I.C.S.: 523150

SOOCHOW SECURITIES CO., LTD.

Soochow Securities Co., Ltd.—(Continued)

Fan Li (Chm & Pres)

SOON LIAN HOLDINGS LIMITED
6 Tuas Lane, Singapore, 638615, Singapore
Tel.: (65) 62618888
Web Site:
  https://www.slmetalsgroup.com
Year Founded: 1983
5MD—(SES)
Rev.: $52,958,133
Assets: $65,614,672
Liabilities: $33,882,179
Net Worth: $31,732,494
Earnings: $5,602,075
Emp.: 100
Fiscal Year-end: 12/31/22
Aluminium Alloy Products Distr
N.A.I.C.S.: 331314
Yee Ho Tan (Chm)

Subsidiaries:

SL Metals (M) Sdn. Bhd. (1)
No 9 Jalan Desa Tropika 1/3, Tropika Industrial Park Ulu Tiram, 81800, Johor, Malaysia
Tel.: (60) 78675888
Aluminum Alloy Product Mfr
N.A.I.C.S.: 331314

SL Metals (Suzhou) Co., Ltd. (1)
Factory Building B No 355 Shanxing Road, Hedong Industrial Park Wuzhong Economic Development Zone, Suzhou, 215124, China
Tel.: (86) 51266623888
Aluminium Alloy Product Mfr
N.A.I.C.S.: 331314

SL Metals (Taiwan) Co., Ltd. (1)
No 51 Lane 620 Section 3 Changping Road, Daya District, Taichung, 42850, Taiwan
Tel.: (886) 425665810
Aluminium Alloy Product Mfr
N.A.I.C.S.: 331313

SL Metals Pte Ltd (1)
6 Tuas Lane, Singapore, 638615, Singapore
Tel.: (65) 62618888
Aluminium Alloy Product Mfr
N.A.I.C.S.: 331313

SOON MINING LIMITED
Level 1 Suite 1A 33 Queen Street, Brisbane, 4000, QLD, Australia
Tel.: (61) 7 3218 7394
Web Site:
  http://www.soonmining.com
Year Founded: 2010
Rev.: $32
Assets: $999,707
Liabilities: $696,868
Net Worth: $302,839
Earnings: ($650,859)
Fiscal Year-end: 12/31/19
Gold Exploration Services
N.A.I.C.S.: 212220
Frederic Ferges (Sec)

SOOR FUEL MARKETING CO. K.S.C.
Mirqab Block 3 - Omar Ben Alkhatab st-KBT Tower, Kuwait, Kuwait
Tel.: (965) 22916114
Web Site: https://www.soor.com.kw
SOOR—(KUW)
Rev.: $485,599,551
Assets: $296,059,651
Liabilities: $67,512,386
Net Worth: $228,547,265
Earnings: $11,389,863
Emp.: 290
Fiscal Year-end: 12/31/22
Fuel Supply Stations, Car Maintenance Shops & Car Washes
N.A.I.C.S.: 457120

Talal Ahmed Al-Khars (Vice Chm & CEO)

SOOSAN HEAVY INDUSTRIES CO., LTD.
260 jeongmunsongsan-ro, Hwaseong, Gyeonggi-Do, Korea (South)
Tel.: (82) 313527733
Web Site:
  https://www.soosanheavy.com
Year Founded: 1984
017550—(KRS)
Rev.: $219,589,622
Assets: $200,747,781
Liabilities: $94,480,967
Net Worth: $106,266,813
Earnings: $12,079,754
Emp.: 187
Fiscal Year-end: 12/31/22
Hydraulic Machinery Mfr.
N.A.I.C.S.: 333998
Seo Seung-min (Asst Mgr)

Subsidiaries:

Soosan Machinery Co., Ltd. (1)
North of Keyun Road East Of Zhengyuan Road, Qingdao National High Tech Industrial Zone, Qingdao, China
Tel.: (86) 53287965655
Construction Equipment Mfr
N.A.I.C.S.: 333120

Soosan USA Inc. (1)
1261 Wiley Rd, Schaumburg, IL 60173
Tel.: (847) 744-5982
Web Site: http://www.soosanmachinery.com
Construction Equipment Mfr
N.A.I.C.S.: 333120

SOOSAN INDUSTRIES CO., LTD.
10 Bamgogaero 1gil Hyundai Ventureville 307, Gangnam-gu, Seoul, 06349, Korea (South)
Tel.: (82) 25141541
Web Site:
  https://www.soosanind.co.kr
Year Founded: 1983
126720—(KRS)
Construction Engineering Services
N.A.I.C.S.: 541330

SOOSAN INT CO.,LTD.
Soosan Building 13 Bamgogae-ro 5-gil, Gangnam-gu, Seoul, 06367, Korea (South)
Tel.: (82) 25410073
Web Site: https://www.soosanint.com
Year Founded: 1998
050960—(KRS)
Rev.: $19,607,152
Assets: $72,743,529
Liabilities: $9,791,932
Net Worth: $62,951,597
Earnings: $1,908,719
Emp.: 95
Fiscal Year-end: 12/31/22
Information Security Solution Services
N.A.I.C.S.: 523150
Eun ha Chung (CEO)

SOOSUNG LIFT MFG. CO., LTD.
673-18 Gyeongseo-dong, Seo-gu, Incheon, 404-170, Korea (South)
Tel.: (82) 328185160
Web Site: http://www.soosung.com
Year Founded: 1970
084180—(KRS)
Rev.: $40,295,897
Assets: $75,765,336
Liabilities: $37,254,682
Net Worth: $38,510,654
Earnings: ($5,318,001)
Emp.: 65
Fiscal Year-end: 12/31/22
Material Handling Equipment Mfr

N.A.I.C.S.: 333924
Jung Tae Kim (Pres)

SOPAF S.P.A.
Foro Buonaparte 24, 20121, Milan, Italy
Tel.: (39) 0272142424
Web Site: http://www.sopafgroup.it
Sales Range: $10-24.9 Million
Real Estate Investment Services
N.A.I.C.S.: 523999
Giorgio Magnoni (Vice Chm & CEO)

SOPARCO
Le Musset, 61110, Conde-sur-Huisne, France
Tel.: (33) 233733011
Web Site: http://www.soparco.com
Year Founded: 1967
Sales Range: $25-49.9 Million
Emp.: 180
Plastics Products
N.A.I.C.S.: 326199

SOPHARMA AD
5 Lachezar Stanchev Str Sopharma Business Towers Building A Fl 11, 1756, Sofia, Bulgaria
Tel.: (359) 28134319   BG
Web Site: https://www.sopharma.bg
Year Founded: 1933
SFA—(BUL)
Rev.: $917,677,960
Assets: $691,964,463
Liabilities: $296,514,733
Net Worth: $395,449,730
Earnings: $42,121,730
Emp.: 4,764
Fiscal Year-end: 12/31/22
Pharmaceuticals Mfr
N.A.I.C.S.: 325412
Vessela Liubenova Stoeva (Deputy Chm)

Subsidiaries:

Biopharm Engineering AD (1)
Trakia 75 Blvd, 8800, Sliven, Bulgaria
Tel.: (359) 44616060
Web Site: https://biopharm.bg
Pharmaceutical Mfr & Distr
N.A.I.C.S.: 325412

Bulgarian Rose Sevtopolis AD (1)
110 23rd Pehoten Shipchenski Polk Blvd, Kazanlak, 6100, Bulgaria
Tel.: (359) 4 316 28 85
Web Site: http://www.bulgarian-rose-sevtopolis.com
Rose Substance Cosmetic & Beauty Products Mfr
N.A.I.C.S.: 325620
Boncho Sholev (Dir-Production)

Medica AD (1)
5 Lachezar Stanchev Str Sopharma Business Towers Building A, Fl 9, Sofia, 1756, Bulgaria   (97.94%)
Tel.: (359) 2 96 00 330
Web Site: http://www.medica.bg
Emp.: 260
Pharmaceuticals Product Mfr
N.A.I.C.S.: 325412

Sopharma Trading JSC (1)
5 Lachezar Stanchev Street Sopharma Business Towers BuildingA Floor 12, Izgrev Region, 1756, Sofia, Bulgaria
Tel.: (359) 28133660
Web Site: https://www.sopharmatrading.bg
Sales Range: $400-449.9 Million
Emp.: 833
Pharmaceutical Products Distr
N.A.I.C.S.: 424990
Ventsislav Marinov (Deputy CEO)

Sopharmacy EOOD (1)
16 Rozhen Blvd, 1220, Sofia, Bulgaria
Tel.: (359) 882740013
Web Site: https://sopharmacy.bg
Pharmaceuticals Mfr
N.A.I.C.S.: 325412

Unipharm JSC (1)

INTERNATIONAL PUBLIC

Traiko Stanoev str No 3, Sofia, 1797, Bulgaria
Tel.: (359) 2 9700305
Web Site: http://www.unipharm.bg
Pharmaceuticals Product Mfr
N.A.I.C.S.: 325412
Ognyan Palaveev (Chm-Mgmt Bd)

Veta Pharma AD (1)
32 Dulga Laka St, 5008, Veliko Tarnovo, Bulgaria
Tel.: (359) 62623400
Web Site: https://www.veta-pharma.com
Emp.: 50
Pharmaceuticals Mfr
N.A.I.C.S.: 325412

SOPHARMA BUILDINGS REIT
5 Lachezar Stanchev str Sopharma Business Towers Complex, Building A Fl 20, 1756, Sofia, 1756, Bulgaria
Tel.: (359) 28134229
Web Site: https://www.sopharma-buildings.com
Year Founded: 2007
SFB—(BUL)
Sales Range: Less than $1 Million
Real Estate Investment Services
N.A.I.C.S.: 531190
Ivanka Panova (Dir-IR)

SOPHARMA PROPERTIES REIT
Lachezar Stanchev Str 5 Building A 20 Fl, Sopharma Business Towers, Sofia, Bulgaria
Tel.: (359) 24250120
Web Site: https://www.sopharma-imoti.com
Year Founded: 2006
SFI—(BUL)
Sales Range: Less than $1 Million
Real Estate Manangement Services
N.A.I.C.S.: 531390
Boriss Borissov (CEO)

SOPHIA CAPITAL S.A.
Ortiz de Ocampo 3302 Edificio I Piso 3 Officina 20, Capital Federal, Buenos Aires, Argentina
Tel.: (54) 11 4803 2326   Ar
Web Site: https://www.sophiacap.com
Oil & Gas Industry Private Equity & Asset Management Services
N.A.I.C.S.: 523999
Federico Schargorodsky (Co-Founder & Mng Partner)

Subsidiaries:

Esferomatic S.A. (1)
Gran Canaria 3010, B 1878 EEJ, Quilmes, Buenos Aires, Argentina
Tel.: (54) 1142783000
Web Site: http://www.esferomatic.com.ar
Industrial Valve Mfr
N.A.I.C.S.: 332911

Industria Y Tecnologia En Aceros S.A. (1)
Antonio Salellas 1391, E3100GBA, Parana, Entre Rios, Argentina   (100%)
Tel.: (54) 343 426 0027
Web Site: www.acerositasa.com
Nonferrou Metal Die-Casting Foundry Mfr
N.A.I.C.S.: 331523
Enrique Sacco (Mgr)

Jefferson Sudamericana S.A. (1)
Av Francisco Fernandez De La Cruz 2016, C1437GYZ, Buenos Aires, Argentina
Tel.: (54) 1149095304
Web Site: http://www.jefferson.com.ar
Industrial Valve Mfr
N.A.I.C.S.: 332911

Subsidiary (US):

Jefferson Solenoid Valves USA, Inc. (2)
20225 NE 15th Ct, Miami, FL 33179
Tel.: (305) 249-8120
Web Site: http://www.jeffersonvalves.com
Industrial Valve Mfr

AND PRIVATE COMPANIES

SOPRA STERIA GROUP S.A.

N.A.I.C.S.: 332911

Norpatagonica S.A. (1)
Ruta 7 S N Parque Industrial Neuquen, Neuquen, 8300, Argentina
Tel.: (54) 2994413033
Web Site: http://www.norpatagonica.com.ar
Oil & Gas Field Support Services
N.A.I.C.S.: 213112

Valvulas Worcester de Argentina S.A. (1)
Osvaldo Cruz 3333, Buenos Aires, Argentina
Tel.: (54) 11 5533 5200
Web Site: http://www.valbol.com.ar
Emp.: 220
Industrial Valve Mfr & Distr
N.A.I.C.S.: 332911

SOPHIA GENETICS SA
Rue du Centre 172, CH-1025, Saint Sulpice, Switzerland
Tel.: (41) 216941060   CH
Web Site:
  https://www.sophiagenetics.com
Year Founded: 2011
SOPH—(NASDAQ)
Rev.: $62,371,000
Assets: $206,156,000
Liabilities: $54,714,000
Net Worth: $151,442,000
Earnings: ($78,981,000)
Emp.: 449
Fiscal Year-end: 12/31/23
Biotechnology Research & Development Services
N.A.I.C.S.: 541714
Jurgi Camblong *(Founder & CEO)*

SOPHIA TRAEXPO LIMITED
Flat No 401 D No 6-3- 1085/D Dega Towers Raj Bhavan Road Somajiguda, Hyderabad, 500082, Telangana, India
Tel.: (91) 4023818475
Web Site:
  https://www.sophiatraexpo.com
Year Founded: 1983
541633—(BOM)
Assets: $715,919
Liabilities: $54,002
Net Worth: $661,917
Earnings: ($20,309)
Paper Product Distr
N.A.I.C.S.: 424130
Yerrapragada Mallikarjuna Rao *(CFO)*

SOPHORA UNTERNEHMERKAPITAL GMBH
Brienner Str. 41, 80333, Munich, Germany
Tel.: (49) 89143677
Web Site: https://www.sophora.de
Year Founded: 2022
Private Equity
N.A.I.C.S.: 523940
Neil MacDougall *(Chm)*

Subsidiaries:

FLOW-TRONIC S.A. (1)
19 A Rue J- H Cool, 4840, Welkenraedt, Belgium
Tel.: (32) 87899799
Web Site: http://www.flow-tronic.com
Emp.: 12
Liquid Flow Measuring Instrumentation Mfr
N.A.I.C.S.: 334519
Dominic Angelini *(Gen Mgr)*

SOPRA STERIA GROUP S.A.
6 avenue Klebe, 75016, Paris, France
Tel.: (33) 140672929   FR
Web Site:
  https://www.soprasteria.com
SOP—(EUR)
Rev.: $5,505,288,150
Assets: $5,337,578,243
Liabilities: $3,294,193,827
Net Worth: $2,043,384,416
Earnings: $267,429,311
Emp.: 48,391
Fiscal Year-end: 12/31/22
Information Technology Consulting Services
N.A.I.C.S.: 541690
Vincent Paris *(CEO)*

Subsidiaries:

2MoRO SAS (1)
Batiment A Cre ticite 374 Allee Antoine d Abbadie, 64210, Bidart, France
Tel.: (33) 559013005
Web Site: https://www.2moro.com
Software Services
N.A.I.C.S.: 541511
Pierre Dagois *(Gen Mgr)*

CIMPA S.A.S. (1)
Centreda 1 4 avenue Didier Daurat, 31700, Blagnac, France (100%)
Tel.: (33) 532110110
Sales Range: $100-124.9 Million
Emp.: 1,400
Product Lifecycle Management Services
N.A.I.C.S.: 541618

Subsidiary (Non-US):

CIMPA GmbH (2)
Notkestrasse 9, 22607, Hamburg, Germany (100%)
Tel.: (49) 40881300
Product Lifecycle Management Services
N.A.I.C.S.: 541618
Alexander Popkes *(Mng Dir)*

CIMPA Ltd. (2)
Nibley Court 3 Turner Drive, Westerleigh Business Park, Bristol, BS37 5YX, United Kingdom (100%)
Tel.: (44) 1173190282
Product Lifecycle Management Services
N.A.I.C.S.: 541618

CS Group SA (1)
22 avenue Galilee, 92350, Le Plessis-Robinson, France (75.06%)
Tel.: (33) 141284000
Web Site: http://www.c-s.fr
Rev.: $257,517,406
Earnings: $3,368,539
Emp.: 1,700
Fiscal Year-end: 12/31/2019
Mission Critical Systems Designer, Integrator & Operator
N.A.I.C.S.: 334290
Barbara Goarant *(Head-Mktg & Comm)*

Subsidiary (Non-US):

CS Canada Inc. (2)
3333 Boulevard de la Cote-Vertu, Montreal, H4R 2N1, QC, Canada
Tel.: (514) 748-8258
Web Site: http://www.cscanada.ca
Sales Range: $25-49.9 Million
Emp.: 80
System Design & Integration Services
N.A.I.C.S.: 541512
Laurent Pieraut *(CEO)*

CS Romania SA (2)
CS Romania Str Pacii nr 29, Craiova, 200692, Dolj, Romania
Tel.: (40) 251412850
Web Site: http://www.c-s.ro
Sales Range: $50-74.9 Million
Emp.: 70
Foreign Missions Services
N.A.I.C.S.: 928120

Ecsat D.O.O. (2)
Zrinjsko Frankopanska bb, Split, 21000, Croatia
Tel.: (385) 21347700
Web Site: http://www.ecsat.hr
Sales Range: $25-49.9 Million
Emp.: 40
Computer Software Whslr
N.A.I.C.S.: 423430
Branko Vujovic *(Mgr-Bus Dev)*

RTI Systems Ltd. (2)
Unit 11 Swan Business Park, Sandpit Rd, Dartford, DA1 SED, United Kingdom
Tel.: (44) 1322286866
Sales Range: $50-74.9 Million
Emp.: 3
Foreign Missions Services
N.A.I.C.S.: 928120

USB GmbH (2)
Beta Str 13 a, Unterfohring, 85774, Germany
Tel.: (49) 8999894283
Web Site: http://www.usb-muc.com
Sales Range: $25-49.9 Million
Emp.: 30
Aeronautics Embedded System Mfr
N.A.I.C.S.: 334511
Detlef Haesner *(Gen Mgr)*

Galitt SAS (1)
17 route de la Reine, 92100, Boulogne, France
Tel.: (33) 177702800
Web Site: http://www.galitt.com
Information Technology Services
N.A.I.C.S.: 541519

Kentor AB (1)
Vasagatan 38 6 tr, Stockholm, Sweden
Tel.: (46) 8 587 650 00
Web Site: http://www.kentor.se
Sales Range: $50-74.9 Million
Emp.: 330
Information Technology Consulting Services
N.A.I.C.S.: 541690
Fredrik Arbman *(Mng Dir)*

Ordina N.V. (1)
Ringwade 1, 3439 LM, Nieuwegein, Netherlands (98.01%)
Tel.: (31) 306637000
Web Site: http://www.ordina.nl
Rev.: $453,506,740
Assets: $351,392,095
Liabilities: $132,997,512
Net Worth: $218,394,583
Earnings: $27,377,470
Emp.: 2,586
Fiscal Year-end: 12/31/2020
Information & Communication Technology Services
N.A.I.C.S.: 561499
Jo Maes *(CEO & Member-Mgmt Bd)*

Subsidiary (Domestic):

Bergson Holding B.V. (2)
Sint Antoniusstraat 9, Eindhoven, Netherlands (100%)
Tel.: (31) 402508600
Computer Programming Services
N.A.I.C.S.: 541511

Bergson Software Factory Services B.V. (2)
Sint Antoniusstraat 9, Eindhoven, Netherlands (100%)
Tel.: (31) 402508600
Computer Programming Services
N.A.I.C.S.: 541511

Bergson Technical Automation B.V. (2)
Sint Antoniusstraat 9, Eindhoven, Netherlands (100%)
Tel.: (31) 402508600
Computer Programming Services
N.A.I.C.S.: 541511

Clockwork B.V. (2)
Ringwade 1, 3439 LM, Nieuwegein, Netherlands
Tel.: (31) 20 6077000
Online Marketing Services
N.A.I.C.S.: 541613

IFS Probity B.V. (2)
Albert Plesmanstraat 2, 3772 MN, Barneveld, Netherlands
Tel.: (31) 34 242 0120
Web Site: http://www.ifsprobity.nl
Sales Range: $1-9.9 Million
Utilities Industry Consulting Services
N.A.I.C.S.: 541690

Magentis B.V. (2)
Kadijk 1, Groningen, Netherlands (100%)
Tel.: (31) 598666100
Computer & Software Stores
N.A.I.C.S.: 449210

Ordina (2)
Europaweg 31-33, Groningen, 9723 AS, Netherlands (100%)
Tel.: (31) 508516000
Web Site: http://www.ordina.com
Sales Range: $50-74.9 Million
Emp.: 250
Data Processing Services
N.A.I.C.S.: 518210

Ordina Application Management B.V. (2)
Ringwade 1, Nieuwegein, Netherlands (100%)
Tel.: (31) 306637000
Web Site: http://www.ordina.no
Emp.: 500
Data Processing Services
N.A.I.C.S.: 518210
Stepan Bredvelt *(Pres)*

Ordina Application Outsourcing en Projecten B.V. (2)
Europaweg 31-33, 9723 AS, Groningen, Netherlands
Tel.: (31) 508516000
Sales Range: $25-49.9 Million
Emp.: 25
Business Process Outsourcing Services
N.A.I.C.S.: 561499

Subsidiary (Non-US):

Ordina Belgium N.V. (2)
Blarenberglaan 3B, 2800, Mechelen, Belgium (100%)
Tel.: (32) 15295858
Web Site: http://www.ordina.be
Sales Range: $75-99.9 Million
Emp.: 500
Information & Communication Technology Services
N.A.I.C.S.: 541519
Ilse Pauwels *(Mgr-Mktg)*

Subsidiary (Domestic):

Ordina E-Chain Management Financials BVBA (3)
Blarenberglaan 3B, 2800, Mechelen, Belgium
Tel.: (32) 15 29 58 58
Web Site: http://www.ordina.be
Financial Management Services
N.A.I.C.S.: 523999

Subsidiary (Domestic):

Ordina Business & Enterprise Solutions B.V. (2)
Ringwade 1, Nieuwegein, 3439 LM, Netherlands (100%)
Tel.: (31) 306637000
Web Site: http://www.ordina.nl
Sales Range: $100-124.9 Million
Emp.: 300
Data Processing Services
N.A.I.C.S.: 518210

Ordina Consulting B.V. (2)
Ringwade 1, Nieuwegein, 3439 LM, Netherlands
Tel.: (31) 306637500
Web Site: http://www.ordina.nl
Sales Range: $150-199.9 Million
Emp.: 500
Software Consulting Services
N.A.I.C.S.: 541512

Ordina Enterprise Application Services B.V. (2)
Ring Wade No 1, Dordrecht, 3318 JX, Netherlands (100%)
Tel.: (31) 786526000
Web Site: http://www.ordina.nl
Sales Range: $25-49.9 Million
Emp.: 55
Data Processing Services
N.A.I.C.S.: 518210

Ordina Enterprise Applications B.V. (2)
Ringwade 1, 3439 LM, Nieuwegein, Netherlands (100%)
Tel.: (31) 306637000
Web Site:
  http://www.activitybasedbudgeting.com
Sales Range: $75-99.9 Million
Emp.: 400
Management Consulting Services
N.A.I.C.S.: 541611

Ordina Holding B.V. (2)

SOPRA STERIA GROUP S.A.

Sopra Steria Group S.A.—(Continued)

Ringwade 1, Nieuwegein, 3439, Netherlands **(100%)**
Tel.: (31) 306637000
Web Site: http://www.ordina.nl
Sales Range: $150-199.9 Million
Emp.: 400
Computer Equipment & Software Whslr
N.A.I.C.S.: 423430

Ordina ICT B.V. (2)
Ringwade 1, 3439 LM, Nieuwegein, Netherlands
Tel.: (31) 30 663 7315
Information Technology Consulting Services
N.A.I.C.S.: 541512

Ordina J. Technogies B.V. (2)
Ringwade 1, 3439LM, Nieuwegein, Netherlands **(100%)**
Tel.: (31) 306637788
Web Site: http://www.ordina.nl
Sales Range: $50-74.9 Million
Emp.: 500
Computer & Software Stores
N.A.I.C.S.: 449210

Subsidiary (Non-US):

Ordina Luxembourg SA (2)
Rue de l'industrie 13, 8399, Windhof, Luxembourg
Tel.: (352) 263033
Information Technology Services
N.A.I.C.S.: 541519

Subsidiary (Domestic):

Ordina Nederland B.V. (2)
Ringwade 1, 3439 LM, Nieuwegein, Netherlands **(100%)**
Tel.: (31) 306637000
Web Site: http://www.ordina.nl
Sales Range: $150-199.9 Million
Emp.: 2,500
Holding Company
N.A.I.C.S.: 551112

Ordina System Integration & Development B.V. (2)
Ringwade 1, PO Box 3439 LM, Nieuwegein, 3439LM, Netherlands **(100%)**
Tel.: (31) 306637000
Web Site: http://www.ordina.nl
Sales Range: $700-749.9 Million
Computer Programming Services
N.A.I.C.S.: 541511

SourcePower B.V.
Ringwade 1, 3439 LM, Nieuwegein, Netherlands
Tel.: (31) 30 663 8700
Web Site: https://www.sourcepower.nl
Human Resouce Services
N.A.I.C.S.: 541612

The Missing Link B.V. (2)
Europaweg 31/33, 9723 AS, Groningen, Netherlands **(100%)**
Tel.: (31) 503688888
Sales Range: $25-49.9 Million
Emp.: 70
Computer Programming Services
N.A.I.C.S.: 541511

Wisdom Tmic B.V. (2)
Helperpark 288, Groningen, Netherlands **(100%)**
Tel.: (31) 503688887
Sales Range: $25-49.9 Million
Emp.: 70
Data Processing Services
N.A.I.C.S.: 518210

SOPRAntic Casablanca (1)
17 Rue El Oraibi Jilali, BP 20 000, Casablanca, 20000, Morocco
Tel.: (212) 522427400
Information Technology Consulting Services
N.A.I.C.S.: 541512

Sodifrance SA (1)
11 rue Nina Simone BP 70908, 44009, Nantes, Cedex 1, France **(94.03%)**
Tel.: (33) 299234600
Web Site: http://www.sodifrance.fr
Information Technology Services
N.A.I.C.S.: 541512
Franck Mazin *(Pres)*

Sopra Banking Cote d'Ivoire SARL (1)
Tour SAMA Avenue Lamblin 01, BP 2185, Abidjan, Cote d'Ivoire
Tel.: (225) 20224307
Software Services
N.A.I.C.S.: 541511

Sopra Banking Software Luxembourg SA (1)
89E Pafebruch Parc d'Activites, Mamer-Capellen, L - 8308, Capellen, Luxembourg
Tel.: (352) 4665481
Software Services
N.A.I.C.S.: 541511

Sopra Banking Software Netherlands BV (1)
De Cuserstraat 93, 1081 CN, Amsterdam, Netherlands
Tel.: (31) 208949122
Software Services
N.A.I.C.S.: 541511

Sopra Banking Software Senegal SASU (1)
Azur 15 Building 12 Bd Djily Mbaye- Le Plateau, Dakar, Senegal
Tel.: (221) 338296453
Software Services
N.A.I.C.S.: 541511

Sopra Financial Technology GmbH (1)
Frankenstrasse 146, 90461, Nuremberg, Germany
Tel.: (49) 91192910
Web Site: https://www.sopra-financial-technology.com
Software Services
N.A.I.C.S.: 541511
Eric Guyot *(CEO)*

Sopra HR Software (1)
Immeuble LATITUDE - 1 Rue Serpentines, La Defense, 92400, Courbevoie, Cedex, France
Tel.: (33) 157005353
Web Site: https://www.soprahr.com
Services to Human Resources Departments
N.A.I.C.S.: 561499

Sopra HR Software GmbH (1)
Banter Deich 18, 26382, Wilhelmshaven, Germany
Tel.: (49) 44213683810
Software Services
N.A.I.C.S.: 541511

Sopra HR Software SL (1)
Avenida de Manoteras num 48 Edificio, 28050, Madrid, Spain
Tel.: (34) 911128000
Software Services
N.A.I.C.S.: 541511
Celia Fernandez Santamaria *(Mgr-Bus Dev)*

Sopra HR Software SPRL (1)
Avenue Arnaud Fraiteur 23, 1050, Brussels, Belgium
Tel.: (32) 25666153
Software Services
N.A.I.C.S.: 541511

Sopra HR Software Sarl (1)
Marina Immeuble IVOIRE 5 Boulevard des Almohades, 20000, Casablanca, Morocco
Tel.: (212) 522645700
Software Services
N.A.I.C.S.: 541511
Nabil Ouardi *(Mgr-Sls East Africa)*

Sopra HR Software Sarl (1)
Rue de la Feuille d Erable Bloc B Cite les Pins Lac II 1053, 1053, Tunis, Tunisia
Tel.: (216) 71167300
Software Services
N.A.I.C.S.: 541511

Sopra HR Software Sarl (1)
89E Pafebruch-Parc d Activites Mamer, 8308, Capellen, Luxembourg
Tel.: (352) 466548269
Software Services
N.A.I.C.S.: 541511
Julia Mateffi *(Country Mgr)*

Sopra HR Software Srl (1)
Strada 4 Palazzo A7-Centro direzionale Milanofiori, 20090, Assago, Italy

Tel.: (39) 0289229353
Software Services
N.A.I.C.S.: 541511

Sopra India Private Ltd (1)
A 67 Sector 64, Noida, 201301, Uttar Pradesh, India
Tel.: (91) 1204056100
Web Site: http://www.in.sopragroup.com
Emp.: 2,000
Information Technology Consulting Services
N.A.I.C.S.: 541511

Sopra Steria A/S (1)
Skindergade 45-47, 1159, Copenhagen, Denmark **(100%)**
Tel.: (45) 44506000
Web Site: https://www.soprasteria.dk
Emp.: 130
Information Technology Services
N.A.I.C.S.: 541519
Kjell Rusti *(Mng Dir)*

Sopra Steria AB (1)
Vasagatan 38, PO Box 169, 111 20, Stockholm, Sweden **(100%)**
Tel.: (46) 858765000
Web Site: https://www.soprasteria.se
Emp.: 600
Information Technology Services
N.A.I.C.S.: 541519
Kjell Rusti *(Mng Dir)*

Sopra Steria AG (1)
Steinackerstrasse 47, 8902, Urdorf, Switzerland **(100%)**
Tel.: (41) 435474343
Web Site: http://www.soprasteria.ch
Information Technology & Consulting Services
N.A.I.C.S.: 541519
Nicolas Vezin *(CEO)*

Sopra Steria AS (1)
Biskop Gunnerus Gate 14A, 57, Oslo, Norway **(100%)**
Tel.: (47) 22575600
Web Site: https://www.soprasteria.no
Sales Range: $300-349.9 Million
Emp.: 1,200
Information Technology Services
N.A.I.C.S.: 541519
Kjell Rusti *(Gen Mgr)*

Sopra Steria Asia Pte. Ltd. (1)
3 Fusionopolis Way 12-27 Symbiosis, Singapore, 138633, Singapore
Tel.: (65) 65789988
Web Site: http://www.soprasteria.sg
Emp.: 55
Information Technology Services
N.A.I.C.S.: 541519

Sopra Steria Belgium (1)
Avenue Arnaud Fraiteurlaan 15-23, 1050, Brussels, Belgium
Tel.: (32) 25666666
Web Site: http://www.soprasteria.be
Consulting, Software Development & Information Technology Services
N.A.I.C.S.: 541511

Sopra Steria Benelux SA (1)
15- 23 Avenue Arnaud Fraiteurlaan, Ixelles, 1050, Brussels, Belgium
Tel.: (32) 56666666
Web Site: http://www.soprasteria.be
Software Services
N.A.I.C.S.: 541511
Astrid Anciaux *(CFO)*

Sopra Steria Espana, S.A. (1)
Avenida de Manoteras 48 Edificio B, 28050, Madrid, Spain
Tel.: (34) 911128000
Web Site: http://www.soprasteria.es
Consulting, Information Technology & Software Development Services
N.A.I.C.S.: 541611

Subsidiary (Domestic):

Sopra Group Euskadi SL (2)
Calle Portal De Gamarra 1 Ed Deba Ofic 412, Vitoria, 1013, Spain **(100%)**
Tel.: (34) 945200736
Web Site: http://www.sopragroup.es
Software Development Consulting Services
N.A.I.C.S.: 541511

Sopra Group Informatica (2)

INTERNATIONAL PUBLIC

Calle Alcala 494, 28027, Madrid, Spain
Tel.: (34) 915681111
Web Site: http://www.soprasteria.es
Software Development Services
N.A.I.C.S.: 541511

Sopra Steria GmbH (1)
Hans-Henny-Jahnn Weg 29, 22085, Hamburg, Germany **(100%)**
Tel.: (49) 40227030
Web Site: http://www.soprasteria.de
Management Consulting & Information Technology Services
N.A.I.C.S.: 541611

Subsidiary (Domestic):

ISS Software GmbH (2)
Hans-Henny-Jahnn Weg 29, 22085, Hamburg, Germany **(100%)**
Tel.: (49) 40227030
Web Site: http://www.iss.soprasteria.de
Sales Range: $25-49.9 Million
Emp.: 60
Computer Storage Device Mfr
N.A.I.C.S.: 334112

Subsidiary (Non-US):

Steria Mummert Consulting GmbH (2)
Kaernt 5, A 1010, Vienna, Austria **(100%)**
Tel.: (43) 151238550
Sales Range: $25-49.9 Million
Emp.: 200
Management Consulting Services
N.A.I.C.S.: 541618

Sopra Steria GmbH (1)
Obere Donaustrasse 95, 1020, Vienna, Austria
Tel.: (43) 121286100
Web Site: http://www.soprasteria.at
Software Services
N.A.I.C.S.: 541511

Sopra Steria Group SpA (1)
Centro Direzionale Milanofiori Strada 4 Palazzo A7, 20057, Assago, MI, Italy
Tel.: (39) 02892291
Web Site: http://www.soprasteria.it
Information Technology Services
N.A.I.C.S.: 541519

Sopra Steria Limited (1)
Three Cherry Trees Lane, Hemel Hempstead, HP2 7AH, Herts, United Kingdom **(100%)**
Tel.: (44) 3706004466
Web Site: http://www.soprasteria.co.uk
Information Technology Services
N.A.I.C.S.: 518210

Affiliate (Domestic):

NHS Shared Business Services Limited (2)
Phoenix House Topcliffe Lane, Tingley, Wakefield, WF3 1WE, United Kingdom **(50%)**
Tel.: (44) 1133071500
Web Site: https://www.sbs.nhs.uk
Sales Range: $150-199.9 Million
Emp.: 360
Financial Transactions Processing Reserve & Clearinghouse Activities
N.A.I.C.S.: 522320
John Neilson *(Mng Dir)*

Subsidiary (Domestic):

Sopra Group Holding Ltd. (2)
30 Old Broad Street, London, EC2N 1HT, United Kingdom
Tel.: (44) 2077865800
Web Site: http://www.sopragroup.co.uk
Information Technology Consulting Services
N.A.I.C.S.: 541690

Subsidiary (Domestic):

Sopra Group Limited (3)
4th Floor 30 Old Broad Street, London, EC2N 1HT, United Kingdom
Tel.: (44) 207 786 5800
Web Site: http://www.sopra.co.uk
Sales Range: $25-49.9 Million
Emp.: 80
Consulting Services
N.A.I.C.S.: 541611

AND PRIVATE COMPANIES

Subsidiary (Domestic):

Sopra Steria Holdings Limited (2)
Three Cherry Trees Lane, Hemel Hempstead, HP2 7AH, Herts, United Kingdom
Tel.: (44) 845 601 8877
Web Site: http://www.soprasteria.co.uk
Holding Company
N.A.I.C.S.: 551112

Subsidiary (Domestic):

Druid Group Limited (3)
Thompson House 420 Thames Valley Park Drive, Reading, RG6 1PU, Berks, United Kingdom
Tel.: (44) 8702 416181
Information Technology Consulting Services
N.A.I.C.S.: 541690

Zansa Limited (3)
300 Maylands Ave The Campus, Hemel Hempstead, HP2 7GG, Hertforshire, United Kingdom
Tel.: (44) 8702416181
Business Process Outsourcing Services
N.A.I.C.S.: 561499

Subsidiary (Domestic):

Sopra Steria Recruitment Limited (2)
1010 Winnersh, Winnersh Triangle, Reading, RG41 5TS, United Kingdom
Tel.: (44) 370 0107715
Web Site:
   http://www.soprasteriarecruitment.co.uk
Human Resource Consulting Services
N.A.I.C.S.: 541612

Sopra Steria Services Limited (2)
Three Cherry Trees Lane, Hemel Hempstead, HP2 7AH, Herts, United Kingdom
Tel.: (44) 3706004466
Web Site: http://www.soprasteria.co.uk
Information Technology Consulting Services
N.A.I.C.S.: 541512

Sopra Steria Luxembourg S.A. (1)
2-4 rue du Chateau d'eau, 3364, Leudelange, Luxembourg
Tel.: (352) 4550021
Web Site: http://www.soprasteria.lu
Information Technology & Consulting Services
N.A.I.C.S.: 541990

Subsidiary (Domestic):

Sopra Steria PSF Luxembourg S.A. (2)
Rue du Kiem 145, 8030, Strassen, Luxembourg (100%)
Tel.: (352) 4550021
Web Site: http://www.steria-psf.lu
Emp.: 60
Financial Sector Computer Related Services
N.A.I.C.S.: 541519
Jean-Jacques Genser (Mng Dir)

Sopra Steria Polska z o.o. (1)
Uniwersytecka 13, 40-007, Katowice, Poland
Tel.: (48) 323549400
Web Site: https://www.soprasteria.pl
Information Technology Services
N.A.I.C.S.: 541519
Karolina Milczarek (Dir-HR)

Sopra Steria Services (1)
6 avenue Kleber, 75016, Paris, France
Tel.: (33) 140672929
Web Site: https://www.soprasteria.com
Management Consulting Services
N.A.I.C.S.: 541618

it-economics GmbH (1)
Bothestrasse 11, 81675, Munich, Germany
Tel.: (49) 8921548800
Web Site: https://www.it-economics.de
Emp.: 300
Information Technology Services
N.A.I.C.S.: 541519
Torsten Klein (CEO, Partner & Mng Dir)

SOPRANO DESIGN LIMITED

L 11 132 Arthur Street, North Sydney, 2060, NSW, Australia
Tel.: (61) 2 9900 2200
Web Site: http://www.soprano.com.au
Enterprise Messaging Solutions for Mobile Network Operators
N.A.I.C.S.: 513210
Richard Favero (Chm)

SOPREMA SAS

14 rue de Saint-Nazaire, Strasbourg, 67025, France
Tel.: (33) 3 88 79 84 00
Web Site: http://www.soprema.fr
Year Founded: 1908
Sales Range: $1-4.9 Billion
Emp.: 5,334
Waterproofing, Roofing & Insulation Systems Mfr
N.A.I.C.S.: 324122
Pierre Etienne Bindschedle (CEO)

Subsidiaries:

Chignolo d'Isola Flag SpA (1)
Via Industriale dell'Isola 3, 24040, Chignolo d'Isola, Italy
Tel.: (39) 0350951011
Insulation Material Whslr
N.A.I.C.S.: 423330

ESSERTEC (1)
Berghauschensweg 77, 41464, Neuss, Germany
Tel.: (49) 2131 183 0
Web Site: http://www.essertec.de
Skylight Dome Installation & Sheet Metal Roofing Services
N.A.I.C.S.: 423330
Karla Schroder (Co-CEO)

SOPREMA AG (1)
Hardlistrasse 1 2, 8957, Spreitenbach, Switzerland
Tel.: (41) 564185930
Web Site: http://www.soprema.ch
Plastic Material & Resin Mfr
N.A.I.C.S.: 325211

SOPREMA Canada Inc. (1)
1688 Jean-Berchmans-Michaud, Drummondville, J2C 8E9, QC, Canada
Tel.: (819) 478-8163
Web Site: https://www.soprema.ca
Emp.: 650
Asphalt Shingle & Coating Materials MFR
N.A.I.C.S.: 324122

Plant (Domestic):

SOPREMA Canada Inc. - Chilliwack Plant (1)
44955 Yale Road West, Chilliwack, V2R 4H3, BC, Canada
Tel.: (604) 793-7100
Insulation Material Whslr
N.A.I.C.S.: 423330

SOPREMA Canada Inc. - Drummondville Plant (2)
1675 rue Haggerty, Drummondville, J2C 5P7, QC, Canada
Tel.: (819) 478-8163
Insulation Material Whslr
N.A.I.C.S.: 423330

SOPREMA GmbH (1)
Mallaustr 59, 68219, Mannheim, Germany
Tel.: (49) 621 73 60 30
Web Site: http://www.soprema.de
Asphalt Shingle & Coating Materials Mfr
N.A.I.C.S.: 324122
Christophe Feist (Mng Dir)

SOPREMA NV (1)
Bouwelven 5, 2280, Grobbendonk, Belgium
Tel.: (32) 14 23 07 07
Web Site: http://www.soprema.be
Synthetic Resin Mfr
N.A.I.C.S.: 325211
Marc Geerts (Dir-Comml)

Plant (Domestic):

SOPREMA NV - Andenne Plant (2)
Chaussee Moncheur 83, 5300, Andenne, Belgium
Tel.: (32) 85849749
Insulation Material Whslr
N.A.I.C.S.: 423330
Ann Bisschops (Controller-Fin)

SOPREMA SAS - Val de Reuil Plant (1)
Voie futur-Z A Parc des Affaires des Portes, 27100, Val-de-Reuil, France
Tel.: (33) 232402298
Insulation Material Whslr
N.A.I.C.S.: 423330

SOPREMA SAS Barcelona Plant (1)
C/ Ferro 7 Poligono Can Pelegri, 08755, Castellbisbal, Spain
Tel.: (34) 936351400
Insulation Material Whslr
N.A.I.C.S.: 423330

SOPREMA SAS Cestas Plant (1)
ZI Auguste 3/4 chemin des Arrestieux, 33610, Cestas, France
Tel.: (33) 557959596
Insulation Material Whslr
N.A.I.C.S.: 423330

SOPREMA SAS Colomiers Plant (1)
Chemin du Garrabot, 31770, Colomiers, France
Tel.: (33) 561301673
Insulation Material Whslr
N.A.I.C.S.: 423330

SOPREMA SAS IJlst Plant (1)
Geeuwkade 21, Postbus 2, 8650 AA, IJlst, Netherlands
Tel.: (31) 515533000
Insulation Material Whslr
N.A.I.C.S.: 423330

SOPREMA SAS La Chapelle Saint-Luc Plant (1)
Rue de la douane, 10600, La Chapelle-Saint-Luc, France
Tel.: (33) 325744326
Insulation Material Whslr
N.A.I.C.S.: 423330

SOPREMA SAS Sorgues Plant (1)
162 Allee de la Traille, 84700, Sorgues, France
Tel.: (33) 490876178
Insulation Material Whslr
N.A.I.C.S.: 423330

SOPREMA SAS Zona Industrial de Alpiarca Plant (1)
Rua A Lote 4 B, 2090-242, Alpiarca, Portugal
Tel.: (351) 243240020
Insulation Material Whslr
N.A.I.C.S.: 423330

SOPREMA, Inc. (1)
310 Quadral Dr, Wadsworth, OH 44281-4281
Tel.: (330) 334-0066
Web Site: http://www.soprema.us
Asphalt Shingle & Coating Materials Mfr
N.A.I.C.S.: 324122

Plant (Domestic):

SOPREMA, Inc. - Gulfport Plant (2)
12251 Seaway Rd, Gulfport, MS 39503
Tel.: (228) 701-1900
Insulation Material Whslr
N.A.I.C.S.: 423330

Branch (Domestic):

SOPREMA, Inc. - Southeast (2)
111 Holt Industrial Cir, Acworth, GA 30101-2016
Tel.: (770) 792-0302
Web Site: http://www.soprema.us
Asphalt Shingle & Coating Materials Mfr
N.A.I.C.S.: 324122

SOPREMA, Sarl. (1)
14C avenue de Pekin, 16209, Algiers, Algeria
Tel.: (213) 21694496
Insulation Material Whslr
N.A.I.C.S.: 423330

Soprema Ltda (1)
Av Councilman Joao Batista Fitipaldi 500, Suzano, Sao Paulo, 08685-000, Brazil
Tel.: (55) 1147416000
Web Site: https://soprema.com.br
Waterproofing, Roofing & Insulation Systems Mfr
N.A.I.C.S.: 324122

SORGENTE GROUP S.P.A.

Subsidiary (Domestic):

Pulvitec do Brasil Industria e Comercio de Colas e Adesivos Ltda (2)
Av Presidente Altino 2600, Jaguare, Sao Paulo, 05323-903, Brazil
Tel.: (55) 113 716 9000
Web Site: https://www.pulvitec.com.br
Adhesive Mfr
N.A.I.C.S.: 325520

Soprema Polska Sp. z o.o. (1)
ul Stefana Batorego 7 Pass, 05-870, Blonie, Poland
Tel.: (48) 224369302
Web Site: http://www.soprema.pl
Insulation Material Mfr
N.A.I.C.S.: 326140

Soprema Singapore Pte. Ltd (1)
Level 39-01 MBFC Tower 2 Marina Boulevard, Singapore, 018983, Singapore
Tel.: (65) 68186353
Insulation Material Whslr
N.A.I.C.S.: 423330

Villa S. Stefano Flag SpA (1)
Via Selvapiana 1, 03020, Villa Santo Stefano, Italy
Tel.: (39) 0775625439
Insulation Material Whslr
N.A.I.C.S.: 423330

SOPROCAL CALERIAS & INDUSTRIAS SA

Avda Pedro de Valdivia 0193 of 31, Santiago, Chile
Tel.: (56) 2318874
Year Founded: 1940
SOPROCAL—(SGO)
Sales Range: Less than $1 Million
Chemical Products Mfr
N.A.I.C.S.: 325998
Alfonso Rozas Ossa (Pres)

SOPURA S.A.

Rue de Trazegnies 199, 6180, Courcelles, Belgium
Tel.: (32) 71 46 80 10
Web Site: http://www.sopura.com
Cleaning & Disinfection Product Mfr
N.A.I.C.S.: 325611
Monique Coppieters (CEO)

SOR JOINT STOCK COMPANY

2nd Khoroo, Khan Uul District, Ulaanbaatar, Mongolia
Tel.: (976) 11 342335
Peltry Production Services
N.A.I.C.S.: 115210

SORENSEN & KOFOED A/S

Smedeholm 7 9, 2730, Herlev, Denmark
Tel.: (45) 44921088
Web Site: http://www.skdk.dk
Sales Range: $25-49.9 Million
Emp.: 100
Distr of Chemical Containment Parts
N.A.I.C.S.: 424690
Fleming Soerensen (Mng Dir)

Subsidiaries:

Linatex A/S (1)
3 5 Snedeholm, 2730, Herlev, Denmark (100%)
Tel.: (45) 43538844
Web Site: http://www.linatex.dk
Sales Range: $25-49.9 Million
Emp.: 25
Distr of Chemical Containment Parts
N.A.I.C.S.: 424690
Ole Klaumann (CEO)

SORGENTE GROUP S.P.A.

Via del Tritone 132, 00187, Rome, Italy
Tel.: (39) 06 5833 2919   IT
Web Site:
   http://www.sorgentegroup.com
Year Founded: 2001

SORGENTE GROUP S.P.A.

Sorgente Group S.p.A.—(Continued)
Holding Company; Real Estate Investment & Asset Management Services
N.A.I.C.S.: 551112
Ilaria Fasano *(Dir-Art & Comm)*

Subsidiaries:

Nova Re SIIQ S.p.A. (1)
Via Vittor Pisani n 19, 20124, Milan, Italy (85%)
Tel.: (39) 02 4968 8268
Web Site: http://www.novare.it
Rev.: $4,461,886
Assets: $620,018,095
Liabilities: $212,773,425
Net Worth: $407,244,669
Earnings: ($706,452,017)
Emp.: 1
Fiscal Year-end: 12/31/2015
Real Estate Development Services
N.A.I.C.S.: 531390
Stefano Cervone *(Mng Dir & Gen Mgr)*

SORGENTI EMILIANE MODENA SPA
Via Capanna Tassoni 219/D, Fanano, 41020, Modena, Italy
Tel.: (39) 0536901511
Web Site: http://www.grupposem.it
Sales Range: $25-49.9 Million
Emp.: 120
Mineral Water & Soft Drink Mfr
N.A.I.C.S.: 312112
Vittorio Balugani *(Chm)*

SORGHUM JAPAN HOLDINGS CORP.
Watanabe Corporation Building
5-9-15 Kitashinagawa, Shinagawa-ku, Tokyo, 141-0001, Japan
Tel.: (81) 3 34493939   JP
Web Site: http://www.sorghum-jp.com
Year Founded: 1970
Rev.: $13,196,905
Assets: $14,772,226
Liabilities: $11,094,539
Net Worth: $3,677,688
Earnings: $20,837,311
Emp.: 84
Fiscal Year-end: 03/31/18
Holding Company
N.A.I.C.S.: 551112
Rei Nakahara *(Pres)*

Subsidiaries:

SUPER SORGHUM ASIA HOLDINGS PTE. LTD. (1)
11 Collyer Quay 11-05 The Arcade, Singapore, 49317, Singapore
Tel.: (65) 33449 3700
Web Site: http://www.super-sorghum.jp
Seed Whslr
N.A.I.C.S.: 424910

SUPER SORGHUM MEXICO S.A. DE C.V. (1)
Av Chapultepec 480 Torre Tribeca 17-D Col Americana, 44160, Guadalajara, Jalisco, Mexico
Tel.: (52) 13336400147
Web Site: http://www.supersorgo.mx
Seed Whslr
N.A.I.C.S.: 424910

THAI SUPER SORGHUM CO., LTD (1)
689 Bhiraj Tower At Emquartier Unit 1813 18th Floor, Sukhumvit road Klongtoey-nua Wattana, Bangkok, 10110, Thailand
Tel.: (66) 22612970
Seed Whslr
N.A.I.C.S.: 424910

SORIBADA INC.
617 4 5F Eonju-ro, Gangnam- gu, Seoul, Korea (South)
Tel.: (82) 15777334
Web Site: http://www.soribada.com
Year Founded: 2000

053110—(KRS)
Rev.: $2,933,528
Assets: $10,793,695
Liabilities: $13,899,959
Net Worth: ($3,106,264)
Earnings: ($2,205,171)
Emp.: 19
Fiscal Year-end: 12/31/22
Online Music Services
N.A.I.C.S.: 519210
Ho-Kyun Cho *(CEO)*

SORIL INFRA RESOURCES LIMITED
Tower-1 Senapati Bapat Marg, Elphinstone Road, Mumbai, 400 013, Haryana, India
Tel.: (91) 2261899700
Web Site: http://www.sorilinfraresources.com
Year Founded: 2005
SORILINFRA—(NSE)
Rev.: $26,352,690
Assets: $94,047,135
Liabilities: $58,431,555
Net Worth: $35,615,580
Earnings: $2,641,275
Emp.: 263
Fiscal Year-end: 03/31/21
Retail Stores
N.A.I.C.S.: 459999
Vikas Khandelwal *(Compliance Officer & Sec)*

Subsidiaries:

Indiabulls Rural Finance Private Limited (1)
One International Center Tower -1 4th Floor S B Marg,Elphinstone W, Mumbai, 400013, Maharashtra, India
Tel.: (91) 2261891200
Web Site: http://www.indiabullsruralfinance.com
Financial Services
N.A.I.C.S.: 523999
Sameer Gehlaut *(Founder & Chm)*

SOROC TECHNOLOGY INC.
607 Chrislea Road, Woodbridge, L4L 8A3, ON, Canada
Tel.: (905) 265-8000
Web Site: http://www.soroc.com
Year Founded: 1981
Rev.: $132,997,194
Emp.: 300
IT Services
N.A.I.C.S.: 423430
Rob McGill *(COO)*

SORRENTO RESOURCES LTD.
2080 - 777 Hornby Street, Vancouver, V6Z 1S4, BC, Canada
Tel.: (604) 290-6152
Web Site: https://sorrentoresources.ca
Year Founded: 2021
SRS—(CNSX)
Assets: $643,469
Liabilities: $163,441
Net Worth: $480,028
Earnings: ($447,823)
Fiscal Year-end: 06/30/24
Mineral Exploration Services
N.A.I.C.S.: 212390
T. Joshua Taylor *(Dir)*

SORTED GROUP HOLDINGS PLC
20 Eastbourne Terrace, London, W2 6LG, United Kingdom
Tel.: (44) 2074238000   UK
Web Site: http://www.locationsciences.ai
Year Founded: 2013
LSAI—(AIM)
Rev.: $139,934
Assets: $5,665,636

Liabilities: $199,273
Net Worth: $5,466,363
Earnings: ($957,108)
Emp.: 1
Fiscal Year-end: 12/31/22
Mobile Software & Services
N.A.I.C.S.: 513210
Mark Slade *(CEO)*

SOS CONSULTING AND RECRUITMENT
Al Khaleej Tower 4th Floor Abu Bakr Street Qiblah Area, PO Box 29273, Kuwait, Kuwait
Tel.: (965) 22243900
Web Site: http://www.soshr.net
Year Founded: 1975
Sales Range: $25-49.9 Million
Emp.: 13
Recruitment Services
N.A.I.C.S.: 561311
V. Jumana *(Deputy Gen Mgr)*

SOS LIMITED
No 6 Building Oriental Ocean View 298 Ocean View Rd, Yinzhu Community Huangdao District, Qingdao, 266400, Shandong, China
Tel.: (86) 53286617117   DE
Web Site: https://service.sosyun.com
Year Founded: 2004
SOS—(NYSE)
Rev.: $92,416,000
Assets: $483,892,000
Liabilities: $61,519,000
Net Worth: $422,373,000
Earnings: ($6,421,000)
Emp.: 181
Fiscal Year-end: 12/31/23
Consumer Lending Services
N.A.I.C.S.: 522291
Zhengyu Wang *(Founder)*

Subsidiaries:

SOS Information Technology Co., Ltd. (1)
Building 6 East Seaview Park 298 Haijing Road Yinzhu Str, West Coast New District, Qingdao, China
Tel.: (86) 53286617117
Web Site: http://www.service.sosyun.com
Satellite Communication Services
N.A.I.C.S.: 517410

SOSANDAR PLC
5-7 Cranwood Street Finsgate, London, EC1 V9EE, United Kingdom
Tel.: (44) 2079338780   UK
Web Site: http://www.orogen.co.uk
Sales Range: Less than $1 Million
Gold Exploration Services
N.A.I.C.S.: 212220
Mark Collingbourne *(Grp Dir-Fin)*

SOSILA LOGISTICS REIT, INC.
1-17-10 Kyobashi, Chuo-ku, Tokyo, 104-8345, Japan
Tel.: (81) 343460579
Web Site: https://www.sosila-reit.co.jp
Year Founded: 2019
2979—(TKS)
Real Estate Investment Services
N.A.I.C.S.: 531190
Masaaki Yano *(Exec Dir)*

SOSTENEO SGR S.P.A.
Piazza Tre Torri, 1 Level 33, 20145, Milan, Italy
Web Site: https://sosteneo.com
Investment Management
N.A.I.C.S.: 523999

SOSTENYA GROUP PLC
44 Welbeck Street, London, W1G 8DY, United Kingdom
Tel.: (44) 20 3393 9393   UK
Web Site: http://www.sostenya.co.uk

INTERNATIONAL PUBLIC

Environment & Renewable Energy Industry Investment Holding Company
N.A.I.C.S.: 551112
Pietro Colucci *(Mng Dir & Sec)*

SOSTRAVEL.COM S.P.A.
via Olona 183/G, 21013, Gallarate, VA, Italy
Tel.: (39) 03311587117
Web Site: https://www.sostravel.com
Year Founded: 2017
SOSAF—(OTCQB)
Rev.: $21,734,322
Assets: $9,431,712
Liabilities: $4,526,305
Net Worth: $4,905,407
Earnings: $1,291,117
Emp.: 16
Fiscal Year-end: 12/31/23
Travel Tour Operator
N.A.I.C.S.: 561520
Rudolph Gentile *(Chm & CEO)*

SOTETSU HOLDINGS, INC.
2-9-14 Kita-Saiwai, Nishi-ku, Yokohama, 220-0004, Japan
Tel.: (81) 453192054
Web Site: http://www.sotetsu.co.jp
Year Founded: 1917
9003—(TKS)
Rev.: $1,784,957,790
Assets: $4,728,681,630
Liabilities: $3,639,803,110
Net Worth: $1,088,878,520
Earnings: $106,288,800
Emp.: 10,194
Fiscal Year-end: 03/31/24
Holding Company; Commuter Train & Bus Operator
N.A.I.C.S.: 551112
Hidekazu Hayashi *(Chm)*

Subsidiaries:

Capital Properties Co., Ltd. (1)
2-9-14 Kitasaiwai, Nishi-ku, Yokohama, 220-0004, Japan
Tel.: (81) 453192368
Real Estate Lending Services
N.A.I.C.S.: 531390
Mikio Morimura *(CEO)*

Hayama Bonjour Co., Ltd. (1)
2-9-14 Kitasaiwai, Nishi-ku, Yokohama, 220-0004, Japan
Tel.: (81) 453197270
Emp.: 96
Bakery Products Mfr
N.A.I.C.S.: 311812

Sagami Railway Co., Ltd. (1)
2-9-14 Kitasaiwai, Nishi-ku, Yokohama, 220-0004, Japan
Tel.: (81) 453192092
Web Site: https://www.sotetsu.co.jp
Emp.: 1,120
Railway Services
N.A.I.C.S.: 488210
Hiroshi Chihara *(Pres)*

Soei Foods Co., Ltd. (1)
2-9-14 Kitasaiwai Building 4th Floor, Nishi-ku, Yokohama, 220-0004, Japan
Tel.: (81) 45 594 6122
Web Site: https://www.soei-f.co.jp
Emp.: 1,195
Processed Meat Product Mfr
N.A.I.C.S.: 311612

Sotetsu Building Management Co., Ltd. (1)
2-1-22 Minamisaiwai, Nishi-ku, Yokohama, 220-0005, Japan
Tel.: (81) 453263032
Building Management Services
N.A.I.C.S.: 531311

Sotetsu Bus Co., Ltd. (1)
2-9-14 Kitasaiwai, Nishi-ku, Yokohama, 220-0004, Japan
Tel.: (81) 453192144
Web Site: https://www.sotetsu.co.jp
Emp.: 567

AND PRIVATE COMPANIES

Cargo Transportation Services
N.A.I.C.S.: 488490

Sotetsu Business Service Co., Ltd. (1)
2-9-14 Kitasaiwai, Nishi-ku, Yokohama, Japan
Tel.: (81) 453192343
Web Site: https://www.sotetsu.co.jp
Emp.: 241
Recruitment Services
N.A.I.C.S.: 561311

Sotetsu Hotel Management Co., Ltd. (1)
Building 2F 2-9-14 Kitasaiwai, Nishi-ku, Yokohama, 220-0004, Kanagawa, Japan
Tel.: (81) 453192566
Home Management Services
N.A.I.C.S.: 721110
Takamasa Kato *(Pres)*

Sotetsu Insurance Service Co., Ltd. (1)
2-9-14 Kitasai, Nishi-ku, Yokohama, 220-0004, Japan
Tel.: (81) 453127525
Insurance Agency Services
N.A.I.C.S.: 524210

Sotetsu International Korea Co., Ltd. (1)
Namdaemun-ro 5-gil, Jung-gu, Seoul, 04526, Korea (South)
Tel.: (82) 27720900
Web Site: https://sotetsu-hotels.com
Emp.: 65
Home Management Services
N.A.I.C.S.: 721110
Takamasa Kato *(CEO)*

Sotetsu Kigyo Co., Ltd. (1)
2-9-14 Kitasaiwai, Nishi-ku, Yokohama, 220-0004, Japan
Tel.: (81) 453192361
Emp.: 1,964
Real Estate Lending Services
N.A.I.C.S.: 531390

Sotetsu Living Support Co., Ltd. (1)
2-9-14 Kitasaiwai, Nishi-ku, Yokohama, 220-0004, Japan
Tel.: (81) 456207602
Emp.: 313
Real Estate Services
N.A.I.C.S.: 531390

Sotetsu Next Stage Co., Ltd. (1)
2-9-14 Kitasaiwai, Nishi-ku, Yokohama, 220-0004, Japan
Tel.: (81) 453192456
Emp.: 10
Worker Dispatch Services
N.A.I.C.S.: 561311

Sotetsu Pure Water Co., Ltd. (1)
4-3-28 Midorien, Izumi-ku, Yokohama, 245-0002, Kanagawa, Japan
Tel.: (81) 455679077
Emp.: 34
Water Treatment Equipment Mfr
N.A.I.C.S.: 333310

Sotetsu Real Estate Co., Ltd. (1)
2-9-14 Kitasaiwai, Nishi-ku, Yokohama, 220-0004, Japan
Tel.: (81) 453192165
Real Estate Services
N.A.I.C.S.: 531390

Sotetsu Real Estate Sales Co., Ltd. (1)
2-9-14 Kitasaiwai, Nishi-ku, Yokohama, 220-0004, Japan
Tel.: (81) 453192100
Emp.: 105
Real Estate Services
N.A.I.C.S.: 531390

Sotetsu Reform Co., Ltd. (1)
3-2-8 Arcus Building 3F Midorien, Izumi-ku, Yokohama, 245-0002, Japan
Tel.: (81) 120127158
Emp.: 42
Detached House Remodeling Services
N.A.I.C.S.: 236118

Sotetsu RenUPs Co., Ltd. (1)
Arcus Building 3F 3-2-8 Arcus Building 3F Midorien, Izumi-ku, Yokohama, 245-0002, Japan

Tel.: (81) 120127158
Emp.: 42
Real Estate Services
N.A.I.C.S.: 531390

Sotetsu Rosen Co., Ltd. (1)
2-9-14 Kitasaiwai, Nishi-ku, Yokohama, 220-0004, Japan
Tel.: (81) 453197060
Emp.: 2,324
All Grocery Product Distr
N.A.I.C.S.: 445110

Sotetsu Rosen Fresh Foods Co., Ltd. (1)
2-9-14 North Saiwai, Nishi Ward, Yokohama, 220-0004, Kanagawa, Japan
Tel.: (81) 455946122
Web Site: https://www.soei-f.co.jp
Emp.: 1,248
Marine Food Mfr & Distr
N.A.I.C.S.: 311710

Sotetsu Station Retail Co., Ltd. (1)
2-9-14 Kitasaiwai, Nishi-ku, Yokohama, 220-0004, Japan
Tel.: (81) 453192208
Web Site: https://www.sotetsu.co.jp
Emp.: 321
Merchandise Distr
N.A.I.C.S.: 455219

Sotetsu Urban Creates Co., Ltd. (1)
2-1-22 Minamisaiwai, Nishi-ku, Yokohama, 220-0005, Kanagawa, Japan
Tel.: (81) 453163111
Web Site: https://www.sotetsu-urban.jp
Emp.: 69
Real Estate Leasing Business Services
N.A.I.C.S.: 531190

Sotetsu Urban Creators Co., Ltd. (1)
2-1-22 Minamisaiwai, Nishi-ku, Yokohama, 220-0005, Japan
Tel.: (81) 453163111
Emp.: 69
Real Estate Services
N.A.I.C.S.: 531390

Sotetsu Wish Co., Ltd. (1)
35-6 Kashiwa-cho, Asahi-ku, Yokohama, Japan
Tel.: (81) 453607866
Web Site: https://www.sotetsu.co.jp
Emp.: 33
Disability Work Services
N.A.I.C.S.: 624120

Thanh Van Hotel Development Investment Joint Stock Company (1)
8 Ly Tu Trong Street, Ben Nghe Ward District 1, 700000, Ho Chi Minh City, Vietnam
Tel.: (84) 2839101848
Web Site: https://sotetsu-hotels.com
Home Management Services
N.A.I.C.S.: 721110
Shigeru Oshima *(CEO)*

Yokohama District Heating & Cooling Co., Ltd. (1)
2-9-14 Kitasaiwai, Nishi-ku, Yokohama, 220-0004, Japan
Tel.: (81) 453192488
Emp.: 5
Heat Supply Services
N.A.I.C.S.: 221330

SOTHEMA
Bouskoura Industrial Zone, BP 20180, Bouskoura, 27182, Casablanca, Morocco
Tel.: (212) 522437040
Web Site: https://www.sothema.com
Year Founded: 1976
SOT—(CAS)
Sales Range: Less than $1 Million
Pharmaceutical Preparation Mfr
N.A.I.C.S.: 325412

SOTKAMO SILVER AB
Nybrogatan 34, PO Box 5216, SE-102 45, Stockholm, Sweden
Tel.: (46) 8304920
Web Site: https://www.silver.fi
SOSI1—(HEL)
Rev.: $34,739,198
Assets: $60,177,770

Liabilities: $37,352,365
Net Worth: $22,825,405
Earnings: ($2,603,801)
Emp.: 138
Fiscal Year-end: 12/31/22
Silver, Gold & Zinc Mining
N.A.I.C.S.: 212220
Eeva-Liisa Virkkunen *(Chm)*

Subsidiaries:

Sotkamo Silver Oy (1)
Isokatu 32 B, 90100, Oulu, Finland
Tel.: (358) 500 37 47 43
Silver & Gold Ore Mining Services
N.A.I.C.S.: 212220
Ilkka Tuokko *(Mng Dir)*

SOTOH CO., LTD.
5-1-1 Kagoya, Ichinomiya, 494-8501, Aichi, Japan
Tel.: (81) 586451121
Web Site: https://www.sotoh.co.jp
Year Founded: 1923
3571—(TKS)
Rev.: $70,786,490
Assets: $124,320,880
Liabilities: $30,022,620
Net Worth: $94,298,260
Earnings: $17,873,440
Fiscal Year-end: 03/31/24
Textile Products Mfr
N.A.I.C.S.: 313310
Yasuhiko Ueda *(Pres)*

SOUCY HOLDING INC.
5450 St-Roch Street, Drummondville, J2B 6W3, QC, Canada
Tel.: (819) 474-9008
Web Site: http://www.soucy-group.com
Year Founded: 1967
Sales Range: $125-149.9 Million
Emp.: 1,700
Recreational, Industrial & Military Vehicle Parts Mfr & Distr
N.A.I.C.S.: 551112
Gilles Soucy *(Pres)*

Subsidiaries:

Soucy Baron Inc. (1)
851 Baron Street, Saint-Jerome, J7Y 4E1, QC, Canada (100%)
Tel.: (450) 436-2433
Web Site: https://soucybaron.soucy-group.com
Sales Range: $50-74.9 Million
Emp.: 200
Rubber Products Mfr
N.A.I.C.S.: 326299
Gilles Soucy *(Pres)*

Soucy Belgen Inc. (1)
4475 Saint-Joseph Blvd, Drummondville, J2B 1T8, QC, Canada
Tel.: (819) 477-2434
Web Site: http://www.soucybelgen.com
Iron Mfr
N.A.I.C.S.: 331511
Jean-Francois Moreau *(Dir-Bus Dev)*

Soucy International Inc. (1)
5450 Saint-Roch street south, Drummondville, J2B 6W3, QC, Canada (100%)
Tel.: (819) 474-9008
Web Site: http://www.soucyinternational.com
Sales Range: $50-74.9 Million
Emp.: 200
Rubber Products Mfr
N.A.I.C.S.: 326299

Soucy Koutou Ltee (1)
1825 Power Street, Drummondville, J2C 5X4, QC, Canada
Tel.: (819) 478-9032
Web Site: http://www.soucykoutou.com
Emp.: 25
Polyurethane Products Mfr
N.A.I.C.S.: 325211
Gilles Soucy *(Founder)*

Soucy Plastiques Inc. (1)
5755 Place Kubota, Drummondville, J2B 6V4, QC, Canada (100%)

Tel.: (819) 474-5151
Web Site: http://www.soucygroup.com
Sales Range: $50-74.9 Million
Emp.: 130
Plastics Product Mfr
N.A.I.C.S.: 326199

Soucy Rivalair Inc. (1)
650 Rocheleau street, Drummondville, J2C 7R8, QC, Canada (100%)
Tel.: (819) 474-2908
Web Site: http://www.rivalair.com
Sales Range: $50-74.9 Million
Emp.: 175
Iron & Steel Forging
N.A.I.C.S.: 332111
Gasmim Villeneuve *(Gen Mgr)*

Soucy Techno Inc (1)
2550 Chemin Saint-Roch S, Sherbrooke, J1N 2R6, QC, Canada
Tel.: (819) 864-4284
Web Site: http://www.soucytechno.com
Rev.: $22,075,200
Emp.: 170
Rubber Custom Mixing Preparer
N.A.I.C.S.: 326299
Andre Archambrault *(Gen Mgr)*

SOUDAL NV
Everdongenlaan 18-20, Turnhout, 2300, Belgium
Tel.: (32) 1 442 42 31
Web Site: http://www.soudal.com
Sales Range: $800-899.9 Million
Emp.: 2,000
Silicone, Polyurethane, Marine Sealants & Acrylics Mfr
N.A.I.C.S.: 326150
Vic Swerts *(Founder & Chm)*

Subsidiaries:

Accumetric LLC (1)
350 Ring Rd, Elizabethtown, KY 42701
Tel.: (270) 769-3385
Web Site: http://www.accumetricinc.com
Sales Range: $50-74.9 Million
Emp.: 150
Adhesives, Sealants, Silicones & Lubricants Mfr
N.A.I.C.S.: 325520
Allen Hartlage *(VP)*

Subsidiary (Non-US):

Accumetric Silicones Private Limited (2)
245 GST Road, Urapakkam Kancheepuram District, Chennai, 603202, Tamil Nadu, India
Tel.: (91) 44 40260345
Adhesives, Sealants & Silicones Mfr
N.A.I.C.S.: 325520

Soudal Inc. (1)
12775 Randolph Ridge Ln, Manassas, VA 20109
Tel.: (817) 319-1433
Web Site: http://www.soudalusa.com
Adhesives, Sealants & Silicones Mfr & Distr
N.A.I.C.S.: 424690
Geert Paepen *(Dir-North America)*

SOUFIAN CEMENT CO.
Km 33 Marand Rd, PO Box 4713-51385, Tabriz, East Azarbaijan, Iran
Tel.: (98) 2188953986
Web Site: https://www.soufiancement.com
Year Founded: 1966
Sales Range: $50-74.9 Million
Cement Mfr
N.A.I.C.S.: 327120
M. Dadash *(Chm)*

SOUGOU SHOUKEN CO., LTD.
448 Higashinaebo 2jo 3chome, Higashi-ku, Sapporo, 007-0802, Hokkaido, Japan
Tel.: (81) 117805677
Web Site: https://www.shouken.co.jp
Year Founded: 1972
7850—(TKS)
Rev.: $98,251,120
Assets: $47,713,620

SOUGOU SHOUKEN CO., LTD.

SOUGOU SHOUKEN CO., LTD.—(Continued)
Liabilities: $29,706,720
Net Worth: $18,006,900
Earnings: $1,704,280
Emp.: 381
Fiscal Year-end: 07/31/24
Commercial Printing Services
N.A.I.C.S.: 323113
Masaru Kato (Chm)

SOUKEN ACE CO.,LTD.
2F Axia Aoyama 8-5-28 Akasaka, Minato-ku, Tokyo, 107-0052, Japan
Tel.: (81) 357752100
Web Site: http://www.crea-hd.co.jp
Year Founded: 1965
1757—(TKS)
Rev.: $10,443,800
Assets: $8,361,650
Liabilities: $6,894,230
Net Worth: $1,467,420
Earnings: $(9,974,490)
Emp.: 547
Fiscal Year-end: 03/31/24
Holding Company
N.A.I.C.S.: 551112
Takashi Kuroda (Pres)

SOULBRAIN HOLDINGS CO., LTD.
34 Pangyo-ro 255beon-gil, Bundang-gu, Seongnam, Gyeonggi-do, Korea (South)
Tel.: (82) 317190700
Web Site: https://www.soulbrain.co.kr
Year Founded: 1986
036830—(KRS)
Rev.: $433,436,514
Assets: $1,295,678,579
Liabilities: $389,249,709
Net Worth: $906,428,870
Earnings: $49,233,320
Emp.: 60
Fiscal Year-end: 12/31/22
Electronic Components Mfr
N.A.I.C.S.: 334419
Byungchang Kang (CEO)

Subsidiaries:

Fect Co., Ltd. (1)
Chemical Products Mfr
N.A.I.C.S.: 325998

MC Solution Co., Ltd. (1)
725-15 Geomsang-dong, Gongju, Choongcheongnam-do, Korea (South)
Electronic Components Mfr
N.A.I.C.S.: 334419

NAU IB capital Co., Ltd. (1)
11 floor Golden Tower 511 Samseong-Ro, Gangnam-Gu, Seoul, Korea (South)
Tel.: (82) 2 565 6234
Web Site: http://www.nauib.com
Financial Investment Services
N.A.I.C.S.: 523940
Seung Wee (CEO)

Soulbrain Co., Ltd. - China Plant (1)
Rm 707 Baishida 6 Changjiang bei-lu, Wuxi, Jiangsu-sheng, China
Tel.: (86) 52 256 0682
Electronic Components Mfr
N.A.I.C.S.: 334419

Soulbrain Co., Ltd. - Gongju Plant (1)
34-19 Gongdan-gil, Gongju, Choongcheongnam-do, Korea (South)
Tel.: (82) 41 852 1636
Electronic Components Mfr
N.A.I.C.S.: 334419

Soulbrain Co., Ltd. - Janghang Plant (1)
78-11 Jangam-ri, Janghang, Choongcheongnam-do, Korea (South)
Tel.: (82) 41 956 7814
Electronic Components Mfr
N.A.I.C.S.: 334419

Soulbrain Co., Ltd. - Paju Plant (1)
29 Donyu 2-ro, Munsan, Gyeonggi-do, Korea (South)
Tel.: (82) 31 954 1636
Electronic Components Mfr
N.A.I.C.S.: 334419

Soulbrain Co., Ltd. - Ulsan Plant (1)
203-2 Seongnam-dong, Nam-gu, Ulsan, Korea (South)
Tel.: (82) 52 256 0682
Electronic Components Mfr
N.A.I.C.S.: 334419

soulbrain LTK Co., Ltd. (1)
Rm 507 Jungang Induspia 5 138-6 Sangdaewon1-dong, Jungwon-gu, Seongnam, Gyeonggi-do, Korea (South)
Tel.: (82) 31 739 5050
Web Site: http://www.soulbrainltk.com
Electronic Components Mfr
N.A.I.C.S.: 334419
Ji Wan Chung (CEO)

soulbrain MI (1)
47050 Five Mile Rd, Northville, MI 48168
Tel.: (248) 869-3000
Chemical Products Distr
N.A.I.C.S.: 424690
Ji Wan Chung (CEO)

soulbrain Nanotec Co., Ltd. (1)
78 Gasan-ro 9-gil, Geumcheon-gu, 153-801, Seoul, Korea (South)
Tel.: (82) 2 3282 7000
Web Site: http://www.soulbrainnanotech.com
Semiconductor Equipment Mfr
N.A.I.C.S.: 333242
Seong Hwan Park (CEO)

soulbrain SLD Co., Ltd. (1)
725-6 Geomsang-dong, Gongju, Choongcheongnam-do, Korea (South)
Tel.: (82) 41 851 4550
Web Site: http://www.soulbrainsld.co.kr
Electronic Components Mfr
N.A.I.C.S.: 334419
Ji Heung Chung (CEO)

soulbrain Savings Bank (1)
1094 Joongandae-ro, Yeonje-gu, Busan, Korea (South)
Tel.: (82) 51 861 8600
Web Site: http://www.soulbrainsb.co.kr
Commercial Banking Services
N.A.I.C.S.: 522110

soulbrain optos Co., Ltd (1)
36 Dolkkotji-gil, Yangseong-myeon, Anseong, Gyeonggi-do, Korea (South)
Tel.: (82) 316713009
Web Site: https://www.soulbrainoptos.com
Electronic Components Mfr
N.A.I.C.S.: 334419
Hwan Chul Rho (CEO)

SOULGATE INC.
22/F SCG Parkside 868 Yinghua Road, Pudong New Area, Shanghai, China
Tel.: (86) 21 2613 5821   Ky
Year Founded: 2017
SSR—(NASDAQ)
Rev.: $76,300,565
Assets: $107,447,935
Liabilities: $297,580,158
Net Worth: $(190,132,223)
Earnings: $(92,058,932)
Emp.: 144
Fiscal Year-end: 12/31/20
Software Development Services
N.A.I.C.S.: 541511
Lu Zhang (Founder, Chm & CEO)

SOUND CAVE TECHNOLOGY, INC.
43 Cathy Jean Crescent, Toronto, M9V 4T2, ON, Canada
Tel.: (417) 322-6228   WY
Year Founded: 2021
Assets: $1,463
Liabilities: $12,457
Net Worth: $(10,994)
Earnings: $(2,993)
Fiscal Year-end: 12/31/23
Apparel Product Mfr
N.A.I.C.S.: 315990

SOUND ENERGY PLC
20 St Dunstan's Hill, Kent, London, EC3R 8HL, United Kingdom
Tel.: (44) 2037953200
Web Site: https://www.soundenergyplc.com
SOU—(AIM)
Rev.: $48,180
Assets: $255,426,270
Liabilities: $40,916,865
Net Worth: $214,509,405
Earnings: $5,986,365
Fiscal Year-end: 12/31/22
Oil & Gas Exploration Services
N.A.I.C.S.: 213112
Mohammed Seghiri (COO)

SOUND GLOBAL LTD.
460 Alexandra Road PSA Building 15-04, Singapore, 119963, Singapore
Tel.: (65) 62726678   SG
Web Site: http://www.soundglobal.com.sg
Sales Range: $400-449.9 Million
Emp.: 1,394
Water & Wastewater Treatment Plant Engineering Services
N.A.I.C.S.: 237110
Yibo Wen (Founder & Chm)

Subsidiaries:

Advanced Resources Holdings Pte. Ltd. (1)
460 Alexandra Road Unit 15-04 PSA Bldg, Singapore, 119963, Singapore
Tel.: (65) 6272 6678
Holding Company; Wastewater Treatment Plant Development & Operation Services
N.A.I.C.S.: 551112

Subsidiary (Non-US):

Advanced Water Reclamation (Chengdu) Co., Ltd. (2)
Block 2 No 12 03 Greenwich Village No 1 Wangjiang Road, Chengdu, 610041, Sichuan, China
Tel.: (86) 28 8529 2768
Wastewater Treatment Plant Development & Operation Services
N.A.I.C.S.: 237110

SOUND GROUP INC.
60 Anson Road Mapletree Anson 09-01/02, Singapore, 079914, Singapore
Tel.: (65) 62021360   Ky
Web Site: https://www.soundgroupinc.com
Year Founded: 2010
SOGP—(NASDAQ)
Rev.: $291,803,000
Assets: $79,800,000
Liabilities: $38,954,000
Net Worth: $40,846,000
Earnings: $(18,947,000)
Emp.: 563
Fiscal Year-end: 12/31/23
Holding Company
N.A.I.C.S.: 551112
Jinnan Lai (Co-Founder & CEO)

SOUNDS FANTASTIC LTD.
48 Bonaccord St, Moncton, E1C 5K7, NB, Canada
Tel.: (506) 857-0000
Web Site: http://www.soundfantastic.ca
Year Founded: 1981
Sales Range: $10-24.9 Million
Emp.: 30
Audio/Video Solutions, Furniture & Installation Services
N.A.I.C.S.: 423620
Georgio Paulin (Gen Mgr)

SOUNDSTORM DIGITAL, INC.
Suite 1500 - 885 West Georgia Street, Vancouver, V6C 3E8, BC, Canada
Tel.: (604) 861-8980   NV
Sales Range: Less than $1 Million
Digital Music Platform
N.A.I.C.S.: 516210
Geoffrey Lee (Pres)

SOUNDVEST SPLIT TRUST
100 Sparks Street Suite 900, Ottawa, K1P 5B7, ON, Canada
Tel.: (613) 236-7361
Web Site: http://www.brookfieldsoundvest.com
Year Founded: 2005
Rev.: $4,160,037
Assets: $17,380,518
Liabilities: $14,056,493
Net Worth: $3,324,024
Earnings: $2,827,368
Fiscal Year-end: 12/31/16
Financial Investment Services
N.A.I.C.S.: 523999

SOUNDWILL HOLDINGS LIMITED
21st Fl Soundwill Plaza No 38 Russell Street, Causeway Bay, China (Hong Kong)
Tel.: (852) 28034260
Web Site: http://www.soundwill.com.hk
0878—(OTCIQ)
Rev.: $61,136,657
Assets: $2,840,103,263
Liabilities: $389,449,052
Net Worth: $2,450,654,210
Earnings: $(33,533,682)
Emp.: 302
Fiscal Year-end: 12/31/22
Property Development
N.A.I.C.S.: 531312
Wai Ling Chan (Exec Dir)

SOUP HOLDINGS LIMITED
150 Kampong Ampat 04-01 KA Centre, Singapore, 368324, Singapore
Tel.: (65) 62224668
Web Site: https://www.souprestaurant.com.sg
5KI—(SES)
Rev.: $31,127,307
Assets: $24,317,721
Liabilities: $15,326,880
Net Worth: $8,990,841
Earnings: $1,246,070
Emp.: 243
Fiscal Year-end: 12/31/23
Home Management Services
N.A.I.C.S.: 721110
Khek Koon Then (Exec Dir)

Subsidiaries:

Pot Luck F & B Singapore Pte. Ltd. (1)
36 Boat Quay, Singapore, 049825, Singapore
Tel.: (65) 92719219
Event Management Services
N.A.I.C.S.: 561920

Samsui Supplies & Services Pte. Ltd. (1)
150 Kampong Ampat KA Centre 04-01, Singapore, 368324, Singapore
Tel.: (65) 66459341
Web Site: http://www.samsui.com
Catering Services
N.A.I.C.S.: 722320

Soup Restaurant (Causeway Point) Pte. Ltd. (1)
1 Woodlands Square 05-11 Causeway Point, Singapore, 738099, Singapore
Tel.: (65) 68942322
Web Site: http://www.souprestaurant.com.sg

Soup Restaurant (Jurong Point) Pte Ltd (1)
1 Jurong W Central 2 02-33 Jurong Point, Singapore, 64886, Singapore
Tel.: (65) 67907797
Restaurant Operating Services
N.A.I.C.S.: 722511

Soup Restaurant Investments Pte. Ltd. (1)
KA Foodlink 03-11 171 Kampong Ampat, Singapore, 368330, Singapore
Tel.: (65) 63339886
Restaurant Operating Services
N.A.I.C.S.: 722511

Soup Restaurant Singapore Pte. Ltd. (1)
150 Kampong Ampat KA Centre 04-01, Singapore, 368324, Singapore
Tel.: (65) 62224668
Web Site: http://www.souprestaurant.com.sg
Restaurant Services
N.A.I.C.S.: 551112
Irin Lau (Head-Mktg)

Sure Food Pte. Ltd. (1)
KA Foodlink 03-11 171 Kampong Ampat, Singapore, 368330, Singapore
Tel.: (65) 63339886
Restaurant Operating Services
N.A.I.C.S.: 722511

SOURCE ATLANTIC INDUSTRIAL DISTRIBUTION & SERVICES GROUP
331 Chesley Drive, PO Box 967, Saint John, E2L 4E4, NB, Canada
Tel.: (506) 632-1000
Web Site: http://www.sourceatlantic.ca
Year Founded: 2001
Sales Range: $50-74.9 Million
Emp.: 500
Holding Company; Industrial, Commercial & Dealer Markets Tool & Equipment Warehouser & Distr
N.A.I.C.S.: 551112
Steve Drummond (Pres)

Subsidiaries:

Thornes (1)
331 Chesley Dr, Saint John, E2L 4E4, NB, Canada
Tel.: (506) 632-1000
Web Site: http://www.sourceatlantic.ca
Sales Range: $125-149.9 Million
Industrial, Commercial & Dealer Markets Tool & Equipment Warehouser & Distr
N.A.I.C.S.: 423610
Steve Drummond (Gen Mgr)

SOURCE ENERGY SERVICES LTD.
500 1060 - 7th Street SW, Calgary, T2R 0C4, AB, Canada
Tel.: (403) 262-1312
Web Site: https://www.sourceenergy.com
SHLE—(TSX)
Rev.: $250,220,863
Assets: $208,110,731
Liabilities: $203,005,571
Net Worth: $5,105,159
Earnings: ($19,089,979)
Fiscal Year-end: 12/31/21
Construction Materials Distr
N.A.I.C.S.: 423390
Derren Newell (CFO)

Subsidiaries:

RWR Trucking Inc. (1)
33297 Westwood Dr, Dade City, FL 33523-9051
Tel.: (780) 312-0006
Web Site: https://rwrtrucking.com
Specialized Freight Trucking; Long-Distance

N.A.I.C.S.: 484230
Malena Sanderson (Mgr)

SOURCE INDUSTRIES (INDIA) LIMITED
Flat No-301 Dbn Padmavathi Arcade, 6-3-709/A/10/A Punjagutta Officers Colony, Hyderabad, 500082, TG, India
Tel.: (91) 4042014389
Web Site: https://www.sourceindustries.com
Year Founded: 1984
521036—(BOM)
Rev.: $6,902
Assets: $679,078
Liabilities: $37,253
Net Worth: $641,825
Earnings: ($15,962)
Emp.: 5
Fiscal Year-end: 03/31/21
Civil Engineering Services
N.A.I.C.S.: 237990
Venubabu Munduri (CFO)

SOURCE NATURAL FOODS & HERBAL SUPPLEMENTS LIMITED
No 201 Sumeru Towers 54-46 Second Floor, 11th Main Road 39th A Cross 4th T Block Jayanagar, Bengaluru, 560 041, India
Tel.: (91) 8026087733
Web Site: https://www.source-natural.com
Year Founded: 1995
531398—(BOM)
Rev.: $3,442,506
Assets: $2,350,968
Liabilities: $554,193
Net Worth: $1,796,775
Earnings: $460,548
Emp.: 57
Fiscal Year-end: 03/31/21
Dietary Supplements Mfr
N.A.I.C.S.: 325412
Arvind Varchaswi Narasimhan (Mng Dir)

SOURCENEXT CORPORATION
Shiodome City Center 33F 1-5-2 Higashi, Shimbashi Minato-ku, Tokyo, 105-7133, Japan
Tel.: (81) 362545231
Web Site: http://www.sourcenext.com
Year Founded: 1996
4344—(TKS)
Rev.: $74,917,740
Assets: $111,120,710
Liabilities: $55,669,420
Net Worth: $55,451,290
Earnings: ($14,337,090)
Emp.: 381
Fiscal Year-end: 03/31/24
Personal Computer Software Sales
N.A.I.C.S.: 423430
Noriyuki Matsuda (Founder, Pres & CEO)

Subsidiaries:

Rosetta Stone Japan Co., Ltd. (1)
Shiodome City Center 33F 1-5-2 Higashi, Shimbashi Minato-ku, Tokyo, 105-7133, Japan
Tel.: (81) 362545231
Language Learning Solutions Including Software, Online Services & Audio Practice Tools
N.A.I.C.S.: 513210

SOURIS MINI INC.
1450 rue Esther Blondin, Quebec, G1Y 3N7, QC, Canada
Tel.: (418) 524-6464
Web Site: http://www.sourismini.com
Year Founded: 1989
Family Clothing Stores

N.A.I.C.S.: 458110
Steeve Beaudet (Owner)

SOUTER CAPITAL LLP
68-70 George Street 4th Floor, Edinburgh, EH2 2LR, United Kingdom
Tel.: (44) 1312257688
Web Site: http://www.souterinvestments.com
Portfolio Management
N.A.I.C.S.: 523940
Brian Souter (Owner)

Subsidiaries:

Tracerco Limited (1)
Measurement Technology Centre The Moat Belasis Hall Technology Park, Billingham, TS23 4ED, United Kingdom
Tel.: (44) 1642375500
Web Site: https://www.tracerco.com
Diagnostic & Measurement Equipment Mfr
N.A.I.C.S.: 334519

SOUTH AFRICAN AIRWAYS (PTY) LTD.
Airways Park Jones Rod, O R Tambo Intl Airport, Johannesburg, South Africa
Tel.: (27) 119781111
Web Site: http://www.flysaa.com
Sales Range: $1-4.9 Billion
Emp.: 10,057
Airline Travel
N.A.I.C.S.: 481111
Tleli Makhetha (Gen Mgr-Cargo)

Subsidiaries:

Air Chefs (Pty) Ltd. (1)
Durban International Airport, PO Box 57745, Durban, 4029, South Africa (100%)
Tel.: (27) 314690770
Web Site: http://www.airchefs.co.za
Sales Range: $10-24.9 Million
Emp.: 84
Catering for Aircrafts
N.A.I.C.S.: 722320

Mango Airlines SOC Ltd (1)
Mezzanine Level Domestic Departure Terminal, PO Box 1273, OR Tambo International Airport, 1627, Johannesburg, South Africa
Tel.: (27) 11 086 6100
Web Site: http://www.flymango.com
Oil Transportation Services
N.A.I.C.S.: 481111

SAA-South African Airways (1)
Lowenstrasse 29, PO Box 6439, 8023, Zurich, Switzerland (100%)
Tel.: (41) 442151115
Web Site: http://www.flysaa.com
Sales Range: $25-49.9 Million
Emp.: 16
Airline Travel
N.A.I.C.S.: 481111

South African Airways (1)
St Georges House 61 Conduit St, W1S 2NE, London, Central London, United Kingdom - England (100%)
Tel.: (44) 2073125005
Web Site: http://www.flysaa.com
Sales Range: $25-49.9 Million
Emp.: 70
Airline
N.A.I.C.S.: 481111

South African Travel Centre (1)
1 Jones Rd Kemptom Park, Parktown, Johannesburg, 2026, South Africa
Tel.: (27) 11 616 7956
Web Site: http://www.satravelcentre.com
Oil Transportation Services
N.A.I.C.S.: 481111
Bulelwa Koyana (CEO)

Subsidiary (Domestic):

South African Bassie Travel Centre (2)
23 Chamberlain Rd, Berea, East London, 5241, Eastern Cape, South Africa
Tel.: (27) 43 726 2542
Web Site: http://www.bassietravel.co.za

Oil Transportation Services
N.A.I.C.S.: 481111
Bassie Ngozwana (Mng Dir)

SOUTH AFRICAN BROADCASTING CORPORATION
Artillery and Henley Rd Auckland Park, PO Box 11, Johannesburg, 2006, South Africa
Tel.: (27) 117149111
Web Site: http://www.sabc.co.za
Year Founded: 1936
Sales Range: $650-699.9 Million
Emp.: 6,000
Television & Radio Broadcasting Services
N.A.I.C.S.: 516120
Bongumusa Makhathini (Chm)

Subsidiaries:

SABC Airwave Travel Proprietary Limited (1)
Radio Park Bldg Henly St, Johannesburg, 2001, Gauteng, South Africa
Tel.: (27) 117144853
Radio & Television Broadcasting Services
N.A.I.C.S.: 516110

SOUTH AFRICAN PROPERTY OPPORTUNITIES PLC
Millennium House 46 Athol Street, Douglas, IM1 1JB, Isle of Man
Tel.: (44) 1624 692 600   IM
Year Founded: 1966
Financial Services
N.A.I.C.S.: 523999

SOUTH AMERICAN LITHIUM CORP
, Calgary, AB, Canada
Tel.: (587) 577-9878
Web Site: https://southamericanlithium.com
Mineral Exploration Services
N.A.I.C.S.: 212220

SOUTH ATLANTIC GOLD INC.
Landmark 3 3351632 Dickson Avenue, Kelowna, V1Y 7T2, BC, Canada
Tel.: (250) 762-5777   BC
Web Site: https://southatlanticgold.com
Year Founded: 2006
JLRRF—(OTCIQ)
Rev.: $3,203
Assets: $3,092,346
Liabilities: $351,600
Net Worth: $2,740,746
Earnings: ($962,796)
Fiscal Year-end: 02/29/24
Mineral Exploration Services
N.A.I.C.S.: 212390
Xiaolin Charlie Cheng (Pres & CEO)

Subsidiaries:

South Atlantic Gold Brasil Explotacao Mineral Ltda. (1)

SOUTH AUSTRALIAN GOVERNMENT FINANCING AUTHORITY
State Administration Centre 200 Victoria Square, Adelaide, 5000, SA, Australia
Tel.: (61) 882269444
Web Site: http://www.safa.sa.gov.au
Year Founded: 1983
Rev.: $820,939,028
Assets: $23,325,737,078
Liabilities: $23,033,900,778
Net Worth: $291,836,300
Earnings: $27,566,224
Emp.: 72
Fiscal Year-end: 06/30/19
Financial Services

SOUTH AUSTRALIAN GOVERNMENT FINANCING AUTHORITY

South Australian Government Financing Authority—(Continued)
N.A.I.C.S.: 921130

SOUTH CHINA ASSETS HOLDINGS LIMITED
28/F Bank of China Tower No 1 Garden Road, Central, China (Hong Kong)
Tel.: (852) 2820 6333 Ky
Web Site: http://www.scland.co
Rev.: $2,442,615
Assets: $53,359,106
Liabilities: $48,690,247
Net Worth: $4,668,859
Earnings: ($2,425,408)
Emp.: 12
Fiscal Year-end: 12/31/19
Property Development Services
N.A.I.C.S.: 531390
Hung Sang Ng *(Chm)*

Subsidiaries:

South China Financial Credits Limited (1)
Wanchai Branch-Room 1209 12th Floor Integration Centre, 302-308 Hennessy Road, Wanchai, China (Hong Kong)
Tel.: (852) 38980908
Web Site: http://www.sccredit.com
Credit Financial Services
N.A.I.C.S.: 522299

SOUTH CHINA FINANCIAL HOLDINGS LIMITED
28th Floor Bank of China Tower 1 Garden Road, Central, China (Hong Kong)
Tel.: (852) 21112222
Web Site: http://www.sctrade.com
0619—(HKG)
Rev.: $8,716,410
Assets: $161,610,330
Liabilities: $118,967,700
Net Worth: $42,642,630
Earnings: ($19,336,523)
Emp.: 181
Fiscal Year-end: 12/31/22
Investment Holding Company
N.A.I.C.S.: 523940
Hung Sang Ng *(Chm)*

SOUTH CHINA HOLDINGS COMPANY LIMITED
28/F Bank of China Tower No 1 Garden Road, Central, China (Hong Kong)
Tel.: (852) 28206333
Web Site: http://www.scholding.com
0413—(HKG)
Rev.: $486,249,555
Assets: $1,725,996,315
Liabilities: $898,622,678
Net Worth: $827,373,638
Earnings: $8,369,610
Emp.: 10,006
Fiscal Year-end: 12/31/22
Investment Holding Company
N.A.I.C.S.: 551112
Richard Howard Gorges *(Vice Chm)*

Subsidiaries:

Tianjin South China Leesheng Sporting Goods Co. Ltd. (1)
No 116 Kunwei Road, Hebei District, Tianjin, 300140, China
Tel.: (86) 2226222277
Web Site: http://www.leeshengsport.com
Emp.: 200
Sporting Goods Mfr
N.A.I.C.S.: 339920

Wah Shing Toys Company Limited (1)
5/F Wah Shing Centre 5 Fung Yip Street, Chai Wan, China (Hong Kong)
Tel.: (852) 2 557 0185
Web Site: https://www.wahshing.com
Toy Mfr
N.A.I.C.S.: 339930

SOUTH CHINA VOCATIONAL EDUCATION GROUP CO., LTD.
No 492 Da Guan Zhong Road, Tianhe, Guangzhou, Guangdong, China Ky
Web Site:
https://www.scvedugroup.com
Year Founded: 1993
6913—(HKG)
Rev.: $77,010,966
Assets: $341,393,720
Liabilities: $112,778,162
Net Worth: $228,615,557
Earnings: $15,580,555
Emp.: 1,476
Fiscal Year-end: 12/31/23
Educational Support Services
N.A.I.C.S.: 611710

SOUTH CLEVELAND GARAGES
Skippers Ln Industrial Estate, Trunk Rd, Middlesbrough, TS6 6UW, Cleveland, United Kingdom
Tel.: (44) 1642 461451
Car Dealership Owner & Operator
N.A.I.C.S.: 441110

SOUTH COUNTRY EQUIPMENT LTD.
Hwy #2 North, Assiniboia, S0H 0B0, SK, Canada
Tel.: (306) 642-3366
Web Site: http://www.southcountry.ca
Year Founded: 1913
Emp.: 125
Farm & Garden Machinery Equipment Mfr
N.A.I.C.S.: 333111
Kip Kyle *(Supvr-Parts)*

SOUTH EAST WATER LIMITED
WatersEdge 101 Wells Street, Frankston, 3199, VIC, Australia
Tel.: (61) 395523000 AU
Web Site:
http://www.southeastwater.com.au
Rev.: $729,802,275
Assets: $3,105,001,353
Liabilities: $1,688,374,319
Net Worth: $1,416,627,034
Earnings: $72,467,295
Emp.: 541
Fiscal Year-end: 06/30/19
Water & Sewerage Services
N.A.I.C.S.: 221310
Philip Johnson *(Gen Mgr-Future Water Strategy)*

SOUTH ELECTRONICS COMPANY PLC
PO Box 850236, Amman, 11185, Jordan
Tel.: (962) 65699245
Year Founded: 1993
SECO—(AMM)
Rev.: $2,000,804
Assets: $24,235,734
Liabilities: $21,606,594
Net Worth: $2,629,141
Earnings: ($352,580)
Emp.:
Fiscal Year-end: 12/31/20
Electronic Product Whslr
N.A.I.C.S.: 423690

SOUTH HARZ POTASH LIMITED
Unit 13 6-10 Douro Place, West Perth, 6005, WA, Australia
Tel.: (61) 408447493 AU
Web Site:
https://southharzpotash.com
Year Founded: 2015

SHP—(ASX)
Rev.: $1,123
Assets: $1,723,283
Liabilities: $1,398,887
Net Worth: $324,396
Earnings: ($6,110,456)
Fiscal Year-end: 06/30/24
Mineral Exploration Services
N.A.I.C.S.: 213115
Ian Farmer *(Chm)*

SOUTH LONDON INFINITI NISSAN
1055 Wharncliffe Road South, London, N6L 1J9, ON, Canada
Tel.: (519) 685-5497
Web Site:
http://www.londoninfiniti.com
Year Founded: 1988
Rev.: $27,822,384
Emp.: 48
New & Used Car Dealers
N.A.I.C.S.: 441110
Mark McCarville *(Gen Mgr)*

SOUTH MALAYSIA INDUSTRIES BERHAD
Suite 1301 13th Floor City Plaza Jalan Tebrau, 80300, Johor Bahru, Johor Darul Takzim, Malaysia
Tel.: (60) 73322088
Web Site: https://www.smib.com.my
SMI—(KLS)
Rev.: $14,191,162
Assets: $33,878,790
Liabilities: $5,593,869
Net Worth: $28,284,920
Earnings: ($1,987,982)
Fiscal Year-end: 06/30/23
Property Development Services
N.A.I.C.S.: 531312
Chee Yin Wong *(Co-Sec)*

Subsidiaries:

Anastoria Sdn. Bhd. (1)
220 Jalan Sultan Iskandar, 30000, Ipoh, Perak, Malaysia
Tel.: (60) 52558688
Investment Holding & Property Development Services
N.A.I.C.S.: 531390

SMI Wire Sdn. Bhd. (1)
12th Floor Menara SMI No 6 Lorong P Ramlee, 50250, Kuala Lumpur, Malaysia
Tel.: (60) 320781522
Web Site: http://www.smiwire.com
Steel Wire & Hard Drawn Steel Wire Mfr
N.A.I.C.S.: 331222

SOUTH OCEAN HOLDINGS LIMITED
16 Botha Street, PO Box 123738, Alrode, 1451, South Africa
Tel.: (27) 118641606
Web Site:
https://www.southocean.co.za
SOH—(JSE)
Rev.: $128,720,294
Assets: $59,134,792
Liabilities: $22,623,174
Net Worth: $36,511,618
Earnings: $4,827,008
Emp.: 454
Fiscal Year-end: 12/31/23
Cables, Wires & Other Electrical Products Mfr
N.A.I.C.S.: 335931
Hung-Lung Li *(Deputy Vice Chm)*

Subsidiaries:

Radiant Group (Proprietary) Limited (1)
72 5th St, PO Box 590, 2037, Randburg, Wynberg, South Africa
Tel.: (27) 113860000
Web Site: http://www.radiant.co.za

INTERNATIONAL PUBLIC

Sales Range: $100-124.9 Million
Emp.: 400
Lighting Fixture Mfr
N.A.I.C.S.: 335131

South Ocean Electric Wire Company (Proprietary) Limited (1)
12 Botha Street, PO Box 123738, Alrode, 1451, Gauteng, South Africa
Tel.: (27) 11 864 1606
Web Site: https://www.soew.co.za
Sales Range: $100-124.9 Million
Emp.: 400
Wires & Cables Mfr
N.A.I.C.S.: 331420

SOUTH PACIFIC STOCK EXCHANGE LIMITED
Shop 1 and 11 Sabrina Building Victoria Parade, GPO Box 11689, Suva, Fiji
Tel.: (679) 3304130
Web Site: http://www.spse.com.fj
Year Founded: 1979
Rev.: $2,099,330
Assets: $6,327,608
Liabilities: $4,688,015
Net Worth: $1,639,593
Earnings: $533,089
Emp.: 11
Fiscal Year-end: 12/31/19
Stock Exchange Services
N.A.I.C.S.: 523210
Saiyad Hussain *(Deputy Chm)*

SOUTH PORT NEW ZEALAND LIMITED
Island Harbour 251 Foreshore Road, PO Box 1, Bluff, 9842, New Zealand
Tel.: (64) 32128159
Web Site:
https://www.southport.co.nz
SPN—(NZX)
Rev.: $32,050,837
Assets: $58,556,220
Liabilities: $22,729,067
Net Worth: $35,827,153
Earnings: $7,004,785
Emp.: 124
Fiscal Year-end: 06/30/23
Cost Management Services
N.A.I.C.S.: 488310
Rex Thomas Chapman *(Chm)*

SOUTH SHORE HOLDINGS LTD.
33/F, 250 Hennessy 250 Hennessy Road, Wanchai, China (Hong Kong)
Tel.: (852) 25776113
Web Site: http://www.southshore-holdings.com
0577—(HKG)
Rev.: $1,399,577,700
Assets: $1,114,406,442
Liabilities: $1,319,322,735
Net Worth: ($204,916,293)
Earnings: ($130,799,068)
Emp.: 2,141
Fiscal Year-end: 03/31/20
Investment Services
N.A.I.C.S.: 523999
Joanna Ching Hung Mui *(Sec)*

Subsidiaries:

Paul Y. Construction & Engineering Pte Limited (1)
629 Geylang Road 02-03, Singapore, 389564, Singapore
Tel.: (65) 6 588 1600
Web Site: https://www.pyengineering.com
Emp.: 2,000
Real Estate Services
N.A.I.C.S.: 531311
Paul Lin *(Technical Dir)*

Paul Y. Engineering Group Limited (1)
11/F Paul Y Centre 51 Hung To Road, Kwun Tong, Kowloon, China (Hong Kong)
Tel.: (852) 2831 8338

Web Site: http://www.pyengineering.com
Sales Range: $5-14.9 Billion
Construction Engineering Services
N.A.I.C.S.: 541330
Joanna Mui Ching Hung (Sec)

SOUTH STAR BATTERY METALS CORP.
750 West Pender Street Suite 1200,
Vancouver, V6C 2T8, BC, Canada
Tel.: (604) 506-2502   BC
Web Site:
http://www.southstarmining.ca
Year Founded: 1984
STSBF—(OTCQB)
Assets: $4,554,425
Liabilities: $560,848
Net Worth: $3,993,577
Earnings: ($573,976)
Emp.: 1
Fiscal Year-end: 12/31/20
Mineral Properties Exploration Services
N.A.I.C.S.: 213114
Dave McMillan (Chm)

Subsidiaries:

Canada Gold Colombia S.A.S.   (1)
Calle 16 41 210 Of 806, Medellin, Colombia
Tel.: (57) 46041981
Gold Ore Mining Services
N.A.I.C.S.: 212220
Ian Park (Gen Mgr)

SOUTH WEST PINNACLE EXPLORATION LTD.
Ground Floor Plot No 15 Sector44
Gurgaon 122003, DLF City Phase IV,
Gurgaon, 122003, Haryana, India
Tel.: (91) 1244235400
Web Site:
https://www.southwestpinnacle.com
Year Founded: 2006
SOUTHWEST—(NSE)
Rev.: $15,400,815
Assets: $23,707,296
Liabilities: $10,072,873
Net Worth: $13,634,422
Earnings: $1,075,499
Emp.: 633
Fiscal Year-end: 03/31/23
Surveying & Mapping Services
N.A.I.C.S.: 541370
Vikas Jain (Mng Dir)

SOUTH32 LIMITED
Level 35 108 St Georges Terrace,
Perth, 6000, WA, Australia
Tel.: (61) 893249000   AU
Web Site: https://www.south32.net
Year Founded: 2000
SHTLF—(OTCIQ)
Rev.: $7,429,000,000
Assets: $14,564,000,000
Liabilities: $5,189,000,000
Net Worth: $9,375,000,000
Earnings: ($173,000,000)
Emp.: 9,616
Fiscal Year-end: 06/30/23
Holding Company; Metals & Minerals Mining
N.A.I.C.S.: 551112
Brendan Harris (Chief HR & Comml Officer)

Subsidiaries:

Groote Eylandt Mining Company Pty. Ltd.   (1)
Rowell Highway, Alyangula, Groote Eylandt, 0885, NT, Australia   (60%)
Tel.: (61) 889874444
Web Site: https://www.south32.net
Manganese Ore Mining
N.A.I.C.S.: 212290
Rob Jackson (Pres)

South32 Aluminium (Holdings) Pty Ltd.   (1)

Level 35, 108 St Georges Terrace, Perth, 6000, WA, Australia
Tel.: (61) 893249000
Mining & Metals Company
N.A.I.C.S.: 213114

Subsidiary (Non-US):

Minera Sud Argentina S.A.   (2)
Esmeralda 684 piso 13, Buenos Aires, 1007, Argentina   (50.1%)
Tel.: (54) 11 4328 4067
Precious Metal Exploration Services
N.A.I.C.S.: 212220
Carlos Massa (Pres & CEO)

South32 SA Ltd.   (1)
39 Melrose Boulevard Melrose Arch, Johannesburg, 2076, South Africa
Tel.: (27) 113762000
Mining Engineering Services
N.A.I.C.S.: 541330

South32 Sierra Gorda S.p.A.   (1)
Cerro El Plomo 5630 -Oficina 1104 Edificio Las Artes, Las Condes, Santiago, Chile
Tel.: (56) 223665263
Copper Mining Services
N.A.I.C.S.: 212230

South32 Worsley Alumina Pty. Ltd.   (1)
Gastaldo Road, PO Box 344, Collie, 6225, WA, Australia   (86%)
Tel.: (61) 89 734 8311
Web Site: http://www.south32.net
Sales Range: $700-749.9 Million
Emp.: 1,800
Alumina Mining & Refining
N.A.I.C.S.: 212290
Jackie Donnan (Mgr-HR)

SOUTHAMPTON FOOTBALL CLUB LIMITED
St Mary Stadium Britannia Road, Britannia Rd, Southampton, SO14 5FP, Hants, United Kingdom
Tel.: (44) 8456889448
Web Site:
http://www.southamptonfc.com
Sales Range: $25-49.9 Million
Emp.: 100
Football Club
N.A.I.C.S.: 711211
Martin Hunter (Dir-Technical)

SOUTHEAST ASIA PROPERTIES & FINANCE LIMITED
Units 407-410 4th Floor Tower 2 Silvercord 30 Canton Road, Tsimshatsui, Kowloon, China (Hong Kong)
Tel.: (852) 27231128   HK
Web Site: http://www.seapnf.com.hk
0252—(HKG)
Rev.: $35,394,046
Assets: $203,469,159
Liabilities: $64,917,008
Net Worth: $138,552,151
Earnings: $3,448,618
Emp.: 276
Fiscal Year-end: 03/31/22
Investment Management Service
N.A.I.C.S.: 523930
Nai Tuen Chua (Chm & Mng Dir)

Subsidiaries:

Hotel Benito Management Limited   (1)
7-7B Cameron Road, Tsimshatsui, Kowloon, China (Hong Kong)
Tel.: (852) 3653 0388
Web Site: http://www.hotelbenito.com
Home Management Services
N.A.I.C.S.: 721110

Stockwell Commodities Limited   (1)
V Heun Bldg, Sheung Wan, China (Hong Kong)
Tel.: (852) 2509 4384
Commodities Dealing Services
N.A.I.C.S.: 523160

Stockwell Securities Limited   (1)
Room 406-410 4th Floor Tower 2 Sunshine

Centre 30 Canton Road, Tsim Tsa Tsui, Kowloon, China (Hong Kong)
Tel.: (852) 23135110
Web Site: http://www.stockwellonline.com
Stock Brokerage Services
N.A.I.C.S.: 523150

SOUTHEAST BANK PLC
Eunoos Trade Center 52-53 Dilkusha C/A, Dhaka, 1000, Bangladesh
Tel.: (880) 247115321
Web Site:
https://www.southeastbank.com.bd
Year Founded: 1995
SOUTHEASTB—(CHT)
Rev.: $160,424,415
Assets: $4,497,791,095
Liabilities: $4,217,159,162
Net Worth: $280,631,933
Earnings: $15,984,452
Emp.: 3,084
Fiscal Year-end: 12/31/22
Commercial Banking Services
N.A.I.C.S.: 522110
Duluma Ahmed (Vice Chm)

SOUTHEAST CEMENT CO., LTD.
No 21 Wu Fu 3 Road, Kaohsiung, Taiwan
Tel.: (886) 72711121
Web Site:
https://www.southeastcement.com
Year Founded: 1956
1110—(TAI)
Rev.: $74,348,995
Assets: $386,590,848
Liabilities: $91,445,891
Net Worth: $295,144,958
Earnings: $5,103,273
Fiscal Year-end: 12/31/23
Cement Mfr
N.A.I.C.S.: 327310
Min Tuan Chen (Chm)

SOUTHERN ACIDS (M) BERHAD
Level 29 Centro Tower No 8 Jalan Batu Tiga Lama, 41300, Kelang, Selangor Darul Ehsan, Malaysia
Tel.: (60) 332583333
Web Site:
https://www.southernacids.com
SAB—(KLS)
Rev.: $298,423,868
Assets: $239,699,790
Liabilities: $35,920,665
Net Worth: $203,779,125
Earnings: $29,234,700
Emp.: 1,671
Fiscal Year-end: 03/31/22
Chemicals Mfr
N.A.I.C.S.: 327110
Kui Suang Lim (Co-Sec)

SOUTHERN ADVERTISING
9 Eastgate Ave Eastgate Bus Park, Little Island, Cork, Ireland
Tel.: (353) 21 431 3744
Year Founded: 1955
Advetising Agency
N.A.I.C.S.: 541810
Pat Lemasney (Owner)

Subsidiaries:

Southern Advertising   (1)
Killoran House Catherine Pl, Limerick, Ireland
Tel.: (353) 61 310 286
Emp.: 12
Advetising Agency
N.A.I.C.S.: 541810
Dave O'Hora (Dir)

SOUTHERN ALLIANCE MINING LTD.
8th Floor Menara Zenith Jalan Putra

Square 6, 25200, Kuantan, Pahang, Malaysia
Tel.: (60) 95488888   SG
Web Site:
https://www.southernalliance.com
Year Founded: 2019
QNS—(CAT)
Rev.: $91,951,834
Assets: $282,903,298
Liabilities: $25,972,582
Net Worth: $256,930,715
Earnings: ($5,762,875)
Emp.: 213
Fiscal Year-end: 07/31/23
Iron Ore Mining Services
N.A.I.C.S.: 212210
Sam Kok Pek (Founder & CEO)

SOUTHERN ARC MINERALS INC.
Suite 650 669 Howe St, Vancouver, V6C 0B4, BC, Canada
Tel.: (778) 725-1490   Ca
Web Site:
https://www.southernarcmineral.com
Year Founded: 1997
SA—(OTCIQ)
Rev.: $5,171,280
Assets: $12,794,276
Liabilities: $1,165,256
Net Worth: $11,629,021
Earnings: $3,387,937
Fiscal Year-end: 06/30/19
Mineral Exploration Services
N.A.I.C.S.: 213114
John Graham Proust (Chm & CEO)

SOUTHERN ARCHIPELAGO LTD.
201 Henderson Road 05-19, Singapore, 159545, Singapore
Tel.: (65) 63329488   SG
Web Site:
https://southernarchipelago.com
Year Founded: 1993
A33—(SES)
Rev.: $3,935,737
Assets: $6,730,748
Liabilities: $4,616,798
Net Worth: $2,113,951
Earnings: $33,654
Emp.: 70
Fiscal Year-end: 12/31/23
Investment Holding Company
N.A.I.C.S.: 551112

SOUTHERN CABLE GROUP BERHAD
Lot 42 Jalan Merbau Pulas Kawasan Perusahaan, Kuala Ketil, 09300, Kedah, Malaysia
Tel.: (60) 44161600   MY
Web Site:
https://www.southerncable.com.my
Year Founded: 1993
SCGBHD—(KLS)
Rev.: $185,371,310
Assets: $120,747,512
Liabilities: $59,830,850
Net Worth: $60,916,662
Earnings: $3,078,175
Emp.: 677
Fiscal Year-end: 12/31/22
Wire & Cable Mfr
N.A.I.C.S.: 331491
Ooi In Keong (Gen Mgr)

SOUTHERN CAPITAL GROUP PTE. LTD.
501 Orchard Road 17-01 Whellock Place, Singapore, 238880, Singapore
Tel.: (65) 6836 8600   SG
Web Site:
http://www.southerncapitalgroup.com
Sales Range: $25-49.9 Million
Emp.: 15

SOUTHERN CAPITAL GROUP PTE. LTD.

Southern Capital Group Pte, Ltd.—(Continued)
Privater Equity Firm
N.A.I.C.S.: 523999
Teong Hean Tan (Chm)

Subsidiaries:

Adventa Berhad (1)
No 21 Jalan Tandang 51/205A Seksyen 51,
46050, Petaling Jaya, Kelantan,
Malaysia (70%)
Tel.: (60) 392130520
Web Site: https://www.adventa.com.my
Sales Range: $125-149.9 Million
Health Care Products Mfr
N.A.I.C.S.: 339113
Seng Wee Pan (Mgr-Factory)

Subsidiary (Domestic):

Adventa Health Sdn. Bhd. (2)
1 Jalan 8 Pengkalan Chepa 2 Industrial
Zone, Kota Baharu, 16100, Kelantan, Malaysia
Tel.: (60) 97747171
Web Site: http://www.adventa-health.com
Medical Glove & Hospital Disposables Mfr
N.A.I.C.S.: 339113
Kwek Siew Leng (CFO)

Profit Point Manufacturing Sdn. Bhd. (2)
Plo 7 Jln Masuri Off Jalan Mersing, Kawasan Industries, 86000, Keluang, Johor, Malaysia
Tel.: (60) 77879001
Rubber Glove Mfr
N.A.I.C.S.: 326299

Purnabina Sdn. Bhd. (2)
No 2 & 6 Jalan Mahsuri 1 Kawasan Perindustrian Kluang 1, 86000, Keluang, Johor Darul Takzim, Malaysia (97.2%)
Tel.: (60) 77879731
Surgical Gloves Mfr
N.A.I.C.S.: 339113

Sun Healthcare (M) Sdn. Bhd. (2)
18 Jalan 19 1 Block C, Kepong, 46300, Petaling Jaya, Malaysia
Tel.: (60) 379555121
Web Site: http://www.sunhealthcare.com.my
Medical Equipment Distr
N.A.I.C.S.: 423450

Terang Nusa (Malaysia) Sdn. Bhd. (2)
2 Jalan 8 Pengkalan Chepa 2 Industrial
Zone, 16100, Kota Baharu, Kelantan, Malaysia
Tel.: (60) 97747171
Surgical Gloves Mfr
N.A.I.C.S.: 339113

Subsidiary (Non-US):

Ulma International GmbH (2)
Arzt- und Krankenhausbedarf Pfaffenweg 35, 89231, Neu-Ulm, Germany
Tel.: (49) 7319260430
Web Site: https://www.ulma.de
Sales Range: $25-49.9 Million
Emp.: 10
Medical Disposable Products Distr
N.A.I.C.S.: 423450

Subsidiary (Domestic):

Utama Associates Sdn. Bhd. (2)
607 Jalan 22 Taman Perindustrian Ehsan Jaya, Kepong, 52100, Kuala Lumpur, Federal Territory, Malaysia
Tel.: (60) 3 62773877
Medical & Healthcare Devices Distr
N.A.I.C.S.: 423450

Greatearth Pte. Ltd. (1)
12 Ang Mo Kio Street 64 #03-13 UE BizHub
Central Block B, Singapore, 569088, Singapore
Tel.: (65) 6818 8666
Web Site: http://www.ueec.sg
Sales Range: $250-299.9 Million
Mechanical & Electrical Engineering Services
N.A.I.C.S.: 541330
Tuck Lee Chan (Exec VP)

Subsidiary (Domestic):

Greatearth Construction Pte Ltd (2)
10 Ang Mo Kio Street 65 05-12 Techpoint, Singapore, 569059, Singapore
Tel.: (65) 68188666
Web Site: http://www.greatearth.sg
Construction Management Services
N.A.I.C.S.: 236220

Greatearth Corporation Pte Ltd (2)
10 Ang Mo Kio Street 65 05-12 Techpoint, Singapore, 569059, Singapore
Tel.: (65) 68188666
Web Site: http://www.greatearth.sg
Commercial Building Construction Services
N.A.I.C.S.: 236220

UG M&E Pte Ltd (2)
12 Ang Mo Kio Street 64 03-15 UE BizHub
Central Block B, Singapore, 569088, Singapore
Tel.: (65) 68188788
Web Site: http://www.greatearth.sg
Civil Engineering Services
N.A.I.C.S.: 541330

HELP International Corporation Berhad (1)
15 Jalan Street Semantan Off Jalan Semantan, Bukit Damansara, 50490, Kuala Lumpur, Malaysia
Tel.: (60) 320942000
Web Site: http://www.hic.com.my
Sales Range: $25-49.9 Million
Education Services
N.A.I.C.S.: 611310
Adam Chan (Dir-Corp Plng & IR)

SOUTHERN CHARTER FINANCIAL GROUP LIMITED

Level 2 Tower Building 50 Customhouse, Quay, Wellington, 6011, New Zealand
Tel.: (64) 4844319
Web Site: http://www.snc.co.nz
IPR—(NZX)
Rev.: $15,623
Assets: $1,039,329
Liabilities: $66,638
Net Worth: $972,691
Earnings: ($167,528)
Fiscal Year-end: 03/31/23
Mobile Applications & Advertising Related Services
N.A.I.C.S.: 513210
Roger Grice (CEO)

SOUTHERN CHINA LIVESTOCK, INC.

88 Guihuayuan Guanjingcheng, Yujiang, Yingtan, Jiangxi, China
Tel.: (86) 7015680890
Year Founded: 2007
Sales Range: $25-49.9 Million
Emp.: 398
Pig Farming Services
N.A.I.C.S.: 112210
Shu Kaneko (Dir-Bus Dev)

SOUTHERN COMMUNICATIONS LTD.

Glebe Farm Down Street, Dummer, Basingstoke, RG25 2AD, Hampshire, United Kingdom
Tel.: (44) 8456344008
Web Site: http://www.southern-comms.co.uk
Year Founded: 1965
Sales Range: $10-24.9 Million
Emp.: 80
Business-to-Business Telecommunications Services
N.A.I.C.S.: 517810
Paul Bradford (CEO)

SOUTHERN CONCRETE PILE PUBLIC COMPANY LIMITED

SSP Tower Floor 17 555 Sukhumvit 63 Road North Klongton, Watthana, Bangkok, 10110, Thailand
Tel.: (66) 27115134
Web Site: http://www.scp.co.th

Year Founded: 1979
SCP—(THA)
Rev.: $54,281,390
Assets: $73,154,938
Liabilities: $10,537,292
Net Worth: $62,617,646
Earnings: $4,277,258
Emp.: 1,249
Fiscal Year-end: 12/31/23
Concrete Products Mfr
N.A.I.C.S.: 327390
Nittaya Chunualsri (Sec-Acctg Consultant & Sr Mgr-Acctg)

SOUTHERN CROSS CAPITAL MANAGEMENT SA

Av Libertador 602 Floor 5, Buenos Aires, C1001ABT, Argentina
Tel.: (54) 11 5129 5400
Web Site: http://www.southerncrossgroup.com
Year Founded: 1998
Emp.: 50
Privater Equity Firm
N.A.I.C.S.: 523999
Norberto Morita (Co-Founder, Chm & Gen Partner)

Subsidiaries:

Southern Cross Group, LLC (1)
41 W Putnam Ave 2nd Fl, Greenwich, CT 06830
Tel.: (203) 629-8272
Web Site: http://www.southerncrossgroup.com
Privater Equity Firm
N.A.I.C.S.: 523999
Rodrigo Lowndes (Mng Dir)

Ultrapetrol (Bahamas) Limited (1)
Ocean Centre Montagu Foreshore East Bay St, PO Box SS-19084, Nassau, Bahamas
Tel.: (242) 364 4755
Web Site: http://www.ultrapetrol.net
Sales Range: $300-349.9 Million
Emp.: 1,332
Marine Transportation Services
N.A.I.C.S.: 483111
Ricardo Menendez Ross (Exec VP)

Subsidiary (Non-US):

Agencia Maritima Argenpar S.A. (2)
C Colon 1817, San Lorenzo, Santa Fe, Argentina
Tel.: (54) 3476 42 0603
Marine Cargo Handling Services
N.A.I.C.S.: 488320

Agriex Agenciamentos, Afretamentos e Apoio Maritimo Ltda. (2)
Rua Bras Cubas n 03 sala 20 9 andar, Santos, 11013-161, Brazil
Tel.: (55) 13 3222 4128
Ship Chartering Services
N.A.I.C.S.: 483111

Cedarino, S.L. (2)
C/ Ayala 66 - Primero Izquierda, Madrid, 28001, Spain
Tel.: (34) 914260700
Management Consulting Services
N.A.I.C.S.: 541618

Subsidiary (Domestic):

Kingly Shipping Ltd. (2)
Fifty Shirley St, Nassau, Bahamas
Tel.: (242) 3222670
Marine Shipping Services
N.A.I.C.S.: 488510

Subsidiary (US):

Lowrie Shipping LLC (2)
2711 Centerville Rd 400, Wilmington, DE 19808-1660
Tel.: (800) 686-8134
Transportation Equipment Distr
N.A.I.C.S.: 423860

Subsidiary (Non-US):

Ravenscroft Holdings Ltd. (2)
Vartan Ravenscroft The Singing Men's

INTERNATIONAL PUBLIC

Chambers 19 Minster Precincts, London, Peterborough, United Kingdom
Tel.: (44) 1733315155
Web Site: http://www.ravenscroftgroup.com
Sales Range: $50-74.9 Million
Emp.: 20
Investment Management Service
N.A.I.C.S.: 523999
Leonard Hoskinson (Gen Mgr)

Subsidiary (US):

Ravenscroft Ship Management Inc. (2)
3251 Ponce De Leon Blvd, Coral Gables, FL 33134
Tel.: (305) 507-2000
Ship Management Services
N.A.I.C.S.: 488330
Leonard Hoskinson (Gen Mgr)

Ship Management Services Inc (2)
3251 Ponce De Leon Blvd, Coral Gables, FL 33134
Tel.: (305) 507-2000
Web Site: http://www.shipmanservices.com
Ship Management Services
N.A.I.C.S.: 488330
Len Hoskinson (Gen Mgr)

Subsidiary (Non-US):

UABL Paraguay S.A (2)
Benjamin Constant 835 Piso 1 Edificio Jacaranda, Asuncion, 1206, Paraguay
Tel.: (595) 21445415
Marine Cargo Handling Services
N.A.I.C.S.: 488320

UABL S.A. (2)
Leandro N Alem 986 11 Fl, Buenos Aires, 1001, Argentina
Tel.: (54) 11 4875 1611
Web Site: http://www.uabl.net
Emp.: 4
Shipping & Terminal Handling Services
N.A.I.C.S.: 488310
Omar Meggiolaro (Mgr-Comml)

UP Offshore Apoio Maritimo Ltda (2)
Alfandega Street 33 54 Centro, Rio de Janeiro, 20070000, Brazil
Tel.: (55) 21 2112 4545
Web Site: http://www.upoffshore.com.br
Marine Cargo Handling Services
N.A.I.C.S.: 488320
Atul Sethe (Gen Mgr)

Ultrapetrol S.A. (2)
Leandro N Alem 986 11th Fl, Buenos Aires, Argentina
Tel.: (54) 1148750400
Web Site: http://www.ultrapetrol.net
Bulk Petroleum Transportation Services
N.A.I.C.S.: 484230

SOUTHERN CROSS ELECTRICAL ENGINEERING LIMITED

Level 15 225 St Georges Tce, Perth, 6000, WA, Australia
Tel.: (61) 892368300
Web Site: https://www.scee.com.au
Year Founded: 1978
SXE—(ASX)
Rev.: $368,502,937
Assets: $243,560,362
Liabilities: $115,915,464
Net Worth: $127,644,898
Earnings: $14,633,413
Fiscal Year-end: 06/30/24
Electrical, Control & Instrumentation Installation & Testing Services
N.A.I.C.S.: 238210
Derek Parkin (Chm)

Subsidiaries:

Cruz Del Sur Ingenieria Electra (Peru) S.A. Ltd. (1)
Av Benjamin Franklin No 220, Ate-Vitarte Dist, Lima, Peru
Tel.: (51) 13267436
Sales Range: $25-49.9 Million
Emp.: 12
Electrical & Instrumentation Installation Services
N.A.I.C.S.: 238210

Heyday5 Pty. Limited (1)
Level 1 3 Apollo Place, Lane Cove, 2066, NSW, Australia
Tel.: (61) 298556666
Web Site: https://www.heyday.com.au
Electrical Contractor; Electrical & Data Communication Systems & Services
N.A.I.C.S.: 238210
David Hammond *(Exec Dir)*

Southern Cross Electrical Engineering (WA) Pty. Ltd. (1)
41 Macedonia Street, Naval Base, Perth, 6165, WA, Australia
Tel.: (61) 892368300
Web Site: http://www.scee.com.au
Sales Range: $25-49.9 Million
Emp.: 75
Electrical Control & Instrument Installation Services
N.A.I.C.S.: 238210
Simon High *(Mng Dir)*

Southern Cross Electrical Engineering Limited-Perth (1)
Level 15 225 St Georges Terrace, Naval Base, Perth, 6000, WA, Australia
Tel.: (61) 89 236 8300
Web Site: https://www.scee.com.au
Sales Range: $25-49.9 Million
Emp.: 80
Electrical Engineering & Contracting Services
N.A.I.C.S.: 238210

Trivantage Pty Ltd. (1)
76 Commercial Drive, Thomastown, 3074, VIC, Australia
Tel.: (61) 394663977
Web Site: https://www.trivantage.com.au
Electrical Equipment Mfr & Distr
N.A.I.C.S.: 335313

SOUTHERN CROSS EXPLORATION NL
Level 29 2 Chifley Square, Sydney, 2000, NSW, Australia
Tel.: (61) 29375 2337 AU
Web Site: http://www.sxxgroup.com
Year Founded: 1970
Rev.: $1,156,718
Assets: $4,009,517
Liabilities: $3,987,753
Net Worth: $21,764
Earnings: ($1,042,636)
Emp.: 7
Fiscal Year-end: 06/30/18
Oil, Gas, Gold & Other Metals Exploration & Mining Services
N.A.I.C.S.: 211120
Stephen Baghdadi *(Exec Dir)*

SOUTHERN CROSS GOLD LTD.
Level 6 350 Collins St, Melbourne, 3000, VIC, Australia
Tel.: (61) 415153122 AU
Web Site: https://www.southerncrossgold.com
Year Founded: 2021
SXG—(ASX)
Rev.: $107
Assets: $21,358,924
Liabilities: $1,029,229
Net Worth: $20,329,694
Earnings: ($2,578,950)
Fiscal Year-end: 05/31/23
Gold Exploration Services
N.A.I.C.S.: 212220
Justin Mouchacca *(Sec)*

SOUTHERN CROSS MEDIA GROUP LIMITED
Level 2 257 Clarendon Street, PO Box 345, South Melbourne, 3205, VIC, Australia
Tel.: (61) 392521019
Web Site: https://www.southerncross.com.au
SXL—(ASX)
Rev.: $333,470,218
Assets: $462,284,320
Liabilities: $326,842,947
Net Worth: $135,441,372
Earnings: ($149,975,961)
Emp.: 1,388
Fiscal Year-end: 06/30/24
Media Investment Services
N.A.I.C.S.: 551112
Leon Pasternak *(Deputy Chm)*

Subsidiaries:

Southern Cross Media Australia Pty Limited (1)
Level 2 257 Clarendon Street, PO Box 345, South Melbourne, 3205, VIC, Australia **(100%)**
Tel.: (61) 392521019
Sales Range: $25-49.9 Million
Radio & Television Broadcasting Services
N.A.I.C.S.: 516210
Leanne Hulm *(Gen Mgr)*

Subsidiary (Domestic):

Austereo Group Limited (2)
Level 2 257 Clarendon Street, Melbourne, 3205, VIC, Australia **(52.5%)**
Tel.: (61) 392521019
Web Site: http://www.southerncrossaustereo.com.au
Radio Broadcasting Services
N.A.I.C.S.: 516210
Rick Lenarcic *(Head-Reg Media)*

Branch (Domestic):

Southern Cross Media (2)
Level 15 50 Goulburn Street World Square, Sydney, 2000, NSW, Australia
Tel.: (61) 293751041
Web Site: http://www.southerncrossaustereo.com.au
Sales Range: $25-49.9 Million
Emp.: 20
Radio Station Owner & Operator
N.A.I.C.S.: 516110

SOUTHERN CROSS PAYMENTS LIMITED
456 Victoria Parade, Melbourne, 3002, VIC, Australia
Tel.: (61) 386400990
Web Site: http://www.isignthis.com
SP1—(ASX)
Rev.: $34,341
Assets: $7,869,366
Liabilities: $599,825
Net Worth: $7,269,541
Earnings: ($1,938,932)
Fiscal Year-end: 12/31/21
Oil & Gas Exploration & Development Services
N.A.I.C.S.: 211120
Nickolas John Karantzis *(Founder, CEO & Mng Dir)*

Subsidiaries:

Lowell Capital Limited (1)
8 Chapel St, Richmond, 3121, VIC, Australia
Tel.: (61) 398152444
Web Site: http://www.lowellcapital.com.au
Fund Management Services
N.A.I.C.S.: 541618

SOUTHERN EMPIRE RESOURCES CORP.
Suite 420 789 West Pender Street, Vancouver, V6C 1H2, BC, Canada
Tel.: (778) 889-5476 BC
Web Site: https://www.smp.gold
Year Founded: 2017
SMPEF—(OTCQB)
Assets: $12,217,606
Liabilities: $407,296
Net Worth: $11,810,310
Earnings: ($554,876)
Fiscal Year-end: 10/31/22
Mining Exploration
N.A.I.C.S.: 212220
Ronald Netolitzky *(Chm)*

Subsidiaries:

SMP Gold Corp. (1)

SOUTHERN ENERGY CORP.
Suite 2400 333 - 7th Avenue SW, Calgary, T2P 2Z1, AB, Canada
Tel.: (587) 287-5400 Ca
Web Site: https://southernenergycorp.com
Year Founded: 2008
0M1—(DEU)
Rev.: $19,313,000
Assets: $67,305,000
Liabilities: $41,494,000
Net Worth: $25,811,000
Earnings: ($46,817,000)
Emp.: 13
Fiscal Year-end: 12/31/23
Mineral Mining Services
N.A.I.C.S.: 212290
Erin Buschert *(VP-Land)*

Subsidiaries:

Southern Energy LA, LLC (1)

SOUTHERN ENERGY HOLDINGS GROUP LIMITED
31/F Fuzhong International Plaza Xinhua Road Nanming District, Guiyang, 550002, Guizhou, China
Tel.: (86) 85185855789 Ky
Web Site: http://www.nfny.hk
Year Founded: 2011
Rev.: $93,222,759
Assets: $237,222,395
Liabilities: $64,234,901
Net Worth: $172,987,494
Earnings: $29,996,574
Emp.: 1,586
Fiscal Year-end: 12/31/18
Anthracite Mining Services
N.A.I.C.S.: 213113
Xu Bo *(Founder, Chm & CEO)*

SOUTHERN GAS JOINT STOCK COMPANY
PetroVietnam Tower 4th Floor, No 1-5 Le Duan Street Ben Nighe Ward District 1, Ho Chi Minh City, Vietnam
Tel.: (84) 839100108
Web Site: https://www.pgs.com.vn
Year Founded: 2000
PGS—(HNX)
Rev.: $682,068,900
Assets: $238,945,100
Liabilities: $137,045,900
Net Worth: $101,899,200
Earnings: $9,885,900
Fiscal Year-end: 12/31/22
Petroleum Product Whslr
N.A.I.C.S.: 424720

SOUTHERN GOLD LIMITED
10 George Street, Stepney, 5069, SA, Australia
Tel.: (61) 883688888
Web Site: http://www.southerngold.com.au
ION—(ASX)
Rev.: $27,003
Assets: $3,334,875
Liabilities: $639,843
Net Worth: $2,695,032
Earnings: ($4,085,958)
Fiscal Year-end: 06/30/24
Discovery, Acquisition & Development of Mineral Resources
N.A.I.C.S.: 327999
Daniel L. Hill *(Sec)*

SOUTHERN HEMISPHERE MINING LIMITED
Tel.: (61) 861440590
Web Site: https://www.shmining.com.au
SUH—(ASX)
Rev.: $379
Assets: $1,191,278
Liabilities: $149,629
Net Worth: $1,041,648
Earnings: ($958,681)
Emp.: 3
Fiscal Year-end: 06/30/21
Copper Mining Services
N.A.I.C.S.: 212230
Trevor Tennant *(CEO)*

Subsidiaries:

Mineras Hemisferio Sur S.C.M. (1)
Zurich 255 Apt 41, 8320000 7550137, Las Condes, Santiago, Chile
Tel.: (56) 24745071
Mineral Exploration & Development Services
N.A.I.C.S.: 213115

Southern Hemisphere Mining Pty Limited (1)
1200 Hay Street, West Perth, Perth, 6005, WA, Australia
Tel.: (61) 894812122
Web Site: http://www.shmining.com.au
Sales Range: $75-99.9 Million
Metal Mining Services
N.A.I.C.S.: 212210

SOUTHERN HYDROPOWER JOINT STOCK COMPANY
Unit 106 1st Floor Citilight Building 45 Vo Thi Sau street, Da Kao Ward District 1, Ho Chi Minh City, Vietnam
Tel.: (84) 838207795
Web Site: https://www.shp.vn
Year Founded: 2004
SHP—(HNX)
Hydroelectric Power Generation Services
N.A.I.C.S.: 221111
Doan Duc Hung *(Chm)*

SOUTHERN INFOSYS LIMITED
402-A Arunachal Building 19 Barakhamba Road, New Delhi, 110 001, India
Tel.: (91) 1123354236
Web Site: https://www.southerninfosys.com
Year Founded: 1994
540174—(BOM)
Rev.: $1,320,173
Assets: $3,455,992
Liabilities: $2,806,259
Net Worth: $649,733
Earnings: $7,254
Emp.: 9
Fiscal Year-end: 03/31/23
Software Development Services
N.A.I.C.S.: 541512
Kriti Bareja *(Compliance Officer)*

SOUTHERN INTERNATIONAL LOGISTICS JOINT STOCK COMPANY
1B Hoang Dieu St Ward 13 District 4, Ho Chi Minh City, Vietnam
Web Site: http://www.sotrans.com.vn
Year Founded: 1975
STG—(HOSE)
Rev.: $73,980,203
Assets: $118,189,534
Liabilities: $25,298,160
Net Worth: $92,891,374
Earnings: $6,208,016
Fiscal Year-end: 12/31/23
Freight Forwarding Services
N.A.I.C.S.: 488320
Tran Tuan Anh *(Chm)*

Subsidiaries:

Sotrans Ha Tinh One Member Limited Company (1)
Do Go Ky Thinh Ward, Ky Anh, Ha Tinh, Vietnam

Southern International Logistics Joint Stock Company—(Continued)
Tel.: (84) 2393864658
Logistic Services
N.A.I.C.S.: 541614

Sotrans Logistics One Member Company Limited (1)
1B Hoang Dieu St Ward 13, District 4, Ho Chi Minh City, Vietnam
Tel.: (84) 2862685858
Logistic Services
N.A.I.C.S.: 541614

South Port Joint Stock Company (1)
Km 9 Ha Noi highway, Truong Tho Ward Thu Duc District, Ho Chi Minh City, Vietnam
Tel.: (84) 2837310033
Freight Forwarding & Transportation Services
N.A.I.C.S.: 488510

Southern Waterborne Transport Joint Stock Corporation (1)
298 Huynh Tan Phat st, Tan Thuan Tay Ward Dist 7, Ho Chi Minh City, Vietnam
Tel.: (84) 2838729748
Web Site: http://www.sowatco.com.vn
Cargo Handling Services
N.A.I.C.S.: 488320

Vietranstimex Multimodal Transport Holding Company (1)
1B Hoang Dieu, Ward 13 District 4, Ho Chi Minh City, Vietnam
Tel.: (84) 2838263621
Web Site: http://www.vietranstimex.com.vn
Transportation Services
N.A.I.C.S.: 485999

SOUTHERN ISPAT & ENERGY LIMITED
19 629 1 Sreyas West Yakkara P O, Palakkad, 678 001, Kerala, India
Tel.: (91) 4912531698
Web Site:
http://www.southernispat.com
Year Founded: 1995
Sales Range: $100-124.9 Million
Steel Products Mfr
N.A.I.C.S.: 331110
Vivek Agarwal (Chm & Mng Dir)

SOUTHERN LATEX LIMITED
B - 11 / W Sipcot Industrial Complex Gummidipoodi, Chengai M G R District, Tiruvallur, 601201, India
Tel.: (91) 4426601313
Web Site:
https://www.southernlatexltd.com
514454—(BOM)
Rev.: $64,627
Assets: $776,638
Liabilities: $20,687
Net Worth: $755,951
Earnings: $28,188
Emp.: 4
Fiscal Year-end: 03/31/23
Rubberized Coir Product Mfr
N.A.I.C.S.: 339999
Namasivayam Pillai Neelakanda (Mng Dir)

SOUTHERN MAGNESIUM & CHEMICALS LIMITED
5th Floor 63666B Deccan Chambers Somajiguda, Hyderabad, 500 082, Telangana, India
Tel.: (91) 4023311789
Web Site:
https://www.southernmag.com
513498—(BOM)
Rev.: $278,212
Assets: $541,340
Liabilities: $205,045
Net Worth: $336,295
Earnings: ($12,614)
Emp.: 23
Fiscal Year-end: 03/31/21
Magnesium Metal Mfr & Distr
N.A.I.C.S.: 332999

N. Ravi Prasad (CEO & Co-Mng Dir)

SOUTHERN ONLINE BIO TECHNOLOGIES LTD
A3 3rd Floor Office Block Samrat Complex Saifabad, Hyderabad, 500 004, Telangana, India
Tel.: (91) 40 2324 1999
Web Site: http://www.sol.net.in
Rev.: $1,447,877
Assets: $26,341,117
Liabilities: $58,515,245
Net Worth: ($32,174,128)
Earnings: ($20,837,724)
Emp.: 60
Fiscal Year-end: 03/31/18
Bio-diesel Production
N.A.I.C.S.: 333618
Devaiah Pagidipati (Exec Dir)

Subsidiaries:

Southern Online Bio Technologies Ltd - Biodiesel Division (1)
A3 3rd Fl Ofc Block Samrat Complex, Saifabad, Hyderabad, 500004, Andhra Pradesh, India
Tel.: (91) 4023241999
Web Site: http://www.sol.net.in
Sales Range: $25-49.9 Million
Emp.: 90
Biodiesel Mfr
N.A.I.C.S.: 324110
B. N. Swami (Gen Mgr)

Southern Online Bio Technologies Ltd - Internet Services Division (1)
No A3 3rd Fl Ofc Block Samrat Complex Saifabad, Hyderabad, 500004, Andhra Pradesh, India
Tel.: (91) 4023241999
Sales Range: $25-49.9 Million
Emp.: 40
Broadband Internet Services
N.A.I.C.S.: 517810
Sathis Kumar (Mng Dir)

SOUTHERN PACKAGING GROUP LIMITED
30 Cecil Street No 19-08 Prudential Tower, Singapore, 49712, Singapore
Tel.: (65) 67350968
Web Site: https://www.southern-packaging.com
BQP—(SES)
Rev.: $90,452,479
Assets: $166,483,548
Liabilities: $80,597,885
Net Worth: $85,885,663
Earnings: $724,791
Fiscal Year-end: 12/31/20
Plastic Packaging Bags Mfr
N.A.I.C.S.: 333993
Yong Hua Li (COO)

Subsidiaries:

Foshan Southern Packaging Co.,Ltd. (1)
No 9 Foping Road 4 Guicheng, Nanhai District, Foshan, 528251, Guangdong, China
Tel.: (86) 75786788388
Packaging Materials Mfr.
N.A.I.C.S.: 326112

Southern (HK) Packaging Company Limited (1)
Room 1301-2 13 F Lippo Center Tower 2 89 Queensway, Admiralty, Central, China (Hong Kong)
Tel.: (852) 28992230
Sales Range: $25-49.9 Million
Emp.: 2
Packaging Materials Mfr
N.A.I.C.S.: 326199

Southern Packaging (Jiangsu) Co., Ltd. (1)
No 255 Wuyi Road, Wujin District, Changzhou, 213000, Jiangsu, China
Tel.: (86) 51983811088
Plastic Packaging Products Mfr
N.A.I.C.S.: 326112

SOUTHERN PALACE GROUP OF COMPANIES (PTY) LTD.
No 1 Sandton Drive 1st Floor, Sandton, Johannesburg, 2196, Gauteng, South Africa
Tel.: (27) 11 656 3437
Web Site:
http://www.southernpalace.co.za
Holding Company
N.A.I.C.S.: 551112
Sello Mahlangu (Founder & Chm)

Subsidiaries:

Genrec Engineering (Pty) Ltd. (1)
Cnr Dekema & Niemann Roads, Wadeville, 1422, South Africa
Tel.: (27) 118762300
Web Site: http://www.genrec.co.za
Steel Building Construction Services
N.A.I.C.S.: 238120
Johann Botha (Mgr-IT)

SOUTHERN PETROCHEMICAL INDUSTRIES CORPORATION LIMITED
SPIC House 88 Mount Road, Guindy, Chennai, 600032, India
Tel.: (91) 4422350245
Web Site: https://www.spic.in
Year Founded: 1969
SPIC—(NSE)
Rev.: $212,465,403
Assets: $233,703,752
Liabilities: $163,302,253
Net Worth: $70,401,499
Earnings: $10,111,278
Emp.: 636
Fiscal Year-end: 03/31/21
Petrochemical Products Mfr & Distr
N.A.I.C.S.: 325110
Ashwin C. Muthiah (Chm)

SOUTHERN PROVINCE CEMENT COMPANY
King Fahad Road, PO Box 548, Abha, 61421, Saudi Arabia
Tel.: (966) 172271500
Web Site: https://www.spcc.sa
Year Founded: 1978
3050—(SAU)
Rev.: $325,932,276
Assets: $1,032,345,993
Liabilities: $177,634,932
Net Worth: $854,711,061
Earnings: $80,178,158
Emp.: 1,670
Fiscal Year-end: 12/31/22
Cement Mfr & Whslr
N.A.I.C.S.: 327310
Abdullah Musaed Abdulrahman Al Saud (Chm)

SOUTHERN PUBLISHING & MEDIA COMPANY LIMITED
No 11 Shuiyin Road, Yuexiu District, Guangzhou, 510075, Guangdong, China
Tel.: (86) 2037600020
Web Site: http://www.nfcb.com.cn
Year Founded: 2009
601900—(SHG)
Rev.: $1,271,263,874
Assets: $2,080,424,638
Liabilities: $950,521,001
Net Worth: $1,129,903,637
Earnings: $132,447,590
Fiscal Year-end: 12/31/22
Books Publishing Services
N.A.I.C.S.: 513130
Juntie Tan (Chm)

SOUTHERN SCORE BUILDERS BERHAD
Unit 21-3 3rd Floor, Platinum Hill PV7, 53100, Kuala Lumpur, Selangor Darul Ehsan, Malaysia
Tel.: (60) 41628289
Web Site: https://www.gneptune.com
SSB8—(KLS)
Rev.: $20,078
Assets: $2,480
Liabilities: $2,043,303
Net Worth: ($2,040,823)
Earnings: ($492,984)
Fiscal Year-end: 06/30/21
Information Technology Solutions Services
N.A.I.C.S.: 541512
Tham Poh Chai (Exec Dir)

SOUTHERN SILVER EXPLORATION CORP.
Suite 1100 1199 West Hastings St, Vancouver, V6E 3T5, BC, Canada
Tel.: (604) 806-0626
Web Site:
https://www.southernsilver.com
Year Founded: 1963
SSVFF—(OTCQX)
Rev.: $14,320
Assets: $32,323,770
Liabilities: $4,299,226
Net Worth: $28,024,544
Earnings: ($156,560)
Fiscal Year-end: 04/30/21
Mineral Exploration Services
N.A.I.C.S.: 213114
Lawrence Page (Pres)

SOUTHERN STATES SIGN COMPANY
Viale Bruno Buozzi 83, Rome, Italy
Tel.: (39) 0680692582
Year Founded: 2008
Sales Range: $1-9.9 Million
Emp.: 4
Hotels & Spas
N.A.I.C.S.: 721110
Fillipo Fucile (CFO)

SOUTHERN STEEL BERHAD
2723 Lorong Perusahaan 12 Prai Industrial Estate, 13600, Prai, Pulau Pinang, Malaysia
Tel.: (60) 43906540
Web Site:
https://www.southsteel.com
Year Founded: 1963
SSTEEL—(KLS)
Rev.: $505,065,608
Assets: $407,748,148
Liabilities: $274,132,910
Net Worth: $133,615,238
Earnings: ($28,794,709)
Emp.: 268
Fiscal Year-end: 06/30/23
Steel Mfrs
N.A.I.C.S.: 331110
Leng San Kwek (Chm)

Subsidiaries:

Southern PC Steel Sdn. Bhd. (1)
No 5 Jalan Utas 15/7 Seksyen 15, 40200, Shah Alam, Selangor Darul Ehsan, Malaysia
Tel.: (60) 355105166
Prestress Concrete Product Mfr & Distr
N.A.I.C.S.: 327390

Southern Pipe Industry (Malaysia) Sdn Bhd (1)
4457 MK 15 Jalan Chain Ferry Butterworth, 12100, Pulau Penang, Malaysia
Tel.: (60) 43317393
Web Site: http://www.southsteel.com
Emp.: 315
Steel Pipe Mfr & Distr
N.A.I.C.S.: 331110
Tan Eng Siong (Gen Mgr)

Southern Steel Mesh Sdn. Bhd. (1)
5 1/2 Miles Jalan Kapar, 42100, Klang, Selangor Darul Ehsan, Malaysia
Tel.: (60) 332912116
Steel Wire Mesh Mfr & Distr

SOUTHERN TRAVEL HOLDINGS LIMITED
Level 6 52 Swanson Street, PO Box 3719, Auckland, 1140, New Zealand
Tel.: (64) 9 302 5247
Web Site:
  http://www.southerntravel.co.nz
Sales Range: $10-24.9 Million
Emp.: 108
Tourism Services
N.A.I.C.S.: 561510
Jacqui Walshe *(Mng Dir)*

Subsidiaries:

Hawaii Tourism Australia PTY Limited (1)
Level 11 117 York Street, Sydney, 2000, NSW, Australia
Tel.: (61) 292868951
Web Site: http://www.hawaiitourism.co.au
Travel & Tour Operating Agencies
N.A.I.C.S.: 561520

Southern Travelnet Limited (1)
Level 6 52 Swanson Street, PO Box 3719, Auckland, 1010, New Zealand
Tel.: (64) 93089747
Web Site: http://www.stravelnet.com
Travel & Tour Operating Agency Services
N.A.I.C.S.: 561520
Michael Hall *(Gen Mgr-Bus Dev)*

Southern Travelnet PTY Limited (1)
Level 8 117 York St, Sydney, 2000, NSW, Australia
Tel.: (61) 292215311
Web Site: http://www.stravelnet.com
Emp.: 5
Travel & Tour Operating Agencies
N.A.I.C.S.: 561520
Michael Hall *(Gen Mgr)*

The Walshe Group (Singapore) PTE. Ltd (1)
7500A Beach Road Unit 04-222 The Plaza, Singapore, 199591, Singapore
Tel.: (65) 6333 4818
Airline Ticket Booking Agencies
N.A.I.C.S.: 561599

The Walshe Group Limited Hong Kong (1)
Room 1804-5 Jubilee Centre 18 Fenwick Street, Wanchai, China (Hong Kong)
Tel.: (852) 3678 8500
Airline Ticket Booking Agencies
N.A.I.C.S.: 561599
Anne De Jesus *(Mgr)*

SOUTHGATE CHEVROLET BUICK GMC LTD.
13103 Lake Fraser Drive SE, Calgary, T2J 3H5, AB, Canada
Tel.: (403) 256-4960
Web Site:
  http://www.southgatechev.ca
Sales Range: $25-49.9 Million
New & Used Car Dealers
N.A.I.C.S.: 441110
Robson Armitage *(Gen Mgr)*

SOUTHGATE VOLKSWAGEN
1223 101 Street SW, Edmonton, T6X 1A1, AB, Canada
Tel.: (780) 438-8888
Web Site: http://www.southgatevw.ca
Year Founded: 1970
Sales Range: $25-49.9 Million
New & Used Car Dealers
N.A.I.C.S.: 441110
Marvin Henschel *(Gen Mgr)*

SOUTHLAND INTERNATIONAL TRUCKS LTD.
905 44 St N, Lethbridge, T1H 7H4, AB, Canada
Tel.: (403) 328-0808
Web Site:
  https://southlandnationaltrucks.com
Year Founded: 1985
Truck & Trailer Dealers
N.A.I.C.S.: 423110
George Kirkham *(Owner)*

SOUTHLAND TRAILER CORP.
1405 41 Street North, Lethbridge, T1H 6G3, AB, Canada
Tel.: (403) 327-8212
Web Site:
  http://www.southlandtrailers.com
Year Founded: 1980
Emp.: 175
Motor Vehicle Parts Distr
N.A.I.C.S.: 423120
Monty Sailer *(Founder)*

SOUTHMEDIC INC.
50 Alliance Blvd, Barrie, L4M 5K3, ON, Canada
Tel.: (705) 726-9383
Web Site:
  https://www.southmedic.com
Year Founded: 1983
Surgical & Medical Instruments Distr
N.A.I.C.S.: 339113
Lisette McDonald *(Founder)*

SOUTHSIDE DODGE CHRYSLER JEEP & RV CENTRE
2804 Gaetz Avenue, Red Deer, T4R 1M4, AB, Canada
Tel.: (403) 346-5577
Web Site:
  http://www.southsidedodge.ca
Year Founded: 1971
New & Used Car Dealers
N.A.I.C.S.: 441110
Wayne Whiteside *(Mgr-Sls-New Vehicle)*

SOUTHSIDE NISSAN LTD
290 SW Marine Drive, Vancouver, V5X 2R5, BC, Canada
Tel.: (604) 324-4644
Web Site:
  http://www.southsidenissan.ca
Year Founded: 1972
New & Used Car Dealers
N.A.I.C.S.: 441110
Jerry Scarfo *(Mgr-Fleet & Lease)*

SOUTHSTONE MINERALS LIMITED
2751 Graham Street, Victoria, V8T 3Z1, BC, Canada
Tel.: (604) 696-4236 BC
Web Site:
  https://www.southstonemineral.com
SML—(TSXV)
Rev.: $967,187
Assets: $151,893
Liabilities: $1,075,904
Net Worth: ($924,011)
Earnings: ($140,437)
Fiscal Year-end: 08/31/23
Gold Mining Services
N.A.I.C.S.: 212220
Terry L. Tucker *(Chm)*

SOUTHVIEW ACURA
9820 34th Ave NW, Edmonton, T6E 6L1, AB, Canada
Tel.: (780) 989-8888
Web Site:
  https://www.southviewacura.com
Rev.: $13,347,016
Emp.: 30
New & Used Car Dealers
N.A.I.C.S.: 441110

SOUTHWEST PROPERTIES LTD
Suite 100 1475 Lower Water Street, Halifax, B3J 3Z2, NS, Canada
Tel.: (902) 422-6412
Web Site: https://www.southwest.ca
Year Founded: 1950
Emp.: 150
Construction Services
N.A.I.C.S.: 236220
Jim Spatz *(Chm & CEO)*

SOUTHWEST SECURITIES CO., LTD.
Southwest Securities Headquarters Building No 32 Jinshamen Road, Jiangbei District, Chongqing, 400025, China
Tel.: (86) 2363786633
Web Site: https://www.swsc.com.cn
Year Founded: 1999
600369—(SHG)
Rev.: $250,872,589
Assets: $11,371,614,181
Liabilities: $7,870,621,768
Net Worth: $3,500,992,413
Earnings: $43,442,049
Emp.: 2,061
Fiscal Year-end: 12/31/22
Securities Brokerage
N.A.I.C.S.: 523150

Subsidiaries:

Southwest Securities International Securities Limited (1)
40F Lee Garden One 33 Hysan Avenue, Causeway Bay, China (Hong Kong)
Tel.: (852) 28028838
Web Site: http://www.swsc.hk
Rev.: $1,026,503
Assets: $103,140,998
Liabilities: $105,835,583
Net Worth: ($2,694,585)
Earnings: ($30,745,095)
Emp.: 45
Fiscal Year-end: 12/31/2022
Investment Management Service
N.A.I.C.S.: 523940
Rui Pu *(CEO)*

Tanrich Asset Management Limited (1)
Room 1601 1606-1608 16/F Central Plaza 18 Harbour Road, Wanchai, China (Hong Kong)
Tel.: (852) 2238 9190
Asset Management Services
N.A.I.C.S.: 531390

SOUVIGNET
15 Boulevard De Chaucheres, 42380, Saint Etienne, France
Tel.: (33) 477500657
Web Site: http://www.souvignet.fr
Rev.: $25,500,000
Emp.: 168
Upholstered Household Furniture
N.A.I.C.S.: 337121
Bernard Jegou *(Dir)*

SOUYU TE GROUP CO., LTD.
The First Bldg Daojiao Town, Changping Second Industrial Zone, Dongguan, 523170, Guangdong, China
Tel.: (86) 7698 133 3505 CN
Web Site: http://www.souyute.com
Year Founded: 2005
002503—(SSE)
Rev.: $1,321,808,550
Assets: $1,615,841,522
Liabilities: $994,938,080
Net Worth: $620,903,442
Earnings: ($271,334,910)
Emp.: 2,500
Fiscal Year-end: 12/31/20
Apparel Product Mfr
N.A.I.C.S.: 315990

SOVCOMBANK PJSC
Prospekt Tekstilschikov 46, 156000, Kostroma, Russia
Tel.: (7) 4959880000 RU
Web Site: http://www.sovcombank.ru
Year Founded: 1991
Rev.: $888,279,100
Assets: $18,310,679,220
Liabilities: $16,067,254,300
Net Worth: $2,243,424,920
Earnings: $486,206,590
Emp.: 15,664
Fiscal Year-end: 12/31/19
Commericial Banking
N.A.I.C.S.: 522110
Gusev Dmitry Vladimirovich *(Chm-Mgmt Bd)*

Subsidiaries:

CB Poidem JSC (1)
Blvd Leningradskii Dom 76 Korpus 4, Moscow, 125315, Russia
Tel.: (7) 3832 12 57 43
Web Site: http://www.poidem.ru
Commercial Banking Services
N.A.I.C.S.: 522110
V. P. Kolosov *(Founder)*

Vitabank PJSC (1)
17/4 Nepokorennykh Avenue, Saint Petersburg, 195220, Russia
Tel.: (7) 8123259999
Web Site: http://www.vitabank.ru
Sales Range: Less than $1 Million
Commercial Banking Services
N.A.I.C.S.: 522110

SOVEREIGN CAPITAL PARTNERS LLP
25 Victoria Street, London, SW1H 0EX, United Kingdom
Tel.: (44) 20 7340 8800 UK
Web Site:
  http://www.sovereigncapital.co.uk
Year Founded: 2001
Sales Range: $25-49.9 Million
Emp.: 40
Privater Equity Firm
N.A.I.C.S.: 523999
Andrew Hayden *(Mng Partner)*

Subsidiaries:

Education Placement Group Limited (1)
2nd Floor Sir Wilfrid Newton House, Thorncliffe Park Chapeltown, Sheffield, S35 2PH, United Kingdom
Tel.: (44) 20 7788 9441
Holding Company; Specialty Education Recruitment Services
N.A.I.C.S.: 551112
Julian Harley *(Chm)*

Subsidiary (Domestic):

Supply Desk Limited (2)
2nd Floor Sir Wilfrid Newton House Newton Chambers Road, Thorncliffe Park Chapeltown, Sheffield, S35 2PH, United Kingdom
Tel.: (44) 114 272 5535
Web Site: http://www.supplydesk.co.uk
Education Employment Agency
N.A.I.C.S.: 561311

Division (Domestic):

Supply Desk Limited - Teach In Division (3)
2nd Floor Sir Wilfrid Newton House Newton Chambers Road, Thorncliffe Park Chapeltown, Sheffield, S35 2PH, United Kingdom
Tel.: (44) 114 272 5535
Web Site: http://www.teachin.co.uk
Educational Support Staff Employment Agency
N.A.I.C.S.: 561320

SOVEREIGN CLOUD HOLDINGS LIMITED
Unit 7 15-21 Beaconsfield St, Fyshwick, 2609, ACT, Australia
Tel.: (61) 18002825683 AU
Web Site:
  https://www.australiacloud.com.au
Year Founded: 2017
SOV—(ASX)
Rev.: $4,430,655

Sovereign Cloud Holdings Limited—(Continued)

Assets: $22,131,187
Liabilities: $5,893,430
Net Worth: $16,237,757
Earnings: ($13,877,170)
Emp.: 64
Fiscal Year-end: 06/30/23
Holding Company
N.A.I.C.S.: 551112
Brad Bastow (COO)

SOVEREIGN DIAMONDS LIMITED

11-A Sovereign House, Chakala MIDC Mahal Industrial Estate, Mahakali Caves Road Andheri East Chakala, Mumbai, 400 093, Maharashtra, India
Tel.: (91) 9820030104
Web Site: https://sovereigndiamondsltd.com
Year Founded: 1974
523826—(BOM)
Rev.: $3,485,188
Assets: $3,850,062
Liabilities: $1,988,660
Net Worth: $1,861,402
Earnings: $169,190
Emp.: 36
Fiscal Year-end: 03/31/23
Diamond Jewelry Mfr
N.A.I.C.S.: 339910
Ajay R. Gehani (Chm, Mng Dir & Compliance Officer)

SOVEREIGN METALS LIMITED

Level 9 28 The Esplanade, Perth, 6000, WA, Australia
Tel.: (61) 893226322
Web Site: https://www.sovereignmetal.com.au
SVMLF—(OTCQX)
Rev.: $1,216,530
Assets: $25,825,071
Liabilities: $2,882,514
Net Worth: $22,942,557
Earnings: ($12,420,469)
Fiscal Year-end: 06/30/24
Architectural & Structural Metals Mfg
N.A.I.C.S.: 212290
Ian P. Middlemas (Chm)

SOVEREIGN SPEED GMBH

Frankenstrasse 12, 20097, Hamburg, Germany
Tel.: (49) 40226317200
Web Site: http://www.sovereignspeed.com
Year Founded: 1997
Rev.: $14,926,676
Emp.: 89
Transport & Logistics Services
N.A.I.C.S.: 541614
Martin Araman (Mng Dir)

Subsidiaries:

Activ Cars GmbH (1)
Oskar-Schulze-Strasse 4, 28832, Achim, Germany
Tel.: (49) 4219496033
Freight Transportation Services
N.A.I.C.S.: 481112

SOVEREIGN SPEED (UK) LTD. (1)
Unit B2X Skyway 14 Calder Way, Colnbrook, Slough, SL3 0BQ, United Kingdom
Tel.: (44) 1753687768
Freight Transportation Services
N.A.I.C.S.: 481112

SOVEREIGN SPEED MUC GMBH (1)
Isarweg 6A, 85375, Neufahrn, Germany
Tel.: (49) 816593449300
Airport Cargo Handling Services
N.A.I.C.S.: 488119

SOVILEG

119 Rue Camille Pelletan, 79100, Thouars, Deux Sevres, France
Tel.: (33) 549962266
Web Site: http://www.sovileg.fr
Rev.: $20,700,000
Emp.: 50
Slaughterhouse & Meat Processing
N.A.I.C.S.: 311611
Rodolphe Lepoureau (Mgr)

SOVLINK LLC

Kremlevskaya Naberezhnaya 1 Building 2, 119019, Moscow, Russia
Tel.: (7) 4959671300
Web Site: http://www.sovlink.ru
Year Founded: 1990
Sales Range: Less than $1 Million
Securities Brokerage Services
N.A.I.C.S.: 523150
Irina Udintseva (CEO)

SOWBHAGYA MEDIA LIMITED

Plot no 79 D no 8-3-230 P-30 Sravanthi Nagar, Jubilee Hills, Hyderabad, 500 045, India
Tel.: (91) 40 23422222
Web Site: http://www.sowbhagya.in
Year Founded: 1994
Rev.: $520,265
Assets: $1,565,627
Liabilities: $75,513
Net Worth: $1,490,114
Earnings: ($126,979)
Fiscal Year-end: 03/31/18
Video Production & Distribution Services
N.A.I.C.S.: 512110
Pasupuleti Pakeeraiah (CFO)

SOYEA TECHNOLOGY CO., LTD.

No 1 Jiaogong Road, Xihu District, Hangzhou, 310016, Zhejiang, China
Tel.: (86) 57188271018
Web Site: http://www.cccme.org.cn
Year Founded: 1999
000909—(SSE)
Rev.: $131,955,839
Assets: $607,403,801
Liabilities: $393,790,157
Net Worth: $213,613,644
Earnings: ($54,148,602)
Fiscal Year-end: 12/31/22
Audio & Video Equipment Mfr
N.A.I.C.S.: 334310
Yang Yusong (Chm & Gen Mgr)

SP CHEMICALS LIMITED

15 Beach Road 05-01 Beach Centre, Singapore, 189677, Singapore
Tel.: (65) 63366188
Web Site: http://www.spchemicals.com
Year Founded: 1996
Sales Range: $1-4.9 Billion
Emp.: 1,300
Ion Membrane Chlor-alkali Mfr
N.A.I.C.S.: 325180
Hian Siang Chan (CEO)

Subsidiaries:

SP Chemicals (Taixing) Co., Ltd. (1)
North Binjiang Road Taixing Economic, Development Zone, Taixing, 225404, Jiangsu, China
Tel.: (86) 5237672400
Web Site: http://www.spchemicals.com
Chemicals Mfr
N.A.I.C.S.: 325180

SP GROUP A/S

Snavevej 6-10, 5471, Sonderso, Denmark
Tel.: (45) 70232379
Web Site: https://www.sp-group.com
SPG—(CSE)
Rev.: $301,758,636
Assets: $308,606,975
Liabilities: $202,110,611
Net Worth: $106,496,364
Earnings: $21,027,726
Emp.: 2,114
Fiscal Year-end: 12/31/19
Molded Plastic Components & Coatings Mfr
N.A.I.C.S.: 326199
Frank Gad (CEO & Member-Exec Bd)

Subsidiaries:

Accoat A/S (1)
Munkegaardsvej 16, DK - 3490, Kvistgaard, Denmark
Tel.: (45) 49126800
Web Site: https://accoat.com
Plastic Mfr
N.A.I.C.S.: 326199
Susie-Ann Spiegelhauer (CEO)

Atlantic Floats Denmark A/S (1)
Fragevej 39, 4760, Vordingborg, Denmark
Tel.: (45) 55980901
Web Site: https://atlanticfloats.com
Trawl Floats Mfr & Distr
N.A.I.C.S.: 326199

Baltic Rim SIA (1)
Kapsedes Street 2, Liepaja, LV-3402, Latvia
Tel.: (371) 26536689
Web Site: https://www.balticrim.lv
Molding Plastic Component Mfr
N.A.I.C.S.: 333511

Bovil ApS (1)
M P Allerups Vej 7-9, 5220, Odense, Denmark
Tel.: (45) 70222122
Web Site: https://bovil.dk
Plastics Product Mfr
N.A.I.C.S.: 326199

Broderna Bourghardt AB (1)
Arendalsvagen 33J, SE-434 39, Kungsbacka, Sweden
Tel.: (46) 30072350
Web Site: https://www.bourghardt.se
Molding Plastic Component Mfr
N.A.I.C.S.: 333511
David Bourghardt (CEO)

DAVINCI 3D A/S (1)
Hedegardsvej 9, 7190, Billund, Denmark
Tel.: (45) 76502850
Web Site: https://www.davinci.dk
3D Printing & Art Services
N.A.I.C.S.: 541430

Ergomat, Inc. (1)
7395 Industrial Pkwy, Lorain, OH 44053
Tel.: (440) 282-4651
Web Site: http://www.ergomat.com
Sales Range: $1-9.9 Million
Emp.: 30
Ergonomic Mats & Molded & Extruded Safety Products Mfr
N.A.I.C.S.: 326199

Ergomat-Nederland B.V. (1)
De Steenbok 24, 5215 ME, 's-Hertogenbosch, Netherlands
Tel.: (31) 73 613 0530
Web Site: https://www.ergomat.com
Molding Plastic Component Distr
N.A.I.C.S.: 423830

Gibo Plast A/S (1)
Ferrodanvej 16, 6900, Skjern, Denmark
Tel.: (45) 87828700
Web Site: https://giboplast.com
Plastic Fabrication Mfr
N.A.I.C.S.: 326199
Egon Madsen (Fin Mgr)

Gibo Poland z o.o. (1)
Stawiszcze 4, 98-200, Sieradz, Poland
Tel.: (48) 436569723
Plastic Mold Mfr
N.A.I.C.S.: 333511

Jollmax Coating Oy (1)
Kiertokatu 11, 24280, Salo, Finland
Tel.: (358) 407260904
Web Site: https://www.jollmax.fi
Painting & Surface Treatment Services
N.A.I.C.S.: 238320

MM Composite A/S (1)
Industrivaenget 2B, Norre Aaby, DK-5580, Middelfart, Denmark
Tel.: (45) 72301015
Web Site: https://mmcomposite.dk
Renewable Energy Semiconductor Mfr
N.A.I.C.S.: 334413
Michael V. Terkelsen (CEO)

MedicoPack A/S (1)
Industrivej 6, DK-5550, Langeskov, Denmark
Tel.: (45) 63381000
Web Site: https://www.medicopack.com
Sales Range: $25-49.9 Million
Emp.: 80
Plastic Packaging Mfr
N.A.I.C.S.: 326199

Meditec Plaststobning A/S (1)
Fabriksvej 17c, 3000, Helsingor, Denmark
Tel.: (45) 48483636
Web Site: https://www.meditec.dk
Medical Equipment Mfr & Distr
N.A.I.C.S.: 339112

Nycopac AB (1)
Eskilstunavagen 3, SE-611 56, Nykoping, Sweden
Tel.: (46) 15598050
Web Site: https://www.nycopac.com
Plastic Material Product Mfr
N.A.I.C.S.: 326112
Mikael Wennerlund (Mgr)

SP Medical Sp. z o.o. (1)
Ul Ceramiczna 2K, PL-98 220, Zdunska Wola, Poland
Tel.: (48) 438242460
Molding Plastic Component Mfr
N.A.I.C.S.: 333511

TPI Polytechniek B.V. (1)
De Steenbok 24, 5215 ME, 's-Hertogenbosch, Netherlands
Tel.: (31) 736569194
Web Site: https://www.tpi-polytechniek.com
Ventilation Component Distr
N.A.I.C.S.: 423730
Loic Van Der Heijden (Mng Dir)

Tinby AB (1)
Sollerovagen 80, 792 91, Mora, Sweden
Tel.: (46) 70 554 5939
Web Site: https://tinby.se
Plastic Mfr
N.A.I.C.S.: 326199

Tinby Skumplast A/S (1)
Sunekaer 13-15, 5471, Sonderso, Denmark
Tel.: (45) 7 517 6060
Web Site: https://tinbyskumplast.dk
Plastic Mfr
N.A.I.C.S.: 326199

Tinby Sp. z o.o. (1)
Tel.: (48) 438232346
Molding Plastic Component Mfr
N.A.I.C.S.: 333511

SP NEW ENERGY CORPORATION

20th Floor PhilamLife Tower Paseo de Roxas Avenue, Makati, Philippines
Tel.: (63) 9985621251
Web Site: https://www.spnec.ph
SPNEC—(PHI)
Rev.: $11,473,345
Assets: $924,127,721
Liabilities: $158,216,832
Net Worth: $765,910,889
Earnings: $107,386,128
Fiscal Year-end: 12/31/23
Solar Electric Power Generation Services
N.A.I.C.S.: 221114

SP REFRACTORIES LIMITED

M-10 M-11/1 & M-11/2 MIDC Industrial Area Hingna Road, Nagpur, 440016, India
Tel.: (91) 7104235399
Web Site: https://www.sprefractories.com
Year Founded: 2007
SPRL—(NSE)
Rev.: $430,349,338

Assets: $208,616,940
Liabilities: $94,991,948
Net Worth: $113,624,991
Earnings: $13,438,239
Emp.: 20
Fiscal Year-end: 03/31/22
Refractory Material Mfr
N.A.I.C.S.: 327120

SP SYSTEMS CO., LTD.
123 Eogokgongdan-No, Yangsan,
Gyeongsang Nam-do, Korea (South)
Tel.: (82) 553715600
Web Site:
https://www.spsystems.co.kr
Year Founded: 1988
317830—(KRS)
Rev.: $40,745,654
Assets: $61,363,083
Liabilities: $22,644,547
Net Worth: $38,718,536
Earnings: $2,108,026
Emp.: 79
Fiscal Year-end: 12/31/22
Industrial Robots Mfr
N.A.I.C.S.: 333998
Sang-Gyun Shim (Chm & CEO)

SPA CAPITAL SERVICES LIMITED
25 C-Block Community Centre
Janakapuri, New Delhi, 110058, India
Tel.: (91) 1145675500
Web Site: https://www.spacapital.com
Year Founded: 1995
542376—(BOM)
Financial Advice Services
N.A.I.C.S.: 523940
Sanjay Goel (CFO)

Subsidiaries:

SPA Capital Advisors Limited (1)
25 C-Block Community Centre, Janak Puri,
New Delhi, 110058, India
Tel.: (91) 114 567 5500
Investment Banking Services
N.A.I.C.S.: 523150

SPA Valuation Advisors Private
Ltd. (1)

SPACE CO., LTD.
3-9-4 Nihonbashi Ningyo-cho, Chuo-ku, Tokyo, 103-0013, Japan
Tel.: (81) 336694008
Web Site: https://www.space-tokyo.co.jp
Year Founded: 1948
9622—(TKS)
Rev.: $374,302,370
Assets: $266,761,250
Liabilities: $48,722,480
Net Worth: $218,038,770
Earnings: $11,946,650
Emp.: 852
Fiscal Year-end: 12/31/23
Construction Services
N.A.I.C.S.: 236220
Fujio Hayashi (Chm)

Subsidiaries:

SPACE Japan Co., Ltd. (1)
Unit 702 7/F CLI Building 313 Hennessy
Road, Wanchai, China (Hong Kong)
Tel.: (852) 2884 0644
Building Construction Services
N.A.I.C.S.: 236220

SPACE Shanghai Co., Ltd. (1)
Tel.: (86) 2162351452
Building Construction Services
N.A.I.C.S.: 236220

SPACE GROUP HOLDINGS LIMITED
Avendia De Marciano Baptista No 26
28 5C, Edificio Centro Comercial
Chong Fok, Macau, China (Macau)
Tel.: (853) 28558103 Ky
Web Site:
http://www.spacegroup.com.mo
Year Founded: 2007
2448—(HKG)
Rev.: $33,954,187
Assets: $140,247,575
Liabilities: $68,738,734
Net Worth: $71,508,841
Earnings: ($15,775,363)
Emp.: 78
Fiscal Year-end: 12/31/23
Construction Work Services
N.A.I.C.S.: 236220
Chan U. Che (Founder & Chm)

Subsidiaries:

Space Construction & Engineering
Co., Ltd. (1)
Avendia De Marciano Baptista No 26 28
8C, Edificio Centro Comercial Chong Fok,
Macau, China (Macau)
Tel.: (853) 28938185
Construction Services
N.A.I.C.S.: 236220
Chan Jack (Deputy Dir-Project)

Space Financial Holdings
Limited (1)
Unit 1008A Ocean Centre Harbour City 5
Canton Rd, Tsim Sha Tsui, Kowloon, China
(Hong Kong)
Tel.: (852) 25100603
Web Site:
https://www.spacefinancial.com.hk
Financial Investment Advisory Services
N.A.I.C.S.: 522320

SPACE HELLAS SA
Messogion Ave 312, Ag Paraskevi,
15341, Athens, Greece
Tel.: (30) 2106504100
Web Site: https://www.space.gr
Year Founded: 1985
SPACE—(ATH)
Rev.: $138,771,854
Assets: $188,939,132
Liabilities: $155,880,639
Net Worth: $33,058,493
Earnings: $5,417,656
Emp.: 844
Fiscal Year-end: 12/31/22
Telecommunication & Information
Technology Services
N.A.I.C.S.: 517810
Spyridon D. Manolopoulos (Chm)

Subsidiaries:

METROLOGY HELLAS S.A. (1)
302 Messogeion Ave, Cholargos, Athens,
15562, Greece
Tel.: (30) 210 682 8090
Web Site: http://www.metrology.gr
Calibration Services
N.A.I.C.S.: 541380

SPACE HOLDING SRL
via Turati 7, 20121, Milan, Italy
Tel.: (39) 02 92853375 IT
Web Site: http://www.spaceholding.it
Investment Holding Company
N.A.I.C.S.: 551112
Sergio Erede (Sr Partner)

SPACE INCUBATRICS TECHNOLOGIES LIMITED
Pawan Puri Near Canal, Muradnagar
Distt, Ghaziabad, 201206, Uttar
Pradesh, India
Tel.: (91) 1232261288
Web Site:
http://www.spaceincubatrics.com
Year Founded: 2016
541890—(BOM)
Rev.: $67,574
Assets: $1,101,457
Liabilities: $25,142
Net Worth: $1,076,314
Earnings: ($633,283)
Emp.: 6
Fiscal Year-end: 03/31/23
Information Technology Services
N.A.I.C.S.: 541511
Nishant Mittal (Mng Dir)

SPACE NORWAY AS
Drammensveien 165 Skoyen, Oslo,
0277, Norway
Tel.: (47) 22510000
Web Site: https://spacenorway.no
Space Research & Technology
N.A.I.C.S.: 927110
Dag H. Stolan (CEO)

Subsidiaries:

Telenor Satellite AS (1)
Snaroyveien 30 C7c, 1360, Fornebu, Norway
Tel.: (47) 67073470
Web Site: https://www.telenorsat.com
Satellite Telecommunication Services
N.A.I.C.S.: 517410

SPACE SHOWER SKIYAKI HOLDINGS INC
East Roppongi Bldg 3-16-35 Roppongi, Minato-Ku, Tokyo, 106-8011,
Japan
Tel.: (81) 335853242
Web Site: https://sssk-hd.com
Year Founded: 1996
4838—(TKS)
Rev.: $108,152,820
Assets: $53,964,040
Liabilities: $27,914,030
Net Worth: $26,050,010
Earnings: $1,850,800
Fiscal Year-end: 03/31/24
Music Program Broadcasting Services
N.A.I.C.S.: 512230
Yoshito Hayashi (Co-Pres)

Subsidiaries:

SKIYAKI, Inc. (1)
HUMAX-Shibuya-building 3F 1-14-6 dogenzaka Shibuyaku, Tokyo, 150-0043, Japan
Tel.: (81) 354288378
Web Site: http://skiyaki.com
Rev.: $47,499,760
Assets: $35,515,920
Liabilities: $24,277,440
Net Worth: $11,238,480
Earnings: $1,171,280
Fiscal Year-end: 01/31/2022
Software Development Services
N.A.I.C.S.: 541511
Takuya Miyase (Pres)

SPACE SHUTTLE HI-TECH CO., LTD.
9nd Floor 2 No 23 Huanke 1st Road,
Wu-Lung Village, Zhubei, 307, Hsin-Chu, Taiwan
Tel.: (886) 35935588
Web Site: https://www.spaces.com.tw
Year Founded: 1985
2440—(TAI)
Rev.: $96,711,040
Assets: $70,957,942
Liabilities: $30,641,746
Net Worth: $40,316,196
Earnings: ($4,495,765)
Emp.: 500
Fiscal Year-end: 12/31/23
Telecommunication Cables Mfr &
Distr
N.A.I.C.S.: 335921
Hsuan-Hui Wang (Chm & Pres)

Subsidiaries:

Space Shuttle (Suz-Hou) Hi-Tech
Co., Ltd. (1)
Guangfu Town Wuzhong District, Suzhou,
Jiangshu, China
Tel.: (86) 512 669 50127
Telecommunications Equipment Mfr
N.A.I.C.S.: 517810

SPACE SOLUTION INC
33 Digital-ro 9-gil Geumcheon-gu,
Seoul, 08511, Korea (South)
Tel.: (82) 220275932
Web Site:
http://www.spacesolution.kr
Business Software Development Services
N.A.I.C.S.: 541511
Chu Eun-Duk (CEO)

SPACE4 S.P.A.
Via Mauro Macchi 27, 20124, Milan,
Italy
Tel.: (39) 02 9285 3375 IT
Web Site: http://www.space4spa.com
Assets: $613,651,280
Liabilities: $20,415,693
Net Worth: $593,235,587
Earnings: ($124,639)
Fiscal Year-end: 12/31/17
Investment Holding Company
N.A.I.C.S.: 551112
Roberto Italia (Chm)

SPACEANDPEOPLE PLC
3rd Floor Delta House 50 West Nile
Street, Glasgow, G1 2NP, United
Kingdom
Tel.: (44) 3333401500
Web Site:
http://www.spaceandpeople.co.uk
SAL—(AIM)
Rev.: $6,979,298
Assets: $13,308,508
Liabilities: $9,455,945
Net Worth: $3,852,562
Earnings: ($2,163,595)
Emp.: 49
Fiscal Year-end: 12/31/22
Promotional Space for Shopping
Centers & Other Venues
N.A.I.C.S.: 561920
Nancy J. Cullen (CEO)

Subsidiaries:

Retail Profile GmbH (1)
Borsteler Bogen 27b, 22453, Hamburg,
Germany
Tel.: (49) 40357040120
Web Site: http://www.popretall.de
Leather Good & Cosmetic Retailer
N.A.I.C.S.: 458110

SpaceandPeople GmbH (1)
Borsteler Bogen 27b Studioloft 13, 22453,
Hamburg, Germany
Tel.: (49) 40357040100
Web Site: http://www.spaceandpeople.de
Real Estate Services
N.A.I.C.S.: 531210

SpaceandPeople India Pvt Ltd. (1)
Unit No 1B 1st Floor Steelmade Industrial
Estate Marol Maroshi Road, Marol Udyog
Premises Co-Op Society Ltd Andheri East,
Mumbai, 400059, India
Tel.: (91) 2249185678
Web Site: http://www.spaceandpeople.in
Marketing Agent Services
N.A.I.C.S.: 541810
Paresh Khivesara (Mng Dir)

SPACEFRAME BUILDINGS PTY. LTD.
225 Queensport Road North, Murarrie, 4172, QLD, Australia
Tel.: (61) 738909500
Web Site:
http://www.spaceframe.com
Sales Range: $25-49.9 Million
Emp.: 60
Industrial Building & Construction
Services
N.A.I.C.S.: 236210
Werner Raspotnik (Mng Dir)

SPACEFY, INC.

SPACEFY, INC.

Spacefy, Inc.—(Continued)
110 Spadina Ave Unit 300, Toronto, M5V 2K4, ON, Canada
Web Site: https://corp.spacefy.com
SPFY—(CNSX)
Rev: $867
Assets: $16,851
Liabilities: $417,435
Net Worth: ($400,584)
Earnings: ($95,613)
Fiscal Year-end: 12/31/22
Media Advertising Services
N.A.I.C.S.: 541840
Judeh Siwady (Co-Founder)

SPACEMARKET, INC.
6-15-1 Nishi-Shinjuku, Shinjuku-Ku, Tokyo, 160-0023, Japan
Tel.: (81) 5017449969
Web Site:
https://www.spacemarket.co.jp
Year Founded: 2014
4487—(TKS)
Rev: $11,088,760
Assets: $14,499,050
Liabilities: $10,592,460
Net Worth: $3,906,590
Earnings: ($1,191,120)
Fiscal Year-end: 12/31/23
Booking Services
N.A.I.C.S.: 561599
Daisuke Shigematsu (Founder, Chm & Pres)

SPACENET ENTERPRISES INDIA LIMITED
Plot No 114 Survey No 66/2 Raidurgam Prashant Hills Gachibowli, Nav Khalsa Serilingampally Ranga Reddy, Hyderabad, 500008, Telangana, India
Tel.: (91) 4029345781
Web Site:
https://www.spacenetent.com
Year Founded: 2010
Rev: $91,816
Assets: $28,213
Liabilities: $1,517,420
Net Worth: ($1,489,207)
Earnings: ($4,610)
Fiscal Year-end: 03/31/19
Internet Advertising Services
N.A.I.C.S.: 541810
Avinash Karingam (Exec Dir)

SPACESAVER SOLUTIONS, INC.
115 Engelhard Drive, Aurora, L4G 3V1, ON, Canada
Tel.: (905) 726-3933
Web Site: https://www.spacesaver.ca
Computer Storage & Document Mfr
N.A.I.C.S.: 334112
Michael Thompson (CEO)

Subsidiaries:

SpaceSaverCCS Inc. (1)
10045 111 St NW, Edmonton, T5J 2M5, AB, Canada
Tel.: (780) 423-3100
Sales Range: $25-49.9 Million
Emp.: 100
Business Management Services
N.A.I.C.S.: 541618
Heather McEwan (Gen Mgr)

SPACETALK LTD.
154 Fullarton Road, Rose Park, 5067, SA, Australia
Tel.: (61) 881049588 AU
Web Site: https://spacetalk.co
Year Founded: 2001
SPA—(ASX)
Rev: $11,961,177
Assets: $5,247,667
Liabilities: $7,826,673
Net Worth: ($2,579,006)
Earnings: ($3,803,454)
Fiscal Year-end: 06/30/24
Wireless Products & Services
N.A.I.C.S.: 517112
Mark Fortunatow (CEO)

Subsidiaries:

Spacetalk Holdings Pty Ltd (1)
154 Fullarton Road, Rose Park, 5067, SA, Australia
Tel.: (61) 881049588
Web Site: http://www.spacetalkwatch.com
Information Technology Services
N.A.I.C.S.: 541519

SPACIOTEMPO
Parc d'Activites Les Hauts Du Val De Nievre, 80420, Flixecourt, Somme, France
Tel.: (33) 322515151
Rev: $26,200,000
Emp.: 123
Equipment Rental & Leasing
N.A.I.C.S.: 532490
Michel Lebrun (Dir)

SPACKMAN ENTERTAINMENT GROUP LTD.
Proom Building 82 Nonhyun-Dong, Gangnam-Gu, Seoul, 135-818, Korea (South)
Tel.: (82) 234434296
Web Site:
https://www.spackmangroup.com
40E—(CAT)
Rev: $9,480,762
Assets: $50,220,297
Liabilities: $17,585,121
Net Worth: $32,635,176
Earnings: ($23,125,181)
Emp.: 30
Fiscal Year-end: 12/31/20
Film Production
N.A.I.C.S.: 512110
Eugene Lee (Exec Dir)

Subsidiaries:

Novus Mediacorp Co., Ltd. (1)
3F 38-17 Jamwon-dong, Seocho-gu, Seoul, Korea (South)
Tel.: (82) 7046106760
Web Site: http://www.novusmediacorp.com
Broadcasting Services
N.A.I.C.S.: 516120

SPACKMAN EQUITIES GROUP INC.
Suite 2502 Scotia Plaza 40 Street West, Toronto, M5H 3Y2, ON, Canada
Tel.: (416) 304-1231
Web Site:
https://spackmanequitiesgroup.com
6QH—(DEU)
Assets: $398,185
Liabilities: $1,314,982
Net Worth: ($916,796)
Earnings: ($374,452)
Fiscal Year-end: 12/31/23
Investment Management Service
N.A.I.C.S.: 523999
Richard Lee (Chm & CEO)

SPACTIV S.P.A.
Piazza Caneva 5, 20154, Milan, Italy
Tel.: (39) 02 8718 9232
Web Site: http://www.spactiv.com
Asset Management Services
N.A.I.C.S.: 523940
Gabriele Bavagnoli (Co-CEO)

SPAENAUR INC.
815 Victoria St N, Kitchener, N2G 4B1, ON, Canada
Tel.: (519) 744-6305
Web Site: http://www.spaenaur.com
Year Founded: 1936
Rev: $36,000,000
Emp.: 122
Hardware Components Distr
N.A.I.C.S.: 423840
Roy Spaetzel (Co-Founder)

SPAL
Via Per Carpi n 26/B, 42015, Correggio, Emilia-Romagna, Italy
Tel.: (39) 0522731311 IT
Web Site:
http://www.spalautomotive.it
Year Founded: 1959
Sales Range: $75-99.9 Million
Emp.: 1,000
Automotive Accessory Mfr
N.A.I.C.S.: 333413
Spaggiari Alexondro (Pres)

Subsidiaries:

SPAL Automotive Components (Shanghai) Co., Ltd. (1)
Part B, The 1st Fl, No 31 of Lot F12-3, No 390, Ai Du Rd, Wai Gao Qiao Free Trade Zone, Shanghai, 200131, China (100%)
Tel.: (86) 2150463637
Web Site: http://www.spal-china.com
Sales Range: $25-49.9 Million
Emp.: 15
Automotive Accessory Mfr
N.A.I.C.S.: 441330

SPAL Automotive UK Limited (1)
Unit 3 Great Western Business Park McKenzie Way Tolladine Road, Worcester, WR4 9PT, United Kingdom
Tel.: (44) 1905 613 714
Web Site: http://www.spalautomotive.co.uk
Axial Fan & Blower Distr
N.A.I.C.S.: 423830
Matthew Morris (Mng Dir)

SPAL China (1)
No 343 Mei Gui North Road Wai Gao Qiao Pilot Free Trade Zone, Shanghai, 200131, China
Tel.: (86) 21 50463637
Web Site: http://www.spal-china.com
Axial Fan & Blower Distr
N.A.I.C.S.: 423830

SPAL RUS LLC (1)
Avenue Sofiyskaya 66 liter A, 192289, Saint Petersburg, Russia
Tel.: (7) 89219632033
Axial Fan & Blower Distr
N.A.I.C.S.: 423830

SPAL USA (1)
1731 SE Oralabor Rd, Ankeny, IA 50021 (100%)
Tel.: (515) 289-7000
Web Site: http://www.spalusa.com
Sales Range: $25-49.9 Million
Emp.: 30
Automotive Accessories Mfr
N.A.I.C.S.: 441330

SPAL do BRASIL Ltda. (1)
R Periperi 158, Socorro, Sao Paulo, 047060-060, Brazil
Tel.: (55) 11 5541 5151
Web Site: http://www.spalbrasil.com
Axial Fan & Blower Distr
N.A.I.C.S.: 423830

SPAN DIVERGENT LTD.
9th Floor Rajhans Bonista Behind Ram Chowk Ghod Dod Road, Surat, 395007, Gujarat, India
Tel.: (91) 2612663232
Web Site: https://www.span.in
Year Founded: 1972
524727—(BOM)
Rev: $1,274,113
Assets: $4,700,509
Liabilities: $3,715,483
Net Worth: $985,025
Earnings: ($840,674)
Emp.: 7
Fiscal Year-end: 03/31/21
Diagnostic Reagent Mfr
N.A.I.C.S.: 325413
Viral P. Desai (Mng Dir)

INTERNATIONAL PUBLIC

Subsidiaries:

Biospan Contamination Control Solutions Pvt. Ltd. (1)
9th Floor Rajhans Bonista Behind Ram Chowk Ghod Dod Road, Surat, 395 007, India
Tel.: (91) 2612663232
Web Site: https://ccs.biospan.in
Cleaning Product Mfr & Distr
N.A.I.C.S.: 325611

Dryfruit Factory LLP (1)
902-904 Rajhans Bonista Behind Ram Chowk Ghod Dod Road, Surat, 395 001, India
Tel.: (91) 9106555488
Web Site: https://demo.dryfruitfactory.in
Dry Fruit & Nut Distr
N.A.I.C.S.: 424490

Span Diagnostics LLP (1)
Ground Floor No 79 40th Main M E I Road, 2nd Stage Yeshwanthpur Industrial Suburb Yeshwanthpur, Bengaluru, 560022, India
Tel.: (91) 9888799994
Web Site: https://spandiagno.com
Diagnostics Instrument Mfr & Distr
N.A.I.C.S.: 334516

SPANCRETE CORPORATION
5F Hongo 3-chome TH Building 2-40-8 Hongo, Bunkyo-Ku, Tokyo, 113-0033, Japan
Tel.: (81) 356896311
Web Site:
https://www.spancretecorp.com
Year Founded: 1963
52770—(TKS)
Sales Range: Less than $1 Million
Prestressed Concrete Plate Mfr
N.A.I.C.S.: 327390

SPANDANA SPHOORTY FINANCIAL LIMITED
Plot no 31 and 32 Ramky Selinium Towers Ground Floor Nanakramguda, Gachibowli, Hyderabad, 500032, India
Tel.: (91) 4044386648 In
Web Site:
http://www.spandanaindia.com
Year Founded: 1998
Rev: $149,380,927
Assets: $702,378,506
Liabilities: $431,872,474
Net Worth: $270,506,032
Earnings: $44,274,463
Emp.: 6,656
Fiscal Year-end: 03/31/19
Financial Services
N.A.I.C.S.: 525990
G. Padmaja Reddy (Founder)

Subsidiaries:

Criss Financial Holdings Limited (1)
Plot No 31 and 32 Ramky Selinium towers Tower A Ground floor, Financial Dist Nanakramguda Gachibowli, Hyderabad, 500032, Telangana, India
Tel.: (91) 4044386648
Web Site: http://www.crissfinancial.com
Financial Services
N.A.I.C.S.: 523999
Padmaja Reddy (Founder & Mng Dir)

SPANDAUER VELOURS GMBH & CO.KG
Hartensteiner Strasse 60, Lichtenstein, 9350, Germany
Tel.: (49) 37204310
Web Site: http://www.spandauer-velours.de
Year Founded: 1987
Rev: $39,714,840
Emp.: 120
Textile Products Mfr
N.A.I.C.S.: 313310
Rainer Georg Ott (Mgr-Sls-Technical Textiles Worldwide)

SPANISH MOUNTAIN GOLD LTD.
Suite 910 1111 Melville Street, Vancouver, V6E 3V6, BC, Canada
Tel.: (604) 398-4377
Web Site: https://www.spanishmountain.com
SPA—(OTCIQ)
Rev.: $16,456
Assets: $59,670,782
Liabilities: $1,073,381
Net Worth: $58,597,401
Earnings: ($607,842)
Fiscal Year-end: 12/31/19
Gold Exploration Services
N.A.I.C.S.: 212220
Morris Beattie *(Chm)*

SPANJAARD LIMITED
748-750 Fifth Street, Wynberg, Sandton, 2090, South Africa
Tel.: (27) 113867100
Web Site: http://www.spanjaard.biz
SPA—(JSE)
Rev.: $9,330,794
Assets: $5,151,501
Liabilities: $1,596,173
Net Worth: $3,555,329
Earnings: $313,994
Emp.: 92
Fiscal Year-end: 02/28/21
Lubricants & Chemical Products Mfr
N.A.I.C.S.: 325998
Clinton Keith Tew Palmer *(Exec Dir)*

SPAR AUSTRALIA LIMITED
Fox Road, Acacia Ridge, 4110, QLD, Australia
Tel.: (61) 737153000
Web Site: http://www.spar.com.au
Year Founded: 2002
Grocery Distr
N.A.I.C.S.: 445110
Lou Jardin *(Mng Dir)*

SPAR CONSTRUCTION LTD.
14415 114 Avenue, Edmonton, T5M 2Y8, AB, Canada
Tel.: (780) 453-3555
Web Site: https://www.sparconstruction.com
Year Founded: 1985
Construction Services
N.A.I.C.S.: 236220
Keith May *(Project Mgr)*

SPAR NORD BANK A/S
Skelagervej 15, PO Box 162, 9100, Aalborg, Denmark
Tel.: (45) 96344000 DK
Web Site: https://www.sparnord.dk
Year Founded: 1824
SPNO—(OMX)
Rev.: $322,814,024
Assets: $17,932,890,567
Liabilities: $16,128,691,525
Net Worth: $1,804,199,042
Earnings: $205,032,484
Emp.: 1,628
Fiscal Year-end: 12/31/22
Retail Banking Services
N.A.I.C.S.: 522110
John Lundsgaard *(Mng Dir & Member-Exec Bd)*

Subsidiaries:

Finans Nord A/S (1)
Skelagervej 15, PO Box 162, 9100, Aalborg, Denmark
Tel.: (45) 9634 4100
Web Site: http://www.finansnord.dk
Sales Range: $100-124.9 Million
Emp.: 130
Financial Lending Services
N.A.I.C.S.: 522220

Spar Nord Ejendomsselskab A/S (1)
Skelagervej 15, 9000, Aalborg, Denmark
Tel.: (45) 96342918
Web Site: http://www.sparnord.dk
Sales Range: $150-199.9 Million
Emp.: 400
Property Management Services
N.A.I.C.S.: 531311

SPARA CAPITAL PARTNERS INC.
1315 N Service Rd E Ste 300, Oakville, L6H 1A7, ON, Canada
Tel.: (905) 829-5757
Web Site: http://www.sparacapital.com
Year Founded: 2001
Emp.: 10
Investment Advisory & Management Services
N.A.I.C.S.: 523940
Jason P. Sparaga *(CEO)*

SPARC SYSTEMS LIMITED
16 Ground Floor Lovely Sector 2, Airoli West, Navi Mumbai, 400708, India
Tel.: (91) 2227792473
Web Site: http://www.sparcsys.com
Year Founded: 1989
Rev.: $34,198
Assets: $507,398
Liabilities: $12,415
Net Worth: $494,982
Earnings: $15,657
Fiscal Year-end: 03/31/19
Electronic Software Development Services
N.A.I.C.S.: 541511
J. T. D'souza *(Mng Dir)*

SPARC TECHNOLOGIES LIMITED
Level 2 480 Collins Street, Melbourne, 3000, VIC, Australia
Tel.: (61) 894820560
Web Site: https://sparctechnologies.com.au
SPN—(ASX)
Rev.: $967,662
Assets: $2,311,812
Liabilities: $353,321
Net Worth: $1,958,491
Earnings: ($2,851,557)
Fiscal Year-end: 06/30/24
Coal Exploration & Development Services
N.A.I.C.S.: 213113
Stephen B. Hunt *(Exec Chm)*

SPAREBANK 1 GRUPPEN AS
Hammersborggata 2, N 0106, Oslo, Norway
Tel.: (47) 21025050 NO
Web Site: http://www2.sparebank1.no
Sales Range: $350-399.9 Million
Emp.: 1,400
Bank Holding Company
N.A.I.C.S.: 551111
Finn Haugan *(Chm)*

Subsidiaries:

BN Bank ASA (1)
Sondre gate 10B, 7011, Trondheim, Norway
Tel.: (47) 22825600
Web Site: http://www.bnbank.no
Sales Range: $75-99.9 Million
Emp.: 100
Commercial Banking
N.A.I.C.S.: 522110
Svein Tore Samdal *(CEO)*

Subsidiary (Domestic):

Bolig- og Naeringskreditt ASA (2)
Sondregata 10, 7011, Trondheim, Norway (100%)
Tel.: (47) 73892000
Web Site: http://www.bnbank.no
Sales Range: $100-124.9 Million
Emp.: 120
Mortgage & Nonmortgage Loan Brokers
N.A.I.C.S.: 522310

Conecto AS (1)
Grini Naringspark 17, PO Box 85, Oslo, Norway
Tel.: (47) 67 15 78 80
Web Site: http://www.conecto.no
Financial Services
N.A.I.C.S.: 522320

SpareBank 1 Forsikring AS (1)
PO Box 778 Sentrum, 0106, Oslo, Norway
Tel.: (47) 21025050
Web Site: http://www.sparebank1.no
Insurance Brokerage Services
N.A.I.C.S.: 524210

SpareBank 1 Gruppen Finans AS (1)
PO Box 1347 Sentrum, Alesund, 6001, Norway
Tel.: (47) 70113600
Web Site: http://www.factoring.no
General Insurance Services
N.A.I.C.S.: 524113

SpareBank 1 Nord-Norge (1)
Storgata 65, 9008, Tromso, Norway
Tel.: (47) 91502244
Web Site: https://www.sparebank1.no
Rev.: $353,223,721
Assets: $11,317,291,705
Liabilities: $9,827,821,910
Net Worth: $1,489,469,795
Earnings: $170,977,277
Emp.: 824
Fiscal Year-end: 12/31/2022
Banking Services
N.A.I.C.S.: 522110
Hans-Tore Bjerkaas *(Deputy Chm)*

SpareBank 1 SMN (1)
Sondre gate 4, 7011, Trondheim, Norway
Tel.: (47) 91507300
Web Site: https://www.sparebank1.no
Rev.: $480,971,735
Assets: $20,627,378,533
Liabilities: $18,317,291,705
Net Worth: $2,310,086,828
Earnings: $257,251,062
Emp.: 1,515
Fiscal Year-end: 12/31/2022
Banking Services
N.A.I.C.S.: 522110
Bard Benum *(Deputy Chm)*

Sparebank 1 Ringerike Hadeland (1)
Sondre Torv 6, 3510, Honefoss, Norway
Tel.: (47) 91502130
Web Site: https://www.sparebank1.no
Sales Range: $25-49.9 Million
Emp.: 173
Banking Services
N.A.I.C.S.: 522110
Kirsten Ideboeen *(CEO)*

SPAREBANK 1 NORDMORE
Langveien 21, Postboks 23, 6501, Kristiansund, Norway
Tel.: (47) 91503900
Web Site: https://www.sparebank1.no
SNOR—(OSL)
Sales Range: Less than $1 Million
Commercial Banking Services
N.A.I.C.S.: 522110

SPAREBANK 1 OESTLANDET
Tel.: (47) 91507040
Web Site: https://www.sparebank1.no
SPOL—(OSL)
Rev.: $331,516,290
Assets: $18,140,510,710
Liabilities: $15,957,707,570
Net Worth: $2,182,803,140
Earnings: $235,947,180
Emp.: 654
Fiscal Year-end: 12/31/21
Commercial Banking Services
N.A.I.C.S.: 522110
Richard Herman Heiberg *(CEO)*

Subsidiaries:

EiendomsMegler 1 Innlandet AS (1)
Torggt 12/14, 2317, Hamar, Norway
Tel.: (47) 91241730
Web Site: https://www.eiendomsmegler1.no
Emp.: 85
Real Estate Services
N.A.I.C.S.: 531390

Totens Sparebank (1)
Tel.: (47) 61141200
Web Site: https://www.totenbanken.no
Sales Range: Less than $1 Million
Commercial Banking Services
N.A.I.C.S.: 522110
Rolf Endre Delingsrud *(CEO)*

SPAREBANK 1 OSTFOLD AKERSHUS
Varnaveien 43E, PO Box 130, 1501, Moss, Norway
Tel.: (47) 91505700
Web Site: https://www.sparebank1.no
SOAG—(OSL)
Sales Range: Less than $1 Million
Commercial Banking Services
N.A.I.C.S.: 522110
Arild Bjorn Hansen *(CEO)*

SPAREBANKEN MORE
Keiser Wilhelmsgt 29-33, PO Box 121, 6001, Alesund, Norway
Tel.: (47) 70113000 NO
Web Site: https://www.sbm.no
Year Founded: 1985
MORG—(OSL)
Rev.: $252,170,700
Assets: $8,267,227,046
Liabilities: $7,518,843,525
Net Worth: $748,383,521
Earnings: $71,771,661
Emp.: 374
Fiscal Year-end: 12/31/22
Commercial Banking Services
N.A.I.C.S.: 522110
Terje Krovel *(Exec VP-Corp Banking)*

Subsidiaries:

More Boligkreditt AS (1)
Kipervigata 6, PO Box 121, 6003, Alesund, Norway
Tel.: (47) 70113000
Web Site: https://www.sbm.no
Sales Range: $200-249.9 Million
Mortgage Banking
N.A.I.C.S.: 522390
Ole Andre Kjerstad *(Mng Dir)*

More Eiendomsmegling AS (1)
Storgata 41/43, 6413, Molde, Norway
Tel.: (47) 71195000
Web Site: https://www.moremegling.no
Real Estate Broker
N.A.I.C.S.: 531210
Bendik Joten Tangen *(CEO)*

SPAREBANKEN OST
Web Site: http://www.oest.no
SPOG—(OSL)
Rev.: $220,685,388
Assets: $4,460,953,256
Liabilities: $3,977,920,727
Net Worth: $483,032,529
Earnings: $43,313,280
Emp.: 193
Fiscal Year-end: 12/31/23
Commercial Banking Services
N.A.I.C.S.: 522110
Pal Strand *(CEO & Mng Dir)*

Subsidiaries:

AS Financiering (1)
Roald Amundsens gt 6, 0161, Oslo, Norway
Tel.: (47) 40002259
Web Site: http://www.financiering.no
Car Loan Financing Services
N.A.I.C.S.: 522220

Ost Prosjekt AS (1)
Svinesundsveien 334, 1788, Halden, Norway
Tel.: (47) 69192508
Web Site: http://www.ost.as
Construction Contracting Services

SPAREBANKEN OST

Sparebanken Ost—(Continued)
N.A.I.C.S.: 236220

Sparebanken Ost Eiendom AS (1)
Stasjonsgata 14, 3300, Hokksund, Norway
Tel.: (47) 33513855
Web Site: http://www.spoe.no
Real Estate Development Services
N.A.I.C.S.: 531390

SPAREBANKEN SOR ASA
Postboks 200, 4662, Kristiansand, Norway
Tel.: (47) 937894538
Web Site: https://www.sor.no
Year Founded: 1824
SOR—(OSL)
Rev.: $638,555,330
Assets: $14,539,719,195
Liabilities: $12,992,333,272
Net Worth: $1,547,385,923
Earnings: $163,772,400
Emp.: 618
Fiscal Year-end: 12/31/23
Commercial Banking Services
N.A.I.C.S.: 522110

SPAREBANKEN VEST
Tel.: (47) 91505555
Web Site: https://www.spv.no
Commercial Banking Services
N.A.I.C.S.: 522110
Jan Erik Kjerpeseth (CEO)

SPAREKASSEN SJAELLAND-FYN A/S
Isefjords Alle 5, 4300, Holbaek, Denmark
Tel.: (45) 59481111
Web Site: https://www.spks.dk
Year Founded: 2015
SPKSJF—(CSE)
Rev.: $184,869,268
Assets: $4,287,479,562
Liabilities: $3,690,091,302
Net Worth: $597,388,259
Earnings: $53,793,173
Emp.: 558
Fiscal Year-end: 12/31/22
Banking Services
N.A.I.C.S.: 522110
Jan Kolbye Jensen (Deputy CEO)

SPARK EDUCATION LTD.
Block A No 101 Wangjing Lize Zhongyuan, Chaoyang District, Beijing, China
Tel.: (86) 10 8414 8552 Ky
Year Founded: 2016
SPRK—(NASDAQ)
Rev.: $179,923,542
Assets: $377,211,600
Liabilities: $702,122,208
Net Worth: ($324,910,608)
Earnings: ($163,322,626)
Emp.: 8,743
Fiscal Year-end: 12/31/20
Educational Support Services
N.A.I.C.S.: 611710
Jian Luo (Co-Founder, Chm & CEO)

SPARK ENERGY MINERALS INC.
Suite 702 - 595 Howe St, Vancouver, V6C 2T5, BC, Canada
Tel.: (604) 484-0355 BC
Web Site: https://www.maxtech-ventures.com
Year Founded: 2000
SPARF—(OTCIQ)
Rev.: $76,573
Assets: $4,933,068
Liabilities: $648,312
Net Worth: $4,284,756
Earnings: ($1,169,949)
Emp.: 3
Fiscal Year-end: 07/31/23

Mineral Exploration Services
N.A.I.C.S.: 213114
Peter Wilson (CEO)

SPARK INFRASTRUCTURE GROUP
Level 29 259 George Street, Sydney, 2000, NSW, Australia
Tel.: (61) 290863600
Web Site: http://www.sparkinfrastructure.com
SKI—(OTCIQ)
Rev.: $209,074,096
Assets: $2,338,036,447
Liabilities: $1,115,173,455
Net Worth: $1,222,862,992
Earnings: $80,452,249
Emp.: 5,400
Fiscal Year-end: 12/31/20
Utility Infrastructure Investment Group
N.A.I.C.S.: 523999
Richard Francis (CEO & Mng Dir)

Subsidiaries:

Spark Infrastructure Holdings No. 2 Pty Limited (1)
Level 29 225 George Street, Sydney, 2000, NSW, Australia
Tel.: (61) 29 086 3600
Electric Power Distribution Services
N.A.I.C.S.: 221122

Spark Infrastructure Trust (1)
Level 29 225 George Street, Sydney, 2000, NSW, Australia
Tel.: (61) 290863600
Web Site: http://www.sparkinfrastructure.com
Sales Range: $75-99.9 Million
Emp.: 9
Gas Distribution Services
N.A.I.C.S.: 221210

SPARK NETWORKS SE
Kohlfurter Strasse 41/43, 10999, Berlin, 10999, Germany
Tel.: (49) 30868000102 De
Web Site: https://www.spark.net
Year Founded: 2017
LOV—(NASDAQ)
Rev.: $187,763,000
Assets: $164,377,000
Liabilities: $171,163,000
Net Worth: ($6,786,000)
Earnings: ($44,190,000)
Emp.: 271
Fiscal Year-end: 12/31/22
Online Dating Website
N.A.I.C.S.: 513140
Colleen Birdnow Brown (Chm & Interim CEO)

Subsidiaries:

Affinitas GmbH (1)
Kohlfurter Strasse 41/43, 10999, Berlin, Germany
Tel.: (49) 30 868 000 100
Web Site: http://www.affinitas.de
Online Dating Services
N.A.I.C.S.: 516210

Spark Networks Inc. (1)
524 Broadway, New York, NY 10013
Tel.: (310) 893-0550
Web Site: http://www.spark.net
Internet & Mobile Dating App Services
N.A.I.C.S.: 812990
Colleen Birdnow Brown (Chm & Interim CEO)

Subsidiary (Domestic):

Kizmeet, Inc. (2)
8383 Wilshire Blvd Ste 800, Beverly Hills, CA 90211
Tel.: (323) 658-3000
Online Dating & Social Networking Services
N.A.I.C.S.: 812990

Smooch Labs, Inc. (2)
240 Bedford Ave, Brooklyn, NY 11211
Tel.: (508) 415-5237

Mobile Dating Apps
N.A.I.C.S.: 541511
David Yarus (Founder)

Zoosk, Inc. (1)
555 Mission St 3rd Fl, San Francisco, CA 94105
Tel.: (800) 722-4400
Web Site: http://www.zoosk.com
Online Dating Services
N.A.I.C.S.: 812990
Shayan Zadeh (Founder)

SPARK NEW ZEALAND LIMITED
Level 2 Spark City 167 Victoria Street West, Auckland, 1010, New Zealand
Tel.: (64) 44711638 NZ
Web Site: http://www.sparknz.co.nz
Year Founded: 1987
SPKKY—(OTCIQ)
Rev.: $2,686,004,785
Assets: $2,680,622,010
Liabilities: $1,520,334,928
Net Worth: $1,160,287,081
Earnings: $678,827,751
Emp.: 5,432
Fiscal Year-end: 06/30/23
Telecommunication Services
N.A.I.C.S.: 517111
Joe McCollum (Dir-HR)

Subsidiaries:

Entelar Group Limited (1)
Lvl 3 46 Sale Street, Auckland CBD, Auckland, New Zealand
Tel.: (64) 800234784
Web Site: https://entelargroup.co.nz
Telecommunication Engineering Services
N.A.I.C.S.: 541330

Telecom New Zealand USA Limited (1)
99 S Lake Ave Ste 500, Pasadena, CA 91101 (100%)
Tel.: (626) 432-4300
Web Site: http://www.tnzi.com
Sales Range: $25-49.9 Million
Emp.: 5
Telecommunications Services Whslr
N.A.I.C.S.: 517111

SPARK VC S.A.
Ul Grzegorzecka 67D/26, 31-559, Krakow, Poland
Tel.: (48) 223781474
Web Site: https://www.sparkvc.pl
Year Founded: 2011
SPK—(WAR)
Investment Management Service
N.A.I.C.S.: 523999

SPARKASSE KOLNBONN
Hahnenstrasse 57, D 50667, Cologne, Germany
Tel.: (49) 2212261
Web Site: http://www.sparkasse-koelnbonn.de
Year Founded: 1826
Sales Range: $1-4.9 Billion
Emp.: 5,112
Banking Services
N.A.I.C.S.: 523150
Joachim Schmalzl (Member-Mgmt Bd-Org & Process Mgmt)

SPARKLING (INDIA) FINSHARES LIMITED
Commercial Unit no 355 3rd floor Building Aggarwal Kodli Plaza, Plot No 8 LSC-I Kondli Gharoli Mised Housing Sector Mayur Vihar, New Delhi, 110096, India
Tel.: (91) 1165678111 In
Web Site: http://www.sparklingfinshares.com
Year Founded: 1994
540211—(BOM)
Rev.: $7,917
Assets: $530,985

INTERNATIONAL PUBLIC

Liabilities: $104,150
Net Worth: $426,836
Earnings: ($38,766)
Fiscal Year-end: 03/31/21
Consumer Lending Services
N.A.I.C.S.: 522291
Kancharla Mahidhar (CEO)

SPARKY AD
1 Rozova dolina Str, Ruse, 7000, Bulgaria
Tel.: (359) 82885400
Web Site: http://www.sparkygroup.com
Year Founded: 1907
SPRK—(BUL)
Sales Range: Less than $1 Million
Industrial Machinery Equipment Mfr
N.A.I.C.S.: 333248
Sofia Kirilova Argirova (Dir-IR)

SPARKY ELTOS AD
9 Kubrat Street, Lovech, 5500, Bulgaria
Tel.: (359) 68 600 550
Web Site: http://www.sparkygroup.com
Power Tool Mfr
N.A.I.C.S.: 333517
Sofia Kirilova Argirova (Dir-IR)

SPARQ SYSTEMS INC.
Innovation Park 945 Princess Street, PO Box 212, Kingston, K7L 0E9, ON, Canada
Tel.: (226) 750-9914
Web Site: https://www.sparqsys.com
SPRQ—(TSXV)
Rev.: $510,435
Assets: $8,047,185
Liabilities: $505,068
Net Worth: $7,542,117
Earnings: ($6,106,538)
Fiscal Year-end: 12/31/21
Asset Management Services
N.A.I.C.S.: 523940
Bryan Van Engelen (CEO & CFO)

SPARROW EARLY LEARNING PTY LIMITED
2/44 Borthwick Ave, Murarrie, 4172, QLD, Australia
Tel.: (61) 1300441441 AU
Web Site: https://www.sparrow.edu.au
Child Education & Care Services
N.A.I.C.S.: 624410

SPARTA AG
Ziegelhauser Landstrasse 3, 69120, Heidelberg, Germany
Tel.: (49) 6221649240
Web Site: https://www.sparta.de
Year Founded: 1995
SPT6—(DEU)
Rev.: $6,561,623
Assets: $195,305,418
Liabilities: $47,086,121
Net Worth: $148,219,296
Earnings: ($15,896,827)
Emp.: 2
Fiscal Year-end: 12/30/23
Financial Investment Services
N.A.I.C.S.: 523940
Jens-Martin Juettner (Member-Mgmt Bd)

Subsidiaries:

BETA Systems Software AG (1)
Alt-Moabit 90d, 10559, Berlin, Germany (75%)
Tel.: (49) 307261180
Web Site: https://www.betasystems.com
Rev.: $84,203,204
Assets: $70,426,906
Liabilities: $47,179,404
Net Worth: $23,247,502

AND PRIVATE COMPANIES

Earnings: $7,804,361
Emp.: 659
Fiscal Year-end: 09/30/2023
Infrastructure Software Publisher
N.A.I.C.S.: 513210
Heiko Wenzel-Schinzer *(Deputy Chm-Supervisory Bd)*

Subsidiary (Domestic):

Auconet GmbH (2)
Stromstrasse 5, 10555, Berlin, Germany
Tel.: (49) 302546900
Web Site: https://www.infraray.com
Information Technology Services
N.A.I.C.S.: 541519

Subsidiary (Non-US):

BETAnn Systems AB. (2)
Hornakersvagen 10, 18365, Taby, Sweden
Tel.: (46) 8 733 0045
Web Site: http://www.betasystems.com
Sales Range: $25-49.9 Million
Emp.: 5
Data Processing Services
N.A.I.C.S.: 518210

Subsidiary (Domestic):

Beta Systems DCI Software AG (2)
Alt-Moabit 90d, 10559, Berlin, Germany
Tel.: (49) 307261180
Web Site: http://www.betasystems-dci.com
Information Technology Services
N.A.I.C.S.: 541519
Wolfgang Schlaak *(Chm)*

Subsidiary (Domestic):

HORIZONT Software GmbH (3)
Schaufeleinstr 7, 80687, Munich, Germany
Tel.: (49) 895401620
Web Site: https://horizont-it.com
Emp.: 25
Software Development Services
N.A.I.C.S.: 541511
Josef Dirnberger *(Mng Dir)*

Subsidiary (Non-US):

Beta Systems EDV Software Ges.m.b.H. (2)
Spaces Square One Stiege 2 1 Stock Leopold-Ungar-Platz 2, 1190, Vienna, Austria
Tel.: (43) 12536216031
Web Site: http://www.betasystems.com
Sales Range: $25-49.9 Million
Emp.: 1
Application Software & Data Processing Services
N.A.I.C.S.: 518210

Beta Systems Software Espana, S.L. (2)
c/ Zurbano 73 6A Planta Esc Int Izq, 28010, Madrid, Spain
Tel.: (34) 913077675
Web Site: http://www.betasystems.com
Sales Range: $25-49.9 Million
Emp.: 2
Application Software & Data Processing Services
N.A.I.C.S.: 518210

Beta Systems Software France S.A.R.L. (2)
5 Avenue de Verdun, 94200, Ivry-sur-Seine, France
Tel.: (33) 143901740
Web Site: http://www.betasystems.com
Sales Range: $25-49.9 Million
Emp.: 8
Application Software & Data Processing Services
N.A.I.C.S.: 518210

Beta Systems Software Ltd. (2)
60 High Street, Chobham, GU24 8AA, Surrey, United Kingdom
Tel.: (44) 1189885175
Web Site: http://www.betasystems.com
Sales Range: $25-49.9 Million
Emp.: 6
Data Processing Services
N.A.I.C.S.: 518210
Gernot Sagl *(CEO)*

Beta Systems Software SPRL. (2)
Centre Monnet Avenue Jean Monnet 1, 1348, Louvain-la-Neuve, Belgium
Tel.: (32) 10230140
Web Site: http://www.betasystems.com
Sales Range: $25-49.9 Million
Emp.: 3
Application Software & Data Processing Services
N.A.I.C.S.: 541511

Beta Systems Software SRL (2)
Condominio C1 Via IV Novembre 92, 20021, Bollate, MI, Italy
Tel.: (39) 0233202251
Information Technology Services
N.A.I.C.S.: 541519
Gregorio Alampi *(Sls Mgr)*

Subsidiary (US):

Beta Systems of North America, Inc. (2)
8300 Greensboro Dr Ste L1-633, McLean, VA 22102
Tel.: (571) 348-4450
Application Software Development & Data Processing Services
N.A.I.C.S.: 541511
Guy Schroen *(VP-Sls-Americas & Gen Mgr)*

Subsidiary (Non-US):

Beta Systems Software of Canada, Inc. (3)
Suite 600 736 Eighth Avenue SW, Calgary, T2P 1H4, AB, Canada
Tel.: (403) 231-9800
Web Site: http://www.betasystems.com
Documents Data Processing Services
N.A.I.C.S.: 518210

Subsidiary (Domestic):

DETEC Decision Technology Software GmbH. (2)
Im Neugrund 16, 64521, Gross-Gerau, Germany
Tel.: (49) 615271230
Web Site: https://www.detec.de
Sales Range: $25-49.9 Million
Emp.: 35
Software Development Services
N.A.I.C.S.: 541511
Corry Homg *(Mgr)*

LYNET Kommunikation AG (2)
Niels-Bohr-Ring 15, 23568, Lubeck, Germany
Tel.: (49) 21173067300
Web Site: https://www.convotis.com
Emp.: 600
Information Technology Services
N.A.I.C.S.: 541519
Henning Hach *(CEO)*

PROXESS GmbH (2)
Untere Hauptstrasse 1 - 5, Rietheim-Weilheim, 78604, Tuttlingen, Germany
Tel.: (49) 746193530
Web Site: https://www.proxess.de
Information Technology Services
N.A.I.C.S.: 541519

SI Software Innovation GmbH. (2)
Europastrasse 3, Neustadt, 67433, Germany
Tel.: (49) 63214991500
Web Site: http://www.si-software.com
Sales Range: $25-49.9 Million
Emp.: 24
Application Software & Data Processing Services
N.A.I.C.S.: 518210
Andreas Kroeber *(Dir-Dev)*

Subsidiary (Non-US):

infinIT Codelab Sp. z o.o. (2)
Plac Brama Portowa 1, 70-225, Szczecin, Poland
Tel.: (48) 918199116
Web Site: https://www.codelab.eu
Information Technology Services
N.A.I.C.S.: 541519
Radoslaw Borek *(Mng Dir)*

Falkenstein Nebenwerte AG (1)
Brook 1, 20457, Hamburg, Germany
Tel.: (49) 04037411020
Web Site: https://www.falkenstein-ag.de

Sales Range: Less than $1 Million
Investment Services
N.A.I.C.S.: 523999
Christoph Schaefers *(Member-Mgmt Bd)*

SPARTA CAPITAL LTD.
1400 - 390 Bay Street, Toronto, M5H 2Y2, ON, Canada
Tel.: (905) 751-8004 AB
Web Site: https://www.spartagroup.ca
Year Founded: 1988
SAY—(TSXV)
Rev.: $7,118,829
Assets: $1,390,705
Liabilities: $2,346,774
Net Worth: ($956,070)
Earnings: ($56,718)
Fiscal Year-end: 09/30/23
Investment Services
N.A.I.C.S.: 523999
Peter Quattrociocchi *(Chm & CEO)*

Subsidiaries:

SuperNova Performance Technologies Ltd. (1)
390 Bay Street Suite 1202, Toronto, M5H 2Y2, ON, Canada
Tel.: (647) 560-4220
Web Site: http://www.supernovatech.info
Emissions Reduction Technologies Developer & Mfr
N.A.I.C.S.: 336390

SPARTAN CONTROLS LTD.
305 - 27 Street SE, Calgary, T2A 7V2, AB, Canada
Tel.: (403) 207-0700
Web Site: https://www.spartancontrols.com
Year Founded: 1963
Rev.: $117,880,648
Emp.: 1,000
Industrial Machinery & Equipment Distr
N.A.I.C.S.: 333248
Barry Blight *(VP)*

SPARTAN DELTA CORP.
Suite 1920 800 - 5th Avenue SW, Calgary, T2P 3T6, AB, Canada
Tel.: (403) 265-8011
Web Site: http://www.spartandeltacorp.com
4YJ0—(DEU)
Rev.: $492,918,927
Assets: $618,838,963
Liabilities: $294,351,062
Net Worth: $324,487,901
Earnings: ($500,725,358)
Fiscal Year-end: 12/31/23
Oil & Natural Gas Exploration
N.A.I.C.S.: 211120
Richard F. McHardy *(Chm)*

SPARTON RESOURCES INC.
81A Front Street E Suite 216, Toronto, M5E 1Z7, ON, Canada
Tel.: (647) 344-7734
Web Site: https://www.spartonres.ca
SPNRF—(OTCIQ)
Rev.: $720,458
Assets: $1,688,260
Liabilities: $426,909
Net Worth: $1,261,351
Earnings: ($251,732)
Fiscal Year-end: 12/31/23
Mineral Exploration Services
N.A.I.C.S.: 213114

Subsidiaries:

Edcor Drilling Services Inc. (1)
81A Front Street E Suite 216, Toronto, M5E 1Z7, ON, Canada
Tel.: (416) 716-5762
Web Site: https://www.edcor.ca
Exploration Drilling Services
N.A.I.C.S.: 238910

VStar Industries Limited (1)

SPARX GROUP CO., LTD.

The Chestnuts Pill Road, Abbots Leigh, Bristol, BS8 3QY, United Kingdom
Tel.: (44) 7859001200
Web Site: https://www.vstarindustries.co.uk
Construction Management Services
N.A.I.C.S.: 541330

SPARTOO SAS
41 rue Boissy d'Anglas, 75008, Paris, France
Tel.: (33) 8 9268 4447 FR
Web Site: http://www.spartoo.com
Year Founded: 2006
Emp.: 400
Online Shoe Retailer
N.A.I.C.S.: 455110
Boris Saragaglia *(Co-Founder & CEO)*

SPARX GROUP CO., LTD.
Shinagawa Season Terrace 6F 1-2-70 Konan, Minato-ku, Tokyo, 108-0075, Japan
Tel.: (81) 367119100
Web Site: https://www.sparxgroup.com
Year Founded: 1989
8739—(TKS)
Rev.: $109,051,780
Assets: $304,800,320
Liabilities: $97,120,730
Net Worth: $207,679,590
Earnings: $43,090,590
Emp.: 186
Fiscal Year-end: 03/31/24
Investment Advisory Services
N.A.I.C.S.: 523940
Masatoshi Fukami *(Deputy Pres & COO)*

Subsidiaries:

IJTT Co., Ltd. (1)
Yokohama Daiya Bldg 18F 1-7 Kinkocho, Kanagawa-ku, Yokohama, 221-0056, Kanagawa, Japan
Tel.: (81) 457775560
Web Site: http://www.ijtt-hd.co.jp
Rev.: $1,397,404,800
Assets: $1,277,914,880
Liabilities: $452,907,840
Net Worth: $825,007,040
Earnings: $27,365,360
Emp.: 4,097
Fiscal Year-end: 03/31/2022
Holding Company; Truck & Construction Vehicle Parts Mfr & Distr
N.A.I.C.S.: 551112
Masashi Harada *(Exec VP)*

Subsidiary (Domestic):

I Metal Technology Co., Ltd. (2)
4-2 Kitakandatsu-machi, Tsuchiura, 300-0015, Ibaraki, Japan
Tel.: (81) 298311788
Web Site: http://www.imetal.co.jp
Cast Iron Parts Mfr & Distr
N.A.I.C.S.: 331511

Subsidiary (Domestic):

I Metal Technology Co., Ltd. - Kitaibaraki Materials Processing Factory (3)
1130-6 Isohara, Isohara-cho, Kitaibaraki, 319-1541, Ibaraki, Japan
Tel.: (81) 293432500
Cast Iron Parts Mfr
N.A.I.C.S.: 331511

Plant (Domestic):

I Metal Technology Co., Ltd. - Kitakami-kita Factory (3)
2-106-6 Goto Waga-cho, Kitakami, 024-0335, Iwate, Japan
Tel.: (81) 197738501
Web Site: http://www.ijtt-hd.co.jp
Cast Iron Parts Mfr
N.A.I.C.S.: 331511

Subsidiary (Domestic):

Jidosha Buhin Kogyo Co., Ltd. (2)

SPARX GROUP CO., LTD.

SPARX Group Co., Ltd.—(Continued)

4-3-1 Kamigo, Ebina, 243-0434, Kanagawa, Japan
Tel.: (81) 462313111
Web Site: http://www.jbk.co.jp
Industrial & Automotive Diesel Engine & Engine Components Mfr
N.A.I.C.S.: 336310

Subsidiary (Domestic):

JM steel Co., Ltd. (3)
5-16 Nigatahonmachi 3-Chome, Kure, 737-0152, Hiroshima, Japan
Tel.: (81) 823791350
Automotive Component Mfr & Distr
N.A.I.C.S.: 336390

Subsidiary (Non-US):

Jibuhin (Thailand) Co., Ltd. (3)
Amata Nakorn Industrial Estate 700/14 M 6 KM 57 th Bangna-Trad Road, Tambol Nongmaidaeng Amphur Muang, Chon Buri, 20000, Chonburi, Thailand (89%)
Tel.: (66) 38213027
Web Site: http://www.jibuhin.co.th
Emp.: 543
Industrial & Automotive Diesel Engine Components Mfr
N.A.I.C.S.: 336310
Toshiaki Takakuwa (Mng Dir)

Subsidiary (Domestic):

Jidosha Buhin Kogyo Co., Ltd. - Moka Factory (3)
21-2 Matsuyama-cho, Moka, 321-4346, Tochigi, Japan
Tel.: (81) 285821151
Industrial & Automotive Diesel Engine & Engine Components Mfr
N.A.I.C.S.: 336310

Subsidiary (Non-US):

PT. Jibuhin Bakrie Indonesia (3)
Jl Maligi II Lot C-7D, KIIC Sukaluyu Industrial Area Teluk Jambe Timur, Karawang, 41361, West Java, Indonesia
Tel.: (62) 218904216
Industrial & Automotive Diesel Engine Components Mfr
N.A.I.C.S.: 336310

Subsidiary (Domestic):

TDF Corporation (2)
39 Honosaku Numabe Murata-cho, Shibata-gun, Miyagi, 989-1321, Japan
Tel.: (81) 224525411
Web Site: http://www.tdforge.co.jp
Forged Automotive Components Mfr & Distr
N.A.I.C.S.: 336390

SPARX Asia Investment Advisors Limited (1)
1706 17th Floor Central Plaza 18 Harbour Road, Wanchai, China (Hong Kong)
Tel.: (852) 31027500
Investment Management Service
N.A.I.C.S.: 523940

SPARX Asset Management Korea Co., Ltd. (1)
2nd Floor S-Tower 82 Saemunan-ro, Jongno-gu, Seoul, 03185, Korea (South) (70.1%)
Tel.: (82) 25701600
Emp.: 23
Investment Management Service
N.A.I.C.S.: 523940
Takeshi Suzuki (Co-CEO)

SPARX Green Energy & Technology Co., Ltd. (1)
6th Floor Shinagawa Season Terrace 1-2-70 Konan, Minato-ku, Tokyo, 108-0075, Japan
Tel.: (81) 367119150
Web Site: https://www.sget.co.jp
Power Generation & Renewable Energy Consulting Services
N.A.I.C.S.: 221118

SPASCIANI S.P.A.

Via Saronnino 72, 21040, Origgio, Italy
Tel.: (39) 019695181
Web Site: http://www.spasciani.com
Year Founded: 1892
Military Masks Mfr
N.A.I.C.S.: 928110
Andrea Spasciani (Area Mgr)

Subsidiaries:

NUEVA SIBOL S.L.U. (1)
Torrelarragoiti 2, 48170, Zamudio, Spain
Tel.: (34) 94 452 30 24
Web Site: http://www.sibol.es
Personal Protective Equipment Distr
N.A.I.C.S.: 423990

SPB CANADA INC.

6240 avenue du Parc, Montreal, H2V 4H7, QC, Canada
Tel.: (514) 273-0411
Web Site: http://www.spb.ca
Year Founded: 1903
Rev.: $96,000,000
Emp.: 600
Paper Box & Corrugated Box Mfr
N.A.I.C.S.: 322219
Andre Moisan (Pres)

SPC POWER CORPORATION

7th Floor Cebu Holdings Center Archbishop Reyes Avenue Cebu, Business Park, Cebu, 6000, Philippines
Tel.: (63) 22320377 PH
Web Site:
http://www.spcpowergroup.com
Year Founded: 1994
SPC—(PHI)
Rev.: $51,363,193
Assets: $215,326,279
Liabilities: $19,341,213
Net Worth: $195,985,066
Earnings: $24,765,596
Emp.: 387
Fiscal Year-end: 12/31/21
Electric Power Transmission Services
N.A.I.C.S.: 221122
Alfredo L. Henares (Chm & Treas)

SPCG PUBLIC COMPANY LIMITED

1 Capital Work Place Building 10th Floor Soi Jamjan, Klongton Nua Sub-District Wattana, Bangkok, 10110, Thailand
Tel.: (66) 20118111
Web Site: https://www.spcg.co.th
Year Founded: 1993
SPCG—(THA)
Rev.: $120,434,245
Assets: $697,597,354
Liabilities: $59,799,400
Net Worth: $637,797,954
Earnings: $57,622,818
Emp.: 122
Fiscal Year-end: 12/31/23
Roof Sheet Mfr
N.A.I.C.S.: 332322
Wandee Khunchornyakong (Chm, CEO & Acting Exec VP-Acctg & Fin)

Subsidiaries:

Solar Power Engineering Company Limited (1)
1 Capital Work Place Building 9th Floor, Soi Jamjan Klongton Nua Sub-District Wattana, Bangkok, 10110, Thailand
Tel.: (66) 2 011 8111
Web Site: https://www.spe.co.th
Solar Inverter Mfr & Distr
N.A.I.C.S.: 335999

Steel Roof Company Limited (1)
8/88 Moo 12 Soi King Kaew 11 King Kaew Road, Racha Thewa, Bang Phli, 10540, Samut Prakan, Thailand
Tel.: (66) 27502380
Web Site: https://www.steelroof.co.th
Metal Sheet Roof Mfr & Distr
N.A.I.C.S.: 332322

Steel and Solar Roof Company Limited (1)
8/88 Moo 12 Soi King-Kaew 11 King-Kaew Road, Rachathewa, Bang Phli, 10540, Samutprakarn, Thailand
Tel.: (66) 2750 2380
Web Site: http://www.steelsolarroof.com
Metal Roofing Sheet Distr
N.A.I.C.S.: 423330

SPEAKEASY CANNABIS CLUB LTD.

1520-6 Myers Creek Road West, Rock Creek, V0H 1Y0, BC, Canada
Tel.: (778) 738-2988 ON
Web Site:
https://www.speakeasygrowers.com
Year Founded: 2010
EASY—(CNSX)
Assets: $13,244,873
Liabilities: $2,381,550
Net Worth: $10,863,323
Earnings: ($10,416,773)
Fiscal Year-end: 07/31/19
Cannabis Product Mfr
N.A.I.C.S.: 325320
Merv Geen (Chm)

SPEARMINT RESOURCES INC.

2905 - 700 West Georgia Street, PO Box 10112, Vancouver, V7Y 1C6, BC, Canada
Tel.: (604) 646-6903 BC
Web Site:
https://www.spearmintresources.ca
Year Founded: 2009
SPMTF—(OTCIQ)
Rev.: $14,089
Assets: $3,258,919
Liabilities: $49,696
Net Worth: $3,209,222
Earnings: ($1,066,469)
Fiscal Year-end: 01/31/24
Mineral Exploration Services
N.A.I.C.S.: 212390
James Nelson (Pres & Sec)

SPECIAL PIPING MATERIALS LTD.

Broadway Globe Industrial Estate, Dukinfield, SK16 4UU, Cheshire, United Kingdom
Tel.: (44) 161 343 7005
Web Site:
http://www.specialpiping.com
Year Founded: 1989
Sales Range: $50-74.9 Million
Emp.: 51
Plumbing Material Whslr
N.A.I.C.S.: 423720

Subsidiaries:

Special Bar Materials LLC (1)
4615 Kennedy Commerce Dr, Houston, TX 77032
Tel.: (281) 921-1050
Web Site:
http://www.specialbarmaterials.com
Steel Products Mfr
N.A.I.C.S.: 331221
Bobby Feiertag (Mgr-Sls)

Special Piping Materials (Singapore) Pte Ltd (1)
43 Kian Teck Drive, Singapore, 628856, Singapore
Tel.: (65) 62648884
Piping Material Distr
N.A.I.C.S.: 423510

Special Piping Materials Australia Pty Ltd (1)
11 Purser Loop, Bassendean, 6054, WA, Australia
Tel.: (61) 892259500
Web Site:
http://www.specialpipingmaterials.com.au
Piping Material Distr
N.A.I.C.S.: 423510

INTERNATIONAL PUBLIC

Ian Hutchinson (Mng Dir)

Special Piping Materials Fze. (1)
PO Box 120667, Sharjah Airport Free Zone, Sharjah, United Arab Emirates
Tel.: (971) 505640523
Piping Material Distr
N.A.I.C.S.: 423510

SPECIALISED CLEANING & RESTORATION INDUSTRY ASSOCIATION, INC.

207 The Parade, Norwood, 5067, Australia
Tel.: (61) 1800 621 872
Web Site: http://www.scria.com.au
Operates & Administers Cleaning Association
N.A.I.C.S.: 813910
Gidon Kabaker (Pres)

Subsidiaries:

International Sanitary Supply Association, Inc. (1)
3300 Dundee Rd, Northbrook, IL 60062
Tel.: (847) 982-0800
Web Site: http://www.issa.com
Sanitary Supplies Whslr
N.A.I.C.S.: 423850
Lisa Veeck (Dir-Media Comm & Publ)

SPECIALIST COMPUTER HOLDINGS LTD.

James House Warwick Rd, Birmingham, B11 2LE, United Kingdom
Tel.: (44) 1217667000 UK
Web Site:
http://www.specialistcomputer.com
Year Founded: 1975
Sales Range: $1-4.9 Billion
Emp.: 6,000
Holding Company; Information Technology Software Asset Management Services
N.A.I.C.S.: 551112
Peter Rigby (Chm & CEO)

Subsidiaries:

Compu'Train BV (1)
Stationsplein 109, 3511 ED, Utrecht, Netherlands
Tel.: (31) 302315714
Sales Range: $25-49.9 Million
Emp.: 80
Information Systems
N.A.I.C.S.: 541512

Specialist Computer Centres (1)
Tolnasingel 2, 2411 PV, Bodegraven, Netherlands
Tel.: (31) 172634200
Web Site: http://www.miscosolutions.nl
Sales Range: $150-199.9 Million
Emp.: 250
Information Systems
N.A.I.C.S.: 541512
Patrick Van De Coolwik (Mng Dir)

Specialist Computer Centres (1)
James House Warwick Road, Birmingham, B11 2LE, United Kingdom
Tel.: (44) 1217667000
Web Site: http://www.scc.com
Sales Range: $100-124.9 Million
Emp.: 500
Information Technology Software Asset Management Services
N.A.I.C.S.: 541513

Subsidiary (Non-US):

Scc Services Romania Srl (2)
Niciman Street 2, Jud Iasi, 700521, Iasi, Romania
Tel.: (40) 33 24 03 030
Information Technology Consulting Services
N.A.I.C.S.: 541512
Adina Tapalaga (Dir-Gen)

SPECIALIST INVESTMENT PROPERTIES PLC

Burleigh Manor Peel Road, Douglas, IM1 5EP, Isle of Man
Tel.: (44) 1624 626586   IM
Web Site:
    http://www.specialistinvestment.com
Sales Range: $200-249.9 Million
Real Estate Services
N.A.I.C.S.: 531390

SPECIALITIES GROUP HOLDING CO. K.S.C.C.
Amghara Industrial Area Block 4 Plot 173, PO Box 23595, 13096, Kuwait, 13096, Kuwait
Tel.: (965) 1802550   KW
Web Site: https://www.spec-kw.com
Year Founded: 1988
SPEC—(KUW)
Rev.: $73,148,906
Assets: $133,371,123
Liabilities: $31,995,958
Net Worth: $101,375,165
Earnings: $4,825,424
Emp.: 350
Fiscal Year-end: 12/31/21
Holding Company
N.A.I.C.S.: 551112
Mubarak Woqayan Khalid Al Woqayan (CEO)

SPECIALITY RESTAURANTS LTD
B25 4th Floor Morya Landmark I Veera Industrial Estate, Off New Link Road Andheri West, Mumbai, 400053, India
Tel.: (91) 22837964
Web Site: https://www.speciality.co.in
SPECIALITY—(NSE)
Rev.: $22,786,355
Assets: $45,386,114
Liabilities: $26,913,705
Net Worth: $18,472,409
Earnings: ($4,005,456)
Emp.: 2,721
Fiscal Year-end: 03/31/21
Restaurant Owner & Operator
N.A.I.C.S.: 722511
Anjan Chatterjee (Chm & Mng Dir)

SPECIALIZED BUSINESS SYSTEM AD
24 Bessarabia St, 1517, Sofia, Bulgaria
Tel.: (359) 291945
Web Site: https://new.sbs.bg
Year Founded: 1990
SBS—(BUL)
Sales Range: Less than $1 Million
Computer Accessory Distr
N.A.I.C.S.: 423430

SPECIALIZED INVESTMENT COMPOUNDS COMPANY, PLC.
Alsitteen Street Sahab, PO Box 1, Amman, 11636, Jordan
Tel.: (962) 64027525
Web Site:
    http://www.altajamouat.com
Year Founded: 1994
SPIC—(AMM)
Rev.: $3,220,505
Assets: $21,826,678
Liabilities: $3,634,430
Net Worth: $18,192,248
Earnings: ($733,335)
Emp.: 35
Fiscal Year-end: 12/31/23
Real Estate Development Services
N.A.I.C.S.: 531120
Maen Hyasat (Fin Dir)

Subsidiaries:

Al Tajamouat Investment Company   (1)
41 Gizert Al Arab, Mohandseen, Giza, Egypt
Tel.: (20) 33038000
Web Site: http://www.altajamouategypt.com
Real Estate Development Services
N.A.I.C.S.: 531120

SPECIALIZED JORDANIAN INVESTMENTS COMPANY P.L.C.
Jabal Amman - City Center Building, PO Box 815442, Amman, 11180, Jordan
Tel.: (962) 64632166
SIJC—(AMM)
Rev.: $13,168
Assets: $2,234,145
Liabilities: $617,197
Net Worth: $1,616,948
Earnings: ($174,976)
Emp.: 4
Fiscal Year-end: 12/31/21
Financial Investment Services
N.A.I.C.S.: 523999
Yusri Barakat (Gen Mgr)

SPECIALIZED TRADING INVESTMENTS CO.
Abdulla Gosheh Street Building No 53, 6th Floor Office No 603, Amman, Jordan
Tel.: (962) 65868768
Web Site: https://www.sptic.com
Year Founded: 1992
SPTI—(AMM)
Rev.: $1,742,740
Assets: $2,158,475
Liabilities: $629,788
Net Worth: $1,528,687
Earnings: ($198,141)
Emp.: 9
Fiscal Year-end: 12/31/20
Steel Products Whslr
N.A.I.C.S.: 423510

SPECIALTY LIQUID TRANSPORTATION CORP.
610-700 West Pender Street, Vancouver, V6C 1G8, BC, Canada
Tel.: (713) 961-2795
Year Founded: 2017
SPQDF—(TSXV)
Sales Range: Less than $1 Million
Packaging Products Mfr
N.A.I.C.S.: 339991

SPECIALTY POWDERS HOLDINGS LTD.
46 Morley Road, Tonbridge, TN9 1RA, Kent, United Kingdom
Tel.: (44) 1732 362611   UK
Web Site: http://www.dryteccp.com
Powder Processing Servies
N.A.I.C.S.: 238990
Philip Bradlley (Gen Mgr)

Subsidiaries:

Phoenix Foods, Inc.   (1)
723 Cowan St, Nashville, TN 37207
Tel.: (615) 742-4989
Web Site: http://www.phoenixfoods.com
Poultry Processing
N.A.I.C.S.: 311615
Roy Lee Maguire (Pres)

Specialty Powders Limited   (1)
Unit 7 Monkswell Park Manse Lane, Knaresborough, HG5 8NQ, North Yorkshire, United Kingdom
Tel.: (44) 1423868411
Chemical Products Distr
N.A.I.C.S.: 424690
Paul Cannings (Gen Mgr)

SPECO LTD.
313 Soi-ro Soi-myeon, Eumseong, 369-872, Chungchongbuk-Do, Korea (South)
Tel.: (82) 438714711
Web Site: http://www.speco.co.kr
Year Founded: 1979
013810—(KRS)
Rev.: $23,838,043
Assets: $65,793,443
Liabilities: $26,879,402
Net Worth: $38,914,041
Earnings: $468,781
Emp.: 64
Fiscal Year-end: 12/31/22
Asphalt Mixing Machinery Mfr
N.A.I.C.S.: 333120
Kim Jae-Hyun (CEO)

Subsidiaries:

SPECO (SHANGHAI) MACHINERY CO., LTD.   (1)
No 28 Huajia Road, Songjang Industry Area, Shanghai, China
Tel.: (86) 21 6774 8003
Web Site: http://www.speco.sh.cn
Industrial Machinery Mfr
N.A.I.C.S.: 333248

SPECO WIND POWER S.A. DE. C.V.   (1)
Antiguo Camino a Hermanas 200 Fracc Estancias de San Juan Bautista, Monclova, 25733, Coahuila, Mexico
Tel.: (52) 866 636 1010
Industrial Machinery Mfr
N.A.I.C.S.: 333248

SPECSAVERS OPTICAL GROUP LIMITED
La Villiaze, Saint Andrew's, GY6 8YP, Guernsey
Tel.: (44) 345 2020 241
Web Site:
    http://www.specsavers.co.uk
Year Founded: 1984
Sales Range: $1-4.9 Billion
Emp.: 32,500
Eyeglass & Contact Lens Mfr
N.A.I.C.S.: 333310
Doug Perkins (Co-Founder & Chm)

Subsidiaries:

Specsavers Finland Oy   (1)
Neilikkatie 17, 01300, Vantaa, Finland
Tel.: (358) 102184380
Web Site: http://www.specsavers.fi
Emp.: 50
Contact Lens Mfr
N.A.I.C.S.: 339115

Specsavers International BV   (1)
Huizermaatweg 320-322, Huizen, 1276 LJ, Netherlands
Tel.: (31) 356288311
Web Site: http://www.specsavers.nl
Contact Lens Mfr
N.A.I.C.S.: 339115

Specsavers New Zealand Ltd   (1)
Unit A 26 Triton Drive Mairangi Bay, Auckland, 0632, New Zealand
Tel.: (64) 94755434
Web Site: http://www.specsavers.co.nz
Contact Lens Mfr
N.A.I.C.S.: 339115

Specsavers Norway AS   (1)
PO Box 6061, Etterstad, 0601, Oslo, Norway
Tel.: (47) 48309040
Web Site: http://www.specsavers.no
Emp.: 5,000
Contact Lens Mfr
N.A.I.C.S.: 339115
Stine Melfald (Mgr-Learning & Dev)

Specsavers Sweden AB   (1)
Torsgatan 5B, PO Box 205, Gothenburg, Sweden
Tel.: (46) 317719800
Web Site: http://www.specsavers.se
Contact Lens Mfr
N.A.I.C.S.: 339115

SPECTACLE VENTURES LIMITED
Office 1 1st Floor 22/24/26 Shipping House Kumpta Street, Fort, Mumbai, 400 001, India
Tel.: (91) 22 2265 6051
Web Site:
    http://www.spectacleindustries.com
Information Technology Services
N.A.I.C.S.: 541519
Shaikh Fazal Mehmood (Mng Dir & Compliance Officer)

SPECTEST SDN. BHD.
40 Jalan Desa Serdang 4, Serdang Lama, Serdang, 43300, Selangor, Malaysia
Tel.: (60) 389438850   MY
Web Site:
    http://www.spectest.com.my
Year Founded: 1992
Geotechnical Engineering Services
N.A.I.C.S.: 541330
Sieng Kai Lee (Founder & Mng Dir)

Subsidiaries:

Glostrext Technology Sdn. Bhd.   (1)
No 38 Jalan Desa Serdang 4, Serdang Lama, 43300, Serdang, Selangor, Malaysia
Tel.: (60) 389438850
Web Site: http://www.glostrext.com.my
Sales Range: $25-49.9 Million
Emp.: 20
Piles Instrumentation Installation & Testing Services
N.A.I.C.S.: 237990
Lee Sieng Kai (Mng Dir)

Subsidiary (Non-US):

Glostrext Technology (S) Pte. Ltd.   (2)
30 Kaki Bukit Road 3 01-02 Empire Techno Centre, Singapore, 417819, Singapore
Tel.: (65) 86469808
Web Site: http://www.glostrext.com.sg
Soil Investigation Services
N.A.I.C.S.: 541380
Li Hai Gang (Gen Mgr)

SPECTR INVEST LLC
2-Ya Zvenigorodskaya Street 13 Bldg 41, 123022, Moscow, Russia
Tel.: (7) 4959026909
Web Site: http://www.spectrinvest.ru
Sales Range: Less than $1 Million
Investment Brokerage Services
N.A.I.C.S.: 523150
Vladislav Valerievich Slitinsky (Gen Dir)

SPECTRA ALUMINUM PRODUCTS INC.
95 Reagens Industrial Parkway, Bradford, L3Z 2A4, ON, Canada
Tel.: (905) 778-8093
Web Site:
    https://www.spectraaluminum.com
Year Founded: 1978
Rev.: $25,330,800
Emp.: 140
Aluminium Products Mfr
N.A.I.C.S.: 331318
David Hudson (Pres & CEO)

SPECTRA INC.
41 Horner Avenue Unit 2, Toronto, M8Z 4X4, ON, Canada
Tel.: (416) 252-2355
Web Site:
    https://www.spectraproducts.ca
Year Founded: 1994
SPKTF—(OTCIQ)
Rev.: $1,568,329
Assets: $1,642,298
Liabilities: $261,367
Net Worth: $1,380,931
Earnings: $214,940
Fiscal Year-end: 12/31/23
Safety Equipment Mfr
N.A.I.C.S.: 335999

SPECTRA INC.

Spectra Inc.—(Continued)
Andrew J. Malion *(Chm & Pres)*

Subsidiaries:

Spectra Products Inc. (1)
41 Horner Avenue Unit 2, Toronto, M8Z 4X4, ON, Canada (100%)
Tel.: (416) 252-2355
Web Site: https://www.spectraproducts.ca
Automobile Parts Mfr
N.A.I.C.S.: 441330
Andre J. Malion *(Pres)*

SPECTRA INDUSTRIES LIMITED

Plot No 9 Spectra Compound Ramchandra Lane Extension Kanchpada II, Malad West, Mumbai, 400 064, India
Tel.: (91) 2228893933
Web Site:
 https://www.spectraindustries.co.in
Year Founded: 1992
513687—(BOM)
Rev.: $368
Assets: $1,290,521
Liabilities: $7,560,398
Net Worth: ($6,269,877)
Earnings: ($400,351)
Emp.: 1
Fiscal Year-end: 03/31/23
Automobile Mfr
N.A.I.C.S.: 336110
Jaidev Gupta *(Chm)*

SPECTRA PREMIUM INDUSTRIES INC.

1421 Rue Ampere, Boucherville, J4B 5Z5, QC, Canada
Tel.: (450) 641-3090
Web Site:
 http://www.spectrapremium.com
Year Founded: 1993
Sales Range: $200-249.9 Million
Emp.: 1,580
Automotive Component Mfr & Distr
N.A.I.C.S.: 336390
Jack Gordon *(Mgr-Sls-Midwest)*

Subsidiaries:

Spectra Premium (USA) Corp. (1)
3052 N Distribution Way, Greenfield, IN 46140-6602
Tel.: (317) 891-1700
Automotive Part Whslr
N.A.I.C.S.: 423120
Matt Verger *(VP-Sls & Mktg-Grasonville)*

Trimag Die Castings (1)
634 Magnesium Rd, Haley Station, K0J 1Y0, ON, Canada (90%)
Tel.: (613) 432-6668
Web Site: http://www.trimag.ca
Sales Range: $25-49.9 Million
Emp.: 100
High-Pressure Die Casting Products
N.A.I.C.S.: 331523

SPECTRACURE AB

Gasverksgatan 1, 222 29, Lund, Sweden
Tel.: (46) 709367412
Web Site: https://spectracure.com
SPEC—(OMX)
Rev.: $149,859
Assets: $15,212,566
Liabilities: $1,135,182
Net Worth: $14,077,383
Earnings: $2,377,139
Emp.: 13
Fiscal Year-end: 12/31/22
Medical Device Mfr
N.A.I.C.S.: 339112
Masoud Khayyami *(CEO)*

SPECTRAL MEDICAL INC.

135 The West Mall Unit 2, Toronto, M9C 1C2, ON, Canada
Tel.: (416) 626-3233
Web Site:
 https://www.spectraldx.com
Year Founded: 1991
SD4—(DEU)
Rev.: $1,231,440
Assets: $8,861,638
Liabilities: $10,725,419
Net Worth: ($1,863,781)
Earnings: ($8,310,556)
Emp.: 31
Fiscal Year-end: 12/31/22
Disease Management Medical Technology Developer; Reagents, Calibrators & Diagnostic Controls Supplier
N.A.I.C.S.: 541711
Anthony P. Bihl III *(Chm)*

SPECTRAMI DMCC

2402 Mazaya Business Avenue, PO Box 487840, BB1 Tower JLT, Dubai, United Arab Emirates
Tel.: (971) 44357209
Web Site: http://www.spectrami.com
Year Founded: 2011
Information Security Solutions
N.A.I.C.S.: 518210
Anand Choudha *(Pres & CEO)*

Subsidiaries:

SPECTRAMI GmbH (1)
Martin-Behaiim-Str 22, D-63263, Neu-Isenburg, Germany
Tel.: (49) 6102 7487 0
Web Site: http://www.de.spectrami.com
Management Consulting Services
N.A.I.C.S.: 541618

SPECTRE CAPITAL CORP.

409 Granville Street Suite 1000, Vancouver, V6C 1T2, BC, Canada
Tel.: (604) 602-0001
Year Founded: 2018
SOO.P—(TSXV)
Assets: $20
Liabilities: $103,489
Net Worth: ($103,469)
Earnings: ($796,055)
Fiscal Year-end: 08/31/23
Business Consulting Services
N.A.I.C.S.: 522299
Geoff Balderson *(CEO & CFO)*

SPECTRIS PLC

5th Floor Melbourne House 44-46 Aldwych, London, WC2B 4LL, Surrey, United Kingdom
Tel.: (44) 3713842030
Web Site: https://www.spectris.com
Year Founded: 1915
SEPJY—(OTCIQ)
Rev.: $1,675,586,973
Assets: $2,458,975,006
Liabilities: $645,165,362
Net Worth: $1,813,809,644
Earnings: $506,816,460
Emp.: 7,608
Fiscal Year-end: 12/31/22
Electronic Controls, Process Instrumentation & Filtration Systems Mfr
N.A.I.C.S.: 335314
Mark D. Williamson *(Chm)*

Subsidiaries:

Beta LaserMike, Inc. (1)
8001 Technology Blvd, Dayton, OH 45424 (100%)
Tel.: (937) 233-9535
Web Site: http://www.betalasermike.com
Laser Measuring Devices Mfr
N.A.I.C.S.: 332216

Subsidiary (Domestic):

DCM Industries, Inc. (2)
20900 Corsair Blvd, Hayward, CA 94545
Tel.: (510) 670-7200
Web Site: http://www.dcmindustries.com
Instrument Mfr for Measuring & Testing Electricity & Electrical Signals
N.A.I.C.S.: 334515

Bruel & Kjaer Sound & Vibration Measurement A/S (1)
Skodsborgvej 307, Naerum, 2850, Denmark (100%)
Tel.: (45) 800500
Web Site: http://www.bksv.com
Sales Range: $150-199.9 Million
Emp.: 500
Mfr of Motors & Generators
N.A.I.C.S.: 335312
Soren Holst *(Pres)*

Subsidiary (US):

Bruel & Kjaer (2)
2815 Colonnades Ct, Norcross, GA 30071-1588 (100%)
Tel.: (770) 209-6907
Web Site: http://www.bksv.com
Sales Range: $25-49.9 Million
Emp.: 100
Mfr of Instrumentation For Sound, Vibration, Thermal Environment & Gas Measurements, Signal Analysis & Medical Diagnostics
N.A.I.C.S.: 423830

Subsidiary (Domestic):

Bruel & Kjaer Sound & Vibration (2)
Skodsborgvej 307, 2850, Naerum, Denmark (100%)
Tel.: (45) 800500
Web Site: http://www.bksv.com
Sales Range: $75-99.9 Million
Emp.: 500
Mfr of Control Devices
N.A.I.C.S.: 334519

Subsidiary (Non-US):

Bruel & Kjaer UK Ltd (2)
Jarman Way, Royston, SG8 5BQ, Hertfordshire, United Kingdom
Tel.: (44) 1223389800
Web Site: http://www.bksv.com
Sales Range: $50-74.9 Million
Emp.: 100
High Speed Data Acquisition Systems & Realtime Signal Analyzers
N.A.I.C.S.: 334515

Subsidiary (Domestic):

Bruel & Kjaer Vibro (2)
Skodsborgvej 307 B, Naerum, 2850, Denmark
Tel.: (45) 45800500
Web Site: http://www.bkvibro.com
Sales Range: $25-49.9 Million
Emp.: 40
Mfr of Control Devices
N.A.I.C.S.: 334519
Torben Ekvall *(Pres)*

CMLabs Simulations Inc. (1)
645 Wellington 301, Montreal, H3C 1T2, QC, Canada
Tel.: (514) 287-1166
Web Site: https://www.cm-labs.com
Construction Management Services
N.A.I.C.S.: 236220

Capstone Technology Corp. (1)
14300 SE 1st St Ste 200, Vancouver, WA 98684
Tel.: (360) 619-5010
Web Site:
 http://www.capstonetechnology.com
Sales Range: $1-9.9 Million
Emp.: 43
Engineering Software & Programming Services
N.A.I.C.S.: 541330
Mike Myers *(CFO)*

Concept Life Sciences Integrated Discovery & Development Services Limited (1)
Frith Knoll Road, Chapel-en-le-Frith, High Peak, SK23 0PG, United Kingdom
Tel.: (44) 1298816700
Web Site:
 https://www.conceptlifesciences.com
Pharmaceutical Laboratory Services
N.A.I.C.S.: 541380

INTERNATIONAL PUBLIC

Concurrent Real-Time, Inc. (1)
800 NW 33rd St, Pompano Beach, FL 33064
Tel.: (954) 974-1700
Web Site: https://concurrent-rt.com
Software Development Services
N.A.I.C.S.: 541511

DISCOM Elektronische Systeme und Komponenten GmbH (1)
Maschmuhlenweg 81, 37081, Gottingen, Germany
Tel.: (49) 551548330
Web Site: https://discom.de
Software Development Services
N.A.I.C.S.: 541511

Dytran Instruments, Inc. (1)
21592 Marilla St, Chatsworth, CA 91311
Tel.: (818) 700-7818
Web Site: http://www.dytran.com
Sales Range: $1-9.9 Million
Emp.: 50
Electronic Components Mfr
N.A.I.C.S.: 334419
Anne Hackney *(CFO & VP)*

HBM FiberSensing SA (1)
Rua Vasconcelos Costa 277, 4470-640, Maia, Portugal
Tel.: (351) 229613010
Instrument & Displaying Product Mfr
N.A.I.C.S.: 334513

HBM Prenscia Inc. (1)
5210 E Williams Cir 2nd Fl Ste 240, Tucson, AZ 85711-4410
Tel.: (520) 886-0410
Web Site: http://www.hbmprenscia.com
Health Care Srvices
N.A.I.C.S.: 621999

HBM Prenscia Pte. Ltd. (1)
31 Kaki Bukit Road 3 06-04/05 Techlink, Singapore, 417818, Singapore
Tel.: (65) 62727422
Health Care Srvices
N.A.I.C.S.: 621999

HBM Prenscia s.p. z.o.o. (1)
Tel.: (48) 224366770
Health Care Srvices
N.A.I.C.S.: 621999

Hottinger Baldwin (Suzhou) Electronic Measurement Technology Ltd. (1)
106 Heng Shan Road, Suzhou, 215009, Jiangsu, China
Tel.: (86) 51268247776
Instrument & Displaying Product Mfr
N.A.I.C.S.: 334513
Fang Chen *(Dir-WT & R&D)*

Hottinger Baldwin Messtechnik GmbH (1)
Im Tiefen See 45, 64293, Darmstadt, Germany (100%)
Tel.: (49) 61518030
Web Site: http://www.hbm.com
Measuring Devices
N.A.I.C.S.: 334519
Andreas Huellhorst *(CEO)*

Subsidiary (Non-US):

HBM Danmark ApS (2)
Nydamsvej 19 D, 8362, Horning, Denmark
Tel.: (45) 87680500
Web Site: http://www.hbm.com
Products & Services for Measurement Applications
N.A.I.C.S.: 334519
Peter Dalum *(Sls Engr)*

HBM France SAS (2)
46 rue du Champoreux, BP 60076, 91540, Mennecy, Cedex, France
Tel.: (33) 1 699 063 70
Web Site: http://www.hbm.com
Products & Services for Measurement Applications
N.A.I.C.S.: 334519

HBM Iberica, S. L. U. (2)
Plaza de la Encina 10-11 Nucleo 3 1 A Tres Cantos, 28760, Madrid, Spain
Tel.: (34) 918062610
Web Site: http://www.hbm.com
Products & Services for Measurement Applications

AND PRIVATE COMPANIES — SPECTRIS PLC

N.A.I.C.S.: 334519
Sergio Adanero *(Mgr-Sls)*

HBM Italia s.r.l. (2)
Via Pordenone 8, 20132, Milan, Italy
Tel.: (39) 0245471616
Web Site: http://www.hbm.com
Products & Services for Measurement Applications
N.A.I.C.S.: 334519
Gian Luca Marengo *(Gen Mgr-Sls)*

HBM Norge AS (2)
Rosenholmveien 25, 1414, Trollasen, Norway
Tel.: (47) 48300700
Web Site: http://www.hbm.com
Products & Services for Measurement Applications
N.A.I.C.S.: 334519
Bjarne Hauge *(Sls Engr)*

HBM United Kingdom Limited (2)
Millbrook Proving Ground Station Lane, Millbrook, Bedford, MK45 2RA, Beds, United Kingdom
Tel.: (44) 1525304980
Web Site: http://www.hbm.com
Test & Measurement Research, Sales & Mfr
N.A.I.C.S.: 334515
Brian Dabell *(Pres)*

Hottinger Baldwin Measurement (Suzhou) Co. Ltd. (2)
106 Heng Shan Rd, Suzhou, 215009, Jiangsu, China
Tel.: (86) 51268247776
Web Site: http://www.hbm.com
Data Acquisition & Analysis
N.A.I.C.S.: 541519

Subsidiary (US):

Hottinger Baldwin Measurement Inc. (2)
19 Bartlett St, Marlborough, MA 01752
Tel.: (508) 485-7400
Web Site: http://www.hbm.com
Data Acquisition & Analysis
N.A.I.C.S.: 541519

Subsidiary (Domestic):

HBM nCode Federal LLC (3)
26555 Evergreen Rd Ste 700, Southfield, MI 48076
Tel.: (248) 350-8300
Web Site: http://www.ncode.com
Software Consultancy & Supply
N.A.I.C.S.: 541511

The Omnicon Group, Inc. (3)
50 Engineers Rd, Hauppauge, NY 11788
Tel.: (631) 223-7043
Web Site: http://www.omnicongroup.com
Hardware & Software Engineering Services
N.A.I.C.S.: 541519
Karen J. Frank *(Exec VP)*

Subsidiary (Non-US):

Hottinger Baldwin Messtechnik AG (2)
Chriesbaumstrasse 6, Volketswil, 8604, Switzerland
Tel.: (41) 449436080
Sales Range: $25-49.9 Million
Emp.: 8
Products & Services for Measurement Applications
N.A.I.C.S.: 334519
Juergen Kirsche *(Head-Sls)*

Hottinger Baldwin Messtechnik GmbH (2)
Lembockgasse 63/2, A-1230, Vienna, Austria
Tel.: (43) 186584410
Web Site: http://www.hbm.com
Products & Services for Measurement Applications
N.A.I.C.S.: 334519
Walter Weilinger *(Branch Mgr-Sls)*

Hottinger Bruel & Kjaer Austria GmbH (1)
Lembockgasse 63/2, 1230, Vienna, Austria
Tel.: (43) 186584410
Measuring Instrument Mfr & Distr
N.A.I.C.S.: 334513

Hottinger Bruel & Kjaer Benelux B.V. (1)
Schutweg 15a, 5145 NP, Waalwijk, Netherlands
Tel.: (31) 416286040
Measuring Instrument Mfr & Distr
N.A.I.C.S.: 334513

Hottinger Bruel & Kjaer Co., Ltd. (1)
106 Heng Shan Road, Suzhou, 215009, Jiangsu, China
Tel.: (86) 51268247776
Control & Measurement Product Mfr
N.A.I.C.S.: 334519

Hottinger Bruel & Kjaer GmbH (1)
Im Tiefen See 45, 64293, Darmstadt, Germany
Tel.: (49) 61518030
Measuring Instrument Mfr & Distr
N.A.I.C.S.: 334513

Hottinger Bruel & Kjaer Iberica, S.L.U. (1)
C/ Teide 5, San Sebastian de los Reyes, 28703, Madrid, Spain
Tel.: (34) 916590820
Measuring Instrument Mfr & Distr
N.A.I.C.S.: 334513

Hottinger Bruel & Kjaer Italy S.R.L. (1)
Via Pordenone 8, 20132, Milan, MI, Italy
Tel.: (39) 025768061
Measuring Instrument Mfr & Distr
N.A.I.C.S.: 334513

Hottinger Bruel & Kjaer Norway AS (1)
Rosenholmveien 25, 1414, Trollasen, Norway
Tel.: (47) 67792770
Measuring Instrument Mfr & Distr
N.A.I.C.S.: 334513

Hottinger Bruel & Kjaer Poland Sp. z.o.o. (1)
Aleje Jerozolimskie 181A, 02-222, Warsaw, Poland
Tel.: (48) 228589392
Measuring Instrument Mfr & Distr
N.A.I.C.S.: 334513

Hottinger Bruel & Kjaer UK Limited (1)
Jarman Way, Royston, SG8 5BQ, Hertfordshire, United Kingdom
Tel.: (44) 1223389800
Measuring Instrument Mfr & Distr
N.A.I.C.S.: 334513

LORD Corporation MicroStrain Sensing Systems (1)
459 Hurricane Ln Ste 102, Williston, VT 05495
Tel.: (802) 862-6629
Web Site: http://www.microstrain.com
Sales Range: $1-9.9 Million
Emp.: 3,000
Electronic Sensor Components Mfr
N.A.I.C.S.: 334419

Malvern Instruments Ltd (1)
Enigma Business Park Grovewood Rd, Malvern, WR14 1XZ, Worcestershire, United Kingdom (100%)
Tel.: (44) 1684892456
Web Site: http://www.malvern.com
Sales Range: $100-124.9 Million
Emp.: 360
Mfr of Control Instruments
N.A.I.C.S.: 334513

Malvern Panalytical (Pty.) Limited (1)
Unit 4 Bush Hill Office Park Jan Frederick Avenue, Randpark Ridge, Randburg, 2169, Gauteng, South Africa
Tel.: (27) 115770880
Laboratory Instrument Mfr & Distr
N.A.I.C.S.: 334516

Malvern Panalytical B.V. (1)
Tel.: (31) 402766660
Measurement Instrument Equipment Mfr
N.A.I.C.S.: 334515

Malvern Panalytical GmbH (1)
Tel.: (49) 56157420
Measurement Instrument Equipment Mfr

N.A.I.C.S.: 334515

Malvern Panalytical Inc. (1)
Tel.: (508) 768-6400
Measurement Instrument Equipment Mfr
N.A.I.C.S.: 334515

Malvern Panalytical Limited (1)
Enigma Business Park Grovewood Road, Malvern, WR14 1XZ, United Kingdom
Tel.: (44) 1684892456
Web Site: https://www.malvernpanalytical.com
Pharmaceutical Instrument Mfr
N.A.I.C.S.: 325412

Malvern Panalytical Nordic AB (1)
Tel.: (46) 18552455
Measurement Instrument Equipment Mfr
N.A.I.C.S.: 334515

Malvern Panalytical S.A.S. (1)
Tel.: (33) 169351808
Measurement Instrument Equipment Mfr
N.A.I.C.S.: 334515

Malvern Panalytical srl (1)
Tel.: (39) 0392434501
Measurement Instrument Equipment Mfr
N.A.I.C.S.: 334515

Malvern-Aimil Instruments Pvt Limited (1)
Naimex House A-8 Mathura Road, Mohan Co-operative Industrial Estate, New Delhi, 110 044, India
Tel.: (91) 1161310200
Measurement Instrument Equipment Mfr
N.A.I.C.S.: 334515

Millbrook Revolutionary Engineering GmbH (1)
Hermann-Kohl-Strasse 7, 28199, Bremen, Germany
Tel.: (49) 4219601485
Measuring & Instrument Testing Mfr
N.A.I.C.S.: 334515
Marco Anlauf *(Mgr-Sls Europe)*

Millbrook Special Vehicles Limited (1)
Millbrook, Bedford, MK45 2JQ, United Kingdom
Tel.: (44) 1525404242
Web Site: http://www.millbrookspecialvehicles.co.uk
Automotive Engineering Services
N.A.I.C.S.: 541330
Kirsty Andrew *(Mng Dir)*

N-TRON, Corp. (1)
3101 International Dr Bldg 6, Mobile, AL 36606
Tel.: (251) 342-2164
Web Site: http://www.n-tron.com
Sales Range: $10-24.9 Million
Emp.: 60
Mfr & Designer of Industrial Ethernet Products
N.A.I.C.S.: 334413

NDC Infrared Engineering Inc. (1)
5314 N Irwindale Ave, Irwindale, CA 91706-2089 (100%)
Tel.: (626) 960-3300
Web Site: http://www.ndcinfrared.com
Sales Range: $25-49.9 Million
Emp.: 85
Measurement, Control & Laboratory Analysis Devices Wholesaler
N.A.I.C.S.: 334513
Terry Patterson *(VP-Global Customer Care-Sensors, Sys & Metals)*

PANalytical B.V. (1)
Lelyweg 1, 7602 EA, Almelo, Netherlands (100%)
Tel.: (31) 546534444
Web Site: http://www.panalytical.com
Sales Range: $150-199.9 Million
Emp.: 450
Instrumentation & Software for X-ray Diffractometry & X-ray Fluorescence Spectrometry Supplier
N.A.I.C.S.: 423450

Subsidiary (US):

Analytical Spectral Devices, Inc. (2)
2555 55th St Ste 100, Boulder, CO 80301
Tel.: (303) 444-6522

Web Site: http://www.asdi.com
Sales Range: $1-9.9 Million
Emp.: 40
Measuring & Controlling Device Mfr
N.A.I.C.S.: 334519

Subsidiary (Non-US):

PANalytical, Inc. (2)
4995 Levy St, Saint Laurent, H4R 2N9, QC, Canada (100%)
Tel.: (514) 956-2132
Web Site: http://www.panalytical.com
Sales Range: $25-49.9 Million
Emp.: 9
Mfr of Electrical Appliances
N.A.I.C.S.: 423620

Particle Measuring Systems S.R.L. (1)
Via di Grotte Portella 34, 00044, Frascati, Italy
Tel.: (39) 0690530130
Measuring Instrument Mfr & Distr
N.A.I.C.S.: 334513

Particle Measuring Systems, Inc. (1)
5475 Airport Blvd, Boulder, CO 80301-2339 (100%)
Tel.: (303) 443-7100
Web Site: https://www.pmeasuring.com
Sales Range: $50-74.9 Million
Emp.: 160
Measuring Device Mfr
N.A.I.C.S.: 334516
Amy Allen *(CFO)*

Servomex Group Ltd (1)
Jarvis Brook, Crowborough, TN6 3FB, East Sussex, United Kingdom (100%)
Tel.: (44) 1892652181
Web Site: https://www.servomex.com
Sales Range: $50-74.9 Million
Emp.: 200
Mfr of Gas Measuring Devices
N.A.I.C.S.: 334519

Subsidiary (Non-US):

Servomex Asia Pacific Ltd (2)
13F-1 NO 128 Sec 3 Min Sheng E Road, Chung Shan N Rd, Taipei, Taiwan (100%)
Tel.: (886) 225462988558
Web Site: http://www.servomex.com
Sales Range: $25-49.9 Million
Emp.: 14
Mfr of Gas Measuring Devices
N.A.I.C.S.: 334519

Servomex BV (2) (100%)
Tel.: (31) 1892652181
Sales Range: $25-49.9 Million
Emp.: 15
Mfr of Gas Measuring Devices
N.A.I.C.S.: 334519

Servomex Inc (2) (100%)
Tel.: (281) 295-5800
Sales Range: $25-49.9 Million
Emp.: 40
Mfr of Gas Measuring Devices
N.A.I.C.S.: 423490

Servomex S.A. (2) (100%)
Tel.: (33) 149462250
Sales Range: $25-49.9 Million
Emp.: 9
Mfr of Gas Measuring Devices
N.A.I.C.S.: 334519

Servomex Middle East LLC (1)
PO Box 147939, Abu Dhabi, United Arab Emirates
Tel.: (971) 25056638
Software Development Services
N.A.I.C.S.: 541511

Spectraseis Inc. (1)
1900 West Loop S Ste 1425, Houston, TX 77027
Tel.: (403) 668-6812
Web Site: http://www.spectraseis.com
Seismic Monitoring Services
N.A.I.C.S.: 541360

Spectris Canada Inc. (1)
82 Boul Arthur-Sauve, Saint-Eustache, J7R 2H7, QC, Canada

SPECTRIS PLC

Spectris Plc—(Continued)
Web Site: https://www.omega.ca
Control & Measurement Product Mfr
N.A.I.C.S.: 334519

Spectris Company Limited (1)
Tel.: (81) 445893068
Web Site: https://www.spectris.co.jp
Sales Range: $50-74.9 Million
Emp.: 181
Electronic Component Mfr & Distr
N.A.I.C.S.: 334419

Spectris Do Brasil Instrumentos Eletronicos Ltda. (1)
Rua Luis Correia de Melo 92-25 Andar, Santo Amaro, Sao Paulo, CEP 04726-220, SP, Brazil
Tel.: (55) 1149508608
Measuring Instrument Mfr & Distr
N.A.I.C.S.: 334513

VI-grade GmbH
Im Tiefen See 45, 64293, Darmstadt, Germany
Tel.: (49) 61518702834
Web Site: https://www.vi-grade.com
Automotive Spare Parts Mfr & Distr
N.A.I.C.S.: 336390

VI-grade S.R.L. (1)
Via Galileo Galilei 42, 33010, Tavagnacco, UD, Italy
Tel.: (39) 0432689151
Automotive Spare Parts Mfr & Distr
N.A.I.C.S.: 336390

VI-grade Systems GmbH (1)
Im Tiefen See 45, 64293, Darmstadt, Germany
Tel.: (49) 61518702834
Software Development Services
N.A.I.C.S.: 541511

SPECTROGON AB
Tillverkarvagen 1, 187 66, Taby, Sweden
Tel.: (46) 86382800 SE
Web Site: http://www.spectrogon.com
Year Founded: 1980
Sales Range: $1-9.9 Million
Emp.: 60
Optical Instrument & Lense Mfr
N.A.I.C.S.: 333310
Petter Jacobsson (CEO)

Subsidiaries:

Spectrogon UK, Ltd. (1)
Whitworth Rd, Southfield Industrial Estate, Glenrothes, KY62TF, United Kingdom (100%)
Tel.: (44) 1592770000
Web Site: http://www.spectrogon.com
Photographic Film Paper Plate & Chemical Mfr
N.A.I.C.S.: 325992
Fred Kumesu (Mgr)

Spectrogon US, Inc. (1)
24B Hill Rd, Parsippany, NJ 07054-1001
Tel.: (973) 331-1191
Web Site: http://www.spectrogon.com
Interference Filters Mfr
N.A.I.C.S.: 333310
Sam Ponzo (VP & Gen Mgr)

SPECTRUM ELECTRICAL INDUSTRIES LIMITED
Gat No 139/1 and 139/2 Umala, Jalgaon, 425003, Maharashtra, India
Tel.: (91) 2572210192
Web Site: https://www.spectrum-india.com
Year Founded: 2008
SPECTRUM—(NSE)
Rev.: $30,968,083
Assets: $30,626,593
Liabilities: $19,586,224
Net Worth: $11,040,369
Earnings: $1,013,189
Emp.: 632
Fiscal Year-end: 03/31/23
Electric Equipment Mfr
N.A.I.C.S.: 335311

Deepak Chaudhari (Chm & Mng Dir)

SPECTRUM FOODS LIMITED
Surya House L-3 B II Krishna Marg C-Scheme, Jaipur, 302001, India
Tel.: (91) 1412379483
Web Site: https://www.suryasalt.com
531982—(BOM)
Rev.: $1,686,840
Assets: $2,337,766
Liabilities: $2,356,418
Net Worth: ($18,652)
Earnings: ($257,757)
Fiscal Year-end: 03/31/21
Salt Whslr
N.A.I.C.S.: 424490
Girdhar Gopal Saboo (CEO & Mng Dir)

SPECTRUM TECHNOLOGIES PLC
Western Avenue, Bridgend, CF31 3RT, Mid Glamorgan, United Kingdom
Tel.: (44) 1656655437 UK
Web Site: http://www.spectrumtech.com
Year Founded: 1989
Sales Range: $10-24.9 Million
Emp.: 65
Development & Mfr of Laser Equipment for Manufacturing Processes
N.A.I.C.S.: 333992
Peter H. Dickinson (Chm & CEO)

Subsidiaries:

Shanghai Imperial Laser Systems Trading Co. Ltd. (1)
Room 905 Building 4 500 Jianyun Road, Pudong District, Shanghai, 201318, China
Tel.: (86) 2160523365
Web Site: http://www.spectrumtech.cn
Industrial Supplies Whslr
N.A.I.C.S.: 423840

Spectrum Technologies USA, Inc. (1)
Fossil Creek Tech Ctr 3934 Sandshell Dr, Fort Worth, TX 76137
Tel.: (817) 232-2373
Web Site: http://www.spectrumtech.com
Laser Wire Processing Technologies Mfr & Distr
N.A.I.C.S.: 335999
Steve Hill (Mgr)

SPECTUR LIMITED
12 Fargo Way, Welshpool, Perth, 6106, WA, Australia
Tel.: (61) 1300802960 AU
Web Site: https://www.spectur.com.au
SP3—(ASX)
Rev.: $5,465,994
Assets: $3,047,853
Liabilities: $2,994,952
Net Worth: $52,901
Earnings: ($1,721,573)
Emp.: 26
Fiscal Year-end: 06/30/24
Security Surveillance Product Distr
N.A.I.C.S.: 423420
Suzie Jayne Foreman (Sec)

SPECTUS MANUFACTURING LIMITED
Telford, Hurdsfield Industrial Estate, Stafford, TF3 3AT, United Kingdom
Tel.: (44) 1625420400 UK
Web Site: http://www.spectus.co.uk
Year Founded: 2009
Holding Company
N.A.I.C.S.: 551112
Ian Blackhurst (Chm & CEO)

Subsidiaries:

Spectus Window Systems Limited (1)
Stafford Park 6, Telford, TF3 3AT, Shropshire, United Kingdom (40%)
Tel.: (44) 1952283344
Web Site: http://www.spectussystems.com
Sales Range: $25-49.9 Million
Emp.: 120
Plastic Window Slider Systems Mfr
N.A.I.C.S.: 326199
Peter Colclough (Dir-Production)

SPEDITION ANSORGE GMBH & CO.KG
Gewerbepark 2, Biessenhofen, 87640, Germany
Tel.: (49) 83429130
Web Site: http://www.ansorge-logistik.de
Year Founded: 1961
Rev.: $65,005,068
Emp.: 410
Logistics & Warehousing Services
N.A.I.C.S.: 493110
Wolfgang Thoma (Mng Dir)

Subsidiaries:

Ansorge Logistica s.r.l. (1)
Via Spluga 130, 23015, Sondrio, Italy
Tel.: (39) 0342687239
Emp.: 25
Logistics Consulting Servies
N.A.I.C.S.: 541614
Sebastian Thelen (Branch Mgr)

SPEDITION SERVICES LTD
Spedition House 1-2 Blenheim Court Brook Way, Leatherhead, KT22 7NA, Surrey, United Kingdom
Tel.: (44) 1372 384900
Web Site: http://www.spedition.co.uk
Year Founded: 1990
Sales Range: $25-49.9 Million
Emp.: 40
Freight Transportation Arrangement
N.A.I.C.S.: 488510
Jens Rastorp (Mng Dir)

SPEECH MODULES LTD.
33 Yavetz St, Tel Aviv, 6525832, Israel
Tel.: (972) 3 794 8845
Web Site: http://www.speechmodules.com
Sales Range: $1-9.9 Million
Information Technology Services
N.A.I.C.S.: 541512

SPEED RABBIT PIZZA SA
28 Garden Street, 59000, Lille, France
Tel.: (33) 366211880
Web Site: https://www.speedrabbitpizza.com
MLSRP—(EUR)
Sales Range: $1-9.9 Million
Pizza Delivery Shop Operator
N.A.I.C.S.: 722513
Daniel Sommer (Chm & CEO)

SPEED TECH CORP.
No 568 Sec 1 Minsheng N Road Kweishan Hsiang, Taoyuan, 33393, Taiwan
Tel.: (886) 32120088
Web Site: https://www.speedtech.com.tw
Year Founded: 1990
5457—(TPE)
Rev.: $602,172,404
Assets: $698,190,132
Liabilities: $402,194,885
Net Worth: $295,995,247
Earnings: $49,282,431
Fiscal Year-end: 12/31/22
Electronic Components Mfr
N.A.I.C.S.: 334419
Chen-Lung Tsai (Chm & CEO)

INTERNATIONAL PUBLIC

SPEEDAGE COMMERCIALS LIMITED
Bhansali House A-5 Off Veera Desai Road, Andheri West, Mumbai, 400 053, India
Tel.: (91) 2226731779
Web Site: http://www.speedagecommercials.net
Year Founded: 1984
512291—(BOM)
Rev.: $310,437
Assets: $10,478,053
Liabilities: $1,846
Net Worth: $10,476,206
Earnings: $218,068
Fiscal Year-end: 03/31/23
Financial Investment Management Services
N.A.I.C.S.: 523940
S. Prakash Singh (Co-CEO)

SPEEDCAST INTERNATIONAL LIMITED
Unit 4F Level 1 Lakes Business Park 12 Lord Street, Botany, 2019, NSW, Australia
Tel.: (61) 9531 7555 AU
Web Site: http://www.speedcast.com
Year Founded: 1989
Rev.: $623,095,000
Assets: $1,220,018,000
Liabilities: $938,258,000
Net Worth: $281,760,000
Earnings: $1,928,000
Emp.: 1,500
Fiscal Year-end: 12/31/18
Network & Satellite Communications Services
N.A.I.C.S.: 517410
Stephen Wilks (Chm)

Subsidiaries:

Globecomm Systems Inc. (1)
45 Oser Ave, Hauppauge, NY 11788
Tel.: (631) 231-9800
Web Site: http://www.globecommsystems.com
Rev.: $319,614,000
Assets: $308,241,000
Liabilities: $63,788,000
Net Worth: $244,453,000
Earnings: $15,239,000
Emp.: 220
Fiscal Year-end: 06/30/2013
Satellite-Based Network Solutions
N.A.I.C.S.: 334220
Paul J. Johnson (Sr VP-Strategic Mktg & Corp Bus Dev)

Subsidiary (Domestic):

Cachendo LLC (2)
9115-K Whiskey Bottom Rd, Laurel, MD 20723
Tel.: (240) 553-9477
Web Site: http://www.cachendo.com
Sales Range: $50-74.9 Million
Technology Consulting Services
N.A.I.C.S.: 541690
Alan Pashkowitz (Bus Mgr)

ComSource Inc. (2)
8430 Gas House Pike Ste B, Frederick, MD 21701
Tel.: (240) 379-1700
Web Site: http://www.comsourceinc.com
Engineering Services, Software Development & Equipment Evaluation for Telecommunications Industry
N.A.I.C.S.: 513210
F. Byron Parker (Pres)

Subsidiary (Non-US):

Globecomm Asia Pte. Ltd (2)
33 Ubi Avenue 3 08-40 Vertex Tower A, Singapore, 408868, Singapore
Tel.: (65) 6732 1930
Sales Range: $10-24.9 Million
Emp.: 7
Voice & Data Communication Services
N.A.I.C.S.: 517810
Trevor Whitworth (Sr VP-Sls & Mktg)

AND PRIVATE COMPANIES

Globecomm Europe BV (2)
Plantweg 8, 8256 SH, Biddinghuizen, Netherlands
Tel.: (31) 321335100
Web Site:
http://www.globecommsystems.com
Sales Range: $10-24.9 Million
Emp.: 50
Satellite Telecommunications
N.A.I.C.S.: 517410
Albert Jan Post *(VP-Engrg)*

Subsidiary (Domestic):

Globecomm Network Services Corporation (2)
45 Oser Ave, Hauppauge, NY 11788
Tel.: (631) 231-9800
Web Site: http://www.globecomm.com
Sales Range: $100-124.9 Million
Emp.: 220
Broadband Satellite-Delivered Internet & Intranet Access, Web Hosting & Network Management Services
N.A.I.C.S.: 517810
Jason Jurenek *(CFO)*

Subsidiary (Domestic):

Globecomm Services Maryland LLC (3)
9115 Whiskey Bottom Rd Ste H, Savage, MD 20723
Tel.: (301) 490-6414
Sales Range: $25-49.9 Million
Designs, Assembles & Installs Satellite Ground Systems & Networks
N.A.I.C.S.: 334220

Subsidiary (Non-US):

Globecomm Systems SA Proprietary Ltd (2)
1st Floor Building Four Esplanade Road Central Park Century City, Cape Town, 7441, South Africa
Tel.: (27) 214883940
Web Site:
http://www.globecommsystems.com
Emp.: 16
Network Communication Solutions
N.A.I.C.S.: 517810

Subsidiary (Domestic):

Telaurus Communications LLC (2)
210 Malapardis Rd Ste 202, Cedar Knolls, NJ 07927
Tel.: (973) 889-8990
Sales Range: $10-24.9 Million
Emp.: 26
Voice & Data Communication Services
N.A.I.C.S.: 517810
Malcolm McMaster *(Pres)*

NewCom International, Inc. (1)
15590 NW 15th Ave, Miami, FL 33169
Tel.: (305) 627-6000
Web Site:
http://www.newcominternational.com
Sales Range: $1-9.9 Million
Emp.: 13
Voice, Video, Data & Content Solutions
N.A.I.C.S.: 517410
Jaime Dickinson *(Pres)*

Speedcast Communications, Inc. (1)
4400 S Sam Houston Pkwy E, Houston, TX 77048
Tel.: (832) 668-2300
Web Site: http://www.speedcast.com
Fiber-Optic Network, Microwave & Satellite Communications Services for Energy, Government & Maritime Companies
N.A.I.C.S.: 517121
Jimmie Keith Johnson *(VP)*

UltiSat, Inc. (1)
708 Quince Orchard Rd Ste 120, Gaithersburg, MD 20878
Tel.: (240) 243-5100
Satellite Communication Infrastructure & Services
N.A.I.C.S.: 517410
Miguel Hernandez *(CFO)*

Wideband Interactive Networks via Satellites Ltd. (1)
219 - 221 Parilja Street, Santa Vennera, SVR 1936, Malta

Tel.: (356) 2149 8680
Web Site: http://www.winsystems.com
Telecommunication Servicesb
N.A.I.C.S.: 517810
Tony Mejlaq *(Chm)*

SPEEDPROP GLOBAL, INC.
190 Toa Payoh Lorong 6 02-514, Singapore, 310190, Singapore
Tel.: (65) 6681 6667 NV
Year Founded: 2015
Emp.: 3
Investment Services
N.A.I.C.S.: 523999
Leong Kwok Heng *(CEO)*

SPEEDY AD
ul Abagar 22 Sofiya Siti Lodzhistik Park Adm sgrada et 5, 5th Floor, Sofia, Bulgaria
Tel.: (359) 70017001
Web Site: http://www.speedy.bg
Year Founded: 1998
SPDY—(BUL)
Sales Range: Less than $1 Million
Courier & Postal Services
N.A.I.C.S.: 492110
Krasimir Tahichev *(Dir-IR)*

SPEEDY GLOBAL HOLDINGS LIMITED
Flat B 13/F Wing Chai Industrial Building 27-29 Ng Fong Street, San Po Kong, Kowloon, China (Hong Kong)
Tel.: (852) 35831111
Web Site: http://www.speedy-global.com
0540—(HKG)
Rev.: $71,629,118
Assets: $40,781,768
Liabilities: $31,164,315
Net Worth: $9,617,453
Earnings: ($4,393,395)
Emp.: 1,171
Fiscal Year-end: 12/31/22
Apparel Mfr & Distr
N.A.I.C.S.: 315990
Chih Shen Huang *(Chm & CEO)*

Subsidiaries:

Jointex Garment Manufactory Limited (1)
Rm C 13/F Wing Chai Industrial Bldg San Po Kong, Hong Kong, China (Hong Kong)
Tel.: (852) 23230636
Apparel Distr
N.A.I.C.S.: 424350
Yiu Wen Chang *(Dir-Mktg)*

SPEEDY HIRE PLC
Chase House 16 The Parks, Newton-le-Willows, WA12 0JQ, Merseyside, United Kingdom
Tel.: (44) 8005003993
Web Site:
https://www.speedyservices.com
SDY—(LSE)
Rev.: $525,166,096
Assets: $659,444,604
Liabilities: $352,056,796
Net Worth: $307,387,808
Earnings: $29,326,752
Emp.: 3,554
Fiscal Year-end: 03/31/22
Tool & Building Equipment Rental
N.A.I.C.S.: 444110
Russell Down *(CEO)*

Subsidiaries:

Allen Investments Limited (1)
Chase House 16 The Parks, Newton-Le-Willows Merseyside, Liverpool, United Kingdom (100%)
Tel.: (44) 1942720000
Sales Range: $50-74.9 Million
Emp.: 90
Real Estate Property Lessors

N.A.I.C.S.: 531190

Speedy Asset Services Limited (1)
Chase House 16 The Parks, Newton-le-Willows, WA12 0JQ, Merseyside, United Kingdom
Tel.: (44) 1942 277 132
Construction Equipment & Tools Hiring Services
N.A.I.C.S.: 532412

Speedy Generators Limited (1)
3 Telford Rd Green Zone 3B, Bayton Rd Industrial Estate, Exhall, CV7 98S, United Kingdom (100%)
Tel.: (44) 2476361333
Web Site: http://www.speedyhire.co.uk
Sales Range: $75-99.9 Million
Emp.: 55
Electric Power Generation
N.A.I.C.S.: 221118
Gary Lowerson *(Gen Mgr)*

Speedy Hire (Ireland) Limited (1)
Unit 2 Glen Industrial Estate Broombridge Road, Dublin, Ireland
Tel.: (353) 1 830 1101
Web Site: http://www.speedyhire.com
Emp.: 20
Equipment & Tools Hiring Services
N.A.I.C.S.: 532490
Paul Carroll *(Gen Mgr)*

Speedy Hire Centres (Northern) Limited (1)
Ashton House 1 The Parks, Lakeside Bldg Alexandra Park Newton-le-Willows, Saint Helens, WA12 0KQ, United Kingdom (100%)
Tel.: (44) 1942327333
Web Site: http://www.speedyhire.com
Commercial & Industrial Machinery & Equipment Rental & Leasing
N.A.I.C.S.: 532490

Speedy Hire Centres (Southern) Limited (1)
73 Wide Bargate, Boston, PE21 6SG, Boston, United Kingdom
Tel.: (44) 1205 366333
Web Site: http://www.speedyhire.plc.uk
Emp.: 4
Equipment & Tools Hiring Services
N.A.I.C.S.: 532490

Speedy Hire Centres (Western) Limited (1)
Clarence Road, Clarence House, BS20NR, Bristol, United Kingdom (100%)
Tel.: (44) 1179555588
Sales Range: $50-74.9 Million
Emp.: 25
Commercial & Industrial Machinery & Equipment Rental & Leasing
N.A.I.C.S.: 532490

Speedy Hire Direct Limited (1)
Newmarket House 20 The Parks, Merseyside, Newton-le-Willows, WA12 0JQ, United Kingdom (100%)
Tel.: (44) 1942277000
Web Site: http://www.speedyservices.com
Sales Range: $75-99.9 Million
Emp.: 140
Commercial & Industrial Machinery & Equipment Rental & Leasing
N.A.I.C.S.: 532490
Keith Ferguson *(Mng Dir)*

Speedy International Asset Services Equipment Rental LLC (1)
PO Box 1436, Boushar, 112, Muscat, Oman
Tel.: (968) 93212446
Emp.: 45
Equipment Rental & Leasing Services
N.A.I.C.S.: 532490
Karim Jaffer *(Dir-Fin)*

Speedy International Asset Services LLC (1)
106 Town Center Commercial Area 1st Section 1st Floor Shop 104, New Cairo, Helwan, Egypt
Tel.: (20) 1 99 958 124
Web Site: http://www.speedyservices.com
Sales Range: $25-49.9 Million
Emp.: 30
Equipment Rental & Leasing Services
N.A.I.C.S.: 532490

SPEEE, INC.

Speedy LCH Generators Limited (1)
37 Downiebrae Road, Rutherglen, Glasgow, G73 1PW, Lanarkshire, United Kingdom
Tel.: (44) 1360440764
Sales Range: $25-49.9 Million
Emp.: 48
Equipment & Tools Hiring Services
N.A.I.C.S.: 532490

Speedy LGH Limited (1)
Bolton Road Atherton, M469YZ, Manchester, United Kingdom (100%)
Tel.: (44) 1942878081
Web Site: http://www.lgh.co.uk
Commercial & Industrial Machinery & Equipment Rental & Leasing
N.A.I.C.S.: 532490

Speedy Lifting Limited (1)
Pentagon Island Nottingham Road, Derby, DE21 6BW, Derbyshire, United Kingdom (100%)
Tel.: (44) 1332200330
Web Site: http://www.speedyservices.com
Sales Range: $25-49.9 Million
Emp.: 30
Commercial & Industrial Machinery & Equipment Rental & Leasing
N.A.I.C.S.: 532490

Speedy Power Limited (1)
Fleet House Pye Close, Old Boston Trading Estate, WA119SJ, Haydock, United Kingdom (100%)
Tel.: (44) 1942723700
Sales Range: $25-49.9 Million
Emp.: 30
Industrial Machinery & Equipment Whslr
N.A.I.C.S.: 423830
Andy Carter *(Mng Dir)*

Speedy Pumps Limited (1)
Fleet House Pye Close, Old Boston Trading Estate, Haydock, WA11 9SJ, United Kingdom (100%)
Tel.: (44) 1942723700
Sales Range: $25-49.9 Million
Emp.: 30
Electrical Equipment & Component Mfr
N.A.I.C.S.: 335999

Speedy Support Services Limited (1)
Chase House 16 The Parks, Newton-Le-Willows, Liverpool, WA12 0JQ, United Kingdom (100%)
Tel.: (44) 1942720000
Web Site: http://www.speedyservices.com
Sales Range: $25-49.9 Million
Emp.: 120
Support Services
N.A.I.C.S.: 561990
Mark Rogerson *(CEO)*

Speedy Transport Limited (1)
Newmarket Ho 20 The Parks, Newton-le-Willows, WA12 0JQ, Merseyside, United Kingdom
Tel.: (44) 1942 720000
Emp.: 200
Equipment Rental & Leasing Services
N.A.I.C.S.: 532490

Waterford Hire Services Limited (1)
Unit 4 Kingsmeadow Retail Park Inner Ring Road, Waterford, X91 TH24, Ireland
Tel.: (353) 5 183 3333
Web Site: http://www.waterfordservices.com
Sales Range: $50-74.9 Million
Emp.: 8
Industrial Equipment Rental & Leasing Services
N.A.I.C.S.: 532490

SPEEE, INC.
3-2-1 Roppongi Roppongi Grand Tower 35th and 39th floors, Minato-ku, Tokyo, 106-0032, Japan
Tel.: (81) 351141943
Web Site: https://www.speee.jp
Year Founded: 2007
4499—(TKS)
Rev.: $96,459,450
Assets: $80,081,550
Liabilities: $44,319,590
Net Worth: $35,761,960
Earnings: ($7,387,780)

Speee, Inc.—(Continued)
Fiscal Year-end: 09/30/23
Digital Marketing Services
N.A.I.C.S.: 541870
Otsuka Hideki (Chm & Pres)

SPEIRS GROUP LIMITED
Speirs Foods Hair Street, PO Box 108, Marton, New Zealand
Tel.: (64) 6 327 5700
Web Site: http://www.speirs.co.nz
Rev.: $10,773,466
Assets: $5,852,683
Liabilities: $3,065,691
Net Worth: $2,786,992
Earnings: $94,463
Fiscal Year-end: 06/30/19
Fresh Food Mfr & Whslr
N.A.I.C.S.: 424480
Lee Simpson (Sec)

Subsidiaries:

Speirs Foods Limited (1)
Hair Street, PO Box 108, Marton, 4710, Manawatu-Wanganui, New Zealand
Tel.: (64) 63275700
Sales Range: $25-49.9 Million
Emp.: 100
Salads Mfr & Distr
N.A.I.C.S.: 311991
Chris Newton (Gen Mgr)

SPEKTA A.D.
Kralja Milutina 13, Belgrade, Serbia
Tel.: (381) 11 2195 073
Year Founded: 1964
Sales Range: Less than $1 Million
Technical Testing & Analysis Services
N.A.I.C.S.: 541990

SPEKTAR INVEST AD
Vojvode Misica 37, 35250, Paracin, Serbia
Tel.: (381) 35 562 819
Web Site: http://www.spektarinvest.rs
Year Founded: 1992
SPIN—(BEL)
Sales Range: Less than $1 Million
Emp.: 18
Construction Engineering Services
N.A.I.C.S.: 541330
Vladan Pekic (Exec Dir)

SPENDA LIMITED
Part G Building B The Garden Office Park 355 Scarborough Beach Road, Osborne Park, 6017, WA, Australia
Tel.: (61) 1300682521 AU
Web Site: https://spenda.co
Year Founded: 2001
SPX—(ASX)
Rev.: $1,720,841
Assets: $41,624,338
Liabilities: $8,372,455
Net Worth: $33,251,883
Earnings: ($38,494,312)
Fiscal Year-end: 06/30/22
Mobile Marketing Services
N.A.I.C.S.: 541613
Adrian Floate (Mng Dir & Exec Dir)

SPENTA INTERNATIONAL LTD.
Plot No 13-16 Dewan Industrial Estate Village Navali, Palghar, 401404, Maharashtra, India
Tel.: (91) 2525254932
Web Site: https://www.spentasocks.com
Year Founded: 1994
526161—(BOM)
Rev.: $6,425,672
Assets: $6,704,210
Liabilities: $3,425,285
Net Worth: $3,278,925
Earnings: $137,391
Emp.: 75
Fiscal Year-end: 03/31/23

Textile Products & Socks Distr
N.A.I.C.S.: 314999
Sanjay S. Gadodia (Chm & CEO)

SPEQTA AB
Kungsgatan 64 3tr, 111 22, Stockholm, Sweden
Tel.: (46) 840026340
Web Site: http://www.speqta.com
Year Founded: 2010
SPEQTA—(OMX)
Rev.: $1,348,731
Assets: $12,746,448
Liabilities: $1,045,267
Net Worth: $11,701,181
Earnings: $6,794,234
Emp.: 76
Fiscal Year-end: 12/31/22
Website Owner & Operator
N.A.I.C.S.: 518210
Andereas Friis (Chief Strategy Officer)

SPEX SERVICES LTD.
Dunnottar House Howe Moss Drive Kirkhill Industrial Estate, Dyce, AB21 0FN, Aberdeen, United Kingdom
Tel.: (44) 1224 727840
Web Site: http://www.spex-group.com
Year Founded: 2009
Sales Range: $10-24.9 Million
Emp.: 80
Oil Engineering Services
N.A.I.C.S.: 213112
Jamie Oag (CEO)

SPEXIS LTD
Hegenheimermattweg 125, CH-4123, Allschwil, Switzerland
Tel.: (41) 615671600
Web Site: https://spexisbio.com
Year Founded: 1996
SPEX—(SWX)
Rev.: $1,753,034
Assets: $69,013,363
Liabilities: $14,642,990
Net Worth: $54,370,372
Earnings: ($33,479,849)
Fiscal Year-end: 12/31/23
Pharmaceuticals Product Mfr
N.A.I.C.S.: 325412
Dennis A. Ausiello (Vice Chm)

Subsidiaries:

EnBiotix, Inc. (1)
197 W Springfield St, Boston, MA 02118-3406
Tel.: (508) 400-1856
Research & Development in Biotechnology
N.A.I.C.S.: 541714
Diane Joseph-Mccarthy (VP-Chemistry & Computational Science)

SPEY RESOURCES CORP.
1315 Moody Avenue, North Vancouver, V7L 3T5, BC, Canada
Tel.: (604) 637-6373
Web Site: http://www.speyresources.ca
Year Founded: 2017
Assets: $102,778
Liabilities: $14,934
Net Worth: $87,844
Earnings: ($237,194)
Fiscal Year-end: 11/30/19
Metal Exploration Services
N.A.I.C.S.: 213114
Phillip Thomas (CEO)

SPEYMILL DEUTSCHLAND IMMOBILIEN COMPANY PLC
Clinch's House Lord Street, Douglas, IM99 1RZ, Isle of Man
Tel.: (44) 1624 683229
Web Site: http://www.speymilldeutsche.com
Sales Range: $150-199.9 Million

Real Estate Investment Services
N.A.I.C.S.: 525990
Nigel Caine (CFO)

SPG CO., LTD.
45 Cheongneung-daero 289 beon-gil, Namdong-gu, Incheon, Korea (South)
Tel.: (82) 328208200
Web Site: https://www.spg.co.kr
Year Founded: 1991
058610—(KRS)
Rev.: $337,845,412
Assets: $271,781,702
Liabilities: $108,032,752
Net Worth: $163,748,950
Earnings: $15,096,563
Emp.: 418
Fiscal Year-end: 12/31/22
Motor Mfr
N.A.I.C.S.: 335312
Young Gil Yeo (CEO)

Subsidiaries:

SPG USA, Inc. (1)
1726 Wright Blvd, Schaumburg, IL 60193
Tel.: (847) 439-4949
Web Site: http://www.spg-usa.com
Geared Motor Mfr
N.A.I.C.S.: 333612

SPHERA FRANCHISE GROUP SA
239 Calea Dorobantilor 2nd floor, 10567, Bucharest, Romania
Tel.: (40) 212011757
Web Site: https://spheragroup.com
Year Founded: 1997
SFG—(BUC)
Rev.: $319,100,801
Assets: $152,324,233
Liabilities: $121,348,363
Net Worth: $30,975,869
Earnings: $15,583,284
Emp.: 5,152
Fiscal Year-end: 12/31/23
Restaurant Operators
N.A.I.C.S.: 722511
Georgios Argentopoulos (CEO)

SPHERE 3D CORPORATION
895 Don Mills Road Bldg 2 Suite 900, Toronto, M3C 1W3, ON, Canada
Tel.: (858) 571-5555 ON
Web Site: http://www.sphere3d.com
Year Founded: 2007
ANY—(NASDAQ)
Rev.: $6,077,000
Assets: $83,016,000
Liabilities: $11,984,000
Net Worth: $71,032,000
Earnings: ($192,801,000)
Emp.: 27
Fiscal Year-end: 12/31/22
Computer Technology Services
N.A.I.C.S.: 541512
Kurt L. Kalbfleisch (CFO & Sr VP)

Subsidiaries:

Guangzhou Tandberg Electronic Components Co. Ltd. (1)
No 2 Zhongyuan Rd Pingshan Village No 1 Shibi Street Panyu District, Guangzhou, Guangdong, China
Tel.: (86) 2039169001
Computer Technology Services
N.A.I.C.S.: 541512

Sphere 3D Inc. (1)
895 Don Mills Road Bldg 2 Suite 900, Toronto, M3C 1W3, ON, Canada
Tel.: (416) 749-5999
Web Site: http://www.sphere3d.com
3D Virtualization Services
N.A.I.C.S.: 518210

SPHERE GLOBAL SERVICES LIMITED
A-52 Road No 70 Journalist Colony,

Jubilee Hills, Hyderabad, 500 033, Andhra Pradesh, India
Tel.: (91) 4023552284
Web Site: https://www.sphereglobal.in
532172—(BOM)
Business Management Services
N.A.I.C.S.: 561499
S. Sudha Kiran Reddy (Mng Dir)

Subsidiaries:

Adroit Infotech Private Limited (1)
Office No 304 3rd Floor Pentagon 1, Magarpatta City Hadapsar, Pune, 411013, Maharashtra, India
Tel.: (91) 2067258700
Web Site: http://www.adroitinfotech.com
Information Technology Development Services
N.A.I.C.S.: 541519
S. Sudhakiran Reddy (Mng Dir)

SPHERE POWER INC.
309 58 Wangsimni-ro Seongdong-gu, Seoul, Korea (South)
Tel.: (82) 25452818
Web Site: https://www.prostemics.com
Year Founded: 2005
203690—(KRS)
Rev.: $20,383,483
Assets: $39,484,867
Liabilities: $31,947,672
Net Worth: $7,537,195
Earnings: ($4,265,017)
Emp.: 73
Fiscal Year-end: 12/31/22
Investment Services
N.A.I.C.S.: 523999
Jong Lee Won (CEO)

SPHERE SA
3 rue Scheffer, 75116, Paris, France
Tel.: (33) 153652300
Web Site: http://www.sphere.eu
Rev.: $21,000,000
Emp.: 750
Household Wraps & Waste Collection Packaging Producer
N.A.I.C.S.: 326112
Daniel Fouquet (Gen Mgr)

Subsidiaries:

BIOTEC Biologische Naturverpackungen GmbH & Co. KG (1)
Werner-Heisenberg-Strasse 32, Emmerich am Rhein, 46446, Germany
Tel.: (49) 282292510
Web Site: http://www.biotec.de
Emp.: 35
Starch-Based Polymer Packaging Mfr
N.A.I.C.S.: 322220
Peter Brunk (Mng Dir)

SPHERE BELGIUM S.A. (1)
Avenue Louise 222 Louisahas Bruxelles, Brussels, Belgium
Tel.: (32) 2 647 53 25
Web Site: http://www.sphere-belgium.be
Plastic Product Mfr & Distr
N.A.I.C.S.: 326111

SPHERE CONSUMER PRODUCTS plc (1)
Unit 15 Bridge Bank Close Yew Tree Way, Stone Cross Park, Golborne, WA3 3JD, United Kingdom
Tel.: (44) 1942 528 130
Web Site: http://www.sphere-uk.eu
Plastic Product Mfr & Distr
N.A.I.C.S.: 326111
Hugh McAulay (Mng Dir)

SPHERE GERMANY GmbH (1)
Hansemann strasse 1, 41468, Neuss, Germany
Tel.: (49) 2131 403 86 00
Web Site: http://www.sphere-germany.de
Plastic Product Mfr & Distr
N.A.I.C.S.: 326111

SPHERE GROUP SPAIN S.L. (1)
P I El Aguila Av Miguel Servet s/n, Utebo, 50180, Zaragoza, Spain

Tel.: (34) 976 792 030
Web Site: http://www.sphere-spain.es
Plastic Product Mfr & Distr
N.A.I.C.S.: 326111
Isabel Cortes *(Mgr-Fin)*

SPHERE NEDERLAND B.V. (1)
Postbus 11, 7770 AA, Hardenberg, Netherlands
Tel.: (31) 523 208500
Web Site: http://www.sphere-nederland.nl
Emp.: 80
Plastic Product Mfr & Distr
N.A.I.C.S.: 326111
Lex Van Den Elst *(CEO)*

SPHERE PROFESSIONAL UK Ltd. (1)
South Park Business Centre 310 Green Lane Suite 11, 1st Floor, Ilford, IG1 1SF, United Kingdom
Tel.: (44) 208 553 4563
Plastic Product Mfr & Distr
N.A.I.C.S.: 326111

SPHERIA EMERGING COMPANIES LIMITED
Level 25 Australia Square Tower 264 George Street, Sydney, 2000, NSW, Australia
Tel.: (61) 433489870   AU
Web Site:
https://www.spheria.com.au
Year Founded: 2017
SEC—(ASX)
Rev.: $8,072,917
Assets: $90,473,424
Liabilities: $90,384,011
Net Worth: $89,412
Earnings: $5,070,780
Fiscal Year-end: 06/30/24
Investment Management Service
N.A.I.C.S.: 525910
Calvin Kwok *(Sec)*

SPHINX INVESTMENT CORP.
Evagorou 31 2nd Fl Office 21, 1066, Nicosia, Cyprus
Tel.: (357) 22010610   MH
Investment Services
N.A.I.C.S.: 523999

SPHINX RESOURCES LTD.
1000 De La Gauchetiere Suite 2100, Montreal, H3B 4W5, QC, Canada
Tel.: (514) 979-4746   BC
Web Site:
http://www.sphinxresources.ca
Year Founded: 2005
SFX—(DEU)
Rev.: $132
Assets: $199,903
Liabilities: $183,548
Net Worth: $16,355
Earnings: ($433,558)
Fiscal Year-end: 02/28/21
Zinc, Copper & Nickel Mining Services
N.A.I.C.S.: 212230
Jeremie Ryan *(Pres & CEO)*

SPI ENERGY CO., LTD.
1128 11/F No 52 Hung To Road, Kwun Tong, Kowloon, China (Hong Kong)
Tel.: (852) 22916020   Ky
Web Site: http://www.spigroups.com
Year Founded: 2015
SPI—(NASDAQ)
Rev.: $177,518,000
Assets: $231,095,000
Liabilities: $213,223,000
Net Worth: $17,872,000
Earnings: ($33,421,000)
Emp.: 316
Fiscal Year-end: 12/31/22
Solar Power Systems Mfr & Installer
N.A.I.C.S.: 333414
Xiaofeng Peng *(Chm & CEO)*

Subsidiaries:

International Assembly Solutions, Limited (1)
A18 Lian He Industrial Park Nan Yue Village, Long Gang, Shenzhen, China
Tel.: (86) 755 89901332
Web Site: http://www.intlassembly.com
Electronic Cable & Parts Mfr
N.A.I.C.S.: 334419

SPI China (1)
Kenan 2, Haidian, Beijing, 100090, China
Tel.: (86) 10 5982 2143
Sales Range: $25-49.9 Million
Emp.: 5
Business Support Services
N.A.I.C.S.: 561499

Solar Green Technology S.p.A. (1)
via Procaccini 48, 20154, Milan, Italy   (70%)
Tel.: (39) 0287242052
Web Site: http://www.solargreentech.it
Engineering Services; Design, Installation & Construction of Photovoltaic Plants
N.A.I.C.S.: 541330

SPIC DONGFANG NEW ENERGY CORP.
No 161 Jianhua South Street, Yuhua District, Shijiazhuang, 050031, Hebei, China
Tel.: (86) 31185053913
000958—(SSE)
Rev.: $858,320,939
Assets: $6,485,055,347
Liabilities: $2,552,091,067
Net Worth: $3,932,964,280
Earnings: $140,296,623
Emp.: 2,303
Fiscal Year-end: 12/31/22
Power Generation Services
N.A.I.C.S.: 221118

SPICE ISLANDS APPARELS LIMITED
Unit 43-48 Bhandup Industrial Pannalal Silk Mills Compound, L B S Marg Bhandup West, Mumbai, 400 078, India
Tel.: (91) 2225968069   In
Web Site:
http://www.spiceislandsapparels.in
Year Founded: 1988
526827—(BOM)
Rev.: $129,441
Assets: $233,502
Liabilities: $308,426
Net Worth: ($74,925)
Earnings: ($14,663)
Emp.: 2
Fiscal Year-end: 03/31/23
Woven & Knitted Garment Mfr
N.A.I.C.S.: 313210
Umesh Katre *(Chm, Mng Dir & Compliance Officer)*

SPICEJET LTD.
319 Udyog Vihar Phase IV, Gurgaon, 122 016, Haryana, India
Tel.: (91) 1243913939
Web Site: https://www.spicejet.com
Year Founded: 1984
500285—(BOM)
Rev.: $1,180,011,870
Assets: $931,667,526
Liabilities: $1,633,141,418
Net Worth: ($701,473,892)
Earnings: ($181,397,638)
Emp.: 7,131
Fiscal Year-end: 03/31/23
Oil Transportation Services
N.A.I.C.S.: 488190
Ajay Singh *(Chm & Mng Dir)*

Subsidiaries:

SpiceJet Technic Private Limited (1)
319 Phase-IV Udyog Vihar, Gurgaon, 122016, Haryana, India

Tel.: (91) 1243913939
Web Site: https://www.spicejet-technic.com
Emp.: 100
Aircraft Maintenance Services
N.A.I.C.S.: 488190

SPICY ENTERTAINMENT & MEDIA LIMITED
68 R K Chatterjee Road Kasba Rash Behari Connector 3rd Floor, Kolkata, 700 042, West Bengal, India
Tel.: (91) 9163452925
Web Site: http://www.spicyy.in
Year Founded: 2012
540084—(BOM)
Rev.: $537,869
Assets: $17,010,827
Liabilities: $14,965,086
Net Worth: $2,045,741
Earnings: $4,568
Emp.: 4
Fiscal Year-end: 03/31/22
Film Production Services
N.A.I.C.S.: 512191
Anindya Bikas Datta *(Mng Dir)*

SPIDER N. PETSIOS & SONS S.A.
Industrial Area of Ioannina, 45 500, Ioannina, Greece
Tel.: (30) 26510 25514
Web Site: http://www.spidersa.com
Year Founded: 1972
Emp.: 300
Metal Furniture & Other Products Mfr
N.A.I.C.S.: 337126
Konstantinos N. Petsios *(Chm & Mng Dir)*

Subsidiaries:

Spider Italia S.R.L. (1)
Strada Provinciale 231, Modugno-bitonto Km 1+ 200, 70026, Modugno, BA, Italy
Tel.: (39) 08056 11107
Web Site: http://www.spideritalia.it
Metal Products Mfr
N.A.I.C.S.: 332999

Spider N. Petsios & Sons S.A. - Kardamitsia Factory (1)
5th km National Road Igoumenitsa, 45 500, Ioannina, Greece
Tel.: (30) 26510 24446
Metal Container & Armed Force Equipment Mfr
N.A.I.C.S.: 332439

Spider UK Ltd. (1)
Chilton Airfield Great Waldingfield Road, Sudbury, CO10 0RB, Suffolk, United Kingdom
Tel.: (44) 1787 375302
Web Site: http://www.spideruk.co.uk
Metal Products Mfr
N.A.I.C.S.: 332999

SPIDERPLUS & CO.
Sumitomo Real Estate Toranomon Tower 27th floor 2-2-1 Toranomon, Minato-ku, Tokyo, 105-0001, Japan
Tel.: (81) 367092830
Web Site:
https://www.spiderplus.co.jp
Year Founded: 1997
4192—(TKS)
Application Development Services
N.A.I.C.S.: 541511
Kenji Ito *(CEO)*

SPIE NUCLEAIRE SAS
Campus Saint-Christophe, 95865, Cergy-Pontoise, France
Tel.: (33) 134418383
Web Site: http://www.spie.com
Year Founded: 1999
Emp.: 2,100
Nuclear Services Provider
N.A.I.C.S.: 221113
Olivier Domergue *(Gen Mgr-SPIE France)*

Subsidiaries:

SPIE Deutschland & Zentraleuropa GmbH (1)
Balcke-Durr-Allee 7, 40882, Ratingen, Germany
Tel.: (49) 210237080
Web Site: http://www.spie.de
Multi-Technology Services
N.A.I.C.S.: 541511
Markus Holzke *(CEO)*

SPIE Nederland B.V (1)
Huifakkerstraat 15, 4815 PN, Breda, Netherlands
Tel.: (31) 881195444
Web Site: http://www.spie-nl.com
Multi-Technology Services
N.A.I.C.S.: 541511

SPIE Switzerland AG (1)
Industriestrasse 50a, 8304, Wallisellen, Switzerland
Tel.: (41) 583011111
Web Site: http://www.spie.ch
IT Services
N.A.I.C.S.: 541519
Pierre Savoy *(CEO)*

SPIE UK Limited (1)
33 Gracechurch Street, London, EC3V 0BT, United Kingdom
Tel.: (44) 2071052300
Web Site: http://www.spieuk.com
Technical Services
N.A.I.C.S.: 541990

Spie Building Solutions Sp. z o.o (1)
Woloska 5 Street, 02-675, Warsaw, Poland
Tel.: (48) 224308300
Web Site: http://www.spie.com.pl
Technical Services
N.A.I.C.S.: 541990
Artur Tomczyk *(CEO)*

Spie Citynetworks Sas (1)
1/3 Place de la Berline, Saint-Denis, 93287, Paris, France
Tel.: (33) 148134242
Energy Network Services
N.A.I.C.S.: 237130
Amelie Dupart *(Comm Mgr)*

SPIEGEL-VERLAG RUDOLF AUGSTEIN GMBH & CO.
Ericusspitze 1, 20457, Hamburg, Germany
Tel.: (49) 4030070
Web Site: http://www.spiegel.de
Sales Range: $350-399.9 Million
Emp.: 1,000
Magazine Publisher; Television Broadcasting Services; Online Information Services
N.A.I.C.S.: 513120
Haauke Janssen *(Mng Dir)*

Subsidiaries:

SPIEGEL TV GmbH (1)
Ericusspitze 1, Hamburg, 20457, Germany   (100%)
Tel.: (49) 40301080
Web Site: http://www.spiegel.de
Sales Range: $100-124.9 Million
Emp.: 200
Television Broadcasting Services
N.A.I.C.S.: 516120
Steffen Krug *(Gen Mgr)*

Affiliate (Domestic):

ASPEKT Telefilm-Produktion GmbH (2)
Jefelder Allee 80, 22045, Hamburg, Germany   (50%)
Tel.: (49) 4066885455
Web Site: http://www.aspekt-telefilm.de
Sales Range: $25-49.9 Million
Emp.: 5
Television & Motion Picture Production Services
N.A.I.C.S.: 512110
Markus Trebitsch *(Mng Dir)*

Subsidiary (Domestic):

a+i art and information GmbH & Co. KG (2)

SPIEGEL-VERLAG RUDOLF AUGSTEIN GMBH & CO.

SPIEGEL-Verlag Rudolf Augstein GmbH & Co.—(Continued)

Ericusstitzi 1, Hamburg, 20457, Germany **(100%)**
Tel.: (49) 40301080
Web Site: http://www.spiegel-tv.de
Sales Range: $100-124.9 Million
Emp.: 1,500
Television Production Services
N.A.I.C.S.: 512110
Thomas Hass *(Mng Dir)*

SPIEGELnet GmbH (1)
Brandstwiete 19, 20457, Hamburg, Germany **(93%)**
Tel.: (49) 40380800
Web Site: http://www.spiegelgruppe.de
Online Information Services
N.A.I.C.S.: 513199
Fried von Bismarck *(Mng Dir)*

Subsidiary (Domestic):

Quality Channel GmbH (2)
Brandstwiete 19, 20457, Hamburg, Germany **(100%)**
Tel.: (49) 4030108502
Web Site: http://www.quality-channel.de
Sales Range: $25-49.9 Million
Emp.: 40
Television Programming Services
N.A.I.C.S.: 516120

SPIEGEL ONLINE GmbH (2)
Ericusspitze 1 Brandstwiete 19, 20457, Hamburg, Germany **(100%)**
Tel.: (49) 40380800
Web Site: http://www.spiegel.com
Online Information Services
N.A.I.C.S.: 513199
Thomas Hass *(Mng Dir)*

manager magazin Verlagsgesellschaft GmbH (2)
Ericusspitze 1, 20457, Hamburg, Germany
Tel.: (49) 403080050
Web Site: http://www.manager-magazin.de
Sales Range: $25-49.9 Million
Emp.: 40
Magazine Publishing
N.A.I.C.S.: 513120
Arno Balzer *(Editor-in-Chief)*

Subsidiary (Domestic):

manager magazin Online GmbH (3)
Brandstwiete 19, 20457, Hamburg, Germany
Tel.: (49) 4038080291
Web Site: http://www.manager-magazin.de
Sales Range: $25-49.9 Million
Online Magazine
N.A.I.C.S.: 513120

STORY HOUSE Productions GmbH (1)
Michael kirchstrasse 17&18, Berlin, 10179, Germany
Tel.: (49) 302809310
Web Site: http://www.storyhousepro.com
Television & Motion Picture Production Services
N.A.I.C.S.: 512110
Andreas Gutzeit *(Co-Pres)*

SPIFFBET AB
Bobergsgatan 48 111 93, 111 93, Stockholm, Sweden
Tel.: (46) 8150858
Web Site: https://www.spiffbet.se
SPIFF—(OMX)
Rev.: $2,229,181
Assets: $9,489,278
Liabilities: $5,607,134
Net Worth: $3,882,144
Earnings: ($3,672,166)
Emp.: 12
Fiscal Year-end: 12/31/20
Buying & Selling Online Platform
N.A.I.C.S.: 513210
Per Ganstrand *(CFO-Interim)*

SPIGEN KOREA CO., LTD.
1709 128 Gasandigital1-ro, Geumcheon-gu, Seoul, Korea (South)
Tel.: (82) 267516041

Web Site:
http://www.spigenkorea.co.kr
Year Founded: 2009
192440—(KRS)
Rev.: $342,002,559
Assets: $363,539,723
Liabilities: $37,649,023
Net Worth: $325,890,699
Earnings: $25,324,063
Emp.: 345
Fiscal Year-end: 12/31/22
Phone Accessory Mfr
N.A.I.C.S.: 339999
Dae Young Kim *(CEO)*

SPIIRE AUSTRALIA PTY LTD
Level 6 414 La Trobe Street, Melbourne, 3000, VIC, Australia
Tel.: (61) 399937888
Web Site: http://www.spiire.com.au
Emp.: 290
Engineering Consulting Services
N.A.I.C.S.: 541330
Mark Breuer *(Mng Dir)*

SPILKER GMBH
Handelsstr 21-23, 33818, Leopoldshohe, Germany
Tel.: (49) 520291000
Web Site: http://www.spilker.de
Year Founded: 1963
Sales Range: $25-49.9 Million
Emp.: 180
Industrial Tools Mfr
N.A.I.C.S.: 333517

Subsidiaries:

Spilker France S.A.R.L. (1)
4 rue Andre Schaaff, 57200, Sarreguemines, France
Tel.: (33) 354291177
Web Site: http://www.spilker.fr
Machine Tool Distr
N.A.I.C.S.: 423830

Spilker Italia S.r.l. (1)
Via Della Vecchia Chimica 5/B, Riozzo di Cerro al Lambro, 20070, Milan, Italy
Tel.: (39) 0298128209
Web Site: http://www.spilker.it
Machine Tool Distr
N.A.I.C.S.: 423830
Alessandro Fadda *(Mgr)*

Spilker Polska Sp. z o.o. (1)
ul Wojska Polskiego 2, 66-200, Swiebodzin, Poland
Tel.: (48) 684754676
Web Site: http://www.spilker.pl
Machine Tool Distr
N.A.I.C.S.: 423830

Spilker UK Ltd. (1)
12 Ranelagh Drive North, Liverpool, L19 9DS, United Kingdom
Tel.: (44) 7738288988
Machine Tool Distr
N.A.I.C.S.: 423830

SPIN MASTER CORP.
225 King Street West, Toronto, M5V 3M2, ON, Canada
Tel.: (416) 364-6002
Web Site:
https://www.spinmaster.com
Year Founded: 1994
TOY—(TSX)
Rev.: $2,042,400,000
Assets: $1,736,700,000
Liabilities: $684,300,000
Net Worth: $1,052,400,000
Earnings: $198,600,000
Emp.: 1,800
Fiscal Year-end: 12/31/21
Holding Company; Toys, Games & Other Entertainment Products Designer, Mfr & Whslr
N.A.I.C.S.: 551112
Mark L. Segal *(CFO & Exec VP)*

Subsidiaries:

Aerobie, Inc. (1)
5816 Ward Ct, Virginia Beach, VA 23455
Tel.: (757) 460-1156
Web Site: http://www.aerobie.com
Sporting Goods Retailer
N.A.I.C.S.: 459110
Alex Tennant *(Gen Mgr)*

Gund, Inc. (1)
1 Runyons Ln, Edison, NJ 08817
Tel.: (732) 248-1500
Web Site: http://www.gund.com
Plush Toy Mfr
N.A.I.C.S.: 339930

Melissa & Doug, LLC (1)
141 Danbury Rd, Wilton, CT 06897
Tel.: (203) 762-4500
Web Site: http://www.melissaanddoug.com
Educational Toys & Children's Products Designer & Mfr
N.A.I.C.S.: 339930
Ilana Berstein *(Head-HR)*

Sago Sago Toys Inc. (1)
487 Adelaide St W Suite 301, Toronto, M5V 1T4, ON, Canada
Tel.: (416) 703-6459
Web Site: https://sagomini.com
Application Software Development Services
N.A.I.C.S.: 541511
Anne-Sophie Brieger *(VP-Ops)*

Spin Master Ltd. (1)
225 King Street West, Toronto, M5V 3M2, ON, Canada **(100%)**
Tel.: (416) 364-6002
Web Site: http://www.spinmaster.com
Sales Range: $700-749.9 Million
Toys, Games & Entertainment Products Designer, Mfr & Whslr
N.A.I.C.S.: 339930
Mark L. Segal *(Exec VP)*

Subsidiary (Non-US):

Meccano SA (2)
363 av de Saint-Exupery, 62100, Calais, Hauts De Seine, France
Tel.: (33) 3 21 46 37 37
Web Site: http://www.meccano.com
Rev.: $37,500,000
Emp.: 142
N.A.I.C.S.: 339930

Spin Master Dongguan Technical Consultancy Servicing Co., Ltd. (2)
1/F-3F & 5/F Home Inn Building Lang Bei Section, Chang Ping Dadao Chang Ping, Dongguan, 523580, China
Tel.: (86) 769 8108 0068
Business Management Services
N.A.I.C.S.: 541611

Spin Master France (2)
36 Rue de Silly, 92100, Boulogne, France
Tel.: (33) 141109360
Sales Range: $50-74.9 Million
Emp.: 10
Toy Sales

Spin Master International S.a.r.l. (2)
Kingsfordweg 151, 1043GR, Amsterdam, Netherlands
Tel.: (31) 20 491 9098
Toy & Hobby Goods Distr
N.A.I.C.S.: 423920

Spin Master Italy S.r.l. (2)
Corso Venezia 40, 20121, Milan, Italy
Tel.: (39) 02 36572230
Toy & Hobby Goods Distr
N.A.I.C.S.: 423920

Spin Master Mexico, S.A. de C.V. (2)
Guillermo Gonzalez Camarena 1450 Piso 5A, Col Centro de Ciudad Santa Fe Alvaro Obregon, Mexico, 01210, Mexico
Tel.: (52) 55 5351 4400
Toy & Hobby Goods Distr
N.A.I.C.S.: 423920

Spin Master Toys Far East Limited (2)
Room 1113 11/F Chinachem Golden Plaza 77 Mody Road, Tsimshatsui Eas, Kowloon, China (Hong Kong)

INTERNATIONAL PUBLIC

Tel.: (852) 2301 3822
Toy & Hobby Goods Distr
N.A.I.C.S.: 423920

Spin Master Toys UK Ltd. (2)
Secure trust House Boston Dr, Bourne End, SL8 5YS, Bucks, United Kingdom
Tel.: (44) 1628535000
Web Site: http://www.spinmastertoys.co.uk
Sales Range: $25-49.9 Million
Emp.: 30
Toy Sales
N.A.I.C.S.: 423920

Subsidiary (US):

Spin Master, Inc. (2)
5880 W Jefferson Blvd Ste A, Los Angeles, CA 90016
Tel.: (310) 826-4914
Web Site: http://www.spinmaster.com
Sales Range: $75-99.9 Million
Emp.: 150
Toy Marketing & Brand Management
N.A.I.C.S.: 423920

Subsidiary (Domestic):

Cardinal Industries, Inc. (3)
21-01 51st Ave, Long Island City, NY 11101
Tel.: (718) 784-3000
Web Site: http://www.cardinalgames.com
Puzzles & Games Mfr & Whslr
N.A.I.C.S.: 339930

Swimways Corporation (1)
5816 Ward Ct, Virginia Beach, VA 23455-3455 **(100%)**
Tel.: (757) 460-1156
Web Site: http://www.swimways.com
Sales Range: $75-99.9 Million
Emp.: 149
Outdoor Water Sports Mfr
N.A.I.C.S.: 339920
Kim Coats *(Dir-HR)*

Toca Boca AB (1)
Lumaparksvagen 9, 120 31, Stockholm, Sweden
Tel.: (46) 7 05 66 19 46
Web Site: http://www.tocaboca.com
Game Software Development Services
N.A.I.C.S.: 541511
Jonas Carlsson *(VP-Brand & Mktg)*

SPINDEX INDUSTRIES LIMITED
8 Boon Lay Way 1003 8 TradeHub 21, Singapore, 609964, Singapore
Tel.: (65) 62680078
Web Site:
https://www.spindex.com.sg
564—(SES)
Rev.: $135,938,496
Assets: $152,468,322
Liabilities: $39,756,947
Net Worth: $112,711,375
Earnings: $8,020,007
Emp.: 634
Fiscal Year-end: 06/30/23
Precision Machined Components Mfr
N.A.I.C.S.: 332216
Choo Pie Tan *(Chm)*

Subsidiaries:

Spindex Industries (Hanoi) Co., Ltd. (1)
Lot No 7A Noi Bai Industrial Zone Quang, Tien Commune Soc Son, Hanoi, Vietnam
Tel.: (84) 2435821633
Web Site: http://www.spindex.com.sg
Sales Range: $100-124.9 Million
Emp.: 400
Precision Machined Components Mfr
N.A.I.C.S.: 332216
Phan Duy Khanh *(Mgr-Bus Dev)*

Spindex Precision Engineering (Shanghai) Co., Ltd. (1)
475 Fa Sai Road Waigaoqiao Free Trade Zone, Shanghai, 200131, China
Tel.: (86) 2150481183
Web Site: http://www.spindex.com.sg
Sales Range: $50-74.9 Million
Emp.: 200
Precision Tool Mfr

AND PRIVATE COMPANIES — SPIRAX-SARCO ENGINEERING PLC

N.A.I.C.S.: 333514

Spindex Precision Engineering (Suzhou) Co., Ltd. (1)
No 58 Yin Sheng Road ShengPu Development Zone, Suzhou Industrial Park, Suzhou, 215126, Jiangsu, China
Tel.: (86) 51267010598
Precision Machine Tools Mfr
N.A.I.C.S.: 332216

Synturn (M) Sdn. Bhd. (1)
No 6 Jalan Istimewa 7 Taman Perindustrian Cemerlang, 81800, Ulu Tiram, Johor Darul Tazim, Malaysia
Tel.: (60) 78632633
Emp.: 800
Metal Stamping Mfr
N.A.I.C.S.: 332119

SPINEGUARD S.A.
10 Cours Louis Lumiere, 94300, Vincennes, France
Tel.: (33) 145184519
Web Site:
   https://www.spineguard.com
Year Founded: 2009
ALSGD—(EUR)
Sales Range: $1-9.9 Million
Emp.: 24
Medical Equipment Mfr
N.A.I.C.S.: 339112
Pierre Jerome (Co-Founder)

SPINELLI S.R.L.
Via Scarsellini 171, 16149, Genoa, GE, Italy
Tel.: (39) 010 46371   IT
Web Site:
   http://www.gruppospinelli.com
Integrated Supply Chain & Logistics Services
N.A.I.C.S.: 488510
Mirco Panariello (Sls Mgr-Terminal Div)

SPINEWAY SA
7 allee Moulin Berger, 69130, Ecully, France
Tel.: (33) 472770152
Web Site: https://www.spineway.com
ALSPW—(EUR)
Rev.: $5,619,457
Assets: $14,305,092
Liabilities: $7,033,841
Net Worth: $7,271,251
Earnings: ($3,220,717)
Emp.: 30
Fiscal Year-end: 12/31/19
Medical Device Mfr
N.A.I.C.S.: 339112
Stephane Le Roux (Pres)

SPINNAKER CAPITAL GROUP
6 Grosvenor Street, London, W1K 4DJ, United Kingdom
Tel.: (44) 2079032900
Web Site:
   http://www.spinnakercapital.com
Year Founded: 1999
Sales Range: $25-49.9 Million
Emp.: 35
Investment Management Firm
N.A.I.C.S.: 523999
Alexis Habib (Principal)
Subsidiaries:

Spinnaker Capital (Asia) Pte Ltd (1)
16 Collyer Quay 34-02 Hitachi Tower, Singapore, 049318, Singapore
Tel.: (65) 6303 9900
Financial Management Services
N.A.I.C.S.: 523999

Spinnaker Capital (Hong Kong) Limited (1)
Suite 2901 Two Exchange Square 8 Connaught Place, Central, China (Hong Kong)
Tel.: (852) 2867 7808
Web Site: http://www.spinnakercapital.com

Emp.: 3
Financial Management Services
N.A.I.C.S.: 523999
Clara Poon (Office Mgr)

Spinnaker Capital (Middle East) Limited (1)
Level 3 Gate Village 10 Dubai International Financial Centre, PO Box 50675, Dubai, United Arab Emirates
Tel.: (971) 4 4019678
Financial Management Services
N.A.I.C.S.: 523999

Spinnaker Capital C.G.R. Ltda. (1)
Alameda Santos 1940 14 andar, Sao Paulo, 01418-200, Brazil
Tel.: (55) 11 4505 2255
Web Site: http://www.spinnaker.com.br
Emp.: 20
Financial Management Services
N.A.I.C.S.: 523999
Marcos Momose (Head-Ops)

SPINNAKER INDUSTRIES INC.
27 Leading Road, Newmarket, M9V 4B7, ON, Canada
Tel.: (416) 742-0598
Web Site:
   http://www.spinnakerindustries.com
Year Founded: 1983
Rev.: $19,562,614
Emp.: 150
Air Conditioning & Refrigeration Equipment Mfr
N.A.I.C.S.: 333415
Stephen Pilling (VP)

SPINNOVA PLC
Palokarjentie 2-4, 40320, Jyvaskyla, Finland
Tel.: (358) 207012430   FI
Web Site: https://www.spinnova.com
Year Founded: 2014
SPINN—(HEL)
Rev.: $11,482,840
Assets: $106,425,642
Liabilities: $12,180,013
Net Worth: $94,245,629
Earnings: ($21,148,284)
Emp.: 76
Fiscal Year-end: 12/31/23
Textile Products Mfr
N.A.I.C.S.: 314999
Ben Selby (CFO)

SPIR GROUP ASA
Dronning Mauds gate 10, 0250, Oslo, Norway
Tel.: (47) 90530049   NO
Web Site: https://spirgroup.com
SIKRI—(OSL)
Rev.: $95,280,990
Assets: $204,192,315
Liabilities: $108,435,341
Net Worth: $95,756,974
Earnings: $2,490,763
Emp.: 490
Fiscal Year-end: 12/31/22
Holding Company
N.A.I.C.S.: 551112

SPIRAL GROUP
Le Millenaire 425 Av Alfred Nobel, Montpellier, Cedex, France
Tel.: (33) 499526757
Web Site: http://www.spiralnet.net
Rev.: $19,108,500
Emp.: 140
Management Consulting Services
N.A.I.C.S.: 541618
Robert Durant (Gen Mgr)

SPIRAX-SARCO ENGINEERING PLC
Charlton House Cirencester Road, Cheltenham, GL53 8ER, Gloucestershire, United Kingdom
Tel.: (44) 1242521361   UK

Web Site:
   http://www.spiraxengineering.com
Year Founded: 1888
SPX—(OTCIQ)
Rev.: $1,939,967,700
Assets: $3,354,412,050
Liabilities: $1,945,387,950
Net Worth: $1,409,024,100
Earnings: $271,012,500
Fiscal Year-end: 12/31/22
Steam Traps, Temperature Controls, Heating Specialties, Strainers, Condensate Return Systems, Pumps, Pressure Reducing Valves, Boiler Controls, Flowmeters Mfr
N.A.I.C.S.: 332911
Neil H. Daws (Mng Dir-Steam Specialties)
Subsidiaries:

Aflex Hose Ltd. (1)
Dyson Wood Way Bradley Business Park, Spring Bank Industrial Estate, Huddersfield, HD2 1GZ, West Yorkshire, United Kingdom
Tel.: (44) 1422317200
Web Site: https://www.aflex-hose.com
Pharmaceutical & Chemical Industrial Machinery Mfr
N.A.I.C.S.: 325199
Peter Millen (Dir-Fin)

BioPure Technology Ltd. (1)
Unit 5 Dunsbury Park, Horndean, Havant, PO9 4EE, Hampshire, United Kingdom
Tel.: (44) 2392499000
Pump Equipment Mfr
N.A.I.C.S.: 333914
Steve Stubbs (Mgr-Ops)

Chromalox (Asia Pacific) Ltd. (1)
383/2 The Village Business Centre Unit D16-A Moo 12 Sukhumvit Road, Nongprue, Bang Lamung, 20151, Chonburi, Thailand
Tel.: (66) 381909169
Industrial Equipment Mfr
N.A.I.C.S.: 333248

Chromalox (UK) Ltd. (1)
AMP House 2nd Floor Dingwall Road, Croydon, CR0 2LX, Surrey, United Kingdom
Tel.: (44) 2086658900
Industrial Equipment Mfr
N.A.I.C.S.: 333248
Robert Kerrigan (Mgr-Area Sls)

Chromalox Engenharia Ltda. (1)
Avenida Manoel Lages do Chao 268 Bairro Portao, Cotia, Sao Paulo, 06705-050, Brazil
Tel.: (55) 11997631541
Industrial Equipment Mfr
N.A.I.C.S.: 333248

Chromalox Gulf DWC, LLC (1)
Office No E-2-0226 Business Park, PO Box 390012, Dubai, United Arab Emirates
Tel.: (971) 48879776
Industrial Equipment Mfr
N.A.I.C.S.: 333248

Chromalox, Inc. (1)
2711 Centerville Rd Ste 400, Wilmington, DE 19808
Tel.: (412) 967-3940
Web Site: https://www.chromalox.com
Industrial Electric Heating Equipment & Temperature Control System Mfr
N.A.I.C.S.: 333414
Mike Sutter (Pres & CEO)

Colima S r l (1)
Via Mestre 11, Cernusco, 20063, Milan, Italy
Tel.: (39) 0292393220
Web Site: http://www.colimaitaly.com
Sales Range: $25-49.9 Million
Emp.: 7
Mechanical Control Tools Mfr
N.A.I.C.S.: 334513
Mark Scrivani (CEO)

Etirex SAS (1)
23 Route De Chateau Thierry Noyant-et-Aconin, 02203, Soissons, Cedex, France
Tel.: (33) 323743939
Industrial Equipment Mfr
N.A.I.C.S.: 333248

GESTRA AG (1)

Munchener Str 77, 28215, Bremen, Germany
Tel.: (49) 4 213 5030
Web Site: https://www.gestra.com
Steam Traps, Check Valves Non-Return Flaps & Other Special Valves; Industrial Electrics Mfr
N.A.I.C.S.: 332919
Lutz Oelsmner (Chm)

Subsidiary (Non-US):

GESTRA Polonia SP. Z.o.o (2)
Ul Ku Ujsciu 19, 80-701, Gdansk, Poland   (100%)
Tel.: (48) 583061010
Web Site: http://pl.gestra.de
Flow Control Products Mfr
N.A.I.C.S.: 333914

Gestra Espanloa SA (1)
Luis Cabrera 86-88, 28002, Madrid, Spain
Tel.: (34) 915152032
Industrial Equipment Mfr
N.A.I.C.S.: 333248

Gestra Portugal, Lda. (1)
Av Dr Antunes Guimaraes 1159, 4100-082, Porto, 4100-082, Portugal
Tel.: (351) 226198770
Industrial Equipment Mfr
N.A.I.C.S.: 333248

Gestra Singapore Pte. Ltd. (1)
21 Changi South Avenue 2 01-01, Singapore, 486630, Singapore
Tel.: (65) 63490480
Industrial Equipment Mfr
N.A.I.C.S.: 333248

Gestra UK Ltd. (1)
Unit 1 Sopwith Park Royce Close West Portway Business Park, Andover, SP10 3TS, Hampshire, United Kingdom
Tel.: (44) 163546999
Industrial Equipment Mfr
N.A.I.C.S.: 333248

Gestra USA, Inc. (1)
1101 Carolina Pines Dr, Blythewood, SC 29016
Industrial Equipment Mfr
N.A.I.C.S.: 333248

Italgestra Srl (1)
Via Per Cinisello 18, 20834, Nova Milanese, Monza and Brianza, Italy
Tel.: (39) 03624917400
Industrial Equipment Mfr
N.A.I.C.S.: 333248

M & M Iberica SL (1)
C/colom 453 Ship C-17 Pi Sta Margarida Ii, 08223, Terrassa, Barcelona, Spain
Tel.: (34) 937892777
Web Site: http://www.mmiberica.com
Industrial Equipment Distr
N.A.I.C.S.: 423830

PT Spirax Sarco Indonesia (1)
Taman Tekno Bumi Serpong Damai Jl Tekno IV Block C Kav 9-9A, Kel Setu Kec Setu, Tangerang, 15314, Banten, Indonesia
Tel.: (62) 2183797233
Fabricated Metal & Hardware Mfr
N.A.I.C.S.: 332999
Lenny Candra (Mgr-Fin)

ProTrace Engineering, Inc. (1)
Suite 205 6204 6A Street SE, Calgary, T2H 2B7, AB, Canada
Tel.: (403) 252-2566
Web Site: https://www.protrace.ca
Building Construction Services
N.A.I.C.S.: 541330
Michael Slade (Dir-Mng & Technical & Mng Dir)

Spirax Inter Valf Sanayi ve Ticaret Ltd (1)
Serifali Mevkii Edep Sok No 27, Maltepe, Istanbul, 34775, Yukaridudullu Umrani, Turkiye
Tel.: (90) 2164417373
Web Site: http://www.spiraxsarco.com.tr
Emp.: 30
Steam Equipment Mfr
N.A.I.C.S.: 333414

Spirax Oy (1)
Niittytie 25 A 24, 01300, Vantaa, Finland

SPIRAX-SARCO ENGINEERING PLC — INTERNATIONAL PUBLIC

Spirax-Sarco Engineering plc—(Continued)
Tel.: (358) 941361611
Web Site: http://www.spiraxsarco.com.fi
Sales Range: $25-49.9 Million
Emp.: 20
Industrial Supplies Whslr
N.A.I.C.S.: 423840
Timo Tarjomaa (Product Mgr)

Spirax Sarco (Japan) Ltd. (1)
2-37 Hamada, Mihama-ku, Chiba, 261-0025, Japan
Tel.: (81) 43 274 4811
Web Site: https://www.spirax-sarco.co.jp
Sales Range: $50-74.9 Million
Emp.: 45
Industrial Machinery & Equipment Whslr
N.A.I.C.S.: 423830

Spirax Sarco (Thailand) Ltd. (1)
38 Krungthepkreeta Road, Klongsongton-nun Latkrabang, 10520, Bangkok, 10520, Thailand
Tel.: (66) 20550888
Web Site: https://www.spiraxsarco.com
Sales Range: $25-49.9 Million
Emp.: 38
Industrial Supplies Whslr
N.A.I.C.S.: 423840

Spirax Sarco Canada Ltd. (1)
383 Applewood Crescent, Concord, L4K 4J3, ON, Canada
Tel.: (905) 660-5510
Web Site: https://www.spiraxsarco.com
Sales Range: $50-74.9 Million
Emp.: 60
Warm Air Heating & Air-Conditioning Equipment & Supplies Whslr
N.A.I.C.S.: 423730

Spirax Sarco Co. Ltd. (1)
6th Floor No 12 Lane 270 Section 3 Beishen Road, Shenkeng District, New Taipei City, 222, Taiwan
Tel.: (886) 226626689
Sales Range: $25-49.9 Million
Industrial Supplies Whslr
N.A.I.C.S.: 423840

Spirax Sarco East Africa Ltd. (1)
Savannah Business Park Godown 8 Mombasa Road, PO Box 38919, 00623, Nairobi, Kenya
Tel.: (254) 204443340
Fabricated Metal & Hardware Mfr
N.A.I.C.S.: 332999
Sriram Vaidyanathan (Gen Mgr)

Spirax Sarco Egypt L.L.C. (1)
19 Farid St El Orouba St, Heliopolis, Cairo, Egypt
Tel.: (20) 224174491
Fabricated Metal & Hardware Mfr
N.A.I.C.S.: 332999

Spirax Sarco Engineering (China) Ltd, (1)
No 800 Xinjunhuan Road Pujiang Hi-Tech Park, Minhang District, Shanghai, 201114, China
Tel.: (86) 2124163666
Web Site: https://www.spiraxsarco.com
Emp.: 500
Engineeering Services
N.A.I.C.S.: 541330

Spirax Sarco Ges. mbH (1)
Duckegasse 7/2/8, 1220, Vienna, Austria
Tel.: (43) 16996411
Web Site: http://www.SpiraxSarco.com.de
Fabricated Pipe & Pipe Fitting Mfr
N.A.I.C.S.: 332996

Spirax Sarco Ind. e Com. Ltda. (1)
Estr Manoel Lages do Chao 268 - Jardim Caiapia, Cotia, 06705-050, SP, Brazil
Tel.: (55) 11996339490
Web Site: http://www.spiraxsarco.com.br
Sales Range: $50-74.9 Million
Emp.: 220
Pump & Pumping Equipment Mfr
N.A.I.C.S.: 333914

Spirax Sarco Ltd. (1)
6 Nandina Ave, PO Box 76 - 170, East Tamaki, Auckland, 2013, New Zealand
Tel.: (64) 800800229
Web Site: https://www.spiraxsarco.com
Sales Range: $25-49.9 Million
Emp.: 30
Industrial Machinery & Equipment Whslr
N.A.I.C.S.: 423830

Spirax Sarco Maghreb
Oulad M taa Secteur 3 Lot 146 Rue Arfoud 2eme Etage Bureaux 5 et 6, 12000, Temara, Morocco
Tel.: (212) 537603800
Fabricated Metal & Hardware Mfr
N.A.I.C.S.: 332999

Spirax Sarco Peru SAC (1)
Av Guillermo Dansey, 2124, Lima, Peru
Tel.: (51) 13394005
Fabricated Metal & Hardware Mfr
N.A.I.C.S.: 332999

Spirax Sarco S.A. (1)
Autopista Panamericana Colectora Este, Don Torcuato, 24951, Buenos Aires, Argentina
Tel.: (54) 1145891300
Web Site: https://www.spiraxsarco.com
Sales Range: $50-74.9 Million
Emp.: 200
Industrial Valve Mfr
N.A.I.C.S.: 332911

Spirax Sarco Sp. z o.o. (1)
Ul Jutrzenki 98, 02-230, Warsaw, Poland
Tel.: (48) 228533588
Sales Range: $75-99.9 Million
Emp.: 25
Steam & Air-Conditioning Supply
N.A.I.C.S.: 221330

Spirax Sarco Spol. S r.o. (1)
Prazska 1455/18a Hostivar, 10200, Prague, 10, Czech Republic
Tel.: (420) 274001351
Web Site: http://www.spiraxsarco.com.cz
Sales Range: $25-49.9 Million
Emp.: 20
Warm Air Heating & Air-Conditioning Equipment & Supplies Whslr
N.A.I.C.S.: 423730

Spirax Sarco Valf Sanayi ve Ticaret A.S. (1)
Deri Osb Mah Kropon Sok No 3, Tuzla, 34956, Istanbul, Turkiye
Tel.: (90) 2166000800
Fabricated Metal & Hardware Mfr
N.A.I.C.S.: 332999

Spirax Sarco Vietnam Co. Ltd. (1)
4th Floor Nam Song Tien Tower 180 Nguyen Van Troi St, Phu Nhuan District, Ho Chi Minh City, Vietnam
Tel.: (84) 2839976000
Fabricated Metal & Hardware Mfr
N.A.I.C.S.: 332999
Wayne Harvey (Gen Mgr)

Spirax Sarco, Inc. (1)
1150 Northpoint Blvd, Blythewood, SC 29016 (100%)
Tel.: (803) 714-2000
Sales Range: $50-74.9 Million
Emp.: 230
Steam Traps, Temperature Controls, Heating Specialties, Strainers, Condensate Return Systems, Pumps, Pressure Reducing Valves, Boiler Controls, Flowmeters Mfr
N.A.I.C.S.: 332911
Javier Jimena (Pres & Gen Mgr)

Spirax-Sarco (Korea) Ltd. (1)
Steam People House 99 Sadang-ro 30-gil, Dongjak-Gu, 07015, Seoul, Korea (South)
Tel.: (82) 234893489
Web Site: https://www.spiraxsarco.com
Industrial Machinery & Equipment Whslr
N.A.I.C.S.: 423830

Spirax-Sarco (Private) Ltd. (1)
464 Tagore Industrial Ave, 787833, Singapore, Singapore
Tel.: (65) 63490480
Web Site: http://www.spiraxsarco.com.sg
Sales Range: $25-49.9 Million
Emp.: 35
Plumbing & Heating Equipment & Supplies Whslr
N.A.I.C.S.: 423720

Spirax-Sarco A.B. (1)
Evenemangsgatan 40 plan 2, 169 56, Solna, Sweden
Tel.: (46) 85 563 2230
Web Site: https://www.spiraxsarco.com
Sales Range: $25-49.9 Million
Emp.: 18
Retail Stores
N.A.I.C.S.: 459999
Gavin Hugstabal (Gen Mgr)

Spirax-Sarco A.G. (1)
Gustav-Maurer-Strasse 9, 8702, Zollikon, Switzerland
Tel.: (41) 44 396 8000
Web Site: https://www.spiraxsarco.com
Sales Range: $25-49.9 Million
Emp.: 23
Instruments & Related Products Mfr for Measuring Displaying & Controlling Industrial Process Variables
N.A.I.C.S.: 334513
Laurent Viatte (CEO)

Spirax-Sarco AS (1)
Vestvollveien 14 A, Oslo, 2019, Skedsmokorset, Norway
Tel.: (47) 67067680
Heating Equipment Mfr
N.A.I.C.S.: 333414

Spirax-Sarco Chile Ltda. (1)
Calle Las Garzas 930 Region Metropolitana, Santiago, Chile
Tel.: (56) 226162550
Fabricated Metal & Hardware Mfr
N.A.I.C.S.: 332999

Spirax-Sarco Engineering LLC (1)
Vozrozhdeniya Street The House 20a lit A, 198188, Saint Petersburg, Russia
Tel.: (7) 8126409044
Web Site: https://www.spiraxsarco.com
Sales Range: $25-49.9 Million
Emp.: 40
Industrial Machinery & Equipment Whslr
N.A.I.C.S.: 423830

Spirax-Sarco Engineering S.L. (1)
Sant Josep 130, Poligon El Pla, 08980, San Feliu de Llobregat, Spain
Tel.: (34) 936857929
Web Site: https://www.spiraxsarco.com
Steam System Engineering
N.A.I.C.S.: 541330

Spirax-Sarco Europe Ltd. (1)
Charlton House, Cheltenham, United Kingdom
Tel.: (44) 1142475599
Business Services
N.A.I.C.S.: 561499

Spirax-Sarco GmbH (1)
Reichenaustrasse 210, Postfach 10 20 42, D - 78467, Konstanz, Germany
Tel.: (49) 753158060
Web Site: http://www.spiraxsarco.com.de
Sales Range: $25-49.9 Million
Emp.: 60
Fabricated Pipe & Pipe Fitting Mfr
N.A.I.C.S.: 332996

Spirax-Sarco India Private Ltd. (1)
Plot No 6 Central Avenue Mahindra World City, Kancheepuram District, Chengalpattu, 603 004, India
Tel.: (91) 4467414800
Fabricated Metal & Hardware Mfr
N.A.I.C.S.: 332999

Spirax-Sarco International Ltd. (1)
Charlton House, Cheltenham, GL53 8ER, United Kingdom
Tel.: (44) 1242521361
Web Site: http://www.spiraxsarco.com
Sales Range: $400-449.9 Million
Emp.: 2,000
Metal Valve & Pipe Fitting Mfr
N.A.I.C.S.: 332919

Spirax-Sarco Investments Ltd. (1)
Charlton House Cirencester Road, Cheltenham, GL53 8ER, Gloucestershire, United Kingdom
Tel.: (44) 1242521361
Sales Range: $400-449.9 Million
Emp.: 2,000
Metal Valve & Pipe Fitting Mfr
N.A.I.C.S.: 332919
Mark E. Vernon (CEO)

Spirax-Sarco Kft (1)
Koer U 2/A, 1103, Budapest, Hungary
Tel.: (36) 12223708
Fabricated Metal & Hardware Mfr
N.A.I.C.S.: 332999

Spirax-Sarco Mexicana S.A. de C.V. (1)
Boulevard Alianza 30B, Parque Industrial CPA, 65550, Cienega de Flores, Nuevo Leon, Mexico
Tel.: (52) 8182203600
Web Site: https://www.spiraxsarco.com
Sales Range: $50-74.9 Million
Industrial Machinery & Equipment Whslr
N.A.I.C.S.: 423830

Spirax-Sarco N.V. (1)
Industriepark 5, 9052, Zwijnaarde, Belgium
Tel.: (32) 92446710
Web Site: https://www.spiraxsarco.com
Sales Range: $25-49.9 Million
Emp.: 35
Industrial Machinery & Equipment Whslr
N.A.I.C.S.: 423830

Spirax-Sarco Netherlands BV (1)
Oslo 9, 2993 LD, Barendrecht, Netherlands
Tel.: (31) 108920386
Web Site: https://www.spiraxsarco.com
Fabricated Metal & Hardware Mfr
N.A.I.C.S.: 332999

Spirax-Sarco Overseas Ltd. (1)
Charlton House Cirencester Road, Cheltenham, GL53 8ER, Gloucestershire, United Kingdom
Tel.: (44) 1242521361
Sales Range: $250-299.9 Million
Emp.: 1,000
Industrial Machinery & Equipment Whslr
N.A.I.C.S.: 423830
Mark E. Vernon (CEO)

Spirax-Sarco Philippines Inc. (1)
2308 Natividad Bldg Chino Roces Ave Ext, Makati, 1231, Philippines
Tel.: (63) 288128654
Web Site: https://www.spiraxsarco.com
Fabricated Metal & Hardware Mfr
N.A.I.C.S.: 332999
Larry Yuseco (Gen Mgr)

Spirax-Sarco Pty. Ltd. (1)
Delivery Ctr, PO Box 6308, Blacktown, 2148, NSW, Australia
Tel.: (61) 296214100
Web Site: http://www.spiraxsarco.com.au
Sales Range: $25-49.9 Million
Emp.: 35
Plumbing & Heating Equipment & Supplies Whslr
N.A.I.C.S.: 423720

Spirax-Sarco S.A.S. (1)
ZI des bruyeres 8 Avenue Le Verrier, BP 61, 78190, Trappes, France
Tel.: (33) 130664343
Web Site: http://www.spiraxsarco.com.fr
Sales Range: $75-99.9 Million
Emp.: 150
Industrial Supplies Whslr
N.A.I.C.S.: 423840

Spirax-Sarco S.r.l. (1)
Via Per Cinisello 18, 20834, Nova Milanese, MB, Italy
Tel.: (39) 036249171
Web Site: https://www.spiraxsarco.com
Sales Range: $50-74.9 Million
Emp.: 200
Metal Valve & Pipe Fitting Mfr
N.A.I.C.S.: 332919

Spirax-Sarco SAU (1)
Sant Josep 130 Poligon El Pla, Sant Feliu de Llobregat, Barcelona, Spain
Tel.: (34) 936857929
Fabricated Metal & Hardware Mfr
N.A.I.C.S.: 332999

Spirax-Sarco Sdn. Bhd. (1)
No 10 Temasya 18 Jalan Pelukis U1/46A, 40150, Shah Alam, Selangor, Malaysia
Tel.: (60) 355699650
Sales Range: $25-49.9 Million
Emp.: 30
Plumbing & Heating Equipment & Supplies Whslr
N.A.I.C.S.: 423720

Spirax-Sarco South Africa (Pty.) Ltd. (1)

Corner Brine ave & Horn str Ext 23, Chloorkop, Kempton Park, 1624, Gauteng, South Africa
Tel.: (27) 112301300
Web Site: https://www.spiraxsarco.com
Sales Range: $50-74.9 Million
Emp.: 62
Turbine & Turbine Generator Set Units Mfr
N.A.I.C.S.: 333611

Watson Marlow FZCO (1)
Office 2005 JAFZA One Tower A, PO Box 263629, Dubai, United Arab Emirates
Tel.: (971) 48868840
Pump Equipment Mfr
N.A.I.C.S.: 333914

Watson-Marlow Austria GmbH (1)
Rathaus-Viertel 3 / 1 OG / 311, 2353, Guntramsdorf, Austria
Tel.: (43) 223632009820
Web Site: https://www.wmfts.com
Pump Equipment Mfr
N.A.I.C.S.: 333914

Watson-Marlow Bombas Chile Ltda. (1)
Calle Las Garzas N 930 Galpon E, Quilicura, Santiago, Chile
Tel.: (56) 226162565
Pump Equipment Mfr
N.A.I.C.S.: 333914

Watson-Marlow Canada Inc. (1)
383 Applewood Crescent, Concord, L4K 4J3, ON, Canada
Tel.: (289) 588-1988
Pump Equipment Mfr
N.A.I.C.S.: 333914

Watson-Marlow Co. Ltd. (1)
1F No 5 Lane 270 Sec Bei Shen Rd, Shen Keng District, New Taipei City, 222, Taiwan
Tel.: (886) 277287026
Pump Equipment Mfr
N.A.I.C.S.: 333914

Watson-Marlow Co. Ltd. (1)
Maruta 7F 2-7-53 Nishimiyahara, Yodogawa-ku, Osaka, 532-0004, Japan
Tel.: (81) 648674840
Pump Equipment Mfr
N.A.I.C.S.: 333914

Watson-Marlow Colombia SAS (1)
Carrera 100 5 169 CC Unicentro Torre B Yoffice Piso 6 Oficina 27, Valle del Cauca, 760032, Cali, Colombia
Tel.: (57) 25190822
Pump Equipment Mfr
N.A.I.C.S.: 333914

Watson-Marlow India Private Ltd. (1)
Mahalaxmi Icon Survey No 132/2A, Near Sai HP Petrol Pump Pune-Mumbai Bypass Road Tathawade, Pune, 411 033, Maharashtra, India
Tel.: (91) 2067115600
Pump Equipment Mfr
N.A.I.C.S.: 333914

Watson-Marlow LLC (1)
Room 19 Premises I Shosse Entuziastov 34, 105118, Moscow, Russia
Tel.: (7) 4956403580
Pump Equipment Mfr
N.A.I.C.S.: 333914

Watson-Marlow Limited (1)
Bickland Water Road, Falmouth, TR11 4RU, Cornwall, United Kingdom
Tel.: (44) 1326763106
Web Site: https://www.wmfts.com
Emp.: 270
Medical Pump Mfr
N.A.I.C.S.: 339112

Subsidiary (US):

ASEPCO Corp. (2)
355 Pioneer Way, Mountain View, CA 94041
Tel.: (650) 691-9500
Web Site: http://www.asepco.com
Sales Range: $1-9.9 Million
Emp.: 18
Aseptic Valves & Magnetic Mixer Mfr
N.A.I.C.S.: 333248
Mark Embury *(VP-Sls & Mktg)*

Subsidiary (Non-US):

Bredel Hose Pumps B.V. (2)
Sluisstraat 7, 7490AA, Delden, Netherlands
Tel.: (31) 743770000
Web Site: http://www.bredel.com
Sales Range: $25-49.9 Million
Emp.: 42
Industrial Machinery & Equipment Whslr
N.A.I.C.S.: 423830

Watson Marlow Bredel S.A. (Pty.) Ltd. (2)
Unit 6 Cradleview Industrial Park Cnr Beyers Naude Drive & Johan Road, Laser Park Honeydew, Johannesburg, 2170, South Africa
Tel.: (27) 11 796 2960
Web Site: https://www.wmftg.com
Sales Range: $25-49.9 Million
Emp.: 20
Retailers Stores
N.A.I.C.S.: 459999

Watson-Marlow Alitea AB (2)
Hammarby Fabriksvag 29-31, 120 30, Stockholm, Sweden
Tel.: (46) 85 565 5609
Web Site: http://www.watson-marlow.se
Sales Range: $25-49.9 Million
Emp.: 40
Peristaltic Pump Mfr
N.A.I.C.S.: 333914

Watson-Marlow B.V. (2)
Oslo 9, 2993 LD, Barendrecht, Netherlands
Tel.: (31) 855360010
Web Site: http://www.watson-marlow.com.mx
Sales Range: $50-74.9 Million
Emp.: 8
Electrical Apparatus & Equipment Wiring Supplies & Construction Material Whslr
N.A.I.C.S.: 423610

Watson-Marlow Bredel Holdings BV (2)
Sluisstraat 7, PO Box 47, 7491 GA, Delden, Netherlands
Tel.: (31) 743770000
Web Site: http://www.bredel.com
Emp.: 60
Investment Management Service
N.A.I.C.S.: 523999

Watson-Marlow Bredel Ind e Com de Bombas (2)
Watson-Marlow Fluid Technology Solutions, Polo Empresarial - Alameda Oceania 63 - Tambore, Santana de Parnaiba, 06543-308, Sao Paulo, Brazil
Tel.: (55) 1121554000
Web Site: http://www.watson-marlow.com.br
Sales Range: $25-49.9 Million
Emp.: 18
Industrial Pump Mfr
N.A.I.C.S.: 333914

Watson-Marlow Flexicon A/S (2)
Frejasvej 2-6, 4100, Ringsted, Denmark
Tel.: (45) 57671155
Web Site: http://www.flexicon.dk
Sales Range: $25-49.9 Million
Emp.: 35
Diagnostic Equipment Mfr
N.A.I.C.S.: 325412
Henrik Corneliussen *(Mgr-Sls & Factory)*

Subsidiary (US):

Watson-Marlow Flow Smart Inc. (2)
213 Nesbitt Dr, Seaford, DE 19973
Tel.: (302) 536-6388
Web Site: http://www.flowsmartinc.com
Sales Range: $1-9.9 Million
Sanitary Gaskets, Silicone Transfer Tubing & Silicone Hoses Mfr
N.A.I.C.S.: 339991

Subsidiary (Non-US):

Watson-Marlow GmbH (2)
Kurt-Alder-Strasse 1, 41569, Rommerskirchen, Germany
Tel.: (49) 218042040
Web Site: http://www.watson-marlow.de
Sales Range: $25-49.9 Million
Emp.: 11
Industrial Machinery & Equipment Whslr
N.A.I.C.S.: 423830

Watson-Marlow Ltd (2)
Unit F 6 Polaris Place East Tamaki, PO Box 259-283, Botany, Manukau, 2013, New Zealand
Tel.: (64) 9 273 3166
Web Site: https://www.wmftg.com
Emp.: 2
Industrial Pump Mfr
N.A.I.C.S.: 333914

Watson-Marlow Ltd (2)
Hardturmstrasse 253, 8005, Zurich, Switzerland
Tel.: (41) 445521700
Web Site: http://www.waatson-marlow.co.uk
Peristaltic Pump Mfr
N.A.I.C.S.: 333914
John Engels *(Gen Mgr)*

Watson-Marlow N.V. (2)
Industriepark 5, 9052, Zwijnaarde, Belgium
Tel.: (32) 92259457
Web Site: https://www.wmftg.com
Emp.: 12
Business Services
N.A.I.C.S.: 561499

Watson-Marlow Pty Ltd (2)
5 Hexham Place, Wetherill Park, Sydney, 2164, NSW, Australia
Tel.: (61) 287871400
Web Site: http://www.wmbpumps.com.au
Industrial Pump Mfr
N.A.I.C.S.: 333914

Watson-Marlow S de R I de C V (2)
Blvd Alianza 30-B Parque Industrial Cpa Business Center & C P, 65550, Cienega de Flores, Nuevo Leon, Mexico
Tel.: (52) 8182203614
Web Site: https://www.wmftg.com
Sales Range: $50-74.9 Million
Emp.: 10
Industrial Pump Sales & Maintenance Services
N.A.I.C.S.: 423830

Watson-Marlow S.A. (2)
302 Ave de Neuville, ZA Les Chenes Batiment n9, 78950, Gambais, France
Tel.: (33) 134871212
Web Site: http://www.watson-marlow.fr
Sales Range: $25-49.9 Million
Emp.: 18
Industrial Supplies Whslr
N.A.I.C.S.: 423840
Eric Blief *(Gen Mgr)*

Watson-Marlow S.r.l. (2)
Via dell Artigianato 6, Mazzano, 25080, Brescia, Italy
Tel.: (39) 0306871184
Durable Goods Whslr
N.A.I.C.S.: 423990

Subsidiary (US):

Watson-Marlow, Inc. (2)
37 Upton Technology Park, Wilmington, MA 01887-1018
Tel.: (978) 658-6168
Web Site: http://www.watson-marlow.com
Sales Range: $25-49.9 Million
Emp.: 40
Industrial Machinery & Equipment Whslr
N.A.I.C.S.: 423830

Watson-Marlow Pte. Ltd. (1)
4010 Ang Mo Kio Avenue 10 TechPlace1 06-01/02, Singapore, 569626, Singapore
Tel.: (65) 64557411
Pump Equipment Mfr
N.A.I.C.S.: 333914

Watson-Marlow Sdn. Bhd. (1)
No 10 Temasya 18 Jln Pelukis U1/46A, 40150, Shah Alam, Selangor, Malaysia
Tel.: (60) 355699650
Pump Equipment Mfr
N.A.I.C.S.: 333914

Watson-Marlow Sp Zoo (1)
Al Jerzego Waszyngtona 146, 04-074, Warsaw, Poland
Tel.: (48) 228530453
Pump Equipment Mfr
N.A.I.C.S.: 333914

SPIRE HEALTHCARE GROUP PLC
Eastern Avenue, Southend-on-Sea, SS2 4XH, Essex, United Kingdom
Tel.: (44) 9084066   UK
Web Site: https://www.spirehealthcare.com
Year Founded: 2007
SPI—(LSE)
Rev.: $1,443,593,250
Assets: $2,601,479,100
Liabilities: $1,728,096,150
Net Worth: $873,382,950
Earnings: $9,876,900
Fiscal Year-end: 12/31/22
Healthcare Services
N.A.I.C.S.: 621511
Justin Ash *(CEO)*

Subsidiaries:

Classic Hospitals, Ltd. (1)
3 Dorset Rise, London, EC4Y 8EN, United Kingdom
Tel.: (44) 1618503931
Web Site: http://www.classichospitalsltd.com
Hospital Operator
N.A.I.C.S.: 622110

Soma Health Limited (1)
Suite 9A Malvern Gate Business Park Bromwich Road, Worcester, Worcestershire, United Kingdom
Tel.: (44) 1905422808
Web Site: https://www.somahealth.co.uk
Occupational Health Services
N.A.I.C.S.: 621498

Spire Thames Valley Hospital Limited (1)
Wexham Street, Wexham, SL3 6NH, Bucks, United Kingdom
Tel.: (44) 1753468174
Healthcare Services
N.A.I.C.S.: 621999
Angela Drennan *(Mgr-Clinical Svcs)*

SPIRENT COMMUNICATIONS PLC
Origin One 108 High Street, Crawley, RH10 1BD, West Sussex, United Kingdom
Tel.: (44) 1293767676   UK
Web Site: https://www.spirent.com
Year Founded: 1936
SPT—(OTCIQ)
Rev.: $607,500,000
Assets: $705,300,000
Liabilities: $240,100,000
Net Worth: $465,200,000
Earnings: $99,900,000
Emp.: 1,600
Fiscal Year-end: 12/31/22
Network Equipment Mfr & Services
N.A.I.C.S.: 517111
Angus Iveson *(Gen Counsel & Sec)*

Subsidiaries:

Bowthorpe-Hellermann Distributors (1)
Brickyard Rd, Aldridge, WS9 8SR, Walsall, United Kingdom   (100%)
Tel.: (44) 001922458151
Web Site: http://www.hellermanntyton.co.uk
Sales Range: $25-49.9 Million
Emp.: 50
Suppliers to Electrical Whslr
N.A.I.C.S.: 423620

Spirent Communications (1)
26750 Agoura Rd, Calabasas, CA 91302   (100%)
Tel.: (818) 676-2300
Web Site: http://www.spirentcom.com
Sales Range: $75-99.9 Million
Emp.: 215
Network Performance Measurement Systems
N.A.I.C.S.: 423690
Gene Zhang *(VP-Spirent Comm-Asia)*

Division (Domestic):

Spirent Communications - CEM (2)
100 Matawan Rd Ste 300, Matawan, NJ 07747
Tel.: (732) 203-1784
Web Site: http://www.daxtechnologies.com

SPIRENT COMMUNICATIONS PLC

Spirent Communications plc—(Continued)
Sales Range: $1-9.9 Million
Emp.: 32
Customer Experience Management Software Mfr
N.A.I.C.S.: 513210

Branch (Domestic):

Spirent Communications - Germantown (2)
20324 Seneca Meadows Pkwy, Germantown, MD 20841 (100%)
Tel.: (301) 444-2400
Web Site: http://www.spirent.com
Sales Range: $25-49.9 Million
Emp.: 100
Test Equipment for the Telecommunications Industry Mfr
N.A.I.C.S.: 334515

Spirent Communications - Honolulu (2)
737 Bishop St Ste 1900, Honolulu, HI 96813-3293 (100%)
Tel.: (808) 734-3300
Web Site: http://www.spirent.com
Sales Range: $25-49.9 Million
Emp.: 58
Communication Equipment Mfr
N.A.I.C.S.: 334118
Cathy Adan (Office Mgr)

Division (Domestic):

Spirent Communications - TAS (2)
541 Industrial Way W, Eatontown, NJ 07724-2211 (100%)
Tel.: (732) 544-8700
Telecommunications Test Instrumentation Mfr
N.A.I.C.S.: 334515

Spirent Communications (Asia) Limited
51 Goldhill Plaza 19-06 Goldhill Plaza, Singapore, Singapore
Tel.: (65) 63559370
Telecommunication Servicesb
N.A.I.C.S.: 517810

Spirent Communications (India) Pvt Limited (1)
2nd Flr Umiya Business Bay Tower Marathahalli-Sarjapur Ring Road, 1 Cessna Business Park kadubeesanahalli, Bengaluru, 560103, Karnataka, India
Tel.: (91) 8041233421
Sales Range: $25-49.9 Million
Emp.: 35
Testing & Measurement Equipment Distr
N.A.I.C.S.: 423830

Spirent Communications SAS
2 Rue Rene Caudron Building G, Voisins-le-Bretonneux, 78960, France
Tel.: (33) 161372250
Sales Range: $25-49.9 Million
Emp.: 25
Telecommunication Servicesb
N.A.I.C.S.: 517810

Spirent Communications Technology (Beijing) Limited (1)
Suite 1302 Shining Tower No 35 Xue Yuan Road, Haidian District, Beijing, 100083, China
Tel.: (86) 1085182539
Telecommunication Servicesb
N.A.I.C.S.: 517810

Spirent Federal Systems Inc. (1)
1402 W State Rd, Pleasant Grove, UT 84062
Tel.: (801) 785-1448
Web Site: https://www.spirentfederal.com
Telecommunication Equipment Distr
N.A.I.C.S.: 423690
Robert Lollini (Chm)

Staeng Limited (1)
Bridge Rd Goonhaven, Truro, TR4 9QL, Cornwall, United Kingdom (100%)
Tel.: (44) 1900000000
Web Site: http://www.staeng.co.uk
Sales Range: $25-49.9 Million
Emp.: 15
Electrical Cable Harnesses Mfr
N.A.I.C.S.: 336320

Joan Cook (Gen Mgr)

Testing Technologies IST GmbH (1)
Michaelkirchstrasse 17/18, 10179, Berlin, Germany (58%)
Tel.: (49) 30 726 19 19 0
Web Site: http://www.testingtech.com
Software-based Testing Tools Developer
N.A.I.C.S.: 513210

SPIRIT BLOCKCHAIN CAPITAL INC.
Suite 1570 505 Burrard Street One Bentall Centre, Vancouver, V7X 1M5, BC, Canada
Tel.: (604) 757-0331
Web Site:
https://www.spiritblockchain.com
Year Founded: 2017
SPIR—(CNSX)
Asset Management Services
N.A.I.C.S.: 523999

SPIRIT EXPLORATION, INC.
118 Howe Street, Victoria, V8V 4K4, BC, Canada
Tel.: (250) 384-2077
Year Founded: 1998
Mining Exploration Services
N.A.I.C.S.: 213114
Terry Fields (CEO & Sec)

SPIRITUS MUNDI PLC
8th Floor The Broadgate Tower 20 Primrose Street, London, EC2A 2EW, United Kingdom UK
Web Site:
https://www.spiritusmundiplc.com
Year Founded: 2021
SPMU—(LSE)
Assets: $1,289,920
Liabilities: $30,213
Net Worth: $1,259,706
Earnings: ($969,756)
Fiscal Year-end: 09/30/22
Asset Management Services
N.A.I.C.S.: 523999
Zaccheus Peh (Founder & Chm)

SPIROX CORPORATION
No 95 Shuiyuan St, Hsin-chu, 300042, Taiwan
Tel.: (886) 35738099
Web Site: https://www.spirox.com.tw
Year Founded: 1987
3055—(TAI)
Rev.: $43,909,708
Assets: $118,519,372
Liabilities: $33,590,894
Net Worth: $84,928,477
Earnings: ($1,806,207)
Emp.: 180
Fiscal Year-end: 12/31/23
Semiconductor Manufacturing Equipment, Software & Accessories
N.A.I.C.S.: 334413
Alex Huang (VP-Customer Svc Div)

Subsidiaries:

Spirox (Shanghai) Corporation (1)
1077 Zu Chongzhi Road, Zhangjiang Hi-Tech Park, Shanghai, China
Tel.: (86) 2161081858
Web Site: http://www.spirox.com.tw
Electronic Components Distr
N.A.I.C.S.: 423690

Spirox Corporation Malaysia Sdn. Bhd. (1)
No 10 Lorong Perusahaan Maju 12 Pelangi Industrial Park,, 13600, Perai, Penang, Malaysia
Tel.: (60) 45080488
Web Site: http://www.spirox.com.tw
Sales Range: $25-49.9 Million
Emp.: 5
Electronic Components Mfr & Distr
N.A.I.C.S.: 334413

Spirox Corporation USA Inc. (1)
135 Commercial St, Sunnyvale, CA 94086 (100%)
Tel.: (408) 739-3334
Instrument Mfr for Measuring & Testing Electricity & Electrical Signals
N.A.I.C.S.: 334515

SPIT BUCOVINA SA
Calea Unirii Street 25 bis, Suceava, Romania
Tel.: (40) 761334125
Web Site:
https://www.spitbucovina.ro
SPTU—(BUC)
Rev.: $428,006
Assets: $3,476,364
Liabilities: $53,621
Net Worth: $3,422,743
Earnings: $81,383
Emp.: 12
Fiscal Year-end: 12/31/20
Motor Vehicle Parts Mfr
N.A.I.C.S.: 336390

SPITFIRE OIL LIMITED
Level 9 BGC Centre 28 The Esplanade, Perth, 6000, WA, Australia
Tel.: (61) 893210544 BM
Web Site: http://www.spitfireoil.com
Year Founded: 2007
SRO—(AIM)
Rev.: $18,713
Assets: $1,541,531
Liabilities: $40,628
Net Worth: $1,500,904
Earnings: ($658,286)
Fiscal Year-end: 06/30/19
Liquid Hydrocarbon Mfr
N.A.I.C.S.: 211130
Catharine Lymberry (Sec)

SPK ACQUISITION CORP.
Room 368 302 Buwei 211 Fute North Road, Pilot Free Trade Zone, Shanghai, 200131, China
Tel.: (86) 1343 912 9879 DE
Year Founded: 2020
SPKAU—(NASDAQ)
Rev.: $1,556
Assets: $51,280,943
Liabilities: $52,566,176
Net Worth: ($1,285,233)
Earnings: ($421,194)
Fiscal Year-end: 12/31/21
Investment Services
N.A.I.C.S.: 523999
Sophie Ye Tao (Chm & CEO)

SPK CORPORATION
5-6-28 Fukushima, Fukushima-ku, Osaka, 553-0003, Japan
Tel.: (81) 664542506 JP
Web Site: https://www.spk.co.jp
Year Founded: 1917
7466—(TKS)
Rev.: $418,426,220
Assets: $255,417,010
Liabilities: $92,870,500
Net Worth: $162,546,510
Earnings: $15,811,120
Emp.: 566
Fiscal Year-end: 03/31/24
Automotive Part Whslr
N.A.I.C.S.: 423120
Kyoichiro Oki (Pres & Pres)

Subsidiaries:

Maruyasu Shokai Ltd. (1)
8-18-14 Fukushima, Fukushima-ku, Osaka, 553-0003, Japan
Tel.: (81) 664525211
Web Site: https://www.maruyasu-s.co.jp
Automobile Parts Distr
N.A.I.C.S.: 423120

SPK EUROPE B.V. (1)
Westblaak 140 3012KM, Rotterdam, Netherlands
Tel.: (31) 104137132

INTERNATIONAL PUBLIC

Automobile Parts Distr
N.A.I.C.S.: 423120

SPK MOTORPARTS CO., LTD. (1)
168/4 Soi Watcharapol 2/1, Tharang Bangkhen, Bangkok, 10230, Thailand
Tel.: (66) 23470356
Automobile Parts Distr
N.A.I.C.S.: 423120

SPK Singapore PTE. Ltd. (1)
No 5 Kallang Pudding Road 02-01 Isetan Warehouse, Singapore, 349309, Singapore
Tel.: (65) 67496616
Web Site: https://www.spk.sg
Automobile Parts Distr
N.A.I.C.S.: 423120

SPK VEHICLE PRODUCTS SDN. BHD. (1)
No 727 4 1/2 Miles Jalan Ipoh, 51200, Kuala Lumpur, Malaysia
Tel.: (60) 362502642
Emp.: 4
Automobile Parts Distr
N.A.I.C.S.: 423120
Yosida Cherokee (Gen Mgr)

Tanikawa Yuka Kogyo Co., Ltd. (1)
13-11 Yako-1 chome, Tsurumi-ku, Yokohama, 230-0001, Kanagawa, Japan
Tel.: (81) 455816635
Brake Fluid Mfr
N.A.I.C.S.: 325998

Plant (Domestic):

Tanikawa Yuka Kogyo Co., Ltd. - Kanazawa Factory (2)
10-10 Fukuura-1 chome, Kanazawa-ku, Yokohama, Kanagawa, Japan
Tel.: (81) 457841231
Brake Fluid Mfr
N.A.I.C.S.: 325998

SPL INDUSTRIES LIMITED
Plot No 21 Sector- 6, Faridabad, 121006, India
Tel.: (91) 1292240411
Web Site: https://www.spllimited.com
Year Founded: 1994
532651—(BOM)
Rev.: $35,773,119
Assets: $25,070,523
Liabilities: $2,595,300
Net Worth: $22,475,223
Earnings: $2,857,850
Emp.: 382
Fiscal Year-end: 03/31/23
Garments Mfr
N.A.I.C.S.: 315250
Mukesh Kumar Aggarwal (Mng Dir)

SPLENDID MEDIEN AG
Lichtstr 25, 50825, Cologne, Germany
Tel.: (49) 2219542320
Web Site:
https://www.splendidmedien.com
SPM—(MUN)
Rev.: $42,653,537
Assets: $36,880,297
Liabilities: $23,865,669
Net Worth: $13,014,627
Earnings: $2,428,514
Emp.: 130
Fiscal Year-end: 12/31/23
Cinema Producer
N.A.I.C.S.: 512120
Ralph Drouven (Chm-Supervisory Bd)

Subsidiaries:

Early Learning Group GmbH (1)
Neumuhlen 17, 22763, Hamburg, Germany
Tel.: (49) 89 420 03 50
Web Site:
http://www.earlylearninggroup.com
Sales Range: $10-24.9 Million
Emp.: 20
Educational Products for Children Ages 2 Through 7
N.A.I.C.S.: 611710
Alexander Welzhofer (Mng Dir)

AND PRIVATE COMPANIES

Enteractive GmbH (1)
Stadtdeich 2-4, 20097, Hamburg, Germany
Tel.: (49) 404600180
Web Site: https://www.enteractive.de
Sales Range: $25-49.9 Million
Emp.: 35
Digital Video & Blu Ray Disc Production Services
N.A.I.C.S.: 334610

Polyband Medien GmbH. (1)
Kistlerhofstr 111, D - 81379, Munich, Germany
Tel.: (49) 89420030
Web Site: https://www.polyband.de
Sales Range: $25-49.9 Million
Emp.: 11
Movie Digital Video Disc & Blu Ray Discs Retailer
N.A.I.C.S.: 423990
Swetlana Winkel (Mng Dir)

Splendid Entertainment GmbH (1)
Lichtstr 25, 50825, Cologne, Germany
Tel.: (49) 2219542320
Movie Entertainment Services
N.A.I.C.S.: 512110
Dirk Schweitzer (Mng Dir)

Splendid Film B.V. (1)
Ellermanstraat 12, 1114 AK, Amsterdam, Netherlands
Tel.: (31) 202380700
Web Site: https://www.splendid-film.nl
Movie Entertainment Services
N.A.I.C.S.: 512110
Laurens Van Laake (Sls Mgr-Theatrical)

Splendid Film GmbH. (1)
Lichtstr 25 / Eingang F, D-50825, Cologne, Germany
Tel.: (49) 2219542320
Web Site: https://splendid-film.de
Emp.: 60
Blu Ray & Digital Video Disc Movies Whslr
N.A.I.C.S.: 423990
Andreas Ralf Klein (Mng Dir)

Splendid Studios GmbH (1)
Lichtstrasse 25, 50825, Cologne, Germany
Tel.: (49) 22196447178
Web Site: http://www.splendidstudios.webflow.io
Movie Entertainment Services
N.A.I.C.S.: 512110
Carolin Engstfeld (Head-Dev)

Splendid Synchron GmbH (1)
Alsdorfer Str 3, 50933, Cologne, 50933, Germany
Tel.: (49) 22195423247
Web Site: https://www.splendid-synchron.com
Motion Picture Dubbing & Audio Post Production Services
N.A.I.C.S.: 512191
Vera Diakhate (Mgr-Studio & Talent)

Videociety GmbH (1)
Am Stadtdeich 2-4, 20097, Hamburg, Germany
Tel.: (49) 4071661380
Web Site: https://store.maxdome.de
Movie Entertainment Services
N.A.I.C.S.: 512110

WVG Medien GmbH (1)
Neumuhlen 17, 22763, Hamburg, Germany
Tel.: (49) 4089085505
Web Site: http://www.wvg.com
Rev.: $40,394,700
Emp.: 22
Movie Digital Video Disc & Blue Ray Discs Retailer
N.A.I.C.S.: 449210
Alexander Welzhofer (Mng Dir)

SPLENDID METAL PRODUCTS LIMITED
18 Nagarjuna Hills, Punjagutta, Hyderabad, 500 082, Andhra Pradesh, India
Tel.: (91) 4023351882
Web Site: http://www.sujana.com
Rev.: $65,779,157
Assets: $196,943,122
Liabilities: $359,683,480
Net Worth: ($162,740,358)
Earnings: ($98,878,473)
Emp.: 306
Fiscal Year-end: 03/31/19
Steel Products Mfr
N.A.I.C.S.: 331110
Shaik Ibraheem (Compliance Officer & Sec)

SPLIETHOFF'S BEVRACHTINGSKANTOOR B.V.
Radarweg 36, 1042 AA, Amsterdam, Netherlands
Tel.: (31) 20 4488 400   NI
Web Site: http://www.spliethoff.com
Year Founded: 1921
Dry Cargo Shipping Services
N.A.I.C.S.: 483111
Michel Fransen (Fin Dir & Member-Exec Bd)

Subsidiaries:

BigLift Shipping B.V. (1)
Radarweg 36, 1042 AA, Amsterdam, Netherlands
Tel.: (31) 20 4488300
Web Site: http://www.bigliftshipping.com
Cargo Handling Services
N.A.I.C.S.: 488320
Arne Hubregtse (Mng Dir)

Subsidiary (US):

BigLift Shipping inc (2)
1415 Louisiana St Ste 3460, Houston, TX 77002
Tel.: (713) 812-0913
Cargo Handling Services
N.A.I.C.S.: 488320
Peter Ludwig (Mgr-Sls & Mktg)

BigLift Shipping FZE (1)
PO Box 28512, Dubai, United Arab Emirates
Tel.: (971) 50 6544 795
Web Site: http://www.bigliftshipping.com
Emp.: 300
Cargo Handling Services
N.A.I.C.S.: 488320
Suresh Iyer (Gen Mgr)

Bore Ltd. (1)
Bulevardi 46, 00120, Helsinki, Finland
Tel.: (358) 9 132 6300
Web Site: http://www.bore.eu
Sales Range: $25-49.9 Million
Emp.: 214
Shipping Services
N.A.I.C.S.: 488510
Hakan Modig (CEO)

OOO Transfennica Russia (1)
Gladky ostrov 1 Office 22, 198095, Saint Petersburg, Russia
Tel.: (7) 8123399189
Cargo Handling Services
N.A.I.C.S.: 488320

Sevenstar Yacht Transport B.V. (1)
Radarweg 36, Amsterdam, 1042AA, Netherlands
Tel.: (31) 2044 88590
Web Site: http://www.sevenstar-yacht-transport.com
Emp.: 15
Yacht Shipping Services
N.A.I.C.S.: 483111
Richard Klabbers (Mng Dir)

Subsidiary (US):

Dockwise Yacht Transport, LLC (2)
1535 SE 17th St Ste 200, Fort Lauderdale, FL 33316
Tel.: (954) 525-8707
Web Site: http://www.yacht-transport.com
Sales Range: $25-49.9 Million
Emp.: 30
Yacht Shipping Services
N.A.I.C.S.: 483111
Gina Last (Gen Sls Mgr)

Transfennica (UK) Ltd (1)
Finland House 47 Berth Tilbury port, Tilbury, RM18 7EH, Essex, United Kingdom
Tel.: (44) 1375 363 900
Cargo Handling Services
N.A.I.C.S.: 488320

Andrew Clarke (Dir-Sls)

Transfennica Belgium B.V.B.A. (1)
Land van Waaslaan Haven 1211, 9130, Kallo, Belgium
Tel.: (32) 3 570 9292
Web Site: http://www.transfennica.com
Emp.: 17
Cargo Handling Services
N.A.I.C.S.: 488320
Mario Vanlancker (Mgr-Sls)

Transfennica Deutschland GmbH (1)
Seelandstrasse 31, 23569, Lubeck, Germany
Tel.: (49) 451 484 850
Cargo Handling Services
N.A.I.C.S.: 488320

Transfennica Ltd (1)
Etelaranta 12, 00130, Helsinki, Finland
Tel.: (358) 9 132 62
Cargo Handling Services
N.A.I.C.S.: 488320
Sami Rokka (Mgr-Ops)

Transfennica OU (1)
Rae poik 10, 76806, Paldiski, Estonia
Tel.: (372) 6 318 870
Cargo Handling Services
N.A.I.C.S.: 488320

Transfennica Polska Sp. z o.o. (1)
Al Solidarnosci 1 C, 81336, Gdynia, Poland
Tel.: (48) 58 660 1260
Cargo Handling Services
N.A.I.C.S.: 488320

Wijnne & Barends' cargadoors-en agentuurkantoren bv (1)
Handelskade Oost 5, 9934 AR, Delfzijl, Netherlands
Tel.: (31) 596 63 77 77
Web Site: http://www.wijnnebarends.com
Cargo Handling Services
N.A.I.C.S.: 488320

SPLITIT PAYMENTS LTD.
Rialto South Tower 525 Collins St, Melbourne, 3000, VIC, Australia
Tel.: (61) 396142444
Web Site: https://www.splitit.com
SPT—(ASX)
Rev.: $10,638,000
Assets: $103,686,000
Liabilities: $77,198,000
Net Worth: $26,488,000
Earnings: ($22,614,000)
Fiscal Year-end: 12/31/22
Payment Management Services
N.A.I.C.S.: 522320
Nandan Sheth (CEO)

SPM JOINT STOCK COMPANY
Lot 51 Road No 2 Tan Tao Industrial Park, Binh Tan District, Ho Chi Minh City, Vietnam
Tel.: (84) 2837507496
Web Site: https://www.spm.com.vn
SPM—(HOSE)
Rev.: $16,731,526
Assets: $42,286,609
Liabilities: $9,078,544
Net Worth: $33,208,065
Earnings: $499,220
Fiscal Year-end: 12/31/23
Pharmaceuticals Product Mfr
N.A.I.C.S.: 325412
Dao Huu Hoang (Chm)

SPML INFRA LIMITED
F-27/2 Okhla Industrial Area Phase-II, New Delhi, 110020, India
Tel.: (91) 1126387091
Web Site: https://www.spml.co.in
Year Founded: 1981
SPMLINFRA—(NSE)
Rev.: $101,914,654
Assets: $371,345,930
Liabilities: $333,489,306
Net Worth: $37,856,623
Earnings: ($15,998,769)
Emp.: 325

Fiscal Year-end: 03/31/21
Engineeering Services
N.A.I.C.S.: 541330
Subhash Chand Sethi (Chm)

Subsidiaries:

SPML Technologies Limited (1)
16 Apple Villa 3rd Floor Left Wing Lalbagh Road, Bengaluru, 560027, India
Tel.: (91) 80 22110461
Web Site: http://www.sums.in
Sales Range: $25-49.9 Million
Emp.: 85
Information Technology Consulting Services
N.A.I.C.S.: 541512
Deepak Sethi (Mng Dir)

Uttarkashi Tons Hydro Power Private Ltd. (1)
F-27/2 Okhla Industrial Area Phase II, New Delhi, 110 020, India
Tel.: (91) 11 26387091
Sales Range: $1-4.9 Billion
Hydroelectric Power Generation Services
N.A.I.C.S.: 221111

SPO GLOBAL INC.
27/F Block A Jinan Pharma Valley, Shandong, 33634, China
Tel.: (86) 53158708846   DE
Web Site: http://www.gerpanghealthcare.com
Year Founded: 1981
SPOM—(OTCIQ)
Rev.: $19,444,000
Assets: $7,811,000
Liabilities: $242,000
Net Worth: $7,569,000
Earnings: $526,000
Fiscal Year-end: 12/31/20
Medical Device Mfr
N.A.I.C.S.: 339112
Fengyou Lu (CEO)

SPOBAG AG
Alter Hof 5, 40212, Munich, Germany
Tel.: (49) 895527580
Web Site: https://www.spobag-ag.de
SBE—(DEU)
Assets: $319,860
Liabilities: $639,720
Net Worth: ($319,860)
Earnings: ($74,634)
Fiscal Year-end: 12/31/22
Asset Management Services
N.A.I.C.S.: 531390
Maik Brockmann (Member-Mgmt Bd)

SPODE LIMITED
Church St, Stoke-on-Trent, ST4 1BX, United Kingdom
Tel.: (44) 1782744011
Web Site: http://www.spode.co.uk
Year Founded: 1770
Sales Range: $75-99.9 Million
Emp.: 500
China Tableware & Giftware Mfr
N.A.I.C.S.: 327110
David Benjamin (Mng Dir)

Subsidiaries:

The Royal China & Porcelain Companies Inc. (1)
107 Olympic Club Ct, Blue Bell, PA 19422-1282
Tel.: (856) 866-2900
Rev.: $30,000,000
Emp.: 100
Distr of Fine Bone China, Porcelain & Oven-to-Tableware; Fine Stone China & Earthenware & Giftware Products
N.A.I.C.S.: 339910

SPOHN & BURKHARDT GMBH & CO. KG
Mauergasse 5, 89143, Blaubeuren, Germany
Tel.: (49) 73441710
Web Site: http://www.spobu.de

Spohn & Burkhardt GmbH & Co. KG—(Continued)
Year Founded: 1920
Rev.: $30,200,000
Emp.: 230
Controlling Equipment Mfr
N.A.I.C.S.: 335314
Markus Seifert *(Mng Dir)*

SPOLYTECH CO., LTD.
275 Hansam-ro Deoksan-eup, Jincheon, 27850, Chungcheongbuk-do, Korea (South)
Tel.: (82) 435369191
Web Site: https://www.spolytech.com
Year Founded: 1991
050760—(KRS)
Rev.: $63,246,458
Assets: $83,325,431
Liabilities: $33,138,174
Net Worth: $50,187,257
Earnings: ($2,168,811)
Emp.: 142
Fiscal Year-end: 12/31/22
Plastics Product Mfr
N.A.I.C.S.: 326112
Hyuck Yul Lee *(CEO)*

SPONSOR CAPITAL OY
Mannerheimintie 4, 00100, Helsinki, Finland
Tel.: (358) 96803300
Web Site: http://www.sponsor.fi
Year Founded: 1926
Sales Range: $25-49.9 Million
Emp.: 11
Privater Equity Firm
N.A.I.C.S.: 523999
Matti Suutarinen *(Chm & Partner)*

Subsidiaries:

Hittapunktse AB (1)
Celsius Gatam 10, Stockholm, 11230, Sweden
Tel.: (46) 8 444 95 00
Web Site: http://www.hitta.se
Emp.: 45
Advertising Agencies
N.A.I.C.S.: 541810
Alexander Hannerland *(Gen Mgr)*

SPONSORSONE INC.
2 Campbell Drive Suite 307C, Uxbridge, L9P 1H6, ON, Canada
Tel.: (647) 400-6927
Web Site:
 https://www.sponsorsone.com
SPONF—(OTCEM)
Rev.: $189,124
Assets: $417,220
Liabilities: $1,718,053
Net Worth: ($1,300,833)
Earnings: ($19,822,900)
Fiscal Year-end: 12/31/21
Cloud-Based Marketing Platform Connecting Brands With Social Marketing
N.A.I.C.S.: 541890
Myles Bartholomew *(Pres & CEO)*

Subsidiaries:

HS Brands Inc. (1)
36 Scotts Road, Bromley, BR1 3QD, United Kingdom
Tel.: (44) 294454511
Web Site: https://hsbrands.eu
Social Media Monitoring Services
N.A.I.C.S.: 541511

SPOONER INDUSTRIES LTD.
Railway Road, Ilkley, LS29 8JB, W Yorkshire, United Kingdom
Tel.: (44) 1943609505 UK
Web Site: http://www.spooner.co.uk
Sales Range: $10-24.9 Million
Emp.: 104
Mfr of Drying Equipment
N.A.I.C.S.: 333414

Steve Newell *(Dir-Sls & Mktg)*

SPORT LISBOA E BENFICA - FUTEBOL SAD
18 Av Eusebio da Silva Ferreira, 1500, Lisbon, Portugal
Tel.: (351) 217219500
Web Site: https://www.slbenfica.pt
SLBEN—(EUR)
Sales Range: $125-149.9 Million
Football Club Operator
N.A.I.C.S.: 711211

SPORT1 MEDIEN AG
Munchener Strasse 101g, 85737, Ismaning, Germany
Tel.: (49) 89995000 De
Web Site: http://www.constantin-medien.de
Rev.: $136,200,226
Assets: $104,128,354
Liabilities: $35,329,386
Net Worth: $68,798,969
Earnings: ($4,966,336)
Emp.: 583
Fiscal Year-end: 12/31/18
Sports Segment Media Company
N.A.I.C.S.: 541840
Paul Graf *(Chm-Supervisory Bd)*

Subsidiaries:

Plazamedia GmbH (1)
Munchener Strasse 101, 85737, Ismaning, Germany
Tel.: (49) 89996330
Web Site: https://www.plazamedia.com
Emp.: 150
Media Production Services
N.A.I.C.S.: 512110

Tridem Sports AG (1)
Wolleraustrasse 15n, 8807, Freienbach, Schwyz, Switzerland
Tel.: (41) 442246900
Web Site: http://www.tridemsports.com
Sales Range: $50-74.9 Million
Emp.: 6
Sports Management Services
N.A.I.C.S.: 711211
Christian Pirze *(Founder)*

SPORTECH PLC
Icarus House Hawkfield Business Park, Bristol, BS14 0BN, United Kingdom
Tel.: (44) 1179029000 UK
Web Site:
 http://www.sportechplc.com
SPO—(LSE)
Rev.: $27,108,238
Assets: $77,237,975
Liabilities: $43,079,098
Net Worth: $34,158,877
Earnings: ($17,422,263)
Emp.: 379
Fiscal Year-end: 12/31/20
Holding Company; Online Gambling Sites, Gaming Venues & Sport Betting Pools Operator
N.A.I.C.S.: 551112
Ted Taylor *(Pres-Sportech Venues)*

Subsidiaries:

Sportech Gaming Limited (1)
Walton House 55 Charnock Road, Liverpool, L67 1AA, Merseyside, United Kingdom
Tel.: (44) 1515253677
Web Site: http://www.sportechplc.com
Gambling Industries
N.A.I.C.S.: 713290

Sportech Racing GmbH (1)
Leesdorfer Haupstrasse 96/3/12, Baden, 2500, Austria
Tel.: (43) 17261035
Football Pools Operating Services
N.A.I.C.S.: 611620

Sportech Racing GmbH (1)
Katernberger St 107, Essen, 45327, Germany
Tel.: (49) 2018306300
Web Site: http://www.sportechplc.com
Sales Range: $25-49.9 Million
Emp.: 30
Online Gambling Services
N.A.I.C.S.: 517810

Sportech Racing LLC (1)
1095 Windward Ridge Pkwy Ste 170, Alpharetta, GA 30005-1728
Tel.: (678) 710-2937
Web Site: http://www.sportechplc.com
Sales Range: $25-49.9 Million
Tote Gaming Services
N.A.I.C.S.: 924120

Sportech Trustees Limited (1)
Walton House 55 Charnock Road, Liverpool, L67 1AA, Merseyside, United Kingdom
Tel.: (44) 1515253677
Holding Company
N.A.I.C.S.: 551112

Sportech Venues Inc (1)
600 Long Wharf Dr, New Haven, CT 06511
Tel.: (203) 946-3100
Betting Services
N.A.I.C.S.: 713290

Sports Hub Private Limited (1)
Ugf 30 1st Floor Vyapar Kendra Sushant Lok-I, Gurgaon, 122001, Haryana, India
Tel.: (91) 1242573583
Online Gaming Site Operation Services
N.A.I.C.S.: 517810
Bryn Jones *(Chm & Acting CEO)*

SPORTING CLUBE DE BRAGA
Parque Norte Ap 12, PT-4710-251, Braga, Portugal
Tel.: (351) 253206860
Web Site: https://www.scbraga.pt
SCB—(EUR)
Sales Range: $10-24.9 Million
Football Sport Club Services
N.A.I.C.S.: 711211
Antonio Manuel Rodrigues Marques *(CEO)*

SPORTING CLUBE DE PORTUGAL - FUTEBOL, SAD
Rua Professor Fernando da Fonseca, PO Box 4120, 1501-806, Lisbon, Portugal
Tel.: (351) 217516000
Web Site: https://www.sporting.pt
Year Founded: 1906
SCP—(EUR)
Sales Range: $75-99.9 Million
Emp.: 268
Soccer Club Operator
N.A.I.C.S.: 711211
Bruno de Carvalho *(Pres)*

SPORTKING INDIA LTD.
Village Kanech Near Sahnewal GT Road, Ludhiana, 141120, Punjab, India
Tel.: (91) 1612845456
Web Site: https://www.sportking.co.in
539221—(BOM)
Rev.: $180,840,592
Assets: $140,868,191
Liabilities: $92,154,631
Net Worth: $48,713,560
Earnings: $11,538,168
Emp.: 5,550
Fiscal Year-end: 03/31/21
Textile Products Mfr
N.A.I.C.S.: 314999
Munish Avasthi *(Mng Dir)*

Subsidiaries:

Sobhagia Sales Pvt. Ltd. (1)
G T Road, Village Sahnewal Khurd, Ludhiana, 141120, Punjab, India
Tel.: (91) 1612846387
Web Site: http://www.sportking.co.in
Garments Mfr

N.A.I.C.S.: 315250
Parveen Kumar Gupta *(CFO)*

SPORTON INTERNATIONAL, INC.
6F No 106-B Sec 1 Sintai 5th Rd, Sijhih Dist, New Taipei City, Taiwan
Tel.: (886) 226962468
Web Site:
 https://www.sporton.com.tw
Year Founded: 1986
6146—(TPE)
Rev.: $156,809,055
Assets: $224,137,604
Liabilities: $57,554,826
Net Worth: $166,582,778
Earnings: $50,058,938
Emp.: 758
Fiscal Year-end: 12/31/22
Electromagnetic Product Mfr
N.A.I.C.S.: 334513
Wen-Liang Huang *(Chm & Pres)*

SPORTRADAR GROUP AG
Feldlistr 2, CH-9000, Saint Gallen, Switzerland
Tel.: (41) 715177200 CH
Web Site: https://sportradar.com
Year Founded: 2018
SRAD—(NASDAQ)
Rev.: $947,141,161
Assets: $2,425,372,329
Liabilities: $1,483,394,129
Net Worth: $941,978,200
Earnings: $36,578,891
Emp.: 4,383
Fiscal Year-end: 12/31/23
Holding Company
N.A.I.C.S.: 551112
Lynn S. McCreary *(Chief Legal Officer & Sec)*

Subsidiaries:

NSoft d.o.o. (1)
Dubrovacka bb, 88000, Mostar, Bosnia & Herzegovina
Tel.: (387) 36317710
Web Site: https://www.nsoft.com
Emp.: 300
Information Technology Services
N.A.I.C.S.: 541511

Optima BEG d.o.o. (1)
Cara Dusana br 1, 21000, Novi Sad, Serbia
Tel.: (381) 216622111
Web Site: https://www.optima.rs
Mechanical Equipment Whslr
N.A.I.C.S.: 423830

Ortec Sports B.V. (1)
Houtsingel 5, 2719 EA, Zoetermeer, Netherlands
Tel.: (31) 886783265
Web Site: https://ortec.com
Information Technology Services
N.A.I.C.S.: 541511

Sportradar AB (1)
Gamla Brogatan 11, 11120, Stockholm, Sweden
Tel.: (46) 855803090
Sports Technology Services
N.A.I.C.S.: 711219

Sportradar AS (1)
Ferjemannsveien 10, 7042, Trondheim, Norway
Tel.: (47) 73101416
Sports Technology Services
N.A.I.C.S.: 711219

Sportradar Germany GmbH (1)
Dingolfinger Str 4, 81673, Munich, Germany
Tel.: (49) 8920008451259
Sports Technology Services
N.A.I.C.S.: 711219

Sportradar Informacijske Tehnologije d.o.o. (1)
Brnciceva ulica 41G, Crnuce, 1231, Ljubljana, Slovenia
Tel.: (386) 17774200
Sports Technology Services
N.A.I.C.S.: 711219

AND PRIVATE COMPANIES / SPRAYKING AGRO EQUIPMENT LIMITED

Sportradar Media Services GmbH (1)
Hosnedigasse 25, 1220, Vienna, Austria
Tel.: (43) 125631410
Gaming Technology Services
N.A.I.C.S.: 713290

Sportradar OU (1)
Mustamae tee 16, 10617, Tallinn, Estonia
Tel.: (372) 6681867
Gaming Technology Services
N.A.I.C.S.: 713290

Sportradar SA (Pty.) Ltd. (1)
Suite 1 3 Douglas Crowe Drive, Ballito, South Africa
Tel.: (27) 311002319
Sports Technology Services
N.A.I.C.S.: 711219

Sportradar Virtual Gaming GmbH (1)
Konsul-Smidt-Strasse 8f, 28217, Bremen, Germany
Tel.: (49) 4216195640
Gaming Technology Services
N.A.I.C.S.: 713290

SPORTS EXCELLENCE CORPORATION INC.
151 Alston suite 100, Pointe-Claire, H9R 5V9, QC, Canada
Tel.: (418) 687-0133
Web Site: https://sportsexcellence.com
Year Founded: 1950
Rev.: $38,947,575
Emp.: 45
Sporting Stores
N.A.I.C.S.: 459110
Rachelle Chicoine (Controller)

SPORTS RECRUITMENT INTERNATIONAL LTD.
150 Buckingham Palace Road, London, SW1 9TR, United Kingdom
Tel.: (44) 207 092 6950   UK
Web Site: http://www.sportsrecruitment.com
Year Founded: 2001
Consulting Firm
N.A.I.C.S.: 541618
Michael Squires (Chm)

Subsidiaries:

SRI Cheyenne, Inc. (1)
The French Bldg 551 5th Ave Ste 417, New York, NY 10176
Tel.: (212) 471-5008
Web Site: http://www.sricheyenne.com
Professional, Scientific & Technical Services
N.A.I.C.S.: 541990
Jay Hussey (CEO)

SPORTSFIELD CO., LTD.
FORECAST Ichigaya 4F 3-29 Honmuracho Ichigaya, Shinjuku-Ku, Tokyo, 162-0845, Japan
Tel.: (81) 352251481
Web Site: https://www.sports-f.co.jp
Year Founded: 2010
7080—(TKS)
Rev.: $24,233,620
Assets: $16,377,900
Liabilities: $6,529,890
Net Worth: $9,848,010
Earnings: $4,310,720
Emp.: 272
Fiscal Year-end: 12/31/23
Management Consulting Services
N.A.I.C.S.: 541613
Katsushi Shinozaki (Chm & Pres)

SPORTSNET
ATA Center Ahi Evren Cad No1 Kat G1, Maslak, 34398, Istanbul, Turkiye
Tel.: (90) 212 329 26 00
Web Site: http://www.sportsnet.com.tr
Emp.: 110
N.A.I.C.S.: 541810

Ahmet Gulum (CEO)

SPORTSOUL CO., LTD.
No 3 Ronghai 2nd Road, Chengyang District, Qingdao, 266111, Shandong, China
Tel.: (86) 53255678903
Web Site: https://www.sportsoul.com
Year Founded: 2004
001300—(SSE)
Rev.: $79,625,501
Assets: $177,237,633
Liabilities: $24,032,184
Net Worth: $153,205,449
Earnings: $9,224,505
Emp.: 1,130
Fiscal Year-end: 12/31/22
Fitness Equipment Mfr & Distr
N.A.I.C.S.: 339920
Zhu Xilong (Chm & Gen Mgr)

SPORTSWIFT LIMITED
Century House, Brunel Road, Wakefield, WF2 0XG, West Yorkshire, United Kingdom
Tel.: (44) 1924 839 150
Web Site: http://www.cardfactory.eu.com
Year Founded: 1997
Sales Range: $300-349.9 Million
Emp.: 5,200
Gifts & Novelties Retailer
N.A.I.C.S.: 459420
Karen Hubbard (CEO)

Subsidiaries:

Getting Personal Ltd (1)
1st Floor Southmoor House Southmoor Ind Est Southmoor Road, Wythenshawe, Manchester, M23 9XD, United Kingdom
Tel.: (44) 3303334220
Web Site: http://www.gettingpersonal.co.uk
Sales Range: $10-24.9 Million
Emp.: 30
Online Gift Retailer
N.A.I.C.S.: 423990
John Smith (Founder)

SPORTSWORLD MEDIA GROUP PLC
6 Henrietta Street Covent Garden, London, WC2E 8PU, United Kingdom
Tel.: (44) 207 240 9626
Television Broadcasting Services
N.A.I.C.S.: 516120
Christopher Robin Akers (Chm)

SPORTTOTAL AG
Am Coloneum 2, 50829, Cologne, Germany
Tel.: (49) 221788770
Web Site: https://www.sporttotal.com
WIG1—(MUN)
Rev.: $49,210,525
Assets: $16,403,508
Liabilities: $50,402,704
Net Worth: ($33,999,196)
Earnings: ($9,460,166)
Emp.: 102
Fiscal Year-end: 12/31/23
Television Broadcasting Services
N.A.I.C.S.: 516120
Peter Lauterbach (Chm-Exec Bd & CEO)

Subsidiaries:

SPORTTOTAL Content Marketing GmbH (1)
Am Coloneum 2, 50829, Cologne, Germany
Tel.: (49) 221788770
TV Broadcasting Services
N.A.I.C.S.: 516120

SPORTTOTAL Event GmbH (1)
Am Coloneum 2, 50829, Cologne, Germany
Tel.: (49) 221788770
TV Broadcasting Services
N.A.I.C.S.: 516120

SPORTTOTAL Venues GmbH (1)
Industriestrasse 33, 53359, Rheinbach, Germany
Tel.: (49) 221788770
TV Broadcasting Services
N.A.I.C.S.: 516120

SPOT COFFEE (CANADA) LTD.
130 Queens Quay East Suite 611, Toronto, M5A 0P6, ON, Canada
Tel.: (416) 368-2220
Web Site: https://www.spotcoffee.com
Year Founded: 2007
33O—(DEU)
Rev.: $5,908,649
Assets: $4,483,071
Liabilities: $7,666,341
Net Worth: ($3,183,270)
Earnings: ($577,149)
Emp.: 100
Fiscal Year-end: 12/31/22
Cafe Development Services
N.A.I.C.S.: 722310

Subsidiaries:

Spot Coffee Glen (1)
221 Glen St, Glens Falls, NY 12801
Tel.: (518) 223-0192
Coffee Distr
N.A.I.C.S.: 424490

Spot Coffee Saratoga LLC (1)
55 Railroad Pl, Saratoga Springs, NY 12866
Tel.: (518) 306-5323
Coffee Distr
N.A.I.C.S.: 424490

Spot Coffee Transit Inc. (1)
5205 Transit Rd, Clarence, NY 14221
Tel.: (716) 276-8158
Coffee Distr
N.A.I.C.S.: 424490

SPOTIFY AB
Birger Jarlsgatan 61 10tr, 113 56, Stockholm, Sweden
Tel.: (46) 72224000   SE
Web Site: http://www.spotify.com
Year Founded: 2006
Sales Range: $200-249.9 Million
Emp.: 500
Holding Company; Online Music Streaming Services
N.A.I.C.S.: 551112
Daniel Ek (Founder, Chm & CEO)

Subsidiaries:

Spotify Hong Kong Ltd. (1)
45/F The Lee Gardens, Causeway Bay, China (Hong Kong)
Tel.: (852) 25266898
Web Site: http://www.spotify.com
Online Music Streaming Services
N.A.I.C.S.: 518210
Ong Sea Yen (VP-Sls-Asia)

Spotify Limited (1)
4th Floor 25 Argyll Street, London, W1F 7TU, United Kingdom
Tel.: (44) 2032 879 990
Web Site: http://www.spotify.com
Online Music Streaming Services
N.A.I.C.S.: 518210
Nikki Lambert (Mktg Dir-Europe)

Spotify USA Inc. (1)
45 W 18th St 7th Fl, New York, NY 10011
Tel.: (646) 837-5380
Web Site: http://www.spotify.com
Sales Range: $50-74.9 Million
Emp.: 125
Online Music Streaming Services
N.A.I.C.S.: 518210
Seth Farbman (CMO-Global)

SPOTIFY TECHNOLOGY S.A.
5 Place de la Gare, L- 1616, Luxembourg, Luxembourg
Tel.: (352) 46702204607   LU
Web Site: https://www.spotify.com
Year Founded: 2006
SPOT—(NYSE)
Rev.: $12,221,682,200
Assets: $7,700,019,600
Liabilities: $5,372,299,800
Net Worth: $2,327,719,800
Earnings: ($490,823,200)
Emp.: 9,123
Fiscal Year-end: 12/31/23
Music Streaming Services
N.A.I.C.S.: 512250
Daniel Ek (Founder, Chm & CEO)

Subsidiaries:

Megaphone, LLC (1)
1255 23rd St NW Ste 650, Washington, DC 20037
Tel.: (646) 693-5823
Web Site: http://www.megaphone.fm
Emp.: 55
Advertising Periodical Publisher
N.A.I.C.S.: 513120

SPOTLIGHT PTY. LTD.
Level 6 111 Cecil Street, South Melbourne, 3205, VIC, Australia
Tel.: (61) 396820866
Web Site: http://www.spotlightstores.com
Year Founded: 1973
Apparel & Accessory Distr
N.A.I.C.S.: 458110
Quentin Gracanin (CEO)

SPOTLIO A.S.
Sorkedalsveien 6, 0369, Oslo, Norway
Tel.: (47) 7795953849
Web Site: https://www.spotlio.com
Year Founded: 2016
SPOT—(OSL)
Rev.: $8,507,518
Assets: $28,106,070
Liabilities: $6,951,457
Net Worth: $21,154,613
Earnings: ($16,804,527)
Emp.: 3
Fiscal Year-end: 05/31/21
Holding Company
N.A.I.C.S.: 551112
James Price (CFO)

SPOTLITE360 IOT SOLUTIONS, INC.
810 - 789 West Pender Street, Vancouver, BC V6C 1H2, Canada
Tel.: (604) 687-2038
Web Site: https://www.spotlite360.com
Year Founded: 2014
LITE—(CNSX)
Rev.: $8,326
Assets: $2,465,235
Liabilities: $2,247,453
Net Worth: $217,782
Earnings: ($7,861,708)
Fiscal Year-end: 12/31/22
Software Development; Logistics Technologies Solutions
N.A.I.C.S.: 513210
Gene McConnell (CFO)

SPRAYKING AGRO EQUIPMENT LIMITED
Plot No 237/B Shop No 4 GIDC Phase II Dared, Jamnagar, 361 005, Gujarat, India
Tel.: (91) 2882730750
Web Site: https://www.spraykingagro.com
Year Founded: 1980
540079—(BOM)
Rev.: $2,798,777
Assets: $1,339,835
Liabilities: $145,520
Net Worth: $1,194,315

Sprayking Agro Equipment Limited—(Continued)
Earnings: $84,681
Emp.: 17
Fiscal Year-end: 03/31/21
Metal Product Mfr & Distr
N.A.I.C.S.: 332323

SPREA EDITORI S.P.A.
Via Torino 51, 20063, Cernusco sul Naviglio, Italy
Tel.: (39) 02924321
Web Site: http://www.sprea.it
Sales Range: $25-49.9 Million
Emp.: 100
Periodical Publishers
N.A.I.C.S.: 513120
Luca Sprea (Pres)

Subsidiaries:

Sprea Media Italy SpA (1)
Via Torino 51, 20063, Cernusco sul Naviglio, MI, Italy
Tel.: (39) 02924321
Web Site: http://www.sprea.it
Sales Range: $25-49.9 Million
Emp.: 89
Magazine Publisher
N.A.I.C.S.: 513120
Bernardo Notarangelo (Mng Dir)

SPREHE GEFLUGEL- UND TIEFKUHLFEINKOST HANDELS GMBH & CO. KG
Ziepelkamp 8, 26901, Lorup, Germany
Tel.: (49) 59 54 9215 0   De
Web Site: http://www.sprehe.de
Meat & Poultry Processing, Packaging & Foods Whslr
N.A.I.C.S.: 311612

Subsidiaries:

Bernard Matthews Oldenburg GmbH (1)
Wilhelmshavener Heerstrasse 100, 26125, Oldenburg, Germany
Tel.: (49) 441930950
Web Site: http://www.bernard-matthews.de
Sales Range: $50-74.9 Million
Emp.: 128
Poultry Processing & Food Products Whslr
N.A.I.C.S.: 311615
Stefan Geisler (Mng Dir)

Sprehe Geflugel- und Tiefkuhlfeinkost Handels GmbH & Co. KG - Cloppenburg Plant (1)
Muhlenstrasse 21, 49661, Cloppenburg, Germany
Tel.: (49) 4471 85031 0
Web Site: http://www.sprehe.de
Animal Slaughtering & Meat Packing Services
N.A.I.C.S.: 311612

SPRIND D.D. SARAJEVO
Rajlovacka Cesta bb, Rajlovac, 71000, Sarajevo, Bosnia & Herzegovina
Tel.: (387) 3 372 5400
Web Site: http://www.sprind.ba
Year Founded: 1982
SPRDR—(SARE)
Rev.: $2,308,731
Assets: $14,550,903
Liabilities: $11,008,035
Net Worth: $3,542,868
Earnings: ($84,320)
Emp.: 123
Fiscal Year-end: 12/31/20
Bakery Products Mfr
N.A.I.C.S.: 311813

SPRING AIRLINES CO., LTD.
Building No 2 No 528 Konggang 1st Road, Changning District, Shanghai, 200335, China
Tel.: (86) 2122353088
Web Site: http://www.ch.com

Year Founded: 2004
601021—(SHG)
Rev.: $1,175,002,869
Assets: $6,096,123,283
Liabilities: $4,173,641,428
Net Worth: $1,922,481,854
Earnings: ($426,229,577)
Fiscal Year-end: 12/31/22
Airline Transportation Services
N.A.I.C.S.: 481111

SPRING ART HOLDINGS BERHAD
Lot Plo 49 Jalan Rami 4 Kawasan Persindustrian, Bukit Pasir, 84300, Muar, Malaysia
Tel.: (60) 69859971   MY
Web Site: https://www.springart.com
Year Founded: 1996
SPRING—(KLS)
Rev.: $9,592,407
Assets: $22,192,711
Liabilities: $5,227,636
Net Worth: $16,965,074
Earnings: $459,244
Emp.: 183
Fiscal Year-end: 12/31/22
Holding Company
N.A.I.C.S.: 551112
Christine Teo (CFO)

SPRING PHARMACEUTICAL GROUP, INC.
c/o Shandong Spring Pharmaceutical Co., Ltd., Economic Development Zone Gucheng Road Sishui, Shandong, 373200, China
Tel.: (86) 537 4268271   DE
Web Site: http://www.yctgroup.com
Rev.: $64,942,737
Assets: $110,138,099
Liabilities: $1,982,809
Net Worth: $108,155,290
Earnings: $11,386,333
Emp.: 313
Fiscal Year-end: 03/31/18
Pharmaceuticals Mfr
N.A.I.C.S.: 325412
Tinghe Yan (Chm & CEO)

SPRING VENTURES LTD.
94 Yigal Alon St, Tel Aviv, 6789139, Israel
Tel.: (972) 035434060   Il
Web Site: https://springv.com
Year Founded: 1999
SPRG—(TAE)
Assets: $34,194,501
Liabilities: $1,153,750
Net Worth: $33,040,751
Earnings: ($9,915,458)
Emp.: 48
Fiscal Year-end: 12/31/23
Miscellaneous Financial Investment Activities
N.A.I.C.S.: 523999
Aviv Refuah (Founder)

SPRINGER & JACOBY OSTERREICH GMBH
Schonbrunner Strasse 31/31, 1050, Vienna, Austria
Tel.: (43) 1 715 10 50 50
Web Site: http://www.sjaustria.com
Advertising Services
N.A.I.C.S.: 541810
Ralf Kober (Mng Dir-Consulting)

Subsidiaries:

Springer & Jacoby El Laboratorio S.L. (1)
Paseo De La Castellana 165, 28046, Madrid, Spain
Tel.: (34) 91 310 72 60
Web Site: http://www.sj.com

Sales Range: $10-24.9 Million
N.A.I.C.S.: 541810
Marisa De Madariaga (Mng Dir)

Springer & Jacoby International B.V. (1)
Keizersgracht 253, 1016 EB, Amsterdam, Netherlands
Tel.: (31) 20 794 06 00
N.A.I.C.S.: 541810

SPRINGFIELD PROPERTIES PLC
Alexander Fleming House 8 Southfield Drive Elgin, Elgin, IV30 6GR, United Kingdom
Tel.: (44) 1343552550   UK
Web Site:
https://www.springfield.co.uk
Year Founded: 1956
SPR—(AIM)
Rev.: $337,109,520
Assets: $377,232,240
Liabilities: $189,035,704
Net Worth: $188,196,536
Earnings: $21,070,984
Fiscal Year-end: 05/31/22
Real Estate Development Services
N.A.I.C.S.: 531210
Sandy Adam (Founder & Chm)

Subsidiaries:

Dawn Homes Limited (1)
220 West George Street, Glasgow, G2 2PG, United Kingdom
Tel.: (44) 1412856700
Web Site: http://www.dawn-homes.co.uk
Residential Construction
N.A.I.C.S.: 236118

Walker Group (Scotland) Limited (1)
Springfield House 3 Central Park Avenue, Larbert, FK5 4RX, United Kingdom
Tel.: (44) 1506413101
Web Site: http://www.walkergroup.co.uk
Residential Construction
N.A.I.C.S.: 236118

SPRINGLAND INTERNATIONAL HOLDINGS LIMITED
Suite 1508 15/F Cityplaza Four 12 Taikoo Wan Road, Taikoo Shang Island East, Hong Kong, China (Hong Kong)
Tel.: (852) 35863665   Ky
Web Site:
http://www.springlandgroup.com.cn
Rev.: $669,948,833
Assets: $1,823,908,827
Liabilities: $1,073,721,143
Net Worth: $750,187,684
Earnings: $57,625,181
Emp.: 8,833
Fiscal Year-end: 12/31/18
Department Stores
N.A.I.C.S.: 455110
Jianqiang Chen (Founder, Chm & CEO)

SPRINGWALL SLEEP PRODUCTS INC.
PO Box 745, Scoudouc, E1C 8M9, NB, Canada
Tel.: (506) 532-4481
Web Site: http://www.springwall.com
Year Founded: 1949
Rev.: $18,953,999
Emp.: 150
Mattresses & Sleep Sets Mfr
N.A.I.C.S.: 337910
Robert G. Kay (Founder & Chm)

SPRINGWATER CAPITAL LLC
Rue Neuve 5 Nyon, 1260, Geneva, Switzerland
Tel.: (41) 22 5950777
Web Site:
http://www.springwatercapital.ch
Year Founded: 2002

Privater Equity Firm
N.A.I.C.S.: 523999
Martin Gruschka (Founder, Chm & Mng Partner)

Subsidiaries:

Nautalia Viajes, S.L. (1)
c/Mahonia No 2 5th Floor, Madrid, Spain
Tel.: (34) 902 811 811
Web Site: http://www.nautaliaviajes.com
Travel Arrangement Services
N.A.I.C.S.: 561599

Pullmantur SA (1)
Calle Mahonia 2, Madrid, 28043, Spain (51%)
Tel.: (34) 915561114
Web Site: http://www.pullmantur.es
Tour Operator
N.A.I.C.S.: 483112
Richard Vogel (Pres & CEO)

Sociedad General Espanola de Libreria S.A. (1)
Valdelaparra 29 Pol Ind, 28108, Alcobendas, Madrid, Spain
Tel.: (34) 91 657 69 00
Web Site: http://www.sgel.es
Newspaper & Magazine Distr
N.A.I.C.S.: 424920

SPRINT BIOSCIENCE AB
Novum Halsovagen 7 Floor 8 Elevator A, 141 57, Huddinge, Sweden
Tel.: (46) 84114455
Web Site:
https://www.sprintbioscience.com
SPRINT—(OMX)
Rev.: $3,288,469
Assets: $7,412,403
Liabilities: $813,922
Net Worth: $6,598,481
Earnings: ($2,349,040)
Emp.: 29
Fiscal Year-end: 12/31/21
Pharmaceuticals Mfr
N.A.I.C.S.: 325412
Martin Andersson (Co-Founder & Chief Scientific Officer)

SPRINTEX LIMITED
Tel.: (61) 892627277   AU
Web Site:
https://www.sprintex.com.au
Year Founded: 2008
SIX—(ASX)
Rev.: $798,696
Assets: $2,995,377
Liabilities: $4,257,082
Net Worth: ($1,261,704)
Earnings: ($3,003,549)
Fiscal Year-end: 06/30/24
Supercharger Mfr & Distr
N.A.I.C.S.: 335312
Richard John Siemens (Chm)

Subsidiaries:

Sprintex Clean Air (Malaysia) Sdn. Bhd. (1)
No 2 Jalan Peguam U1/25 Hicom-glenmarie Industrial Park, 40150, Shah Alam, Selangor, Malaysia
Tel.: (60) 358822661
Twin Screw Compressors Mfr & Distr
N.A.I.C.S.: 333912

Sprintex USA, Inc. (1)
4325 Giddings Rd, Auburn Hills, MI 48326
Web Site:
https://www.sprintexsuperchargers.com
Twin Screw Compressor Mfr
N.A.I.C.S.: 336390

SPRINTQUIP PTY. LTD.
109B Vanessa Street, Kingsgrove, NSW, Australia
Tel.: (61) 1800 500 994
Web Site:
http://www.sprintquip.com.au
Cost Management Services
N.A.I.C.S.: 561499

John Petty (Chm)
Subsidiaries:

Banking Automation Ltd. (1)
Unit 510 Eskdale Road Winnersh Triangle, Wokingham, RG41 5TU, Berks, United Kingdom
Tel.: (44) 1189186327
Web Site:
http://www.bankingautomation.co.uk
Automated Banking Equipment Mfr
N.A.I.C.S.: 333310
David Tew (Exec Dir)

SPRITZER BHD.
Lot 898 Jalan Reservoir Off Jalan Air Kuning, 34000, Taiping, Perak Darul Ridzuan, Malaysia
Tel.: (60) 58012663
Web Site:
https://www.spritzer.com.my
SPRITZER—(KLS)
Rev.: $91,703,704
Assets: $127,186,032
Liabilities: $22,745,820
Net Worth: $104,440,212
Earnings: $7,823,280
Emp.: 960
Fiscal Year-end: 12/31/22
Bottled Water Mfr & Distr
N.A.I.C.S.: 312112
Yeng Chong Sow (Sec & Controller-Grp Fin)
Subsidiaries:

Chuan Sin Cactus Sdn Bhd (1)
Lot 898 Jalan Reservoir Off Jalan Air Kurning, 34000, Taiping, Perak, Malaysia
Tel.: (60) 58073536
Pet Bottle Mfr
N.A.I.C.S.: 326160

Golden PET Industries Sdn Bhd (1)
No 33 Lebuh Perusahaan Klebang 11 Kawasan Perusahaan IGB, 31200, Chemor, Perak, Malaysia
Tel.: (60) 5 291 2130
Web Site: https://www.goldenpet.com.my
Pet Bottle Mfr
N.A.I.C.S.: 326160

SPRIX INC.
1-11-1 Nishiikebukuro Metropolitan Plaza Building, Toshima-Ku, Tokyo, 171-0021, Japan
Tel.: (81) 359271695
Web Site: http://www.sprix.jp
7030—(TKS)
Rev.: $215,273,670
Assets: $142,813,870
Liabilities: $73,998,330
Net Worth: $68,815,540
Earnings: $3,977,490
Fiscal Year-end: 09/30/23
Educational Support Services
N.A.I.C.S.: 611710
Hiroyuki Tsuneishi (Pres)
Subsidiaries:

Programming Research Institute Co., Ltd. (1)
1-11-1 Nishiikebukuro, Toshima-ku, Tokyo, Japan
Tel.: (81) 369128202
Web Site: https://programming-ri.com
Software Development Services
N.A.I.C.S.: 541511

Qureo, Inc. (1)
Shibuya Scramble Square 2-24-12 Shibuya, Shibuya-ku, Tokyo, Japan
Tel.: (81) 342180011
Web Site: https://qureo.jp
Software Development Services
N.A.I.C.S.: 541511

Shonan Seminar Co., Ltd. (1)
Yokohama East Exit Wisport Building 21F 2-6-32 Takashima, Nishi Ward, Yokohama, 220-0011, Kanagawa Prefecture, Japan
Tel.: (81) 455655100
Web Site: https://www.shozemi.com

Educational Institution Services
N.A.I.C.S.: 611710

Shonan Seminar Ocean Co., Ltd. (1)
Yokohama East Exit Wisport Building 21F 2-6-32 Takashima, Nishi Ward, Yokohama, 220-0011, Kanagawa, Japan
Tel.: (81) 455655100
Web Site: https://ss-ocean.com
Emp.: 28
Learning Support Business Services
N.A.I.C.S.: 611710

SPROCOMM INTELLIGENCE LIMITED
5D-506 F1 6 Block Tianfa Building Tianan Chegongmiao Industrial Park, Futian District, Shenzhen, China Ky
Web Site:
https://www.sprocomm.com
Year Founded: 2009
1401—(HKG)
Rev.: $222,212,260
Assets: $223,838,125
Liabilities: $174,702,299
Net Worth: $49,135,826
Earnings: $974,569
Emp.: 890
Fiscal Year-end: 12/31/22
Mobile Phone Mfr & Distr
N.A.I.C.S.: 334111
Chengjun Li (Chm)

SPRONKEN ORTHOPEDIE NV
Transportlaan 9, 3600, Genk, Belgium
Tel.: (32) 89 50 05 00
Web Site: http://www.spronken.com
Healthcare & Medical Aids Services
N.A.I.C.S.: 621999
Leon Spronken (CEO)
Subsidiaries:

Kinetec S.A. (1)
Zone Industrielle de Tournes Rue Maurice Perin, 08090, Tournes, France
Tel.: (33) 3 24 29 85 05
Web Site: http://www.kinetec.fr
Sales Range: $10-24.9 Million
Emp.: 32
Healthcare Equipment Mfr & Distr
N.A.I.C.S.: 339112

SPROTT FOCUS TRUST, INC.
Royal Bank Plaza South Tower 200 Bay Street Suite 2600, Toronto, M5J 2J1, ON, Canada
FUND—(NASDAQ)
Rev.: $5,615,763
Assets: $249,435,215
Liabilities: $14,112,773
Net Worth: $235,322,442
Earnings: $3,284,572
Fiscal Year-end: 12/31/19
Investment Management Service
N.A.I.C.S.: 525990

SPROTT INC.
Royal Bank Plaza South Tower 200 Bay Street Suite 2600, Toronto, M5J 2J1, ON, Canada
Tel.: (416) 945-3279 ON
Web Site: https://www.sprott.com
Year Founded: 1981
SII—(NYSE)
Rev.: $145,182,000
Assets: $383,748,000
Liabilities: $106,477,000
Net Worth: $277,271,000
Earnings: $17,632,000
Emp.: 173
Fiscal Year-end: 12/31/22
Alternative Investment Fund Management Services
N.A.I.C.S.: 523940
W. Whitney George (Pres, Chief Investment Officer & Chm-Sprott U.S. Holdings)

Subsidiaries:

Sprott Asset Management LP (1)
Suite 2700 South Tower Royal Bank Plaza 200 Bay Street, Toronto, M5J 2J1, ON, Canada (100%)
Tel.: (416) 943-8099
Web Site: http://www.sprott.com
Investment Asset Management Services
N.A.I.C.S.: 523940
W. Whitney George (Chief Investment Officer)

Affiliate (Domestic):

Sprott Physical Gold Trust (2)
Suite 2600 South Tower Royal Bank Plaza 200 Bay Street, PO Box 26, Toronto, M5J 2J1, ON, Canada
Tel.: (416) 203-2310
Web Site:
http://www.sprottphysicalgoldtrust.com
Rev.: $324,000
Assets: $5,746,239,000
Liabilities: $144,000
Net Worth: $5,746,095,000
Earnings: ($82,470,000)
Fiscal Year-end: 12/31/2022
Gold Bullion Closed-End Investment Trust
N.A.I.C.S.: 525990
John Ciampaglia (CEO)

Subsidiary (Domestic):

Sprott Physical Gold and Silver Trust (2)
Royal Bank Plaza South Tower 200 Bay Street Suite 2600, Toronto, M5J 2J1, ON, Canada
Tel.: (416) 943-8099
Web Site: https://www.sprott.com
Rev.: $23,724,000
Assets: $3,999,515,000
Liabilities: $1,189,000
Net Worth: $3,998,326,000
Earnings: $4,727,000
Emp.: 56
Fiscal Year-end: 12/31/2022
Closed-End Investment Fund
N.A.I.C.S.: 525990
John Ciampaglia (CEO)

Affiliate (Domestic):

Sprott Physical Platinum and Palladium Trust (2)
Royal Bank Plaza South Tower 200 Bay Street Suite 2600, PO Box 26, Toronto, M5J 2J1, ON, Canada
Tel.: (416) 203-2310
Web Site: http://sprott.com
Rev.: $5,000
Assets: $138,347,000
Liabilities: $59,000
Net Worth: $138,288,000
Earnings: ($5,354,000)
Fiscal Year-end: 12/31/2022
Platinum & Palladium Closed-End Investment Trust
N.A.I.C.S.: 525990
John Ciampaglia (CEO)

Sprott Physical Silver Trust (2)
Suite 2600 South Tower Royal Bank Plaza 200 Bay Street, PO Box 26, Toronto, M5J 2J1, ON, Canada
Tel.: (416) 203-2310
Web Site:
http://www.sprottphysicalsilvertrust.com
Rev.: $168,000
Assets: $4,100,987,000
Liabilities: $9,738,000
Net Worth: $4,091,249,000
Earnings: $103,219,000
Fiscal Year-end: 12/31/2022
Silver Bullion Closed-End Investment Trust
N.A.I.C.S.: 525990
John Ciampaglia (CEO)

Sprott Private Wealth LP (1)
Royal Bank Plz S Tower 200 Bay St Ste 2700, PO Box 27, Toronto, M5J 2J1, ON, Canada
Tel.: (416) 943-6707
Web Site: http://www.sprott.com
Emp.: 147
Investment Services
N.A.I.C.S.: 523999

Sprott Resource Lending Corp. (1)
Royal Bank Plaza South Tower 200 Bay Street Suite 2700, Toronto, M5J 2J2, ON, Canada (100%)
Tel.: (416) 362-7172
Web Site: http://www.sprottlending.com
Sales Range: $10-24.9 Million
Emp.: 10
Renting Services
N.A.I.C.S.: 525990
Peter F. Grosskopf (Mng Dir)

Three Valley Copper Corp. (1)
18 King St E Suite 902, Toronto, M5C 1C4, ON, Canada
Tel.: (647) 749-5859
Web Site: http://www.sprottresource.com
Assets: $3,178,000
Liabilities: $58,000
Net Worth: $3,120,000
Earnings: ($1,534,000)
Fiscal Year-end: 12/31/2023
Natural Resource Investment Holding Company
N.A.I.C.S.: 551112
Terrence A. Lyons (Chm)

Toscana Capital Corporation (1)
Suite 2550 700 2nd Street SW, Calgary, T2P 2W2, AB, Canada
Tel.: (403) 410-6793
Web Site: http://www.toscanacapital.com
Corporate Debt Financing & Lending Asset Management Services
N.A.I.C.S.: 523940

SPROULE HOLDINGS LIMITED
140 - 4th Avenue SW Suite 900, Calgary, T2P 3N3, AB, Canada
Tel.: (403) 294-5500
Web Site: https://sproule.com
Emp.: 100
Holding Company
N.A.I.C.S.: 551112

SPROUTLY CANADA, INC.
3318-1055 Dunsmuir Street, Vancouver, V7X 1L2, BC, Canada
Tel.: (778) 945-6868
Web Site: http://www.sproutly.ca
38G—(BER)
Rev.: $484,792
Assets: $3,131,678
Liabilities: $7,319,490
Net Worth: ($4,187,812)
Earnings: ($12,243,312)
Fiscal Year-end: 02/28/23
Pharmaceutical Products Distr
N.A.I.C.S.: 424210
Craig Loverock (CFO)

SPRUCE RIDGE RESOURCES LTD.
110 Yonge St Suite 1601, Toronto, M5C 1T4, ON, Canada
Tel.: (905) 407-9586 ON
Web Site:
https://homelandnickel.com
Year Founded: 1989
SHL—(TSXV)
Assets: $10,657,202
Liabilities: $178,696
Net Worth: $10,478,507
Earnings: ($5,337)
Fiscal Year-end: 04/30/24
Mineral Exploration Services
N.A.I.C.S.: 213114
John Ryan (Pres & CEO)

SPRUCELAND FORD SALES LTD.
4144 Kepler St, Whitecourt, T7S 1N5, AB, Canada
Tel.: (780) 778-4777
Web Site:
http://www.sprucelandford.com
Year Founded: 1993
New & Used Car Dealers
N.A.I.C.S.: 441110
Rob Button (Mgr-Svc & Parts)

SPS FINQUEST LIMITED

Spruceland Ford Sales Ltd.—(Continued)

SPS FINQUEST LIMITED
R-514 5th Floor Rotunda Building BS
Marg Fort, Mumbai, 400 001, India
Tel.: (91) 2222722488
Web Site:
https://www.spsfinquest.co.in
538402—(BOM)
Rev.: $3,182,466
Assets: $8,975,835
Liabilities: $4,353,854
Net Worth: $4,621,980
Earnings: $1,039,093
Emp.: 11
Fiscal Year-end: 03/31/21
Business Lending Services
N.A.I.C.S.: 522310
Pramod P. Shah (Chm)

SPS INTERNATIONAL LIMITED
15/1 Ground Floor Main Mathura
Road, Faridabad, 121003, Haryana,
India
Tel.: (91) 1297117719
Web Site: https://www.spsintl.co.in
530177—(BOM)
Rev.: $16,602
Assets: $484,661
Liabilities: $3,745
Net Worth: $480,915
Earnings: ($13,924)
Emp.: 4
Fiscal Year-end: 03/31/23
Automatic Data Processing Services
N.A.I.C.S.: 518210
Surendra Kumar Jain (Mng Dir)

SPT ENERGY GROUP INC.
5th Floor Hongmao Business Building
No 8 A Hongjunying East Road, Cha-
oyang District, Beijing, 100012, China
Tel.: (86) 1062068888   Ky
Web Site:
http://www.sptenergygroup.com
1251—(HKG)
Rev.: $246,705,545
Assets: $404,711,143
Liabilities: $232,706,542
Net Worth: $172,004,602
Earnings: $1,046,963
Emp.: 4,331
Fiscal Year-end: 12/31/22
Oil & Gas Exploration Services
N.A.I.C.S.: 213112
Qiang Li (CFO & VP)

Subsidiaries:

Enecal Pte. Limited   (1)
78 Tuas South Street 5, Singapore,
637810, Singapore
Tel.: (65) 6 933 9433
Web Site: https://www.enecal.com
Tool Product Mfr & Distr
N.A.I.C.S.: 333515
Benny Wan (Ops Mgr)

Pioneer Petrotech Services Inc.   (1)
1 1431-40 Ave NE, Calgary, T2E 8N6, AB,
Canada
Tel.: (403) 282-7669
Web Site: https://www.pioneerps.com
Measurement Gauge Mfr
N.A.I.C.S.: 334519

SPUR CORPORATION
14 Edison Way Century Gate Busi-
ness Park, Century City, Cape Town,
7441, South Africa
Tel.: (27) 215555100
Web Site:
https://www.spurcorporation.com
Year Founded: 1967
SUR—(JSE)
Rev.: $160,817,129
Assets: $61,626,813
Liabilities: $21,929,044
Net Worth: $39,697,768
Earnings: $11,671,543

Emp.: 669
Fiscal Year-end: 06/30/23
Restaurant Services
N.A.I.C.S.: 492210
Kevin Robertson (COO-Spur Steak Ranches)

Subsidiaries:

John Dory's Advertising (Pty) Ltd.   (1)
Shop FCCL20 Pavilion Shopping Centre
Jack Martens Drive, Durban, Westville,
4001, KwaZulu-Natal, South Africa
Tel.: (27) 312650106
Web Site: http://www.johndorys.co.za
Advertising Agencies
N.A.I.C.S.: 541810

John Dory's Franchise (Pty) Ltd   (1)
Block B 2 Derby Downs Ofc Park, West-
ville, Kwazulu Natal, South Africa
Tel.: (27) 312672174
Web Site: http://www.johndorys.co.za
Sales Range: $10-24.9 Million
Emp.: 7
Restaurant Management Services
N.A.I.C.S.: 722511
Leonard Coetzee (Mng Dir)

RocoMamas Franchise Co (Pty). Ltd.   (1)
14 Edison Way, Century City, Cape Town,
South Africa
Tel.: (27) 860888772
Web Site: http://www.rocomamas.com
Restaurant Services
N.A.I.C.S.: 722511

Spur Corporation Australia Pty Ltd   (1)
Unit 4 37 Borec Rd, Penrith, 2750, NSW,
Australia
Tel.: (61) 247325399
Web Site: http://www.spur.com.au
Restaurant Management Services
N.A.I.C.S.: 722511

Steak Ranches International BV   (1)
Surinameplein 124, 1058 GV, Amsterdam,
Netherlands
Tel.: (31) 208884119
Web Site: http://www.spurcorp.nl
Sales Range: $10-24.9 Million
Emp.: 4
Restaurant Management Services
N.A.I.C.S.: 722511
Lisa Stout (Mgr-Fin)

The Hussar Grill Advertising (Pty). Ltd.   (1)
14 Edison Way Century Gate Business
Park, Century City, Cape Town, 7441,
South Africa
Tel.: (27) 215555100
Web Site: https://www.hussargrill.co.za
Restaurant Services
N.A.I.C.S.: 722511

SPV GLOBAL TRADING LIMITED
Binani Bhawan 2nd Floor 28/30
Anant Wadi, Bhuleshwar, Mumbai,
400002, Maharashtra, India
Tel.: (91) 22 22014001
Sales Range: Less than $1 Million
Financial Services
N.A.I.C.S.: 523999

SPVGG UNTERHACHING FOOTBALL GMBH & CO. KGAA
Am Sportpark 9, 82008, Unterhach-
ing, Germany
Tel.: (49) 8961559160
Web Site:
https://www.spvgunterhaching.de
Year Founded: 1925
S6P—(DEU)
Rev.: $2,196,710
Assets: $17,363,947
Liabilities: $29,285,793
Net Worth: ($11,921,846)
Earnings: ($7,484,270)

Emp.: 115
Fiscal Year-end: 12/31/23
Sports Club Operator
N.A.I.C.S.: 711211
Daniel Eyer (VP)

SPYGLASS RESOURCES CORP.
1700 - 250 Second Street SW, Cal-
gary, T2P 0C1, AB, Canada
Tel.: (403) 303-8500   AB
Web Site:
http://www.spyglassresources.com
Year Founded: 2013
Oil & Gas Exploration & Extraction
N.A.I.C.S.: 211120
Thomas W. Buchanan (Chm)

SPYKER N.V.
Oogstweg 27a, 3899 BJ, Zeewolde,
Netherlands
Tel.: (31) 365358787   Nl
Web Site: http://www.spykernv.com
Year Founded: 1999
Sales Range: $1-9.9 Million
Emp.: 56
Holding Company; Automobile Mfr & Distr
N.A.I.C.S.: 551112
Victor R. Muller (CEO & Member-Mgmt Bd)

Subsidiaries:

Spyker Automobielen B.V.   (1)
Edisonweg 2, Zeewolde, 3899AZ, Nether-
lands
Tel.: (31) 365358787
Web Site: http://www.spykercars.nl
Automobile Mfr & Distr
N.A.I.C.S.: 336110
M. Muller (Mgr)

Subsidiary (Domestic):

Spyker Events & Branding B.V.   (2)
Edisonweg 2, 3899, Zeewolde, Netherlands
Tel.: (31) 365358787
Web Site: http://www.spykercars.com
Car Mfr
N.A.I.C.S.: 336110

Joint Venture (Non-US):

Spyker of China Ltd.   (2)
West Third Ring North Road, Beijing Eco-
nomic & Trade Build, Beijing, Haidian,
China
Tel.: (86) 1068484266
Automobile Mfr; Sportscars
N.A.I.C.S.: 336110
Martyn Schilte (Mng Dir)

SPYROSOFT S.A.
Pl Nowy Targ 28, 50-141, Wroclaw,
Poland
Tel.: (48) 500104042
Web Site: https://www.spyro-soft.com
Year Founded: 2016
2NP—(DEU)
Information Technology Services
N.A.I.C.S.: 541512
Konrad Weiske (Chm)

Subsidiaries:

Better Software Group S.A.   (1)
Nowy Targ 28, 50-141, Wroclaw, Poland
Tel.: (48) 795945870
Web Site: https://bsgroup.eu
Telecommunication Servicesb
N.A.I.C.S.: 532490

Spyrosoft Ecommerce S.A.   (1)
Pl Nowy Targ 28, 50-141, Wroclaw, Poland
Tel.: (48) 500104042
Information Technology Consulting Services
N.A.I.C.S.: 541512

Spyrosoft Synergy S.A.   (1)
Cyfrowa 4, 71-441, Szczecin, Poland
Tel.: (48) 797484563
Software Development Services
N.A.I.C.S.: 541330

INTERNATIONAL PUBLIC

Unravel S.A.   (1)
Pl Nowy Targ 28, 50-141, Wroclaw, Poland
Tel.: (48) 500104042
Web Site: https://www.unravel.cc
Emp.: 1,300
Digital Product Design & Management Services
N.A.I.C.S.: 541810

SQ-M2 LTD
3rd Fl Boundary House 7-17 Jewry
Street, London, EC3N 2EX, United
Kingdom
Tel.: (44) 20 7481 6450
Web Site: http://www.square-metre.com
Year Founded: 2003
Sales Range: $10-24.9 Million
Emp.: 30
Interior Design Services
N.A.I.C.S.: 541410
Steve Hart (Founder)

SQI DIAGNOSTICS INC.
36 Meteor Drive, Toronto, M9W 1A4,
ON, Canada
Tel.: (416) 674-9500   Ca
Web Site:
https://www.sqidiagnostics.com
SQD—(OTCIQ)
Rev.: $717,351
Assets: $7,090,586
Liabilities: $5,896,827
Net Worth: $1,193,759
Earnings: ($8,258,530)
Emp.: 52
Fiscal Year-end: 09/30/21
Microarray Diagnostics Products
N.A.I.C.S.: 339112
Peter Lea (Founder)

SQID TECHNOLOGIES LIMITED
L14 440 Collins Street, Melbourne,
3000, VIC, Australia
Tel.: (61) 1800697729
Web Site:
https://sqidtechnologies.com
Year Founded: 2006
SQID—(CNSX)
Rev.: $778,042
Assets: $1,646,565
Liabilities: $477,533
Net Worth: $1,169,032
Earnings: ($2,621,223)
Fiscal Year-end: 12/31/21
Electronic Payment Processing Services
N.A.I.C.S.: 522320
Athan Lekkas (Chm & CEO)

SQUAMISH TERMINALS LTD.
37500 Third Avenue, PO Box 1520,
Squamish, V8B 0B1, BC, Canada
Tel.: (604) 892-3511
Web Site:
https://www.sqterminals.com
Year Founded: 1972
Rev.: $19,675,795
Emp.: 110
Marine Cargo Handling Services
N.A.I.C.S.: 488320

SQUARE 1 PRODUCTS LTD.
Bollin Court Mill Lane, Lymm, WA13
9SX, Cheshire, United Kingdom
Tel.: (44) 1925 530 111
Web Site:
http://www.square1products.com
Year Founded: 1991
Sales Range: $25-49.9 Million
Emp.: 30
Computer Peripheral Whslr
N.A.I.C.S.: 423690
Terry Dorricott (Mgr-Technical)

AND PRIVATE COMPANIES

SQUARE ENIX HOLDINGS CO. LTD.
Shinjuku Eastside Square 6-27-30
Shinjuku, Shinjuku-ku, Tokyo, 160-8430, Japan
Tel.: (81) 352928000
Web Site: https://www.hd.square-enix.com
Year Founded: 2003
9684—(TKS)
Rev.: $2,355,433,840
Assets: $2,715,890,360
Liabilities: $619,667,670
Net Worth: $2,096,222,690
Earnings: $98,568,320
Emp.: 4,770
Fiscal Year-end: 03/31/24
Video Game Developer & Publisher
N.A.I.C.S.: 513210
Hideaki Sato (CIO)

Subsidiaries:

Eidos Ltd. (1)
Wimbledon Bridge House 1 Hartfield Rd, London, FE1 8NW, United Kingdom
Tel.: (44) 2086363000
Web Site: http://www.squareenix.com
Sales Range: $200-249.9 Million
Emp.: 240
Video Game Developer & Publisher
N.A.I.C.S.: 513210
Phil Rogers (CEO)

Huang Long Co., Ltd. (1)
161 Meng Tzu Road, Kaohsiung, Taiwan
Tel.: (886) 73484945
Game Software Publsihers
N.A.I.C.S.: 513210

IO Interactive A/S (1)
Gammel Moent 2-4, 1117, Copenhagen, Denmark
Tel.: (45) 33732900
Web Site: https://www.ioi.dk
Sales Range: $50-74.9 Million
Emp.: 200
Internet Entertainment Services
N.A.I.C.S.: 516210
Alexander Patrick Strandlod (Gen Counsel)

Smile-Lab Co., Ltd. (1)
Ariake Park Building 20F 3-7-11 Ariake, Koto-ku, Tokyo, 135-0063, Japan
Tel.: (81) 362739851
Web Site: https://www.smile-lab.com
Entertainment Websites Development & Hosting Services
N.A.I.C.S.: 518210

Square Enix (China) Co. Ltd. (1)
Room 716 Gaode Building No 10 Huayuan East Rd, Haidian District, Beijing, 100083, China
Tel.: (86) 1082039311
Web Site: https://www.square-enix.net.cn
Online Game Publishers
N.A.I.C.S.: 516210

Square Enix Co., Ltd. (1)
6-27-30 Shinjuku Shinjuku Eastside Square, Shinjuku-ku, Tokyo, 160-8430, Japan
Tel.: (81) 352928100
Web Site: https://www.jp.square-enix.com
Online Game Development Services
N.A.I.C.S.: 541511

Square Enix GmbH (1)
Domstrassee 17, 20095, Hamburg, Germany
Tel.: (49) 4030633400
Web Site: http://www.eidos.com
Entertainment Content Publisher & Distr
N.A.I.C.S.: 516210

Square Enix Ltd. (1)
12th & 13th Floor 240 Blackfriars Road, London, SE1 8NW, United Kingdom
Tel.: (44) 2086363000
Video Game Services
N.A.I.C.S.: 713120

Square Enix MobileStudio, CO., LTD. (1)
1-2-5 Kita 1-Jo Higashi Building, Chuo-ku, Sapporo, 060-0031, Hokkaido, Japan
Tel.: (81) 353330926

Web Site: http://www.square-enix-mobilestudio.com
Mobile Media Content Development Services
N.A.I.C.S.: 541511

Square Enix, Inc. (1)
999 N Sepulveda Blvd 3rd Fl, El Segundo, CA 90245
Tel.: (310) 846-0400
Web Site: http://www.square-enix.com
Sales Range: $75-99.9 Million
Emp.: 150
Entertainment Software & Games Development & Publishing Services
N.A.I.C.S.: 423430

SQUARE FOUR PROJECTS INDIA LIMITED
238A Square Four Group 2nd Floor Suit No 2B A J C Bose Road, Kolkata, 700020, West Bengal, India
Tel.: (91) 3322903185
Web Site: https://www.squarefourgroup.in
526532—(BOM)
Rev.: $340,813
Assets: $830,985
Liabilities: $7,248
Net Worth: $823,737
Earnings: $89,066
Emp.: 2
Fiscal Year-end: 03/31/21
Epoxy Resin Mfr
N.A.I.C.S.: 325211
Ganesh Kumar Singhania (Mng Dir)

SQUARE PHARMACEUTICALS LTD.
Square Centre 48 Mohakhali C/A, Dhaka, 1212, Bangladesh
Tel.: (880) 29859007
Web Site: http://www.squarepharma.com.bd
Year Founded: 1958
Rev.: $588,529,655
Assets: $834,729,828
Liabilities: $49,351,088
Net Worth: $785,378,741
Earnings: $146,388,281
Fiscal Year-end: 06/30/19
Pharmaceuticals Mfr
N.A.I.C.S.: 325412
Tapan Chowdhury (Mng Dir)

SQUARE TECHNOLOGY GROUP CO., LTD.
No 3888 Jintong Road, Xingren Town Tongzhou District, Nantong, 226371, JiangSu, China
Tel.: (86) 51381658162
Web Site: http://www.ntsquare.com
Year Founded: 1990
603339—(SHG)
Rev.: $284,227,501
Assets: $450,381,452
Liabilities: $140,733,801
Net Worth: $309,647,651
Earnings: $42,914,762
Fiscal Year-end: 12/31/22
Freezing Equipment Mfr & Distr
N.A.I.C.S.: 333415
Jie Huang (Chm & Gen Mgr)

Subsidiaries:

Nantong Tank Container CO., Ltd. (1)
3888 Jintong Rd, Xingren, Tongzhou, China
Tel.: (86) 51381601166
Web Site: https://www.nttank.com
Tank Container Mfr
N.A.I.C.S.: 332420

SQUARE TEXTILE LTD.
48 Mohakhali CA, Dhaka, 1212, Bangladesh
Tel.: (880) 2883304756

Web Site: https://www.textile.squaregroup.com
Year Founded: 1997
SQUARETEXT—(DHA)
Rev.: $150,580,701
Assets: $175,225,415
Liabilities: $87,052,433
Net Worth: $88,172,982
Earnings: $10,447,513
Emp.: 4,563
Fiscal Year-end: 06/30/23
Textile Products Mfr
N.A.I.C.S.: 314999
Tapan Chowdhury (Chm)

SQUARELIFE LEBENSVERSI-CHERUNGS AKTIENGESELL-SCHAFT S.A.
Landstrasse 33, 9491, Ruggell, Liechtenstein
Tel.: (423) 2371565
Web Site: http://www.squarelife.li
Year Founded: 2013
Insurance Management Services
N.A.I.C.S.: 524113
Hansueli Edelmann (Pres)

SQUARESTONE BRASIL LIMITED
1st Floor Royal Chambers, Saint Julian's Avenue, Saint Peter Port, GY1 3JX, Guernsey
Tel.: (44) 1481 810102
Year Founded: 2007
Real Estate Investment Services
N.A.I.C.S.: 531390
Chris Coulson (Dir-Dev)

SQUATEX ENERGY & RESOURCES, INC.
7055 boul Taschereau suite 500, Brossard, J4Z 1A7, QC, Canada
Tel.: (450) 766-0861
Web Site: https://www.squatex.com
Year Founded: 2001
SQX—(CNSX)
Assets: $20,388
Liabilities: $1,941,504
Net Worth: ($1,921,116)
Earnings: ($249,626)
Fiscal Year-end: 03/31/24
Oil & Gas Exploration Services
N.A.I.C.S.: 213112
Jean-Claude Caron (Pres)

SQX RESOURCES LIMITED
Level 1 371 Queen St, Brisbane, 4000, QLD, Australia AU
Web Site: https://www.sqxresources.com
Year Founded: 2022
SQX—(ASX)
Rev.: $49,725
Assets: $2,212,966
Liabilities: $70,039
Net Worth: $2,142,927
Earnings: ($505,131)
Fiscal Year-end: 06/30/24
Exploration & Mining Services
N.A.I.C.S.: 213115
Craig McPherson (CFO & Sec)

SR ACCORD LTD.
Klausner 10, PO Box 520038670, Beit Zim, Ramla, 7243224, Israel
Tel.: (972) 723305482
Web Site: https://sr-accord.com
Asset Management Services
N.A.I.C.S.: 523940
Gil Dekel Hochboim (CFO)

SR BIOTEK, INC.
B101 B101-1 3 Sicox Tower 484 Dunchon-daero, Jungwon-gu, Seongnam, Gyeonggi-do, Korea (South)
Tel.: (82) 317263134

Web Site: https://www.srbiotek.com
Year Founded: 2005
Cosmetics Products Mfr
N.A.I.C.S.: 325620
Byungho Song (CEO & Chief Sls Officer)

SR WEBATEX GMBH
Tunnelstrasse 6, 95408, Bayreuth, Germany
Tel.: (49) 9212860
Web Site: http://www.sr-webatex.de
Year Founded: 1853
Sales Range: $10-24.9 Million
Emp.: 123
Fabrics Mfr & Whslr
N.A.I.C.S.: 313310
Berthold Galonska (Mng Dir)

SRA HOLDINGS INC
2-32-8 Minamiikebukuro, Toshima-ku, Tokyo, 171-0022, Japan
Tel.: (81) 359792666
Web Site: https://www.sra-hd.co.jp
3817—(TKS)
Rev.: $311,496,250
Assets: $312,844,690
Liabilities: $119,654,220
Net Worth: $193,190,470
Earnings: $30,300,240
Emp.: 272
Fiscal Year-end: 03/31/24
Planning, Development & Maintenance Of Computer Systems
N.A.I.C.S.: 541513
Toru Kashima (Pres)

Subsidiaries:

Advanced Integration Technology, Inc. (1)
Eitai OT Building 1-5-6 Saga, Koto-ku, Tokyo, 135-0031, Japan
Tel.: (81) 352457771
Web Site: https://www.ait.co.jp
Emp.: 120
Software Consulting Services
N.A.I.C.S.: 541511

CreDist, Inc. (1)
Eitai OT Bldg 1-5-6 Saga, Koutou-ku, Tokyo, 135-0031, Japan
Tel.: (81) 352458640
Web Site: http://www.credist.co.jp
Sales Range: $25-49.9 Million
Emp.: 10
Networking & Software Consulting Services
N.A.I.C.S.: 541511

SRA IP Solutions (Asia Pacific) Pte. Ltd. (1)
133 Cecil Street 13-03 Keck Seng Tower, Singapore, 069535, Singapore
Tel.: (65) 62209289
Web Site: https://www.sraips.sg
Sales Range: $25-49.9 Million
Emp.: 7
Software Development & Computer Systems Management Services
N.A.I.C.S.: 541511
Shota Kondo (Mng Dir)

SRA India Private Limited (1)
80 EPIP Industrial Area, Whitefield, Bengaluru, 560066, Karnataka, India
Tel.: (91) 8028416491
Web Site: http://www.sraindia.com
Software Development Services
N.A.I.C.S.: 541511

SRA Professional Service, Inc. (1)
2-32-8 Minamiikebukuro, Toshima-ku, Tokyo, 171-0022, Japan
Tel.: (81) 359792777
Web Site: http://www.sra-ps.co.jp
Emp.: 65
Recruiting & Temporary Staffing Services
N.A.I.C.S.: 541612

SRA Tohoku, Inc. (1)
3-1-2 Kokubuncho Urban Net Jozenji Building 5th floor, Aoba-ku, Sendai, 980-0803, Miyagi, Japan
Tel.: (81) 222219061
Web Site: http://www.sra-tohoku.co.jp

SRA HOLDINGS INC / INTERNATIONAL PUBLIC

SRA Holdings Inc—(Continued)
Sales Range: $25-49.9 Million
Software Development & Consulting Services
N.A.I.C.S.: 541511
Hideki Aizawa (Operating Officer)

Software Research Associates, Inc. (1)
2-32-8 Minami-Ikebukuro, Toshima-ku, Tokyo, 171-8513, Japan
Tel.: (81) 359792111
Emp.: 878
Software Services & Products
N.A.I.C.S.: 541512
Toru Kashima (Chm & CEO)

Subsidiary (Non-US):

Turbolinux, Japan K.K. (2)
Tel.: (81) 357661660
Web Site: http://www.turbolinux.co.jp
Computer Software & Services
N.A.I.C.S.: 541512

Subsidiary (Non-US):

SRA (Europe) B.V. (3)
Tel.: (31) 204535667
Web Site: https://www.sra-europe.com
Sales Range: $25-49.9 Million
Emp.: 8
Information Technology Solutions
N.A.I.C.S.: 519290

TurboLinux, Inc. (3)
Tel.: (86) 4006220178
Developer of Computer Software
N.A.I.C.S.: 541512

Software Science, Inc. (1)
2-32-8 Minamiikebukuro Ikebukuro Daiichi Building 7F, Toshima-ku, Tokyo, 171-0022, Japan
Tel.: (81) 359521311
Web Site: http://www.ssi.co.jp
Emp.: 165
Software Development Services
N.A.I.C.S.: 541511
Masatoshi Kurihara (Pres)

SRBIJA TIS A.D.
Nikole Pasica bb, 19000, Zajecar, Serbia
Tel.: (381) 631140389
Web Site: https://www.srbijatis.co.rs
Year Founded: 2003
STIS—(BEL)
Rev.: $1,032,968
Assets: $1,230,283
Liabilities: $565,016
Net Worth: $665,266
Earnings: $31,952
Emp.: 46
Fiscal Year-end: 12/31/22
Home Management Services
N.A.I.C.S.: 721110
Snezana Mitrovic (Exec Dir)

SRBIJA TURIST A.D.
Trg Kralja Milana bb, Nis, Serbia
Tel.: (381) 18 505 700
Year Founded: 1951
SRTU—(BEL)
Sales Range: Less than $1 Million
Emp.: 65
Home Management Services
N.A.I.C.S.: 721110
Petar Ilic (Exec Dir)

SRBIJAPUT A.D.
Bulevar Kralja Aleksandra 282, Belgrade, Serbia
Tel.: (381) 113040645
Web Site: http://www.srbijaput.rs
Year Founded: 1998
SRPU—(BEL)
Rev.: $20,167,189
Assets: $8,705,070
Liabilities: $7,728,712
Net Worth: $976,358
Earnings: $4,036
Emp.: 55
Fiscal Year-end: 12/31/23
Road Construction & Maintenance Services
N.A.I.C.S.: 237310
Dragan Vujnovic (Gen Dir)

SRBIJATRANSPORT A.D.
Poincares 16, 11000, Belgrade, Serbia
Tel.: (381) 112767447
Web Site: https://www.srbijatransport.rs
Year Founded: 1951
STRN—(BEL)
Rev.: $99,875
Assets: $52,857
Liabilities: $19,221
Net Worth: $33,636
Earnings: ($5,574)
Emp.: 2
Fiscal Year-end: 12/31/22
Food Transportation Services
N.A.I.C.S.: 484121
Gazimir Gavric (Asst Dir Gen)

SRE GROUP LIMITED
Level 11 Admiralty Center Tower II 18 Harcourt Road Admiralty, Hong Kong, China (Hong Kong)
Tel.: (852) 28913618
Web Site: http://www.sre.com.cn
1207—(HKG)
Rev.: $109,453,172
Assets: $1,976,898,690
Liabilities: $1,347,428,066
Net Worth: $629,470,624
Earnings: $3,890,344
Emp.: 407
Fiscal Year-end: 12/31/22
Real Estate Services
N.A.I.C.S.: 531312
Chao Chen (Exec Dir)

SRE HOLDINGS CORPORATION
14F Akasaka Intercity Air 1-8-1 Akasaka, Minato-Ku, Tokyo, 107-0052, Japan
Tel.: (81) 362746550
Web Site: https://sre-group.co.jp
Year Founded: 2014
2980—(TKS)
Rev.: $160,080,980
Assets: $158,752,370
Liabilities: $76,391,770
Net Worth: $82,360,600
Earnings: $9,174,680
Fiscal Year-end: 03/31/24
Holding Company
N.A.I.C.S.: 551112
Akio Kukuminato (Exec Officer)

SREDNJA BACKA A.D.
Marsala Tita 236, Kula, Serbia
Tel.: (381) 25722172
Year Founded: 1979
SBAC—(BEL)
Sales Range: Less than $1 Million
Emp.: 8
Mobile Food Services
N.A.I.C.S.: 722330
Jasminka Stamenic (Board of Directors & Exec Dir)

SREDNJI BANAT A.D.
Partizanski Put br 54, 23240, Secanj, Serbia
Tel.: (381) 23 841 055
Web Site: http://www.prpsvetinikola.com
Year Founded: 1991
SBNT—(BEL)
Sales Range: Less than $1 Million
Emp.: 1
Agricultural Raw Material Whslr
N.A.I.C.S.: 424590

Danilo Vukoje (Exec Dir)

SREE JAYALAKSHMI AUTOSPIN LIMITED
Sanjana Davangere Road, Chitradurga, 577501, India
Tel.: (91) 8194223040
Web Site: https://www.sjlal.com
Year Founded: 1991
530037—(BOM)
Rev.: $10,923
Assets: $126,911
Liabilities: $347,653
Net Worth: ($220,742)
Earnings: ($7,170)
Fiscal Year-end: 03/31/23
Cotton Product Mfr & Whslr
N.A.I.C.S.: 313110
Kuruvatappa Veerabhadrappa Prabhakar (Chm & Mng Dir)

SREE RAYALASEEMA HI-STRENGTH HYPO LIMITED
216 K J S Complex Bhagya Nagar, Kurnool, 518 004, Andhra Pradesh, India
Tel.: (91) 8518228750
Web Site: https://www.srhhl.com
532842—(BOM)
Rev.: $201,933,445
Assets: $107,601,535
Liabilities: $17,547,881
Net Worth: $90,053,654
Earnings: $18,494,587
Emp.: 516
Fiscal Year-end: 03/31/23
Chemical Compound Mfr
N.A.I.C.S.: 325180
T. G. Bharath (Chm)

SREECHEM RESINS LIMITED
23A Netaji Subhas Road 11th Floor Room No -11, Kolkata, 700 001, India
Tel.: (91) 3322313149
Web Site: https://www.sreechem.in
Year Founded: 1988
514248—(BOM)
Rev.: $4,712,882
Assets: $2,748,166
Liabilities: $1,721,976
Net Worth: $1,026,190
Earnings: $253,108
Emp.: 80
Fiscal Year-end: 03/31/21
Building Material Mfr & Distr
N.A.I.C.S.: 327120
Binod Sharma (Mng Dir)

SREELEATHERS LIMITED
6 Tottee Lane, Kolkata, 700016, West Bengal, India
Tel.: (91) 3322861506
Web Site: https://www.sreeleathers.com
SREEL—(NSE)
Rev.: $11,439,818
Assets: $45,066,479
Liabilities: $2,214,724
Net Worth: $42,851,756
Earnings: $1,522,139
Emp.: 139
Fiscal Year-end: 03/31/21
Footwear & Other Leather Accessories Retailer
N.A.I.C.S.: 458210
Satyabrata Dey (Mng Dir)

SREMPUT A.D.
Trg Osloboenja 12, Ruma, Serbia
Tel.: (381) 22 474 100
Web Site: http://www.sremput.co.rs
Year Founded: 1962
SPRU—(BEL)
Sales Range: $10-24.9 Million
Emp.: 335

Road Construction & Maintenance Services
N.A.I.C.S.: 237310
Zoran Vukicevic (Gen Mgr)

SRESTHA FINVEST LIMITED
Door No 19&20 General Muthiah Mudali Street Sowcarpet, Chennai, 600003, India
Tel.: (91) 4440057044
Web Site: https://www.srestha.co.in
539217—(BOM)
Rev.: $645,278
Assets: $6,345,065
Liabilities: $4,051,161
Net Worth: $2,293,904
Earnings: ($73,608)
Fiscal Year-end: 03/31/21
Financial Support Services
N.A.I.C.S.: 523999
Kamlesh Parasmal (CFO)

SRETEN GUDURIC A.D.
Pekarska 1, Uzice, Serbia
Tel.: (381) 31 561 466
Year Founded: 1949
Sales Range: $1-9.9 Million
Emp.: 280
Bakery Products Mfr
N.A.I.C.S.: 311813

SRF LIMITED
Block-C Sector-45, Gurgaon, 122003, Haryana, India
Tel.: (91) 1244354400
Web Site: https://www.srf.com
Year Founded: 1970
SRF—(NSE)
Rev.: $1,155,662,235
Assets: $1,764,864,465
Liabilities: $828,963,135
Net Worth: $935,901,330
Earnings: $163,518,810
Emp.: 6,386
Fiscal Year-end: 03/31/21
Chemicals Mfr
N.A.I.C.S.: 325998
Arun Bharat Ram (Chm)

SRG GLOBAL LIMITED
Level 2 500 Hay Street, Subiaco, 6008, WA, Australia
Tel.: (61) 892675400
Web Site: https://www.srgglobal.com.au
Year Founded: 1961
SRG—(ASX)
Rev.: $713,981,701
Assets: $427,673,609
Liabilities: $223,978,364
Net Worth: $203,695,245
Earnings: $22,994,124
Emp.: 4,300
Fiscal Year-end: 06/30/24
Construction Services Company
N.A.I.C.S.: 541330
Peter McMorrow (Deputy Chm)

Subsidiaries:

CASC Constructions Pty. Ltd. (1)
2 Redcliffe Rd, Redcliffe, 6104, WA, Australia
Tel.: (61) 894782922
Web Site: http://www.gcs-group.com.au
Sales Range: $50-74.9 Million
Emp.: 160
Concrete Formwork Services
N.A.I.C.S.: 238190

Subsidiary (Domestic):

Newave Contracting Pty. Ltd. (2)
2 Redcliffe Rd, Redcliffe, 6104, WA, Australia
Tel.: (61) 29 479 7990
Web Site: http://www.gcs-group.com.au
Concrete Contractor
N.A.I.C.S.: 238110

AND PRIVATE COMPANIES

GCS Hire Pty. Ltd. (1)
25B Jackson St, Bassendean, 6054, WA, Australia
Tel.: (61) 893096177
Web Site: http://www.gcs-group.com.au
Sales Range: $25-49.9 Million
Emp.: 7
Temporary Fencing Services
N.A.I.C.S.: 237990

GCS Northwest Pty. Ltd. (1)
Lot 1103 Lambden Way, Karratha, 6714, WA, Australia
Tel.: (61) 891437500
Web Site: http://www.gcs-group.com.au
Sales Range: $25-49.9 Million
Emp.: 14
Industrial Scaffolding & Formwork Contractors
N.A.I.C.S.: 238190
Kieran Steadman (Gen Mgr)

GCS Security Scaffolding Pty. Ltd. (1)
15-17 Smokebush Ave, Bunbury, 6230, WA, Australia
Tel.: (61) 897256223
Web Site: http://www.gcs-group.com.au
Emp.: 14
Commercial Formwork Services
N.A.I.C.S.: 237990
Antonio Multari (Mgr-Bus Dev)

Refobar Australia Pty Ltd (1)
642 Old Gympie Rd, Narangba, 4504, QLD, Australia
Tel.: (61) 738886655
Web Site: http://www.refobar.com.au
Emp.: 17
Construction Component Mfr & Distr
N.A.I.C.S.: 332313
Russell Wheeler (Gen Mgr)

SRG HOUSING FINANCE LTD
321 SM Lodha Complex Near Shastri Circle, Udaipur, 313001, Rajasthan, India
Tel.: (91) 2942561882
Web Site: https://www.srghousing.com
534680—(BOM)
Rev.: $10,022,977
Assets: $53,689,995
Liabilities: $40,912,135
Net Worth: $12,777,861
Earnings: $2,570,841
Emp.: 298
Fiscal Year-end: 03/31/21
Real Estate Financial Services
N.A.I.C.S.: 525990
Vinod Kumar Jain (Mng Dir)

SRG INTERNATIONAL INC.
211 Boulevard Brien #8 Suite 131, Repentigny, J6A 0A4, QC, Canada
Tel.: (514) 886-8274 Sc
Alertness Detection Software
N.A.I.C.S.: 513210
Claude Brun (Chm, Pres & CEO)

SRG MINING INC.
1320 Graham suite 132, Mount-Royal, H3P 3C8, QC, Canada
Tel.: (604) 443-3835
Web Site: https://srgmining.com
Year Founded: 1996
18Y—(DEU)
Rev.: $255
Assets: $7,086,771
Liabilities: $509,672
Net Worth: $6,577,100
Earnings: $4,146,203
Fiscal Year-end: 12/31/23
Mineral Exploration Services
N.A.I.C.S.: 213114
Patrick Moryoussef (COO)

SRG MINING INC.
1320 Graham Suite 132, Ville Mont-Royal, Montreal, H3P 3C8, QC, Canada
Tel.: (604) 443-3835
Web Site: https://srgmining.com
Year Founded: 1996
SRGMF—(OTCIQ)
Rev.: $255
Assets: $7,086,810
Liabilities: $509,674
Net Worth: $6,577,135
Earnings: ($4,146,226)
Fiscal Year-end: 12/31/23
Newspaper & Magazine Publisher
N.A.I.C.S.: 513110
Benoit La Salle (Chm)

SRG SSR IDEE SUISSE
Giacomettistrasse 1, Bern, 3006, Switzerland
Tel.: (41) 313509111
Web Site: http://www.srgssr.ch
Sales Range: $400-449.9 Million
Emp.: 4,800
Holding Company; Radio & Television Broadcast Media Services
N.A.I.C.S.: 551112
Gilles Marchand (Member-Exec Bd & Dir Gen)

Subsidiaries:

MCDT AG (1)
Brunnenhofstrasse 22, PO Box 8042, 8057, Zurich, Switzerland
Tel.: (41) 44 366 11 47
Web Site: http://www.mcdt.ch
Marketing Consulting Services
N.A.I.C.S.: 541613
Beatrice Merlach (CEO)

Mxlab AG (1)
bollwerk 21, 3011, Bern, Switzerland
Tel.: (41) 31 311 72 73
Web Site: http://www.mxlab.ch
Event Management Services
N.A.I.C.S.: 711310

Publisuisse SA (1)
Giacomettistrasse 1, Bern, 3006, Switzerland
Tel.: (41) 31 358 3111
Web Site: http://www.publisuisse.ch
Marketing & Advertising Services
N.A.I.C.S.: 541613
Beatrice Kniel-May (Dir-Sls)

Schweizer Mediendatenbank (SMD) AG (1)
Badenerstrasse 119, 8036, Zurich, Switzerland
Tel.: (41) 443156080
Web Site: http://www.smd.ch
Sales Range: $1-9.9 Million
Emp.: 20
Online Operator & Services
N.A.I.C.S.: 812990
Mumprecht Jurg (Gen Mgr)

Schweizerische Teletext AG (1)
Alexander-Schoni-Strasse 40, Postfach 1136, 2501, Biel, Switzerland
Tel.: (41) 32 329 29 29
Web Site: http://www.swisstxt.ch
Marketing & Advertising Services
N.A.I.C.S.: 541613

Swiss TXT AG (1)
Alexander-Schoni Strasse 40, 2501, Biel, Switzerland
Tel.: (41) 58 136 4000
Web Site: https://www.swisstxt.ch
Video & Audio Streaming Services
N.A.I.C.S.: 518210
Bettina Manta (Mgr-Sales)

Technology and Production Center Switzerland AG (1)
Fernsehstrasse 1- 4, 8052, Zurich, Switzerland
Tel.: (41) 44 305 40 00
Web Site: http://www.tpcag.ch
Emp.: 1,000
Television Broadcasting Services
N.A.I.C.S.: 516120
Jurg Kaser (Mgr-Bus Dev)

Telvetia S.A. (1)
Giacomettistrasse 1, 3000, Bern, Switzerland
Tel.: (41) 58 136 1093
Television Broadcasting Services
N.A.I.C.S.: 516120

SRH HOLDING GMBH
Bonhoefferstrasse 1, 69123, Heidelberg, Germany
Tel.: (49) 6221 8223 0
Web Site: http://www.srh.de
Year Founded: 1966
Holding Company Services
N.A.I.C.S.: 551112
Hans-Joachim Eucker (Deputy CEO)

Subsidiaries:

SRH Fachkrankenhaus Neresheim GmbH (1)
Kosinger Strasse 11, 73450, Neresheim, Germany
Tel.: (49) 732696080
Web Site: http://www.fachkrankenhaus-neresheim.de
Hospital Management Services
N.A.I.C.S.: 622110

SRH Gesundheitszentrum Bad Wimpfen GmbH (1)
Bei der alten Saline 2, 74206, Bad Wimpfen, Germany
Tel.: (49) 7063520
Web Site: http://www.gesundheitszentrum-badwimpfen.de
Hospital Management Services
N.A.I.C.S.: 622110
Andreas Christopeit (CEO)

SRH Klinikum Karlsbad-Langensteinbach GmbH (1)
Langensteinbach Guttmannstrasse 1, 76307, Karlsbad, Germany
Tel.: (49) 7202610
Web Site: http://www.klinikum-karlsbad.de
Hospital Management Services
N.A.I.C.S.: 622110

SRH Krankenhaus Oberndorf a.N. GmbH (1)
Uhlandstrasse 2, 78727, Oberndorf, Germany
Tel.: (49) 74238130
Web Site: http://www.krankenhaus-oberndorf.de
Hospital Management Services
N.A.I.C.S.: 622110
Harald Smooth (CEO)

SRH Krankenhaus Waltershausen-Friedrichroda GmbH (1)
Reinhardsbrunner Str 17, Friedrichsdorf, 99894, Grumbach, Germany
Tel.: (49) 36233500
Web Site: http://www.krankenhaus-waltershausen-friedrichroda.de
Emp.: 300
Hospital Management Services
N.A.I.C.S.: 622110
Annett Gratz (Mng Dir)

SRH Kurpfalzkrankenhaus Heidelberg GmbH (1)
Bonhoefferstrasse 5, 69123, Heidelberg, Germany
Tel.: (49) 6221884010
Web Site: http://www.kurpfalzkrankenhaus.de
Hospital Management Services
N.A.I.C.S.: 622110

SRH Wald-Klinikum Gera GmbH (1)
Road of Peace 122, 07548, Gera, Germany
Tel.: (49) 3658280
Web Site: http://www.waldklinikumgera.de
Hospital Management Services
N.A.I.C.S.: 622110

SRH Zentralklinikum Suhl GmbH (1)
Albert-Schweitzer-Strasse 2, 98527, Suhl, Germany
Tel.: (49) 3681359
Web Site: http://www.zentralklinikum-suhl.de
Hospital Management Services
N.A.I.C.S.: 622110

SRHHL INDUSTRIES LIMITED
216 K J S Complex Bhagya Nagar, Hyderabad, 518 004, Andhra Pradesh, India

SRI KRISHNA CONSTRUCTIONS (INDIA) LIMITED

Tel.: (91) 8518228750
Web Site: http://www.srhhl.com
Sales Range: Less than $1 Million
Inorganic Chemical Mfr
N.A.I.C.S.: 325180
E. Thirupalu Babu (CEO & Compliance Officer)

SRI AMARNATH FINANCE LIMITED
4883-84 Second Floor Main Road, Kuch Ustad Dag Chandni Chowk, Delhi, 110006, India
Tel.: (91) 9999505033
Web Site: https://www.sriamarnathfinance.in
Year Founded: 1985
538863—(BOM)
Rev.: $586,079
Assets: $8,489,785
Liabilities: $70,918
Net Worth: $8,418,866
Earnings: $310,539
Emp.: 8
Fiscal Year-end: 03/31/23
Financial Support Services
N.A.I.C.S.: 523999
Priti Jain (Mng Dir)

SRI HAVISHA HOSPITALITY & INFRASTRUCTURE LTD.
Venus Plaza Adjacent to Old Airport Begumpet, Hyderabad, 500 016, India
Tel.: (91) 4027902929
Web Site: https://www.srihavisha.in
Year Founded: 1993
HAVISHA—(NSE)
Rev.: $2,157,616
Assets: $4,943,301
Liabilities: $871,866
Net Worth: $4,071,435
Earnings: $179,534
Emp.: 3
Fiscal Year-end: 03/31/23
Gas Fuel Retailer
N.A.I.C.S.: 457210
V. Subrahmanyam (Chm)

SRI KPR INDUSTRIES LIMITED
K P R House 5th Floor Sardar Patel Road Near Anand Theatre, Secunderabad, 500003, India
Tel.: (91) 4027847121
Web Site: https://www.kprindustries.in
Year Founded: 1988
514442—(BOM)
Rev.: $2,748,025
Assets: $17,959,864
Liabilities: $3,195,716
Net Worth: $14,764,148
Earnings: $1,314,575
Emp.: 25
Fiscal Year-end: 03/31/22
Plastic Product Mfr & Whslr
N.A.I.C.S.: 326199
Nalla Kishan Reddy (Mng Dir)

SRI KRISHNA CONSTRUCTIONS (INDIA) LIMITED
No 224 3rd Floor SS Complex 14th cross Sampige Road, Malleshwaram, Bengaluru, 560003, India
Tel.: (91) 8023318189
Web Site: https://skcil.in
Year Founded: 2005
539363—(BOM)
Rev.: $754,153
Assets: $12,019,479
Liabilities: $8,082,020
Net Worth: $3,937,460
Earnings: $101,179
Emp.: 8
Fiscal Year-end: 03/31/20
Landscape Architectural Services

SRI KRISHNA CONSTRUCTIONS (INDIA) LIMITED

Sri Krishna Constructions (India) Limited—(Continued)
N.A.I.C.S.: 541320
Jignesh Dhirendra Dubal (CFO)

SRI LAKSHMI SARASWATHI TEXTILES (ARNI) LTD.
16 Krishnama Road Nungambakkam, Chennai, 600 034, Tamil Nadu, India
Tel.: (91) 4428277344
Web Site: https://www.slstindia.com
521161—(BOM)
Rev.: $18,186,979
Assets: $4,884,048
Liabilities: $8,191,991
Net Worth: ($3,307,943)
Earnings: ($2,377,735)
Emp.: 1,010
Fiscal Year-end: 03/31/23
Cotton Yarn Mfr
N.A.I.C.S.: 313110
S. Balakrishna (Chm, CEO & Co-Mng Dir)

SRI LANKA TELECOM PLC
Lotus Road, PO Box 503, 1, Colombo, 1, Sri Lanka
Tel.: (94) 112021000
Web Site: https://www.slt.lk
Year Founded: 1991
SLTL.N0000—(COL)
Rev.: $358,543,324
Assets: $800,852,169
Liabilities: $492,979,595
Net Worth: $307,872,574
Earnings: $15,861,656
Emp.: 8,058
Fiscal Year-end: 12/31/22
Telecommunication Servicesb
N.A.I.C.S.: 517112
Indrani Hissalle (Chief Innovation & Culture Officer)

Subsidiaries:

EChannelling PLC (1)
No 108 W A D Ramanayake Mawatha, Colombo, Sri Lanka
Tel.: (94) 710225225
Web Site: https://www.echannelling.com
Emp.: 30
Software Development Services
N.A.I.C.S.: 541511

Mobitel (Private) Limited (1)
No 108 W A D Ramanayake Mawatha, Colombo, 02, Western Province, Sri Lanka
Tel.: (94) 71 275 5777
Web Site: https://www.mobitel.lk
Cellular Phone Communcation Carriers
N.A.I.C.S.: 517112
Nalin Perera (CEO)

SLT Campus (Private) Limited (1)
Ingiriya Road, Padukka, Colombo, Sri Lanka
Tel.: (94) 112100500
Web Site: http://www.sltc.ac.lk
Education Services
N.A.I.C.S.: 611710
Ranjith G. Rubasinghe (Founder, Pres & CEO)

SLT Digital Info Services (Private) Limited (1)
No 17 H K Dharmadasa Mawatha, Colombo, Sri Lanka
Tel.: (94) 11 239 9399
Web Site: https://www.sltds.lk
Digital Marketing Services
N.A.I.C.S.: 541613
P. G. Kumarasinghe Sirisena (Chm)

SLT Digital Services Pvt Ltd (1)
No 17 HK Dharmadasa Mawatha, 200, Colombo, Western Province, Sri Lanka
Tel.: (94) 112399399
Web Site: https://www.rainbowpages.lk
Emp.: 100
Telephone Directory Publishing Services
N.A.I.C.S.: 513140

SLT Human Capital Solutions (Private) Limited (1)
Sri Lanka Telecom Office Maradana road, Colombo, 01000, Sri Lanka
Tel.: (94) 112558558
Web Site: http://www.hcs.lk
Consultancy Services
N.A.I.C.S.: 541618
Roshan Kaluarachchi (CEO)

Subsidiary (Domestic):

Talentfort (Pvt.) Ltd. (2)
No 800 Maradana Road, Colombo, Sri Lanka
Tel.: (94) 11 269 4406
Web Site: https://www.talentfort.lk
Consultancy Services
N.A.I.C.S.: 541618
Diwan Ruwanpura (Sec)

SLT Manpower Solutions (Private) Limited (1)
Sri Lanka Telecom Office Maradana Road, Colombo, 00800, Western Province, Sri Lanka
Tel.: (94) 112694416
Web Site: http://www.manpower.lk
Contract Manpower Services
N.A.I.C.S.: 561320

SLT Property Management (Private) Limited (1)
No 07 Anderson Road, Colombo, Sri Lanka
Tel.: (94) 112556060
Web Site: http://www.sltproperty.lk
Real Estate Services
N.A.I.C.S.: 531390
Dileepa Wijesundera (Grp CEO)

SLT VisionCom (Private) Limited (1)
Lotus Road, PO Box 503, Colombo, 01, Western Province, Sri Lanka
Tel.: (94) 11 200 5511
Web Site: https://www.sltvisioncom.lk
Internet Protocol Television Services
N.A.I.C.S.: 516210
Thusha Weerasooriya (CEO)

Sky Network (Private) Limited (1)
No 5 Anderson Road, Colombo, 00500, Western Province, Sri Lanka
Tel.: (94) 112559401
Sales Range: $25-49.9 Million
Emp.: 40
Internet Service Provider
N.A.I.C.S.: 517111
Nimal Welgama (Chm)

Sri Lanka Telecom (Services) Limited (1)
148/15 Lesley Ranagala Mawatha, Nugegoda, Colombo, 08, Western Province, Sri Lanka
Tel.: (94) 11 281 8652
Web Site: https://www.slts.lk
Sales Range: $50-74.9 Million
Emp.: 120
Satellite Telecommunication Services
N.A.I.C.S.: 517410
Nimal Welgama (Co-Chm)

SRI MALINI SPINNING MILLS LTD.
Trichy Main Road, Sandhiyur Mallur, Salem, 636 203, Tamil Nadu, India
Tel.: (91) 4272422936
Textile Products Mfr
N.A.I.C.S.: 313110
K. S. S. Prakkaash (Exec Dir)

SRI NACHAMMAI COTTON MILLS LIMITED
Door No 181 Vasantham 4th Cross Street New Fairlands, Salem, 636016, India
Tel.: (91) 4272330847
Web Site: https://www.sncmindia.com
Year Founded: 1980
521234—(BOM)
Rev.: $21,735,332
Assets: $17,379,535
Liabilities: $14,395,167
Net Worth: $2,984,368
Earnings: $72,877
Emp.: 150
Fiscal Year-end: 03/31/21

Textile Products Mfr
N.A.I.C.S.: 314999
P. Palaniappan (Chm & Co-Mng Dir)

SRI PANWA HOSPITALITY REAL ESTATE INVESTMENT TRUST
2922/198 10thFl Charn Issara Tower II New Petchburi Road, Bangkapi Huay Kwang, Bangkok, 10310, Thailand
Tel.: (66) 23082022
SRIPANWA—(THA)
Rev.: $8,429,473
Assets: $127,638,094
Liabilities: $25,633,761
Net Worth: $102,004,333
Earnings: $2,483,653
Fiscal Year-end: 12/31/23
Real Estate Investment Trust Services
N.A.I.C.S.: 531190

SRI RAMAKRISHNA MILLS (COIMBATORE) LIMITED
1493 Sathyamangalam Road, Ganapathy Post, Coimbatore, 641 006, Tamil Nadu, India
Tel.: (91) 4222531022
Web Site:
    https://www.ramakrishnamills.com
521178—(BOM)
Rev.: $4,781,464
Assets: $6,916,756
Liabilities: $5,482,225
Net Worth: $1,434,530
Earnings: $33,463
Emp.: 116
Fiscal Year-end: 03/31/23
Yarn Mfr
N.A.I.C.S.: 313110
D. Lakshminarayanaswamy (CEO & Mng Dir)

SRI SRUMUGA ENTERPRISE LIMITED
No 1 Sundaram Brothers Layout, Opp All India Radio Trichy Road, Coimbatore, 641 045, Tamil Nadu, India
Tel.: (91) 422 2322340
Web Site:
    http://www.arumugaenterprise.com
Year Founded: 1995
Sales Range: $1-9.9 Million
Textile Products Mfr
N.A.I.C.S.: 314999
T. Rajkumar (Chm & Mng Dir)

Subsidiaries:

Sri Mahasakthi Mills Limited (1)
2nd Floor 180 Race Course, Coimbatore, 641018, Tamilnadu, India
Tel.: (91) 422 2222845
Web Site: http://www.mahasakthimills.com
Textile Products Mfr
N.A.I.C.S.: 314999
T. Rajkumar (Chm)

SRI TRANG AGRO-INDUSTRY PUBLIC COMPANY LIMITED
10 Soi 10 Phetkasem Road Hatyai, Songkhla, 90110, Thailand
Tel.: (66) 74344663
Web Site:
    https://www.sritranggroup.com
Year Founded: 1987
NC2—(SES)
Rev.: $2,459,274,853
Assets: $3,261,837,648
Liabilities: $1,272,513,669
Net Worth: $1,989,323,979
Earnings: ($13,310,335)
Emp.: 15,852
Fiscal Year-end: 12/31/23
Holding Company; Rubber & Rubber Products Mfr
N.A.I.C.S.: 551112

INTERNATIONAL PUBLIC

Viyavood Sincharoenkul (Chm & Mng Dir)

Subsidiaries:

Anvar Parawood Co., Ltd. (1)
No 101 Moo 3 Samnakkham, Sadao, 90120, Songkhla, Thailand
Tel.: (66) 744127568
Wood Preservation
N.A.I.C.S.: 321114

Nam Hua Rubber Co., Ltd. (1)
41 and 99 Moo 3, Samnuk Kham Subdistrict, Sadao, 90120, Songkhla, Thailand
Tel.: (66) 7 441 2268
Web Site: http://www.sritranggroup.com
Block Rubber Mfr
N.A.I.C.S.: 326299

PT Sri Trang Lingga Indonesia (1)
Jalan TPA 2 RT 26 and 29 Keramasan, Palembang, 30259, South Sumatera, Indonesia
Tel.: (62) 711445666
Rubber Products Mfr
N.A.I.C.S.: 326299

PT Star Rubber (1)
Jalan Trans Kalimantan KM 16 Desa Jawa Tengah Kec Kab Kubu Raya-Kalbar, PO Box 7864, Sungai Ambawang, Pontianak, Kalimantan Barat, Indonesia
Tel.: (62) 561724888
Rubber Products Mfr
N.A.I.C.S.: 326299

Pattana Agro Futures Co., Ltd. (1)
No 33-84 Wallstreet Tower 17th Fl, Surawong Rd Bangrak, 10500, Bangkok, Thailand (40%)
Tel.: (66) 26328826
Web Site: http://www.pafutures.com
Sales Range: $25-49.9 Million
Emp.: 20
Wholesale Trade Agents & Brokers
N.A.I.C.S.: 425120
Leelasithorn Nipon (Mng Dir)

Premier System Engineering Co., Ltd. (1)
123 Moo 8, Ban Phru Sub-District, Hat Yai, 90250, Songkhla, Thailand
Tel.: (66) 74471480
Web Site: http://www.pse-cal.com
Industrial Machinery Design, Engineering & Maintenance Services
N.A.I.C.S.: 811310

Rubberland Products Co., Ltd. (1)
109 Karnchanawanich Road, Pahtong Subdistrict, Hat Yai, 90230, Songkhla, Thailand
Tel.: (66) 74 291 2234
Web Site: http://www.sritranggroup.com
Concentrated Latex Mfr
N.A.I.C.S.: 325212

Sadao P.S. Rubber Co., Ltd. (1)
No 207-1 Padang Besar Road, Sadao, 90120, Songkhla, Thailand
Tel.: (66) 7441 1838
Ribbed Smoked Rubber Sheet Mfr
N.A.I.C.S.: 326299

Semperflex Shanghai Ltd. (1)
1255 Cang Gong Road, Shanghai Chemical Industrial Park Fengxian Subzone, Shanghai, 201417, China (50%)
Tel.: (86) 2137581133
Rubber Products Mfr
N.A.I.C.S.: 326299

Shi Dong Shanghai Rubber Co., Ltd. (1)
5F East Block D F W square No 1686 Wuzhong Road, Minhang District, Shanghai, 201103, China
Tel.: (86) 216413 786 0603
Web Site: http://www.sritranggroup.com
Rubber Product Distr
N.A.I.C.S.: 423840

Sri Trang Ayeyar Rubber Industry Co., Ltd. (1)
848/1221 Kankalay Plot, Kyone Phite Village Mudon Township Mawlamyine District, Yangon, 12081, Mon, Myanmar
Tel.: (95) 9976994561
Rubber Products Mfr
N.A.I.C.S.: 326299

AND PRIVATE COMPANIES

Sri Trang Gloves (Singapore) Pte. Ltd. (1)
50 Raffles Place 27-01 Land Tower, Singapore, Singapore
Tel.: (65) 325210
Industrial Glove Distr
N.A.I.C.S.: 423450

Sri Trang Gloves (Thailand) Co., Ltd. (1)
17th Floor Park Venture Ecoplex Unit 1701 1707-1712 57 Wireless Road, Lumpini Pathumwan, Bangkok, 10330, Thailand
Tel.: (66) 20074500
Web Site: http://www.sritranggloves.com
Medical Gloves Mfr
N.A.I.C.S.: 339113
Thanawan Sangiamsak (CFO)

Sri Trang Gloves Global Pte. Ltd. (1)
50 Raffles Place 27-01 Land Tower, Singapore, Singapore
Tel.: (65) 325210
Financial Investment Services
N.A.I.C.S.: 522320

Sri Trang Gloves Vietnam Co., Ltd. (1)
Room No7 01A 7th Floor Vietnam Business Center Building, 57-59 Ho Tung Mau Street Ben Nghe Ward District 1, Ho Chi Minh City, Vietnam
Tel.: (84) 838216869
Industrial Glove Distr
N.A.I.C.S.: 423450

Sri Trang IBC Co., Ltd. (1)
10 Soi 10 Phetkasem Road, Hatyai, Songkhla, 90110, Thailand
Tel.: (66) 74344663
Information Technology Services
N.A.I.C.S.: 541512

Sri Trang Indochina (Vietnam) Co., Ltd. (1)
Room No 7 01A 7th Floor Vietnam Business Center Building 57-59, Ho tung Mau Street Ben Nghe Ward District 1, Ho Chi Minh City, Vietnam
Tel.: (84) 838216869
Rubber Products Mfr
N.A.I.C.S.: 326299

Sri Trang International Pte. Ltd. (1)
1 Wallich Street 25-02 Guoco Tower, Singapore, 078881, Singapore (100%)
Tel.: (65) 6 532 5210
Web Site: http://www.sritrang.com
Sales Range: $25-49.9 Million
Emp.: 28
Rubber Products Mfr
N.A.I.C.S.: 326299

Sri Trang Rubber & Plantation Co., Ltd. (1)
121 Moo 4, Nong Pa Khrang Sub-district Muang Chiang Mai District, Chiang Mai, 50000, Thailand
Tel.: (66) 53106198
Rubber Products Mfr
N.A.I.C.S.: 326299

Sri Trang USA, Inc. (1)
5820 W Cypress St Ste H, Tampa, FL 33607-1785 (100%)
Tel.: (813) 606-4301
Web Site: http://www.sritranggroup.com
Rubber Products Mfr
N.A.I.C.S.: 326299

Starlight Express Transport Co., Ltd. (1)
13/1 Jingjit Road Tubtiang, Mueang trang, Trang, 92000, Thailand
Tel.: (66) 755029002
Web Site: http://www.sritranggroup.com
Freight Transportation Services
N.A.I.C.S.: 484110

Startex Rubber Corporation Limited (1)
No 10 Soi 10 Phetkasem Road, Hat Yai, 90110, Thailand
Tel.: (66) 74344663
Web Site: http://www.sritranggroup.com
Sales Range: $25-49.9 Million
Emp.: 80
Synthetic Rubber Mfr
N.A.I.C.S.: 325212

Thai Tech Rubber Corporation Limited (1)
2 Juti Utit 3 Road, Hatyai Subdistrict Hatyai District, Hat Yai, 90110, Songkhla, Thailand (33.5%)
Tel.: (66) 7 423 0768
Web Site: http://www.thaitechglobal.com
Sales Range: $200-249.9 Million
Emp.: 1,000
Rubber Products Mfr
N.A.I.C.S.: 326299
Chansak Chansaci (Mgr)

SRI VAJRA GRANITES LIMITED
Survey No 225 Baswapoor Village, Bhiknoor Mandal Kamareddy, Hyderabad, 503101, Telangana, India
Tel.: (91) 4023355695
Web Site: http://www.srivajragranites.com
Rev.: $18,121
Assets: $594,181
Liabilities: $1,179,265
Net Worth: ($585,084)
Earnings: ($119,384)
Fiscal Year-end: 03/31/18
Granite Mfr
N.A.I.C.S.: 327991
Leela Annapareddy (Mng Dir)

SRILANKAN AIRLINES LTD.
Airline Ctr Bandaranaike International Airport, Katunayake, Sri Lanka
Tel.: (94) 197335555
Web Site: http://www.srilankan.com
Year Founded: 1979
Sales Range: $550-599.9 Million
Emp.: 5,508
Passenger & Cargo Airline Services
N.A.I.C.S.: 481111
Peter Hill (CEO)

Subsidiaries:

SriLankan Airlines Ltd.-Thailand (1)
942 34 35 Charn Issara Tower Rama IV Rd Suriyawongse, Bangrak, Bangkok, 10500, Thailand
Tel.: (66) 223692923
Web Site: http://www.srilankan.com
Sales Range: $25-49.9 Million
Emp.: 20
Passenger & Cargo Airline Services
N.A.I.C.S.: 481111
Jayan Tha Abeysinghe (Country Mgr)

SriLankan Catering Limited (1)
Airline Centre Bandaranaike International Airport, Katunayake, Negombo, Katunayake, Sri Lanka
Tel.: (94) 197 334111
Web Site: http://www.srilankancatering.com
Catering Services
N.A.I.C.S.: 722320
Nishantha Wickremasinghe (Chm)

SRINIVASA HATCHERIES LTD.
Plot No 169 Rd No 13 Jubilee Hills, Hyderabad, 500 033, Telangana, India
Tel.: (91) 40 23633500
Web Site: http://srinivasa.co
Year Founded: 1978
Poultry Breeding Services & Animal Feed Distr
N.A.I.C.S.: 112340
C. Jagapati Rao (Chm)

Subsidiaries:

Srinivasa Hatcheries Ltd. - Broiler Division (1)
54-13-7/A/1 Near SBI T S No 3 Seethammadhara, Visakhapatnam, 530 013, India
Tel.: (91) 891 6701104
Poultry Breeding Services
N.A.I.C.S.: 115210

SRIRACHA CONSTRUCTION PUBLIC COMPANY LIMITED
97 Village No 3, Surasak Subdistrict, Chon Buri, 20110, Thailand
Tel.: (66) 38317555
Web Site: https://www.sricha.com
SRICHA—(THA)
Rev.: $64,895,048
Assets: $73,323,027
Liabilities: $21,186,053
Net Worth: $52,136,974
Earnings: $3,914,765
Emp.: 2,629
Fiscal Year-end: 12/31/23
Industrial Building Construction
N.A.I.C.S.: 236210
Boonkrua Khemapiratana (Mng Dir)

SRISAWAD CORPORATION PUBLIC COMPANY LIMITED
99/392 Srisawad Building 4 6 Floor Chaeng Watthana Road Thungsonghong, Laksi, Bangkok, 10210, Thailand
Tel.: (66) 26935555 TH
Web Site: http://www.meebaanmeerod.com
Year Founded: 1979
SAWAD—(THA)
Rev.: $366,287,693
Assets: $1,732,885,635
Liabilities: $930,877,300
Net Worth: $802,008,335
Earnings: $159,630,489
Emp.: 7,580
Fiscal Year-end: 12/31/20
Loan Broker
N.A.I.C.S.: 522310
Sukont Kanjana-Huttakit (Chm)

Subsidiaries:

SWP Asset Management Co., Ltd. (1)
99/392 2nd Floor SoiChaengwattana 10 Intersection 3 Benjamitr, Chaengwattana Road Thung Song Hong Subdistrict Lak Si District, Bangkok, 10210, Thailand
Tel.: (66) 655203474
Web Site: https://www.swpamc.com
Asset Management Services
N.A.I.C.S.: 531390

Srisawad Capital Co., Ltd. (1)
99/392 Srisawad Building 5 6 floor Chaeng Wattana Road, Thung Song Hong Subdistrict Lak Si District, Bangkok, 10210, Thailand
Tel.: (66) 26915600
Web Site: https://www.srisawadcapital.co.th
Financial Loan Services
N.A.I.C.S.: 522310

SRISAWAD FINANCE PUBLIC COMPANY LIMITED
No 99/392 Srisawad Bldg 1 3 5 6 Fl Soi Chaeng Wattana 10, Yak 3 Benjamitre Chaeng Wattana Rd, Bangkok, 10210, Thailand
Tel.: (66) 20730677 TH
Web Site: http://www.bfit.co.th
Year Founded: 1969
BFIT—(THA)
Rev.: $114,036,001
Assets: $652,473,687
Liabilities: $332,713,435
Net Worth: $319,760,252
Earnings: $52,218,881
Fiscal Year-end: 12/31/20
Investment Banking Services
N.A.I.C.S.: 523150
Thititham Rojanapruk (Mng Dir)

Subsidiaries:

Cathay Leasing Co., Ltd. (1)
No 134 Cholasin Building 2nd Floor Surawong Road, Si Phraya Subdistrict Bang Rak District, Bangkok, 10500, Thailand
Tel.: (66) 21614519
Web Site: https://www.cathayleasing.co.th
Loan Providing Services
N.A.I.C.S.: 522310

SRITHAI SUPERWARE PUBLIC COMPANY LIMITED
15 Suksawat Rd Soi 36 Bangpakok, Rasburana, Bangkok, 10140, Thailand
Tel.: (66) 24270088 TH
Web Site: https://www.srithaisuperware.com
Year Founded: 1963
SITHAI—(THA)
Rev.: $249,597,144
Assets: $220,739,598
Liabilities: $88,537,303
Net Worth: $132,202,295
Earnings: $10,969,683
Emp.: 1,414
Fiscal Year-end: 12/31/23
Household & Industrial Plastic Products Mfr
N.A.I.C.S.: 326199
Sanan Angubolkul (Chm & Pres)

Subsidiaries:

Korat Thai Tech Company Limited (1)
325-328 Suranaree Industrial Estate Moo 6 Ratchasima-Chok Chai Road, Amphoe Mueang, Nakhon Ratchasima, Thailand
Tel.: (66) 4421 8766
Plastic Product Mfr & Distr
N.A.I.C.S.: 325211

Srithai (Vietnam) Company Limited (1)
No 9 Street 2 Song Than 1 Industrial Park, 75300, Di An, Binh Duong, Vietnam
Tel.: (84) 2743801653
Web Site: https://www.srithaivietnam.com
Emp.: 500
Plastic Product Mfr & Distr
N.A.I.C.S.: 326199

Srithai Miyagawa Company Limited (1)
539 M 4 Soi 8B Bangpoo Industrial Estate Sukhumvit Rd, Phraeksa Subdistrict Mueang Samut Prakan District, Samut Prakan, 10280, Thailand
Tel.: (66) 23240425
Web Site: https://www.st-miyagawa.com
Emp.: 452
Plastic Product Mfr & Distr
N.A.I.C.S.: 326199

Srithai Moulds Company Limited (1)
55/1 55/6 Moo 1 Tambon Nong samsak, Amphur Banbung, Chon Buri, 20170, Thailand
Tel.: (66) 38476525
Web Site: https://www.srithai-moulds.co.th
Emp.: 140
Plastics Product Mfr
N.A.I.C.S.: 326199
Sanan Angubolkul (Chm & Pres)

Srithai Superware India Limited (1)
507 Udyog Vihar Phase-V, Gurgaon, 122001, Haryana, India
Tel.: (91) 124 411 0404
Plastic Product Distr
N.A.I.C.S.: 423840
Seema Bhardwaj Vashisht (Mgr-Mktg)

Srithai Superware Manufacturing Private Limited (1)
SM-22 GIDC Sanand-II Bol, Taluka Sanand, Ahmedabad, 382170, Gujarat, India
Tel.: (91) 9909947903
Web Site: https://www.srithaisuperware.in
Plastic Product Mfr & Distr
N.A.I.C.S.: 326199

Srithai Superware Public Company Limited - Amata Nakorn Chonburi Factory (1)
70013 Moo 1 Chonburi Industrial Estate, Mueang Chonburi, Chon Buri, 20000, Thailand
Tel.: (66) 38203000
Web Site: http://www.srithaisuperware.com
Plastics Product Mfr
N.A.I.C.S.: 326199

SRITHAI SUPERWARE PUBLIC COMPANY LIMITED

Srithai Superware Public Company Limited—(Continued)

Srithai Superware Public Company Limited - Bangpoo Factory (1)
610 Soi 8A Bangpoo Industrial Estate Tambon Prak-Sa, Amphoe Mueang, Samut Prakan, 10280, Thailand
Tel.: (66) 2324 0922
Plastics Product Mfr
N.A.I.C.S.: 326199

Srithai Superware Public Company Limited - Korat Factory (1)
335 Moo 6 Suranaree Industrial Estate Ratchasima-Chok Chai Road, Amphoe Mueang, Nakhon Ratchasima, 30000, Thailand
Tel.: (66) 4421 2100
Plastics Product Mfr
N.A.I.C.S.: 326199

Srithai-Otto (Thailand) Company Limited (1)
15 Suksawat Rd Soi 36 Bangpakok, Rasburana, Bangkok, Thailand
Tel.: (66) 24270088
Plastic Product Mfr & Distr
N.A.I.C.S.: 326199

SRIVARI SPICES & FOODS LIMITED
4-1-878 876 877 & 877/1 207 Second Floor RDB Blue Hope, Abids, Hyderabad, 500001, Telangana, India
Tel.: (91) 9055234567
Web Site:
  https://www.srivarispices.com
Year Founded: 2019
SSFL—(NSE)
Rev.: $4,355,724
Assets: $3,122,870
Liabilities: $2,011,726
Net Worth: $1,111,144
Earnings: $375,926
Emp.: 94
Fiscal Year-end: 03/31/23
Packaged Food Distr
N.A.I.C.S.: 424420
Aradhana Puranlal Kawde (Officer)

Subsidiaries:

Srivari Supply Chain Private Limited (1)

SRIVARU HOLDING LIMITED
2nd Floor, Regatta Office Park, West Bay Road, Grand Cayman, KY1-1006, Cayman Islands
Tel.: (888) 227-8066
Web Site: https://svmh.ai
Year Founded: 2021
SVMH—(NASDAQ)
Rev.: $42,538
Assets: $1,586,159
Liabilities: $1,693,783
Net Worth: ($107,624)
Earnings: ($11,482,294)
Emp.: 45
Fiscal Year-end: 03/31/24
Holding Company
N.A.I.C.S.: 551112

Subsidiaries:

Mobiv Acquisition Corp. (1)
850 Library Ave Ste 204, Newark, DE 19711
Tel.: (302) 738-6680
Investment Management Service
N.A.I.C.S.: 523999

Srivaru Motors Private Limited. (1)
224/2, Trichy Rd, Naicken Thottam, Selvaraja Puram, Kannampalayam, Sulur,, Tamil Nadu, 641402, India
Tel.: (91) 8098202030
Web Site: https://srivarumotors.com
Vehicles Mfg.
N.A.I.C.S.: 336211

SRIVEN MULTI-TECH LIMITED
4A Kautilya - Amrutha Estates Near Errum Manzil Metro Station, Somajiguda, Hyderabad, 500082, Andhra Pradesh, India
Tel.: (91) 4049538120
Web Site:
  https://www.srivenmultitech.com
Year Founded: 1995
531536—(BOM)
Software Development Services
N.A.I.C.S.: 541511
V. V. Subrahmanyam (Chm & Mng Dir)

SRIVICHAIVEJVIVAT PUBLIC COMPANY LIMITED
74/5 Moo 4 Phetkasem Road, Omnoi Krathumbaen, Samut Sakhon, 74130, Thailand
Tel.: (66) 2 441 7899
Web Site: http://www.vichaivej.com
VIH—(THA)
Rev.: $157,595,525
Assets: $121,260,701
Liabilities: $34,776,054
Net Worth: $86,484,647
Earnings: $41,990,226
Emp.: 2,289
Fiscal Year-end: 12/31/21
Health Care Srvices
N.A.I.C.S.: 524114
Vichai Vanadurongwan (Chm & Pres)

Subsidiaries:

Saivichai Development Company Limited (1)
456-456/8 Phetkasem Road Nongkhang Plue, Nongkhaem, Bangkok, 10160, Thailand
Tel.: (66) 24416999
General Hospital Services
N.A.I.C.S.: 622110

Srisakornvejavivat Company Limited (1)
93/256 Sethakit 1 Road Tambon Tasai, Amphur Muang, 74000, Samutsakhon, Thailand
Tel.: (66) 3482670829
General Hospital Services
N.A.I.C.S.: 622110

Srivichai Vocational College Company Limited (1)
74/5 Moo 4 Phetkasem Road, Omnoi Krathumbaen, Samut Sakhon, 74130, Thailand
Tel.: (66) 24310070
Vocational School Operating Services
N.A.I.C.S.: 611519

The Bangkok Orthopedic Hospital Company Limited (1)
240/2-4 Charunsanitwong Road Banchanghlor, Bangkoknoi, Bangkok, 10700, Thailand
Tel.: (66) 2412005560
General Hospital Services
N.A.I.C.S.: 622110

SRJ TECHNOLOGIES GROUP PLC
Level 25 108 St Georges Terrace, Perth, 6000, WA, Australia
Tel.: (61) 861626199
Web Site: https://www.srj-technologies.com
Year Founded: 2014
SRJ—(ASX)
Rev.: $1,970,487
Assets: $1,628,480
Liabilities: $1,100,490
Net Worth: $527,990
Earnings: ($1,625,442)
Emp.: 11
Fiscal Year-end: 12/31/23
Management Consulting Services
N.A.I.C.S.: 541618
Alex Wood (CEO)

Subsidiaries:

SRJ Technology Limited (1)

Unit 2 Waterside House Port Hamble Satchell Lane Hamble, Southampton, SO31 4QD, United Kingdom
Tel.: (44) 2382549818
Civil Engineering Services
N.A.I.C.S.: 541330

SRM ENERGY LIMITED
21 Basant Lok Complex, Vasant Vihar, New Delhi, 110 057, India
Tel.: (91) 1141403205
Web Site: https://www.srmenergy.in
523222—(BOM)
Rev.: $5,156
Assets: $148,792
Liabilities: $5,578,203
Net Worth: ($5,429,411)
Earnings: ($272,646)
Emp.: 2
Fiscal Year-end: 03/31/23
Electric Power Generation & Distribution Services
N.A.I.C.S.: 221118
Vishal Rastogi (Mng Dir)

SRP GROUPE SA
1 rue des Bles ZAC Montjoie, 93210, La Plaine Saint-Denis, Cedex, France
Tel.: (33) 149460567   FR
Web Site:
  https://www.showroomprive.com
Year Founded: 2006
SRP—(EUR)
Sales Range: $1-9.9 Million
Online Product Distribution Services
N.A.I.C.S.: 561422
David Dayan (Co-Founder, Chm & CEO)

SRPSKA BANKA A.D
25 Savska St, 11000, Belgrade, Serbia
Tel.: (381) 113607200
Web Site:
  https://www.srpskabanka.rs
SRBN—(BEL)
Rev.: $5,197,364
Assets: $256,528,116
Liabilities: $230,889,306
Net Worth: $25,638,809
Earnings: $327,795
Emp.: 82
Fiscal Year-end: 12/31/22
Commercial Banking Services
N.A.I.C.S.: 522110
Zoran Ovuka (Dir-Comml Banking Dept)

SRS FINANCE LTD.
SRS Tower 306 3rd Floor, Near Metro Station Mewla Maharajpur G T Road, Faridabad, 121 003, Delhi, India
Tel.: (91) 1294323118
Web Site: http://www.srsparivar.com
Rev.: $2,669,262
Assets: $35,035,768
Liabilities: $19,103,523
Net Worth: $15,932,245
Earnings: ($2,209,435)
Emp.: 19
Fiscal Year-end: 03/31/17
Financial Investment Services
N.A.I.C.S.: 523999
Rakhi Mehta (Compliance Officer & Sec)

SRS HOLDINGS CO.,LTD.
Osaka International Building 30th floor 2-3-13 Azuchi-ch, Chuo-ku, Osaka, 541-0052, Japan
Tel.: (81) 672223101
Web Site: https://www.srs-holdings.co.jp
Year Founded: 1968
8163—(TKS)
Rev.: $398,107,080

INTERNATIONAL PUBLIC

Assets: $236,195,130
Liabilities: $129,384,140
Net Worth: $106,810,990
Earnings: $11,884,780
Emp.: 1,402
Fiscal Year-end: 03/31/24
Holding Company; Japanese Restaurant Operator
N.A.I.C.S.: 551112
Masahiko Shigesato (Pres & CEO)

Subsidiaries:

KAZOKUTEI Co., Ltd. (1)
Fushimi-cho 4-chome No 2 No 14 WAKITA Midosuji building second floor, Fujimura Chuo-ku, Osaka, 541-0044, Japan
Tel.: (81) 662276030
Web Site: http://www.kazokutei.co.jp
Sales Range: $125-149.9 Million
Emp.: 1,783
Restaurant Operators
N.A.I.C.S.: 722511
Kazuaki Irie (Pres & CEO)

SRS REAL INFRASTRUCTURE LIMITED
SRS Tower 3th Floor Near Metro Station Mewla Maharajpur GT Road, Faridabad, 121 003, Delhi, India
Tel.: (91) 1294323100
Web Site: http://www.srsparivar.com
Year Founded: 1990
Commercial Building Construction Services
N.A.I.C.S.: 236220
Anil Jindal (Chm)

SRT MARINE SYSTEMS PLC
Wireless House Westfield Industrial Estate, Midsomer Norton, Bath, BA3 4BS, United Kingdom
Tel.: (44) 1761409500   UK
Web Site: https://www.srt-marine.com
Year Founded: 2005
SRT—(LSE)
Rev.: $37,882,540
Assets: $32,791,577
Liabilities: $19,991,576
Net Worth: $12,800,001
Earnings: $86,330
Emp.: 90
Fiscal Year-end: 03/31/23
Wireless Communication Equipment Mfr
N.A.I.C.S.: 334220
Simon Tucker (CEO)

Subsidiaries:

Em-track Marine Electronics Limited (1)
Wireless House Westfield Industrial Estate, Midsomer Norton, Bath, BA3 4BS, United Kingdom
Tel.: (44) 1761409559
Web Site: http://www.em-trak.com
Marine Electronic Equipment Mfr
N.A.I.C.S.: 335999

SRT Marine Technology Limited (1)
Wireless House Westfield Industrial Estate, Midsomer Norton, Bath, BA3 4BS, United Kingdom
Tel.: (44) 1761 409 500
Web Site: http://www.srt-marine.com
Emp.: 45
Marine Electronic Equipment Distr
N.A.I.C.S.: 423690
Simon Cutker (Mng Dir)

Software Radio Technology (UK) Limited (1)
Wireless House Westfield Industrial Estate, Midsomer Norton, Bath, BA3 4BS, United Kingdom
Tel.: (44) 1761 409 500
Web Site: http://www.srtmarine.com
Sales Range: $25-49.9 Million
Emp.: 40
Wireless Communication Device Mfr
N.A.I.C.S.: 334220
Simon Tucker (CEO)

AND PRIVATE COMPANIES

SRU STEELS LIMITED
A-48 1st Floor Wazirpur Industrial Area, New Delhi, 110 052, India
Tel.: (91) 1127373622
Web Site: http://www.srusteels.in
Year Founded: 1995
540914—(BOM)
Rev.: $3,696,359
Assets: $2,453,416
Liabilities: $754,858
Net Worth: $1,698,558
Earnings: $28,871
Emp.: 14
Fiscal Year-end: 03/31/21
Construction Materials Distr
N.A.I.C.S.: 423390
Ramesh Agarwal *(Chm & Mng Dir)*

SRV GROUP PLC
Derby Business Park Tarvonsalmenkatu 15, PO Box 555, FIN-02601, Espoo, Finland
Tel.: (358) 201455200
Web Site: http://www.srv.fi
SRV1V—(HEL)
Rev.: $831,079,214
Assets: $484,024,390
Liabilities: $326,260,522
Net Worth: $157,763,868
Earnings: ($92,447,658)
Emp.: 834
Fiscal Year-end: 12/31/22
Construction Services
N.A.I.C.S.: 236220
Timo Nieminen *(Deputy CEO, Exec VP & Sr VP-Project Dev)*

Subsidiaries:

Jupiter Realty B.V (1)
Prins Bernhardplein 200, Amsterdam, 1097 JB, Noord-Holland, Netherlands
Tel.: (31) 205214777
Residential Building Construction Services
N.A.I.C.S.: 531120

OOO SRV Development (1)
Pr Shaumyana 4 Block 1 Letter A Business Centre Bazen Office 208, 195027, Saint Petersburg, Russia
Tel.: (7) 812 449 00 55
Web Site: http://www.srv.fi
Real Estate Development Services
N.A.I.C.S.: 531390

Rakennusliike Purmonen Oy (1)
Koskikatu 11 D 56, 80100, Joensuu, Finland
Tel.: (358) 13 126 636
Web Site: http://www.rakennusliikepurmonen.fi
Construction Engineering Services
N.A.I.C.S.: 541330

SRV Baltia Oy
Derby Business Park Tarvonsalmenkatu 15, 02600, Espoo, Finland
Tel.: (358) 201455200
Web Site: http://www.srv.fi
Construction Engineering Services
N.A.I.C.S.: 541330

SRV Construction Ltd
Derby Business Park Tarvonsalmenkatu 15, 02600, Espoo, Finland
Tel.: (358) 201455200
Web Site: http://www.srv.fi
Construction Engineering Services
N.A.I.C.S.: 541330

SRV Ehitused AS
Roosikrantsi 11, 10119, Tallinn, Estonia
Tel.: (372) 6662400
Web Site: https://srv.ee
Industrial Building Construction Services
N.A.I.C.S.: 236210

SRV Kaakkois-Suomi oy (1)
Kaivokatu 7 B, 53100, Lappeenranta, Finland
Tel.: (358) 201455850
Web Site: http://www.srv.fi
Sales Range: $25-49.9 Million
Emp.: 20
Construction Engineering Services

SRV Keski-Suomi Oy (1)
Puistokatu 2 A, 40100, Jyvaskyla, Finland
Tel.: (358) 201455200
Web Site: http://www.srv.fi
Emp.: 30
Property Development Services
N.A.I.C.S.: 531390
Timo Kauppi *(Reg Dir)*

SRV Kinnisvara AS (1)
Ravala Pst 3, Tallinn, 10143, Estonia
Tel.: (372) 666 2400
Web Site: http://www.srv.ee
Real Estate Development Services
N.A.I.C.S.: 531390

SRV Lounais-Suomi Oy (1)
Kurjenmaenkatu 10 B 42, 20700, Turku, Finland
Tel.: (358) 201455200
Web Site: https://www.srv.fi
Sales Range: $25-49.9 Million
Construction Engineering Services
N.A.I.C.S.: 237990
Heikki Kallio *(Reg Dir)*

SRV Pirkanmaa Oy (1)
Tampellan Esplanadi 2, 33100, Tampere, Finland
Tel.: (358) 201 455 740
Construction Engineering Services
N.A.I.C.S.: 541330
Virpi Ekholm *(Reg Mgr)*

SRV Pohjois-Suomi (1)
Hallituskatu 13-17 F 57, 90100, Oulu, Finland
Tel.: (358) 201455200
Web Site: http://www.srv.fi
Sales Range: $25-49.9 Million
Construction Engineering Services
N.A.I.C.S.: 541330

SRV Russia Oy (1)
Derby Business Park Tarvonsalmenkatu 15, 02600, Espoo, Finland
Tel.: (358) 201455200
Web Site: https://www.srv.fi
Construction Engineering Services
N.A.I.C.S.: 541330

SRV Stroi OOO (1)
33 Schepkina Street, 129090, Moscow, Russia
Tel.: (7) 495 228 1709
Construction Engineering Services
N.A.I.C.S.: 541330

TBE-Construction Oy (1)
Niittytaival 13, Espoo, 02200, Uusimaa, Finland
Tel.: (358) 201455200
Construction Engineering Services
N.A.I.C.S.: 541330
Juha Ojala *(CEO)*

SRV YHTIOT OYJ
Derby Business Park Tarvonsalmenkatu 15, 2600, Espoo, Finland
Tel.: (358) 201455200
Web Site: https://www.srv.fi
Year Founded: 1987
SRV1V—(HEL)
Rev.: $831,079,214
Assets: $484,024,390
Liabilities: $326,260,522
Net Worth: $157,763,868
Earnings: ($92,447,658)
Emp.: 834
Fiscal Year-end: 12/31/22
Building Construction Services
N.A.I.C.S.: 236115
Saku Sipola *(Pres & CEO)*

Subsidiaries:

SRV Infra Ltd. (1)
Alikeravantie 83, 04260, Kerava, Finland
Tel.: (358) 201455200
Construction Services
N.A.I.C.S.: 236220

SSAB AB
Klarabergsviadukten 70 D6, PO Box 70, 101 21, Stockholm, Sweden

Tel.: (46) 84545700 SE
Web Site: https://www.ssab.com
Year Founded: 1978
SSAB.A—(OMX)
Rev.: $10,969,090,200
Assets: $9,899,620,200
Liabilities: $3,661,993,800
Net Worth: $6,237,626,400
Earnings: $1,196,888,400
Emp.: 14,715
Fiscal Year-end: 12/31/23
Steel Sheet & Steel Plate Producer
N.A.I.C.S.: 331221
Olavi Huhtala *(Exec VP & Head-Europe)*

Subsidiaries:

Abraservice Holding SAS (1)
2 rue Jean-Baptiste Perrin, 71380, Saint Marcel, France
Tel.: (33) 385906000
Web Site: https://www.abraservice.com
Stainless Steel Mfr
N.A.I.C.S.: 331110

Subsidiary (Non-US):

Abraservice Deutschland GmbH (2)
Ronsdorfer Str 24, 40233, Dusseldorf, Germany
Tel.: (49) 211995500
Web Site: https://www.abraservice.com
Stainless Steel Mfr
N.A.I.C.S.: 331110

Subsidiary (Domestic):

Abraservice Lyon SAS (2)
4 rue Jean Mace, 69330, Meyzieu, France
Tel.: (33) 472229090
Web Site: https://www.abraservice.com
Stainless Steel Mfr
N.A.I.C.S.: 331110

Subsidiary (Non-US):

Abraservice Nederland BV (2)
Nijverheidsweg 10, 1442 LD, Purmerend, Netherlands
Tel.: (31) 299792003
Web Site: https://www.abraservice.com
Stainless Steel Mfr
N.A.I.C.S.: 331110

Abraservice UK Limited (1)
Arley Road, Saltley, Birmingham, B8 1BB, United Kingdom
Tel.: (44) 1213263100
Steel Distr
N.A.I.C.S.: 423510

Borlange Handelsstal AB (1)
Hantverkargatan 9, 781 71, Borlange, Sweden
Tel.: (46) 24392160
Web Site: https://www.borlangehandelsstal.se
Steel Distr
N.A.I.C.S.: 423510

Goteborgs Stal AB (1)
Marieholmsgatan 72, 415 02, Gothenburg, Sweden
Tel.: (46) 31800880
Web Site: https://www.goteborgsstal.se
Steel Distr
N.A.I.C.S.: 423510

Hardox Wearparts Center Stirling Ltd. (1)
Unit 1-4 Bandeath Industrial Estate, Throsk, Stirling, FK7 7NP, United Kingdom
Tel.: (44) 1786817081
Wear Parts Distr
N.A.I.C.S.: 423120

Mjolby Handelsstal AB (1)
Florettgatan 3, 595 43, Mjolby, Sweden
Tel.: (46) 14218811
Web Site: https://www.mjolbyhandelsstal.se
Steel Distr
N.A.I.C.S.: 423510

Norrkopings Handelsstal AB (1)
Kommendantvagen 6, 602 38, Norrkoping, Sweden
Tel.: (46) 11157300

Web Site: https://www.norrkopingshandelsstal.se
Steel Distr
N.A.I.C.S.: 423510

Norsk Staal Tynnplater AS (1)
Harborveien 60, Fredrikstad, Norway (50%)
Tel.: (47) 69358400
Web Site: http://www.tynnplater.com
Steel Sheets, Plates & Stainless Steel Products Distr
N.A.I.C.S.: 423510

Piristeel Oy (1)
Metallitie 4, 62200, Kauhava, Finland
Tel.: (358) 64338800
Web Site: https://piristeel.fi
Steel Mfr & Distr
N.A.I.C.S.: 331110

Plannja Siba (1)
Vastra Varvsgatan 3, PO Box 143, Jarnforsen, Lulea, 97436, Sweden
Tel.: (46) 49517500
Web Site: https://www.plannja.se
Fabricated Structural Metal Mfr
N.A.I.C.S.: 332312
Thom Mathisen *(Gen Mgr)*

Rautaruukki Oyj (1)
Panuntie 11, 00620, Helsinki, Finland
Tel.: (358) 2059150
Sales Range: $1-4.9 Billion
Steel Products Mfr
N.A.I.C.S.: 331221
Sami Eronen *(Pres)*

Subsidiary (Non-US):

LLC Ruukki Ukraine (2)
Fridrikha Angelsa 60 Office 114, 54001, Mariupol, Ukraine
Tel.: (380) 629 41 08 65
Web Site: http://www.ruukki.com
Sales Range: $75-99.9 Million
Emp.: 150
Seal Products Distr
N.A.I.C.S.: 423510

Rautaruukki Stalservis Spbl (2)
Domostroiteinaja Ulitsa 16, Saint Petersburg, 194292, Russia (100%)
Tel.: (7) 8123466969
Web Site: http://www.rukki.com
Sales Range: $75-99.9 Million
Emp.: 150
Provider of Steel Services
N.A.I.C.S.: 423510
Vazim Perfiliez *(CEO)*

Division (Domestic):

Rautaruukki Steel (2)
Rautaruukintie 155, PO Box 93, FIN 92101, Raahe, Finland (100%)
Tel.: (358) 205911
Web Site: http://www.ruukki.com
Sales Range: $1-4.9 Billion
Emp.: 3,000
Coal Prodcuts Mfr
N.A.I.C.S.: 324199
Sakari Akallo *(Sr VP)*

Subsidiary (Domestic):

JIT Trans Oy (3)
Rautaruukintie 155, PO Box 84, FIN 92101, Raahe, Finland
Tel.: (358) 88493880
Web Site: http://www.jittrans.fi
Sales Range: $25-49.9 Million
Emp.: 60
Coal Prodcuts Mfr
N.A.I.C.S.: 324199

Presteel Oy (3)
Lapaluodontie 320, PO Box 106, 92100, Raahe, Finland (80%)
Tel.: (358) 205911
Web Site: https://www.presteel.fi
Coal Prodcuts Mfr
N.A.I.C.S.: 324199

Unit (Domestic):

Rautaruukki Steel - Kankaanpaa Works (3)
Rautatienkatu 19, 38700, Kankaanpaa, Finland (100%)
Tel.: (358) 205911
Web Site: http://www.ruukki.com

SSAB AB

SSAB AB—(Continued)
Sales Range: $25-49.9 Million
Emp.: 75
Coal Prodcuts Mfr
N.A.I.C.S.: 324199
Pauli Heinonen (Mgr-Works)

Subsidiary (Domestic):

Velsa Oy (3)
Paulaharjuntie 6, FIN 61301, Kurikka, Finland
Tel.: (358) 205911
Web Site: http://www.rukki.com
Sales Range: $75-99.9 Million
Emp.: 350
Mobile Logistics Capping Mfr
N.A.I.C.S.: 541230

Division (Domestic):

Rautaruukki Steel Structure (2)
Harvialantie 420, FIN 13300, Hameenlinna, Finland (100%)
Tel.: (358) 2059125312
Web Site: http://www.ruukki.com
Sales Range: $600-649.9 Million
Emp.: 1,500
Roofing Product Mfr
N.A.I.C.S.: 423330
Petri Nieminen (Sr VP)

Unit (Non-US):

Ruukki CZ s.r.o. (3)
Pekarska 695/10a, 155 00, Prague, Czech Republic (100%)
Tel.: (420) 25 731 1040
Web Site: https://www.ruukki.com
Sales Range: $25-49.9 Million
Building & Construction Products Mfr
N.A.I.C.S.: 236220

Ruukki L.L.C (3)
Domostroitelnaja Ulitsa 16, 194292, Saint Petersburg, Russia (100%)
Tel.: (7) 495) 032 10 45
Web Site: http://www.ruukki.ru
Provider of Repair Services
N.A.I.C.S.: 423510

Ruukki Latvia S.I.A. (3)
Delu Iela 4, Riga, 1004, Latvia (100%)
Tel.: (371) 67044900
Web Site: http://www.ruukki.com
Sales Range: $10-24.9 Million
Emp.: 100
Coal Prodcuts Mfr
N.A.I.C.S.: 324199
Guntis Duas (Mng Dir)

Ruukki Lithuania (3)
Pramomes St 16, Vilnius, 14149, Lithuania (100%)
Tel.: (370) 52322314
Sales Range: $25-49.9 Million
Emp.: 100
Coal Prodcuts Mfr
N.A.I.C.S.: 324199

Unit (Domestic):

Ruukki Metals Toijalan (3)
Hameentie 100, PO Box 96, Toijala, 37801, Finland (100%)
Tel.: (358) 205911
Web Site: http://www.ruukki.com
Sales Range: $200-249.9 Million
Emp.: 50
N.A.I.C.S.: 324199
Sakari Tamminen (Pres & CEO)

Unit (Non-US):

Ruukki Product AS (3)
Turba 7, Parnu, 80010, Estonia (100%)
Tel.: (372) 447 9900
Web Site: https://www.ruukki.com
Sales Range: $50-74.9 Million
Emp.: 260
Coal Prodcuts Mfr
N.A.I.C.S.: 324199

Ruukki Slovakia, s.r.o. (3)
Stara Vajnorska 37, 831 04, Bratislava, Slovakia (100%)
Tel.: (421) 23 213 1411
Web Site: https://www.ruukki.com

Sales Range: $25-49.9 Million
Metal & Metal Ore Whslr
N.A.I.C.S.: 324199

ZAO Rannila Minsk (3)
Amuratorskaya 7 11, Minsk, 220004, Belarus (100%)
Tel.: (375) 172267814
Web Site: http://www.yandix.au
Sales Range: $25-49.9 Million
Emp.: 20
Coal Prodcuts Mfr
N.A.I.C.S.: 324199

ZAT Ruukki Ukraina (3)
35A Mashinostroivna Street, 03067, Kiev, UA, Ukraine (100%)
Tel.: (380) 95 364 4545
Web Site: https://www.ruukki.com
Sales Range: $50-74.9 Million
Steel Services
N.A.I.C.S.: 423510
Anna Melithtnko (Sec)

Subsidiary (Domestic):

Ruukki Construction Oy (2)
Panuntie 11, 00620, Helsinki, Finland
Tel.: (358) 2059150
Sales Range: $700-749.9 Million
Emp.: 350
Construction Engineering Services
N.A.I.C.S.: 541330
Tommi Matomaki (Exec VP)

Subsidiary (Non-US):

Ruukki Danmark A/S (2)
Banemarksvej 50 1 sal, DK 2605, Brondby, Denmark (100%)
Tel.: (45) 45 70 2502 40
Web Site: http://www.ruukki.com
Sales Range: $25-49.9 Million
Emp.: 20
Steel Mfr & Exporter
N.A.I.C.S.: 331222

Ruukki France SARL (2)
121 Avenue Paul Doumer, Rueil-Malmaison, 92500, France
Tel.: (33) 1 41 39 99 00
Emp.: 5
Commercial Building Construction Services
N.A.I.C.S.: 236220
Jose Moutinho (Mgr-Sls)

Ruukki Holding B.V. (2)
Twenteepoort West 10-5, Almelo, 7609 RD, Netherlands
Tel.: (31) 546578535
Web Site: https://www.ruukki.com
Sales Range: $50-74.9 Million
Emp.: 11
Investment Management Service
N.A.I.C.S.: 523999

Subsidiary (Domestic):

Ruukki Benelux B.V. (3)
Twenteepoort West 10-5, 7609 RD, Almelo, Netherlands
Tel.: (31) 546 57 85 35
Sales Range: $50-74.9 Million
Emp.: 11
Metal Mining Services
N.A.I.C.S.: 212290
Robert Wesdijk (Mng Dir)

Ruukki Finance B.V. (3)
Twenteepoort West 10-5, Almelo, 7609 RD, Netherlands
Tel.: (31) 546578535
Financial Management Services
N.A.I.C.S.: 523999

Subsidiary (Non-US):

Ruukki Holding GmbH (2)
Schifferstr 92, Duisburg, 47059, Germany
Tel.: (49) 203317390
Web Site: http://www.ruukki.com
Sales Range: $50-74.9 Million
Emp.: 5
Investment Management Service
N.A.I.C.S.: 523999

Ruukki Hungary Kft (2)
Erdoalja U 1, Biatorbagy, 2051, Hungary
Tel.: (36) 23814700
Construction Engineering Services
N.A.I.C.S.: 541330

Ruukki Metals Polska Sp. z.o.o. (2)
Ul Jaktorowska 13, 96300, Zyrardow, Poland (100%)
Tel.: (48) 468554660
Web Site: http://www.ruukkimetalspolska.pl
Sales Range: $10-24.9 Million
Emp.: 100
Mechanical Engineering & Construction
N.A.I.C.S.: 541330

Ruukki Norge (2)
Prof Birkelandsvei 21, Furuset, Oslo, 1001, Norway (100%)
Tel.: (47) 22909000
Web Site: http://www.ccb.no
Sales Range: $50-74.9 Million
Emp.: 100
Coal Prodcuts Mfr
N.A.I.C.S.: 324199
John Borge Halvorsen (Mng Dir)

Ruukki Polska Sp. z o.o. (2)
Ul Jaktorowska 13, 96 300, Zyrardow, Poland (100%)
Tel.: (48) 468581600
Web Site: https://www.ruukki.com
Sales Range: $50-74.9 Million
Emp.: 100
Petroleum & Coal Products Manufacturing
N.A.I.C.S.: 324199

Ruukki Products AS (2)
Jarvevana Tee 5, Tallinn, 10132, Estonia (100%)
Tel.: (372) 6512771
Web Site: http://www.ruukki.ee
Sales Range: $50-74.9 Million
Emp.: 15
Steel Mfrs
N.A.I.C.S.: 522220

Ruukki Romania s.r.l. (2)
Ithaca 220, 087015, Bolintin-Deal, Romania
Tel.: (40) 346220000
Web Site: https://www.ruukki.com
Sales Range: $50-74.9 Million
Emp.: 200
Prefabricated Metal Mfr
N.A.I.C.S.: 332311

Ruukki Spain S.L. (2)
Calle Ramon y Cajal 7-9 Bajo-Oficina 13, 1007, Vitoria, Spain
Tel.: (34) 945 23 11 60
Sales Range: $50-74.9 Million
Emp.: 5
Steel Product Distr
N.A.I.C.S.: 423510
Cameron Michael Clark (Gen Mgr)

Subsidiary (Domestic):

Ruukki Stainless Steel & Aluminium Oy (2)
Suolakivenkatu 1, PL 138, 811, Helsinki, Finland
Tel.: (358) 20 5911
Metal Mining Services
N.A.I.C.S.: 212290

Subsidiary (Non-US):

Ruukki Sverige AB (2)
Olof Asklunds gata 6, PO Box 506, 421 30, Vastra Frolunda, Sweden (100%)
Tel.: (46) 10 787 8000
Web Site: https://www.ruukki.com
Sales Range: $150-199.9 Million
Steel Services
N.A.I.C.S.: 423510

Branch (Domestic):

Ruukki Sverige AB (3)
Olof Asklunds gata 6, PO Box 100, 421 30, Vastra Frolunda, Sweden (100%)
Tel.: (46) 10 787 8000
Web Site: https://www.ruukki.com
Sales Range: $50-74.9 Million
Coal Prodcuts Mfr
N.A.I.C.S.: 324199
Ulf Wuopeo (Mng Dir)

Ruukki Sverige AB (3)
Landsvagen 68, PO Box 7, Anderslov, SE2 3108, Sweden (100%)
Tel.: (46) 41021400
Web Site: http://www.gasell.com
Sales Range: $75-99.9 Million
Coal Prodcuts Mfr
N.A.I.C.S.: 324199

Yuham Magnussom (Mng Dir)
Subsidiary (Non-US):

Ruukki UK Ltd. (2)
Cranmore Place Cranmore Business Park Suite 6, Solihull, B90 4RZ, United Kingdom
Tel.: (44) 1217047300
Web Site: https://www.ruukki.com
Sales Range: $50-74.9 Million
Emp.: 10
Metal Products Sales
N.A.I.C.S.: 423510

SIA Ruukki Latvija (2)
Vienibas Gatre 204, LV 1058, Riga, Latvia (100%)
Tel.: (371) 7677707
Web Site: http://www.asva.lv
Sales Range: $25-49.9 Million
Emp.: 50
Coal Prodcuts Mfr
N.A.I.C.S.: 324199
Ivars Enims (Mng Dir)

UAB Ruukki Lietuva (2)
Pramones str 16, vaidotai, 14149, Vilnius, Lithuania (100%)
Tel.: (370) 52322315
Web Site: http://www.ruukki.com
Sales Range: $50-74.9 Million
Emp.: 100
Coal Prodcuts Mfr
N.A.I.C.S.: 324199

SSAB EMEA AB (1)
Jarnverket, Oxelosund, 613 31, Sweden
Tel.: (46) 155254000
Web Site: http://www.ssab.com
Steel Mfrs
N.A.I.C.S.: 331110

SSAB Enterprises, LLC (1)
801 Warrenville Rd Ste 800, Lisle, IL 60532-4314
Tel.: (630) 810-4800
Web Site: http://www.ssab.com
Sales Range: $1-4.9 Billion
Emp.: 100
Steel Products Mfr
N.A.I.C.S.: 331110

SSAB Merox (1)
Jarnverket, Oxelosund, 61380, Oxelosund, Sweden
Tel.: (46) 155254400
Web Site: http://www.ssab.com
Sales Range: $25-49.9 Million
Emp.: 25
Secondary Smelting Refining & Alloying Nonferrous Metal
N.A.I.C.S.: 331492

SSAB Oxelosund (1)
Jarnverket, Oxelosund, 61380, Linkoping, Sweden
Tel.: (46) 155254000
Web Site: http://www.ssabox.com
Sales Range: $400-449.9 Million
Emp.: 2,400
Iron & Steel Mills
N.A.I.C.S.: 331110

SSAB Swedish Steel BV (1)
IJzerwerf 3, 6641 TK, Beuningen, Netherlands
Tel.: (31) 246790550
Web Site: https://www.ssab.com
Emp.: 25
Steel Product Distr
N.A.I.C.S.: 423510

SSAB Swedish Steel Ltd (1)
5-26-20 Shiba Kenchiku Ksikan 5F, Minato-Ku, Tokyo, 108-0014, Japan
Tel.: (81) 33 456 3447
Steel Distr
N.A.I.C.S.: 423510

SSAB Swedish Steel Ltd (1)
Narrowboat Way, Brierley Hill, DY5 1UF, West Midlands, United Kingdom
Tel.: (44) 1384472300
Web Site: https://www.ssab.com
Steel Products Mfr
N.A.I.C.S.: 331110

SSAB Swedish Steel Trading Kft (1)
Lover Krt 31-A, 9400, Sopron, Hungary
Tel.: (36) 99510510
Web Site: http://www.ssab.hu

AND PRIVATE COMPANIES

Iron & Steel Mills
N.A.I.C.S.: 331110

SSAB Swedish Steel, S.L (1)
Paseo de la Castellana 149 7th Floor Left,
28046, Madrid, Spain
Tel.: (34) 91 300 54 22
Web Site: http://www.ssab.es
Steel Distr
N.A.I.C.S.: 423510

SSAB Technology AB (1)
Klarabergsviadukten 70 D6, PO Box 70,
101 21, Stockholm, Sweden
Tel.: (46) 84545700
Web Site: https://www.ssab.com
Steel Mfrs
N.A.I.C.S.: 331110

SSAB Tunnplat (1)
Kontorsvagen, 78184, Borlange, Sweden
Tel.: (46) 24370000
Web Site: http://www.ssab.com
Sales Range: $400-449.9 Million
Emp.: 1,700
Iron & Steel Mfrs
N.A.I.C.S.: 331110

SSAB Wear Solutions LLC (1)
8915 Energy Lne, Northport, AL 35476
Tel.: (205) 333-7828
Web Site: https://ssabwearsolutions.com
Steel Fabrication
N.A.I.C.S.: 332111

Subsidiary (Domestic):

Astralloy Steel Products Inc. (2)
251 Wheeler St, Sharon, PA 16146
Tel.: (724) 230-5100
Web Site: https://ssabwearsolutions.com
Metals Service Centers & Offices
N.A.I.C.S.: 423510

Sundsvalls Stal AB (1)
Montarvagen 7, 853 50, Sundsvall, Sweden
Tel.: (46) 607004550
Web Site: https://www.sundsvallsstal.se
Steel Distr
N.A.I.C.S.: 423510

Tibnor AB (1)
Sundbybergsvagen 1, 171 73, Solna, Sweden
Tel.: (46) 104840000
Web Site: https://www.tibnor.se
Sales Range: $600-649.9 Million
Emp.: 1,000
Metals Service Center
N.A.I.C.S.: 423510
Mikael Nyquist (CEO)

Subsidiary (Domestic):

EM Eriksson Steel Service Center AB (2)
Hejargatan 8, 781 71, Borlange, Sweden
Tel.: (46) 243 79 45 00
Web Site: http://www.emeab.com
Steel Service Center
N.A.I.C.S.: 423510
Anders Larsson (Acting Mng Dir)

EO Stal AB (2)
Bryggaregatan 2, PO Box 66, Lersaters industrial area, 665 32, Kil, Sweden
Tel.: (46) 55 468 9770
Web Site: https://www.eostal.se
Metals Service Center
N.A.I.C.S.: 423510
Anders Broms (CEO)

Linkopings Stal AB (2)
Haradskarsgatan 2, 582 78, Linkoping, Sweden
Tel.: (46) 13315015
Web Site: https://www.lkpgstal.se
Metals & Steel Whslr
N.A.I.C.S.: 423510
Hakan Lindqvist (CEO)

Platedepan AB (2)
Hejargatan 4, PO Box 816, 781 71, Borlange, Sweden
Tel.: (46) 24 379 4430
Web Site: https://www.platdepan.se
Emp.: 1
Sheet Metal & Plate Whslr
N.A.I.C.S.: 423510
Per Lahger (CEO)

Tappers Stal & Metaller AB (2)
Mossvagen 23, 521 30, Falkoping, Sweden
Tel.: (46) 515721670
Web Site: https://www.tappers.se
Metal Whslr
N.A.I.C.S.: 423510
Hakan Lindqvist (CEO)

Subsidiary (Non-US):

Tibnor A/S (2)
Klokkestobervej 18, 5230, Odense, Denmark
Tel.: (45) 4 323 7700
Web Site: https://www.tibnor.dk
Metals Service Center
N.A.I.C.S.: 423510

Tibnor A/S (2)
Tevlingveien 15, PO Box 27, NO-1081, Oslo, Norway
Tel.: (47) 22909000
Web Site: https://www.tibnor.no
Metals Service Center
N.A.I.C.S.: 423510

Tibnor SIA (2)
Delu iela 4, Babites Pagasts, LV 2107, Riga, Latvia
Tel.: (371) 67677418
Web Site: http://www.tibnor.lv
Metals Service Center
N.A.I.C.S.: 423510

UAB Tibnor (1)
Erdves 39, Ramuciai Kaunas District, 52114, Kaunas, Lithuania
Tel.: (370) 68681158
Web Site: https://www.tibnor.lt
Steel Material Mfr & Distr
N.A.I.C.S.: 332312

SSANGYONG INFORMATION & COMMUNICATIONS CORP.
5F City Center Tower 34 Supyo-ro, Jung-gu, Seoul, 100-748, Korea (South)
Tel.: (82) 222628114
Web Site: http://www.sicc.co.kr
Year Founded: 1981
010280—(KRS)
Rev.: $249,439,507
Assets: $202,043,506
Liabilities: $154,969,731
Net Worth: $47,073,775
Earnings: $9,217,286
Emp.: 525
Fiscal Year-end: 12/31/22
Software Development Services
N.A.I.C.S.: 541511
Kyeong-Sang Kim (CEO)

Subsidiaries:

Comtec Information Co., Ltd. (79.5%)
ITCEN Bldg 13 Banpo-Daero, Seocho-gu, Seoul, Korea (South)
Tel.: (82) 234976980
Information Technology Services
N.A.I.C.S.: 541511

SSAW HOTELS & RESORTS GROUP CO., LTD.
No 29 Xueyuan Road, Xihu District, Hangzhou, 310030, Zhejiang, China
Tel.: (86) 57186750888
Web Site: https://www.ssawhotels.com
Year Founded: 2007
301073—(CHIN)
Rev.: $75,208,296
Assets: $341,520,393
Liabilities: $204,076,028
Net Worth: $137,444,366
Earnings: $4,298,577
Fiscal Year-end: 12/31/23
Resort Operator
N.A.I.C.S.: 721120
Qiyuan Wu (Chm)

SSC GROUP
Torggatan 15, Solna, 17104, Sweden
Tel.: (46) 8 627 62 00

Web Site: http://www.sscspace.com
Year Founded: 1972
Sales Range: $125-149.9 Million
Emp.: 150
Space & Satellite Communications Equipment Mfr
N.A.I.C.S.: 336419
Lennart Poromaa (Pres-Science Svcs Div)

Subsidiaries:

SSC Space Canada Corporation (1)
3528 30 St, Lethbridge, T1H 6Z4, AB, Canada
Tel.: (403) 332-6018
Wireless Telecommunication Services
N.A.I.C.S.: 517410

Universal Space Network, Inc. (1)
1501 Quail St Ste 102, Newport Beach, CA 92660
Tel.: (949) 476-3432
Web Site: http://www.uspacenetwork.com
Sales Range: $1-9.9 Million
Emp.: 50
Space & Satellite Communications Equipment Mfr
N.A.I.C.S.: 336419

SSC MANDARIN FINANCIAL SERVICES LIMITED
Room 1402 14/F China Resources Bldg, 26 Harbour Road, Wanchai, China (Hong Kong)
Tel.: (852) 25042333 HK
Web Site: http://www.sscmandarin.com
Year Founded: 1998
Sales Range: $50-74.9 Million
Emp.: 15
Financial Advisory, Portfolio Management & Investment Services
N.A.I.C.S.: 523940
Robin Seng Leong Lee (Chm & CEO)

Subsidiaries:

China Mining Resources Holdings Limited (1)
Room 1402 14/F China Resources Bldg, 26 Harbour Road, Wanchai, China (Hong Kong)
Tel.: (852) 25042333
Holding Company
N.A.I.C.S.: 551112

SSC SECURITY SERVICES CORP.
300 - 1914 Hamilton Street, Regina, S4P 3N6, SK, Canada
Tel.: (306) 347-3006 SK
Web Site: https://securityservicescorp.ca
Year Founded: 2012
SECU—(TSXV)
Rev.: $82,349,317
Assets: $64,015,546
Liabilities: $12,904,445
Net Worth: $51,111,100
Earnings: $65,802
Emp.: 3,000
Fiscal Year-end: 09/30/23
Agriculture Streaming Company
N.A.I.C.S.: 926140
Doug Emsley (Chm, Pres & CEO)

Subsidiaries:

Logixx Security Inc. (1)
1955 Leslie Street, Toronto, M3B 2M3, ON, Canada
Tel.: (416) 760-0000
Web Site: http://www.logixxsecurity.com
Security Firm Services
N.A.I.C.S.: 561621
Craig Campbell (Chm)

SRG Security Resource Group Inc. (1)
303 - 2114 11th Avenue, Regina, S4P 0J5, SK, Canada
Tel.: (306) 525-2108

Web Site: https://securityresourcegroup.com
Guard & Patrol Security Services
N.A.I.C.S.: 561612

SSE PLC

SSE PLC
Inveralmond House 200 Dunkeld Road, Perth, PH1 3AQ, United Kingdom
Tel.: (44) 3031231113 UK
Web Site: https://www.sse.com
Year Founded: 1998
SSEZF—(OTCIQ)
Rev.: $9,268,339,808
Assets: $29,315,347,152
Liabilities: $20,244,284,060
Net Worth: $9,071,063,092
Earnings: $3,153,712,016
Emp.: 11,691
Fiscal Year-end: 03/31/21
Natural Gas Distribution Services
N.A.I.C.S.: 221210
Richard Gillingwater (Chm)

Subsidiaries:

Airtricity Energy Supply (Northern Ireland) Limited (1)
2nd Floor 83-85 Great Victoria Street, Belfast, BT2 7AF, United Kingdom
Tel.: (44) 28 9043 7470
Web Site: http://www.airtricity.com
Sales Range: $50-74.9 Million
Emp.: 30
Eletric Power Generation Services
N.A.I.C.S.: 221118

Fusion Heating Limited (1)
Unit 14 Maryland Industrial Estate Ballygowan Road, Belfast, BT23 6BL, United Kingdom
Tel.: (44) 289 044 9499
Web Site: https://fusionheating.co.uk
Heating & Air-Conditioning Services
N.A.I.C.S.: 238220

SSE Airtricity Energy Services (NI) Limited (1)
Unit 14 Maryland Industrial Estate Ballygowan Road, Newtownards, BT23 6BL, United Kingdom
Tel.: (44) 3458508940
Web Site: https://www.sseairtricity.com
Emp.: 200
Electric Power Distribution Services
N.A.I.C.S.: 221122

SSE Airtricity Limited (1)
Red Oak South South County Business Park, Leopardstown, Dublin, 18, Ireland
Tel.: (353) 818812220
Emp.: 1,000
Electric Power Distribution Services
N.A.I.C.S.: 221122
Christina Martindale (Mgr-Operations-Sls,Retention)

SSE E&P UK Limited (1)
Inveralmond House 200 Dunkeld Road, Perth, PH1 3AQ, United Kingdom
Tel.: (44) 845 076 0530
Web Site: http://www.sse.com
Eletric Power Generation Services
N.A.I.C.S.: 221111
Alistair Phillips-Davies (CEO)

SSE Generation Ltd (1)
No 1 Forbury Place 43 Forbury Road, Reading, RG1 3JH, United Kingdom (100%)
Tel.: (44) 1738456660
Electricity Supplier
N.A.I.C.S.: 221122

Subsidiary (Domestic):

Dunlop BTL Ltd. (2)
MPT House Brunswick Road, Cobbs Wood Industrial Estate, Ashford, TN23 1EL, Kent, United Kingdom (100%)
Tel.: (44) 1233663340
Web Site: http://www.dunlopbtl.com
Sales Range: $50-74.9 Million
Emp.: 70
Bearings, Ball Joints, Belts & Pulleys Mfr
N.A.I.C.S.: 332991

Subsidiary (Non-US):

Endesa Ireland Ltd (2)

SSE PLC

SSE Plc—(Continued)
Red Oak South South County Business Park Leopardstown, Grand Canal Street Upper, Dublin, 18, Ireland
Tel.: (353) 15228300
Web Site: http://www.sse.com
Sales Range: $100-124.9 Million
Emp.: 11
Power Plant Operations
N.A.I.C.S.: 221118

SSE Hornsea Ltd (1)
No 1 Forbury Place 43 Forbury Road, Reading, RG1 3JH, United Kingdom (100%)
Tel.: (44) 1738453960
Sales Range: $25-49.9 Million
Emp.: 10
Gas Storage
N.A.I.C.S.: 486210

SSE Power Distribution Ltd (1)
200 Dunkeld Road, Perth, PH1 3AQ, United Kingdom (100%)
Tel.: (44) 738456000
Sales Range: $1-4.9 Billion
Emp.: 1,500
Electricity Supplier
N.A.I.C.S.: 221122

Subsidiary (Domestic):

Scottish Hydro Electric Power Distribution Ltd (2)
Inveralmond House 200 Dunkeld Road, Perth, PH1 3AQ, United Kingdom (100%)
Tel.: (44) 738456000
Sales Range: $1-4.9 Billion
Electricity Supplier
N.A.I.C.S.: 221122

Scottish Hydro Electric Transmission Ltd (2)
Inveralmond House 200 Dunkeld Road, Perth, PH1 3AQ, United Kingdom (100%)
Tel.: (44) 738456000
Electronic Services
N.A.I.C.S.: 221122

SSE Renewables Holdings (UK) Limited (1)
3rd Floor Millennium House 17-25 Great Victoria Street, Belfast, BT2 7AQ, United Kingdom
Tel.: (44) 2890437470
Sales Range: $50-74.9 Million
Emp.: 30
Eletric Power Generation Services
N.A.I.C.S.: 221118

SSE Renewables Holdings Limited (1)
Red Oak South South County Business Park, Leopardstown, Dublin, 18, Ireland
Tel.: (353) 16556400
Sales Range: $250-299.9 Million
Emp.: 600
Eletric Power Generation Services
N.A.I.C.S.: 221118
Stephen Wheeler (CEO)

Subsidiary (Domestic):

Airtricity Limited (2)
Red Oak South South County Business Park Leopardstown, Sandyford, Dublin, 18, Ireland
Tel.: (353) 1 6556400
Web Site: http://www.airtricity.com
Emp.: 550
Gas Distribution Services
N.A.I.C.S.: 221210
Steven Wheeler (Mng Dir)

SSE Renewables (Ireland) Limited (2)
Red Oak South South County Bus Park, Leopardstown, Dublin, 18, Ireland
Tel.: (353) 16556400
Emp.: 550
Eletric Power Generation Services
N.A.I.C.S.: 221118

SSE Renewables Wind (Ireland) Holdings Limited (1)
Red Oak South, South County Business Park Leopardstown, Dublin, 18, Ireland
Tel.: (353) 16556400
Renewable Energy Services

N.A.I.C.S.: 221118

SSE Services plc (1)
No 1 Forbury Place 43 Forbury Road, Reading, RG1 3JH, Berkshire, United Kingdom
Tel.: (44) 1964530115
Eletric Power Generation Services
N.A.I.C.S.: 221118

SSE Telecommunications Limited (1)
Inveralmond House 200 Dunkeld Road, Perth, PH1 3AQ, United Kingdom
Tel.: (44) 3450701997
Web Site: http://www.ssetelecoms.com
Telecommunication Servicesb
N.A.I.C.S.: 517810
Colin Douglas Sempill (Mng Dir)

Southern Electric Gas Limited (1)
55 Vastern Road, Reading, Berkshire, United Kingdom
Tel.: (44) 8450260654
Electric Power Generation & Distribution Services
N.A.I.C.S.: 221118

SSF HOME GROUP BERHAD
C-11-08 & C-11-09 Sunway Nexis No 1 Jalan PJU 5/1, Kota Damansara, 47810, Petaling Jaya, Selangor, Malaysia
Tel.: (60) 386053643 **MY**
Web Site: https://www.ssf.com.my
Year Founded: 2015
SSF—(KLS)
Rev.: $37,895,753
Assets: $32,337,170
Liabilities: $7,797,480
Net Worth: $24,539,690
Earnings: $3,481,933
Emp.: 528
Fiscal Year-end: 04/30/23
Furniture Product Distr
N.A.I.C.S.: 423210

SSH COMMUNICATIONS SECURITY CORPORATION
Karvaamokuja 2 B, Suite 600, 00380, Helsinki, Finland
Tel.: (358) 205007000
Web Site: https://www.ssh.com
Year Founded: 1995
SSH1V—(HEL)
Rev.: $19,565,236
Assets: $44,125,893
Liabilities: $29,355,399
Net Worth: $14,770,494
Earnings: ($2,847,544)
Emp.: 123
Fiscal Year-end: 12/31/21
Data Protection & Network Security Software
N.A.I.C.S.: 513210
Tatu Ylonen (Founder)

Subsidiaries:

SSH CommSec Singapore Pte. Ltd. (1)
6 Raffles Boulevard Marina Square 03-308, Singapore, 039594, Singapore
Tel.: (65) 63387160
Software Development Services
N.A.I.C.S.: 541511

Tectia Ltd. (1)
2/F Shui On Centre 6-8 Harbour Road, Wanchai, China (Hong Kong)
Tel.: (852) 2824 8361
Security Software Development Services
N.A.I.C.S.: 541511

Tectia Operations Ltd. (1)
Lintorfer Str 7, 40878, Ratingen, North Rhine, Germany
Tel.: (49) 2102 309790
Business Management Services
N.A.I.C.S.: 561110

Tectia, Inc. (1)
333 Twin Dolphin Dr Ste 100, Redwood City, CA 94065-1410

Tel.: (650) 559-2220
Web Site: http://www.ssh.com
Sales Range: $25-49.9 Million
Emp.: 5
Security Software Services
N.A.I.C.S.: 513210

SSH GROUP LIMITED
Tel.: (61) 894632463
Web Site:
https://www.sshgroup.com.au
Year Founded: 2013
SSH—(ASX)
Rev.: $7,275,142
Assets: $25,833,230
Liabilities: $21,227,577
Net Worth: $4,605,653
Earnings: ($867,441)
Fiscal Year-end: 06/30/23
Construction Engineering Services
N.A.I.C.S.: 237990
Daniel Cowley-Cooper (Mng Dir)

Subsidiaries:

Complete Equipment Australia Pty. (1)
1 Casswell Terrace McDougalls Hill, PO Box 391, Singleton, 2330, NSW, Australia
Tel.: (61) 265711228
Web Site:
https://completepartsandequipment.com
Earthmoving Equipment Mfr & Distr
N.A.I.C.S.: 333112

Tru Fleet Pty. Ltd. (1)
100 Daddow Rd, Kewdale, 6105, WA, Australia
Tel.: (61) 894754602
Web Site: https://trufleet.com.au
Fleet Hire & Transportation Services
N.A.I.C.S.: 532411

SSHT S&T GROUP LTD.
46 Reeves Road, Pakuranga, 2010, Auckland, New Zealand
Tel.: (61) 405223877 **NV**
Year Founded: 2007
SSHT—(OTCIQ)
Business Consulting Services
N.A.I.C.S.: 541611
Zonghan Wu (Chm & CEO)

SSI GROUP, INC.
6/F Midland Buendia Bldg 403 Sen Gil Puyat Avenue, Makati, 1200, Philippines
Tel.: (63) 28908034
Web Site:
https://www.ssigroup.com.ph
Year Founded: 1987
SSI—(PHI)
Rev.: $500,965,257
Assets: $421,307,086
Liabilities: $156,874,279
Net Worth: $264,432,807
Earnings: $46,575,446
Emp.: 4,415
Fiscal Year-end: 12/31/23
Specialty Retailer
N.A.I.C.S.: 459999
Zenaida R. Tantoco (Chm & CEO)

Subsidiaries:

Stores Specialists, Inc. (1)
4/F Midland Buendia Bldg 403 Sen Gil Puyat Avenue, Makati, 1200, Philippines
Tel.: (63) 28908034
Non-Durable Goods Retailer
N.A.I.C.S.: 424990
Anthony T. Huang (Pres)

SSI SCHAFER SHOP GMBH
Industriestrasse 65, 57518, Betzdorf, Germany
Tel.: (49) 27412860
Web Site: http://www.schaefer-shop.de
Sales Range: $200-249.9 Million
Emp.: 750

INTERNATIONAL PUBLIC

Furniture & Office Supplies Mail Order & Electronic Shopping
N.A.I.C.S.: 423210
Gerhard Schafer (Member-Mgmt Bd)

SSI SECURITIES CORPORATION
72 Nguyen Hue Ben Nghe Ward District 1, Ho Chi Minh City, Vietnam
Web Site: http://www.ssi.com.vn
Year Founded: 1999
SSI—(HOSE)
Rev.: $633,582,306
Assets: $5,222,638,289
Liabilities: $2,984,250,092
Net Worth: $2,238,388,196
Earnings: $169,931,990
Emp.: 1,603
Fiscal Year-end: 12/31/22
Securities Brokerage Services
N.A.I.C.S.: 523150
Nguyen Duy Hung (Founder, Chm & CEO)

Subsidiaries:

SSI Asset Management Ltd. (1)
1C Ngo Quyen, Ly Thai To Ward Hoan Kiem District, Hanoi, Vietnam
Tel.: (84) 2439366321
Financial Services
N.A.I.C.S.: 523999

SSIAL FOOD, INC.
85 Bio Valley1-ro, Jecheon, 390250, Chungbuk, Korea (South)
Tel.: (82) 436454100
Web Site:
http://www.ssialfoo.tradekorea.com
Year Founded: 2007
Food & Beverage Product Mfr
N.A.I.C.S.: 311999
Sang-Bum Lee (Board of Directors & CEO)

SSK CORPORATION
1-2-19 Uehonmachi Nishi, Chuo-ku, Osaka, 542-8585, Japan
Tel.: (81) 667681111 **JP**
Web Site: http://www.ssksports.com
Year Founded: 1946
Sales Range: $450-499.9 Million
Emp.: 551
Sporting Goods Mfr & Whslr
N.A.I.C.S.: 339920
Kyoichi Sasaki (Chm & Pres)

Subsidiaries:

Xiamen Kyosei Sporting Goods Co. Ltd (1)
2/F 1 Building No 10 Yangguang Road, Xinyang Industrial Area Haicha, Xiamen, 361022, China
Tel.: (86) 592 6514100
Web Site: http://www.kyoseisports.com
Sporting Goods Mfr
N.A.I.C.S.: 339920

SSK FOODS CO., LTD.
11-1 Irifune-cho, Shimizu-ku, Shizuoka, Japan
Tel.: (81) 0542219351
Web Site: http://www.sskfoods.co.jp
Year Founded: 1978
Mayonnaise, Dressing & Other Prepared Sauce Mfr; Bottled Beverages Mfr & Sales
N.A.I.C.S.: 311941
Eiichi Shimoyamada (Pres & CEO)

SSLJ.COM LIMITED
23/F Block 4 Oceanwide International SOHO Town, Jianghan District, Wuhan, 430000, China
Tel.: (86) 2783668638 **Ky**
Web Site: http://www.sslj.com
Year Founded: 2016
YGTYF—(OTCEM)

Sales Range: $10-24.9 Million
Emp.: 692
Interior Design & Furnishing Services
N.A.I.C.S.: 541410

SSM HOLDING AB
Torsgatan 13, 111 23, Stockholm, Sweden
Tel.: (46) 850103300 SE
Web Site:
http://www.ssmlivinggroup.com
Year Founded: 1993
Rev.: $72,603,675
Assets: $149,569,134
Liabilities: $64,258,425
Net Worth: $85,310,709
Earnings: $1,702,431
Emp.: 65
Fiscal Year-end: 12/31/18
Residential Property Development Services
N.A.I.C.S.: 531311
Mikael Ranes *(Chm)*

SSNEWTECH CO., LTD.
170 Donyu 2-ro Munsan-eup, Pajusi, Seoul, Gyeonggido, Korea (South)
Tel.: (82) 319522147
Web Site: http://www.ssntech.kr
Year Founded: 2006
Mobile & Electronic Parts, Printing & Optical Coating Mfr
N.A.I.C.S.: 321991
Hae Gwi You *(Chm)*

Subsidiaries:

Korea Electro-Optics Co., Ltd.   (1)
8 Seokcheon ro 398 Beon Gil, Bucheon, 421-809, Gyeonggi-Do, Korea (South)
Tel.: (82) 326806100
Web Site: http://www.keoc.kr
Optical Components & Lens Mfr & Supplier
N.A.I.C.S.: 333310
Haegui Yoo *(CEO)*

SSP GROUP PLC
8 Canada Square, London, E14 5HQ, United Kingdom
Tel.: (44) 2075433300
Web Site:
https://www.foodtravelexperts.com
Year Founded: 1992
SSPG—(LSE)
Rev.: $3,737,445,460
Assets: $3,598,984,760
Liabilities: $3,199,000,980
Net Worth: $399,983,780
Earnings: $69,664,980
Emp.: 42,000
Fiscal Year-end: 06/30/23
Restaurant Operating Services
N.A.I.C.S.: 722511
Jonathan Davies *(CFO)*

Subsidiaries:

SSP America, Inc.   (1)
330 N Brand Blvd, Glendale, CA 91203
Tel.: (281) 233-7620
Food & Catering Services
N.A.I.C.S.: 722310
Michael Svagdis *(CEO)*

Subsidiary (Domestic):

SSP America Gladco, Inc.   (2)
600 N 2nd St Ste 401, Harrisburg, PA 17101-1071
Tel.: (703) 729-2333
Food & Catering Services
N.A.I.C.S.: 722310

SSP Canada Food Services Inc.   (1)
2406-3880 Grant McConachie Way, Richmond, V7B 0A5, BC, Canada
Tel.: (604) 278-2755
Food & Catering Services
N.A.I.C.S.: 722310

SSP Nederland BV   (1)
Leidseveer 2-10, 3511 SB, Utrecht, Netherlands
Tel.: (31) 206532268
Food & Catering Services
N.A.I.C.S.: 722310

SSP Taiwan Limited   (1)
13 He 1st Road Lane 84 202, Keelung, Taiwan
Tel.: (886) 222477339
Food & Catering Services
N.A.I.C.S.: 722310

Scandinavian Service Partner AB   (1)
Box 67, Arlanda, 190 45, Stockholm, Sweden
Tel.: (46) 87977500
Web Site: http://www.ssp.se
Emp.: 300
Food & Catering Services
N.A.I.C.S.: 722310

Select Service Partner (Schweiz) AG   (1)
Postfach 2472, Zurich-Flughafen, Zurich, 8060, Switzerland
Tel.: (41) 438168484
Emp.: 320
Food & Catering Services
N.A.I.C.S.: 722310
Michael Jupitz *(Gen Mgr)*

Select Service Partner Finland Oy   (1)
Helsinki-Vantaan Lentoasema, 01530, Vantaa, Finland
Tel.: (358) 207629732
Web Site: https://www.sspfinland.fi
Emp.: 250
Restaurant Operators
N.A.I.C.S.: 722511
Anne Immonen *(Dir-Ops & HR)*

Societe D'Exploitation du Chalet de la Porte Jaune SASU   (1)
Avenue De Nogent, 75012, Paris, France
Tel.: (33) 143288011
Web Site: http://www.chaletportejaune.com
Event Management Services
N.A.I.C.S.: 711310

SSPDL LIMITED
3rd Floor Serene Towers 8-2-623/A Road No 10 Banjara Hills, Hyderabad, 500 034, Telangana, India
Tel.: (91) 4066637560
Web Site: https://www.sspdl.com
530821—(BOM)
Rev.: $1,091,767
Assets: $23,292,483
Liabilities: $23,206,289
Net Worth: $86,194
Earnings: ($2,358,240)
Emp.: 32
Fiscal Year-end: 03/31/21
Property Development Services
N.A.I.C.S.: 531311
Prakash Challa *(Chm & Mng Dir)*

SSPI GMBH
Grossmatte 4, CH-6014, Lucerne, Switzerland
Tel.: (41) 259 43 00 CH
Web Site: http://www.sspi-chemical.ch
Emp.: 23
Specialty Materials & Process Technology Solutions for Semiconductor & Electronics Mfr
N.A.I.C.S.: 334419
Andreas Eisenbart *(CEO)*

SSPN FINANCE LIMITED
Shop no 187 B 1st floor Powai plaza, S V Road Vile Parle W, Mumbai, 400076, Maharashtra, India
Tel.: (91) 1142334804
Web Site: https://sspnfin.com
Year Founded: 2012
539026—(BOM)
Rev.: $32,467
Assets: $757,097
Liabilities: $233,508
Net Worth: $523,588
Earnings: $39

Fiscal Year-end: 03/31/23
Investment Management, Venture Capital & Consulting Services
N.A.I.C.S.: 523999
Ankur Krishnakant Choksi *(CFO)*

SSR MINING INC.
Suite 800 - 1055 Dunsmuir Street, PO Box 49088 Bentall Postal Station, Vancouver, V7X 1G4, BC, Canada
Tel.: (604) 689-3846 BC
Web Site: http://www.ssrmining.com
Year Founded: 1946
SSRM—(NASDAQ)
Rev.: $1,426,927,000
Assets: $5,385,773,000
Liabilities: $1,081,570,000
Net Worth: $4,304,203,000
Earnings: ($98,007,000)
Emp.: 2,500
Fiscal Year-end: 12/31/23
Precious Metal Exploration, Development & Mining Services
N.A.I.C.S.: 212220
Michael J. Sparks *(CFO & Exec VP)*

Subsidiaries:

Alacer Gold Corp.   (1)
7001 E Belleview Ave Ste 800, Denver, CO 80237
Tel.: (303) 292-1299
Web Site: http://www.alacergold.com
Gold & Mineral Exploration & Mining
N.A.I.C.S.: 212220
F. Edward Farid *(Chief Dev Officer & Exec VP)*

SSR, INC.
111 Digital-Ro 26-Gil, Guro-Gu, Seoul, 08390, Korea (South)
Tel.: (82) 262406000
Web Site: https://www.ssrinc.co.kr
Year Founded: 2010
275630—(KRS)
Rev.: $9,594,698
Assets: $24,182,745
Liabilities: $2,829,882
Net Worth: $21,352,862
Earnings: $1,455,367
Emp.: 96
Fiscal Year-end: 12/31/22
Software Development Services
N.A.I.C.S.: 541511
Go Pil-Ju *(CEO)*

SST SPEDITION GMBH
Peuter Elbdeich 5-9, Hamburg, 20539, Germany
Tel.: (49) 405590060 De
Web Site: http://www.sst.de
Sales Range: $25-49.9 Million
Emp.: 8
Special Freight Transportation Services
N.A.I.C.S.: 484220
Ralph Walter *(CEO & Chm-Mgmt Bd)*

SSY GROUP LIMITED
Rooms 4902-03 49th Floor Central Plaza 18 Harbour Road, Wanchai, China (Hong Kong)
Tel.: (852) 26880869
Web Site:
http://www.ssygroup.com.hk
2005—(HKG)
Rev.: $820,338,188
Assets: $1,398,230,280
Liabilities: $563,637,720
Net Worth: $834,592,560
Earnings: $151,667,625
Emp.: 5,000
Fiscal Year-end: 12/31/22
Pharmaceuticals Product Mfr
N.A.I.C.S.: 325412
Xianjun Wang *(Exec Dir)*

Subsidiaries:

Shijiazhuang No. 4 Pharmaceutical Co., Ltd.   (1)
No 288 Zhujiang Road, High-tech Industrial Development, Shijiazhuang, 52165, Hebei, China
Tel.: (86) 3116 716 7137
Web Site: https://ssypc.com
Emp.: 2,800
Pharmaceutical Product Mfr & Distr
N.A.I.C.S.: 325412
Qu Jiguang *(Chm)*

Subsidiary (Domestic):

Hebei Hanlin Biotechnology Co., Ltd.   (2)
238 Long River Blvd Hongchang Hi-tech Industrial Park, Shijiazhuang, 050000, Hebei, China
Tel.: (86) 13393019193
Web Site:
https://www.hanlinbiotechnology.com
Pharmaceutical Product Mfr & Distr
N.A.I.C.S.: 325412
Zhou Ximing *(CEO)*

ST BARBARA LIMITED
Level 19 58 Mounts Bay Road, Perth, 6000, WA, Australia
Tel.: (61) 894765555 AU
Web Site:
https://www.stbarbara.com.au
SBM—(ASX)
Rev.: $149,307,558
Assets: $379,696,179
Liabilities: $146,461,004
Net Worth: $233,235,175
Earnings: ($36,000,935)
Fiscal Year-end: 06/30/24
Gold Exploration & Mining
N.A.I.C.S.: 212220
Garth Campbell-Cowan *(CFO)*

Subsidiaries:

Atlantic Gold Corporation   (1)
Suite 3083 Three Bentall Centre, PO Box 49298, 595 Burrard Street, Vancouver, V7X 1L3, BC, Canada
Tel.: (604) 689-5564
Web Site:
http://www.atlanticgoldcorporation.com
Sales Range: $150-199.9 Million
Gold Exploration & Mining
N.A.I.C.S.: 213114
Steven G. Dean *(CEO)*

Subsidiary (Non-US):

Atlantic Gold Exploration Pty. Ltd.   (2)
Suite 506 815 Pacific Highway, Chatswood, 2067, NSW, Australia
Tel.: (61) 2 9410 0993
Web Site:
http://www.atlanticgoldcorporation.com
Gold Exploration & Mine Development; Regional Managing Office
N.A.I.C.S.: 213114

Bardoc Gold Pty Ltd   (1)
130 Stirling Highway, North Fremantle, 6159, WA, Australia
Tel.: (61) 862150090
Web Site: http://www.bardocgold.com
Gold Exploration & Mining
N.A.I.C.S.: 212290

NSGold Corp.   (1)
P O Box 48053, Mill Cove, Bedford, B4A 3Z2, NS, Canada
Tel.: (902) 798-1148
Web Site: http://www.nsgoldcorp.com
Assets: $1,905,017
Liabilities: $50,540
Net Worth: $1,854,476
Earnings: ($95,092)
Fiscal Year-end: 12/31/2019
Investment Services
N.A.I.C.S.: 523999
Johannes H. C. van Hoof *(Chm, Pres & CEO)*

ST DUPONT S.A.

ST DUPONT S.A.

ST Dupont S.A.—(Continued)
92 Boulevard du Montparnasse,
75014, Paris, France
Tel.: (33) 157953010
Web Site: https://www.st-dupont.com
DPT—(EUR)
Sales Range: $50-74.9 Million
Emp.: 78
Luxury Goods & Accessories Mfr For Men
N.A.I.C.S.: 315250
Alain Crevet *(Dir-Publ)*

Subsidiaries:

Lotus Mjyx LLC (1)
30 Coronado Rd 2nd Fl, Warwick, RI 02886-1405
Tel.: (401) 921-5216
Sales Range: $50-74.9 Million
Emp.: 10
Stationery & Leather Goods Whslr
N.A.I.C.S.: 424120
Christine Collins *(Mng Dir)*

S.T. Dupont Marketing Limited (1)
13/F South Block Skyway House No 3 Sham Mong Road, Tai Kok Tsui, Kowloon, China (Hong Kong)
Tel.: (852) 2 311 8838
Web Site: https://hk.st-dupont.com
Lighter, Pen & Leather Good Mfr
N.A.I.C.S.: 316990
Selina Lam *(Sr Mgr-Sls Admin)*

S.T.DUPONT ITALIA S.P.A. (1)
Via A Correggio 19, 20149, Milan, Italy
Tel.: (39) 0243995356
Sales Range: $50-74.9 Million
Emp.: 7
Stationery Product Whslr
N.A.I.C.S.: 424120

S.T.Dupont (Malaysia) Sdn Bhd. (1)
N 7K Jalan 1/57 D Off Jalan Segambut, 51200, Kuala Lumpur, Federal Territory, Malaysia
Tel.: (60) 362580122
Sales Range: $25-49.9 Million
Emp.: 20
Stationery Product Distr
N.A.I.C.S.: 424120

S.T.Dupont Deutschland Gmbh (1)
Toyota-Allee 99, 50858, Cologne, Germany
Tel.: (49) 2234953000
Web Site: http://www.st-dupont.com
Stationery & Leather Accessories Distr
N.A.I.C.S.: 424120
Thierry Lemaire *(Mng Dir)*

S.T.Dupont Ltd. (1)
67 Brampton Rd, London, NW9 9DE, United Kingdom
Tel.: (44) 1626821990
Stationery & Leather Goods Whslr
N.A.I.C.S.: 424120

S.T.Dupont Marketing Ltd. (1)
12 F S Block Skwy House 3 Sham Mong Rd, Tai Kok Tsui, Kowloon, China (Hong Kong)
Tel.: (852) 23118838
Stationery Product Whslr
N.A.I.C.S.: 424120

Savings Pros, Inc. (1)
10 W 47th St Ste 56, New York, NY 10036
Tel.: (212) 921-1144
Web Site: http://www.st-dupont-usa.com
Stationery & Leather Goods Whslr
N.A.I.C.S.: 424120

ST GEORGE MINING LIMITED

Suite 2 28 Ord Street, West Perth, 6005, WA, Australia
Tel.: (61) 861182118
Web Site: https://www.stgm.com.au
SGQ—(ASX)
Rev.: $122,446
Assets: $2,041,371
Liabilities: $666,717
Net Worth: $1,374,654
Earnings: ($5,530,577)
Fiscal Year-end: 06/30/24
Gold Mining Services
N.A.I.C.S.: 212220
John Prineas *(Chm)*

ST GROUP FOOD INDUSTRIES HOLDINGS LIMITED

120 Turner Street, Port Melbourne, 3207, VIC, Australia
Tel.: (61) 396454667
Web Site: https://www.stgroup.net.au
SG
DRX—(SES)
Rev.: $35,989,425
Assets: $44,258,416
Liabilities: $29,222,010
Net Worth: $15,036,406
Earnings: ($704,675)
Fiscal Year-end: 06/30/22
Full-Service Restaurants
N.A.I.C.S.: 722511
Tatt Ghee Saw *(Chm & CEO)*

Subsidiaries:

HBCT (Aust) Pty Ltd. (1)
22 Red Cape Lane Lonsdale St & Swanston Street, Melbourne, 3000, VIC, Australia
Tel.: (61) 386523970
Web Site: http://www.hbctaus.com.au
Food Service
N.A.I.C.S.: 722330

NNC Food Industries Malaysia Sdn. Bhd. (1)
13 Jalan Mivo 1, Taman Perindustrian Desa Aman, 47000, Sungai Besar, Malaysia
Tel.: (60) 362629198
Web Site: http://www.nenechicken.com.my
Food Service
N.A.I.C.S.: 722330

Pafu Australia Pty Ltd. (1)
120 Turner Street, Port Melbourne, 3207, VIC, Australia
Tel.: (61) 396454667
Web Site: http://www.pafu.com.au
Food Service
N.A.I.C.S.: 722330

Papparich Outlets Pty Ltd. (1)
35 M-City 2107-2125 Dandenong Road, Clayton, 3168, VIC, Australia
Tel.: (61) 385221266
Web Site: http://www.papparich.net.au
Food Service
N.A.I.C.S.: 722330

iDarts Australia Pty Ltd. (1)
120 Turner Street, Port Melbourne, 3207, VIC, Australia
Tel.: (61) 385264498
Web Site: http://www.idarts.com.au
Bar Services
N.A.I.C.S.: 722410

ST INSTRUMENTS B.V.

Energieweg 20B, 2964 LE, Groot-Ammers, Netherlands
Tel.: (31) 184640000
NI
Web Site: http://www.stinstruments.com
Laboratory Equipment Distr
N.A.I.C.S.: 423490
Ries de Leeuw *(Mng Dir)*

ST INTERNATIONAL HOLDINGS CO., LTD.

Room 1006 10/F Center Point 181-185 Gloucester Road, Wanchai, China (Hong Kong)
Tel.: (852) 36110268
Ky
Web Site: http://www.smart-team.cn
8521—(HKG)
Rev.: $12,890,250
Assets: $22,782,083
Liabilities: $6,493,958
Net Worth: $16,288,125
Earnings: ($1,405,688)
Emp.: 63
Fiscal Year-end: 12/31/22
Textile Product Mfr & Distr
N.A.I.C.S.: 313240
Kelvin Kai Hung Wong *(Founder, Chm & Compliance Officer)*

ST LAURENT VOLVO

1300 Michael St, Ottawa, K1B 3N2, ON, Canada
Tel.: (613) 749-8658
Web Site: http://www.stlaurentvolvo.com
Rev.: $23,973,621
Emp.: 55
New & Used Car Dealers
N.A.I.C.S.: 441110

ST MARK HOMES PLC

1 Railshead Road, Twickenham, TE7 7EP, United Kingdom
Tel.: (44) 2089032442
Web Site: https://www.stmarkhomes.co.uk
Year Founded: 1999
Building Construction Services
N.A.I.C.S.: 236210
Bernard Tansey *(Chm)*

ST PETER PORT CAPITAL LIMITED

3rd Floor 1 Le Truchot, Saint Peter Port, GY1 1WD, Guernsey
Tel.: (44) 1481 749360
GY
Web Site: http://www.stpeterportcapital.com
Year Founded: 2007
Rev.: $10,152
Assets: $14,148,304
Liabilities: $121,826
Net Worth: $14,026,478
Earnings: ($2,810,879)
Fiscal Year-end: 03/31/19
Investment Management Service
N.A.I.C.S.: 525990
Elizabeth Lynn Bruce *(Chm)*

ST SHINE OPTICAL CO., LTD.

5F No 276 Section 1 Tatung Road, Xizhi District, New Taipei City, 22146, Taiwan
Tel.: (886) 226471578
Web Site: https://www.stshine.com.tw
Year Founded: 1981
1565—(TPE)
Rev.: $156,442,454
Assets: $259,565,863
Liabilities: $63,594,191
Net Worth: $195,971,672
Earnings: $31,862,364
Emp.: 2,796
Fiscal Year-end: 12/31/22
Optical Lens Product Mfr
N.A.I.C.S.: 333310
Ming-Hsien Chen *(Chm)*

ST THOMAS FORD LINCOLN SALES LIMITED

1012 Talbot Street, Saint Thomas, N5P 1G3, ON, Canada
Tel.: (519) 637-3673
Web Site: http://www.stthomasford.com
Rev.: $38,544,721
Emp.: 48
New & Used Car Dealers
N.A.I.C.S.: 441110
Billy Eansor *(VP)*

ST-GEORGES ECO-MINING CORP.

Suite 2700 1000 Rue Sherbrooke O, Montreal, H3A 3G4, QC, Canada
Tel.: (514) 996-6342
AB
Web Site: https://www.st-georgescorp.com
Year Founded: 2002
SXOOF—(OTCQB)
Rev.: $48,340
Assets: $35,498,913
Liabilities: $14,327,764
Net Worth: $21,171,149
Earnings: $2,240,992

INTERNATIONAL PUBLIC

Fiscal Year-end: 03/31/23
Platinum & Base Metal Mining
N.A.I.C.S.: 212290
Frank Dumas *(COO)*

Subsidiaries:

Iceland Resources EHF (1)
Skipasund 82, 104, Reykjavik, Iceland
Tel.: (354) 4216293
Web Site: http://www.icelandresources.is
Precious Metal Mining Services
N.A.I.C.S.: 212290
Thordis Bjork Sigurbjornsdottir *(CEO)*

ST. ALBERT DODGE CHRYSLER LTD.

184 St Albert Road, Saint Albert, T8N 0P7, AB, Canada
Tel.: (780) 458-8660
Web Site: http://www.stalbertdodge.com
Sales Range: $10-24.9 Million
New & Used Car Dealers
N.A.I.C.S.: 441110
Alan Wack *(Principal-Dealer)*

ST. AUGUSTINE GOLD AND COPPER LIMITED

No 21 Greenwood Lane, Singapore, 286949, Singapore
Tel.: (65) 63822250884
Web Site: https://www.sagcmining.com
Year Founded: 2010
RTLGF—(OTCIQ)
Rev.: $1,344,177
Assets: $113,420,245
Liabilities: $2,056,383
Net Worth: $111,363,862
Earnings: $381,586
Emp.: 20
Fiscal Year-end: 12/31/23
Gold Ore & Silver Ore Mining
N.A.I.C.S.: 212220
Manuel Paolo A. Villar *(Chm, Pres & CEO)*

ST. AUSTELL BREWERY COMPANY LIMITED

63 Trevarthian Road, Saint Austell, PL25 4BY, Cornwall, United Kingdom
Tel.: (44) 8452411122
Web Site: http://www.staustellbrewery.co.uk
Sales Range: $125-149.9 Million
Emp.: 1,000
Pub, Brewery & Hotel Owner & Operator
N.A.I.C.S.: 722410
Will Michelmore *(Chm)*

ST. CONSTANTINE AND HELENA HOLDING JSC

St St Constantine and Helena Resort, 9006, Varna, Bulgaria
Tel.: (359) 52383900
Web Site: http://www.stconstantine.bg
Year Founded: 1991
Home Management Services
N.A.I.C.S.: 721110
Ilko Kolev Zapryanov *(Chm-Mgmt Bd)*

ST. COUSAIR CO., LTD.

1260 Imogawa Iizuna, Kamiminochi District, Nagano, 389-1201, Japan
Tel.: (81) 120537002
Web Site: https://stcousair.co.jp
Year Founded: 1979
2937—(TKS)
Rev.: $126,660,820
Assets: $62,279,420
Liabilities: $30,934,800
Net Worth: $31,344,620
Earnings: $5,406,980
Emp.: 265

Fiscal Year-end: 03/31/24
Packaged Food Mfr
N.A.I.C.S.: 327213
Mayumi Kuze *(Co-Founder)*
Subsidiaries:

St. Cousair, Inc. (1)
8951 NE St Paul Hwy, Newberg, OR 97132
Tel.: (503) 538-2929
Web Site: https://www.stcousair-oregon.com
Emp.: 800
Food & Beverage Packing Services
N.A.I.C.S.: 561910

ST. GALLER KANTONALBANK AG
St Leonhardstrasse 25, 9001, Saint Gallen, Switzerland
Tel.: (41) 712313131
Web Site: http://www.sgkb.ch
Year Founded: 1868
SGKN—(SWX)
Sales Range: Less than $1 Million
Banking Services
N.A.I.C.S.: 523940
Thomas A. Gutzwiller *(Chm)*
Subsidiaries:

St. Galler Kantonalbank Germany Ltd. (1)
Prannerstrasse 11, 80333, Munich, Germany
Tel.: (49) 8912501830
Web Site: http://www.sgkb.de
Sales Range: $50-74.9 Million
Emp.: 60
Banking Services
N.A.I.C.S.: 522110

ST. JAMES GOLD CORP.
Suite 1128 789 West Pender Street, Vancouver, V6C 1H2, BC, Canada
Tel.: (604) 687-2038
Web Site: http://www.bardventures.com
Year Founded: 2005
BVU3—(DEU)
Assets: $634,484
Liabilities: $5,938,105
Net Worth: ($5,303,621)
Earnings: ($14,012,939)
Emp.: 5
Fiscal Year-end: 09/30/22
Mineral Exploration Services
N.A.I.C.S.: 213114
George Drazenovic *(Pres & CEO)*

ST. JAMES VOLKSWAGEN LTD.
670 Century Street, Winnipeg, R3H 0A1, MB, Canada
Tel.: (204) 788-1100
Web Site: http://www.stjamesvw.com
Rev.: $25,003,537
Emp.: 70
New & Used Car Dealers
N.A.I.C.S.: 441110
Sean McCreary *(Mgr-Collision Centre)*

ST. JAMES'S PLACE PLC
St James's Place House 1 Tetbury Road, Cirencester, GL7 1FP, Glos, United Kingdom
Tel.: (44) 1285640302 UK
Web Site: http://www.sjpc.co.uk
Year Founded: 1996
STJ—(LSE)
Rev.: $49,169,150
Assets: $209,783,748,290
Liabilities: $208,276,073,970
Net Worth: $1,507,674,320
Earnings: $387,425,960
Emp.: 2,673
Fiscal Year-end: 12/31/21
Holding Company; Investment Advisory & Wealth Management Services
N.A.I.C.S.: 551112

Mark FitzPatrick *(CEO)*
Subsidiaries:

St. James's Place Wealth Management Group Limited (1)
1Tetbury Rd, Cirencester, GL7 1FP, Gloucestershire, United Kingdom
Tel.: (44) 285640302
Sales Range: $150-199.9 Million
Emp.: 300
Wealth Management Services
N.A.I.C.S.: 523940

ST. JOHNS PACKAGING LTD.
80 Moreau, Saint-Jean-sur-Richelieu, J2W 2M4, QC, Canada
Tel.: (450) 349-5871
Web Site: http://www.sjpack.com
Emp.: 500
Flexible Packaging Mfr
N.A.I.C.S.: 326112
Jacques LeClair *(Pres)*
Subsidiaries:

N.S. Flexibles LLC (1)
2619 Phoenix Dr, Greensboro, NC 27406-6321
Tel.: (336) 292-9911
Web Site: http://www.nsflexibles.com
Sales Range: $25-49.9 Million
Emp.: 200
Flexible Plastic Packing
N.A.I.C.S.: 322220

St. Johns Packaging (Kunshan) Ltd. (1)
80 Yun Que Road Kunshan economic & technology development zone, Kunshan, 215300, Jiangsu, China
Tel.: (86) 51257007200
Packaging Product Mfr & Distr
N.A.I.C.S.: 326112

ST. JOSEPH COMMUNICATIONS INC.
50 MacIntosh Blvd, Concord, L4K 4P3, ON, Canada
Tel.: (905) 660-3111
Web Site: http://www.stjoseph.com
Year Founded: 1956
Sales Range: $200-249.9 Million
Emp.: 350
Magazine Publisher; Commercial Printing & Related Services
N.A.I.C.S.: 323111
Subsidiaries:

St. Joseph Media Inc. (1)
111 Queen St E Ste 320, Toronto, M5C 1S2, ON, Canada
Tel.: (416) 364-3333
Web Site: http://www.stjosephmedia.com
Sales Range: $50-74.9 Million
Emp.: 200
Magazine Publisher
N.A.I.C.S.: 513120

Unit (Domestic):

Canadian Family (2)
111 Queen St E Ste 320, Toronto, M5C 1S2, ON, Canada
Tel.: (416) 364-3333
Web Site: http://www.canadianfamily.ca
Sales Range: $50-74.9 Million
Emp.: 200
Magazine Publisher
N.A.I.C.S.: 513120

FASHION Magazine (2)
111 Queen St E Suite 320, Toronto, M5C 1S2, ON, Canada
Tel.: (416) 364-3333
Web Site: https://www.fashionmagazine.com
Sales Range: $25-49.9 Million
Emp.: 50
Magazine Publisher
N.A.I.C.S.: 513120
Dora Brenndorfer *(Controller)*

Mariage Quebec (2)
Robert-Bourassa Bureau 1301, Montreal, H3B 3A7, QC, Canada
Tel.: (514) 284-2552

Web Site: http://www.mariagequebec.com
Sales Range: $25-49.9 Million
Emp.: 8
Magazine Publisher
N.A.I.C.S.: 513120

Ottawa Magazine (2)
43 Eccles St, Ottawa, K1R 6S3, ON, Canada
Tel.: (613) 230-0333
Sales Range: $25-49.9 Million
Emp.: 20
Magazine Publisher
N.A.I.C.S.: 513120

Quill & Quire (2)
15 Benton Road, Toronto, M6M 3G2, ON, Canada
Tel.: (416) 248-4868
Web Site: https://www.quillandquire.com
Sales Range: $25-49.9 Million
Emp.: 30
Magazine Publisher
N.A.I.C.S.: 513120
Alison Jones *(Publr-Adv Sls)*

Toronto Life (2)
111 Queen St E Ste 320, Toronto, M5C 1S2, ON, Canada
Tel.: (416) 364-3333
Web Site: http://www.torontolife.com
Sales Range: $50-74.9 Million
Emp.: 250
Magazine Publisher
N.A.I.C.S.: 513120

WEDDINGBELLS (2)
111 Queen St E Ste 320, Toronto, M5C 1S2, ON, Canada
Tel.: (416) 364-3333
Web Site: http://www.weddingbells.ca
Sales Range: $25-49.9 Million
Emp.: 30
Magazine Publisher Services
N.A.I.C.S.: 513120
Sandy Sternthal *(Dir-Retail Adv Sls)*

St. Joseph Print Inc. (1)
50 MacIntosh Boulevard, Concord, L4K 4P3, ON, Canada
Tel.: (905) 660-3111
Web Site: https://www.stjoseph.com
Sales Range: $125-149.9 Million
Emp.: 300
Commercial Printing Services
N.A.I.C.S.: 323111

ST. KITTS NEVIS ANGUILLA TRADING & DEVELOPMENT CO., LTD.
Fort Street, PO Box 142, Basseterre, Saint Kitts & Nevis
Tel.: (869) 465 2511
Web Site: http://www.tdcgrouplimited.com
Year Founded: 1973
Rev.: $57,265,027
Assets: $161,160,443
Liabilities: $93,213,555
Net Worth: $67,946,888
Earnings: ($1,595,695)
Emp.: 648
Fiscal Year-end: 01/31/20
Diverse Trading & Development Services
N.A.I.C.S.: 425120
Earle Austin Kelly *(Chm)*
Subsidiaries:

Ocean Terrace Inn Ltd. (1)
Wigley Avenue, PO Box 65, Fortlands, Saint Kitts & Nevis (91.88%)
Tel.: (869) 4652754
Web Site: http://www.oceanterraceinn.com
Sales Range: $10-24.9 Million
Emp.: 10
Hotel Owner & Operator
N.A.I.C.S.: 721110

Sands Development (1)
PO Box 142, Basseterre, Saint Kitts & Nevis
Tel.: (869) 4652511
Commercial & Residential Complex
N.A.I.C.S.: 531390

St. Kitts-Nevis Finance Company Ltd. (1)
Central Street, Basseterre, Saint Kitts & Nevis
Tel.: (869) 4656516
Sales Range: $75-99.9 Million
Emp.: 25
Consumer Financing & Loan Services
N.A.I.C.S.: 522291

TDC Airlines Services Ltd. (1)
PO Box 142, Basseterre, Saint Kitts & Nevis
Tel.: (869) 4656035
Web Site: http://www.tdclimited.com
Airport Services
N.A.I.C.S.: 488119

TDC Nevis Ltd. (1)
PO Box 142, Fort Street, Basseterre, Saint Kitts & Nevis
Tel.: (869) 465 2511
Web Site: http://www.tdclimited.com
Wholesale Trade Broker
N.A.I.C.S.: 425120
Earle Kelly *(Chm)*

TDC Rentals Ltd. (1)
West Indepence Square, Basseterre, Saint Kitts & Nevis
Tel.: (869) 4652991
Web Site: http://www.tdclimited.com
Sales Range: $50-74.9 Million
Car Rental Services
N.A.I.C.S.: 532111

Subsidiary (Domestic):

TDC Rentals (Nevis) Ltd. (2)
Main St, Charlestown, Saint Kitts & Nevis
Tel.: (869) 4695430
Web Site: http://www.tdclimited.com
Car Rental Services
N.A.I.C.S.: 532111

TDC Shipping Ltd. (1)
Fort Street Box 142, PO Box 142, Basseterre, Saint Kitts & Nevis (100%)
Tel.: (869) 4652511
Web Site: http://www.tdclimited.com
Sales Range: $25-49.9 Million
Shipping Services
N.A.I.C.S.: 483211
Elvis Bassue *(Asst Mgr)*

ST. KITTS-NEVIS-ANGUILLA NATIONAL BANK LIMITED
Central Street, PO Box 343, West Indies, Basseterre, 00265, Saint Kitts & Nevis
Tel.: (869) 4652204
Web Site: http://www.sknanb.com
Year Founded: 1971
SKNB—(ECA)
Rev.: $27,555,556
Assets: $1,404,657,407
Liabilities: $1,209,995,185
Net Worth: $194,662,222
Earnings: $18,401,111
Emp.: 289
Fiscal Year-end: 06/30/23
Banking Services
N.A.I.C.S.: 522110
Donald Thompson *(CEO)*
Subsidiaries:

National Bank Trust Company (St. Kitts-Nevis-Anguilla) Ltd. (1)
Central St, PO Box 343, Basseterre, Saint Kitts & Nevis
Tel.: (869) 4652204
Web Site: https://www.sknanb.com
Sales Range: $50-74.9 Million
Emp.: 100
Long Term Mortgage Financing, Property Management, Real Estate Development & Investment Services
N.A.I.C.S.: 921130

National Caribbean Insurance Company (1)
Church Street, Basseterre, Saint Kitts & Nevis
Tel.: (869) 4652694
Web Site: https://www.nci-biz.com

ST. KITTS-NEVIS-ANGUILLA NATIONAL BANK LIMITED

St. Kitts-Nevis-Anguilla National Bank Limited—(Continued)
Sales Range: $75-99.9 Million
Emp.: 65
Insurance Services
N.A.I.C.S.: 524113

St. Kitts-Nevis Mortgage & Investment Co., Ltd. (1)
Central Street, PO Box 343, Basseterre, Saint Kitts & Nevis
Tel.: (869) 4668101
Web Site: http://www.micoonline.com
Real Estate Mortgage Services
N.A.I.C.S.: 522310
Calvin Buchanan *(CFO)*

ST. LUCIA ELECTRICITY SERVICES LTD.
Lucelec Building Sans Soucis John Compton Highway, Castries, Saint Lucia
Tel.: (758) 4574400
Web Site: http://www.lucelec.com
Year Founded: 1964
SLES—(ECA)
Rev.: $143,322,963
Assets: $228,661,111
Liabilities: $76,054,074
Net Worth: $152,607,037
Earnings: $15,406,296
Emp.: 260
Fiscal Year-end: 12/31/23
Electricity Power Distr
N.A.I.C.S.: 221122
Trevor M. Louisy *(Mng Dir)*

ST. MARYS PAPER CORP.
75 Huron St, Sault Sainte Marie, P6A 5P4, ON, Canada
Tel.: (705) 942-6070
Web Site: http://www.stmaryspaper.com
Year Founded: 1994
Sales Range: $150-199.9 Million
Emp.: 300
Paper Mills
N.A.I.C.S.: 322120
Gord Acton *(Pres)*

ST1 NORDIC OY
Purotie 1, 00380, Helsinki, Finland
Tel.: (358) 1055711
Web Site: http://www.st1.fi
Sales Range: $1-4.9 Billion
Emp.: 160
Alternative Fuel Producer & Gas Station Operator
N.A.I.C.S.: 457120
Mika Wiljanen *(CEO & Mng Dir)*

Subsidiaries:

St1 Sverige AB (1)
Lofstroms Alle 5, PO Box 1029, Sundbyberg, 172 66, Sweden
Tel.: (46) 0771 369 369
Alternative Fuel Producer & Gas Station Operator
N.A.I.C.S.: 457120

STA. LUCIA LAND, INC.
Penthouse Building III Sta Lucia East Grand Mall Cainta, Rizal, 1900, Philippines
Tel.: (63) 286817332
Web Site: https://www.stalucialand.com.ph
SLI—(PHI)
Rev.: $204,301,948
Assets: $1,117,614,703
Liabilities: $638,882,030
Net Worth: $478,732,673
Earnings: $67,412,673
Emp.: 223
Fiscal Year-end: 12/31/23
Real Estate Services
N.A.I.C.S.: 531120
Pancho G. Umali *(Asst Sec)*

STAATL MINERALBRUNNEN AG BAD BRUECKENAU
Buchstr 5, 97763, Bad Bruckenau, Germany
Tel.: (49) 97418030
Web Site: https://www.badbrueckenauer.de
Bottled Product Mfr
N.A.I.C.S.: 312112
Ingo Vialon *(Chm-Mgmt Bd & CEO)*

STACK CAPITAL GROUP INC.
155 Wellington St West Suite 3140, Toronto, M5V 3H1, ON, Canada
Tel.: (647) 802-3351 ON
Web Site: https://www.stackcapitalgroup.com
Year Founded: 2021
STCGF—(OTCIQ)
Rev.: $1,794,528
Assets: $76,411,803
Liabilities: $276,626
Net Worth: $76,135,178
Earnings: ($633,136)
Fiscal Year-end: 12/31/22
Investment Management Service
N.A.I.C.S.: 523999
Brian Viveiros *(VP)*

STACKE HYDRAULIK AB
Skillingaryd, PO Box 154, Varnamo, 568, Sweden
Tel.: (46) 37078900
Web Site: http://www.stackehydraulik.se
Sales Range: $25-49.9 Million
Emp.: 115
Hydraulic Systems Mfr & Marketer
N.A.I.C.S.: 333310
Anders Stacke *(Mng Dir)*

STACO LINK CO., LTD.
15-1 Yangpyungdong2ga, Youngdngpogu, Seoul, 08506, Korea (South)
Tel.: (82) 3180686602
Web Site: http://www.longtukorea.com
Year Founded: 1993
060240—(KRS)
Rev.: $22,308,969
Assets: $32,507,699
Liabilities: $4,297,416
Net Worth: $28,210,283
Earnings: ($22,900,453)
Emp.: 42
Fiscal Year-end: 12/31/22
Online Education Services
N.A.I.C.S.: 611691

STADCO LTD.
Queensway Hortonwood, Telford, TF1 7LL, Shropshire, United Kingdom
Tel.: (44) 1952 222111
Web Site: http://www.stadco.co.uk
Year Founded: 2010
Sales Range: $300-349.9 Million
Emp.: 1,198
Automobile Body Mfr
N.A.I.C.S.: 336211
Dermot Sterne *(Mng Dir)*

Subsidiaries:

Stadco Automotive India Pvt. Ltd. (1)
S-15 Economist House 3rd Floor 1st Cross Rd, Industrial Estate Guindy, Chennai, 600032, India
Tel.: (91) 4445532113
Web Site: http://www.stadco.co.in
Automotive Body Parts Mfr & Distr
N.A.I.C.S.: 336370
Peter Spackman *(Dir-Indian Ops)*

Stadco Saarlouis Ltd. & Co. KG (1)
Henry Ford Strasse, 66740, Saarlouis, Germany
Tel.: (49) 68318952290

Web Site: http://www.stadco.de
Emp.: 300
Automotive Body Parts Mfr & Distr
N.A.I.C.S.: 336370

STADEMOS HOTELS PLC
60 Amathus Avenue, PO Box 56767, 3310, Limassol, Cyprus
Tel.: (357) 25 828333
Web Site: http://www.stademos.com.cy
Year Founded: 1989
Home Management Services
N.A.I.C.S.: 721110

STADIO HOLDINGS LTD.
Office 101 The Village Square Corners Oxford Queen Streets, Durbanville, Cape Town, 7550, South Africa
Tel.: (27) 872883220
Web Site: https://www.stadio.co.za
SDO—(JSE)
Rev.: $76,987,379
Assets: $126,128,706
Liabilities: $24,713,186
Net Worth: $101,415,521
Earnings: $12,866,829
Emp.: 1,193
Fiscal Year-end: 12/31/23
Financial Investment Services
N.A.I.C.S.: 523999
Samara Totaram *(CFO)*

Subsidiaries:

Southern Business School Proprietary Limited (1)
Plot 10 R28 Service Road Diswilmar, Krugersdorp, 1739, South Africa
Tel.: (27) 116621444
Web Site: http://www.sbs.ac.za
Education & Training Services
N.A.I.C.S.: 611710

STADLER RAIL AG
Ernst Stadler Strasse 1, 9565, Bussnang, Switzerland
Tel.: (41) 716262120 CH
Web Site: http://www.stadlerrail.com
Year Founded: 1942
Holding Company; Rail Vehicle Mfr
N.A.I.C.S.: 551112
Peter Spuhler *(Owner, Chm & CEO)*

Subsidiaries:

Stadler Algerie Eurl (1)
Stadler Algerie Eurl 14bis Rue de l'ALN Caroubier, 16005, Algiers, Algeria
Tel.: (213) 21 498 329
Web Site: http://www.stadlerrail.com
Emp.: 70
Maintenance of Rail Vehicle Services
N.A.I.C.S.: 488210
Toniato Massimo *(Gen Mgr)*

Stadler Altenrhein AG (1)
Park Altenrhein for Industry & Trade, Altenrhein, 9423, Switzerland
Tel.: (41) 71 858 41 41
Streetcars, Double-Decker Trains, Rail Vehicles & Passenger Coaches Mfr
N.A.I.C.S.: 336510
Markus Sauerbruch *(Gen Mgr)*

Stadler Bussnang AG (1)
Ernst-Stadler-Strasse 4, Bussnang, 9565, Switzerland
Tel.: (41) 716262120
Web Site: http://www.stadlerrail.com
Emp.: 1,000
Rail Vehicle Mfr
N.A.I.C.S.: 336510
Georg Kapeller *(CEO)*

Stadler Netherlands B.V (1)
Koppelstraat 3, 7391 AK, Twello, Netherlands
Tel.: (31) 58 23 34910
Railway Vehicle Distr
N.A.I.C.S.: 423860
Hein van der Schoot *(Gen Mgr)*

Stadler Pankow GmbH (1)

INTERNATIONAL PUBLIC

Lessingstrasse 102, Berlin, 13158, Germany (100%)
Tel.: (49) 30 91 91 16 16
Web Site: http://www.stadlerrail.com
Development, Sales & Export of Streetcars
N.A.I.C.S.: 488210
Michael Daum *(Gen Mgr-Sls)*

Subsidiary (Domestic):

Stadler Reinickendorf GmbH (2)
Lessingstrasse 102, 13158, Berlin, Germany
Tel.: (49) 30 91910
Railway Vehicle Mfr
N.A.I.C.S.: 336510

Stadler Polska Sp. z o.o. (1)
ul Targowa 50, 08 110, Siedlce, Poland
Tel.: (48) 25 746 45 00
Web Site: http://www.stadlerrail.com
Rail Vehicle Assembly
N.A.I.C.S.: 336510
Christian Spichiger *(Gen Mgr)*

Stadler Praha, s.r.o. (1)
Kutvirtova 339/5, 150 00, Prague, Czech Republic
Tel.: (420) 257 404 900
Web Site: http://www.stadlerrail.com
Rail Vehicle Engineering & Development Services
N.A.I.C.S.: 541330
Bohumir Kracmar *(Gen Mgr)*

Stadler Rail Valencia S.A.U (1)
Calle Mitjera 6, 46550, Albuixech, Valencia, Spain
Tel.: (34) 961415000
Web Site: http://www.stadlerrail.es
Emp.: 900
Locomotive Mfr
N.A.I.C.S.: 336510
Juan Jose Sanchis *(Mgr-Comm & Mktg)*

Stadler Service Sweden AB (1)
Box 1071, SE-101 39, Stockholm, Sweden
Tel.: (46) 76 105 90 14
Web Site: http://www.stadlerrail.com
Rail Vehicles Maintenance
N.A.I.C.S.: 488210
Walter Neureiter *(CEO)*

Stadler Stahlguss AG (1)
Johann-Renfer-Str 51-55, 2504, Biel/Bienne, Switzerland
Tel.: (41) 32 344 45 00
Web Site: http://www.stadlerstahlguss.ch
Sales Range: $25-49.9 Million
Emp.: 100
Steel Foundry
N.A.I.C.S.: 331513

Stadler Szolnok Vasuti Jarmugyarto Kft. (1)
Banki Donat u, Ipari Park (Piroskai ut), 5000, Szolnok, Hungary
Tel.: (36) 56 888 500
Web Site: http://www.stadlerrail.com
Emp.: 400
Mfr of Aluminum Rail Car Bodies
N.A.I.C.S.: 336510
Jens Hofmann *(Gen Mgr)*

Stadler US Inc. (1)
231 N Ave W No 112, Westfield, NJ 07090
Tel.: (908) 232-2778
Web Site: http://www.stadlerrail.com
Sales & Service of Rail Vehicles & Products
N.A.I.C.S.: 488210
Stephen Bonina *(Pres)*

Stadler Ungarn Kft. (1)
Varosligeti fasor 47-49, Budapest, 1071, Hungary
Tel.: (36) 1 327 40 60
Web Site: http://www.stadlerrail.com
Emp.: 100
Sales, Marketing & Servicing of Rail Vehicles
N.A.I.C.S.: 488210
Dunai Zoltan *(Gen Mgr)*

Stadler Winterthur AG (1)
Sulzer-Allee 11, 8404, Winterthur, Switzerland
Tel.: (41) 52 224 61 00
Web Site: http://www.stadlerrail.com
Rail Vehicles & Locomotives Mfr
N.A.I.C.S.: 336510
Hartmut Dietrich *(Gen Mgr)*

AND PRIVATE COMPANIES

Zentrallager Weinfelden der Stadler Bussnang AG **(1)**
Fohlenweide 3/5, 8570, Weinfelden, Switzerland
Tel.: (41) 71 626 20 20
Railway Vehicle Distr
N.A.I.C.S.: 423860

STADTREINIGUNG HAMBURG A.O.R.

Bullerdeich 19, Hamburg, 20537, Germany
Tel.: (49) 4025760
Web Site: http://www.stadtreinigung.hamburg
Environmental Services
N.A.I.C.S.: 541620
Heiko Laas *(Ops Mgr)*

Subsidiaries:

MVR Mullverwertung Rugenberger Damm GmbH & Co. KG **(1)**
Rugenberger Damm, 21129, Hamburg, Germany **(100%)**
Tel.: (49) 40 74 186 100
Web Site: http://www.mvr-hh.de
Waste Recycling Services
N.A.I.C.S.: 562920
Martin Mineur *(Mng Dir)*

STADTSPARKASSE MUNCHEN GMBH

Sparkassenstrasse 2, Munich, 80331, Germany
Tel.: (49) 8921670 De
Web Site: http://www.sskm.de
Year Founded: 1824
Sales Range: $1-4.9 Billion
Emp.: 3,100
Municipal Savings Bank
N.A.I.C.S.: 522219
Harald Strotgen *(Chm-Exec Bd)*

STADTWERKE BIELEFELD GMBH

Schildescher Strasse 16, 33611, Bielefeld, Germany
Tel.: (49) 521 51 90 De
Web Site: http://www.stadtwerke-bielefeld.de
Year Founded: 1856
Emp.: 1,240
Electricity, Water, Heat & Gas Utility Administration Services
N.A.I.C.S.: 926130
Martin Uekmann *(Mng Dir)*

Subsidiaries:

Interargem GmbH **(1)**
Schelpmilser Weg 30, 33609, Bielefeld, Germany
Tel.: (49) 521 3398 106
Web Site: http://www.interargem.de
Waste Disposal Services
N.A.I.C.S.: 562219

Subsidiary (Domestic):

Enertec Hameln GmbH **(2)**
Heinrich-Schoormann-Weg 1, 31789, Hameln, Germany
Tel.: (49) 5 151 81 2901
Web Site: http://www.interargem.de
Eletric Power Generation Services
N.A.I.C.S.: 221118

STADTWERKE GELNHAUSEN GMBH

Philipp-Reis-Strasse 1-3, 63571, Gelnhausen, Germany
Tel.: (49) 6051 838 01 De
Web Site: http://www.stadtwerke-gelnhausen.de
Electric Power & Water Utility Administration Services
N.A.I.C.S.: 926130
Siegfried Ruckriegel *(Mng Dir)*

STADTWERKE HANNOVER AG

Ihmeplatz 2, 30449, Hannover, Germany
Tel.: (49) 5114300 De
Web Site: http://www.enercity.de
Emp.: 2,417
Electricity, Water, Heat, Communications & Gas Utility Administration Services
N.A.I.C.S.: 926130
Susanna Zapreva *(Chm-Mgmt Bd)*

Subsidiaries:

Danpower GmbH **(1)**
Otto-Braun-Platz 1, 14467, Potsdam, Germany **(84%)**
Tel.: (49) 331 23782 0
Web Site: http://www.danpower.de
Sales Range: $150-199.9 Million
Emp.: 400
Energy & Heat Supplier
N.A.I.C.S.: 221121
Hartmut Liebisch *(Mng Dir)*

Subsidiary (Domestic):

Bitterfelder Fernwarme GmbH **(2)**
Bahnhofstr 30, 06749, Bitterfeld-Wolfen, Germany
Tel.: (49) 3493 3751 0
Web Site: http://www.btf-waerme.de
Thermal Energy Supplier
N.A.I.C.S.: 221116
Mario Engler *(Mng Dir)*

Danpower Biomasse Pfaffenhofen GmbH **(2)**
Posthofstrasse 2, 85276, Pfaffenhofen, Germany
Tel.: (49) 8441 4984 90
Biomass Energy Services
N.A.I.C.S.: 221117
Mario Sonntag *(Mng Dir)*

Subsidiary (Non-US):

Danpower Eesti AS **(2)**
Vilja 14, 65605, Voru, Estonia
Tel.: (372) 786415 2
Web Site: http://www.danpower.ee
Heat Supply Services
N.A.I.C.S.: 221122
Valter Banhard *(Mgr-Production)*

Subsidiary (Domestic):

Danpower Energie Service GmbH **(2)**
Charlottenstr 40, 14467, Potsdam, Germany **(100%)**
Tel.: (49) 331 23782 0
Energy Generation & Contracting Services
N.A.I.C.S.: 221122
Hartmut Liebisch *(Mng Dir)*

EKT Energie und Kommunal-Technologie GmbH **(2)**
Otto Brown Humboldtstrasse 1, 14467, Potsdam, Germany **(100%)**
Tel.: (49) 331 23782 0
Web Site: http://www.danpower-gruppe.de
Heat Supply & Contracting Services
N.A.I.C.S.: 238220
Hartmut Liebisch *(Mng Dir)*

ELW Energieversorgung Leinefelde-Worbis GmbH **(2)**
Boschstrasse 25, 37327, Leinefelde, Germany
Tel.: (49) 3605 5521 53
Heat Generation Services
N.A.I.C.S.: 221122
Heinrich Schmidt *(Mng Dir)*

IEP Innovative Energien Potsdam GmbH **(2)**
Charlottenstrasse 40, 14467, Potsdam, Germany
Tel.: (49) 331 23782 0
Web Site: http://www.iep-innovative-energien-potsdam.de
Energy Generation Plants Builder & Operator
N.A.I.C.S.: 221122
Karsten Krieg *(Mng Dir)*

IEW Innovative Energien Wolgast GmbH **(2)**
Burgstrasse 6a, 17438, Wolgast, Germany

Tel.: (49) 331 23782 43
Web Site: http://www.iew-innovative-energien-wolgast.de
Biogas Production & Sales
N.A.I.C.S.: 221117
Antje Tiedt-Schimanski *(Mng Dir)*

PD Energy GmbH **(2)**
Zorbiger Strasse 22, 06749, Bitterfeld-Wolfen, Germany
Tel.: (49) 3493 723 45
Web Site: http://www.pd-energy.de
Emp.: 27
Thermal Residue Treatment Services
N.A.I.C.S.: 562998
Michael Polk *(Mng Dir)*

PME Projekmanagement & Engineering GmbH **(2)**
Charlottenstr 40, 14467, Potsdam, Germany
Tel.: (49) 331 23782 0
Web Site: http://www.pme-potsdam.de
Energy Generation Engineering Services
N.A.I.C.S.: 541330
Ingo Schauer *(Mng Dir)*

Stadtwerk Elsterwerda GmbH **(2)**
Lauchhammerstrasse 45, 04910, Elsterwerda, Germany **(51%)**
Tel.: (49) 3533 4867 0
Web Site: http://www.stadtwerk-elsterwerda.de
Biomass & District Heating Supplier
N.A.I.C.S.: 221118
Mario Sonntag *(Mng Dir)*

Vigoris Handels GmbH **(2)**
Lauchhammer Strasse 45, 04910, Elsterwerda, Germany
Tel.: (49) 331 23782 0
Energy Trading Services
N.A.I.C.S.: 561499
Nico Blume *(Mng Dir)*

WVZ-Warmeversorgung Zinnowitz GmbH **(2)**
Wiesenweg 2, Postfach 1236, 17454, Zinnowitz, Germany
Tel.: (49) 38377 40796
Heating Supply Services
N.A.I.C.S.: 221122
Antje Tiedt-Schimanski *(Mng Dir)*

Warmeversorgung Wolgast GmbH **(2)**
Burgstr 6a, 17438, Wolgast, Germany
Tel.: (49) 3836 28952 0
Web Site: http://www.wolgast.de
Heat Generation Services
N.A.I.C.S.: 221122
Antje Tiedt-Schimanski *(Mng Dir)*

STADTWERKE INGOLSTADT BETEILIGUNGEN GMBH

Ringlerstrasse 28, 85057, Ingolstadt, Germany
Tel.: (49) 841 80.0 De
Web Site: http://www.sw-i.de
Year Founded: 1863
Electricity, Natural Gas, Heat & Other Public Utility Administration Services
N.A.I.C.S.: 926130
Matthias Bolle *(Mng Dir)*

Subsidiaries:

Stadtwerke Ingolstadt Energie GmbH **(1)**
Ringlerstrasse 28, 85057, Ingolstadt, Germany
Tel.: (49) 841800
Web Site: http://www.sw-i.de
Electricity, Gas & Heat Distr
N.A.I.C.S.: 221122
Matthias Bolle *(CEO)*

STADTWERKE KOLN GMBH

Parkgurtel 26, 50823, Cologne, Germany
Tel.: (49) 2211780 De
Web Site: http://www.stadtwerkekoeln.de
Year Founded: 1960

STADTWERKE MUNCHEN GMBH

Holding Company Electricity Water Heat & Gas Utility Administration & Distribution Services
N.A.I.C.S.: 551112
Jurgen Fenske *(Mng Dir)*

Subsidiaries:

Hafen und Guterverkehr Koln AG **(1)**
Bayenstrasse 2, 50678, Cologne, Germany **(54.5%)**
Tel.: (49) 2213900
Web Site: http://www.hgk.de
Sales Range: $200-249.9 Million
Emp.: 700
Rail Transportation Services
N.A.I.C.S.: 482111

Subsidiary (Domestic):

HTAG Hafen und Transport AG **(2)**
Baumstrasse 31, 47 198, Duisburg, Germany **(100%)**
Tel.: (49) 20662090
Web Site: http://www.htag-duisburg.de
Sales Range: $25-49.9 Million
Emp.: 50
Inland Navigation
N.A.I.C.S.: 488210

Subsidiary (Domestic):

NESKA Schiffahrts- und Speditionskontor GmbH **(3)**
Neumarkt 7-11, 47119, Duisburg, Germany **(65%)**
Tel.: (49) 20347989301
Web Site: http://www.neska.com
Sales Range: $125-149.9 Million
Cargo, Transportation, Storage & Logistic Services; Joint Venture of Imperial Logistics International GmbH (65%) & HTAG Hafen und Transport AG (35%)
N.A.I.C.S.: 493190
Stefan Hutten *(Member-Mgmt Bd)*

Navigare Stauerei und Speditions GmbH **(3)**
Baumstrasse 31, 47198, Duisburg, Germany **(100%)**
Tel.: (49) 2066209121
Web Site: http://www.navigare-stauerei.de
Sales Range: $50-74.9 Million
Coal Transport Services
N.A.I.C.S.: 488510
Carsten Borgards *(Mgr-Ops)*

STADTWERKE MUNCHEN GMBH

Emmy-Noether-Strasse 2, 80992, Munich, Germany
Tel.: (49) 89 2361 0 De
Web Site: http://www.swm.de
Rev.: $12,227,227,246
Assets: $12,521,052,753
Liabilities: $6,162,296,177
Net Worth: $6,358,756,576
Earnings: $149,678,248
Emp.: 9,444
Fiscal Year-end: 12/31/19
Electricity, Water, Heat, Communications & Gas Utility Administration Services
N.A.I.C.S.: 926130
Florian Bieberbach *(Member-Mgmt Bd)*

Subsidiaries:

Bayerngas Energy GmbH **(1)**
Poccistr 9, 80336, Munich, Germany
Tel.: (49) 897200123
Web Site: http://www.bayerngas-energy.de
Natural Gas Exploration & Production Services
N.A.I.C.S.: 211130
Dimitri Semenchenko *(Portfolio Mgr-Energy)*

Bayerngas GmbH **(1)**
Poccistrasse 9, 80336, Munich, Germany **(56.3%)**
Tel.: (49) 8972000
Web Site: http://www.bayerngas.de
Sales Range: $75-99.9 Million
Natural Gas Purchasing & Distribution Services

7161

Stadtwerke München GmbH—(Continued)

N.A.I.C.S.: 221210
Thomas Meerpohl *(Chm-Supervisory Bd)*

Subsidiary (Domestic):

bayernugs GmbH (2)
Poccistrasse 9, 80336, Munich, Germany
Tel.: (49) 897200700
Web Site: http://www.bayernugs.de
Gas Storage Services
N.A.I.C.S.: 457120

Bioenergie Taufkirchen GmbH & Co. KG (1)
Lanzenhaarer Weg 2, 82024, Taufkirchen, Germany
Tel.: (49) 8921236360
Web Site: http://www.bioenergie-taufkirchen.de
Electric Power Utility Services
N.A.I.C.S.: 221122

Hanse Windkraft GmbH (1)
Neuer Wall 38, 20354, Hamburg, Germany
Tel.: (49) 4068875510
Web Site: http://www.hanse-windkraft.de
Wind Electric Power Generation Services
N.A.I.C.S.: 221115

LHM Services GmbH (1)
Emmy-Noether-Strasse 2, 80992, Munich, Germany
Tel.: (49) 8915704927
Web Site: http://www.lhm-services.de
Information Technology Services
N.A.I.C.S.: 541511
Hartmut Menzel *(Mgr-Svcs & Implementation)*

M-net Telekommunikations GmbH (1)
Frankfurter Ring 158, 80807, Munich, Germany
Tel.: (49) 89452000
Web Site: http://www.m-net.de
Internet Provider Services
N.A.I.C.S.: 517111
Mirjam Hug *(Mktg Mgr)*

Munchner Verkehrsgesellschaft mbH (1)
Emmy-Noether-Strasse 2, 80992, Munich, Germany
Tel.: (49) 8921910
Web Site: http://www.mvg.de
Public Transportation Services
N.A.I.C.S.: 485999
Johannes Reiter *(Product Mgr-Mobile Svcs)*

Praterkraftwerk GmbH (1)
Emmy-Noether-Strasse 2, 80992, Munich, Germany
Tel.: (49) 8923612433
Web Site: http://www.praterkraftwerk.de
Eletric Power Generation Services
N.A.I.C.S.: 221118

eta Energieberatung GmbH (1)
Loewenstr 11, 85276, Pfaffenhofen, Germany
Tel.: (49) 844149460
Web Site: http://www.eta-energieberatung.de
Consultancy Services
N.A.I.C.S.: 541618
Olaf Barck *(Head-Sls)*

STADTWERKE SCHWERIN GMBH

Eckdrift 43-45, 19061, Schwerin, Germany
Tel.: (49) 3856330 De
Web Site: http://www.stadtwerke-schwerin.de
Year Founded: 1991
Electricity, Water, Heat & Gas Utility Administration Services
N.A.I.C.S.: 926130
Josef Wolf *(CEO & Member-Mgmt Bd)*

STADTWERKE SOLINGEN GMBH

Beethovenstrasse 210, 42655, Solingen, Germany

Tel.: (49) 212 295 0 De
Web Site: http://www.stadtwerke-solingen.de
Sales Range: $10-24.9 Million
Emp.: 400
Energy, Water Resource & Public Transportation Administration Services
N.A.I.C.S.: 926130
Andreas Schwarberg *(Mng Dir)*

Subsidiaries:

Stadtwerke Solingen Netz GmbH (1)
Beethovenstrasse 210, 42655, Solingen, Germany (100%)
Tel.: (49) 2122950
Web Site: http://www.sws-solingen.de
Energy Holding Company
N.A.I.C.S.: 551112

enserva GmbH (1)
Beethovenstrasse 210, 42655, Solingen, Germany (100%)
Tel.: (49) 2122480180
Web Site: http://www.enserva.de
Energy Consulting Services
N.A.I.C.S.: 541690

STAEDTLER MARS GMBH & CO KG

Moosaeckerstrasse 3, 90427, Nuremberg, Germany
Tel.: (49) 91193650
Web Site: http://www.staedtler.com
Year Founded: 1835
Sales Range: $750-799.9 Million
Emp.: 3,000
Pen Pencil Marker & Inkjet Cartridge Mfr
N.A.I.C.S.: 339940
Axel Marx *(Mng Dir-Comml)*

Subsidiaries:

P.T. STAEDTLER Indonesia (1)
Jalan Raya Serang Km 80, Cimiung Serang, Bandung, 10120, Jawa Barat, Indonesia
Tel.: (62) 254281371
Office Equipment Whslr
N.A.I.C.S.: 424120

STAEDTLER (Korea) Co. Ltd. (1)
3 Floors Kyungwon Building 663-4 Bokjeong-Dong, Sujeong-Gu, Seongnam, 461-831, Gyeonggi-Do, Korea (South)
Tel.: (82) 317217664
Web Site: http://www.staedtler.co.kr
Office Equipment Whslr
N.A.I.C.S.: 424120

STAEDTLER (NZ) Ltd. (1)
9 Ashfield Road North Shore Mail Centre, PO Box 100640, Auckland, New Zealand
Tel.: (64) 94444090
Web Site: http://www.staedtler.co.nz
Office Equipment Whslr
N.A.I.C.S.: 424120
Emily Jankuloska *(Mgr-Admin)*

STAEDTLER (Pacific) Pty. Ltd. (1)
Level 3 18 Aquatic Drive Frenchs Forest, Sydney, 2086, NSW, Australia
Tel.: (61) 299713500
Web Site: http://www.staedtler.com.au
Office Equipment Whslr
N.A.I.C.S.: 424120

STAEDTLER (S.A.) (PTY.) Ltd. (1)
Longmeadow Business Estate West 10 Drakensburg Drive, Edenvale, 1609, South Africa
Tel.: (27) 115791600
Web Site: http://www.staedtler.co.za
Office Equipment Whslr
N.A.I.C.S.: 424120
Janine Howarth *(Acct Mgr)*

STAEDTLER (Singapore) Pte. Ltd. (1)
17 Mandai Estate 06-02A Hwa Yew Industrial Building, Singapore, 729934, Singapore
Tel.: (65) 67608755
Office Equipment Whslr
N.A.I.C.S.: 424120

STAEDTLER (Thailand) Ltd. (1)
59 Soi Barbos 2 Sukhumvit 42 Road Prakanong, Klongtoey, Bangkok, 10110, Thailand
Tel.: (66) 27120701
Web Site: http://www.staedtler.co.th
Office Equipment Whslr
N.A.I.C.S.: 424120
Markus Handfest *(Mng Dir)*

STAEDTLER (U.K.) LTD. (1)
1st Floor 31 Old Field Road Bocam Park, Pencoed, Bridgend, CF35 5LJ, Mid Glamorgan, United Kingdom
Tel.: (44) 1656778668
Web Site: http://www.staedtler.co.uk
Office Equipment Whslr
N.A.I.C.S.: 424120

STAEDTLER Benelux N.V./S.A. (1)
Fountain Business Centre - Building 5 C Van Kerckhovenstraat 110, 2880, Bornem, Belgium
Tel.: (32) 38906170
Web Site: http://www.staedtler.be
Office Equipment Whslr
N.A.I.C.S.: 424120

STAEDTLER IBERIA, S.A. (1)
Poligono Industrial Agripina C/Comunicacions 12, Castellbisbal, 08755, Barcelona, Spain
Tel.: (34) 937724005
Web Site: http://www.staedtler.es
Office Equipment Whslr
N.A.I.C.S.: 424120
Jose Antonio Camacho Ruiz *(Area Mgr)*

STAEDTLER Italia S.p.A. (1)
V Priv Archimede 5, 20094, Corsico, Italy
Tel.: (39) 02399341
Office Equipment Whslr
N.A.I.C.S.: 424120

STAEDTLER Marketing Sdn Bhd (1)
Lot 8 Jalan P10/10 Kawasan Perusahaan Bangi, Bandar Baru Bangi, 43650, Bangi, Selangor, Malaysia
Tel.: (60) 389268057
Office Equipment Whslr
N.A.I.C.S.: 424120
Christopher Huehn *(CEO)*

STAEDTLER Nippon K.K. (1)
6-3 Iwamoto-cho 1-chome, Chiyoda-ku, Tokyo, 101-0032, Japan
Tel.: (81) 358352811
Office Equipment Whslr
N.A.I.C.S.: 424120

STAEDTLER Nordic A/S (1)
Hoffdingsvej 22, 2500, Valby, Denmark
Tel.: (45) 36174344
Web Site: http://www.staedtler.dk
Office Equipment Whslr
N.A.I.C.S.: 424120
Gitte Kjaer Nielsen *(Acct Mgr)*

STAEDTLER de Mexico, S.A. de C.V. (1)
Avenida Las Partidas Kilometro 3 Lote 6 Manzana 2, Colonia Cerrillo II, Lerma, 52004, Mexico
Tel.: (52) 7222625200
Web Site: http://www.staedtler.com.mx
Office Equipment Whslr
N.A.I.C.S.: 424120

Staedtler, Inc. (1)
2160 Meadow Brook Ct, Thousand Oaks, CA 91362-5311
Tel.: (818) 882-6000
Sales Range: $10-24.9 Million
Emp.: 45
Pens, Pencils & Other Stationery Products Mfr & Distr
N.A.I.C.S.: 424120

STAFFLINE GROUP PLC

19-20 The Triangle NG2 Business Park, Nottingham, NG2 1AE, United Kingdom
Tel.: (44) 1159500885
Web Site: https://www.staffline.co.uk
STAF—(AIM)
Rev.: $1,194,394,274
Assets: $270,145,454
Liabilities: $200,253,911
Net Worth: $69,891,543
Earnings: ($14,003,770)
Fiscal Year-end: 12/31/23
Human Resouce Services
N.A.I.C.S.: 541612
Albert Ellis *(CEO)*

Subsidiaries:

A4e Ltd. (1)
19-20 The Triangle Ng2 Business Park, Nottingham, NG2 1AE, United Kingdom
Tel.: (44) 0800345666
Web Site: http://www.peopleplus.co.uk
Human Resource Consulting Services
N.A.I.C.S.: 541612

Driving Plus Limited (1)
Blenwood Court Suite 3001 Backstone Business Centre 451 Cleckheaton Rd, Bradford, BD12 0NY, United Kingdom
Tel.: (44) 1274952133
Web Site: https://www.driversplus.co.uk
Employment Placement Agency Services
N.A.I.C.S.: 561311

PeoplePlus Group Limited (1)
PO Box 509, Saint Helens, WA10 9JT, United Kingdom
Tel.: (44) 800345666
Web Site: https://www.peopleplus.co.uk
Staffing Recruitment Services
N.A.I.C.S.: 561311

STAFFORD PRIVATE EQUITY PTY. LIMITED

Terrace 1 66 Gloucester Street, The Rocks, Sydney, 2000, NSW, Australia
Tel.: (61) 2 9252 9788 AU
Web Site: http://www.staffordcp.com
Privater Equity Firm
N.A.I.C.S.: 523999
Geoff Norman *(Co-Founder)*

Subsidiaries:

Stafford Private Equity Inc. (1)
700 Larkspur Landing Cir Ste 267, Larkspur, CA 94939
Tel.: (415) 793-9275
Web Site: http://www.staffordcp.com
Privater Equity Firm
N.A.I.C.S.: 523999
Ian Deas *(Partner)*

Stafford Private Equity Limited (1)
24 Old Bond Street 4th Floor, London, W1S 4AW, United Kingdom
Tel.: (44) 20 7535 4916
Web Site: http://www.staffordcp.com
Emp.: 3
Privater Equity Firm
N.A.I.C.S.: 523999
Lucy Nicholls *(Partner)*

Stafford Timberland Limited (1)
24 Old Bond Street 4th Floor, London, W1S 4AW, United Kingdom
Tel.: (44) 20 7535 4915
Web Site: http://www.staffordcp.com
Emp.: 35
Fund Management & Investment Advisory Services
N.A.I.C.S.: 523940
Richard Bowley *(Co-Founder)*

STAFFORD RAILWAY BUILDING SOCIETY

4 Market Square, Stafford, ST16 2JH, United Kingdom
Tel.: (44) 1785 223212
Web Site: http://www.srbs.co.uk
Rev.: $8,664,430
Assets: $340,509,722
Liabilities: $311,790,929
Net Worth: $28,718,794
Earnings: $1,129,288
Emp.: 37
Fiscal Year-end: 10/31/19
Mortgage Lending & Other Financial Services
N.A.I.C.S.: 522310
Michael Richard Smith *(CEO)*

STAFFORD TEXTILES LIMITED

1 Eva Road Suite 101, Toronto, M9C 4Z5, ON, Canada
Tel.: (416) 252-3133
Web Site: http://www.staftex.com
Year Founded: 1945
Rev.: $13,563,412
Emp.: 65
Carbon Footprint & Apparels Whslr
N.A.I.C.S.: 424310
David Schwartz *(Pres)*

STAGE CAPITAL LLP
8-10 Hill Street, London, W1J 5NQ, United Kingdom
Tel.: (44) 207661 5656   UK
Web Site: http://www.stagecap.com
Year Founded: 2000
Privater Equity Firm
N.A.I.C.S.: 523999
Graham Thomas *(Mng Partner)*

Subsidiaries:

Bright Blue Foods Limited   (1)
Sett End Road, Blackburn, BB1 2PT, Lancs, United Kingdom
Tel.: (44) 1254 277700
Web Site: http://www.brightbluefoods.com
Emp.: 1,000
Bakery Products Mfr
N.A.I.C.S.: 311812

STAGE ELECTRICS PARTNERSHIP LTD.
Third Way, Avonmouth, BS11 9YL, Bristol, United Kingdom
Tel.: (44) 117 938 4000
Web Site: http://www.stage-electrics.co.uk
Year Founded: 1979
Sales Range: $25-49.9 Million
Emp.: 239
Electrical Equipment Distr
N.A.I.C.S.: 423610
Dan Aldridge *(Dir-Comml)*

STAGE TECHNOLOGIES LIMITED
9 Falcon Park, 9 Neasden Lane, London, NW10 1RZ, United Kingdom
Tel.: (44) 2082086000
Web Site: http://www.stagetech.com
Year Founded: 1995
Sales Range: $25-49.9 Million
Emp.: 104
Stage Equipment Design & Engineering Svcs
N.A.I.C.S.: 541330
Nikki Scott *(Mng Dir)*

STAGECOACH GROUP PLC
10 Dunkeld Road, Perth, PH1 5TW, United Kingdom
Tel.: (44) 1738442111   UK
Web Site: http://www.stagecoachgroup.com
Year Founded: 1980
SGC—(LSE)
Rev.: $1,260,235,704
Assets: $2,275,402,948
Liabilities: $2,192,582,028
Net Worth: $82,820,920
Earnings: $45,483,620
Emp.: 23,762
Fiscal Year-end: 05/01/21
Buses, Railways, Ferries & Airport Services Operator
N.A.I.C.S.: 485510
Brian Souter *(Co-Founder)*

Subsidiaries:

Busways Travel Services Ltd.   (1)
North Bridge St, The Wheatsheaf, Sunderland, SR51AQ, United Kingdom   (100%)
Tel.: (44) 1915675251
Web Site: http://www.stagecoach.com
Sales Range: $50-74.9 Million
Emp.: 200
Bus & Motor Vehicle Transit Systems
N.A.I.C.S.: 485113

Cambus Limited   (1)
100 Cowley Road, Cambridge, CB4 0DL, United Kingdom
Tel.: (44) 1223 423578
Web Site: http://www.stagecoachbus.com
Sales Range: $125-149.9 Million
Emp.: 400
Bus & Coach Operating Services
N.A.I.C.S.: 485210
Andy Campbell *(Mng Dir)*

Cleveland Transit Ltd.   (1)
Church Rd, Stockton-on-Tees, TS182HW, United Kingdom
Tel.: (44) 1642602112
Web Site: http://www.stagecoachbus.com
Sales Range: $50-74.9 Million
Emp.: 200
Bus & Motor Vehicle Transit Systems
N.A.I.C.S.: 485113
John Conroy *(Mng Dir)*

East Kent Road Car Company Ltd.   (1)
Ticket Office St Georges La, Canterbury, United Kingdom
Tel.: (44) 2084777204
Transit & Ground Passenger Transportation
N.A.I.C.S.: 485999

East Midlands Trains Limited   (1)
1 Prospect Place Millennium Way, Pride Park, Derby, DE24 8HG, United Kingdom
Tel.: (44) 8457 125 678
Web Site: http://www.eastmidlandstrains.co.uk
Rail Transportation Services
N.A.I.C.S.: 488210

Gray Line New York Tours Inc.   (1)
1430 Broadway Ste 507, New York, NY 10018
Tel.: (212) 397-2600
Web Site: http://www.newyorksiteseeing.com
Charter Bus Industry
N.A.I.C.S.: 485510
Thomas Louis *(Mng Dir)*

Greater Manchester Buses South Ltd.   (1)
Dawbank, Stockport, SK3 0DU, United Kingdom
Tel.: (44) 1612733377
Web Site: http://www.stagecoachbus.com
Sales Range: $25-49.9 Million
Emp.: 30
Charter Bus Industry
N.A.I.C.S.: 485510

Lakefront Lines, Inc.   (1)
13315 Brookpark Rd, Cleveland, OH 44142
Tel.: (216) 267-8810
Web Site: http://www.lakefrontlines.com
Chartered Bus Transportation Services
N.A.I.C.S.: 485510

Orkney Coaches Limited   (1)
Scotts Road Hatson Industrial Estate, Kirkwall, KW15 1GR, United Kingdom
Tel.: (44) 18 5687 8014
Web Site: http://www.stagecoaches.com
Sales Range: $25-49.9 Million
Emp.: 50
Rural Bus Transportation Services
N.A.I.C.S.: 485210
Steven Reid *(Gen Mgr)*

PSV Claims Bureau Ltd.   (1)
10 Dunkeld Rd, Perth, PH15TX, United Kingdom   (100%)
Tel.: (44) 17384417
Sales Range: $50-74.9 Million
Emp.: 100
Claim Adjusting Services
N.A.I.C.S.: 524291

South East London & Kent Bus Company Limited   (1)
Plumstead Bus Garage Pettman Crescent, London, SE28 0BJ, United Kingdom
Tel.: (44) 2088559022
Web Site: http://www.southeasternrailway.co.uk
Rural Bus Transportation Services
N.A.I.C.S.: 485210

South West Trains Ltd.   (1)
Blackfriars Road, Friars Bridge Ct 41-45, London, SE1 8NZ, United Kingdom
Tel.: (44) 8456000650
Web Site: http://www.southwesttrains.co.uk
Line-Haul Railroads
N.A.I.C.S.: 482111
Stewart Palmer *(Mng Dir)*

Stagecoach (South) Ltd.   (1)
The Bus Station, Southgate, Chichester, PO19 8DG, United Kingdom   (100%)
Tel.: (44) 1243755850
Web Site: http://www.stagecoachbus.com
Sales Range: $50-74.9 Million
Emp.: 150
Bus Transportation Services
N.A.I.C.S.: 485113

Stagecoach Bus Holdings Limited   (1)
10 Dunkeld Rd, Perth, PH1 5TW, United Kingdom   (100%)
Tel.: (44) 1738442111
Web Site: http://www.stagecoachbus.com
Sales Range: $50-74.9 Million
Emp.: 120
Transit & Ground Passenger Transportation
N.A.I.C.S.: 485999
Robert Speirs *(Chm)*

Stagecoach Cambridgeshire   (1)
100 Cowley Road, Cambridge, CB4 0DN, United Kingdom   (100%)
Tel.: (44) 1223433250
Web Site: http://www.stagecoachbus.com
Sales Range: $125-149.9 Million
Emp.: 450
Charter Bus Industry
N.A.I.C.S.: 485510
Andrew Campbell *(Mng Dir)*

Stagecoach Scotland Ltd.   (1)
10 Dunkeld Rd, Perth, PH15TW, United Kingdom   (100%)
Tel.: (44) 1738442111
Web Site: http://www.stagecoachbus.com
Sales Range: $25-49.9 Million
Emp.: 100
Transit & Ground Passenger Transportation
N.A.I.C.S.: 485999

Stagecoach Services Limited   (1)
Dawbank, Stockport, SK3 0DU, Cheshire, United Kingdom
Tel.: (44) 1612762577
Charter Bus Industry
N.A.I.C.S.: 485510

Stagecoach South Western Trains Ltd.   (1)
41-45 Blackfriars Road, Friars Bridge Ct 41-45, London, SE1 8NZ, United Kingdom
Tel.: (44) 8700005151
Web Site: http://www.southwesttrains.co.uk
Line-Haul Railroads
N.A.I.C.S.: 482111
Tim Shoveller *(Mng Dir)*

Stagecoach Transport Holdings PLC   (1)
10 Dunkeld Rd, Perth, PH1 5TW, Scotland, United Kingdom   (100%)
Tel.: (44) 1738442111
Web Site: http://www.stagecoachgroup.com
Sales Range: $25-49.9 Million
Emp.: 120
Transportation Services
N.A.I.C.S.: 561599

Stagecoach West Limited   (1)
3rd Floor 65 London Road, Gloucester, GL1 3HF, United Kingdom
Tel.: (44) 1452418630
Web Site: http://www.stagecoach.com
Sales Range: $50-74.9 Million
Emp.: 168
Bus & Coach Operating Services
N.A.I.C.S.: 485510
Rupert Cox *(Mng Dir-Bus Ops-England)*

STAGECOACH THEATRE ARTS PLC
The Courthouse Elm Grove, Walton-on-Thames, KT12 1LZ, Surrey, United Kingdom
Tel.: (44) 8009150199
Web Site: http://www.stagecoach.co.uk
Sales Range: $1-9.9 Million
Emp.: 55
Artistic Performance Education Services
N.A.I.C.S.: 711310
Nicola Cutcliffe *(Partner-Northampton)*

Subsidiaries:

Stagecoach Agency (UK) Limited   (1)
1 St Flr Offices Ste Cantilute Chambers Cantilute Rd, Ross-on-Wye, HR9 7AN, Herefordshire, United Kingdom
Tel.: (44) 8454082468
Web Site: http://www.stagecoachagency.co.uk
Theater Arts Schools
N.A.I.C.S.: 611610
Tarquin Shaw-Young *(Mng Dir)*

Stagecoach Theatre Arts Schools GmbH   (1)
Emilienstrasse 8, 90411, Nuremberg, Germany
Tel.: (49) 9115677580
Web Site: http://www.stagecoach.de
Theater Arts Schools
N.A.I.C.S.: 611610

STAGEZERO LIFE SCIENCES, LTD.
30-70 East Beaver Creek Road, Richmond Hill, L4B 3B2, ON, Canada
Tel.: (905) 209-2030   ON
Web Site: https://www.stagezerosciences.com
Year Founded: 1998
SZLS—(OTCIQ)
Rev.: $138,704
Assets: $1,964,760
Liabilities: $6,456,047
Net Worth: ($4,491,287)
Earnings: ($3,481,802)
Emp.: 22
Fiscal Year-end: 12/31/19
Bio Technology Services
N.A.I.C.S.: 541714
James R. Howard-Tripp *(Chm & CEO)*

Subsidiaries:

GeneNews Corporation   (1)
2 E Beaver Creek Rd Bldg 2, L4B 2N3, Richmond Hill, ON, Canada
Tel.: (905) 739-2035
Sales Range: $10-24.9 Million
Molecular Diagnostics Services
N.A.I.C.S.: 621512

StageZero Life Sciences, Inc.   (1)
3705 Saunders Ave, Richmond, VA 23227
Tel.: (804) 261-3340
Cancer Treatment Center Services
N.A.I.C.S.: 622310

STAHLER SUISSE SA
Henzmannstrasse 17A, Zofingen, 4800, Switzerland
Tel.: (41) 62 746 8000
Web Site: http://www.staehler.ch
Sales Range: $25-49.9 Million
Emp.: 35
Plant Protection Chemicals Mfr
N.A.I.C.S.: 325320
Stephan Lack *(Mng Dir)*

STAHLGRUBER OTTO GRUBER GMBH & CO. KG
Gruber Strasse 65, 85586, Poing, Germany
Tel.: (49) 81217070
Web Site: http://www.stahlgruber.de
Year Founded: 1923
Sales Range: $1-4.9 Billion
Emp.: 4,400
Tire Repair Product Mfr & Distr
N.A.I.C.S.: 441340
Bernhard Strauch *(CEO & Mng Dir)*

STAHLGRUBER OTTO GRUBER GMBH & CO. KG

Stahlgruber Otto Gruber GmbH & Co. KG—(Continued)

Subsidiaries:

ATR International AG (1)
Otto-Hirsch-Brucken 17, 70329, Stuttgart, Germany
Tel.: (49) 711 91 89 79 0
Web Site: http://www.atr.de
Emp.: 26
Automotive Part Whslr
N.A.I.C.S.: 423120
Roland Dilmertz *(Mng Dir)*

Autobenex, spol. s.r.o. (1)
Prumyslova 1385 areal Tulipan park, 253 01, Hostivice, Czech Republic
Tel.: (420) 225 983 225
Web Site: http://www.autobenex.cz
Automotive Part Whslr
N.A.I.C.S.: 423120

Autocora Obchodni Spol s.r.o (1)
Vsechromy 65, Strancice, Prague, 251 63, Czech Republic
Tel.: (420) 322 310 103
Web Site: http://www.autocora.cz
Automotive Part Whslr
N.A.I.C.S.: 423120
Jan Chaloupka *(CIO)*

ISST Handels GmbH (1)
Furt 43, 4754, Andrichsfurt, Austria
Tel.: (43) 775221270
Web Site: http://www.issc.at
Firearms Mfr & Distr
N.A.I.C.S.: 332994

Klaus Berger Autozubehor Grosshandel GmbH (1)
Hilgardring 12, 67657, Kaiserslautern, Germany
Tel.: (49) 631 341500
Web Site: http://www.autoteile-berger.de
Automotive Part Whslr
N.A.I.C.S.: 423120

NEIMCKE GmbH & Co. KG (1)
Am Industriepark 21, 84453, Muhldorf, Germany
Tel.: (49) 8631 618 0
Web Site: http://www.neimcke.de
Automotive Part Whslr
N.A.I.C.S.: 423120

PV Automotive GmbH (1)
Langemarckstrasse 34, 45141, Essen, Germany
Tel.: (49) 2 01 84 85 50
Web Site: http://www.pvautomotive.de
Sales Range: $450-499.9 Million
Emp.: 1,600
Automotive Part Whslr
N.A.I.C.S.: 423120
Martin Conrad *(Mng Dir)*

Rema Tip Top/North America, Inc. (1)
119 Rockland Ave, Northvale, NJ 07647
Tel.: (201) 768-8100
Web Site: http://www.rema.com
Tire Repair Product Distr
N.A.I.C.S.: 423130

STAHLGRUBER S.r.l (1)
Via T Signorini 2/4, 20092, Cinisello Balsamo, Italy
Tel.: (39) 026185488
Web Site: http://www.stahlgruber.it
Automotive Part Whslr
N.A.I.C.S.: 423120
Marco Porcinai *(CEO)*

STAIDSON (BEIJING) BIO-PHARMACEUTICALS CO., LTD.

No 36 Jinghai 2nd Road Economic and Technological Development Zone, Beijing, 100176, China
Tel.: (86) 1067875255
Web Site: https://www.staidson.com
Year Founded: 2002
300204—(CHIN)
Rev.: $51,294,105
Assets: $187,643,229
Liabilities: $43,882,156
Net Worth: $143,761,074
Earnings: ($56,184,051)
Fiscal Year-end: 12/31/23
Pharmaceutical Product Mfr & Distr
N.A.I.C.S.: 325412
Zhiwen Zhou *(Chm)*

STAKEHOLDER GOLD CORP.

130 Queens Quay E Suite 607, Toronto, M5A 3Y5, ON, Canada
Tel.: (416) 525-6869 YT
Web Site: https://www.stakeholdergold.com
Year Founded: 2011
SRC—(OTCIQ)
Assets: $205,603
Liabilities: $110,176
Net Worth: $95,426
Earnings: ($900,123)
Fiscal Year-end: 12/31/20
Gold Mining Services
N.A.I.C.S.: 212220
Artie Hao Li *(CFO)*

Subsidiaries:

Victoria Mining Corporation (1)
Carlos Gomes N 207 Apt 101 Centro, Capivari de Baixo, 29730-000, Espirito Santo, Brazil
Tel.: (55) 27998584972
Web Site: https://victoriaminingcorp.ca
Quarry Product Mfr & Distr
N.A.I.C.S.: 327120

STAKHANOV RAILWAY CAR BUILDING WORKS, PJSC

67 Lenina ave c, Stakhanov, 94013, Ukraine
Tel.: (380) 6444 9 70 01
Web Site: http://www.stakhanovvz.com
Rail Wagon Building & Stock Mfr
N.A.I.C.S.: 336510

STAKLOREKLAM A.D.

Dragise Misovica 14, Lucani, Serbia
Tel.: (381) 32 817 138
Web Site: http://www.stakloreklam.com
Year Founded: 2001
Sales Range: Less than $1 Million
Emp.: 13
Painting & Glazing Contracting Services
N.A.I.C.S.: 238320

STALEXPORT AUTOSTRADY S.A.

ul Piaskowa 20, 41-404, Myslowice, Poland
Tel.: (48) 327627545 PL
Web Site: https://www.stalexport-autostrady.pl
Year Founded: 1963
STX—(WAR)
Rev.: $103,976,787
Assets: $359,462,644
Liabilities: $153,316,837
Net Worth: $206,145,807
Earnings: $21,521,630
Fiscal Year-end: 12/31/22
Motorways Construction Services
N.A.I.C.S.: 237310
Emil Wasacz *(Chm-Mgmt Bd & Gen Dir)*

Subsidiaries:

Biuro Centrum Sp. z o.o. (1)
ul Mickiewicza 29, 40-085, Katowice, Poland (40.63%)
Tel.: (48) 32 207 21 82
Web Site: http://www.biurocentrum.pl
Real Estate Administration & Management Services
N.A.I.C.S.: 531390

Stalexport Autostrada Malopolska S.A. (1)
ul Piaskowa 20, 41-404, Myslowice, Poland (100%)
Tel.: (48) 32 76 27 555
Web Site: http://www.autostrada-a4.com.pl
Highway & Street Construction Services
N.A.I.C.S.: 237310

VIA4 S.A. (1)
ul Piaskowa, 41-404, Myslowice, Poland (55%)
Tel.: (48) 327627333
Web Site: https://www.via4.pl
Highway Maintenance & Safety Services
N.A.I.C.S.: 488490
Henri Skiba *(Chm-Mgmt Bd & Gen Dir)*

STALLION GOLD CORP.

700-838 West Hastings St, Vancouver, V6C 0A6, BC, Canada
Tel.: (778) 686-0973 BC
Web Site: https://stallionuranium.com
Year Founded: 2011
FE0—(DEU)
Rev.: $58,581
Assets: $19,362,102
Liabilities: $898,876
Net Worth: $18,463,226
Earnings: ($1,679,930)
Emp.: 1
Fiscal Year-end: 12/31/23
Metal Mining
N.A.I.C.S.: 212290

STALPRODUKT S.A.

Tel.: (48) 146151000
Web Site: https://www.stalprodukt.com.pl
Year Founded: 1992
STP—(WAR)
Rev.: $1,483,286,942
Assets: $1,301,651,761
Liabilities: $337,904,587
Net Worth: $963,747,174
Earnings: $119,137,567
Fiscal Year-end: 12/31/22
Steel Products Mfr
N.A.I.C.S.: 331110
Piotr Janeczek *(Chm-Mgmt Bd & CEO)*

Subsidiaries:

Cynk-Mal S.A. (1)
Ul Patnowska 48, 59-220, Legnica, Poland
Tel.: (48) 768551500
Web Site: https://www.cynkmal.pl
Steel Products Mfr
N.A.I.C.S.: 331110
Lidia Alina Klarkowska *(Co-Chm)*

Go Steel Frydek Mistek a.s. (1)
Miru 3777, 738 01, Frydek-Mistek, Czech Republic
Tel.: (420) 558482445
Web Site: http://www.gosteel.cz
Rolled Steel Strip Mfr
N.A.I.C.S.: 331221
Ivo Chmelik *(CEO)*

STP Elbud Sp. z o.o. (1)
Pulkownika Stanislawa Dabka 9 Street, 30-732, Krakow, Poland
Tel.: (48) 123702321
Web Site: https://www.stpelbud.com
Steel Products Mfr
N.A.I.C.S.: 331110
Zbigniew Kowal *(Pres & CEO)*

Stalprodukt-Wamech Sp. z o.o. (1)
Ul Wygoda 69, 32-700, Bochnia, Poland
Tel.: (48) 146151691
Web Site: https://www.wamech.stalprodukt.pl
Emp.: 120
Electromagnetic Steel Mfr
N.A.I.C.S.: 332312

Stalprodukt-Zamosc Sp. z o.o. (1)
Ul Kilinskiego 86, 22-400, Zamosc, Poland
Tel.: (48) 846393441
Web Site: https://www.futryna.com.pl
Steel Door Mfr
N.A.I.C.S.: 332321

ZGH Boleslaw S.A. (1)
Ul Kolejowa 37, 32-332, Bukowno, Poland

INTERNATIONAL PUBLIC

Tel.: (48) 322955100
Web Site: https://www.zghboleslaw.pl
Zinc Alloy Mfr
N.A.I.C.S.: 331529

Subsidiary (Domestic):

Boltech Sp. z o.o (2)
Ul Kolejowa 37, 32-332, Bukowno, Poland
Tel.: (48) 326421717
Web Site: https://www.boltech.com.pl
Metal Products Mfr
N.A.I.C.S.: 332999
Jozef Sarecki *(Chm)*

Subsidiary (Non-US):

Gradir Montenegro d.o.o. Niksic (2)
Ratnih Vojnih Invalida bb, Pljevlja, 84210, Podgorica, Montenegro
Tel.: (382) 52324111
Web Site: http://www.gradirmontenegro.com
Steel Product Distr
N.A.I.C.S.: 423510

Subsidiary (Domestic):

Huta Cynku Miasteczko Slaskie S.A (2)
Ul Hutnicza 17, Miasteczko slaskie, 42-610, Katowice, Poland
Tel.: (48) 322888444
Web Site: http://www.hcm.com.pl
Steel Products Mfr
N.A.I.C.S.: 331110

Karo Sp. z o.o. (2)
Zielona Wies 14 b, Nowa Karczma, 83-404, Nowa Sarzyna, Poland
Tel.: (48) 797558764
Web Site: https://www.karo-poland.eu
Saddle Pad Mfr
N.A.I.C.S.: 316990

Polska Technika Zabezpieczen Sp. z o.o. (2)
Ul Sasankowa 8, Sulejowek, 05-070, Warsaw, Poland
Tel.: (48) 228130303
Web Site: https://www.ptz.pl
Steel Door Mfr
N.A.I.C.S.: 332321

STALPROFIL S.A.

Ul Rozdzienskiego 11a, 41 308, Dabrowa Gornicza, Poland
Tel.: (48) 322616034
Web Site: https://www.stalprofil.com.pl
Year Founded: 1988
STF—(WAR)
Rev.: $389,682,926
Assets: $258,580,538
Liabilities: $133,057,418
Net Worth: $125,523,120
Earnings: $3,965,701
Fiscal Year-end: 12/31/23
Steel Mfrs
N.A.I.C.S.: 331110
Henryk Orczykowski *(Chm-Mgmt Bd, Pres & CEO)*

Subsidiaries:

Izostal S.A. (1)
ul Opolska 29, 47-113, Kolonowskie, Poland (60.28%)
Tel.: (48) 774056500
Web Site: https://www.izostal.com.pl
Rev.: $190,812,245
Assets: $129,864,837
Liabilities: $65,906,250
Net Worth: $63,958,587
Earnings: $3,032,266
Fiscal Year-end: 12/31/2023
Steel Pole Mfr
N.A.I.C.S.: 331210
Jerzy Bernhard *(Chm-Supervisory Bd)*

KOLB Sp. z o.o. (1)
ul Kosciuszki 3 A, 47-110, Kolonowskie, Poland
Tel.: (48) 774611703
Web Site: http://www.kolb.pl
Stainless Steel Mfr
N.A.I.C.S.: 331110

AND PRIVATE COMPANIES

STALWART TANKERS INC.
St Ave 184A chalandiri, Maroussi,
15125, Athens, Greece
Tel.: (30) 2106801136   MH
Year Founded: 2013
Deep Sea Freight Transportation
N.A.I.C.S.: 483111

STAMEN CO., LTD.
1-1 Ibukacho, Nakamura-Ku, Nagoya,
453-0012, Japan
Tel.: (81) 524621428
Web Site: http://www.stmn.co.jp
Year Founded: 2016
4019—(TKS)
Rev.: $13,322,110
Assets: $13,031,420
Liabilities: $4,417,070
Net Worth: $8,614,350
Earnings: $886,250
Fiscal Year-end: 12/31/23
Software Development Services
N.A.I.C.S.: 541511
Atsushi Kato (Chm & Pres)

STAMFORD LAND CORPORATION LTD.
200 Cantonment Road 09-01 Southpoint, Singapore, 089763, Singapore
Tel.: (65) 62366888
Web Site: https://www.stamfordland.com
Year Founded: 1935
H07—(SES)
Rev.: $112,472,768
Assets: $846,432,753
Liabilities: $201,746,573
Net Worth: $644,686,180
Earnings: $91,459,800
Emp.: 709
Fiscal Year-end: 03/31/23
Hotel Management Services; Travel Agency & Trading Services; Property Investment & Development
N.A.I.C.S.: 721110
Thomas Ong (COO-Hotel Div)

Subsidiaries:

Fabric House Pte. Ltd.   (1)
5 Little Rd Level 6-01 Cemtex Industrial Building, Singapore, 536983, Singapore   (100%)
Tel.: (65) 64792822
Web Site: http://www.singwall.com.sg
Sales Range: $25-49.9 Million
Emp.: 15
Fur & Leather Apparel Mfr
N.A.I.C.S.: 315250
Patrene Yap (Gen Mgr)

Singapore Wallcoverings Centre (Private) Limited   (1)
5 Little Rd 06-01 Cemtex Industrial Building, 536983, Singapore, Singapore   (100%)
Tel.: (65) 64792822
Web Site: http://www.singwall.com.sg
Sales Range: $25-49.9 Million
Emp.: 15
Paint Varnish & Supplies Whslr
N.A.I.C.S.: 424950
Patrene Yap (CEO)

Sir Stamford at Circular Quay Pty. Ltd.   (1)
93 Macquarie Street, Sydney, 2000, NSW, Australia   (100%)
Tel.: (61) 292524600
Web Site: http://www.stamford.com.au
Sales Range: $10-24.9 Million
Emp.: 100
Hotels & Motels
N.A.I.C.S.: 721110

Stamford Heritage Pty Ltd   (1)
Cnr Edward and Margaret Sts, Brisbane, 4000, QLD, Australia
Tel.: (61) 732211999
Web Site: http://www.stamford.com.au
Sales Range: $25-49.9 Million
Emp.: 200
Home Management Services
N.A.I.C.S.: 721110

Stamford Hotels & Resorts Pte. Ltd.   (1)
200 Cantonment Road, Singapore, Singapore   (100%)
Tel.: (65) 62366888
Web Site: http://www.stamford.com
Sales Range: $25-49.9 Million
Emp.: 200
Hotels & Motels
N.A.I.C.S.: 721110

Stamford Hotels & Resorts Pty Limited   (1)
Suite 222 Level 2 Stamford Plaza Sydney Airport Corner, Robey and O'Riordan Streets, Mascot, 2020, NSW, Australia   (100%)
Tel.: (61) 297707707
Web Site: http://www.stamford.com.au
Sales Range: $10-24.9 Million
Emp.: 40
Hotel & Property Management
N.A.I.C.S.: 721110

Subsidiary (Domestic):

Stamford Heritage Plaza Hotel Pty. Ltd.   (2)
Edward Street Corner Margaret Street, Brisbane, 4000, QLD, Australia   (100%)
Tel.: (61) 732211999
Web Site: http://www.stamford.com.au
Hotels & Motels
N.A.I.C.S.: 721110
Luke Pearl (Gen Mgr)

Stamford Hotels Pty. Limited   (2)
Corner Epping & Herring Rd, North Ryde, 2113, NSW, Australia   (100%)
Tel.: (61) 298881077
Web Site: http://www.stamford.com.au
Hotels & Motels
N.A.I.C.S.: 721110
C. K. Ow (CEO)

Stamford Plaza Hotels Pty. Limited   (2)
150 North Terrace, Adelaide, 5000, SA, Australia   (100%)
Tel.: (61) 884611111
Web Site: http://www.stamford.com.au
Hotels & Motels
N.A.I.C.S.: 721110
Russell Cool (Gen Mgr)

Stamford Plaza Sydney Airport Pty. Ltd.   (2)
241 O Riordan Street, Mascot, 2020, NSW, Australia   (100%)
Tel.: (61) 293172200
Web Site: http://www.stamford.com.au
Hotels & Motels
N.A.I.C.S.: 721110

Stamford Land Management Pte. Ltd.   (1)
200 Cantonment Road 09-01 South Point, Singapore, 089763, Singapore   (100%)
Tel.: (65) 62366888
Web Site: http://www.stamfordland.com
Emp.: 100
Freight Transportation Arrangement
N.A.I.C.S.: 488510

Stamford Plaza Auckland Hotel   (1)
22-26 Albert Street, Auckland, 1010, New Zealand   (100%)
Tel.: (64) 93098888
Web Site: http://www.stamford.com.au
Sales Range: $25-49.9 Million
Emp.: 200
Hotels & Motels
N.A.I.C.S.: 721110

Stamford Sydney Airport Pty Ltd   (1)
CNR O'RIORDAN & ROBEY ST, Mascot, 2020, NSW, Australia
Tel.: (61) 293172200
Web Site: http://www.stamford.com.au
Property Management Services
N.A.I.C.S.: 531312
Lean Wood (Gen Mgr)

Terrace Hotel (Operations) Pty Ltd   (1)
150 North Tce, Adelaide, 5000, SA, Australia
Tel.: (61) 884611111
Home Management Services
N.A.I.C.S.: 721110
Cameron Jeffrey (Gen Mgr)

Varimerx S.E. Asia Pte. Ltd.   (1)
5 Little Rd 06-01, Cemtex Industrial Bldg, Singapore, 536983, Singapore   (100%)
Tel.: (65) 64792822
Web Site: http://www.singwall.com.sg
Sales Range: $25-49.9 Million
Emp.: 15
Furniture Retailer
N.A.I.C.S.: 449110
Patrene Yap (Gen Mgr)

Voyager Travel Pte. Ltd.   (1)
200 Cantonment Road 09-01 Southpoint, Singapore, 089763, Singapore
Tel.: (65) 64767133
Web Site: https://www.voyagertravel.com.sg
Travel Agency Services
N.A.I.C.S.: 561510
Winnie Seet (Sr Mgr-Bus Dev)

STAMFORD TYRES CORPORATION LIMITED
19 Lok Yang Way, Jurong, Singapore, 628635, Singapore
Tel.: (65) 62683111
Web Site: https://www.stamfordtyres.com
S29—(SES)
Rev.: $140,992,219
Assets: $156,083,735
Liabilities: $73,117,451
Net Worth: $82,966,284
Earnings: $4,451,278
Emp.: 300
Fiscal Year-end: 04/30/24
Wheels & Tyres Mfr
N.A.I.C.S.: 336390
Dawn Wai Ying Wee (Exec Dir)

Subsidiaries:

PT Stamford Tyres Distributor Indonesia   (1)
Jl Boulevard Raya PA 19, No 4-5 Kelapa Gading Permai, Jakarta, 14240, Indonesia
Tel.: (62) 214504388
Wheels & Tires Mfr
N.A.I.C.S.: 336390

PT Stamford Tyres Indonesia   (1)
Jl Kuala Kuningan L I P, Timika, Kuala Kencana, 99920, Papua, Indonesia
Tel.: (62) 901301889
Motor Vehicle Tire Mfr
N.A.I.C.S.: 326211

Stamford Sport Wheels Company Limited   (1)
111/2 5 8 9 Moo 2 Highway 340 Suphanburi Road, Tambon Saiyai Amphur Sainoi, Nonthaburi, 11150, Thailand
Tel.: (66) 2 967 7100
Web Site: https://www.stamfordwheels.com
Aluminum Alloy Wheel Tire Mfr & Distr
N.A.I.C.S.: 336390
Kunnatee Kalayanakupt (Sr Mgr-Sls)

Stamford Tires Distributor Co, Ltd   (1)
Tel.: (66) 26782355
Wheels & Tires Mfr
N.A.I.C.S.: 336390

Stamford Tyre Mart Sdn Bhd   (1)
16 Jalan Jurunilai U1/20 Section U1, Hicom Glenmarie Industrial Park, 40150, Shah Alam, Selangor Darul Ehsan, Malaysia
Tel.: (60) 3 5569 3090
Web Site: http://www.stamfordtyres.com.my
Emp.: 100
Tire Mfr & Distr
N.A.I.C.S.: 326211
Cham Soon Kian (CEO & Exec VP)

Stamford Tyres (Africa) (Proprietary) Limited   (1)
10 Ferrule Avenue Montague Gardens, Hout Bay, Cape Town, 7441, South Africa
Tel.: (27) 860522322
Web Site: https://www.stamford.co.za
Tire Distr
N.A.I.C.S.: 423130

Stamford Tyres (Australia) Pty Ltd   (1)
97A Lisbon Street, Fairfield, NSW 2165, Australia
Tel.: (61) 2 9727 2955
Wheels & Tires Mfr
N.A.I.C.S.: 336390

Stamford Tyres (B) Sdn. Bhd.   (1)
Unit 5 and 6 Lot No 47701 EDR No BD40018 Spg 128-11-26 Jalan Tungku, Link kg Pengkalan Gadong, Bandar Seri Begawan, Brunei Darussalam
Tel.: (673) 2428194
Motor Vehicle Tire Mfr
N.A.I.C.S.: 326211

Stamford Tyres (Hong Kong) Limited   (1)
560 Kam Tin Road Shek Kong, Yuen Long, New Territories, China (Hong Kong)
Tel.: (852) 24062381
Tire Whslr
N.A.I.C.S.: 423130

Stamford Tyres (M) Sdn Bhd   (1)
16 Jalan Jurunilai U1 20 Section U1, Hicom Glenmarie Indus Park, 40150, Shah Alam, Malaysia
Sales Range: $25-49.9 Million
Emp.: 100
Wheels & Tires Mfr
N.A.I.C.S.: 336390

Stamford Tyres Distributors India Pvt Ltd   (1)
No 2 3&4 B Tower 9th Floor Aggarwal Trade Center, Sector 11 CBD Belapur, Mumbai, 400614, India
Tel.: (91) 22 41020111
Wheels & Tires Mfr
N.A.I.C.S.: 336390

Stamford Tyres Durban   (1)
No 9 Leeukop Road Mahogany Ridge, Pinetown, 3608, Durban, South Africa
Tel.: (27) 31 700 3092
Web Site: http://www.stamfordtyres.com
Tire Distr
N.A.I.C.S.: 423130

Stamford Tyres Guangzhou Limited   (1)
Room 2703 Jia Ye Building, No 318 Middle Dong Feng Road, Guangzhou, Yue Xiu, China
Tel.: (86) 2033201467
Wheels & Tires Mfr
N.A.I.C.S.: 336390

Stamford Tyres International Pte Ltd   (1)
19 Lok Yang Way Jurong, Singapore, 628635, Singapore
Tel.: (65) 62683111
Tire Mfr & Whslr
N.A.I.C.S.: 326211
Peter Hofmann (Sr VP)

Stamford Tyres Johannesburg   (1)
Horn Street & Brine Rd Chloorkop Extension 1, Johannesburg, 1624, South Africa
Tel.: (27) 11 393 7125
Tire Distr
N.A.I.C.S.: 423130

Stamford Tyres Pty. Ltd.   (1)
Unit 6 36 Victoria Ave, Hout Bay 7806, Cape Town, South Africa
Tel.: (27) 217901302
Wheels & Tires Mfr
N.A.I.C.S.: 336390

Stamford Tyres Vietnam Company Limited   (1)
4th Floor No 20/13 Nguyen Truong To Street, District 4, Ho Chi Minh City, Vietnam
Tel.: (84) 839430558
Motor Vehicle Tire Mfr
N.A.I.C.S.: 326211
Cheng-Kang Chao (Mgr-Fin & Operation)

Tyre Pacific (HK) Ltd   (1)
13th Fl Sandoz Ctr, 178/182 Texaco Rd, Hong Kong, China (Hong Kong)
Tel.: (852) 24078268
Web Site: http://tyrepacific.com.hk
Wheels & Tires Mfr
N.A.I.C.S.: 336390

STAMPARIJA BORBA A.D.

STAMPARIJA BORBA A.D.

Stamparija Borba a.d.—(Continued)
Kosovska 26, 11000, Belgrade, Serbia
Tel.: (381) 113398272
Web Site:
 https://www.stamparija.ad.co.rs
Year Founded: 1944
SBRB—(BEL)
Rev.: $2,795,546
Assets: $2,612,455
Liabilities: $858,471
Net Worth: $1,753,983
Earnings: ($664,269)
Fiscal Year-end: 12/31/22
Newspaper Printing Services
N.A.I.C.S.: 323111
Vladimir Guduric *(Exec Dir)*

STAMPARIJA D.D.KLJUC
Branilaca BiH 125, Kljuc, 79280, Sarajevo, Bosnia & Herzegovina
Tel.: (387) 37660039
STMKRK5—(SARE)
Rev.: $11,978
Assets: $206,966
Liabilities: $206,965
Net Worth: $1
Earnings: ($20,256)
Fiscal Year-end: 12/31/19
Commercial Printing Services
N.A.I.C.S.: 323113

STAMPEDE CAPITAL LIMITED
A Z Elite 1st Floor Plot No 197 Guttala Begumpet Village Madhapur, Hyderabad, 500081, Telangana, India
Tel.: (91) 40 2354 0763
Web Site:
 http://www.stampedecap.com
Rev.: $23,287,704
Assets: $5,119,870
Liabilities: $3,620,771
Net Worth: $1,499,099
Earnings: ($8,808,021)
Fiscal Year-end: 03/31/19
Securities Brokerage Services
N.A.I.C.S.: 523150
J. V. Tirupati Rao *(Mng Dir)*

STAMPEDE DRILLING INC.
2600 700 - 9 Avenue SW South Tower, Calgary, T2P 3V7, AB, Canada
Tel.: (403) 984-5042 AB
Web Site:
 https://stampededrilling.com
Year Founded: 2009
STPDF—(OTCIQ)
Rev.: $64,907,095
Assets: $89,533,068
Liabilities: $22,836,339
Net Worth: $66,696,729
Earnings: $7,931,780
Emp.: 25
Fiscal Year-end: 12/31/23
Oil & Gas Well Drilling Services
N.A.I.C.S.: 213111
Thane Russell *(Chm)*

STAMPEN AB
Polhemsplatsen 5, 405 02, Gothenburg, Sweden
Tel.: (46) 31624300
Web Site:
 http://www.stampenmedia.se
Sales Range: $800-899.9 Million
Emp.: 1,500
Newspaper Publishing; Radio Station Operator
N.A.I.C.S.: 513110
Peter Hjorne *(Chm)*

Subsidiaries:

Stampen Media Partner AB (1)
St Clemens Gata 32, Gothenburg, 405 02, Sweden

Tel.: (46) 850556200
Printing Services
N.A.I.C.S.: 323111
Pelle Mattisson *(Pres)*

Subsidiary (Domestic):

Hello There Holding AB (2)
Vallgatan 36, 411 16, Gothenburg, Sweden
Tel.: (46) 313 331 600
Web Site: http://www.hellothere.se
Sales Range: $1-9.9 Million
Emp.: 17
Game & Application Developer
N.A.I.C.S.: 513210
Oskar Eklund *(CEO)*

STAMPER OIL & GAS CORP.
Suite 401 - 750 West Pender Street, North Vancouver, Vancouver, V6C 2T7, BC, Canada
Tel.: (604) 341-1531 BC
Web Site:
 https://www.stamperoilandgas.com
Year Founded: 1984
STMGF—(OTCIQ)
Assets: $642,200
Liabilities: $220,431
Net Worth: $421,770
Earnings: ($422,919)
Fiscal Year-end: 06/30/24
Oil & Gas Exploration
N.A.I.C.S.: 211120
Natasha Sever *(CFO)*

STAMPFLI AG
Wolfli strasse 1, PO Box 8326, 3001, Bern, Switzerland
Tel.: (41) 313006666
Web Site: http://www.staempfli.com
Year Founded: 1799
Sales Range: $100-124.9 Million
Emp.: 380
Print & Electronic Publishing Services
N.A.I.C.S.: 513199
Daniel Sinn *(Member-Mgmt Bd & Dir-Sls & Mktg)*

Subsidiaries:

Lokal-Nachrichten Muri-Gumligen AG (1)
Worbstrasse 190, PO Box 157, 3073, Gumligen, Switzerland
Tel.: (41) 31 952 56 60
Web Site: http://www.lokalnachrichten.ch
Magazine Publisher
N.A.I.C.S.: 513120

Stampfli Polska Sp. z o.o. (1)
Aleje Jerozolimskie 99 31, 02 001, Warsaw, Poland
Tel.: (48) 22 664 44 61
Web Site: http://www.staempfli.com.pl
Magazine Publisher
N.A.I.C.S.: 513120
Rafal Cwenk *(Mng Dir)*

Stampfli Verlag AG (1)
Wolflistrasse 1, PO Box 8326, Bern, 3000, Switzerland
Tel.: (41) 313006666
Web Site: http://www.staempfliverlag.com
Sales Range: $25-49.9 Million
Emp.: 50
Legal Publishing Services
N.A.I.C.S.: 513130

STANBIC IBTC HOLDINGS PLC
I B T C Place Walter Carrington Crescent, Victoria Island, Lagos, Nigeria
Tel.: (234) 14222222
Web Site:
 https://www.stanbicibtc.com
STANBIC—(NIGE)
Rev.: $212,834,292
Assets: $2,242,078,772
Liabilities: $1,940,322,282
Net Worth: $301,756,490
Earnings: $59,818,355
Emp.: 3,008

Fiscal Year-end: 12/31/22
Commercial Banking Services
N.A.I.C.S.: 522110
Yinka Sanni *(CEO)*

Subsidiaries:

Stanbic IBTC Asset Management Limited (1)
The Wealth House Plot 1678 Olakunle Bakare Close Off, Sanus Fafunwa Street Victoria Island, Lagos, Nigeria
Tel.: (234) 12805595
Web Site:
 https://www.stanbicibtcmanagement.com
Non Pension Fund Management Services
N.A.I.C.S.: 525110

Stanbic IBTC Capital Limited (1)
IBTC Place Walter Carrington Crescent, Victoria Island, Lagos, Nigeria
Tel.: (234) 14228855
Web Site:
 https://www.stanbicibtccapital.com
Investment Banking & Financial Services
N.A.I.C.S.: 523999

Stanbic IBTC Insurance Brokers Limited (1)
The Wealth House 1678 Olakunle Bakare Close Off Sanusi Fafunwa, Victoria Island, Lagos, Nigeria
Tel.: (234) 1012770394
Web Site:
 https://www.stanbicibtcinsurance.com
Life & General Insurance Broker Services
N.A.I.C.S.: 524210

Stanbic IBTC Insurance Limited (1)
The Wealth House 1678 Olakunle Bakare Close Off Sanusi Fanfunwa Street, Victoria Island, Lagos, Nigeria
Tel.: (234) 12706801
Web Site:
 https://www.stanbicibtcinsurance.com
Life Insurance Agency Services
N.A.I.C.S.: 524210

Stanbic IBTC Nominees Limited (1)
IBTC Place Walter Carrington Crescent, 23401 Victoria Island, Lagos, Nigeria
Tel.: (234) 14227827
Web Site:
 https://www.stanbicibtcnominees.com
Non Pension Fund Management Services
N.A.I.C.S.: 525110

Stanbic IBTC Pension Managers Limited (1)
The Wealth House 1678 Olakunle Bakare Close Off Sanusi Fanfunwa Street, Victoria Island, Lagos, Nigeria
Tel.: (234) 12716000
Web Site:
 https://www.stanbicibtcpension.com
Pension Fund Management Services
N.A.I.C.S.: 525110

Stanbic IBTC Stockbrokers Limited (1)
IBTC Place Walter Carington Crescent, Victoria Island, Lagos, Nigeria
Tel.: (234) 14220004
Web Site:
 https://www.stanbicibtcstockbrokers.com
Stock Broking Services
N.A.I.C.S.: 561730

STANDARD A.D.
Bulevar Oslobodenja 92, 16000, Leskovac, Serbia
Tel.: (381) 16244530
Web Site: https://www.standard-ad.co
Year Founded: 1965
STLE—(BEL)
Sales Range: Less than $1 Million
Emp.: 8
Wall Cladding Services
N.A.I.C.S.: 238390
Miodrag Ilic *(Exec Dir)*

STANDARD A.D.
Serdar Janka 21, 73220, Rogatica, Bosnia & Herzegovina
Tel.: (387) 58 415 260
Year Founded: 2001

Sales Range: Less than $1 Million
Emp.: 2
Building Construction Services
N.A.I.C.S.: 236116
Ivica Bozic *(Chm-Mgmt Bd)*

STANDARD BANK LIMITED
Metropolitan Chamber Building 122-124 Motijheel C/A 3rd Floor, Dhaka, 1000, Bangladesh
Tel.: (880) 29578385
Web Site:
 https://www.standardbankbd.com
Year Founded: 1999
STANDBANKL—(CHT)
Rev.: $61,370,733
Assets: $2,133,770,098
Liabilities: $1,972,295,721
Net Worth: $161,474,376
Earnings: $10,232,632
Emp.: 1,981
Fiscal Year-end: 12/31/22
Banking Services
N.A.I.C.S.: 523150
Muhammed Zahedul Hoque *(Vice Chm)*

Subsidiaries:

SBL Capital Management Limited (1)
2 D I T Avenue Extension 3rd Floor, Motijheel C/A, Dhaka, 1000, Bangladesh
Tel.: (880) 29585984
Portfolio Management Services
N.A.I.C.S.: 523150
Kazi Akram Uddin Ahmed *(Chm)*

Standard Bank Securities Ltd. (1)
2 DIT Avenue Extension 1st Floor, Motijheel C/A, Dhaka, 1000, Bangladesh
Tel.: (880) 29585837
Brokerage Services
N.A.I.C.S.: 523150
Kazi Akram Uddin Ahmed *(Chm)*

STANDARD CAPITAL MARKETS LIMITED
G-17 Krishna Apra Business Square Netaji Subhash Place, Pitampura, Delhi, 110034, India
Tel.: (91) 9871652224
Web Site: https://www.stancap.co.in
Year Founded: 1987
511700—(BOM)
Rev.: $51,052
Assets: $719,227
Liabilities: $153,267
Net Worth: $565,960
Earnings: $3,269
Emp.: 5
Fiscal Year-end: 03/31/20
Investment Management Service
N.A.I.C.S.: 523999

STANDARD CERAMIC INDUSTRIES LTD.
Amin Court 3rd Floor 62-63 Motijheel C/A, Dhaka, 1000, Bangladesh
Tel.: (880) 29561947
Web Site:
 https://www.standardceramic.net
STANCERAM—(CHT)
Rev.: $2,229,958
Assets: $2,960,513
Liabilities: $3,834,073
Net Worth: ($873,559)
Earnings: ($1,121,647)
Emp.: 600
Fiscal Year-end: 06/30/23
Ceramic Products Mfr
N.A.I.C.S.: 335220
Helal Uddin Ahmed *(Mng Dir)*

STANDARD CHARTERED PLC
1 Basinghall Avenue, London, EC2V 5DD, United Kingdom
Tel.: (44) 2078858888 UK
Web Site: https://www.sc.com

STANDARD CHARTERED PLC

AND PRIVATE COMPANIES

Year Founded: 1853
2888—(HKG)
Rev.: $27,227,000,000
Assets: $822,844,000,000
Liabilities: $772,491,000,000
Net Worth: $50,353,000,000
Earnings: $3,462,000,000
Emp.: 85,000
Fiscal Year-end: 12/31/23
Commercial Banking Services
N.A.I.C.S.: 551111
Simon N. Cooper *(CEO-Corp, Comml & Institutional Banking)*

Subsidiaries:

Mox Bank Limited (1)
39/F Oxford House Taikoo Place 979 King's Road, Quarry Bay, China (Hong Kong)
Tel.: (852) 2 888 8228
Web Site: https://mox.com
Banking Services
N.A.I.C.S.: 522110

Standard Chartered Bank (1)
1 Basinghall Avenue, London, EC2V 5DD, United Kingdom **(100%)**
Tel.: (44) 2078858888
Emp.: 1,736
Private & Wholesale Banking
N.A.I.C.S.: 523150
Benjamin Pi Cheng Hung *(CEO-Retail Banking-Global)*

Subsidiary (Non-US):

Banco Standard Totta de Moçambique, SARL (2)
Praca 25 de Junho No 1, Box 2086, Maputo, Mozambique **(100%)**
Tel.: (258) 1301959
Sales Range: $50-74.9 Million
Emp.: 16
International Banking
N.A.I.C.S.: 522299

Affiliate (Non-US):

Seychelles International Mercantile Banking Corporation Limited (2)
Nouvobanq House Francis Rachel Street, PO Box 241, Victoria, Victoria, Seychelles **(22%)**
Tel.: (248) 4293000
Web Site: https://www.nouvobanq.sc
Sales Range: $50-74.9 Million
Emp.: 66
International Banking
N.A.I.C.S.: 522299

Subsidiary (Non-US):

Standard Chartered Bank (China) Limited (2)
18th Floor Standard Chartered Bank Building No 201 Century Avenue, Pudong New District, Shanghai, 200127, China **(100%)**
Tel.: (86) 75533382730
Web Site: https://www.sc.com
International Banking
N.A.I.C.S.: 522299
Benjamin Hung *(CEO-Greater China)*

Standard Chartered Bank (Hong Kong) Limited (2)
32nd Floor 4-4A Des Voeux Road, Central, China (Hong Kong) **(100%)**
Tel.: (852) 28203333
Web Site: http://www.sc.com
Sales Range: $1-4.9 Billion
Merchant Banking
N.A.I.C.S.: 522210

Standard Chartered Bank (Singapore) Pty. Ltd. (2)
6 Battery Road, Singapore, 049909, Singapore **(100%)**
Tel.: (65) 67477000
Sales Range: $75-99.9 Million
Emp.: 125
Commercial Banking Services
N.A.I.C.S.: 522110
Patrick Lee *(CEO)*

Subsidiary (Domestic):

Standard Chartered Equitor Trustee Singapore Limited (3)
6 Battery Road, Singapore, 049909, Singapore **(100%)**
Tel.: (65) 67477000
Web Site: http://www.standardchartered.com.sg
Sales Range: $50-74.9 Million
Emp.: 100
Trust Services
N.A.I.C.S.: 523991

Subsidiary (Non-US):

Standard Chartered Bank (Taiwan) Limited (2)
No 168 Dunhua N Rd, Songshan Dist, Taipei, 105, Taiwan **(100%)**
Tel.: (886) 227166261
Sales Range: $300-349.9 Million
Emp.: 600
Full Banking Services
N.A.I.C.S.: 522320

Standard Chartered Bank (Thai) Public Co. Ltd. (2)
140 Wireless Road Lumpini, Patumwan, Bangkok, 10330, Thailand **(100%)**
Tel.: (66) 21061000
Sales Range: $600-649.9 Million
Emp.: 1,800
Banking
N.A.I.C.S.: 522299

Subsidiary (Domestic):

Standard Chartered Bank Thailand - Global Markets (3)
8th Fl Sathorn Nakorn Twr 100 N Sathorn Rd Bangrak, Bangkok, 10500, Thailand
Tel.: (66) 027248880
Web Site: http://www.standardchartered.co.th
Sales Range: $200-249.9 Million
Emp.: 500
Financial Services
N.A.I.C.S.: 523999

Standard Chartered Thailand Limited (3)
90 N Sathorn Rd, Bangkok, 10500, Silom Bangrak, Thailand **(100%)**
Tel.: (66) 27248001
Web Site: http://www.standardchartered.com
Sales Range: $50-74.9 Million
Emp.: 100
Merchant Banking
N.A.I.C.S.: 522210

Representative Office (Non-US):

Standard Chartered Bank - Colombia Representative Office (2)
Carrera 7 71-52, Torre A Of 702, Bogota, 110231, Colombia
Tel.: (57) 13264030
Web Site: https://www.sc.com
Sales Range: $25-49.9 Million
Emp.: 42
Banking
N.A.I.C.S.: 522110

Standard Chartered Bank - India Representative Office (2)
Crescenzo C-38/39 G Block Bandra Kurla Complex, Bandra East, Mumbai, 400 051, India
Tel.: (91) 2261157000
Sales Range: $1-4.9 Billion
Full Banking Services
N.A.I.C.S.: 522110

Standard Chartered Bank - Japan Representative Office (2)
21-1 Sanno Park Tower 21st floor Nagatacho, Chiyoda-ku, Tokyo, 100-6155, Japan
Tel.: (81) 355111200
Web Site: https://www.sc.com
Merchant Banking
N.A.I.C.S.: 522110

Standard Chartered Bank - Jersey Representative Office (2)
15 Castle Street, PO Box 80, Saint Helier, JE4 8PT, Jersey
Tel.: (44) 1534704000
Sales Range: $75-99.9 Million
Emp.: 200
Banking
N.A.I.C.S.: 522299

Representative Office (US):

Standard Chartered Bank - USA Representative Office (2)
1095 Avenue of the Americas, New York, NY 10036-6797
Tel.: (212) 667-0700
Web Site: http://www.standardchartered.com
Sales Range: $150-199.9 Million
Emp.: 450
Banking
N.A.I.C.S.: 522110
Julio Rojas *(CEO-Americas)*

Subsidiary (Non-US):

Standard Chartered Bank Australia Limited (2)
Level 5 345 George Street, Sydney, 2000, NSW, Australia **(100%)**
Tel.: (61) 292329315
Sales Range: $50-74.9 Million
Emp.: 50
Commercial Bank
N.A.I.C.S.: 522110

Standard Chartered Bank Botswana Limited (2)
5th Floor Standard House Building The Mall Queens Road, PO Box 496, Gaborone, 9267, Botswana **(100%)**
Tel.: (267) 3615800
Web Site: http://www.standardchartered.com
Sales Range: $300-349.9 Million
Emp.: 700
International Banking
N.A.I.C.S.: 522299
Mpho Masupe *(CEO & Mng Dir)*

Standard Chartered Bank Cameroon S.A. (2)
Akwa Boulevard de la Liberte, PO Box 1784, Douala, Cameroon **(100%)**
Tel.: (237) 233435200
Sales Range: $50-74.9 Million
Emp.: 100
International Banking
N.A.I.C.S.: 522299

Standard Chartered Bank Gambia Ltd. (2)
8 Ecowas Avenue, PO Box 259, Banjul, 259, Gambia **(100%)**
Tel.: (220) 4202275
Web Site: https://www.sc.com
Emp.: 140
International Banking
N.A.I.C.S.: 522110
Albert Saltson *(CEO & Mng Dir-Uganda)*

Standard Chartered Bank Kenya Limited (2)
Number 48 Westlands Road, PO Box 30003, Moi Avenue, 100, Nairobi, Kenya **(100%)**
Tel.: (254) 203293900
Web Site: http://www.standardchartered.com
International Banking
N.A.I.C.S.: 522110
Lamin Manjang *(CEO & Mng Dir-Nigeria)*

Standard Chartered Bank Korea Limited (2)
47 Jong-ro, Jongno-gu, Seoul, 03160, Korea (South) **(100%)**
Tel.: (82) 2 730 5442
Web Site: https://www.standardchartered.co.kr
Commercial Banking Services
N.A.I.C.S.: 522110
J. B. Park *(CEO)*

Standard Chartered Bank Malaysia Berhad (2)
Level 26 Equatorial Plaza Jalan Sultan Ismail, 50250, Kuala Lumpur, Malaysia **(100%)**
Tel.: (60) 377118888
Web Site: https://www.sc.com
Rev.: $852,000,000
Emp.: 2,126
International Banking
N.A.I.C.S.: 522299
Aaron Loo *(Head-Retail Clients)*

Standard Chartered Bank Nepal Limited (2)
New Baneshwor Branch, PO Box 3990, Kathmandu, Nepal **(70.21%)**
Tel.: (977) 14782333
Web Site: https://www.sc.com
Rev.: $95,501,809
Assets: $1,134,402,875
Liabilities: $983,456,734
Net Worth: $150,946,141
Earnings: $25,968,635
Emp.: 504
Fiscal Year-end: 07/16/2023
Commercial Banking Services
N.A.I.C.S.: 522110
Michael Siddhi *(Head-Transaction Banking)*

Standard Chartered Bank PLC (2)
Standard Chartered Bank Building 6 John Evans Atta Mills High Street, PO Box 768, Accra, Ghana **(100%)**
Tel.: (233) 302740100
Web Site: https://www.sc.com
Rev.: $173,875,347
Assets: $1,365,464,897
Liabilities: $1,116,093,549
Net Worth: $249,371,348
Earnings: $81,315,103
Emp.: 811
Fiscal Year-end: 12/31/2020
Banking Services
N.A.I.C.S.: 522110
Mansa Nettey *(CEO)*

Standard Chartered Bank Sierra Leone Ltd. (2)
Lightfoot Boston Street, 9-12 Lightfoot Boston St, Freetown, Sierra Leone **(100%)**
Tel.: (232) 76505609
Web Site: https://www.sc.com
Emp.: 151
International Banking
N.A.I.C.S.: 522299
Idrissa Kamara *(CEO)*

Standard Chartered Bank Tanzania Limited (2)
1st - 3rd Floor International House Corner Shaaban Robert Street, PO Box 9011, Garden Avenue, Dar es Salaam, Tanzania **(100%)**
Tel.: (255) 2221221601
Sales Range: $150-199.9 Million
Emp.: 330
International Banking
N.A.I.C.S.: 522299

Standard Chartered Bank Uganda Ltd. (2)
5 Speke Rd, Kampala, 7111, Uganda **(100%)**
Tel.: (256) 200524100
Web Site: https://www.sc.com
Sales Range: $75-99.9 Million
Emp.: 180
International Banking
N.A.I.C.S.: 522299
Albert Richard Saltson *(CEO & Mng Dir)*

Standard Chartered Bank Zambia Ltd. (2)
Standard Chartered House Cairo Road, PO Box 32238, Lusaka, 10101, Zambia **(100%)**
Tel.: (260) 966999990
Web Site: https://www.sc.com
Sales Range: $300-349.9 Million
Emp.: 400
International Banking
N.A.I.C.S.: 522299
Herman Kasekende *(CEO & Mng Dir)*

Standard Chartered Bank Zimbabwe Limited (2)
1st Floor AUSQ Building 68 Nelson Mandela Ave, PO Box 373, Harare, Zimbabwe **(100%)**
Tel.: (263) 242253801
Web Site: https://www.sc.com
Sales Range: $300-349.9 Million
Emp.: 700
International Banking
N.A.I.C.S.: 522110
Christopher Mwerenga *(CFO)*

Standard Chartered Finance (Brunei) Berhad (2)
51-55 Jalan Sultan Omar Ali Saifuddien Jalan Sultan Complex, Bandar Seri, Bandar Seri Begawan, BS8811, Brunei Darussalam **(100%)**

STANDARD CHARTERED PLC

Standard Chartered PLC—(Continued)
Tel.: (673) 265 8000
Web Site: https://www.sc.com
Emp.: 300
Finance Company
N.A.I.C.S.: 522291
Annie Ng (CFO)

Standard Chartered Securities Investment Consulting Ltd (2)
1st Fl 168 Tun Hwa North Rd, Taipei, 10549, Taiwan (100%)
Tel.: (886) 227172866
Web Site:
    http://www.standardchartered.com.tw
Sales Range: $300-349.9 Million
Emp.: 700
Stockbroking
N.A.I.C.S.: 523910
Pruce Chien (Head-Fin)

Standard Chartered Bank (Vietnam) Limited (1)
Room 1810-1815 Level 18 Keangnam Hanoi Landmark Tower Pham Hung Road, Me Tri Ward Nam Tu Liem District, Hanoi, 10000, Vietnam
Tel.: (84) 24 936 8000
Financial Services
N.A.I.C.S.: 523999

Standard Chartered Bank AG (1)
Taunusanlage 16, 60325, Frankfurt am Main, Germany
Tel.: (49) 69 770 7500
Web Site: https://www.sc.com
Financial Services
N.A.I.C.S.: 523999
Heinz Hilger (CEO & Head-Banking-Global)

Standard Chartered Bank Angola S.A. (1)
Kilamba Building 7th Floor Avenida 4 de Fevereiro Marginal de Luanda, Ingombota Urban District, Luanda, Angola
Tel.: (244) 22 263 6800
Web Site: https://www.sc.com
Commercial Banking Services
N.A.I.C.S.: 522110

Standard Chartered Bank Cote d'Ivoire SA (1)
Plateau 23 Boulevard De La Republique 17, BP 1141, Abidjan, Cote d'Ivoire
Tel.: (225) 2 030 3200
Web Site: https://www.sc.com
Financial Services
N.A.I.C.S.: 523999

Standard Chartered Capital (Saudi Arabia) Ltd. (1)
16th Floor Al Faisaliah Tower King Fahad Street, PO Box 92224, 11653, Riyadh, Saudi Arabia
Tel.: (966) 11 288 8540
Financial Services
N.A.I.C.S.: 523999

Standard Chartered Global Business Services Spolka z ograniczona odpowiedzialnoscia (1)
Rondo Daszynskiego 2b, 00-843, Warsaw, Poland
Tel.: (48) 22 359 7000
Web Site: https://www.sc.com
Banking Services
N.A.I.C.S.: 522110

Standard Chartered Nominees South Africa Proprietary Limited (1)
2nd Floor 115 West Street, Sandton, 2196, Gauteng, South Africa
Tel.: (27) 11 217 6600
Web Site: https://www.sc.com
Financial Services
N.A.I.C.S.: 523999
Kweku Bedu-Addo (CEO)

Standard Chartered Representacao Ltda. (1)
Av Brig Faria Lima 3 477 - Tower A 6th Floor Room 62 Itaim Bibi, Sao Paulo, Brazil
Tel.: (55) 113 073 7000
Web Site: https://www.sc.com
Financial Services
N.A.I.C.S.: 523999
Germana Cruz (CEO & Head)

Standard Chartered Securities (India) Limited (1)

2nd Floor 23-25 MG Road Fort, Mumbai, 400001, India
Tel.: (91) 226 135 5635
Web Site:
    https://standardcharteredtrade.co.in
Banking Services
N.A.I.C.S.: 522110

Standard Chartered Trustees (UK) Limited (1)
1 Basinghall Avenue, London, EC2V 5DD, United Kingdom
Tel.: (44) 207 885 8888
Financial Services
N.A.I.C.S.: 522320

Standard Chartered Wealth Management Limited Company (1)
Standard Chartered Bank Building 6 John Evans Atta Mills High Street, PO Box 768, Accra, Ghana
Tel.: (233) 30 274 0100
Financial Services
N.A.I.C.S.: 523999

Standard Chartered Yatirim Bankasi Turk Anonim Sirketi (1)
Buyukdere Cad Yapi Kredi Plaza C Blok Kat 15, Levent, Istanbul, 34330, Turkiye
Tel.: (90) 212 339 3700
Web Site: https://www.sc.com
Financial Services
N.A.I.C.S.: 523150

STANDARD CHEM. & PHARM. CO., LTD.
No 154 Kaiyuan Road, Xinying District, T'ainan, 73055, Taiwan
Tel.: (886) 66361516
Web Site:
    https://www.standard.com.tw
1720—(TAI)
Rev.: $204,054,016
Assets: $365,895,666
Liabilities: $99,787,007
Net Worth: $266,108,659
Earnings: $37,866,803
Emp.: 1,713
Fiscal Year-end: 12/31/23
Pharmaceutical Products Mfr & Distr
N.A.I.C.S.: 325412
Tzu-Ting Fan (Pres)

Subsidiaries:

Adv Pharma ,Inc. (1)
6F No 90 Hsin-Tai Wu Road Sec 1, Hsi-Chih Town, Taipei, Taiwan
Tel.: (886) 226963922
Web Site: https://www.advpharma.com.tw
Sales Range: $50-74.9 Million
Emp.: 10
Pharmaceuticals Import & Distr
N.A.I.C.S.: 424210

Boscogen Inc (1)
11 Morgan, Irvine, CA 92618
Tel.: (949) 380-4317
Web Site: http://www.boscogen.com
Sales Range: $25-49.9 Million
Emp.: 50
Nutritional Supplements Mfr & Distr
N.A.I.C.S.: 311119
Harry Fan (Owner)

Jiangsu Standard-Dia Biopharma Co., Ltd. (1)
No 8 Peilan Road, China medicine city, Taizhou, Jiangsu, China
Tel.: (86) 52386200328
Web Site: http://www.jsdymedical.com
Research & Development Services
N.A.I.C.S.: 541715

Souriree Biotech & Pharm. Co., Ltd. (1)
No 6 Ln 26 Zixin Rd, Sanxia Dist, New Taipei City, 237, Taiwan
Tel.: (886) 226726032
Web Site: http://www.souriree.com.tw
Medical Product Mfr & Distr
N.A.I.C.S.: 325412

Stason Pharmaceuticals,Inc. (1)
11 Morgan, Irvine, CA 92618
Tel.: (949) 380-4327
Web Site: http://www.stasonpharma.com

Pharmaceutical Products Mfr & Distr
N.A.I.C.S.: 325412

Sunstar Chem & Pharm. Corp. (1)
45 Tong Cheng 10th Str, Hsin-Ying, Taiwan
Tel.: (886) 6 636 2898
Web Site: http://www.sun-pharm.com
Sales Range: $50-74.9 Million
Emp.: 5
Pharmaceuticals Products Import & Distr
N.A.I.C.S.: 424210
Rock Wu (Gen Mgr)

Syngen Biotech International Sdn. Bhd. (1)
3-4-2 No 14 Persiaran Anggerik Vanilla, Kota Kemuning Seksyen 31, 40460, Shah Alam, Selangor, Malaysia
Tel.: (60) 358853735
Preventive Medicine Distr
N.A.I.C.S.: 423450

Syntech Chemicals, Inc. (1)
168 Kai Yuan Road, Hsin-Ying, 73055, Taiwan
Tel.: (886) 66362121
Web Site: http://www.syn-tech.com.tw
Sales Range: $25-49.9 Million
Emp.: 100
Pharmaceutical Chemicals Mfr
N.A.I.C.S.: 325412

STANDARD COMMUNICATIONS PTY. LTD.
Winston Hills, North Ryde, 2153, NSW, Australia
Tel.: (61) 288676000
Web Site: http://www.gme.net.au
Sales Range: $50-74.9 Million
Emp.: 200
Radio Communication Products Designer & Mfr
N.A.I.C.S.: 334220
Sean Griffin (Bus Mgr-Product Dev)

Subsidiaries:

Standard Communications (NZ) Ltd. (1)
Unit 2 24 Bishop Dunn Place, East Tamaki, Manukau, 2013, New Zealand
Tel.: (64) 9 274 0955
Communication Equipment Distr
N.A.I.C.S.: 423690

STANDARD DEVELOPMENT GROUP LIMITED
21/F Po Shau Centre No 115 How Ming Street, Kwun Tong, Kowloon, China (Hong Kong)
Tel.: (852) 35291864
Year Founded: 2005
1867—(HKG)
Rev.: $28,619,888
Assets: $19,271,031
Liabilities: $4,089,440
Net Worth: $15,181,591
Earnings: $129,754
Emp.: 60
Fiscal Year-end: 03/31/21
Interior Design Services
N.A.I.C.S.: 541410
Wan Sze Wong (Chm & Officer-Compliance)

STANDARD FIRM CO., LTD.
621-18 Yeok Sam-Dong Gangham-Gu, Seoul, Korea (South)
Tel.: (82) 2 584 3963
Web Site: http://www.sfal.kr
Year Founded: 2007
Nonferrous Alloys Mfr
N.A.I.C.S.: 331529
Sang-Baek Kim (CEO)

STANDARD FOODS CORPORATION
10F No 610 Ruiguang Rd, Neihu Dist, Taipei, 114727, Taiwan
Tel.: (886) 227092323

INTERNATIONAL PUBLIC

Web Site:
    https://www.sfworldwide.com
Year Founded: 1979
1227—(TAI)
Rev.: $909,255,272
Assets: $841,283,562
Liabilities: $263,725,553
Net Worth: $577,558,008
Earnings: $41,471,335
Emp.: 2,878
Fiscal Year-end: 12/31/23
Food Products Mfr
N.A.I.C.S.: 311991
Ter-Fung Tsao (Chm)

Subsidiaries:

Dermalab S.A. (1)
Dufourstrasse 20, 8702, Zollikon, Switzerland
Tel.: (41) 443961060
Web Site: https://www.swissline-cosmetics.com
Cosmetic Product Mfr & Distr
N.A.I.C.S.: 325620

Domex Technology Corporation (1)
No 6 Hsin-Ann Rd Hsinchu Science Park, Hsinchu, 30078, Taiwan
Tel.: (886) 35772115
Web Site: http://www.domex.com.tw
Computer Peripheral Equipment Mfr & Distr
N.A.I.C.S.: 334118

STANDARD FORMS FRANCE SAS
Rue de Fleteau, PO Box 76, ZI du Boulay, 37110, Chateau-Renalt, France
Tel.: (33) 247298040
Web Site:
    http://www.standardforms.fr
Sales Range: $1-9.9 Million
Emp.: 23
Business Forms Direct Distr
N.A.I.C.S.: 459410

STANDARD GREASES & SPECIALITIES PVT LTD.
101 Ketan Apartments 233 R B Mehta Marg, Ghatkopar East, Mumbai, 400077, India
Tel.: (91) 22 25013641
Web Site:
    http://www.standardgreases.co.in
Year Founded: 1983
Grease Mfr
N.A.I.C.S.: 324191
D. S. Chandavarkar (Chm & Mng Dir)

STANDARD INDUSTRIES LIMITED
Vijyalaxmi Mafatlal Centre 57A Dr G Deshmukh Marg, Mumbai, 400 026, India
Tel.: (91) 2223527600
Web Site:
    https://www.standardindustries.co
Year Founded: 1892
530017—(BOM)
Rev.: $7,965,230
Assets: $23,092,848
Liabilities: $5,445,861
Net Worth: $17,646,988
Earnings: $2,596,751
Emp.: 12
Fiscal Year-end: 03/31/23
Real Estate Development Services
N.A.I.C.S.: 531390
Dhansukh H. Parekh (Exec Dir)

STANDARD INSURANCE COMPANY LIMITED
2nd Floor Standard Insurance House II Chundrigar Road, Karachi, Pakistan
Tel.: (92) 3 242 7559
Insurance Management Services
N.A.I.C.S.: 524298
J. Greg Ness (Chm, Pres & CEO)

AND PRIVATE COMPANIES

STANDARD INSURANCE LIMITED
Civil Engineers Bhaban 69 Mohakhali C/A Level 05, Dhaka, 1212, Bangladesh
Tel.: (880) 9888548
Web Site: https://www.standardinsurance.com
Year Founded: 1999
STANDARINS—(CHT)
Sales Range: $1-9.9 Million
Emp.: 234
Insurance Services Including Fire, Marine, Engineering & Motor Insurance
N.A.I.C.S.: 524126
Md Ali Imam *(Asst Mng Dir)*

STANDARD INVESTMENT MANAGEMENT B.V.
Leidsegracht 3, 1017 NA, Amsterdam, Netherlands
Tel.: (31) 23375430   NI
Web Site: http://www.standard.nl
Year Founded: 2004
Privater Equity Firm
N.A.I.C.S.: 523999
Idgar van Kippersluis *(Co-Founder & Partner)*

Subsidiaries:

HYET Sweet S.A.S.   (1)
Port 7516 7516 Route de La Grande Hernesse, 59820, Gravelines, France
Tel.: (33) 3 28 22 74 00
Web Site: http://www.hyetsweet.com
Emp.: 73
Sweetener Mfr & Distr
N.A.I.C.S.: 311999
Satoshi Inamori *(Pres)*

Micro Machining Holding B.V.   (1)
Granaatstraat 15, 7554 TN, Hengelo, Netherlands
Tel.: (31) 74 243 8866
Web Site: http://www.micromachininggroup.nl
Emp.: 90
Holding Company; Industrial Machinery Components & Assemblies Mfr & Whslr
N.A.I.C.S.: 551112
Roel Klein *(Mng Dir)*

Subsidiary (Domestic):

Germefa B.V.   (2)
Ivoorstraat 6, 1812 RE, Alkmaar, Netherlands   (100%)
Tel.: (31) 725350000
Web Site: http://www.germefa.nl
Precision Industrial Tools Mfr
N.A.I.C.S.: 333991

Machinefabriek Technology Twente B.V.   (2)
Granaatstraat 15, 7554 TN, Hengelo, Netherlands
Tel.: (31) 74 2438866
Web Site: http://www.technologytwente.nl
Emp.: 50
Precision Engineered Mechanical Components Mfr
N.A.I.C.S.: 333613
Roel Klein *(Mng Dir)*

RKW ACE SA.   (1)
Rue de Renory 499, 4030, Liege, Belgium
Tel.: (32) 4 349 86 86
Web Site: http://www.ace-films.be
N.A.I.C.S.: 326199
Guy Pinchard *(CEO)*

Riedel B.V.   (1)
Frankeneng 12, Ede, 6717 AG, Gelderland, Netherlands
Tel.: (31) 318679911
Web Site: http://www.riedel.nl
Beverages Mfr & Distr
N.A.I.C.S.: 311411

STANDARD LITHIUM LTD.
1625 1075 West Georgia Street, Vancouver, V6E 3C9, BC, Canada
Tel.: (604) 409-8154   Ca
Web Site: https://www.standardlithium.com
Year Founded: 1999
SLI—(NYSEAMEX)
Rev.: $2,497,608
Assets: $129,428,762
Liabilities: $10,534,266
Net Worth: $118,894,496
Earnings: ($31,323,794)
Emp.: 12
Fiscal Year-end: 06/30/23
Lithium Exploration Services
N.A.I.C.S.: 327999
Robert Mintak *(CEO)*

STANDARD MERCANTILE ACQUISITION CORP.
1700-745 Thurlow Street, Vancouver, V6E 0C5, BC, Canada
Tel.: (604) 689-0821   Ca
Web Site: http://www.trezcapital.com
Year Founded: 2012
TZZ—(TSX)
Sales Range: $1-9.9 Million
Emp.: 80
Mortgage Investment Services
N.A.I.C.S.: 523999
Alexander Manson *(Pres & CEO)*

STANDARD MERCANTILE ACQUISITION CORP.
1700-745 Thurlow Street, Vancouver, V6E 0C5, BC, Canada
Tel.: (416) 972-1741   Ca
Web Site: https://www.standardmercantile.com
Year Founded: 2012
TZS—(TSX)
Rev.: $1,055,558
Assets: $18,022,624
Liabilities: $602,724
Net Worth: $17,419,900
Earnings: ($371,769)
Fiscal Year-end: 12/31/19
Investment Services
N.A.I.C.S.: 523999
Jordan M. Kupinsky *(Chm)*

STANDARD MOTORS LTD.
44 2nd Ave NW, Swift Current, S9H 0N9, SK, Canada
Tel.: (306) 773-3131
Web Site: http://www.standardmotors.ca
Year Founded: 1910
Rev.: $26,244,691
Emp.: 45
New & Used Car Dealers
N.A.I.C.S.: 441110
Jim Plewis *(Partner)*

STANDARD NEKRETNINE D.D. SARAJEVO
Dzemala Bijedica 182, Ilidza, Sarajevo, Bosnia & Herzegovina
Tel.: (387) 973290
SNKSR—(SARE)
Assets: $6,292,136
Liabilities: $1,102,009
Net Worth: $5,190,126
Earnings: ($107,322)
Emp.: 1
Fiscal Year-end: 12/31/20
Building Construction Services
N.A.I.C.S.: 236220

STANDARD PRODUCTS, INC.
5905 Chemin de la Cote de Liesse, Saint Laurent, H4T 1C3, QC, Canada
Tel.: (514) 342-1199
Web Site: http://www.standardpro.com
Year Founded: 1961
Rev.: $37,290,231
Emp.: 180
Commercial, Industrial & Residential Lighting Provider
N.A.I.C.S.: 335132
David Nathaniel *(CEO)*

STANDARD SHOE SOLE & MOULD (INDIA) LIMITED
95 Park Street 2nd Floor, Kolkata, 700 016, West Bengal, India
Tel.: (91) 3322261175
Web Site: https://www.sssmil.com
Year Founded: 1973
523351—(BOM)
Rev.: $31
Assets: $22,959
Liabilities: $191,098
Net Worth: ($168,139)
Earnings: ($17,072)
Emp.: 2
Fiscal Year-end: 03/31/21
Shoe Mfr & Whslr
N.A.I.C.S.: 316210
Mukund Bhatter *(Exec Dir)*

STANDARD SUPPLY AS
Sjolystplass 2, 0278, Oslo, Norway
Tel.: (47) 95204493
Web Site: https://www.standard-supply.com
Year Founded: 2010
STSU—(OSL)
Rev.: $73,292,392
Assets: $106,675,953
Liabilities: $6,887,350
Net Worth: $99,788,603
Earnings: $41,603,014
Fiscal Year-end: 12/31/23
Air Conditioning Distr
N.A.I.C.S.: 423730
Eldar Paulsrud *(CFO)*

STANDARD SURFACTANTS LTD.
8/15 Arya Nagar, Kanpur, 208002, Uttar Pradesh, India
Tel.: (91) 5122531762
Web Site: https://www.standardsurfactant.com
Year Founded: 1990
526231—(BOM)
Rev.: $18,359,091
Assets: $7,645,309
Liabilities: $4,718,458
Net Worth: $2,926,851
Earnings: $186,835
Emp.: 60
Fiscal Year-end: 03/31/23
Chemical Products Mfr
N.A.I.C.S.: 325998
Pawan Kumar Garg *(Chm & Mng Dir)*

STANDARD URANIUM LTD.
918 - 1030 West Georgia St, Vancouver, V6E 2Y3, BC, Canada
Tel.: (306) 850-6699
Web Site: https://www.standarduranium.ca
STTDF—(OTCQB)
Assets: $751,154
Liabilities: $321,741
Net Worth: $429,413
Earnings: ($661,096)
Fiscal Year-end: 04/30/20
Mineral Exploration Services
N.A.I.C.S.: 213115
Jon Bey *(Chm & CEO)*

STANFIELD'S LIMITED
1 Logan St, PO Box 190, Truro, B2N 5C2, NS, Canada
Tel.: (902) 895-5406
Web Site: http://www.stanfields.com
Year Founded: 1856
Sales Range: $50-74.9 Million
Emp.: 500
Sportswear, Underwear & Lounge Wear Mfr & Seller
N.A.I.C.S.: 315250
F. Thomas Stanfield *(Chm & Pres)*

Subsidiaries:

Longworth Industries, Inc.   (1)
565 Air Tool Dr Ste K, Southern Pines, NC 28387
Tel.: (910) 974-3068
Web Site: http://www.polarmax.com
Apparels Mfr
N.A.I.C.S.: 315250
Randy Black *(Pres & CEO)*

Stanfield's Limited Marketing & Sales Division   (1)
136 Tycos Dr., Toronto, M6B 1W8, ON, Canada
Sportswear, Baselayers & Underwear Retailer
N.A.I.C.S.: 458110

STANHILL OPERATIONS LTD.
32 Saint James's Street, London, SW1A 1HD, United Kingdom
Tel.: (44) 203 301 9330   UK
Web Site: http://www.stanhillcapital.com
Privater Equity Firm
N.A.I.C.S.: 523999
Ilyas Khan *(Founder & Sr Partner)*

Subsidiaries:

Stanhill (Hong Kong) Limited   (1)
2401 Winsome House 73 Wyndham Street, Central, China (Hong Kong)
Tel.: (852) 2167 8137
Web Site: http://www.stanhillcapital.com
Privater Equity Firm
N.A.I.C.S.: 523999
Cathleen Wu *(Sec & Office Mgr)*

Tengri Resources Limited   (1)
32 Saint James's Street, London, SW1A1HD, United Kingdom   (87.3%)
Tel.: (44) 203 301 9346
Web Site: http://www.tengriresources.co.uk
Metal & Other Commodity Trading Services
N.A.I.C.S.: 523160

STANHOME WORLD FRANCE
62 Avenue d'iena, Paris, 75016, France
Tel.: (33) 153673900
Web Site: http://www.stanhome-world.com
Year Founded: 1972
Sales Range: $10-24.9 Million
Emp.: 50
Personal & Home Care Products
N.A.I.C.S.: 456199
Jonas Hedberg *(Dir Gen)*

Subsidiaries:

Stanhome Panamericana, C.A.   (1)
Avenia Maracay, Zona Industrial San Vicente, Maracay, 2101, Aragua, Venezuela
Tel.: (58) 2435536874
Web Site: http://www.stanhome.com.ve
Home Cleaning Items Mfr & Whslr
N.A.I.C.S.: 325612

Stanhome S.A.   (1)
Tuset 32 2nd Fl, 08006, Barcelona, Spain
Tel.: (34) 932374900
Web Site: http://www.stanhome.es
Cosmetic & Household Product Distr
N.A.I.C.S.: 456120

Stanhome S.p.A.   (1)
Via Zoe Fontana 200, 131, Rome, Italy
Tel.: (39) 06 45081
Wholesale of Home Cleaning Items
N.A.I.C.S.: 561720

Stanhome World Mexico, S.A. de C.V.   (1)
Napoles Num 47 Col Juarez Deleg Cuauhtemoc, Mexico, 06600, Mexico
Tel.: (52) 5511020300
Web Site: http://www.stanhome.com.mx
Sanitary & Cleaning Products Mfr
N.A.I.C.S.: 325612

STANHOME WORLD FRANCE

INTERNATIONAL PUBLIC

Stanhome World France—(Continued)

Stanhome World Philippines, Inc. (1)
4th Floor Montivar Building 34 Jupiter St,
Bel-Air, Makati, 1209, Philippines
Tel.: (63) 9178264663
Beauty Product Whslr
N.A.I.C.S.: 424210

STANLEY AGRICULTURAL GROUP CO., LTD.

Shidanli Road, Linshu County, Linyi, 276700, Shandong, China
Tel.: (86) 5396263620
Web Site: http://www.shidanli.cn
Year Founded: 1992
002588—(SSE)
Rev.: $1,268,984,242
Assets: $1,451,808,039
Liabilities: $606,736,480
Net Worth: $845,071,559
Earnings: $61,901,812
Emp.: 2,070
Fiscal Year-end: 12/31/22
Fertilizer Mfr
N.A.I.C.S.: 325314

Subsidiaries:

Stanley Fertilizer Co., Ltd. (1)
Base Of Circulation Industry Sundu Town, Fengcheng, 331100, Jiangxi, China
Tel.: (86) 7958358888
Fertilizer Mfr
N.A.I.C.S.: 325311

Stanley Fertilizer Co., Ltd. (1)
West Side Of Beici Road Economic Development Zone Dangyang, Hubei, 444165, China
Tel.: (86) 7173328888
Fertilizer Mfr
N.A.I.C.S.: 325311

Stanley Fertilizer Co., Ltd. (1)
Intersection of Industrial Avenue & Huanghe Road, Henan, 476700, Ningling County, China
Tel.: (86) 3707757777
Fertilizer Mfr
N.A.I.C.S.: 325311

Stanley Fertilizer Co., Ltd. (1)
North Side of Hope Avenue Industrial Agglomeration Area, Henan, 463100, Suiping County, China
Tel.: (86) 3964717777
Fertilizer Mfr
N.A.I.C.S.: 325311

Stanley Fertilizer Co., Ltd. (1)
315 West Side of Provincial Road Eastern Economic Development Zone, Shandong, 253100, Pingyuan County, China
Tel.: (86) 5342166666
Fertilizer Mfr
N.A.I.C.S.: 325311

Stanley Fertilizer Co., Ltd. (1)
Street No 345 Kunlun Economic & Technological Development Zone, Jilin, 132115, Jilin, China
Tel.: (86) 43262017777
Fertilizer Mfr
N.A.I.C.S.: 325311

Stanley Fertilizer Co., Ltd. (1)
Jiangnan Industrial Park Zhuang Autonomous Region, Guiyang, 537100, Guangxi, China
Tel.: (86) 7755968888
Fertilizer Mfr
N.A.I.C.S.: 325311

STANLEY ELECTRIC CO., LTD.

2-9-13 Nakameguro, Meguro-ku, Tokyo, 153-8636, Japan
Tel.: (81) 368662222
Web Site: https://www.stanley.co.jp
Year Founded: 1920
STAEF—(OTCIQ)
Rev.: $3,138,954,300
Assets: $4,514,310,870
Liabilities: $670,273,110
Net Worth: $3,844,037,760
Earnings: $189,976,320
Emp.: 16,964
Fiscal Year-end: 03/31/23
Electronic Components Mfr
N.A.I.C.S.: 334419
Takanori Kitano (Pres)

Subsidiaries:

Asian Stanley International Co., Ltd. (1)
48 1 Moo 1 Tambol Kukwang Amphur, Ladlumkaew, Pathumthani, 12140, Thailand
Tel.: (66) 25991260
Sales Range: $200-249.9 Million
Emp.: 900
Electronic Parts
N.A.I.C.S.: 334419

Chongqing Hua-yu Stanley Electric Co., Ltd (1)
No 68 Long-Shan Road, Yubei District, Chongqing, 400021, Sichuan, China
Tel.: (86) 2367659032
Web Site: http://www.stanley.co.jp
Lighting Fixtures
N.A.I.C.S.: 335139

Guangzhou Stanley Electric Co., Ltd (1)
No 138 Jun Ye Road Eastern Section GETDD, Guangzhou, 510530, China
Tel.: (86) 208 226 6668
Web Site: http://www.stanley.co.jp
Vehicle Lighting
N.A.I.C.S.: 336320

Hella-Phil., Inc. (1)
Km 38 Aguinaldo Highway, 4114, Dasmarinas, Cavite, Philippines (90%)
Tel.: (63) 464165704
Automotive Spare Parts Distr
N.A.I.C.S.: 423120

Matsuo Electric Co., Ltd. (1)
10392-2 Kamitokura Daiwacho, Daiwa-chou Kamo-gun, Mihara, 729-1405, Hiroshima, Japan
Tel.: (81) 84 733 0158
Web Site: http://www.stanley.co.jp
Vehicle Parts
N.A.I.C.S.: 336390

P.T. Indonesia Stanley Electric (1)
Jl Bhumimas I No 17 Kawasan Industri Cikupamas Desa Talaga, Kecamatan Cikupa Kabupaten, Tangerang, 15710, Banten, Indonesia
Tel.: (62) 215 940 4506
Web Site: http://www.stanley.co.jp
Engine Electrical Equipment
N.A.I.C.S.: 333618

Shanghai Stanley Electric Co., Ltd. (1)
A-C8F Sun Tong Infoport Plaza 55 Huai Hai Road, Shanghai, China
Tel.: (86) 2152989431
Sales Range: $50-74.9 Million
Emp.: 100
Electrical Parts & Equipment
N.A.I.C.S.: 423690

Shenzhen Stanley Electric Co., Ltd (1)
No 16 Jianan Road Taifeng Industrial Bogang, Shajing Town Bao An District, Shenzhen, 518104, China
Tel.: (86) 7552 975 5074
Web Site: http://www.stanley.co.jp
Electronic Equipment Mfr & Sales
N.A.I.C.S.: 334419

Stanley Denka Co., Ltd. (1)
920 Soya, Hadano, 257-0031, Kanagawa, Japan
Tel.: (81) 463810087
Metal Stamping
N.A.I.C.S.: 332119

Stanley Electric (Asia Pacific) Ltd. (1)
Suites 2001-4 20 F Tower 1 The Gateway 25 Canton Road, Tsimshatsui, Kowloon, Japan
Tel.: (81) 27301738
Web Site: http://www.stanley.co.jp
Sales Range: $25-49.9 Million
Emp.: 30
Electronic Parts

Stanley Electric (Asia Pacific) Ltd. (1)
7F No375 Sung-Chiang Rd, Taipei, 104, Taiwan
Tel.: (886) 225121758
Sales Range: $25-49.9 Million
Emp.: 13
Electronics Equipment
N.A.I.C.S.: 334419

Stanley Electric (Asia Pacific) Ltd. (1)
Suites 2002-4 Tower I The Gateway 25 Canton Road, Tsim Tsa Tsui, China (Hong Kong)
Tel.: (852) 2730 1738
Web Site: http://www.stanley.co.jp
Semiconductor Device Whslr
N.A.I.C.S.: 423690

Stanley Electric (UK) Co. Ltd. (1)
Suite 3C Part 3rd Floor The Columbia Centre Station Road, Bracknell, RG12 1LP, Berkshire, United Kingdom
Tel.: (44) 134 483 0450
Web Site: http://www.stanley.co.jp
Sales Range: $25-49.9 Million
Emp.: 20
Electronic Parts
N.A.I.C.S.: 334419

Stanley Electric Co., Ltd. - Hamamatsu Factory (1)
1705 Nakagawa, Hosoecho Kitaku, Hamamatsu, 431-1304, Shizuoka, Japan
Tel.: (81) 53 527 2222
Web Site: https://www.stanley.co.jp
Automobile Equipment Mfr
N.A.I.C.S.: 336390

Stanley Electric Co., Ltd. - Hatano Factory (1)
400 Soya, Hadano, 257-8555, Kanagawa, Japan
Tel.: (81) 463 81 1111
Motor Vehicle Lamp Mfr
N.A.I.C.S.: 336320

Stanley Electric Co., Ltd. - Hiroshima Factory (1)
1866 Okuya, Shiwacho, Higashi-hiroshima, 739-0266, Hiroshima, Japan
Tel.: (81) 82 433 2711
Web Site: https://www.stanley.co.jp
Automobile Equipment Mfr
N.A.I.C.S.: 336390

Stanley Electric Co., Ltd. - Iida Factory (1)
7302-1 Matuoteradokoro, Iida, 395-0822, Nagano, Japan
Tel.: (81) 265 56 9301
Automobile Equipment Mfr
N.A.I.C.S.: 336390

Stanley Electric Co., Ltd. - Okazaki Factory (1)
3-33 Azaiwata Makihiracho, Okazaki, 444-3698, Aichi, Japan
Tel.: (81) 564 82 2111
Automobile Equipment Mfr
N.A.I.C.S.: 336390

Stanley Electric Co., Ltd. - Yamagata Factory (1)
271-6 Nihonkoku Aza Daihouji, Tsuruoka, 997-0017, Yamagata, Japan
Tel.: (81) 235 25 3111
Emp.: 3,500
Automobile Equipment Mfr
N.A.I.C.S.: 336390

Stanley Electric GmbH (1)
Waldecker Strasse 5, 64546, Morfelden, Germany
Tel.: (49) 6105930530
Web Site: http://www.stanley-electric.de
Sales Range: $25-49.9 Million
Emp.: 12
Electrical Equipment
N.A.I.C.S.: 335999
Koji Oe (Mng Dir)

Stanley Electric Holding Asia-Pacific Pte. Ltd. (1)
80 Robinson Road 10-01A, Singapore, 068898, Singapore
Tel.: (65) 6 420 6220

Electric Light Mfr
N.A.I.C.S.: 335131

Stanley Electric Holding of America, Inc. (1)
1500 Hill-Brady Rd, Battle Creek, MI 49037
Tel.: (616) 660-2315
Web Site: http://www.stanley.co
Sales Range: $150-199.9 Million
Emp.: 400
Holding Company
N.A.I.C.S.: 551112

Subsidiary (Domestic):

Hexatech, Inc. (2)
991 Aviation Pkwy Ste 800, Morrisville, NC 27560
Tel.: (919) 481-4412
Web Site: https://www.hexatechinc.com
Rev.: $1,600,000
Emp.: 13
Radio, Television & Other Electronics Stores
N.A.I.C.S.: 449210
Raoul Schlesser (Co-Founder & Co-CTO)

I I Stanley Co., Inc. (2)
1500 Hill Brady Rd, Battle Creek, MI 49037
Tel.: (269) 660-7777
Web Site: https://www.iistanley.com
Sales Range: $75-99.9 Million
Lighting Fixtures
N.A.I.C.S.: 336320

Stanley Electric Sales of America, Inc. (2)
1 Musick, Irvine, CA 92618
Tel.: (949) 222-0777
Web Site: http://www.stanleyelectric.com
Sales Range: $25-49.9 Million
Emp.: 25
Electronic Parts Sales
N.A.I.C.S.: 423690

Stanley Electric U.S. Co., Inc. (2)
420 E High St, London, OH 43140
Tel.: (740) 852-5200
Web Site: https://www.stanleyelectricus.com
Lighting Fixtures
N.A.I.C.S.: 336320

Stanley Electric Hungary KFT (1)
Gabor Denes ut 1, 3200, Gyongyos, Hungary
Tel.: (36) 3 751 1200
Web Site: https://www.stanleyelectrichungary.hu
Sales Range: $50-74.9 Million
Emp.: 245
Vehicle Parts
N.A.I.C.S.: 336390
Kurihara Masataka (Mng Dir)

Stanley Electric Korea Co., Ltd. (1)
Daechi-dong Keumkang Tower 1204 410 Teheran-ro, Gangnam-gu, Seoul, 06192, Korea (South)
Tel.: (82) 23 453 7190
Web Site: http://www.stanley.co.jp
Electronic Parts
N.A.I.C.S.: 334419

Stanley Electric Manufacturing Mexico S.A. de C.V. (1)
Av Rita Perez de Moreno 2045 Col Parque Industrial Colinas de Lagos, 47515, Lagos de Moreno, Jalisco, Mexico
Tel.: (52) 474 403 3600
Automobile Equipment Mfr
N.A.I.C.S.: 336310

Stanley Electric do Brasil Ltda. (1)
Rodovia Deputado Laercio Corte SP 147 Km 120 Lots Nr 04 05 & 06, Geada District, 13480-000, Limeira, Sao Paulo, Brazil
Tel.: (55) 1934465703
Sales Range: $25-49.9 Million
Emp.: 7
Automotive Lighting Equipment Mfr & Whslr
N.A.I.C.S.: 336320
Yasumi Motokawa (Pres)

Stanley IDESS S.A.S (1)
Immeuble MB6 41 rue des Trois Fontanot, 92000, Nanterre, France
Tel.: (33) 14 781 8585
Web Site: http://www.stanley.co.jp
Sales Range: $25-49.9 Million
Emp.: 13
Electronic Parts

N.A.I.C.S.: 334419

Stanley Ina Works Co., Ltd. (1)
7302-1 Matsuoteradoko, Iida, 395-0821, Nagano, Japan
Tel.: (81) 26 524 4711
Web Site: https://www.stanley.co.jp
Emp.: 95
Manufacture & Sales of LCDs Application Products
N.A.I.C.S.: 423430

Stanley Iwaki Works Co., Ltd. (1)
3-1 Chubu Industrial Park, Iwaki, 972-8338, Fukushima, Japan
Tel.: (81) 24 672 2222
Web Site: https://www.stanley.co.jp
Sales Range: $100-124.9 Million
Emp.: 212
Lighting Mfr & Sales
N.A.I.C.S.: 335132

Stanley Miyagi Works Co., Ltd. (1)
260 Aza-Jumonji Kuronuma Takarae, Nakada-chou Tome-gun, Miyagi, 987-0621, Japan
Tel.: (81) 220346655
Emp.: 150
Lighting Fixtures
N.A.I.C.S.: 335132

Stanley Niigata Works Co., Ltd. (1)
497-28 Miyashita Kitada Naka, Minami-ku, Niigata, 950-1237, Japan
Tel.: (81) 25 362 7100
Web Site: https://www.stanley.co.jp
Emp.: 95
Vehicle Parts
N.A.I.C.S.: 336390

Stanley Pal Co., Ltd. (1)
2-5-26 Nakameguro, Meguro-ku, Tokyo, 153-8636, Japan
Tel.: (81) 36 866 2602
Web Site: http://www.stanley.co.jp
Credit Services
N.A.I.C.S.: 522390

Stanley Shiga Works Co., Ltd. (1)
372-1 Funaki Imajuku, Shiga-chou Shiga-gun, 520-0524, Shiga, Japan
Tel.: (81) 775940700
Web Site: http://www.stanley.co.jp
Lighting Fixtures
N.A.I.C.S.: 335132

Stanley Tsuruoka Works Co., Ltd. (1)
45 Aza-Ootsubo Ooaza-Watamae Fujishima-machi, Higasitagawa-gun, Yamagata, 999-7695, Japan
Tel.: (81) 235643111
Emp.: 600
Semiconductors
N.A.I.C.S.: 333242

Stanley Well Corp. (1)
434 Soya, Hadano, 257-0031, Kanagawa, Japan
Tel.: (81) 46 381 3000
Web Site: http://www.stanley.co.jp
Vehicle Parts
N.A.I.C.S.: 336390

Suzhou Stanley Electric Co., Ltd. (1)
No 158-70A Huashan Road Fehgqiao, New District, Suzhou, 215129, Jiansu, China
Tel.: (86) 5126 661 6450
Web Site: http://www.stanley.co.jp
Sales Range: $200-249.9 Million
Emp.: 650
Mfr & Sales of Semiconductors & Electronic Equipment
N.A.I.C.S.: 333242

Suzhou Stanley LED Lighting Technology Co., Ltd. (1)
NO 158-70A Huashan Road Fengqiao, Suzhou, 215129, Jiangsu, China
Tel.: (86) 5126 661 6450
Web Site: https://www.stanley.co.jp
Semiconductor Lighting Equipment Mfr & Whslr
N.A.I.C.S.: 423690

Tian Jin Stanley Electric Co., Ltd. (1)
No 140 Nanhai Road TEDA, Tianjin, China
Tel.: (86) 226 517 9797
Web Site: http://www.stanley.co.jp
Vehicle Lighting
N.A.I.C.S.: 336320

Tianjin Stanley Electric Technology Co., Ltd. (1)
No 99 6th Avenue Teda, Tianjin, China
Tel.: (86) 226 517 9988
Automobile Equipment Mfr
N.A.I.C.S.: 336310

Vietnam Stanley Electric Co., Ltd. (1)
Duongxa, Gia Lam District, Hanoi, Vietnam
Tel.: (84) 243 876 6245
Web Site: http://www.stanley.co.jp
Electronic Parts
N.A.I.C.S.: 334419

Wuhan Stanley Electric Co., Ltd. (1)
No 818 Gexin road, Dongxihu District, Wuhan, 430040, China
Tel.: (86) 278 326 5953
Automobile Equipment Mfr
N.A.I.C.S.: 336310

STANMORE RESOURCES LIMITED
Level 32 12 Creek Street, Brisbane, 4000, QLD, Australia
Tel.: (61) 732381000
Web Site: https://stanmore.au
SMR—(ASX)
Rev.: $2,806,900,000
Assets: $3,605,400,000
Liabilities: $1,851,900,000
Net Worth: $1,753,500,000
Earnings: $472,400,000
Emp.: 3
Fiscal Year-end: 12/31/23
Coal Mining Services
N.A.I.C.S.: 212115
Daniel Clifford *(Mng Dir)*

STANOVI JADRAN D.D
Kralja Zvonimira 14 / IX, 21000, Split, Croatia
Tel.: (385) 21482367
Web Site: https://www.stanovijadran.com
Real Estate Manangement Services
N.A.I.C.S.: 531390

STANPACKS (INDIA) LTD.
S K Enclave New No 4 Nowroji Road, Chetpet, Chennai, 600 031, India
Tel.: (91) 4426451722
Web Site: https://www.blissgroup.com
530931—(BOM)
Rev.: $4,153,067
Assets: $3,085,596
Liabilities: $2,870,827
Net Worth: $214,769
Earnings: ($183,975)
Emp.: 50
Fiscal Year-end: 03/31/21
Packaging Materials Mfr
N.A.I.C.S.: 326112
G. P. N. Gupta *(Chm)*

STANPRO LIGHTING SYSTEMS INC.
2233 Rue de l'Aviation Dorval, Dorval, H9P 2X6, QC, Canada
Tel.: (514) 739-9984
Web Site: http://www.stanprols.com
Year Founded: 1997
Lighting Product Mfr
N.A.I.C.S.: 335139
Sam Rimoin *(Pres)*

STANROSE MAFATLAL INVESTMENTS & FINANCE LIMITED
6th Floor Popular House Ashram Road, Ahmedabad, 380 009, India
Tel.: (91) 7926580067 In

Web Site: https://www.stanrosefinvest.com
Year Founded: 1980
506105—(BOM)
Rev.: $385,696
Assets: $7,433,799
Liabilities: $397,266
Net Worth: $7,036,533
Earnings: ($58,510)
Emp.: 10
Fiscal Year-end: 03/31/23
Investment Management Service
N.A.I.C.S.: 523999
Madhusudan J. Mehta *(CEO)*

STANS ENERGY CORP.
1 Yonge Street Suite 1011, Toronto, M5E 1E5, ON, Canada
Tel.: (647) 426-1865 ON
Web Site: http://www.stansenergy.com
Year Founded: 2008
HRE—(OTCIQ)
Rev.: $12,073,404
Assets: $102,182
Liabilities: $1,435,153
Net Worth: ($1,332,971)
Earnings: $11,364,819
Fiscal Year-end: 12/31/20
Uranium, Gold & Other Metal Mining Services
N.A.I.C.S.: 212290
Rodney Irwin *(CEO-Interim)*

STANTEC INC.
300 - 10220-103 Avenue, Edmonton, T5J 0K4, AB, Canada
Tel.: (780) 917-7000 AB
Web Site: https://www.stantec.com
Year Founded: 1954
STN—(NYSE)
Rev.: $4,441,160,016
Assets: $4,422,150,612
Liabilities: $2,633,545,620
Net Worth: $1,788,604,992
Earnings: $193,223,160
Emp.: 26,000
Fiscal Year-end: 12/31/22
Engineering, Design & Architectural Project Management & Consulting Services
N.A.I.C.S.: 541330
Douglas K. Ammerman *(Chm)*

Subsidiaries:

Communication Arts, Inc. (1)
1112 Pearl St, Boulder, CO 80302
Tel.: (303) 447-8202
Web Site: http://www.commartsdesign.com
Sales Range: $25-49.9 Million
Emp.: 25
Architectural Services
N.A.I.C.S.: 541310

MWH Global, Inc. (1)
370 Interlocken Blvd Ste 300, Broomfield, CO 80021-8012
Tel.: (303) 410-4000
Web Site: http://www.stantec.com
Civil Engineering Services in the Areas of Energy, Infrastructure, Water & Wastewater
N.A.I.C.S.: 541330

Subsidiary (Non-US):

MWH Europe Limited (2)
92 Avenue de Reine Astrid, 1310, La Hulpe, Belgium
Tel.: (32) 2655230
Web Site: http://www.stantec.com
Civil Engineering Services in the Areas of Energy, Infrastructure, Water & Wastewater Provider
N.A.I.C.S.: 541330
Christophe Leroy *(Dir-Ops)*

Subsidiary (Domestic):

Stantec Inc. - Belgium (3)
92 Avenue de Reine Astrid, 1310, La Hulpe, Belgium
Tel.: (32) 26552230

Web Site: http://www.stantec.com
Environmental Engineering
N.A.I.C.S.: 541330
Christophe Leroy *(Dir-Ops)*

Subsidiary (Non-US):

Stantec Inc. - Italy (3)
Centro Direzionale Milano 2 Palazzo Canova, 20090, Milan, Segrate, Italy
Tel.: (39) 0294757240
Web Site: http://www.stantec.com
Provider of Civil Engineering Services in the Areas of Energy, Infrastructure, Water & Wastewater
N.A.I.C.S.: 541330
Matteo Bellinello *(Dir-Intl Bus Dev)*

Subsidiary (Non-US):

MWH Arabtech-Jardaneh (4)
Ayman Krayyem Al Ma aytah st Building 3, PO Box 9532, Amman, 11191, Jordan
Tel.: (962) 65857167
Provider of Civil Engineering Services in the Areas of Energy, Infrastructure, Water & Wastewater
N.A.I.C.S.: 541330

Subsidiary (Non-US):

MWH Treatment Limited (2)
Soapworks Colgate Lane, Salford, M5 3LZ, United Kingdom
Tel.: (44) 1706367555
Web Site: https://mwhtreatment.com
Waste Water System Engineering & Design Services
N.A.I.C.S.: 221320

Subsidiary (Domestic):

MWH Farrer Limited (3)
Soapworks Colgate Lane, Salford, M5 3LZ, England, United Kingdom
Tel.: (44) 1706367555
Engineeering Services
N.A.I.C.S.: 541330

Branch (Domestic):

Stantec Inc. - Cleveland (2)
1001 Lakeside Ave E Ste 1600, Cleveland, OH 44114-1193
Tel.: (216) 621-2407
Web Site: http://www.stantec.com
Enviromental Engineering
N.A.I.C.S.: 237110
Carol Malesky *(Principal-Fin Svcs)*

Subsidiary (Domestic):

Stantec Inc. - Illinois (2)
350 N Orleans St Ste 1301, Chicago, IL 60654-1983
Tel.: (312) 831-3000
Web Site: http://www.stantec.com
Consulting Services in Engineering, Hydroelectric Generation & Power Systems
N.A.I.C.S.: 541330
Beth Knackstedt *(VP)*

Subsidiary (Domestic):

Stantec Inc. - Bellevue (3)
1687 114th Ave SE Ste 100, Bellevue, WA 98004-6965
Tel.: (425) 289-7300
Environmental Engineering
N.A.I.C.S.: 541330
Heidi Wahto *(Principal)*

Subsidiary (Non-US):

Stantec Inc. - New Zealand (2)
Tel.: (64) 33667449
Web Site: http://www.stantec.com
Civil Engineering Services in the Areas of Energy, Infrastructure, Water & Wastewater
N.A.I.C.S.: 541330
Chris Maguire *(Mgr-Grp)*

Stantec India Pvt. Ltd. (2)
5th Floor Bajaj Brandview 38 Wakdewadi Shivaji Nagar, Pune, 411 005, Maharashtra, India
Tel.: (91) 2066419000
Web Site: http://www.stantec.com
Civil Engineering Services
N.A.I.C.S.: 541330

Project Control Group Inc. (1)

STANTEC INC.

Stantec Inc.—(Continued)
207 Queens Quay West Suite 420, Toronto, M5J 1A7, ON, Canada
Tel.: (416) 203-1010
Project Planning & Implementation Services
N.A.I.C.S.: 541611

QuadraTec Inc. (1)
430-434 Water Street Suite 230, Saint John's, A1C 1E2, NL, Canada
Tel.: (709) 738-0122
Web Site: http://www.quadratec.ca
Sales Range: $25-49.9 Million
Emp.: 4
Mechanical & Electrical Engineering Services
N.A.I.C.S.: 541330
Ralph Mondeaux (CMO)

RiverMorph, LLC (1)
9200 Shelbyville Rd Ste 800, Louisville, KY 40222-5136
Web Site: https://www.rivermorph.com
Sales Range: $25-49.9 Million
Emp.: 80
Stream Restoration Software Development Services
N.A.I.C.S.: 541511

Roth Hill Engineering Partners, LLC (1)
11130 NE 33rd Pl Ste 200, Bellevue, WA 98004
Tel.: (425) 869-9448
Web Site: http://www.rothhill.com
Sales Range: $1-4.9 Billion
Emp.: 12,000
Engineeering Services
N.A.I.C.S.: 541330

Sparling, Inc. (1)
4100 194th St SW Ste 400, Lynnwood, WA 98036-4613 (100%)
Tel.: (206) 667-0555
Web Site: http://www.sparling.com
Emp.: 130
Engineering, IT Architecture, Acoustics, Security & Lighting Services
N.A.I.C.S.: 541330
Basel H. Jurdy (Principal)

Stantec Australia Pty. Ltd. (1)
Level 25 55 Collins Street, Melbourne, 3000, VIC, Australia
Tel.: (61) 39 851 9600
Construction Engineering Services
N.A.I.C.S.: 541330
Simon Davis (Dir-Business Development)

Stantec Consulting Caribbean Ltd. (1)
Winslow House Black Rock, Saint Michael, BB12056, Barbados
Tel.: (246) 4258505
Emp.: 15
Business Management Consulting Services
N.A.I.C.S.: 541611

Stantec Consulting Colombia S.A.S. (1)
Calle 70 A 4 41, Bogota, Colombia
Tel.: (57) 17442244
Management Consulting Services
N.A.I.C.S.: 541618

Stantec Consulting Group Inc. (1)
Three Columbia Cir Ste 6, Albany, NY 12203
Tel.: (518) 464-1717
Web Site: http://www.stantec.com
Rev.: $6,000,000
Emp.: 45
Engineeering Services
N.A.I.C.S.: 541330

Stantec Consulting International Ltd. (1)
49 Frederick St, Kitchener, N2H 6M7, ON, Canada
Tel.: (519) 579-4410
Web Site: http://www.stantec.com
Sales Range: $75-99.9 Million
Emp.: 350
Architecture Consulting Services
N.A.I.C.S.: 541690

Stantec Consulting Ltd. (1)
10160 112th St, Edmonton, 25KT2L6, Canada (100%)
Tel.: (780) 917-7000
Web Site: http://www.santec.com
Emp.: 1,200
Engineering Services
N.A.I.C.S.: 541330

Branch (Domestic):

Stantec Consulting Ltd. - Winnipeg Office (2)
199 Henlow Bay, Winnipeg, R3Y 1G4, MB, Canada
Tel.: (204) 488-6999
Web Site: http://www.stantec.com
Sales Range: $25-49.9 Million
Emp.: 100
Materials Testing Facility & Concrete Technology Consulting
N.A.I.C.S.: 541380

Stantec Consulting Services Inc. (1)
19 Technology Dr Ste 200, Irvine, CA 92618-2334
Tel.: (949) 923-6000
Web Site: http://www.stantec.com
Sales Range: $25-49.9 Million
Emp.: 120
Planning & Engineering Consulting Services
N.A.I.C.S.: 541690

Subsidiary (Domestic):

Stantec Consulting International LLC (2)
8211 S 48th St, Phoenix, AZ 85044
Tel.: (602) 438-2200
Engineeering Services
N.A.I.C.S.: 541330
Krista Bourque (Principal-Boston)

Stantec Consulting Michigan Inc. (2)
1168 Oak Valley Dr Ste 100, Ann Arbor, MI 48108-9200
Tel.: (734) 761-1010
Sales Range: $25-49.9 Million
Emp.: 40
Business Management Consulting Services
N.A.I.C.S.: 541611
Brian Simons (Principal)

Branch (Domestic):

Stantec Consulting Services Inc. - Bakersfield (2)
5500 Ming Ave Ste 410, Bakersfield, CA 93309-4631
Tel.: (661) 396-3770
Sales Range: $50-74.9 Million
Emp.: 100
Engineeering Services
N.A.I.C.S.: 541330
Kanna Meyyappan (VP-Engrg Ops)

Stantec Consulting Services Inc. - Baton Rouge (2)
1200 Brickyard Ln Ste 400, Baton Rouge, LA 70802
Tel.: (225) 765-7400
Sales Range: $10-24.9 Million
Engineeering Services
N.A.I.C.S.: 541330
Steve M. Boudreaux (Mng Principal)

Stantec Consulting Services Inc. - Tampa (2)
777 S Harbour Island Blvd Ste 600, Tampa, FL 33602-5729
Tel.: (813) 223-9500
Emp.: 160
Engineering & Environmental Services
N.A.I.C.S.: 541330
Dave Kemper (Sr Principal-Community Dev)

Stantec Experts-conseils ltee (1)
100 Alexis-Nihon Blvd Ste 110, Saint Laurent, H4M 2N6, QC, Canada
Tel.: (514) 739-0708
Web Site: http://www.stantec.com
Sales Range: $25-49.9 Million
Emp.: 55
Professional Consulting Services
N.A.I.C.S.: 813920

Stantec Holding (2017) Limited (1)
Buckingham Court Kingsmead Business Park Frederick Place London Road, High Wycombe, HP11 1JU, Buckinghamshire, United Kingdom
Tel.: (44) 149 452 6240
Web Site: https://www.stantec.com

Construction Engineering Services
N.A.I.C.S.: 541330
Ian Cranshaw (Dir)

Stantec Inc. - China (1)
2016 Yi-San Road, Shanghai, 200051, China
Tel.: (86) 2162370588
Web Site: http://www.stantec.com
Civil Engineering Services in the Areas of Energy, Infrastructure, Water & Wastewater
N.A.I.C.S.: 541330
Luke Long (Country Mgr-China)

Stantec Inc. - Manama (1)
Office No 13 Building 596 Rd 3819 Block 338 Adliya, PO Box 5150, Manama, Bahrain
Tel.: (973) 17712542
Web Site: http://www.stantec.com
Civil Engineering Services in the Areas of Energy, Infrastructure, Water & Wastewater
N.A.I.C.S.: 541330

Stantec Inc. - Taiwan (1)
9F 167 Tun Hua N Road, Taipei, 105, Taiwan
Tel.: (886) 2 8712 3866
Web Site: http://www.stantec.com
Civil Engineering Services in the Areas of Energy, Infrastructure, Water & Wastewater
N.A.I.C.S.: 541330
Adam Liu (Sr Dir)

Stantec Newfoundland & Labrador Ltd. (1)
118 Humphrey Rd, Labrador City, A2V 2J8, NL, Canada
Tel.: (709) 944-5228
Engineeering Services
N.A.I.C.S.: 541330

Stantec Technology International Inc. (1)
8211 S 48th St, Phoenix, AZ 85044-5355
Tel.: (602) 438-2200
Construction Engineering Services
N.A.I.C.S.: 237990

VOA Associates Incorporated (1)
224 S Michigan Ave, Chicago, IL 60604-2505
Tel.: (312) 554-1400
Web Site: http://www.voa.com
Architectural Design Services
N.A.I.C.S.: 541310

WilsonMiller, Inc. (1)
3200 Bailey Ln Ste 200, Naples, FL 34105-8507
Tel.: (239) 649-4040
Web Site: http://www.wilsonmiller.com
Sales Range: $25-49.9 Million
Emp.: 50
Engineering Services & Property Development
N.A.I.C.S.: 541330

STANWICK MANAGEMENT CONSULTANTS
Axxes Business Park Gebouw B, Guldensporenpark 20, Merelbeke, 9820, Belgium
Tel.: (32) 92105950 BE
Web Site: http://www.stanwick.be
Sales Range: $10-24.9 Million
Emp.: 23
Management Consulting
N.A.I.C.S.: 541611

Subsidiaries:

Asenta Management Consultants (1)
C Ibanez De Bilbao 28 6C, E-48009, Bilbao, Vizcaya, Spain
Tel.: (34) 944355190
Web Site: http://www.asenta.es
Management Consulting Services
N.A.I.C.S.: 541611

BCF Management Consultants (1)
276 Av De La Marne, Marcq-en-Baroeul, 59700, France (100%)
Tel.: (33) 3 28 33 02 33
Web Site: http://www.bcs.fr
Management Consulting Services
N.A.I.C.S.: 541611
Ven Loy (Sec)

INTERNATIONAL PUBLIC

STAPLES ARGENTINA S.A.
Vieytes Av 1690, Buenos Aires, Argentina
Tel.: (54) 1141362626 Ar
Web Site: http://www.staples.com.ar
Office Supplies Retailer
N.A.I.C.S.: 459410

STAPRING A.S.
Piaristicka Ul C 2, 949 01, Nitra, Slovakia
Tel.: (421) 376542131
Web Site: http://www.stapring.sk
Civil Engineering & Construction Services
N.A.I.C.S.: 541330
Lubos Kovac (Fin Mgr)

STAR ADHESIVES LTD.
Shanta Western Tower Level-13 Bir Uttam Mir Shawkat Road, 186 Tejgaon I/A, Dhaka, 1208, Bangladesh
Tel.: (880) 288 788 0011
Web Site: https://www.staradhesives.com.bd
Year Founded: 2013
Rev.: $4,784,004
Assets: $5,055,573
Liabilities: $2,870,317
Net Worth: $2,185,255
Earnings: $312,383
Fiscal Year-end: 06/30/21
N.A.I.C.S.: 325520
Zulfikar Ali (CFO)

STAR AG
Wiesholz 35, CH-8262, Ramsen, Switzerland
Tel.: (41) 52 742 92 00 CH
Web Site: http://www.star-group.net
Year Founded: 1984
Software Development Services
N.A.I.C.S.: 513210
Altaf Alimohamed (Pres-Digital Program Grp)

STAR ASIA INVESTMENT CORPORATION
18th Floor Atago Green Hills MORI Tower 2-5-1 Atago Minato, Tokyo, 105-6218, Japan
Tel.: (81) 354251340
Web Site: https://www.starasia-reit.com
Year Founded: 2015
3468—(TKS)
Sales Range: Less than $1 Million
Real Estate Investment Services
N.A.I.C.S.: 531210
Taro Masuyama (Co-Founder & Mng Partner)

Subsidiaries:

Sakura Sogo REIT Investment Corporation (1)
3-8-11 Kudan Minami Chiyoda-ku, Tokyo, 102-0074, Japan
Tel.: (81) 362726608
Web Site: http://www.sakurasogoreit.com
Real Estate Investment Services
N.A.I.C.S.: 531210
Makoto Muranaka (Exec Dir)

STAR ASIA VISION CORPORATION
No 1 Li-Hsin 5th Road Hsinchu Science Park, Hsinchu, 30078, Taiwan
Tel.: (886) 35638951
Web Site: https://en.tascsemi.com
Year Founded: 1983
2340—(TAI)
Rev.: $129,902,183
Assets: $408,513,311
Liabilities: $130,606,261
Net Worth: $277,907,050

Earnings: $9,938,225
Emp.: 1,077
Fiscal Year-end: 12/31/23
Sensor Chips Mfr
N.A.I.C.S.: 334413
Tsun-Chia Tai *(Vice Chm)*

Subsidiaries:

Opto Plus Technology Co., Ltd. (1)
No 696 Yangming North Road, Yuecheng District, Shaoxing, 202400, Zhejiang, China
Tel.: (86) 57588623888
Light Emitting Diode Lamps & Displays Mfr
N.A.I.C.S.: 334413

Opto Tech (Macao) Co., Ltd. (1)
Alameda Dr Carlos D'Assumpcao No 258 Praca Kin Heng Long 13 Andar P, Andar B, Macau, China (Macau)
Tel.: (853) 28723657
Light Emitting Diode Displays Mfr33411
N.A.I.C.S.: 334419

Opto Tech (Suzhou) Co., Ltd. (1)
No 735 Changjiang Road, Suzhou New District, Suzhou, 225300, Jiangsu, China
Tel.: (86) 512 66655226
Web Site: http://www.optosz.com
Light Emitting Diode Displays Mfr
N.A.I.C.S.: 334419

ProAsia Semiconductor Corporation Ltd. (1)
8F No 1 Li-Hsin 5th Road Hsinchu Science Park, Hsinchu, Taiwan
Tel.: (886) 35795070
Semiconductor Power Component Mfr & Distr
N.A.I.C.S.: 334413

STAR BULK CARRIERS CORP.
c/o Star Bulk Management Inc 40 Agiou Konstantinou Str, Maroussi, 15124, Athens, Greece
Tel.: (30) 2106178400 DE
Web Site: https://www.starbulk.com
SBLK—(NASDAQ)
Rev.: $949,269,000
Assets: $3,028,255,000
Liabilities: $1,368,185,000
Net Worth: $1,660,070,000
Earnings: $173,556,000
Emp.: 216
Fiscal Year-end: 12/31/23
Global Shipping Services
N.A.I.C.S.: 483111
Simos Spyrou *(Co-CFO)*

Subsidiaries:

Eagle Bulk Shipping Inc. (1)
300 1st Stamford Pl 5th Fl, Stamford, CT 06902
Tel.: (203) 276-8100
Web Site: https://www.eagleships.com
Rev.: $719,847,000
Assets: $1,237,209,000
Liabilities: $418,028,000
Net Worth: $819,181,000
Earnings: $248,009,000
Emp.: 96
Fiscal Year-end: 12/31/2022
Dry Bulk Shipping Services
N.A.I.C.S.: 483111

Subsidiary (Non-US):

Eagle Bulk Europe A/S (2)
Nyhavn 43 b 1st floor, 1051, Copenhagen, Denmark
Tel.: (45) 98800900
Sea Shipping Services
N.A.I.C.S.: 483111
Christian Vang Christensen *(Mgr-Chartering)*

Eagle Bulk Europe GmbH (2)
Zippelhaus 2, 20457, Hamburg, Germany
Tel.: (49) 4046000800
Freight Transportation Services
N.A.I.C.S.: 483111
Claus Frantzheld *(Mgr-Ops)*

Eagle Bulk Pte. Ltd. (2)
9 Raffles Place Ste 14-02 Republic Plaza 1, Singapore, 048619, Singapore
Tel.: (65) 65088180
Web Site: https://www.eagleships.com
Freight Transportation Services
N.A.I.C.S.: 483111

Subsidiary (Domestic):

Eagle Shipping International (USA) LLC (2)
477 Madison Ave Ste 1405, New York, NY 10022 (100%)
Tel.: (212) 785-2500
Web Site: http://www.eagleships.com
Sales Range: $100-124.9 Million
Emp.: 50
Deep Sea Freight Transportation Services
N.A.I.C.S.: 483111

OLDENDORFF GmbH & Co. KG (1)
Willy-Brandt-Allee 6, 23554, Lubeck, Germany
Tel.: (49) 45115000
Web Site: https://www.oldendorff.com
Cargo Transportation Services
N.A.I.C.S.: 488320

STAR CAPITAL PARTNERS LIMITED
15th Floor 33 Cavendish Square, London, W1G 0PW, United Kingdom
Tel.: (44) 2070168500 UK
Web Site: http://www.star-capital.com
Year Founded: 1999
Sales Range: $25-49.9 Million
Emp.: 22
Investment Management Service
N.A.I.C.S.: 523940
Tony Mallin *(Founder, Chm & Mng Partner)*

Subsidiaries:

ASL Aviation Holdings DAC (1)
No 3 Malahide Road, Swords, Dublin, K67 PP52, Ireland (51%)
Tel.: (353) 1 892 8100
Web Site: http://www.aslaviationgroup.com
Sales Range: $400-499.9 Million
Holding Company; Passenger & Freight Air Transportation Services
N.A.I.C.S.: 551112
Ulf Weber *(CEO-ASL Airlines Belgium)*

Subsidiary (Domestic):

ASL Airlines (Ireland) Limited (2)
No 3 Malahide Rd, Swords, Dublin, Ireland
Tel.: (353) 18121900
Web Site: http://www.aslairlines.ie
Freight Air Transportation Services
N.A.I.C.S.: 481112
Hugh Flynn *(CEO)*

Blohm + Voss Repair GmbH (1)
Hermann-Blohm-Strasse 2, 20457, Hamburg, Germany
Tel.: (49) 4031191139
Web Site: http://www.blohmvoss-repair.com
Sales Range: $100-124.9 Million
Emp.: 450
Ship Repair & Conversion Services
N.A.I.C.S.: 336611

STAR Capital Partnership LLP (1)
15th Floor 33 Cavendish Square, London, W1G 0PW, United Kingdom
Tel.: (44) 20 7016 8500
Web Site: http://www.star-capital.com
Investment Services
N.A.I.C.S.: 523999
Tony Mallin *(Chm & Mng Partner)*

Joint Venture (Domestic):

Vouvray Acquisition Limited (2)
1st Floor 63 Queen Victoria Street, London, EC4N 4UA, United Kingdom
Tel.: (44) 2380 258 381
Web Site: http://www.vgrouplimited.com
Holding Company; Ship Management & Shipping Industry Support Services
N.A.I.C.S.: 551112
Graham Westgarth *(CEO)*

Subsidiary (US):

Global Marine Travel LLC (3)
1800 SE 10th Ave Ste 320, Fort Lauderdale, FL 33316-2907
Tel.: (954) 761-9595
Web Site: http://www.flygmt.com
Ship Crew & Seafarers Travel Arrangement Agency
N.A.I.C.S.: 561510
Timothy D. Davey *(Mng Dir)*

Subsidiary (Domestic):

V.Scope Risk Management Ltd. (3)
1st Floor 63 Queen Victoria Street, London, EC4N 4UA, United Kingdom
Tel.: (44) 20 7332 8540
Web Site: http://www.vgrouplimited.com
Marine Insurance Brokerage Services
N.A.I.C.S.: 524210
John Sullivan *(Mng Dir)*

Subsidiary (Non-US):

V.Ships Group Ltd. (3)
2 Rue du Gabian, Les Industries Cedex, Monaco, 98013, Monaco
Tel.: (377) 92051010
Web Site: http://www.vgrouplimited.com
Ship Management & Support Services
N.A.I.C.S.: 488390
Franck Kayser *(CEO)*

Subsidiary (Domestic):

V.Ships Leisure Ltd. (4)
2 Rue du Gabaian, PO Box 639, 24 Ave de Fontvieille, Monaco, 98013, Monaco
Tel.: (377) 92051010
Web Site: http://www.vgrouplimited.com
Passenger Ship Management Support Services
N.A.I.C.S.: 488390
Lucy Hodgson *(Mgr-Recruitment-Global)*

Subsidiary (US):

V.Ships Leisure (USA) LLC (5)
1800 SE 10th Ave Ste 320, Fort Lauderdale, FL 33316
Tel.: (305) 455-0101
Passenger Vessel Management Support Services
N.A.I.C.S.: 488390

Subsidiary (Non-US):

V.Ships Offshore (Asia) Pte. Ltd. (4)
Prudential Tower 24/01-02 30 Cecil Street, Singapore, 049721, Singapore
Tel.: (65) 6603 9270
Ship Management Services
N.A.I.C.S.: 541618

V.Ships UK Ltd. (4)
Skypark 8 Elliot Place, Glasgow, G3 8EP, United Kingdom
Tel.: (44) 1412432435
Web Site: http://www.vgrouplimited.com
Technical & Personnel Ship Support Services
N.A.I.C.S.: 488390
John Adams *(Mng Dir)*

Subsidiary (Domestic):

Seatec UK Ltd. (5)
1st Floor Skypark 8 Elliot Place, Glasgow, G3 8EP, United Kingdom
Tel.: (44) 1413051300
Web Site: http://www.seatec-services.com
Ship Repair, Maintenance, Inspection & Ship Building Support Project Services
N.A.I.C.S.: 488390
Johannes Paulus Henricus Engels *(Gen Mgr-UK)*

Subsidiary (Domestic):

U.M.C. International Plc (6)
Warrior Close Chandlers Ford, Eastleigh, SO53 4TE, Southants, United Kingdom
Tel.: (44) 2380269866
Web Site: http://www.seatec-services.com
Commercial & Naval Ship Underwater Maintenance, Repair & Support Services
N.A.I.C.S.: 336611
Alan Trevarthen *(Mng Dir)*

Synergy Health Managed Services Limited (1)
Ascot Drive, Derby, DE24 8HE, United Kingdom
Tel.: (44) 330 0535 737
Web Site: http://www.synergylms.co.uk

Linen Management Services
N.A.I.C.S.: 812331
Mike Langhorn *(Mng Dir)*

STAR CM HOLDINGS LIMITED
17th floor No 300 Hankou Road, Huangpu District, Shanghai, China
Tel.: (86) 2152032888 Ky
Web Site:
  https://www.starcmgroup.com
Year Founded: 2006
6698—(HKG)
Rev.: $133,817,444
Assets: $765,656,404
Liabilities: $79,537,286
Net Worth: $686,119,117
Earnings: $12,954,978
Emp.: 367
Fiscal Year-end: 12/31/22
Holding Company
N.A.I.C.S.: 551112
Ming Tian *(CEO)*

Subsidiaries:

Fortune Star Media Limited (1)
Unit A 9/F MG Tower 133 Hoi Bun Road, Kwun Tong, Kowloon, China (Hong Kong)
Tel.: (852) 39963700
Web Site:
  https://www.fortunestarentertainment.com
Television Network Services
N.A.I.C.S.: 512120

Shanghai CanXing Culture & Media Co., Ltd. (1)
17th Floor No 300 Hankou Road, Huangpu District, Shanghai, China
Tel.: (86) 2152032888
Web Site: https://www.canxingmedia.com
Television & Internet Program Operator
N.A.I.C.S.: 512110

STAR COMBO PHARMA LTD.
171-177 Woodpark Rd, Smithfield, 2164, NSW, Australia
Tel.: (61) 297566555 AU
Web Site:
  https://www.starcombo.com.au
Year Founded: 2004
S66—(ASX)
Rev.: $17,373,865
Assets: $28,589,498
Liabilities: $6,213,264
Net Worth: $22,376,234
Earnings: $499,018
Fiscal Year-end: 06/30/24
Dietary Supplement Product Mfr
N.A.I.C.S.: 325412
Star Zhang *(Founder & Mng Dir)*

Subsidiaries:

CoStar Pharma Laboratory Pty Ltd (1)
171-177 Woodpark Road, Smithfield, 2164, NSW, Australia
Tel.: (61) 29 756 6555
Web Site: https://www.costarpharma.com.au
Pharmaceutical Preparation Mfr
N.A.I.C.S.: 325412

STAR DELTA TRANSFORMERS LIMITED
92-A Industrial Area Govindpura, Bhopal, 462023, India
Tel.: (91) 7552586680
Web Site:
  https://www.startransformers.com
Year Founded: 1980
539255—(BOM)
Rev.: $10,547,649
Assets: $10,290,886
Liabilities: $2,785,924
Net Worth: $7,504,962
Earnings: $690,442
Emp.: 35
Fiscal Year-end: 03/31/23
Electric Power Transformer Mfr
N.A.I.C.S.: 335311
Kishore Gupta *(Chm & Mng Dir)*

Star Delta Transformers Limited—(Continued)

STAR DIAMOND CORPORATION
600 224-4th Avenue South, Saskatoon, S7K 5M5, SK, Canada
Tel.: (306) 664-2202   Ca
Web Site:
https://www.stardiamondcorp.com
Year Founded: 1985
DIAM—(TSX)
Rev.: $66,494
Assets: $56,819,343
Liabilities: $1,746,049
Net Worth: $55,073,294
Earnings: ($4,794,594)
Emp.: 5
Fiscal Year-end: 12/31/20
Natural Resource Exploration
N.A.I.C.S.: 212290
Rick Johnson *(CFO)*

STAR ENERGY
Wisma Barito Star Energy Tower
Jalan Let Jen S Parman Kav 62-63, Jakarta Barat, 11410, Indonesia
Tel.: (62) 21 5325828   Id
Web Site: http://www.starenergy.co.id
Year Founded: 2003
Oil & Gas Production & Exploration; Geothermal Electricity Production
N.A.I.C.S.: 211120
Rudy Suparman *(Pres & CEO)*

STAR ENERGY GROUP PLC
Barfield Lane Off Wragby Road, Sudbrooke, Lincoln, LN2 2QX, United Kingdom
Tel.: (44) 2079939899   UK
Web Site:
https://www.starenergygroupplc.com
STAR—(AIM)
Sales Range: $50-74.9 Million
Emp.: 155
Crude Petroleum Extraction Services
N.A.I.C.S.: 211120
Stephen Bowler *(CEO)*

Subsidiaries:

Star Energy Group Ltd. (1)
Grand Buildings 1st Floor 1 3 Strand, London, W1J 7AJ, United Kingdom
Tel.: (44) 2079552121
Web Site: http://www.starenergy.co.uk
Sales Range: $75-99.9 Million
Emp.: 148
Oil & Gas Exploration Services
N.A.I.C.S.: 211120
Abigail Ford *(Office Mgr)*

STAR FASHION CULTURE HOLDINGS LIMITED
12F No 611 Sishui Road, Huli District, Xiamen, China
Tel.: (86) 13063138565   Ky
Web Site: https://www.xmxingji.com
Year Founded: 2015
STFS—(NASDAQ)
Rev.: $14,971,610
Assets: $8,239,723
Liabilities: $5,153,292
Net Worth: $3,086,431
Earnings: $1,542,430
Emp.: 17
Fiscal Year-end: 06/30/24
Holding Company
N.A.I.C.S.: 551112

STAR FERRO & CEMENT LIMITED
Satyam Towers Unit No 9B 1st Floor 3 Alipore Road, Kolkata, 700 027, India
Tel.: (91) 33 24484169   In
Web Site:
http://www.starferrocement.com
Year Founded: 2011
Rev.: $260,455,819
Assets: $364,324,884
Liabilities: $200,466,829
Net Worth: $163,858,055
Earnings: $20,443,246
Emp.: 2
Fiscal Year-end: 03/31/16
Ferro Alloy Mfr
N.A.I.C.S.: 331110
Sajjan Bhajanka *(Chm)*

STAR FLYER INC.
Airport Headquarters Building 6 Kuko Kitamachi, Kokuraminami-ku Kitakyushu, Fukuyama, 800-0306, Japan
Tel.: (81) 935554500
Web Site: https://www.starflyer.jp
Year Founded: 2002
9206—(TKS)
Sales Range: $200-249.9 Million
Emp.: 490
Oil Transportation Services
N.A.I.C.S.: 481111
Sadami Matsuishi *(Pres)*

STAR GROUP COMPANY LIMITED
11/F TG Place TG Place 10 Shing Yip Street Kwun Tong Kowloon, Hong Kong, China (Hong Kong)
Tel.: (852) 36536387   Ky
Web Site:
http://www.starproperties.com.hk
Year Founded: 2016
1560—(HKG)
Rev.: $216,661,260
Assets: $651,283,770
Liabilities: $432,324,195
Net Worth: $218,959,575
Earnings: $42,216,143
Emp.: 122
Fiscal Year-end: 12/31/22
Property Development Services
N.A.I.C.S.: 531210
Wai Shuen Cheung *(Sec)*

Subsidiaries:

Metropolitan Wine Cellar Limited (1)
Unit 402 Block A Sea View Estate 2 Watson Road, Tin Hau, Hong Kong, China (Hong Kong)
Tel.: (852) 251 2093
Web Site: https://metrowine.hk
Wine Distr
N.A.I.C.S.: 424820

STAR HEALTH & ALLIED INSURANCE CO. LTD.
No 1 New Tank Street Valluvarkottam High Road Nungambakkam, Chennai, 600034, India
Tel.: (91) 28288800
Web Site: https://www.starhealth.in
Year Founded: 2006
543412—(BOM)
Insurance Services
N.A.I.C.S.: 524210
V. Jagannathan *(Chm & CEO)*

STAR HOUSING FINANCE LTD.
603 Western Edge 1 Above Metro Mall Borivali East, Mumbai, 400066, Rajasthan, India
Tel.: (91) 8828036610
Web Site: https://www.starhfl.com
539017—(BOM)
Rev.: $4,465,332
Assets: $34,231,533
Liabilities: $21,472,250
Net Worth: $12,759,283
Earnings: $836,868
Emp.: 148
Fiscal Year-end: 03/31/23
Home & Mortgage Lending Services
N.A.I.C.S.: 522310

Nirmal Kumar Jain *(Exec Dir)*

STAR LAKE BIOSCIENCE CO., INC.
No 67 Gongnong Road North, Zhaoqing, 526040, Guangdong, China
Tel.: (86) 7582290061
Web Site:
https://www.starlake.com.cn
Year Founded: 1964
600866—(SHG)
Rev.: $2,455,078,865
Assets: $2,246,182,857
Liabilities: $1,273,323,486
Net Worth: $972,859,371
Earnings: $85,408,984
Emp.: 2,000
Fiscal Year-end: 12/31/22
Pharmaceuticals Product Mfr
N.A.I.C.S.: 325412
Wu Chen *(Board of Directors & Gen Mgr)*

STAR MEDIA GROUP BERHAD
Lot 2 Jalan Astaka U8/88 Section U8, Bukit Jelutong, 40150, Shah Alam, Selangor Darul Ehsan, Malaysia
Tel.: (60) 379671388
Web Site:
https://www.thestar.com.my
STAR—(KLS)
Rev.: $45,891,217
Assets: $164,092,698
Liabilities: $26,071,323
Net Worth: $138,021,376
Earnings: $1,456,931
Emp.: 940
Fiscal Year-end: 12/31/22
Publishing Services
N.A.I.C.S.: 513110
Esther Ng *(Chief Content Officer)*

Subsidiaries:

Star Publications (Singapore) Pte. Ltd. (1)
Block 115A Commonwealth Drive 05-12 Tanglin Halt Industrial Park, Singapore, 149596, Singapore
Tel.: (65) 64796800
Web Site: http://www.starpub.com.sg
Books Publishing Services
N.A.I.C.S.: 513130

STAR MICA CO., LTD.
28F Shiroyama Trust Tower 4-3-1 Toranomon, Minato-ku, Tokyo, 105-6028, Japan
Tel.: (81) 33 568 1091
Web Site: http://www.starmica.co.jp
Year Founded: 2001
Rev.: $268,895,280
Assets: $564,199,680
Liabilities: $411,774,480
Net Worth: $152,425,200
Earnings: $19,127,520
Emp.: 82
Fiscal Year-end: 11/30/18
Real Estate Investment Services
N.A.I.C.S.: 531390
Masashi Mizunaga *(Chm, Pres & CEO)*

STAR MICA HOLDINGS CO., LTD.
28F Shiroyama Trust Tower 4-3-1 Toranomon, Minato-ku, Tokyo, 105-6028, Japan
Tel.: (81) 357762785
Web Site: http://www.starmica-holdings.co.jp
Year Founded: 1998
2975—(TKS)
Rev.: $346,537,930
Assets: $673,422,380
Liabilities: $508,714,590
Net Worth: $164,707,790
Earnings: $18,887,760

Emp.: 144
Fiscal Year-end: 11/30/23
Holding Company
N.A.I.C.S.: 551112
Masashi Mizunaga *(Chm, Pres & CEO)*

Subsidiaries:

SMAiT Co., Ltd. (1)
28th Floor of Shiroyama Trust Tower 4-3-1, Toranomon Minato-ku, Tokyo, 105-6028, Japan
Tel.: (81) 357762820
Web Site: https://www.smait.co.jp
Real Estate Asset Management Services
N.A.I.C.S.: 531311

Star Mica Asset Partners Co., Ltd. (1)
28th Floor of Shiroyama Trust Tower 4-3-1, Toranomon Minato-ku, Tokyo, 105-6028, Japan
Tel.: (81) 357762561
Web Site: https://www.starmica-ap.co.jp
Real Estate Brokerage Services
N.A.I.C.S.: 531210

Star Mica Property Co., Ltd. (1)
28th Floor Shiroyama Trust Tower 4-3-1, Toranomon Minato-ku, Tokyo, 105-6028, Japan
Tel.: (81) 357762703
Web Site: https://www.starmica-property.co.jp
Real Estate Rental Management Services
N.A.I.C.S.: 531311

Star Mica Residence Co., Ltd. (1)
Shiroyama Trust Tower 28F 4-3-1, Toranomon Minato-ku, Tokyo, 105-6028, Japan
Tel.: (81) 357762688
Web Site: https://www.starmica-r.co.jp
Condominium Brokerage Services
N.A.I.C.S.: 531311

STAR MICRONICS CO LTD
20-10 Nakayoshida, Suruga-ku, Shizuoka, 422-8654, Japan
Tel.: (81) 542631111
Web Site: https://www.star-m.jp
Year Founded: 1947
7718—(TKS)
Rev.: $626,428,560
Assets: $713,687,460
Liabilities: $189,646,500
Net Worth: $524,040,960
Earnings: $73,836,660
Emp.: 470
Fiscal Year-end: 12/31/22
Electronic Components Mfr
N.A.I.C.S.: 334419
Hajime Sato *(Chm)*

Subsidiaries:

Micro Sapporo Company (1)
705-2 Shinkouminami 3-chome, Ishikari, Hokkaido, Japan
Tel.: (81) 133643663
Computer Peripheral Equipment Mfr
N.A.I.C.S.: 334118

Smart Solution Technology, Inc. (1)
8F Kagurazaka 1-chome Building 1-15 Kagurazaka, Shinjuku-ku, Tokyo, 162-0825, Japan
Tel.: (81) 362650009
Web Site: https://www.sstinc.co.jp
Emp.: 51
Software Development Services
N.A.I.C.S.: 541511

Star CNC Machine Tool Corporation (1)
123 Powerhouse Rd, Roslyn Heights, NY 11577
Tel.: (516) 484-0500
Web Site: http://www.starcnc.com
Machine Tool Distr
N.A.I.C.S.: 423830
George Bursac *(Gen Mgr-Sls)*

Star Metal Company (1)
1500-133 Kitanoya Misawa, Kikugawa, Shizuoka, Japan
Tel.: (81) 537350026

AND PRIVATE COMPANIES — STARA SA-INDUSTRIA DE IMPLEMENTOS AGRICOLAS

Computer Peripheral Equipment Mfr
N.A.I.C.S.: 334118

Star Micronics AG (1)
Lauetstrasse 3, 8112, Otelfingen, Switzerland
Tel.: (41) 434116060
Web Site: https://www.starmicronics.ch
Machine Tool Distr
N.A.I.C.S.: 423830
Jörg Pekeler (Mgr-Sls-Europe)

Star Micronics GmbH (1)
Robert-Grob-Str 1, 75305, Neuenburg, Germany
Tel.: (49) 708279200
Web Site: https://www.starmicronics.de
Lathe Machine Tool Distr
N.A.I.C.S.: 423830

Star Micronics Manufacturing (Thailand) Co., Ltd. (1)
Suranaree Industrial Zone 888 Moo 6 Nongraweing, Amphur Muang, 30000, Nakhonratchasima, Thailand
Tel.: (66) 44327588
Machine Tools Mfr
N.A.I.C.S.: 333517

Star Micronics Precision (Thailand) Co., Ltd. (1)
42 Moo 4 Rojana Industrial Park Tambol Banchang Amphur U-Thai, Ayutthaya, 13210, Thailand
Tel.: (66) 35746569
Industrial Precision Component Mfr
N.A.I.C.S.: 333310

Star Micronics Pty. Ltd. (1)
Unit A 15 Lagana Place, Wetherill Park, 2164, NSW, Australia
Tel.: (61) 287881500
Web Site: https://www.starmicronics.com.au
Printer Distr
N.A.I.C.S.: 423430

Star Micronics Southeast Asia Co., Ltd. (1)
399 Interchange 21 Building Unit 2105 21st Floor Sukhumvit Road, Klongtoey-Nua Wattana, Bangkok, 10110, Thailand
Tel.: (66) 225846312
Web Site: https://www.starmicronics.co.th
Computer Peripheral Equipment Mfr & Distr
N.A.I.C.S.: 334118

Star-Asia Technology Ltd. (1)
Unit 1905-08 19/F Enterprise Square Two 3 Sheung Yuet Road Kowloon Bay, Kowloon, China (Hong Kong)
Tel.: (852) 27996682
Web Site: http://www.starasia.com
Industrial Precision Component Mfr
N.A.I.C.S.: 333310

Triple Industries Taiwan Corp. (1)
1F No 31 Lane 245 Sec 4 Pa-Teh Rd, Taipei, Taiwan
Tel.: (886) 227632715
Web Site: http://www.sankotriple.com.tw
Printer Distr
N.A.I.C.S.: 423430

STAR MINERALS LIMITED
191B Carr Place, Leederville, 6007, WA, Australia
Tel.: (61) 92261860
Web Site: https://www.starminerals.com.au
Year Founded: 2021
SMS—(ASX)
Rev.: $131,927
Assets: $4,179,390
Liabilities: $140,486
Net Worth: $4,038,904
Earnings: ($765,023)
Fiscal Year-end: 06/30/23
Mineral Exploration Services
N.A.I.C.S.: 212390

STAR MONEY PUBLIC COMPANY LIMITED
204/1-8 Sukhumvit Road, Thang Kwian Subdistrict Klaeng District, Rayong, 21110, Thailand
Tel.: (66) 613939988
Web Site: https://www.starmoney.co.th
Year Founded: 1987
SM—(THA)
Rev.: $40,280,664
Assets: $86,396,745
Liabilities: $53,479,077
Net Worth: $32,917,668
Earnings: $1,802,595
Emp.: 438
Fiscal Year-end: 12/31/23
Consumer Electronics Retailer
N.A.I.C.S.: 423620
Visit Ongpipattanakul (Chm)

STAR NAVIGATION SYSTEMS GROUP LTD.
11 Kenview Blvd, Brampton, L6T 5G5, ON, Canada
Tel.: (416) 252-2889
Web Site: https://www.star-navigation.com
SNA—(CNSX)
Rev.: $93,340
Assets: $719,684
Liabilities: $3,081,565
Net Worth: ($2,361,881)
Earnings: ($4,199,556)
Fiscal Year-end: 06/30/24
Aerospace Safety Monitoring System Mfr
N.A.I.C.S.: 334511

Subsidiaries:

Star Navigation Systems Inc. (1)
2970 Lake Shore Blvd W, Etobicoke, M8V 1J7, ON, Canada
Tel.: (416) 252-2889
Web Site: http://www.star-navigation.com
Emp.: 22
Aerospace Safety Monitoring System Mfr
N.A.I.C.S.: 334511
Firaf Kapadia (CEO)

STAR PAPER MILLS LIMITED
Duncan House 2nd Floor 31-Netaji Subhas Road, Kolkata, 700 001, West Bengal, India
Tel.: (91) 3322427380
Web Site: https://www.starpapers.com
STARPAPER—(NSE)
Rev.: $33,150,663
Assets: $88,770,209
Liabilities: $20,262,647
Net Worth: $68,507,562
Earnings: $2,390,920
Emp.: 417
Fiscal Year-end: 03/31/21
Paper Mfr
N.A.I.C.S.: 322299
G. P. Goenka (Chm)

STAR PHARMACEUTICAL LIMITED
Six Battery Road 10-01, Singapore, 049909, Singapore
Tel.: (65) 6381 6972
Web Site: http://www.star-pharm.com
Year Founded: 2005
Rev.: $35,229,596
Assets: $39,670,243
Liabilities: $18,435,016
Net Worth: $21,235,227
Earnings: $1,704,116
Fiscal Year-end: 12/31/18
Drug Product Mfr & Distr
N.A.I.C.S.: 325412
Zhi Bin Xu (Chm)

STAR PHOENIX GROUP LTD
Level 1 8 St Georges Terrace, Perth, 6000, WA, Australia
Tel.: (61) 862053012
Web Site: https://www.starphoenixgroup.com
STA—(AIM)
Rev.: $2,792
Assets: $5,030,649
Liabilities: $10,993,091
Net Worth: ($5,962,442)
Earnings: ($1,336,247)
Fiscal Year-end: 06/30/22
Crude Petroleum Extraction Services
N.A.I.C.S.: 211120
Zhiwei Gu (Chm)

Subsidiaries:

Star Phoenix Group UK Limited (1)
Studio F8 Battersea Studios 80 Silverthorne Road, London, SW8 3HE, United Kingdom
Tel.: (44) 2038658430
Oil Field Services
N.A.I.C.S.: 213112
Evgenia Bezruchko (Sec & Mgr-Corp Dev)

STAR PORTFOLIO CORP.
1 First Canadian Place 100 King Street West 3rd Floor Podium, Toronto, M5X 1H3, ON, Canada
Tel.: (866) 864-7760
Year Founded: 2010
Investment Services
N.A.I.C.S.: 523999

STAR PRODUCE LTD.
366 Edson Street, Saskatoon, S7J 0P9, SK, Canada
Tel.: (306) 934-3372
Web Site: http://www.starproduce.com
Year Founded: 1989
Rev.: $22,337,347
Emp.: 55
Fruits & Vegetables Distr
N.A.I.C.S.: 424480
Glenn Baty (Pres & COO)

STAR SANITARYWARE (THAILAND) CO., LTD.
410/7-9 Ratchadapisek 22 Rd Samsennok, Huaykwang, Bangkok, 10310, Thailand
Tel.: (66) 2541 5588
Web Site: http://www.starsanitaryware.com
Year Founded: 1990
Ceramic Toilet & Wash Basin Mfr
N.A.I.C.S.: 326191
Somchai Wongaroon (Chm)

STAR UNIVERSAL NETWORK PUBLIC COMPANY LIMITED
57 Park Ventures Ecoplex Building Unit 1607A 16th Floor, Wireless Road Lumpini Patumwan, Bangkok, 10330, Thailand
Tel.: (66) 20418162
Web Site: http://www.staruniversal.com
STAR—(THA)
Sales Range: $1-9.9 Million
Holding Company
N.A.I.C.S.: 551112
Chirarak Sithiphand (Chm)

STAR WEALTH GROUP INC.
Rm 1316 13/F Tower A New Mandarin Plaza Science Museum Road, Tsim Sha Tsui, Kowloon, China (Hong Kong)
Tel.: (852) 65197111
Web Site: http://starwealth.group
Year Founded: 2014
SWGI—(OTCBB)
Assets: $11,000
Liabilities: $50,823
Net Worth: ($39,823)
Earnings: ($55,256)
Fiscal Year-end: 09/30/19
Investment Services
N.A.I.C.S.: 523999

Bum Chul Kim (Pres, CEO, CFO, Treas & Sec)

STAR7 S.P.A.
Via Alessandria 37/B, Valle San Bartolomeo, 15122, Alessandria, AL, Italy
Tel.: (39) 013119788
Web Site: https://www.star-7.com
Year Founded: 2000
STAR7—(ITA)
Rev.: $116,594,359
Assets: $116,668,286
Liabilities: $81,484,049
Net Worth: $35,184,237
Earnings: $2,463,531
Emp.: 566
Fiscal Year-end: 12/31/23
Information Technology Services
N.A.I.C.S.: 541512

Subsidiaries:

STAR7 Gmbh (1)
Am Belvedere 8, 1100, Vienna, Austria
Tel.: (43) 171728756
Printing Services
N.A.I.C.S.: 561410

Star Comunicacao E Servicos Ltda. (1)
Rua Gaturana 112 Bairro Santo Antonio, Betim, 32684-010, MG, Brazil
Tel.: (55) 3121233484
Printing Services
N.A.I.C.S.: 561410

Vertere S.R.L. (1)
Via Calciati 16, 29122, Piacenza, Italy
Tel.: (39) 03420116532
Web Site: https://vertere.net
Information Technology Services
N.A.I.C.S.: 541930

STAR8 CORP.
467 Edgeley Blvd Unit3, Vaughan, L4K4E9, ON, Canada
Tel.: (416) 568-5267
Year Founded: 1987
STRH—(OTCIQ)
Sales Range: Less than $1 Million
Emp.: 1
Computer Peripheral Distr
N.A.I.C.S.: 423430

STARA PLANINA HOLD PLC
20 Fr Joliot Curie Str Floor 9, 1113, Sofia, Bulgaria
Tel.: (359) 29634161
Web Site: https://www.sphold.com
Year Founded: 1996
SPH—(BUL)
Rev.: $207,584,356
Assets: $180,162,687
Liabilities: $33,759,312
Net Worth: $146,403,375
Earnings: $22,165,316
Emp.: 2,353
Fiscal Year-end: 12/31/23
Hydraulic Cylinder Mfr
N.A.I.C.S.: 333995
Evgeniy Vasilev Uzunov (Chm)

Subsidiaries:

Boriana JSC (1)
St Struga 1 Industrial Zone, Cherven Bryag, 5980, Bulgaria
Tel.: (359) 659 9 24 38
Web Site: http://www.boriana.bg
Knitwear Mfr
N.A.I.C.S.: 315120

Patstroyinjenering JSC (1)
Boulevard Belomorski N 79, 6600, Kardjhali, Bulgaria
Tel.: (359) 361 66033
Road Construction & Repair Services
N.A.I.C.S.: 237310

STARA SA-INDUSTRIA DE IMPLEMENTOS AGRICOLAS
Avenida Stara 519, PO Box 53, Nao-

STARA SA-INDUSTRIA DE IMPLEMENTOS AGRICOLAS

Stara SA-Industria De Implementos Agricolas—(Continued)
Me-Toque, Rio Grande, 99470-000, Brazil
Tel.: (55) 5433322800
Web Site: http://www.stara.com.br
STTR3—(BRAZ)
Sales Range: Less than $1 Million
Agricultural Machine & Equipment Mfr
N.A.I.C.S.: 333111
Atila Stapelbroek Trennepohl *(CEO)*

STARBOX GROUP HOLDINGS LTD.
VO20305 Velocity Office 2 Lingkaran SV Sunway Velocity, 55100, Kuala Lumpur, Malaysia
Tel.: (60) 327819066   Ky
Web Site: https://www.starboxholdings.com
Year Founded: 2021
STBX—(NASDAQ)
Rev.: $11,740,852
Assets: $153,026,585
Liabilities: $11,968,253
Net Worth: $141,058,332
Earnings: $2,148,236
Emp.: 104
Fiscal Year-end: 09/30/23
Holding Company
N.A.I.C.S.: 551112
Choon Wooi Lee *(CEO & Chm)*

STARBREEZE AB
Regeringsgatan 38, PO Box 7731, 103 95, Stockholm, Sweden
Tel.: (46) 8209208
Web Site: https://www.starbreeze.com
Year Founded: 1998
STAR.B—(OMX)
Rev.: $62,889,393
Assets: $110,339,411
Liabilities: $21,526,099
Net Worth: $88,813,312
Earnings: $20,611,909
Emp.: 194
Fiscal Year-end: 12/31/23
Game Software Developer
N.A.I.C.S.: 513210
Mikael Nermark *(CEO-Acting)*

Subsidiaries:

StarVR Corp.
25F 88 Section 1 Xintai 5 Road, Xizhi District, New Taipei City, 22175, Taiwan
Tel.: (886) 226960567
Electronic Components Mfr
N.A.I.C.S.: 334419
Gregoire Colombet *(Program Mgr)*

STARCAN CORPORATION
161 Bay St, BCE Pl, Toronto, M5J 2S1, ON, Canada
Tel.: (416) 361-0255   ON
Year Founded: 1972
Sales Range: $50-74.9 Million
Emp.: 200
Holding Company
N.A.I.C.S.: 551112
L. Grant Burton *(Pres)*

STARCOM INFORMATION TECHNOLOGY LTD
73/1 Sheriff Centre 5th Floor St Marks Road, Bengaluru, 560 001, India
Tel.: (91) 8022278283
Web Site: https://starcominfotech.com
Year Founded: 1995
531616—(BOM)
Rev.: $242,204
Assets: $3,995,900
Liabilities: $5,325,808
Net Worth: ($1,329,908)

Earnings: ($628,619)
Emp.: 32
Fiscal Year-end: 03/31/23
Software Publisher
N.A.I.C.S.: 513210
Ziaulla Sheriff *(Chm & Mng Dir)*

STARCORE INTERNATIONAL MINES LTD.
Suite 750 - 580 Hornby Street, Box 113, Vancouver, V6C 3B6, BC, Canada
Tel.: (604) 602-4935   BC
Web Site: https://www.starcore.com
SAM—(OTCIQ)
Rev.: $20,964,322
Assets: $36,353,334
Liabilities: $7,972,215
Net Worth: $28,381,118
Earnings: ($801,055)
Emp.: 197
Fiscal Year-end: 04/30/21
Gold & Silver Exploration & Mining Services
N.A.I.C.S.: 212220
Robert Eadie *(CEO)*

STARCREST EDUCATION LIMITED
Cricket Square Hutchins Drive, PO Box 2681, Georgetown, KY3-1111, Grand Cayman, Cayman Islands   Ky
Web Site: https://www.starcresteducation.com
Year Founded: 2018
OBOR—(LSE)
Assets: $59,560
Liabilities: $846,701
Net Worth: ($787,141)
Earnings: ($1,889,106)
Fiscal Year-end: 12/31/21
Educational Support Services
N.A.I.C.S.: 611710
Nigel Cartwright *(Sec)*

STARDYNE TECHNOLOGIES INC.
1632 Dickson Avenue Suite 400, Kelowna, V1Y 7T2, BC, Canada
Tel.: (250) 469-7676
Web Site: http://www.stardynetech.com
Year Founded: 2001
Sales Range: $25-49.9 Million
Emp.: 350
Holding Company; Government, Education & Asset Management Sector Software Solutions
N.A.I.C.S.: 551112
Dave A. Love *(Pres-SRB Education Solutions)*

Subsidiaries:

Dreamstalk Studios Inc.   (1)
1201 Kingsway Avenue SE, Medicine Hat, T1A 2Y2, AB, Canada
Tel.: (403) 488-2433
Web Site: http://www.dreamstalk.ca
Website Designing Services
N.A.I.C.S.: 541511

PATHFIVE LTD   (1)
1632 Dickson Ave, Kelowna, V1Y 9X1, BC, Canada
Tel.: (866) 578-5157
Web Site: http://www.pathfive.ca
Application Software Development Services
N.A.I.C.S.: 541511
Brad Leitch *(Dir-Product Delivery)*

Pacific Alliance Technologies Inc.   (1)
Suite 200 - 4170 Still Creek Drive, Burnaby, V5C 6C6, BC, Canada
Tel.: (604) 676-6000
Web Site: http://www.pat.ca
Emp.: 15
Application Software Development Services
N.A.I.C.S.: 541511

Stone Orchard Software Inc.   (1)

17665 Leslie St, Newmarket, L3Y 3E3, ON, Canada
Tel.: (905) 953-0700
Web Site: http://www.stoneorchardsoftware.com
Emp.: 8
Application Software Development Services
N.A.I.C.S.: 541511
Ken Munday *(Dir-Ops)*

Tempest Development Group Inc.   (1)
103 - 8431 160 St, Surrey, V4N 0V6, BC, Canada
Tel.: (604) 597-2846
Web Site: http://www.tempestdg.com
Application Software Development Services
N.A.I.C.S.: 541511
Dave Baines *(Mgr-Customer Svc)*

United Systems Technology, Inc.   (1)
1430 Valwood Pkwy Ste 130, Carrollton, TX 75006
Tel.: (972) 402-8600
Web Site: http://www.unitedsystech.com
Sales Range: $10-24.9 Million
Emp.: 34
Government Software Publisher
N.A.I.C.S.: 513210
Thomas E. Gibbs *(Chm, Pres & CEO)*

Vadim Computer Management Group Ltd.   (1)
1632 Dickson Avenue Suite 400, Kelowna, V1Y 7T2, BC, Canada
Tel.: (250) 763-7654
Web Site: http://www.vadimsoftware.com
Emp.: 30
Government Software Publisher & Support Services
N.A.I.C.S.: 513210
Wendy Jarvis *(Gen Mgr)*

Subsidiary (US):

VERSYSS Commercial Systems, Inc.   (2)
1 Davol Sq Ste 204, Providence, RI 02903
Tel.: (401) 351-9101
Application Software Development Services
N.A.I.C.S.: 541511

WorkTech Inc.   (1)
290 Glendale Ave Unit 6B, Saint Catharines, L2T 2L3, ON, Canada
Tel.: (905) 309-6054
Web Site: http://www.worktech.ca
Application Software Development Services
N.A.I.C.S.: 541511

Yfactor Inc.   (1)
1100-151 Yonge St, Toronto, M5C 2W7, ON, Canada
Tel.: (416) 977-9724
Web Site: http://www.yfactor.com
Website Designing Services
N.A.I.C.S.: 541511

STARFIRE MINERALS INC.
3B - 19299 94th Avenue, Surrey, V4N 4E6, BC, Canada
Tel.: (604) 455-0484   Ca
Web Site: http://www.starfireminerals.ca
Sales Range: Less than $1 Million
Mineral Exploration Services
N.A.I.C.S.: 213114
Dan Mosher *(Pres & CEO)*

STARFLEX CO., LTD.
CBS B/D 11F 158-701 Mok-dong Yangcheon-ku, Seoul, Chungchonbuk-do, Korea (South)
Tel.: (82) 438784071
Web Site: https://www.star-flex.com
Year Founded: 1996
115570—(KRS)
Rev.: $79,823,608
Assets: $89,008,019
Liabilities: $29,283,180
Net Worth: $59,724,838
Earnings: $5,013,882
Emp.: 96
Fiscal Year-end: 12/31/22
Plastics Product Mfr

INTERNATIONAL PUBLIC

N.A.I.C.S.: 326199
Kim Se-Kwon *(CEO)*

STARFLEX PUBLIC COMPANY LIMITED
189/48-49 M3 Theparak Rd, Bangprieng Bangbo District, Samut Prakan, 10560, Thailand
Tel.: (66) 27082555   TH
Web Site: https://www.starflex.co.th
Year Founded: 2003
SFLEX—(THA)
Rev.: $53,144,491
Assets: $59,437,690
Liabilities: $30,230,856
Net Worth: $29,206,834
Earnings: $5,378,628
Emp.: 556
Fiscal Year-end: 12/31/23
Packaging Product Mfr & Distr
N.A.I.C.S.: 333993
Sompote Valyasevi *(CEO)*

STARGATE CAPITAL GMBH
Brienner Strasse 10, 80333, Munich, Germany
Tel.: (49) 89 2877 9371
Web Site: http://www.stargate-capital.com
Privater Equity Firm
N.A.I.C.S.: 523999
Boris Levin *(Mng Dir)*

Subsidiaries:

Beissbarth Automotive Testing Solutions GmbH   (1)
Hanauer Strasse 101, 80993, Munich, Germany
Tel.: (49) 89149010
Web Site: http://www.beissbarth.com
Automobile Component Distr
N.A.I.C.S.: 423120

Loewe Technologies GmbH   (1)
Industriestrasse 11, 96317, Kronach, Germany
Tel.: (49) 9261 99 0
Web Site: http://www.loewe.tv
Television & Related Electronics Mfr & Whslr
N.A.I.C.S.: 334310
Mark Husges *(Mng Dir)*

Subsidiary (Non-US):

Loewe France S.A.S.   (2)
13 rue Du Depot, 67207, Niederhausbergen, Bas-Rhin, France
Tel.: (33) 388797250
Television Mfr
N.A.I.C.S.: 334220

Loewe Opta Benelux N.V./S.A   (2)
Uilenbaan 84, Wommelgem, 2160, Belgium
Tel.: (32) 32709930
Web Site: http://www.loewe.be
Emp.: 15
Home Appliance Mfr
N.A.I.C.S.: 334310
Bavo Mareels *(Mgr-Product & Sls)*

SICAM S.r.l.   (1)
Via G Corradini 1, 42015, Reggio Emilia, Italy
Tel.: (39) 0522643311
Web Site: http://www.sicam.it
Automobile Parts Distr
N.A.I.C.S.: 423120
Matteo Malagoli *(Mgr-IT)*

STARGLORY HOLDINGS COMPANY LIMITED
6th Floor Southland Building 48 Connaught Road Central, Central, China (Hong Kong)
Tel.: (852) 37528133   Ky
Web Site: http://www.starglorhcl.com
8213—(HKG)
Rev.: $20,719,770
Assets: $9,274,223
Liabilities: $24,419,693

Net Worth: ($15,145,470)
Earnings: ($1,788,188)
Emp.: 115
Fiscal Year-end: 03/31/23
Restaurant Management Services
N.A.I.C.S.: 722511
Chao Huang (Chm)

Subsidiaries:

Epicurean Management (Asia) Limited (1)
10/F Silver Fortune Plaza 1 Wellington Street, Central, China (Hong Kong)
Tel.: (852) 25326200
Web Site: http://www.epicurean.com.hk
Restaurant Operators
N.A.I.C.S.: 722511
Erik Dam (Sr Mgr)

STARGUIDE GROUP, INC.
275 Jatwada Dasna Gate near Old Bus Stand, Ghaziabad, Ghaziabad, 201002, Uttar Pradesh, India
Tel.: (91) 7029966002   NV
Year Founded: 2017
Rev.: $4,370
Assets: $2,246
Liabilities: $252,581
Net Worth: ($250,335)
Earnings: ($202,345)
Fiscal Year-end: 01/31/24
Art & Craft Product Distr
N.A.I.C.S.: 459920
Vicky Sharma (Pres, CEO, CFO, Treas & Sec)

STARHEDGE S.A.
Plac Defilad 1 17th floor, 00-901, Warsaw, Poland
Tel.: (48) 226203176
Web Site: https://www.starhedge.pl
SHG—(WAR)
Rev.: $9,415,904
Assets: $24,524,390
Liabilities: $7,648,882
Net Worth: $16,875,508
Earnings: $934,197
Fiscal Year-end: 12/31/23
Eletric Power Generation Services
N.A.I.C.S.: 221118
Andrzej Jasinski (Chm-Supervisory Bd)

STARHILL GLOBAL REIT
391B Orchard Road 24-03 Ngee Ann City Tower B, Singapore, 238874, Singapore
Tel.: (65) 68358633
Web Site: https://www.starhillglobalreit.com
P40U—(SES)
Rev.: $139,141,904
Assets: $2,119,519,081
Liabilities: $823,390,886
Net Worth: $1,296,128,196
Earnings: $23,729,529
Emp.: 30
Fiscal Year-end: 06/30/23
Trust Management Services
N.A.I.C.S.: 523940
Ho Sing (CEO)

STARHUB LTD.
67 Ubi Avenue 1 05-01 StarHub Green, Singapore, 408942, Singapore
Tel.: (65) 68201633   SG
Web Site: https://www.starhub.com
Year Founded: 2000
Telecommunication Servicesb
N.A.I.C.S.: 517810
Nikhil Eapen (CEO & Exec Dir)

STARI DERAM A.D.
Mirijevski venac 20, Belgrade, Serbia
Tel.: (381) 11 3422 030
Year Founded: 1959

Sales Range: Less than $1 Million
Mobile Food Services
N.A.I.C.S.: 722330

STARI GRAD A.D.
Brace Stefanovica Bb, 75400, Zvornik, Bosnia & Herzegovina
Tel.: (387) 56260449
Year Founded: 1952
STGR—(BANJ)
Sales Range: Less than $1 Million
Emp.: 1
Home Management Services
N.A.I.C.S.: 721110
Ivo Jokic (Chm-Supervisory Bd)

STARI GRAD A.D.
Obiliceva bb, Cacak, Serbia
Tel.: (381) 32 375 739
Web Site: http://www.starigrad.co.rs
Year Founded: 1965
Sales Range: Less than $1 Million
Emp.: 1
Building Construction Services
N.A.I.C.S.: 236220
Aleksandar Terzic (Exec Dir)

STARI GRAD GP A.D.
Skender Begova 22, Belgrade, Serbia
Tel.: (381) 64 230 50 55
Year Founded: 1957
STRG—(BEL)
Sales Range: Less than $1 Million
Heavy Construction Services
N.A.I.C.S.: 237990
Milos Coric (Exec Dir)

STARI TAMIS A.D.
Kestenova 4, Pancevo, Serbia
Tel.: (381) 13 2638 201
Web Site: http://www.tamis.rs
Year Founded: 1975
STTM—(BEL)
Sales Range: $10-24.9 Million
Emp.: 170
Cereal Crop Farming Services
N.A.I.C.S.: 111998
Goran Radic (Dir)

STARK CORPORATION PUBLIC COMPANY LIMITED
Maneeya Building 518/5 Ploenchit Road lumpinee, Pathumwan, Bangkok, 10330, Thailand
Tel.: (66) 26805800
Web Site: https://www.starkcorporation.com
Year Founded: 1990
STARK—(THA)
Rev.: $903,220,353
Assets: $1,304,215,011
Liabilities: $1,084,594,420
Net Worth: $219,620,591
Earnings: $93,129,018
Emp.: 1,875
Fiscal Year-end: 12/31/21
Cartoon & Packet Books Publisher, Printing & Retailer; Television Stations & Satellite Programs
N.A.I.C.S.: 513130
Chanin Yensudchai (Chm)

Subsidiaries:

Adisorn Songkhla Co., Ltd. (1)
39/15 Soi 29 Karnjanavanich Road, Muang Songkhla, Songkhla, Thailand
Tel.: (66) 74302500
Web Site: http://www.adisorn-skl.com
Construction Services
N.A.I.C.S.: 236220

STARK FOCUS GROUP INC.
505 6th Street SW Suite 3001, Calgary, T2P 1X5, AB, Canada
Tel.: (352) 562-0289   NV
Year Founded: 2018
SFG—(OTCIQ)

Assets: $5,967
Liabilities: $67,370
Net Worth: ($61,403)
Earnings: ($49,273)
Fiscal Year-end: 12/31/22
Apparel Product Distr
N.A.I.C.S.: 424350
Zhi Fen Cao (CEO, Treas, Pres & CFO)

STARK TECHNOLOGY, INC.
12F No 83 Sec 2 Dongda Rd, North Dist, Hsinchu, Taiwan
Tel.: (886) 35425566
Web Site: https://www.sti.com.tw
Year Founded: 1993
2480—(TAI)
Rev.: $237,773,038
Assets: $218,072,820
Liabilities: $111,138,293
Net Worth: $106,934,526
Earnings: $25,613,688
Emp.: 714
Fiscal Year-end: 12/31/23
Computer System Integration & Design Services
N.A.I.C.S.: 541512
Hsing-Chou Chen (VP)

Subsidiaries:

Shanghai Stark Technology Inc. (1)
Unit2307 No 1 Lane 600 TianShan Road, Shanghai, China
Tel.: (86) 2160909192
Software Development Services
N.A.I.C.S.: 541511

Stark (Ningbo) Technology Inc. (1)
1102 11F Ningbo FTZ International Development Edifice, Beilun, Ningbo, 315000, Zhejiang, China
Tel.: (86) 57486820669
Web Site: http://www.sti.com.tw
Software Consulting Services
N.A.I.C.S.: 541512

Stark Technology Inc. (1)
1209 Mayberry Ln, San Jose, CA 95131
Tel.: (408) 452-7600
Web Site: http://www.sti.com.tw
Enterprise Management Software Development Services
N.A.I.C.S.: 541511

U.S.A Stark Technology Inc. (1)
1209 Mayberry Lan, San Jose, CA 95131
Tel.: (408) 452-7600
Information & Communication Technology Services
N.A.I.C.S.: 541430

STARKOT CORP.
2-57 A Hanuman Irukupakem Muppalla Mandal, Guntur, 522403, India
Tel.: (91) 601 522 7236   NV
Web Site: http://www.starkotcorp.com
Year Founded: 2016
Embroidery Pillow Mfr
N.A.I.C.S.: 313210
Ravi Kiran Inturi (Pres, Treas & Sec)

STARKS PLUMBING & HEATING LTD.
724 14th Street SW, Medicine Hat, T1A 4V7, AB, Canada
Tel.: (403) 527-2929
Web Site: http://www.starks.ca
Year Founded: 1956
Rev.: $11,100,000
Emp.: 55
Plumbing Heating Air Conditioning Suppliers
N.A.I.C.S.: 423720

STARLIGHT ADVERTISING PTE. LTD.
10 Ubi Crescent #02-61, UBI Techpark Lobby D, Singapore, 408564, Singapore
Tel.: (65) 6336 2733   SG

Web Site: http://www.starlight.com.sg
Year Founded: 1952
Sales Range: $1-9.9 Million
Advetising Agency
N.A.I.C.S.: 541810
Kien Choong Liew (Mng Dir)

STARLIGHT INVESTMENTS LTD.
3300 Bloor Street West Suite 1801 West Tower, Toronto, M8X 2X2, ON, Canada
Tel.: (416) 234-8444
Web Site: http://www.rentstarlight.com
Year Founded: 1995
Sales Range: $50-74.9 Million
Emp.: 70
Real Estate Asset Management Services
N.A.I.C.S.: 531311
Daniel Drimmer (Pres & CEO)

Subsidiaries:

Northview Canadian High Yield Residential Fund (1)
6131 6 St SE Suite 200, Calgary, T2H 1L9, AB, Canada
Tel.: (403) 531-0720
Web Site: https://www.northviewfund.com
Holding Company
N.A.I.C.S.: 551112
Todd R. Cook (CEO)

Joint Venture (Domestic):

Northview Apartment Real Estate Investment Trust (2)
6131 - 6th Street SE Suite 200, Calgary, T2H 1L9, AB, Canada
Tel.: (403) 531-0720
Web Site: http://www.northviewreit.com
Rev.: $300,404,145
Assets: $3,501,154,362
Liabilities: $1,896,566,990
Net Worth: $1,604,587,372
Earnings: $185,162,827
Emp.: 937
Fiscal Year-end: 12/31/2019
Real Estate Investment Trust
N.A.I.C.S.: 525990

Subsidiary (Domestic):

Northern Property R.E.I.T. Holdings Inc. (3)
203 4508 42nd St, Bonnyville, T9N 1K5, AB, Canada
Tel.: (780) 826-3304
Real Estate Property Management Services
N.A.I.C.S.: 531311

True North Commercial Real Estate Investment Trust (1)
3280 Bloor Street West Suite 1400 Centre Tower, Toronto, M8X 2X3, ON, Canada
Tel.: (416) 234-8444
Web Site: http://www.truenorthreit.com
Rev.: $109,074,083
Assets: $1,099,011,091
Liabilities: $688,148,248
Net Worth: $410,862,843
Earnings: $31,097,195
Fiscal Year-end: 12/31/2020
Real Estate Investment Trust
N.A.I.C.S.: 525990
Tracy Sherren (Pres & CFO)

STARLINEPS ENTERPRISES LTD.
Shop-F/1 1St Floor Athwa Ark Shopping Centre Opp Yatim Khana, Athwa Gate, Surat, 395001, India
Tel.: (91) 2612600343
Web Site: https://www.starlineps.com
Year Founded: 2011
540492—(BOM)
Rev.: $2,452,597
Assets: $2,974,310
Liabilities: $38,577
Net Worth: $2,935,733
Earnings: $73,418
Emp.: 5

Starlineps Enterprises Ltd.—(Continued)
Fiscal Year-end: 03/31/23
Investment Management Service
N.A.I.C.S.: 523940
Shwet Koradiya (Chm & Mng Dir)

STARLINGER & CO. GMBH
Sonnenuhrgasse 4, 1060, Vienna, Austria
Tel.: (43) 1599550
Web Site: http://www.starlinger.com
Year Founded: 1970
Sales Range: $250-299.9 Million
Emp.: 750
Textile Machinery Mfr
N.A.I.C.S.: 333248
Angelika Huemer (Mng Partner)

Subsidiaries:

Georg Sahm GmbH & Co. KG (1)
Maschinenfabrik Sudetenlandstrasse 33, 37269, Eschwege, Germany
Tel.: (49) 56518040
Web Site: http://www.sahmwinder.de
Sales Range: $25-49.9 Million
Emp.: 150
Textile Machinery Mfr
N.A.I.C.S.: 333248
Uwe Baldewein (Area Mgr-Sls)

Affiliate (US):

American Starlinger-Sahm, Inc. (2)
11 Jack Casey Ct Fountain Inn, Greenville, SC 29644
Tel.: (864) 297-1900
Web Site: http://www.starlingersahm.com
Sales Range: $25-49.9 Million
Emp.: 22
Mfr of Bi-Directional Tensioners, Marketing & Sale of Winders
N.A.I.C.S.: 423830
Bernd Budaschik (Mgr-Technical)

PT. Starlinger SEA (1)
Water Place Residence Apartment Tokan B-12 Jl Pakuwon Indah, Lontar Timur No 3-5, 60126, Surabaya, Indonesia
Tel.: (62) 31 7393394
Woven Plastic Sack Mfr
N.A.I.C.S.: 314910

STARLINGER SOUTHERN AFRICA (Pty) Ltd (1)
Unit 5A Barbeque Corner Dytchley Road Barbeque Downs, Kyalami, 1600, Gauteng, South Africa
Tel.: (27) 730950802
Plastic Machinery Whslr
N.A.I.C.S.: 423830

Starlinger & Co. GmbH - Factory 1 (1)
Hauptstrasse 43, 2564, Vienna, Austria
Tel.: (43) 2674 800 0
Woven Plastic Sack Mfr
N.A.I.C.S.: 314910

Starlinger & Co. GmbH - Factory 2 (1)
Furtherstrasse 47, 2564, Weissenbach an der Triesting, Austria
Tel.: (43) 2674 808
Woven Plastic Sack Mfr
N.A.I.C.S.: 314910

Starlinger Export GmbH (1)
811A-812 Block E Intl Trade Tower Nehru Place, 110019, New Delhi, India
Tel.: (91) 11 41617820
Web Site: http://www.starlinger.com
Emp.: 10
Industrial Supplies Whslr
N.A.I.C.S.: 423840
Ruchi Singh (Engr)

Starlinger Plastics Machinery (Taicang) Co., Ltd. (1)
No 19 Factory Premises No 111 North Dongting Road Taicang, 215400, 215400, Taicang, Jiangsu, China
Tel.: (86) 512 5337 5800
Plastic Machine Mfr
N.A.I.C.S.: 423830
Dominick Fortuna (Gen Mgr)

Starlinger do Brasil Ltda. (1)
Rua Barao de Triunfo 73 - Conjunto 41/47, Brooklin Novo, 04602-000, Sao Paulo, Brazil
Tel.: (55) 11 3361 3675
Plastic Material Distr
N.A.I.C.S.: 424610

STARLINK AVIATION INC.
9025 Ryan Avenue, Dorval, H9P 1A2, QC, Canada
Tel.: (514) 631-7500
Web Site: http://www.starlinkaviation.com
Year Founded: 1981
Oil Transportation Services
N.A.I.C.S.: 481212
Gilles Bruneau (Pres)

STARLIT POWER SYSTEMS LTD
A-1/51 LGF Safdarjung Enclave, New Delhi, 110029, India
Tel.: (91) 1146027970
Web Site: http://www.starlitpower.com
538733—(BOM)
Rev.: $2,459,784
Assets: $4,836,375
Liabilities: $6,562,550
Net Worth: ($1,726,175)
Earnings: ($654,761)
Emp.: 43
Fiscal Year-end: 03/31/21
Lead-Based Products Recycling, Refining, Manufacturing, Trade, Import & Export
N.A.I.C.S.: 332999
Yogesh Kumar Gupta (Chm & Mng Dir)

STARLITE COMPONENTS LTD.
F-108 MIDC Area Satpur, Nashik, 422007, India
Tel.: (91) 8004154452
Web Site: https://www.starlitecomponents.com
Year Founded: 1991
517548—(BOM)
Rev.: $275,471
Assets: $1,593,419
Liabilities: $2,866,077
Net Worth: ($1,272,658)
Earnings: ($165,124)
Emp.: 3
Fiscal Year-end: 03/31/21
Electric Equipment Mfr
N.A.I.C.S.: 335999
Arvind Bharati (Mng Dir)

STARLITE HOLDINGS LIMITED
3/F Perfect Industrial Building 31 Tai Yau Street Sanpokong, Kowloon, China (Hong Kong)
Tel.: (852) 34031111
Web Site: https://www.hkstarlite.com
0403—(HKG)
Rev.: $135,261,326
Assets: $134,071,614
Liabilities: $47,571,822
Net Worth: $86,499,792
Earnings: $46,106,868
Emp.: 3,000
Fiscal Year-end: 03/31/22
Printing & Manufacturing of Packaging Materials
N.A.I.C.S.: 561910
Chui Yeung (Co-Founder)

Subsidiaries:

Guangzhou Starlite Environmental Friendly Center Ltd. (1)
189 Kaifa Avenue, Economic and Technological Development District, Guangzhou, 510730, China
Tel.: (86) 2082211211
Packaging & Labeling Services
N.A.I.C.S.: 561910

Shaoguan Fortune Creative Industries Co., Ltd. (1)
Muxi Industrial Zone, Shaoguan, 512028, Guangdong, China
Tel.: (86) 7518801111
Packaging & Labeling Services
N.A.I.C.S.: 561910

Starlite Enterprise (Shanghai) Inc. (1)
Room 2203 2204 No 1 Lane 829 Wan Hang Du Road, Shanghai, 200042, China
Tel.: (86) 62323111
Packaging & Labeling Services
N.A.I.C.S.: 561910

Starlite Printers (Far East) Pte Ltd (1)
49 Sungei Kadut Ave, Singapore, Singapore
Tel.: (65) 62666111
Packaging & Labeling Services
N.A.I.C.S.: 561910

Starlite Printers (Shenzhen) Co., Ltd. (1)
Starlite Southern China Development Centre, Industrial District 2 Xi Xiang Zhen Bao An Qu, Shenzhen, 518126, China
Tel.: (86) 75527496111
Packaging & Labeling Services
N.A.I.C.S.: 561910

Starlite Printers (Suzhou) Co., Ltd. (1)
98 Hu Tai Xin Road, Suzhou, 215431, Jiangsu, China
Tel.: (86) 51253600111
Packaging & Labeling Services
N.A.I.C.S.: 561910

Starlite Printers Limited (1)
3rd Floor Perfect Industrial Building 31 Tai Yau Street, Sanpokong, Kowloon, China (Hong Kong)
Tel.: (852) 34031111
Packaging & Labeling Services
N.A.I.C.S.: 561910

STARLO VENTURES LTD.
400 Burrard Street Suite 1400, Vancouver, V6C 3A6, BC, Canada
Tel.: (604) 628-1110 BC
Year Founded: 2021
SLO—(CNSX)
Mineral Exploration Services
N.A.I.C.S.: 213115
Patrick De Witt (CEO)

STARLOG ENTERPRISES LIMITED
501 Sukh Sagar N S Patkar Marg, Mumbai, 400 007, India
Tel.: (91) 2269071234
Web Site: https://www.starlog.in
Year Founded: 1983
520155—(BOM)
Rev.: $25,695,320
Assets: $110,558,489
Liabilities: $118,459,887
Net Worth: ($7,901,398)
Earnings: ($7,023,676)
Emp.: 16
Fiscal Year-end: 03/31/21
Logistics & Physical Distribution Services
N.A.I.C.S.: 541614
Pranali Sulakhe A. (Sec)

Subsidiaries:

Dakshin Bharat Gateway Terminal Private Limited (1)
Berth No 8 V O C Port Trust Tuticorin Container Terminal Rd, Harbour Estate Muttayyapuram, Thoothukudi, 628 004, Tamil Nadu, India
Tel.: (91) 4612382241
Web Site: http://www.dbgt.in
Port Warehousing & Harbor Services
N.A.I.C.S.: 488310
Senthilkumar Subramanian (CEO)

STARMET VENTURES INC.
303-1687 W Broadway, Vancouver, V6J 1X2, BC, Canada
Tel.: (604) 833-6820
Year Founded: 2019
STAR—(CNSX)
Mineral Exploration Services
N.A.I.C.S.: 213114
Nir Eliyahu (Dir)

STARNBERGER KLINIKEN GMBH
Osswaldstr 1, 82319, Starnberg, Germany
Tel.: (49) 08151 18 0
Web Site: http://www.starnberger-kliniken.de
Healthcare facility Dist & Services
N.A.I.C.S.: 456199
Thomas Weiler (Mng Dir)

Subsidiaries:

Privatklinik Dr. Robert Schindlbeck GmbH & Co. KG (1)
Seestrasse 43, 82211, Herrsching am Ammersee, Germany
Tel.: (49) 8152290
Web Site: http://www.klinik-schindlbeck.de
Health Care Srvices
N.A.I.C.S.: 621610
Christian Doerk (CIO)

Subsidiary (Domestic):

MVZ Fur Molekulardiagnostik GmbH (2)
Candidplatz 13, Munich, 81543, Germany
Tel.: (49) 89809115780
Web Site: http://www.mvzmolekulardiagnostik.de
Medical Laboratory Services
N.A.I.C.S.: 621511

STARPHARMA HOLDINGS LIMITED
4-6 Southampton Cresent, Abbotsford, 3067, VIC, Australia
Tel.: (61) 385322700
Web Site: http://www.starpharma.com
SPL—(OTCIQ)
Rev.: $2,671,705
Assets: $56,114,223
Liabilities: $8,380,586
Net Worth: $47,733,637
Earnings: ($15,118,461)
Emp.: 45
Fiscal Year-end: 06/30/21
Holding Company; Nanotechnology-Based Pharmaceuticals Mfr
N.A.I.C.S.: 551112
Jacinth K. Fairley (CEO)

Subsidiaries:

Starpharma Pty. Ltd. (1)
4-6 Southampton Cresent, Abbotsford, 3067, VIC, Australia
Tel.: (61) 385322700
Web Site: http://www.starpharma.com
Sales Range: $25-49.9 Million
Nanotechnology-Based Pharmaceuticals Mfr
N.A.I.C.S.: 325412

STARPOWER SEMICONDUCTOR LTD.
No 988 Kexing Road, Nanhu, Jiaxing, 314006, Zhejiang, China
Tel.: (86) 57382586699
Web Site: https://www.powersemi.cc
Year Founded: 2005
603290—(SHG)
Rev.: $379,851,975
Assets: $1,000,737,181
Liabilities: $194,681,560
Net Worth: $806,055,621
Earnings: $114,797,063
Emp.: 1,000
Fiscal Year-end: 12/31/22

AND PRIVATE COMPANIES

STARTS CORPORATION, INC.

Semiconductor Product Mfr & Distr
N.A.I.C.S.: 334413
Hua Shen *(Chm & Gen Mgr)*

STARR PEAK MINING LTD.
Suite 300 - 1055 West Hastings Street, Vancouver, V6E 2E9, BC, Canada
Tel.: (515) 401-7479
Web Site:
https://starrpeakminingltd.com
Year Founded: 1981
STE—(TSXV)
Assets: $18,476,265
Liabilities: $1,521,222
Net Worth: $16,955,042
Earnings: ($8,105,410)
Fiscal Year-end: 07/31/21
Metal Exploration Services
N.A.I.C.S.: 213114
Thomas Kennedy *(CEO)*

STARRAG GROUP HOLDING AG
Seebleichestrasse 61, 9404, Rorschacherberg, Switzerland
Tel.: (41) 718588111
Web Site: https://www.starrag.com
STGN—(SWX)
Rev.: $352,097,561
Assets: $370,192,905
Liabilities: $178,973,392
Net Worth: $191,219,512
Earnings: $12,321,508
Emp.: 1,280
Fiscal Year-end: 12/31/22
Holding Company; Machine Tool Mfr
N.A.I.C.S.: 551112
Gunther Eller *(Member-Exec Bd & Head-Customer Svc)*

Subsidiaries:

Dorries Scharmann Technologie GmbH (1)
Hugo-Junkers-Strasse 12-32, 41236, Monchengladbach, Germany
Tel.: (49) 21664540
Web Site: http://www.ds-technologie.de
Sales Range: $150-199.9 Million
Emp.: 800
Machine Tool Distr
N.A.I.C.S.: 423830

Subsidiary (US):

DS Technology (USA), Inc. (2)
Skyport Business Park 2379 Progress Dr, Hebron, KY 41048
Tel.: (859) 534-5201
Web Site: http://www.starrag.com
Sales Range: $25-49.9 Million
Emp.: 10
Grinding Machine Mfr
N.A.I.C.S.: 327910

Subsidiary (Domestic):

Dorries Scharmann Technologie Service Center GmbH & Co KG (2)
Am Sulzenbruckener Weg 14, 99334, Ichtershausen, Germany
Tel.: (49) 36202 77980
Industrial Milling & Grinding Machinery Repair Services
N.A.I.C.S.: 811310

Societe d'Instruments de Precision SA (1)
19 Rue de la Pre-de-la-Fontaine, Meyrin, 1217, Switzerland
Tel.: (41) 227190200
Web Site: http://www.starrag.com
Sales Range: $25-49.9 Million
Emp.: 30
Precision Tool Mfr
N.A.I.C.S.: 332721

Starrag (Shanghai) Co. Ltd. (1)
B8-1F 912 Bibo Road, Zhangjiang Hi-tech Park Pudong, Shanghai, 201203, China
Tel.: (86) 2120249800
Machine Tool Mfr & Distr
N.A.I.C.S.: 333517

Starrag AG (1)
Seebleichestrasse 61, 9404, Rorschacherberg, Switzerland
Tel.: (41) 718588111
Web Site: https://www.starrag.com
Emp.: 200
Precision Tool Mfr
N.A.I.C.S.: 332721

Starrag GmbH (1)
Otto-Schmerbach-Strasse 15/17, 09117, Chemnitz, Germany
Tel.: (49) 3718362288
Machine Tools Mfr
N.A.I.C.S.: 333517

Starrag India Private Limited (1)
No 66 KIADB Bengaluru Aerospace Park, Singahalli Village Budigere Post Bangalore North Taluk, Bengaluru, 562129, India
Tel.: (91) 8071070600
Machine Tools Mfr
N.A.I.C.S.: 333517

Starrag Italia Srl (1)
Corso SUSA 242, 10098, Rivoli, TO, Italy
Tel.: (39) 01119171637
Machine Tool Mfr & Distr
N.A.I.C.S.: 333517

Starrag RU Ltd. (1)
B Novodmitrovskaya str 23c3, Moscow, RF - 127015, Russia
Tel.: (7) 4952698041
Machine Tools Mfr
N.A.I.C.S.: 333517

Starrag S.A.S. (1)
5 rue Barrouin, 42029, Saint-Etienne, Cedex 1, France
Tel.: (33) 477923992
Machine Tools Mfr
N.A.I.C.S.: 333517

Starrag UK Ltd. (1)
43 Phoenix Park Avenue Close, Nechells, Birmingham, B7 4 NU, United Kingdom
Tel.: (44) 1213593637
Machine Tools Mfr
N.A.I.C.S.: 333517

Starrag USA Inc. (1)
Skyport Business Park 2379 Progress Dr, Hebron, KY 41048
Tel.: (859) 534-5201
Machine Tools Mfr
N.A.I.C.S.: 333517

Starrag Vuadens SA (1)
Rue du Moleson 41, 1628, Vuadens, Switzerland
Tel.: (41) 263510000
Machine Tools Mfr
N.A.I.C.S.: 333517

Toolroom Technology Ltd. (1)
Unit 1a and 1b, Haddenham Business Park Pegasus Way Haddenham Aylesbury, Buckingham, HP17 8LJ, Buckinghamshire, United Kingdom
Tel.: (44) 1844296650
Web Site: https://www.ttl-solutions.com
Automation Machinery Mfr
N.A.I.C.S.: 333998

STARREX INTERNATIONAL LTD.
1250 639 5th Avenue SW Standard Life Building, Calgary, T2P 0M9, AB, Canada
Tel.: (281) 406-8337
Web Site: https://www.starrexintl.com
STXMF—(OTCQB)
Rev.: $3,808,611
Assets: $11,454,825
Liabilities: $3,260,211
Net Worth: $8,194,614
Earnings: $4,155,976
Fiscal Year-end: 12/31/22
Holding Company
N.A.I.C.S.: 551112
Ronald K. Mann *(COO & Officer-IR)*

Subsidiaries:

Olympia Capital Managment Inc. (1)
3001 N Rockey Point Dr E Ste 200, Tampa, FL 33602
Tel.: (727) 741-7926
Web Site: http://www.olympiacm.com
Consulting Services for Mortgage Industry
N.A.I.C.S.: 541618
Greg Thompson *(CEO)*

Property Interlink, LLC (1)
Tel.: (970) 243-6808
Web Site: http://www.propertyinterlink.com
Emp.: 50
Real Estate Appraisal Services
N.A.I.C.S.: 531320

Subsidiary (Domestic):

Brownlee Appraisal Services Inc. (2)
PO Box 4484, Grand Junction, CO 81502
Tel.: (970) 243-6808
Web Site:
http://www.brownleeappraisals.com
Emp.: 5
Real Estate Appraisal Services
N.A.I.C.S.: 531320
Dan Dancooter *(Gen Mgr)*

STARS MICROELECTRONICS (THAILAND) PUBLIC COMPANY LIMITED
Bang Pa-In Industrial Estate I-EA-T Free Zone 605-606 Moo 2 Klongjig, Bang Pa-In, Ayutthaya, 13160, Thailand
Tel.: (66) 35258555
Web Site:
https://www.starsmicro.com
SMT—(THA)
Rev.: $77,277,429
Assets: $69,682,318
Liabilities: $9,349,782
Net Worth: $60,332,536
Earnings: $6,889,470
Emp.: 1,033
Fiscal Year-end: 12/31/23
Semiconductor Devices Mfr
N.A.I.C.S.: 334413
Yunyong Sawasdi *(CFO, Chief Admin Officer & Sec)*

Subsidiaries:

Stars Microelectronics USA, Inc. (1)
2157 O Toole Ave Ste, San Jose, CA 95131
Tel.: (408) 894-8160
Electronic Products Mfr
N.A.I.C.S.: 334419
Robert Luthi *(Pres)*

STARTECH.COM LTD.
45 Artisans Crescent, London, N5V 5E9, ON, Canada
Tel.: (519) 455-9675
Web Site: https://www.startech.com
Year Founded: 1985
Rev.: $16,917,543
Emp.: 400
Computer Equipment Mfr
N.A.I.C.S.: 334118
Paul Seed *(Co-Founder & CEO)*

STARTECK FINANCE LIMITED
5th Floor Sunteck Centre, 37-40 Subhash Road Vileparle E, Mumbai, 400 057, India
Tel.: (91) 2242877800
Web Site:
https://www.starteckfinance.com
512381—(BOM)
Rev.: $10,389,506
Assets: $111,128,404
Liabilities: $91,121,148
Net Worth: $20,007,255
Earnings: $5,135,567
Emp.: 7
Fiscal Year-end: 03/31/21
Financial Support Services
N.A.I.C.S.: 523999
Anand Shroff *(Exec Dir)*

STARTIA HOLDINGS, INC.
Shinjuku Monolith 19th Floor 2-3-1 Nishi Shinjuku, Shinjuku-ku, Tokyo, 163-0919, Japan
Tel.: (81) 363880415
Web Site:
https://www.startiaholdings.com
Year Founded: 1996
3393—(TKS)
Rev.: $129,364,310
Assets: $97,094,290
Liabilities: $52,027,310
Net Worth: $45,066,980
Earnings: $10,219,060
Emp.: 908
Fiscal Year-end: 03/31/24
Information Technology Services
N.A.I.C.S.: 541512
Hideyuki Hongo *(Founder, Pres & CEO)*

Subsidiaries:

BCMEDIA Co., Ltd. (1)
17-25 Ichijo-dori, Sakai-ku Sakai Ward, Sakai, 590-0048, Osaka, Japan
Tel.: (81) 722321233
Office Automation Equipment Distr
N.A.I.C.S.: 423430
Yoshinori Fujiwara *(Pres)*

Crosscheck, inc. (1) (14.58%)
1-17-4 Nishi-Shimbashi 2nd floor, Minato-ku, Tokyo, 105-0003, Japan
Tel.: (81) 355019500
Web Site: https://www.crosscheck.co.jp
Telecommunication Servicesb
N.A.I.C.S.: 517810
Kimura Ikusei *(CEO)*

NOS Ltd. (1)
1019-35 Sakamoto-cho, Kagoshima, Japan
Tel.: (81) 992477007
Emp.: 27
Office Automation Equipment Distr
N.A.I.C.S.: 423430
Yoshinobu Nagata *(Pres)*

STARTIA SHANGHAI INC.
519Room 5F North Wulumuqi Road 207, Shanghai, China
Tel.: (86) 2152895361
Web Site: http://www.startia.cn
Year Founded: 2013
Software Development Services
N.A.I.C.S.: 541511
Atsushi Shibata *(Gen Mgr)*

STARTMONDAY TECHNOLOGY CORP.
1500-1055 W Georgia St, Vancouver, V6E 4N7, BC, Canada
Tel.: (604) 343-4547
Mobile Application Development Services
N.A.I.C.S.: 541511
Sean Kingsley *(CEO & Sec)*

STARTS CORPORATION, INC.
Starts Yaesu Central Building 3-4-10 Nihonbashi, Chuo-ku, Tokyo, 103-0027, Japan
Tel.: (81) 362020111
Web Site: https://www.starts.co.jp
Year Founded: 1969
8850—(TKS)
Rev.: $1,902,875,040
Assets: $2,645,418,160
Liabilities: $1,409,514,480
Net Worth: $1,235,903,680
Earnings: $162,352,960
Emp.: 8,591
Fiscal Year-end: 03/31/22
Holding Company
N.A.I.C.S.: 551112
Hisaji Muraishi *(Chm)*

Subsidiaries:

Myanmar Starts Corporate Services Co., Ltd. (1)
4th Fl Yuzana Hotel 130 Shwe Gon Taing Road, Bahan Township, Yangon, Myanmar
Tel.: (95) 1 860 3390

STARTS CORPORATION, INC.

Starts Corporation, Inc.—(Continued)
Real Estate Services
N.A.I.C.S.: 531210
Kengo Shida *(Mng Dir)*

PT. Starts International Indonesia (1)
Midplaza2 Building 12th Floor Jl Jend Sudirman Kav 10-11, Jakarta, 10220, Indonesia
Tel.: (62) 21 570 7632
Real Estate Services
N.A.I.C.S.: 531210

STARTS SINGAPORE PTE. LTD.
1 Wallich Street 14-01 Guoco Tower, Singapore, 078881, Singapore
Tel.: (65) 62200320
Web Site: https://kaigai.starts.co.jp
Sales Range: $50-74.9 Million
Emp.: 4
Real Estate Manangement Services
N.A.I.C.S.: 531390

Starts (Guangzhou) Consulting Service Co., Ltd.
Room 410 No 138 Taiyu East Road, Tianhe District, Guangzhou, China (100%)
Tel.: (86) 2038770041
Web Site: http://www.starts.co.jp
Real Estate Agents & Brokers
N.A.I.C.S.: 531210

Starts Amenity Corporation
1-9-1 Nakase, Mihama-ku, Chiba, 261-0023, Japan
Tel.: (81) 432741001
Web Site: https://www.amenity-net.co.jp
Emp.: 1,074
Real Estate Manangement Services
N.A.I.C.S.: 531390

Starts CAM Co., Ltd. (1)
Starts Kasai Building 8F 3-37-4 Nakakasai, Edogawa-ku, Tokyo, 134-0083, Japan
Tel.: (81) 368957700
Emp.: 810
Construction Engineering Services
N.A.I.C.S.: 541330
Akira Fukasawa *(Exec Dir)*

Starts Construction & Asset Management Co. Ltd. (1)
Starts Kasai Building 8F 3-37-4 Nakakasai, Edogawa-ku, Tokyo, 134-0083, Japan
Tel.: (81) 368957700
Web Site: http://www.starts-cam.co.jp
Emp.: 810
Construction & Engineering Services
N.A.I.C.S.: 237990

Subsidiary (Domestic):

S-Tech Resource Co., Ltd. (2)
3-4-17 Etchujima Koto-ku, Tokyo, 135-8530, Japan
Tel.: (81) 356391335
Sales Range: $25-49.9 Million
Emp.: 13
Seismic Isolation System Design & Construction Services
N.A.I.C.S.: 541330

Starts Development Corporation (1)
5F Nihonbashi Building 3-1-8 Nihonbashi, Chuo-ku, Tokyo, 103-0027, Japan
Tel.: (81) 120598001
Web Site: https://www.starts-development.co.jp
Emp.: 30
Real Estate Manangement Services
N.A.I.C.S.: 531390

Starts Guam Golf Resort Inc. (1)
Starts Guam Golf Resort 2991 Route 3, Yigo, GU 96929
Tel.: (671) 632-1111
Web Site: https://www.startsguamgolf.com
Hotel Services
N.A.I.C.S.: 721110

Starts International (Thailand) Co., Ltd. (1)
29th Fl United Center Building 323 Silom Road Silom, Bangrak, Bangkok, 10500, Thailand (100%)
Tel.: (66) 26304848
Web Site: http://www.starts.co.th
Sales Range: $50-74.9 Million
Emp.: 3
Real Estate Agents & Brokers
N.A.I.C.S.: 531210

Starts International Australia Pty., Ltd. (1)
Level 5 115 Pitt Street, Sydney, 2000, NSW, Australia
Tel.: (61) 291137223
Web Site: http://www.startsaustralia.com
Emp.: 5
Real Estate Agents & Brokers
N.A.I.C.S.: 531210

Starts International Hawaii, Inc. (1)
1953 S Beretania St Ste PH-C, Honolulu, HI 96826
Tel.: (808) 947-2280
Web Site: https://startshawaii.com
Real Estate Services
N.A.I.C.S.: 531210

Starts International Malaysia Sdn. Bhd. (1)
Suite 8 01 Level 8 Menara Binjai No 2 Jalan Binjai, 50450, Kuala Lumpur, Malaysia
Tel.: (60) 32 386 7818
Real Estate Services
N.A.I.C.S.: 531210

Starts International Vietnam Co., Ltd. (1)
Unit 4 11 CornerStone Building 16 Phan Chu Trinh Str, Hoan Kiem Dist, Hanoi, Vietnam
Tel.: (84) 243 936 9884
Real Estate Services
N.A.I.C.S.: 531210

Starts New York Realty LLC (1)
1460 Broadway Ste 6024, New York, NY 10036 (100%)
Tel.: (212) 599-7697
Sales Range: $50-74.9 Million
Emp.: 5
Real Estate Agents & Brokers
N.A.I.C.S.: 531210

Starts Pacific Inc. (1)
21151 S Western Ave 227, Torrance, CA 90501
Tel.: (310) 782-7877
Real Estate Services
N.A.I.C.S.: 531210

Starts Real Estate Consultants (Shanghai) Co., Ltd. (1)
Junyao International Plaza 6F No 789 Hajimhaha Road, Xuhui District, Shanghai, 200032, China
Tel.: (86) 216 125 6888
Rental Brokerage Services
N.A.I.C.S.: 531210

Starts Securities Co., Ltd. (1)
6-10-6 Kasai, Edogawa-ku, Tokyo, 134-0088, Japan
Tel.: (81) 336862511
Web Site: https://www.starts-sc.co.jp
Sales Range: $50-74.9 Million
Emp.: 100
Financial Management Services
N.A.I.C.S.: 523999

STARTS PROCEED INVESTMENT CORPORATION
318 Nihonbashi, Chuo-ku, Tokyo, 103-0027, Japan
Tel.: (81) 362020856
Web Site: https://www.sp-inv.co.jp
Year Founded: 2005
8979—(TKS)
Sales Range: $10-24.9 Million
Investment Management Service
N.A.I.C.S.: 523940
Kazuya Hiraide *(Exec Officer)*

STARTUP300 AG
Peter Behrens Platz 10, 4020, Linz, Austria
Tel.: (43) 66488387402
Web Site: http://www.startup300.at
S300—(VIE)
Sales Range: Less than $1 Million
Business Services
N.A.I.C.S.: 561499

Michael Eisler *(Chm-Mgmt Bd & CEO)*

STARVEST PLC
33 St James s Square, London, SW1Y 4JS, Surrey, United Kingdom
Tel.: (44) 207 769 6876   UK
Web Site: http://www.starvest.co.uk
Year Founded: 2000
SVE—(AIM)
Rev.: $76,032
Assets: $19,253,423
Liabilities: $2,385,124
Net Worth: $16,868,298
Earnings: ($4,790,691)
Fiscal Year-end: 09/30/21
Investment Management Service
N.A.I.C.S.: 523940
Callum Newton Baxter *(Chm & CEO)*

Subsidiaries:

Kefi Minerals Plc (1)
Wisdom Tower 1st Floor 2 Ayiou Pavlou and Kadmou Street, 1105, Nicosia, Cyprus
Tel.: (357) 22256161
Web Site: https://www.kefi-goldandcopper.com
Gold & Copper Mining Services
N.A.I.C.S.: 212290
Harry Anagnostaras-Adams *(Chm)*

STARWARD INDUSTRIES S.A.
ul Przemyslowa 12, 30-701, Krakow, Poland
Web Site: https://www.starwardindustries.com
Year Founded: 2018
4T6—(DEU)
Rev.: $72,049,807
Assets: $355,168,645
Liabilities: $83,786,142
Net Worth: $271,382,503
Earnings: ($44,422,262)
Emp.: 27
Fiscal Year-end: 12/31/22
Software Development Services
N.A.I.C.S.: 541511
Maciej Dobrowolski *(CMO)*

STARWIN PRODUCTS LIMITED
Plot 16 Adjuma Crescent South Industrial Area, PO Box 5760, Accra, Ghana
Tel.: (233) 243690232
Year Founded: 1960
Pharmaceuticals Mfr
N.A.I.C.S.: 325412
Kwasi Yirenkyi *(Chief Corp Affairs Officer)*

STARWOOD EUROPEAN REAL ESTATE FINANCE LIMITED
1 Royal Plaza Royal Avenue, Saint Peter Port, GY1 2HL, Guernsey
Tel.: (44) 1481713843   GY
Web Site: https://www.starwoodeuropean.com
Year Founded: 2008
SWEF—(LSE)
Rev.: $44,500,460
Assets: $418,790,186
Liabilities: $2,072,546
Net Worth: $416,717,640
Earnings: $32,146,380
Fiscal Year-end: 12/31/23
Real Estate Investment Services
N.A.I.C.S.: 531390
Andrew Whittaker *(Mgr-Investment)*

STARZEN COMPANY LIMITED
Starzen Shinagawa Building 2-4-13 Konan, Minato-ku, Tokyo, 108-0075, Japan
Tel.: (81) 334715521
Web Site: https://www.starzen.co.jp
Year Founded: 1948

INTERNATIONAL PUBLIC

8043—(TKS)
Rev.: $2,713,629,740
Assets: $1,065,399,800
Liabilities: $549,813,190
Net Worth: $515,586,610
Earnings: $49,654,320
Emp.: 2,723
Fiscal Year-end: 03/31/24
Meat Product Mfr & Distr
N.A.I.C.S.: 311615
Kazuhiko Yokota *(Co-Pres, Co-CEO & Dir-Rep, Digital Entertainment Ops, and Publ Dept)*

STASSEN EXPORTS LTD.
833 Sirimavo Bandaranaike Mawatha, PO Box 1970, Colombo, 14, Sri Lanka
Tel.: (94) 112522155
Web Site: http://www.stassengroup.com
Year Founded: 1977
Sales Range: $75-99.9 Million
Emp.: 125
Import & Export Business; Dairy Products; Banking Services; Insurance Services; Manufacturing Business;
N.A.I.C.S.: 425120
Harry Jayawardena *(Chm)*

STATCOUNTER LTD.
Guinness Enterprise Centre Taylor's Lane, Dublin, 8, Ireland
Tel.: (353) 1 4100 658
Web Site: http://www.statcounter.com
Sales Range: $1-9.9 Million
Web Analytics Software
N.A.I.C.S.: 513210

STATE ATOMIC ENERGY CORPORATION ROSATOM
24 Bolshaya Ordynka Ul, 119017, Moscow, Russia
Tel.: (7) 4999494535   RU
Web Site: http://www.rosatom.ru
Year Founded: 2007
Sales Range: $1-9.9 Million
Emp.: 258,000
Holding Company; Nuclear Energy & Defense Services
N.A.I.C.S.: 551112
Sergey Kirienko *(Chm-Supervisory Bd)*

Subsidiaries:

JSC Atomenergoprom (1)
Bolshaya Ordynka Str 24, 119017, Moscow, Russia (100%)
Tel.: (7) 4959692939
Web Site: http://www.atomenergoprom.ru
Holding Company; Nuclear Plant Engineering & Power Generation Services
N.A.I.C.S.: 551112

Subsidiary (Domestic):

JSC Atomredmetzoloto (2)
22 B Drovyanoi Lane, 109004, Moscow, Russia (80.47%)
Tel.: (7) 495 508 8808
Web Site: http://www.armz.ru
Holding Company; Uranium Mining
N.A.I.C.S.: 551112
Verkhovtsev Vladimir *(Gen Dir)*

Holding (Non-US):

Uranium One Inc. (3)
Suite 1250-10 KING ST E, PO Box 43070, Toronto, M2N 6N1, ON, Canada
Tel.: (647) 788-8500
Web Site: https://www.uranium1.com
Rev.: $394,100,000
Assets: $2,661,200,000
Liabilities: $1,128,500,000
Net Worth: $1,532,700,000
Earnings: ($1,000,000)
Emp.: 2,630
Fiscal Year-end: 12/31/2019

AND PRIVATE COMPANIES

Uranium & Gold Resources Exploration & Development
N.A.I.C.S.: 212290
Jane Luck *(VP-Legal)*

Subsidiary (Non-US):

Southern Cross Resources Australia Pty. Ltd. (4)
75A Magill Rd, Stepney, 5069, SA, Australia
Tel.: (61) 883637006
Web Site: http://www.uranium1.com
Sales Range: $50-74.9 Million
Emp.: 5
Explorer & Developer of Uranium & Gold Resources
N.A.I.C.S.: 212290

Subsidiary (US):

UrAsia Energy (U.S.A.) Holdings Inc (4)
8055 E Tufts Ave Ste 400, Denver, CO 80237-2755
Tel.: (303) 325-2370
Sales Range: $25-49.9 Million
Emp.: 20
Uranium Exploration Services
N.A.I.C.S.: 331410

Subsidiary (Non-US):

Uranium One Africa Ltd (4)
Second Floor Selborne Building Fourways Golf Park Roos St, Johannesburg, 2191, Fourways, South Africa
Tel.: (27) 114653772
Web Site: http://www.uranium1.com
Uranium Metal Mining Services
N.A.I.C.S.: 212290

Subsidiary (US):

Uranium One Americas, Inc (4)
907 No Poplar St Ste 260, Casper, WY 82601
Tel.: (307) 234-8235
Web Site: http://www.uranium1.com
Uranium Ore Mining Services
N.A.I.C.S.: 212290

Subsidiary (Non-US):

Uranium One Netherlands B.V. (4)
Jan Van Goyenkade 8, 1075 HP, Amsterdam, North-Holland, Netherlands
Tel.: (31) 205214777
Uranium Metal Mining Services
N.A.I.C.S.: 212290

Subsidiary (US):

Uranium One USA, Inc. (4)
11850 S Hwy 191 A5, Moab, UT 84532-3923
Tel.: (435) 259-2443
Uranium Ore Mining Services
N.A.I.C.S.: 212290

Subsidiary (Domestic):

JSC TVEL (2)
Kashirskoe shosse 49, 115409, Moscow, Russia (100%)
Tel.: (7) 4959888282
Web Site: http://www.tvel.ru
Rev.: $3,004,068,000
Earnings: $770,616,000
Emp.: 22,328
Fiscal Year-end: 12/31/2016
Nuclear Fuel Production
N.A.I.C.S.: 325180
Olenin Yury Aleksandrovich *(Pres)*

Subsidiary (Domestic):

JSC Mashinostroitelny Zavod (3)
Karl Marx Str 12 Elektrostal, 144001, Moscow, Russia (96.41%)
Tel.: (7) 4957029901
Web Site: http://www.elemash.ru
Emp.: 10,000
Nuclear Fuel Mfr
N.A.I.C.S.: 339999

Subsidiary (Domestic):

OOO MSZ Mekhanika (4)
Karl Marx Str 12, 144001, Moscow, Russia
Tel.: (7) 4965776026
Web Site: http://mszm.ru

Nuclear Fuel & Material Equipment Mfr
N.A.I.C.S.: 334519

Subsidiary (Domestic):

Kovrovskiy mekhanicheskiy zavod OAO (3)
26 Sotsialisticheskaya Str Kovrovskiy R-N, Vladimir, Kovrov, 601909, Russia (65.23%)
Tel.: (7) 4923294004
Web Site: https://www.kvmz.ru
Sales Range: Less than $1 Million
Centrifuge Equipment Mfr
N.A.I.C.S.: 333998
Anatoly Gavrikov *(Gen Dir)*

JSC Rusatom Overseas Company (1)
Simonov Plaza Business Centre Leninskaya Sloboda Str 26 building 5, 115280, Moscow, Russia
Tel.: (7) 4952800014
Web Site: http://rusatom-overseas.com
Eletric Power Generation Services
N.A.I.C.S.: 221113

ROSATOM AFRICA (PTY) LTD (1)
7th Floor Sandton City Office Tower Sandton, 2196, Johannesburg, South Africa
Tel.: (27) 11 7842554
Eletric Power Generation Services
N.A.I.C.S.: 221113

ROSATOM ASIA PTE. LTD. (1)
One Raffles Place Tower 2 19-61, Singapore, 048616, Singapore
Tel.: (65) 6808 5692
Web Site: http://www.rosatom.com.sg
Eletric Power Generation Services
N.A.I.C.S.: 221113

ROSATOM FRANCE, sarl (1)
103 rue de Grenelle, 75007, Paris, France
Tel.: (33) 1 70 91 72 23
Eletric Power Generation Services
N.A.I.C.S.: 221113

Rosatom Central Europe s.r.o.
Antala Staska 2027/79 - Budejovicka alej, 140 00, Prague, Czech Republic
Tel.: (420) 244 402 646
Web Site: http://www.rosatom.hu
Eletric Power Generation Services
N.A.I.C.S.: 221113

Rosatom Eastern Europe, LLC (1)
Gogolevskaya str 17 office 49, Kiev, 01054, Ukraine
Tel.: (380) 44 220 28 48
Web Site: http://www.rosatom.com.ua
44 220 28 48
N.A.I.C.S.: 221113

STATE BANK OF INDIA
State Bank Bhavan 16th Floor
Madam Cama Road, Nariman Point,
Mumbai, 400 021, Maharashtra, India
Tel.: (91) 9449112211 In
Web Site: https://www.sbi.co.in
Year Founded: 1806
SBIN—(NSE)
Rev.: $56,756,566,297
Assets: $713,916,230,082
Liabilities: $669,342,411,066
Net Worth: $44,573,819,016
Earnings: $6,672,042,779
Emp.: 235,858
Fiscal Year-end: 03/31/23
Financial Investment Services
N.A.I.C.S.: 523999
Dinesh Kumar Khara *(Chm)*

Subsidiaries:

PT Bank SBI Indonesia (1)
Gedung Graha Mandiri Lantai 11 15 & 24 Jl Imam Bonjol No 61, Jakarta Pusat, 10310, Indonesia
Tel.: (62) 213 983 8747
Web Site: https://www.sbiindo.com
Banking Services
N.A.I.C.S.: 522110
Pranab Ranjan Das *(Pres)*

SBI Cards & Payments Services Pvt. Ltd. (1)

Unit 401 & 402 4th Floor Aggarwal Millennium Tower E-1 2 3, Netaji Subhash Place Wazirpur, New Delhi, 110034, India (74%)
Tel.: (91) 124 458 9803
Web Site: http://www.sbicard.com
Credit Card Issuing & Financial Transaction Processing Services
N.A.I.C.S.: 522210
Ugen Bhutia *(Exec VP & Head-Legal)*

SBI Life Insurance Company Limited (1)
MV Road Western Express Highway Junction, Andheri East, Mumbai, 400 069, India (62.1%)
Tel.: (91) 226 191 0000
Web Site: https://www.sbilife.co.in
Life Insurance Services; Joint Venture of BNP Paribas Assurance & State Bank of India
N.A.I.C.S.: 524113
Anand Pejawar *(Pres-Ops, IT & Intl Bus)*

SBICAP Ventures Ltd. (1)
A Wing 12th Floor Marathon Futurex, Mafatlal Mills Compound NM Joshi Marg Lower Pare, Mumbai, 400013, India
Tel.: (91) 226 911 2800
Web Site: https://www.sbicapventures.com
Financial Services
N.A.I.C.S.: 523999
Suresh Kozhikote *(CEO & Mng Dir)*

State Bank Operations Support Services Pvt. Ltd. (1)
2 Floor NBCC Place South Wing Bhisham Pitamah Marg Pragati Vihar, Lodhi Road, New Delhi, 110003, India
Tel.: (91) 1124309745
Web Site: https://sboss.net.in
Bank Financial Services
N.A.I.C.S.: 521110

State Bank of India (UK) Limited (1)
15 King Street, London, EC2V 8EA, United Kingdom
Tel.: (44) 207 454 4338
Web Site: https://sbiuk.statebank
Banking Services
N.A.I.C.S.: 522110

State Bank of India-Chicago Branch (1)
19 S LaSalle St Ste 200, Chicago, IL 60603-1453 (100%)
Tel.: (312) 621-1200
Web Site: http://www.sbichicago.com
Sales Range: $50-74.9 Million
International Banking
N.A.I.C.S.: 522110

State Bank of Mysore (1)
K G Road, Bengaluru, 560254, India
Tel.: (91) 80 22353901
Web Site: http://www.statebankofmysore.co.in
Rev.: $1,172,420,076
Assets: $12,255,408,061
Liabilities: $11,481,195,590
Net Worth: $774,212,472
Earnings: $52,854,223
Emp.: 10,650
Fiscal Year-end: 03/31/2016
Commercial Banking Services
N.A.I.C.S.: 522110

STATE BANK OF MAURITIUS LTD.
SBM Tower 1 Queen Elizabeth Avenue, Port Louis, Mauritius
Tel.: (230) 2021111
Web Site: http://www.sbmgroup.mu
Rev.: $205,853,392
Assets: $5,178,492,938
Liabilities: $4,649,439,903
Net Worth: $529,053,034
Earnings: $75,257,464
Emp.: 1,100
Fiscal Year-end: 12/31/17
Banking Services
N.A.I.C.S.: 522110
Nayen Koomar Ballah *(Chm)*

Subsidiaries:

Banque SBM Madagascar SA (1)

1 Rue Andriannary Ratianarivo Antsahavola, 10, Antananarivo, Madagascar (100%)
Tel.: (261) 202266607
Web Site: http://www.sbmgroup.mu
Sales Range: $50-74.9 Million
Emp.: 100
Commericial Banking
N.A.I.C.S.: 522110

SBM Asset Management Limited (1)
SBM Tower 1 Queen Elizabeth II Avenue, Port Louis, Mauritius
Tel.: (230) 202 1111
Web Site: http://www.sbmgroup.mu
Sales Range: $50-74.9 Million
Emp.: 10
Asset Management Services
N.A.I.C.S.: 523940

SBM Capital Management Limited (1)
Suite 2005 level 2 Alexander House 35 Cybercity, Ebene, Mauritius
Tel.: (230) 4048800
Financial Management Services
N.A.I.C.S.: 523999

SBM Financials Limited (1)
Queen Elizabeth 2 Avenue State Bank Tower, 1 Queen Elizabeth II Avenue, Port Louis, Mauritius (100%)
Tel.: (230) 2021111
Web Site: http://www.sbmgroup.com
Trust Fiduciary & Custody Activities
N.A.I.C.S.: 523991

SBM Global Investment Limited (1)
State Bank Tower, 1 Queen Elizabeth II Ave, Port Louis, Mauritius (100%)
Tel.: (230) 2021111
Investment Banking & Securities Dealing
N.A.I.C.S.: 523150

SBM IT Limited (1)
State Bank Tower, 1 Queen Elizabeth II Avenue, Port Louis, 152, Mauritius (100%)
Tel.: (230) 2021111
Web Site: http://www.sbmgroup.com
All Other Professional Scientific & Technical Services
N.A.I.C.S.: 541990

SBM International Investments Limited (1)
SBM Tower 1 Queen Elizabeth II Avenue, Port Louis, Mauritius
Tel.: (230) 202 1111
Investment Management Service
N.A.I.C.S.: 523999
Jairaj Sonoo *(CEO)*

SBM Investments Limited (1)
State Bank Tower, 1 Queen Elizabeth II Avenue, Port Louis, Mauritius (100%)
Tel.: (230) 2021111
Investment Banking & Securities Dealing
N.A.I.C.S.: 523150

SBM Lease Limited (1)
State Bank Tower, 1 Queen Elizabeth II Ave, Port Louis, Mauritius (100%)
Tel.: (230) 2021111
Web Site: http://www.sbmgroup.mu
Commericial Banking
N.A.I.C.S.: 522110

SBM Mauritius Asset Managers Ltd (1)
State Bank Tower 1 Queen Elizabeth II Avenue, Port Louis, Mauritius (100%)
Tel.: (230) 2021111
Pension Funds
N.A.I.C.S.: 525110

SBM Securities Ltd (1)
State Bank Tower, 1 Queen Elizabeth II Avenue, Port Louis, Mauritius (100%)
Tel.: (230) 2021111
Sales Range: $350-399.9 Million
Emp.: 1,000
Securities Brokerage
N.A.I.C.S.: 523150

STATE BANK OF PAKISTAN
II Chundrigar Road, Karachi, Pakistan
Tel.: (92) 111727111
Web Site: http://www.sbp.org.pk
Year Founded: 1947
Rev.: $358,661,169

STATE BANK OF PAKISTAN

State Bank of Pakistan—(Continued)
Assets: $82,332,575,056
Liabilities: $77,262,257,769
Net Worth: $5,070,317,286
Earnings: ($7,490,916)
Emp.: 1,275
Fiscal Year-end: 06/30/19
Banking Services
N.A.I.C.S.: 521110
Mohammad Mansoor Ali *(Sec)*

Subsidiaries:

National Bank of Pakistan **(1)**
NBP Building I I Chundrigar Road, Karachi,
Pakistan **(75.2%)**
Tel.: (92) 2199220100
Web Site: https://www.nbp.com.pk
Rev.: $707,844,544
Assets: $20,172,400,126
Liabilities: $18,631,806,872
Net Worth: $1,540,593,254
Earnings: $107,207,916
Emp.: 15,188
Fiscal Year-end: 12/31/2019
Savings, Commercial & Investment Banking Services
N.A.I.C.S.: 522110
Muhammad Ali Zamin *(Exec VP)*

Affiliate (Domestic):

First Credit and Investment Bank
Limited **(2)**
2nd Floor Sidco Avenue Centre Stratchen
Road R A Lines, Karachi, 74200, Pakistan
Tel.: (92) 2135658750
Web Site: http://www.fcibank.com.pk
Rev.: $832,651
Assets: $12,744,623
Liabilities: $8,262,010
Net Worth: $4,482,613
Earnings: $50,856
Emp.: 24
Fiscal Year-end: 06/30/2022
Financial Management & Investment Services
N.A.I.C.S.: 523940
Muhammad Mohsin Ali *(Pres & CEO)*

Subsidiary (Domestic):

NBP Capital Limited **(2)**
4th Fl PIC Tower 32 A Lalazar Drive MT
Khan Road, 75400, Karachi,
Pakistan **(100%)**
Tel.: (92) 215610369
Web Site: http://www.nbp.com.pk
Financial Transactions Processing Reserve
& Clearinghouse Activities
N.A.I.C.S.: 522320

Affiliate (Domestic):

National Fullerton Asset Management
Limited **(2)**
7th Floor Clifton Diamond Building Block No
4 Scheme No 5, I.I. Chundrigar Rd, Karachi, Pakistan **(27%)**
Tel.: (92) 21 111 111 632
Web Site: http://www.nafafunds.com
Asset Management Services
N.A.I.C.S.: 523940
Amjad Waheed *(CEO)*

Subsidiary (Domestic):

Taurus Securities Limited **(2)**
Suite 604 6th Floor Progressive Plaza,
Beaumont Road, Karachi, 75530,
Pakistan **(58.32%)**
Tel.: (92) 21 568 4962
Web Site: http://www.taurus.com.pk
Sales Range: $75-99.9 Million
Emp.: 60
Equity Investment, Securities Brokerage &
Financial Advisory Services
N.A.I.C.S.: 523999
Zain Hussain *(CEO)*

Joint Venture (Non-US):

United National Bank Limited **(2)**
2 Brook Street, London, W1S 1BQ, United Kingdom
Tel.: (44) 2072908000
Web Site: http://www.unbankltd.com

Sales Range: $600-649.9 Million
Emp.: 1,500
Commercial Banking & Treasury Services;
Owned 55% by United Bank Limited & 45%
by National Bank of Pakistan
N.A.I.C.S.: 522110
Mansoor Khan *(CEO)*

STATE CAPITAL INVESTMENT CORPORATION

Floors 23-24 Charmvit Building, 117
Tran Duy Hung Cau Giay District,
Hanoi, Vietnam
Tel.: (84) 024 3824 07 03 **VN**
Web Site: http://www.scic.vn
Holding Company
N.A.I.C.S.: 551112
Quoc Huy Nguyen *(Chm)*

STATE ENERGY GROUP INTERNATIONAL ASSETS HOLDINGS LIMITED

Unit 13 5/F Tower 1 Harbour Centre,
1 Hok Cheung Street Hung Hom,
Kowloon, China (Hong Kong)
Tel.: (852) 2 123 8460 **BM**
Web Site: http://www.seiah.com
Year Founded: 1977
0918—(HKG)
Rev.: $35,713,272
Assets: $46,989,736
Liabilities: $31,994,263
Net Worth: $14,995,473
Earnings: $1,322,045
Emp.: 44
Fiscal Year-end: 03/31/21
Holding Company; Financial Services
N.A.I.C.S.: 551112
Jinbing Zhang *(Chm)*

STATE GAS LIMITED

Suite 4 Level 1 40 Edward Street,
Brisbane, 4000, QLD, Australia
Tel.: (61) 283551819 **AU**
Web Site: https://www.stategas.com
Year Founded: 2017
GAS—(ASX)
Natural Gas Exploration Service
N.A.I.C.S.: 211130
Doug McAlpine *(CEO)*

STATE GRID CORPORATION OF CHINA

No 86 Changan Street, Xicheng District, Beijing, 100031, China
Tel.: (86) 1063415242
Web Site: http://www.sgcc.com.cn
Year Founded: 2002
Sales Range: $75-99.9 Billion
Power Transmission
N.A.I.C.S.: 335311
Liu Zehong *(Exec VP)*

Subsidiaries:

Anhui Electric Power Company **(1)**
No 133 Susong Road, Baohe District, Hefei,
230022, Anhui, China
Tel.: (86) 55163882114
Eletric Power Generation Services
N.A.I.C.S.: 221118

CPFL Energia S.A. **(1)**
Rua Jorge de Figueiredo Correa No 1 632
Parte, Jardim Professora Tarcilia Campinas,
13087-397, Sao Paulo, Brazil **(94.76%)**
Tel.: (55) 1937566211
Web Site: http://www.cpfl.com.br
Rev.: $7,925,653,605
Assets: $14,950,887,825
Liabilities: $11,185,913,052
Net Worth: $3,764,974,773
Earnings: $1,102,223,751
Emp.: 13,302
Fiscal Year-end: 12/31/2023
Electrical Products Distr
N.A.I.C.S.: 423610
Yumeng Zhao *(Exec VP)*

Subsidiary (Domestic):

CERAN - Companhia Energetica Rio
das Antas **(2)**
Av Carlos Gomes 300 8 andar, Bairro Boa
Vista, Porto Alegre, 90480-000, Rio Grande
do Sul, Brazil
Tel.: (55) 51 3025 6700
Web Site: http://www.ceran.com.br
Sales Range: $25-49.9 Million
Emp.: 65
Power Plant Construction Services
N.A.I.C.S.: 237990

CPFL Bio Buriti S.A. **(2)**
Rodovia Campinas-Mogi Mirim Km 2 5,
Jardim Santana, Campinas, 13088-900,
Sao Paulo, Brazil
Tel.: (55) 19 3847 5910
Eletric Power Generation Services
N.A.I.C.S.: 221118

CPFL Bio Pedra S.A. **(2)**
Rodovia Campinas-Mogi Mirim Km 2 5,
Jardim Santana, Campinas, 13088-900,
Sao Paulo, Brazil
Tel.: (55) 19 3847 5910
Thermal Power Plant Construction Services
N.A.I.C.S.: 237130

CPFL Bioenergia S.A. **(2)**
Rua Gomes de Carvalho n 1510 14 Andar
Conjunto 1402 Sala 04, Vila Olimpia,
04547-005, Sao Paulo, Brazil
Tel.: (55) 11 3841 8507
Eletric Power Generation Services
N.A.I.C.S.: 221118

CPFL Comercializacao Cone Sul
S.A. **(2)**
Rua Gomes De Carvalho 1 510 14 Andar
Conjunto 1402 Sala 3, Vila Olimpia, 04547-005, Sao Paulo, Brazil
Tel.: (55) 11 3841 8507
Web Site: http://www.cpfl.com.br
Electric Power Distr
N.A.I.C.S.: 221122

CPFL Santa Cruz **(2)**
Rua Gomes de Carvalho 1510, 14 andar
CJ 142 Sala 02, Vila Olimpia, 04547-005,
Sao Paulo, Brazil
Tel.: (55) 19 3754 7648
Electricity Distr
N.A.I.C.S.: 221122
Wilson Pinto Ferreira Jr. *(CEO)*

CPFL Servicos, Equipamentos, Industria e Comercio S.A. **(2)**
Avenida dos Bragheta 364, Sao Jose do
Rio Pardo, 13720-000, Sao Paulo, Brazil
Tel.: (55) 19 3687 8200
Electric Power Generation & Distribution
Services
N.A.I.C.S.: 221118

Centrais Eletricas da Paraiba
S.A. **(2)**
Avenida Fernando Simoes Barbosa 266,
Boa Viagem, 51020-390, Recife, Pernambuco, Brazil
Tel.: (55) 19 3756 8844
Thermal Power Plant Construction Services
N.A.I.C.S.: 237130

Companhia Jaguari de Energia **(2)**
Rua Vigato 1620, Sao Paulo, 13820-000,
Jaguariuna, Brazil
Tel.: (55) 19 3847 5945
Web Site: http://www.cpfl.com.br
Electric Power Distr
N.A.I.C.S.: 221122

Companhia Jaguari de Geracao de
Energia Ltda. **(2)**
Rua Vigato 1620 Terreo Sala 2, Jaguariuna, 13820-000, Sao Paulo, Brazil
Tel.: (55) 19 3847 5910
Electric Power Generation Services
N.A.I.C.S.: 221118

Companhia Paulista de Energia Eletrica Ltda. **(2)**
Rua Vigato 1 620 1 andar sala 1, Jaguariuna, 13820-000, Sao Paulo, Brazil
Tel.: (55) 19 3847 5900
Web Site: http://www.cpfl.com.br
Electric Power Distr
N.A.I.C.S.: 221122

INTERNATIONAL PUBLIC

Companhia Sul Paulista de
Energia **(2)**
Rua Vigato 1 620 1 andar sala 2, Jaguariuna, 13820-000, Sao Paulo, Brazil
Tel.: (55) 19 3847 5900
Electric Power Generation & Distribution
Services
N.A.I.C.S.: 221118

RGE Sul Distribuidora de Energia
S/A **(2)**
Avenida Sao Borja n 2 801r, Rio Grande,
Sao Paolo, Brazil
Tel.: (55) 1123915509
Web Site: http://www.rgesul.com.br
Electric Power Distribution Services
N.A.I.C.S.: 221122
Jose Carlos Saciloto Tadiello *(Pres)*

Subsidiary (Domestic):

RGE Rio Grande Energia S.A. **(3)**
Rua Sao Luiz 77 8th Floor, Porto Alegre,
Brazil
Tel.: (55) 5132183210
Web Site: http://www.rge-rs.com.br
Electric Power Distribution
N.A.I.C.S.: 221122
Wilson Pinto Ferreira Jr. *(Pres)*

Subsidiary (Domestic):

SPE Alto Irani Energia S.A. **(2)**
Rua Sao Pedro 2987 E, Jardim America,
89803-903, Chapeco, Santa Catarina, Brazil
Tel.: (55) 49 3328 6199
Eletric Power Generation Services
N.A.I.C.S.: 221118

Subsidiary (Non-US):

United Iron & Steel Manufacturing
Co. P.L.C. **(2)**
PO Box 125, Amman, 16010, Jordan
Tel.: (962) 64460577
Sales Range: $1-9.9 Million
Iron & Steel Product Mfr
N.A.I.C.S.: 331110
Oday Al Manaseer *(Acting Gen Mgr)*

China Electric Power Equipment and
Technology Co., Ltd. **(1)**
No 8 Nanrui Road, Gulou District, Nanjing,
210003, China
Tel.: (86) 2581092820
Web Site: http://www.narigroup.com
Electric Power Distribution Services
N.A.I.C.S.: 221122

East China Grid Company
Limited **(1)**
No 201 East Nan Jing Road, Shanghai,
200002, China
Tel.: (86) 21 2301 5607
Electric Power Distribution Services
N.A.I.C.S.: 221122

Fujian Electric Power Company **(1)**
No 1032 Liedong Street, Meilie District,
Sanming, 365000, Fujian, China
Tel.: (86) 5988202928
Eletric Power Generation Services
N.A.I.C.S.: 221118

Gansu Electric Power Company **(1)**
No 628 Xijin East Road, Lanzhou, 730050,
Gansu, China
Tel.: (86) 9312952235
Electric Power Generation Services
N.A.I.C.S.: 221118

Henan Electric Power Company **(1)**
No 168 Hongli Avenue, Weibin District,
Xinxiang, 453002, Henan, China
Tel.: (86) 3732884096
Eletric Power Generation Services
N.A.I.C.S.: 221118

Hubei Electric Power Company **(1)**
No 175 Xudong Road, Wuchang District,
Wuhan, 430077, Hubei, China
Tel.: (86) 2788566881
Electric Power Generation Services
N.A.I.C.S.: 221118

Hunan Electric Power Company **(1)**
No 1 Chuanshan W Rd, Zhengxiang Dist,
Hengyang, 421001, Hunan, China
Tel.: (86) 7348252153

AND PRIVATE COMPANIES   **STATE GRID YINGDA CO., LTD.**

Eletric Power Generation Services
N.A.I.C.S.: 221118

Jiangsu Electric Power Company (1)
No 215 Shanghai Rd, Nanjing, 210024, Jiangsu, China
Tel.: (86) 2585851529
Eletric Power Generation Services
N.A.I.C.S.: 221118

Jilin Electric Power Company (1)
No 4629 Renmin St, Chaoyang Dist, Changchun, 130021, Jilin, China
Tel.: (86) 43185792222
Electric Power Generation Services
N.A.I.C.S.: 221118

Luneng Group Co., Ltd. (1)
No 5 Courtyard Chaowai Avenue, Chaoyang District, Beijing, China
Tel.: (86) 10 85727222
Web Site: http://www.en.luneng.com
Electric Power Distribution Services
N.A.I.C.S.: 221122

NARI Technology Co., Ltd. (1)
No 19 Chengxin Avenue, Jiangning District, Nanjing, 211106, China
Tel.: (86) 4000095598
Web Site: https://www.naritech.cn
Rev.: $6,574,786,391
Assets: $10,763,844,273
Liabilities: $4,395,530,515
Net Worth: $6,368,313,758
Earnings: $905,043,840
Fiscal Year-end: 12/31/2022
Electric Equipment Mfr
N.A.I.C.S.: 335999

National Grid Corporation of the Philippines (1)
Quezon Avenue cor BIR Road, Diliman, Quezon City, Philippines
Tel.: (63) 2 298 12100
Web Site: http://www.ngcp.ph
Electric Power Distr
N.A.I.C.S.: 221122

Ningxia Electric Power Company (1)
No 288 Changcheng East Road, Ningxia, Yinchuan, 750001, China
Tel.: (86) 9514912209
Eletric Power Generation Services
N.A.I.C.S.: 221118

North China Grid Company Limited (1)
482 Guang'anmenneidajie, Xuanwu District, Beijing, 100053, China
Tel.: (86) 10 83583114
Web Site: http://www.nc.sgcc.com.cn
Electric Power Distribution Services
N.A.I.C.S.: 221122

Subsidiary (Domestic):

Beijing Electric Power Company (2)
No 41 Qianmen West Ave, Beijing, 100031, China
Tel.: (86) 1066154598
Electric Power Distribution Services
N.A.I.C.S.: 221122

Beijing Power Equipment Group (2)
No 12 Haotian Street, Liangxiang Fangshan District, Beijing, 102401, China
Tel.: (86) 10 69372305
Web Site: http://www.bpeg.cn
Rev.: $31,770,000
Emp.: 3,000
Mechanical Power Transmission Equipment Mfr
N.A.I.C.S.: 333613
Li Yueming (Deputy Gen Mgr-Mechanical Products)

Chengde Power Supply Company (2)
No 10 North To Xinhua Road, Shuangqiao District, Chengde, 067000, Hebei, China
Tel.: (86) 3142173203
Electric Power Distribution Services
N.A.I.C.S.: 221122

Qinhuangdao Power Generation Co., Ltd. (2)
181 East Street, Qinhuangdao, 066000, China
Tel.: (86) 335 5898537
Eletric Power Generation Services
N.A.I.C.S.: 221118

North China International Power Economic and Trade Corp. (1)
No 32 Zaolinqianjie Street, Xuanwu District, Beijing, 100053, China
Tel.: (86) 108 3583382
Web Site: http://www.nipc.com.cn
Electric Power Distr
N.A.I.C.S.: 221122
Guo Dejiang (Pres)

Northwest China Grid Company Limited (1)
No 50 Middle Segment of East Huancheng, Xi'an, 710048, China
Tel.: (86) 29 85425678
Web Site: http://www.nw.sgcc.com.cn
Eletric Power Generation Services
N.A.I.C.S.: 221118

Pinggao Group Co., Ltd. (1)
Nanhuandong Road, Pingdingshan, Henan, China
Tel.: (86) 375 3506739
Web Site: http://www.pinggaogroup.com.cn
Switchgear Mfr
N.A.I.C.S.: 335313

Subsidiary (Domestic):

Henan Pinggao Electric Co., Ltd (2)
No 22 Nanhuan East Road, Pingdingshan, 467000, Henan, China
Tel.: (86) 3753804064
Web Site: https://en.pinggao.com
Rev.: $1,302,108,350
Assets: $2,505,689,892
Liabilities: $1,138,308,655
Net Worth: $1,367,381,237
Earnings: $29,778,521
Emp.: 4,797
Fiscal Year-end: 12/31/2022
Switchgear Mfr
N.A.I.C.S.: 335313
Qingping Pang (Gen Mgr)

Joint Venture (Domestic):

Henan Pinggao Toshiba High-Voltage Switchgear Co., Ltd. (3)
Dongduan Jianshe Road, Pingdingshan, 467013, Henan, China
Tel.: (86) 3753988888
Sales Range: $25-49.9 Million
Emp.: 27
High-Voltage Switchgear Mfr
N.A.I.C.S.: 335313

Qinghai Electric Power Company (1)
No 14 Xinning Road, Chenxi Dist, Xining, Qinghai, China
Tel.: (86) 971 6178298
Eletric Power Generation Services
N.A.I.C.S.: 221118

SGSP (Australia) Assets Pty. Ltd. (1)
Level 16 567 Collins Street, Melbourne, 3000, VIC, Australia (60%)
Tel.: (61) 3 9173 7000
Holding Company; Energy & Water Transportation Assets
N.A.I.C.S.: 551112
Paul Adams (Mng Dir-Jemena)

Subsidiary (Domestic):

Jemena Limited (2)
Level 16 567 Collins Street, Melbourne, 3000, VIC, Australia
Tel.: (61) 3 9173 7000
Web Site: http://www.jemena.com.au
Energy Infrastructure Asset Management Services
N.A.I.C.S.: 523940
Shaun Reardon (Exec Gen Mgr-Strategy, Regulation & Markets)

Shaanxi Electric Power Company (1)
No 16 Wanshou North Road, Xincheng District, Xi'an, 710043, Shaanxi, China
Tel.: (86) 2982546308
Eletric Power Generation Services
N.A.I.C.S.: 221118

Shandong Electric Power Company (1)
No150 Jingsan Road, Shizhong District, Jinan, 250001, China
Tel.: (86) 53186932222

Electric Power Distribution Services
N.A.I.C.S.: 221122

Shandong Power (Group) Corporation (1)
No 150 Jingsan Road, Shizhong District, 250001, Jinan, China
Tel.: (86) 531 86932222
Electric Power Distr
N.A.I.C.S.: 221122

Shandong Power Equipment Co., Ltd. (1)
N0 3 Jiyixichang Road, Jinan, 250022, Shandong, China
Tel.: (86) 15066662917
Web Site: http://www.speco.com.cn
Electric Power Distribution Services
N.A.I.C.S.: 221122

Shanghai Municipal Electric Power Company (1)
No 1122 Yuanshen Road, Pudong New District, Shanghai, 200122, China
Tel.: (86) 21 2892 5222
Eletric Power Generation Services
N.A.I.C.S.: 221118

State Grid International Development Limited (1)
No 88 West Chang'an Street, Xicheng District, Beijing, 100031, China (100%)
Tel.: (86) 1060616923
Web Site: http://www.stategrid.com.cn
Investment Management Service
N.A.I.C.S.: 523999
Jiang Xiaojun (Sr VP)

Subsidiary (Non-US):

Compania General de Electricidad S.A. (2)
Avda Presidente Riesco N 5561 Piso 17, Las Condes, Santiago, Chile (96.04%)
Tel.: (56) 800800767
Web Site: https://www.cge.cl
Sales Range: $1-4.9 Billion
Electric Power Generation & Distribution
N.A.I.C.S.: 221118
Carlos Alvarez Fernandez (Pres)

Subsidiary (Domestic):

CGE Distribucion S.A. (3)
Av Presidente Riesco 5561 Piso 14, Las Condes, Santiago, Chile
Tel.: (56) 600 624 3243
Web Site: http://www.cgedistribucion.cl
Power Distribution Services
N.A.I.C.S.: 221118
C. Lorena Leon (Head-Fin Plng & IR)

CGE Magallanes S.A. (3)
Pdte Riesco 5561 Piso 17, Las Condes, Santiago, Chile
Tel.: (56) 56 2 680 7104
Web Site: http://www.cge.cl
Eletric Power Generation Services
N.A.I.C.S.: 221118

Subsidiary (Domestic):

Empresa Electrica de Magallanes S.A. (4)
Croacia 444, Punta Arenas, Chile
Tel.: (56) 800800400
Web Site: https://www.edelmag.cl
Sales Range: $25-49.9 Million
Power Generation Services
N.A.I.C.S.: 221118
Jorge Iardan Franulic (Chm)

Subsidiary (Domestic):

Empresa Electrica de Antofagasta S.A. (3)
Avenida Pedro Aguirre Cerda 5558, Antofagasta, Chile
Tel.: (56) 55 681401
Web Site: http://www.elecda.cl
Electric Power Distribution Services
N.A.I.C.S.: 221122
Eduardo Apablaza Dau (CEO)

Inmobiliaria Coronel S.A. (3)
Avenida Cordillera 3633 Of 3, Coronel, Chile
Tel.: (56) 41 2790400
Real Estate Manangement Services
N.A.I.C.S.: 531390

Transformadores TUSAN S.A. (3)
Av Gladys Marin 6030, Estacion Central, Santiago, Chile
Tel.: (56) 2 899 6800
Web Site: http://www.tusan.cl
Electric Power Transmission Equipment Mfr
N.A.I.C.S.: 333613
Aogusto Wiegand Puyssegur (Gen Mgr)

Subsidiary (Domestic):

Energy Sur S.A. (4)
Parque Industrial Michaihue - Calle Local N 55, San Pedro de la Paz, Concepcion, Chile
Tel.: (56) 41 2798266
Web Site: http://energysur.cl
Electric Power Transformer Maintenance Services & Distr
N.A.I.C.S.: 811210

Ingenieria y Desarrollo Tecnologico S.A. (4)
Avda Las Parcelas 5490, Estacion Central, Santiago, Chile
Tel.: (56) 2 719 2200
Web Site: http://www.idt.cl
Power Electronic Equipment Mfr
N.A.I.C.S.: 334419
Patricio Lagos (Gen Mgr)

Subsidiary (Domestic):

Transnet S.A. (3)
Presidente Riesco 5561 Piso 12, Las Condes, 8340434, Santiago, Chile
Tel.: (56) 2 280 7000
Web Site: http://www.transnet.cl
Electric Power Transmission Services
N.A.I.C.S.: 221121
Eduardo Apablaza Dau (Gen Mgr)

Tianjin Electric Power Company (1)
No 39 Wujing Rd, Hebei District, Tianjin, China
Tel.: (86) 222 4406114
Electric Power Distr
N.A.I.C.S.: 221122

Xinjiang Electric Power Company (1)
No 123 Jianshe Road, Tianshan District, 830002, Urumqi, China
Tel.: (86) 991 2920376
Electric Power Distr
N.A.I.C.S.: 221122

Yingda Security Corporation Ltd. (1)
Shennan Road Huaneng Building 30th Floor, Shenzhen, China
Tel.: (86) 75526982993
Electric Power Distribution Services
N.A.I.C.S.: 221122

Zhejiang Electric Power Company (1)
No 8 Huanglong Road, Xihu Dist, Hangzhou, 311100, Zhejiang, China
Tel.: (86) 57185162219
Eletric Power Generation Services
N.A.I.C.S.: 221118

STATE GRID INFORMATION & COMMUNICATION CO LTD
No 390 Lazi Road, Tianfu New District, Chengdu, 610041, Sichuan, China
Tel.: (86) 2887333131
Web Site: https://www.sgitc.com
Year Founded: 1997
600131—(SHG)
Rev.: $1,069,160,531
Assets: $1,689,335,299
Liabilities: $884,188,459
Net Worth: $805,146,840
Earnings: $112,541,888
Fiscal Year-end: 12/31/22
Hydroelectric Power Generation & Distribution Services
N.A.I.C.S.: 221111
Wang Ben (Chm)

STATE GRID YINGDA CO., LTD.
9F Tower C No 211 Guoyao Road,

STATE GRID YINGDA CO., LTD.

State Grid Yingda Co., Ltd.—(Continued)
Pilot Free Trade Zone, Shanghai, 200126, China
Tel.: (86) 2151531111
Web Site: http://www.zhixindianqi.com
Year Founded: 1997
600517—(SHG)
Rev.: $1,453,238,217
Assets: $6,880,486,441
Liabilities: $3,604,369,433
Net Worth: $3,276,117,008
Earnings: $187,516,783
Fiscal Year-end: 12/31/21
Transformer Mfr
N.A.I.C.S.: 335311
Yang Dongwei (Chm)

STATE OIL CO. OF AZERBAIJAN REPUBLIC
121 Haydar Aliyev Avenue, Baku, AZ1029, Azerbaijan
Tel.: (994) 125210282
Web Site: http://www.socar.az
Oil & Gas Production Services
N.A.I.C.S.: 213111
Rovnag Ibrahim Abdullayev (Pres)

Subsidiaries:

Azerbaijan (BTC) Ltd (1)
4th floor Zakir 11a str Babek avenue, Baku, Azerbaijan
Tel.: (994) 12 514 82 28
Web Site: http://www.azbtc.com
Petroleum Product Distr
N.A.I.C.S.: 424710
Rashad Shabanov (Mng Dir)

Azerbaijan (SCP) LTD (1)
3rd floor 6 Ali Veliyev str, AZ1060, Baku, Azerbaijan
Tel.: (994) 12 520 03 03
Web Site: http://www.az-scpc.com
Emp.: 35
Natural Gas Distr
N.A.I.C.S.: 221210
Fuad M. Ahmadov (Exec Dir)

Caspian Drilling Company JV (1)
86 Nasibbay Yusifbayli Street, AZ1007, Baku, Azerbaijan
Tel.: (994) 12 404 41 80
Web Site: http://www.caspiandrilling.com
Oil & Gas Field Drilling Services
N.A.I.C.S.: 213111
Farid Akhundov (Gen Dir)

SOCAR Energy Georgia LLC (1)
300 Aragveli Str 24, Tbilisi, Georgia
Tel.: (995) 32 2 439 275
Web Site: http://www.socar.ge
Petroleum Product Distr
N.A.I.C.S.: 424710
Mahir Mammedov (Gen Dir)

SOCAR Energy Switzerland GmbH (1)
Nuschelerstrasse 24, Zurich, 8001, Switzerland
Tel.: (41) 44.214.41 11
Web Site: http://www.socarenergy.ch
Sales Range: $300-349.9 Million
Emp.: 900
Marketer of Petroleum Products; Gasoline Service Stations
N.A.I.C.S.: 424720
Edgar Bachmann (CEO)

SOCAR Energy Ukraine (1)
52-A B Khmelnitsky str, Kiev, 01030, Ukraine
Tel.: (380) 44 207 10 10
Web Site: http://www.socar.com.ua
Petroleum Product Distr
N.A.I.C.S.: 424710
Sergey Tashchi (Head-Legal Dept)

SOCAR Turkey Enerji A.S. (1)
Eski Buyukdere Cad Socar Bosphorus Plaza No 231 Kat 6/7 Maslak, Istanbul, 34398, Turkiye
Tel.: (90) 212 305 00 00
Web Site: http://www.socar.com.tr
Oil & Gas Field Exploration Services
N.A.I.C.S.: 213111

Kenan Yavuz (Pres & CEO)

Subsidiary (Domestic):

EWE Turkey Holding A.S. (2)
Buyukdere Caddesi No 127 Astoria A Blok Kat 25, 34394, Esentepe, Istanbul, Turkiye
Tel.: (90) 212 355 26 00
Sales Range: $200-249.9 Million
Emp.: 397
Investment Management Service
N.A.I.C.S.: 523940

SOCAR Gaz Ticareti A.S. (2)
Eski Buyukdere Cad Socar Bosphorus Plaza No 231 Floor 3 Maslak, Istanbul, Turkiye
Tel.: (90) 232 616 12 40
Natural Gas Distr
N.A.I.C.S.: 221210
Abdullah Nezihi Erdem (Gen Mgr)

SOCAR Turkey Petrol Enerji Dagitim A.S. (2)
Cengiz Topel Cad Le Meridien Is Merkezi No 39 Etiler Besiktas, Istanbul, Turkiye
Tel.: (90) 212 350 12 00
Petroleum Product Distr
N.A.I.C.S.: 424710
Mutluay Dogan (CEO)

STATE OIL FUND OF THE REPUBLIC OF AZERBAIJAN
Heydar Aliyev av 165, Baku, AZ1029, Azerbaijan
Tel.: (994) 124987753
Web Site: http://www.oilfund.az
Year Founded: 1999
Sales Range: $650-699.9 Million
Emp.: 75,000
Oil & Gas Exploration Services
N.A.I.C.S.: 541360
Heydar Aliyev (Pres)

Subsidiaries:

AzBTC Co. (1)
4th Floor Zakir 11a Str Babek Avenue, Baku, Azerbaijan
Tel.: (994) 12 514 82 28
Web Site: http://www.azbtc.com
Crude Oil Pipeline Transportation Services
N.A.I.C.S.: 486110

STATE OIL LIMITED
York House 45 Seymour Street, London, W1H 7JT, United Kingdom
Tel.: (44) 2075800033
Web Site: https://www.prax.com
Year Founded: 1999
Oil & Gas Distribution
N.A.I.C.S.: 213112
Sanjeev Kumar Soosaipillai (Chm & CEO)

Subsidiaries:

Prax Exploration & Production PLC (1)
Harvest House Horizon Business Village 1 Brooklands Road Weybridge, Surrey, KT13 0TJ, United Kingdom
Tel.: (44) 2075800033
Web Site: https://www.prax.com
Oil & Gas Exploration
N.A.I.C.S.: 211130

Subsidiary (Domestic):

Hurricane Energy plc (2)
The Wharf Abbey Mill Business Park, Lower Eashing, Godalming, GU7 2QN, Surrey, United Kingdom
Tel.: (44) 1483862820
Web Site: http://www.hurricaneenergy.com
Rev.: $240,540,000
Assets: $248,257,000
Liabilities: $161,379,000
Net Worth: $86,878,000
Earnings: $18,236,000
Emp.: 55
Fiscal Year-end: 12/31/2021
Oil & Gas Exploration
N.A.I.C.S.: 211120
Steven James McTiernan (Chm)

STATE POWER INVESTMENT CORPORATION
Building 3 No 28 Financial Street, Xicheng District, Beijing, 100033, China
Tel.: (86) 1066298000
Web Site: http://www.spic.com.cn
Sales Range: $25-49.9 Billion
Emp.: 140,000
Holding Company; Electric Power Generation Plant & Infrastructure Investment, Development, Construction & Management Services
N.A.I.C.S.: 551112
Zhenping Meng (Pres)

Subsidiaries:

Pacific Hydro Australia (1)
Level 11 474 Flinders St, Melbourne, 3000, VIC, Australia
Tel.: (61) 386216000
Web Site: http://www.pacifichydro.com.au
Hydroelectric & Wind Power Generation Services
N.A.I.C.S.: 221111
Michael Fuge (CEO)

SPIC Yuanda Environmental-Protection Co., Ltd. (1)
Building 1 No 10 Huanghuan North Road, Liangjiang New District, Chongqing, 401122, China
Tel.: (86) 2365933055
Web Site: https://www.zdydep.com
Rev.: $580,805,190
Assets: $1,459,594,707
Liabilities: $683,464,645
Net Worth: $776,130,063
Earnings: ($3,948,216)
Fiscal Year-end: 12/31/2022
Environment Protection Servivces
N.A.I.C.S.: 541330
Chen Bin (Chm)

STATE POWER RIXIN TECH. CO., LTD.
Room 227 F2 N6 BBMG Intelligent Manufacturing Workshop 27, Jiancaicheng Middle Road Xisanqi Haidian District, Beijing, 100096, China
Tel.: (86) 1083458100
Web Site: https://www.sprixin.com
Year Founded: 2008
301162—(CHIN)
Rev.: $64,256,774
Assets: $196,985,704
Liabilities: $45,836,929
Net Worth: $151,148,774
Earnings: $11,865,704
Fiscal Year-end: 12/31/23
Electrical Component Mfr & Distr
N.A.I.C.S.: 335210
Zheng Yong (Chm)

STATE PROPERTY FUND OF UKRAINE
18/9 (metro station Pecherskay), 133 st. Kutuzov, 01601, Kiev, Ukraine
Tel.: (380) 442003333
Web Site: http://www.spfu.gov.ua
Year Founded: 1991
Sales Range: $800-899.9 Million
Emp.: 4,500
State Government Economic Programs
N.A.I.C.S.: 926110
Oleksandr V. Ryabchenko (Mng Dir)

STATE TRADING CORPORATION OF INDIA LTD
Jawahar Vyapar Bhavan Tolstoy Marg, New Delhi, 110001, India
Tel.: (91) 1123313177
Web Site: https://www.stclimited.co.in
Year Founded: 1956
STCINDIA—(NSE)
Rev.: $41,962,830
Assets: $322,275,135
Liabilities: $960,196,965

INTERNATIONAL PUBLIC

Net Worth: ($637,921,830)
Earnings: ($6,886,425)
Emp.: 212
Fiscal Year-end: 03/31/21
Trading
N.A.I.C.S.: 323111
Sanjeev K. Sharma (Dir-Personnel)

Subsidiaries:

STCL Limited (1)
Tel.: (91) 8022286925
Web Site: http://www.stclindia.com
Sales Range: $50-74.9 Million
Emp.: 56
Agricultural Products Trading Services
N.A.I.C.S.: 926140

STATE TRANSPORT LEASING COMPANY PJSC
31a/1 Leningradsky Prospekt, 125284, Moscow, Russia
Tel.: (7) 4952210012
Web Site: http://www.gtlk.ru
Sales Range: Less than $1 Million
Freight Transportation Services
N.A.I.C.S.: 481212
E. I. Ditrikh (Gen Dir)

STATEHOUSE HOLDINGS INC.
77 King Street West Suite 2905, Toronto, M5K 1H1, ON, Canada
Tel.: (416) 840-3798
Web Site: http://www.investharborside.com
STHZF—(OTCQX)
Rev.: $62,625,364
Assets: $153,820,929
Liabilities: $106,218,165
Net Worth: $47,602,764
Earnings: ($26,158,466)
Emp.: 620
Fiscal Year-end: 12/31/21
Investment Services
N.A.I.C.S.: 523999
Zed Schlott (VP-Retail)

STATKRAFT AS
Lilleakerveien 6, N-0283, Oslo, Norway
Tel.: (47) 24067000
Web Site: http://www.statkraft.com
Year Founded: 1895
Rev.: $5,442,792,150
Assets: $20,160,575,400
Liabilities: $8,718,823,200
Net Worth: $11,441,752,200
Earnings: $1,286,180,850
Emp.: 4,000
Fiscal Year-end: 12/31/19
Power Distribution & Generation
N.A.I.C.S.: 221122
Christian Rynning-Tonnesen (Pres & CEO)

Subsidiaries:

Agua Imara ACA Pte Ltd (1)
16 Collyer Quay 29-02 Hitachi Tower, Singapore, 049318, Singapore
Tel.: (65) 6513 2189
Power Generation Services
N.A.I.C.S.: 221111

Subsidiary (Non-US):

Fountain Intertrade Corporation (2)
Edificio Plaza Credicorp Bank Panama Calle 50, Panama, 833-0125, Panama
Tel.: (507) 2101111
Power Generation Services
N.A.I.C.S.: 221111

Lunsemfwa Hydro Power Company Ltd (2)
Plot 5047 Former Mine Complex, Kabwe, Zambia
Tel.: (260) 215 22 4597
Power Generation Services
N.A.I.C.S.: 221111

Aktieselskabet Tyssefaldene (1)

AND PRIVATE COMPANIES

Salthellervegen 2, Tyssedal, Hordaland, 5770, Norway
Tel.: (47) 53653000
Web Site: http://www.tyssefaldene.no
Power Generation Services
N.A.I.C.S.: 221122

Baltic Cable AB (1)
Nobelvaegen 66, 205 09, Malmo, Sweden
Tel.: (46) 40256130
Web Site: http://www.balticcable.com
Sales Range: $25-49.9 Million
Emp.: 3
Telecommunications Services; Owned 66.7% by Statkraft Energy Europe AS & 33.3% by E.ON Sverige AB
N.A.I.C.S.: 517111
Jan Brewitz *(Mng Dir)*

Empresa de Generacion Electrica Cheves S.A (1)
Camino Real 456 7th Floor, San Isidro, Lima, Peru
Tel.: (51) 1 7008100
Power Generation Services
N.A.I.C.S.: 221111

Fjordkraft AS (1)
Folke Bernadottesvei 38, Fyllingsdalen, 5147, Bergen, Norway **(51.15%)**
Tel.: (47) 23006100
Web Site: http://www.fjordkraft.no
Electric Power Distr
N.A.I.C.S.: 221122

Harrsele AB (1)
Sveavagen 9, 111 57, Stockholm, Sweden
Tel.: (46) 300562400
Power Generation Services
N.A.I.C.S.: 221122

Himal Power Limited (1)
Bijaya Niwas Jhamsikhel, PO Box 12740, Lalitpur, Kathmandu, Nepal
Tel.: (977) 48410031
Web Site: http://www.hpl.com.np
Power Generation Services
N.A.I.C.S.: 221122
Tima Ayer Utne *(Chm)*

Hitra Vind AS (1)
Eldsfjellet, 7240, Hitra, Norway
Tel.: (47) 24 06 70 00
Power Generation Services
N.A.I.C.S.: 221111

Kargi Kizilirmak Enerji A.S. (1)
A Corekci Cad Yeni Cami Sok Selale Apt No 1, Osmancik, 19500, Corum, Turkiye
Tel.: (90) 3646001103
Power Generation Services
N.A.I.C.S.: 221111

Knapsack Power GmbH & Co KG (1)
Niederkasseler Lohweg 175, Dusseldorf, 40547, Germany
Tel.: (49) 211 6024 4000
Power Generation Services
N.A.I.C.S.: 221111

Rheidol 2008 Trustees Ltd. (1)
41 Moorgate Liverpool Street, London, EC2R 6PP, United Kingdom
Tel.: (44) 20 7448 8200
Web Site: http://www.statkfrat.com
Power Generation Services
N.A.I.C.S.: 221111

SN Power Chile Inversiones Electricas Ltda. (1)
Avenida Vitacura 2939 Of 2802 Edificio Millenium Piso 28, Las Condes, 7550011, Santiago, Chile
Tel.: (56) 2 2592 9200
Power Generation Services
N.A.I.C.S.: 221111
Marco-Antonya Bardas *(Gen Mgr)*

SN Power Energia do Brasil Ltda (1)
Avenida das Americas 3500 - salas 211/212 Condominio, Le Monde - Edificio Londres Barra da Tijuca, Rio de Janeiro, 22640-102, Brazil
Tel.: (55) 21 3873 7500
Emp.: 50
Power Generation Services
N.A.I.C.S.: 221111
Fernando Lapuerta *(Gen Mgr)*

Skagerak Energi AS (1)
Floodelokka 1, 3915, Porsgrunn, Norway **(66.62%)**
Tel.: (47) 3593 5000
Web Site: http://www.skagerakenergi.no
Electric Power Distr
N.A.I.C.S.: 221122

Joint Venture (Domestic):

Air Liquide Skagerak AS (2)
Floodelokka 1, 3915, Porsgrunn, Norway **(49%)**
Tel.: (47) 94 13 13 00
Web Site: http://skagerak.airliquide.com
Natural Gas Distr
N.A.I.C.S.: 221210
Forde Halvorsen *(CEO)*

Smakraft AS (1)
Kokstadvegen 37, 5020, Bergen, Norway
Tel.: (47) 5512 7320
Web Site: http://www.smaakraft.no
Electric Power Distr
N.A.I.C.S.: 221122

Statkraft Agder Energi Vind DA (1)
PO Box 603, Lundsiden, 4606, Kristiansand, Norway
Tel.: (47) 24 06 85 00
Power Generation Services
N.A.I.C.S.: 221111

Statkraft Brasil AS (1)
Statkraft Brasil AS, Florianopolis, 88010-300, Santa Catarina, Brazil
Tel.: (55) 48 3877 7100
48 3877 7100
N.A.I.C.S.: 221122

Statkraft Chile Inversiones Electricas Ltd. (1)
Av Vitacura 2939 Of 2801 Edificio Millenium, Las Condes, Santiago, Chile
Tel.: (56) 2 592 9200
Power Generation Services
N.A.I.C.S.: 221122

Statkraft Energia do Brasil Ltda. (1)
Rua Tenente Silveira 94 - 4th Floor Edificio Schweidson, Florianopolis, 88010-300, Santa Catarina, Brazil
Tel.: (55) 4838777100
Power Generation Services
N.A.I.C.S.: 221122

Statkraft Enerji A.S. (1)
Unalan Mah Libadiya Cad EMAAR Square No 82F / 58-59, Uskudar, 34700, Istanbul, Turkiye
Tel.: (90) 212 340 1900
Web Site: http://www.statkraft.com.tr
Power Generation Services
N.A.I.C.S.: 221111

Subsidiary (Domestic):

Anadolu Elektrik A.S. (2)
Industry Caddesi No 23/36, 06080, Ankara, Turkiye
Tel.: (90) 312324 30 30
Web Site: http://www.anadoluelektrik.com.tr
Power Generation Services
N.A.I.C.S.: 221111

Subsidiary (Non-US):

Skagerak Elektro AS (2)
Floodmyrveien 17 Pb 244, 3901, Porsgrunn, Norway
Tel.: (47) 35 51 61 30
Web Site: http://www.skagerak-elektro.no
Power Generation Services
N.A.I.C.S.: 221111

Statkraft Varme AS (2)
Sluppenvegen 17 B, PO Box 2400, 7005, Trondheim, Norway
Tel.: (47) 91502450
Web Site: http://www.statkraftvarme.no
Heating System Mfr
N.A.I.C.S.: 334512

Statkraft Financial Energy AB (1)
Hitechbuilding 92, 101 52, Stockholm, Sweden
Tel.: (46) 8 545 11260
Power Generation Services
N.A.I.C.S.: 221111

Statkraft France SAS (1)
Cite Internationale de Lyon 66 Quai Charles de Gaulle, 69463, Lyon, Cedex, France
Tel.: (33) 4 78 94 94 86
Web Site: http://www.statkraft.fr
Power Generation Services
N.A.I.C.S.: 221122

Statkraft India Pvt. Ltd. (1)
Block-A Plot-A/2 4th Floor MGF Metropolitan Mall, Saket District, New Delhi, 110017, India
Tel.: (91) 1166005000
Power Generation Services
N.A.I.C.S.: 221122
Mohammed Faisal Jafri *(Project Mgr)*

Statkraft Markets BV (1)
Gustav Mahlerplein 100, NL-1082 MA, Amsterdam, Netherlands
Tel.: (31) 20 795 7800
Electric Power Distr
N.A.I.C.S.: 221122

Subsidiary (Non-US):

Devoll Hydropower Sh.A. (2)
ABA Business Center Office no 1206 Rruga Papa Gjon Pali II, Tirana, Albania
Tel.: (355) 445 01450
Web Site: http://www.devollhydropower.al
Power Generation Services
N.A.I.C.S.: 221122

Statkraft Markets GmbH (1)
Derendorfer Allee 2a, 40476, Dusseldorf, Germany
Tel.: (49) 211 60244 000
Web Site: http://www.statkraft.de
Emp.: 300
Electric Power Distr
N.A.I.C.S.: 221122

Subsidiary (Non-US):

Statkraft South East Europe EOOD (2)
10 Tri Ushi Str office 5, 1000, Sofia, Bulgaria
Tel.: (359) 2 400 1380
Web Site: http://www.statkraft.com
Electric Power Distr
N.A.I.C.S.: 221122

Statkraft Norfund Power Invest AS (1)
PO Box 200 Lilleaker, 0216, Oslo, Norway
Tel.: (47) 2406 8620
Electric Power Distr
N.A.I.C.S.: 221122

Statkraft Romania SRL (1)
Strada Povernei 15 - 17 Sector 1, 010642, Bucharest, Romania
Tel.: (40) 314 251 764
Web Site: http://www.statkraft.eu
Emp.: 1
Electric Power Distr
N.A.I.C.S.: 221122

Statkraft Sodra Vindkraft AB (1)
Framtidsvagen 16, 351 96, Vaxjo, Sweden
Tel.: (46) 300 56 24 00
Web Site: http://www.statkraftsodra.com
Power Generation Services
N.A.I.C.S.: 221111

Statkraft Suomi Oy (1)
Kolsintie 230, 32800, Kokemaki, Finland
Tel.: (358) 10 77 67 600
Power Generation Services
N.A.I.C.S.: 221111

Statkraft Sverige AB (1)
Nipan 51, 881 52, Solleftea, Sweden
Tel.: (46) 620 13080
Power Generation Services
N.A.I.C.S.: 221111
Urban Blom *(Sr Project Mgr)*

Subsidiary (Domestic):

Statkraft Sverige Vattendel 3 AB (2)
Lagavagen, Laholm, 312 30, Halland, Sweden
Tel.: (46) 43073405
Power Generation Services
N.A.I.C.S.: 221111

Statkraft Treasury Centre SA (1)
Rue Archimede 15-21, 1000, Brussels, Belgium
Tel.: (32) 2 280 24 64

Power Generation Services
N.A.I.C.S.: 221111
Laurent Drion Du Chapois *(Mgr-Treasury front Office)*

Statkraft UK Ltd. (1)
41 Moorgate, London, EC2R 6PP, United Kingdom
Tel.: (44) 20 7448 8200
Web Site: http://www.statkraft.com
Emp.: 4
Electric Power Distr
N.A.I.C.S.: 221122
Jon Datnaland *(Pres)*

Statkraft Varme AB (1)
Smorhalevagen 21, Kungsbacka, 434 22, Sweden
Tel.: (46) 3 00 56 24 00
Power Generation Services
N.A.I.C.S.: 221111

Statkraft Western Balkans d.o.o. (1)
Francuska 17/05, Belgrade, 11000, Serbia
Tel.: (381) 11 3038 688
Electric Power Distr
N.A.I.C.S.: 221122
Dragan Vignjevic *(Gen Mgr)*

Trondheim Energi AS (1)
Sluppenvegen 6, 7005, Trondheim, Norway **(100%)**
Tel.: (47) 7396 1011
Web Site: http://www.trondheimenergi.no
Electric Power Distr
N.A.I.C.S.: 221122

Trondheim Kraft AS (1)
Sluppenvegen 17B, 7037, Trondheim, Norway
Tel.: (47) 73506161
Web Site: http://www.trondelagkraft.no
Power Generation Services
N.A.I.C.S.: 221122

Vattenkraftens Miljofond Sverige AB (1)
Ostra Hamngatan 30-34, 41109, Gothenburg, Sweden
Tel.: (46) 3204499
Web Site: https://vattenkraftensmiljofond.se
Hydroelectric Power Generation Services
N.A.I.C.S.: 221111

STATRON AG

Almuesenacherstrasse 1, 5506, Magenwil, Switzerland
Tel.: (41) 628874887
Web Site: http://www.statron.com
Sales Range: $10-24.9 Million
Emp.: 50
Electrical Supply & Safety System Mfr
N.A.I.C.S.: 335910
Peter Limacher *(Chm)*

Subsidiaries:

Andre Technologies & Statron SA (1)
En Vallaire Ouest D7, 1024, Ecublens, Switzerland
Tel.: (41) 21 691 08 80
Inverter Mfr & Distr
N.A.I.C.S.: 335999

STAVOLT NON STOP POWER GmbH (1)
Pforzheimer Str 134, Ettlingen, 76275, Germany
Tel.: (49) 7243 72555 0
Web Site: http://www.stavolt.de
Inverter Mfr & Distr
N.A.I.C.S.: 335999
Ulrich Durr *(Office Mgr)*

Statron (UK) Ltd. (1)
Unit 5 Godwin Road, Corby, NN17 4DS, United Kingdom
Tel.: (44) 1536 445 485
Web Site: http://www.statron.com
Emp.: 5
Inverter Mfr & Distr
N.A.I.C.S.: 335999

Statron B.V. (1)
New Yorkstreet 33, 1175 RD, Lijnden, Netherlands
Tel.: (31) 20 44 99 424

Statron AG—(Continued)
Emp.: 4
Inverter Mfr & Distr
N.A.I.C.S.: 335999
Rene Farenhorst (Gen Mgr)

Statron GmbH (1)
Gewerbepark 11, Grafenschachen, 7423, Austria
Tel.: (43) 33 59 32 0 90
Web Site: http://www.statron.com
Inverter Mfr & Distr
N.A.I.C.S.: 335999

Statron Middle East FZCO (1)
4E A Block 231 Dubai Airport Free Zone, PO Box 54596, Dubai, 54596, United Arab Emirates
Tel.: (971) 42045231
Inverter Mfr & Distr
N.A.I.C.S.: 335999
S. Surendra Naidu (Mgr-Fin)

STAUFEN GMBH & CO. KG
Obere Hauptstrasse 58, 78573, Tuttlingen, Germany
Tel.: (49) 74619240
Web Site: http://www.paperteam.de
Year Founded: 1862
Rev.: $69,263,564
Emp.: 70
Book Binding Services
N.A.I.C.S.: 333248
Rals Banholzer (Mng Dir)

STAVELY MINERALS LIMITED
168 Stirling Hwy, Nedlands, 6009, WA, Australia
Tel.: (61) 892877630
Web Site: https://www.stavely.com.au
SVY—(ASX)
Rev.: $1,330,440
Assets: $6,260,879
Liabilities: $598,843
Net Worth: $5,662,037
Earnings: ($3,735,921)
Fiscal Year-end: 06/30/24
Copper & Gold Mining
N.A.I.C.S.: 212230
Christopher Cairns (Chm & Mng Dir)

Subsidiaries:

Energy Metals Australia Pty. Ltd. (1)
Level 2 5 Ord Street, West Perth, WA, Australia
Tel.: (61) 893226904
Web Site: https://energymetals.net
Uranium Exploration Services
N.A.I.C.S.: 541219

STAVROPOLENERGOSBYT OJSC
Bolshevistskaya street 59A, Stavropol region, Yessentuki, 357600, Russia
Tel.: (7) 8793442180
Web Site: https://www.staves.ru
STSB—(MOEX)
Sales Range: Less than $1 Million
Electric Power Distribution Services
N.A.I.C.S.: 221122

STAX TRADE CENTRES PLC
Holloway Drive Wardley Industrial Estate, Worsley, Manchester, M28 2LA, United Kingdom
Tel.: (44) 1617288000
Web Site: http://www.staxtradecentres.co.uk
Sales Range: $10-24.9 Million
Emp.: 495
Household Products Retailer
N.A.I.C.S.: 423220
Eddie Brady (Chm & Co-Mng Dir-Car Care, Housewares & Christmas)

STAYSURE.CO.UK LIMITED
McGowan House Waterside The Lakes Bedford Road, Northampton, NN4 7XD, United Kingdom
Tel.: (44) 1604 210845
Web Site: http://www.staysure.co.uk
Year Founded: 2004
Sales Range: $10-24.9 Million
Emp.: 200
Health & Life Insurance Services
N.A.I.C.S.: 524114

STC CONCRETE PRODUCT PUBLIC COMPANY LIMITED
220/26 Moo 6 Sukhumvit Rd, Naklua Banglamung, Chon Buri, 20150, Thailand
Tel.: (66) 384231156
Web Site: https://www.stc.co.th
Year Founded: 1988
STC—(THA)
Rev.: $15,709,367
Assets: $23,177,257
Liabilities: $12,484,822
Net Worth: $10,692,435
Earnings: $279,659
Fiscal Year-end: 12/31/23
Concrete Product Mfr & Distr
N.A.I.C.S.: 327390
Narongrit Tavornvisitporn (Chm)

STCUBE, INC.
2201 Trade Center Trade Tower 511 Yeongdong-daero, Gangnam-gu, Seoul, 06164, Korea (South)
Tel.: (82) 25513370
Web Site: https://www.stcube.com
Year Founded: 1989
052020—(KRS)
Rev.: $4,833,892
Assets: $46,840,260
Liabilities: $7,554,772
Net Worth: $39,285,488
Earnings: ($14,490,070)
Emp.: 16
Fiscal Year-end: 12/31/22
Robot Mfr
N.A.I.C.S.: 334419
Junyong Park (CFO)

Subsidiaries:

STCube Pharmaceuticals, Inc. (1)
Ste 125 15000 Conference Center Dr, Chantilly, VA 20151
Tel.: (832) 426-4573
Pharmaceutical Products Distr
N.A.I.C.S.: 424210

STE APOSTROPHE
43 R Du Faubourg, Saint Honore, Paris, 75008, France
Tel.: (33) 140069160
Rev.: $25,500,000
Emp.: 116
Womens & Misses Suits & Coats
N.A.I.C.S.: 315250
Marie-France Dupuis (Personnel Dir)

STE COOP AGRIC PERIGORD TABAC
35 Avenue Benoit Frachon, 24750, Boulazac, Dordogne, France
Tel.: (33) 553356444
Web Site: http://www.perigordtabac.com
Sales Range: $25-49.9 Million
Emp.: 18
Wheat
N.A.I.C.S.: 111140
Jacques Beaudoin (Pres)

STE DE DISTRIBUTION DU DON
33 Route De Besle, Guemene-Penfao, 44290, Nantes, France
Tel.: (33) 240792211
Web Site: http://www.societe.com
Year Founded: 1976
Sales Range: $25-49.9 Million
Emp.: 99
Miscellaneous General Merchandise Stores,
N.A.I.C.S.: 444180
Danielle Ferre (Chm)

STE DE TRANSPORT NEGOCE AUTOMOBILE
154 av Victor Hugo, 92350, Paris, France
Tel.: (33) 146422061
Sales Range: $25-49.9 Million
Emp.: 49
New & Used Car Dealers
N.A.I.C.S.: 441110
Gerard Alard (Gen Mgr)

STE DU GRAND GARAGE DES CHANTIERS
Zae Saltgourde Avenue De L Industrie, Marsac Sur L Isle, 24430, Bordeaux, France
Tel.: (33) 139535252
Sales Range: $25-49.9 Million
Emp.: 45
New & Used Car Dealers
N.A.I.C.S.: 441110
Gerard Alard (Gen Mgr)

STE DU PIPELINE SUD-EUROPEEN
195 Avenue Charles De Gaulle, 92200, Neuilly-sur-Seine, Hauts De Seine, France
Tel.: (33) 141432150
Rev.: $29,400,000
Emp.: 175
Pipeline
N.A.I.C.S.: 486990
Pierre Abert (Personnel Dir)

STE ECONOMIE MIXTE LOGEMENT DE EURE
20 Rue Josephine, 27000, Evreux, Eure, France
Tel.: (33) 232388585
Web Site: http://www.secomile.fr
Sales Range: $25-49.9 Million
Emp.: 68
Apartment Building Operator
N.A.I.C.S.: 531110
Marcel Larmanou (Chm)

STE EDIT ARTISTES PEIGNANT BOUCHE PIED
Route Ecospace, 67120, Molsheim, Bas Rhin, France
Tel.: (33) 388479698
Rev.: $25,400,000
Emp.: 63
Miscellaneous Publishing
N.A.I.C.S.: 513199
Brigitte Wernert (Dir-Mktg)

STE ELECTRIQUE DE L'OUR SA
Tel.: (352) 28271
Web Site: https://seo.lu
Year Founded: 1951
SEO—(LUX)
Sales Range: Less than $1 Million
Electric Power Distribution Services
N.A.I.C.S.: 221118

STE EQUIPEMENT DU DEPART MAINE ET LOIRE
79 Rue Desjardins, 49100, Angers, Maine Et Loire, France
Tel.: (33) 241182121
Web Site: http://www.sodemel.fr
Rev.: $25,300,000
Emp.: 31
Real Estate Agents & Managers
N.A.I.C.S.: 531110
Michel Ballarini (Dir)

STE ESSARTAISE DE DISTRIBUTION
Route De La Roche, Les Essarts, 85140, Paris, France
Tel.: (33) 251484343 FR
Web Site: http://www.societe.com
Miscellaneous General Merchandise Stores,
N.A.I.C.S.: 444180

STE EUROPEENNE LOGISTIQUE INTERNATIONALE
250 rue des Droits de l'Homme, ZAC de la Garosse, 33240, Saint-Andre-de-Cubzac, France
Tel.: (33) 557426030
Web Site: http://www.seli.fr
Rev.: $22,200,000
Emp.: 28
Logistics & Transportation
N.A.I.C.S.: 488510
Nadine Antonioli (Mgr)

Subsidiaries:

SELI GmbH (1)
Werfthallenstrasse 43, 68159, Mannheim, Germany
Tel.: (49) 621 125063 0
Transportation Services
N.A.I.C.S.: 484230

SELI PROTRANS (1)
101 chemin des Huguenots, BP 127, 26905, Valence, Cedex, France
Tel.: (33) 4 75 82 60 60
Transportation Services
N.A.I.C.S.: 484230

STE EXPLOITATION MATERIELS MARTIN BAKER
98 T Boulevard Heloise, 95100, Argenteuil, Val D Oise, France
Tel.: (33) 139617884
Rev.: $20,500,000
Emp.: 34
Pilot Escape Systems Mfr & Maintainer
N.A.I.C.S.: 423830
Andre Margot (Dir)

STE GARAGE MOISON
60 Rue De La Ville Halluard, 44600, Saint Nazaire, Loire Atlantique, France
Tel.: (33) 240226571
Rev.: $25,200,000
Emp.: 42
New & Used Car Dealers
N.A.I.C.S.: 441110
Jean Rouyer (Pres)

STE GRAND GARAGE DU BOULEVARD
Route de Toulouse, BP 82, 46002, Cahors, France
Tel.: (33) 565350202
Web Site: http://concessions.peugeot.fr
Sales Range: $10-24.9 Million
Emp.: 52
Automobile Dealership
N.A.I.C.S.: 441110
Thomas Chardard (Pres)

STE INSULAIRE AUTOMOBILES
Quartier Monte Carlo, 20600, Furiani, Corse, France
Tel.: (33) 495542020
Web Site: http://concessions.peugeot.fr
Rev.: $21,400,000
Emp.: 51
Automobile Dealership
N.A.I.C.S.: 441110
Philippe Martinez (Pres)

STE JOSEPH HUWER

Zone indusrielle de Ruitz, PO Box
62620, Millery, 54670, Barlin, France
Tel.: (33) 321524041
Web Site: http://www.huwer.com
Rev.: $28,600,000
Emp.: 97
Motor Vehicles & Car Bodies
N.A.I.C.S.: 336110
Jean-Pierre Corby *(Dir)*

STE MONTOISE DU BOIS
59 B Avenue De Sabres, Mont-de-
Marsan, 40000, Landes, France
Tel.: (33) 558757777
Web Site: http://www.montoise-
bois.com
Sales Range: $10-24.9 Million
Emp.: 64
Sawmills & Planing Mills, General
N.A.I.C.S.: 321113
Jean-Loup Farbos *(Gen Dir)*

**STE MULHOUSIENNE DES
CITES OUVRIERES**
20 Porte Du Miroir, Mulhouse, 67100,
Haut Rhin, France
Tel.: (33) 389462020
Rev.: $21,500,000
Emp.: 33
Lodging
N.A.I.C.S.: 531110
Véronique Dabrainville *(DP Mgr)*

STEADFAST GROUP LIMITED
Level 4 99 Bathurst Street, Sydney,
2000, NSW, Australia
Tel.: (61) 294956500   AU
Web Site:
https://www.steadfast.com.au
Year Founded: 1996
SDF—(ASX)
Rev.: $999,465,808
Assets: $3,809,962,591
Liabilities: $2,095,085,462
Net Worth: $1,714,877,130
Earnings: $182,759,080
Emp.: 45
Fiscal Year-end: 06/30/24
Insurance & Underwriting Brokers
N.A.I.C.S.: 524210
Robert Kelly *(Founder, CEO & Mng
Dir)*

Subsidiaries:

Axis Underwriting Services Pty
Ltd   (1)
Level 5 90 Collins Street, Melbourne, 3000,
VIC, Australia
Tel.: (61) 38 660 7000
Web Site:
https://www.axisunderwriting.com.au
Insurance Brokerage Services
N.A.I.C.S.: 524210
Ivan Verescuk *(CEO)*

Body Corporate Brokers Pty Ltd   (1)
Level 11 23 Hunter Street, Sydney, 2000,
NSW, Australia
Tel.: (61) 290243850
Web Site: https://bcb.au
Emp.: 80
Insurance Underwriting Services
N.A.I.C.S.: 524113
Alistair Gibney *(Mng Dir)*

CHU Underwriting Agencies Pty.
Ltd.   (1)
Level 33/101 Miller St, North Sydney, 2060,
NSW, Australia
Tel.: (61) 130 036 1263
Web Site: https://www.chu.com.au
Insurance Underwriting Services
N.A.I.C.S.: 524113

Calliden Group Limited   (1)
Level 7 100 Arthur Street, North Sydney,
2060, NSW, Australia
Tel.: (61) 1300002255
Web Site: http://www.calliden.com.au
Insurance Services
N.A.I.C.S.: 524298

Subsidiary (Domestic):

Dawes Underwriting Australia Pty.
Limited   (2)
Level 7 100 Arthur Street, North Sydney,
2060, NSW, Australia
Tel.: (61) 130 018 8299
Web Site: https://www.dawes.com.au
Automobile Insurance Services
N.A.I.C.S.: 524128

SGUAS Pty Ltd.   (2)
Level 5 97-99 Bathurst Street, Sydney,
2000, NSW, Australia
Tel.: (61) 130 073 8308
Web Site: https://www.mansions.com.au
Emp.: 5
Property Insurance Services
N.A.I.C.S.: 524126

Subsidiary (Domestic):

AIG Australia Limited   (3)
Level 19 2 Park Street, Sydney, 2000,
NSW, Australia
Tel.: (61) 130 003 0886
Web Site: https://www.aig.com.au
Insurance Services
N.A.I.C.S.: 524298
Debbie Wilson *(CFO)*

ARGIS Limited   (3)
Level 21 150 Lonsdale Street, Melbourne,
3000, VIC, Australia
Tel.: (61) 130 079 4364
Web Site: https://www.argis.com.au
Insurance Underwriting Agencies
N.A.I.C.S.: 524298

GSA Insurance Brokers Pty Ltd   (1)
The Old Presbytery 137 Harrington Street,
Sydney, 2000, NSW, Australia
Tel.: (61) 28 274 8100
Web Site: https://www.gsaib.com.au
Insurance Brokerage Services
N.A.I.C.S.: 524210
Paul Hines *(Chm)*

Galaxy Insurance Consultants Pte
Ltd   (1)
101 Cecil Street 17-01 Tong Eng Building,
Singapore, 069533, Singapore
Tel.: (65) 6 222 8737
Web Site:
https://www.galaxyconsultants.com
Insurance Brokerage Services
N.A.I.C.S.: 524210
Uttam Kripalani *(Founder & Chm)*

Great Wall Insurance Services Pty
Ltd   (1)
205 Springvale Road, Springvale, 3171,
VIC, Australia
Tel.: (61) 39 574 2833
Web Site: https://www.gwinsurance.com.au
Underwriting Insurance Agency Services
N.A.I.C.S.: 524210
Chuck Wong *(Sr Acct Mgr)*

HMIA Pty Ltd   (1)
1 Castlereagh St, Sydney, 2000, NSW,
Australia
Tel.: (61) 29 227 8400
Web Site: https://www.hmia.com.au
Insurance Brokerage Services
N.A.I.C.S.: 524210
Michael Zaknic *(CEO)*

Holdfast Insurance Brokers Pty.
Ltd.   (1)
Level 1 62 Greenhill Road, Wayville, SA,
Australia
Tel.: (61) 882730900
Web Site: https://www.holdfast.com.au
Insurance Broker Services
N.A.I.C.S.: 524210

Ian Bell Insurance Brokers Pty.
Ltd.   (1)
Suite 1/ 33 Harbour Drive, Coffs Harbour,
NSW, Australia
Tel.: (61) 266515522
Web Site: https://www.ibinsurance.com.au
Insurance Broker Services
N.A.I.C.S.: 524210

Joe Vella Insurance Brokers Pty
Ltd   (1)
Level 1 108 Mulgrave Road, Cairns, 4870,
QLD, Australia
Tel.: (61) 74 040 4444
Web Site: https://www.jvib.com.au
Insurance Brokerage Services
N.A.I.C.S.: 524210
Joe Vella *(Mng Dir)*

Miramar Underwriting Agency Pty
Ltd   (1)
Level 5 97-99 Bathurst Street, Sydney,
2000, NSW, Australia
Tel.: (61) 29 307 6600
Web Site: https://www.miramaruw.com.au
Insurance Brokerage Services
N.A.I.C.S.: 524210
James Fitzpatrick *(Mgr)*

Network Insurance Group Pty
Ltd   (1)
Level 35 140 William Street, Melbourne,
3000, VIC, Australia
Tel.: (61) 38 420 8700
Web Site:
https://www.networksteadfast.com.au
Insurance Brokerage Services
N.A.I.C.S.: 524210

Newsure Insurance Brokers Pty
Ltd   (1)
Level 3 50 Hunter Street, Newcastle, 2300,
NSW, Australia
Tel.: (61) 24 969 8100
Web Site: https://www.newsure.com.au
Insurance Brokerage Services
N.A.I.C.S.: 524210
Brett Edmonds *(Gen Mgr)*

Phoenix Insurance Brokers Pty
Ltd   (1)
Level 1/1 Preston St, Como, 6152, WA,
Australia
Tel.: (61) 89 367 7399
Web Site: https://www.phoenixins.com.au
Insurance Brokerage Services
N.A.I.C.S.: 524210
David White *(Mng Dir)*

Platinum Placement Solutions Pty
Ltd   (1)
Level 4 97-99 Bathurst Street, Sydney,
2000, NSW, Australia
Tel.: (61) 41 266 2262
Web Site:
https://www.platinumplacements.com.au
Insurance Brokerage Services
N.A.I.C.S.: 524210

Pollard Advisory Services Pty.
Ltd.   (1)
Suite 12 395 Nepean Hwy, PO Box 261,
Frankston, VIC, Australia
Tel.: (61) 300733981
Web Site:
https://www.pollardinsurance.com.au
Insurance Brokerage Services
N.A.I.C.S.: 524126

Primassure (Australia) Pty. Ltd.   (1)
119 Glen Osmond Road, Eastwood, SA,
Australia
Tel.: (61) 883732289
Web Site: https://www.primassure.com.au
Jewellers Block Insurance Services
N.A.I.C.S.: 524210

Procover Underwriting Agency Pty
Ltd   (1)
Level 5 97-99 Bathurst Street, Sydney,
2000, NSW, Australia
Tel.: (61) 29 307 6600
Web Site: https://www.procover.com.au
Underwriting Agency Services
N.A.I.C.S.: 524210
Jayson Grossman *(Mgr)*

Quanta Insurance Group Pty.
Ltd.   (1)
Lvl 26 Tower 1 International Towers Syd-
ney, Barangaroo, NSW, Australia
Tel.: (61) 1300782682
Web Site: https://www.quanta.com.au
Insurance Brokerage Services
N.A.I.C.S.: 524298

Risk Broking Pty. Ltd.   (1)
Level 2 86 Pirie Street, Adelaide, SA, Aus-
tralia
Tel.: (61) 882322311
Web Site: https://riskbroking.com.au
Insurance Brokerage Services
N.A.I.C.S.: 524210

Risk Partners Pty Ltd   (1)
23 Cremorne Street, Cremorne, 3121, VIC,
Australia
Tel.: (61) 39 929 9800
Web Site: https://riskpartners.com.au
Insurance Services
N.A.I.C.S.: 524210

Rose Stanton Insurance Brokers Pty.
Ltd.   (1)
Suite 104 Level 1 3 Eden Street, North
Sydney, NSW, Australia
Tel.: (61) 1300665311
Web Site: https://www.rosestanton.com.au
Travel Insurance Services
N.A.I.C.S.: 524210

SRB Management Pty. Ltd.   (1)
2/37 Benwerrin Drive, Burwood East, VIC,
Australia
Tel.: (61) 398866654
Web Site: https://www.srbbuilders.com.au
Residential Building Construction Services
N.A.I.C.S.: 237990

Scott & Broad Pty Ltd   (1)
Level 2 924 Pacific Highway, Gordon, 2072,
NSW, Australia
Tel.: (61) 29 932 6444
Web Site: https://www.scottbroad.com.au
Insurance Brokerage Services
N.A.I.C.S.: 524210
Andrew Miller *(Mng Dir)*

Scott Winton Nominees Pty Ltd   (1)
Level 1 222 St Kilda Road, Saint Kilda,
3182, VIC, Australia
Tel.: (61) 38 598 9411
Web Site: https://www.scottwinton.com.au
Insurance Brokerage Services
N.A.I.C.S.: 524210
Avi Tatarka *(CEO)*

Simplex Insurance Solutions Pty.
Ltd.   (1)
72 Mair Street, Ballarat, VIC, Australia
Tel.: (61) 353315633
Web Site: https://simplexinsurance.com.au
Insurance Brokerage Services
N.A.I.C.S.: 524298

Sports Underwriting Australia Pty.
Ltd.   (1)
46 Kilby Road, PO Box 288, Kew, VIC,
Australia
Tel.: (61) 388622600
Web Site: https://sportsunderwriting.com.au
Sports & Leisure Insurance Services
N.A.I.C.S.: 524210

Steadfast Distribution Services Pte
Ltd   (1)
160 Robinson Rd 17-09 SBF Centre, Singa-
pore, 068914, Singapore
Tel.: (65) 6 282 8809
Web Site: https://www.steadfast.com.sg
Insurance Brokerage Services
N.A.I.C.S.: 524210
Derek Teo *(CEO)*

Steadfast NZ Ltd.   (1)
Level 11 Shortland Centre 55 Shortland St,
Auckland, 1010, New Zealand
Tel.: (64) 9 309 6379
Web Site: https://www.steadfastnz.nz
Insurance Brokerage Services
N.A.I.C.S.: 524210
Bruce Oughton *(CEO)*

Steadfast Placement Solutions UK
Ltd.   (1)
1 Creechurch Lane, London, EC3A 5AF,
United Kingdom
Tel.: (44) 207 398 4897
Web Site:
https://www.steadfastplacements.co.uk
Wholesale Broking Services
N.A.I.C.S.: 425120
Tash Annalingam *(Ops Mgr)*

Steadfast Taswide Insurance Brokers
Pty Ltd   (1)
Level 4 142 Elizabeth Street, Hobart, 7000,
TAS, Australia
Tel.: (61) 36 231 3360
Web Site:
https://www.steadfasttaswide.com.au
Insurance Brokerage Services

STEADFAST GROUP LIMITED

Steadfast Group Limited—(Continued)
N.A.I.C.S.: 524210
Cameron Gill (Acct Exec)

Steadfast Underwriting Agencies Holdings Pty Ltd (1)
Level 5 99 Bathurst Street, Sydney, 2000, NSW, Australia
Tel.: (61) 29 307 6600
Web Site:
https://www.steadfastagencies.com.au
Insurance Brokerage Services
N.A.I.C.S.: 524210

Timjamway Pty. Ltd. (1)
2/55 West Fyans St, Newtown, VIC, Australia
Tel.: (61) 352296008
Web Site: https://wkkinsurance.com.au
Insurance Brokerage Services
N.A.I.C.S.: 524126

Trident Insurance Group Pty Ltd (1)
1st Floor 186 Scarborough Beach Rd, Mount Hawthorn, Perth, 6015, WA, Australia
Tel.: (61) 89 202 8000
Web Site:
https://www.tridentinsurance.com.au
Insurance Brokerage Services
N.A.I.C.S.: 524210
Rick Wolozny (Mng Dir)

Underwriting Agencies of Australia Pty. Ltd. (1)
Suite 202 19 Honeysuckle Drive, PO Box 656, Newcastle, 2300, NSW, Australia
Tel.: (61) 24 925 6600
Web Site: https://www.uaa.com.au
Insurance Underwriting Services
N.A.I.C.S.: 524113
Michael Murphy (CEO)

Underwriting Agencies of New Zealand Limited (1)
Suite 2 506 South Titirangi Road, Auckland, 0604, New Zealand
Tel.: (64) 9 980 3447
Web Site: https://www.uanz.co.nz
Insurance Brokerage Services
N.A.I.C.S.: 524210
Matthew Ziegler (Head)

Underwriting Agencies of Singapore Pte Ltd (1)
1 Raffles Quay 29-10 South Tower, Singapore, 048583, Singapore
Tel.: (65) 9 068 9315
Web Site: https://www.uas.sg
Underwriting Insurance Agency Services
N.A.I.C.S.: 524210
Mark Crossman (Reg Mgr)

unisonSteadfast AG (1)
Chilehaus C Burchardstr 13, 20095, Hamburg, Germany
Tel.: (49) 408 090 7290
Web Site: https://www.unisonsteadfast.com
Insurance Brokerage Services
N.A.I.C.S.: 524210
Wolfgang Mercier (Pres & CEO)

STEADFAST MARINE TBK
Graha Corner Stone Jl Rajawali Selatan II No 1 Kemayoran, Jakarta Pusat, 10720, Indonesia
Tel.: (62) 2164713088
Web Site: http://www.steadfast-marine.co.id
Year Founded: 2005
KPAL—(INDO)
Sales Range: $1-9.9 Million
Ship Building Material Mfr
N.A.I.C.S.: 336611
Rudy Kurniawan Logam (Board of Directors & Chm)

STEADRIGHT CRITICAL MINERALS INC
Suite 216-1 Crescent Rd, Huntsville, P1H 1Z6, ON, Canada
Tel.: (647) 637-8608
Web Site: https://steadright.ca
Year Founded: 2019
SCM—(CNSX)
Mineral Exploration Services
N.A.I.C.S.: 213114

STEADY SAFE TBK
Gedung Istana Kana Lt 2 Jl RP Soeroso No 24, Jakarta, 10330, Indonesia
Tel.: (62) 213922222
Web Site:
https://www.steadysafetbk.co.id
Year Founded: 1971
SAFE—(INDO)
Rev.: $15,766,953
Assets: $15,410,074
Liabilities: $17,893,478
Net Worth: ($2,483,404)
Earnings: $1,277,265
Emp.: 6
Fiscal Year-end: 12/31/23
Public Transportation Services
N.A.I.C.S.: 485999
John Pieter Sembiring (Chm)

STEAK GROUP
62-70 Shorts Gardens, Covent Garden, London, WC2H 9AH, United Kingdom
Tel.: (44) 20 7420 3500
Web Site:
http://www.steakdigital.co.uk
Year Founded: 2005
Sales Range: $10-24.9 Million
Emp.: 80
Advertising, Digital/Interactive
N.A.I.C.S.: 541810
Oliver Bishop (CEO)

Subsidiaries:

Steak (1)
648 Broadway Ste 703, New York, NY 10012
Tel.: (646) 556-6585
Emp.: 70
Media Buying Agency
N.A.I.C.S.: 541830
Oliver Bishop (CEO)

Steak (1)
Ste 904 530 Little Collins St, 3000, Melbourne, VIC, Australia
Tel.: (61) 3 9649 7760
N.A.I.C.S.: 541810

STEAKHOLDER FOODS LTD.
David fikes st 5, PO Box 4061, Rehovot, 7632805, Israel
Tel.: (972) 775412206
Web Site:
https://www.steakholderfoods.com
Year Founded: 2018
STKH—(NASDAQ)
Assets: $10,823,000
Liabilities: $4,941,000
Net Worth: $5,882,000
Earnings: $16,864,000
Emp.: 43
Fiscal Year-end: 12/31/23
Veal Product Mfr
N.A.I.C.S.: 311612
Arik Kaufman (Executives)

STEALTH BIOTHERAPEUTICS CORP.
190 Elgin Avenue, Georgetown, KY1-9005, Grand Cayman, Cayman Islands
Tel.: (345) 617 600 6888   Ky
Web Site: http://www.stealthbt.com
Year Founded: 2006
MITO—(NASDAQ)
Rev.: $3,000
Assets: $50,226,000
Liabilities: $95,521,000
Net Worth: ($45,295,000)
Earnings: ($52,527,000)
Emp.: 38
Fiscal Year-end: 12/31/21

Biopharmaceutical Product Mfr & Distr
N.A.I.C.S.: 325412
Reenie P. McCarthy (CEO)

STEALTH GLOBAL HOLDINGS LTD.
Level 2 Unit 10 43 Cedric Street, Stirling, 6021, WA, Australia
Tel.: (61) 864657800   AU
Web Site: https://www.stealthgi.com
Year Founded: 2014
SGI—(ASX)
Rev.: $75,908,296
Assets: $56,885,928
Liabilities: $43,285,793
Net Worth: $13,600,135
Earnings: $904,968
Emp.: 250
Fiscal Year-end: 06/30/24
Consumer Goods Distr
N.A.I.C.S.: 423990
Michael Arnold (Founder & Mng Dir)

Subsidiaries:

Heatleys Safety & Industrial Limited (1)
50 Vinnicombe Drive, Canning Vale, 6155, WA, Australia
Tel.: (61) 892565200
Web Site: http://www.heatleys.com.au
Industrial Product Distr
N.A.I.C.S.: 423840

STEALTH MINERALS LIMITED
590 East Kings Road, North Vancouver, V7N 1J3, BC, Canada
Tel.: (604) 924-5504
Web Site:
http://www.stealthminerals.com
Year Founded: 1997
Gold Exploration Services
N.A.I.C.S.: 212220

STEALTH VENTURES INC.
Suite 3300 Bow Valley Square II 205 5th Avenue Southwest, Calgary, T2P 2V7, AB, Canada
Tel.: (403) 514-9998   AB
Web Site:
http://www.stealthventures.ca
Year Founded: 1996
Sales Range: Less than $1 Million
Oil & Gas Exploration & Production Services
N.A.I.C.S.: 211120

STEALTHGAS INC.
331 Kifisias Ave, 14561, Athens, Greece
Tel.: (30) 2106250001
Web Site:
https://www.stealthgas.com
Year Founded: 2004
GASS—(NASDAQ)
Rev.: $152,760,888
Assets: $821,533,307
Liabilities: $303,607,956
Net Worth: $517,925,351
Earnings: $34,253,365
Emp.: 560
Fiscal Year-end: 12/31/22
Liquefied Petroleum Transport Services
N.A.I.C.S.: 483111
Michael G. Jolliffe (Chm)

Subsidiaries:

Geneve Butane Inc (1)
331 Kifissias Avenue Erithrea, Athens, 14561, Greece
Tel.: (30) 210 625 0001
Web Site: http://www.stealthgas.com
Emp.: 70
Petroleum Transportation Services
N.A.I.C.S.: 457210

International Gases Inc (1)
331 Kifissias Avenue Erithrea, Athens, 14561, Greece
Tel.: (30) 210 625 0001
Emp.: 80
Industrial Gas Mfr
N.A.I.C.S.: 325120
Despina Bacha (Gen Mgr-Legal)

Northern Yield Shipping Ltd (1)
331 Kifissias Avenue Erithrea, Athens, 14561, Greece
Tel.: (30) 2106250001
Petroleum Transportation Services
N.A.I.C.S.: 457210

Studio City Inc. (1)
23 Fraser Ave, Toronto, M6K 1Y7, ON, Canada
Tel.: (416) 532-5100
Motion Picture & Video Production Services
N.A.I.C.S.: 512110

Ventspils Gases Ltd (1)
331 Kifissias Avenue Erithrea, Athens, 14561, Greece
Tel.: (30) 210 625 0001
Industrial Gas Mfr
N.A.I.C.S.: 325120

STEAM FRANCE SA
Rue de la Valsiere Parc Euromedecine II, 34090, Montpellier, France
Tel.: (33) 4 99 52 62 32
Web Site: http://www.steam.fr
Year Founded: 1999
Sterilization & Disinfection Equipment Mfr
N.A.I.C.S.: 339112

STEAMSHIPS TRADING COMPANY LIMITED
Levels 1-2 Stanley Esplanade, PO Box 1, NCD 121, Port Moresby, NCD 121, Papua New Guinea
Tel.: (675) 3137400
Web Site:
https://www.steamships.com.pg
SST—(PNGX)
Rev.: $179,459,983
Assets: $456,289,051
Liabilities: $169,488,405
Net Worth: $286,800,646
Earnings: $15,730,527
Emp.: 3,010
Fiscal Year-end: 12/31/23
Shipping Services; Hotel Operations; Hardware Retailer
N.A.I.C.S.: 483111
G. L. Cundle (Chm)

Subsidiaries:

Kavieng Port Services Limited (1)
PO Box 293, Kavieng, New Ireland, Papua New Guinea
Tel.: (675) 9842599
Web Site: http://www.steamships.com
Sales Range: $25-49.9 Million
Emp.: 20
Shipping Services
N.A.I.C.S.: 483111

Laga Industries Limited (1)
PO Box 1441, Port Moresby, Papua New Guinea
Tel.: (675) 4757387
Web Site: http://www.lagaindustries.com.pg
Sales Range: $100-124.9 Million
Emp.: 350
Ice Cream & Health Products Mfr
N.A.I.C.S.: 311520

Laurabada Shipping Services Limited (1)
PO Box 390, Port Moresby, Papua New Guinea
Tel.: (675) 321 1344
Shipping Services
N.A.I.C.S.: 483111

Madang Port Services Limited (1)
Modilon Rd, PO Box 226, Madang, 511, Papua New Guinea
Tel.: (675) 4222225
Web Site: http://www.steamships.com.pg
Emp.: 25

Shipping Services
N.A.I.C.S.: 483111

Pacific Towing (PNG) Limited (1)
PO Box 701, Port Moresby, Papua New Guinea
Tel.: (675) 321 1206
Web Site:
https://pacifictowingmarineservices.com
Marine Services
N.A.I.C.S.: 488390
Neil Papenfus *(Gen Mgr)*

Progressive Traders Limited (1)
LC-40 Landhi Industrial Area, Karachi, Pakistan
Tel.: (92) 111786784
Web Site: https://progressivetraders.com
Industrial Raw Material Mfr
N.A.I.C.S.: 333248

STEARMAN RESOURCES INC.
Suite 170-422 Richards Street, Vancouver, V6B 2Z4, BC, Canada
Tel.: (604) 377-8994 BC
Year Founded: 2022
STMN—(CNSX)
Mineral Mining Services
N.A.I.C.S.: 213115
Howard Milne *(CEO)*

STEAUA ELECTRICA S.A.
1 Garii Street, Jud Dambovita, 135100, Fieni, Romania
Tel.: (40) 245606031
Web Site: http://www.selum.ro
Year Founded: 1936
Electrical Equipment Distr
N.A.I.C.S.: 423610
Georgeta Corina Popescu *(CEO)*

STEED ORIENTAL (HOLDINGS) COMPANY LIMITED
Room 2104 21/F OfficePlus Wan Chai, No 303 Hennessy Road, Wanchai, China (Hong Kong)
Tel.: (852) 3 595 6556 Ky
Web Site:
http://www.steedoriental.com.hk
Year Founded: 2013
8277—(HKG)
Rev.: $12,102,451
Assets: $55,160,103
Liabilities: $50,452,591
Net Worth: $4,707,512
Earnings: ($649,930)
Emp.: 224
Fiscal Year-end: 03/31/22
Holding Company
N.A.I.C.S.: 551112
Xue Song Sun *(Chm & Compliance Officer)*

Subsidiaries:

Jiangmen Changda Wood Products Company Limited (1)
No 29 Du Ruan North Third Road, Pengjiang District, Jiangmen, 529030, Guangdong, China
Tel.: (86) 7503291688
Web Site: http://www.changdawood.com
Plywood Product Mfr & Retailer
N.A.I.C.S.: 321211

Million Champ Trading Limited (1)
Office D 15/F MG Tower No 133 Hoi Bun Road, Kwun Tong, Kowloon, China (Hong Kong)
Tel.: (852) 29561808
Plywood Product Mfr & Retailer
N.A.I.C.S.: 321211

STEEL & TUBE HOLDINGS LIMITED
7 Bruce Roderick Drive East Tamaki, Auckland, New Zealand
Tel.: (64) 45705000
Web Site:
http://www.steelandtube.co.nz
STU—(NZX)
Rev.: $352,319,378
Assets: $217,756,579
Liabilities: $93,262,560
Net Worth: $124,494,019
Earnings: $10,165,670
Emp.: 851
Fiscal Year-end: 06/30/23
Steel Products Mfr & Distr
N.A.I.C.S.: 331110
Susan Marie Paterson *(Chm)*

Subsidiaries:

Composite Floor Decks Limited (1)
30 Business Parade, East Tamaki, Auckland, 2013, New Zealand
Tel.: (64) 92731111
Web Site: http://www.studwelders.co.nz
Steel & Tube Product Mfr
N.A.I.C.S.: 331210

Manufacturing Suppliers Limited (1)
560 Rosebank Road, Avondale, New Zealand
Tel.: (64) 98282777
Web Site: https://www.fortress.kiwi
Construction Materials Distr
N.A.I.C.S.: 423390
Michael Thompson *(Natl Mgr)*

S & T Stainless Limited (1)
7 Bruce Roderick Drive, East Tamaki, Auckland, 2013, New Zealand
Tel.: (64) 92711781
Web Site: https://steelandtube.co.nz
Steel & Tube Product Mfr
N.A.I.C.S.: 331210
Mark Malpass *(CEO)*

STEEL AUTHORITY OF INDIA LIMITED
Ispat Bhawan Lodhi Road, New Delhi, 110 003, India
Tel.: (91) 2436748186
Web Site: https://www.sail.co.in
Year Founded: 1973
500113—(NSE)
Rev.: $12,636,901,864
Assets: $15,644,276,722
Liabilities: $9,080,320,125
Net Worth: $6,563,956,597
Earnings: $260,959,175
Emp.: 59,186
Fiscal Year-end: 03/31/23
Iron & Steel Product Mfr
N.A.I.C.S.: 331110
Soma Mondal *(Chm)*

Subsidiaries:

Indian Iron & Steel Company (1)
7 The Ridge Burnpur, PO Box 325, Burdwan, 713 325, India (100%)
Tel.: (91) 3412240441
Web Site: http://www.sail.co.in
Sales Range: $25-49.9 Million
Emp.: 17
Iron & Steel Mills
N.A.I.C.S.: 331513

NTPC SAIL Power Company Pvt. Ltd (1)
4th Fl NBCC Tower 15 Bhikaiji Cama Place, Bikaji Kama Place, New Delhi, 110 066, India
Tel.: (91) 112 671 7379
Web Site: https://www.nspcl.co.in
Sales Range: $5-14.9 Billion
Emp.: 120
Electric Power Supply; Owned 50% by National Thermal Power Corp. Ltd. & 50% by Steel Authority of India Limited
N.A.I.C.S.: 221122
Saptarshi Roy *(Chm)*

Romelt-SAIL (India) Ltd (1)
A-47 (FF) Friends Colony East, New Delhi, 110065, India (15%)
Tel.: (91) 11 2692 3982
Sales Range: $25-49.9 Million
Emp.: 20
Management Consulting Services
N.A.I.C.S.: 541611

SAIL Central Marketing Organization (1)
Ispat Bhawan 40 JL Nehru Road, Kolkata, 700071, West Bengal, India
Tel.: (91) 3322886151
N.A.I.C.S.: 331513

SAIL Centre for Engineering and Technology (1)
RDCIS Lab Bldg 4th Fl, Ranchi, 834002, Jharkhand, India
Tel.: (91) 6512411165
Web Site: http://www.sailcet.com
Sales Range: $75-99.9 Million
Emp.: 300
N.A.I.C.S.: 541330
Jagdish Arora *(Exec Dir)*

SAIL Consultancy Division (1)
Scope Minar 19th Floor Core -1 Laxmi Nagar, District Centre, New Delhi, 110 092, India (100%)
Tel.: (91) 1122531242
Web Site: http://www.sail.co.in
Sales Range: $25-49.9 Million
Emp.: 1,000
Design, Engineering, Technical, Management & Training Consultancy & Services
N.A.I.C.S.: 541690

SAIL Environment Management Division (1)
SAIL House 3rd Floor 50 Jawaharlal Nehru Road, Kolkata, 700071, India
Tel.: (91) 3322821352
Web Site: http://www.sail.co.in
Soil & Plants Conservation, Recovery & Recycling, to Manage Wastes Associated with Steel Making
N.A.I.C.S.: 813312
Meenakshi Kakkar *(Dir & Gen Mgr)*

SAIL International Trade Division (1)
Hindustan Times House 13th Fl 18 20 Kasturba Ghandi Marg, 110001, New Delhi, India (100%)
Tel.: (91) 1123355733
Web Site: http://www.sail.com
Sales Range: $25-49.9 Million
Emp.: 50
N.A.I.C.S.: 331513

SAIL Management Training Institute (1)
RDCIS Lab Bldg, Ranchi, 834002, Bihar, India
Tel.: (91) 6512411165
N.A.I.C.S.: 331513

SAIL Raw Materials Division (1)
Industry House 10 Camac Street, Kolkata, 700017, West Bengal, India
Tel.: (91) 3322821457
Sales Range: $1-4.9 Billion
Emp.: 5,400
Rolled Steel Products Mfr
N.A.I.C.S.: 331513
C. S. Varma *(Chm)*

SAIL Research and Development Centre for Iron and Steel (1)
PO Doranda, Ranchi, 834002, Bihar, India
Tel.: (91) 6512411084
Sales Range: $200-249.9 Million
Emp.: 700
N.A.I.C.S.: 331513

Steel Authority of India Limited - IISCO Steel Plant (1)
7 Ridge, Burnpur, 713 325, West Bengal, India
Tel.: (91) 341 2240441
Steel Products Mfr
N.A.I.C.S.: 331110

Steel Authority of India Limited - SAIL Refractory Unit (1)
Indira Gandhi Marg Sector-IV, Bokaro, 827 004, Jharkhand, India
Tel.: (91) 6542 233179
Web Site: http://sail.co.in
Sales Range: $50-74.9 Million
Emp.: 1,600
Steel Products Mfr
N.A.I.C.S.: 331110

Steel Authority of India Limited - Visvesvaraya Iron and Steel Plant (1)
Sail-Visl New Town, Shimoga District, Bhadravati, 577301, Karnataka, India
Tel.: (91) 8282 271621 9
Sales Range: $200-249.9 Million
Emp.: 900
Steel Products Mfr
N.A.I.C.S.: 331110

UEC SAIL Information Technology Limited (1)
Piccadily House 1st Floor 275-276, Captain Gaur Marg Srinivaspuri, New Delhi, 110003, India
Tel.: (91) 1126845393
Sales Range: $50-74.9 Million
Emp.: 120
Business & Management Services; owned 40% by Steel Authority of India Limited & 60% by USX Engineers Consultants (US Steel)
N.A.I.C.S.: 541611

mjunction Services Limited (1)
Godrej Waterside 3rd Floor Tower 1 Plot V Block DP Sector V, Salt Lake, Kolkata, 700091, India
Tel.: (91) 3366106100
Web Site: http://www.mjunction.in
Emp.: 900
Procurement & Selling Services
N.A.I.C.S.: 561499
Vinaya Varma *(CEO & Mng Dir)*

STEEL CANADA LTD.
375 Traders Blvd East, Mississauga, L4Z 2E5, ON, Canada
Tel.: (905) 890-0209
Web Site:
https://www.steelcanada.com
Year Founded: 1982
Rev.: $48,825,015
Emp.: 30
Steel Service Center
N.A.I.C.S.: 331513
Feroz Jassani *(Pres)*

STEEL CITY SECURITIES LIMITED
50-81-18 Main Road Seethammapeta, Visakhapatnam, 530016, India
Tel.: (91) 8912563581
Web Site:
https://www.steelcitynettrade.com
Year Founded: 1995
STEELCITY—(NSE)
Rev.: $7,051,088
Assets: $21,994,053
Liabilities: $8,619,999
Net Worth: $13,374,054
Earnings: $1,343,924
Emp.: 341
Fiscal Year-end: 03/31/23
Retail Stock Broking Services
N.A.I.C.S.: 523150
K. Satyanarayana *(Chm)*

STEEL CRAFT DOOR PRODUCTS LTD.
13504 St Albert Trail, Edmonton, T5L 4P4, AB, Canada
Tel.: (780) 453-3761
Web Site: https://www.steel-craft.ca
Year Founded: 1963
Rev.: $16,739,464
Emp.: 150
Door Mfr
N.A.I.C.S.: 332321
Art Mihalcheon *(Founder)*

STEEL EXCHANGE INDIA LTD.
Block-A Greencity Near Apparel Export Park, Vadlapudi Post, Visakhapatnam, 530 046, Andhra Pradesh, India
Tel.: (91) 8912587175
Web Site: https://www.seil.co.in
STEELXIND—(NSE)
Rev.: $167,059,900
Assets: $135,718,578
Liabilities: $73,712,140
Net Worth: $62,006,438
Earnings: ($7,056,064)
Emp.: 526
Fiscal Year-end: 03/31/23
Electronic Steel Shopping Services
N.A.I.C.S.: 459999

STEEL EXCHANGE INDIA LTD.

Steel Exchange India Ltd.—(Continued)

Bandi Satish Kumar *(Chm & Co-Mng Dir)*

STEEL FLOWER CO., LTD.
25F KNN Tower 30 Centurm deo-ro, Haeundae-gu, Busan, Korea (South)
Tel.: (82) 51 745 3000
Web Site: http://www.steelflower.co.kr
Year Founded: 1999
087220—(KRS)
Sales Range: $75-99.9 Million
Pipe Product Mfr
N.A.I.C.S.: 332919
Byeongkwon Kim *(CEO)*

Subsidiaries:

Steel Flower Co., Ltd. - JINYOUNG PLANT (1)
4-38 Bonsan 2-ro 79beon-gil, Jinyeong-eup, Gimhae, Gyeongsangnam-Do, Korea (South)
Tel.: (82) 55 340 7777
Steel Pole Mfr
N.A.I.C.S.: 331210

Steel Flower Co., Ltd. - POHANG PLANT (1)
138 Songdeok-ro 212beon-gil Daesong-Myeong, Nam-gu, Pohang, 790-841, Gyeongsangbuk-Do, Korea (South)
Tel.: (82) 54 280 2000
Steel Pole Mfr
N.A.I.C.S.: 331210

STEEL STRIPS WHEELS LTD.
SCO 49-50 Sector 26 Madhya Marg, Chandigarh, 160 019, India
Tel.: (91) 1722792385
Web Site: https://www.sswlindia.com
Year Founded: 1991
513262—(BOM)
Rev.: $485,935,747
Assets: $333,476,326
Liabilities: $197,427,780
Net Worth: $136,048,546
Earnings: $23,235,298
Emp.: 2,486
Fiscal Year-end: 03/31/23
Automotive Steel Wheels Mfr
N.A.I.C.S.: 336390
Dheeraj Garg *(Mng Dir)*

Subsidiaries:

SAB Infotech Ltd. (1)
41 1st Flr Chikhal House 455 Kalbadevi Road, Mumbai, 400002, Uttar Pradesh, India
Tel.: (91) 9320044748
Web Site: http://www.saberp.com
Sales Range: $25-49.9 Million
Emp.: 100
Software Development Services
N.A.I.C.S.: 513210

Steel Strips & Tubes Ltd. (1)
Somalheri Lehli PO Dappar, Tehsil Rajpura, Patiala, 147105, Punjab, India
Tel.: (91) 1722793112
Web Site: http://www.ssll.com
Sales Range: $50-74.9 Million
Emp.: 130
Wheel Rim Mfr
N.A.I.C.S.: 336390

STEEL STRUCTURE MANUFACTURE JOINT STOCK COMPANY
Road No 9 Hoa Khanh Industrial Zone, Lien Chieu District, Da Nang, Vietnam
Tel.: (84) 511732998
Web Site: https://www.ssm.com.vn
Year Founded: 2001
SSM—(HNX)
Rev.: $13,755,700
Assets: $14,366,300
Liabilities: $8,405,300
Net Worth: $5,961,000
Earnings: $148,600

Emp.: 257
Fiscal Year-end: 12/31/23
Steel Products Mfr
N.A.I.C.S.: 332312
Ho Thai Hoa *(Chm-Mgmt Bd)*

STEELASIA MANUFACTURING CORPORATION
2nd Floor B2 Bonifacio High Street, Taguig, 1634, Metro Manila, Philippines
Tel.: (63) 2 856 6888
Web Site: http://www.steelasia.com
Year Founded: 1965
Steel Bars Mfr & Distr
N.A.I.C.S.: 331110
Benjamin O. Yao *(Chm & Pres)*

STEELCAST LTD
Ruvapari Road, Bhavnagar, 364 005, Gujarat, India
Tel.: (91) 2782519062
Web Site: https://www.steelcast.net
513517—(NSE)
Rev.: $41,271,553
Assets: $37,680,061
Liabilities: $16,310,426
Net Worth: $21,369,635
Earnings: $4,541,614
Emp.: 887
Fiscal Year-end: 03/31/22
Steel Casting Mfr
N.A.I.C.S.: 331513
Chetankumar Manmohanbhai Tamboli *(Mng Dir & Chm)*

Subsidiaries:

Steelcast Ltd - Manufacturing Plant (1)
Ruvapari Rd, Bhavnagar, 364005, Gujarat, India
Tel.: (91) 2782519062
Web Site: http://www.steelcast.net
Sales Range: $200-249.9 Million
Heavy Electrical Equipment Mfr
N.A.I.C.S.: 335999

STEELCO GUJARAT LTD.
Plot No 2 G I D C Estate Palej, Bharuch, 392220, Gujarat, India
Tel.: (91) 2642277479
Web Site: https://www.steelcogujarat.com
Year Founded: 1989
Rev.: $10,614,411
Assets: $22,983,693
Liabilities: $63,652,478
Net Worth: $(40,668,785)
Earnings: $(13,969,082)
Emp.: 325
Fiscal Year-end: 03/31/19
Steel Products Mfr
N.A.I.C.S.: 331221
Mitesh H. Shah *(Mng Dir)*

STEELE FORD LINCOLN
3773 Windsor Street, Halifax, B3K 5M2, NS, Canada
Tel.: (902) 453-1130
Web Site: http://www.steeleford.com
New & Used Car Dealers
N.A.I.C.S.: 441110
Jim MacLellan *(Controller)*

STEELE VOLKSWAGEN LIMITED
696 Windmill Road, Dartmouth, B3B 2A5, NS, Canada
Tel.: (902) 468-6411
Web Site: http://www.steelevw.ca
Rev.: $14,190,950
Emp.: 31
New & Used Car Dealers
N.A.I.C.S.: 441110
Corey Mosher *(Mgr-Parts)*

STEELHEAD PETROLEUM LTD.
Suite 2500 240 4th Avenue SW, Calgary, T2P 4H4, AB, Canada
Tel.: (403) 536-8050
Web Site: http://www.steelheadpetroleum.com
Oil & Gas Exploration Services
N.A.I.C.S.: 213112
Chris Seasons *(Chm)*

STEELMAN TELECOM PRIVATE LIMITED
Street No 0315 DH Block Newtown Action Area 1D, Newtown Rajarhat, Kolkata, 700156, West Bengal, India
Tel.: (91) 8443022233
Web Site: https://www.steelmantelecom.com
Year Founded: 2003
543622—(BOM)
Rev.: $12,306,162
Assets: $4,976,101
Liabilities: $3,246,010
Net Worth: $1,730,090
Earnings: $227,916
Fiscal Year-end: 03/31/21
Telecommunication Servicesb
N.A.I.C.S.: 517810

STEELSERIES APS
Dirch Passers Alle 27 5th Floor, DK-2000, Frederiksberg, Denmark
Tel.: (45) 70 25 00 75
Web Site: http://steelseries.com
Gaming Peripherals & Computer Equipment Mfr
N.A.I.C.S.: 334118
Ehtisham Rabbani *(CEO)*

Subsidiaries:

Kontrolfreek, LLC (1)
2020 Howell Mill Rd NW, Atlanta, GA 30318-1732
Web Site: http://www.kontrolfreek.com
Doll, Toy & Game Mfr
N.A.I.C.S.: 339930
Ashish Mistry *(CEO)*

STEELTOWN FORD SALES
933 Manitoba Avenue, Selkirk, R1A 3T7, MB, Canada
Tel.: (204) 482-3841
Web Site: https://www.steeltownford.com
Year Founded: 1979
Sales Range: $10-24.9 Million
New & Used Car Dealers
N.A.I.C.S.: 441110
Kevin Barnhart *(Fin Mgr)*

STEEN RIVER OIL & GAS LTD.
Suite 400 606 4th Street SW, Calgary, T2P 1T1, AB, Canada
Tel.: (403) 335-2101
Sales Range: $10-24.9 Million
Emp.: 29
Oil & Gas Exploration Services
N.A.I.C.S.: 211120
W. Jeffrey Huckle *(VP-Ops)*

STEEP GMBH
Justus-von-Liebig-Strasse 18, 53121, Bonn, Germany
Tel.: (49) 228 6681 0
Web Site: http://www.steep.de
Year Founded: 1961
Sales Range: $125-149.9 Million
Emp.: 600
Engineering & Administrative Support Services for Defense Sector
N.A.I.C.S.: 541990
Matthias Moseler *(CEO)*

Subsidiaries:

BetaTech GmbH (1)

INTERNATIONAL PUBLIC

Justus-von-Liebig-Str 18, 53121, Bonn, Germany
Tel.: (49) 228 6 68 96 0
Web Site: http://www.betatech.de
Radio Network & Link System Installation Services
N.A.I.C.S.: 237130

STEEP HILL INC.
5160 Explorer Drive Unit 8, Mississauga, L4W 4T7, ON, Canada
Tel.: (905) 614-0272
Web Site: http://www.canbudcorp.com
CBDX—(CNSX)
Rev.: $2,998
Assets: $1,332,144
Liabilities: $431,699
Net Worth: $900,445
Earnings: $(1,658,329)
Fiscal Year-end: 12/31/20
Pharmaceutical Products Distr
N.A.I.C.S.: 424210
Steve Singh *(Co-Founder & CEO)*

STEER DAVIES & GLEAVE LIMITED
28 32 Upper Ground, London, SE1 9PD, United Kingdom
Tel.: (44) 2079105000
Web Site: http://www.steerdaviesgleave.com
Year Founded: 1978
Rev.: $61,539,962
Emp.: 376
Transport Consultancy Service
N.A.I.C.S.: 541614
John Lawrence *(Chm)*

STEERING HOLDINGS LTD.
6/F The Suns Group Centre 200 Gloucester Road, Wanchai, China (Hong Kong)
Tel.: (852) 31885595
Web Site: http://www.steering.com.hk
Year Founded: 2015
Rev.: $166,071,754
Assets: $125,620,036
Liabilities: $70,636,286
Net Worth: $54,983,749
Earnings: $14,969,653
Emp.: 567
Fiscal Year-end: 12/31/19
Building Consulting Services
N.A.I.C.S.: 541420
Sammy Ip *(Dir-MEP & Licensing Consultancy Dept)*

STEF SA
93 boulevard Malesherbes, 75008, Paris, France
Tel.: (33) 140742900
Web Site: https://www.stef.com
STF—(EUR)
Rev.: $4,601,935,031
Assets: $3,610,275,200
Liabilities: $2,487,940,859
Net Worth: $1,122,334,341
Earnings: $157,952,730
Emp.: 21,718
Fiscal Year-end: 12/31/22
Frozen & Refrigerated Goods Transportation, Logistics & Warehousing Services
N.A.I.C.S.: 488510
Bernard Jolivet *(Vice Chm)*

Subsidiaries:

Nagel Airfreight France SAS (1)
8 Quai de Boulogne, BP 30525, F-94539, Rungis, Cedex, France
Tel.: (33) 145122525
Community Food Services
N.A.I.C.S.: 624210

STEF Bodegraven BV (1)
Tolnasingel 4 Pays-Bas, 2411 PV, Bodegraven, Netherlands
Tel.: (31) 172613963

AND PRIVATE COMPANIES — STEF SA

Transportation Infrastructure Services
N.A.I.C.S.: 488510

STEF Eurofrischfracht SASU (1)
35 rue de Calais, 67100, Strasbourg, France
Tel.: (33) 388102000
Sea Freight Transportation & Logistics Services
N.A.I.C.S.: 488510

STEF Logistics Courcelles SA (1)
Rue du Hainaut 40, 6180, Courcelles, Belgium
Tel.: (32) 71469800
Transportation Infrastructure Services
N.A.I.C.S.: 488510

STEF Logistics Saintes SA (1)
Avenue Zenobe Gramme 13, 1480, Saintes, Belgium
Tel.: (32) 24663355
Transportation Infrastructure Services
N.A.I.C.S.: 488510

STEF Logistique Aulnay-Sous-Bois SA (1)
47 Boulevard Andre Citroen, 93600, Aulnay-sous-Bois, France
Tel.: (33) 141846001
Sea Freight Transportation & Logistics Services
N.A.I.C.S.: 488510

STEF Logistique Aurice SAS (1)
Lieu-dit Guillon, 40500, Saint-Sever, France
Tel.: (33) 558053300
Sea Freight Transportation & Logistics Services
N.A.I.C.S.: 488510

STEF Logistique Darvault SAS (1)
Z A C de la pierre levee-Lieu-dit Les Moines, Darvault, 77140, Seine-et-Marne, France
Tel.: (33) 160552100
Sea Freight Transportation & Logistics Services
N.A.I.C.S.: 488510

STEF Logistique Fuveau SA (1)
Parc Saint-Charles-Avenue de l Etoile, Fuveau, 13710, Marseille, France
Tel.: (33) 442331031
Sea Freight Transportation & Logistics Services
N.A.I.C.S.: 488510

STEF Logistique Givors SA (1)
Z I de la Vallee du GIER-Rue de la democratie, 69700, Givors, France
Tel.: (33) 472492055
Sea Freight Transportation & Logistics Services
N.A.I.C.S.: 488510

STEF Logistique Le Plessis Belleville SAS (1)
Z I des Meuniers 19 rue des Meuniers, 60330, Le Plessis-Belleville, France
Tel.: (33) 344604210
Sea Freight Transportation & Logistics Services
N.A.I.C.S.: 488510

STEF Logistique Le Plessis-Pate SA (1)
15 Rue de la Mare aux Joncs, 91220, Le Plessis-Pate, France
Tel.: (33) 164859930
Sea Freight Transportation & Logistics Services
N.A.I.C.S.: 488510

STEF Logistique Lesquin SA (1)
106 rue du Fort CRT N 3, Fretin, 59273, Lesquin, France
Tel.: (33) 320887440
Sea Freight Transportation & Logistics Services
N.A.I.C.S.: 488510

STEF Logistique Mions SAS (1)
Z A C Pesseliere 2 rue Joseph Marie Jacquard, 69780, Mions, France
Tel.: (33) 426205418
Sea Freight Transportation & Logistics Services
N.A.I.C.S.: 488510

STEF Logistique Moulins Les Metz SA (1)
Z A C de la Rotonde 108 route de Jouy, Moulins-les-Metz, 57160, Metz, France
Tel.: (33) 387624411
Sea Freight Transportation & Logistics Services
N.A.I.C.S.: 488510

STEF Logistique Nemours SA (1)
4 rue des Palis, 77140, Nemours, France
Tel.: (33) 160515000
Sea Freight Transportation & Logistics Services
N.A.I.C.S.: 488510

STEF Logistique Niort SAS (1)
Centre Routier-Rue Charles Tellier, La Creche, 79260, Sevres, France
Tel.: (33) 549053232
Sea Freight Transportation & Logistics Services
N.A.I.C.S.: 488510

STEF Logistique Pessac SAS (1)
Z I Bersol-8 rue Thoms Edison, 33600, Pessac, France
Tel.: (33) 557265260
Sea Freight Transportation & Logistics Services
N.A.I.C.S.: 488510

STEF Logistique Plouenan EFL (1)
Route de Mespaul, Plouenan, 29420, Morlaix, France
Tel.: (33) 298695007
Transportation Infrastructure Services
N.A.I.C.S.: 488510

STEF Logistique St Pierre Des Corps SA (1)
149 Avenue Yves Farges, 37700, Saint-Pierre-des-Corps, France
Tel.: (33) 247462360
Sea Freight Transportation & Logistics Services
N.A.I.C.S.: 488510

STEF Logistique Tigery SAS (1)
4 boulevard des Pays-Bas-Parc d Activites de Parisud, 91250, Tigery, France
Tel.: (33) 169138101
Sea Freight Transportation & Logistics Services
N.A.I.C.S.: 488510

STEF Logistique Toussieu SASU (1)
Parc d activites-Le Logis Neuf, 69780, Toussieu, France
Tel.: (33) 472096740
Sea Freight Transportation & Logistics Services
N.A.I.C.S.: 488510

STEF Logistique Venissieux SA (1)
Parc d activites de l Arsenal-2 rue Andre Sentuc, 69200, Venissieux, France
Tel.: (33) 472909930
Sea Freight Transportation & Logistics Services
N.A.I.C.S.: 488510

STEF TSA Orleans Nord SAS (1)
Lieudit vers Artenay et Villeneuve, Poupry, 28140, Orleans, France
Tel.: (33) 238654092
Sea Freight Transportation & Logistics Services
N.A.I.C.S.: 488510

STEF Transport Angers SASU (1)
Z I d Ecouflant 7 rue des 4 Routes Batiment Totem 3, 49009, Angers, France
Tel.: (33) 241439797
Sea Freight Transportation & Logistics Services
N.A.I.C.S.: 488510

STEF Transport Avignon SAS (1)
91 Espace d Activite Sainte-Anne, 84700, Sorgues, France
Tel.: (33) 490232829
Sea Freight Transportation & Logistics Services
N.A.I.C.S.: 488510

STEF Transport Bordeaux Begles SAS (1)
3 Rue du Lugan, 33323, Begles, France
Tel.: (33) 556844330
Sea Freight Transportation & Logistics Services
N.A.I.C.S.: 488510

STEF Transport Boulogne SAS (1)
41 rue Alexandre Adam, 62204, Boulogne-sur-Mer, France
Tel.: (33) 321100321
Sea Freight Transportation & Logistics Services
N.A.I.C.S.: 488510

STEF Transport Chaulnes SAS (1)
Z I Route d Hallu, Chaulnes, 80320, Amiens, France
Tel.: (33) 322835510
Sea Freight Transportation & Logistics Services
N.A.I.C.S.: 488510

STEF Transport Clermont-Ferrand SA (1)
Z I de Ladoux 3 rue Verte, 63118, Cebazat, France
Tel.: (33) 473235656
Sea Freight Transportation & Logistics Services
N.A.I.C.S.: 488510

STEF Transport Dijon SA (1)
Z A E de Boulouze, Fauverney, 21110, Dijon, France
Tel.: (33) 380282500
Sea Freight Transportation & Logistics Services
N.A.I.C.S.: 488510

STEF Transport Landivisiau SAS (1)
Z A du Vern 2-Rue du Ponant, 29400, Landivisiau, France
Tel.: (33) 298244848
Sea Freight Transportation & Logistics Services
N.A.I.C.S.: 488510

STEF Transport Langres SA (1)
Faubourg de la Colliniere, BP 155, 52201, Langres, Cedex, France
Tel.: (33) 325874712
Sea Freight Transportation & Logistics Services
N.A.I.C.S.: 488510

STEF Transport Laval SA (1)
Boulevard de la Communication Zone Autoroutiere 2, Louverne, 53950, Mayenne, France
Tel.: (33) 243493900
Sea Freight Transportation & Logistics Services
N.A.I.C.S.: 488510

STEF Transport Le Mans SAS (1)
16 rue Mickael Faraday CS 42731 Z I Sud, 72027, Le Mans, France
Tel.: (33) 243612233
Sea Freight Transportation & Logistics Services
N.A.I.C.S.: 488510

STEF Transport Lesquin SAS (1)
17 Rue des Seringats, Fretin, 59273, Calais, France
Tel.: (33) 320887483
Sea Freight Transportation & Logistics Services
N.A.I.C.S.: 488510

STEF Transport Limoges SASU (1)
3 rue Enzo Ferrari, 87280, Limoges, France
Tel.: (33) 555389370
Sea Freight Transportation & Logistics Services
N.A.I.C.S.: 488510

STEF Transport Macon SAS (1)
Zone Macon Est Les Brosses, Replonges, 01750, Bourgogne, France
Tel.: (33) 385318989
Sea Freight Transportation & Logistics Services
N.A.I.C.S.: 488510

STEF Transport Marseille SA (1)
Z A C de l Anjoly-Voie d Irlande, 13741, Vitrolles, France
Tel.: (33) 442462400
Sea Freight Transportation & Logistics Services
N.A.I.C.S.: 488510

STEF Transport Montpellier SA (1)
205 rue Terre de Roy, 34740, Vendargues, France
Tel.: (33) 467874740
Sea Freight Transportation & Logistics Services
N.A.I.C.S.: 488510

STEF Transport Mulhouse SA (1)
6 rue de l Europe, Burnhaupt-le-Bas, 68520, Colmar, France
Tel.: (33) 389627610
Sea Freight Transportation & Logistics Services
N.A.I.C.S.: 488510

STEF Transport Nantes Carquefou SA (1)
10 rue Vega, 44470, Carquefou, France
Tel.: (33) 251885400
Sea Freight Transportation & Logistics Services
N.A.I.C.S.: 488510

STEF Transport Niort 1 La Creche SA (1)
Centre Routier 12 rue Charles Tellier, La Creche, 79260, Sevres, France
Tel.: (33) 549053232
Sea Freight Transportation & Logistics Services
N.A.I.C.S.: 488510

STEF Transport Niort 2 La Creche SAS (1)
2 allee des grands champs, La Creche, 79260, Sevres, France
Tel.: (33) 549053883
Sea Freight Transportation & Logistics Services
N.A.I.C.S.: 488510

STEF Transport Orleans SA (1)
1001 rue du Champ Rouge, 45770, Saran, France
Tel.: (33) 238363636
Sea Freight Transportation & Logistics Services
N.A.I.C.S.: 488510

STEF Transport Paris Rungis SAS (1)
2 avenue de Boulogne Maree 326, 94569, Rungis, Cedex, France
Tel.: (33) 145607777
Sea Freight Transportation & Logistics Services
N.A.I.C.S.: 488510

STEF Transport Reims SA (1)
Allee Attilio Marzin Zone d Activites de la Pompelle, 51100, Reims, France
Tel.: (33) 326462720
Sea Freight Transportation & Logistics Services
N.A.I.C.S.: 488510

STEF Transport Rouen SAS (1)
Rouen Multi Marchandises Rue du Long Boel, 76807, Saint Etienne-du-Rouvray, France
Tel.: (33) 232919393
Sea Freight Transportation & Logistics Services
N.A.I.C.S.: 488510

STEF Transport Saint-Brieuc SA (1)
Z I du Moulin a Vent rue dJean Monet, 22120, Yffiniac, France
Tel.: (33) 296638150
Sea Freight Transportation & Logistics Services
N.A.I.C.S.: 488510

STEF Transport Saint-Sever SA (1)
Z I d Aurice, Saint-Sever, 40500, Rion-des-Landes, France
Tel.: (33) 558053737
Sea Freight Transportation & Logistics Services
N.A.I.C.S.: 488510

STEF Transport St-Etienne SASU (1)
Z I de Verpilleux 6 rue Necker, 42000, Saint Etienne, France
Tel.: (33) 477481818
Sea Freight Transportation & Logistics Services
N.A.I.C.S.: 488510

STEF Transport Toulouse SA (1)
Z A Eurocentre 2 avenue de la Tuilerie, Villeneuve-les-Bouloc, 31620, Toulouse, France

STEF SA

STEF SA—(Continued)
Tel.: (33) 561159255
Sea Freight Transportation & Logistics Services
N.A.I.C.S.: 488510

STEFANEL S.P.A.
Via Postojna 85, Ponte di Piave, 31047, Treviso, Italy
Tel.: (39) 04228191809
Web Site: http://www.stefanel.it
Year Founded: 1959
Sales Range: $200-249.9 Million
Emp.: 2,619
Men & Women's Clothing Mfr
N.A.I.C.S.: 315250

Subsidiaries:

Interfashion S.p.A. (1)
Via Coriano 58 90, 47900, Rimini, Italy
Tel.: (39) 0541706911
Web Site: http://www.hi.com
Sales Range: $25-49.9 Million
Emp.: 150
Mens & Boys Cut & Sew Work Clothing Mfr
N.A.I.C.S.: 315250
Federica Inbrunetti *(Mgr-Adv)*

Lara Stefanel SAS (1)
54 Rue De Rennes, 75006, Paris, France
Tel.: (33) 145440607
Web Site: http://www.stefanel.com
Sales Range: $25-49.9 Million
Emp.: 4
Family Clothing Stores
N.A.I.C.S.: 458110

Stefanel Polonia Sp. z o.o. (1)
Nowy Swiat 1-10, 00-496, Warsaw, Poland
Tel.: (48) 227453220
Web Site: http://www.stefanel.pl
Sales Range: $25-49.9 Million
Emp.: 60
Mens & Boys Cut & Sew Work Clothing Mfr
N.A.I.C.S.: 315250
Renata Ciszewska *(Gen Mgr)*

Stefanel Romania S.r.l. (1)
8 Sector 6 Brasov, Bucharest, Romania
Tel.: (40) 216137986
Web Site: http://www.stefanel.com
Piece & Goods Notions & Dry Goods Whslr
N.A.I.C.S.: 424310

Stefpraha s.r.o. (1)
Zelezna 14, 11000, Prague, Czech Republic
Tel.: (420) 224223500
Family Clothing Stores
N.A.I.C.S.: 458110

STEFANINI CONSULTORIA E ASSESSORIA EM INFORMATICA, LTDA.
Avenida Azenita Eusebio Matoso 1375 & 1385 8th Floor, Butanta, 05423-905, Brazil
Tel.: (55) 1130392000
Web Site: http://www.stefanini.com
Year Founded: 1987
Sales Range: $600-649.9 Million
Emp.: 14,000
IT Services
N.A.I.C.S.: 541512
Marco Stefanini *(Founder & CEO)*

Subsidiaries:

Stefanini International Corp. (1)
6301 NW 5th Way Ste 2700, Fort Lauderdale, FL 33309
Tel.: (954) 229-9150
IT Services
N.A.I.C.S.: 541511
Spencer Gracias *(CEO-North America & Asia Pacific)*

Subsidiary (Non-US):

Stefanini TechTeam Akela SRL (2)
IRIDE Industrial Park 9-9A Dimitrie Pompei Blvd, Cladirea 2A2 Sector 2, 020335, Bucharest, Romania
Tel.: (40) 213051400
Web Site: http://www.akelasoftware.com

Sales Range: $1-9.9 Million
Emp.: 150
Software Application Development
N.A.I.C.S.: 513210

Stefanini TechTeam Global GmbH (2)
Im Zollhafen 24, 50678, Cologne, Germany
Tel.: (49) 221 650 78 466
Web Site: http://www.techteam.com
Sales Range: $25-49.9 Million
Emp.: 10
Outsourced Computer Help Desk Support, Systems Integration & Technical Staffing & Training Services
N.A.I.C.S.: 541512
Ernst Voegtle *(Gen Mgr)*

Stefanini TechTeam Global Ltd. (2)
Lakeside House 1 Furzground Way, Stockley Park, Uxbridge, UB11 1BD, United Kingdom
Tel.: (44) 208 622 3490
Web Site: http://www.techteam.com
Outsourced Computer Help Desk Support, Systems Integration & Technical Staffing & Training Services
N.A.I.C.S.: 541512

Stefanini TechTeam Global NV/SA (2)
Zweefvliegtuigstraat 10 Rue du Planeur, 1130, Brussels, Belgium
Tel.: (32) 26202020
Web Site: http://www.techteam.com
Sales Range: $150-199.9 Million
Emp.: 300
Outsourced Computer Help Desk Support, Systems Integration & Technical Staffing & Training Services
N.A.I.C.S.: 541512

Stefanini TechTeam Global SRL (2)
24 Calea Dumbravii, Royal Business Center 4th Flr, 550324, Sibiu, Romania
Tel.: (40) 21 301 23 56
Web Site: http://www.techteam.com
Outsourced Computer Help Desk Support, Systems Integration & Technical Staffing & Training Services
N.A.I.C.S.: 541512

STEFANUTTI STOCKS HOLDINGS LIMITED
No 9 Palala Street Protec Park, Cnr Zuurfontein Avenue and Oranjerivier Drive, Johannesburg, 1619, South Africa
Tel.: (27) 115714300 ZA
Web Site: https://stefanuttistocks.com
Rev.: $685,230,579
Assets: $446,413,040
Liabilities: $326,523,849
Net Worth: $119,889,191
Earnings: ($7,706,753)
Emp.: 10,746
Fiscal Year-end: 02/28/19
Civil Engineering & Building Construction Services
N.A.I.C.S.: 237990
William Somerville *(Sec)*

Subsidiaries:

Al Tayer Stocks LLC (1)
30th 31st Floor API Trio Office Towers Al Barsha 1, PO Box 2623, Garhoud, Dubai, 2623, United Arab Emirates **(49%)**
Tel.: (971) 45034888
Web Site: http://www.altayerstocks.com
Sales Range: $50-74.9 Million
Emp.: 150
Interior-Contracting; Plastering, Furnishing & Electrical & Mechanical Systems Installation
N.A.I.C.S.: 236220

ECMP (Pty) Ltd (1)
Block 6 Stratford Office Pk c/o Valley & Cedar Roads, Broad Acres, 2021, Johannesburg, South Africa
Tel.: (27) 117051111
Sales Range: $25-49.9 Million
Emp.: 70
Mining Engineering Services
N.A.I.C.S.: 237990

Stefanutti Stocks Building (Pty) Ltd (1)
Protec Park Cnr Zuurfontein Avenue & Oranjerivier Drive, PO Box 12394 Aston Manor1630, Chloorkop, Kempton Park, South Africa
Tel.: (27) 115714300
Web Site: http://www.stefanutti.co.za
Sales Range: $900-999.9 Million
Emp.: 3,000
Commercial Construction
N.A.I.C.S.: 236220

Subsidiary (Non-US):

Stefanutti Stocks Botswana (Pty) Limited (2)
Plot 21307 Phakalane, Gaborone, Botswana
Tel.: (267) 3974773
Web Site: http://www.stefanutti.co.za
Sales Range: $50-74.9 Million
Emp.: 126
Engineeering Services
N.A.I.C.S.: 236210
Lucas Labuschagne *(Mng Dir)*

Subsidiary (Domestic):

Stefanutti Stocks Building Gauteng (Pty) Limited (2)
176 Barbara Road Elandsfontein, Germiston, 1684, South Africa
Tel.: (27) 118204600
Sales Range: $1-4.9 Billion
Emp.: 1,200
Construction Services
N.A.I.C.S.: 236210

Stefanutti Stocks Building KZN (Pty) Ltd (2)
14 Circuit Road Westmead Pinetown, Durban, 3610, South Africa
Tel.: (27) 317001416
Web Site: http://www.Stefanuttistocks.co.za
Sales Range: $25-49.9 Million
Emp.: 100
Engineeering Services
N.A.I.C.S.: 236210

Stefanutti Stocks Building W Cape (Pty) Limited (2)
Manhattan Close Airport Industria, 7525, Cape Town, South Africa
Tel.: (27) 213866336
Sales Range: $100-124.9 Million
Emp.: 300
Construction Services
N.A.I.C.S.: 236210

Subsidiary (Non-US):

Stefanutti Stocks Construcoes (Mocambique) Lda (2)
Av De Mocambique Parcela 7160/A En1 km 13 2, Zimpeto, Maputo, Mozambique
Tel.: (258) 21 471 604
Web Site: http://www.stefanutti.co.za
Engineeering Services
N.A.I.C.S.: 236210

Subsidiary (Domestic):

Stefanutti Stocks Housing (Pty) Limited (2)
85 Neptune Avenue, Crowthorne, 1685, Kyalami, South Africa
Tel.: (27) 114682735
Web Site: http://www.stefanutti.co.za
Sales Range: $25-49.9 Million
Emp.: 30
Engineeering Services
N.A.I.C.S.: 236210

Stefanutti Stocks Civils (Pty) Ltd (1)
Protec Park Cnr Zuurfontein Avenue & Oranjerivier Drive, Chloorkop, Kempton Park, 1624, South Africa
Tel.: (27) 115714300
Web Site: http://www.stefanuttisocks.com
Civil Structures Construction
N.A.I.C.S.: 237990

Subsidiary (Domestic):

Stefanutti Stocks Geotechnical (Pty) Limited (2)
Protec Park Cnr Zuurfontein Avenue and Oranjerivier Drive, Chloorkop, Kempton Park, 1630, South Africa
Tel.: (27) 115714300
Web Site: http://www.stefstocks.co.za
Sales Range: $100-124.9 Million
Emp.: 320
Civil Engineering
N.A.I.C.S.: 237990

Stefanutti Stocks Civils Gauteng (Pty) Limited (1)
Protec Park Cnr Zuurfontein Avenue & Oranjerivier Drive, PO Box 12394, Chloorkop Aston Manor, Kempton Park, 1630, South Africa
Tel.: (27) 11 571 4300
Emp.: 1,300
Civil Engineering Construction Services
N.A.I.C.S.: 237990
Kosance Dimitrijevic *(Chm)*

Stefanutti Stocks Civils KZN (Pty) Limited (1)
14 Circuit Road Westmede, PO Box 1567, Westmead, 3600, Pinetown, South Africa
Tel.: (27) 31 700 1416
Sales Range: $25-49.9 Million
Emp.: 15
Civil Engineering Construction Services
N.A.I.C.S.: 237990

Stefanutti Stocks Earthworks (Pty) Ltd (1)
6 Mulalani Street Protec Park Cnr Zuurfontein Avenue & Oranjerivier, PO Box 12394, Chloorkop, Kempton Park, 1630, South Africa
Tel.: (27) 115524200
Web Site: http://www.stefanutti.co.za
Sales Range: $400-449.9 Million
Emp.: 2,000
Mining & Road Construction
N.A.I.C.S.: 237310

Subsidiary (Non-US):

Stefanutti Stocks Swaziland (Pty) Limited (2)
Plot 238, Matsapha, Eswatini
Tel.: (268) 5185006
Web Site: http://www.stefanutti.co.za
Sales Range: $25-49.9 Million
Emp.: 9
Highway Construction
N.A.I.C.S.: 237310

Stefanutti Stocks Gulf FZE (1)
Jafza Tower 18, 17th Floor Office 5, Jebel Ali, United Arab Emirates
Tel.: (971) 4 8864751
Construction, Interior Fitting, Refurbishment & Electromechanical Installations
N.A.I.C.S.: 236220

Subsidiary (Domestic):

Zener Steward LLC (2)
Office No 702 Mostafawi Building Khalid Bin Al Walid Rd, Zariba AreaBur Dibai, Dubai, United Arab Emirates
Tel.: (971) 43523494
Web Site: http://www.zenersteward.me
Sales Range: $100-124.9 Million
Emp.: 300
Residential, Commercial & Industrial Plumbing Systems Design & Installation
N.A.I.C.S.: 238220
Drevor Arkle *(Gen Mgr)*

Stefanutti Stocks Holdings Limited - Stefanutti Stocks Building Business Unit (1)
176 Barbara Road Elandsfontein, Germiston, 1630, South Africa
Tel.: (27) 118204600
Web Site: http://www.stefanuttistocks.com
Real Estate Manangement Services
N.A.I.C.S.: 531390

Subsidiary (Non-US):

Stefanutti Stocks Building Botswana (Pty) Ltd (2)
Plot 21307 Phakalane, PO Box 402127, Gaborone, Botswana
Tel.: (267) 397 4773
Emp.: 30
Commercial Building Construction Services
N.A.I.C.S.: 236220
Shaun Cross *(Mng Dir)*

AND PRIVATE COMPANIES

Division (Domestic):

Stefanutti Stocks Building Business Unit - Stefanutti Stocks Building Major Projects Division (2)
Protec Park Cnr Zuurfontein Avenue & Oranjerivier Drive, Chloorkop, Kempton Park, 1619, South Africa
Tel.: (27) 112440300
Construction Engineering Services
N.A.I.C.S.: 541330
Howard Jones *(Gen Mgr)*

Stefanutti Stocks Holdings Limited - Stefanutti Stocks Building Western Cape Division (1)
Manhattan Close Airport Industria, PO Box 6221, Cape Town, 7525, South Africa
Tel.: (27) 21 386 6336
Sales Range: $50-74.9 Million
Emp.: 12
Commercial Building Construction Engineering Services
N.A.I.C.S.: 236220
Brindom Goldsworthy *(Dir-Comml)*

Stefanutti Stocks Holdings Limited - Stefanutti Stocks Housing Division (1)
85 Neptune Avenue, Private Bag X72, Crowthorne Halfway House, Midrand, 1685, South Africa
Tel.: (27) 11 468 2735
Web Site: http://www.stefanuttistocks.com
Construction Engineering Services
N.A.I.C.S.: 541330

Stefanutti Stocks Holdings Limited - Stefanutti Stocks North West Division (1)
12 Waterval Street Industrial Area, PO Box 1795, Rustenburg, 0299, South Africa
Tel.: (27) 14 597 3321
Web Site: http://www.stefanuttistocks.com
Sales Range: $150-199.9 Million
Emp.: 1,000
Construction Engineering Services
N.A.I.C.S.: 541330

Stefanutti Stocks Holdings Limited - Stefanutti Stocks Roads & Earthworks Unit
6 Mulalani Street Protec Park Cnr Zuurfontein Ave & Oranjerivier Drive, PO Box 12394, Chloorkop Aston Manor, Kempton Park, 1618, South Africa
Tel.: (27) 11 552 4200
Highway Construction Services
N.A.I.C.S.: 237310

Stefanutti Stocks International Holdings (Pty) Limited (1)
Protec Pk-Cnr Zuurfontein Av Oranjerivier D, Kempton Park, 1624, South Africa
Tel.: (27) 115714300
Investment Management Service
N.A.I.C.S.: 523999

Stefanutti Stocks Material Handling (Pty) Limited (1)
9 Hoop Street, Middelburg, 1050, South Africa
Tel.: (27) 132432225
Sales Range: $100-124.9 Million
Emp.: 13
Coal Mining Services
N.A.I.C.S.: 213113
Marco Pasquali *(Dir-Contract)*

Stefanutti Stocks Mechanical & Electrical (1)
176 Barbara Road Elandsfontein, Germiston, 1401, South Africa
Tel.: (27) 11 820 4600
Energy Transmission; Power Instrumentation, Engineering & Construction Services
N.A.I.C.S.: 237130

Division (Domestic):

Stefanutti Stocks (2)
176 Barbara Road, Elandsfontein, Private Bag, X2032, Isando, South Africa
Tel.: (27) 112545700
Web Site: http://www.sp.co.za
Sales Range: $75-99.9 Million
Emp.: 300
Electrical & Instrumentation Construction Services

N.A.I.C.S.: 335999

Stefanutti Stocks Holdings Limited - Stefanutti Stocks Electrical & Instrumentation Division (2)
176 Barbara Road, PO Box 1491, Elandsfontein, Germiston, 1401, South Africa
Tel.: (27) 118204600
Web Site: http://www.stefanuttistocks.com
Mining Industry Equipment Mfr
N.A.I.C.S.: 333131

Stefanutti Stocks Holdings Limited - Stefanutti Stocks Mechanical Division (2)
Midrand Industrial Park 05 Musket Road Chloorkop Ext 5, PO Box 1491, Halfway House, Kempton Park, 1685, South Africa
Tel.: (27) 11 254 5700
Web Site: http://www.stefanuttistocks.com
Sales Range: $50-74.9 Million
Emp.: 200
Steel Pipe Installation Services
N.A.I.C.S.: 238120
Vincent Olley *(Mng Dir)*

Stefanutti Stocks Holdings Limited - Stefanutti Stocks Power Division (2)
Midrand Industrial Park 05 Musket Road Chloorkop Ext 5, PO Box 1491, Halfways House, Kempton Park, 1685, South Africa
Tel.: (27) 11 254 5700
Sales Range: $100-124.9 Million
Emp.: 30
Power Plant Construction Engineering Services
N.A.I.C.S.: 237130
Vince Olley *(Mng Dir)*

Subsidiary (Non-US):

Zener Steward Electromechanical (2)
Office No R1 3rd Floor Al Fardan Building Al Mankhool Road, PO Box 111500, Bur Dubai, Dubai, United Arab Emirates
Tel.: (971) 43523494
Web Site: http://www.zenersteward.ae
Sales Range: $50-74.9 Million
Emp.: 196
Mechanical & Electrical Construction Services
N.A.I.C.S.: 423390

Stefanutti Stocks Middle East FZE (1)
Office No 702 317/301 Building Khalid Bin Al Walid Road Zariba Area, PO Box 389, Burdubai, Dubai, United Arab Emirates
Tel.: (971) 4 352 3494
Web Site: http://www.stefanuttistocks.com
Sales Range: $25-49.9 Million
Emp.: 60
Construction Engineering Services
N.A.I.C.S.: 541330

Stefanutti Stocks Property & Concessions (Pty) Ltd (1)
2nd Floor 109 Monza Close, Kyalami Business Park, 1684, Johannesburg, South Africa
Tel.: (27) 114668010
Sales Range: $50-74.9 Million
Emp.: 6
Real Estate
N.A.I.C.S.: 531390
Rob King *(Mng Dir)*

Stefanutti Stocks Workshops (Pty) Limited (1)
Protech Bldng Cnr Zuurfontein Ave Oranje St, Kempton Park, 481, Gauteng, South Africa
Tel.: (27) 115714300
Property Management Services
N.A.I.C.S.: 531311

STEGGLES FOODS
642 Great Western Highway, PO Box 21, Pendle Hill, 2145, NSW, Australia
Tel.: (61) 298421000
Web Site: http://www.steggles.com.au
Sales Range: $25-49.9 Million
Emp.: 1,000
Fresh & Frozen Poultry

N.A.I.C.S.: 424440
Simon Camilleri *(CEO)*

STEILMANN HOLDING AG
Industriestrasse 42, Bergkamen, 59192, Germany
Tel.: (49) 2389 783 0   De
Web Site: http://www.steilmann-holding.de
Year Founded: 2006
Holding Company; Men's & Women's Apparel & Home Textiles Designer, Mfr & Whslr
N.A.I.C.S.: 551112
Michele Puller *(CEO)*

Subsidiaries:

Adler Modemarkte AG (1)
Industriestrasse Ost 1-7, 63808, Haibach, Germany   (54.76%)
Tel.: (49) 60216331828
Web Site: http://www.adlermode.com
Rev.: $554,737,209
Assets: $458,446,047
Liabilities: $384,434,500
Net Worth: $74,011,547
Earnings: $5,749,361
Emp.: 3,612
Fiscal Year-end: 12/31/2019
Holding Company; Family Clothing Stores Owner & Operator
N.A.I.C.S.: 551112
Karsten Odemann *(CFO, Exec Bd-Fin, Controlling, Audits, Legal, IT & IR)*

ERTW GmbH (1)
Webersteig 2-6, 09471, Barenstein, Germany
Tel.: (49) 37347 81 0
Web Site: http://www.ertw.de
Carpet Mfr
N.A.I.C.S.: 314110

Hermann van Dillen Asiatex GmbH (1)
Industrieweg 17, 48493, Wettringen, Germany
Tel.: (49) 2557 9397 0
Web Site: http://www.vandillenasiatex.com
Textile Products Distr
N.A.I.C.S.: 424990

Division (Domestic):

Hermann van Dillen Asiatex GmbH - Global Labels Division (2)
Wernher-von-Braun-Str 10 a, 85640, Putzbrunn, Germany
Tel.: (49) 89 457094 0
Web Site: http://www.global-labels.de
Textile Products Distr
N.A.I.C.S.: 424990

Kettenbach GmbH (1)
Carl-Zeiss-Strasse 4, 72636, Frickenhausen, Germany
Tel.: (49) 7022 40593 0
Web Site: http://www.kettenbach.eu
Textile Product Mfr & Distr
N.A.I.C.S.: 315990

Kirsten Modedesign GmbH & Co. KG (1)
Emschermulde 6, 45891, Gelsenkirchen, Germany
Tel.: (49) 209 97629 0
Web Site: http://www.kirsten-mode.de
Apparel Product Distr
N.A.I.C.S.: 458110

Klaus Steilmann GmbH & Co. KG (1)
Industriestrasse 24, 59192, Bergkamen, Germany
Tel.: (49) 2389 9007 0
Web Site: http://www.steilmann.com
Sales Range: $900-999.9 Million
Emp.: 3,000
Women's Fashionwear & Outerwear Designer, Mfr & Whslr
N.A.I.C.S.: 315250

Marcona GmbH & Co. KG (1)
Industriestr 22, 59192, Bergkamen, Germany
Tel.: (49) 238 90080 60
Apparel Product Retailer

NTS Ltd. (1)
3rd Floor No 1415 Nan Su Zhou Road, 200041, Shanghai, China
Tel.: (86) 21 5119 6900
Web Site: http://www.ntsasia.cn
Emp.: 172
Apparel Product Mfr
N.A.I.C.S.: 315990
Josef Kaemmerer *(Chm & Gen Mgr)*

Sprugel Hometex GmbH (1)
Daimlerstr 2, 91161, Hilpoltstein, Germany
Tel.: (49) 9174 9730
Textile Products Distr
N.A.I.C.S.: 424990

Steilmann Osteuropa GmbH & Co. KG (1)
Mariendorfer Damm 1-3, 12099, Berlin, Germany
Tel.: (49) 30 7628 91 100
Web Site: http://www.steilmann-osteuropa.de
Textile Products Distr
N.A.I.C.S.: 424990
Carla Korn *(Mng Dir)*

Steilmann-Boecker Fashion Point GmbH & Co. KG (1)
Baumstrasse 22 - 24, 44623, Herne, Germany
Tel.: (49) 1801 26 32 53 7
Web Site: http://www.boecker-mode.com
Apparel Product Retailer
N.A.I.C.S.: 458110

Sym SAS (1)
139 rue de la Belle Etoile ZAC Paris Nord II, 95948, Roissy-en-France, France
Tel.: (33) 1 48 17 20 99
Web Site: http://www.sym.fr
Apparel Product Retailer
N.A.I.C.S.: 458110

STEILMANN SE
Industriestr 42, Bergkamen, 59192, Germany
Tel.: (49) 23897830
STE—(DUS)
Holding Company
N.A.I.C.S.: 551112
Michele Puller *(Chm & CEO)*

STEINBACH DODGE CHRYSLER LTD.
208 Main Street, Steinbach, R5G 1Y6, MB, Canada
Tel.: (204) 326-4461
Web Site: http://www.steinbachdodge.ca
Year Founded: 1982
Rev.: $21,083,184
Emp.: 45
New & Used Car Dealers
N.A.I.C.S.: 441110

STEINBEIS PAPIER GLUCKSTADT GMBH & CO. KG
Stadtstrasse 20, 25348, Gluckstadt, Germany
Tel.: (49) 41249110   De
Web Site: http://www.stp.de
Year Founded: 1911
Rev.: $217,836,900
Emp.: 321
Recycled Paper Mfr
N.A.I.C.S.: 322120
Michael Soffge *(CEO)*

Subsidiaries:

Steinbeis Temming Papier GmbH & Co. (1)
Statstrasse 2-14, Gluckstadt, 25348, Germany
Tel.: (49) 412491101
Web Site: http://www.stp.de
Sales Range: $125-149.9 Million
Recycled Paper
N.A.I.C.S.: 322120
Michael Hunold *(Mng Dir)*

STEINHOFF INTERNATIONAL HOLDINGS N.V.

Steinhoff International Holdings N.V.—(Continued)

STEINHOFF INTERNATIONAL HOLDINGS N.V.
Building B2 Vineyard Office Park Cnr Adam Tas and Devon Valley Road, Stellenbosch, 7600, South Africa
Tel.: (27) 21 808 0700 **NL**
Web Site:
http://www.steinhoffnational.com
Year Founded: 2015
SNH—(DEU)
Rev.: $627,238,390
Assets: $1,029,181,320
Liabilities: $813,506,290
Net Worth: $215,675,030
Earnings: ($57,995,500)
Emp.: 90,731
Fiscal Year-end: 09/30/21
Holding Company; Bedding, Case Goods, Lounge Furniture & Household Goods Mfr & Distr
N.A.I.C.S.: 551112
Louis Du Preez (Mng Dir, Member-Mgmt Bd & Comml Dir)

Subsidiaries:

Abacus Insurance Limited (1)
171 Katherine Street Building 3, Sandown, Sandton, 2031, South Africa
Tel.: (27) 87 654 8222
Web Site: https://www.abacus-insurance.co.za
Insurance Services
N.A.I.C.S.: 524298

Ackermans Proprietary Limited (1)
4 Produksie St Kuilsriver Industrial, Cape Town, 7580, South Africa
Tel.: (27) 21 928 1040
Web Site: https://www.ackermans.co.za
Clothing Distr
N.A.I.C.S.: 458110
Thabo Moyo (Mgr)

DCLSA Proprietary Limited (1)
119 Landmarks Avenue, Samrand Business Park, Centurion, 0187, South Africa
Tel.: (27) 10 591 3988
Web Site: https://www.dclsa.co.za
Lockset Product Distr
N.A.I.C.S.: 423710

Fantastic Holdings Limited (1)
62 Hume Hwy, Chullora, 2190, NSW, Australia
Tel.: (61) 287172600
Sales Range: $300-349.9 Million
Wooden Furniture Mfr
N.A.I.C.S.: 337211
Debra Singh (CEO-Retail-Grp)

Subsidiary (Domestic):

FHL Distribution Centre Pty Ltd (1)
10-28 Bildela Street, Villawood, 2163, NSW, Australia
Tel.: (61) 287172600
Web Site:
http://www.fantasticholdings.com.au
Emp.: 75
Household Furniture Distr
N.A.I.C.S.: 423210
Stephen Heath (Gen Mgr)

Fantastic Furniture (Licensing) Pty Ltd (2)
62 Hume Highway, PO Box 445, Chullora, 2190, NSW, Australia
Tel.: (61) 287138713
Web Site:
http://www.fantasticfurniture.com.au
Furniture Retailer
N.A.I.C.S.: 449110

Fantastic Furniture Limited (2)
62 Hume Highway, Chullora, 2091, NSW, Australia
Tel.: (61) 287138713
Web Site:
http://www.fantasticfurniture.com.au
Sales Range: $25-49.9 Million
Emp.: 90
Furniture Retailer Distr
N.A.I.C.S.: 449110

Fantastic Furniture Pty Limited (2)
62 Hume Highway, Chullora, 2091, NSW, Australia
Tel.: (61) 287082600
Furniture Retailer
N.A.I.C.S.: 449110

Subsidiary (Non-US):

Original Mattress Factory Pty Ltd (2)
Web Site: http://www.omf.net.au
Sales Range: $25-49.9 Million
Emp.: 4
Mattress Retailer
N.A.I.C.S.: 449110

Subsidiary (Domestic):

Plush - Think Sofas Pty Ltd (2)
419 Townsend Street, Albury, 2640, NSW, Australia
Tel.: (61) 260413311
Web Site: https://www.plush.com.au
Sales Range: $50-74.9 Million
Emp.: 5
Sofa Retailer
N.A.I.C.S.: 423210

Royal Comfort Bedding Pty Ltd (2)
1333 The Horsley Drive, Wetherill Park, Sydney, 2164, NSW, Australia
Tel.: (61) 287876600
Mattress Mfr
N.A.I.C.S.: 337910

G&G Furniture Imports Pty. Ltd. (2)
2 Harvey Road, PO Box 4227, Kings Park, Marayong, 2148, NSW, Australia
Tel.: (61) 29 068 7840
Web Site: https://ggfurniture.com.au
Furniture Product Distr
N.A.I.C.S.: 423210
Philip Tyler (Mng Dir)

Greenlit Brands Proprietary Limited (1)
Level 4 1 Epping Road, North Ryde, Australia
Tel.: (61) 298829000
Web Site:
https://www.greenlitbrands.com.au
Household Goods Mfr & Distr
N.A.I.C.S.: 335220

Lodge Stock & Barrel Proprietary Limited (1)
232-15th Road Between George and Olifantsfontein Roads, Randjespark Midrand, Johannesburg, 1685, South Africa
Tel.: (27) 11 452 8658
Web Site: https://lodgestockandbarrel.co.za
Logistic Services
N.A.I.C.S.: 541614

MacNeil George Proprietary Limited (1)
18 Ring Street George Industrial, George, 6536, South Africa
Tel.: (27) 44 874 2632
Sanitary Ware Product Mfr & Distr
N.A.I.C.S.: 322291

MacNeil Proprietary Limited (1)
Kapbro Industrial Park Bedford Street Dudley Street, Gqeberha, Port Elizabeth, South Africa
Tel.: (27) 41 451 0400
Sanitary Ware Product Mfr & Distr
N.A.I.C.S.: 322291

Maplewave Holdings (Pty) Ltd. (1)
Longmeadow Business Estate Extension 7 12 Platinum Drive, Johannesburg, 1609, South Africa
Tel.: (27) 10 003 2440
Software Development Services
N.A.I.C.S.: 541511

Mattress Firm Group Inc. (1)
10201 S Main St, Houston, TX 77025
Web Site: https://www.mattressfirm.com
Rev.: $4,392,900,000
Assets: $3,539,100,000
Liabilities: $3,461,900,000
Net Worth: $77,200,000
Earnings: ($165,100,000)
Emp.: 8,600
Fiscal Year-end: 09/28/2021
Holding Company
N.A.I.C.S.: 551112

John W. Eck (Pres & CEO)

Online Poundshop Limited (1)
Unit 8 Parkway Pacific Ave, Wednesbury, United Kingdom
Tel.: (44) 1216472569
Web Site: https://www.poundshop.com
Online Shopping Services
N.A.I.C.S.: 561439

Pepco Group Limited (1)
Unit B 120 Weston Street, London, SE1 4GS, United Kingdom
Tel.: (44) 203 735 9210
Web Site: https://www.pepcogroup.eu
Grocery Product Distr
N.A.I.C.S.: 445110
Richard Burrows (Chm)

Pepco Slovakia s.r.o. (1)
Ul Nevadzova 6, 821 01, Bratislava, Slovakia
Tel.: (421) 23 305 6067
Web Site: https://pepco.sk
Clothing Store Distr
N.A.I.C.S.: 458110

Pepkor Holdings Limited (1)
36 Stellenberg Road, Parow, 7493, South Africa
Tel.: (27) 219294800
Web Site: https://www.pepkor.co.za
Rev.: $4,760,239,680
Assets: $5,921,980,400
Liabilities: $2,705,954,020
Net Worth: $3,216,026,380
Earnings: ($69,708,800)
Emp.: 50,000
Fiscal Year-end: 09/30/2023
Discount, Value & Specialized Goods Retailer
N.A.I.C.S.: 423990
Leon Lourens (CEO)

Poundland Stores Ltd. (1)
Poundland CSC Midland Road, Walsall, WS1 3TX, United Kingdom
Tel.: (44) 333 234 1877
Web Site: https://www.poundland.co.uk
Grocery Product Distr
N.A.I.C.S.: 445110
Barry Williams (Mng Dir)

Steinhoff International Holdings Limited (1)
Building B2 Vineyard Office Park Cnr Adam Tas Devon Valley Road, Stellenbosch, 7600, South Africa (100%)
Tel.: (27) 218080700
Web Site:
https://www.steinhoffinternational.com
Holding Company; Bedding, Case Goods, Lounge Furniture & Household Goods Mfr & Distr
N.A.I.C.S.: 551112

Steinhoff Investment Holdings Limited (1)
28 6th Street Wynberg, Sandton, 2090, Johannesburg, South Africa (100%)
Tel.: (27) 114453000
Holding Company
N.A.I.C.S.: 551112

Affiliate (Domestic):

KAP Limited (2)
Unit G7 Stellenpark Business Park Cnr R44 and School Road, Jamestown, Stellenbosch, 7600, South Africa (42.98%)
Tel.: (27) 218080900
Web Site: http://www.kap.co.za
Rev.: $1,909,007,170
Assets: $2,013,126,150
Liabilities: $1,211,423,650
Net Worth: $801,702,500
Earnings: $120,494,180
Emp.: 19,425
Fiscal Year-end: 06/30/2022
Investment Holding Company
N.A.I.C.S.: 551112
Ugo Frigerio (CEO-Automotive Components Div)

Subsidiary (Domestic):

Feltex Automotive (Pty) Ltd. (3)
291 Paisley Road Jacobs, Durban, 4026, Kwazulu-Natal, South Africa
Tel.: (27) 314604200
Web Site: https://www.feltex.co.za

INTERNATIONAL PUBLIC

Automotive Acoustic & Trim Components Supplier
N.A.I.C.S.: 423120
Ugo Frigerio (Mng Dir)

Joint Venture (Domestic):

Autoneum Feltex (Pty) Ltd. (4)
Automotive Supplier Park Unit A9 30 Helium Road, Rosslyn, Pretoria, 0200, Gauteng, South Africa (49%)
Tel.: (27) 873546671
Motor Vehicle Interior Product Mfr
N.A.I.C.S.: 336360

Unit (Domestic):

Feltex Automotive (Pty) Ltd. - Feltex Foam (4)
291 Paisley Rd, Jacobs, Durban, 4026, South Africa
Tel.: (27) 314604200
Web Site: http://www.feltex.co.za
Polyurethane Foam Mfr
N.A.I.C.S.: 326150

Subsidiary (Domestic):

Feltex Automotive Trim Ltd (4)
291 Paisley Rd, Jacobs, Durban, 4026, Kwazulu-Natal, South Africa
Tel.: (27) 314604200
Automotive Acoustic & Trim Components Supplier
N.A.I.C.S.: 423930
Robert Gooch (Gen Mgr)

Feltex Fehrer (Pty) Ltd. (4)
291 Paisley Rd, Jacobs, Durban, 4026, I, South Africa
Tel.: (27) 314604200
Web Site: http://www.feltex.co.za
Moulded Polyurethane Products Mfr
N.A.I.C.S.: 326150
Andrew Pillay (Gen Mgr)

Subsidiary (Domestic):

Glodina (Pty) Ltd. (3)
1 Anderson Road Hammarsdale, PO Box 12, Hammarsdale, 3700, KwaZulu-Natal, South Africa
Tel.: (27) 317367600
Web Site: http://www.glodina.co.za
Towels Mfr
N.A.I.C.S.: 313210
Grant Robertson (CFO)

PG Bison Holdings (Pty) Limited (3)
Brakpan & Lonie Roads, Boksburg, 1459, Gauteng, South Africa
Tel.: (27) 118975200
Web Site: https://www.pgbison.co.za
Holding Company
N.A.I.C.S.: 551112
Elize King (Mgr-Risk)

Safripol (Pty) Ltd (3)
The Campus Business Park 57 Sloane Street, Private Bag X52, Bryanston, 2191, South Africa
Tel.: (27) 115754549
Web Site: http://www.safripol.com
Plastic Mfr
N.A.I.C.S.: 325211
Willem Els (CFO)

Unitrans Holdings (Pty) Ltd. (3)
Block W Greenford Office Park Punters Way, Kenilworth, 7700, South Africa (100%)
Tel.: (27) 217620061
Web Site: https://unitransafrica.com
Emp.: 8,500
Holding Company
N.A.I.C.S.: 551112
Adriaan De Beer (CFO)

Subsidiary (Domestic):

Unitrans Passenger (Pty) Limited (4)
40 Lepus Road Crown Mine, Wynberg, Johannesburg, 2092, South Africa
Tel.: (27) 112498700
Bus Transportation Services
N.A.I.C.S.: 485113

Unitrans Supply Chain Solutions (Pty) Ltd. (4)
14 Punters Way Kenilworth, Cape Town, 7708, South Africa

AND PRIVATE COMPANIES

Tel.: (27) 217620061
Total Supply Chain Logistics Services
N.A.I.C.S.: 541614

Division (Domestic):

Unitrans Freight & Logistics
Division (5)
6 Eastern Service Road Eastgate Ext 3, Sandton, 2090, South Africa
Tel.: (27) 11 445 5000
Specialized Freight Transportation, Warehousing, Logistics & Supply Chain Services
N.A.I.C.S.: 488510
Bruce Arnold (CFO)

Subsidiary (US):

Mattress Firm, Inc. (2)
10201 S Main St, Houston, TX 77025
Tel.: (713) 923-1090
Web Site: https://www.mattressfirm.com
Distr & Retailer of Mattresses & Furniture
N.A.I.C.S.: 449110
Hendre Ackermann (CFO & COO)

Subsidiary (Domestic):

Sleep Experts Partners, L.P. (3)
5100 Belt Line Rd Ste 1052, Addison, TX 75254
Tel.: (469) 801-4000
Web Site: http://www.sleepexperts.com
Furniture Whslr & Mattress Whslr & Retailer
N.A.I.C.S.: 449110

Subsidiary (Non-US):

Poundland Group Limited (2)
Poundland CSC Midland Road, Willenhall West Midlands, Walsall, WS1 3TX, United Kingdom
Tel.: (44) 1215687000
Web Site: https://www.poundland.co.uk
Sales Range: $1-4.9 Billion
Holding Company; Discount Store Operator
N.A.I.C.S.: 551112
Andy Garbutt (Dir-Bus Dev)

Subsidiary (Domestic):

Poundland Limited (3)
23 New Road, Willenhall, WV13 2BG, W Midlands, United Kingdom
Tel.: (44) 1902601289
Web Site: http://www.poundland.co.uk
Discount Store Operator
N.A.I.C.S.: 455110
Austin Cooke (COO)

Subsidiary (Domestic):

Steinhoff Africa Holdings (Proprietary) Limited (2)
28 6th Street, Wynberg, Johannesburg, 2090, South Africa
Tel.: (27) 11 445 3080
Household Furniture Mfr
N.A.I.C.S.: 337121

Subsidiary (Domestic):

JD Group Limited (3)
6 Eastern Service Road, Sandton, 2090, South Africa
Tel.: (27) 114080408
Web Site: http://www.jdg.co.za
Emp.: 15,000
Holding Company; Furniture, Appliances & Electronics Retailer
N.A.I.C.S.: 551112

Pepkor Retail Limited (3)
36 Stellenberg Road, Parow, 7493, Industria, South Africa (100%)
Tel.: (27) 21 929 4800
Web Site: http://pepkor.co.za
Holding Company; Apparel & Accessory Stores
N.A.I.C.S.: 458110

Subsidiary (Non-US):

Best & Less Pty. Limited (4)
657-673 Parramatta Road, Leichhardt, 2040, NSW, Australia
Web Site: http://www.bestandless.com.au
Apparel Store Owner & Operator
N.A.I.C.S.: 458110
Rodney Orrock (CEO)

Subsidiary (Domestic):

John Craig (Pty) Ltd. (4)
43 Bradford Rd, Bedfordview, 2007, Gauteng, South Africa
Tel.: (27) 100063268
Web Site: https://www.johncraig.co.za
Men's Clothing & Accessory Stores
N.A.I.C.S.: 458110
Lily Moreira (Mng Dir)

Pep Stores (Pty) Ltd (4)
Radnor St Parow Industrial, Parow, 7500, South Africa
Tel.: (27) 219372300
Web Site: https://www.pepstores.com
Clothing Accessories Stores
N.A.I.C.S.: 458110

Subsidiary (Non-US):

Pepco Poland Sp. Z o.o. (4)
ul Strzeszynska 73A, 60-479, Poznan, Poland
Tel.: (48) 616684300
Web Site: https://pepco.pl
Emp.: 12,000
Clothing & Household Goods Store Operator
N.A.I.C.S.: 458110
Janusz Ratajczak (Officer-Health & Safety)

Postie Plus Group Limited (4)
Level 1 646 Great South Road, Ellerslie, 1051, Auckland, New Zealand
Tel.: (64) 800767843
Web Site: https://www.postie.co.nz
Family Clothing Stores
N.A.I.C.S.: 458110

Subsidiary (Domestic):

Shoe City (Pty) Ltd. (4)
Shop 119 Canal Walk Shopping Centre Century Boulevard St, Milnerton, 7441, Western Cape, South Africa
Tel.: (27) 215553053
Web Site: http://www.shoecity.co.za
Shoes & Accessories Whslr
N.A.I.C.S.: 459999

Subsidiary (Non-US):

Steinhoff Asia Pacific Holdings Proprietary Limited (2)
Level 4 1 Epping Road, North Ryde, 2133, NSW, Australia
Tel.: (61) 98829100
Web Site: http://www.freedom.com.au
Furniture Retailer
N.A.I.C.S.: 449110

Steinhoff Finance Holding GmbH (2)
Rennweg 77, Brunn am Gebirge, 2345, Austria
Tel.: (43) 2236316710
Holding Company
N.A.I.C.S.: 551112

Subsidiary (Domestic):

Steinhoff Europe AG (3)
Rennweg 77, Brunn, 2345, Austria
Tel.: (43) 2236316710
Holding Company
N.A.I.C.S.: 551112

Subsidiary (Non-US):

Abra S.A. (4)
ul Lagiewnicka 33a, 30-417, Krakow, Poland
Tel.: (48) 122907150
Web Site: https://www.abra-meble.pl
Furnishings & Furnitures Retailer
N.A.I.C.S.: 449110
James D. Robinson IV (Co-Founder)

Relyon Group Limited (4)
Tel.: (44) 1823667501
Web Site: http://www.relyon.co.uk
Upholstered Household Furniture Mfr
N.A.I.C.S.: 337121

Subsidiary (Non-US):

Relyon Limited (5)
Tel.: (44) 1823 667501
Web Site: http://www.relyon.co.uk
Household Furniture Mfr
N.A.I.C.S.: 337121

Subsidiary (Non-US):

Steinhoff Service GmbH (4)
Langebruegger Strasse 5, 26655, Westerstede, Germany (100%)
Tel.: (49) 4488580
Web Site: http://www.steinhoff-moebel.de
Holding Company
N.A.I.C.S.: 551112
Duke Schreiber (Mng Dir)

Steinhoff UK Retail Limited (4)
Festival House Jessop Avenue, Cheltenham, GL50 3SH, Glos, United Kingdom
Tel.: (44) 3448472626
Web Site: http://www.sukf.co.uk
Furniture Retailer
N.A.I.C.S.: 423210
John Henry Robins (Sec)

Subsidiary (Non-US):

Bensons for Beds (5)
Tel.: (44) 3332226800
Web Site: http://www.bensonsforbeds.co.uk
Bed Retailer
N.A.I.C.S.: 449110
Chris Howell (Chm)

Unitrans Asia Pacific Pty. Ltd. (1)
2-4 Harvey Road, Kings Park, 2148, NSW, Australia
Tel.: (61) 28 822 8822
Web Site: https://unitrans.com.au
Warehousing Services
N.A.I.C.S.: 493110
Wayne Twigge (CFO)

STEINIGKE SHOWTECHNIC GMBH
Andreas-Bauer-Str 5, Waldbuttelbrunn, 97297, Wurzburg, Germany
Tel.: (49) 9314061700
Web Site: http://www.steinigke.de
Year Founded: 1979
Rev.: $19,820,850
Emp.: 170
Musical Instrument Distr
N.A.I.C.S.: 459140
Bernd Steinigke (Mng Dir)

STEL HOLDINGS LIMITED
24/1624 Bristow Road, Willingdon Island, Cochin, 682 003, Kerala, India
Tel.: (91) 4846624335 IN
Web Site: https://www.stelholdings.com
Year Founded: 1990
STEL—(NSE)
Rev.: $1,674,485
Assets: $106,816,403
Liabilities: $653,426
Net Worth: $106,162,976
Earnings: $1,181,374
Emp.: 3
Fiscal Year-end: 03/31/21
Tea Distr
N.A.I.C.S.: 424490
Sivarama Neelakantan Krishnan (CFO)

STELAR METALS LIMITED
22 Greenhill Road, Wayville, 5034, SA, Australia
Tel.: (61) 883727881 AU
Web Site: https://www.stelarmetals.com.au
Year Founded: 2021
SLB—(ASX)
Rev.: $31,908
Assets: $4,744,511
Liabilities: $155,525
Net Worth: $4,588,986
Earnings: ($619,334)
Fiscal Year-end: 06/30/23
Metal Exploration Services
N.A.I.C.S.: 213114
Colin Skidmore (CEO)

STELLA CHEMIFA CORPORATION

STELLA INTERNATIONAL HOLDINGS LIMITED

Meiji Yasuda Seimei Osaka Midosuji Building 10F 4-1-1 Fushimi-machi, Chuo-ku, Osaka, 541-0044, Japan
Tel.: (81) 647071511
Web Site: https://www.stella-chemifa.co.jp
Year Founded: 1916
4109—(TKS)
Rev.: $201,248,060
Assets: $387,464,980
Liabilities: $93,313,370
Net Worth: $294,151,610
Earnings: $12,195,450
Fiscal Year-end: 03/31/24
Chemical Products Mfr
N.A.I.C.S.: 325998
Kiyonori Saka (Sr Mng Exec Officer)

Subsidiaries:

STELLA PHARMA CORPORATION (1)
ORIX Koraibashi Bldg 5F 3-2-7 Koraibashi, Chuo-ku, Osaka, 541-0043, Japan
Tel.: (81) 647071516
Web Site: https://www.stella-pharma.co.jp
Pharmaceuticals Product Mfr
N.A.I.C.S.: 325412

Stella Chemifa Corporation - Izumi Factory (1)
1-41 Rinkai-cho, Izumiotsu, 595-0075, Osaka, Japan
Tel.: (81) 725216801
Chemical Products Mfr
N.A.I.C.S.: 325998

Stella Chemifa Corporation - Kitakyushu Factory (1)
1-1 Shiroishi Kurosaki, Yahatanishi-ku, Kitakyushu, 806-0004, Fukuoka, Japan
Tel.: (81) 938836417
Chemical Products Mfr
N.A.I.C.S.: 325998

Stella Chemifa Corporation - Sanpo Factory (1)
7-227 Kaisan-cho, Sakai-ku, Sakai, 590-0982, Osaka, Japan
Tel.: (81) 722293101
Chemical Products Mfr
N.A.I.C.S.: 325998

Stella Express (Singapore) Pte Ltd. (1)
36 Robinson Rd Ste 12-02 City House, Singapore, 68877, Singapore
Tel.: (65) 62 257 911
Logistics Consulting Servies
N.A.I.C.S.: 541614

STELLA HOLDINGS BERHAD
A-13A Pusat Komersial Arena Bintang Jalan Zuhal U5/178 Seksyen U5, 40150, Shah Alam, Selangor, Malaysia
Tel.: (60) 327794003 MY
Web Site: https://www.stella-holdings.com.my
Year Founded: 1981
VARIA—(KLS)
Rev.: $6,211,733
Assets: $14,818,542
Liabilities: $6,981,987
Net Worth: $7,836,555
Earnings: ($2,408,961)
Emp.: 56
Fiscal Year-end: 03/31/23
Construction Engineering Services
N.A.I.C.S.: 541330
Siew Yen Yeoh (Sec)

Subsidiaries:

Paramount Ventures Sdn. Bhd. (1)
A-13A Pusat Komersial Arena Bintang Jalan Zuhal U5/178 Seksyen U5, 40150, Shah Alam, Selangor, Malaysia
Tel.: (60) 378472900
Property Development Services
N.A.I.C.S.: 531311

STELLA INTERNATIONAL HOLDINGS LIMITED

STELLA INTERNATIONAL HOLDINGS LIMITED — INTERNATIONAL PUBLIC

Stella International Holdings Limited—(Continued)
Flat C 20/F MG Tower 133 Hoi Bun Road, Kowloon, China (Hong Kong)
Tel.: (852) 29561339
Web Site: http://www.stella.com.hk
1836—(HKG)
Rev.: $1,630,771,000
Assets: $1,258,083,000
Liabilities: $242,134,000
Net Worth: $1,015,949,000
Earnings: $117,187,000
Emp.: 42,500
Fiscal Year-end: 12/31/22
Footwear Manufacturing
N.A.I.C.S.: 316210
Stephen Lo-Jen Chi *(CEO)*

STELLA MCCARTNEY LIMITED
3 Olaf Street, London, W11 4BE, United Kingdom
Tel.: (44) 2078982710   UK
Web Site:
http://www.stellamccartney.com
Year Founded: 2001
Luxury Goods Retailer
N.A.I.C.S.: 456120
Stella Nina McCartney *(Founder, Owner & Designer)*

Subsidiaries:

Stella McCartney America Inc. (1)
112 Green St, New York, NY 10012
Tel.: (212) 255-1556
Web Site: http://www.stellamccartney.com
Womens Clothing Online Retail Store Operating Services
N.A.I.C.S.: 458110

Stella McCartney France SAS (1)
114-121 Galerie de Valois Jardins du Palais Royal, 75001, Paris, France
Tel.: (33) 1 47 03 03 80
Web Site: http://www.stellamccartney.com
Fashion Apparel & Clothing Distr
N.A.I.C.S.: 458110

Stella McCartney Italia Srl (1)
Via Don Lorenzo Perosi 6, Scandicci, 50018, Florence, Italy
Tel.: (39) 055759221
Web Site: http://www.stellamccartney.com
Footwear Retailer
N.A.I.C.S.: 458210

STELLA-JONES, INC.
3100 de la Cote-Vertu Boulevard Ste 300, Saint Laurent, H4R 2J8, QC, Canada
Tel.: (514) 934-8666   Ca
Web Site: https://www.stella-jones.com
Year Founded: 1992
SJ—(TSX)
Rev.: $2,151,270,000
Assets: $2,084,776,200
Liabilities: $952,034,760
Net Worth: $1,132,741,440
Earnings: $177,577,560
Emp.: 2,402
Fiscal Year-end: 12/31/21
Pressure Treated Wood Products Mfr
N.A.I.C.S.: 321999
Brian McManus *(Pres & CEO)*

Subsidiaries:

Cahaba Timber, Inc. (1)
PO Box 160, Brierfield, AL 35035
Tel.: (205) 926-9888
Web Site: https://cahabatimber.com
Sales Range: $1-9.9 Million
Emp.: 50
Wood Products Mfr
N.A.I.C.S.: 321999
Kermit L. Stephens *(Pres)*

Guelph Utility Pole Company Ltd. (1)
7818 Wellington Road 22 R R 5, PO Box 154, Guelph, N1H 6J2, ON, Canada (100%)
Tel.: (519) 822-3901
Web Site: http://www.guelphpole.com
Sales Range: $25-49.9 Million
Emp.: 50
Wood Preservation
N.A.I.C.S.: 321114

McFarland Cascade Holdings, Inc. (1)
1640 E Marc Ave, Tacoma, WA 98421
Tel.: (253) 572-3033
Web Site: http://www.mcfarlandcascade.com
Sales Range: $100-124.9 Million
Emp.: 250
Holding Company; Lumber & Wood Products Mfr
N.A.I.C.S.: 551112

Subsidiary (Domestic):

Lufkin Creosoting Co., Inc. (2)
5865 US Hwy 69 S, Lufkin, TX 75901
Tel.: (936) 634-4923
Rev.: $34,200,000
Emp.: 81
Fiscal Year-end: 12/31/2015
Wood Preservation Services
N.A.I.C.S.: 321114
David F. Vines *(Pres & CEO)*

Plant (Domestic):

McFarland Cascade - Sheridan (2)
22125 Rock Creek Rd, Sheridan, OR 97378
Tel.: (503) 843-2122
Sales Range: $10-24.9 Million
Emp.: 60
Wood Treatment & Preservation
N.A.I.C.S.: 321114
Roland Mueller *(Mgr-Production)*

McFarland Cascade - Silver Springs (2)
1680 E Spruce Ave, Silver Springs, NV 89429
Tel.: (775) 577-2000
Web Site: http://www.mcfarlandcascade.com
Sales Range: $10-24.9 Million
Emp.: 45
Wood Treatment & Preservation
N.A.I.C.S.: 321114

Subsidiary (Domestic):

McFarland Cascade Pole & Lumber Company (2)
1640 E Marc St, Tacoma, WA 98421 (100%)
Tel.: (253) 572-3033
Web Site: http://www.ldm.com
Sales Range: $125-149.9 Million
Poles, Lumber & Wood Products
N.A.I.C.S.: 321113

Stella-Jones Canada, Inc. (1)
4661 60th Street SE, Salmon Arm, V1E 1X2, BC, Canada (100%)
Tel.: (250) 832-1180
Web Site: http://www.stella-jones.com
Sales Range: $25-49.9 Million
Emp.: 17
Miscellaneous Wood Product Mfr
N.A.I.C.S.: 321999

Stella-Jones Corp. - Bangor (1)
W1038 County Rd U, Bangor, WI 54614
Tel.: (608) 486-2700
Web Site: http://www.stella-jones.com
Sales Range: $25-49.9 Million
Emp.: 50
Miscellaneous Wood Product Mfr
N.A.I.C.S.: 321999

Stella-Jones Corp. - Eloy (1)
850 W Chambers St, Eloy, AZ 85131
Tel.: (520) 466-7801
Emp.: 40
Wood Treatment & Preservation
N.A.I.C.S.: 321114

Unit (Domestic):

Stella-Jones Corp. - Livingston (2)
1355 State Hwy Loop 116, Livingston, TX 77351
Tel.: (936) 398-5745
Emp.: 20
Wood Incising, End-Plating & Cross-Tie Manufacturing
N.A.I.C.S.: 321114
Yancey Long *(Reg Mgr)*

Stella-Jones Corp. - Montevallo (1)
1051 Hwy 25 S, Montevallo, AL 35115-0372
Tel.: (205) 679-4005
Sales Range: $50-74.9 Million
Emp.: 100
Mfr & Distr of Creosote & Borate-Treated Crossties, Switch Ties, Tie Plugs & Bridge Timbers
N.A.I.C.S.: 321114

The Burke-Parsons-Bowlby Corporation (1)
1315 S Church St, Ripley, WV 25271
Tel.: (304) 372-2211
Web Site: http://www.bpbcorp.com
Pressure Treated Wood Products Mfr
N.A.I.C.S.: 321999

Wood Preservers, Inc. (1)
15939 Historyland Hwy, Warsaw, VA 22572
Tel.: (804) 333-4022
Web Site: https://www.woodpreservers.com
Wood & Lumber Whslr
N.A.I.C.S.: 321114

STELLANT SECURITIES (INDIA) LIMITED
305 Regent Chambers Jamnalal Bajaj Marg Nariman Point, Churchgate, Mumbai, 400 021, India
Tel.: (91) 2222021824
Web Site:
https://www.stellantsecurities.com
526071—(BOM)
Rev.: $18,920
Assets: $34,147
Liabilities: $3,417
Net Worth: $30,730
Earnings: ($17,877)
Emp.: 2
Fiscal Year-end: 03/31/23
Securities Brokerage Services
N.A.I.C.S.: 523150
Kalpesh Fifadra *(CFO)*

STELLANTIS N.V.
Taurusavenue 1, 2132 LS, Hoofddorp, Netherlands
Tel.: (31) 203421707   Nl
Web Site: https://www.stellantis.com
Year Founded: 2014
STLA—(NYSE)
Rev.: $204,558,601,338
Assets: $218,139,434,492
Liabilities: $129,514,353,551
Net Worth: $88,625,080,941
Earnings: $20,100,366,933
Emp.: 258,275
Fiscal Year-end: 12/31/23
Holding Company; Automobile & Motor Vehicle Components Designer, Mfr & Whslr
N.A.I.C.S.: 551112
Richard Schwarzwald *(Chief Customer Experience Officer)*

Subsidiaries:

AC Austro Car Handelsgesellschaft mbh & Co. (1)
Breitenfurter Strase 142-144, 1230, Vienna, Austria
Tel.: (43) 180 12 10
New Car Dealers
N.A.I.C.S.: 441110

Automotive Lighting Reutlingen GmbH (1)
Tubinger Str 123, Reutlingen, 72770, Germany
Tel.: (49) 7121 35 6000
Web Site: http://www.al-lighting.de
Rev.: $2,378,502,000
Emp.: 13,480
Automotive Lighting Equipment Mfr
N.A.I.C.S.: 336320
E. Ferrari *(Pres)*

Subsidiary (Domestic):

Automotive Lighting Brotterode GmbH (2)
Liebensteiner Str 36, 98596, Brotterode-Trusetal, Germany
Tel.: (49) 36840830
Web Site: http://www.al-lighting.de
Automotive Lighting Equipment Mfr
N.A.I.C.S.: 336320

Subsidiary (Non-US):

Automotive Lighting Italia S.p.A. (2)
Via Cavallo 18, Venaria Reale, 10078, Torino, Italy
Tel.: (39) 011 6870 111
Web Site: http://www.al-lighting.com
Lighting Equipment Mfr
N.A.I.C.S.: 336320

Subsidiary (Non-US):

Automotive Lighting Rear Lamps France S.a.s. (3)
Z I des Manteaux, 89330, Saint-Julien-du-Sault, France
Tel.: (33) 3 866339 39
Web Site: http://www.al-lighting.de
Automotive Lighting Equipment Mfr
N.A.I.C.S.: 336320

Subsidiary (Non-US):

Automotive Lighting Japan K.K. (2)
Benex S-2 Building 8F 3-17-5 Shinyokohama, Kohoku-ku, Yokohama, 222-0033, Japan
Tel.: (81) 45 478 0045
Web Site: http://www.al-lighting.com
Sales Range: $25-49.9 Million
Emp.: 50
Automotive Lighting Equipment Mfr
N.A.I.C.S.: 336320

Automotive Lighting Polska Sp. z o.o. (2)
Ul Gen M Zaruskiego 11, 41-200, Sosnowiec, Poland
Tel.: (48) 32 2960 111
Web Site: http://www.al-lighting.de
Automotive Lighting Equipment Mfr
N.A.I.C.S.: 336320

Automotive Lighting S.R.O. (2)
Pavov 113, 586 01, Jihlava, Czech Republic
Tel.: (420) 567 562 601
Web Site: http://www.al-lighting.cz
Sales Range: $350-399.9 Million
Emp.: 2,000
Automotive Lighting Equipment Mfr
N.A.I.C.S.: 336320

Malaysian Automotive Lighting SDN. BHD (2)
Plot 45 Phase 4 Bayan Lepas Industrial Park, 11900, Bayan Lepas, Penang, Malaysia
Tel.: (60) 4 8206 000
Web Site: http://www.al-lighting.de
Automotive Lighting Equipment Mfr
N.A.I.C.S.: 336320

BMI S.p.A. (1)
Vle Brigata Bisagno 2, 16129, Genoa, Italy
Tel.: (39) 010534011
New Car Dealers
N.A.I.C.S.: 441110

Business Solutions S.p.A. (1)
Corso Marconi 10, 10125, Turin, Italy (100%)
Tel.: (39) 0110061911
Web Site: http://www.bsolutions.it
Sales Range: $200-249.9 Million
Emp.: 651
Human Resource Management & Consulting Services
N.A.I.C.S.: 541611

Subsidiary (Domestic):

Easy Drive S.r.l. (2)
Corso Marconi 10, 10125, Turin, Italy
Tel.: (39) 0110063341
Automobile Consulting Services
N.A.I.C.S.: 541611

Fiat Services S.p.A. (2)
Corso Giovanni Agnelli 200, 10135, Turin, Italy

STELLANTIS N.V.

Tel.: (39) 01100311111
Web Site: http://www.fiat.it
Sales Range: $100-124.9 Million
Emp.: 300
Automobile Outsourcing Services
N.A.I.C.S.: 541612

Subsidiary (Non-US):

Fiat Argentina S.A. (3)
Carlos Maria Della Paolera 299 25th floor,
Buenos Aires, Argentina
Tel.: (54) 8007778000
Web Site: https://www.fiat.com.ar
New Car Dealers
N.A.I.C.S.: 441110

Fiat Finance et Services S.A. (3)
Za Trappes Elancourt, Trappes, 78190,
Yvelines, France
Tel.: (33) 130169200
Financial Services
N.A.I.C.S.: 525990

Fiat GmbH (3)
Nicolaus-Otto-Str 4, Ulm, 89079, Baden-Wurttemberg, Germany
Tel.: (49) 73120740
Automobile Mfr
N.A.I.C.S.: 336110

Fiat Iberica S.A. (3)
Paseo de la Habana 74-A, Madrid, 28036,
Spain
Tel.: (34) 914572211
New Car Dealers
N.A.I.C.S.: 441110

Subsidiary (Domestic):

Fiat Information Technology, Excellence and Methods S.p.A. (3)
Via Plava 86, Turin, 10135, Italy
Tel.: (39) 0110057611
Software Development Services
N.A.I.C.S.: 541511

Subsidiary (Non-US):

Fiat Services Polska Sp. z o.o. (3)
Weglowa 72, Bielsko-Biala, Poland
Tel.: (48) 33 813 2242
Financial Management Services
N.A.I.C.S.: 523999

Subsidiary (Domestic):

Servizi e Attivita Doganali per l'Industria S.p.A. (3)
Corso Francesco Ferrucci 112/A, Turin,
10138, Italy
Tel.: (39) 0110057611
Freight Transportation Services
N.A.I.C.S.: 488510

Subsidiary (Non-US):

Sadi Polska-Agencja Celna Sp. z o.o. (4)
Ul Konwojowa 57, 43-346, Bielsko-Biala,
Poland
Tel.: (48) 33 813 53 23
Web Site: http://www.sadipolska.pl
Freight Transportation Services
N.A.I.C.S.: 488510

Subsidiary (Domestic):

Human Resources Services S.p.A. (2)
Via Marothetti 11, 10126, Turin,
Italy (100%)
Tel.: (39) 0110066111
Web Site: http://www.humanresourcesservices.it
Human Resouce Services
N.A.I.C.S.: 541611

Isvor Fiat S.C.p.A. (2)
Via Giacosa 38, 10125, Turin, Italy
Tel.: (39) 0110065773
Web Site: http://www.isvor.it
Technical Training & Consulting Services
N.A.I.C.S.: 611430

KeyG Consulting S.p.A. (2)
Corso Ferrucci 112/A, 10138, Turin, Italy
Tel.: (39) 0110058109
Web Site: http://www.keyg.it
Administrative & Management Consulting Services

N.A.I.C.S.: 541611

Sestrieres S.p.A. (2)
Piazza Agnelli 4, Sestriere, 10058, Turin,
Italy
Tel.: (39) 0122799411
Web Site: http://www.vialattea.it
Sales Range: $25-49.9 Million
Emp.: 50
Ski Complex Management Services
N.A.I.C.S.: 713940

Comau S.p.A. (1)
Via Rivalta 30, 10095, Grugliasco, Italy
Tel.: (39) 0116849111
Web Site: http://www.comau.com
Machine Tool & Production Systems Mfr
N.A.I.C.S.: 333310

Subsidiary (Non-US):

Comau (Kunshan) Automation Co. Ltd. (2)
No 232 Yuanfeng Road Kunshan Hi-Tech
Park, Kunshan, 215300, Jiangsu, China
Tel.: (86) 51236821000
Industrial Automation System Repair & Maintenance Services
N.A.I.C.S.: 811310

Comau (Shanghai) International Trading Co. Ltd. (2)
Room 402 Sanlian Building No 8 Huajing
Road, Songjiang Dist, Shanghai, 201601,
China
Tel.: (86) 2137616222
Automobile Parts Distr
N.A.I.C.S.: 423120

Comau Argentina S.A. (2)
Tel.: (54) 3514103311
Web Site: http://www.comau.com
Industrial Machinery Mfr
N.A.I.C.S.: 333998

Comau Deutschland GmbH (2)
Hugo-Eckener-Strasse 20, 50829, Cologne,
Germany
Tel.: (49) 221 76 0060
Web Site: http://www.comau.com
Industrial Automation Machinery Distr
N.A.I.C.S.: 423830

Comau France S.A.S. (2)
5-7 rue Albert Einstein, 78197, Trappes,
France
Tel.: (33) 1 30166100
Web Site: http://www.comau.com
Automotive Components Mfr
N.A.I.C.S.: 336390

Comau India Private Limited (2)
34Km Milestone - Pune-Nagar Rd, Shikrapur, Pune, 412 208, India
Tel.: (91) 2137678100
Sales Range: $75-99.9 Million
Industrial Automation Machinery Mfr
N.A.I.C.S.: 333248
Aman Garg *(Mgr-Robotics & Simulation)*

Subsidiary (US):

Comau Pico Holdings Corporation (2)
21000 Telegraph Rd, Southfield, MI 48033
Tel.: (248) 353-8888
Welding & Soldering Equipment Mfr
N.A.I.C.S.: 333992
Riccardo Tarantini *(CEO)*

Subsidiary (Domestic):

Comau Inc. (3)
21000 Telegraph Rd, Southfield, MI 48033
Tel.: (248) 353-8888
Web Site: http://www.comau.com
Welding & Soldering Equipment Mfr
N.A.I.C.S.: 333992

Subsidiary (Non-US):

Comau Pico Mexico S.de R.l. de C.V. (2)
Av Acceso Lotes 12 Y 13, Tepotzotlan,
Mexico
Tel.: (52) 5558996900
Automobile Parts Mfr
N.A.I.C.S.: 336390

Subsidiary (Domestic):

Comau Pico Pitex S.de R.L. C.V (3)

Av Acceso Lotes 12 y 13 Fracc Ind El Trebol 2 Secc, Tepotzotlan, 54610, Mexico
Tel.: (52) 55 5899 69 00
Automobile Parts Mfr
N.A.I.C.S.: 336390

Comau Pico Trebol S.de R.l. de C.V. (3)
Av Acceso Lotes 12 Y 13, Tepotzotlan,
54610, Mexico
Tel.: (52) 5558996900
Sales Range: $150-199.9 Million
Emp.: 300
Real Estate Development Services
N.A.I.C.S.: 531390
Luca Gandino *(Gen Mgr)*

Comau Pico Iaisa S.de R.L. de C.V. (3)
Av Acceso Lotes 12 Y 13, Tepotzotlan,
54610, Mexico
Tel.: (52) 5558996900
Business Management Consulting Services
N.A.I.C.S.: 541618

Subsidiary (Non-US):

Comau Romania S.R.L. (2)
Calea Borsului 53 B, 410605, Oradea, Bihor, Romania
Tel.: (40) 259414769
Sales Range: $75-99.9 Million
Emp.: 450
Automotive Welding Equipment Mfr
N.A.I.C.S.: 333992

Comau Russia OOO (2)
Street SH-2 2/7 SEZ Alabuga, The Republic of Tatarstan, 423600, Yelabuga, Russia
Tel.: (7) 8555752209
Web Site: http://www.comau.com
Automotive Components Mfr
N.A.I.C.S.: 336390

Comau Service Systems S.L. (2)
Avenida Aragon 402, 28022, Madrid, Spain
Tel.: (34) 913252851
Sales Range: $25-49.9 Million
Emp.: 1
Automotive Repair & Maintenance Services
N.A.I.C.S.: 811111

Comau U.K. Limited (2)
10 Midland Road, Luton, LU2 0HR, Bedfordshire, United Kingdom
Tel.: (44) 1582 817600
Web Site: http://www.comau.com
Industrial Automation Machinery Distr
N.A.I.C.S.: 423830

Ergom do Brasil Ltda (1)
Rodovia MG 431 - Km 51 7, Itauna, 35680-142, Minas Gerais, Brazil
Tel.: (55) 37 3243 4400
Web Site: http://www.ergom.com.br
Automobile Parts Mfr
N.A.I.C.S.: 336390

FCA Australia Pty. Ltd. (1)
437 Plummer Street, Port Melbourne, 3207,
VIC, Australia
Tel.: (61) 29 284 9749
Web Site: https://www.fiatchrysler.com.au
Automobile Mfr
N.A.I.C.S.: 336110

FCA Mexico, S.A. de C.V. (1)
Prol Paseo de La Reforma 1240 Desarrollo
Santa Fe, Distrito Federal, 05348, Mexico,
Mexico
Tel.: (52) 555 081 3000
Web Site: https://www.fcamexico.com.mx
Automobile Mfr
N.A.I.C.S.: 336110

Fiat Finance S.p.A. (1)
Via Nizza 250, 10126, Turin, Italy
Tel.: (39) 011 006 3710
Treasury Services for Fiat Group Companies
N.A.I.C.S.: 525990

Subsidiary (US):

Fiat Chrysler Finance North America, Inc. (2)
7 Times Sq Tower, New York, NY 10036
Tel.: (212) 355-2600
Web Site: http://www.fcagroup.com
Art Finance Services
N.A.I.C.S.: 522299

Subsidiary (Non-US):

Fiat Financas Brasil Ltda (2)
Rua Senador Milton Campos 175 5 andar - Parte, Nova Lima, 34000-000, Minas
Gerais, Brazil
Tel.: (55) 3121234500
Business Management Consulting Services
N.A.I.C.S.: 541618

Fiat Finance and Trade Ltd S.A. (2)
24 boulevard Royal, 2449, Luxembourg,
Luxembourg
Tel.: (352) 262 05621
Sales Range: $50-74.9 Million
Emp.: 7
Financial Investment Services
N.A.I.C.S.: 525990

Fiat Gestione Partecipazioni S.p.A. (1)
62 Via Volturno, 25126, Brescia, Italy
Tel.: (39) 0306 597 111
Automobile Design & Mfr
N.A.I.C.S.: 336110

Subsidiary (Domestic):

Fiat Group Purchasing S.r.l. (2)
Corso Giovanni Agnelli 200, Turin, 10135,
Italy
Tel.: (39) 0110031111
Procurement Services
N.A.I.C.S.: 541990

Subsidiary (Non-US):

Fiat Group Purchasing France S.a.r.l. (3)
6 Rue Nicolas Copernic, 78190, Trappes,
France
Tel.: (33) 130167000
Car Dealer
N.A.I.C.S.: 441110

Fiat Group Purchasing Poland Sp. z o.o (3)
Ul Grazynskiego 141, Bielsko-Biala, Poland
Tel.: (48) 338132549
Automotive Distr
N.A.I.C.S.: 423110

Fiat Group Automobiles S.p.A. (1)
Corso Agnelli 200, 10135, Turin,
Italy (100%)
Tel.: (39) 0110031111
Web Site: http://www.fiat.com
Sales Range: $25-49.9 Billion
Emp.: 44,691
Automobile Mfr & Sales
N.A.I.C.S.: 336110

Subsidiary (Domestic):

Alfa Romeo - FCA Italy S.p.A. (2)
Corso Agnelli 200, 10135, Turin, Italy
Tel.: (39) 0110031111
Web Site: http://www.alfaromeo.com
Automobile Mfr
N.A.I.C.S.: 336110

Subsidiary (Domestic):

Alfa Romeo U.S.A. S.p.A. (3)
Corso Francesco Ferrucci 112/A, Turin,
10138, Italy
Tel.: (39) 0110057611
Sales Range: $25-49.9 Million
Emp.: 200
Financial Administration Services
N.A.I.C.S.: 541611

Subsidiary (Domestic):

C.R.F. Societa Consortile per Azioni (2)
50 Strada Torino, 10043, Orbassano, Italy
Tel.: (39) 0119 083 111
Web Site: http://www.crf.it
Sales Range: $150-199.9 Million
Emp.: 1,000
Automotive Research & Development Services
N.A.I.C.S.: 541715

Subsidiary (Non-US):

CMP Componentes e Modulos Plasticos Industria e Comercio Ltda. (2)
Rua Americo Santiago Piacenza 651 - Cinco, Contagem, 32010-030, MG, Brazil

STELLANTIS N.V.

INTERNATIONAL PUBLIC

Stellantis N.V.—(Continued)
Tel.: (55) 3121053401
Web Site: https://cmp-componentes-e-modulos-plasticos.negocio.site
Plastics Product Mfr
N.A.I.C.S.: 326199

Subsidiary (Domestic):

CODEFIS Societa consortile per azioni (2)
Corso Giovanni Agnelli 200, Turin, 10135, Italy
Tel.: (39) 0116866111
Investment Management Service
N.A.I.C.S.: 523940

Centro Ricerche Fiat S.C.p.A. (2)
Strada Torino 50, Orbassano, 10043, Italy (100%)
Tel.: (39) 0119083111
Web Site: http://www.crf.it
Sales Range: $350-399.9 Million
Emp.: 1,200
Automotive Research & Development Services
N.A.I.C.S.: 541715

Customer Services Centre S.r.l. (2)
V le Luraghi Snc, 20020, Arese, Italy
Tel.: (39) 0293776360
Web Site: http://www.customercenter.fiat.com
Customer Service Center Operator
N.A.I.C.S.: 561422

Elasis-Societa Consortile per Azioni (2)
Via Ex Aeroporto s n, Pomigliano d'Arco, 80038, Naples, Italy
Tel.: (39) 08119695011
Scientific Research & Development Services
N.A.I.C.S.: 541990

Subsidiary (Non-US):

FCA Austria GmbH (2)
Gross-Enzersdorfer Strasse 59, 1220, Vienna, Austria
Tel.: (43) 1680010
Web Site: https://www.fiat.at
Automobile Whslr
N.A.I.C.S.: 423110
Ulrich Hoernke (Mng Dir)

Subsidiary (Domestic):

Motor Village Austria GmbH (3)
Schonbrunner Strasse 297-307, 1120, Vienna, Austria
Tel.: (43) 1 810 11 48
Web Site: http://www.motorvillageaustria.com
New & Used Car Distr
N.A.I.C.S.: 441110

Subsidiary (Non-US):

FCA Belgium SA (2)
Bourgetlaan 20 B, 1130, Brussels, Belgium (100%)
Tel.: (32) 80034280000
Web Site: https://www.fiat.be
Sales Range: $50-74.9 Million
Emp.: 100
Automobile Marketer & Sales
N.A.I.C.S.: 423110

Subsidiary (Domestic):

Italian Automotive Center S.A. (3)
Leuvensesteenweg 770, Brussels, 1030, Brussel-Hoofdstad, Belgium
Tel.: (32) 27023124
Car Dealer
N.A.I.C.S.: 441110

Subsidiary (Non-US):

FCA Denmark A/S (2)
Hovedvejen 1, 2600, Glostrup, Denmark
Tel.: (45) 43228800
Web Site: https://www.fiat.dk
Automobile Whslr
N.A.I.C.S.: 423110

FCA Germany AG (2)
Hanauerlanp Strasse 176, 60314, Frankfurt, Germany
Tel.: (49) 69669880
Web Site: http://www.fiat.de
Sales Range: $50-74.9 Million
Emp.: 400
Automobile Mfr
N.A.I.C.S.: 423110
Norbert Tschrepp (Member-Mgmt Bd)

FCA Netherlands B.V. (2)
Singaporestraat 92-100, 1175 RA, Lijnden, Netherlands
Tel.: (31) 203421700
Web Site: http://www.fiat.nl
Automobile Whslr
N.A.I.C.S.: 423110

FCA Switzerland SA (2)
Zurcherstrasse 111, 8952, Schlieren, Switzerland (100%)
Tel.: (41) 445514800
Web Site: https://www.fiat.ch
Automobile Marketer & Sales
N.A.I.C.S.: 423110

Subsidiary (Domestic):

FGA Investimenti S.p.A. (2)
Corso Giovanni Agnelli 200, Turin, 10135, Italy
Tel.: (39) 01170941
Investment Management Service
N.A.I.C.S.: 523940

FGA Russia S.r.l. (2)
Corso Giovanni Agnelli 200, Turin, 10135, Italy
Tel.: (39) 011 00 31111
Investment Management Service
N.A.I.C.S.: 523940

FGA officine Automobilistiche Grugliasco S.p.A. (2)
Via San Paolo 67/71 Grugliasco, Turin, Italy
Tel.: (39) 011683111
Automobile Parts Distr
N.A.I.C.S.: 423120

Subsidiary (Non-US):

Fiat Auto Argentina S.A (2)
Ruta 9 Km 690, Ferreyra, Cordoba, 5123, Argentina
Tel.: (54) 11 5776 5100
Web Site: http://www.fiat.com.ar
Emp.: 1,000
Automobile Mfr & Distr
N.A.I.C.S.: 336110

Subsidiary (Domestic):

Fiat Auto S.A. de Ahorro para Fines Determinados (3)
Balcarce 548 Piso 2, 1064, Buenos Aires, Argentina
Tel.: (54) 1143445700
Financial Management Consulting Services
N.A.I.C.S.: 541611

Subsidiary (Non-US):

Fiat Auto Ireland Ltd. (2)
Fiat House Tpke Rd Naas Rd 22, Dublin, 22, Ireland
Tel.: (353) 14034433
Web Site: http://www.fiat.com
Sales Range: $25-49.9 Million
Emp.: 15
Automobiles & Light Commercial Vehicles Distr
N.A.I.C.S.: 423110

Fiat Auto Poland S.A. (2)
ul Grazynskiego 141, 43-300, Bielsko-Biala, Poland
Tel.: (48) 338132100
Web Site: http://www.fiat.pl
Sales Range: $450-499.9 Million
Emp.: 1,370
Automobile Whslr
N.A.I.C.S.: 423110

Subsidiary (Domestic):

GESTIN POLSKA Sp. z o.o. (3)
ul Grazynskiego 141, 43-300, Bielsko-Biala, Poland
Tel.: (48) 338132272
Web Site: https://fcagroup.pl
Facility Management Services
N.A.I.C.S.: 561210

Subsidiary (Non-US):

Fiat Auto Portuguesa SA (2)
Ave Jose Gomes Ferreira 15, Edificio Atlas IV Miraflores, Alges, 1495-139, Portugal (100%)
Tel.: (351) 214125400
Web Site: http://www.fiat.pt
Sales Range: $25-49.9 Million
Emp.: 60
Automobiles Marketer & Sales
N.A.I.C.S.: 423110

Subsidiary (Domestic):

Fiat Auto Var S.r.l. (2)
Corso Luigi Settembrini 215, Turin, 10135, Italy
Tel.: (39) 0110042111
Automotive Distr
N.A.I.C.S.: 423110

Fiat Automobiles S.p.A. (2)
Corso Giovanni Agnelli 200, 10135, Turin, Italy
Tel.: (39) 080034280000
Web Site: https://www.fiat.com
Sales Range: $150-199.9 Million
Emp.: 1,000
Automobile Mfr
N.A.I.C.S.: 336110

Subsidiary (Non-US):

Fiat Automobiles Service Co. Ltd. (2)
No 188 Guangzhou Road, 210024, Nanjing, China
Tel.: (86) 13002590482
Automobile Maintenance & Repair Services
N.A.I.C.S.: 811111

Fiat CR Spol. S R.O. (2)
F Automobili Import sro Olbrachtova 2006/9, 140 00, Prague, 4, Czech Republic
Tel.: (420) 800200233
Web Site: https://www.fiat.cz
Automobile Whslr
N.A.I.C.S.: 423110

Fiat Chrysler Automobiles UK Ltd. (2)
Fiat House 240 Bath Rd, Slough, SL1 4DX, Berks, United Kingdom
Tel.: (44) 1753511431
Web Site: http://www.fiat.co.uk
Sales Range: $150-199.9 Million
Emp.: 300
Automobile Sales & Services
N.A.I.C.S.: 423110
Steve Zanlunghi (Mng Dir)

Fiat France SA (2)
6 Rue Copemic, 78083, Trappes, Cedex, France (100%)
Tel.: (33) 130167000
Web Site: http://www.fiat.fr
Sales Range: $75-99.9 Million
Emp.: 200
Automobile Importer & Sales
N.A.I.C.S.: 423110

Fiat Group Automobiles Hellas S.A. (2)
Vouliagmeni Avenue no 580A, Argyroupolis, 16452, Athens, Greece
Tel.: (30) 2109988630
Web Site: https://www.fiat.gr
Automobile Mfr & Distr
N.A.I.C.S.: 336110

Fiat Group Automobiles Ireland Ltd. (2)
Agnelli House Naas Road, Dublin, Ireland
Tel.: (353) 14034460
Web Site: http://www.fiat.ie
Automobile Mfr & Distr
N.A.I.C.S.: 336110

Fiat Group Automobiles Japan K.K. (2)
Mita Belliu Building 5-36-7 Shiba, Minato-Ku, Tokyo, 108-0014, Japan
Tel.: (81) 354601913
New Car Dealers
N.A.I.C.S.: 441110

Fiat Group Automobiles Maroc S.A.
Mandarona 300 Lot 9 Route de Sidi Maar-ouf, Casablanca, Morocco
Tel.: (212) 5 22 42 40 00
Web Site: http://www.fiat.com
Automotive Distr
N.A.I.C.S.: 423110

Fiat Group Automobiles South Africa (Proprietary) Ltd (2)
Waterfall Park Howick Close Bekker Street, Voma Valley, Midrand, 1685, Gauteng, South Africa
Tel.: (27) 11 205 3700
Web Site: http://www.fiat.co.za
Sales Range: $25-49.9 Million
Emp.: 50
New Car Dealers
N.A.I.C.S.: 441110

Fiat Group Automobiles Spain S.A. (2)
Carretera Comarcal M-300 Km 28 5, 28802, Alcala de Henares, Madrid, Spain (100%)
Tel.: (34) 918853700
Web Site: http://www.fiat.es
Automobile Marketer & Sales
N.A.I.C.S.: 423110
Jaevier Marijuan (Mng Dir)

Subsidiary (Domestic):

Fiat Auto Espana Marketing Instituto Agrupacion de Interes Economico (3)
Carretera Madrid-Barcelona N-II Km 27 500, Alcala De Henares, Madrid, Spain
Tel.: (34) 913251125
Dealer Training Services
N.A.I.C.S.: 611430

Subsidiary (Non-US):

Fiat Group Automobiles Sweden AB (2)
Farogatan 33, Kista, 16440, Stockholm, Sweden
Tel.: (46) 858837200
Web Site: http://www.fiat.se
New & Used Car Distr
N.A.I.C.S.: 441110

Subsidiary (Domestic):

Fiat Group Marketing & Corporate Communication S.p.A. (2)
Via Nizza 250, 10126, Turin, Italy
Tel.: (39) 0110061111
Sales Range: $25-49.9 Million
Emp.: 100
Direct Marketing Services
N.A.I.C.S.: 541840

Subsidiary (Non-US):

Fiat Magyarorszag Kft (2)
Andre Citroen u1, 1194, Budapest, Hungary
Tel.: (36) 14583100
Web Site: https://www.fiat.hu
Sales Range: $25-49.9 Million
Emp.: 30
Automobile Whslr
N.A.I.C.S.: 423110

Fiat Netherlands Holding B.V. (2)
Schiphol Blvd 217WTC Airport, 1118 BH, Schiphol, Netherlands
Tel.: (31) 204460429
Web Site: http://www.fiat.com
Holding Company
N.A.I.C.S.: 551112

Subsidiary (US):

Fiat North America LLC (2)
1000 Chrysler Dr, Auburn Hills, MI 48326
Tel.: (248) 512-2950
Holding Company
N.A.I.C.S.: 551112

Subsidiary (Domestic):

Alfa Romeo Inc. (3)
375 Park Ave Ste 2703, New York, NY 10152-2704
Tel.: (212) 355-2600
New Car Dealers
N.A.I.C.S.: 441110
Tim Kuniskis (Head-Global)

FCA US LLC (3)
1000 Chrysler Dr, Auburn Hills, MI 48326-2766

AND PRIVATE COMPANIES

Tel.: (800) 334-9200
Web Site: http://www.fcanorthamerica.com
Motor Vehicles Mfr
N.A.I.C.S.: 336110
Laura J. Soave (Executives)

Subsidiary (Domestic):

AutoDie LLC (4)
44 Coldbrook NW, Grand Rapids, MI 49503
Tel.: (616) 454-9361
Web Site: https://www.autodie-llc.com
Emp.: 300
Automotive Stamping Die Mfr
N.A.I.C.S.: 333514
Charlie Murphy (CFO)

CG Co-Issuer Inc. (4)
1000 Chrysler Dr, Auburn Hills, MI 48326
Tel.: (248) 512-3984
Emp.: 10,000
Financial Management Consulting Services
N.A.I.C.S.: 541611

Subsidiary (Non-US):

CHRYSLER GROUP DO BRASIL COMERCIO DE VEICULOS Ltda. (4)
Chrysler 6th floor, PO Box 3042, 06210-970, Sao Paulo, Brazil
Tel.: (55) 1149493900
Web Site: http://www.chrysler.com.br
Emp.: 18
New Car Dealers
N.A.I.C.S.: 441110

Subsidiary (Domestic):

CHRYSLER GROUP INTERNATIONAL LLC
1000 Chrysler Dr, Auburn Hills, MI 48326-2766
Tel.: (248) 576-2850
Automobile Parts Distr
N.A.I.C.S.: 423120

CHRYSLER GROUP INTERNATIONAL SERVICES LLC
1000 Chrysler Dr, Auburn Hills, MI 48326
Tel.: (248) 512-3984
New Car Dealers
N.A.I.C.S.: 441110

CHRYSLER GROUP REALTY COMPANY LLC
1000 Chrysler Dr, Auburn Hills, MI 48326
Tel.: (248) 512-3984
Investment Management Service
N.A.I.C.S.: 523940

Subsidiary (Non-US):

Chrysler & Jeep Vertriebsgesellschaft mbH (4)
Franklinstrasse 26 A, 10587, Berlin, Germany
Tel.: (49) 30437360
Web Site: http://www.berlin.motorvillage.de
Sales Range: $25-49.9 Million
Emp.: 8
Automotive Repair & Maintenance Services
N.A.I.C.S.: 811198

Unit (Domestic):

Chrysler (Atlanta) Parts Distribution Center (4)
1149 Citizens Pkwy, Morrow, GA 30260-2929
Tel.: (770) 960-3300
Sales Range: $25-49.9 Million
Emp.: 80
Motor Vehicle Supplies & New Parts Distr
N.A.I.C.S.: 423120

Chrysler (Cleveland) Parts Distribution Center (4)
9777 Mopar Dr, Streetsboro, OH 44241-5220
Tel.: (330) 626-7600
Sales Range: $25-49.9 Million
Emp.: 142
Motor Vehicle Supplies & New Parts Distr
N.A.I.C.S.: 423120

Chrysler (Dallas) Parts Distribution Center (4)
2205 E Belt Line Rd, Carrollton, TX 75006-5608
Tel.: (972) 418-4699
Sales Range: $25-49.9 Million
Emp.: 97
Motor Vehicle Supplies & New Parts Distr
N.A.I.C.S.: 423120

Chrysler (Memphis) Parts Distribution Center (4)
4175 Chrysler Dr, Memphis, TN 38118
Tel.: (901) 797-3806
Sales Range: $25-49.9 Million
Emp.: 54
Motor Vehicle Supplies & New Parts Distr
N.A.I.C.S.: 423120

Chrysler (Portland) Parts Distribution Center (4)
10030 SW Allen Blvd, Beaverton, OR 97005-4123
Tel.: (503) 526-5570
Sales Range: $25-49.9 Million
Emp.: 59
Motor Vehicle Supplies & New Parts Distr
N.A.I.C.S.: 423120

Chrysler (Warren) Parts Distribution Center (4)
21035 Sherwood Ave, Warren, MI 48091
Tel.: (586) 497-2698
Sales Range: $25-49.9 Million
Emp.: 98
Motor Vehicle Supplies & New Parts Distr
N.A.I.C.S.: 423120
Kim Kosak (Mgr-Ops)

Plant (Domestic):

Chrysler - Conner Street Assembly Plant (4)
20000 Conner St, Detroit, MI 48234-3227
Tel.: (313) 369-6700
Sales Range: $50-74.9 Million
Emp.: 115
Automobile Assembly
N.A.I.C.S.: 336110

Chrysler - Detroit Axle Plant (4)
6700 Lynch Rd, Detroit, MI 48234-4119
Tel.: (313) 252-5400
Sales Range: $450-499.9 Million
Emp.: 1,646
Motor Vehicle Axle Mfr
N.A.I.C.S.: 336390

Chrysler - Detroit Engine Plant (4)
11570 E Warren St, Detroit, MI 48214-1692
Tel.: (313) 252-6601
Sales Range: $350-399.9 Million
Emp.: 1,200
Automotive Engine Mfr
N.A.I.C.S.: 336310

Chrysler - Kokomo Casting Plant (4)
1001 E Blvd, Kokomo, IN 46902
Tel.: (765) 454-1005
Sales Range: $200-249.9 Million
Emp.: 915
Automotive Transmission, Transaxle & Other Aluminum Parts Casting
N.A.I.C.S.: 331523

Chrysler - Kokomo Transmission Plant (4)
2401 S Reed Rd, Kokomo, IN 46902
Tel.: (765) 454-1000
Sales Range: $800-899.9 Million
Emp.: 3,168
Motor Vehicle Transmission Mfr
N.A.I.C.S.: 336350
Bob Lee (VP-Power Train Engrg)

Chrysler - Newark Assembly Plant (4)
550 S College Ave, Newark, DE 19713-1383
Tel.: (302) 453-5115
Sales Range: $350-399.9 Million
Emp.: 1,125
Light Truck Assembly
N.A.I.C.S.: 336110

Chrysler - Plymouth Road Office Complex (PROC) (4)
14250 Plymouth Rd, Detroit, MI 48227-3042
Tel.: (313) 493-2101
Sales Range: $500-549.9 Million
Emp.: 1,596
Motor Vehicle Engineering, Development, Procurement & Advance Manufacturing Services
N.A.I.C.S.: 336110

Unit (Domestic):

Chrysler - Port Operations (4)
2901 Childs St, Baltimore, MD 21226-1015
Tel.: (410) 355-2705
Deep Sea Automobile Transport Services
N.A.I.C.S.: 483111

Plant (Domestic):

Chrysler - Sterling Assembly Plant (4)
35777 Van Dyke Ave, Sterling Heights, MI 48312-1138
Tel.: (586) 978-6001
Sales Range: $800-899.9 Million
Emp.: 2,718
Automobile Assembly
N.A.I.C.S.: 336110

Chrysler - Sterling Stamping Plant (4)
35777 Van Dyke Ave, Sterling Heights, MI 48312-3565
Tel.: (586) 977-4700
Web Site: http://www.Chryslercouriers.com
Sales Range: $350-399.9 Million
Emp.: 2,000
Automotive Stampings
N.A.I.C.S.: 336370

Chrysler - Toledo Machining Plant (4)
8000 Chrysler Dr, Perrysburg, OH 43551-4813
Tel.: (419) 661-3500
Web Site: http://www.fcagroup.com
Steering Columns & Torque Converters Mfr
N.A.I.C.S.: 336330

Chrysler - Toledo North Assembly Plant (4)
4400 Chrysler Dr, Toledo, OH 43608
Tel.: (419) 727-7700
Sales Range: $800-899.9 Million
Emp.: 3,408
Automobile Assembly
N.A.I.C.S.: 336110

Chrysler - Trenton Engine Plant (4)
2000 Van Horn Rd, Trenton, MI 48183-4204
Tel.: (313) 956-9129
Sales Range: $350-399.9 Million
Emp.: 1,630
Automotive Engine Mfr
N.A.I.C.S.: 336310

Chrysler - Warren Stamping Plant (4)
22800 Mound Rd, Warren, MI 48091
Tel.: (586) 497-3630
Sales Range: $450-499.9 Million
Emp.: 1,425
Automotive Body Stampings & Assembly
N.A.I.C.S.: 336370

Chrysler - Warren Truck Assembly Plant (4)
21500 Mound Rd, Warren, MI 48091-4840
Tel.: (586) 497-2400
Sales Range: $800-899.9 Million
Emp.: 2,791
Assembly of Pickup Trucks
N.A.I.C.S.: 336120

Subsidiary (Non-US):

Chrysler Asia pacific Investment Ltd. (4)
5/F Third Office Building No 555 Dongchuan Road, Minhang Dist, Shanghai, China
Tel.: (86) 2161927800
Investment Management Service
N.A.I.C.S.: 523940

Chrysler Australia Pty. Ltd. (4)
437 Plummer Street, Melbourne, 3207, VIC, Australia
Tel.: (61) 386980200
Web Site: https://www.chrysler.com.au
New & Used Car Dealer
N.A.I.C.S.: 441110

Group (Non-US):

Chrysler Canada Inc. (4)
1 Riverside Dr W, Windsor, N9A 5K3, ON, Canada

STELLANTIS N.V.

Tel.: (519) 973-2000
Web Site: http://www.chryslercanada.ca
Sales Range: $1-4.9 Billion
Emp.: 9,000
Motor Vehicles Mfr & Distr
N.A.I.C.S.: 336110

Plant (Domestic):

Chrysler Canada - Brampton Assembly Plant (5)
2000 Williams Parkway East, Brampton, L6S 6B3, ON, Canada
Tel.: (905) 458-1330
Web Site: http://www.chryslercanada.com
Sales Range: $600-649.9 Million
Emp.: 3,750
Automobile Assembly
N.A.I.C.S.: 336110

Chrysler Canada - Etobicoke Casting Plant (5)
15 Brown's Line, Toronto, M8W 3S3, ON, Canada
Tel.: (416) 253-2300
Web Site: http://www.chryslercanada.ca
Sales Range: $100-124.9 Million
Emp.: 400
Automotive Aluminium Die Casting & Parts Mfr
N.A.I.C.S.: 331523

Affiliate (Domestic):

Cpk Interior Products Inc. (5)
128 Peter Street, Port Hope, L1A 3W4, Canada (100%)
Tel.: (905) 885-7231
Web Site: https://www.cpkip.com
Sales Range: $50-74.9 Million
Emp.: 700
Automotive Trim & Interior Parts Mfr
N.A.I.C.S.: 336360
Doug Gouin (CEO)

Unit (Domestic):

National Fleet & Lease (5)
6500 Mississauga Rd N, Mississauga, L5N 1A8, ON, Canada
Tel.: (905) 821-6046
Web Site: http://www.fcacanada.ca
Automobile Fleet Sales & Services
N.A.I.C.S.: 423110

Unit (Domestic):

Chrysler Corporation (4)
7700 Irvine Ctr Dr Ste 400, Irvine, CA 92618-2923
Tel.: (949) 450-5111
Web Site: http://www.chrysler.com
Sales Range: $25-49.9 Million
Emp.: 97
Business Support Services
N.A.I.C.S.: 561499

Chrysler Corporation (4)
5790 Campus Pkwy, Hazelwood, MO 63042-2337
Tel.: (314) 895-0740
Sales Range: $25-49.9 Million
Emp.: 59
Automobile Parts, Sales & Services
N.A.I.C.S.: 423110

Subsidiary (Non-US):

Chrysler Czech Republic s.r.o. (4)
Karolinska 650/1, 186 00, Prague, Czech Republic
Tel.: (420) 224 806 111
Web Site: http://www.chrysler.cz
Car Dealer
N.A.I.C.S.: 441110

Chrysler France S.A.S. (4)
Za Trappes Elancourt, Trappes, 78190, Yvelines, France
Tel.: (33) 130167666
Web Site: http://www.chrysler.fr
New & Used Car Distr
N.A.I.C.S.: 441110

Subsidiary (Domestic):

Chrysler Group Transport LLC (4)
8555 Lynch Rd, Detroit, MI 48234-4154
Tel.: (313) 252-2578
General Freight Trucking Services
N.A.I.C.S.: 484110

STELLANTIS N.V.

INTERNATIONAL PUBLIC

Stellantis N.V.—(Continued)

Chrysler Investment Holdings LLC (4)
1000 Chrysler Dr, Auburn Hills, MI 48326-2766
Tel.: (248) 576-5741
Investment Management Service
N.A.I.C.S.: 523940

Subsidiary (Non-US):

Chrysler Italia S.r.l. (4)
Viale Manzoni 67, 00185, Rome, Italy
Tel.: (39) 06418821
Web Site: http://www.chrysler.it
Motor Vehicle Parts Distr
N.A.I.C.S.: 423120

Chrysler Jeep Ticaret S.A. (4)
Pazarlama Merkezi TEM Otoyolu Hadimkoey Cikisi, Buekuekcekmece, Istanbul, 34900, Türkiye
Tel.: (90) 2128674000
New Car Dealers
N.A.I.C.S.: 441110

Chrysler Korea, Ltd. (4)
Gangnam Finance Center 737 Yeoksamdong 14 floors, Gangnam-gu, Seoul, 135-984, Korea (South)
Tel.: (82) 2 2112 2666
Web Site: http://www.chryslergroup.co.kr
New Car Dealers
N.A.I.C.S.: 441110

Chrysler Management Austria GmbH (4)
Bundesstrasse 83, Gossendorf, 8077, Austria
Tel.: (43) 3164080
Sales Range: $10-24.9 Million
Emp.: 40
Automobile Repair & Maintenance Services
N.A.I.C.S.: 811114
Anthony Picknell (Gen Mgr)

Chrysler Polska sp. zo.o. (4)
Aleja Wyscigowa 6, Warsaw, 02-681, Poland
Tel.: (48) 22 312 76 11
Web Site: http://www.chrysler.pl
New & Used Car Distr
N.A.I.C.S.: 441110

Chrysler South Africa (Pty) Limited (4)
270 George Street, Noordwyk, Midrand, 1685, Gauteng, South Africa
Tel.: (27) 12 666 3600
Web Site: http://www.chryslergroup.co.za
Used & New Car Dealer
N.A.I.C.S.: 441110

Chrysler de Venezuela LLC. (4)
Avenida Pancho Pepe Croquer Zona Industrial Norte, Valencia, Venezuela
Tel.: (58) 241 6132400
Web Site: http://www.chryslerdevenezuela.com.ve
Used & New Car Dealer
N.A.I.C.S.: 441120

Subsidiary (Domestic):

Downriver Dodge, Inc. (4)
5535 Gatewood Dr, Sterling Heights, MI 48310-2227
Tel.: (586) 264-3700
Sales Range: $25-49.9 Million
Emp.: 2
Office Administrative & Accounting Services
N.A.I.C.S.: 561110
Patrick Long (Gen Mgr)

FCA Foundation (4)
1000 Chrysler Dr, Auburn Hills, MI 48326
Tel.: (800) 334-9200
Web Site: http://www.fcanorthamerica.com
Fund Management Services
N.A.I.C.S.: 523940

Subsidiary (Non-US):

FCA Nederland B.V. (4)
Postbus 203, 1170 AE, Badhoevedorp, Netherlands
Tel.: (31) 80016921692
Web Site: https://www.chrysler.nl
Car Dealer
N.A.I.C.S.: 441110

Fundacion Chrysler de Mexico I.A.P (4)
Prolongacion Paseo De La Reforma No 1240, Santa Fe, 05109, Mexico, Mexico
Tel.: (52) 5550813221
Engineeering Services
N.A.I.C.S.: 541330

Subsidiary (Domestic):

Gulfgate Dodge, Inc. (4)
7250 Gulf Fwy, Houston, TX 77017
Tel.: (281) 949-6344
Web Site: https://www.gulfgatedodge.com
New & Used Car Dealer
N.A.I.C.S.: 441110
Stacy McCourt (Dir-Parts)

North Tampa Chrysler Jeep Dodge, Inc. (4)
10909 N Florida Ave, Tampa, FL 33612-6633
Tel.: (813) 638-0436
Web Site: https://www.chryslerdodgetampabay.com
New & Used Car Dealer
N.A.I.C.S.: 441110
Jim Browne (Owner)

Subsidiary (Domestic):

Fiat U.S.A., Inc. (3)
7 Times Sq, New York, NY 10036 (100%)
Tel.: (212) 355-2600
Web Site: https://www.fiatusa.com
Automobile Whslr
N.A.I.C.S.: 423110

Subsidiary (Domestic):

Fiat Partecipazioni S.p.A. (2)
Via Nizza 250, Turin, 10126, Italy
Tel.: (39) 01 10 06 11 11
Investment Management Service
N.A.I.C.S.: 523940

Subsidiary (Non-US):

Fiat do Brasil SA (2)
Senador Milton Campos 175, 34000-000, Serra, Nova Lima MG, Brazil
Tel.: (55) 3121234366
Web Site: http://www.fiat.com.br
Sales Range: $450-499.9 Million
Emp.: 1,200
Automobile Importer & Sales
N.A.I.C.S.: 423110

Subsidiary (Domestic):

Fiat professional S.p.A. (2)
Corso Giovanni Agnelli 200, 10135, Turin, Italy
Tel.: (39) 080034280000
Web Site: https://www.fiatprofessional.com
New Car Dealers
N.A.I.C.S.: 441110

Lancia Automobiles S.p.A. (2)
C so G Agnelli 200, 10135, Turin, Italy
Tel.: (39) 0110042111
Web Site: https://www.lancia.com
New Car Dealers
N.A.I.C.S.: 441110

Maserati S.p.A. (2)
322 Viale Ciro Menotti, 41121, Modena, Italy (100%)
Tel.: (39) 059590511
Web Site: http://www.maserati.com
Sales Range: $650-699.9 Million
Emp.: 649
Luxury Automobile Mfr
N.A.I.C.S.: 336110

Subsidiary (Non-US):

Maserati Deutschland GmbH (3)
Stielstrasse 3b, Wiesbaden, 65201, Germany
Tel.: (49) 6112840980
Car Mfr
N.A.I.C.S.: 336110

Maserati GB Ltd. (3)
275 Leigh Rd, Slough, SL1 4HF, United Kingdom
Tel.: (44) 01753878888
Web Site: http://www.maserati.com

Sales Range: $25-49.9 Million
Emp.: 12
Luxury Automobile Importer & Distr
N.A.I.C.S.: 423110

Maserati Japan KK (3)
22 Mori Bldg 1-12-32 Akasaka, Minato-ku, Tokyo, Japan
Tel.: (81) 120965120
Web Site: https://www.maserati.com
New Car Dealers
N.A.I.C.S.: 441110

Subsidiary (US):

Maserati North America, Inc. (3)
40 Sylvan Ave, Englewood Cliffs, NJ 07632
Tel.: (551) 303-6344
Sales Range: $75-99.9 Million
Emp.: 150
Sports Cars Importer & Distr
N.A.I.C.S.: 423110

Subsidiary (Domestic):

Sisport Fiat S.p.A. (2)
Corso Moncalieri 346 12, 10133, Turin, Italy
Tel.: (39) 0116619801
Sports Activities Promotion & Recreational Facilities Management Services
N.A.I.C.S.: 711310

Joint Venture (Non-US):

Tofas Turk Otomobil Fabrikasi A.S. (2)
Buyukdere Cad No 145, Tofas Han Zincirlikuyu, 34394, Istanbul, Türkiye (37.9%)
Tel.: (90) 2122753390
Web Site: http://www.tofas.com.tr
Rev: $2,024,535,652
Assets: $1,247,110,160
Liabilities: $897,659,496
Net Worth: $349,450,665
Earnings: $264,465,136
Emp.: 5,928
Fiscal Year-end: 12/31/2022
Automobile Mfr
N.A.I.C.S.: 336110
Altan Aytac (Dir-Fiat Bus Unit)

Subsidiary (Domestic):

i-FAST Automotive logistics S.r.l. (2)
Corso Agnelli 200, 10135, Rivalta di Torino, Italy
Tel.: (39) 0110031111
Web Site: http://www.i-fast.it
Automotive Logistics Consulting Services
N.A.I.C.S.: 541614

Fiat Powertrain Technologies S.p.A. (1)
Strada Torino 50, 10043, Orbassano, Italy
Tel.: (39) 0119080617
Web Site: http://www.fiatpowertrain.com
Sales Range: $5-14.9 Billion
Emp.: 18,924
Automobile Engine & Transmission Mfr
N.A.I.C.S.: 336350

Joint Venture (Domestic):

VM Motori S.p.A. (2)
Via Ferrarese 29, 44042, Cento, Ferrara, Italy
Tel.: (39) 0516837511
Web Site: http://www.vmmotori.it
Sales Range: $200-249.9 Million
Emp.: 1,200
Diesel Engine Mfr
N.A.I.C.S.: 336310

Fiat Revi S.c.r.l. (1)
Via Nizza 250, 10126, Turin, Italy
Tel.: (39) 0110063160
Accounting & Internal Auditing Services
N.A.I.C.S.: 541219

Industrial Yorka de Tepoztotlan S.A. de C.V (1)
Av De La Industria No 21, Tepoztotlan, 54600, Mexico
Tel.: (52) 5558760511
Automobile Parts Distr
N.A.I.C.S.: 423120

International Metropolitan Automotive promotion (France) S.A. (1)
365 route de Vienne, 69200, Venissieux, France
Tel.: (33) 899962694
New Car Dealers
N.A.I.C.S.: 441110

Italian Motor Village S.A. (1)
Avenida Jose Gomes Ferreira 15, Alges, Oeiras, 1495-139, Portugal
Tel.: (351) 214166300
New Car Dealers
N.A.I.C.S.: 441110

Italiana Edizioni S.p.A (1)
Via Marenco 32, 10126, Turin, Italy
Tel.: (39) 0110063893
Web Site: http://www.lastampa.it
Sales Range: $500-549.9 Million
Emp.: 836
Publishing & Communication Services
N.A.I.C.S.: 513110

Subsidiary (Domestic):

Editrice La Stampa S.p.A. (2)
Via Lugaro 15, 10126, Turin, Italy
Tel.: (39) 0116568111
Web Site: http://www.lastampa.it
Sales Range: $100-124.9 Million
Emp.: 400
Newspaper Publishers
N.A.I.C.S.: 513110

Mako Elektrik Sanayi Ve Ticaret A.S. (1)
Tel.: (90) 2242195600
Web Site: http://www.mako.com.tr
Automotive Lighting & Air Conditioning Device Mfr
N.A.I.C.S.: 336320

Mugello Circuit S.p.A. (1)
Via Senni 15, 50038, Scarperia, FI, Italy
Tel.: (39) 0558499111
Web Site: https://www.mugellocircuit.com
Automotive Race Track Operator
N.A.I.C.S.: 711212

Nexta Srl (1)
Via Lugaro 15, 10126, Turin, Italy
Tel.: (39) 06 993 452 04
Web Site: http://www.nexta.com
Business Directory Publisher
N.A.I.C.S.: 513140

Peugeot S.A. (1)
7 rue Henri Ste Claire Deville, CS 60125, Rueil-Malmaison, 92563, Paris, France
Tel.: (33) 155948100
Web Site: https://www.groupe-psa.com
Rev.: $83,688,257,660
Assets: $78,128,152,760
Liabilities: $53,714,084,900
Net Worth: $24,414,067,860
Earnings: $4,013,578,240
Emp.: 209,000
Fiscal Year-end: 12/31/2019
Holding Company; Automobile Mfr & Distr
N.A.I.C.S.: 551112
Carlos Tavares (Chm-Mgmt Bd)

Subsidiary (Non-US):

Adam Opel GmbH (2)
Bahnhofsplatz, 65423, Russelsheim, Germany
Tel.: (49) 6142770
Web Site: https://www.opel.de
Car Mfr & Distr
N.A.I.C.S.: 336110

Subsidiary (Non-US):

Opel Austria Vertrieb GmbH (3)
Grossenzersdorfer Strasse 59, 1220, Vienna, Austria (100%)
Tel.: (43) 1 360 27 71 904
Web Site: http://www.opel.at
Mfr of Engines & Transmissions; Import of Opel & other GM Products
N.A.I.C.S.: 336110

Opel Danmark A/S (3)
Main road 1, 2600, Glostrup, Denmark
Tel.: (45) 43451622
Automobile Mfr
N.A.I.C.S.: 336110

Subsidiary (Domestic):

Opel Group Warehousing GmbH (3)

AND PRIVATE COMPANIES
STELLANTIS N.V.

Hauptstrasse 63, 44894, Bochum, Germany
Tel.: (49) 2349892226
Motor Vehicle Storage & Logistics Services
N.A.I.C.S.: 493110

Subsidiary (Non-US):

Opel Ireland (3)
Gowan House Naas Road, Walkinstown,
D12 RCC4, Ireland (100%)
Tel.: (353) 12161026
Web Site: http://www.opel.ie
Automobile Mfr
N.A.I.C.S.: 336110
Gillian Whittall *(Gen Mgr)*

Opel Norge AS (3)
Kjeller Vest 6, 2007, Kjeller, Norway
Tel.: (47) 23 02 46 44
Web Site: http://www.opel.no
Automobile Mfr & Distr
N.A.I.C.S.: 336110

Subsidiary (Domestic):

Opel Service GmbH (3)
Friedrich-Lutzmann-Ring, 65428, Russelsheim, Germany
Tel.: (49) 06142 8729750
Web Site: http://www.opel.de
Automotive Distr
N.A.I.C.S.: 441110

Subsidiary (Non-US):

Opel Sverige AB (3)
Arstaangsvagen 17, Stockholm, 117 43, Sweden
Tel.: (46) 86328500
Web Site: http://www.opel.se
Automobile Mfr
N.A.I.C.S.: 336110
Nicholas Parts *(Gen Mgr)*

Opel Wien GmbH (3)
Gross-Enzersdorfer Strasse 59, 1220, Vienna, Austria
Tel.: (43) 1288990
Automotive Distr
N.A.I.C.S.: 441110

Subsidiary (Non-US):

Asientos de Castilla Leon, S.A. (2)
Carretera Nacional 620 Km 120 - Pg Ind El Berrocal, Valladolid, 47009, Spain
Tel.: (34) 983360079
Motor Vehicle Parts Distr
N.A.I.C.S.: 423120

Asientos de Galicia, S.L. (2)
Calle 3 Pq Tecnologico Y Logistico Parc 2, Vigo, 36214, Spain
Tel.: (34) 986828800
Automobile Parts Distr
N.A.I.C.S.: 423120

Asientos del Norte, S.A. (2)
Avenida Los Huetos 73 - 75, Vitoria, 01010, Spain
Tel.: (34) 945188422
Motor Vehicle Seats Mfr
N.A.I.C.S.: 336360

Subsidiary (Domestic):

Autobiz SA (2)
4 Place des Vosges, 92400, Courbevoie, France
Tel.: (33) 141449100
Car Whslr
N.A.I.C.S.: 441110
Nacera Aggoun *(Sr Project Mgr)*

Subsidiary (Non-US):

Autobutler ApS (2)
Artillerivej 86, 2300, Copenhagen, Denmark
Tel.: (45) 77343221
Web Site: https://www.autobutler.dk
Automotive Services
N.A.I.C.S.: 811111
Christian Legene *(CEO & Partner)*

Subsidiary (Domestic):

Automobiles Citroen SA (2)
6 rue Fructidor, 75017, Paris, France
Tel.: (33) 158797979
Web Site: http://www.citroen.com
Car Whslr
N.A.I.C.S.: 441110

Olivier Bodet *(Mgr-B2B)*

Automobiles Peugeot SA (2)
75 Avenue de la Grande Armee, Paris, 75116, France
Tel.: (33) 140665511
Web Site: http://www.psa-peugeot-citroen.com
Holding Company
N.A.I.C.S.: 551112
Carlos Tavares *(Chm-Mgmt Bd)*

Automotive Sandouville (2)
2 Rue Hennape, 92000, Nanterre, France
Tel.: (33) 172367000
Automobile Parts Mfr
N.A.I.C.S.: 336390

Subsidiary (Non-US):

Automotores Franco-Chilena S.A. (2)
Camino San Rafael S No, Los Andes, Chile (100%)
Tel.: (56) 34422231
Sales Range: $50-74.9 Million
Emp.: 130
Mfr of Automobiles
N.A.I.C.S.: 336110

Automoveis Citroen S.A. (2)
Rua Vasco da Gama 20, Portela, 2685-244, Sacavem, Portugal
Tel.: (351) 808203776
Web Site: http://www.citroen.pt
Car Whslr
N.A.I.C.S.: 441110
Marcio Lourenco *(Reg Mgr)*

BPF Mexico S.A. DE CV (2)
Av Insurgentes Sur No 1898 Piso 6 Florida Alvaro Obregon, Mexico, 01030, Mexico
Tel.: (52) 5553504070
Financial Management Services
N.A.I.C.S.: 523999

Subsidiary (Domestic):

Banque PSA Finance S.A. (2)
75 Avenue de la Grande-Armee, 75116, Levallois-Perret, France (100%)
Tel.: (33) 146396633
Web Site: http://www.banquepsafinance.com
Sales Range: $100-124.9 Million
Emp.: 964
Motor Vehicle Retail Sales & Commercial Wholesale Financing Services
N.A.I.C.S.: 522220
Frederic Legrand *(Officer-Lion Project)*

Subsidiary (Non-US):

BPF PAZARLAMA ACENTELIK HIZMETLERI A.S. (3)
Kar Plaza E Kat 16 Kayisdagi Caddesi Karamanciftlik Yolu, Istanbul, 34752, Turkiye
Tel.: (90) 2165799400
Sales Range: $25-49.9 Million
Emp.: 8
Motor Vehicle Distr
N.A.I.C.S.: 423110

Subsidiary (Domestic):

CREDIPAR SA (3)
12 Avenue Andre Malraux, Levallois-Perret, 92300, France
Tel.: (33) 146396633
Automobile Financing Services
N.A.I.C.S.: 522220

Subsidiary (Non-US):

PSA FINANCE SUISSE S.A. (3)
Untere Zollgasse 28, Ostermundigen, 3072, Bern, Switzerland
Tel.: (41) 319392211
Financial Management Services
N.A.I.C.S.: 523999

PSA FINANCIAL HOLDING B.V. (3)
Goudsesingel 136, Rotterdam, 3011 KD, Netherlands
Tel.: (31) 102012600
Investment Management Service
N.A.I.C.S.: 523999

Subsidiary (Non-US):

PSA FINANCE BELUX S.A (4)

Rue De L'Etoile 99, Brussels, 1180, Belgium
Tel.: (32) 23707711
Web Site: http://www.psafinance.com
Financial Management Services
N.A.I.C.S.: 523999

PSA FINANCE CESKA REPUBLIKA S.R.O. (4)
Hbeddova 1716 4, 186 00, Prague, Czech Republic
Tel.: (420) 224 835 451
Web Site: http://www.psa.com
Emp.: 25
Financial Management Services
N.A.I.C.S.: 523999
Hitesh Lokhandwala *(Gen Mgr)*

Subsidiary (Domestic):

PSA FINANCE NEDERLAND B.V. (4)
Hoofdweg 256, 3011 KD, Rotterdam, Netherlands
Tel.: (31) 102012600
Financial Management Services
N.A.I.C.S.: 523999

Affiliate (Non-US):

Dongfeng Peugeot Citroen Auto Finance Co., Ltd. (5)
East Section 9/F Hanwei Building No 7 Guanghua Road, Chaoyang Dist, Beijing, 100004, China (50%)
Tel.: (86) 1065628000
Automobile Financing Services
N.A.I.C.S.: 522220

Subsidiary (Non-US):

PSA FINANCIAL d.o.o. (4)
Bani 75, Buzin, 10010, Zagreb, Croatia
Tel.: (385) 1 6612669
Financial Management Services
N.A.I.C.S.: 523999

Subsidiary (Non-US):

PSA WHOLESALE Ltd (3)
Quadrant House Princess Way, Redhill, RH1 1QA, United Kingdom
Tel.: (44) 1293800800
Sales Range: $50-74.9 Million
Emp.: 25
Automotive Distr
N.A.I.C.S.: 423110
Cruciano Infosino *(Mng Dir)*

Subsidiary (Domestic):

Centrauto SARL (2)
Chemin De Blainville, Vernouillet, 28500, Eure-et-Loir, France
Tel.: (33) 237464265
Motor Vehicle Distr
N.A.I.C.S.: 423110

Subsidiary (Non-US):

Circulo de Inversiones S.A. (2)
Maipu 942-18th Floor, CP 1006, Buenos Aires, Argentina
Tel.: (54) 8108886666
Web Site: http://www.autoplan-peugeot.com.ar
Institute Services
N.A.I.C.S.: 522180

Citroen Belux SA NV (2)
Avenue du Bourget 20, 1130, Brussels, Belgium
Tel.: (32) 22066800
Web Site: http://www.citroen.be
Car Whslr
N.A.I.C.S.: 441110
Stefan De Smet *(Sls Dir)*

Citroen Deutschland AG (2)
Bahnhofsplatz, 65423, Russelsheim, Germany
Tel.: (49) 6142747122
Web Site: https://www.citroen.de
Car Lending Services
N.A.I.C.S.: 532112
Wolfgang Schlimme *(Mng Dir)*

Subsidiary (Domestic):

Citroen Dunkerque S.A.S. (2)

75 Ave De La Grande Armee, 75016, Paris, France
Tel.: (33) 328259700
Motor Vehicle Distr
N.A.I.C.S.: 423110

Citroen Orleans S.A.S. (2)
740 Rue De Bourges, 45160, Olivet, France
Tel.: (33) 2 38 25 21 21
Automotive Distr
N.A.I.C.S.: 423110

Subsidiary (Non-US):

Citroen Polska Sp. z.o.o. (2)
Al Krakowska 206, 02-219, Warsaw, Poland
Tel.: (48) 224442244
Web Site: http://www.citroen.pl
Car Whslr
N.A.I.C.S.: 441110

Citroen Suisse S.A. (2)
27 Rue Des Acacias, Geneva, 1211, Switzerland (99.75%)
Tel.: (41) 223080239
Web Site: http://www.citroen.ch
Sales Range: $75-99.9 Million
Emp.: 110
Citroen Vehicles Distr
N.A.I.C.S.: 423120

Clicars Spain SL (2)
Av Laboral 10, 28021, Madrid, Spain
Tel.: (34) 919015000
Web Site: https://www.clicars.com
Car Whslr
N.A.I.C.S.: 441110
Ivan Velasco *(CTO)*

Comercial Citroen S.A. (2)
Guipuzcoa 177-191, 08020, Barcelona, Spain
Tel.: (34) 934987950
Motor Vehicle Distr
N.A.I.C.S.: 423110

Subsidiary (Domestic):

Compagnie Generale de Credit aux Particuliers S.A (2)
12 Av Andre Malraux, 92300, Levallois-Perret, France
Tel.: (33) 1 46 39 66 33
Sales Range: $350-399.9 Million
Emp.: 900
Financial Management Services
N.A.I.C.S.: 523999
Philippe Miralles *(Gen Mgr)*

Subsidiary (Non-US):

ET Mexico Holdings II, S. de R.L. de C.V. (2)
Km 9 5 Carretera Constitucion, Queretaro, 76120, Mexico
Tel.: (52) 4422383000
Exhaust System Mfr
N.A.I.C.S.: 336390

European Automobile Co. (2)
184 Surawong Rd, 10500, Bangkok, Thailand
Tel.: (66) 2 234 09 21
Web Site: http://www.psa-peugeot-citroen.com
Automobile Mfr
N.A.I.C.S.: 336110

Subsidiary (Domestic):

Financiere Pergolese (2)
75 Avenue De La Grande Armee, 75116, Paris, France
Tel.: (33) 140665511
Financial Management Services
N.A.I.C.S.: 523999

GIE PSA TRESORERIE (2)
75 Avenue De La Grande Armee, 75116, Paris, France
Tel.: (33) 140665151
Financial Management Services
N.A.I.C.S.: 523999
Tavareses Carlor *(CEO)*

Subsidiary (Non-US):

Garaje Eloy Granollers S.A. (2)
Jordi Camp 40, 08403, Granollers, Barcelona, Spain
Tel.: (34) 938404999

STELLANTIS N.V.

Stellantis N.V.—(Continued)

New Car Dealers
N.A.I.C.S.: 441110

Subsidiary (Domestic):

Grands Garages du Limousin (2)
357 Rue De Toulouse A20 Sortie 36, Limoges, 87000, France
Tel.: (33) 555314444
Automotive Distr
N.A.I.C.S.: 423110

Subsidiary (Non-US):

Groupe PSA Automotiv Pazarlama AS (2)
Buyukhanli Plaza Kucukbakkalkoy Mah Defne Sok No 3, Atasehir, 34750, Istanbul, Turkiye
Tel.: (90) 2165799400
Web Site: http://www.groupe-psa.com.tr
Car Whslr
N.A.I.C.S.: 441110

Lowen Garage AG (2)
Gewerbestrasse 17, Moosseedorf, 3302, Switzerland
Tel.: (41) 31 850 28 28
Automobile Parts Mfr
N.A.I.C.S.: 336390

Subsidiary (Domestic):

Mister Auto SAS (2)
19 rue Alfred de Musset, 69100, Villeurbanne, France
Tel.: (33) 426707077
Web Site: https://www.mister-auto.com
Auto Parts Whslr
N.A.I.C.S.: 423120
Matthieu Rubin (Mgr-Sls & Mktg)

Subsidiary (Non-US):

Motor Talavera SA (2)
Avenida Portugal 84, 45600, Talavera de la Reina, Toledo, Spain
Tel.: (34) 925811843
New Car Dealers
N.A.I.C.S.: 441110

NAZA Automotive Manufacturing Sdn. Bhd. (2)
Lot 6744 and 7270 Kawasan Perinudstrian, 08300, Gurun, Kedah, Malaysia
Tel.: (60) 44669100
Web Site: http://www.nam.com.my
Automobile Mfr
N.A.I.C.S.: 336110
Yusof Mohamed (Gen Mgr)

Opel Austria GmbH (2)
Gross-Enzersdorfer Strasse 59, 1220, Vienna, Austria
Tel.: (43) 13602771904
Web Site: https://www.opel.at
Car Whslr
N.A.I.C.S.: 441110
Werner Spissak (Mgr-Bus Dev)

Opel Automobile GmbH (2)
Bahnhofsplatz, 65423, Russelsheim, Germany
Tel.: (49) 6142770
Web Site: http://www.opel.de
Automobile Mfr
N.A.I.C.S.: 441110
Andreas Hofer (Dir-Mktg & IT)

Opel Belgium NV (2)
Avenue Bourget 20, 1130, Brussels, Belgium
Tel.: (32) 34506329
Web Site: https://www.opel.be
Car Whslr
N.A.I.C.S.: 441110
Peter Audenaert (Mktg Mgr)

Subsidiary (Domestic):

Opel France S.A.S. (2)
7 rue Henri Sainte-Claire Deville, 92500, Rueil-Malmaison, France
Tel.: (33) 821980006
Web Site: https://www.opel.fr
Car Whslr
N.A.I.C.S.: 441110
Stephane Le Guevel (Mng Dir)

Subsidiary (Non-US):

Opel Italia S.r.l. (2)
Via Gallarate 199, 20151, Milan, Italy
Tel.: (39) 02307031
Web Site: http://www.opel.it
Car Whslr
N.A.I.C.S.: 441110
Stefano Virgilio (Mgr-PR)

Opel Manufacturing Poland Sp.z o.o. (2)
ul Adama Opel 1, 44-100, Gliwice, Poland
Tel.: (48) 322709000
Automobile Mfr
N.A.I.C.S.: 336110
Andrzej Korpak (Mng Dir)

Opel Nederland B.V. (2)
Lemelerbergweg 12, 1101 AJ, Amsterdam, Netherlands
Tel.: (31) 206545751
Web Site: https://www.opel.nl
Car Whslr
N.A.I.C.S.: 441110
Robin Uebbing (Mng Dir)

Opel Poland Sp.z o.o. (2)
Aleja Krakowska 206, 02-219, Warsaw, Poland
Tel.: (48) 225830092
Web Site: https://www.opel.pl
Car Whslr
N.A.I.C.S.: 441110
Tomasz Chudzik (Mktg Dir)

Opel Portugal, Lda. (2)
Rua Vasco da Gama 20, Portela, 2685-244, Sacavem, Portugal
Tel.: (351) 808200700
Web Site: https://www.opel.pt
Car Whslr
N.A.I.C.S.: 441110
Nuno Alves (Mgr-Technical Field & Customer Care)

Opel Sibiu SRL (2)
Str Banu Antonache 40-44 etaj 4, Bucharest, 011665, Romania
Tel.: (40) 216550709
Web Site: http://www.opel.ro
Car Whslr
N.A.I.C.S.: 441110
Andreas Blauert (Mng Dir)

PCA Automobiles India Private Limited (2)
Adhigattur Village Kadambathur, Tiruvallur, Chennai, 631203, India
Tel.: (91) 18002671000
Web Site: https://www.citroen.in
Car Whslr
N.A.I.C.S.: 441110
Sakhivel Kumaravel (Mgr-Mfg)

PSA AVTEC Powertrain Private Ltd. (2)
Mathagondapalli Post, Poonapalli Village, Hosur, 635114, Tamil Nadu, India
Tel.: (91) 4344405445
Web Site: https://www.psa-avtec.com
Car Whslr
N.A.I.C.S.: 441110
Vinod Kawthekar (Gen Mgr)

PSA Insurance Solutions Ltd. (2)
MIB House 53 Abate Rigord Street, Ta' Xbiex, Malta
Tel.: (356) 22583492
Web Site: http://www.psa-insurance-solutions.be
Insurance Services
N.A.I.C.S.: 524210
Joanne Grima (CFO)

PSA International S.A. (2)
62 Quai Gustave Ador, Geneva, 1207, Switzerland (99.9%)
Tel.: (41) 227077000
Web Site: http://www.psai.ch
Sales Range: $50-74.9 Million
Emp.: 20
Management of the Group's Foreign Exchange Operations
N.A.I.C.S.: 522299
Bertrand Champion (Mng Dir)

Unit (Domestic):

PSA Peugeot Citroen (2)

PO Box 1403, 68071, Mulhouse, France
Tel.: (33) 389092170
Sales Range: $1-4.9 Billion
Emp.: 10,000
Mfr of Automobiles
N.A.I.C.S.: 336110

PSA Peugeot Citroen (2)
45 Rue Jean Pierre Timbaud, 78307, Poissy, France (100%)
Tel.: (33) 130193000
Web Site: http://www.mpsa.com
Sales Range: $1-4.9 Billion
Emp.: 9,000
Automotive Distr
N.A.I.C.S.: 423110

Subsidiary (Non-US):

PSA Retail Austria GmbH (2)
Triester Strasse 50A, 1100, Vienna, Austria
Tel.: (43) 19959481
Car Whslr
N.A.I.C.S.: 441110
Sophie Thomasitz (Mgr-Digital Mktg)

PSA Retail Rent Poland SP Z O.O. (2)
ul Radzyminska 112, 03-574, Warsaw, Poland
Tel.: (48) 502442244
Web Site: https://www.psaretailrent.pl
Car Whslr
N.A.I.C.S.: 441110

Peugeot Autohaus GmbH (2)
Plateaustrasse 1, 4060, Leonding, Austria
Tel.: (43) 732 77 04 81 0
Automotive Distr
N.A.I.C.S.: 423110

Peugeot Belgique-Luxembourg SA (2)
Avenue du Bourget 20, 1130, Brussels, Belgium
Tel.: (32) 78151615
Web Site: http://www.peugeot.be
Car Whslr
N.A.I.C.S.: 441110

Peugeot Bratislava S.r.o (2)
Jasovska 22/A, 821 07, Bratislava, Slovakia
Tel.: (421) 221290777
Automotive Distr
N.A.I.C.S.: 423110

Peugeot Citroen Retail Italia S.p.A. (2)
Via Gattamelata 41, 20149, Milan, Italy
Tel.: (39) 0239761
Car Whslr
N.A.I.C.S.: 441110
Sergio Corona (Head-B2B & Mgr-DS)

Peugeot Citroen Rus LLC (2)
2nd Syromyatnichesky per 1 room 1 24, 105120, Moscow, Russia
Tel.: (7) 8001001150
Web Site: http://www.citroen.ru
Car Whslr
N.A.I.C.S.: 441110

Peugeot Delegation Office (2)
Gaya Motor Selatan No 1, Jakarta, 14330, Indonesia
Tel.: (62) 216509595
Sales Range: $200-249.9 Million
Emp.: 750
Automobile Mfr
N.A.I.C.S.: 336110

Peugeot Deutschland GmbH (2)
Edmund-Rumpler-Strasse 4, 51149, Cologne, Germany
Tel.: (49) 8001111999
Web Site: http://www.peugeot.de
Motor Vehicle Mfr & Whslr
N.A.I.C.S.: 336110
Alberic Chopelin (Mng Dir)

Subsidiary (Domestic):

PSA Retail GmbH (3)
Edmund-Rumpler-Strasse 4, Gremberghoven, 51149, Cologne, Germany
Tel.: (49) 61426927582
Web Site: https://www.stellantisandyou.com
New Car Dealers
N.A.I.C.S.: 441110
Florian Mueller (Mng Dir)

Peugeot Motocycles Deutschland GmbH (3)
Kurhessenstrasse 13, 64546, Morfelden, Germany
Tel.: (49) 6105 20930
Web Site: http://www.peugeot-scooter.de
Motor Vehicle Mfr & Distr
N.A.I.C.S.: 336110
Oliver Kurtz (Gen Mgr)

Peugeot Rheinland GmbH (3)
Vorgebirgsstrasse 94, 53119, Bonn, Germany
Tel.: (49) 228725980
Automobile Parts Distr
N.A.I.C.S.: 423140

Peugeot Sudbaden GmbH (3)
Botzinger Strasse 37, Freiburg, 79111, Germany
Tel.: (49) 761490530
Web Site: http://www.peugeot-commerce.de
Emp.: 38
Automotive Distr
N.A.I.C.S.: 423110
Wolfgang Doereyng (Gen Mgr)

Peugeot Weser-EMS GmbH (3)
Stresemannstrasse 47, Bremen, 28207, Germany
Tel.: (49) 421434240
Web Site: http://www.peugeot-commerce.de
Emp.: 37
Automotive Distr
N.A.I.C.S.: 423110
Thomas Fischer (Mgr)

Subsidiary (Non-US):

Peugeot Milan (2)
Via Gallarate 199, 20151, Milan, Italy
Tel.: (39) 023008071
Automotive Distr
N.A.I.C.S.: 423110

Peugeot Motor Co. Plc (2)
Pinley House 2 Sunbeam Way, Coventry, CV3 1ND, United Kingdom (100%)
Tel.: (44) 2476884831
Web Site: https://www.peugeot.co.uk
Sales Range: $800-899.9 Million
Emp.: 4,500
Automobiles Mfr; Car Importing & Wholesale Distr
N.A.I.C.S.: 336110
David Peel (Mng Dir-Peugeot UK)

Subsidiary (Domestic):

Robins & Day Ltd (3)
Pinley House 2 Sunbeam Way, PO Box 227, Coventry, CV3 1ND, West Midlands, United Kingdom
Tel.: (44) 2476851458
Web Site: https://www.stellantisandyou.co.uk
Sales Range: $75-99.9 Million
Used Car Dealers
N.A.I.C.S.: 441120

Subsidiary (Non-US):

Peugeot Motors South Africa Ltd (2)
44 Saturn Crescent Linbro Business Park, Johannesburg, 2090, Gauteng, South Africa
Tel.: (27) 118797400
Web Site: http://www.peugeot.co.za
Sales Range: $50-74.9 Million
Emp.: 10
Motor Vehicle Distr
N.A.I.C.S.: 423110
Francis Harnie (Mng Dir)

Subsidiary (US):

Peugeot Motors of America Inc. (2)
150 Clove Rd, Little Falls, NJ 07424 (100%)
Tel.: (973) 812-4444
Web Site: http://www.peugeot.com
Sales Range: $50-74.9 Million
Emp.: 3
Provider of Automobile Parts & Services
N.A.I.C.S.: 423120

Subsidiary (Non-US):

Peugeot Polska S.p. z.o.o. (2)
Al Krakowska 206, 02-219, Warsaw, Poland
Tel.: (48) 224442244
Web Site: https://www.peugeot.pl

AND PRIVATE COMPANIES — STELLANTIS N.V.

Motor Vehicle Distr
N.A.I.C.S.: 423110

Subsidiary (Domestic):

Peugeot SODEXA (2)
18 Rue des Fauvelles La Garenne, BP 323, 92400, Colombes, Cedex, France **(100%)**
Tel.: (33) 1 56 47 30 30
Web Site:
http://www.peugeot-diplomates.com
Rev.: $284,978,880
Emp.: 70
Wholesale Marketing, Export & Sales of Peugeot Automobiles to Diplomats, Expatriates & International Organizations
N.A.I.C.S.: 425120

Peugeot Saint-Denis Automobiles (2)
43 Boulevard de la Liberation, 93200, Saint Denis, France
Tel.: (33) 149336060
Web Site: http://concessions.peugeot.fr
Automotive Distr
N.A.I.C.S.: 423110

Subsidiary (Non-US):

Peugeot Tokyo Co., Ltd (2)
5-1-3 Himonya, Meguro-Ku, Tokyo, 152-0003, Japan
Tel.: (81) 357044511
Automobile Parts Distr
N.A.I.C.S.: 423110

Subsidiary (Domestic):

Peugeot-Citroen Moteurs (2)
49 Rue Noel Pons, 92000, Nanterre, France **(99.96%)**
Tel.: (33) 0146494900
Web Site: http://www.pcm.psa.fr
Sales Range: $25-49.9 Million
Emp.: 68
Sale of PSA Peugeot Citroen Engines to Other Car Manufacturers & Industries
N.A.I.C.S.: 455219

Subsidiary (Non-US):

Automoviles Citroen Espana S.A. (3)
Dr Esquerdo 62, 28007, Madrid, Spain **(94.88%)**
Tel.: (34) 1902445566
Web Site: https://profesionales.citroen.es
Sales Range: $25-49.9 Million
Mfr of Citroen Automobiles
N.A.I.C.S.: 336110

PSA Peugeot Citroen (3)
Montes de Oca 1102, Caba, CP 1270, Buenos Aires, Argentina **(100%)**
Tel.: (54) 11 4121 0100
Web Site: http://www.peugeot.com.ar
Sales Range: $400-449.9 Million
Emp.: 2,025
Mfr of Automobiles
N.A.I.C.S.: 336110

PSA Peugeot Citroen (3)
Avda Citroen 3 and 5, 36210, Vigo, Pontevedra, Spain **(100%)**
Tel.: (34) 986215000
Sales Range: $1-4.9 Billion
Emp.: 7,500
Mfr of Automobiles
N.A.I.C.S.: 336110

PSA Peugeot Citroen Automobiles Espana (3)
Citroen Ave 395 Zona Franca De Vigo, 36210, Madrid, Spain **(94.97%)**
Tel.: (34) 986215000
Sales Range: $1-4.9 Billion
Emp.: 10,500
Production of Citroen Vehicles
N.A.I.C.S.: 336211

Subsidiary (Domestic):

Peugeot Citroen Automobiles S.A. (3)
2-10 Boulevard De l'Europe, 78092, Yvelines, France
Tel.: (33) 1 61 45 14 14
Automobile Mfr
N.A.I.C.S.: 336110

Subsidiary (Non-US):

Peugeot Citroen Automoviles Espana S.A (3)
Citroen - 3 5, 36210, Vigo, Spain
Tel.: (34) 986 20 00 18
Motor Vehicle Distr
N.A.I.C.S.: 423110

Subsidiary (Non-US):

Peugeot Citroen Argentina S.A. (4)
Juan Domingo Peron 1001, 1682, Villa Bosch, Buenos Aires, Argentina
Tel.: (54) 11 4734 3000
Motor Vehicle Parts Mfr
N.A.I.C.S.: 336390

Peugeot Citroen Automoveis Portugal S.A. (4)
Quinta Do Bacelo, 3531, Mangualde, Portugal
Tel.: (351) 232 619 300
Automobile Mfr
N.A.I.C.S.: 336110

Subsidiary (Domestic):

Peugeot Citroen Mecanique du Nord Ouest S.N.C. (3)
11 Boulevard De L Esperance, 14123, Cormelles-le-Royal, France
Tel.: (33) 231784545
Automobile Parts Mfr
N.A.I.C.S.: 336390

Peugeot Citroen Pieces de Rechange S.N.C. (3)
Chemin De Gizy, Velizy-Villacoublay, 78140, France
Tel.: (33) 157593000
Automobile Mfr
N.A.I.C.S.: 336110
Cavares Paulos (Gen Mgr)

Peugeot Citroen Poissy S.N.C. (3)
45 Rue Jean Pierre Timbaud, 78300, Poissy, France
Tel.: (33) 130742305
Automobile Parts Mfr
N.A.I.C.S.: 336390

Peugeot Citroen Rennes S.N.C. (3)
Rte De Nante Usine La Janais, 35131, Chartres-de-Bretagne, France
Tel.: (33) 223363131
Automobile Parts Mfr
N.A.I.C.S.: 336390
Jean-Luc Perrard (Gen Mgr)

Peugeot Citroen Sochaux S.N.C. (3)
57 Avenue Du General Leclerc, 25600, Sochaux, France
Tel.: (33) 381331234
Automobile Mfr
N.A.I.C.S.: 336110

Societe Mecanique Automobile de l'Est (3)
Pole Industriel Nord Metropole Lorraine, 57300, Tremery, France
Tel.: (33) 387403131
Automobile Parts Mfr
N.A.I.C.S.: 336390

Subsidiary (Non-US):

S.A. Peugeot Distribution Service N.V. (2)
Avenue Jacques Georgin 15-19, Brussels, 1030, Belgium
Tel.: (32) 27026232
Automobile Parts Distr
N.A.I.C.S.: 423120

Subsidiary (Domestic):

Siedoubs SA (2)
14 Avenue D Helvetie, 25200, Montbeliard, France
Tel.: (33) 381994400
Automotive Seat Distr
N.A.I.C.S.: 423120

Societe Fonciere pour l'Equipement (2)
2 Rue Hennape, 92000, Nanterre, France
Tel.: (33) 172367000
Motor Vehicle Parts Mfr
N.A.I.C.S.: 336390

Subsidiary (Non-US):

Tekoto Motorlu Tastlar Ankara (2)
Eskisehir Yolu 12 Km No 354, Umitkoy, 06810, Ankara, Turkiye
Tel.: (90) 312 236 36 80
Web Site: http://www.goral.com.tr
Emp.: 200
Motor Vehicle Distr
N.A.I.C.S.: 423110
Nezih Allioglu (CEO)

Tekoto Motorlu Tastlar Istanbul (2)
89 Meclis Mahallesi Semih Sancar Caddesi, Istanbul, Turkiye
Tel.: (90) 2166210500
Automobile Distr
N.A.I.C.S.: 423110

Valencia Modulos de Puerta, S.L. (2)
Moli De Paneros 2 Polig Ind Juan Carlos I, Almusafes, 46440, Spain
Tel.: (34) 961797058
Emp.: 300
Motor Vehicle Parts Mfr
N.A.I.C.S.: 336390

Vauxhall Motors Limited (2)
Griffin House Osborne Rd, Luton, LU1 3YT, Bedfordshire, United Kingdom **(100%)**
Tel.: (44) 1582721122
Web Site: http://www.vauxhall.co.uk
Automobile Mfr
N.A.I.C.S.: 336110
Stephen Norman (Grp Mng Dir)

Subsidiary (Domestic):

IBC Vehicles Limited (3)
Kimpton Road, PO Box 163, Luton, LU2 0JX, Bedfordshire, United Kingdom
Tel.: (44) 01582721122
Mfr of Medium-Duty Vans
N.A.I.C.S.: 336110

Plastic Components and Modules Holding S.p.A. (1)
Viale Carlo Emanuele 118, Venaria Reale, 10078, Italy
Tel.: (39) 0116879111
Web Site: http://www.magnetimarelli.com
Plastics Product Mfr
N.A.I.C.S.: 326199

Subsidiary (Domestic):

Ergom Soffiaggio S.r.l. (2)
Via B Castelli 18, 25024, Leno, Brescia, Italy
Tel.: (39) 030 9038257
Web Site: http://www.ergomsoff.com
Thermoplastic Container Mfr
N.A.I.C.S.: 326199

Subsidiary (Non-US):

Plastic Components and Modules Poland S.A. (2)
Generala Mariusza Zaruskiego 11, Sosnowiec, Poland
Tel.: (48) 32 368 12 00
Automotive Plastic Component & Module Mfr
N.A.I.C.S.: 326199

Subsidiary (Domestic):

Plastic Components and Modules Fuel Systems Poland Sp. z o.o. (3)
ul Jednosci 44, Sosnowiec, 41200, Poland
Tel.: (48) 32 368 12 23
Web Site: http://www.magnetimarelli.com
Emp.: 500
Plastics Product Mfr
N.A.I.C.S.: 326199

Powertrain Mekanik Sanayi ve Ticaret Anoniom Sirketi (1)
Organize Sanayi Bolgesi Yesil Cd No 28 Nilufer, Bursa, Turkiye
Tel.: (90) 224 261 03 50
Automobile Parts Distr
N.A.I.C.S.: 423120

Publikompass S.p.A. (1)
Via Washington 70, 20123, Milan, Italy
Tel.: (39) 0224424611
Web Site: http://www.publikompass.it
Advertising Space Sales
N.A.I.C.S.: 541890

Risk Management S.p.A. (1)
Via Giacosa 38, Turin, 10125, Italy
Tel.: (39) 0110057611
Risk Managemeng Srvices
N.A.I.C.S.: 523940

SIRIO - Sicurezza Industriale S.c.p.a. (1)
Corso Marconi 20, 10125, Turin, Italy
Tel.: (39) 0110062759
Corporate Security Services
N.A.I.C.S.: 561621

Servicios Administrativos Corp. IPASA S.A. (1)
Retorno Ave De La Industria Lote 20 Y 21, Tepotzotlan, 54600, Mexico
Tel.: (52) 5558760511
Automobile Parts Distr
N.A.I.C.S.: 423120

Sistemi Sospensioni S.p.A. (1)
Corso Unione Sovietica 600, Turin, 10135, Italy
Tel.: (39) 0110046844
Automobile Parts Mfr
N.A.I.C.S.: 336390

TCA - Tecnologia em Componentes Automotivos. SA (1)
Rod Prestes Maia Br - 101 Sul S/N, Jaboatao dos Guararapes, 54335-180, Pernambuco, Brazil
Tel.: (55) 8121196715
Automobile Parts Distr
N.A.I.C.S.: 423120

Teksid S.p.A. (1)
Via Plava 86, 10138, Turin, Italy **(84.8%)**
Tel.: (39) 0119794111
Web Site: http://www.teksid.com
Sales Range: $1-4.9 Billion
Emp.: 8,342
Metallurgical Component Mfr
N.A.I.C.S.: 336390
Paolo Airaldi (Pres & CEO)

Subsidiary (Non-US):

Funfrap-Fundicao Portuguesa S.A. (2)
Apartado 3, 3801-652, Aveiro, Portugal
Tel.: (351) 234 301700
Web Site: http://www.teksid.com
Iron Casting Product Mfr
N.A.I.C.S.: 331511

Teksid Aluminum S.r.l. (2)
Tel.: (39) 0119794111
Web Site: http://www.teksid.com
Emp.: 1,000
Metal Casting Equipment Mfr
N.A.I.C.S.: 333248

Teksid Hierro de Mexico S.A. de C.V. (2)
Libramiento Carlos Salinas de Gortari 2001 PTE C D Frontera Coah, Mexico, 25616, Mexico
Tel.: (52) 86 66494078
Web Site: http://www.teksid.com
Cast Iron Mfr
N.A.I.C.S.: 331511

Subsidiary (Domestic):

Compania Industrial Frontera S.A. de C.V. (3)
Libramiento Carlos Salinas De Gortari No 2001 Pte, Villa Frontera, 25616, Mexico
Tel.: (52) 8666494100
Automobile Metallurgical Product Mfr
N.A.I.C.S.: 423120

Subsidiary (US):

Teksid Inc. (2)
21000 Telegraph Rd, Southfield, MI 48033
Tel.: (248) 624-3040
Web Site: http://www.teksid.com
Cast Iron Mfr
N.A.I.C.S.: 331511

Subsidiary (Non-US):

Teksid Iron Poland Sp. z o.o. (2)
Ul Ciezarowa 49, 43-300, Skoczow, Poland
Tel.: (48) 338538200

STELLANTIS N.V.

Stellantis N.V.—(Continued)
Sales Range: $75-99.9 Million
Emp.: 500
Metal Casting Equipment Mfr
N.A.I.C.S.: 333248
M. Kanafek (Plant Mgr)

STELLAR AFRICAGOLD INC.
4908 Pine Crescent, Vancouver, V6M 3P6, BC, Canada
Tel.: (604) 618-4262
Web Site:
https://www.stellarafricagold.com
Year Founded: 2006
6YP—(DEU)
Assets: $153,129
Liabilities: $552,509
Net Worth: ($399,380)
Earnings: ($500,990)
Fiscal Year-end: 07/31/24
Gold Exploration Services
N.A.I.C.S.: 212220
Maurice Giroux (COO & VP-Exploration)

Subsidiaries:

Stelmine Canada Ltd. (1)
8255 boul Henri Bourassa office 230, Quebec, G1G 4C8, QC, Canada
Tel.: (418) 626-6333
Web Site: https://www.stelmine.com
Assets: $7,776,439
Liabilities: $960,322
Net Worth: $6,816,117
Earnings: ($1,320,338)
Fiscal Year-end: 07/31/2022
Mineral Exploration Services
N.A.I.C.S.: 213114
Andre Proulx (Chm)

STELLAR CALL CENTRES PTY. LIMITED
Level 5 12 Church St, Sydney, 2060, NSW, Australia
Tel.: (61) 294652222
Web Site: http://www.stellarbpo.com
Year Founded: 1998
Sales Range: $75-99.9 Million
Emp.: 3,000
Customer Contact Solutions
N.A.I.C.S.: 561422
Richard Mann (Gen Mgr-Bus Dev)

STELLAR CAPITAL PARTNERS LIMITED
4th Floor The Terraces 25 Protea Road, Cape Town, 7708, South Africa
Tel.: (27) 21 657 8772
Web Site:
http://www.stellarcapital.co.za
Year Founded: 2005
SCP—(JSE)
Sales Range: $25-49.9 Million
Holding Company; Information & Communications Technology Products & Services
N.A.I.C.S.: 551112
Peter J. van Zyl (CEO)

Subsidiaries:

Cadiz Holdings (Pty) Ltd (1)
4th Floor The Terraces 25 Protea Road, Claremont, 7708, South Africa (100%)
Tel.: (27) 21 657 8300
Web Site: http://www.cadiz.co.za
Financial Services
N.A.I.C.S.: 541611
Fraser Shaw (CEO, COO & Dir-Fin)

Subsidiary (Domestic):

Cadiz Asset Management (Pty) Ltd (2)
4th Floor The Terraces 25 Protea Road, Claremont, 7708, South Africa
Tel.: (27) 21 657 8300
Web Site: http://www.cadiz.co.za
Asset Management Services
N.A.I.C.S.: 531390
Fraser Shaw (CEO, COO & Fin Dir)

Interface Network Technology (Pty) Ltd (1)
22 Westbrook, PO BOX 10524, Centurion, Pretoria, 0046, Gauteng, South Africa
Tel.: (27) 126442466
Web Site: http://www.intafrica.co.za
Sales Range: $25-49.9 Million
Emp.: 12
Data Communication Software Development Services
N.A.I.C.S.: 541511
Christian de Waal (Project Mgr-Sls)

Navix Distribution (Pty) Ltd (1)
7 Monza Close, Kyalami Business Park, Kyalami, 1684, South Africa
Tel.: (27) 11 466 3936/7
Information & Communication Technology Services
N.A.I.C.S.: 541430

Sizwe Africa IT Group (Pty) Ltd (1)
Cnr's Landmark 35 Waterloo Ave Kosmosdal, Samrand, Centurion, 0157, Gauteng, South Africa
Tel.: (27) 126575300
Web Site: http://www.sizwegroup.co.za
Sales Range: $75-99.9 Million
Emp.: 500
Information & Communication Technology Services
N.A.I.C.S.: 541430
Hanno van Dyk (CEO)

Subsidiary (Domestic):

Sizwe Business Networking (Pty) Ltd (2)
Sizwe House Corner Landmarks and Waterloo Ave, Centurion, 0158, Kosmosdel, South Africa
Tel.: (27) 126575300
Web Site: http://www.sizwegroup.co.za
Information Communications Technology Support Services
N.A.I.C.S.: 517111
Hanno Vandyk (CEO)

Smart Box Support Services (Pty) Ltd (2)
35 Landmarks Rd Sizwe House, Samrand, Pretoria, 0002, Gauteng, South Africa
Tel.: (27) 126570619
Information Communications Technology Support Services
N.A.I.C.S.: 517111

Subsidiary (Domestic):

Leboa IT Solutions (Pty) Ltd (3)
58B King Edward Dr Willows, Bloemfontein, 9300, Free State, South Africa
Tel.: (27) 514472206
Web Site: http://www.leboa.co.za
Sales Range: $25-49.9 Million
Emp.: 10
Information & Communication Technology Services
N.A.I.C.S.: 517810
Faye Delport Cader (Mng Dir)

Setsibi IT Support Services (Pty) Ltd (3)
91 Retief St, Potchefstroom, 2520, South Africa
Tel.: (27) 182978518
Web Site: http://www.setsibi.co.za
Sales Range: $25-49.9 Million
Emp.: 11
Information Technology Support Services
N.A.I.C.S.: 541511

Structured Connectivity Solutions (Pty) Ltd (1)
Unit 14 a Wild Fig Bus Park 1494 Cranberry St Honeydew Ext 1919, Johannesburg, 2170, Gauteng, South Africa
Tel.: (27) 117942240
Web Site: http://www.scs-za.com
Sales Range: $25-49.9 Million
Emp.: 15
Information Technology Solutions
N.A.I.C.S.: 541512
Andrew Scheepers (Exec Dir)

Tellumat (Pty) Ltd. (1)
64-74 White Road, Retreat, Cape Town, 7945, South Africa (48.9%)
Tel.: (27) 21 710 2911

Web Site: http://www.tellumat.com
Electronics Mfr
N.A.I.C.S.: 334220
Graham Meyer (Dir-Fin)

XDSL Networking Solutions (Pty) Ltd (1)
977 Schoeman Street, Arcadia, Pretoria, 0083, South Africa
Tel.: (27) 86 100 9375
Information & Communication Technology Services
N.A.I.C.S.: 541430

netXcom (Pty) Ltd (1)
Prosperitas Building Unit 5 Tiger Valley Office Park, Silver Lakes Drive, Pretoria, 0081, South Africa
Tel.: (27) 128093368
Web Site: http://www.convergenet.com
Sales Range: $25-49.9 Million
Emp.: 2
Information & Communication Technology Services
N.A.I.C.S.: 541430

STELLAR CAPITAL SERVICES LIMITED
402 4th Floor Solitaire Plaza MG Road, Gurgaon, 122002, Haryana, India
Tel.: (91) 8587000091
Web Site: https://www.stellarcapital.in
536702—(BOM)
Rev.: $376,610
Assets: $5,869,437
Liabilities: $209,773
Net Worth: $5,659,665
Earnings: ($93,263)
Emp.: 12
Fiscal Year-end: 03/31/23
Securities & Loan Brokerage Services
N.A.I.C.S.: 523150
Pranay Aneja (Mng Dir)

STELLAR RESOURCES LIMITED
Level 4 96-100 Albert Road, South Melbourne, 3205, VIC, Australia
Tel.: (61) 396927222
Web Site:
https://www.stellarresources.com.au
SRZ—(ASX)
Rev.: $71,447
Assets: $7,284,971
Liabilities: $167,764
Net Worth: $7,117,207
Earnings: ($1,503,160)
Fiscal Year-end: 06/30/24
Gold Mining & Mineral Exploration Services
N.A.I.C.S.: 212220
Melanie J. Leydin (Sec)

STELLARIS GROWTH ACQUISITION CORP.
Tower B Suite #308 18 Parc Place SCBD, Jl. Jendral Sudirman Kav. 52 - 53, Jakarta, 12190, Indonesia
Tel.: (62) 21 5080 8585
Year Founded: 2021
STLRU—(NASDAQ)
Investment Services
N.A.I.C.S.: 523999
Ronald Felt (Chm & CEO)

STELMET SA
Ul Gorzowska 20, 65-127, Gora Zielona, Poland
Tel.: (48) 683293800
Web Site: http://www.stelmet.com
Year Founded: 1985
Wood Products Mfr
N.A.I.C.S.: 321999
Stanislaw Bienkowski (Founder & Chm-Mgmt Bd)

STELRAD GROUP PLC

INTERNATIONAL PUBLIC

69-75 Side, New Castle Upon Tyne, NE1 3JE, Tyne And Wear, United Kingdom
Tel.: (44) 2613301
Web Site: https://www.stelradplc.com
Year Founded: 2021
SRAD—(LSE)
Heating Radiators Mfr
N.A.I.C.S.: 333414
Bob Ellis (Chm)

Subsidiaries:

DL Radiators Srl (1)
Strada Statale 54 21, 33040, Moimacco, Udine, Italy
Tel.: (39) 0421303811
Web Site: http://www.dlradiators.com
Raditor Mfr & Distr
N.A.I.C.S.: 333414

STELUX HOLDINGS INTERNATIONAL LIMITED
27th Floor Stelux House 698 Prince Edward Road East San Po Kong, Kowloon, China (Hong Kong)
Tel.: (852) 21132288
Web Site: https://www.irasia.com
0084—(HKG)
Rev.: $89,319,553
Assets: $152,458,229
Liabilities: $102,833,432
Net Worth: $49,624,797
Earnings: ($13,731,211)
Emp.: 910
Fiscal Year-end: 03/31/22
Retailing, Trading & Property Investment Services
N.A.I.C.S.: 523999
Joseph C. C. Wong (Chm & CEO)

Subsidiaries:

City Chain (M) Sdn Bhd (1)
Unit 10 01 10th Floor NCB Plaza, No 6 Changkat Raja Chulan, 50200, Kuala Lumpur, Malaysia (92.5%)
Tel.: (60) 320261125
Web Site: http://www.citychain.com
Jewelry Stores
N.A.I.C.S.: 458310

City Chain Company Limited (1)
27th Floor Stelux Hse, Kowloon, China (Hong Kong) (100%)
Tel.: (852) 21132288
Web Site: http://www.hkite.com
Sales Range: $25-49.9 Million
Emp.: 100
Jewelry Stores
N.A.I.C.S.: 458310
Joseph Wong (CEO)

Optical 88 Eyecare (M) Sdn Bhd (1)
Unit 10 01 10th Floor MCB Plaza 6 Changkat 18, Raja Chulan, 50200, Kuala Lumpur, Malaysia (70%)
Tel.: (60) 320261125
Web Site: http://www.optical88.com.cn
Professional Equipment & Supplies Whslr
N.A.I.C.S.: 423490
Eric Wong (Mng Dir)

Optical 88 Limited (1)
19/F Stelux House 698 Prince Edward Road, East San Po Kong, Kowloon, China (Hong Kong) (100%)
Tel.: (852) 21132363
Web Site: http://www.optical88.com.hk
Sales Range: $25-49.9 Million
Emp.: 100
Optical Goods Stores
N.A.I.C.S.: 456130

Pronto Watch S.A. (1)
Ch du Grand Puits 38, Meyrin, 1217, Switzerland (100%)
Tel.: (41) 223077880
Emp.: 2
Watch Clock & Part Mfr
N.A.I.C.S.: 334519
Vernier Nicolas (Gen Mgr)

Solvil Et Titus SA (1)
Route Des Acacias 6, 1227, Geneva, Switzerland (100%)

Tel.: (41) 223480480
Jewelry Stores
N.A.I.C.S.: 458310

Stelux Properties Limited (1)
3rd Floor Kader Building, Kowloon, China
(Hong Kong) **(100%)**
Tel.: (852) 23522668
Web Site: http://www.cityshain.com
Sales Range: $25-49.9 Million
Emp.: 100
Land Subdivision
N.A.I.C.S.: 237210

Stelux Trading (International) Ltd (1)
27th Floor Stelux House 698 Prince Edward Road East, San Po Kong, Kowloon, China (Hong Kong)
Tel.: (852) 21132288
Web Site: http://www.ellessewatch.com
Watch Clock & Part Mfr
N.A.I.C.S.: 334519

Stelux Watch Limited (1)
3rd Floor Kader Bldg, Kowloon, China
(Hong Kong) **(100%)**
Tel.: (852) 23522668
Watch Clock & Part Mfr
N.A.I.C.S.: 334519
Joseph Wong *(CEO)*

Thong Sia Co (S) Pte Ltd (1)
31 Ubi Road 1 02-06, Singapore, 408694, Singapore **(100%)**
Tel.: (65) 67376122
Web Site: http://www.thongsia.com.sg
Sales Range: $25-49.9 Million
Emp.: 80
Watch Clock & Part Mfr
N.A.I.C.S.: 334519

Thong Sia Sdn Bhd (1)
CP27 Suite 2601-04 26th floor Wisma Chuang No 34 Jalan Sultan Ismail, 50250, Kuala Lumpur, Malaysia **(96.4%)**
Tel.: (60) 21415163
Web Site: http://www.thongsia.com.my
Sales Range: $25-49.9 Million
Emp.: 50
Jewelry Stores
N.A.I.C.S.: 458310

Thong Sia Watch Co. Ltd (1)
21/F Po Kwong Commercial Centre 698 Prince Edward Road East, Kowloon, China
(Hong Kong) **(96%)**
Tel.: (852) 27360235
Web Site: http://www.thongsia.com.hk
Sales Range: $25-49.9 Million
Emp.: 50
Watch Clock & Part Mfr
N.A.I.C.S.: 334519

STEMA METALLEICHTBAU GMBH
Riesaer Strasse 50, 01558, Grossenhain, Germany
Tel.: (49) 352230940
Web Site: http://www.stema-grossenhain.de
Rev.: $34,164,697
Emp.: 150
Truck Trailer Mfr
N.A.I.C.S.: 336212
Michael Jursch *(Mng Dir)*

STEMCELL HOLDINGS, INC.
5-9-15-3F Minamiaoyama Minato-ku, Tokyo, 107-0062, Japan
Tel.: (81) 334000077 DE
Web Site: http://www.stemcoordinate.com
Year Founded: 2015
STMM—(OTCIQ)
Sales Range: $1-9.9 Million
Emp.: 28
Biotechnology Research & Development Services
N.A.I.C.S.: 541714
Takaaki Matsuoka *(Pres, CEO, Treas & Sec)*

STEMCELL TECHNOLOGIES CANADA INC.
1618 Station St, Vancouver, V6A 1B6, BC, Canada
Tel.: (604) 877-0713
Web Site: https://www.stemcell.com
Biotechnology Research & Development Services
N.A.I.C.S.: 541714

Subsidiaries:

Stemcell Technologies Inc (1)
12698 Gateway Dr S, Tukwila, WA 98168
Tel.: (206) 244-0440
Web Site: http://www.stemcell.com
Rev.: $2,237,100
Emp.: 11
Stem Cell Products Mfr & Distr
N.A.I.C.S.: 325414
Allen C. Eaves *(Pres & CEO)*

STEMCELL UNITED LIMITED
Level 12 680 George Street, Sydney, 2000, NSW, Australia
Tel.: (61) 2 8280 7355
Web Site: http://scu.com.sg
Year Founded: 1989
Rev.: $1,092,048
Assets: $1,700,535
Liabilities: $244,745
Net Worth: $1,455,789
Earnings: ($1,585,595)
Fiscal Year-end: 06/30/19
Investment Services
N.A.I.C.S.: 523999
Chow-Yee Koh *(Sec)*

Subsidiaries:

Yunnan HuaFang Industrial Hemp Co., Ltd. (1)
13 Xinyuan Villa, Kunming, YunNan, China
Tel.: (86) 18666562181
Web Site: http://www.hfhemp.com
Cannabis Product Mfr
N.A.I.C.S.: 325411

STEMCOR HOLDINGS LIMITED
Longbow House 4th Floor 14-20 Chiswell Street, London, EC1Y 4TW, United Kingdom
Tel.: (44) 2077753600
Web Site: http://www.stemcor.com
Year Founded: 1951
Sales Range: $5-14.9 Billion
Emp.: 2,000
Steel & Raw Material Distr
N.A.I.C.S.: 423510
Steven M. Graf *(CEO)*

Subsidiaries:

Estac Industrial Agencies Ltd. (1)
232A Spanish Town Road, Kingston, 11, Jamaica
Tel.: (876) 9018708
Steel & Raw Materials Distr
N.A.I.C.S.: 331221

Eurosteel (Portugal) Comercio Internacional LDA (1)
Rotumda Roffio Dolezante 2B, Vila Expo, Lisbon, 1990-374, Portugal
Tel.: (351) 218922960
Web Site: http://www.pt.stemcor.com
Sales Range: $25-49.9 Million
Emp.: 5
Steel & Raw Materials Distr
N.A.I.C.S.: 331221
Jule Rofino *(Mng Dir)*

L.W. Lambourn Nigeria Ltd. (1)
23 Warehouse Road, Apapa, Lagos, Nigeria
Tel.: (234) 15876026
Steel & Raw Materials Distr
N.A.I.C.S.: 331221

Stemcor (Contistahl) Beijing Ltd. (1)
Room 1709B Tengda Plaza No 168 Xiwai Street, Haidian District, Beijing, 100044, China
Tel.: (86) 10 885 75 868
Steel Product Distr
N.A.I.C.S.: 423390

Stemcor (S.E.A.) PTE Ltd. (1)
541 Orchard Rd, Unit 17-00 Liat Tower, Singapore, 238881, Singapore
Tel.: (65) 67327666
Sales Range: $25-49.9 Million
Emp.: 40
Steel & Raw Materials Distr
N.A.I.C.S.: 331221
Jerry Craggs *(Pres)*

Stemcor AG (1)
Grafenauweg 4, Zug, 6300, Switzerland
Tel.: (41) 41 619 8700
Steel Product Distr
N.A.I.C.S.: 423390

Stemcor Australia Pty. Ltd. (1)
Level 18 55 11th Street, Milsons Point, 2061, NSW, Australia
Tel.: (61) 299593088
Sales Range: $25-49.9 Million
Emp.: 80
Steel & Raw Materials Distr
N.A.I.C.S.: 331221
Stephen Baker *(Mgr)*

Stemcor Bangkok (1)
Bangkok, Bangkok, 10330, Thailand
Tel.: (66) 2 254 8340 5
Steel Product Distr
N.A.I.C.S.: 423390

Stemcor Bielefeld (1)
Ludwig-Erhard-Allee 53, 33719, Bielefeld, Germany
Tel.: (49) 521 163964 0
Steel Product Distr
N.A.I.C.S.: 423390

Stemcor Bucharest (1)
1 Titulescu Blvd Bloc A 7 SC 2 3rd Floor Apartment 37, Bucharest, Romania
Tel.: (40) 1 21 3185668
Steel Product Distr
N.A.I.C.S.: 423390

Stemcor Budapest Ltd. (1)
Fogado u 4, Budapest, 1107, Hungary
Tel.: (36) 1 886 4975
Steel Product Distr
N.A.I.C.S.: 423390

Stemcor Chile SpA (1)
Almirante Pastene 185 Of 1103, Providencia, Santiago, 750053, Chile
Tel.: (56) 2 2434 9153
Emp.: 2
Steel Product Distr
N.A.I.C.S.: 423390
Sam Andrus *(Gen Mgr)*

Stemcor Deutschland Holding GmbH (1)
Breite Strasse 31, 40213, Dusseldorf, Germany
Tel.: (49) 211 4585 5 0
Holding Company
N.A.I.C.S.: 551112

Stemcor Dis Ticaret Ltd. STI (1)
Dikilitas, Bestekar Sokak no 5, Istanbul, 34349, Turkiye
Tel.: (90) 2122369088
Web Site: http://www.stemcor.com
Sales Range: $25-49.9 Million
Emp.: 25
Steel & Raw Materials Distr
N.A.I.C.S.: 331221

Stemcor Dnepropetrovsk (1)
Chkalova Street 40 Room 5, Dnepropetrovsk, 49000, Ukraine
Tel.: (380) 562 473 706
Steel Product Distr
N.A.I.C.S.: 423390

Stemcor Egypt (1)
13 Al Esraa Street Sixth floor Apartment No 602, Mohandessin, Cairo, Egypt
Tel.: (20) 2 305 9432
Steel Product Distr
N.A.I.C.S.: 423390

Stemcor Flachstahl GmbH (1)
Jagdschankenstrasse 17, 09117, Chemnitz, Germany
Tel.: (49) 371 4819 04110
Steel Product Distr
N.A.I.C.S.: 423390

Stemcor France SAS (1)
39 Rue de Courcelles, 75008, Paris, France
Tel.: (33) 1 58 18 66 66
Steel Product Distr
N.A.I.C.S.: 423390

Stemcor Gdansk (1)
Ul Majewskich 13, 80-457, Gdansk, Poland
Tel.: (48) 58 346 5460
Steel Product Distr
N.A.I.C.S.: 423390

Stemcor GmbH (1)
Tersteegenstrasse 28, 40474, Dusseldorf, Germany
Tel.: (49) 21145853
Web Site: http://www.stemcor.com
Steel & Raw Materials Distr
N.A.I.C.S.: 331221

Stemcor Hamburg (1)
Ferdinand Strasse 36, 20095, Hamburg, Germany
Tel.: (49) 40 321 103
Steel Product Distr
N.A.I.C.S.: 423390

Stemcor Hanoi (1)
194 Tran Quang Khai Street, Hoan Kiem District, Hanoi, Vietnam
Tel.: (84) 4 3 935 0798
Steel Product Distr
N.A.I.C.S.: 423390

Stemcor Hellas Ltd (1)
13 G Lambraki Street, Glyfada, 16675, Athens, Greece
Tel.: (30) 210 894 4490
Steel Product Distr
N.A.I.C.S.: 423390

Stemcor Hong Kong Ltd. (1)
12th Fl Infinitus Plaza 199 Des Voeux Rd Central, Sheung Wan, China (Hong Kong)
Tel.: (852) 2527 7861
Steel Product Distr
N.A.I.C.S.: 423390

Stemcor India Pvt Ltd (1)
No 25 2nd Floor 9th Main 36th Cross Road 5th Block, Jayanagar, Bengaluru, 560 041, India
Tel.: (91) 80 2664 4076
Steel Product Distr
N.A.I.C.S.: 423390

Stemcor Italia s.r.l. (1)
Palazzo Torre Tonda Piazza Don Giovanni Mapelli 1, Sesto San Giovanni, Milan, 20099, Italy
Tel.: (39) 0224124511
Sales Range: $25-49.9 Million
Emp.: 25
Steel & Raw Materials Distr
N.A.I.C.S.: 331221

Stemcor Japan Ltd. (1)
Takeda Edobashi Building 14-3 Room 201, 3-chome Nihonbashi Chuo-ku, Tokyo, 103-0027, Japan
Tel.: (81) 362029391
Sales Range: $25-49.9 Million
Emp.: 3
Steel & Raw Materials Distr
N.A.I.C.S.: 331221

Stemcor Kiev (1)
Tolstoho Street 11 Appt 56, Kiev, 01004, Ukraine
Tel.: (380) 44 495 22 89
Steel Product Distr
N.A.I.C.S.: 423390

Stemcor Krakow (1)
Ul Kamienskiego 51, 30-644, Krakow, Poland
Tel.: (48) 12 255 1446
Steel Product Distr
N.A.I.C.S.: 423390

Stemcor Lahore (1)
FB-3 1st Floor Awami Complex, New Garden Town, Lahore, Pakistan
Tel.: (92) 25 3940 1423
Steel Product Distr
N.A.I.C.S.: 423390

Stemcor MESA DMCC (1)
Level 21 Silver Tower AG Jumeirah Lake Towers, PO Box 37324, Dubai, United Arab Emirates
Tel.: (971) 4 4270452

STEMCOR HOLDINGS LIMITED

Stemcor Holdings Limited—(Continued)
Steel Product Distr
N.A.I.C.S.: 423390
Bill Attenborough (Mng Dir)

Stemcor Morocco Sarl (1)
Residence Maryamo 18 Oumaima Essayeh Bureau n 5 - 2eme Etage, Casablanca, Morocco
Tel.: (212) 5 225 396529
Steel Product Distr
N.A.I.C.S.: 423390

Stemcor Moscow (1)
Ducat Place II 7 Gasheka Street Office 420, Moscow, 123056, Russia
Tel.: (7) 495 363 0630
Steel Product Distr
N.A.I.C.S.: 423390

Stemcor New Zealand (1)
Level 2 41 Bath Street, Parnell, Auckland, 1151, New Zealand
Tel.: (64) 9 309 5775
Steel Product Distr
N.A.I.C.S.: 423390

Stemcor Norway AS (1)
Taerudgata 1, Lillestrom, 2004, Norway
Tel.: (47) 63 81 50 70
Steel Product Distr
N.A.I.C.S.: 423390

Stemcor Odessa (1)
Uspenskaya Street Home 6 Flat 64, Odessa, Ukraine
Tel.: (380) 482 34 6218
Steel Product Distr
N.A.I.C.S.: 423390

Stemcor SA (1)
Hubertusstigen 11, 974 55, Lulea, Sweden
Tel.: (46) 920 66400
Steel Product Distr
N.A.I.C.S.: 423390

Stemcor Shanghai Ltd. (1)
2201 East Tower Room 3-7 Floor 27 Lujiazui Plaza, Shanghai, 200122, China
Tel.: (86) 21 5836 0788
Steel Product Distr
N.A.I.C.S.: 423390

Stemcor Skopje (1)
Mitropolit Teodosij Gologanov N 28/2/21, Centar, Skopje, 1000, North Macedonia
Tel.: (389) 2 3296 055
Steel Product Distr
N.A.I.C.S.: 423390

Stemcor South Africa (Proprietary) Ltd. (1)
193 Cnr Bryanston Dr & William Nicol Bryanston, Brystan, Cramerview, 2060, South Africa
Tel.: (27) 115166000
Sales Range: $25-49.9 Million
Emp.: 18
Steel & Raw Materials Distr
N.A.I.C.S.: 331221

Stemcor Special Steels Gulf FZE (1)
Jebil Ali Free Zone, PO Box 17437, Dubai, United Arab Emirates
Tel.: (971) 4 8809249
Steel Product Distr
N.A.I.C.S.: 423390

Stemcor Special Steels Pte Ltd (1)
No 1 Kian Teck Crescent, Singapore, 628880, Singapore
Tel.: (65) 6862 035
Steel Product Distr
N.A.I.C.S.: 423390
Maggie Koh (Gen Mgr)

Stemcor Steel, S.L. (1)
Paseo de la Castellana 14964 Dcha 149 6 Floor, 28046, Madrid, Spain
Tel.: (34) 917241400
Sales Range: $25-49.9 Million
Emp.: 11
Steel & Raw Materials Distr
N.A.I.C.S.: 331221
Alejandro Ciudad Real Calder (Mgr)

Subsidiary (Non-US):

Global Metals Pty Ltd (2)
64-66 Venture Place, Dandenong South, 3175, VIC, Australia
Tel.: (61) 3 9799 6111
Web Site: http://www.globalmetals.com.au
Steel Product Distr
N.A.I.C.S.: 423390
Rod Gregory (Mng Dir)

OKS Otto Knauf GmbH (2)
Zollhausstrasse 38, 58640, Iserlohn, Germany
Tel.: (49) 2371 9456 0
Web Site: http://www.oks-knauf.com
Steel Product Distr
N.A.I.C.S.: 423390

Semi-Produtos de Metais, Lda (2)
Rua Caminho do Senhor 938, 4410-083, Serzedo, Portugal
Tel.: (351) 22 753 60 10
Web Site: http://www.semimetais.com
Metal Product Distr
N.A.I.C.S.: 423510

Subsidiary (Domestic):

Servichap S.L. (2)
Poligono Industrial San Colombar, 31360, Funes, Navarre, Spain
Tel.: (34) 948 753 027
Web Site: http://www.servichap.com
Steel Product Distr
N.A.I.C.S.: 423390

Subsidiary (Non-US):

Steel Plate & Sections Ltd (2)
Mill House Forge Lane, Minworth, Sutton Coldfield, B76 1AH, West Midlands, United Kingdom
Tel.: (44) 12 1313 4300
Web Site: http://www.steelplate.co.uk
Emp.: 20
Steel Product Distr
N.A.I.C.S.: 423390

Subsidiary (US):

Stemcor Special Steels LLC (2)
32703 Tamina Rd, Magnolia, TX 77354
Tel.: (281) 252-3625
Metal Product Distr
N.A.I.C.S.: 423510
Tom Turnipseede (Pres & CEO)

Subsidiary (Non-US):

Stemcor Special Steels Ltd (2)
Pottery Lane East Whittington Moor, Chesterfield, S41 9BH, Derbyshire, United Kingdom
Tel.: (44) 1246 458100
Web Site: http://www.stemcorspecialsteels.com
Metal Product Distr
N.A.I.C.S.: 423510
Michael Naylor (Mgr-Comml)

Stemcor Tubes (2)
Office 6 Liverpool Barclay & Mathieson Byng Street, Bootle, Liverpool, L20 1EE, United Kingdom
Tel.: (44) 151 933 0671
Steel Product Distr
N.A.I.C.S.: 423390

Stemcor UK Ltd. (2)
Level 27 CityPoint 1 Ropemaker Street, London, EC2Y 9ST, United Kingdom
Tel.: (44) 20 7775 3600
Web Site: http://www.stemcor.com
Steel Product Distr
N.A.I.C.S.: 423390

Subsidiary (Domestic):

Barclay & Mathieson Ltd. (2)
Shieldhall Works 180 Hardgate Road, Glasgow, G51 4TB, United Kingdom
Tel.: (44) 207 775 3592
Web Site: http://www.bmsteel.co.uk
Steel Stockholding & Fabrication Services
N.A.I.C.S.: 332420
Alain Huys (Mgr-Sls & Solution Architects)

Unit (Domestic):

Stemcor Architectural (2)
Coleford Road, Darnall, Sheffield, S9 5NF, United Kingdom
Tel.: (44) 114 2543226
Steel Product Distr
N.A.I.C.S.: 423390

Vicky Bradley (Mgr-Technical Sls)

Stemcor Sections (2)
Grove Cottage Neap House Road, Gunness, Scunthorpe, DN15 8TY, United Kingdom
Tel.: (44) 1724 782825
Steel Product Distr
N.A.I.C.S.: 423390

Stemcor Stainless UK (2)
Hints Hall Rookery Lane Hints, Tamworth, B78 3DP, Staffordshire, United Kingdom
Tel.: (44) 1543 483020
Web Site: http://www.stemcor.com
Emp.: 4
Steel Product Distr
N.A.I.C.S.: 423390
Martin Adams (Mgr-Bus Dev)

Stemcor USA Inc. (1)
350 5th Ave Ste 1526, New York, NY 10118-1593
Tel.: (212) 563-0262
Web Site: http://www.stemcor.com
Steel & Raw Materials Distr
N.A.I.C.S.: 331221
Shawn Gill (VP)

Stemcor Vietnam Co. (1)
Level 1 Somerset Chancellor Court 21-23 Nguyen Thi Minh Khai Street, District 1, Ho Chi Minh City, Vietnam
Tel.: (84) 8 3 824 7071
Steel Product Distr
N.A.I.C.S.: 423390

Stemcor de Mexico, S.A. de C.V. (1)
Calvario No 7 Col Tlalpan Centro Del Tlalpan, Mexico, 14000, Mexico
Tel.: (52) 55 5171 6209
Steel Product Distr
N.A.I.C.S.: 423390
Javier Escartin (Gen Mgr)

STEMLAB, INC.
602-4 Techno Complex of Korea University 145 Anam-dong, Sungbuk-gu, Seoul, 136-701, Korea (South)
Tel.: (82) 220701177
Web Site: https://www.stemlab.co.kr
Year Founded: 2011
Medical Device Mfr
N.A.I.C.S.: 334510
Donghoon Oh (CEO)

STEMRIM, INC.
Saito Bio-Incubator 3F 7-7-15 Saito-Asagi, Ibaraki City, Osaka, 567-0085, Japan
Tel.: (81) 726487152
Web Site: https://www.stemrim.com
Year Founded: 2006
4599—(TKS)
Emp.: 58
Medicinal Product Mfr
N.A.I.C.S.: 339112
Kensuke Tomita (Chm & CEO)

STEMTECH CORPORATION
2302-3 Pacific Plaza 410 Des Voeux Road West, Hong Kong, China (Hong Kong)
Tel.: (852) 2528637   NV
Web Site: http://www.globenetwireless.com
Year Founded: 2009
STEK—(OTCQB)
Rev.: $4,559,399
Assets: $4,266,941
Liabilities: $7,438,859
Net Worth: ($3,171,918)
Earnings: ($8,632,828)
Fiscal Year-end: 12/31/22
Internet & Wireless Connectivity Systems Developer & Sales
N.A.I.C.S.: 334220
Kirk Reed (Pres, CEO, CFO, Sec)

STENA AB
Masthuggskajen, SE-40519, Gothenburg, Sweden
Tel.: (46) 31855000   SE

INTERNATIONAL PUBLIC

Web Site: http://www.stena.com
Year Founded: 1939
Rev.: $3,980,508,140
Assets: $13,908,201,090
Liabilities: $8,758,682,590
Net Worth: $5,149,518,500
Earnings: $1,393,210
Emp.: 11,813
Fiscal Year-end: 12/31/19
Holding Company; Transportation & Shipping Services; Investment Services
N.A.I.C.S.: 551112
Dan Sten Olsson (CEO)

Subsidiaries:

Austen Maritime Services Pte Ltd (1)
30 Pandan Road, Singapore, 609277, Singapore
Tel.: (65) 66537700
Web Site: http://www.austenmaritime.com
Emp.: 35
Freight Transportation Services
N.A.I.C.S.: 481212
Christopher Cher (Head-Marine Projects)

Blomsterlandet AB (1)
Antennvagen 39, 863 33, Sundsbruk, Sweden
Tel.: (46) 313857440
Web Site: http://www.blomsterlandet.se
Freight Transportation Services
N.A.I.C.S.: 481212

Mediatec Broadcast Sweden AB (1)
Ranhammarsvagen 12-14, 168 67, Bromma, Sweden
Tel.: (46) 10 454 03 00
Web Site: http://www.mepsweden.com
Emp.: 60
Television Broadcasting Services
N.A.I.C.S.: 516120
Patrik Nygren (Mgr-Fin)

Mediatec Solutions Sweden AB (1)
Bultgatan 31, PO Box 634, 442 17, Kungalv, Sweden
Tel.: (46) 10 454 01 00
Television Broadcasting Services
N.A.I.C.S.: 516120
Olof Bull (Project Mgr)

Northern Marine Group (1)
Alba House 2 Central Avenue, Clydebank, Glasgow, G81 2QR, United Kingdom
Tel.: (44) 141 876 3000
Web Site: http://www.nmm-stena.com
Emp.: 300
Marine Support Services
N.A.I.C.S.: 488510
Jackie Tierney (Sec & Dir-Fin)

Stena Adactum AB (1)
Rosenlundsgatan 3, Box 7123, 402 33, Gothenburg, Sweden
Tel.: (46) 31 855 000
Web Site: http://www.stenaadactum.com
Financial Investment Services
N.A.I.C.S.: 523940
Martin Svalstedt (CEO)

Subsidiary (Domestic):

Blomsterlandet AB (2)
Antennvagen 39, 863 33, Sundsbruk, Sweden
Tel.: (46) 060 740 40 40
Web Site: http://www.blomsterlandet.se
Freight Transportation Services
N.A.I.C.S.: 481212

Envac AB (2)
Fleminggatan 7 3 tr, 112 26, Stockholm, Sweden
Tel.: (46) 8 785 00 10
Web Site: http://www.envac.se
Emp.: 13
Hazardous Waste Collection Services
N.A.I.C.S.: 562112

Stena Renewable AB (2)
Rosenlundsgatan 3, Box 7123, 402 33, Gothenburg, Sweden
Tel.: (46) 31 85 53 90
Web Site: http://www.stenarenewable.se
Freight Transportation Services
N.A.I.C.S.: 481212

AND PRIVATE COMPANIES

Stena Bulk AB (1)
44-01 Suntec Tower 4 6 Temasek Boulevard, Singapore, 038986, Singapore
Tel.: (65) 63 36 59 53
Web Site: http://www.stenabulk.com
Freight Transportation Services
N.A.I.C.S.: 481212
Lars Malmbratt *(Gen Mgr-Bunker Procurement)*

Stena Drilling (Holdings) Ltd (1)
Ullevi House Greenbank Crescent East Tullos, Aberdeen, AB12 3BG, United Kingdom
Tel.: (44) 1224 401180
Web Site: http://www.stena-drilling.com
Emp.: 150
Freight Transportation Services
N.A.I.C.S.: 481212
Erik Ronsberg *(CEO)*

Stena Fastigheter AB (1)
Varmlandsgatan 2, Box 31157, 400 32, Gothenburg, Sweden
Tel.: (46) 75 24 15 000
Web Site: http://www.stenafastigheter.se
Freight Transportation Services
N.A.I.C.S.: 481212
Dan Sten Olsson *(Chm)*

Stena Holding (Cyprus) Ltd. (1)
Lophitis Business Centre II 28 October Street 4th Floor Office No 401, Limassol, Cyprus
Tel.: (357) 25871207
Web Site: http://www.stenaholding.com
Tanker & Ferry Operation Services
N.A.I.C.S.: 483212

Stena International S.A. (1)
26b Boulevard Royal, Luxembourg, 2449, Luxembourg
Tel.: (352) 26 48 67 00
Freight Transportation Services
N.A.I.C.S.: 481212

Stena Line AB (1)
Danmarksterminalen, 405 19, Gothenburg, Sweden
Tel.: (46) 31858000
Web Site: http://www.stenaline.com
Sales Range: $1-4.9 Billion
Emp.: 4,300
Transoceanic Freight Shipping, Passenger Lines & Ferries
N.A.I.C.S.: 483111

Unit (Non-US):

Buro Scandinavia B.V. (2)
Hogehilweg 6, 1101 CC, Amsterdam, Netherlands
Tel.: (31) 204621040
Web Site: http://www.buroscanbrit.nl
Sales Range: $25-49.9 Million
N.A.I.C.S.: 483111

Affiliate (Domestic):

Concordia Maritime AB (2)
Denmark Terminal, SE 405 19, Gothenburg, Sweden **(52.2%)**
Tel.: (46) 31855000
Web Site: http://www.concordia-maritime.se
Sales Range: $75-99.9 Million
Emp.: 200
Tanker Shipping Company
N.A.I.C.S.: 483211
Martin Nerfeldt *(CFO)*

Unit (Non-US):

Stena Line (Belfast) (2)
W Punk Road, Belfast, BT3 9JL, United Kingdom
Tel.: (44) 2890747747
Web Site: http://www.stenaline.co.uk
Sales Range: $25-49.9 Million
Emp.: 100
Waterfront Terminal
N.A.I.C.S.: 488310

Stena Line (Dun Laoghaire) (2)
Ferry Terminal Dun Laoghaire Harbour, Dun Laoghaire, 5565, Ireland
Tel.: (353) 12047700
Web Site: http://www.stenaline.ie
Sales Range: $25-49.9 Million
Emp.: 100
Waterfront Terminal
N.A.I.C.S.: 488310
Nicola Marsh *(Mgr-Customer Svcs)*

Stena Line (Fishguard) (2)
Fishguard Harbour, Goodwick, SA64 0BU, Pembrokeshire, United Kingdom
Tel.: (44) 1348404404
Web Site: http://www.stenaline.com
Emp.: 300
N.A.I.C.S.: 483111
Carl Johan Hagman *(Pres)*

Stena Line (Frederikshavn) (2)
Trafikhavnen 10, 9900, Frederikshavn, Denmark
Tel.: (45) 96200225
Web Site: http://www.stenaline.dk
Sales Range: $25-49.9 Million
Emp.: 50
Waterfront Terminal
N.A.I.C.S.: 488310
Dent Kobperup *(Mng Dir)*

Stena Line (Grena) (2)
Faergevej 1, PO Box 150, 8500, Grena, Denmark
Tel.: (45) 96200200
Web Site: http://www.stenaline.dk
Sales Range: $25-49.9 Million
Ship Charter Services
N.A.I.C.S.: 483111

Stena Line (Harwich) (2)
Harwich International Port Parkeston Quay Parkeston, Harwich, CO12 4SR, Essex, United Kingdom
Tel.: (44) 3447707070
Web Site: http://www.stenaline.co.uk
Sales Range: $25-49.9 Million
Emp.: 40
Deep Sea Freight Transportation
N.A.I.C.S.: 483111

Stena Line (Hoek van Holland) (2)
Stationsweg 10, 3151 HS, Hoek van Holland, Netherlands
Tel.: (31) 174389333
Web Site: http://www.stenaline.nl
Sales Range: $100-124.9 Million
Emp.: 500
Waterfront Terminal
N.A.I.C.S.: 488310

Unit (Domestic):

Stena Line (Karlskrona) (2)
Verkoterminalen, PO Box 6047, 371 06, Lyckeby, Sweden
Tel.: (46) 455366300
Web Site: http://www.stenaline.com
Sales Range: $25-49.9 Million
Emp.: 25
Waterfront Terminal
N.A.I.C.S.: 488310

Unit (Non-US):

Stena Line (Kiel) (2)
Schwedenkai 1, 24103, Kiel, Germany
Tel.: (49) 431909312
Web Site: http://www.stenaline.de
Sales Range: $50-74.9 Million
Emp.: 120
Waterfront Terminal
N.A.I.C.S.: 488310

Stena Line (Rosslare) (2)
The Ferry Terminal, Rosslare, Co Wexford, Ireland
Tel.: (353) 19075555
Web Site: http://www.stenaline.ie
Sales Range: $25-49.9 Million
Emp.: 15
Waterfront Terminal
N.A.I.C.S.: 488310

Stena Line (Stranraer) (2)
Burns House 32 Harbour St, Stranraer, DG9 7RA, Wigtownshire, United Kingdom
Tel.: (44) 1776 802136
Web Site: http://www.stenaline.co.uk
Sales Range: $100-124.9 Million
Emp.: 500
Waterfront Terminal
N.A.I.C.S.: 488310

Unit (Domestic):

Stena Line Freight (2)
Danmarksterminalen, 405 19, Gothenburg, Sweden
Tel.: (46) 31858000
Web Site: http://www.stenaline.com

Sales Range: $25-49.9 Million
Emp.: 19
Waterfront Terminal
N.A.I.C.S.: 488310

Unit (Non-US):

Stena Line Scandic Hotel Frederikshavn (2)
Tordenskjoldsgade 14, 9900, Frederikshavn, Denmark
Tel.: (45) 9 843 3233
Web Site: https://www.scandichotels.dk
Sales Range: $50-74.9 Million
Emp.: 110
Ship Charter Services
N.A.I.C.S.: 483111

Stena Line UK (2)
Stena House Station Approach, Holyhead, LL65 1DQ, Anglesey, United Kingdom
Tel.: (44) 3447707070
Web Site: http://www.stenaline.co.uk
Sales Range: $200-249.9 Million
Emp.: 550
Freight & Passenger Ferry Services
N.A.I.C.S.: 488310

Unit (Domestic):

Stena Metall AB (2)
Box 4088, 400 40, Gothenburg, Sweden
Tel.: (46) 104450000
Web Site: http://www.stenametall.com
Metals, Paper, Electronics, Hazardous Waste & Chemicals Recycling & Processing
N.A.I.C.S.: 423930

Subsidiary (Domestic):

IL Recycling AB (3)
Linnegatan 2, 102 49, Stockholm, Sweden
Tel.: (46) 86712700
Web Site: http://www.ilrecycling.com
Sales Range: $100-124.9 Million
Emp.: 450
Recycling Services
N.A.I.C.S.: 423930
Lars Gummar Almryd *(Pres & Mng Dir)*

Stena Recycling AB (3)
Fiskhamnsgatan 8 B, 414 58, Gothenburg, Sweden
Tel.: (46) 104450000
Web Site: http://www.stenarecycling.se
Sales Range: $50-74.9 Million
Emp.: 2
Recycling Operations for Stena Metall Group
N.A.I.C.S.: 423930

Stena Maritime AG (1)
Bahnhofplatz, Zug, 6300, Switzerland
Tel.: (41) 417288121
Freight Transportation Services
N.A.I.C.S.: 481212

Stena Realty B.V. (1)
Burgemeester Haspelslaan 61, 1181 NB, Amstelveen, Netherlands
Tel.: (31) 20 426 16 16
Web Site: http://www.stenarealty.com
Emp.: 16
Freight Transportation Services
N.A.I.C.S.: 481212
Ronald R. M. Visscher *(Mng Dir)*

Stena Rederi AB (1)
Kungsportsavenyn 2, Gothenburg, 400 10, Sweden
Tel.: (46) 3 17 74 35 30
Freight Transportation Services
N.A.I.C.S.: 481212

Stena Ropax Ltd (1)
45 Albemarle Street, London, W1S 4JL, United Kingdom
Tel.: (44) 2074 090 124
Freight Transportation Services
N.A.I.C.S.: 481212

STENIEL MANUFACTURING CORPORATION

STENDER AG
Alte Poststrasse 121, 46514, Schermbeck, Germany
Tel.: (49) 28 53 9 69 0   De
Web Site: http://www.stender.de
Year Founded: 1984
Rev.: $63,850,027
Emp.: 98

Compost & Substrates Mfr & Distr
N.A.I.C.S.: 325311
Heinrich-Gerhard Hengstermann *(CEO)*

Subsidiaries:

Gartenhilfe Ges.m.b.H. (1)
Pillweinstrasse 30, A 4020, Linz, Donau, Austria
Tel.: (43) 732771977
Web Site: http://www.gartenhilfe.at
Sales Range: $25-49.9 Million
Emp.: 20
Gardening Product Mfr
N.A.I.C.S.: 325311

STENFLEX RUDOLF STENDER GMBH
Robert-Koch-Str 17, 22851, Norderstedt, Germany
Tel.: (49) 40529030
Web Site: http://www.stenflex.com
Year Founded: 1965
Rev.: $21,863,490
Emp.: 80
Pipe Connectors & Hoses Supplier
N.A.I.C.S.: 423840
Birgit Stender *(Mng Dir)*

Subsidiaries:

STENFLEX S.A. (1)
Poligono Industrial el Praderon Calle Tanger no 6, 28700, San Sebastian, Spain
Tel.: (34) 916637896
Web Site: http://www.stenflex.com
Industrial Supplies Whslr
N.A.I.C.S.: 423840

STENFLEX S.a.r.l. (1)
ZI les Chanoux 38 rue des Freres Lumiere, 93330, Neuilly-sur-Marne, France
Tel.: (33) 143004837
Web Site: http://www.stenflex.com
Industrial Supplies Whslr
N.A.I.C.S.: 423840

STENHUS FASTIGHETER I NORDEN AB
Arstaangsvagen 11, 117 43, Stockholm, Sweden
Tel.: (46) 0841022100   SE
Web Site: https://www.stenhusfastigheter.se
Year Founded: 2020
SFAST—(OMX)
Rev.: $101,156,513
Assets: $1,456,780,258
Liabilities: $889,460,376
Net Worth: $567,319,882
Earnings: ($41,013,958)
Emp.: 38
Fiscal Year-end: 12/31/23
Real Estate Services
N.A.I.C.S.: 531390
Elias Georgiadis *(CEO)*

Subsidiaries:

Halla Shopping Fastighets AB (1)
Hallagatan 14, 721 34, Vasteras, Sweden
Tel.: (46) 21186207
Web Site: http://www.hallashopping.com
Shopping Mall
N.A.I.C.S.: 531120

STENIEL MANUFACTURING CORPORATION
Gateway Business Park, Brgy Javalera General Trias, Cavite, Philippines
Tel.: (63) 464330066
Web Site: https://steniel.com.ph
Year Founded: 1963
STN—(PHI)
Rev.: $61,512,449
Assets: $76,887,370
Liabilities: $60,800,288
Net Worth: $16,087,081
Earnings: $2,126,605
Emp.: 261

STENIEL MANUFACTURING CORPORATION

Steniel Manufacturing Corporation—(Continued)
Fiscal Year-end: 12/31/23
Corrugated Box Mfr
N.A.I.C.S.: 322211
Eliza C. Macuray *(CFO, Treas & VP)*

STENOCARE A/S
Frederiksborgvej 54, Allerod, 3450, Denmark
Tel.: (45) 31770060
Pharmaceutical Product Mfr & Distr
N.A.I.C.S.: 325412
Peter Bugge Johansen *(CFO)*

STENTORIUS
34 Rue Pierre Et Marie Curie, Ivry-sur-Seine, 94004, Val De Marne, France
Tel.: (33) 146707520
Web Site: http://www.stentorius.com
Rev.: $20,900,000
Emp.: 45
Communications & Security Equipment Distr
N.A.I.C.S.: 423690
Jean-Paul Grall *(Mgr-DP)*

STENTYS S.A.
18 Rue d Hauteville, 75010, Paris, France
Tel.: (33) 1 44 53 99 42
Web Site: http://www.stentys.com
Rev.: $10,148,849
Earnings: ($6,174,178)
Emp.: 35
Fiscal Year-end: 12/31/18
Medicinal Product Mfr
N.A.I.C.S.: 339112

STENVALLS TRA AB
Vargbackenvagen 1, Sikfors, 942 94, Lulea, Sweden
Tel.: (246) 911251000
Web Site: https://www.stenvalls.se
Emp.: 100
Paper & Forest Products Mfr
N.A.I.C.S.: 321999

Subsidiaries:

Genesis-IT AB (1)
Norrsagsvaegen 41, Lulea, 972 31, Sweden **(100%)**
Tel.: (46) 920272700
Web Site: http://www.genesis.se
Security System Services
N.A.I.C.S.: 561621
Tommy Flink *(CEO)*

STEP CO., LTD.
602 Fujisawa, Fujisawa, 251-0052, Kanagawa, Japan
Tel.: (81) 466208000
Web Site: https://www.stepnet.co.jp
Year Founded: 1979
9795—(TKS)
Sales Range: $75-99.9 Million
Cram School Operator
N.A.I.C.S.: 611710
Kyoji Tatsui *(Chm, Pres & Exec Officer)*

STEP D.D.
Halilovici 2, 71000, Sarajevo, Bosnia & Herzegovina
Tel.: (387) 33776850
Web Site: http://www.step.ba
STEPR—(SARE)
Sales Range: $1-9.9 Million
Emp.: 117
Railway Construction Services
N.A.I.C.S.: 237990

STEP ENERGY SERVICES LTD.
Bow Valley Square II 1200 205 - 5th Ave SW, Calgary, T2P 2V7, AB, Canada
Tel.: (403) 457-1772
Web Site: http://www.stepenergyservices.com
Year Founded: 2011
STEP—(TSX)
Oil Field Service Company
N.A.I.C.S.: 213112
Douglas C. Freel *(Chm)*

Subsidiaries:

Tucker Energy Services Holdings, Inc. (1)
411 N Sam Houston Pkwy E Ste 300, Houston, TX 77060-3555
Tel.: (281) 442-9095
Web Site: http://www.tuckerenergy.com
Oil & Gas Operations
N.A.I.C.S.: 213112

STEP ONE CLOTHING LIMITED
Level 2 120 Chalmers Street, Surry Hills, 2010, NSW, Australia
Tel.: (61) 280956350 AU
Web Site: https://www.stepone.group
Year Founded: 2017
STP—(ASX)
Rev.: $42,501,141
Assets: $43,114,038
Liabilities: $5,901,415
Net Worth: $37,212,623
Earnings: $5,617,787
Emp.: 43
Fiscal Year-end: 06/30/23
Clothing Accessory Distr
N.A.I.C.S.: 458110
Greg Taylor *(Founder & CEO)*

STEP TWO CORPORATION LIMITED
21 Hemant Basu Sarani 5th Floor Room No 507, Kolkata, 700001, India
Tel.: (91) 3322318207
Web Site: https://www.steptwo.in
Year Founded: 1994
531509—(BOM)
Rev.: $108,360
Assets: $730,433
Liabilities: $17,703
Net Worth: $712,731
Earnings: $59,413
Emp.: 6
Fiscal Year-end: 03/31/23
Securities Brokerage Services
N.A.I.C.S.: 523150
Raj Kumar Agarwal *(Founder & Mng Partner)*

STEPHANOTIS FINANCE LIMITED
3 Ground Floor Durga Chambers Veena Industrial Estate, Off Veera Desai Road Andheri West, Mumbai, 400053, Maharashtra, India
Tel.: (91) 9820446355
Web Site: https://www.stephanotis.in
Year Founded: 1985
512215—(BOM)
Rev.: $101,571
Assets: $3,738,280
Liabilities: $303,591
Net Worth: $3,434,690
Earnings: $2,203
Emp.: 5
Fiscal Year-end: 03/31/21
Security Brokerage Services
N.A.I.C.S.: 523150
Sonu Sureshbabu Malge *(CEO)*

STEPPE CEMENT LTD.
Suite 10 1 10th Floor Rohas Perkasa West Wing No 8 Jalan Perak, 50450, Kuala Lumpur, Malaysia
Tel.: (60) 321660361
Web Site: https://www.steppecement.com
STCM—(AIM)
Rev.: $81,762,548
Assets: $95,819,433
Liabilities: $25,124,401
Net Worth: $70,695,032
Earnings: $4,525,421
Emp.: 794
Fiscal Year-end: 12/31/23
Construction Materials Mfr
N.A.I.C.S.: 327310
Peter Durnev *(Gen Dir-Central Asia Cement JSC)*

Subsidiaries:

Central Asia Cement JSC (1)
Aktau settlement accounting quarter No 114 building 46, 101408, Karaganda, Kazakhstan
Tel.: (7) 7213941117
Web Site: https://cac.kz
Cement & Cement Products Mfr & Sales
N.A.I.C.S.: 327310

STEPPE GOLD LTD.
Shangri-La office Suite 1201 Olympic street 19A, Sukhbaatar District 1, Ulaanbaatar, 14241, Mongolia
Tel.: (976) 77321914
Web Site: https://www.steppegold.com
STGO—(TSX)
Rev.: $78,725,069
Assets: $91,716,738
Liabilities: $69,976,016
Net Worth: $21,740,722
Earnings: $19,839,687
Emp.: 290
Fiscal Year-end: 12/31/22
Metal Exploration Services
N.A.I.C.S.: 213114
Bataa Tumur-Ochir *(Chm & CEO)*

STER GROUP
Gulan St, Erbil, Iraq
Tel.: (964) 7502569200
Web Site: http://www.stergroup.com
Year Founded: 2002
Holding Company Services
N.A.I.C.S.: 551112
Sirwan A. Aziz *(Chm & CEO)*

Subsidiaries:

Kani Water (1)
, Erbil, Iraq
Tel.: (964) 750 448 6774
Mineral Water Producer
N.A.I.C.S.: 312112

StarKar Insurance Company (1)
156 Permam St Shorish, Erbil, Iraq
Tel.: (964) 6622446413
Web Site: http://www.sic-iq.com
Insurance Services
N.A.I.C.S.: 524126
Nawzad A. Rafiq *(Gen Mgr)*

Ster Company (1)
Gulan Street Ster Tower 12th Floor, Erbil, Iraq
Tel.: (964) 750 256 9200
Web Site: http://www.stergroup.com
Construction Services
N.A.I.C.S.: 237990

Ster Petroleum LLC (1)
, Erbil, Iraq
Tel.: (964) 750 461 1850
Oil & Gas Exploration
N.A.I.C.S.: 211120

Ster Security (1)
1st Floor Ster Tower Gulan Street, Erbil, Iraq
Tel.: (964) 7504271690
Web Site: http://www.stergroup.com
Security Consulting & Planning Services
N.A.I.C.S.: 561612

TarinNet Company (1)
Gulan Street Ster Tower Bldg, Erbil, Iraq
Tel.: (964) 662537500
Web Site: http://www.tarinnet.info

INTERNATIONAL PUBLIC

Sales Range: $25-49.9 Million
Emp.: 40
Internet Services
N.A.I.C.S.: 517810

STERIHEALTH LIMITED
34-36 Cahill Street, Dandenong, 3175, VIC, Australia
Tel.: (61) 387628300 AU
Web Site: http://www.sterihealth.com.au
Sales Range: $50-74.9 Million
Emp.: 222
Healthcare Products & Services
N.A.I.C.S.: 339113
Jenny Storey *(Officer-Privacy)*

Subsidiaries:

SteriHealth Services Pty. Ltd. (1)
34-36 Cahill Street, Dandenong Sth, Melbourne, 3175, VIC, Australia
Tel.: (61) 3 8762 8300
Web Site: http://www.sterihealth.com.au
Medical Waste Disposal Services
N.A.I.C.S.: 562211

STERIS PLC
70 Sir John Rogerson s Quay, Dublin, D02 R296, Ireland
Tel.: (353) 12322000 IE
Web Site: https://www.steris.com
Year Founded: 1985
STE—(NYSE)
Rev.: $5,138,701,000
Assets: $11,063,697,000
Liabilities: $4,748,351,000
Net Worth: $6,315,346,000
Earnings: $380,079,000
Emp.: 18,000
Fiscal Year-end: 03/31/24
Holding Company; Medical & Surgical Instruments Mfr & Whslr
N.A.I.C.S.: 551112
Mohsen M. Sohi *(Chm)*

Subsidiaries:

Cantel Medical Corp. (1)
150 Clove Rd 9th Fl, Little Falls, NJ 07424-2139
Tel.: (973) 890-7220
Web Site: http://www.cantelmedical.com
Rev.: $1,016,048,000
Assets: $2,071,754,000
Liabilities: $1,342,155,000
Net Worth: $729,599,000
Earnings: $13,708,000
Emp.: 3,669
Fiscal Year-end: 07/31/2020
Endoscopy & Scientific Instrumentation Products
N.A.I.C.S.: 339112
Seth M. Yellin *(Exec VP-Strategy & Corp Dev)*

Subsidiary (Non-US)

Aexis Medical BVBA (2)
Kabbeekvest 67A, 3300, Tienen, Belgium
Tel.: (32) 16210913
Software Development Services
N.A.I.C.S.: 513210

BHT Hygienetechnik GmbH (2)
Messerschmittstrasse 11, 86368, Gersthofen, Germany
Tel.: (49) 821278930
Web Site: http://www.bht.de
Medical Equipment Mfr & Distr
N.A.I.C.S.: 334510

Bior Medica S.r.l. (2)
Via A Volta 7, 41037, Mirandola, Italy
Tel.: (39) 053530038
Web Site: http://www.biormedica.com
Surgical & Medical Instrument Mfr
N.A.I.C.S.: 339112

Subsidiary (Domestic):

CHIPS Manufacturing LLC (2)
741 Winston St, West Chicago, IL 60185-5121
Tel.: (630) 682-4477
Web Site: https://www.chipsmfg.com

AND PRIVATE COMPANIES — STERIS PLC

Precision Machining Product Mfr
N.A.I.C.S.: 332721
Jim Jett *(Pres)*

Subsidiary (Non-US):

Camark S.A. (2)
Industrial Park Axioupoli, Axioupoli, 61400, Kilkis, Greece
Tel.: (30) 2343032043
Web Site: https://www.camark.gr
Surgical & Medical Instrument Mfr
N.A.I.C.S.: 339112

Cantel (Australia) Pty. Ltd. (2)
300 Lorimer Street, Port Melbourne, 3207, VIC, Australia
Tel.: (61) 1300211422
Medical Equipment Distr
N.A.I.C.S.: 423450

Cantel (Canada) Inc. (2)
6-88B East Beaver Creek Road, Richmond Hill, L4B 4W2, ON, Canada
Web Site: https://www.cantelcanada.com
Surgical & Medical Instrument Mfr
N.A.I.C.S.: 339112

Cantel (France) SAS (2)
3 rue du Pre Ferme, 31200, Toulouse, France
Tel.: (33) 561245275
Medical Equipment Mfr
N.A.I.C.S.: 334510

Cantel (Germany) GmbH (2)
Messerschmittstr 11, 86368, Gersthofen, Germany
Tel.: (49) 21190980750
Medical Equipment Distr
N.A.I.C.S.: 423450

Cantel (Production) Germany GmbH (2)
Zur Ohmdwiesen 5, 88633, Heidelberg, Germany
Tel.: (49) 75549999500
Web Site: https://www.cantelmedical.eu
Medical Equipment Mfr
N.A.I.C.S.: 334510

Cantel (UK) Limited (2)
Campfield Road, Shoeburyness, London, SS3 9BX, Essex, United Kingdom
Tel.: (44) 1702291878
Web Site: http://www.cantelmedical.co.uk
Medical Equipment Mfr
N.A.I.C.S.: 334510

Cantel Lanka (Pvt.) Ltd. (2)
No 10 1/3 Prince Alfred Tower Alfred House Gardens, Colombo, 00300, Sri Lanka
Tel.: (94) 112598236
Web Site: http://www.cantel.lk
Software Development Services
N.A.I.C.S.: 541511
Dries Vanbiervliet *(CEO)*

Cantel Medical (Hong Kong) Limited (2)
Unit 919-922 41 Heung Yip Road Wong Chuk Hang, Hong Kong, China (Hong Kong)
Tel.: (852) 21573220
Medical Equipment Distr
N.A.I.C.S.: 423450

Cantel Medical (Italy) S.r.l. (2)
Via Laurentina 169, 00040, Pomezia, RM, Italy
Tel.: (39) 069145399
Medical Equipment Mfr
N.A.I.C.S.: 334510

Cantel Medical (Malaysia) Sdn. Bhd. (2)
No 2 Jalan Tandang 51/205A Seksyen 51, Selangor Darul Ehsan, 46050, Petaling Jaya, Malaysia
Tel.: (60) 77720220
Surgical & Medical Instrument Mfr
N.A.I.C.S.: 339112

Cantel Medical (UK) Limited (2)
Campfield Road Shoeburyness, Stafford, SS3 9BX, Essex, United Kingdom
Tel.: (44) 1702291878
Web Site: http://www.cantelmedical.co.uk
Medical Equipment Distr
N.A.I.C.S.: 423450

Cantel Medical Devices (China) Co., Ltd. (2)
Unit 804-805 Innov Tower Block A 1801 Hongmei Road, Xuhui, Shanghai, 200233, China
Tel.: (86) 2160161380
Medical Equipment Distr
N.A.I.C.S.: 423450

Cantel Medical Middle East FZ-LLC (2)
Executive Office 11 3rd Floor Dubai Science Park Laboratory Complex, Dubai, United Arab Emirates
Tel.: (971) 566699872
Medical Equipment Distr
N.A.I.C.S.: 423450

Subsidiary (Domestic):

Crosstex International Inc. (2)
10 Ranick Rd, Hauppauge, NY 11788
Tel.: (631) 582-6777
Web Site: http://www.crosstex.com
Sales Range: $10-24.9 Million
Emp.: 50
Infection Control & Single-Use Disposable Products Mfr
N.A.I.C.S.: 334516

Subsidiary (Domestic):

ConFirm Monitoring Systems, Inc. (3)
109 Inverness Dr E Ste F, Englewood, CO 80112-5105
Tel.: (303) 699-3356
Web Site: http://www.confirmmonitoring.com
Sales Range: $10-24.9 Million
Emp.: 22
Biological Monitoring Services
N.A.I.C.S.: 334516
Gary Goldberg *(Pres)*

SPS Medical Supply Corp. (3)
6789 W Henrietta Rd, Rush, NY 14543
Tel.: (585) 359-0130
Web Site: http://www.spsmedical.com
Sales Range: $10-24.9 Million
Emp.: 50
Medical Supplies Mfr
N.A.I.C.S.: 339113

Subsidiary (Non-US):

ESCAD Medical GmbH (2)
Zur Ohmdwiesen 5, Heiligenberg, 88633, Heidelberg, Germany
Tel.: (49) 75549999500
Medical Equipment Distr
N.A.I.C.S.: 423450

Ecode Lanka Software (Private) Limited (2)
No 10 1/3 Prince Alfred Towe Alfred House Gardens, Colombo, 00300, Sri Lanka
Tel.: (94) 112598236
Web Site: http://www.ecode.lk
Software Development Services
N.A.I.C.S.: 513210
Dries Vanbiervliet *(CEO)*

Hu-Friedy Italy SRL (2)
Via Mauro Macchi 27, 20124, Milan, Italy
Tel.: (39) 0236589600
Dental Instrument Mfr & Distr
N.A.I.C.S.: 339114

Hu-Friedy Japan GK (2)
6-13-10 Prostech Akihabara Building 6F Sotokanda, Chiyoda-ku, Tokyo, 101-0021, Japan
Tel.: (81) 345500660
Web Site: https://www.hu-friedy.co.jp
Dental Instruments Mfr
N.A.I.C.S.: 339114

Hu-Friedy Medical Instrument (Shanghai) China Co. Ltd. (2)
Building 29 1365 Kangqiao Road E, Shanghai, 201319, China
Tel.: (86) 2168183182
Dental Instrument Mfr & Distr
N.A.I.C.S.: 339114
Xu Jimei *(Mgr-Quality)*

Jet Prep. Ltd. (2)
71 HaNadiv St, Herzliya Pituach, 46485, Israel
Tel.: (972) 99506712
Web Site: http://www.jetprep.com
Surgical & Medical Instrument Mfr
N.A.I.C.S.: 339112
David Nitsan *(CEO)*

Subsidiary (Domestic):

Karl Schumacher Dental, LLC (2)
1666 E Touhy Ave, Des Plaines, IL 60018
Tel.: (215) 322-0511
Web Site: https://www.karlschumacher.com
Medical Device & Instrument Mfr
N.A.I.C.S.: 339112

MEDIVATORS, Inc. (2)
14605 28th Ave N, Minneapolis, MN 55447-4822
Web Site: http://www.medivators.com
Medical Devices, Sterilants & Water Purification Products Mfr & Marketer
N.A.I.C.S.: 339112

Branch (Non-US):

Mar Cor Purification (3)
85 Lindsay Ave, Dorval, H9P 2S6, QC, Canada (100%)
Tel.: (514) 636-0032
Web Site: http://www.mcpur.com
Water Purification Services
N.A.I.C.S.: 221310

Subsidiary (Domestic):

Mar Cor Purification, Inc. (2)
14550 28th Ave N, Plymouth, MN 55447
Tel.: (484) 991-0220
Web Site: https://www.mcpur.com
Water Purification Products & Services
N.A.I.C.S.: 221310

Subsidiary (Non-US):

Mar Cor Purification Canada (3)
3250 Harvester Rd Unit 6, Burlington, L7N 3W9, ON, Canada (100%)
Tel.: (905) 639-7025
Sales Range: $25-49.9 Million
Emp.: 50
Water Purifying Services
N.A.I.C.S.: 221310

Subsidiary (Non-US):

Medivators B.V. (2)
Sourethweg 11, 6422 PC, Heerlen, Netherlands
Tel.: (31) 455471471
Web Site: http://www.cantelmedical.com
Emp.: 30
Medical Equipment Distr
N.A.I.C.S.: 423450
Yoost Hettwnga *(Mng Dir)*

Omnia Dental S.L. (2)
Calle Alberto Bosch 10 Bajo Izqda, 28014, Madrid, Spain
Tel.: (34) 910609731
Web Site: http://www.omnia-dental.com
Surgical & Medical Instrument Mfr
N.A.I.C.S.: 339112

Subsidiary (Domestic):

Omnia LLC (2)
301 Pleasant St, Abbottstown, PA 17301
Surgical & Medical Instrument Mfr
N.A.I.C.S.: 339112

Subsidiary (Non-US):

Omnia SpA (2)
Via Francesco Delnevo 190 Loc S Michele Campagna, 43036, Fidenza, Parma, Italy
Tel.: (39) 0524527453
Web Site: http://www.omniaspa.eu
Curtain & Drapery Mills
N.A.I.C.S.: 314120

STERIS Corporation (1)
5960 Heisley Rd, Mentor, OH 44060-1834
Tel.: (440) 354-2600
Web Site: http://www.steris.com
Infection Prevention, Contamination Prevention, Microbial Reduction & Surgical Support Products & Services
N.A.I.C.S.: 339113
Walter M. Rosebrough Jr. *(Pres & CEO)*

Subsidiary (Domestic):

Black Diamond Video, Inc. (2)
503 Canal Blvd, Point Richmond, CA 94804-3517
Tel.: (510) 439-4500
Web Site: http://www.blackdiamondvideo.com
Electronic Components Mfr
N.A.I.C.S.: 334419

Subsidiary (Non-US):

HAMO Switzerland AG/SA/Ltd. (2)
Zurichstrasse 3, CH-2504, Biel, Switzerland (100%)
Tel.: (41) 323443500
Web Site: http://www.amsonic-hamo.com
Sales Range: $25-49.9 Million
Emp.: 60
Medical Sterilization Services
N.A.I.C.S.: 621511
Alex Moser *(Pres)*

IDtek Identifikationslosungen GmbH (2)
Tel.: (49) 89998209000
Track & Trace Solutions
N.A.I.C.S.: 541511
Dieter Salomon *(Exec Dir)*

Subsidiary (Domestic):

Integrated Medical Systems International, Inc. (2)
3316 2nd Ave N, Birmingham, AL 35222
Tel.: (205) 879-3840
Web Site: https://www.steris-ims.com
Sales Range: $150-199.9 Million
Emp.: 350
Medical Equipment & Supplies Repair Services
N.A.I.C.S.: 423450
Mark Pinson *(Pres-Ops)*

Isomedix Inc. (2)
5960 Heisley Rd, Mentor, OH 44060
Tel.: (440) 354-2600
Web Site: http://www.isomedix.com
Holding Company; Contract Sterilization & Laboratory Testing Services
N.A.I.C.S.: 551112

Subsidiary (Domestic):

Biotest Laboratories, Inc. (3)
9303 W Broadway Ave, Minneapolis, MN 55445
Tel.: (763) 315-1200
Web Site: http://www.biotestlabs.com
Laboratory Equipment Mfr
N.A.I.C.S.: 334516
Tonia Bevers *(Asst Mgr-Laboratory)*

Isomedix Operations Inc. (3)
5960 Heisley Rd, Mentor, OH 44060
Tel.: (440) 354-2600
Contract Sterilization & Decontamination Services
N.A.I.C.S.: 561910
Robert E. Moss *(Pres)*

Plant (Domestic):

Isomedix Operations Inc. - Chester (4)
23 Elizabeth Dr, Chester, NY 10918-1367
Tel.: (845) 469-4087
Web Site: http://www.isomedix.com
Emp.: 85
Contract Gamma Sterilization & Decontamination Services
N.A.I.C.S.: 561910

Isomedix Operations Inc. - El Paso I (4)
1435 Isomedix Pl, El Paso, TX 79936-6801
Tel.: (915) 855-2001
Web Site: http://www.isomedix.com
Emp.: 50
Contract Gamma & Ethylene Oxide Sterilization & Decontamination Services
N.A.I.C.S.: 561910

Isomedix Operations Inc. - El Paso II (4)
1441 Don Haskins Dr, El Paso, TX 79936
Tel.: (915) 849-8908
Web Site: http://www.isomedix.com
Emp.: 50
Contract Ethylene Oxide Sterilization & Decontamination Services
N.A.I.C.S.: 561910

STERIS PLC

STERIS plc—(Continued)

Isomedix Operations Inc. - Groveport (4)
4405 Marketing Pl, Groveport, OH 43125-5757
Tel.: (614) 836-5757
Web Site: http://www.isomedix.com
Contract Gamma Sterilization & Decontamination Services
N.A.I.C.S.: 561910

Isomedix Operations Inc. - Libertyville North (4)
1880 Industrial Dr, Libertyville, IL 60048-9439
Tel.: (847) 367-1911
Web Site: http://www.isomedix.com
Contract Gamma Sterilization & Decontamination Services
N.A.I.C.S.: 561910

Isomedix Operations Inc. - Libertyville South (4)
2500 Commerce Dr, Libertyville, IL 60048
Tel.: (847) 247-0970
Web Site: http://www.steris.com
Contract Gamma Sterilization & Decontamination Services
N.A.I.C.S.: 561910

Isomedix Operations Inc. - Minneapolis (4)
380 90th Ave NW, Minneapolis, MN 55433-5826
Tel.: (763) 786-2929
Web Site: http://www.isomedix.com
Contract Ethylene Oxide Sterilization & Decontamination Services
N.A.I.C.S.: 561910

Isomedix Operations Inc. - Sandy (4)
9120 S 150th E, Sandy, UT 84070-2734
Tel.: (801) 561-0052
Web Site: http://www.isomedix.com
Contract Gamma Sterilization & Decontamination Services
N.A.I.C.S.: 561910

Isomedix Operations Inc. - Spartanburg (4)
2072 Southport Rd, Spartanburg, SC 29306-6299
Tel.: (864) 582-3041
Web Site: http://www.isomedix.com
Emp.: 50
Contract Gamma & Ethylene Oxide Sterilization & Decontamination Services
N.A.I.C.S.: 561910

Isomedix Operations Inc. - Temecula (4)
43425 Business Park Dr, Temecula, CA 92590
Tel.: (951) 694-9340
Web Site: http://www.isomedix.com
Emp.: 15
Contract Ethylene Oxide Sterilization & Decontamination Services
N.A.I.C.S.: 561910

Isomedix Operations Inc. - Whippany (4)
9 Apollo Dr, Whippany, NJ 07981
Tel.: (973) 887-2754
Web Site: http://www.isomedix.com
Contract Gamma Sterilization & Decontamination Services
N.A.I.C.S.: 561910

Subsidiary (Domestic):

Key Surgical, LLC (2)
8101 Wallace Rd, Eden Prairie, MN 55344
Tel.: (952) 914-9789
Web Site: https://www.keysurgical.com
Medical & Hospital Equipment Whslr
N.A.I.C.S.: 423450
Brandon Van Hee *(Sr Mgr-Clinical Education)*

Subsidiary (Non-US):

Key Surgical GmbH (3)
Zum Windpark 1, 23788, Lensahn, Germany
Tel.: (49) 407237470
Web Site: https://www.keysurgical.de
Medical Device Mfr

N.A.I.C.S.: 339112

Subsidiary (Non-US):

STERIS (India) Private Limited (2)
8th Floor Eternity Building Block - DN-1 Sector V, Salt Lake, Kolkata, 700 091, India
Tel.: (91) 3323675150
Sales Range: $10-24.9 Million
Emp.: 12
Surgical Equipment Mfr & Distr
N.A.I.C.S.: 339113

Subsidiary (Domestic):

STERIS Barrier Products Solutions, Inc. (2)
1725 N 6th St, Philadelphia, PA 19122
Tel.: (215) 763-8200
Web Site: http://sterisbps.com
Surgical Appliance & Supplies Mfr
N.A.I.C.S.: 339113

Subsidiary (Non-US):

STERIS Brasil Servicos Administrativos Ltda. (2)
Av Ibirapuera 2907 - Cj 1401, Sao Paulo, 04029-200, Brazil
Tel.: (55) 1150539823
Surgical Equipment Mfr
N.A.I.C.S.: 339112

Subsidiary (Domestic):

STERIS Canada Corporation (2)
490 Boul Armand-Paris, Quebec, G1C 8A3, QC, Canada (100%)
Tel.: (418) 664-1549
Sales Range: $50-74.9 Million
Emp.: 230
Sterilization Products Mfr
N.A.I.C.S.: 339113

STERIS Canada, Inc. (2)
490 Boul Armand-Paris, Quebec, G1C 8A3, QC, Canada (100%)
Tel.: (418) 664-1549
Web Site: http://www.steris.com
Sales Range: $25-49.9 Million
Emp.: 30
Distr of Sterilization Products
N.A.I.C.S.: 423450

Plant (Domestic):

STERIS Corporation - Montgomery Plant (2)
2720 Gunther Park Dr E, Montgomery, AL 36109
Tel.: (334) 277-6660
Web Site: http://www.steris.com
Sales Range: $100-124.9 Million
Emp.: 310
Patient Handling Equipment Mfr
N.A.I.C.S.: 339113

Subsidiary (Non-US):

STERIS Deutschland GmbH (2)
Eupener Str 70, 50933, Cologne, Germany
Tel.: (49) 22146612090
Sales Range: $25-49.9 Million
Emp.: 35
Surgical Equipment Mfr & Distr
N.A.I.C.S.: 339112

STERIS Finn-Aqua (2)
Teollisuustie 2, 4300, Tuusula, Finland (100%)
Tel.: (358) 925851
Sales Range: $25-49.9 Million
Emp.: 170
Sterilization Products Mfr
N.A.I.C.S.: 339113
Petri Huhti *(Mng Dir)*

STERIS GmbH (2)
Bielstrasse 76, 2542, Pieterlen, Switzerland
Tel.: (41) 323760200
Pharmaceuticals Product Mfr
N.A.I.C.S.: 325412

STERIS Japan, Inc. (2)
(100%)
Tel.: (81) 352101521
Web Site: https://www.steris.co.jp
Sales Range: $1-9.9 Million
Emp.: 13
Sterilization Equipment Vendors
N.A.I.C.S.: 339112

STERIS Limited (2)

Steris House Jays Close, Viables, Basingstoke, RG22 4AX, Hampshire, United Kingdom (100%)
Tel.: (44) 1256840400
Sales Range: $10-24.9 Million
Emp.: 25
Sterilization Equipment Vendors
N.A.I.C.S.: 339113

Subsidiary (Domestic):

Albert Browne Limited (3)
Chancery House 190 Waterside Road Hamilton Industrial Park, Leicester, LE5 1QZ, United Kingdom
Tel.: (44) 1162768636
Laboratory Equipment Mfr
N.A.I.C.S.: 334516

Eschmann Holdings Limited (3)
Eschmann House 15 Peter Rd, Lancing, BN15 8TJ, West Sussex, United Kingdom
Tel.: (44) 1903753322
Web Site: https://www.eschmann.co.uk
Holding Company; Diagnostics, Medical Devices & Equipment Design & Mfr
N.A.I.C.S.: 551112

Subsidiary (Non-US):

Eschmann Holdings Pte Limited (4)
No 3 International Business Park #01-20A Nordic European Center, Singapore, 609927, Singapore
Tel.: (65) 64119843
Web Site: http://www.eschmann.co.uk
Diagnostics, Medical Devices & Equipment Design & Mfr
N.A.I.C.S.: 339112

Subsidiary (Domestic):

ReNOVA Surgical Limited (3)
Spring Hill Office Park Harborough Road, Northampton, NN6 9AA, United Kingdom
Tel.: (44) 1604973355
Web Site: http://www.renovasurgical.co.uk
Medical Device Repair Services
N.A.I.C.S.: 811210

STERIS Solutions Limited (3)
Chancery House Rayns Way, Syston, LE7 1PF, Leicester, United Kingdom
Tel.: (44) 1162768636
Medical Product Mfr & Distr
N.A.I.C.S.: 339112

Synergy Health Limited (3)
Ground Floor Stella Windmill Hill Business Park Whitehill Way, Swindon, SN5 6NX, United Kingdom
Tel.: (44) 1793 601000
Web Site: http://www.synergyhealthplc.com
Surgical Instruments & Linen Management Supplier; Patient Support Services
N.A.I.C.S.: 423450

Subsidiary (Non-US):

Synergy Health (Suzhou) Limited (4)
No 26 Xinchang Road, Suzhou Industrial Park, Suzhou, 215125, Jiangsu, China
Tel.: (86) 51282289099
Hospital Sterilization Services
N.A.I.C.S.: 811210

Synergy Health (Suzhou) Sterilization Technologies Limited (4)
No 26 Xinchang Road Suzhou Industrial Park, Suzhou, 215125, Jiangsu, China
Tel.: (86) 512 8228 9099
Web Site: http://www.synergyhealthplc.com
Medical Device Sterilisation Services
N.A.I.C.S.: 621511

Synergy Health Allershausen GmbH (4)
Kesselbodenstrasse 7, 85391, Allershausen, Germany
Tel.: (49) 816668800
Medical Device Sterilisation Services
N.A.I.C.S.: 621511
Reiner Eidenberger *(Mng Dir)*

Subsidiary (US):

Synergy Health Americas (4)
401 E Jackson St Ste 3100, Tampa, FL 33602
Tel.: (813) 891-9550
Web Site: http://www.synergyhealthplc.com

INTERNATIONAL PUBLIC

Health Care Products & Services
N.A.I.C.S.: 339112

Subsidiary (Domestic):

Synergy Health AST, LLC (5)
500 W 4th St, Lima, OH 45804-1900
Tel.: (419) 225-1288
Web Site: http://www.synergyhealthplc.com
Hospital Sterilization Services
N.A.I.C.S.: 811210

Synergy Health Outsourcing Solutions, Inc. (5)
401 E Jackson St Ste 3100, Tampa, FL 33602
Tel.: (813) 891-9550
Web Site: http://www.synergyhealthplc.com
Health Care Srvices
N.A.I.C.S.: 621498

Subsidiary (Non-US):

Synergy Health Daniken AG (4)
Hogenweidstrasse 6, 4658, Daniken, Switzerland
Tel.: (41) 622889060
Radiation Processing Services
N.A.I.C.S.: 541380

Subsidiary (Domestic):

Synergy Health Investments Limited (4)
Ground Floor Stella Windmill Hill Business Park, Whitehall Way, Swindon, SN5 6NX, Wilts, United Kingdom
Tel.: (44) 1793601000
Web Site: http://www.synergyhealthplc.com
Investment Management Service
N.A.I.C.S.: 523999

Subsidiary (Non-US):

Synergy Health (Thailand) Limited (5)
700/465 Amata Nakorn Industrial Moo 7, Tambon Donhuaroh Amphur Muang, Chon Buri, 20000, Thailand
Tel.: (66) 38450092
Medical Device Sterilisation Services
N.A.I.C.S.: 621511

Synergy Health Ireland Limited (5)
IDA Business Technology Park Sragh Industrial Estate, Offaly, Tullamore, R35 X865, Ireland
Tel.: (353) 579349999
Medical Device Sterilisation Services
N.A.I.C.S.: 621511

Synergy Sterilisation (M) Sdn Bhd (5)
Plot 203 Kuala Ketil Industrial Park, Kuala Ketil, 09300, Kedah, Malaysia
Tel.: (60) 44152111
Web Site: http://www.synergyhealthplc.com
Medical Device Sterilisation Services
N.A.I.C.S.: 621511

Synergy Sterilisation South Africa (Pty) Limited (5)
5 Waterpas Street Kempton Park, Isando Ext 3, Johannesburg, 1600, South Africa
Tel.: (27) 119748851
Web Site: http://www.synergyhealthplc.com
Medical Device Sterilisation Services
N.A.I.C.S.: 621511
Graham Reeves *(Mng Dir)*

Subsidiary (Non-US):

Synergy Health Marseille sas (4)
MIN 712 Les Arnavaux, 13323, Marseille, Cedex 14, France
Tel.: (33) 491214214
Radiation Processing Services
N.A.I.C.S.: 541380

Synergy Health Nederland B.V. (4)
Fokkerstraat 574, Schiedam, 3125 BE, Netherlands
Tel.: (31) 102322666
Web Site: http://www.synergyhealthplc.com
Regional Head Office; Medical Device Sterilisation Services
N.A.I.C.S.: 621511

Subsidiary (Domestic):

Synergy Health Amsterdam B.V. (5)

Sterilisatie Dienst DO-310 Academisch Medisch Centrum, Postbus 22660, Amsterdam, 1100 DD, Netherlands
Tel.: (31) 205662510
Web Site: http://www.synergyhealthplc.com
Hospital Sterilization Services
N.A.I.C.S.: 811210

Synergy Health Ede B.V. (5)
Morsestraat 3, 6716 AH, Ede, Netherlands
Tel.: (31) 318637476
Medical Device Sterilisation Services
N.A.I.C.S.: 621511

Synergy Health Hoorn B.V. (5)
Neutronweg 1, Hoorn, 1627 LG, Netherlands
Tel.: (31) 229219041
Web Site: http://www.synergyhealthplc.com
Linen Management Services
N.A.I.C.S.: 812331

Synergy Health Utrecht B.V. (5)
Reactorweg 47A, Utrecht, 3542 AD, Netherlands
Tel.: (31) 302843010
Web Site: http://www.synergyhealthplc.com
Medical Laboratory Services
N.A.I.C.S.: 621511

Subsidiary (Non-US):

Synergy Health Radeberg GmbH (4)
Juri-Gagarin-Strasse 15, 01454, Radeberg, Germany
Tel.: (49) 352843640
Medical Device Sterilisation Services
N.A.I.C.S.: 621511

Subsidiary (Domestic):

Synergy Health Sterilisation UK Limited (4)
Unit 2 Marcus Close, Tilehurst, Reading, RG30 4EA, Berks, United Kingdom
Tel.: (44) 1189421061
Radiation Processing Services
N.A.I.C.S.: 541380

Subsidiary (Non-US):

Synergy Sterilisation Kulim (M) Sdn Bhd (4)
Lot 71 Kulim Industrial Estate, 09000, Kulim, Kedah, Malaysia
Tel.: (60) 44892158
Medical Device Sterilisation Services
N.A.I.C.S.: 541380

Synergy Sterilisation Rawang (M) Sdn Bhd (4)
Lot 42 Jalan Industri 2/1, Rawang Integrated Industrial Park, 48000, Rawang, Selangor, Malaysia
Tel.: (60) 360999600
Medical Device Sterilisation Services
N.A.I.C.S.: 541380

Subsidiary (Domestic):

Vernon and Co. Limited (3)
Belgrave House 58 High Street Gargrave, Skipton, BD23 3LX, United Kingdom
Tel.: (44) 1756748000
Web Site: https://www.vernon.co.uk
Real Estate Agency Services
N.A.I.C.S.: 531210
Peter Vernon (Dir)

Subsidiary (Non-US):

STERIS NV (2)
Uitbreidingstraat 80 - 3e Verdieping, 2600, Berchem, Belgium
Tel.: (32) 33691197
Surgical Equipment Mfr & Distr
N.A.I.C.S.: 339112

STERIS S.r.l. (2)
Strada Cassanese 224 Centro Direzionale Milano, Oltre Palazzo Tintoretto, 20090, Segrate, Italy
Tel.: (39) 022130341
Sales Range: $25-49.9 Million
Emp.: 33
Surgical Equipment Mfr
N.A.I.C.S.: 339112
Luca Danesi (Pres)

STERIS SPRL/BVRA (2)
De Keyserlei 58-60, Anderlecht, 1070, Brussels, Belgium
Tel.: (32) 25232488
Web Site: http://www.steris.com
Sales Range: $1-9.9 Million
Emp.: 12
Sterilization Equipment Sales
N.A.I.C.S.: 339113

STERIS Singapore Pte. Ltd. (2)
29 Media Circle 04-01 ALICE MEDIAPOLIS North Tower, Singapore, 138565, Singapore
Tel.: (65) 68417677
Surgical Equipment Mfr & Distr
N.A.I.C.S.: 339112

Subsidiary (Domestic):

STERIS USA Distribution Corporation (2) (100%)
5960 Heisley Rd, Mentor, OH 44060
Tel.: (440) 354-2600
Web Site: http://www.steris.com
Sales Range: $100-124.9 Million
Emp.: 500
Healthcare Product Distr
N.A.I.C.S.: 339113

Subsidiary (Non-US):

STERIS sas (2)
116 Avenue de Magudas, CS 10033, Le Haillan, 33187, Bordeaux, France
Tel.: (33) 556939494
Web Site: http://www.steris.com
Surgical Equipment Mfr & Distr
N.A.I.C.S.: 339112

STERIS-Austar Pharmaceutical Systems Hong Kong Limited (2)
Web Site: http://www.austar.com.hk
Emp.: 100
Pharmaceuticals Product Mfr
N.A.I.C.S.: 325412

Subsidiary (Domestic):

Strategic Technology Enterprise, Inc. (2)
5960 Heisley Rd, Mentor, OH 44060
Tel.: (440) 354-2600
Sales Range: $10-24.9 Million
Emp.: 20
Decontamination Equipment Mfr
N.A.I.C.S.: 333310

United States Endoscopy Group, Inc. (2)
5976 Heisley Rd, Mentor, OH 44060
Tel.: (440) 639-4494
Web Site: http://www.usendoscopy.com
Surgical Instrument Design & Mfr
N.A.I.C.S.: 339112
Tony Siracusa (VP & Gen Mgr)

Subsidiary (Domestic):

Genii, Inc. (3)
2155 Woodlane Dr Ste 104, Saint Paul, MN 55125-1920
Tel.: (855) 501-4810
Electromedical & Electrotherapeutic Apparatus Mfr
N.A.I.C.S.: 334510

STERLING & WILSON SOLAR LIMITED
Universal Majestic 9th Floor P L Lokhande Marg, Chembur West, Mumbai, 400043, India
Tel.: (91) 2225485300
Web Site: https://www.sterlingandwilsonre.com
Year Founded: 2011
542760—(BOM)
Rev.: $254,885,199
Assets: $382,515,437
Liabilities: $411,326,659
Net Worth: ($28,811,222)
Earnings: ($140,874,048)
Emp.: 835
Fiscal Year-end: 03/31/23
Solar Electric Power Generation Services
N.A.I.C.S.: 221114

Jagannadha Rao (Compliance Officer & Sec)

STERLING AIRLINES A/S
Copenhagen Airport South, 2791, Dragor, Denmark
Tel.: (45) 70333370
Web Site: http://www.sterlingticket.com
Sales Range: $150-199.9 Million
Emp.: 612
Oil Transportation Services
N.A.I.C.S.: 481111
Michael T. Hansen (Chief Comml Officer)

STERLING BANK PLC
Sterling Towers 20 Marina Lagos Island, Lagos, Nigeria
Tel.: (234) 07008220000
Web Site: http://www.sterling.ng
STERLNBANK—(NIGE)
Rev.: $9,506,362
Assets: $1,375,281,830
Liabilities: $1,261,292,830
Net Worth: $113,989,001
Earnings: $14,284,340
Emp.: 3,043
Fiscal Year-end: 12/31/22
Commercial Banking Services
N.A.I.C.S.: 522110
Abubakar Suleiman (CEO & Mng Dir)

Subsidiaries:

Pace Registrars Limited (1)
8th Floor Knight Frank Building 24 Campbell Street, Lagos, Nigeria
Tel.: (234) 27907979
Web Site: https://www.paceregistrars.com
Securities Register Administration Services
N.A.I.C.S.: 523210
Oladunni Ismael (Head-Fin & Admin)

SCM Capital Limited (1)
2 - 4 Customs Street 19th Floor Nigerian Stock Exchange House, Ikoyi, Lagos, 23401, Marina, Nigeria
Tel.: (234) 128022279
Web Site: https://www.scmcapitalng.com
Emp.: 30
Investment Banking Services
N.A.I.C.S.: 523150
Alhassan Gwarzo (Head-Corp Fin)

STERLING BIOTECH LTD.
C - 25 Laxmi Towers A - 601 6th Floor Bandra Kurla Complex, Bandra East, Mumbai, 400051, India
Tel.: (91) 22 26509076
Web Site: http://www.sterlingbiotech.in
Year Founded: 1985
Pharmaceutical Gelatin Mfr & Distr
N.A.I.C.S.: 325412
Nitin J. Sandesara (Chm & Co-Mng Dir)

STERLING FORD SALES (OTTAWA) INC.
1425 Ogilvie Rd, Ottawa, K1J 7P3, ON, Canada
Tel.: (613) 741-3720
Web Site: http://www.sterlingford.ca
Year Founded: 1988
Rev.: $21,083,184
Emp.: 45
New & Used Car Dealers
N.A.I.C.S.: 441110

STERLING GREENWOODS LTD.
25 Sunrise Center opp Indraprasth Towers, Drive-in Cinema Road, Ahmedabad, 380054, Gujarat, India
Tel.: (91) 7926851680
Web Site: https://www.sterlinggreenwood.com

526500—(BOM)
Rev.: $467,202
Assets: $3,984,569
Liabilities: $2,230,238
Net Worth: $1,754,331
Earnings: ($144,212)
Emp.: 48
Fiscal Year-end: 03/31/23
Restaurant Operating Services
N.A.I.C.S.: 722511
Umesh Ghanshyambhai Lavingia (Chm)

STERLING GROUP HOLDINGS LIMITED
18/F-19/F Win Plaza 9 Sheung Hei Street, San Po Kong, Kowloon, China (Hong Kong)
Tel.: (852) 35886111 Ky
Web Site: http://www.sterlingapparel.com.hk
1825—(HKG)
Rev.: $79,487,708
Assets: $38,450,685
Liabilities: $32,457,803
Net Worth: $5,992,883
Earnings: $2,540,693
Emp.: 1,444
Fiscal Year-end: 03/31/23
Apparel Product Mfr & Distr
N.A.I.C.S.: 315250
Alice Mei Wai Wong (Exec Dir)

STERLING GROUP VENTURES, INC.
Unit 520 409 Granville Street, Vancouver, V6C 1T2, BC, Canada
Tel.: (604) 564-0765 NV
Web Site: http://www.mojo.game
Year Founded: 2001
SGGV—(OTCBB)
Online Gaming Company
N.A.I.C.S.: 713290
Chris MacPherson (CFO)

STERLING GUARANTY & FINANCE LTD.
Office No 3rd & 4th 3rd Floor The Centrium Village Kurla Kirol Kurla W, Nariman Point, Mumbai, 400070, India
Tel.: (91) 2222840019
Web Site: https://www.sterlingguaranty.com
Year Founded: 1983
508963—(BOM)
Rev.: $18,683
Assets: $3,545
Liabilities: $86,351
Net Worth: ($82,806)
Earnings: $4,187
Fiscal Year-end: 03/31/23
Financial Investment Services
N.A.I.C.S.: 523999
Dhiren D. Mehta (Chm)

STERLING INTERNATIONAL ENTERPRISES LIMITED
43 Atlanta Building, Nariman Point, Mumbai, 400 021, India
Tel.: (91) 22 66306732 In
Web Site: http://www.sterinternational.com
Year Founded: 1984
Sales Range: $50-74.9 Million
Oil Exploration Services
N.A.I.C.S.: 213112

STERLING MARKING PRODUCTS INC.
349 Ridout Street North, London, N6A 2N8, ON, Canada
Tel.: (519) 434-5785
Web Site: http://www.sterling.ca
Year Founded: 1945
Rev.: $11,579,118

STERLING MARKING PRODUCTS INC.

Sterling Marking Products Inc.—(Continued)
Emp.: 160
Rubber & Other Stampings Mfr
N.A.I.C.S.: 339940
Bob Schram (Pres)

STERLING METALS CORP.
217 Queen St W Suite 401, Toronto, M5V 0R2, ON, Canada
Tel.: (416) 643-7630   Ca
Web Site: https://sterlingmetals.ca
LACB—(DEU)
Assets: $9,188,591
Liabilities: $252,682
Net Worth: $8,935,908
Earnings: ($1,138,175)
Fiscal Year-end: 12/31/22
Metal Mining
N.A.I.C.S.: 212290
Chris Irwin (Sec)

STERLING PLANTATIONS LIMITED
Ground Floor Suite 1 437 Roberts Road, Subiaco, 6008, WA, Australia
Tel.: (61) 863802555   AU
Web Site:
    http://www.sterlingplantations.com
Year Founded: 2006
Rev.: $1,278,443
Assets: $26,402,416
Liabilities: $63,541,252
Net Worth: ($37,138,836)
Earnings: ($2,059,713)
Fiscal Year-end: 06/30/18
Oil Palm Developer & Biodiesel Mfr
N.A.I.C.S.: 111120
C. R. S. Paragash (Chm)

STERLING POWERGENSYS LIMITED
Office No 121 Runwal Commercial Complex Co-Op Premises Ltd L B S Marg, Mulund, Mumbai, 400080, Maharashtra, India
Tel.: (91) 9619572230   In
Web Site: https://splsolar.in
Year Founded: 1984
513575—(BOM)
Rev.: $39,855
Assets: $1,751,599
Liabilities: $2,066,713
Net Worth: ($315,114)
Earnings: ($84,864)
Emp.: 8
Fiscal Year-end: 03/31/23
Solar Power Engineering Services
N.A.I.C.S.: 541330
Sankaran Venkata Subramanian (Mng Dir)

STERLING TOOLS LIMITED
5A DLF Industrial Estate, Faridabad, 121 003, Haryana, India
Tel.: (91) 1292270621
Web Site:
    https://www.stlfasteners.com
Year Founded: 1979
STERTOOLS—(NSE)
Rev.: $48,936,765
Assets: $70,475,046
Liabilities: $25,228,107
Net Worth: $45,246,938
Earnings: $3,208,992
Emp.: 571
Fiscal Year-end: 03/31/21
Fasteners Marketing & Mfr
N.A.I.C.S.: 339993
Manohar Lal Aggarwal (Chm)

STERLING WHITE HALIBUT AS
Hundsnesveien 205, 4130, Hjelmeland, Norway
Tel.: (47) 51752027

Web Site:
    http://www.sterlingwhitehalibut.com
Sales Range: $10-24.9 Million
Emp.: 11
White Halibut Farming Services
N.A.I.C.S.: 114111
Magnus Skretting (Mng Dir)

STERLITE TECHNOLOGIES LIMITED
Godrej Millenium 9 Koregaon Road, Pune, 411001, Maharashtra, India
Tel.: (91) 2030514000
Web Site: https://www.stl.tech
532374—(BOM)
Rev.: $835,201,727
Assets: $1,062,885,918
Liabilities: $811,701,936
Net Worth: $251,183,982
Earnings: $15,226,905
Emp.: 3,140
Fiscal Year-end: 03/31/23
Power Transmission Conductors, Optical Fibers & Telecommunication Cables Mfr
N.A.I.C.S.: 335921
Pravin Agarwal (Vice Chm)

Subsidiaries:

Metallurgica Bresciana S.p.A   (1)
Viale G Marconi 31, Dello, 25020, Brescia, Italy
Tel.: (39) 0309771911
Web Site:
    https://www.metallurgicabresciana.it
Optical Fiber Mfr
N.A.I.C.S.: 335921

Optotec S.p.A.   (1)
Largo Boccioni 1, 21040, Origgio, VA, Italy
Tel.: (39) 02995151
Web Site: https://www.optotec.com
Telecommunication Servicesb
N.A.I.C.S.: 517810

Sterlite Conduspar Industrial Ltda   (1)
Dr Murici Street 4000 Airport, Sao Jose dos Pinhais, 83015-290, Parana, Brazil
Tel.: (55) 4121096037
Web Site:
    http://www.sterliteconduspar.com.br
Optical Fiber Mfr
N.A.I.C.S.: 335921
Marco Antonio Scocco (Mgr-Technical)

Sterlite Technologies DMCC   (1)
Unit No 1101 1109 The Dome Tower Jumeirah Lakes Towers, Dubai, United Arab Emirates
Tel.: (971) 565452766
Digital Marketing Services
N.A.I.C.S.: 541613

Sterlite Technologies S.p.A   (1)
Via G Marconi 31 Dello, 25020, Brescia, Italy
Tel.: (39) 0309771911
Software Services
N.A.I.C.S.: 541511

Vulcan Data Centre Solutions Limited   (1)
Unit 501 Centennial Park Elstree, Borehamwood, WD6 3FG, Hampshire, United Kingdom
Tel.: (44) 2036334570
Web Site: http://www.vulcan.global
Data Solution Services
N.A.I.C.S.: 518210

STERN IMMOBILIEN AG
Tolzer Str. 4, 82031, Grunwald, Germany
Tel.: (49) 89 64954442
Web Site: http://www.stern-immobilien.com
Real Estate Services
N.A.I.C.S.: 531390
Hans Kilger (Chm-Supervisory Bd)

STERN PARTNERS INC.
Suite 2900 650 West Georgia Street, Vancouver, V6B 4N8, BC, Canada
Tel.: (604) 681-8817
Web Site:
    https://www.sternpartners.com
Emp.: 7,000
Investment Management Service
N.A.I.C.S.: 523940
Ronald N. Stern (Founder & Pres)

Subsidiaries:

TerraLink Horticulture Inc.   (1)
464 Riverside Rd, Abbotsford, V2S 7M1, BC, Canada
Tel.: (604) 864-9044
Web Site: https://www.tlhort.com
Fertilizer Distr
N.A.I.C.S.: 424910

Division (Domestic):

TerraLink Horticulture Inc. - Delta Division   (2)
4119 - 40th Street, Delta, V4K 3N2, BC, Canada
Tel.: (604) 946-8338
Farm Equipment Mfr
N.A.I.C.S.: 333111

TerraLink Horticulture Inc. - Grotec Equipment Division   (2)
1050 Riverside Road, Abbotsford, V2S 7P6, BC, Canada
Tel.: (604) 504-2838
Farm Equipment Mfr
N.A.I.C.S.: 333111

West Linn Paper Company   (1)
4800 Mill St, West Linn, OR 97068
Tel.: (503) 557-6500
Web Site: http://www.westlinnpaper.com
Sales Range: $10-24.9 Million
Emp.: 250
Paper Mill Operator
N.A.I.C.S.: 322120
Ronald N. Stern (Chm & CEO)

Subsidiary (Non-US):

Port Hawkesbury Paper Limited Partnership   (2)
120 Pulp Mill Road, PO Box 9500, Port Hawkesbury, B9A 1A1, NS, Canada
Tel.: (902) 625-2460
Web Site:
    http://www.porthawkesburypaper.com
Emp.: 700
Paper Mill Operator
N.A.I.C.S.: 322120
Marc Dube (Mgr-Dev)

STERN STEWART & CO. GMBH
Salvatorplatz 4, 80333, Munich, Germany
Tel.: (49) 89 242 0710   De
Web Site:
    http://www.sternstewart.com
Management Consulting Services
N.A.I.C.S.: 541611
Dimitri Belobokov (Partner)

Subsidiaries:

Stern Stewart Capital GmbH   (1)
Salvatorplatz 4, 80333, Munich, Germany
Tel.: (49) 89 242071 0
Web Site:
    http://www.sternstewartcapital.com
Investment Services
N.A.I.C.S.: 523999
Markus Pertl (Mng Partner)

Holding (Domestic):

Siteco Lighting GmbH   (2)
Georg-Simon-Ohm-Str 50, 83301, Traunreut, Bavaria, Germany
Tel.: (49) 8669330
Emp.: 900
Lighting Equipment Mfr
N.A.I.C.S.: 335139

STERNE ACURA
15795 Yonge St, Aurora, L4G 1P4, ON, Canada

INTERNATIONAL PUBLIC

Tel.: (905) 841-1400
Web Site:
    http://www.sterneacura.com
Year Founded: 1987
Rev.: $16,258,706
Emp.: 35
New & Used Car Dealers
N.A.I.C.S.: 441110
David Horvath (Gen Mgr-Sls)

STETSON MOTORS 2000 LTD
2451 50th Street, Drayton Valley, T7A 1S4, AB, Canada
Tel.: (780) 542-5391
Web Site: http://www.stetsongm.com
Sales Range: $125-149.9 Million
New & Used Car Dealers
N.A.I.C.S.: 441110
Scott Swendseid (Owner)

STEVANATO GROUP S.P.A.
Via Molinella 17, 35017, Piombino Dese, Padua, Italy
Tel.: (39) 0499318111   IT
Web Site:
    https://www.stevanatogroup.com
Year Founded: 1949
STVN—(NYSE)
Rev.: $1,171,329,592
Assets: $2,235,675,588
Liabilities: $1,013,307,792
Net Worth: $1,222,367,796
Earnings: $157,230,736
Emp.: 5,635
Fiscal Year-end: 12/31/23
Holding Company; Pharmaceutical Glass Parenteral Packaging Designer, Mfr & Whslr
N.A.I.C.S.: 551112
Franco Stevanato (Chm)

Subsidiaries:

Balda Medical GmbH & Co. KG   (1)
    (100%)
Tel.: (49) 57345130
Web Site: http://www.balda-group.com
Emp.: 200
Medical Glass Product Mfr
N.A.I.C.S.: 327212

Subsidiary (Non-US):

Balda Medical Verwaltungsgesellschaft mbH   (2)
    (100%)
Tel.: (49) 57349220
Medical Glass Product Whslr
N.A.I.C.S.: 423450

Nuova Ompi S.r.l.   (1)
Via Molinella 17, 35017, Piombino Dese, PD, Italy
Tel.: (39) 0499318111
Web Site: http://www.ompipharma.com
Pharmaceutical Glass Parenteral Packaging Designer, Mfr & Whslr
N.A.I.C.S.: 327212
Alessandro Morandotti (Product Mgr-EZ-fill Syringes)

Subsidiary (US):

Ompi of America, Inc.   (2)
41 University Dr Ste 400, Newtown, PA 18940
Tel.: (267) 757-8747
Web Site: http://www.ompipharma.com
Pharmaceutical Glass Parenteral Packaging Whslr
N.A.I.C.S.: 423450
Howard Drake (VP & Gen Mgr)

S.P.A.M.I. S.r.l.   (1)
Via Molinella 17, 35017, Piombino Dese, PD, Italy
Tel.: (39) 049 931 8111
Web Site: http://www.spami.it
Tubular Glass & Packaging Machinery Designer & Mfr
N.A.I.C.S.: 333248
Franco Stevanato (CEO)

Division (Domestic):

Optrel (2)
Via Molinella 17, 35017, Piombino Dese, PD, Italy
Tel.: (39) 049 931 8111
Web Site: http://www.optrelinspection.com
Glass Pharmaceutical Tubing Container Inspection Machinery Designer & Mfr
N.A.I.C.S.: 333248

SG Lab S.r.l. (1)
Via delle Tofane 38/A, 40134, Bologna, Italy
Tel.: (39) 0514122793
Web Site: https://www.sglab.it
Architectural Services
N.A.I.C.S.: 541310

STEVE LEUNG DESIGN GROUP LTD.
30/F Manhattan Place 23 Wang Tai Road, Kowloon Bay, China (Hong Kong)
Tel.: (852) 25271600
Web Site: http://www.sldgroup.com
Year Founded: 1997
2262—(HKG)
Rev.: $48,577,755
Assets: $66,693,083
Liabilities: $23,444,445
Net Worth: $43,248,638
Earnings: ($7,635,720)
Emp.: 442
Fiscal Year-end: 12/31/22
Interior Designing Services
N.A.I.C.S.: 541410
Chong Chiu Fung (Chief Creative Officer)

Subsidiaries:

Everyday Living (Guangzhou) Trading Limited (1)
Unit 3B-3C Zone 6 Tongchuang Hui 88 Xinjiao Middle Road, Haizhu District, Guangzhou, 510300, China
Tel.: (86) 2089772168
Interior Decorative Product Distr
N.A.I.C.S.: 423620

Steve Leung Designers (Beijing) Limited (1)
4/F Block 15 Building No 6 Court Jingshun East Road, Chaoyang District, Beijing, 100015, China
Tel.: (86) 1065863988
Interior Design Services
N.A.I.C.S.: 541410

Steve Leung Exchange Limited (1)
30/F Manhattan Place 23 Wang Tai Road Kowloon Bay, Hong Kong, China (Hong Kong)
Tel.: (852) 25271600
Interior Design Services
N.A.I.C.S.: 541410

STEVE MARSHALL FORD LINCOLN
3851 Shenton Road, Nanaimo, V9T 2H1, BC, Canada
Tel.: (250) 758-7311
Web Site: https://www.stevemarshallford.com
Year Founded: 1966
Rev.: $28,186,600
Emp.: 70
New & Used Car Dealers
N.A.I.C.S.: 441110
Ann Marie Clark (Owner)

STEVE MARSHALL GROUP LTD.
2300 North Island Highway, Campbell River, V9W 2G8, BC, Canada
Tel.: (250) 287-9211
Web Site: https://www.stevemarshall.com
Car Dealer
N.A.I.C.S.: 441110
Steve Marshall (Pres)

Subsidiaries:

Inter-Pacific Motors Inc. (1)
1030 Kanoelehua Ave, Hilo, HI 96720
Tel.: (808) 935-1191
Web Site: http://www.fordhawaii.com
Sales Range: $10-24.9 Million
Emp.: 56
New & Used Car Dealers
N.A.I.C.S.: 441110
J. Walsh Hanley (CEO)

STEVEDORING SERVICES LTD.
Stevedore House 38 Front Street, Hamilton, HM 12, Bermuda
Tel.: (441) 2923366
Web Site: http://www.stevedoring.bm
Sales Range: $10-24.9 Million
Port & Harbor Services
N.A.I.C.S.: 488310
Peter L. Aldrich (Gen Mgr)

STEVENSON LOGISTICS PTY. LTD.
Rous Head Terminal Lot R111 Kooringa Place, North Fremantle, 6159, WA, Australia
Tel.: (61) 8 9358 7777
Web Site: http://www.stevensonlogistics.com
Year Founded: 1930
Sales Range: $25-49.9 Million
Emp.: 50
Container Transport, Warehousing & Logistics Services
N.A.I.C.S.: 541614
Jim Stevenson (Chm)

STEVIA NUTRA CORP.
37 Bannisters Road, Corner Brook, A2H 1M5, NL, Canada
Tel.: (709) 660-3056
Web Site: http://www.stevianutra.com
Year Founded: 2010
Sweetner Mfr
N.A.I.C.S.: 311314
Brian W. Dicks (Pres)

STEWART & WIGHT PLC
845 Finchley Road, London, NW11 8NA, United Kingdom
Tel.: (44) 2084551111
Web Site: http://www.stewartandwightplc.co.uk
Year Founded: 1898
Sales Range: $1-9.9 Million
Property Investment Services
N.A.I.C.S.: 523999
Michael B. Conn (Chm)

STEWART INVESTMENT & FINANCIAL PRIVATE LIMITED
36A, Elgin Road, Ground Floor, Kolkata, 700 020, India
Tel.: (91) 03346020843
Year Founded: 1985
Financial Services
N.A.I.C.S.: 523999

STEWARTS & LLOYDS OF INDIA LTD
Kanak Building 1st Floor 41 Chowringhee Road, Kolkata, 700 071, India
Tel.: (91) 3322888194
Web Site: https://www.slofindia.com
Year Founded: 1937
Construction Engineering Services
N.A.I.C.S.: 237990
Dipankar Banerjee (CEO)

STEYR MOTORS CO., LTD.
3F Customs House No 66 Yanghu West Road Wujin National Hi-tech Zone, Changzhou, 213164, Jiangsu, China
Tel.: (86) 5198 159 5631
Web Site: http://www.steyr-motors.cn
000760—(SSE)
Rev.: $1,392,206
Assets: $93,169,891
Liabilities: $51,638,064
Net Worth: $41,531,827
Earnings: ($26,005,262)
Fiscal Year-end: 12/31/19
Automotive Components Mfr
N.A.I.C.S.: 336110
Zhang Jie (Chm-Interim)

STF S.P.A
Strada Robecco 20, 20013, Magenta, Italy
Tel.: (39) 02972091
Web Site: http://www.stf.it
Year Founded: 1937
Sales Range: $75-99.9 Million
Emp.: 300
Power Plant Equipment Mfr
N.A.I.C.S.: 332410
Salvatore Trifone (Chm)

Subsidiaries:

Burmeister & Wain Energy A/S (1)
Lundtoftegardsvej 93A, 2800, Lyngby, Denmark
Tel.: (45) 39452000
Web Site: http://www.bwe.dk
Sales Range: $10-24.9 Million
Emp.: 100
Power Plant Equipment Mfr
N.A.I.C.S.: 332410
Paolo Danesi (VP-Sls)

Subsidiary (Non-US):

BWE Energy India Pvt. Ltd. (2)
Guna Towers No 2 North Boag Road, T Nagar, Chennai, TamilNadu, India
Tel.: (91) 44 49173300
Web Site: http://www.bweenergy.in
Boiler Distr
N.A.I.C.S.: 423720
R. Paramasivam (Sr Mgr-Proposals)

BWE International B.V. (2)
Drentestraat 24 Bg, 1083HK, Amsterdam, Netherlands
Tel.: (31) 205408989
Boiler Distr
N.A.I.C.S.: 423720

STF ENERJI LIMITED (1)
Cumhuriyet cd N 44 D 2 Elmadag Sisli, Istanbul, Turkiye
Tel.: (90) 212 232 30 30
Boiler Distr
N.A.I.C.S.: 423720

STF SLOVAKIA S.R.O. (1)
Palarikova 25, 811 04, Bratislava, Slovakia
Tel.: (421) 2 33221100
Boiler Distr
N.A.I.C.S.: 423720

STG CO., LTD.
Tel.: (81) 729280212
Web Site: https://www.stgroup.jp
5858—(TKS)
Rev.: $34,649,620
Assets: $38,939,510
Liabilities: $27,662,850
Net Worth: $11,276,660
Earnings: $1,308,780
Emp.: 160
Fiscal Year-end: 03/31/24
Metal Products Mfr
N.A.I.C.S.: 331314
Teruaki Sato (CEO)

Subsidiaries:

STX Precision (JB) Sdn. Bhd. (1)
Lot 153 No 17A Jalan Angkasa Mas 6 Kawasan Perindustrian Tebrau II, 81100, Johor Bahru, Malaysia
Tel.: (60) 73533940
Web Site: https://stx.com.my
Metal Component Mfr & Distr
N.A.I.C.S.: 331523

Sanki Eastern (Thailand) Co., Ltd. (1)
113/4 Moo4 Nakhon Luang Industrial Estate Tambol Bangphrakru, Amphur Nakhonlung, Ayutthaya, 13260, Thailand
Tel.: (66) 35364101
Automobile Parts Mfr & Distr
N.A.I.C.S.: 336390

Sanki Fine Technology (Hong Kong) Co., Ltd. (1)
Room 604 6th Floor Emperor Group Center 288Hennessy Road, Wanchai, Hong Kong, China (Hong Kong)
Tel.: (852) 75525249522
Automobile Parts Mfr & Distr
N.A.I.C.S.: 336390

Shenzhen Sanhui Precision Hardware Co., Ltd. (1)
101 Plant NO 8 Niujiao Road, Industrial Zone in the 2nd of Yanchuan Community Songgang Baoan, Shenzhen, China
Tel.: (86) 75527148589
Magnesium Molded Product Mfr & Distr
N.A.I.C.S.: 332999

STG INTERNATIONAL LTD
53 Derech Hashalom St, Givatayim, 53454, Israel
Tel.: (972) 37331400
Web Site: https://www.stggroup.co.il
Year Founded: 1965
STG—(TAE)
Rev.: $47,170,050
Assets: $50,876,640
Liabilities: $15,874,844
Net Worth: $35,001,795
Earnings: $5,199,337
Emp.: 60
Fiscal Year-end: 12/31/23
Other Electronic Parts & Equipment Merchant Wholesalers
N.A.I.C.S.: 423690

Subsidiaries:

STARTRONICS (1)
53 Derech Hashalom St, Givatayim, Israel
Tel.: (972) 37331414
Web Site: http://www.startronics.co.il
Sales Range: $25-49.9 Million
Emp.: 10
Electronic Components Mfr
N.A.I.C.S.: 334416

Unisor MultiSystems Ltd. (1)
Giborei Israel 10 Entrance A, Netanya, 42505, Israel
Tel.: (972) 97726410
Web Site: http://www.unisor.com
Industrial Computing Mfr
N.A.I.C.S.: 334111

STG LIFECARE LIMITED
1/26 Lalita Park Laxmi Nagar, New Delhi, 110092, India
Tel.: (91) 1147587113
Web Site: http://www.stgglobal.com
Sales Range: Less than $1 Million
Software Development Services
N.A.I.C.S.: 541511

Subsidiaries:

Software Technology Group Inc. (1)
555 S 300 E, Salt Lake City, UT 84111
Tel.: (801) 595-1000
Web Site: http://www.softwaretechnologygroup.com
Emp.: 84
Software Development Services
N.A.I.C.S.: 541511
Jeff Soderberg (CEO)

STHALER LIMITED
International House Floor 6 1 St Katharine's Way, St Katharine's Docks, London, E1W 1UN, United Kingdom
Tel.: (44) 2031891460
Web Site: http://www.sthaler.com
Financial Services
N.A.I.C.S.: 523999

STHALER LIMITED

Sthaler Limited—(Continued)

Nick Dryden (CEO)

STHREE PLC.
1st Floor 75 King William Street, London, EC4N 7BE, United Kingdom
Tel.: (44) 2072686000 UK
Web Site: https://www.sthree.com
Year Founded: 1986
STEM—(LSE)
Rev.: $2,117,335,464
Assets: $601,276,896
Liabilities: $317,528,964
Net Worth: $283,747,932
Earnings: $71,357,098
Emp.: 3,441
Fiscal Year-end: 11/30/23
Permanent & Contract Staffing Services
N.A.I.C.S.: 561311
Alex Smith (CFO)

Subsidiaries:

Huxley Associates Limited (1)
1st Floor 75 King William Street, London, EC4N 7BE, United Kingdom
Tel.: (44) 2074695000
Web Site: https://www.huxley.com
Recruitment Services
N.A.I.C.S.: 561311

Huxley BV (1)
Keizersgracht 281 5th Floor, 1016 ED, Amsterdam, Netherlands
Tel.: (31) 205221250
Staffing & Recruiting Services
N.A.I.C.S.: 561311

Jobboard Enterprises GmbH (1)
Grosse Bockenheimer Str 50, Frankfurt am Main, 60313, Hessen, Germany
Tel.: (49) 6913385177
Human Resource Consulting Services
N.A.I.C.S.: 541612

Real Staffing Group Limited (1)
1st Floor 75 King William Street, London, EC4N 7BE, United Kingdom
Tel.: (44) 2077587322
Web Site: https://www.realstaffing.com
Recruitment Services
N.A.I.C.S.: 561311

SThree Belgium NV (1)
Kreupelenstraat 9 5de en 6de verdieping, 1000, Brussels, Belgium
Tel.: (32) 26453311
Emp.: 90
Human Resource Consulting Services
N.A.I.C.S.: 541612
Kurt Schreurs (Mng Dir)

Division (Domestic):

Computer Futures Solutions NV (2)
Post X Gebouw 8 5th Floor Borsbeeksebrug 36, Berchem, 2600, Antwerp, Belgium
Tel.: (32) 36133000
Emp.: 350
Recruitment Services
N.A.I.C.S.: 561311

Huxley Associates Belgium NV (2)
5th Floor Rue Des Boiteux 9, 1000, Brussels, Belgium
Tel.: (32) 25577188
Web Site: https://www.huxley.com
Emp.: 50
Human Resource Consulting Services
N.A.I.C.S.: 541612

SThree GmbH (1)
Querstrasse 7, 60322, Frankfurt am Main, Germany
Tel.: (49) 89242939893
Recruitment Services
N.A.I.C.S.: 561311

SThree LLC (1)
9th Floor Office 9012-9014 Smolenskaya Square 3, 121099, Moscow, Russia
Tel.: (7) 4959378277
Recruitment Services
N.A.I.C.S.: 561311

SThree Pte. Ltd. (1)
WeWork 30 Raffles Place 17th Floor 12 - 01, Singapore, 048622, Singapore
Tel.: (65) 65915640
Web Site: https://www.sthree.com
Recruitment Services
N.A.I.C.S.: 561311

SThree S.a r.l (1)
33 Boulevard Prince Henri, 1724, Luxembourg, Luxembourg
Tel.: (352) 26453390
Recruitment Services
N.A.I.C.S.: 561311

SThree SAS (1)
170 boulevard de la Villette, 75017, Paris, Cedex, France
Tel.: (33) 142998337
Web Site: https://www.sthree.com
Recruitment Services
N.A.I.C.S.: 561311
Adrien Prime (Sr Mgr-Relationship)

STI CO. LTD.
No 21 Bonggigil Gongdo-eup, Anseong, 17558, Gyeonggi-do, Korea (South)
Tel.: (82) 316534380
Web Site: https://www.sti.co.kr
Year Founded: 1997
039440—(KRS)
Rev.: $323,995,184
Assets: $252,248,794
Liabilities: $84,060,970
Net Worth: $168,187,824
Earnings: $22,891,868
Emp.: 378
Fiscal Year-end: 12/31/22
Semiconductor Machinery Mfr
N.A.I.C.S.: 333242
Woo Seok Lee (CEO)

Subsidiaries:

PNST Co., Ltd. (1)
117 Seochon-ro Namsa-myeon, Cheoin-gu, Yongin, Gyeonggi-do, Korea (South)
Tel.: (82) 3180142100
Web Site: http://www.pnst.co.kr
Electrical Products Mfr
N.A.I.C.S.: 335999
In-Soo Kim (CEO)

STI EDUCATION SYSTEMS HOLDINGS INC.
7F STI Holdings Center 6764 Ayala Avenue, Makati, 1226, Philippines
Tel.: (63) 288449553
Web Site:
https://www.stiholdings.com
Year Founded: 1928
STI—(PHI)
Rev.: $60,594,437
Assets: $268,379,234
Liabilities: $104,506,518
Net Worth: $163,872,716
Earnings: $15,548,376
Emp.: 2,911
Fiscal Year-end: 06/30/23
Holding Company
N.A.I.C.S.: 551112
Paolo Martin O. Bautista (CIO & VP)

Subsidiaries:

STI Education Services Group, Inc. (1)
STI Academic Center Ortigas Avenue Extension, Cainta, Rizal, Philippines
Tel.: (63) 288121784
Web Site: https://www.sti.edu
School Education Services
N.A.I.C.S.: 611710

STI West Negros University, Inc. (1)
Burgos Street, Bacolod, 6100, Negros, Philippines
Tel.: (63) 344344561
School Education Services
N.A.I.C.S.: 611710

STI FOODS HOLDINGS, INC.
1-15-14 Minami-Aoyama, Minato-Ku, Tokyo, 107-0062, Japan
Tel.: (81) 334796956
Web Site: https://www.stifoods-hd.com
Year Founded: 1988
2932—(TKS)
Rev.: $225,348,560
Assets: $107,073,180
Liabilities: $54,281,040
Net Worth: $52,792,140
Earnings: $11,074,580
Emp.: 1,168
Fiscal Year-end: 12/31/23
Holding Company
N.A.I.C.S.: 551112
Yutaka Jumi (Founder, Chm, Pres & CEO)

Subsidiaries:

STI Sanyo, Inc. (1)
5-7-3 Yaizu, Yaizu, 425-0026, Shizuoka, Japan
Tel.: (81) 546287211
Web Site: https://www.stisanyo.com
Emp.: 93
Pet Food Mfr & Distr
N.A.I.C.S.: 311111

STI PRODUCTS INDIA LTD.
Suite-B Lakeview Farm Ramagondanahalli Varthur Main Road, Bengaluru, 560066, Karnataka, India
Tel.: (91) 8041482091
Iron & Steel Product Mfr
N.A.I.C.S.: 332111

STICHTING BEHEER SNS REAAL
Maliebaan 12, 3581 CN, Utrecht, Netherlands
Tel.: (31) 302334420
Web Site:
http://www.beheersnsreaal.nl
Year Founded: 1997
Sales Range: $5-14.9 Billion
Emp.: 7,113
Holding Company
N.A.I.C.S.: 551112
Jan Overmeer (Pres)

Subsidiaries:

SRH N.V. (1)
Hojel City Center Building A Croeselaan 1, NL 3521 BJ, Utrecht, Netherlands (54.3%)
Tel.: (31) 302915200
Web Site: http://www.srh.nl
Sales Range: Less than $1 Million
Bank Holding Company; Commercial Banking & Insurance Services
N.A.I.C.S.: 551111
Wim Henk Steenpoorte (Member-Exec Bd)

Division (Domestic):

SNS REAAL Invest N.V. (2)
Croeselaan 1, Utrecht, 3521 BJ, Netherlands (100%)
Tel.: (31) 302915200
Web Site: http://www.snsreaal.nl
Sales Range: $1-4.9 Billion
Trusts Estates & Agency Accounts
N.A.I.C.S.: 525920
Gerard van Olphen (CEO)

Subsidiary (Domestic):

SNS Asset Management N.V. (3)
PO Box 70053, 5201 DZ, 's-Hertogenbosch, Netherlands
Tel.: (31) 736833355
Web Site: http://www.snsbank.nl
Sales Range: $350-399.9 Million
Emp.: 700
Investment Management Service
N.A.I.C.S.: 523999

STICHTING INGKA FOUNDATION
Postbus 75505, 1070AM, Amsterdam, Netherlands
Tel.: (31) 205772000 NI
Year Founded: 1982

INTERNATIONAL PUBLIC

Sales Range: $10-24.9 Million
Emp.: 16
Non-profit Foundation
N.A.I.C.S.: 813211
Ingvar Feodor Kamprad (Chm)

Subsidiaries:

INGKA Holding B.V. (1)
Bargelaan 20, NL 2333CT, Leiden, Netherlands
Tel.: (31) 7105657100
Web Site: http://www.ikea.com
Holding Company
N.A.I.C.S.: 551112
Anders Dahlvig (Grp Pres & CEO)

Subsidiary (Non-US):

Ikea International A/S (2)
Sjogatan 1, Helsingborg, 252 25, Sweden (100%)
Tel.: (46) 42267100
Web Site: http://www.ikea.com
Sales Range: $25-49.9 Billion
Furniture Retailer
N.A.I.C.S.: 449110
Anders Dahlvig (Pres)

Subsidiary (Domestic):

Ikea Svenska AB (3)
Ikeagatan 7, PO Box 701, Almhult, 343 36, Sweden (100%)
Tel.: (46) 47681000
Web Site: http://www.ikea.se
Furniture Retailer
N.A.I.C.S.: 449110

Subsidiary (Domestic):

IKEA Industry AB (4)
Kuvettgatan 2, 26271, Angelholm, Sweden
Tel.: (46) 431442800
Web Site: http://www.swedwood.com
Wood Based Furniture Mfr & Distr
N.A.I.C.S.: 337122
Gonnor Kursell (Pres)

Subsidiary (US):

Ikea North America Services LLC (4)
420 Alan Wood Rd, Conshohocken, PA 19428
Tel.: (610) 834-0180
Web Site: http://www.ikea.com
Furniture Stores; Nonresidential Building Operators
N.A.I.C.S.: 541611
Leontyne Green Sykes (COO)

Subsidiary (Domestic):

Ikea Svenska Forsaljnings AB (4)
PO Box 200, 26035, Odakra, Sweden (100%)
Tel.: (46) 42252600
Web Site: http://www.ikea.se
Floor Covering Stores
N.A.I.C.S.: 449121

Subsidiary (Non-US):

SWEDSPAN International s.r.o. (3)
Rontgenova 28, 85101, Bratislava, Slovakia
Tel.: (421) 2 3278 2126
Web Site: http://www.swedspan.com
Wood Based Panel Mfr
N.A.I.C.S.: 321219
Jorgen Lindquist (CEO)

Subsidiary (Non-US):

IKEA Indastri Novgorod, OOO (4)
Zentralnaya street 106, 173502, Podbereze, Russia
Tel.: (7) 8162943700
Web Site: http://www.swedspan.ru
Wood Products Mfr
N.A.I.C.S.: 321219
Alexander Kozlov (Mng Dir)

Joint Venture (Non-US):

Inter IKEA Centre Group A/S (2)
Amager Strandvej 390, 2770, Kastrup, Denmark (49%)
Tel.: (45) 3262 6880
Web Site: http://www.iicg.com
Emp.: 600

Shopping Center Operator
N.A.I.C.S.: 531190
John Tegner (CEO)

Subsidiary (US):

Made4net LLC (2)
400 Frank W. Burr Boulevard Suite 10, Teaneck, NJ 07666
Tel.: (201) 645-4345
Web Site: https://made4net.com
Emp.: 140
Supply Chain Execution
N.A.I.C.S.: 541614
Joe McManus (Exec VP-Sls)

Subsidiary (Domestic):

Zethcon Corp. (3)
200 W 22nd St Ste 218, Lombard, IL 60148
Tel.: (847) 318-0800
Web Site: http://www.zethcon.com
Emp.: 100
Custom Computer Programming Services
N.A.I.C.S.: 541511
Christopher J. Oechsel (Pres & CEO)

STICHTING SURF

Hoog Overborch Office Building Hoog Catharijne Moreelspark 48, 3511 EP, Utrecht, Netherlands
Tel.: (31) 887873000
Web Site: http://www.surf.nl
Year Founded: 1987
Sales Range: $10-24.9 Million
Emp.: 50
Research Services
N.A.I.C.S.: 541715
W. B. G. Liebrand (Sec)

Subsidiaries:

SURFmarket bv (1)
Radboudkwartier 217, 3511 CJ, Utrecht, Netherlands
Tel.: (31) 881269700
Web Site: http://www.surfspot.nl
Educational Support Services
N.A.I.C.S.: 611710
Danique Aaftink (Mgr-Mktg & Comm)

SURFnet BV (1)
Hoog Overborch Moreelspark 48, 3511 EP, Utrecht, Netherlands
Tel.: (31) 887873000
Web Site: http://www.surf.nl
Rev.: $23,363,812
Assets: $27,157,715
Liabilities: $10,627,164
Net Worth: $16,530,551
Earnings: $804,717
Emp.: 92
Fiscal Year-end: 12/31/2014
Research Facilities, Colleges & Libraries Networking Services
N.A.I.C.S.: 517111
Erwin Bleumink (Member-Exec Bd)

SURFsara BV (1)
SURF Science Park Building Science Park 140, 1098 XG, Amsterdam, Netherlands
Tel.: (31) 20 800 1300
Web Site: http://www.surfsara.nl
Computer Research Services
N.A.I.C.S.: 541715

STICK INVESTMENT CO., LTD.

12 Teheran-ro 78-gil, Gangnam-gu, Seoul, Korea (South)
Tel.: (82) 234047800
Web Site: http://www.dpc.co.kr
Year Founded: 1982
026890—(KRS)
Rev.: $47,754,345
Assets: $200,619,977
Liabilities: $17,101,274
Net Worth: $183,518,704
Earnings: $12,526,019
Emp.: 68
Fiscal Year-end: 12/31/22
Transformer Mfr
N.A.I.C.S.: 334416
Yong Hwan Do (CEO)

Subsidiaries:

DPC Foshan Co., Ltd. (1)
22 3 Road West D/C Guanghua-Baian Industrial Park, Xingtan Shunde, Foshan, Guangdong, China
Tel.: (86) 75726667008
Coil & Transformer Mfr
N.A.I.C.S.: 334416

DPC Nantong Co., Ltd. (1)
No 8 Binjiang Road, Huifeng Town, Qidong, Jiangsu, China
Tel.: (86) 5133699320
Coil & Transformer Mfr
N.A.I.C.S.: 334416

DY Power Systems (M) Sdn. Bhd. (1)
Lot 17245 4th Mile Jalan Gentingoff Jalan Kapar, 42100, Klang, Selangor, Malaysia
Tel.: (60) 332912794
Coil & Transformer Mfr
N.A.I.C.S.: 334416

STIC Investment, Inc. (1)
10 Fl MSA Bldg 12 Teheran-ro 78-gil, Gangnam-gu, Seoul, 06194, Korea (South)
Tel.: (82) 2340407800
Privater Equity Firm
N.A.I.C.S.: 523999
Joon Ha An (Mng Dir)

STICKIT TECHNOLOGIES INC.

666 Burrard Street, Vancouver, V6C 3P6, BC, Canada
Tel.: (604) 608-5454   BC
Web Site: https://www.stickit-labs.com
Year Founded: 2021
STKT—(CNSX)
Pharmaceutical Product Mfr & Distr
N.A.I.C.S.: 325412

STIEBEL ELTRON GMBH & CO. KG

Dr Stiebel Strasse 33, Holzminden, Germany
Tel.: (49) 55 31702702
Web Site: http://www.stiebel-eltron.de
Year Founded: 1924
Appliance Mfr
N.A.I.C.S.: 335220
Axel Frhr V. Ruedorffer (Chm-Supervisory Bd)

Subsidiaries:

Thermia AB (1)
Thermia Varmepumpar Snickaregatan 1, Arvika, 671 29, Sweden
Tel.: (46) 570 813 00
Web Site: http://www.thermia.se
Pumps Mfr
N.A.I.C.S.: 333914

STIF FRANCE SAS

ZA de la Lande, 49171, Saint-Georges-sur-Loire, France
Tel.: (33) 41721680
Web Site: https://www.stifnet.com
Year Founded: 1984
ALSTI—(ITA)
Metal Component Mfr
N.A.I.C.S.: 332420

STIG GP A.D.

Trg Radomira Vujevica 16, Pozarevac, Serbia
Tel.: (381) 12221275
Year Founded: 1965
STIG—(BEL)
Sales Range: Less than $1 Million
Heavy Construction Services
N.A.I.C.S.: 237990
Radomir Mircic (Board of Directors & Exec Dir)

STILLCANNA INC.

2922 Mount Seymour Parkway, Vancouver, V7H 1E9, BC, Canada
Tel.: (604) 725-2255   BC

Year Founded: 2011
Natural Resource Company Handling Acquisitions, Exploration & Development of Mineral Properties
N.A.I.C.S.: 213114
Henry Lees-Buckley (CEO)

STILLE AB

Ekbacken 11, 644 30, Torshalla, Sweden
Tel.: (46) 858858000
Web Site: http://www.stille.se
Year Founded: 1841
Medical Supplies & Equipment
N.A.I.C.S.: 423450
Goran Brorsson (Chm)

Subsidiaries:

Arcoma North America Inc. (1)
23112 Alcalde Dr Ste A, Laguna Hills, CA 92653-1458
Tel.: (704) 897-0305
Medical, Dental & Hospital Equipment & Supplies Merchant Whslr
N.A.I.C.S.: 423450
Michael Cordes (Pres)

STILLFRONT GROUP AB

Hitech Building Sveavagen 9 5th floor, 111 57, Stockholm, Sweden
Tel.: (46) 7 6850 2050
Web Site: http://www.stillfront.com
Year Founded: 2010
Rev.: $147,432,750
Assets: $289,079,460
Liabilities: $167,127,540
Net Worth: $121,951,920
Earnings: $17,469,390
Fiscal Year-end: 12/31/18
Software Publisher & Online Gaming Studios
N.A.I.C.S.: 513210
Jorgen Larsson (CEO)

Subsidiaries:

Storm8, Inc. (1)
901 Mariners Island Blvd Ste 300, San Marino, CA 94065
Tel.: (650) 394-4910
Web Site: http://www.storm8.com
Sales Range: $10-24.9 Million
Emp.: 50
Social Network Video Game Developer
N.A.I.C.S.: 513210
Perry Tam (Founder & CEO)

STILLWATER CRITICAL MINERALS CORP.

Suite 904 - 409 Granville Street, Vancouver, V6C 1T2, BC, Canada
Tel.: (604) 357-4790   BC
Web Site: https://criticalminerals.com
Year Founded: 2006
PGEZF—(OTCQB)
Rev.: $7,354
Assets: $3,547,708
Liabilities: $348,311
Net Worth: $3,199,397
Earnings: ($3,212,689)
Emp.: 6
Fiscal Year-end: 03/31/23
Mineral Exploration Services
N.A.I.C.S.: 213114
Michael Rowley (Pres & CEO)

STILO ENERGY S.A.

Ul Heweliusza 11 premises 811, 80-890, Gdansk, Poland
Tel.: (48) 517884635
Web Site: https://www.stiloenergy.pl
Year Founded: 2017
CD60—(DEU)
Solar Component Distr
N.A.I.C.S.: 423720
Alfonso Kalinauskas (Pres)

STILO INTERNATIONAL PLC

Windmill Hill Business Park Whitehill Way, Swindon, SN5 6QR, United Kingdom
Tel.: (44) 1793 441 444
Web Site: http://www.stilo.com
Rev.: $1,887,033
Assets: $5,285,468
Liabilities: $558,369
Net Worth: $4,727,100
Earnings: $224,617
Emp.: 18
Fiscal Year-end: 12/31/18
Software Solutions Provider
N.A.I.C.S.: 513210
Leslie Burnham (Chm)

Subsidiaries:

Stilo Corporation (1)
440 Laurier Avenue West Suite 200, Ottawa, K1R 7X6, ON, Canada
Tel.: (613) 745-4242
Web Site: http://www.stilo.com
Emp.: 12
Customized Software Publishers
N.A.I.C.S.: 541511

Stilo Technology Limited (1)
Regus House Windmill Hill Bus Park, Whitehill Way, Swindon, SN5 6QR, Wiltshire, United Kingdom
Tel.: (44) 1793441444
Sales Range: $25-49.9 Million
Emp.: 5
Customized Software Publishers
N.A.I.C.S.: 541511
Les Burnham (Mng Dir)

STIMET SA

Str Mihai Viteazu 96, Sighisoara, Mures, Romania
Tel.: (40) 265 771071
Sales Range: Less than $1 Million
Emp.: 7
Glass Products Mfr
N.A.I.C.S.: 327215

STINAG STUTTGART INVEST AG

Tubinger Strasse 41, 70178, Stuttgart, Germany
Tel.: (49) 71193313600
Web Site: https://www.stinag-ag.de
STG—(MUN)
Rev.: $30,996,670
Assets: $357,124,022
Liabilities: $190,340,304
Net Worth: $166,783,718
Earnings: $6,954,381
Emp.: 20
Fiscal Year-end: 12/31/23
Real Estate Manangement Services
N.A.I.C.S.: 531390

STINGRAY GROUP INC.

730 Wellington, Montreal, H3C 1T4, QC, Canada
Tel.: (514) 664-1244
Web Site: https://www.stingray.com
RAY—(TSX)
Emp.: 300
Internet Publishing & Broadcasting Services
N.A.I.C.S.: 516210
Lloyd Feldman (Gen Counsel & Sr VP)

Subsidiaries:

DJ Matic N.V. (1)
Oscar Romerolaan 16, 1216 TK, Hilversum, Netherlands
Tel.: (31) 352077000
Web Site: https://www.djmatic.nl
Media Entertainment Services
N.A.I.C.S.: 541810

Newfoundland Capital Corporation Limited (1)
8 Basinview Drive, Dartmouth, B3B 1G4, NS, Canada
Tel.: (902) 468-7557
Rev.: $135,317,540

STINGRAY GROUP INC.

Stingray Group Inc.—(Continued)
Assets: $294,023,759
Liabilities: $163,575,774
Net Worth: $130,447,985
Earnings: $21,260,987
Emp.: 800
Fiscal Year-end: 12/31/2017
Holding Company; Radio Station Owner & Operator; Real Estate & Hotel Owner & Operator
N.A.I.C.S.: 551112
Robert G. Steele *(Chm, Pres & CEO)*

Subsidiary (Domestic):

NewCap Radio (2)
3770 Kemp Rd Ste 200, Halifax, B3K 4X8, NS, Canada (100%)
Tel.: (902) 453-4004
Web Site: http://www.ncc.com
Sales Range: $10-24.9 Million
Emp.: 50
N.A.I.C.S.: 561311

The Glynmill Inn Incorporated (2)
1b Cobb Ln, Corner Brook, A2H 2V3, NL, Canada
Tel.: (709) 634-5181
Web Site: http://www.steelhotel.com
Sales Range: $10-24.9 Million
Emp.: 50
Home Management Services
N.A.I.C.S.: 721110

Stingray Music USA Inc. (1)
6420-A1 Rea Rd Ste 161, Charlotte, NC 28277
Tel.: (704) 817-1530
Music Store Operator
N.A.I.C.S.: 512230
Steve Boone *(Mgr-Digital Media)*

STINS COMAN INCORPORATED

Pervomayskaya str 126, Moscow, 105203, Russia
Tel.: (7) 2952313040
Web Site:
http://www.stinscoman.com
Holding Company
N.A.I.C.S.: 551112
Sergey Anisimov *(Founder & Pres)*

Subsidiaries:

RIT Technologies Ltd. (1)
20 Atir Yeda, Kfar Saba, 69719, Israel (68.3%)
Tel.: (972) 772707270
Web Site: https://www.rittech.com
Sales Range: $1-9.9 Million
Emp.: 66
Real-Time Physical Layer Management Software & Hardware; Premise Wiring & Networking Products Developer & Mfr
N.A.I.C.S.: 334290
Sergey Anisimov *(Chm)*

Subsidiary (US):

RiT Technologies Inc. (2)
900 Corporate Dr, Mahwah, NJ 07430-3611
Tel.: (201) 512-1970
Web Site: http://www.rittech.com
Sales Range: $25-49.9 Million
Emp.: 2
Network Management
N.A.I.C.S.: 334118
Maria Repetti *(Office Mgr)*

STIRLING PRODUCTS LIMITED

Level 1 275 George St, 2001, Sydney, New South Wales, Australia
Tel.: (61) 292999270
Sales Range: Less than $1 Million
Emp.: 20
Metabolic Modifiers Development & Commercialization
N.A.I.C.S.: 112990
Neil Covey *(Dir-Sls & Mktg)*

STIRLING SQUARE CAPITAL PARTNERS LLP

Liscarton House 4th Fl, 127-131 Sloane Street, London, SW1X 9AX, United Kingdom
Tel.: (44) 2078084130 UK
Web Site:
http://www.stirlingsquare.com
Year Founded: 2002
Rev.: $1,880,685,000
Emp.: 16
Private Equity Investment Firm
N.A.I.C.S.: 523999
Stefano Bonfiglio *(Co-Founder)*

Subsidiaries:

3SI Security Systems, Inc. (1)
550 Castle Manor Ct, Indianapolis, IN 46214
Tel.: (317) 487-0443
Security Solution Providing Services
N.A.I.C.S.: 561621

Axitea S.p.A (1)
Via Gallarate 207, 20151, Milan, Italy
Tel.: (39) 02 3003131
Security Consulting Services
N.A.I.C.S.: 561621

Docu Group Sweden AB (1)
Lojtnantsgatan 9, 82781, Ljusdal, Sweden
Tel.: (46) 651552500
Web Site: http://www.docunordic.com
Business Information Services
N.A.I.C.S.: 561499
Stefan Lindqvist *(CEO)*

Subsidiary (Domestic):

Byggfakta Group (2)
Lojtnantsgatan 9, 82781, Ljusdal, Sweden
Tel.: (46) 651552500
Web Site: http://byggfaktagroup.com
Market Data & Business Intelligence Services
N.A.I.C.S.: 561499
Stefan Lindqvist *(CEO)*

Itelyum Group S.r.l. (1)
Via Tavernelle 19, 26854, Pieve Fissiraga, Italy
Tel.: (39) 037125031
Web Site: https://www.itelyum.com
Waste Management Services
N.A.I.C.S.: 562998
Marco Codognola *(CEO)*

Subsidiary (Domestic):

Itelyum Regeneration S.p.A. (2)
Via Tavernelle 19, 26854, Pieve Fissiraga, Italy
Tel.: (39) 037125031
Web Site: https://www.itelyum-regeneration.com
Waste Management Services
N.A.I.C.S.: 562998

Subsidiary (Non-US):

SAFECHEM Europe GmbH (3)
Tersteegenstrasse 25, 40474, Dusseldorf, Germany
Tel.: (49) 2114389300
Web Site: http://www.safechem-europe.com
Chemicals Mfr
N.A.I.C.S.: 325998
Manfred Holzleg *(Gen Mgr)*

Subsidiary (Domestic):

Dow Deutschland Anlagengesellschaft mbH (4)
Buetzflether Sand 2, 21683, Stade, Germany
Tel.: (49) 4146910
Chemical Products Mfr
N.A.I.C.S.: 325199

Dow Wolff Cellulosics GmbH & Co. KG (4)
August-Wolff-Str 13, Bomlitz, 29699, Germany
Tel.: (49) 5161443901
Web Site:
http://www.dowwolffcellulosics.com
Cellulosic Products Mfr
N.A.I.C.S.: 325220

Unit (US):

Dow Wolff Cellulosics LLC (5)
7330 S Madison St, Willowbrook, IL 60527-5588
Tel.: (630) 789-8440
Cellulosic Casings & Film Mfr
N.A.I.C.S.: 325220

Jeckerson (1)
Via Savona 97, 20144, Milan, Italy
Tel.: (39) 02 89092166
Web Site: http://www.jeckerson.com
Fashion Apparels Retailer
N.A.I.C.S.: 458110

Omni Helicopters International S.A. (1)
Avenida D Joao II n9 - I Edificio Adamastor Torre B - 9 andar, Lisbon, 1990-077, Portugal
Tel.: (351) 21 898 7000
Web Site: http://www.ohi.pt
Helicopter Charter Services
N.A.I.C.S.: 481211
Rui de Almeida *(Founder & Chm)*

SAR AS (1)
Verkstedveien 29, Hammerfest, 9600, Finnmark, Norway
Tel.: (47) 51944444
Web Site: http://www.sargruppen.no
Waste Management Services
N.A.I.C.S.: 562119
Per Kristian Nagell *(CEO)*

Vernet SAS (1)
21-27 Route d'Arpajon, 91340, Ollainville, France
Tel.: (33) 169268282
Web Site: http://www.vernet.fr
Sales Range: $150-199.9 Million
Emp.: 350
Thermostatic Regulation Components Mfr
N.A.I.C.S.: 334519
Jean Sebastien Frank *(Dir-Publication)*

Viscolube S.p.A (1)
Via Tavernelle 19, Pieve Fissiraga, 26854, Italy
Tel.: (39) 037 125031
Web Site: http://www.viscolube.it
Waste Oil Refining Services
N.A.I.C.S.: 324191
Giorgio Carriero *(Pres)*

STJENIK A.D.

Milutina Mandica bb, Cacak, Serbia
Tel.: (381) 32 374 544
Year Founded: 1947
Sales Range: Less than $1 Million
Emp.: 43
Food Store Operator
N.A.I.C.S.: 445298

STL GLOBAL LTD.

Plot No 207-208 Sector 58, Faridabad, 121004, Haryana, India
Tel.: (91) 1294275900
Web Site: https://www.stl-global.com
532730—(BOM)
Rev.: $12,092,033
Assets: $7,974,426
Liabilities: $4,442,228
Net Worth: $3,532,198
Earnings: $26,269
Emp.: 186
Fiscal Year-end: 03/31/23
Textile Mfr
N.A.I.C.S.: 314999
Vishal Aggarwal *(Chm & Mng Dir)*

STL TECHNOLOGY CO., LTD.

No 1 West 15th St, Cianjhen Dist, Kaohsiung, 806011, Taiwan
Tel.: (886) 78411501
Web Site: https://www.stl-tech.com
Year Founded: 2004
4931—(TPE)
Rev.: $57,863,284
Assets: $48,358,660
Liabilities: $13,956,672
Net Worth: $34,401,988
Earnings: $2,249,625
Fiscal Year-end: 12/31/20
Battery Product Mfr & Distr
N.A.I.C.S.: 335910

George Chang *(Chm)*

Subsidiaries:

STL Technology SIP Co., Ltd. (1)
East Unit Building D Phase 2 Export Processing Zone, No 200 Su Hong Road Suzhou Industrial Park, Suzhou, 215021, China
Tel.: (86) 5126 258 3887
Battery Pack Mfr
N.A.I.C.S.: 335910

STLLR GOLD INC.

65 Third Avenue, Timmins, P4N 1C2, ON, Canada
Tel.: (705) 264-2296 ON
Web Site:
https://www.monetaporcupine.com
Year Founded: 1910
MEAUF—(OTCQX)
Rev.: $97,166
Assets: $5,329,325
Liabilities: $1,575,411
Net Worth: $3,753,914
Earnings: ($2,557,300)
Fiscal Year-end: 12/31/19
Gold Mining Services
N.A.I.C.S.: 212220
Ian C. Peres *(Pres, Pres, CFO & CFO)*

Subsidiaries:

Nighthawk Gold Corp. (1)
141 Adelaide St W Suite 301, Toronto, M5H 3L5, ON, Canada
Tel.: (647) 794-4313
Web Site: https://www.nighthawkgold.com
Rev.: $363,377
Assets: $74,555,063
Liabilities: $10,134,974
Net Worth: $64,420,089
Earnings: ($3,544,436)
Emp.: 3
Fiscal Year-end: 12/31/2019
Gold Exploration & Mining Services
N.A.I.C.S.: 213114
Allan Candelario *(VP)*

STM GROUP PLC

18 Athol Street, Douglas, IM1 1JA, Isle of Man
Tel.: (44) 35020042686
Web Site:
https://info.stmgroupplc.com
STM—(AIM)
Rev.: $30,414,037
Assets: $68,352,689
Liabilities: $24,295,632
Net Worth: $44,057,056
Earnings: $1,078,011
Emp.: 289
Fiscal Year-end: 12/31/22
Financial Services
N.A.I.C.S.: 521110
Alan Roy Kentish *(CEO)*

Subsidiaries:

London & Colonial (Trustee Services) Limited (1)
3rd Floor 55 Line Wall Road, GX11 1AA, Gibraltar, Gibraltar
Tel.: (350) 20074311
Medical Financial Services
N.A.I.C.S.: 524114

Options Corporate Pensions UK Limited (1)
1 st Floor Lakeside House Shirwell Crescent, Furzton Lake, Milton Keynes, MK4 1GA, United Kingdom
Tel.: (44) 3301241510
Web Site:
https://www.optionsautoenrolment.co.uk
Pension Fund Services
N.A.I.C.S.: 525110

Options UK Personal Pensions LLP (1)
1 st Floor Lakeside House Shirwell Crescent, Furzton Lake, Milton Keynes, MK4 1GA, United Kingdom

AND PRIVATE COMPANIES

Tel.: (44) 3301241505
Web Site:
https://www.optionspensions.co.uk
Pension Fund Services
N.A.I.C.S.: 525110

STM Nummos Life S.L. (1)
Edif Sotovila Plaza Mayor, Pueblo Nuevo de Guadiaro Sotogrande, 11311, Cadiz, Spain
Tel.: (34) 956796148
Web Site:
https://privatehealthcarespain.com
Health Insurance Services
N.A.I.C.S.: 524114

STM Swiss AG (1)
Dreikonigstrasse 45, 8027, Zurich, Switzerland
Tel.: (41) 442066070
Web Site: http://www.stmswiss.com
Sales Range: $25-49.9 Million
Emp.: 3
Corporate Administration Services
N.A.I.C.S.: 561110

STMICROELECTRONICS N.V.

39 Chemin du Champ des Filles, 1228, Plan-les-Ouates, Geneva, Switzerland
Tel.: (41) 229292929 NL
Web Site: https://www.st.com
Year Founded: 1987
STM—(NYSE)
Rev.: $17,286,000,000
Assets: $24,453,000,000
Liabilities: $7,601,000,000
Net Worth: $16,852,000,000
Earnings: $4,211,000,000
Emp.: 51,323
Fiscal Year-end: 12/31/23
Holding Company; Semiconductor Integrated Circuits & Discrete Devices Designer, Mfr & Distr
N.A.I.C.S.: 551112
Marco Luciano Cassis *(Pres-Sls, Mktg, Comm & Strategy Dev)*

Subsidiaries:

Anatec AG (1)
Sumpfstrasse 7, 6312, Steinhausen, Switzerland
Tel.: (41) 7483232
Web Site: https://www.anatec.ch
Electronic Components Distr
N.A.I.C.S.: 423690

Anglia Components PLC (1)
Sandall Road, Wisbech, United Kingdom
Tel.: (44) 1945474747
Web Site: https://www.anglia.co.uk
Electronic Components Distr
N.A.I.C.S.: 423690

Avnet Max Limited (1)
No 304 3rd Fl Baani Corporate One Plot 5 Phase 3, New Delhi, India
Tel.: (91) 1146481100
Electronic Components Mfr
N.A.I.C.S.: 334419

Bs Micro Electronics (S) Pte Ltd. (1)
3rd Floor 228 Soi LadPrao 94 LadPrao Road, Phlab Phla Wang Thong Lang, Bangkok, Thailand
Tel.: (66) 20620611
Electronic Equipment Whslr
N.A.I.C.S.: 423690

Dacom Multimedia Internet Co., Ltd. (1)
6/F Dacom Bldg 706 - 1 Yeoksam-Dong, Gangnam-Gu, Seoul, 135-080, Korea (South)
Tel.: (82) 220860694
Online Educational Content Publishing Services
N.A.I.C.S.: 513199

Digi-Key Electronics Shanghai Company Ltd. (1)
Units 3202 3203 3205 3206 32nd Floor Office Building T1 Raffles City, No 1133 Road Changning District, Shanghai, China
Tel.: (86) 4009201199
Web Site: https://www.digikey.cn

Electric Component Whslr
N.A.I.C.S.: 423690

Future Electronics Mktg Services Co, Ltd. (1)
No 1 MD Tower 7th floor Unit C3 E Soi Bangna - Trad 25, Kweng Bangna Khet Bangna, Bangkok, Thailand
Tel.: (66) 27829800
Electronic Components Mfr
N.A.I.C.S.: 334419

Future Electronics Services Sdn. Bhd. (1)
Suite 801-1 Tower 1 Wisma Am First Jalan SS7/15, Kelana Jaya, 47301, Petaling Jaya, Selangor, Malaysia
Tel.: (60) 376516888
Electronic Components Distr
N.A.I.C.S.: 423690

Hakuto Enterprises Ltd. (1)
Suites 1401-6 14/F North Tower World Finance Centre Harbour City, 17-19 Canton Road Tsim Sha Tsui, Kowloon, China (Hong Kong)
Tel.: (852) 25784921
Web Site: https://www.hakuto.com.hk
Electronic Components Distr
N.A.I.C.S.: 423690

Infinity Informatica Inc. (1)
5846 S Flamingo Rd Ste 239, Cooper City, FL 33330
Tel.: (954) 534-9378
Web Site: https://www.infinity-info.net
Electronic Product Distr
N.A.I.C.S.: 423690

Lierda Science And Technology Group Co. Ltd. (1)
Lierda IoT Science Park No 1326 West Wenyi Road, Hangzhou, Zhejiang, China
Tel.: (86) 18067988206
Web Site: https://lierda.com
Information Technology Services
N.A.I.C.S.: 541511

Proton World International N.V. (1)
Lambroekstraat 5, 1930, Diegem, Belgium
Tel.: (32) 27245111
Web Site: http://www.st.com
Sales Range: $25-49.9 Million
Emp.: 68
Smart Card System Software Development Services
N.A.I.C.S.: 541511

Ramakrishna Electro Components Hk Pvt Ltd. (1)
Unit 415 4th Floor World Wide Industrial Centre 43-47 Sham MEI Street, Fotan, China (Hong Kong)
Tel.: (852) 37055232
Electronic Equipment Distr
N.A.I.C.S.: 423690

Ramakrishna Electro Components Pvt Ltd. (1)
B-79 Wazirpur industrial Area, New Delhi, India
Tel.: (91) 1141423100
Web Site: https://www.rkelectro.com
Emp.: 100
Electronic Components Distr
N.A.I.C.S.: 423690

Reigncom Tech Ltd. (1)
A-1201 1203 Woolim Lions Valley 5 302 Galmachi-ro, Jungwon-gu, Seongnam, Gyeonggi-do, Korea (South)
Tel.: (82) 25257942
Web Site: https://www.reigncomtech.com
Electric Component Whslr
N.A.I.C.S.: 423690

Rs Components Amidata S.A.U. (1)
Avenida de Bruxelles 6, Alcobendas, 28108, Madrid, Spain
Tel.: (34) 915129699
Web Site: https://es.rs-online.com
Electronic Components Mfr
N.A.I.C.S.: 334419

STMicroelectronics (Canada), Inc. (1)
165 Commerce Valley Dr W, Thornhill, L3T 7V8, ON, Canada **(100%)**
Tel.: (905) 889-5400
Web Site: http://www.st.com

Microelectronic Design & Mfr
N.A.I.C.S.: 541420

STMicroelectronics (China) Investment Co. Ltd (1)
No 88 Zihai Road ZiZhu SciencePark, Minhang, Shanghai, 200241, China
Tel.: (86) 2124188688
Sales Range: $200-249.9 Million
Emp.: 30
Investment Management Service
N.A.I.C.S.: 523999

STMicroelectronics (Grenoble 2) SAS (1)
12 Rue Jules Horowitz, BP 217, 38000, Grenoble, France
Tel.: (33) 476585000
Electronic Components Mfr
N.A.I.C.S.: 334419

STMicroelectronics (Malta) Ltd. (1)
Industry Road, Kirkop, KKP 9042, Malta **(100%)**
Tel.: (356) 21642214
Microelectronic Products Industrial Center
N.A.I.C.S.: 334419

STMicroelectronics (North America) Holding, Inc. (1)
750 Canyon Dr Ste 300, Coppell, TX 75019
Tel.: (972) 466-6000
Holding Company
N.A.I.C.S.: 551112
Bruce Quill *(Mgr-HR)*

STMicroelectronics (Shanghai) R&D Co. Ltd (1)
No 88 Zihai Rd Shanghai Zizhu Scientific Park, Shanghai, 200241, China
Tel.: (86) 2124188688
Sales Range: $75-99.9 Million
Emp.: 300
Electronic Component Research & Development Services
N.A.I.C.S.: 541715

STMicroelectronics (Shenzhen) R&D Co. Ltd (1)
Unit D E 48/F CES Tower 3099 Keyuan Road, Nanshan District, Shenzhen, 518057, China
Tel.: (86) 75586012228
Electronic Component Research & Development Services
N.A.I.C.S.: 541715

STMicroelectronics (Thailand) Ltd (1)
24th Floor Unit 2404 Q House Lumpini Building 1 South Sathorn Road, Tungmahamek, Sathorn, 10120, Thailand
Tel.: (66) 2 343 8944
Web Site: http://www.st.com
Electronic Parts Distr
N.A.I.C.S.: 423690

STMicroelectronics AB (1)
Kista Science Tower Farogatan 33, 164 51, Kista, Sweden
Tel.: (46) 858774400
Sales Range: $25-49.9 Million
Emp.: 26
Microelectronic R&D & Design Center
N.A.I.C.S.: 334419

STMicroelectronics Asia Pacific Pte. Ltd. (1)
5A Serangoon North Avenue 5, Singapore, 554574, Singapore **(100%)**
Tel.: (65) 62165000
Semiconductor Design & Products Mfr
N.A.I.C.S.: 334413

Subsidiary (Non-US):

STMicroelectronics (Shanghai) Co., Ltd. (2)
No 88 ZiHai Road Zizhu Science Park, Min-Hang District, Shanghai, 200241, China **(100%)**
Tel.: (86) 2124188688
Web Site: http://www.st.com
Sales Range: $10-24.9 Million
Emp.: 50
Microelectronic Manufacturing & Industrial Design
N.A.I.C.S.: 541420

STMicroelectronics (Shenzhen) Co. Ltd. (2)

B501 - B503 6F Block B TCL R D Tower No 6 Southern N 1 Road, South District Hi-Tech Industrial Park Nanshan, Shenzhen, 518057, China
Tel.: (86) 75586012000
Microelectronic Product Sales
N.A.I.C.S.: 541420

Subsidiary (Domestic):

Shenzhen STS Microelectronics Co. Ltd. (3)
16Tao Hua Rd Futian Free Trade Zone, Shenzhen, 518038, China **(60%)**
Tel.: (86) 75583488000
Microelectronics Manufacturing & Industrial Design
N.A.I.C.S.: 541420

Subsidiary (Non-US):

STMicroelectronics Ltd. (2)
16/F Tower 1 The Gateway 25 Canton Road, Tsim Sha Tsui Kowloon, Hong Kong, China (Hong Kong) **(100%)**
Tel.: (852) 28615700
Microelectronics Industrial Designer
N.A.I.C.S.: 541420

Subsidiary (Domestic):

STMicroelectronics Pte. Ltd.-AMK5 (2)
28 Ang Mo Kio - Industrial Park 2, 569508, Singapore, Singapore **(100%)**
Tel.: (65) 64277558
Web Site: http://www.st.com
Sales Range: $1-4.9 Billion
Emp.: 8,000
Semiconductor Design & Products Mfr
N.A.I.C.S.: 334413

Plant (Domestic):

STMicroelectronics-AMK6 (3)
18 Ang Mo Kio Industrial Park 2, Singapore, 569505, Singapore **(100%)**
Tel.: (65) 64276000
Web Site: http://www.st.com
Microelectronic Design Center
N.A.I.C.S.: 541420

STMicroelectronics-AMK8 (3)
28 Ang Mo Kio Industrial Part 2, Singapore, 569508, Singapore **(100%)**
Tel.: (65) 64821411
Web Site: http://www.st.com
Sales Range: $1-4.9 Billion
Emp.: 8,000
Microelectronics Designer
N.A.I.C.S.: 541420

Subsidiary (Non-US):

STMicroelectronics Pvt. Ltd. (2)
Plot No 1 Knowledge Park III, Greater Noida, Noida, 201 308, Uttar Pradesh, India **(100%)**
Tel.: (91) 1204003000
Sales Range: $700-749.9 Million
Emp.: 4,000
Mfr & Design of Microelectronic Products
N.A.I.C.S.: 334111

STMicroelectronics Sdn Bhd (2)
Unit 13A Lower Level 5 Hotel Equatorial 1 Jalan, Bukit Jambul, 11900, Penang, Malaysia **(100%)**
Tel.: (60) 46428291
Semiconductor Product Mfr
N.A.I.C.S.: 334413

STMicroelectronics Design and Application s.r.o. (1)
Pobrezni 620/3, Prague, 186 00, Czech Republic
Tel.: (420) 222336111
Web Site: http://www.st.com
Semiconductor Devices Mfr
N.A.I.C.S.: 334413

STMicroelectronics GmbH (1)
Bahnhofstrasse 18, Aschheim, 85609, Germany **(100%)**
Tel.: (49) 89460060
Web Site: http://www.st.com
Microelectronics Design & Mfr
N.A.I.C.S.: 334419

STMicroelectronics K.K. (1)
Shinagawa INTERCITY Tower A 2-15-1 Ko-

STMICROELECTRONICS N.V.

STMicroelectronics N.V.—(Continued)
nan, Minato-ku, Tokyo, 108-6017, Japan
Tel.: (81) 357838200
Sales Range: $50-74.9 Million
Emp.: 200
Semiconductor Integrated Circuits & Other Electronic Components Designer, Mfr & Distr
N.A.I.C.S.: 334413
Marco Luciano Cassis (Pres)

Unit (Domestic):

STMicroelectronics K.K. - Japan Regional Warehouse (2)
KWE 2nd Terminal 3F 1953-7 Koya, Ichikawa-shi, Chiba, 272-0013, Japan
Tel.: (81) 473205001
Web Site: http://www.tkt.st.com
Sales Range: $25-49.9 Million
Emp.: 200
Semiconductor Integrated Circuit & Other Electronic Component Warehousing & Distribution Services
N.A.I.C.S.: 493110

STMicroelectronics Limited (100%)
Atlas House Third Avenue Globe Park, Marlow, SL7 1EY, Buckinghamshire, United Kingdom
Tel.: (44) 1628890800
Web Site: http://www.st.com
Sales Range: $25-49.9 Million
Emp.: 36
Sales & Design Center for Microelectronic Products
N.A.I.C.S.: 334419

Unit (Domestic):

STMicroelectronics (R&D) Ltd. - Bristol (2)
1000 Aztec West Almondsbury, Bristol, BS32 4SQ, United Kingdom
Tel.: (44) 1454616616
Web Site: http://www.st.com
Research & Development & Design Center for Microelectronic Products
N.A.I.C.S.: 334419

STMicroelectronics (R&D) Ltd. - Edinburgh (2)
33 Pinkhill, Edinburgh, EH12 7BF, United Kingdom
Tel.: (44) 1313366000
Sales Range: $75-99.9 Million
Research & Development & Design Center for Microelectronic Products
N.A.I.C.S.: 334419
Linsey Grant (Gen Mgr)

STMicroelectronics Ltda (1)
Av Brigadeiro Faria Lima 201 - room 152, Pinheiros, Sao Paulo, 05426-100, Brazil
Tel.: (55) 1121011650
Sales Range: $25-49.9 Million
Emp.: 25
Electronic Components Distr
N.A.I.C.S.: 423690

STMicroelectronics Marketing SDN BHD (1)
Suite 8 07 Level 8 The Gardens North Tower, Mid Valley City Lingkaran Syed Putra, 59200, Kuala Lumpur, Malaysia
Tel.: (60) 322825951
Sales Range: $50-74.9 Million
Emp.: 8
Electronic Components Distr
N.A.I.C.S.: 423690

STMicroelectronics Marketing, S. de R.L. de C.V. (1)
Av Mariano Otero No 1249 Piso 11 Rincon, Del Bosque, Guadalajara, 44530, Jalisco, Mexico
Tel.: (52) 3350004900
Semiconductor Device Distr
N.A.I.C.S.: 423690

STMicroelectronics PTY Ltd (1)
Wheelers Hill Business Centre Suite G10 202 Jells Road, Wheelers Hill, Melbourne, 3150, VIC, Australia
Tel.: (61) 395619879
Electronic Components Distr
N.A.I.C.S.: 423690

STMicroelectronics S.A. (1)
Chemin du Champ-des-Filles 39, 1228, Plan-les-Ouates, Geneva, Switzerland
Tel.: (41) 229292929
Electronic Connector Mfr
N.A.I.C.S.: 334417

STMicroelectronics S.r.l. (1)
Via C Olivetti 2, I 20041, Agrate Brianza, Italy (100%)
Tel.: (39) 0396031
Web Site: http://www.st.com
Sales Range: $800-899.9 Million
Emp.: 3,000
Research & Development, Design & Industrial Center for Microelectronic Products
N.A.I.C.S.: 334419

Plant (Domestic):

STMicroelectronics S.r.l. - Castelletto Plant (2)
Palazzo Quadrifoglio Via Tolomeo 1, 20010, Cornaredo, MI, Italy
Tel.: (39) 0293519000
Web Site: http://www.st.com
Microelectronics Mfr
N.A.I.C.S.: 334419

STMicroelectronics S.r.l. - Catania Plant (2)
Stradale Primosole 50, 95121, Catania, Italy
Tel.: (39) 0957401111
Web Site: http://www.st.com
Sales Range: $700-749.9 Million
Research & Development, Design & Industrial Center for Microelectronic Products
N.A.I.C.S.: 334419

Division (Domestic):

STMicroelectronics S.r.l. - Incard Division (2)
ZI Marcianise Sud, 81025, Marcianise, Italy
Tel.: (39) 0823630111
Smartcard Mfr
N.A.I.C.S.: 334118

Plant (Domestic):

STMicroelectronics S.r.l. - Napoli Plant (2)
Via Remo De Feo 1, IT-80022, Arzano, Italy
Tel.: (39) 0812381117
Web Site: http://www.st.com
Sales Range: $25-49.9 Million
Emp.: 90
Research & Development, Design & Industrial Center for Microelectronic Products
N.A.I.C.S.: 334419

STMicroelectronics SA (1)
29 Boulevard Romain Rolland, 75669, Paris, France (100%)
Tel.: (33) 158077575
Web Site: http://www.st.com
Sales of Microelectronic Products
N.A.I.C.S.: 334419

Plant (Domestic):

STMicroelectonics (Grenoble 2) SAS (2)
12 rue Jules Horowitz, BP 217, Cedex, F 38019, Grenoble, France (100%)
Tel.: (33) 476585000
Web Site: http://www.st.com
Sales Range: $350-399.9 Million
Emp.: 2,400
IP & Design of Microelectronic Components
N.A.I.C.S.: 334419

STMicroelectronics (Crolles 2) SAS (2)
850 rue Jean Monnet, F-38926, Crolles, Cedex, France (100%)
Tel.: (33) 476926000
Web Site: http://www.st.com
Sales Range: $700-749.9 Million
Emp.: 4,000
Research & Development, Design & Industrials for Microelectronic Components
N.A.I.C.S.: 334419

Unit (Domestic):

STMicroelectronics - Europe Manufacturing & Design (2)
BP 323, 06906, Sophia-Antipolis, France
Tel.: (33) 497288400
Web Site: http://www.st.com
Mfr & Design of Microelectronic Components
N.A.I.C.S.: 334419

STMicroelectronics - Rennes Industrial & Design Center (2)
3 Rue de Suisse, CS 60816, 35208, Rennes, France
Tel.: (33) 299264800
Sales Range: $25-49.9 Million
Emp.: 70
Industrial & Design Center of Microelectronic Components
N.A.I.C.S.: 334419

Plant (Domestic):

STMicroelectronics Rousset SAS (2)
190 Ave Celestin Coq, Zone Industrielle, F-13106, Rousset, France
Tel.: (33) 442688800
Web Site: http://www.st.com
Sales Range: $75-99.9 Million
Emp.: 300
Microelectronic Designs
N.A.I.C.S.: 334419

STMicroelectronics Tours SAS (2)
16 Rue Pierre et marie Curie, BP 7155, 37071, Tours, France (100%)
Tel.: (33) 247424000
Web Site: http://www.st.com
Sales Range: $150-199.9 Million
Emp.: 1,000
Mfr & Design of Microelectronic Components
N.A.I.C.S.: 334419

STMicroelectronics s.r.o. (1)
(100%)
Tel.: (420) 222336111
Web Site: http://www.st.com
Design & Application Sales of Microelectronic Components
N.A.I.C.S.: 334419

STMicroelectronics, Inc. (1)
750 Kanyon Dr Ste 300, Coppell, TX 75019
Tel.: (972) 466-6000
Web Site: http://www.st.com
Sales Range: $400-449.9 Million
Emp.: 250
Integrated Circuits & Computer Component Systems Mfr
N.A.I.C.S.: 334413

Subsidiary (Domestic):

Faroudja Inc. (2)
180 Baytech Dr Ste 110, San Jose, CA 95134 (100%)
Tel.: (408) 919-8700
Web Site: http://www.faroudja.com
Sales Range: $25-49.9 Million
Emp.: 35
Video Technology Services
N.A.I.C.S.: 541715

Genesis Microchip Inc. (2)
2755 Great America Way, Santa Clara, CA 95054
Tel.: (408) 919-8400
Sales Range: $200-249.9 Million
Emp.: 600
Image & Video Display Processing Systems
N.A.I.C.S.: 334413

Stmicroelctronics (China) Investment Co., Ltd. (1)
Room A1908 Suzhou International Science and Technology Park, No 1355 Jinjihu Road Suzhou Industrial Park, Suzhou, China
Tel.: (86) 51268093198
Electric Component Whslr
N.A.I.C.S.: 423690

Stmicroelectronics Software Ab (1)
Science Park Jonkoping Gjuterigatan 7, 55318, Jonkoping, Sweden
Tel.: (46) 363303000
Electric Component Whslr
N.A.I.C.S.: 423690

Toyota Tsusho Nexty Electronics (Dalian) Co., Ltd. (1)
No 04-02 03 04 No 7 Huixian Garden, Gaoxinyuan District, Dalian, Liaoning, China
Tel.: (86) 41139776788
Web Site: https://www.dl.cn.nexty-ele.com
Vehicle Related Software Services

INTERNATIONAL PUBLIC

N.A.I.C.S.: 541511

Toyota Tsusho Nexty Electronics (Thailand) Co., Ltd. (1)
15th - 16th Floor Mercury Tower 540 Ploenchit Road, Lumpini Pathumwan, Bangkok, Thailand
Tel.: (66) 26393500
Web Site: https://www.th.nexty-ele.com
Electronic Components Distr
N.A.I.C.S.: 423690

Toyota Tsusho Nexty Electronics Hong Kong Co., Ltd. (1)
Room 2702 Block 1 27/F Admiralty Centre 18 Harcourt Road, Hong Kong, China (Hong Kong)
Tel.: (852) 23126229
Electronic Components Distr
N.A.I.C.S.: 423690

Toyota Tsusho Nexty Electronics Shanghai Co., Ltd. (1)
2nd/F Wheelock Square 1717 Nanjing Road West, Jingan Dist, Shanghai, China
Tel.: (86) 2168764727
Electric Component Whslr
N.A.I.C.S.: 423690

Toyota Tsusho Nexty Electronics Shenzhen Co., Beijing Branch Ltd. (1)
Room 220 Beijing Fortune Building No 5 East 3rd Ring North Road, Chaoyang, Beijing, China
Tel.: (86) 6611
Electric Component Whslr
N.A.I.C.S.: 423690

Toyota Tsusho Nexty Electronics Shenzhen Co., Chengdu Branch Ltd. (1)
No 1004 T2 Raffles Place Section 4 South Remin Road, Wuhou, Chengdu, China
Tel.: (86) 2885068745
Electronic Components Distr
N.A.I.C.S.: 423690

Toyota Tsusho Nexty Electronics Shenzhen Co., Wuhan Branch Ltd. (1)
Room 2212-15 22 Floor World City plaza office building, Optics valley Plaza East Lake High-tech Development Zone, Wuhan, Hubei, China
Tel.: (86) 2787598301
Electric Component Whslr
N.A.I.C.S.: 423690

Vissa Electronic Ltd. (1)
78 Masherov ave 3-rd floor, 220035, Minsk, Belarus
Tel.: (375) 172032139
Electronic Components Distr
N.A.I.C.S.: 423690

STO CO., LTD.

5 F, B-dong Woolim Bluenine Business Center 583 Yangcheon-ro, Gangseo-Gu, Seoul, Korea (South)
Tel.: (82) 220932500
Web Site: http://www.thesto.kr
098660—(KRS)
Rev.: $56,115,323
Assets: $46,338,906
Liabilities: $23,393,594
Net Worth: $22,945,312
Earnings: $1,228,360
Emp.: 87
Fiscal Year-end: 12/31/22
Apparel Product Distr
N.A.I.C.S.: 424310
Kim Heung-Soo (CEO)

STO EXPRESS CO., LTD.

No 425 Jiadian Road, Qingpu District, Shanghai, 201706, China
Tel.: (86) 2160376669
Web Site: https://www.sto.cn
Year Founded: 1993
002468—(SSE)
Rev.: $4,727,365,339
Assets: $2,854,633,214
Liabilities: $1,702,301,576
Net Worth: $1,152,331,638

AND PRIVATE COMPANIES — STOCKCUBE PLC

Earnings: $40,395,677
Fiscal Year-end: 12/31/22
Logistic Services
N.A.I.C.S.: 541614
Dejun Chen *(Chm)*

STO SE & CO. KGAA
Ehrenbachstrasse 1, D-79780, Stuhlingen, Germany
Tel.: (49) 7744570   De
Web Site: https://www.sto.com
Year Founded: 1835
STO3—(MUN)
Rev.: $1,896,481,776
Assets: $1,285,787,776
Liabilities: $480,768,501
Net Worth: $805,019,275
Earnings: $95,021,130
Emp.: 5,815
Fiscal Year-end: 12/31/23
Paints, Lacquers & Varnishes Mfr
N.A.I.C.S.: 325510
Jochen Stotmeister *(Chm-Supervisory Bd)*

Subsidiaries:

Beissier S.A.S.   (1)
Quartier de la Gare, La Chapelle-la-Reine, 77760, La Chapelle, France
Tel.: (33) 160396110
Web Site: https://www.beissier.fr
Building Materials Mfr
N.A.I.C.S.: 327120

Beissier S.A.U.   (1)
Txirrita Maleo 14, 20100, Errenteria, Gipuzkoa, Spain
Tel.: (34) 943344070
Web Site: https://www.beissier.es
Building Materials Mfr
N.A.I.C.S.: 327120

Gepadi Fliesen GmbH   (1)
Kasseler Str 41, 35683, Dillenburg, Germany
Tel.: (49) 27713910
Web Site: https://www.gepadi.de
Building Materials Mfr
N.A.I.C.S.: 327120

Innolation GmbH   (1)
Hanns-Martin-Schleyer-Str 3, D-89415, Lauingen, Germany
Tel.: (49) 907270270
Web Site: https://www.innolation.de
Paint & Coating Mfr
N.A.I.C.S.: 325510

Liaver GmbH & Co. KG   (1)
Gewerbepark Am Wald 17, D-98693, Ilmenau, Germany
Tel.: (49) 367786290
Web Site: https://www.liaver.com
Glass Mfr
N.A.I.C.S.: 327215
Ronald Tschiersch *(Mng Dir)*

OOO Sto   (1)
Varshavskoe shosse 118 bld1 office XLI 5, 117587, Moscow, Russia
Tel.: (7) 4956646400
Web Site: https://www.sto.ru
Building Materials Mfr
N.A.I.C.S.: 327120

Shanghai Sto Ltd.   (1)
288 Qingda Road, Pudong, 201201, Shanghai, China
Tel.: (86) 2158972295
Web Site: https://www.sto.com.cn
Building Materials Mfr
N.A.I.C.S.: 327120

Skyrise Prefab Building Solutions Inc.   (1)
896 Brock Road - Unit 1, Pickering, L1W 1Z9, ON, Canada
Tel.: (289) 275-4419
Web Site: https://www.skyriseprefab.com
Building Materials Mfr
N.A.I.C.S.: 327120
Joe Aprile *(Exec Dir)*

Sto Brasil Revestimentos e Fachadas Ltda.   (1)
Rua Flor de Noiva 886 Quinta da Boa Vista, Itaquaquecetuba, 08597-630, SP, Brazil
Tel.: (55) 1121450011
Web Site: https://www.stobrasil.com.br
Building Materials Mfr
N.A.I.C.S.: 327120

Sto Canada Ltd.   (1)
1821 Albion Rd 1, Etobicoke, M9W 5W8, ON, Canada
Tel.: (587) 436-9428
Building Materials Mfr
N.A.I.C.S.: 327120

Sto Colombia S.A.S.   (1)
Carrera 70 19-52, 110931, Bogota, Colombia
Tel.: (57) 17451280
Web Site: https://stocolombia.com
Paint & Coating Mfr
N.A.I.C.S.: 325510

Sto Danmark A/S   (1)
Avedoreholmen 48, 2650, Hvidovre, Denmark
Tel.: (45) 70270143
Web Site: https://www.sto.dk
Building Materials Mfr
N.A.I.C.S.: 327120

Sto Epitoanyag Kft.   (1)
Jedlik Anyos u 17, 2330, Dunaharaszti, Hungary
Tel.: (36) 24510210
Web Site: https://www.sto.hu
Building Materials Mfr
N.A.I.C.S.: 327120

Sto Finexter OY   (1)
Suokallionkuja 8 G, FI-01740, Vantaa, Finland
Tel.: (358) 201104728
Web Site: https://www.sto.fi
Building Materials Mfr
N.A.I.C.S.: 327120

Sto Ges.m.b.H.   (1)
Richtstrasse 47, A-9500, Villach, Austria
Tel.: (43) 4242331330
Web Site: https://www.sto.at
Building Materials Mfr
N.A.I.C.S.: 327120

Sto Isoned B.V.   (1)
Lingewei 107, 4004 LH, Tiel, Netherlands
Tel.: (31) 344620666
Web Site: https://www.sto.nl
Building Materials Mfr
N.A.I.C.S.: 327120

Sto Italia Srl   (1)
Via G Di Vittorio 1-3, Empoli, 50053, Florence, Italy
Tel.: (39) 057194701
Web Site: https://www.stoitalia.it
Building Materials Mfr
N.A.I.C.S.: 327120

Sto Mexico S. de R.L. de C.V.   (1)
Prol Reforma 51 - 803 Paseo de las Lomas Santa Fe, Alvaro Obregon, DF 01330, Mexico, Mexico
Tel.: (52) 5563840999
Web Site: https://www.stomexico.com
Building Materials Mfr
N.A.I.C.S.: 327120

Sto N.V.   (1)
Z 5 Mollem 43, 1730, Asse, Belgium
Tel.: (32) 24530110
Web Site: https://www.sto.be
Building Materials Mfr
N.A.I.C.S.: 327120

Sto Norge AS   (1)
Facade Coatings Facade Insulation Systems and Concrete Restoration, Waldemar Thranes gate 98B, 0175, Oslo, Norway
Tel.: (47) 66813500
Web Site: http://www.sto.no
Building Materials Mfr
N.A.I.C.S.: 327120

Sto S.A.S.   (1)
224 Rue Michel Carre, CS 40045, F-95872, Bezons, Cedex, France
Tel.: (33) 134345700
Web Site: https://www.sto.fr
Building Materials Mfr
N.A.I.C.S.: 327120

Sto SDF Iberica S.L.U.   (1)
Riera del Fonollar 13, E-08830, Sant Boi de Llobregat, Barcelona, Spain
Tel.: (34) 937415972
Web Site: https://www.sto.es
Building Materials Mfr
N.A.I.C.S.: 327120

Sto SEA Pte. Ltd.   (1)
159 Sin Ming Road 06-02 Amtech Building, Singapore, 575625, Singapore
Tel.: (65) 64533080
Building Materials Mfr
N.A.I.C.S.: 327120

Sto SEA Sdn. Bhd.   (1)
No 15 Jalan Teknologi 3/3A, Surian Industrial Park Kota Damansara, 47810, Petaling Jaya, Malaysia
Tel.: (60) 361566133
Web Site: http://www.sto-sea.com
Building Materials Mfr
N.A.I.C.S.: 327120

Sto Scandinavia AB   (1)
Gesallgatan 6, 582 77, Linkoping, Sweden
Tel.: (46) 13377100
Web Site: https://www.sto.se
Building Materials Mfr
N.A.I.C.S.: 327120

Sto Slovensko s.r.o.   (1)
Pribylinska 2, 831 04, Bratislava, Slovakia
Tel.: (421) 244648142
Web Site: https://www.sto.sk
Building Materials Mfr
N.A.I.C.S.: 327120

Sto Sp. z o.o.   (1)
ul Zabraniecka 15, 03-872, Warsaw, Poland
Tel.: (48) 225116102
Web Site: https://www.sto.pl
Building Materials Mfr
N.A.I.C.S.: 327120

Sto Yapi Sistemleri Sanayi ve Ticaret A.S.   (1)
Goztepe Mah Ataturk Cad Semazen Sok No 8 A Hisari, Beykoz, 34815, Istanbul, Turkiye
Tel.: (90) 2163305100
Web Site: https://www.sto.com.tr
Paint & Coating Mfr
N.A.I.C.S.: 325510

Sto s.r.o.   (1)
Cestlice 271, 251 70, Dobrejovice, Czech Republic
Tel.: (420) 225996311
Web Site: https://www.sto.cz
Building Materials Mfr
N.A.I.C.S.: 327120

StoCretec Flooring AS   (1)
Vaerftsgata 7A Pb 1023, Jeloy, 1510, Moss, Norway
Tel.: (47) 66813500
Web Site: https://www.stocretec.no
Building Materials Mfr
N.A.I.C.S.: 327120
Richard Spoletini *(Mgr-Market)*

StoCretec GmbH   (1)
Gutenbergstrasse 6, D-65 830, Kriftel, Germany   (100%)
Tel.: (49) 6192401104
Web Site: https://www.stocretec.de
Concrete Protection Products & Repair Services
N.A.I.C.S.: 444180
Alexander Gansler *(Mng Dir)*

Stroher GmbH   (1)
Stroherstrasse 2-10, D-35683, Dillenburg, Germany
Tel.: (49) 27713910
Web Site: https://www.stroeher.com
Building Materials Mfr
N.A.I.C.S.: 327120

UAB Tech-Coat   (1)
Vieversiu g 1a, Ginduliai, LT- 91284, Klaipeda, Lithuania
Tel.: (370) 68552104
Web Site: https://www.techcoat.lt
Building Materials Mfr
N.A.I.C.S.: 327120

Unitex Australia Pty Ltd.   (1)
96 Prosperity Way, Dandenong South, 3175, VIC, Australia
Tel.: (61) 397684900
Web Site: https://www.unitex.com.au
Building Materials Mfr
N.A.I.C.S.: 327120

Verotec GmbH   (1)
Hanns-Martin-Schleyer-Str 1, Donau, 89415, Lauingen, Germany
Tel.: (49) 90729900
Web Site: https://www.verotec.de
Building Materials Mfr
N.A.I.C.S.: 327120

Viacor Polymer GmbH   (1)
Graf-Bentzel-Str 78, 72108, Rottenburg am Neckar, Germany   (100%)
Tel.: (49) 7472949990
Web Site: https://www.viacor.de
Paint & Coating Mfr
N.A.I.C.S.: 325510
Ralf Jooss *(CEO)*

STOCAR A.D.
Tel.: (387) 51305520
Year Founded: 2001
STOR-R-A—(BANJ)
Rev.: $171,540
Assets: $3,981,283
Liabilities: $3,639,493
Net Worth: $341,790
Earnings: ($273,252)
Emp.: 14
Fiscal Year-end: 12/31/12
Veal Product Mfr
N.A.I.C.S.: 311612
Stanko Barisic *(Chm-Mgmt Bd)*

STOCK TREND CAPITAL INC.
301 - 217 Queen Street West, Toronto, M5V 0R2, ON, Canada
Tel.: (604) 473-9569
Web Site: https://stocktrend.com
PUMP—(CNSX)
Rev.: $7,543,336
Assets: $12,239,576
Liabilities: $4,619,751
Net Worth: $7,619,826
Earnings: ($3,509,557)
Fiscal Year-end: 04/30/21
Cannabis Extracting Services
N.A.I.C.S.: 459999
Anthony John Durkacz *(CEO)*

STOCK3 AG
Balanstrasse 73 House 11/3rd floor, 81541, Munich, Germany
Tel.: (49) 89767369123
Web Site: https://www.stock3.com
Year Founded: 2000
BOG—(MUN)
Rev.: $13,202,285
Assets: $10,078,333
Liabilities: $5,044,686
Net Worth: $5,033,647
Earnings: ($1,633,728)
Emp.: 84
Fiscal Year-end: 12/31/23
Asset Management Services
N.A.I.C.S.: 523999

STOCKCUBE PLC
58 Bradbourne Street, London, SW6 3TE, United Kingdom
Tel.: (44) 20 7352 4001
Web Site: http://www.stockcube.com
Sales Range: $1-9.9 Million
Emp.: 20
Financial Services
N.A.I.C.S.: 522320

Subsidiaries:

Chartcraft Inc.   (1)
30 Church St, New Rochelle, NY 10801-6357
Tel.: (914) 632-0422
Investment Banking & Securities Dealing Services
N.A.I.C.S.: 523150

Stockcube Research Limited   (1)
Ste 120-123 Plz 535 Kings Rd, London,

STOCKCUBE PLC

Stockcube Plc—(Continued)
SW10 0SZ, United Kingdom
Tel.: (44) 2073524001
Web Site:
http://www.stockcuberesearch.com
Sales Range: $50-74.9 Million
Institutional Fund Management Research Services
N.A.I.C.S.: 523940

STOCKFISH GEORGE FORD SALES (1987) LTD.
Hwy 17 East, North Bay, P1B 8J5, ON, Canada
Tel.: (705) 476-1506
Web Site: http://www.stockfish.ca
Year Founded: 1987
Rev.: $37,300,000
Emp.: 65
New & Used Car Dealers
N.A.I.C.S.: 441110

STOCKLAND CORPORATION LTD.
Level 25 133 Castlereagh Street, Sydney, 2000, NSW, Australia
Tel.: (61) 290352000
Web Site:
https://www.stockland.com.au
Year Founded: 1952
SGP—(OTCIQ)
Rev.: $2,111,619,640
Assets: $14,791,297,950
Liabilities: $7,448,132,990
Net Worth: $7,343,164,960
Earnings: $846,639,950
Emp.: 1,600
Fiscal Year-end: 06/30/21
Real Estate Investment Trust
N.A.I.C.S.: 525990
Andrew Whitson *(CEO-Communities)*

STOCKLIN LOGISTIK AG
Dornacherstrasse 197, CH-4143, Dornach, Switzerland
Tel.: (41) 617058111
Web Site: http://www.stocklin.com
Year Founded: 1934
Sales Range: $100-124.9 Million
Emp.: 520
Conveyor Systems, Logistics & Warehousing Software, Forklifts & Industrial Trucks Mfr
N.A.I.C.S.: 333922
Urs Grutter *(Chm & CEO)*

Subsidiaries:

Walter Stocklin Ges.m.b.H. (1)
Industriestrasse 23, A-2353, Guntramsdorf, Austria
Tel.: (43) 2236255660
Web Site: http://www.stocklin.at
Sales Range: $25-49.9 Million
Emp.: 33
Forklifts & Industrial Trucks Mfr
N.A.I.C.S.: 333924
Christian Schwartz *(CEO)*

STOCKMANN OYJ ABP
Aleksanterinkatu 52 B, PO Box 220, Helsinki, 00101, Finland
Tel.: (358) 91211
Web Site:
http://www.stockmanngroup.com
LINDEX—(HEL)
Rev.: $1,021,575,784
Assets: $1,406,397,596
Liabilities: $986,152,856
Net Worth: $420,244,740
Earnings: $55,495,921
Emp.: 6,062
Fiscal Year-end: 12/31/23
Clothing Apparel Distr
N.A.I.C.S.: 458110
Jari Latvanen *(CEO)*

STOCKMANN PLC
Aleksanterinkatu 52 B, PO Box 220, 00101, Helsinki, Finland
Tel.: (358) 91211
Web Site:
http://www.stockmanngroup.com
Year Founded: 1862
STCAS—(HEL)
Rev.: $1,059,464,710
Assets: $1,384,524,066
Liabilities: $1,022,339,737
Net Worth: $362,184,330
Earnings: $109,648,176
Emp.: 2,121
Fiscal Year-end: 12/31/22
Department Stores, Fashion Stores & Mail-Order Retailing
N.A.I.C.S.: 455110
Pekka Vahahyyppa *(CFO)*

Subsidiaries:

AB Lindex (1)
Nils Ericsonplatsen 3, Postboks 223, 401 23, Gothenburg, Sweden
Tel.: (46) 317395000
Web Site: http://www.lindex.com
Sales Range: $700-749.9 Million
Emp.: 300
Clothing Stores
N.A.I.C.S.: 458110
Peter Andersson *(Dir-Fin)*

AS Stockmann (1)
Liivalaia 53, 10145, Tallinn, Estonia
Tel.: (372) 6 339 632
Web Site: http://www.stockmann.ee
Sales Range: $125-149.9 Million
Emp.: 400
Department Stores Operation Services
N.A.I.C.S.: 458110

Lindex Ou Eesti (1)
Paldiski Mnt 102, 13522, Tallinn, Estonia
Tel.: (372) 6108787
Women Clothing Distr
N.A.I.C.S.: 458110
Mart Magi *(Dir Gen)*

Lindex UK Fashion Ltd. (1)
Wey House Farnham Road, Guildford, GU1 4YD, United Kingdom
Tel.: (44) 2030050009
Women Clothing Distr
N.A.I.C.S.: 458110

Stockmann plc - Department Store Division (1)
Takomotie 1-3, PL 147, 00381, Helsinki, Finland
Tel.: (358) 912151
Web Site: http://www.stockmann.com
Sales Range: $1-4.9 Billion
Emp.: 6,000
Department Stores
N.A.I.C.S.: 455110

TOV Stockmann (1)
Antonovicha St 172, 03680, Kiev, Ukraine
Tel.: (380) 442204024
Fashion Apparels Retailer
N.A.I.C.S.: 458110

ZAO Stockmann (1)
Nevsky Prospect 112, 191025, Saint Petersburg, Russia
Tel.: (7) 812 676 0790
Apparel Retailer
N.A.I.C.S.: 458110

STOCKMEIER HOLDING GMBH
Eckendorfer Str 10, 33609, Bielefeld, Germany
Tel.: (49) 521 30370
Web Site: http://www.stockmeier.com
Year Founded: 1920
Sales Range: $450-499.9 Million
Emp.: 700
Holding Company
N.A.I.C.S.: 551112
Peter-August Stockmeier *(Member-Mgmt Bd)*

Subsidiaries:

KAPP-CHEMIE GmbH & Co. KG (1)
Industriestrasse 2-4, 56357, Miehlen, Germany
Tel.: (49) 6772 9311 0
Web Site: http://www.kapp-chemie.de
Emp.: 100
Chemical Mfr & Distr
N.A.I.C.S.: 325998
Marco Hamann *(Gen Mgr)*

SFC STOCKMEIER GmbH (1)
Afrikanergasse 3/3, 1020, Vienna, Austria
Tel.: (43) 12121085
Web Site: http://www.sfc-stockmeier.at
Chemical Products Distr
N.A.I.C.S.: 423830

STOCKMEIER Chemie Austria GmbH (1)
Ricoweg 32 B, 2351, Wiener Neudorf, Austria
Tel.: (43) 223662340
Chemical Products Distr
N.A.I.C.S.: 423830

STOCKMEIER Chemie BVBA (1)
Belgicastraat 1C Haven 2290, 9042, Gent, Belgium
Tel.: (32) 93268933
Chemical Products Distr
N.A.I.C.S.: 423830

STOCKMEIER Chemie Dillenburg GmbH & Co. KG (1)
Am Guterbahnhof 28, 35683, Dillenburg, Germany
Tel.: (49) 277187100
Chemical Products Mfr
N.A.I.C.S.: 325199

STOCKMEIER Chemie Eilenburg GmbH & Co. KG (1)
Gustav-Adolf-Ring 5, 04838, Eilenburg, Germany
Tel.: (49) 342369000
Chemical Products Mfr
N.A.I.C.S.: 325199

STOCKMEIER Chemie Polen Sp z o.o. (1)
ul Obornicka 277, 60-691, Poznan, Poland
Tel.: (48) 616661066
Chemical Products Distr
N.A.I.C.S.: 423830
Leszek Walkowiak *(Mgr-Sls)*

STOCKMEIER Food GmbH & Co. KG (1)
Zeppelinstrasse 7, 32051, Herford, Germany
Tel.: (49) 522193390
Chemical Products Mfr
N.A.I.C.S.: 325199

STOCKMEIER Urethanes France S.A. (1)
8 Rue de L'Industrie Z I Est, 68700, Cernay, France
Tel.: (33) 389 75 70 70
Web Site: http://www.stockmeier-urethanes.de
Polyurethane Resin Mfr & Distr
N.A.I.C.S.: 325211

Subsidiary (Non-US):

STOCKMEIER Urethanes UK Ltd (2)
Mylestone House Sowerby New Road, Sowerby Bridge, HX6 1AA, West Yorkshire, United Kingdom
Tel.: (44) 1422835835
Chemical Products Distr
N.A.I.C.S.: 423830
Tim Blundell *(Dir-Technical)*

Stockmeier Urethanes GmbH & Co. KG (1)
Im Hengstfeld 15, 32657, Lemgo, Germany
Tel.: (49) 5261 660 68 0
Web Site: http://stockmeier-urethanes.com
Polyurethane Mfr
N.A.I.C.S.: 325211

Subsidiary (US):

Stockmeier Urethanes USA, Inc. (2)
20 Columbia Blvd, Clarksburg, WV 26301
Tel.: (304) 624-7002
Web Site: http://www.stockmeier.com

INTERNATIONAL PUBLIC

Sales Range: $25-49.9 Million
Emp.: 15
Polyurethane Mfr
N.A.I.C.S.: 325211
Chris Martinkat *(Pres)*

STOCKWIK FORVALTNING AB
Frosundaviks alle1 169 70 Solna
SeatCounty seat, municipal seat
Solna, 16970, Stockholm, Sweden
Tel.: (46) 855696500
Web Site: https://www.stockwik.se
STWK—(OMX)
Rev.: $71,613,888
Assets: $87,330,355
Liabilities: $62,884,599
Net Worth: $24,445,756
Earnings: $355,915
Emp.: 462
Fiscal Year-end: 12/31/22
Telecommunication Servicesb
N.A.I.C.S.: 517810
Leif Rune Rinnan *(Chm)*

STOCZNIA GDYNIA S.A.
ul Czechoslowacka 3, 81-969, Gdynia, Poland
Tel.: (48) 586277000
Web Site:
http://www.stocznia.gdynia.pl
Year Founded: 1922
Sales Range: $450-499.9 Million
Emp.: 6,700
Ship Building & Repairing Services
N.A.I.C.S.: 336611
Konopka Jerzy *(Vice Chm-Supervisory Bd)*

Subsidiaries:

EURO RUSZTOWANIA Grupa Stoczni Gdynia Sp. z o.o. (1)
ul Golebia 1, 81-185, Gdynia, Poland
Tel.: (48) 586271630
Web Site: http://www.e-rusztowania.com.pl
Scaffolding Services for Ship Building & Repairing
N.A.I.C.S.: 336611

EURO-CYNK Gdynia Sp, z o.o. (1)
Ul Czechoslowacka 3, 81-969, Gdynia, Poland
Tel.: (48) 586271777
Sales Range: $25-49.9 Million
Emp.: 100
Ship Building & Repairing Services
N.A.I.C.S.: 336611

EUROMAL Grupa Stoczni Gdynia Sp. z o.o. (1)
Ul Czechoslowacka 3, 81963, Gdynia, Poland
Tel.: (48) 586271431
Web Site: http://www.euromal.gdynia.pl
Sales Range: $25-49.9 Million
Emp.: 50
Ship Painting, Cleaning & Maintenance Services
N.A.I.C.S.: 811310

POL-SUPPLY Sp. z o.o. (1)
ul Janka Wisniewskiego 20, 81-969, Gdynia, Poland
Tel.: (48) 586278638
Web Site: http://www.polsupply.com.pl
Sales Range: $25-49.9 Million
Emp.: 20
Industrial Supplies Distr
N.A.I.C.S.: 423840

Polskie Linie Oceaniczne S.A. (1)
Building 24 No 10 Lutego Street, 81-364, Gdynia, Poland
Tel.: (48) 586900670
Web Site: http://www.pol.com.pl
Sales Range: $25-49.9 Million
Emp.: 50
Conventional & Container Shipping, Transportation & Shiphandler's Services
N.A.I.C.S.: 483111

Stocznia Gdanska Grupa Stoczni Gdynia S.A. (1)
Ul Na Ostrowiu 15/20, 80-873, Gdansk, Poland

Tel.: (48) 587691607
Web Site: http://www.gdanskshipyard.pl
Ship Building & Repairing Services
N.A.I.C.S.: 336611

STOKKAN LYS
Mellomila 56, 7018, Trondheim, Norway
Tel.: (47) 958 58 800 NO
Web Site: http://www.stokkanlys.no
Functional Lighting Product Mfr
N.A.I.C.S.: 335132
Nils Gronningsaeter *(Partner)*

STOKVIS NIG PLC.
50 Ogunlana Drive, Surulere, Nigeria
Tel.: (234) 1920775
Financial Services
N.A.I.C.S.: 523999

STOLT-NIELSEN LIMITED
1 Bermudiana Road, Po Box HM 3143, Hamilton, HM08, Bermuda
Tel.: (441) 2927337 BM
Web Site: https://www.stolt-nielsen.com
SNI—(OSL)
Rev.: $2,820,218,000
Assets: $4,983,723,000
Liabilities: $3,077,669,000
Net Worth: $1,906,054,000
Earnings: $296,651,000
Emp.: 6,682
Fiscal Year-end: 11/30/23
Logistic Services
N.A.I.C.S.: 541614
Niels G. Stolt-Nielsen *(CEO)*

Subsidiaries:

Italy Vado Tank Cleaning s.r.l. (1)
Via G Bertola 53, Vado Ligure, Sv, Italy
Tel.: (39) 0192160106
Web Site: https://www.vadotankcleaning.com
Tank Cleaning Services
N.A.I.C.S.: 562112

Jo Tankers AS (1)
Kokstadflaten 5 2nd Floor, NO-5257, Kokstad, Norway
Tel.: (47) 55998730
Web Site: http://www.jotankers.com
Marine Shipping Services
N.A.I.C.S.: 488510
Nils-Petter Sivertsen *(Pres & CEO)*

NC Stolt Chukyo Transportation Services Co. Ltd. (1)
(50%)
Web Site: http://www.sntg.com
Sales Range: $1-9.9 Million
Emp.: 16
Logistic Services
N.A.I.C.S.: 541614

P.T. Komaritim (1)
Ventura Building Suite 501, PO Box 26, Outr Ring Road South, Jakarta, 12430, Indonesia **(50%)**
Tel.: (62) 217504540
Web Site: http://www.stoltoffshore.com
Sales Range: $25-49.9 Million
Emp.: 30
Offshore Contracting Services
N.A.I.C.S.: 237120

Stolt Sea Farm Holdings Ltd (1)
Grev Wedels Plass 5, Sentrum, 0102, Oslo, Norway **(100%)**
Tel.: (47) 22401400
Web Site: http://www.stoltseafarm.com
Sales Range: $50-74.9 Million
Emp.: 30
Fish Farms Operator
N.A.I.C.S.: 112511

Subsidiary (US):

Sterling Caviar LLC (2)
9149 E Levee Rd, Elverta, CA 95626 **(100%)**
Tel.: (916) 991-4420
Web Site: http://www.sterlingcaviar.com
Emp.: 45

Fish Farming
N.A.I.C.S.: 112519
Shaoching Bihop *(VP-Mktg & Sls)*

Stolt Sea Farm Americas (2)
Ste 750 1600 S Federal Hwy, Pompano Beach, FL 33062-7519 **(100%)**
Tel.: (305) 629-9162
Web Site: http://www.stoltseafarm.com
Seafood Whslr
N.A.I.C.S.: 424460

Subsidiary (Non-US):

Stolt Sea Farm Inc. (2)
1 Fundy Bay Dr, Saint George, E5C 3E2, NB, Canada **(100%)**
Tel.: (506) 755-6421
Web Site: http://www.stoltseafarm.com
Sales Range: $10-24.9 Million
Emp.: 18
Fish Farming
N.A.I.C.S.: 112512

Stolt Sea Farm Inc. (2)
4100 Yonge Street Suite 513, Toronto, M2P 2B5, ON, Canada **(100%)**
Tel.: (416) 221-0404
Web Site: http://www.stoltseafarm.com
Sales Range: $10-24.9 Million
Emp.: 20
Fish Farming
N.A.I.C.S.: 112512

Stolt Sea Farm S.A. (2)
Lira Site Punta De Los Remedios, 15292, La Coruna, Carnota, Spain **(100%)**
Tel.: (34) 981837501
Web Site: http://www.stoltseafarm.com
Sales Range: $25-49.9 Million
Fish Farming
N.A.I.C.S.: 112512

Stolt Sea Farm Taiwan (2)
32 F No 87 7 Chung Cheng E Rd Sec 2, Hsien, Taiwan **(100%)**
Tel.: (886) 288097299
Web Site: http://www.stoltseafarm.com
Sales Range: $25-49.9 Million
Seafood Whslr
N.A.I.C.S.: 445250

Stolt-Nielsen Japan Co., Ltd. (2)
Urban Shibakoen 4F 3-1-13 Shibakoen, Minato-ku, Tokyo, 105-0011, Japan **(100%)**
Tel.: (81) 368417001
Web Site: http://www.stolt-nielsen.com
Fish Farming
N.A.I.C.S.: 112512

Stolt Tank Containers BV (1)
1 5 Oldchurch Road, Romford, RM7 0BQ, Assex, United Kingdom **(100%)**
Tel.: (44) 1708746070
Sales Range: $25-49.9 Million
Emp.: 30
Logistic Services
N.A.I.C.S.: 541614

Stolt Tank Containers France S.A.S. (1)
(100%)
Tel.: (33) 232796300
Sales Range: $25-49.9 Million
Emp.: 30
Logistic Services
N.A.I.C.S.: 541614

Stolt Tank Containers Italy Srl (1)
Piazza Ilaria Alpi 2 int 5, 17100, Savona, Italy
Tel.: (39) 0199420020
Bulk Liquid Chemical & Food Logistics Services
N.A.I.C.S.: 541614

Stolt Tank Containers Saudi Arabia Ltd. (1)
Eastern Cement Tower 3rd Floor Office 305, PO Box 1634, Al Khobar, 31952, Saudi Arabia
Tel.: (966) 138870969
Bulk Liquid Chemical & Food Logistics Services
N.A.I.C.S.: 541614

Stolt Tankers B.V. (1)
Westerlaan 12, 3016CK, Rotterdam, Netherlands **(100%)**
Tel.: (31) 102996666

Sales Range: $75-99.9 Million
Emp.: 350
Logistic Services
N.A.I.C.S.: 541614

Stolt Tankers B.V. & Middle East Service Ltd.
API Tower Ste 1303 Sheikh Zayed Rd, PO Box 8612, Dubai, United Arab Emirates **(100%)**
Tel.: (971) 43328444
Web Site: http://www.sntg.com
Sales Range: $25-49.9 Million
Emp.: 10
Logistic Services
N.A.I.C.S.: 541614

Stolt Tankers Singapore Pte. Ltd. (1)
10-01 mTower 460 Alexandra Road, Singapore, 119963, Singapore
Tel.: (65) 62734844
Chemical Liquid Transportation Services
N.A.I.C.S.: 522320

Stolt-Nielsen Argentina S.A. (1)
684 Marcelo T de Alvear St, Office A 2nd Fl, C1058AAH, Buenos Aires, Argentina **(100%)**
Tel.: (54) 1143455001
Sales Range: $25-49.9 Million
Emp.: 5
Logistic Services
N.A.I.C.S.: 541614

Stolt-Nielsen Australia Pty Ltd. (1)
(100%)
Tel.: (61) 398203288
Sales Range: $1-9.9 Million
Emp.: 10
Logistic Services
N.A.I.C.S.: 541614

Stolt-Nielsen Brasil Ltda. (1)
Al Santos 2224 3 Andar Cerqueira Cesar, Sao Paulo, 01418-200, Brazil **(100%)**
Tel.: (55) 1138974999
Web Site: http://www.stolt-nielsen.com
Sales Range: $25-49.9 Million
Emp.: 20
Logistic Services
N.A.I.C.S.: 541614

Stolt-Nielsen Mexico S.A. de C.V. (1)
Calle Violeta No 16 Col San Jose de Jaral Atizapan de Zaragoza, CP 52924, Mexico, Mexico
Tel.: (52) 5553082609
Chemical Liquid Transportation Services
N.A.I.C.S.: 522320

Stolt-Nielsen Philippines, Inc. (1)
(100%)
Tel.: (63) 28307900
Sales Range: $25-49.9 Million
Emp.: 50
Logistic Services
N.A.I.C.S.: 541614

Stolt-Nielsen Singapore Pte. Ltd. (1)
460 Alexandra Road 10-01 PSA Building, Singapore, 119963, Singapore **(100%)**
Tel.: (65) 62734844
Sales Range: $25-49.9 Million
Emp.: 9
Logistic Services
N.A.I.C.S.: 541614

Stolt-Nielsen Switzerland AG (1)
Baarerstrasse 149, 6300, Zug, Switzerland
Tel.: (41) 417663020
Chemical Liquid Transportation Services
N.A.I.C.S.: 522320

Stolt-Nielsen Transportation (Shanghai) Ltd. (1)
Room1703 Tower A Future Plaza 103 WeiDi Road, HeXi District, Tianjin, 300201, China
Tel.: (86) 222 837 2278
Chemical Logistics Services
N.A.I.C.S.: 541614

Stolt-Nielsen USA Inc. (1)
15635 Jacintoport Blvd, Houston, TX 77015-6533 **(100%)**
Tel.: (281) 860-6800
Web Site: http://www.stolt-nielsen.com
Sales Range: $50-74.9 Million
Emp.: 200
Freight Transportation Arrangement

N.A.I.C.S.: 488510
Mike Kramer *(Pres)*

Stolt-Nielsen USA Inc. (1)
800 Connecticut Ave 4th Fl E, Norwalk, CT 06854
Tel.: (203) 299-3600
Web Site: http://www.stoltnielsen.com
Sales Range: $1-4.9 Billion
Deep Sea Foreign Transportation Of Freigh
N.A.I.C.S.: 488390

Stolthaven Houston Inc. (1)
15602 Jacintoport Blvd, Houston, TX 77015-6533 **(100%)**
Tel.: (281) 860-6800
Sales Range: $25-49.9 Million
Emp.: 150
Bulk-Liquid Terminal Operator
N.A.I.C.S.: 424710

Stolthaven New Orleans LLC (1)
2444 English Turn Rd, Braithwaite, LA 70040
Tel.: (504) 682-9989
Emp.: 50
Bulk-Liquid Terminal Operator
N.A.I.C.S.: 424710
Ron Luebbe *(Mgr-Engrg & Construction)*

Stolthaven Singapore Pte. Ltd. (1)
22 Tembusu Crescent, Jurong Island, Singapore, 627611, Singapore
Tel.: (65) 64774530
Chemical Logistics Services
N.A.I.C.S.: 541614

STONE BOAT MINING CORP.
6325 Rincon del Palmito, CP31216, Chihuahua, Mexico
Tel.: (52) 6144558383 NV
Year Founded: 2011
Copper & Other Metal Mining
N.A.I.C.S.: 212230
Adam Whyte *(Pres, CEO, CFO, Treas & Sec)*

STONE COMPANY SPILIT
8A room 9th floor Vincom Center building 72 Le Thanh Ton, Ben Nghe ward District 1, Ho Chi Minh City, Vietnam
Tel.: (84) 02866501585
Web Site: http://www.spilit.com.vn
SPI—(HNX)
Rev.: $4,609,400
Assets: $12,748,680
Liabilities: $6,060,440
Net Worth: $6,688,240
Earnings: $8,483
Fiscal Year-end: 12/31/19
Stone Quarrying Services
N.A.I.C.S.: 212319
Pham Duc Thang *(Chm)*

STONE GOLD INC.
82 Richmond Street East, Toronto, M5C 1P1, ON, Canada
Tel.: (416) 849-7773 ON
Web Site: https://copperroad.ca
Year Founded: 2002
STGDF—(OTCIQ)
Assets: $31,923
Liabilities: $123,150
Net Worth: ($91,227)
Earnings: ($847,756)
Fiscal Year-end: 12/31/23
Metal Mining Exploration Service
N.A.I.C.S.: 213114
Mark E. Goodman *(Founder & Chm)*

STONE GROUP HOLDINGS LIMITED
8th Fl Pico Tower 66 Gloucester Rd, Wanchai, China (Hong Kong)
Tel.: (852) 25791166
Web Site: http://www.stone.com.hk
Sales Range: $400-449.9 Million
Emp.: 15,000

STONE GROUP HOLDINGS LIMITED

Stone Group Holdings Limited—(Continued)
Investment Services, Electronic Products Mfr & Consumer Healthcare Products Distr
N.A.I.C.S.: 334419
Guojun Shen *(Exec Dir)*

Subsidiaries:

Stone Advance Technology Limited (1)
8 fl pico tower 66 Gloucester Rd Wan Chai Dist, 8 Cotton Tree Drive, Hong Kong, China (Hong Kong) **(100%)**
Tel.: (852) 25791166
Web Site: http://www.stoneresources.cn
Electronic Parts & Equipment Whslr
N.A.I.C.S.: 423690

STONE MASTER CORPORATION BERHAD
Unit 02-3 Medan Klang Lama 28 No 419 Jalan Klang Lama, 58100, Kuala Lumpur, Wilayah Persekutuan, Malaysia
Tel.: (60) 3 2382 1777
Web Site:
 http://www.stonemaster.com.my
Rev.: $10,378,736
Assets: $10,958,315
Liabilities: $11,394,599
Net Worth: ($436,284)
Earnings: ($1,230,311)
Fiscal Year-end: 09/30/18
Ceramic Mfr
N.A.I.C.S.: 327120
Han Ching Chew *(CEO & Exec Dir)*

Subsidiaries:

Rainbow Marble & Tiling Sdn. Bhd. (1)
No 41 43 and 45 Batu 7 Jalan Kota Tinggi Pandan, 81100, Johor Bahru, Johor Darul Takzim, Malaysia
Tel.: (60) 7 354 3816
Sanitaryware Distr
N.A.I.C.S.: 423720

Stone Master Design & Build Sdn. Bhd. (1)
Unit 02-03 Medan Klang Lama 28 No 419 Jalan Klang Lama, Wilayah Persekutuan, 58100, Kuala Lumpur, Malaysia
Tel.: (60) 323821777
Ceramic Mfr
N.A.I.C.S.: 327120

STONEBRIDGE RESOURCES EXPLORATIONS LTD.
1962 Hartland Drive, Mississauga, L5J 1M6, ON, Canada
Tel.: (702) 490-4735 NV
Year Founded: 2004
SRCX—(OTCIQ)
Sales Range: Less than $1 Million
Metal Mining Services
N.A.I.C.S.: 213114
Patrick Webb *(Treas & Sec)*

STONEBRIDGE VENTURES INC.
14th floor KFAS Building 211 Teheran-ro, Gangnam-gu, Seoul, Korea (South)
Tel.: (82) 261824700
Web Site:
 https://www.stonebridgeventures.vc
330730—(KRS)
Rev.: $22,688,417
Assets: $75,224,222
Liabilities: $9,376,883
Net Worth: $65,847,339
Earnings: $5,476,576
Emp.: 25
Fiscal Year-end: 12/31/22
Investment Management Service
N.A.I.C.S.: 523999

STONECO LTD.
R Fidencio Ramos 308 Vila Olimpia 10th floor, Sao Paulo, 04551-010, SP, Brazil
Tel.: (55) 1130049680 Ky
Web Site: http://www.stone.co
Year Founded: 2014
STNE—(NASDAQ)
Rev.: $1,843,474,676
Assets: $8,121,685,840
Liabilities: $5,632,043,726
Net Worth: $2,489,642,114
Earnings: ($101,199,631)
Emp.: 16,685
Fiscal Year-end: 12/31/22
Electronic Financial Transaction Processing Services
N.A.I.C.S.: 522320
Roberta Noronha *(Head-IR)*

Subsidiaries:

Cappta S.A. (1)
Rua Gomes de Carvalho 1609, Vila Olimpia, Sao Paulo, 04547-006, Brazil
Tel.: (55) 1143026199
Web Site: http://www.cappta.com.br
Electronic Payment Services
N.A.I.C.S.: 522320

Equals S.A. (1)
Av Dra Ruth Cardoso 7221 - 7 andar, Pinheiros, Sao Paulo, 05425-902, Brazil
Tel.: (55) 1126550800
Web Site: https://equals.com.br
Financial Management Platform Services
N.A.I.C.S.: 541611

Linx S.A. (1)
Avenida Doutora Ruth Cardoso 7221, Ed Birmann 21-Pinheiros, 05425-902, Sao Paulo, Brazil
Tel.: (55) 1121032400
Web Site: https://www.linx.com.br
Rev.: $168,483,478
Assets: $514,909,519
Liabilities: $203,452,215
Net Worth: $311,457,304
Earnings: ($15,394,226)
Emp.: 3,938
Fiscal Year-end: 12/31/2020
Software Publisher
N.A.I.C.S.: 513210

Mundipagg Tecnologia em Pagamento S.A. (1)
Rua Fidencio Ramos 308 Av General Justo 375 Centro, Rio de Janeiro, Sao Paulo, Brazil
Tel.: (55) 1131573207
Web Site: http://www.mundipagg.com
Online Payment Services
N.A.I.C.S.: 522320

Pagar.me Pagamentos S.A. (1)
Web Site: http://www.pagar.me
Online Payment Services
N.A.I.C.S.: 522320
Henrique Coelho *(Founder)*

STONEGATE PUB COMPANY LIMITED
500 Capability Green, Luton, LU1 3LS, United Kingdom
Tel.: (44) 1582211631
Web Site:
 http://www.stonegatepubs.com
Managed Pub Operators
N.A.I.C.S.: 532310
Simon Longbottom *(CEO)*

Subsidiaries:

EI Group Limited (1)
3 Monkspath Hall Road, Solihull, B90 4SJ, W Midlands, United Kingdom
Tel.: (44) 1212725000
Pub Leasing & Management Services
N.A.I.C.S.: 722410

Subsidiary (Domestic):

Unique Pub Properties Limited (2)
3 Monkspath Hall Rd Solihull, Shirley, B90 4SJ, West Midlands, United Kingdom
Tel.: (44) 1217337700
Web Site: http://www.enterpriseinn.com

Sales Range: $150-199.9 Million
Emp.: 300
Real Estate Management Services
N.A.I.C.S.: 531390

STONEHAGE FLEMING FAMILY & PARTNERS LIMITED
15 Suffolk Street, London, SW1Y 4HG, United Kingdom
Tel.: (44) 20 7087 0000
Web Site:
 http://www.stonehagefleming.com
Investment Management Service
N.A.I.C.S.: 523940
Giuseppe Ciucci *(CEO)*

Subsidiaries:

Stonehage Fleming Investment Management (Suisse) AG (1)
Todistrasse 38, 8022, Zurich, Switzerland
Tel.: (41) 44 217 9600
Web Site: http://www.stonehagefleming.com
Emp.: 13
Investment Services
N.A.I.C.S.: 523999
Pawel Sniegocki *(Portfolio Mgr)*

STONEHENGE INTER PCL
163 Soi Chokchai Ruammit Ratchada 19 Ratchadaphisek Road, Din Daeng, Bangkok, 10400, Thailand
Tel.: (66) 26907462
Web Site: https://www.sti.co.th
Year Founded: 2004
STI—(THA)
Rev.: $36,450,158
Assets: $63,513,901
Liabilities: $34,156,533
Net Worth: $29,357,368
Earnings: $2,701,520
Emp.: 1,489
Fiscal Year-end: 12/31/22
Building Construction Services
N.A.I.C.S.: 236220

Subsidiaries:

Stonehenge Company Limited (1)
No 163 Soi Chokchai Ruammit Ratchadaphisek 19, Din Daeng, Bangkok, 10400, Thailand
Tel.: (66) 26907460
Web Site: https://www.stonehenge.co.th
Construction Services
N.A.I.C.S.: 236220
Somsak Seubsai *(Deputy Dir-Engrg)*

STONEMARTIN PLC
New Broad Street House, 35 New Broad Street, London, EC2M 1NH, United Kingdom
Tel.: (44) 20 7194 7500
Web Site:
 http://www.stonemartin.co.uk
Year Founded: 1999
Sales Range: $25-49.9 Million
Emp.: 30
Fully-Equipped & Serviced Business Virtual Office Leasing & Operation Services
N.A.I.C.S.: 561499
Colin Peacock *(Chm-Stonemartin Properties)*

STONESET EQUITY DEVELOPMENT CORP.
3915 8th Street Southeast, Calgary, T2G 3A5, AB, Canada
Tel.: (403) 237-8822 AB
Year Founded: 2006
Sales Range: Less than $1 Million
Emp.: 10
Real Estate Investment Services
N.A.I.C.S.: 531390
Tony Argento *(Chm & CEO)*

STONEWEG SA
8 Bvd Georges Favon, 1204, Geneva, Switzerland

INTERNATIONAL PUBLIC

Tel.: (41) 225524030
Web Site: https://www.stoneweg.com
Real Estate Investment Services
N.A.I.C.S.: 531210

STONEY CREEK FURNITURE
395 Lewis Road, Stoney Creek, L8E 5N5, ON, Canada
Tel.: (905) 643-4121
Web Site:
 http://www.stoneycreekfurniture.com
Rev.: $15,469,833
Emp.: 125
Furniture Store
N.A.I.C.S.: 449110
Lori Negrinotti *(Mgr-Mdse)*

STOR-AGE PROPERTY REIT LTD.
First Floor 216 Claremont Main Road, Claremont, Cape Town, 7735, South Africa
Tel.: (27) 216713233
Web Site: https://www.stor-age.co.za
Year Founded: 2006
SSS—(JSE)
Rev.: $56,548,337
Assets: $636,688,336
Liabilities: $256,740,354
Net Worth: $379,947,982
Earnings: $38,639,297
Emp.: 480
Fiscal Year-end: 03/31/23
Real Estate Manangement Services
N.A.I.C.S.: 531390
Gavin Mark Lucas *(Founder & CEO)*

STORA ENSO OYJ
Kanavaranta 1, PO Box 309, FI-00101, Helsinki, Finland
Tel.: (358) 2046111 FI
Web Site: https://www.storaenso.com
Year Founded: 1998
STERV—(HEL)
Rev.: $10,140,297,863
Assets: $22,398,014,246
Liabilities: $10,646,449,385
Net Worth: $11,751,564,861
Earnings: ($465,141,377)
Emp.: 20,822
Fiscal Year-end: 12/31/23
Packaging & Forest Products Mfr
N.A.I.C.S.: 322220
Per Lyrvall *(Gen Counsel, Exec VP-Legal & Country Mgr-Sweden)*

Subsidiaries:

AS Stora Enso Latvija (1)
Maskavas Street 4 Spikeri, Riga, LV-1050, Latvia
Tel.: (371) 67670051
Door Distr
N.A.I.C.S.: 423310

Eufores, S.A. (1)
Luis Alberto de Herrera 1248 Complejo World Trade Center, Torre 3 Piso 9, Montevideo, Uruguay **(50%)**
Tel.: (598) 2 623 6300
Web Site:
 https://www.montesdelplata.com.uy
Sales Range: $50-74.9 Million
Emp.: 250
Forest Nurseries & Wood Pulp Mills
N.A.I.C.S.: 113210

Herman Andersson Oy (1)
Poikkimaantie 12, PO Box 37, FI-90401, Oulu, Finland
Tel.: (358) 83150131
Web Site: https://www.hermanandersson.fi
Rev.: $21,142,240
Emp.: 88
Logistics Consulting Servies
N.A.I.C.S.: 541614
Jari Erkkila *(Mgr-Customer Svc)*

RETS Timber Oy Ltd. (1)
Urho Kekkosen katu 3B, 00100, Helsinki, Finland **(100%)**
Tel.: (358) 94132630

AND PRIVATE COMPANIES — STORA ENSO OYJ

Sales Range: $50-74.9 Million
Emp.: 20
Sawn Timber Wholesale Trading Agency
N.A.I.C.S.: 425120

Stora Enso (HK) Limited (1)
25 Fl 88 Hingfat St, Causeway Bay, China
(Hong Kong) **(100%)**
Tel.: (852) 23121223
Web Site: https://www.storaenso.com
Sales Range: Less than $1 Million
Emp.: 10
Mfr of Paper & Paperboard
N.A.I.C.S.: 424130

Stora Enso (Schweiz) AG (1)
Uberlandstrasse 109, 8600, Dubendorf,
Switzerland
Tel.: (41) 44 435 38 24
Web Site: http://www.storaenso.com
Packaging Paper Products Mfr
N.A.I.C.S.: 322220

Stora Enso AB (1)
World Trade Center Klarabergsviadukten 70
C4, PO Box 70395, SE 107 24, Stockholm,
Sweden **(100%)**
Tel.: (46) 104646000
Sales Range: $25-49.9 Million
Emp.: 70
Producers of Pulp, Fine Paper, Newsprint,
Sawn Timber, Electric Power
N.A.I.C.S.: 322110
Gunnar Brock *(Chm)*

Subsidiary (Domestic):

Design Force AB (2)
Vastra Bravikenvagen 1, 602 38, Norrkoping, Sweden
Tel.: (46) 11 15 52 50
Web Site: http://www.designforce.se
Sales Range: $25-49.9 Million
Emp.: 20
Cardboard Paper Products Mfr
N.A.I.C.S.: 322220

June Emballage AB (2)
Momarken 38, 556 50, Jonkoping, Sweden
Tel.: (46) 36367100
Web Site: http://www.juneemballage.se
Corrugated Board Mfr
N.A.I.C.S.: 322130
Mikael Sandberg *(CEO)*

Stora Enso Fine Paper AB (2)
Sgatan 22, Falun, 791 80, Sweden
Tel.: (46) 104680000
Web Site: http://www.storaenso.com
Sales Range: $50-74.9 Million
Emp.: 150
Paper Product Distr
N.A.I.C.S.: 424130

Stora Enso Forest (2)
Asgatan 22, 791 80, Falun,
Sweden **(100%)**
Tel.: (46) 705948520
Web Site: http://www.storaenso.com
Sales Range: $10-24.9 Million
Emp.: 50
Group Forest Management
N.A.I.C.S.: 115310

Subsidiary (Domestic):

Stora Enso Skog AB (3)
Asgatan 22, 791 80, Falun,
Sweden **(100%)**
Tel.: (46) 104640000
Web Site: https://www.storaensoskog.se
Wood Products Mfr
N.A.I.C.S.: 423310
Daniel Forsberg *(Mgr-IT)*

Subsidiary (Domestic):

Stora Enso Bioenergi AB (4)
Norra Oskarsgatan 27 C, 582 73, Linkoping, Sweden
Tel.: (46) 1046 385 00
Sales Range: $10-24.9 Million
Emp.: 12
Forest Management Services
N.A.I.C.S.: 115310
Peter Sondelius *(Gen Mgr)*

Subsidiary (Domestic):

Stora Enso Fors AB (2)
Kopparforsvagen 3, 774 97, Fors, Sweden

Tel.: (46) 104635000
Emp.: 707
Packaging Carton Board Mfr
N.A.I.C.S.: 322130
Richard Moren *(Mgr-Mill)*

Stora Enso Hylte AB (2)
Gamla Nissastigen 16, 314 81, Hyltebruk,
Sweden
Tel.: (46) 1046 190 00
Newsprint Paper Products Mfr
N.A.I.C.S.: 322299
Lars Lundin *(Mgr-Mill)*

Stora Enso Kvarnsveden AB (2)
Kvarnsveden Mill, 781 83, Borlange, Sweden
Tel.: (46) 1046 650 00
Emp.: 800
Newsprint Paper Products Mfr
N.A.I.C.S.: 322299
Rickard Eriksson *(Mgr-Mill)*

Stora Enso Logistics AB (2)
Lilla Bommen 1, Box 2556, Gothenburg,
411 04, Sweden
Tel.: (46) 1046 150 00
Web Site: http://www.storaenso.com
Sales Range: $25-49.9 Million
Emp.: 70
Logistics Consulting Servies
N.A.I.C.S.: 541614
Knut Hansen *(Sr VP)*

Stora Enso Nymolla AB (2)
Nymolla Mill, 295 80, Nymolla, Sweden
Tel.: (46) 1046 440 00
Emp.: 771
Paper Products Mfr
N.A.I.C.S.: 322299
Michael Lindemann *(Gen Mgr)*

Stora Enso Pulp (2)
Gavlegatan 1, PO Box 34, 814 81,
Skutskar, Sweden **(100%)**
Tel.: (46) 104685000
Sales Range: $25-49.9 Million
Emp.: 420
Mfr & Marketing of Paper & Fluff Pulp
N.A.I.C.S.: 322120
Henrik Holm *(VP)*

Stora Enso Research (2)
Sodra Mariegatan 18, S 791 80, Falun,
Sweden **(100%)**
Tel.: (46) 23788100
Sales Range: $25-49.9 Million
Emp.: 55
Renewable Materials Business
N.A.I.C.S.: 113110

Stora Enso Skoghall AB (2)
Bruksgatan, PO Box 501, 663 30, Skoghall,
Sweden
Tel.: (46) 1046 500 00
Web Site: http://www.storaenso.com
Emp.: 700
Packaging Carton Board Mfr
N.A.I.C.S.: 322130

Stora Enso Timber AB (2)
Svardsjogatan 8, 791 80, Falun, Sweden
Tel.: (46) 104680000
Sales Range: $125-149.9 Million
Timber Products Distr
N.A.I.C.S.: 423990
Gorgan Ormanson *(Sr VP)*

Stora Enso Amsterdam B.V. (1)
Arena Blvd 83, PO Box 12386, Amsterdam,
1101 DM, Netherlands **(100%)**
Tel.: (31) 206505555
Web Site: https://www.storaenso.com
Sales Range: $25-49.9 Million
Emp.: 13
Marketing of Paper & Paperboard
N.A.I.C.S.: 424130

Stora Enso Argentina S.A. (1)
Alicia Moreau de Justo 1848-1st Floor Office 27, C1107AFJ, Buenos Aires, Argentina
Tel.: (54) 11 4313 0330
Web Site: http://www.storaenso.com
Paper Product Distr
N.A.I.C.S.: 424130

Stora Enso Austria GmbH (1)
Mooslackengasse 17, 2290, Vienna, Austria
Tel.: (43) 154655
Sales Range: $50-74.9 Million
Emp.: 6
Paper Product Distr

N.A.I.C.S.: 424130
Henrik Stjernvall *(Mng Dir)*

Subsidiary (Domestic):

Stora Enso Lumber Trading GmbH (2)
Mooslackengasse 17, 1190, Vienna, Austria
Tel.: (43) 154655
Sales Range: $25-49.9 Million
Emp.: 6
Timber Products Sales
N.A.I.C.S.: 113110

Stora Enso Base Industries Group (1)
Havurinne 3, 55800, Imatra,
Finland **(100%)**
Tel.: (358) 2046131
Sales Range: $25-49.9 Million
Emp.: 13
Renewable Solutions in Packaging, Biomaterials, Wood & Paper
N.A.I.C.S.: 321999
Ari Johansson *(Gen Mgr)*

Subsidiary (Domestic):

Enocell Oy (2)
PO Box 2, 81281, Uimaharju,
Finland **(100%)**
Tel.: (358) 2046122
Web Site: http://www.storaenso.com
Emp.: 258
Sulphate Pulp Mill
N.A.I.C.S.: 322120

Ladenso Oy (2)
PO Box 309, FIN 00101, Helsinki, Finland
Tel.: (358) 204623155
N.A.I.C.S.: 113110

Division (Domestic):

Stora Enso Forest (2)
Tainiontehtaantie 25, 55800, Imatra,
Finland **(100%)**
Tel.: (358) 2046121
Web Site: http://www.storaenso.com
Sales Range: $25-49.9 Million
Emp.: 820
Forestry Management; Logging; Supplies
Raw Wood For Enso-Gutzeit's Mills, Factories & Sawmills
N.A.I.C.S.: 115310

Stora Enso Belgium NV (1)
Rue de Genval 20, Bierges, 1301, Wavre,
Belgium
Tel.: (32) 28886420
Sales Range: $150-199.9 Million
Emp.: 500
Paper Product Distr
N.A.I.C.S.: 424130
Erkki Majorin *(Mng Dir)*

Subsidiary (Domestic):

Lumipaper N.V. (2)
Haven 1204, Kallo, 9130, Belgium
Tel.: (32) 35750606
Sales Range: $50-74.9 Million
Emp.: 115
Printing Paper Products Mfr
N.A.I.C.S.: 322299
Pekka Korhonen *(Mgr-Mill)*

S.A. Comptoir Finlandais N.V. (2)
Ave des Gaulois 7, 1040, Brussels, Belgium
Tel.: (32) 27341360
Marketing of Paper, Paperboard & Lumber
N.A.I.C.S.: 424130

Stora Enso Brasil Ltda (1)
Av Pres Jucelino Kubitschek 1400, 01421-001, Sao Paulo, Brazil
Tel.: (55) 1130655200
Web Site: https://www.storaenso.com
Emp.: 60
Paper Product Distr
N.A.I.C.S.: 424130

Subsidiary (Domestic):

SAMAB Cia. Industria e Comercio de Papel (2)
Rua Epicaba 90/222/260 Parque Fongaro,
Sao Paulo, SP, Brazil
Tel.: (55) 11 3670 0800
Web Site: http://www.samab.com.br
Marketing of Paper & Paperboard Products

N.A.I.C.S.: 424130

Stora Enso Deutschland GmbH (1)
Srankem strasse 35, 20097, Hamburg,
Germany **(100%)**
Tel.: (49) 2115810
Web Site: http://www.storaenso.com
Marketing of Paper & Paperboard
N.A.I.C.S.: 424130

Subsidiary (Domestic):

Altpapier Verw Wattenschied GmbH (2)
Coloniastrasse 13, 44892, Bochum, Germany
Tel.: (49) 234 92090
Paper Products Mfr
N.A.I.C.S.: 322299

FPB Holding GmbH & Co. KG (2)
Krefelder Str 560, Monchengladbach,
41066, Germany
Tel.: (49) 2161 60 96 314
Web Site: http://www.storaenso.com
Paper Products Mfr
N.A.I.C.S.: 322299

Stora Enso Kabel GmbH & Co. KG (2)
Schwerter Str 263, 58099, Hagen, Germany
Tel.: (49) 2331 6990
Web Site: http://www.storaenso.com
Emp.: 60
Pulp Product Mfr
N.A.I.C.S.: 322110

Stora Enso Kabel Verwaltungs Gmbh (2)
Schwerter Strasse 263, 58099, Hagen, Germany
Tel.: (49) 2331 699 0
Magazine Paper Mfr
N.A.I.C.S.: 322120

Stora Enso Logistics GmbH (2)
Moskauer Strasse 27, Dusseldorf, 14237,
Germany
Tel.: (49) 211 581 04
Web Site: http://www.storaenso.com
Logistics Consulting Servies
N.A.I.C.S.: 541614

Stora Enso Magazine Paper (2)
Moskauer Strasse 27, 40227, Dusseldorf,
Germany **(100%)**
Tel.: (49) 21158101
Sales Range: $25-49.9 Million
Emp.: 220
N.A.I.C.S.: 113110
Jouko A. Karvinen *(CEO)*

Stora Enso Maxau GmbH (2)
Mitscherlichstrasse, 76187, Karlsruhe, Germany
Tel.: (49) 721 9566 0
Sales Range: $200-249.9 Million
Emp.: 64
Magazine Paper Mfr
N.A.I.C.S.: 322120
Joachim Grunewald *(Mgr-Mill)*

Stora Enso Newsprint Sachsen Mill (2)
Am Schanzberg 1, 4838, Eilenburg,
Germany **(100%)**
Tel.: (49) 34236500
Sales Range: $75-99.9 Million
Emp.: 320
N.A.I.C.S.: 113110

Stora Enso Publication Paper (2)
Grafenberger Allee 293, PO Box 101014,
40227, Dusseldorf, Germany **(100%)**
Tel.: (49) 211581200
Web Site: http://www.stora.com
Sales Range: $75-99.9 Million
Emp.: 300
N.A.I.C.S.: 113110

Stora Enso Sachsen GmbH (2)
Am Schanzberg 1, 04838, Eilenburg, Germany
Tel.: (49) 3423 650 0
Web Site: http://www.storaenso.com
Sales Range: $100-124.9 Million
Printing Paper Mfr
N.A.I.C.S.: 322120

Stora Enso Timber (Deutschland) (2)

STORA ENSO OYJ

Stora Enso Oyj—(Continued)

Max-Breiherr-Strasse 20, 84347, Pfarrkirchen, Germany **(100%)**
Tel.: (49) 856130050
Web Site: http://www.storaenso.com
Sales Range: $25-49.9 Million
Emp.: 96
Marketing of Lumber, Plywood & Paper
N.A.I.C.S.: 423310

Stora Enso Transport GmbH (2)
Posener Str 30, 23554, Lubeck, Germany **(100%)**
Tel.: (49) 451470060
Web Site: http://www.storaenso.com
Sales Range: $25-49.9 Million
Emp.: 30
Port Terminal
N.A.I.C.S.: 488310

Stora Enso Eesti AS (1)
Liivalaia 13, 10118, Tallinn, Estonia
Tel.: (372) 7140050
Sales Range: $25-49.9 Million
Emp.: 20
Forest Management Services
N.A.I.C.S.: 115310
Marakaa Kasa *(Gen Mgr)*

Subsidiary (Domestic):

Puumerkki AS (2)
Sinikivi Tee 2, 75306, Harjumaa, Estonia
Tel.: (372) 6646960
Sales Range: $25-49.9 Million
Emp.: 14
Wood Product Distr
N.A.I.C.S.: 423310

Subsidiary (Non-US):

Stora Enso Latvia A/S (2)
Tiraines Iela 5, Riga, 1058, Latvia **(100%)**
Tel.: (371) 67670077
Web Site: http://www.storaenso.com
Sales Range: $25-49.9 Million
Mfr of Paper Products
N.A.I.C.S.: 322120

UAB Stora Enso Lietuva (2)
Naujoji str 134, 62175, Alytus, Lithuania
Tel.: (370) 31556910
Web Site: https://www.storaenso.com
Emp.: 264
Packaging Paper Products Mfr
N.A.I.C.S.: 322220

Subsidiary (Domestic):

UAB Puumerkki (3)
Geliu g 2B Avizieniai, Vilnius, 11419, Lithuania
Tel.: (370) 52403952
Web Site: http://www.Puumerkki.lt
Sales Range: $50-74.9 Million
Emp.: 7
Building Materials Distr
N.A.I.C.S.: 423310
Raivo Olgo *(Gen Mgr)*

Stora Enso Espana S.A.U. (1)
quintanavides 17 3 Fl, 28050, Madrid, Spain **(100%)**
Tel.: (34) 915674400
Web Site: https://www.storaenso.com
Sales Range: $25-49.9 Million
Emp.: 20
Paper & Paperboard, Plywood & Lumber Distr
N.A.I.C.S.: 424130

Subsidiary (Domestic):

Stora Enso Grafic S.A.U. (2)
Parque Empresarial Via Norte Quintanavides 17 Edificio 3-Planta, 3a - Modulo E, 28050, Madrid, Spain
Tel.: (34) 91 567 44 00
Sales Range: $25-49.9 Million
Emp.: 20
Paper Products Mfr
N.A.I.C.S.: 322299
Edwardo Poledo *(Gen Mgr)*

Stora Enso France SAS (1)
15 25 Blvd de l'Amiral Bruix, F 75782, Paris, France **(100%)**
Tel.: (33) 153647900
Sales Range: $25-49.9 Million
Emp.: 100
Sales & Marketing, Timber Pulp, Chemicals
N.A.I.C.S.: 424130

Subsidiary (Domestic):

Stora Enso Corbehem SAS (2)
Rue de Brebieres, Corbehem, 62112, France
Tel.: (33) 327923200
Web Site: https://www.storaenso.com
Sales Range: $125-149.9 Million
Magazine Paper Products Mfr
N.A.I.C.S.: 322122

Stora Enso Holdings UK Ltd (1)
1 Kingfisher House New Mill Rd, Orpington, BR5 3QJ, Kent, United Kingdom
Tel.: (44) 1689836911
Holding Company
N.A.I.C.S.: 551112

Subsidiary (Domestic):

Lumipaper Ltd (2)
Norwich Rd, Stowmarket, IP14 5ND, United Kingdom
Tel.: (44) 1449767173
Web Site: https://www.storaenso.com
Emp.: 6
Paper Product Distr
N.A.I.C.S.: 424130

Stora Enso International Ltd. (2)
West Wing, 1 Sheldon Sq, London, W2 6TT, United Kingdom **(100%)**
Tel.: (44) 2071210880
Holding Company
N.A.I.C.S.: 551112
Jouko A. Karvinen *(CEO)*

Stora Enso Timber UK Ltd (2)
1 Kingfisher House New Mill Road, Orpington, BR5 3QG, Kent, United Kingdom
Tel.: (44) 1689 883220
Emp.: 15
Timber Products Distr
N.A.I.C.S.: 423990

Stora Enso UK Ltd. (2)
Stora Enso House New Mill Road, Orpington, BR5 3QA, Kent, United Kingdom **(100%)**
Tel.: (44) 1689836911
Web Site: https://www.storaenso.com
Marketing of Newsprint
N.A.I.C.S.: 424110

Stora Enso Hungary Kft (1)
M1 Uzleti Park B Epulet, 2071, Paty, Hungary **(100%)**
Tel.: (36) 23 555 600
Sales Range: $1-9.9 Million
Emp.: 9
Paper Sales
N.A.I.C.S.: 322299
Peter Racz *(Mgr-Sls)*

Stora Enso Ingerois Oy (1)
Inkeroisten Kartonkitehdas, 46900, Kouvola, Finland
Tel.: (358) 2046117
Sales Range: $50-74.9 Million
Emp.: 25
Coated Folding Board Mfr
N.A.I.C.S.: 322130
Ari Johansson *(Gen Mgr)*

Stora Enso Italia Srl (2)
Via Cadorna 67, Vimodrone, Milan, Italy
Tel.: (39) 0225037033
Web Site: https://www.storaenso.com
Paper Product Distr
N.A.I.C.S.: 424130

Stora Enso Japan K.K. (1)
3-2-11 Kudankita Chiyoda-ku, Tokyo, 102-0073, Japan **(100%)**
Tel.: (81) 332395211
Sales Range: $25-49.9 Million
Emp.: 12
Marketing of Paper & Plywood
N.A.I.C.S.: 423310
Tuomo Kuuppo *(Pres)*

Stora Enso Korea Co., Ltd. (1)
11F Haesung 2 Building 942 10 Daechi dong, Kangnam ku, Seoul, 135 283, Korea (South)
Tel.: (82) 234532323
Web Site: http://www.storaenso.com
Sales Range: $50-74.9 Million
Emp.: 7
Marketing of Paper, Paperboard & Plywood
N.A.I.C.S.: 424130

Stora Enso Langerbrugge N.V. (1)
Wondelgemkaai 200, 9000, Gent, Belgium
Tel.: (32) 92577211
Sales Range: $125-149.9 Million
Emp.: 377
Magazine Paper Products Mfr
N.A.I.C.S.: 322122
Chris de Hollander *(Mgr-Mill)*

Stora Enso Mexico S.A. (1)
Montecity No 38 37 Floor Suite 32 Colonia Napoles, Delegacion Benito Juarez, Mexico, 03810, Mexico
Tel.: (52) 5590008530
Web Site: https://www.storaenso.com
Emp.: 3
Paper Product Distr
N.A.I.C.S.: 424130

Stora Enso Middle East JLT (1)
Dubai Media City Bldg No 9 Office 46 47, PO Box 502165, Dubai, United Arab Emirates **(100%)**
Tel.: (971) 43904994
Web Site: http://www.storaenso.com
Sales Range: $50-74.9 Million
Emp.: 7
Paper, Packaging & Wood Product Mfr
N.A.I.C.S.: 322120

Subsidiary (Non-US):

Fouad & Toufic Fadel & Co. (2)
St Joseph s street T Fadel Bldg no 11 1st Floor Bauchrieh, PO Box 90-444, Jdeideh, Beirut, Jdeideh, Lebanon
Tel.: (961) 1248000
Web Site: http://www.fadelgroup.com
Marketing of Lumber, Paper & Paper Products
N.A.I.C.S.: 423310

Stora Enso North America (1)
Cantenbury Green 201 Broad St, Stamford, CT 06901
Tel.: (203) 541-5100
Web Site: http://www.storaenso.com
Sales Range: $25-49.9 Million
Emp.: 25
Specialty Paper Mfr
N.A.I.C.S.: 322220

Subsidiary (Domestic):

Enso International, Inc. (2)
281 Tresser Blvd 15th Fl, Stamford, CT 06901-3284
Tel.: (203) 978-1755
Marketing of Paper & Paperboard
N.A.I.C.S.: 424130

Stora Enso Oulu Holding Oy (1)
Oulu Mill Paperitehtaantie 1/ Nuottasaarentie 17, PO Box 196, 90101, Oulu, Finland
Tel.: (358) 204 6124
Emp.: 400
Pulp Mfr
N.A.I.C.S.: 322110

Stora Enso Packagent Oy (1)
Kanavaranta 1, 00160, Helsinki, Finland
Tel.: (358) 2046131
Sales Range: $125-149.9 Million
Emp.: 500
Packaging Paper Products Mfr
N.A.I.C.S.: 322220
Jouko A. Karvinen *(CEO)*

Stora Enso Packaging Boards Group (1)
Hennalankatu 270, 15701, Lahti, Finland **(100%)**
Tel.: (358) 2046118
Web Site: http://www.storaenso.com
Emp.: 312
N.A.I.C.S.: 113110

Subsidiary (Domestic):

Stora Enso Packaging Oy (2)
Hennalankatu 270, 15701, Lahti, Finland **(100%)**
Tel.: (358) 2046118
Web Site: https://www.storaenso.com
Sales Range: $100-124.9 Million
Emp.: 342
Corrugated Board Mfr
N.A.I.C.S.: 322130

INTERNATIONAL PUBLIC

Plant (Domestic):

Stora Enso Packaging - Lahti Mill (3)
Hennalankatu 270, 15701, Lahti, Finland
Tel.: (358) 2046118
Web Site: http://www.storaenso.com
Corrugated Board Mill; Carton Factory
N.A.I.C.S.: 322130

Division (Domestic):

Consumer Packages (4)
Pentti Hallenkatu, Imatra, 55800, Finland **(100%)**
Tel.: (358) 2046121
Sales Range: $250-299.9 Million
N.A.I.C.S.: 113110

Imatra Paperboards (4)
Pentti Hallen Street 7, 55800, Imatra, Finland
Tel.: (358) 204 6121
Web Site: https://www.storaenso.com
Sales Range: $25-49.9 Million
Emp.: 100
N.A.I.C.S.: 113110
Ari Johansson *(Mng Dir)*

Subsidiary (Non-US):

Stora Enso Packaging AB (3)
Klockarehemsvagen 6, Box 1055, 556 33, Jonkoping, Sweden
Tel.: (46) 104636000
Emp.: 200
Packaging Corrugated Board Mfr
N.A.I.C.S.: 322212
Tomas Rosenskold *(Mgr-Sls-Pkg Board)*

Stora Enso Packaging AS (3)
Piirimae 10 Tanassilma Tehnopark, Saku vald, Harjumaa, 76401, Estonia
Tel.: (372) 655 8960
Web Site: http://www.storaensopack.ee
Sales Range: $25-49.9 Million
Corrugated Board Mfr
N.A.I.C.S.: 322130

Stora Enso Packaging Kft (3)
M1 Business Park Building A, 2071, Paty, Hungary
Tel.: (36) 23 555 600
Sales Range: $50-74.9 Million
Emp.: 15
Printed Corrugated Board Mfr
N.A.I.C.S.: 322130
Horvath Zsolt *(VP)*

Stora Enso Packaging SIA (3)
5 Tiraines Iela, 1058, Riga, Latvia
Tel.: (371) 67670077
Sales Range: $50-74.9 Million
Emp.: 13
Corrugated Board Mfr
N.A.I.C.S.: 322130
Aiga Zemribo *(Dir-Baltic)*

Stora Enso Polska S.A. (1)
Aleja Wojska Polskiego 21, 07-401, Ostroleka, Poland **(100%)**
Tel.: (48) 297640200
Web Site: http://www.storaenso.com
Pulp & Paper Mills; Corrugating Packaging
N.A.I.C.S.: 322110

Subsidiary (Domestic):

Scantrans Sp. z.o.o (2)
Ul Warecka 7, 91-202, Lodz, Poland
Tel.: (48) 42 652 98 78
Sales Range: $25-49.9 Million
Emp.: 3
Transportation Services
N.A.I.C.S.: 488999

Stora Enso Narew Sp. z.o.o (2)
Ul I Armii Wojska Polskiego 21, 07-401, Ostroleka, Poland
Tel.: (48) 297640100
Packaging Paper Products Mfr
N.A.I.C.S.: 322220

Stora Enso Praha s.r.o. (1)
U Uranie 18, PO Box 7, 170 00, Prague, Czech Republic **(100%)**
Tel.: (420) 281080555
Web Site: https://www.storaenso.com
Sales Range: $75-99.9 Million
Emp.: 6
N.A.I.C.S.: 113110

AND PRIVATE COMPANIES

Subsidiary (Domestic):

Stora Enso WP HV s.r.o. (2)
Nadrazni 66, 582 63, Zdirec, Czech Republic
Tel.: (420) 569776611
Emp.: 100
Wood Products Mfr
N.A.I.C.S.: 321999
Pavel Urban *(Mgr-Mill & KVH)*

Stora Enso Publication Paper Oy Ltd. (1)
Kanavaranta 1, PO Box 309, 100, Helsinki, Finland **(100%)**
Tel.: (358) 20 46 131
Sales Range: $25-49.9 Million
Paper, Wood & Packaging Products Mfr
N.A.I.C.S.: 333243

Subsidiary (Domestic):

Laminating Papers Ltd. (1)
PO Box 62 63, FIN 48101, Kotka, Finland **(100%)**
Tel.: (358) 2046112
Web Site: http://www.storaenso.com
Sales Range: $50-74.9 Million
Laminating Papers
N.A.I.C.S.: 322220

Plant (Domestic):

Stora Enso Publication Paper Oy Ltd. - Veitsiluoto Mill (2)
Veitsiluoto Mill Pl 244, 94101, Kemi, Finland
Tel.: (358) 2046125
N.A.I.C.S.: 113110

Stora Enso South East Asia Pte Ltd (1)
438 Alexandra Road 04-03 Alexandra Point, Singapore, 119958, Singapore
Tel.: (65) 62136900
Web Site: https://www.storaenso.com
Sales Range: $25-49.9 Million
Emp.: 2
Paper Product Distr
N.A.I.C.S.: 424130

Subsidiary (Non-US):

Stora Enso Laos Co. Ltd (2)
46 Kaysone Phomvihane Avenue, Ban Phonesaat, Vientiane, Lao People's Democratic Republic
Tel.: (856) 21 451841 2
Sales Range: $25-49.9 Million
Forest Management Services
N.A.I.C.S.: 115310

Subsidiary (Domestic):

Stora Enso Singapore (2)
438 Alexandra Rd 04-03 Alexandra Point, Singapore, 119958, Singapore
Tel.: (65) 62136900
Web Site: http://www.storaenso.com
Sales Range: $25-49.9 Million
Marketing of Paper & Paperboard
N.A.I.C.S.: 424130

Branch (Non-US):

Stora Enso Singapore Pte Ltd.- Malaysian Office (3)
Block 154 2 11 Kompleks Maluri, Jalan Jejaka Taman Maluri, Kuala Lumpur, 55100, Malaysia **(100%)**
Tel.: (60) 392818122
Sales Range: $25-49.9 Million
Emp.: 8
N.A.I.C.S.: 113110

Subsidiary (Non-US):

Stora Enso South East Asia (2)
Wisma 46 Kota BNI 43 Floor Jendal, Sudirman Kav 1, Jakarta, 10220, Indonesia **(100%)**
Tel.: (62) 215748935
Web Site: http://www.storaenso.com
Marketing of Paper, Paperboard & Pulp
N.A.I.C.S.: 424130

Stora Enso Southern Africa Ltd. (1)
1st Floor Divot House, PO Box 12900, 7463, Cape Town, South Africa **(100%)**
Tel.: (27) 215950942
Web Site: https://www.storaenso.com

Sales Range: $25-49.9 Million
Emp.: 80
N.A.I.C.S.: 113110

Stora Enso Wood Products Oy Ltd (1)
Lintulahdenkuja 10, Helsinki, 500, Finland
Tel.: (358) 2046 114
Wood Building Mfr
N.A.I.C.S.: 321992

Subsidiary (Domestic):

Eridomic Oy (2)
Yrittajantie 7, 36600, Palkane, Finland
Tel.: (358) 3 534 1129
Web Site: http://www.eridomic.fi
Sales Range: $25-49.9 Million
Emp.: 3
Wooden Building Products Mfr
N.A.I.C.S.: 321999

Subsidiary (Non-US):

OOO Setles (2)
Sortavalskoe Shosse 70 Pitkaranta Area, 186801, Impilakhti, Russia
Tel.: (7) 8143326241
Web Site: http://www.storaenso.com
Wood Products Mfr
N.A.I.C.S.: 321999

Stora Enso Timber Japan K.K. (2)
Kouji-Machi Park Side Bldg 401 Kouji-Machi 4-7, Chiyoda-ku, Tokyo, 101-0083, Japan
Tel.: (81) 3 3239 5381
Sales Range: $25-49.9 Million
Emp.: 5
Timber Products Distr
N.A.I.C.S.: 423990
Masao Fukuchi *(Mgr-Sls)*

Stora Enso Timber d.o.o (2)
Vojkovo Nabrezje 32, 6000, Koper, Slovenia
Tel.: (386) 5631 4201
Emp.: 6
Timber Products Distr
N.A.I.C.S.: 423990
Ales Azman *(Gen Mgr)*

Stora Enso Wood Products GmbH (2)
Bahnhofstr 31, A-3370, Ybbs an der Donau, Austria
Tel.: (43) 502454400
Emp.: 450
Timber Products Distr
N.A.I.C.S.: 423990
Eduard Reutner *(Mgr-Ops)*

Subsidiary (Non-US):

Euro Timber Spol s.r.o. (3)
Bajkalska 31, 82105, Bratislava, Slovakia
Tel.: (421) 911356281
Timber Products Distr
N.A.I.C.S.: 423990

Stora Enso Timber Sp. z.o.o. (3)
Wolnosci 4, 46-030, Murow, Poland
Tel.: (48) 774 270 235
Web Site: http://www.storaenso.com
Sales Range: $25-49.9 Million
Emp.: 300
Timber Products Distr
N.A.I.C.S.: 423990

Subsidiary (Domestic):

Stora Enso WP Bad St Leonhard GmbH (3)
Wisperndorf 4, 9462, Bad Sankt Leonhard, Austria
Tel.: (43) 502453100
Sales Range: $125-149.9 Million
Emp.: 285
Wood Products Mfr
N.A.I.C.S.: 321113
Christian Scharf *(Mgr-Mill)*

Stora Enso WP Holzverarbetungs GmbH (3)
Industriestrasse 260, 2601, Sollenau, Austria
Tel.: (43) 2826 7001 0
Sales Range: $25-49.9 Million
Emp.: 100
Paper Product Distr
N.A.I.C.S.: 424130
Raener Schrenk *(Dir)*

Subsidiary (Non-US):

Stora Enso Wood products Zdirec s.r.o. (3)
Nadrazni 66, Zdirec nad Doubravou, 58263, Zdirec, Czech Republic
Tel.: (420) 569776611
Wood Product Distr
N.A.I.C.S.: 423990
Tomas Krcil *(Mgr-Mktg)*

Sunilan Puhdistamo Oy (1)
Sunilantie 1, Kotka, 48900, Finland
Tel.: (358) 52298111
Paper Product Distr
N.A.I.C.S.: 424130

ZAO Stora Enso (1)
1 Golutvinksy Per 3/1 6th Floor, PO Box 28, Moscow, 119180, Russia
Tel.: (7) 495 935 76 60
Sales Range: $25-49.9 Million
Emp.: 20
Paper Product Distr
N.A.I.C.S.: 424130

Subsidiary (Domestic):

OAO Olonetsles (2)
21 Ul Lenina, Olonets, 186000, Russia
Tel.: (7) 8127024343
Forest Management Services
N.A.I.C.S.: 115310

OOO Stora Enso Forest West (2)
37 Nab R Moiki, Saint Petersburg, 191186, Russia
Tel.: (7) 8127024343
Web Site: http://www.storaenso.com
Emp.: 10
Forest Management Services
N.A.I.C.S.: 115310

OOO Stora Enso Packaging KG (2)
Lermontov Str 2, Balabanovo, 249000, Kaluga, Russia
Tel.: (7) 48438 6 07 40
Web Site: http://www.storaenso.com
Packaging Paper Products Distr
N.A.I.C.S.: 424130

Predstavitelstvo firmy Enso (2)
Moika emb 37, Saint Petersburg, 191065, Russia
Tel.: (7) 8121024343
N.A.I.C.S.: 113110

STORAGE DROP
Eli Horovitz 19, Rehovot, 7608802, Israel
Tel.: (972) 774008515
Web Site: https://www.storagedrop.co.il
Year Founded: 2017
STRG—(TAE)
Assets: $162,453
Liabilities: $478,243
Net Worth: ($315,789)
Earnings: ($1,796,104)
Fiscal Year-end: 12/31/23
Renewable Energy Storage Services
N.A.I.C.S.: 541690
Gad Eisenkot *(Chm)*

STORAGEFLEX, INC.
15 West Pearce Street Unit 3, Richmond, L4B 1H6, ON, Canada
Tel.: (905) 475-1380
Web Site: http://www.storageflex.com
Year Founded: 1983
Sales Range: $25-49.9 Million
Emp.: 500
Data Storage Products
N.A.I.C.S.: 334610

STORAGEVAULT CANADA INC.
100 Canadian Rd, Scarborough, Toronto, M1R 4Z5, ON, Canada
Tel.: (416) 288-2402 AB
Web Site: https://storagevaultcanada.com
Year Founded: 2007

STORCK GMBH & CO.

OSV—(DEU)
Rev.—$218,021,729
Assets: $1,543,629,863
Liabilities: $1,395,721,690
Net Worth: $147,908,173
Earnings: ($1,283,823)
Emp.: 800
Fiscal Year-end: 12/31/23
Portable & Self Storage Rental Services
N.A.I.C.S.: 531130
Alan A. Simpson *(Co-Founder)*

Subsidiaries:

Sentinel Self-Storage Corporation (1)
#1970-10123-99 Street, Edmonton, T5J 3H1, AB, Canada **(100%)**
Tel.: (780) 424-8945
Web Site: http://www.sentinel.ca
Self-Service & Mini-Warehousing Services
N.A.I.C.S.: 493110
Shelley Bowes *(CFO)*

STORCK GMBH & CO.
Waldstrasse 27, Berlin, 13403, Germany
Tel.: (49) 304177303 De
Web Site: http://www.storck.com
Year Founded: 1903
Sales Range: $500-549.9 Million
Emp.: 6,000
Chocolates & Candy Mfr
N.A.I.C.S.: 311351
Axel Oberwelland *(Chm)*

Subsidiaries:

Merci Gmbh & Co KG (1)
Waldstrabe 27, Berlin, 13403, Germany **(100%)**
Tel.: (49) 304177301
Web Site: http://www.storck.com
Sales Range: $50-74.9 Million
Emp.: 120
Chocolates & Candy Mfr
N.A.I.C.S.: 311351

OOO Storck (1)
Letnikovskaya Street 2 House 2 Building 1 10 floor, 115114, Moscow, Russia **(100%)**
Tel.: (7) 4952321620
Web Site: http://www.storck.ru
Sales Range: $25-49.9 Million
Emp.: 18
Chocolates & Candy Mfr
N.A.I.C.S.: 311351

STORCK ADRIA D.O.O. (1)
Brdnikova ul 44, 1000, Ljubljana, Slovenia
Tel.: (386) 1 24437 50
Web Site: http://www.storck.si
Emp.: 18
Confectionary Product Mfr
N.A.I.C.S.: 311351
Michael Zink *(Dir)*

STORCK ASIA PACIFIC PTE LTD (1)
302 Orchard Road 18-01 Tong Building, Singapore, 238862, Singapore
Tel.: (65) 67 389488
Web Site: http://www.storck.sg
Emp.: 23
Confectionary Product Mfr
N.A.I.C.S.: 311351
Klaus Kaiser *(Mng Dir)*

STORCK B.V. (1)
Hogebrinkerweg 10, 3871 KN, Hoevelaken, Netherlands
Tel.: (31) 33 2541800
Web Site: http://www.storck.nl
Confectionary Product Mfr
N.A.I.C.S.: 311351
Michael Zink *(Co-Mng Dir)*

STORCK B.V.B.A. (1)
Berchemstadionstraat 76, PO Box 5, 2600, Antwerp, Belgium
Tel.: (32) 3 235 2288
Web Site: http://www.storck.be
Emp.: 12
Confectionary Product Mfr
N.A.I.C.S.: 311351

STORCK GMBH & CO.

Storck GmbH & Co.—(Continued)

STORCK CANADA INC. (1)
100 City Centre Dr, PO Box 2103, Mississauga, L5B 3C6, ON, Canada
Tel.: (905) 272-4480
Web Site: http://www.storck.ca
Emp.: 18
Confectionary Product Mfr
N.A.I.C.S.: 311351

STORCK CESKA REPUBLIKA, S.R.O. (1)
Meteor Office Park Sokolovska 100/94, 180 00, Prague, Czech Republic
Tel.: (420) 221 181 411
Web Site: http://www.storck.cz
Confectionery Product Mfr
N.A.I.C.S.: 311351
Michael Zink (Co-Mng Dir)

STORCK CROATIA D.O.O. (1)
Radnicka 34a, 10000, Zagreb, Croatia
Tel.: (385) 1 5634 880
Web Site: http://www.storck.com
Confectionery Product Mfr
N.A.I.C.S.: 311351

STORCK DANMARK A/S (1)
Hyllie Stationsvag 42, 215 32, Malmo, Sweden
Tel.: (46) 40 37 19 60
Web Site: http://www.storck.dk
Confectionery Product Mfr
N.A.I.C.S.: 311351
Magnus Franzen (Dir)

STORCK GES.M.B.H. (1)
Maxglaner Hauptstrasse 72, 5020, Salzburg, Austria
Tel.: (43) 662 82 7885 0
Web Site: http://www.storck.at
Confectionery Product Mfr
N.A.I.C.S.: 311351
Ronald Munster (Co-Mng Dir)

STORCK HUNGARIA KFT. (1)
Aradi u 8-10, 1062, Budapest, Hungary
Tel.: (36) 6 1 354 25 20
Web Site: http://www.storck.hu
Confectionery Product Mfr
N.A.I.C.S.: 311351
Janos Fabian (Co-Mng Dir)

STORCK IBERICA, S.L.U. (1)
Ctra Real 340 n 122 A 5 Planta, 08960, Sant Just Desvern, Spain
Tel.: (34) 93 470 05 82
Web Site: http://www.storck.es
Confectionery Product Mfr
N.A.I.C.S.: 311351
Michael Zink (Co-Mng Dir)

STORCK SP. Z O.O. (1)
ul Prosta 70, 00-838, Warsaw, Poland
Tel.: (48) 22 33 66 366
Web Site: http://www.storck.pl
Confectionery Product Mfr
N.A.I.C.S.: 311351
Iwona K. Piatkowska (Co-Mng Dir)

STORCK UK LTD. (1)
Matrix House Basing View, Basingstoke, RG21 4DZ, Hampshire, United Kingdom
Tel.: (44) 1256340300
Web Site: http://www.storck.co.uk
Emp.: 35
Confectionery Product Mfr
N.A.I.C.S.: 311351
Thomas Huber (Mng Dir)

Storck (Schweiz) GmbH (1)
Josefstrasse 84, 8005, Zurich, Switzerland (100%)
Tel.: (41) 442764545
Web Site: http://www.storck.ch
Sales Range: $25-49.9 Million
Emp.: 20
Chocolates & Candy Mfr
N.A.I.C.S.: 311351

Storck Middle East & Africa FZ-LLC (1)
Aurora Tower 14th Floor Office 1401 Media City, PO Box 502431, Dubai, United Arab Emirates
Tel.: (971) 44228393
Web Site: http://www.storck.ae
Chocolate Sugar Confectionery Product Mfr
N.A.I.C.S.: 311352
Mahmoud Zayed (Reg Mgr-Mktg)

Storck Sverige AB (1)
Hyllie Stationsvag 42, 215 32, Malmo, Sweden
Tel.: (46) 40371960
Web Site: http://www.storck.se
Chocolate Sugar Confectionery Product Mfr & Distr
N.A.I.C.S.: 311352
Daniel Hansson (Acct Mgr)

Storck Travel Retail Ltd (1)
Moorside Road Winnall, Winchester, SO23 7SA, Hampshire, United Kingdom (100%)
Tel.: (44) 1962 84 4800
Web Site: http://www.storck-travel-retail.com
Sales Range: $50-74.9 Million
Emp.: 100
Chocolates & Candy Supplier
N.A.I.C.S.: 424450
Paul Ridgway (Mng Dir)

Storck USA, L.P. (1)
325 N LaSalle Ste 400, Chicago, IL 60654 (100%)
Tel.: (312) 467-5700
Web Site: http://www.storck.com
Sales Range: $25-49.9 Million
Emp.: 50
Mfr & Distr of Candy Products
N.A.I.C.S.: 424450

STOREBRAND ASA

Professor Kohts vei 9, PO Box 500, NO-1327, Lysaker, Norway
Tel.: (47) 91508880 NO
Web Site: https://www.storebrand.no
STB—(OSL)
Year Founded: 1861
Rev.: $794,106,780
Assets: $82,850,544,984
Liabilities: $80,122,760,022
Net Worth: $2,727,784,962
Earnings: $311,934,232
Emp.: 2,308
Fiscal Year-end: 12/31/23
Financial Investment Services
N.A.I.C.S.: 551112
Lars Aa. Loddesol (CFO)

Subsidiaries:

Hadrian Eiendom AS (1)
Olav Vs Gate 1, 0161, Oslo, Norway
Tel.: (47) 2 201 4040
Web Site: https://www.hadrian.no
Sales Range: $50-74.9 Million
Emp.: 6
Commercial Property Development Services
N.A.I.C.S.: 531210

Norsk Pensjon AS (1)
Hansteens Gate 2, Oslo, 253, Norway
Tel.: (47) 90913004
Web Site: http://www.norskpensjon.no
Sales Range: $50-74.9 Million
Emp.: 2
Financial & Pension Services
N.A.I.C.S.: 524113

Oslo Reinsurance Company AS (1)
c/o Storebrand Skadeforsikring AS, PO Box 500, 1327, Lysaker, Norway
Tel.: (47) 22312828
Web Site: http://www.storebrand.no
Reinsurance Services
N.A.I.C.S.: 524130

Ring Eiendomsmegling AS (1)
Professor Kohts Vei 9, 1366, Lysaker, Norway
Tel.: (47) 22314200
Web Site: http://www.ringeiendom.no
Residential Property Development Services
N.A.I.C.S.: 531390

SPP Livforsakring AB (1)
Torsgatan 14, SE 105 39, Stockholm, Sweden
Tel.: (46) 84517000
Web Site: http://www.spp.se
Sales Range: $650-699.9 Million
Emp.: 590
Fire Insurance Services
N.A.I.C.S.: 524113
Bo Frogner (Chief Acctg Officer)

Subsidiary (Non-US):

Benco Insurance Holding BV (2)
Strawinskylaan 411, Amsterdam, North Holland, Netherlands
Tel.: (31) 205752727
General Insurance Services
N.A.I.C.S.: 524113

Subsidiary (Domestic):

SPP Fastigheter AB (2)
Vasagatan 10, 105 39, Stockholm, Sweden
Tel.: (46) 84517000
Web Site: http://www.storebrandfastigheter.se
Emp.: 100
Real Estate Investment Services
N.A.I.C.S.: 525990
Marita Loft (CEO)

Storebrand (1)
Tel.: (47) 2 231 5050
Web Site: https://www.storebrand.no
Insurance & Banking Services
N.A.I.C.S.: 524113
Kjetil R. Krokje (Head-Fin, Strategy & M&A)

Storebrand Bank ASA (1)
Proffeser Kohts Rd No 9 1366, PO Box 500, 0120, Lysaker, Norway
Tel.: (47) 22315050
Sales Range: $50-74.9 Million
Emp.: 153
Banking Services
N.A.I.C.S.: 522110

Subsidiary (Domestic):

Bjorndalen Panorama AS (2)
Professor Kohts Vei 9, 1366, Lysaker, Norway (100%)
Tel.: (47) 22315050
Sales Range: $50-74.9 Million
Residential Property Development Services
N.A.I.C.S.: 236116

Storebrand Eiendom AS (1)
Professor Kohts Vei 9, 1366, Lysaker, Akershus, Norway
Tel.: (47) 93480533
Sales Range: $50-74.9 Million
Emp.: 30
Commercial Banking Services
N.A.I.C.S.: 522110

Storebrand Eiendom Holding AS (1)
Professor Kohts Vei 9, 1366, Lysaker, Akershus, Norway
Tel.: (47) 22312105
Web Site: http://www.storebrand.no
Sales Range: $650-699.9 Million
Emp.: 700
Real Estate Property Holding Services
N.A.I.C.S.: 531210

Storebrand Finans AS (1)
Professor Kohts vei 9, PO Box 500, 1327, Lysaker, Norway (100%)
Tel.: (47) 22315050
Web Site: http://www.storebrand.com
Sales Range: $300-349.9 Million
Emp.: 1,600
Financial Services
N.A.I.C.S.: 561499

Storebrand Fonder AB (1)
Vasagatan 10, 105 39, Stockholm, Sweden
Tel.: (46) 86142450
Web Site: https://www.storebrandfonder.se
Sales Range: $50-74.9 Million
Emp.: 13
Fund Management Services
N.A.I.C.S.: 524292

Storebrand Helseforsikring AS (1)
Havedkontr Filitstad Brygge 1, PO Box 1382, N 0114, Oslo, Vica, Norway (50%)
Tel.: (47) 22311330
Web Site: http://www.storebrandhelse.no
Sales Range: $50-74.9 Million
Emp.: 60
Insurance Services
N.A.I.C.S.: 524298

Storebrand I AS (1)
Filipstad Brygge 1, 0114, Oslo, Norway
Tel.: (47) 22315050
Fire Insurance Services
N.A.I.C.S.: 524113

INTERNATIONAL PUBLIC

Storebrand Kapitalforvaltning (1)
Vasagatan 10, PO Box 5541, Stockholm, 10539, Sweden (100%)
Tel.: (46) 86142400
Web Site: http://www.storebrand.se
Sales Range: $50-74.9 Million
Emp.: 10
Investment Services
N.A.I.C.S.: 523940

Storebrand Leieforvaltning AS (1)
Po Box 500, 1327, Lysaker, Norway
Tel.: (47) 22315050
Portfolio Management Services
N.A.I.C.S.: 523940
Hans Aasnaes (Mng Dir)

Storebrand Livsforsikring AS (1)
Professor Kohts Vei 9, 1366, Lysaker, Akershus, Norway
Tel.: (47) 22315050
Web Site: http://www.storebrand.com
Emp.: 2,000
Fire Insurance Services
N.A.I.C.S.: 524113
Geir Holmgren (Mng Dir)

Subsidiary (Domestic):

Danica Pensjonsforsikring AS (2)
Nordregt 12, 7011, Trondheim, Norway
Tel.: (47) 7 356 3200
Web Site: https://www.danica.no
Sales Range: $50-74.9 Million
Emp.: 120
Investment Management Service
N.A.I.C.S.: 523999

Ullensaker Boligbyggelag AS (1)
Solvangtun 55, 2040, Klofta, Norway
Tel.: (47) 63980595
Web Site: http://www.ubbl.no
Residential Property Development Services
N.A.I.C.S.: 236115

STORM CAPITAL MANAGEMENT LTD.

Berger House 36-38 Berkeley Square, London, W1J 5AE, United Kingdom
Tel.: (44) 2074093378
Web Site: http://www.stormcapital.co.uk
Year Founded: 2006
Rev.: $175,043,700
Emp.: 15
Investment & Portfolio Management Services
N.A.I.C.S.: 523999
Morten E. Astrup (Partner)

STORM EXPLORATION INC

Suite 1480 885 West Georgia Street, Vancouver, V6C 3E8, BC, Canada
Tel.: (604) 506-2804
Web Site: https://stormex.ca
CWVWF—(OTCIQ)
Assets: $339,054
Liabilities: $213,957
Net Worth: $125,097
Earnings: ($2,742,438)
Fiscal Year-end: 03/31/23
Mineral Exploration Services
N.A.I.C.S.: 212390
Bruce Counts (Pres & CEO)

STORM RESOURCES LTD.

Suite 600 215-2 Street SW, Calgary, T2P 1M4, AB, Canada
Tel.: (403) 817-6145 AB
Web Site: http://www.stormresourcesltd.com
Year Founded: 2010
SRMLF—(TSX)
Rev.: $122,049,761
Assets: $493,047,616
Liabilities: $161,724,656
Net Worth: $331,322,960
Earnings: ($167,408)
Emp.: 28
Fiscal Year-end: 12/31/20
Oil & Gas Exploration Services

AND PRIVATE COMPANIES

STORSKOGEN GROUP AB

N.A.I.C.S.: 211120
Brian Lavergne *(Pres & CEO)*

STORMTECH PERFORMANCE APPAREL LTD.
2550 Boundary Road, Burnaby, V5M 3Z3, BC, Canada
Tel.: (604) 454-1492
Web Site: https://www.stormtech.ca
Year Founded: 1977
Sales Range: $25-49.9 Million
Technical Outdoor Apparel Mfr
N.A.I.C.S.: 315990

STORNOWAY DIAMOND CORPORATION
1111 St-Charles Ouest Tour Ouest Suite 400, Longueuil, J4K 5G4, QC, Canada
Tel.: (450) 616-5555 BC
Web Site: https://www.stornowaydiamond.com
Year Founded: 1986
SWY—(OTCIQ)
Sales Range: Less than $1 Million
Emp.: 586
Diamond & Mineral Property Acquisition, Exploration & Development for Mining Operations
N.A.I.C.S.: 213115
Patrick Sevigny *(COO)*

STORSKOGEN GROUP AB
Hovslagargatan 3 6fl, 11148, Stockholm, Sweden
Tel.: (46) 739209400
Web Site: http://www.storskogen.com
Year Founded: 2012
Rev.: $1,090,540,640
Assets: $1,465,204,160
Liabilities: $822,819,200
Net Worth: $642,384,960
Earnings: $70,073,920
Emp.: 3,565
Fiscal Year-end: 12/31/20
Holding Company
N.A.I.C.S.: 551112
Daniel Kaplan *(Co-Founder & CEO)*

Subsidiaries:

2M2 Group AB (1)
Kopmansgatan 23, 269 33, Bastad, Sweden
Tel.: (46) 43170580
Web Site: https://www.2m2.se
Home Decorative Product Distr
N.A.I.C.S.: 423220

A Lot Decoration Sweden AB (1)
Sodermannagatan 2, 521 36, Falkoping, Sweden
Tel.: (46) 515711100
Web Site: https://www.alot.se
Home Decorative Product Retailer
N.A.I.C.S.: 449129

A&K Die Frische Kuche GmbH (1)
Blitzkuhlenstr 152, 45659, Recklinghausen, Germany
Tel.: (49) 23619605400
Web Site: https://www.die-frische-kueche.de
Veal Product Mfr
N.A.I.C.S.: 311999

AGIO System och Kompetens i Skandinavien AB (1)
Vastra Varvsgatan 3 Plan 3A, 972 36, Lulea, Sweden
Tel.: (46) 920225114
Web Site: https://agio.se
Computer Support Services
N.A.I.C.S.: 541511

ARAT AB (1)
Olvagen 4, 342 50, Vislanda, Sweden
Tel.: (46) 33272560
Web Site: https://arat.se
Wood Products Mfr
N.A.I.C.S.: 321999

Albin Components AB (1)
Hantverkargatan 3, 681 42, Kristinehamn, Sweden
Tel.: (46) 550410500
Web Site: https://albincomponents.se
Gear Mfr & Distr
N.A.I.C.S.: 333612

Alfta Kvalitetsindustri AB (1)
Vastra Osavagen 24E, 822 40, Alfta, Sweden
Tel.: (46) 27158860
Web Site: https://www.alfta-kvalitetslego.se
Lathe Mfr
N.A.I.C.S.: 333243

Allan Eriksson Mark AB (1)
Fabriksgatan 26, 733 39, Sala, Sweden
Tel.: (46) 22414570
Web Site: https://aemark.se
Construction Contracting Services
N.A.I.C.S.: 236210

Baldacci AB (1)
August Barks Gata 1, 421 32, Vastra Frolunda, Sweden
Tel.: (46) 31476000
Web Site: https://baldacci.se
Hairdressing Product Whslr
N.A.I.C.S.: 424210

Bergendahls El Gruppen AB (1)
Omvagen 2H, 412 75, Gothenburg, Sweden
Tel.: (46) 317251200
Web Site: https://bergendahlsel.se
Eletric Power Generation Services
N.A.I.C.S.: 221116

Bombayworks AB (1)
Birger Jarlsgatan 32B, 114 29, Stockholm, Sweden
Tel.: (46) 841005940
Web Site: https://www.bombayworks.com
Computer Support Services
N.A.I.C.S.: 541511

Brandprojekting Sverige AB (1)
Sodra Metallvagen 2, Skovde, Sweden
Tel.: (46) 500424130
Web Site: https://brandprojektering.se
Business Consulting Services
N.A.I.C.S.: 541611

Brenderup Group AB (1)
Fosievagen 13, 213 41, Malmo, Sweden
Tel.: (46) 36 18 19 50
Web Site: http://www.brenderupgroup.com
Trailer Mfr & Distr
N.A.I.C.S.: 336212
Lotta Castell *(CEO & Mng Dir)*

Subsidiary (Non-US):

Brenderup A/S (2)
Sivmosevaenget 2C, 5260, Odense, S, Denmark (100%)
Tel.: (45) 63422200
Web Site: http://www.brenderup.dk
Travel Trailer Mfr & Whslr
N.A.I.C.S.: 336214
Susanne Knudsen *(Dir-Mktg)*

Budettan AB (1)
Hedentorpsvagen 5, 291 59, Kristianstad, Sweden
Tel.: (46) 44126400
Web Site: https://www.budettan.se
Transportation Services
N.A.I.C.S.: 488510

Christ & Wirth Haustechnik GmbH (1)
Spengler Allee 19, 04442, Zwenkau, Germany
Tel.: (49) 3420343340
Web Site: https://cuw-ht.de
Plumbing Contracting Services
N.A.I.C.S.: 238220

Cuben Utbildning AB (1)
Regnbagsgatan 7, 417 55, Gothenburg, Sweden
Tel.: (46) 313896200
Web Site: https://www.cubenutbildning.se
Educational Support Services
N.A.I.C.S.: 611710

Danmatic Automated Bakery Systems A/S (1)
Lundvej 16, Viborg, Denmark
Tel.: (45) 87259800
Web Site: https://www.danmatic.dk
Food Product Machinery Mfr & Distr
N.A.I.C.S.: 333241

Dansforum i Goteborg AB (1)
Frihamnen 16 A, 417 70, Gothenburg, Sweden
Tel.: (46) 317016680
Web Site: https://www.dansforum.se
Dance School Studio Services
N.A.I.C.S.: 611610

Delikatesskungen AB (1)
Heliosgatan 30, 120 61, Stockholm, Sweden
Tel.: (46) 87222233
Web Site: https://www.delikatesskungen.se
Confectionery Distr
N.A.I.C.S.: 424450

Dimbay GmbH (1)
Schmiedehof 16, 10965, Berlin, Germany
Tel.: (49) 30992119200
Web Site: https://www.dimabay.com
Marketing Services
N.A.I.C.S.: 541613

EVIAB Gruppen AB (1)
Gamla vagen 7B, 702 27, Orebro, Sweden
Tel.: (46) 19100500
Web Site: https://www.eviabgruppen.se
Building Automation System Installation Services
N.A.I.C.S.: 238210

El & Projektering Vetlanda AB (1)
Industrigatan 29, 574 38, Vetlanda, Sweden
Tel.: (46) 38317840
Web Site: https://www.el-projektering.se
Electrical Installation Services
N.A.I.C.S.: 238210

Elcommunication Sweden AB (1)
Strommvagen 3, 374 32, Karlshamn, Sweden
Tel.: (46) 454566300
Web Site: https://www.elcom.se
Electrical Contracting Services
N.A.I.C.S.: 238210

Elektroautomatik i Sverige AB (1)
Karrlyckegatan 20 B, 418 78, Gothenburg, Sweden
Tel.: (46) 317207300
Web Site: https://elektroautomatik.se
Automobile Parts Distr
N.A.I.C.S.: 423120

Extra UK Ltd. (1)
Domino House Morris Close, Park Farm Industrial Estate, Wellingborough, NN8 6XF, Northants, United Kingdom
Tel.: (44) 1933672170
Web Site: https://www.extrauk.co.uk
Cycling Products Distr
N.A.I.C.S.: 423910

Fon Anlegg AS (1)
Nordre Fokserod 24, Sandefjord, Norway
Tel.: (47) 95896000
Web Site: https://fon.no
Construction Contracting Services
N.A.I.C.S.: 238990

Frends AS (1)
Ringtunveien 4, Gralum, Norway
Tel.: (47) 69221599
Web Site: https://www.frends.no
Hairdressing Product Whslr
N.A.I.C.S.: 424210

Gullangets Mekaniska Verkstad AB (1)
Bjornavagen 78, 891 42, Ornskoldsvik, Sweden
Tel.: (46) 66082240
Web Site: https://www.gmek.se
Machine Tool Mfr & Distr
N.A.I.C.S.: 333517

HK Immobilien GmbH (1)
Hauptstrasse 11, 85579, Neubiberg, Germany
Tel.: (49) 8960060408
Web Site: https://huk-immobilien.com
Real Estate Services
N.A.I.C.S.: 531390

Harrysson Entreprenad Aktiebolag (1)
Ostra Promenaden 1, 694 31, Hallsberg, Sweden
Tel.: (46) 58216035
Web Site: https://www.heabent.se
Marine Construction Services
N.A.I.C.S.: 237990

Hedson Technologies AB (1)
Hammarv gen 4, 232 37, Arlov, Sweden
Tel.: (46) 40534200
Web Site: http://www.hedson.com
Automotive Products
N.A.I.C.S.: 336340
Magnus Bjornstrom *(CEO)*

Subsidiary (Non-US):

Hedson North America, Inc. (2)
466 Speers Rd 3rd floor, Oakville, L6K 3W9, ON, Canada
Tel.: (905) 339-2800
Automobile Product Distr
N.A.I.C.S.: 441330

Herkules Hebetechnik GmbH (2)
Falderbaumstrasse 34, Kassel, 34123, Germany
Tel.: (49) 561589070
Web Site: http://www.herkules.de
Pneumatic Lifts
N.A.I.C.S.: 423440

IRT North America, Inc. (2)
86 Guided Court Unit C, Toronto, M9V 4K6, ON, Canada
Tel.: (416) 744-8371
Web Site: http://www.hedson.com
Car Refinishing Equipment
N.A.I.C.S.: 333248

Hudikshus AB (1)
Kravellgatan 1, 824 55, Hudiksvall, Sweden
Tel.: (46) 65010008
Web Site: https://www.hudikhus.se
House Mfr
N.A.I.C.S.: 321991

IMS Maskinteknik AB (1)
Tillinge Nykvarn 2, 745 94, Enkoping, Sweden
Tel.: (46) 171442090
Web Site: https://www.imsmaskinteknik.se
Mailing Machine Mfr
N.A.I.C.S.: 333517

INBEGO AB (1)
Delary Mill 6, 343 95, Almhult, Sweden
Tel.: (46) 47633080
Web Site: https://inbego.se
Flooring Contracting Services
N.A.I.C.S.: 238330

IVEO AB (1)
Ostermalmgatan 87B, 114 59, Stockholm, Sweden
Tel.: (46) 735270731
Web Site: https://www.iveo.se
Software Development Services
N.A.I.C.S.: 541511

Imazo AB (1)
Gradgatan 1, 534 50, Vara, Sweden
Tel.: (46) 512270700
Web Site: https://imazo.se
Poultry Product Distr
N.A.I.C.S.: 424440

Innovative Logistics Umea AB (1)
Umea Port Magasin 11, 913 32, Holmsund, Sweden
Tel.: (46) 727321918
Web Site: https://ilogistics.se
Logistic Services
N.A.I.C.S.: 541614

Jacob Lindh AB (1)
Spanvagen 15B, 245 34, Staffanstorp, Sweden
Tel.: (46) 2610400
Web Site: https://jacoblindh.se
Building Construction Services
N.A.I.C.S.: 236210

Jata Cargo AB (1)
Olsgardsgatan 14, 215 79, Malmo, Sweden
Tel.: (46) 40552350
Web Site: https://www.jatacargo.se
Cargo Transportation Services
N.A.I.C.S.: 484110

Julian Bowen Ltd. (1)
Bentinck House Park Lane Business Park, Kirkby in Ashfield, NG17 9LE, United Kingdom

STORSKOGEN GROUP AB

Storskogen Group AB—(Continued)
Tel.: (44) 1623727374
Web Site: https://julian-bowen.co.uk
Furniture Product Distr
N.A.I.C.S.: 423210

Karriarkonsulten Sverige AB (1)
Turebergsvagen 5 3 TR, 191 47, Sollentuna, Sweden
Tel.: (46) 868428871
Web Site: https://www.karriarkonsulten.se
Recruitment Services
N.A.I.C.S.: 561311

L'anza EP Sweden AB (1)
Murmansgatan126, 212 25, Malmo, Sweden
Tel.: (46) 31476000
Web Site: https://www.lanza.se
Hair Salon Services
N.A.I.C.S.: 812112

Lan Assistans Sverige AB (1)
Malmgatan 5, 602 23, Norrkoping, Sweden
Tel.: (46) 114708400
Web Site: https://www.lanassistans.se
Information Technology Services
N.A.I.C.S.: 541511

Lindberg Stenberg Arkitekter AB (1)
Pustegrand 3, 118 20, Stockholm, Sweden
Tel.: (46) 84068700
Web Site: https://lindbergstenberg.se
Building Rental Services
N.A.I.C.S.: 531110

NetRed AB (1)
Norra Ringvagen 2A, 522 31, Tidaholm, Sweden
Tel.: (46) 50217770
Web Site: https://netred.se
Computer Support Services
N.A.I.C.S.: 541511

Newton Kompetensutveckling AB (1)
Malmvagen 1, 115 41, Stockholm, Sweden
Tel.: (46) 841045600
Web Site: https://www.newton.se
Educational Support Services
N.A.I.C.S.: 611710

Noa: s Snickeri i Tibro AB (1)
Fabriksgatan 2, 543 50, Tibro, Sweden
Tel.: (46) 504495100
Web Site: https://www.noassweden.se
Home Interior Product Mfr
N.A.I.C.S.: 332913

Nordic Wheel & Autosupply AB (1)
Vaxnasgatan 150, 653 43, Karlstad, Sweden
Tel.: (46) 54141600
Web Site: https://www.nordicwheels.se
Motor Vehicle Tire Distr
N.A.I.C.S.: 423130

Ornsberg El Tele & Data AB (1)
Olaus Magnus Vag 12, 141 40, Johanneshov, Sweden
Tel.: (46) 8999949
Web Site: https://www.ornsbergsel.se
Electrical Installation Services
N.A.I.C.S.: 238210

PR Home of Scandinavia AB (1)
Viaredsvagen 32, 504 64, Boras, Sweden
Tel.: (46) 33133349
Web Site: https://www.prhome.se
Lamp Light Retailer
N.A.I.C.S.: 335131

PV System AB (1)
Skaftgatan 1, 522 30, Tidaholm, Sweden
Tel.: (46) 50223500
Web Site: https://www.pvs.se
Machine Tool Mfr & Distr
N.A.I.C.S.: 333517

Pierre Entreprenad i Gavle AB (1)
Kungsladuvage 10, 802 67, Gavle, Sweden
Tel.: (46) 26544500
Web Site: https://www.pierre.se
Construction Contracting Services
N.A.I.C.S.: 236210

Plathuset i Malardalen AB (1)
Stenvretsgatan 1, 749 40, Enkoping, Sweden
Tel.: (46) 171440075
Web Site: https://plathuset.com
Construction Services
N.A.I.C.S.: 541330

Primulator AS (1)
Johan Scharffenbergsvei 95, Oslo, Norway
Tel.: (47) 23031760
Web Site: https://primulator.no
Food Processing Machinery Distr
N.A.I.C.S.: 423830

Roslagsgjuteriet AB (1)
Herrangsvagen 38, Herrang, 763 71, Stockholm, Sweden
Tel.: (46) 17515500
Web Site: https://www.roslagsgjut.se
Iron Product Mfr & Distr
N.A.I.C.S.: 331110

SF Tooling Group GmbH (1)
Goethestrasse 72, 89150, Laichingen, Germany
Tel.: (49) 733396080
Web Site: https://schaufler.de
Machine Tool Mfr & Distr
N.A.I.C.S.: 333517

Sag & Betongborrning i Uddevalla AB (1)
Graskarrsvagen 6, 451 55, Uddevalla, Sweden
Tel.: (46) 52234620
Web Site: https://www.sagobetongborrning.se
Floor & Wall Sawing Services
N.A.I.C.S.: 238910

Schalins Ringar AB (1)
Box 3036, 831 03, Ostersund, Sweden
Tel.: (46) 107771515
Web Site: https://schalins.com
Jewelry Mfr
N.A.I.C.S.: 339910

Smederna Sverige AB (1)
Skyttbrinksvagen 12, 147 39, Tumba, Sweden
Tel.: (46) 855645500
Web Site: https://smederna.se
Forging Product Mfr
N.A.I.C.S.: 332111

Specialfalgar i Kungsbacka Holding AB (1)
Borgasvagen 2, 434 39, Kungsbacka, Sweden
Tel.: (46) 30072900
Web Site: https://www.specialfalgar.se
Motor Vehicle Tire Distr
N.A.I.C.S.: 423130

Stal & Rormontage i Solvesborg AB (1)
Ysanevagen 390, 294 92, Solvesborg, Sweden
Tel.: (46) 45631205
Web Site: https://www.srmab.com
Structural Steel Mfr & Distr
N.A.I.C.S.: 332312

Stockholms Internationella Handelsskola AB (1)
Karlavagen 108, 115 26, Stockholm, Sweden
Tel.: (46) 8322212
Web Site: https://sih.se
Education Training Services
N.A.I.C.S.: 611710

Stop Start Transport Ltd. (1)
Unit 1A Berkeley Business Park Wainwright Road, Worcester, WR4 9FA, United Kingdom
Tel.: (44) 7885329393
Web Site: https://www.stop-start.co.uk
Logistic Services
N.A.I.C.S.: 541614

Strand i Jonkoping AB (1)
Kabelvagen 12, 553 02, Jonkoping, Sweden
Tel.: (46) 36184580
Web Site: https://www.strand-mark.se
Construction Contracting Services
N.A.I.C.S.: 236210

Svenska Grindmatriser AB (1)
Brigadgatan 16, 587 58, Linkoping, Sweden
Tel.: (46) 13364660
Web Site: https://www.sga.se
Semiconductor Mfr & Distr
N.A.I.C.S.: 334413

Swedwise AB (1)
Fack 517, Box 3037, 831 03, Ostersund, Sweden
Tel.: (46) 54136302
Web Site: https://swedwise.com
Software Development Services
N.A.I.C.S.: 541511

TRELLEGRAV AB (1)
Vannhogsgatan 5, 231 66, Trelleborg, Sweden
Tel.: (46) 41015680
Web Site: https://www.trellegrav.se
Machinery Rental Services
N.A.I.C.S.: 532490

Tepac Entreprenad AB (1)
Smedjegatan 6, 131 54, Nacka, Sweden
Tel.: (46) 87753076
Web Site: https://www.tepac.co
Plumbing Services
N.A.I.C.S.: 238220

Tornado Group Ltd. (1)
Bldg No 51 Aradah St Al Nahyan, PO Box 52069, Abu Dhabi, United Arab Emirates
Tel.: (971) 26664110
Web Site: https://www.tornado-group.com
Engineering Construction Services
N.A.I.C.S.: 541330

Tunga Lyft i Sverige AB (1)
Hammarvagen 17, 232 37, Arlov, Sweden
Tel.: (46) 104740340
Web Site: https://www.tungalyft.se
Escalator Installation Services
N.A.I.C.S.: 238290

Vardvaskan AB (1)
Oktanvagen 17, 311 32, Falkenberg, Sweden
Tel.: (46) 34612212
Web Site: https://foretag.vardvaskan.se
Shoes Mfr & Retailer
N.A.I.C.S.: 316210

Viametrics Group AB (1)
Anasvagen 44, 416 68, Gothenburg, Sweden
Tel.: (46) 317504030
Web Site: https://viametrics.com
Software Development Services
N.A.I.C.S.: 541511

Vikingsun AB (1)
Karduansmakargatan 2 C, 111 52, Stockholm, Sweden
Tel.: (46) 854511880
Web Site: https://www.vikingsun.se
Kitchen Appliance Distr
N.A.I.C.S.: 423220

Vokus Personal AG (1)
Lowenstrasse 43, 8001, Zurich, Switzerland
Tel.: (41) 442138000
Web Site: https://www.vokuspersonal.ch
Recruitment Services
N.A.I.C.S.: 561311

STORY TELECOM LTD.

Olympia House 1 Armitage Road, London, NW11 8RQ, United Kingdom
Tel.: (44) 208 497 9210
Web Site: http://www.storytelecom.com
Year Founded: 2002
Sales Range: $200-249.9 Million
Emp.: 10
N.A.I.C.S.: 517810
Telecommunication Servicesb
Paris Karatzas (Dir-Comml)

STORY-I LIMITED

Suite 1 GF 437 Roberts Road, Subiaco, 6008, WA, Australia
Tel.: (61) 8 6380 2555
Web Site: http://www.story-i.com
Rev.: $28,980,552
Assets: $25,652,545
Liabilities: $14,211,023
Net Worth: $11,441,522
Earnings: $790,823
Fiscal Year-end: 06/30/19
Consumer Electronic Products Distr
N.A.I.C.S.: 423690
Djohan Widodo (Chm)

INTERNATIONAL PUBLIC

STORYTEL AB

Tryckerigatan 4, PO Box 24 167, 104 51, Stockholm, Sweden
Tel.: (46) 812042500
Web Site: https://storytelgroup.com
Year Founded: 2005
STORY.B—(OMX)
Rev.: $285,451,118
Assets: $231,882,414
Liabilities: $88,298,022
Net Worth: $143,584,392
Earnings: ($22,404,122)
Emp.: 577
Fiscal Year-end: 12/31/20
Media Advertising Services
N.A.I.C.S.: 541840
Jonas Tellander (Founder & CEO)

STOTEKS A.D.

Bulevar Mihajla Pupina 6/6, 21000, Novi Sad, Serbia
Tel.: (381) 21423722
Web Site: https://www.stoteks.com
Year Founded: 1994
STOTN—(BEL)
Rev.: $745,224
Assets: $11,742,522
Liabilities: $6,595,759
Net Worth: $5,146,763
Earnings: $86,988
Fiscal Year-end: 12/31/23
Grain Product Whslr
N.A.I.C.S.: 424510
Slavica Latinovic (Exec Dir)

STOVE KRAFT LIMITED

81/1 Harohalli Industrial Area, Kanakapura Taluk Ramanagara, Bengaluru, 562112, Karnataka, India
Tel.: (91) 8026985800
Web Site: https://www.stovekraft.com
Year Founded: 1999
STOVEKRAFT—(BOM)
Rev.: $117,458,796
Assets: $77,769,237
Liabilities: $36,621,585
Net Worth: $41,147,652
Earnings: $11,118,744
Emp.: 3,312
Fiscal Year-end: 03/31/21
Kitchen Appliances Mfr
N.A.I.C.S.: 335220
Rajendra Gandhi (Mng Dir)

STP SCHMIEDETECHNIK PLETTENBERG GMBH & CO.

Daimlerstrasse 9, 58840, Plettenberg, Germany
Tel.: (49) 23918166
Web Site: http://www.stplettenberg.de
Sales Range: $100-124.9 Million
Emp.: 600
Metal Forgings
N.A.I.C.S.: 333517
Egon Ambaum (Mng Dir)

Subsidiaries:

CNC-Zerspanungstechnik Blug GmbH (1)
Gewerbegebiet Keltenweg 9, 66636, Tholey, Germany
Tel.: (49) 685391420
Web Site: http://www.cnc-blug.de
Sales Range: $10-24.9 Million
Emp.: 0
Metal Forgings
N.A.I.C.S.: 332111
Cornel Mueller (Mng Dir)

STP&I PUBLIC COMPANY LIMITED

32/24 3rd Floor Sino-Thai Tower Sukhumvit 21 Road Asoke Klongtoey Nua, Wattana, Bangkok, 10110, Thailand
Tel.: (66) 22601181
Web Site: https://www.stpi.co.th

AND PRIVATE COMPANIES

Year Founded: 1975
STPI—(THA)
Rev.: $116,609,609
Assets: $357,424,087
Liabilities: $129,137,025
Net Worth: $228,287,062
Earnings: $3,637,585
Emp.: 4,073
Fiscal Year-end: 12/31/23
Fabricating Pipe Mfr
N.A.I.C.S.: 332996
Masthawin Charnvirakul (Mng Dir & Member-Exec Bd)

Subsidiaries:

STIT Co., Ltd. (1)
25 Moo 13 Bueng Kham Phroi Subdrict, Lam Luk Ka District, Pathumthani, 12150, Thailand
Tel.: (66) 21506833
Web Site: http://www.sino-thai.com
Fabricated Structural Steel Mfr
N.A.I.C.S.: 332312
Masthawin Charnvirakul (Mng Dir)

STP&I Public Company Limited - Chonburi Fabrication Facility (1)
69 Moo 3 Bangna-Trad Km 53 5 Rd, Klong-Tamru Muang, Chon Buri, 20000, Thailand
Tel.: (66) 38 214 131 8
Web Site: http://www.stpi.co.th
Emp.: 600
Fabricated Structural Steel Mfr
N.A.I.C.S.: 332312

STP&I Public Company Limited - Laem Chabang Yard Facility (1)
48/1 Moo 3 Sukhumvit Rd Tungsukla, Si Racha, 20230, Chonburi, Thailand
Tel.: (66) 38 407 900
Fabricated Pipe Mfr
N.A.I.C.S.: 332996

STP&I Public Company Limited - Rayong Fabrication Facility (1)
45/10 Moo 4 Banlang-Nongbon Rd Nikompattana, King Amphur Nikompattana, Rayong, 21180, Thailand
Tel.: (66) 38 606 302 14
Fabricated Structural Steel Mfr
N.A.I.C.S.: 332312

STP&I Public Company Limited - Sriracha Fabrication Facility (1)
389/34 Moo 4 NongKham, Si Racha, 20230, Chonburi, Thailand
Tel.: (66) 38 320 000
Fabricated Steel Pipe Mfr
N.A.I.C.S.: 332996

STPI GROUP
58 Avenue Claude Vellefaux, 75010, Paris, France
Tel.: (33) 142039420
Web Site: http://www.stpigroup.com
Sales Range: $50-74.9 Million
Emp.: 150
Relay Mfr
N.A.I.C.S.: 335314
Michel Nespoulous (CEO)

Subsidiaries:

STPI ESPANOLA S.L. (1)
Paseo de la Castellana n 167 Piso 13 D, 28046, Madrid, Spain
Tel.: (34) 91 57 95 884
Relay Mfr
N.A.I.C.S.: 334513

STRABAG SE
Donau-City-Strasse 9, 1220, Vienna, Austria
Tel.: (43) 1224220   AT
Web Site: https://www.strabag.com
Year Founded: 1835
STR—(VIE)
Rev.: $18,374,538,096
Assets: $13,688,494,496
Liabilities: $9,344,394,561
Net Worth: $4,344,099,935
Earnings: $509,879,128
Emp.: 71,219
Fiscal Year-end: 12/31/22
Construction Engineering Services
N.A.I.C.S.: 236220
Christian Harder (CFO & Member-Mgmt Bd)

Subsidiaries:

ABR Abfall Behandlung und Recycling GmbH (1)
Am Mullnerstrassl 3, 2432, Schwadorf, Austria
Tel.: (43) 2230291670
Web Site: http://www.abr-gmbh.at
Waste Management Services
N.A.I.C.S.: 562998
Heinrich Riegler (Officer)

AKA Zrt. (1)
Lajos Utca 26, Budapest, 1023, Hungary
Tel.: (36) 13260555
Web Site: http://www.aka.hu
Emp.: 14
Construction Engineering Services
N.A.I.C.S.: 541330

ANTREPRIZA DE REPARATII SI LUCRAR I A R L CLUJ S.A.
Fabricii Str No 131, 400632, Cluj-Napoca, Romania
Tel.: (40) 264418620
Web Site: http://www.arlcluj.ro
Sales Range: $125-149.9 Million
Emp.: 300
Asphalt Mix Mfr
N.A.I.C.S.: 324121
Karoly Kacso (Head-Quality Assurance)

ASIA Center Kft. (1)
Szentmihalyi ut 167-169, 1152, Budapest, Hungary
Tel.: (36) 1 688 8888
Web Site: http://www.asiacenter.hu
Shopping Mall Management Services
N.A.I.C.S.: 531120

Alpines Hartschotterwerk Georg Kassbohrer & Sohn GmbH & Co. KG
Kemptenerstrasse 101, 89250, Senden, Germany
Tel.: (49) 730794940
Construction Materials Distr
N.A.I.C.S.: 423320

Asphalt & Beton GmbH (1)
Molzbichlerstr 6, 9800, Spittal an der Drau, Austria
Tel.: (43) 4762200
Building Construction Services
N.A.I.C.S.: 236220

Asphalt Gesellschaft Riegler GmbH (1)
Klagenfurt Str 48, 9100, Volkermarkt, Carinthia, Austria
Tel.: (43) 4232370800
Highway & Street Construction Engineering Services
N.A.I.C.S.: 237310

August & Jean Hilpert GmbH & Co. KG (1)
Kilianstr 118-120, 90425, Nuremberg, Bavaria, Germany
Tel.: (49) 91193530
Construction Engineering Services
N.A.I.C.S.: 541330

Autocesta Zagreb-Macelj d.o.o. (1)
Garicgradska 18, 10000, Zagreb, Croatia
Tel.: (385) 13689600
Web Site: http://www.azm.hr
Road Construction Services
N.A.I.C.S.: 237310
Milos Savic (Pres)

BHG Bitumenhandelsgesellschaft mbH (1)
Brauhausstrasse 15a, Hamburg, 22041, Germany
Tel.: (49) 4067048980
Construction Materials Distr
N.A.I.C.S.: 423320

BHG CZ s.r.o. (1)
Vrbenska 1931-29, Ceske Budejovice, 370 06, Czech Republic
Tel.: (420) 387004221

Sales Range: $25-49.9 Million
Emp.: 7
Construction Engineering Services
N.A.I.C.S.: 541330

BHG Sp. z o.o. (1)
Brechta 7, 03-472, Warsaw, Poland
Tel.: (48) 227322747
Construction Engineering Services
N.A.I.C.S.: 541330

BITUNO VA Baustofftechnik Gesellschaft m.b.H (1)
Wiener Strasse 24, 3382, Loosdorf, Austria
Tel.: (43) 27546981
Web Site: http://www.bitunova.at
Sales Range: $25-49.9 Million
Construction Machinery Mfr
N.A.I.C.S.: 333120
Herwig Sumetzberger (Mng Dir)

BLT Baulogistik und Transport GmbH (1)
Ungargasse 64-66-4-2, 1030, Vienna, Austria
Tel.: (43) 1224220
Logistics Transportation Services
N.A.I.C.S.: 541614

BMTI CR s.r.o. (1)
Tovarni 3, Brno, 620 00, Czech Republic
Tel.: (420) 545423750
Construction Engineering Services
N.A.I.C.S.: 541330
Rezl Yan (Gen Mgr)

BMTI Polska sp.z.o.o. (1)
Blonska 6, Pruszkow, 05-8004, Masovian, Poland
Tel.: (48) 227384050
Web Site: http://www.stranet.strabag.com
Sales Range: $25-49.9 Million
Emp.: 50
Construction Machinery Repair & Maintenance Services
N.A.I.C.S.: 811310
Jacek Kobus (Mng Dir)

BOHEMIA ASFALT , s.r.o. (1)
Na Svadlackach 478/II, Sobeslav, Czech Republic
Tel.: (420) 384541151
Construction Materials Distr
N.A.I.C.S.: 423990

BRVZ Bau- Rechen- u. Verwaltungszentrum Gesellschaft m.b.H. (1)
Siegburger Strasse 241, 50679, Cologne, Germany
Tel.: (49) 221 824 01
Construction Engineering Services
N.A.I.C.S.: 541330

BRVZ Bau-, Rechen- und Verwaltungszentrum AG (1)
Victory Strasse 241, 50679, Cologne, Germany
Tel.: (49) 2218242330
Civil Engineering Services
N.A.I.C.S.: 541330

BRVZ center za racunovodstvo in upravljanje d.o.o. (1)
33 Letaliska Cesta, Ljubljana, 1000, Slovenia
Tel.: (386) 15466727
Sales Range: $25-49.9 Million
Emp.: 150
Financial Accounting Management Services
N.A.I.C.S.: 541219
Anamarija Krpicandrejek (Mng Dir)

BRVZ s.r.o. (1)
Mlynske nivy 61/a, Bratislava, 825 18, Slovakia
Tel.: (421) 232621111
Software Development Services
N.A.I.C.S.: 541511

Bau Holding Beteiligungs AG (1)
Ortenburger Strasse 27, Spittal an der Drau, 9800, Austria
Tel.: (43) 47626200
Sales Range: $200-249.9 Million
Emp.: 700
Highway Construction Services
N.A.I.C.S.: 237310

Bautragergesellschaft Olande mbH (1)

STRABAG SE

Luebecker Strasse 128, 22087, Hamburg, Germany
Tel.: (49) 40202080
Commercial Property Development Services
N.A.I.C.S.: 236220
Christian Hattendorf (Mng Dir)

Bitumen Handelsgesellschaft m.b.H. & Co KG (1)
Wiener Strasse 24, Loosdorf, 3382, Lower Austria, Austria
Tel.: (43) 275464860
Construction Engineering Services
N.A.I.C.S.: 541330

Bitunova GmbH & Co. KG (1)
Neuhofer Bruckenstrasse 103, 21107, Hamburg, Germany
Tel.: (49) 407524960
Web Site: http://www.bitunova.de
Sales Range: $50-74.9 Million
Emp.: 57
Bitumen Emulsion Mfr & Distr
N.A.I.C.S.: 325180

Bitunova Kft. (1)
Gabor Denes U 2 Infopark D Building, 1117, Budapest, Hungary
Tel.: (36) 13585051
Web Site: http://www.bitunova.hu
Road Construction Services
N.A.I.C.S.: 237310

Bitunova Sp. z o.o. (1)
ul Wolczynska 237, 01-919, Warsaw, Poland
Tel.: (48) 227144930
Web Site: http://www.bitunova.com.pl
Sales Range: $25-49.9 Million
Emp.: 40
Bitumen Emulsion Mfr
N.A.I.C.S.: 325510

Bitunova Spol. S.r.o. (1)
Neresnicka Cesta 3, 960 01, Zvolen, Slovakia
Tel.: (421) 455243300
Web Site: http://www.bitunova.sk
Road Construction Services
N.A.I.C.S.: 237310

Blees-Kolling-Bau GmbH (1)
Siegburger Strasse 229a, 50679, Cologne, Germany
Tel.: (49) 2218242043
Building Construction Services
N.A.I.C.S.: 236220

Bohemia Bitunova, spol s.r.o. (1)
Kosovska 1122/16, Jihlava, 586 01, Czech Republic
Tel.: (420) 567310670
Construction Engineering Services
N.A.I.C.S.: 541330

Bohm Stadtbaumeister & Gebaudetechnik GmbH (1)
Donau-City-Str 9, 1220, Vienna, Austria
Tel.: (43) 1224221499
Web Site: http://www.boehmgmbh.at
Building Construction Services
N.A.I.C.S.: 236220

Bug-AluTechnic GmbH (1)
Bergstrasse 17, 88267, Vogt, Germany
Tel.: (49) 75299990
Web Site: http://www.bug.de
Aluminium Extruding Product Mfr
N.A.I.C.S.: 331318

C.S. Bitunova s.r.o. (1)
Neresnicka 3, 960 01, Zvolen, Slovakia
Tel.: (421) 455243300
Web Site: http://www.csbitunova.sk
Road & Railway Transportation Services
N.A.I.C.S.: 488490

CESTAR d.o.o. (1)
Sjeverna Vezna Cesta Bb, Slavonski Brod, 35000, Croatia
Tel.: (385) 35270015
Sales Range: $25-49.9 Million
Emp.: 83
Road Construction Services
N.A.I.C.S.: 237310
Walter Renner (CEO)

CLS Construction Legal Services GmbH (1)
Siegburger Street 241, Cologne, 50679, Germany

7229

STRABAG SE

STRABAG SE—(Continued)
Tel.: (49) 22182401
Construction Engineering Services
N.A.I.C.S.: 541330
Christian Schulz (Atty)

Carb SA (1)
Romania Calea Feldioarei nr 31 R1,
500471, Brasov, Romania
Tel.: (40) 268418774
Web Site: http://www.mineral.eu
Emp.: 55
Stone Quarrying Services
N.A.I.C.S.: 212319

Center Communication Systems BVBA/SPRL (1)
Bruxelles West Point Park T Hofveld 6 D 3, 1702, Groot-Bijgaarden, Belgium
Tel.: (32) 24649490
Sales Range: $50-74.9 Million
Emp.: 160
Telecommunication Equipment Mfr & Distr
N.A.I.C.S.: 334290

Center Communication Systems GmbH (1)
Gewerbepark, 5506, Magenwil, Switzerland
Tel.: (41) 628872333
Web Site: http://www.centersystems.at
Sales Range: $25-49.9 Million
Emp.: 5
Communication Equipment Mfr & Distr
N.A.I.C.S.: 334290

Center Systems (Deutschland) GmbH (1)
Nonnendammallee 42, Berlin, 13599, Germany
Tel.: (49) 3035530850
Web Site: http://www.centersystems.com
Sales Range: $25-49.9 Million
Emp.: 16
Construction Engineering Services
N.A.I.C.S.: 541330

DIW Instandhaltung GmbH (1)
Waldburgstr 19, 70563, Stuttgart, Germany
Tel.: (49) 7117823820
Web Site: http://www.diw-facility.de
Cleaning, Facility Management, Maintenance, Personnel Leasing & Infrastructural Facility Management Services
N.A.I.C.S.: 561210
Mike Kirschnereit (Chm-Mgmt Bd)

DOMIZIL Bautrager GmbH (1)
Ungarg 64, 1030, Vienna, Austria
Tel.: (43) 1360700
Emp.: 3
Construction Engineering Services
N.A.I.C.S.: 541330
Manfred Trnka (Gen Mgr)

DYWIDAG -Holding GmbH (1)
Siegburger Street 241, 50679, Cologne, Germany
Tel.: (49) 22182401
Construction Engineering Services
N.A.I.C.S.: 541330

DYWIDAG International GmbH (1)
Klausenburger Strasse 9, D-81677, Munich, Germany (100%)
Tel.: (49) 899210480
Web Site: http://www.dywidag.com
Sales Range: $100-124.9 Million
Emp.: 120
Construction Company
N.A.I.C.S.: 236210

Deutsche Asphalt GmbH (1)
Hermann-Kirchner-Strasse 6, 36251, Bad Hersfeld, Germany
Tel.: (49) 6621162224
Web Site: http://www.deutsche-asphalt.de
Emp.: 251
Road Construction Services
N.A.I.C.S.: 237310

Diw Instandhaltung Gmbh (1)
Eichsfelder Strasse 7, 40595, Dusseldorf, Germany
Tel.: (49) 2117052010
Web Site: http://www.diw-facility.de
Repair Shops & Related Services
N.A.I.C.S.: 811412

Dywidag Saudi Arabia Co. Ltd. (1)
1261 Al Jubail Industrial Area, Al Jubayl, 31951, Saudi Arabia
Tel.: (966) 33416306
Bridges & Building Contracting Services
N.A.I.C.S.: 238390

ECS European Construction Services GmbH (1)
Waldeckerstr 11, Morfelden, 64546, Hesse, Germany
Tel.: (49) 6105 40830
Construction Engineering Services
N.A.I.C.S.: 541330

EFKON AG (1)
Dietrich Keller Strasse 20, 8074, Raaba, Austria (75.6%)
Tel.: (43) 31669900
Web Site: https://www.efkon.com
Sales Range: $100-124.9 Million
Emp.: 200
Electronic Toll Collection Systems & Services
N.A.I.C.S.: 488490

Subsidiary (Non-US):

EFKON Bulgaria Ltd. (2)
Expo 2000 Business Center 55 Nikola Vaptsarov Boulevard, Sofia, 1407, Bulgaria
Tel.: (359) 2 962 5116
Web Site: http://www.efkon.com
Telecommunication Servicesb
N.A.I.C.S.: 517810

EFKON India Private Limited (2)
1405-1408 14th Floor Supremus E Wing, I-Think Techno Campus Kanjurmarg E, Mumbai, 400 042, Maharashtra, India
Tel.: (91) 2242949494
Web Site: http://www.efkonindia.com
Sales Range: $25-49.9 Million
Toll & Telematics System Installation & Support Services
N.A.I.C.S.: 541511
Sandeep Murarka (CFO)

EFKON Romania SRL (2)
Sector 2 Soseaua Mihai Bravu Nr 194 bl 203 Scara A Etaj 1 Apartament 2, Bucharest, Romania
Tel.: (40) 722394721
Software Development Services
N.A.I.C.S.: 541511

TolLink (Pty) Ltd (2)
Route 21 Corporate Park 34 Sovereign Drive, Irene, 0157, Pretoria, South Africa
Tel.: (27) 861 865 546
Web Site: http://www.tollink.co.za
Toll System Software Development & Maintenance Services
N.A.I.C.S.: 541511
Peter Filbey (CEO)

iFleet Solutions & Services Pvt. Ltd. (2)
701 7th Flr B-wing Lbs Mark Tricolli W, Sanpada, Navi Mumbai, 400705, Maharashtra, India
Tel.: (91) 2267148200
Web Site: http://www.ifleet.in
Vehicle Tracking & Telemetry Services
N.A.I.C.S.: 561990

ERMATEC Maschinen Technische Anlagen Gesellschaft m.b.H. (1)
Donau City Strasse 9, 1220, Vienna, Austria
Tel.: (43) 43122422
Sales Range: $150-199.9 Million
Emp.: 1,000
Construction Engineering Services
N.A.I.C.S.: 541330

ETG Erzgebirge Transportbeton GmbH (1)
Fuchsmuhlenweg, Freiberg, 9599, Germany
Tel.: (49) 3731211023
Industrial Building Construction Services
N.A.I.C.S.: 236210

Eberhard Pohner Unternehmen fur Hoch- und Tiefbau GmbH (1)
Hirschbaumstrasse 1 A, 95448, Bayreuth, Bavaria, Germany
Tel.: (49) 9209914000
Web Site: http://www.poehner-bayreuth.de
Sales Range: $50-74.9 Million
Emp.: 200
Civil Engineering Services
N.A.I.C.S.: 237990

Ed. Zublin AG (1)
Albstadtweg 3, 70567, Stuttgart, Germany
Tel.: (49) 71178830
Web Site: http://www.zueblin.de
Building Construction Services
N.A.I.C.S.: 236220

Eduard Hachmann Gesellschaft mit beschrankter Haftung (1)
Koogchaussee 24, 25774, Lunden, Schleswig-Holstein, Germany
Tel.: (49) 48825990
Construction Engineering Services
N.A.I.C.S.: 541330

Egolf AG Strassen- und Tiefbau (1)
Walkestrasse 101, 8570, Weinfelden, Switzerland
Tel.: (41) 71 626 29 29
Web Site: http://www.egolf.ch
Sales Range: $25-49.9 Million
Emp.: 80
Road Construction Services
N.A.I.C.S.: 237310

Ezel Bauunternehmung Sindelfingen GmbH (1)
Maybachstrasse 21, 71069, Sindelfingen, Germany
Tel.: (49) 70 31 73 610
Civil Engineering Services
N.A.I.C.S.: 541330

F. Lang u. K. Menhofer Baugesellschaft m.b.H. & Co. KG (1)
Tritolstrasse Parzelle 846-10, 2492, Eggendorf, Austria
Tel.: (43) 2622 23574 0
Road Construction Services
N.A.I.C.S.: 237310

F.K. Systembau GmbH (1)
Dottinger Strasse 87, 72525, Munsingen, Germany
Tel.: (49) 738193060
Web Site: http://www.fk-systembau.de
Emp.: 150
Civil Engineering Services
N.A.I.C.S.: 541330

FK Systembau Beteiligungs-GmbH (1)
Dottinger Strasse 87, 72525, Munsingen, Germany
Tel.: (49) 738193060
Web Site: https://www.fk-systembau.de
Construction Engineering Services
N.A.I.C.S.: 541330

FUSSENEGGER Hochbau und Holzindustrie GmbH (1)
Gutlestrasse 5, 6850, Dornbirn, Austria
Tel.: (43) 5572243810
Construction Engineering Services
N.A.I.C.S.: 541330

Fahrleitungsbau GmbH (1)
Wolbeckstr 19, Essen, 45329, Germany
Tel.: (49) 201364020
Construction Engineering Services
N.A.I.C.S.: 541330

Frischbeton s.r.o. (1)
Kacirkova 982/4, Jinonice, 158 00, Prague, Czech Republic
Tel.: (420) 222868264
Web Site: http://www.frischbeton.cz
Road Construction Services
N.A.I.C.S.: 237310

Frissbeton Kft. (1)
Papa Kopja u 10, 8500, Budapest, Hungary
Tel.: (36) 89 322489
Construction Materials Distr
N.A.I.C.S.: 423390

GRADBENO PO DJETJE IN KAMNOLOM GRASTO d.o.o (1)
33 Letaliska Cesta, Ljubljana, 1000, Slovenia
Tel.: (386) 546 67 19
Construction Engineering Services
N.A.I.C.S.: 541330

Gaul GmbH (1)
Heiligenwiesen 33, 70327, Stuttgart, Germany
Tel.: (49) 7114090000
Web Site: http://www.gaul.de
Building Construction Services
N.A.I.C.S.: 236220

Goldeck Bergbahnen GmbH (1)
Schwaig 38, Baldramsdorf, 9805, Spittal an der Drau, Austria
Tel.: (43) 4762 2864
Web Site: http://www.sportberg-goldeck.at
Travel & Tour Operating Services
N.A.I.C.S.: 561599

Griproad Spezialbelage und Baugesellschaft mbH (1)
Wikinkerstrasse 85, 51107, Cologne, Germany
Tel.: (49) 22129020775
Web Site: http://www.griproad.de
Industrial Building Construction Services
N.A.I.C.S.: 236210

H-TPA Kft. (1)
Gabor Danas St 2d, Budapest, 1117, Hungary
Tel.: (36) 13715701
Web Site: http://www.tpaqe.com
Sales Range: $25-49.9 Million
Emp.: 70
Construction Engineering Services
N.A.I.C.S.: 541330
Gyozo Kepes (Mgr)

HUMMEL Systemhaus GmbH & Co. KG (1)
In den Gernackern 13, 72636, Frickenhausen, Germany
Tel.: (49) 7025912710
Web Site: https://hummel-systemhaus.de
Construction Engineering Services
N.A.I.C.S.: 236220

Hermann Kirchner Bauunternehmung GmbH (1)
Gruppe Kassel Hauptstrasse 67, 34253, Lohfelden, Germany
Tel.: (49) 561 31690927
Civil Engineering Services
N.A.I.C.S.: 541330

Hermann Kirchner Hoch- und Ingenieurbau GmbH (1)
Zweigniederlassung Erfurt Hagansplatz 1, 99085, Erfurt, Germany
Tel.: (49) 361 7832 400
Civil Engineering Services
N.A.I.C.S.: 541330

Hermann Kirchner Projektgesellschaft mbH (1)
Hermann Kirchner Strasse 6, Bad Hersfeld, 36251, Germany
Tel.: (49) 66211620
Civil Engineering Services
N.A.I.C.S.: 237990

Ilbau GmbH Deutschland (1)
Bessemerstr 42b, Berlin, 12103, Germany
Tel.: (49) 30754770
Construction Engineering Services
N.A.I.C.S.: 541330

Ilbau Liegenschaftsverwaltung GmbH (1)
Ortenburger Strasse 27, Spittal an der Drau, 9800, Austria
Tel.: (43) 47626200
Web Site: http://www.strabag.at
Sales Range: $150-199.9 Million
Emp.: 700
Construction Engineering Services
N.A.I.C.S.: 541330

Industrielles Bauen Betreuungsgesellschaft mbH (1)
Albstadtweg 3, 70567, Stuttgart, Germany
Tel.: (49) 71178830
Construction Engineering Services
N.A.I.C.S.: 541330

InfoSys Informationssysteme GmbH (1)
Ortenburger Strasse 27, Spittal an der Drau, 9800, Austria
Tel.: (43) 47626200
Web Site: http://www.infosys-aachen.de
Software Consulting Services
N.A.I.C.S.: 541512

Innsbrucker Nordkettenbahnen Betriebs GmbH (1)
Hohenstrasse 145, 6020, Innsbruck, Austria
Tel.: (43) 512293344

AND PRIVATE COMPANIES

Web Site: http://www.nordkette.com
Building Construction Services
N.A.I.C.S.: 236220

JHP spol. s.r.o. (1)
Ustredni 423/62 Praha 10, 102 00, Prague, Czech Republic
Tel.: (420) 272701667
Web Site: http://www.jhp-mosty.cz
Emp.: 50
Construction Engineering Services
N.A.I.C.S.: 541330
Irena Sedmikova *(Mgr-Economic Dev)*

Josef Mobius Bau-Aktiengesellschaft (1)
Brandstucken 18, Hamburg, 22549, Germany
Tel.: (49) 40 800 903 0
Web Site: http://www.moebiusbau.com
Sales Range: $100-124.9 Million
Emp.: 400
Road Construction Services
N.A.I.C.S.: 237990
Rauben Heimer *(Mng Dir-Technical)*

Josef Riepl Unternehmen fur Hoch- und Tiefbau GmbH (1)
Im Gewerbepark D 55, 93059, Regensburg, Germany
Tel.: (49) 941 5682 300
Web Site: http://www.josef-riepl.de
Civil Engineering Services
N.A.I.C.S.: 541330

Josef Riepl Unternehmen fur Ingenieur- und Hochbau GmbH (1)
Im Gewerbepark D 55, 93059, Regensburg, Germany
Tel.: (49) 941 5682 300
Web Site: http://www.josef-riepl.de
Construction Engineering Services
N.A.I.C.S.: 541330

KAB Strabensanierung GmbH & Co KG (1)
Ernst Maerker Str 20, 3106, Saint Polten, Austria
Tel.: (43) 274226444
Web Site: http://www.kab.at
Road Construction Services
N.A.I.C.S.: 237310
Klaus Palle *(Mgr-Fleet-Vienna, Lower Austria & Burgenland)*

KAB Strassensanierung GmbH & Co KG (1)
Ernst Maerker Str 20, 3106, Saint Polten, Austria
Tel.: (43) 274226444
Web Site: https://www.kab.at
Road Construction Services
N.A.I.C.S.: 237310

KAMENOLO MY CR s.r.o. (1)
Polanecka 849, Svinov, 721 00, Ostrava, Czech Republic
Tel.: (420) 596964468
Web Site: http://www.mineral-cesko.com
Crushed Stone Quarrying & Sales
N.A.I.C.S.: 212319
Radmila Zapletalova *(Dir-Direction RM)*

KOKA Kft. (1)
Vagohid u 7/b, 4030, Debrecen, Hungary
Tel.: (36) 52440281
Web Site: http://www.kokakontener.hu
Waste Collection & Disposal Services
N.A.I.C.S.: 562219

Kamenolomy SR , s.r.o. (1)
Neresnicka cesta 3, 960 01, Zvolen, Slovakia
Tel.: (421) 455333102
Web Site: http://www.minera-slovensko.com
Sales Range: $25-49.9 Million
Emp.: 75
Construction Engineering Services
N.A.I.C.S.: 541330
Peter Brtanyi *(Head-RT & CC)*

Kanzelsteinbruch Gratkorn GmbH (1)
Pail 2, 8101, Gratkorn, Steiermark, Austria
Tel.: (43) 3166958650
Construction Services
N.A.I.C.S.: 236220

Kirchhoff Asphalt-Mischwerke GmbH & Co. KG (1)
Esslinger Strasse 1, 70771, Leinfelden-Echterdingen, Germany
Tel.: (49) 711 61924 0
Civil Engineering Services
N.A.I.C.S.: 541330

Kirchner & Volker Bauunternehmung GmbH (1)
Hagansplatz 1, 99085, Erfurt, Germany
Tel.: (49) 36178320
Construction Engineering Services
N.A.I.C.S.: 541330

Kirchner Holding GmbH (1)
Hermann Kirchner Strasse 6, 36251, Bad Hersfeld, Germany
Tel.: (49) 66211620
Web Site: http://www.kirchner.de
Highway Construction Services
N.A.I.C.S.: 237310

Leitner Gesellschaft m.b.H (1)
Rauscher Strasse 10, Amstetten, 3363, Austria
Tel.: (43) 7475522210
Construction Engineering Services
N.A.I.C.S.: 541330

Leonhard Moll Hoch- und Tiefbau GmbH (1)
Niederlassung Rhein Main Birkenweiherstrasse 9, 63505, Langenselbold, Germany
Tel.: (49) 618492500
Sales Range: $25-49.9 Million
Emp.: 100
Civil Engineering Services
N.A.I.C.S.: 541330

MAV Kelheim GmbH (1)
Sud-Chemie-Str 3, 93309, Kelheim, Germany
Tel.: (49) 944170966
Web Site: https://mav-gmbh.com
Construction Equipment Services
N.A.I.C.S.: 532412

MAV Lunen GmbH (1)
Buchenberg 38a-70, 44532, Lunen, Germany
Tel.: (49) 2306203430
Industrial Waste Disposal Services
N.A.I.C.S.: 562111

MAV Mineralstoff - Aufbereitung und - Verwertung GmbH (1)
Bataverstr 9, 47809, Krefeld, Germany
Tel.: (49) 2151 574 810
Web Site: http://mav-gmbh.com
Emp.: 160
Construction Waste Treatment Services
N.A.I.C.S.: 562211

MAV Mineralstoff - Aufbereitung und Verwertung Lunen GmbH (1)
Buchenburg 38a, 44532, Lunen, Germany
Tel.: (49) 2306203430
Civil Engineering Services
N.A.I.C.S.: 541330

MINERAL IGM d.o.o. (1)
Zapuzane BB, 23420, Benkovac, Croatia
Tel.: (385) 23662730
Construction Engineering Services
N.A.I.C.S.: 541330

Metallica Stahl- und Fassadentechnik GmbH (1)
Donau-City-Strasse 1, 1220, Vienna, Austria
Tel.: (43) 1224220
Web Site: https://www.metallica-fassade.com
Construction Services
N.A.I.C.S.: 236220

MiTTaG spo.s. r.o. (1) (100%)
Kosinova 785/24, 612 00, Brno, Czech Republic
Tel.: (420) 541556200
Web Site: http://www.mittag.cz
Construction Engineering Services
N.A.I.C.S.: 541330
Jiri Dohnal *(Co-CEO)*

Mineral Abbau GmbH (1)
Trigalv Strasse 9, 9500, Villach, Austria
Tel.: (43) 42423033700
Web Site: http://www.mineral.eu.com
Emp.: 5
Mineral Exploration Services
N.A.I.C.S.: 213115

Mineral Polska Sp. z o.o. (1)
ul Wesola 12, 58-379, Czarny Bor, Poland
Tel.: (48) 748866830
Web Site: http://www.mineral-polska.com
Mineral Mining
N.A.I.C.S.: 212390

Mineral Rom Srl (1)
Calea Feldioarei-31R1, Brasov, Romania
Tel.: (40) 268418774
Construction Equipment Services
N.A.I.C.S.: 532412

Mischek Bautrager Service GmbH (1)
Ungargasse 64-66 Stiege 4 Top 302, 1030, Vienna, 1030, Austria
Tel.: (43) 1360700
Web Site: http://www.mischek.at
Construction Engineering Services
N.A.I.C.S.: 541330

Mischek Leasing eins Gesellschaft m.b.H. (1)
Ungargasse 64-66 Stiege 4 Top 302, Vienna, 1030, Austria
Tel.: (43) 136070
Web Site: http://www.mischek.at
Construction Engineering Services
N.A.I.C.S.: 541330

Mischek Systembau GmbH (1)
Hugo Mischek Strasse 10, 2201, Garasdorf, Austria
Tel.: (43) 224625010
Web Site: http://www.mischek-systembau.at
Sales Range: $50-74.9 Million
Industrial Building Construction Services
N.A.I.C.S.: 236210

Mobil Baustoffe GmbH (1)
Erlenweg 1, 9463, Reichenfels, Austria
Tel.: (43) 4359 21 20 0
Web Site: http://www.mobil-baustoffe.com
Concrete Products Mfr
N.A.I.C.S.: 327390
Rudolf Kauper *(Mng Dir)*

N.V. STRABAG Benelux S.A. (1)
Noorderlaan 139, 2030, Antwerp, Belgium
Tel.: (32) 35404500
Web Site: http://www.strabag.be
Sales Range: $75-99.9 Million
Emp.: 400
Construction Engineering Services
N.A.I.C.S.: 541330
Carl Vermeer *(Dir-Comml)*

N.V. Strabag Belgium S.A. (1)
Noorderlaan 139, 2030, Antwerp, Belgium
Tel.: (32) 35404500
Web Site: https://www.strabag.be
Construction Services
N.A.I.C.S.: 236220

NOSTRA Cement Kft. (1)
Szegedi Ut 35-37, Budapest, 1135, Hungary
Tel.: (36) 18721400
Cement Mfr
N.A.I.C.S.: 327310

Nimab Entreprenad AB (1)
Akaregrand 6, PO Box 115, 275 23, Sjobo, Sweden
Tel.: (46) 41625000
Web Site: http://www.nimab.se
Building Construction Services
N.A.I.C.S.: 236220

OAT - Bohr- und Fugentechnik Gesellschaft m.b.H. (1)
Molzbichler Strasse 6, 9800, Spittal an der Drau, Austria
Tel.: (43) 47626200
Web Site: http://www.oat.at
Sales Range: $25-49.9 Million
Concrete Repair & Maintenance Services
N.A.I.C.S.: 561990
Willibald Traschitzker *(Mng Dir)*

OAT Kft. (1)
1097 Bp Gubacsi u 8/b, Budapest, Hungary
Tel.: (36) 614566144
Web Site: http://www.oat.hu
Road Construction Services
N.A.I.C.S.: 237310

OAT s.r.o. (1)
Nedokoncena 363 Praha 10, 102 00, Prague, Czech Republic
Tel.: (420) 272700072

Web Site: http://www.oat-cr.cz
Industrial Building Construction Services
N.A.I.C.S.: 236210

PL-BITUNOVA Sp. z o.o. (1)
ul Gliwicka 9, 47-240, Bierawa, Poland
Tel.: (48) 774830730
Web Site: http://www.pl-bitunova.com.pl
Sales Range: $25-49.9 Million
Emp.: 2
Road Construction Services
N.A.I.C.S.: 488490
Valdimir Czawsk *(Gen Mgr)*

PZC SPLIT d.d. (1)
Sv Mihovila 1, 21204, Dugopolje, Croatia
Tel.: (385) 21687000
Road Construction Services
N.A.I.C.S.: 488490
Marko Milardovic *(Gen Mgr)*

Pansuevia GmbH & Co. KG (1)
Carl-von-Linde-Strasse 2 Scheppach, 89343, Jettingen, Germany
Tel.: (49) 8225307690
Web Site: http://www.pansuevia.de
Building Construction Services
N.A.I.C.S.: 236220

Pobogel & Partner Strassen- und Tiefbau GmbH Hermdorf/Thur (1)
An der Autobahnabfahrt 1, 07629, Sankt Gangloff, Germany
Tel.: (49) 366017920
Web Site: http://www.possoegel.com
Construction Engineering Services
N.A.I.C.S.: 541330

Polski Asfalt Sp. z o. o. (1)
ul Parzniewska 10, 05-800, Pruszkow, Masovian, Poland
Tel.: (48) 227144100
Web Site: http://www.polskiasfalt.pl
Asphalt Mixture Products Mfr
N.A.I.C.S.: 324121

Pomgrad Inzenjering d.o.o. (1)
Stinice 26 B, Split, 21000, Croatia
Tel.: (385) 21340740
Web Site: http://www.pomgrad.hr
Emp.: 180
Dam & Shipyards Construction & Reconstruction Services
N.A.I.C.S.: 237990

Preduzece za puteve Zajecar a.D. (1)
Generala Gambete 68, Zajecar, 19000, Serbia
Tel.: (381) 19 422 528
Web Site: http://www.strabag.com
Emp.: 200
Construction Engineering Services
N.A.I.C.S.: 541330

Prinzing Gebaudetechnik GmbH (1)
Goerdelerstrasse 21, 91058, Erlangen, Germany
Tel.: (49) 9131687300
Web Site: https://www.prinzing-gt.de
Sales Range: $25-49.9 Million
Emp.: 120
Construction Engineering Services
N.A.I.C.S.: 541330

Projekt Elbpark GmbH & Co. KG (1)
Siegburger Strasse 229 C, 50679, Cologne, Nordrhein-Westfalen, Germany
Tel.: (49) 22182401
Real Estate Manangement Services
N.A.I.C.S.: 531390

Protecta Gesellschaft fur Oberflachenschutzschichten mit beschrankter Haftung (1)
Bataverstr 7-9, Krefeld, 47809, Germany
Tel.: (49) 2151 574700
Web Site: http://www.protecta-strassenerhalt.de
Road Maintenance Services
N.A.I.C.S.: 488490

Przedsiebiorstwo Budownictwa Ogolnego i Uslug Technicznych Slask Sp. z o.o (1)
Ul Wojska Polskiego 136A, 41-208, Sosnowiec, Poland
Tel.: (48) 322514442
Web Site: http://www.pboslask.com.pl
Construction Engineering Services

STRABAG SE

STRABAG SE—(Continued)
N.A.I.C.S.: 541330

Putevi Cacak doo (1)
Ulica 600 br 2, 32000, Cacak, Serbia
Tel.: (381) 32374590
Web Site: http://www.putevicacak.rs
Building Construction Services
N.A.I.C.S.: 236220

RBS Rohrbau Schweistechnik GmbH (1)
Westbahnstrasse 62, 4614, Marchtrenk, Austria
Tel.: (43) 7243508000
Web Site: http://www.rbs.at
Directional Drilling Services & Pipeline Mfr
N.A.I.C.S.: 213111

RBS Rohrbau-Schweisstechnik Gesellschaft m.b.H (1)
Westbahnstrasse 62, 4614, Marchtrenk, Austria
Tel.: (43) 7243508000
Web Site: https://www.rbs.at
Well Drilling Services
N.A.I.C.S.: 237110

Repass-Sanierungstechnik GmbH Korrosionsschutz Und Betoninstandsetzung (1)
Riedstrasse 9, 89597, Munderkingen, Germany
Tel.: (49) 73932088
Web Site: http://www.repass.de
Building Construction Services
N.A.I.C.S.: 236220

Rm Asphalt Gmbh & Co. Kg (1)
AMA Buttelborn Auf der Hardt / On The B42, 64572, Buttelborn, Germany
Tel.: (49) 615259789
Web Site: https://www.rm-asphalt.de
Asphalt Mixture Distr
N.A.I.C.S.: 423320

Rodinger Ingenieurbau GmbH (1)
Alaunweg 8, 93426, Roding, Germany (100%)
Tel.: (49) 946194000
Construction Engineering Services
N.A.I.C.S.: 541330

SAT Sp. z o.o (1)
ul Opolska 9, 55-200, Olawa, Poland
Tel.: (48) 607760052
Web Site: http://www.satpolska.com.pl
Road Maintenance Services
N.A.I.C.S.: 488490

SAT Strassensanierung GmbH (1)
Alfred-Schutte-Allee 10, 50679, Cologne, Germany
Tel.: (49) 2218240
Web Site: http://www.sat-roads.com
Building Construction Services
N.A.I.C.S.: 236220

SAT Utjavito Kft. (1)
1097 Gubacsi Street 8B, Budapest, 1135, Hungary
Tel.: (36) 14566149
Construction Engineering Services
N.A.I.C.S.: 541330

SAT s.r.o. (1)
Kacirkova 982/4 Praha 5, Jinonice, 158 00, Prague, Czech Republic
Tel.: (420) 417569443
Web Site: http://www.sat-roads.cz
Road Maintenance Services
N.A.I.C.S.: 488490

SBS Strabag Bau Holding Service GmbH (1)
Ortenburger Strasse 27, Spittal an der Drau, 9800, Austria
Tel.: (43) 47626200
Web Site: http://www.strabag.at
Sales Range: $75-99.9 Million
Emp.: 350
Construction Engineering Services
N.A.I.C.S.: 541330

SC Bitunova Romania SRL (1)
Sector 3 Traian No 2 block F1 Section Unirea Stairscase 3 Floor 7, Bucharest, 030574, Romania
Tel.: (40) 213228622
Web Site: http://www.bitunova.eu

Public Utility Construction Services
N.A.I.C.S.: 237990

SF-Ausbau GmbH (1)
Zuger Strasse 1, 09599, Freiberg, Germany
Tel.: (49) 373178780
Web Site: http://www.sf-ausbau.de
Emp.: 125
Construction Engineering Services
N.A.I.C.S.: 541330

SILO II LBG 57 - 59 Liegenschaftsverwertung GmbH & Co KG (1)
Donau-City-Strasse 1, 1220, Vienna, Austria
Tel.: (43) 1224227100
Web Site: http://www.silo-offices.at
Building Construction Services
N.A.I.C.S.: 236220
Erwin Gross *(Mng Dir)*

STRAB IL STRABAG Bildung im Lauenburgischen GmbH (1)
Siegburger Strasse 229c, Cologne, 50679, Germany
Tel.: (49) 22182401
Industrial Building Construction Services
N.A.I.C.S.: 236210
Karsten Richter *(Gen Mgr)*

STRABAG - ZIPP Development s.r.o. (1)
Mlynske Nivy 61/A, Bratislava, 825 18, Slovakia
Tel.: (421) 232621111
Web Site: http://www.starbag.sk
Construction Engineering Services
N.A.I.C.S.: 541330
Jarmila Povazanova *(Mng Dir)*

STRABAG AG (1)
Unterrohrstr 5, 8952, Schlieren, Switzerland
Tel.: (41) 448742600
Web Site: http://www.strabag.ch
Construction Engineering Services
N.A.I.C.S.: 541330

STRABAG Aszfalt Kft. (1)
Gabor Denes u 2, 1117, Budapest, Hungary
Tel.: (36) 13585000
Construction Services
N.A.I.C.S.: 236220

STRABAG Bau GmbH (1)
Indutriestrasse 4 2, 9360, Friesach, Carinthia, Austria
Tel.: (43) 4268 25 77 0
Emp.: 100
Construction Engineering Services
N.A.I.C.S.: 541330
Vancanta Thomas *(Gen Mgr)*

STRABAG Beograd d.o.o. (1)
Antifasisticke Borbe 13a, Novi Beograd, 11070, Belgrade, Serbia
Tel.: (381) 112221700
Construction Engineering Services
N.A.I.C.S.: 541330
Dragon Pavelic *(Gen Mgr)*

STRABAG Beton GmbH & Co. KG (1)
Neukollnische Allee 1-3, 12057, Berlin, Germany
Tel.: (49) 30754770
Construction Materials Distr
N.A.I.C.S.: 423390

STRABAG EAD (1)
1 Kukush Street, Sofia, 1309, Bulgaria
Tel.: (359) 29330201
Industrial Building Construction Services
N.A.I.C.S.: 236210

STRABAG Facility Management GmbH (1)
Kilianstr 120, Nuremberg, 90425, Bavaria, Germany
Tel.: (49) 9118336500
Web Site: http://www.strabag-pfs.de
Emp.: 600
Construction Engineering Services
N.A.I.C.S.: 541330

STRABAG GmbH (1)
Hermann Kirchner Strasse 6, 36251, Bad Hersfeld, Germany
Tel.: (49) 66211620
Web Site: http://www.strabag.com
Construction Engineering Services
N.A.I.C.S.: 541330

STRABAG IMOBILIJA-agencija za posrednistvo v prometu z nepre micninami d.o.o. (1)
Letaliska Cesta 33, 1000, Ljubljana, 1000, Slovenia
Tel.: (386) 15466727
Web Site: http://www.strabag.si
Construction Engineering Services
N.A.I.C.S.: 541330
Dietmar Cerjak *(Mgr-Bus Dev)*

STRABAG International GmbH (1)
Siegburger Strasse 241, Cologne, 50679, Germany
Tel.: (49) 2218242989
Web Site: http://www.strabag-international.com
Sales Range: $25-49.9 Million
Emp.: 50
Construction Engineering Services
N.A.I.C.S.: 541330
Christian Zoller *(Mng Dir)*

STRABAG Off-Shore Wind GmbH (1)
Segelckestrasse 45-47, Cuxhaven, 27472, Germany
Tel.: (49) 4721699770
Web Site: http://www.strabag-offshore.de
Sales Range: $25-49.9 Million
Emp.: 30
Offshore Engineering Services
N.A.I.C.S.: 541330
Klaus Weber *(Member-Exec Bd)*

STRABAG PFS Polska Sp. z o.o. (1)
Al Jerozolimskie 179, 02-222, Warsaw, Poland
Tel.: (48) 228238811
Web Site: https://www.strabag-pfs.pl
Construction Services
N.A.I.C.S.: 236220

STRABAG Pipeline- und Rohrleitungsbau GmbH (1)
Im Gewerbepark 55, Regensburg, 93059, Germany
Tel.: (49) 941798890
Construction Engineering Services
N.A.I.C.S.: 541330

STRABAG Pozemni a inzenyrske stavitelstvi s.r.o. (1)
Kacirkova 982/4, 158 00, Prague, Czech Republic
Tel.: (420) 222868111
Web Site: https://www.strabag-pozemni.cz
Construction Services
N.A.I.C.S.: 236220

STRABAG Projektentwicklung GmbH (1)
Siegburger Strasse 229c, Cologne, 50679, Germany
Tel.: (49) 2218242010
Construction Engineering Services
N.A.I.C.S.: 541330
Guenter Nikelowski *(Gen Mgr)*

STRABAG Property and Facility Services GmbH (1)
Bleichstrasse 52, 60313, Frankfurt am Main, Germany
Tel.: (49) 69 13029 0
Web Site: http://www.strabag-pfs.com
Sales Range: $75-99.9 Million
Emp.: 110
Real Estate Manangement Services
N.A.I.C.S.: 531390

STRABAG Property and Facility Services GmbH (1)
Leopold-Bohm-Strasse 10 Office 1 4th Fl top 437 454, A1030, Vienna, Austria
Tel.: (43) 505990
Construction Services
N.A.I.C.S.: 532412
Stefan Babsch *(CEO)*

Subsidiary (Non-US):

Caverion Polska Sp.z.o.o. (2)
ul Klobucka 25, 02-699, Warsaw, Poland
Tel.: (48) 22 823 88 11
Web Site: http://www.caverion.pl
Building Maintenance Services
N.A.I.C.S.: 561790
Michal Wolicki *(Dir-Technical)*

INTERNATIONAL PUBLIC

STRABAG Rail Fahrleitungen GmbH (1)
Marzahner Strasse 34, Berlin, 13053, Germany
Tel.: (49) 3098612440
Web Site: http://www.strabag-rail.com
Railway Construction Management Services
N.A.I.C.S.: 488210

STRABAG Rail GmbH (1)
Bessemerstr 42b, 12103, Berlin, Germany
Tel.: (49) 30670690962
Web Site: http://www.strabag-rail.com
Civil Engineering Services
N.A.I.C.S.: 237990
Jurgen Wetscheck *(Mng Dir)*

STRABAG Real Estate GmbH (1)
Siegburger Str 241, 50679, Cologne, Germany
Tel.: (49) 2218242000
Web Site: http://www.strabag-real-estate.com
Sales Range: $50-74.9 Million
Real Estate Development Services
N.A.I.C.S.: 531390

STRABAG Sp.z o.o. (1)
ul Parzniewska 10, 05-800, Pruszkow, Poland
Tel.: (49) 227144800
Web Site: http://www.strabag.pl
Construction Engineering Services
N.A.I.C.S.: 541330

STRABAG Sportstattenbau GmbH (1)
Schaferstrasse 49, 44147, Dortmund, Germany
Tel.: (49) 231 98 20 23 0
Web Site: http://www.strabag-sportstaettenbau.de
Sports Field Construction Services
N.A.I.C.S.: 237990

STRABAG Umwelttechnik GmbH (1)
Vogelsanger Weg 111, 40470, Dusseldorf, Germany
Tel.: (49) 211610450
Web Site: http://www.strabag-umwelttechnik.com
Emp.: 300
Environmental Engineering Services
N.A.I.C.S.: 541330
Marian Kloss *(Head-Comml Bus Unit)*

STRABAG Unterstutzungskasse GmbH (1)
Siegburger Strasse 241, 50679, Cologne, Nordrhein-Westfalen, Germany
Tel.: (49) 22182402
Road Construction Services
N.A.I.C.S.: 237310
Thomas Birtel *(Gen Mgr)*

STRABAG gradbene storitve d.o.o (1)
Letaliska cesta 33, 1000, Ljubljana, Slovenia
Tel.: (386) 15466700
Sales Range: $25-49.9 Million
Emp.: 140
Civil Engineering Services
N.A.I.C.S.: 541330
Dietmar Cerjak *(Dir-Tech)*

STRABAG s.r.o. (1)
Mlynske Nivy 61 A, 825 18, Bratislava, Slovakia
Tel.: (421) 232621111
Web Site: http://www.strabag.sk
Civil Engineering Services
N.A.I.C.S.: 541330

STRABAG-MML Kft. (1)
Daroczi Ut 30, Budapest, 1113, Hungary
Tel.: (36) 13728219
Civil Engineering Services
N.A.I.C.S.: 541330

STRABIL STRABAG Bildung im Lauenburgischen GmbH (1)
Siegburger Strasse 229c, Cologne, 50679, Germany
Tel.: (49) 22182401
Sales Range: $25-49.9 Million
Emp.: 50
Real Estate Manangement Services
N.A.I.C.S.: 531390

AND PRIVATE COMPANIES — STRABAG SE

Slovasfalt, spol.s.r.o. (1)
Mlynske Nivy 61 A, 825 18, Bratislava, Slovakia
Tel.: (421) 41 500 26 84
Web Site: http://www.slovasfalt.sk
Asphalt Mixture Products Mfr
N.A.I.C.S.: 324121

Square One GmbH & Co KG (1)
Talstrasse 66, 40217, Dusseldorf, Germany
Tel.: (49) 21115924960
Web Site: http://www.squareonegmbh.de
Building Construction Services
N.A.I.C.S.: 236220

StraBAG Strassenbau und Beton AG (1)
Waffenplatzstr 18, 8002, Zurich, Switzerland
Tel.: (41) 433444444
Construction Engineering Services
N.A.I.C.S.: 541330

Strabag AG (1)
Siegburger Str 241, 50679, Cologne, Germany
Tel.: (49) 22182401
Web Site: http://www.mobile.strabag.com
Building Construction Services
N.A.I.C.S.: 236220

Strabag Altalanos Epito Kft. (1)
Gabor Denes Utca 2 Infopark D Building, 1117, Budapest, Hungary
Tel.: (36) 13585000
Web Site: http://www.strabag.hu
Road Construction Services
N.A.I.C.S.: 237310

Strabag Asfalt s.r.o. (1)
Svadlackach 478 II, 392 01, Sobeslav, Czech Republic
Tel.: (420) 381541178
Web Site: http://www.strabagasfalt.cz
Road Construction Services
N.A.I.C.S.: 237310

Strabag Building & Industrial Services GmbH (1)
Waldburgstr 19, 70563, Stuttgart, Germany
Tel.: (49) 117823820
Web Site: https://www.strabag-bis.de
Construction Services
N.A.I.C.S.: 236220

Strabag Development Belgium NV (1)
Noorderlaan 139, 2030, Antwerp, Belgium
Tel.: (32) 35404650
Web Site: https://www.strabag.be
Construction Services
N.A.I.C.S.: 236220

Strabag Epito Zartkoruen Mukodo Reszvenytarsasag (1)
Szegedi Ut 35-37, Budapest, 1135, Hungary
Tel.: (36) 13728100
Construction Engineering Services
N.A.I.C.S.: 541330

Strabag Grossprojekte GmbH (1)
Leopoldstrasse 250 c, 80807, Munich, Germany
Tel.: (49) 8936055550
Web Site: http://www.grossprojekte.strabag.de
Building Construction Services
N.A.I.C.S.: 236220

Strabag Inc. (1)
6790 Century Avenue Suite 401, Mississauga, L5N 2V8, ON, Canada
Tel.: (416) 848-6353
Emp.: 40
Construction Engineering Services
N.A.I.C.S.: 541330
Teri O'Neill *(Mgr-HR)*

Strabag Infrastructure & Safety Solutions GmbH (1)
Ignaz-Kock-Strasse 19, 1210, Vienna, Austria
Tel.: (43) 1901990
Web Site: http://www.strabag-iss.com
Building Construction Services
N.A.I.C.S.: 236220
Egon Manhartseder *(Gen Mgr)*

Strabag Kieserling Flooring Systems GmbH (1)
Reeperbahn 1, 20359, Hamburg, Germany
Tel.: (49) 40202083390
Web Site: http://www.kieserling.strabag.de
Construction Equipment Services
N.A.I.C.S.: 532412

Strabag Oman L.L.C. (1)
Way No 5007 Building No 700 Near Athaiba Interchange, PO Box 444, Ghala, Muscat, 100, Oman
Tel.: (968) 2452900
Web Site: http://www.strabag-oman.com
Building Construction Services
N.A.I.C.S.: 236220

Strabag Qatar W.L.L. (1)
Al Emadi Enterprises C-Ring Road 2nd Floor Room 12, PO Box 23041, Doha, Qatar
Tel.: (974) 44990300
Construction Engineering Services
N.A.I.C.S.: 541330

Strabag Rail a.s. (1)
Zeleznicarska 1385/29 Strekov, 400 03, Usti nad Labem, Czech Republic
Tel.: (420) 475300111
Web Site: http://www.strabagrail.cz
Road Construction Services
N.A.I.C.S.: 237310

Strabag SIA (1)
Slokenbeka-5 Smardes Pagasts Engures nov, Milzkalne, LV-3148, Latvia
Tel.: (371) 63181552
Web Site: http://www.strabag.lv
Building Construction Services
N.A.I.C.S.: 236220

Strabag SRL (1)
Calea 13 Septembrie Nr 90 et 5 cam 5 14 Sector 5, 050720, Bucharest, Romania
Tel.: (40) 2140343
Web Site: http://www.strabag.ro
Building Construction Services
N.A.I.C.S.: 236220

Strabag Sverige AB (1)
Vallgatan 9, PO Box 7017, 170 07, Solna, Sweden
Tel.: (46) 86260750
Web Site: http://www.mobile.strabag.com
Building Construction Services
N.A.I.C.S.: 236220

Strabag UK Limited (1)
3rd Floor The Tower 65 Buckingham Gate, London, SW1E 6AS, United Kingdom
Tel.: (44) 2081544670
Construction Services
N.A.I.C.S.: 236220

Strabag Wasserbau GmbH (1)
Reeperbahn 1, 20359, Hamburg, Germany
Tel.: (49) 40202082032
Web Site: http://www.strabag-wasserbau.com
Construction Equipment Services
N.A.I.C.S.: 532412

Strabag a.s. (1)
Kacirkova 982/4, 158 00, Prague, Czech Republic
Tel.: (420) 222868111
Web Site: http://www.strabag.cz
Civil Engineering Construction Services
N.A.I.C.S.: 237990

Strabag d.o.o. (1)
Zmaja od Bosne 11-Objekat B, 71000, Sarajevo, Bosnia & Herzegovina
Tel.: (387) 33569700
Commercial & Institutional Building Construction Services
N.A.I.C.S.: 236220

Strabag d.o.o. (1)
Ulica Petra Hektorovica 2, 10000, Zagreb, Croatia
Tel.: (385) 16392000
Web Site: http://www.strabag.hr
Building Construction Services
N.A.I.C.S.: 236220

Stratebau GmbH (1)
North Div Bayern Donaustaufer Strasse 176, 93059, Regensburg, Germany
Tel.: (49) 94140210
Web Site: http://www.stratebau.de
Sales Range: $100-124.9 Million
Emp.: 500
Highway Construction Services & Materials

N.A.I.C.S.: 237310

Affiliate (Domestic):

Bayerische Asphalt-Mischwerke GmbH & Co. (2)
Ottostrasse 7, Hofolding, 85649, Munich, Germany
Tel.: (49) 81046610
Web Site: http://www.bam-net.de
Sales Range: $50-74.9 Million
Highway Construction Materials
N.A.I.C.S.: 237310

Szamito- es Ugyviteli Kozpont Korlatolt Felelossegu Tarsasag (1)
Szegedi Ut 35-37, Budapest, 1135, Hungary
Tel.: (36) 12708300
Construction Engineering Services
N.A.I.C.S.: 541330

Szentesi Vasutepito Kft. (1)
Baross Utca 2, Szentes, 6600, Hungary
Tel.: (36) 63311974
Emp.: 76
Railroad Construction Services
N.A.I.C.S.: 488210

TPA CR s.r.o. (1)
Vrbenska 1821/31, 370 06, Ceske Budejovice, Czech Republic
Tel.: (420) 387004552
Road Construction Services
N.A.I.C.S.: 237310

TPA Gesellschaft fur Qualitatssicherung und Innovation GmbH (1)
Polgarstrasse 30, Vienna, 1220, Austria
Tel.: (43) 121728600
Web Site: http://www.tpaqi.com
Sales Range: $25-49.9 Million
Emp.: 25
Road Construction Services
N.A.I.C.S.: 488490

TPA Hu Kft. (1)
Scented Road 8, 1097, Budapest, Hungary
Tel.: (36) 12113220
Road Construction Services
N.A.I.C.S.: 237310

TPA INST YTUT BA DAN TECHNICZNYCH Sp.z o.o. (1)
ul Warszawska 43, Poznan, 61-028, Poland
Tel.: (48) 616503132
Web Site: http://www.tpaqi.com
Emp.: 100
Construction Engineering Services
N.A.I.C.S.: 541330

TPA Societate pentru asigurarea calitatii si inovatii SRL (1)
90 Calea 13 Septembrie, Bucharest, 050726, Romania
Tel.: (40) 372715875
Sales Range: $25-49.9 Million
Emp.: 50
Construction Engineering Services
N.A.I.C.S.: 541330

TPA Sp. z o.o. (1)
Ul Parzniewska 8, 05-800, Pruszkow, Poland
Tel.: (48) 227382200
Building Construction Services
N.A.I.C.S.: 236220

Tech Gate Vienna Wissenschafts- und Technologiepark GmbH (1)
Donau-City-Strasse 1, 1220, Vienna, Austria
Tel.: (43) 1224221175
Web Site: http://www.techgate.at
Consulting Management Services
N.A.I.C.S.: 541618

The Intolligent Ltd (1)
Skahanagh North, Watergrasshill, Cork, Ireland
Tel.: (353) 214889968
Web Site: http://www.the-intolligent.ie
Highway Maintenance Services
N.A.I.C.S.: 561990

Torkret GmbH (1)
Langemarckstr 39, 45141, Essen, Germany
Tel.: (49) 20129430
Web Site: http://www.torkret.de
Construction Equipment Services
N.A.I.C.S.: 532412

Trema Engineering 2 sh p.k (1)
Rruga Bardhok Biba Old Tirana Building, Tirana, Albania
Tel.: (355) 42266618
Web Site: http://www.tremaengineering2.com.al
Construction Engineering Services
N.A.I.C.S.: 541330

UN IPRO JEKT Bau- und Innenbau GmbH (1)
Donau City Strasse 9, 1220, Vienna, Austria
Tel.: (43) 1224220
Construction Engineering Services
N.A.I.C.S.: 541330

Vojvodinaput-Pancevo a.d. (1)
Zarka Zrenjanina 12, Pancevo, 26000, Vojvodina, Serbia
Tel.: (381) 13 346 755
Web Site: http://www.strabag.com
Emp.: 82
Roads & Bridges Construction Services
N.A.I.C.S.: 237310

WMB Drogbud Sp. z o.o. (1)
Prosta 78/80, 42-209, Czestochowa, Poland
Tel.: (48) 343627812
Construction Materials Mfr
N.A.I.C.S.: 327120

Wolfer & Goebel Bau GmbH (1)
Vaihinger Str 169, 70567, Stuttgart, Germany
Tel.: (49) 71125860
Web Site: http://www.wolfer-goebel.de
Building Construction Services
N.A.I.C.S.: 236220

Xaver Bachner GmbH (1)
Landshuter Strasse 63, Straubing, 94315, Germany
Tel.: (49) 942133197
Emp.: 8
Civil Engineering Services
N.A.I.C.S.: 541330

Z-Bau GmbH (1)
Friedrich-Ebert-Strasse 62, Magdeburg, 39114, Germany
Tel.: (49) 391 636 7092
Construction Engineering Services
N.A.I.C.S.: 541330
Andreas Freustedt *(Mng Dir)*

ZIPP BRATISLAVA spol. sr.o. (1)
Mlynske Nivy 61 A, 825 18, Bratislava, Slovakia
Tel.: (421) 232621111
Web Site: http://www.strabag.com
Sales Range: $150-199.9 Million
Emp.: 320
Real Estate Manangement Services
N.A.I.C.S.: 531390

ZIPP PRAHA, s.r.o (1)
Na Belidle 198-21 Praha 5, 150 00, Prague, Czech Republic
Tel.: (420) 224301130
Web Site: http://www.zipp.cz
Construction Engineering Services
N.A.I.C.S.: 541330

ZUBLIN Timber Gaildorf GmbH (1)
Gartenstr 40, 74405, Gaildorf, Germany
Tel.: (49) 79712580
Construction Engineering Services
N.A.I.C.S.: 541330

ZUBLIN Timber GmbH (1)
Industriestrasse 2, 86551, Aichach, Germany
Tel.: (49) 82519080
Web Site: http://www.zueblin-timber.com
Construction Engineering Services
N.A.I.C.S.: 541330

Zentrum Rennweg S-Bahn Immobilienentwicklung GmbH (1)
Donau City Strasse 9, 1220, Vienna, Austria
Tel.: (43) 1 22422 0
Industrial Building Construction Services
N.A.I.C.S.: 236210

Zublin A/S (1)
Haestvej 46D, Trige, 8380, Arhus, Denmark
Tel.: (45) 86121582
Web Site: http://www.zueblin.dk
Construction Engineering Services
N.A.I.C.S.: 541330

Zublin Baugesellschaft m.b.H. (1)

STRABAG SE

STRABAG SE—(Continued)
Ungargasse 64 Stg 2 TOP 306, 1030, Vienna, Austria
Tel.: (43) 1601450
Web Site: http://www.zueblin.de
Construction Engineering Services
N.A.I.C.S.: 541330

Zublin Chimney & Refractory GmbH
Siegburger Str 229a, 50679, Cologne, Germany
Tel.: (49) 221 824 2943
Web Site: http://www.ooms-ittner-hof.de
Sales Range: $25-49.9 Million
Emp.: 120
Construction Engineering Services
N.A.I.C.S.: 541330

Zublin Construct s.r.l. (1)
Str Miss Ruxandra 12 et 1 Sector 2, 020562, Bucharest, Romania
Tel.: (40) 212120889
Web Site: http://www.zueblin.ro
Emp.: 100
Construction Engineering Services
N.A.I.C.S.: 541330

Zublin Ground and Civil Engineering LLC (1)
PO Box 111556, Dubai, United Arab Emirates
Tel.: (971) 4 3344324
Web Site: http://www.zublin-groundengineering.com
Civil Engineering Services
N.A.I.C.S.: 541330

Zublin Inc. (1)
6790 Century Ave Suite 401, Mississauga, L5N 2V8, ON, Canada
Tel.: (416) 840-9524
Building Construction Services
N.A.I.C.S.: 236220

Zublin International Chile Ltda. (1)
Cerro Portezuelo 9760 Quilicura, Santiago, 8720023, Chile
Tel.: (56) 24989600
Web Site: http://www.zublin.cl
Civil Engineering Services
N.A.I.C.S.: 237990

Zublin International GmbH (1)
Albstadtweg 3, 70567, Stuttgart, Germany
Tel.: (49) 7117883583
Web Site: http://www.zueblin-international.com
Sales Range: $75-99.9 Million
Emp.: 500
Construction Engineering Services
N.A.I.C.S.: 541330

Zublin K.f.t (1)
Daroci Ut 30, Budapest, 1113, Hungary
Tel.: (36) 13728117
Web Site: http://www.zueblin.hu
Construction Engineering Services
N.A.I.C.S.: 541330

Zublin Nederland B.V. (1)
Lage Mosten 61-63, 4822 NK, Breda, Netherlands
Tel.: (31) 881332000
Building Construction Services
N.A.I.C.S.: 236220

Zublin Romania S.R.L. (1)
Str Domnita Ruxandra Nr 12 Sector 2, 020562, Bucharest, Romania
Tel.: (40) 212120889
Web Site: https://www.zublin.ro
Construction Engineering Services
N.A.I.C.S.: 541330
Toma Ioan (Mgr)

Zublin Sp.z o.o (1)
ul Ziebicka 35, 60-164, Poznan, Poland
Tel.: (48) 61 8649 400
Web Site: http://www.zueblin.pl
Construction Engineering Services
N.A.I.C.S.: 541330

Zublin Spezialtiefbau Ges.m.b.H. (1)
Ungargasse 64, 1030, Vienna, Austria
Tel.: (43) 1 8773588 0
Web Site: http://www.zueblin.at
Sales Range: $50-74.9 Million
Emp.: 140
Civil Engineering Services
N.A.I.C.S.: 237990

Zublin Spezialtiefbau GmbH (1)
Albstadtweg 1, 70567, Stuttgart, Germany
Tel.: (49) 711 7883 454
Web Site: http://www.spt.zueblin.de
Civil Engineering Services
N.A.I.C.S.: 237990

Subsidiary (Non-US):

Zublin Scandinavia AB (2)
Vallgatan 9, 170 67, Solna, Sweden
Tel.: (46) 855335300
Web Site: http://www.zueblin.se
Construction Engineering Services
N.A.I.C.S.: 541330

Zublin Stahlbau GmbH (1)
Bahnhofstrasse 13, Hosena, 01996, Senftenberg, Germany
Tel.: (49) 35756710
Web Site: http://www.zueblin-stahlbau.de
Sales Range: $75-99.9 Million
Emp.: 360
Construction Engineering Services
N.A.I.C.S.: 541330
Jochen Schneider (Dir-Comml)

Zublin Umwelttechnik GmbH (1)
Maulbronner Weg 32, 71706, Markgroningen, Germany
Tel.: (49) 71459324
Web Site: http://www.zueblin-umwelttechnik.com
Sales Range: $25-49.9 Million
Environmental Engineering Services
N.A.I.C.S.: 541330

Zublin stavebni spol s.r.o. (1)
Kolbenova 5 A Praha 9, 190 00, Prague, Czech Republic
Tel.: (420) 283061610
Web Site: http://www.zueblin.cz
Construction Engineering Services
N.A.I.C.S.: 541330

Zucotec-Sociedade de Construcoes Lda (1)
Av da Quinta Grande 53 1 Edificio Prime, Alfragide, 2610-156, Amadora, Lisbon, Portugal
Tel.: (351) 21 01706 00
Web Site: http://www.zucotec.com
Construction Engineering Services
N.A.I.C.S.: 237990

STRACO CORPORATION, LTD.
10 Anson Road 30-15 International Plaza, Singapore, 079903, Singapore
Tel.: (65) 62233082
Web Site: https://www.stracocorp.com
Year Founded: 2002
S85—(SES)
Rev.: $62,209,738
Assets: $265,687,432
Liabilities: $59,380,704
Net Worth: $206,306,728
Earnings: $20,667,650
Emp.: 433
Fiscal Year-end: 12/31/23
Tourism Related Business Services
N.A.I.C.S.: 561520
Hsioh Kwang Wu (Founder, Chm & CEO)

Subsidiaries:

Shanghai Ocean Aquarium Co., Ltd. (1)
No 1388 Lujiazui Ring Road, Pudong New Area, Shanghai, 200120, China
Tel.: (86) 2158779988
Web Site: http://www.sh-aquarium.com
Underwater Aquarium Operator
N.A.I.C.S.: 712130

Straco Leisure Pte Ltd (1)
30 Raffles Avenue Singapore Flyer 02-05, Singapore, 039803, Singapore
Tel.: (65) 63333311
Web Site: https://www.singaporeflyer.com
Giant Observation Wheel Operator
N.A.I.C.S.: 713990

Underwater World Xiamen Co., Ltd. (1)
Gulang Park Gulangyu, Xiamen, 361002, China
Tel.: (86) 592 257 1668
Web Site: https://www.xm-hdsj.com
Underwater Aquarium Operator
N.A.I.C.S.: 712130
Charles Yiwei Cai (Gen Mgr)

STRAD ENERGY SERVICES LTD.
440 - 2nd Avenue SW Suite 1200, Calgary, T2P 5E9, AB, Canada
Tel.: (403) 232-6900   AB
Web Site: http://www.stradinc.com
Year Founded: 2005
Rev.: $99,661,797
Assets: $132,530,385
Liabilities: $33,045,359
Net Worth: $99,485,026
Earnings: $836,407
Emp.: 174
Fiscal Year-end: 12/31/19
Oil & Gas Exploration & Production Services
N.A.I.C.S.: 211120
Andy Pernal (CEO)

Subsidiaries:

Strad Controls Ltd (1)
11001 78 Ave, Grande Prairie, T8W 2J7, AB, Canada
Tel.: (780) 539-7114
Sales Range: $50-74.9 Million
Emp.: 100
Oil & Gas Drilling Services
N.A.I.C.S.: 213111
Tali Hughes (Owner)

Strad Energy Services USA Ltd. (1)
600 17th St Ste 1400N, Denver, CO 80202
Tel.: (720) 292-2200
Web Site: http://stradusa.stradenergy.com
Sales Range: $25-49.9 Million
Emp.: 12
Environmental Engineering Services
N.A.I.C.S.: 541330

Strad Manufacturing Inc (1)
602 - 25 Avenue, Nisku, T9E 0G6, AB, Canada
Tel.: (780) 955-9393
Web Site: http://www.stradenergy.com
Sales Range: $50-74.9 Million
Emp.: 85
Oil & Gas Drilling Services
N.A.I.C.S.: 213111

Strad Oilfield Rentals Ltd (1)
5 61072 Highway 668, County of Grande Prairie No 1, Grande Prairie, T8W 5A9, AB, Canada
Tel.: (780) 830-5470
Oilfield Equipment Rental Services
N.A.I.C.S.: 532412

Subsidiary (Domestic):

Strad Downhole Services Ltd. (2)
Ste1200 440 2nd Ave SW, Calgary, T2P 5E9, AB, Canada
Tel.: (403) 232-6900
Sales Range: $50-74.9 Million
Emp.: 10
Oilfield Equipment Rental Services
N.A.I.C.S.: 532412

STRADA AUTO PASSION
4 Avenue Auguste Ferrier, 38130, Echirolles, Isere, France
Tel.: (33) 476333231
Web Site: http://www.strada-entreprise.fr
Rev.: $24,100,000
Emp.: 46
Automobile Dealership
N.A.I.C.S.: 441110
Aldo Diaferia (Mgr-Ford)

STRADIM-ESPACE FINANCE SA
3 rue Pegase, 67960, Entzheim, France
Tel.: (33) 388154060   FR

INTERNATIONAL PUBLIC

Web Site: https://www.stradim.fr
Year Founded: 1990
ALSAS—(EUR)
Sales Range: $100-124.9 Million
Real Estate Support Services
N.A.I.C.S.: 531390
Francis Ebel (CEO)

STRAFFIC CO,. LTD.
C Block Withen Tower 56 Geumto-ro 80beon-gil, Sujeong-gu, Seongnam, Gyeonggi-do, Korea (South)
Tel.: (82) 317399500
Web Site: https://www.go-straffic.com
Year Founded: 2013
234300—(KRS)
Rev.: $101,297,462
Assets: $137,268,085
Liabilities: $84,735,566
Net Worth: $52,532,519
Earnings: $24,576,604
Emp.: 211
Fiscal Year-end: 12/31/22
Software Development Services
N.A.I.C.S.: 541511
Moon Chan-Jong (CEO)

STRAIT INNOVATION INTERNET CO., LTD.
6F Tianji Building No 181 Tianmushan Road, Xihu District, Hangzhou, 310063, Zhejiang, China
Tel.: (86) 57189938397
Web Site: http://www.hakim.com.cn
Year Founded: 2002
300300—(CHIN)
Rev.: $23,006,478
Assets: $187,780,044
Liabilities: $136,010,548
Net Worth: $51,769,495
Earnings: ($24,757,715)
Fiscal Year-end: 12/31/22
Information Software & Services, Entertainment Media & Innovative Finance Business
N.A.I.C.S.: 513210
Yang Cao (Chm)

STRAITS ENERGY RESOURCES BERHAD
B-07-06 Plaza Mont Kiara 2 Jalan Kiara Mont Kiara, 50480, Kuala Lumpur, Malaysia
Tel.: (60) 364191266
Web Site: https://www.straits-interlogistics.com
Year Founded: 1996
STRAITS—(KLS)
Rev.: $658,360,102
Assets: $119,345,017
Liabilities: $81,882,765
Net Worth: $37,462,252
Earnings: $1,470,537
Fiscal Year-end: 12/31/22
Filter Equipment Mfr
N.A.I.C.S.: 333413
Ho Kam Choy (Mng Dir)

Subsidiaries:

Quest Technology Sdn. Bhd. (1)
No 8 Jalan Astaka U8/88A Seksyen U8, Bukit Jelutong, 40150, Shah Alam, Selangor, Malaysia
Tel.: (60) 35 879 1493
Web Site: https://www.qts.com.my
Clean Room Equipment Mfr
N.A.I.C.S.: 339113

Sinar Maju Logistik Sdn. Bhd. (1)
NO 8-B Jalan Molek 1/9, Taman Molek, 81100, Johor Bahru, Malaysia
Tel.: (60) 73583881
Web Site: https://smlsb.com
Vessel Husbandry Services
N.A.I.C.S.: 541614

Straits Marine Services Pte Ltd (1)
No 2 International Business Park The Strat-

egy 10-06, Singapore, 609930, Singapore (100%)
Tel.: (65) 6 255 2737
Web Site: https://www.straits-services.com
Vessel Management Services
N.A.I.C.S.: 713930

Victoria STS (Labuan) Sdn. Bhd. (1)
Unit No 5-1 Level 5 Office Lot Labuan Times Square, 87000, Labuan, Malaysia
Tel.: (60) 87583050
Web Site: https://victoria-sts.com
Shipping Operation Services
N.A.I.C.S.: 541614

STRAKER LIMITED
Level 2 Building 3 61 Constellation Drive Rosedale, Auckland, 0632, New Zealand
Tel.: (64) 98010648 NZ
Web Site: http://www.strakertranslations.com
Year Founded: 1999
STG—(ASX)
Rev.: $35,531,100
Assets: $33,697,967
Liabilities: $10,936,005
Net Worth: $22,761,962
Earnings: ($1,648,923)
Emp.: 221
Fiscal Year-end: 03/31/23
Translation Agency Services
N.A.I.C.S.: 518210
Merryn Straker (COO)

Subsidiaries:

Hong Kong Translations Limited (1)
Level 19 China Building 29 Queens Road Central, Central, China (Hong Kong)
Tel.: (852) 27369622
Web Site: https://www.hongkong-translation.com
Translation Agency Services
N.A.I.C.S.: 541930

IDEST Communication S.A. (1)
6 Rue de l Eclipse, 1000, Brussels, Belgium
Tel.: (32) 25431860
Web Site: https://www.idestnet.com
Translation Services
N.A.I.C.S.: 541930

Lingotek, Inc. (1)
3400 N Ashton Blvd Ste 150, Lehi, UT 84043-5350
Tel.: (801) 331-7777
Web Site: http://www.lingotek.com
Software Publisher
N.A.I.C.S.: 513210
Kirk Langston (VP-Sls)

New Zealand Translations Centre Limited (1)
Level 2 49 Parkway Drive, Rosedale, Auckland, 0632, New Zealand
Tel.: (64) 98010648
Cloud-Enabled Translation Services
N.A.I.C.S.: 518210

Straker Germany GmbH (1)
Luxemburger Str 259, 50939, Cologne, Germany
Tel.: (49) 22116899331
Translation Agency Services
N.A.I.C.S.: 541930

Straker Lingotek LLC (1)
3400 N Ashton Blvd Ste 150, Lehi, UT 84043
Tel.: (801) 331-7777
Web Site: https://lingotek.com
Translation & Localization Services
N.A.I.C.S.: 541930

Straker Translations Australia Pty Limited (1)
Level 26 44 Market Street, Sydney, 2000, NSW, Australia
Tel.: (61) 280152744
Cloud-Enabled Translation Services
N.A.I.C.S.: 518210

Straker Translations UK Limited (1)
71-75 Shelton Street Covent Garden, London, WC2H 9JQ, United Kingdom
Tel.: (44) 8455911640
Translation Services
N.A.I.C.S.: 541930

STRANDBAGS GROUP PTY. LTD.
2 Minna Close Austlink Corporate Park, Belrose, 2085, NSW, Australia
Tel.: (61) 294797777
Web Site: http://www.strandbags.com.au
Year Founded: 1927
Leather Product Distr
N.A.I.C.S.: 424990
Felicity McGahan (Mng Dir)

STRANDLINE RESOURCES LIMITED
London House Level 9 216 St Georges Terrace, Perth, 6000, WA, Australia
Tel.: (61) 892263130
Web Site: https://www.strandline.com.au
STA—(ASX)
Rev.: $57,483,652
Assets: $231,284,267
Liabilities: $226,192,153
Net Worth: $5,092,115
Earnings: ($128,717,354)
Emp.: 127
Fiscal Year-end: 06/30/24
Metal Mineral Exploration
N.A.I.C.S.: 212290
Luke Edward Graham (CEO & Mng Dir)

STRATA POWER CORPORATION
500 - 4th Avenue SW Suite 2500, Calgary, T2P 2V6, AB, Canada
Tel.: (403) 237-5443 AB
Web Site: https://www.strataoil.com
Year Founded: 1998
SPOWF—(OTCIQ)
Rev.: $398,427
Assets: $236,478
Liabilities: $445,469
Net Worth: ($208,991)
Earnings: $477,657
Fiscal Year-end: 12/31/22
Oil & Gas Exploration Services
N.A.I.C.S.: 211120
Dave Mahowich (VP-Ops)

STRATABOUND MINERALS CORP.
100 King Street West Suite 5700, Toronto, M5X 1C7, ON, Canada
Tel.: (416) 915-4157 AB
Web Site: https://stratabound.com
Year Founded: 1986
SB—(OTCIQ)
Assets: $21,110,715
Liabilities: $4,653,675
Net Worth: $16,457,040
Earnings: ($1,282,355)
Fiscal Year-end: 12/31/21
Base & Precious Metals Exploration
N.A.I.C.S.: 213114
Terrence Harry Byberg (Exec VP)

Subsidiaries:

California Gold Mining Inc. (1)
150 King St W Suite 2106, Toronto, M5H 1J9, ON, Canada
Tel.: (647) 977-9267
Web Site: http://www.caligold.ca
Assets: $7,228,139
Liabilities: $1,654,255
Net Worth: $5,573,883
Earnings: ($2,671,469)
Fiscal Year-end: 08/31/2019
Metal Exploration Services
N.A.I.C.S.: 213114
Louis R. Nagy (CFO & Sec)

Subsidiary (US):

Fremont Gold Mining LLC (2)
7585 Hwy 49 N, Mariposa, CA 95338
Tel.: (209) 377-8488
Web Site: http://www.caligold.ca
Emp.: 1
Gold Exploration Services
N.A.I.C.S.: 212220
Vishal Gupta (CEO)

STRATASYS LTD.
1 Holtzman Street Science Park, PO Box 2496, Rehovot, 7612401, Israel
Tel.: (972) 747454314 II
Web Site: https://www.stratasys.com
Year Founded: 1998
SSYS—(NASDAQ)
Rev.: $651,483,000
Assets: $1,259,790,000
Liabilities: $300,358,000
Net Worth: $959,432,000
Earnings: ($28,974,000)
Emp.: 2,062
Fiscal Year-end: 12/31/22
3D Printing, Prototyping & Additive Mfr
N.A.I.C.S.: 333248
Dov Ofer (Chm)

Subsidiaries:

Additive Flight Solutions Pte. Ltd. (1)
9 Loyang Way 04-04 Krislite Building, Singapore, 508722, Singapore
Tel.: (65) 65134770
Web Site: http://www.additiveflightsolutions.com
Aerospace Parts Mfr
N.A.I.C.S.: 336413

Stratasys, Inc. (1)
7665 Commerce Way, Eden Prairie, MN 55344-2020
Tel.: (952) 937-3000
Web Site: http://www.stratasys.com
3D Printing, Prototyping & Additive Mfr
N.A.I.C.S.: 339999
Richard Garrity (Pres)

Subsidiary (Non-US):

Stratasys GmbH (2)
Airport Boulevard B 120, 77836, Rheinmunster, Germany
Tel.: (49) 69420994
Rapid Prototyping Systems Sales
N.A.I.C.S.: 541519

Technimold, S.R.L. (2)
Via Romairone 42 / E red, Genoa, 16152, Italy
Tel.: (39) 0106018463
Web Site: http://www.technimoldsistemi.com
Sales Range: $25-49.9 Million
Emp.: 7
3D Printers Distr
N.A.I.C.S.: 423430

STRATCO B.V.
Bosboomplantsoen 21, 4907 NT, Oosterhout, Netherlands
Tel.: (31) 6 21566774
Web Site: http://www.stratco.nl
Investment & Management Consulting Services
N.A.I.C.S.: 523999
Ad Timmermans (Owner)

STRATEC SE
Gewerbestrasse 37, 75217, Birkenfeld, Germany
Tel.: (49) 708279160
Web Site: https://www.stratec.com
Year Founded: 1979
SBS—(STU)
Rev.: $296,379,236
Assets: $428,992,014
Liabilities: $185,970,214
Net Worth: $243,021,800
Earnings: $31,537,880
Emp.: 1,420
Fiscal Year-end: 12/31/22
Automated Analyzer Systems Mfr
N.A.I.C.S.: 339112
Marcus Wolfinger (Chm-Mgmt Bd)

Subsidiaries:

DIATRON MI Zrt. (1)
Tablas u 39, 1097, Budapest, Hungary
Tel.: (36) 1 436 9800
Web Site: http://www.diatron.com
Medical Equipment Mfr
N.A.I.C.S.: 334510
Roberto Marcos (Key Acct Mgr-Intl)

Diatron (US), Inc. (1)
12601 NW 115th Ave, Medley, FL 33178
Tel.: (305) 805-7010
Web Site: https://www.diatron.com
Hematology Analyzer Distr
N.A.I.C.S.: 327910
Frank Matuszak (Gen Mgr)

Diatron Medicinai Instrumentumok Laboratoriumi Diagnosztikai Fejleszto-Gyarto Zrt. (1)
Tablas u 39, 1097, Budapest, Hungary
Tel.: (36) 4369800
Web Site: http://www.diatron.com
Clinical Chemistry Analyzer & Reagent Mfr
N.A.I.C.S.: 334516
Jim Schepp (CEO)

Natech Plastics, Inc. (1)
1750 Julia Goldbach Ave, Ronkonkoma, NY 11779
Tel.: (631) 580-3506
Web Site: http://www.natechplastics.com
Sales Range: $1-9.9 Million
Emp.: 45
Plastics Products, Nec, Nsk
N.A.I.C.S.: 326199
Seemab Yousuf (Engr-Application)

Robion AG (1)
Gewerbestrasse 6, 8212, Neuhausen, Schaffhausen, Switzerland
Tel.: (41) 526700955
Web Site: http://www.robion.ch
Sales Range: $25-49.9 Million
Emp.: 31
Diagnostic System Mfr
N.A.I.C.S.: 334510

STRATEC Biomedical Data Management Systems (1)
1 Barberry Court Callister Way, Burton-on-Trent, DE14 2UE, Staffs, United Kingdom
Tel.: (44) 1283 741144
Web Site: http://www.stratec.com
Sales Range: $25-49.9 Million
Emp.: 25
Laboratory System Software Design Services
N.A.I.C.S.: 541380

Subsidiary (US):

Sanguin International Inc. (2)
1020 Sherman Ave, Hamden, CT 06514-1337
Tel.: (203) 288-8608
Software Publisher
N.A.I.C.S.: 513210

STRATEC Biomedical Inc. (1)
1020 Sherman Ave, Hamden, CT 06514-1337
Tel.: (203) 288-8608
Web Site: http://www.stratec.com
Sales Range: $50-74.9 Million
Emp.: 2
Diagnostic Equipment Distr
N.A.I.C.S.: 423450

STRATEC Molecular GmbH (1)
Robert-Roessle-Str 10, 13125, Berlin, 13125, Germany
Tel.: (49) 30 9489 2901
Web Site: http://www.stratec.com
Sales Range: $25-49.9 Million
Emp.: 27
Nucleic Acid Sample Collection, Stabilization & Both Manual & Automated Purification Diagnostic Preparations Mfr
N.A.I.C.S.: 325412

STRATEC NewGen GmbH (1)
Gewerbestr 37, Birkenfeld, 75217, Baden-Wurttemberg, Germany
Tel.: (49) 708279160
Sales Range: $25-49.9 Million
Emp.: 2
Diagnostics Preparation Mfr
N.A.I.C.S.: 325412
Marcus Wolfinger (Mng Dir)

STRATECO RESOURCES INC.

Strateco Resources Inc.—(Continued)

STRATECO RESOURCES INC.
186 de Normandie Suite 106,
Boucherville, J4B 7J1, QC, Canada
Tel.: (450) 641-0775 Ca
Web Site: http://www.stratecoinc.com
Year Founded: 2000
Sales Range: Less than $1 Million
Uranium Mining Exploration & Development
N.A.I.C.S.: 213114
Guy Hebert (Pres & CEO)

STRATEGEM CAPITAL CORPORATION
210-240 11 Ave SW, Calgary, T2R 0C3, AB, Canada
Tel.: (604) 692-0073
Web Site:
    https://www.strategmcapital.com
Year Founded: 1994
SGE—(TSXV)
Rev.: $360,192
Assets: $7,410,748
Liabilities: $23,409
Net Worth: $7,387,339
Earnings: ($1,305,602)
Fiscal Year-end: 12/31/23
Investment Management Service
N.A.I.C.S.: 523940
Jo-Anne O'Connor (Pres & CEO)

STRATEGEX GROUP CHARTERED PROFESSIONAL ACCOUNTANTS
Suite 520-900 West Hastings Street, Vancouver, V6C 1E5, BC, Canada
Tel.: (604) 688-2355
Web Site: https://strategexgroup.ca
Year Founded: 2002
Accounting Services
N.A.I.C.S.: 541219
Lakh Multani (Partner)

STRATEGIC ELEMENTS LTD.
138 Churchill Avenue, Subiaco, 6008, WA, Australia
Tel.: (61) 892782788
Web Site:
    https://www.strategicelements.com
SOR—(ASX)
Rev.: $304,445
Assets: $4,008,474
Liabilities: $415,152
Net Worth: $3,593,321
Earnings: ($1,727,573)
Fiscal Year-end: 06/30/24
Metal Mining
N.A.I.C.S.: 212290
Matthew Howard (Sec)

Subsidiaries:

Strategic Materials Pty Ltd. (1)
Labouchere Road Suite 6/57, South Perth, Perth, 6151, SA, Australia
Tel.: (61) 892782788
Web Site:
    http://www.strategicelements.com.au
Metal Exploration Services
N.A.I.C.S.: 213114

STRATEGIC ENERGY RESOURCES LIMITED
Level 4 100 Albert Road, South Melbourne, 3205, VIC, Australia
Tel.: (61) 396927222
Web Site:
    https://www.strategicenergy.com.au
SER—(ASX)
Rev.: $274,093
Assets: $5,649,812
Liabilities: $562,728
Net Worth: $5,087,084
Earnings: ($974,199)
Fiscal Year-end: 06/30/24
Petroleum Exploration Services

N.A.I.C.S.: 213112
Stuart Rechner (Exec Dir)

STRATEGIC EQUITY CAPITAL PLC
The Pavilions Bridgwater Road, Bristol, BS13 8AE, United Kingdom
Tel.: (44) 8707020000 UK
Web Site:
    https://www.strategicequitycap.com
SEC—(LSE)
Rev.: $4,046,905
Assets: $218,833,616
Liabilities: $4,322,282
Net Worth: $214,511,334
Earnings: $2,973,314
Fiscal Year-end: 06/30/19
Investment Fund Management Services
N.A.I.C.S.: 523940
Jeff Harris (Mgr-Fund)

STRATEGIC HOSPITALITY EXTENDABLE FREEHOLD & LEASEHOLD REIT
Unit 1107 11th Floor Abdulrahim Place No.990 Rama IV Road, Silom Bank Rak, Bangkok, 10500, Thailand
Tel.: (66) 943101810
Web Site: http://www.sh-reit.com
SHREIT—(THA)
Rev.: $3,324,897
Assets: $134,407,213
Liabilities: $57,617,689
Net Worth: $76,789,524
Earnings: ($8,522,507)
Fiscal Year-end: 12/31/20
Real Estate Investment Trust Services
N.A.I.C.S.: 523991
Christophe Forsinetti (Mng Dir)

STRATEGIC INTERNET INVESTMENTS, INCORPORATED
Jood Palace Hotel 36-A Off Al Rigga Road, PO Box 42111, Suite 1058 Deira, Dubai, United Arab Emirates
Tel.: (971) 4065521170 DE
Web Site:
    http://www.siiincorporated.com
SIII—(OTCIQ)
Investment Services
N.A.I.C.S.: 523999
Abbas Salih (Chm, Pres, CEO & CFO)

STRATEGIC INVESTMENTS A/S
August Bournville's Passage 1, 1055, Copenhagen, Denmark
Tel.: (45) 38401550
Web Site:
    https://www.strategicinvestments.dk
STRINV—(CSE)
Rev.: $7,794,477
Assets: $81,363,737
Liabilities: $9,224,846
Net Worth: $72,138,891
Earnings: $6,368,550
Emp.: 3
Fiscal Year-end: 12/31/23
Holding Company
N.A.I.C.S.: 551112
Lars Stoltze (Chm)

STRATEGIC INVESTORS GROUP, INC.
Building Balboa Bank Trust Calle 50 y Beatriz Maria Cabal, PO Box 0823-05813, Panama, Panama
Tel.: (507) 208 7300
Holding Company
N.A.I.C.S.: 551112

STRATEGIC METALS LTD.

510-1100 Melville Street, Vancouver, V6E 4A6, BC, Canada
Tel.: (604) 687-2522
Web Site:
    https://www.strategicmetalsltd.com
SMD—(OTCIQ)
Rev.: $128,202
Assets: $61,352,258
Liabilities: $3,455,090
Net Worth: $57,897,168
Earnings: ($1,852,828)
Fiscal Year-end: 12/31/19
Metal Mining Services
N.A.I.C.S.: 212290
Glenn R. Yeadon (Sec)

Subsidiaries:

CAVU Energy Metals Corp. (1)
Suite 2133 - 1177 West Hastings Street, Vancouver, V6A 2K3, BC, Canada
Tel.: (604) 493-2997
Web Site: https://cavuenergymetals.com
Mineral Exploration Services
N.A.I.C.S.: 213115

STRATEGIC MINERALS CORPORATION NL
Level 4 240 Queen Street, Brisbane, 4000, QLD, Australia
Tel.: (61) 861413500 AU
Web Site: http://www.stratmin.com.au
Year Founded: 1979
SMC—(ASX)
Rev.: $7,826
Assets: $20,092,226
Liabilities: $227,107
Net Worth: $19,865,118
Earnings: ($548,410)
Fiscal Year-end: 12/31/19
Gold Exploration Services
N.A.I.C.S.: 212220

Subsidiaries:

Alpha Uranium Ltd. (1)
58 Jersey Street, Jolimont, 6008, Western Australia, Australia
Tel.: (61) 89284125
Web Site: http://www.stratmin.com.au
Uranium Ore Exploration & Mining Services
N.A.I.C.S.: 212290

Signature Resources Pty. Ltd. (1)
15 Shannon St, Floreat, Perth, 6014, WA, Australia
Tel.: (61) 893888399
Web Site: http://www.stratmin.com.au
Sales Range: $50-74.9 Million
Mineral Exploration Services
N.A.I.C.S.: 213115
Wally Martin (Mng Dir)

STRATEGIC MINERALS PLC
27/28 Eastcastle Street, London, W1W 8DH, United Kingdom
Tel.: (44) 2079306009 UK
Web Site:
    https://www.strategicminerals.net
SML—(AIM)
Rev.: $1,580,000
Assets: $6,600,000
Liabilities: $2,750,000
Net Worth: $3,850,000
Earnings: ($9,190,000)
Fiscal Year-end: 12/31/23
Iron Ore Mining
N.A.I.C.S.: 212210
John Peters (Mng Dir)

Subsidiaries:

Southern Minerals Group LLC (1)
303 Fierro Rd, Hanover, NM 88041
Tel.: (575) 912-5484
Metal Mining Services
N.A.I.C.S.: 213114

STRATEGIC NATURAL RESOURCES PLC
Suite 4 Claridge House 32 Davies

INTERNATIONAL PUBLIC

Street, London, W1K 4ND, United Kingdom
Tel.: (44) 2033285668 UK
Web Site: http://www.snrplc.co.uk
SNRP—(LSE)
Sales Range: Less than $1 Million
Emp.: 18
Natural Resources Extraction Services
N.A.I.C.S.: 212114

STRATEGIC OIL & GAS LTD.
1100 645 7 Avenue SW, Calgary, T2P 4G8, AB, Canada
Tel.: (403) 767-9000
Web Site: https://www.sogoil.com
SOGFF—(OTCIQ)
Sales Range: $25-49.9 Million
Emp.: 37
Oil & Gas Exploration
N.A.I.C.S.: 211120
Thomas E. Claugus (Chm)

STRATEGIC PUBLIC RELATIONS GROUP LIMITED
Unit A 29/F Admiralty Centre I 18 Harcourt Rd Fl 24 Rm 2402, Hong Kong, China (Hong Kong)
Tel.: (852) 2527 0490 HK
Web Site:
    http://www.strategic.com.hk
Year Founded: 1995
Emp.: 120
Public Relations Agency
N.A.I.C.S.: 541820
Richard Tsang (Chm & Mng Dir)

Subsidiaries:

Strategic Public Relations (1)
80 Robinson Road 22-01A, Singapore, 068898, Singapore
Tel.: (65) 6325 8260
Web Site: http://www.sprg.com.sg
N.A.I.C.S.: 541810

Strategic Public Relations (1)
Room 510 Tower C SoHo New Town 88 Jianguo Rd, Chaoyang District, Beijing, 100022, China
Tel.: (86) 10 8680 4258
N.A.I.C.S.: 541810

Strategic Public Relations (1)
Rm 705 Taipan Bus Ctr No 22 Donghu Rd, Xuhui District, Shanghai, China
Tel.: (86) 21 5404 2778
N.A.I.C.S.: 541810

Strategic Public Relations (1)
Rm 1809 Dongshan Plz 69 Xianlie Rd Central, Guangzhou, 510095, China
Tel.: (86) 20 8732 0980
Emp.: 8
N.A.I.C.S.: 541810

Strategic Public Relations (1)
Unit 503 5F No 112 Sec 1 Zhongxiao E Rd, Jhongjheng District, Taipei, 10052, Taiwan
Tel.: (886) 2 2394 9002
Web Site: http://www.sprg.com.tw
N.A.I.C.S.: 541810

STRATEGIC RESOURCES INC.
410 - 625 Howe Street, Vancouver, V6C 2T6, BC, Canada
Tel.: (604) 646-1890 ON
Web Site: https://www.strategic-res.com
Year Founded: 2004
SR—(TSXV)
Assets: $68,487,688
Liabilities: $15,476,328
Net Worth: $53,011,360
Earnings: ($53,554,530)
Fiscal Year-end: 06/30/24
Rare Earth Metals Exploration Services
N.A.I.C.S.: 212290
Scott Hicks (CEO)

STRATEGX ELEMENTS CORP.

55 Water Street Unit 514, Vancouver, V6B 1A1, BC, Canada **BC**
Web Site:
https://www.strategxcorp.com
Year Founded: 2018
STGX—(CNSX)
Assets: $1,908,170
Liabilities: $290,975
Net Worth: $1,617,195
Earnings: ($452,737)
Fiscal Year-end: 12/31/21
Natural Gas Distribution Services
N.A.I.C.S.: 221210
Andrea Yuan *(CFO)*

STRATEGY INTERNATIONAL INSURANCE GROUP, INC.
200 Yorkland Blvd Suite 710, Toronto, M2J 5C1, ON, Canada
Tel.: (416) 496-9988
SGYI—(OTCIQ)
Sales Range: Less than $1 Million
Financial Investment Services
N.A.I.C.S.: 524210
Stephen Stonhill *(Chm & CEO)*

STRATEVIC FINANCE GROUP AB
PO Box 5109, 102 43, Stockholm, Sweden
Tel.: (46) 101388644
Web Site: http://www.stratevic.com
Year Founded: 2009
Commercial Banking Services
N.A.I.C.S.: 522110

STRATFORD MOTOR PRODUCTS
824 Ontario Street, Stratford, N5A 3K1, ON, Canada
Tel.: (519) 271-5900
Web Site: http://www.buysmp.com
New & Used Car Dealers
N.A.I.C.S.: 441110

STRATHALLEN CAPITAL CORP.
2 Bloor Street West Suite 1001, Toronto, M4W 3E2, ON, Canada
Tel.: (416) 922-5553
Web Site: http://www.strathallen.com
Year Founded: 2003
Emp.: 90
Commercial Real Estate Investment, Asset Management & Leasing Services
N.A.I.C.S.: 531390
David Wright *(Founder)*

STRATHMORE PLUS URANIUM CORP
Suite 750 - 1620 Dickson Ave, Kelowna, V1Y 9Y2, BC, Canada
Tel.: (250) 868-8177 **BC**
Web Site: https://www.strathmoreplus.com
Year Founded: 2007
TO3—(DEU)
Rev.: $88,891
Assets: $3,026,690
Liabilities: $374,001
Net Worth: $2,652,689
Earnings: ($2,719,768)
Fiscal Year-end: 07/31/24
Mineral Exploration Services
N.A.I.C.S.: 327999
Devinder Randhawa *(CEO)*

Subsidiaries:

Wyoming Uranium LLC (1)

STRATMONT INDUSTRIES LIMITED
505 5th Floor VIP Plaza Co-operative Premises Society Limited, Veera Industrial Estate New Link Road Andheri West, Mumbai, 400 053, Maharastra, India
Tel.: (91) 2249792103 **In**
Web Site:
https://www.stratmontindustries.com
Year Founded: 1994
530495—(BOM)
Rev.: $96,897
Assets: $697,351
Liabilities: $468,553
Net Worth: $228,798
Earnings: $1,202
Fiscal Year-end: 03/31/21
Coal Product Mfr & Distr
N.A.I.C.S.: 324199
Gayatari Devi Goyal *(Chm)*

STRATUM OY
Hankikuja 2, 01390, Vantaa, Finland
Tel.: (358) 75 30 500 329
Web Site: http://www.stratum.fi
Sales Range: $25-49.9 Million
Emp.: 50
Plating, Coating & Engineering
N.A.I.C.S.: 332812
Pekka Laukkanen *(Mng Dir)*

Subsidiaries:

Stratum Oy - Stratum Tuusula Unit (1)
Repsikantie 1, PO Box 5, 04500, Helsinki, Finland
Tel.: (358) 75 30 500 300
Industrial Engineering Services
N.A.I.C.S.: 541330
Pertti Niemi-Impola *(Mgr-Tech)*

Stratum Oy - Stratum Vantaa Unit (1)
Hankikuja 2, PO Box 5, 01390, Vantaa, Finland
Tel.: (358) 75 30 500 329
Industrial Engineering Services
N.A.I.C.S.: 541330
Petteri Soranta *(Dir-Production)*

Stratum Pori (1)
Kuparitie 5, 28330, Pori, Finland
Tel.: (358) 26266111
Web Site: http://www.luvata.com
Copper Plating
N.A.I.C.S.: 332813
Jan Snrha *(Dir-Production)*

STRATUS GESTAO DE CARTEIRAS LTDA.
Rua Funchal 418 28th andar, CEP 04551-060, Sao Paulo, SP, Brazil
Tel.: (55) 11 2166 8800 **BR**
Web Site: http://www.stratusbr.com
Year Founded: 1999
Privater Equity Firm
N.A.I.C.S.: 523999
Alvaro Goncalves *(Co-Founder & Exec Mng Partner)*

Subsidiaries:

BBM Logistica S.A. (1)
Alameda Bom Pastor 2216 - Barro Preto, CEP 83015-140, Sao Jose dos Pinhais, PR, Brazil
Tel.: (55) 41 2169 0005
Web Site: http://www.bbmlogistica.com.br
Freight Transportation & Logistics Services
N.A.I.C.S.: 484121
Marcos Battistella *(Partner)*

STRAUMANN HOLDING AG
Peter Merian-Weg 12, CH-4052, Basel, Switzerland
Tel.: (41) 619651111 **CH**
Web Site:
https://www.straumann.com
Year Founded: 1954
STMN—(SWX)
Rev.: $2,572,932,373
Assets: $3,739,950,111
Liabilities: $1,684,689,579
Net Worth: $2,055,260,532
Earnings: $482,017,738
Emp.: 10,333
Fiscal Year-end: 12/31/22
Holding Company
N.A.I.C.S.: 551112
Beat Luthi *(Vice Chm)*

Subsidiaries:

Abutment Direct Inc. (1)
102-7351 Victoria Park Ave, Markham, L3R 3A5, ON, Canada
Tel.: (905) 604-0465
Dental Services
N.A.I.C.S.: 621210

Anthogyr S.A. (1)
8 um Mierscherbierg, B P 184, 7526, Mersch, Luxembourg
Tel.: (352) 2664041
Dental Equipment Mfr
N.A.I.C.S.: 339114

Anthogyr SAS (1)
2 237 Avenue Andre Lasquin, 74700, Sallanches, France
Tel.: (33) 450580237
Dental Equipment Mfr
N.A.I.C.S.: 339114

Batigroup Dental Dis Urunleri Ticaret AS (1)
The Paragon Plaza B Blok 2 / 10-11, Cukurambar-Cankaya, Ankara, Turkiye
Tel.: (90) 312 419 0191
Web Site: https://www.batigrupodeme.com
Dental Equipment Mfr & Distr
N.A.I.C.S.: 339114

Biora AB (1)
Per Albin Hanssons vag 41 Medeon Science Park, SE-214 32, Malmo, Sweden
Tel.: (46) 40321333
Dental Equipment Mfr & Distr
N.A.I.C.S.: 339114

Createch Medical S.L.U. (1)
Pol Kurutz Gain 3, Mendaro, 20850, Guipuzcoa, Spain
Tel.: (34) 943708951
Web Site: https://www.createchmedical.com
Dental Equipment Mfr & Distr
N.A.I.C.S.: 339114

Dental Wings GmbH (1)
Dusseldorfer Platz 1, 09111, Chemnitz, Germany
Tel.: (49) 37127390370
Dental Equipment Mfr & Distr
N.A.I.C.S.: 339114

Dental Wings Inc. (1)
160 Rue St-Viateur E Suite 701, Montreal, H2T 1A8, QC, Canada
Tel.: (514) 807-8485
Web Site: https://www.dentalwings.com
Dental Equipment Mfr & Distr
N.A.I.C.S.: 339114

DrSmile Iberia S.L. (1)
Illarza Dental Clinic Pl Dominican Republic 7 1 B, 28016, Madrid, Spain
Tel.: (34) 910782123
Web Site: https://drsmile.es
Dental Services
N.A.I.C.S.: 621210

DrSmile Italia S.R.L. (1)
Via Borgogna 2, 20122, Milan, Italy
Tel.: (39) 0238590587
Web Site: https://dr-smile.it
Dental Clinic Services
N.A.I.C.S.: 621210

Equinox Implants LLP (1)
301-C Pooname Chambers A Wing Dr Annie Besant Road, Worli, 400018, Mumbai, India
Tel.: (91) 2224934400
Dental Equipment Mfr & Distr
N.A.I.C.S.: 339114

Etkon (Schweiz) AG (1)
Theodorshofweg 22, 4310, Rheinfelden, Switzerland
Tel.: (41) 800810817
Dental Equipment Mfr & Distr
N.A.I.C.S.: 339114

GalvoSurge Dental AG (1)
Nollenstrasse 15a, 9443, Widnau, Switzerland
Tel.: (41) 717471144
Web Site: https://www.galvosurge.com
Dental Equipment Mfr & Distr
N.A.I.C.S.: 339114

Institut Straumann AG (1)
Peter Merian-Weg 12, 4002, Basel, Switzerland
Tel.: (41) 61 965 1111
Web Site: https://www.straumann.com
Sales Range: $400-449.9 Million
Emp.: 1,342
Dentistry Products
N.A.I.C.S.: 339114

Subsidiary (Non-US):

Straumann AB (2)
Krokslatts Fabriker 45, SE-431 37, Molndal, Sweden
Tel.: (46) 317087500
Web Site: https://www.straumann.com
Sales Range: $25-49.9 Million
Emp.: 25
Dentistry Products
N.A.I.C.S.: 456199

Straumann AS (2)
Nils Hansens vei 7, NO - 0667, Oslo, Norway
Tel.: (47) 23354488
Web Site: https://www.straumann.com
Sales Range: $25-49.9 Million
Emp.: 10
Dentistry Products
N.A.I.C.S.: 456199

Straumann Australia P/L (2)
7 Gateway Crt, Port Melbourne, 3207, VIC, Australia
Tel.: (61) 39 261 1300
Web Site: http://www.straumann.com.au
Sales Range: $25-49.9 Million
Emp.: 15
Medical Supplies Distr
N.A.I.C.S.: 423450

Straumann B.V. (2)
Einsteinweg 15, 3404 LE, IJsselstein, Netherlands
Tel.: (31) 306008900
Web Site: https://www.straumann.com
Sales Range: $25-49.9 Million
Emp.: 50
Dentistry Products
N.A.I.C.S.: 456199

Straumann Belgium (2)
Belgicastraat 3, Box 3, BE-1930, Zaventem, Belgium
Tel.: (32) 27901000
Web Site: https://www.straumann.com
Sales Range: $1-9.9 Million
Emp.: 20
Dentistry Products
N.A.I.C.S.: 456199

Straumann Biologics Division (2)
Medeon Science Park, SE 205 12, Malmo, Sweden
Tel.: (46) 40321333
Web Site: http://www.biora.se
Sales Range: $25-49.9 Million
Emp.: 35
Distr & Developer of Products for the Treatment of Mouth Diseases
N.A.I.C.S.: 456199

Straumann Brasil Ltda (2)
Rua Benjamin Lins 742, Batel, 04551-060, Curitiba, Parana, Brazil
Tel.: (55) 800 707 2526
Web Site: https://www.straumann.com
Dentistry Products
N.A.I.C.S.: 456199

Straumann GmbH (2)
Heinrich-von-Stephan-Strasse 21, 79100, Freiburg, Germany
Tel.: (49) 76145010
Web Site: https://www.straumann.com
Sales Range: $25-49.9 Million
Emp.: 150
Dentistry Products
N.A.I.C.S.: 456199

Straumann Ltd (2)
3 Pegasus Place Gatwick Road, Crawley, RH10 9AY, West Sussex, United Kingdom
Tel.: (44) 1293651230
Web Site: https://www.straumann.com

STRAUMANN HOLDING AG

Straumann Holding AG—(Continued)
Sales Range: $25-49.9 Million
Emp.: 20
Dentistry Products
N.A.I.C.S.: 456199

Straumann Oy (2)
Ayritie 12 A, 01510, Vantaa, Finland
Tel.: (358) 942729200
Web Site: https://www.straumann.com
Sales Range: $1-9.9 Million
Emp.: 14
Dentistry Products
N.A.I.C.S.: 456199

Subsidiary (US):

Straumann USA, LLC (2)
60 Minuteman Rd, Andover, MA 01810
Tel.: (978) 747-2500
Web Site: https://www.straumann.com
Sales Range: $50-74.9 Million
Emp.: 250
Dentistry Products
N.A.I.C.S.: 423450

Subsidiary (Non-US):

Straumann Canada Limited (3)
1109 Clay Avenue Unit 8, Burlington, L7L 0A1, ON, Canada
Tel.: (905) 319-2900
Web Site: https://www.straumann.com
Sales Range: $25-49.9 Million
Emp.: 20
Dentistry Products
N.A.I.C.S.: 339114

Manohay Argentina SA (1)
Direccion Juana Manso 555 Piso 7 E, C1107CBK, Buenos Aires, Argentina
Tel.: (54) 1121506540
Dental Equipment Mfr & Distr
N.A.I.C.S.: 339114

Manohay Dental SA (1)
Calle Anabel Segura 16 Edificio 3 - Planta Baja Alcobendas, 28108, Madrid, Spain
Tel.: (34) 916308214
Web Site: https://www.straumann.com
Dental Equipment Mfr & Distr
N.A.I.C.S.: 339114

Manohay Mexico SA de CV (1)
Direccion Comercial y Fiscal Lago Alberto 319 Int 1401, Col Granada Del Miguel Hidalgo, 11520, Mexico, Mexico
Tel.: (52) 5552826262
Web Site: https://www.straumann.com
Dental Equipment Mfr & Distr
N.A.I.C.S.: 339114

Medentika GmbH (1)
Hammweg 8-10, Hugelsheim, 76549, Rastatt, Germany
Tel.: (49) 722969912120
Web Site: https://www.straumann.com
Dental Equipment Mfr & Distr
N.A.I.C.S.: 339114

Smilink Servicos Ortodonticos Ltda. (1)
Rua Augusta N 2 840 Cj 71 and 72, Sao Paulo, 01412-100, Brazil
Tel.: (55) 11197968385
Web Site: https://www.smilink.com.br
Dental Services
N.A.I.C.S.: 621210

Straumann (Beijing) Medical Device Consulting Co., Ltd. (1)
3Fl Tower B Jiaming Centre 27 Dongsanhuan Beilu, Chaoyang District, Beijing, 100020, China
Tel.: (86) 105 775 6555
Web Site: https://www.straumann.cn
Surgical Implants Mfr
N.A.I.C.S.: 339113

Straumann CADCAM GmbH (1)
Lochhamer Schlag 6, Munich, 82166, Germany
Tel.: (49) 89 30 90 75 116
Sales Range: $25-49.9 Million
Emp.: 35
Dental Care Software Development Services
N.A.I.C.S.: 541511

Straumann Danmark ApS (1)
Nygards Plads 21 1, DK-2605, Brondby, Denmark
Tel.: (45) 46160666
Web Site: https://www.straumann.com
Dental Surgical Implant Mfr
N.A.I.C.S.: 339113

Straumann Dental India LLP (1)
Tel.: (91) 1244310600
Web Site: https://www.straumann.com
Dental Equipment Mfr & Distr
N.A.I.C.S.: 339114

Straumann Dental Korea Inc (1)
Tel.: (82) 221493800
Web Site: https://www.straumann.com
Dental Implant System Distr
N.A.I.C.S.: 423450

Straumann Dental s.r.l. (1)
Str Av Popisteanu Nr 54A Cladirea 1 et 1, 012095, Bucharest, Romania
Tel.: (40) 790015165
Web Site: https://straumanndental.ro
Dental Equipment Mfr & Distr
N.A.I.C.S.: 339114

Straumann Digital Planning Services (Private) Ltd. (1)
961-962 Block L Main Boulevard, Johar Town, Lahore, Pakistan
Tel.: (92) 42353038016
Orthodontic Digital Treatment Services
N.A.I.C.S.: 621210

Straumann Group & Clear Correct Singapore Pte. Ltd. (1)
19-05 Raffles City Tower 250 North Bridge Road, Singapore, 179101, Singapore
Tel.: (65) 63519193
Dental Care Services
N.A.I.C.S.: 621210

Straumann Group (Taiwan) Co. Ltd. (1)
Tel.: (886) 281786199
Dental Equipment Mfr & Distr
N.A.I.C.S.: 339114

Straumann Group (Thailand) Limited (1)
Tel.: (66) 21091234
Web Site: https://www.straumann.com
Dental Equipment Mfr & Distr
N.A.I.C.S.: 339114

Straumann Group Adriatic d.o.o. (1)
Stefanovecka cesta 10, 10000, Zagreb, Croatia
Tel.: (385) 17987361
Dental Care Services
N.A.I.C.S.: 621210

Straumann Group Costa Rica S.A. (1)
Corporate Center El Cafetal 2, Belen, 40703, Heredia, Costa Rica
Tel.: (506) 40023337
Dental Equipment Mfr & Distr
N.A.I.C.S.: 339114

Straumann Group Peru SA (1)
Av Primavera 517 Oficina 401 Urb Chacarilla del Estanque, San Borja, San Borja, Lima, Peru
Tel.: (51) 1 289 9709
Web Site: https://www.straumann.com
Dental Equipment Mfr & Distr
N.A.I.C.S.: 339114

Straumann Group Sdn. Bhd. (1)
B03-B-15-01 Menara 3A No 3 Jalan Bangsar, KL Eco City, 59200, Kuala Lumpur, Malaysia
Tel.: (60) 162102062
Dental Equipment Mfr & Distr
N.A.I.C.S.: 339114

Straumann Group South Africa (Pty) Ltd. (1)
15 Huising Street, Somerset West, 7130, Western Cape, South Africa
Tel.: (27) 21 850 0823
Web Site: https://www.straumann.com
Dental Equipment Mfr & Distr
N.A.I.C.S.: 339114

Straumann Holding Deutschland GmbH (1)
Jechtinger Str 9, Freiburg, 79111, Baden-Wurttemberg, Germany
Tel.: (49) 76145010
Dental Surgical Implant Mfr
N.A.I.C.S.: 339113

Straumann Italia srl (1)
Viale Bodio 37/A - Palazzo 4, 20158, Milan, Italy
Tel.: (39) 023932831
Web Site: https://www.straumann.com
Dental Surgical Implant Mfr
N.A.I.C.S.: 339113

Straumann Japan KK (1)
Tel.: (81) 368581188
Web Site: https://www.straumann.com
Surgical Dental Implant Mfr
N.A.I.C.S.: 339114

Straumann Latvia SIA (1)
Cesu iela 31-k-3, Riga, LV-1012, Latvia
Tel.: (371) 29568888
Web Site: https://www.straumann.lv
Dental Care Services
N.A.I.C.S.: 621210

Straumann Lithuania UAB (1)
A Vivulskio g 7-101, LT-03162, Vilnius, Lithuania
Tel.: (370) 60069839
Web Site: https://www.straumann.lt
Dental Care Services
N.A.I.C.S.: 621210

Straumann Mexico SA de C V (1)
Ruben Dario 281 Int 1702 Piso 17, Col Bosque de Chapultepec, Piso, 11580, Mexico
Tel.: (52) 55 5282 6262
Web Site: http://www.straumann.com.mx
Emp.: 25
Dental Surgical Implant Mfr
N.A.I.C.S.: 339113

Straumann Middle East PJS (1)
Tel.: (98) 218866631125
Web Site: https://www.straumann.com
Dental Equipment Mfr & Distr
N.A.I.C.S.: 339114

Straumann Pty. Ltd. (1)
Tel.: (61) 392611300
Web Site: https://www.straumann.com.au
Dental Equipment Mfr & Distr
N.A.I.C.S.: 339114

Straumann SA (1)
Edificio Arroyo A Avda de Bruselas 38 Planta 1, 28108, Alcobendas, Madrid, Spain
Tel.: (34) 902 400 979
Web Site: http://www.straumann.es
Sales Range: $25-49.9 Million
Emp.: 80
Dental Surgical Implant Mfr
N.A.I.C.S.: 339113
Alejandro Camino *(Gen Mgr)*

Straumann Singapore Pte Ltd (1)
19-05 Raffles City Tower 250 North Bridge Road, Singapore, 179101, Singapore
Tel.: (65) 63519193
Web Site: http://www.straumann.com.sg
Dental Equipment Mfr & Distr
N.A.I.C.S.: 339114
Frank Hemm *(Gen Mgr)*

Straumann Villeret SA (1)
Champs du Clos 2, Case postale 32, 2613, Villeret, Switzerland
Tel.: (41) 329428787
Dental Implant Mfr
N.A.I.C.S.: 339114

Straumann sro (1)
Na zertvach 2196/34, 180 00, Prague, 8, Czech Republic
Tel.: (420) 284094650
Web Site: https://www.straumann.com
Emp.: 10
Dental Surgical Implant Distr
N.A.I.C.S.: 423450

T Plus Implant Tech Co. Ltd. (1)
No 41 Wuquan 6th Rd 248, Wugu Dist, New Taipei City, Taiwan
Tel.: (886) 222981950
Web Site: https://www.tplus.com.tw
Dental Equipment Mfr & Distr
N.A.I.C.S.: 339114

Urban Technology GmbH (1)
Brunnenstrasse 128, 13355, Berlin, Germany
Tel.: (49) 3041735850
Web Site: https://www.drsmile.de
Dental Care Services
N.A.I.C.S.: 621210

Yller Biomateriais S.A. (1)
Av Sao Francisco de Paula, Bairro Areal, 3852, Brazil
Tel.: (55) 5132727460
Web Site: https://www.yller.com.br
Dental Material Mfr & Distr
N.A.I.C.S.: 339114

etkon GmbH (1)
Lochhamer Schlag 6, 82166, Grafelfing, Germany
Tel.: (49) 893090750
Dental Equipment Mfr & Distr
N.A.I.C.S.: 339114

STRAUSS GROUP LTD.

49 Hasivim St, PO Box 194, 49517, Petach Tikva, 49517, Israel
Tel.: (972) 36752499
Web Site: https://www.strauss-group.com
Year Founded: 1933
STRS—(TAE)
Rev.: $1,877,331,094
Assets: $2,257,217,812
Liabilities: $1,341,345,469
Net Worth: $915,872,344
Earnings: $153,059,812
Emp.: 17,860
Fiscal Year-end: 12/31/23
Offices of Other Holding Companies
N.A.I.C.S.: 551112
Ofra Strauss *(Chm)*

Subsidiaries:

Doncafe International Doo (1)
Put Famosa 38, 71000, Sarajevo, Bosnia & Herzegovina **(100%)**
Tel.: (387) 33475720
Web Site: http://www.strauss-group.ba
Coffee & Tea Mfr
N.A.I.C.S.: 311920

Max Brenner Second Avenue LLC (1)
841 Broadway, New York, NY 10003 **(90%)**
Tel.: (646) 467-8803
Web Site: http://www.maxbrenner.com
Sales Range: $25-49.9 Million
Chocolate & Confectionery Mfr
N.A.I.C.S.: 311351

Sabra Dipping Company LLC (1)
777 Westchester Ave Fl 3, White Plains, NY 10604
Tel.: (718) 932-9000
Web Site: http://www.sabra.com
Sales Range: $50-74.9 Million
Dip & Spread Mfr
N.A.I.C.S.: 311919
Meiky Tollman *(VP-Growth & Capabilities-Global)*

Strauss Cafe Poland Sp. z o.o. (1)
Derezolimskie 179, Blue city 1st floor, Warsaw, 02-222, Poland **(100%)**
Tel.: (48) 225333600
Web Site: http://www.strauss-group.pl
Sales Range: $25-49.9 Million
Emp.: 35
Coffee & Tea Mfr
N.A.I.C.S.: 311920
Christopher Klimczak *(Mng Dir)*

Strauss Coffee B.V. (1)
Beechavenue 162, 1119PS, Schiphol-Rijk, Netherlands
Tel.: (31) 206541166
Web Site: https://www.strauss-group.com
Sales Range: $50-74.9 Million
Emp.: 6,000
Coffee Mfr & Sales
N.A.I.C.S.: 311920
Amir Levin *(CFO)*

Strauss Commodities AG (1)
Baarerstrasse 63, 6300, Zug, Switzerland **(100%)**
Tel.: (41) 41 723 1060
Web Site: http://www.strauss-group.com

Procurement of Green Coffee Raw Materials, Logistics & Coffee Blends
N.A.I.C.S.: 311920

Strauss Russia LLC (1)
Bagrationovskiy proyezd 18 Floor 5, Moscow, 121087, Russia
Tel.: (7) 4952300077
Coffee Product Retailer
N.A.I.C.S.: 722515

STRAUSS INNOVATION GMBH
Retourenabteilung Strauss Platz 1, 42697, Solingen, Germany
Tel.: (49) 21 73 99 00 01   De
Web Site: http://www.strauss-innovation.de
Year Founded: 1902
Emp.: 1,200
Apparel Accessory Store Operator
N.A.I.C.S.: 458110
Thorsten Hollger *(Mng Dir)*

STRAWBEAR ENTERTAINMENT GROUP
Room 2508 Building A Wanda Plaza No 98 Jiangdong Zhong Road, Jianye, Nanjing, Jiangsu, China
Tel.: (86) 255805551   Ky
Web Site: http://www.strawbearentertain.com
Year Founded: 2014
2125—(HKG)
Motion Picture Technology Services
N.A.I.C.S.: 512132
Liu Xiaofeng *(Chm)*

STRAX AB
Master Samuelsgatan 10, 111 44, Stockholm, Sweden
Tel.: (46) 854501750
Web Site: https://www.strax.com
Year Founded: 1997
STRAX—(OMX)
Rev.: $112,661,343
Assets: $107,484,351
Liabilities: $114,479,819
Net Worth: ($6,995,467)
Earnings: ($21,182,819)
Emp.: 203
Fiscal Year-end: 12/31/22
Mobile Accessories & Connected Devices Design, Mfr & Distr
N.A.I.C.S.: 334417
Johan Heijbel *(CFO)*

Subsidiaries:

Brandvault Global Services Ltd. (1)
Unit B11 in Arena Business Centre 9 Nimrod Way, Wimborne, BH21 7UH, Dorset, United Kingdom
Tel.: (44) 333 577 8044
Web Site: https://www.brandvault.com
Ecommerce Services
N.A.I.C.S.: 541618
Michael Bartlett *(Mng Dir)*

Strax Americas, Inc. (1)
2606 NW 97th Ave, Doral, FL 33172   (100%)
Tel.: (305) 209-4299
Web Site: https://www.strax.com
Mobile Device Accesories Mfr & Distr
N.A.I.C.S.: 334417

Subsidiary (Non-US):

Strax (UK) Ltd. (2)
13 Parkbury Handley Page Way Colney, Saint Albans, AL2 2DQ, Herts, United Kingdom
Tel.: (44) 1923852900
Sales Range: $10-24.9 Million
Emp.: 9
Wireless & Mobile Telecommunications Services
N.A.I.C.S.: 517112

Strax Asia Ltd. (1)
703 7/F Sunbeam Plaza 1155 Canton Road, Mongkok, Kowloon, China (Hong Kong)
Tel.: (852) 23140670
Mobile Accessory Mfr & Distr
N.A.I.C.S.: 334210

Strax France Sarl (1)
16 Bis Rue Grange Dame Rose, 78140, Velizy-Villacoublay, France
Tel.: (33) 139463707
Mobile Accessory Mfr & Distr
N.A.I.C.S.: 334210

Strax Germany GmbH (1)
Belgische Allee 52 54, 53842, Troisdorf, Germany
Tel.: (49) 224 195 1270
Mobile Accessory Mfr & Distr
N.A.I.C.S.: 334210

Strax Norway S.A. (1)
Hangarveien 21, 3241, Sandefjord, Norway
Tel.: (47) 33478000
Mobile Accessory Mfr & Distr
N.A.I.C.S.: 334210

Strax Shenzhen Limited (1)
6-R39 6F China Mercants Port Plaza No 1 Gongye 3rd Street, Shekou, Shenzhen, China
Tel.: (86) 75521615493
Mobile Accessory Mfr & Distr
N.A.I.C.S.: 334210

Strax Sp. z o.o. (1)
Ul Minska 25, 03-741, Warsaw, Poland
Tel.: (48) 22 556 6590
Mobile Accessory Mfr & Distr
N.A.I.C.S.: 334210

Telecom Lifestyle Fashion B.V. (1)
Kraaivenstraat 25-34, 5048 AB, Tilburg, Netherlands
Tel.: (31) 138200163
Web Site: https://www.tlfmobile.com
Mobile Accessory Mfr & Distr
N.A.I.C.S.: 334210

STREAKSAI PLC
9th Floor 16 Great Queen Street, London, WC2B 5DG, United Kingdom   UK
Web Site: https://playstreaks.com
Year Founded: 2021
STK—(LSE)
Custom Computer Programming Services
N.A.I.C.S.: 541511
Nicholas Lyth *(CFO)*

STREAM CO., LTD.
5F Sumitomo Real Estate Onarimon Ekimae Building 6-17-21 Shinbashi, Minato-ku, Tokyo, 105-0004, Japan
Tel.: (81) 368231125
Web Site: https://www.stream-jp.com
3071—(TKS)
Rev.: $194,620,500
Assets: $43,979,270
Liabilities: $22,787,260
Net Worth: $21,192,010
Earnings: $212,700
Emp.: 1,168
Fiscal Year-end: 01/31/24
Internet Electronics Retailer
N.A.I.C.S.: 455219
Satoshi Matsui *(Pres)*

Subsidiaries:

X-One Co., Ltd. (1)
Barbizon104 Bldg 5F 5-4-27, Minami-Aoyama Minato-ku, Tokyo, 105-0014, Japan   (80%)
Tel.: (81) 368223570
Web Site: https://www.x-one.co.jp
Sales Range: $25-49.9 Million
Health Foods & Cosmetics Retailer
N.A.I.C.S.: 456120

STREAM IDEAS GROUP LTD.
Unit 402A 4/F Benson Tower 74 Hung To Road, Kwun Tong, China (Hong Kong)
Tel.: (852) 35831143   Ky
Web Site: http://www.stream-ideas.com
Year Founded: 2010
8401—(HKG)
Rev.: $1,925,888
Assets: $3,304,800
Liabilities: $1,048,815
Net Worth: $2,255,985
Earnings: ($2,084,498)
Emp.: 33
Fiscal Year-end: 03/31/23
Online Advertising Services
N.A.I.C.S.: 541810
Jenny Cheung *(Co-Founder & Gen Mgr)*

Subsidiaries:

JAG Ideas (Malaysia) Sdn. Bhd. (1)
B-7-20 Empire Soho Empire Subang Jalan SS16/1, 47500, Subang Jaya, Selangor, Malaysia
Tel.: (60) 386012434
Social Media Marketing Services
N.A.I.C.S.: 541890

JAG Ideas Company Limited (1)
Unit 402A 4/F Benson Tower 74 Hung To Road, Kwun Tong, China (Hong Kong)
Tel.: (852) 35831143
Web Site: https://www.jagideasgroup.com
Social Media Marketing Services
N.A.I.C.S.: 541890
Hin Lau *(Mgr-Adv)*

STREAMAX TECHNOLOGY CO., LTD.
21-23/F B1 Building Zhiyuan No 1001 Xueyuan Avenue, Nanshan Dsitrict, Shenzhen, 518055, Guangdong, China
Tel.: (86) 75533601988
Web Site: https://www.streamax.com
Year Founded: 2002
002970—(SSE)
Rev.: $194,284,706
Assets: $281,198,764
Liabilities: $90,042,353
Net Worth: $191,156,411
Earnings: ($20,585,336)
Emp.: 2,200
Fiscal Year-end: 12/31/22
Application Development Services
N.A.I.C.S.: 541511
Zhijian Zhao *(Chm & Gen Mgr)*

STREAMPLAY STUDIO LIMITED
Level 5 126 - 130 Phillip Street, Sydney, 2000, NSW, Australia
Tel.: (61) 296808777   AU
Web Site: https://www.streamplay.studio
SP8—(ASX)
Rev.: $6,505,318
Assets: $17,196,141
Liabilities: $2,422,047
Net Worth: $14,774,094
Earnings: $5,218,132
Fiscal Year-end: 06/30/22
Metal Exploration & Mining Services
N.A.I.C.S.: 212290

STREAMWIDE S.A.
84 Rue d Hauteville, 75010, Paris, France
Tel.: (33) 170220101
Web Site: https://www.streamwide.com
Year Founded: 2001
ALSTW—(EUR)
Sales Range: $10-24.9 Million
Emp.: 44
Software Development Services
N.A.I.C.S.: 541511
Pascal Beglin *(CEO)*

Subsidiaries:

Beijing StreamWIDE Technology Company Limited (1)
1009 10th Floor Cultural Plaza 59 Zhong Guan Cun Street, Hai Dian District, Beijing, 100872, China
Tel.: (86) 10 82503365
Software Development Services
N.A.I.C.S.: 541511

StreamWIDE Romania S.R.L. (1)
25 Fagaras Street Sector 1, Bucharest, 010897, Romania
Tel.: (40) 21 327 55 50
Software Development Services
N.A.I.C.S.: 541511

StreamWIDE Tunisia Sarl (1)
rue Lac Mazurie Immeuble SILAC 3ieme etage - B11 Les Berges du Lac, 1053, Tunis, Tunisia
Tel.: (216) 97 235 460
Software Development Services
N.A.I.C.S.: 541511

StreamWIDE, Inc. (1)
Copper Ridge Plz 9 Polito Ave Ste 1005, Lyndhurst, NJ 07071
Tel.: (201) 933-5700
Software Development Services
N.A.I.C.S.: 541511

Streamwide Pte. Ltd. (1)
141 Cecil Street 10-01, Singapore, 069541, Singapore
Tel.: (65) 63245808
Telecommunication Servicesb
N.A.I.C.S.: 517810
Lindy Wong *(Gen Mgr)*

STRECKFUSS SYSTEMS GMBH & CO. KG
Kruppstrasse 10, Eggenstein, D-76344, Germany
Tel.: (49) 72197710
Web Site: http://www.streckfuss.de
Sales Range: $1-9.9 Million
Emp.: 10
Soldering Systems Mfr
N.A.I.C.S.: 333992
Michael Streckfuss *(CEO)*

STREDOSLOVENSKA ENERGETIKA, A.S.
Pri Rajcianke 8591/4B, 010 47, Zilina, Slovakia
Tel.: (421) 41 519 1111
Web Site: http://www.sse.sk
Electric Power Supply Services
N.A.I.C.S.: 221121
Szilard Mangult *(Dir-Sls & Svcs)*

Subsidiaries:

Elektroenergeticke montaze, a. s. (1)
Pri Rajcianke 292610, Zilina, 010 01, Slovakia
Tel.: (421) 415192721
Web Site: http://www.eem.sk
Electric Equipment Mfr
N.A.I.C.S.: 327110

Stredoslovenska energetika - Distribucia, a. s. (1)
Pri Rajcianke 2927/8, 010 47, Zilina, Slovakia
Tel.: (421) 850166007
Web Site: http://www.sse-d.sk
Electric Equipment Mfr
N.A.I.C.S.: 327110

STREET MOTOR SALES LTD.
24 Family Lane, Smiths Falls, K7A 5B8, ON, Canada
Tel.: (888) 603-3486
New & Used Car Dealers
N.A.I.C.S.: 441110

STREET ONE GMBH
Imkerstrasse 4, 30916, Isernhagen, Germany
Tel.: (49) 513697730
Web Site: http://www.street-one.de
Year Founded: 1983
Rev.: $326,490,186
Emp.: 120
Apparel Whslr
N.A.I.C.S.: 424350

STREET ONE GMBH

Street One GmbH—(Continued)

Thomas Kromik (Co-Mng Dir)

STREIF GMBH
Josef-Streif-Strasse 1 Eifel, 54595, Weinsheim, Germany
Tel.: (49) 65511200
Web Site: http://www.streif.de
Sales Range: $25-49.9 Million
Emp.: 200
Construction & Engineering Services
N.A.I.C.S.: 236115
Joerg-Achim Vette (Owner & Mng Dir)

Subsidiaries:

SFH Fertighaus AG (1)
Landstrasse 41, 5430, Wettingen, Switzerland
Tel.: (41) 56 426 50 30
Web Site: http://www.sfh-fertighaus.ch
Residential & Commercial Building Construction Services
N.A.I.C.S.: 236115

Streif GmbH (1)
3-5 Route De Stadtbredimus, 5570, Remich, Luxembourg
Tel.: (352) 26708330
Web Site: http://www.streif.lu
Residential & Commercial Building Construction Services
N.A.I.C.S.: 236115

Streif UK Ltd (1)
Metro House Northgate, Chichester, PO19 1BE, West Sussex, United Kingdom
Tel.: (44) 1243 790 075
Web Site: http://www.streif.co.uk
Residential & Commercial Building Construction Services
N.A.I.C.S.: 236115

STREIT MECANIQUE SA
21 rue Gaston Renault, 25340, Santoche, France
Tel.: (33) 381906670
MLSTR—(EUR)
Sales Range: $50-74.9 Million
Automobile Parts Mfr
N.A.I.C.S.: 334515
Celine Jeannin (Chief HR Officer)

STRENESSE NEW GMBH
Eichendorffplatz 3, 86720, Nordlingen, Germany
Tel.: (49) 90818070   De
Web Site: http://www.strenesse.com
Year Founded: 1949
Women Clothing & Accessories Designer & Retailer
N.A.I.C.S.: 315250
Jurgen Gessler (CEO)

STRESS ANALYSIS AND DESIGN ENGINEERING LTD.
Peachley Court Peachley Lane, Lower Broadheath, Worcester, WR2 6QR, Worcestershire, United Kingdom
Tel.: (44) 1905 640025
Web Site: http://www.strandeng.com
Year Founded: 1997
Aerospace Analysis & Engineering
N.A.I.C.S.: 541330
Anthony Bedborough (Founder & Mng Dir)

Subsidiaries:

Strand Aerospace Malaysia (1)
PJ Trade Centre, B13 02 & B13 03 Menara BATA, No 8 Jalan PJU 8/8A, 47820, Petaling Jaya, Selangor, Malaysia
Tel.: (60) 3 7495 5222
Emp.: 150
Aerospace & Engineering Services
N.A.I.C.S.: 541330
Naguib Mohd Nor (CEO)

STRIA LITHIUM INC.
945 Princess Street, Kingston, K7L 0E9, ON, Canada
Tel.: (613) 702-0789   Ca
Web Site: https://strialithium.com
Year Founded: 2011
S35A—(DEU)
Rev.: $59,882
Assets: $2,942,039
Liabilities: $164,342
Net Worth: $2,777,697
Earnings: ($935,918)
Fiscal Year-end: 09/30/23
Investment Services
N.A.I.C.S.: 523999
Judith Mazvihwa-MacLean (CFO & Sec)

STRICKLAND METALS LIMITED
Level 4 15 Ogilvie Road, Mount Pleasant, 6153, WA, Australia
Tel.: (61) 863179875   AU
Web Site: https://www.stricklandmetals.com.au
Year Founded: 2004
STK—(ASX)
Rev.: $336,371
Assets: $58,043,867
Liabilities: $4,875,898
Net Worth: $53,167,969
Earnings: ($4,390,662)
Fiscal Year-end: 06/30/24
Mineral Exploration Services
N.A.I.C.S.: 213115
Andrew Viner (Chm)

STRIDERS CORPORATION
Nihonbashi Muromachi 4-6-2 Ryoka Building 9th floor, Chuo-Ku, Tokyo, 103-0022, Japan
Tel.: (81) 369108390
Web Site: https://www.striders.co.jp
Year Founded: 1965
9816—(TKS)
Rev.: $50,764,800
Assets: $30,597,690
Liabilities: $13,808,290
Net Worth: $16,789,400
Earnings: $542,020
Emp.: 135
Fiscal Year-end: 03/31/24
Information Technology Services
N.A.I.C.S.: 541511
Ryoichi Hayakawa (Chm)

Subsidiaries:

Kurashiki Royal Art Hotel Co., Ltd. (1)
3-21-19 Achi, Kurashiki, 710-0055, Okayama Prefecture, Japan
Tel.: (81) 864232400
Web Site: https://www.royal-art-hotel.co.jp
Hotel Services
N.A.I.C.S.: 721110

M&A Global Partners Co. Ltd. (1)
Shimbashi MCV Bldg 8th Floor 5-13-5 Shimbashi, Minato-ku, Tokyo, 105-0004, Japan
Tel.: (81) 102818888
Web Site: http://www.ma-gp.co.jp
Advisory Services
N.A.I.C.S.: 541611

Mirai Intellectual Property & Technology Research Center Co., Ltd. (1)
Sumitomo Seimei Yotsuya Building 4-41 Yotsuyahonshiocho, Shinjuku-ku, Tokyo, 160-0003, Japan
Tel.: (81) 364578044
Web Site: https://www.mirai-iptrc.co.jp
Emp.: 80
Patent Search Services
N.A.I.C.S.: 541199

Mobile Link Inc. (1)
2-1-3 Ichigaya Higashi Building 1F Ichigaya Tacho, Shinjuku-ku, Tokyo, 162-0843, Japan
Tel.: (81) 352271375
Web Site: https://www.mobile-link.co.jp

Sales Network Construction Services
N.A.I.C.S.: 236220

Narita Gateway Hotel Co., Ltd. (1)
658 Oyama, Narita, Chiba Prefecture, Japan
Tel.: (81) 476355511
Web Site: http://www.gateway-hotel.co.jp
Hotel Services
N.A.I.C.S.: 721110

Trust Advisers Corporation (1)
1-3-5 Tanmachi Shoji Building 5F Taito, Taito-ku, Tokyo, 110-0016, Japan
Tel.: (81) 358468240
Web Site: https://www.trust-advisers.co.jp
Emp.: 60
Trading Services
N.A.I.C.S.: 425120

STRIDES PHARMA SCIENCE LIMITED
Strides House Bilekahalli Bannerghatta Road, Bengaluru, 560076, India
Tel.: (91) 8067840000   In
Web Site: https://www.strides.com
Year Founded: 1990
532531—(BOM)
Rev.: $453,056,172
Assets: $795,925,904
Liabilities: $535,403,993
Net Worth: $260,521,911
Earnings: ($25,457,706)
Emp.: 2,850
Fiscal Year-end: 03/31/23
Pharmaceutical Mfr & Distr
N.A.I.C.S.: 325412
Arun Kumar (Founder)

Subsidiaries:

Akorn Strides LLC (1)
1925 W Field Ct Ste 300, Lake Forest, IL 60045   (50%)
Tel.: (847) 279-6100
Web Site: http://www.akorn.com
Emp.: 100
Pharmaceutical Preparation Mfr
N.A.I.C.S.: 325412
Raj Rai (Pres)

Arco Lab Private Limited (1)
19/2 15th Cross Rd Dollar Layout 4th Phase J P Nagar, Sarakki Village, Bengaluru, 560078, Karnataka, India
Tel.: (91) 8067840000
Web Site: https://www.arcolab.com
Emp.: 400
Business Support Services
N.A.I.C.S.: 561499

Arcolab SA (1)
Chemin du Grand-Puits 28, 1217, Meyrin, Switzerland   (100%)
Tel.: (41) 227829525
Drugs & Druggists Sundries Whslr
N.A.I.C.S.: 424210

Beltapharm S.p.A (1)
Via Stelvio 66, 20095, Cusano Milanino, Italy   (70%)
Tel.: (39) 0266401216
Web Site: http://www.beltapharm.com
Sales Range: $25-49.9 Million
Emp.: 35
Pharmaceutical Preparation Mfr
N.A.I.C.S.: 325412

Co Pharma Ltd. (1)
Unit 4 Metro Centre Tolpits Lane, Watford, WD18 9SS, Herts, United Kingdom
Tel.: (44) 1923 255580
Web Site: http://www.co-pharma.co.uk
Sales Range: $25-49.9 Million
Emp.: 6
Pharmaceuticals Product Mfr
N.A.I.C.S.: 325412
John Vaughan (Gen Mgr)

Fairmed Healthcare GmbH (1)
Dorotheenstrasse 48, 22301, Hamburg, Germany
Tel.: (49) 4030085678
Web Site: https://www.fair-med.de
Pharmaceuticals Product Mfr
N.A.I.C.S.: 325412

INTERNATIONAL PUBLIC

Global Remedies Ltd. (1)
#124 Sipcot Industrial Complex, 635126, Hosur, India   (100%)
Tel.: (91) 4344277372
Sales Range: $25-49.9 Million
Emp.: 100
Pharmaceutical Preparation Mfr
N.A.I.C.S.: 325412

Inbiopro Solutions Private Limited (1)
Lab Office 138-B 2nd-3rd Floors Udayagiri Complex Kiadb, Peenya 3rd Phase, Bengaluru, 560058, India
Tel.: (91) 80 4160 8141
Web Site: http://www.inbiopro.com
Sales Range: $25-49.9 Million
Emp.: 3
Biotechnology Research Services
N.A.I.C.S.: 541714
Erich Fric (CEO)

Infabra Industria Farmaceutica Ltd. (1)
AV Das Americas 8445, Room 801-804, Barra Tower, Rio de Janeiro, 22793 080, Brazil
Tel.: (55) 21 24876305
Pharmaceutical Mfr & Distr
N.A.I.C.S.: 325412

Onco Therapies Limited (1)
284/B part Bglr Industrial Area, Hobli Anekal Taluka, Bengaluru, 560076, Karnataka, India
Tel.: (91) 8067840000
Web Site: http://www.stridesarco.com
Emp.: 100
Medical Instrument Mfr & Distr
N.A.I.C.S.: 334510
Peter Jensen-Muir (Gen Mgr)

Pharma Strides Canada Corporation (1)
33rd Ave Fort, Saint-Lambert, J4P3S9, QC, Canada   (100%)
Tel.: (450) 672-4455
Drugs & Druggists Sundries Whslr
N.A.I.C.S.: 424210

PharmaPar Inc. (1)
1565 boul Lionel-Boulet, Varennes, J3X 1P7, QC, Canada
Web Site: https://www.pharmapar.ca
Pharmaceuticals Mfr
N.A.I.C.S.: 325412

SVADS Holdings SA (1)
Rue Fritz-Courvoisier 40, 2300, La Chaux-de-Fonds, Suisse, Switzerland
Tel.: (41) 329679595
Emp.: 2
Pharmaceutical Product Mfr & Distr
N.A.I.C.S.: 325412

Shasun (Dudley) Ltd (1)
Dudley, Cramlington, NE23 7QG, United Kingdom   (100%)
Tel.: (44) 1912500471
Sales Range: $125-149.9 Million
Emp.: 300
Chemicals Mfr
N.A.I.C.S.: 325998
John Wiper (Dir-Ops)

Shasun Pharma Solutions Inc. (1)
1001 Sheldon Dr Ste 101, Cary, NC 27513
Tel.: (919) 678-0702
Web Site: https://www.sterlingpharmasolutions.com
Pharmaceuticals Product Mfr
N.A.I.C.S.: 325412
Kevin Cook (CEO)

Solara S.A. De C.V. (1)
Monte Elbruz 124 Oficina 401 4to piso, Col Palmitas Polanco Miguel Hidalgo, 11560, Mexico, Mexico   (74%)
Tel.: (52) 5591260860
Web Site: http://www.solara.com.mx
Pharmaceutical Preparation Mfr
N.A.I.C.S.: 325412

Strides Arcolab (FA) Ltd. (1)
BP 1834 Rue Dubois de Saligny, Douala, Cameroon
Tel.: (237) 343 0435
Pharmaceutical Mfr & Distr
N.A.I.C.S.: 325412

AND PRIVATE COMPANIES

Strides Arcolab Polska Sp.z o.o (1)
ul Daniszewska 10, 03-320, Warsaw, Poland
Tel.: (48) 22 614 00 81
Web Site: http://www.strides.pl
Sales Range: $25-49.9 Million
Emp.: 100
Pharmaceuticals Product Mfr
N.A.I.C.S.: 325412
Pawel Stanislaw Wronski *(Gen Mgr)*

Strides Chemicals Private Limited (1)
Plot No. N 39/N39-1 Additional MIDC, Anand Nagar Ambernath, Thane, 431 506, India
Tel.: (91) 251 3983420 45 48
Private Label, Over-the-Counter, Pharmaceuticals & Nutritionals Mfr
N.A.I.C.S.: 325412

Strides Pharma UK Limited (1)
Units 4 Dwight Road, Tolpits Lane, Watford, WD18 9SS, Hertfordshire, United Kingdom
Tel.: (44) 1923255580
Web Site: https://www.stridespharma.co.uk
Pharmaceuticals Product Mfr
N.A.I.C.S.: 325412

Strides Pharma., Inc. (1)
2 Twr Ctr Blvd Ste 1102, East Brunswick, NJ 08816 **(84.93%)**
Tel.: (609) 773-5000
Sales Range: $25-49.9 Million
Emp.: 5
Pharmaceutical Preparation Mfr
N.A.I.C.S.: 325412

Subsidiary (Domestic):

Shasun USA Inc. (2)
197 Route 18 Ste 102, East Brunswick, NJ 08816
Tel.: (732) 465-0700
Pharmaceutical Product Mfr & Distr
N.A.I.C.S.: 325412
Chaitanya Devendra *(Mgr-Bus Dev)*

Strides Singapore Pte Ltd. (1)
Strides House Bilekahalli Bannerghatta Road, Bengaluru, 560 076, India
Tel.: (91) 8057580738
Pharmaceuticals
N.A.I.C.S.: 325412

Trinity Pharma Proprietary Limited (1)
Tel.: (27) 105945610
Web Site: https://www.trinitypharma.co.za
Pharmaceuticals Product Mfr
N.A.I.C.S.: 325412
Gaby Simaan *(Mng Dir)*

Vensun Pharmaceuticals Inc. (1)
790 Township Line Rd Ste 250, Yardley, PA 19067
Tel.: (215) 543-3737
Web Site: https://www.vensunrx.com
Pharmaceuticals Product Mfr
N.A.I.C.S.: 325412
Hemanshu Pandya *(Pres & CEO)*

STRIKE CO., LTD.
15F Mitsui and Co Building 1-2-1 Otemachi, Chiyoda-ku, Tokyo, 100-0004, Japan
Tel.: (81) 368480101
Web Site: https://www.strike.co.jp
Year Founded: 1997
6196—(TKS)
Rev.: $63,419,720
Assets: $82,942,650
Liabilities: $17,918,180
Net Worth: $65,024,470
Earnings: $20,192,340
Fiscal Year-end: 08/31/20
Merger Acquisition Consulting Services
N.A.I.C.S.: 541611
Kunihiko Arai *(Pres & CEO)*

STRIKE ENERGY LIMITED
Level 1 40 Kings Park Road, PO Box 569, West Perth, 6005, WA, Australia
Tel.: (61) 870997400 AU
Web Site: https://strikeenergy.au

STX—(ASX)
Rev.: $30,446,047
Assets: $352,021,233
Liabilities: $49,911,191
Net Worth: $302,110,041
Earnings: $5,731,838
Fiscal Year-end: 06/30/24
Crude Petroleum Extraction Services
N.A.I.C.S.: 211120
Neville Joseph Power *(Deputy Chm)*

Subsidiaries:

Talon Energy Ltd. (1)
1202 Hay Street, West Perth, 6005, WA, Australia
Tel.: (61) 863191900
Web Site: http://www.talonpetroleum.com.au
Rev.: $30,767
Assets: $19,948,667
Liabilities: $1,940,944
Net Worth: $18,007,723
Earnings: $8,640,890
Fiscal Year-end: 12/31/2022
Petroleum Exploration & Development
N.A.I.C.S.: 213112
Matt Worner *(Exec Dir)*

Subsidiary (US):

Texoz E&P I, Inc. (2)
20445 State Hwy 249 Ste 280, Houston, TX 77070
Tel.: (281) 419-4976
Petroleum Exploration Services
N.A.I.C.S.: 213112

STRIKE LIMITED
650 The Crescent Colchester Business Park, Colchester, Essex, United Kingdom
Tel.: (44) 3300571637
Web Site: https://strike.co.uk
Year Founded: 2011
Real Estate Lending Services
N.A.I.C.S.: 531190
Sam Mitchell *(CEO)*

STRIKE MINERALS INC.
80 Richmond Street West Suite 1101, Toronto, M5H 2A4, ON, Canada
Tel.: (416) 603-7200
Web Site: http://www.strikeminerals.com
Year Founded: 1987
Sales Range: Less than $1 Million
Mineral Exploration & Drilling Services
N.A.I.C.S.: 213114
Denis G. Crane *(Chm)*

STRIKE RESOURCES LIMITED
Suite 1 Level 1 680 Murray Street, West Perth, 6005, WA, Australia
Tel.: (61) 892149700 AU
Web Site: https://www.strikeresources.com.au
SRK—(ASX)
Rev.: $3,583,118
Assets: $5,245,405
Liabilities: $770,729
Net Worth: $4,474,675
Earnings: $503,821
Fiscal Year-end: 06/30/24
Mineral Development Services
N.A.I.C.S.: 213114
William M. Johnson *(Mng Dir)*

STRIKEPOINT GOLD INC.
Suite 3123 - 595 Burrard Street, PO Box 49139, Three Bentall Centre, Vancouver, V7X 1J1, BC, Canada
Tel.: (604) 602-1440
Web Site: https://www.strikepointgold.com
SKP—(OTCIQ)
Rev.: $741
Assets: $479,877
Liabilities: $78,939
Net Worth: $400,938

Earnings: ($3,031,271)
Fiscal Year-end: 12/31/19
Gold Exploration Services
N.A.I.C.S.: 212220
Shawn Khunkhun *(CEO)*

STRIKEWELL ENERGY CORP.
RPO Box 60610, Granville Park, Vancouver, V6H 4B9, BC, Canada
Tel.: (604) 331-3395
Web Site: https://www.strikewellenergy.com
SKK—(TSXV)
Rev.: $463,231
Assets: $737,474
Liabilities: $18,783,186
Net Worth: ($18,045,712)
Earnings: ($1,507,167)
Fiscal Year-end: 12/31/23
Oil & Gas Exploration Services
N.A.I.C.S.: 213112
David Hislop *(Pres & CEO)*

STRIP TINNING HOLDINGS PLC
Arden Business Park Arden Road, Birmingham, B45 0JA, United Kingdom
Tel.: (44) 1214577675 UK
Web Site: https://www.striptinning.com
Year Founded: 1957
STG—(AIM)
Emp.: 130
Offices of Other Holding Companies
N.A.I.C.S.: 551112

Subsidiaries:

Strip Tinning Limited (1)
Arden Business Park Arden Road, Birmingham, B45 0JA, United Kingdom
Tel.: (44) 1214577675
Web Site: https://www.striptinning.com
Emp.: 130
Automotive Glazing Product Distr
N.A.I.C.S.: 423120

STRIVE CAPITAL LLP
34 St James Street, London, SW1A 1HD, United Kingdom
Tel.: (44) 7814 858 227 UK
Web Site: http://www.strivecapital.co.uk
Privater Equity Firm
N.A.I.C.S.: 523999
Andrew Harman *(Co-Founder)*

Subsidiaries:

Academia Ltd. (1)
8 Kinetic Crescent Innova Park, Enfield, EN3 7XH, United Kingdom
Tel.: (44) 8456 120 118
Web Site: http://www.academia.co.uk
Sales Range: $10-24.9 Million
Emp.: 75
Software Licensing Services
N.A.I.C.S.: 423430
Mike Bacon *(CEO)*

STRIX GROUP PLC
Tel.: (44) 1624829829 IM
Web Site: https://www.strixplc.com
Year Founded: 2017
KETL—(AIM)
Rev.: $134,965,918
Assets: $264,082,302
Liabilities: $217,062,610
Net Worth: $47,019,692
Earnings: $21,276,193
Emp.: 850
Fiscal Year-end: 12/31/22
Filtration Device Mfr & Distr
N.A.I.C.S.: 333414
Mark Bartlett *(CEO)*

Subsidiaries:

Strix (U.K.) Limited (1)
Dodleston House Bell Meadow Business Park Park Lane, Pulford, Chester, CH4 9EP, United Kingdom
Tel.: (44) 1624829829
Electronic Product Mfr & Distr
N.A.I.C.S.: 334111

Strix Guangzhou Ltd. (1)
383 Xiayuan Road, Huangpu District, Guangzhou, 510735, China
Tel.: (86) 2082222903
Electronic Product Mfr & Distr
N.A.I.C.S.: 334111

Strix Hong Kong Ltd. (1)
Room 2002-03 20/F World Trade Centre 280 Gloucester Road, Causeway Bay, China (Hong Kong)
Tel.: (852) 28325878
Electronic Product Mfr & Distr
N.A.I.C.S.: 334111

Strix Limited (1)
Forrest House, Ronaldsway, IM9 2RG, Ballasalla, Isle of Man
Tel.: (44) 1624829829
Web Site: http://www.strix.com
Household Appliances Mfr
N.A.I.C.S.: 335220

STROBELGASSE WERBEAGENTUR GMBH
Strobelgasse 2, 1010, Vienna, Austria
Tel.: (43) 1 512 18 02 AT
Web Site: http://www.st-stephens.at
Year Founded: 1984
Rev.: $12,000,000
Emp.: 14
N.A.I.C.S.: 541810
Gerd Babits *(Mng Partner)*

STROC INDUSTRIE
4 rue des Tabors, Oasis district, Casablanca, Morocco
Tel.: (212) 522991570
Web Site: https://www.stroc.com
Year Founded: 1989
STR—(CAS)
Sales Range: $1-9.9 Million
Engineeering Services
N.A.I.C.S.: 541330
Nabil Ziat *(Chm & CEO)*

STROER SE & CO. KGAA
Stroer Allee 1, 50999, Cologne, Germany
Tel.: (49) 223696450 De
Web Site: https://www.stroeer.com
SAX—(EUR)
Holding Company; Out-of-Home Media & Marketing Services
N.A.I.C.S.: 551112
Christoph Vilanek *(Chm & Chm-Supervisory Bd)*

Subsidiaries:

Ambient-TV Sales & Services GmbH (1)
Oberstrasse 88, 20149, Hamburg, Germany
Tel.: (49) 40226162510
Web Site: http://www.dooh-media.de
Digital Advertising Services
N.A.I.C.S.: 541810

Asam Betriebs-GmbH (1)
Altenzeller Weg 23 Aschbuch, 92339, Beilngries, Germany
Tel.: (49) 846170060
Web Site: http://www.asam-cosmetics.com
Emp.: 200
Cosmetics Products Mfr
N.A.I.C.S.: 325620

BBelements Sp. z.o.o. (1)
Usypiskowa 3, Warsaw, Poland
Tel.: (48) 225924601
Advertising Services
N.A.I.C.S.: 541810

Business Advertising GmbH (1)
Tersteegenstrasse 30, 40474, Dusseldorf, Germany
Tel.: (49) 21117934750
Web Site: http://www.businessad.de
Online Marketing Services

STROER SE & CO. KGAA

Stroer SE & Co. KGaA—(Continued)
N.A.I.C.S.: 541613

Content Fleet GmbH (1)
Kehrwieder 8, 20457, Hamburg, Germany
Tel.: (49) 40600800600
Web Site: http://www.contentfleet.com
Integrated Content Marketing Services
N.A.I.C.S.: 541613
Kirsten Becker *(Head-Ops)*

D+S communication center management GmbH (1)
Mexikoring 33, 22297, Hamburg, Germany
Tel.: (49) 40 4114 0
Call Center Services
N.A.I.C.S.: 561422

DSM Krefeld Aussenwerbung GmbH (1)
Mevissenstrasse 54, 47803, Krefeld, Germany
Tel.: (49) 2151878870
Advertising Services
N.A.I.C.S.: 541810

Delta Concept S.a.r.l. (1)
6 rue de Chamechaude, 38360, Sassenage, France
Tel.: (33) 476535581
Web Site: http://www.delta-concept.fr
Thermo Bimetal Component Mfr
N.A.I.C.S.: 334513
Gilbert Pitone *(CEO)*

ECE flatmedia GmbH (1)
Heegbarg 30, 22391, Hamburg, Germany
Tel.: (49) 4060607766
Web Site: http://www.ece-flatmedia.com
Digital Advertising Services
N.A.I.C.S.: 541850
Christiane Nickel *(Acct Mgr)*

Edgar Ambient Media Group GmbH (1)
Kehrwieder 8, 20457, Hamburg, Germany
Tel.: (49) 4069638250
Web Site: http://www.edgar.de
Media Advertising Services
N.A.I.C.S.: 541810
Peter Kruezner *(Sls Mgr)*

GIGA Digital AG (1)
Wohlertstr 12-13, Berlin, 10115, Germany
Tel.: (49) 309210640
Digital Advertising Services
N.A.I.C.S.: 541850

GIGA fixxoo GmbH (1)
Torstr 49, 10119, Berlin, Germany
Tel.: (49) 3039749002
Web Site: http://www.fixxoo.de
Advertising Services
N.A.I.C.S.: 541810
Flavio Trillo *(Mgr-ECommerce)*

Grapevine Marketing GmbH (1)
Tengstrasse 9, 80798, Munich, Germany
Tel.: (49) 89588031770
Web Site: http://www.grapevine-marketing.com
Branding & Personnel Marketing Services
N.A.I.C.S.: 541613
Enrico Geigle *(Mng Dir)*

HanXX Media GmbH (1)
Am Buchel 77, 53173, Bonn, Germany
Tel.: (49) 22167789300
Web Site: http://www.hanxx.de
Media Advertising Services
N.A.I.C.S.: 541840

INFOSCREEN GmbH (1)
Staffelseestrasse 8, 81477, Munich, Germany
Tel.: (49) 897489890
Web Site: http://www.infoscreen.de
Media Advertising Services
N.A.I.C.S.: 541840
Alexander Furthner *(Mng Dir)*

Internet BillBoard a.s. (1)
Novoveska 1262/95, 709 00, Ostrava, Czech Republic
Tel.: (420) 553615555
Web Site: http://www.ibillboard.com
Online Advertising Services
N.A.I.C.S.: 541810
Barbora Rackova *(Head-Customer Svc)*

Kajomi GmbH (1)
Semmelweisstrasse 8, 82152, Planegg, Germany
Tel.: (49) 8945228390
Web Site: http://www.kajomi.de
Email Marketing Services
N.A.I.C.S.: 541860
Manuela Pehle *(Head-Acct)*

Kolner Aussenwerbung Gesellschaft mit beschrankter Haftung (1)
Bonner Wall 33, 50677, Cologne, Germany
Tel.: (49) 221376020
Advertising Services
N.A.I.C.S.: 541810

Kultur-Medien Hamburg GmbH Gesellschaft fur Kulturinformationsanlagen (1)
Oehleckerring 22-24, 22419, Hamburg, Germany
Tel.: (49) 402294230
Web Site: http://www.kulturmedien-hh.de
Media Advertising Services
N.A.I.C.S.: 541840

LSP Digital GmbH & Co. KG (1)
Johannes-Brahms-Platz 1, 20355, Hamburg, Germany
Tel.: (49) 40284841750
Web Site: http://www.lsp.de
Business Management Consulting Services
N.A.I.C.S.: 541611
Madlen Jesswein *(Office Mgr)*

MBR Targeting GmbH (1)
Hobrechtstr 65, 12047, Berlin, Germany
Tel.: (49) 3069817113
Web Site: http://www.mbr-targeting.com
Online Advertising Services
N.A.I.C.S.: 541810
Pablo Metz *(CEO)*

Media-Direktservice GmbH (1)
Stroer-Allee 1, 50999, Cologne, Germany
Tel.: (49) 20149869400
Web Site: http://www.media-direktservice.de
Online Marketing Services
N.A.I.C.S.: 541613

Nachsendeauftrag DE Online GmbH (1)
Ustav-Heinemann-Ufer 74B, 50968, Cologne, Germany
Tel.: (49) 22164308941
Web Site: http://www.nachsendeauftrag.net
Mail Forwarding Services
N.A.I.C.S.: 561431

Neo Advertising GmbH (1)
Kehrwieder 10, 20457, Hamburg, Germany
Tel.: (49) 4030384150
Web Site: http://www.neo-group.de
Digital Marketing Services
N.A.I.C.S.: 541613

Optimise-it GmbH (1)
Kehrwieder 9, 20457, Hamburg, Germany
Tel.: (49) 40466666110
Web Site: http://www.optimise-it.de
Live Chat Operating Services
N.A.I.C.S.: 561499
Jorn Stampehl *(Mng Dir)*

Outsite Media GmbH (1)
Sophienstrasse 33, 41065, Monchengladbach, Germany
Tel.: (49) 2161307050
Web Site: http://www.outsite-media.de
Media Marketing Services
N.A.I.C.S.: 541810
Walter Ehren *(Mng Dir)*

Permodo GmbH (1)
Derendorfer Allee 6, 40476, Dusseldorf, Germany
Tel.: (49) 89413240264
Web Site: http://www.permodo.com
Mobile Marketing Services
N.A.I.C.S.: 541613

PosterSelect Media-Agentur fur Aubenwerbung GmbH (1)
Fremersbergstrasse 67a, 76530, Baden-Baden, Germany
Tel.: (49) 7221973320
Web Site: http://www.posterselect.com
Outdoor Advertising Services
N.A.I.C.S.: 541850
Andre Barth *(Head-Sls-Intl)*

RegioHelden GmbH (1)
Rotebuhlstrasse 50, 70178, Stuttgart, Germany
Tel.: (49) 7111285010
Web Site: http://www.stroeer-online-marketing.de
Online Marketing Services
N.A.I.C.S.: 541613

Retail Media GmbH (1)
Stroer Allee 1, 50999, Cologne, Germany
Tel.: (49) 223638696222
Web Site: http://www.retailmedia.de
Web Advertising Services
N.A.I.C.S.: 541810

SEM Internet Reklam Hizmetleri ve Danismanlik A.S. (1)
Esentepe Mah Kore Sehitleri Cad NO 19, Zincirlikuyu, Istanbul, Turkiye
Tel.: (90) 2127055200
Web Site: http://www.semtr.com
Online Advertising Services
N.A.I.C.S.: 541810

Sales Holding GmbH (1)
Parsevalstrasse 11, 40468, Dusseldorf, Germany
Tel.: (49) 21120008300
Web Site: http://www.sales-holding.com
Sale Marketing Services
N.A.I.C.S.: 541613
Tobias Mehrer *(CEO)*

Service Planet GmbH (1)
Am Teich 1, 99427, Weimar, Germany
Tel.: (49) 36434370
Web Site: http://www.serviceplanet-online.de
Financial Accounting Services
N.A.I.C.S.: 541219

Sign You Mediascreen GmbH (1)
Kirchhellener Strasse 46, 46145, Oberhausen, Germany
Tel.: (49) 20862581780
Web Site: http://www.signyou-mediascreen.de
Web Advertising Services
N.A.I.C.S.: 541810

Statista GmbH (1)
Johannes-Brahms-Platz 1, 20355, Hamburg, Germany
Tel.: (49) 402848410
Statistical Data Analysis Services
N.A.I.C.S.: 518210

Statista Inc. (1)
55 Broad St 30th Fl, New York, NY 10004
Tel.: (212) 433-2270
Statistical Data Analysis Services
N.A.I.C.S.: 518210
Arne Wolter *(CMO, Chief Sls Officer & Chief Revenue Officer)*

Statista Ltd. (1)
209-215 Blackfriars Road 5th Floor, London, SE1 8NL, United Kingdom
Tel.: (44) 2081897000
Statistical Data Analysis Services
N.A.I.C.S.: 518210

Statista Pte. Ltd. (1)
138 Market Street, Singapore, 048946, Singapore
Tel.: (65) 66796229
Statistical Data Analysis Services
N.A.I.C.S.: 518210

Statista S.a.r.l. (1)
20 rue Cambon, 75001, Paris, France
Tel.: (33) 184889671
Statistical Data Analysis Services
N.A.I.C.S.: 518210

StayFriends GmbH (1)
Salzufer 8, 10587, Berlin, Germany
Tel.: (49) 3023607850
Web Site: http://www.stayfriends.de
Social Networking Site Operator
N.A.I.C.S.: 541910

Stroer Dialog Group GmbH (1)
Georgiring 3, 04103, Leipzig, Germany
Tel.: (49) 34122900100
Web Site: http://www.stroer-dialog.de
Telemarketing Services
N.A.I.C.S.: 561422

Stroer Digital Media GmbH (1)
Stresemannstrasse 2, 22769, Hamburg, Germany
Tel.: (49) 40468567100
Web Site: http://www.stroeerdigitalmedia.de
Online Advertising Services
N.A.I.C.S.: 541810
Luminita Ciumacu *(Mgr-Tech Adv)*

Stroer Digital Publishing GmbH (1)
Kastor Tower Platz der Einheit 1, 60327, Frankfurt, Germany
Tel.: (49) 69921017610
Web Advertising Services
N.A.I.C.S.: 541810

Stroer Media Brands Apps d.o.o. (1)
Ulica Farkasa Vukotinovica 4, Zagreb, Croatia
Tel.: (385) 18894214
Web Site: http://www.smbapps.hr
Application Software Development Services
N.A.I.C.S.: 541511
Marko Curkovic *(Co-CEO)*

Stroer Media Brands GmbH (1)
Torstrasse 49, 10119, Berlin, Germany
Tel.: (49) 3059001130
Web Site: http://www.stroeermediabrands.de
Web Advertising Services
N.A.I.C.S.: 541810
Michael Ittner *(Sls Dir)*

Stroer Media Sp. z.o.o. (1)
ul Belwederska 6A, 00-762, Warsaw, Poland
Tel.: (48) 224442600
Web Site: http://www.stroer.pl
Advertising Services
N.A.I.C.S.: 541810
Anna Bialobrzeska *(Bus Mgr)*

Stroer Mobile Media GmbH (1)
Torstrasse 49, 10119, Berlin, Germany
Tel.: (49) 3094050176
Web Site: http://www.stroeermobilemedia.de
Media Advertising Services
N.A.I.C.S.: 541840
Sascha Luger *(Mgr-Campaign)*

SuperM&N UG (1)
Stroer Allee 1, 50999, Cologne, Germany
Tel.: (49) 22197598960
Web Site: http://www.super-mn.de
Web Advertising Services
N.A.I.C.S.: 541810

Yieldlove GmbH (1)
Kehrwieder 9, 20457, Hamburg, Germany
Tel.: (49) 40882157810
Web Site: http://www.yieldlove.com
Web Advertising Services
N.A.I.C.S.: 541810

adscale GmbH (1)
Ungererstrasse 40, 80802, Munich, Germany
Tel.: (49) 89 330 668 10 0
Web Site: http://www.adscale.de
Online Advertising Services
N.A.I.C.S.: 541810
Christina Pfluegler *(Mgr-PR)*

Subsidiary (Non-US):

adscale Laboratories Ltd. (2)
5 Ayr St, PO Box 19895, Riccarton, Christchurch, 8011, New Zealand
Tel.: (64) 33430494
Web Site: http://www.adscale.co.nz
Emp.: 50
Online Advertising Services
N.A.I.C.S.: 541810

blowUP media Benelux B.V. (1)
Singel 259, 1012 WG, Amsterdam, Netherlands
Tel.: (31) 206764164
Web Site: http://www.blowup-media.nl
Advertising Services
N.A.I.C.S.: 541810
Ernst Vos *(Chief Comml Officer)*

blowUP media Espana S.A. (1)
Nunez de Balboa 114 5-13, 28006, Madrid, Spain
Tel.: (34) 915159413
Web Site: http://www.blowup-media.es
Advertising Services
N.A.I.C.S.: 541810
Laura Carranza *(Mng Dir)*

AND PRIVATE COMPANIES / STS GLOBAL INCOME & GROWTH TRUST PLC

blowUP media GmbH (1)
Nordstrasse 116, 40477, Dusseldorf, Germany
Tel.: (49) 2114913700
Web Site: http://www.blowup-media.de
Advertising Services
N.A.I.C.S.: 541810
Carsten Kramer *(Mgr-Dev)*

iBillBoard Internet Reklam Hizmetleri ve Bilisim Teknolojileri A.S. (1)
Prf Ali Nihat Tarlan Cd Demircioglu Ism No 108 K 2 D 2, Atasehir, Istanbul, Turkiye
Tel.: (90) 2125322948
Advertising Services
N.A.I.C.S.: 541810

iBillBoard Poland Sp. z.o.o. (1)
Pl Konstytucji 5/ 75, 00-657, Warsaw, Poland
Tel.: (48) 221017913
Web Site: http://www.ibillboard.com
Online Advertising Services
N.A.I.C.S.: 541810
Magdalena Paciorek *(Mgr-Traffic)*

servtag GmbH (1)
Schonhauser Allee 6/7, 10119, Berlin, Germany
Tel.: (49) 30 492 092 27
Web Site: http://www.radcarpet.de
Mobile Advertising Services
N.A.I.C.S.: 541890

stylefruits GmbH (1)
Sonnenstrasse 31, 80331, Munich, Germany
Tel.: (49) 89540412924
Web Site: http://www.stylefruits.pr.co
Furniture Product Mfr
N.A.I.C.S.: 337127

STRONG PETROCHEMICAL HOLDINGS LIMITED
1604 Far East Finance Centre 16 Harcourt Road Admiralty, Hong Kong, China (Hong Kong)
Tel.: (852) 28343393   Ky
Web Site:
  http://www.strongpetrochem.com
Year Founded: 2000
0852—(HKG)
Rev.: $117,697,163
Assets: $188,518,695
Liabilities: $10,512,248
Net Worth: $178,006,448
Earnings: $731,085
Emp.: 93
Fiscal Year-end: 12/31/22
Petrochemical Mfr
N.A.I.C.S.: 325110
Jian Sheng Wang *(Chm)*

Subsidiaries:

Strong Petrochemical Limited (1)
Rua de Pequim No 230-246 17B and C Edif Macau Finance Centre, Macau, China (Macau)
Tel.: (853) 28700098
Emp.: 5
Petroleum Product Distr
N.A.I.C.S.: 424720
Ivan Sun *(Gen Mgr)*

STRONGLED LIGHTING SYSTEM (CAYMAN) CO., LTD.
The Grand Pavilion Commercial Centre Oleander Way 802 West Bay Road, PO Box 32052, Grand Cayman, Georgetown, KY1-1208, Cayman Islands
Tel.: (345) 51282868008
Web Site: http://www.strongled.com
5281—(TPE)
Rev.: $40,945,347
Assets: $57,660,587
Liabilities: $29,065,288
Net Worth: $28,595,299
Earnings: $1,062,105
Fiscal Year-end: 12/31/19
LED Lighting Mfr
N.A.I.C.S.: 335132

Chia-Jui Chang *(Chm)*

Subsidiaries:

ShangHai Grand Canyon LED Lighting Systems Co., Ltd. (1)
Room 501 Tower C Building 27-7 Lane 958 Fuli Yuedu Shenhong Road, Minhang District, Shanghai, China
Tel.: (86) 2164659597
LED Floodlight Mfr
N.A.I.C.S.: 335139

StrongLED Smart Lighting (Suzhou) Co., Ltd. (1)
No 2888 Linhu Avenue Foho Economic Development Zone, Wujiang, Suzhou, 215200, China
Tel.: (86) 51282868008
Light-Emitting Diode Lighting System Mfr & Distr
N.A.I.C.S.: 334511

Strongled Lighting Systems (Cayon) Co., Ltd. (1)
5F No 30 Sichuan 2nd St, Xitun Dist, Taichung, 407, Taiwan
Tel.: (886) 423171919
LED Floodlight Mfr
N.A.I.C.S.: 335139

STRONGPOINT ASA
Brynsengveien 10, 667, Oslo, Norway
Tel.: (47) 93403254   NO
Web Site:
  https://www.strongpoint.com
Year Founded: 2000
STRO—(OSL)
Rev.: $131,964,731
Assets: $99,729,663
Liabilities: $53,049,232
Net Worth: $46,680,430
Earnings: $3,362,039
Emp.: 524
Fiscal Year-end: 12/31/23
Software Developer
N.A.I.C.S.: 513210
Julius Stulpinas *(Sr VP-Tech & Supply Chain)*

Subsidiaries:

StrongPoint Cub AB (1)
Kemistvagen 1 B, 183 79, Taby, Sweden
Tel.: (46) 86388850
Ecommerce Services
N.A.I.C.S.: 459999

StrongPoint UAB (1)
Zalgirio str 90, LT 09303, Vilnius, Lithuania
Tel.: (370) 70070022
Web Site: https://www.strongpoint.com
Emp.: 500
IT Services
N.A.I.C.S.: 541519
Evaldas Budvilaitis *(Mng Dir)*

STRONTIUM PLC
Atlantic House Imperial Way, Reading, RG2 0TD, United Kingdom
Tel.: (44) 1189036035
Web Site:
  http://www.strontiumplc.com
Sales Range: $25-49.9 Million
Emp.: 30
Investment Services
N.A.I.C.S.: 523999
David Barker *(Mng Dir)*

Subsidiaries:

MiAD UK Limited (1)
1st Fl Estate House 2 Pembroke Rd, Sevenoaks, TN13 1XR, Kent, United Kingdom
Tel.: (44) 1732457200
Web Site: http://www.miaduk.com
Sales Range: $10-24.9 Million
Emp.: 10
Doctors Management Training Services
N.A.I.C.S.: 611430
Alan Wills *(Mgr-Bus Dev)*

STROUD RESOURCES LTD.
1090 Don Mills Road Suite 404, Toronto, M3C 3R6, ON, Canada
Tel.: (416) 888-8731   Ca
Web Site:
  https://www.stroudsilver.com
Year Founded: 1983
3X21—(DEU)
Rev.: $27,112
Assets: $272,992
Liabilities: $82,032
Net Worth: $190,960
Earnings: ($210,845)
Fiscal Year-end: 12/31/23
Mineral Exploration Services
N.A.I.C.S.: 213114

STROYINVEST HOLDING AD
Bul Gen Totleben 34 sgrada 6 et 3 ofis 12, Sofia, 1606, Bulgaria
Tel.: (359) 24224178
HSTR—(BUL)
Sales Range: Less than $1 Million
Professional & Other Technical Services
N.A.I.C.S.: 541990

STRUCT-CON CONSTRUCTION LTD.
2051 Williams Parkway East Unit 14, Brampton, L6S 5T3, ON, Canada
Tel.: (905) 791-5445
Web Site: http://www.struct-con.ca
Rev.: $17,164,743
Emp.: 40
Building Construction
N.A.I.C.S.: 236220
Mo Shariati *(CEO)*

STRUCTURAL MONITORING SYSTEMS PLC
1 Kyle Way Suite 116, Claremont, 6010, WA, Australia
Tel.: (61) 861617412
SMN—(ASX)
Rev.: $18,663,862
Assets: $21,915,732
Liabilities: $12,152,778
Net Worth: $9,762,954
Earnings: ($695,112)
Emp.: 143
Fiscal Year-end: 06/30/24
Crack Detection Sensor Mfr
N.A.I.C.S.: 334516
Sam Michael Wright *(Sec)*

Subsidiaries:

Structural Monitoring Systems Ltd. (1)
1 Kyle Way Suite 116, Claremont, 6010, WA, Australia
Tel.: (61) 861617412
Web Site: http://www.smsystems.com.au
Sales Range: $25-49.9 Million
Emp.: 3
Monitoring Equipments Mfr
N.A.I.C.S.: 334511

STRUCTURLAM PRODUCTS LTD.
2176 Government St, Penticton, V2A 8B5, BC, Canada
Tel.: (250) 492-8912
Web Site: http://www.structurlam.com
Year Founded: 1962
Rev.: $13,883,759
Emp.: 85
Wood Packages & Wood Laminations Mfr
N.A.I.C.S.: 321999
Mark Rufiange *(Owner)*

STRUIK HOLDING N.V.
Voorthuizerweg 9, Nijkerk, 3862 PZ, Netherlands
Tel.: (31) 342471841
Web Site: http://www.struik.nl
Year Founded: 1987
Sales Range: $100-124.9 Million
Emp.: 343
Food Products Mfr
N.A.I.C.S.: 311999
Johannes Struik *(Pres & Mng Dir)*

Subsidiaries:

Chillfis BvBa (1)
Brechtsebaan 913, 2900, Schoten, Belgium
Tel.: (32) 3 217 14 00
Food Retailer
N.A.I.C.S.: 445298

Struik Foods Deutschland GmbH (1)
Clara Zetkinstrasse 8 15, 14547, Beelitz, Germany
Tel.: (49) 332043900
Web Site: http://www.sonnenbassermann.de
Canned Soup Mfr
N.A.I.C.S.: 311422
Edwin van Veldhuizen *(Mng Dir)*

Struik Foods Europe N.V. (1)
PO Box 70, 3780 AA, Voorthuizen, Netherlands
Tel.: (31) 342 47 48 48
Web Site: http://www.struik.com
Emp.: 250
Convenience Foods Mfr
N.A.I.C.S.: 311999
Gert Mandersloot *(Mgr-Corp HR)*

Struik Foods Group Moscow (1)
World Trade Center Krasnopresnenskaya NAB 12, 123610, Moscow, Russia
Tel.: (7) 495 258 1299
Food Products Distr
N.A.I.C.S.: 424490

Ye Olde Oak Foods Ltd (1)
No 2 the Warehouse whars, PO Box 801, Halifax, HX62qj, United Kingdom
Tel.: (44) 14 22 83 30 44
Web Site: http://www.yeoldeoak.co.uk
Emp.: 4
Food Products Distr
N.A.I.C.S.: 424490
Liam Racktoo *(Natl Acct Mgr)*

STRUMICA TABAK AD
Ul Vanco Kitanov br 1, Strumica, North Macedonia
Tel.: (389) 34346562
Web Site:
  http://www.strumicatabak.com.mk
STTB—(MAC)
Sales Range: $25-49.9 Million
Tobacco Product Mfr
N.A.I.C.S.: 312230
Tony Veta *(Head-IT Dept)*

STRUST CO., LTD.
4-1-22 Takezakicho, Shimonoseki, 750-0025, Yamaguchi, Japan
Tel.: (81) 832291456
Web Site: https://www.strust.co.jp
3280—(TKS)
Rev.: $127,931,960
Assets: $252,715,960
Liabilities: $193,776,790
Net Worth: $58,939,170
Earnings: $5,182,790
Fiscal Year-end: 02/29/24
Real Estate Sales & Management
N.A.I.C.S.: 531210
Tomonari Sasahara *(Founder & Chm)*

STRUWE & PARTNER AGENTUR KOMMUNKATION GMBH
Zimmerstrasse 15A, 40215, Dusseldorf, Germany
Tel.: (49) 211 968 040
Year Founded: 1972
Rev.: $25,000,000
Emp.: 25
Co-op Advertising, Consumer Marketing
N.A.I.C.S.: 541810
Goerg Struwe *(Mng Dir)*

STS GLOBAL INCOME & GROWTH TRUST PLC
28 Walker Street, Edinburgh, EH3 7HR, United Kingdom

STS Global Income & Growth Trust plc—(Continued)

Tel.: (44) 1313780500 UK
Web Site: https://stsplc.co.uk
Year Founded: 2006
STS—(LSE)
Rev.: $11,410,920
Assets: $259,930,265
Liabilities: $36,348,371
Net Worth: $223,581,894
Earnings: ($19,742,203)
Fiscal Year-end: 03/31/20
Securities Brokerage Services
N.A.I.C.S.: 523150
John Evans (Chm)

Subsidiaries:

Troy Income & Growth Trust plc (1)
10 St Colme Street, Edinburgh, EH3 6AA, United Kingdom
Tel.: (44) 1315386610
Web Site: http://www.tigt.co.uk
Investment Trust
N.A.I.C.S.: 523999
Francis Brooke (Fund Mgr)

Subsidiary (Domestic):

Cameron Investors Trust Plc (2)
21 Walker Street, Edinburgh, EH3 7HX, United Kingdom
Tel.: (44) 1315381400
Web Site: http://www.cameroninvestors.co.uk
Investment Trust Management Services
N.A.I.C.S.: 523940

STUART ALEXANDER & CO., PTY. LTD.

Level 3 1 Smail Street, Ultimo, 2007, NSW, Australia
Tel.: (61) 292827700
Web Site: http://www.stuartalexander.com.au
Year Founded: 1884
Consumer Goods Distr
N.A.I.C.S.: 423620
Garry Browne (Chm)

STUART KIA LTD

265 Robie St, Truro, B2N 1K8, NS, Canada
Tel.: (902) 895-1671
Web Site: https://www.stuartkia.com
Year Founded: 1978
Sales Range: $10-24.9 Million
Emp.: 12
Car Dealer
N.A.I.C.S.: 441110

STUDEC

51 B Rue Piat, Paris, 75020, France
Tel.: (33) 144623232
Sales Range: $25-49.9 Million
Engineeering Services
N.A.I.C.S.: 541330
Grossi Laurent (Dir-Fin & Admin)

STUDEN & CO. HOLDING GMBH

Wilhelminenstrasse 91/19/2, Vienna, 1160, Austria
Tel.: (43) 14862424 De
Web Site: http://www.sco-group.com
Year Founded: 1992
Sales Range: $50-74.9 Million
Emp.: 200
Holding Company
N.A.I.C.S.: 551112
Ilija Studen (Pres)

Subsidiaries:

AGRANA-STUDEN Serbia d.o.o. (1)
5 V Milentija Popovica, 11000, Novi Beograd, Serbia
Tel.: (381) 116149145
Food Products Distr
N.A.I.C.S.: 424490
Aleksandar Cancarevic (Mgr-Mktg & Sls)

MINGOS COFFEE d.o.o. (1)
Ledenice Donje bb, Gradacac, Brcko, Bosnia & Herzegovina
Tel.: (387) 35 850 180
Emp.: 19
Coffee Product Mfr
N.A.I.C.S.: 311920

SCO - AREX Holding Ges.m.b.H. (1)
Wilhelminenstr 91 19 2, 1160, Vienna, Austria
Tel.: (43) 14862424
Web Site: http://www.scogroup.com
Emp.: 400
Holding Company
N.A.I.C.S.: 551112

Subsidiary (Domestic):

Seed Oil Holdings Ges.m.b.H. (2)
Wilhelminenstr 91 19 2, 1160, Vienna, 1160, Austria
Tel.: (43) 14862424
Web Site: http://www.sco-group.com
Holding Company
N.A.I.C.S.: 551112

Studen & CO Ltd. (1)
Letaliska cesta 16, 1000, Ljubljana, Slovenia
Tel.: (386) 1 548 30 36
Web Site: http://www.agragold.com
Emp.: 6
Coffee Distr
N.A.I.C.S.: 424490
Mitja Kovacic (Mng Dir)

STUDENTBOSTADER I NORDEN AB

Kungsgatan 47A, 753 21, Uppsala, Sweden
Tel.: (46) 841049130
Web Site: https://sbsstudent.se
Year Founded: 2006
STUDBO—(NASDAQ)
Rev.: $6,295,657
Assets: $213,420,311
Liabilities: $191,424,457
Net Worth: $21,995,854
Earnings: ($65,434,549)
Emp.: 12
Fiscal Year-end: 12/31/18
Multifamily Home Developer
N.A.I.C.S.: 236116
Lars Wikstrom (CEO & CFO)

STUDIO 100 NV

Halfstraat 80, 2627, Schelle, Belgium
Tel.: (32) 38776035 BE
Web Site: http://www.studio100.tv
Year Founded: 1996
Sales Range: $100-124.9 Million
Emp.: 1,000
Television Production & Broadcasting
N.A.I.C.S.: 516120
Hans Bourlon (Co-Founder & Co-CEO)

Subsidiaries:

Little Airplane Productions, Inc. (1)
207 Front St, New York, NY 10038
Tel.: (212) 965-8999
Web Site: http://www.littleairplane.com
Children's Television Programming Production Studio
N.A.I.C.S.: 512110
Josh Selig (CEO)

Studio 100 Animation SAS (1)
105 rue La Fayette, 75010, Paris, France
Tel.: (33) 1 56 92 30 00
Web Site: http://www.studio100animation.net
Animation Studio
N.A.I.C.S.: 516120
Katell France (Mng Dir)

Studio 100 Media GmbH (1)
Neumarkter Str 18-20 1, 81673, Munich, Germany
Tel.: (49) 89 960 855 0
Web Site: http://www.studio100media.com
Television Production & Distr

N.A.I.C.S.: 512191
Hans Ulrich Stoef (Mng Dir)

Subsidiary (Domestic):

m4e AG (2)
Neumarkter Str 18-20, 81673, Munich, Germany (68%)
Tel.: (49) 89960855155
Web Site: https://www.studio100international.com
Sales Range: $10-24.9 Million
Brand Management & Media Services
N.A.I.C.S.: 512110
Hans Ulrich Stoef (CEO & Member-Mgmt Bd)

STUDIO ALICE CO., LTD.

Osaka Daiichi Life Building 7F 1-8-17 Umeda, Kita-ku, Osaka, 530-0001, Japan
Tel.: (81) 663432600
Web Site: https://www.studio-alice.co.jp
Year Founded: 1974
2305—(TKS)
Rev.: $258,047,640
Assets: $300,233,140
Liabilities: $80,755,100
Net Worth: $219,478,040
Earnings: $8,203,130
Fiscal Year-end: 02/29/24
Children Photography Services
N.A.I.C.S.: 541921
Masatsugu Motomura (Chm)

STUDIO ATAO CO., LTD.

6-1-8 Miyukidori, Chuo-ku, Kobe, 651-0087, Hyogo, Japan
Tel.: (81) 362262772
Web Site: https://www.studioatao.jp
Year Founded: 2006
3550—(TKS)
Rev.: $28,373,850
Assets: $29,062,350
Liabilities: $9,447,750
Net Worth: $19,614,600
Earnings: ($1,744,200)
Fiscal Year-end: 02/28/23
Bag Product Distr
N.A.I.C.S.: 458110

STUDIO CITY INTERNATIONAL HOLDINGS LIMITED

C/O 38/F The Centrium 60 Wyndham Street, Hong Kong, China (Hong Kong)
Tel.: (852) 25983600 Ky
Year Founded: 2000
MSC—(NYSE)
Rev.: $11,548,000
Assets: $3,593,522,000
Liabilities: $2,717,377,000
Net Worth: $876,145,000
Earnings: ($326,451,000)
Emp.: 3,571
Fiscal Year-end: 12/31/22
Holding Company
N.A.I.C.S.: 551112
Geoffrey Stuart Davis (CFO)

STUDIO PRESS NIGERIA PLC.

Israel Adebajo Close, Ikeja, Lagos, Nigeria
Tel.: (234) 17930001
STUDPRESS—(NIGE)
Rev.: $28,451,132
Assets: $22,310,335
Liabilities: $14,577,647
Net Worth: $7,732,688
Earnings: $781,875
Emp.: 246
Fiscal Year-end: 12/31/19
Commercial Printing Services
N.A.I.C.S.: 323120
M. Ayo Oni (Chm)

STUDIO SANTA CLAUS ENTERTAINMENT CO., LTD.

201 37-37 Dokseodang-ro 39-gil, Seongdong-gu, Seoul, Korea (South)
Tel.: (82) 222998089 KR
Web Site: http://studiosantaent.com
Year Founded: 2005
204630—(KRS)
Rev.: $14,600,072
Assets: $95,047,969
Liabilities: $43,158,635
Net Worth: $51,889,334
Earnings: ($26,031,780)
Emp.: 30
Fiscal Year-end: 12/31/22
Movie Production Services
N.A.I.C.S.: 512110
Jung Woon Sim (Founder)

STUDIOUL CINEMATOGRAFIC ANIMAFILM SA

Str Franceza Nr 10 Sect 3, Bucharest, Romania
Tel.: (40) 786623657
ANIM—(BUC)
Rev.: $53,018
Assets: $391,338
Liabilities: $299,144
Net Worth: $92,194
Earnings: ($16,316)
Emp.: 1
Fiscal Year-end: 12/31/23
Motion Picture & Video Production Services
N.A.I.C.S.: 512110
Florin Minea (Pres)

STUDSVIK AB

Tel.: (46) 155221000
Web Site: http://www.studsvik.com
SUDKY—(OTCEM)
Rev.: $82,000,716
Assets: $99,989,082
Liabilities: $61,352,772
Net Worth: $38,636,310
Earnings: $4,822,900
Emp.: 530
Fiscal Year-end: 12/31/23
Nuclear Waste Services
N.A.I.C.S.: 562211
Joakim Lundstrom (Pres-Bus Area-Fuel,Materials Tech)

Subsidiaries:

AB SVAFO (1)
V Tradgardsg 38, 61182, Nykoping, Sweden
Tel.: (46) 15 520 6090
Web Site: https://www.svafo.se
Sales Range: $25-49.9 Million
Emp.: 60
Radio Active Waste Management Services
N.A.I.C.S.: 562998
Sven Ordeus (Mng Dir)

ALARA Engineering AB (1)
Stensborgsgatan 4, SE-721 32, Vasteras, Sweden
Tel.: (46) 214480760
Web Site: http://www.alara.se
Nuclear Waste Management Services
N.A.I.C.S.: 562998

Studsvik Engineering Technology (Beijing) Co., Ltd. (1)
Level 26 Fortune Financial Center No 5 Central East 3rd Ring Rd, Chaoyang District, Beijing, China
Tel.: (86) 1057750535
Engineering Consulting Services
N.A.I.C.S.: 541330

Studsvik Germany GmbH (1)
Baden Wurttemberg, Bundesrepublik Deutschland, 75179, Pforzheim, Germany
Tel.: (49) 72315869501
Web Site: http://www.studsvik.de
Sales Range: $10-24.9 Million
Emp.: 30
Nuclear Waste Management Services
N.A.I.C.S.: 562998

Studsvik GmbH & Co. KG (1)

Walter-Krause-Str 11, 68163, Mannheim, Germany
Tel.: (49) 62195040301
Web Site: https://www.studsvik.com
Sales Range: $10-24.9 Million
Emp.: 40
Nuclear Waste Management Services
N.A.I.C.S.: 562998

Studsvik Japan Ltd (1)
Nakamura Bldg 3F 2-7-14 Shibuya, Shibuya-ku, Tokyo, 150 0002, Japan
Tel.: (81) 354643771
Web Site: http://www.studsvik.se
Sales Range: $25-49.9 Million
Emp.: 2
Nuclear Technology & Radiological Services.
N.A.I.C.S.: 541330

Studsvik Nuclear AB (1)
Stensborgsgatan 4, 61182, Nykoping, Sweden
Tel.: (46) 155221000
Web Site: http://www.studsvik.se
Emp.: 400
Radioactive Waste Processing Services
N.A.I.C.S.: 562211

Studsvik SAS (1)
Ctr d Affaires Euripole 17 rue de Sancey, ZA des Vauguillettes III, Sens, F 89100, France
Tel.: (33) 386666075
Web Site: http://www.studsvik.se
Sales Range: $10-24.9 Million
Emp.: 45
Nuclear Waste Management Services
N.A.I.C.S.: 562998

Studsvik Scandpower GmbH (1)
Rathausallee 28, DE 22846, Norderstedt, Germany
Tel.: (49) 40309808810
Web Site: http://www.studsvikscandpower.com
Sales Range: $25-49.9 Million
Emp.: 5
Waste Management Services
N.A.I.C.S.: 562998

Studsvik Scandpower Suisse GmbH (1)
Klausenstrasse 21, Fischbach Goslikon, Aarau, 5525, Switzerland
Tel.: (41) 56 221 7359
Sales Range: $25-49.9 Million
Emp.: 2
Nuclear Technology & Radiological Services
N.A.I.C.S.: 541330
Alejandro Noel *(Mgr)*

Studsvik Scandpower, Inc (1)
1087 Beacon St Ste 301, Newton, MA 02459
Tel.: (617) 965-7450
Web Site: http://www.studsvikscandpower.com
Sales Range: $25-49.9 Million
Emp.: 35
Computer Software Services
N.A.I.C.S.: 541511
Axel Becker *(Mgr)*

Studsvik UK Ltd (1)
Unit 14 Princes Park Fourth Ave, Team Vly Trading Estate, Gateshead, NE11 0NF, Tyne & Wear, United Kingdom
Tel.: (44) 1914821744
Web Site: http://www.studsvik.com
Sales Range: $25-49.9 Million
Emp.: 10
Waste Collection & Treatment Services
N.A.I.C.S.: 562219

STUDYRAMA
34-38 Rue Camille Pelletan, 92300, Levallois-Perret, Hauts De Seine, France
Tel.: (33) 141065900
Web Site: http://www.studyrama.com
Rev.: $18,200,000
Emp.: 100
Study Guide Publisher
N.A.I.C.S.: 513120
Jean-Cyrille Boutmy *(Pres)*

STUHINI EXPLORATION LTD.
105-1245 West Broadway, Vancouver, V6H 1G7, BC, Canada
Tel.: (604) 835-4019
Web Site: https://www.stuhini.com
STXPF—(OTCQB)
Assets: $7,156,940
Liabilities: $387,366
Net Worth: $6,769,574
Earnings: ($618,151)
Fiscal Year-end: 02/28/23
Metal Exploration Services
N.A.I.C.S.: 213115
Tony Fogarassy *(Chm)*

STUP VRSAC A.D.
Stepe Stepanovica 9, 26300, Vrsac, Serbia
Tel.: (381) 13 839 917
Web Site: http://www.stup.rs
Year Founded: 1975
STUP—(BEL)
Sales Range: $1-9.9 Million
Emp.: 210
Passenger Transportation Services
N.A.I.C.S.: 485999
Milan Prokin *(Dir-Gen Ops)*

STURDY INDUSTRIES LTD.
Village Bhatoli Khurd, Baddi Nalagarh District, Solan, 173205, Himachal Pradesh, India
Tel.: (91) 1792232570
Web Site:
https://www.sturdyindustries.com
Rev.: $28,029,896
Assets: $40,836,204
Liabilities: $40,681,347
Net Worth: $154,858
Earnings: ($2,628,479)
Emp.: 100
Fiscal Year-end: 03/31/19
Aluminum Casting Mfr
N.A.I.C.S.: 331523
Gurwinder Singh *(Compliance Officer & Sec)*

STV GROUP PLC
Pacific Quay, Glasgow, G51 1PQ, United Kingdom
Tel.: (44) 1413003704 UK
Web Site: https://www.stvplc.tv
STVG—(LSE)
Rev.: $165,980,100
Assets: $186,095,250
Liabilities: $196,092,600
Net Worth: ($9,997,350)
Earnings: $20,958,300
Fiscal Year-end: 12/31/22
Holding Company; Television Broadcasting, Program Production & Media Advertising Services
N.A.I.C.S.: 551112
Jane E. A. Tames *(Sec)*

Subsidiaries:

Primal Media Limited (1)
40 Great Portland Street, London, W1W 7LZ, United Kingdom
Tel.: (44) 2038715289
Web Site: http://www.primalmedia.co.uk
Television Production Services
N.A.I.C.S.: 512110
Mat Steiner *(Co-Founder & Co-Mng Dir)*

STV Central Limited (1)
Pacific Quay, Glasgow, G51 1PQ, United Kingdom (100%)
Tel.: (44) 1413003333
Web Site: http://www.stv.tv
Sales Range: $25-49.9 Million
Television Broadcasting
N.A.I.C.S.: 516120

STV North Limited (1)
Craigshaw Business Park, West Tullos, Aberdeen, AB12 3QH, United Kingdom (100%)
Tel.: (44) 1224 848 828
Web Site: http://www.stv.tv
Television Broadcasting
N.A.I.C.S.: 516120
Linda Grimes-Douglas *(Head-News & Current Affairs)*

STV Productions Limited (1)
Pacific Quay, Glasgow, G51 1PQ, United Kingdom (100%)
Tel.: (44) 1413003000
Web Site: http://www.stv.tv
Sales Range: $50-74.9 Million
Emp.: 150
Television Program Production
N.A.I.C.S.: 512110
Peter Collins *(Head-Specialist Factual)*

Subsidiary (Domestic):

Ginger Television Productions Limited (2)
2nd Floor Garfield House 86-88 Edgware Road, London, W2 2EA, United Kingdom (100%)
Tel.: (44) 20 7535 7250
Web Site: http://www.ginger.tv
Television Program Production
N.A.I.C.S.: 512110

Unit (Domestic):

Solutions.tv (2)
Pacific Quay, Glasgow, G51 1PQ, United Kingdom
Tel.: (44) 1413003400
Web Site: http://www.solutions.tv
Sales Range: $25-49.9 Million
Emp.: 300
Television Production Resource & Post Production Services
N.A.I.C.S.: 512191
Rob Woodward *(CEO)*

STX CORPORATION
13th floor of the west wing 100 Cheonggyecheon-ro, Jung-gu, Seoul, Korea (South)
Tel.: (82) 23169600
Web Site: https://stx.co.kr
Year Founded: 2004
011810—(KRS)
Rev.: $911,637,025
Assets: $568,948,328
Liabilities: $490,402,159
Net Worth: $78,546,169
Earnings: ($14,304,550)
Emp.: 75
Fiscal Year-end: 12/31/22
Holding Company
N.A.I.C.S.: 551112
Sang Jun Park *(CEO)*

Subsidiaries:

DTK Oceanic Limited (1)
Plot 1637 Oko-Awo Street, Victoria Island, Lagos, Nigeria
Tel.: (234) 806 560 8522
Web Site: http://www.dtkoceanic.com
Precision Engineered Products Mfr
N.A.I.C.S.: 332216

STX Architectural Design Co., Ltd. (1)
Bachagou Changxing Island Harbor Industrial Zone, Dalian, 116323, China
Tel.: (86) 411 3939 5001
Precision Engineered Products Mfr
N.A.I.C.S.: 332216

STX Engine Co., Ltd. (1)
36 Gongdan-ro 474beon-gil, Seongsan-gu, Changwon, 51574, Gyeongsangnam-do, Korea (South)
Tel.: (82) 552800114
Web Site: https://www.stxengine.co.kr
Rev.: $417,264,107
Assets: $654,548,596
Liabilities: $454,940,681
Net Worth: $199,607,915
Earnings: ($20,465,861)
Emp.: 877
Fiscal Year-end: 12/31/2022
Ship Engine Mfr & Whslr
N.A.I.C.S.: 333618
Jong-geun Song *(Pres & CEO)*

STX Global Logix Co., Ltd (1)
5th Floor Toranomon 1-Chome Mori Building 1-19-5 Toranomon, Minato-Ku, Tokyo, Japan
Tel.: (81) 355101326
Emp.: 10
Precision Engineered Products Mfr
N.A.I.C.S.: 332216

STX Japan Corporation (1)
7th Floor ShinToranomon Jitsuyo Kaikan 1-1-21 Toranomon, Minato-Ku, Tokyo, 105-0001, Japan
Precision Engineered Products Mfr
N.A.I.C.S.: 332216

STX Marine Service Co., Ltd. (1)
STX Busan Bldg 83-5 Jungang-Dong, Jung-ku, Busan, 600-725, Korea (South)
Tel.: (82) 514612138
Web Site: http://www.stxmarine.co.kr
Sales Range: $150-199.9 Million
Emp.: 600
Marine Engineering Services; Ship Management
N.A.I.C.S.: 541330

STX Metal Co., Ltd. (1)
Tel.: (82) 552800700
Sales Range: $800-899.9 Million
Emp.: 424
Machinery Parts, Cast Steel & Machine Tool Mfr, Importer, Exporter & Sales
N.A.I.C.S.: 333998
Chun-il Yu *(Pres)*

STX Middle East FZE (1)
LOB 19-1907 Jafza, PO Box No 262099, Dubai, United Arab Emirates
Tel.: (971) 4 886 5154
Web Site: http://www.stx.co.kr
Sales Range: $25-49.9 Million
Emp.: 3
Ship Building Services
N.A.I.C.S.: 336611
Alex Lim *(Gen Mgr)*

STX Offshore & Shipbuilding Co. Ltd. (1)
60 Myeongje-ro, Jinhae-gu, Changwon, 51624, Gyeongsangnam-do, Korea (South)
Tel.: (82) 555481122
Web Site: https://www.kshipbuilding.com
Sales Range: $5-14.9 Billion
Emp.: 935
Ship Building & Offshore Services
N.A.I.C.S.: 336611

Subsidiary (Non-US):

STX Brazil Offshore SA (2)
Praca Alcides Pereira 1-Parte Ilha da Conceicao, Niteroi, 24050 350, Rio de Janeiro, Brazil
Tel.: (55) 21 27 18 90 90
Emp.: 700
Ship Building Services
N.A.I.C.S.: 336611
Jan Bronstein *(CEO)*

STX Solar Co., Ltd. (1)
Sindang-Ri Sandong-Myeon, Gumi, Korea (South)
Tel.: (82) 2 317 2576
Web Site: http://www.stxsolar.co.kr
Solar Cell Mfr
N.A.I.C.S.: 334413

STYLAM INDUSTRIES LIMITED
SCO 14 Sec 7C Madhya Marg, Chandigarh, 160 019, UT, India
Tel.: (91) 1725021555
Web Site: https://www.stylam.com
STYLAMIND—(NSE)
Rev.: $114,330,939
Assets: $64,515,233
Liabilities: $15,109,394
Net Worth: $49,405,839
Earnings: $11,507,727
Emp.: 1,142
Fiscal Year-end: 03/31/23
Decorative Laminates Mfr
N.A.I.C.S.: 322220
Jagdish Rai Gupta *(Founder & Mng Dir)*

STYLAND HOLDINGS LIMITED
28th Floor Aitken Vanson Centre 61

STYLAND HOLDINGS LIMITED

Styland Holdings Limited—(Continued)
Hoi Yuen Road, Kwun Tong, Kowloon, China (Hong Kong)
Tel.: (852) 29593123 BM
Web Site: http://www.styland.com
Year Founded: 1977
0211—(HKG)
Rev.: $23,926,268
Assets: $100,726,913
Liabilities: $48,307,583
Net Worth: $52,419,330
Earnings: ($8,758,485)
Emp.: 67
Fiscal Year-end: 03/31/23
Financial Management Services
N.A.I.C.S.: 523999
Hoo Win Cheung (CEO)

Subsidiaries:

Ever-Long Securities Company Limited (1)
Room 1101-1102 & 1111-1112 11/F Wing On Centre 111 Connaught Road, Sheung Wan, China (Hong Kong)
Tel.: (852) 2815 3522
Web Site: http://www.everlong.com
Securities Brokerage Services
N.A.I.C.S.: 523150

STYLECRAFT LIMITED

Red Crescent Concord Tower 17 Mohakhali Commercial Area 14th Floor, Dhaka, Bangladesh
Tel.: (880) 9897877
Web Site:
    https://www.stylecraftltd.com
Year Founded: 1983
STYLECRAFT—(DHA)
Rev.: $11,656,851
Assets: $15,706,593
Liabilities: $14,176,262
Net Worth: $1,530,330
Earnings: ($616,291)
Emp.: 2,071
Fiscal Year-end: 06/30/23
Garments Mfr
N.A.I.C.S.: 315250
Omar Golam Rabbany (Chm)

STYLES & WOOD GROUP PLC

Cavendish House Cross Street, Sale, M33 7BU, United Kingdom
Tel.: (44) 1619266000 UK
Web Site:
    http://www.stylesandwood.co.uk
Year Founded: 2014
Sales Range: $125-149.9 Million
Holding Company; Commercial Property Development & Management Services
N.A.I.C.S.: 551112
Philip Lanigan (Fin Dir-Grp)

STYROMATIC A/S

Sintrupvej 25A, 8220, Brabrand, Denmark
Tel.: (45) 8745 3100
Web Site: http://www.styromatic.dk
Electronic Control System Mfr
N.A.I.C.S.: 334513
Asmus Hamborg-Petersen (CEO)

Subsidiaries:

Styromatic (Thailand) Co., Ltd. (1)
99 Moo 6 Baan Wang Pla Fa Tambol Baanchan, Amphur Muang, Udon Thani, 41000, Thailand
Tel.: (66) 42 123 030 1
Web Site: http://www.styromatic.dk
Electronic Control System Distr
N.A.I.C.S.: 423690
Padungsak Duangmatpol (CTO)

SU GROUP HOLDINGS LIMITED

7 F, The Rays 71 Hung To Road, Kwun Tong, Kowloon, China (Hong Kong)
Tel.: (852) 23418183 Ky
Web Site:
    https://www.sugroup.com.hk
Year Founded: 1998
SUGP—(NASDAQ)
Rev.: $1,279,899,663
Assets: $894,807,290
Liabilities: $453,623,804
Net Worth: $441,183,486
Earnings: $75,823,728
Emp.: 257
Fiscal Year-end: 09/30/23
Holding Company
N.A.I.C.S.: 551112
Dave Chan (Founder, Chm & CEO)

SU-HOLDINGS CO.,LTD.

7th floor 20 Yeongdong-daero 96-gil, Gangnam-gu, Seoul, 06173, Korea (South)
Tel.: (82) 221065417
Web Site: https://su-holdings.com
Year Founded: 1979
031860—(KRS)
Rev.: $6,403,380
Assets: $63,605,595
Liabilities: $17,692,310
Net Worth: $45,913,284
Earnings: ($11,126,968)
Emp.: 32
Fiscal Year-end: 12/31/22
Mobile Phone Camera Module Mfr
N.A.I.C.S.: 334413

SU-MARKETI A.D

Main 55 A, 24300, Backa Topola, Serbia
Tel.: (381) 24715898
Web Site: https://www.sumarketi.ip.rs
Year Founded: 2004
SMRK—(BEL)
Rev.: $4,348
Assets: $10,489
Liabilities: $4,009
Net Worth: $6,480
Earnings: ($9,601)
Fiscal Year-end: 12/31/23
Advertising Agency Services
N.A.I.C.S.: 541810

SUASHISH DIAMONDS LTD.

Mehta Mahal 11th 12th Floor 15 Mathew Road Opera House, Mumbai, 400 004, India
Tel.: (91) 22 4040 1111
Web Site: http://www.suashish.com
Sales Range: $200-249.9 Million
Jewelry & Lapidary Work Mfr
N.A.I.C.S.: 339910
Ashish R. Goenka (Chm & Mng Dir)

Subsidiaries:

Suashish Diamonds (Botswana) (Pty.) Ltd. (1)
Plot 20617 Block 3 Industrial, Gaborone, Botswana
Tel.: (267) 3971 450
Emp.: 97
Jewelry Mfr
N.A.I.C.S.: 339910
Sriram Valluri (Mgr)

Suashish Diamonds (HK) Limited (1)
Unit 1001 10/F Guard Force Center, 3 Hok Yuen Street East Hunghorn, Kowloon, China (Hong Kong)
Tel.: (852) 2314 8514
Jewelry Mfr
N.A.I.C.S.: 339910

Suashish Jewelry India Ltd. (1)
Gala No 207 & 208 2nd Floor Multistoried Building, SEEPZ-SEZ Andheri East, Mumbai, 400 096, India
Tel.: (91) 22 2829 2677
Jewelry Mfr
N.A.I.C.S.: 339910

Suashish Jewels Canada Inc. (1)
Suite 205 301 Moodie Drive, Ottawa, K2H 9C4, ON, Canada
Tel.: (613) 828-7726
Jewelry Whslr
N.A.I.C.S.: 423940
Natacha Saud (Coord-Logistics)

Suashish Jewels Inc. (1)
5525 MacArthur Blvd Ste 538, Irving, TX 75038
Tel.: (972) 891-3150
Jewelry Whslr
N.A.I.C.S.: 423940

SUBA SEEDS COMPANY SRL

Via Emilia 1818, 47020, Longiano, Italy
Tel.: (39) 0547 56191
Web Site: http://www.subaseeds.com
Seed Distribution
N.A.I.C.S.: 444240

Subsidiaries:

W. Brotherton Seed Co , Inc. (1)
451 S Milwaukee Ave, Moses Lake, WA 98837
Tel.: (509) 765-1816
Web Site: http://www.brothertonseed.net
Sales Range: $1-9.9 Million
Emp.: 22
Farm Supplies Merchant Whslr
N.A.I.C.S.: 424910
John Wamatu (Dir-Res)

SUBARU CO., LTD.

Ebisu Subaru Bldg 1-20-8 Ebisu, Shibuya-ku, Tokyo, 150-8554, Japan
Tel.: (81) 364478000
Web Site: https://www.subaru.co.jp
Year Founded: 1972
9778—(TKS)
Rev.: $24,938,671,952
Assets: $26,059,795,177
Liabilities: $12,118,949,455
Net Worth: $13,940,845,722
Earnings: $1,315,388,173
Emp.: 17,228
Fiscal Year-end: 03/31/23
Cram School Operator
N.A.I.C.S.: 611710
Michiko Nishimura (Pres)

Subsidiaries:

Chiba Subaru Inc. (1)
176-2 Shinko, Mihama Ward, Chiba, 261-0002, Japan
Tel.: (81) 432432261
Web Site: https://www.chibasubaru.com
Emp.: 553
Automotive Parts Retailer
N.A.I.C.S.: 811121

Fukuoka Subaru Inc. (1)
4-14-12 Chihaya, Higashi Ward, Fukuoka, Japan
Tel.: (81) 927100111
Web Site: https://fukuoka.kyushu-subaru.jp
Emp.: 381
Automobile Parts Distr
N.A.I.C.S.: 423110

Hiroshima Subaru Inc. (1)
1-3-17 Nakahirocho, West Ward, Hiroshima, 733-0012, Japan
Tel.: (81) 822914355
Web Site: https://www.hiroshima-subaru.co.jp
Emp.: 250
New Car & Used Car Distr
N.A.I.C.S.: 441110

Hokkaido Subaru Inc. (1)
14-1-1 Nishimachi Minami, Nishi Ward, Sapporo, 063-0062, Japan
Tel.: (81) 116682210
Web Site: https://www.hokkaido-subaru.com
Emp.: 498
New & Used Car Distr
N.A.I.C.S.: 441120

Kanagawa Subaru Inc. (1)
1-18-1 Shin-Yokohama, Kohoku-ku, Yokohama, 222-8571, Kanagawa, Japan
Tel.: (81) 454783625

INTERNATIONAL PUBLIC

Web Site: https://www.kanagawa-subaru.com
Emp.: 704
Automotive Parts Retailer
N.A.I.C.S.: 811121

Miyagi Subaru Inc. (1)
1-5-26 Hinodecho, Miyagino Ward, Sendai, 983-0035, Japan
Tel.: (81) 222359113
Web Site: https://www.miyagi-subaru.co.jp
Emp.: 297
New & Used Car Distr
N.A.I.C.S.: 441120

Nagoya Subaru Inc. (1)
233 Ochiai-cho, Kita-ku, Nagoya, 462-0017, Japan
Tel.: (81) 529018611
Web Site: https://www.nagoya-subaru.co.jp
Emp.: 584
Automotive Parts Retailer
N.A.I.C.S.: 811121

Niigata Subaru Inc. (1)
2307 Yamada, Nishi Ward, Niigata, 950-1182, Japan
Tel.: (81) 252669177
Web Site: https://www.niigata-subaru.co.jp
Emp.: 343
Automotive Parts Retailer
N.A.I.C.S.: 811121

SUBARU CORPORATION

Ebisu Subaru Bldg 1-20-8 Ebisu, Shibuya-ku, Tokyo, 150-8554, Japan
Tel.: (81) 364478000 JP
Web Site: https://www.subaru.co.jp
Year Founded: 1953
7270—(TKS)
Rev.: $31,086,479,670
Assets: $31,821,524,890
Liabilities: $14,864,270,550
Net Worth: $16,957,254,340
Earnings: $2,545,405,240
Emp.: 37,693
Fiscal Year-end: 03/31/24
Heavy Machinery Mfr
N.A.I.C.S.: 333996
Tomomi Nakamura (Pres & CEO)

Subsidiaries:

Changzhou Fuji Changchai Robin Gasoline Engine Co.,Ltd. (1)
No 28 Changjiang M Road, Xinbei District, Changzhou, 213022, Jiangsu, China
Tel.: (86) 51985109370
Combustion Gasoline Engine Mfr
N.A.I.C.S.: 336310

Daiwa Shoko Co., Ltd (1)
1-4-1 Ebara, Shinagawa-Ku, Tokyo, 142-0063, Japan
Tel.: (81) 337839131
Web Site: http://www.daiwa-sk.jp
Industrial Machinery & Equipment Distr
N.A.I.C.S.: 423830

Fuji Aerospace Corporation (1)
1-2-15 Yonan, Utsunomiya, 320-0834, Tochigi, Japan
Tel.: (81) 286459509
Aircraft Parts & Equipment Mfr
N.A.I.C.S.: 336412

Fuji Aerospace Technology Co.,Ltd. (1)
1-1-11 Yonan, Utsunomiya, 320-8564, Tochigi, Japan
Tel.: (81) 286597436
Web Site: http://www.fatec.jp
Emp.: 96
Aircraft System & Equipment Mfr
N.A.I.C.S.: 336413

Fuji Aircraft Maintenance Co.,Ltd. (1)
1-28 Kanda-Sudacho, Chiyoda-ku, Tokyo, 101-0041, Japan
Tel.: (81) 332571533
Emp.: 190
Aircraft Maintenance Services
N.A.I.C.S.: 488190

Fuji Heavy Industries (Singapore) Pte. Ltd. (1)
8 Jurong Town Hall Rd 23-02, Singapore,

609434, Singapore
Tel.: (65) 68968960
Web Site:
http://www.fujiheavyindustries.com
Sales Range: $10-24.9 Million
Emp.: 5
N.A.I.C.S.: 336110

Fuji Heavy Industries Ltd., China Office (1)
Beijing Landmark Towers Office Bldg 2-1501, 8 North Dongsanhuan Rd, Beijing, 100004, Chaoyang District, China (100%)
Tel.: (86) 10 8527 6164
Web Site: http://www.fhi.co.jp
Manufacture, Repair & Sales of Heavy Duty Trucks
N.A.I.C.S.: 336120

Fuji Heavy Industries U.S.A. Inc. (1)
Subaru Plz 2235 Route 70 W, Cherry Hill, NJ 08002 (100%)
Tel.: (856) 488-8500
Web Site: http://www.subaru.com
Sales Range: $150-199.9 Million
Emp.: 400
Distribution & Sales of Subaru Automobiles
N.A.I.C.S.: 423110

Fuji Heavy Industries U.S.A. Inc. (1)
4040 Lake Washington Blvd NE Ste 314, Kirkland, WA 98033-7874 (100%)
Tel.: (425) 822-0762
Web Site: http://www.fhi.co.jp
Sales Range: $25-49.9 Million
Emp.: 7
Heavy Machinery & Aerospace Distr
N.A.I.C.S.: 336413

Fuji Heavy Industries, Ltd. - Air Space Div. (1)
1 11 Yonan 1 Chome, Utsunomiya, Tochigi, 320 8564, Japan (100%)
Tel.: (81) 286847777
Web Site: http://www.fhi.co.jp
Sales Range: $800-899.9 Million
Emp.: 2,600
Mfr of Aircraft Rolling Stock, Containers & Special Purpose Vehicles
N.A.I.C.S.: 336110
Hisasha Nagano *(Pres)*

Fuji Heavy Industries, Ltd. - Gunma Main Plant (1)
1-1 Subaru-cho, Ota, 373-8555, Gunma, Japan
Tel.: (81) 276 26 2011
Web Site: http://www.fhi.co.jp
Emp.: 4,026
Automobile Parts Mfr
N.A.I.C.S.: 336390

Fuji Heavy Industries, Ltd. - Gunma Oizumi Plant (1)
1-1-1 Izumi Oizumi-machi, Oura-gun, Gunma, 370-0531, Japan
Tel.: (81) 276482881
Sales Range: $400-449.9 Million
Emp.: 1,533
Automobile Engines & Transmissions Mfr
N.A.I.C.S.: 336360

Fuji Heavy Industries, Ltd. - Gunma Yajima Plant (1)
1-1 Shoya-cho, Ota, 373-0822, Gunma, Japan
Tel.: (81) 276 48 2701
Web Site: http://www.fhi.co.jp
Emp.: 2,929
Automobile Parts Mfr
N.A.I.C.S.: 336390

Fuji Heavy Industries, Ltd. - Handa Plant (1)
1-27 Ushioi-cho, Handa, 475-0032, Aichi, Japan
Tel.: (81) 569294801
Sales Range: $50-74.9 Million
Emp.: 181
Aircraft Mfr
N.A.I.C.S.: 336411

Fuji Heavy Industries, Ltd. - Handa West Plant (1)
102 Kamihama-cho, Handa, 475-0804, Aichi, Japan
Tel.: (81) 569 32 2501
Web Site: http://www.fhi.co.jp
Sales Range: $25-49.9 Million
Emp.: 23
Aircraft Mfr
N.A.I.C.S.: 336411

Fuji Heavy Industries, Ltd. - Omiya Subaru Building Facility (1)
1-1-2 Miyahara-cho, Kita-ku, Saitama, 331-0812, Japan
Tel.: (81) 486535722
Sales Range: $25-49.9 Million
Emp.: 41
Automobile Parts Mfr
N.A.I.C.S.: 336390

Fuji Heavy Industries, Ltd. - Saitama Plant (1)
4-410 Asahi, Kitamoto, 364-8511, Saitama, Japan
Tel.: (81) 485937755
Sales Range: $200-249.9 Million
Emp.: 551
Engine & Generator Mfr
N.A.I.C.S.: 335312

Fuji Heavy Industries, Ltd. - Utsunomiya Plant (1)
1-1-11 Yonan, Utsunomiya, 320-8564, Tochigi, Japan
Tel.: (81) 28 684 7777
Sales Range: $400-449.9 Million
Emp.: 212
Aircraft Mfr
N.A.I.C.S.: 336411

Fuji Heavy Industries, Ltd., Aircraft Div. (1)
1 11 Yonan 1 Chome, 320 8564, Tochigi, Japan (100%)
Tel.: (81) 286847777
Web Site: http://www.fhi.co.jp
Sales Range: Less than $1 Million
Emp.: 2,500
Mfr of Aircraft
N.A.I.C.S.: 336411
Hisashi Nagano *(Pres)*

Fuji Heavy Industries, Ltd., Automobile Div. (1)
9 6 Osawa 3 Chome, Tokyo, 1818577, Japan (100%)
Tel.: (81) 422337000
Web Site: http://www.fhi.co.jp
Rev.: $4,339,716,096
Emp.: 10,405
Mfr of Subcompact Cars & Minivehicles
N.A.I.C.S.: 336110

Fuji Heavy Industries, Ltd., Engine & Machinery Div. (1)
Asahi 4 Hiahong 4 410, Kitamoto, 364-8511, Saitama, Japan
Tel.: (81) 485937755
Rev.: $225,532,000
Emp.: 600
Mfr of Industrial Gasoline, Kerosene & Diesel Engines, Generators, Pumps
N.A.I.C.S.: 325998

Fuji Heavy Industries, Ltd., Industrial Products (1)
4 410 Asahi Kitamoto, Saitama, 3648511, Japan (100%)
Tel.: (81) 485937723
Sales Range: $25-49.9 Million
Emp.: 600
Kamimura Kazuto *(Mgr-Gen Affairs & Dept)*

Fuji Heavy Industries, Ltd., Manufacturing Div. (1)
1-1 Subaru-cho, Ota, 373 8555, Gunma, Japan (100%)
Tel.: (81) 276260011
Web Site: http://www.fhi.co.jp
Sales Range: $1-4.9 Billion
Automobile Mfr
N.A.I.C.S.: 336211

Fuji Houren Co., Ltd. (1)
100 Suehirocho, Isesaki, 372-0057, Gunma, Japan
Tel.: (81) 270303147
Sales Range: $10-24.9 Million
Emp.: 44
Housing Rental & Leasing Services
N.A.I.C.S.: 624229

Fuji Machinery Co., Ltd. (1)
2-24-3 Iwagamimachi, Maebashi, 371-0035, Gunma, Japan (100%)
Tel.: (81) 272313111
Web Site: https://www.fuji-machinery.co.jp

Sales Range: $100-124.9 Million
Emp.: 403
Automobile & Industrial Parts Mfr & Sales
N.A.I.C.S.: 336390
Tamaki Kamogawa *(Pres)*

Fuji Techno Service Co.,Ltd. (1)
1-2-5 Arato, Chuo-ku, Fukuoka, 810-0062, Japan
Tel.: (81) 927415539
Web Site: http://www.fujts.com
Hydraulic Machinery Maintenance Service
N.A.I.C.S.: 811310

Ichitan Co., Ltd. (1)
74 Shindocho, Ohta, Ota, 373-0037, Gunma, Japan (51%)
Tel.: (81) 276312331
Sales Range: $100-124.9 Million
Emp.: 280
Automobile & Industrial Casting Products Mfr & Sales
N.A.I.C.S.: 336390

Kiryu Industry Co., Ltd. (1)
2-704 Aioi-cho, Kiryu-shi, Gunma, 376-0011, Japan
Tel.: (81) 277531111
Web Site: https://kkc.subaru.co.jp
Emp.: 420
Car Parts Mfr
N.A.I.C.S.: 441330
Nobuyuki Shiroguchi *(CEO)*

N.V. Subaru Benelux (1)
Leuvensesteenweg 555 bus 1, Zaventem, Belgium
Tel.: (32) 880881600
Web Site: http://www.subaru.nl
Import & Export Services
N.A.I.C.S.: 522299
Kristel Reniers *(Fin Mgr)*

Osaka Subaru Inc. (1)
1-21-23 Yakumo Higashicho, Moriguchi, 570-0021, Osaka, Japan
Tel.: (81) 669083131
Web Site: https://osaka.kinki-subaru.jp
Emp.: 599
Automobile Dealers
N.A.I.C.S.: 441110

Robin America Inc. (1)
905 Telser Rd, Lake Zurich, IL 60047
Tel.: (847) 540-7300
Web Site: http://www.robinamerica.com
Sales Range: $25-49.9 Million
Emp.: 30
Industrial Machinery Mfr & Distr
N.A.I.C.S.: 333248
Michael Magolan *(Mgr-Sls-Reg)*

Robin Europe GmbH (1)
Willicher Damm, 3541066, Willich, Germany
Tel.: (49) 2161636200
Web Site: http://www.robin-europe.de
Sales Range: $25-49.9 Million
Emp.: 13
Engine, Generator & Pump Distr
N.A.I.C.S.: 336110

Robin Manufacturing USA, Inc. (1)
1201 Industrial St, Hudson, WI 54016-9361
Tel.: (715) 381-5902
Sales Range: $25-49.9 Million
Emp.: 30
General Purpose, Four-Wheel Buggy & Golf Cart Engine Mfr
N.A.I.C.S.: 333618

Subaru Auto Accessory Co.,Ltd. (1)
1-1-2 Miyahara-cho, Saitama, 330-0038, Japan
Tel.: (81) 486525603
Emp.: 50
Automobile Parts Distr
N.A.I.C.S.: 336390
Masaki Okawara *(Gen Mgr-Mfg & Gunma Plant)*

Subaru Canada, Inc. (1)
560 Suffolk Court, Mississauga, L5R 4J7, ON, Canada (100%)
Tel.: (905) 568-4959
Web Site: https://www.subaru.ca
Sales Range: $50-74.9 Million
Emp.: 100
Distribution & Sales of Subaru Automobiles
N.A.I.C.S.: 423120

Subaru Distributor Corp. (1)
6 Ramland Rd, Orangeburg, NY 10962-2606
Tel.: (845) 359-2500
Rev.: $124,594,000
Emp.: 67
Automobile & Parts Wholesale; Independent Distributor
N.A.I.C.S.: 423110
Nicholas Tenore *(VP & Controller)*

Subaru Europe N.V./S.A. (1)
Leuvensesteenweg 555 B 8, 1930, Zaventem, Belgium (100%)
Tel.: (32) 27140300
Web Site: https://www.subaru.eu
Sales Range: $25-49.9 Million
Emp.: 40
Automobiles, Parts & Accessories Distr & Sales
N.A.I.C.S.: 423120

Subaru Finance Co., Ltd. (1)
Unosawa Tokyu Building 2F 1-19-15 Ebisu, Shibuya-ku, Tokyo, 150-0013, Japan (100%)
Tel.: (81) 334452111
Web Site: https://www.subaru-finance.co.jp
Emp.: 244
Automobile Rental, Leasing & Financial Services
N.A.I.C.S.: 561499
Toshiaki Okada *(CEO)*

Subaru IT Creations Corporation (1)
1-854-1 Miyahara-cho Omiya Subaru Building, Kita-ku, Saitama, 331-0812, Japan
Tel.: (81) 486535752
Emp.: 306
Information Technology Services
N.A.I.C.S.: 541511

Subaru Italia S.p.A. (1)
L go Negrelli 1, 38061, Ala, TN, Italy
Tel.: (39) 0289040200
Automotive Products Whslr
N.A.I.C.S.: 423690
Graziana Marchi *(Area Mgr-Sls)*

Subaru Kohsan Co., Ltd. (1)
Ebisu Subaru Building 5F 1-20-8 Ebisu, Shibuya-ku, Tokyo, 150-0013, Japan
Tel.: (81) 364478900
Emp.: 96
Real Estate Services
N.A.I.C.S.: 531390

Subaru Kosan Co., Ltd (1)
1-20-8 Ebisu Ebisu Subaru Bldg 3F, Shibuya-ku, Tokyo, 150-0013, Japan
Tel.: (81) 364478900
Emp.: 118
Automobile Parts Mfr
N.A.I.C.S.: 336390

Subaru Living Service Co.,Ltd. (1)
3-9-6 Osawa, Mitaka, 181-8577, Tokyo, Japan
Tel.: (81) 422336100
Web Site: https://sls.subaru.co.jp
Emp.: 561
Online Shopping Services
N.A.I.C.S.: 561990

Subaru Logistics Co.,Ltd. (1)
558-1 Asahi-cho, Ota, 373-0814, Gunma, Japan
Tel.: (81) 276 48 3131
Web Site: http://www.subaru-logistics.co.jp
Emp.: 385
Packaging & Freight Transportation Services
N.A.I.C.S.: 488510

Subaru Research & Development (1)
6431 Global Dr, Cypress, CA 90630-5227 (100%)
Tel.: (714) 828-1875
Web Site: http://www.fhi.co.jp
Sales Range: $25-49.9 Million
Emp.: 10
Research & Development of Subaru Cars
N.A.I.C.S.: 541910
Brent Crary *(Asst Mgr)*

Subaru Research & Development, Inc. (1)
50255 Michigan Ave, Van Buren Township, MI 48111
Tel.: (734) 623-0075

SUBARU CORPORATION

Subaru Corporation—(Continued)
Sales Range: $25-49.9 Million
Emp.: 20
N.A.I.C.S.: 336110
Tiffany Garth *(Mgr-HR)*

Subaru Robin Power Products (1)
905 Telser Rd, Lake Zurich, IL 60047
Tel.: (847) 540-7300
Web Site: http://www.robinamerica.com
Sales Range: $25-49.9 Million
Emp.: 30
Small Industrial Engines Mfr
N.A.I.C.S.: 423830
David Quance *(Controller)*

Subaru Tecnica International Inc. (1)
3-9-6 Osawa, Mitaka, 181-0015, Tokyo, Japan
Tel.: (81) 422337848
Web Site: https://www.sti.jp
Motor Sport Engine & Chassis Mfr
N.A.I.C.S.: 333618

Subaru Test & Development Center in Europe (1)
Konrad Adenauer Strasse 34, 55218, Ingelheim, Ingelheim, Germany **(100%)**
Tel.: (49) 613276370
Sales Range: $50-74.9 Million
Emp.: 7
N.A.I.C.S.: 336110

Subaru Vehicle Distribution BV (1)
Merseyweg 40 Botlek, 3197 KG, Rotterdam, Netherlands
Tel.: (31) 181290499
Emp.: 1
Automobile Whslr
N.A.I.C.S.: 423110
Masashi Tajiri *(Gen Mgr)*

Subaru of America, Inc. (1)
2235 Marlton Pike W, Cherry Hill, NJ 08002 **(100%)**
Tel.: (856) 488-8500
Web Site: http://www.subaru.com
Sales Range: $1-4.9 Billion
Emp.: 1,000
Automobile Whslr
N.A.I.C.S.: 423110
Tadashi Yoshida *(Chm & CEO)*

Subsidiary (Domestic):

Subaru Acceptance Corporation (2)
2235 Route 70 W, Cherry Hill, NJ 08002-6000 **(100%)**
Tel.: (856) 488-8500
Web Site: http://www.subaru.com
Sales Range: $50-74.9 Million
Emp.: 5
Financial Services
N.A.I.C.S.: 522220
Yishil Hasunuma *(Chm, Pres & CEO)*

Subaru Financial Services, Inc. (2)
PO Box 6000, Cherry Hill, NJ 08034-6000
Tel.: (856) 488-8770
Web Site: http://www.subaru.com
Sales Range: $10-24.9 Million
Emp.: 20
Financing of Automobiles
N.A.I.C.S.: 522220

Subaru Leasing Corporation (2)
2235 Route 70 W, Cherry Hill, NJ 08002-6000
Tel.: (856) 488-8500
Web Site: http://www.subaru.com
Sales Range: $150-199.9 Million
Emp.: 500
Distribution & Sales of Subaru Automobiles
N.A.I.C.S.: 423110
Kurt Allen *(Controller)*

Division (Domestic):

Subaru Western Region, Inc. (2)
22100 E 26th Ave Ste 140, Aurora, CO 80019
Tel.: (303) 371-3820
Web Site: http://www.subaru.com
Rev.: $84,808,000
Emp.: 50
Automotive Parts Sales & Distribution
N.A.I.C.S.: 423110
Anthony Graziano *(Reg VP)*

Subaru of America Northwest Region (2)
5216 NE 158th Ave, Portland, OR 97230-4937
Tel.: (503) 262-1250
Web Site: http://www.subaru.com
Sales Range: $25-49.9 Million
Emp.: 35
Regional Office of Subaru Vehicles & Replacement Parts
N.A.I.C.S.: 423110

Subaru of America Southeast Region (2)
220 The Bluffs, Austell, GA 30168
Tel.: (770) 732-3200
Web Site: http://www.subaru.com
Sales Range: $50-74.9 Million
Emp.: 70
Mfr of Vehicles & Replacement Parts
N.A.I.C.S.: 423120

Subaru of America, Inc. - Central Region (2)
500 Park Blvd Ste 255C, Itasca, IL 60143-1253
Tel.: (630) 250-4740
Web Site: http://www.subaru.com
Sales Range: $25-49.9 Million
Emp.: 40
Regional Office of Subaru Vehicles & Replacement Parts
N.A.I.C.S.: 423110
Thomas. J. Doll *(Pres & COO)*

Subaru of New England, Inc. (2)
95 Morse St, Norwood, MA 02062-4623
Tel.: (781) 769-5100
Web Site: http://www.subaru.com
Rev.: $225,000,000
Emp.: 65
Automobiles & Parts Wholesale
N.A.I.C.S.: 423110
Jeffrey Ruble *(Exec VP & Gen Mgr)*

Subaru of China, Inc. (1)
Tel.: (86) 4008184860
Web Site: https://www.subaru-china.cn
Sales Range: $25-49.9 Million
Emp.: 50
Automobile Mfr
N.A.I.C.S.: 336390

Subaru of Indiana Automotive, Inc. (1)
5500 State Rd 38 E, Lafayette, IN 47905
Tel.: (765) 449-1111
Web Site: https://www.subaru-sia.com
Sales Range: $25-49.9 Million
Emp.: 34
Mfr of Pickup Trucks Sports Utility Vehicles & Passenger Cars; Joint Venture of Fuji Heavy Industries, Ltd. & Isuzu Motors Limited
N.A.I.C.S.: 336110
Toshiaki Tamegai *(Sr Gen Mgr)*

Tokyo Subaru Inc. (1) **(100%)**
Tel.: (81) 120390486
Web Site: https://www.tokyo-subaru.co.jp
Sales Range: $400-449.9 Million
Emp.: 1,064
Automobile Sales & Service
N.A.I.C.S.: 441227
Kazuhiko Miyazawa *(CEO)*

Yusoki Kogyo K.K. (1)
102 Kamihama-cho, Handa, 475-0804, Aichi, Japan
Tel.: (81) 569213311
Web Site: https://yusoki.subaru.co.jp
Emp.: 160
Aircraft Parts Mfr & Distr
N.A.I.C.S.: 336413
Norio Ando *(CEO)*

SUBARU ENTERPRISE CO., LTD.
1-5-2 Yurakucho, Chiyoda-ku, Tokyo, 100-0006, Japan
Tel.: (81) 332132861
Web Site: https://www.subaru-kougyou.jp
Year Founded: 1946
9632—(TKS)
Rev.: $207,347,050
Assets: $274,546,070
Liabilities: $36,577,310
Net Worth: $237,968,760
Earnings: $23,276,470
Emp.: 685
Fiscal Year-end: 01/31/24
Road Maintenance Services
N.A.I.C.S.: 237310
Kenji Kobayashi *(Pres)*

SUBARU MONTREAL
4900 Pare, Montreal, H4P 1P3, QC, Canada
Tel.: (514) 737-1880
Web Site: http://www.subaru-montreal.com
Year Founded: 1977
Sales Range: $10-24.9 Million
Emp.: 35
Car Dealership
N.A.I.C.S.: 441110
Robert Scott *(Gen Mgr)*

SUBAYE, INC.
A 536-537 13 Block 232 Waihuandong Road, Xiaoguwei Street, University City, Guangzhou, 510006, China
Tel.: (86) 20 39990266 DE
Web Site: http://www.subaye.com
Sales Range: $25-49.9 Million
Emp.: 1,539
Wireless Entertainment & Information Content
N.A.I.C.S.: 517112
King Rong *(Sr VP-Sls & Mktg)*

SUBEX LTD
RMZ Ecoworld Devarabisanahalli Outer Ring Road, Bengaluru, 560103, India
Tel.: (91) 806 659 8700
Web Site: http://www.subex.com
532348—(NSE)
Rev.: $51,429,105
Assets: $99,189,090
Liabilities: $24,312,015
Net Worth: $74,877,075
Earnings: $7,059,780
Emp.: 1,023
Fiscal Year-end: 03/31/21
Communications Services Provider
N.A.I.C.S.: 517112
Vinod Kumar Padmanabhan *(CEO & Mng Dir)*

Subsidiaries:

Subex (Asia Pacific) Pte. Limited (1)
175A Bencoolen Street 08-03 Burlington Square, Singapore, 189650, Singapore
Tel.: (65) 63381218
Sales Range: $25-49.9 Million
Telecommunication Servicesb
N.A.I.C.S.: 517810

Subex (UK) Limited (1)
1st Floor Rama Apartment 17 St Ann's Road, Middlesex, Harrow, HA1 1JU, United Kingdom
Tel.: (44) 2078265300
Information Technology Services
N.A.I.C.S.: 541519

Subex Inc. (1)
Tel.: (303) 301-6200
Sales Range: $25-49.9 Million
Telecommunication Servicesb
N.A.I.C.S.: 517810

Subex Technologies Inc. (1)
255 Old New Brunswick Rd Ste S 240, Piscataway, NJ 08854
Tel.: (732) 981-1333
Sales Range: $50-74.9 Million
Emp.: 150
IT Consulting Services
N.A.I.C.S.: 519290

SUBHASH SILK MILLS LTD.
G-15 Prem Kutir Gr Floor 177 Marine Drive, Mumbai, 400020, India
Tel.: (91) 2222825309

INTERNATIONAL PUBLIC

Web Site: https://www.subhashsilkmills.com
Year Founded: 1949
530231—(BOM)
Rev.: $320,707
Assets: $2,057,034
Liabilities: $731,746
Net Worth: $1,325,288
Earnings: $42,429
Emp.: 5
Fiscal Year-end: 03/31/21
Textile Product Mfr & Whslr
N.A.I.C.S.: 314999
Sumeet Subhash Mehra *(Chm)*

SUBLIME CHINA INFORMATION CO., LTD.
No 186 North Beijing Road, Zhangdian District, Zibo, 255095, Shandong, China
Tel.: (86) 5335075233
Web Site: https://www.sci99.com
Year Founded: 2004
301299—(CHIN)
Rev.: $39,259,886
Assets: $135,633,529
Liabilities: $42,428,583
Net Worth: $93,204,946
Earnings: $7,208,781
Emp.: 1,000
Fiscal Year-end: 12/31/21
Information Technology Services
N.A.I.C.S.: 541512

SUBROS LTD
LGF World Trade Centre Barakhamba Lane, New Delhi, 110001, India
Tel.: (91) 1123414946
Web Site: https://www.subros.com
517168—(NSE)
Rev.: $246,514,182
Assets: $197,833,258
Liabilities: $89,300,129
Net Worth: $108,533,129
Earnings: $6,468,885
Emp.: 2,776
Fiscal Year-end: 03/31/21
Auto Air Conditioning Systems Mfr
N.A.I.C.S.: 333415
Ramesh Suri *(Founder & Chm)*

SUBSEA 7 S.A.
40 Brighton Road, Surrey, Sutton, SM2 5BN, United Kingdom
Tel.: (44) 2082105500 LU
Web Site: https://www.subsea7.com
Year Founded: 1973
ACGYF—(OTCIQ)
Rev.: $5,010,000,000
Assets: $6,988,300,000
Liabilities: $2,499,100,000
Net Worth: $4,489,200,000
Earnings: $36,400,000
Emp.: 5,067
Fiscal Year-end: 12/31/21
Underwater Engineering & Construction Services for Oil & Gas Producers
N.A.I.C.S.: 237120
John Evans *(CEO)*

Subsidiaries:

4Subsea AS (1)
Hagalokkveien 26 NO-1383, Asker, Norway
Tel.: (47) 6 698 2700
Web Site: https://www.4subsea.com
Subsea Equipment Whslr
N.A.I.C.S.: 423830

Acergy France S.A. (1)
1 Quai Marcel Dassault, 92156, Suresnes, Cedex, France
Tel.: (33) 140976300
Sales Range: $100-124.9 Million
Emp.: 400
Underwater Engineering & Construction Services for Oil & Gas Producers
N.A.I.C.S.: 237120
Jean Cahuzac *(CEO)*

AND PRIVATE COMPANIES

Green Light Environment Pty Limited (1)
Unit 19/210 Queen Victoria St, North Fremantle, 6159, WA, Australia
Tel.: (61) 458887791
Web Site:
https://www.greenlightenvironmental.com
Environmental Consulting Services
N.A.I.C.S.: 541620

Seaway Heavy Lifting Contracting Germany GmbH (1)
Neuer Wall 63, 20354, Hamburg, Germany
Tel.: (49) 40808093146
Engineering Fabrication & Heavy Lifting Mfr
N.A.I.C.S.: 333998
Richard Van Aurich *(Mgr-Bus Dev)*

Seaway Heavy Lifting Limited (1)
Lophitis Business Centre 1 249 28th October Street, 3035, Limassol, Cyprus
Tel.: (357) 25029090
Engineering Fabrication & Heavy Lifting Mfr
N.A.I.C.S.: 333998
Constans Kootstra *(Mng Dir)*

Seaway Offshore Cables GmbH (1)
Bavinkstrasse 23 Block E, 26789, Leer, Germany
Tel.: (49) 491912430
Cable Installation Repair & Maintenance Services
N.A.I.C.S.: 238210

Seaway Offshore Cables Limited (1)
Prospect Road Arnhall Business Park, Westhill, AB32 6FE, Aberdeenshire, United Kingdom
Tel.: (44) 1224526000
Cable Installation Repair & Maintenance Services
N.A.I.C.S.: 238210

Subsea 7 (Singapore) Pte. Ltd. (1)
150 Beach Road 27-01 Gateway West, Singapore, 189720, Singapore
Tel.: (65) 63094700
Web Site: http://www.subsea7.com
Sales Range: $25-49.9 Million
Underwater Engineering & Construction Services for Oil & Gas Producers
N.A.I.C.S.: 237120

Subsea 7 (UK) (1)
Prospect Road Arnhall Business Park, Westhill, AB32 6FE, Aberdeenshire, United Kingdom
Tel.: (44) 1224526000
Web Site: http://www.subsea7.com
Sales Range: $400-449.9 Million
Oil Field Services & Products; Engineering & Construction
N.A.I.C.S.: 541330

Subsea 7 (US) LLC (1)
17220 Katy Fwy Ste 100, Houston, TX 77094
Tel.: (713) 430-1100
Web Site: http://www.subsea7.com
Holding Company; Regional Managing Office
N.A.I.C.S.: 551112

Subsidiary (Domestic):

Subsea 7 (GOM) Inc. (2)
10787 Clay Rd, Houston, TX 77041
Tel.: (713) 430-1100
Web Site: http://www.subsea7.com
Sales Range: $50-74.9 Million
Emp.: 150
Underwater Engineering & Construction Services for Oil & Gas Producers
N.A.I.C.S.: 237120

Division (Domestic):

Subsea 7 - i-Tech & Veripos Divisions (3)
15990 N Barkers Landing Ste 200, Houston, TX 77079
Tel.: (281) 966-7600
Web Site: http://www.subsea7.com
Sales Range: $50-74.9 Million
Emp.: 150
Manned Or Unmanned Submersible Marine Robots
N.A.I.C.S.: 236210

Subsea 7 (Vessel Company) Limited (1)
17th Floor Quadrant House The Quadrant, Sutton, SM2 5AS, United Kingdom
Tel.: (44) 2087226220
Sales Range: $100-124.9 Million
Emp.: 150
Oil & Gas Extraction Services
N.A.I.C.S.: 213112

Subsea 7 Asia Pacific Sdn. Bhd. (1)
Suite 9 02 Level 9 GTower 199 Jalan Tun Razak, 50400, Kuala Lumpur, Malaysia
Tel.: (60) 32 174 7777
Web Site: https://www.subsea7.com
Sales Range: $25-49.9 Million
Emp.: 28
Construction Engineering Services
N.A.I.C.S.: 541330

Subsea 7 Australia Pty. Ltd. (1)
Australia Place Level 7 15-17 Williams Street, Perth, 6000, WA, Australia
Tel.: (61) 89 326 0600
Web Site:
http://www.interventiontechnogy.com
Sales Range: $50-74.9 Million
Emp.: 7
Oil & Gas Exploration Services
N.A.I.C.S.: 213112

Subsea 7 B.V. (1)
Weena 327, 3013 AL, Rotterdam, Zuid-Holland, Netherlands
Tel.: (31) 102064600
Engineeering Services
N.A.I.C.S.: 541330

Subsea 7 Blue Space Limited (1)
Prospect Road Arnhall Business Park Westhill, Aberdeen, AB32 6FE, United Kingdom
Tel.: (44) 1224526000
Sales Range: $100-124.9 Million
Underwater Engineering & Construction Services for Oil & Gas Producers
N.A.I.C.S.: 237120

Subsea 7 Brasil S.A. (1)
Rua Engenheiro Fabio Goulart 155 Ilha da Conceicao, Niteroi, Rio de Janeiro, 24050-090, Brazil (100%)
Tel.: (55) 213 370 9723
Web Site: https://www.subsea7.com
Sales Range: $25-49.9 Million
Emp.: 10
Underwater Engineering & Construction Services for Oil & Gas Producers
N.A.I.C.S.: 237120

Subsidiary (Domestic):

Subsea 7 do Brasil Servicos Ltda (2)
Rua Eng Fabio Goulart 155 Ilha da Conceicao, Niteroi, 20361320, Brazil
Tel.: (55) 21 2621 9800
Web Site: http://www.subsea7.com
Oil & Gas Plant Construction Services
N.A.I.C.S.: 237120

Subsea 7 Canada Inc. (1)
351 Water Street 6th Floor, Saint John's, A1C 1C2, NL, Canada
Tel.: (709) 753-0500
Construction & Offshore Services
N.A.I.C.S.: 541330

Subsea 7 Contracting (Norway) AS (1)
Kanalsletta 9, Stavanger, 4033, Norway
Tel.: (47) 51845000
Web Site: http://www.subsea7.com
Sales Range: $200-249.9 Million
Emp.: 500
Underwater Engineering & Construction Services for Oil & Gas Producers
N.A.I.C.S.: 213112

Subsea 7 Mocambique Lda (1)
Avenida Marginal n 9149A Bairro do Triunfo, Maputo, Mozambique
Tel.: (258) 21451690
Engineeering Services
N.A.I.C.S.: 541330

Subsea 7 Pipeline Production Limited (1)
Prospect Road, Arnhall Business Park, Westhill, AB32 6FE, Aberdeenshire, United Kingdom
Tel.: (44) 122 452 6000
Web Site: https://www.subsea7.com
Emp.: 1,200
Construction Engineering Services
N.A.I.C.S.: 541330

Subsea 7 Portugal, Limitada (1)
Avenida Dom Joao II Lote 1 17 01 Edificio Torre Zen - 7, Piso Parque das Nacoes, Lisbon, 1990-084, Portugal
Tel.: (351) 210434904
Engineeering Services
N.A.I.C.S.: 541330

Subsea 7 Shipping AS (1)
Kanalsletta 9, Royneberg, 4065, Stavanger, Norway
Tel.: (47) 51725000
Civil Engineering Services
N.A.I.C.S.: 237990

Subsea 7 i-Tech Mexico S. de R.L. de C.V. (1)
Veracruz Calle Laurel Lote 33 Manzana entre Av Arrayanes y Araucarias, Col Ciudad Industrial Bruno Pagliai Tejeria, 91697, Veracruz, Mexico
Tel.: (52) 2291302500
Engineeering Services
N.A.I.C.S.: 541330

Subsea 7 i-Tech Norway AS (1)
Kanalsletta 9 Rosenberg, 4052, Trondheim, Norway
Tel.: (47) 51725000
Engineeering Services
N.A.I.C.S.: 541330
Gert Juel Rasmussen *(Mgr-Bus)*

Subsea 7 i-Tech US Inc. (1)
22330 Merchants Way Ste 100, Katy, TX 77449
Tel.: (713) 430-1100
Engineeering Services
N.A.I.C.S.: 541330

Swagelining Limited (1)
Swagelining River Clyde House Erskine Ferry Road, Old Kilpatrick, Glasgow, G60 5EU, United Kingdom
Tel.: (44) 1389801820
Web Site: http://www.swagelining.com
Oil & Gas Pipeline Services
N.A.I.C.S.: 237120

Xodus Group Ltd. (1)
Xodus House 50 Huntly Street, Aberdeen, AB10 1RS, United Kingdom
Tel.: (44) 1224628300
Web Site: http://www.xodusgroup.com
Commercial Services
N.A.I.C.S.: 561499

SUBSRITHAI PUBLIC COMPANY LIMITED

No 2044/25-27 New Petchaburi Extension Bangkapi Huaykwang, Bangkok, 10310, Thailand
Tel.: (66) 23185514
Web Site:
https://www.subsrithai.co.th
Year Founded: 1976
SST—(THA)
Rev.: $119,405,374
Assets: $222,768,010
Liabilities: $163,445,256
Net Worth: $59,322,754
Earnings: ($15,180)
Emp.: 241
Fiscal Year-end: 12/31/23
Transportation & Logistics Services
N.A.I.C.S.: 488999
Supasith Sukhanindr *(Chm, Pres & CEO)*

Subsidiaries:

Mudman Public Company Limited (1)
33/4 The 9th Towers Grand Rama 9 18th Fl Tower A Rama 9 Road Huaykwang, Huaykwang, Bangkok, 10310, Thailand
Tel.: (66) 20799765
Web Site: http://www.mudman.co.th
Food Product Retailer
N.A.I.C.S.: 445298
Nadim Xavier Salhani *(CEO)*

SUBURBAN MINERALS CORP.

SUBSTRATE ARTIFICIAL INTELIGENCE SA

C/Correos 10-Pta 7, 46002, Valencia, Spain
Tel.: (34) 961237015 ES
Web Site: https://www.substrate.ai
Year Founded: 2010
SAI—(MAD)
Rev.: $9,503,032
Assets: $49,078,174
Liabilities: $22,738,313
Net Worth: $26,339,861
Earnings: ($9,344,597)
Emp.: 131
Fiscal Year-end: 12/31/23
Software Development Services
N.A.I.C.S.: 541511
Bern Worth *(CTO)*

Subsidiaries:

Cuarta Dimension Medica, S.L. (1)
Pol Ind Cami Reial C/ LLaurardors 8, L Alcudia, 46250, Valencia, Spain
Tel.: (34) 910020252
Web Site: https://www.4dmedica.com
X-ray Equipment Mfr & Distr
N.A.I.C.S.: 339112

Kau Market EAF, S.L. (1)
C/ Ruiz de Lihory 5, 46003, Valencia, Spain
Tel.: (34) 961237015
Web Site: https://www.kaumarkets.com
Real Estate & Financial Advisory Services
N.A.I.C.S.: 531390

Substrate AI Spain, S.L. (1)
C/ Maria de Molina 41 Office 503, 28006, Madrid, Spain
Tel.: (34) 680692738
Web Site: https://substrate.ai
Artificial Intelligence Technology Development Services
N.A.I.C.S.: 541715

Zona Value Global, S.L. (1)
C/ Cronista Carreres 10 bajo, 46003, Valencia, Spain
Tel.: (34) 961237015
Web Site: https://zonavueglobal.com
Financial Investment Services
N.A.I.C.S.: 522220

SUBUR TIASA HOLDINGS BERHAD

No 66-78 Pusat Suria Permata Jalan Upper Lanang CDT 123, 96000, Sibu, Sarawak, Malaysia
Tel.: (60) 84211555
Web Site:
https://www.suburtiasa.com
SUBUR—(KLS)
Rev.: $127,067,864
Assets: $330,787,564
Liabilities: $185,662,343
Net Worth: $145,125,221
Earnings: $9,709,492
Fiscal Year-end: 12/31/22
Plywood Mfr
N.A.I.C.S.: 321211
Chieh Min Ling *(Co-Sec)*

Subsidiaries:

Subur Tiasa Particleboard Sdn. Bhd. (1)
No 66-78 Pusat Suria Permata Jalan Upper Lanang CDT 123, 96000, Sibu, Sarawak, Malaysia
Tel.: (60) 84212155
Emp.: 175
Laminate Particleboard Mfr & Distr
N.A.I.C.S.: 337110
Wong Siekwong *(Mgr-Factory)*

SUBURBAN MINERALS CORP.

300 North Main Street, PO Box 487, Vancouver, 26807, BC, Canada
Tel.: (304) 358-2311
Mineral Exploration Services
N.A.I.C.S.: 213115
Tim Sperling *(Pres & CEO)*

SUBURBIA ADVERTISING

Suburban Minerals Corp.—(Continued)

SUBURBIA ADVERTISING
590 Beaver Lake Road RR3, Victoria, V9E 2J7, BC, Canada
Tel.: (250) 744-1231
Web Site:
http://www.suburbiastudios.com
Year Founded: 1988
Emp.: 13
Advertising Agencies
N.A.I.C.S.: 541810
Mary-Lynn Bellamy-Williams (Partner & CEO)

Subsidiaries:

Suburbia Advertising - Delta (1)
3-1363 56th St, Delta, V4L 2P7, BC, Canada
Tel.: (604) 943-6414
Advertising Agencies
N.A.I.C.S.: 541810

SUBWAY FINANCE & INVESTMENT COMPANY LIMITED
B/101 Eastern Court Junction of Tejpal and Parleshwar Road, Vile Parle East, Mumbai, 400 057, Maharastra, India
Tel.: (91) 22 26165960
Web Site:
http://www.subwayfinance.in
Year Founded: 1983
Rev.: $21,800
Assets: $291,126
Liabilities: $48,550
Net Worth: $242,576
Earnings: $11,414
Fiscal Year-end: 03/31/17
Financial Investment Management Services
N.A.I.C.S.: 523940

SUBZERO GROUP LIMITED
39-43 Thomas Mitchell Drive, PO Box 561, Muswellbrook, 2333, NSW, Australia
Tel.: (61) 2 6540 9400
Year Founded: 1999
Sales Range: $25-49.9 Million
Emp.: 350
Mining Engineering Services
N.A.I.C.S.: 541330
John W. Dickson (CFO)

Subsidiaries:

DMST Pty Limited (1)
28 Amber Grove, Bolwarra Heights, Maitland, 2320, NSW, Australia
Tel.: (61) 4 3839 2961
Mining Engineering Services
N.A.I.C.S.: 541330

Harness Master Wiring Systems (NSW) Pty Limited (1)
U 2/49 Racecourse Rd, Maitland, 2320, NSW, Australia
Tel.: (61) 2 4932 8054
Mining Engineering Services
N.A.I.C.S.: 541330

SF Auto Australia Pty Limited (1)
10 Carramere Dr, Muswellbrook, 2333, NSW, Australia
Tel.: (61) 265411945
Mining Engineering Services
N.A.I.C.S.: 541330

SUCCESS DRAGON INTERNATIONAL HOLDINGS LIMITED
Room 903 9/F Tower A New Mandarin Plaza, 14 Science Museum Road Tsim Sha Tsui East, Kowloon, China (Hong Kong)
Tel.: (852) 3 576 3309
Web Site:
http://successdragonintl.com
1182—(HKG)
Rev.: $23,478,487
Assets: $18,304,326

Liabilities: $11,870,803
Net Worth: $6,433,522
Earnings: $262,087
Emp.: 60
Fiscal Year-end: 03/31/22
Investment Services in Gaming Industry
N.A.I.C.S.: 523999
Lei Ding (Chm & CEO)

Subsidiaries:

Success Dragon Kingbox Limited (1)
Room 901 Fabrico Industrial Building 78-84 Kwai Cheong Road, Kwai Chung, New Territories, China (Hong Kong)
Tel.: (852) 23101237
Web Site: http://www.kingbox.com
Packaged Box Mfr
N.A.I.C.S.: 322212

SUCCESS GLOBAL MEDIA LIMITED
Level 9 368 Sussex Street, Sydney, 2000, NSW, Australia
Tel.: (61) 2 8098 8100 AU
Web Site:
http://successglobalmedia.com
Year Founded: 1992
Holding Company; Seminar Management Services
N.A.I.C.S.: 551112
Richard Poh Choon Tan (Chm & Mng Dir)

Subsidiaries:

Success Resources Pte. Ltd. (1)
190 MacPherson Road #08-01, Wisma Gulab, Singapore, 348548, Singapore
Tel.: (65) 6299 4677
Web Site: http://www.srpl.net
Seminar Management Services
N.A.I.C.S.: 923110
Richard Poh Choon Tan (CEO)

Subsidiary (Non-US):

Success Resources Sdn. Bhd. (2)
23-2 Block D2 Jalan PJU 1/39, Dataran Prima, Petaling Jaya, 47301, Selangor Darul Ehsan, Malaysia
Tel.: (60) 3 7801 2888
Web Site: http://www.srpl.net
Emp.: 30
Seminar Management Services
N.A.I.C.S.: 923110
Chong Koh (Country Mgr)

Success Resources UK Ltd. (2)
19 Bolsover Street, London, W1W 5NA, United Kingdom
Tel.: (44) 20 7665 8261
Seminar Management Services
N.A.I.C.S.: 923110

SUCCESS PRIME CORPORATION
2F No 11 Kezhong Rd, Zhunan Township, 350, Miao-li, Taiwan
Tel.: (886) 37586999
Web Site: http://www.pofc.com
Year Founded: 1991
2496—(TAI)
Rev.: $25,011,118
Assets: $44,651,916
Liabilities: $16,725,465
Net Worth: $27,926,452
Earnings: $3,384,251
Emp.: 15
Fiscal Year-end: 12/31/23
Optical Fiber Product Mfr
N.A.I.C.S.: 335921

Subsidiaries:

Chen Li Education Co., Ltd. (1)
11 22nd Floor No 50 Section 1 Zhongxiao West Road, Zhongzheng District, Taipei, Taiwan
Tel.: (886) 223899200
Web Site: https://www.chenliedu.com
Education Training & Support Services
N.A.I.C.S.: 611710

SUCCESS TRANSFORMER CORPORATION BERHAD
No 3 5 7 Jalan TSB 8 Taman Industri Sungai Buloh, 47000, Sungai Buloh, Selangor, Malaysia
Tel.: (60) 362792800
Web Site:
https://www.success.com.my
SUCCESS—(KLS)
Rev.: $57,233,390
Assets: $105,794,427
Liabilities: $12,351,620
Net Worth: $93,442,807
Earnings: $5,262,528
Emp.: 1,244
Fiscal Year-end: 06/30/22
Lighting Services
N.A.I.C.S.: 335132

Subsidiaries:

Global-Pacific Manufacturing Sdn. Bhd. (1)
No 6 Lot 10473 Jalan Kamunting 3 Perindustrian Jalan Kamunting, Bukit Beruntung, 48300, Rawang, Selangor, Malaysia
Tel.: (60) 360211668
Web Site: https://globalpm.com.my
Electrical Part Mfr & Distr
N.A.I.C.S.: 336320

Kare For U Sdn. Bhd. (1)
No 3 5 & 7 Jalan TSB 8 Taman Industri, 47000, Sungai Buloh, Selangor, Malaysia
Tel.: (60) 123319206
Web Site: https://kareforu.com
Medical Equipment Retailer
N.A.I.C.S.: 524114

Ningbo Success Gushi International Trading Co. Ltd. (1)
No 238-2 Keba Road Sci-Tech Park Taoyuan Street, Ninghai, Ningbo, 315600, Zhejiang, China
Tel.: (86) 57465389976
Web Site: https://nbqfgs.jngruinano.com
Outdoor Lighting Mfr
N.A.I.C.S.: 335139

Omega Metal Industries Sdn. Bhd. (1)
Lot 102 Jalan Industri 3/4, Taman Industri Integrasi Rawang, 48000, Rawang, Selangor, Malaysia
Tel.: (60) 362792900
Web Site: https://www.omegametal.com.my
Metal Casing Product Mfr
N.A.I.C.S.: 332322

PT. Boxon Nikkon Jayaindo (1)
Jl Agung perkasa 8 blok k1 no 40 sunterjakarta Utara, Jakarta Utara, 14350, Indonesia
Tel.: (62) 2122652860
Web Site:
https://www.boxonnikkonjayaindo.com
Emp.: 24
Voltage Transformer & Lighting Equipment Mfr
N.A.I.C.S.: 335311

Success Electronics & Transformer Manufacturer Sdn. Bhd. (1)
3 5 7 Jalan TSB 8, Taman Industri Sungai Buloh, 47000, Sungai Buloh, Selangor, Malaysia
Tel.: (60) 362792800
Web Site: https://store-success.business.site
Voltage Transformer & Lighting Equipment Mfr
N.A.I.C.S.: 335311

Success Transformer Pte. Ltd. (1)
Block 3 Kaki Bukit Road 1 03-15 Eunos Technolink, Singapore, 415935, Singapore
Tel.: (65) 67424808
Voltage Transformer & Lighting Equipment Mfr
N.A.I.C.S.: 335311

Subsidiary (Domestic):

Nikkon Lighting & Electrical Pte. Ltd. (2)
No 7 Kaki Bukit Road 1 03-15 Eunos Technolink, Singapore, 415937, Singapore

INTERNATIONAL PUBLIC

Tel.: (65) 67424377
LED Lighting Mfr & Distr
N.A.I.C.S.: 335139

SUCCESS UNIVERSE GROUP LIMITED
Suite 1601-2 and 8-10 16/F Great Eagle Centre 23 Harbour Road, Wanchai, China (Hong Kong)
Tel.: (852) 31018668
Web Site: http://www.successug.com
0487—(HKG)
Rev.: $14,634,195
Assets: $162,072,518
Liabilities: $70,353,480
Net Worth: $91,719,038
Earnings: ($36,601,680)
Emp.: 68
Fiscal Year-end: 12/31/22
Travel & Tourism Services
N.A.I.C.S.: 561510
Agnes Nam Ying Chiu (Sec)

Subsidiaries:

Jade Travel Ltd. (1)
254 Canal St Ste 5005, New York, NY 10013
Tel.: (212) 227-0061
Web Site: http://www2.jadetours.com
Travel & Tour Operating Agencies
N.A.I.C.S.: 561520

Jade Travel Ltd. (1)
4940 No 3 Road Suite 210, Richmond, V6X 3A5, BC, Canada
Tel.: (604) 689-5885
Web Site: http://en.jadetours.com
Travel & Tour Operating Agencies
N.A.I.C.S.: 561520

SUCCESSMORE BEING PUBLIC COMPANY LIMITED
10/1-2 Ratchadapisek Road, Chatuchak, Bangkok, 10900, Thailand
Tel.: (66) 25115955 TH
Web Site:
https://www.successmore.com
Year Founded: 2012
SCM—(THA)
Rev.: $28,696,173
Assets: $25,910,500
Liabilities: $5,370,452
Net Worth: $20,540,048
Earnings: $2,600,197
Emp.: 179
Fiscal Year-end: 12/31/23
Personal Care Product Mfr
N.A.I.C.S.: 326299
Sitthawee Kriatchawanun (Co-Founder, Chm & Vice Chm)

SUCESORES DE RIVADENEYRA SA
Torneros 16 Poligono Industrial Los Angeles, 28906, Getafe, Spain
Tel.: (34) 912089150 ES
Web Site:
http://www.rivadeneyra.com
Sales Range: $10-24.9 Million
Commercial Printing Services
N.A.I.C.S.: 323111
Arakil Gosamaria (Mng Dir)

SUCHUANG GAS CORPORATION LIMITED
116 Loujiangnan Road Taicang, Suzhou, Jiangsu, China
Tel.: (86) 512 53521392 Ky
Web Site:
http://www.suchuanggas.com
Year Founded: 2013
1430—(HKG)
Rev.: $180,959,395
Assets: $352,457,766
Liabilities: $114,180,825
Net Worth: $238,276,942
Earnings: $8,313,787

Emp.: 415
Fiscal Year-end: 12/31/20
Natural Gas Distribution
N.A.I.C.S.: 221210
Shaozhou Du (CEO & Gen Mgr)

SUCOCITRICO CUTRALE LTDA.

Avenida Padre Jose de Anchieta 470
Araraquara, Sao Paulo, 14807-900,
Brazil
Tel.: (55) 16 3301 1100   BR
Web Site: http://www.cutrale.com.br
Year Founded: 1967
Sales Range: $500-549.9 Million
Emp.: 3,500
Citrus Farming & Production Mfr
N.A.I.C.S.: 311411
Jose Luis Cutrale (Chm)

Subsidiaries:

Chiquita Brands International, Inc.   (1)
4757 The Grove Drive Ste 260, Windermere, FL 34786
Tel.: (800) 468-9716
Web Site: http://www.chiquita.com
Rev.: $3,090,224,000
Assets: $1,612,038,000
Liabilities: $1,288,704,000
Net Worth: $323,334,000
Earnings: ($62,536,000)
Emp.: 120
Fiscal Year-end: 12/31/2014
Food Producer, Processor & Distr
N.A.I.C.S.: 311411
Allyson Bouldon (Chief Compliance Officer & VP)

Subsidiary (Non-US):

Chiquita Brands International Sarl   (2)
Batiment B4 A-One Business Center Route de l'Etraz, 1180, Rolle, Switzerland
Tel.: (41) 58 272 2000
Holding Company; Regional Managing Office; Fruit Distr
N.A.I.C.S.: 551112
Mario Pacheco (Sr VP-Global Logistics)

Subsidiary (Non-US):

Boeckmans Belgie NV   (3)
Van Meterenkaai 1 bus 4, B-2000, Antwerp, Belgium
Tel.: (32) 3202 0202
Web Site: http://www.boeckmans.be
Maritime Freight Transport Services
N.A.I.C.S.: 483111
Thierry Denave (Gen Mgr)

Boeckmans Nederland b.v.   (3)
Spui 16, 3161 ED, Rhoon, Netherlands
Tel.: (31) 10 5030000
Web Site: http://www.boeckmans.nl
Shipping & Forwarding Freight Services
N.A.I.C.S.: 483111
Caroline Naaktgeboren (Gen Mgr-Customer Svc)

Chiquita Banana Company BV   (3)
Franklinweg 35, 4207 HX, Gorinchem, Netherlands
Tel.: (31) 183 69 31 11
Web Site: http://www.chiquita.nl
Sales Range: $125-149.9 Million
Banana Import & Export
N.A.I.C.S.: 111339

Subsidiary (Non-US):

Chiquita Deutschland GmbH   (4)
Neue Groninger Strasse 13, D-20457, Hamburg, Germany
Tel.: (49) 40 360239 200
Web Site: http://www.chiquita.de
Fruit & Vegetable Canning Services
N.A.I.C.S.: 311421
Marc Speidel (Mng Dir, Member-Mgmt Bd & Country Dir-Germany)

Subsidiary (Domestic):

Chiquita Fruit Bar (Germany) GmbH   (5)
Trankgasse 11, 50667, Cologne, Germany
Tel.: (49) 221 1608711
Web Site: http://www.chiquita-fruitbar.com
Emp.: 20
Fresh Fruit & Vegetable Juices & Smoothies
N.A.I.C.S.: 311421
Christiane Kruse (Office Mgr)

Subsidiary (Non-US):

Processed Fruit Ingredients, BVBA   (4)
Rijnkaai 37, Antwerp, 2000, Belgium
Tel.: (32) 26494961
Fruit & Vegetable Canning Services
N.A.I.C.S.: 311421

Subsidiary (Non-US):

Great White Fleet, Ltd.   (3)
Van Meterenkaai 1, B-2000, Antwerp, Belgium
Tel.: (32) 3 2020202
Web Site: http://www.boeckmans.be
Air Freight & Shipping Cargo Transport Services
N.A.I.C.S.: 484230
Thierry de Nave (Gen Mgr-Agency)

Subsidiary (Domestic):

Chiquita Brands LLC   (2)
2051 SE 35th St, Fort Lauderdale, FL 33316-4019
Tel.: (954) 453-1201
Web Site: http://www.chiquita.com
Tree Fruits
N.A.I.C.S.: 111339
Darcilo Santos (CEO & CFO)

Plant (Domestic):

Chiquita Brands LLC - Bethlehem   (3)
2777 Brodhead Rd, Bethlehem, PA 18020-9448
Tel.: (610) 866-1851
Web Site: http://www.chiquita.com
Sales Range: $50-74.9 Million
Emp.: 14
Banana Ripening & Distribution Center
N.A.I.C.S.: 424480
Alvaro Alevedo (Branch Mgr)

Chiquita Brands LLC - Fort Lauderdale   (3)
DCOTA Office Center 1855 Griffin Rd Ste C436, Fort Lauderdale, FL 33004-2275
Tel.: (954) 527-7816
Web Site: http://www.chiquita.com
Sales Range: $75-99.9 Million
Emp.: 80
Fresh Fruit & Vegetable Service
N.A.I.C.S.: 424480

Chiquita Brands LLC - Freeport   (3)
1100 Cherry St, Freeport, TX 77541-5863
Tel.: (979) 233-0844
Web Site: http://www.chiquita.com
Sales Range: $50-74.9 Million
Emp.: 7
Bananas Ripening & Freight Transportation
N.A.I.C.S.: 483111
Tony Caranna (Gen Mgr)

Chiquita Brands LLC - Gulfport   (3)
1000 30th Ave, Gulfport, MS 39501
Tel.: (228) 864-5046
Web Site: http://www.chiquita.com
Sales Range: $10-24.9 Million
Emp.: 16
Bananas Freight Transportation
N.A.I.C.S.: 488510

Chiquita Brands LLC - Wilmington   (3)
101 River Rd, Wilmington, DE 19801
Tel.: (302) 571-9781
Web Site: http://www.chiquita.com
Sales Range: $50-74.9 Million
Emp.: 100
Import & Distribution of Bananas
N.A.I.C.S.: 424480
Mario Pacheco (Sr VP-Global Logistics)

Subsidiary (Domestic):

Chiquita Fresh North America LLC   (3)
2051 SE 35th St, Fort Lauderdale, FL 33316-4019
Tel.: (954) 453-1201
Web Site: http://www.chiquita.com
Sales Range: $100-124.9 Million
Fresh Fruit Distr
N.A.I.C.S.: 424480
Darcilo Santos (CEO & CFO)

Fresh Express Incorporated   (3)
950 E Blanco Rd, Salinas, CA 93901-4409
Tel.: (831) 775-2300
Sales Range: $50-74.9 Million
Fresh Salads & Vegetables Mfr & Whslr
N.A.I.C.S.: 424480
Kenneth Diveley (CEO-Chiquita Fruit Solutions & Fresh Express)

Plant (Domestic):

Fresh Express Inc. - Chicago   (4)
9501 Nevada Ave, Franklin Park, IL 60131
Tel.: (847) 451-1452
Sales Range: $125-149.9 Million
Emp.: 300
Pre-Cut Vegetable Supplier to Fast-Food Chains
N.A.I.C.S.: 424480
Kevin Drves (Plant Mgr)

Fresh Express Inc. - Grand Prairie   (4)
2370 W Warrior Trail, Grand Prairie, TX 75052-7254
Tel.: (972) 595-3600
Wholesale Produce
N.A.I.C.S.: 424480

Subsidiary (Domestic):

TransFRESH Corporation   (3)
40 Ragsdale Dr Ste 200, Monterey, CA 93940
Tel.: (831) 772-6086
Web Site: http://www.transfresh.com
Sales Range: Less than $1 Million
Emp.: 17
Transportation of Fresh Fruits & Vegetables
N.A.I.C.S.: 311421
Jean-Yves Pamart (Gen Mgr-Europe)

Subsidiary (Non-US):

Chiquita Guatemala, S.A.   (2)
9a Calle entre 1ra y 2da av Puerto Barrios, Izabal, Guatemala, Guatemala
Tel.: (502) 24 793 17000
Web Site: http://www.chiquita.com
Fruit & Vegetable Freight & Shipping Services
N.A.I.C.S.: 311421
Manrique Bermudez (Dir-Latin American Logistics)

Chiquita Logistic Services El Salvador Ltda.   (2)
Paseo General Escalon Villas Espanolas, San Salvador, El Salvador
Tel.: (503) 22638017
Fruit & Vegetable Logistics & Canning Services
N.A.I.C.S.: 311421
Edwin Polanco (Country Mgr)

Cutrale Citrus Juices USA, Inc.   (1)
602 McKean St, Auburndale, FL 33823-4070
Tel.: (863) 965-5000
Web Site: http://www.cutrale.com
Sales Range: $150-199.9 Million
Emp.: 400
Frozen Fruits & Vegetables
N.A.I.C.S.: 311411

SUDAL INDUSTRIES LTD.

26A Nariman Bhavan 227 Nariman Point, Mumbai, 400 021, India
Tel.: (91) 2261577100
Web Site: https://www.sudal.co.in
Year Founded: 1979
506003—(BOM)
Rev.: $19,388,190
Assets: $7,372,795
Liabilities: $19,713,686
Net Worth: ($12,340,891)
Earnings: ($4,001,942)
Emp.: 118
Fiscal Year-end: 03/31/23
Aluminum Extrusions Mfr
N.A.I.C.S.: 331318
Sudarshan S. Chokhani (Mng Dir)

SUDANESE FRENCH BANK

Al Qasr Street, Khartoum, Sudan
Tel.: (249) 183 771730
Year Founded: 1979
Banking Services
N.A.I.C.S.: 522110

SUDANESE ISLAMIC BANK

Khartoum University Street, Khartoum, Sudan
Tel.: (249) 183777610
SIBA—(KHAR)
Sales Range: Less than $1 Million
Banking Services
N.A.I.C.S.: 522110
Ali Mohammed Osman Mirghani (Chm)

SUDARSHAN CHEMICAL INDUSTRIES LTD.

162 Wellesley Road, Pune, 411 001, India
Tel.: (91) 2068281200   In
Web Site: https://www.sudarshan.com
Year Founded: 1952
SUDARSCHEM—(NSE)
Rev.: $255,408,836
Assets: $273,464,783
Liabilities: $171,966,659
Net Worth: $101,498,124
Earnings: $19,261,652
Emp.: 1,192
Fiscal Year-end: 03/31/21
Pigments, Agrochemicals & Specialty Chemicals Sales & Mfr; Environmental Management Consulting Services
N.A.I.C.S.: 325130
Pradeep R. Rathi (Chm)

Subsidiaries:

Sudarshan Europe B.V.   (1)
Tel.: (31) 204919417
Sales Range: $25-49.9 Million
Emp.: 10
Organic & Inorganic Pigments Mfr
N.A.I.C.S.: 325998

SUDARSHAN PHARMA INDUSTRIES LIMITED

301 3rd Floor Aura Biplex Landmark Kalyan Jewellers S V Road, Borivali West, Mumbai, 400092, Maharashtra, India
Tel.: (91) 9769628096
Web Site: https://www.sudarshanpharma.com
Year Founded: 2008
543828—(BOM)
Rev.: $55,446,196
Assets: $27,873,389
Liabilities: $15,767,004
Net Worth: $12,106,385
Earnings: $843,678
Emp.: 56
Fiscal Year-end: 03/31/23
Pharmaceutical Product Mfr & Distr
N.A.I.C.S.: 325412
Hemal V. Mehta (Chm)

SUDATEL TELECOM GROUP LIMITED

Sinkat Street, PO Box 11155, Khartoum, Sudan
Tel.: (249) 183782322
Web Site: https://www.sudatel.sd
Year Founded: 1993
SUDATEL—(ABU)
Rev.: $400,191,428
Assets: $1,100,891,204
Liabilities: $732,081,907
Net Worth: $368,809,297
Earnings: $19,937,320

SUDATEL TELECOM GROUP LIMITED

Sudatel Telecom Group Limited—(Continued)
Fiscal Year-end: 12/31/23
Telecommunication Servicesb
N.A.I.C.S.: 517810
Hassan Osman Sakota *(Deputy Chm)*

SUDDEUTSCHE ZUCKERRUBEN-VERWERTUNGS-GENOSSENSCHAFT EG

Marktbreiter Str 74, 97199, Ochsenfurt, Germany
Tel.: (49) 933191256
Web Site: http://www.szvg.de
Sales Range: $25-49.9 Million
Emp.: 8
Sugar Beet Farming Services
N.A.I.C.S.: 111991
Fred Zeller *(Mng Dir)*

Subsidiaries:

Sudzucker AG (1)
Maximilianstrabe 10, 68165, Mannheim, Germany (55%)
Tel.: (49) 6214210
Web Site: https://www.suedzucker.de
Rev.: $11,357,765,759
Assets: $11,345,623,139
Liabilities: $6,628,766,973
Net Worth: $4,716,856,166
Earnings: $715,310,741
Emp.: 19,160
Fiscal Year-end: 02/29/2024
Holding Company; Agricultural Raw Materials Processor & Products Mfr
N.A.I.C.S.: 551112
Hans-Jorg Gebhard *(Chm-Supervisory Bd)*

Subsidiary (Domestic):

BGD Bodengesundheitsdienst GmbH (2)
Marktbreiter Strasse 74, 97199, Ochsenfurt, Germany
Tel.: (49) 933191481
Web Site: http://www.bodengesundheitsdienst.de
Sugar Mfr
N.A.I.C.S.: 311313

CropEnergies AG (2)
Maximilianstrasse 10, D-68165, Mannheim, Germany (100%)
Tel.: (49) 62171419000
Web Site: https://www.cropenergies.com
Rev.: $1,827,956,430
Assets: $1,285,807,609
Liabilities: $323,174,509
Net Worth: $962,633,100
Earnings: $241,417,941
Emp.: 464
Fiscal Year-end: 02/28/2023
Bioethanol Mfr
N.A.I.C.S.: 325193
Markwart Kunz *(Chm-Supervisory Bd)*

Freiberger Lebensmittel GmbH & Co. (2)
Zerpenschleuser Ring 1, 13439, Berlin, Germany
Tel.: (49) 30 40704 0
Web Site: http://www.freiberger.de
Emp.: 2,500
Frozen Pizza, Pasta, Snacks & Baguettes Mfr & Distr
N.A.I.C.S.: 311412
Holger Seidel *(Dir-Sls)*

Subsidiary (Non-US):

Freiberger France Sarl (3)
12 Rue Claude Chappe, Parc d'Affaires de Crecy, 69370, Saint Didier, France
Tel.: (33) 4 78 64 33 70
Web Site: http://www.freiberger.de
Frozen Food Distr
N.A.I.C.S.: 424420
Philippe Balcon *(Mng Dir)*

Freiberger Polska Sp.z.o.o. (3)
ul Pory 78, 02-757, Warsaw, Poland
Tel.: (48) 22 456 1830
Web Site: http://www.freiberger.de
Frozen Food Distr
N.A.I.C.S.: 424420

Pawel Rytarowski *(Dir)*

Freiberger UK Ltd. (3)
Broadgate House Westlode Street, Spalding, PE11 2AF, Lincolnshire, United Kingdom
Tel.: (44) 1775 767655
Web Site: http://www.freiberger.de
Frozen Food Product Mfr
N.A.I.C.S.: 311412
Andrew Thorne *(Mng Dir)*

Subsidiary (US):

Freiberger USA, Inc. (3)
6 Upper Pond Rd #3A, Parsippany, NJ 07054
Tel.: (781) 786-6837
Web Site: http://www.freiberger-pizza.com
Frozen Food Distr
N.A.I.C.S.: 424420
Claudia Willison *(Dir-Supply Chain)*

Subsidiary (Domestic):

Richelieu Group, LLC (4)
222 Forbes Rd Ste 400, Braintree, MA 02184
Tel.: (781) 961-1537
Web Site: http://www.richelieufoods.com
Sales Range: $10-24.9 Million
Emp.: 80
Holding Company; Frozen Food Mfr
N.A.I.C.S.: 551112
Tim O'Connor *(Pres & CEO)*

Subsidiary (Domestic):

Richelieu Foods, Inc. (5)
222 Forbes Rd Ste 4400, Braintree, MA 02184
Tel.: (781) 786-6800
Web Site: http://www.richelieufoods.com
Frozen Pizza, Salad Dressing & BBQ Sauce Products Mfr
N.A.I.C.S.: 311423

Subsidiary (Domestic):

Lady Cake-Feine Kuchen GmbH (2)
Bucher Str 137, 90419, Nuremberg, Germany
Tel.: (49) 9119380
Web Site: http://www.nestle.de
Sales Range: $25-49.9 Million
Cake Mfr
N.A.I.C.S.: 311812

Moennich GmbH (2)
Leipziger Str 363-365, 34123, Kassel, Germany
Tel.: (49) 561951640
Web Site: http://www.muesli-moennich.de
Sales Range: $25-49.9 Million
Sugar Mfr
N.A.I.C.S.: 311313
Gabriela Koering *(Gen Mgr)*

Palatinit GmbH (2)
Maximilianstrasse 10, Mannheim, 68165, Germany
Tel.: (49) 621421150
Web Site: http://www.beneo.com
Sales Range: $25-49.9 Million
Sugar Ingredient Developer & Mfr
N.A.I.C.S.: 311313

Subsidiary (Non-US):

Raffinerie Tirlemontoise S.A. (2)
Tervurenlaan 182, 1150, Brussels, Belgium (99.61%)
Tel.: (32) 27758020
Web Site: http://www.tiensegroup.com
Sugar Refinery
N.A.I.C.S.: 311313
Geert Van Aelst *(Mgr-Mktg)*

Subsidiary (Domestic):

BENEO-Orafti N.V. (3)
Aandorenstraat 1, 3300, Tienen, Belgium
Tel.: (32) 16 801 301
Web Site: http://www.beneo.com
Fruit Processing Services
N.A.I.C.S.: 111336

Subsidiary (Domestic):

BENEO-Remy N.V. (4)
Remylaan 4, Leuven, 3018, Wijgmaal, Belgium

Tel.: (32) 16248511
Web Site: http://www.beneo-remy.com
Sales Range: $25-49.9 Million
Emp.: 160
Rice Derivatives Producer & Sales
N.A.I.C.S.: 311212
Claudia Meissner *(Mgr-Corp Comm)*

Subsidiary (Non-US):

Saint Louis Sucre S.A. (2)
23-25 Ave Franklin D Roosevelt, F 75008, Paris, France (100%)
Tel.: (33) 140767472
Web Site: http://www.saintlouis-sucre.com
Mfr & Refining of Sugar Products
N.A.I.C.S.: 311314
Carsten Stahn *(Pres)*

Joint Venture (Non-US):

Eastern Sugar BV (3)
Zwanebloem 31, 4823 MV, Breda, Netherlands
Tel.: (31) 765424994
Holding Company
N.A.I.C.S.: 551112

Plant (Domestic):

Sudzucker AG - Zeitz Plant (2)
Albrechtstrasse 54, Zeitz, 6712, Germany
Tel.: (49) 34418990
Web Site: http://www.suedzucker.de
Sales Range: $25-49.9 Million
Beet Sugar Refining
N.A.I.C.S.: 311313
Philip Schluter *(Plant Mgr)*

SUDESTE S.A.

Av Presidente Wilson 231 - 28 Andar/parte, 20030021, Rio de Janeiro, Brazil
Tel.: (55) 2138043700
Web Site: http://www.sudestenet.com.br
OPSE3—(BRAZ)
Assets: $21,749,879
Liabilities: $21,749,879
Earnings: ($222,198)
Fiscal Year-end: 12/31/23
Financial Management Services
N.A.I.C.S.: 523999

SUDHAUS GMBH & CO. KG

Teichstr 5, 58644, Iserlohn, Germany
Tel.: (49) 23719060   De
Web Site: http://www.sudhaus.de
Year Founded: 1844
Sales Range: $25-49.9 Million
Racking Systems Mfr
N.A.I.C.S.: 337215
Michael Hartmann *(Mng Dir)*

SUDITI INDUSTRIES LIMITED

C-253/254 MIDC TTC Industrial Area Pawne Village, Behind Savita Chemicals Navi Mumbai, Mumbai, 400 705, India
Tel.: (91) 67368600
Web Site: https://www.suditi.in
Year Founded: 1991
521113—(BOM)
Rev.: $13,970,805
Assets: $7,410,899
Liabilities: $8,607,769
Net Worth: ($1,196,871)
Earnings: ($2,107,476)
Emp.: 154
Fiscal Year-end: 03/31/23
Fabric Material Mfr
N.A.I.C.S.: 313240
Pawan Agarwal *(Chm)*

SUDU TRADING HONG KONG LIMITED

The Executive Centre Level 1 - 25 28 Stanley Street Central, Hong Kong, China (Hong Kong)
Tel.: (852) 24366210
Web Site: https://www.sudutrade.com
Year Founded: 2009

INTERNATIONAL PUBLIC

Investment Holding Company
N.A.I.C.S.: 551112
Barney Esterhuyzen *(Founder)*

SUDWESTDEUTSCHE MEDIENHOLDING GMBH

Plieninger Strasse 150, 70567, Stuttgart, Germany
Tel.: (49) 711 7205 0
Web Site: http://www.swmh.de
Emp.: 7,000
Media Holding Services
N.A.I.C.S.: 551112
Alexander Paasch *(CFO)*

Subsidiaries:

Suddeutscher Verlag GmbH (1)
Hultschiner Strasse 8, 81677, Munich, Germany (81.25%)
Tel.: (49) 89 2183 0
Web Site: http://www.sueddeutscher-verlag.de
Newspaper & Periodicals Publishing
N.A.I.C.S.: 513110

Subsidiary (Domestic):

Medical Tribune Verlagsgesellschaft mbH (2)
Unter den Eichen 5, 65195, Wiesbaden, Germany (100%)
Tel.: (49) 611 9746 0
Web Site: http://www.medical-tribune.de
Sales Range: $25-49.9 Million
Emp.: 50
Newspaper Publishers
N.A.I.C.S.: 513110

SUDWESTFALEN ENERGIE UND WASSER AG

Kornerstrasse 40, 58095, Hagen, Germany
Tel.: (49) 23 31 3565 0
Web Site: http://www.sewag-gruppe.de
Emp.: 900
Utility Services
N.A.I.C.S.: 221122

Subsidiaries:

Nuon Deutschland GmbH (1)
Egellsstrasse 21, 13507, Berlin, Germany
Tel.: (49) 30409020
Web Site: http://www.nuon.de
Sales Range: $300-349.9 Million
Electric Power Services
N.A.I.C.S.: 221122

SUEDWESTDEUTSCHE SALZWERKE AG

Salzgrund 67, 74076, Heilbronn, Germany
Tel.: (49) 71319590
Web Site: https://www.salzwerke.de
Year Founded: 1883
SSH—(STU)
Sales Range: Less than $1 Million
Spice Mfr
N.A.I.C.S.: 311942
Wolfgang Ruether *(Member-Mgmt Bd)*

SUEK LTD

3 Georgiou Katsounotou Kitallides Bldg 3rd Floor, 3036, Limassol, Cyprus
Tel.: (357) 2550 9110   CY
Web Site: http://www.suek.com
Year Founded: 2011
Sales Range: $5-14.9 Billion
Emp.: 33,583
Holding Company; Coal Mining, Processing & Distribution
N.A.I.C.S.: 551112
Vladimir Rashevsky *(Chm-Mgmt Bd & CEO)*

Subsidiaries:

OJSC Siberian Coal Energy Company (1)
29 Serebryanicheskaya nab, 109028, Moscow, Russia **(100%)**
Tel.: (7) 4957952538
Web Site: http://www.suek.ru
Sales Range: $5-14.9 Billion
Emp.: 30,000
Holding Company; Coal Mining, Processing & Distribution Services
N.A.I.C.S.: 551112

SUEK AG (1)
Wassergasse 7, Saint Gallen, 9000, Switzerland
Tel.: (41) 712268500
Web Site: http://www.suekag.com
Coal Mining Services
N.A.I.C.S.: 213113
Victoria Pokrovskaya *(Mgr-Freight)*

SUELOPETROL C.A. S.A.C.A.
Av San Juan Bosco Edifcio Centro Altamira Piso 9, Urbanizacion Altamira, Caracas, 1061, Venezuela
Tel.: (58) 2122653733
Web Site: http://www.suelopetrol.com
Sales Range: $10-24.9 Million
Hydrocarbons Production Services
N.A.I.C.S.: 211130

Subsidiaries:

Suelopetrol Corp. (1)
770 S Post Oak Ln Ste 325, Houston, TX 77056-1913
Tel.: (713) 960-1148
Oilfield Support Services
N.A.I.C.S.: 561990

SUERYAA KNITWEAR LIMITED
408 Industrial Area-A, Ludhiana, 141 001, Punjab, India
Tel.: (91) 1612433793
Web Site: https://www.sueryaaknitwear.com
Year Founded: 1995
540318—(BOM)
Rev.: $11,833
Assets: $277,002
Liabilities: $2,258
Net Worth: $274,744
Earnings: ($20,163)
Emp.: 3
Fiscal Year-end: 03/31/23
Textile Product Mfr & Distr
N.A.I.C.S.: 313110
Rajiv Jain *(Mng Dir)*

SUEZ ASIA HOLDINGS PTE. LTD.
6 Raffles Quay No 10-07 John Hancock Tower, Singapore, 48580, Singapore
Tel.: (65) 6538 5383
Year Founded: 1995
Investment & Holding Company
N.A.I.C.S.: 551112
Janine Tran *(Mng Dir)*

Subsidiaries:

Inner Mongolia King Deer Cashmere Group Co. (1)
S Donghe Bridge Bayantal St, Donghe District, Baotou, 140040, Inner Mongolia, China **(51.2%)**
Tel.: (86) 472 4171155
Web Site: http://www.kingdeer.com.cn
Sales Range: $200-249.9 Million
Emp.: 7,000
Cashmere Mfr
N.A.I.C.S.: 313210
Kang Zhongkui *(VP & Gen Mgr-Capital & Raw Matls Mgmt)*

Subsidiary (Non-US):

Mongolia Gao Feng Cashmere Co., Ltd. (2)
Former Shoe Leather Factory 5th Little District, Hanshan District, Ulaanbaatar, 210136, Mongolia
Tel.: (976) 99113621
Web Site: http://www.moniiveel.com
Sales Range: $25-49.9 Million
Emp.: 15
Textile & Fabric Finishing Mills
N.A.I.C.S.: 313310

SUEZ CANAL BANK SAE
7 and 9 Abdel Kader Hamza St, Garden City, Cairo, Egypt
Tel.: (20) 237743276
Web Site: https://www.scbank.com.eg
Year Founded: 1978
CANA—(EGX)
Rev.: $319,747,196
Assets: $3,330,523,892
Liabilities: $3,077,733,557
Net Worth: $252,790,335
Earnings: $74,200,031
Emp.: 1,473
Fiscal Year-end: 12/31/23
Banking Services
N.A.I.C.S.: 522110
Hussein Ahmed Ismail Refaei *(Chm & Mng Dir)*

SUEZ CANAL COMPANY FOR TECHNOLOGY SETTLING
9 Abdel Qader Hamza Street Garden City, Agricultural Bank of Egypt Building, Cairo, Egypt
Tel.: (20) 227931982
Web Site: https://www.scts-eg.com
Year Founded: 1996
Software Development Services
N.A.I.C.S.: 541511
Amr Ali Al-Jarhi *(Chm)*

SUFA TECHNOLOGY INDUSTRY CO., LTD., CNNC
No 501 Zhujiang Road, High-tech Zone, Suzhou, 215129, Jiangsu, China
Tel.: (86) 51266672245
Web Site: https://www.chinasufa.com.cn
Year Founded: 1997
000777—(SSE)
Rev.: $210,607,076
Assets: $424,465,142
Liabilities: $172,349,185
Net Worth: $252,115,957
Earnings: $24,140,530
Fiscal Year-end: 12/31/22
Industrial Valve Mfr
N.A.I.C.S.: 332911
Ma Ying *(Chm & Sec)*

Subsidiaries:

Sue valve science and technology industrial co., Ltd. (1)
Pearl River Road 501, China Suzhou New District, Suzhou, 215129, China
Tel.: (86) 51267533655
Industrial Valve Mfr & Distr
N.A.I.C.S.: 332911

SUFRIN HOLDINGS LTD.
Jabotinsky 9, Bnei Brak, Israel
Tel.: (972) 36123965
Web Site: https://www.sufrin.io
Year Founded: 2009
SFRN—(TAE)
Rev.: $17,941,428
Assets: $84,009,392
Liabilities: $40,666,113
Net Worth: $43,343,279
Earnings: $408,896
Fiscal Year-end: 12/31/23
Offices of Other Holding Companies
N.A.I.C.S.: 551112

SUGA INTERNATIONAL HOLDINGS LIMITED
22/F Tower B Billion Centre, No 1 Wang Kwong Road Kowloon Bay, Kowloon, China (Hong Kong)
Tel.: (852) 29530383
Web Site: https://www.suga.com.hk
0912—(HKG)
Rev.: $239,370,758
Assets: $171,963,359
Liabilities: $67,494,847
Net Worth: $104,468,512
Earnings: $7,324,645
Emp.: 2,530
Fiscal Year-end: 03/31/22
Printed Circuit Board Assembly; Electronics Mfr
N.A.I.C.S.: 334418
Chi Ho Ng *(Founder, Chm & Mng Dir)*

Subsidiaries:

Net-Tech Products Limited (1)
Units 1904-1907 19th Floor Chevalier Commercial Centre, 8 Wang Hoi Road Kowloon Bay, Kowloon, China (Hong Kong) **(100%)**
Tel.: (852) 29530121
Web Site: http://www.suga.com.hk
Computer & Computer Peripheral Equipment & Software Whslr
N.A.I.C.S.: 423430

P & S Macao Commercial Offshore Ltd. (1)
Unit 6E 6/F I Tak Commercial Centre, No 126 Rua De Pequim, Macau, China (Macau) **(100%)**
Tel.: (853) 853780130
Other Electronic Parts & Equipment Whslr
N.A.I.C.S.: 423690

Precise Computer Tooling Co. Limited (1)
22/F Tower B Billion Centre No 1 Wang Kwong Road Kowloon Bay, Kowloon, China (Hong Kong) **(100%)**
Tel.: (852) 29530383
Web Site: http://www.suga.com.hk
Computer Services
N.A.I.C.S.: 541519

Suga Digital Technology Limited (1)
22F Tower B Billion Centre No 1 Wang Kwong Road, Kowloon Bay, Kowloon, China (Hong Kong) **(100%)**
Tel.: (852) 29531515
Digital Entertainment, Imaging, Audio & Video Consumer Electronics Mfr & Developer
N.A.I.C.S.: 335999
Chi Ho Ng *(Mng Dir)*

Suga Electronics (Shenzhen) Co. Ltd. (1)
Upper Le Lang Village, Buji Town, Shenzhen, 518112, China **(100%)**
Tel.: (86) 75533820999
Web Site: http://www.suga.com.hk
Sales Range: $200-249.9 Million
Emp.: 1,000
Telephone Apparatus Mfr
N.A.I.C.S.: 334210

Suga Electronics Limited (1)
22/F Tower B Billion Centre No 1 Wang Kwong Road Kowloon Bay, Kowloon, China (Hong Kong) **(100%)**
Tel.: (852) 29530383
Web Site: http://www.suga.com.hk
Sales Range: $25-49.9 Million
Other Electronic Parts & Equipment Whslr
N.A.I.C.S.: 423690

Suga Networks Hong Kong Limited (1)
22nd Fl Tower B Billion Centre 1 Wang Kwong Road, Kowloon Bay, Kowloon, China (Hong Kong) **(100%)**
Tel.: (852) 29530383
Sales Range: $50-74.9 Million
Emp.: 50
Other Electronic Parts & Equipment Merchant Whslr
N.A.I.C.S.: 423690

SUGA STEEL CO., LTD.
3-8-1 Terashima, Itoigawa, 941-0066, Niigata, Japan
Tel.: (81) 255530121
Web Site: https://www.suga-steel.com
Year Founded: 1996
3448—(TKS)
Rev.: $19,638,310
Assets: $15,150,120
Liabilities: $12,400,360
Net Worth: $2,749,760
Earnings: ($171,860)
Emp.: 37,693
Fiscal Year-end: 03/31/24
Steel Sheet Product Mfr & Distr
N.A.I.C.S.: 332216
Yoichi Hoshino *(Pres)*

SUGACH SOCAPI
14 Rue De Turenne, 90300, Valdole, France
Tel.: (33) 384366120
Rev.: $29,500,000
Emp.: 49
Grocery Stores
N.A.I.C.S.: 445110
Alain Moissenot *(Dir)*

SUGAI CHEMICAL IND. CO., LTD.
4-4-6 Uzu, Wakayama-shi, Wakayama, 641-0043, Japan
Tel.: (81) 734221171
Web Site: https://www.sugai-chem.co.jp
Year Founded: 1928
4120—(TKS)
Sales Range: $50-74.9 Million
Emp.: 172
Pharmaceutical Product Mfr & Distr
N.A.I.C.S.: 325412
Haruo Takeda *(Pres)*

Subsidiaries:

Sugai Chemical Ind. Co., Ltd. - Wakayama Nishi Factory (1)
1280 Minato, Wakayama, Japan
Tel.: (81) 734236341
Pharmaceuticals Product Mfr
N.A.I.C.S.: 325412

SUGAL & DAMANI SHARE BROKERS LTD
Siyat House 3rd Floor No 961 Poonamallee High Road, Purasaiwalkkam, Chennai, 600 084, India
Tel.: (91) 28587105
Web Site: https://www.sugalshare.com
511654—(BOM)
Rev.: $688,649
Assets: $2,510,157
Liabilities: $255,997
Net Worth: $2,254,161
Earnings: ($48,801)
Emp.: 11
Fiscal Year-end: 03/31/21
Financial Advisory & Security Brokerage Services
N.A.I.C.S.: 523940
S. Vinodh Kumar Jain *(Exec Dir)*

SUGALIDAL INDUSTRIAS DE ALIMENTACAO SA
Fonte das Somas Apartado 6, 2131 901, Benavente, Portugal
Tel.: (351) 263500501
Web Site: http://www.sugal.pt
Year Founded: 1984
Sales Range: $50-74.9 Million
Emp.: 300
Tomatoes & Tomato Products Mfr
N.A.I.C.S.: 111219
Isabel Dinis *(Dir-HR)*

Subsidiaries:

Sugal Chile Limitada (1)
Torre Santa Maria-Los Conquistadores 1700 floor 29 - Providencia, Santiago, Chile
Tel.: (56) 223323600

SUGALIDAL INDUSTRIAS DE ALIMENTACAO SA

Sugalidal Industrias de Alimentacao SA—(Continued)
Web Site: http://www.sugalchile.cl
Food Products Mfr
N.A.I.C.S.: 311919
Joao Ortigao Costa (CEO)

Plant (Domestic):

Sugal Chile Limitada Tilcoco Factory (2)
The Sauce n 026-030, PO Box 5, Santiago, Chile
Tel.: (56) 72541160
Food Products Mfr
N.A.I.C.S.: 311919

Tomates del Sur S.L. (1)
Carretera de la Estacion Km 3 5, Las Cabezas de San Juan, 41730, Sevilla, Spain
Tel.: (34) 955871201
Food Products Mfr
N.A.I.C.S.: 311919

SUGAR NAGHSHE JAHAN COMPANY
Gom Street Beside Hospital Gom Block44-Block3, Tehran, Iran
Tel.: (98) 2188847645
Year Founded: 1966
Confectionary Product Mfr
N.A.I.C.S.: 311351

SUGAR TERMINALS LIMITED
Level 11, 348 Edward Street, Brisbane, 4000, QLD, Australia
Tel.: (61) 732217017
Web Site:
  http://www.sugarterminals.com.au
Year Founded: 2000
SUG—(NSXA)
Rev.: $75,694,209
Assets: $286,879,925
Liabilities: $29,967,989
Net Worth: $256,911,935
Earnings: $20,781,371
Fiscal Year-end: 06/30/21
Bulk Sugar Terminals Owner & Manager
N.A.I.C.S.: 493130
Peter M. Bolton (CFO & Sec)

SUGENTECH INC.
206 Techno 2-ro Yuseong-gu 2nd floor office building, Daejeon, Korea (South)
Tel.: (82) 423645001
Web Site:
  https://www.sugentech.com
Year Founded: 2011
253840—(KRS)
Rev.: $77,773,229
Assets: $132,918,644
Liabilities: $25,096,128
Net Worth: $107,822,516
Earnings: $20,491,656
Emp.: 130
Fiscal Year-end: 12/31/22
In-Vitro Diagnostic Services
N.A.I.C.S.: 621511

SUGI HOLDINGS CO., LTD.
1-8-4 Mikawa Anjo-cho, Anjo, 446-0056, Aichi, Japan
Tel.: (81) 562452700
Web Site: https://www.sugi-hd.co.jp
Year Founded: 1982
7649—(TKS)
Rev.: $5,278,341,930
Assets: $2,769,091,670
Liabilities: $1,114,555,090
Net Worth: $1,654,536,580
Earnings: $155,831,110
Emp.: 8,724
Fiscal Year-end: 02/29/24
Holding Company
N.A.I.C.S.: 551112
Eiichi Sakakibara (Chm)

SUGIKO GROUP HOLDINGS CO., LTD.
14F 1-7 Kinko-cho, Kanagawa-ku, Yokohama, Japan
Tel.: (81) 45 444 0835 JP
Web Site:
  http://www.sugikohldgs.com
Year Founded: 2012
Holding Company
N.A.I.C.S.: 551112
Nobuo Sugiyama (Pres & CEO)

Subsidiaries:

Nakakin Lease Co., Ltd. (1)
4-2-10 Hoeidou 5 Bldg 54 Halamachida, Machida, 194-0013, Japan (100%)
Tel.: (81) 427101181
Web Site: http://www.nakakin-l.com
Sales Range: $10-24.9 Million
Emp.: 62
Construction Materials Leasing Services
N.A.I.C.S.: 532412
Kazutaka Iwase (Pres)

SUGIMOTO & CO., LTD.
5-7-27 Itachibori, Nishi-ku, Osaka, 550-8502, Japan
Tel.: (81) 665382661
Web Site: https://www.sugi-net.co.jp
Year Founded: 1938
9932—(TKS)
Rev.: $308,263,960
Assets: $281,579,390
Liabilities: $43,897,010
Net Worth: $237,682,380
Earnings: $12,400,360
Emp.: 505
Fiscal Year-end: 03/31/24
Measuring Machine Whslr
N.A.I.C.S.: 423830
Masahiro Sugimoto (Mgr, Pres & Exec Officer)

SUGIMURA SEIKO CO., LTD.
2-13-32 Osachigosho, Okaya, 394-0082, Nagano, Japan
Tel.: (81) 266282478 JP
Web Site:
  https://www.sugimuraseiko.co.jp
Metal Press Die Mfr
N.A.I.C.S.: 333514

SUGIMURA WAREHOUSE CO., LTD.
1-1-57 Fukusaki, Minato-ku, Osaka, 552-0013, Japan
Tel.: (81) 665711221
Web Site: https://www.sugimura-wh.co.jp
Year Founded: 1919
9307—(TKS)
Rev.: $71,718,500
Assets: $145,975,240
Liabilities: $40,228,460
Net Worth: $105,746,780
Earnings: $5,704,430
Fiscal Year-end: 03/31/24
Warehousing & Transportation Services
N.A.I.C.S.: 493110

SUGITA ACE CO., LTD.
2-14-15 Midori, Sumida-Ku, Tokyo, 130-0026, Japan
Tel.: (81) 336335150
Web Site: https://www.sugita-ace.co.jp
Year Founded: 1948
7635—(TKS)
Rev.: $541,838,000
Assets: $357,366,240
Liabilities: $257,042,720
Net Worth: $100,323,520
Earnings: $2,197,360
Fiscal Year-end: 03/31/22
Construction Hardware Material Distr
N.A.I.C.S.: 423710

Naoyoshi Sugita (Chm)

SUHAIL BAHWAN GROUP (HOLDING) LLC
Al Riwaq Building No 10/1 Block 205 Plot 20 Way No 207 Street 7, Al Qurum, 100, Muscat, Oman
Tel.: (968) 24650000
Web Site:
  http://www.suhailbahwangroup.com
Year Founded: 1965
Sales Range: $1-4.9 Billion
Emp.: 15,000
Holding Company
N.A.I.C.S.: 551112
Suhail Salim Bahwan (Chm)

Subsidiaries:

Al-Mutawaa Trading Company LLC (1)
PO Box 17, Muttrah, 114, Muscat, Oman
Tel.: (968) 2459 1871
Web Site: http://www.al-mutawaa.com
Emp.: 100
Building Materials Mfr
N.A.I.C.S.: 327120
Sheikh Suhail Salim Bahwan (Chm)

Bahwan Engineering Company L.L.C. (1)
PO Box 703, Ruwi, Oman
Tel.: (968) 24597510
Web Site:
  http://www.bahwanengineering.com
Sales Range: $700-749.9 Million
Emp.: 4,000
Engineeering Services
N.A.I.C.S.: 541330

Subsidiary (Domestic):

Bahwan Contracting Company (2)
PO Box 1098, Ruwi, 112, Muscat, Oman
Tel.: (968) 24591092
Emp.: 3,200
Civil Engineering Construction Services
N.A.I.C.S.: 237990
Navaneethakrishnan Manaharan (Engr-Site)

Universal Engineering Services LLC (2)
PO Box 2688, Ruwi, 112, Muscat, Oman
Tel.: (968) 24597531
Power Generation Services
N.A.I.C.S.: 221118
Mark Israel (CEO)

Subsidiary (US):

GEOServices, LLC (3)
2561 Willow Point Way, Knoxville, TN 37931-3162
Tel.: (865) 539-8242
Web Site: http://www.geoservicesllc.com
Engineeering Services
N.A.I.C.S.: 541330
Byron Barton (Mgr)

Bahwan Foods (Khalijana) Company L.L.C. (1)
PO Box 711, Ruwi, Oman
Tel.: (968) 24592492
Web Site: http://www.iffco.com
Sales Range: $25-49.9 Million
Emp.: 160
Snack Food Mfr & Distr
N.A.I.C.S.: 311919

Bahwan IT LLC (1)
5th Floor Al-Rawaq Building Next to Nissan Showroom, PO Box 169, Qurum, Muscat, Oman
Tel.: (968) 2465 0366
Web Site: http://www.bahwanit.com
Information Technology Consulting Services
N.A.I.C.S.: 541512
Shyam Sundar (Deputy Gen Mgr)

Bahwan Projects & Telecoms LLC (1)
Al Rawaq Building Way No 207, Muscat, Oman
Tel.: (968) 24793741
Telecommunication Servicesb
N.A.I.C.S.: 517810

Bahwan Travel Agencies (1)

INTERNATIONAL PUBLIC

PO Box 282, Muscat, 100, Oman
Tel.: (968) 24704455
Web Site: http://www.bahwantravels.com
Sales Range: $25-49.9 Million
Emp.: 150
Travel Services
N.A.I.C.S.: 561510
Shankar K. Bose (Gen Mgr)

Bilad Oman LLC (1)
Sohar Industrial Estate, PO Box 6, 124, Muscat, Oman
Tel.: (968) 24502024
Steel Construction Services
N.A.I.C.S.: 238120

Mercantile Information & Telecommunication Technology Co. LLC (1)
004 Office Floor Sheikha Ayesha Building Salam Street Tourist Club Are, PO Box 41175, Abu Dhabi, United Arab Emirates
Tel.: (971) 2 6458909
Web Site: http://www.mittco.ae
Telecommunication Servicesb
N.A.I.C.S.: 517810
Baiju Pushpangathan (Mgr-Telecom & IT Networking)

SIXT Rent-a-Car LLC (1)
1850 SE 17th St Causeway Ste 207, Fort Lauderdale, FL 33316
Web Site: https://www.sixt.com
Car Rental Services
N.A.I.C.S.: 532111
V. Todd Sazera (Exec VP-Ops)

Sogex Oman Co. L.L.C (1)
Villa No 2478 Street No 3036 Near Grand Hyatt Hotel Shatti Al Qurm, PO Box 1739/1170, 112, Muscat, Oman
Tel.: (968) 2469 4970
Web Site: http://www.sogexoman.com
Fossil Fuel Electric Power Generation Services
N.A.I.C.S.: 221112
Abdulraouf Abudayyeh (CEO)

Suhail Bahwan Automotive Group (1)
PO Box 156, Ruwi, 112, Muscat, Oman
Tel.: (968) 24567108
Web Site:
  http://www.suhailbahwanautogroup.com
Automobile Parts Distr
N.A.I.C.S.: 441330

Utmost Building Materials LLC (1)
PO Box 55014, Dubai, United Arab Emirates
Tel.: (971) 4 355 3883
Web Site:
  http://www.utmostbuildingmaterials.com
Building Materials Mfr
N.A.I.C.S.: 327120

SUHAIL JUTE MILLS LIMITED
14-B Civil Lines, Rawalpindi, Pakistan
Tel.: (92) 515146534
Web Site: https://sjmlimited.com
Year Founded: 1981
SUHJ—(PSX)
Assets: $5,393,747
Liabilities: $2,866,159
Net Worth: $2,527,588
Earnings: $(245,289)
Emp.: 51
Fiscal Year-end: 06/30/23
Textile Mill Operator
N.A.I.C.S.: 314999
Sohail Farooq Shaikh (CEO)

SUHEUNG CO., LTD.
Suheung Bldg 40 Janghan-Ro, Dongdaemun-Gu, Seoul, 130-845, Korea (South)
Tel.: (82) 2222108177
Web Site: https://www.suheung.com
Year Founded: 1973
008490—(KRS)
Rev.: $487,018,983
Assets: $710,563,017
Liabilities: $350,284,619
Net Worth: $360,278,398
Earnings: $26,066,201
Emp.: 758

Fiscal Year-end: 12/31/22
Chemical Products Mfr
N.A.I.C.S.: 325998
Joohwan Yang (CEO)

Subsidiaries:

Chemplus Ltd. (1)
Morc St Andre Plaine des Papayes, 20903, Triolet, Mauritius
Tel.: (230) 2613100
Web Site: https://chemplusltd.com
Healtcare Services
N.A.I.C.S.: 621999

Levi Dis Ticaret A.S. (1)
No 6 Kemeralti Caddesi Oney Is Hani, Beyoglu, 34425, Istanbul, Turkiye
Tel.: (90) 2122517520
Web Site: http://www.levi.com.tr
Pharmaceutical Ingredient Mfr
N.A.I.C.S.: 325412
Murat Yagizer (Mgr-Sls)

Suheung Veitnam Co., Ltd. (1)
2nd floor Saigon Finance center 9 Dinh Tien Hoang Street, Dakao Ward District 1, Ho Chi Minh City, Vietnam
Tel.: (84) 854222357
Web Site: https://www.suheung-vietnam.com
Capsule Mfr
N.A.I.C.S.: 325412

Suheung-America Corporation (1)
428 E Saturn St, Brea, CA 92821
Tel.: (714) 854-9887
Capsule Mfr
N.A.I.C.S.: 325412

Welding Gmbh & Co (1)
Esplanade 39, 20354, Hamburg, Germany
Tel.: (49) 40359080
Web Site: https://www.welding.eu
Capsule Mfr
N.A.I.C.S.: 325412
Torsten Knecht (CEO & Mng Dir)

SUI NORTHERN GAS PIPELINES LTD.
Gas House 21 Kashmir Road, PO Box 56, Lahore, 54000, Pakistan
Tel.: (92) 9908200006 PK
Web Site: https://www.sngpl.com.pk
Year Founded: 1963
SNGP—(PSX)
Rev.: $5,062,882,572
Assets: $5,845,963,063
Liabilities: $5,687,781,048
Net Worth: $158,182,015
Earnings: $36,656,053
Emp.: 8,278
Fiscal Year-end: 06/30/23
Natural Gas Pipeline Transmission & Distribution Services
N.A.I.C.S.: 221210
Uzma Adil Khan (Sr Gen Mgr-Fin)

SUI SOUTHERN GAS COMPANY LIMITED
ST-4/B Block 14 Sir Shah Suleman Road, Gulshan-e-Iqbal, Karachi, 75300, Pakistan
Tel.: (92) 2199021000 PK
Web Site: https://www.ssgc.com.pk
Year Founded: 1954
SSGC—(PSX)
Rev.: $1,896,573,192
Assets: $4,028,507,084
Liabilities: $4,046,558,046
Net Worth: ($18,050,962)
Earnings: ($57,630,696)
Emp.: 6,849
Fiscal Year-end: 06/30/22
Natural Gas Distr
N.A.I.C.S.: 221210
Yusuf Jamil Ansari (Sec & Sr Gen Mgr-Mgmt Svcs)

Subsidiaries:

Inter State Gas Systems (Pvt) Ltd. (1)
517 Margalla Rd F-10-2, Islamabad, Pakistan
Tel.: (92) 512215493
Pipeline Transportation
N.A.I.C.S.: 486210

Pakistan Tourism Development Corporation (1)
Agha Khan Rd, PO Box 1465, 44000, Islamabad, Pakistan
Tel.: (92) 519212760
Web Site: http://www.tourism.gov.pk
Sales Range: $75-99.9 Million
Emp.: 500
Tour Operator
N.A.I.C.S.: 561520
Kabir Ahmed Khan (Mng Dir)

SUIWAH CORPORATION BERHAD
1-20-1 Suntech at Penang Cybercity Lintang Mayang Pasir 3, Bayan Baru, 11950, Penang, Malaysia
Tel.: (60) 46431111
Web Site: http://www.suiwah.com.my
Rev.: $102,469,812
Assets: $117,708,618
Liabilities: $60,904,879
Net Worth: $56,803,739
Earnings: $2,866,076
Emp.: 800
Fiscal Year-end: 05/31/18
Supermarket Services
N.A.I.C.S.: 445110
Sook Fun Thum (Sec)

SUJALA TRADING & HOLDINGS LTD.
1A Grant Lane Room No 202 2nd Floor, Kolkata, 700012, India
Tel.: (91) 3322364330
Web Site: https://www.sujalagroup.com
Year Founded: 1981
539117—(BOM)
Rev.: $204,933
Assets: $4,436,880
Liabilities: $2,268,165
Net Worth: $2,168,715
Earnings: $16,220
Emp.: 7
Fiscal Year-end: 03/31/21
Financial Management Services
N.A.I.C.S.: 523999
Subhadeep Mukherjee (Chm & Mng Dir)

SUJANA UNIVERSAL INDUSTRIES LIMITED
18 Nagarjuna Hills, Panjagutta, Hyderabad, 500 082, Telangana, India
Tel.: (91) 4023351882
Web Site: http://www.sujana.com
Year Founded: 1986
Rev.: $72,447,220
Assets: $365,648,579
Liabilities: $326,852,131
Net Worth: $38,796,448
Earnings: ($19,166,046)
Emp.: 21
Fiscal Year-end: 03/31/18
Bearing Mfr
N.A.I.C.S.: 332991
G. Srinivasa Raju (Mng Dir)

SUKEGAWA ELECTRIC CO., LTD.
3333-23 Kamitezuna, Takahagi, 318-0004, Ibaraki, Japan
Tel.: (81) 293236411
Web Site: https://www.sukegawadenki.co.jp
Year Founded: 1949
7711—(TKS)
Sales Range: $1-4.9 Billion
Emp.: 260
Electric Machinery Equipment Mfr
N.A.I.C.S.: 334513
Osamu Kotaki (Pres)

SUKGYUNG AT CO., LTD.
24 Byeolmang-Ro 459Beon-Gil, Danwon-Ku, Ansan, 15599, Gyeonggi-do, Korea (South)
Tel.: (82) 314930955
Web Site: https://www.sukgyung.com
Year Founded: 1994
357550—(KRS)
Rev.: $9,469,195
Assets: $25,531,263
Liabilities: $2,741,225
Net Worth: $22,790,038
Earnings: $3,292,529
Emp.: 61
Fiscal Year-end: 12/31/22
Inorganic Chemical Mfr
N.A.I.C.S.: 325180
Ki-Joung Kim (Gen Mgr)

SUKHJIT STARCH & CHEMICALS LTD.
Sukhjit Road, Phagwara, 144401, PB, India
Tel.: (91) 1824468800
Web Site: https://www.sukhjitgroup.com
524542—(BOM)
Rev.: $96,484,561
Assets: $108,822,386
Liabilities: $63,411,853
Net Worth: $45,410,533
Earnings: $2,853,874
Emp.: 1,167
Fiscal Year-end: 03/31/21
Starch Mfr & Distr
N.A.I.C.S.: 311221
V. P. Kapahi (Chm)

Subsidiaries:

Sukhjit Mega Food Park & Infra Ltd. (1)
Village Rehana Jattan Tehsil Phagwara, Adjoining the Phagwara-Hoshiarpur State Highway, Kapurthala, 144407, India
Tel.: (91) 9815342794
Web Site: https://sukhjitmfp.com
Maize Starch Mfr & Distr
N.A.I.C.S.: 311221

The Vijoy Steel & General Mills Co. Ltd. (1)
GT Road Opposite Sugar Mill, Phagwara, 144 401, India
Tel.: (91) 1824261656
Maize Starch Mfr
N.A.I.C.S.: 311221

SUKI SUSHI PTE LTD.
26 Tai Seng Street #03-01 J'Forte, Singapore, 534057, Singapore
Tel.: (65) 6858 0880 SG
Web Site: http://www.sukigroup.com.sg
Year Founded: 2002
Japanese Restaurant Operator
N.A.I.C.S.: 722511
Jason Lee (Founder)

Subsidiaries:

Mary Chia Holdings Limited (1)
151 Lorong Chuan New Tech Park 06-07A Lobby G, Singapore, 556741,
Singapore (67.57%)
Tel.: (65) 62529651
Web Site: http://www.marychia.com
Rev.: $4,631,345
Assets: $2,148,944
Liabilities: $10,250,463
Net Worth: ($8,101,519)
Earnings: ($4,118,562)
Emp.: 70
Fiscal Year-end: 03/31/2024
Holding Company; Spas & Beauty Salons Owner & Operator
N.A.I.C.S.: 551112
Simon Ooi (Mng Dir-MCU Holdings Sdn Bhd)

SUL 116 PARTICIPACOES S.A.
Av Rio Branco 311 - Sala 523/parte, 20040903, Rio de Janeiro, Brazil
Tel.: (55) 2121967200
Year Founded: 1997
OPTS3—(BRAZ)
Rev.: $49,516
Assets: $2,060,743
Liabilities: $765,449
Net Worth: $1,295,293
Earnings: $4,290
Fiscal Year-end: 12/31/23
Investment Management Service
N.A.I.C.S.: 523940
Luis Henrique De Carvalho Vieira Goncalves (CFO & Chief HR Officer)

SULA VINEYARDS LIMITED
901 Hubtown Solaris N S Phadke Marg Andheri E, Mumbai, 400069, Maharashtra, India
Tel.: (91) 2261280606
Web Site: https://www.sulavineyards.com
Year Founded: 1999
543711—(BOM)
Rev.: $66,749,595
Assets: $105,673,521
Liabilities: $41,882,981
Net Worth: $63,790,540
Earnings: $10,075,415
Emp.: 729
Fiscal Year-end: 03/31/23
Wine Product Mfr & Distr
N.A.I.C.S.: 312130

SULI CO., LTD.
No 7-1 Runhua Road, Lingang Town, Jiangyin, 214444, Jiangsu, China
Tel.: (86) 51086631388
Web Site: https://www.suli.com
Year Founded: 1994
603585—(SHG)
Rev.: $442,283,980
Assets: $746,150,577
Liabilities: $276,896,768
Net Worth: $469,253,809
Earnings: $44,269,791
Fiscal Year-end: 12/31/22
Pesticide Mfr & Distr
N.A.I.C.S.: 325320
Miao Jinfeng (Chm & Gen Mgr)

Subsidiaries:

Jiangyin Suli Pharmaceutical Technology Co. Ltd. (1)
Building No 10 3399 Kangxin Road Century Medicine Park, Pudong District, Shanghai, 201318, China
Tel.: (86) 2158086325
Web Site: http://www.sulipharma.com
Pharmaceuticals Mfr
N.A.I.C.S.: 325412
Meihua Zhao (Mgr-Sls)

Suli Pharmaceutical Technology Jiangyin Co., Ltd. (1)
2 Runhua Road Ligang Industrial Park, Jiangyin, 214444, China
Tel.: (86) 51086631886249
Web Site: https://www.sulipharma.com
Pharmaceutical Product Mfr & Distr
N.A.I.C.S.: 325412

SULIRAN CORPORATION
Suliran Avenue 16th Km of Old Karaj Road, Tehran, 37571, Iran
Tel.: (98) 21 66282267
Steel Structural Mfr
N.A.I.C.S.: 331110
Mansour Shahsavari (Mng Dir)

SULLIDEN MINING CAPITAL INC.
800-65 Queen Street West, Toronto, M5H 2M5, ON, Canada
Tel.: (416) 861-2267 ON
Web Site: https://www.sulliden.com

SULLIDEN MINING CAPITAL INC.

Sulliden Mining Capital Inc.—(Continued)
Year Founded: 2014
SMC—(TSX)
Rev.: $19,303
Assets: $10,251,568
Liabilities: $432,198
Net Worth: $9,819,370
Earnings: ($16,702,717)
Fiscal Year-end: 07/31/19
Gold & Other Metal Ore Exploration & Development
N.A.I.C.S.: 213114
Roger Marcel Lemaitre (VP)

SULLIVAN STREET PARTNERS LIMITED
110 Wigmore St, Marylebone, W1U 3RW, United Kingdom
Tel.: (44) 2037272210   UK
Web Site: https://sullivanstreet.co.uk
Privater Equity Firm
N.A.I.C.S.: 523999

Subsidiaries:

Tracerco Limited   (1)
Measurement Technology Centre The Moat Belasis Hall Technology Park, Billingham, TS23 4ED, United Kingdom
Tel.: (44) 1642375500
Web Site: https://www.tracerco.com
Diagnostic & Measurement Equipment Mfr
N.A.I.C.S.: 334519

SULNOX GROUP PLC
Tel.: (44) 2034415363
Web Site: https://www.sulnoxgroup.com
Year Founded: 2012
3U4—(DEU)
Rev.: $252,180
Assets: $10,114,452
Liabilities: $447,896
Net Worth: $9,666,556
Earnings: ($2,363,907)
Emp.: 7
Fiscal Year-end: 03/31/23
Fuel Dealers
N.A.I.C.S.: 457210

Subsidiaries:

Sulnox Fuel Fusions Ltd.   (1)
10 Orange Street Haymarket, London, WC2H 7DQ, United Kingdom
Tel.: (44) 2034415363
Web Site: https://www.sulnox.com
Fuel Oil Distr
N.A.I.C.S.: 424720

SULTAN CENTER FOOD PRODUCTS CO. KSCC
Airport road 6th ring road Sultan ben Essa complex-Dajeej, PO Box 26567, Building 44 Sons Of Sultan Bin Essa Company Safat, Kuwait, 13126, Kuwait
Tel.: (965) 1844449
Web Site: https://www.sultan-center.com
Year Founded: 1976
SULTAN—(KUW)
Rev.: $627,753,729
Assets: $943,636,959
Liabilities: $776,897,712
Net Worth: $166,739,247
Earnings: $8,342,403
Emp.: 5,000
Fiscal Year-end: 12/31/22
Food Service & Various Other Investments
N.A.I.C.S.: 523999
Tareq Abdulaziz Sultan Eissa (Chm)

Subsidiaries:

Gulf United Real Estate & Tourism Investment Company - K.S.C.   (1)
PO Box 3805, Doha, Qatar
Tel.: (974) 44355501

Web Site: http://www.guc.qa
Portfolio Management Services
N.A.I.C.S.: 523940

SULTAN RESOURCES LIMITED
Suite 11 Level 2 23 Railway Rd, Subiaco, 6008, WA, Australia
Tel.: (61) 865591792   AU
Web Site: https://www.sultanresources.com.au
Year Founded: 2018
SLZ—(ASX)
Rev.: $7,458
Assets: $6,554,561
Liabilities: $159,734
Net Worth: $6,394,827
Earnings: ($585,390)
Fiscal Year-end: 06/30/24
Mineral Exploration Services
N.A.I.C.S.: 213114
Steven Groves (Mng Dir)

SULZER LTD.
Neuwiesenstrasse 15, 8401, Winterthur, Switzerland
Tel.: (41) 522623000   CH
Web Site: https://www.sulzer.com
Year Founded: 1834
SUN—(SWX)
Rev.: $3,900,285,256
Assets: $5,193,130,519
Liabilities: $3,887,449,506
Net Worth: $1,305,681,013
Earnings: $273,948,183
Emp.: 13,130
Fiscal Year-end: 12/31/23
Measuring, Dispensing & Other Pumping Equipment Manufacturing
N.A.I.C.S.: 333914
Greg Poux-Guillaume (CEO)

Subsidiaries:

Alba Power Limited   (1)
Mill of Monquich, Netherley, Liverpool, AB39 3QR, Aberdeenshire, United Kingdom
Tel.: (44) 1569730088
Web Site: http://www.albapower.com
Gas Turbine Mfr
N.A.I.C.S.: 333611
Neil McKenzie (Mng Dir)

Medmix Systems AG   (1)
Grundstrasse 12, 6343, Rotkreuz, Switzerland
Tel.: (41) 417980680
Web Site: http://www.medmix.ch
Medicinal & Botanical Product Mfr
N.A.I.C.S.: 325411
Stefan Kugler (CEO)

Nordic Water GmbH   (1)
Hansemannstrasse 41, 414 68, Neuss, Germany
Tel.: (49) 213131060
Waste Treatment Services
N.A.I.C.S.: 221310

Nordic Water Products (Beijing) Co. Ltd.   (1)
Unit 08 10th floor Block 1 Bright China Chang An Building, No 7 Jian Guo Men Nei Avenue Dong Cheng District, Beijing, CN-100005, China
Tel.: (86) 1085118120
Waste Treatment Services
N.A.I.C.S.: 221310

Nordic Water Products A/S   (1)
Idrettsvegen 144, NO-5353, Straume, Norway
Tel.: (47) 56317730
Waste Treatment Services
N.A.I.C.S.: 221310

PT. Sulzer Indonesia   (1)
Tel.: (62) 2648631300
Industrial Machinery & Equipment Mfr
N.A.I.C.S.: 333914

Process Laboratories Netherlands (PROLAB NL) B.V.   (1)

Leemansweg 13, 6827 BX, Arnhem, Netherlands
Tel.: (31) 263760000
Web Site: http://www.prolabnl.com
Oil & Gas Equipment Distr
N.A.I.C.S.: 423830
Kurt Breu (Mng Dir)

Sulzer (South Africa) Holdings (Pty) Ltd.   (1)
9 Gerhardus Road, Elandsfontein, 1406, South Africa
Tel.: (27) 118206000
Fluid Power Product Mfr
N.A.I.C.S.: 333996

Sulzer (UK) Holdings Ltd.   (1)
Manor Mill Lane, Leeds, LS11 8BR, United Kingdom
Tel.: (44) 1132701244
Investment Management Service
N.A.I.C.S.: 523999

Sulzer Bombas Chile Ltda.   (1)
Parque Industrial Ejercito Avenida Interlaguna 478, Concepcion, Chile
Tel.: (56) 413832828
Industrial Machinery & Equipment Mfr
N.A.I.C.S.: 333914

Sulzer Chemtech AG   (1)
Neuwiesenstrasse 15, 8401, Winterthur, Switzerland
Tel.: (41) 522621122   (100%)
Sales Range: $125-149.9 Million
Emp.: 300
Provider of Chemical Technology Services
N.A.I.C.S.: 325998
Oliver Bailer (Pres)

Subsidiary (Non-US):

EC Chemical Technologies (S) Pte. Ltd.   (2)
No 1 International Business Park, 01 01 The Synergy, SG 609917, Singapore, Singapore   (30%)
Tel.: (65) 68991193
Provider of Chemical Technology Products
N.A.I.C.S.: 325998

Inher S.A. (Pty) Ltd.   (2)
41 Mopedi St, Sebenza, 1609, Edenglin, South Africa   (100%)
Tel.: (27) 116092116
Web Site: http://www.inhersa.co.za
Sales Range: $25-49.9 Million
Provider of Chemical Technology Products
N.A.I.C.S.: 325998

Subsidiary (US):

Medmix US Inc.   (2)
8 Willow St, Salem, NH 03079-2060
Tel.: (603) 893-2727
Web Site: https://www.coxdispensers.com
Emp.: 25
Dispensing Pump Mfr
N.A.I.C.S.: 333914
Richard Wilson (Gen Mgr)

Subsidiary (Non-US):

Sulzer Chemtech (France) SASU   (2)
1 Blvd Des Bouvets, Nanterre, 92022, France   (100%)
Tel.: (33) 155691888
Web Site: http://www.sulzer.com
Sales Range: Less than $1 Million
Emp.: 3
Provider of Chemical Technology Products
N.A.I.C.S.: 325998
Martin Vogique (Mgr-Sls)

Sulzer Chemtech (UK) Ltd.   (2)
2 Sedgefield Way, Stockton-on-Tees, TS18 2SG, United Kingdom   (100%)
Tel.: (44) 1252525413
Sales Range: $25-49.9 Million
Emp.: 30
Chemical Technology Services
N.A.I.C.S.: 325998
Jonathan Marley (Mng Dir)

Subsidiary (Domestic):

Sulzer Chemtech (UK) Ltd.   (3)
2 Sedgefield Way, Stockton, TS18 2SG, United Kingdom   (100%)
Tel.: (44) 1642873520
Web Site: http://www.sulzer.com

INTERNATIONAL PUBLIC

Sales Range: $25-49.9 Million
Emp.: 30
Provider of Chemical Technology Products
N.A.I.C.S.: 424690
Johnson Marley (Mng Dir)

Subsidiary (Domestic):

Sulzer Chemtech AG (Buchs)   (2)
Sulzer Allee 48, PO Box 65, Winterthur, 8404, Switzerland   (100%)
Tel.: (41) 522621122
Web Site: http://www.sulzerchemtech.com
Sales Range: $100-124.9 Million
Emp.: 300
Provider of Chemical Technology Products
N.A.I.C.S.: 325998
Oliver Bailer (Gen Mgr)

Subsidiary (Non-US):

Sulzer Chemtech Canada Inc.   (2)
5218 68 Ave NW, Edmonton, T6B 2X7, AB, Canada
Tel.: (780) 577-7979
Chemical Engineering Consulting Services
N.A.I.C.S.: 541330

Sulzer Chemtech GmbH   (2)
Friedrichstaler Strasse 19, 66540, Neuenkirchen, Germany   (100%)
Tel.: (49) 68217920
Web Site: http://www.sulzerchemtech.com
Sales Range: $25-49.9 Million
Emp.: 8
Mfr & Sales of Chemical Technology Products
N.A.I.C.S.: 325998

Subsidiary (Domestic):

Sulzer Chemtech GmbH (Neuenkirchen)   (3)
Friedrichsthaler St 19, DE 66540, Neuenkirchen, Germany   (100%)
Tel.: (49) 68217920
Web Site: http://www.sulzerchemtech.com
Sales Range: $25-49.9 Million
Chemical Technology Products Whslr
N.A.I.C.S.: 424690

Subsidiary (Non-US):

Sulzer Chemtech Italia S.r.l.   (2)
Piazza Duca d'Aosta 12, 20124, Milan, Italy   (100%)
Tel.: (39) 02 667 2131
Web Site: http://www.sulzerchemtech.com
Sales Range: $25-49.9 Million
Emp.: 6
Mfr & Sales of Chemical Technology Products
N.A.I.C.S.: 325998
Alessandro Comar (Gen Mgr)

Sulzer Chemtech Nederland B.V.   (2)
Buitenbulkweg 2, NL 4000 LA, Tiel, Netherlands   (100%)
Tel.: (31) 344636600
Sales Range: $25-49.9 Million
Emp.: 25
Provider of Chemical Technology Services
N.A.I.C.S.: 325998

Sulzer Chemtech Tower Field Services (India) Pvt. Ltd.   (2)
248 1 Bosco Mansion, Wadla, Mumbai, India
Tel.: (91) 22 2414 7211
Tower Installation & Maintenance Services
N.A.I.C.S.: 237130

Subsidiary (US):

Sulzer Chemtech USA, Inc.   (2)
8505 E North Belt Dr, Humble, TX 77396   (100%)
Tel.: (281) 604-4100
Web Site: http://www.sulzerchemtech.com
Sales Range: $25-49.9 Million
Emp.: 40
Provider of Chemical Technology Services in Mass Transfer
N.A.I.C.S.: 332312
Ana Herrera (Sec)

Division (Domestic):

Sulzer Chemtech USA, Inc.   (3)
1 Sulzer Way, Tulsa, OK 74131   (100%)
Tel.: (918) 446-6672

Web Site: http://www.sulzer.com
Sales Range: $50-74.9 Million
Emp.: 80
Provider of Chemical Technology Services
N.A.I.C.S.: 332312
Gregoire Poux-Guillaume *(CEO)*

Subsidiary (Non-US):

Sulzer Chemtech, S. de R.L. de C.V. (2)
Calzada A La Venta No 19, Complejo Industrial Cuamatla, 54730, Cuautitlan, Mexico **(100%)**
Tel.: (52) 5550016883
Web Site:
   http://www.sulzerchemtech.com.mx
Sales Range: $1-9.9 Million
Emp.: 142
Provider of Chemical Technology Services
N.A.I.C.S.: 325998

Subsidiary (Domestic):

Sulzer Mixpac AG (2)
Ruetistrasse 7, 9469, Sennwald, Switzerland
Tel.: (41) 814147000
Web Site: http://www.sulzer.com
Adhesive Mfr
N.A.I.C.S.: 325520

Subsidiary (Non-US):

Sulzer Shanghai Engineering & Machinery Works Limited (2)
68 Bei Dou Lu, Minhang, 200245, Shanghai, China **(100%)**
Tel.: (86) 2164306868
Web Site: http://www.sulzer.com
Sales Range: $25-49.9 Million
Emp.: 100
Provider of Chemical Technology Services
N.A.I.C.S.: 325998

Sulzer Ensival Moret France SASU (1)
Lieu dit le Grillons, 33810, Ambes, France
Tel.: (33) 556770878
Fluid Power Product Mfr
N.A.I.C.S.: 333996

Sulzer Italy S.r.l. (1)
Via del Lavoro 87, Casalecchio di Reno, 40033, Bologna, Italy
Tel.: (39) 0516169511
Industrial Machinery & Equipment Mfr
N.A.I.C.S.: 333914

Sulzer Ltd - Rotating Equipment Services (1)
Neuwiesenstrasse 15, 8401, Winterthur, Switzerland
Tel.: (41) 522623441
Web Site: http://www.sulzer.com
Sales Range: $400-449.9 Million
Repair, Refurbishment & Maintenance of Rotating Equipment
N.A.I.C.S.: 811310
Peter Alexander *(Pres)*

Subsidiary (Non-US):

Sulzer Electro Mechanical Services (UK) Limited (2)
6502 Solihull Parkway, Birmingham Business Park Marston Green, Birmingham, B37 7WL, United Kingdom - England
Tel.: (44) 1217666161
Rotating Electrical Equipment Services
N.A.I.C.S.: 541330

Subsidiary (Non-US):

Dowding & Mills Limited (3)
342 South Pine Road, Brendale, 4500, QLD, Australia
Tel.: (61) 732053233
Web Site: http://www.sulzer.com
Emp.: 74
Engineering & Electronics Services
N.A.I.C.S.: 541330

Subsidiary (US):

Equipment Maintenance Services, Inc. (3)
2412 W Durango Rd, Phoenix, AZ 85009
Tel.: (602) 258-8545
Web Site: http://www.emsusa.com

Sales Range: $25-49.9 Million
Emp.: 85
Engineering & Electronics Services
N.A.I.C.S.: 541330
Rick Hooper *(COO)*

Subsidiary (US):

Sulzer Turbo Services Houston Inc. (2)
11518 Old La Porte Rd, La Porte, TX 77571-9516 **(100%)**
Tel.: (713) 567-2700
Sales Range: $75-99.9 Million
Turbomachinery Repair Services
N.A.I.C.S.: 811310

Sulzer Management AG (1)
Neuwiesenstrasse 15, PO Box 414, 8401, Winterthur, Switzerland **(100%)**
Tel.: (41) 522623000
Sales Range: $300-349.9 Million
Provider of Business Services
N.A.I.C.S.: 561499

Subsidiary (Domestic):

Centre Suisse d'Electronique et de Microtechnique S.A. (2)
Rue Jaquet-Droz 1, 2002, Neuchatel, Switzerland
Tel.: (41) 32 720 5111
Web Site: https://www.csem.ch
Sales Range: $75-99.9 Million
Emp.: 450
Marketing & Technology Services
N.A.I.C.S.: 927110
Claude Nicollier *(Chm)*

Subsidiary (Non-US):

Ensival-Moret France SAS (2)
Chemin des Ponts et Chaussees, 02100, Saint-Quentin, France
Tel.: (33) 323629100
Web Site: http://www.ensival-moret.com
Industrial Pumping Equipment Mfr
N.A.I.C.S.: 333914

GEKA GmbH (2)
Waizendorf 3, 91572, Bechhofen, Germany
Tel.: (49) 9 822 8701
Web Site: https://www.geka-world.com
Cosmetic Brush, Applicator & Packaging System Mfr
N.A.I.C.S.: 326199

Subsidiary (US):

GTC Technology US, LLC (2)
900 Threadneedle St Ste 800, Houston, TX 77079
Tel.: (281) 597-4800
Business Support Services
N.A.I.C.S.: 561499
Pinti Wang *(Pres & CEO)*

JWC Environmental, LLC (2)
2850 S Red Hill Ave Ste 125, Santa Ana, CA 92705
Tel.: (949) 833-3888
Web Site: https://www.jwce.com
Wastewater Treatment Equipment Designer & Mfr
N.A.I.C.S.: 333310
Greg Queen *(Pres)*

Subsidiary (Domestic):

FRC Systems International (3)
505 Industrial Way, Cumming, GA 30040
Tel.: (770) 534-3681
Web Site: http://www.frcsystems.com
Engineering Services
N.A.I.C.S.: 541330
Adriaan Vanderbeak *(Pres)*

Subsidiary (Non-US):

PT Sulzer Turbo Services Indonesia (2)
Kawasan Industri Kota Bukit Indah Blok AII Kav IC-ID, Purwakarta, 41181, Indonesia
Tel.: (62) 264 351 920
Web Site: http://www.sulzer.com
Rotating Equipment Repair & Maintenance Services
N.A.I.C.S.: 811310

Subsidiary (US):

Sulzer EMS Inc. (2)
2412 W Durango, Phoenix, AZ 85009
Tel.: (602) 258-8545
Web Site: http://www.emsusa.com
Mechanical Equipment Repair & Maintenance Services
N.A.I.C.S.: 811310

Subsidiary (Non-US):

Sulzer Turbo Services Argentina S.A. (2)
Talcahuano 736 7th Floor, C1013AAP, Buenos Aires, Argentina
Tel.: (54) 1143736327
Turbine Mfr
N.A.I.C.S.: 333611

Sulzer Turbo Services Canada Ltd. (2)
5218 68 Ave NW, Edmonton, T6B 2X7, AB, Canada
Tel.: (780) 577-9200
Sales Range: $25-49.9 Million
Emp.: 15
Industrial Equipment Repair & Maintenance Services
N.A.I.C.S.: 811310
Henry Karusewicz *(Gen Mgr)*

Subsidiary (US):

Sulzer Turbo Services New Orleans Inc. (2)
1516 Engineers Rd, Belle Chasse, LA 70037
Tel.: (504) 392-1800
Oil & Gas Exploration Services
N.A.I.C.S.: 213112

Subsidiary (Non-US):

Sulzer Turbo Services Rotterdam B.V. (2)
Moezelweg 190, Europoort, 3198 LS, Rotterdam, Netherlands
Tel.: (31) 18 128 2000
Web Site: http://www.sulzer.com
Sales Range: $25-49.9 Million
Emp.: 54
Rotating Equipment Repair & Maintenance Services
N.A.I.C.S.: 811310

Sulzer Turbo Services Venlo B.V (2)
Spikweien 36, 5943 AD, Lomm, Netherlands
Tel.: (31) 774738659
Web Site: https://www.sulzer.com
Emp.: 134
Gas Turbine Component Repair Services
N.A.I.C.S.: 811310

Sulzer Markets and Technology AG (1)
Zurcherstrasse 12, PO Box 414, CH 8401, Winterthur, Switzerland **(100%)**
Tel.: (41) 522621122
Web Site: http://www.sulzerinnotec.com
Sales Range: $50-74.9 Million
Emp.: 130
Provider of Industrial Equipment & Technology Services
N.A.I.C.S.: 333310

Subsidiary (Non-US):

Amasscom Co., Ltd. (2)
909 8/5 Floor Ample Tower, Bangna-Trad Road, 10260, Bangkok, Bangna, Thailand **(49%)**
Tel.: (66) 27441691
Web Site: http://www.sulzerpumps.com
Marketing & Technology Services
N.A.I.C.S.: 541613

Martina & Technologies S.A.C. (2)
Avenida Salaverry 3240, Lima, 27, Peru **(100%)**
Tel.: (51) 012640250
Sales Range: $25-49.9 Million
Emp.: 5
Provider of Industrial Equipment
N.A.I.C.S.: 333310

Semax Argentina S.A. (2)
Avenida Belgrano 863 2nd Floor, C1092AAI, Buenos Aires, Argentina **(100%)**
Tel.: (54) 1143319201

Sales Range: $25-49.9 Million
Emp.: 45
Provider of Industrial Equipment
N.A.I.C.S.: 333310

Sulzer India Ltd. (2)
Sulzer House Baner Road, Aundh, Pune, 411 007, India
Tel.: (91) 2025888991
Web Site: http://www.sulzerindia.com
Sales Range: $25-49.9 Million
Emp.: 50
Provider of Industrial Products
N.A.I.C.S.: 333310

Subsidiary (Domestic):

Sulzer Innotec AG (2)
Sulzer Allee 25, PO Box 414, CH-8404, Winterthur, Switzerland **(100%)**
Tel.: (41) 522622121
Web Site: http://www.sulzerinnotec.com
Sales Range: $25-49.9 Million
Emp.: 100
Provider of Research & Development Services
N.A.I.C.S.: 541715

Subsidiary (Non-US):

Sulzer Portugal Lda. (2)
Rua Castillo 1-6 Dto, P-1250, Lisbon, Portugal **(100%)**
Tel.: (351) 213512912
Provider of Industrial Equipment
N.A.I.C.S.: 333310

Sulzer Pumps (UK) Ltd. (2)
Manor Mill Lane, Leeds, LS11 8BR, W Yorks, United Kingdom **(100%)**
Tel.: (44) 1132724502
Sales Range: $125-149.9 Million
Holding Company
N.A.I.C.S.: 551112

Sulzer Sistemas e Instalaciones (Chile) S.A. (2)
Jaime Eyzaguirre 9 Piso 1 Oficina 13, PO Box 51666, Santiago, Chile **(97%)**
Tel.: (56) 26343457
Provider of Industrial Equipment
N.A.I.C.S.: 333310

Sulzer de Venezuela S.A. (2)
Calle San Rafael Con Calle Urape, Central Commercial, Lomas De La Trinidad, 1081, Caracas, Venezuela **(100%)**
Tel.: (58) 2129458222
Sales Range: $25-49.9 Million
Emp.: 3
Industrial Equipment Supplier
N.A.I.C.S.: 333310

Sulzer Mixpac (UK) Ltd. (1)
1 Tealgate Charnham Park, Telford Way Industrial Estate, Hungerford, RG17 0YT, Berkshire, United Kingdom
Tel.: (44) 1488647800
Web Site: https://www.coxdispensers.com
Mixer & Dispenser Mfr
N.A.I.C.S.: 325910

Sulzer Netherlands Holding B.V. (1)
Buitenbulkweg 2, NL 4005 LA, Tiel, Netherlands **(100%)**
Tel.: (31) 344636615
Sales Range: $50-74.9 Million
Emp.: 10
Provider of Corporate Financial Services
N.A.I.C.S.: 523999

Sulzer Pumpen AG (1)
Zuercherstrasse 12, Winterthur, 8401, Switzerland **(100%)**
Tel.: (41) 522621155
Web Site: http://www.sulzerpumps.com
Emp.: 8,200
Pumping Equipment Mfr
N.A.I.C.S.: 333914

Subsidiary (Non-US):

ABS Pumps AS (2)
Kobli Str 25, PO Box 290, 10412, Tallinn, Estonia **(100%)**
Tel.: (372) 6563398
Web Site: http://www.abspumps.com
Sales Range: $1-9.9 Million
Emp.: 7
Mfr of Pumps
N.A.I.C.S.: 333914

SULZER LTD. — INTERNATIONAL PUBLIC

Sulzer Ltd.—(Continued)

Cardo Production Lohmar GmbH (2)
Scheiderhoher Str 3, 53797, Lohmar, Germany
Tel.: (49) 2246 9000
Industrial Pump Mfr
N.A.I.C.S.: 333914

Compagnie de Construction Mecanique Sulzer S.A. (2)
28 Blvd Roger Salengro, 78202, Mantes-la-Jolie, France **(100%)**
Tel.: (33) 134777000
Sales Range: $1-9.9 Million
Emp.: 60
Corporate Services
N.A.I.C.S.: 541430

Pumpex AB (2)
Rokerigatan 20, PO Box 5207, Johanneshov, 121 18, Stockholm, Sweden **(100%)**
Tel.: (46) 87254930
Web Site: http://www.pumpex.com
Submersible Pump Mfr
N.A.I.C.S.: 333914

Plant (Domestic):

Pumpex AB (3)
Asgatan, PO Box 57, SE 914 32, Nordmaling, Sweden
Tel.: (46) 93039500
Sales Range: $25-49.9 Million
Emp.: 100
Submersible Pump Mfr
N.A.I.C.S.: 333914

Subsidiary (Non-US):

Sulzer (South Africa) Ltd. (2)
9 Gerhardus Road, PO Box 823, Elandsfontein, 1406, Gauteng, South Africa **(100%)**
Tel.: (27) 11 820 6000
Web Site: http://www.sulzerpumps.com
Sales Range: $25-49.9 Million
Emp.: 400
Provider of Pumping Equipment
N.A.I.C.S.: 333914
Shaune Chester (Gen Mgr)

Sulzer Brasil S.A. (2)
Avenida Eng Joao Fernandes Gimenez Molina 905, Distrito Industrial, Jundiai, 13213-080, Sao Paulo, Brazil **(100%)**
Tel.: (55) 1145892000
Sales Range: $150-199.9 Million
Pumps Mfr
N.A.I.C.S.: 333914

Subsidiary (Domestic):

Sulzer Brasil S.A. (Chemtech) (3)
Rua Pref Aristeu Ferreira da Silva 213, Macae, Rio de Janeiro, 27930-070, Brazil **(100%)**
Tel.: (55) 1133795631
Web Site: http://www.sulzerchamtech.com
Sales Range: $25-49.9 Million
Emp.: 4
Provider of Chemical Technology Products
N.A.I.C.S.: 325998

Joint Venture (Non-US):

Sulzer Daiichi K.K. (2)
PMO Ochanomizu 6F 4-4-1 Kandasurugadai, Chiyoda-ku, Tokyo, 101-0062, Japan **(60%)**
Tel.: (81) 363708550
Web Site: http://www.sulzerpumps.com
Sales Range: $25-49.9 Million
Emp.: 8
Joint Venture of Sulzer Ltd. & Daichi Jitsugyo Co. Ltd.; Pulp & Paper Machinery & Equipment Sales
N.A.I.C.S.: 333243

Subsidiary (Non-US):

Sulzer Dalian Pumps & Compressors Ltd. (2)
No 6 dd 7th Street dd Port, Dalian, 116600, China **(54%)**
Tel.: (86) 41187581888
Web Site: http://www.sulzerpumps.com
Sales Range: $75-99.9 Million
Emp.: 386
Sales & Servicer of Pumping Equipment
N.A.I.C.S.: 333914

Sulzer Korea Ltd. (2)
Boam Bldg Rm 401 528 Shinsa Dong, Kangnam Ku, Seoul, 135888, Korea (South) **(100%)**
Tel.: (82) 234454800
Web Site: http://www.sulzertunts.com
Sales Range: $25-49.9 Million
Emp.: 10
Provider of Pumping Equipment
N.A.I.C.S.: 333914
Young Tae Kim (Gen Mgr)

Sulzer Pompes France S.A., Mantes-la-Jolie, France (2)
28 Blvd Logar Salengro 31217, BP 1217, 78202, Mantes-la-Jolie, France **(100%)**
Tel.: (33) 134777200
Web Site: http://www.sulzer.com
Sales Range: $25-49.9 Million
Emp.: 140
Mfr of Pumps; Repair & Maintenance of Pumps & Pump Components
N.A.I.C.S.: 333914

Sulzer Pompes Process S.A. (2)
Zone Industrielle, Haguenau, 67590, France **(100%)**
Tel.: (33) 388072600
Web Site: http://www.sulzer.com
Sales Range: $25-49.9 Million
Emp.: 9
Pumping Equipment
N.A.I.C.S.: 333914
Riva Laurenge (Mng Dir)

Subsidiary (US):

Sulzer Pump Solutions (US) Inc. (2)
140 Pond View Dr, Meriden, CT 06450-7142 **(100%)**
Tel.: (203) 238-2700
Sales Range: $25-49.9 Million
Emp.: 70
Pump Equipment Mfr
N.A.I.C.S.: 333914
Paul Bellivaeu (Pres)

Subsidiary (Non-US):

Sulzer Pump Solutions AB (2)
Roskildevagen 1, PO Box 394, 201 23, Malmo, Sweden
Tel.: (46) 104747200
Web Site: http://www.absgroup.com
Mfr of Pumps & Other Flow Devices
N.A.I.C.S.: 333914

Sulzer Pump Solutions Finland Oy (2)
Turvekuja 6, 700, Helsinki, Finland **(100%)**
Tel.: (358) 7 5324 0300
Web Site: http://www.absgroup.com
Sales Range: $25-49.9 Million
Emp.: 15
Pumps Mfr
N.A.I.C.S.: 333914

Sulzer Pump Solutions Germany GmbH (2)
Scheiderhoher Strasse 30-38, D 53797, Lohmar, Germany
Tel.: (49) 2246 900 0
Sales Range: $25-49.9 Million
Emp.: 117
Pump Equipment Mfr
N.A.I.C.S.: 333914
Johan Sandstrom (Mng Dir)

Sulzer Pump Solutions Ireland Ltd. (2)
Riverview Business Park New Nangor Road, Dublin, D12 DY90, Ireland **(100%)**
Tel.: (353) 14608888
Sales Range: $75-99.9 Million
Pump Equipment Mfr
N.A.I.C.S.: 333914

Sulzer Pump Solutions Nordmaling AB (2)
Asgatan 3, PO Box 57, SE 914 32, Nordmaling, Sweden **(100%)**
Tel.: (46) 93039500
Web Site: http://www.absgroup.com
Sales Range: $25-49.9 Million
Emp.: 70
Mfr of Pumps
N.A.I.C.S.: 333914
Juan Vargues (Gen Mgr)

Sulzer Pump Solutions Sweden AB (2)
Taljegardsgatan 11, PO Box 1, SE 431 21, Molndal, Sweden **(100%)**
Tel.: (46) 104747390
Web Site: http://www.scanpump.com
Rev.: $350,822,112
Emp.: 40
Mfr of Pumps, Mixers & Aerators for Water & Wastewater Treatment, Pulp & Paper, Plumbing, Heating & Ventilation
N.A.I.C.S.: 333914

Subsidiary (Non-US):

Sulzer Pompa Cozumleri Ltd. Sti. (3)
Ataseher Duilure Abs Pl No 40, 34758, Istanbul, Atasehir, Turkiye
Tel.: (90) 2164552256
Sales Range: $25-49.9 Million
Emp.: 20
Pumps Mfr
N.A.I.C.S.: 333914
Kerem Yorganci (Mng Dir)

Subsidiary (Non-US):

Sulzer Pump Solutions Sweden AB - Arlov (3)
Virvelvagen 5, 232 36, Arlov, Sweden **(100%)**
Tel.: (46) 10 130 1730
Web Site: http://www.abspumps.com
Sales Range: $25-49.9 Million
Emp.: 4
Mfr of Pumps for Water & Wastewater Treatement, Plumbing, Heating & Ventilation
N.A.I.C.S.: 333914

Sulzer Pump Solutions Vadstena AB (2)
Kvarnbacksvagen 9, 592 41, Vadstena, Sweden **(100%)**
Tel.: (46) 10 47 47 231
Sales Range: $25-49.9 Million
Emp.: 15
Mfr of Pumps for Water & Wastewater Treatment, Plumbing, Heating & Ventilation
N.A.I.C.S.: 333914

Sulzer Pumpen (Deutschland) GmbH (2)
Darmstader Strasse 9, 64404, Bickenbach, Germany **(100%)**
Tel.: (49) 625793170
Sales Range: $25-49.9 Million
Emp.: 5
Marketer & Retailer of Pumps
N.A.I.C.S.: 423830

Sulzer Pumpen (Deutschland) GmbH (2)
Industriepark Schwarze Pumpe / An der Heide 10, Spreetal, 02979, Mannheim, Germany **(100%)**
Tel.: (49) 3564386850
Sales Range: $75-99.9 Million
Emp.: 500
Pump Mfr & Whslr
N.A.I.C.S.: 333914
Walter Reinhart (Mng Dir)

Sulzer Pumpen GmbH (2)
Ernst-Blickle-Str 29, 76646, Bruchsal, Germany **(100%)**
Tel.: (49) 7251760
Web Site: http://www.sulzerpumps.com
Sales Range: $75-99.9 Million
Emp.: 500
Marketing & Sales of Equipment for the Pulp & Paper Machinery
N.A.I.C.S.: 333243
Walton Reinhard (Mgr)

Sulzer Pumpen Oesterreich GmbH (2)
Kienzlstrasse 13, 4600, Wels, Austria **(100%)**
Tel.: (43) 724260692
Sales Range: $25-49.9 Million
Emp.: 5
Pumps Mfr
N.A.I.C.S.: 333914
Harald Sonntagbauer (Gen Mgr)

Sulzer Pumps (ANZ) Pty Ltd. (2)
28 Lancaster Road, Perth, 6065, WA, Australia
Tel.: (61) 8 9309 1171
Web Site: http://www.sulzer.com

Pumping Equipment Mfr
N.A.I.C.S.: 333914

Sulzer Pumps (China) Ltd. (2)
Rm 9 C Hang Seng Causeway Bay Bldg 28, 34 Yee Wo St, Causeway Bay, China (Hong Kong) **(100%)**
Tel.: (852) 25213230
Web Site: http://www.sulzerpumps.com
Sales Range: $25-49.9 Million
Emp.: 4
Provider of Pumping Equipment
N.A.I.C.S.: 333914

Sulzer Pumps (South Africa) (Pty) Ltd. (2)
9 Gerhardus Road, Elandsfontein, 1406, South Africa
Tel.: (27) 118206000
Web Site: https://www.sulzer.com
Sales Range: $75-99.9 Million
Emp.: 321
Pump & Pumping Equipment Mfr
N.A.I.C.S.: 333914

Sulzer Pumps (UK) Ltd. (2)
Manor Mill Lane, Leeds, LS11 8BR, West Yorkshire, United Kingdom **(100%)**
Tel.: (44) 1132724502
Web Site: https://www.sulzer.com
Pumps Mfr
N.A.I.C.S.: 333914

Subsidiary (US):

Sulzer Pumps (US) Inc. (2)
4126 Caine Ln, Chattanooga, TN 37421
Tel.: (423) 296-1919
Web Site: http://www.sulzerpumps.com
Sales Range: $1-9.9 Million
Emp.: 30
Pump & Pumping Equipment Mfr
N.A.I.C.S.: 333914

Subsidiary (Non-US):

Sulzer Pumps (Venezuela) S.A. (2)
Centro Comercial Marisandra Galpon 9, Barcelona, Venezuela
Tel.: (58) 281 274 0819
Pumping Equipment Mfr
N.A.I.C.S.: 333914

Sulzer Pumps Asia Pacific Pte Ltd. (2)
10 Benoi Sector, Singapore, 629845, Singapore **(100%)**
Tel.: (65) 68000000
Web Site: https://www.sulzer.com
Sales Range: $25-49.9 Million
Emp.: 50
Pumping Equipment
N.A.I.C.S.: 333914

Sulzer Pumps Benelux B.V. (2)
Vincent Van Goghstraat 43, NL 4812 AP, Breda, Netherlands **(100%)**
Tel.: (31) 765339639
Web Site: http://www.sulzerpumps.com
Sales Range: $25-49.9 Million
Emp.: 3
Provider of Pumping Equipment
N.A.I.C.S.: 333914

Sulzer Pumps Canada (2)
4129 Lozells Avenue, Burnaby, V5A 2Z5, BC, Canada **(100%)**
Tel.: (604) 415-7800
Web Site: http://www.sulzer.com
Sales Range: $25-49.9 Million
Emp.: 55
Production & Engineering; Sales & Services
N.A.I.C.S.: 541330
Dave Chan (Mgr-Intl Part Sls)

Sulzer Pumps Canada Incorporated (2)
4129 Lozells Avenue, Burnaby, V5A 2Z5, BC, Canada **(100%)**
Tel.: (604) 415-7800
Sales Range: $25-49.9 Million
Emp.: 13
Mfr of Equipment & Machinery for the Pulp & Paper Industry
N.A.I.C.S.: 333243

Sulzer Pumps Denmark A/S (2)
Farum Gydevej 89, 3520, Farum, Denmark **(100%)**
Tel.: (45) 48171110

Web Site: http://www.sulzer.com
Sales Range: $25-49.9 Million
Pumps Mfr
N.A.I.C.S.: 333914

Sulzer Pumps Finland Oy (2)
Vasamakuja 1, 01740, Vantaa, Finland
Tel.: (358) 102343333
Pumps Mfr
N.A.I.C.S.: 333914

Subsidiary (US):

Sulzer Pumps Inc. (2)
2800 NW Frnt Ave, Portland, OR
97210-1502 **(100%)**
Tel.: (503) 226-5200
Web Site: http://www.sulzerpumps.com
Sales Range: $25-49.9 Million
Emp.: 200
Sales of Custom Pumps; Repair & Maintenance of Pumps & Pump Components
N.A.I.C.S.: 333996
Andre Martins (Engr-Oil & Gas Application)

Subsidiary (Non-US):

Sulzer Pumps India Ltd. (2)
Unit No B Plot No B-8 midc Industrial area, Digha, Mumbai, 400 709, Maharashtra, India **(100%)**
Tel.: (91) 865 730 2470
Web Site: http://www.sulzerpumps.com
Sales Range: $75-99.9 Million
Emp.: 350
Mfr & Sales of Pumping Equipment
N.A.I.C.S.: 333914

Sulzer Pumps Mexico, S.A. de C.V. (2)
Calzada a la Venta 19, Fracc Industrial Cuamatla, 54730, Cuautitlan Izcalli, Estado de Mexico, Mexico **(100%)**
Tel.: (52) 5515004780
Web Site: http://www.sulzer.com.mx
Sales Range: $75-99.9 Million
Emp.: 300
Pumping Equipment Mfr & Whslr
N.A.I.C.S.: 333914
Jeanette Inclan (Mgr-HR)

Sulzer Pumps Rus LLC (2)
Novo-Leningradskaya street, Solnechnogorskiy district, 141580, Moscow, Russia
Tel.: (7) 4953632458
Web Site: http://www.sulzer.com
Sales Range: $25-49.9 Million
Centrifugal Pump Mfr
N.A.I.C.S.: 333914
Arnold Van Sinderen (Gen Dir)

Subsidiary (US):

Sulzer Pumps Solutions Inc. (2)
155 Ahlstrom Way, Easley, SC
29640 **(100%)**
Tel.: (864) 850-5684
Mfr of Pumps for the Pulp & Paper Industry
N.A.I.C.S.: 333914
Alan Crawford (Pres)

Subsidiary (Non-US):

Sulzer Pumps Spain S.A. (2)
Ctra M 106, 28110, Algete, Spain **(100%)**
Tel.: (34) 916293207
Sales Range: $25-49.9 Million
Emp.: 10
Provider of Pumping Equipment
N.A.I.C.S.: 333914

Sulzer Pumps Suzhou Ltd. (2)
No 433 Jianlin Rd, New District, Suzhou, 215151, China
Tel.: (86) 51281873928
Web Site: https://www.sulzer.com
Sales Range: $75-99.9 Million
Pumps Mfr
N.A.I.C.S.: 333914

Sulzer Pumps Sweden AB (2)
Soderleden 104 B, Norrkoping, 60116, Sweden
Tel.: (46) 10 130 15 00
Web Site: http://www.sulzer.com
Emp.: 5
Centrifugal Pump Whslr
N.A.I.C.S.: 423830
Peter Sundberg (Gen Mgr)

Subsidiary (US):

Sulzer Pumps US, Inc. (2)
3400 Meador Dr, Mobile, AL 36607
Tel.: (832) 886-2304
Web Site: http://www.sulzer.com
Sales Range: $25-49.9 Million
Pump & Pumping Equipment Mfr
N.A.I.C.S.: 333914

Subsidiary (Non-US):

Sulzer Pumps Wastewater Asia Pacific Pte Ltd. (2)
25 International Business Park No 03-51 55
German Ctr, Singapore, 609916, Singapore **(100%)**
Tel.: (65) 64633933
Sales Range: $25-49.9 Million
Emp.: 40
Pumps Mfr
N.A.I.C.S.: 333914
Wongjin Yong (Mng Dir)

Sulzer Pumps Wastewater Austria GmbH (2)
IZ NO Sud Strasse 2 Obj M27, AT-2351, Wiener Neudorf, Austria **(100%)**
Tel.: (43) 223664261
Web Site: http://www.sulzerpumps.com
Sales Range: $25-49.9 Million
Emp.: 25
Pump Equipment Mfr
N.A.I.C.S.: 333914
Michael Wurm (Gen Mgr)

Sulzer Pumps Wastewater Belgium NV/SA (2)
Tollaan 101b, 5222, Saint-Stevens-Woluwe, Belgium
Tel.: (32) 27257900
Web Site: http://www.sulzer.com
Sales Range: $25-49.9 Million
Emp.: 15
Pumps Mfr
N.A.I.C.S.: 333914
Maarcen Bake (Mng Dir)

Sulzer Pumps Wastewater Brasil Ltda. (2)
Rua Hasdrubal Bellegard 701 CIC, Curitiba, 81460-120, Brazil **(100%)**
Tel.: (55) 4121088100
Sales Range: $25-49.9 Million
Emp.: 100
Pumps Mfr
N.A.I.C.S.: 333914

Sulzer Pumps Wastewater France SAS (2)
26 alle du Plateau, 93250, Villemomble, France
Tel.: (33) 149352450
Sales Range: $25-49.9 Million
Emp.: 25
Pumps Mfr
N.A.I.C.S.: 333914

Sulzer Pumps Wastewater Germany GmbH (2)
Putzchens Chaussee 202, 53229, Bonn, Germany **(100%)**
Tel.: (49) 224 6130
Web Site: http://www.absdeutschland.com
Sales Range: $25-49.9 Million
Emp.: 8
Pumps Mfr
N.A.I.C.S.: 333914

Sulzer Pumps Wastewater Hungary Kft. (2)
Kiss Erno u 1-3, HU 1046, Budapest, Hungary **(100%)**
Tel.: (36) 12316070
Sales Range: $1-9.9 Million
Emp.: 20
Pumps Mfr
N.A.I.C.S.: 333914

Sulzer Pumps Wastewater Netherlands B.V. (2)
Amerikalaan 63, Maastricht-Airport, 6199 AE, Maastricht, Netherlands
Tel.: (31) 433525050
Sales Range: $25-49.9 Million
Pumps Mfr
N.A.I.C.S.: 333914

Sulzer Pumps Wastewater Norway AS (2)
Industriveien 44, PO Box 473, 1337, Sandvika, Norway **(100%)**
Tel.: (47) 6 755 4700
Web Site: http://www.absgroup.com
Sales Range: $25-49.9 Million
Emp.: 36
Pumps Mfr
N.A.I.C.S.: 333914

Sulzer Pumps Wastewater Poland Sp. z o.o. (2)
Ul Rydygiera 8, 01 793, Warsaw, Poland **(100%)**
Tel.: (48) 226338287
Sales Range: $25-49.9 Million
Emp.: 33
Pumps Mfr
N.A.I.C.S.: 333914
Maciej Lewandowski (Mng Dir)

Sulzer Pumps Wastewater Spain S.A. (2)
Madera 8-16 Pol Ind Santa Ana, Rivas Vaciamadrid, Madrid, 28522, Spain **(100%)**
Tel.: (34) 916702851
Sales Range: $25-49.9 Million
Emp.: 60
Pumps Mfr
N.A.I.C.S.: 333914
Marima Aica (Mgr-Mktg)

Sulzer Pumps Wastewater UK Limited (2)
Unit 24 Parkview Industrial Estate, Hartlepool, TS25 1PE, United Kingdom **(100%)**
Tel.: (44) 1429266749
Web Site: http://www.sulzer.com
Sales Range: $25-49.9 Million
Mfr of Pumps for Water & Wastewater Treatment, Plumbing, Heating & Ventilation
N.A.I.C.S.: 333914

Wastetech (2)
4 Dimitsanas str, Moschato, 18346, Athens, Greece
Tel.: (30) 210 483 9930
Web Site: https://www.wastetech.gr
Emp.: 4
Pump Mfr & Distr
N.A.I.C.S.: 333914
Dimitris Pyrlis (Engr-Sls)

Sulzer Pumps (Nigeria) Ltd. (1)
Danjuma Drive, Port Harcourt, Nigeria
Tel.: (234) 84463734
Industrial Machinery & Equipment Mfr
N.A.I.C.S.: 333914

Sulzer Pumps Colombia S.A.S. (1)
Km 1 5 via Siberia-Cota Parque Industrial Potrero Chico Parque, Empresarial San Miguel Bodega No 10 Cota, Cundinamarca, Colombia
Tel.: (57) 3188915133
Industrial Machinery & Equipment Mfr
N.A.I.C.S.: 333914

Sulzer Pumps Norway A/S (1)
Orstadvegen 124 Stasjon, 4353, Klepp, Norway
Tel.: (47) 51634282
Industrial Machinery & Equipment Mfr
N.A.I.C.S.: 333914

Sulzer Pumps Wastewater Malaysia Sdn. Bhd. (1)
Jalan Subang 3, 47610, Subang Jaya, Selangor Darul Ehsan, Malaysia
Tel.: (60) 356313118
Industrial Machinery & Equipment Mfr
N.A.I.C.S.: 333914

Sulzer Singapore Pte. Ltd. (1)
43 Gul Avenue, Singapore, 629578, Singapore
Tel.: (65) 68000000
Industrial Machinery & Equipment Mfr
N.A.I.C.S.: 333914

Sulzer Turbo Services Rus LLC (1)
Frontovykh Brigad St 18, 620017, Ekaterinburg, Russia
Tel.: (7) 3433006833
Industrial Machinery & Equipment Mfr
N.A.I.C.S.: 333914

Sulzer Zambia Ltd. (1)
Chingola service center Stand 603 Station Road, PO Box 10472, Chingola, Zambia
Tel.: (260) 212311740
Industrial Machinery & Equipment Mfr
N.A.I.C.S.: 333914

Tefag AG (1)
Grossfeldstrasse 5, PO Box 164, 8887, Mels, Switzerland
Tel.: (41) 817204900
Web Site: https://www.tefag.demmel-group.com
Emp.: 20
Electronic Products Mfr
N.A.I.C.S.: 333914
Marlise Stirnimann (Head-Fin & HR)

ZAO Sulzer Pumps (1)
Mashinnaya Str 42A, 620089, Ekaterinburg, Russia
Tel.: (7) 3432531911
Industrial Machinery & Equipment Mfr
N.A.I.C.S.: 333914

SUMADIJA A.D.
Karadordeva 2, Raca, Serbia
Tel.: (381) 34 751 509
Year Founded: 2003
Sales Range: Less than $1 Million
Emp.: 2
Retail Store Operator
N.A.I.C.S.: 459999

SUMADIJA TRANSPORT A.D.
Dorda Tomasevica 97/1, Cacak, Serbia
Tel.: (381) 32 356 980
Year Founded: 1989
Sales Range: Less than $1 Million
Food Transportation Services
N.A.I.C.S.: 484121

SUMAPROJEKT D.D. SARAJEVO
Vilsonovo Setaliste 10, 71000, Sarajevo, Bosnia & Herzegovina
Tel.: (387) 33720750
Web Site: http://www.sumaprojekt.ba
SMPJRK1—(SARE)
Rev.: $219,656
Assets: $4,366,275
Liabilities: $213,314
Net Worth: $4,152,962
Earnings: $233,937
Emp.: 2
Fiscal Year-end: 12/31/21
Wood Design & Engineering Services
N.A.I.C.S.: 321999
Ljiljana Pasic (Pres)

SUMARIA GROUP
Selous House 368 Msasani Road Oysterbay Office Complex Block B, PO Box 3016, 3rd Floor, Dar es Salaam, Tanzania
Tel.: (255) 222165100
Web Site: http://www.sumaria.biz
Year Founded: 1956
Sales Range: $800-899.9 Million
Emp.: 3,500
Holding Company; Manufacturing & Consumer Services & Goods
N.A.I.C.S.: 551112
Jayesh G. Shah (Mng Dir & CEO)

Subsidiaries:

Nyanza Bottling Company Limited (1)
PO Box 2086, Mwanza, Tanzania
Tel.: (255) 6842185
Web Site: http://www.nbcl.biz
Soft Drink Bottler
N.A.I.C.S.: 312112

Royal Dairy Products Limited (1)
PO Box 3016, Dar es Salaam, Tanzania
Tel.: (255) 222451152
Dairy Products Producer
N.A.I.C.S.: 445298

S&C Ginning Company Limited (1)
Libya Band St, PO Box 3016, Dar es Salaam, Tanzania
Tel.: (255) 222119265

SUMARIA GROUP

Sumaria Group—(Continued)
Sales Range: $100-124.9 Million
Emp.: 400
Cotton Lint Producer
N.A.I.C.S.: 115111

SDL Limited (1)
PO Box 483, Tanga, Tanzania
Tel.: (255) 5347686
Soap & Detergent Mfr
N.A.I.C.S.: 325611

Shelys Pharmaceuticals Limited (1)
New Bagamoyo Road Mwenge Plot No 696 Block No 32, PO Box 3016, Dar es Salaam, Tanzania
Tel.: (255) 222771715
Web Site: http://www.shelys.com
Pharmaceuticals Mfr
N.A.I.C.S.: 325412

SUMARSTVO PRENJ D.D. KONJIC
Sarajevska br 31, 88400, Konjic, Bosnia & Herzegovina
Tel.: (387) 3 672 6209
Web Site: http://www.sumarstvo-prenj.ba
SUMPR—(SARE)
Rev.: $2,947,665
Assets: $2,309,752
Liabilities: $794,904
Net Worth: $1,514,848
Earnings: $3,917
Emp.: 148
Fiscal Year-end: 12/31/20
Wildlife & Forest Protection Services
N.A.I.C.S.: 813312

SUMAS SUNI TAHTA VE MOBILYA SANAYI A.S.
Yoloren mah asagi/2 sok Sumas blok No 28, Edremit, 10300, Balikesir, Turkiye
Tel.: (90) 2663921169
Web Site: https://www.sumas.com.tr
Year Founded: 1976
SUMAS—(IST)
Sales Range: Less than $1 Million
Paper Products Mfr
N.A.I.C.S.: 322120
Hilmi Evin Ertur *(Chm)*

SUMATRA COPPER & GOLD PLC
Amberley Business Centre IBM Building Level 3 1060 Hay Street, West Perth, 6005, WA, Australia
Tel.: (61) 8 9480 0620
Web Site:
http://www.sumatracoppergold.com
Rev.: $32,560,000
Assets: $53,715,000
Liabilities: $79,269,000
Net Worth: ($25,554,000)
Earnings: $25,829,000)
Emp.: 435
Fiscal Year-end: 12/31/17
Copper & Gold Mining Services
N.A.I.C.S.: 212230
Robert Gregory *(CEO)*

Subsidiaries:

PT Dwinad Nusa Sejahtera (1)
International Finance Centre 9th Floor Jl Jendral Sudirman Kav 22-23, Jakarta, 12920, Indonesia
Tel.: (62) 2157903050
Gold Ore Mining Services
N.A.I.C.S.: 212220

SUMAVISION TECHNOLOGIES CO., LTD.
Sumavision Plaza No 15 KaiTuo Road, Haidian District, Beijing, 100085, China
Tel.: (86) 1082345950

Web Site:
https://www.sumavision.com
Year Founded: 2000
300079—(CHIN)
Rev.: $153,948,600
Assets: $676,434,564
Liabilities: $79,626,456
Net Worth: $596,808,108
Earnings: $15,639,156
Emp.: 1,000
Fiscal Year-end: 12/31/22
Digital Video Broadcasting Products Mfr
N.A.I.C.S.: 334310
Haitao Zheng *(Founder)*

Subsidiaries:

Fuzhou Sumavision Smart Cards Co., Ltd. (1)
No 386 Changyang Road Chang an Investment Zone, Tingjiang Town Mawei District, Fuzhou, China
Tel.: (86) 59183547993
Web Site: http://www.sumabank.com
Smart Card Mfr & Distr
N.A.I.C.S.: 326199

SUMCO CORPORATION
Seavance North 1-2-1 Shibaura, Minato-ku, Tokyo, 105-8634, Japan
Tel.: (81) 354440808   JP
Web Site: https://www.sumcosi.com
Year Founded: 1999
SUMCF—(OTCIQ)
Rev.: $3,053,996,970
Assets: $7,694,033,790
Liabilities: $3,137,305,200
Net Worth: $4,556,728,590
Earnings: $518,857,050
Emp.: 9,847
Fiscal Year-end: 12/31/23
Silicon Wafers Mfr
N.A.I.C.S.: 334413
Michiharu Takii *(Vice Chm)*

Subsidiaries:

High-Purity Silicon America Corporation (1)
7800 Mitsubishi Ln, Theodore, AL 36582
Tel.: (251) 443-6440
Web Site: https://www.hpsacorp.com
Semiconductor Equipment Mfr & Distr
N.A.I.C.S.: 334413

Japan Super Quartz Corporation (1)
5-14-3 Barajima, Akita, 010-0065, Japan
Tel.: (81) 18 862 1692
Web Site: http://www.sumcosi.com
Quartz Crucible Mfr
N.A.I.C.S.: 334419

Minamata Denshi Co., Ltd. (1)
57-6 Hamamatsu-cho, Minamata, 867-0068, Kumamoto, Japan
Tel.: (81) 966 63 2194
Web Site: http://www.sumcosi.com
Silicon Wafers Mfr
N.A.I.C.S.: 334419

PT. SUMCO Indonesia (1)
MM2100 Industrial Town Block GG-6, Cikarang Barat, Bekasi, 17520, West Java, Indonesia
Tel.: (62) 218980003
Web Site: http://www.sumcosi.com
Silicon Wafers Mfr
N.A.I.C.S.: 335999

SUMCO Corporation - Chitose Plant (1)
1007-62 Izumisawa, Chitose, 066-0051, Hokkaido, Japan
Tel.: (81) 123281877
Silicon Wafers Mfr
N.A.I.C.S.: 334413

SUMCO Corporation - Imari Factory (1)
826-1 Nagahama Higashiyamashiro-cho, Imari, 849-4271, Saga, Japan
Tel.: (81) 95 522 7015
Web Site: http://www.sumcosi.com
Silicon Wafers Mfr

N.A.I.C.S.: 334419

SUMCO Corporation - Kansai Factory (Amagasaki) (1)
1 Higashihama-cho, Amagasaki, 660-0844, Hyogo, Japan
Tel.: (81) 664307645
Monocrystalline Silicon Ingots Mfr
N.A.I.C.S.: 332999

SUMCO Corporation - Saga Factory (1)
2201 Oaza Kamioda Kohoku-cho, Kishima-gun, Saga, 849-0597, Japan
Tel.: (81) 952716555
Silicon Wafers Mfr
N.A.I.C.S.: 334413

SUMCO Corporation - Yonezawa Plant (1)
4-3146-12 Hachimanpara, Yonezawa, 992-1128, Yamagata, Japan
Tel.: (81) 238283131
Silicon Wafers Mfr
N.A.I.C.S.: 334413

SUMCO Europe Sales plc (1)
Tel.: (44) 2032143800
Sales Range: $25-49.9 Million
Emp.: 20
Distr of Silicon Wafers
N.A.I.C.S.: 334413

SUMCO Insurance Service Corp. (1)
1324-2 Masuragahara, Omura, 856-8555, Nagasaki, Japan
Tel.: (81) 957547209
Semiconductor Equipment Mfr
N.A.I.C.S.: 333242

SUMCO Korea Corporation (1)
Tel.: (82) 317095732
Silicon Wafer Mfr & Distr
N.A.I.C.S.: 423690

SUMCO Phoenix Corporation (1)
19801 N Tatum Blvd, Phoenix, AZ 85050-4201
Tel.: (480) 473-6000
Web Site: https://www.sumcousa.com
Sales Range: $100-124.9 Million
Emp.: 500
Mfr of Silicon Wafers
N.A.I.C.S.: 334413

SUMCO Service Corporation (1)
2201 Oaza Kamioda Kohoku-cho, Kishima-gun, Saga, 849-0506, Japan
Tel.: (81) 952716577
Web Site: https://www.sumcosi.com
Silicon Wafers Mfr
N.A.I.C.S.: 334413

SUMCO Shanghai Corporation (1)
Room 2509-2511 Shanghai Maxdo Center No 8 Xingyi Rd, Shanghai, 200336, China
Tel.: (86) 2152080333
Web Site: https://www.sumcosi.com
Semiconductors Mfr & Distr
N.A.I.C.S.: 334413

SUMCO Singapore Pte. Ltd. (1)
7 Temasek Boulevard 22-01 Suntec Tower One, Singapore, 038987, Singapore
Tel.: (65) 68831570
Emp.: 10
Silicon Wafers Mfr & Sales
N.A.I.C.S.: 334413

SUMCO Solar Corporation (1)
260-100 Funao, Kainan, 642-0001, Wakayama, Japan
Tel.: (81) 734838187
Sales Range: $50-74.9 Million
Emp.: 250
Solar Cell Silicon Wafers Mfr
N.A.I.C.S.: 334413

SUMCO Southwest Corporation (1)
19801 N Tatum Blvd, Phoenix, AZ 85050
Tel.: (480) 473-6000
Web Site: http://www.sumcousa.com
Semiconductors Devices Mfr & Distr
N.A.I.C.S.: 334413

SUMCO Support Corp. (1)
826-1 Nagahama Higashiyamashiro-cho, Imari, 849-4271, Saga, Japan
Tel.: (81) 955227063
Silicon Wafers Mfr
N.A.I.C.S.: 334419

INTERNATIONAL PUBLIC

SUMCO Taiwan Technology Corporation (1)
9F No 417 Sec 2 Gongdao 5th Road, Hsinchu, 237, Taiwan
Tel.: (886) 35712838
Sales Range: $25-49.9 Million
Emp.: 10
Silicon Wafers Mfr & Distr
N.A.I.C.S.: 334419

SUMCO TechXIV Corporation (1)
(100%)
Tel.: (81) 957520111
Web Site: https://www.sumcotechxiv.com
Sales Range: $750-799.9 Million
Emp.: 1,738
Mfr & Sales of Semiconductor Silicon Wafers
N.A.I.C.S.: 334413
Miyaji Politics *(CEO)*

Subsidiary (Non-US):

Formosa Sumco Technology Corporation (2)
8F A1 Building No 380 Sec 6 Nanjing E Rd, Neihu Dist, Taipei, 105, Taiwan
Tel.: (886) 227122211
Web Site: https://www.fstech.com.tw
Sales Range: $25-49.9 Million
Emp.: 1,000
Mfr & Sales of Semiconductor Silicon Wafers; Joint Venture of Komatsu Ltd., Asia Pacific Development Company & Formosa Plastic Corporation
N.A.I.C.S.: 334413

SUMCO TechXIV Europe NV (2)
Mechelsesteenweg 586, 1800, Vilvoorde, Belgium
Tel.: (32) 22512412
Sales Range: $25-49.9 Million
Emp.: 5
Sales of Semiconductor Silicon Wafers
N.A.I.C.S.: 334413

SUMCO Technology Corporation (1)
314 Nishisangao, Noda, 278-0015, Chiba, Japan
Tel.: (81) 471241621
Web Site: http://www.stecsi.com
Sales Range: $50-74.9 Million
Emp.: 200
Silicon Wafers Mfr
N.A.I.C.S.: 334413

SUMTEC Service Corporation (1)
1324-2 Masuragaharamachi, Omura, 856-8555, Nagasaki, Japan
Tel.: (81) 957520078
Emp.: 90
Silicon Wafers Mfr
N.A.I.C.S.: 334419

SUME TK D.D. KLADANJ
Fadila Kurtagica 1, 75280, Kladanj, Bosnia & Herzegovina
Tel.: (387) 3 562 1212
Web Site: http://www.jpsumetk.ba
SMTKR—(SARE)
Rev.: $10,609,223
Assets: $3,390,718
Liabilities: $3,314,213
Net Worth: $76,505
Earnings: ($267,350)
Emp.: 518
Fiscal Year-end: 12/31/20
Silviculture & Forestry Services
N.A.I.C.S.: 115310

SUMEDHA FISCAL SERVICES LTD.
8B Middleton Street 6A Geetanjali, Kolkata, 700 071, India
Tel.: (91) 3322298936
Web Site:
https://www.sumedhafiscal.com
530419—(BOM)
Rev.: $2,732,735
Assets: $6,587,920
Liabilities: $182,476
Net Worth: $6,405,444
Earnings: $1,181,440
Emp.: 47
Fiscal Year-end: 03/31/21

Financial Services
N.A.I.C.S.: 523999
Ratan Lal Gaggar *(Chm)*

SUMEEKO INDUSTRIES CO., LTD.
No 20 Huaxi Rd, Ta-Fa Industrial Dist, Kaohsiung, 831, Taiwan
Tel.: (886) 77889168
Web Site: https://www.sumeeko.com
Year Founded: 1988
2066—(TPE)
Rev.: $89,146,234
Assets: $100,512,491
Liabilities: $44,460,776
Net Worth: $56,051,715
Earnings: $9,259,669
Fiscal Year-end: 12/31/22
Carbon Steel Screw Mfr
N.A.I.C.S.: 332722
Wu Seng-Fu *(Pres)*

SUMEET INDUSTRIES LTD
504 Trividh Chamber Opp Fire Brigade Station Ring Road, Surat, 395 002, Gujarat, India
Tel.: (91) 2612328902
Web Site: https://www.sumeetindustries.com
Rev.: $124,839,322
Assets: $116,104,255
Liabilities: $103,974,092
Net Worth: $12,130,163
Earnings: ($16,764,837)
Emp.: 627
Fiscal Year-end: 03/31/19
Textile Industry
N.A.I.C.S.: 313220
Anil Kumar Jain *(Compliance Officer & Sec)*

Subsidiaries:

Ambaji Syntex Private Limited (1)
Plot No 19 Goodluck Compound NR Manhar Dyeing Bamrolil Rd, Surat, 394210, Gujarat, India
Tel.: (91) 2612630639
Sales Range: $25-49.9 Million
Emp.: 20
Cotton Fabrics Mfr
N.A.I.C.S.: 313240

SUMER COMMERICAL BANK
Uqba Bin Nafi, Baghdad, Iraq
Tel.: (964) 7833399890
Web Site: https://sumerbank.iq
Year Founded: 1999
BSUC—(IRAQ)
Rev.: $5,162,525
Assets: $224,532,457
Liabilities: $42,931,949
Net Worth: $181,600,508
Earnings: $708,151
Fiscal Year-end: 12/31/22
Banking Services
N.A.I.C.S.: 522110

SUMER FAKTORING A.S.
Keskin Kalem Sok No 39/1 Esentepe, Sisli, 34394, Istanbul, Turkiye
Tel.: (90) 2123472250
Web Site: http://www.sumerfaktoring.com
SMRFA—(IST)
Sales Range: Less than $1 Million
Financial Advisory Services
N.A.I.C.S.: 523940
Vakkas Altinbas *(Vice Chm)*

SUMER VARLIK YONETIMI A.S.
Esentepe Mah Buyukdere CD No 124 Ozsezen is Merkezi B Blok K 1-2-3, Sisli, Istanbul, Turkiye
Tel.: (90) 2122176900
Web Site: http://www.sumervarlik.com.tr
SMRVA—(IST)
Sales Range: Less than $1 Million
Asset Management Services
N.A.I.C.S.: 531390
Sofu Altinbas *(Chm)*

SUMIDA CORPORATION
KDX Ginza East Building 7F 3-7-2 Irifune, Chuo-ku, Tokyo, 104-0042, Japan
Tel.: (81) 367582470
Web Site: https://www.sumida.com
Year Founded: 1956
6817—(TKS)
Rev.: $1,046,994,480
Assets: $1,012,352,740
Liabilities: $606,010,660
Net Worth: $406,342,080
Earnings: $35,903,760
Emp.: 15,464
Fiscal Year-end: 12/31/23
Electronic Components Mfr
N.A.I.C.S.: 335312
Shigeyuki Yawata *(Chm & CEO)*

Subsidiaries:

Dongguan Sumida (Tai Ping) Electric Co., Ltd. (1)
Tel.: (86) 76985111118
Electronic Components Mfr
N.A.I.C.S.: 334416

Guangzhou Sumida Electric Co., Ltd. (1)
3 of No 4 Jiu Chun Dong Road Da Long Street, Panyu District, Guangzhou, Guangdong, China
Tel.: (86) 2034569688
Electronic Components Mfr
N.A.I.C.S.: 334416

Pontiac Coil Inc. (1)
5800 Moody Dr, Clarkston, MI 48348-4768
Tel.: (248) 922-1100
Web Site: http://www.pontiaccoil.com
Electronic Coils & Transformers Mfr
N.A.I.C.S.: 334416
Don Nelson *(Mgr-Quality)*

Sumida Corporate Service Company Limited (1)
2201-3 Berkshire House 25 Westlands Road, Quarry Bay, China (Hong Kong)
Tel.: (852) 28806688
Web Site: http://www.sumida.com
Sales Range: $25-49.9 Million
Emp.: 100
Electronic Components Mfr & Whslr
N.A.I.C.S.: 334419

Sumida Corporate Service Incorporated (1)
Yaesu Ctr Bldg 1-6-6 Yaesu, Chuo-ku, Tokyo, Japan
Tel.: (81) 332727100
Web Site: http://www.sumida.com
Sales Range: $25-49.9 Million
Emp.: 30
Electronic Components Mfr
N.A.I.C.S.: 334419

Sumida Corporation - Electric Factory (1)
Economic Industrial Development Zone, Kou Shui Heng Village Dalong Sub-district Panyu District, Guangzhou, 511450, Guangdong, China
Tel.: (86) 208 461 6928
Web Site: http://www.sumida.com
Electronic Components Mfr
N.A.I.C.S.: 334419

Sumida EMS GmbH (1)
Dr Hans-Vogt-Platz 1, 94130, Obernzell, Germany
Tel.: (49) 8591937100
Web Site: http://www.sumida-eu.com
Sales Range: $75-99.9 Million
Emp.: 200
Electronic Components Distr
N.A.I.C.S.: 423690

Sumida Electric (Changde) Co., Ltd. (1)
Electronic Information Industrial Pioneer Park, Deshan Economic Development District, Changde, Hunan, China
Tel.: (86) 7367308168
Electronic Components Mfr
N.A.I.C.S.: 334416

Sumida Electric (Guangxi) Co., Ltd. (1)
China-Asean Advanced Business Park No 3 Zongbu Road, Nanning, Guangxi, China
Tel.: (86) 7713216866
Electronic Components Mfr
N.A.I.C.S.: 334416

Sumida Electric (India) Private Limited (1)
Room 2236 Regus World Trade Centre Brigade Gateway Campus, Rajajinagar Extn Malleshwaram W, Bengaluru, 560055, India
Tel.: (91) 8067935885
Electronic Components Distr
N.A.I.C.S.: 423690

Sumida Electric (JI'AN) Co., Ltd. (1)
Tel.: (86) 7968400666
Electronic Components Mfr
N.A.I.C.S.: 334416

Sumida Electric (Thailand) Co., Ltd. (1)
148 Moo 5 Tiwanon Road, Bangkadi Sub-District Pathumthani District, Amphur Muang, 12000, Pathumthani, Thailand
Tel.: (66) 25011611
Electronic Coil Mfr & Distr
N.A.I.C.S.: 334416

Sumida Electric Co., Ltd. (Osaka) (1)
Shin-Osaka Trust Tower 12th Fl 3-5-36 Miyahara, Yodogawa-ku, Osaka, 532-0003, Japan
Tel.: (81) 663918855
Web Site: http://www.sumida.co.jp
Sales Range: $25-49.9 Million
Emp.: 20
Electronic Components Distr
N.A.I.C.S.: 423690

Sumida Electric Co., Ltd. - Aomori Factory (1)
97-3 Ueno Ohata-machi, Mutsu, 039-4401, Aomori, Japan
Tel.: (81) 175345511
Coil Component Mfr
N.A.I.C.S.: 334416

Sumida Electronic Components Co., Ltd (1)
7F Kdx Ginza East Building 3-7-2 Irifune, Chuo-ku, Tokyo, 104-0042, Japan
Tel.: (81) 363627200
Web Site: http://www.sumida.com
Electronic Components Supplier
N.A.I.C.S.: 423690

Subsidiary (US):

Sumida America Components Inc. (2)
1251 N Plum Grove Rd Ste 150, Schaumburg, IL 60173
Tel.: (847) 545-6700
Web Site: http://www.sumida.com
Sales Range: $25-49.9 Million
Electronic Components Distr
N.A.I.C.S.: 423690

Subsidiary (Non-US):

Sumida Electric (H.K.) Company Limited (2)
2201-3 Berkshire House 25 Westlands Road, Quarry Bay, China (Hong Kong)
Tel.: (852) 28806688
Web Site: http://www.sumida.com
Sales Range: $25-49.9 Million
Electronic Components Mfr & Supplier
N.A.I.C.S.: 334416

Subsidiary (Domestic):

Sumida Electric Co., Ltd. (2)
KDX Ginza East Building 7F 3-7-2 Irifune, Chuo-ku, Tokyo, 104-0042, Japan
Tel.: (81) 36 362 7200
Web Site: http://www.sumida.com
Electric Component Whslr
N.A.I.C.S.: 423690

Subsidiary (Non-US):

Sumida Service Company Limited (2)
2201-3 DCH Commercial Centre 25 Westlands Rd, Quarry Bay, China (Hong Kong)
Tel.: (852) 2880 6688
Web Site: http://www.sumida.com
Sales Range: $25-49.9 Million
Emp.: 40
Electronic Components Distr & Sales
N.A.I.C.S.: 423690

Sumida Service Company Limited (2)
1507-8 Westlands Centre 20 Westlands Rd, Quarry Bay, China (Hong Kong)
Tel.: (852) 28806781
Web Site: http://www.sumida.com
Sales Range: $25-49.9 Million
Electronic Components Mfr & Sales
N.A.I.C.S.: 334419

Sumida Trading (Korea) Company Limited (2)
5F 134 Hangang-daero, Yongsan-gu, Seoul, Korea (South)
Tel.: (82) 26 237 0777
Web Site: http://www.sumida.com
Sales Range: $25-49.9 Million
Emp.: 4
Electric Component Whslr
N.A.I.C.S.: 423690

Sumida Trading (Shanghai) Company Limited (2)
Unit 15-022 15/F No 1000 Lujiazui Ring Road, Shanghai Pilot Free Trade Zone, Shanghai, 200120, China
Tel.: (86) 2158363299
Web Site: http://www.sumida.com
Sales Range: $25-49.9 Million
Electronic Components Supplier
N.A.I.C.S.: 423690

Sumida Trading Company Limited (2)
14 F Eastern Ctr 1065 Kings Rd, Quarry Bay, China (Hong Kong)
Tel.: (852) 28806688
Electric Component Whslr
N.A.I.C.S.: 423690
Winwood Lam *(Gen Mgr)*

Sumida Trading Pte Ltd. (2)
28 Genting Lane 01-02 Platinum 28, Singapore, 349585, Singapore
Tel.: (65) 6 296 3388
Web Site: http://www.sumida.com
Sales Range: $25-49.9 Million
Electronic Components Distr
N.A.I.C.S.: 423690

Taiwan Sumida Trading Company Limited (2)
8/F-1 No 75 Jhouzih Street, Neihu District, Taipei, 114, Taiwan
Tel.: (886) 287512737
Sales Range: $25-49.9 Million
Emp.: 15
Electronic Components Distr
N.A.I.C.S.: 423690

Sumida Electronic Quang Ngai Co., Ltd. (1)
Lot CN 03 Street No 2 Tinh Phong Industrial Park, Son Tinh, Quang Ngai, Vietnam
Tel.: (84) 2553526688
Electronic Components Mfr
N.A.I.C.S.: 334416

Sumida Electronic SuQian Co., Ltd. (1)
Buzi Town Industrial Park A2 Building, Sucheng District, Suqian, Jiangsu, China
Tel.: (86) 52784601686
Electronic Components Mfr
N.A.I.C.S.: 334416

Sumida Electronic Vietnam Co., Ltd. (1)
Standard factory B1 and B2 Japan-Hai Phong Industrial Zone, An Duong District, Haiphong, Vietnam
Tel.: (84) 2253290119
Electronic Components Mfr
N.A.I.C.S.: 334416

Sumida Europe GmbH (1)

SUMIDA CORPORATION

Sumida Corporation—(Continued)
Kerschensteinerstrasse 21, 92318, Neumarkt, Germany
Tel.: (49) 9181 450 9110
Web Site: http://www.sumida.com
Electronic Components Mfr & Supplier
N.A.I.C.S.: 334416

Subsidiary (Domestic):

Sumida AG (2)
Dr Hans-Vogt-Platz 1, Passau, 94130, Obernzell, Germany
Tel.: (49) 85919370
Web Site: http://www.sumida-eu.com
Sales Range: $50-74.9 Million
Emp.: 150
Electronic Components Mfr & Sales
N.A.I.C.S.: 334416

Subsidiary (Domestic):

Sumida Components & Modules GmbH (3)
Dr Hans-Vogt-Platz 1, 94130, Obernzell, Germany
Tel.: (49) 859 193 7100
Sales Range: $125-149.9 Million
Electronic Components Mfr & Supplier
N.A.I.C.S.: 334416

Subsidiary (Non-US):

Sumida Austria GmbH (4)
Drautendorff 48, Rohrbach, 4174, Niederwaldkirchen, Austria
Tel.: (43) 7231 3131 0
Electronic Components Mfr
N.A.I.C.S.: 334416

Sumida Electronic Shanghai Co., Ltd. (4)
Building 6 No 88 XuTang Road, Songjiang District, Shanghai, 201613, China
Tel.: (86) 2167696150
Sales Range: $25-49.9 Million
Emp.: 100
Electronic Components Mfr & Supplier
N.A.I.C.S.: 334416

Sumida Romania S.R.L. (4)
Str Corneliu Coposu Nr 1A, jud Timis, 305400, Jimbolia, Timis, Romania
Tel.: (40) 25 640 9900
Web Site: http://www.sumida.com
Electrical Component Mfr
N.A.I.C.S.: 334416

Vogtronics GmbH (4)
Tel.: (49) 85919370
Sales Range: $25-49.9 Million
Emp.: 9
Electronic Components Mfr & Supplier
N.A.I.C.S.: 334416
Thomas Moetsch (Mng Dir)

Subsidiary (Non-US):

Sumida Slovenija d.o.o (5)
Blejska Dobrava 124, 4273, Blejska Dobrava, Slovenia
Tel.: (386) 46209211
Web Site: https://www.sumida.si
Sales Range: $100-124.9 Million
Emp.: 238
Electronic Components Mfr
N.A.I.C.S.: 334416
Janez Locniskar (Mgr)

Sumida Power Electronics Co., Ltd. (1)
7F Kdx Ginza East Building 3-7-2 Irifune, Chuo-ku, Tokyo, 104-0042, Japan
Tel.: (81) 363627200
Web Site: http://www.sumida.com
Electronic Components Mfr
N.A.I.C.S.: 334419

Subsidiary (Domestic):

Concord Electronics Industries Co., Ltd. (2)
604-1 Motohara Sanadamachi, Ueda, Nagano, Japan
Tel.: (81) 268728810
Web Site: http://www.concord-ei.co.jp
Sales Range: $25-49.9 Million
Emp.: 120
Electronic Components Mfr
N.A.I.C.S.: 334419

Sumida Power Technology Co., Ltd. (1)
604-1 Motohara Sanadamachi, Ueda, 386-2202, Nagano, Japan
Tel.: (81) 268728810
Electronic Component Mfr & Distr
N.A.I.C.S.: 334416

Sumida Trading (Shanghai) Company Limited (Shenzhen) (1)
Room 3905 Block A United Plaza 5022 Binhe Road, Futian District, Shenzhen, 518026, Guangdong, China
Tel.: (86) 7558 291 0228
Web Site: http://www.sumida.com
Sales Range: $25-49.9 Million
Electric Component Whslr
N.A.I.C.S.: 423690

Sumida Trading (Shanghai) Company Limited - Guangzhou Panyu Sumida Kou Shui Heng Electric Factory (1)
Economic & Industrial Development Zone, Kou Shui Heng Village Dalong Sub-District Panyu District, Guangzhou, 511450, Guangdong, China
Tel.: (86) 2084616928
Electronic Components Mfr
N.A.I.C.S.: 334416

SUMINOE TEXTILE CO., LTD.
11-20 Minami-Semba 3-Chome, Chuo-ku, Osaka, 542-8504, Japan
Tel.: (81) 662516801
Web Site: https://www.suminoe.co.jp
Year Founded: 1883
3501—(TKS)
Rev.: $683,989,580
Assets: $609,435,390
Liabilities: $360,324,320
Net Worth: $249,111,070
Earnings: $5,777,140
Emp.: 2,812
Fiscal Year-end: 05/31/24
Interior Fitting Product Mfr
N.A.I.C.S.: 326150
Ichizo Yoshikawa (Chm)

Subsidiaries:

PT. Suminoe Surya Techno (1)
Tel.: (62) 226120690
Textile Products Distr
N.A.I.C.S.: 424310

RUNON CO., LTD. (1)
BR Gotanda-Building 30-4 Nishi-Gotanda 2-Chome, Shinagawa, 141-0031, Tokyo, Japan
Tel.: (81) 334927341
Web Site: https://www.runon.co.jp
Wallpaper Distr
N.A.I.C.S.: 424950

SPM Automotive Textile Co., Ltd. (1)
Liu Chong Tong Xing County Wan Qing Sha Town, Nansha, Guangzhou, China
Tel.: (86) 2084945588
Emp.: 136
Textile Products Distr
N.A.I.C.S.: 424310

SUMINOE Co., Ltd. (1)
Naniwa-suji SIA Building 2-4-2, Shinmachi Nishi-ku, Osaka, 550-0013, Japan
Tel.: (81) 665376301
Curtain & Rug Mfr
N.A.I.C.S.: 326150

Suminoe Logistics Co., Ltd. (1)
634-1 Kubota Ando-cho, Ikoma-gun, Nara, 639-1064, Japan
Tel.: (81) 743572060
Web Site: https://suminoe-logistics.co.jp
Emp.: 117
Interior Design Services
N.A.I.C.S.: 541410

Suminoe Techno Co., Ltd. (1)
634-1 Kubota Ando-cho, Ikoma-gun, Nara, 639-1064, Japan
Tel.: (81) 743573181
Interior Fitting Product Mfr
N.A.I.C.S.: 326150

Plant (Domestic):

Suminoe Techno Co., Ltd. - Shiga Factory (2)

Kokacho Jinbo, Koka-shi, Shiga, 520-3404, Japan
Tel.: (81) 748 88 5727
Interior Fitting Product Mfr
N.A.I.C.S.: 326150

Suminoe Teijin Techno Krishna India Pvt. Ltd. (1)
Plot no 437 Sector 8 IMT Manesar, Gurgaon, 122050, Haryana, India
Tel.: (91) 1244956762
Web Site: https://stk.co.in
Automotive Fabric Mfr
N.A.I.C.S.: 336360

Suminoe Textile Shanghai Co., Ltd. (1)
W2A7 Sun Plaza No 88 Xianxia Rd, Chang Ning Area, Shanghai, China
Tel.: (86) 2152131538
Textile Products Distr
N.A.I.C.S.: 424310

Suminoe Textile de Mexico, S.A. de C.V. (1)
Av Rio San Lorenzo 931 Parque Industrial Castro del Rio, CP 36810, Irapuato, Guanajuato, Mexico
Tel.: (52) 4626937141
Textile Products Distr
N.A.I.C.S.: 424310

Suminoe Textile of America Corporation (1)
10 Commerce Dr, Gaffney, SC 29340
Tel.: (864) 488-0053
Web Site: https://www.suminoe.us
Textile Products Mfr
N.A.I.C.S.: 314999

Suminoe Works Co., Ltd. (1)
BR Gotanda-Building 30-4 Nishi-Gotanda 2-Chome, Shinagawa-ku, Tokyo, 141-0031, Japan
Tel.: (81) 35 434 2970
Interior Product Installation Services
N.A.I.C.S.: 541410

Suzhou Suminoe Koide Automotive Accessories Co., Ltd. (1)
Xi shan Gong Ye Yuan 9 Xi shan Zhen Jin Ting Lu77, Wu Zhong Qu, Suzhou, China
Tel.: (86) 51266372581
Textile Products Distr
N.A.I.C.S.: 424310

Suzhou Suminoe Textiles Co., Ltd. (1)
Xijiao Caohu Science and Technology Park C403, No 1 Guantang Road Caohu Street Xiangcheng District, Suzhou, Jiangsu Province, China
Tel.: (86) 51265796318
Carpet Distr
N.A.I.C.S.: 423220

T.C.H. Suminoe Co., Ltd. (1)
Bangpa-in Industrial Estate 157 Moo16 Tumbol Bangkrasun, Amphur Bangpa-in, Ayutthaya, Thailand, Thailand
Tel.: (66) 35258419
Textile Products Distr
N.A.I.C.S.: 424310
Damrong Ruenjinda (Mgr-Quality Assurance)

SUMISEKI HOLDINGS, INC.
1-7-14 Nishi-Shinbashi, Minato-ku, Tokyo, 105-0003, Japan
Tel.: (81) 355111400
Web Site: https://www.sumiseki.co.jp
1514—(TKS)
Rev.: $149,379,390
Assets: $205,815,570
Liabilities: $27,418,280
Net Worth: $178,397,290
Earnings: $49,773,300
Fiscal Year-end: 03/31/24
Holding Company; Coal, New Material, Quarry, Construction Material & Equipment
N.A.I.C.S.: 551112
Komaki Nagasaki (Pres)

SUMIT WOODS LIMITED

INTERNATIONAL PUBLIC

B-1101 Express Zone Diagonally Opp To Oberoi Mall W E Highway, Malad East, Mumbai, 400097, India
Tel.: (91) 2228749966
Web Site: https://www.sumitwoods.com
Year Founded: 1997
SUMIT—(NSE)
Rev.: $12,337,462
Assets: $5,364,271
Liabilities: $5,180,637
Net Worth: $183,634
Earnings: $837,000
Emp.: 37
Fiscal Year-end: 03/31/23
Real Estate Development Services
N.A.I.C.S.: 531390
Mitaram Jangid (Co-Founder)

SUMITA OPTICAL GLASS, INC.
4-7-25 Harigaya, Urawa-ku, Saitama, 330-8565, Japan
Tel.: (81) 488323165
Web Site: http://www.sumita-opt.co.jp
Year Founded: 1953
Emp.: 350
Optical Glass & Fiberoptics Products
N.A.I.C.S.: 327215
Toshiaki Sumita (Pres)

Subsidiaries:

Sumita Optical Glass Europe GmbH (1)
Andernacher Strasse 23, 90411, Nuremberg, Germany
Tel.: (49) 911 376 6836 0
Web Site: http://www.sumita.com.de
Optical Glasses Mfr
N.A.I.C.S.: 333310
Daisuke Sumita (Mng Dir)

Sumita Optical Glass, Inc. - Tajima Factory (1)
174-1 Tabehara Tajima Minamiaizu-cho, Minamiaizu-gun, Fukushima, 957-0004, Japan
Tel.: (81) 241 62 2626
Optical Glasses Mfr
N.A.I.C.S.: 333310

SUMITOMO BAKELITE CO., LTD.
Tennozu Parkside Building 2-5-8 Higashishinagawa, Shinagawa-ku, Tokyo, 140-0002, Japan
Tel.: (81) 354624111
Web Site: https://www.sumibe.co.jp
Year Founded: 1932
4203—(TKS)
Rev.: $1,898,834,870
Assets: $2,916,080,820
Liabilities: $908,445,350
Net Worth: $2,007,635,470
Earnings: $144,302,910
Emp.: 7,953
Fiscal Year-end: 03/31/24
Chemicals, Resins & Plastics Mfr
N.A.I.C.S.: 325998
Shigeru Hayashi (Chm)

Subsidiaries:

Akita Sumitomo Bakelite Co., Ltd. (1)
27-4 Aza-Nakajimashita Souzen-Machi, Tsuchizakiminato, Akita, 011-8510, Japan
Tel.: (81) 188451181
Plastics Material & Resin Mfr
N.A.I.C.S.: 325211

Changchun SB (Changshu) Co., Ltd. (1)
Changchun Road Riverside Industrial Park, Changshu Economic Development Zone, Changshu, 215537, China
Tel.: (86) 51252648000
Plastics Material & Resin Mfr
N.A.I.C.S.: 325211

Durez Canada Co., Ltd. (1)
100 Dunlop Street, Fort Erie, L2A 4H9, ON, Canada

AND PRIVATE COMPANIES — SUMITOMO BAKELITE CO., LTD.

Tel.: (905) 346-8700
Emp.: 70
Phenolic Moulding Compound & Phenolic Resins Mfr
N.A.I.C.S.: 325211

Hokkai Taiyo Plastic Co., Ltd. (1)
2-763-7 Shinko-Chuo, Ishikari, 061-3242, Japan
Tel.: (81) 133646611
Emp.: 28
Polyethylene Film & Pipe Mfr
N.A.I.C.S.: 326113

Kawasumi Laboratories Incorporated (1)
Shinagawa Intercity Tower B 9th Floor
2-15-2 Konan, Minato-ku, Tokyo, 108-6109, Japan (100%)
Tel.: (81) 337631155
Web Site: http://www.kawasumi.jp
Rev.: $218,382,240
Assets: $400,361,400
Liabilities: $52,747,320
Net Worth: $347,614,080
Earnings: $1,685,160
Emp.: 2,404
Fiscal Year-end: 03/31/2019
Medical Devices & Pharmaceuticals Mfr & Sales
N.A.I.C.S.: 325412
Takeshi Saino *(Pres & COO)*

Subsidiary (Non-US):

Kawasumi Laboratories (Thailand) Co., Ltd. (2)
Nava Nakorn Industrial Promotion Zone 55/26 MU 13 Phahon Yothin Road, KM-46 Tambon Khlong Nueng Amphoe Khlong Luang Changwat, Pathumthani, 12120, Thailand
Tel.: (66) 29660911
Disposable Medical Devices Mfr
N.A.I.C.S.: 334517

Subsidiary (US):

Kawasumi Laboratories America Inc.
10002 Princess Palm Ave Ste 324, Tampa, FL 33619
Tel.: (813) 630-5554
Web Site: http://www.kawasumiamerica.com
Sales Range: $50-74.9 Million
Emp.: 20
Blood Kits & Medical Instruments Distr
N.A.I.C.S.: 423450
Crystal Karlson *(Mgr-Ops)*

Plant (Domestic):

Kawasumi Laboratories Incorporated - Mie Plant (2)
7-1 Tamada, Mie-cho, Bungo-ono, 879-7153, Oita, Japan
Tel.: (81) 974224111
Web Site: http://www.kawasumi.jp
Sales Range: $100-124.9 Million
Emp.: 400
Medical Equipment Mfr
N.A.I.C.S.: 339112

Kawasumi Laboratories Incorporated - Saiki Plant (2)
1077 Oda Yayoi Oaza, Saiki, 876-0121, Oita, Japan
Tel.: (81) 972461212
Web Site: http://www.kawasumi.jp
Medical Equipment Mfr
N.A.I.C.S.: 339112

Kawasumi Laboratories Incorporated - Yayoi Plant (2)
2051 Osakamoto, Yayoi, Saiki, 876-0101, Oita, Japan
Tel.: (81) 972460229
Web Site: http://www.kawasumi.jp
Medical Equipment Mfr
N.A.I.C.S.: 339112

Kyushu Sumitomo Bakelite Co., Ltd. (1)
40-1 Oaza-Kamizakai, Nogata, Fukuoka, 822-0006, Japan
Tel.: (81) 949231911
Plastics Material & Resin Mfr
N.A.I.C.S.: 325211

P.T. Indopherin Jaya (1)
Nusantara Bldg 6th Floor 59 Jl Mh Thamrin, Jakarta, 10350, Indonesia
Tel.: (62) 213914010
Emp.: 120
Phenolic Resins Mfr & Distr
N.A.I.C.S.: 325211

P.T. SBP Indonesia (1)
Blok NN Kawasan Industri MM2100 Jl Irian VI Kec, Cikarang Bar, Bekasi, 17520, jawa barat, Indonesia
Tel.: (62) 218980540
Web Site: https://www.sbpindonesia.co.id
Emp.: 87
Polycarbonate Extruded Resin Sheet Mfr & Distr
N.A.I.C.S.: 325211

Promerus, LLC (1)
225 W Bartges St, Akron, OH 44307
Tel.: (440) 922-0300
Web Site: https://info.promerus.com
Emp.: 30
Semiconductor Mfr & Distr
N.A.I.C.S.: 334413

S.B. Information System Co., Ltd. (1)
2-5-8 Higashi-Shinagawa, Shinagawa-ku, Tokyo, 140-0002, Japan
Tel.: (81) 354624864
Plastics Material & Resin Mfr
N.A.I.C.S.: 325211

S.B. Recycle Co., Ltd. (1)
2100 Takayanagi, Fujieda, 426-0041, Japan
Tel.: (81) 546356445
Plastics Material & Resin Mfr
N.A.I.C.S.: 325211

S.B. Research Co., Ltd. (1)
20-7 Kiyohara Kogyodanchi, Utsunomiya, 321-3231, Japan
Tel.: (81) 286676226
Plastics Material & Resin Mfr
N.A.I.C.S.: 325211

S.B. Sheet Waterproof Systems Co., Ltd. (1)
2-5-8 Higashi-Shinagawa, Shinagawa-ku, Tokyo, 140-0002, Japan
Tel.: (81) 354628950
Plastics Material & Resin Mfr
N.A.I.C.S.: 325211

S.B. Techno Plastics Co., Ltd. (1)
300-2 Motohara, Kamikawa-cho Kodamagun, Saitama, 367-0241, Japan
Tel.: (81) 495774601
Plastics Material & Resin Mfr
N.A.I.C.S.: 325211

SB-Kawasumi Laboratories, Inc. (1)
3-25-4 Tonomachi, Kawasaki-ku, Kawasaki, 210-8602, Kanagawa, Japan
Tel.: (81) 445898070
Chemical Products Mfr
N.A.I.C.S.: 325998

SNC Industrial Laminates Sdn. Bhd. (1)
Plo 38 Jalan Keluli Satu Pasir Gudang Industrial Estate, 81700, Pasir Gudang, Malaysia
Tel.: (60) 72512199
Emp.: 94
Phenolic Resin Copper Clad Laminate Mfr
N.A.I.C.S.: 326112

Seibu Jushi Co., Ltd. (1)
8-40 Futamatase-Shinmachi, Higashi-ku, Fukuoka, 812-0065, Japan
Tel.: (81) 926244688
Plastics Material & Resin Mfr
N.A.I.C.S.: 325211

SumiDurez Singapore Pte. Ltd. (1)
9 Tanjong Penjuru Crescent, Singapore, 608972, Singapore
Tel.: (65) 62651717
Emp.: 62
Phenolic Moulding Compound Mfr & Distr
N.A.I.C.S.: 325991

Sumibe Korea Co., Ltd. (1)
Rm 2014 Sungjee Heights III Bldg 507, Nonhyeon-ro Gangnam-Gu, Seoul, Korea (South)
Tel.: (82) 25691860
Chemical Products Mfr
N.A.I.C.S.: 325998

Sumitomo Bakelite (Dongguan) Co., Ltd. (1)
No 2 Qiao Lin Road, Ling Tou Industrial District Qiao Tou Town, Dongguan, China
Tel.: (86) 76983343022
Plastics Material & Resin Mfr
N.A.I.C.S.: 325211

Sumitomo Bakelite (Nantong) Co., Ltd. (1)
No81 Tongda Road Port Industrial Park3, Economic Technological Development Area, Nantong, 226017, China
Tel.: (86) 51385997104
Plastics Material & Resin Mfr
N.A.I.C.S.: 325211

Sumitomo Bakelite (Shanghai) Co., Ltd. (1)
No 88 Aidu Road Pilot Free Trade Zone, Shanghai, 200131, China
Tel.: (86) 2150460091
Plastics Material & Resin Mfr
N.A.I.C.S.: 325211

Sumitomo Bakelite (Suzhou) Co., Ltd. (1)
140 Zhongxin Avenue West Suzhou Industrial Park, Suzhou, 215021, China
Tel.: (86) 51267613850
Epoxy Resin Moulding Compound Mfr
N.A.I.C.S.: 325991

Sumitomo Bakelite (Taiwan) Corporation Limited (1)
No 1 Hwa Syi Road, Ta Fa Industries District Ta Liao, Kaohsiung, Taiwan
Tel.: (886) 77871285
Web Site: http://www.sumibe.co.jp
Epoxy Moulding Compound Mfr
N.A.I.C.S.: 325211

Sumitomo Bakelite (Thailand) Co., Ltd. (1)
90 Cw Tower B 17th Floor Suite 1703 Ratchadapisek Road, Huai Khwang, Bangkok, 10310, Thailand
Tel.: (66) 21683238
Phenolic Resins Mfr
N.A.I.C.S.: 325211

Sumitomo Bakelite Europe (Barcelona), S.L.U. (1)
Gran Vial 4, Montornes del Valles, 08170, Barcelona, Spain
Tel.: (34) 935799040
Web Site: https://www.sbhpp-europe.com
Emp.: 90
Phenolic Resins Mfr
N.A.I.C.S.: 325211

Sumitomo Bakelite Europe N.V. (1)
Henry Fordlaan 80, 3600, Genk, Belgium
Tel.: (32) 89320300
Phenolic Resin & Polyester Resin Mfr
N.A.I.C.S.: 325211

Sumitomo Bakelite Hong Kong Co., Ltd. (1)
Unit 7 on 20th Floor Greenfield Tower Concordia Plaza, No1 Science Museum Road Tsim Sha Tsui East, Kowloon, China (Hong Kong)
Tel.: (852) 27393993
Plastics Material & Resin Mfr
N.A.I.C.S.: 325211

Sumitomo Bakelite Macau Co., Ltd. (1)
Zona Ind do Aterro Sanitario de Seac Pai Van Lote A, junto a Estrada de Seac Pai Van, Coloane, China (Macau)
Tel.: (853) 28881020
Plastics Material & Resin Mfr
N.A.I.C.S.: 325211

Sumitomo Bakelite North America Holding, Inc. (1)
4400 Haggerty Rd, Commerce Township, MI 48390
Tel.: (248) 313-7000
Phenolic Moulding Compound Mfr & Distr
N.A.I.C.S.: 325991

Sumitomo Bakelite Singapore Pte. Ltd. (1)
1 Senoko South Road, Singapore, 758069, Singapore
Tel.: (65) 67526431

Emp.: 225
Epoxy Moulding Compound Mfr & Distr
N.A.I.C.S.: 325991

Sumitomo Plastics America, Inc. (1)
900 Lafayette St Ste 510, Santa Clara, CA 95050
Tel.: (408) 243-8402
Phenolic Resins Mfr
N.A.I.C.S.: 325211

Tsutsunaka Kosan Co., Ltd. (1)
2-22 Ishikawa-cho, Kashiwara, 582-0029, Japan
Tel.: (81) 729773851
Plastics Material & Resin Mfr
N.A.I.C.S.: 325211

Vaupell China (Dongguan) Co., Ltd. (1)
No 2 Qiao Lin Road, Ling Tou Industrial District Qiao Tou Town, Dongguan, China
Tel.: (86) 76983343022
Plastics Material & Resin Mfr
N.A.I.C.S.: 325211

Vaupell Holdings, Inc (1)
1144 N W 53rd, Seattle, WA 98107
Tel.: (206) 784-9050
Web Site: http://www.vaupell.com
Sales Range: $125-149.9 Million
Emp.: 1,000
Plastic Components & Assemblies Mfr
N.A.I.C.S.: 326199

Subsidiary (Domestic):

Vaupell Inc. (2)
1144 NW 53rd, Seattle, WA 98107
Tel.: (206) 784-9050
Web Site: http://www.vaupell.com
Sales Range: $10-24.9 Million
Emp.: 400
Plastic Mfr
N.A.I.C.S.: 326199
Joe Jahn *(CEO)*

Subsidiary (Domestic):

Russell Plastics Technology Company, Inc. (3)
521 W Hoffman Ave, Lindenhurst, NY 11757
Tel.: (631) 226-3700
Web Site: http://www.vaupell.com
Sales Range: $10-24.9 Million
Emp.: 115
Plastics Product Mfr
N.A.I.C.S.: 326199

Division (Non-US):

Vaupell Inc. - Vaupell China Molding & Tooling Division (3)
Building B32 Tantou Xibu Industrial Park, Songgang Town, Shenzhen, 518105, Guangdong, China
Tel.: (86) 755 29710863
Aircraft Part Mfr
N.A.I.C.S.: 336413
Sumit Nandedkar *(Gen Mgr)*

Division (Domestic):

Vaupell Inc. - Vaupell Midwest Molding & Tooling Division (3)
485 Florence Rd, Constantine, MI 49042
Tel.: (269) 435-8414
Thermoplastic & Composite Product Mfr
N.A.I.C.S.: 326199
Ted Duggan *(Gen Mgr)*

Vaupell Inc. - Vaupell NW Molding & Tooling Division (3)
1144 NW 53rd St, Seattle, WA 98107
Tel.: (206) 784-9050
Web Site: http://www.vaupell.com
Emp.: 360
Aircraft Part Mfr
N.A.I.C.S.: 336413

Vaupell Inc. - Vaupell Northeast Molding & Tooling Division (3)
101 HP Almgren Dr, Agawam, MA 01001
Tel.: (413) 233-3700
Aviation Aftermarket Part Distr
N.A.I.C.S.: 423860
Steve Ettelson *(VP-Medical & Comml)*

Vaupell Inc. - Vaupell Rapid Solutions Division (3)

SUMITOMO BAKELITE CO., LTD.

Sumitomo Bakelite Co., Ltd.—(Continued)
20 Executive Dr, Hudson, NH 03051
Tel.: (603) 577-9970
Aviation Aftermarket Part Distr
N.A.I.C.S.: 336413

Vaupell Industrial Plastics, Inc. (1)
11323 Commando Rd W, Everett, WA 98204
Tel.: (425) 610-2300
Web Site: https://vaupell.com
Emp.: 122
Pneumatic Tube Mfr
N.A.I.C.S.: 333922

Vaupell Molding & Tooling, Inc. (1)
101 Hp Almgren Dr, Agawam, MA 01001
Tel.: (413) 233-3700
Emp.: 142
Medical Device Parts Mfr
N.A.I.C.S.: 339112

Vyncolit N.V. (1)
Wiedauwkaai 6, 9000, Gent, Belgium (100%)
Tel.: (32) 92950100
Web Site: http://www.vyncolit.com
Sales Range: $25-49.9 Million
Emp.: 150
Phenolic Resins Mfr
N.A.I.C.S.: 325211

Subsidiary (US):

Sumitomo Bakelite North America Inc (2)
46820 Magellan Dr Ste C, Novi, MI 48377
Tel.: (248) 313-7000
Web Site: http://www.sbna-inc.com
Sales Range: $50-74.9 Million
Emp.: 135
Phenolic Resins Mfr
N.A.I.C.S.: 325211

Yamaroku Kasei Industry Co., Ltd. (1)
19-10 Katayama-cho, Kashiwara, 582-0020, Japan
Tel.: (81) 729773321
Plastics Material & Resin Mfr
N.A.I.C.S.: 325211

SUMITOMO CHEMICAL COMPANY, LIMITED
Tokyo Nihombashi Tower 2-7-1 Nihonbashi, Chuo-ku, Tokyo, 103-6020, Japan
Tel.: (81) 352010215 JP
Web Site: https://www.sumitomo-chem.co.jp
Year Founded: 1913
4005—(TKS)
Rev.: $16,173,962,730
Assets: $26,009,146,980
Liabilities: $18,312,687,720
Net Worth: $7,696,459,260
Earnings: ($2,061,249,180)
Emp.: 32,161
Fiscal Year-end: 03/31/24
Chemical Products Mfr
N.A.I.C.S.: 325998
Masakazu Tokura (Chm)

Subsidiaries:

Asahi Chemical Co., Ltd. (1)
2-10-23 Kyomachibori, Nishi-ku, Osaka, 550-0003, Japan (100%)
Tel.: (81) 664484051
Web Site: http://www.asachemi.co.jp
Sales Range: $50-74.9 Million
Emp.: 90
Inorganic Chemicals Mfr & Sales
N.A.I.C.S.: 325180
Jun Sakurai (Pres)

Bara Chemical Co., Ltd (1)
225 Moo 4 Soi Sukhumvit 2 C Sukhumvit Km 34 Rd Phraeksa, Muang, Samut Prakan, 10280, Thailand
Tel.: (66) 232316336
Synthetic Resin Mfr
N.A.I.C.S.: 325211

Career Support Co., Ltd. (1)
3-12-2 Nihombashikayabacho Dai17arai Bldg Ask Bldg 9f, Chuo-Ku, Tokyo, 103-0025, Japan
Tel.: (81) 3 5614 2285
Temporary Staffing Services
N.A.I.C.S.: 561320

Ceratec Co., Ltd. (1)
1-10-1 Kikumotocho, Niihama, 792-0801, Ehime, Japan
Tel.: (81) 897 33 8541
Metal Products Mfr
N.A.I.C.S.: 332999

Chiba General Service Co., Ltd. (1)
5-1 Anesakikaigan, Ichihara, 299-0107, Chiba, Japan
Tel.: (81) 436 61 2563
Web Site: http://www.cgs-chiba.co.jp
Waste Water Treatment Services
N.A.I.C.S.: 221310
Ryuichi Hirayama (Pres)

Dalian Sumika Chemphy Chemical Co., Ltd. (1)
488 Dongbei Street Haiqingdao Development Zone, Dalian, Liaoning, China
Tel.: (86) 41187516068
Emp.: 50
Crop Protection Chemical Intermediates Mfr
N.A.I.C.S.: 325320

Dalian Sumika Jingang Chemicals Co., Ltd. (1)
No 77 Economic Technology Development Zone, Dalian, 116600, Liaoning, China
Tel.: (86) 41187511015
Emp.: 120
Chemical Products Mfr
N.A.I.C.S.: 325998
Kzuro Kato (Mgr)

Dongwoo Fine-Chem Co., Ltd. (1)
8F City Air Tower 159-9 Samsung-dong, Kangnam-gu, Seoul, 135 973, Korea (South) (100%)
Tel.: (82) 262501100
Web Site: http://www.dwchem.co.kr
Sales Range: $1-4.9 Billion
Emp.: 2,655
Mfr & Sales of Fine Chemicals, Optical Functional Films & Color Filter
N.A.I.C.S.: 325180
Sang Yoon Kim (Mng Dir)

EGS Co., Ltd. (1)
3-1-39 Shindencho Sobiraki Bldg 1f, Niihama, 792-0003, Ehime, Japan
Tel.: (81) 897 37 1233
Civil Engineering Services
N.A.I.C.S.: 237990

Japan-Singapore Petrochemicals Co., Ltd (1)
2-27-1 Shinkawa Tokyo Sumitomo Twin Bldg Higaikan, Chuo-Ku, Tokyo, 104-0033, Japan
Tel.: (81) 3 5543 5867
Petrochemical Mfr
N.A.I.C.S.: 325110

Jilin Dongcheng Sumika Polymer Compounds Co., Ltd. (1)
Jingkai Street, Gongzhuling, Jilin, China
Tel.: (86) 4346597772
Polypropylene Compound Mfr
N.A.I.C.S.: 325211

Keiyo Ethylene Co., Ltd. (1)
1-1 Irifune 2-chome, Chuo-ku, Tokyo, 104-0042, Japan
Tel.: (81) 335529373
Petrochemical Products Mfr
N.A.I.C.S.: 325110

Koei Chemical Co., Ltd. (1)
1-8 Nihonbashi Koamicho, Chuo-ku, Tokyo, 103-0016, Japan (55.7%)
Tel.: (81) 368379300
Web Site: https://www.koeichem.com
Sales Range: $150-199.9 Million
Emp.: 397
Mfr of Chemicals
N.A.I.C.S.: 325998
Shigenori Tsuda (Pres)

LG Mma Corp. (1)
23F LG Seoulstation Bldg 98 Huam-ro, Jung-gu, Seoul, 04637, Korea (South)
Tel.: (82) 269303800
Web Site: http://www.lgmma.com
Petrochemical Products Mfr
N.A.I.C.S.: 325110
Park Jong-il (CEO)

LX MMA Corp. (1)
98 Huam-ro, Jung-gu, Seoul, 04637, Korea (South)
Tel.: (82) 269303800
Petrochemical Products Mfr
N.A.I.C.S.: 325110

Mycorrhizal Applications, LLC (1)
710 NW E St, Grants Pass, OR 97526
Tel.: (541) 476-3985
Web Site: http://www.mycorrhizae.com
Micro Organism Crop Enhancement Product Mfr
N.A.I.C.S.: 325320
Blair Busenbark (Acct Mgr-Sls-Western States)

NOC Asia Limited (1)
45/F The Lee Gardens 33 Hysan Avenue Causeway Bay, Hong Kong, China (Hong Kong)
Tel.: (852) 3180 7707
Propylene Oxide Distr
N.A.I.C.S.: 424690

Nihon Ecoagro Co., Ltd (1)
10-11 Nihombashikodemmacho Fukawa Bldg 3fc, Chuo-ku, Tokyo, 103-0001, Japan
Tel.: (81) 3 3523 8280
Web Site: http://www.nihon-ecoagro.co.jp
Farm Supplies Distr
N.A.I.C.S.: 424910

Nihon Medi-Physics Co., Ltd. (1)
3-4-10 Shinsuna, Koto-ku, Tokyo, 136-0075, Japan
Tel.: (81) 35 634 7006
Web Site: https://www.nmp.co.jp
Emp.: 818
Pharmaceuticals Product Mfr
N.A.I.C.S.: 325412
Nobuhiko Tamura (Pres)

Nihon Singapore Polyolefin Co., Ltd (1)
2-27-1 Shinkawa Tokyo Sumitomo Twin Bldg, Chuo-Ku, Tokyo, 104-0033, Japan
Tel.: (81) 3 5543 5319
Chemical Products Mfr
N.A.I.C.S.: 325998

Niihama Coal Center Co., Ltd. (1)
1-10-1 Kikumotocho, Niihama, 792-0801, Ehime, Japan
Tel.: (81) 897 32 8320
Coal Warehousing Services
N.A.I.C.S.: 493110

Nippon A&L, Inc. (1)
Sumitomo Bldg 5-33 Kitahama 4-Chome, Chuo-ku, Osaka, 541-8550, Japan
Tel.: (81) 662203656
Web Site: https://www.n-al.co.jp
Sales Range: $125-149.9 Million
Emp.: 350
Resins & Latexes Mfr & Sales; Owned 85% by Sumitomo Chemical Company, Ltd. & 15% by Mitsui Chemicals, Inc.
N.A.I.C.S.: 325211
Toshiro Kojima (Chm)

Nippon Thermo Co., Ltd. (1)
3-2-1 Takata-nishi, Kohoku-ku, Yokohama, 223-0066, Japan
Tel.: (81) 45 592 3131
Web Site: https://www.nippon-thermo.co.jp
Emp.: 100
Electronic Components Mfr
N.A.I.C.S.: 334419
Takashi Nozawa (Pres & Owner)

Oita General Service Co., Ltd. (1)
2200 Tsurusaki, Oita, 870-0106, Japan
Tel.: (81) 975231183
Web Site: http://www.ogs-oita.co.jp
Emp.: 191
Precision Cleaning Services
N.A.I.C.S.: 561720

Osaka General Service Co., Ltd. (1)
3-1-98 Kasugadenaka, Konohana-Ku, Osaka, 554-0022, Japan
Tel.: (81) 6 6466 5035
Landscaping Services
N.A.I.C.S.: 561730

Petrochemical Corporation of Singapore (Pte.) Ltd. (1)
100 Ayer Merbau Road, Singapore, 628277, Singapore
Tel.: (65) 68672000
Web Site: http://www.pcs.com.sg
Emp.: 390
Petrochemical Products Mfr
N.A.I.C.S.: 325110

Philagro South Africa (Pty) Ltd. (1)
1st Floor The Corner Office 410 Lynnwood Road, Straat Lynnwood, Pretoria, 0081, South Africa
Tel.: (27) 12 348 8808
Web Site: http://www.philagro.co.za
Sales Range: $25-49.9 Million
Emp.: 13
Crop Protection Chemical Mfr & Distr
N.A.I.C.S.: 325320
Henk van der Westhuizen (Mng Dir)

S-RACMO Co., Ltd. (1)
i33-94 Enoki-cho, Suita, 564-0053, Osakai, Japan
Tel.: (81) 663370180
Web Site: https://www.s-racmo.co.jp
Pharmaceuticals Product Mfr
N.A.I.C.S.: 325412

SC Environmental Science Co., Ltd. (1)
2-8 Doshomachi 2-Chome, Chuo-Ku, Osaka, 541-0045, Japan
Tel.: (81) 662237530
Web Site: https://www.sumika-env-sci.jp
Environmental Consulting Services
N.A.I.C.S.: 541620

SanTerra Co., Ltd. (1)
4th floor Takagi Building Kayabacho 1-8 Nihonbashi Koamicho, Chuo-ku, Tokyo, 103-0016, Japan
Tel.: (81) 3 6837 9030
Web Site: http://www.santerra.jp
Agricultural Films Mfr & Distr
N.A.I.C.S.: 326130
Shigeru Oya (Pres)

Sanritz Corporation (1)
40-1 Shimouwano Nyuzen-cho, Shimoniikawa-gun, Toyama, 939-0641, Japan
Tel.: (81) 765747220
Web Site: http://www.sanritz-corp.co.jp
Polarizing Film Mfr
N.A.I.C.S.: 325992

Sciocs Company Limited (1)
880 Isagozawa-cho, Hitachi, 319-1418, Ibaraki-ken, Japan
Tel.: (81) 29 442 5027
Web Site: https://www.sciocs.com
Semiconductor Material Mfr
N.A.I.C.S.: 334413
Toshiya Saito (Pres)

Shanghai Lifetech Household Products Co., Ltd. (1)
2006 Jiangchuan Road, Minhang District, Shanghai, 201111, China
Tel.: (86) 21 5159 3281
Household Insecticide Mfr & Distr
N.A.I.C.S.: 325320

Shinto Paint Co., Ltd. (1)
10-73 6-Chome Minamitsukaguchi-cho, Amagasaki, 661-8511, Hyogo, Japan (45.1%)
Tel.: (81) 664263355
Web Site: http://www.shintopaint.co.jp
Sales Range: $125-149.9 Million
Emp.: 455
Mfr & Sales of Paints
N.A.I.C.S.: 325510
Satoshi Takazawa (Pres)

Sumika Acryl Co., Ltd (1)
3rd Floor Kayabacho Takagi Building 1-8 Nihonbashi Koamicho, Chuo-ku, Tokyo, 103-0016, Japan
Tel.: (81) 36 837 9090
Web Site: https://www.sumika-acryl.co.jp
Sales Range: $25-49.9 Million
Emp.: 13
Acrylic Sheet Distr
N.A.I.C.S.: 424610
Akinobu Yoshino (Pres)

Sumika Agro Manufacturing Co., Ltd. (1)
1-3 Higashikaigandori, Kudamatsu, 744-

AND PRIVATE COMPANIES — SUMITOMO CHEMICAL COMPANY, LIMITED

0002, Yamaguchi Prefecture, Japan
Tel.: (81) 833418100
Web Site: http://www.sumika-agro.co.jp
Pesticide & Horticultural Product Mfr
N.A.I.C.S.: 325320

Sumika Agrotech Co., Ltd. (1)
Sumika Fudosan Yokobori Bldg 4-6-17 Koraibashi, Chuo-ku, Osaka, 541-0043, Japan **(100%)**
Tel.: (81) 662041245
Web Site: http://www.sumika-agrotech.com
Sales Range: $75-99.9 Million
Emp.: 200
Mfr & Sales of Agricultural & Horticultural Materials
N.A.I.C.S.: 325320

Sumika Alchem Co., Ltd. (1)
Sumika Fudosan Yokobori Building 6-17 Koraibashi 4-chome, Chuo-ku, Osaka, 541-0043, Japan
Tel.: (81) 66 204 1291
Web Site: https://www.sumika-alchem.co.jp
Emp.: 17
Synthetic Resin Product Mfr & Distr
N.A.I.C.S.: 325211
Toshiharu Yamabayashi (Pres)

Sumika Assembly Techno Co., Ltd. (1)
1-1 Oecho, Niihama, 792-0015, Ehime Prefecture, Japan
Tel.: (81) 897371220
Web Site: http://www.sat-sumika.jp
Polarizing Film Mfr
N.A.I.C.S.: 325992

Sumika Chemical Analysis Service, Ltd. (1)
Sumika Fudosan Yokobori Building 4F 6-17 Koraibashi 4-chome, Chuo-ku, Osaka, 541-0043, Japan
Tel.: (81) 66 202 1810
Web Site: https://www.scas.co.jp
Emp.: 1,128
Pharmaceutical Products Research & Development Services
N.A.I.C.S.: 541715
Osamu Maruyama (Pres)

Sumika Chemtex Co., Ltd (1)
1-98 Kasugade-Naka 3-Chome, Konohana-Ku, Osaka, 554-8558, Japan
Tel.: (81) 664665317
Web Site: http://www.chemtex.co.jp
Sales Range: $25-49.9 Million
Emp.: 60
Synthetic Resin Mfr
N.A.I.C.S.: 325211
Hiroyuki Yokoyama (Co-Pres)

Sumika Color Co., Ltd. (1)
4-6-17 Koraibashi 6th floor Sumika Real Estate Yokobori Building, Chuo-ku, Osaka, 541-0043, Japan **(87.8%)**
Tel.: (81) 662054300
Web Site: http://www.sumikacolor.co.jp
Sales Range: $125-149.9 Million
Mfr & Sales of Organic Pigments & Color Compounds
N.A.I.C.S.: 325130

Sumika Dx Accent Co., Ltd. (1)
2-27-1 Shinkawa, Chuo-ku, Tokyo, Japan
Tel.: (81) 355435102
Chemical & Pharmaceutical Products Mfr
N.A.I.C.S.: 325110

Sumika Electronic Materials (Changzhou) Co., Ltd. (1)
No 1 Gangqu Middle Road, Xinbei District, Changzhou, Jiangsu, China
Tel.: (86) 51988811218
Chemical Products Mfr
N.A.I.C.S.: 325998

Sumika Electronic Materials (Chengdu) Co., Ltd. (1)
No 171 Tianba West street, Pidu District, Chengdu, Sichuan, China
Tel.: (86) 2863198889
Sensor Module Mfr
N.A.I.C.S.: 334419

Sumika Electronic Materials (Chongqing) Co., Ltd. (1)
No 4 Shuishan Road, Beibei District, Chongqing, China
Tel.: (86) 2361309530
Chemical Products Mfr
N.A.I.C.S.: 325998

Sumika Electronic Materials (Hefei) Co., Ltd. (1)
South of Xinbianhe Road, Industrial Park Xinzhan District, Hefei, 230011, China
Tel.: (86) 5515190908
Chemical Products Mfr
N.A.I.C.S.: 325998

Sumika Electronic Materials (Shanghai) Co., Ltd. (1)
1802-03 No 398 Jiangsu Road, Changning District, Shanghai, 200050, China
Tel.: (86) 21 5046 2296
Web Site: http://www.sumika.com.cn
Mfr & Sales of Optical Functional Films
N.A.I.C.S.: 334419

Sumika Electronic Materials (Shenzhen) Co., Ltd. (1)
29H Tower A of World Finance Centre No 4003 Shennan Road East, Luohu, Shenzhen, 518001, China
Tel.: (86) 755 2598 1598
Chemical Product Whslr
N.A.I.C.S.: 424690

Sumika Electronic Materials (Wuxi) Co., Ltd. (1)
No 61 Xinmei Road, Wuxi, 214028, China
Tel.: (86) 51085322688
Heat Resistant Splitter Mfr
N.A.I.C.S.: 332410

Sumika Electronic Materials (Xi'An) Co., Ltd. (1)
No 853 Baosan Road Integrated Free Trade Zone, High-tech Development District, Xi'an, Shaanxi, China
Tel.: (86) 2989384836
Chemical Products Mfr
N.A.I.C.S.: 325998

Sumika Electronic Materials Poland Sp. zo.o. (1)
Ostaszewo 57i, 87-148, Lysomice, Poland
Tel.: (48) 56 621 42 00
Web Site: http://www.sumikapoland.pl
Liquid Crystal Display Panel Mfr
N.A.I.C.S.: 334419

Sumika Enviro-Science Co., Ltd (1)
4-3-4 Kamikoshien, Nishinomiya, 663-8114, Hyogo, Japan
Tel.: (81) 798 38 2330
Web Site: http://www.sumika-env-sci.jp
Household Insecticides Mfr
N.A.I.C.S.: 325320

Sumika Farm Ibaraki Co., Ltd. (1)
2-27-1 Sumitomo Twin Building East Wing Shinkawa, Chuo-ku, Tokyo, 104-8260, Japan
Tel.: (81) 355435214
Leafy Vegetable Farming Services
N.A.I.C.S.: 111219

Sumika Farm Mie Co., Ltd. (1)
1619-1 Isobe-cho, Shima-shi, Mie, 517-0214, Japan
Tel.: (81) 355435214
Vegetable Farming Services
N.A.I.C.S.: 111219

Sumika Farm Oita Co., Ltd. (1)
88 Miyano Miemachi, Bungo-ono, 879-7101, Oita Prefecture, Japan
Tel.: (81) 974228330
Vegetable Farming Services
N.A.I.C.S.: 111219

Sumika Finance Co., Ltd (1)
2-27-1 Shinkawa Tokyo Sumitomo Twin Bldg Higashi Kan 19f, Chuo-Ku, Tokyo, 104-0033, Japan
Tel.: (81) 3 5543 5163
Financial Management Services
N.A.I.C.S.: 523999

Sumika Green Co., Ltd. (1)
4-5-4 Hacchobori, Chuo-ku, Tokyo, 104-0032, Japan
Tel.: (81) 3 3523 8070
Web Site: http://www.sumika-green.jp
Crop Protection Chemical Mfr & Distr
N.A.I.C.S.: 325320

Sumika High-purity Gas Company (1)
5-1 Soubiraki-cho, Niihama, 792-0001, Ehime, Japan
Tel.: (81) 897 37 1716
Oxygen & Nitrogen Mfr
N.A.I.C.S.: 325120

Sumika Huabei Electronic Materials (Beijing) Co., Ltd. (1)
No 21 Kechuang 10th Street, Beijing Economic and Technological Development Zone, Beijing, 100176, China
Tel.: (86) 1080849328
Flat Panel Display Material Mfr
N.A.I.C.S.: 334419

Sumika Life Tech Co., Ltd. (1)
4-5-33 Kitahama Sumitomo Bldg 6f, Chuo-Ku, Osaka, 541-0041, Japan
Tel.: (81) 662203640
Sales Range: $25-49.9 Million
Emp.: 27
Household Insecticide Distr
N.A.I.C.S.: 325320

Sumika Logistics Co., Ltd. (1)
5th floor Kayabacho Takagi Building 1-8 Nihonbashi Koamicho, Chuo-ku, Tokyo, 103-0016, Chiba, Japan
Tel.: (81) 36 837 9450
Web Site: https://www.sumika-logi.co.jp
Emp.: 850
Logistics Consulting Servies
N.A.I.C.S.: 541614

Sumika Plastech Co., Ltd. (1)
1-8 Nihonbashikoamicho, Chuo-ku, Tokyo, 103-0016, Japan **(100%)**
Tel.: (81) 368379201
Web Site: http://www.sumikapla.co.jp
Sales Range: $25-49.9 Million
Emp.: 40
Mfr & Sales of Plastic Sheets & Films
N.A.I.C.S.: 322220
Ryuji Shibata (Pres)

Sumika Polycarbonate Limited (1)
Kayabacho-Takagi Bldg 1-8 Nihonbashi-Koamicho, Chuo-ku, Tokyo, 103-0016, Japan
Tel.: (81) 36 837 9220
Web Site: https://www.scpc.jp
Emp.: 130
Polycarbonate Resin Mfr.
N.A.I.C.S.: 325211
Yasunobu Ida (Exec VP)

Sumika Polymer Compounds Dalian Co., Ltd. (1)
No 133 Tieshan Zhong Road Dalian Development Area, Dalian, Liaoning, China
Tel.: (86) 41139253518
Polypropylene Compound Mfr
N.A.I.C.S.: 325211

Sumika Polymer Compounds Europe Ltd. (1)
28 New Lane, Havant, PO9 2NQ, Hampshire, United Kingdom
Tel.: (44) 2392486350
Web Site: http://www.sumikaeurope.com
Thermoplastic Compound Mfr
N.A.I.C.S.: 325211

Sumika Polymers North America LLC (1)
27555 Executive Dr Ste 380, Farmington Hills, MI 48331
Tel.: (248) 284-4797
Petrochemical Products Mfr
N.A.I.C.S.: 325110

Sumika Real Estate Co., Ltd (1)
4-6-17 Koraibashi Sumikafudosanyokohori Bldg, Chuo-ku, Osaka, 541-0043, Japan
Tel.: (81) 6 6220 3263
Real Estate Manangement Services
N.A.I.C.S.: 531390

Sumika Sekisui Film Co., Ltd. (1)
5-9 Akihabara Meiji Yasuda Seimei Akihabara Building 5F, Taito-ku, Tokyo, 110-0006, Japan
Tel.: (81) 352898668
Web Site: http://www.ss-film.co.jp
Polyolefin Film Product Mfr
N.A.I.C.S.: 326113

Sumika Styron Polycarbonate Limited (1)
Nakajima Building 8-8 Nihonbashi-Kabutocho, Chuo-ku, Tokyo, 103-0026, Japan **(50%)**
Tel.: (81) 356444750
Web Site: http://www.sspc.jp
Sales Range: $25-49.9 Million
Emp.: 120
Polycarbonate Resins Mfr & Sales; Owned 50 % by Trinseo S.A. & 50% by Sumitomo Chemical Company, Ltd.
N.A.I.C.S.: 325998
Shin-Ichi Nakano (VP)

Sumika Technical Information Service, Inc. (1)
6-17 Koraibashi 4-chome, Chuo-ku, Osaka, 541-0043, Japan
Tel.: (81) 662203001
Web Site: http://www.stis.co.jp
Sales Range: $25-49.9 Million
Emp.: 7
Research, Analysis & Information Services
N.A.I.C.S.: 541618

Sumika Technology Co., Ltd. (1)
32 Huan E Rd Sec 2, Shanhwa Chen, T'ainan, 74144, Taiwan
Tel.: (886) 65053456
Web Site: http://www.sumika.com.tw
Optical Functional Film Mfr
N.A.I.C.S.: 326113

Sumika Technoservice Corporation1989 (1)
4-2-1 Takatsukasa, Takarazuka, 665-0051, Hyogo, Japan
Tel.: (81) 797742120
Web Site: http://www.sc-sts.co.jp
Syntheses Research Services
N.A.I.C.S.: 541715

Sumika-Kakoushi Co., Ltd. (1)
4F Kayabacho Takagi Bldg 1-8 Nihonbashi-Koamicho, Chuo-ku, Tokyo, 103-0016, Japan **(100%)**
Tel.: (81) 368379052
Web Site: http://www.sumika-kakoushi.co.jp
Sales Range: $50-74.9 Million
Mfr & Sales of Paper
N.A.I.C.S.: 322220
Hiroyuki Shiraishi (Mgr-Sls Div & Mgr-Sls Div)

Sumipex (Thailand) Co., Ltd. (1)
526 M 4 Soi 9C Pattana3 Road Preakkasa Muang, Samut Prakan, 10280, Thailand
Tel.: (66) 2324009091
Web Site: http://www.sumipex.co.th
Emp.: 20
Cast Acrylic Sheet Mfr
N.A.I.C.S.: 326113

Sumipex TechSheet Co., Ltd. (1)
No 39 Chung Yang Road, Nanzih Dist, Kaohsiung, 81170, Taiwan
Tel.: (886) 7 365 8126
Web Site: https://www.sumipex.com
Sales Range: $50-74.9 Million
Cell Cast Acrylic Sheet Mfr & Distr
N.A.I.C.S.: 339999
Tsuyoshi Masuda (Pres)

Sumitomo Chemical Agro Seoul, Ltd. (1)
2nd Fl KTF Tower 890-20 Daechi-Dong, Gangnam-Gu, Seoul, 135-737, Korea (South)
Tel.: (82) 2 558 4814
Crop Protection Chemical Whslr
N.A.I.C.S.: 424690
Y. S. Lim (Gen Mgr)

Sumitomo Chemical America, Inc. (1)
150 E 42nd St Ste 701, New York, NY 10017-5688 **(100%)**
Tel.: (212) 572-8200
Web Site: http://www.sumitomochemicalamerica.com
Sales Range: $25-49.9 Million
Regional Managing Office; Chemicals Mfr & Distr
N.A.I.C.S.: 424690

Subsidiary (Domestic):

McLaughlin Gormley King Company (2)
8810 10th Ave N, Minneapolis, MN 55427 **(82.36%)**
Tel.: (763) 544-0341

SUMITOMO CHEMICAL COMPANY, LIMITED

Sumitomo Chemical Company, Limited—(Continued)
Web Site: http://www.mgk.com
Sales Range: $50-74.9 Million
Emp.: 60
Pesticide & Other Agricultural Chemicals Mfr & Distr
N.A.I.C.S.: 325320
Steven M. Gullickson *(Pres)*

Subsidiary (Domestic):

Valent BioSciences Corporation (3)
870 Technology Way, Libertyville, IL 60048-5350
Tel.: (847) 968-4700
Web Site: http://www.valentbiosciences.com
Agricultural Chemicals Developer, Mfr & Distr
N.A.I.C.S.: 325320
Ted Melnik *(COO & Exec VP)*

Subsidiary (Domestic):

FBSciences Holdings, Inc. (4)
153 North Main St Ste 100, Collierville, TN 38017
Tel.: (901) 221-1200
Web Site: https://fbsciences.com
Emp.: 100
Holding Company
N.A.I.C.S.: 551112

Subsidiary (Domestic):

Fbsciences Inc. (5)
153 N Main St Ste 100, Collierville, TN 38017
Tel.: (901) 221-1200
Web Site: http://www.fbsciences.com
Chemicals Mfr
N.A.I.C.S.: 325320
John Bradley *(VP-Tech Sls)*

Subsidiary (Domestic):

Sumika Polymer Compounds America, Inc. (2)
121 Hudson Industrial Dr, Griffin, GA 30224-4541
Tel.: (770) 227-6400
Sales Range: $25-49.9 Million
Emp.: 45
Polypropylene Compound Mfr & Distr
N.A.I.C.S.: 325211
Teruhiko Doi *(Pres)*

Sumitomo Chemical Advanced Technologies (2)
3832 E Watkins St, Phoenix, AZ 85034
Tel.: (602) 659-2500
Web Site: https://sumichem-at.com
Sales Range: $25-49.9 Million
Emp.: 25
Mfr & Sales of IT-Related Materials
N.A.I.C.S.: 334413

Sumitomo Pharma America Holdings, Inc. (2)
84 Waterford Dr, Marlborough, MA 01752
Tel.: (508) 481-6700
Web Site: http://www.ds-pharma.com
Sales Range: $50-74.9 Million
Emp.: 130
Holding Company; Pharmaceutical Products Mfr
N.A.I.C.S.: 551112

Valent U.S.A. Corporation (2)
1600 Riviera Ave Ste 200, Walnut Creek, CA 94596-8025 **(100%)**
Tel.: (925) 256-2700
Web Site: http://www.valent.com
Agricultural Chemicals Developer, Mfr & Distr
N.A.I.C.S.: 325320
John Pawlak *(Sr Mgr-Product Dev)*

Sumitomo Chemical Argentina S.A. (1)
Intecons Building Arias 3751 Piso 20, Caba, C1430CRG, Buenos Aires, Argentina
Tel.: (54) 1132200000
Web Site: https://www.sumitomochemical.com
Crop Protection Chemical Mfr & Distr
N.A.I.C.S.: 325320

Sumitomo Chemical Asia Pte. Ltd. (1)
3 Fraser Street 07-28 DUO Tower, Singapore, 189352, Singapore **(100%)**
Tel.: (65) 63035188
Web Site: http://www.sumitomo-chem.com.sg
Sales Range: $75-99.9 Million
Emp.: 448
Petrochemical Products Mfr & Sales
N.A.I.C.S.: 325110

Sumitomo Chemical Australia Pty. Ltd. (1)
Level 5 51 Rawson Street, Epping, 2121, NSW, Australia
Tel.: (61) 287529000
Web Site: http://www.sumitomo-chem.com.au
Sales Range: $25-49.9 Million
Emp.: 24
Crop Protection Chemical Mfr
N.A.I.C.S.: 325320
Doug Paton *(Mgr-R&D-Agrosolutions)*

Sumitomo Chemical Colombia S.A.S. (1)
Calle 35 Norte 6 A Bis 100 Centro Empresarial Carvajal, Santa Monica, 760046, Cali, Colombia
Tel.: (57) 6023308000
Chemical Products Mfr
N.A.I.C.S.: 325998

Sumitomo Chemical Company, Ltd. - Chiba Works (1)
5-1 Anesaki-Kaigan, Ichihara, 299-0195, Chiba, Japan
Tel.: (81) 436 61 1313
Chemical Products Mfr
N.A.I.C.S.: 325998

Sumitomo Chemical Company, Ltd. - Ehime Works (1)
5-I Sobiraki-cho, Niihama, 792-8521, Ehime, Japan
Tel.: (81) 897 37 1711
Web Site: http://www.sumitomo-chem.co.jp
Crop Protection Chemical Mfr
N.A.I.C.S.: 325320

Sumitomo Chemical Company, Ltd. - Gifu Plant (1)
3750 Jyuhachicho Makiaza Anpachi-cho, Gifu, 503-0125, Japan
Tel.: (81) 584 64 2099
Emp.: 160
Pharmaceutical Chemicals Mfr
N.A.I.C.S.: 325998

Sumitomo Chemical Company, Ltd. - Misawa Works (1)
Aza-Sabishirotai, Oaza-Misawa, Misawa, 033-0022, Aomori, Japan
Tel.: (81) 176 54 2111
Web Site: http://www.sumitomo-chem.co.jp
Household Insecticides Mfr
N.A.I.C.S.: 325320

Sumitomo Chemical Company, Ltd. - Ohe Works (1)
1-1 Ohe-cho, Niihama, 792-0015, Ehime, Japan
Tel.: (81) 897 65 1800
Polarizing Film Mfr
N.A.I.C.S.: 326113

Sumitomo Chemical Company, Ltd. - Oita Works (1)
2200 Tsurusaki, Oita, 870-0106, Japan
Tel.: (81) 97 523 1111
Agricultural Chemical Mfr
N.A.I.C.S.: 325320

Sumitomo Chemical Company, Ltd. - Okayama Plant (1)
4-1 Kojimatanokuchi 6-chome, Kurashiki, 711-0903, Okayama, Japan
Tel.: (81) 86 477 7771
Web Site: http://www.sumitomo-chem.co.jp
Sales Range: $50-74.9 Million
Chemical Products Mfr
N.A.I.C.S.: 325998

Sumitomo Chemical Company, Ltd. - Osaka Works (1)
1-98 Kasugade-naka 3-chome, Konohana-ku, Osaka, 554-8558, Japan
Tel.: (81) 6 6466 5022
Emp.: 800
Crop Protection Chemical Mfr

N.A.I.C.S.: 325320
Kazuhumi Yokugawa *(Gen Mgr)*

Sumitomo Chemical Engineering Co., Ltd. (1)
Building 7-1 Nakase 1-chome, Mihama-ku, Chiba, 261-8568, Japan **(100%)**
Tel.: (81) 432990200
Web Site: http://www.scec.co.jp
Sales Range: $50-74.9 Million
Emp.: 170
Chemical Engineering Services & Construction of Chemical Plants
N.A.I.C.S.: 541330

Sumitomo Chemical Enviro-Agro Asia Pacific Sdn. Bhd. (1)
62A Persiaran Bunga Senawang Industrial Park Tanjung 1, Seremban, 70400, Malaysia
Tel.: (60) 66793711
Sales Range: $25-49.9 Million
Emp.: 30
Crop Protection Chemical Mfr
N.A.I.C.S.: 325320

Sumitomo Chemical Europe S.A./N.V. (1)
Woluwelaan 57, 1830, Machelen, Belgium **(100%)**
Tel.: (32) 22510650
Web Site: http://www.sumitomochemicaleurope.eu
Sales Range: $100-124.9 Million
Sales & Marketing of Chemical Products
N.A.I.C.S.: 424690

Subsidiary (Non-US):

Kenogard S.A. (2)
Diputacion 279, 08007, Barcelona, Catalonia, Spain
Tel.: (34) 934881270
Web Site: http://www.kenogard.es
Sales Range: $25-49.9 Million
Emp.: 45
Crop Protection Chemical Mfr & Distr
N.A.I.C.S.: 325320

Sumitomo Chemical (U.K.) PLC (2)
Hythe House 200 Shepherds Bush Road, London, W6 7NL, United Kingdom **(100%)**
Tel.: (44) 2074713730
Web Site: http://www.sumitomo-chemical.co.uk
Sales Range: $25-49.9 Million
Financing & Marketing of Chemicals
N.A.I.C.S.: 424690

Subsidiary (Domestic):

CDT Holdings Ltd. (3)
Building 2020 Cambourne Business Park, Caxton, CB23 6DW, Cambridgeshire, United Kingdom
Tel.: (44) 1954 713600
Web Site: http://www.cdtltd.co.uk
Sales Range: $25-49.9 Million
Emp.: 45
Electronic Display Mfr
N.A.I.C.S.: 334419
Jim Veninger *(Gen Mgr)*

Cambridge Display Technology Ltd. (3)
Building 2020, Cambourne Business Park, Cambridge, CB23 6DW, Cambridgeshire, United Kingdom
Tel.: (44) 1954713600
Web Site: http://www.cdtltd.co.uk
Sales Range: $1-9.9 Million
Emp.: 114
Display Technology & Diodes Developer
N.A.I.C.S.: 334419
David Fyfe *(CEO)*

Subsidiary (Non-US):

Sumitomo Chemical Agro Europe S.A.S. (2)
Parc d affaires de Crecy 10A rue de la Voie Lactee, 69370, Saint-Didier-au-Mont-d'Or, France **(100%)**
Tel.: (33) 4 7864 3260
Web Site: http://www.sumitomo-chem-agro.com
Sales Range: $50-74.9 Million
Development & Sls of Crop Protection Chemicals
N.A.I.C.S.: 325320

Sho Arimoto *(Dir-Bus Plng)*

Subsidiary (Domestic):

Philagro France S.A.S. (3)
Parc d Affaires de Crecy 10A rue de la Voie Lactee, 69370, Saint-Didier-au-Mont-d'Or, France
Tel.: (33) 478643264
Web Site: http://www.philagro.fr
Sales Range: $25-49.9 Million
Emp.: 76
Agrochemical Mfr
N.A.I.C.S.: 325320
Denis Troalen *(Mng Dir & Dir-Publication)*

Subsidiary (Non-US):

Sumitomo Chemical Italia S.r.l. (2)
Via Caldera 21, 20153, Milan, Italy
Tel.: (39) 0 2 45280 1
Web Site: http://www.sumitomo-chem.it
Sales Range: $25-49.9 Million
Crop Protection Chemicals Distr
N.A.I.C.S.: 424690

Sumitomo Chemical Nederland B.V. (2)
Officia I De Boelelaan 7, 1083 HJ, Amsterdam, Netherlands **(100%)**
Financing
N.A.I.C.S.: 522299

Sumitomo Chemical Garden Products Co., Ltd. (1)
5F Kayabacho Takagi Building 1-8 Nihonbashi Koamicho, Chuo-ku, Tokyo, 103-0016, Japan
Tel.: (81) 336631128
Web Site: http://www.sc-engei.co.jp
Home Gardening Fertilizer Mfr
N.A.I.C.S.: 325312

Sumitomo Chemical India Private Limited (1)
6th Floor Moti Mahal 195 J Tata Rd, Samrat Hotel Church Gate, Mumbai, 400020, Maharashtra, India
Tel.: (91) 2222892610
Sales Range: $25-49.9 Million
Emp.: 42
Crop Protection Chemical Mfr & Distr
N.A.I.C.S.: 325320
Akira Harada *(Mng Dir)*

Subsidiary (Domestic):

Excel Crop Care Limited (2)
13/14 Aradhana Industrial Development Corporation, Near Virwani Industrial Estate Goregaon East, Mumbai, 400063, India
Tel.: (91) 2242522200
Web Site: http://www.excelcropcare.com
Agrochemical Product Mfr
N.A.I.C.S.: 325320
Mukul G. Asher *(Chm)*

Sumitomo Chemical Intellectual Property Service, Ltd. (1)
4-5-33 Kitahama, Chuo-ku, Osaka, 541-8550, Japan
Tel.: (81) 6 6220 3410
Patent Translation & Research Services
N.A.I.C.S.: 541199

Sumitomo Chemical Philippines, Inc. (1)
Unit 4-C 4th Floor MAPFRE Insular Corporate Center 1220 Acacia Avenue, Madrigal Business Park Ayala Alabang, Muntinlupa, 1770, Philippines
Tel.: (63) 28214768
Chemical Products Mfr
N.A.I.C.S.: 325998

Sumitomo Chemical Shanghai Co., Ltd. (1)
Room S2402-2404 Shanghai Stock Exchange Building, No 528 South Pudong Road, Shanghai, 200120, China
Tel.: (86) 2168817700
Web Site: http://www.sumitomochemical-china.com.cn
Crop Protection Chemical Mfr & Distr
N.A.I.C.S.: 325320

Sumitomo Chemical Singapore Pte. Ltd. (1)
3 Fraser Street 07-28 DUO Tower, Gateway

West, Singapore, 189352, Singapore **(100%)**
Tel.: (65) 63035188
Web Site: http://www.sumitomo-chem.com.sg
Sales Range: $75-99.9 Million
Chemicals Mfr & Sales
N.A.I.C.S.: 424690

Sumitomo Chemical System Service Co., Ltd. (1)
Takagi Building Kayabacho 1-8 Koamicho, Nihonbashi Chuo-ku, Tokyo, 103-0016, Japan
Tel.: (81) 368379100
Web Site: http://www.sc-sss.co.jp
IT Professional Services
N.A.I.C.S.: 541512

Sumitomo Chemical Taiwan Co., Ltd. (1)
13 F 4 206 Nanking E Rd Sec 2, Taipei, 104, Taiwan **(100%)**
Tel.: (886) 225068180
Sales Range: $25-49.9 Million
Emp.: 3
Chemical Products Mfr
N.A.I.C.S.: 325998

Sumitomo Chemical Vietnam Co., Ltd. (1)
Floor 5 No 40 Pham Ngoc Thach Street, Ward 6 District 3, Ho Chi Minh City, Vietnam
Tel.: (84) 2838220127
Web Site: http://www.scvcl-chem.com.vn
Sales Range: $50-74.9 Million
Crop Protection Chemicals Whslr
N.A.I.C.S.: 424910

Sumitomo Dainippon Pharma Oncology, Inc. (1)
640 Memorial Dr, Cambridge, MA 02139
Tel.: (617) 674-6800
Web Site: http://www.sdponcology.com
Pharmaceutical Research & Development Services
N.A.I.C.S.: 541714
Patricia S. Andrews *(CEO & Global Head-Oncology)*

Sumitomo Joint Electric Power Co., Ltd. (1)
16-5 Isoura-cho, Niihama, 792-8520, Ehime, Japan
Tel.: (81) 897 37 2142
Web Site: http://www.sumikyo.co.jp
Emp.: 400
Electric Power Distr
N.A.I.C.S.: 221122

Joint Venture (Domestic):

Kawasaki Biomass Power Generation Co., Ltd. (2)
12-6 Ogimachi, Kawasaki, 2100867, Japan **(53%)**
Tel.: (81) 897372142
Emp.: 50
Eletric Power Generation Services
N.A.I.C.S.: 221117

Sumitomo Pharma (China) Co., Ltd. (1)
7th Floor Tower A China Overseas International Center Lane 838, South Huangpi Road Huangpu District, Shanghai, China
Tel.: (86) 2123065600
Chemical & Pharmaceutical Products Mfr
N.A.I.C.S.: 325110

Sumitomo Pharma Co., Ltd. (1)
6-8 Doshomachi 2-chome, Chuo-ku, Osaka, 541-0045, Japan **(50.22%)**
Tel.: (81) 662035321
Web Site: https://www.sumitomo-pharma.com
Rev.: $2,079,228,380
Assets: $5,998,614,660
Liabilities: $4,966,555,700
Net Worth: $1,032,058,960
Earnings: ($2,081,945,090)
Emp.: 4,767
Fiscal Year-end: 03/31/2024
Pharmaceuticals Preparation & Research & Development
N.A.I.C.S.: 325412
Antony Loebel *(Exec Officer)*

Subsidiary (Domestic):

DS Pharma Animal Health Co., Ltd. (2)
1-5-51 Ebie Fukushima-ku, Osaka City, Osaka, Japan
Tel.: (81) 664548823
Veterinary Medicine Mfr
N.A.I.C.S.: 541940

DS Pharma Biomedical Co., Ltd. (2)
33-94 Enoki-Cho, Suita, Osaka, 564-0053, Japan
Tel.: (81) 663375940
Web Site: http://www.dspbio.co.jp
Emp.: 90
In-Vitro Diagnostics & Research Materials Research & Development
N.A.I.C.S.: 325413
Yukio Takano *(Pres)*

DSP Distribution Service Co., Ltd. (2)
1-5-51 Ebie Fukushima-ku, Osaka, Japan
Tel.: (81) 6 6453 3179
Pharmaceuticals Product Mfr
N.A.I.C.S.: 325412

DSP Gokyo Food & Chemical Co., LTD. (2)
HERBIS OSAKA 20th floor 2-5-25 Umeda, Kita-ku, Osaka, 530-0001, Japan
Tel.: (81) 671776866
Web Site: http://www.dsp-gokyo-fc.co.jp
Food Additives & Fine Chemicals Mfr
N.A.I.C.S.: 325199

Subsidiary (Non-US):

Dainippon Sumitomo Pharma Europe Ltd. (2)
First Fl Southside, 97-105 Victoria St, London, SW1E 6QT, United Kingdom
Tel.: (44) 2078212840
Web Site: http://www.dsp-e.com
Sales Range: $25-49.9 Million
Emp.: 20
Pharmaceuticals Preparation & Research & Development
N.A.I.C.S.: 325412

Subsidiary (Domestic):

Eiko Service Co., Ltd. (2)
1-33 Nozaki-cho, Kita-ku, Osaka, Japan
Tel.: (81) 6 6314 0795
Building Management Services
N.A.I.C.S.: 541618

Marupi Lifetech Co., Ltd. (2)
103 Fushio-cho, Ikeda, 563-0011, Osaka, Japan
Tel.: (81) 72 753 0335
Web Site: https://www.m-lt.co.jp
Clinical Pathology Testing Services
N.A.I.C.S.: 622310

NS Life Corporation (2)
28F Seiruka Tower 8-1 Akashi-cho, Osaka, Japan
Tel.: (81) 335427666
Pharmaceuticals Producut Sales
N.A.I.C.S.: 325412

Nichiei Sangyo Co., Ltd. (2)
1-33 Nozaki-cho, Kita-ku, Osaka, Japan
Tel.: (81) 663143455
Insurance Services
N.A.I.C.S.: 524298

Subsidiary (Non-US):

Sumitomo Pharmaceuticals(Suzhou)Co., Ltd. (2)
Suchun Industrial Estate 22, No 428 Xinglong Street, Suzhou, 215126, China
Tel.: (86) 51262837896
Pharmaceuticals Preparation & Research & Development
N.A.I.C.S.: 325412

Subsidiary (US):

Sunovion (2)
84 Waterford Dr, Marlborough, MA 01752
Tel.: (508) 481-6700
Web Site: https://www.sunovion.com
Sales Range: $1-4.9 Billion
Emp.: 1,620
Pharmaceutical & Biopharmaceutical Compounds Mfr
N.A.I.C.S.: 325412
Antony Loebel *(CEO-Marlborough)*

Tolero Pharmaceuticals, Inc. (2)
3900 N Traverse Mtn Blvd Ste 100, Lehi, UT 84043
Tel.: (801) 769-0796
Web Site: http://www.sdponcology.com
Pharmaceuticals Product Mfr
N.A.I.C.S.: 325412
David J. Bearss *(CEO)*

Sumitomo Pharma Co., Ltd. (1)
6-8 Doshomachi 2-chome, Chuo-ku, Osaka, 541-0045, Japan
Tel.: (81) 662035321
Web Site: https://www.sumitomo-pharma.com
Pharmaceutical Product Mfr & Distr
N.A.I.C.S.: 325412

Sumitomo Pharma Malaysia Sdn. Bhd. (1)
Suite 7 Level 27 Axiata Tower 9 Jalan Stesen Sentral 5, Kuala Lumpur Sentral, 50470, Kuala Lumpur, Malaysia
Tel.: (60) 327766917
Pharmaceutical Products Distr
N.A.I.C.S.: 424210

Sumitomo Pharma Taiwan Co., Ltd. (1)
15F-2 & 3 No 62 Nanjing W Rd, Datong Dist, Taipei, 103, Taiwan
Tel.: (886) 225559962
Pharmaceutical Products Distr
N.A.I.C.S.: 424210

Sumitomo Pharmaceuticals (Thailand) Co., Ltd. (1)
Unit No 1501 15th Floor Athenee Tower 63 Wireless Road, Witthayu Lumpini Pathumwan, Bangkok, 10330, Thailand
Tel.: (66) 21688515
Pharmaceuticals Product Mfr
N.A.I.C.S.: 325412

Sumitomo Pharmaceuticals Asia Pacific Pte. Ltd. (1)
3 Fraser Street 07-28 DUO Tower, Singapore, 189352, Singapore
Tel.: (65) 65818761
Pharmaceutical Research & Development Services
N.A.I.C.S.: 541714

Sumitovant Biopharma Ltd. (1)
151 W 42nd St 15th Fl, New York, NY 10036
Tel.: (716) 235-5983
Web Site: http://www.sumitovant.com
Pharmaceuticals Product Mfr
N.A.I.C.S.: 325412
Adele M. Gulfo *(Chief Bus & Comml Dev Officer)*

Subsidiary (Non-US):

Myovant Sciences Ltd. (2)
Suite 1 3rd Floor 11-12 St James s Square, London, SW1Y 4LB, United Kingdom **(52%)**
Tel.: (44) 207 400 3351
Web Site: http://www.myovant.com
Rev.: $230,972,000
Assets: $520,011,000
Liabilities: $993,488,000
Net Worth: ($473,477,000)
Earnings: ($205,981,000)
Emp.: 579
Fiscal Year-end: 03/31/2022
Biopharmaceutical Research & Development
N.A.I.C.S.: 541715
Adele M. Gulfo *(Interim Chief Comml Officer)*

Sunovion Pharmaceuticals Europe Ltd. (1)
First Floor Southside 97-105 Victoria Street, London, SW1E 6QT, United Kingdom
Tel.: (44) 2078212840
Web Site: http://www.sunovion.eu
Emp.: 1,620
Pharmaceuticals Product Mfr
N.A.I.C.S.: 325412

Sunrise Farm Saijo Co., Ltd. (1)
150-1 Saijo Industrial Information Support Center in the Kanbaiko, Yubinbango, Saijo, 104-8260, Ehime Prefecture, Japan
Tel.: (81) 897586510
Vegetable Farming Services

N.A.I.C.S.: 111219

Sunrise Farm Toyota Co., Ltd. (1)
1209 Nishikawa Mitsukuri-cho, Toyota, 470-0424, Aichi Prefecture, Japan
Tel.: (81) 565762600
Vegetable Farming Services
N.A.I.C.S.: 111219

Tanaka Chemical Corporation (1)
45-5-10 Shirakata-cho, Fukui, 910-3131, Japan **(50.1%)**
Tel.: (81) 776851801
Web Site: https://www.tanaka-chem.co.jp
Rev.: $220,258,720
Assets: $328,093,920
Liabilities: $205,912,960
Net Worth: $122,180,960
Earnings: ($4,007,520)
Emp.: 307
Fiscal Year-end: 03/31/2021
Chemical Products & Battery Materials Mfr
N.A.I.C.S.: 325180
Tamotsu Tanaka *(Pres)*

Taoka Chemical Co., Ltd. (1)
4-2-11 Nishi Mikuni, Yodogawa-ku, Osaka, 532 0006, Japan **(50.2%)**
Tel.: (81) 663941221
Web Site: https://www.taoka-chem.co.jp
Rev.: $188,675,840
Assets: $196,449,200
Liabilities: $82,684,490
Net Worth: $113,764,710
Earnings: $5,420,200
Emp.: 374
Fiscal Year-end: 03/31/2024
Dyestuffs, Industrial Chemicals & Adhesives Mfr & Sales
N.A.I.C.S.: 325998
Takeshi Hioki *(Sr Mng Dir)*

The Polyolefin Company (Singapore) Pte. Ltd. (1)
10-00 Gateway West 150 Beach Road, Singapore, 189720, Singapore **(70%)**
Tel.: (65) 62929622
Web Site: http://www.tpc.com.sg
Sales Range: $150-199.9 Million
Emp.: 320
Mfr & Sales of Polyethylene & Polypropylene
N.A.I.C.S.: 326199
Ikhiri Tamaru *(Mng Dir)*

Urovant Sciences Ltd. (1)
Ste 1 3rd Floor 11-12 St James's Square, London, SW1Y 4LB, United Kingdom
Tel.: (44) 207 400 3347
Web Site: http://www.urovant.com
Assets: $63,295,000
Liabilities: $121,301,000
Net Worth: ($58,006,000)
Earnings: ($146,745,000)
Fiscal Year-end: 03/31/2020
Pharmaceutical Product Mfr & Distr
N.A.I.C.S.: 325412
Christine G. Ocampo *(Chief Acctg Officer)*

Subsidiary (US):

Urovant Sciences, Inc. (2)
5281 California Ave Ste 100, Irvine, CA 92617
Biopharmaceutical Research & Development Services
N.A.I.C.S.: 541714
James Robinson *(Pres & CEO)*

Yashima Sangyo Co., Ltd (1)
2-9-14 Ohkusu, Minami-ku, Fukuoka, 815-8529, Japan
Tel.: (81) 925245464
Web Site: http://www.yashimasangyo.co.jp
Emp.: 54
Chemical Products Mfr
N.A.I.C.S.: 325998

ZS Elastomers Co., Ltd. (1)
1-6-2 Marunouchi, Chiyoda-ku, Tokyo, 100-0005, Japan
Tel.: (81) 332160620
Web Site: https://www.zs-elastomers.com
Synthetic Rubber Products Mfr
N.A.I.C.S.: 325212
Kei Itoh *(Pres & Pres)*

Zhuhai Sumika Polymer Compounds Co., Ltd. (1)
Fushan Industrial Zone Qianwu Town, Dou-

SUMITOMO CHEMICAL COMPANY, LIMITED

Sumitomo Chemical Company, Limited—(Continued)
men Dist, Zhuhai, 519175, Guangdong, China
Tel.: (86) 756 5655 689
Polypropylene Compound Mfr
N.A.I.C.S.: 325998

SUMITOMO CORPORATION
OTEMACHI PLACE EAST TOWER
3-2 Otemachi 2-Chome, Chiyoda-ku, Tokyo, 100-8601, Japan
Tel.: (81) 362855000 JP
Web Site:
https://www.sumitomocorp.com
Year Founded: 1919
SSUMF—(OTCIQ)
Rev.: $48,884,142,240
Assets: $72,455,574,600
Liabilities: $43,943,445,810
Net Worth: $28,512,128,790
Earnings: $4,052,326,260
Emp.: 79,513
Fiscal Year-end: 03/31/23
Iron & Steel Raw Materials Whslr
N.A.I.C.S.: 425120
Koichi Takahata *(CFO & Exec VP)*

Subsidiaries:

Aimo Solution AB (1)
Formansvagen 11, 117 43, Stockholm, Sweden
Tel.: (46) 10 456 3939
Web Site: https://www.aimoshare.se
Motor Vehicles Mfr
N.A.I.C.S.: 336110

Alcedo S.R.L. (1)
Strada Alexandru Constantinescu 63, Bucharest, 011472, Romania
Tel.: (40) 21 310 8350
Web Site: https://www.alcedo.ro
Agricultural Material Distr
N.A.I.C.S.: 424910

Alcut Co., Ltd. (1)
1-17-33 Miyahara, Yodogawa-Ku, Osaka, 532-0003, Japan
Tel.: (81) 648073233
Aluminium Sheet Mfr & Distr
N.A.I.C.S.: 331315

Asama Giken Co., Ltd. (1)
450 Mimitori, Komoro, 384-0084, Nagano, Japan
Tel.: (81) 267228118
Web Site: http://www.asamagiken.co.jp
Automobile Parts Mfr
N.A.I.C.S.: 336390

Plant (Domestic):

Asamagiken Co., Ltd. - Misato Plant (2)
450 Mimitori, Komoro, 384-0084, Nagano, Japan
Tel.: (81) 267 22 8118
Automotive Parts Molding Mfr
N.A.I.C.S.: 336390

Subsidiary (Non-US):

P.T TSUZUKI & ASAMA MANUFACTURING (2)
Jl Surya Lestari Kav 1-2 B, Teluk Jambe, Karawang, 41361, Indonesia
Tel.: (62) 267 440026
Sales Range: $25-49.9 Million
Emp.: 24
Automobile Parts Mfr
N.A.I.C.S.: 336390
Haruo Shomura *(Pres)*

Asian Steel Company Ltd. (1)
10 Gul Circle, Jurong, 629566, Singapore
Tel.: (65) 68616000
Web Site: http://www.asiansteel.sg
Emp.: 120
Steel Service Center & Distr
N.A.I.C.S.: 423510

Aver Asia (S) Pte. Ltd. (1)
14 Benoi Place, Singapore, 629953, Singapore
Tel.: (65) 6 861 5550
Web Site: https://www.averasia.com

Construction & Infrastructure Equipment Rental Services
N.A.I.C.S.: 532412

B&L Pipeco Services Inc. (1)
20465 SH 249 Ste 200, Houston, TX 77070
Tel.: (281) 955-3500
Web Site: https://www.blpipeco.com
Emp.: 100
Oil & Gas Mfg.
N.A.I.C.S.: 333132

BWA Japan Ltd. (1)
2-3-2 Otemachi Otemachi Place East Tower, Chiyoda-ku, Tokyo, 100-8601, Japan
Tel.: (81) 36 285 5190
Web Site: https://bwajapan.co.jp
Telecommunication Servicesb
N.A.I.C.S.: 517810

Bluewell Corporation (1)
19 Floor Triton Square Tower Z 1-8-12, Chuo-ku, Tokyo, 104-6219, Japan
Tel.: (81) 3 5144 0525
Web Site: http://www.bluewell.co.jp
Risk Management Consulting Services
N.A.I.C.S.: 541618

Bluewell Insurance Brokers Ltd. (1)
OTEMACHI PLACE EAST TOWER 20th Floor 3-2 Otemachi 2-Chome, Chiyoda-ku, Tokyo, 100-8601, Japan
Tel.: (81) 362857456
Web Site: http://www.bluewellbro.com
Insurance Brokerage Services
N.A.I.C.S.: 524210

CS Metal Co., Ltd. (1)
92 M5 Wellgrow Industrial Estate KM 36 Bangna-Trad Rd, Bangsamak, Bang Pakong, 24180, Chachoengsao, Thailand
Tel.: (66) 385 707 4453
Web Site: https://www.csmetal.co.th
Steel Products Mfr
N.A.I.C.S.: 331110

Chiba Kyodo Silo Co., Ltd. (1)
16 Shinminato, Mihama-Ku, Chiba, 261-0002, Japan
Tel.: (81) 432411231
Web Site: https://www.kyodosilo.co.jp
Sales Range: $10-24.9 Million
Emp.: 35
General Warehousing & Freight Transportation Services
N.A.I.C.S.: 493110
Yoshikatsu Nakamura *(Pres & CEO)*

Chongqing Sumisho Yunxin Logistics Co., Ltd. (1)
No 18 Tianming Village Yudong Town Banan, Chongqing, China
Tel.: (86) 2386998077
Logistics & Freight Transportation Services
N.A.I.C.S.: 541614

Dragon Logistics Co., Ltd. (1)
Plot E4A Thang Long Industrial Park, Kim Chung Commune Dong Anh District, Hanoi, Vietnam
Tel.: (84) 243 881 2488
Web Site: https://draco.com.vn
Transportation Services
N.A.I.C.S.: 488510

EWEL, Inc. (1)
3-6 Kioicho Kioicho Park Building, Chiyoda-ku, Tokyo, 102-0094, Japan
Tel.: (81) 33 511 1445
Web Site: https://www.ewel.co.jp
Emp.: 1,167
Business Process Outsourcing Services
N.A.I.C.S.: 541611

Fyffes Limited (1)
M1 Bussiness Park Courtlough, balbriggan, Dublin, k32 KV20, Ireland
Tel.: (353) 35315740070
Web Site: https://www.fyffes.us
Emp.: 6,000
Tropical Produce Importer & Distr
N.A.I.C.S.: 424480
David V. McCann *(Chm)*

Subsidiary (Domestic):

Banana Importers of Ireland Limited (2)
Charles McCann Building Rampant Road, Dundalk, Ireland
Tel.: (353) 429135451

Web Site: http://www.fyffes.us
Fresh Produce Distr
N.A.I.C.S.: 445230
Gerard Cunningham *(Mng Dir)*

Fyffes Bananas (Swords) Limited (2)
Swords Business Park, Dublin, Ireland
Tel.: (353) 1807 4882
Web Site: http://www.fyffes.us
Fresh Fruit & Vegetable Distr
N.A.I.C.S.: 424480

Fyffes International Holdings Limited (2)
29 North Anne Street, Dublin, D07 PH36, Ireland
Tel.: (353) 18872700
Web Site: http://www.fyffes.us
Holding Company
N.A.I.C.S.: 551112

Subsidiary (Non-US):

Fyffe BV (3)
Marconistraat 19, Rotterdam, 3029 AE, Netherlands
Tel.: (31) 102445300
Web Site: http://www.fyffes.us
Fresh Produce Importer & Distr
N.A.I.C.S.: 445230

Fyffes Group Limited (2)
Houndmills Road, Houndmills Industrial Estate, Basingstoke, RG21 6XL, Hants, United Kingdom
Tel.: (44) 1256383200
Web Site: http://www.fyffes.us
Fresh Produce Distributor
N.A.I.C.S.: 445230

Subsidiary (US):

Fyffes North America Inc. (3)
999 Ponce de Leon Blvd Ste 900, Coral Gables, FL 33134
Tel.: (305) 445-1542
Web Site: http://www.fyffes.us
Fresh Produce Distr
N.A.I.C.S.: 311991

Subsidiary (Domestic):

Sol Group Marketing Company Inc. (4)
1751 SW 8th St, Pompano Beach, FL 33069-4517
Tel.: (954) 781-0003
Web Site: http://www.solmelons.com
Fruits & Vegetable Mfr & Distr
N.A.I.C.S.: 311411

Subsidiary (Non-US):

Internationale Fruchtimport Gesellschaft Weichert & Co. KG (3)
Banksstrasse 28, 20097, Hamburg, Germany
Tel.: (49) 40329000
Web Site: https://www.interweichert.de
Fruits & Vegetables Distr
N.A.I.C.S.: 424480
Andre Weichert *(Mng Dir)*

Subsidiary (Domestic):

Fyffes Tropical (Ireland) Limited (2)
29 North Anne Street, Dublin, D07 PH36, Ireland
Tel.: (353) 18872700
Web Site: http://www.fyffes.us
Fruit & Vegetables Mfr & Sales
N.A.I.C.S.: 311411

Subsidiary (Non-US):

Highline Produce Limited (2)
506 Mersea Road 5, Leamington, N8H 3V5, ON, Canada
Tel.: (519) 326-8643
Web Site:
http://www.highlinemushrooms.com
Mushroom Producer
N.A.I.C.S.: 111411

Plant (Domestic):

Highline Produce Limited - Highline Distribution Facility (3)
1509 Antonio-Barbeau, Montreal, H4N 2R5, QC, Canada
Tel.: (514) 381-4804

Web Site:
http://www.highlinemushrooms.com
Mushroom Distr
N.A.I.C.S.: 424480

Highline Produce Limited - Kingsville Mushroom Farm Facility (3)
2646 Division Rd N, Kingsville, N9Y 2E5, ON, Canada
Tel.: (519) 733-5215
Web Site:
http://www.highlinemushrooms.com
Mushroom Farming Services
N.A.I.C.S.: 111411

Highline Produce Limited - Wellington Mushroom Farm Facility (3)
339 Conley Rd, Bloomfield, K0K 1G0, ON, Canada
Tel.: (613) 399-3121
Web Site:
http://www.highlinemushrooms.com
Mushroom Farming Services
N.A.I.C.S.: 111411

Grape One Co., Ltd. (1)
1-3-9 Iwamotocho Hakusei Building 4th Floor, Chiyoda-ku, Tokyo, 101-0032, Japan
Tel.: (81) 36 240 9638
Web Site: https://www.grapeone.co.jp
Telecommunication Servicesb
N.A.I.C.S.: 517810

Green San-ai Inc. (1)
6-1-1 Morino, Machida, 194-0022, Tokyo, Japan
Tel.: (81) 42 728 9801
Wastepaper Processing Services
N.A.I.C.S.: 322110

Hanoi Steel Center Co., Ltd. (1)
Plot M5B Thang Long Industrial Park, Dong Anh Dist, Hanoi, Vietnam
Tel.: (84) 2439590109
Web Site: http://www.hanoisteel.com
Steel Sheet Mfr
N.A.I.C.S.: 331221

Hanoi Steel Center Co., Ltd. - Factory 1 (1)
Plot B13 Thanglong Industrial Park, Donganh Dist, Hanoi, Vietnam
Tel.: (84) 4 38813107
Metal Sheet Mfr
N.A.I.C.S.: 331221

Hidd Power Company BSC (1)
Hidd Power Station, Hidd Industrial Area, Hidd, Bahrain
Tel.: (973) 1 767 9479
Web Site: https://www.hpc.com.bh
Water & Electric Utility Services
N.A.I.C.S.: 221112
Radhakrishnan Kaiparambath *(Mgr-Engrg, Plng & Performance)*

IG Kogyo Co., Ltd. (1)
Food Building 5F 2-7 South Hondori 19-chome, Shiroishi-ku, Sapporo, 003-0026, Hokkaido, Japan
Tel.: (81) 118630303
Web Site: http://www.igkogyo.co.jp
Insulated Metal Siding Mfr
N.A.I.C.S.: 332999

Inamoto Manufacturing Co., Ltd. (1)
948 Genpeijima-machi Ishikawa-cho, Hakusan, 924-0052, Japan
Tel.: (81) 76 277 2211
Web Site: http://www.inamoto.co.jp
Emp.: 128
Industrial Washing Machine Mfr
N.A.I.C.S.: 333248
Sasaki Tawaman *(Pres)*

India Steel Summit Private Limited (1)
2F-2G Ecotech III Udyog Kendra, Noida, 201306, Uttar Pradesh, India
Tel.: (91) 120 610 3000
Web Site: https://www.indiasteelsummit.com
Emp.: 373
Steel Product Mfr & Distr
N.A.I.C.S.: 331110
Tomotsugu Takashima *(Mng Dir)*

Interacid Trading (Chile) S.A. (1)
Isidora Goyenechea Nr 3600 - Office 301, PO Box 13476, Las Condes, Santiago, Chile

AND PRIVATE COMPANIES — SUMITOMO CORPORATION

Tel.: (56) 223347141
Web Site: http://www.interacid-trading.com
Chemical Product Whslr
N.A.I.C.S.: 424690

Interacid Trading S.A. (1)
En Budron H-14, 1052, Le Mont-sur-Lausanne, Switzerland
Tel.: (41) 216545352
Web Site: http://www.interacid-trading.com
Emp.: 22
Chemical Distr & Logistics Services
N.A.I.C.S.: 424690

Subsidiary (Non-US):

Interacid Australia Pty Ltd. (2)
Suite 915 1 Queens Road, Melbourne, 3004, VIC, Australia
Tel.: (61) 3 9863 9777
Emp.: 4
Chemical Product Whslr
N.A.I.C.S.: 424690
Kevin Hunter (Gen Mgr)

Ishida Metal Co., Ltd. (1)
4-1-22 Tatsumikita, Ikuno-Ku, Osaka, 544-0004, Japan
Tel.: (81) 6 6751 3366
Web Site: http://www.ishida-metal.com
Sales Range: $25-49.9 Million
Emp.: 40
Stainless Steel Whslr
N.A.I.C.S.: 423510

Ishihara Kohtetu Co., Ltd. (1)
2-51-3 Akabane Ns3 Bldg 6kai, Kita-Ku, Tokyo, 115-0045, Japan
Tel.: (81) 352495215
Tool Steel Stocking, Processing & Sales
N.A.I.C.S.: 423510

Japan Charge Network Co., Ltd. (1)
Queen's Tower C Building 2-3-5 Minatomirai, Nishi-ku, Yokohama, 220-6208, Kanagawa, Japan
Tel.: (81) 57 020 0588
Web Site: https://www.evcharger-network.com
Electric Charging Station Services
N.A.I.C.S.: 221122
Naoko Yotsuyanagi (Pres & CEO)

Juice Products New Zealand Ltd. (1)
55 Sheffield Street, Washdyke, Timaru, 7910, New Zealand
Tel.: (64) 3 687 4170
Web Site: https://www.jp-nz.com
Fresh Fruit Product Mfr
N.A.I.C.S.: 311421
Akinari Yamaguchi (CEO)

Jupiter Golf Network Co., Ltd. (1)
2-5-10 Aomi Telecom Center Building West Building 18F, Koto-ku, Tokyo, 135-0064, Japan
Tel.: (81) 12 056 2034
Web Site: https://www.golfnetwork.co.jp
Television Broadcasting Services
N.A.I.C.S.: 516120

Jupiter Telecommunications Co., Ltd. (1)
Marunouchi Trust Tower North 1-8-1 Marunouchi, Chiyoda-ku, Tokyo, 100-0005, Japan
Tel.: (81) 367658000
Web Site: http://www.jcom.co.jp
Sales Range: $1-4.9 Billion
Emp.: 11,500
Cable Telecommunication Systems Owner & Operator
N.A.I.C.S.: 516210
Daisuke Mikogami (Exec VP & Gen Mgr - Bus Strategy Unit)

Subsidiary (Domestic):

Asmik Ace, Inc. (2)
Lapiross Roppongi 3/F 6-1-24 Roppongi, Minato-ku, Tokyo, 106-8553, Japan
Tel.: (81) 354134313
Web Site: http://www.asmik-ace.co.jp
Sales Range: $50-74.9 Million
Emp.: 100
Motion Picture Production & Distribution Services
N.A.I.C.S.: 512110
Masanori Miyata (Pres)

Joint Venture (Domestic):

Jupiter Shop Channel Co., Ltd. (2)
7-2-18 Toyo, Kotu-ku, Tokyo, 104-0033, Japan
Tel.: (81) 355416885
Web Site: https://www.shopch.jp
Emp.: 994
Television Shopping Channel Broadcasting Services
N.A.I.C.S.: 516120

KI Fresh Access, Inc. (1)
Sumitomo Nakano Sakagami Building 15th floor 1-36-1, Chuo Nakano-ku, Tokyo, 164-0011, Japan (50%)
Tel.: (81) 33 227 8700
Web Site: https://www.kifa.co.jp
Emp.: 367
Fresh Fruits & Vegetables Whslr
N.A.I.C.S.: 424480
Shoichi Kato (Pres)

KIRIU Corporation (1)
2 Omata-minami-cho, Ashikaga, 326-0142, Tochigi, Japan
Tel.: (81) 284622321
Web Site: http://www.kiriu.co.jp
Sales Range: $200-249.9 Million
Emp.: 517
Automotive Parts & Machine Tools Mfr
N.A.I.C.S.: 336390
Makoto Yoshimoto (Pres)

KISHIWADA CANCAN BAYSIDE MALL CORPORATION (1)
Minatomidori-cho 2-1, Kishiwada, 596-0014, Osaka, Japan
Tel.: (81) 72 436 9955
Web Site: http://www.k-cancan.jp
Shopping Mall Operation Services
N.A.I.C.S.: 445110

KS Summit Steel Co., Ltd. (1)
Kiba 5-5-2 CN-1 BLDG 4 floor, Koto-Ku, Tokyo, 135-0042, Japan
Tel.: (81) 356218065
Web Site: http://www.ks-summit.co.jp
Steel Products Mfr & Distr
N.A.I.C.S.: 331110

Kienle + Spiess GmbH (1)
Bahnhofstrasse 23, 74343, Sachsenheim, Germany
Tel.: (49) 714 7290
Web Site: https://www.kienle-spiess.com
Passenger Vehicle Mfr & Distr
N.A.I.C.S.: 336110

Kiriu (Thailand) Co., Ltd. (1)
300/37 Moo1 T Tasit A, Pluakdaeng, Rayong, 21140, Thailand
Tel.: (66) 3 310 3700
Automotive Components Mfr
N.A.I.C.S.: 336390

Kiriu Techno Corp. (1)
5842 Mimuro-Cho, Isesaki, 379-2235, Gunma, Japan
Tel.: (81) 27 040 0660
Web Site: https://www.kiriu.co.jp
Automotive Component Mfr & Distr
N.A.I.C.S.: 336390
Yoshio Onoguchi (Pres & CEO)

Kiriu USA Corporation (1)
359 Mitch McConnell Way, Bowling Green, KY 42101
Tel.: (270) 843-4160
Web Site: https://www.kiriuusacorp.com
Automotive Components Mfr
N.A.I.C.S.: 336390
Mark Perdue (Pres)

Krisumi Corporation Private Limited (1)
461-462 Udyog Vihar Phase-3, Gurgaon, 122001, Haryana, India
Tel.: (91) 951 327 0083
Web Site: https://www.krisumi.com
Condominium Development Services
N.A.I.C.S.: 531311

LLC Russian Quartz (1)
3 Kaslinskoe highway, Kyshtym, 456870, Chelyabinsk, Russia
Tel.: (7) 3515143845
Web Site: https://www.russianquartz.com
High Purity Quartz Mfr
N.A.I.C.S.: 327991

Mactan Steel Center Inc. (1)
Mactan Economic Processing Zone I, Lapu-Lapu, 6015, Cebu, Philippines
Tel.: (63) 323402852
Sales Range: $25-49.9 Million
Emp.: 30
Steel Service Center & Distr
N.A.I.C.S.: 423510
Tsubota Yukiyasu (Gen Mgr)

Mason Metal Industry Co., Ltd. (1)
7f 649-6 Chung Cheng Rd, Hsinchuang, Taipei, 24257, Taiwan
Tel.: (886) 229085669
Sales Range: $50-74.9 Million
Emp.: 110
Metal Service Center & Distr
N.A.I.C.S.: 423510
Fujio Hiroaki (Gen Mgr)

Mazda Steel Co., Ltd. (1)
1-5-27 Ueda Sakamachi, Aki, 731-4321, Hiroshima, Japan
Tel.: (81) 828852225
Web Site: http://www.mazdastl.co.jp
Steel Sheet Shearing & Slitting Services
N.A.I.C.S.: 331110

Mezon Stainless Steel FZCO (1)
Jebel Ali Free Zone South Zone Plot No S10904, PO Box 261084, Dubai, 261084, United Arab Emirates
Tel.: (971) 4 8861180
Web Site: http://www.mezonss.com
Sales Range: $25-49.9 Million
Emp.: 30
Stainless Steel Distr
N.A.I.C.S.: 423510

Montrive Corporation (1)
8-10-6 Nishigotanda, Shinagawa-ku, Tokyo, 141-0031, Japan
Tel.: (81) 354870353
Web Site: http://www.montrive.co.jp
Chenille Fabrics Mfr & Whslr
N.A.I.C.S.: 313240

Moto-Pfohe EOOD (1)
444 Slivnitsa Blvd, Sofia, 1360, Bulgaria
Tel.: (359) 2 984 2222
Web Site: https://www.motopfohe.bg
Automobile Component Distr
N.A.I.C.S.: 423120

Naracamicie Co., Ltd. (1)
Nakayama Building 5F 3-17-15 Minami-aoyama, Minato-ku, Tokyo, 107-0062, Japan
Tel.: (81) 3 3746 8751
Web Site: www.naracamicie.co.jp
Apparel & Accessories Retailer
N.A.I.C.S.: 458110

Nippon Katan Co., Ltd. (1)
13-1 Isojima Minamicho, Hirakata, 573-1020, Osaka, Japan
Tel.: (81) 728401382
Web Site: http://www.nipponkatan.co.jp
Sales Range: $25-49.9 Million
Emp.: 92
Transmission Equipment Distr
N.A.I.C.S.: 423610

Nippon Steel Pipe America, Inc. (1)
1515 E 4th St Rd, Seymour, IN 47274
Tel.: (812) 523-3638
Web Site: https://www.nipponsteelpipeamerica.com
Emp.: 470
Steel Pipe Mfr & Distr
N.A.I.C.S.: 331210

Nusa Tenggara Mining Corporation (1)
Harumi Island Toriton Square W To 7f, Chuo-Ku, Tokyo, 104-0053, Japan
Tel.: (81) 351444030
Gold Mining & Exploration Services
N.A.I.C.S.: 212220

P.T. Satomo Indovyl Polymer (1)
UIC Building 4th Floor JL Jend Gatot Subroto Kav 6-7, Jakarta, 12930, Indonesia
Tel.: (62) 215264618
PVC Resins Mfr & Whslr
N.A.I.C.S.: 325211

PM Care Sdn. Bhd. (1)
No 1 Jalan USJ 21/10 UEP, 47630, Subang Jaya, Selangor, Malaysia
Tel.: (60) 38 026 6888

Web Site: https://www.pmcare.com.my
Health Care Management Services
N.A.I.C.S.: 541611
Adzahar Wahid (CEO)

PT MonotaRO Indonesia (1)
Wisma 46 Lantai 6 Jl Jend Sudirman Kav 1, Kota Jakarta Pusat, Jakarta, 10220, Indonesia (37.3%)
Tel.: (62) 8557 467 8400
Web Site: https://www.monotaro.id
Electronic Shopping Services
N.A.I.C.S.: 423840

PT. Kiriu Indonesia (1)
Jarakosta RT 07 / RW 04, Sukadanau, Cikarang, 17520, Bekasi, Indonesia
Tel.: (62) 21 890 0760
Automotive Components Mfr
N.A.I.C.S.: 336390

PT. Sumitomo Indonesia (1)
Summitmas I 12th Floor JL Jenderal Sudirman Kaveling 61-62, Jakarta Selatan, 12190, Indonesia
Tel.: (62) 21 525 1550
Web Site: https://www.sumitomocorp-indonesia.co.id
Sales Range: $25-49.9 Million
Emp.: 170
Ferrous & Non Ferrous Material Whslr
N.A.I.C.S.: 423510
Kanji Tojo (Chm)

Subsidiary (Domestic):

P.T. East Jakarta Industrial Park (2)
EJIP Industrial Park Plot 3A Cikarang Selatan, Lemahabang, Bekasi, 17550, West Java, Indonesia
Tel.: (62) 218970001
Web Site: http://www.ejip.co.id
Sales Range: $75-99.9 Million
Emp.: 89
Real Estate Management Services
N.A.I.C.S.: 531390

P.T. Super Steel Karawang (2)
Jl Surya Utama Kav 1-22A Kawasan Industri Suryacipta, Karawang, 41361, Indonesia
Tel.: (62) 267 440244
Steel Products Whslr
N.A.I.C.S.: 423510

PT Sumisho Global Logistics Indonesia (2)
EJIP Industrial Park Plot 1 E 2 Cikarang, Selatan, Bekasi, 17750, Indonesia
Tel.: (62) 21 897 0171
Web Site: http://www.sgl.co.id
Logistics Consulting Servies
N.A.I.C.S.: 541614

PT. Sumitronics Indonesia (2)
EJIP Industrial Park Plot 1E-2, Cikarang Selatan, Bekasi, 17550, Indonesia
Tel.: (62) 21 897 5220
Web Site: http://www.sumitronics.co.jp
Sales Range: $25-49.9 Million
Emp.: 83
Electronic Components Distr
N.A.I.C.S.: 423690
Tetsuya Saito (Gen Mgr)

Pacific Bioenergy Corporation (1)
9988 Willow Cale Forest Road, Prince George, V2N 7A8, BC, Canada
Tel.: (250) 562-7220
Web Site: https://www.pacificbioenergy.ca
Wood Biomass Pellet Mfr & Distr
N.A.I.C.S.: 321999
John Stirling (Pres & CEO)

Petro Summit Pte. Ltd. (1)
182 cecil street fresers tower unit22 01, Singapore, 069547, Singapore
Tel.: (65) 65386138
Sales Range: $25-49.9 Million
Emp.: 35
Petrol & Oil Whslr
N.A.I.C.S.: 424720
Maikawa Tadamase (Mng Dir)

S.C. Cement Co., Ltd. (1)
OTEMACHI PLACE EAST TOWER 3-2 Otemachi 2-Chome, Chiyoda-ku, Tokyo, 100-8601, Japan
Tel.: (81) 362855636
Web Site: http://www.sc-cement.co.jp
Sales Range: $25-49.9 Million
Emp.: 60
Construction Materials Distr

SUMITOMO CORPORATION

Sumitomo Corporation—(Continued)
N.A.I.C.S.: 423320

SC Foods Co., Ltd. (1)
13th Floor Sumitomo Corporation Takebashi Building 1-2-2 Hitotsubashi, Chiyoda-ku, Tokyo, 100-0003, Japan
Tel.: (81) 36 369 0111
Web Site: https://www.scfoods.co.jp
Emp.: 237
Beverages & Food Products Distr
N.A.I.C.S.: 424820
Tetsuro Tajima *(Pres)*

SC Machinery & Service Co., Ltd. (1)
Hamamatsu Act Tower 21F 111-2 Itayamachi, Naka-ku, Hamamatsu, 430-7721, Shizuoka, Japan
Tel.: (81) 53 401 0780
Web Site: https://www.scms.jp
Machine Tool Mfr & Distr
N.A.I.C.S.: 333248
Osamu Sato *(Pres)*

SC Machinery & Service Co., Ltd. (1)
Hamamatsu Act Tower 21F 111-2 Itayamachi, Naka-ku, Hamamatsu, 430-7721, Shizuoka, Japan
Tel.: (81) 53 401 0780
Web Site: https://www.scms.jp
Emp.: 23
Machine Tools Mfr & Distr
N.A.I.C.S.: 333517

SC Mineral Resources Pty. Ltd. (1)
L 18 88 Phillip St, Sydney, 2000, NSW, Australia
Tel.: (61) 2 9335 3730
Gold Ore Mining Services
N.A.I.C.S.: 212220

SC Motors Sweden AB (1)
Kanalvagen 10 A, 194 61, Upplands Vasby, Sweden
Tel.: (46) 850605060
Web Site: http://www.sc-motors.se
Sales Range: $25-49.9 Million
Emp.: 70
Auto Parts & Accessories Distr
N.A.I.C.S.: 423120

SC Pipe Solutions Co., Ltd. (1)
3F RBM Tsukiji Bldg 2-15-5 Shintomi, Chuo-ku, Tokyo, 104-0041, Japan **(100%)**
Tel.: (81) 362800131
Web Site: http://www.sumishokokan.co.jp
Sales Range: $400-449.9 Million
Emp.: 458
Metal Pipe Mfr & Distr
N.A.I.C.S.: 332323
Shigeru Moriguchi *(Pres & CEO)*

SC Tubular and Steel Products (M.E.) FZCO (1)
10th Floor Ja View 18, 262517, Jebel Ali, United Arab Emirates
Tel.: (971) 4 8865900
Web Site: http://www.sctsp.com
Sales Range: $25-49.9 Million
Emp.: 35
Tabular Steel Products Distr
N.A.I.C.S.: 423510
Akira Shima *(Mng Dir)*

SC Tubulars Co., Ltd. (1)
1-8-12 Harumi Toriton Square Office Tower Z To 10f, Chuo-Ku, Tokyo, Japan
Tel.: (81) 351444094
Web Site: http://www.sc-tubulars.co.jp
Sales Range: $25-49.9 Million
Emp.: 78
Steel Pipe Distr
N.A.I.C.S.: 423510
Nobuhiko Tsuchihiro *(Pres)*

SC-ABeam Automotive Consulting (1)
Otemachi Place East Tower 3-2 Otemachi 2-chome, Chiyoda-ku, Tokyo, 100-8601, Japan
Tel.: (81) 36 285 4600
Web Site: https://www.sc-abeam.com
Sales Range: $25-49.9 Million
Emp.: 7
Automotive Consulting Services
N.A.I.C.S.: 541690
Shinya Omori *(Pres & CEO)*

SCSK Corporation (1)
Toyosu Front 3-2-20 Toyosu, Koto-ku, Tokyo, 135-8110, Japan
Tel.: (81) 351662500
Web Site: https://www.scsk.jp
Rev.: $3,174,829,270
Assets: $3,115,954,000
Liabilities: $1,113,718,900
Net Worth: $2,002,235,100
Earnings: $267,447,210
Emp.: 16,296
Fiscal Year-end: 03/31/2024
Information Technology Services
N.A.I.C.S.: 541512
Tetsuya Fukunaga *(Sr Mng Exec Officer)*

Subsidiary (Domestic):

CSK Administration Service Corporation (2)
CSK Aoyama Building 2-26-1 Minamiaoyama, Minato-ku, Tokyo, 107 0062, Japan
Tel.: (81) 364383001
Web Site: http://www.csk.com
Sales Range: $75-99.9 Million
Emp.: 394
IT Business Services
N.A.I.C.S.: 561499

CSK Agricole Corporation (2)
Floral City Nishinohara N 9-205, Nishinohara, Inzai, 207 1334, Chiba, Japan
Tel.: (81) 476407893
Sales Range: $25-49.9 Million
Emp.: 7
Agricultural Services; Production & Distribution of Farm Produce, Farm Workers Contracts/Compensation & Farm Land Management
N.A.I.C.S.: 115116

CSK Nearshore Systems Corporation (2)
CSK Aoyama Building 2-26-1 Minamiaoyama, Minato-ku, Tokyo, 107 0062, Japan
Tel.: (81) 3 6438 3001
Web Site: http://www.csk.com
Information Technology Services
N.A.I.C.S.: 541519
Mizuki Saeki *(Pres)*

CSK Prescendo Corporation (2)
CSK Aoyama Building 2-26-1 Minamiaoyama, Minato-ku, Tokyo, 107 0062, Japan
Tel.: (81) 364383471
Web Site: http://www.csk.com
IT Services
N.A.I.C.S.: 541519

CSK ServiceWare Corporation (2)
CSK Aoyama Building 2-26-1 Minamiaoyama, Minato-ku, Tokyo, 107 0062, Japan **(100%)**
Tel.: (81) 3 6438 4860
Information Technology Services
N.A.I.C.S.: 541519
Yasuhiko Tanaka *(Exec Officer)*

CSK System Management Corporation (2)
CSK Aoyama Building 2-26-1 Minamiaoyama, Minato-ku, Tokyo, 107-0062, Japan
Tel.: (81) 364383131
Web Site: http://www.csk.com
IT Management Services
N.A.I.C.S.: 541512

Subsidiary (Non-US):

CSK Systems (Shanghai) Co., Ltd. (2)
18F East Tower Hi-Tech King World, 668 Beijing East Road, Shanghai, 200001, China
Tel.: (86) 2161032518
Web Site: http://www.cskchina.com
Sales Range: $25-49.9 Million
Emp.: 125
Information Technology Services
N.A.I.C.S.: 541519

Subsidiary (Domestic):

CSK Systems Corporation (2)
CSK Aoyama Building 2-26-1 Minamiaoyama, Minato-ku, Tokyo, 107 0062, Japan
Tel.: (81) 364383000
Web Site: http://www.csk.com
Sales Range: $800-899.9 Million
Emp.: 3,687
Computer Systems Development Services
N.A.I.C.S.: 541512

CSK WinTechnology Corporation (2)
Nishi Shinjuku Mitsui Building 20th Floor 6-24-1 Nishi Shinjuku, Shinjuku-ku, Tokyo, 160 0023, Japan
Tel.: (81) 333432500
Web Site: http://www.cskwin.com
Sales Range: $50-74.9 Million
Emp.: 150
Systems Development Services & IT Consulting
N.A.I.C.S.: 541519

Fukuoka CSK Corporation (2)
Hakata Station 30 23rd Fan 3 chome Bodo Orchestral Hikaru Bldg 4F, Chuo-ku, Fukuoka, 812 0011, Fukuoka-ken, Japan
Tel.: (81) 92 686 7373
Web Site: http://www.csk.com
Sales Range: $25-49.9 Million
Emp.: 119
Information Technology Services
N.A.I.C.S.: 541519

Hokkaido CSK Corporation (2)
Urbannet Sapporo Building 4th Floor Kita 1 Nishi 6-1-2, Chuo-ku, Sapporo, 060 0001, Japan
Tel.: (81) 11 206 3700
Web Site: http://www.hokkaidocsk.jp
Sales Range: $25-49.9 Million
Emp.: 114
Information Technology Services
N.A.I.C.S.: 541519

JIEC Co., Ltd. (2)
20F Nishi-Shinjuku Mitsui Building 6-24-1, Shinjuku-ku, Tokyo, 160-0023, Japan **(97.9%)**
Tel.: (81) 3 5326 3331
Web Site: http://www.jiec.co.jp
Sales Range: $125-149.9 Million
Emp.: 818
Information Technology Services
N.A.I.C.S.: 541512
Koji Ueda *(Exec Officer)*

Net One Systems Co Ltd (2)
24th Floor JP Tower 2-7-2 Marunouchi, Chiyoda-ku, Tokyo, 100-7025, Japan **(79.69%)**
Tel.: (81) 362560600
Web Site: https://www.netone.co.jp
Rev.: $1,355,889,470
Assets: $1,090,048,490
Liabilities: $582,307,950
Net Worth: $507,740,540
Earnings: $90,689,200
Emp.: 2,579
Fiscal Year-end: 03/31/2024
Network Integration Services
N.A.I.C.S.: 541512
Toru Arai *(Pres & COO)*

Subsidiary (Domestic):

Net One Connect G.K. (3)
JP Tower 2-7-2 Marunouchi, Chiyoda-ku, Tokyo, Japan
Tel.: (81) 362560690
Web Site: https://netone-con.co.jp
Software Package Development Services
N.A.I.C.S.: 513210

Net One Next Co., Ltd. (3)
JP Tower 2-7-2 Marunouchi, Chiyoda-ku, Tokyo, 100-7024, Yubinbango, Japan
Tel.: (81) 362560730
Web Site: https://www.netone-next.co.jp
ICT Equipment Whslr
N.A.I.C.S.: 423430

Net One Partners Co., Ltd. (3)
JP Tower 2-7-2 Marunouchi, Chiyoda-ku, Tokyo, 100-7024, Yubinbango, Japan
Tel.: (81) 362560700
Web Site: https://www.netone-pa.co.jp
Emp.: 247
Network Integration Business Services
N.A.I.C.S.: 541519

Division (Domestic):

Net One Systems Co Ltd - Chugoku (3)
10-12 Teppocho Hiroshima Teppocho Building 5F, Naka Ward, Hiroshima, 730-0017, Japan
Tel.: (81) 825112661
Web Site: http://www.netone.co.jp
Network Integration Services
N.A.I.C.S.: 541512

Subsidiary (Domestic):

eXtreak, Inc. (3)
5F Shibahama Building 4-9-4 Shiba, Minato-ku, Tokyo, 108-0014, Japan
Tel.: (81) 354447677
Web Site: https://www.extreak.co.jp
IT Facility Support Services
N.A.I.C.S.: 561210

Subsidiary (Domestic):

Plaza Asset Management Co., Ltd. (2)
Riviera Minami Aoyama Building A 4th Floor 3-3-3 Minami-Aoyama, Minato-ku, Tokyo, 107 0062, Japan
Tel.: (81) 3 5771 6414
Financial Services
N.A.I.C.S.: 523999

Tokyo Green Systems Corporation (2)
2-3-3 Sannoshita SCSK Tama Center EAST, Tama, 206-0042, Tokyo, Japan
Tel.: (81) 423101261
Web Site: http://www.tgs.co.jp
Business Support Services; Flower Sales & Rental to Government Offices & Businesses; Website Creation & Maintenance for Government Services
N.A.I.C.S.: 561499

VeriServe Corporation (2)
14F Nishi-Shinjuku Mitsui Building 6-24-1, Nishi-Shinjuku-ku, Tokyo, 160-0023, Japan **(94.76%)**
Tel.: (81) 5037338440
Web Site: http://www.veriserve.co.jp
Security Verification Services
N.A.I.C.S.: 561621
Yoshihisa Tsurumaki *(Mng Exec Officer)*

SMAS Auto Leasing India Private Limited (1)
404 4th Floor Worldmark 2 Asset No 8, Aerocity Hospitality District, New Delhi, 110037, India
Tel.: (91) 114 828 8300
Web Site: https://www.smasindia.com
Motor Vehicle Leasing Services
N.A.I.C.S.: 532112
Yoshimi Akiyama *(Mng Dir)*

SMBC Aero Engine Lease B.V. (1)
World Trade Center Office Tower B/16F Strawinskylaan 1639, 1077 XX, Amsterdam, Netherlands
Tel.: (31) 20 705 4982
Web Site: https://www.sael.aero
Aircraft Engine Leasing Services
N.A.I.C.S.: 532411
Roger Welaratne *(CEO & Mng Dir)*

SMS Equipment (Alaska) Inc. (1)
8895 King St, Anchorage, AK 99515
Tel.: (907) 275-3300
Mining Equipment Distr
N.A.I.C.S.: 423830

SMS Equipment Inc. (1)
11285 - 274 Street, Acheson, T7X 6P9, AB, Canada **(100%)**
Tel.: (780) 948-2200
Web Site: http://www.smsequipment.com
Sales Range: $75-99.9 Million
Emp.: 250
Construction & Mining Machinery
N.A.I.C.S.: 532412

Division (Domestic):

SMS Equipment Inc. (2)
19520 Telegraph Trail, Surrey, V4N 4H1, BC, Canada **(100%)**
Tel.: (604) 888-9700
Web Site: http://www.smsequipment.com
Sales Range: $25-49.9 Million
Emp.: 50
Construction & Mining Machinery Mfr
N.A.I.C.S.: 333120

SUMISHO BUILDING MANAGEMENT CO., LTD. (1)
3-26 Kandanishikicho 7th floor Hitotsubashi SI Building, Chiyoda-ku, Tokyo, 101-0054, Japan
Tel.: (81) 352823700
Web Site: http://www.sumisho-bm.co.jp
Emp.: 214
Property Management Services
N.A.I.C.S.: 531312

SUMISHO TATEMONO CO., LTD. (1)
6-floor Hitotsubashi SI Building 3-26 Kanda, Chiyoda-ku Nishikicho, Tokyo, 101-0054, Japan
Tel.: (81) 352171057
Web Site: http://www.sumisho-tatemono.co.jp
Real Estate Manangement Services
N.A.I.C.S.: 531390
Koichi Nishimura (Exec Dir)

Saci Cfpa (1)
9 rue du Chevalier de St George, 75008, Paris, France (90%)
Tel.: (33) 14 260 1283
Web Site: https://www.saci-cfpa.com
Emp.: 19
Cosmetics & Related Products Mfr & Distr
N.A.I.C.S.: 456120

Saigon Steel Service & Processing Co., Ltd. (1)
No 5 Road 4A, Bien Hoa 2 Industrial Park Long Binh Tan Ward, Bien Hoa, Dong Nai, Vietnam
Tel.: (84) 251 383 3001
Web Site: https://saigonsteel-sgc.com.vn
Steel Product Distr
N.A.I.C.S.: 423510

Sakura Ferroalloys Sdn. Bhd. (1)
Unit 30-01 Level 30 Tower A Vertical Business Suite Avenue 3, Bangsar South N 8 Jalan Kerinchi, 59200, Kuala Lumpur, Malaysia
Tel.: (60) 8 629 8800
Web Site: https://sakuraferroalloys.com.my
Steel Mfrs
N.A.I.C.S.: 331110

Servilamina Summit Mexicana S.A. de C.V. (1)
Acceso III No 15-A Fraccionamiento Industrial Benito Juarez, Queretaro, 76120, Mexico
Tel.: (52) 442 1538100
Web Site: http://www.summitmx.com
Emp.: 250
Steel Processing Service Center & Distr
N.A.I.C.S.: 423510

Shanghai Hi-Tec Metal Products Co., Ltd. (1)
No 5111 Bao-an Rd An-ting Zhen, Jia-ding District, Shanghai, China
Tel.: (86) 21 3950 3088
Metal Products Mfr & Distr
N.A.I.C.S.: 332999

Shanghai Nikka Metal Products Co., Ltd. (1)
No 858 Lixue Rd, Jiading District, Shanghai, China
Tel.: (86) 21 6915 7288
Web Site: http://www.summital.com.cn
Steel Products Whslr
N.A.I.C.S.: 423510

Shanghai Summit Metal Products Co., Ltd. (1)
No 5111 Bao-an Rd An-ting Zhen, Jia-ding Disctric, Shanghai, China
Tel.: (86) 2139503088
Web Site: http://www.summital.com.cn
Processed Steel Product Mfr
N.A.I.C.S.: 331221

Shenzhen Sumitomo Corporation Ltd. (1)
Room 802 21/F Anlian Plaza 4018 Jintian Road, Futian District, Shenzhen, 518026, Guangdong, China
Tel.: (86) 75533355200
Web Site: http://www.sumitomocorp.co.jp
Sales Range: $25-49.9 Million
Emp.: 10
Industrial Metal Services & Distr
N.A.I.C.S.: 423510

Soda Ash Japan Co., Ltd. (1)
Harumi Island Triton Square Office Tower Z Wing 1-8-12 Harumi, Chuo-Ku, Tokyo, 104-6216, Japan
Tel.: (81) 3 6219 7531
Web Site: http://www.s-a-j.com
Soda Ash Distr
N.A.I.C.S.: 424690

Steel Center Europe, S.R.O. (1)
Prazska 1669, 396 01, Humpolec, Czech Republic
Tel.: (420) 56 545 0313
Web Site: https://steelcentereurope.com
Steel Product Mfr & Distr
N.A.I.C.S.: 331110

Steel Centre Malaysia Sdn. Bhd. (1)
Plo 61 Senai Iii Industrial Area, Senai, 81400, Johor, Malaysia
Tel.: (60) 75992939
Steel Service Center Operating Services
N.A.I.C.S.: 423510

Strohm Holding B.V. (1)
Monnickendamkade 1, 1976 EC, IJmuiden, Netherlands
Tel.: (31) 25 576 3500
Web Site: http://www.strohm.eu
Thermoplastic Composite Pipe Mfr & Distr
N.A.I.C.S.: 326199

Sumi Agro Europe Limited (1)
Vintners Place 68 Upper Thames Street, London, EC4V 3BJ, United Kingdom
Tel.: (44) 20 7246 3697
Farm Supplies Mfr
N.A.I.C.S.: 339999
Hideo Ozaki (Pres & CEO)

Sumi-Thai International Limited (1)
25th Floor Unit 1-5 and 7 26th Floor 32nd Floor Unit 2-3 CRC Tower, All Seasons Place 87/2 Wireless Road Lumpini Phatumwan, Bangkok, 10330, Thailand
Tel.: (66) 26540002
Web Site: http://www.sumitomothailand.co.th
Sales Range: $50-74.9 Million
Emp.: 180
Automotive Metal Products Distr
N.A.I.C.S.: 423120

Sumifert Sdn. Bhd. (1)
64-66 Jln 52/4 Seksyen 52, Petaling Jaya, 46200, Selangor, Malaysia
Tel.: (60) 3 79552882
Sales Range: $25-49.9 Million
Emp.: 2
Fertilizer & Farm Products Distr
N.A.I.C.S.: 424590

Sumifru Corporation (1)
TN Koishikawa Building 1-15-17 Koishikawa, Bunkyo-ku, Tokyo, 112-0002, Japan
Tel.: (81) 358050573
Web Site: http://www.sumifru.co.jp
Sales Range: $25-49.9 Million
Emp.: 50
Fruits & Vegetable Mfr & Distr
N.A.I.C.S.: 311411

Sumiputeh Steel Centre Sdn, Bhd. (1)
Lot 10 Persiaran Selangor, PO Box 7089, 40702, Shah Alam, Selangor, Malaysia
Tel.: (60) 3 5519 5411
Web Site: http://www.sumiputeh.com.my
Emp.: 270
Metal Products Mfr
N.A.I.C.S.: 332999

Sumisho Administration Services Co., Ltd. (1)
Otemachi Place East Tower 2-3-2 Otemachi, Chiyoda-ku, Tokyo, 100-8601, Japan
Tel.: (81) 36 285 6784
Web Site: https://www.sumisho-admin.co.jp
Emp.: 147
Personnel & General Affairs Services
N.A.I.C.S.: 923130
Tsuneyuki Okada (Pres & CEO)

Sumisho Aero-Systems Corporation (1)
1-2-2 Hitotsubashi Takebashi Building 5F, Chiyoda-ku, Tokyo, 100-0003, Japan
Tel.: (81) 365512074
Web Site: http://www.sc-aero.co.jp
Emp.: 147
Aircraft Equipment Whslr
N.A.I.C.S.: 423860

Sumisho Airbag Systems Co., Ltd. (1)
851 No 11 Shimen, Matsukawa-cho, Matsuura, 859-4536, Nagasaki, Japan
Tel.: (81) 956279111
Web Site: http://www.scairbag.jp
Emp.: 380
Automotive Parts Mfr & Distr
N.A.I.C.S.: 336390

Sumisho Aircraft Asset Management B.V. (1)
World Trade Center Amsterdam Tower A 9F Strawinskylaan 907, 1077XX, Amsterdam, Netherlands
Tel.: (31) 20 575 2573
Web Site: http://www.saambv.com
Sales Range: $25-49.9 Million
Emp.: 15
Aircraft Leasing Services
N.A.I.C.S.: 532411

Sumisho Capital Management (Singapore) Pte. Ltd. (1)
60 Anson Road 05-04 Maple Tree and Sons, Singapore, 079914, Singapore
Tel.: (65) 64382528
Sales Range: $50-74.9 Million
Emp.: 9
Financial Management Services
N.A.I.C.S.: 523999

Sumisho Global Logistics (China) Co., Ltd. (1)
Room 1001 Building 108 Building 108 Building Jing'An Road, Jing'An District, Shanghai, 200040, China
Tel.: (86) 21 635 2881
Web Site: https://www.sglchina.com.cn
Global Logistics Services
N.A.I.C.S.: 541614

Sumisho Global Logistics (Shanghai) Co., Ltd. (1)
Rm 1801 Haiyang Mansion No 550 Yanan East Road, Yangpu Distr, Shanghai, 200001, China
Tel.: (86) 2163528811
Sales Range: $10-24.9 Million
Emp.: 40
Logistics Consulting Servies
N.A.I.C.S.: 541614

Sumisho Global Logistics (Thailand) Co., Ltd. (1)
55/20 Moo 13 Tumbol Amphur, Klongnueng, Khlong Luang, 12120, Pathum Thani, Thailand
Tel.: (66) 2 529 2361
Web Site: https://www.sgl.co.th
Sales Range: $75-99.9 Million
Emp.: 332
Logistics & Freight Transportation Services
N.A.I.C.S.: 541614

Sumisho Global Logistics Co., Ltd. (1)
Takebashi Building 1-2-2 Hitotsubashi, Chiyoda-ku, Tokyo, 100-0003, Japan
Tel.: (81) 362666000
Web Site: http://www.sglogi.co.jp
Emp.: 639
Marine Shipping Services
N.A.I.C.S.: 483111

Sumisho Global Logistics Europe GmbH (1)
Georg Glock Str 8, 40474, Dusseldorf, Germany
Tel.: (49) 211 4570 290
Web Site: http://www.sgleurope.com
Logistics Consulting Servies
N.A.I.C.S.: 541614

Sumisho Global Logistics Europe s.r.o. (1)
Skretova 490/12 Vinohrady, 120 00, Prague, Czech Republic
Tel.: (420) 37 822 9650
Web Site: https://www.sgleurope.cz
Emp.: 75
Global Logistics Services
N.A.I.C.S.: 541614

Sumisho Global Logistics South China Co., Ltd. (1)
Rm 3107 Shum Yip Center No 5045 Shennan E Rd, Luohu Dist, Shenzhen, 518031, Guangdong, China
Tel.: (86) 75582110115
Web Site: http://www.sglogi-sc.com.cn
Logistics Consulting Servies
N.A.I.C.S.: 541614

Sumisho Inax Corporation (1)
5-1-11 Osaki, Shinagawa-Ku, Tokyo, 141-0032, Japan
Tel.: (81) 3 34935391
Web Site: http://www.inax-corp.co.jp
Sales Range: $25-49.9 Million
Emp.: 170
Industrial Washing Machine Mfr & Distr
N.A.I.C.S.: 333248
Kazuo Sasada (Pres)

Sumisho Interior International Inc. (1)
1F 3-26 Kanda Nishiki-cho, Chiyoda-ku, Tokyo, 101-0054, Japan
Tel.: (81) 35 577 1761
Web Site: https://www.interior-i.jp
Emp.: 76
Interior Design Services
N.A.I.C.S.: 541410
Naoki Hisano (Pres)

Sumisho Machinery Trade Corporation (1)
Triton Square Office Tower Z 21-22F 1-8-12 Harumi, Chuo-ku, Tokyo, 104-6222, Japan
Tel.: (81) 351449000
Web Site: http://www.smtcorp.co.jp
Rev.: $2,757,366,000
Emp.: 321
Industrial Machinery & Equipment Distr
N.A.I.C.S.: 423830
Kenjiro Hachiya (Pres)

Sumisho Marine Co., Ltd. (1)
1-8-12 Harumi, Chuo-Ku, Tokyo, 104-8610, Japan
Tel.: (81) 351440886
Sales Range: $25-49.9 Million
Emp.: 20
Marine Shipping Services
N.A.I.C.S.: 488330
Keichihuga Hyuga (Pres)

Sumisho Materials Corporation (1)
1-4-3 Kanda Nishikicho Kanda Square Front 4F, Chiyoda-ku, Tokyo, 101-0054, Japan
Tel.: (81) 35 280 9260
Web Site: https://www.smc-gold.jp
Emp.: 20
Precious Metal Distr
N.A.I.C.S.: 423940
Toshikatsu Ohashi (Mng Dir)

Sumisho Metalex Corporation (1)
Kanda Square Front 1-4-3 Kandanishikicho, Chiyoda-ku, Tokyo, 101-0054, Japan
Tel.: (81) 355777500
Web Site: http://www.metalex.co.jp
Sales Range: $200-249.9 Million
Emp.: 258
Residential Water Supply System Distr
N.A.I.C.S.: 221310
Yoshimitsu Matsuda (Pres)

Sumisho Montblanc Co., Ltd. (1)
4-7-28 Kitahama, Chuo-ku, Osaka, 541-0041, Japan
Tel.: (81) 66 228 8051
Web Site: https://www.scmb.jp
Emp.: 142
Uniforms Mfr
N.A.I.C.S.: 315120
Tomohisa Ishida (Mng Dir & Gen Mgr-Sls Dept)

Sumisho Motor Finance Corporation (1)
12th Floor PSBank Center 777 Paseo de Roxas corner Sedeno Street, Makati, Philippines
Tel.: (63) 28 802 6888
Web Site: https://www.sumisho.com.ph
Financial Motor Cycle Services
N.A.I.C.S.: 525990

SUMITOMO CORPORATION

Sumitomo Corporation—(Continued)

Sumisho Paper Co., Ltd. (1)
Harumi Island Triton Square Office Tower W
11th Floor 1-8-8 Harumi, Chuo-Ku, Tokyo,
104-0053, Japan
Tel.: (81) 351667300
Web Site: http://www.sumishopaper.co.jp
Sales Range: $50-74.9 Million
Emp.: 102
Paper & Packaging Materials Distr
N.A.I.C.S.: 423840

Sumisho Realty Management Co., Ltd. (1)
Sumitomo Corporation Kyobashi Bldg 9F
1-17-10 Kyobashi, Chuo-ku, Tokyo, 104-0031, Japan
Tel.: (81) 34 346 0571
Web Site: https://www.sumisho-rm.co.jp
Emp.: 69
Asset Management Services
N.A.I.C.S.: 523940
Hideki Yano *(Pres & CEO)*

Sumisho Steel Sheets Works Co., Ltd. (1)
1-1-78 Tsuneyoshi, Konohana-Ku, Osaka, 554-0052, Japan
Tel.: (81) 664624151
Web Site: http://www.skk-osaka.co.jp
Sales Range: $50-74.9 Million
Emp.: 187
Steel Product Distr
N.A.I.C.S.: 423510

Sumisho Tekko Hanbai Co., Ltd. (1)
1-8-12 Harumi Triton Square Tower Z 18f, Chuo-ku, Tokyo, 104-6218, Japan
Tel.: (81) 351668811
Web Site: http://www.scit.co.jp
Structured Steel Shapes Mfr
N.A.I.C.S.: 331221

Sumitec International, Ltd. (1)
40 bld 2 Bolshaya Ordynka str, 119017, Moscow, Russia
Tel.: (7) 4957972848
Web Site: http://www.sumitec.ru
Sales Range: $25-49.9 Million
Emp.: 50
Construction Machinery Distr
N.A.I.C.S.: 423810

Sumitex Hong Kong Limited (1)
Units 4012-4615 Level46 Metroplaza Tower1 No 223 Hing Fong Road, Salisbury Road, Kwai Fong, China (Hong Kong)
Tel.: (852) 23137700
Sales Range: $25-49.9 Million
Emp.: 15
Textile Products & Accessories Distr
N.A.I.C.S.: 424350

Sumitex International Co., Ltd (1)
5th Floor Hitotsubashi SI Building 3-26 Kanda Nishiki-cho, Chiyoda-ku, Tokyo, 101-0054, Japan
Tel.: (81) 352598130
Web Site: http://www.stx.co.jp
Sales Range: $100-124.9 Million
Emp.: 243
Textile Products Mfr & Distr
N.A.I.C.S.: 314999
Masahiro Ikeda *(Mng Exec Officer)*

Sumitomo Australia Pty Ltd (1)
Level 33 Grosvenor Place 225 George Street, Sydney, 2000, NSW, Australia
Tel.: (61) 29 335 3700
Web Site: https://www.sumitomocorp.com
Sales Range: $25-49.9 Million
Emp.: 40
Industrial & Consumer Goods Distr
N.A.I.C.S.: 424990
Frank Palatucci *(Mgr-Commercial-Carbon,Chemicals,Machinery)*

Sumitomo Benelux S.A./N.V. (1)
Triumph Building II Avenue A Fraiteur 15-23, 1050, Brussels, Belgium
Tel.: (32) 25097811
Building Materials Distr
N.A.I.C.S.: 423390

Sumitomo Canada Ltd. (1)
150 King Street West Suite 2304, Toronto, M5H 1J9, ON, Canada (100%)
Tel.: (416) 860-3800
Web Site: http://www.sumitomocanada.com
Sales Range: $100-124.9 Million
Emp.: 10
Import & Export of Steel Products, Telecommunications Equipment, Chemical Products, Tires, Glass & Malt
N.A.I.C.S.: 325998

Sumitomo Corporation (Central Eurasia) LLC (1)
Sadovnicheskaya street building 9A 3rd floor, 115035, Moscow, Russia
Tel.: (7) 4957972888
Web Site: http://www.sumitomocorp.com
Financial Services
N.A.I.C.S.: 523999
Haruo Matsuzaki *(Pres & CEO)*

Sumitomo Corporation (Chile) Limitada (1)
Orinoco 90 Office 2002 20th Floor, Las Condes, Santiago, Chile
Tel.: (56) 224306300
Web Site: http://www.sumitomochile.cl
Sales Range: $25-49.9 Million
Emp.: 27
Non Ferrous Metal Mining Services
N.A.I.C.S.: 213114

Sumitomo Corporation (China) Holding Ltd. (1)
23rd Floor China World Tower No 1 Jian Guo Men Wai Avenue, Beijing, 100004, China
Tel.: (86) 105 798 6800
Construction Machinery Mfr
N.A.I.C.S.: 333120

Sumitomo Corporation (Guangzhou) Ltd. (1)
39/F Citic Plaza 233 Tian He North Road, Guangzhou, 510613, China
Tel.: (86) 20 8752 0068
Electronic Parts & Equipment Whslr
N.A.I.C.S.: 423690
Kurihara Jun *(Office Mgr)*

Sumitomo Corporation (Hong Kong) Limited (1)
23rd Fl United Centre No 95, GPO Box 3619, Queensway, Hong Kong, China (Hong Kong)
Tel.: (852) 28609300
Metal Product Whslr
N.A.I.C.S.: 423510

Sumitomo Corporation (Qingdao) Ltd. (1)
1101-1103 11F No 9 Xiang Gang Middle Road Qingdao, Shangri-La Centre Office Tower, Qingdao, 266071, China
Tel.: (86) 532 8388 3939
Automobile Parts Distr
N.A.I.C.S.: 423120

Sumitomo Corporation (Shanghai) Limited (1)
10F Shanghai World Financial Center 100 Century Avenue, Pudong New Area, Shanghai, 200120, China
Tel.: (86) 21 6146 1888
Web Site: http://www.sumitomocorp.co.jp
Sales Range: $50-74.9 Million
Emp.: 200
Metal Product Whslr
N.A.I.C.S.: 423510

Sumitomo Corporation (Tianjin) Ltd. (1)
Room 2801 28th Floor The Exchange Tower No 1 189 Nanjing Road, Heping District, Tianjin, 300051, China
Tel.: (86) 222 331 8000
Construction Machinery Mfr
N.A.I.C.S.: 333120

Sumitomo Corporation - Osaka Office (1)
4-5-33 Kitahama Chuo-ku, Chuo-ku, Osaka, 541-8666, Japan
Tel.: (81) 6 6220 6000
Metals Service Centers & Offices
N.A.I.C.S.: 423510

Sumitomo Corporation Andes S.A.S. (1)
Carrera 9 No 115-06 Oficina 1904 Edificio Tierra Firme, Bogota, 110111, Colombia
Tel.: (57) 317 379 5457
Construction Machinery Mfr
N.A.I.C.S.: 333120

Sumitomo Corporation Argentina S.A. (1)
Carlos Pellegrini 719 Piso 10, C1009ABO, Buenos Aires, Argentina
Tel.: (54) 1152743040
Web Site: http://www.sumitomocorp.co.jp
Industrial Equipment Mfr
N.A.I.C.S.: 333248

Sumitomo Corporation Asia & Oceania Pte. Ltd. (1)
182 Cecil Street 22-01 Frasers Tower, Singapore, 069547, Singapore
Tel.: (65) 6 533 7722
Metal Product Distr
N.A.I.C.S.: 423510

Sumitomo Corporation Asia Pte. Ltd. (1)
60 Anson Road 05-01 Mapletree Anson, Singapore, 079914, Singapore
Tel.: (65) 6533 7722
Web Site: http://www.sumitomocorp.com.sg
Emp.: 250
Oil & Gas Consumable Fuels Distr
N.A.I.C.S.: 457210
Masao Sekiuchi *(Pres & CEO)*

Sumitomo Corporation Capital Europe Plc (1)
Vintners' Place 68 Upper Thames Street, London, EC4V 3BJ, United Kingdom
Tel.: (44) 2072463600
Web Site: http://www.sumitomocorpeurope.com
Financial Management Services
N.A.I.C.S.: 523999
Kiyoshi Sunobe *(Mng Dir)*

Sumitomo Corporation Colombia S.A. (1)
Apartado Aereo DC 8 Calle 113 No 7-21 Oficina 1111, PO Box 94325, Torre A Distrito Capital, Bogota, Colombia
Tel.: (57) 16292171
Web Site: http://www.sumitomocorp.co.jp
Chemical Products Mfr & Distr
N.A.I.C.S.: 325998

Sumitomo Corporation Dis Ticaret A.S. (1)
Beybi Giz Plaza Meydan Sokak No 1 Kat 18, Maslak, Istanbul, 34398, Turkiye
Tel.: (90) 212 2902560
Sales Range: $25-49.9 Million
Emp.: 50
Industrial Machinery Distr
N.A.I.C.S.: 423830
Robert Schilton *(Gen Mgr)*

Sumitomo Corporation Equity Asia Limited (1)
Unit B1 23/F United Centre 95 Queensway, No 1 Harbour View Street, Hong Kong, China (Hong Kong)
Tel.: (852) 2 295 0300
Web Site: https://www.scequity.com.hk
Financial Management Services
N.A.I.C.S.: 523999
Francis Wong *(Exec Dir)*

Sumitomo Corporation Espana S.A. (1)
Calle Insanta Mercedes 90 7th Floor, 28020, Madrid, Spain
Tel.: (34) 91 555 3033
Emp.: 18
Industrial Product Distr
N.A.I.C.S.: 423840
Damingo Cerdates *(Mng Dir)*

Sumitomo Corporation Europe Holding Limited (1)
Vintners Place 68 Upper Thames Street, London, EC4V 3BJ, United Kingdom
Tel.: (44) 2072463600
Web Site: http://www.sumitomocorp.com
Emp.: 200
Investment Management Service
N.A.I.C.S.: 523999

Sumitomo Corporation Global Commodities Limited (1)
Vintners Place 68 Upper Thames Street, London, EC4V 3BJ, United Kingdom
Tel.: (44) 20 7246 3716
Sales Range: $50-74.9 Million
Emp.: 21
Commodities Trading Services

INTERNATIONAL PUBLIC

N.A.I.C.S.: 523160

Sumitomo Corporation Global Research Co. Ltd. (1)
1-8-11 Harumi Island Triton Square Office Tower Y, Chuo-ku, Tokyo, 104-0053, Japan (100%)
Tel.: (81) 351663182
Web Site: http://www.scgr.co.jp
Emp.: 38
Market Research & Surveying Services
N.A.I.C.S.: 541910
Hiroyuki Takai *(Pres)*

Sumitomo Corporation Hokkaido Co., Ltd. (1)
Fukamiya Odori Building 2 Odori-nishi 8-chome, Chuo-ku, Sapporo, 060-0042, Hokkaido, Japan
Tel.: (81) 11 261 9131
Web Site: http://www.sumitomocorp.com
Specialty Chemicals & Industrial Machinery Distr
N.A.I.C.S.: 424690

Sumitomo Corporation India Private Limited (1)
4th Floor DLF Centre, Sansad Marg, New Delhi, 110001, India
Tel.: (91) 1123737181
Sales Range: $25-49.9 Million
Emp.: 65
Industrial Metal Products Mfr
N.A.I.C.S.: 332999
Rajiv Mishra *(Gen Mgr)*

Sumitomo Corporation Iran, Ltd. (1)
3rd Floor Maadiran Building No 3 Aftab St Khoddami Ave Vanak Sq, PO Box 11155-4667, 1994834574, Tehran, Iran
Tel.: (98) 218 862 3760
Metal Product Distr
N.A.I.C.S.: 423510

Sumitomo Corporation Italia S.p.A. (1)
Viale Piero e Alberto Pirelli 6 Torre U7, Milan, 20126, Italy
Tel.: (39) 0269721
Web Site: http://www.sumitomocorp.com
Emp.: 10
Agriculture & Industrial Products Distr
N.A.I.C.S.: 423840

Sumitomo Corporation Korea Ltd. (1)
20th Fl Kyobo Life Insurance Bldg 1 Jongro, Jongno-gu, Seoul, 03154, Korea (South)
Tel.: (82) 2 721 1114
Web Site: http://www.sumitomocorp.com
Emp.: 80
Specialty Chemical & Steel Products Distr
N.A.I.C.S.: 423510

Sumitomo Corporation Kyushu Co., Ltd. (1)
Hakata Kangen Building 6F 30-23 Hakataekimae 3-chome, Hakata-ku, Fukuoka, 812-0011, Japan
Tel.: (81) 924414111
Web Site: http://www.sumitomocorp.com
Industrial Machinery Whslr
N.A.I.C.S.: 423830

Sumitomo Corporation Middle East FZE (1)
Level 2 The Offices 3 One Central Dubai World Trade Centre, PO Box 340744, Dubai, United Arab Emirates
Tel.: (971) 48178000
Web Site: http://www.sumitomocorp.com
Steel Products Mfr
N.A.I.C.S.: 331110

Sumitomo Corporation Saudi Arabia Ltd. (1)
Al-Hugayet Skyline Tower 17th Floor King Fahd Road, PO Box 3229, Al Khobar, 31952, Saudi Arabia
Tel.: (966) 13 882 3662
Construction Machinery Mfr
N.A.I.C.S.: 333120

Sumitomo Corporation Thailand, Ltd. (1)
25th Floor Unit 1-5 and 7 26th Floor 32nd Floor Unit 2-3 CRC Tower, All Seasons Place 87/2 Wireless Road Lumpini Phatumwan, Bangkok, 10330, Thailand

AND PRIVATE COMPANIES — SUMITOMO CORPORATION

Tel.: (66) 26540002
Web Site: http://www.sumitomocorp.com
Sales Range: $50-74.9 Million
Emp.: 222
Automotive Metal Products Whslr
N.A.I.C.S.: 423120

Sumitomo Corporation Tohoku Co., Ltd. (1)
Sendai Capital Tower 15F 10-3 Chuo 4-chome, Aoba-ku, Sendai, 980-0021, Miyagi, Japan
Tel.: (81) 222626232
Web Site: http://www.sumitomocorp.com
Sales Range: $25-49.9 Million
Emp.: 15
Specialty Chemicals & Industrial Machinery Mfr
N.A.I.C.S.: 325180

Sumitomo Corporation Vietnam LLC (1)
Hanoi Tower 49 Hai Ba Trung Street, Hanoi, Vietnam
Tel.: (84) 4 3825 8818
Sales Range: $25-49.9 Million
Emp.: 30
Seal Products Distr
N.A.I.C.S.: 423510

Sumitomo Corporation de Mexico S.A. de C.V. (1)
Jaime Blames No 8-801 Col Los Morales, Polanco, Mexico, 11510, Mexico
Tel.: (52) 5521223500
Waste Water Treatment Services
N.A.I.C.S.: 221310

Sumitomo Corporation del Ecuador S.A. (1)
Av Amazonas 4080 Edificio Puerta del Sol, Torre Oeste Piso 7, Quito, Ecuador
Tel.: (593) 22261751
Sales Range: $10-24.9 Million
Emp.: 20
Flower Farming Services
N.A.I.C.S.: 111998

Sumitomo Corporation del Peru S.A. (1)
Av Jose Pardo 513 Ofic 701, Miraflores, Lima, Peru
Tel.: (51) 1 242 7991
Web Site: http://www.sumitomocorp.co.jp
Seal Products Distr
N.A.I.C.S.: 423510

Sumitomo Corporation do Brasil S.A. (1)
Avenida Paulista 37-14 e 20 andares, Bela Vista, Sao Paulo, 01311-902, Brazil
Tel.: (55) 1131794800
Web Site: http://www.sumitomo.com.br
Sales Range: $25-49.9 Million
Emp.: 60
Industrial Machinery Mfr
N.A.I.C.S.: 333248
Hiroshi Tomishima *(Pres)*

Sumitomo Corporation of America (1)
300 Madison Ave, New York, NY 10017 **(100%)**
Tel.: (212) 207-0700
Web Site: http://www.sumitomocorpofamericas.com
Sales Range: $75-99.9 Million
Emp.: 200
Distribution, Project Management, Supply Chain Management, Technology Transfer, Trade & Transportation Services
N.A.I.C.S.: 488999

Subsidiary (Domestic):

123 Mission LLC (2)
123 Mission St Fl 10, San Francisco, CA 94105-1551
Tel.: (415) 495-3623
Office Building Leasing Services
N.A.I.C.S.: 531120

Cantex Inc. (2)
2101 SE 1st St, Mineral Wells, TX 76067-5601
Tel.: (940) 325-3344
Web Site: http://www.cantexinc.com
Sales Range: $125-149.9 Million
Electrical Conduit Mfr
N.A.I.C.S.: 326122

Dave Milius *(VP-Sls & Mktg)*

Champion Cinco Pipe & Supply LP (2)
4 City N 16945 Northchase Dr Ste 200, Houston, TX 77060
Tel.: (713) 468-6555
Web Site: http://championscinco.com
Textile Product Mills
N.A.I.C.S.: 314999

Diversified CPC International, Inc. (2)
24338 W Durkee Rd, Channahon, IL 60410
Tel.: (815) 424-2000
Web Site: http://www.diversifiedcpc.com
Sales Range: $25-49.9 Million
Emp.: 30
Aerosol Propellants Mfr & Distr
N.A.I.C.S.: 325180
George K. Sehringer *(VP-Sls & Mktg)*

Edgen Group Inc. (2)
18444 Highland Rd, Baton Rouge, LA 70809
Tel.: (225) 756-9868
Web Site: http://www.edgengroup.com
Sales Range: $1-4.9 Billion
Steel Pipes, Valves & Other Related Products Distr
N.A.I.C.S.: 423510
Daniel J. O'Leary *(Chm, Pres & CEO)*

Subsidiary (Domestic):

EM Holdings LLC (3)
18444 Highland Rd, Baton Rouge, LA 70809
Tel.: (225) 756-9868
Web Site: http://www.edgenmurray.com
Emp.: 50
Investment Management Service
N.A.I.C.S.: 551112
Erika Fortenberry *(Gen Mgr)*

Subsidiary (Non-US):

EMGH Limited (3)
20-22 Bedford Row, London, WC1R 4JS, United Kingdom
Tel.: (44) 1313333333
Sales Range: $25-49.9 Million
Emp.: 5
Investment Management Service
N.A.I.C.S.: 551112

Edgen Murray (India) Pvt, Ltd (3)
215 Atrium C-Wing Unit 320 3rd Floor Andheri Kurla Road, Mumbai, 400 069, India
Tel.: (91) 2261270519
Web Site: http://www.edgenmurray.com
Emp.: 4
Energy Infrastructure Steel Product Distr
N.A.I.C.S.: 423510

Subsidiary (Domestic):

Edgen Murray Corporation (3)
18444 Highland Rd, Baton Rouge, LA 70809
Tel.: (225) 756-9868
Web Site: http://www.edgenmurray.com
Sales Range: $250-299.9 Million
Emp.: 238
Specialty Pipe & Components
N.A.I.C.S.: 332111

Branch (Domestic):

Edgen Murray Corp. - Houston Office (4)
10370 Richmond Ave Ste 900, Houston, TX 77042
Tel.: (713) 268-7200
Web Site: http://www.edgenmurray.com
Sales Range: $10-24.9 Million
Emp.: 60
Carbon Products
N.A.I.C.S.: 331210

Subsidiary (Non-US):

Edgen Murray Europe Limited (3)
Newbridge Industrial Estate, Newbridge, EH28 8PJ, United Kingdom
Tel.: (44) 1313333333
Web Site: http://www.edgenmurray.com
Emp.: 80
Specialty Steel Product Distr
N.A.I.C.S.: 423510

David Kemp *(VP-Europe, Middle East, and Africa)*

Edgen Murray FZE (3)
PO Box 61225, Jebel Ali, Dubai, United Arab Emirates
Tel.: (971) 48834486
Web Site: http://www.edgenmurray.com
Sales Range: $25-49.9 Million
Emp.: 40
Energy Infrastructure Steel Product Distr
N.A.I.C.S.: 423510

Edgen Murray France S.A.S. (3)
11-11bis rue Louis Philippe, Neuilly-sur-Seine, 92200, France
Tel.: (33) 170614050
Web Site: http://www.edgenmurray.com
Emp.: 12
Specialty Steel Product Distr
N.A.I.C.S.: 423510

Edgen Murray Pte. Ltd. (3)
7 Tuas South Street 5, Singapore, 637136, Singapore
Tel.: (65) 62233334
Energy Infrastructure Steel Product Distr
N.A.I.C.S.: 423510

Edgen Murray do Brasil Limitada (3)
Centro Empresarial Mario Henrique Simonsen Avenida das Americas, 3434-Bloco 5-Sala 413, Rio de Janeiro, 22640-102, Brazil
Tel.: (55) 2134311280
Sales Range: $25-49.9 Million
Emp.: 10
Energy Infrastructure Steel Product Distr
N.A.I.C.S.: 423510
Alex Collazo *(Dir-Dev)*

HS Pipequipment (Aberdeen) Limited (3)
6 Minto Place, Altens, Aberdeen, AB12 3SN, Aberdeenshire, United Kingdom
Tel.: (44) 1224249900
Web Site: http://www.hspvalves.com
Sales Range: $25-49.9 Million
Emp.: 15
Oil & Gas Industrial Valve Supplier
N.A.I.C.S.: 423840

HS Pipequipment (Northern) Limited (3)
Units 12/13 Primrose Hill Industrial Estate, Orde Wingate Way, Stockton-on-Tees, TS19 0GA, United Kingdom
Tel.: (44) 1642608999
Web Site: http://www.hspvalves.com
Emp.: 16
Specialty Steel Product Distr
N.A.I.C.S.: 423510

HSP Group Limited (3)
Red Shute Hill Industrial Estate, Thatcham, RG18 9QL, United Kingdom
Tel.: (44) 1635201329
Web Site: http://www.hspvalves.com
Sales Range: $25-49.9 Million
Emp.: 15
Oil & Gas Industrial Valve Supplier
N.A.I.C.S.: 423840
Peter Everett *(Gen Mgr)*

Subsidiary (Domestic):

Global Stainless Supply, Inc. (2)
8900 Railwood Dr Ste A, Houston, TX 77078
Tel.: (713) 980-5089
Web Site: http://www.onestoppvf.com
Stainless Steel Wire Distr
N.A.I.C.S.: 423510
Steve Martinez *(Mgr-Los Angeles Branch)*

Subsidiary (Domestic):

Forgings Flanges & Fittings, LLC (3)
8900 Railwood Dr Ste B, Houston, TX 77078
Tel.: (713) 695-5400
Web Site: http://www.onestoppvf.com
Stainless Steel Services & Distr
N.A.I.C.S.: 423510
Steve Martinez *(Mgr-Los Angeles Branch)*

Subsidiary (Domestic):

Ipanema Shoe Corporation (2)
350 5th Ave Ste 7100, New York, NY 10118-7193

Importer & Distributor of Shoes from Brazil
N.A.I.C.S.: 316210

Linder Industrial Machinery Company (2)
1601 S Frontage Rd, Plant City, FL 33563-2014
Tel.: (813) 754-2727
Web Site: http://www.linderco.com
Sales Range: $50-74.9 Million
Emp.: 100
Construction & Mining Machinery
N.A.I.C.S.: 423810
Polly Van Valkenburg *(Dir-HR)*

Subsidiary (Domestic):

Southern Tractor & Outdoors (3)
1205 Veterans Pkwy N, Moultrie, GA 31788-1934
Tel.: (229) 998-3882
Web Site: http://www.southerntractoroutdoors.com
Farm & Garden Machinery & Equipment Merchant Whslr
N.A.I.C.S.: 423820
Mike Horne *(Mgr)*

Subsidiary (Domestic):

Pacific Summit Energy LLC (2)
2010 Main St Ste 1200, Irvine, CA 92614
Tel.: (949) 777-3200
Web Site: http://www.pacificsummitenergy.com
Emp.: 80
Natural Gas Distribution Services
N.A.I.C.S.: 221210

Premier Pipe LLC (2)
15600 JFK Blvd Ste 200, Houston, TX 77032
Tel.: (832) 300-8100
Web Site: http://www.prempipe.com
Sales Range: $25-49.9 Million
Emp.: 50
Industrial Supplies Distr
N.A.I.C.S.: 423840
Joe Schumacher *(Exec VP-Sls)*

Presperse, Inc. (2)
19 Schoolhouse Rd, Somerset, NJ 08873
Tel.: (732) 356-5200
Web Site: http://www.presperse.com
Sales Range: $25-49.9 Million
Emp.: 34
Chemicals Mfr
N.A.I.C.S.: 325199

SMS International Corporation (2)
1601 S Frontage Rd, Plant City, FL 33563
Tel.: (813) 754-2727
Construction Materials Distr
N.A.I.C.S.: 423390
Shingo Kato *(Pres)*

Subsidiary (Domestic):

Sunstate Equipment Co. LLC (3)
5552 E Washington St, Phoenix, AZ 85034
Tel.: (602) 275-2398
Web Site: http://www.sunstateequip.com
Sales Range: $150-199.9 Million
Emp.: 391
Heavy Construction Equipment Rental
N.A.I.C.S.: 532412
Chris Watts *(Pres & CEO)*

Subsidiary (Domestic):

Steel Summit International, Inc. (2)
6450 Poe Ave Ste 102, Dayton, OH 45414-2646
Tel.: (937) 264-0537
Emp.: 6
Steel Product Distr
N.A.I.C.S.: 423510

SteelSummit Holdings, Inc. (2)
1718 JP Hennessy Dr, La Vergne, TN 37086
Tel.: (615) 641-3300
Web Site: http://www.steelsummit.com
Sales Range: $50-74.9 Million
Emp.: 100
Flat Rolled Steel Products Mfr & Whslr
N.A.I.C.S.: 423510
Eddie Luz *(CFO)*

Sumisho Global Logistics (USA) Corporation (2)

SUMITOMO CORPORATION

Sumitomo Corporation—(Continued)
1979 Marcus Ave Ste 220, Lake Success, NY 11042
Tel.: (516) 684-3100
Web Site: http://www.sglusa.com
Emp.: 40
Logistics & Freight Transportation Services
N.A.I.C.S.: 541614

Sumitomo Corporation of America (2)
300 Madison Ave, New York, NY 10017
Tel.: (212) 207-0379
Web Site: http://www.sumitomo.com
Sales Range: $50-74.9 Million
Emp.: 15
Import & Export of Specialty Chemical Products
N.A.I.C.S.: 424690

Subsidiary (Domestic):

Werner Aero Services, LLC (3)
19 Industrial Ave, Mahwah, NJ 07430 (51%)
Tel.: (201) 785-9700
Sales Range: $1-9.9 Million
Emp.: 25
Asset Management & Logistical Solution Provider
N.A.I.C.S.: 423860
Brenda Ruditzky *(Dir-Bus Dev)*

Subsidiary (Domestic):

Summit Stainless (2)
9838 Geary Ave, Santa Fe Springs, CA 90670-3238
Tel.: (562) 946-1591
Web Site: http://www.summitstainless.com
Sales Range: $25-49.9 Million
Emp.: 30
Metal Bars
N.A.I.C.S.: 423510

Summit Stainless Steel, LLC (2)
2001 Elizabeth St, North Brunswick, NJ 08902-4901
Tel.: (732) 297-9505
Web Site: http://www.summitstainless.com
Sales Range: $25-49.9 Million
Emp.: 50
Steel Products Mfr
N.A.I.C.S.: 423510
Rich Husar *(VP-Admin & Controller)*

TBC Corporation (2)
4300 TBC Way, Palm Beach Gardens, FL 33410
Tel.: (561) 383-3100
Web Site: http://www.tbccorp.com
Wholesale Distr of Automotive Replacement Tires; Operator of Automotive Service Centers & Franchisor of Tire Retail Centers
N.A.I.C.S.: 423130
Scott Hurd *(CFO & Exec VP)*

Subsidiary (Domestic):

Big O Tires, Inc. (3)
4280 Professional Ctr Dr Ste 400, Palm Beach Gardens, FL 33410
Tel.: (561) 383-3100
Web Site: http://www.bigotires.com
Sales Range: $25-49.9 Million
Emp.: 90
Franchisor of Tire Retail Centers
N.A.I.C.S.: 441340

Group (Domestic):

Midas, Inc. (3)
1300 Arlington Heights Rd, Itasca, IL 60143
Tel.: (630) 438-3000
Sales Range: $300-349.9 Million
Emp.: 765
Holding Company; General Auto Repair Service Stations Owner, Operator & Franchisor
N.A.I.C.S.: 551112

Subsidiary (Domestic):

Midas International, Inc. (4)
823 Donald Ross Rd, Juno Beach, FL 33408
Tel.: (630) 438-3000
Web Site: http://www.midas.com
Sales Range: $100-124.9 Million
Emp.: 140
Franchisor of Muffler Shops; Automotive Aftermarket Mufflers, Exhausts, Brakes & Suspension Products & Services
N.A.I.C.S.: 423110

Subsidiary (Non-US):

Corporacion Mexicana De Servicio Automotriz, S.A. de C.V. (5)
Rio Rosas 330 (esq. Vasconcelos), Garza Garcia, 66268, Mexico
Tel.: (52) 8378 0464
Auto Parts Stores
N.A.I.C.S.: 441330

Corporativo Midas Mexico (5)
Av Gomez Morin No 900 Col Carrizalejo Torre Plaza Vita Piso 7, Despacho 701, 66267, Garza Garcia, Nuevo Leon, Mexico
Tel.: (52) 8183780464
Web Site: http://www.midas.com.mx
Auto Parts Stores
N.A.I.C.S.: 441330
Richard Mattenberger *(Mng Dir)*

Midas Asia Pacific Pty. Ltd. (5)
76-92 Station St, Nunawading, 3131, VIC, Australia
Tel.: (61) 388781111
Web Site: http://www.midas.com.au
Auto Parts Stores
N.A.I.C.S.: 441330

Midas Canada Inc. (5)
4601 Highway 7 East, Markham, L3R 1M6, ON, Canada
Tel.: (289) 806-0546
Web Site: http://www.midas.com
Sales Range: $25-49.9 Million
Emp.: 12
Auto Parts Stores
N.A.I.C.S.: 441330

Midas Europe SAM (5)
Gildo Pastor Center, 7 rue du Gobain, MC 98000, Monaco, Monaco
Tel.: (377) 93 10 13 50
Auto Parts Stores
N.A.I.C.S.: 441330

Subsidiary (Non-US):

Midas Belgique (6)
Potvlietlaan 6, 2600, Berchem, Belgium
Tel.: (32) 868350
Web Site: http://www.midas.be
Sales Range: $25-49.9 Million
Emp.: 60
Auto Parts Stores
N.A.I.C.S.: 441330

Midas Espana (6)
St Jose Echegaray 10, PO Box 28100, 28760, Alcobendas, Spain
Tel.: (34) 918066000
Web Site: http://www.midas.es
Sales Range: $50-74.9 Million
Emp.: 110
Auto Parts Stores
N.A.I.C.S.: 441330
Ramon Rueda *(Gen Mgr)*

Midas France SAS (6)
108 Ave Jean Moulin 78170 La Celle Saint Cloud, Paris, France
Tel.: (33) 130825656
Web Site: http://www.midas.sr
Sales Range: $150-199.9 Million
Auto Parts Stores
N.A.I.C.S.: 441330

Midas Italia S.p.A. (6)
viale Carlo Emanuele II, 150, 10078 Venaria Reale, Turin, Italy
Tel.: (39) 011 6879 396
Sales Range: $150-199.9 Million
Auto Parts Stores
N.A.I.C.S.: 441330

Midas Polska (6)
ul Jubielerska 10, 04-190, Warsaw, Poland
Tel.: (48) 0226116263
Web Site: http://www.midas.polska.pl
Sales Range: $25-49.9 Million
Emp.: 23
Auto Parts Stores
N.A.I.C.S.: 441330

Subsidiary (Non-US):

Midas Portugal (5)
Rua dos Ciprestes 48 - Office no Estoril Alto dos Gaios, 2765-623, Estoril, Portugal
Tel.: (351) 210115017
Web Site: http://www.midas.pt
Auto Parts Stores
N.A.I.C.S.: 441330

United Auto Service & Maintenance Co Ltd (5)
Khorais Road, PO Box 1321, Riyadh, Saudi Arabia
Tel.: (966) 14936333
Auto Parts Stores
N.A.I.C.S.: 441330

Subsidiary (Domestic):

Midas Properties (4)
1067 5th Ave Ste 1, New York, NY 10128-0101
Tel.: (212) 813-9797
Web Site: http://www.bgsa.com
Sales Range: Less than $1 Million
Emp.: 10
Commercial Real Estate Management
N.A.I.C.S.: 531390

Division (Domestic):

TBC Private Brands (4)
4770 Hickory Hills Rd, Memphis, TN 38141
Tel.: (901) 363-8030
Mfr, Marketer & Distr of Tires
N.A.I.C.S.: 326211

Subsidiary (Domestic):

Tennessee Steelsummit (4)
1718 JP Hennessy Dr, La Vergne, TN 37086-3525
Tel.: (615) 641-3300
Web Site: http://www.steelsummit.com
Steel Mfrs
N.A.I.C.S.: 423510

Joint Venture (Domestic):

The Hartz Mountain Corporation (2)
400 Plz Dr, Secaucus, NJ 07094-3605 (49%)
Tel.: (201) 271-4800
Web Site: https://www.hartz.com
Sales Range: $125-149.9 Million
Pet Care Products & Accessories Mfr & Distr
N.A.I.C.S.: 311111
Vitor Oliveira *(Engr-Pkg)*

Subsidiary (Domestic):

Unique Machine, LLC (2)
8875 King St, Anchorage, AK 99515
Tel.: (907) 563-3012
Web Site: http://www.umalaska.com
Sales Range: $25-49.9 Million
Emp.: 100
Machine Tool Distr
N.A.I.C.S.: 423830
Patrick D. Hanley *(Gen Mgr)*

Sumitomo Corporation of the Philippines (1)
35th Floor Philamlife Tower 8767 Paseo de Roxas, PO Box 2351, Makati, 1226, Metro Manila, Philippines
Tel.: (63) 2 885 0671
Web Site: http://www.sumitomocorp.co.jp
Emp.: 22
Industrial Machinery Mfr
N.A.I.C.S.: 333248
Hiroshi Shiraishi *(Pres)*

Sumitomo Deutschland GmbH (1)
Georg-Glock-Strasse 8, 40474, Dusseldorf, Germany
Tel.: (49) 21145700
Web Site: http://www.sumitomocorp.com
Sales Range: $25-49.9 Million
Emp.: 60
Construction & Agriculture Machinery Distr
N.A.I.C.S.: 423810

Sumitomo France S.A.S. (1)
152 Avenue des Champs - Elysees, 75008, Paris, France
Tel.: (33) 14 067 8400
Web Site: http://www.sumitomocorp.com
Emp.: 6
Chemical Products Distr
N.A.I.C.S.: 424690
Naoyuki Ishii *(Pres)*

INTERNATIONAL PUBLIC

Sumitomo Mitsui Auto Service Company, Limited (1)
Tokyo Opera City Tower 3-20-2 Nishishinjuku, Shinjuku-Ku, Tokyo, 163-1434, Japan
Tel.: (81) 35 302 5610
Web Site: http://www.smauto.co.jp
Emp.: 1,979
Automobile Parts Distr
N.A.I.C.S.: 423120
Akira Tsuyuguchi *(Pres & CEO)*

Subsidiary (Domestic):

Cedyna Auto Lease Co., Ltd. (2)
2-8-12 Sakae, Naka-Ku, Nagoya, 460-0008, Aichi, Japan
Tel.: (81) 52 212 1081
Web Site: https://www.cedyna-al.jp
Automobile Leasing Services
N.A.I.C.S.: 532112
Hideo Shiraki *(Pres)*

Sumitomo Mitsui Finance & Leasing Co., Ltd. (1)
1-3-2 Marunouchi, Chiyoda-ku, Tokyo, 100-8287, Japan (50%)
Tel.: (81) 352196400
Web Site: http://www.smfl.co.jp
Commercial Office Equipment Finance & Leasing Services
N.A.I.C.S.: 532420

Subsidiary (Non-US):

PT. SMFL Leasing Indonesia (2)
Menara BTPN 31st Floor Jl Dr Ide Anak Agung Gde Agung Kav 5 5-5 6, Mega Kuningan, Jakarta Selatan, 12950, Indonesia
Tel.: (62) 2180628710
Web Site: http://www.smfl.co.jp
Emp.: 48
Commercial Office Equipment Finance & Leasing Services
N.A.I.C.S.: 532420

SMBC Aviation Capital Limited (2)
IFSC House, IFSC, Dublin, 1, Ireland
Tel.: (353) 1 859 9000
Web Site: https://www.smbc.aero
Sales Range: $50-74.9 Million
Emp.: 90
Commercial Aircraft Acquisition & Leasing Services
N.A.I.C.S.: 532411
Peter Barrett *(CEO)*

SMFL Leasing (Malaysia) Sdn. Bhd. (2)
Suite 16D Level 16 Vista Tower The Intermark No 348, Jalan Tun Razak, 50400, Kuala Lumpur, Malaysia
Tel.: (60) 327100170
Web Site: http://www.smfl.co.jp
Commercial Office Equipment Finance & Leasing Services
N.A.I.C.S.: 532420

SMFL Leasing (Thailand) Co., Ltd. (2)
30th Floor Q House Lumpini Building 1 South Sathorn Road, Tungmahamek Sathorn, Bangkok, 10120, Thailand
Tel.: (66) 26777400
Sales Range: $50-74.9 Million
Emp.: 60
Commercial Office Equipment Finance & Leasing Services
N.A.I.C.S.: 532420

Subsidiary (Domestic):

SMFL MIRAI Partners Co., Ltd (2)
1-5-1 Otemachi, Chiyoda-ku, Tokyo, 100-0004, Japan
Tel.: (81) 3 6695 8320
Web Site: http://www.smfl-mp.co.jp
Emp.: 118
Investment Services
N.A.I.C.S.: 523999
Tatsurou Terada *(Pres)*

Subsidiary (Domestic):

SMFL MIRAI Partners Investment 2 Co., Ltd. (3)
5-1 Otemachi-chome, Chiyoda-ku, Tokyo, 100-0004, Japan
Tel.: (81) 366958320
Holding Company
N.A.I.C.S.: 551112

AND PRIVATE COMPANIES — SUMITOMO CORPORATION

Hiroyasu Komiya (Dir)

Subsidiary (Domestic):

Kenedix, Inc. (4)
Hibiya Parkfront 2-1-6 Uchisaiwaicho, Chiyoda-ku, Tokyo, 100-0011, Japan (70%)
Tel.: (81) 351576100
Web Site: http://www.kenedix.com
Rev.: $644,889,420
Assets: $1,576,524,740
Liabilities: $662,560,010
Net Worth: $913,964,730
Earnings: $97,871,410
Emp.: 339
Fiscal Year-end: 12/31/2019
Real Estate Investment Advisory, Acquisition, Brokerage, Real Estate Consulting & Asset Management
N.A.I.C.S.: 531210
Soushi Ikeda (Mng Dir & Head-Strategic Investment Dept)

Subsidiary (Domestic):

CRES Co., Ltd. (5)
Hiei Kudankita Building 2nd floor 4-1-3 Kudankita, Chiyoda-ku, Tokyo, 102-0073, Japan
Tel.: (81) 332228011
Web Site: https://www.cres-c.com
Real Estate Manangement Services
N.A.I.C.S.: 531312

Kenedix Advisors Co., Ltd (5)
2-2-9 Shimbashi, Tokyo, 105-0004, Minato-ku, Japan
Tel.: (81) 335194056
Web Site: http://www.kenedix.com
Sales Range: $50-74.9 Million
Emp.: 30
Financial Advisors
N.A.I.C.S.: 523999

Subsidiary (Non-US):

Sumitomo Mitsui Auto Leasing & Service (Thailand) Co., Ltd. (2)
87/2 CRC Tower All Seasons Place 41st Floor Wireless Road, Pathumwan, Bangkok, 10330, Thailand
Tel.: (66) 22529511
Web Site: https://www.smauto.co.th
Automobile Finance Leasing Services
N.A.I.C.S.: 522220

Sumitomo Mitsui Finance & Leasing (China) Co., Ltd. (2)
Unit 2302 TaiKoo Hui Tower 1385 Tianhe Road, 385 Tianhe Rd, Guangzhou, 510620, China
Tel.: (86) 2087550021
Sales Range: $50-74.9 Million
Emp.: 50
Commercial Office Equipment Finance & Leasing Services
N.A.I.C.S.: 532420

Branch (Domestic):

Sumitomo Mitsui Finance & Leasing (China) Co., Ltd. - Shanghai Branch (3)
10F Pingan Riverfront Financial Center 757 Mengzi Road, Huangpu District, Shanghai, China
Tel.: (86) 2153965522
Commercial Office Equipment Finance & Leasing Services
N.A.I.C.S.: 532420

Subsidiary (Non-US):

Sumitomo Mitsui Finance & Leasing (Hong Kong) Ltd. (2)
Units 4206-8 42/F Dah Sing Financial Centre 248 Queen's Road East, 18 Harcourt Road, Hong Kong, China (Hong Kong)
Tel.: (852) 25232280
Sales Range: $50-74.9 Million
Emp.: 30
Commercial Office Equipment Finance & Leasing Services
N.A.I.C.S.: 532420

Sumitomo Mitsui Finance & Leasing (Singapore) Pte. Ltd. (2)
152 Beach Road 05-06/08 Gateway East, Singapore, 189721, Singapore
Tel.: (65) 62242955
Web Site: http://www.smfl.co.jp
Sales Range: $50-74.9 Million
Emp.: 10
Commercial Office Equipment Finance & Leasing Services
N.A.I.C.S.: 532420

Sumitomo Precision Products Co., Ltd. (1)
1-10 Fuso-cho, Amagasaki, 660-0891, Hyogo, Japan (83.4%)
Tel.: (81) 664828811
Web Site: http://www.spp.co.jp
Rev.: $423,993,680
Assets: $741,933,280
Liabilities: $459,112,720
Net Worth: $282,820,560
Earnings: $22,380,160
Emp.: 1,694
Fiscal Year-end: 03/31/2022
Aerospace & Industrial Equipment
N.A.I.C.S.: 334511
Machi Nakata (Exec VP-Corp R&D, Environmental Sys & Heat Exchangers)

Subsidiary (Domestic):

MET Co., Ltd. (2)
8F Office Tower Y 1-8-11 Harumi, Chuo-Ku, Tokyo, 104-6108, Japan
Tel.: (81) 362200726
Semiconductor Equipment Mfr
N.A.I.C.S.: 334413

Plant (Domestic):

MET Co., Ltd. - Amagasaki Factory (3)
1-10 Fuso-cho, Amagasaki, 660-0891, Hyogo, Japan
Tel.: (81) 664895900
Semiconductor Equipment Mfr
N.A.I.C.S.: 334413

Subsidiary (Domestic):

Shinsen Seiki Co., Ltd. (2)
1 Higashi-Mukojima Higashino-cho, Amagasaki, 660-0835, Hyogo, Japan
Tel.: (81) 664111531
Precision Machining Tools Mfr
N.A.I.C.S.: 332721

Sumisei Engineering Co., Ltd. (2)
1-10 Fuso-cho, Amagasaki, 660-0891, Japan
Tel.: (81) 664895893
Sales Range: $25-49.9 Million
Design Drawing & Engineering Services
N.A.I.C.S.: 541330

Sumisei Hydraulic Systems Co., Ltd. (2)
2-2-227 Tsujido Shindai, Fujisawa, 251-0041, Kanagawa, Japan
Tel.: (81) 466 35 1520
Web Site: http://www.spp.co.jp
Sales Range: $25-49.9 Million
Emp.: 20
Hydraulic Equipment Mfr & Distr
N.A.I.C.S.: 333248

Sumisei Sangyo Co., Ltd. (2)
1-8 Fuso-cho, Amagasaki, 660-0891, Japan
Tel.: (81) 664823444
Industrial Machinery & Equipment Distr
N.A.I.C.S.: 423830

Sumisei Service Co., Ltd. (2)
1-10 Fuso-cho, Amagasaki, 660-0891, Japan
Tel.: (81) 664895892
Industrial Equipment Mfr
N.A.I.C.S.: 333248

Sumisei Techno Service Co., Ltd. (2)
1-10 Fuso-cho, Amagasaki, 660-0891, Hyogo, Japan
Tel.: (81) 664895896
Sales Range: $150-199.9 Million
Emp.: 1,000
Industrial Machinery Repair & Maintenance Services
N.A.I.C.S.: 811310

Plant (Domestic):

Sumitomo Precision Products Co., Ltd. - Shiga Plant (2)
1000-15 Okamoto-cho, Kusatsu, 525-0044, Shiga, Japan
Tel.: (81) 775643811
Web Site: http://www.spp.co.jp
Sales Range: $50-74.9 Million
Emp.: 105
Aerospace Products Mfr
N.A.I.C.S.: 334511

Sumitomo Precision Products Co., Ltd. - Wakayama Plant (2)
1850 Minato, Wakayama, 640-8404, Japan
Tel.: (81) 73 457 2557
Web Site: http://www.spp.co.jp
Heat Exchanger Mfr
N.A.I.C.S.: 332410

Subsidiary (Non-US):

Sumitomo Precision Shanghai Co., Ltd. (2)
Rm 2201 Zhongxin Mansion No 1468 Nanjing West Road, Shanghai, 200040, China
Tel.: (86) 2162884747
Precision Machining Tools Mfr
N.A.I.C.S.: 332721

Subsidiary (US):

Sumitomo Precision USA, Inc. (2)
1639 Falcon Dr, Desoto, TX 75115
Tel.: (972) 228-9300
Web Site: http://www.spu-usa.com
Sales Range: $25-49.9 Million
Emp.: 10
Heat Exchanger Repair Services
N.A.I.C.S.: 811210
Lynn Lacey (Gen Mgr)

Subsidiary (Non-US):

Surface Technology Systems plc (2)
Imperial Park, Newport, NP10 8UJ, United Kingdom
Tel.: (44) 1633652400
Web Site: http://www.stsystems.com
Sales Range: $50-74.9 Million
Emp.: 190
Surface Deposition & Etching Equipment Mfr
N.A.I.C.S.: 333242

Sumitomo Shoji Chemicals Co., Ltd. (1)
8F Sumitomo Shoji Takebashi Bldg 2-2 Hitotsubashi 1-Chome, Chiyoda-ku, Tokyo, 100-0013, Japan
Tel.: (81) 35 220 8200
Web Site: https://www.sc-chem.co.jp
Emp.: 267
Plastic & Chemical Products Mfr
N.A.I.C.S.: 325211
Rei Ito (Pres)

Sumitomo Shoji Financial Management Co., Ltd. (1)
Otemachi Place East Tower 13-14F 2-3-2, Chiyoda-ku Otemachi, Tokyo, 100-8601, Japan
Tel.: (81) 362856482
Web Site: http://ssfm.co.jp
Sales Range: $150-199.9 Million
Emp.: 440
Financial Management Services
N.A.I.C.S.: 523999

Sumitomo Shoji Machinex Co., Ltd. (1)
10th 11th Floor Sumitomo Corporation Takebashi Building, 1-2-2 Hitotsubashi Chiyoda-ku, Tokyo, 100-0003, Japan
Tel.: (81) 34 531 3900
Web Site: https://www.smx.co.jp
Emp.: 465
Optical Communication System Sales, Computer Peripheral Devices & Environment-Related Machinery
N.A.I.C.S.: 423690
Meizo Sahashi (Pres)

Sumitronics Corporation (1)
10F Sumitomo Shoji Takebashi Bldg 1-2-2 Hitotsubashi, Chiyoda-ku, Tokyo, 100-0003, Japan
Tel.: (81) 36 259 1411
Web Site: https://www.sumitronics.co.jp
Emp.: 2,690
Electronic Parts Distr
N.A.I.C.S.: 423690
Keiya Endo (Pres & CEO)

Subsidiary (Non-US):

Sumitronics (Shenzhen) Ltd (2)
19F Ping An Bank Building No 1099 Shennan Road Central, Shenzhen, 518031, China
Tel.: (86) 755 2587 8000
Electronic Components Mfr
N.A.I.C.S.: 334419

Sumitronics (Thailand) Co., Ltd. (2)
18th Floor Column Tower 199 Ratchadapisek Road, Khlong Toei, Bangkok, 10110, Thailand
Tel.: (66) 2 663 0510
Web Site: http://www.sumitronics.co.jp
Sales Range: $25-49.9 Million
Emp.: 80
Electronic Equipment & Parts Distr
N.A.I.C.S.: 423690

Sumitronics Shanghai Co., Ltd. (2)
Room 302 Gubei International Fortune Center Phase II 1438, Hongqiao Road Changning District, Shanghai, 200050, China
Tel.: (86) 21 6082 5188
Web Site: http://www.sumitronics.co.jp
Electronic Component Mfr & Distr
N.A.I.C.S.: 334419

Sumitronics Hong Kong Ltd (1)
Unit 803A 8th Floor East Ocean Centre 98 Granville Road, Tsim Sha Tsui, Kowloon, China (Hong Kong)
Tel.: (852) 2722 6303
Sales Range: $25-49.9 Million
Emp.: 24
Financial Accounting Services
N.A.I.C.S.: 541219

Sumitronics Philippines, Inc. (1)
3-A Mountain Drive Light Industry Science Park II Brgy La Mesa, Calamba, 4130, Laguna, Philippines
Tel.: (63) 49 545 0144
Web Site: http://www.sumitronics.co.jp
Sales Range: $25-49.9 Million
Emp.: 50
Industrial Machinery Equipment Mfr & Distr
N.A.I.C.S.: 333248

Sumitronics Taiwan Co., Ltd. (1)
8F No 415 Gongdao 5th Road Sec 2, Hsinchu, 30069, Taiwan
Tel.: (886) 3 571 1499
Web Site: https://www.sumitronics.com.tw
Emp.: 80
Semiconductor Mfr & Distr
N.A.I.C.S.: 334413
Shin Udatsu (CEO & Chm)

Summit Agri-Business Corporation (1)
8th floor Kanda Izumicho Building 1 Kanda Izumicho, Chiyoda-Ku, Tokyo, 101-0024, Japan
Tel.: (81) 358392400
Web Site: http://www.summit-agri.co.jp
Fertilizer & Farm Products Mfr
N.A.I.C.S.: 325312

Summit Agro China Co., Ltd. (1)
Room306 Building One Office Area No 23 JinZhong Road, Huangpu District, Guangzhou, China
Tel.: (86) 203 781 2286
Web Site: https://www.summitagro.com
Agricultural Material Distr
N.A.I.C.S.: 424910

Summit Agro International, Ltd. (1)
Sumitomo Corporation Takebashi Bld 9F 1-2-2 Hitotsubashi, Chiyoda-ku, Tokyo, 100-0003, Japan
Tel.: (81) 36 259 1212
Web Site: https://www.summit-agro.co.jp
Emp.: 114
Insecticides & Herbicides Mfr
N.A.I.C.S.: 325320
Yukihiko Miki (Pres)

Summit Auto Lease Australia Pty Limited (1)
Unit 7 38-46 South Street, Rydalmere, 2116, NSW, Australia
Tel.: (61) 29 638 7833
Web Site: https://www.summitfleet.com.au
Sales Range: $25-49.9 Million
Emp.: 49
Automotive Fleet Leasing Services

SUMITOMO CORPORATION

INTERNATIONAL PUBLIC

Sumitomo Corporation—(Continued)
N.A.I.C.S.: 532112
David Clinch (Gen Mgr)

Summit Auto Poland Sp. z.o.o. (1)
ul Malownicza 29a, Warsaw, 02-272, Poland
Tel.: (48) 224310000
Web Site: http://www.hondaplaza.pl
Emp.: 50
Automobile Component Distr
N.A.I.C.S.: 423120
Mirek Rekawek (Gen Mgr)

Summit Auto Trade Facilities (1)
Madina Munawara St, Amman, Jordan
Tel.: (962) 65537602
Automobile Financing Services
N.A.I.C.S.: 522220
Yasuo Sekine (Gen Mgr)

Summit CRM, Ltd. (1)
Sumitomo Shoji Takebashi Building 9F 1-2-2 Hitotsubashi, Chiyoda-ku, Tokyo, 100-0003, Japan
Tel.: (81) 35 219 3800
Web Site: https://www.scrm.co.jp
Emp.: 52
Fuel & Coke Whslr
N.A.I.C.S.: 423520

Summit Capital Leasing Co., Ltd. (1)
968 Floor 11 U Chu Liang Building Rama 4 Road, Silom Subdistrict Bangrak, Bangkok, 10500, Thailand
Tel.: (66) 21072222
Web Site: http://www.summitcapital.co.th
Automobile Finance Leasing Services
N.A.I.C.S.: 522220

Summit Colmo, Inc. (1)
3-37-7 Eifuku, Suginami-Ku, Tokyo, 168-0064, Japan
Tel.: (81) 333185045
Web Site: https://www.summitcolmo.co.jp
Clothing & Retail Store Operations
N.A.I.C.S.: 459999

Subsidiary (Domestic):

Summit, Inc. (2)
3-57-14 Eifuku, Suginami-ku, Tokyo, 168-8686, Japan (100%)
Tel.: (81) 33 318 5000
Web Site: https://www.summitstore.co.jp
Rev.: $2,279,975,520
Fiscal Year-end: 03/31/2017
Supermarket & Lifestyle Store
N.A.I.C.S.: 445110
Hiroki Takeno (Pres)

Summit Cosmetics Corporation (1)
Takebashi Building 12F 1-2-2 Hitotsubashi, Chiyoda-ku, Tokyo, 100-0003, Japan
Tel.: (81) 36 212 0125
Web Site: https://www.summitcosme.com
Cosmetic Product Mfr & Distr
N.A.I.C.S.: 325620
Koh Akiyama (Pres & CEO)

Summit Exploration & Production Limited (1)
23 College Hill, London, EC4R 2RP, United Kingdom
Tel.: (44) 207 429 3500
Web Site: https://www.summiteandp.com
Organic Chemical Mfr
N.A.I.C.S.: 325199
John Austin (CEO)

Summit Finance Slovakia s.r.o. (1)
Tuhovska 9, Zlate Piesky, 831 07, Bratislava, Slovakia
Tel.: (421) 2 33 526 200
Web Site: http://www.summit.sk
Automotive Financial Leasing Services
N.A.I.C.S.: 522220
Vladimir Sman (Gen Mgr)

Summit Minerals GmbH (1)
Bahnhofstrasse 10, 6300, Zug, Switzerland
Tel.: (41) 41 726 16 00
Emp.: 5
Seal Products Distr
N.A.I.C.S.: 423510
Yoshitaka Ise (Gen Mgr)

Summit Motors Ljubljana d.o.o. (1)
Flajsmanova Ulica 3, 1000, Ljubljana, Slovenia

Tel.: (386) 12525110
Web Site: http://www.ford.si
Emp.: 42
Automotive Consulting Services
N.A.I.C.S.: 541690
David Uhrig (Gen Mgr)

Summit Motors Poland Sp. z.o.o. (1)
ul Sokratesa 11a, 01-909, Warsaw, Poland
Tel.: (48) 228350000
Web Site: http://www.autoplaza.com.pl
Automobile Dealers
N.A.I.C.S.: 441110

Summit Motors Slovakia, spol. s r.o. (1)
Tuhovska 9, 831 07, Bratislava, Slovakia
Tel.: (421) 233526255
Web Site: http://fordstore.sk
Automotive Distr
N.A.I.C.S.: 423110

Summit Oil Mill Co., Ltd. (1)
38-18 Shinko, Mihama-Ku, Chiba, 261-0002, Japan
Tel.: (81) 432423351
Web Site: http://www.summit-oilmill.com
Vegetable Oil Mfr
N.A.I.C.S.: 311225

Summit Pharmaceuticals China Limited (1)
Room 302 Building 1 Kerry Enterprise Center No 128 Tianmu West Road, Jing'an District, Shanghai, 200070, China
Tel.: (86) 216 473 3311
Web Site: https://www.summitpharmachina.com
Pharmaceutical Products Distr
N.A.I.C.S.: 424210

Summit Pharmaceuticals Europe Srl (1)
Viale Piero e Alberto Pirelli 6, 20126, Milan, Italy
Tel.: (39) 0269 5511
Web Site: https://www.summitpharmaeurope.com
Pharmaceuticals Product Mfr
N.A.I.C.S.: 325412

Summit Pharmaceuticals International Corporation (1)
1-2-2 Hitotsubashi Sumitomo Corporation Takebashi BLD 12F, Chiyoda-ku, Tokyo, 100-0003, Japan
Tel.: (81) 35 220 1500
Web Site: https://www.summitpharma.co.jp
Emp.: 158
Pharmaceutical Products Import & Distr
N.A.I.C.S.: 424210
Kenichi Nakamura (Pres & CEO)

Summit Power Holdings Limited (1)
Harumi Toriton Square Y To 21f, Chuo-Ku, Tokyo, 104-0053, Japan
Tel.: (81) 351665375
Eletric Power Generation Services
N.A.I.C.S.: 221118

Summit Rural (WA) Pty Limited (1)
29 Ocean Street, Kwinana Beach, Perth, 6167, WA, Australia
Tel.: (61) 89 439 8999
Web Site: https://www.summitfertz.com.au
Fertilizer Mfr & Distr
N.A.I.C.S.: 325314

Summit Steel (M.E.) FZCO (1)
Jebel Ali Free Zone, PO Box 17428, Jebel Ali, United Arab Emirates
Tel.: (971) 4 8860006
Sales Range: $25-49.9 Million
Emp.: 36
Steel Service Center & Distr
N.A.I.C.S.: 423510
Akihiro Kuromi (Mng Dir)

Summit Steel Corporation (1)
3F Tokyo Park Side Building 5-8-40 Kiba, Koto-ku, Tokyo, 135-0042, Japan
Tel.: (81) 356465020
Web Site: http://www.summitsteel.co.jp
Emp.: 60
Metal Service Center & Whslr
N.A.I.C.S.: 423510

Summit Steel Oita Co., Ltd. (1)
38 Kanaedai, Bungotakada, 879-0600, Oita, Japan

Tel.: (81) 978220977
Steel Products Services & Whslr
N.A.I.C.S.: 423510

Summit Sunrise Energy Co., Ltd. (1)
87 M Thai Tower All Seasons Place 22nd Floor Wireless Road, Lumpini Phatumwan, Bangkok, 10330, Thailand
Tel.: (66) 26540500
Web Site: http://www.ssenergy.co.th
Power Plant Management Services
N.A.I.C.S.: 541618

Summit Tubulars Corp. (1)
2300 350 7th Ave SW First Canadian Centre, Calgary, T2P 3N9, AB, Canada (100%)
Tel.: (403) 232-6066
Web Site: http://www.summit-tubulars.com
Sales Range: Less than $1 Million
Emp.: 20
Metals Service Centers & Offices
N.A.I.C.S.: 423510

Summit Wool Spinners Limited (1)
Weaver Street, Private Bag 50052, Oamaru, 9444, New Zealand
Tel.: (64) 34330040
Web Site: http://www.summitwool.co.nz
Sales Range: $75-99.9 Million
Emp.: 275
Spinning Yarn Mfr & Distr
N.A.I.C.S.: 313110

Sumur Cahaya Sdn. Bhd. (1)
35th Floor UBN Tower No 10 Jalan P Ramlee, 50250, Kuala Lumpur, Malaysia
Tel.: (60) 320280600
Web Site: http://www.sumitomocorp.co.jp
Sales Range: $25-49.9 Million
Emp.: 40
Pest Control Chemical Mfr
N.A.I.C.S.: 325320

Tasmanian Advanced Minerals Pty. Ltd. (1)
38a Saunders St, Wynard, 7325, TAS, Australia
Tel.: (61) 3 6442 116
Mineral Mining Services
N.A.I.C.S.: 212390

Thai Steel Service Center Ltd. (1)
47 Moo 7 Soi Wat Mahawong Phoochaosamingprai Rd Samrong, Prapradaeng, Samut Prakan, Thailand
Tel.: (66) 23980153
Web Site: http://www.tsscthai.com
Steel Sheet Processing & Distr
N.A.I.C.S.: 423510

Thang Long Industrial Park II Corporation (1)
Thang Long Industrial Park II, Lieu Xa Commune, Yen My, Hung Yen, Vietnam
Tel.: (84) 221 397 4620
Web Site: https://tlip2.com
Sales Range: $25-49.9 Million
Emp.: 72
Industrial Park Construction Services
N.A.I.C.S.: 236210
Akito Shiraishi (Gen Dir)

Tortoise Co., Ltd. (1)
4-15-5 Higashinippori, Arakawa-Ku, Tokyo, 116-0014, Japan
Tel.: (81) 338071395
Interior Goods Mfr & Distr
N.A.I.C.S.: 337212

Toyota Canarias, S.A. (1)
C Diego Vega Sarmiento 5, 35014, Las Palmas, Spain
Tel.: (34) 928447600
Web Site: http://www.toyota-canarias.es
Emp.: 150
New Car Dealers
N.A.I.C.S.: 441110

Toyota Central Asia FZE (1)
Level 2 The Offices 3 One Central Dubai World Trade Centre, PO Box 263790, Dubai, United Arab Emirates
Tel.: (971) 4 803 8999
Web Site: http://www.toyota-centralasia.com
Motor Vehicle Distr
N.A.I.C.S.: 423110

Toyota Ly Thuong Kiet (1)
151A Ly Thuong Kiet P 6, Tan Binh, Ho Chi Minh City, Vietnam
Tel.: (84) 901818818
Web Site: http://www.toyotalythuongkiet.com.vn
Automotive Repair & Maintenance Services
N.A.I.C.S.: 811198

Toyota Ukraine (1)
Mechnikova St, Kiev, Ukraine
Tel.: (380) 44 492 7000
Web Site: http://www.toyota.ua
Automotive Distr
N.A.I.C.S.: 423110

Transwest Mongolia LLC (1)
Erchim Khuch Street-32 20th Khoroo, PO Box 242, Bayangol District, Ulaanbaatar, 18031, Mongolia
Tel.: (976) 7 577 9905
Web Site: https://www.transwest.mn
Construction Equipment Distr
N.A.I.C.S.: 423810

Union Harvest (M) Sdn.Bhd (1)
4th Floor Menara PKNS-PJ No 17 Jalan Yong Shook Lin, 46050, Petaling Jaya, Selangor, Malaysia
Tel.: (60) 37 957 2122
Web Site: https://www.unionharvest.com
Fertilizer Mfr & Distr
N.A.I.C.S.: 325314

WAM!NET Japan K.K. (1)
Eiha Shinkawa 9F 1-5-17 Shinkawa, Chuo-Ku, Tokyo, 104-0033, Japan
Tel.: (81) 351172160
Web Site: http://www.wamnet.jp
Data Transfer & Storage Services
N.A.I.C.S.: 518210

SUMITOMO DENSETSU CO., LTD.

2-1-4 Awaza, Nishi-ku, Osaka, 550-8550, Japan
Tel.: (81) 665373400
Web Site: https://www.sem.co.jp
1949—(TKS)
Rev.: $1,226,313,640
Assets: $1,200,799,040
Liabilities: $467,538,520
Net Worth: $733,260,520
Earnings: $66,496,600
Emp.: 3,466
Fiscal Year-end: 03/31/24
Electric Facilities Construction Services
N.A.I.C.S.: 237130
Masao Sakazaki (Pres)

Subsidiaries:

Hokkaido Sumiden Dengyo Co., Ltd. (1)
14-9-1 Kita12-Jyo Higashi, Higashi-ku, Sapporo, 065-0012, Hokkaido, Japan
Tel.: (81) 117411131
Mechanical & Electrical Engineering Services
N.A.I.C.S.: 541330

Meiwa Dengyo Co., Ltd. (1)
2-26 Tsuchiichi-machi, Mizuho-ku, Nagoya, 467-0843, Aichi, Japan
Tel.: (81) 528521251
Mechanical & Electrical Engineering Services
N.A.I.C.S.: 541330

P.T. Taiyo Sinar Raya Teknik (1)
7th Floor Jl Jenderal Sudirman Kav 61-62, Jakarta Selatan, Indonesia
Tel.: (62) 215253400
Electrical Power Mfr
N.A.I.C.S.: 335311

SEMEC Corporation (1)
1-2-29 Himesato, Nishiyodogawa-ku, Osaka, 550-0025, Japan
Tel.: (81) 664756832
Mechanical & Electrical Engineering Services
N.A.I.C.S.: 541330

Shanghai Sumisetsu Trading Co., Ltd. (1)
Room 311 Tianxiang Building No 1068 Maotai Road, Changning District, Shanghai, 200336, China

AND PRIVATE COMPANIES

Tel.: (86) 2152067700
Electrical Power Mfr
N.A.I.C.S.: 335311

Sumisetsu China Co., ltd. (1)
Room311 Tianxiang Building No 1068
Maotai Road, Changning District, Shanghai, 200336, China
Tel.: (86) 2152067700
Building Construction Services
N.A.I.C.S.: 236115

Sumisetsu Philippines, Inc. (1)
8th floor GC Corporate Plaza 150 Legaspi St, Legaspi Village, Makati, 1229, Philippines
Tel.: (63) 288175571
Web Site: https://www.sumisetsu.com.ph
Mechanical Services
N.A.I.C.S.: 541380

Sumisetsu Vietnam CO., Ltd. (1)
Hata Building 1st Floor 115 Pham Viet Chanh Street, Ward 19 Binh Thanh District, Ho Chi Minh City, Vietnam
Tel.: (84) 2838407888
Electronic Services
N.A.I.C.S.: 541330

Temacon Engineering Sdn. Bhd. (1)
Lot 2-49 Jalan SU8 Taman Perindustrian Subang Utama, 40300, Shah Alam, Selangor Darul Ehsan, Malaysia
Tel.: (60) 351927711
Web Site: https://www.temacon.com.my
Mechanical & Electrical Engineering Installation Services
N.A.I.C.S.: 238220

Thai Semcon Co., Ltd. (1)
252 15th Floor SPE Tower Phaholyothin Rd Samsen nai, Phayathai, Bangkok, 10400, Thailand
Tel.: (66) 20447888
Electric Design & Installation Services
N.A.I.C.S.: 238210
Norifumi Kikuchi *(Mng Dir)*

Toyo Denki Kouji Co., Ltd. (1)
2-11-22 Minamikaneden, Suita, 564-0044, Osaka, Japan
Tel.: (81) 668217560
Web Site: https://www.vvv1.co.jp
Mechanical & Electrical Engineering Services
N.A.I.C.S.: 541330

Tsc Tech Asia Co., Ltd. (1)
700/256 Moo 1, Tambon Ban Kao, Phan Thong, 20160, Chonburi province, Thailand
Tel.: (66) 38465060
Electronic Services
N.A.I.C.S.: 541330

SUMITOMO ELECTRIC INDUSTRIES, LTD.
4-5-33 Kitahama, Chuo-ku, Osaka, 541-0041, Japan
Tel.: (81) 662204141   JP
Web Site:
   https://sumitomoelectric.com
Year Founded: 1897
SMTOF—(OTCIQ)
Rev.: $29,102,600,540
Assets: $28,855,274,170
Liabilities: $12,780,494,490
Net Worth: $16,074,779,680
Earnings: $989,669,030
Emp.: 293,266
Fiscal Year-end: 03/31/24
Fabricated Wires Mfr
N.A.I.C.S.: 332618
Akira Nishimura *(Sr Mng Dir & Gen Mgr-R&D-Unit-Electronics Grp)*

Subsidiaries:

A.L.M.T. Corp. (1)
Sumitomo Fudosan Shiba Building 14F
1-11-11 Shiba, Minato-ku, Tokyo, 105-0014, Japan
Tel.: (81) 354181801
Web Site: http://www.allied-material.co.jp
Sales Range: $25-49.9 Million
Emp.: 1,334
Alloys & Diamond Tools Mfr
N.A.I.C.S.: 333514

Nobuyuki Kitagawa *(Pres)*

Subsidiary (Non-US):

A.L.M.T. (Thailand) Co., Ltd. (2)
90/2 Moo 9 Wellgrow Industrial Estate
Bangna-Trad Road Km 36, Bangwua, Bang Pakong, 24180, Chachoensao, Thailand
Tel.: (66) 38522291
Industrial Machinery Mfr
N.A.I.C.S.: 333248
Janusz Matusik *(Mng Dir)*

Plant (Domestic):

A.L.M.T. (Thailand) Co., Ltd. - Korat Factory (3)
Mooban Bannaklang 567 Moo 1 T Naklang A Soongnuen, A Soongnuen, Nakhon Ratchasima, 30380, Thailand
Tel.: (66) 44335190
Web Site: http://www.allied-material.co.jp
Electronic Components Mfr
N.A.I.C.S.: 334419

Subsidiary (Non-US):

A.L.M.T. Asia Pacific Pte. Ltd. (2)
No 2 Boon Leat Terrace 03-02/03 Harbourside 2, Singapore, 119844, Singapore
Tel.: (65) 62719252
Sales Range: $25-49.9 Million
Emp.: 3
Industrial Equipment Distr
N.A.I.C.S.: 423830
Eiji Takeuchi *(Mng Dir)*

Subsidiary (Domestic):

A.L.M.T. TECH Inc. (2)
398-16 Murahigashiyama Jurizuka, Sakata, 998-0114, Yamagata, Japan   (100%)
Tel.: (81) 234312222
Web Site: http://www.allied-material.co.jp
Heatspreader Materials for Telecommunications, Semiconductors & Electronics Mfr
N.A.I.C.S.: 334419
Yoshitsugu Kurosawa *(Dir)*

Division (Domestic):

A.L.M.T. TECH Inc. - Itami Division (3)
1-1-1 Koya-Kita, Itami, 664-0016, Hyogo, Japan
Tel.: (81) 727710551
Web Site: http://www.allied-material.co.jp
Composite Alloys Mfr
N.A.I.C.S.: 335999
Masao Sujimoeo *(Gen Mgr)*

A.L.M.T. TECH Inc. - Sakata Division (3)
398-16 Murahigashiyama Jurizuka, Sakata, 998-0114, Yamagata, Japan
Tel.: (81) 234312222
Electronic Components Mfr
N.A.I.C.S.: 334419

A.L.M.T. TECH Inc. - Sakata Division (Ohama Plant) (3)
2-1-12 Ohama, Sakata, 998-0064, Yamagata, Japan
Tel.: (81) 234333311
Web Site: http://www.allied-material.co.jp
Emp.: 300
Automotive Electronic Parts Mfr
N.A.I.C.S.: 336320
Hiroshi Yokoyama *(Deputy Mgr)*

A.L.M.T. TECH Inc. - Sakata Division No.2 Plant (3)
398-15 Murahigashiyama Jurizuka, Sakata, 998-0114, Yamagata, Japan
Tel.: (81) 234312222
Web Site: http://www.allied-material.co.jp
Powder Metallurgy Product Mfr
N.A.I.C.S.: 332117

A.L.M.T. TECH Inc. - Sakata Division No.3 Plant (3)
398-16 Murahigashiyama Jurizuka, Sakata, 998-0114, Yamagata, Japan
Tel.: (81) 234312222
Electric Powder Product Mfr
N.A.I.C.S.: 332117

A.L.M.T. TECH Inc. - Toyama Division (3)

2 Iwase-koshi-machi, Toyama, 931-8543, Japan
Tel.: (81) 764377401
Electronic Parts Mfr
N.A.I.C.S.: 334419

AutoNetworks Technologies, Ltd. (1)
1-14 Nishisuehiro-cho, Yokkaichi, 510-8503, Mie, Japan
Tel.: (81) 593546320
Web Site: https://www.autonetworks.co.jp
Automobile Wiring Harnesses Product Mfr
N.A.I.C.S.: 335931
Masataka Inoue *(Pres & CEO)*

Autosistemas de Torreon S.A. de C.V. (1)
Blvd Pedro Rodriguez Triana No 2143 Sur Col Villas La Merced, 27297, Torreon, Coah, Mexico
Tel.: (52) 8717307940
Web Site: http://www.sws.co.jp
Wiring Harness Mfr & Distr
N.A.I.C.S.: 332618

Axismateria Ltd. (1)
1 Takumidai, Ono, 675-1322, Hyogo, Japan
Tel.: (81) 794628535
Web Site: https://www.axismateria.co.jp
Emp.: 290
Cemented Carbide Tool & Cutting Tool Mfr
N.A.I.C.S.: 333515
Yoshimitsu Sawazono *(Pres)*

Beijing Zhuli Diantong Optoelectronics Technology Co., Ltd. (1)
2 Daliushu-lu Xizhimenwai, Beijing, Haidan, China
Tel.: (86) 62228043
Sales Range: $50-74.9 Million
Emp.: 90
Electronic Products & Components Mfr
N.A.I.C.S.: 332618

Broad Net Mux Corporation (1)
Rivage Shinagawa 4-1-8 Konan, Minato-ku, Tokyo, 108-0075, Japan
Tel.: (81) 357831035
Web Site: http://www.bnmux.co.jp
Telecommunication Network Construction Services
N.A.I.C.S.: 237130

Changchun SE Bordnetze Co., Ltd. (1)
5599 Fanrong Road, Changchun, 130012, China
Tel.: (86) 43188570818
Wiring Harnesses Product Mfr
N.A.I.C.S.: 335931

Chengdu SE Bordnetze Company Ltd. (1)
No 369 Nanyi Road Economic and Technological Development Zone, Chengdu, Sichuan, China
Tel.: (86) 2865081387
Wiring Harnesses Product Mfr
N.A.I.C.S.: 335931

Chengdu SEI Optical Fiber Co., Ltd. (1)
No 56 Xiyuan Avenue, Gaoxin West District, Chengdu, 611731, China
Tel.: (86) 2887838170
Web Site: http://www.cdsei.com
Optical Fiber & Cable Mfr
N.A.I.C.S.: 327212

Chongqing Jin-Zhu Wiring Systems Co., Ltd. (1)
No 1995 Jinkai Road Jingkai Garden, Economy Tech Devel District, Chongqing, China
Tel.: (86) 2386002265
Automotive Components Mfr
N.A.I.C.S.: 336320

Chuetsu Sumidenso, Ltd (1)
993-1 Oaza Iwasawa, Ojiya, 949-8724, Niigata, Japan
Tel.: (81) 258866111
Wiring Harnesses Product Mfr
N.A.I.C.S.: 335931

Conductores Technologicos de Juarez, S.A. de C.V. (1)
Av Parque Industrial Aztecas 1550, Col Parque Industrial Aztecas, 32679, Mexico, Mexico

SUMITOMO ELECTRIC INDUSTRIES, LTD.

Tel.: (52) 6566298600
Automobile Wiring Harnesses Product Mfr
N.A.I.C.S.: 335931

Daikoku Electric Wire Co., Ltd. (1)
767-90 Takawarabi Hachisu, Otawara, 324-0244, Tochigi, Japan
Tel.: (81) 287543581
Rev.: $36,484,000
Emp.: 141
Electric Wire Mfr & Distr
N.A.I.C.S.: 332618
Yoshiki Kishikawa *(Pres)*

Subsidiary (Non-US):

DAIKOKU ELECTRONICS (PHILS.), INC. (2)
Lot 32 Phase 1B Special Economic Zone, First Philippine Industrial Park, Tanauan, 4232, Batangas, Philippines
Tel.: (63) 495549210
Web Site: http://www.daikokudensen.co.jp
Sales Range: $50-74.9 Million
Relay Coil Mfr
N.A.I.C.S.: 334416

DAIKOKU ELECTRONICS (THAILAND.), LTD (2)
75/19 Moo 11 Paholyothin Road Klong Nueng, Khlong Luang, 12120, Pathumthani, Thailand
Tel.: (66) 25292715
Web Site: http://www.daikokudensen.co.jp
Emp.: 94
Relay & Miniature Coil Mfr
N.A.I.C.S.: 334416

Plant (Domestic):

Daikoku Electric Wire Co., Ltd. - KUROBANE Factory (2)
767-90 Takawarabi Hachisu, Otawara, 324-0244, Tochigi, Japan
Tel.: (81) 287543581
Emp.: 6
Electrical Wire Mfr
N.A.I.C.S.: 332618
Kishikawa Yoshiki *(Pres)*

Daikoku Electric Wire Co., Ltd. - MUIKAMACHI Factory (2)
629-16 Niibori Shinden, Minami-Uonuma, 949-7135, Niigata, Japan
Tel.: (81) 257752595
Relay & Miniature Coil Mfr
N.A.I.C.S.: 334416

Daikoku Electric Wire Co., Ltd.- SENMAYA Factory (2)
321 Shimokiroku, Senmaya-Town, Ichinoseki, 290803, Iwate, Japan
Tel.: (81) 191532895
Sales Range: $25-49.9 Million
Emp.: 4
Transformer Coil & Parts Mfr
N.A.I.C.S.: 334416
Hideki Yamamura *(Gen Mgr)*

Dyden Corporation (1)
15-1 Minami 2-chome, Kurume, 830-8511, Fukuoka, Japan
Tel.: (81) 942221111
Web Site: https://en.dyden.co.jp
Communication Power Cable Mfr
N.A.I.C.S.: 335929
Shinichi Toyofuku *(Pres)*

Electronic Harnesses (U.K.) Ltd. (1)
Unit 5 Llantrisant Business Park, Llantrisant, Pontyclun, CF72 8LF, Mid Glamorgan, United Kingdom
Tel.: (44) 1443237511
Web Site: http://www.ehuk.co.uk
Electric Wiring Harnesses Mfr
N.A.I.C.S.: 336340

First Sumiden Circuits, Inc. (1)
Ampere St Corner Main Ave, Light Industry and Science Park Barrio Diezmo, Cabuyao, 4025, Laguna, Philippines
Tel.: (63) 277309999
Web Site: http://www.fsci.com.ph
Printed Circuit Mfr
N.A.I.C.S.: 334418

Fujian JK Wiring Systems Co., Ltd. (1)
No 4 Section 2 Cangshan Zone of Fuzhou High-Tech Park, Bai Hu Ting Cangshan Dis-

SUMITOMO ELECTRIC INDUSTRIES, LTD.

Sumitomo Electric Industries, Ltd.—(Continued)
trict, Fuzhou, 350007, Fujian, China
Tel.: (86) 59183449234
Wiring Harnesses Product Mfr
N.A.I.C.S.: 335931

Fuzhou Zhu Wiring Systems Co., Ltd. (1)
No 5 Fuwan Park Jinshan Industrial Zone, Fuzhou, 350008, China
Tel.: (86) 59188005505
Automobile Harness Mfr & Distr
N.A.I.C.S.: 336320

Gokoh Shoji Co., Ltd. (1)
MPR Hommachi Bldg 2Fl 1-8 Minami Kyuhoji Machi 3-Chome, Chuo-Ku, Osaka, 541-0058, Japan
Tel.: (81) 662516020
Web Site: https://www.gokoh.co.jp
Sales Range: $25-49.9 Million
Emp.: 50
Automobile Parts Distr
N.A.I.C.S.: 423120

Subsidiary (Non-US):

GOKOH TRADING (SHANGHAI) CO., LTD. (2)
Room 309 Shanghai Airport City Terminal No 1600 Nanjing Road W, Shanghai, 200040, China
Tel.: (86) 2162256622
Web Site: http://www.gokoh.co.jp
Industrial Machinery Distr
N.A.I.C.S.: 423830

Hangzhou SEI-Futong Optical Fiber Co., Ltd. (1)
No 1089 Yucai West Road, Fuyang, 311400, Zhejiang, China
Tel.: (86) 57123276666
Fiber Optic Cable Mfr
N.A.I.C.S.: 335921

Hangzhou Walsin Power Cable & Wire Co., Ltd. (1)
No9 Rd 12 Xiasha Economic & Technological Development Zone, Hangzhou, 310018, China
Tel.: (86) 57186912466
Web Site: http://www.walsin.com
High-Voltage Power Cables Mfr
N.A.I.C.S.: 237130

Hitachi Chemical Sumiden Power Products, Ltd. (1)
5-1-1 Hidaka-cho, Hitachi, 319-1414, Ibaraki, Japan
Tel.: (81) 294427194
Rising Molded Product Mfr
N.A.I.C.S.: 325211

Hokkaido Electric Industries Ltd. (1)
776 Naie, Naie-cho Sorachi-gun, Hokkaido, 079-0304, Japan
Tel.: (81) 125655501
Electric Power Cable & Wire Mfr
N.A.I.C.S.: 335929

Hokkaido Sumiden Precision Co., Ltd. (1)
776 Naie, Naie-cho Sorachi-gun, Hokkaido, 079-0304, Japan
Tel.: (81) 125655501
Cemented Carbide Tool Mfr
N.A.I.C.S.: 333515

Hokkaido Sumiden Steel Wire Co., Ltd. (1)
12 Nakamachi, Muroran, 050-0087, Hokkaido, Japan
Tel.: (81) 143466552
Oil Tempered Wire Mfr
N.A.I.C.S.: 331222

Hokkoh Transportation Inc. (1)
3-2-1 Kasugadekita, Konohana-ku, Osaka, 554-0021, Japan
Tel.: (81) 6646623131
Web Site: http://www.hokkohu.co.jp
Domestic Transportation Services
N.A.I.C.S.: 488510

Hoshi Industries Co., Ltd. (1)
2-1-40 Minato, Izumisano, 598-0063, Osaka, Japan
Tel.: (81) 724622606
Welding Wire Mfr

N.A.I.C.S.: 333992

Huizhou Sumiden Wiring Systems Co., Ltd. (1)
The First Industry Zone Xiqu Daya Bay, Huizhou, 516083, Guangdong, China
Tel.: (86) 7525288388
Wiring Harnesses Product Mfr
N.A.I.C.S.: 335931

Huizhou Zhu Guang Auto Wiring Systems Co., Ltd. (1)
6th Buildong 388 Zhongkai Avenue, Huizhou, Guangdong, China
Tel.: (86) 7525795566
Wiring Harnesses Product Mfr
N.A.I.C.S.: 335931

Huizhou Zhucheng Wiring Systems, Co., Ltd. (1)
Xinliao Dongfeng Car City, Dayawan, Huizhou, 516085, Guangdong, China
Tel.: (86) 7525202835
Web Site: http://www.sws.co.jp
Automotive Wiring Harness Mfr & Distr
N.A.I.C.S.: 336320

Huizhou Zhurun Automotive Wire Co., Ltd. (1)
Jiu long High Technology Industrial Park, Xiao Jin Kou, Huizhou, 516023, Guangdong, China
Tel.: (86) 7522821600
Automobile Electric Wire Mfr & Sales
N.A.I.C.S.: 336320

IWS Realty Corporation (1)
Luisita Industrial Park Special Export Processing Zone San Miguel, Tarlac, 2301, Philippines
Tel.: (63) 459850080
Real Estate Manangement Services
N.A.I.C.S.: 531390

Innovation Core SEI, Inc. (1)
2355 Zanker Rd, San Jose, CA 95131-1138
Tel.: (408) 232-9511
Web Site: http://sei-innovation.com
Sales Range: $25-49.9 Million
Emp.: 10
Electric Equipment Research & Development Services
N.A.I.C.S.: 541715
Makoto Katayama (Pres)

International Electric Wires Phils. Corp. (1)
Specia Export Processing Zone San Miguel, Luisita Industrial Park, Tarlac, 2301, Philippines
Tel.: (63) 459851590
Web Site: http://www.global-sei.com
Emp.: 40
Automotive Electric Wire Mfr & Distr
N.A.I.C.S.: 336320

J-Power Systems Corporation (1)
5-1-1 Hidaka-cho, Hitachi, 319-1414, Ibaraki, Japan
Tel.: (81) 364062792
Web Site: https://www.jpowers.co.jp
Sales Range: $700-749.9 Million
Emp.: 900
Electric Power Cables & Accessories, Overhead Power Transmission Lines & Related Systems Research, Development & Mfr
N.A.I.C.S.: 423610
Tomoki Osawa (Pres)

Affiliate (Non-US):

Thai Sumiden Engineering and Construction Co., Ltd. (2)
164 166 168 Srinakarin Road Hua Mak, Bangkapi, Bangkok, 10240, Thailand
Tel.: (66) 27316647
Web Site: http://www.thaisumiden.com
Sales Range: $25-49.9 Million
Emp.: 40
Power Cable Installation Services
N.A.I.C.S.: 238210
Veeraphong Jiraphanphong (Pres & Mng Dir)

Jiang Xi Wiring Systems Co., Ltd. (1)
Ji Zhou Industrial Park, Jian, Jiangxi, China
Tel.: (86) 7968251717
Web Site: http://www.sws.co.jp
Automotive Wiring Harness Mfr

N.A.I.C.S.: 336320

Judd Wire, Inc. (1)
124 Tpke Rd, Turners Falls, MA 01376-2699
Tel.: (413) 863-4357
Web Site: http://www.juddwire.com
Sales Range: $75-99.9 Million
Emp.: 300
Electronic Wire & Component Mfr
N.A.I.C.S.: 332618
Hidetoshi Kanuta (CEO)

Kaifeng Zhucheng Wiring Systems, Co., Ltd. (1)
West Section Weidu Road Kaifeng New Area, Kaifeng, 475000, Henan, China
Tel.: (86) 3783381063
Automobile Electric Wire Product Mfr
N.A.I.C.S.: 336320

Kansai Pipe Industries, Ltd. (1)
4-8-4 Kami Kita, Hirano-ku, Osaka, 547-0001, Japan
Tel.: (81) 667930700
Web Site: http://www.kansaipipe.co.jp
Aluminum & Copper Alloy Product Mfr
N.A.I.C.S.: 331491

Keystone Powdered Metal Company (1)
251 State St, Saint Marys, PA 15857-1697
Tel.: (814) 781-1591
Web Site: http://www.keystonepm.com
Powder Metal Parts Mfr
N.A.I.C.S.: 331221
Michael Stauffer (VP-Sls & Mktg)

Plant (Domestic):

Keystone Powdered Metal Company - Cherryville (2)
Sunbeam Industrial Complex 100 Commerce Dr, Cherryville, NC 28021 (100%)
Tel.: (704) 435-4036
Web Site: http://www.keystonepm.com
Bearing Mfr
N.A.I.C.S.: 331221

Keystone Powdered Metal Company - Lewis Run (2)
8 Hanley Dr, Lewis Run, PA 16738
Tel.: (814) 368-5320
Web Site: http://www.keystonepm.com
Automotive Powertrain Mfr
N.A.I.C.S.: 331221

Subsidiary (Domestic):

Sumitomo Electric U.S.A. Holdings, Inc. (2)
160 Mine Lake Ct Ste 200, Raleigh, NC 27615
Tel.: (704) 528-7500
Powered Metal Structural Parts for Drivetrain & Engine Accessory Applications in Cars, Light Trucks & Off-Highway Vehicles
N.A.I.C.S.: 332111

Kiyohara Sumiden, Ltd. (1)
18-5 Kiyohara Kogyodanchi, Utsunomiya, 321-3231, Tochigi, Japan
Tel.: (81) 286701270
Web Site: http://www.global-sei.com
Sales Range: $75-99.9 Million
Emp.: 300
Fiber Optic Cable Mfr
N.A.I.C.S.: 335921

Korea Sintered Metal Co., Ltd. (1)
43 Nongongro 87Gil Nongong-Eup, Dalsung-Gun, Daegu, 711855, Korea (South)
Tel.: (82) 536100700
Web Site: https://www.iksm.co.kr
Sales Range: $75-99.9 Million
Emp.: 450
Powdered Metallurgical Parts Mfr
N.A.I.C.S.: 333131
Kun Jin Lee (Pres & CEO)

Korloy, Inc. (1)
Holystar B/D 1350 Nambusunhwan-ro, Geumcheon-gu, Seoul, 153-823, Korea (South)
Tel.: (82) 25223184
Web Site: http://www.korloy.com
Sales Range: $75-99.9 Million
Emp.: 500
Hard Metal Tools & Alloys Mfr

INTERNATIONAL PUBLIC

N.A.I.C.S.: 333991
Hye-Sub Yun (Chm)

Kyungshin Corporation (1)
98 Gaetbeol-ro, Yeonsu-gu, Incheon, 21999, Korea (South)
Tel.: (82) 327147100
Automotive Components Mfr
N.A.I.C.S.: 336390

Kyushu Sumiden Seimitsu Ltd. (1)
2374 Fukumo, Omachi-cho Kishima-gun, Saga, 849-2102, Japan
Tel.: (81) 952823225
Cemented Carbide Tool Mfr
N.A.I.C.S.: 333515

Misawa Trading Co., Ltd. (1)
Kitahankyu Bldg 7th Fl No 4-8 1-chome, Kita-ku, Shibata, 530-0012, Osaka, Japan
Tel.: (81) 663733191
Web Site: https://www.misawa-kosan.jp
Emp.: 60
Steel & Metal Product Mfr
N.A.I.C.S.: 331110
Koshu Kono (Pres)

Nissin Electric Co., Ltd. (1)
47 Umezu-Takase-cho, Ukyo-ku, Kyoto, 615-8686, Japan (100%)
Tel.: (81) 758613151
Web Site: http://www.nissin.co.jp
Rev.: $1,278,999,040
Assets: $1,890,378,160
Liabilities: $586,608,000
Net Worth: $1,303,770,160
Earnings: $115,008,080
Emp.: 5,382
Fiscal Year-end: 03/31/2022
Electrical Power Equipment & Switchgear Mfr
N.A.I.C.S.: 335313
Hideaki Obata (Chm)

Subsidiary (Domestic):

Auland Co., Ltd. (2)
47 Umezu-Takase-cho, Ukyo-ku, Kyoto, 615-8686, Japan
Tel.: (81) 758825991
Web Site: https://www.auland.co.jp
Power Transformer Mfr & Distr
N.A.I.C.S.: 335311
Kenjiro Mizuta (Pres & CEO)

Subsidiary (Non-US):

Beijing Hongda Nissin Electric Co., Ltd. (2)
No 8 Hongda Nan Lu Jingji Jishu Kaifa Qu, Beijing, 100176, China
Tel.: (86) 1067802698
Gas Insulated Switchgear Mfr & Distr
N.A.I.C.S.: 335313

NHV Accelerator Technologies Shanghai Co., Ltd. (1)
No 1118 Pinghai Road, Situan Town Fengxian District, Shanghai, 201413, China
Tel.: (86) 2169216030
Web Site: https://www.nhvat.com
Electron Processing System Mfr
N.A.I.C.S.: 335999

Subsidiary (US):

NHV America Inc. (2)
100 Griffin Brook Dr, Methuen, MA 01844
Tel.: (978) 682-4900
Web Site: http://www.nhv.jp
Sales Range: $50-74.9 Million
Emp.: 5
Electrical Apparatus & Equipment Wiring Supplies & Related Equipment Whslr
N.A.I.C.S.: 423610
Kanji Asao (Pres)

Subsidiary (Domestic):

Nippon I.T.F Inc. (2)
575 Kuzetonoshirocho, Minami-ku, Kyoto, 601-8205, Japan
Tel.: (81) 759316040
Web Site: http://nippon-itf.co.jp
Sales Range: $50-74.9 Million
Emp.: 200
Motor Vehicle Electrical & Electronic Equipment Mfr
N.A.I.C.S.: 336320

AND PRIVATE COMPANIES   SUMITOMO ELECTRIC INDUSTRIES, LTD.

Subsidiary (Non-US):

Nissin Advanced Coating (Shenyang) Co., Ltd. (2)
No 8 Yuanhangdong Road, Hunnan New, Shenyang, 110168, China
Tel.: (86) 2424689990
Thinfilm Coating Services
N.A.I.C.S.: 332812

Nissin Advanced Coating Indo Co., Private Ltd. (2)
B-135 Sector-63, Noida, 201301, Uttar Pradesh, India
Tel.: (91) 1204313016
Pipe Coating Services
N.A.I.C.S.: 332812
Ajay Dulloo (COO)

Nissin Allis Electric Co., Ltd. (2)
No 10 Ronggong S Rd, Guanyin Industrial Park, Taoyuan, 32849, Taiwan
Tel.: (886) 34836601
Web Site: https://www.nactw.com.tw
Power Electric Products Mfr
N.A.I.C.S.: 423610

Nissin Allis Ion Equipment (Shanghai) Co., Ltd. (2)
Suite 12 3F Tomson Commercial Bldg 710 Dongfang Rd, Shanghai, 200122, China
Tel.: (86) 215 831 4024
Web Site: https://www.nissin-ion.co.jp
Electronic Component Mfr & Distr
N.A.I.C.S.: 334419

Nissin Allis Union Ion Equipment Co. Ltd (2)
4th Floor - 6 371 Kuang Fu Rd Sec 1, Hsinchu, Taiwan
Tel.: (886) 35640991
Web Site: https://www.nissin-ion.co.jp
Industrial Machinery & Equipment Whslr
N.A.I.C.S.: 423830

Subsidiary (Domestic):

Nissin Denki Shouji Co., Ltd. (2)
1-2-10 Omikacho Hitachi, Ibaraki, 319-1221, Japan
Tel.: (81) 294538477
Electrical Equipment Whslr
N.A.I.C.S.: 423610

Subsidiary (Non-US):

Nissin Electric (Thailand) Co. Ltd (2)
60/64 Moo 19 Navanakorn 2 Phaholyothin Rd, Khlong Luang, Pathumthani, 12120, Thailand
Tel.: (66) 25290968
Web Site: http://www.nissin-thai.com
Sales Range: $150-199.9 Million
Emp.: 813
Electrical Apparatus & Equipment Wiring Supplies & Related Equipment Whslr
N.A.I.C.S.: 423610
Hiroyuki Ubukata (Pres)

Subsidiary (Non-US):

Nissin Electric Vietnam Co., Ltd. (3)
Tien Son Industrial Zone, Hoan Son, Bac Ninh, Vietnam
Tel.: (84) 241714434
Web Site: https://en.nissinelectric-vietnam.vn
Sales Range: $1-9.9 Million
Emp.: 490
Fiscal Year-end: 12/31/2022
Electrical Equipment Mfr & Distr
N.A.I.C.S.: 335999

Subsidiary (Non-US):

Nissin Electric Myanmar Co., Ltd. (2)
Unit No C1 Lot C24 C25 Zone A, Thilawa Special Economic Zone, Yangon, Myanmar
Tel.: (95) 12309338
Electrical Equipment Mfr & Distr
N.A.I.C.S.: 335311

Nissin Electric Wuxi Co. Ltd (2)
No 28 Xinhua Road, New Wu District, Wuxi, 214028, Jiangsu, China
Tel.: (86) 51082255800
Web Site: http://www.nissin-wuxi.com
Emp.: 600

Electrical Apparatus & Equipment Wiring Supplies & Related Equipment Whslr
N.A.I.C.S.: 423610

Subsidiary (Domestic):

Nissin Ion Equipment Co., Ltd. (2)
4F Grand Kyoto 75 Nishikujo Higashihieijocho, Minami-ku, Kyoto, 601-8438, Japan
Tel.: (81) 756329700
Web Site: http://www.nissin-ion.co.jp
Emp.: 266
Semiconductor Machinery Mfr & Distr
N.A.I.C.S.: 333242
Nobuo Nagai (Pres)

Subsidiary (US):

Nissin Ion Equipment USA, Inc. (2)
8701 N Mopac Expy Ste 130 Austin Office Ctr, Austin, TX 78759
Tel.: (512) 340-1423
Web Site: https://www.nissinimplanter.com
Electric Equipment Mfr
N.A.I.C.S.: 334419
Tom Schettino (Mgr-Field Svc)

Subsidiary (Non-US):

Nissin Ion HighTech (Yangzhou) Co., Ltd. (2)
Yangzhou Export Processing Zone No 9 South Yangzijiang Road, Yangzhou, 225131, Jiangsu, China
Tel.: (86) 51487887757
Electronic Component Mfr & Distr
N.A.I.C.S.: 334419

Nissin Ion Korea Co., Ltd. (2)
Starplaza 11F 53 Metapolis-ro, Hwaseong, 445-160, Gyeonggi, Korea (South)
Tel.: (82) 312731480
Electric Equipment Mfr
N.A.I.C.S.: 334419

Subsidiary (Domestic):

Nissin Pulse Electronics Co., Ltd. (2)
2744-3 yamazaki, Noda, 278-0022, Chiba, Japan
Tel.: (81) 471230611
Web Site: https://nissin-pulse.jp
Emp.: 41
High Voltage Equipment Mfr & Distr
N.A.I.C.S.: 335999
Noboru Tsuchiya (Gen Mgr)

Nissin Systems Co., Ltd. (2)
293-1 Ayahorikawa-cho Ayanokoji-dori Horikawa-dori Shijo Building, Shimogyo-ku, Kyoto, 600-8482, Japan
Tel.: (81) 753447880
Web Site: https://www.co-nss.co.jp
Sales Range: $25-49.9 Million
Emp.: 219
Software Development & Distribution Services
N.A.I.C.S.: 541511
Katsuhide Sakai (Exec Officer)

O & S California, Inc. (1)
9731 Siempre Viva Rd Ste E, San Diego, CA 92154-7217
Tel.: (619) 661-1800
Web Site: http://www.osca-arcosa.com
Sales Range: $25-49.9 Million
Emp.: 1,071
Wiring Harnesses For Electric Appliances
N.A.I.C.S.: 334419

OCC Corporation (1)
Queen's Tower C 15F 2-3-5, Minato-Mirai Nishi-ku, Yokohama, 220-6215, Japan
Tel.: (81) 453306600
Web Site: https://www.occjp.com
Emp.: 296
Optic Cable Mfr
N.A.I.C.S.: 335921
Tomokazu Ito (Pres)

P.T. IKI Indah Kabel (1)
Jl Raya Tangerang Serang Km 7 8, Desa Pasirjaya Kec Jatiuwung, Tangerang, 15135, Indonesia
Tel.: (62) 215922404
Sales Range: $200-249.9 Million
Emp.: 600
Wire Harnesses Mfr
N.A.I.C.S.: 332618
Chigeki Osawa (Pres)

P.T. Karya Sumiden Indonesia (1)
Jln Gatot Subroto Km 7 8 Kel Pasir Jaya, Kec Jatiuwung, Tangerang, Indonesia
Tel.: (62) 215922404
Copper Wire Mfr & Distr
N.A.I.C.S.: 335929

P.T. Sumi Indo Kabel Tbk (1)
Jln Gatot Subroto Km 7 8 Kel Pasir Jaya, Kec Jatiuwung, Tangerang, 15135, Indonesia
Tel.: (62) 215922404
Web Site: https://www.sikabel.com
Sales Range: $150-199.9 Million
Emp.: 500
Mfr of Electric Wire & Cable
N.A.I.C.S.: 335139
Toshihiko Terao (Chm)

P.T. Sumiden Serasi Wire Products (1)
Jalan pahlawan J East Karang Asam Timor Capaureut, Bogor, 16810, Indonesia
Tel.: (62) 218754706
Sales Range: $75-99.9 Million
Emp.: 500
PC Strand, Grooved PC Wire & Plain PC Wire Mfr
N.A.I.C.S.: 332618
Katsuyuki Nagaiae (Pres)

PT. SEI Consulting Jakarta (1)
88 Office Kota Kasablanca Tower A, 11th Floor Unit D Jl Casablanca Raya Kav 88, Jakarta Selatan, 12870, Indonesia
Tel.: (62) 2129568510
Administrative Support Services
N.A.I.C.S.: 561110

PT. Sumi Indo Wiring Systems (1)
Kota Bukit Indah Blok D II No 27-29 Ds Dangdeur Kec Bungursari, Kawasan Industri, Purwakarta, 41181, Jawa Barat, Indonesia
Tel.: (62) 264351657
Wiring Harnesses Product Mfr
N.A.I.C.S.: 335931

PT. Sumiden Hardmetal Manufacturing Indonesia (1)
Jl Permata Raya Lot C-2A, Kawasan Industri Kiic, Karawang, 41361, Indonesia
Tel.: (62) 2129620626
Cemented Carbide Tool Mfr
N.A.I.C.S.: 333515

PT. Sumiden Sintered Components Indonesia (1)
Jl Rotan Plot F27-26, Kawasan Industri Delta Silicon 3 Lippo Cikarang, Bekasi, 17530, West Java, Indonesia
Tel.: (62) 2129577711
Web Site: http://www.sumiden-sintered.co.id
Automotive Components Mfr
N.A.I.C.S.: 336390

PT. Sumitomo Electric Hardmetal Indonesia (1)
88 Office Kota Kasablanca Tower A, 11th Floor Unit D Jl Casablanca Raya Kav 88, Jakarta Selatan, 12870, Indonesia
Tel.: (62) 2129568508
Cemented Carbide Tool & Cutting Tool Mfr
N.A.I.C.S.: 333515

PT. Sumitomo Electric Wintec Indonesia (1)
Block T-7 MM2100 Industrial Town, Cikarang Barat, Bekasi, 17520, West Java, Indonesia
Tel.: (62) 218980589
Sales Range: $50-74.9 Million
Emp.: 180
Magnet Wire Mfr & Distr
N.A.I.C.S.: 335929

Pilipinas Kyohritsu Inc. (1)
Km75 Laurel Highway Brgy Inosloban, Lipa, 4217, Batangas, Philippines
Tel.: (63) 434042116
Wiring Harnesses Product Mfr
N.A.I.C.S.: 335931

S D Engineering - Hui Zhou, Ltd. (1)
Jiulong Baigang Industry Xiaojinkou, Huicheng District, Huizhou, 516023, Guangdong, China
Tel.: (86) 7522367828
Jig & Equipment Mfr
N.A.I.C.S.: 333514

S&S Components Co., Ltd. (1)
3500-8 Hitaki Oaza, Suzaka, 382-0000, Nagano, Japan
Tel.: (81) 262512620
Wiring Harnesses Terminal Mfr
N.A.I.C.S.: 335931

S.D. Engineering, Ltd. (1)
1-14 Nishisuehiro-cho, Yokkaichi, 510-8503, Mie, Japan
Tel.: (81) 593546291
Web Site: http://www.sws.co.jp
Machine Tools Mfr
N.A.I.C.S.: 333517

S.E.I. Thai Holding Co., Ltd. (1)
54 BB 10th Floor Room 1012-1013 Sukhumvit 21 Road Asoke, North Klongtoey Watthana, Bangkok, 10110, Thailand
Tel.: (66) 22607092
Investment Management Service
N.A.I.C.S.: 523999

SD Engineering (Europe) Sp. z.o.o. (1)
Ul Lesna 1, 64-100, Leszno, Poland
Tel.: (48) 655252673
Web Site: http://www.sws.co.jp
Sales Range: $25-49.9 Million
Emp.: 22
Assembly Board & Jig Mfr & Distr
N.A.I.C.S.: 334418

SDE (Philippines) Corp. (1)
Luisita Industrial Park Special Export Processing Zone San Miguel, Tarlac, 2301, Philippines
Tel.: (63) 459850080
Assembly Board & Jig Mfr & Distr
N.A.I.C.S.: 333514

SE Bordnetze Morocco S.A.R.L. (1)
Lot 32-Zone Franche de, Tangiers, Morocco
Tel.: (212) 531069200
Wiring Harnesses Product Mfr
N.A.I.C.S.: 335931

SE Bordnetze Tunisia S.A.R.L. (1)
Zone Industrielle de El Irtyah, 8117, Jendouba, Tunisia
Tel.: (216) 70013120
Web Site: http://www.sebn.com
Wire Harness Mfr & Distr
N.A.I.C.S.: 332618
Mohamed Adel Bedioui (COO)

SE Bordnetze-Bulgaria EOOD (1)
Photen Sipcenski Polk No 114 Bulevard 23-Ti, 6100, Kazanlak, Bulgaria
Tel.: (359) 55928906
Wiring Harness Mfr & Distr
N.A.I.C.S.: 332618

SE Bordnetze-Mexico S.A. de C.V. (1)
Carretera Puebla-Santa ana km 17 2, 90860, Acuamanala de Miguel Hidalgo, Tlaxcala, Mexico
Tel.: (52) 2464652300
Web Site: http://www.sws.co.jp
Sales Range: $400-449.9 Million
Emp.: 200
Wiring Harness Mfr & Distr
N.A.I.C.S.: 332618
Horacio Martinez (Mgr)

SE Bordnetze-Polska Sp. z.o.o. (1)
Podmiejskastrabe ul Walczaka 25, 66-400, Gorzow, Wielkopolski, Poland
Tel.: (48) 957335703
Wiring Harness Mfr & Distr
N.A.I.C.S.: 332618

SE Bordnetze-Slovakia S.r.o. (1)
Novozamocka 67, 949 05, Nitra, Slovakia
Tel.: (421) 376569200
Web Site: http://www.sebn.sk
Emp.: 800
Wiring Harness Mfr
N.A.I.C.S.: 332618

SE Wiring Systems Egypt S.A.E (1)
Port Said Private Free Zone, South Industrial Area, Port-Said, Egypt
Tel.: (20) 663798000
Wiring Harnesses Product Mfr
N.A.I.C.S.: 335931

SE Wiring Systems TR Trading and Services Ltd. (1)
Esentepe Mah Ali Kaya Sok Pol Center A-B

SUMITOMO ELECTRIC INDUSTRIES, LTD.

Sumitomo Electric Industries, Ltd.—(Continued)
Blok Apt No1/B 69 Kat1 Levent, Sisli, Istanbul, Turkiye
Tel.: (90) 2643192467
Web Site: http://www.sws.co.jp
Wire Harness Distr
N.A.I.C.S.: 423610
Ruhsar Bozkurt *(Gen Mgr)*

SEAPS Vietnam Co., Ltd. (1)
21st Floor TNR Tower 54A Nguyen Chi Thanh Street, Thuong Ward Dong Da District, Hanoi, Vietnam
Tel.: (84) 2432444375
Wiring Harness Component Whslr
N.A.I.C.S.: 423690

SEAUTO-E GmbH (1)
Peter Sander Strasse 32, 55252, Mainz-Kastel, Germany
Tel.: (49) 6134204710
Sales Range: $25-49.9 Million
Emp.: 2
Information Technology Consulting Services
N.A.I.C.S.: 541512

SEI (Philippines) Incorporated (1)
4F King's Court 1 Building 2129 Chino Roces Ave, Makati, 1231, Philippines
Tel.: (63) 28112755
Cemented Carbide Tool & Cutting Tool Mfr
N.A.I.C.S.: 333515

SEI ANTech-Europe GmbH (1)
Peter Sander Strasse 32, 55252, Mainz-Kastel, Germany
Tel.: (49) 6134204715
Emp.: 11
Wiring Harness Distr
N.A.I.C.S.: 423610
Naohiro Kondo *(Mng Dir)*

SEI Business Creates, Inc. (1)
4-3-18 Imahashi, Chuo-ku, Osaka, 541-0042, Japan
Tel.: (81) 662045500
Sales Range: $100-124.9 Million
Emp.: 37
Electrical Equipment Mfr & Distr
N.A.I.C.S.: 335999

SEI Carbide Australia Pty., Ltd. (1)
2/89 Batt Street, Penrith, 2750, NSW, Australia
Tel.: (61) 247212000
Web Site: http://www.sumitool.com.au
Sales Range: $25-49.9 Million
Emp.: 15
Hard Metal Tools Mfr
N.A.I.C.S.: 333517

SEI Consulting Vietnam Co., Ltd. (1)
10th Floor Pacific Place 83B Ly Thuong Kiet Street, Tran Hung Dao Ward Hoan Kiem Dist, Hanoi, Vietnam
Tel.: (84) 2439461036
Administrative Support Services
N.A.I.C.S.: 561110

SEI Electronic Components (Vietnam), Ltd. (1)
Lot C-6, Thang Long Industrial Park Dong Anh District, Hanoi, Vietnam
Tel.: (84) 2438811531
Printed Circuit Board Mfr
N.A.I.C.S.: 334412

SEI Electronics Materials Ltd. (1)
No 19 Kon Ye No 5 Rd Fon San Tsuen Fukow Shan, Hsin-chu, 303, Hsien, Taiwan
Tel.: (886) 35984518
Web Site: http://www.global-sei.com
Sales Range: $25-49.9 Million
Emp.: 50
Compound Semiconductor & Electronic Materials Mfr
N.A.I.C.S.: 334413
Yoshiki Miura *(Pres)*

SEI Interconnect Products (Europe) Ltd. (1)
317 Square des Champs Elysees, 91026, Evry, Cedex, France
Tel.: (33) 169111380
Electric Wire & Cable Mfr
N.A.I.C.S.: 335929

SEI Interconnect Products (Europe) Ltd. (1)
Oststrasse 89, 22844, Norderstedt, Germany
Tel.: (49) 4052650160
Automotive Wire & Cable Mfr
N.A.I.C.S.: 336320

SEI Interconnect Products (Europe) Ltd. (1)
Via Belvedere 45, 22100, Como, Italy
Tel.: (39) 031526833
Automotive Wire & Cable Mfr
N.A.I.C.S.: 336320

SEI Interconnect Products (Europe), Ltd. (1)
Axis 10 Axis Court, Mallard Way, Swansea, SA7 0AJ, United Kingdom
Tel.: (44) 1792487290
Web Site: http://www.sumi-electric.eu
Sales Range: $25-49.9 Million
Emp.: 7
Electrical Wire Mfr
N.A.I.C.S.: 332618

SEI Interconnect Products (Hungary), Kft. (1)
Jaszapati u 1, Alattyan, 5142, Szolnok, Hungary
Tel.: (36) 57561207
Electronic Wire Product Mfr & Whslr
N.A.I.C.S.: 332618

SEI Loginet Co., Ltd. (1)
3-3-24 Kasugadekita, Konohana-ku, Osaka, 554-0021, Japan
Tel.: (81) 664665968
Web Site: http://www.global-sei.com
Electrical Wire Mfr
N.A.I.C.S.: 332618

SEI Optifrontier Co., Ltd. (1)
1 Taya-Cho, Sakae-ku, Yokohama, 244-8589, Kanagawa, Japan
Tel.: (81) 458537100
Web Site: http://seof.co.jp
Sales Range: $150-199.9 Million
Emp.: 800
Fiber Optic Cable Mfr
N.A.I.C.S.: 335921
Suetsugu Yoshiyuki *(Pres)*

Unit (Domestic):

SEI Optifrontier Co., Ltd. - Saitama Works (2)
4125 Sakitama, Gyoda, 361-8604, Saitama, Japan
Tel.: (81) 485592151
Sales Range: $150-199.9 Million
Fiber Optic Cable Mfr
N.A.I.C.S.: 335921
Akio Kawabata *(Mng Dir)*

SEI Optifrontier Co., Ltd. - Shonan Works (2)
1-5-1 Shimomachiya, Chigasaki, 253-0087, Kanagawa, Japan
Tel.: (81) 467854881
Web Site: http://www.seof.co.jp
Sales Range: $150-199.9 Million
Emp.: 800
Fiber Optic Cable Mfr
N.A.I.C.S.: 335921

SEI Optifrontier Co., Ltd. - Suwa Works (2)
11211 Ochiai Fujimi-machi, Suwa-gun, Nagano, 399-0214, Japan
Tel.: (81) 266623155
Optical Product Mfr
N.A.I.C.S.: 335921

SEI Optifrontier Vietnam, Ltd. (1)
Land Plot No B-3, Thang Long Industrial Park Thien Ke Commune, Binh Xuyen, Vinh Phuc, Vietnam
Tel.: (84) 2113555777
Cable & Optical Connector Mfr
N.A.I.C.S.: 334417

SEI Professional Staffs Inc. (1)
2-1-3 Nishimiyahara, Yodogawa-ku, Osaka, 532-0004, Japan
Tel.: (81) 663946748
Human Resource Consulting Services
N.A.I.C.S.: 541612

SEI Thai Electric Conductor Co., Ltd. (1)
7/414 Moo 6 Tambol Mabyangporn Amphur, Pluak Daeng, 21140, Rayong, Thailand
Tel.: (66) 3891373234
Web Site: http://www.stec-sei.com
Copper Wire Rod Mfr
N.A.I.C.S.: 331420

SEI Trading India Pte, Ltd. (1)
802 Vatika City Point M G Road Near M G Road Metro Station, Gurgaon, 122 002, Haryana, India
Tel.: (91) 1244577470
Web Site: https://www.seti.co.in
Sales Range: $25-49.9 Million
Emp.: 10
Electronic Components Distr
N.A.I.C.S.: 423610
Kan Kinoshita *(Pres)*

SEWS Asia Technical Center, Ltd. (1)
1778 Summer Hub 4th-5th Floor Sukhumvit Road, Kwaeng Prakhanong Khet Klongtoey, Bangkok, 10110, Thailand
Tel.: (66) 2029043045
Automobile Wiring Harnesses Product Mfr
N.A.I.C.S.: 335931

SEWS Australia Pty Ltd. (1)
23 Scanlon Dr, Epping, Melbourne, 3076, VIC, Australia
Tel.: (6) 399122803
Web Site: http://www.sws.com.au
Emp.: 10
Construction Engineering Services
N.A.I.C.S.: 541330
Hideaki Higashimura *(Mng Dir)*

SEWS Canada, Ltd. (1)
8771 George Bolton Parkway, Bolton, L7E 2X8, ON, Canada
Tel.: (905) 951-2037
Web Site: http://www.sws.co.jp
Customer Support Services
N.A.I.C.S.: 561990

SEWS Components (Huizhou) Limited (1)
Jiu long High Technology Industrial Park, Xiao Jin Kou Town, Huizhou, 516023, Guangdong, China
Tel.: (86) 7522783887
Automotive Electronic Product Mfr
N.A.I.C.S.: 336320

SEWS Hungary Wiring Harness, Ltd. (1)
Mor Akai u 12, 8060, Mor, Hungary
Tel.: (36) 22563530
Sales Range: $100-124.9 Million
Emp.: 80
Wiring Harness Mfr & Distr
N.A.I.C.S.: 332618

SEWS Mexico S.A. de C.V. (1)
AV Japon 126, Parque Industrial, 20300, San Francisco de los Romo, Aguascalientes, Mexico
Tel.: (52) 4499100600
Automobile Wiring Harnesses Product Mfr
N.A.I.C.S.: 335931

SEWS Polska Sp. Zo. o. (1)
Lesna 1, 64-100, Leszno, Poland
Tel.: (48) 655252600
Sales Range: $25-49.9 Million
Emp.: 10
Wire Harness Mfr & Distr
N.A.I.C.S.: 332618
Martin Urban *(Gen Mgr)*

SEWS Romania S.R.L. (1)
Calea Zarandului nr 166 DN7 Loc, Deva, 330182, Hunedoara, Romania
Tel.: (40) 254206600
Web Site: http://www.sws.co.jp
Wire Harness Mfr & Distr
N.A.I.C.S.: 332618

SEWS South Africa Pty Ltd. (1)
6/8 Prospecton Road, Prospecton, Durban, 4133, Kwazulu-Natal, South Africa
Tel.: (27) 319130700
Emp.: 50
Automobile Component Mfr & Distr
N.A.I.C.S.: 336390
Inus Dewet *(Gen Mgr-Production)*

SEWS Taiwan Ltd. (1)
12F-6 No 101 Fu-Hsin N Rd, Taipei, 105, Taiwan
Tel.: (886) 6287121468
Wiring Harnesses Product Mfr
N.A.I.C.S.: 335931

SEWS-Automotive Wire Hungary Ltd. (1)
Batthyany-Puszta Ipartelep 4, 2870, Kisber, Hungary
Tel.: (36) 34552206
Web Site: http://www.sws.co.jp
Sales Range: $25-49.9 Million
Emp.: 100
Automotive Electric Wire Mfr & Distr
N.A.I.C.S.: 336320
Shinji Kotaka *(Gen Mgr)*

SEWS-CABIND Maroc S.A.S. (1)
Zone Industrielle Ahmed Ben Ichou Km 9 Route de Rabat Ain Harrouda, BP130, 28632, Mohammedia, Morocco
Tel.: (212) 552749494
Web Site: http://www.sws.co.jp
Wire Harness Mfr & Distr
N.A.I.C.S.: 332618

SEWS-CABIND Poland Sp. z.o.o. (1)
ul Lesnianka 73, 34-300, Zywiec, Poland
Tel.: (48) 338604827
Web Site: http://www.sews-cabind.pl
Emp.: 1,100
Wiring Harness Mfr
N.A.I.C.S.: 332618

Plant (Domestic):

SEWS-CABIND Poland Sp. z.o.o. - Lesnianka Plant (2)
Lesnianka Str 73, Zywiec, 34300, Poland
Tel.: (48) 338604840
Web Site: http://www.sews-cabind.pl
Automotive Wiring Harness Mfr
N.A.I.C.S.: 336320

SEWS-CABIND S.p.A. (1)
Corso Pastrengo 40, 10093, Collegno, Torino, Italy
Tel.: (39) 01140106611
Automotive Wire Mfr & Distr
N.A.I.C.S.: 336320

SEWS-Components (Thailand) Ltd. (1)
7/129 Moo 4 Mabyangporn, Amata City Industrial Estate, Pluak Daeng, 21140, Rayong, Thailand
Tel.: (66) 38956318
Automobile Wiring Harnesses Product Mfr
N.A.I.C.S.: 335931

SEWS-Components Changshu Ltd. (1)
No 710 DongNan Road, Changshu New and Hi-tech Industrial Development Zone, Changshu, 215500, Jinangsu, China
Tel.: (86) 51251937588
Wiring Harnesses Product Mfr
N.A.I.C.S.: 335931

SEWS-Components Europe Hungary Ltd. (1)
Akai u 14, 8061, Mor, Hungary
Tel.: (36) 22563800
Web Site: http://www.sews-ceh.hu
Sales Range: $150-199.9 Million
Automobile Parts Mfr
N.A.I.C.S.: 336390
Magi Bobs *(Mng Dir)*

SEWS-Components Vietnam Co., Ltd. (1)
Plot D-2 and D-3, Thang Long Industrial Park II Lieu Xa, Yen My, Hung Yen, Vietnam
Tel.: (84) 2213974741
Electric & Electronic Component Mfr
N.A.I.C.S.: 335999

SEWS-Maroc SARL (1)
Lotissement Al Menzeh TF 9547 Bir Rami Z I, Kenitra, Morocco
Tel.: (212) 530774000
Wiring Harnesses Product Mfr
N.A.I.C.S.: 335931

SEWS-STC, Inc. (1)
6F World Plaza 855 Pudong Nan Road, Pudong New Area, Shanghai, 200120, China
Tel.: (86) 2168598668

AND PRIVATE COMPANIES

SUMITOMO ELECTRIC INDUSTRIES, LTD.

Sales Range: $25-49.9 Million
Emp.: 34
Automotive Wiring Harness Mfr
N.A.I.C.S.: 336320

SHC Co., Ltd. (1)
1845 Toba, Imizu, 939-0351, Toyama, Japan
Tel.: (81) 766562360
Rubber Goods Mfr & Whslr
N.A.I.C.S.: 326291

SWS Australia Pty., Ltd. (1)
23 Scanlon Dr Epping, 3076, Somerton, VIC, Australia
Tel.: (61) 393089177
Web Site: http://www.seaps.com.sg
Sales Range: $25-49.9 Million
Emp.: 50
Automotive Wiring Harness Mfr
N.A.I.C.S.: 336320

SWS CHINA LTD (1)
Room 1503-1506 Tower B City Center of Shanghai 100 Zunyi Rd, Chang Ning District, Shanghai, 200051, China
Tel.: (86) 2120286588
Web Site: http://www.sws.co.jp
Wiring Supplies Distr
N.A.I.C.S.: 423610

SWS East Japan, Ltd. (1)
50-30 Higashidai Ichinoseki, Iwate, 021-0822, Japan
Tel.: (81) 191212185
Sales Range: $75-99.9 Million
Emp.: 500
Electrical Wire Mfr
N.A.I.C.S.: 332618
Naoki Sawada *(Gen Mgr-Admin)*

SWS India Management Support & Service Pvt, Ltd. (1)
Plot No 1 8th Floor Sector-127 Noida-Greater Noida Expressway, Noida, 201301, Uttar Pradesh, India
Tel.: (91) 1206693687
Automobile Wiring Harnesses Product Mfr
N.A.I.C.S.: 335931

SWS Korea Co., Ltd. (1)
402 8 Seongnam-daero 331beon-gil, Bundang-gu, Seongnam, 13558, Gyeonggi-do, Korea (South)
Tel.: (82) 317199710
Web Site: http://www.sws.co.jp
Emp.: 8
Automobile Wiring Harness Mfr & Distr
N.A.I.C.S.: 336320
Hitomi Manabu *(Pres)*

SWS Logistics & Marketing (Thailand) Co., Ltd. (1)
35th Floor CRC Tower All Seasons Pl 87/2 Wireless Road, Lumpini, 10330, Bangkok, Pathumwan, Thailand
Tel.: (66) 24014129
Web Site: http://www.sws.co.jp
Harness Components Whslr
N.A.I.C.S.: 336320

SWS Management Support, Ltd. (1)
1-14 Nishisuehiro-cho, Yokkaichi, 510-8503, Mie, Japan
Tel.: (81) 593646532
Web Site: http://www.sws.co.jp
Business Support Services
N.A.I.C.S.: 561499

SWS Sales & Marketing (Thailand) Co., Ltd. (1)
33/4 The 9th Towers Grand Rama 9 Tower A 15th Fl Rama 9 Rd, Huaykwang, Bangkok, 10310, Thailand
Tel.: (66) 20014301
Wiring Harness Component Whslr
N.A.I.C.S.: 423690

SWS West Japan, Ltd. (1)
25-2 Otsuka-cho, Matsusaka, 515-0813, Mie, Japan
Tel.: (81) 598533800
Electrical Wire Distr
N.A.I.C.S.: 423610

SWS do Brasil Comercial Ltda. (1)
AV General Valdomiro De Lime, 275 Parque Jabaquara, 04344 070, Sao Paulo, Brazil
Tel.: (55) 1150132300

Wire Harnesses Mfr
N.A.I.C.S.: 332618

Sistemas de Arneses K&S Mexicana, S.A. de C.V. (1)
AV Japon 126 Parque Industrial, San Francisco de los Romo, Aguascalientes, 20300, Mexico
Tel.: (52) 4499100600
Web Site: http://www.sws.co.jp
Wiring Harness Mfr & Distr
N.A.I.C.S.: 332618

Sumi (Cambodia) Wiring Systems Co., Ltd. (1)
P1-047 P1-048 P1-049 Phnom Penh Special Economic Zone, National Road No 4 Sangkat Khantouk Khan Kambol, Phnom Penh, Cambodia
Tel.: (855) 23968338
Wiring Harnesses Product Mfr
N.A.I.C.S.: 335931

Sumi Philippines Wiring Systems Corporation (1)
Parkway Drive, Hermosa Ecozone Industrial Park Palihan Hermosa, Bataan, 2111, Philippines
Tel.: (63) 476331201
Automobile Wiring Harnesses Product Mfr
N.A.I.C.S.: 335931

Sumi Texas Wire, Inc. (1)
6500 N Desert Blvd, El Paso, TX 79912-8401
Tel.: (915) 845-7700
Electrical Wire Mfr
N.A.I.C.S.: 332618
Roberto Ornelas *(Coord-Safety)*

Sumi Vietnam Wiring System Co., Ltd. (1)
Lot B-1, Dong Van II Industrial Zone Duy Minh Ward Duy Tien Town, Ha Nam, Vietnam
Tel.: (84) 2266262081
Electric Wire Harnesses Mfr & Whslr
N.A.I.C.S.: 335931

Sumi-Pac Construction Co., Ltd. (1)
1671 Sec 1 Wan Shou Wan Rd Kuei Shan Hsiang, Taoyuan, 333, Hsien, Taiwan
Tel.: (886) 33205936
Sales Range: $25-49.9 Million
Emp.: 30
Power Cable Installation
N.A.I.C.S.: 238210

Sumi-Pac Corporation (1)
No 2 Kon Ye 5 Rd Fon San Tsuenfu Kow Shan, Hsin Chu, Hsien, 303, Taiwan
Tel.: (886) 35984147
Web Site: http://www.sumi-pac.com
Sales Range: $25-49.9 Million
Emp.: 190
Electronic Components Mfr
N.A.I.C.S.: 334419

Subsidiary (Non-US):

Sumiden Fine Conductors Co., Ltd. (2)
2-3 Sanra-higashi-machi, Neyagawa, 572-0813, Osaka, Japan
Tel.: (81) 728252223
Metallic Wire & Electronic Parts Mfr & Distr
N.A.I.C.S.: 332618

Plant (Domestic):

Sumiden Fine Conductors Co., Ltd. - Himejima Plant (3)
3-2-23 Himejima, Nishiyodogawa-ku, Osaka, 555-0033, Japan
Tel.: (81) 664722461
Web Site: http://www.sfc-hp.co.jp
Electrical Wire Mfr
N.A.I.C.S.: 332618

Sumiden Fine Conductors Co., Ltd. - Maebashi Plant (3)
2118 Soja Soja-machi, Maebashi, 371-0852, Gunma, Japan
Tel.: (81) 272537360
Electrical Wire Mfr
N.A.I.C.S.: 332618

Sumi-Pac Electro-Chemical Corporation (1)
15 Kung Yeh 5 Rd, Taipei, 303, Taiwan

Tel.: (886) 35984165
Heat-Shrinkable Tubing Mfr
N.A.I.C.S.: 423690

Sumiden Asia (Shenzhen) Co., Ltd. (1)
Rm 3407-3410 Tower 4 Excellence Century Center Fuhua 3 Rd, Futian District, Shenzhen, 518033, China
Tel.: (86) 75582706880
Fiber Optic Cable Mfr
N.A.I.C.S.: 335921

Sumiden Carbide Manufacturing (Tianjin) Co., Ltd. (1)
No 2 Saida Huiya Industrial Park, Xiqing Economic Develop Area, Tianjin, 300385, China
Tel.: (86) 2223889100
Web Site: http://www.sumitool.com
Cemented Carbide Tools Manufacture & Sales
N.A.I.C.S.: 333515

Sumiden Communication Engineering Co., Ltd. (1)
501-11 Maeda-cho, Totsuka-ku, Yokohama, 244-0804, Kanagawa, Japan
Tel.: (81) 458256111
Automotive Electronic Product Mfr
N.A.I.C.S.: 336320

Sumiden Dengyo Co., Ltd. (1)
3-12-15 Mita, Minato-ku, Tokyo, 108-8303, Japan
Tel.: (81) 334546961
Construction Equipment Mfr
N.A.I.C.S.: 333120

Sumiden Device Innovations Vietnam Co., Ltd. (1)
Plot 105/5 Amata Road 5 Amata Industrial Park, Long Binh Ward, Bien Hoa, Dong Nai, Vietnam
Tel.: (84) 613936516
Sales Range: $150-199.9 Million
Emp.: 64
Electric Device Mfr
N.A.I.C.S.: 335999

Sumiden Electronic Materials (M) Sdn. Bhd. (1)
No 16A Jalan Jenjarum 28/39 Section 28, 40400, Shah Alam, Selangor Darul Ehsan, Malaysia
Tel.: (60) 351922955
Web Site: http://www.sumiden.com.my
Sales Range: $25-49.9 Million
Emp.: 70
Mfr of Lead Wire for Electonic Components
N.A.I.C.S.: 334419
Yuichi Sugino *(Mng Dir)*

Sumiden Friend, Ltd. (1)
1-1-1 Koyakita, Itami, 664-0016, Hyogo, Japan
Tel.: (81) 727710767
Emp.: 35
Environmental Consulting Services
N.A.I.C.S.: 541620
Yasuo Homa *(Pres)*

Sumiden Hitachi Cable Ltd. (1)
Sumitomo Nakanoshima Building 3F 3-2-18 Nakanoshima, Kita-ku, Osaka, 530-0005, Japan
Tel.: (81) 661314624
Web Site: http://www.hst-cable.co.jp
Electric Cable & Wire Product Mfr
N.A.I.C.S.: 335929

Sumiden International Trading (Shanghai) Co., Ltd. (1)
Room 601 108 Yuyuan Road, Jing'an District, Shanghai, China
Tel.: (86) 2162491100
Automotive Electronic Product Mfr
N.A.I.C.S.: 336320

Sumiden International Trading (Vietnam) Co., Ltd. (1)
201B 2F Floor V-Tower 649 Kim Ma, Ba Dinh, Hanoi, Vietnam
Tel.: (84) 2439336436
Automotive Electronic Product Mfr
N.A.I.C.S.: 336320

Sumiden Light Alloy (Changzhou) Co., Ltd. (1)
No 7 Xinyong Road, Wujin High-Tech In-

dustrial Development Zone, Changzhou, Jinangu, China
Tel.: (86) 51981690218
Web Site: http://www.zdqhj.cn
Magnesium Alloy Product Mfr
N.A.I.C.S.: 331529

Sumiden Opcom, Ltd. (1)
112 Iijima-cho, Sakae-ku, Yokohama, 244-0842, Japan
Tel.: (81) 454109390
Communication Equipment Mfr & Distr
N.A.I.C.S.: 334290

Sumiden Powder Metallurgy (Wuxi) Co., Ltd. (1)
No 2 Xing Chuang 4Th Road, Wuxi-Singapore Industrial, Wuxi, 214028, Jiangsu, China
Tel.: (86) 51085280577
Rev.: $10,700,000
Cemented Carbide Tool Mfr
N.A.I.C.S.: 333515

Sumiden Semiconductor Materials Co., Ltd. (1)
1-9-2 Takatsukadai, Nishi-ku, Kobe, 651-2271, Hyogo, Japan
Tel.: (81) 789901304
Sales Range: $100-124.9 Million
Emp.: 26
Semiconductor Device Mfr & Distr
N.A.I.C.S.: 334413

Sumiden Shoji (Thailand) Co., Ltd. (1)
15th Fl BB Bldg 54 Soi Asoke, Bangkok, 10110, Thailand
Tel.: (66) 22607059
Sales Range: $25-49.9 Million
Emp.: 20
Electric Wire & Cable Mfr
N.A.I.C.S.: 335929
Ryuji Matsubara *(Mng Dir)*

Sumiden Shoji Co., Ltd. (1)
5-8-11 Itachibori, Nishi-Ku, Osaka, 550-0012, Japan
Tel.: (81) 665385241
Web Site: https://www.sumidenshoji.co.jp
Emp.: 435
Electronic Component Mfr & Distr
N.A.I.C.S.: 334419

Sumiden Sizai Kakou Co., Ltd. (1)
1-1-19 Tsuneyoshi, Konohana-ku, Osaka, 554-0052, Japan
Tel.: (81) 664621691
Web Site: http://www.sei-skc.co.jp
Recycled Wires Mfr
N.A.I.C.S.: 335929

Sumiden Steel Wire (Thailand) Co., Ltd. (1)
7/325 Moo 6, Amata City Rayong Industrial Estate Tambol Mabyabgpom Amphur, Pluak Daeng, 21140, Rayong, Thailand
Tel.: (66) 38036410
Steel Tire Cord Mfr
N.A.I.C.S.: 314994

Sumiden Transmission & Distribution System Products, Ltd. (1)
6-1-3 Kitagawara, Itami, 664-0837, Hyogo, Japan
Tel.: (81) 727820671
Electric Cable & Wire Product Mfr
N.A.I.C.S.: 335929

Sumiden Vietnam Automotive Wire Co., Ltd. (1)
Dai An Industrial Zone Km 51 Highway No 5, Hai Duong, Vietnam
Tel.: (84) 3203555833
Sales Range: $100-124.9 Million
Emp.: 300
Automobile Electric Wire Mfr & Distr
N.A.I.C.S.: 336320
Kazunori Tsuji *(Gen Dir)*

Sumiden Wire Products Corporation (1)
1412 El Pinal Dr, Stockton, CA 95205-2642
Tel.: (209) 466-8924
Web Site: http://www.sumidenwire.com
Sales Range: $25-49.9 Million
Emp.: 33
Construction Wire Mfr & Whslr
N.A.I.C.S.: 331222

SUMITOMO ELECTRIC INDUSTRIES, LTD.

INTERNATIONAL PUBLIC

Sumitomo Electric Industries, Ltd.—(Continued)

Division (Domestic):

Sumiden Wire Products Corporation (2)
710 Marshall Stuart Dr, Dickson, TN 37055-3004
Tel.: (615) 446-3199
Web Site: http://www.sumidenwire.com
Sales Range: $25-49.9 Million
Stainless Steel Wire Mfr
N.A.I.C.S.: 331222

Sumidenso Mediatech (Huizhou)Ltd. (1)
Xian Ke Road Side Xia-cun, RuHu Town Huicheng District, Huizhou, 516021, Guangdong, China
Tel.: (86) 7522806026
Automobile Wire Harness Mfr & Distr
N.A.I.C.S.: 336320

Sumidenso Mediatech Suzhou Co., Ltd. (1)
NO 15 Chun Qiu Road Pan Yang Industrial Park Huang Dai Town, Xiang Cheng, Suzhou, 215143, Jiang Su, China
Tel.: (86) 51265710060
Wire Harness Mfr & Distr
N.A.I.C.S.: 332618

Sumidenso Platech, Ltd. (1)
127 Nakashimizu, Gotemba, 412-0037, Shizuoka, Japan
Tel.: (81) 550871714
Web Site: http://www.sws.co.jp
Synthetic Resin & Metal Products Mfr & Distr
N.A.I.C.S.: 325211

Sumidenso Service, Ltd. (1)
1-14 Nishisuehiro-cho, Yokkaichi, 510-8503, Mie, Japan
Tel.: (81) 593546288
Web Site: http://www.sws.co.jp
Electric Wire Dismantling & Insurance Services
N.A.I.C.S.: 238210

Sumidenso Vietnam Co., Ltd. (1)
Dai An Industrial Zone Km 51 Highway No 5, Hai Duong, Vietnam
Tel.: (84) 3203784568
Wiring Harness Mfr & Distr
N.A.I.C.S.: 332618

Sumidenso do Brasil Industrias Electricas Ltda. (1)
Estrada Municipal do Varjao 6400 Jd, Novo Horizonte Jundiai, Sao Paulo, Brazil
Tel.: (55) 1144316400
Automotive Wiring Harness Mfr
N.A.I.C.S.: 332618

Sumidenso do Brasil Industrias Eletricas Ltda. (1)
Avenida Fagundes Filho 141-11 Andar Jardim Monte Alegre, Sao Paulo, 04304-000, Brazil
Tel.: (55) 1155842300
Automobile Wiring Harnesses Product Mfr
N.A.I.C.S.: 335931

Suminet Communication Technologies (Shanghai) Co., Ltd. (1)
3F- 4F 3Bld 647 Long Song Tao Road, Zhangjiang High-tech Park, Shanghai, 201203, China
Tel.: (86) 2150273600
Web Site: http://www.suminet-sh.com
Broadband Internet Access Equipment Mfr
N.A.I.C.S.: 334290

Sumisetsu Techno Co., Ltd. (1)
6-1 Kaminarashirogaito, Yawata, 614-8155, Kyoto, Japan
Tel.: (81) 759721210
Industrial Machinery Mfr & Distr
N.A.I.C.S.: 333248

Sumitomo (SEI) Electronic Wire, Inc. (1)
3-3 Satsuki-cho, Kanuma, 322-8585, Tochigi, Japan
Tel.: (81) 289760301
Electric Wire Mfr & Distr
N.A.I.C.S.: 332618

Sumitomo (SEI) Steel Wire Corp. (1)
1-1-1 Koyakita, Itami, 664-0016, Hyogo, Japan
Tel.: (81) 727722228
Web Site: http://www.sei-ssw.co.jp
Steel Wire Mfr & Distr
N.A.I.C.S.: 331222
Hiroyasu Torii *(Gen Mgr)*

Sumitomo Corporation Europe Limited (1)
Vintners Place 68 Upper Thames Street, London, EC4V 3BJ, United Kingdom
Tel.: (44) 2072463600
Web Site: http://www.sumitomocorp.com
Sales Range: $50-74.9 Million
Emp.: 250
Wire & Cable Mfr
N.A.I.C.S.: 332618

Sumitomo Electric (Korea) Electronics, Ltd. (1)
14F Gyeongwon Bldg 340 Gangnam-daero, Gangnam-gu, Seoul, 06242, Korea (South)
Tel.: (82) 234534511
Web Site: http://www.global-sei.com
Sales Range: $25-49.9 Million
Emp.: 2
Electrical Wire Distr
N.A.I.C.S.: 423610
Hara Masanori *(CEO)*

Sumitomo Electric (Shanghai) Electronics, Ltd. (1)
Room 2015 Shanghai International Trade Center 2201 Yan An Road W, Chang Ning District, Shanghai, China
Tel.: (86) 2162195959
Automobile Electric Wire Product Mfr
N.A.I.C.S.: 336320

Sumitomo Electric (Thailand) Ltd. (1)
Room 1406 Sakura Tower 339 Bogyoke Aung San Road, Kyauktada Township, Yangon, Myanmar
Tel.: (95) 9788205567
Communication & Power Cable Wire Mfr
N.A.I.C.S.: 335929

Sumitomo Electric (Thailand) Ltd. (1)
15th Floor B B Building No 54 Sukhumvit 21 Road, North Klongtoey Wattana, Bangkok, 10110, Thailand
Tel.: (66) 226072315
Web Site: http://www.set-th.com
Sales Range: $25-49.9 Million
Emp.: 36
Electric Wire & Cable Mfr
N.A.I.C.S.: 332618

Sumitomo Electric Asia Pacific Pte. Ltd. (1)
31 International Business Park 02 -10, Singapore, 609921, Singapore
Tel.: (65) 62613388
Web Site: http://www.seap.com.sg
Electronic Products Mfr
N.A.I.C.S.: 334419

Sumitomo Electric Asia, Ltd. (1)
Room 2624-2637 Sun Hung Kai Centre 30 Harbour Road, 30 Harbor Road, Wanchai, China (Hong Kong)
Tel.: (852) 25760080
Web Site: http://www.sei.pl.jp
Sales Range: $25-49.9 Million
Emp.: 25
Wire & Fiber Optics Mfr
N.A.I.C.S.: 332618

Sumitomo Electric Automotive Products (Singapore) Pte., Ltd. (1)
460 Alexandra Road 25-01 PSA Building, Singapore, 119963, Singapore
Tel.: (65) 63925441
Web Site: http://www.seaps.com.sg
Sales Range: $25-49.9 Million
Emp.: 16
Seller of Wiring Harnesses & Harness Components for Automobiles
N.A.I.C.S.: 336340

Sumitomo Electric Bordnetze GmbH (1)
Brandgehaege 11, Hattorf, 38444, Wolfsburg, Germany
Tel.: (49) 5308400400
Web Site: http://www.sebn.com
Sales Range: $100-124.9 Million
Emp.: 35
Automotive Wiring System Mfr & Distr
N.A.I.C.S.: 336320
Tomoyuki Miyake *(CEO)*

Sumitomo Electric Carbide Manufacturing, Inc. (1)
5635 S Westbridge Dr, New Berlin, WI 53151-1110
Tel.: (262) 938-6700
Sales Range: $25-49.9 Million
Emp.: 83
Hard Metal Tools Mfr
N.A.I.C.S.: 333515
Ben Nakamura *(Pres)*

Sumitomo Electric Carbide, Inc. (1)
1001 Business Ctr Dr, Mount Prospect, IL 60056-2181
Tel.: (847) 635-0044
Web Site: http://www.sumicarbide.com
Sales Range: $50-74.9 Million
Emp.: 65
Storage & Distribution of Hard Metal Tools
N.A.I.C.S.: 423830

Subsidiary (Domestic):

Master Tool Corp. (2)
210 River St, Grand River, OH 44045
Tel.: (440) 354-0600
Web Site: http://www.mtctools.com
Sales Range: $25-49.9 Million
Emp.: 50
Machine Tools, Metal Cutting Type
N.A.I.C.S.: 333517

Sumitomo Electric Device Innovations U.S.A., Inc. (1)
2355 Zanker Rd, San Jose, CA 95131-1138
Tel.: (408) 232-9500
Web Site: http://www.sei-device.com
Sales Range: $25-49.9 Million
Emp.: 100
Provider of Computer Systems, Peripherals & Internet Services
N.A.I.C.S.: 334118

Sumitomo Electric Device Innovations, Inc. (1)
1 Kanai-cho, Sakae-ku, Yokohama, 244-0845, Kanagawa, Japan
Tel.: (81) 458538150
Web Site: https://www.sedi.co.jp
Electric Device Mfr
N.A.I.C.S.: 335999
Yuichi Hasegawa *(Pres)*

Plant (Domestic):

Sumitomo Electric Device Innovations Inc. - Yamanashi Plant (2)
1000 Kamisukiawara Showa-cho, Nakakoma-gun, Yamanashi, 409-3883, Japan
Tel.: (81) 552754411
Web Site: http://www.sedi.co.jp
Wireless Communication Equipment Mfr
N.A.I.C.S.: 334290

Sumitomo Electric Europe Ltd. (1)
Viale Piero e Alberto Pirelli 6, 20126, Milan, Italy
Tel.: (39) 0249638601
Fiber Optic Cable Mfr
N.A.I.C.S.: 335921

Sumitomo Electric Europe Ltd. (1)
220 Centennial Park, Elstree, WD6 3SL, Hertfordshire, United Kingdom
Tel.: (44) 2089538118
Web Site: http://www.sumielectric.com
Fiber Optic Cable Distr
N.A.I.C.S.: 423610

Sumitomo Electric Finance U.K. Ltd. (1)
220 Centennial Park, London, WD6 3SL, United Kingdom
Tel.: (44) 2079290345
Corporate Financial Services
N.A.I.C.S.: 561499

Sumitomo Electric Finance U.S.A., Inc. (1)
600 5th Ave 18th Fl, New York, NY 10020-2320
Tel.: (212) 490-6610
Financing Activity Services
N.A.I.C.S.: 523999

Sumitomo Electric Fine Polymer (Suzhou) Ltd. (1)
No 232 Jinfeng Road, Suzhou New District, Suzhou, 215129, Jiangsu, China
Tel.: (86) 51289186680
Heat Shrinkable Tubing & Roller Mfr
N.A.I.C.S.: 326220

Sumitomo Electric Fine Polymer, Inc. (1)
950 1-chome Asashiro-nishi, Kumatori-cho Sennan-gun, Osaka, 590-0458, Japan
Tel.: (81) 724521301
Web Site: https://www.sei-sfp.co.jp
Sales Range: $100-124.9 Million
Emp.: 480
Polymer Material Mfr
N.A.I.C.S.: 325211

Subsidiary (Non-US):

Sumitomo Electric Schrumpf-Produkte GmbH (2)
Oststr 89, 22844, Norderstedt, Germany
Tel.: (49) 405265010
Web Site: http://www.sesp.de
Sales Range: $25-49.9 Million
Electric Component Mfr & Distr
N.A.I.C.S.: 335999
Thomas Deckert *(Plant Mgr)*

Sumitomo Electric Hardmetal Asia Pacific Pte Ltd (1)
6 New Industrial Road 03-03/04 New Century, Singapore, 536199, Singapore
Tel.: (65) 62824334
Web Site: https://www.sumitool.com.sg
Cutting Tool Mfr
N.A.I.C.S.: 333515
Murayama Atsushi *(Mng Dir)*

Sumitomo Electric Hardmetal Corp. (1)
1-1-1 Koyakita, Itami, 664-0016, Hyogo, Japan
Tel.: (81) 727724531
Web Site: http://www.sumitool.com
Cutting Tool Mfr
N.A.I.C.S.: 333515

Sumitomo Electric Hardmetal Ltd. (1)
50 Summerleys Road, Princes Risborough, HP27 9PW, Buckinghamshire, United Kingdom
Tel.: (44) 1844342081
Web Site: http://www.sumitomo-hardmetal.co.uk
Sales Range: $25-49.9 Million
Emp.: 10
Hard Metal Tools Mfr
N.A.I.C.S.: 333991

Sumitomo Electric Hardmetal Manufacturing (Changzhou) Co., Ltd. (1)
Factory Building 12 Xihu Road 8 Wujin High-Tech Industrial Zone, Changzhou, 213164, China
Tel.: (86) 51986220306
Sales Range: $50-74.9 Million
Emp.: 12
Industrial Tool Mfr & Distr
N.A.I.C.S.: 333515

Sumitomo Electric Hardmetal Manufacturing (Thailand), Ltd. (1)
No 102 Moo 9 Bangna-Trad Road, Wellgrow Industrial Estate, Bang Pakong, 24180, Chachoengsao, Thailand
Tel.: (66) 38571940
Cemented Carbide Tool & Cutting Tool Mfr
N.A.I.C.S.: 333515

Sumitomo Electric Hardmetal Manufacturing India Pvt. Ltd. (1)
Community Centre Bhageria House, 43 New Friends Colony, Noida, 110065, India
Tel.: (91) 1184510048
Web Site: http://www.sews-deutschland.de
Hard Metal Tools Mfr
N.A.I.C.S.: 332510

Sumitomo Electric Hardmetal Trading (Shanghai) Co., Ltd. (1)
Room J 6/F Huamin Empire Plz No 728 Yan An Rd, Shanghai, 200050, China
Tel.: (86) 2152381199

AND PRIVATE COMPANIES / SUMITOMO ELECTRIC INDUSTRIES, LTD.

Emp.: 4
Industrial Cutting Tool Distr
N.A.I.C.S.: 423830
Akihiro Tanaka *(Gen Mgr)*

Sumitomo Electric Hardmetal de Mexico. S.A. de C.V. (1)
Eugenio Garza Sada 42 Colonia Los Pocitos, 20328, Aguascalientes, Mexico
Tel.: (52) 4499932740
Web Site: http://www.sumitool.mx
Cutting Tool Mfr
N.A.I.C.S.: 333515

Sumitomo Electric Hartmetal GmbH (1)
Konrad-Zuse-Str 9, 47877, Willich, Germany
Tel.: (49) 215449920
Web Site: https://www.sumitomotool.com
Sales Range: $25-49.9 Million
Emp.: 60
Hard Metal Tools Mfr
N.A.I.C.S.: 333991

Sumitomo Electric Hartmetallfabrik GmbH (1)
Industrie Strasse 2, 73466, Lauchheim, Germany
Tel.: (49) 7363870
Web Site: http://www.sumitomotool.com
Sales Range: $25-49.9 Million
Emp.: 100
Hard Metal Tools Mfr
N.A.I.C.S.: 333991

Sumitomo Electric Industrial Wire & Cable Inc. (1)
Sumiden Tomita Shoji Bldg 5F 5-8-11 Itachibori, Nishi-ku, Osaka, 550-0012, Japan
Tel.: (81) 665312000
Web Site: http://www.global-sei.com
Electric Wire & Cable Mfr & Distr
N.A.I.C.S.: 332618

Sumitomo Electric Industries, Ltd. (1)
Akasaka Center Building 1-3-13 Motoakasaka, Minato-ku, Tokyo, 107-8468, Japan
Tel.: (81) 364062600
Web Site: http://global-sei.com
Sales Range: $250-299.9 Million
Emp.: 500
International Wire & Electric Parts Sales
N.A.I.C.S.: 221122

Sumitomo Electric Industries, Ltd. - Itami Works (1)
1-1-1 Koyakita, Koyakita, Itami, 664-0016, Hyogo, Japan
Tel.: (81) 727723300
Web Site: http://www.global-sei.com
Steel Wires & Powdered Alloys Mfr
N.A.I.C.S.: 332618

Sumitomo Electric Industries, Ltd. - Osaka Works (1)
1-1-3 Shimaya, Konohana-ku, Osaka, 554-0024, Japan
Tel.: (81) 664665651
Web Site: http://www.global-sei.com
Human Resource Management & Administration Services
N.A.I.C.S.: 541612

Sumitomo Electric Industries, Ltd. - Yokohama Works (1)
1 Taya-cho, Sakae-ku, Yokohama, 244-8588, Japan
Tel.: (81) 458537182
Web Site: http://www.global-sei.com
Fiber Optic Cable Mfr
N.A.I.C.S.: 335921

Sumitomo Electric Information Systems Co., Ltd. (1)
Sora Shin-Osaka 21 Bldg 2-1-3 Nishimiyahara, Yodogawa-ku, Osaka, 532-0004, Japan
Tel.: (81) 663946751
Web Site: http://www.global-sei.com
Software Development Services
N.A.I.C.S.: 541511

Sumitomo Electric Intellectual Property & Technology Center, Ltd. (1)
1-1-3 Shimaya, Konohana-ku, Osaka, 554-0024, Japan
Tel.: (81) 664666539
Web Site: http://www.global-sei.com
Sales Range: $450-499.9 Million
Emp.: 2,000
Industrial Machinery Distr
N.A.I.C.S.: 423830

Sumitomo Electric Interconnect Hong Kong Ltd (1)
Rm 1005-1006 10/F West Wing Center 66 Mody Road, Tsin Sha Tsui, Kowloon, China (Hong Kong)
Tel.: (852) 28056777
Sales Range: $25-49.9 Million
Emp.: 40
Flexible Printed Circuit Mfr
N.A.I.C.S.: 334412

Sumitomo Electric Interconnect Products (Hong Kong), Ltd. (1)
Suites 1003-7 10F Tower1 The Gateway Harbour City, Tsim Sha Tsui, Kowloon, China (Hong Kong)
Tel.: (852) 28056777
Web Site: http://www.sei.co.jp
Electric Wire & Cable Distr
N.A.I.C.S.: 423610

Sumitomo Electric Interconnect Products (M) Sdn. Bhd. (1)
No 1 Jalan Angkasa Mas Utama Kawasan Perindustrian Tebrau II, 81100, Johor Bahru, Johor, Malaysia
Tel.: (60) 73602000
Web Site: http://www.sepm.com.my
Sales Range: $150-199.9 Million
Emp.: 906
TV High Voltage Wire & Insulated Wires Mfr
N.A.I.C.S.: 336320

Sumitomo Electric Interconnect Products (Shanghai), Ltd. (1)
No 35 Building No 281 Fa Sai Road, Pilot Free Trade Zone, Shanghai, 200131, China
Tel.: (86) 2150481064
Web Site: http://www.global-sei.com
Flat Cable Wiring System Mfr & Distr
N.A.I.C.S.: 335929

Sumitomo Electric Interconnect Products (Shenzhen), Ltd. (1)
No 20 Songtang Road, Tongfuyu Industrial Area Tangxiayong Songgang Bao An, Shenzhen, 518127, Guangdong, China
Tel.: (86) 75527058903
Web Site: http://www.global-sei.com
Wiring Harness Mfr
N.A.I.C.S.: 332618

Sumitomo Electric Interconnect Products (Singapore) Pte., Ltd. (1)
31 International Business Park 02-10, Singapore, 609921, Singapore
Tel.: (65) 62613388
Web Site: http://www.seps.com.sg
Sales Range: $25-49.9 Million
Emp.: 43
Electric Product Sales & Mktg
N.A.I.C.S.: 336320
Akitoshi Umemoto *(Mng Dir)*

Sumitomo Electric Interconnect Products (Suzhou), Ltd. (1)
No 232 Jinfeng Rd, Suzhou, '215129, China
Tel.: (86) 51266653090
Electrical Wire Mfr
N.A.I.C.S.: 335929

Sumitomo Electric Interconnect Products (Vietnam), Ltd. (1)
Lot3 Ts 6 Street Tien Son Industrial Zone, Bac Ninh, Vietnam
Tel.: (84) 2223714880
Web Site: http://www.sei-sfp.co.jp
Roller Products Mfr & Distr
N.A.I.C.S.: 332991

Sumitomo Electric Interconnect Products Inc. (1)
915 Armorite Dr, San Marcos, CA 92069-1440
Tel.: (760) 761-0600
Web Site: http://www.seipusa.com
Sales Range: $25-49.9 Million
Emp.: 7
Heat-Shrinkable Tubing Mfr & Sales
N.A.I.C.S.: 326299

Sumitomo Electric International (Singapore) Pte. Ltd. (1)
100 Beach Road Shaw Tower 24-09, Singapore, 189702, Singapore
Tel.: (65) 62917525
Web Site: http://www.seaps.com.sg
Sales Range: $25-49.9 Million
Emp.: 20
Cable & Fiber Optics Mfr
N.A.I.C.S.: 332618
Yoshinobu Matsumura *(Mng Dir)*

Sumitomo Electric Lightwave Corp. (1)
201 S Rogers Ln Ste 100, Raleigh, NC 27610
Tel.: (919) 541-8100
Web Site: http://www.sumitomoelectric.com
Sales Range: $50-74.9 Million
Emp.: 450
Optical Fiber Cable, Components & Equipment Mfr
N.A.I.C.S.: 332618
Rob Sutton *(Reg Mgr-Sls-North Central & West Canada)*

Sumitomo Electric Magnet Wire (M) Sdn. Bhd. (1)
Lot 499 and 500 Persiaran Sabak Bernam, Seksyen 26, Shah Alam, 40000, Darul Ehsan, Malaysia
Tel.: (60) 351912299
Web Site: http://www.sumitomo.com
Sales Range: $75-99.9 Million
Emp.: 270
Magnet Wire Mfr
N.A.I.C.S.: 332618
Masaya Mori *(Mng Dir)*

Sumitomo Electric Management (Shanghai) Co., Ltd. (1)
Room 2015 Shanghai International Trade Center 2201 Yan An Road W, Chang Ning District, Shanghai, China
Tel.: (86) 2162785978
Corporate Governance & Administration Services
N.A.I.C.S.: 561110

Sumitomo Electric Optical Components (Wuxi) Co., Ltd. (1)
113-1-1 Ximei Road, Xinwu District, Wuxi, Jiangsu, China
Tel.: (86) 51085202036
Optical Coupler & Optical Connector Mfr
N.A.I.C.S.: 334417

Sumitomo Electric Optifrontier Co., Ltd. (1)
1 Taya-Cho, Sakae-ku, Yokohama, 244-8589, Kanagawa, Japan
Tel.: (81) 458537100
Web Site: https://www.seof.co.jp
Emp.: 900
Optical Coupler & Optical Connector Mfr
N.A.I.C.S.: 334417
Suetsugu Yoshiyuki *(Pres)*

Sumitomo Electric Photo-Electronics Components (Suzhou), Ltd. (1)
No 199 Putuoshan Road Snd, Suzhou, 215153, Jiangsu, China
Tel.: (86) 51266070768
Electronic Components Mfr
N.A.I.C.S.: 334419

Sumitomo Electric Printed Circuits, Inc. (1)
30 Hinokigaoka, Minakuchi-cho, Koka, 528-0068, Shiga, Japan
Tel.: (81) 748653400
Web Site: https://www.sei-sect.co.jp
Printed Circuit Board Mfr
N.A.I.C.S.: 334412
Hiroshi Tatsuta *(Pres)*

Sumitomo Electric Semiconductor Materials, Inc. (1)
7230 NW Evergreen Pkwy, Hillsboro, OR 97124-5827
Tel.: (503) 693-3100
Semiconductor Mfr & Distr
N.A.I.C.S.: 334413

Sumitomo Electric Sintered Alloy Ltd. (1)
2901 Nariwa Nariwa-cho, Takahashi, 716-0192, Okayama, Japan
Tel.: (81) 866424161
Web Site: http://www.sei.co.jp
Sintered Products Mfr
N.A.I.C.S.: 332117

Sumitomo Electric Sintered Components (Germany) GmbH (1)
Dischinger Str 1, Oberseifersdorf, 2763, Germany
Tel.: (49) 3583518488
Sales Range: $50-74.9 Million
Emp.: 12
Sintered Component Mfr & Distr
N.A.I.C.S.: 332999
Naoki Inui *(Mng Dir)*

Sumitomo Electric Sintered Components (M) Sdn. Bhd. (1)
No 16 Jalan Jenjarum 28/39 Seksyen 28, 40400, Shah Alam, Selangor, Malaysia
Tel.: (60) 351912700
Web Site: https://www.sesc.com.my
Sales Range: $75-99.9 Million
Emp.: 330
Powdered Metallurgical Parts Mfr
N.A.I.C.S.: 333131
Ang Ean Chuan *(Mng Dir)*

Sumitomo Electric Sintered Components (Thailand) Co., Ltd. (1)
700/471 Moo Amata Nakorn Industrial Estate Tambol Donhua-Roh, Amphur Muangchonburi, Chon Buri, 20000, Thailand
Tel.: (66) 38469555
Sintered Parts Mfr & Distr
N.A.I.C.S.: 336390

Sumitomo Electric System Solutions Co., Ltd. (1)
1-43-5 Sekiguchi, Bunkyo-ku, Tokyo, 112-0014, Japan
Tel.: (81) 352867575
Web Site: https://www.seiss.co.jp
Emp.: 625
Communication Software Development Services
N.A.I.C.S.: 541511
Koichi Washimi *(Pres)*

Subsidiary (Domestic):

Sumitomo Electric System Solutions Co., Ltd. - Konohana Works (2)
1-1-3 Shimaya, Konohana-ku, Osaka, 554-0024, Japan
Tel.: (81) 664665984
Web Site: http://www.seiss.co.jp
Communication Software Development Services
N.A.I.C.S.: 541511

Sumitomo Electric Technical Solutions, Inc. (1)
No 2 Sumitomo Bldg 4F 4-7-28 Kitahama, Chuo-ku, Osaka, 541-0041, Japan
Tel.: (81) 662323700
Web Site: https://www.sei-sts.co.jp
Emp.: 580
Steel Pole Mfr
N.A.I.C.S.: 331110

Sumitomo Electric Tochigi Co., Ltd. (1)
18-4 Kiyohara-Kogyodanchi, Utsunomiya, 321-3281, Tochigi, Japan
Tel.: (81) 286676313
Sales Range: $75-99.9 Million
Emp.: 300
Steel Pole Mfr
N.A.I.C.S.: 331221

Sumitomo Electric Tool Net, Inc. (1)
No 2 Sumitomo Bldg 4F 4-7-28 Kitahama, Chuo-ku, Osaka, 541-0041, Japan
Tel.: (81) 662213011
Web Site: http://www.global-sei.com
Industrial Cutting Tool Distr
N.A.I.C.S.: 423830

Sumitomo Electric Toyama Co., Ltd. (1)
10-2 Nagonoe, Imizu, 934-8852, Toyama, Japan
Tel.: (81) 766847122
Web Site: http://www.sei-toyama.co.jp
Sales Range: $125-149.9 Million
Emp.: 40
Electric Wire & Metal Products Mfr & Distr
N.A.I.C.S.: 332618

Sumitomo Electric U.S.A., Inc. (1)
21241 S Western Ave Ste 120, Torrance, CA 90501

SUMITOMO ELECTRIC INDUSTRIES, LTD.

Sumitomo Electric Industries, Ltd.—(Continued)
Tel.: (310) 782-0227
Web Site: http://www.sumitomoelectricusa.com
Sales Range: $25-49.9 Million
Emp.: 25
Electrical Wire Distr
N.A.I.C.S.: 423610

Sumitomo Electric Windtech America, Inc. (1)
909 Industrial Dr, Edmonton, KY 42129-8944
Tel.: (270) 432-2233
Web Site: http://www.sewaus.com
Sales Range: $25-49.9 Million
Emp.: 5
Magnet Wire Mfr
N.A.I.C.S.: 238210
Ted Hayashi (Pres)

Sumitomo Electric Wintec (Malaysia) Sdn. Bhd. (1)
Lot Pt 499 and 500 Persiran Sabak Bernam Seksyen 26, 40000, Shah Alam, Selangor Durul Ehsan, Malaysia
Tel.: (60) 351912299
Web Site: http://www.global-sei.com
Sales Range: $50-74.9 Million
Emp.: 180
Magnet Wire & Coil Mfr & Distr
N.A.I.C.S.: 334416

Sumitomo Electric Wintec (Singapore) Pte Ltd (1)
24 Penjuru Rd 01 06B, 609128, Jurong, Singapore
Tel.: (65) 68614477
Sales Range: $25-49.9 Million
Emp.: 6
Magnet Wire & Bare Copper Wire Mfr; Sales of Hard Metal Tools
N.A.I.C.S.: 333991

Sumitomo Electric Wintec (Thailand) Co., Ltd. (1)
Bangpoo Industrial Estate Soi 1B 649 Moo 2 Tambol Bangpoomai, Amphur Muang, Samut Prakan, 10280, Thailand
Tel.: (66) 27094252
Electric Wire Mfr & Distr
N.A.I.C.S.: 332618

Sumitomo Electric Wintec (Wuxi) Co., Ltd. (1)
No3 Xing Chuang 4 Road Wuxi-Singapore Industrial Park, Wuxi, China
Tel.: (86) 51085280011
Electric Wire Mfr & Distr
N.A.I.C.S.: 335929

Sumitomo Electric Wintec America, Inc. (1)
909 Industrial Dr, Edmonton, KY 42129
Tel.: (270) 432-2233
Web Site: http://www.sewaus.com
Copper Magnet Wire Mfr
N.A.I.C.S.: 331420

Sumitomo Electric Wintec, Inc. (1)
1073 Eda Shigaraki-cho, Koka, 529-1811, Shiga, Japan
Tel.: (81) 748827800
Electrical Wire Mfr
N.A.I.C.S.: 332618

Sumitomo Electric Wiring Systems (Europe) Ltd. (1)
Prospect House Cemetery Road, Silverdale, Newcastle-under-Lyme, ST5 6PA, Staffordshire, United Kingdom
Tel.: (44) 1782664700
Web Site: http://www.sews-e.com
Automotive Components Mfr
N.A.I.C.S.: 336390

Sumitomo Electric Wiring Systems (Thailand) Ltd. (1)
Siam Eastern Industrial Park 60/2 Moo 3 Mabyangporn, Pluak Daeng, 21140, Rayong, Thailand
Tel.: (66) 38891140
Web Site: http://www.global-sei.com
Electric Wire Mfr & Distr
N.A.I.C.S.: 332618

Sumitomo Wiring Systems (U.S.A.) Inc. (1)
39555 Orchard Hill Pl Ste L60, Novi, MI 48375-5523
Tel.: (248) 347-9450
Web Site: http://www.swsusainc.com
Emp.: 44
Wiring Harness Component Distr
N.A.I.C.S.: 423610

Sumitomo Wiring Systems, Ltd. (1)
5-28 Hamada-cho, Yokkaichi, 510-8528, Mie, Japan
Tel.: (81) 593546200
Web Site: https://www.sws.co.jp
Emp.: 7,255
Wiring Harnesses, Harness Components & Other Electric Wires Mfr & Sales
N.A.I.C.S.: 332618
Masami Makido (Exec VP)

Subsidiary (Non-US):

H.K. Wiring Systems, Ltd. (2)
Units Nos 08 and 09 23rd Floor CDW Building 388 Castle Peak Road, Tsuen Wan, Hong Kong, NT, China (Hong Kong)
Tel.: (852) 24110806
Web Site: http://www.sws.co.jp
Sales Range: $25-49.9 Million
Emp.: 28
Information Systems & Wiring Harness Equipment Mfr
N.A.I.C.S.: 332618

Huizhou Zhurun Wiring Systems Co. Ltd. (2)
Jiu Long High Technology Industry Park, Xiao Jin Kou Town, 516023, Huizhou, Guangdong, China
Tel.: (86) 7522820000
Automotive Wiring Harness Mfr
N.A.I.C.S.: 332618

International Wiring Systems (Phils.) Corporation (2)
Luisita Indus Pk Special Export Processing Zn San Miguel, Tarlac, 2301, Philippines
Tel.: (63) 459850080
Web Site: http://www.iwspc.com
Sales Range: $1-4.9 Billion
Emp.: 7,000
Automotive Wiring Harness Sales
N.A.I.C.S.: 335931
Hirofumi Shimizu (Pres)

J.K. Wire Harness Sdn. Bhd. (2)
No 7 9 and 11 Jalan Firma 2/2 Kawasan Perindustrian Tebrau 1, 81100, Johor Bahru, Johor, Malaysia (100%)
Tel.: (60) 73548886
Web Site: http://www.jkwh.com.my
Sales Range: $150-199.9 Million
Emp.: 1,200
Automotive Wiring Harness Mfr
N.A.I.C.S.: 335931

Nigerian Wire and Cable Co., Ltd. (2)
Owode Industrial Estate Km 9 Ibadan-Abeokuta Road, PMB 5573, Ibadan, PMB 5573, Oyo, Nigeria
Tel.: (234) 208095905301
Web Site: http://www.nwcplc.com
Sales Range: $50-74.9 Million
Emp.: 118
Electrical & Telecommunication Conductors Mfr
N.A.I.C.S.: 332618

P.T. Sumitomo Wiring Systems Batam Indonesia (2)
Kawasan Industri Batamindo Kav 8, Muka Kuning, Batam, 29433, Indonesia
Tel.: (62) 770611553
Web Site: http://www.sws.co.jp
Emp.: 2,500
Mfr of Wiring Harnesses for Automobiles
N.A.I.C.S.: 336340

SEWS Hungary Wiring Harness, Ltd. (2)
Mor Akai u 12, 8060, Mor, Hungary
Tel.: (36) 22563530
Sales Range: $150-199.9 Million
Automotive Wiring Harness Mfr & Sales
N.A.I.C.S.: 332618
Jeno Kenyeres (Gen Mgr)

SEWS-Components Europe Polska Sp.Zo.o (Poland) (2)
Ul Okrenza 27, 64 100, Leszno, Poland (100%)
Tel.: (48) 655258700
Sales Range: $150-199.9 Million
Emp.: 1,000
Automotive Wiring Harness Mfr
N.A.I.C.S.: 332618
Grzegorz Lebioda (Mng Dir)

SUMI-HANEL Wiring Systems Co., Ltd. (2)
Sai Dong B Industrial Zone Thach Ban, Long Bien, Hanoi, Vietnam
Tel.: (84) 438750511
Web Site: http://www.sumi-hanel.com
Automotive Wiring Harnesses Mfr & Sales
N.A.I.C.S.: 332618

Sumidenso Automotive Technologies Asia Corporation (2)
N2835 Jose Abad Santos Ave corner Bayanihan Street, Clark Freeport Zone, 2023, Pampanga, Philippines
Tel.: (63) 455995518
Web Site: http://www.sat-a.com.ph
Sales Range: $50-74.9 Million
Emp.: 20
Automotive Wiring Harness Mfr
N.A.I.C.S.: 336320

Sumitomo Electric (Thailand), Ltd. (2)
15th Fl BB Bldg 54 Soi Sukhurnvit 21 Sukhurnvit Rd, Bangkok, 10110, Thailand
Tel.: (66) 22607231
Web Site: http://www.set-ps.com
Sales Range: $25-49.9 Million
Emp.: 38
Automotive Wiring Harness Mfr
N.A.I.C.S.: 335931
Yasuo Nakazawa (Mng Dir)

Sumitomo Electric Wiring Systems (Slovakia) Ltd. (2)
UL Pivovarnicka, 955 01, Topolcany, Slovakia (100%)
Tel.: (421) 385320840
Web Site: http://www.sews-e.com
Sales Range: $450-499.9 Million
Emp.: 2,080
Automotive Wiring Harness Mfr
N.A.I.C.S.: 327110

Subsidiary (US):

Sumitomo Electric Wiring Systems, Inc. (2)
1018 Ashley St, Bowling Green, KY 42103
Tel.: (270) 782-7397
Web Site: http://www.sewsus.com
Sales Range: $25-49.9 Million
Emp.: 70
Mfr of Wiring Harnesses for Automobiles
N.A.I.C.S.: 336320

Branch (Domestic):

Sumitomo Electric Wiring Systems - Nashville Distribution Center (3)
323 Mason Rd Ste A, La Vergne, TN 37086
Tel.: (615) 793-7516
Emp.: 20
Electric Wiring Supplies Distr
N.A.I.C.S.: 423610
Masayoshi Fuse (Pres & CEO)

Unit (Domestic):

Sumitomo Wiring Systems, Ltd. - Ibaraki Automotive Wire Works (2)
4311-1 Oaza-Hiratsuka, Yachiyo-cho Yukigun, Ibaraki, 300-3561, Japan
Tel.: (81) 296493311
Automotive Wire Harness Mfr
N.A.I.C.S.: 336320

Sumitomo Wiring Systems, Ltd. - Kameyama Works (2)
250-12 Ooishiki, Chomyoji-Cho, Kameyama, 519-0214, Mie, Japan
Tel.: (81) 595820080
Automotive Wire Harness Mfr
N.A.I.C.S.: 336320

Plant (Domestic):

Sumitomo Wiring Systems, Ltd. - Suzuka Plant (2)
1820 Aza-Nakanoike Mikkaichi-cho, Suzuka, 513-8631, Mie, Japan

Tel.: (81) 593828700
Web Site: http://www.sws.co.jp
Sales Range: $350-399.9 Million
Emp.: 2,500
Electrical Wire Mfr
N.A.I.C.S.: 332618

Sumitomo Wiring Systems, Ltd. - Tsu Plant (2)
530-1 Ninomi-cho, Tsu, 514-1116, Mie, Japan
Tel.: (81) 592568400
Web Site: http://www.sws.co.jp
Emp.: 90
Electrical Wire Mfr
N.A.I.C.S.: 332618

Subsidiary (Non-US):

Tianjin Jin-Zhu Wiring Systems Components Co., Ltd. (2)
271 Xiqing Rd, Xiqing District, Tianjin, 300112, China
Tel.: (86) 2287912668
Web Site: http://www.sws.co.jp
Automotive Wiring Harness Components Mfr
N.A.I.C.S.: 332618

Tianjin Jinzhu Wiring Systems Co., Ltd. (2)
Opposite Cao Zhuang Station Xiqing Road, Xiqing District, Tianjin, 300111, China
Tel.: (86) 2287912668
Mfr of Wiring Harness Components
N.A.I.C.S.: 332618

Sunray Reinetsu Co., Ltd. (1)
3-25 Shodai Tajika, Hirakata, 573-1132, Osaka, Japan
Tel.: (81) 728563221
Automotive Electronic Product Mfr
N.A.I.C.S.: 336320

Suzhou Bordnetze Electrical Systems Ltd. (1)
Linhu Road, Lu Xu Town Wujiang, Suzhou, Jiangsu, China
Tel.: (86) 51263259863
Wiring Harnesses Product Mfr
N.A.I.C.S.: 335931

Suzhou Sumiden Automotive Wire Co., Ltd. (1)
No 88 Chun Feng Road, Pan Yang Industrial Park Huang Dai Town Xiang Cheng District, Suzhou, Jiangsu, China
Tel.: (86) 51265715596
Automobile Electric Wire Product Mfr
N.A.I.C.S.: 336320

Suzhou Sumiden Electronic Materials Co., Ltd. (1)
No 232 Jinfeng Rd, Suzhou, 215129, Jiangsu, China
Tel.: (86) 51266903318
Electronic Parts Mfr & Distr
N.A.I.C.S.: 334419
Terai Takashi (Gen Mgr)

Suzuki-Sumiden Stainless Wire Co., Ltd. (1)
7-5-1 Higashi-Narashino, Narashino, 275-0001, Chiba, Japan
Tel.: (81) 474764052
Web Site: http://www.ss-stainless.co.jp
Emp.: 114
Stainless Steel Wire Mfr & Whslr
N.A.I.C.S.: 332618
Yoshio Horikawa (Pres & CEO)

Takara Sangyo Co., Ltd. (1)
I S Minamimorimachi Bldg 5F 2-6-5 Higashi-temma, Kita-ko, Osaka, 530-0044, Japan
Tel.: (81) 663545678
Web Site: http://www.takara-co.com
Sales Range: $25-49.9 Million
Emp.: 5
Cutting & Machine Tool Distr
N.A.I.C.S.: 423830

Techno Associe Co., Ltd. (1)
3-3-17 Tosabori, Nishi-ku, Osaka, 550-0001, Japan (100%)
Tel.: (81) 664592101
Web Site: http://www.technoassocie.co.jp
Rev.: $832,663,920
Assets: $721,314,880
Liabilities: $200,724,480

AND PRIVATE COMPANIES

SUMITOMO FORESTRY CO., LTD.

Net Worth: $520,590,400
Earnings: $23,435,280
Emp.: 1,841
Fiscal Year-end: 03/31/2022
Hardware Merchant Whslr
N.A.I.C.S.: 423710
Jun Ito *(Sr Mng Dir)*

Subsidiary (Non-US):

Accurate Metal Machining Co., Ltd. (2)
No189 East Baoqun Road, Yaozhuang Town, Jiashan, 314117, Zhejiang, China
Tel.: (86) 5738 477 5298
Web Site: https://www.technoassocie.co.jp
Hardware Whslr
N.A.I.C.S.: 423710

F&T KUNSHAN TECHNO CO., LTD. (2)
No 1 Rencheng Road, Shipu Village Qiandeng Kunshan, Jiangsu, 215343, China
Tel.: (86) 5125 747 2416
Web Site: https://www.technoassocie.co.jp
Hardware Whslr
N.A.I.C.S.: 423710

Subsidiary (Domestic):

Funakoshi Co., Ltd. (2)
572-20 Kamiuwada, Satte, 340-0124, Saitama, Japan
Tel.: (81) 480 48 7855
Hardware Whslr
N.A.I.C.S.: 423710

Subsidiary (Non-US):

MALAYSIAN PRECISION MANUFACTURING SDN. BHD. (2)
No 3 Lorong Perak3 Kawasan Perusahaan, Kuala Langat, 42500, Teluk Panglima Garang, Selangor, Malaysia
Tel.: (60) 3 31227405
Hardware Whslr
N.A.I.C.S.: 423710
K. B. Tee *(Mgr-Quality Assurance)*

Subsidiary (US):

T.A. America Corporation (2)
12414 McCann Dr, Santa Fe Springs, CA 90670
Tel.: (562) 946-6064
Web Site: https://www.taamericacorp.com
Precision Component Mfr
N.A.I.C.S.: 322220

Subsidiary (Non-US):

TA AUTOMOTIVE PARTS (THAILAND) CO., LTD. (2)
203/2 Moo 2 T Nongbondeang, Ban Bueng, 20170, Chonburi, Thailand
Tel.: (66) 3819 2630
Automotive Parts Mfr & Distr
N.A.I.C.S.: 336211

Plant (Non-US):

TECHNO ASSOCIE DE MEXICO, S.A. DE C.V. - AGUASCALIENTES FACILITY (2)
2Do Piso Av Aguascalientes Sur 2729-17 Fracc, 20290, Aguascalientes, Mexico
Tel.: (52) 449 912 3133
Hardware Mfr
N.A.I.C.S.: 332510

TECHNO ASSOCIE DE MEXICO, S.A. DE C.V. - MONTERREY FACILITY (2)
Blvd Interamerican 305 Furaccionamiento Interamerican Parque, 66600, Nuevo Leon, Mexico
Tel.: (52) 81 8145 0652
Hardware Mfr
N.A.I.C.S.: 332510

TECHNO ASSOCIE DE MEXICO, S.A. DE C.V. - TIJUANA FACILITY (2)
Blvd Hector Teran 20120 Edificio 9-A Ciudad Industrial Mesa De Otay, 22444, Tijuana, Mexico
Tel.: (52) 664 623 6518
Hardware Mfr
N.A.I.C.S.: 332510

Subsidiary (Non-US):

Techno Associe (Dalian F.T.Z.) Co., Ltd. (2)
406K Huineng Building 24 Haitian Road, Dalian FTZ, Dalian, 116600, China
Tel.: (86) 411 8754 2455
Hardware Whslr
N.A.I.C.S.: 423710

Techno Associe (Guangzhou) Co., Ltd. (2)
No 12 Canghai San Road Yonghe Street, Huangpu, Guangzhou, 511356, China
Tel.: (86) 203 202 0918
Web Site: https://www.technoassocie.co.jp
Hardware Whslr
N.A.I.C.S.: 423710

Techno Associe (Thailand) Co., Ltd. (2)
825 Phairojkijja Tower 14th Floor Bangna-Trad Road, Bangna, Bangkok, 10260, Thailand
Tel.: (66) 2 361 4491
Hardware Whslr
N.A.I.C.S.: 423710

Techno Associe Czech s.r.o. (2)
Dedinska 893/29, Prague, 6, Czech Republic
Tel.: (420) 2 3331 2782
Hardware Whslr
N.A.I.C.S.: 423710

Techno Associe Hong Kong Co., Ltd. (2)
Unit A 11/F KC100 No 100 Kwai Cheong Road, Kwai Chung, NT, China (Hong Kong)
Tel.: (852) 2754 1188
Web Site: http://www.technoassocie.co.jp
Hardware Whslr
N.A.I.C.S.: 423710

Techno Associe Shanghai Co., Ltd. (2)
C/21F East Tower New Hua Lian Mansion, No 755 Huai Hai Rd, Shanghai, 200020, China
Tel.: (86) 21 64318971
Hardware Whslr
N.A.I.C.S.: 423710

Techno Associe Singapore Pte. Ltd. (2)
19 Jalan Kilang Barat 06-07 Acetech Centre, Singapore, 159361, Singapore
Tel.: (65) 6590 0300
Hardware Whslr
N.A.I.C.S.: 423710

Techno Associe Taiwan Co., Ltd. (2)
10F-4 No 23 Sec 1 Chang-An East Rd, Jhongshan District, Taipei, 10442, Taiwan
Tel.: (886) 2 2571 1777
Hardware Whslr
N.A.I.C.S.: 423710

Subsidiary (Domestic):

Tobutsu Techno Co., Ltd. (2)
2-7-10 Kusune, Higashiosaka, 577-0006, Osaka, Japan
Tel.: (81) 6 6745 8900
Web Site: http://www.technoassocie.co.jp
Hardware Whslr
N.A.I.C.S.: 423710

Tohoku Sumiden Precision Co., Ltd. (1)
10-1 Fukasaku, Miharu-machi, Tamura, 963-7700, Fukushima, Japan
Tel.: (81) 247616325
Cemented Carbide Tool & Cutting Tool Mfr
N.A.I.C.S.: 333515

Tokai Sumiden Precision Co., Ltd. (1)
2500-5 Ogohara, Komono-cho, Mie, 510-1222, Japan
Tel.: (81) 593943170
Cemented Carbide Tool Mfr
N.A.I.C.S.: 333515

United Electric Industries Co., Ltd. (1)
No 39 Technology 7th Rd Kueishan Taoyuan Hsien, 333, Taipei, Taiwan
Tel.: (886) 33960101
Web Site: http://www.uei.com.tw

Sales Range: $25-49.9 Million
Emp.: 50
Cable Accessories Mfr
N.A.I.C.S.: 332618

Wuhan Sumiden Wiring Systems Co., Ltd. (1)
GuanShan 1st Road East Lake New Technology Development Zone, Wuhan Automobile Electronic Industry Park, Wuhan, China
Tel.: (86) 2781691193
Wiring Harnesses Product Mfr
N.A.I.C.S.: 335931

Wuzhou SE Bordnetze Company Ltd. (1)
No 86 Yuanqu 3 Road, Wuzhou Industrial Park, Wuzhou, Guangxi, China
Tel.: (86) 7743105804
Wiring Harnesses Product Mfr
N.A.I.C.S.: 335931

Zhongshan Sumiden Hybrid Products Co. Ltd. (1)
Jing Ye Road Zhongshan Torch Hi-Tech Industrial Development Zone, Zhongshan Port, Zhongshan, 528437, Guangdong, China
Tel.: (86) 76085592038
Web Site: http://www.sumiden-zs.com
Wire Harnesses Mfr
N.A.I.C.S.: 332618

SUMITOMO FORESTRY CO., LTD.

Keidanren Kaikan 3-2 Otemachi 1-chome, Chiyoda-ku, Tokyo, 100-8270, Japan
Tel.: (81) 332142270
Web Site: https://sfc.jp
Year Founded: 1691
1911—(TKS)
Rev: $11,451,397,423
Assets: $11,977,020,152
Liabilities: $6,537,337,298
Net Worth: $5,439,682,854
Earnings: $677,099,438
Emp.: 21,254
Fiscal Year-end: 12/31/23
Construction Engineering Services
N.A.I.C.S.: 541330
Akira Ichikawa *(Chm)*

Subsidiaries:

An Cuong Wood-Working Joint Stock Company (1)
702/1K Su Van Hanh, Ward 12 District 10, Ho Chi Minh City, Vietnam
Tel.: (84) 283 862 5726
Web Site: https://ancuong.com
Woodworking Product Mfr
N.A.I.C.S.: 337212

Dalian Sumirin Information Technology Service Co., Ltd. (1)
2nd floor No 3 Hui xian yuan Dalian High-tech Zone, Shahekou District, Dalian, 116025, Liaoning, China
Tel.: (86) 41183658755
Web Site: https://en.sumirin-its.com
Delivery Data Processing Services
N.A.I.C.S.: 518210
Yu Xiojun *(Mgr)*

Edge Homes Group Ltd. (1)
13702 S 200 W B12, Draper, UT 84020
Tel.: (801) 905-8163
Web Site: https://www.edgehomes.com
Floor Plan Design Services
N.A.I.C.S.: 541310
Drew Detrick *(Chief Sls & Mktg Officer)*

Fill Care Co., Ltd. (1)
219 Nakayama-cho Ru Chido Building 5F, Midori-ku, Yokohama, 226-0011, Kanagawa, Japan
Tel.: (81) 459371205
Web Site: http://www.fillcare.co.jp
Sales Range: $50-74.9 Million
Emp.: 300
Nursing Care Facilities Management Services
N.A.I.C.S.: 623110

Gehan Homes Ltd. (1)
15725 N Dallas Pkwy Ste 300, Addison, TX 75001
Tel.: (972) 383-4300
Web Site: http://www.gehanhomes.com
Emp.: 65
Home Design, Remodelling & Construction Services
N.A.I.C.S.: 236115

Henley Arch Pty. Ltd. (1)
395 Ferntree Gully Road, Mount Waverley, Melbourne, 3149, VIC, Australia
Tel.: (61) 395745333
Web Site: http://www.henley.com.au
Residential Building Construction Services
N.A.I.C.S.: 236116
John Harvey *(Mng Dir)*

Igeto Co. Ltd. (1)
1-15 Juichiya, Minato-ku, Nagoya, 455-0831, Aichi, Japan
Tel.: (81) 527473118
Web Site: https://www.igeto.co.jp
Emp.: 561
Building Materials Distr
N.A.I.C.S.: 444180

Kawasaki Biomass Power Generation Co., Ltd. (1)
12-6 Ogimachi, Kawasaki, 2100867, Japan (34%)
Tel.: (81) 897372142
Emp.: 50
Eletric Power Generation Services
N.A.I.C.S.: 221117

Kowa Lumber Co., Ltd. (1)
1-9-13 Asakusabashi, Taito-ku, Tokyo, 111-0053, Japan
Tel.: (81) 338659080
Sales Range: $50-74.9 Million
Emp.: 10
Lumber Whslr
N.A.I.C.S.: 423310

Meikan Honchosha PFI Co., Ltd. (1)
3-4-6 Nishiki, Naka-ku, Nagoya, 460-0003, Aichi, Japan
Tel.: (81) 529730671
Construction Engineering Services
N.A.I.C.S.: 541330

Nihei Co., Ltd. (1)
Miyanosawa Terminal Building 2F 1-1-1-30, Nishi-ku, Sapporo, 063-0051, Hokkaido, Japan
Tel.: (81) 116681280
Web Site: http://www.nihei.co.jp
Wood Construction Materials Whslr
N.A.I.C.S.: 423310

Northern Tech Co., Ltd. (1)
2-10-6 Yonesato 1jo, Shiroishi-ku, Sapporo, 003-0871, Hokkaido, Japan
Tel.: (81) 118748550
Home Remodeling Services
N.A.I.C.S.: 236118

Open Bay Timber Ltd. (1)
Sect 40 Lot 1, PO Box 66, Kenabot, Kokopo, East New Britain, Papua New Guinea
Tel.: (675) 9829827
Web Site: https://openbaytimber.com
Sales Range: $150-199.9 Million
Emp.: 600
Forestry Plantation Services
N.A.I.C.S.: 115310

P.T. AST Indonesia (1)
KITW Technopark Blok A-01 JL Raya Semarang Kendal KM 12, Semarang, 50152, Central Java, Indonesia
Tel.: (62) 248664800
Web Site: http://www.ast.co.id
Speaker Boxes Mfr
N.A.I.C.S.: 321999

P.T. Kutai Timber Indonesia (1)
Jl Tanjung Tembaga Baru Pelabuhan, Probolinggo, East Java, 67201, Indonesia
Tel.: (62) 335422412
Web Site: https://www.kti.co.id
Plywood Mfr & Distr
N.A.I.C.S.: 321212

Plant (Domestic):

P.T. Kutai Timber Indonesia - Probolinggo Factory (2)
Jl Tanjung Tembaga Baru, Pelabuhan,

SUMITOMO FORESTRY CO., LTD.

Sumitomo Forestry Co., Ltd.—(Continued)

Probolinggo, 67201, Jawa Timur, Indonesia
Tel.: (62) 335422412
Particleboard & Plywood Mfr
N.A.I.C.S.: 321212

PT. Kubu Mulia Forestry (1)
Jl Surya Gang Surya Nila No 8 Kel Parit
Tokaya Kec Pontianak Selatan, Pontianak,
Kalimantan Barat, Indonesia
Tel.: (62) 56 172 1122
Real Estate Services
N.A.I.C.S.: 531210

PT. Sumitomo Forestry Indonesia (1)
Summitmas II 8th Fl JL Jend Sudirman Kav
61-62, Jakarta, 12190, Indonesia
Tel.: (62) 21 520 0268
Building Material Mfr & Distr
N.A.I.C.S.: 327120

Pan Asia Packing Ltd. (1)
789/5-7 Pinthong Industrial Estate Moo 1,
Nongkham A Sriracha, Chon Buri, 20230,
Thailand
Tel.: (66) 3 834 8319
Web Site: https://panasiapacking.com
Wood Packaging Material Mfr & Distr
N.A.I.C.S.: 321920

Paragon Wood Product (Dalian) Co., Ltd. (1)
Room 312 Market Building Free Trade
Zone, Dalian, 116600, Liaoning, China
Tel.: (86) 41187187980
Web Site: http://www.sfc.jp
Design & Construction of Wooden Houses
& Office Interiors
N.A.I.C.S.: 236115

Paragon Wood Product (Shanghai) Co., Ltd. (1)
D902 9th Fl Pufa Plz Bldg D 1759 N
Zhongshan Rd, Shanghai, China
Tel.: (86) 2161405828
Wooden Trusses Mfr
N.A.I.C.S.: 321215

Scott Park Group Pty. Ltd. (1)
16 Frobisher Street, Osborne Park, 6017,
WA, Australia
Tel.: (61) 89 202 7700
Building Material Mfr & Distr
N.A.I.C.S.: 327120

Shouei Furniture Co., Ltd. (1)
68/2 Nong Kankrao Road Tang Khwian,
Klaeng, Rayong, 21110, Thailand
Tel.: (66) 38672003
Household Furniture Distr
N.A.I.C.S.: 423210

Sumikyo Co., Ltd. (1)
4-22-25 Shima, Ibaraki, 567-0854, Osaka,
Japan
Tel.: (81) 72 630 0321
Web Site: https://www.sumikyou.co.jp
Emp.: 63
Building Materials Distr
N.A.I.C.S.: 423390

Sumikyo Wintec Co., Ltd. (1)
763-2 Ouchida, Kita-ku, Okayama, 701-0165, Japan
Tel.: (81) 862925200
Web Site: https://www.sk-wintec.co.jp
Sales Range: $50-74.9 Million
Emp.: 56
Door & Window Sashes Whslr
N.A.I.C.S.: 423310

Sumirin Enterprises Co., Ltd. (1)
Shinjuku Monolith 27F 2-3-1 Nishi-Shinjuku,
Shinjuku-ku, Tokyo, 163-0927, Japan
Tel.: (81) 368647700
Web Site: https://www.sumirin-sep.co.jp
Emp.: 163
Insurance & Leasing Services
N.A.I.C.S.: 524210

Sumirin Sash Co., Ltd. (1)
1650-38 Okubaracho, Ushiku, 300-1283,
Ibaraki, Japan
Tel.: (81) 298751271
Web Site: https://www.sumirin-sc.co.jp
Sales Range: $25-49.9 Million
Emp.: 50
Secondary Processing & Sales of Aluminum
Sashes & Exterior Finishes
N.A.I.C.S.: 321911

Sumitomo Forestry (Dalian) Ltd. (1)
3304A Units ST2 Eton International Tower
No 280 Changjiang Rd, Zhongshan District,
Dalian, 116001, Liaoning, China
Tel.: (86) 41183678060
Timber Products Distr
N.A.I.C.S.: 423310

Sumitomo Forestry (Singapore) Ltd. (1)
55 Market Street 11-02, Singapore, 048941,
Singapore
Tel.: (65) 64350150
Web Site: http://www.sfspore.com.sg
Sales Range: $50-74.9 Million
Emp.: 10
Wood Product Distr
N.A.I.C.S.: 423990

Sumitomo Forestry America, Inc. (1)
121 3rd Ave, Kirkland, WA 6160
Tel.: (425) 454-2355
Wooden Housing Construction Services
N.A.I.C.S.: 236115
Atsushi Iwasaki (Pres)

Subsidiary (Domestic):

Bloomfield Homes (2)
981 Crystal Falls Dr, Prosper, TX 75078-9209
Tel.: (972) 347-6224
Web Site: http://www.bloomfieldhomes.net
Home Center Operator
N.A.I.C.S.: 444110
Matt Becton (Mgr)

Crescent Communities, LLC (2)
601 S Tyron St Ste 800, Charlotte, NC 28202
Tel.: (980) 321-6000
Web Site: http://www.crescentcommunities.com
Rev.: $1,000,000,000
Real Estate Development, Management &
Investment Services
N.A.I.C.S.: 237210
Kevin H. Lambert (CFO)

Edge Homes LLC (2)
13702 S 200 W B12, Draper, UT 84020 (70%)
Tel.: (801) 800-8127
Web Site: http://www.edgehomes.com
Single-Family & Custom Built Home Construction
N.A.I.C.S.: 236115
Jed Stewart (VP-Land Acq)

Mark III Properties, LLC (2)
170-C Camelot Dr, Spartanburg, SC 29301
Tel.: (864) 595-1735
Web Site: https://www.markiiiproperties.com
Land Subdivision
N.A.I.C.S.: 237210
John Beeson (Owner)

Sumitomo Forestry Archi Techno Co., Ltd. (1)
1-3 Nakase Makuhari Techno Garden Building B 8-9F, Mihama-ku, Chiba, 261-0023, Japan
Tel.: (81) 433108061
Web Site: http://www.sumirin-at.co.jp
Rev.: $81,792,000
Emp.: 677
Wooden Housing Construction Management Services
N.A.I.C.S.: 236115

Sumitomo Forestry Australia Pty. Ltd. (1)
Suite7 395 Ferntree Gully Rd, Mount Waverley, 3149, VIC, Australia
Tel.: (61) 39 574 5500
Building Material Mfr & Distr
N.A.I.C.S.: 327120

Sumitomo Forestry Crest Co., Ltd. (1)
3-10-33 Nishiki, Naka-ku, Nagoya, 460-0003, Aichi, Japan
Tel.: (81) 522058401
Web Site: https://www.sumirin-crest.co.jp
Plywood & Furnitures Mfr
N.A.I.C.S.: 321211
Kazutaka Horita (Pres)

Sumitomo Forestry Home Engineering Co., Ltd. (1)
1-24-1 Nishi-Shinjuku, Shinjuku-ku, Tokyo, 160-0023, Japan
Tel.: (81) 369113341
Web Site: https://www.sumirin-he.co.jp
Emp.: 1,044
Wooden Housing Construction Services
N.A.I.C.S.: 236115
Kanpei Tokunaga (Pres)

Sumitomo Forestry Home Service Co., Ltd. (1)
3-2-11 Nishishinjuku Shinjukumitsui Building
Nigokan 11F, Shinjuku-ku, Tokyo, 160-0023, Japan
Tel.: (81) 353817921
Web Site: http://www.sumirin-hs-jinzai.jp
Real Estate Brokerage Services
N.A.I.C.S.: 531210

Sumitomo Forestry India Pvt. Ltd. (1)
Unit No 52A Ground Floor Centrum Plaza
Sector 53 Golf Course Road, Gurgaon, 122002, Haryana, India
Tel.: (91) 124 437 0351
Real Estate Services
N.A.I.C.S.: 531210

Sumitomo Forestry Information Systems Co., Ltd. (1)
7th floor Makuhari Techno Garden Building
B 1-3 Nakase, Mihama-ku, Chiba, 261-8501, Japan
Tel.: (81) 432966834
Web Site: https://www.sumirin.co.jp
Emp.: 189
Information Technology Consulting Services
N.A.I.C.S.: 541690

Sumitomo Forestry Landscaping Co., Ltd. (1)
1-38-1 Tyuo, Nakano-ku, Tokyo, 164-0011, Japan
Tel.: (81) 368322200
Web Site: http://www.sumirin-sfl.co.jp
Sales Range: $25-49.9 Million
Emp.: 100
Landscaping Services
N.A.I.C.S.: 561730
Yutaka Kamiya (Pres)

Sumitomo Forestry Residential Co., Ltd. (1)
4F Biggs Shinjuku Building 2-19-1 Shinjuku,
Shinjuku-ku, Tokyo, 160-0022, Japan
Tel.: (81) 333508731
Web Site: https://www.sumirin-residential.co.jp
Emp.: 354
Condominiums & Apartments Management Services
N.A.I.C.S.: 531311

Toclas Corporation (1)
1370 Nishiyama-cho, Nishi-ku, Hamamatsu, 432-8001, Shizuoka, Japan
Tel.: (81) 534851201
Web Site: https://www.toclas.co.jp
Emp.: 688
Designs, Constructs & Manufactures Bathroom & Kitchen Systems
N.A.I.C.S.: 327110
Ryo Sasaki (Pres)

Toyo Rikuun Co., Ltd. (1)
3-11-9 Oike, Suzuka, 510-0201, Mie, Japan
Tel.: (81) 593878881
Web Site: http://www.toyo-rikuun.co.jp
General Freight Trucking Services
N.A.I.C.S.: 484110

Vina Eco Board Co., Ltd. (1)
Lot D2-D7 Phu An Thanh IP, An Thanh
Commune Ben Luc Dist, Ho Chi Minh City, 70999, Long An Prov, Vietnam
Tel.: (84) 723640199
Sales Range: $25-49.9 Million
Emp.: 15
Particleboard Mfr & Distr
N.A.I.C.S.: 321219

SUMITOMO HEAVY INDUSTRIES, LTD.

1-1 Osaki 2-chome, Shinagawa-ku,
Shinagawa-ku, Tokyo, 141-6025, Japan
Tel.: (81) 367372000   JP
Web Site: https://www.shi.co.jp

INTERNATIONAL PUBLIC

Year Founded: 1934
SOHVF—(OTCIQ)
Rev.: $6,123,846,810
Assets: $8,237,397,900
Liabilities: $4,100,867,160
Net Worth: $4,136,530,740
Earnings: $41,456,940
Emp.: 25,211
Fiscal Year-end: 12/31/22
Industrial Machinery Mfr
N.A.I.C.S.: 333248
Shunsuke Betsukawa (Chm)

Subsidiaries:

Dalian Spindle Environmental Facilities Co., Ltd. (1)
Add No 8 North East Street 4, Eco & Tech
Development Zone, Dalian, 116033, China
Tel.: (86) 4000361116
Web Site: http://en.spindle.cn
Cooling Tower Mfr
N.A.I.C.S.: 333415

Demag Plastics Machinery (Ningbo) Co., Ltd. (1)
No 28 Baiyunshan Road Modern Logistics
Park, Beilun District, Ningbo, 315800, Zhejiang, China
Tel.: (86) 57426906600
Injection Molding Machine Mfr
N.A.I.C.S.: 333511
Zhen Zhou (Mgr-SAP Project)

Hansen Industrial Transmissions NV (1)
Leonardo da Vincilaan 1, Edegem, Belgium
Tel.: (32) 34501211
Web Site: http://www.emeia.sumitomodrive.com
Gear Mfr
N.A.I.C.S.: 336350

Invertek Drives Ltd. (1)
Offas Dyke Business Park, Welshpool, SY21 8JF, United Kingdom
Tel.: (44) 1938556868
Web Site: https://www.invertekdrives.com
Construction Machinery Mfr
N.A.I.C.S.: 333120

Izumi Food Machinery Co., Ltd. (1)
4-2-30 Shioe, Amagasaki, 661-8510, Hyogo, Japan
Tel.: (81) 66 718 6150
Web Site: https://www.izumifood.shi.co.jp
Sales Range: $75-99.9 Million
Emp.: 150
Industrial Machinery Distr
N.A.I.C.S.: 423830
Keiji Yoshimoto (Pres & CEO)

Plant (Domestic):

Izumi Food Machinery Co., Ltd. - Awaji-Plant (2)
552-1 Hirota, Minamiawaji, 656-0122, Hyogo, Japan
Tel.: (81) 79 945 1121
Web Site: http://www.izumifood.shi.co.jp
Food Product Machinery Mfr
N.A.I.C.S.: 333241
Ken Nanataki (Pres)

Izumi Support Corporation (1)
ThinkPark Tower 1 1 Osaki 2 chome,
Shinagawa-ku, Tokyo, 141-6025, Japan
Tel.: (81) 367372666
Real Estate Services
N.A.I.C.S.: 531390

JSC Sumitomo (SHI) Demag Plastics Machinery (1)
Kantemirovskaya Str 65 room number 1, 115477, Moscow, Russia
Tel.: (7) 4959379764
Web Site: http://russia.sumitomo-shi-demag.eu
Injection Molding Machine Mfr
N.A.I.C.S.: 333511

Kenki Engineering Chiba Co., Ltd. (1)
731 1 Naganumahara-cho, Inage-ku, Chiba, 263-0001, Japan
Tel.: (81) 434201514
Web Site: http://kenki-eng-chiba.jp
Hydraulic Excavator Mfr

AND PRIVATE COMPANIES — SUMITOMO HEAVY INDUSTRIES, LTD.

N.A.I.C.S.: 333120

LBX do Brasil Comerico de Equipmentos Industriais Ltda (1)
Avenida Jerome Case 2900 Eden, Sorocaba, 18087-220, Sao Paulo, Brazil
Tel.: (55) 1533256402
Web Site: http://lbx-do-brasil-comercio-de.negocio.site
Construction Machinery Whslr
N.A.I.C.S.: 423210

Lafert (Suzhou) Co., Ltd. (1)
No 3 Industrial Plant Building Yue Xi Phase 3 Tian E Dang Lu 2011, Wuzong Economic Development Zone, Suzhou, 215104, China
Tel.: (86) 5126 687 0618
Web Site: http://www.lafert.com
Electric Motor Mfr
N.A.I.C.S.: 335312
Eros Rinaldi *(Gen Mgr)*

Lafert Elektromotorji D.o.o. (1)
Cesta Goriske fronte 46, 5290, Sempeter pri Gorici, Slovenia
Tel.: (386) 5 393 6430
Web Site: https://www.lafert.si
Electric Motor Mfr
N.A.I.C.S.: 335312
Matej Vuga *(Mng Dir)*

Lafert GmbH (1)
Wolf Hirth Strasse 10, 71034, Boblingen, Germany
Tel.: (49) 1755504526
Electric Motor Mfr
N.A.I.C.S.: 335312
Holger Klein *(Gen Mgr)*

Lafert S.p.A. (1)
J F Kennedy 43, 30027, San Dona di Piave, VE, Italy
Tel.: (39) 0421229611
Web Site: http://lafert.com
Electric Motor Mfr
N.A.I.C.S.: 335312
Elisa Maddalozzo *(Mgr-HR)*

Lafert Servo Drives S.r.l. (1)
E Mattei 84 25, 40138, Bologna, Italy
Tel.: (39) 051780294
Electric Motor Mfr
N.A.I.C.S.: 335312
Mattia Calanchi *(Mgr-Technical)*

Lafert Servo Motors S.p.A. (1)
E Majorana 2 a, Noventa di Piave, 30020, Venice, Italy
Tel.: (39) 0421572211
Electric Motor Mfr
N.A.I.C.S.: 335312

Leifeld Metal Spinning GmbH (1)
Feldstr 2-20, 59229, Ahlen, Germany
Tel.: (49) 2382966070
Web Site: https://leifeldms.com
Automotive & E-Mobility Mfr
N.A.I.C.S.: 332119

Lightwell Co., Ltd (1)
Motoasakusa 3-18-10 Ueno NS building, Taito-Ku, Tokyo, 111-0041, Japan (100%)
Tel.: (81) 358289230
Web Site: http://www.lightwell.co.jp
Sales Range: $75-99.9 Million
Emp.: 188
Software Development Services
N.A.I.C.S.: 541511
Yutaka Yoshikawa *(Pres)*

Link-Belt Construction Equipment Co. (1)
2651 Palumbo Dr, Lexington, KY 40509-1233
Tel.: (859) 263-5200
Web Site: http://www.linkbelt.com
Sales Range: $100-124.9 Million
Emp.: 400
Construction Crane Mfr & Distr
N.A.I.C.S.: 333120
Melvin Porter *(Pres & CEO)*

Division (Domestic):

Link-Belt Construction Equipment Co. - Mid Atlantic (2)
10020 Lickinghole Rd, Ashland, VA 23005
Tel.: (804) 798-2290
Web Site: http://www.linkbelt.com
Sales Range: $25-49.9 Million
Emp.: 15
Construction Crane Mfr & Distr
N.A.I.C.S.: 333120

Nihon Spindle Manufacturing Co., Ltd. (1)
4-2-30 Shioe, Amagasaki, 661-8510, Hyogo, Japan
Tel.: (81) 66 499 5551
Web Site: https://spindle.co.jp
Emp.: 861
Industrial Machinery Mfr
N.A.I.C.S.: 333248
Shigeo Kondo *(Mng Dir)*

Nihon Spindle Mfg. Co., Ltd. (1)
4-2-30 Shioe, Amagasaki, 661-8510, Hyogo, Japan
Tel.: (81) 6 6499 5551
Web Site: http://www.spindle.co.jp
Sales Range: $100-124.9 Million
Emp.: 320
Spinning Machine Mfr
N.A.I.C.S.: 333248
Hiroshi Arito *(Pres)*

Subsidiary (Non-US):

Nihon Spindle Cooling Towers Sdn. Bhd. (2)
20 B Jalan Perusahaan Prai Industrial Estate 4, 13600, Perai, Pulau Pinang, Malaysia
Tel.: (60) 4 5013 322
Web Site: http://www.spindle.com.my
Sales Range: $25-49.9 Million
Emp.: 60
Cooling Tower Mfr
N.A.I.C.S.: 333415

Ningbo Sumiju Machinery, Ltd (1)
No 775 Hengshan W Rd, Beilun Dist, Ningbo, 315800, Zhejiang, China
Tel.: (86) 57426890132
Industrial Machinery Mfr
N.A.I.C.S.: 333248

PT SHI Plastics Machinery (Indonesia) (1)
Jl Tebet Raya No 5B, Tebet, Jakarta, 12810, Indonesia
Tel.: (62) 21 829 3872
Web Site: http://www.shi.co.jp
Plastic Molding Machinery Repair Services
N.A.I.C.S.: 811310

PT SM-Cyclo Indonesia (1)
Cikarang Jalan Sungkai Blok F 25 No 09K Delta Silicon 3, Lippo Cikarang, Bekasi, Jawa Barat, Indonesia
Tel.: (62) 2129612100
Industrial Machinery Mfr
N.A.I.C.S.: 333248
Nur Heliyani *(Mgr-Acct & Admin)*

PT Sumitomo S.H.I. Construction Machinery Indonesia (1)
Jl Maligi VIII Lot T 1 Kawasan Industri KIIC, Karawang, 41361, Jawa Barat, Indonesia
Tel.: (62) 2189108686
Construction Machinery Mfr
N.A.I.C.S.: 333120
Andri Hardiansyah *(Mgr-Manufacturing Ops)*

PT Sumitomo S.H.I. Construction Machinery Southeast Asia (1)
Wisma GKBI 16th Floor Jl Jend Sudirman No 28, Jakarta Pusat, 10210, Indonesia
Tel.: (62) 2157952254
Web Site: http://sumitomokenki-asean.com
Construction Machinery Mfr
N.A.I.C.S.: 333120
Kazumi Yasunobu *(Pres)*

PT. Sumitomo Heavy Industries Indonesia (1)
Wisma GKBI 1606 Jl Jend Sudirman No 28, Jakarta, 10210, Indonesia
Tel.: (62) 21 5795 2120
Emp.: 25
Industrial Machinery Mfr
N.A.I.C.S.: 333248

Parks Koushinetsu Co., Ltd. (1)
6729 1 Imai, Matsumoto, 399-0033, Nagano Prefecture, Japan
Tel.: (81) 263870152
Web Site: http://pax-k.co.jp
Construction Machine Maintenance Services
N.A.I.C.S.: 811490

Persimmon Technologies Corporation (1)
178 Albion St Ste 100, Wakefield, MA 01880
Tel.: (781) 587-0677
Web Site: http://www.persimmontech.com
Vacuum Robotics & Hybrid-Field Motor Technology Services
N.A.I.C.S.: 423690
Mark Hanna *(VP-Sls)*

S.H.I. Plastics Machinery (S) Pte. Ltd. (1)
67 Ayer Rajah Crescent 01-15 to 20, Singapore, 139950, Singapore
Tel.: (65) 67797544
Web Site: http://www.shi.co.jp
Sales Range: $25-49.9 Million
Emp.: 15
Plastic Injection Molding Machine Mfr
N.A.I.C.S.: 333248
Koichi Kasamatsu *(Mng Dir)*

S.H.I. Plastics Machinery (Vietnam) Llc (1)
Floor 1A Hongkong tower 243A La Thanh Street, Lang Thuong Ward Dong Da District, Hanoi, Vietnam
Tel.: (84) 2437280105
Construction Machinery Mfr
N.A.I.C.S.: 333120

SEISA Gear, Ltd. (1)
16-1 Wakihama 4-chome, Kaizuka, 597-8555, Osaka, Japan
Tel.: (81) 724313021
Web Site: http://www.seisa.co.jp
Sales Range: $100-124.9 Million
Emp.: 350
Gear Mfr
N.A.I.C.S.: 333612

SEN Corporation (1)
Think Park Tower 2-1-1 Osaki, Shinagawa, Tokyo, 141-6025, Japan
Tel.: (81) 3 6737 2690
Sales Range: $100-124.9 Million
Emp.: 35
Ion Implementation System Mfr
N.A.I.C.S.: 334516
Takeshi Ogasawara *(Auditor)*

Plant (Domestic):

SEN Corporation - Ehime Plant (2)
1501 Imazaike, Saijo, 799-1362, Ehime, Japan
Tel.: (81) 898 64 1912
Semiconductor Equipment Mfr
N.A.I.C.S.: 334413

SFK Co., Ltd. (1)
500 Kobe, Tsuyama, 708-0015, Okayama, Japan
Tel.: (81) 868281161
Web Site: http://sfm.co.jp
Industrial Machinery Mfr
N.A.I.C.S.: 333248

SHI Accelerator Service Ltd. (1)
Nissho Building 1 17 6 Osaki, Shinagawa-ku, Tokyo, 141-0032, Japan
Tel.: (81) 354348468
Accelerator Maintenance Services
N.A.I.C.S.: 811490

SHI Airport System Co., Ltd. (1)
1 South Senshu Airport, Sennan, 549-0021, Osaka Prefecture, Japan
Tel.: (81) 724566255
Web Site: http://www.skk-kix.co.jp
Water Maintenance Services
N.A.I.C.S.: 221310

SHI Cryogenics Group (1)
1-1 Osaki 2-Chome, Shinagawa-ku, Tokyo, 141-6025, Japan
Tel.: (81) 367372550
Web Site: http://www.shicryogenics.com
Mfr of Laboratory Cryogenic Refrigeration Equipment, Miniature Heat Exchangers, Recondensers & Shield Coolers For Superconducting Magnets & Cryopumps
N.A.I.C.S.: 333248

Subsidiary (Non-US):

SHI Cryogenics of Korea, Ltd. (2)
3F 280-3 Saneop-ro 155beon-gil, Gweonseon-Gu, Suwon, Gyeonggi-Do, Korea (South)
Tel.: (82) 312783050
Web Site: http://www.shicryogenics.com
Sales Range: $25-49.9 Million
Emp.: 13
Mfr of Laboratory Cryogenic Refrigeration Equipment, Miniature Heat Exchangers, Recondensers & Shield Coolers For Superconducting Magnets & Cryopumps
N.A.I.C.S.: 333248
Won Bum Lee *(Gen Mgr)*

Subsidiary (US):

Sumitomo (SHI) Cryogenics of America, Inc. (2)
1833 Vultee St, Allentown, PA 18103-4742 (100%)
Tel.: (610) 791-6700
Web Site: http://www.shicryogenics.com
Sales Range: $25-49.9 Million
Emp.: 100
Mfr of Laboratory Cryogenic Refrigeration Equipment, Miniature Heat Exchangers, Recondensers & Shield Coolers For Superconducting Magnets & Cryopumps
N.A.I.C.S.: 333248
David Devman *(CEO)*

Branch (Domestic):

Sumitomo (SHI) Cryogenics of America, Inc. (3)
1800 Wyatt Dr Ste 13, Santa Clara, CA 95054 (100%)
Tel.: (408) 736-4406
Web Site: http://www.shicryogenics.com
Sales Range: $25-49.9 Million
Emp.: 5
N.A.I.C.S.: 334512
Mark Derakhshan *(Pres)*

Subsidiary (Non-US):

Sumitomo (SHI) Cryogenics of Europe GmbH (2)
Daimlerweg 5a, Darmstadt, 64293, Germany
Tel.: (49) 6151860610
Web Site: http://www.shicryogenics.com
Sales Range: $25-49.9 Million
Emp.: 18
Mfr of Laboratory Cryogenic Refrigeration Equipment, Miniature Heat Exchangers, Recondensers & Shield Coolers For Superconducting Magnets & Cryopumps
N.A.I.C.S.: 333248

Sumitomo (SHI) Cryogenics of Europe, Ltd. (2)
3 Hamilton Close Houndmills Industrial Estate, Basingstoke, RG21 6YT, Hampshire, United Kingdom (100%)
Tel.: (44) 1256853333
Web Site: http://www.shicryogenics.com
Sales Range: $25-49.9 Million
Emp.: 14
N.A.I.C.S.: 335999

SHI Designing & Manufacturing Inc. (1)
20/F One Corporate Centre Building Julia Vargas Avenue corner, Meralco Avenue Ortigas Center, Pasig, 1605, Metro Manila, Philippines
Tel.: (63) 26366010
Web Site: http://shi-sdmi.com
Engineering Software Development Services
N.A.I.C.S.: 541511

SHI Electro-Mechanical Systems (Taiwan) Co., Ltd. (1)
1F No81 Sec 3 Chung-hsin Rd, Sang Chung District, New Taipei City, Taiwan
Tel.: (886) 229877071
Machinery Mfr
N.A.I.C.S.: 333517

SHI Examination & Inspection, Ltd. (1)
1501 Imazaike, Saijo, 799-1393, Ehime, Japan
Tel.: (81) 898654868
Web Site: http://www.shiei.co.jp
Emp.: 158
Nondestructive Inspection & Cyclotron Services

SUMITOMO HEAVY INDUSTRIES, LTD.

Sumitomo Heavy Industries, Ltd.—(Continued)
N.A.I.C.S.: 561499
Masahiro Akiyama (Pres)

SHI FW Energia Fakop Sp. Z.o.o. (1)
ul Staszica 31, 41-200, Sosnowiec, Poland
Tel.: (48) 323681300
Web Site: https://fakop.com
Power Plant Services
N.A.I.C.S.: 237130

SHI Industrial Equipment (Taiwan) Co., Ltd. (1)
Rm A 30F-1 No 97 Sec 4 Chongxin Rd, Sanchong Dist, New Taipei City, 24161, Taiwan
Tel.: (886) 229740200
Chemical Products Mfr
N.A.I.C.S.: 325998

SHI Manufacturing & Services (Philippines), Inc (1)
First Phillippine Industrial Park Barangay Sta Anastacia, Sto Tomas, 4234, Batangas, Philippines
Tel.: (63) 434056263
Web Site: http://www.global-shi.com
Sales Range: $50-74.9 Million
Emp.: 200
Precision Parts Mfr
N.A.I.C.S.: 332216

SHI Material Handling Machinery (Shanghai) Co., Ltd. (1)
10F SMEG Plaza No 1386 Hongqiao Road, Shanghai, 200336, China
Tel.: (86) 2164876795
Textile Machinery Mfr
N.A.I.C.S.: 333248

SHI Plastics Machinery (Hong Kong) Ltd (1)
EM Room 601 Telford House 12-16 Wang Hoi Road, Kowloon Bay, Kowloon, China (Hong Kong)
Tel.: (852) 27506630
Web Site: http://www.spm-northasia.com
Emp.: 20
Plastic Injection Molding Machine Mfr
N.A.I.C.S.: 333248

SHI Plastics Machinery (India) Private Ltd. (1)
Unit No 22-25 1st Floor JMD Galleria Sohna Road, Gurgaon, 122 001, Haryana, India
Tel.: (91) 1242217056
Construction Machinery Mfr
N.A.I.C.S.: 333120

SHI Plastics Machinery (Korea) Co, Ltd. (1)
203 JEIPLATZ 459-11 Gasan-dong, Geumcheon-gu, Seoul, 153-792, Korea (South)
Tel.: (82) 2 757 8656
Web Site: http://www.spm-northasia.com
Plastic Molding Machinery Mfr
N.A.I.C.S.: 333248

SHI Plastics Machinery (Malaysia) Sdn. Bhd. (1)
Lot AG 16 17&18 PJ Industrial Park Jalan Kemajuan Section 13, 46200, Petaling Jaya, Selangor, Malaysia
Tel.: (60) 379582079
Emp.: 15
Plastic Molding Machinery Distr
N.A.I.C.S.: 423830
Ichiro Okazaki (Gen Mgr)

SHI Plastics Machinery (Phils) Inc. (1)
Lot 2-B No14 Victoria Street, Cor EDSA Magallanes Village, Makati, 1232, Philippines
Tel.: (63) 2 844 0632
Web Site: http://www.global-shi.com
Plastic Molding Machinery Repair Services & Distr
N.A.I.C.S.: 811310

SHI Plastics Machinery (Taiwan) Inc. (1)
6F No 33 Dexing W Rd, Shilin Dist, Taipei, 11158, Taiwan
Tel.: (886) 22 831 4500

Web Site: http://www.global-shi.com
Emp.: 20
Plastic Molding Machinery Distr
N.A.I.C.S.: 423830
Yoichi Saito (Mng Dir)

SHI Plastics Machinery (Thailand) Ltd. (1)
317 Debaratna Road, Kwaeng Bangna Nuea Khet Bangna, Bangkok, 10260, Bangna, Thailand
Tel.: (66) 2 747 4053
Web Site: http://www.spm-northasia.com
Emp.: 35
Injection Molding Machine Mfr
N.A.I.C.S.: 333248
Shigeo Takahashi (Mng Dir)

SHI Plastics Machinery de Mexico, S.A.de C.V. (1)
Missouri River 400 crosses Rosas River, Mexico, Mexico
Tel.: (52) 8183561714
Construction Machinery Mfr
N.A.I.C.S.: 333120

SHI-ATEX Co., Ltd. (1)
1501 Imazaike, Saijo, 799-1393, Ehime Prefecture, Japan
Tel.: (81) 898654868
Web Site: http://shi-atex.com
Medical Instrument Mfr
N.A.I.C.S.: 339112

SM Cyclo Colombia, S.A.S. (1)
Parque Industrial Celta Km 7 0 Autopista Medellin Costado Occidental, Cun, 250057, Funza, Colombia
Tel.: (57) 18269766
Motor & Motor Equipment Distr
N.A.I.C.S.: 423830

SM Cyclo Turkey Guc Aktarim Sis. Tic. Ltd. (1)
Barbaros Mh Cigdem Sk Agaoglu Office Mrk No 1 Kat 4 D 18, Atasehir, Istanbul, Turkiye
Tel.: (90) 2162506069
Construction Machinery Mfr
N.A.I.C.S.: 333120

SM Cyclo de Peru S.A.C (1)
Jr Monte Rosa 255 Office 702, Santiago de Surco, Lima, Peru
Tel.: (51) 17130342
Industrial Machinery Mfr
N.A.I.C.S.: 333248

SM-CYCLO (Malaysia) Sdn. Bhd. (1)
No 2 Jalan BP 4 1 Bandar Bukit Puchong, 47100, Puchong, Selangor Darul Ehsan, Malaysia
Tel.: (60) 380612909
Gear Mfr & Whslr
N.A.I.C.S.: 333248

SM-CYCLO (Thailand) Co., Ltd. (1)
1 Empire Tower 21st Floor Unit 2103 4 South Sathorn Road, Yan Nawa, Bangkok, Thailand
Tel.: (66) 26700998
Cycloid & Gear Box Whslr
N.A.I.C.S.: 423210
Wuttiphan Wangteeranon (Asst Mgr)

SM-Cyclo (Vietnam) Co., Ltd. (1)
Factory 2B Lot K1 2 5 Road No 2 3 5A, Le Minh Xuan Industrial Park Binh Chanh District Ho Chi Minh, Ho Chi Minh City, Vietnam
Tel.: (84) 837663709
Cycloid & Gear Box Whslr
N.A.I.C.S.: 423210
Duy Linh Ta (Engr-Sls)

SM-Cyclo France S.A.S. (1)
8 Avenue Christian Doppler, 77700, Serris, France
Tel.: (33) 164171717
Industrial Machinery Mfr
N.A.I.C.S.: 333248
Martin De Grom (Gen Mgr)

SM-Cyclo Iberia, S.L. (1)
C Gran Via n 63 BIS planta 1 Departamento 1B, 48011, Bilbao, Vizcaya, Spain
Tel.: (34) 944805389
Industrial Machinery Mfr
N.A.I.C.S.: 333248

Pedro Roncero Arostegi (Dir Gen)

SM-Cyclo Italy Srl (1)
Via dell Artigianato 23, 20010, Cornaredo, MI, Italy
Tel.: (39) 0293481101
Industrial Machinery Mfr
N.A.I.C.S.: 333248
Gian Matteo Marzano (Area Mgr)

SM-Cyclo Redutores Do Brasil Ltda. (1)
Ave Fagundes Filho 191 Metro Sao Judas, Edificio Houston Sala H123, 04304 010, Sao Paulo, Brazil **(100%)**
Tel.: (55) 1155853600
Web Site: http://www.smcyclo.com
Sales Range: $25-49.9 Million
Emp.: 3
N.A.I.C.S.: 335312
Marcelo Kuramoto (Gen Mgr)

SM-Cyclo Turkey Ltd. Sti. (1)
Barbaros Mh Cigdem SK Agaoglu My Office is Mrk No 1 Kat 4 D18, Atasehir, 34746, Istanbul, Turkiye
Tel.: (90) 2162506069
Industrial Machinery Mfr
N.A.I.C.S.: 333248

SM-Cyclo UK Ltd. (1)
29 Bergen Way, Hull, HU7 0YQ, United Kingdom
Tel.: (44) 1482790340
Industrial Machinery Mfr
N.A.I.C.S.: 333248

SM-Cyclo de Argentina S.A. (1)
Ing Delpini 2230 Malvinas Argentinas, Grand Bourg, B1615KGB, Buenos Aires, Argentina
Tel.: (54) 3327454095
Cycloid, Bevel Buddy Box & Hypoxic Whslr
N.A.I.C.S.: 423210
Diego Alberto Arballo (Gen Mgr)

SM-Cyclo de Chile, Ltda. (1)
Camino Lo Echevers 550 Bodegas 5 y 6 Region Metropolitana, Quilicura, Santiago, Chile
Tel.: (56) 28927000
Web Site: http://www.sumitomodrive.com
Industrial Drive Technologies Mfr & Distr
N.A.I.C.S.: 333612
Hector Fuentes (Gen Mgr)

SM-Cyclo de Colombia Ltda. (1)
Parque Industrial Celta Km 7 0 Autopista Medellin Costado Occidental, Funza, Colombia
Tel.: (57) 18269766
Industrial Machinery Mfr
N.A.I.C.S.: 333248

SM-Cyclo de Mexico, S.A. de C.V. (1)
Av Desarrollo 541 Finsa, Parque Industrial Almacentro, 67132, Guadalupe, NL, Mexico **(99%)**
Tel.: (52) 81 8144 5130
Web Site: http://www.smcyclo.com
Sales Range: $25-49.9 Million
Emp.: 95
N.A.I.C.S.: 335312

SM-Cyclo of Canada, Ltd. (1)
1453 Cornwall Road, Oakville, L6J 7T5, ON, Canada **(100%)**
Tel.: (905) 469-1050
Web Site:
  https://canada.sumitomodrive.com
Sales Range: $25-49.9 Million
Emp.: 20
Distr of Heat Reducers
N.A.I.C.S.: 423730
Denny Bozinovic (Mgr-Sls)

Branch (Domestic):

SM-Cyclo of Canada, Ltd. (2)
740 Chester Road, Annacis Island, Delta, V3M 6J1, BC, Canada **(100%)**
Tel.: (604) 525-5403
Web Site: http://www.sumitomodrive.com
Sales Range: $25-49.9 Million
Emp.: 10
Assembly of Power Transmission Products
N.A.I.C.S.: 333613
Greg Banero (Pres & CEO)

SM-Cyclo of Hong Kong Co., Ltd. (1)

Room 19 28 F Metropole Square No 2 On Yiu Street, Sha Tin, China (Hong Kong)
Tel.: (852) 24601881
Gear Mfr & Whslr
N.A.I.C.S.: 333248

Shin Nippon Machinery Co., Ltd. (1)
ThinkPark Tower 1-1 Osaki 2-Chome, Shinagawa-ku, Tokyo, 141-6025, Japan
Tel.: (81) 36 737 2630
Web Site: https://www.snm.co.jp
Emp.: 512
Steam Turbine Mfr & Distr
N.A.I.C.S.: 333611
Akio Yoshikawa (Pres)

Sociedad Industrial de Transmissiones S.A. (1)
Paseo de Ubarburu 67 Poliigono 27, Martutene, 20014, San Sebastian, Spain
Tel.: (34) 94 345 7200
Web Site: https://sitsa.es
Transmission Repair Services
N.A.I.C.S.: 811114
Jose Ignacio Vergara (Dir-Comml)

Sumi-Cyclo Drive India Private Limited (1)
Gat No 186 Alandi Markal Road, Raisoni Industrial Park Fulgaon, Pune, 412216, Maharashtra, India
Tel.: (91) 9607745353
Industrial Machinery Mfr
N.A.I.C.S.: 333248

Sumiju Business, Ltd (1)
2-1-1 Yato-Cho, Nishi-Tokyo, 188-8585, Tokyo, Japan
Tel.: (81) 424 68 43 11
Web Site: http://www.shi.co.jp
Industrial Machinery Mfr
N.A.I.C.S.: 333248

Sumiju Environmental Engineering, Inc. (1)
7-1-1 Nishigotanda Sumitomogotanda Bldg, Shinagawa-Ku, Tokyo, 141-0031, Japan
Tel.: (81) 357195020
Web Site: http://www.ske.shi.co.jp
Sales Range: $500-549.9 Million
Emp.: 700
Waste Water Treatment Services
N.A.I.C.S.: 221310
Katsuske Yamuse (Pres)

Sumiju Environmental Technologies, Ltd. (1)
Nishigotanda ES Building 7 25 9 Nishigotanda, Shinagawa-ku, Tokyo, 141-0031, Japan
Tel.: (81) 367372800
Bridge & Marine Structure Mfr & Maintenance Services
N.A.I.C.S.: 331110

Sumiju Logitech Co., Ltd. (1)
731-1 Naganumahara-cho, Inage-ku, Chiba, 263-0001, Japan
Tel.: (81) 434201680
Web Site: http://www.shi.co.jp
Plastic Injection Molding Machine Mfr
N.A.I.C.S.: 333248

Sumiju Magnet (Kunshan) Co., Ltd. (1)
No 1333 Jinmao Road Luyang Zhoushi Town, Kunshan, China
Tel.: (86) 51257689200
Magnetic Field Shielding Product Mfr & Distr
N.A.I.C.S.: 335999

Sumiju Plant Engineering Co., Ltd. (1)
7-25-9 Nishigotanda, Shinagawa-ku, Tokyo, 141-0031, Japan
Tel.: (81) 367372890
Web Site: http://www.spe.shi.co.jp
Sales Range: $25-49.9 Million
Emp.: 80
Plant Construction Engineering Services
N.A.I.C.S.: 236210
Shiro Matsumura (Pres & CEO)

Plant (Domestic):

Sumiju Plant Engineering Co., Ltd. - Niihama Works (2)
5-2 Soubiraki-Cho, Niihama, 792-8588, Ehime, Japan

AND PRIVATE COMPANIES SUMITOMO HEAVY INDUSTRIES, LTD.

Tel.: (81) 897 32 6227
Web Site: http://www.spe.shi.co.jp
Emp.: 10
Plant Construction Engineering Services
N.A.I.C.S.: 236210

Sumiju Platec Co., Ltd (1)
731-1 Naganumaharacho, Inage-Ku, Chiba, 263-0001, Japan
Tel.: (81) 434201558
Emp.: 100
Plastic Injection Molding Machine Mfr
N.A.I.C.S.: 333248
Junichi Koga *(Gen Mgr)*

Sumiju Precision Forging Co., Ltd. (1)
19 Natsushima-cho, Yokosuka, 237-8555, Kanagawa, Japan
Tel.: (81) 46 869 1881
Web Site: http://www.spf.shi.co.jp
Emp.: 300
Precision Forging Mfr
N.A.I.C.S.: 332111

Sumiju SCE (Xiamen) Construction Machinery Co., Ltd. (1)
7F Block 2 Zhongjun Group Building No 210 South 5th Road Gaoqi, Xiamen, 361012, China
Tel.: (86) 5925207968
Web Site: http://sscm-cn.com
Construction Machinery Mfr
N.A.I.C.S.: 333120

Sumiju Tokki Service Co., Ltd. (1)
2 1 1 Yato cho, Nishitokyo, Tokyo, 188-8585, Japan
Tel.: (81) 424684451
Cryogenic Product Mfr & Distr
N.A.I.C.S.: 332811

Sumiju Yokosuka Kogyo Co., Ltd. (1)
19 Natsushima-cho, Yokosuka, 237-8555, Kanagawa, Japan
Tel.: (81) 46 869 1707
Web Site: https://shi.co.jp
Emp.: 168
Bridge & Marine Structure Mfr & Maintenance Services
N.A.I.C.S.: 331110
Atsushi Ishikawa *(Pres & CEO)*

Sumimec Engineering Inc. (1)
3 4 23 Shindencho, Niihama, 792-0003, Ehime Prefecture, Japan
Tel.: (81) 897341421
Web Site: http://sumimec.jp
Industrial Machinery Mfr
N.A.I.C.S.: 333248

Sumitomo (S.H.I.) Construction Machinery (Tangshan) Co., Ltd. (1)
No 33 Yuanqu Road Modern Equipment Manufacturing Industry Park, Tangshan, 063021, Hebei, China
Tel.: (86) 3153391000
Construction Machinery Mfr
N.A.I.C.S.: 333120

Sumitomo (S.H.I.) Construction Machinery Co., Ltd. (1)
2-1-1 Osaki, Shinagawa-ku, Tokyo, 141-6025, Japan
Tel.: (81) 367372600
Web Site: http://www.sumitomokenki.co.jp
Construction Machinery Mfr
N.A.I.C.S.: 333120
Shinji Shimomura *(Pres & CEO)*

Subsidiary (US):

LBX Company LLC (2)
2004 Buck Ln, Lexington, KY 40511-1073
Tel.: (859) 245-3900
Web Site: http://en.lbxco.com
Sales Range: $25-49.9 Million
Emp.: 60
Construction Machinery Mfr
N.A.I.C.S.: 333120
Eric Sauvage *(Pres & CEO)*

Sumitomo (S.H.I.) Construction Machinery Sales Co., Ltd. (1)
2-1-1 Osaki, Shinagawa-ku, Tokyo, 141-6025, Japan
Tel.: (81) 367372610
Construction Machinery Distr
N.A.I.C.S.: 423810

Eetsukawa Shunsuke *(CEO)*

Sumitomo (SHI) Cryogenics Korea Co., Ltd. (1)
Room 619-620 Venture Valley 958 Goseck-Dong, Kwonsun-Gu, Suwon, Gyeonggi-Do, Korea (South)
Tel.: (82) 31 278 3050
Laboratory Cryostat Mfr
N.A.I.C.S.: 334516

Sumitomo (SHI) Cryogenics Shanghai, Ltd. (1)
Building 15 Lane 333 Zhujian Road, Minhang District, Shanghai, 201107, China
Tel.: (86) 2154866318
Book Publishers
N.A.I.C.S.: 513130

Sumitomo (SHI) Cryogenics Taiwan Co., Ltd. (1)
4th Floor No 3 Lane 216 Gongyuan Rd, Hsinchu, 300, Taiwan
Tel.: (886) 35612101
Refrigeration Equipment Distr
N.A.I.C.S.: 423740

Sumitomo (SHI) Cyclo Drive Asia Pacific Pte. Ltd. (1)
15 Kwong Min Road, Singapore, 628718, Singapore
Tel.: (65) 6 591 7800
Web Site: http://www.sumitomodrive.com
Sales Range: $25-49.9 Million
Emp.: 50
Industrial Machinery Mfr
N.A.I.C.S.: 333248
Rico Docena *(Country Mgr-Philippines)*

Sumitomo (SHI) Cyclo Drive China, Ltd. (1)
201600 Building 2 No 301 Shuya Road, Songjiang District, Shanghai, 201103, China
Tel.: (86) 2157748866
Web Site: http://www.smcyclo.com.cn
Sales Range: $100-124.9 Million
Emp.: 300
Gear Control Device Mfr
N.A.I.C.S.: 334513
Okada Norio *(Gen Mgr)*

Sumitomo (SHI) Cyclo Drive Germany GmbH (1)
Cyclostrasse 92, 85229, Markt Indersdorf, Germany
Tel.: (49) 8136 66 0
Web Site: www.sumitomodriveeurope.com
Sales Range: $100-124.9 Million
Emp.: 300
Power Transmission Equipment Mfr
N.A.I.C.S.: 333613

Sumitomo (SHI) Cyclo Drive Korea, Ltd. (1)
913 Royal Building 19 Saemunan-ro 5-gil, Jongno - gu, Seoul, 110-721, Korea (South)
Tel.: (82) 2 730 0151
Web Site: http://www.sck.co.kr
Emp.: 37
Power Transmission & Control Equipment Mfr
N.A.I.C.S.: 333613
Kim Hakchul *(Pres)*

Sumitomo (SHI) Cyclo Drive Logistics, Ltd. (1)
Building 2 No 301 Shuya Road, Songjiang District, Shanghai, China
Tel.: (86) 2157748866
Industrial Machinery Mfr
N.A.I.C.S.: 333248

Sumitomo (SHI) Cyclo Drive Shanghai, Ltd. (1)
11F SMEG Plaza No 1386 Hongqiao Road, Changning District, Shanghai, 200336, China
Tel.: (86) 2134627877
Power Transmission Device Mfr & Distr
N.A.I.C.S.: 333612

Sumitomo (SHI) Demag Plastics Machinery (France) S.A.S. (1)
ZAC du Mandinet 9 rue des Campanules, Lognes, 77437, Marne-la-Vallee, Cedex, France
Tel.: (33) 160332010
Web Site: http://fance.sumitomo-shi-demag.eu

Injection Molding Machine Mfr
N.A.I.C.S.: 333511

Sumitomo (SHI) Demag Plastics Machinery (Italia) S.r.l. (1)
Strada del Portone 61 A, 10137, Turin, Italy
Tel.: (39) 0119595057
Injection Molding Machine Mfr
N.A.I.C.S.: 333511

Sumitomo (SHI) Demag Plastics Machinery (UK) Ltd. (1)
Accent House Triangle Business Park Wendover Road, Stoke Mandeville, Aylesbury, HP22 5BL, Buckinghamshire, United Kingdom
Tel.: (44) 129 673 9500
Web Site: https://sumitomo-shi-demag.co.uk
Injection Molding Machine Mfr
N.A.I.C.S.: 333511
Darren Herron *(Natl Sls Mgr)*

Sumitomo (SHI) Demag Plastics Machinery Espana S.L. (1)
Plaza de America 4 2-3, 46004, Valencia, Spain
Tel.: (34) 961116311
Injection Molding Machine Mfr
N.A.I.C.S.: 333511

Sumitomo (SHI) Demag Plastics Machinery GmbH (1)
Altdorfer Str 15, 90571, Schwaig, Germany
Tel.: (49) 911 5061 0
Web Site: http://www.sumitomo-shi-demag.eu
Plastic Injection Molding Machine Mfr
N.A.I.C.S.: 333248
Gerd Liebig *(CEO)*

Sumitomo (SHI) Demag Plastics Machinery Hungaria Kft. (1)
FSD Park 2 Fsz 2, 2045, Torokbalint, Hungary
Tel.: (36) 23531290
Injection Molding Machine Mfr
N.A.I.C.S.: 333511

Sumitomo (SHI) Demag Plastics Machinery North America, Inc. (1)
11792 Alameda Dr, Strongsville, OH 44149
Tel.: (440) 876-8960
Web Site: http://sumitomo-shi-demag.us
Plastic Injection Molding Machine Mfr
N.A.I.C.S.: 333248

Division (Domestic):

Van Dorn Demag (2)
11792 Alameda Dr, Strongsville, OH 44149 (100%)
Tel.: (440) 876-8960
Web Site: http://www.sumitomo-shi-demag.us
OEM Aftersales for Van Dorn & Demag Injection Molding Machine Parts, Service, Training & Support
N.A.I.C.S.: 333248

Sumitomo (SHI) Demag Plastics Machinery Sp. z.o.o. (1)
o ul Jagiellonska 81 83, 42-200, Czestochowa, Poland
Tel.: (48) 343709540
Web Site: http://poland.sumitomo-shi-demag.eu
Injection Molding Machine Mfr
N.A.I.C.S.: 333511

Sumitomo (SHI) Hansen Australia Pty. Ltd. (1)
181 Power Street, Glendenning, 2761, NSW, Australia
Tel.: (61) 292083000
Cycloid & Gear Box Whslr
N.A.I.C.S.: 423210
Steve Wightman *(Gen Mgr-Ops)*

Sumitomo Construction Machinery Co., Ltd. (1)
2-1-1 Osaki, Shinagawa-ku, Tokyo, 141-6025, Japan
Tel.: (81) 36 737 2600
Web Site: https://www.sumitomokenki.com
Construction Machinery Mfr & Distr
N.A.I.C.S.: 333120
Yasunobu Kazumi *(Pres & CEO)*

Sumitomo Construction Machinery Sales Co., Ltd. (1)

2 1 1 Osaki, Shinagawa-ku, Tokyo, 141-6025, Japan
Tel.: (81) 367372610
Construction Machinery Mfr & Distr
N.A.I.C.S.: 333120
Kazumi Yasunobu *(Pres)*

Sumitomo Eaton Nova Corporation (1)
SBS Tower 9F, 10-1 Yoga 4chome, Setagaya-ku, Tokyo, 158 0097, Japan
Tel.: (81) 354917800
Sales Range: $200-249.9 Million
Emp.: 403
Ion Implantation Systems; Owned 50% by Sumitomo Heavy Industries, Ltd. & 50% Axcelis Technologies, Inc.
N.A.I.C.S.: 334516

Sumitomo Heavy Industries (China), Ltd. (1)
10F SMEG Plaza No 1386 Hongqiao Road, Shanghai, 200336, China
Tel.: (86) 2134627660
Marketing Support Services
N.A.I.C.S.: 541613

Sumitomo Heavy Industries (Tangshan), Ltd. (1)
No 35 Yuanqu Road Modern Equipment Manufacturing Industrial Park, Kaiping District, Tangshan, 063021, China
Tel.: (86) 315 3390880
Web Site: http://www.shts.shi.co.jp
Sales Range: $100-124.9 Million
Emp.: 320
Construction Machinery Mfr
N.A.I.C.S.: 333120

Sumitomo Heavy Industries (USA), Inc. (1)
1833 Vultee St, Allentown, PA 18103-4783
Tel.: (610) 791-6782
Web Site: http://www.global-shi.com
Sales Range: $25-49.9 Million
Emp.: 5
Industrial Supplies Sales & Repair Services
N.A.I.C.S.: 811310

Sumitomo Heavy Industries (Vietnam) Co., Ltd. (1)
17 Thang Long Industrial Park, Dong Anh District, Hanoi, Vietnam
Tel.: (84) 439550004
Power Transmission Equipment Mfr
N.A.I.C.S.: 333613

Sumitomo Heavy Industries Business Associates, Ltd. (1)
ThinkPark Tower 1 1 Osaki 2 chome, Shinagawa-ku, Tokyo, 141-6025, Japan
Tel.: (81) 367372445
Information Technology & Services
N.A.I.C.S.: 561210
Hiroo Morita *(Pres & CEO)*

Sumitomo Heavy Industries Construction Cranes Co., Ltd. (1)
6F Sumitomo Fudosan Ueno Bldg 9 3 Higashi Ueno 6 chome, Taito-ku, Tokyo, 110-0015, Japan
Tel.: (81) 338451387
Industrial Machinery Mfr
N.A.I.C.S.: 333248

Sumitomo Heavy Industries Engineering and Services Co., Ltd. (1)
Think Park Tower 1-1 Osaki 2-chome, Shinagawa-ku, Tokyo, 141-6025, Japan
Tel.: (81) 367372643
Web Site: http://www.shi.co.jp
Sales Range: $100-124.9 Million
Emp.: 450
Material Handling Machinery Mfr
N.A.I.C.S.: 333248

Unit (Domestic):

Sumitomo Heavy Industries Engineering & Services Co., Ltd. - Niihama Works (2)
5-2 Sobiraki-cho, Niihama, 792-8588, Ehime, Japan
Tel.: (81) 897 32 1605
Industrial Machinery Mfr
N.A.I.C.S.: 333248

Sumitomo Heavy Industries Environment Co., Ltd. (1)

SUMITOMO HEAVY INDUSTRIES, LTD.

Sumitomo Heavy Industries, Ltd.—(Continued)
Lucid Square Gotanda 10-4 Nishigotanda 7-chome, Shinagawa-ku, Tokyo, 141-0031, Japan
Tel.: (81) 367372700
Web Site: http://www.shiev.shi.co.jp
Waste Water Treatment Services
N.A.I.C.S.: 221310

Sumitomo Heavy Industries Finetech, Ltd. (1)
8230 Tamashima Otoshima, Kurashiki, 713-8501, Okayama, Japan
Tel.: (81) 86 525 6281
Web Site: https://www.shi-ftec.co.jp
Emp.: 200
Grinding Machine Mfr
N.A.I.C.S.: 333517
Masakazu Muta *(Pres)*

Sumitomo Heavy Industries Gearbox Co., Ltd. (1)
16 1 Wakihama 4 chome, Kaizuka, 597-8555, Osaka, Japan
Tel.: (81) 724313021
Web Site: http://shigearbox.com
Gear Mfr
N.A.I.C.S.: 333612

Sumitomo Heavy Industries Himatex Co., Ltd. (1)
5-2 Soubiraki-cho, Niihama, 792-0001, Ehime, Japan
Tel.: (81) 89 732 6484
Web Site: https://www.shi.co.jp
Emp.: 117
Rolling Mill Rolls Mfr
N.A.I.C.S.: 331511
Takaaki Kido *(Pres)*

Sumitomo Heavy Industries Ion Technology Co., Ltd. (1)
ThinkPark Tower 1-1 Osaki 2-chome, Shinagawa-ku, Tokyo, 141-6025, Japan
Tel.: (81) 36 737 2690
Web Site: https://shi-ion.jp
Emp.: 513
Semiconductor Mfr & Distr
N.A.I.C.S.: 334413
Mitsukuni Tsukihara *(Pres)*

Sumitomo Heavy Industries Marine & Engineering Co., Ltd. (1)
ThinkPark Tower 1-1 Osaki 2-chome, Shinagawa-ku, Tokyo, 141-6025, Japan
Tel.: (81) 367372620
Web Site: http://www.shi.co.jp
Sales Range: $125-149.9 Million
Emp.: 500
Marine Shipping Services
N.A.I.C.S.: 488320

Sumitomo Heavy Industries Material Handling Systems Co., Ltd. (1)
5th Floor Sumitomo Fudosan Hibiya Building 8-6 Nishishimbashi 2-Chome, Minato-Ku, Tokyo, 105-0003, Japan
Tel.: (81) 36 891 2160
Web Site: https://shi.co.jp
Emp.: 750
Crane Mfr & Maintenance Services
N.A.I.C.S.: 333120
Tatsuya Endo *(Pres)*

Sumitomo Heavy Industries Mechatronics, Ltd. (1)
2-1-1 Osaki Thinkpark Tower, Shinagawa-ku, Tokyo, 141-6025, Japan
Tel.: (81) 367372530
Web Site: http://www.shi-mechatronics.jp
Sales Range: $25-49.9 Million
Emp.: 50
Semiconductor Equipment Mfr
N.A.I.C.S.: 334413

Sumitomo Heavy Industries Modern, Ltd. (1)
8-32-16 Shinyoshida-Higashi, Kohoku-Ku, Yokohama, 223-8511, Japan
Tel.: (81) 45 547 7777
Sales Range: $50-74.9 Million
Emp.: 13
Industrial Machinery Mfr
N.A.I.C.S.: 333248
Shingo Tsuda *(Pres)*

Subsidiary (Non-US):

SHI Plastics Machinery (Shanghai) Ltd (2)
Rm 6308 Ruijin Business Center Ruijin Hotel No 118 Ruijin Er Rd, Shanghai, 200020, China
Tel.: (86) 21 5466 1226
Industrial Machinery Mfr
N.A.I.C.S.: 333248

Plant (Domestic):

Sumitomo Heavy Industries Modern, Ltd. - Futtsu Plant (2)
93-8 Shintomi, Futtsu, 293-0011, Chiba, Japan
Tel.: (81) 439 88 6288
Extrusion Coating Lines Mfr
N.A.I.C.S.: 332999

Sumitomo Heavy Industries PTC Sales Co., Ltd. (1)
2-1-1 Osaki Shinkupakutawa, Shinagawa-Ku, Tokyo, 141-0032, Japan
Tel.: (81) 367372580
Transmissions & Gear Reducer Whslr
N.A.I.C.S.: 423840
Nobuhiko Kawamura *(Gen Mgr)*

Sumitomo Heavy Industries Process Equipment Co., Ltd. (1)
1501 Imazaike, Saijo, 799-1393, Ehime, Japan
Tel.: (81) 89 864 6936
Web Site: https://www.shi-pe.shi.co.jp
Emp.: 240
Industrial Machinery Mfr
N.A.I.C.S.: 333248
Shigeru Tajima *(Pres)*

Sumitomo Heavy Industries Techno-Fort Co., Ltd. (1)
5-2 Soubiraki-cho, Niihama, 792-0001, Ehime, Japan
Tel.: (81) 897326397
Sales Range: $50-74.9 Million
Emp.: 240
Steel Making Machinery Mfr & Installation Services
N.A.I.C.S.: 333248

Sumitomo Heavy Industries, Ltd. - Chiba Works (1)
731-1 Naganumahara-machi, Inage-ku, Chiba, 263-0001, Japan
Tel.: (81) 43 420 1351
Industrial Machinery Mfr
N.A.I.C.S.: 333248

Sumitomo Heavy Industries, Ltd. - Engineering and Sales Division (1)
731-1 Naganumahara-Cho, Inage-Ku, Chiba, 263-0001, Japan
Tel.: (81) 43 420 1471
Web Site: http://www.shi.co.jp
Injection Molding Machine Mfr
N.A.I.C.S.: 333248

Sumitomo Heavy Industries, Ltd. - Mechatronics Division (1)
2-1-1 Osaki, Shinagawa-ku, Tokyo, 141-6025, Japan
Tel.: (81) 3 6737 2545
Sales Range: $100-124.9 Million
Emp.: 50
Laser Processing System Mfr
N.A.I.C.S.: 334419
Shinji Shimomura *(CEO)*

Sumitomo Heavy Industries, Ltd. - Nagoya Works (1)
1 Asahi-machi 6-chome, Obu, 474-8501, Aichi, Japan
Tel.: (81) 562 48 5111
Web Site: http://www.shi.co.jp
Industrial Machinery Mfr
N.A.I.C.S.: 333248

Sumitomo Heavy Industries, Ltd. - Niihama Plant (1)
5-2 Soubiraki-cho, Niihama, 792-8588, Ehime, Japan
Tel.: (81) 897 32 6211
Industrial Machinery Mfr
N.A.I.C.S.: 333248

Sumitomo Heavy Industries, Ltd. - Okayama Works (1)
8230 Tamashima Otoshima, Kurashiki, 713-8501, Okayama, Japan
Tel.: (81) 86 525 6101
Web Site: http://www.shi.co.jp
Industrial Machinery Mfr
N.A.I.C.S.: 333248

Sumitomo Heavy Industries, Ltd. - Power Transmission & Controls Division (1)
1-1 Osaki 2-chome, Shinagawa-ku, Tokyo, 141-6025, Japan
Tel.: (81) 3 6737 2300
Web Site: http://www.shi.co.jp
Hyponic Gear Motors Mfr
N.A.I.C.S.: 333612

Sumitomo Heavy Industries, Ltd. - Quantum Equipment Division (1)
2-1-1 Osaki, Shinagawa-ku, Tokyo, 141-6025, Japan
Tel.: (81) 3 6737 2565
Web Site: http://www.shi.co.jp
Metal Products Mfr
N.A.I.C.S.: 332999

Sumitomo Heavy Industries, Ltd. - Saijo Plant (1)
1501 Imazaike, Saijo, 799-1393, Ehime, Japan
Tel.: (81) 898 64 4811
Industrial Machinery Mfr
N.A.I.C.S.: 333248

Sumitomo Heavy Industries, Ltd. - Tanashi Works (1)
1-1 Yato-cho 2-chome, Nishi-Tokyo, 188-8585, Japan
Tel.: (81) 42 468 4104
Web Site: http://www.shi.co.jp
Industrial Machinery Mfr
N.A.I.C.S.: 333248

Sumitomo Heavy Industries, Ltd. - Yokosuka Works (1)
19 Natsushima-cho, Yokosuka, 237-8555, Kanagawa, Japan
Tel.: (81) 46 869 1842
Web Site: http://www.shi.co.jp
Industrial Machinery Mfr
N.A.I.C.S.: 333248

Sumitomo Industrias Pesadas do Brasil Ltda. (1)
Rodovia do Acucar km 26 S N, Itu, Sao Paulo, Brazil
Tel.: (55) 1144039292
Industrial Machinery Mfr
N.A.I.C.S.: 333248

Sumitomo Machinery Corporation of America (1)
4200 Holland Blvd, Chesapeake, VA 23323-1525
Tel.: (757) 485-3355
Web Site: www.sumitomodrive.com
Power Transmissions, Speed Reducers & Gear Motors Mfr
N.A.I.C.S.: 423610
James Solomon *(Pres & CEO)*

Sumitomo NAACO Materials Handling Co., Ltd. (1)
2-75 Daito-cho Obu-shi, Nagoya, 474-8555, Japan (50%)
Tel.: (81) 562485251
Web Site: http://www.sumitomonacco.co.jp
Sales Range: $125-149.9 Million
Emp.: 1,200
Fork-Lift Trucks & Logistic Handling Equipment Mfr & Distr
N.A.I.C.S.: 333924

Subsidiary (Domestic):

Sumitomo NACCO Materials Handling Sales Co., Ltd. (2)
2-75 Daito-cho Obu-shi, Nagoya, 474-8555, Japan
Tel.: (81) 562485251
Web Site: http://www.sumitomonacco.co.jp
Emp.: 1,200
Sales, Lease, Repair & Service of Forklift Trucks & Logistics Machinery & Equipment
N.A.I.C.S.: 423830

Sumitomo NACCO Forklift Co., Ltd. (1)
2-75 Daito-cho, Obu, 474-8555, Aichi, Japan
Tel.: (81) 36 721 5696
Web Site: https://sumitomonacco.co.jp
Emp.: 1,200

INTERNATIONAL PUBLIC

Forklift Truck Mfr & Whslr
N.A.I.C.S.: 333924
Minoru Kato *(Pres)*

Sumitomo SHI FW Brazil Management Ltda. (1)
Rua Boa Vista 254 13 andar Centro, Sao Paulo, Brazil
Tel.: (55) 1132925054
Boiler Services
N.A.I.C.S.: 238220

Sumitomo SHI FW Energie B.V. (1)
Naritaweg 165 Telestone 8, 1043 BW, Amsterdam, Netherlands
Tel.: (31) 205214777
Web Site: http://www.shi-fw.com
Holding Company; Circulating Fluidized Bed Boiler Mfr & Whslr
N.A.I.C.S.: 551112

Subsidiary (Non-US):

Sumitomo SHI FW Energie GmbH (2)
Petersstrasse 120, 47798, Krefeld, Germany
Tel.: (49) 15110851366
CFB Boiler Maintenance Services
N.A.I.C.S.: 238220

Sumitomo SHI FW Energy Management (Shanghai) Co., Ltd. (2)
8th Floor UC Tower 500 Fushan Road, Pudong, 200122, Shanghai, China
Tel.: (86) 2150582266
CFB Boiler Mfr
N.A.I.C.S.: 332410

Sumitomo SHI FW Power Group Asia Ltd. (2)
Unit1502 15 F Westley Square 48 Hoi Yuen Road, Kwun Tong, Kowloon, China (Hong Kong)
Tel.: (852) 35965860
CFB Boiler Whslr
N.A.I.C.S.: 423720

Sumitomo SHI FW Power Service Philippine Corporation (2)
Unit 901A 9th Floor Vicente Madrigal Bldg, Ayala Ave, Makati, 6793, Philippines
Tel.: (63) 27289662
CFB Boiler Maintenance Services
N.A.I.C.S.: 238220

Sumitomo SHI FW Power Vietnam Ltd. (2)
31 Hai Ba Trung Street, Hoan Kiem Dist, Hanoi, Vietnam
Tel.: (84) 2439393809
CFB Boiler Maintenance Services
N.A.I.C.S.: 238220

Sumitomo Shi FW Energia Oy (2)
Metsanneidonkuja 8, PO Box 7, 02130, Espoo, Finland (100%)
Tel.: (358) 1039311
Web Site: http://www.shi-fw.com
Engineering & Construction Services
N.A.I.C.S.: 541330
Eiji Kojima *(Chm)*

Subsidiary (Non-US):

Sumitomo Shi FW Energi Aktiebolag (3)
Lindovagen 75, 602 28, Norrkoping, Sweden
Tel.: (46) 1 128 5330
Web Site: http://www.shi-fw.com
Fluid Bed Boiler Distr
N.A.I.C.S.: 423720
Claes Moqvist *(Mng Dir)*

Sumitomo Shi FW Energia Polska Sp. z o.o. (3)
ul Mlynarska 42, 01-171, Warsaw, Poland
Tel.: (48) 225355065
Web Site: http://www.shi-fw.com
Industrial Boiler Mfr & Distr
N.A.I.C.S.: 332410

Subsidiary (Domestic):

Sumitomo Shi FW Energy FAKOP Sp. z o.o. (4)
Ul Staszica 31, Sosnowiec, 41-200, Poland
Tel.: (48) 32 368 13 00
Web Site: http://www.shi-fw.com

Power Boiler & Heat Exchanger Mfr
N.A.I.C.S.: 332410

Sumitomo SHI FW Service (Thailand) Ltd. (1)
20th Floor Bhiraj Tower at EmQuartier 689 Sukhumvit Rd, Klongton Nuea Wattana, Bangkok, 10110, Thailand
Tel.: (66) 204171403
Circulating Fluidized Bed Boiler Mfr & Distr
N.A.I.C.S.: 332410

SUMITOMO LIFE INSURANCE COMPANY
1-4-35 Shiromi, Chuo-ku, Osaka, 540-8512, Japan
Tel.: (81) 669371435 JP
Web Site: https://www.sumitomolife.co.jp
Year Founded: 1907
Rev.: $31,966,372,410
Assets: $354,347,598,500
Liabilities: $339,985,086,000
Net Worth: $14,362,512,500
Earnings: $47,748,190
Emp.: 43,168
Fiscal Year-end: 03/31/20
Life Insurance
N.A.I.C.S.: 524113
Yoshio Sato (Chm)

Subsidiaries:

CSS Co., Ltd. (1)
Sono-cho 709, Iwakura, 482-0003, Aichi, Japan
Tel.: (81) 587 379131
Web Site: http://www.css-corp.jp
Software Development Services
N.A.I.C.S.: 541511

Sumisei Business Service Co., Ltd. (1)
1-4-35 Shiromi, Chuo-Ku, Osaka, 540-0001, Japan
Tel.: (81) 669 371480
Fire Insurance Services
N.A.I.C.S.: 524113

Sumisei Insurance Service Corporation (1)
2F Dome-mae Izumi Building 1-2-20 Kujominami, Nishi-ku, Osaka, 550-0025, Japan
Tel.: (81) 665836661
Web Site: https://www.sumisei-sis.co.jp
Fire Insurance Services
N.A.I.C.S.: 524113

Sumisei-Support & Consulting Co., Ltd. (1)
6-14-1 Nishi-Shinjuku Shinjuku Green Tower Building 19th floor, Shinjuku-ku, Tokyo, 160-0023, Japan
Tel.: (81) 333420085
Web Site: https://www.sumisei-agc.co.jp
Fire Insurance Services
N.A.I.C.S.: 524113

Sumitomo Life Insurance Company - New York (1)
1350 Ave of the Americas Ste 1140, New York, NY 10019 (100%)
Tel.: (212) 521-8340
Sales Range: $50-74.9 Million
Emp.: 6
Insurance Research Services
N.A.I.C.S.: 524210
Tomo Matsubara (Sr Mgr)

Symetra Financial Corporation (1)
777 108th Ave NE Ste 1200, Bellevue, WA 98004
Tel.: (800) 796-3872
Web Site: http://www.symetra.com
Holding Company; Life Insurance, Annuities, Retirement Plans & Employee Benefits Administration Services
N.A.I.C.S.: 551112
Tommie D. Brooks (Sr VP & Chief Actuary)

Subsidiary (Domestic):

Symetra Life Insurance Company (2)
777 108th Ave NE Ste 1200, Bellevue, WA 98004

Tel.: (800) 796-3872
Web Site: http://www.symetra.com
Fire Insurance Services
N.A.I.C.S.: 524113
Michael W. Fry (Exec VP-Benefits Div)

Subsidiary (Domestic):

First Symetra National Life Insurance Company of New York (3)
PO Box 34690, Seattle, WA 98124-1690 (100%)
Web Site: http://www.symetra.com
Life Insurance
N.A.I.C.S.: 524113
Margaret A. Meister (Pres)

SUMITOMO METAL MINING CO., LTD.
11-3 Shimbashi 5-chome Shimbashi Sumitomo Building, Minato-ku, Tokyo, 105-8716, Japan
Tel.: (81) 334367701
Web Site: https://www.smm.co.jp
Year Founded: 1950
SMMYY—(OTCIQ)
Rev.: $10,202,831,130
Assets: $19,415,635,830
Liabilities: $6,586,383,510
Net Worth: $12,829,252,320
Earnings: $1,151,394,450
Emp.: 7,330
Fiscal Year-end: 03/31/23
Metals Mfr
N.A.I.C.S.: 331410
Yoshiaki Nakazato (Chm)

Subsidiaries:

Coral Bay Nickel Corporation (1)
Rio Tuba, Bataraza, Palawan, Philippines
Tel.: (63) 27501536
Web Site: http://www.smm.co.jp
Sales Range: $50-74.9 Million
Emp.: 200
Nickel & Cobalt Products Mfr; Joint Venture Owned 54% by Sumitomo Metal Mining Co., Ltd. & 18% by Mitsui & Co., Ltd. & 18% by Nissho Iwai Corp. & 10% by Rio Tuba Nickel Mining Corp.
N.A.I.C.S.: 331491

Dongguan Sumiko Electronic Paste Co., Ltd. (1)
No 1 North Industry Road 4 Songshan Lake Sci & Tech Industry Park, Small-Medium Enterprises, Dongguan, 523808, Guangdong, China
Tel.: (86) 769 22899277
Sales Range: $25-49.9 Million
Emp.: 11
Thick Film Paste Mfr & Distr
N.A.I.C.S.: 325520
Yoshiyuki Uesaka (Pres)

FIGESBAL (1)
21 23 Rue De L Alma, BP C4, Noumea, Cedex, New Caledonia
Tel.: (687) 272031
N.A.I.C.S.: 331410

Hyuga Smelting Co., Ltd. (1)
5 Funaba-cho, Hyuga, 883-8585, Miyazaki, Japan (60%)
Tel.: (81) 98 252 8101
Web Site: https://www.smm.co.jp
Sales Range: $100-124.9 Million
Emp.: 162
Smelting & Refining of Nickel
N.A.I.C.S.: 331410
Takuya Takemoto (Pres)

Igeta Heim Co., Ltd. (1)
16-11 Takadanobaba 2-chome, Shinjuku-ku, Tokyo, 169-0075, Japan
Tel.: (81) 3 5292 0816
Sales Range: $25-49.9 Million
Emp.: 2
Steel Frame & Construction Material Mfr
N.A.I.C.S.: 332311
Shoichiro Kuwahata (Pres)

JCO Co., Ltd. (1)
2600 Ishigamitojuku Takai-mura, Naka-gun, Ibaraki, 319-1101, Japan
Tel.: (81) 29 287 0511

Sales Range: $10-24.9 Million
Emp.: 4
Uranium Waste Management Services
N.A.I.C.S.: 562998
Kenji Kirishima (Pres)

Japan Irradiation Service Co., Ltd. (1)
11-3 Shimbashi 5-chome, Minato-ku, Tokyo, 105-8716, Japan
Tel.: (81) 3 5403 7711
Sales Range: $25-49.9 Million
Emp.: 6
Irradiation Sterilization Services
N.A.I.C.S.: 561499
Koike Kouji (Pres)

M-SMM Electronics Sdn. Bhd. (1)
Lots 5 7 And 9 Jalan Ragum 15,17, 40200, Shah Alam, Selangor Darul Ehsan, Malaysia (100%)
Tel.: (60) 355198140
Web Site: http://www.msmm.com.my
Sales Range: $25-49.9 Million
Emp.: 400
N.A.I.C.S.: 331410
Ishak Yacob (Mgr-HR)

Malaysian Electronics Materials Sdn. Bhd (1)
Lots 5 Jalan Ragum 15-17, 40200, Shah Alam, Selangor Darul Ehsan, Malaysia (100%)
Tel.: (60) 355198302
Web Site: http://www.memwire.com
Sales Range: $150-199.9 Million
Emp.: 190
N.A.I.C.S.: 331410

N.E. ChemCat Corporation (1)
27th floor World Trade Center Building South Tower 2-4-1 Hamamatsucho, Minato-ku, Tokyo, 105-5127, Japan
Tel.: (81) 334355490
Sales Range: $200-249.9 Million
Emp.: 681
Chemical Catalysts, Precious Metal Coating & Automotive Exhaust Catalysts Mfr
N.A.I.C.S.: 325998

Niihama Electronics Co., Ltd. (1)
1-10 Oji-cho, Niihama, 792-0008, Ehime, Japan
Tel.: (81) 897 37 2411
Web Site: http://www.niihamadenshi.jp
Sales Range: $125-149.9 Million
Emp.: 303
Manufacture of Adhesiveless Copperclad Polymide Film
N.A.I.C.S.: 326113
Hiroki Hata (Pres)

Nippon Ketjen Co., Ltd. (1)
1-2-1 Shibaura 20F Seavans N Building, Minato-ku, Tokyo, 105-6791, Japan (50%)
Tel.: (81) 354425061
Web Site: http://www.nippon-ketjen.co.jp
Sales Range: $50-74.9 Million
Emp.: 159
Development, Production & Sales of Hydroprocessing Catalysts
N.A.I.C.S.: 325998
Hiromasa Ooba (Pres)

Nittosha Co., Ltd. (1)
524 Higashiyama, Station on the Sanyo train, Himeji, 672-8014, Hyogo, Japan (100%)
Tel.: (81) 79 246 1561
Web Site: https://www.nitto-sha.co.jp
Sales Range: Less than $1 Million
Emp.: 140
Metal Product Plating & Electromagnetic Shielding Services
N.A.I.C.S.: 332813
Shunji Inagaki (Pres)

Ohkuchi Electronics Co., Ltd. (1)
1755-0 Okuchiushio, Isa, 895-2501, Kagoshima, Japan (100%)
Tel.: (81) 99 522 7511
Web Site: https://www.ohkuchielectronics.co.jp
Sales Range: $200-249.9 Million
Emp.: 479
Electronic Components Mfr
N.A.I.C.S.: 334413
Hiroyuki Sakata (Pres)

Ohkuchi Materials Co., Ltd. (1)
1746-2 Ohkuchi-Ushio Isa, Kagoshima, 895-2501, Japan
Tel.: (81) 99 522 8421
Lead Frames Mfr
N.A.I.C.S.: 334413

SMM KOREA Co., Ltd. (1)
503 Seocho Plaza 286 Seocho-daero, Seocho-gu, Seoul, Korea (South)
Tel.: (82) 2 553 2430
Web Site: http://www.smm.co.jp
Sales Range: $50-74.9 Million
Emp.: 4
Semiconductor Equipment Sales & Distribution
N.A.I.C.S.: 423690
Kenichi Dehara (Pres)

SMM Precision Co., Ltd. (1)
4-4 Ougibuchi Ougida, Noshiro, 016-0122, Akita, Japan
Tel.: (81) 185 70 1161
Web Site: http://www.smm.co.jp
Emp.: 74
Optical Communication Component Mfr
N.A.I.C.S.: 334290
Hiroshi Matsumoto (Pres)

SMM Solomon LIMITED (1)
Mendana Avenue, PO Box 912, Honiara, Solomon Islands
Tel.: (677) 27074
Web Site: http://www.smm.co.jp
Nickel Mining Services
N.A.I.C.S.: 212230
Yoritoshi Ochi (Mng Dir)

Shinko Co., Ltd. (1)
12238 Nakaminowa Minowama-machi, Kamiina-gun, Nagano, 399-4692, Japan (97%)
Tel.: (81) 265790121
Web Site: http://www.shinko-jp.biz
Sales Range: $75-99.9 Million
Emp.: 280
Printed Circuit Boards Design, Sales & Mfr
N.A.I.C.S.: 334412
Koichi Uzawa (Pres)

Shisaka Smelting Co., Ltd. (1)
5-3 Nishibara-cho 3-chome, Niihama, 792-0011, Ehime, Japan
Tel.: (81) 89 734 6820
Crude Zinc Oxide Mfr
N.A.I.C.S.: 325180

Sicoxs Corporation (1)
Shimbashi Sumitomo Building 7F 5-11-3 Shimbashi, Minato-ku, Tokyo, 105-0004, Japan
Tel.: (81) 33 437 5220
Web Site: https://www.sicoxs.com
Emp.: 37
Semiconductor & Related Device Mfr
N.A.I.C.S.: 334413
Takayuki Iino (Pres)

Sumico Lubricant Co., Ltd. (1)
5-11-3 Shimbashi 7th floor Shimbashi Sumitomo Building, Minato-ku, Tokyo, 105-0004, Japan (100%)
Tel.: (81) 35 425 6702
Web Site: https://www.sumico.co.jp
Sales Range: $25-49.9 Million
Emp.: 112
Lubricating Oil Mfr & Distr
N.A.I.C.S.: 324191
Shinichirou Imai (Pres)

Sumiko Consultants Co., Ltd. (1)
Ikenohata Nisshoku Bldg 9-7 Ikenohata 2-chome, Tokyo, 110 0008, Taito-ku, Japan (100%)
Tel.: (81) 338276134
Web Site: http://www.sumicon.co.jp
Sales Range: $25-49.9 Million
Emp.: 100
Engineeering Services
N.A.I.C.S.: 541330

Sumiko Electronics Suzhou Co., Ltd. (1)
No 123 Longtan Rd 3rd District Suzhou Industrial Park, Suzhou, 215126, Jiangsu, China
Tel.: (86) 512 62836501
Web Site: http://www.smm.co.jp
Sales Range: $200-249.9 Million
Emp.: 534

SUMITOMO METAL MINING CO., LTD.

Sumitomo Metal Mining Co., Ltd.—(Continued)
Semiconductor Package Material Mfr & Distr
N.A.I.C.S.: 334413
Tay Hwee Cheng (Pres)

Sumiko Electronics Taiwan Co., Ltd. (1)
16 East 7th St, Kaohsiung, Taiwan
Tel.: (886) 73653592
N.A.I.C.S.: 331410

Sumiko Kunitomi Denshi Co., Ltd. (1)
351-1 Kunitomi, Kyowa-cho, Iwanai, 048-2143, Hokkaido, Japan
Tel.: (81) 135 72 1211
Sales Range: $50-74.9 Million
Emp.: 157
Crystal Products & Magnetic Material Mfr
N.A.I.C.S.: 333517
Koichi Uzawa (Pres)

Sumiko Logistics Co., Ltd. (1)
3-5-3 Nishibara-cho, Niihama, 792-0011, Ehime, Japan
Tel.: (81) 897 37 2474
Web Site: http://sklco.com
Sales Range: $25-49.9 Million
Emp.: 113
Logistics Consulting Servies
N.A.I.C.S.: 541614
Nobuo Tai (Mng Dir)

Sumiko Plantech Co., Ltd. (1)
3-20 Shinden 3-chome, Niihama, 792-0003, Ehime, Japan
Tel.: (81) 897 33 2651
Sales Range: $25-49.9 Million
Emp.: 7
Metal Processing Machinery Repair Services & Mfr
N.A.I.C.S.: 333248
Hiromasa Ohba (Pres)

Sumiko Resources Exploration & Development Co., Ltd. (1)
Toranomon 33 Mori Building 5F 3-8-21, Toranomon Minato-ku, Tokyo, 105-0001, Japan
Tel.: (81) 354052173
Web Site: http://www.sred.co.jp
Emp.: 101
Non Ferrous Metal Mining & Smelting Services
N.A.I.C.S.: 331491
Yu Yamato (Pres)

Sumiko Tec Co., Ltd. (1)
2-3-19 Shin-Yokohama 4th floor Shin-Yokohama Mineta Building, Kohoku-ku, Yokohama, 222-0033, Kanagawa, Japan
Tel.: (81) 452852341
Web Site: http://www.sumiko-tec.co.jp
Emp.: 319
Electronic Device Terminal & Connector Mfr
N.A.I.C.S.: 335931
Kazuo Iijima (Pres)

Sumiko Technical Service Co., Ltd. (1)
1-6 Soubiraki-cho, Niihama, 792-0001, Ehime, Japan
Tel.: (81) 897 33 1050
Emp.: 219
Business Support Services
N.A.I.C.S.: 561499

Sumiko Techno-Research Co., Ltd. (1)
17-2 Isoura-cho, Niihama, 792-0002, Ehime, Japan
Tel.: (81) 897 34 3411
Sales Range: $50-74.9 Million
Emp.: 13
Non Ferrous Metal Analyzing Services
N.A.I.C.S.: 331491
Katsuaki Watanabe (Pres)

Sumitomo Metal Mining America Inc. (1)
701 5th Ave Ste 2150, Seattle, WA 98104 (100%)
Tel.: (206) 405-2800
Web Site: https://www.smm.co.jp
Sales Range: $50-74.9 Million
Emp.: 7
Holding Office
N.A.I.C.S.: 213114

Subsidiary (Domestic):

SMM Pogo LLC (2)
701 5th Ave Ste 2150, Seattle, WA 98104
Tel.: (206) 405-2800
Web Site: http://www.smn.co.jp
Sales Range: $50-74.9 Million
Holding Company
N.A.I.C.S.: 551112

Sumitomo Metal Mining Arizona Inc. (2)
701 5th Ave Ste 2150, Seattle, WA 98104
Tel.: (206) 405-2800
Sales Range: $25-49.9 Million
Emp.: 7
N.A.I.C.S.: 331410
Yoshinao Koeayashi (Mgr)

Sumitomo Metal Mining Asia Pacific Pte. Ltd. (1)
10 Eunos Road 8, Singapore, 339163, Singapore (100%)
Tel.: (65) 62934377
Web Site: http://wwwsmmap.com
Sales Range: $25-49.9 Million
Emp.: 45
N.A.I.C.S.: 331410
Kengi Higuehi (Gen Mgr)

Subsidiary (Non-US):

P.T. Sumiko Leadframe Bintan (2)
Lots D6 & D7 Bintan Industrial Estate, 98104, Bintan, Riau, Indonesia
Tel.: (62) 770696020
Web Site: http://www.smmap.com
Lead Frame Production
N.A.I.C.S.: 334413

Sumiko Leadframe (Thailand) Co., Ltd. (2)
1 49 Moo 5 Rojana Industrial Pk, T Kanham A U Thai, Ayutthaya, 13210, Thailand (100%)
Tel.: (66) 35226303
Web Site: http://www.sumiko.com
Sales Range: Less than $1 Million
Lead Frame Production
N.A.I.C.S.: 334413

Sumiko Leadframe Chengdu Co., Ltd. (2)
No 7 Nan'er Road Singapore Industrial Park, Airport Road, Chengdu, 610041, Sichuan, China
Tel.: (86) 2885155577
Web Site: http://www.smm.co.jp
Sales Range: $25-49.9 Million
Lead Frame Production
N.A.I.C.S.: 334413

Subsidiary (Domestic):

Sumiko Leadframe Singapore Pte Ltd (2)
No 35/41 Kallang Place, 339163, Singapore, Singapore
Tel.: (65) 62934377
Sales Range: $75-99.9 Million
Lead Frame Production
N.A.I.C.S.: 334419

Sumitomo Metal Mining Brass and Copper Co., Ltd. (1)
656-1 Futatsumiya, Saitama, Ageo, 362-0017, Saitama, Japan (100%)
Tel.: (81) 48 775 7111
Web Site: https://www.msmmbc.co.jp
Sales Range: $50-74.9 Million
Emp.: 450
Copper Rolling
N.A.I.C.S.: 331420

Sumitomo Metal Mining Canada Ltd. (1)
818-700 West Georgia Street, Vancouver, V7Y 1A1, BC, Canada (100%)
Tel.: (604) 685-3274
Web Site: http://www.sumitomo.gr.jp
Sales Range: $50-74.9 Million
Emp.: 4
Mining & Exploration Services
N.A.I.C.S.: 212290

Sumitomo Metal Mining Chile Ltda. (1)
Isidora Goyenechea 3477 Ofic 151 Piso 15, Las Condes, 7550106, Santiago, Chile
Tel.: (56) 2 362 9250
Sales Range: $50-74.9 Million
Emp.: 15
Metal Mining Services
N.A.I.C.S.: 213114

Sumitomo Metal Mining Co., Ltd. - Besshi-Niihama District Division (1)
Besshi Main Building General Affairs Center Safe, Niihama, 792-8555, Ehime, Japan
Tel.: (81) 89 737 4800
Web Site: https://www.smm.co.jp
Sales Range: $1-4.9 Billion
Emp.: 800
Smelting & Refining of Non-Ferrous Metals
N.A.I.C.S.: 331410

Sumitomo Metal Mining Co., Ltd. - Energy & Environment Business Div. Research & Development Center (1)
2600 Ishigama Tojuku Tokai Mura, Naka, 319 1101, Ibaraki, Japan (100%)
Tel.: (81) 292827518
Sales Range: $25-49.9 Million
Emp.: 30
N.A.I.C.S.: 331410

Sumitomo Metal Mining Co., Ltd. - Harima District Division (1)
346 4 Miyanishi Harima Cho, Hyogo, 675 0145, Japan
Tel.: (81) 794378651
Sales Range: $50-74.9 Million
Emp.: 184
N.A.I.C.S.: 331410
Kaikake Atsushi (Gen Mgr)

Sumitomo Metal Mining Co., Ltd. - Harima Smelter Facility (1)
346-4 Miyanishi Harima-cho, Kako-gun, Hyogo, 675-0145, Japan
Tel.: (81) 79 437 8651
Emp.: 17
Zinc Smelting Services
N.A.I.C.S.: 331410

Sumitomo Metal Mining Co., Ltd. - Ichikawa Research Laboratory (1)
18-5 Nakakokubun 3-chome, Ichikawa, 272-8588, Chiba, Japan
Tel.: (81) 47 372 7221
Web Site: http://www.smm.co.jp
Sales Range: $25-49.9 Million
Emp.: 100
Research Laboratories
N.A.I.C.S.: 541380

Sumitomo Metal Mining Co., Ltd. - Isoura Plant (1)
17-3 Isoura-cho, Niihama, 792-0002, Ehime, Japan
Tel.: (81) 897 34 9743
Web Site: http://www.smm.co.jp
Metallic Compound Materials Mfr
N.A.I.C.S.: 332999

Sumitomo Metal Mining Co., Ltd. - Kunitomi District Division (1)
84 Kunitomi Kyowa Cho, Iwanai, 048 21, Japan
Tel.: (81) 135721211
Sales Range: $50-74.9 Million
Emp.: 140
N.A.I.C.S.: 331410

Sumitomo Metal Mining Co., Ltd. - Niihama Nickel Refinery Facility (1)
5-1 Nishibara-cho 3-chome, Niihama, 792-8555, Ehime, Japan
Tel.: (81) 897 37 4830
Web Site: http://www.smm.co.jp
Emp.: 180
Nickel & Metal Refining Services
N.A.I.C.S.: 331492

Sumitomo Metal Mining Co., Ltd. - Niihama Research Laboratory (1)
17-5 Isoura-cho, Niihama, 792 0006, Ehime, Japan
Tel.: (81) 897377171
Sales Range: $25-49.9 Million
Emp.: 60
N.A.I.C.S.: 331410

Sumitomo Metal Mining Co., Ltd. - Ome District Division (1)
1-6-1 Suehiro-cho, Ome, 198-8601, Tokyo, Japan
Tel.: (81) 42 831 1181

INTERNATIONAL PUBLIC

Web Site: http://www.smm.co.jp
Sales Range: $200-249.9 Million
Electronics Materials & Components Mfr
N.A.I.C.S.: 334419

Sumitomo Metal Mining Co., Ltd. - Sagami Plant (1)
7-1 Chuorinkan West 3-chome, Yamato, 242-0008, Kanagawa, Japan
Tel.: (81) 46 275 1481
Metal Mining Services
N.A.I.C.S.: 212290

Sumitomo Metal Mining Co., Ltd. - Toyo Smelter & Refinery Facility (1)
145-1 Funaya-Aza-Shinchi-Otu, Saijo, 793-0005, Ehime, Japan
Tel.: (81) 897 56 1222
Web Site: http://www.smm.co.jp
Metal Smelting & Refining Services
N.A.I.C.S.: 331492

Sumitomo Metal Mining Electronics Parts Pte. Ltd. (1)
No 6 Tues Ave 20, Singapore, 638820, Singapore (100%)
Tel.: (65) 68631123
Sales Range: $25-49.9 Million
Emp.: 100
Metal Mining
N.A.I.C.S.: 331410

Sumitomo Metal Mining Engineering Co., Ltd. (1)
5-11-3 Shimbashi Shimbashi Sumitomo Building 11th floor, Minato-ku, Tokyo, 105-8716, Ehime, Japan
Tel.: (81) 354254431
Web Site: http://www.smmec.co.jp
Sales Range: $50-74.9 Million
Emp.: 122
Non-ferrous Metal Smelting Services
N.A.I.C.S.: 331492
Yoshinobu Ono (Pres & CEO)

Sumitomo Metal Mining Oceania Pty. Ltd. (1)
Level 25 Citigroup Ctr 2 Park Street, Sydney, 2000, NSW, Australia (89%)
Tel.: (61) 292660400
Sales Range: $25-49.9 Million
Emp.: 5
N.A.I.C.S.: 331410
Katsuya Tanaka (Mng Dir)

Sumitomo Metal Mining Peru S.A. (1)
Av Santo Toribio 173 y Via Central 125 Edificio Real 8 Oficina 702, San Isidro, Lima, Peru
Tel.: (51) 1 222 3290
Web Site: http://www.smm.co.jp
Sales Range: $50-74.9 Million
Emp.: 15
Metal Mining Services
N.A.I.C.S.: 212290
Koji Ueda (Pres)

Sumitomo Metal Mining Siporex Co., Ltd. (1)
5-11-3 Shimbashi Shimbashi Sumitomo Building, Minato-ku, Tokyo, 105-0004, Japan
Tel.: (81) 33 435 4660
Web Site: https://www.sumitomo-siporex.co.jp
Sales Range: $25-49.9 Million
Emp.: 398
Manufacture & Distribution of Autoclaved Lightweight Aerated Concrete (ALC) & Other Construction Materials
N.A.I.C.S.: 423390

Sumitomo Metal Mining do Brasil Ltda. (1)
Alameda Santos 200 - Suite 12, Cerqueira Cesar, Sao Paulo, 01418-000, Brazil
Tel.: (55) 113 587 1365
Mining Exploration Services
N.A.I.C.S.: 212290

Taganito HPAL Nickel Corporation (1)
24th Floor Pacific Star Building Makati Ave Cor Sen Gil Puyat Ave, Makati, 1200, Philippines
Tel.: (63) 2 856 3929
Nickel Mining Services
N.A.I.C.S.: 212230

AND PRIVATE COMPANIES

Takanori Fujimura *(Pres)*

Taihei Metal Industry Co., Ltd. (1)
3860 Shimotsuruma, Yamato, 242 8555, Kanagawa, Japan
Tel.: (81) 462741606
Web Site: http://www.taiheikinzoku.co.jp
Sales Range: $25-49.9 Million
Emp.: 140
Steel Casting
N.A.I.C.S.: 331523
Hisashi Wata *(CEO)*

Taiwan Sumiko Materials Co., Ltd. (1)
5F No 16 East 7th St N E P Z, Kaohsiung, Taiwan
Tel.: (886) 7 363 3134
Sales Range: $25-49.9 Million
Emp.: 95
Bonding Wire & Thin Film Materials Mfr
N.A.I.C.S.: 332618
Mikio Fukasawa *(Pres)*

SUMITOMO MITSUI FINANCIAL GROUP, INC.

SUMITOMO MITSUI FINANCIAL GROUP, INC.
1-2 Marunouchi 1-chome, Chiyoda-ku, Tokyo, 100-0005, Japan
Tel.: (81) 332828111   JP
Web Site: https://www.smfg.co.jp
Year Founded: 2002
83160—(TKS)
Rev.: $19,517,636,666
Assets: $1,749,745,850,315
Liabilities: $1,648,476,186,313
Net Worth: $101,269,664,002
Earnings: $3,204,199,163
Emp.: 120,000
Fiscal Year-end: 03/31/24
Financial Services Holding Company
N.A.I.C.S.: 551111
Takeshi Kunibe *(Chm)*

Subsidiaries:

SBCS Co., Limited. (1)
1 Q House Lumpini Building 16th Floor South Sathorn Road Tungmahamek, Sathorn, Bangkok, 10120, Thailand
Tel.: (66) 267772705
Web Site: https://sbcs.co.th
Commercial Banking Services
N.A.I.C.S.: 522110

SMBC Friend Securities Co., Ltd. (1)
7-12 Nihonbashi-Kabutocho, Chuo-ku, Tokyo, 103-8221, Japan
Tel.: (81) 336693211
Web Site: http://www.smbc-friend.co.jp
Sales Range: $900-999.9 Million
Emp.: 2,104
Securities Brokerage & Dealing Services
N.A.I.C.S.: 523150
Osamu Endo *(Pres)*

SMFG Card & Credit, Inc. (1)
1-2 Yurakucho 1-chome, Chiyoda-ku, Tokyo, 100-0006, Japan   (100%)
Tel.: (81) 3 5512 3411
Web Site: http://www.smfg.co.jp
Holding Company; Credit Card Products & Services
N.A.I.C.S.: 551112

Subsidiary (Domestic):

Sumitomo Mitsui Card Co., Ltd. (2)
SMBC Toyosu Building 2-2-31 Toyosu, Koto-ku, Tokyo, Japan   (65.99%)
Tel.: (81) 366341700
Web Site: https://www.smbc-card.com
Sales Range: $900-999.9 Million
Emp.: 3,190
Credit Card Products & Services
N.A.I.C.S.: 522210

Subsidiary (Domestic):

SMBC Finance Service Co., Ltd. (3)
16-4 Konan 2-chome, Minato-ku, Tokyo, 108-8117, Japan
Tel.: (81) 367147713
Web Site: http://www.smbc.co.jp
Emp.: 3,515

Holding Company; Credit Card, Sales Financing, Lending, Collection & Settlement Services
N.A.I.C.S.: 551112
Satoru Nakanishi *(Pres)*

Subsidiary (Domestic):

BLOCKLINE Inc. (4)
16-4 Konan 2-chome, Minato-ku, Tokyo, 108-8117, Japan
Tel.: (81) 367147743
Web Site: http://www.blockline.com
Sales Range: $25-49.9 Million
Emp.: 10
Data Processing Services
N.A.I.C.S.: 518210

CF Shinyohosho Co., Ltd. (4)
23-20 Marunouchi 3-Chome, Naka-Ku, Nagoya, 460-0002, Aichi, Japan
Tel.: (81) 523101578
Business Loan Guarantee Services
N.A.I.C.S.: 522390

CLO Inc. (4)
621 Ginza, Chuo-ku, Tokyo, 104-0061, Japan
Tel.: (81) 335692374,
Driving Schools
N.A.I.C.S.: 611692

Cedyna Servicer, Inc. (4)
20-25 Marunouchi 2-chome, Naka-ku, Nagoya, 460-0002, Aichi, Japan
Tel.: (81) 522196140
Web Site: http://www.cedyna.co.jp
Credit Collection & Collection Outsourcing Services
N.A.I.C.S.: 522390

Cedyna Total Service Co., Ltd. (4)
3-23-20 Marunouchi, Naka-ku, Nagoya, 460-8670, Aichi, Japan
Tel.: (81) 529620682
Data Processing & Business Process Outsourcing Services
N.A.I.C.S.: 518210

MCS Servicer Co., Ltd. (4)
17-2 Kikukawa 3 Chome, Sumida-ku, Tokyo, 130-8583, Japan
Tel.: (81) 356005201
Web Site: http://www.mcs.co.jp
Credit Management & Collection Services
N.A.I.C.S.: 522299

Procent Inc. (4)
17 2 Kikukawa 3 Chome, Sumida-Ku, Tokyo, 130-0024, Japan
Tel.: (81) 356385501
Web Site: http://www.procent.co.jp
Credit Card Processing Services
N.A.I.C.S.: 522390

Sumitomo Mitsui Asset Management Co., Ltd. (1)
Atago Green Hills MORI Tower 28F 2-5-1 Atago, Minato-ku, Tokyo, 105-6228, Japan   (60%)
Tel.: (81) 354050555
Web Site: http://www.smam-jp.com
Emp.: 635
Investment Advisory & Trust Management Services
N.A.I.C.S.: 523940
Takashi Matsushita *(Chm)*

Subsidiary (Non-US):

Sumitomo Mitsui Asset Management (Hong Kong) Limited (2)
6/F One International Finance Centre 1 Harbour View Street, Central, China (Hong Kong)
Tel.: (852) 25218883
Web Site: https://www.smd-am.co.jp
Investment Management Service
N.A.I.C.S.: 523940

Subsidiary (US):

Sumitomo Mitsui Asset Management (New York) Inc. (2)
300 Park Ave 16th Fl, New York, NY 10022
Tel.: (212) 418-3030
Web Site: http://www.smam-jp.com
Investment Management Service
N.A.I.C.S.: 523940

Sumitomo Mitsui Auto Service Company, Limited (1)
Tokyo Opera City Tower 3-20-2 Nishishinjuku, Shinjuku-Ku, Tokyo, 163-1434, Japan
Tel.: (81) 35 302 5610
Web Site: http://www.smauto.co.jp
Emp.: 1,979
Automobile Parts Distr
N.A.I.C.S.: 423120
Akira Tsuyuguchi *(Pres & CEO)*

Subsidiary (Domestic):

Cedyna Auto Lease Co., Ltd. (2)
2-8-12 Sakae, Naka-Ku, Nagoya, 460-0008, Aichi, Japan
Tel.: (81) 52 212 1081
Web Site: https://www.cedyna-al.jp
Automobile Leasing Services
N.A.I.C.S.: 532112
Hideo Shiraki *(Pres)*

Sumitomo Mitsui Banking Corporation (1)
1-1-2 Marunouchi, Chiyoda-ku, Tokyo, 100-0005, Japan
Tel.: (81) 57128891111
Web Site: https://www.smbc.co.jp
Emp.: 28,191
Commercial & Investment Banking, Credit Card, Leasing, Mortgage, Consumer Lending, Custody & Trade Financing Services
N.A.I.C.S.: 522110
Toru Nakashima *(Sr Mng Exec Officer)*

Affiliate (Domestic):

At-Loan Co., Ltd. (2)
27th Floor Shiodome Sumitomo Building 1-9-2, Higashi-Shimbashi Minatu-ku, Tokyo, Japan
Tel.: (81) 35324 6909
Web Site: http://www.at-loan.jp
Sales Range: $150-199.9 Million
Emp.: 280
Consumer Lending Services; Owned 50% by Promise Co., Ltd. & 49.99% by Sumitomo Mitsui Financial Group, Inc.
N.A.I.C.S.: 522291

Subsidiary (Non-US):

Banco Sumitomo Mitsui Brasileiro S.A. (2)
Avenida Paulista 37 11 and 12 floors, 11th Floor, Bela Vista, Sao Paulo, 01311-902, Brazil
Tel.: (55) 31788000
Web Site: https://www.smbcgroup.com.br
Sales Range: $50-74.9 Million
Emp.: 85
Commercial Banking Services
N.A.I.C.S.: 522110

Joint Venture (Domestic):

Daiwa Securities SMBC Principal Investments Co. Ltd. (2)
Gran Tokyo North Tower 1-9-1 Marunouchi, Chiyoda-ku, Tokyo, 100-6754, Japan
Tel.: (81) 35 555 6111
Web Site: https://www.daiwasmbcpi.co.jp
Sales Range: $50-74.9 Million
Emp.: 65
Private Equity, Real Estate & Other Investment Services; Owned 60% by Daiwa Securities Group Inc. & 40% by Sumitomo Mitsui Financial Group, Inc.
N.A.I.C.S.: 523999
Shinya Nishio *(Chm)*

Subsidiary (Domestic):

Financial Link Co., Ltd. (2)
3-1-111 Building 9th Fl Landic Nagatomo Shinbashi, Minato-ku, Tokyo, 105-0004, Japan   (100%)
Tel.: (81) 3 3597 7560
Web Site: http://www.financial-link.jp
Financial Transaction Processing Services
N.A.I.C.S.: 522320
Kitahara Akihiro *(Mng Dir)*

Japan Pension Navigator Co., Ltd. (2)
Sumitomo Mitsui Bank Gofukubashi Building 1-3-4 Yaesu, Chuo-ku, Tokyo, 103-0028, Japan
Tel.: (81) 335162020
Web Site: https://www.j-pec.co.jp

Pension Fund Administration Services
N.A.I.C.S.: 524292
Taro Kubo *(Pres)*

Subsidiary (US):

Manufacturers Bank (2)
515 S Figueroa St 5th Fl, Los Angeles, CA 90071-3301
Tel.: (213) 489-6200
Web Site: https://www.manufacturersbank.com
Sales Range: $150-199.9 Million
Emp.: 278
Commercial Banking Services
N.A.I.C.S.: 522110
Fumihiko Kusakabe *(Chm & CEO)*

Branch (Non-US):

PT Bank BTPN Tbk (2)
Iantai GF Jl Dr Ide Anak Agung Gde Agung Kav 5 5 5 6, Menara BTPN, Jakarta, 12950, Indonesia   (92.43%)
Tel.: (62) 2130026200
Web Site: http://www.btpn.com
Rev.: $865,620,630
Assets: $12,821,618,460
Liabilities: $9,959,450,130
Net Worth: $2,862,168,330
Earnings: $140,397,390
Emp.: 19,370
Fiscal Year-end: 12/31/2020
General Banking Services
N.A.I.C.S.: 522180
Ongki Wanadjati Dana *(Chm)*

Subsidiary (Non-US):

PT Bank Sumitomo Mitsui Indonesia (2)
Summitmas II 10th Fl Jl Jendral Sudirman Kav 61 62, Jakarta, 12069, Indonesia
Tel.: (62) 215227011
Web Site: http://www.smbc-jakt.co.id
Sales Range: $100-124.9 Million
Emp.: 300
Commercial Banking Services
N.A.I.C.S.: 522110

Subsidiary (Domestic):

SMBC Business Servicing Co., Ltd. (2)
Tsukiji Muromachi Building 16-9 Tsukiji 3-chome, Chuo-ku, Tokyo, Japan
Tel.: (81) 335446004
Business Servicing Solutions
N.A.I.C.S.: 561499

SMBC Business Support Co., Ltd. (2)
2-11-1 Sugamo Sugamomuromachi Bldg 5f, Toshima-Ku, Tokyo, 170-0002, Japan
Tel.: (81) 359745021
Web Site: http://www.smbc-bs.co.jp
Business Support Services
N.A.I.C.S.: 561499

Subsidiary (Non-US):

SMBC Capital Markets (Asia) Limited (2)
7/F One International Finance Centre, 1 Harbour View Street, Central, China (Hong Kong)
Tel.: (852) 2532 8500
Emp.: 20
Commercial Banking Services
N.A.I.C.S.: 522110
Anthony Sewell *(Head-Mktg)*

Subsidiary (US):

SMBC Capital Markets, Inc. (2)
277 Park Ave, New York, NY 10172-0003
Tel.: (212) 224-5100
Web Site: http://www.smbc-cm.com
Sales Range: $50-74.9 Million
Emp.: 100
Derivatives, Interest Rate & Currency Trading Services
N.A.I.C.S.: 523160
Vernice Gamble *(Sr VP)*

Subsidiary (Non-US):

SMBC Capital Markets Limited (3)
One New Change, London, EC4M 9AF, United Kingdom
Tel.: (44) 2077861400

SUMITOMO MITSUI FINANCIAL GROUP, INC.

Sumitomo Mitsui Financial Group, Inc.—(Continued)

Web Site: http://www.smbc-cm.com
Sales Range: $50-74.9 Million
Emp.: 100
Derivatives, Interest Rate & Currency Trading Services
N.A.I.C.S.: 523160

Subsidiary (Domestic):

SMBC Center Service Co., Ltd. (2)
4-3-4 Shibaura Tamachikiyota Bldg 7f, Minato-Ku, Tokyo, 108-0023, Japan
Tel.: (81) 354413706
Commercial Banking Services
N.A.I.C.S.: 522110

SMBC Consulting Co., Ltd. (2)
Sumitomo Mitsui Bank Gofukubashi Building 1-3-4 Yaesu, Chuo-ku, Tokyo, 103-0028, Japan (75%)
Tel.: (81) 352555551
Web Site: https://www.smbc-consulting.co.jp
Sales Range: $25-49.9 Million
Emp.: 100
Corporate Management & Human Resource Consulting Services
N.A.I.C.S.: 541611

SMBC Consumer Finance Co Ltd. (2)
SMBC Toyosu Building 2-2-31 Toyosu, Koto-ku, Tokyo, 135-0061, Japan (100%)
Tel.: (81) 368871515
Web Site: https://www.smbc-cf.com
Emp.: 2,145
Consumer Loan & Financing Services
N.A.I.C.S.: 522291
Ryota Naito *(Mng Exec Officer)*

Subsidiary (Domestic):

Abilio Servicer Co., Ltd. (2)
8F SMBC Toyosu Building 2-2-31 Toyosu, Koto-ku, Tokyo, 135-0061, Japan
Tel.: (81) 368544672
Web Site: https://www.abilio-servicer.co.jp
Loan Management & Collection Services
N.A.I.C.S.: 522291

Car Conveni Club Co., Ltd. (3)
2-16-4 Higashinihombashi, Chuo-ku, Tokyo, 103-0004, Japan
Tel.: (81) 358251701
Car Repair & Maintenance Services
N.A.I.C.S.: 811111

Do Financial Service Co., Ltd. (3)
1-3-3 Uchisaiwai-cho, Chiyoda-ku, Tokyo, 135-0016, Japan
Tel.: (81) 368919270
Web Site: https://www.do-fs.co.jp
Financial Support Services
N.A.I.C.S.: 523999

Subsidiary (Non-US):

Liang Jing Co., Ltd. (3)
9th Floor No 6 Sec 3Min Chuan E Rd, Taipei, 104, Taiwan
Tel.: (886) 225151598
Financial Lending & Management Services
N.A.I.C.S.: 522291

Subsidiary (Domestic):

Net Future Co., Ltd. (3)
1-2-4 Otemachi, Chiyoda-ku, Tokyo, 100-0004, Japan
Tel.: (81) 332873755
Web Site: http://www.netfuture.co.jp
Automatic Teller Machines Management & Maintenance Services
N.A.I.C.S.: 238290

PAL Life Co., Ltd. (3)
1-2-4 Otemachi, Chiyoda-ku, Tokyo, 100-0004, Japan
Tel.: (81) 332873761
Real Estate Manangement Services
N.A.I.C.S.: 531390

Subsidiary (Non-US):

Promise (Hong Kong) Co., Ltd. (3)
G/F Ying King Building 196-198 Hennessy Road, Wanchai, China (Hong Kong) (100%)
Tel.: (852) 28041233
Web Site: https://www.promise.com.hk

Sales Range: $75-99.9 Million
Emp.: 200
Consumer Financing
N.A.I.C.S.: 522291

Promise (Shenyang) Co., Ltd. (3)
5F No 1 Yuebin Street, Shenhe District, Shenyang, 110013, Liaoning, China
Tel.: (86) 2422506200
Web Site: http://www.bangmin-sy.com
Consumer Financial Services
N.A.I.C.S.: 522291

Promise (Thailand) Co., Ltd. (3)
159/19-20 Serm-mit Tower Unit 1201 12th Floor Sukhumvit, 21 Asoke Road North Klongtoey Wattana, Bangkok, 10110, Thailand
Tel.: (66) 26326700
Web Site: http://www.promise.co.th
Consumer Financial Services
N.A.I.C.S.: 522291

Subsidiary (Domestic):

Sun Life Co., Ltd. (3)
2-7-6 Kawaramachi, Takamatsu, 760-0052, Japan (100%)
Tel.: (81) 878372727
Consumer Financing
N.A.I.C.S.: 522291

Subsidiary (Domestic):

SMBC Delivery Service Co., Ltd. (2)
4-3-4 Shibaura Tamachikiyota Bldg 6f, Minato-Ku, Tokyo, 108-0023, Japan
Tel.: (81) 354413678
Emp.: 27
Commercial Banking Services
N.A.I.C.S.: 522110

SMBC Electronic Monetary Claims Recording Co., Ltd. (2)
Sumitomo Mitsui Banking Gofukubashi Building 4F 1-3-4 Yaesu, Chuo-ku, Tokyo, 108-6363, Japan
Tel.: (81) 332728675
Web Site: https://www.smbc-emcr.co.jp
Electronic Monetary Claims Recording Services
N.A.I.C.S.: 524291

SMBC Green Service Co., Ltd. (2)
4-9-16 Tsudanuma, Narashino, Tokyo, 275-0016, Japan
Tel.: (81) 474545751
Web Site: https://www.smbc-green.co.jp
Commercial Banking Services
N.A.I.C.S.: 522110

SMBC Guarantee Co., Ltd. (2)
6-1-21 Roppongi, Minato-ku, Tokyo, 106-0032, Japan
Tel.: (81) 337463200
Financial Management Services
N.A.I.C.S.: 523999
Ashiee Masaki *(Pres)*

SMBC International Business Co., Ltd. (2)
13-6 Nihombashikodemmacho Yusen Odemmacho Bldg, Chuo-Ku, Tokyo, 103-0001, Japan
Tel.: (81) 356955351
Commercial Banking Services
N.A.I.C.S.: 522110

SMBC Learning Support Co., Ltd. (2)
17th Floor Nishi-shimbashi Square 3-1 Nishi-shimbashi 1-chome, Minato-ku, Tokyo, 105-0003, Japan
Tel.: (81) 335933301
Web Site: https://www.smbcls.jp
Educational Support Services
N.A.I.C.S.: 611710

Subsidiary (US):

SMBC Leasing & Finance, Inc. (2)
277 Park Ave 5th Fl, New York, NY 10172
Tel.: (212) 224-5200
Web Site: http://www.smbcgroup.com
Sales Range: $50-74.9 Million
Emp.: 16
Leasing & Sales Financing Services
N.A.I.C.S.: 532420

Subsidiary (Domestic):

SMBC Loan Business Service Co., Ltd. (2)

1-21-2 Nihombashi Sakuraedobashi Bldg, Chuo-Ku, Tokyo, 103-0027, Japan
Tel.: (81) 332725525
Commercial Banking Services
N.A.I.C.S.: 522110

SMBC Loan Servicer Co., Ltd. (2)
16-9 Tsukiji 3-chome, Chuo-ku, Tokyo, Japan
Tel.: (81) 33546310
Loan Management & Collection Services
N.A.I.C.S.: 522390

SMBC Market Service Co., Ltd. (2)
13-6 Nihombashikodemmacho, Chuo-ku, Tokyo, 103-0001, Japan
Tel.: (81) 356406600
Web Site: http://www.smbc.co.jp
Commercial Banking Services
N.A.I.C.S.: 522110

Subsidiary (Non-US):

SMBC Metro Investment Corp. (2)
6th Floor Unit 600 Rufino Building, 6784 Ayala Avenue cor V A Rufino Street Legaspi Village, Makati, 1230, Philippines (100%)
Tel.: (63) 288110845
Web Site: http://www.smbc.co.jp
Sales Range: $50-74.9 Million
Emp.: 9
Financial Services
N.A.I.C.S.: 522299

SMBC Nikko Capital Markets Limited (2)
100 Liverpool Street, London, EC2M 2AT, United Kingdom
Tel.: (44) 2077861400
Web Site: https://www.smbcgroup.com
Investment Management Service
N.A.I.C.S.: 523999

Subsidiary (Domestic):

SMBC Nikko Securities Inc. (2)
3-1 Marunouchi 3-chome, Chiyoda-ku, Tokyo, 100-8325, Japan (100%)
Tel.: (81) 356443111
Web Site: http://www.smbcnikko.co.jp
Rev.: $3,437,590,640
Assets: $136,895,227,920
Liabilities: $127,725,112,240
Net Worth: $9,170,115,680
Earnings: $482,044,640
Emp.: 9,255
Fiscal Year-end: 03/31/2022
Investment Banking & Securities Trading Services
N.A.I.C.S.: 523150
Hiroaki Toyoda *(Sr Mng Exec Officer)*

Subsidiary (Domestic):

Nikko Systems Solutions, Ltd. (3)
12-1 Daitocho, Tsurumi-ku, Yokohama, 230-0032, Kanagawa, Japan
Tel.: (81) 455068811
Web Site: https://www.nksol.co.jp
Sales Range: $200-249.9 Million
Emp.: 485
Financial & Securities Technology Services
N.A.I.C.S.: 541512

Branch (US):

Nikko Systems Solutions (4)
1875 S Grant St Ste 560, San Mateo, CA 94402-7022
Tel.: (650) 345-1900
Web Site: http://www.nksol.com
Sales Range: $10-24.9 Million
Emp.: 2
Financial Technology Systems Services
N.A.I.C.S.: 541512

Subsidiary (US):

SMBC Nikko Securities America, Inc. (3)
277 Park Ave, New York, NY 10172-0003
Tel.: (212) 224-5300
Securities Brokerage Services
N.A.I.C.S.: 523150
Michael Baisley *(Co-Head-Mergers & Acq)*

Subsidiary (Domestic):

SMBC PERSONNEL SUPPORT CO., LTD. (2)
1-1-2 Marunouchi, Chiyoda-Ku, Tokyo, 100-

0005, Japan
Tel.: (81) 343335285
Web Site: http://www.smbc.co.jp
Investment Banking Services
N.A.I.C.S.: 523150

Subsidiary (US):

SMBC Securities, Inc. (2)
277 Park Ave 5th Fl, New York, NY 10172 (100%)
Tel.: (212) 224-5300
Securities Dealing & Brokerage Services
N.A.I.C.S.: 523150

Subsidiary (Domestic):

SMBC Servicer Co., Ltd. (2)
3-16-9 Tsukiji Muromachitsukiji Bldg, Chuo-Ku, Tokyo, 104-0045, Japan
Tel.: (81) 335446003
Financial Management Services
N.A.I.C.S.: 523999

SMBC Staff Service Co., Ltd. (2)
6F Kanda Muromachi Building 1-1 Kanda Ogawamachi, Chiyoda-ku, Tokyo, 101-0052, Japan
Tel.: (81) 352813211
Web Site: https://www.smbc-staff.com
Emp.: 160
Temporary Staffing Services
N.A.I.C.S.: 561320

SMBC Venture Capital Co., Ltd. (2)
Sumitomo Mitsui Banking Gofukubashi Building 1-3-4 Yaesu, Chuo-ku, Tokyo, 103-0028, Japan
Tel.: (81) 362621190
Web Site: https://www.smbc-vc.co.jp
Emp.: 82
Investment Management Service
N.A.I.C.S.: 523999

SMM Auto Finance, Inc. (2)
3-3-23 Nakanoshima Dai Building 21st floor Nakanoshima Dai Building, Kita-ku, Osaka, 530-6121, Japan (56%)
Tel.: (81) 677390590
Web Site: https://www.mazdacr.co.jp
Sales Range: $200-249.9 Million
Emp.: 186
Automobile Sales Financing Services
N.A.I.C.S.: 522220

Sakura Card Co., Ltd. (2)
8-12 Nihombashi-Horidomecho 1-chome, Chuo-ku, Tokyo, Japan
Tel.: (81) 336633331
Web Site: http://www.sakura-card.co.jp
Sales Range: $100-124.9 Million
Emp.: 163
Credit Card Products & Services
N.A.I.C.S.: 522390

Sakura KCS Corporation (2)
21-1 Harimacho, Chuo-ku, Kobe, 650-0036, Japan (50.22%)
Tel.: (81) 783916571
Web Site: https://www.kcs.co.jp
Rev.: $150,503,090
Assets: $160,199,960
Liabilities: $33,420,160
Net Worth: $126,779,800
Earnings: $5,915,950
Emp.: 63
Fiscal Year-end: 03/31/2024
Information Technology Services & Product Whslr
N.A.I.C.S.: 541512
Takanori Kato *(Pres & CEO)*

Joint Venture (Domestic):

Sakura Information Systems Co., Ltd. (3)
1-17-3 NBF Platinum Tower Shirokane, Minato-ku, Tokyo, 108-8650, Japan
Tel.: (81) 367577200
Web Site: https://www.sakura-is.co.jp
Emp.: 1,170
Information Technology Network Construction, Support & Data Processing Services; Owned 51% by Osaka Gas Co., Ltd. & 49% by Sumitomo Mitsui Financial Group, Inc.
N.A.I.C.S.: 541512
Hiroaki Shigesada *(Pres & CEO)*

Subsidiary (Non-US):

Sumitomo Mitsui Banking Corporation (China) Limited (2)

AND PRIVATE COMPANIES SUMITOMO MITSUI FINANCIAL GROUP, INC.

11F Shanghai World Financial Center 100 Century Avenue, Pudong New Area, Shanghai, 200120, China **(100%)**
Tel.: (86) 2138609000
Web Site: http://www.smbc.co.jp
Emp.: 700
Commercial Banking Services
N.A.I.C.S.: 522110

Branch (Non-US):

Sumitomo Mitsui Banking Corporation - Bahrain (2)
No 406 & 407 Entrance 3 4th Fl Manama Ctr, Government Rd, Manama, 20483, Bahrain
Tel.: (973) 17223211
Web Site: http://www.smbcgroup.com
Commercial Banking Services
N.A.I.C.S.: 522110

Sumitomo Mitsui Banking Corporation - Bangkok (2)
8th-10th Floor Q House Lumpini Building 1 South Sathorn Road, Tungmahamek Sathorn, Bangkok, 10120, Thailand **(100%)**
Tel.: (66) 23538000
Web Site: http://www.smbc.co.jp
Sales Range: $200-249.9 Million
Emp.: 260
Commercial Banking Services
N.A.I.C.S.: 522110

Sumitomo Mitsui Banking Corporation - Dusseldorf (2)
Prinzenallee 7, 40549, Dusseldorf, Germany
Tel.: (49) 21136190
Sales Range: $50-74.9 Million
Emp.: 50
Commercial Banking Services
N.A.I.C.S.: 522110

Sumitomo Mitsui Banking Corporation - Hong Kong (2)
8/F One International Finance Centre 1 Harbour View Street, Central, China (Hong Kong)
Tel.: (852) 22062000
Web Site: http://www.smbc.co.jp
Sales Range: $200-249.9 Million
Emp.: 300
Commercial Banking Services
N.A.I.C.S.: 522110

Subsidiary (Non-US):

Sumitomo Mitsui Banking Corporation Europe Limited (2)
100 Liverpool Street, London, EC2M 2AT, United Kingdom **(100%)**
Tel.: (44) 2077861000
Sales Range: $400-449.9 Million
Emp.: 900
Commercial Banking Services
N.A.I.C.S.: 522110

Sumitomo Mitsui Banking Corporation of Canada (2) **(100%)**
Tel.: (416) 368-4766
Sales Range: $50-74.9 Million
Emp.: 35
Commercial Banking Services
N.A.I.C.S.: 522110

Joint Venture (Domestic):

Sumitomo Mitsui DS Asset Management Company, Limited (2)
Toranomon Hills Business Tower 26F 1-17-1 Toranomon, Minato-ku, Tokyo, 105-6426, Japan
Tel.: (81) 36 205 0200
Web Site: https://www.smd-am.co.jp
Emp.: 1,009
Financial Advisory Services
N.A.I.C.S.: 523940
Takashi Saruta (Pres & CEO)

Subsidiary (Non-US):

Sumitomo Mitsui Finance Australia Limited (2)
Level 35 The Chifley Tower 2 Chifley Square, Sydney, 2000, NSW, Australia **(100%)**
Tel.: (61) 293761800

Sales Range: $25-49.9 Million
Emp.: 80
Banking & Financial Services
N.A.I.C.S.: 522299

Subsidiary (Domestic):

The Japan Net Bank, Limited (2)
6 Fl Shinjuku-Mitsui Building 1-1 Nishi-Shinjuku 2-chome, Tokyo, Japan **(59.7%)**
Tel.: (81) 3 3344 5210
Web Site: http://www.japannetbank.co.jp
Online Banking Services
N.A.I.C.S.: 522180
Ikeda Kojiro (Exec VP-HR & Risk Mgmt Dept & Gen Mgr)

Subsidiary (Non-US):

ZAO Sumitomo Mitsui Rus Bank (2)
Presnenskaya Naberezhnaya House 10 Block C, 123112, Moscow, Russia
Tel.: (7) 4952878200
Web Site: http://www.smbc.co.jp
Emp.: 75
Commercial Banking Services
N.A.I.C.S.: 522110
Takaaki Ando (Pres)

Sumitomo Mitsui Finance & Leasing Co., Ltd. (1)
1-3-2 Marunouchi, Chiyoda-ku, Tokyo, 100-8287, Japan **(50%)**
Tel.: (81) 352196400
Web Site: http://www.smfl.co.jp
Commercial Office Equipment Finance & Leasing Services
N.A.I.C.S.: 532420

Subsidiary (Non-US):

PT. SMFL Leasing Indonesia (2)
Menara BTPN 31st Floor Jl Dr Ide Anak Agung Gde Agung Kav 5 5-5 6, Mega Kuningan, Jakarta Selatan, 12950, Indonesia
Tel.: (62) 2180628710
Web Site: http://www.smfl.co.jp
Emp.: 48
Commercial Office Equipment Finance & Leasing Services
N.A.I.C.S.: 532420

SMBC Aviation Capital Limited (2)
IFSC House, IFSC, Dublin, 1, Ireland
Tel.: (353) 1 859 9000
Web Site: https://www.smbc.aero
Sales Range: $50-74.9 Million
Emp.: 90
Commercial Aircraft Acquisition & Leasing Services
N.A.I.C.S.: 532411
Peter Barrett (CEO)

SMFL Leasing (Malaysia) Sdn. Bhd. (2)
Suite 16D Level 16 Vista Tower The Intermark No 348, Jalan Tun Razak, 50400, Kuala Lumpur, Malaysia
Tel.: (60) 327100170
Web Site: http://www.smfl.co.jp
Commercial Office Equipment Finance & Leasing Services
N.A.I.C.S.: 532420

SMFL Leasing (Thailand) Co., Ltd. (2)
30th Floor Q House Lumpini Building 1 South Sathorn Road, Tungmahamek Sathorn, Bangkok, 10120, Thailand
Tel.: (66) 26777400
Sales Range: $50-74.9 Million
Emp.: 60
Commercial Office Equipment Finance & Leasing Services
N.A.I.C.S.: 532420

Subsidiary (Domestic):

SMFL MIRAI Partners Co., Ltd (2)
1-5-1 Otemachi, Chiyoda-ku, Tokyo, 100-0004, Japan
Tel.: (81) 3 6695 8320
Web Site: http://www.smfl-mp.co.jp
Emp.: 118
Investment Services
N.A.I.C.S.: 523999
Tatsurou Terada (Pres)

Subsidiary (Domestic):

SMFL MIRAI Partners Investment 2 Co., Ltd. (3)

5-1 Otemachi-chome, Chiyoda-ku, Tokyo, 100-0004, Japan
Tel.: (81) 366958320
Holding Company
N.A.I.C.S.: 551112
Hiroyasu Komiya (Dir)

Subsidiary (Domestic):

Kenedix, Inc. (4)
Hibiya Parkfront 2-1-6 Uchisaiwaicho, Chiyoda-ku, Tokyo, 100-0011, Japan **(70%)**
Tel.: (81) 351576100
Web Site: http://www.kenedix.com
Rev.: $644,889,420
Assets: $1,576,524,740
Liabilities: $662,560,010
Net Worth: $913,964,730
Earnings: $97,871,410
Emp.: 339
Fiscal Year-end: 12/31/2019
Real Estate Investment Advisory, Acquisition, Brokerage, Real Estate Consulting & Asset Management
N.A.I.C.S.: 531210
Soushi Ikeda (Mng Dir & Head-Strategic Investment Dept)

Subsidiary (Domestic):

CRES Co., Ltd. (5)
Hiei Kudankita Building 2nd floor 4-1-3 Kudankita, Chiyoda-ku, Tokyo, 102-0073, Japan
Tel.: (81) 332228011
Web Site: https://www.cres-c.com
Real Estate Manangement Services
N.A.I.C.S.: 531312

Kenedix Advisors Co., Ltd (5)
2-2-9 Shimbashi, Tokyo, 105-0004, Minato-ku, Japan
Tel.: (81) 335194056
Web Site: http://www.kenedix.com
Sales Range: $50-74.9 Million
Emp.: 30
Financial Advisors
N.A.I.C.S.: 523999

Subsidiary (Non-US):

Sumitomo Mitsui Auto Leasing & Service (Thailand) Co., Ltd. (2)
87/2 CRC Tower All Seasons Place 41st Floor Wireless Road, Pathumwan, Bangkok, 10330, Thailand
Tel.: (66) 22529511
Web Site: https://www.smauto.co.th
Automobile Finance Leasing Services
N.A.I.C.S.: 522220

Sumitomo Mitsui Finance & Leasing (China) Co., Ltd. (2)
Unit 2302 TaiKoo Hui Tower 1385 Tianhe Road, 385 Tianhe Rd, Guangzhou, 510620, China
Tel.: (86) 2087550021
Sales Range: $50-74.9 Million
Emp.: 50
Commercial Office Equipment Finance & Leasing Services
N.A.I.C.S.: 532420

Branch (Domestic):

Sumitomo Mitsui Finance & Leasing (China) Co., Ltd. - Shanghai Branch (3)
10F Pingan Riverfront Financial Center 757 Mengzi Road, Huangpu District, Shanghai, China
Tel.: (86) 2153965522
Commercial Office Equipment Finance & Leasing Services
N.A.I.C.S.: 532420

Subsidiary (Non-US):

Sumitomo Mitsui Finance & Leasing (Hong Kong) Ltd. (2)
Units 4206-8 42/F Dah Sing Financial Centre 248 Queen's Road East, 18 Harcourt Road, Hong Kong, China (Hong Kong)
Tel.: (852) 25232280
Sales Range: $50-74.9 Million
Emp.: 30
Commercial Office Equipment Finance & Leasing Services
N.A.I.C.S.: 532420

Sumitomo Mitsui Finance & Leasing (Singapore) Pte. Ltd. (2)
152 Beach Road 05-06/08 Gateway East, Singapore, 189721, Singapore
Tel.: (65) 62242955
Web Site: http://www.smfl.co.jp
Sales Range: $50-74.9 Million
Emp.: 10
Commercial Office Equipment Finance & Leasing Services
N.A.I.C.S.: 532420

TT International (1)
62 Threadneedle Street, London, EC2R 8HP, United Kingdom
Tel.: (44) 2075091000
Web Site: https://www.ttint.com
Sales Range: $75-99.9 Million
Emp.: 110
Investment Management Service
N.A.I.C.S.: 523999
Dean Smith (Head-Intl & Emerging Markets Equities)

Subsidiary (Non-US):

TT International (Hong Kong) Limited (2)
20/F 18 On Lan Street, Central, China (Hong Kong)
Tel.: (852) 34766200
Investment Advisory Services
N.A.I.C.S.: 523940

Subsidiary (US):

TT International Advisors Inc. (2)
400 Madison Ave Ste 14 C, New York, NY 10017
Tel.: (917) 814-2590
Investment Advisory Services
N.A.I.C.S.: 523940

The Japan Research Institute, Limited (1)
2-18-1 Higashi-Gotanda, Tokyo, 141-0022, Japan
Tel.: (81) 368330900
Web Site: http://www.jri.co.jp
Sales Range: $450-499.9 Million
Emp.: 2,962
Economic Research, Data Processing, System Development & Management Consulting Services
N.A.I.C.S.: 541720

Subsidiary (US):

JRI America, Inc. (2)
277 Park Ave, New York, NY 10172
Tel.: (212) 224-4200
Web Site: https://www.jri-america.com
Business Application Software Development Services
N.A.I.C.S.: 541511

Subsidiary (Non-US):

JRI Europe, Limited (2)
100 Liverpool Street, London, EC2M 2AT, United Kingdom
Tel.: (44) 2045071000
Web Site: https://www.jri.co.jp
Sales Range: $25-49.9 Million
Emp.: 50
Software Development Services
N.A.I.C.S.: 541511
Tomoyuki Kawanaka (Pres)

Joint Venture (Domestic):

JSOL Corporation (2)
Harumi Center Bldg 2-5-24 Harumi, Chuo-ku, Tokyo, 104-0053, Japan
Tel.: (81) 358596001
Web Site: http://www.jsol.co.jp
Sales Range: $400-449.9 Million
Emp.: 1,300
Information Technology Consulting & Management Services; Owned 50% by Nippon Telegraph & Telephone Corporation & 50% by Sumitomo Mitsui Financial Group, Inc.
N.A.I.C.S.: 541690
Masatoshi Maekawa (Pres & CEO)

Subsidiary (Non-US):

The Japan Research Institute (Shanghai) Consulting Co., Ltd. (2)
18F HSBC Tower 1000 Lujiazui Ring Road,

SUMITOMO MITSUI FINANCIAL GROUP, INC.

Sumitomo Mitsui Financial Group, Inc.—(Continued)
Pudong New Area, Shanghai, 200120, China
Tel.: (86) 21 6841 1288
Web Site: http://www.jris.com.cn
Business Management Consulting Services
N.A.I.C.S.: 541611

The Japan Research Institute (Shanghai) Solution Co., Ltd. (2)
Unit T40 17F SWFC 100 Century Avenue, Pudong New Area, Shanghai, 200120, China
Tel.: (86) 2168412788
Web Site: https://www.jri.co.jp
Communication System Research Services
N.A.I.C.S.: 541715

SUMITOMO MITSUI TRUST HOLDINGS, INC.
1-4-1 Marunouchi, Chiyoda-ku, Tokyo, 100-8233, Japan
Tel.: (81) 362566000 JP
Web Site: https://www.smth.jp
Year Founded: 2002
CMTDF—(OTCIQ)
Rev.: $16,361,752,830
Assets: $501,546,342,050
Liabilities: $480,806,237,590
Net Worth: $20,740,104,460
Earnings: $363,550
Emp.: 13,181
Fiscal Year-end: 03/31/24
Bank Holding Company
N.A.I.C.S.: 551111
Masaru Hashimoto (Exec Officer)

Subsidiaries:

ASAHI KAGAKU KOGYO CO.,LTD. (1)
133-3 Hiromi Jogairi-cho, Anjo, 444-1205, Japan
Tel.: (81) 566924181
Web Site: https://www.asahikagakukogyo.co.jp
Rev.: $51,874,800
Assets: $43,253,880
Liabilities: $8,832,400
Net Worth: $34,421,480
Earnings: $578,460
Fiscal Year-end: 08/31/2024
Plastics Product Mfr
N.A.I.C.S.: 326199
Takeshi Sugiura (Pres)

Nikko Asset Management Co., Ltd. (1)
Midtown Tower 9-7-1, Akasaka Minato-ku, Tokyo, 107-6242, Japan
Tel.: (81) 36 447 6000
Web Site: https://www.nikkoam.com
Sales Range: $150-199.9 Billion
Emp.: 250
Asset & Open-End Investment Fund Management Services
N.A.I.C.S.: 523940
Yu-Ming Wang (Deputy Pres, CIO-Intl & Head-Investment-Global)

Subsidiary (US):

Nikko Asset Management Americas, Inc. (2)
605 3rd Ave 38th Fl, New York, NY 10158
Tel.: (212) 610-6100
Web Site: https://americas.nikkoam.com
Sales Range: $1-4.9 Billion
Emp.: 32
Asset & Open-End Investment Fund Management Services
N.A.I.C.S.: 525910
Fred DeSerio (Sr Mng Dir & Head-Sales)

Subsidiary (Non-US):

Nikko Asset Management Asia Limited (2)
12 Marina View 18-02 Asia Square Tower 2, Singapore, 018961, Singapore (100%)
Tel.: (65) 6 500 5700
Web Site: https://www.nikkoam.com.sg
Sales Range: $50-74.9 Million
Emp.: 100
Investment Management Service
N.A.I.C.S.: 523940

Eleanor Seet (Pres)

Nikko Asset Management Europe Ltd. (2)
Level 5 City Tower 40 Basinghall Street, London, EC2V 5DE, United Kingdom
Tel.: (44) 207 796 9866
Web Site: https://emea.nikkoam.com
Asset & Open-End Investment Fund Management Services
N.A.I.C.S.: 523940
John Howland-Jackson (CEO)

Tyndall Investment Management Limited (2)
L 10 321 Kent Street, Sydney, NSW, Australia (100%)
Tel.: (61) 282753000
Web Site: http://www.tyndall.com.au
Sales Range: $15-24.9 Million
Investment Management & Advice
N.A.I.C.S.: 523940
Andrew Julius (Head-Retail)

Subsidiary (Domestic):

Tasman Asset Management Limited (3)
GPO Box 3881, Sydney, 2001, NSW, Australia
Tel.: (61) 280726300
Web Site: http://www.tyndall.com.au
Asset Management
N.A.I.C.S.: 523999
Robert Van Munster (Head-Equities)

Sumitomo Mitsui Trust Bank, Limited (1)
1-4-1 Marunouchi, Chiyoda-ku, Tokyo, 100-8233, Japan (100%)
Tel.: (81) 36 256 3449
Web Site: https://www.smtb.jp
Sales Range: $1-4.9 Billion
Emp.: 13,469
Trust & Banking Services
N.A.I.C.S.: 522110
Kunitaro Kitamura (Co-Chm)

Joint Venture (Domestic):

SBI Sumishin Net Bank, Ltd. (2)
Sumitomo Fudosan Roppongi Grand Tower 2-1 Roppongi 3-chome, Minato-ku, Tokyo, Japan (50%)
Tel.: (81) 353637381
Web Site: http://www.netbk.co.jp
Rev.: $783,429,138
Assets: $70,541,235,547
Liabilities: $69,539,530,889
Net Worth: $1,001,704,658
Earnings: $164,155,930
Fiscal Year-end: 03/31/2024
Internet Banking
N.A.I.C.S.: 522110

Subsidiary (Domestic):

NetMove Corporation (3)
KDC Shibuya Bldg 5F 3-9-10 Shibuya, Shibuya-ku, Tokyo, 150-0002, Japan
Tel.: (81) 357667835
Web Site: http://www.netmove.co.jp
Sales Range: $25-49.9 Million
Emp.: 30
Corporate Website Communication & Support Services
N.A.I.C.S.: 541519

Subsidiary (Non-US):

Sumitomo Mitsui Trust (Hong Kong) Limited (2)
25/F AIA Central 1 Connaught Road, Central, China (Hong Kong) (100%)
Tel.: (852) 2 801 8800
Web Site: http://www.smtb.jp
Sales Range: $25-49.9 Million
Emp.: 40
Commericial Banking
N.A.I.C.S.: 522110

Sumitomo Mitsui Trust (Ireland) Limited (2)
Block 5 Harcourt Centre Harcourt Road, Dublin, 2, Ireland
Tel.: (353) 1 603 9900
Web Site: http://www.sumitrustgas.com
Emp.: 150
Holding Company; Trust & Fund Management Services

N.A.I.C.S.: 551112

Subsidiary (Domestic):

SMT Fund Services (Ireland) Limited (3)
Block 5 Harcourt Centre Harcourt Road, D02 DR5, Dublin, Ireland
Tel.: (353) 1 603 9900
Sales Range: $350-399.9 Million
Fund Management Services
N.A.I.C.S.: 523940

SMT Trustees (Ireland) Limited (3)
Block 5 Harcourt Centre Harcourt Road, Dublin, 1002, Ireland
Tel.: (353) 1 603 9900
Web Site: http://www.sumitrustgas.com
Sales Range: $50-74.9 Million
Emp.: 11
Trust Management Services
N.A.I.C.S.: 523991

Subsidiary (Non-US):

Sumitomo Mitsui Trust (UK) Limited (2)
3rd Floor 17 Dominion Street, London, EC2M 2EF, United Kingdom (100%)
Tel.: (44) 20 7826 4200
Sales Range: $25-49.9 Million
Emp.: 32
Global Asset & Treasury Services
N.A.I.C.S.: 522299

Sumitomo Mitsui Trust Bank (Luxembourg) S.A. (2)
2 r Peternelchen, PO Box 882, Howald, 2370, Luxembourg (100%)
Tel.: (352) 4779851
Sales Range: $50-74.9 Million
Emp.: 21
International Banking
N.A.I.C.S.: 522110
Natsuhiko Okumura (Mng Dir)

Representative Office (Non-US):

Sumitomo Mitsui Trust Bank, Ltd. - Singapore Branch (2)
One Raffles Quay 24-01 North Tower, Singapore, 048583, Singapore
Tel.: (65) 6 224 9055
Web Site: https://www.smtb.jp
Sales Range: $50-74.9 Million
Emp.: 145
Commercial Bank
N.A.I.C.S.: 522110
Tetsuaya Yamawaki (CEO)

Representative Office (US):

Sumitomo Mitsui Trust Bank, Ltd. - USA Branch (2)
1251 Avenue of the Americas, New York, NY 10020
Tel.: (212) 326-0600
Web Site: https://www.smtb.jp
Sales Range: $75-99.9 Million
Emp.: 150
Banking Services
N.A.I.C.S.: 522110
Keiji Tanaka (Exec Gen Mgr)

Subsidiary (Domestic):

Sumitomo Mitsui Trust Club Co., Ltd. (2)
Triton Square X Building 1-8-10 Harumi, Chuo-ku, Tokyo, 104-6035, Japan
Tel.: (81) 36 770 2800
Web Site: https://www.sumitclub.jp
Credit Card Issuing & Services
N.A.I.C.S.: 522210
Koji Nohara (Pres, CEO & Mgr)

Subsidiary (Non-US):

Sumitomo Mitsui Trust International Limited (2)
155 Bishopsgate, London, EC2M 3XU, United Kingdom (100%)
Tel.: (44) 207 562 8400
Web Site: https://uk.sumitrust-am.com
Investment Management Service
N.A.I.C.S.: 523940
Akimichi Oi (Head)

SUMITOMO OSAKA CEMENT CO LTD

INTERNATIONAL PUBLIC

20th floor Shiodome Sumitomo Building 1-9-2, Chiyoda-Ward, Tokyo, 105-8641, Japan
Tel.: (81) 363702700
Web Site: https://www.soc.co.jp
Year Founded: 1907
5232—(TKS)
Rev.: $1,470,738,220
Assets: $2,355,030,630
Liabilities: $1,054,347,880
Net Worth: $1,300,682,750
Earnings: $101,390,790
Emp.: 2,886
Fiscal Year-end: 03/31/24
Cement & Construction Materials Mfr
N.A.I.C.S.: 327332
Fukuichi Sekine (Chm)

Subsidiaries:

CLICON Co., Ltd. (1)
961 Toendo, Aisho-cho Aichi-gun, Shiga, 529-1383, Japan
Tel.: (81) 749423111
Web Site: https://kuricon-soc.co.jp
Emp.: 60
Cement Product Mfr
N.A.I.C.S.: 327310

Cap Co., Ltd. (1)
3415-42 Shinyoshidacho, Kohoku-ku, Yokohama, 223-0056, Kanagawa, Japan
Tel.: (81) 455951701
Web Site: https://www.cap-co.jp
Sales Range: $25-49.9 Million
Emp.: 22
Mold Mfr
N.A.I.C.S.: 331511

Chiyoda Engineering Co., Ltd. (1)
2-3-12 Shiba-daimon, Minato-ku, Tokyo, 105-0012, Japan
Tel.: (81) 334322621
Sales Range: $25-49.9 Million
Emp.: 85
Electric Smelting Furnace & Industrial Furnace Mfr
N.A.I.C.S.: 333994
Takeo Matsuura (Pres)

Chuken Consultant Co., Ltd. (1)
7-1-55 Minamiokajima, Taisho-ku, Osaka, 551-0021, Japan
Tel.: (81) 665562380
Web Site: http://www.chuken.co.jp
Sales Range: Less than $1 Million
Emp.: 120
Concrete Materials Research & Consulting Services
N.A.I.C.S.: 541618
Okamoto Hideaki (Pres)

Hachinohe Cement Co., Ltd. (1)
7 1 Shimotakamachiba, Niida, Hachinohe, 031 0813, Aomori, Japan
Tel.: (81) 178330111
Cement Mfr
N.A.I.C.S.: 327310

Izumi Industry Co., Ltd. (1)
715 Tsuiji-cho, Sano, 327-0502, Tochigi, Japan
Tel.: (81) 283862225
Web Site: https://www.izumi-kougyo.co.jp
Recycling Services
N.A.I.C.S.: 562920

Izumi Transport Co., Ltd. (1)
2 26-10 Kameido Tachibana Kameido Building 2nd floor, Koto-ku, Tokyo, Japan
Web Site: http://izumi-unyu.jp
Emp.: 90
Transportation Services
N.A.I.C.S.: 484110

Kitaura SOC Co., Ltd. (1)
3rd floor Namba Smithou Building 1-4-19 Minamihorie, Nishi-ku, Osaka, 550-0015, Japan
Tel.: (81) 665362660
Web Site: https://kitaurasoc.co.jp
Construction Materials Whslr
N.A.I.C.S.: 423320

Kurimoto Concrete Industry Co., Ltd. (1)
961 Toendo Aisyo cho, Echi-gun, Shiga, 529-1383, Japan

Tel.: (81) 749423111
Web Site: https://kuricon-soc.co.jp
Emp.: 60
Concrete Pipe Mfr
N.A.I.C.S.: 327332

SEO Engineering Co., Ltd. (1)
7-1-55 Minami-okajima, Taisho-Ward, Osaka, 551-0021, Japan
Tel.: (81) 665562020
Cement & Reinforcement Materials Mfr
N.A.I.C.S.: 327310

SNC Co., Ltd. (1)
90 Shime Shime-cho, Kasuya-gun, Fukuoka, 811-2202, Japan
Tel.: (81) 929351382
Web Site: https://www.snc-inc.co.jp
Concrete Product Mfr & Whslr
N.A.I.C.S.: 327320

SOC Kenzai Co., Ltd. (1)
Naniwa Bldg Higashi Kan 7f 4 12, Banzaicho Kita Ku, Osaka, Japan
Tel.: (81) 663157051
Construction Materials Mfr
N.A.I.C.S.: 423320

SOC Logistics Co., Ltd. (1)
3-4 Kanda Surugadai Ryumeikan Main Store Building 10F, Chiyoda-ku, Tokyo, 101-0062, Japan
Tel.: (81) 352982311
Web Site: http://www.soc-logistics.jp
Emp.: 25
Transportation Services
N.A.I.C.S.: 484110

SOC Marine Co., Ltd. (1)
10th floor Ryumeikan Main Store Building 3-4 Kanda Surugadai, Chiyoda-ku, Tokyo, 101-0062, Japan
Tel.: (81) 352982315
Web Site: https://www.soc-marine.jp
Emp.: 180
Ship Rental Services
N.A.I.C.S.: 532284

Shiga Mining Co., Ltd. (1)
200 Harusho, Maibara, 521-0314, Shiga, Japan
Tel.: (81) 749581218
Web Site: https://shigakosan.jp
Emp.: 41
Limestone Mining Services
N.A.I.C.S.: 212312

Sumise Kenzai Co., Ltd. (1)
2 2 23 Koraku Sumitomo Realty Development Iidabashi Building 11 Floor, Bunkyo Ward, Tokyo, Japan
Tel.: (81) 358053601
Cement Whslr
N.A.I.C.S.: 423320

Sumitec Co., Ltd. (1)
369-3 Bansho, Noda, 278-0041, Chiba, Japan
Tel.: (81) 471296380
Web Site: https://www.sumitec.jp
Sales Range: $25-49.9 Million
Emp.: 60
Optoelectronics & Advanced Materials Mfr
N.A.I.C.S.: 334413

Sumitomo Cement Computer Systems Co., Ltd. (1)
3F Shiba NBF Tower 1-1-30 Shiba Daimon, Minato-ku, Tokyo, 105-0012, Japan
Tel.: (81) 364037860
Web Site: https://sumitem.co.jp
Emp.: 130
Ready Mix Concrete Mfr & Whslr
N.A.I.C.S.: 327320

Taiyo Kisen Co., Ltd. (1)
2-1-3 Dojimahama, Kita-ku, Osaka, 530-0004, Japan
Tel.: (81) 663463434
Web Site: http://www.taiyo-shipping.co.jp
Emp.: 5
Shipping Services
N.A.I.C.S.: 488510

Taiyo Shipping Co., Ltd. (1)
Yamayo Bldg 1 11 Dojima Hama 2 chome, Kita ku, Osaka, Japan
Tel.: (81) 663463434
Shipping Mfr
N.A.I.C.S.: 332439

Tokai Sumice Sales Co., Ltd. (1)
Sumitomoseimei Chikusa No 2 Bldg 4f, Aoi Higashi Ku, Fukuoka, 31531, Japan
Tel.: (81) 529305970
Construction Materials Whslr
N.A.I.C.S.: 423810

Tokai Sumise Sales Co., Ltd. (1)
5th floor Imaike General Building 5-24-32 Imaike, Chikusa-ku, Nagoya, 464-0850, Japan
Tel.: (81) 527455210
Web Site: https://www.t-sumise.jp
Emp.: 25
Construction Materials Whslr
N.A.I.C.S.: 423320

Tokyo SOC Co., Ltd. (1)
7F Higashimatsu Building 16-1 Hakozaki-cho Nihonbashi, Chuo-ku, Tokyo, 103-0015, Japan
Tel.: (81) 336688186
Web Site: https://tokyosoc.co.jp
Ready Mix Concrete Mfr & Whslr
N.A.I.C.S.: 327320

SUMITOMO REALTY & DEVELOPMENT CO., LTD.
Shinjuku NS Building 4-1 Nishi-Shinjuku 2-chome, Shinjuku-ku, Tokyo, 163-0820, Japan
Tel.: (81) 333461325
Web Site: https://english.sumitomo-rd.co.jp
Year Founded: 1949
SURDF—(OTCIQ)
Rev.: $6,739,118,850
Assets: $45,640,176,120
Liabilities: $32,738,678,880
Net Worth: $12,901,497,240
Earnings: $1,161,009,420
Emp.: 12,957
Fiscal Year-end: 03/31/23
Real Estate & Construction Services
N.A.I.C.S.: 531190
Kenichi Onodera (Chm)

Subsidiaries:

Sumitomo Fudosan Bellesalle Co., Ltd. (1)
2-6-1 Nishi-Shinjuku Shinjuku Sumitomo Building 33rd Floor, Shinjuku-ku, Tokyo, 163-0290, Japan
Tel.: (81) 33 346 1398
Web Site: https://www.bellesalle.co.jp
Emp.: 179
Conference & Meeting Hall Rental Services
N.A.I.C.S.: 531120

Sumitomo Fudosan Esforta Co., Ltd. (1)
2-6-1 Nishishinjuku Shinjukusumitomo Building, Shinjuku-ku, Tokyo, 160-0023, Japan
Tel.: (81) 353203460
Real Estate Manangement Services
N.A.I.C.S.: 531390

Sumitomo Fudosan Finance Co., Ltd. (1)
2-6-1 Nishishinjuku Shinjukusumitomo Building B1, Shinjuku-ku, Tokyo, 160-0023, Japan
Tel.: (81) 333461071
Financial Management Consulting Services
N.A.I.C.S.: 541611

Sumitomo Fudosan Reform Co., Ltd. (1)
2-6-1 Nishishinjuku Shinjuku Sumitomo Building 2nd Floor, Shinjuku-ku, Tokyo, 160-0023, Japan
Tel.: (81) 482402111
Home Renovation Services
N.A.I.C.S.: 236118

Sumitomo Fudosan Syscon Co., Ltd. (1)
2-6-1 Nishishinjuku Sumitomofudosan Building 33F, Shinjuku-ku, Tokyo, 160-0023, Japan
Tel.: (81) 333465311
Home Renovation Services
N.A.I.C.S.: 236118

Sumitomo Fudosan Tatemono Service Co., Ltd. (1)
7-22-12 Nishi-Shinjuku Izumi Hoshiichi Building, Shinjuku-ku, Tokyo, 160-0023, Japan
Tel.: (81) 33 363 3409
Web Site: https://www.sumitate.co.jp
Emp.: 3,487
Office Buildings & Luxury Condominiums Management Services
N.A.I.C.S.: 531120

Sumitomo Fudosan Villa Fontaine Co., Ltd. (1)
2-6-1 Nishishinjuku Shinjukuns Building Sumitomofudosannai, Shinjuku-ku, Tokyo, 160-0023, Japan
Tel.: (81) 333461736
Web Site: http://www.hvf.jp
Emp.: 300
Home Management Services
N.A.I.C.S.: 561110
Mari Miyoshi (Pres)

Sumitomo Real Estate Sales Co., Ltd. (1)
Sumitomo Fudosan Yaesu building 9F 4-1 Yaesu 2 chome, Chuo-ku, Tokyo, 104-0028, Japan
Tel.: (81) 33 548 8167
Web Site: https://global.sumitomo-res.com
Emp.: 3,642
Real Estate Brokerage, Rental & Leasing Services
N.A.I.C.S.: 531210
Shunji Onishi (Sr Mng Exec Officer)

Subsidiary (US):

Sumitomo Real Estate Sales (N.Y) Inc. (2)
800 2nd Ave Ste 300, New York, NY 10017
Tel.: (212) 596-0800
Web Site: http://www.sumitomo-ny.com
Sales Range: $25-49.9 Million
Emp.: 20
Real Estate & Brokerage Services
N.A.I.C.S.: 531210

SUMITOMO RIKO COMPANY LIMITED
1 Higashi 3-chome, Komaki, 485-8550, Aichi, Japan
Tel.: (81) 568772121
Web Site: https://www.sumitomoriko.co.jp
Year Founded: 1929
5191—(TKS)
Rev.: $4,068,117,890
Assets: $2,920,060,040
Liabilities: $1,449,619,270
Net Worth: $1,470,440,770
Earnings: $123,217,010
Emp.: 25,692
Fiscal Year-end: 03/31/24
Motor Vehicle Component Mfr
N.A.I.C.S.: 326291
Tetsu Matsui (Chm)

Subsidiaries:

Anvis Group GmbH (1)
Karl-Winnacker-Str 22a, D 36396, Steinau an der Strasse, Germany
Tel.: (49) 6663 9128 0
Web Site: http://www.anvisgroup.com
Sales Range: $400-449.9 Million
Emp.: 2,000
Automotive Anti-Vibration Products Mfr
N.A.I.C.S.: 336390
Olaf Hahn (Mng Dir)

Subsidiary (Non-US):

Anvis (Wuxi) Rubber Anti-Vibration Co., Ltd. (2)
No 2 Lingjiang Road, New Development Zone, Wuxi, 214028, Jiangsu, China
Tel.: (86) 5108 5217 088
Web Site: http://www.anvisgroup.com
Emp.: 412
Automotive Anti-Vibration Products Mfr
N.A.I.C.S.: 336390

Anvis AVT s.r.o. (2)
Benatky 904, 75501, Vsetin, Czech Republic
Tel.: (420) 571428707
Web Site: http://www.anvisgroup.com
Emp.: 7
Administrative Services for Automotive Parts Mfr
N.A.I.C.S.: 561110

Plant (Domestic):

Anvis AVT s.r.o. (3)
Drnovice 146, 763 25, Ujezd, Czech Republic
Tel.: (420) 577 311411
Web Site: http://www.anvisgroup.com
Emp.: 314
Automotive Anti-Vibration Products Mfr
N.A.I.C.S.: 336390

Subsidiary (Non-US):

Anvis Automotive Spain S.A.U. (2)
Poligono Industrial, Las Casas Calle F, E 42005, Soria, Spain
Tel.: (34) 975233105
Web Site: http://www.anvisgroup.com
Emp.: 133
Automotive Anti-Vibration Products Mfr
N.A.I.C.S.: 336390

Subsidiary (Domestic):

Anvis Deutschland GmbH (2)
Karl-Winnacker-Strasse 22a, D 36396, Steinau an der Strasse, Germany
Tel.: (49) 666391280
Automotive Anti-Vibration Products Mfr
N.A.I.C.S.: 336390
Olaf Hahn (Mng Dir)

Subsidiary (Non-US):

Anvis France Decize S.A.S. (2)
Web Site: http://www.anvisgroup.com
Emp.: 327
Automotive Anti-Vibration Products Mfr
N.A.I.C.S.: 336390

Anvis France Epinal S.A.S. (2)
Route d'Archettes, F 88000, Epinal, France
Emp.: 114
Automotive Anti-Vibration Products Mfr
N.A.I.C.S.: 336390

Anvis Industry S.A.S. (2)
Usine des Caillots, B P 101, F 58302, Decize, France
Tel.: (33) 130974141
Web Site: http://www.anvisgroup.com
Emp.: 104
Automotive Anti-Vibration Products Mfr
N.A.I.C.S.: 336390

Anvis Rom SRL (2)
Park Industrial 11, 440186, Satu-Mare, Romania
Tel.: (40) 261706750
Web Site: http://www.anvisgroup.com
Emp.: 319
Automotive Anti-Vibration Products Mfr
N.A.I.C.S.: 336390
Popovici Florinn (Plant Mgr)

Anvis Rus (2)
1 Industrialnaya Street, Togliatti, 445035, Samara, Russia
Tel.: (7) 8482 5119 10
Web Site: http://www.anvisgroup.com
Emp.: 85
Automotive Anti-Vibration Products Mfr
N.A.I.C.S.: 336390

Anvis SD France S.A.S. (2)
Usine des Caillots, B P 101, F 58302, Decize, France
Tel.: (33) 3867 73232
Web Site: http://www.anvisgroup.com
Emp.: 63
Automotive Anti-Vibration Products Mfr
N.A.I.C.S.: 336390

Anvisgroup Mexico S.A.P.I. de C.V. (2)
Av de las Fuentes No 19 Parque Industrial Bernardo Quintana, El Marques, Queretaro, CP 76246, Mexico
Tel.: (52) 4421 019400
Web Site: http://www.anvisgroup.com
Emp.: 189

SUMITOMO RIKO COMPANY LIMITED

Sumitomo Riko Company Limited—(Continued)

Automotive Anti-Vibration Products Mfr
N.A.I.C.S.: 336390

Bel-Anvis Antivibration System (Pty) Ltd. (2)
130 Paterson Road, North End, Port Elizabeth, 6056, South Africa
Tel.: (27) 4148 45456
Web Site: http://www.anvisgroup.com
Emp.: 166
Automotive Anti-Vibration Products Mfr
N.A.I.C.S.: 336390
Clive Vanienseurg *(Plant Mgr)*

S-Riko Automotive Hose de Chihuahua, S.A.P.I. de C.V. (1)
Carretera A CD Juarez 19100 Esquina Con AV, Ishiwaka Parque Industrial Supra, 31183, Chihuahua, Mexico
Tel.: (52) 614 426 0240
Plastic Tubing Parts Mfr
N.A.I.C.S.: 326122

SumiRiko AVS Germany GmbH (1)
Karl-Winnacker-Strasse 19, 36396, Steinau an der Strasse, Germany
Tel.: (49) 66 639 1280
Web Site: https://avs.sumiriko.com
Anti-Vibration Rubber Mfr & Distr
N.A.I.C.S.: 326299

SumiRiko AVS RUS LLC (1)
337 Frunze str 14B, 445037, Togliatti, Samara, Russia
Tel.: (7) 8482556310
Anti-Vibration Rubber Mfr & Distr
N.A.I.C.S.: 326299

SumiRiko AVS Spain S.A.U. (1)
Poligono Industrial Las Casas Calle, 42005, Soria, Spain
Tel.: (34) 97 523 3105
Anti-Vibration Rubber Mfr & Distr
N.A.I.C.S.: 326299

SumiRiko Eastern Rubber (Thailand) Ltd. (1)
111/3 Moo 2 Soi Nikom 13 Rd T Makhamkoo A, Rayong, 21180, Nikompattana, Thailand
Tel.: (66) 3 891 8088
Web Site: https://www.er.sumiriko.com
Anti-Vibration Rubber Mfr & Distr
N.A.I.C.S.: 326299
Yuichi Ogawa *(Mng Dir)*

SumiRiko Rubber Compounding France S.A.S. (1)
ZI des Caillots, BP 101, 58302, Decize, Cedex, France
Tel.: (33) 38 677 3232
Web Site: https://srk-rcf.fr
Rubber Compound Mfr & Distr
N.A.I.C.S.: 326299

SumiRiko South Africa (Pty) Ltd. (1)
130 Paterson Road North End, Port Elizabeth, 6056, South Africa
Tel.: (27) 41 484 5312
Anti-Vibration Rubber Mfr & Distr
N.A.I.C.S.: 326299

SumiRiko Yamagata Company Limited (1)
3-4452-33 Hachimanpara, Yonezawa, 992-1128, Yamagata, Japan
Tel.: (81) 23 829 1460
Anti-Vibration Rubber Mfr
N.A.I.C.S.: 326299

Sumitomo Riko America, Inc. (1)
41441 11 Mile Rd, Novi, MI 48375
Tel.: (248) 946-4915
Electric Equipment Mfr
N.A.I.C.S.: 335311

Sumitomo Riko Hosetex, Ltd. (1)
1 Toyosaka Town, Ayabe, 623-0117, Kyoto, Japan
Tel.: (81) 77 340 5250
Web Site: https://ht.sumitomoriko.co.jp
Hydraulic Hoses Rubber Mfr & Distr
N.A.I.C.S.: 326220
H. Ninagawa *(Pres)*

TRI (Poland) Sp.zo.o. (1)
ul 1 Maja 100, 32 340, Wolbrom, Poland
Tel.: (48) 326472500
Motor Vehicle Component Mfr

N.A.I.C.S.: 326220

TRI Engineering, Ltd. (1)
3-1 Higashi, Komaki, 485-8550, Aichi, Japan
Tel.: (81) 568 75 4444
Web Site: http://www.trie.co.jp
Emp.: 35
Machine Tool & Cutting Tool Mfr
N.A.I.C.S.: 333517

TRI Hose Sales, Ltd. (1)
86 Wakakusacho, Komaki, 485-0031, Aichi, Japan
Tel.: (81) 568775544
Web Site: http://www.tri-hs.jp
Hydraulic Hose Mfr
N.A.I.C.S.: 326220

TRI Logitech, Ltd. (1)
Higashi 2-322 Aichi, Komaki, 485-0831, Japan
Tel.: (81) 568 77 2986
Web Site: http://www.tri-logitech.co.jp
Sales Range: $25-49.9 Million
Emp.: 50
Logistic Services
N.A.I.C.S.: 541614

TRI Metex, Ltd. (1)
3-1 Higashi, Komaki, 485-0831, Aichi, Japan
Tel.: (81) 568 77 3171
Web Site: http://www.tri-metex.com
Metal Products Mfr
N.A.I.C.S.: 332999

TRI Oita Advanced Elastomer, Ltd. (1)
Kanaedai 1 Bungotakada, Oita, 879-0603, Japan
Tel.: (81) 978 23 1111
Web Site: http://www.tri-oitaae.co.jp
Emp.: 420
Office Equipment Component Mfr
N.A.I.C.S.: 326291
Takehiro Ohashi *(Pres)*

TRI Techno, Ltd. (1)
3-1 Higashi, Komaki, 485-8550, Aichi, Japan
Tel.: (81) 568 77 0908
Web Site: http://www.tri-techno.co.jp
Technical Services
N.A.I.C.S.: 541330

TRI USA, Inc. (1)
320 Snider Rd, Bluffton, OH 45817
Tel.: (419) 358-2121
Emp.: 600
Motor Vehicle Component Mfr
N.A.I.C.S.: 326220
Jason Brandt *(Mgr-HR)*

Subsidiary (Domestic):

SumiRiko Ohio, Inc. (2)
320 Snider Rd, Bluffton, OH 45817
Tel.: (419) 358-2121
Web Site: http://www.dtroh.com
Emp.: 500
Motor Vehicle Component Mfr
N.A.I.C.S.: 326220

SumiRiko Tennessee, Inc. (2)
199 Pottertown Rd, Midway, TN 37809
Tel.: (423) 422-4454
Web Site: http://www.srk.com
Emp.: 900
Motor Vehicle Component Mfr
N.A.I.C.S.: 326220

TRI Technical Center USA, Inc. (2)
25825 Meadowbrook Rd, Novi, MI 48375
Tel.: (248) 374-6600
Sales Range: $25-49.9 Million
Emp.: 12
Motor Vehicle Component Testing & Analysis Services
N.A.I.C.S.: 541380

Tokai Chemical (Tianjin) Auto Parts Co., Ltd. (1)
No 6 Juying Road Jinnan Economic Development Area, Dist Jinnan, Tianjin, 300350, China
Tel.: (86) 2258790768
Web Site: https://en.tcttokai.com.cn
Motor Vehicle Component Mfr
N.A.I.C.S.: 326220

Tokai Chemical Industries, Ltd. (1)
Mitake 2192-30, Kanigun, Mitake, 505-0116, Gifu, Japan **(80%)**
Tel.: (81) 574672033
Web Site: https://www.tci.tokai.co.jp
Emp.: 743
Automotive Components Mfr
N.A.I.C.S.: 336360
Isao Mizukami *(Pres)*

Tokai Chemical Kyushu, Ltd. (1)
Kanaedai 1, Bungotakada, 879-0603, Oita, Japan
Tel.: (81) 97 823 1661
Automobile Inner Parts Mfr & Distr
N.A.I.C.S.: 336390

Tokai Dalian Hose Co., Ltd. (1)
No 25 Bay Road Pulandian Zone, Dalian, Liaoning, China
Tel.: (86) 41186591166
Motor Vehicle Component Mfr
N.A.I.C.S.: 326220

Tokai Eastern Rubber (Thailand) Co., Ltd. (1)
111/3 Moo 2 Soi Nikom 13 Road T Makhamkoo, Tambol Makhamkoo, 21180, Rayong, Thailand
Rubber Motor Vehicle Component Mfr
N.A.I.C.S.: 326220

Tokai Imperial Rubber India Private Limited (1)
45 Milestone VPO Prithla Delhi-Mathura Road, Palwal, 121 102, Haryana, India
Tel.: (91) 1275262102
Motor Vehicle Hose Mfr
N.A.I.C.S.: 326220

Tokai Rubber (Dongguan) Co., Ltd. (1)
No 4 Area 2 Jin He Industrial zone, Zhang mu tou, Dongguan, Guang dong, China
Tel.: (86) 76987195711
Rubber Component Mfr
N.A.I.C.S.: 326299

Tokai Rubber (Guangzhou) Co., Ltd. (1)
No 331 Xinan Road Yonghe Economic Zone GETDD, Guangzhou, Guang dong, China
Tel.: (86) 2032221291
Rubber Motor Vehicle Components Mfr
N.A.I.C.S.: 326220

Tokai Rubber (Jiaxing) Co., Ltd. (1)
No 500 Gangshan Road Economic Development Zone, Jiaxing, Zhejiang, China
Tel.: (86) 57382215569
Motor Vehicle Component Mfr
N.A.I.C.S.: 326291

Tokai Rubber (Tianjin) Co., Ltd. (1)
No 6 Juying Rd Jinnan Economic Development Area, Dist Jinnan, Tianjin, China
Tel.: (86) 2228512121
Motor Vehicle Component Mfr
N.A.I.C.S.: 326220

Tokai Rubber Auto-Parts India Private Ltd. (1)
Plot No 337 Harohalli Industrial Area Phase 2, Kanakapura, 562112, Karnataka, India
Tel.: (91) 80 3991 9900
Web Site: http://www.tri.com
Motor Vehicle Anti-Vibration Rubber Components Mfr
N.A.I.C.S.: 326291
Naoki Hayashi *(Mng Dir)*

Tokai Rubber Industries (H.K.) Ltd. (1)
Suite 1215-1216 12/F DELTA HOUSE 3 On Yiu Street, Shatin, Hong Kong, NT, China (Hong Kong)
Tel.: (852) 23149305
Rubber Component Mfr
N.A.I.C.S.: 326299
Motohiko Mizuno *(Gen Mgr)*

Tokai Rubber Moldings (Tianjin) Co., Ltd. (1)
No 6 Juying Rd Jinnan Economic Development Area, Dist Jinnan, Tianjin, China
Tel.: (86) 22 8851 8088
Rubber Motor Vehicle Components Mfr
N.A.I.C.S.: 326220
Kenichi Naka *(Gen Mgr)*

Tokai Rubber Technical Center (China) Co., Ltd. (1)
No 151 Baigongqiao Road Economic Development Zone, Jiaxing, 314001, Zhejiang, China
Tel.: (86) 573 8338 3770
Web Site: http://www.tokai.co.jp
Rubber Motor Vehicle Component Mfr
N.A.I.C.S.: 326220
Suzuki Tatsuya *(Gen Mgr)*

SUMITOMO RUBBER INDUSTRIES, LTD.

3-6-9 Wakinohama-cho, Chuo-ku, Kobe, 651-0072, Hyogo, Japan
Tel.: (81) 8007232553 JP
Web Site: https://www.srigroup.co.jp
Year Founded: 1909
5110—(TKS)
Rev: $8,347,758,910
Assets: $8,981,129,880
Liabilities: $4,433,391,180
Net Worth: $4,547,738,700
Earnings: $262,670,320
Emp.: 7,705
Fiscal Year-end: 12/31/23
Holding Company; Rubber Tire, Sporting Good & Other Rubber Products Mfr
N.A.I.C.S.: 551112
Ikuji Ikeda *(Chm)*

Subsidiaries:

Abbotsinch Tyres & Exhausts Ltd. (1)
17 James Little Street, Ayrshire, Kilmarnock, KA1 4AT, United Kingdom
Tel.: (44) 1563340172
Web Site: https://www.kilmarnock-tyresandservice.co.uk
Tyre Mfr & Distr
N.A.I.C.S.: 326211

Changshu Srixon Sports Co., Ltd. (1)
Room 301 Block AB 27 Fenglin Road Yushan street, Commercial Center of Changshu Economic Technology Development Zone, Changshu, Jiangsu, China
Tel.: (86) 5125 269 2000
Golf Equipment Distr
N.A.I.C.S.: 423910

Corby Tyres and Exhausts Limited (1)
Unit 5 Curie Courtyard Cockerell Road, Corby, NN17 5DU, United Kingdom
Tel.: (44) 1536614053
Web Site: https://www.corbytyres.co.uk
Tyre Mfr & Distr
N.A.I.C.S.: 326211

Cribb Tyre & Battery Ltd. (1)
Wareham Road, Holton Heath Dorset, Poole, BH16 6JW, United Kingdom
Tel.: (44) 1202631122
Web Site: https://www.holtonheathtyres.co.uk
Tyre Mfr & Distr
N.A.I.C.S.: 326211

Dunlop Golf Club Corp. (1)
3 Tohoku-cho, Miyakonojo, Miyazaki, Japan
Tel.: (81) 986384679
Golf Club Mfr
N.A.I.C.S.: 339920

Dunlop Goodyear Tires Ltd. (1)
3-3-3 Toyosu, Koto Ku, Tokyo, 135 6005, Japan
Tel.: (81) 355460111
Web Site: http://www.dunlop.co.jp
Sales Range: $25-49.9 Million
Emp.: 30
Mfr of Tires, Sporting Goods & Other Rubber Related Products
N.A.I.C.S.: 326211

Dunlop Home Products, Ltd. (1)
4-6-10 Bakuromachi Honey Bldg 5f, Chuo-Ku, Osaka, 541-0059, Japan
Tel.: (81)
Web Site: http://www.dhp-dunlop.co.jp
Emp.: 30
Rubber Glove Mfr
N.A.I.C.S.: 315990

AND PRIVATE COMPANIES — SUMITOMO RUBBER INDUSTRIES, LTD.

Dunlop Sports Korea Co., Ltd. (1)
1st floor Logit Building 76 Sapyeong-daero, Seocho-gu, Seoul, Korea (South)
Tel.: (82) 234623960
Web Site: https://www.dunlopkorea.co.kr
Golf Equipment Distr
N.A.I.C.S.: 423910

Dunlop Sports Marketing Co., Ltd. (1)
Shinagawa Crystal Square 1-6-41 Konan, Minato-ku, Tokyo, Japan
Tel.: (81) 354637320
Sports Equipment Whslr
N.A.I.C.S.: 423910

Dunlop Srixon Sports (Thailand) Co., Ltd. (1)
317 Kamol Sukosol BLD FL 10 Silom RD, Bangrak, Bangkok, 10500, Thailand
Tel.: (66) 26311441
Web Site: https://www.srixonthailand.co.th
Golf Equipment Distr
N.A.I.C.S.: 423910

Dunlop Srixon Sports Asia Sdn. Bhd. (1)
1 Jalan Pengetua U1/32 HICOM-Glenmarie Industrial Park, 40150, Shah Alam, Selangor, Malaysia
Tel.: (60) 355693438
Web Site: https://srixonasia.com
Golf Equipment Whslr
N.A.I.C.S.: 423910

Dunlop Srixon Sports Hong Kong Co., Ltd. (1)
Unit 509 5th floor Tower 1 Silvercord 30 Canton Road, Tsimshatsui, Kowloon, China (Hong Kong)
Tel.: (852) 23162286
Golf Equipment Distr
N.A.I.C.S.: 423910

Dunlop Srixon Sports Manufacturing (Thailand) Co., Ltd. (1)
612/9 Moo 9 Kabinburi Indutrial Zone Tumbon NongKi, Amphur Kabinburi, Prachin Buri, 25110, Thailand
Tel.: (66) 37204868
Web Site: https://www.dunlop-srixon.co.th
Emp.: 455
Tennis Ball Mfr
N.A.I.C.S.: 339920
Satoshi Tanaka (Mng Dir)

Dunlop Srixon Sports South Africa (Pty.) Ltd. (1)
Unit 6 Capital Hill Commercial Estate K101, Midrand, 1685, South Africa
Tel.: (27) 118056339
Web Site: https://za.dunlopsports.com
Golf Equipment Mfr & Distr
N.A.I.C.S.: 339920

Dunlop Tech GmbH (1)
Offenbacher Landstrasse 8, 63456, Hanau, Germany
Tel.: (49) 618193940
Web Site: https://www.dunloptech.com
Sales Range: $25-49.9 Million
Emp.: 25
Tiles Mfr
N.A.I.C.S.: 326211
Bernd Schuchhardt (Mng Dir)

Dunlop Tire (Thailand) Co., Ltd. (1)
909 Ample Tower 4th Floor Room 4/1 Debaratana Road, Bangna Nua Bangna, Bangkok, 10260, Thailand
Tel.: (66) 27440199
Web Site: http://www.dunloptire.co.th
Tier Dealer & Retailer
N.A.I.C.S.: 441340

Falken Tire Corporation (1)
8656 Haven Ave, Rancho Cucamonga, CA 91730
Tel.: (909) 466-1116
Web Site: http://www.falkentire.com
Sales Range: $25-49.9 Million
Tiles Mfr
N.A.I.C.S.: 326211
Rick Brennan (VP-Mktg)

Falken Tyre Europe GmbH (1)
Berliner Strasse 74-76, 63065, Offenbach, Germany
Tel.: (49) 69247525210
Web Site: https://www.falkentyre.com
Emp.: 55
Automotive Tire Mfr
N.A.I.C.S.: 326211
Markus Bogner (Mng Dir)

Falken Tyre India Private Limited (1)
Unit 312 J K L M N P Q Centrum Plaza Golf Course Road Sector 53, Gurgaon, 122002, Haryana, India
Tel.: (91) 1244638989
Web Site: http://www.falkentyre.in
Tier Dealer & Retailer
N.A.I.C.S.: 441340

Hong Kong Sumirubber, Ltd. (1)
Unit 9 5/F Tower 1 Silvercord 30 Canton Road Tsimshatsui KLN, Hong Kong, China (Hong Kong)
Tel.: (852) 27361217
Web Site: http://www.dunlop-care.com
Health Care Products Mfr
N.A.I.C.S.: 339112

Lonstroff AG (1)
Riedstrasse 368, Hallwil, 5634, Lenzburg, Switzerland (100%)
Tel.: (41) 628363737
Web Site: https://www.lonstroff.com
Elastomers Mfr
N.A.I.C.S.: 326291

Lonstroff Medicinski Elastomeri d.o.o. (1)
Obrtna cona Logatec 31, 1370, Logatec, Slovenia
Tel.: (386) 17800900
Tire Mfr & Distr
N.A.I.C.S.: 326211

Micheldever Tyre Services Ltd. (1)
Micheldever Station, Winchester, SO21 3AP, Hampshire, United Kingdom
Tel.: (44) 1962388258
Web Site: https://www.micheldever.co.uk
Tire Distr
N.A.I.C.S.: 423130

Mid Devon Tyres Limited (1)
Apple Lane, Devon, Exeter, EX2 5GL, United Kingdom
Tel.: (44) 1392914737
Web Site: https://www.middevontyres.com
Tyre Mfr & Distr
N.A.I.C.S.: 326211

Nakata Engineering Co., Ltd. (1)
619 Minami Kande-cho, Nishi-ku, Kobe, 651-2312, Japan
Tel.: (81) 789651015
Web Site: https://www.nakata-eng.co.jp
Emp.: 150
Tyre Mfr & Distr
N.A.I.C.S.: 326211
Ippei Oda (Pres)

P.T. Sumi Rubber Indonesia (1)
Wisma Indomobil 12th Floor Jl Letjen M T Haryono Kav 8, Jakarta, 13330, Indonesia
Tel.: (62) 218512561
Web Site: http://www.dunlop.co.id
Sales Range: $25-49.9 Million
Emp.: 110
N.A.I.C.S.: 326211
Mitsuru Nagai (Dir & Pres)

SRI Hybrid Ltd. (1)
6 9 3 Chome Wakinohama cho, 651 0072, Kobe, Chuo ku, Japan
Tel.: (81) 782653057
Web Site: http://www.sri-hybrid.co.jp
Sales Range: $125-149.9 Million
Emp.: 400
Rubber Mfr
N.A.I.C.S.: 326299

Selecta Tyre Limited (1)
Waterside Road, Derbyshire, Ashbourne, DE6 1DG, United Kingdom
Tel.: (44) 1335470074
Web Site: https://www.selectatyre.co.uk
Tyre Mfr & Distr
N.A.I.C.S.: 326211

Srixon Sports Europe Ltd. (1)
3 Newman Lane Industrial Estate, Alton, GU34 2QR, Hampshire, United Kingdom
Tel.: (44) 1420541709
Web Site: https://eu.dunlopsports.com
Golf Equipment Distr
N.A.I.C.S.: 423910

Srixon Sports Manufacturing (Thailand) Co., Ltd. (1)
612/9 Moo 9 Kabinburi Industrial Zone soi 14 Nongki, Kabinburi, Bangkok, 25110, Prachinburi, Thailand
Tel.: (66) 3720486876
Web Site: http://www.srixon.co.th
Golf Apparel Equipment Mfr & Distr
N.A.I.C.S.: 339920

Srixon Sports South Africa (Pty) Ltd. (1)
Unit 6 Pentagon Park Capital Hill Commercial Estate Le Roux Road, Midrand, Johannesburg, South Africa
Tel.: (27) 11 805 6339
Golf Equipment Distr
N.A.I.C.S.: 423910

Sumigomu Takasago Integrate, Ltd. (1)
Kobe Commerce Industry and Trade Center Building 716 5-1-4 Hamabedori, Chuo-ku, Kobe, 651-0083, Hyogo, Japan
Tel.: (81) 78 221 1706
Web Site: https://www.st-integrate.co.jp
Electric Equipment Mfr
N.A.I.C.S.: 335311
Seiji Tomono (CEO)

Sumigomusangyo, Ltd. (1)
4-6-10 Bakurocho Honey Building, Chuo-Ku, Osaka, 541-0059, Japan
Tel.: (81) 662527080
Web Site: https://www.sumigs.co.jp
Emp.: 157
Industrial Rubber Product Mfr
N.A.I.C.S.: 326299

Sumirubber Industries (Malaysia) Sdn. Bhd. (1)
Lot 44 45 And 86 Bakar Arang Industrial Estate, 8000, Sungai Petani, Kedah, Malaysia (100%)
Tel.: (60) 44213121
Web Site: http://www.sumirubber.com
Sales Range: $10-24.9 Million
Emp.: 600
Mfr of Rubber Gloves
N.A.I.C.S.: 339113

Sumirubber Malaysia Sdn. Bhd. (1)
Lot 44 45 86 Bakar Arang Industrial Estate, 08000, Sungai Petani, Kedah, Malaysia
Tel.: (60) 44213121
Web Site: https://www.sumirubber.com
Sales Range: $250-299.9 Million
Emp.: 600
Rubber Tire Mfr
N.A.I.C.S.: 326211

Sumirubber Vietnam, Ltd. (1)
Lot A11 Nomura Industrial Zone, An Duong Dist, Haiphong, Vietnam
Tel.: (84) 31 3743270
Precision Rubber Products Distr
N.A.I.C.S.: 423840

Sumitomo Rubber (Changshu) Co., Ltd. (1)
No 1 Avenue Yanjiang Industrial Zone Economic, Xinhuagang District, Changshu, 215513, Jiangsu, China
Tel.: (86) 51252695000
Radial Tires Mfr
N.A.I.C.S.: 327910
Masafumi Takami (Pres)

Sumitomo Rubber (Thailand) Co., Ltd. (1)
7/232 Moo 6 Soi Pornprapa Amata City Rayong Industrial Estate, Tambol Mabyangporn Amphur Pluakdaeng, Rayong, 21140, Thailand
Tel.: (66) 38953000
Web Site: https://www.sumitomorubberthailand.com
Emp.: 7,391
Tire Mfr & Whslr
N.A.I.C.S.: 326211

Sumitomo Rubber AKO Lastik Sanayi ve Ticaret A.S. (1)
Yakinkent Org San Bolg 1 Cad No 1 Tuney Koyu Mevki, Istanbul, Cankiri, Turkiye
Tel.: (90) 376218910001
Web Site: https://www.sumitomorubberako.com.tr
Emp.: 2,650
Car Tire Mfr & Whslr

Sumitomo Rubber Asia (Tyre) Pte, Ltd. (1)
1 Maritime Square 09-39 Harbourfront Centre, Singapore, 099253, Singapore
Tel.: (65) 62786975
Sales Range: $25-49.9 Million
Emp.: 9
Car Tire Whslr
N.A.I.C.S.: 441340
Yasuhiro Nemoto (Mng Dir)

Sumitomo Rubber Industries, Ltd. - Changshu Factory (1)
Economic Development Zone, Changshu, Jiangsu, China
Tel.: (86) 512 5269 0502
Automotive Tire Mfr
N.A.I.C.S.: 326211

Sumitomo Rubber Industries, Ltd. - Indonesia Factory (1)
Bukit Indah City Blok H Sektor 1A, 41373, Cikampek, Indonesia
Tel.: (62) 264 351346
Automotive Tire Mfr
N.A.I.C.S.: 326211

Sumitomo Rubber Industries, Ltd. - Izumiohtsu Factory (1)
9-1 Kawahara-cho, Izumiotsu, 595-8650, Osaka, Japan
Tel.: (81) 725 21 1286
Automotive Tire Mfr
N.A.I.C.S.: 326211

Sumitomo Rubber Industries, Ltd. - Kakogawa Factory (1)
410-1 Kitano Noguchi-cho, Kakogawa, 675-0011, Hyogo, Japan
Tel.: (81) 79 424 0111
Automotive Tire Mfr
N.A.I.C.S.: 326211

Sumitomo Rubber Industries, Ltd. - Miyazaki Factory (1)
3 Tohoku-cho, Miyakonojo, 855-0004, Miyazaki, Japan
Tel.: (81) 986 38 1311
Automotive Tire Mfr
N.A.I.C.S.: 326211

Sumitomo Rubber Industries, Ltd. - Nagoya Factory (1)
4-1 Shinsei-cho, Toyota, 471-0837, Aichi, Japan
Tel.: (81) 56 528 2345
Web Site: http://www.srigroup.co.jp
Automotive Tire Mfr
N.A.I.C.S.: 326211
Ikuji Ikeda (Chm)

Sumitomo Rubber Industries, Ltd. - Shirakawa Factory (1)
1 Hirokubo Kurabeish, Shirakawa, 961-0017, Fukushima, Japan
Tel.: (81) 248 22 3311
Automotive Tire Mfr
N.A.I.C.S.: 326211

Sumitomo Rubber Industries, Ltd. - Sports Business (1)
3-6-9 Wakinohama-cho, Chuo-ku, Kobe, Hyogo, Japan
Tel.: (81) 782653200
Web Site: http://www.dunlopsports.co.jp
Sales Range: $600-649.9 Million
Sporting Goods Mfr
N.A.I.C.S.: 339920

Subsidiary (Domestic):

Dunlop Sports Enterprises Ltd. (2)
La Mour Ashiya 2F 2-6 Ohara-cho, Ashiya, 6590092, Hyogo, Japan
Tel.: (81) 797311618
Emp.: 80
Golf Tournaments Operation Services
N.A.I.C.S.: 713910
Sezo Panaka (Pres)

Plant (Domestic):

Dunlop Sports Limited - Ichijima Factory (2)
5 Kajiwara Ichijima-cho, Tanba, 669-4323, Hyogo, Japan
Tel.: (81) 795 85 3000

SUMITOMO RUBBER INDUSTRIES, LTD.

Sumitomo Rubber Industries, Ltd.—(Continued)
Web Site: http://www.dunlopsports.co.jp
Golf Balls Mfr
N.A.I.C.S.: 339920

Subsidiary (Domestic):

Dunlop Sports Wellness Co. Ltd. (2)
Kitts Building 1-10-1 Nakase, Mihama-ku, Chiba, 261-8577, Japan (100%)
Tel.: (81) 432991795
Web Site: https://www.wellness-dunlopsports.jp
Emp.: 1,432
Sports Club Services
N.A.I.C.S.: 711211
Masato Nagano (Auditor)

Subsidiary (US):

Roger Cleveland Golf Company, Inc. (2)
5601 Skylab Rd, Huntington Beach, CA 92647
Tel.: (714) 889-1300
Web Site: https://us.dunlopsports.com
Sales Range: $75-99.9 Million
Golfing Equipment & Apparel Mfr
N.A.I.C.S.: 339920

Subsidiary (Non-US):

Cleveland Golf Asia Co., Ltd. (3)
1 Kanda Izumicho Building 14F, Chiyoda Ku, Tokyo, 101 0024, Japan
Tel.: (81) 3 5822 0696
Golf Equipment & Apparel Mfr & Distr
N.A.I.C.S.: 339920

Cleveland Golf Canada Corp. (3)
6900 S Service Rd, Pointe-Claire, H9R 5W1, QC, Canada
Tel.: (604) 542-0911
Web Site: http://www.clevelandgolf.com
Sales Range: $25-49.9 Million
Emp.: 10
Golf Equipment & Apparel Mfr & Distr
N.A.I.C.S.: 339920

Cleveland Golf Deutschland GmbH (3)
Landsbergerstrasse 302, 80687, Munich, Germany
Tel.: (49) 89 90405223
Golf Equipment & Apparel Mfr & Distr
N.A.I.C.S.: 339920

Subsidiary (Non-US):

Srixon Sports Australasia Pty Ltd. (2)
2-707 Forest Road, Peakhurst, 2210, NSW, Australia
Tel.: (61) 295848111
Web Site: http://www.srixon.com.au
Sales Range: $25-49.9 Million
Sporting Goods Mfr
N.A.I.C.S.: 339920

Subsidiary (US):

Srixon Sports USA Inc. (2)
3505 Newpoint Pl, Lawrenceville, GA 30043
Tel.: (678) 518-5121
Web Site: http://www.srixon.com
Sales Range: $25-49.9 Million
Emp.: 25
Sporting Good Equipment
N.A.I.C.S.: 423910

Sumitomo Rubber Middle East FZE (1)
Office 5WA 118 Dubai Airport Free Zone, Dubai, 54901, United Arab Emirates
Tel.: (971) 42146959
Web Site: http://www.srigroup.co.jp
Sales Range: $25-49.9 Million
Emp.: 35
Tire Distr
N.A.I.C.S.: 423130

Sumitomo Rubber North America, Inc. (1)
8656 Haven Ave, Rancho Cucamonga, CA 91730
Web Site: https://www.falkentire.com
Automobile Tyre Mfr & Distr
N.A.I.C.S.: 326211

Sumitomo Rubber South Africa (Pty) Limited (1)
892 Umgeni Road, Congella, 4001, South Africa
Tel.: (27) 31 242 1111
Sales Range: $250-299.9 Million
Emp.: 1,700
Tires Mfr & Distr
N.A.I.C.S.: 326211
Csaba Makos (Head-Hungary)

Sumitomo Rubber USA, LLC (1)
200 Innovation Way, Akron, OH 44316-0001 (100%)
Tel.: (716) 879-8200
Tiles Mfr
N.A.I.C.S.: 326211
Shannon Ross (Mgr-Bus Center-Consumer Div)

Suzhou Dunlop Srixon Sports Co., Ltd. (1)
Room 301 block AB 27 Fenglin Road Yushan street, Changshu, Jiangsu, China
Tel.: (86) 51252692000
Golf Equipment Distr
N.A.I.C.S.: 423910

Wellingborough Tyres Limited (1)
Leyland Trading Estate, Northamptonshire, Wellingborough, NN8 1RT, United Kingdom
Tel.: (44) 1933558032
Web Site: https://www.wellingboroughtyres.co.uk
Tyre Mfr & Distr
N.A.I.C.S.: 326211

Zhongshan Sumirubber Precision Rubber Ltd. (1)
No 21 Huoju Avenue Huoju Development Zone, Zhongshan, 528436, Guangdong, China
Tel.: (86) 76085314774
Rubber Products Mfr
N.A.I.C.S.: 326299

SUMITOMO SEIKA CHEMICALS COMPANY LIMITED

The Sumitomo Building 4-5-33 Kitahama Chuo, Osaka, 541 0041, Japan
Tel.: (81) 662208508 JP
Web Site: https://www.sumitomoseika.co.jp
Year Founded: 1944
4008—(TKS)
Rev.: $945,137,460
Assets: $900,976,050
Liabilities: $272,688,940
Net Worth: $628,287,110
Earnings: $40,757,260
Emp.: 1,402
Fiscal Year-end: 03/31/24
Fine Chemical & Gas Products & Functional Polymers Mfr; Engineering Services
N.A.I.C.S.: 325998
Kazuhiro Hamatani (Sr Mng Exec Officer & Gen Mgr-Gen Affairs & Personnel Office)

Subsidiaries:

Seika Engineering Co., Ltd. (1)
346-1 Miyanishi Harima-cho, Kako-gun, Hyogo, 675-0145, Japan (100%)
Tel.: (81) 794372153
Web Site: http://www.sumitomoseika.co.jp
Plants & Tanks Designer & Constructor
N.A.I.C.S.: 237990

Sumisei Chemical Company Limited (1)
8th Fl Superior Tower 528 Teheran-ro, Gangnam-gu, Seoul, 06181, Korea (South)
Tel.: (82) 25617091
Sales Range: $50-74.9 Million
Emp.: 7
Chemicals Mfr & Whslr
N.A.I.C.S.: 325211

Sumisei Taiwan Technology Co., Ltd. (1)
13F No 255 Dong Sec 1 Guangming 6th Rd, Zhubei, 30264, Hsinchu, Taiwan
Tel.: (886) 36578811

Sales Range: $50-74.9 Million
Emp.: 5
Electronic Gases Mfr & Sales
N.A.I.C.S.: 325120

Sumitomo Seika America, Inc. (1)
150 E 42nd St Ste 701, New York, NY 10017
Tel.: (212) 572-8245
Web Site: http://www.sumitomoseika.co.jp
Sales Range: $50-74.9 Million
Emp.: 2
Industrial Chemical Whslr
N.A.I.C.S.: 424690

Sumitomo Seika Asia Pacific Pte. Ltd. (1)
1 Raffles Place Suite 19-03 One Raffles place, Singapore, 048616, Singapore
Tel.: (65) 65342276
Sales Range: $50-74.9 Million
Emp.: 60
Chemicals Mfr & Whslr
N.A.I.C.S.: 325211
Helen Choon (Mgr-Sls)

Sumitomo Seika Europe S.A./N.V. (1)
Woluwelaan 57, B-1830, Machelen, Belgium
Tel.: (32) 22557660
Sales Range: $50-74.9 Million
Emp.: 11
Chemicals Whslr
N.A.I.C.S.: 424690

Sumitomo Seika Singapore Pte. Ltd. (1)
1 Raffles Place Suite 19-03, One Raffles place, Singapore, 048616, Singapore
Tel.: (65) 342276
Sales Range: $50-74.9 Million
Emp.: 8
Absorbent Resins Mfr & Sales
N.A.I.C.S.: 325211

SUMMA GROUP

Bolshoi Savvinski Per 10A, Moscow, 119435, Russia
Tel.: (7) 495 771 6060
Web Site: http://www.summagroup.ru
Investment Holding Company
N.A.I.C.S.: 551112
Ziyavudin Magomedov (Chm)

Subsidiaries:

GlobalElectroService, OJSC (1)
Podolskoe highway 8/5, Moscow, 115093, Russia
Tel.: (7) 495 287 20 22
Web Site: http://www.global-es.ru
Engineeering Services
N.A.I.C.S.: 541330
Orevkov Alexander Borisovich (Chief Engr)

Stroynovatsiya, LLC (1)
Bldg 54 Unit 1 Bolshaya Polyanka St, Moscow, 119180, Russia
Tel.: (7) 495 223 31 94
Web Site: http://www.stroynov.com
Engineering Consulting Services
N.A.I.C.S.: 541330
Wolski Aleksandr Stanislavovich (CEO)

Summa Telecom LLC (1)
8 1-st Kozhevnicheskiy sidestreet, 115114, Moscow, Russia
Tel.: (7) 4956629090
Telecommunication Servicesb
N.A.I.C.S.: 517111

SUMMA SILVER CORP.

918-1030 West Georgia St, Vancouver, V6E 2Y3, BC, Canada
Tel.: (604) 288-8004
Web Site: https://www.summasilver.com
SSVR—(OTCIQ)
Assets: $16,796,382
Liabilities: $431,179
Net Worth: $16,365,204
Earnings: ($4,257,593)
Fiscal Year-end: 08/31/21
Mineral Exploration Services
N.A.I.C.S.: 213115

Martin Bajic (CFO)

SUMMER FRESH SALADS INC.

181 Sharer Road, Woodbridge, L4L 8Z3, ON, Canada
Tel.: (905) 856-8816
Web Site: http://www.summerfresh.com
Year Founded: 1991
Emp.: 125
Food Products Mfr
N.A.I.C.S.: 311999
Susan Niczowski (Owner & Pres)

SUMMERHILL VENTURE PARTNERS

22 St Clair Ave E Ste 1010, Toronto, M4T 2S3, ON, Canada
Tel.: (416) 408-0070
Web Site: http://www.summerhillvp.com
Year Founded: 2007
Sales Range: $25-49.9 Million
Emp.: 7
Venture Capital Firm
N.A.I.C.S.: 523999
Gary Rubinoff (Mng Partner-Toronto & Boston)

SUMMERSET GROUP HOLDINGS LIMITED

Level 27 Majestic Centre 100 Willis Street, Wellington, 6011, New Zealand
Tel.: (64) 48947320
Web Site: https://www.summerset.co.nz
SNZ—(ASX)
Rev.: $435,509,180
Assets: $4,235,573,217
Liabilities: $2,645,867,939
Net Worth: $1,589,705,278
Earnings: $266,226,735
Emp.: 2,799
Fiscal Year-end: 12/31/23
Retirement Villages & Aged Care Facilities Operator
N.A.I.C.S.: 623311
Julian Cook (CEO)

Subsidiaries:

Summerset Villages (Aotea) Limited (1)
15 Aotea Drive, Porirua, 5024, Wellington, New Zealand
Tel.: (64) 42350011
Retirement Village Operator
N.A.I.C.S.: 623311
Becky Smith (Mgr-Village)

Summerset Villages (Avonhead) Limited (1)
120 Hawthornden Road, Avonhead, Christchurch, 8042, New Zealand
Tel.: (64) 33573200
Retirement Living Care Services
N.A.I.C.S.: 623312
Stephanie Meehan (Mgr)

Summerset Villages (Bell Block) Limited (1)
70 Pohutukawa Place, Bell Block, New Plymouth, 4312, New Zealand
Tel.: (64) 68248530
Residential Care Services
N.A.I.C.S.: 623990
Martin Hook (Mgr)

Summerset Villages (Blenheim) Limited (1)
183 Old Renwick Road, Springlands, Blenheim, 7272, New Zealand
Tel.: (64) 35206042
Residential Care Services
N.A.I.C.S.: 623990

Summerset Villages (Cambridge) Limited (1)
1 Mary Ann Drive, Cambridge, 3434, New Zealand

AND PRIVATE COMPANIES — SUMMIT ASCENT HOLDINGS LIMITED

Tel.: (64) 78399482
Residential Care Services
N.A.I.C.S.: 623990

Summerset Villages (Dunedin) Limited (1)
36 Shetland Street, Wakari, Dunedin, 9010, New Zealand
Tel.: (64) 39503100
Emp.: 50
Retirement Village Operator
N.A.I.C.S.: 623311
Mark Ryan (Mgr-Village)

Summerset Villages (Ellerslie) Limited (1)
8 Harrison Road, Auckland, 1060, New Zealand
Tel.: (64) 99507960
Retirement Village Operator
N.A.I.C.S.: 623311
Tonchi Begovich (Grp Sr Mgr-Construction)

Summerset Villages (Half Moon Bay) Limited (1)
25 Thurston Place, Half Moon Bay, Auckland, 2012, New Zealand
Tel.: (64) 93061422
Residential Care Services
N.A.I.C.S.: 623990

Summerset Villages (Hamilton) Limited (1)
206 Dixon Road, Hamilton, 3206, New Zealand
Tel.: (64) 78430157
Web Site: http://www.summerset.co.nz
Retirement Village Operator
N.A.I.C.S.: 623311

Summerset Villages (Hastings) Limited (1)
1228 Ada Street, Parkvale, Hastings, 4122, New Zealand
Tel.: (64) 69741310
Emp.: 4
Retirement Village Operator
N.A.I.C.S.: 623311
Alan den Boer (Mgr-Village)

Summerset Villages (Havelock North) Limited (1)
249 Te Mata Road, Havelock, 4130, New Zealand
Tel.: (64) 68771185
Retirement Village Operator
N.A.I.C.S.: 623311
Cherie Adams (Mgr-Sls)

Summerset Villages (Hobsonville) Limited (1)
1 Squadron Drive, Hobsonville, Auckland, 0618, New Zealand
Tel.: (64) 99518920
Retirement Village Operator
N.A.I.C.S.: 623311
Diane McShane (Mgr-Sls)

Summerset Villages (Karaka) Limited (1)
49 Pararekau Road, Karaka, 2580, New Zealand
Tel.: (64) 99518900
Retirement Village Operator
N.A.I.C.S.: 623311
Kaye Jensen (Mgr-Village)

Summerset Villages (Katikati) Limited (1)
181 Park Road, Katikati, 3129, New Zealand
Tel.: (64) 79856890
Retirement Village Operator
N.A.I.C.S.: 623311
Susan Hough (Mgr-Village)

Summerset Villages (Kenepuru) Limited (1)
1-3 Bluff Road, Kenepuru, Porirua, 5022, New Zealand
Tel.: (64) 42306720
Residential Care Services
N.A.I.C.S.: 623990
Howard Woodley (Mgr)

Summerset Villages (Levin) Limited (1)
104 - 112 Liverpool Street, Levin, 5510, New Zealand
Tel.: (64) 63670337
Residential Care Services
N.A.I.C.S.: 623311
Joanne Welch (Mgr-Sls)

Summerset Villages (Lower Hutt) Limited (1)
1a Boulcott Street, Boulcott, Lower Hutt, 5010, New Zealand
Tel.: (64) 45681442
Retirement Village Operator
N.A.I.C.S.: 623311

Summerset Villages (Manukau) Limited (1)
7 Flat Bush School Road, Manukau, Auckland, 2019, New Zealand
Tel.: (64) 92723950
Web Site: http://www.sumersetgroup.co.nz
Retirement Village Operator
Rhonda Edlin (Mgr-Village)

Summerset Villages (Napier) Limited (1)
79 Merlot Drive, Greenmeadows, Napier, 4112, New Zealand
Tel.: (64) 68452840
Emp.: 60
Retirement Village Operator
N.A.I.C.S.: 623311
Russell Walters (Mgr-Village)

Summerset Villages (Nelson) Limited (1)
16 Sargeson Street, Stoke, Nelson, 7011, New Zealand
Tel.: (64) 35380000
Emp.: 50
Retirement Village Operator
N.A.I.C.S.: 623311
James Hamilton (Mgr-Village)

Summerset Villages (New Plymouth) Limited (1)
35 Fernbrook Drive, Vogeltown, New Plymouth, 4371, New Zealand
Tel.: (64) 68248900
Web Site: http://www.summerset.co.nz
Emp.: 30
Retirement Village Operator
N.A.I.C.S.: 623311

Summerset Villages (Palmerston North) Limited (1)
180 Ruapehu Drive, Fitzherbert, Palmerston North, 4410, New Zealand
Tel.: (64) 63544964
Retirement Village Operator
N.A.I.C.S.: 623311
Sue Gould (Mgr-Village)

Summerset Villages (Papamoa) Limited (1)
35 Manawa Road, Papamoa Beach, Tauranga, 3118, New Zealand
Tel.: (64) 75429080
Residential Care Services
N.A.I.C.S.: 623990
Izak Luther (Mgr)

Summerset Villages (Paraparaumu) Limited (1)
104 Realm Drive, Paraparaumu, 5032, New Zealand
Tel.: (64) 42983540
Web Site: http://www.summerset.co.nz
Retirement Village Operator
N.A.I.C.S.: 623311

Summerset Villages (Parnell) Limited (1)
23 Cheshire Street, Auckland, 1052, New Zealand
Tel.: (64) 99508212
Residential Care Services
N.A.I.C.S.: 623990

Summerset Villages (Rangiora) Limited (1)
141 South Belt, Rangiora, 7400, New Zealand
Tel.: (64) 33641312
Residential Care Services
N.A.I.C.S.: 623990

Summerset Villages (Rototuna) Limited (1)
39 Kimbrae Drive, Rototuna North, Hamilton, 3210, New Zealand
Tel.: (64) 79817820
Residential Care Services
N.A.I.C.S.: 623990
Joanna Smith (Mgr)

Summerset Villages (St Johns) Limited (1)
188 St Johns Road, St Johns, Auckland, 1072, New Zealand
Tel.: (64) 99507982
Residential Care Services
N.A.I.C.S.: 623990

Summerset Villages (Taupo) Limited (1)
2 Wharewaka Road, Wharewaka, Taupo, 3330, New Zealand
Tel.: (64) 73769470
Retirement Village Operator
N.A.I.C.S.: 623311
Helen Cooney (Mgr-Village)

Summerset Villages (Te Awa) Limited (1)
136 Eriksen Road, Te Awa, Napier, 4110, New Zealand
Tel.: (64) 68335852
Residential Care Services
N.A.I.C.S.: 623990
Jacqueline Cowan (Mgr)

Summerset Villages (Trentham) Limited (1)
20 Racecourse Road, Trentham, Upper Hutt, 5018, New Zealand
Tel.: (64) 45272980
Retirement Village Operator
N.A.I.C.S.: 623311
Margaret Sharp (Mgr-Village)

Summerset Villages (Wanganui) Limited (1)
40 Burton Avenue, Wanganui East, Wanganui, 4500, New Zealand
Tel.: (64) 63433133
Web Site: http://www.summerset.co.nz
Emp.: 40
Retirement Village Operator
N.A.I.C.S.: 623311

Summerset Villages (Warkworth) Limited (1)
31 Mansel Drive, Warkworth, 0910, New Zealand
Tel.: (64) 94251200
Web Site: http://www.summerset.co.nz
Emp.: 63
Retirement Village Operator
N.A.I.C.S.: 623311

Summerset Villages (Whangarei) Limited (1)
7 Par Lane, Tikipunga, Whangarei, 0112, New Zealand
Tel.: (64) 94700282
Residential Care Services
N.A.I.C.S.: 623990
Kat Symonds (Mgr)

SUMMI (GROUP) HOLDINGS LIMITED
Room 1012 Block A Hung Hom Commercial Centre 37 Ma Tau Wai Road, Hong Hum, Causeway Bay, China (Hong Kong)
Tel.: (852) 3163 1000   Ky
Year Founded: 1993
756—(HKG)
Juice Mfr & Whslr
N.A.I.C.S.: 311411
Shaohao Wu (Chm)

Subsidiaries:

Chongqing Tianbang Food Co. Limited (1)
Zhaojia Town Zone B Kai County Industrial Park, Chongqing, China
Tel.: (86) 23 5267 8888
Juice Mfr & Whslr
N.A.I.C.S.: 311411

Summi (Fujian) Food Co. Limited (1)
Industrial Zone North of Luoyang Town, Hui, Quanzhou, 362121, Fujian, China
Tel.: (86) 595 87491420

Juice Mfr & Whslr
N.A.I.C.S.: 311411

SUMMIT ALLIANCE PORT LIMITED
Katghar South Patenga, Chittagong, 4204, Bangladesh
Tel.: (880) 2333300067
Web Site: https://www.saplbd.com
Year Founded: 2003
SAPORTL—(CHT)
Rev.: $16,857,434
Assets: $110,488,130
Liabilities: $37,880,393
Net Worth: $72,607,737
Earnings: $2,703,585
Emp.: 956
Fiscal Year-end: 06/30/23
Shipping & Port Services
N.A.I.C.S.: 488310
Ali Jowher Rizvi (Mng Dir)

Subsidiaries:

Summit Alliance Port East Gateway India Pvt Ltd. (1)
20 Garden Reach Road Garden Reach Jetty II Near Bhut Ghat, Kolkata, 70043, India
Tel.: (91) 6292338585
Web Site: http://www.saplindia.in
Inland Water Way Terminal Services
N.A.I.C.S.: 483211

SUMMIT ASCENT HOLDINGS LIMITED
Unit 1704 17th Floor West Tower Shun Tak Centre, 200 Connaught Road Central, Hong Kong, China (Hong Kong)
Tel.: (852) 37292135   BM
Web Site:
https://www.saholdings.com.hk
0102—(HKG)
Rev.: $47,469,015
Assets: $476,148,113
Liabilities: $30,636,465
Net Worth: $445,511,648
Earnings: $3,937,328
Emp.: 996
Fiscal Year-end: 12/31/22
Holding Company; Building Materials & Engineering Equipment Distr
N.A.I.C.S.: 551112
Eric Daniel Landheer (Exec Dir)

Subsidiaries:

Arnhold & Company, Limited (1)
6th Fl Victoria Ctr 15 Watson Rd, North Point, China (Hong Kong)
Tel.: (852) 28064600
Building Materials Trading & Engineering Services
N.A.I.C.S.: 444180

Arnhold (Macau) Limited (1)
Level 20 AIA Tower Nos 251A - 301 251A - 301, Avenida Comercial De, Macau, China (Macau)
Tel.: (853) 82942220
Building Materials Distr
N.A.I.C.S.: 444180

Arnhold Design Centres Limited (1)
G/F Lucky Plaza 315-321 Lockhart Road, Wanchai, China (Hong Kong)
Tel.: (852) 28650318
Web Site: http://www.arnhold.com.hk
Bathroom Hardware Fixtures Sales
N.A.I.C.S.: 423220

Arnhold Investments Limited (1)
6F Victoria Ctr 15 Watson Rd, North Point, China (Hong Kong)
Tel.: (852) 28079400
Web Site: http://www.arnhold.com
Emp.: 100
Investment Management Service
N.A.I.C.S.: 523999

Arnhold Marble Limited (1)
6F Victoria Ctr 15 Watson Rd, North Point, China (Hong Kong)

SUMMIT ASCENT HOLDINGS LIMITED

Summit Ascent Holdings Limited—(Continued)
Tel.: (852) 28079400
Sales Range: $25-49.9 Million
Building Materials Whslr
N.A.I.C.S.: 444180

Arnhold Sourcing Limited (1)
6F Victoria Ctr 15 Watson Rd, North Point, China (Hong Kong)
Tel.: (852) 28079400
Web Site: http://www.arnhold.com.hk
Emp.: 150
Building Materials Export Services
N.A.I.C.S.: 444180
Michael John Green *(Mng Dir)*

SUMMIT FOREST PRODUCTS INC.
407 McGill Ave 315, Montreal, H2Y 2G3, QC, Canada
Tel.: (514) 745-1331
Web Site: http://www.summitforest.ca
Rev.: $30,000,000
Emp.: 5
Lumber Distr
N.A.I.C.S.: 423310
Christian Labbe *(Mng Partner)*

SUMMIT HEALTHCARE ACQUISITION CORP.
Unit 1101 11th Floor 1 Lyndhurst Tower 1 Lyndhurst Terrace, Central, China (Hong Kong)
Tel.: (852) 9 162 5199   Ky
Year Founded: 2020
SMIH—(NASDAQ)
Rev.: $3,452
Assets: $201,034,150
Liabilities: $220,352,001
Net Worth: ($19,317,851)
Earnings: ($545,727)
Emp.: 2
Fiscal Year-end: 12/31/21
Investment Services
N.A.I.C.S.: 523999
Bo Tan *(CEO & Co-Chief Investment Officer)*

SUMMIT HOMES GROUP
242 Leach Hwy, Myaree, 6154, WA, Australia
Tel.: (61) 893170141
Web Site: http://www.summithomes.com.au
Year Founded: 1978
Emp.: 340
Residential Building Construction Services
N.A.I.C.S.: 236116
Kim Anthony *(Mgr-Construction)*

SUMMIT NETWORKS INC.
3010-8888 Odlin Cresent, Richmond, V6X 3Z8, BC, Canada
Tel.: (604) 232-3968   NV
Year Founded: 2014
SNTW—(OTCQB)
Rev.: $189,140
Assets: $164,377
Liabilities: $702,847
Net Worth: ($538,470)
Earnings: $23,778
Fiscal Year-end: 09/30/23
Glass Craft Product Distr
N.A.I.C.S.: 423220
Stephen Kok Koon Tan *(CEO)*

SUMMIT PIPELINE SERVICES LTD.
46 Cooper Rd RR 2 Site 13 1, Thunder Bay, P7C 4V1, ON, Canada
Tel.: (807) 939-1100
Web Site: http://www.summitpipeline.com
Rev.: $10,000,000
Emp.: 10

Pipeline Construction & Maintenance Services
N.A.I.C.S.: 237120
Neil Gillingham *(Pres)*

SUMMIT POWER LTD.
Summit Centre 18 Karwan Bazar C/A, Dhaka, 1215, Bangladesh
Tel.: (880) 255012255
Web Site: https://summitpowernational.com
SUMITPOWER—(CHT)
Rev.: $510,842,937
Assets: $1,019,517,954
Liabilities: $524,845,878
Net Worth: $494,672,076
Earnings: $15,881,547
Emp.: 497
Fiscal Year-end: 06/30/23
Electric Power Generation & Distribution Services
N.A.I.C.S.: 221122
Muhammad Latif Khan *(Vice Chm)*

SUMMIT REAL ESTATE HOLDINGS LTD.
66 Hahistadrut Ave, Haifa, Israel
Tel.: (972) 48408091
Web Site: http://www.smt.co.il
Year Founded: 1965
Sales Range: $75-99.9 Million
Emp.: 250
Real Estate Services
N.A.I.C.S.: 531390
Yair Bernat *(CFO)*

Subsidiaries:

Summit Germany Limited (1)
1st and 2nd Floors Elizabeth House, Les Ruettes Brayes, Saint Peter Port, GY1 1EW, Guernsey   (79.17%)
Tel.: (44) 1481700300
Web Site: http://www.summitgermany.com
Rev.: $200,445,716
Assets: $2,084,590,978
Liabilities: $953,473,991
Net Worth: $1,131,116,987
Earnings: ($68,204,187)
Emp.: 50
Fiscal Year-end: 12/31/2023
Commercial Property Investment & Management Services
N.A.I.C.S.: 531390
Zohar Levy *(Mng Dir)*

Subsidiary (Non-US):

Deutsche Real Estate AG (2)
Oudenarder Str 16, 13347, Berlin, Germany   (76%)
Tel.: (49) 3024008640
Web Site: https://www.drestate.de
Rev.: $24,185,193
Assets: $577,088,280
Liabilities: $101,974,962
Net Worth: $475,113,318
Earnings: ($15,939,996)
Emp.: 27
Fiscal Year-end: 12/31/2022
Real Estate Development Services
N.A.I.C.S.: 531210
Boaz Rosen *(Member-Mgmt Bd)*

SUMMIT SECURITIES LTD.
213 Bezzola Complex B Wing 71 Sion-Trombay Road, Chembur, Mumbai, 400 071, Maharashtra, India
Tel.: (91) 2246098668
Web Site: https://www.summitsecurities.net
Year Founded: 1997
SUMMIT—(NSE)
Rev.: $2,058,420
Assets: $336,447,425
Liabilities: $29,973,448
Net Worth: $306,473,977
Earnings: $1,182,622
Emp.: 8
Fiscal Year-end: 03/31/21
Investment Services
N.A.I.C.S.: 523999

Jiya Gangwani *(Sec)*

SUMMITVIEW CAPITAL MANAGEMENT LTD.
Pudong New Area Shanghai Zhang Jiang Songtao Road 506 1 Dongfang Road, Shanghai, 2001203, China
Tel.: (86) 21 58206180
Web Site: http://www.summitviewcapital.com
Year Founded: 2011
Privater Equity Firm
N.A.I.C.S.: 523999
Feng Li *(Co-Founder & Partner)*

Subsidiaries:

Integrated Silicon Solution, Inc. (1)
1623 Buckeye Dr, Milpitas, CA 95035
Tel.: (408) 969-6600
Web Site: http://www.issi.com
Memory Semiconductors Designer & Mfr
N.A.I.C.S.: 334413
Kong-Yeu Han *(CEO)*

Subsidiary (Non-US):

Giantec Semiconductor Inc. (2)
No.12 Lane 647 Songtao Road Zhangjiang Hi-Tech Park, Pudong New Area, Shanghai, China
Tel.: (86) 2150802030
Web Site: http://www.giantec-semi.com
Integrated Circuits Mfr
N.A.I.C.S.: 333242

ISSI Japan, Inc. (2)
18F Shinjuku Green Tower Bldg 6-14-1 Nishishinjuku, Shinjuku-ku, Tokyo, 160-0023, Japan
Tel.: (81) 353392950
Web Site: http://www.issi.com
Semiconductor Equipment Mfr
N.A.I.C.S.: 333242
Miura Naoki *(Pres)*

Integrated Silicon Solution Israel Ltd. (2)
38 Habarzel St, Tel Aviv, 69710, Israel
Tel.: (972) 37696222
Web Site: http://www.issi.com
Software Embedded Microchip Mfr
N.A.I.C.S.: 334413

SUMMUS SOLUTIONS N.V.
RPO Box 60610, Granville Park, Vancouver, V6H 4B9, BC, Canada
Tel.: (604) 331-3393   NL
Web Site: http://www.summus-solutions.com
Year Founded: 1993
Rev.: $66,039
Assets: $555,624
Liabilities: $2,249,529
Net Worth: ($1,693,905)
Earnings: ($230,671)
Fiscal Year-end: 06/30/19
Exploration, Development & Production of Petroleum & Natural Gas
N.A.I.C.S.: 211120
Urs Meisterhans *(Pres & CEO)*

SUMNER GROUP HEALTH LIMITED
89 Leigh Road, Eastleigh, SO50 9DQ, Hants, United Kingdom
Tel.: (44) 207 118 8815
Web Site: http://www.healthperm.com
Sales Range: $1-9.9 Million
Healthcare Recruiting Services
N.A.I.C.S.: 561311
David Sumner *(CEO)*

Subsidiaries:

JR Orion Services Pte. Ltd. (1)
400 Orchard Road #20-05 Orchard Towers, Singapore, 238875, Singapore
Tel.: (65) 62262963
Web Site: http://www.jrorion.com.sg
Shipping Services
N.A.I.C.S.: 483111
Joseph Ting *(Mng Dir)*

INTERNATIONAL PUBLIC

SUMO GROUP PLC
Unit 32 Jessops Riverside Brightside Lane, Sheffield, S9 2RX, United Kingdom
Tel.: (44) 1142426766   UK
Web Site: http://www.sumogroupplc.com
Year Founded: 2003
SUMO—(AIM)
Rev.: $93,612,079
Assets: $230,687,490
Liabilities: $100,548,670
Net Worth: $130,138,820
Earnings: $2,233,449
Emp.: 875
Fiscal Year-end: 12/31/20
Video Software Development Services
N.A.I.C.S.: 541511
Carl Cavers *(Co-Founder & CEO)*

Subsidiaries:

Atomhawk Design Limited (1)
RIGA Business Centre Baltic Business Quarter Quarryfield Road, Gateshead, NE8 3DF, United Kingdom
Tel.: (44) 1914909160
Web Site: http://www.atomhawk.com
Game Developing Services
N.A.I.C.S.: 541430

SUMO RESOURCES PLC
Kemp House 152 City Road, London, EC1V 2NX, United Kingdom
Tel.: (44) 2036933820
Web Site: https://www.sumoresources.com
MLSUM—(EUR)
Rev.: $190,081
Assets: $116,824
Liabilities: $224,616
Net Worth: ($107,792)
Earnings: ($36,899)
Emp.: 5
Fiscal Year-end: 12/31/21
Other Metal Ore Mining
N.A.I.C.S.: 212290
Andre Odendaal *(CEO)*

SUMOL+COMPAL
Estrada da Portela 9, 2790-124, Carnaxide, Portugal
Tel.: (351) 214243500
Web Site: http://www.sumolcompal.pt
Rev.: $371,623,351
Earnings: $9,131,683
Fiscal Year-end: 12/31/15
Beverage Mfr & Distr
N.A.I.C.S.: 312120

Subsidiaries:

Sumol+Compal - Pombal Factory (1)
Rua Manuel da Mota 35 Zona Industrial da Formiga, Pombal, 3100 - 517, Portugal
Tel.: (351) 236 210 800
Web Site: http://www.en.sumolcompal.pt
Sales Range: $50-74.9 Million
Emp.: 250
Soft Drink & Beer Mfr
N.A.I.C.S.: 312111
Serjio Eusebio *(Gen Mgr)*

SUMUKA AGRO INDUSTRIES LIMITED
Plot no 89 AB CTS No 319, Opposite NKGSB Bank Kandivali West Kandivali village, Mumbai, 400 067, India
Tel.: (91) 9538441419
Web Site: https://www.sumukaagro.com
Year Founded: 1989
532070—(BOM)
Rev.: $146,907
Assets: $385,633
Liabilities: $172,762
Net Worth: $212,871
Earnings: $58,543

Emp.: 3
Fiscal Year-end: 03/31/21
Dry Fruits Products Trader & Retailer
N.A.I.C.S.: 111336
Paresh Thakker *(Chm & Mng Dir)*

SUMUP PAYMENTS LIMITED
32-34 Great Marlborough St, London, London, W1F 7JB, United Kingdom
Tel.: (44) 2035100160
Web Site: http://sumup.com
Mobile Payments Company
N.A.I.C.S.: 522320
Daniel Klein *(CEO)*

Subsidiaries:

Five Stars Loyalty, Inc. (1)
500 3rd St Ste 405, San Francisco, CA 94107
Tel.: (860) 578-2770
Web Site: http://www.fivestars.com
Marketing Consulting Services
N.A.I.C.S.: 541613
Victor Ho *(Co-Founder & CEO)*

SUN A. KAKEN CO., LTD.
1-7-4 Nihonbashi Honcho, Chuo-ku, Tokyo, Japan
Tel.: (81) 332415701
Web Site: https://www.sun-a-kaken.co.jp
Year Founded: 1942
4234—(TKS)
Rev.: $181,836,751
Assets: $247,373,568
Liabilities: $104,644,834
Net Worth: $142,728,734
Earnings: $2,299,306
Fiscal Year-end: 03/31/24
Packaging Materials Mfr
N.A.I.C.S.: 326199
Akihiro Yamamoto *(Pres)*

SUN BROTHERS DEVELOPMENT CO., LTD.
No 50 Minquan Rd, Luzhu District, Taoyuan, 33846, Taiwan
Tel.: (886) 33267897
Web Site:
http://www.sunbrothers.com.tw
Year Founded: 1980
3489—(TPE)
Rev.: $28,869,587
Assets: $123,101,054
Liabilities: $82,484,789
Net Worth: $40,616,265
Earnings: $759,997
Fiscal Year-end: 12/31/22
Building Construction Services
N.A.I.C.S.: 236220
Yuan-Cheng Chien *(Chm)*

SUN CHEONG CREATIVE DEVELOPMENT HOLDINGS LIMITED
Flat B-F 23/F Blk 4 Golden Dragon Industrial Centre, 182-190 Tai Lin Pai Road, Kwai Chung, New Territories, China (Hong Kong)
Tel.: (852) 24273933   Ky
Web Site: http://www.clip-fresh.com
Year Founded: 1979
Rev.: $43,538,715
Assets: $72,139,104
Liabilities: $43,322,280
Net Worth: $28,816,824
Earnings: $4,320,647
Emp.: 452
Fiscal Year-end: 12/31/18
Household Product Mfr & Distr
N.A.I.C.S.: 337110
Chiu Ying Tong *(Founder & Chm)*

SUN CONTRACTORS LTD
258 Belsize Rd, London, NW6 4BT, United Kingdom
Tel.: (44) 20 7316 1850
Web Site:
http://www.suncontractors.co.uk
Year Founded: 2004
Sales Range: $10-24.9 Million
General Contractors
N.A.I.C.S.: 238190
Yaser Salman *(Mng Dir)*

SUN CORPORATION
GLOBAL GATE 20F 4-60-12 Hiraikecho Nakamuraku Nagoya-shi, Nagoya, 453-6120, Aichi, Japan
Tel.: (81) 587552201
Web Site: https://www.sun-denshi.co.jp
6736—(TKS)
Rev.: $66,397,450
Assets: $309,599,180
Liabilities: $63,317,190
Net Worth: $246,281,990
Earnings: ($24,965,970)
Emp.: 301
Fiscal Year-end: 03/31/24
Information Technology Services
N.A.I.C.S.: 541511
Yoshimi Kimura *(Sr Mng Dir)*

Subsidiaries:

Cellebrite DI Ltd. (1)
94 Shlomo shmelzer Rd, PO Box 3925, Petah Tiqwa, 49130, Israel (51.08%)
Tel.: (972) 39260900
Web Site: https://www.cellebrite.com
Rev.: $325,110,000
Assets: $532,885,000
Liabilities: $498,673,000
Net Worth: $34,212,000
Earnings: ($81,100,000)
Emp.: 1,008
Fiscal Year-end: 12/31/2023
Mobile Software Development Services
N.A.I.C.S.: 541511
Ron Serber *(Co-CEO)*

Subsidiary (Non-US):

Cellebrite APAC PTE Ltd (2)
150 Beach Road Suite 08-05/08 Gateway West, Singapore, 189720, Singapore
Tel.: (65) 64386240
Emp.: 4
Mobile Application Software Distr
N.A.I.C.S.: 423430

Cellebrite GmbH (2)
Herzog-Heinrich-Strasse 20, 80336, Munich, Germany
Tel.: (49) 89262017000
Emp.: 11
Mobile Application Software Distr
N.A.I.C.S.: 423430

Cellebrite Ltda. (2)
Av Engenheiro Luiz Carlos Berrini 550 -12 Andar Brooklin, Andar Brooklin, Sao Paulo, 04794-000, Brazil
Tel.: (55) 113 216 3800
Web Site: https://www.cellebrite.com
Mobile Application Software Distr
N.A.I.C.S.: 423430

Subsidiary (US):

Cellebrite USA Inc. (2)
7 Campus Dr Ste 210, Parsippany, NJ 07054
Tel.: (201) 848-8552
Emp.: 46
Mobile Application Software Distr
N.A.I.C.S.: 423430
James H. Grady *(CEO)*

TWC Tech Holdings II Corp. (2)
4 Embarcadero Ctr Ste 2110, San Francisco, CA 94111
Tel.: (415) 780-9971
SPAC
N.A.I.C.S.: 525990
Adam Clammer *(CEO)*

SUN COUNTRY TOYOTA
1355 Cariboo Pl, Kamloops, V2C 5Z3, BC, Canada
Tel.: (250) 828-7966
Web Site: https://www.suncountrytoyota.ca
Emp.: 50
New & Used Car Dealers
N.A.I.C.S.: 441110
Rod McCaskill *(Mgr-Parts)*

SUN FOOK KONG GROUP
43/F Hopewell Centre 183 Queens Road East, Wanchai, China (Hong Kong)
Tel.: (852) 2828 1688
Web Site: http://www.sfk.com.hk
Year Founded: 1948
Holding Company
N.A.I.C.S.: 551112
Kai Shui Lo *(Chm)*

Subsidiaries:

SFK Construction Holdings Limited (1)
Rm 3207-10 Great Eagle Centre 23 Harbour Road, Wanchai, China (Hong Kong)
Tel.: (852) 28281688
Web Site: http://www.sfkchl.com
Sales Range: $25-49.9 Million
Emp.: 925
Building Construction & Civil Engineering Services
N.A.I.C.S.: 236220
Ki Chun Chan *(Chm)*

Subsidiary (Domestic):

Biwater Man Lee Limited (2)
Suite 202 Block 1 Hofai Commercial Centre 218 Sai Lau Kok Road, Tsuen Wan, Hong Kong, China (Hong Kong)
Tel.: (852) 24162828
Waste Water Treatment Services
N.A.I.C.S.: 221320

SUN FRONTIER FUDOUSAN CO. LTD.
14F Toho Hibiya Building 1-2-2 Yurakucho, Chiyoda-ku, Tokyo, 100-0006, Japan
Tel.: (81) 355211301
Web Site: https://www.sunfrt.co.jp
Year Founded: 1999
8934—(TKS)
Rev.: $527,927,480
Assets: $1,247,049,210
Liabilities: $622,959,450
Net Worth: $624,089,760
Earnings: $78,771,370
Emp.: 1,719
Fiscal Year-end: 03/31/24
Real Estate Services
N.A.I.C.S.: 531210
Seiichi Saito *(Exec Officer & Exec VP)*

Subsidiaries:

Navd Co., Ltd. (1)
2-24-9 Higashi-Nihonbashi, Chuo-ku, Tokyo, Japan
Tel.: (81) 361616453
Web Site: https://www.navd.co.jp
Interior Design Services
N.A.I.C.S.: 541410

SF Building Maintenance Co., Ltd. (1)
5th floor TM Building 2-5-4 Chitose, Sumida-ku, Tokyo, 130-0025, Japan
Tel.: (81) 366594601
Web Site: https://www.sfbm.co.jp
Emp.: 166
Building Management Services
N.A.I.C.S.: 531311

SF Building Support Inc. (1)
8th floor Toho Hibiya Building 1-2-2 Yurakucho, Chiyoda-ku, Tokyo, 100-0006, Japan
Tel.: (81) 355211350
Web Site: https://www.sfbs.co.jp
Real Estate Services
N.A.I.C.S.: 531390

SF Engineering Inc. (1)
1-17-6 6th Floor Terukoku Building, Ryogoku Sumida-ku, Tokyo, 130-0026, Japan

Tel.: (81) 336324425
Web Site: http://www.sfen.co.jp
Interior & Residential Construction Services
N.A.I.C.S.: 236220

Sky Heart Hotel Co., Ltd. (1)
1-2-2 8th Floor Toho Hibiya Building Yurakucho, Chiyoda-ku, Tokyo, 100-0006, Japan
Tel.: (81) 368582010
Web Site: http://www.sky-hotel.jp
Hotel Services
N.A.I.C.S.: 721110

Sun Frontier Community Arrangement Co., Ltd. (1)
8th Floor Toho Hibiya Building 1-2-2 Yurakucho, Chiyoda-ku, Tokyo, 100-0006, Japan
Tel.: (81) 368580540
Web Site: http://www.sfca.co.jp
Real Estate Services
N.A.I.C.S.: 531390

Sun Frontier Sado Co., Ltd. (1)
79-3 Chigusa, Sado, 952-1209, Niigata, Japan
Tel.: (81) 259587030
Web Site: http://www.sfsado.co.jp
Home Management Services
N.A.I.C.S.: 721110

Sun Frontier Space Management Co., Ltd. (1)
2-8-14 Hamamatsucho, Minato-ku, Tokyo, 105-0013, Japan
Tel.: (81) 362623636
Web Site: https://www.sfsm.co.jp
Residential Rental Services
N.A.I.C.S.: 531120

SUN GRANITE EXPORT LIMITED
Vill Paniora PO Palaspur, Khordha, 752054, Odisha, India
Tel.: (91) 6742584194
Web Site: http://www.sungranite.co.in
531013—(BOM)
Rev.: $49,984
Assets: $3,489,567
Liabilities: $1,515,206
Net Worth: $1,974,361
Earnings: $178,613
Fiscal Year-end: 03/31/14
Stone Product Mfr
N.A.I.C.S.: 327991
Smitarani Sutar *(Compliance Officer & Sec)*

SUN HING PRINTING HOLDINGS LIMITED
4/F Sze Hing Industrial Building 35-37 Lee Chung Street, Chai Wan, China (Hong Kong)
Tel.: (852) 2 557 0181   Ky
Web Site:
http://www.sunhingprinting.com
1975—(HKG)
Rev.: $49,024,008
Assets: $63,227,028
Liabilities: $13,533,871
Net Worth: $49,693,156
Earnings: $10,038,771
Emp.: 971
Fiscal Year-end: 06/30/21
Printing Product Mfr & Distr
N.A.I.C.S.: 323113
Chan Kenneth Kin Chi *(CEO)*

SUN HING VISION GROUP HOLDINGS LIMITED
1001C 10th Floor Sunbeam Centre 27 Shing Yip Street Kwun Tong, Kowloon, China (Hong Kong)
Tel.: (852) 2 341 7698
Web Site:
http://www.sunhingoptical.com
0125—(HKG)
Rev.: $113,082,054
Assets: $134,187,568
Liabilities: $33,391,632

SUN HING VISION GROUP HOLDINGS LIMITED

SUN HING VISION GROUP HOLDINGS LIMITED—(Continued)
Net Worth: $100,795,935
Earnings: $1,116,322
Emp.: 3,500
Fiscal Year-end: 03/31/22
Design & Manufacture of Optical Products
N.A.I.C.S.: 333310
Sau Ching Ma *(Exec Dir-Mktg Dev)*

Subsidiaries:

101 Studio Limited (1)
25/F EGL Tower 83 Hung To Road, Kwun Tong, Kowloon, China (Hong Kong)
Tel.: (852) 23417698
Web Site: http://www.101studio.com
Optical Instrument & Lens Mfr
N.A.I.C.S.: 333310

SUN HUNG KAI PROPERTIES LIMITED

45th Floor Sun Hung Kai Centre 30 Harbour Road, Hong Kong, China (Hong Kong)
Tel.: (852) 28278111 **HK**
Web Site: https://www.shkp.com
Year Founded: 1972
SUHJY—(OTCIQ)
Rev.: $9,098,751,390
Assets: $103,005,993,840
Liabilities: $25,457,206,027
Net Worth: $77,548,787,813
Earnings: $3,140,695,490
Emp.: 40,000
Fiscal Year-end: 06/30/23
Real Estate Management Services
N.A.I.C.S.: 531190
Raymond Ping-luen Kwok *(Chm & Mng Dir)*

Subsidiaries:

Airport Freight Forwarding Centre Company Limited (1)
6/F Sun Hung Kai Centre 30 Harbour Road, Hong Kong, China (Hong Kong)
Tel.: (852) 2 827 2002
Web Site: https://www.affc.com.hk
Freight Forwarding Services
N.A.I.C.S.: 488510

Ever Fast Limited (1)
Unit B 13Th Floor No 17 Sheung Hei Street, Success Industrial Building San Po Kong, Kowloon, China (Hong Kong)
Tel.: (852) 3 152 3688
Web Site: https://www.everfast.com.hk
Battery & Power Supply Mfr
N.A.I.C.S.: 335999

Group Allied Limited (1)
22nd Floor Allied Kajima Building 138 Gloucester Road, Wanchai, China (Hong Kong)
Tel.: (852) 2 519 2288
Web Site: https://www.alliedgroup.com.hk
Property Trading & Investment Services
N.A.I.C.S.: 523940
Lee Seng Hui *(CEO)*

Hong Kong Business Aviation Centre Limited
12 South Perimeter Road Hong Kong International Airport Lantau, Hong Kong, China (Hong Kong)
Tel.: (852) 2 949 9000
Web Site: https://www.hkbac.com
Flight Handling Services
N.A.I.C.S.: 488119
Madonna W. Y. Fung *(Gen Mgr)*

Hong Kong Sky Deck Limited (1)
100/F International Commerce Centre 1 Austin Road West, Kowloon, China (Hong Kong)
Tel.: (852) 2 613 3888
Web Site: https://www.sky100.com.hk
Indoor Observation Deck Services
N.A.I.C.S.: 713990

Kai Shing Management Services Limited (1)
Room 2301 23/F Sun Hung Kai Centre 30 Harbour Road, Wanchai, China (Hong Kong)
Tel.: (852) 2 828 5123
Web Site: https://www.kaishing.hk
Property Management Services
N.A.I.C.S.: 531311

Nixon Cleaning Company Limited (1)
5/F Hong Kong Plaza 188 Connaught Road West, Hong Kong, China (Hong Kong)
Tel.: (852) 2 563 0118
Web Site: https://www.nixon.com.hk
Emp.: 4,000
Contracting Cleaning Services
N.A.I.C.S.: 238140

SUNeVision Holdings Ltd. (1)
Unit 3110 31/F Standard Chartered Tower Millennium City 1, 388 Kwun Tong Road Kwun Tong, Kowloon, China (Hong Kong) **(73.82%)**
Tel.: (852) 26279000
Web Site: http://www.sunevision.com
Rev.: $269,032,288
Assets: $2,340,056,022
Liabilities: $1,747,839,809
Net Worth: $592,216,313
Earnings: $109,224,262
Emp.: 410
Fiscal Year-end: 06/30/2022
Internet Infrastructure & Enabling Services
N.A.I.C.S.: 517810
Raymond Ping-luen Kwok *(Chm)*

Sanfield Building Contractors Limited (1)
44 Fl Sun Hung Kai Centre, 30 Harbour Road, Wanchai, China (Hong Kong) **(100%)**
Tel.: (852) 2827 8111
Sales Range: $550-599.9 Million
Emp.: 1,500
Building Construction
N.A.I.C.S.: 236220

Shanghai Central Plaza Property Co., Ltd. (1)
No 381 Middle Huaihai Road, Huang Pu District, Shanghai, 200040, China
Tel.: (86) 216 311 1111
Web Site: https://www.shanghaicentralplaza.com.cn
Property Investment Services
N.A.I.C.S.: 523940

SmarTone Telecommunications Holdings Limited (1)
31/F Millennium City 2 378 Kwun Tong Road, Kwun Tong, Kowloon, China (Hong Kong) **(67.05%)**
Tel.: (852) 31282828
Web Site: https://www.smartoneholdings.com
Rev.: $897,350,619
Assets: $1,622,714,405
Liabilities: $957,979,345
Net Worth: $664,735,060
Earnings: $54,548,995
Emp.: 1,737
Fiscal Year-end: 06/30/2022
Mobile Telecommunications Services
N.A.I.C.S.: 517112
Raymond Ping-luen Kwok *(Chm)*

Subsidiary (Domestic):

SmarTone Mobile Communications Limited (2)
31F Millennium City 2 378 Kwun Tong Road, Kwun Tong, Kowloon, China (Hong Kong) **(100%)**
Tel.: (852) 31282828
Web Site: http://www.smartone.com
Mobile Telecommunications
N.A.I.C.S.: 517112
Patrick Kai-lung Chan *(Exec Dir)*

Sun Hung Kai Development (China) Limited (1)
45/F Sun Hung Kai Centre, 30 Harbour Road, Wanchai, China (Hong Kong)
Tel.: (852) 2827 8111
Sales Range: $50-74.9 Million
Emp.: 70
Investment Holding
N.A.I.C.S.: 551112

Sun Hung Kai Properties Insurance Ltd. (1)
Room 2305-16 Sun Hung Kai Centre 30 Harbour Road, 30 Harbour Rd, Wanchai, China (Hong Kong) **(100%)**
Tel.: (852) 2 828 7886
Web Site: https://www.shkpi.com.hk
Sales Range: $50-74.9 Million
Emp.: 5
General Insurance
N.A.I.C.S.: 524126
Fanny Yeung *(Mgr-Mktg)*

WTC (Club) Limited (1)
38/F World Trade Centre 280 Gloucester Road, Causeway Bay, China (Hong Kong)
Tel.: (852) 2 808 2288
Web Site: https://www.wtcchk.com
Private Club Services
N.A.I.C.S.: 813410

SUN INTERNATIONAL LIMITED

6 Sandown Valley Crescent, Sandton, 2196, South Africa
Tel.: (27) 117807000 **ZA**
Web Site: http://www.suninternational.com
SUI—(JSE)
Rev.: $658,748,160
Assets: $739,022,200
Liabilities: $629,557,600
Net Worth: $109,464,600
Earnings: $66,168,900
Emp.: 3,634
Fiscal Year-end: 12/31/23
Gaming & Hospitality Services
N.A.I.C.S.: 721110
Anthony M. Leeming *(CEO)*

Subsidiaries:

Afrisun KZN (Pty) Limited (1)
1 Sibaya Dr, Umhlanga, 4320, Kwazulu-Natal, South Africa
Tel.: (27) 315805000
Web Site: http://www.suninternational.com
Sales Range: $200-249.9 Million
Emp.: 1,300
Casino Resort Operation Services
N.A.I.C.S.: 721120

Mangaung Sun (Pty) Limited (1)
Corner N1 and Jan Pierewiet, Bloemfontein, 9301, Free State, South Africa
Tel.: (27) 514102127
Casino Resort Operation Services
N.A.I.C.S.: 721120
Yasheen Sookdeo *(Gen Mgr)*

Meropa Leisure and Entertainment (Pty) Limited (1)
59 Sterkloop Farm Roodepoort Rd, Polokwane, 0700, Limpopo, South Africa
Tel.: (27) 152905400
Web Site: http://www.suninternational.com
Emp.: 300
Casino Operation Services
N.A.I.C.S.: 713210
Thenbh Marasha *(Gen Mgr)*

Sun Dreams S.A. (1)
Panamerica Sur Km 57 Sun Monticello, San Francisco de Mostazal, Rancagua, Chile **(55%)**
Tel.: (56) 72 2951 100
Web Site: http://www.mundodreams.com
Rev.: $230,352,883
Assets: $767,423,089
Liabilities: $269,465,030
Net Worth: $497,958,059
Earnings: $7,815,258
Emp.: 4,026
Fiscal Year-end: 12/31/2016
Holding Company; Casinos & Casino Hotels Operator
N.A.I.C.S.: 551112
Claudio Felix Fischer Llop *(Chm)*

Sun International (South Africa) Limited (1)
6 Sandown Valley Crescent, Sandton, 2031, Gauteng, South Africa
Tel.: (27) 117807444
Web Site: http://www.suninternational.com
Sales Range: $75-99.9 Million
Emp.: 450
Home Management Services
N.A.I.C.S.: 561110

INTERNATIONAL PUBLIC

Subsidiary (Domestic):

SunWest International (Pty) Limited (2)
Q6 Viena Waterfront, Cape Town, 8003, South Africa
Tel.: (27) 214065000
Home Management Services
N.A.I.C.S.: 561110
Graham Stevens *(CEO)*

Sun International Management Limited (1)
6 Sandown Valley Crescent, Sandown, Johannesburg, 2196, Gauteng, South Africa
Tel.: (27) 117807000
Web Site: http://www.suninternational.com
Emp.: 500
Home Management Services
N.A.I.C.S.: 561110

Sun International Travel (Pty) Limited (1)
6 Sandown Valley Crescent, Sandton, 2146, Gauteng, South Africa
Tel.: (27) 117807685
Web Site: http://www.suninternational.com
Home Management Services
N.A.I.C.S.: 561110

Swazispa Holdings Limited (1)
Ezulwini Valley Private Bag, Ezulwini, Eswatini
Tel.: (268) 4161001
Sales Range: $200-249.9 Million
Holding Company
N.A.I.C.S.: 551112

SUN KONG HOLDINGS LTD.

20/F Glass View Commercial Building No 65 Castle Peak Road, Yuen Long, New Territories, China (Hong Kong)
Tel.: (852) 28844226 **Ky**
Web Site: http://www.skhl.com.hk
8631—(HKG)
Rev.: $8,634,555
Assets: $7,424,580
Liabilities: $2,329,935
Net Worth: $5,094,645
Earnings: ($1,538,415)
Emp.: 18
Fiscal Year-end: 03/31/23
Diesel Oil Distr
N.A.I.C.S.: 424710
Ming Yik Law *(Chm)*

SUN KWANG CO., LTD.

37 Chukhang-daero 211beon-gil, Jung-gu, Incheon, Korea (South)
Tel.: (82) 328806500
Web Site: https://www.sun-kwang.co.kr
Year Founded: 1948
003100—(KRS)
Rev.: $132,032,482
Assets: $486,762,867
Liabilities: $224,766,692
Net Worth: $261,996,175
Earnings: $11,117,290
Emp.: 240
Fiscal Year-end: 12/31/22
Logistic Services
N.A.I.C.S.: 541614
Choung-Shik Shim *(CEO)*

Subsidiaries:

Sun Kwang Co., Ltd. - Container Division (1)
112-7 Hang-dong-7-ga, Jung-gu, Incheon, Korea (South)
Tel.: (82) 32 880 6700
Logistics Management Services
N.A.I.C.S.: 541614

Sun Kwang Co., Ltd. - Logistics Division (1)
Logistics Management Services
N.A.I.C.S.: 541614

Sun Kwang Co., Ltd. - Sea Sand Division (1)
1539 Oryu-dong, Seo-gu, Incheon, Korea (South)

AND PRIVATE COMPANIES

Tel.: (82) 32 584 8871
Logistics Management Services
N.A.I.C.S.: 541614

Sun Kwang Logistics Co., Ltd (1)
Tel.: (82) 328806840
Logistics Management Services
N.A.I.C.S.: 541614
Kim Duck-il *(Pres)*

Sun Kwang New Container Terminal Co., Ltd (1)
1711 Jesi-dong Songdo the shap first world Songdo-dong, Yeonsu-gu, Incheon, Korea (South)
Tel.: (82) 32 880 6530
Ship Building Services
N.A.I.C.S.: 336611
Shim Bo *(Pres)*

Sun Myung Aham Logistics Co., Ltd (1)
Tel.: (82) 328830109
Logistics Management Services
N.A.I.C.S.: 541614
Kim Young-Eum *(Mng Dir)*

SUN LIFE CORPORATION
13-11 Banyuhon-cho, Hiratsuka, 254-0024, Kanagawa, Japan
Tel.: (81) 463 221233
Web Site: http://www.sunlife.jp
Year Founded: 1970
Rev.: $105,352,320
Assets: $323,507,280
Liabilities: $267,438,960
Net Worth: $56,068,320
Earnings: $6,571,200
Fiscal Year-end: 03/31/18
Holding Company; Hotel, Insurance, Nursing Care & Special Event Services
N.A.I.C.S.: 551112
Takeshi Hiki *(Pres)*

SUN LIFE FINANCIAL INC.
1 York Street, Toronto, M5J 0B6, ON, Canada
Tel.: (416) 979-9966 ON
Web Site: https://www.sunlife.com
Year Founded: 1871
SLF—(NYSE)
Rev.: $28,668,294,400
Assets: $447,342,718,400
Liabilities: $414,856,638,400
Net Worth: $32,486,080,000
Earnings: $4,142,646,400
Emp.: 30,941
Fiscal Year-end: 12/31/23
Life Insurance & Financial Services
N.A.I.C.S.: 525910
Robert W. Dumas *(Pres/CEO-Sun Life Financial Quebec)*

Subsidiaries:

Advisors Asset Management, Inc. (1)
18925 Base Camp Rd Ste 203, Monument, CO 80132 **(51%)**
Tel.: (719) 488-9956
Web Site: http://www.aam.us.com
Sales Range: $100-124.9 Million
Emp.: 335
Investment Solutions Partner for Brokers/Dealers & Advisors
N.A.I.C.S.: 523940
Scott Colyer *(CEO & CIO)*

Bentall Kennedy (U.S.) Limited Partnership (1)
1215 4th Ave Ste 2400, Seattle, WA 98101
Tel.: (206) 623-4739
Emp.: 100
Real Estate Investment & Management Services
N.A.I.C.S.: 531390
Amy Price *(Pres)*

Subsidiary (Domestic):

Reiner Communities L.P. (2)
100 Spectrum Ctr Dr Ste 830, Irvine, CA 92618
Tel.: (949) 753-0555
Web Site: http://www.reinercommunities.com
Real Estate Services
N.A.I.C.S.: 531190
Ken Reiner *(Owner)*

BentallGreenOak Advisors (Korea) Limited (1)
Posco P and S Tower 16th Floor Teheran-ro 134, Gangnam-gu, Seoul, 135-923, Korea (South)
Tel.: (82) 22 015 7755
Real Estate Services
N.A.I.C.S.: 531390

BestServe Financial Limited (1)
10/F One Harbourfront 18 Tak Fung Street Hunghom, Kowloon, China (Hong Kong)
Tel.: (852) 3183 1833
Web Site: http://www.bestserve.com
Pension Fund & Administrative Services
N.A.I.C.S.: 525110

California Benefits Dental Plan (1)
18881 Von Karman Ave Ste 950, Irvine, CA 92612
Tel.: (949) 757-0152
Web Site: http://www.sunlifedistributors.com
Administrative Services
N.A.I.C.S.: 541611

Crescent Capital Group LP (1)
11100 Santa Monica Blvd Ste 2000, Los Angeles, CA 90025
Tel.: (310) 235-5900
Web Site: https://www.crescentcap.com
Emp.: 200
Financial Services
N.A.I.C.S.: 523999
Elizabeth E. Ko *(Mng Dir)*

Crescent Credit Europe LLP (1)
2 Cavendish Square, London, United Kingdom
Tel.: (44) 2036965420
Financial Investment Services
N.A.I.C.S.: 523940

DentaQuest, LLC (1)
465 Medford St, Boston, MA 02129-1454
Tel.: (800) 417-7140
Web Site: http://www.dentaquest.com
Oral Healthcare Company
N.A.I.C.S.: 456199
Steve Pollock *(Pres & CEO)*

Subsidiary (Domestic):

DCP Holding Company (2)
100 Crowne Point Pl, Sharonville, OH 45241
Tel.: (513) 554-1100
Rev.: $112,522,054
Assets: $66,785,493
Liabilities: $49,763,929
Net Worth: $17,021,564
Earnings: $2,557,072
Emp.: 96
Fiscal Year-end: 12/31/2018
Investment Management Service
N.A.I.C.S.: 523940
Robert C. Hodgkins Jr. *(Pres, CEO & CFO)*

MFS Fund Distributors, Inc. (1)
111 Huntington Ave, Boston, MA 02199-7610
Tel.: (617) 954-5000
Web Site: https://www.mfs.com
Fund Management Services
N.A.I.C.S.: 541611
Karen Gray *(Head)*

MFS Institutional Trust (1)
111 Huntington Ave, Boston, MA 02199
Tel.: (617) 954-5000
Investment Management Service
N.A.I.C.S.: 523999
Steven E. Buller *(Trustee)*

MFS International (U.K.) Limited (1)
One Carter Lane London EC4V 5ER, London, EC4V 5ER, United Kingdom
Tel.: (44) 20 7429 7200
Sales Range: $50-74.9 Million
Emp.: 130
Investment Management Service
N.A.I.C.S.: 523999
Anton Commissaris *(Mng Dir-Switzerland & Austria)*

SUN LIFE FINANCIAL INC.

MFS Investment Management Company (LUX) S.a.r.l. (1)
111 Huntington Ave, Boston, MA 02199
Tel.: (617) 954-5000
Web Site: http://www.mfs.com
Closed End Fund Investment Services
N.A.I.C.S.: 523999

MFS Investment Management K.K. (1)
1-4-2 Kasumigaseki Daidoseimeikasumigaseki Bldg 16f, Chiyoda-Ku, Tokyo, 100-0013, Japan
Tel.: (81) 355108550
Sales Range: $50-74.9 Million
Emp.: 26
Investment Management Service
N.A.I.C.S.: 523999
Yoshinori Inoue *(Mgr-Sls)*

Massachusetts Financial Services Company (1)
1011 Huntington Ave, Boston, MA 02199
Tel.: (617) 954-5000
Sales Range: $700-749.9 Million
Emp.: 1,500
Financial Services
N.A.I.C.S.: 523999

NewTower Trust Company (1)
7315 Wisconsin Ave Ste 300 W, Bethesda, MD 20814
Tel.: (240) 235-9960
Web Site: https://www.newtowertrust.com
Trust Services
N.A.I.C.S.: 525920
Robert Edwards *(Pres)*

PT Sun Life Indonesia (1)
Jl Dr Ide Anak Agung Gde Agung Blok 6 3 Kawasan Mega Kuningan, Jakarta Selatan, 12950, Indonesia
Tel.: (62) 215 289 0000
Web Site: https://www.sunlife.co.id
Financial Services
N.A.I.C.S.: 523999
Elin Waty *(Pres)*

Pinnacle Care International, LLC (1)
250 W Pratt St 1100, Baltimore, MD 21201
Tel.: (410) 752-1712
Web Site: https://www.pinnaclecare.com
Health Care Advisory Services
N.A.I.C.S.: 621498

Prime Advisors, Inc. (1)
Redmond Ridge Corp Ctr 22635 NE Marketplace Dr Ste 160, Redmond, WA 98053
Tel.: (425) 202-2000
Web Site: http://www.primeadvisors.com
Rev.: $13,000,000,000
Emp.: 44
Investment Advice
N.A.I.C.S.: 523940

Ryan Labs Asset Management Inc. (1)
500 Fifth Avenue Suite 2520, New York, NY 10110
Tel.: (212) 635-2300
Web Site: http://www.ryanlabs.com
Sales Range: $1-9.9 Million
Emp.: 100
Managed Fixed Income & Mutual Funds
N.A.I.C.S.: 523999
Michael P. Donelan *(Sr Portfolio Mgr)*

Sun Life Assurance Company of Canada (1)
100 Simcoe St Ste 115, Toronto, M5H 3G2, ON, Canada **(100%)**
Tel.: (647) 788-2415
Web Site: https://www.sunlife.ca
Sales Range: $50-74.9 Million
Emp.: 10
Distibutor of Mutual Funds
N.A.I.C.S.: 523150

Subsidiary (Domestic):

Sun Life Assurance (2)
227 King St W, Waterloo, N2J 4C5, ON, Canada **(100%)**
Tel.: (416) 408-8100
Web Site: http://www.sunlife.ca
Provider of Residential Mortgages & Deposit Services
N.A.I.C.S.: 523991

Sun Life Assurance (2)
1155 Metcalfe Street, Montreal, H3B 2V9, QC, Canada **(100%)**
Tel.: (514) 866-6411
Web Site: http://www.sunlife.ca
Administrative Claims & Actuarial Services
N.A.I.C.S.: 523940

Joint Venture (Non-US):

Sun Life Everbright Life Insurance Company Limited (2)
4th Floor Tianjin International Building 75 Nanjing Road, Heping District, Tianjin, 300050, China **(24.99%)**
Tel.: (86) 22 2339 1188
Web Site: http://www.sunlife-everbright.com
Life Insurance Products & Services
N.A.I.C.S.: 524113

Subsidiary (Domestic):

Sun Life Financial Insurance (2)
227 King St S, Waterloo, N2J 4C5, ON, Canada **(100%)**
Tel.: (519) 888-3900
Web Site: http://www.sunlife.ca
Emp.: 2,300
Insurance
N.A.I.C.S.: 524210

Sun Life Financial Investment Services (Canada) Inc. (2)
227 King St S, Waterloo, N2J 4C5, ON, Canada
Tel.: (519) 888-2290
Web Site: http://www.sunlife.com
Financial Investment Services
N.A.I.C.S.: 523999

Subsidiary (Domestic):

Excel Funds Management, Inc. (3)
2810 Matheson Blvd E Ste 800, Mississauga, L4W 4X7, ON, Canada
Tel.: (905) 813-7111
Investment Fund Management Services
N.A.I.C.S.: 523999
Bhim D. Asdhir *(Pres & CEO)*

Subsidiary (Non-US):

Sun Life Financial Investments (Bermuda) Ltd. (2)
Victoria Hall-2nd Floor 11 Victoria Street, PO Box HM 3070, Hamilton, HM11, Bermuda
Tel.: (441) 2946050
Web Site: http://www.salesnet.sunlife.com
Sales Range: $25-49.9 Million
Financial & Insurance Services
N.A.I.C.S.: 524298

Subsidiary (Domestic):

Sun Life Financial Trust Inc. (2)
227 King St S, PO Box 1601, Waterloo, N2J 4C5, ON, Canada **(100%)**
Tel.: (519) 888-8000
Web Site: http://www.sunlife.ca
Trust Services
N.A.I.C.S.: 523991

Sun Life Information Services Canada, Inc. (2)
150 King St W, Toronto, M5H 1J9, ON, Canada
Tel.: (416) 979-9966
Financial Management Services
N.A.I.C.S.: 523999

Subsidiary (Non-US):

Sun Life Information Services Ireland Limited (2)
Unit 324 Ida Industrial Park Cork Road, Waterford, Ireland
Tel.: (353) 51 333300
Web Site: http://www.sunlife.ie
Sales Range: $75-99.9 Million
Software Development Services
N.A.I.C.S.: 541511

Sun Life Assurance Company of Canada (U.K.) Limited (1)
Matrix House Basing View, Basingstoke, RG21 4DZ, United Kingdom
Tel.: (44) 1256841414
Web Site: http://www.sloc.co.uk
Insurance Management Services
N.A.I.C.S.: 524298

SUN LIFE FINANCIAL INC.

Sun Life Financial Inc.—(Continued)

Sun Life Financial Of Canada (U.K.) Limited (1)
Matrix House, Basing View, Basingstoke, RG21 4DZ, Hampshire, United Kingdom (100%)
Tel.: (44) 8701646060
Web Site: http://www.sunlifefinancialofcanada.co.uk
Sales Range: $350-399.9 Million
Emp.: 600
Life Insurance, Health Insurance & Pension Plans
N.A.I.C.S.: 524292

Subsidiary (Domestic):

Sun Life of Canada Unit Managers Limited (2)
Matrix House, Basing View, Basingstoke, RG21 4DZ, Hampshire, United Kingdom (100%)
Tel.: (44) 8701611111
Web Site: http://www.sunlifeofcanada.co.uk
Sales Range: $50-74.9 Million
Emp.: 100
Insurance Services
N.A.I.C.S.: 524128

Sun Life Financial Plans, Inc. (1)
2/F Sun Life Centre 5th Avenue corner Rizal Drive, Bonifacio Global City, Taguig, 1634, Philippines
Tel.: (63) 28 555 8888
Financial Services
N.A.I.C.S.: 523999

Sun Life Financial Reinsurance (Barbados) Limited (1)
Orena St Law Main Rd, Christ Church, Bridgetown, BB15029, Barbados
Tel.: (246) 418 9945
Reinsurance Management Services
N.A.I.C.S.: 524130
Chris Evans (CFO & VP)

Sun Life Financial of Canada Trustee Limited (1)
Matrix House, Basingstoke, RG21 4DZ, United Kingdom
Tel.: (44) 8701611111
Insurance Brokerage Services
N.A.I.C.S.: 524210

Sun Life Global Investments (Canada) Inc. (1)
1 York Street, Toronto, M5J 0B6, ON, Canada
Web Site: http://www.sunlifeglobalinvestments.com
Investment Management Service
N.A.I.C.S.: 523999

Sun Life Grepa Financial, Inc. (1)
21 Sen Gil Puyat Avenue, Makati, Philippines
Tel.: (63) 28161726
Web Site: http://www.sunlifegrepa.com
Sales Range: $25-49.9 Million
Life Insurance & Other Insurance Products & Services
N.A.I.C.S.: 524113

Subsidiary (Domestic):

Great Life Financial Assurance Corporation (2)
21/F Tower 2 RCBC Plz, 6819 Ayala Ave, Makati, 1200, Philippines (80%)
Tel.: (63) 27532151
Web Site: http://grepalife.node27.com
Emp.: 200
Life, Health, Property & Casualty Insurance Products & Services
N.A.I.C.S.: 524113

Grepalife Asset Management Corporation (2)
6/F GREPALIFE Bldg 221 Sen Gil Puyat Avenue, Makati, Philippines (100%)
Tel.: (63) 28456408
Web Site: http://www.grepafunds.com
Emp.: 8
Asset & Fund Management Services
N.A.I.C.S.: 523940

Sun Life India Service Centre Private Limited (1)
Uni-Tech World Cyber Park Sector-39 Ground Floor, Gurgaon, 122001, Haryana, India
Tel.: (91) 124 4565500
Business Support Services
N.A.I.C.S.: 561990
Shiney Prasad (Mng Dir)

Sun Life Malaysia Assurance Berhad (1)
Level 11 338 Jalan Tuankku Abdul Rahman, 50100, Kuala Lumpur, Malaysia (49%)
Tel.: (60) 3 2612 3600
Web Site: http://www.sunlifemalaysia.com
Life Insurance & Financial Planning Services
N.A.I.C.S.: 524113

Subsidiary (Domestic):

Sun Life Malaysia Takaful Berhad (2)
Level 11 338 Jalan Tuanku Abdul Rahman, 50100, Kuala Lumpur, Malaysia
Tel.: (60) 3 2612 3600
Web Site: http://www.sunlifemalaysia.com
Insurance Services
N.A.I.C.S.: 524298
Jeffry Azmi Mohd Shah (CEO)

Sun Life of Canada (U.S.) Holdings, Inc. (1)
1 Sun Life Exec Pk, Wellesley, MA 02481
Tel.: (781) 237-6030
Web Site: http://www.sunlife.com
Investment Management Service
N.A.I.C.S.: 327910

SynchroSERV Inc. (1)
Suite 770 One Bentall Centre 505 Burrard Street, PO Box No 89, Vancouver, V7X 1M4, BC, Canada
Tel.: (604) 628-5973
Web Site: https://www.synchroserv.com
Real Estate Services
N.A.I.C.S.: 531210

The Mortgage Works (UK) Plc (1)
Nationwide House Pipers Way, Swindon, SN38 1NW, United Kingdom (100%)
Tel.: (44) 8454545400
Web Site: https://www.themortgageworks.co.uk
Sales Range: $75-99.9 Million
Emp.: 100
Mortgage Lender
N.A.I.C.S.: 522310

SUN LIFE HOLDING CO., LTD.
13-11 Banyu Honmachi, Hiratsuka, 254-0024, Kanagawa, Japan
Tel.: (81) 463221233
Web Site: https://sunlife-hd.jp
Year Founded: 2018
7040—(TKS)
Rev.: $89,248,220
Assets: $236,862,740
Liabilities: $197,169,690
Net Worth: $39,693,050
Earnings: $7,376,760
Fiscal Year-end: 03/31/24
Holding Company
N.A.I.C.S.: 551112
Keiji Takeuchi (Chm)

SUN LIMITED
Ebene Skies Rue de lInstitut, Ebene, Mauritius
Tel.: (230) 4020000
Web Site: https://www.yoursunlife.com
Year Founded: 1983
SUN—(MAU)
Rev.: $175,285,476
Assets: $500,800,432
Liabilities: $247,113,815
Net Worth: $253,686,617
Earnings: $32,729,749
Emp.: 3,084
Fiscal Year-end: 06/30/23
Home Management Services
N.A.I.C.S.: 721110
Tommy Yun Shing Wong (CFO)

Subsidiaries:

World Leisure Holidays (Pty) Ltd (1)
Ground Floor 292 Surrey Avenue, PO Box 1474, Ferndale, Randburg, 2125, South Africa
Tel.: (27) 112852500
Web Site: https://www.wlh.co.za
Tour Operator
N.A.I.C.S.: 561520

SUN LING & COMPANY
42 Lee Chung St 12/F, Chai Wan, China (Hong Kong)
Tel.: (852) 25565645 HK
Web Site: http://www.sunling.com
Year Founded: 1962
Sales Range: $25-49.9 Million
Emp.: 10
Sourcing of Various Personal & Home Accessory Mfr
N.A.I.C.S.: 339910

Subsidiaries:

Sundial & Co. (1)
42 Lee Chung St., 12/F., Chai Wan, China (Hong Kong)
Personal Care Products
N.A.I.C.S.: 812199

SUN MACHINERY CO., LTD.
843-24 Pureundeulpan-ro, Paltanmyeon, Hwaseong, 445-949, Gyeonggi-do, Korea (South)
Tel.: (82) 313549150
Web Site: https://www.sun-mc.net
Year Founded: 1988
Sales Range: $25-49.9 Million
Emp.: 60
Motor Vehicle Parts & Medical Equipment Mfr
N.A.I.C.S.: 336390
Chang-Yeob Park (CEO)

SUN MARK LIMITED
428 Long Drive, Greenford, UB6 8UH, Middlesex, United Kingdom
Tel.: (44) 20 8575 3700
Web Site: http://www.sunmark.co.uk
Year Founded: 1995
Sales Range: $200-249.9 Million
Emp.: 55
Consumer Products Whslr
N.A.I.C.S.: 445110
Rami Ranger (Chm & Mng Dir)

SUN MARKETING & COMMUNICATIONS LTD./SOLEIL COMMUNICATIONS-MARKETING LTEE
2120 Rue Sherbrooke E Bureau 900, Montreal, H2K 1C3, QC, Canada
Tel.: (514) 521-5464
Web Site: http://www.soleilcom.com
Year Founded: 1973
Sales Range: $10-24.9 Million
Emp.: 20
N.A.I.C.S.: 541810
Gilles Lesage (VP)

SUN MAX TECH LTD.
9F-1 9F No 166 Jian 1st Rd, Zhonghe District, New Taipei City, 23511, Taiwan
Tel.: (886) 282263300
Web Site: https://sun-max.com.tw
Year Founded: 2013
6591—(TAI)
Rev.: $45,201,280
Assets: $85,809,049
Liabilities: $28,301,186
Net Worth: $57,507,863
Earnings: $3,869,028
Emp.: 1,380
Fiscal Year-end: 12/31/23
Industrial Fan Equipment Mfr
N.A.I.C.S.: 333413

Wen-Fang Hsu (Chm & Pres)

SUN MESSE CO., LTD.
7-5-1 Kuzegawa-cho, Ogaki, 503-8518, Gifu, Japan
Tel.: (81) 584819111
Web Site: https://www.sunmesse.co.jp
Year Founded: 1935
7883—(TKS)
Rev.: $109,897,558
Assets: $135,771,353
Liabilities: $55,566,552
Net Worth: $80,204,801
Earnings: $1,698,050
Emp.: 663
Fiscal Year-end: 03/31/24
Commercial Printing Mfr
N.A.I.C.S.: 323111
Katsuhide Tanaka (Vice Chm)

Subsidiaries:

Nippon Event Planning Co., Ltd. (1)
1-1-5 Suga, Gifu, Gifu, Japan
Tel.: (81) 582746334
Web Site: http://www.ne-planning.com
Event Management Services
N.A.I.C.S.: 711310

Sun Messe (Thailand) Co., Ltd. (1)
68/27 North Sathorn Road Silom Bangrak, Bangkok, 10500, Thailand
Tel.: (66) 26320058
Web Site: https://www.sunmessethai.com
Packaging Product Mfr & Distr
N.A.I.C.S.: 322211

Sun Messe Co., Ltd. - Naka Factory (1)
423 Arakawa-Cho, Ogaki, 503-0993, Gifu, Japan
Tel.: (81) 584922111
Paper Packaging Product Mfr.
N.A.I.C.S.: 322211

Sun Messe Co., Ltd. - Nishi Factory (1)
452-1 Arakawa-Cho, Ogaki, 503-0993, Gifu, Japan
Tel.: (81) 584919191
Paper Packaging Product Mfr.
N.A.I.C.S.: 322211

SUN PEAK METALS CORP.
Suite 1400-400 Burrard Street, Vancouver, V6B 0S6, BC, Canada
Tel.: (604) 999-1099
Web Site: https://www.sunpeakmetals.com
SUNPF—(OTCQB)
Rev.: $148,613
Assets: $10,262,110
Liabilities: $166,210
Net Worth: $10,095,900
Earnings: ($2,446,952)
Fiscal Year-end: 12/31/20
Metal Exploration Services
N.A.I.C.S.: 213115
Kaeli Gattens (VP-Corp Dev)

SUN PHARMA ADVANCED RESEARCH COMPANY LTD
17 B Mahal Industrial Estate Mahakali Caves Road, Andheri East, Mumbai, 400 093, India
Tel.: (91) 2266455645
Web Site: https://sparc.life
Year Founded: 2007
532872—(BOM)
Rev.: $35,267,450
Assets: $31,352,658
Liabilities: $54,319,001
Net Worth: ($22,966,343)
Earnings: ($20,630,446)
Emp.: 410
Fiscal Year-end: 03/31/21
Drug Discovery Company
N.A.I.C.S.: 541715
Dilip S. Shanghvi (Chm & Mng Dir)

AND PRIVATE COMPANIES

SUN PHARMACEUTICAL INDUSTRIES LTD.

SUN PHARMACEUTICAL IN-DUSTRIES LTD.
Sun House CTS No 201 B/1 Western Express Highway, Goregaon E, Mumbai, 400063, India
Tel.: (91) 2243244324
Web Site:
  https://www.sunpharma.com
Year Founded: 1983
524715—(NSE)
Rev.: $5,337,833,463
Assets: $9,680,905,222
Liabilities: $2,569,164,918
Net Worth: $7,111,740,303
Earnings: $1,015,955,878
Emp.: 19,124
Fiscal Year-end: 03/31/23
Pharmaceutical Product Mfr & Distr
N.A.I.C.S.: 325412
Dilip S. Shanghvi *(Mng Dir)*

Subsidiaries:

AO Ranbaxy (1)
Electrozavodskaya 27 bld 8 Business center LeFort, Moscow, Russia
Tel.: (7) 4952345611
Pharmaceuticals Product Mfr
N.A.I.C.S.: 325412

Alkaloida Chemical Company Zrt (1)
Kabay Janos Unit 29, Tiszavasvari, 4440, Szabolcs Szatmar Ber, Hungary
Tel.: (36) 42 275 511
Pharmaceutical Products Mfr & Distr
N.A.I.C.S.: 325412

Concert Pharmaceuticals, Inc. (1)
65 Hayden Ave Ste 3000N, Lexington, MA 02421
Tel.: (781) 860-0045
Web Site: http://www.concertpharma.com
Rev.: $32,578,000
Assets: $165,316,000
Liabilities: $53,091,000
Net Worth: $112,225,000
Earnings: ($80,051,000)
Emp.: 64
Fiscal Year-end: 12/31/2021
Pharmaceuticals Mfr
N.A.I.C.S.: 325412
Justine E. Koenigsberg *(Sr VP-Corp Comm & IR)*

Pola Pharma Inc. (1)
8-9-5 Nishi Gotanda, Shinagawa-ku, Tokyo, 141-0031, Japan
Tel.: (81) 357196663
Web Site: http://www.pola-pharma.co.jp
Sales Range: $125-149.9 Million
Emp.: 280
Cosmetics Mfr
N.A.I.C.S.: 325620
Norihiro Araki *(Pres)*

Ranbaxy (Netherlands) B.V. (1)
Polaris avenue 87, 2132 JH, Hoofddorp, Netherlands
Tel.: (31) 23 568 5501
Holding Company
N.A.I.C.S.: 551112

Subsidiary (Non-US):

Basics GmbH (2)
Hemmelrather Weg 201 Building GIZ 1, 51377, Leverkusen, Germany **(100%)**
Tel.: (49) 214 40399 0
Web Site: http://www.sunpharma.com
Sales Range: $25-49.9 Million
Pharmaceuticals Producut Sales
N.A.I.C.S.: 424210

Ranbaxy (Malaysia) Sdn. Bhd. (2)
Peti 8 5th Floor South Block Wisma Selangor Dredging 142-A, Jalan Ampang, 50450, Kuala Lumpur, Malaysia **(71.22%)**
Tel.: (60) 3 216 141 81
Web Site: http://www.sunpharma.com
Sales Range: $10-24.9 Million
Pharmaceutical Products Mfr & Distr
N.A.I.C.S.: 325412

Ranbaxy (Poland) Sp. z o.o. (2)
Ul Kubickiego 11, 02-954, Warsaw, Poland
Tel.: (48) 22 642 07 75
Web Site: http://www.sunpharma.com
Pharmaceutical Products Distr

N.A.I.C.S.: 424210
Przemyslaw Chromiec *(Member-Mgmt Bd)*

Ranbaxy (U.K.) Ltd. (2)
5th Floor Hyde Park Hayes 3 11 Millington Road, Hayes, UB3 4AZ, United Kingdom **(100%)**
Tel.: (44) 2088488688
Web Site: http://www.sunpharma.com
Sales Range: $25-49.9 Million
Pharmaceuticals Distr
N.A.I.C.S.: 424210

Ranbaxy Australia Pty Ltd (2)
Ground Floor 9-13 Waterloo Road, North Ryde, 2113, NSW, Australia **(100%)**
Tel.: (61) 2 9887 2600
Web Site: http://www.sunpharma.com
Sales Range: $25-49.9 Million
Emp.: 35
Pharmaceutical Products Distr
N.A.I.C.S.: 424210
Alexander Evans *(Gen Mgr)*

Ranbaxy Egypt Company L.L.C. (2)
3 Ahmed Nessim St, Giza, Egypt
Tel.: (20) 2 37613973
Sales Range: $25-49.9 Million
Emp.: 10
Pharmaceutical Products Mfr & Distr
N.A.I.C.S.: 325412
Hany Mashaal *(Gen Mgr)*

Ranbaxy Italia SpA (2)
Viale Giulio Richard 1, 20143, Milan, Italy
Tel.: (39) 02 25 066 1
Web Site: http://www.sunpharma.com
Sales Range: $10-24.9 Million
Generic Pharmaceuticals Sales & Distr
N.A.I.C.S.: 424210

Ranbaxy Pharmaceuticals (Pty) Ltd (2)
14 Lautre Road Stormill Ext 1, Roodepoort, 1724, Gauteng, South Africa **(100%)**
Tel.: (27) 114950100
Pharmaceuticals Mfr
N.A.I.C.S.: 325412
Desmond Brothers *(CEO)*

Ranbaxy Pharmaceuticals Canada Inc. (2)
126 East Drive, Brampton, L6T 1C1, ON, Canada
Tel.: (905) 790-5199
Web Site: http://www.sunpharma.com
Sales Range: $25-49.9 Million
Emp.: 22
Pharmaceutical Products Distr
N.A.I.C.S.: 424210
Paul Drake *(Gen Mgr)*

Ranbaxy South Africa Proprietary Limited (2)
Ground Floor Tugela House Riverside Office Park 1303 Heuwel Avenue, Centurion, Pretoria, 1303, South Africa **(100%)**
Tel.: (27) 12 643 2000
Web Site: http://www.sunpharma.com
Sales Range: $25-49.9 Million
Pharmaceutical Products Mfr & Whslr
N.A.I.C.S.: 325412
Desmond Brothers *(CEO)*

Subsidiary (US):

Ranbaxy, Inc. (2)
600 College Rd E Ste 2100, Princeton, NJ 08540-6636 **(100%)**
Tel.: (609) 720-9200
Rev.: $542,832,891
Assets: $865,838,427
Liabilities: $357,105,508
Net Worth: $508,732,919
Earnings: $55,274,669
Fiscal Year-end: 03/31/2016
Pharmaceutical Products Mfr & Whslr
N.A.I.C.S.: 325412

Subsidiary (Domestic):

InSite Vision Incorporated (3)
965 Atlantic Ave, Alameda, CA 94501 **(100%)**
Tel.: (510) 865-8800
Web Site: http://www.insitevision.com
Genetic Glaucoma Research & Ophthalmic Disease Treatment Mfr
N.A.I.C.S.: 325412

Kamran Hosseini *(Chief Medical Officer & VP-Clinical Affairs)*

Ohm Laboratories, Inc. (3)
14 Terminal Rd, New Brunswick, NJ 08901
Tel.: (609) 720-9200
Web Site: http://www.sunpharma.com
Prescription & OTC Drugs Mfr
N.A.I.C.S.: 325412
Chuck Caprariello *(VP-Corp Comm & Govt Affairs)*

Ranbaxy Pharmaceuticals, Inc. (3)
2 independence way, Princeton, NJ 08540-6636
Tel.: (609) 720-9200
Sales Range: $50-74.9 Million
Emp.: 178
Branded Generic Pharmaceuticals Mfr & Pharmaceutical Research
N.A.I.C.S.: 325412
Charles M. Caprariello *(VP-Corp Comm & Govt Affairs)*

Subsidiary (Non-US):

Ranbaxy- PRP (Peru) S.A.C. (2)
534 Dos de Mayo Avenue, Miraflores, Lima, Peru **(100%)**
Tel.: (51) 1 441 4553
Emp.: 5
Pharmaceutical Products Sales & Distr
N.A.I.C.S.: 424210
Theresa Torres Moreno *(Mgr-Fin)*

Sun Pharmaceuticals Morocco LLC (2)
169 Avenue Hassan 1er etage No 3 B 5, Casablanca, 20070, Morocco **(100%)**
Tel.: (212) 522 20 49 81
Web Site: http://www.sunpharma.com
Pharmaceutical Products Sales & Distr
N.A.I.C.S.: 424210
Atul Chhabra *(Gen Mgr)*

Ranbaxy (Thailand) Co., Ltd. (1)
No 475 Siripinyo Building 8 Floor Sri Ayutthaya Road Phayathai Road, Rajathevi, Bangkok, 10400, Thailand
Tel.: (66) 2 246 3300
Pharmaceutical Product Mfr
N.A.I.C.S.: 325412

Ranbaxy Farmaceutica Ltda. (1)
Avenida Doutor Napoleao Rodrigues Laureano n 2821 quadra CH Lote 02, Fazenda Planicie, Goiania, 74690-060, Brazil
Tel.: (55) 623 205 2290
Pharmaceutical Products Distr
N.A.I.C.S.: 424210

Ranbaxy Nigeria Limited (1)
1st Floor Abimbola House 24 Abimbola Street, Ilasmaja, Oshodi, Lagos, Nigeria
Tel.: (234) 803 316 0727
Pharmaceutical Product Mfr & Distr
N.A.I.C.S.: 325412

Ranbaxy Pharmaceuticals Ukraine LLC (1)
175 Kharkivske Shose, Kiev, 02121, Ukraine
Tel.: (380) 44 371 7724
Pharmaceutical Products Distr
N.A.I.C.S.: 424210

Sonke Pharmaceuticals Proprietary Limited (1)
Ground Floor Tugela Building Riverside Office Park 1303 Heuwel Avenue, cnr of Heuwel and Lenchen Avenue North, Centurion, 0046, South Africa
Tel.: (27) 12 643 2000
Web Site:
  https://www.sonkepharmaceuticals.co.za
Pharmaceuticals Product Mfr
N.A.I.C.S.: 325412
Deepakh Sewnarain *(CEO)*

Sun Farmaceutica do Brasil Ltda. (1)
Rodovia Go 080 Km02 Farms 1/2, Jardim Pompeia, Goiania, 74690-170, Brazil
Tel.: (55) 623 205 2290
Pharmaceutical Products Distr
N.A.I.C.S.: 424210

Sun Pharma ANZ Pty. Ltd. (1)
Suite 2 02 Level 2 12 Waterloo Road, Macquarie Park, 2113, NSW, Australia

Tel.: (61) 298872600
Pharmaceutical Product Mfr & Distr
N.A.I.C.S.: 325412

Sun Pharma De Mexico S.A. de C.V. (1)
Av Insurgentes Sur 600 Interior Mezzanine Colonia del Valle, Benito Juarez, 03100, Mexico, Mexico **(75%)**
Tel.: (52) 555 663 2577
Web Site: https://www.sunpharma.com.mx
Pharmaceuticals Product Mfr
N.A.I.C.S.: 325412

Sun Pharma Exports Ltd (1)
Acne Plaza Andheri Kurla Rd Andheri East, Mumbai, 400059, Maharashtra, India
Tel.: (91) 22 28230102
Pharmaceutical Preparation Mfr
N.A.I.C.S.: 325412

Sun Pharma Japan Ltd. (1)
Forecast Gotanda West 8-9-5 Nishigotanda, Shinagawa-ku, Tokyo, 141-0001, Japan
Tel.: (81) 35 719 6663
Web Site: https://jp.sunpharma.com
Pharmaceutical Product Mfr & Distr
N.A.I.C.S.: 325412
Junichi Nakamichi *(Head)*

Sun Pharma Laboratorios, S.L.U. (1)
Rambla De Catalunya 53-55 5th Floor, 08007, Barcelona, Spain
Tel.: (34) 93 342 7890
Pharmaceutical Product Mfr & Distr
N.A.I.C.S.: 325412

Sun Pharmaceutical (Bangladesh) Limited (1)
14th Floor West Side Police Plaza Concord Tower-B, Gulshan-1, Dhaka, 1212, Bangladesh
Tel.: (880) 255 045 0012
Pharmaceuticals Product Mfr
N.A.I.C.S.: 325412

Sun Pharmaceutical Industries (Australia) Pty. Ltd. (1)
Controlled Substances Division Princes Highway, Port Fairy, Melbourne, 3281, VIC, Australia
Tel.: (61) 355680222
Web Site: http://sunpharma.com
Pharmaceuticals Product Mfr
N.A.I.C.S.: 325412

Sun Pharmaceutical Industries Europe B.V (1)
Polarisavenue 87, 2132 JH, Hoofddorp, Netherlands
Tel.: (31) 235685501
Web Site: http://www.sunpharma.com
Sales Range: $25-49.9 Million
Pharmaceutical Products Mfr & Whslr
N.A.I.C.S.: 325412

Sun Pharmaceutical Industries S.A.C. (1)
Av Republica De Panama N 3418-3420 Oficina 1501-A, 15047, San Isidro, Lima, Peru
Tel.: (51) 1 717 4830
Pharmaceutical Product Mfr & Distr
N.A.I.C.S.: 325412

Sun Pharmaceutical Industries, Inc. (1)
1 Commerce Dr, Cranbury, NJ 08512
Tel.: (609) 819-8200
Web Site: http://www.sunpharma.com
Sales Range: $200-249.9 Million
Emp.: 535
Generic & Private Label Prescription Drug Developer
N.A.I.C.S.: 325412
Kirti Ganorkar *(Exec VP-India Bus)*

Subsidiary (Domestic):

Chattem Chemicals, Inc. (2)
3708 St Elmo Ave, Chattanooga, TN 37409-1235
Tel.: (423) 822-5000
Web Site: http://www.chattemchemicals.com
Narcotic Raw Material Importer & Mfr
N.A.I.C.S.: 325199
Rich Redding *(Partner-HR Bus)*

DUSA Pharmaceuticals, Inc. (2)
25 Upton Dr, Wilmington, MA 01887
Tel.: (978) 657-7500

SUN PHARMACEUTICAL INDUSTRIES LTD.

Sun Pharmaceutical Industries Ltd.—(Continued)
Web Site: http://www.dusapharma.com
Sales Range: $25-49.9 Million
Emp.: 96
Pharmaceuticals Mfr
N.A.I.C.S.: 325412

Sun Radiopharma Company (2)
29 Dunham Rd, Billerica, MA 01821
Tel.: (781) 275-7120
Web Site: https://www.pharmalucence.com
Sales Range: $1-9.9 Million
Emp.: 37
Human Injectable Pharmaceuticals Mfr
N.A.I.C.S.: 325412
Jeanne Fiore (VP-Regulatory Affairs & Compliance)

Sun Pharmaceutical UK Limited (1)
1200 Century Way Thorpe Business Park, Colton, Leeds, LS15 8ZA, West Yorkshire, United Kingdom
Tel.: (44) 7787433889
Pharmaceuticals Product Mfr
N.A.I.C.S.: 325412

Sun Pharmaceuticals France (1)
Avant Seine building 11 - 15 quai de Dion Bouton, 92816, Puteaux, Cedex, France
Tel.: (33) 141444450
Web Site: http://sunpharma.fr
Sales Range: $50-74.9 Million
Pharmaceutical Products Distr
N.A.I.C.S.: 424210

Sun Pharmaceuticals Germany GmbH (1)
Hemmelrather Weg 201 Building GIZ 1, 51377, Leverkusen, Germany
Tel.: (49) 214403990
Web Site: http://www.sunpharma.com
Pharmaceuticals Product Mfr
N.A.I.C.S.: 325412

Sun Pharmaceuticals Italia S.R.L. (1)
Via Luigi Rizzo 8, 20151, Milan, Italy
Tel.: (39) 02 33 490 793
Web Site: http://www.sunpharma-europe.it
Pharmaceutical Product Mfr
N.A.I.C.S.: 325412

Sun Pharmaceuticals Spain, SL. (1)
C Bobinadora 1-5 Planta 1a Local 13, Mataro, 08302, Barcelona, Spain
Tel.: (34) 937980285
Web Site: http://www.sunpharma-europe.es
Sales Range: $50-74.9 Million
Emp.: 7
Pharmaceutical Products Distr
N.A.I.C.S.: 424210
Murillo Torra Javier (Mgr-Fin)

TKS Farmaceutica Ltda (1)
Rod GO-080 Km 02 Jardim Pompeia, Goiania, 74690-170, Goias, Brazil
Tel.: (55) 62 3205 2290
Web Site: http://www.tksfarmaceutica.com.br
Pharmaceutical Products Mfr & Distr
N.A.I.C.S.: 325412

Taro Pharmaceutical Industries Ltd. (1)
14 Hakitor Street, Haifa Bay, 2624761, Israel (66.3%)
Tel.: (972) 48475700
Web Site: https://www.taro.com
Rev.: $572,952,000
Assets: $2,135,513,000
Liabilities: $404,654,000
Net Worth: $1,730,859,000
Earnings: $25,445,000
Emp.: 1,554
Fiscal Year-end: 03/31/2023
Pharmaceuticals Mfr & Distr
N.A.I.C.S.: 325412
Dilip S. Shanghvi (Chm)

Subsidiary (US):

Taro Pharmaceuticals U.S.A. Inc. (2)
3 Skyline Dr Ste 120, Hawthorne, NY 10532-2163
Tel.: (914) 345-9001
Web Site: http://www.taro.com
Mfr & Distributor of Generic Pharmaceuticals
N.A.I.C.S.: 424210

Subsidiary (Non-US):

Taro Pharmaceuticals, Inc. (2)
130 East Drive, Brampton, L6T 1C1, ON, Canada (100%)
Tel.: (905) 791-8276
Web Site: http://www.taro.ca
Sales Range: $100-124.9 Million
Emp.: 450
Mfr & Distributor of Generic Pharmaceuticals
N.A.I.C.S.: 325412

Subsidiary (US):

The Alchemee LLC (2)
PO Box 2021, Harlan, IA 51593
Web Site: https://www.alchemee.com
N.A.I.C.S.: 456120
Cosmetic Product Whslr
Shannon Pappas (Head-Global)

Terapia SA (1)
124 Fabricii Street, 400632, Cluj-Napoca, Romania
Tel.: (40) 26 450 1500
Pharmaceutical Product Mfr & Distr
N.A.I.C.S.: 325412
Bogdan Ungureanu (Head)

Vivaldis Health & Foods Private Limited (1)
803/804 Clover Hills Plaza NIBM Road opposite Golds Gym, Pune, 411048, Maharashtra, India
Tel.: (91) 7767922244
Web Site: https://www.vivaldis.co.in
Animal Healthcare Services
N.A.I.C.S.: 541940

Zenotech Laboratories Limited (1)
Survey No 250-252 Turkapally Village, Shameerpet Mandal RR District, Hyderabad, 500 078, Telangana, India (68.84%)
Tel.: (91) 9032044584
Web Site: https://www.zenotechlab.com
Rev.: $3,806,712
Assets: $11,977,560
Liabilities: $5,029,500
Net Worth: $6,948,060
Earnings: $1,508,850
Emp.: 123
Fiscal Year-end: 03/31/2020
Generic Biopharmaceutical Mfr & Distr
N.A.I.C.S.: 325412
Kachappilly Varghese Poly (CFO)

SUN RACE STURMEY-ARCHER INC.

No 51 Haishan Central Street, Luzhu District, Taoyuan, 33856, Taiwan
Tel.: (886) 33543900
Web Site: https://www.sunrace.com
1526—(TAI)
Rev.: $32,543,967
Assets: $87,415,609
Liabilities: $41,758,231
Net Worth: $45,657,378
Earnings: $1,487,982
Fiscal Year-end: 12/31/23
Bicycle Mfr
N.A.I.C.S.: 336991

Subsidiaries:

Sun Race Sturmey Archer USA Inc. (1)
1436 2nd St #409, Napa, CA 94559-2824
Tel.: (707) 259-6700
Bicycle Spare Parts Mfr & Distr
N.A.I.C.S.: 333613

Sun Race Sturmey-Archer Europe BV (1)
Nijverheidsweg 19A, 3641 RP, Mijdrecht, Netherlands
Tel.: (31) 206090221
Web Site: http://www.sunrace.com
Bicycle Spare Parts Mfr & Distr
N.A.I.C.S.: 336991

SUN RESIDENTIAL REAL ESTATE INVESTMENT TRUST

2300-130 King Street West Exchange Tower, Toronto, M5X 1C8, ON, Canada
Tel.: (416) 729-7592
Web Site: https://www.sunresreit.ca
SRES—(TSXV)
Rev.: $5,780,485
Assets: $64,255,183
Liabilities: $32,739,553
Net Worth: $31,515,630
Earnings: ($8,548,041)
Fiscal Year-end: 12/31/23
Real Estate Manangement Services
N.A.I.C.S.: 531210
Gordon Wiebe (CEO)

SUN RETAIL LTD.

722 Gala Empire Drive in Road, Opp Tv Tower Thaltej, Ahmedabad, 380054, India
Tel.: (91) 9512521919
Web Site: https://www.sunretail.in
Year Founded: 2007
542025—(BOM)
Rev.: $1,812,313
Assets: $3,966,621
Liabilities: $2,126,120
Net Worth: $1,840,501
Earnings: ($150,626)
Emp.: 4
Fiscal Year-end: 03/31/23
Cooking Oil Distr
N.A.I.C.S.: 424490
Vikram Ishvarbhai Desai (Chm)

SUN SAVINGS BANK INC.

Ground Floor Door No 8 Rosalie Bldg, Tabunok City of Talisay, Cebu, 6045, Philippines
Tel.: (63) 325208847 PH
Web Site: http://www.sunsavings.ph
Year Founded: 2004
Sales Range: $1-9.9 Million
Retail & Commercial Banking
N.A.I.C.S.: 522110
Augusto S. Gonzales (Treas)

SUN SOURCE (INDIA) LIMITED

One Sonal Industrial Estate (Khoda), Sanand Viramgam Highway, Ahmedabad, 382170, Gujarat, India
Tel.: (91) 265 2358172
Web Site: http://www.sunsource.in
Assets: $1,402,795
Liabilities: $284,981
Net Worth: $1,117,814
Earnings: ($44,719)
Fiscal Year-end: 03/31/18
Power Generating Equipment Mfr
N.A.I.C.S.: 333611

SUN SUMMIT MINERALS CORP.

c/o Suite 704 595 Howe Street, Box 35, Vancouver, V6C 2T5, BC, Canada
Tel.: (778) 588-9606
Web Site: http://www.sanmarcocorp.com
Year Founded: 2005
SMREF—(OTCQB)
Rev.: $37,067
Assets: $1,690,492
Liabilities: $181,672
Net Worth: $1,508,820
Earnings: ($2,805,327)
Emp.: 2
Fiscal Year-end: 11/30/23
Metal Exploration Services
N.A.I.C.S.: 213114
Robert D. Willis (CEO)

SUN TECHNOLOGIES CO., LTD.

56 Yeoui-daero Yongdeungpo-gu, Seoul, Korea (South)
Tel.: (82) 2 2055 4050
Web Site: http://www.ktroll.co.kr
Year Founded: 2002

INTERNATIONAL PUBLIC

Sales Range: $10-24.9 Million
Emp.: 103
Steel Products Mfr
N.A.I.C.S.: 332111
Seung-Jun Lee (Exec Dir)

SUN TOYOTA LTD

5210 Calgary Trail, Edmonton, T6H 4J8, AB, Canada
Tel.: (780) 431-6780
Web Site: http://www.suntoyota.ca
Rev.: $25,424,880
Emp.: 55
New & Used Car Dealers
N.A.I.C.S.: 441110
Nissanka VJ Wijayanayaka (Mgr-Svc)

SUN TV NETWORK LIMITED

Murasoli Maran Towers 73 MRC Nagar Main Road MRC Nagar, Chennai, 600 028, Tamil Nadu, India
Tel.: (91) 4444676767
Web Site: https://www.suntv.in
532733—(BOM)
Rev.: $497,464,181
Assets: $1,216,723,218
Liabilities: $104,419,399
Net Worth: $1,112,303,819
Earnings: $204,654,397
Emp.: 693
Fiscal Year-end: 03/31/24
Television Channels Broadcasting
N.A.I.C.S.: 334220
R. Ravi (Compliance Officer & Sec)

Subsidiaries:

South Asia FM Limited (1)
4 1017 3rd Cross St 9th Ln Nehru Nagar, Kotivakkam, 04444676767, Chennai, Tamil Nadu, India
Tel.: (91) 4443411434
Sales Range: $25-49.9 Million
Emp.: 50
Radio Broadcasting Services
N.A.I.C.S.: 516110

Sun TV Network Limited - Sun Pictures (1)
Murasoli Maran Towers 73 MRC Nagar Main Road MRC Nagar, Chennai, 600 028, Tamil Nadu, India
Tel.: (91) 444 467 6767
Web Site: https://www.sunpictures.in
Emp.: 2,000
Production, Distribution & Acquisition of Content
N.A.I.C.S.: 516120
Kalanithi Maran (Chm)

SUN VALLEY LTD.

Georgia Avenue, Bromborough, CH62 3RD, Wirral, United Kingdom
Tel.: (44) 1514827100
Web Site: http://www.sun-valley.co.uk
Year Founded: 1949
Sales Range: $25-49.9 Million
Emp.: 162
Snack Food Product Mfr
N.A.I.C.S.: 311919
James P. Hacking (Founder & Chm)

SUN YAD CONSTRUCTION CO., LTD.

20-6F No 248 Sec 2 Yong Hua Rd, Anping Dist, T'ainan, 708, Taiwan
Tel.: (886) 62988318
Web Site: https://www.sunyad.com.tw
1316—(TAI)
Rev.: $27,663,984
Assets: $411,307,254
Liabilities: $221,855,056
Net Worth: $189,452,199
Earnings: ($4,868,668)
Fiscal Year-end: 12/31/23
Resin Product Mfr
N.A.I.C.S.: 325211
Youming Zhang (Chm & Gen Mgr)

SUN&L CO., LTD.

96 Wolmi ro, Jung gu, Incheon, Korea (South)
Tel.: (82) 327703000
Web Site: https://www.sunwood.co.kr
Year Founded: 1959
002820—(KRS)
Rev.: $388,632,161
Assets: $402,241,123
Liabilities: $286,848,936
Net Worth: $115,392,187
Earnings: ($14,003,696)
Emp.: 557
Fiscal Year-end: 12/31/22
Wood Products Mfr
N.A.I.C.S.: 321999
Lee Yoon-Gyu (CEO)

Subsidiaries:

Darin Co., Ltd. (1)
111 Jayumuyeok 3-gil, Masanhoewon-gu, Changwon, Gyungnam, Korea (South)
Tel.: (82) 55 294 8801
Web Site: http://www.darin.co.kr
Pump Dispenser Mfr
N.A.I.C.S.: 333914
Kye-Hong Park (CEO)

SunchangITS co., Ltd (1)
101 5-Ra Sihwa Industrial Complex 118 Beonyeong-2 ro, Danwon-gu, Ansan, Gyeonggi-do, Korea (South)
Tel.: (82) 314987863
Furniture Distr
N.A.I.C.S.: 423210

SUN-BRITE FOODS INC.
1532 County Rd 34, Ruthven, N0P 2G0, ON, Canada
Tel.: (519) 326-9033
Web Site: http://www.sun-brite.com
Sales Range: $10-24.9 Million
Emp.: 86
Canned Tomatoes, Sauces, Condiments, Beans & Pasta Mfr
N.A.I.C.S.: 311999
Henry Iacobelli (Founder & Pres)

Subsidiaries:

Primo Foods Inc. (1)
56 Huxley Rd, Toronto, M9M 1H2, ON, Canada
Tel.: (416) 741-9300
Web Site: http://www.primofoods.ca
Macaroni & Spaghetti Mfr
N.A.I.C.S.: 311824
Henry Iacobelli (Pres)

Unico Inc. (1)
8000 Keele Street, Concord, L4K 2A4, ON, Canada
Tel.: (905) 669-9637
Web Site: http://www.unico.ca
Food Products Distr
N.A.I.C.S.: 424490

SUN-SEA CONSTRUCTION CO., LTD.
No 186 Minzu Road, Hsinchu, Taiwan
Tel.: (886) 35348168
Web Site: https://sunsea.com.tw
Year Founded: 1971
5516—(TPE)
Rev.: $76,337,117
Assets: $97,933,402
Liabilities: $71,975,550
Net Worth: $25,957,853
Earnings: $4,027,671
Fiscal Year-end: 12/31/22
Building Construction Services
N.A.I.C.S.: 236210
Jerry H. Chiu (Chm & CEO)

SUN-WA TECHNOS CORPORATION
Tokyo Square Garden 18F 3-1-1 Kyobashi, Chuo-ku, Tokyo, 104-0031, Japan
Tel.: (81) 352024011
Web Site: https://www.sunwa.co.jp

8137—(TKS)
Rev.: $1,098,172,180
Assets: $652,453,270
Liabilities: $335,398,010
Net Worth: $317,055,260
Earnings: $33,096,270
Emp.: 1,109
Fiscal Year-end: 03/31/24
Electrical Apparatus & Equipment Wholesaler
N.A.I.C.S.: 423690
Hiroyuki Tanaka (Pres)

Subsidiaries:

PT. Sunwa Technos Indonesia (1)
Gd Chase Plaza Lantai 6 Jl Jend Sudirman Kav 21 Kel Karet Kec, Setiabudi, Jakarta Selatan, 12920, Indonesia
Tel.: (62) 2129347983
Office Equipments Mfr
N.A.I.C.S.: 337215

SUN-WA TECHNOS (SHENZHEN) CO., LTD (1)
Unit 10-15 32/F Shun Hing Spuare Di Wang Commercial Centre, 5002 Shennan Road East, Shenzhen, 518008, China
Tel.: (86) 75525879800
Web Site: http://www.sunwatec.com
Electronic Connector Mfr
N.A.I.C.S.: 334417

SUN-WA TRINITY CORPORATION (1)
1-6-1 Kitashinjuku, Shinjuku-ku, Tokyo, 169-0074, Japan
Tel.: (81) 333713501
Industrial Machinery & Equipment Mfr
N.A.I.C.S.: 333248

Shanghai Sun-Wa Technos Co., Ltd. (1)
Room 100 Shanghai International Trade Centre No 2201 Yan An Road W, Changning District, Shanghai, 200336, China
Tel.: (86) 2163906600
Office Equipments Mfr
N.A.I.C.S.: 337215

Sun-Wa Technos (Hong Kong) Co. Ltd. (1)
Room 1202-1203 12th Floor Metropolis Tower 10 Metropolis Drive, Hung Hom, Kowloon, China (Hong Kong)
Tel.: (852) 23504827
Web Site: http://sun-wa.com.hk
Electronic Parts & Equipment Whslr
N.A.I.C.S.: 423690
Sei Yamamoto (Pres)

Sun-Wa Technos (Malaysia) Sdn. Bhd. (1)
A-21-1 Level 21 Menara UOA Bangsar No 5 Jalan Bangsar Utama1, 59000, Kuala Lumpur, Malaysia
Tel.: (60) 322828230
Sales Range: $25-49.9 Million
Emp.: 7
Electrical Equipment & Component Mfr
N.A.I.C.S.: 335999

Sun-Wa Technos (Philippines), Inc. (1)
Unit No 1405 Tower One Exchange Plaza 6767 Ayala Avenue, Makati, 1226, Philippines
Tel.: (63) 288866914
Office Equipments Mfr
N.A.I.C.S.: 337215

Sun-Wa Technos (Singapore) Pte Ltd (1)
7500A Beach Road 14-301 The Plaza, Singapore, 199591, Singapore
Tel.: (65) 63388903
Web Site: https://www.sunwa.com.sg
Sales Range: $50-74.9 Million
Emp.: 8
Electronic Parts & Equipment Whslr
N.A.I.C.S.: 423690

Sun-Wa Technos (Vietnam) Co., Ltd. (1)
25th Floor Lim Tower 9-11 Ton Duc Thang Str, Ben Nghe ward 1st Dist, Ho Chi Minh City, Vietnam
Tel.: (84) 2873022988

Office Equipments Mfr
N.A.I.C.S.: 337215

Sun-Wa Technos America, Inc. (1)
1051 Perimeter Dr 625, Schaumburg, IL 60173
Tel.: (847) 969-0081
Web Site: http://www.sunwaus.com
Sales Range: $25-49.9 Million
Emp.: 10
Electrical Equipment & Component Mfr
N.A.I.C.S.: 335999

Sun-Wa Technos Asia (Thailand) Co. Ltd. (1)
43 Thai CC Tower, 31st Floor Room number 314-316 South Sathorn Road, Yannawa, Bangkok, 10120, Thailand
Tel.: (66) 26723581
Web Site: http://www.sunwaus.com
Sales Range: $50-74.9 Million
Emp.: 8
Electronic Parts & Equipment Whslr
N.A.I.C.S.: 423690

Sun-Wa Technos Europe GmbH (1)
Na Brezince 6-930, 15000, Prague, Czech Republic
Tel.: (420) 272781632
Electronic Parts & Equipment Whslr
N.A.I.C.S.: 423690

Sun-Wa Technos Mexico S.A. De C.v. (1)
Av 5 de Febrero 1351 Empresalia Edificio Robel oficina 208, 76120, Queretaro, Mexico
Tel.: (52) 4426901050
Office Equipments Mfr
N.A.I.C.S.: 337215

Sun-Wa Technos Taiwan Co. Ltd. (1)
Room 1003 10th Floor No 18 Section 1 Chang'an East Road, Zhongshan, Taipei, 104, Taiwan
Tel.: (886) 225614060
Web Site: https://www.sunwa.com.tw
Emp.: 13
Industrial Machinery & Equipment Whslr
N.A.I.C.S.: 423830

Sun-wa Technos (Europe) GmbH (1)
World Trade Center LJUBLJANA Room 614 Dunajska cesta 156, 1000, Ljubljana, Slovenia
Tel.: (386) 59084800
Office Equipments Mfr
N.A.I.C.S.: 337215

Sun-wa Technos (Europe) GmbH (1)
Bleichstr 1, 60313, Frankfurt am Main, Germany
Tel.: (49) 691338950
Web Site: https://www.sunwa.eu
Office Equipments Mfr
N.A.I.C.S.: 337215

Sunwa-Logistic Corporation (1)
Tokyo Square Garden 3-1-1 Kyobashi, Chuo-ku, Tokyo, 104-0031, Japan
Tel.: (81) 352024011
Office Equipments Mfr
N.A.I.C.S.: 337215

SUN.KING TECHNOLOGY GROUP LIMITED
Building 9-A KongGangRong HuiYuan Yuhua Road, Tianzhu Airport Industrial Zone B Shunyi District, Beijing, 101300, China
Tel.: (86) 1056301111   Ky
Web Site: http://www.speg.hk
Year Founded: 2002
0580—(HKG)
Rev.: $128,856,312
Assets: $350,525,869
Liabilities: $81,807,570
Net Worth: $268,718,299
Earnings: $3,232,991
Emp.: 778
Fiscal Year-end: 12/31/22
Rail Transportation Equipment Mfr
N.A.I.C.S.: 339999
Jie Xiang (Founder & Chm)

Subsidiaries:

Astrol Electronic AG (1)

Ahornweg 14, Othmarsingen, 5504, Lenzburg, Switzerland
Tel.: (41) 564856020
Electronic Parts Mfr
N.A.I.C.S.: 334419

Jiashan Sunking Power Equipment Technology Co., Ltd. (1)
No 81 Zhijiang Road Economic Development Zone, Jiashan, 314100, Zhejiang, China
Tel.: (86) 573 84296333
Electronic Component Mfr & Distr
N.A.I.C.S.: 334419
Li Tao (Product Mgr-Water Sys Div)

Subsidiary (Domestic):

Jiujiang Sun.king Technology Co., Ltd. (2)
No 59 Gangxing Road, Chengxigang District Jiujiang Economic & Technological Dev Zone, Jiujiang, Jiangxi, China
Tel.: (86) 7928150719
Web Site: https://www.jjzlqc.com.cn
Emp.: 150
Electronic Component Mfr & Distr
N.A.I.C.S.: 334419

Wuhan Langde Electrics Co., Ltd. (1)
No 40 Gaoxin 4th Road, Donghu New Technology Development Zone, Wuhan, 430074, Hubei, China
Tel.: (86) 2787267930
Web Site: https://www.landgroup.com.cn
Online Monitoring Equipment Mfr
N.A.I.C.S.: 334290
Bai Weijie (Product Mgr-Online Monitoring Div)

Wuxi Sunking Power Capacitor Co., Ltd. (1)
No 18 Chunhui Road Huishan Economic Development Zone, Wuxi, 214177, China
Tel.: (86) 51083762888
Emp.: 120
Power Capacitor Mfr & Distr
N.A.I.C.S.: 334416
Geng Feng (Product Mgr-Capacitor Div)

Zhejiang Jiashan Keneng Power Equipment Co., Ltd. (1)
14/F Block D North China Electric Power University Main Building No 2, Beinong Road Zhuxinzhuang Changping District, Beijing, 102206, China
Tel.: (86) 1061772899
Web Site: http://www.jskeneng.com
Electronic Component Mfr & Distr
N.A.I.C.S.: 334419
He Lifeng (Product Mgr-Electricity Power Quality Div)

SUNAC CHINA HOLDINGS LIMITED
10/F Building C7 Magnetic Plaza Binshuixi Road, Nankai District, Tianjin, 300381, China
Tel.: (86) 2223937799
Web Site: https://www.sunac.com.cn
1918—(HKG)
Rev.: $21,654,017,237
Assets: $137,290,730,101
Liabilities: $125,527,194,655
Net Worth: $11,763,535,446
Earnings: ($1,461,773,196)
Emp.: 39,228
Fiscal Year-end: 12/31/23
Residential & Commercial Property Developer
N.A.I.C.S.: 236117
Hongbin Sun (Founder & Chm)

SUNAC SERVICES HOLDINGS LIMITED
Floor 25 Building O1A Sunac Center, Nankai District, Tianjin, China   Ky
Web Site: https://www.sunacservice.com
Year Founded: 2004
1516—(HKG)
Rev.: $970,524,618
Assets: $1,612,321,251

Sunac Services Holdings Limited—(Continued)
Liabilities: $748,687,832
Net Worth: $863,633,418
Earnings: ($54,439,383)
Emp.: 26,795
Fiscal Year-end: 12/31/23
Holding Company
N.A.I.C.S.: 551112
Hongling Cao (CEO)

SUNAM CO., LTD.
52 Seungnyang-Gil, Wongok-Myeon, Anseong, 17554, Gyeonggi-do, Korea (South)
Tel.: (82) 316554336
Web Site: https://www.i-sunam.com
Year Founded: 2004
294630—(KRS)
Rev.: $4,881,656
Assets: $13,547,272
Liabilities: $7,484,735
Net Worth: $6,062,537
Earnings: ($1,622,363)
Emp.: 41
Fiscal Year-end: 12/31/22
Electric Equipment Mfr
N.A.I.C.S.: 334419
Ho-Yeob Lee (CFO)

SUNAUTAS CORPORATION
2-4-15 Shinyokohama 9th Floor Ohta Kosan Building, Kohoku-ku, Yokohama, 222-0033, Kanagawa, Japan
Tel.: (81) 454731211
Web Site: https://www.sunautas.co.jp
Year Founded: 1951
7623—(TKS)
Rev.: $109,950,740
Assets: $77,647,670
Liabilities: $55,438,070
Net Worth: $22,209,600
Earnings: $1,725,210
Fiscal Year-end: 04/30/24
Petroleum Product Distr
N.A.I.C.S.: 424720

SUNBIO, INC.,
95 Sanbon-Ro, Gunpo, 15849, Gyeonggi-do, Korea (South)
Tel.: (82) 314235467　　　　　　　　CA
Web Site: https://www.sunbio.com
Year Founded: 1997
067370—(KRS)
Rev.: $5,862,111
Assets: $33,890,048
Liabilities: $15,057,008
Net Worth: $18,833,040
Earnings: $686,767
Emp.: 25
Fiscal Year-end: 12/31/22
Pharmaceuticals Product Mfr
N.A.I.C.S.: 325412
Nho Kwang (CEO)

SUNBRIDGE GROUP LIMITED
Level 12 680 George Street, Sydney, 2000, NSW, Australia
Tel.: (61) 2 8280 7355
Web Site:
　　http://www.sunbridge.com.au
Rev.: $44,175,279
Assets: $49,657,378
Liabilities: $3,796,880
Net Worth: $45,860,498
Earnings: ($273,398)
Fiscal Year-end: 12/31/17
Menswear Retailer
N.A.I.C.S.: 458110
Jia Yin Xu (Founder, CEO & Mng Dir)

Subsidiaries:

Bangdisidun (Fujian) Dress Development Co., Ltd.　　　　　(1)
ShaoHui Industry Zone LongHu Town, Jinjiang, Fujian, China
Tel.: (86) 59585255677

Web Site: http://www.pandist.com
Fashion Wear Distr
N.A.I.C.S.: 458110

SUNCALL CORPORATION
14 Umezu Nishiura-cho, Ukyo-ku, Kyoto, 615-8555, Japan
Tel.: (81) 758818111
Web Site: https://www.suncall.co.jp
Year Founded: 1943
5985—(TKS)
Rev.: $340,388,560
Assets: $399,554,670
Liabilities: $205,544,560
Net Worth: $194,010,110
Earnings: ($78,103,760)
Emp.: 2,172
Fiscal Year-end: 03/31/24
Metal Stampings, Wire Springs, Steel Springs & Other Steel Products Mfr
N.A.I.C.S.: 332119
Koji Tsutsumi (Mng Exec Officer)

Subsidiaries:

Hirose Technology Co. Ltd.　　　　(1)
635 20 Komugyo Nishi Hirosecho, Toyota, Aichi, Japan　　　　　　　　(100%)
Tel.: (81) 565459777
Sales Range: $25-49.9 Million
Emp.: 100
N.A.I.C.S.: 332618

PT Suncall Indonesia　　　　　　(1)
Jl Maligii I Lot B-5 Kawasan Industri KIIC, 41361, Karawang, West Jawa, Indonesia　　　　　　　　　　　(100%)
Tel.: (62) 218905428
Web Site: http://www.suncall.co.jp
Sales Range: $1-9.9 Million
Emp.: 200
Wire Product Mfr
N.A.I.C.S.: 332618

SUNCALL (Guangzhou) Co., Ltd.　　　　　　　　　　　　　　　(1)
No 6 Checheng Road, Auto City Huadu District, Guangzhou, 510800, Guangdong, China
Tel.: (86) 2086733858
Web Site: http://www.suncall.co.jp
Sales Range: $25-49.9 Million
Emp.: 79
Automotive Components Mfr
N.A.I.C.S.: 336212

Suncall (Guangzhou) Trading Co., Ltd.　　　　　　　　　　　　　　(1)
No 6 Checheng Road Auto City, Huadu District, Guangzhou, 510800, China
Tel.: (86) 208 673 3858
Automotive Parts Mfr & Distr
N.A.I.C.S.: 336390

Suncall (Tianjin) Co., Ltd.　　　　(1)
No 78 TaiHua Road Development District, Tianjin, 300457, China
Tel.: (86) 225 990 1955
Automotive Parts Mfr & Distr
N.A.I.C.S.: 336390

Suncall Co., (H.K.) Ltd.　　　　　(1)
Unit 805-806 Billiton Trade Centre 31 Hung To Road, Kwun Tong, Kowloon, China (Hong Kong)　　　　　　　　　(100%)
Tel.: (852) 23170245
Sales Range: $50-74.9 Million
Emp.: 5
N.A.I.C.S.: 332618

Suncall Corporation - Hirose Plant　　　　　　　　　　　　　　(1)
635-20 Komugyo Nishi-Hirose-cho, Toyota, 470-0309, Aichi, Japan
Tel.: (81) 565459777
Automotive Components Mfr
N.A.I.C.S.: 336330

Suncall Corporation - Suncall Buji Nan Ling Factory　　　　　　(1)
No 23 Nan Xin Road The First Industrial District Nan Ling Village, Buji Town Long Gang, Shenzhen, Guangdong, China
Tel.: (86) 75584709320
Web Site: http://www.suncall.co.jp
Automotive Components Mfr
N.A.I.C.S.: 336390

Suncall Engineering Corp.　　　　(1)
970 Toda, Minami-Alps, 400-0414, Yamanashi, Japan
Tel.: (81) 552842981
Web Site: https://suncall-eng.co.jp
Sales Range: $25-49.9 Million
Emp.: 67
Metal Stamping Mfr
N.A.I.C.S.: 332119
Shojiro Wakabayashi (Pres)

Suncall High Precision (Thailand) Ltd.　　　　　　　　　　　　　　(1)
Tel.: (66) 38454063
Web Site: http://www.suncall.co.jp
Automotive Components Mfr
N.A.I.C.S.: 336320

Suncall Kikuchi Corp.　　　　　　(1)
1950 Akahoshi, Kikuchi, 861-1311, Kumamoto, Japan
Tel.: (81) 968251105
Web Site: http://www.suncall-kc.co.jp
Industrial Spring Mfr
N.A.I.C.S.: 332613

Suncall Technologies (SZ) Co., Ltd.　　　　　　　　　　　　　　(1)
Building 4 Hongbang Technology Park No 30 Cuibao Road Baolong Street, Longgang District, Shenzhen, China
Tel.: (86) 7552 870 6720
Printer Related Product Mfr & Distr
N.A.I.C.S.: 333248

Suncall Technologies Mexico, S.A. de C.V.　　　　　　　　　　　　　(1)
Circuito Cerezos Sur No 106, Parque Industrial San Francisco IV San Francisco De Los Romo, 20355, Aguascalientes, Mexico
Tel.: (52) 449 922 3750
Automotive Parts Mfr & Distr
N.A.I.C.S.: 336390

Suncall Technology Vietnam Co., Ltd.　　　　　　　　　　　　　　(1)
Plot H-1, hang Long Industrial Park Vong La commune Dong Anh Dist, Hanoi, Vietnam
Tel.: (84) 2439516372
Sales Range: $200-249.9 Million
Emp.: 1,000
Automotive Components Mfr
N.A.I.C.S.: 336310

SUNCAR TECHNOLOGY GROUP INC
Suncar Auto Building No 656 Lingshi Road, Jing'an District, Shanghai, 200072, China
Tel.: (86) 2131836200
Web Site: https://suncartech.com
Year Founded: 2007
SDA—(NASDAQ)
Emp.: 528
Insurance Services
N.A.I.C.S.: 524298
Bohong Du (CFO)

SUNCARE TRADERS LTD.
7 Shree Shakti Estate Behind Milan Complex, Sarkhej-Sanand Cross Road, Ahmedabad, 382210, Gujarat, India
Tel.: (91) 7929096047
Web Site: https://www.sctl.shop
Year Founded: 1997
539526—(BOM)
Rev.: $818,356
Assets: $3,834,434
Liabilities: $1,199,496
Net Worth: $2,634,938
Earnings: ($2,211,150)
Emp.: 14
Fiscal Year-end: 03/31/23
Laminate Sales
N.A.I.C.S.: 326130
Pooja Shah (Officer-Compliance & Sec)

SUNCHA TECHNOLOGY CO., LTD.
No 103 Zhucheng Road, Baizhang

Town Yuhang District, Hangzhou, 311100, Zhejiang, China
Tel.: (86) 57188617962
Web Site: https://sqzm.com
Year Founded: 2002
001211—(SSE)
Rev.: $134,118,448
Assets: $197,608,465
Liabilities: $74,306,489
Net Worth: $123,301,976
Earnings: ($2,164,715)
Emp.: 1,500
Fiscal Year-end: 12/31/22
Wood Product Mfr & Distr
N.A.I.C.S.: 321999
Zheng Chenglie (Chm)

SUNCITY SYNTHETICS LTD.
C-8 1st Floor Opp MDM Hospital Shastri Nagar, Jodhpur, 342 002, Rajasthan, India
Tel.: (91) 2912645278
Web Site:
　　https://www.suncitysyntheticsltd.in
Year Founded: 1988
530795—(BOM)
Rev.: $601,007
Assets: $644,781
Liabilities: $650,297
Net Worth: ($5,515)
Earnings: ($14,651)
Emp.: 5
Fiscal Year-end: 03/31/23
Plastics Product Mfr
N.A.I.C.S.: 326199
Suresh Dhanraj Kawar (Mng Dir)

SUNCO BUILDERS & DEVELOPERS LIMITED
Crawford Street, PO Box N-4829, Nassau, Bahamas
Tel.: (242) 3234966
Web Site:
　　http://www.suncobahamas.com
Year Founded: 1977
Sales Range: $50-74.9 Million
Emp.: 200
Professional Building & Development Services Including Construction Management & Development, Project Management & Cost Planning & Interior Design & Outfitting Services
N.A.I.C.S.: 236220
Emmanuel C. Alexiou (Founder & Pres)

SUNCOR ENERGY INC.
150-6th Avenue SW, PO Box 2844, Calgary, T2P 3E3, AB, Canada
Tel.: (403) 296-8000　　　　　　AB
Web Site: https://www.suncor.com
Year Founded: 1979
SU—(NYSE)
Rev.: $59,380,000,000
Assets: $88,539,000,000
Liabilities: $45,260,000,000
Net Worth: $43,279,000,000
Earnings: $5,341,000,000
Emp.: 14,906
Fiscal Year-end: 12/31/23
Renewable Energy Services
N.A.I.C.S.: 221210
Paul Gardner (Chief People Officer)

Subsidiaries:

Montreal Pipe Line Limited　　　(1)
10803 rue Sherbrooke Est, Montreal, H1B 1B3, QC, Canada　　　　　　(23.8%)
Tel.: (514) 645-8797
Web Site: https://www.pmpl.com
Sales Range: $10-24.9 Million
Crude Petroleum Pipelines
N.A.I.C.S.: 486110
Thomas A. Hardison (Pres)

Unit (Domestic):

Montreal Pipe Line Limited　　　(2)

AND PRIVATE COMPANIES

148 Rang De La Pipeline, Saint Cesaire,
J0L 1T0, QC, Canada
Tel.: (450) 469-2394
Web Site: http://www.pmpl.com
Sales Range: $10-24.9 Million
Crude Oil Transportation
N.A.I.C.S.: 486990

Subsidiary (US):

Portland Pipe Line Corporation **(2)**
30 Hill St, South Portland, ME 04106-4201
Tel.: (207) 767-0421
Web Site: https://www.pmpl.com
Sales Range: $10-24.9 Million
Crude Petroleum Pipelines
N.A.I.C.S.: 486110
J. Chris Gillies *(Treas & Sec)*

Suncor Energy (U.S.A.) Inc. **(1)**
717 17th St Ste 2900, Denver, CO 80202
Tel.: (303) 793-8000
Web Site: http://www.suncor.com
Sales Range: $50-74.9 Million
Emp.: 75
Oil & Gas Exploration Services
N.A.I.C.S.: 213112

Suncor Energy Germany GmbH **(1)**
Theodor-Althoff-Str 39, Essen, 45133, Germany
Tel.: (49) 2017260
Petroleum Refining Services
N.A.I.C.S.: 324110

Subsidiary (Domestic):

Suncor Energy Oil (North Africa) GmbH **(2)**
Theodor-Althoff-Str 39, 45133, Essen, Germany
Tel.: (49) 2017260
Oil & Gas Exploration Services
N.A.I.C.S.: 213112

Suncor Energy Marketing Inc. **(1)**
Suncor Energy Centre West Tower 21st Floor 150 - 6th Avenue S W, PO Box 2844, Calgary, T2P 3E3, AB, Canada
Web Site: http://www.suncor.com
Crude Oil & Natural Gas Distr
N.A.I.C.S.: 424720

Suncor Energy UK Limited **(1)**
28b Albyn Place, Aberdeen, AB10 1YL, United Kingdom
Tel.: (44) 1224565600
Sales Range: $50-74.9 Million
Emp.: 4
Oil & Gas Exploration Services
N.A.I.C.S.: 213112
Aidan Campbell *(Mng Dir)*

Sunoco Sarnia Refinery **(1)**
1900 River Rd, PO Box 307, Sarnia, N7T 7J3, ON, Canada **(100%)**
Tel.: (519) 337-2301
Web Site: http://www.sunoco.com
Sales Range: $125-149.9 Million
Emp.: 350
Refinery
N.A.I.C.S.: 324110

Syncrude Canada Ltd. **(1)**
Stn Main, PO Bag 4009, Fort McMurray, T9H 3L1, AB, Canada **(58.74%)**
Tel.: (780) 790-5911
Web Site: http://www.syncrude.ca
Emp.: 5,000
Crude Oil Producer
N.A.I.C.S.: 211120
Kara Flynn *(VP-Govt & Pub Affairs)*

TotalEnergies EP Canada Ltd. **(1)**
4700 888 - 3 Street SW, Calgary, T2P 5C5, AB, Canada
Tel.: (403) 571-7599
Oil & Gas Exploration Services
N.A.I.C.S.: 213112

UPI Energy LP **(1)**
105 Silvercreek Parkway North Suite 200, Guelph, N1H 8M1, ON, Canada
Tel.: (519) 821-2667
Web Site: http://www.upienergylp.com
Sales Range: $25-49.9 Million
Emp.: 50
Petroleum & Propane Product Marketer & Distr; Owned by Suncor Energy Inc. & Growmark, Inc.
N.A.I.C.S.: 424720

Robert P. Sicard *(Pres & CEO)*

SUNCORE, INC.
673-1 Deogeun-ri Wollong-myeon, P'aju, 10844, Gyeonggi-do, Korea (South)
Tel.: (82) 31 937 5000
Web Site: http://www.luboinc.com
Year Founded: 1978
Sales Range: $25-49.9 Million
Emp.: 171
Machine Part Mfr
N.A.I.C.S.: 332991
Choi Kyu Sun *(CEO)*

SUNCORP GROUP LIMITED
Level 23 80 Ann Street, Brisbane, 4000, QLD, Australia
Tel.: (61) 131155 **AU**
Web Site:
  https://www.suncorpgroup.com.au
Year Founded: 1996
SUN—(ASX)
Rev.: $11,967,138,293
Assets: $74,970,985,199
Liabilities: $66,268,501,011
Net Worth: $8,702,484,189
Earnings: $755,688,857
Emp.: 13,000
Fiscal Year-end: 06/30/23
Financial Investment Services
N.A.I.C.S.: 523999
Steve Johnston *(CEO-Grp & Mng Dir)*

Subsidiaries:

AAI Insurance Ltd. **(1)**
Shortland Street, PO Box 992, Auckland, 1140, New Zealand **(50%)**
Tel.: (64) 99272306
Web Site: http://www.aainsurance.co.nz
Direct Life Insurance Carriers
N.A.I.C.S.: 524113
Chris Curtin *(CEO)*

Asteron Life Limited **(1)**
55 Featherston St, PO Box 894, Wellington, New Zealand
Tel.: (64) 4 495 8700
Web Site: http://www.asteron.co.nz
Emp.: 200
Financial Management Services
N.A.I.C.S.: 523940

Graham & Company Limited **(1)**
18th Flr 344 Queen St, Brisbane, 4000, QLD, Australia
Tel.: (61) 732282600
Securities Brokerage Services
N.A.I.C.S.: 523150

Guardianfp Limited **(1)**
Level 10 321 Kent Street, Sydney, 2000, NSW, Australia **(100%)**
Tel.: (61) 282753500
Web Site:
  http://www.guardianadvice.com.au
Sales Range: $25-49.9 Million
Emp.: 40
Management Consulting Services
N.A.I.C.S.: 541618

IIMI (Australia) Pty Ltd. **(1)**
Queen Victoria Building, PO Box 1197, 1230, Melbourne, NSW, Australia **(100%)**
Tel.: (61) 385201555
Other Airport Operations
N.A.I.C.S.: 488119

National Marine Insurance Agency Limited **(1)**
L 13 465 Victoria Ave, Chatswood, NSW, Australia **(100%)**
Tel.: (61) 299789091
Investment Advice
N.A.I.C.S.: 523940

Secure Sentinel Pty Limited **(1)**
Locked Bag 4845, Chatswood, 2057, NSW, Australia **(100%)**
Tel.: (61) 29 411 6898
Web Site:
  https://www.securesentinel.com.au
Sales Range: $50-74.9 Million
Emp.: 30
Investment Banking & Securities Dealing

N.A.I.C.S.: 523150
Suncorp Custodian Services Pty Ltd **(1)**
GPO Box 1453, Brisbane, 4001, QLD, Australia
Tel.: (61) 733622222
Investment Management Service
N.A.I.C.S.: 523940

Suncorp Group Holdings Pty Limited **(1)**
L 18 Suncorp Centre 36 Whickham Tce, Brisbane, 4000, QLD, Australia
Tel.: (61) 733621222
Investment Management Service
N.A.I.C.S.: 523999

Suncorp Insurance Services Limited **(1)**
L 18 36 Wickham Tce, Brisbane, 4000, QLD, Australia
Tel.: (61) 733621222
Insurance Agency Services
N.A.I.C.S.: 524210

Taurus Trade Finance Pty Ltd **(1)**
Level 2 450 Saint Kilda Rd, Melbourne, 3004, VIC, Australia
Tel.: (61) 3 9867 1777
Web Site: http://www.taurustf.com.au
Sales Range: $50-74.9 Million
Emp.: 20
Trade Financing Services
N.A.I.C.S.: 522299

Vero Insurance Limited **(1)**
Level 28 266 George Street, Brisbane, 4000, QLD, Australia
Tel.: (61) 882055477
Web Site: http://www.vero.com.au
Sales Range: $50-74.9 Million
Emp.: 55
General Insurance Management Services
N.A.I.C.S.: 524298

Subsidiary (Domestic):

Terri Scheer Insurance Pty Ltd **(2)**
45 Grenfell Street, GPO Box 1619, Adelaide, 5001, SA, Australia
Tel.: (61) 88 205 5110
Web Site: https://www.terrischeer.com.au
Sales Range: $25-49.9 Million
Emp.: 30
Landlord Insurance Services
N.A.I.C.S.: 524127

Vero Insurance New Zealand Limited **(1)**
Level 13 48 Shortland Street, Auckland, 1010, New Zealand **(100%)**
Tel.: (64) 9 363 2222
Web Site: https://www.vero.co.nz
Sales Range: $200-249.9 Million
Emp.: 500
Direct Property & Casualty Insurance Carriers
N.A.I.C.S.: 524126

Vero Liability Insurance Limited **(1)**
Level 32 ANZ Centre 23-29 Albert Street, Auckland, 1010, New Zealand
Tel.: (64) 9 306 0350
Web Site: https://www.veroliability.co.nz
Property & Liability Insurance Services
N.A.I.C.S.: 524126
Adrian Tulloch *(Mng Dir)*

Vero Marine Insurance Limited **(1)**
Level 15 48 Shortland St, 1010, Auckland, New Zealand **(100%)**
Tel.: (64) 93632600
Web Site: http://www.veromarine.com
Sales Range: $50-74.9 Million
Emp.: 50
Direct Life Insurance Carriers
N.A.I.C.S.: 524113

SUNCORP GROUP LIMITED
Level 28 Brisbane Square 266 George Street, Brisbane, 4000, QLD, Australia
Tel.: (61) 731354155
Web Site:
  http://www.suncorpgroup.com.au
Year Founded: 1902
Banking Financial Services

N.A.I.C.S.: 523150
Steve Johnston *(CEO & Mng Dir)*

SUNCORP TECHNOLOGIES LIMITED
Unit 1201-05 12/F China Resources Building, 26 Harbour Road, Wanchai, China (Hong Kong)
Tel.: (852) 25726111
1063—(OTCIQ)
Rev.: $16,362,928
Assets: $36,061,958
Liabilities: $10,091,761
Net Worth: $25,970,197
Earnings: ($7,329,866)
Emp.: 18
Fiscal Year-end: 12/31/22
Telephones & Related Products Mfr & Sales
N.A.I.C.S.: 334210
Cynthia Sin Fai Wong *(Sec)*

Subsidiaries:

Suncorp Securities Limited **(1)**
Room 2305 23rd Floor Central Centre 99 Queens Road, Central, China (Hong Kong)
Tel.: (852) 38991810
Web Site:
  https://www.suncorpsecurities.com.hk
Banking & Financial Consulting Services
N.A.I.C.S.: 541611

SUNDA ENERGY PLC
2 Leman Street, London, E1W 9US, United Kingdom
Tel.: (44) 2071172849
Web Site: https://sundaenergy.com
SNDA—(AIM)
Rev.: $120,837
Assets: $7,240,721
Liabilities: $883,876
Net Worth: $6,356,845
Earnings: ($1,530,150)
Emp.: 5
Fiscal Year-end: 12/31/21
Crude Petroleum Extraction Services
N.A.I.C.S.: 211120
Geoffrey Kenneth Barnes *(Sec)*

Subsidiaries:

Gold Oil Peru S.A.C **(1)**
Calle General Julian Arias Araguez N 250 Urbanizacion San Antonio, Distrito de Miraflores, Lima, Peru
Tel.: (51) 14442900
Oil & Gas Exploration Services
N.A.I.C.S.: 213112

SUNDANCE RESOURCES LIMITED
45 Ventnor Avenue, West Perth, 6005, WA, Australia
Tel.: (61) 89 220 2300
Web Site:
  http://www.sundanceresources.com
Year Founded: 1993
SDL—(ASX)
Sales Range: $1-9.9 Million
Iron Ore Company
N.A.I.C.S.: 212210
Giulio Casello *(CEO & Mng Dir)*

Subsidiaries:

Cam Iron S.A. **(1)**
PO Box 33059, Yaounde, Cameroon
Tel.: (237) 22019783
Iron Ore Mining Services
N.A.I.C.S.: 212210
Serge Asso'O *(CEO)*

Congo Iron S.A. **(1)**
BP 567, Brazzaville, Congo, Republic of
Tel.: (242) 222810637
Metal Mining Services
N.A.I.C.S.: 213114
Aime Emmanuel Yoka *(Gen Mgr)*

SUNDARAM BRAKE LININGS LIMITED

SUNDARAM BRAKE LININGS LIMITED

Sundaram Brake Linings Limited—(Continued)
Padi, Chennai, 600 050, India
Tel.: (91) 7358033474
Web Site:
https://www.tvsbrakelinings.com
Year Founded: 1976
SUNDRMBRAK—(BOM)
Rev.: $42,875,583
Assets: $24,705,977
Liabilities: $14,465,548
Net Worth: $10,240,429
Earnings: ($573,299)
Emp.: 591
Fiscal Year-end: 03/31/23
Brake Products Mfr
N.A.I.C.S.: 336340
S. Ramabadran (CFO, Chief Compliance Officer, Chief IR Officer & Sec)

Subsidiaries:

Axles India Limited (1)
21 Patullos Road, Chennai, 600002, India
Tel.: (91) 9003181264
Web Site: https://www.axlesindia.com
Commercial Vehicle Mfr
N.A.I.C.S.: 336120

Lucas Indian Service Limited (1)
No 28 Poomagal Main Road Behind Olympia Tech Park, Ekkatuthangal, Chennai, 600 032, India
Tel.: (91) 4422255032
Web Site: https://www.lucas-service.com
Electronic Components Mfr
N.A.I.C.S.: 335931

Lucas-TVS Limited (1)
11 & 13 Patullos Road, Chennai, 600 002, Tamil Nadu, India
Tel.: (91) 4428460063
Web Site: https://www.lucas-tvs.com
Emp.: 6,000
Automotive Electrical Parts Mfr
N.A.I.C.S.: 336320

Southern Roadways Limited (1)
Lakshmi Building Usilampatti Road kochadai, Madurai, 625 016, India
Tel.: (91) 4522381281
Web Site:
https://www.southernroadways.com
Courier Service
N.A.I.C.S.: 624210

Sundaram Brake Linings Limited - Padi Plant
M T H Road Padi, Chennai, 600 050, India
Tel.: (91) 7358033474
Web Site: http://www.tvssbl.com (1)
Emp.: 500
Automobile Parts Mfr
N.A.I.C.S.: 336390
Purushothaman Ram Subramaniam (Pres)

Sundaram Brake Linings Limited - Plant 4 & 5 (1)
Mahindra World City SEZ Natham Sub-Post, Chengalpet, Kanchipuram, 603 002, India
Tel.: (91) 44 47490005
Automobile Parts Mfr
N.A.I.C.S.: 336390

Sundaram Textiles Limited (1)
TSC 47 Maruthur Road Tekkutheru Post Melur Tk, Madurai, 627502, Tamil Nadu, India
Tel.: (91) 9487587137
Web Site: https://www.sundaramtextiles.com
Textile Product Mfr & Distr
N.A.I.C.S.: 314999

SUNDARAM CLAYTON LTD.

Chaitanya No 12 Khader Nawaz Khan Road, Nungambakkam, Chennai, 600 006, Tamil Nadu, India
Tel.: (91) 4428332115
Web Site: https://www.sundaram-clayton.com
Year Founded: 1962
SUNDRMCLAY—(NSE)
Rev.: $2,779,369,320
Assets: $3,199,049,490
Liabilities: $2,562,506,310
Net Worth: $636,543,180
Earnings: $44,182,320
Emp.: 1,721
Fiscal Year-end: 03/31/21
Aluminum Casting Mfr
N.A.I.C.S.: 331318
Venu Srinivasan (Chm & Co-Mng Dir)

Subsidiaries:

Emerald Haven Reality Limited (1)
1st Floor Greenways Tower 119 St Mary's Road Abhiramapuram, Chennai, 600 018, India (77.6%)
Tel.: (91) 8056009200
Web Site: http://www.tvsemerald.com
Real Estate Development Services
N.A.I.C.S.: 531390

PT. TVS Motor Company (1)
Gedung Wirausaha Lt 3 JI HR Rasuna Said Kav C5, kuningan, Jakarta, 12920, Indonesia
Tel.: (62) 2130020570
Web Site: https://www.tvsmotor.co.id
Motor Vehicle Product Mfr & Distr
N.A.I.C.S.: 336991

Sundaram Clayton Ltd. - Chennai Plant (1)
Mahindra world city SEZ, Chennai, 603 002, India
Tel.: (91) 4447490049
Automotive Components Mfr
N.A.I.C.S.: 336110

Sundaram Clayton Ltd. - Kanchipuram Plant (1)
No B14 SIPCOT Industrial Growth Center, Oragadam Sriperumbudur Taluk, Kanchipuram, 602 105, India
Tel.: (91) 4467103300
Automotive Components Mfr
N.A.I.C.S.: 336110

Sundaram-Clayton (USA) Limited (1)
700 Commerce Dr Ste 500, Oak Brook, IL 60523
Tel.: (630) 288-3572
Automobile Component Mfr & Distr
N.A.I.C.S.: 336110

SUNDARAM FINANCE HOLDINGS LIMITED

21 Patullos Road, Chennai, 600002, India
Tel.: (91) 4428881311
Web Site:
https://www.sundaramholdings.in
Year Founded: 1993
SUNDARMHLD—(NSE)
Sales Range: $1-9.9 Million
Emp.: 304
Financial Services
N.A.I.C.S.: 522390
S. Ravi (CEO)

Subsidiaries:

Sundaram Business Services Limited (1)
20 Patullos Road, Chennai, 600002, Tamil Nadu, India
Tel.: (91) 4428599900
Web Site:
https://www.sundarambusiness.com
Emp.: 400
Business Process Outsourcing Services
N.A.I.C.S.: 518210
Ravi S. (CEO)

SUNDARAM FINANCE LTD

21 Patullos Road, Chennai, 600 002, India
Tel.: (91) 4428521181
Web Site:
https://www.sundaramfinance.in
Year Founded: 1954
590071—(BOM)
Rev.: $664,758,708
Assets: $6,722,126,871
Liabilities: $5,206,812,541
Net Worth: $1,515,314,430
Earnings: $179,792,578
Emp.: 4,737
Fiscal Year-end: 03/31/23
Financial Services
N.A.I.C.S.: 522291
S. Viji (Chm)

Subsidiaries:

Royal Sundaram Alliance Insurance Company Limited (1)
Vishranthi Melaram Towers No 2/319 Rajiv Gandhi Salai OMR, Chennai, 600 097, Karapakkam, India (100%)
Tel.: (91) 4471177117
Web Site: http://www.royalsundaram.in
Insurance Services
N.A.I.C.S.: 524298
Sreedhar M. S. (Mng Dir)

Sundaram Alternate Assets Limited (1)
Sundaram Towers I II Floor No 46 Whites Road, Royapettah, Chennai, 600 014, India
Tel.: (91) 7305529179
Web Site:
https://www.sundaramalternates.com
Portfolio Management Services
N.A.I.C.S.: 523940
Harsha Viji (Chm)

Sundaram Asset Management Company Limited (1)
Sundaram Towers I II Floor No 46 Whites Road, Chennai, 600 014, India
Tel.: (91) 4428583362
Web Site: https://www.sundarammutual.com
Asset Management Services
N.A.I.C.S.: 523940
Harsha Viji (Chm)

Sundaram Asset Management Singapore Pte. Limited (1)
50 Armenian Street 02-02 Wilmer Place, Singapore, 179938, Singapore
Tel.: (65) 65577080
Web Site: http://www.sundarammutual.sg
Asset Management Services
N.A.I.C.S.: 523940
Anish Mathew (CEO & Chief Investment Officer)

SUNDARAM MULTI PAP LIMITED

Unit no 5 6 ground floor Papa Industrial Estate, Andheri Kurla Road Andheri east, Mumbai, 400093, Maharashtra, India
Tel.: (91) 2267602200
Web Site:
https://www.sundaramgroups.in
Year Founded: 1995
SUNDARAM—(NSE)
Rev.: $7,240,192
Assets: $20,158,552
Liabilities: $7,747,699
Net Worth: $12,410,853
Earnings: ($1,206,032)
Emp.: 245
Fiscal Year-end: 03/31/21
Stationery Products Marketing & Mfr
N.A.I.C.S.: 322230
Amrut P. Shah (Chm & Mng Dir)

Subsidiaries:

E-Class Education System Ltd (1)
603 Dev Plaza Opp Fire Station S V Road, Andheri West, Mumbai, 400058, India
Tel.: (91) 22 61163030
Web Site: http://www.e-class.in
Interactive Educational Support Services
N.A.I.C.S.: 611710

SUNDART HOLDINGS LIMITED

19/F Millennium City 3 370 Kwun Tong Road, Kowloon, China (Hong Kong)
Tel.: (852) 24132333 VG
Web Site: http://www.sundart.com
1568—(HKG)
Rev.: $596,524,943
Assets: $853,332,128
Liabilities: $439,259,558

INTERNATIONAL PUBLIC

Net Worth: $414,072,570
Earnings: $36,660,075
Emp.: 1,987
Fiscal Year-end: 12/31/22
Fitting-out Contracting Services
N.A.I.C.S.: 236118
Tak Kwan Ng (CEO)

Subsidiaries:

Beijing Sundart Decoration Engineering Co., Ltd. (1)
Building 3 No 277 Yongdeng Road Putuo District, Shanghai, China
Tel.: (86) 2132505580
Building Construction Services
N.A.I.C.S.: 236220

SUNDE AS

Borgundfjordveien 137, 6017, Alesund, Norway
Tel.: (47) 70177000
Web Site: http://www.sundolitt.no
Year Founded: 1917
Sales Range: $125-149.9 Million
Expandable Polystyrene Product Mfr
N.A.I.C.S.: 326140
Karl Johan Sunde (Mng Dir)

Subsidiaries:

Sundolitt Limited (1)
Bath Rd Green Lane Industrial Estate, Gateshead, NE10 0JT, Tyne And Wear, United Kingdom
Tel.: (44) 1914381023
Web Site: http://www.sundolitt.co.uk
Sales Range: $25-49.9 Million
Emp.: 12
Mfr of Packaging Products
N.A.I.C.S.: 326140
Paul Brown (Gen Mgr)

SUNDIRO HOLDING CO., LTD.

03-06 40th floor China Life Financial Center 88 Yincheng Road, Pudong District, Shanghai, 200120, China
Tel.: (86) 2161050111
Web Site: https://sundiro.com
Year Founded: 1988
000571—(SSE)
Rev.: $184,881,009
Assets: $417,666,399
Liabilities: $275,656,249
Net Worth: $142,010,149
Earnings: ($5,290,132)
Emp.: 3,000
Fiscal Year-end: 12/31/22
Coal Mining Services
N.A.I.C.S.: 213113

Subsidiaries:

Lirtix S.A. (1)
Av Islas Canarias 6175, Departamento de, 12900, Montevideo, Uruguay
Tel.: (598) 98305378
Web Site: https://lirtix-uy.com
Beef & Lamb Distr
N.A.I.C.S.: 424470

Sanlorenzo China Co., Ltd. (1)
111-211 Cannes Ave Bansh-anbandao Luhuitou Rd Hedong District, Sanya, 572000, Hainan, China
Tel.: (86) 898 88227585
Motorcycle Mfr
N.A.I.C.S.: 336991

Shanghai Sundiro Logistics Co., Ltd. (1)
3728 Middle Jiasong Road Qingpu District, Shanghai, 201705, China
Tel.: (86) 4008828856
Web Site: http://www.sundiro56.com
Emp.: 600
Logistics Management Services
N.A.I.C.S.: 541614

Shanghai Sundiro Property Management Co., Ltd. (1)
395 Alley Huaqiang Road Qingpu District, Shanghai, 201708, China
Tel.: (86) 2159794991
Motorcycle Mfr

AND PRIVATE COMPANIES / SUNFUN INFO CO., LTD.

N.A.I.C.S.: 336991

Shanghai Yuandun Industrial Co., Ltd. (1)
18 Alley Middle Xinfeng Road Qingpu District, Shanghai, 201708, China
Tel.: (86) 2159796796
Motorcycle Mfr
N.A.I.C.S.: 336991

Sundiro Sanlorenzo Yacht Manufacturing Co., Ltd. (1)
351 Lingui Avenue Guilinyang Development Zone, Hainai, 101300, China
Tel.: (86) 89868591366
Yacht Mfr
N.A.I.C.S.: 336611

Tianjin Sundiro Electric Vehicle Co., Ltd. (1)
5 Guangzhi Road Wangqingtuo Wuqing District, Tianjin, 301713, China
Tel.: (86) 22 29525034
Motorcycle Mfr
N.A.I.C.S.: 336991

Subsidiary (Domestic):

Wuxi Sundiro Electric Mobiles Co., Ltd. (2)
Xihu Road Langxia Villiage Yangjian Town Xishan District, Wuxi, 214108, Jiangsu, China
Tel.: (86) 51368555257
Motorcycle Mfr
N.A.I.C.S.: 336991

SUNDRUG CO., LTD.
1-38-1 Wakamatsu-cho, Fuchu, Tokyo, 183-0005, Japan
Tel.: (81) 423694361
Web Site: https://sundrug-online.com
9989—(TKS)
Rev.: $4,969,245,970
Assets: $2,777,574,880
Liabilities: $1,104,649,980
Net Worth: $1,672,924,900
Earnings: $192,522,860
Emp.: 7,800
Fiscal Year-end: 03/31/24
Drug Stores Owner & Operator
N.A.I.C.S.: 456110
Hiroshi Sadakata (Pres)

SUNDY LAND INVESTMENT CO., LTD.
Songdu Building No 789 Fuchun Road, Hangzhou, 310016, Zhejiang, China
Tel.: (86) 5718 675 9621
Web Site: http://www.songdu.com
600077—(SHG)
Rev.: $1,097,201,158
Assets: $6,590,651,423
Liabilities: $5,714,023,638
Net Worth: $876,627,785
Earnings: $53,989,672
Fiscal Year-end: 12/31/20
Real Estate Development Services
N.A.I.C.S.: 531390
Jianwu Yu (Chm & Pres)

SUNDY SERVICE GROUP CO., LTD.
Cai He Jiaye Mansion 19 Xintang Road, Jianggan, Hangzhou, China
Tel.: (86) 57186821030
Web Site: http://www.songduwuye.com
Year Founded: 1995
9608—(HKG)
Emp.: 1,400
Property Management Services
N.A.I.C.S.: 531311
Yun Yu (Exec Dir)

SUNEX SA
Piaskowa 7, 47-400, Raciborz, Poland
Tel.: (48) 324149212
Web Site: https://www.sunex.pl

SNX—(WAR)
Rev.: $80,214,522
Assets: $68,343,691
Liabilities: $43,263,404
Net Worth: $25,080,287
Earnings: $6,190,610
Fiscal Year-end: 12/31/23
Solar Energy Equipment Mfr
N.A.I.C.S.: 335999
Romuald Kalyciok (Co-Owner)

SUNF PU TECHNOLOGY CO., LTD.
No 3 Ding Hu 5th St, Kwei Shan Dist, Taoyuan, 333, Taiwan
Tel.: (886) 33285480
Web Site: https://www.sunfpu.com
Year Founded: 1983
5488—(TPE)
Rev.: $37,718,944
Assets: $48,867,617
Liabilities: $21,021,199
Net Worth: $27,846,418
Earnings: $565,425
Fiscal Year-end: 12/31/22
Wire & Cable Product Mfr
N.A.I.C.S.: 332618
Kuo-Cheng Lo (Chm & Pres)

Subsidiaries:

New Sunf Pu Electric Wire & Cable (Shenzhen) Co., Ltd. (1)
No 11 Minqing Road Longhua Street, Longhua New District, Shenzhen, 518109, Guangdong, China
Tel.: (86) 75581477635
Cable Products Mfr
N.A.I.C.S.: 332618

Sunf Pu Technology (Dong-guan) Co., Ltd. (1)
No 261 Si-Li South Road, Ta Ping Village Tang Xia Town, Dongguan, 523722, Guangdong, China
Tel.: (86) 76987937608
Cable Products Mfr
N.A.I.C.S.: 332618

SUNFAR COMPUTER CO., LTD.
2 Chien-Kuo 2nd Road, Sanmin District, Kaohsiung, Taiwan
Tel.: (886) 72366221
Web Site: http://www.sunfar.com.tw
6154—(TPE)
Rev.: $136,914,236
Assets: $63,221,305
Liabilities: $22,642,029
Net Worth: $40,579,276
Earnings: $2,788,794
Fiscal Year-end: 12/31/22
Computer Peripheral Equipment Distr
N.A.I.C.S.: 423430
Wu Chin-Chang (Chm & Pres)

SUNFCO LTD.
1-8-3 Kaji-cho, Chiyoda-ku, Tokyo, 101-0044, Japan
Tel.: (81) 3 3255 2460
Web Site: http://www.sunfco.com
Year Founded: 1979
Sales Range: $5-14.9 Billion
Emp.: 30
Dairy & Pharmaceutical Product Whslr
N.A.I.C.S.: 424430
Shigeru Takahara (Auditor)

SUNFIELD HOMES MISSISSAUGA LIMITED
120 Whitmore Road Unit 8 Suite 800, Woodbridge, L4L 6A5, ON, Canada
Tel.: (905) 851-2424
Web Site: http://www.sunfieldhomes.ca
Rev.: $34,281,000
Emp.: 20
House Construction

N.A.I.C.S.: 236115
Larry Lecce (Pres)

SUNFLAG IRON AND STEEL COMPANY LIMITED
33 Mount Road Sadar, Nagpur, 440 001, India
Tel.: (91) 2520356
Web Site: https://www.sunflagsteel.com
Year Founded: 1989
500404—(BOM)
Rev.: $419,098,375
Assets: $592,571,189
Liabilities: $191,663,569
Net Worth: $400,907,619
Earnings: $133,722,199
Emp.: 1,140
Fiscal Year-end: 03/31/23
Steel Mfrs
N.A.I.C.S.: 331110
Pranav Bhardwaj (Mng Dir)

SUNFLEX TECH CO., LTD.
No 522 Nanshang Road, Guishan District, Taoyuan, Taiwan
Tel.: (886) 32220998
Web Site: https://www.sunflex.com.tw
Year Founded: 1998
3390—(TPE)
Rev.: $31,055,436
Assets: $59,666,760
Liabilities: $24,486,133
Net Worth: $35,180,627
Earnings: $2,399,243
Fiscal Year-end: 12/31/22
Printed Circuit Board Mfr
N.A.I.C.S.: 334412
Hsin-Ying Li (Pres)

Subsidiaries:

Sunflex Electronic (Shenzhen) Co., Ltd. (1)
1st Building, 2nd Industrial Area Shasan Village Shajing Town Baoah District, Shenzhen, Guangdong, China
Tel.: (86) 75527269226
Circuit Board Mfr
N.A.I.C.S.: 334412

SUNFLOWER PHARMACEUTICAL GROUP CO., LTD.
No 18 Donghu Road Yingbin Road, Central District Daoli District, Harbin, 150078, Heilongjiang, China
Tel.: (86) 45182307136
Web Site: https://www.kuihuayaoye.com
Year Founded: 2005
002737—(SSE)
Rev.: $715,269,387
Assets: $987,259,904
Liabilities: $364,059,868
Net Worth: $623,200,037
Earnings: $121,752,928
Emp.: 4,500
Fiscal Year-end: 12/31/22
Pharmaceuticals Mfr
N.A.I.C.S.: 325412
Guan Yi (Pres & VP)

SUNFLOWER SUSTAINABLE INVESTMENTS LTD.
Dawn Tower 4 Ariel Sharon 37th floor, Givatayim, 5320045, Israel
Tel.: (972) 733244860
Web Site: https://www.sunflower-sit.com
Year Founded: 1995
SNFL—(TAE)
Rev.: $50,925,818
Assets: $238,291,473
Liabilities: $164,301,420
Net Worth: $73,990,053
Earnings: $1,444,951
Fiscal Year-end: 12/31/23

Miscellaneous Financial Investment Activities
N.A.I.C.S.: 523999

SUNFLY INTELLIGENT TECHNOLOGY CO., LTD.
No 256 Xijian Longmen, Laiyang, 265200, Shandong, China
Tel.: (86) 5357962888
Web Site: https://www.sunflytech.com
Year Founded: 2003
300423—(CHIN)
Rev.: $301,372,812
Assets: $804,347,388
Liabilities: $356,733,936
Net Worth: $447,613,452
Earnings: ($137,799,792)
Emp.: 360
Fiscal Year-end: 12/31/22
Electric Equipment Mfr
N.A.I.C.S.: 335999
Li Zhaoqiang (Chm)

SUNFON CONSTRUCTION CO., LTD.
7 F No 173 Chang An East Road Sec 2, Taipei, Taiwan
Tel.: (886) 227720267
Web Site: https://www.sunfon.com.tw
5514—(TPE)
Rev.: $216,865
Assets: $145,646,750
Liabilities: $60,483,225
Net Worth: $85,163,524
Earnings: ($435,044)
Fiscal Year-end: 12/31/22
Residential Apartment Leasing Services
N.A.I.C.S.: 531110

SUNFONDA GROUP HOLDINGS LIMITED
Sunfonda Auto Group No 1555 1st Ouya Road, Chanba Ecological District, Xi'an, 710021, Shaanxi, China
Tel.: (86) 2986101188
Web Site: http://www.sunfonda.com.cn
1771—(HKG)
Rev.: $1,533,684,391
Assets: $830,253,575
Liabilities: $484,474,349
Net Worth: $345,779,226
Earnings: $11,409,606
Emp.: 3,495
Fiscal Year-end: 12/31/22
Car Dealership Owner & Operator
N.A.I.C.S.: 441110
Tak Lam Wu (Co-Founder & Chm)

Subsidiaries:

Weinan Zongshen Baotai Automobile Sales & Service Co., Ltd. (1)
200 meters west of the intersection of Letian Street and Xinsheng Road, Hightech Zone, Weinan, China
Tel.: (86) 9138139999
Web Site: http://www.wnzsbaotai.bmw.com.cn
Car & Automobile Parts Retailer
N.A.I.C.S.: 441330

SUNFUN INFO CO., LTD.
5F No 37 Sec 3 Roosevelt Rd, Da-an District, Taipei, 106, Taiwan
Tel.: (886) 223650103
5278—(TPE)
Rev.: $57,371,228
Assets: $35,253,854
Liabilities: $21,283,369
Net Worth: $13,970,484
Earnings: $7,701,904
Fiscal Year-end: 12/31/22
Information Technology Consulting Services
N.A.I.C.S.: 513199
Chia-Ming Chang (Chm & Pres)

SUNG GANG CORP LTD.

11th Floor No 50 Section 1
Zhongxiao West Road, Taipei, 10041,
Taiwan
Tel.: (886) 223830383
Web Site: https://sunggang.com.tw
6240—(TPE)
Rev.: $1,501,455
Assets: $31,832,139
Liabilities: $18,860,459
Net Worth: $12,971,679
Earnings: ($337,814)
Fiscal Year-end: 12/31/23
Book Publishers
N.A.I.C.S.: 513130
Wang Yanjun *(Chm)*

SUNG HO ELECTRONICS CORP.

Ace Highend Tower 5th Gasan-dong,
Geumcheon-gu, Seoul, Korea (South)
Tel.: (82) 221047500
Web Site: https://www.sungho.net
Year Founded: 1973
043260—(KRS)
Rev.: $117,792,523
Assets: $178,036,501
Liabilities: $114,383,398
Net Worth: $63,653,104
Earnings: ($3,215,616)
Emp.: 95
Fiscal Year-end: 12/31/22
Film Capacitor Mfr.
N.A.I.C.S.: 334416
Park Sung-Jae *(CEO)*

Subsidiaries:

Sung Ho Electronics Corp. - China (Weihai) Factory   (1)
No 1519 Hexing Road, Weihai, Shandong, China
Tel.: (86) 631 5665661
Emp.: 940
Film Capacitor Mfr
N.A.I.C.S.: 334416

Sung Ho Electronics Corp. - China (Zhuhai) Factory   (1)
No 8 Pingxi Rd Naanpig S&T Industrial Park Zhuhai Avenue E, Zhuhai, Guangdong, China
Tel.: (86) 756 868 0001
Emp.: 650
Film Capacitor Mfr
N.A.I.C.S.: 334416

SUNG WOO ELECTRONICS CO., LTD.

606 4-ma Sihwa Complex 68
Beonnyeong-ro, Danwon-Gu, Ansan,
Gyeonggi-Do, Korea (South)
Tel.: (82) 313623100
Web Site: https://www.swei.co.kr
Year Founded: 1987
081580—(KRS)
Rev.: $127,264,311
Assets: $122,924,754
Liabilities: $38,898,806
Net Worth: $84,025,947
Earnings: $4,325,748
Emp.: 100
Fiscal Year-end: 12/31/22
Wireless Communication Equipment Mfr
N.A.I.C.S.: 334220
Joonho Oh *(Co-CEO)*

Subsidiaries:

Sung Woo Electronics Co., Ltd. - Estech Gwangju Factory   (1)
158-13 Pyeongdong-ro 803beon-gil Okdong Gwangsan-gu, Gwangju, Korea (South)
Tel.: (82) 234128555
Communication Equipment Mfr
N.A.I.C.S.: 334220

Sungwoo NIT, Inc   (1)

6-27 4F 51 Road, Gangnam-gu, Seoul, Korea (South)
Tel.: (82) 25551514
Web Site: http://www.swestec.co.kr
Smart Card Mfr & Distr
N.A.I.C.S.: 326199

SUNG-EUM MUSIC CO., LTD.

356-1 Goam-ri Hoecheon-eup,
Yangju, Seoul, 482-170, Gyeonggi-do, Korea (South)
Tel.: (82) 318587000
Web Site: http://www.crafterguitars.com
Year Founded: 1972
Sales Range: $25-49.9 Million
Emp.: 200
Guitar Mfr & Sales
N.A.I.C.S.: 339992
Hyun-Kwon Park *(Chm)*

SUNGARNER ENERGIES LIMITED

Plot No 113 Udyog Kendra-II Sector Ecotech-III, Gautam Budh Nagar, Noida, 201306, Uttar Pradesh, India
Tel.: (91) 9717558008
Web Site: https://www.sungarner.com
Year Founded: 2015
SEL—(NSE)
Rev.: $2,146,641
Assets: $1,233,851
Liabilities: $845,132
Net Worth: $388,719
Earnings: $90,130
Emp.: 46
Fiscal Year-end: 03/31/23
Solar Component Distr
N.A.I.C.S.: 423720
Akansha Pandey *(CEO)*

Subsidiaries:

Seltrik Electric India Private Limited   (1)

SUNGBO CHEMICAL CO., LTD.

104 Teheran-ro, Gangnam-gu, Seoul, Korea (South)
Tel.: (82) 237893800
Web Site: https://www.sbcc.kr
Year Founded: 1961
003080—(KRS)
Rev.: $50,912,891
Assets: $130,992,315
Liabilities: $25,604,924
Net Worth: $105,387,392
Earnings: $3,019,193
Emp.: 181
Fiscal Year-end: 12/31/22
Agricultural Chemical Mfr
N.A.I.C.S.: 325320
Yun Sun Jung *(CEO)*

SUNGCHANG AUTOTECH CO., LTD.

1785-1 Cheongwon-ro Wongokmyeon, Anseong, Gyeonggi-do, Korea (South)
Tel.: (82) 316505433
Web Site: https://www.sc-autotech.com
Year Founded: 1996
080470—(KRS)
Rev.: $141,729,745
Assets: $95,015,005
Liabilities: $57,504,511
Net Worth: $37,510,494
Earnings: $1,980,058
Emp.: 221
Fiscal Year-end: 12/31/22
Automobile Parts Mfr
N.A.I.C.S.: 336390
Goh Jong Wu *(Chm)*

Subsidiaries:

Sungchang Autotech Co., Ltd. - Asan Plant

132 Dunpo-ro Dunpo-ri Dunpo-myeon, Asan, 336-872, Chungcheongnam-do, Korea (South)
Tel.: (82) 41 532 1951
Automobile Parts Mfr
N.A.I.C.S.: 336360

SUNGCHANG ENTERPRISE HOLDINGS LIMITED

627 Dadae-ro, Saha-gu, Busan, 49526, Korea (South)
Tel.: (82) 512603333
Web Site: https://www.sce.kr
Year Founded: 1916
000180—(KRS)
Rev.: $174,507,608
Assets: $629,181,034
Liabilities: $172,223,305
Net Worth: $456,957,728
Earnings: ($10,124,132)
Emp.: 41
Fiscal Year-end: 12/31/22
Plywood Mfr
N.A.I.C.S.: 321211
Woo In-Seok *(CEO)*

Subsidiaries:

GC Tech Company Limited   (1)
8-21 Seowoncheon-ro 40-gil Namsanmyeon, Gyeongsan, 38573, Gyeongsangbuk-do, Korea (South)
Tel.: (82) 7046524606
Hardwood Veneer & Plywood Mfr
N.A.I.C.S.: 321211

Sungchang Enterprise Board Limited   (1)
35 Gangdang-ro Samnam-myeon, Ulju-gun, Ulsan, 44953, Korea (South)
Tel.: (82) 522553500
Hardwood Veneer & Plywood Mfr
N.A.I.C.S.: 321211

SUNGDO ENG HUNGARY KFT

Bem Rakpart 23, 1011, Budapest, Hungary
Tel.: (36) 709407208
Electronic Product Retailer
N.A.I.C.S.: 449210

SUNGDO ENGINEERING & CONSTRUCTION CO., LTD.

5F-7F Sungdo Venture Tower 42 Yeongdong-daero 106-gil, Gangnamgu, Seoul, Korea (South)
Tel.: (82) 262445200
Web Site: https://www.sungdokorea.com
037350—(KRS)
Rev.: $541,351,273
Assets: $384,727,966
Liabilities: $188,216,076
Net Worth: $196,511,890
Earnings: $562,334
Emp.: 426
Fiscal Year-end: 12/31/22
Construction Engineering Services
N.A.I.C.S.: 236220
In Soo Seo *(Chm & Co-CEO)*

Subsidiaries:

SUNGDO E&C (China) Co., LTD   (1)
811 Jinglian Rd, Minhang District, Shanghai, 201108, China
Tel.: (86) 21 5440 3261
Commercial Building Construction Services
N.A.I.C.S.: 236220

Sungdo Engineering&Construction PVT LTD   (1)
606 Satya Sai Residency Camlet Layout Near Chirec Public School, Kondapur, Hyderabad, 500 084, Andhra Pradesh, India
Tel.: (91) 84649 27890
Commercial Building Construction Services
N.A.I.C.S.: 236220

Sungdo Philippines Construction INC   (1)
1011 Remedios St CorModesto St BGY 689

Zone 07 Malate, Manila, Philippines
Tel.: (63) 927 364 6717
Commercial Building Construction Services
N.A.I.C.S.: 236220
Danilo Perez *(Head-Safety)*

SUNGEI BAGAN RUBBER COMPANY (MALAYA) BERHAD

Suite 9D Level 9 Menara Ansar, 65 Jalan Trus, 80000, Johor Bahru, Johor, Malaysia
Tel.: (60) 72241035
Web Site: https://www.sungeibagan.com
Year Founded: 1958
SBAGAN—(KLS)
Rev.: $8,468,593
Assets: $157,902,216
Liabilities: $3,686,213
Net Worth: $154,216,003
Earnings: $5,610,483
Emp.: 118
Fiscal Year-end: 06/30/24
Oil Palm Fruit Mfr & Distr
N.A.I.C.S.: 311411
Justin Chung-Shih Lee *(Deputy Chm)*

Subsidiaries:

Kuchai Development Berhad   (1)
Suite 9D Level 9 Menara Ansar 65 Jalan Trus, 80000, Johor Bahru, Johor, Malaysia
Tel.: (60) 72241035
Web Site: https://www.kuchaidevelopment.com
Rev.: $2,092,056
Assets: $75,586,151
Liabilities: $513,334
Net Worth: $75,072,818
Earnings: $4,002,834
Fiscal Year-end: 06/30/2023
Property Leasing Services
N.A.I.C.S.: 531120
Justin Chung-Shih Lee *(Deputy Chm)*

SUNGJEE CONSTRUCTION CO., LTD.

51-9 Suji-ro 296 Beon-gil, Suji-gu, Yongin, 16841, Gyeonggi-do, Korea (South)
Tel.: (82) 31 272 0972
Web Site: http://www.sungjee.com
Year Founded: 1969
Civil Engineering Construction Services
N.A.I.C.S.: 541330

SUNGJI TRADING CO., LTD.

604 Woolim e-biz Center 16 Yangpyung-Dong 3GA Yeongdeungpo-Gu, Youngdongpo Gu, Seoul, 150-946, Korea (South)
Tel.: (82) 220687231
Web Site: http://www.sungjis.com
Year Founded: 1982
Sales Range: $10-24.9 Million
Emp.: 15
Semiconductors, Electronics, Chemicals, Food, Healthcare Products, Glass & Film Products Distr, Importer & Exporter
N.A.I.C.S.: 425120
In Sun Chung *(Pres)*

SUNGKWANG BEND CO., LTD.

26 Noksansandan 262-ro, Gangseo-gu, Busan, Korea (South)
Tel.: (82) 513300350
Web Site: https://www.skbend.com
Year Founded: 1963
014620—(KRS)
Rev.: $187,167,593
Assets: $404,296,479
Liabilities: $42,469,816
Net Worth: $361,826,663
Earnings: $30,100,686
Emp.: 323
Fiscal Year-end: 12/31/22
Pipe Fitting Mfr

SUNGMOON ELECTRONICS CO., LTD.
61 Segyosandan-Ro, Pyeongtaek, 17843, Gyeonggi-do, Korea (South)
Tel.: (82) 316502800
Web Site: https://www.smec-korea.co.kr
Year Founded: 1980
014910—(KRS)
Rev.: $38,329,980
Assets: $43,904,089
Liabilities: $19,303,562
Net Worth: $24,600,527
Earnings: $1,564,574
Emp.: 68
Fiscal Year-end: 12/31/22
Electrical & Electronic Component Mfr
N.A.I.C.S.: 335999
Dong Yeol Shin *(Chm)*

Subsidiaries:

CHANG CHUN SUNG MOON ELECTRONICS CO., LTD. (1)
No 215 Chuang Xin Street High New Technology, Industry Development District, Changchun, China
Tel.: (86) 431 701 1602
Electronic Components Mfr
N.A.I.C.S.: 334419

QINGDAO SUNG MOON ELECTRONICS CO., LTD. (1)
No 5 Yantai Road, Economy Develop Area Pingdu, Qingdao, Shandong, China
Tel.: (86) 532 8330 5005
Electronic Components Mfr
N.A.I.C.S.: 334419

Sungmoon Electronics Co., Ltd. - 1ST FACTORY (1)
441-6 Sangdaewon Dong, Jungwon Gu, Seongnam, Kyungki Do, Korea (South)
Tel.: (82) 31 748 4343
Electronic Components Mfr
N.A.I.C.S.: 334419

Sungmoon Electronics Co., Ltd. - 2ND FACTORY (1)
442-13 Sangdaewon Dong, Jungwon Gu, Seongnam, Kyungki Do, Korea (South)
Tel.: (82) 31 734 6704
Electronic Components Mfr
N.A.I.C.S.: 334419

TIANJIN SUNG MOON ELECTRONICS CO., LTD. (1)
Teda Da Zhang Zhuang Town Beichan Qu, Tianjin, China
Tel.: (86) 22 2699 3971
Electronic Components Mfr
N.A.I.C.S.: 334419

SUNGOLD CAPITAL LIMITED
Ground Floor 36 Shri Rang Residency Vadia, Narmada, Rajpipla, 393145, Gujarat, India
Tel.: (91) 8108756812
Web Site: https://www.sungoldcapitalltd.com
Year Founded: 1993
531433—(BOM)
Rev.: $216,282
Assets: $3,686,050
Liabilities: $1,039,398
Net Worth: $2,646,652
Earnings: $3,153
Emp.: 5
Fiscal Year-end: 03/31/23
Financial Services
N.A.I.C.S.: 523999
Rajiv Kotia *(Chm, CEO & Mng Dir)*

SUNGOLD INTERNATIONAL HOLDINGS CORP
300-940 The East Mall, Toronto, M9B 6J7, ON, Canada
Tel.: (416) 621-4519
Web Site: http://www.sungolintl.com
Emp.: 7
Live Race Lottery Event, Virtual Race Lottery Event, Pari-Mutuel & Virtual Horseracing Game
N.A.I.C.S.: 713290
Donald R. Harris *(Chm)*

SUNGOLD MEDIA & ENTERTAINMENT LTD.
102 1st Floor 36 Shri Rang Residency Vadia Rajpipla Narmada, Village- Rajpipla Nandod Narmada, Gujarat, 393145, India
Tel.: (91) 9099018633
Web Site: https://www.sungoldmediaent.com
541799—(BOM)
Rev.: $86,554
Assets: $1,386,488
Liabilities: $1,858
Net Worth: $1,384,629
Earnings: $2,038
Emp.: 6
Fiscal Year-end: 03/31/23
Entertainment Services
N.A.I.C.S.: 711130
Raj Kotia *(Chm & Mng Dir)*

SUNGROW POWER SUPPLY CO., LTD.
No 1699 Xiyou Rd New and High Technology Industrial Development Zone, Hefei, Anhui, China
Tel.: (86) 4001197799
Web Site: https://ind.sungrowpower.com
Year Founded: 1997
300274—(CHIN)
Rev.: $9,233,667,093
Assets: $10,591,652,932
Liabilities: $6,827,355,732
Net Worth: $3,764,297,200
Earnings: $1,206,380,027
Emp.: 2,100
Fiscal Year-end: 12/31/23
Solar Energy Photovoltaic, Wind Energy & Other Power Products Mfr
N.A.I.C.S.: 335311
Renxian Cao *(Founder)*

Subsidiaries:

SUNGROW POWER AUSTRALIA PTY LTD. (1)
Suite 1703 99 Mount Street, North Sydney, 2060, NSW, Australia
Tel.: (61) 299221522
Web Site: http://www.sungrowpower.com.au
Sales Range: $25-49.9 Million
Emp.: 3
Solar Inverter Mfr
N.A.I.C.S.: 335999

Sungrow Canada Inc. (1)
6535 Millcreek Dr Unit 63-64, Mississauga, L5N 2M2, ON, Canada
Tel.: (905) 760-8618
Web Site: http://www.sungrow.ca
Sales Range: $25-49.9 Million
Emp.: 5
Solar Inverter Mfr
N.A.I.C.S.: 335999
Mizhi Zhang *(CEO)*

SUNGSHIN CEMENT CO., LTD.
7F Taehwa Building 29 Insadong 5-gil, Jongno-gu, Seoul, Korea (South)
Tel.: (82) 237827000
Web Site: https://www.sungshincement.co.kr
Year Founded: 1967
004980—(KRS)
Rev.: $790,327,791
Assets: $910,876,163
Liabilities: $606,980,315
Net Worth: $303,895,848
Earnings: $(20,302,867)
Emp.: 587
Fiscal Year-end: 12/31/22
Cement Product Mfr
N.A.I.C.S.: 327310
Sang-gyu Kim *(CEO)*

Subsidiaries:

Sungshin Vina Co., Ltd. (1)
Lai Yen Industrial Zone, Lai Yen commune Hoai Duc district, Hanoi, Vietnam
Tel.: (84) 433213411
Web Site: https://www.sungshinvina.com.vn
Concrete Product Distr
N.A.I.C.S.: 423390
Pham Van Anh *(Mktg Mgr)*

SUNGWOO HITECH CO., LTD.
2-9 Nonggong-gil Jeonggwan-eup, Gijang-gun, Busan, 46020, Korea (South)
Tel.: (82) 7074775501
Web Site: https://www.swhitech.com
Year Founded: 1977
015750—(KRS)
Rev.: $3,050,385,568
Assets: $2,810,419,195
Liabilities: $1,697,800,308
Net Worth: $1,112,618,888
Earnings: $29,538,314
Emp.: 17,500
Fiscal Year-end: 12/31/22
Automobile Parts Mfr
N.A.I.C.S.: 336390
Myung-Keun Lee *(Chm & CEO)*

Subsidiaries:

Asan Sungwoo Hitech Co., Ltd. (1)
591 Seobunam-ro, Sinchang-myeon, Asan, 31535, Chungnam, Korea (South)
Tel.: (82) 7074775700
Automobile Parts Mfr
N.A.I.C.S.: 336390

Beijing Sungwoo Che Hitech Co., Ltd. (1)
28 Xinggu Industrial Development Zone, Pinggu District, Beijing, China
Tel.: (86) 10 6995 8500
Motor Vehicle Body Parts Mfr & Distr
N.A.I.C.S.: 336390

Cangzhou Sungwoo Hitech Automobile Parts Co., Ltd. (1)
Huoju Road 9, Zhongjiegaoxin Technology Industry Development Zone Bohaixin District, Cangzhou, 061000, Hebei, China
Tel.: (86) 3175601380
Automobile Parts Mfr
N.A.I.C.S.: 336390

Chongqing Sungwoo Hitech Automobile Parts Co., Ltd. (1)
Crossing the Streets of Ming Tao Road 1102, Changshou District, Chongqing, China
Tel.: (86) 15213142824
Automobile Parts Mfr
N.A.I.C.S.: 336390

Sungwoo Hitech Automobile Components (Yancheng) Co., Ltd. (1)
26 Kaichuang street Yandu NewZone, Yancheng, Jiangsu, China
Tel.: (86) 515 8885 6800
Web Site: http://www.swhitech.com
Automotive Components Mfr
N.A.I.C.S.: 336390

Sungwoo Hitech Co., Ltd. - Dadae Factory (1)
1503-9 Dade-Dong Saha-Ku, Busan, Korea (South)
Tel.: (82) 51 264 7560
Automotive Part Whslr
N.A.I.C.S.: 441330

Sungwoo Hitech Co., Ltd. - Jeonggwan Factory (1)
2-9 Nonggong-gil, Gijiang-gun, Busan, Korea (South)
Tel.: (82) 7074775450
Automobile Parts Mfr
N.A.I.C.S.: 336390

Sungwoo Hitech Co., Ltd. - Jisa Factory (1)
1213 Jisa-dong, Gangseo-gu, Busan, Korea (South)
Tel.: (82) 70 7477 5400
Automotive Components Mfr
N.A.I.C.S.: 336390

Sungwoo Hitech Co., Ltd. - JungKwan Factory (1)
148-12 Dalsan-ri Chungkwan-myu, Gijang-gun, Busan, Korea (South)
Tel.: (82) 51 728 5317
Automobile Parts Mfr
N.A.I.C.S.: 336110

Sungwoo Hitech Co., Ltd. - JungKwan No.2 Factory (1)
940-15 Yerim-ri Chungkwan-myun, Gijang-Gun, Busan, Korea (South)
Tel.: (82) 517285317
Web Site: http://www.swhitech.co.kr
Sales Range: $200-249.9 Million
Emp.: 700
Automobile Parts Mfr
N.A.I.C.S.: 336110

Sungwoo Hitech Co., Ltd. - Seochang Factory (1)
3-13 Soju-dong, Yangsan, Gyeongnam, Korea (South)
Tel.: (82) 70 7477 5000
Automotive Components Mfr
N.A.I.C.S.: 336390

Sungwoo Hitech India Ltd. (1)
Tel.: (91) 4427256032
Automobile Parts Mfr
N.A.I.C.S.: 336390

Sungwoo Hitech Slovakia s.r.o (1)
Cestarska 1, 010 01, Zilina, Slovakia
Tel.: (421) 41 2240 131
Automobile Component Mfr & Distr
N.A.I.C.S.: 336390
Lukas Durech *(Mgr-Process Engrg & Maintenance)*

Sungwoo Hitech WMU (1)
Gottinger Landstr 2-6, 34346, Hann. Munden, Germany
Tel.: (49) 55 41 98 22 0
Web Site: http://www.wmu.de
Emp.: 600
Automobile Component Distr
N.A.I.C.S.: 423120

Sungwoo Hitech Wuxi Co., Ltd. (1)
25 Xnhua Road, Wuxi National Hi-Tech Industrial Development Zone, Wuxi, Jiangsu, China
Tel.: (86) 51085200591
Automobile Parts Mfr
N.A.I.C.S.: 336390

Sungwoo Hitech s.r.o (1)
Na Rovince 895, Hrabova, 720 00, Ostrava, Czech Republic
Tel.: (420) 552306411
Web Site: https://www.swhitech.cz
Automobile Component Mfr & Distr
N.A.I.C.S.: 336390

Sungwoo Mold Co., Ltd. (1)
118-1 Soji-dong, Yangsan, Gyeongnam, Korea (South)
Tel.: (82) 70 7477 5300
Web Site: http://www.swhitech.com
Motor Vehicle Body Parts Mfr
N.A.I.C.S.: 336390

Weser-Metall-Umformtechnik Bavaria GmbH (1)
Luitpoldpark 15, Niederaichbach, 84100, Landshut, Germany
Tel.: (49) 8702453800
Web Site: http://www.wmu-bavaria.de
Automobile Parts Mfr
N.A.I.C.S.: 336390

Weser-Metall-Umformtechnik GmbH (1)
Tel.: (49) 554198220
Automobile Parts Mfr
N.A.I.C.S.: 336390

SUNGWOO TECHRON CO., LTD.
55 Changwon-daero 1144beon-gil, Changwon, Korea (South)
Tel.: (82) 552798400

Sungwoo Techron Co., Ltd.—(Continued)

Web Site: https://www.swmv.co.kr
045300—(KRS)
Rev.: $34,062,430
Assets: $71,019,317
Liabilities: $17,333,014
Net Worth: $53,686,303
Earnings: $3,690,615
Emp.: 254
Fiscal Year-end: 12/31/22
Semiconductor Equipment Mfr
N.A.I.C.S.: 334413
Chan-Hong Park (CEO)

Subsidiaries:

ATS-Avante Technology & Service Ltd. (1)
No 20-1 Jalan Seit Taman Cheng Baru, 75250, Melaka, Malaysia
Tel.: (60) 63123925
Flat Flexible Cable Mfr
N.A.I.C.S.: 335921

Dongguan City Synpower Co., Ltd. (1)
Room 1313-1315 Parkway Finance Center Dong-Men Middle Road No 121, Chang-An Town, Dongguan, 523850, China
Tel.: (86) 76985093891
Web Site: https://www.synpower.com.tw
Printed Circuit Board Automatic Machine & Raw Material Mfr
N.A.I.C.S.: 334412

SynPower Co., Ltd. (1)
330 No 12 Lane81 Longshout St, Taoyuan Dist, Taoyuan, 330, Taiwan
Tel.: (886) 33690966
Web Site: https://www.synpower.com.tw
Printed Circuit Board Automatic Machine & Raw Material Mfr
N.A.I.C.S.: 334412

SUNGY MOBILE LIMITED

17th Floor Tower A China International Centre No 33 Zhong Shan 3rd, Yue Xiu District, Guangzhou, 510055, China
Tel.: (86) 20 6681 5066   Ky
Web Site:
  http://www.sungymobile.com
Year Founded: 2003
Sales Range: $50-74.9 Million
Mobile Internet Products & Services
N.A.I.C.S.: 513210
Yuqiang Deng (Chm & CEO)

SUNIC SYSTEM CO., LTD.

293 Saneop-ro 155 beon-gil, Gwonseon-gu, Suwon, Gyeonggi, Korea (South)
Tel.: (82) 3180121600
Web Site: https://www.sunic.co.kr
Year Founded: 1990
171090—(KRS)
Rev.: $56,798,388
Assets: $95,775,229
Liabilities: $34,950,396
Net Worth: $60,824,832
Earnings: ($2,482,005)
Emp.: 180
Fiscal Year-end: 12/31/22
Electrical Component Mfr
N.A.I.C.S.: 335999
Lee Young-Jong (CEO)

SUNIL AGRO FOODS LIMITED

1/104 Ahuja Chambers Kumara Krupa Road, Bengaluru, 56 00 01, India
Tel.: (91) 8022251555
Web Site: https://www.sunilagro.in
530953—(BOM)
Rev.: $25,189,125
Assets: $9,109,142
Liabilities: $7,177,951
Net Worth: $1,931,191
Earnings: $106,756
Emp.: 97

Fiscal Year-end: 03/31/23
Wheat Products Mfr
N.A.I.C.S.: 311230
Shantilal Bansilal (Mng Dir)

Subsidiaries:

Brindavan Roller Flour Mills Limited (1)
Plot No 142 K R S Rd Belagola Indl Area Metagalli, Mysore, 570 016, India
Tel.: (91) 821 2582067
Wheat Flour Mfr
N.A.I.C.S.: 311211
Subramania Bhatt (Gen Mgr)

SUNIL HEALTHCARE LIMITED

Vijay Tower 38E/252 - A Shahpur Jat Opp Panchsheel, Park Commercial Complex, New Delhi, 110 049, India
Tel.: (91) 1149435500
Web Site:
  https://www.sunilhealthcare.com
029424—(KOL)
Rev.: $13,786,631
Assets: $14,482,381
Liabilities: $7,768,527
Net Worth: $6,713,854
Earnings: $801,163
Emp.: 221
Fiscal Year-end: 03/31/23
Gelatin Capsules Mfr
N.A.I.C.S.: 325998
Santosh Kumar Sharma (Compliance Officer & Sec)

SUNIL INDUSTRIES LIMITED

D/8 MIDC Phase II Manpada Road, Dombivli E, Thane, 421 203, Maharashtra, India
Tel.: (91) 2512870749
Web Site:
  https://www.sunilgroup.com
Year Founded: 1976
521232—(BOM)
Rev.: $27,308,914
Assets: $15,224,507
Liabilities: $10,060,548
Net Worth: $5,163,959
Earnings: $412,445
Emp.: 29
Fiscal Year-end: 03/31/23
Printed Cotton Fabric Mfr
N.A.I.C.S.: 313210
Vinod Gajanand Lath (Chm & Mng Dir)

SUNING HOLDINGS GROUP CO., LTD.

No 1 Suning Avenue Xuzhuang Software Park, Xuanwu District, Nanjing, Jiangsu, China
Tel.: (86) 2566996699
Web Site:
  http://www.suningholdings.com
Year Founded: 1990
Sales Range: Less than $1 Million
Holding Company
N.A.I.C.S.: 551112
Jindong Zhang (Chm)

Subsidiaries:

Suning.com Co., Ltd. (1)
Floor 1-5 Jinshan Building No 8 Shanxi, Road, Xuanwu District, Nanjing, 210042, Jiangsu, China
Tel.: (86) 2584418888
Web Site: http://www.suning.cn
Rev.: $8,671,280,322
Assets: $16,857,039,627
Liabilities: $15,453,639,233
Net Worth: $1,403,400,393
Earnings: ($566,209,647)
Emp.: 13,390
Fiscal Year-end: 12/31/2023
Household Appliance Stores
N.A.I.C.S.: 449210
Jun Ren (Chm)

Subsidiary (Domestic):

CARREFOUR China, Inc. (2)
Floor 18 Tower A Ce3ntral Towers No 555 Langao Rd, Shanghai, 200333, Putuo District, China   (80%)
Tel.: (86) 21 3878 4500
Super Market Stores Operating Services
N.A.I.C.S.: 445110
Thierry Garnier (Exec Dir-China)

SUNING UNIVERSAL CO., LTD.

No 718 Jiuzhan Street, Jilin Economic and Technological Development Zone, Jilin, 210024, China
Tel.: (86) 2583247946
Web Site: http://www.suning-universal.com
Year Founded: 1993
000718—(SSE)
Rev.: $314,377,039
Assets: $2,161,112,602
Liabilities: $788,079,844
Net Worth: $1,373,032,758
Earnings: $50,255,604
Fiscal Year-end: 12/31/22
Real Estate Development Services
N.A.I.C.S.: 531190
Guiping Zhang (Chm & Pres)

SUNITY ONLINE ENTERTAINMENT LTD.

Level 9 Block A 31 Gaoxin Road, Xi'an, 710075, China
Tel.: (86) 2985227627   Ky
Web Site: http://www.sunity5.com
Year Founded: 2006
Sales Range: $10-24.9 Million
Emp.: 344
Online Game Developer
N.A.I.C.S.: 513210
Fan Zhang (Chm & CEO)

SUNJIN BEAUTY SCIENCE CO., LTD.

43-14 Gasan digital 2-ro, Geumcheon-gu, Seoul, Korea (South)
Tel.: (82) 8533200
Web Site: https://sunjinbs.com
Year Founded: 1978
086710—(KRS)
Rev.: $49,342,818
Assets: $103,982,990
Liabilities: $52,695,918
Net Worth: $51,287,072
Earnings: $15,420,225
Emp.: 122
Fiscal Year-end: 12/31/22
Cosmetic Product Mfr & Distr
N.A.I.C.S.: 325620
Sung Ho Lee (CEO)

Subsidiaries:

Aston Chemicals Ltd. (1)
5 Premus Coldharbour Way, Aylesbury, HP19 8AP, Buckinghamshire, United Kingdom
Tel.: (44) 1296337700
Web Site: https://www.aston-chemicals.com
Personal Care Industries Raw Material Distr
N.A.I.C.S.: 424590

Company Tera Co., Ltd. (1)
KashirskoeShosse d 33 k 1 office 259A, Moscow, 115409, Russia
Tel.: (7) 4959874256
Cosmetic Raw Material Distr
N.A.I.C.S.: 424210

Impag GmbH (1)
Fritz-Remy-str25, 63071, Offenbach, Germany
Tel.: (49) 69850008130
Cosmetic Raw Material Distr
N.A.I.C.S.: 424210

Shantou Mitutoyo Chemical Co., Ltd. (1)
No 33 to 35 4th Street Huanan Square, Xiashan Subdistrict Chaonan District, Shantou, Guangdong, China

Tel.: (86) 13553377199
Cosmetic Raw Material Distr
N.A.I.C.S.: 424210

SUNJIN CO., LTD.

1378 Yangjae-daero, Gangdong-gu, Seoul, 05372, Korea (South)
Tel.: (82) 222250777
Web Site: https://www.sunjin.com
Year Founded: 2011
136490—(KRS)
Rev.: $1,434,889,169
Assets: $702,229,966
Liabilities: $375,229,009
Net Worth: $327,000,957
Earnings: $17,617,818
Emp.: 419
Fiscal Year-end: 12/31/22
Animal Feed Mfr
N.A.I.C.S.: 311119
Bum-Kwon Lee (Pres & CEO)

Subsidiaries:

QINGDAO SUNJIN FEED Co., Ltd. (1)
Agriculture Collaboration Zone, Nancun Pingdu, Qingdao, Shandong, China
Tel.: (86) 15308099568
Animal Food Distr
N.A.I.C.S.: 424910

SUNJIN CHENGDU FEED Co., Ltd. (1)
199 Rongtai Road Chengdu National Cross-Strait Technology, Industrial Development Park Wenjiang, Chengdu, Sichuan, China
Tel.: (86) 13808075285
Animal Food Distr
N.A.I.C.S.: 424910

SUNJIN FARMSCO Co., Ltd. (1)
Section D Pho Noi A Industrial Park, Yen My, Hung Yen, Vietnam
Tel.: (84) 904871588
Animal Food Distr
N.A.I.C.S.: 424910

SUNJIN GENETICS CORPORATION (1)
Roman roxas road sitio abuyod brgy, San jose, Antipolo, Rizal, Philippines
Tel.: (63) 26941982
Animal Food Distr
N.A.I.C.S.: 424910

SUNJIN PHILIPPINES Inc. (1)
Bgy Partida Norzagaray, Bulacan, 3013, Philippines
Tel.: (63) 446942076
Animal Food Distr
N.A.I.C.S.: 424910
Hernie Gajo (Mgr-Production)

SUNJIN VINA Co., Ltd. (1)
Lot II-11 Ho Nai Industrial Park, Ho Nai 3 Commune Trang Bom District, Dong Nai, Vietnam
Tel.: (84) 2517300680
Animal Food Distr
N.A.I.C.S.: 424910
Diep Hoang Huynh Nguyen (Mgr-HR)

SUNJIN VINA MEKONG CO., Ltd. (1)
Lot 82 Long Ging Industrial Zone, Tan Lap 1 Commune Tan Phuoc District, Tan Phuoc, Tien Giang, Vietnam
Tel.: (84) 908648567
Animal Food Distr
N.A.I.C.S.: 424910

TIELING SUNJIN Co., Ltd. (1)
Guantai Industrial park Tieling Economic Development Zone, Tieling, Liaoning, China
Tel.: (86) 18904103877
Animal Food Distr
N.A.I.C.S.: 424910

SUNJUICE HOLDINGS CO., LTD.

No 10 JuJin Road No 500 YuanPu Road, Zhangpu Township, Suzhou, 215321, Jiangsu, China
Tel.: (86) 51257515501   Ky

Web Site:
https://www.myfreshjuice.com
Year Founded: 2010
1256—(TAI)
Rev.: $118,046,744
Assets: $104,626,279
Liabilities: $36,185,510
Net Worth: $68,440,769
Earnings: $18,211,557
Emp.: 768
Fiscal Year-end: 12/31/19
Fruit Juice Mfr & Distr
N.A.I.C.S.: 311421
Kuo-Huang Huang *(Chm & Pres)*

Subsidiaries:

Fresh Juice Industry (Kunshan) Co., Ltd (1)
No 10 JuJin Road No 500 YuanPu Road Zhangpu Township, Kunshan, 215321, Jiangsu, China
Tel.: (86) 512 57515501
Canned & Bottled Juice Mfr
N.A.I.C.S.: 311421

Subsidiary (Domestic):

Fresh Juice Industry (Tianjin) Co., Ltd. (2)
No 98 XinMin Road The West District Economic, Technological Development Zone, Tianjin, China
Tel.: (86) 2258532966
Canned & Bottled Juice Mfr
N.A.I.C.S.: 311421

Guangdong Fresh Juice Biological Technology Company Ltd. (2)
No 3 Xinglong One Street High-tech Zone, Zhaoqing, Guangdong, China
Tel.: (86) 7583981780
Canned & Bottled Juice Mfr
N.A.I.C.S.: 311421

SUNKAR RESOURCES PLC
Suite 5 Floor 2 107 Cheapside, London, EC2V 6DN, United Kingdom
Tel.: (44) 2073973730 UK
Web Site:
http://www.sunkarresources.com
Sales Range: $1-9.9 Million
Emp.: 118
Phosphatic Fertilizer Mfr
N.A.I.C.S.: 325312
Nurdin Damitov *(Dir-Corp Affairs)*

SUNKO INK CO., LTD.
403 5th Floor No 229 Zhongxing Street, West District, Taichung, 403, Taiwan
Tel.: (886) 423215616
Web Site: https://www.sunko.com.tw
1721—(TAI)
Rev.: $71,476,206
Assets: $121,771,996
Liabilities: $52,845,775
Net Worth: $68,926,221
Earnings: ($9,090,127)
Emp.: 505
Fiscal Year-end: 12/31/23
Thermoplastic Polyurethane Mfr
N.A.I.C.S.: 325211

SUNKWAN PROPERTIES GROUP LIMITED
8/F Tower 5 No 1399 Xinzhen Road, Minhang, Shanghai, China
Tel.: (86) 4000152220 Ky
Web Site:
http://www.sunkwan.com.cn
Year Founded: 2018
6900—(HKG)
Real Estate Development Services
N.A.I.C.S.: 531390
Jing Zhu *(Founder, Chm & CEO)*

SUNLAND GROUP LIMITED
140A Alice Street, Brisbane, 4000, QLD, Australia
Tel.: (61) 7 3456 5700 AU
Web Site:
http://www.sunlandgroup.com.au
Year Founded: 1983
SDG—(ASX)
Rev.: $216,260,958
Assets: $400,156,519
Liabilities: $161,368,042
Net Worth: $238,788,477
Earnings: $19,114,908
Emp.: 73
Fiscal Year-end: 06/30/21
Property Development & Construction Services
N.A.I.C.S.: 236220
Soheil Abedian *(Founder & Chm)*

SUNLANDS TECHNOLOGY GROUP
Building 4-6 Chaolai Science Park No 36 Chuangyuan Road, Chaoyang District, Beijing, 100012, China
Tel.: (86) 1052413738 Ky
Web Site: https://www.sunlands.com
Year Founded: 2015
STG—(NYSE)
Rev.: $355,922,304
Assets: $348,716,685
Liabilities: $406,913,656
Net Worth: ($58,196,972)
Earnings: $98,660,958
Emp.: 2,318
Fiscal Year-end: 12/31/22
Online Education Services
N.A.I.C.S.: 611710
Peng Ou *(Founder & Chm)*

SUNLIFE INSURANCE COMPANY LTD.
BTA Tower 7th Floor 29 Kemal Ataturk Avenue Road 17, Banani, Dhaka, 1213, Bangladesh
Tel.: (880) 9821567
Web Site:
http://www.sunlifeinsbd.com
Year Founded: 2000
Fire Insurance Services
N.A.I.C.S.: 524113
Rubina Hamid *(Chm)*

SUNLIGHT (1977) HOLDINGS LTD.
11 Tuas South Street 5, Singapore, 637590, Singapore
Tel.: (65) 62686788 Ky
Web Site:
https://www.sunlightpaper.com.sg
Year Founded: 1977
8451—(HKG)
Rev.: $10,815,858
Assets: $15,055,206
Liabilities: $2,585,402
Net Worth: $12,469,804
Earnings: $481,660
Emp.: 37
Fiscal Year-end: 09/30/23
Tissue Paper Mfr & Distr
N.A.I.C.S.: 322291
Liang Sie Chua *(Chm & CEO)*

SUNLIGHT GROUP ENERGY STORAGE SYSTEMS INDUSTRIAL AND COMMERCIAL SINGLEMEMBER SOCIETE ANONYME
22 Thivaidos Kifissia, 145 64, Athens, Greece
Tel.: (30) 210624540
Web Site: https://www.the-sunlight-group.com
Rev.: $333,962,336
Assets: $445,867,274
Liabilities: $303,015,796
Net Worth: $142,851,478
Earnings: $9,890,110
Emp.: 1,151
Fiscal Year-end: 12/31/21
Innovative Industrial & Off-road Energy storage Solutions
N.A.I.C.S.: 493190
Lampros Bisalas *(CEO)*

Subsidiaries:

Triathlon Holding GmbH (1)
Siemensstrasse 1, 08371, Glauchau, Germany (100%)
Tel.: (49) 376377850
Web Site: https://www.triathlon-batterien.de
Holding Company
N.A.I.C.S.: 551112

SUNLOUR PIGMENT CO., LTD.
No 2 Renmin Road, Zhangguo Xinghua, Taizhou, 225722, Jiangsu, China
Tel.: (86) 52383764200
Web Site: https://www.shuangle.com
Year Founded: 1983
301036—(CHIN)
Rev.: $201,876,675
Assets: $260,728,239
Liabilities: $39,903,127
Net Worth: $220,825,112
Earnings: $6,658,761
Fiscal Year-end: 12/31/23
Pigment Product Mfr & Distr
N.A.I.C.S.: 325130
Hanzhou Yang *(Chm)*

Subsidiaries:

Sunlour Pigment Taixing City Co., Ltd. (1)
No 18 Shugang Road Taixing Economic Development Zone, Taizhou, China
Tel.: (86) 52383764200
Pigment Mfr
N.A.I.C.S.: 325130

SUNLUX
Rue Verte, 63118, Cebazat, France
Tel.: (33) 473258400
Year Founded: 1985
Rev.: $16,200,000
Emp.: 28
Lighting Fixture Mfr & Distr
N.A.I.C.S.: 335132
Frederic Larivaille *(CEO)*

Subsidiaries:

Sunlux Mediterranean (1)
10 boulevard du 2 Mars Appartement 22, Casablanca, Morocco
Tel.: (212) 522 275 299
Lighting Equipment Distr
N.A.I.C.S.: 423610

SUNMART HOLDINGS LIMITED
No 26 E N Rd Xiake, Jiangyin, Jiangsu, China
Tel.: (86) 51086530115
Sales Range: $50-74.9 Million
Spray Pumps Mfr
N.A.I.C.S.: 333111
Sun Bingzhong *(Chm & CEO)*

SUNMIRROR AG
General-Guisan-Strasse 6, 6300, Zug, Switzerland
Tel.: (41) 435051400 CH
Web Site: https://www.sunmirror.com
Year Founded: 2014
ROR—(DEU)
Rev.: $1,448,000
Assets: $41,280,000
Liabilities: $8,429,000
Net Worth: $32,851,000
Earnings: ($18,290,000)
Fiscal Year-end: 06/30/22
Holding Company
N.A.I.C.S.: 551112
Laurent Quelin *(Chm)*

SUNMOON FOOD COMPANY LIMITED
51 Changi Business Park Central 2 0306 The Signature, Singapore, 608840, Singapore
Tel.: (65) 67795688 SG
Web Site:
https://www.sunmoonfood.com
Year Founded: 1977
AAJ—(SES)
Rev.: $31,395,332
Assets: $9,435,346
Liabilities: $5,611,708
Net Worth: $3,823,638
Earnings: ($1,693,220)
Emp.: 31
Fiscal Year-end: 03/31/23
Fruit Farming Services
N.A.I.C.S.: 311411
Gary Loh Hock Chuan *(Deputy Chm)*

SUNNDAL SPAREBANK
Tel.: (47) 71689100
Web Site: https://www.sunndal-sparebank.no
SUNSB-ME—(OSL)
Sales Range: Less than $1 Million
Commercial Banking Services
N.A.I.C.S.: 522110
Jonny Engdahl *(CEO & Mgr-Adm Bank)*

SUNNEXTA GROUP INC.
35 Tansu-cho America TIME24 Building, Shinjuku-ku, Tokyo, 162-0833, Japan
Tel.: (81) 352298748
Web Site: https://www.syataku.co.jp
Year Founded: 1998
8945—(TKS)
Rev.: $52,067,620
Assets: $67,760,680
Liabilities: $18,572,920
Net Worth: $49,187,760
Earnings: $11,040,500
Emp.: 214
Fiscal Year-end: 06/30/24
Real Estate Manangement Services
N.A.I.C.S.: 531390

SUNNIC TECHNOLOGY & MERCHANDISE, INC.
6/F 76 Zhouzi St, NeiHu Dist, Taipei, Taiwan
Tel.: (886) 287973566
Web Site: https://www.sunnic.com
Year Founded: 1985
3360—(TPE)
Rev.: $316,361,442
Assets: $159,592,565
Liabilities: $126,262,296
Net Worth: $33,330,269
Earnings: $752,963
Fiscal Year-end: 12/31/22
Electronic Components Distr
N.A.I.C.S.: 423690
Chien Kang-Min *(Chm & Pres)*

SUNNINGDALE TECH LTD
51 Joo Koon Circle, Singapore, 629069, Singapore
Tel.: (65) 6861 1161
Web Site: http://www.sdaletech.com
Rev.: $499,373,462
Assets: $525,392,664
Liabilities: $251,510,306
Net Worth: $273,882,358
Earnings: $5,920,226
Fiscal Year-end: 12/31/19
Plastic Component Mfr
N.A.I.C.S.: 326199
Dorothy Lai Yong Ho *(Sec)*

Subsidiaries:

AS Sunningdale Tech (Latvia) (1)
2 Sampetera Street, Riga, 1046, Latvia

SUNNINGDALE TECH LTD

Sunningdale Tech Ltd—(Continued)
Tel.: (371) 67804590
Plastic Mould & Product Mfr & Distr
N.A.I.C.S.: 333511

Chi Wo Plastic Moulds Fty. Limited (1)
Suite 6-9 15/F Tower 1 China Hong Kong City 33 Canton Road T S T, Kowloon, China (Hong Kong)
Tel.: (852) 27906130
Web Site: http://www.chiwo.com
Plastic Mould & Product Mfr & Distr
N.A.I.C.S.: 333511

Subsidiary (Non-US):

Zhongshan Zhihe Electrical Equipment Co., Ltd. (2)
Qian Jin Er Lu Xin Qian Jin Cun, Tanzhou Town, Zhongshan, Guangdong, China
Tel.: (86) 76086983333
Plastic Injection Mould Product Mfr & Distr
N.A.I.C.S.: 333511

First Engineering Limited (1)
51 Joo Koon Circle, Singapore, 629069, Singapore
Tel.: (65) 6861 1161
Web Site: http://www.first-engr.com
Plastic Mould & Product Mfr & Distr
N.A.I.C.S.: 333511

Subsidiary (Non-US):

First Engineering (Guangzhou) Co., Ltd. (2)
No 701 Kai Chuang Road GETDD, Guangzhou, 510530, Guangdong, China
Tel.: (86) 2082264470
Plastic Injection Mould Product Mfr & Distr
N.A.I.C.S.: 333511

First Engineering (Shanghai) Co., Ltd. (2)
Block 51 No 199 North Riying Rd Waigaoqiao Free Trade Zone, Pudong, Shanghai, 200131, China
Tel.: (86) 2150460300
Plastic Injection Mould Product Mfr & Distr
N.A.I.C.S.: 333511

First Engineering (Suzhou) Co., Ltd. (2)
Blk 7 8 9 No 777 Kang Yuan Road Xiangcheng Economic Zone, Suzhou, 215131, Jiangsu, China
Tel.: (86) 51265799200
Plastic Injection Mould Product Mfr & Distr
N.A.I.C.S.: 333511

First Engineering Plastics India Private Limited (2)
Plot B72 Sipcot Industrial Park Irrungattukottai, Sriperumbudur Kancheepuram District, Chennai, 602105, Tamil Nadu, India
Tel.: (91) 4447112000
Plastic Injection Mould Product Mfr & Distr
N.A.I.C.S.: 333511

First Engineering Plastics (Malaysia) Sdn Bhd (2)
No 23 Jalan Persiaran Teknologi Taman Teknologi Johor, 81400, Senai, Johor, Malaysia
Tel.: (60) 75978555
Precision Plastic Component Mfr
N.A.I.C.S.: 332721
Syuhada Sabirin (Engr-Lab)

Omni Mold Ltd. (1)
51 Joo Koon Circle, Singapore, 629069, Singapore
Tel.: (65) 6861 1161
Steel Mould Mfr & Distr
N.A.I.C.S.: 331511
Simon Bair Kion Tan (Gen Mgr-Bus Dev & Ops)

Subsidiary (Non-US):

Skan-Tooling SIA (2)
Kruzes Street 2c, Riga, 1046, Latvia
Tel.: (371) 67807794
Web Site: http://www.skantooling.lv
Steel Mould Mfr & Distr
N.A.I.C.S.: 331511

Omni Tech (Suzhou) Co., Ltd. (1)
428 Xinglong Street Unit 7A Suchun Factory Suzhou Industrial Park, Suzhou, 215024, China
Tel.: (86) 51262833860
Plastic Mould & Product Mfr
N.A.I.C.S.: 333511

PT. Sunningdale Tech Batam (1)
Panbil Industrial Estate Factory B2 Lot 8-9 Jl Ahmad Yani Muka Kuning, Batam, 29433, Indonesia
Tel.: (62) 7788071001
Plastic Injection Mould Product Mfr
N.A.I.C.S.: 333511
Rio Geolando (Officer-Pur)

SDP Manufacturing Sdn Bhd (1)
34 Jalan Masyhur Satu, Taman Perindustrian Cemerlang, 81800, Ulu Tiram, Johor, Malaysia
Tel.: (60) 78618000
Precision Plastic Component Mfr
N.A.I.C.S.: 332721
Foo Hee Swan (Gen Mgr)

Sunningdale Precision Industries Ltd. (1)
51 Joo Koon Circle, Singapore, 629069, Singapore
Tel.: (65) 6861 1161
Plastic Injection Mould Product Mfr
N.A.I.C.S.: 333511

Subsidiary (Non-US):

Sunningdale Precision Industries (Shanghai) Co., Ltd. (2)
279 Lizhi Road Wangqiao Industrial Zone, Pudong New Area, Shanghai, 201201, China
Tel.: (86) 2158388000
Plastic Injection Mould Product Mfr
N.A.I.C.S.: 333511

Sunningdale Precision Mold Industries (Tianjin) Co., Ltd. (2)
No 22 Huanghai St 1 Old Avenue 9, Tianjin Economic Technological Development Area, Tianjin, 300457, China
Tel.: (86) 2225328690
Industrial Mold Mfr
N.A.I.C.S.: 333511

Sunningdale Technologies S.A. de C.V. (2)
Camino Al Iteso No 8900-2C Parque Industrial Tecnologico, 45609, Tlaquepaque, Jalisco, Mexico
Tel.: (52) 3331344090
Plastic Injection Mould Product Mfr & Distr
N.A.I.C.S.: 333511
Guadalupe Moreno (Coord-Quality Sys)

Sunningdale Tech (Malaysia) Sdn Bhd (1)
Lot PTD 1261 and 1262 Jalan Tun Mutahir, Kaw Perindustrian Bandar Tenggara, 81000, Kulai, Johor, Malaysia
Tel.: (60) 78961482
Precision Plastic Component Mfr
N.A.I.C.S.: 332721

Sunningdale Tech Inc. (1)
100 W Big Beaver Ste 200, Troy, MI 48084
Tel.: (248) 526-0517
Office Support Services
N.A.I.C.S.: 561439

SUNNIVA, INC.
Suite 400 355-4th Avenue S W, Calgary, T2P 0J1, AB, Canada
Web Site: http://www.sunniva.com
Year Founded: 2014
SNNVF—(CNSX)
Sales Range: $10-24.9 Million
Pharmaceuticals Product Mfr
N.A.I.C.S.: 325412
Anthony F. Holler (Founder, Chm & CEO)

SUNNY DAY AD-VARNA
k k Sunny day resort St St Constantine and Helena, Varna, Bulgaria
Tel.: (359) 52 361 971
Web Site:
http://www.sunnydaybg.com
SDEN—(BUL)
Sales Range: Less than $1 Million
Resort & Hotel Services
N.A.I.C.S.: 721110
Mitko Atanasov (Gen Mgr)

SUNNY ELECTRONICS CORP.
59 Mokhaengsandan 2-ro, Chungju, Chung-buk, Korea (South)
Tel.: (82) 438531760
Web Site: https://www.sunny.co.kr
Year Founded: 1966
004770—(KRS)
Rev.: $13,377,296
Assets: $58,682,932
Liabilities: $2,520,467
Net Worth: $56,162,465
Earnings: $3,863,235
Emp.: 43
Fiscal Year-end: 12/31/22
Electronic Equipment Mfr & Distr
N.A.I.C.S.: 334419
SangKwon Cha (CEO)

Subsidiaries:

Samwoo Communications Industry Co., Ltd. (1)
225-6 2/F Dangjung-dong, Gunpo, Kyunggi, Korea (South)
Tel.: (82) 314286700
Electronic Components Mfr
N.A.I.C.S.: 334419

SUNNY FRIEND ENVIRONMENTAL TECHNOLOGY CO., LTD.
No 1-20 Yuan Dong Rd, Yuancheng Township Yunlin, Hsien, 655, Taiwan
Tel.: (886) 57885788
Web Site:
https://www.sunnyfriend.com.tw
Year Founded: 1994
8341—(TAI)
Rev.: $106,507,632
Assets: $339,158,397
Liabilities: $166,905,713
Net Worth: $172,252,683
Earnings: $13,906,013
Emp.: 349
Fiscal Year-end: 12/31/23
Biomedical Waste Treatment
N.A.I.C.S.: 562211
Fang-Cheng Chang (Chm & Gen Dir)

Subsidiaries:

Chin Hsin Environmental Engineering Co., Ltd. (1)
No 376 Shijia East Road, East District, Taichung, 40153, Taiwan
Tel.: (886) 422150928
Web Site: https://www.chan-hsin.com.tw
Chemical Raw Material Distr
N.A.I.C.S.: 424690

SUNNY HILL ENERGY
3 Grand Canal Plaza Grand Canal Street Upper, Dublin, 4, Ireland
Tel.: (353) 14218300
Web Site: http://www.petroceltic.com
PTIFF—(OTCIQ)
Sales Range: $1-4.9 Billion
Emp.: 171
Oil & Gas Exploration & Production Services
N.A.I.C.S.: 211120
Brian O'Cathain (CEO)

Subsidiaries:

Petroceltic African Holdings Limited (1)
75 St Stephens Green, Dublin, Ireland
Tel.: (353) 14218300
Web Site: http://www.petroceltic.ie
Sales Range: $50-74.9 Million
Emp.: 20
Oil & Gas Field Exploration Services
N.A.I.C.S.: 213112
Brian O'Caghain (Gen Mgr)

Petroceltic Elsa S.R.L. (1)
Via Paola N 24 Int 7, 00186, Rome, Italy
Tel.: (39) 0668216653
Web Site: http://www.petroceltic.ie
Sales Range: $50-74.9 Million
Emp.: 5
Oil & Gas Field Exploration Services
N.A.I.C.S.: 213112

Petroceltic Erris Limited (1)
75 St Stephen's Green, Dublin, Ireland
Tel.: (353) 14218300
Web Site: http://www.petroceltic.com
Sales Range: $50-74.9 Million
Emp.: 18
Oil & Gas Field Exploration Services
N.A.I.C.S.: 213112
Brian O'Cathain (CEO)

Petroceltic Investments Limited (1)
3 Grand Canal Plaza Grand Canal Street Upper, Dublin, 4, Ireland
Tel.: (353) 14218300
Web Site: http://www.petroceltic.com
Sales Range: $50-74.9 Million
Emp.: 18
Oil & Gas Field Exploration Services
N.A.I.C.S.: 213112
O. Brian (Office Mgr)

Petroceltic Isarene Limited (1)
3 Grand Canal Plaza Grand Canal Street Upper, Dublin, 4, Ireland
Tel.: (353) 14218300
Web Site: http://www.petroceltic.com
Sales Range: $50-74.9 Million
Emp.: 20
Oil & Gas Field Exploration Services
N.A.I.C.S.: 213112
Brian O'Cathain (Gen Mgr)

Petroceltic Ksar Hadada Limited (1)
75 St Stephens Green, Dublin, 2, Ireland
Tel.: (353) 14218300
Web Site: http://www.petroceltic.ie
Sales Range: $50-74.9 Million
Emp.: 20
Oil & Gas Field Exploration Services
N.A.I.C.S.: 213112
Brian O'Cathain (Mng Dir)

SUNNY LOAN TOP CO., LTD.
No 158 Xihe Street, Haishu District, Ningbo, Zhejiang, China
Tel.: (86) 57487315310
Web Site:
https://www.sunnyloantop.cn
Year Founded: 1992
600830—(SHG)
Rev.: $35,836,187
Assets: $503,517,531
Liabilities: $119,154,911
Net Worth: $384,362,620
Earnings: $1,250,108
Fiscal Year-end: 12/31/22
Entrusted Loan Services
N.A.I.C.S.: 522299
Fang Guofu (Chm)

SUNNY OPTICAL TECHNOLOGY (GROUP) COMPANY LIMITED
27-29 Shunke Road, Yuyao, 315400, Zhejiang, China
Tel.: (86) 57462538080
Web Site:
https://www.sunnyoptical.com
Year Founded: 1984
SNPTF—(OTCIQ)
Rev.: $4,596,385,827
Assets: $5,953,877,935
Liabilities: $2,882,546,245
Net Worth: $3,071,331,690
Earnings: $342,565,906
Emp.: 26,610
Fiscal Year-end: 12/31/22
Optical Product Mfr
N.A.I.C.S.: 334610
Liaoning Ye (Co-Founder & Chm)

Subsidiaries:

Ningbo Sunny Automotive Optech Co., Ltd. (1)
66-68 Shunyu Road, Yuyao, 315400, Zhejiang, China

Tel.: (86) 57462550637
Optical Product Mfr
N.A.I.C.S.: 423460

Ningbo Sunny Instruments Co., Ltd. (1)
27-29 shunke road, Yuyao, Ningbo, Zhejiang, China
Tel.: (86) 57462525665
Web Site:
  http://www.nboptics.en.chinaningbo.com
Optical Instrument Mfr
N.A.I.C.S.: 333310

Power Optics Co., Ltd. (1)
332-28 Gocheon-dong, Uiwang, 437-801, Korea (South)
Tel.: (82) 314273554
Optical Instrument Distr
N.A.I.C.S.: 423490

Sunny Instruments Singapore Pte. Ltd. (1)
Blk 1003 Bukit Merah Central 01-09/10, Singapore, 159836, Singapore
Tel.: (65) 62788083
Web Site: http://www.sunnyoptical.com
Optical Instrument Mfr & Distr
N.A.I.C.S.: 333310

Sunny Japan Co., Ltd. (1)
2-12-8 Tsukiji 6th floor of Ohiro Building, Chuo-ku, Tokyo, 104-0045, Japan
Tel.: (81) 351481106
Web Site: http://www.sj-tokyo.com
Emp.: 20
Optical Instrument Distr
N.A.I.C.S.: 423490
Kazuyuki Takahashi *(Mgr-Sls)*

Sunny Opotech North America Inc (1)
1735 N 1st St Ste 285, San Jose, CA 95112
Tel.: (408) 329-9001
Web Site: https://www.sunnyopotech.com
Optical Instrument Mfr & Distr
N.A.I.C.S.: 333310

Sunny Optics (Zhongshan) Co., Ltd. (1)
No 20 Shichong Road Torch Development Zone, Zhongshan, 528437, Guang Dong, China
Tel.: (86) 76088295338
Optical Instrument Distr
N.A.I.C.S.: 423490

Wuxi Wissen Intelligent Sensing Technology Co., Ltd. (1)
2F Building C Wangzhuang Technology Innovation Center, No 4 Longshan Road Wuxi New District, Wuxi, 214028, Jiangsu, China
Tel.: (86) 51085388793
Web Site: http://www.wissenstar.com
Emp.: 240
Optical Product Distr
N.A.I.C.S.: 423460

Zhejiang Sunny Optical Intelligence Technology Co., Ltd. (1)
22F Building A DIC No 1190 Bin'an Road, Binjiang District, Hangzhou, Zhejiang, China
Tel.: (86) 57187788280
Optical Product Distr
N.A.I.C.S.: 423460
Xin Tu *(Mgr-Quality)*

SUNNY QUEEN PTY LTD
104 Mica St, Carole Park, 4300, QLD, Australia
Tel.: (61) 739079999
Web Site:
  http://www.sunnyqueen.com.au
Year Founded: 1994
Sales Range: $25-49.9 Million
Emp.: 30
Eggs & Egg Products Producer & Supplier
N.A.I.C.S.: 112310
Julie Proctor *(Dir-Mktg)*

SUNNY SIDE UP GROUP INC.
4-23-5 Sendagaya JPR Sendagaya Building 7F, Shibuya-ku, Tokyo, 151-0051, Japan

Tel.: (81) 368641234
Web Site: https://www.ssu.co.jp
2180—(TKS)
Rev.: $111,387,760
Assets: $52,695,840
Liabilities: $26,969,920
Net Worth: $25,725,920
Earnings: $4,944,900
Emp.: 360
Fiscal Year-end: 06/30/24
Public Relations, Sales Promotion Consulting & Strategic Planning Services; Athletes, Artists & Other Distinguished People Management Services
N.A.I.C.S.: 711410
Etsuko Tsugihara *(Pres)*

Subsidiaries:

Kumnamu Entertainment, Inc. (1)
402 Grand Maison Jingumae 5-13-10, Jingumae Shibuya-ku, Tokyo, 150-0001, Japan
Tel.: (81) 368619676
Web Site: http://www.kumnamu.co.jp
Casting Services
N.A.I.C.S.: 561311

Some Good&Co., Inc. (1)
4-23-5 Sendagaya JPR Sendagaya Building, Shibuya-ku, Tokyo, Japan
Tel.: (81) 368633580
Web Site: https://www.goodandco.jp
Recruiting Services
N.A.I.C.S.: 561311

Steady study Ltd. (1)
5-46-16 Il Centro 3F, Shibuya-ku Jingumae, Tokyo, 150-0001, Japan
Tel.: (81) 354697110
Web Site: https://www.steady-study.co.jp
Emp.: 36
Event Planning & Marketing Research Services
N.A.I.C.S.: 541910

Wise Integration Co., Ltd. (1)
7F JPR Sendagaya Building 4-23-5 Sendagaya, Shibuya-ku, Tokyo, 151-0051, Japan
Tel.: (81) 368641122
Web Site: https://www.wise-int.co.jp
Communication Planning Services
N.A.I.C.S.: 517112

SUNOIL LTD.
Suite 257 8680 Cambie Road, Richmond, V6X 4K1, BC, Canada
Tel.: (604) 285-1811   BC
Web Site:
  http://www.sunoilgroup.com
Year Founded: 2006
Sales Range: Less than $1 Million
Emp.: 10
Oil & Gas Exploration Services
N.A.I.C.S.: 211120
Kevin Sun *(Pres & CEO)*

SUNONWEALTH ELECTRIC MACHINE INDUSTRY COMPANY LIMITED
No 30 Ln 296 Xinya Rd, Qianzhen Dist, Kaohsiung, Taiwan
Tel.: (886) 78135888
Web Site: https://www.sunon.com
Year Founded: 1980
2421—(TAI)
Rev.: $422,338,354
Assets: $412,529,204
Liabilities: $176,461,061
Net Worth: $236,068,142
Earnings: $43,622,550
Emp.: 4,806
Fiscal Year-end: 12/31/23
Current Fans & Related Parts Mfr
N.A.I.C.S.: 333413
Ching-Shen Hong *(Co-Chm & Pres)*

Subsidiaries:

SCT Coolers Canada Technology Inc (1)
8931 Heather St, Richmond, V6Y 2R7, BC, Canada
Tel.: (604) 277-9086
Web Site: http://www.sunonusa.com
Sales Range: $25-49.9 Million
Emp.: 2
Coolers Mfr
N.A.I.C.S.: 333415

Sunon Corporation (1)
Stork Minami Otsuka 4FI 33-1 2 Chome Minami Otsuka, Toshimaku, Tokyo, 170-0005, Japan
Tel.: (81) 353953069
Sales Range: $25-49.9 Million
Emp.: 10
Industrial Fans Mfr & Distr
N.A.I.C.S.: 333413

Sunon Inc. (1)
1075A W Lambert Rd Ste A, Brea, CA 92821
Tel.: (714) 255-0208
Web Site: http://www.sunonusa.com
Sales Range: $25-49.9 Million
Emp.: 20
Industrial Fans Mfr & Distr
N.A.I.C.S.: 333413

Sunon SAS (1)
Parc Medicis 66 Ave des Pepinieres, 94260, Fresnes, France
Tel.: (33) 146154515
Web Site: http://www.sunoneurope.com
Sales Range: $25-49.9 Million
Emp.: 19
Exhaust Fans Distr
N.A.I.C.S.: 423730
Pascal Moraux *(Reg Mgr-Sls)*

SUNOPTA INC.
2233 Argentina Road Suite 401, Mississauga, L5N 2X7, ON, Canada
Tel.: (905) 821-9669   ON
Web Site: http://www.sunopta.com
Year Founded: 1973
STKL—(NASDAQ)
Rev.: $812,624,000
Assets: $755,119,000
Liabilities: $450,135,000
Net Worth: $304,984,000
Earnings: $(8,341,000)
Emp.: 1,380
Fiscal Year-end: 01/01/22
Holding Company; Specialty Foods Mfr
N.A.I.C.S.: 551112
Brian W. Kocher *(CEO)*

Subsidiaries:

Crown of Holland B.V. (1)
Business Park Agriport A7 Agriport 161, 1775 TA, Middenmeer, Netherlands
Tel.: (31) 227504670
Web Site: https://www.crownofholland.com
Food Products Distr
N.A.I.C.S.: 424490

Magnesium Technologies Corporation (1)
4807 Rockside Rd Ste 400, Independence, OH 44131
Tel.: (330) 659-3003
Desulphurization System Distr
N.A.I.C.S.: 423830

Opus Foods Mexico, S.A. de C.V. (1)
La Haciendita 8 Col Los Laureles Jacona, 59800, Michoacan, Mexico
Tel.: (52) 3515161247
Web Site: http://www.opusfoods.com.mx
Specialty Food Packaging & Labeling Services
N.A.I.C.S.: 561910

Organic Land Corporation OOD (1)
Rashko Blaskov Str 210, 7539, Silistra, Bulgaria
Tel.: (359) 24237442
Web Site: http://www.olc.bg
Food Products Distr
N.A.I.C.S.: 424490

SunOpta Aseptic, Inc. (1)
3915 Minnesota St, Alexandria, MN 56308   (100%)
Tel.: (320) 763-9822
Web Site: http://www.sunopta.com
Sales Range: $1-9.9 Million
Emp.: 100
Soymilk & Other Beverage Aseptic Packaging Services
N.A.I.C.S.: 561910

SunOpta Food Group LLC (1)
5850 Opus Pkwy 150, Minnetonka, MN 55343   (100%)
Tel.: (952) 939-3956
Web Site: http://www.sunopta.com
Natural & Organic Food Product Sourcing, Processing & Distribution
N.A.I.C.S.: 424510

SunOpta Foods Europe B.V. (1)
Prims Hendrikkade 14, 1012 TL, Amsterdam, Netherlands
Tel.: (31) 204074499
Agriculture Product Distr
N.A.I.C.S.: 424910

SunOpta Foods Inc. (1)
7301 Ohms Ln Ste 600, Edina, MN 55439
Tel.: (952) 820-2518
Web Site: http://www.sunopta.com
Organic Food Distr
N.A.I.C.S.: 424490

Division (Domestic):

Sunopta Consumer Products Group - SunOpta Food Solutions Division (2)
2100 Delaware Ave, Santa Cruz, CA 95060
Tel.: (831) 685-6565
Web Site: http://www.sunopta.com
Sales Range: $25-49.9 Million
Emp.: 20
Packaged Food Products Retailer
N.A.I.C.S.: 445298

SunOpta Global Organic Ingredients, Inc. (1)
2100 Delaware Ave, Santa Cruz, CA 95060
Tel.: (831) 685-6506
Organic Food Ingredient Mfr & Distr
N.A.I.C.S.: 311999

SunOpta Grains and Foods Inc. (1)
3824 SW 93rd St, Hope, MN 56026
Web Site: http://www.sunopta.com
Emp.: 70
Organic Grain Based Ingredients Producer & Supplier
N.A.I.C.S.: 311999

Division (Domestic):

SunOpta Grains & Foods Inc. - Crookston (2)
1220 Sunflower St, Crookston, MN 56716
Tel.: (218) 281-2985
Sales Range: $75-99.9 Million
Raw & Roasted Sunflower Products
N.A.I.C.S.: 115114
Ron Klinge *(Mgr-Quality Sys)*

SunOpta Ingredients, Inc. (1)
100 Apollo Dr, Chelmsford, MA 01824   (100%)
Tel.: (781) 276-5100
Sales Range: $25-49.9 Million
Emp.: 150
Texturizing Ingredients Added to Prepared Foods
N.A.I.C.S.: 311999

Sunrich LLC (1)
3824 SW 93rd St, Hope, MN 56046   (100%)
Tel.: (507) 451-4724
Web Site: http://www.sunrich.com
Sales Range: $25-49.9 Million
Emp.: 50
Producer of Soybeans & Soybean Products
N.A.I.C.S.: 311224

Sunrise Growers, Inc. (1)
701 W Kimberly Ave Ste 210, Placentia, CA 92870
Tel.: (714) 630-6292
Web Site: http://www.sunrisegrowers.com
Sales Range: $300-349.9 Million
Emp.: 250
Frozen Fruit Products Mfr & Whslr
N.A.I.C.S.: 311411

SUNOPTA INC.

SunOpta Inc.—(Continued)
Maria Gonzalez (Dir-Supply Chain)

The Organic Corporation B.V. (1)
Stationsplein 61-65, 1012 AB, Amsterdam, Netherlands
Tel.: (31) 204074499
Web Site: https://www.tradinorganic.com
Emp.: 70
Organic Food Distr
N.A.I.C.S.: 424490
Gerard Versteegh (Founder)

Subsidiary (Non-US):

SunOpta Food (Dalian) Co., Ltd. (2)
No 6-2 Xinshuini Road, Ganjingzi District, Dalian, 116035, China
Tel.: (86) 411 86429838
Web Site: http://www.sunoptafood.com
Organic Seed Kernel Distr
N.A.I.C.S.: 424490

Subsidiary (US):

Tradin Organics USA, Inc. (2)
15 A Parade St, Aptos, CA 95003
Tel.: (831) 685-6565
Sales Range: $25-49.9 Million
Emp.: 30
Organic Food Distr
N.A.I.C.S.: 424490

Trabocca B.V. (1)
Web Site: http://www.trabocca.com
Sales Range: $25-49.9 Million
Emp.: 10
Natural & Organic Food Producer & Distr
N.A.I.C.S.: 311999
Menno Simons (Founder & Gen Mgr)

WGI Heavy Minerals, LLC (1)
810 E Sherman Ave, Coeur D'Alene, ID 83814
Tel.: (208) 666-2000
Web Site: http://www.wgiheavyminerals.com
Food Products Distr
N.A.I.C.S.: 424490

SUNORA FOODS INC.
205 4616 Valiant Dr NW, Calgary, T3A 0X9, AB, Canada
Tel.: (403) 247-8300 ON
Web Site: https://www.sunora.com
Year Founded: 2011
SNF—(TSXV)
Rev.: $8,860,979
Assets: $4,010,606
Liabilities: $951,545
Net Worth: $3,059,061
Earnings: ($6,208)
Fiscal Year-end: 12/31/20
Investment Services
N.A.I.C.S.: 523999
Steve Bank (Chm & CEO)

SUNPLUS TECHNOLOGY CO., LTD.
No 19 Innovation 1st Road Science Park, Hsin-chu, 30076, Taiwan
Tel.: (886) 35786005 TW
Web Site: https://www.sunplus.com
Year Founded: 1990
2401—(TAI)
Rev.: $181,020,334
Assets: $456,392,638
Liabilities: $103,232,607
Net Worth: $353,160,031
Earnings: ($7,236,109)
Emp.: 1,065
Fiscal Year-end: 12/31/23
Integrated Chips Designer
N.A.I.C.S.: 334118
Wayne Shen (VP)

Subsidiaries:

Beijing Sunplus-EHue Tech Co., Ltd. (1)
Section C 6/F Building 1 Zhongli Science & Technology Garden, Shangdi 3rd Street Haidian District, Beijing, 100085, China
Tel.: (86) 1062981668
Software Development Services
N.A.I.C.S.: 541511

Chongqing CQPlus1 Technology Co., Ltd. (1)
2/F building 3 Jintai Intelligent Industrial Park No 22 Jinyu Avenue, Liangjiang New District, Chongqing, China
Tel.: (86) 2362326628
Software Development Services
N.A.I.C.S.: 541511

HT mMobile Inc (1)
19-1 Innovation 1st Road Hsinchu Science Park, Hsin-chu, Taiwan
Tel.: (886) 3 5799699
Web Site: http://www.htmmi.com
Sales Range: $100-124.9 Million
Emp.: 300
Integrated Circuits Mfr
N.A.I.C.S.: 334419

Jumplux Technology Co., Ltd. (1)
2F No19 Innovation 1st Road Science Park, Hsinchu, 30076, Taiwan
Tel.: (886) 35782385
Web Site: https://www.jumplux.com
Industrial Microcontroller Mfr & Distr
N.A.I.C.S.: 334413

Shanghai Sunplus Technology Co., Ltd. (1)
1077 Zu Chong Zhi Road Zhang Jiang Hi-Tech Park, Pudong New Area, Shanghai, China
Tel.: (86) 21 616 36388
Web Site: http://www.sunplus.com
Sales Range: $25-49.9 Million
Emp.: 150
Multimedia Audio IC Mfr & Distr
N.A.I.C.S.: 334310

SunMedia Technology Co., Ltd (1)
Tel.: (86) 2887848688
Web Site: http://www.sunplus.com
Emp.: 250
Multimedia Integrated Circuit Mfr & Sales
N.A.I.C.S.: 334413

Sunext Technology Co., Ltd. (1)
6F No 19-1 Innovation 1st RD Science Park, Hsinchu, 30076, Taiwan
Tel.: (886) 36661311
Integrated Circuit Product Mfr & Distr
N.A.I.C.S.: 334413

Sunplus Core Technology Co., Ltd (1)
2F No 19-1 Innovation 1st Road Hsinchu Science Park, Hsin-chu, 300, Taiwan
Tel.: (886) 35780216
Web Site: http://www.sunplusct.com
Semiconductor Components Mfr.
N.A.I.C.S.: 334413

Sunplus Innovation Technology Inc. (1)
A2 3F No 1 Li-Hsin 1st Road, Hsinchu Science Park, Hsin-chu, 300, Taiwan
Tel.: (886) 35632822
Web Site: https://www.sunplusit.com
Sales Range: $50-74.9 Million
Emp.: 100
Computer & Computer Peripheral Equipment & Software Whslr
N.A.I.C.S.: 423430
Chih-Hao Kung (Pres)

Sunplus Prof-tek Technology (Shenzhen) Co., Ltd. (1)
9/F 2C Building Software Industries Base No 1003 Keyuan Road, Nanshan District, Shenzhen, China
Tel.: (86) 75526984588
Software Development Services
N.A.I.C.S.: 541511

Sunplus Technology (H.K.) Co., Ltd (1)
Room 810 8F Tower 1 Cheung Sha Wan Plaza No 833 Cheung Sha Wan Road, Kowloon, China (Hong Kong)
Tel.: (852) 27505788
Web Site: http://www.sunplus.com
Sales Range: $25-49.9 Million
Emp.: 6
Integrated Circuit Mfr & Sales
N.A.I.C.S.: 335999

Sunplus mMobile Inc. (1)
No 19-1 Innovation 1st Rd, Hsinchu Science Park, Hsin-chu, Taiwan
Tel.: (886) 35799699
Web Site: http://www.sunplusmm.com
Sales Range: $125-149.9 Million
Mobile Mfr
N.A.I.C.S.: 321991
Chou-Chye Huang (Chm & CEO)

iCatch Technology, Inc. (1)
4F No 19-1 Innovation 1st Rd Hsinchu Science Park, Hsin-chu, 300, Taiwan
Tel.: (886) 3 564 1600
Web Site: http://www.icatchtek.com
Electronic Components Mfr
N.A.I.C.S.: 334419
Weber Hsu (Exec VP)

SUNPOWER GROUP LTD.
No 2111 Chengxin Avenue High-tech Industrial Park, Jiangning District, Nanjing, 211112, Jiangsu, China
Tel.: (86) 2552169777
Web Site:
https://www.sunpower.com.cn
5GD—(SES)
Rev.: $621,849,208
Assets: $1,269,362,776
Liabilities: $965,321,974
Net Worth: $304,040,802
Earnings: ($4,315,160)
Fiscal Year-end: 12/31/20
Heat Pipes & Exchangers Mfr
N.A.I.C.S.: 332410
Ming Ma (Co-Founder)

Subsidiaries:

Jiangsu Sunpower Heat Exchanger & Pressure Vessel Co., Ltd. (1)
2111 Chengxin Avenue Jiangning High-Tech Park, Nanjing, Jiangsu, China
Tel.: (86) 255 216 9777
Web Site: https://pv.sunpowertech.cn
Non Ferrous Metal Equipment Mfr & Distr
N.A.I.C.S.: 332112

Jiangsu Sunpower Piping Technology Co., Ltd. (1)
No 2111 Chengxin Avenue, High-Tech Industrial Park Jiangning District, Nanjing, 211112, Jiangsu, China
Tel.: (86) 255 279 8200
Web Site: https://pe.sunpowertech.cn
Storage Tank Mfr & Distr
N.A.I.C.S.: 332420

Jiangsu Sunpower Technology Co., Ltd. (1)
No 2111 Chengxin Ave, Jiangning Science Park, Nanjing, 211112, Jiangsu, China
Tel.: (86) 2552169777
Web Site: http://www.sunpower.com.cn
Emp.: 2,000
Solar Panel Mfr
N.A.I.C.S.: 334413

Nanjing Shengnue Heat Pipe Co., Ltd. (1)
No 30 Dingjiaqiao, Gulou District, Nanjing, Jiangsu, China
Tel.: (86) 258 332 5444
Pipe Product Mfr
N.A.I.C.S.: 332996

Shandong yangguang Engineering Design Institute Co., Ltd. (1)
4th Floor Block E Yinhe Building No 2008 Xinluo Street, High-Tech Zone, Jinan, Shandong, China
Tel.: (86) 5316 667 5800
Engineeering Services
N.A.I.C.S.: 541330

Sunpower Clean Energy Investment (Jiangsu) Co., Ltd. (1)
2111 Chengxin Avenue Jiangning High-Tech Park, Nanjing, 211112, Jiangsu, China
Tel.: (86) 2551198005
Environmental Services
N.A.I.C.S.: 541620

SUNRAJ DIAMOND EXPORTS LIMITED
616 6th Floor Prasad Chambers Plot No 1487, Tata Road No 2 Opera House, Mumbai, 400 004, Maharashtra, India
Tel.: (91) 2223638559
Web Site:
https://www.sunrajdiamonds.com
Year Founded: 1990
523425—(BOM)
Rev.: $177,084
Assets: $2,225,681
Liabilities: $2,225,483
Net Worth: $198
Earnings: ($365,303)
Emp.: 9
Fiscal Year-end: 03/31/21
Jewellery Product Mfr & Distr
N.A.I.C.S.: 339910
Sunny S. Gandhi (Exec Dir)

SUNRAY ENGINEERING GROUP LIMITED
Unit 802-804 8/F Laford Centre No 838 Lai Chi Kok Road, Kowloon, China (Hong Kong)
Tel.: (852) 39776789
Web Site: http://www.sunray.com.hk
Year Founded: 1988
8616—(HKG)
Rev.: $28,408,148
Assets: $32,831,888
Liabilities: $8,917,605
Net Worth: $23,914,283
Earnings: $702,780
Emp.: 38
Fiscal Year-end: 03/31/23
Commercial Building Maintenance Services
N.A.I.C.S.: 236210
Lam Peter (Founder, Chm & CEO)

Subsidiaries:

Tech Link Construction Engineering Limited (1)
Unit 802 8/F Laford Centre No 838 Lai Chi Kok Road, Cheung Sha Wan, Kowloon, China (Hong Kong)
Tel.: (852) 37011899
Web Site: http://www.techlinkcon.com.hk
Building Protection Product Distr
N.A.I.C.S.: 423390

SUNRESIN NEW MATERIALS CO., LTD.
Sunresin Park No 135 Jinye Road, Xian Hi-tech Industrial Development Zone, Xi'an, 710076, Shaanxi, China
Tel.: (86) 2989182091
Web Site: https://www.seplite.com
Year Founded: 2001
300487—(CHIN)
Rev.: $350,549,987
Assets: $802,146,722
Liabilities: $315,393,193
Net Worth: $486,753,529
Earnings: $100,994,042
Fiscal Year-end: 12/31/23
Resin Mfr
N.A.I.C.S.: 325211
Ivy Gao (Chm)

Subsidiaries:

Puritech Technologies (S) Pte. Ltd. (1)
6 Woodlands Square Wood Square Tower 2 08-01, Singapore, 737737, Singapore
Tel.: (65) 91848
Web Site: https://puritec-group.com
Plant Engineering System & Building Services
N.A.I.C.S.: 541330

SUNREX TECHNOLOGY CORPORATION
No 475 Sec 4 Changping Rd, Daya Dist, Taichung, 428, Taiwan
Tel.: (886) 425686983
Web Site: https://www.sunrex.com.tw
Year Founded: 1975

AND PRIVATE COMPANIES / SUNRISE NEW ENERGY CO., LTD.

2387—(TAI)
Rev.: $768,276,459
Assets: $683,379,670
Liabilities: $366,886,533
Net Worth: $316,493,137
Earnings: $48,892,036
Emp.: 8,187
Fiscal Year-end: 12/31/22
Computer Input Device Mfr
N.A.I.C.S.: 334118
Huo Lu Tsai *(Chm)*

Subsidiaries:

Changsu Sunrex Technology Corp. (1)
Yantai Road New Hi-Tech Industries Park, Changshu Economic Development Area, Jiangsu, China
Tel.: (86) 51252922228
Computer Keyboard Mfr
N.A.I.C.S.: 334118

Jiangxi Sunrex Technology Corp. (1)
Lulin Industrial Area, Guangfeng County, Shangrao, Jiangxi, China
Tel.: (86) 7932629666
Computer Keyboard Mfr
N.A.I.C.S.: 334118

SUNRIDGE PARTNERS (UK), LLP

318 Harbour Yard Third Floor, Chelsea Harbour, London, SW10 0XD, United Kingdom
Tel.: (44) 2038923080
Web Site:
https://sunridgepartners.com
Investment Services
N.A.I.C.S.: 523999

Subsidiaries:

JDM Food Group Limited (1)
Monument Road Bicker, Boston, PE20 3DJ, Lincs, United Kingdom
Tel.: (44) 1775822389
Web Site: https://www.jdmfoodgroup.co.uk
Holding Company
N.A.I.C.S.: 551112

Subsidiary (US):

Henry Broch & Co. (2)
704 Florsheim Dr Ste 12, Libertyville, IL 60048-5002
Tel.: (847) 816-6225
Web Site: http://www.hbroch.com
Sales Range: $10-24.9 Million
Emp.: 7
Whol Groceries
N.A.I.C.S.: 424490

SUNRIGHT LIMITED

1093 Lower Delta Road 02-01/08, Singapore, 169204, Singapore
Tel.: (65) 62725842
Web Site: https://www.sunright.com
Year Founded: 1978
S71—(SES)
Rev.: $65,437,569
Assets: $130,516,488
Liabilities: $36,716,562
Net Worth: $93,799,926
Earnings: ($2,664,691)
Emp.: 962
Fiscal Year-end: 07/31/23
Parallel Test & Burn-In Equipment & Services
N.A.I.C.S.: 333242
Samuel Syn Soo Lim *(Chm & CEO)*

Subsidiaries:

KES Systems, Inc. (1)
1407 W Drivers Way, Tempe, AZ 85284
Tel.: (972) 832-6267
Web Site: https://www.kessystemsinc.com
Semiconductor Related Product Mfr & Distr
N.A.I.C.S.: 334413

Kestronics (S) Pte. Ltd. (1)
1090 Lower Delta Road #07-01/04, Tiong Bahru Industrial Estate, Singapore, 169201, Singapore
Tel.: (65) 62786211
Web Site: http://www.kestronics.com.sg
Semiconductor Distr
N.A.I.C.S.: 423690
Poh Leng Chio *(Gen Mgr)*

Subsidiary (Non-US):

Kestronics (Thailand) Co., Ltd. (2)
3336 The Prim Place 2nd Floor 210 Unit, Phaholyothin Road Chatuchak, Bangkok, Thailand
Tel.: (66) 2 9395 691
Semiconductor Distr
N.A.I.C.S.: 423690

Kestronics Electronics (Shanghai Pudong New Area) Co. Ltd. (2)
Unit A 2nd Floor Factory 5 No 350 Xiya Road, Waigaoqiao Free Trade Zone, Shanghai, 200131, China
Tel.: (86) 21 5046 0703
Emp.: 30
Electronic Components Distr
N.A.I.C.S.: 423690
Luo Wenyao *(Mgr)*

Kestronics Philippines, Inc. (2)
Unit 17L Burgundy Corporate Tower, 252 Sen Gil Puyat Avenue, Makati, Philippines
Tel.: (63) 2 887 6215
Semiconductor Distr
N.A.I.C.S.: 423690

SUNRISE ASIAN LTD

Forbes Building 3rd Floor East Wing Charanjit Rai Marg, Fort, Mumbai, 400001, India
Tel.: (91) 22 67474309
Web Site: http://www.sunriseasian.net
Sales Range: Less than $1 Million
Industrial Supplies Distr
N.A.I.C.S.: 423840
O. P. Gupta *(Chm)*

SUNRISE EFFICIENT MARKETING LIMITED

3rd floor 9292 Building Main Vip Road Near Metro Wholesale, Althan Sarsana Road, Surat, 394221, Gujarat, India
Tel.: (91) 9376660507
Web Site: https://www.sunrisemarketing.com
Year Founded: 2002
MUFTI—(NSE)
Marketing Consulting Services
N.A.I.C.S.: 541613
Hemantrai Thakorbhai Desai *(Chm)*

SUNRISE ENERGY METALS LIMITED

Unit 1 Level 6 10 Queen Street, Melbourne, 3000, VIC, Australia
Tel.: (61) 397976700
Web Site: https://www.sunriseem.com
SREMF—(OTCQX)
Rev.: $399,306
Assets: $6,686,699
Liabilities: $870,726
Net Worth: $5,815,972
Earnings: ($5,247,062)
Fiscal Year-end: 06/30/24
Industrial Water Producer
N.A.I.C.S.: 237110
Robert Martin Friedland *(Chm)*

Subsidiaries:

Clean TeQ Limited (1)
270 280 Hammond Rd, Dandenong S, Melbourne, 3175, Victoria, Australia
Tel.: (61) 397068244
Web Site: http://www.cleanteq.com
Sales Range: $25-49.9 Million
Air & Water Purification Equipment Mfr
N.A.I.C.S.: 333413

SUNRISE FORD SALES

872 Alpine Road, 100 Mile House, V0K 2E0, BC, Canada
Tel.: (250) 395-2414
Web Site: http://www.sunriseford.ca
Rev.: $13,347,016
Emp.: 30
New & Used Car Dealers
N.A.I.C.S.: 441110

SUNRISE GLOBAL SOLAR ENERGY CO., LTD.

No 1 Sec 2 Ligong 1 Road, Yilan County, Wujie, 268, Taiwan
Tel.: (886) 3 990 5511 CN
Web Site: http://www.saswafer.com
Photovoltaic Cell & Panel Mfr & Whslr
N.A.I.C.S.: 334413
Kuei-Chang Hsu *(Co-Founder & CEO)*

Subsidiaries:

aleo solar GmbH (1)
Marius-Eriksen-Strasse 1, 17291, Prenzlau, Germany
Tel.: (49) 3984 8328 0
Web Site: http://www.aleo-solar.de
Solar Module Mfr
N.A.I.C.S.: 334413
William Yau-Min Chen *(CEO & Mng Dir)*

SUNRISE GROUP COMPANY LIMITED

Jingyi Road Economic and Technological Development Zone, Fuzhou, 350015, Fujian, China
Tel.: (86) 59183680888
Web Site: https://www.shengxingholdings.com
Year Founded: 1992
002752—(SSE)
Rev.: $965,621,751
Assets: $1,093,088,229
Liabilities: $686,085,492
Net Worth: $407,002,738
Earnings: $29,383,881
Emp.: 1,500
Fiscal Year-end: 12/31/22
Metal Can & Container Mfr
N.A.I.C.S.: 332431
Lin Yongbao *(Chm & Pres)*

Subsidiaries:

Shengxing (Beijing) Packing Co., Ltd. (1)
No 1 M2-5 Area Xinggu Development Area Pinggu District, Beijing, 101200, China
Tel.: (86) 1069956333
Metal Tank Mfr
N.A.I.C.S.: 332431

Shengxing (Hebei) Packing Co., Ltd. (1)
No 3 of Zhongyue Road Qinhuangdao Economic Development Zone East Area, Qinhuangdao, 66206, Hebei, China
Tel.: (86) 3355180606
Metal Tank Mfr
N.A.I.C.S.: 332431

Shengxing (Hong Kong) Co., Ltd. (1)
Room 2205-2206 22th Floor of Creative Center No 740, Wangjiaomidun Street, Kowloon, China (Hong Kong)
Tel.: (852) 85223963307
Metal Tank Mfr
N.A.I.C.S.: 332431

Shengxing (Shandong) Packing Co., Ltd. (1)
Western side of north end of Lepu Ave Dezhou, Economic & Technological Development Zone, Dezhou, 253000, Shandong, China
Tel.: (86) 5342766333
Metal Tank Mfr
N.A.I.C.S.: 332431

Shengxing (Zhongshan) Packing Co., Ltd. (1)
No 3 Hongchang Industrial City Minzhong Town, Zhongshan, Guangdong, China
Tel.: (86) 76085573666
Metal Tank Mfr
N.A.I.C.S.: 332431

SUNRISE INDUSTRIAL TRADERS LIMITED

503 Commerce House 5th Floor 140 Nagindas Master Road Fort, Mumbai, 400 023, India
Tel.: (91) 8655438454
Web Site: https://www.sunriseindustrial.co.in
Year Founded: 1972
501110—(BOM)
Rev.: $562,844
Assets: $16,069,216
Liabilities: $1,894
Net Worth: $16,067,322
Earnings: $287,932
Emp.: 7
Fiscal Year-end: 03/31/23
Securities Dealing Services
N.A.I.C.S.: 523150
Suresh B. Raheja *(CEO)*

SUNRISE INDUSTRY CO., LTD.

Machioku 603, Kanzaki-gun, Ichikawa, 679-2325, Hyogo, Japan
Tel.: (81) 790 22 5500 JP
Web Site: http://www.sunrise-grp.com
Year Founded: 1975
Sales Range: $25-49.9 Million
Emp.: 250
Automotive Parts Mfr & Distr
N.A.I.C.S.: 336390
Masato Hiraishi *(Chm)*

Subsidiaries:

Sunchirin Industries (Malaysia) Berhad (1)
Lot 7 Jalan Api-Api 26/1 Hicom Industrial Estate Section 26, Shah Alam, 40400, Selangor Darul Ehsan, Malaysia
Tel.: (60) 3 5191 1558
Web Site: http://www.sunchirin.net
Sales Range: $50-74.9 Million
Motor Vehicle Parts Mfr
N.A.I.C.S.: 336390
Mitsuru Ishimoto *(Mng Dir)*

Subsidiary (Non-US):

PT Sunchirin Industries Indonesia (2)
Jl Harapan II Lot KK-5A Kawasan Industri KIIC, Desa Sirnabaya-Kecamatan Teluk Jambe Timur, Karawang, 41361, West Java, Indonesia
Tel.: (62) 21 8911 5033
Automobile Parts Distr
N.A.I.C.S.: 423120

Sunchirin Autoparts India Pvt. Ltd. (2)
Plot No 25 New Municipal No 5 KIADB 3rd Main Road, I Phase Peenya Industrial Area, Bengaluru, 560058, Karnataka, India
Tel.: (91) 80 41179583
Automobile Parts Distr
N.A.I.C.S.: 423120
Gopi Nadh *(Mgr-Production)*

Sunchirin Industry (Thailand) Ltd. (2)
700/865 Moo 3 Amata Nakorn Industrial Estate Bangna-Trad Rd Km 57, Tambol Nongkakha Amphur Panthong, Chon Buri, 20160, Thailand
Tel.: (66) 38 185 500 2
Automobile Parts Distr
N.A.I.C.S.: 423120

SUNRISE NEW ENERGY CO., LTD.

West Zone R&D Building No 69 Sanying Road, Zibo Science & Technology Industrial Entrepreneurship Park Zhangdian, Zibo, Shandong, China
Tel.: (86) 1082967728 Ky
Web Site: https://sunrisenewenergy.com

SUNRISE NEW ENERGY CO., LTD.

Sunrise New Energy Co., Ltd.—(Continued)
Year Founded: 2019
EPOW—(NASDAQ)
Rev.: $45,050,405
Assets: $120,504,530
Liabilities: $109,715,952
Net Worth: $10,788,578
Earnings: ($32,920,724)
Emp.: 25
Fiscal Year-end: 12/31/23
Business Consulting Services
N.A.I.C.S.: 541611
Haiping Hu *(Founder, Chm & CEO)*

SUNRISE POULTRY PROCESSORS LTD.
13542 73A Avenue, Surrey, V3W 1C9, BC, Canada
Tel.: (604) 596-9505
Web Site: http://www.sunrisepoultry.com
Year Founded: 1982
Rev.: $83,697,318
Emp.: 550
Poultry Food Service & Mfr
N.A.I.C.S.: 424440
Peter Shoore *(Pres)*

SUNRISE REAL ESTATE GROUP, INC.
25th floor 638 Hengfeng Road, Shanghai, 201702, China
Tel.: (86) 2160673831   TX
Web Site: https://www.sunrise.sh
Year Founded: 2004
SRRE—(OTCIQ)
Rev.: $24,833,863
Assets: $207,875,056
Liabilities: $91,682,684
Net Worth: $116,192,372
Earnings: ($26,261,818)
Emp.: 78
Fiscal Year-end: 12/31/23
Real Estate Development Services
N.A.I.C.S.: 531390
Hsin Hung Lin *(Chm)*

SUNRISE RESOURCES LTD.
650 Saint Annes Road, Armstrong, V0E 1B5, BC, Canada
Tel.: (250) 546-6559
Web Site: http://www.sunriseresourcesltd.ca
Sales Range: Less than $1 Million
Metal Exploration Services
N.A.I.C.S.: 212290
Lars Glimhagen *(CFO)*

SUNRISE RESOURCES PLC
Silk Point Queens Avenue, Macclesfield, SK10 2BB, Cheshire, United Kingdom
Tel.: (44) 1625838884
Web Site: https://www.sunriseresources.com
SRES—(AIM)
Assets: $3,500,942
Liabilities: $560,151
Net Worth: $2,940,792
Earnings: $496,497
Fiscal Year-end: 09/30/23
Diamond Mining Services
N.A.I.C.S.: 212390
Patrick Cheetham *(Chm)*

SUNRISE SHARES HOLDINGS LTD.
380 Jalan Besar 07-10 ARC 380, Singapore, 209000, Singapore
Tel.: (65) 68121611   SG
Web Site: https://sunriseshares.com
Year Founded: 1983
581—(SES)
Rev.: $870,001
Assets: $4,527,284
Liabilities: $440,921
Net Worth: $4,086,363
Earnings: $113,591
Fiscal Year-end: 12/31/20
Investment Holding Company; Electrical & Control Equipment Mfr & Distr
N.A.I.C.S.: 551112

Subsidiaries:

A-Jung Electric Sdn Bhd   (1)
Ste E 06-08 Block E Block E Plz Mont Kiara 2 Jalan 1/70C, Mont Kiara, 50480, Kuala Lumpur, Malaysia
Tel.: (60) 362019101
Electronic Components Distr
N.A.I.C.S.: 423690
Clement Koh *(Gen Mgr)*

Electech Distribution Systems Pte. Ltd.   (1)
1 Harrison Road ITE Electric Building 07-01, Singapore, 369652, Singapore
Tel.: (65) 62869933
Web Site: http://www.ite.com.sg
Sales Range: $25-49.9 Million
Emp.: 30
Electrical Transmission Products Whslr
N.A.I.C.S.: 423610

SUNRISE SOYA FOODS
729 Powell Street, Vancouver, V6A 1H5, BC, Canada
Tel.: (604) 253-2326
Web Site: https://www.sunrise-soya.com
Year Founded: 1957
Sales Range: $25-49.9 Million
Emp.: 200
Soybean Products Mfr
N.A.I.C.S.: 311224

SUNRISE TOYOTA ABBOTSFORD
30210 Auto Mall Dr, Abbotsford, V2T 5M1, BC, Canada
Tel.: (604) 857-2657
Web Site: http://www.sunriseabbotsford.ca
Year Founded: 1966
New & Used Car Dealers
N.A.I.C.S.: 441110
Mark Smith *(Gen Mgr)*

SUNSEA AIOT TECHNOLOGY CO., LTD.
Unit 1701 17F Majialong Innovation Building No 198 Daxin Road, Nanshan District, Shenzhen, 518052, Guangdong, China
Tel.: (86) 75586185752
Web Site: https://www.sunseagroup.com
Year Founded: 1994
002313—(SSE)
Rev.: $471,849,539
Assets: $685,182,495
Liabilities: $593,182,138
Net Worth: $92,000,357
Earnings: ($179,092,892)
Fiscal Year-end: 12/31/22
Communication Product Mfr
N.A.I.C.S.: 334290
Ping Liu *(Chm)*

Subsidiaries:

SIMCom Wireless Solutions Ltd.   (1)
Building A SIM Technology Building No 633 Jinzhong Road, Changning District, Shanghai, 200335, China   (72.8%)
Tel.: (86) 2132523424
Web Site: http://www.simcomm2m.com
Communication Module Mfr & Distr
N.A.I.C.S.: 334220

SUNSEEKER ENERGY HOLDING AG
Dorfstrasse 3, 8834, Schindellegi, Switzerland
Tel.: (41) 44 687 4550
Web Site: http://www.sunseekerenergy.ch
Emp.: 21
Solar & Hybrid Power Technologies Developer
N.A.I.C.S.: 541715
Antony Howard *(Dir-Tech)*

SUNSET ENERGIETECHNIK GMBH
Industriestrasse 8-22, Alsdorf, 91325, Germany
Tel.: (49) 919594940
Web Site: http://www.sunset-solar.de
Rev.: $37,500,000
Emp.: 75
Solar Power Systems Mfr
N.A.I.C.S.: 221118
Olaf Fleck *(Mng Dir)*

Subsidiaries:

Sunseap Enterprises Pte Ltd.   (1)
18 Boon Lay Way Tradehub21 06-135, Singapore, 609966, Singapore
Tel.: (65) 66028086
Web Site: http://www.sunseap.com
Solar Energy Distr
N.A.I.C.S.: 423690
Shawn Tan *(Mgr-Bus Dev)*

SUNSET PACIFIC PETROLEUM LTD.
938 Howe Street Suite 704, Vancouver, V6Z 1N9, BC, Canada
Tel.: (604) 369-9113
Year Founded: 1981
Assets: $10,568
Liabilities: $1,092,269
Net Worth: ($1,081,701)
Earnings: ($270,750)
Fiscal Year-end: 12/31/18
Oil & Gas Exploration Services
N.A.I.C.S.: 213112
Dennis Luk *(CFO & Sec)*

SUNSET SUITS HOLDINGS, INC.
ul Starlecka 18, 61-361, Poznan, Poland
Tel.: (48) 616424004   NV
Web Site: http://www.sunsetsuits.pl
Sales Range: $10-24.9 Million
Emp.: 443
Men's Clothing Designer & Retailer
N.A.I.C.S.: 458110
Miroslaw Kranik *(Pres, CEO & Acting CFO)*

SUNSHINE 100 CHINA HOLDINGS LIMITED
12th Floor Block D Sunshine 100 Office Building No 2 Guanghua Road, Chaoyang, Beijing, 100026, China
Tel.: (86) 1065060100   Ky
Year Founded: 2007
2608—(HKG)
Rev.: $882,442,411
Assets: $9,339,406,128
Liabilities: $7,474,837,977
Net Worth: $1,864,568,151
Earnings: $196,714,133
Emp.: 3,949
Fiscal Year-end: 12/31/20
Holding Company
N.A.I.C.S.: 551112
Yi Xiaodi *(Chm & Pres)*

SUNSHINE AGRI-TECH INC.
900-885 West Georgia Street, Vancouver, V6C 3H1, BC, Canada
Tel.: (604) 339-7688   BC
Web Site: http://www.sunshine-agri.com
Year Founded: 2009
SAI.H—(TSXV)
Assets: $9,094
Liabilities: $110,015

INTERNATIONAL PUBLIC

Net Worth: ($100,921)
Earnings: ($17,012)
Fiscal Year-end: 12/31/23
Animal Feed Research & Development Services
N.A.I.C.S.: 115210

SUNSHINE BIOPHARMA, INC.
6500 Trans-Canada Highway 4th Floor, Pointe-Claire, H9R 0A5, QC, Canada
Tel.: (514) 426-6161   CO
Web Site: https://www.sunshinebiopharma.com
Year Founded: 2006
SBFM—(NASDAQ)
Rev.: $4,345,603
Assets: $29,243,848
Liabilities: $7,616,278
Net Worth: $21,627,570
Earnings: ($26,744,440)
Emp.: 46
Fiscal Year-end: 12/31/22
Pharmaceutical Researcher, Developer & Mfr
N.A.I.C.S.: 325412
Steve N. Slilaty *(Chm & CEO)*

Subsidiaries:

Atlas Pharma Inc.   (1)
7582 Chemin de la Cote-de-liesse, Montreal, H4T 1E7, QC, Canada
Tel.: (450) 682-8000
Web Site: https://www.atlaspharmainc.ca
Pharmaceutical & Cosmetic Product Mfr
N.A.I.C.S.: 325620

Nora Pharma Inc.   (1)
1565 Boulevard Lionel-Boulet, Varennes, QC, Canada
Web Site: https://norapharma.ca
Generic Drug Distr
N.A.I.C.S.: 424210

SUNSHINE CAPITAL LTD.
Office No 209 Bhanot Plaza-II 3 D B Gupta Road, New Delhi, 110055, India
Tel.: (91) 1123582393
Web Site: https://www.sunshinecapital.in
Year Founded: 1994
539574—(BOM)
Rev.: $925,184
Assets: $12,356,789
Liabilities: $58,017
Net Worth: $12,298,772
Earnings: $214,594
Emp.: 9
Fiscal Year-end: 03/31/23
Financial Support Services
N.A.I.C.S.: 541611
Surender Kumar Jain *(Mng Dir)*

SUNSHINE GLOBAL CIRCUITS CO., LTD.
ShangXing No 2 Bldg B ShaJing, Industry District BaoAn, Shenzhen, China
Tel.: (86) 75527243597
Web Site: https://www.sunshinepcb.com
Year Founded: 2001
300739—(CHIN)
Rev.: $227,986,838
Assets: $490,243,637
Liabilities: $220,847,011
Net Worth: $269,396,626
Earnings: $14,463,886
Emp.: 2,000
Fiscal Year-end: 12/31/23
Printed Circuit Board Mfr & Distr
N.A.I.C.S.: 334412
Zhang Peike *(Chm, Sec & Gen Mgr)*

Subsidiaries:

Sunshine Circuits USA, LLC   (1)

3400 Silverstone Dr Ste 139, Plano, TX 75023
Tel.: (972) 867-8886
Printed Circuit Board Mfr
N.A.I.C.S.: 334412

Sunshine PCB GmbH (1)
Walter-Friday-Str17, D-42899, Remscheid, Germany
Tel.: (49) 219195730
Web Site: https://www.sunshinepcb.de
Printed Circuit Board Mfr
N.A.I.C.S.: 334412

SUNSHINE INSURANCE GROUP COMPANY LIMITED
17th Floor Block A First World Plaza No 7002 Hongli West Road, Futian District, Shenzhen, 518034, China
Tel.: (86) 1058289999 CN
Web Site: https://www.sinosig.com
Year Founded: 2004
6963—(HKG)
Rev.: $10,830,748,782
Assets: $71,124,003,101
Liabilities: $62,568,813,691
Net Worth: $8,555,189,411
Earnings: $535,279,132
Emp.: 50,629
Fiscal Year-end: 12/31/23
Holding Company
N.A.I.C.S.: 551112
Rui Nie (Chief Risk Officer)

SUNSHINE KAIDI NEW ENERGY GROUP CO., LTD.
Kaidi Building 3 Jiangxia Avenue, East Lake New Tech Dev Zone, Wuhan, 430223, China
Tel.: (86) 27 6786 9001 CN
Web Site: http://www.kaidihi.com
Sales Range: $1-4.9 Billion
Renewable Energy Investment Holding Company
N.A.I.C.S.: 551112
Jiawei Li (Gen Counsel)

SUNSHINE OILSANDS LTD.
1910 715-5th Ave SW, Calgary, T2P 2X6, AB, Canada
Tel.: (403) 800-2272 AB
Web Site: https://www.sunshineoilsands.com
Year Founded: 2007
SUNYF—(OTCIQ)
Rev.: $28,019,014
Assets: $557,798,374
Liabilities: $475,731,660
Net Worth: $82,066,714
Earnings: ($49,015,930)
Emp.: 33
Fiscal Year-end: 12/31/22
Oilsands Land Owner
N.A.I.C.S.: 213112
Michael John Hibberd (Vice Chm)

SUNSHINE100 CO LTD
12th Floor Block D Sunshine 100 Office Building No 2 Guanghua Road, Chaoyang District, Beijing, 100026, China
Tel.: (86) 1065060100 Ky
Web Site: http://www.ss100.com.cn
Year Founded: 2007
Rev.: $1,055,592,220
Assets: $8,565,067,061
Liabilities: $7,158,190,829
Net Worth: $1,406,876,232
Earnings: $130,321,263
Emp.: 4,439
Fiscal Year-end: 12/31/17
Real Estate Manangement Services
N.A.I.C.S.: 531210
Xiaodi Yi (Chm)

SUNSPRING METAL CORPORATION
No 11 Keya Rd Taichung Science Park, Taichung, Taiwan
Tel.: (886) 422582062 TW
Web Site: http://www.sunspring.com.tw
Year Founded: 1978
2062—(TAI)
Rev.: $247,453,832
Assets: $419,800,108
Liabilities: $179,549,128
Net Worth: $240,250,980
Earnings: $10,274,371
Emp.: 5,376
Fiscal Year-end: 12/31/23
Metal Products, Including Bathroom & Kitchen Plumbing Fixtures, Door Hardware & Communications Equipment Mfr
N.A.I.C.S.: 332999

Subsidiaries:

Sunspring America, Inc. (1)
1105 5th St, Henderson, KY 42420
Tel.: (270) 826-9573
Web Site: http://www.ssa.sunspring.com
Zinc Die Casting
N.A.I.C.S.: 331523
Mike Shappell (Mgr-Mfg Plant-SSA KY Grp)

Subsidiary (Domestic):

Sunspring North America, LLC (2)
4168 Berkeley Ave, Kinston, NC 28504
Tel.: (252) 520-6578
Web Site: http://www.sunspring.com.tw
Sales Range: $1-9.9 Million
Emp.: 25
Zinc & Copper Products Distr
N.A.I.C.S.: 423510

SUNSTAR REALTY DEVELOPMENT LIMITED
Office No 422 Level 4 Dynasty A Wing Andheri-Kurla Road, Mumbai, 400 059, Maharashtra, India
Tel.: (91) 22 65341988
Web Site: http://www.sunstarrealtors.com
Year Founded: 2008
Rev.: $292,361
Assets: $8,505,404
Liabilities: $1,508,789
Net Worth: $6,996,615
Earnings: $17,065
Fiscal Year-end: 03/31/18
Real Estate Development, Sales & Leasing
N.A.I.C.S.: 236220
Nitin Kishore Boricha (Exec Dir)

SUNSTAR SUISSE S.A.
Route de Pallatex 11, Etoy, 1163, Switzerland
Tel.: (41) 218210500
Web Site: http://www.sunstar.com
Sales Range: $1-4.9 Billion
Emp.: 3,910
Holding Company
N.A.I.C.S.: 551112
Hiroo Kaneda (Chm)

Subsidiaries:

Braking-Sunstar S.p.A. (1)
Via Daneda 8, 20040, Milan, Briosco, Italy
Tel.: (39) 036295699
Preventive Dentistry & Oral Hygiene Products Mfr
N.A.I.C.S.: 339994

Maple Marketing (GFTZ) Ltd (1)
5D Modern Industry Centre 89 Weisan Road Conbo Avenue, 510730, Guangzhou, China
Tel.: (86) 2028397891
Preventive Dentistry & Oral Hygiene Products Mfr
N.A.I.C.S.: 339994

Maple Marketing Ltd. (1)
Flat A5 18th Fl Blk A Elizabeth House 250-254, Gloucester Rd, Hong Kong, Causeway Bay, China (Hong Kong)
Tel.: (852) 28107638
Preventive Dentistry & Oral Hygiene Products Mfr
N.A.I.C.S.: 339994

PT. Sunstar Engineering Indonesia (1)
MM-2100 Industrial Town Block I-2/1, Bekasi, 17520, West-Java, Indonesia
Tel.: (62) 218980892
Preventive Dentistry & Oral Hygiene Products Mfr
N.A.I.C.S.: 339994

Starlecs Inc. (1)
3-1 Asahi-machi Takatsuki, Osaka, 569-1195, Japan
Tel.: (81) 726825552
Preventive Dentistry & Oral Hygiene Products Mfr
N.A.I.C.S.: 339994
Kunio Takizawa (Mng Dir)

Sunstar Americas Inc. (1)
4635 W Foster Ave, Chicago, IL 60630-1709
Tel.: (773) 777-4000
Web Site: http://www.gumbrand.com
Sales Range: $200-249.9 Million
Emp.: 750
Preventive Dentistry & Oral Hygiene Products Mfr
N.A.I.C.S.: 339994
Angel Gonzalez (Dir-Engrg)

Subsidiary (Non-US):

Sunstar Americas Inc. (2)
515 Governors Road, Guelph, N1K 1C7, ON, Canada
Tel.: (519) 837-2500
Web Site: http://www.gumbrand.ca
Sales Range: $10-24.9 Million
Emp.: 60
Distribution of Preventive Dentistry & Oral Aids
N.A.I.C.S.: 423450
Dan Descary (Mng Dir)

Subsidiary (Domestic):

Sunstar Pharmaceutical, Inc. (2)
1300 Abbott Dr, Elgin, IL 60123-1821
Tel.: (847) 888-1141
Rev.: $12,801,000
Emp.: 3
Mfr of Private Label & Generic Over-the-Counter Pharamceuticals
N.A.I.C.S.: 325412

Sunstar Americas, Mexico S. de R.L. de C.V. (1)
Av De La Palma No 8 despacho 205 Col San Fernando La Herradura, 52787, Mexico, Mexico
Tel.: (52) 55 30 88 37 80
Cosmetic Product Distr
N.A.I.C.S.: 424210
Eduardo Perez Rolon (Gen Mgr)

Sunstar Benelux B.V. (1)
Hogeweyselaan 221, 1382 JL, Weesp, Netherlands
Tel.: (31) 29 448 4244
Web Site: https://www.sunstargum.com
Dental Product Distr
N.A.I.C.S.: 423450
Job van Dijk (Gen Mgr)

Sunstar Chemical (Thailand) Co., Ltd. (1)
624 Moo 4 Bangpoo Industrial Estate, Soi 7 Sukhumvit Rd, Samut Prakan, 10280, Thailand
Tel.: (66) 2 709 4531
Preventive Dentistry & Oral Hygiene Products Mfr
N.A.I.C.S.: 339994

Sunstar Co., Ltd. (1)
No 401 Kuen Yang International Business Plaza 798 Zhao Jia Bang Rd, Shanghai, 200030, China
Tel.: (86) 21 6445 3177
Cosmetic Product Distr
N.A.I.C.S.: 424210

Sunstar Deutschland GmbH (1)
Gutenbergstrasse 5, 65830, Kriftel, Germany
Tel.: (49) 6192 95 10 80
Oral Healthcare Products
N.A.I.C.S.: 325412

Sunstar Engineering (Thailand) Co., Ltd. (1)
632 Moo 4 Bangpoo Industrial Estate, Soi 6 Sukhumvit Rd, Samut Prakan, 10280, Thailand
Tel.: (66) 2 324 06524
Preventive Dentistry & Oral Hygiene Products Mfr
N.A.I.C.S.: 339994

Sunstar Engineering Americas Inc. (1)
85 S Pioneer Blvd, Springboro, OH 45066
Tel.: (937) 746-8575
Web Site: http://www.sunstarea.com
Chemical Products Mfr
N.A.I.C.S.: 325199
Eric Aukerman (Sr Engr-Process)

Sunstar Engineering Europe GmbH (1)
Emil Fischer Strasse 1, Rain am Lech, 86641, Donauworth, Germany
Tel.: (49) 9090 574 9220
Living Environment Services
N.A.I.C.S.: 624120

Sunstar Engineering Inc. (1)
3-1 Asahi-machi, Takatsuki, Osaka, 569-1134, Japan
Tel.: (81) 72 681 0351
Web Site: http://www.jp.sunstar-engineering.com
Cosmetic Product Distr
N.A.I.C.S.: 424210

Plant (Domestic):

Sunstar Engineering Inc. - Shiga Plant (2)
1000-16 Aza-Otani, Okamoto-cho, Kusatsu, 525-0044, Shiga, Japan
Tel.: (81) 77 562 6771
Cosmetic Product Distr
N.A.I.C.S.: 424210

Sunstar Engineering Inc. - Yamanashi Plant (2)
181-1 Miyazawa, Minami-Alps, 400-0415, Yamanashi, Japan
Tel.: (81) 552 84 3801
Cosmetic Product Distr
N.A.I.C.S.: 424210

Sunstar Engineering Italy S.r.l. (1)
Via Luciano Manara 2, 20812, Limbiate, MB, Italy
Tel.: (39) 02 97075699
Web Site: http://www.braking.com
Motor Vehicle Parts Distr
N.A.I.C.S.: 423120
Raphael Dalban-Moreynas (Mng Dir)

Sunstar Europe S.A. (1)
Route de Pallatex 11, 1163, Etoy, Switzerland
Tel.: (41) 21 821 0500
Living Environment Services
N.A.I.C.S.: 624120

Sunstar Europe SA (1)
Al Jerozolimskie 181B, 02-222, Warsaw, Poland
Tel.: (48) 79 044 4128
Web Site: https://www.sunstargum.com
Dental Product Distr
N.A.I.C.S.: 423450

Sunstar France S.A.S. (1)
55/63 rue Anatole, Levallois-Perret, 92300, France
Tel.: (33) 141066464
Web Site: http://www.sunstar.fr
Sales Range: $25-49.9 Million
Emp.: 70
Distr of Preventive & Oral Aids
N.A.I.C.S.: 325412

Sunstar Guangzhou Ltd. (1)
BLK D 5/F NO 203 Material Building Conbo Avenue, Guangzhou, 510730, China
Tel.: (86) 20 8222 5199
Cosmetic Product Distr
N.A.I.C.S.: 424210

Sunstar Iberia S.L.U. (1)
Carrer de Frederic Mompou 5 6 planta 3 B Edificio Euro 3, 8960, Sant Just Desvern,

SUNSTAR SUISSE S.A.

Sunstar Suisse S.A.—(Continued)
Barcelona, Spain
Tel.: (34) 93 470 58 80
Cosmetic Product Distr
N.A.I.C.S.: 424210
Gemma Torne *(Mgr-Fin & Admin)*

Sunstar Interbros GmbH (1)
Aiterfeld 1, 79677, Schönau, Germany
Tel.: (49) 7673 885 0
Web Site: http://www.sunstarinterbros.com
Dental Care Product Mfr
N.A.I.C.S.: 339114

Sunstar Italiana Srl (1)
Corso Italia 13, 21047, Saronno, Varese, Italy
Tel.: (39) 02 96319003
Web Site: http://www.sunstargum.com
Dental Care Product Mfr
N.A.I.C.S.: 339114

Sunstar Singapore Pte. Ltd. (1)
3 Fusionopolis Link 02-07, Singapore, 138543, Singapore
Tel.: (65) 67618555
Web Site: http://www.sunstar-engineering.com
Chemicals & Sealants Mfr; Motorcycle Parts Mfr
N.A.I.C.S.: 325998

Sunstar Sverige AB (1)
Hantverksvagen 15, 436 33, Stockholm, Sweden
Tel.: (46) 31 871610
Cosmetic Product Distr
N.A.I.C.S.: 424210
Christer Rydh *(Gen Mgr)*

Sunstar do Brazil Ltda. (1)
Avenida Ibirapuera 2315 - 9 Andar, Sao Paulo, 04029-200, Brazil
Tel.: (55) 115 056 4100
Rural Health Care Services
N.A.I.C.S.: 621210

Sunstar, Inc. (1)
3-1 Asahi-Machi, Takatsuki, 569-1195, Osaka, Japan
Tel.: (81) 726825541
Web Site: http://www.sunstar.com
Sales Range: $700-749.9 Million
Emp.: 300
Oral Care & Health & Beauty Care Products Mfr; Motorcycle Parts & Adhesives Mfr
N.A.I.C.S.: 325620
Nobuyuki Hoshi *(Mgr)*

Plant (Domestic):

Sunstar Inc. - Tokushima Plant (2)
Matsushige-Kogyo-Danchi 139-16 Kazu-Toyohisa-Kaitaku Toyohisa, Matsushige-cho, Itano, 771-0213, Tokushima, Japan
Tel.: (81) 88 699 4611
Cosmetic Product Distr
N.A.I.C.S.: 424210

Tsubamex Co., Ltd. (1)
3283-1 Konomiya, Nishikan-ku, Niigata, 950-1324, Japan
Tel.: (81) 25 375 4945
Web Site: https://www.tsubamex.co.jp
Plastic Molded Product Mfr
N.A.I.C.S.: 333511
Fukuo Yamamura *(Pres & CEO)*

ViSpot Inc. (1)
6-3-5 Minatojima Minamimachi Kobe Medical Innovation Center KCMI 2F, Chuo-ku, Kobe, 650-0047, Hyogo, Japan
Tel.: (81) 78 515 6401
Web Site: https://www.vispot.co.jp
Safety Evaluation Testing Services
N.A.I.C.S.: 541380

SUNSTONE DEVELOPMENT CO., LTD.

North Side of New National Highway 104, Hengyuan Economic Development Zone, Linyi, 251500, Shandong, China
Tel.: (86) 5342148011
Web Site: http://www.sun-stone.com
Year Founded: 2003
603612—(SHG)
Rev.: $2,723,842,260
Assets: $2,436,511,189
Liabilities: $1,410,055,003
Net Worth: $1,026,456,187
Earnings: $127,088,704
Emp.: 200
Fiscal Year-end: 12/31/22
Electrolytic Aluminum Product Mfr & Distr
N.A.I.C.S.: 335991
Lang Guanghui *(Chm)*

SUNSTONE METALS LTD

9 Gardner Close, PO Box 1565, Milton, 4064, QLD, Australia
Tel.: (61) 733689888
Web Site: https://www.sunstonemetals.com.au
STM—(ASX)
Rev.: $61,364
Assets: $20,268,973
Liabilities: $489,412
Net Worth: $19,779,560
Earnings: ($16,127,792)
Emp.: 5
Fiscal Year-end: 06/30/19
Minerals Exploration
N.A.I.C.S.: 213115
Graham Ascough *(Chm)*

Subsidiaries:

Avalon Minerals Adak AB (1)
Kasern gatan 6-981-37, 98138, Kiruna, Vasterbotten, Sweden
Tel.: (46) 98010910
Web Site: http://www.avalonminerals.com
Mineral Mining Services
N.A.I.C.S.: 212323

SUNSTONE REALTY ADVISORS INC.

910-925 West Georgia Street, Vancouver, V6C 3L2, BC, Canada
Tel.: (604) 681-5959 BC
Web Site: http://www.sunstoneadvisors.com
Year Founded: 2002
Emp.: 30
Real Estate Investment Trust Investment Management Services
N.A.I.C.S.: 523940
Stephen J. Evans *(Principal)*

SUNSURIA BERHAD

Suite 8 Main Tower Sunsuria Avenue Persiaran Mahogani Kota Damansar, PJU5, 47810, Petaling Jaya, Selangor Darul Ehsan, Malaysia
Tel.: (60) 361457777 MY
Web Site: https://www.sunsuria.com
SUNSURIA—(KLS)
Rev.: $107,132,063
Assets: $473,070,899
Liabilities: $241,175,450
Net Worth: $231,895,450
Earnings: $6,440,423
Emp.: 238
Fiscal Year-end: 09/30/23
Property Development; Wooden Doors Mfr
N.A.I.C.S.: 236116
Leong Yap Ter *(Chm)*

SUNSWEET PCL

No 9 Moo 1, Toongsatok Sanpatong, Chiang Mai, 50120, Thailand
Tel.: (66) 53106538
Web Site: https://www.sunsweetthai.com
Year Founded: 1997
SUN—(THA)
Rev.: $107,909,531
Assets: $57,746,291
Liabilities: $17,845,254
Net Worth: $39,901,036
Earnings: $10,432,740
Emp.: 960
Fiscal Year-end: 12/31/23

Grocery Product Mfr & Distr
N.A.I.C.S.: 311221
Ongart Kittikhunchai *(CEO)*

SUNTAK TECHNOLOGY CO., LTD.

Suntak Building Fengju Road, Guangming District, Shenzhen, 518132, Guangdong, China
Tel.: (86) 75526068047
Web Site: https://www.suntakpcb.com
Year Founded: 1995
002815—(SSE)
Rev.: $824,278,544
Assets: $1,332,475,480
Liabilities: $563,858,924
Net Worth: $768,616,557
Earnings: $89,391,795
Emp.: 5,000
Fiscal Year-end: 12/31/22
Batch Plate Mfr & Distr
N.A.I.C.S.: 332313
Xuefei Jiang *(Founder)*

Subsidiaries:

Dalian Suntak Circuit Co., Ltd. (1)
No 11 Guangming West Rd Economical Developing Dist Dalian, Liaoning, 116600, China
Tel.: (86) 41187180769
Emp.: 580
Circuit Board Mfr
N.A.I.C.S.: 334412

Jiangmen Suntak Circuit Technology Co., Ltd. (1)
No 363 Lianhai Rd Gaoxin Dist, Jiangmen, 529040, Guangdong, China
Tel.: (86) 7507361888
Emp.: 1,100
Circuit Board Mfr
N.A.I.C.S.: 334412

SUNTAR ECO-CITY LIMITED

3 Tuas Link 1, Singapore, 638584, Singapore
Tel.: (65) 63341514
Year Founded: 2006
BKZ—(SES)
Rev.: $4,988,451
Assets: $16,730,422
Liabilities: $3,946,197
Net Worth: $12,784,225
Earnings: $101,549
Emp.: 800
Fiscal Year-end: 12/31/23
Pharmaceuticals Product Mfr
N.A.I.C.S.: 325412
Lim Siew Choo Sharon *(Sec)*

SUNTAR ENVIRONMENTAL TECHNOLOGY CO., LTD.

No 66 Xinglin Jinting North Road, Jimei, Xiamen, 361022, Fujian, China
Tel.: (86) 5926778100
Web Site: http://www.suntar.com
Year Founded: 2005
688101—(SHG)
Rev.: $176,786,162
Assets: $743,968,368
Liabilities: $238,801,446
Net Worth: $505,166,922
Earnings: $30,593,511
Emp.: 800
Fiscal Year-end: 12/31/22
Application Development Services
N.A.I.C.S.: 541511
Tang Jiajing *(CFO)*

SUNTEC BUSINESS SOLUTIONS PVT. LTD.

Vikramapuram Hills Kuravankonam Kowdiar P O, Trivandrum, 695003, India
Tel.: (91) 4712539600
Web Site: http://www.suntecgroup.com

INTERNATIONAL PUBLIC

Year Founded: 1990
Sales Range: $1-9.9 Million
Telecom & Financial Services Industries Software Developer
N.A.I.C.S.: 513210
K. Nanda Kumar *(Founder & CEO)*

Subsidiaries:

SunTec Business Solutions FZE (1)
2 Executive Suite X4-49, Post Box No 121126, Sharjah, United Arab Emirates
Tel.: (971) 655 760 30
Financial Management Services
N.A.I.C.S.: 523999

SunTec Business Solutions GmbH (1)
Mainzer Landstrasse 27 31, D 60329, Frankfurt am Main, Germany
Tel.: (49) 69274015831
Software Development & Sales
N.A.I.C.S.: 513210

SunTec Business Solutions Inc. (1)
3060 Bristol Rd Apt 104, Bensalem, PA 19020-2134
Tel.: (609) 454-3026
Software Developer
N.A.I.C.S.: 513210
Michael Yesudas *(CTO)*

SunTec Business Solutions Ltd. (1)
3 Harbour Exchange Sq, London, E14 9GD, United Kingdom
Tel.: (44) 2075173670
Software Development & Sales
N.A.I.C.S.: 513210

SunTec Business Solutions Singapore Pte Ltd. (1)
Level 44 SunTec Tower Three 8 Temasek Bouelvard, Singapore, 038988, Singapore
Tel.: (65) 6829 2139
Financial Management Services
N.A.I.C.S.: 523999

SunTec Info Systems Pvt. Ltd. (1)
TC 9/427 Jawahar Nagar, Trivandrum, 695041, India
Tel.: (91) 471 2313670
Financial Management Services
N.A.I.C.S.: 523999

SUNTEC REAL ESTATE INVESTMENT TRUST

5 Temasek Boulevard 12-01 Suntec Tower Five, Singapore, 038985, Singapore
Tel.: (65) 68359232 SG
Web Site: https://suntecreit.listedcompany.com
Year Founded: 2004
T82U—(SES)
Rev.: $350,480,194
Assets: $8,429,317,575
Liabilities: $3,442,647,881
Net Worth: $4,986,669,694
Earnings: $148,694,236
Emp.: 19
Fiscal Year-end: 12/31/23
Trust Management Services
N.A.I.C.S.: 523940
Chan Kong Leong *(CEO)*

SUNTECH CO., LTD.

#217 Hanshin Officetel 11-9 Shincheon-dong Songpa-gu, Seoul, Korea (South)
Tel.: (82) 2 6413 1000
Web Site: http://www.sun-tech.co.kr
Sales Range: $25-49.9 Million
Emp.: 50
Power Generators & Transmitters Mfr
N.A.I.C.S.: 335312

SUNTECH POWER HOLDINGS CO., LTD.

Xinhua Road 9, New District, Wuxi, 214028, Jiangsu, China
Tel.: (86) 510 8531 8888 Ky
Web Site: http://www.suntech-power.com

Sales Range: $1-4.9 Billion
Emp.: 17,693
Solar Electric Systems Mfr
N.A.I.C.S.: 221118
Zhengrong Shi *(Founder, Chm & Chief Strategy Officer)*

Subsidiaries:

KSL Kuttler Automation Systems GmbH (1)
Zeissstrasse 1, Dauchingen, 78083, Germany
Tel.: (49) 7720 9760 0
Web Site: http://www.kuttler.com
Emp.: 24
Automation Equipment Distr
N.A.I.C.S.: 423830
Verner Renz *(Mgr)*

Subsidiary (Non-US):

Kuttler Automation Systems (Suzhou) Co., Ltd. (2)
No 71 Xingwu Rd Wuzhong, Suzhou, 215168, Jiangsu, China
Tel.: (86) 512 6527 9800
Web Site: http://www.ksl-kuttler.com.cn
Solar Cell Equipment Mfr
N.A.I.C.S.: 334413

Subsidiary (Domestic):

Suntech Power Deutschland GmbH (2)
Mainzer Landstr 46, Frankfurt am Main, 60325, Germany
Tel.: (49) 69770394600
Photovoltaic Device Mfr
N.A.I.C.S.: 334413
Jeremy Stokes *(Pres)*

Luoyang Suntech Power Co., Ltd. (1)
No 8 Huaxia Road High-Tech Industry Development Zone, Luoyang, 471003, China
Tel.: (86) 37965191000
Sales Range: $200-249.9 Million
Emp.: 700
Solar Cell Mfr
N.A.I.C.S.: 334413

Nanjing Engge Lanbo Microelectronics Co., Ltd. (1)
No 2405 Sport Mansion No 44 Gongyuan Road, Nanjing, 210002, China
Tel.: (86) 2584647685
Sales Range: $50-74.9 Million
Emp.: 3
Photovoltaic Device Distr
N.A.I.C.S.: 423690
Shijun Cai *(Mgr)*

Shenzhen Suntech Power Co., Ltd. (1)
Rm 801 Breeding Bldg Academy Of Secience & Technology Development, Shenzhen, 518000, China
Tel.: (86) 75582507778
Photovoltaic Device Mfr
N.A.I.C.S.: 334413

Sichuan Suntech Power Co., Ltd. (1)
No 18 Xinggang Middle Rd Economic & Technology Dev Zone, Chengdu, 100076, Sichuan, China
Tel.: (86) 2888431112
Solar Cell Mfr
N.A.I.C.S.: 334413

Suntech America, Inc. (1)
71 Steven Beach St 10 Fl, San Francisco, CA 94105
Tel.: (415) 882-9922
Sales Range: $75-99.9 Million
Emp.: 55
Photovoltaic Cells, Modules & Equipment Mfr
N.A.I.C.S.: 221118

Suntech Australia Pty Ltd (1)
Suite 1101 Level 11 201 Miller Street, North Sydney, 2060, NSW, Australia
Tel.: (61) 2 8188 2450
Sales Range: $25-49.9 Million
Emp.: 7
Solar Panel Mfr
N.A.I.C.S.: 334413

Jijun Shi *(Gen Mgr)*

Suntech Power Australia Pty Ltd (1)
Ste 1101 Level 11 201 Miller Street, North Sydney, 2060, NSW, Australia
Tel.: (61) 296958180
Web Site: http://www.suntech-power.com
Sales Range: $25-49.9 Million
Emp.: 7
Solar Power Heating Equipment Mfr
N.A.I.C.S.: 333414
Jiaying Lu *(Mng Dir)*

Suntech Power International Ltd (1)
Schwertstrasse 1, CH-8200, Schaffhausen, Switzerland
Tel.: (41) 526320090
Web Site: http://ir.suntech-power.com
Photovoltaic Cells, Modules & Equipment Mfr
N.A.I.C.S.: 221118

Subsidiary (US):

Suntech Arizona, Inc. (2)
71 Stevenson St Fl 10, San Francisco, CA 94105
Tel.: (623) 882-8500
Solar Wafer & Panel Mfr
N.A.I.C.S.: 334413

Subsidiary (Non-US):

Suntech Power Italy Co., Srl (2)
Viale Colleoni 25 - Palazzo Pegaso, Agrate Brianza, 20041, Monza and Brianza, Italy
Tel.: (39) 039 9633000
Web Site: http://www.suntech-power.com
Sales Range: $25-49.9 Million
Emp.: 7
Photovoltaic Device Mfr & Distr
N.A.I.C.S.: 334413
Jeremy Stokes *(CEO)*

Suntech Power Japan Corporation (1)
6F Nishishinjuku KS Building 3-6-11 Nishishinjuku, Shinjuku, Tokyo, 160-0023, Japan
Tel.: (81) 3 3342 3838
Solar Module Mfr
N.A.I.C.S.: 334413

Suntech R&D Australia Pty Ltd (1)
82-86 Bay St, Botany, 2019, NSW, Australia
Tel.: (61) 293166811
Sales Range: $25-49.9 Million
Emp.: 2
Photovoltaic Device Research & Development Services
N.A.I.C.S.: 541715
Renate Egan *(Mng Dir)*

Zhenjiang Ren De New Energy Technology Co., Ltd. (1)
No 998 Ganglong Road Economic And Technological Development Zone, Yangzhong, 212215, China
Tel.: (86) 51188280050
Web Site: http://www.rietechsolar.com
Emp.: 1,500
Semiconductor Devices Mfr
N.A.I.C.S.: 334413
Tang Jun *(Gen Mgr)*

Zhenjiang Rietech New Energy Science Technology Co., Ltd. (1)
No 998 Ganglong Road Economic Development Zone, Yangzhong, 212200, China
Tel.: (86) 51188280000
Web Site: http://www.rietech-solar.com
Semiconductor Devices Mfr
N.A.I.C.S.: 334413
Gouzhu Long *(Mgr)*

SUNTECK REALTY LIMITED

5th Floor Sunteck Centre 37-40 Subhash Road Vile Parle E, Mumbai, 400 057, India
Tel.: (91) 2242877800
Web Site:
    https://www.sunteckindia.com
512179—(BOM)
Rev.: $46,864,469
Assets: $870,287,105
Liabilities: $536,031,893
Net Worth: $334,255,213
Earnings: $168,923
Emp.: 511
Fiscal Year-end: 03/31/23
Real Estate Development Services
N.A.I.C.S.: 531390
Kamal Khetan *(Chm & Mng Dir)*

Subsidiaries:

Sunteck Infracon Private Limited (1)
601 Gopal Heights Netaji Subash Place, Pitampura Delhi, New Delhi, 110034, India
Tel.: (91) 9810117013
Web Site: https://suntechinfra.com
Construction Equipment Rental & Construction Services
N.A.I.C.S.: 532412

SUNTORY HOLDINGS LIMITED

2-1-40 Dojimahama, Kita-ku, Osaka, 530-8203, Japan
Tel.: (81) 663461131   JP
Web Site: http://www.suntory.com
Year Founded: 1899
Rev.: $23,559,839,100
Assets: $41,418,863,430
Liabilities: $24,968,919,640
Net Worth: $16,449,943,790
Earnings: $1,672,928,950
Emp.: 40,210
Fiscal Year-end: 12/31/19
Holding Company; Alcoholic & Non-Alcoholic Beverages, Food & Personal Health Products Mfr, Bottler & Distr
N.A.I.C.S.: 551112
Takeshi Niinami *(Pres & CEO)*

Subsidiaries:

Alcoholes Y Vinos, S.A. (1)
Ctra Zancara km 0460, Socuellamos, 13630, Ciudad Real, Spain
Tel.: (34) 926539320
Web Site: http://www.alvisa.es
Alcohol Mfr
N.A.I.C.S.: 312130

Beam Suntory Inc. (1)
510 Lake Cook Rd, Deerfield, IL 60015
Tel.: (847) 948-8888
Web Site: http://www.beamsuntory.com
Rev.: $3,148,400,000
Assets: $8,584,700,000
Liabilities: $3,510,600,000
Net Worth: $5,074,100,000
Earnings: $362,500,000
Emp.: 5,000
Fiscal Year-end: 12/31/2013
Holding Company; Distilled Spirits Mfr & Whslr
N.A.I.C.S.: 551112
Paula K. Erickson *(Chief People, Culture & Comm Officer & Sr VP)*

Subsidiary (Domestic):

Beam Global Spirits & Wine LLC (2)
510 Lake Cook Rd, Deerfield, IL 60015   (100%)
Tel.: (847) 948-8888
Web Site: http://www.beamsuntory.com
Sales Range: $1-4.9 Billion
Emp.: 1,253
Holding Company; Alcoholic Beverages Mfr & Distr
N.A.I.C.S.: 551112
Paula K. Erickson *(Chief HR Officer-Global & Sr VP)*

Subsidiary (Non-US):

Alberta Distillers Limited (3)
1521 34 Ave SE, Calgary, T2G 1V9, AB, Canada   (100%)
Tel.: (403) 265-2541
Web Site: https://www.albertadistillers.com
Sales Range: $75-99.9 Million
Emp.: 100
Rye Whisky Producer
N.A.I.C.S.: 424820

Beam Australia Pty Ltd. (3)
Level 2 Building 2 49 Frenchs Forest Rd, French's Forest, 2086, NSW, Australia
Tel.: (61) 289779700
Web Site: http://www.beamsuntory.com
Emp.: 5
Distillers & Wineries

N.A.I.C.S.: 312140
Scott Blank *(Mng Dir)*

Beam Canada Inc. (3)
67 Mowat Ave Suite 200, Toronto, M6K 3E3, ON, Canada   (100%)
Tel.: (416) 849-7300
Web Site: http://www.beamsuntory.com
Sales Range: $25-49.9 Million
Emp.: 50
Whisky & Malt Distr
N.A.I.C.S.: 312140

Subsidiary (Domestic):

Jim Beam Brands Co. (3)
510 Lake Cook Rd, Deerfield, IL 60015
Tel.: (847) 948-8888
Web Site: http://www.jimbeam.com
Sales Range: $1-9.9 Million
Emp.: 500
Distilled Spirits Mfr, Marketer & Importer
N.A.I.C.S.: 312140
Matthew John Shattock *(Chm & CEO)*

Plant (Domestic):

Jim Beam Brands Co. - Clermont Plant (4)
526 Happy Hollow Rd, Clermont, KY 40110
Tel.: (502) 543-2221
Web Site: http://www.beamsuntory.com
Distilled Beverages Producer
N.A.I.C.S.: 312140
Debbie Faust *(Mgr-Retail)*

Subsidiary (Non-US):

Canadian Club Canada Inc. (2)
2072 Riverside Dr East, Windsor, N8Y 4S5, ON, Canada
Tel.: (519) 973-9503
Web Site: http://www.canadianclub.com
Whisky Distillery
N.A.I.C.S.: 312140
Dan Tullio *(Mng Dir)*

Subsidiary (Domestic):

Cruzan Viril Ltd. (2)
3A Estate Diamond Frederiksted, Saint Croix, VI 00840
Tel.: (340) 692-2280
Web Site: http://www.cruzanrum.com
Rum Production
N.A.I.C.S.: 312140
Kimora Gregoire *(Mgr-DCS Ops)*

Maker's Mark Distillery, Inc. (2)
3350 Burks Spring Rd, Loretto, KY 40037
Tel.: (270) 865-2881
Web Site: http://www.makersmark.com
Sales Range: $25-49.9 Million
Emp.: 70
Whisky Distillery & Retail Shop
N.A.I.C.S.: 312140
Rob Samuels *(COO & Pres)*

Subsidiary (Non-US):

Maxxium Espana S.L. (2)
Calle Mahonia No 2 Edificio Portico, Madrid, 28043, Spain
Tel.: (34) 913 53 4600
Web Site: http://www.maxxium.com
Whisky & Distilled Alcoholic Beverage Merchant Whslr
N.A.I.C.S.: 424820

Maxxium Shanghai Ltd. (2)
Unit 1 19 Fl Tower 1 Grand Gateway 1 Hong Qiao Rd, Shanghai, 200030, China
Tel.: (86) 2164483388
Wine & Distilled Alcoholic Beverage Merchant Whslr
N.A.I.C.S.: 424820
Simon Tsao *(Mng Dir)*

Maxxium UK Ltd. (2)
Maxxium House Castle Business Park, Stirling, FK9 4RT, Scotland, United Kingdom
Tel.: (44) 1786 430 500
Web Site: http://www.maxxium.co.uk
Emp.: 200
Sales, Marketing & Distribution of Mixed Drinks & Cocktails
N.A.I.C.S.: 312140
Mark Riley *(Mng Dir)*

Chateau Lagrange S.A. (1)

SUNTORY HOLDINGS LIMITED

Suntory Holdings Limited—(Continued)
Saint Julien, Pauillac, 33250, Gironde, France **(100%)**
Tel.: (33) 556733838
Web Site: http://www.chateau-lagrange.com
Sales Range: $25-49.9 Million
Produces & Markets Wines
N.A.I.C.S.: 445320
Matthew Bordes *(Mng Dir)*

China Jiangsu Suntory Foods Co., Ltd. **(1)**
118 Tie Xi Road, Haizhou, Lianyungang, 222023, Jiangsu, China
Tel.: (86) 518 543 0600
Web Site: http://www.princebeer.com
Assets: $598,712,000
Liabilities: $707,052,000
Net Worth: ($108,340,000)
Emp.: 750
Beer & Malt Producer & Retailer
N.A.I.C.S.: 312120

Chiyoda Kogyo Co., Ltd. **(1)**
2-4-17 Tagawa, Yodogawa-ku, Osaka, 532-0027, Japan **(100%)**
Tel.: (81) 663091241
Web Site: http://www.chiyoda-kogyo.co.jp
Sales Range: $50-74.9 Million
Emp.: 120
Mfr of Pipe Bending Products
N.A.I.C.S.: 332996
Hideyuki Togoshi *(CEO)*

Connecto Co., Ltd. **(1)**
Success Shibadaimon Building 7F 2-8-13 Shibadaimon, Minato-ku, Tokyo, 105-0012, Japan
Tel.: (81) 354722351
Web Site: https://www.enherb.jp
Herbal Product Retailer
N.A.I.C.S.: 424490

Dynac Corporation **(1)**
1-8-1 Shinjuku hashi Mitake Station Building 8F, Shinjuku-Ku, Tokyo, 160-0022, Japan **(100%)**
Tel.: (81) 333414216
Web Site: http://www.dynac.co.jp
Sales Range: $200-249.9 Million
Emp.: 85
Restaurant Developer & Operator
N.A.I.C.S.: 722511

Dynac Holdings Corporation **(1)**
1-8-1 Shinjuku, Shinjuku-ku, Tokyo, 160-0022, Japan
Tel.: (81) 3 3341 4216
Web Site: http://www.dynac.co.jp
Rev.: $190,657,280
Assets: $106,267,040
Liabilities: $59,135,120
Net Worth: $47,131,920
Earnings: ($86,819,920)
Fiscal Year-end: 12/31/2020
Holding Company
N.A.I.C.S.: 551112
Yasuhiro Itou *(Chm & Pres)*

Fwines Co., Ltd. **(1)**
Ebisu MF Bldg 6F 4-6-1, Ebisu Shibuya-ku, Tokyo, 150-0013, Japan
Tel.: (81) 367328600
Web Site: https://www.fwines.co.jp
Wine Mfr & Distr
N.A.I.C.S.: 312130

Grands Millesimes de France, S.A. **(1)**
18 rue Lafont, F-33290, Ludon-Medoc, France **(37%)**
Tel.: (33) 5 5788 8577
Holding Company; Grape Vineyard & Winery Operator & Mail-Order Wine Distr
N.A.I.C.S.: 551112
Aymar de Baillenx *(Mng Dir)*

Subsidiary (Domestic):

Barriere Freres S.A. **(2)**
18 Rue Lafont, Blanquefort, 33295, Ludon-Medoc, Cedex, France
Tel.: (33) 557888585
Web Site: http://www.barriere-freres.fr
Sales Range: $25-49.9 Million
Emp.: 30
Wine Distr
N.A.I.C.S.: 424820
Laurent Ehrmann *(Mng Dir)*

Chateau Beaumont **(2)**
Cussac fort Medoc, 33460, Gironde, France
Tel.: (33) 556589229
Web Site: http://www.chateau-beaumont.com
Sales Range: $25-49.9 Million
Grape Vineyard & Winery Mfr
N.A.I.C.S.: 312130

Chateau Beychevelle **(2)**
Saint Julien Beychevelle, Pauillac, 33250, Gironde, France
Tel.: (33) 556732070
Web Site: http://www.beychevelle.com
Sales Range: $25-49.9 Million
Grape Vineyard & Winery
N.A.I.C.S.: 312130

Haagen-Dazs Japan, Inc. **(1)**
2-1-1 Kamimeguro, Meguro-ku, Tokyo, 153-0051, Japan
Tel.: (81) 120190821
Web Site: https://www.haagen-dazs.co.jp
Sales Range: $50-74.9 Million
Ice Cream Producer
N.A.I.C.S.: 311520

Hibino Wines & Spirits Co. **(1)**
Nihonbashi Kodenma Cho 16 2 7, Chuo Ku, Tokyo, 103 0001, Japan **(100%)**
Tel.: (81) 336640703
Web Site: http://www.hibino-wine.jp
Sales Range: $50-74.9 Million
Emp.: 8
Leases Real Estate
N.A.I.C.S.: 525990

Iwanohara Vineyard Co., Ltd. **(1)**
1223 Kitakata, Joetsu, Niigata, 943 04, Japan **(100%)**
Tel.: (81) 255284002
Web Site: http://www.iwanohara.sgn.ne.jp
Sales Range: $25-49.9 Million
Emp.: 20
Harvests Grapes; Produces & Markets Wines
N.A.I.C.S.: 445320

Izutsu Maisen Co., Ltd. **(1)**
4-8-5 Jingumae, Shibuya-ku, Tokyo, 150-0001, Japan
Tel.: (81) 120412955
Web Site: https://mai-sen.com
Restaurant Services
N.A.I.C.S.: 722511

Japan Beverage Holdings Inc. **(1)**
Sumitomo Realty and Development Shinjuku Grand Tower 11th Floor 17-1, Nishi-Shinjuku 8-chome Shinjuku-ku, Tokyo, 160-6111, Japan
Tel.: (81) 363040501
Beverage Distr
N.A.I.C.S.: 424490

Kanbaku Co., Ltd. **(1)**
2910 1 Naka Okamoto-cho, Utsunomiya-shi, Tochigi, 329 1105, Japan **(99%)**
Tel.: (81) 286730058
Sales Range: $25-49.9 Million
Emp.: 30
Production, Storage & Warehousing of Malt for Beer Products
N.A.I.C.S.: 312130

Kyushu Suntory Techno Products Ltd.
478 Aza-Hachimansui Oaza-Kitaamagi Kashima-machi, Kamimashiki-gun, Kumamoto, 861-3104, Japan
Tel.: (81) 962371115
Beverages Mfr
N.A.I.C.S.: 312130

Lucozade Ribena Suntory Limited **(1)**
2 Longwalk Road Stockley Park, Uxbridge, UB11 1BA, United Kingdom
Tel.: (44) 2037272420
Beverage Mfr & Distr
N.A.I.C.S.: 312111

MYU Planning and Operations, Inc. **(1)**
3-1-14 Jingumae Tokyo 3rd Floor, Shibuya-ku, Tokyo, 150-0001, Japan **(100%)**
Tel.: (81) 364347430
Web Site: http://www.myuplanning.co.jp
Sales Range: $125-149.9 Million
Emp.: 500

Planning, Design & Operation of Commercial Shops
N.A.I.C.S.: 323111

Monte Bussan K.K. **(1)**
Aoyama Oval Building 6F 5-52-2, Jingumae Shibuya-ku, Tokyo, 150-0001, Japan
Tel.: (81) 354664510
Web Site: https://www.montebussan.co.jp
Beer & Spirit Distr
N.A.I.C.S.: 424820

Morrison Bowmore Distillers, Ltd. **(1)**
Springburn Bond Carlisle Street, Glasgow, G21 1EQ, United Kingdom **(100%)**
Tel.: (44) 415589011
Web Site: http://www.morrisonbowmore.co.uk
Sales Range: $25-49.9 Million
Emp.: 150
Produces & Markets Whiskies
N.A.I.C.S.: 312130

Okinawa Suntory Ltd. **(1)**
628 Aja, Naha, Okinawa, 900-0003, Japan **(100%)**
Tel.: (81) 988682107
Web Site: http://www.okinawa-suntory.sgn.ne.jp
Sales Range: $25-49.9 Million
Markets Bottles & Cans Suntory Products Wholesale
N.A.I.C.S.: 423930
Tsuyoshi Iwanopo *(Mng Dir)*

Orangina Schweppes Holding B.V. **(1)**
Mediarena 5-6, Duivendrecht, 1114BC, Amsterdam, Netherlands
Tel.: (31) 203479170
Web Site: https://orangina.eu
Textile Machinery Mfr & Distr
N.A.I.C.S.: 333248

Restaurant Suntory USA Inc. **(1)**
2233 Kalakaua Ave Ste 307, Honolulu, HI 96815
Tel.: (808) 922-5511.
Authentic Japanese Restaurant Operator
N.A.I.C.S.: 722511
Nobuyuki Aoyama *(Gen Mgr)*

SUN-AD Company Limited **(1)**
A-PLACE Aoyama 2-11-3 Kita Aoyama, Minato-ku, Tokyo, 107-0061, Japan
Tel.: (81) 3 5785 6800
Web Site: http://www.sun-ad.co.jp
Rev.: $25,804,800
Emp.: 100
Advetising Agency
N.A.I.C.S.: 541810
Takashi Ando *(Exec Creative Dir)*

Shintori **(1)**
Al Campinas 600, Jardim Paulista, 01404 000, Sao Paulo, Brazil **(100%)**
Tel.: (55) 1132832455
Web Site: http://www.suntory.com.br
Sales Range: $10-24.9 Million
Emp.: 60
Restaurant
N.A.I.C.S.: 722511

Subway Japan Inc. **(1)**
Akasaka Biz Tower B2F B2-01 5-3-1, Akasaka Minato-ku, Tokyo, 1078515, Japan **(100%)**
Tel.: (81) 355455525
Web Site: https://www.subway.co.jp
Sales Range: $10-24.9 Million
U.S. Sandwich & Salad Restaurant Chain
N.A.I.C.S.: 722511

Sungrain, Ltd. **(1)**
16 Kitahama Cho, Chita, 478 0046, Japan **(50%)**
Tel.: (81) 562326351
Sales Range: $25-49.9 Million
Emp.: 20
Produces Grain Whisky; Makes & Markets Feedstuffs
N.A.I.C.S.: 312130

Suntory (Aust.) Pty. Ltd. **(1)**
Level 3 90-96 Bourke Road, Alexandria, 2015, NSW, Australia **(100%)**
Tel.: (61) 296631877
Web Site: http://www.clubsuntory.com.au
Sales Range: $25-49.9 Million
Emp.: 60
Bottles & Markets Liquors

INTERNATIONAL PUBLIC

N.A.I.C.S.: 312130
Ian Atherton *(Mng Dir)*

Suntory (China) Holding Co., Ltd. **(1)**
Room 3706 InterContinental Center No 100 Yutong Road, Shanghai, 200070, China
Tel.: (86) 21 6263 7999
Beer & Soft Drinks Mfr & Distr
N.A.I.C.S.: 312111

Subsidiary (Domestic):

Suntory (Shanghai) Foods Co., Ltd. **(2)**
600 Chuan Qiao Road, Pudong, Shanghai, China
Tel.: (86) 21 5854 1234
Non-Alcoholic Beverage Mfr
N.A.I.C.S.: 312120

Suntory (Shanghai) Foods Marketing Co., Ltd. **(2)**
Room 3706 BM Intercontinental Business Center No 100 Yutong Road, Shanghai, China
Tel.: (86) 21 6263 7999
Web Site: http://www.princebeer.com
Beverage Mfr & Distr
N.A.I.C.S.: 312120

Suntory Allied Ltd. **(1)**
16th Fl Tradepia Odaiba 2-3-1 Daiba Minato ku, Minato-ku, Tokyo, 135 0091, Japan
Tel.: (81) 355302245
Emp.: 12
Wine & Liquor Distr
N.A.I.C.S.: 445320

Suntory Beverage & Food Europe Ltd. **(1)**
2 Longwalk Road Stockley Park, Uxbridge, United Kingdom
Tel.: (44) 2037272420
Web Site: https://www.suntorybeverageandfood-europe.com
Food & Beverage Mfr
N.A.I.C.S.: 311999

Suntory Beverage & Food Limited **(1)**
3-1-1 Kyobashi, Chuo-ku, Tokyo, 104-0031, Japan
Tel.: (81) 332757310
Web Site: http://www.suntory.com
Rev.: $11,412,646,740
Assets: $13,712,015,550
Liabilities: $5,215,371,960
Net Worth: $8,496,643,590
Earnings: $749,121,600
Emp.: 23,532
Fiscal Year-end: 12/31/2023
Holding Company; Non-Alcoholic Beverage & Food Products Mfr & Distr
N.A.I.C.S.: 551112
Saburo Kogo *(Chm)*

Holding (Non-US):

Cerebos Pacific Limited **(2)**
18 Cross Street #12-01/08, China Square Central, Singapore, 048423, Singapore
Tel.: (65) 6212 0100
Web Site: http://www.cerebos.com
Emp.: 2,686
Produces & Markets Foods & Beverages
N.A.I.C.S.: 312130
Ramlee Buang *(CFO & Exec VP)*

Subsidiary (Non-US):

Cerebos (Australia) Limited **(3)**
92 96 Station Road, Seven Hills, 2147, NSW, Australia **(100%)**
Tel.: (61) 296245200
Web Site: http://www.cerebos.com.au
Sales Range: $75-99.9 Million
Emp.: 400
Produces Sauces, Gravies, Desserts, Fruit Pulps
N.A.I.C.S.: 311941
Robert Vincent Tanna *(Sr VP-Fin & Comml-Australia & New Zealand)*

Subsidiary (Non-US):

Orangina Schweppes S.A.S. **(2)**
133 Rue Victor Hugo, 92309, Levallois-Perret, Cedex, France

AND PRIVATE COMPANIES

Tel.: (33) 149687000
Web Site:
http://www.oranginaschweppes.com
Sales Range: $1-4.9 Billion
Emp.: 2,500
Soft Drinks Mfr
N.A.I.C.S.: 312111
Jacques Steffens (CEO)

Subsidiary (Non-US):

Orangina Schweppes Belgium SA/NV (3)
Rue du Cerf 127, Rixensart, 1332, Genval, Belgium (100%)
Tel.: (32) 26565211
Web Site:
http://www.oranginaschweppes.be
Sales Range: $25-49.9 Million
Emp.: 100
Soft Drinks Mfr
N.A.I.C.S.: 312111
Alexis Daems (Gen Mgr)

Orangina Schweppes International (3)
Bankrashof 3, 1183 NP, Amstelveen, Netherlands (100%)
Tel.: (31) 203479170
Web Site:
http://www.oranginaschweppes.com
Sales Range: $25-49.9 Million
Emp.: 65
Soft Drink Mfr & Distr
N.A.I.C.S.: 312111

Schweppes S.A. (3)
Avenida Bel Partenon 4, 28042, Madrid, Spain (100%)
Tel.: (34) 21 420 9800
Web Site: http://www.schweppes.es
Sales Range: $25-49.9 Million
Emp.: 200
Soft Drink Mfr & Distr
N.A.I.C.S.: 312111

Joint Venture (US):

Pepsi Bottling Ventures LLC (2)
4141 ParkLake Ave Ste 600, Raleigh, NC 27612
Tel.: (919) 865-2300
Web Site:
http://www.pepsibottlingventures.com
Sales Range: $200-249.9 Million
Soft Drinks Bottler; Owned by Suntory Ltd. & PepsiCo, Inc.
N.A.I.C.S.: 312111
Paul Finney (Pres & CEO)

Plant (Domestic):

Pepsi Bottling - Raleigh (3)
Six Forks Ctr 4700 Homewood Ct Ste 380, Raleigh, NC 27609-5711
Tel.: (919) 782-9271
Sales Range: $250-299.9 Million
Emp.: 1,000
Bottles & Markets Pepsi Cola & Other Drinks
N.A.I.C.S.: 312111
Rick Poillon (Pres & CEO)

Subsidiary (Domestic):

Pepsi-Cola Bottling Co of Roxboro, NC, Inc. (3)
605 S Morgan St, Roxboro, NC 27573
Tel.: (336) 599-2166
Rev.: $4,500,000
Emp.: 36
Other Grocery & Related Products Merchant Whslr
N.A.I.C.S.: 424490
Brantly T. Burnett (Pres)

Subsidiary (Domestic):

Suntory Foods, Ltd. (2)
Tamachi Station Tower N 3 1 1, Shibaura Minato ku, Tokyo, 108-8503, Japan (100%)
Tel.: (81) 368095950
Sales Range: $150-199.9 Million
Markets Soft Drinks & Fruit Beverages
N.A.I.C.S.: 312111

Suntory F&B International (H.K.) Co., Ltd. (1)
Unit 1405 14F Causeway Bay Plaza 1 489 Hennessy Road, Hong Kong, China (Hong Kong)
Tel.: (852) 2890 9333
Emp.: 100
Beverage Mfr & Distr
N.A.I.C.S.: 312120
Eiji Kamada (Deputy Gen Mgr)

Suntory F&B International (Sha) Co., Ltd. (1)
6 Bund 2F Zhongshan Dong Yi Lu, Shanghai, China (100%)
Tel.: (86) 21 6339 2770
Restaurant & Bar Opeartor
N.A.I.C.S.: 722410
Hiromasa Kudo (Mng Dir)

Suntory Flowers Ltd. (1)
4th Floor Sotetsu Tamachi Building 4-17-5 Shiba, Minato-ku, Tokyo, 108-0014, Japan
Tel.: (81) 3 5419 1386
Web Site: http://www.suntory.co.jp
Beverage Distr
N.A.I.C.S.: 424810

Suntory International Corp. (1)
600 3rd Ave Fl 21, New York, NY 10016
Tel.: (212) 891-6600
Web Site: http://www.suntory.com
Distilled Spirits, Wine, Beer & Food Products Importer
N.A.I.C.S.: 561499
Yoshihiro Morita (Exec Mgr-Sls & Mktg)

Suntory Investment & Development Ltd. (1)
Suntory Building 2F 2-1-40 Dojimahama, Kita-ku, Osaka, 530-0004, Japan
Tel.: (81) 663461220
Web Site: https://www.kousan.suntory.co.jp
Real Estate Lending Services
N.A.I.C.S.: 531110

Suntory Logistics Ltd. (1)
6th Floor Furukawa Osaka Building Nishi-kan 2-1-9 Dojimahama Kita, Osaka, 530-0004, Japan
Tel.: (81) 6 6345 2880
Logistics Consulting Servies
N.A.I.C.S.: 541614

Suntory Mexicana, S.A. de C.V. (1)
Magdelena 226 Col Del Valle, 03100, Mexico, D.F., Mexico
Tel.: (52) 5555360290
Web Site: http://www.suntory.com
Sales Range: $25-49.9 Million
Emp.: 3
Alcoholic Beveragers Producer & Sales
N.A.I.C.S.: 312130
Fumio Sakurai (Pres)

Suntory Publicity Service Co., Ltd. (1)
3D Akasaka Eight-One Bldg 2-13-5 Nagata-cho, Chiyoda-ku, Tokyo, 100 0014, Japan (100%)
Tel.: (81) 355320611
Sales Range: $10-24.9 Million
Emp.: 45
Guide Service for Suntory Tours & School Programs
N.A.I.C.S.: 561520

Suntory Service Ltd. (1)
Akasaka-Mitsuke MT Building 11th Floor 1 2 3 Moto-akasaka, Minato-ku, Tokyo, 107-0051, Japan (100%)
Tel.: (81) 334791467
Web Site: http://www.suntory.co.jp
Sales Range: $25-49.9 Million
Emp.: 30
Cave du Vin Wine Shops, Stella Silverware Shops & Kirana Jewlery Shops Operator
N.A.I.C.S.: 445220

Suntory Shopping Club, Ltd. (1)
Kyodo Bldg 8th Fl Nihonbashi Horidome Cho 1 10 12, Chuo Ku, Tokyo, 103 8567, Japan (100%)
Tel.: (81) 336678898
Web Site: http://www.suntory-sc.com
Direct-Mail Marketing Services
N.A.I.C.S.: 541910

Suntory Spirits Ltd. (1)
Tamachi Station Tower N 3 1 1, Shibaura Minato ku, Tokyo, 108-8503, Japan
Tel.: (81) 368095715
Beverage Mfr & Distr
N.A.I.C.S.: 312111

Suntory Sports System, Ltd. (1)
1588 1 Shinano Machi, Totsuka Ku, Yokohama, 244, Japan (100%)
Tel.: (81) 458216011
Manages Tennis Clubs
N.A.I.C.S.: 713940

Suntory Trading Hong Kong Ltd. (1)
15/F Cambridge House Taikoo Place 979 King's Road, Quarry Bay, China (Hong Kong)
Tel.: (852) 25062432
Beverage Distr
N.A.I.C.S.: 424490

Suntory U.K. Ltd. (1)
Buchanan House 3 St James Sq, London, FW1Y 4JU, United Kingdom (100%)
Tel.: (44) 2078399370
Web Site: http://www.suntory.com
Sales Range: $25-49.9 Million
Emp.: 7
Imports & Markets Suntory Products; Exports British Goods; Oversees Investment for Operations
N.A.I.C.S.: 312130
Makiko Ono (Gen Mgr-Corp Dev & Plng Dept)

Suntory Wellness Ltd. (1)
2-3-3 Daiba, Minato-ku, Tokyo, 135-8631, Japan
Tel.: (81) 355791000
Healthcare Product Distr
N.A.I.C.S.: 423450

Weingut Robert Weil (1)
Muhlberg 5, Rheingau, 65399, Kiedrich, Germany (50%)
Tel.: (49) 61232308
Web Site: http://www.weingut-robert-weil.com
Sales Range: $1-9.9 Million
Producer & Marketer of Wine Mfr
N.A.I.C.S.: 312130

SUNTRONT TECHNOLOGY CO., LTD.
No 252 Hongsong Road, High and New Tech Industrial Development Zone, Zhengzhou, 450001, China
Tel.: (86) 37156160869
Web Site: https://www.suntront.com
Year Founded: 2000
300259—(CHIN)
Rev.: $157,482,468
Assets: $482,383,512
Liabilities: $79,278,264
Net Worth: $403,105,248
Earnings: $34,513,128
Emp.: 1,300
Fiscal Year-end: 12/31/22
Measurement Instruments & Systems Mfr
N.A.I.C.S.: 334513
Dongling Yang (Sec)

SUNTRUST RESORT HOLDINGS, INC.
26th Floor Alliance Global Tower 36th Street Cor 11th Avenue, Uptown Bonifacio, Taguig, 1634, Philippines
Tel.: (63) 88946300
Web Site:
https://www.suntrusthomedev.com
Year Founded: 1956
SUN—(PHI)
Rev.: $74,779
Assets: $638,256,748
Liabilities: $474,168,968
Net Worth: $164,087,780
Earnings: ($10,501,464)
Emp.: 17
Fiscal Year-end: 12/31/21
Property Development Services
N.A.I.C.S.: 531312

SUNTY DEVELOPMENT CO., LTD.
11F No289 Sec 4 Zhongxiao E Rd, Da-an Dist, Taipei, 106, Taiwan
Tel.: (886) 227771355
Web Site: https://www.sunty.com.tw
Year Founded: 1987
3266—(TAI)
Rev.: $138,734,093
Assets: $429,753,115
Liabilities: $232,399,939
Net Worth: $197,353,176
Earnings: $21,067,235
Emp.: 70
Fiscal Year-end: 12/31/23
Real Estate Development, Construction, Leasing
N.A.I.C.S.: 237210
Kuan-Chen Mai (Chm)

SUNU ASSURANCES NIGERIA PLC
Plot 1196 Bishop Oluwole Street Off Akin Adesola Road, PO Box 1514, Marina Victoria Island, Lagos, Nigeria
Tel.: (234) 12802012
Web Site:
https://www.sunuassurances.com
Year Founded: 1984
SUNUASSUR—(NIGE)
Rev.: $11,166,380
Assets: $18,950,700
Liabilities: $7,505,282
Net Worth: $11,445,418
Earnings: $3,030,915
Emp.: 194
Fiscal Year-end: 12/31/23
All Other Insurance Related Activities
N.A.I.C.S.: 524298
John Nkemakonam Akujieze (Sec & Head-Legal & Compliance)

Subsidiaries:

Sunu Health Nigeria Limited (1)
174B Murtala Mohammed Way Ebute Metta, Lagos, Nigeria
Tel.: (234) 70010008000
Web Site: https://sunuhealthnigeria.com
Healtcare Services
N.A.I.C.S.: 621610

SUNVAULT ENERGY, INC.
Suite 200-10703-181 Street NW, Edmonton, T5S 1N3, AB, Canada
Tel.: (778) 478-9530 NV
SVLT—(OTCIQ)
Sales Range: Less than $1 Million
Renewable Energy Services
N.A.I.C.S.: 221114

SUNVEST CORPORATION LIMITED
Level 57 MLC Center 19-29 Martin Place, Sydney, 2000, NSW, Australia
Tel.: (61) 402841662 AU
Web Site:
http://www.sunvestcorp.com.au
Year Founded: 1987
SVS—(ASX)
Rev.: $1,042,190
Assets: $6,162,810
Liabilities: $214,920
Net Worth: $5,947,890
Earnings: $818,604
Fiscal Year-end: 06/30/21
Financial Services
N.A.I.C.S.: 523999
Bruce David Burrell (Chm & Sec)

SUNVESTA, INC.
Seestrasse 97 Seepark, CH-8942, Oberrieden, Switzerland
Tel.: (41) 43 388 4060 FL
Web Site: http://www.sunvesta.com
Assets: $83,776,000
Liabilities: $153,876,000
Net Worth: ($70,100,000)
Earnings: ($15,414,000)
Emp.: 5
Fiscal Year-end: 12/31/17
Hotel Developer

SUNVESTA, INC.

SunVesta, Inc.—(Continued)
N.A.I.C.S.: 721110
Hans Rigendinger (Chm & CEO)

Subsidiaries:

SunVesta Holding AG (1)
Seestrasse 97 Seepark, 8942, Oberrieden, Switzerland
Tel.: (41) 433884060
Web Site: http://www.sunvesta.com
Holding Company
N.A.I.C.S.: 551112
Charles Fessel (Project Dir)

Subsidiary (Non-US):

SunVesta Costa Rica Limitada (2)
Oficentro Forum 2 Edificio A Piso 4, Santa Ana, San Jose, 10903, Costa Rica
Tel.: (506) 22245757
Hotel & Motel Operator
N.A.I.C.S.: 721110

SUNVIC CHEMICAL HOLDINGS LIMITED
112 Robinson Road 11-01, Singapore, 068902, Singapore
Tel.: (65) 62209070
Web Site: http://www.sunvic-chem.com
A7S—(SES)
Sales Range: $300-349.9 Million
Acrylic Acid Esters Mfr
N.A.I.C.S.: 325199
Wei Hsiung Lee (Co-Sec)

Subsidiaries:

Jiangsu Jurong Chemical Co., Ltd. (1)
Chenjiagang Chemical Zone, Xiangshi, Yancheng, Jiangsu, China
Tel.: (86) 515 6735995
Chemical Products Mfr
N.A.I.C.S.: 325998

SUNVIC TECHNOLOGY CO., LTD.
8F No 33 Ln 221 Gangqian Rd, Neihu Dist, Taipei, 114, Taiwan
Tel.: (886) 277159058
Web Site: https://www.sunvic.com.tw
Year Founded: 1982
4304—(TPE)
Rev.: $16,048,088
Assets: $17,082,763
Liabilities: $10,515,930
Net Worth: $6,566,832
Earnings: ($1,762,530)
Fiscal Year-end: 12/31/22
Wire & Cable Material Mfr
N.A.I.C.S.: 335929
Lin Kuo-Jui (Chm & Pres)

SUNVIM GROUP CO., LTD.
No 1 Furi Street, Gaomi, 261500, Shandong, China
Tel.: (86) 5362308043
Web Site: http://www.sunvim.com
Year Founded: 1987
002083—(SSE)
Rev.: $736,864,170
Assets: $1,039,105,300
Liabilities: $506,669,497
Net Worth: $532,435,803
Earnings: $28,571,428
Fiscal Year-end: 12/31/22
Textile Products Mfr
N.A.I.C.S.: 314999
Zhang Guohua (Chm)

SUNWAH INTERNATIIONAL LIMITED
7/F Tower One Lippo Centre 89 Queensway, Hong Kong, China (Hong Kong)
Tel.: (852) 2283 7000 BM
Web Site: http://www.sunwahinternational.com

Year Founded: 1990
Rev.: $2,041,000
Assets: $27,007,000
Liabilities: $1,760,000
Net Worth: $25,247,000
Earnings: ($3,608,000)
Emp.: 159
Fiscal Year-end: 06/30/19
Investment Banking Services
N.A.I.C.S.: 523150
Douglas C. Betts (Exec Dir)

Subsidiaries:

Kingsway Financial Services Group Limited (1)
Rm 3303 Jin Mao Tower, 88 Century Ave Pudong, Shanghai, 200121, China
Tel.: (86) 2150490358
Web Site: http://www.kingswaygroup.cn
Sales Range: $50-74.9 Million
Emp.: 6
Investment Services
N.A.I.C.S.: 523999

Sunwah Kingsway Capital Holdings Limited (1)
7/F Tower One Lippo Centre 89 Queensway, Hong Kong, China (Hong Kong)
Tel.: (852) 22837000
Web Site: http://www.sunwahkingsway.com
Rev.: $8,890,075
Assets: $214,842,244
Liabilities: $97,363,133
Net Worth: $117,479,111
Earnings: ($10,150,210)
Emp.: 79
Fiscal Year-end: 06/30/2022
Financial Services
N.A.I.C.S.: 523999
Eric Kwok keung Chan (CFO)

SUNWARD INTELLIGENT EQUIPMENT CO., LTD.
Sunward Industrial Park No 1335 Liangtang Road, Xingsha, Changsha, 410100, Hunan, China
Tel.: (86) 4008876230
Web Site: https://www.sunwardmachine.com
Year Founded: 1999
002097—(SSE)
Rev.: $1,025,239,508
Assets: $2,889,470,975
Liabilities: $2,223,209,388
Net Worth: $666,261,587
Earnings: ($159,756,316)
Emp.: 4,800
Fiscal Year-end: 12/31/22
Construction Machinery Mfr
N.A.I.C.S.: 333120
Fu Xiangdong (Chm)

Subsidiaries:

Sunward Europe Heavy Industry NV (1)
Nijverheidspark 3, 3580, Beringen, Belgium
Tel.: (32) 11434666
Web Site: http://www.sunwardeurope.com
Engineering Machinery Equipment Mfr
N.A.I.C.S.: 333991

SUNWAVE COMMUNICATIONS CO., LTD.
No 581 Huoju Avenue, Binjiang District, Hangzhou, 310053, Zhejiang, China
Tel.: (86) 57188923377
Web Site: https://en.sunwave.com
Year Founded: 1993
002115—(SSE)
Rev.: $1,445,568,691
Assets: $641,153,841
Liabilities: $299,309,311
Net Worth: $341,844,530
Earnings: $18,997,356
Emp.: 1,000
Fiscal Year-end: 12/31/22
Communication Equipment Mfr
N.A.I.C.S.: 334290
Li Yuelun (Chm & Gen Mgr)

SUNWAY BERHAD
Level 18 Menara Sunway Jalan Lagoon Timur, 47500, Bandar Sunway, Selangor Darul Ehsan, Malaysia
Tel.: (60) 356398889 MY
Web Site: https://www.sunway.com.my
SUNWAY—(KLS)
Rev.: $1,335,698,529
Assets: $6,221,988,722
Liabilities: $2,956,786,916
Net Worth: $3,265,201,807
Earnings: $186,255,117
Emp.: 11,828
Fiscal Year-end: 12/31/23
Holding Company
N.A.I.C.S.: 551112
Jeffrey Fook Ling Cheah (Founder & Chm)

Subsidiaries:

Kinta Sunway Resort Sdn. Bhd. (1)
No 1 Persiaran Lagun Sunway 3 Sunway City Ipoh Darul Ridzuan, 31150, Ipoh, Perak, Malaysia
Tel.: (60) 52107777
Holding Company Services
N.A.I.C.S.: 551112

PT Sunway Pacific Flow (1)
Complex Union Industrial Park Block A No 1 Gate 3 Batu Ampar, Batam, Kepulauan Riau, Indonesia
Tel.: (62) 778413989
Construction Machinery Mfr
N.A.I.C.S.: 333120

Pasir Mas Holdings Sdn. Bhd. (1)
PT 9312 Bandar Sunway, 46200, Petaling Jaya, Selangor, Malaysia
Tel.: (60) 356116993
Holding Company Services
N.A.I.C.S.: 551112

SUNWAY PALS Loyalty Sdn. Bhd. (1)
Level 12 Menara Sunway, Jalan Lagoon Timur Bandar Sunway, 46150, Petaling Jaya, Selangor, Malaysia (100%)
Tel.: (60) 3 5639 8630
Web Site: http://www.sunway.com.my
Business Support Services
N.A.I.C.S.: 561990

Shahawan (M) Sdn Bhd (1)
Menara Sunway Jalan Lagoon Timur, Bandar Sunway, 46150, Petaling Jaya, Selangor, Malaysia
Tel.: (60) 3 5639 8889
Property Management Services
N.A.I.C.S.: 531311

Sumber Dorongan Sdn. Bhd. (1)
Unit 4 5 Level 4 East Lobby Menara Sunway Annexe Jalan Lagoon, Timur Bandar Sunway, 47500, Subang Jaya, Selangor, Malaysia
Tel.: (60) 356398888
Holding Company Services
N.A.I.C.S.: 551112

Sun Pharmaceutical Sdn. Bhd. (1)
9A Jalan SS5B-6, Kelana Jaya, 47301, Petaling Jaya, Selangor Darul Ehsan, Malaysia
Tel.: (60) 3 7874 1900
Pharmaceutical Product Whslr
N.A.I.C.S.: 424210

Subsidiary (Domestic):

Sunway Pharma Sdn Bhd (2)
Level 5-2 Menara Sunway Jalan Lagoon Timur, Bandar Sunway, 46150, Petaling Jaya, Selangor, Malaysia
Tel.: (60) 3 7491 0761
Pharmaceutical Product Whslr
N.A.I.C.S.: 424210

SunMed Clinics Sdn. Bhd. (1)
Sunway Pyramid Mall 3 Cp2 01 Jalan Pjs 11/1, 46150, Petaling Jaya, Malaysia
Tel.: (60) 3 7491 0121
Emp.: 6
Medical Consultation Services
N.A.I.C.S.: 541611

Sungei Way Ocean Joint Venture Ltd (1)

Nui Dinh Quarry, Long Huang Vlg, Vung Tau, Ba Ria-Vung Tau, Vietnam
Tel.: (84) 64828079
Sales Range: $50-74.9 Million
Emp.: 52
Quarrying Services
N.A.I.C.S.: 212311

Sunway (Tianjin) Management Consultancy Co. Ltd. (1)
Unit 801-802 Level 8 The Landmark Eco-Business Park, No 1620 Zhongtian Road Sino-Singapore Tianjin Eco-City, Tianjin, 300467, China
Tel.: (86) 2258950205
Holding Company Services
N.A.I.C.S.: 551112

Sunway Avila Sdn. Bhd. (1)
Lobby Level Menara Sunway Jalan Lagoon Timur, Bandar Sunway, 47500, Petaling Jaya, Selangor, Malaysia
Tel.: (60) 17 964 0822
Web Site: https://www.sunwayavila.com
Property Development Services
N.A.I.C.S.: 531190

Sunway Berhad - Batang Kali Factory (1)
Lot No 100711 Mukim, Daerah Ulu Selangor, 44300, Batang Kali, Selangor Darul Ehsan, Malaysia
Tel.: (60) 36 057 2407
Web Site: http://www.sunwaybavingpollution.com
Building Construction Services
N.A.I.C.S.: 236116
Lei Shu Ying (Head-HR)

Sunway Berhad - Nibong Tebal Factory (1)
Lot 2788 & 2796 Lorong Industri 3 Kawasan Perindustrian Bukit Panchor, Nibong Tebal, 14300, Penang, Malaysia
Tel.: (60) 4 593 8697
Building Construction Services
N.A.I.C.S.: 236116

Sunway Berhad - Senai Factory (1)
PLO 6 Jalan Lapangan Terbang Fasa 1 Kawasan Perindustrian, 81400, Senai, Johor, Malaysia
Tel.: (60) 75985633
Web Site: http://www.sunway.com.my
Building Construction Services
N.A.I.C.S.: 236116

Sunway Bintang Sdn. Bhd. (1)
No 28 Jalan Anson, 10400, George Town, Penang, Malaysia
Tel.: (60) 4 684 8000
Web Site: https://www.sunwaywellesley.com
Property Development Services
N.A.I.C.S.: 531190

Sunway City (Ipoh) Sdn. Bhd. (1)
No 52 Jalan SCI 1 3 Dataran Sunway Sunway City, 31150, Ipoh, Malaysia
Tel.: (60) 5 548 6668
Holding Company
N.A.I.C.S.: 551112
Wong Van Wooi (Gen Mgr)

Subsidiary (Domestic):

Sunway Lost World Water Park Sdn. Bhd. (2)
No 1 Persiaran Lagun Sunway 1, Sunway City, 31150, Ipoh, Perak, Malaysia
Tel.: (60) 5 542 8888
Web Site: http://www.sunwaylostworldoftambun.com
Theme Park Operator
N.A.I.C.S.: 713110

Sunway City (JB) Sdn. Bhd. (1)
No 65 & 65-01 Jalan Molek 1/29 Taman Molek, 81100, Johor Bahru, Malaysia
Tel.: (60) 7 355 2535
Building Construction Services
N.A.I.C.S.: 236116

Sunway City (S'pore) Pte. Ltd. (1)
9B Duxton Road Tanjong Pagar Conservation Area, Singapore, 89523, Singapore
Tel.: (65) 67345115
Emp.: 5
Holding Company
N.A.I.C.S.: 551112

SUNWAY BERHAD
AND PRIVATE COMPANIES

Subsidiary (Non-US):

Sunway Investment Management Consultancy (Shanghai) Co. Ltd. (2)
No 04 26th Floor 1788 International Center No 1788 Nanjing Road West, Shanghai, China **(100%)**
Tel.: (86) 21 6075 1193
Investment Advisory Services
N.A.I.C.S.: 523940

Sunway Coating Solutions Sdn. Bhd. (1)
No 27 and 29 Jalan Lombong Emas 4 Off Jalan Tun Dr Ismail Seremban, Light Industrial Park, 70200, Seremban, Malaysia
Tel.: (60) 67620573
Hardware Tool Distr
N.A.I.C.S.: 423710

Sunway Concrete Products (M) Sdn. Bhd. (1)
194 Sungai Puyu, 13020, Butterworth, Pulau Pinang, Malaysia
Tel.: (60) 43332853
Web Site: http://www.sgc.com.my
Precast Reinforced Concrete Mfr
N.A.I.C.S.: 327390

Sunway Construction Sdn Bhd (1)
Level 8 Menara Sunway Jalan Lagoon Timur, 47500, Bandar Sunway, Selangor Darul Ehsan, Malaysia
Tel.: (60) 356399696
Web Site: https://www.sunwayconstruction.com.my
Design & Construction Services
N.A.I.C.S.: 541330

Subsidiary (Domestic):

Muhibbah Permai Sdn Bhd (2)
CT-04-11 4 th Fl Subang Sq, Jln Ss 15 4g, 47500, Petaling Jaya, Selangor, Malaysia
Tel.: (60) 3 56317717
Property Management Services
N.A.I.C.S.: 531312

Subsidiary (Non-US):

PT Sunway-Yasa PMI Pile (2)
Sukomanunggal 244, Surabaya, 60188, Indonesia
Tel.: (62) 31 749 5682
Web Site: http://www.sunway.co.id
Sales Range: $25-49.9 Million
Emp.: 100
Heavy Equipment Parts, Hoses & Fittings Mfr & Distr
N.A.I.C.S.: 335999

Subsidiary (Domestic):

Sunway Builders Sdn Bhd (2)
Level 9 Menara Sunway Jalan Lagoon Timur, Bandar Sunway, 46150, Petaling Jaya, Selangor Darul Ehsan, Malaysia
Tel.: (60) 356399333
Sales Range: $25-49.9 Million
Emp.: 150
Civil Engineering Services
N.A.I.C.S.: 541330

Subsidiary (Non-US):

Sunway Concrete Products (S) Pte Ltd (2)
65 Ubi Road 1 Unit No 01-62, Singapore, 408729, Singapore
Tel.: (65) 65828089
Sales Range: $10-24.9 Million
Emp.: 50
Civil Engineering Services
N.A.I.C.S.: 541330
Tzyn Kwong (Gen Mgr)

Subsidiary (Domestic):

Sunway Developments Pte. Ltd. (3)
4 Tampines Industrial Street 62, Singapore, 528817, Singapore
Tel.: (65) 2 6582 8089
Holding Company
N.A.I.C.S.: 551112

Subsidiary (Non-US):

Sunway Construction India Pvt. Ltd. (2)
Survey nos 162p & 164 Ameenpur Village & Bachupalli Road, Patencheru, Medak, 500 032, Andra Pradesh, India
Tel.: (91) 40 2303 8888
Web Site: http://www.sunwayopus.com
Emp.: 40
Building Construction Services
N.A.I.C.S.: 236116
Brijesh Kumar Saxena (Deputy Gen Mgr)

Subsidiary (Domestic):

Sunway Creative Stones Sdn Bhd (2)
Lot 9 Jalan TUDM, 40150, Shah Alam, Malaysia
Tel.: (60) 378467662
Sales Range: $25-49.9 Million
Emp.: 20
Civil Engineering Services
N.A.I.C.S.: 541330

Subsidiary (Non-US):

Sunway Creative Stones (Xiamen) Co., Ltd. (3)
12 D XiangYu Bldg, Free Trade Zone, Xiamen, 361006, China
Tel.: (86) 5926016230
Sales Range: $25-49.9 Million
Emp.: 6
Civil Engineering Services
N.A.I.C.S.: 541330
Dany Lim (Country Mgr)

Subsidiary (Domestic):

Sunway Dimension Stones Sdn Bhd (3)
Lot 9 Jalan TUDM SuBang New Village, 40150, Shah Alam, Selangor Darul Ehsan, Malaysia
Tel.: (60) 378467662
Web Site: http://www.sunway.com.my
Sales Range: $25-49.9 Million
Civil Engineering Services
N.A.I.C.S.: 541330

Subsidiary (Domestic):

Sunway Engineering Sdn Bhd (2)
Level 9 Menara Sunway Jalan Lagoon Timur, 47500, Bandar Sunway, Selangor Darul Ehsan, Malaysia
Tel.: (60) 35 639 9696
Web Site: http://www.sunway.com.my
Electrical Engineering Services
N.A.I.C.S.: 541330

Sunway GD Piling Sdn Bhd (2)
9th Fl Menara Sunway, Jln Lagoon Selatan, 46150, Petaling Jaya, Selangor, Malaysia
Tel.: (60) 3 56399770
Piling Contractors
N.A.I.C.S.: 238910

Sunway Geotechnics (M) Sdn Bhd (2)
Level 7 Menara Sunway Jalan Lagoon Timur, 47500, Bandar Sunway, Selangor Darul Ehsan, Malaysia
Tel.: (60) 35 639 9696
Web Site: http://www.sunway.com.my
Sales Range: $50-74.9 Million
Piling Contractors
N.A.I.C.S.: 238910

Sunway Machineries Services Sdn Bhd (2)
Lot 656 Jalan Subang-2, Off Persiaran Subang, 47500, Petaling Jaya, Selangor Darul Ehsan, Malaysia
Tel.: (60) 356336499
Construction Machinery Rental Services
N.A.I.C.S.: 532412

Sunway Machinery Sdn Bhd (2)
Sunway Enterprise Park Jalan SEP2, Taman Putra Perdana, 47130, Puchong, Selangor Darul Ehsan, Malaysia
Tel.: (60) 38 322 3630
Web Site: http://www.sunway.com.my
Sales Range: $75-99.9 Million
Emp.: 160
Machinery Rental Services
N.A.I.C.S.: 532412

Sunway Credit Sdn. Bhd. (1)
Sunway Innovation Labs Level 1 Menara Sunway Jalan Lagoon Timur, Bandar Sunway, 47500, Selangor, Malaysia
Tel.: (60) 356398889
Web Site: http://www.sunwaycredit.com
Financial Transaction Services
N.A.I.C.S.: 522320

Sunway Daechang Forging (Anhui) Co. Ltd. (1)
No 1 Xu Zhen Industrial Area, Wuhu, 241306, Anhui, China
Tel.: (86) 5532395300
Construction Machinery Mfr
N.A.I.C.S.: 333120

Sunway Damansara Sdn. Bhd. (1)
No 2 Jalan PJU 5/1A Dataran Sunway Kota Damansara, Petaling Jaya, 47810, Malaysia
Tel.: (60) 3 6141 6888
Web Site: http://www.sunwayproperties.com
Emp.: 7
Holding Company
N.A.I.C.S.: 551112

Subsidiary (Domestic):

Sunway Monterez Sdn. Bhd. (2)
No 3 Jalan Pulau Angsa U10/1H Sunway Alam Suria Seksyen U10, 40170, Shah Alam, Selangor, Malaysia
Tel.: (60) 3 7845 5637
Building Construction Services
N.A.I.C.S.: 236116

Sunway Design Sdn. Bhd. (1)
Unit 2 5 Level 2 Menara Sunway Annexe Jalan Lagoon Timur Bandar Sunway, 47500, Subang Jaya, Selangor, Malaysia
Tel.: (60) 356398868
Holding Company Services
N.A.I.C.S.: 551112

Sunway Destiny Sdn. Bhd. (1)
Unit 4-5 Level 4 East Lobby Menara Sunway Annexe Jalan Lagoon Timur, Bandar Sunway, 46150, Selangor, Malaysia
Tel.: (60) 3 5639 8888
Building Construction Services
N.A.I.C.S.: 236116

Sunway Enterprise (1988) Sdn Bhd (1)
Lot 526 Persiaran Subang Permai, Sungai Penaga Industrial Park USJ 1, 47600, Subang Jaya, Selangor, Malaysia
Tel.: (60) 38 021 9228
Web Site: https://www.sunwayenterprise1988.com
Sales Range: $25-49.9 Million
Emp.: 50
Heavy Machinery Maintenance Services
N.A.I.C.S.: 811310
Yeoh Yuen Chee (Gen Mgr)

Subsidiary (Non-US):

PT Sunway Indoquip (2)
Jl Pangeran Jayakarta 26 Blok A No 12 & 13 Kelurahan Mangga 2 Selatan, Kecamatan Sawah Besar, Jakarta, 10730, Indonesia
Tel.: (62) 216 240 288
Industrial Supplies Whslr
N.A.I.C.S.: 423840
Fredericus Bambang (Mgr-Parts & Svc)

Sunway Facility Management Sdn. Bhd. (1)
No 3 Jalan Pjs 11/15 dar Sun Lee, PJS 11/15 Bandar Sunway, 46150, Petaling Jaya, Selangor, Malaysia
Tel.: (60) 374943000
Building Construction Services
N.A.I.C.S.: 236116
Chan Hc (CEO)

Sunway Giza Mall Sdn. Bhd. (1)
Centre Management Office LG Block D Sunway Giza No 2 Jalan PJU 5, Kota Damansara, 47810, Petaling Jaya, Malaysia
Tel.: (60) 36 148 1600
Web Site: https://www.sunwaygizamall.com
Shopping Mall Rental Services
N.A.I.C.S.: 531120
Kevin Tan (COO)

Sunway Giza Parking Sdn. Bhd. (1)
Centre Management Office LG Block D Sunway Giza, No 2 Jalan PJU 5 Kota Damansara, 47810, Petaling Jaya, Selangor, Malaysia
Tel.: (60) 361481600
Holding Company Services
N.A.I.C.S.: 551112

Sunway Guanghao Real Estate (Jiangyin) Co. Ltd. (1)
No 359 Xiangjiang Road Xia Gang, Jiangyin, 214442, JiangSu, China
Tel.: (86) 5 10 8688 0862
Building Construction Services
N.A.I.C.S.: 236116

Sunway Healthy Lifestyle Sdn. Bhd. (1)
Sunway Lagoon Club Lobby Shoplot No 2 No 3 Jalan Lagoon Timur, Bandar Sunway, 47500, Selangor, Malaysia
Tel.: (60) 356399993
Health Screening Programme Services
N.A.I.C.S.: 621999

Sunway Hose Centre Sdn Bhd (1)
Lot 526 Persiaran Subang Permai Sungai Penaga Industrial Park USJ 1, Bandar Sunway, 47600, Subang Jaya, Selangor, Malaysia
Tel.: (60) 38 021 9228
Web Site: https://www.sunwaymarketing.com.my
Emp.: 20
Hoses & Fittings Mfr
N.A.I.C.S.: 326220

Sunway Hotel (Penang) Sdn. Bhd. (1)
33 New Lane Off Macalister Road, 10400, George Town, Penang, Malaysia
Tel.: (60) 42299988
Emp.: 120
Hotel Operator
N.A.I.C.S.: 721120
Prakash Kumaran (Gen Mgr)

Sunway Hotel (Seberang Jaya) Sdn. Bhd. (1)
11 Lebuh Tenggiri Dua, Pusat Bandar Seberang Jaya, 13700, Prai, Penang, Malaysia
Tel.: (60) 43707788
Web Site: https://www.sunwayhotels.com
Hotel Services
N.A.I.C.S.: 721110

Sunway Hotel Hanoi Liability Limited Company (1)
19 Pham Dinh Ho Street, Hai Ba Trung, Hanoi, Vietnam
Tel.: (84) 4 3971 3888
Web Site: http://hanoi.sunwayhotels.com
Hotel Operator
N.A.I.C.S.: 721120

Sunway Hydraulic Industries (Wuhu) Co. Ltd. (1)
No 1 Xuzhen Industrial Park, Wuhu, 241306, Anhui, China
Tel.: (86) 553 237 0003
Web Site: https://www.sunway.me
Emp.: 300
Industrial Hose Whslr
N.A.I.C.S.: 423840

Sunway Hydraulic Industries Sdn Bhd (1)
Lot 526 Persiaran Subang Permai, Sungai Penaga Industrial Park USJ 1, 47600, Subang Jaya, Selangor, Malaysia
Tel.: (60) 38 021 9228
Web Site: https://www.sunwaymarketing.com.my
Sales Range: $25-49.9 Million
Emp.: 12
Hydraulic Hose Mfr
N.A.I.C.S.: 326220

Sunway IFM Sdn. Bhd. (1)
Jalan Todak Pusat Bandar Seberang, Petaling Jaya, 13700, Penang, Malaysia
Tel.: (60) 4 397 9888
Facility Management Services
N.A.I.C.S.: 561210
Chow Heng Wah (Gen Mgr)

Sunway Integrated Properties Sdn. Bhd. (1)
The Property Gallery Lobby Level Menara Sunway Jalan Lagoon Timur, 47500, Bandar Sunway, Selangor Darul Ehsan, Malaysia

7329

SUNWAY BERHAD

Sunway Berhad—(Continued)
Tel.: (60) 3 5639 9000
Web Site: http://www.sunwayproperty.com
Building Construction Services
N.A.I.C.S.: 236116

Sunway International Hotels & Resorts Sdn. Bhd. (1)
Level 15 Sunway Resort Hotel & Spa Persiaran Lagoon Bandar Sunway, 46150, Petaling Jaya, Selangor, Malaysia
Tel.: (60) 3 5639 8894
Web Site: http://www.sihr.com
Hotel Operator
N.A.I.C.S.: 721120

Subsidiary (Non-US):

Sunway Hotel Phnom Penh Ltd. (2)
No 1 Street 92, PO Box 633, Sangkat Wat Phnom, Phnom Penh, 120211, Cambodia
Tel.: (855) 2 343 0333
Web Site: https://www.sunwayhotels.com
Hotel Operator
N.A.I.C.S.: 721120

Sunway International Vacation Club Berhad (1)
Menara Sunway Jalan Lagoon Timur, 47500, Bandar Sunway, Selangor, Malaysia
Tel.: (60) 300880011
Web Site: http://www.sunway.com.my
Pub Operator
N.A.I.C.S.: 713910

Sunway Iskandar Sdn. Bhd. (1)
Sunway Southern Region Office Level 7 Hab Citrine, Iskandar Persiaran Medini 3 Bandar Medini Iskandar, 79250, Iskandar Puteri, Johor, Malaysia
Tel.: (60) 75098800
Holding Company Services
N.A.I.C.S.: 551112

Sunway Keramo Sdn Bhd (1)
Lot 6489 Off 6th Mile, Jalan Kapar, 20588, Kelang, Selangor, Malaysia
Tel.: (60) 332915288
Web Site: http://www.sunway.com
Sales Range: $50-74.9 Million
Emp.: 150
Pipes & Fittings Mfr
N.A.I.C.S.: 326122

Sunway Lagoon Club Berhad (1)
No 3 Jalan Lagoon Timur, Bandar Sunway, 47500, Subang Jaya, Selangor Darul Ehsan, Malaysia
Tel.: (60) 35 639 8600
Web Site: https://www.sunway.com.my
Recreation Club Operator
N.A.I.C.S.: 713990

Sunway Lagoon Sdn. Bhd. (1)
3 Jalan PJS 11/11 Bandar Sunway, 46150, Petaling Jaya, Selangor, Malaysia
Tel.: (60) 3 5639 0000
Theme Park Operator
N.A.I.C.S.: 713110

Sunway Leasing Sdn Bhd (1)
Level 15 Menara Sunway Jalan Lagoon, Timur Bandar Sunway, 46150, Petaling Jaya, Malaysia
Tel.: (60) 356398899
Sales Range: $25-49.9 Million
Emp.: 6
Financial Consulting Services
N.A.I.C.S.: 541611

Sunway Leisure Services Sdn. Bhd. (1)
No 86 Jalan Ampang, 50450, Kuala Lumpur, Malaysia
Tel.: (60) 3 2032 5622
Emp.: 6
Transportation Management Services
N.A.I.C.S.: 541614

Sunway Lost World Hotel Sdn. Bhd. (1)
No 2 Persiaran Lagun Sunway 1 Sunway City Ipoh Darul Ridzuan, 31150, Ipoh, Perak, Malaysia
Tel.: (60) 55408888
Holding Company Services
N.A.I.C.S.: 551112

Sunway Marketing (East Malaysia) Sdn Bhd (1)
S/lot 15 Lot 294 Sibiyu Industrial Estate Jalan Bintulu-tatau, 97000, Bintulu, Sarawak, Malaysia
Tel.: (60) 8 631 3778
Web Site: https://www.sunflex.com.sg
Hoses & Fittings Mfr
N.A.I.C.S.: 326220

Sunway Marketing (S) Pte Ltd (1)
19 Senoko South Road, Singapore, 758078, Singapore
Tel.: (65) 6 758 5454
Web Site: https://www.sunflex.com.sg
Sales Range: $50-74.9 Million
Emp.: 75
Construction Equipment Rental Services
N.A.I.C.S.: 532412

Subsidiary (Non-US):

PT Sunway Flowtech (2)
Complex Union Industrial Park Block A No 1 Gate 3, Batu Ampar, Batam, Riau Islands, Indonesia
Tel.: (62) 778 413 989
Hose Mfr & Distr
N.A.I.C.S.: 326220

PT Sunway Trek Masindo (2)
Jl Kosambi Timur No 47 Komp Pergudangan Sentra Kosambi Blok H1 No A, Kosambi Timur Dadap, Tangerang, 15211, Indonesia
Tel.: (62) 215 595 5445
Web Site: http://www.sunflex.com.sg
Sales Range: $25-49.9 Million
Emp.: 30
Hoses & Fittings Mfr
N.A.I.C.S.: 326220

Sunway Marketing (Shanghai) Pte Ltd (2)
No 588 Jianyun Road, Zhou Pu Town Nan Hui, Shanghai, 201318, China
Tel.: (86) 2168066662
Web Site: http://www.sunflex.com.sg
Sales Range: $25-49.9 Million
Emp.: 42
Bulldozer Parts, Tractor Parts, Hoses & Fittings Importer, Exporter & Sales
N.A.I.C.S.: 423830

Sunway Marketing (Thailand) Ltd. (2)
199/1 Soi Prayasurane 35 Prayasurane Road Bangchan, Klongsamwa, Bangkok, 10510, Thailand
Tel.: (66) 2 907 3955
Hose Mfr & Distr
N.A.I.C.S.: 326220

Sunway Marketing (Vietnam) Co., Ltd. (1)
Warehouse 1 Lot Va 12-10b Road 17 and 22 Industrial Park, Tan Thuan Export Processing Zone Tan Thuan Dong Ward District 7, Ho Chi Minh City, Vietnam
Tel.: (84) 36363300
Holding Company Services
N.A.I.C.S.: 551112
Le Huy Dung *(Mgr-Ops)*

Sunway Marketing Sdn. Bhd. (1)
Level 11 Menara Sunway Jalan Lagoon Timur, Bandar Sunway, 47500, Subang Jaya, Selangor, Malaysia
Tel.: (60) 35 639 9997
Web Site: https://www.sunwaymarketing.com.my
Construction Machinery Mfr
N.A.I.C.S.: 333122
Diane Gan *(Asst Mgr-Mktg & Plng)*

Sunway Medical Centre Berhad (1)
No 5 Jalan Lagoon Selatan, 47500, Bandar Sunway, Selangor, Malaysia
Tel.: (60) 374919191
Web Site: https://www.sunwaymedical.com
Hospital Management Services
N.A.I.C.S.: 622110

Sunway Melawati Sdn. Bhd. (1)
Jalan 6/4 Desa Melawati, 53200, Kuala Lumpur, Malaysia
Tel.: (60) 3 4108 8822
Building Construction Services
N.A.I.C.S.: 236116

Sunway Nexis Parking Sdn. Bhd. (1)
D-B1-02 Sunway Nexis No 1 Jalan PJU 5/1 Kota Damansara, 47810, Petaling Jaya, Selangor, Malaysia
Tel.: (60) 361431039
Holding Company Services
N.A.I.C.S.: 551112

Sunway Paving Solutions Sdn Bhd (1)
3 2 Level 3 Menara Sunway Jalan Lagoon Timur, 47500, Bandar Sunway, Selangor Darul Ehsan, Malaysia
Tel.: (60) 35 639 9325
Web Site: https://www.sunwaypavingsolutions.com
Interlocking Concrete Pavers Mfr
N.A.I.C.S.: 238990

Subsidiary (Non-US):

Sunway Cavity Wall Panel (S) Pte Ltd (2)
19 Senoko S Rd, 758078, Singapore, Singapore
Tel.: (65) 2 67594995
Cavity Wall Panel Mfr
N.A.I.C.S.: 238310

Subsidiary (Domestic):

Sunway Cavity Wall Panel Sdn Bhd (2)
Ste 3-2 Level 3 Menara Sunway Jalan Lagoon Timur, Bandar Sunway, 46150, Petaling Jaya, Selangor Darul Ehsan, Malaysia
Tel.: (60) 3 5639 8282
Cavity Wall Panel Installation Services
N.A.I.C.S.: 238310

Sunway Pipeplus Technology Sdn Bhd (1)
Ste 3-2 Level 3 Menara Sunway Jalan Lagoon Timur, Bandar Sunway, 46150, Petaling Jaya, Selangor, Malaysia
Tel.: (60) 356398282
Concrete Pipe Mfr
N.A.I.C.S.: 327332

Sunway Putra Hotel Sdn. Bhd. (1)
100 Jalan Putra, 50350, Kuala Lumpur, Malaysia
Tel.: (60) 340409888
Web Site: http://www.putra.sunwayhotels.com
Emp.: 400
Hotel Operator
N.A.I.C.S.: 721120

Sunway Pyramid Development Sdn. Bhd. (1)
LL1-10 Sunway Pyramid Shopping Mall No 3 Jalan PJS 11/15, Bandar Sunway, Petaling Jaya, 46150, Malaysia
Tel.: (60) 3 7492 6668
Building Construction Services
N.A.I.C.S.: 236116

Sunway Quarry Industries (Caribbean) Limited (1)
214 The Crossings Santa Rosa West Tempuna Road, Arima, Trinidad & Tobago
Tel.: (868) 868 2222 041
Sand & Gravel Quarrying Services
N.A.I.C.S.: 212321

Sunway Quarry Industries (Melaka) Sdn. Bhd. (1)
7 Jalan PJS 9-5, Bandar Sunway, Petaling Jaya, 6150, Malaysia
Tel.: (60) 65568255
Web Site: http://www.sjqi.com
Sales Range: $50-74.9 Million
Emp.: 30
Granite Quarrying & Road Construction Servies
N.A.I.C.S.: 212311
Dennis Lim *(Mgr)*

Sunway Quarry Industries (Melaka) Sdn. Bhd. (1)
No 7 Jalan PJS 9/5, Bandar Sunway, 46150, Petaling Jaya, Selangor, Malaysia
Tel.: (60) 3 5621 5035
Granite Quarrying Services
N.A.I.C.S.: 212313

Sunway Quarry Industries Sdn Bhd (1)
No 7 Jalan Pjs 9-5, Bandar Sunway, 46150, Petaling Jaya, Selangor Darul Ehsan, Malaysia

INTERNATIONAL PUBLIC

Tel.: (60) 356215035
Web Site: http://www.sunway.com.my
Sales Range: $50-74.9 Million
Emp.: 40
Quarry Operating Services
N.A.I.C.S.: 212311

Sunway Rahman Putra Sdn. Bhd. (1)
Jalan BRP 3/3 Bukit Rahman Putra, 47000, Sungai Buloh, Malaysia
Tel.: (60) 3 5639 9000
Building Construction Services
N.A.I.C.S.: 236116

Sunway Risk Management Sdn Bhd (1)
Level 5 Menara Sunway Jalan Lagoon Timur, Bandar Sunway, Petaling Jaya, 47500, Selangor Darul Ehsan, Malaysia
Tel.: (60) 356399299
Sales Range: $50-74.9 Million
Emp.: 30
Insurance Agency Services
N.A.I.C.S.: 524210
Kenneth Chan *(Gen Mgr)*

Sunway Semenyih Sdn. Bhd. (1)
Jalan Sunway 2 Bandar Sunway, 43500, Semenyih, Selangor, Malaysia
Tel.: (60) 3 8723 3131
Building Construction Services
N.A.I.C.S.: 236116

Sunway Shared Services Centre Sdn Bhd (1)
Menara Sunway Jalan Lagoon Timur, Bandar Sunway, 46150, Petaling Jaya, Selangor, Malaysia
Tel.: (60) 356398889
Web Site: http://www.sunway.com.my
Financial Management Services
N.A.I.C.S.: 541611

Sunway South Quay Sdn. Bhd. (1)
Sunway Lagoon 3, Petaling Jaya, 46150, Malaysia
Tel.: (60) 3 5639 8888
Building Construction Services
N.A.I.C.S.: 236116

Sunway Spun Pile (Zhuhai) Co. Ltd. (1)
Xingang Zone Baijiao Village, Baijiao Science Technology Industrial Park Doumen District, Zhuhai, 519180, Guangdong, China
Tel.: (86) 756 523 2666
Web Site: https://www.sunwayzh.com
Concrete Pipe Mfr & Distr
N.A.I.C.S.: 327332

Sunway Subang Sdn. Bhd. (1)
Lobby Level Menara Sunway Jalan Lagoon Timur, 47500, Bandar Sunway, Selangor, Malaysia
Tel.: (60) 179640490
Web Site: https://www.sunwaysubang.com
Property Development Services
N.A.I.C.S.: 531190

Sunway TotalRubber Services Franchising Pty. Ltd. (1)
6-8 Siddons Way, Hallam, 3803, VIC, Australia
Tel.: (61) 397023331
Holding Company Services
N.A.I.C.S.: 551112

Sunway Trading (Shanghai) Pte. Ltd. (1)
No 588 Jianyun Road Zhou Pu Town, Nanhui District, Shanghai, 201318, China
Tel.: (86) 21 6806 6669
Hose Distr
N.A.I.C.S.: 423840

Subsidiary (Domestic):

Sunway International Trading (Tianjin) Pte. Ltd. (2)
No 8 South Xunhai Road, Dongli District, Tianjin, 300300, China
Tel.: (86) 22 5866 6900
Hose Distr
N.A.I.C.S.: 423840

Sunway Travel Sdn. Bhd. (1)
Unit 1 7 Level 1 West Lobby Menara Sunway Annexe, Jalan Lagoon Timur, 47500, Bandar Sunway, Selangor, Malaysia

Tel.: (60) 3 5632 5622
Web Site: http://www.sunway.travel
Travel Tour Operator
N.A.I.C.S.: 561520

Sunway Tunas Sdn. Bhd. (1)
Unit 1-D 4th Floor Desa Rahmat Jalan Dato Ismail Hashim, Bayan Lepas, 11900, Malaysia
Tel.: (60) 4 643 9898
Building Construction Services
N.A.I.C.S.: 236116

Sunway Velocity Hotel Sdn. Bhd. (1)
Lingkaran SV Sunway Velocity, 55100, Kuala Lumpur, Malaysia
Tel.: (60) 32 726 3988
Web Site: https://www.sunwayhotels.com
Hotel Services
N.A.I.C.S.: 721110

Sunway Velocity Mall Sdn. Bhd. (1)
Lingkaran SV Sunway Velocity, 55100, Kuala Lumpur, Malaysia
Tel.: (60) 32 786 3970
Web Site: https://www.sunwayvelocitymall.com
Property Investment Services
N.A.I.C.S.: 531390
Kevin Gar Peng Tan (COO)

Sunway Winstar Sdn. Bhd. (1)
Lot 526 Persiaran Subang Permai Sungai Penaga Industrial Park USJ1, 47600, Subang Jaya, Selangor Darul Ehsan, Malaysia
Tel.: (60) 38 021 9238
Web Site: https://www.sunwaywinstar.com
Industrial Hardware Product Distr
N.A.I.C.S.: 423840

Subsidiary (Domestic):

Jaya DIY Mart Sdn. Bhd. (2)
Lot 526 Persiaran Subang Permai Sungai Penaga Industrial Park USJ 1, 47600, Subang Jaya, Selangor, Malaysia
Tel.: (60) 380219238
Holding Company Services
N.A.I.C.S.: 551112

Sunway Saf-T-Quip Sdn. Bhd. (2)
No 9 Jalan 3/33B Batu 6 1/2 Jalan Kepong, 52000, Kuala Lumpur, Malaysia
Tel.: (60) 362592006
Hardware Tool Distr
N.A.I.C.S.: 423710

Sunway United Star Sdn. Bhd. (2)
85 and 87 Jalan Metro Perdana Barat 12, Sri Edaran Light Industrial Park Kepong, 52100, Kuala Lumpur, Malaysia
Tel.: (60) 362592366
Hardware Tool Distr
N.A.I.C.S.: 423710

Sunway Xin Long (Anhui) Hydraulic Co. Ltd. (1)
No 1 Xu Zheng Industrial Area, Wuhu, 241306, Anhui, China
Tel.: (86) 553 627 7999
Web Site: https://www.xlah.com
Building Materials Distr
N.A.I.C.S.: 444180

SunwayMas Sdn Bhd (1)
Level 5 Menara Sunway Jalan Lagoon Timur, Bandar Sunway, 46150, Petaling Jaya, Selangor, Malaysia
Tel.: (60) 356399998
Web Site: http://www.sunwaymas.com.my
Property Development & Management Services
N.A.I.C.S.: 531311

Subsidiary (Domestic):

Sunway Bangi Sdn Bhd (2)
A-3A-G, Paragon Point Jalan Medan PB5, Sek 9 Pusat Bandar, 43650, Bandar Baru Bangi, Selangor Darul Ehsan, Malaysia
Tel.: (60) 389253998
Web Site: http://www.sunway.com.my
Sales Range: $250-299.9 Million
Emp.: 1,000
Property Management Services
N.A.I.C.S.: 531311

Sunway Eastwood Sdn. Bhd. (2)
Sunway Eastwood Clubhouse Jalan Equine 3, 43300, Seri Kembangan, Selangor, Malaysia

Tel.: (60) 3 8958 1777
Building Construction Services
N.A.I.C.S.: 236116

Sunway Greenview Sdn Bhd (2)
Level 5 Menara Sunway Jalan Lagoon Timur, Bandar Sunway, Petaling Jaya, Selangor, Malaysia
Tel.: (60) 341475722
Property Development & Management Services
N.A.I.C.S.: 531311

Tianjin Eco-City Sunway Property Development Co., Ltd. (1)
Unit 801-802 Level 8 The Landmark Eco-Business Park, No 1620 Zhongtian Road Sino-Singapore Tianjin Eco-City, Tianjin, 300467, China
Tel.: (86) 2259999589
Holding Company Services
N.A.I.C.S.: 551112

Totalrubber Limited (1)
2 Jamieson Way, Dandenong South, 3175, VIC, Australia
Tel.: (61) 39 799 2388
Web Site: https://www.totalrubber.com.au
Emp.: 15
Rubber & Plastic Products Mfr
N.A.I.C.S.: 326220

SUNWAY CO., LTD.
No 18 Yingbin Avenue High-tech Zone, Leshan, 614012, Sichuan, China
Tel.: (86) 8332595155
Web Site: http://www.sunwayint.com
Year Founded: 2003
603333—(SHG)
Rev.: $283,161,696
Assets: $500,139,605
Liabilities: $204,211,547
Net Worth: $295,928,058
Earnings: $2,570,064
Fiscal Year-end: 12/31/22
Power Cable Mfr & Distr
N.A.I.C.S.: 335929
Guangsheng Li (Chm & Gen Mgr)

Subsidiaries:

Sunway Big Box Sdn. Bhd. (1)
Persiaran Medini 5 Nusajaya, Sunway, 79250, Iskandar Puteri, Malaysia
Tel.: (60) 75331333
Web Site: https://www.sunwaybigbox.com
Shopping Complex & Car Park Operator
N.A.I.C.S.: 561210

Sunway Medical Centre (Singapore) Pte. Ltd. (1)
101 Irrawaddy Rd 09-01 Royal Square, Singapore, 329565, Singapore
Tel.: (65) 69110699
Web Site: https://www.sunwaymedicalsingapore.com
Health Care Srvices
N.A.I.C.S.: 621498

SUNWAY GLOBAL INC.
Daqing Hi-Tech Industry Development Zone, Daqing, 163316, Heilongjiang, China
Tel.: (86) 1061779332 NV
Year Founded: 1971
Sales Range: $1-9.9 Million
Pneumatic Tube Logistic Transport Products Mfr & Sales
N.A.I.C.S.: 332919
Samuel Sheng (CFO)

SUNWAY INTERNATIONAL HOLDINGS LIMITED
3/F Mandarin Commercial House 38 Morrison Hill Road, Wanchai, China (Hong Kong)
Tel.: (852) 27282766 HK
Web Site: http://www.hk0058.com
Year Founded: 1998
0058—(HKG)
Rev.: $57,517,163
Assets: $53,798,625

Liabilities: $27,860,663
Net Worth: $25,937,963
Earnings: ($5,786,460)
Emp.: 378
Fiscal Year-end: 12/31/22
Holding Company: Finance & Industrial
N.A.I.C.S.: 551112
Chongyang Li (Mng Dir)

SUNWAY REAL ESTATE INVESTMENT TRUST
Level 15 Menra Sunway Jalan Lagoon Timur Bandar Sunway, 47500, Subang Jaya, 47500, Selangor Darul Ehsan, Malaysia
Tel.: (60) 356398889 MY
Web Site: https://www.sunwayreit.com
Year Founded: 2010
SUNREIT—(KLS)
Rev.: $137,872,169
Assets: $1,992,247,831
Liabilities: $822,305,397
Net Worth: $1,169,942,434
Earnings: $68,477,884
Emp.: 19
Fiscal Year-end: 12/31/22
Real Estate Investment Trust Services
N.A.I.C.S.: 531110
Ahmad Mohd Don (Chm)

SUNWEST AUTO CENTRE LTD
401 Ryan Rd, Courtenay, V9N 3R5, BC, Canada
Tel.: (250) 338-1221
Web Site: https://www.comoxvalley.com
Rev.: $13,389,522
Emp.: 29
New & Used Car Dealer
N.A.I.C.S.: 441110
Jon Beekman (Mgr-Sls)

SUNWIN STEVIA INTERNATIONAL, INC.
6 Shengwang Ave, Qufu, 273100, Shandong, China
Tel.: (86) 1234561234 NV
Web Site: https://www.sunwininternational.com
Year Founded: 1995
SUWN—(OTCEM)
Rev.: $35,261,479
Assets: $25,491,662
Liabilities: $22,004,906
Net Worth: $3,486,756
Earnings: ($2,910,189)
Emp.: 242
Fiscal Year-end: 04/30/22
Nutraceutical Product Mfr
N.A.I.C.S.: 325411
Chunchun Wang (CEO & Gen Mgr-Web Based Ops)

Subsidiaries:

Qufu Shengren Pharmaceutical Co., Ltd. (1)
No 6 Shengwang Ave, Qufu, Shandong, China
Tel.: (86) 5374913739
Pharmaceuticals Product Mfr
N.A.I.C.S.: 325412

Qufu Shengwang Stevia Biology and Science Co., Ltd. (1)
6 Shengwang Ave, Qufu, China
Tel.: (86) 5374424999
Agricultural Organic Fertilizer Mfr & Distr
N.A.I.C.S.: 325311
Yuyi Liu (Executives)

SUNWING TRAVEL GROUP, INC.
27 Fasken Dr, Toronto, M9W 1K6, ON, Canada

Web Site: http://sunwingtravelgroup.com
Holding Company; Travel & Hotel Agencies
N.A.I.C.S.: 561599
Sabah Mirza (Pres & CEO)

Subsidiaries:

Blue Diamond Resorts, Inc (1)
27 Fasken Dr, Toronto, M9W 1k6, ON, Canada
Tel.: (416) 620-4955
Web Site: http://www.bluediamondresorts.com
Hotels & Resorts
N.A.I.C.S.: 721110
Jordi Pelfort (Pres)

Subsidiary (Non-US):

Grand Lido Negril Resort (2)
Norman Manley Blvd., Negril, Jamaica
Tel.: (876) 6192303
Web Site: http://www.grandlidoresorts.com
Hotel & Resort
N.A.I.C.S.: 721110

Grand Memories Punta Cana (2)
Highway Macao, Playa Arena Gorda Bavaro, Punta Cana, Dominican Republic
Tel.: (809) 552 1617
Web Site: http://www.memoriesresorts.com
Hotel & Resorts
N.A.I.C.S.: 721110
Mauricio Zarate (Gen Mgr)

Grand Memories Santa Maria (2)
Cayo Santa Maria, Jardines del Rey, Ciego de Avila, Cuba
Tel.: (53) 42350600
Web Site: http://www.memoriesresorts.com
Hotel & Resort
N.A.I.C.S.: 721110

Grand Memories Splash (2)
Highway Macao Playa Arena Gorda Bavaro, Punta Cana, Altagracia, Dominican Republic
Tel.: (809) 5521617
Web Site: http://www.memoriesresorts.com
Hotel & Resort
N.A.I.C.S.: 721120

Grand Memories Varadero (2)
Km 18 1/2 Autopista Sur, Punta Hicacos Varadero, Havana, Cuba
Tel.: (53) 45667966
Web Site: http://www.memoriesresorts.com
Hotel & Resort
N.A.I.C.S.: 721110

Memories Caribe Beach Resort (2)
Cayo Coco, Jardines del Rey, Ciego de Avila, Cuba
Tel.: (53) 33302350
Web Site: http://www.memoriesresorts.com
Hotel & Resort
N.A.I.C.S.: 721110

Memories Flamenco Beach Resort (2)
Caya Coco, Jardines del Rey, Ciego de Avila, Cuba
Tel.: (53) 33304100
Web Site: http://www.memoriesresorts.com
Hotel & Resort
N.A.I.C.S.: 721110

Memories Holguin Beach Resort (2)
Carretera a Guardalavaca S/N Playa Yuraguanal, Municipio Rafael Freyre, Holguin, 83300, Cuba
Tel.: (53) 24433540
Web Site: http://www.memoriesresorts.com
Hotel & Resort
N.A.I.C.S.: 721110
Alexander Welch (Dir-Gen)

Memories Jibacao Resort (2)
Arroyo Bermejo Beach, Via Blanca Km 60 Santa Cruz del Norte, Mayabeque, Cuba
Tel.: (53) 47295122
Web Site: http://www.memoriesresorts.com
Hotel & Resort
N.A.I.C.S.: 721110

Memories Miramar Havana (2)
Fifth Avenue between 72 and 76 Fraccionamiento Miramar, Havana, 11300, Cuba

SUNWING TRAVEL GROUP, INC.

Sunwing Travel Group, Inc.—(Continued)
Tel.: (53) 72 043584
Web Site: http://www.memoriesresorts.com
Hotel & Resorts
N.A.I.C.S.: 721110

Memories Paraiso Beach Resort (2)
Cayo Santa Maria, Jardines del Rey, Ciego de Avila, Cuba
Tel.: (53) 42350600
Web Site: http://www.memoriesresorts.com
Hotel & Resort
N.A.I.C.S.: 721110

Memories Trinidad Del Mar (2)
Peninsula Ancon, Casilda, Trinidad, 62600, Cuba
Tel.: (53) 41996500
Web Site: http://www.memoriesresorts.com
Hotel & Resort
N.A.I.C.S.: 721110

Memories Varadero Beach Resort (2)
Autopista Sur km 18 5, Punta Hicacos, Varadero, Cuba
Tel.: (53) 45667599
Web Site: http://www.memoriesresorts.com
Hotel & Resort
N.A.I.C.S.: 721110

Mystique Blue Holbox (2)
Av. Pedro Joaquin Coldwell Entre, calle Chabelita y Paseo Carey Holbox, Lazaro Cardenas, QR, Mexico
Tel.: (52) 9982833924
Web Site: http://www.mystiqueresorts.com
Hotel & Resort
N.A.I.C.S.: 721110

Mystique Royal St. Lucia (2)
Reduit Beach, PO Box 977, Rodney Bay, Gros Islet, West Indies, Saint Lucia
Tel.: (758) 4573131
Web Site: http://www.mystiqueresorts.com
Hotel & Resort
N.A.I.C.S.: 721110

Planet Hollywood Hotels-Adult Scene-Cancun (2)
Carratera a Punta Sam, SM006 MZA2, Cancun, QR, Mexico
Web Site: http://www.planethollywoodhotels.com
Hotel
N.A.I.C.S.: 721110

Planet Hollywood Hotels-Cancun (2)
Carratera a Punta Sam, SM006 MZA2 Lt 7 Salinas, 77400, Cancun, QR, Mexico
Web Site: http://www.planethollywoodhotels.com
Hotel
N.A.I.C.S.: 721120

Planet Hollywood Hotels-Costa Rica (2)
Playa Manzanillo Bahia Culebra Golfo de Papagayo, Guanacaste, Liberia, Costa Rica
Tel.: (506) 21060090
Web Site: http://www.planethollywoodhotels.com
Hotel & Resort
N.A.I.C.S.: 721110
Jonathan Iriarte (Gen Mgr)

Royalton Resorts & Spa (2)
77500 Cancun Benito Juarez, Cancun, Quintan Roo, Mexico
Tel.: (52) 9982833935
Web Site: http://www.royaltonresorts.com
Hotel & Resorts
N.A.I.C.S.: 721110
Daniel Cazarin (Gen Mgr)

Subsidiary (Non-US):

CHIC Punta Cana (3)
Carretera Uvero Alto, Uvero Alto, Punta Cana, Dominican Republic
Web Site: http://www.chicresorts.com
Hotel & Resorts
N.A.I.C.S.: 721110
Jonathan Iriarte (Gen Mgr)

Hideaway at Royalton Negril (3)
Norman Manley Blvd, Negril, A1, Jamaica
Tel.: (876) 8766192303
Web Site: http://www.royaltonresorts.com
Hotel & Resort
N.A.I.C.S.: 721110
Omar Duenas Garcia (Gen Mgr)

Hideaway at Royalton Punta Cana (3)
Playa Arena Gorda Carretera, Punta Cana, 2300, Dominican Republic
Tel.: (809) 2212121
Web Site: http://www.royaltonresorts.com
Hotel & Resort
N.A.I.C.S.: 721110

Subsidiary (Domestic):

Hideaway at Royalton Riviera Cancun (3)
Carretera Federal 307 Cancun, Playa del Carmen Km 322 15 31, 77500, Cancun, QR, Mexico
Tel.: (52) 9982833900
Web Site: http://www.royaltonresorts.com
Hotel & Resort
N.A.I.C.S.: 721110
Francisco Jorge (Gen Mgr)

Subsidiary (Non-US):

Hideaway at Saint Lucia (3)
Cap Estates, Gros Islet, Saint Lucia
Tel.: (758) 7311000
Web Site: http://www.royaltonresorts.com
Hotel & Resort
N.A.I.C.S.: 721110

Royalton Antigua Resort & Spa (3)
Deep Bay Street, Saint John's, 517, Antigua & Barbuda
Tel.: (268) 484 2000
Web Site: http://www.royaltonresorts.com
Hotel & Spa
N.A.I.C.S.: 721110
Christian Langlade (Gen Mgr)

Royalton Bavaro Resort & Spa (3)
Highway Macao, Playa Arena Gorda, Punta Cana, 2300, Dominican Republic
Tel.: (809) 5526888
Web Site: http://www.royaltonresorts.com
Hotel & Resort
N.A.I.C.S.: 721110
Pedro Martorell Moreno (Gen Mgr)

Royalton Blue Waters (3)
Mountain Spring trewlawny A1, Montego Bay, Jamaica
Tel.: (876) 6846200
Web Site: http://www.royaltonresorts.com
Hotel & Resort
N.A.I.C.S.: 721110
Enrico Pezzoli (Gen Mgr)

Royalton Cayo Santa Maria (3)
Cayo Santa Maria, Havana, CP 52610, Villa Clara, Cuba
Tel.: (53) 42350900
Web Site: http://www.royaltonresorts.com
Hotel & Resort
N.A.I.C.S.: 721110
Miguel Del Fraile (Gen Mgr)

Royalton Grenada Resort & Spa (3)
Magazine Beach Point Salines, Saint George's, Grenada
Tel.: (473) 4443333
Web Site: http://www.royaltonresorts.com
Hotrel & Resort
N.A.I.C.S.: 721110

Royalton Hicacos Resort & Spa (3)
Las Morlas Street, Km 15 Varadero, Havana, Cuba
Tel.: (53) 456688444
Web Site: http://www.royaltonresorts.com
Hotel & Resort
N.A.I.C.S.: 721110
Paula Chacin (Gen Mgr)

Royalton Negril (3)
Norman Manley Blvd, Negril, A1, Jamaica
Tel.: (876) 6192303
Web Site: http://www.royaltonresorts.com
Hotel & Resort
N.A.I.C.S.: 721110
Omar Duenas Garcia (Gen Mgr)

Royalton Punta Cana Resort & Casino (3)
Playa Arena Gorda, Carretera Macao, Punta Cana, 2300, Dominican Republic
Tel.: (809) 2212121
Web Site: http://royaltonresorts.com
Hotel & Casino
N.A.I.C.S.: 721120
Wendy Franco (Asst Gen Mgr)

Subsidiary (Domestic):

Royalton Riviera Cancun Resort & Spa (3)
Carretera Federal 307 Cancun-Playa del carmen Km 332 15, SM 31 MZ 03, 77500, Cancun, QR, Mexico
Tel.: (52) 9982833900
Web Site: http://royaltonresorts.com
Hotel & Resort
N.A.I.C.S.: 721110
Francisco Jorge (Gen Mgr)

Subsidiary (Non-US):

Royalton Saint Lucia Resort & Spa (3)
Smugglers Cove Drive, Cap Estate, Gros Islet, Saint Lucia
Tel.: (758) 7311000
Web Site: http://royaltonresorts.com
Hotel & Resort
N.A.I.C.S.: 721110
Anderson Howard (Gen Mgr)

Subsidiary (Domestic):

Royalton Suites Cancun Resort & Spa (3)
5 Manzana 51 lot 13-c Section A Boulevard Kukulcan ZT Kilometer 9, Zone Hotelera, 77500, Cancun, QR, Mexico
Tel.: (52) 9988685900
Web Site: http://www.royaltonresorts.com
Hotel & Resorts
N.A.I.C.S.: 721110

Subsidiary (Non-US):

Royalton White Sands Resort (3)
Highway A1 Mountain Spring Trelawny, Montego Bay, Jamaica
Tel.: (876) 684 6200
Web Site: http://royaltonresorts.com
Hotel & Casino
N.A.I.C.S.: 721110
Marlon D. Honegan (Gen Mgr)

Subsidiary (Non-US):

Sanctuary at Grand Memories Santa Maria (2)
Cayo Santa Maria, Jardines del Rey, Ciego de Avila, Cuba
Tel.: (53) 42350600
Web Site: http://www.memoriesresorts.com
Hotel & Resort
N.A.I.C.S.: 721110

Sanctuary at Grand Memories Varadero (2)
Km 18 1/2 Autopista Sur, Punta Hicacos, Varadero, Matanzas, Cuba
Tel.: (53) 45667966
Web Site: http://www.memoriesresorts.com
Hotel & Resorts
N.A.I.C.S.: 721110
Saskia Jaspers (Mgr)

Starfish Cayo Santa Maria (2)
Pedraplen a Cayo Santa Maria Sin Numero,, Cayo Santa Maria Caibarien, Villa Clara, 56200, Cuba
Tel.: (53) 42350400
Web Site: http://www.starfishresorts.com
Hotel
N.A.I.C.S.: 721110

Starfish Cuarto Palmas (2)
Avenida 1ra entre 60 y 64, Varadero, 42200, Matanzas, Cuba
Tel.: (53) 45667040
Web Site: http://www.starfishresorts.com
Hotel & Resort
N.A.I.C.S.: 721110

Starfish Discovery Bay Resort (2)
Trents Holetown St James BB, BB24017, Holetown, Barbados
Tel.: (246) 4321301
Web Site: http://www.starfishresorts.com
Hotel & Resort
N.A.I.C.S.: 721110

Starfish Halcyon Cove Resort (2)
Dickenson Bay, Antigua, Antigua & Barbuda
Tel.: (268) 4620256
Web Site: http://www.starfishresorts.com
Hotel & Resort
N.A.I.C.S.: 721110

Starfish Jolly Beach Resort (2)
Bolands, Saint Mary, Bolans, Antigua & Barbuda
Tel.: (268) 4620061
Web Site: http://www.starfishresorts.com
Hotel & Beach Resort
N.A.I.C.S.: 721110
Christopher Forbes (Gen Mgr)

Starfish Las Palmas (2)
Avenida 1ra entre 60 y 64, Varadero, 42200, Matanzas, Cuba
Tel.: (53) 45667040
Web Site: http://www.starfishresorts.com
Hotel
N.A.I.C.S.: 721110

Starfish Montehabana (2)
Avenida 70 entre 5ta y 7ma avenida Miramar, Fraccionamiento Miramar, Havana, 11300, Cuba
Tel.: (53) 47668844
Web Site: http://www.starfishresorts.com
Hotel
N.A.I.C.S.: 721110

Starfish St. Lucia (2)
Reduit Beach, PO Box 514, Rodney Bay, Gros Islet, West Indies, Saint Lucia
Tel.: (758) 4573000
Web Site: http://www.starfishresorts.com
Hotel & Resort
N.A.I.C.S.: 721110

Starfish Tobago (2)
1 Courland Bay, Scarborough, Trinidad & Tobago
Web Site: http://www.starfishresorts.com
Hotel & Resort
N.A.I.C.S.: 721110

Starfish Tropical (2)
Pedraplen a Cayo Santa Maria Sin Numero, Cayo Santa Maria Caibarien, Villa Clara, 56200, Cuba
Tel.: (53) 42350400
Web Site: http://www.starfishresorts.com
Hotel & Resort
N.A.I.C.S.: 721110

Starfish Varadero (2)
Carretera las Morlas, Km 14.5. Autopista, Varadero, Matanzas, Cuba
Tel.: (53) 45668243
Web Site: http://www.starfishresorts.com
Hotel & Resort
N.A.I.C.S.: 721110

Travel Smart VIP Club (2)
Carretera Federal 307 Cancun Playa del Carmen, Km. 332 15 SM31, MZ 03, Cancún, QR, Mexico
Tel.: (52) 50115553
Web Site: http://www.travelsmartvip.com
Tour Booking Services
N.A.I.C.S.: 561599

Luxe Destination Weddings Inc. (1)
171 East Liberty Street Suite 139, Toronto, M6K 3P6, ON, Canada
Tel.: (416) 536-7422
Web Site: http://www.luxedestinationweddings.com
Destination Weddings Planning Services
N.A.I.C.S.: 561599

NexusTours Corp. (1)
Camino de Acceso a Rancho Nazaret Mz, 66 Lte Sm 310, Cancun, 77560, Quintana Roo, Mexico
Tel.: (52) 9982516559
Web Site: http://nexustours.com
Travel Destination Booking Services
N.A.I.C.S.: 561599

Signature Vacations, Inc. (1)
27 Fasken Drive, Toronto, M9W 1K6, ON, Canada
Web Site: http://www.signaturevacations.com
Tour Booking Services
N.A.I.C.S.: 561599

Sunwing Jets (1)
27 Fasken Drive, Toronto, M9W 1K6, ON, Canada

AND PRIVATE COMPANIES

Web Site: https://sunwingjets.com
Flights & Travel Booking Services
N.A.I.C.S.: 561599

Sunwing Vacations Inc. (1)
27 Fasken Drive, Toronto, M9W 1K6, ON,
Canada
Tel.: (416) 620-4955
Web Site: http://www.sunwing.ca
Sales Range: $200-249.9 Million
Emp.: 200
Travel & Vacation Arrangement Services
N.A.I.C.S.: 561599

Subsidiary (Domestic):

SellOff Vacations (2)
27 Fasken Drive, Toronto, M9W 1K6, ON,
Canada
Web Site: https://www.selloffvacations.com
Travel Booking Services
N.A.I.C.S.: 561599
Stuart Morris (Gen Mgr)

Subsidiary (US):

Vacation Expess USA Corp. (2)
3500 Piedmont Rd Ste 600, Atlanta, GA
30305
Tel.: (404) 321-7742
Web Site: http://www.vacationexpress.com
Travel Destination Booking Services
N.A.I.C.S.: 561599

SUNWODA ELECTRONICS CO., LTD.
No 2 Yihe Road Shilong Community
Shiyan Street, Baoan District, Shenzhen, 518108, Guangdong, China
Tel.: (86) 75529516888
Web Site: https://www.sunwoda.com
Year Founded: 1997
300207—(CHIN)
Rev.: $7,323,582,708
Assets: $10,459,022,184
Liabilities: $6,765,568,524
Net Worth: $3,693,453,660
Earnings: $149,350,500
Emp.: 42,000
Fiscal Year-end: 12/31/22
Battery Module Mfr
N.A.I.C.S.: 335910
Mingwang Wang (Founder, Chm & Gen Mgr)

Subsidiaries:

Huizhou Winone Precision Technology Co., Ltd. (1)
Sunwoda industrial park Dongpo RD, Yuanzhou Town Boluo County, Huizhou, China
Tel.: (86) 7526388858
Web Site: https://en.hz-winone.com
Injection Molding Machine Mfr
N.A.I.C.S.: 333248

Shenzhen Xinwei Electronic Co., Ltd. (1)
2F A2 Building the first Industrial Road of Xinwei Community, Fuyong street Baoan District, Shenzhen, China
Tel.: (86) 13662561248
Web Site: https://www.xinweikedz.com
Printed Circuit Board Mfr
N.A.I.C.S.: 334412

Shenzhen Yisheng Investment Co., Ltd. (1)
A26F Fulllink Plaza No18 Chaowai St, Chao Yang District, Beijing, 100020, China
Tel.: (86) 1065887799
Web Site: https://www.yishenggroup.cn
Real Estate Services
N.A.I.C.S.: 531390

SUNWOOD CORPORATION
7th Floor Toranomon 30 Mori Building
3-2-2 Toranomon, Minato-ku, Tokyo,
105-0001, Japan
Tel.: (81) 3 5425 2661
Web Site: http://www.sunwood.co.jp
Year Founded: 1997
8903—(JAS)
Sales Range: Less than $1 Million
Emp.: 57

Real Estate Manangement Services
N.A.I.C.S.: 531210
Yoshimi Sasaki (Pres)

SUNY ELECTRONICS LTD.
46 Ben Zion Galis Street, Petach,
Petah Tiqwa, 49277, Israel
Tel.: (972) 39057777
Mobile Phone Retailer
N.A.I.C.S.: 449210
Ilan Ben-Dov (Chm)

Subsidiaries:

Suny Cellular Communication Ltd. (1)
Herakevet 8, Petah Tiqwa, 49277,
Israel (82.33%)
Tel.: (972) 39057701
Rev.: $235,861,579
Assets: $121,456,000
Liabilities: $58,665,837
Net Worth: $62,790,163
Earnings: $6,171,018
Fiscal Year-end: 12/31/2023
Household Appliances, Electric Housewares & Consumer Electronics Merchant Wholesalers
N.A.I.C.S.: 423620
Jacob Luxenburg (Chm)

SUNYARD TECHNOLOGY CO., LTD
Sunyard Technology Building No
3888 Jiangnan Avenue High-tech
Zone, Binjiang Dist, Hangzhou,
310053, Zhejiang, China
Tel.: (86) 57156686888
Web Site: https://www.sunyard.com
Year Founded: 1996
600571—(SHG)
Rev.: $215,934,835
Assets: $254,305,846
Liabilities: $90,812,391
Net Worth: $163,493,455
Earnings: ($21,006,353)
Emp.: 3,000
Fiscal Year-end: 12/31/22
Software Development Services
N.A.I.C.S.: 541511
Geng Junling (Chm)

Subsidiaries:

Dalian Sunyard Software Co., Ltd. (1)
Rm 1102 Nami Tower 3 Huoju Rd, Hi-Tech Zone, Dalian, 116023, China
Tel.: (86) 411 88120508
Software Development Services
N.A.I.C.S.: 541511
Zhang Jack (Mgr)

Hangzhou Sunyard Computer Services Co., Ltd. (1)
6F 452 6th Ave High Technology Incubator Building, Hangzhou Economic & Technology Development Zone, Hangzhou, 310000, China
Tel.: (86) 571 28927512
Software Development Services
N.A.I.C.S.: 541511

Hangzhou Sunyard Sanjia System Engineering Co., Ltd. (1)
Sunyard Science & Technology Building
3888 Jiangnan Ave, Binjiang District,
Hangzhou, 310053, China
Tel.: (86) 57156686769
Business Channel Development Services
N.A.I.C.S.: 541613

Hangzhou Tianming Environmental Protection Engineering Co., Ltd. (1)
No 160 South of 11th Street Economic & Technological Development Zone, Hangzhou, Zhejiang, China
Tel.: (86) 57186799888
Web Site: http://www.hztianming.com
Emp.: 500
Environment Protection Product Mfr
N.A.I.C.S.: 334512
Yu Yunjie (Deputy Mng Dir)

SUNZEN BIOTECH BERHAD
No 11 Jalan Anggerik Mokara 31/47,
Kota Kemuning, 40460, Shah Alam,
Selangor, Malaysia
Tel.: (60) 51229333 MY
Web Site: https://www.sunzen.com.my
Year Founded: 1998
SUNZEN—(KLS)
Rev.: $20,549,037
Assets: $31,948,771
Liabilities: $4,497,064
Net Worth: $27,451,707
Earnings: $1,008,897
Emp.: 36
Fiscal Year-end: 12/31/22
Animal Pharmaceutical Products Researcher, Developer, Mfr & Distr
N.A.I.C.S.: 325412
Yek Ming Teo (CEO & Mng Dir-Grp)

Subsidiaries:

Amplio Ingredients Sdn. Bhd. (1)
21 Jalan Perindustrian SIS 1 Taman Perindustrian SIS 228, 43700, Beranang, Selangor, Malaysia
Tel.: (60) 387270388
Web Site: http://amplio-ingredients.com
Food Product Whslr
N.A.I.C.S.: 424490
Low Yuan Heng (Founder & CEO)

Ecolite Biotech Manufacturing Sdn. Bhd. (1)
Lot 9284 & 9285 Jalan Yong Peng, Sri Medan, 83400, Batu Pahat, Johor, Malaysia (100%)
Tel.: (60) 74850055
Web Site: https://about.ecolite.com.my
Health Foods Retailer
N.A.I.C.S.: 456191

Finsource Credit (M) Sdn. Bhd. (1)
Finsource Credit 22-08 Tower B The Vertical Business Suite, Jalan Kerinchi Bangsar South, 59200, Kuala Lumpur, Malaysia
Tel.: (60) 327124333
Web Site: https://www.finsourcecredit.com
Financial Services
N.A.I.C.S.: 522320

Sunzen Corporation Sdn. Bhd. (1)
11 Jalan Anggerik Mokara 31/47, Kota Kemuning, 40460, Shah Alam, Selangor, Malaysia
Tel.: (60) 351229333
Web Site: https://www.sunzen.com.my
Sales Range: $25-49.9 Million
Emp.: 40
Veterinary Medicinal Products Mfr
N.A.I.C.S.: 325411

SUOFEIYA HOME COLLECTION CO., LTD.
Floor 10 West Bldg Chuangzhan
Center, Tianhe, Guangzhou, 511358,
Guangdong, China
Tel.: (86) 19966204429
Web Site: https://global.suofeiya.com
Year Founded: 1981
002572—(SSE)
Rev.: $1,575,644,813
Assets: $1,692,776,658
Liabilities: $844,242,792
Net Worth: $848,533,865
Earnings: $149,428,239
Emp.: 5,360
Fiscal Year-end: 12/31/22
Household & Kitchen Furniture Mfr
N.A.I.C.S.: 337122
Jiang Ganjun (Chm)

SUOMEN OSUUSKAUPPOJEN KESKUSKUNTA
Fleminginkatu 34, PO Box 1, FI-
00088, Helsinki, Finland
Tel.: (358) 10768011 FI
Web Site: http://www.s-kanava.fi
Year Founded: 1904
Rev.: $8,353,670,265
Assets: $1,979,099,837

SUOMINEN OYJ

Liabilities: $1,223,397,784
Net Worth: $755,702,053
Earnings: $55,702,573
Emp.: 5,474
Fiscal Year-end: 12/31/18
Holding Company
N.A.I.C.S.: 551112
Jorma Bergholm (Mng Dir-Helsinki)

Subsidiaries:

Coop Trading A/S (1)
Helgeshoj Alle 57, Hoje Taastrup, 2620, Denmark
Tel.: (45) 8853 0000
Web Site: http://www.cooptrading.com
Internordic Procurement of Branded Products
N.A.I.C.S.: 455219
Rene Sandberg (Mgr-Strategy & Coordination)

Helsinki Cooperative Society Elanto (1)
Kaupintie 14, 00440, Helsinki, Finland
Tel.: (358) 10 76 600
Web Site: http://www.s-kanava.fi
Grocery Distr
N.A.I.C.S.: 445110

Subsidiary (Domestic):

Oy Center-Inn Ab (2)
Aleksanterinkatu 46, Helsinki, 00100, Finland
Tel.: (358) 9856 8560
Web Site: http://www.center-inn.fi
Grocery Distr
N.A.I.C.S.: 445110

Inex Partners Oy (1)
Karantie 2, 02630, Espoo, Finland
Tel.: (358) 10 76 87000
Web Site: http://www.inex.fi
Semiconductor Product Whslr
N.A.I.C.S.: 423690
Eija Hakosalo (Mgr-Sourcing)

S-Business Oy (1)
PL 80, 0088, Helsinki, Finland
Tel.: (358) 10 768 0820
Web Site: http://www.s-business.fi
Smartcard Mfr
N.A.I.C.S.: 326199

SUOMEN TEOLLISUUSSI-JOITUS OY
Porkkalankatu 1, PO Box 685, FIN-
00101, Helsinki, Finland
Tel.: (358) 96803680 FI
Web Site: http://www.tesi.fi
Year Founded: 1995
Equity Investment Firm
N.A.I.C.S.: 523999
Jani Ramo (Co-CFO)

SUOMINEN OYJ
Keilaranta 13 A, FI-00180, Helsinki,
Finland
Tel.: (358) 10214300 FI
Web Site: https://www.suominen.fi
SUY1V—(HEL)
Rev.: $532,374,272
Assets: $370,650,766
Liabilities: $213,176,128
Net Worth: $157,474,638
Earnings: ($14,961,148)
Emp.: 703
Fiscal Year-end: 12/31/22
Fibre, Nonwovens, Packaging, Lotions & Other Consumer Products Mfr
N.A.I.C.S.: 325220
Lynda A. Kelly (Sr VP-Bus Dev & Sr VP-Interim-Americas Bus Area)

Subsidiaries:

Suominen US Holding, Inc. (1)
3 Chirnside Rd Bldg D, Windsor Locks, CT 06096-2335 (100%)
Tel.: (860) 292-5600
Web Site: http://www.suominen.com
Holding Company; Regional Managing Office; Nonwoven Fabric Mill & Products Mfr
N.A.I.C.S.: 551112

SUOMINEN OYJ

Suominen Oyj—(Continued)

Subsidiary (Domestic):

Bethune Nonwovens, Inc. (2)
500 Chestnut St, Bethune, SC 29009-0982
Tel.: (843) 334-6211
Nonwoven Fabric Mill & Products Mfr
N.A.I.C.S.: 313230

Green Bay Nonwovens, Inc. (2)
1250 Glory Rd, Green Bay, WI 54304
Tel.: (920) 339-9433
Nonwoven Fabric Mill & Products Mfr
N.A.I.C.S.: 313230

Windsor Locks Nonwovens, Inc. (2)
3 Chirnside Rd Bldg D, Windsor Locks, CT 06096-2335
Tel.: (860) 292-5600
Web Site: http://www.Suominen.com
Nonwoven Fabric Mill & Products Mfr
N.A.I.C.S.: 313230

SUPALAI PUBLIC COMPANY LIMITED

Supalai Grand Tower 1011 Rama 3 Road, Chongnonsee Yan Nawa, Bangkok, 10120, Thailand
Tel.: (66) 27258888
Web Site: http://www.supalai.com
SPALI—(THA)
Rev.: $928,832,344
Assets: $2,514,179,469
Liabilities: $1,011,823,337
Net Worth: $1,502,356,132
Earnings: $177,586,328
Emp.: 1,776
Fiscal Year-end: 12/31/23
Property Development & Real Estate Construction Services
N.A.I.C.S.: 531390
Prateep Tangmatitham (Chm & CEO)

SUPER BAKERS (INDIA) LTD.

Near Hirawadi Char Rasta Anil Starch Mills Road, Ahmedabad, 380 025, Gujarat, India
Tel.: (91) 7922201011
Web Site:
https://www.superbread.com
530735—(BOM)
Rev.: $91,482
Assets: $584,302
Liabilities: $30,713
Net Worth: $553,589
Earnings: $38,561
Fiscal Year-end: 03/31/22
Wheat Flour Mfr & Distr
N.A.I.C.S.: 311211
Shankar Tekchand Ahuja (Chm)

SUPER CENTURY INVESTMENTS LIMITED

c/o Simsen International Corp Ltd
26th Floor Top Glory Tower, 262 Gloucester Road, Causeway Bay, China (Hong Kong)
Tel.: (852) 28662332
Year Founded: 2009
Investment Holding Company
N.A.I.C.S.: 551112
Xiadong Peng (Owner)

SUPER CLUBS INTERNATIONAL LTD.

2 St. Lucia Avenue, Kingston, 5, Jamaica
Tel.: (876) 18769601750
Web Site: http://www.superclubs.org
Sales Range: $350-399.9 Million
Emp.: 3,000
Resort & Hotel Owner & Operator
N.A.I.C.S.: 721110
John Issa (Chm)

SUPER CROP SAFE LIMITED

C-1/290 GIDC Estate Phase-1 Naroda, Ahmedabad, 382330, Gujarat, India
Tel.: (91) 7922823907
Web Site:
https://www.supercropsafe.com
Year Founded: 1987
530883—(BOM)
Rev.: $2,703,519
Assets: $7,148,636
Liabilities: $4,062,179
Net Worth: $3,086,458
Earnings: $121,360
Emp.: 60
Fiscal Year-end: 03/31/23
Insecticide & Fungicide Mfr & Distr
N.A.I.C.S.: 325320
Ambalal B. Patel (Exec Dir)

SUPER DRAGON TECHNOLOGY CO., LTD.

No 323 Huanke Rd, Guanyin Dist, Taoyuan, 328, Taiwan
Tel.: (886) 34736566
Web Site: http://www.sdti.com.tw
Year Founded: 1996
9955—(TAI)
Rev.: $37,283,167
Assets: $92,378,786
Liabilities: $49,447,756
Net Worth: $42,931,029
Earnings: ($2,673,043)
Fiscal Year-end: 12/31/23
Industrial Waste Removal & Disposal Services
N.A.I.C.S.: 562119
Chieh-Hsin Wu (Chm & Pres)

SUPER ENERGY CORPORATION PUBLIC COMPANY LIMITED

223/61 14th Floor Country Complex Building A Sanphawut Road, Bangna, Bangkok, 10260, Thailand
Tel.: (66) 23615599
Web Site:
https://www.supercorp.co.th
Year Founded: 1994
SUPER—(THA)
Rev.: $280,840,034
Assets: $2,385,117,094
Liabilities: $1,744,439,935
Net Worth: $640,677,158
Earnings: ($3,439,719)
Emp.: 634
Fiscal Year-end: 12/31/23
Electric Power Generation
N.A.I.C.S.: 221114
Kamtorn Udomritthiruj (Vice Chm)

SUPER FASTENING SYSTEM (SHANGHAI) CO., LTD.

No 39 Lane 100 Fengshuo Road, Jiading, Shanghai, 201822, China
Tel.: (86) 2159907242
Web Site:
http://www.shchaojie.com.cn
Year Founded: 2001
301005—(SSE)
Rev.: $65,943,788
Assets: $159,366,847
Liabilities: $37,512,451
Net Worth: $121,854,396
Earnings: $8,718,040
Emp.: 300
Fiscal Year-end: 12/31/22
Hardware Product Mfr & Distr
N.A.I.C.S.: 332510
Guangdong Song (Chm & Gen Mgr)

SUPER FINE KNITTERS LIMITED

C-5 Focal Point Phase -5, Ludhiana, 141010, Punjab, India
Tel.: (91) 1615049900
Web Site:
https://www.superfineknitters.com
540269—(BOM)
Rev.: $3,341,946
Assets: $4,909,650
Liabilities: $2,177,431
Net Worth: $2,732,219
Earnings: $6,159
Emp.: 62
Fiscal Year-end: 03/31/23
Textile Product Mfr & Distr
N.A.I.C.S.: 315120
Ajit Kumar Lakra (Mng Dir)

SUPER GROUP LIMITED

27 Impala Road, Chislehurston, Sandton, 2196, South Africa
Tel.: (27) 115234000
Web Site:
https://www.supergroup.co.za
SPG—(JSE)
Rev.: $3,154,797,998
Assets: $3,959,335,728
Liabilities: $2,804,365,784
Net Worth: $1,154,969,943
Earnings: $118,464,610
Emp.: 14,934
Fiscal Year-end: 06/30/22
Supply Chain Management Services
N.A.I.C.S.: 493110
Peter Mountford (CEO)

Subsidiaries:

Africa Truck Accident Repairs (Pty) Limited (1)
1 York Place, Pinetown, 3620, Kwazulu-Natal, South Africa
Tel.: (27) 317013822
Web Site: http://www.htar.co.za
Sales Range: $25-49.9 Million
Emp.: 100
Truck Repair & Maintenance Services
N.A.I.C.S.: 811111
Andre Herman (Owner)

Arnold Chatz Cars Constantia Kloof Proprietary Limited (1)
15 JG Strydom Rd, Constantia Kloof, Roodepoort, South Africa
Tel.: (27) 108238154
Web Site: https://www.arnoldchatz.co
Car Retailer
N.A.I.C.S.: 441110

Baleka Freight Proprietary Limited (1)
28 Karee Road, kraaifontein, Cape Town, 7570, South Africa
Tel.: (27) 614051525
Web Site: https://www.balekafreight.co.za
Dry Cargo Transportation Services
N.A.I.C.S.: 484110
Carlo Etzebeth (Controller)

Cargoworks Proprietary Limited (1)
7 Graphite Close, Driehoek, Germiston, 1401, South Africa
Tel.: (27) 118731212
Web Site: https://www.cargoworks.co.za
Bulk Transportation Services
N.A.I.C.S.: 484110
Douglas Driver (Owner)

Digistics Proprietary Limited (1)
Waterfall Distribution Campus 2 Bridal Veil Road, Midrand, 1686, South Africa
Tel.: (27) 116633500
Web Site: https://www.digistics.co.za
Emp.: 1,240
Value Added Logistics Services
N.A.I.C.S.: 541614

EuroAvionics UK Ltd (1)
Maydwell Avenue, Slinfold, London, RH13 0AS, Sussex, United Kingdom
Tel.: (44) 1403790018
Web Site: http://www.euroavionicsuk.com
Software Development Services
N.A.I.C.S.: 541511

Extreme Lifestyle Centre (Pty) Limited (1)
Unit 1 Jurgens St, Isando, 1600, Gauteng, South Africa
Tel.: (27) 115655300

INTERNATIONAL PUBLIC

Sales Range: $50-74.9 Million
Emp.: 92
Conference Center Management Services
N.A.I.C.S.: 531120

FleetAfrica (Pty) Limited (1)
Super Park Cnr Barbara & Brollo Road, Isando, South Africa
Tel.: (27) 113873335
Web Site: http://www.fleetafrica.co.za
Sales Range: $25-49.9 Million
Emp.: 50
Fleet Leasing & Management Services
N.A.I.C.S.: 532112
Craig Soper (Mgr-Application Sys)

GLS Supply Chain Equipment Proprietary Limited (1)
28 Karee Road, kraaifontein, Cape Town, 7570, South Africa
Tel.: (27) 219870190
Web Site: https://www.gls-equipment.com
Material Handling Equipment Distr
N.A.I.C.S.: 423830

IN tIME Express Logistik GmbH (1)
Am Kirchhorster See 1, 30916, Isernhagen, Germany
Tel.: (49) 513697570
Web Site: http://www.intime.de
Emp.: 600
Logistics Consulting Servies
N.A.I.C.S.: 541614

Lieben Logistics Proprietary Limited (1)
28 Karee Road, Kraaifontein, Cape Town, 7570, South Africa
Tel.: (27) 219870190
Web Site: https://www.liebenlogistics.co.za
Refrigerated Distribution Services
N.A.I.C.S.: 493120

MDS Collivery Proprietary Limited (1)
58c Webber Street, Selby, Johannesburg, Gauteng, South Africa
Tel.: (27) 112414900
Web Site: https://www.collivery.net
Courier Service
N.A.I.C.S.: 492110

MzansiGo South Africa Proprietary Limited (1)
The Woodmill Office Park Vredenburg Road, Stellenbosch, Western Cape, South Africa
Tel.: (27) 814322300
Web Site: https://mzansigo.co.za
Logistic Services
N.A.I.C.S.: 541614

Phola Coaches Proprietary Limited (1)
2 Schonland Drive Ferrobank Leraatsfontein, PO Box 13587, Witbank, 2271, South Africa
Tel.: (27) 136962667
Web Site: https://www.pholacoaches.co.za
Emp.: 500
Bus Transport & Charter Services
N.A.I.C.S.: 485210
Julius Sebola (Mgr-)

SG Coal Proprietary Limited (1)
8 Hektaar Street, Middelburg, 1050, South Africa
Tel.: (27) 132462905
Web Site: https://www.sgcoal.co.za
Courier Service
N.A.I.C.S.: 492110

SG Fleet Group Limited (1)
20 Bridge Street, Pymble, 2073, NSW, Australia (50.6%)
Tel.: (61) 294941000
Web Site: https://www.sgfleet.com
Rev.: $752,555,419
Assets: $2,231,726,086
Liabilities: $1,837,284,982
Net Worth: $394,441,104
Earnings: $59,869,791
Emp.: 1,100
Fiscal Year-end: 06/30/2024
Fleet Leasing & Management Services
N.A.I.C.S.: 532112
Andy Mulcaster (Mng Dir-Australia)

SG Fleet Investments Pty Ltd (1)
Level 2 Building 3 20 Bridge St, Pymble,

2073, NSW, Australia
Tel.: (61) 1300138235
Web Site: https://www.sgfleet.com
Fleet Leasing & Management Services
N.A.I.C.S.: 532112

SG Fleet Proprietary Limited (1)
Level 2 Building 3 20 Bridge Street,
Pymble, Sydney, NSW, Australia
Tel.: (61) 294941000
Web Site: https://www.sgfleet.com
Vehicle Leasing Services
N.A.I.C.S.: 532120

Trans-Logo-Tech (TLT) GmbH (1)
Hans-Gruninger-Weg 11, 71706, Markgroningen, Germany
Tel.: (49) 7145142000
Web Site: https://www.tlt-group.com
Logistics Consulting Servies
N.A.I.C.S.: 541614
Alen Cevra (Mng Dir)

Transport Brokers (Pty) Limited (1)
3 Atlas Rd, Germiston, 1429, Gauteng,
South Africa
Tel.: (27) 112550334
Sales Range: $25-49.9 Million
Emp.: 30
Used Trucks Procurement & Sales
N.A.I.C.S.: 441120
Craig Strydom (Mng Dir)

Zultrans Proprietary Limited (1)
69 Riverhorse Road Umgeni Business Park,
PO Box 100, Riverhorse Valley, Durban,
4098, South Africa
Tel.: (27) 315691669
Web Site: https://www.zultrans.co.za
Vehicle Freight Transportation Services
N.A.I.C.S.: 484230
Gavin Cunningham (CEO)

SUPER RETAIL GROUP LIMITED
Tel.: (61) 734827900
Web Site:
http://www.superretailgroup.com.au
SUL—(ASX)
Rev.: $2,646,037,165
Assets: $2,277,576,394
Liabilities: $1,337,844,359
Net Worth: $939,732,035
Earnings: $230,623,190
Emp.: 12,000
Fiscal Year-end: 06/26/21
Automotive & Other Motor Vehicles
Products Sales & Distr
N.A.I.C.S.: 423120
Rebecca Farrell (Gen Counsel & Co-Sec)

Subsidiaries:

BCF Australia Pty Ltd (1)
751 Glympie Road, Lawnton, 4501, QLD,
Australia
Tel.: (61) 734807800
Web Site: http://www.bcf.com.au
Sales Range: $1-4.9 Billion
Emp.: 400
Boating, Camping & Fishing Equipment
Sales & Distr
N.A.I.C.S.: 423910
Nat Cooper (Mgr-Supply Chain Dev)

Goldcross Cycles Pty Ltd. (1)
Showroom 7 Fountain Gate Super Ctr,
Narre Warren, 3805, VIC, Australia
Tel.: (61) 397053333
Web Site: http://www.goldcross.com.au
Sales Range: $25-49.9 Million
Emp.: 30
Bicycles Distr
N.A.I.C.S.: 423110

Macpac New Zealand Limited (1)
4 Mary Muller Drive, PO Box 22-225, Hillsborough, 8022, Christchurch, New Zealand
Tel.: (64) 3 964 9693
Web Site: https://www.macpac.co.nz
Outdoor Goods Distr
N.A.I.C.S.: 459110
Bruce McIntyre (Founder)

Super Cheap Auto Pty Ltd. (1)
751 Gympie Road, Lawnton, 4501, QLD,
Australia

Tel.: (61) 73 881 2800
Web Site:
https://www.supercheapauto.com.au
Sales Range: $100-124.9 Million
Emp.: 350
Automotive Parts & Accessories Distr
N.A.I.C.S.: 441330

Subsidiary (Non-US):

Super Cheap Auto (New Zealand) Pty. Ltd. (2)
180 Savill Drive, PO Box 97059, Mangere
East, Auckland, 2024, New Zealand
Tel.: (64) 80 050 0605
Web Site:
https://www.supercheapauto.co.nz
Sales Range: $25-49.9 Million
Emp.: 49
Automotive Parts & Accessories Retailer
N.A.I.C.S.: 441330

SUPER RIFLE S.P.A.
Viale Matteotti 2b/2c, Barberino di
Mugello, Florence, 50031, Italy
Tel.: (39) 05584761
Web Site: http://www.riflejeans.com
Sales Range: $75-99.9 Million
Emp.: 300
Jean Mfr & Retailer
N.A.I.C.S.: 315250
Sandro Fratini (Pres)

SUPER SALES INDIA LIMITED
34-A Kamaraj Road, Coimbatore, 641
018, Tamil Nadu, India
Tel.: (91) 4222222404
Web Site:
https://www.supersales.co.in
Year Founded: 1981
512527—(BOM)
Sales Range: $25-49.9 Million
Emp.: 881
Yarn, Gears & Gear Box Mfr & Sales
N.A.I.C.S.: 339999
S. K. Radhakrishnan (Officer-Compliance & Sec)

Subsidiaries:

Super Sales India Limited - Marketing Division (1)
34-A Kamaraj Road, Coimbatore, 641 018,
India
Tel.: (91) 422 2222404
Web Site: http://www.supersales.co.in
Sales Range: $25-49.9 Million
Emp.: 50
Industrial Machinery Distr
N.A.I.C.S.: 423830
G. Mani (Mng Dir)

SUPER SPINNING MILLS LTD
Elgi Towers Green Fields 737 D Puliyakulam Road, Coimbatore, 641045,
Tamil Nadu, India
Tel.: (91) 4222311711
Web Site:
https://www.superspinning.com
SUPERSPIN—(NSE)
Rev.: $7,412,987
Assets: $24,868,799
Liabilities: $10,721,802
Net Worth: $14,146,997
Earnings: ($746,450)
Emp.: 156
Fiscal Year-end: 03/31/21
Spinning
N.A.I.C.S.: 313310
Sumanth Ramamurthi (Chm & Mng Dir)

Subsidiaries:

ELGI Building Products Ltd. (1)
ELGI Towers, No 737 Puliakulam Rd, Coimbatore, 641045, Tamil Nadu, India
Tel.: (91) 4224351711
Web Site: http://www.saraelgi.com
Sales Range: $25-49.9 Million
Emp.: 50
Textile Services
N.A.I.C.S.: 314999

ELGI Electric & Industries Ltd. (1)
737 - D Puliakulam Road, Puliakulam Rd,
Coimbatore, 641 045, Tamil Nadu, India
Tel.: (91) 4224351711
Web Site: http://www.elgielectric.com
Sales Range: $25-49.9 Million
Emp.: 30
Electronic Products Mfr
N.A.I.C.S.: 334515
Sumanth Ramamurthi (Mng Dir)

ELGI Software & Technologies Ltd. (1)
ELGI Towers 737 D Green Fields, No 737
Puliakulam Road, Coimbatore, 641 045,
Tamil Nadu, India
Tel.: (91) 422 311711
Web Site: http://www.saraelgi.com
Data Processing Services
N.A.I.C.S.: 518210

ELGI Treads (I) Ltd. (1)
2000 Trichy Rd, Singanallur, Coimbatore,
641005, Tamil Nadu, India
Tel.: (91) 422 4321000
Web Site: http://www.elgitread.co.in
Sales Range: $25-49.9 Million
Emp.: 100
Tire Repair & Maintenance Services
N.A.I.C.S.: 326212
Sudharshan Varatharaj (Mng Dir)

ELGI Ultra Industries Ltd. (1)
India House 1443/1 Trichy Rd, Coimbatore,
641 018, Tamil Nadu, India
Tel.: (91) 4222304141
Web Site: http://www.elgiultra.com
Sales Range: $1-9.9 Million
Emp.: 200
Conveyor Belts Mfr
N.A.I.C.S.: 326220

Super Spinning Mills Ltd - Unit SARA APPAREL & FASHION (1)
SF 458 Poonthottam Thekklur Avinashi TK
Tirupur Dist, 641 654, Coimbatore, Tamil
Nadu, India
Tel.: (91) 4296255030
Sales Range: $150-199.9 Million
Emp.: 800
Cotton Yarn Mfr
N.A.I.C.S.: 313110

Super Spinning Mills Ltd - Unit Super A (1)
Kirikera, Hindupur, 515 211, Andhra
Pradesh, India
Tel.: (91) 8556220522
Web Site: http://www.superspinning.com
Sales Range: $350-399.9 Million
Emp.: 2,000
Cotton Yarn Mfr
N.A.I.C.S.: 313110

Super Spinning Mills Ltd - Unit Super B (1)
Elgi Towers Green Fields 737 D Puliyakulam Road, Coimbatore, 641045, Andhra
Pradesh, India
Tel.: (91) 4222311711
Web Site: http://www.superspinning.com
Sales Range: $150-199.9 Million
Emp.: 1,000
Cotton Yarn Mfr
N.A.I.C.S.: 313110

Super Spinning Mills Ltd - Unit Super C (1)
C Gudalur, 624 620, Vedasandur, Tamil
Nadu, India
Tel.: (91) 4551225310
Web Site:
http://www.superspinningmills.com
Sales Range: $200-249.9 Million
Emp.: 700
Cotton Yarn Mfr
N.A.I.C.S.: 541820

SUPER STRONG HOLDINGS LIMITED
Unit D 3/F Freder Centre 3 Mok
Cheong Street Tokwawan, Kowloon,
China (Hong Kong)
Tel.: (852) 2 332 0521 Ky
Web Site: http://www.wmcl.com.hk
Year Founded: 2015

8262—(HKG)
Rev.: $17,888,494
Assets: $23,155,135
Liabilities: $6,438,166
Net Worth: $16,716,969
Earnings: ($2,959,704)
Emp.: 44
Fiscal Year-end: 06/30/21
Building Construction Services
N.A.I.C.S.: 236220
Tung Keung Kwok (Chm)

SUPER SYNCOTEX (INDIA) LTD.
Sadar Bazar Village Khari-Ka-Lamba,
PO Box 3, Dist Bhilwara, Gulabpura,
311021, Rajasthan, India
Tel.: (91) 1483223167
503297—(BOM)
Textile Products Mfr
N.A.I.C.S.: 313310
B. S. Sacheti (Chm & Mng Dir)

SUPER TANNERY LIMITED
187/170 Jajmau Road, Kanpur,
208010, Uttar Pradesh, India
Tel.: (91) 7522000370
Web Site:
https://www.supertannery.com
523842—(BOM)
Rev.: $27,462,430
Assets: $26,928,565
Liabilities: $15,842,252
Net Worth: $11,086,314
Earnings: $759,439
Emp.: 500
Fiscal Year-end: 03/31/23
Leather Accessories Mfr
N.A.I.C.S.: 316990
Iftikharul Amin (Co-Mng Dir)

SUPER TELECOM CO., LTD.
No 1025 1027 Gaopu Road 4th Floor
Gaotang New Area, Guangzhou
Tianhe Software Park, Guangzhou,
510663, Guangdong, China
Tel.: (86) 2080660188
Web Site: https://www.sts.cn
Year Founded: 1998
603322—(SHG)
Rev.: $284,428,343
Assets: $302,810,564
Liabilities: $258,183,020
Net Worth: $44,627,544
Earnings: $2,132,620
Fiscal Year-end: 12/31/22
Telecommunication Servicesb
N.A.I.C.S.: 517810
Jianhua Liang (Chm)

Subsidiaries:

Chengdu Hop Technology Co., Ltd. (1)
No 8 Wuxing 2 Road, Wuhou District,
Chengdu, 610045, China
Tel.: (86) 15828586717
Web Site: https://www.hopcooling.com
Cabinet Air Conditioner Mfr
N.A.I.C.S.: 333415

Guangdong Connectek IOT Tech Co., Ltd. (1) (51%)
One Floor 4 Building Hongtai Wisdom Valley 17 Sicheng Road, Tianhe District,
Guangzhou, China
Tel.: (86) 2035915666
Web Site: https://www.china-code.com
Software Development Services
N.A.I.C.S.: 541511

SUPER TOOL CO., LTD.
158 Minoyama, Naka-ku, Sakai, 599-
8243, Osaka, Japan
Tel.: (81) 722555521
Web Site: https://www.supertool.co.jp
Year Founded: 1918
5990—(TKS)
Rev.: $38,671,942

Super Tool Co., Ltd.—(Continued)
Assets: $86,574,142
Liabilities: $16,128,175
Net Worth: $70,445,966
Earnings: $2,015,196
Fiscal Year-end: 03/31/24
Machine Tools Mfr
N.A.I.C.S.: 333517
Kazuo Hirano (Pres & CEO)

SUPER TURTLE PUBLIC COMPANY LIMITED
333 Lao Peng Nguan 1 Tower 24th Floor Soi Choeiphuang, Vibhavadi-Rangsit Road Chomphon Chatuchak, Bangkok, 10900, Thailand
Tel.: (66) 20915900
Web Site: https://www.superturtle.co.th
Year Founded: 1996
TURTLE—(THA)
Rev.: $16,406,577
Assets: $124,662,807
Liabilities: $10,897,679
Net Worth: $113,765,129
Earnings: ($8,555,381)
Emp.: 474
Fiscal Year-end: 12/31/23
Children's Book & Media Publisher & Distr
N.A.I.C.S.: 513130
Chaiwat Atsawintarangkun (Chm)

SUPER VALUE CO., LTD.
Miya-cho 4-129 Omiya-ku, Saitama, 330-0802, Japan
Tel.: (81) 487783222
Web Site: http://www.supervalue.jp
Year Founded: 1996
3094—(TKS)
Sales Range: $350-399.9 Million
Emp.: 549
Supermarket & Home Improvement Store Owner & Operator
N.A.I.C.S.: 445110
Shichiro Kishimoto (Pres)

SUPER VALUE FOOD STORES LIMITED
Golden Gates Shopping Centre Carmichael and Blue Hill Roads, Nassau, Bahamas
Tel.: (242) 3615220
Year Founded: 1967
Sales Range: $125-149.9 Million
Emp.: 800
Grocery Store Operator
N.A.I.C.S.: 445110
Rupert W. Roberts Jr. (Pres)

SUPER-DRAGON ENGINEERING PLASTICS CO., LTD.
Longtan Jubao Industrial Zone Village, Aotou Town Conghua, Guangzhou, 510945, Guangdong, China
Tel.: (86) 2087886338
Web Site: https://www.gzselon.com
Year Founded: 1998
301131—(SSE)
Rev.: $183,013,001
Assets: $199,969,221
Liabilities: $91,051,927
Net Worth: $108,917,294
Earnings: $4,843,028
Fiscal Year-end: 12/31/22
Plastic Product Mfr & Distr
N.A.I.C.S.: 326199
Yuanzeng Hao (Chm & Gen Mgr)

SUPERACTIVE GROUP COMPANY LIMITED
Unit 1510 15/F West Tower Shun Tak Centre, 168-200 Connaught Road, Central, China (Hong Kong)
Tel.: (852) 23508100   BM
Web Site: http://www.superactive.com.hk
0176—(HKG)
Rev.: $11,313,075
Assets: $140,447,625
Liabilities: $102,661,598
Net Worth: $37,786,028
Earnings: ($12,154,065)
Emp.: 300
Fiscal Year-end: 12/31/22
Investment Management Service
N.A.I.C.S.: 523940
So Lai Yeung (Chm)

SUPERALLOY INDUSTRIAL CO., LTD.
80 Yun-Ko Road Sec 3, Yunlin County, Douliu, 640111, Taiwan
Tel.: (886) 55512288
Web Site: https://www.superalloy.tw
Year Founded: 1994
1563—(TAI)
Lightweight Metal Product Mfr
N.A.I.C.S.: 332999
Huang Tsung-Jung (Chm)

SUPERB SUMMIT INTERNATIONAL GROUP LIMITED
Unit 2801-03 28F Shui On Centre, 6-8 Harbour Road, Wanchai, China (Hong Kong)
Tel.: (852) 3163 2686   Ky
Web Site: http://www.ssitimber.com.hk
Year Founded: 2001
Sales Range: $50-74.9 Million
Timber Management Services; Timber Products Mfr & Distr
N.A.I.C.S.: 115310
Jilin Yang (Exec Dir)

SUPERBAG CO., LTD.
5-18-11 Nishi-Ikebukuro, Toshima-ku, Tokyo, 171-0021, Japan
Tel.: (81) 339879244
Web Site: https://www.superbag.co.jp
3945—(TKS)
Rev.: $177,392,570
Assets: $103,096,170
Liabilities: $75,644,840
Net Worth: $27,451,330
Earnings: $5,724,260
Emp.: 102
Fiscal Year-end: 03/31/24
Paper Bag Mfr
N.A.I.C.S.: 322220
Hajime Higuchi (Pres & Chm)

Subsidiaries:
Hokkaido Superbag Co., Ltd. (1)
115 Karamatsu Aoyamacho, Mikasa, 068-2137, Hokkaido, Japan
Tel.: (81) 126722114
Paper Bag Mfr
N.A.I.C.S.: 322220

Shanghai Superbag Co., Ltd. (1)
No 508 Yutang Road Songjiang Industrial Zone, Shanghai, China
Tel.: (86) 2157742880
Paper Bag Distr
N.A.I.C.S.: 424130

SUPERBOWL HOLDINGS LIMITED
18 Ah Hood Road 13-51 Hiap Hoe Building at Zhongshan Park, Singapore, 329983, Singapore
Tel.: (65) 6250 2200
Web Site: http://www.superbowl.com.sg
Sales Range: $10-24.9 Million
Emp.: 20
Holding Company; Bowling Alleys & Other Recreation Facilities Owner, Developer & Operator
N.A.I.C.S.: 551112
Beng To Ho (Chm & CEO)

Subsidiaries:
SuperBowl Development Pte. Ltd. (1)
18 Ah Hood Road 13-51 Hiap Hoe Building At Zhongshan Park, Singapore, 329983, Singapore (100%)
Tel.: (65) 62502200
Web Site: http://www.superbowl.com.sg
Bowling Alleys & Other Recreation Facilities Operator
N.A.I.C.S.: 713950
Poh Ho Teo (Mgr-Ops)

SUPERCART PLC
3 The Mews 16 Hollybush Lane, Sevenoaks, TN13 3TH, Kent, United Kingdom
Tel.: (44) 1732459898
Web Site: http://www.supercartplc.com
Year Founded: 1992
Sales Range: $10-24.9 Million
Emp.: 18
Plastic Shopping Cart Mfr
N.A.I.C.S.: 326199
Michael Wolfe (CEO)

Subsidiaries:
Supercart Australia (Pty.) Ltd. (1)
PO Box 457, Coolum Beach, 4573, QLD, Australia
Tel.: (61) 753511305
Web Site: http://www.supercart.com
Shopping Trolley Mfr
N.A.I.C.S.: 336110

Supercart Europe Limited (Germany) (1)
Klausenburger Str 9, 81677, Munich, Bavaria, Germany
Tel.: (49) 8945472231
Web Site: http://www.supercartplc.com
Shopping Trolley Mfr
N.A.I.C.S.: 336110

Supercart South Africa (Pty.) Ltd. (1)
32 Prospecton Rd, Prospecton, Durban, 4110, Kwa Zulu Natal, South Africa
Tel.: (27) 319135270
Web Site: http://www.supercart.com
Emp.: 15
Shopping Trolley Mfr
N.A.I.C.S.: 336110
Bridget Tencrel (Mgr-Sls)

SUPERCITY REALTY DEVELOPMENT CORPORATION
2 F CSP Building 173 EDSA Barangay Wack Wack, Mandaluyong, Philippines
Tel.: (63) 9322561377
Web Site: https://www.supercity.com.ph
Year Founded: 2000
SRDC—(PHI)
Rev.: $269,040
Assets: $1,358,312
Liabilities: $335,924
Net Worth: $1,022,388
Earnings: ($21,215)
Fiscal Year-end: 12/31/23
Construction Services
N.A.I.C.S.: 236220
Ferdinand Z. Soliman (Chm, Pres & CEO)

SUPERCO S.R.O.
Udolni 212/1, 147 00, Prague, Czech Republic
Tel.: (420) 220950531
Web Site: http://www.superco.cz
Year Founded: 1993
Fellow Road Marking Operator
N.A.I.C.S.: 488490
Erich Schreiber (Mng Dir)

SUPERCOM LTD.
3 Rothschild Blvd, Tel Aviv, 6688106, Israel
Tel.: (972) 98890880   II
Web Site: https://www.supercom.com
Year Founded: 1988
SPCB—(NASDAQ)
Rev.: $17,649,000
Assets: $42,040,000
Liabilities: $38,909,000
Net Worth: $3,131,000
Earnings: ($7,457,000)
Emp.: 122
Fiscal Year-end: 12/31/22
Smart Card Technology Developer, Designer & Marketer
N.A.I.C.S.: 541512
Arie Trabelsi (Pres)

Subsidiaries:
Alvarion Technologies (1)
Web Site: http://www.alvarion.com
Point-to-Multipoint Broadband Wireless Access Services
N.A.I.C.S.: 517810

Subsidiary (Non-US):
Alvarion South Africa (Pty) Ltd (2)
Hazel Close Building 1 Suite 1C 141 Witch Hazel Avenue, Highveld Park, Centurion, 0157, Gauteng, South Africa
Tel.: (27) 12 665 1424
Web Site: http://www.alvarion.com
Point-to-Multipoint Broadband Wireless Access Services
N.A.I.C.S.: 517810

PureRFid Inc. (1)
9817 S 13th St, Oak Creek, WI 53154
Tel.: (414) 301-9435
Web Site: http://www.supercom.com
Emp.: 1
Smart Card Technology Developer, Designer & Marketer
N.A.I.C.S.: 541512

SuperCom Ltd. (1)
Suite 3403 China Resources Building, 26 Harbour Road, Wanchai, China (Hong Kong)
Tel.: (852) 28921327
Web Site: http://www.supercom.com.hk
Sales Range: $25-49.9 Million
Emp.: 10
Smart Card Technology Developer, Designer & Marketer
N.A.I.C.S.: 541512

SUPERCOMNET TECHNOLOGIES BERHAD
Lot 172 Jalan PKNK 3/8 Kawasan Perusahaan, Sungai Petani, 08000, Kedah, Malaysia
Tel.: (60) 43719808   MY
Web Site: https://www.supercomnet.com.my
Year Founded: 1990
SCOMNET—(KLS)
Rev.: $33,504,297
Assets: $75,698,604
Liabilities: $6,095,174
Net Worth: $69,603,430
Earnings: $6,962,574
Emp.: 759
Fiscal Year-end: 12/31/22
Wire & Cable Mfr
N.A.I.C.S.: 331491
Jong-Zone Shiue (Mng Dir)

Subsidiaries:
Supercomal Advanced Cable Sdn. Bhd. (1)
Lot 171 Jalan PKNK 3/8, Kawasan Perusahaan, 08000, Sungai Petani, Kedah, Malaysia
Tel.: (60) 43719808
Communication Wire & Cable Mfr
N.A.I.C.S.: 335929

Supercomal Medical Products Sdn. Bhd. (1)
Lot 171 Jalan PKNK 3/8, Kawasan Perusa-

haan, 08000, Sungai Petani, Kedah, Malaysia
Tel.: (60) 43719808
Web Site: https://www.supercomnet.com.my
Medical Device Mfr
N.A.I.C.S.: 339112

SUPERDRY PLC
Unit 60 The Runnings, Cheltenham, GL51 9NW, Glos, United Kingdom
Tel.: (44) 1242578376   UK
Web Site:
    https://corporate.superdry.com
Year Founded: 1985
SEPGF—(OTCIQ)
Rev.: $755,028,092
Assets: $695,424,184
Liabilities: $572,686,296
Net Worth: $122,737,888
Earnings: ($49,013,692)
Emp.: 2,822
Fiscal Year-end: 04/24/21
Clothing & Clothing Accessories Retailers
N.A.I.C.S.: 458110
Julian Dunkerton *(CEO & Founder)*

Subsidiaries:

SuperGroup Internet Limited   (1)
Unit 60 The Runnings, Cheltenham, GL51 9NW, Gloucestershire, United Kingdom
Tel.: (44) 1242578376
Sales Range: $25-49.9 Million
Emp.: 100
Apparels & Accessories Online Retailer
N.A.I.C.S.: 458110

SuperGroup Retail Ireland Limited   (1)
6-10 Suffolk St 2, Dublin, Ireland
Tel.: (353) 16337636
Sales Range: $25-49.9 Million
Emp.: 22
Fashion Wears Retailer
N.A.I.C.S.: 458110

Superdry Germany GmbH   (1)
Sendlingerstrasse 6, 80331, Munich, Germany
Tel.: (49) 8941 112 2100
Web Site: https://www.stores.superdry.de
Clothing Distr
N.A.I.C.S.: 458110

Superdry Norway A/S   (1)
Stoperiveien 5, 2010, Oslo, Norway
Tel.: (47) 4 550 0925
Web Site:
    https://www.stores.superdrystore.no
Clothing Distr
N.A.I.C.S.: 458110

Superdry Sweden AB   (1)
Lilla Strandvagen 2, 444 31, Stenungsund, Sweden
Tel.: (46) 3 035 0660
Web Site: https://www.superdry.se
Clothing Distr
N.A.I.C.S.: 458110

SUPERFUND GOLD, L.P.
Superfund Office Building, PO Box 1479, Grand Anse, Saint George's, Grenada
Tel.: (473) 439 2418   DE
Web Site: http://www.superfund.com
Year Founded: 2008
Sales Range: Less than $1 Million
Investment Services
N.A.I.C.S.: 523999
Christian Baha *(Founder & Owner)*

SUPERFUND GREEN, L.P.
Superfund Office Building, PO Box 1479, Grand Anse, Saint George's, Grenada
Tel.: (473) 439 2418   DE
Sales Range: Less than $1 Million
Investment Services
N.A.I.C.S.: 523999
Craig Lucas *(Mng Dir)*

SUPERGAS ENERGY LTD.
35 Yad Harutzim st, Netanya, Israel
Tel.: (972) 98308103   II
Web Site:
    https://www.supergasenergy.co.il
Year Founded: 1953
SPGE—(TAE)
Rev.: $193,527,553
Assets: $495,583,399
Liabilities: $262,286,307
Net Worth: $233,297,092
Earnings: $11,674,310
Fiscal Year-end: 12/31/21
Natural Gas Distribution Services
N.A.I.C.S.: 211130

SUPERHOUSE LIMITED
150 Feet Road, Jajmau, Kanpur, 208 010, India
Tel.: (91) 9956040004
Web Site: https://www.superhouse.in
Year Founded: 1980
523283—(BOM)
Rev.: $74,413,753
Assets: $92,310,268
Liabilities: $40,329,949
Net Worth: $51,980,319
Earnings: $3,329,986
Emp.: 1,338
Fiscal Year-end: 03/31/21
Leather Goods Mfr
N.A.I.C.S.: 316990
Mukhtarul Amin *(Chm & Co-Mng Dir)*

Subsidiaries:

Briggs Industrial Footwear Ltd.   (1)
Himalayan House Briggs House 430 Thurmaston Boulevard, South Wigston, Leicester, LE4 9LE, Leicestershire, United Kingdom
Tel.: (44) 1162444700
Web Site: https://www.briggsfootwear.co.uk
Footwear Mfr & Distr
N.A.I.C.S.: 316210

Linea De Seguridad S.L.U   (1)
Tel.: (34) 930185589
Web Site: https://www.securityline.es
Leather Product Mfr
N.A.I.C.S.: 316990

Superhouse (U.K.) Ltd.   (1)
66 Commercial Sq Freemens Common, Leicester, LE2 7SR, United Kingdom
Tel.: (44) 1162756555
Web Site: http://www.superhousegroup.com
Leather Product Mfr
N.A.I.C.S.: 316210
Barbara Dodd *(Acct Mgr)*

Superhouse (USA) International Inc.   (1)
Tel.: (732) 581-0452
Leather Product Mfr
N.A.I.C.S.: 316990

Superhouse GMBH   (1)
Am Buchenbaum 40-42, 47051, Duisburg, Germany
Tel.: (49) 20373994801
Web Site:
    http://www.supoerhousegroup.com
Emp.: 5,000
Leather Product Mfr
N.A.I.C.S.: 316990
Ramit Uppal *(Gen Mgr)*

Superhouse Limited - Accessories Factory No.1   (1)
E-55 Industrial Area Site - I, Unnao, Uttar Pradesh, India
Tel.: (91) 515 2829055
Leather Product Mfr
N.A.I.C.S.: 316990

Superhouse Limited - Breeches Division   (1)
A-14 Sector-65 Phase III, Noida, 201303, Uttar Pradesh, India
Tel.: (91) 120 4647777
Web Site: http://www.superhousegroup.com
Emp.: 500
Leather Product Mfr
N.A.I.C.S.: 316990

Superhouse Limited - Finished Leather Facility   (1)
A-1 Site - II Industrial Area, Unnao, Uttar Pradesh, India
Tel.: (91) 515 2829750
Leather Product Mfr
N.A.I.C.S.: 316990
Zafarul Amin *(Mng Dir)*

Superhouse Limited - Footwear Division - I   (1)
D-15 Industrial Area Site - II, Unnao, 209801, Uttar Pradesh, India
Tel.: (91) 515 2829452
Footwear Mfr
N.A.I.C.S.: 316210

Superhouse Limited - Footwear Division - III   (1)
B-6 I Site-I UPSIDC Industrial Area, Unnao, 209801, Uttar Pradesh, India
Tel.: (91) 515 2829384
Footwear Mfr
N.A.I.C.S.: 316210
Iqbal Hussain *(Deputy Gen Mgr)*

Superhouse Limited - Leather Garment Division - I   (1)
C-10 Sector 58, Noida, 201301, Uttar Pradesh, India
Tel.: (91) 120 4648888
Leather Product Mfr
N.A.I.C.S.: 316990
Afzal Alam *(Gen Mgr)*

Superhouse Limited - Safety Footwear Division - I   (1)
150 Feet Road, Jajmau, Kanpur, 208010, Uttar Pradesh, India
Tel.: (91) 512 2460496
Footwear Mfr
N.A.I.C.S.: 316210
Vinay Sanan *(Exec Dir)*

Superhouse Middle East FZC   (1)
W/H No A1-16 Ajman Free Zone, PO Box 20376, Ajman, United Arab Emirates
Tel.: (971) 167442993
Leather Product Mfr
N.A.I.C.S.: 316990

Surephouse (Uk) Ltd.   (1)
Himalayan House 430, Thurmaston Boulevard, West Leicester, LE4 9LE, United Kingdom
Tel.: (44) 1162756555
Footwear Product Mfr & Distr
N.A.I.C.S.: 316210

Surephouse GmbH   (1)
40-42 Am Buchenbaum, 47051, Duisburg, Germany
Tel.: (49) 20373994801
Footwear Product Mfr & Distr
N.A.I.C.S.: 316210

SUPERIOR ALLOY TECHNOLOGY CO
60 Chemin du Tremblay, Boucherville, J4B 6Z5, QC, Canada
Tel.: (450) 645-1330
Web Site: http://www.supalloy.com
Industrial Machinery Mfr
N.A.I.C.S.: 333248
Rick Daigle *(Pres)*

SUPERIOR CABINETS.
747 46th Street West, Saskatoon, S7L 6A1, SK, Canada
Tel.: (306) 667-6600
Web Site:
    http://www.superiorcabinets.ca
Year Founded: 1980
Rev.: $22,103,338
Emp.: 260
Kitchen Cabinet Mfr
N.A.I.C.S.: 337110
Jack Laninga *(Vice Chm)*

SUPERIOR FINLEASE LIMITED
NS-92 Khasra No 33/21 Ranaji Enclave, Najafgarh, New Delhi, 110085, India
Tel.: (91) 9953798335   In
Web Site:
    https://www.superiorfinlease.com
Year Founded: 1994
539835—(BOM)
Rev.: $268,341
Assets: $5,862,850
Liabilities: $5,410,023
Net Worth: $452,827
Earnings: $39,998
Emp.: 4
Fiscal Year-end: 03/31/23
Finance Management Services
N.A.I.C.S.: 522220
Shipali Gupta *(Co-CEO)*

SUPERIOR INDUSTRIAL ENTERPRISES LIMITED
25 Bazar Lane Bengali Market, New Delhi, 110001, India
Tel.: (91) 1143585000   In
Web Site:
    https://www.superiorindustrial.in
Year Founded: 1991
519234—(BOM)
Rev.: $2,201,417
Assets: $10,979,323
Liabilities: $2,015,873
Net Worth: $8,963,450
Earnings: $389,585
Emp.: 39
Fiscal Year-end: 03/31/21
Corrugated Box Mfr
N.A.I.C.S.: 322211
Kamal Aggarwal *(Mng Dir)*

SUPERIOR MINING INTERNATIONAL CORPORATION
300 - 1055 West Hastings St, Vancouver, V6E 2E9, BC, Canada
Tel.: (515) 401-7479
Web Site:
    https://superiorminingnational.com
SUIFF—(OTCIQ)
Assets: $9,103
Liabilities: $241,782
Net Worth: ($232,679)
Earnings: ($1,110,798)
Fiscal Year-end: 07/31/19
Mineral Exploration Services
N.A.I.C.S.: 213114
Brent Butler *(CEO)*

SUPERIOR PLATING TECHNOLOGY CO., LTD.
7F No151 Xin Hu First Rd, Neihu Dist, Taipei, 114, Taiwan
Tel.: (886) 227926918
Web Site:
    https://thesuperiorplating.com
Year Founded: 1999
8431—(TPE)
Rev.: $36,988,923
Assets: $52,483,428
Liabilities: $19,314,297
Net Worth: $33,169,132
Earnings: $4,595,822
Emp.: 1,300
Fiscal Year-end: 12/31/20
Surface Mining Services
N.A.I.C.S.: 212114
S. P. Lee *(Pres)*

SUPERIOR PLUS CORP.
401 200 Wellington Street West, Toronto, M5V 3C7, ON, Canada
Tel.: (416) 345-8050   AB
Web Site:
    https://www.superiorplus.com
Year Founded: 1996
SPB—(TSX)
Rev.: $1,871,683,128
Assets: $2,785,229,712
Liabilities: $1,758,721,896
Net Worth: $1,026,507,816
Earnings: $142,922,556
Fiscal Year-end: 12/31/21

SUPERIOR PLUS CORP.

Superior Plus Corp.—(Continued)
Investment Holding Company
N.A.I.C.S.: 551112
Inder Minhas (Sr VP-Mergers & Acquisitions)

Subsidiaries:

Central Coast Propane, Inc. (1)
6260 Monterey Rd, Paso Robles, CA 93446
Tel.: (805) 237-1001
Web Site:
http://www.centralcoastpropane.com
Fuel Dealers
N.A.I.C.S.: 457210
Brent Wingett (Pres)

Certarus (USA) Ltd. (1)
757 N Eldridge Pkwy Ste 1200, Houston, TX 77079
Gas & Oil Exploration Services
N.A.I.C.S.: 213112

Certarus Ltd. (1)
3400 308 4th Ave SW, Calgary, T2P 0H7, AB, Canada
Tel.: (403) 930-0123
Web Site: https://certarus.com
Emp.: 300
Gas & Oil Exploration Services
N.A.I.C.S.: 213112

Champagne's Energy Inc. (1)
844 Old Post Rd, Arundel, ME 04046-7911
Tel.: (207) 363-5525
Web Site:
http://www.champagnesenergy.com
Petroleum & Petroleum Products Merchant Whslr
N.A.I.C.S.: 424720

Freeman Gas & Electric Co. Inc. (1)
113 Peake Rd, Roebuck, SC 29376
Tel.: (864) 582-5475
Web Site: http://www.freemangas.com
Sales Range: $25-49.9 Million
Emp.: 20
Propane Gas Distr
N.A.I.C.S.: 221210
Jim Cannon (VP & Gen Mgr)

Holden Oil, Inc. (1)
91 Lynnfield St, Peabody, MA 01960
Tel.: (978) 326-9394
Web Site: http://www.holdenoil.com
Liquefied Petroleum Gas Dealers
N.A.I.C.S.: 457210
Chuck Holden (Pres)

Kamps Propane, Inc. (1)
1929 Moffat Blvd, Manteca, CA 95336
Tel.: (209) 823-8924
Web Site: http://www.kampspropane.com
Rev.: $19,314,164
Emp.: 240
Liquefied Petroleum Gas, Delivered To Customers' Premises
N.A.I.C.S.: 457210

Rymes Heating Oils Inc. (1)
257 Sheep Davis Rd, Concord, NH 03301
Tel.: (603) 228-2224
Web Site: http://www.rymes.com
Retailer of Heating Oils & Propane
N.A.I.C.S.: 457210

Superior Gas Liquids Partnership (1)
308 4th Ave SW Suite 2900, Calgary, T2P 0H7, AB, Canada
Tel.: (403) 218-2970
Web Site:
https://www.superiorgasliquids.com
Gas & Oil Exploration Services
N.A.I.C.S.: 213112

Superior General Partner Inc. (1)
605 5 Ave SW Ste 2820, Calgary, T2P 3H5, AB, Canada
Tel.: (403) 218-2970
Web Site: http://www.superiorplus.com
Holding Company
N.A.I.C.S.: 551112

Subsidiary (Domestic):

Superior Plus LP (2)
840 7 Ave Sw Suite 1400, Calgary, T2P 3G2, AB, Canada
Tel.: (403) 218-2970
Petroleum Product Distr

N.A.I.C.S.: 424720

Subsidiary (Domestic):

Canwest Propane Ltd. (3)
1700 440 2nd Avenue SW, Calgary, T2P 5E9, AB, Canada
Tel.: (403) 206-4100
Web Site: https://www.superiorpropane.com
Propane Distr
N.A.I.C.S.: 221210
Rick Carron (Pres)

Subsidiary (Non-US):

Commercial e Industrial ERCO (Chile) Limitada (3)
Camino Publico Antiguo Km 1 Sector Poniente De La Villa, Collipulli, Angol, Chile
Tel.: (56) 24367091
Web Site: http://www.ercoworldwide.com
Sales Range: $25-49.9 Million
Chemical Products Mfr
N.A.I.C.S.: 325998

Subsidiary (US):

Sheldon Gas Company (3)
1 Harbor Ctr Ste 310, Suisun City, CA 94585
Tel.: (707) 425-2951
Web Site: http://www.sheldongas.com
Petroleum & Petroleum Products Merchant Whslr
N.A.I.C.S.: 424720

Subsidiary (Domestic):

Superior Energy Management Electricity LP (3)
6860 Century Ave E Twr Ste 2001, Mississauga, L5N 2W5, ON, Canada
Tel.: (905) 542-5471
Web Site:
http://www.superiorenergymanage.com
Sales Range: $50-74.9 Million
Emp.: 40
Natural Gas Supply Services
N.A.I.C.S.: 213112

Subsidiary (US):

Superior Plus Energy Services Inc. (3)
224 Valley Creek Blvd, Exton, PA 19341
Tel.: (800) 627-4328
Web Site:
http://www.superiorplusenergy.com
Energy Consulting Services
N.A.I.C.S.: 541690
James Devens (VP-Ops)

Subsidiary (Non-US):

Burnwell Gas of Canada Ltd (4)
2364 Ridgemount Rd, Stevensville, Stevensville, L0S 1S0, ON, Canada
Tel.: (905) 382-2902
Emp.: 2
Warehousing & Storage Services
N.A.I.C.S.: 493110
George Burgman (Gen Mgr)

Subsidiary (US):

Superior Plus Propane (3)
19 Industrial Dr, Florida, NY 10921
Tel.: (845) 651-2662
Web Site:
https://www.superiorpluspropane.com
Propane Dealer
N.A.I.C.S.: 457210

Subsidiary (Domestic):

Superior Propane Inc. (3)
1111 49th Ave NE, Calgary, T2E 8V2, AB, Canada
Tel.: (403) 730-7500
Web Site: http://www.superiorpropane.com
Sales Range: $550-599.9 Million
Emp.: 100
Marketing of Propane, Propane Burning Appliances & Related Services
N.A.I.C.S.: 211130
David Passador (VP-Customer Experience)

Subsidiary (US):

United Liquid Gas Company (3)
425 W Plumb Ln, Reno, NV 89509-5163

Tel.: (800) 726-5747
Web Site:
http://www.unitedpacificenergy.com
Petroleum & Petroleum Products Merchant Whslr
N.A.I.C.S.: 424720

Virginia Propane, Inc. (3)
11211 Air Park Dr, Ashland, VA 23005
Tel.: (804) 798-4243
Web Site:
http://www.superiorplusenergy.com
Propane Dealer
N.A.I.C.S.: 457210

Division (Domestic):

Winroc (3)
4949 51 St SE, Calgary, T2B 3S7, AB, Canada (100%)
Tel.: (403) 236-5583
Web Site: http://www.winroc.com
Sales Range: $25-49.9 Million
Emp.: 35
Construction Products for the Walls & Ceilings Industry Distr
N.A.I.C.S.: 423320

SUPERIOR RESOURCES LIMITED

Unit 8 61 Holdsworth Street, PO Box 189, Brisbane, 4151, QLD, Australia
Tel.: (61) 738472887
Web Site:
https://www.superiorresources.com
SPQ—(ASX)
Assets: $10,878,535
Liabilities: $317,341
Net Worth: $10,561,194
Earnings: ($940,403)
Fiscal Year-end: 06/30/24
Exploring for Copper & Lead
N.A.I.C.S.: 213114
Peter Henry Hwang (Mng Dir)

SUPERLAND GROUP HOLDINGS LIMITED

3 F Yin Da Commercial Building 181 Wai Yip Street, Kwun Tong, Kowloon, China (Hong Kong)
Tel.: (852) 28711265 Ky
Web Site: https://www.superland-group.com
Year Founded: 2004
0368—(HKG)
Holding Company
N.A.I.C.S.: 551112
Nga Ling Ho (Exec Dir)

Subsidiaries:

Success Base Engineering Limited (1)
3/F Yin Da Commercial Building 181 Wai Yip Street, Kwun Tong, Kowloon, China (Hong Kong)
Tel.: (852) 28711265
Web Site: http://www.success-base.com
Emp.: 200
Fitting-out Services
N.A.I.C.S.: 541410

SUPERLON HOLDINGS BERHAD

Lot 2567 Jalan Sungai Jati, 41200, Klang, Selangor Darul Ehsan, Malaysia
Tel.: (60) 333723888
Web Site:
https://www.superlon.com.my
SUPERLN—(KLS)
Rev.: $25,010,427
Assets: $42,913,656
Liabilities: $10,502,198
Net Worth: $32,411,458
Earnings: $2,537,454
Emp.: 25
Fiscal Year-end: 04/30/24
Elastomeric Closed Cell Rubber Insulation Products Mfr
N.A.I.C.S.: 326299

INTERNATIONAL PUBLIC

Jessica H. Liu (CEO & Mng Dir)

Subsidiaries:

Superlon Worldwide Sdn Bhd. (1)
Lot 2567 Jalan Sungai Jati, 41200, Klang, Selangor, Malaysia
Tel.: (60) 333821688
Web Site: https://www.superlon.com.my
Building Materials Mfr
N.A.I.C.S.: 332311

SUPERLOOP LIMITED

Level 1 545 Queen Street, Brisbane, 4000, QLD, Australia
Tel.: (61) 1300558406 AU
Web Site: https://www.superloop.com
SLC—(ASX)
Rev.: $280,800,696
Assets: $368,776,108
Liabilities: $123,233,420
Net Worth: $245,542,688
Earnings: ($9,843,823)
Emp.: 950
Fiscal Year-end: 06/30/24
Dark Fiber Telecommunications Network Designer, Constructor & Operator
N.A.I.C.S.: 237130
Drew Kelton (Bd of Dirs, CEO & Mng Dir)

Subsidiaries:

Acurus Pty. Ltd. (1)
Level 26 150 Lonsdale Street, Melbourne, VIC, Australia
Tel.: (61) 1300885220
Web Site: https://acurus.com.au
Strategic Consulting Services
N.A.I.C.S.: 541611

BigAir Group Pty Ltd (1)
Level 1 203 Pacific Highway, Saint Leonards, 2065, NSW, Australia (100%)
Tel.: (61) 2 9993 1300
Web Site: http://www.bigair.com.au
Wireless Communication Services
N.A.I.C.S.: 517112
Jason Ashton (Founder)

CyberHound Pty. Ltd. (1)
Level 2 895 Ann St, PO Box 396, Fortitude Valley, QLD, Australia
Tel.: (61) 730203330
Web Site: https://cyberhound.com
Cyber Security Services
N.A.I.C.S.: 541513

SUPERMAN RESOURCES INC

520 - 3rd Avenue Sw 30th Floor, Calgary, T2P 0r3, AB, Canada
Tel.: (403) 294-1336
Rev.: $14,300,000
Emp.: 30
Natural Gas Extraction Services
N.A.I.C.S.: 211130
Gordon Phillips (Pres)

SUPERMAP SOFTWARE CO., LTD.

6/F Building 107 No A10 Jiuxianqiao North Road, Chaoyang District, Beijing, 100015, China
Tel.: (86) 1059896503
Web Site: https://www.supermap.com
Year Founded: 1997
300036—(CHIN)
Rev.: $224,034,876
Assets: $617,316,336
Liabilities: $221,924,664
Net Worth: $395,391,672
Earnings: ($47,545,056)
Emp.: 4,000
Fiscal Year-end: 12/31/22
Mapping Software Development Services
N.A.I.C.S.: 541511
Song Guanfu (Gen Mgr)

Subsidiaries:

SuperMap Japan Co., Ltd. (1)

2-27-8 Shiba, Minato-ku, Tokyo, Japan
Tel.: (81) 354197911
Web Site: https://supermap.jp
Software Development Services
N.A.I.C.S.: 541511

SUPERMARKET INCOME REIT PLC
10 Bishops Square 3rd Floor, London, E1 6EG, United Kingdom
Tel.: (44) 2038902500   UK
Web Site:
    https://www.supermarketreit.com
Year Founded: 2017
SUPR—(LSE)
Rev.: $118,269,032
Assets: $2,401,305,914
Liabilities: $889,128,800
Net Worth: $1,512,177,114
Earnings: ($179,899,566)
Fiscal Year-end: 06/30/23
Real Estate Investment Services
N.A.I.C.S.: 531390
Nick Hewson *(Chm)*

SUPERMAX CORPORATION BERHAD
Lot 38 Putra Industrial Park Bukit Rahman Putra, 47000, Sungai Buloh, Selangor Darul Ehsan, Malaysia
Tel.: (60) 361452328
Web Site:
    https://www.supermax.com.my
SUPERMX—(KLS)
Rev.: $665,088,720
Assets: $1,474,346,983
Liabilities: $228,896,139
Net Worth: $1,245,450,844
Earnings: $187,387,802
Emp.: 1,698
Fiscal Year-end: 06/30/22
Glove Mfr
N.A.I.C.S.: 326199
Wai Foong Wong *(Co-Sec)*

Subsidiaries:

Aime Supermax K.K.   (1)
4F 1-7-9 Shin-Yokohama, Kouhoku-Ku, Yokohama, 222-0033, Kanagawa, Japan
Tel.: (81) 454759361
Web Site: https://www.aime.jp
Lens Care Product Distr
N.A.I.C.S.: 456130

Maxter Healthcare Pte. Ltd.   (1)
One Commonwealth Lane 07-01 07-02 and 07-09, Singapore, 149544, Singapore
Tel.: (65) 69113208
Web Site: https://www.aureliagloves.com.sg
Medical & Surgical Glove Distr
N.A.I.C.S.: 423450

Maxwell Glove Manufacturing Berhad   (1)
Lot 6070 Jalan Haji Adbul Manan 6th Miles Off Jalan Meru, 41050, Klang, Selangor, Malaysia
Tel.: (60) 333928811
Web Site: https://www.maxwell.my
Disposable Medical Examination Glove Mfr
N.A.I.C.S.: 339113

SuperVision Optimax Sdn. Bhd.   (1)
Lot 38 Putra Industrial Park, Bukit Rahman Putra, 40160, Sungai Buloh, Malaysia
Tel.: (60) 361452328
Web Site: https://www.supervision.com.my
Contact Len Mfr & Distr
N.A.I.C.S.: 339115

Supermax Global (HK) Limited   (1)
Suite E and F 39/F COS Centre 56 Tsun Yip Street, Kwun Tong, Kowloon, China (Hong Kong)
Tel.: (852) 22350700
Web Site: https://www.supermax.hk
Medical & Dental Glove Mfr & Distr
N.A.I.C.S.: 339113

Supermax Healthcare Canada Incorporated   (1)
1001 Jean-Talon, Saint-Bruno-de-Montarville, J3V 0N3, QC, Canada   (67%)
Tel.: (450) 926-2828
Web Site: https://supermaxcanada.com
Medical & Dental Glove Mfr & Distr
N.A.I.C.S.: 339113

Supermax Healthcare Incorporated   (1)
1899 Sequoia Dr, Aurora, IL 60506
Tel.: (630) 898-8886
Web Site: https://www.aureliagloves.com
Medical & Industrial Glove Mfr
N.A.I.C.S.: 339113
C. K. Tan *(CEO)*

Supermax Healthcare Limited   (1)
Unit 12-16 Titan Drive Fengate, Peterborough, PE1 5XN, United Kingdom
Tel.: (44) 1733615215
Web Site: https://www.aureliagloves.co.uk
Disposable Medical Examination Glove Mfr
N.A.I.C.S.: 339113
Iain Crawford *(Mng Dir)*

SUPERMERCADOS LA FAVORITA C.A.
Avenue General Enrique Via Cotogcha, Quito, Ecuador
Tel.: (593) 22996500
Web Site: http://www.supermaxi.com
Sales Range: $550-599.9 Million
Emp.: 3,800
Supermarket Owner & Operator
N.A.I.C.S.: 445110
Ronald Duran-Ballen *(Chm)*

Subsidiaries:

Rey Holdings Corporation   (1)
Calle 50 and Calle 75 San Francisco 9 Zone, PO Box 0830-00682, Panama, Panama
Tel.: (507) 2705535
Sales Range: Less than $1 Million
Holding Company
N.A.I.C.S.: 551112

SUPERNOVA ADVERTISING LIMITED
Shop No G/28 Ground Floor Om Heera Panna Premises, Andheri W, Mumbai, 400 053, Maharashtra, India
Tel.: (91) 22 69997772
Web Site:
    http://www.supernovaads.com
Year Founded: 2008
Advertising Services
N.A.I.C.S.: 541810
Ambreen Khan *(Mgr-Mktg)*

SUPERNOVA METALS CORP.
400 - 1681 Chestnut Street, Vancouver, V6J 4M6, BC, Canada
Tel.: (604) 669-9553   AB
Web Site:
    https://supernovametals.com
Year Founded: 2000
A1S—(DEU)
Assets: $75,616
Liabilities: $43,386
Net Worth: $32,230
Earnings: ($159,963)
Fiscal Year-end: 12/31/23
Oil & Gas Exploration Services
N.A.I.C.S.: 213112
Sean Christopher McGrath *(CEO)*

SUPERROBOTICS HOLDINGS LTD.
Unit 3811 38/F Shun Tak Centre West Tower 168200 Connaught Road, Central, China (Hong Kong)
Tel.: (852) 22688278   Ky
Year Founded: 2014
8176—(HKG)
Rev.: $505,028
Assets: $2,832,158
Liabilities: $28,376,145
Net Worth: ($25,543,988)
Earnings: ($4,913,723)
Emp.: 35
Fiscal Year-end: 12/31/22
Holding Company
N.A.I.C.S.: 551112
Billy Kin Wah Chan *(Chm & Compliance Officer)*

SUPERROBOTICS LIMITED
Room 1405 14/FChina Merchants Tower, Shun Tak Centre 166-200 Connaught Road Central Sheung Wan, Hong Kong, China (Hong Kong)
Tel.: (852) 31089028   Ky
Web Site:
    http://www.superrobotics.com.hk
Rev.: $11,319,984
Assets: $26,485,333
Liabilities: $23,015,952
Net Worth: $3,469,381
Earnings: ($21,099,432)
Emp.: 228
Fiscal Year-end: 12/31/19
Communication Network Services
N.A.I.C.S.: 517112
Charles Chuen Liang Yang *(Sec)*

Subsidiaries:

Engineering Services Inc.   (1)
11 Allstate Parkway Suite 110, Markham, L3R 9T8, ON, Canada
Tel.: (416) 595-5519
Web Site: http://www.esit.com
Wireless Telecommunication Services
N.A.I.C.S.: 517112
Andrew Goldenberg *(Founder & CTO)*

Shenzhen Anzer Intelligent Engineering Co., Ltd.   (1)
Level 5 and 6 F2 International E-City 1001 Zhongshanyuan Rd, Nanshan District, Shenzhen, Guangdong, China
Tel.: (86) 75586638383
Web Site: http://www.anzer.com.cn
Wireless Telecommunication Services
N.A.I.C.S.: 517112
Andrew A. Goldenberg *(CTO)*

SUPERSHAKTI METALIKS LIMITED
39 Shakespeare Sarani Premlata Building 2rd Floor, Kolkata, 700017, India
Tel.: (91) 3322892734
Web Site:
    https://www.supershaktimetalik.com
Year Founded: 2012
541701—(BOM)
Rev.: $87,886,338
Assets: $36,629,279
Liabilities: $8,183,250
Net Worth: $28,446,028
Earnings: $3,992,794
Emp.: 107
Fiscal Year-end: 03/31/23
Wire Rod Mfr
N.A.I.C.S.: 331221
Dilipp Agarwal *(Chm)*

SUPERSONIC IMAGINE SA
Les Jardins de la Duranne Bat E&F 510 Rue Rene Descartes, 13857, Aix-en-Provence, France
Tel.: (33) 4 42 99 24 24
Web Site:
    http://www.supersonicimagine.com
Year Founded: 2005
SSI—(EUR)
Sales Range: $10-24.9 Million
Medical Imaging Products Mfr
N.A.I.C.S.: 334510
Jacques Souquet *(Co-Founder, Chief Strategic & Innovation Officer & Exec VP)*

Subsidiaries:

SuperSonic Imagine (Shanghai) Medical Devices Co. Ltd.   (1)
Room 2304 Block D Ocean International Dong SiHuan ZhongLu, Chaoyang District, Beijing, 100025, China
Tel.: (86) 1085861023
Emp.: 49
Ultrasound Device Mfr
N.A.I.C.S.: 334510

SuperSonic Imagine Ltd.   (1)
18 Upper Walk, Virginia Water, GU25 4SN, Surrey, United Kingdom
Tel.: (44) 8456434516
Ultrasound Imaging System Distr
N.A.I.C.S.: 423450
David Rose *(Gen Mgr)*

SuperSonic Imagine, GmbH   (1)
Zeppelinsrt 71-73, 81669, Munich, Germany
Tel.: (49) 8936036844
Ultrasound Device Mfr
N.A.I.C.S.: 334510

SUPERSTYLE FURNITURE LTD.
123 Ashbridge Circle, Woodbridge, L4L 3R5, ON, Canada
Tel.: (905) 850-6060
Web Site:
    http://www.superstylefurniture.com
Year Founded: 1967
Rev.: $12,259,238
Emp.: 130
Upholstered Furniture Mfr
N.A.I.C.S.: 337121
Danny Colalillo *(Pres)*

SUPERTEX INDUSTRIES LTD.
Balkrishna Krupa 2nd Floor 45/49 Babu Genu Road Princess Street, Mumbai, 400002, Maharashtra, India
Tel.: (91) 2222095630
Web Site: https://www.supertex.in
526133—(BOM)
Rev.: $8,304,142
Assets: $9,229,459
Liabilities: $5,644,710
Net Worth: $3,584,749
Earnings: $6,247
Emp.: 63
Fiscal Year-end: 03/31/23
Textile Machinery & Products Mfr
N.A.I.C.S.: 333248
Ramesh Kumar Mishra *(Chm & Mng Dir)*

SUPORT LOGISTIC BUCURESTI SA
Str Teius Nr 73-77 Sector 5, Bucharest, Romania
Tel.: (40) 214203472
SLBB—(BUC)
Rev.: $77,902
Assets: $491,778
Liabilities: $21,064
Net Worth: $470,714
Earnings: $4,254
Emp.: 3
Fiscal Year-end: 12/31/23
Security Guard Services
N.A.I.C.S.: 561612
Bogdan Mihai Stoicescu *(Pres & Gen Mgr)*

SUPPLY NETWORK LIMITED
Tel.: (61) 286248077   AU
Web Site:
    https://www.supplynetwork.com.au
SNL—(ASX)
Rev.: $124,593,987
Assets: $89,759,925
Liabilities: $51,999,017
Net Worth: $37,760,908
Earnings: $10,608,667
Emp.: 188
Fiscal Year-end: 06/30/21
Commercial Vehicle Industry Sales
N.A.I.C.S.: 423120
Peter William Gill *(Sec)*

SUPPLY NETWORK LIMITED

Supply Network Limited—(Continued)

Subsidiaries:

Globac Limited (1)
1-22 Turnbull close pemulwuy, Guildford, 2145, NSW, Australia
Tel.: (61) 287242150
Web Site: http://www.globac.com.au
Sales Range: $50-74.9 Million
Emp.: 100
Break Friction Parts Whslr
N.A.I.C.S.: 423110
Jeff Stawart (Mng Dir)

Multispares Limited (1)
1 Turnbull Close, Pemulwuy, Sydney, 2145, NSW, Australia
Tel.: (61) 286248001
Web Site: https://www.multispares.com.au
Emp.: 75
Truck & Bus Parts Distr
N.A.I.C.S.: 336110
Geoff Stewart (Mng Dir)

Multispares N.Z. Limited (1)
9 Vestey Drive Mt Wellington, Auckland, 1060, New Zealand
Tel.: (64) 92700715
Web Site: https://www.multispares.co.nz
Sales Range: $25-49.9 Million
Emp.: 6
Truck & Bus Parts Distr
N.A.I.C.S.: 336110

SUPPLY@ME CAPITAL PLC

Eastcastle House 27/28 Eastcastle Street, London, W1W 8DH, United Kingdom
Tel.: (44) 1329243243
Web Site:
  https://www.supplymecapital.com
Year Founded: 1994
SYME—(LSE)
Rev.: $174,198
Assets: $10,535,218
Liabilities: $13,091,391
Net Worth: ($2,556,173)
Earnings: ($12,469,073)
Emp.: 19
Fiscal Year-end: 12/31/22
Software Publisher
N.A.I.C.S.: 513210
Alessandro Zamboni (Founder & CEO)

Subsidiaries:

Tradeflow Capital Management Pte. Ltd. (1)
10 Marina Boulevard 08-05 MBFC Tower 2, Singapore, 018983, Singapore
Tel.: (65) 31052063
Investment Management Service
N.A.I.C.S.: 522320

SUPPLYON AG

Ludwigstrasse 49, 85399, Hallbergmoos, Germany
Tel.: (49) 811999970
Web Site: http://www.supplyon.com
Year Founded: 2000
Sales Range: $25-49.9 Million
Emp.: 150
Supply Chain Management Solutions
N.A.I.C.S.: 513210
Markus Quicken (CEO)

Subsidiaries:

SupplyOn Consulting (Shanghai) Co., Ltd. (1)
Great Wall Building Suite 4502 3000 North Zhongshan Road, Putuo District, Shanghai, 200063, China
Tel.: (86) 21 6040 2280
Emp.: 11
Software Development Services
N.A.I.C.S.: 541511
Zixi Zheng (Gen Mgr)

SupplyOn North America Inc. (1)
7 W Sq Lk Rd, Bloomfield Hills, MI 48302
Tel.: (248) 758-2300
Software Development Services

N.A.I.C.S.: 541511
John Kay (Owner)

SUPPORT BITTIYA SANSTHA LIMITED

Itahari 4, Sunsari, Inaruwa, Nepal
Tel.: (977) 25588177
Web Site:
  https://www.supportfinance.com.np
Year Founded: 2014
SMB—(NEP)
Sales Range: Less than $1 Million
Insurance Advisory Services
N.A.I.C.S.: 524298
Pradip Adhikari (Chm)

SUPPORTINGSMALLBUSINESS, INC.

15 Gottenham St, Glebe, 2037, NSW, Australia
Tel.: (61) 418236985
Investment Services
N.A.I.C.S.: 523999
George Sparsis (Pres & Treas)

SUPPRO CO LTD

27 Gangnam-daero Seocho-gu, Seoul, Korea (South)
Tel.: (82) 263002444
Seedling Services
N.A.I.C.S.: 111421
Chai Il (CEO)

SUPRA PACIFIC FINANCIAL SERVICES LTD.

No 3 Ground Floor Building No 12 Amar Niketan Nr JB Nagar Post Office, JB Nagar Andheri East, Mumbai, 400059, India
Tel.: (91) 8879471948
Web Site:
  https://www.suprapacific.com
Year Founded: 1986
540168—(BOM)
Rev.: $1,482,321
Assets: $9,656,879
Liabilities: $7,090,990
Net Worth: $2,565,889
Earnings: $30,909
Emp.: 174
Fiscal Year-end: 03/31/23
Asset Management Services
N.A.I.C.S.: 523940
Kishor Amichand Shah (Chm & Mng Dir)

SUPRA TRENDS LIMITED

112 A-Block Paragon Venkatadri Appts 3-4-812 Barkatpura, Hyderabad, 500 027, Andhra Pradesh, India
Tel.: (91) 4027560252
Web Site:
  http://www.supratrends.com
Year Founded: 1987
511539—(BOM)
Assets: $326,503
Liabilities: $386,655
Net Worth: ($60,152)
Earnings: ($8,165)
Emp.: 5
Fiscal Year-end: 03/31/23
Textile Product Whslr
N.A.I.C.S.: 424990
M. V. K. Sunil Kumar (Chm & Mng Dir)

SUPRAJIT ENGINEERING LIMITED

No 100 and 101 Bommasandra Industrial Area, Bengaluru, 560 099, Karnataka, India
Tel.: (91) 8043421100
Web Site: https://www.suprajit.com
Year Founded: 1985
532509—(BOM)
Rev.: $334,631,377

Assets: $29,189,137
Liabilities: $14,508,003
Net Worth: $14,681,134
Earnings: $18,237,396
Emp.: 1,823
Fiscal Year-end: 03/31/23
Cable Mfr
N.A.I.C.S.: 336390
K. Ajith Kumar Rai (Chm)

Subsidiaries:

Phoenix Lamps Division (1)
100 Bommasandra Industrial Area Anekal, Taluk, Bengaluru, 560009, India
Tel.: (91) 08043421110
Web Site: http://www.phoenixlamps.co.in
Rev.: $36,614,252
Assets: $39,187,253
Liabilities: $13,176,099
Net Worth: $26,011,154
Earnings: $3,522,908
Fiscal Year-end: 03/31/2017
Automotive Lighting Mfr
N.A.I.C.S.: 335139
N. S. Mohan (CEO)

Suprajit Europe Limited (1)
25 Apollo Lichfield Road, Tamworth, B79 7TA, West Midlands, United Kingdom (61.9%)
Tel.: (44) 1827304777
Web Site: http://www.suprajit.com
Fabricated Cable Mfr
N.A.I.C.S.: 335921

Trifa Lamps, Germany GmbH (1)
Gebruder-Seibel-Strasse 6, DE-76846, Hauenstein, Germany
Tel.: (49) 6392999900
Web Site: https://www.trifa.de
Automobile Parts Mfr
N.A.I.C.S.: 332119

Wescon Controls, LLC (1)
2533 S W St, Wichita, KS 67217
Tel.: (316) 942-7266
Web Site: https://wesconcontrols.com
Mechanical Controls, Injection Molded Products & Wire Parts Mfr
N.A.I.C.S.: 334514

SUPREMA HQ INC.

17F Parkview Tower 248, Jeongjail-ro Bundang-gu, Seongnam, 13554, Gyeonggi, Korea (South)
Tel.: (82) 317834502
Web Site: https://www.suprema.co.kr
Year Founded: 2000
094840—(KRS)
Rev.: $24,853,172
Assets: $156,880,081
Liabilities: $7,230,702
Net Worth: $149,649,379
Earnings: $10,520,007
Emp.: 48
Fiscal Year-end: 12/31/22
Biometric Device Mfr
N.A.I.C.S.: 334118
Lee Jae-Won (Chm & CEO)

Subsidiaries:

Suprema Europe S.A.R.L. (1)
366 T Rue de Vaugirard, 75015, Paris, France
Tel.: (33) 184732943
Biometrics System Services
N.A.I.C.S.: 561611

Suprema Middle East FZCO (1)
Dubai Airport Freezone Building 1E 206, Dubai, United Arab Emirates
Tel.: (971) 509405133
Biometrics System Services
N.A.I.C.S.: 561611

Suprema Systems Japan Ltd. (1)
8-6 604 Nihonbashi Kobunacho, Chuo-ku, Tokyo, 103-0024, Japan
Tel.: (81) 335272114
Biometric Security Products Mfr
N.A.I.C.S.: 334118

Suprema Systems UK Ltd. (1)
12 St Pauls Square, Birmingham, B3 1RB, United Kingdom

INTERNATIONAL PUBLIC

Tel.: (44) 8003688123
Biometrics System Services
N.A.I.C.S.: 561611

SUPREME ELECTRONICS CO., LTD.

7F No 189 Kangchien Rd, Nei-Hu, Taipei, Taiwan
Tel.: (886) 226578809
Web Site:
  http://www.supreme.com.tw
Year Founded: 1987
8112—(TAI)
Rev.: $4,975,478,997
Assets: $1,702,504,400
Liabilities: $1,095,020,299
Net Worth: $607,484,100
Earnings: $79,760,094
Emp.: 455
Fiscal Year-end: 12/31/23
Semiconductor Product Whslr
N.A.I.C.S.: 423690
Eric Hsing (Vice Chm)

Subsidiaries:

Go-Tech Energy Co., Ltd. (1)
11F No 175 Sec 2 Datong Rd, Sijhih Dist, New Taipei City, 22183, Taiwan
Tel.: (886) 277080899
Web Site: http://www.gtenergy.com.tw
Lithium Ion Battery Mfr & Distr
N.A.I.C.S.: 325180

Golden Supreme International Trading (Shanghai) Co., Ltd. (1)
Room A 28 Floor Huamin Empire Plaza No 726 Yan An Road W, Shanghai, 200050, China
Tel.: (86) 2151096065
Semiconductor Mfr & Distr
N.A.I.C.S.: 334413

Hk Xzj Digital Co., Ltd. (1)
Workshop No 8 5th Floor No 1 Huang To Road, Kwun Tong, Hong Kong, China (Hong Kong)
Tel.: (852) 27550033
Web Site: https://www.hkxzj.com
Electronic Component Mfr & Distr
N.A.I.C.S.: 334419

SUPREME ENGINEERING LIMITED

R-223 Midc Complex Thane-Belapur Road, Rabale, Navi Mumbai, 400701, India
Tel.: (91) 2227692232
Web Site:
  https://www.supremesteels.com
Year Founded: 1987
SUPREMEENG—(NSE)
Rev.: $2,260,056
Assets: $6,734,608
Liabilities: $14,674,180
Net Worth: ($7,939,572)
Earnings: ($12,609,556)
Emp.: 29
Fiscal Year-end: 03/31/23
Steel & Wire Product Mfr
N.A.I.C.S.: 331110
Sanjay Chowdhri (Chm & Mng Dir)

SUPREME GROUP

28169 96 Ave, Acheson, T7X 6J7, AB, Canada
Tel.: (780) 483-3278
Web Site:
  http://www.supremegroup.com
Year Founded: 1972
Emp.: 200
Structural Steel Products Mfr & Distr
N.A.I.C.S.: 332313
John Leder (Pres)

Subsidiaries:

Canron Western Constructor LP (1)
1168 Derwent Way Annacis Island, Delta, V3M 5R1, BC, Canada
Tel.: (604) 524-4421
Web Site: http://www.supremegroup.com

AND PRIVATE COMPANIES — SUPRIYA LIFESCIENCE LTD.

Emp.: 150
Construction Services
N.A.I.C.S.: 237310
Terry Burns *(Gen Mgr)*

Canron Western Constructors Inc (1)
4600 NE 138th Ave, Portland, OR 97230
Tel.: (503) 255-8634
Web Site: http://www.supremegroup.com
Emp.: 112
Bridge & Highway Construction Services
N.A.I.C.S.: 237310

Hopkins Steel Works Limited (1)
2 Broadway Ave, Welland, L3B 5G4, ON, Canada
Tel.: (905) 732-6108
Sales Range: $25-49.9 Million
Emp.: 17
Fabricated Metal Products Mfr
N.A.I.C.S.: 332312

Quality Fabricating & Supply LP (1)
3751 76 Avenue, Edmonton, T6B 2S8, AB, Canada
Tel.: (780) 468-6762
Drilling Equipment Mfr & Distr
N.A.I.C.S.: 333131
Bob Angerman *(Gen Mgr)*

Supreme Group - Supreme Steel Bridge Division (1)
10496 Knightsbridge Rd NW, Edmonton, T6P 1W4, AB, Canada
Tel.: (780) 467-2266
Bridge Construction Services
N.A.I.C.S.: 237310
Brian Hofstede *(Mgr-Production)*

Supreme Steel Saskatoon (1)
1 North Corman Industrial Park, Box 26002, Lawson Heights, Saskatoon, S7K 3J8, SK, Canada
Tel.: (306) 975-1177
Web Site: http://www.supremegroup.com
Structural Steel Product Distr
N.A.I.C.S.: 423510
Ross Fraser *(Gen Mgr)*

Supreme Steel Winnipeg (1)
1001 Jarvis Avenue, Winnipeg, R2X 0A1, MB, Canada
Tel.: (204) 589-7371
Emp.: 60
Fabricated Structural Steel Products Mfr
N.A.I.C.S.: 332312
Miroslav Mackic *(Mgr-Ops)*

SUPREME GROUP BV
De Lairessesraat 154, 1075 HL, Amsterdam, Netherlands
Tel.: (31) 20 471 01 28
Web Site: http://www.supreme-group.net
Supply Chain Solutions
N.A.I.C.S.: 488510
Theo Reichert *(CEO)*

Subsidiaries:

EMS Seven Seas ASA (1)
Strandveien 37, N-1366, Lysaker, Norway
Tel.: (47) 67 52 60 60
Web Site: http://www.ems-sevenseas.com
Sales Range: $400-449.9 Million
Emp.: 1,095
Maritime Transportation Services
N.A.I.C.S.: 488390
Ole Anton Gulsvik *(CFO)*

SUPREME HOLDINGS & HOSPITALITY (INDIA) LTD.
Office No 510-513 5th Floor Platinum Square, Shri Satpal Malhotra Marg Nagar Road, Pune, 411 014, Wadgaonsheri, India
Tel.: (91) 9607600044
Web Site: https://www.supremeholdings.net
Year Founded: 1982
530677—(BOM)
Rev.: $9,194,353
Assets: $71,840,177
Liabilities: $7,444,290
Net Worth: $64,395,888
Earnings: $1,431,545
Emp.: 19
Fiscal Year-end: 03/31/23
Home Management Services
N.A.I.C.S.: 721110
Vidip Vinod Jatia *(Chm, Mng Dir & CFO)*

SUPREME IMPORTS LTD.
4 Beacon Rd Trafford Park, Stretford, Manchester, M17 1AF, United Kingdom
Tel.: (44) 1618725151
Web Site: http://www.supreme-imports.co.uk
Year Founded: 1970
Sales Range: $50-74.9 Million
Emp.: 66
Electric Bulb Whslr
N.A.I.C.S.: 423610
Sandy Chadha *(Mng Dir)*

SUPREME INFRASTRUCTURE INDIA LIMITED
Supreme House 94c Pratap gad Apna bazar road Opp IIT main gate, Powai, Mumbai, 400076, Maharashtra, India
Tel.: (91) 2261289700
Web Site: https://www.supremeinfra.com
Rev.: $152,534,556
Assets: $505,021,880
Liabilities: $482,300,250
Net Worth: $22,721,630
Earnings: ($77,818,999)
Emp.: 579
Fiscal Year-end: 03/31/18
Infrastructure Development Projects
N.A.I.C.S.: 236115
Vikram B. Sharma *(Mng Dir)*

SUPREME OFFICE PRODUCTS LIMITED
310 Henderson Drive, Regina, S4N 5W7, SK, Canada
Tel.: (306) 566-8888
Web Site: http://www.supremebasics.com
Year Founded: 1974
Rev.: $55,564,968
Emp.: 324
Office Stationery Supplier
N.A.I.C.S.: 459410
Irene Schramm *(Mgr-Customer Svc)*

SUPREME PETROCHEM LIMITED
Solitaire Corporate Park Building No 11 5th Floor, 167 Guru Hargovindji Marg Chakala Andheri East, Mumbai, 400093, India
Tel.: (91) 2267091900
Web Site: http://www.supremepetrochem.com
SUPPETRO—(NSE)
Rev.: $437,680,589
Assets: $239,603,596
Liabilities: $94,252,281
Net Worth: $145,351,315
Earnings: $65,177,617
Emp.: 361
Fiscal Year-end: 03/31/21
Polystyrene Product Mfr
N.A.I.C.S.: 326140
Rakesh Nayyar *(CFO & Exec Dir-Fin & Corp Affairs)*

SUPREME PLC
4 Beacon Road Trafford Park, Manchester, M17 1AF, United Kingdom   UK
Year Founded: 2006
SUP—(AIM)
Rev.: $193,238,982
Assets: $111,940,819
Liabilities: $62,323,458
Net Worth: $49,617,361
Earnings: $14,861,862
Emp.: 354
Fiscal Year-end: 03/31/23
Battery Product Mfr & Distr
N.A.I.C.S.: 335910

Subsidiaries:

Liberty Flights Limited (1)
4 Beacon Rd, Stretford, Manchester, M17 1AF, United Kingdom
Tel.: (44) 3330345050
Web Site: https://www.liberty-flights.co.uk
Chemical Product Mfr & Distr
N.A.I.C.S.: 325998

VN Labs Limited (1)
4 Beacon Rd Trafford Park, Stretford, Manchester, M17 1AF, United Kingdom
Tel.: (44) 1614133564
Web Site: https://vn-labs.com
Sports Nutrition Mfr & Distr
N.A.I.C.S.: 325411

SUPREME POWER EQUIPMENT LIMITED
No 55 Sidco Industrial Estate Thirumazhisai, Chennai, 600124, Tamilnadu, India
Tel.: (91) 9444237858
Web Site: https://www.supremepower.in
Year Founded: 1994
SUPREMEPWR—(NSE)
Rev.: $9,441,634
Assets: $5,758,128
Liabilities: $3,569,629
Net Worth: $2,188,498
Earnings: $1,311,739
Emp.: 61
Fiscal Year-end: 03/31/23
Electrical Equipment Mfr & Distr
N.A.I.C.S.: 331110

SUPREME TEX MART LIMITED
B-72 Focal Point Phase-8, Ludhiana, 141010, Punjab, India
Tel.: (91) 161 6614400
Web Site: http://www.supremetexmart.com
Year Founded: 2001
Rev.: $49,173,614
Assets: $38,125,081
Liabilities: $86,411,013
Net Worth: ($48,285,932)
Earnings: $18,440,514
Emp.: 1,099
Fiscal Year-end: 03/31/18
Cotton Yarn Mfr
N.A.I.C.S.: 313110
Ajay Gupta *(Mng Dir)*

SUPREME VENTURES LIMITED
9a Retirement Crescent Cross Roads, Kingston, 5, Jamaica
Tel.: (876) 7546526
Web Site: https://www.supremeventures.com
Year Founded: 1995
Rev.: $245,373,424
Assets: $49,285,065
Liabilities: $24,810,638
Net Worth: $24,474,427
Earnings: $15,633,140
Emp.: 500
Fiscal Year-end: 12/31/18
Holding Company; Lottery, Gaming, Hospitality, Financial Services & Pin Codes
N.A.I.C.S.: 551112
Gary H. Peart *(Chm)*

Subsidiaries:

Supreme Ventures Financial Services Limited (1)
9a Retirement Crescent, Kingston, 5, Jamaica
Tel.: (876) 906 8603
Web Site: http://www.supremeventures.com
Financial Remittance Services
N.A.I.C.S.: 525990

Supreme Ventures Lotteries Limited (1)
4th Floor Sagicor Centre 28-48 Barbados Avenue, Kingston, Jamaica
Tel.: (876) 754 6526
Web Site: http://www.supremeventures.com
Online Lottery Game Operating Services
N.A.I.C.S.: 713290
Brian George *(Pres & CEO)*

SUPREME WINDOWS (CALGARY) INC.
4705 102 Avenue SE, Calgary, T2C 2X7, AB, Canada
Tel.: (403) 279-2797
Web Site: http://www.supremewindows.net
Year Founded: 1967
Rev.: $12,751,926
Emp.: 98
Windows & Doors Mfr
N.A.I.C.S.: 321911
Ann MacKenna *(Pres)*

SUPREMEX INC.
7213 Cordner Street LaSalle, Montreal, H8N 2J7, QC, Canada
Tel.: (514) 595-0555   Ca
Web Site: https://www.supremex.com
SXP—(TSX)
Rev.: $146,672,902
Assets: $137,474,523
Liabilities: $78,954,248
Net Worth: $58,520,274
Earnings: $5,423,945
Emp.: 935
Fiscal Year-end: 12/31/19
Envelopes, Labels & Mailing Products Mfr
N.A.I.C.S.: 322230
Robert B. Johnston *(Chm)*

Subsidiaries:

Bowers Envelope Company, Inc. (1)
5331 N Tacoma Ave, Indianapolis, IN 46220-3613   (100%)
Tel.: (317) 253-4321
Web Site: http://www.bowersenvelope.com
Sales Range: $1-9.9 Million
Emp.: 50
Custom Envelope Mfr
N.A.I.C.S.: 322230

Buffalo Envelope Inc. (1)
2914 Walden Ave, Depew, NY 14043
Tel.: (716) 686-0100
Web Site: http://www.buffaloenvelope.com
Sales Range: $1-9.9 Million
Emp.: 12
Envelope Mfr & Whslr
N.A.I.C.S.: 322230
Sandy Morley *(Coord-Admin & Acctg)*

Enveloppe Quebec (2008) Inc. (1)
6 Rue des Gouverneurs, Sainte-Helene-de-Breakeyville, Levis, G0S 1E2, QC, Canada
Tel.: (418) 832-8500
Web Site: http://www.enveloppe-quebec.com
Envelope Mfr
N.A.I.C.S.: 322230

Royal Envelope Corp. (1)
4114 South Peoria St, Chicago, IL 60609
Tel.: (773) 376-1212
Web Site: http://www.royalenv.com
Envelope Mfr
N.A.I.C.S.: 322230
Mike Pusatera *(Pres & Sls Mgr)*

SUPRIYA LIFESCIENCE LTD.
207/208 Udyog Bhavan Sonawala Road, Goregoan East, Mumbai, 400063, India
Tel.: (91) 2226860012

SUPRIYA LIFESCIENCE LTD.

Supriya Lifescience Ltd.—(Continued)

Web Site:
https://www.supriyalifescience.com
Year Founded: 1987
543434—(BOM)
Pharmaceuticals Product Mfr
N.A.I.C.S.: 325412
Satish Waman Wagh *(Founder, Chm & Mng Dir)*

SURA DEVELOPMENT & INVESTMENT PLC

Abdulhameed Sharaf Street Building No 84, Box 954140, Al-Shmisani, Amman, 11954, Jordan
Tel.: (962) 795880302
Year Founded: 2008
SURA—(AMM)
Rev.: $7,045
Assets: $9,224,293
Liabilities: $990,931
Net Worth: $8,233,362
Earnings: ($63,982)
Fiscal Year-end: 12/31/20
Home Management Services
N.A.I.C.S.: 721110
Mohammad Ghazalih *(Gen Mgr)*

SURAJ COTTON MILLS LIMITED

Tricon Corporate Center 8th Floor 73E Main Jail Road Gulberg 2, Lahore, Pakistan
Tel.: (92) 4235760381
Web Site: https://www.suraj.com
SURC—(PSX)
Rev.: $67,850,132
Assets: $76,184,541
Liabilities: $37,340,801
Net Worth: $38,843,741
Earnings: ($1,483,172)
Emp.: 2,227
Fiscal Year-end: 06/30/23
Woven Fabrics Mfr
N.A.I.C.S.: 313110
Nadeem Maqbool *(CEO)*

SURAJ ESTATE DEVELOPERS LIMITED

301 3rd Floor Aman Chambers Veer Savarkar Marg Opp Bengal Chemicals, Prabhadevi, Mumbai, 400025, Maharashtra, India
Tel.: (91) 2240154746
Web Site:
https://www.surajestate.com
Year Founded: 1986
544054—(BOM)
Rev.: $37,316,268
Assets: $114,240,696
Liabilities: $105,573,199
Net Worth: $8,667,497
Earnings: $3,886,157
Emp.: 126
Fiscal Year-end: 03/31/23
Engineeering Services
N.A.I.C.S.: 541330

SURAJ GHEE INDUSTRIES LIMITED

Al-Fateh Building 13-Link Mecleod Road, Lahore, Pakistan
Tel.: (92) 62178
Refined Oil & Ghee Mfr
N.A.I.C.S.: 311225

SURAJ INDUSTRIES LTD.

F-32/3 First Floor Okhla Industrial Area Phase-II, New Delhi, 110020, India
Tel.: (91) 1142524455
Web Site:
https://www.surajindustries.org
526211—(BOM)
Rev.: $8,179,905
Assets: $12,439,746
Liabilities: $4,716,336
Net Worth: $7,723,410
Earnings: $888,244
Emp.: 26
Fiscal Year-end: 03/31/23
Drilling Machines Mfr
N.A.I.C.S.: 333517
Suraj Prakash Gupta *(Mng Dir)*

SURAJ LTD.

Suraj House Opp Usmanpura Garden Ashram Road, Ahmedabad, 380014, Gujarat, India
Tel.: (91) 7927540720
Web Site:
https://www.surajgroup.com
531638—(BOM)
Rev.: $44,638,079
Assets: $17,474,852
Liabilities: $5,034,770
Net Worth: $12,440,082
Earnings: $2,412,793
Fiscal Year-end: 03/31/23
Stainless Steel Pipe Mfr & Distr
N.A.I.C.S.: 331210
Ashok T. Shah *(Chm & CFO)*

SURAJ PRODUCTS LIMITED

Vill Barpali PO Kesaramal, Rajgangpur, Sundergarh, 770017, Odisha, India
Tel.: (91) 9437049074
Web Site:
https://www.surajproducts.com
Year Founded: 1991
518075—(BOM)
Rev.: $29,744,775
Assets: $17,679,929
Liabilities: $10,195,271
Net Worth: $7,484,658
Earnings: $1,251,352
Fiscal Year-end: 03/31/21
Sponge Iron Mfr
N.A.I.C.S.: 331110
Yogesh Kumar Dalmia *(Mng Dir)*

SURALA NET CO., LTD.

7F PMO Uchikanda 1-14-10 Uchikanda, Chiyoda-ku, Tokyo, 101-0047, Japan
Tel.: (81) 352835158
Web Site: https://surala.co.jp
Year Founded: 2008
3998—(TKS)
Rev.: $15,208,050
Assets: $19,199,720
Liabilities: $3,240,130
Net Worth: $15,959,590
Earnings: $2,155,360
Emp.: 88
Fiscal Year-end: 12/31/23
Online Education Services
N.A.I.C.S.: 611710
Takahiko Yunokawa *(Founder & CEO)*

SURANA INDUSTRIES LTD.

29 Whites Road II Floor, Royapettah, Chennai, 600014, India
Tel.: (91) 44 28525127
Web Site: http://www.suranaind.com
Year Founded: 1991
513597—(BOM)
Steel Products Mfr
N.A.I.C.S.: 331110
G. R. Surana *(Founder & Chm)*

Subsidiaries:

Surana Mines and Minerals Limited (1)
Maxwell House 08-01N 20 Maxwell Road, Singapore, 069113, Singapore
Tel.: (65) 6223 9731
Coal Mining Services
N.A.I.C.S.: 212114

SURANA SOLAR LIMITED

Plot No 212/3 and 4 Phase II IDA, Cherlapally, Hyderabad, 500051, Telangana, India
Tel.: (91) 4027845119
Web Site:
https://www.suranasolar.com
Year Founded: 1978
SURANASOL—(NSE)
Rev.: $3,869,881
Assets: $8,733,099
Liabilities: $1,321,727
Net Worth: $7,411,372
Earnings: $28,806
Emp.: 7
Fiscal Year-end: 03/31/21
Solar Photovoltaic Modules, Home Lighting, Street Lighting & LED Lighting
N.A.I.C.S.: 334413
Manish Surana *(CFO, Dir-Fin & Tech)*

SURANA TELECOM AND POWER LIMITED

2nd 3rd and 5th Floors Surya Towers S P Road, Secunderabad, 500 003, Andhra Pradesh, India
Tel.: (91) 4044665729
Web Site:
https://www.suranatele.com
Year Founded: 1978
517530—(BOM)
Rev.: $4,476,638
Assets: $18,066,219
Liabilities: $3,292,680
Net Worth: $14,773,539
Earnings: $518,446
Emp.: 18
Fiscal Year-end: 03/31/23
Telecommunication Products Mfr
N.A.I.C.S.: 339999
Baunakar Shekarnath *(Exec Dir)*

Subsidiaries:

Bhagyanagar Green Energy Private Limited (1)
5th Floor Surya Towers S P Road, Secunderabad, 500 003, India
Tel.: (91) 4027175891
Web Site:
https://www.bhagyanagarindia.com
Copper Product Mfr & Distr
N.A.I.C.S.: 331420

SURANI STEEL TUBES LIMITED

Sr No 110 115 Opp Vinayak Tmt Bayad Road, Village Sampa Ta Dahegam Dist, Gandhinagar, 382315, Gujarat, India
Tel.: (91) 9099759497
Web Site:
https://www.suranisteel.com
Year Founded: 2012
SURANI—(NSE)
Rev.: $14,844,925
Assets: $4,962,185
Liabilities: $2,230,718
Net Worth: $2,731,467
Earnings: ($215,011)
Emp.: 52
Fiscal Year-end: 03/31/23
Steel Tube Mfr & Distr
N.A.I.C.S.: 331210
Gaurav Rajeshbhai Patel *(CFO)*

SURAPON FOODS PUBLIC COMPANY LIMITED

247 Moo 1 Theparak Road, Theparak Muang, Samut Prakan, 10270, Thailand
Tel.: (66) 23853038
Web Site: https://www.surapon.com
Year Founded: 1977
SSF—(THA)
Rev.: $156,893,685
Assets: $121,325,271
Liabilities: $52,018,150

INTERNATIONAL PUBLIC

Net Worth: $69,307,121
Earnings: $8,858,349
Emp.: 2,854
Fiscal Year-end: 12/31/23
Frozen Seafood Mfr & Exporter
N.A.I.C.S.: 311710
Patt Somchaikulsup *(Sec & VP-CEO Office)*

Subsidiaries:

Chantaburi Marine Farm Co., Ltd. (1)
247 Moo 1 Theparak Road, Theparak Muang, Samut Prakan, 10270, Thailand
Tel.: (66) 23853054
Web Site: www.surapon.com
Sales Range: $300-349.9 Million
Emp.: 1,200
Shrimp Farming Services
N.A.I.C.S.: 112512

Surapon Aquaculture Co., Ltd. (1)
247 Moo 1 Theparak Road, Theparak Muang, Samut Prakan, 10270, Thailand
Tel.: (66) 2 385 3038
Web Site: http://www.surapon.com
Sales Range: $25-49.9 Million
Emp.: 10
Shrimp Production & Farming Services
N.A.I.C.S.: 112512
Phont Chai Thongchai *(Mgr-Mktg)*

Surapon Foods Public Company Limited - Factory 1 (1)
247 Theparak Road, Theparak Muang, Samut Prakan, 10270, Thailand
Tel.: (66) 23853627
Sales Range: $200-249.9 Million
Emp.: 1,000
Frozen Seafood Mfr & Distr
N.A.I.C.S.: 311710

Surapon Nichirei Foods Co., Inc. (1)
22/5 Moo 4 Theparak Rd, Samut Prakan, 10540, Thailand
Tel.: (66) 2 385 3051
Web Site: https://www.test.surapon.com
Sales Range: $150-199.9 Million
Food Processor; Owned by Nichirei Corporation & by Surapon Foods Public Company Limited
N.A.I.C.S.: 311999

Surat Seafoods Company Limited (1)
247 Moo 61 Teparak Rd, Muang, Bangkok, Thailand (94%)
Tel.: (66) 2385303854
Fresh & Frozen Seafood Processing
N.A.I.C.S.: 311710

SURAT TEXTILE MILLS LIMITED

Tulsi Krupa Arcade 6 th Floor, Near Aai Mata Chowk Puna-Kumbharia Road Dumbhal, Surat, 395 010, India
Tel.: (91) 2612311198
Web Site:
https://www.surattextilemillsltd.com
Year Founded: 1945
530185—(BOM)
Rev.: $18,547,088
Assets: $19,563,685
Liabilities: $724,665
Net Worth: $18,839,020
Earnings: $1,977,162
Emp.: 58
Fiscal Year-end: 03/31/21
Textile Mill Operator
N.A.I.C.S.: 314999
Manikant R. Momaya *(Mng Dir)*

SURATWWALA BUSINESS GROUP LTD.

4/38 Sumangal Building Office No 2 1St Floor Sahakar Colony, Behind Sbi Bank Karve Road Erandawane, Pune, 411004, India
Tel.: (91) 2025434392
Web Site:
https://www.suratwwala.co.in
Year Founded: 2008

SBGLP—(NSE)
Rev.: $7,488,975
Assets: $14,421,414
Liabilities: $12,924,789
Net Worth: $1,496,625
Earnings: $2,537,378
Emp.: 48
Fiscal Year-end: 03/31/23
Construction Services
N.A.I.C.S.: 236220
Jatin Dhansukhlal Suratwala *(Chm & Mng Dir)*

SURBHI INDUSTRIES LIMITED
Surbhi House 2nd Floor Fp No 206 B/H Old Subjail Ring Road, Khatodra, Surat, 395002, India
Tel.: (91) 2612209500
Web Site: https://www.surbhi.com
Year Founded: 1976
514260—(BOM)
Rev.: $2,600,128
Assets: $2,918,249
Liabilities: $749,221
Net Worth: $2,169,027
Earnings: $211,735
Emp.: 84
Fiscal Year-end: 03/31/21
Textile Products Mfr
N.A.I.C.S.: 313110
Naimish Patel *(Head-Rapier Weaving)*

SURE VENTURES PLC
51 Lime Street, London, EC3M 7DQ, United Kingdom
Tel.: (44) 2039317000
Web Site:
    https://www.sureventuresplc.com
SURE—(LSE)
Assets: $10,226,335
Liabilities: $337,624
Net Worth: $9,888,710
Earnings: ($533,524)
Fiscal Year-end: 03/31/23
Commericial Banking
N.A.I.C.S.: 522110
Perry Wilson *(Chm)*

SUREFIRE RESOURCES NL
45 Ventnor Avenue, West Perth, 6005, WA, Australia
Tel.: (61) 894298846   AU
Web Site:
    https://www.surefireresources.com
GBL—(DEU)
Rev.: $436,347
Assets: $9,668,959
Liabilities: $8,232,653
Net Worth: $1,436,306
Earnings: ($2,049,000)
Emp.: 2
Fiscal Year-end: 06/30/24
Mineral Exploration & Development Services
N.A.I.C.S.: 213115
Vladimir Nikolaenko *(Chm & Mng Dir)*

SURERUS PIPELINE INC.
9312 109th Street, Fort Saint John, V1J 6G9, BC, Canada
Tel.: (250) 785-2423   BC
Web Site: http://www.surerus.com
Year Founded: 1969
Pipeline Installation Services
N.A.I.C.S.: 237120
John Steward *(Project Coord)*
Subsidiaries:

Grizzly Equipment Company   (1)
10912 91st Avenue, Fort Saint John, V1J 6G7, BC, Canada
Tel.: (250) 785-4334
Web Site: https://www.grizzlyequipment.com
Construction Equipment Rental Services
N.A.I.C.S.: 532412

SUREWAY INTERNATIONAL INC
3151 Wharton Way, Mississauga, L4X 2B7, ON, Canada
Tel.: (905) 624-0077
Web Site: http://www.surelite.ca
Year Founded: 1982
Rev.: $11,998,403
Emp.: 55
Electrical Apparatus & Equipment Supplier
N.A.I.C.S.: 423610
Maria Vento *(Gen Mgr)*

SURF COMMUNICATION SOLUTIONS, LTD.
7 Hamada St Yoqneam Hi-Tech Park, PO Box 343, 2069205, Yokneam, Israel
Tel.: (972) 737140715
Web Site:
    http://www.surfsolutions.com
Year Founded: 1996
Sales Range: $25-49.9 Million
Emp.: 24
Voice & Video Computer Systems & Software Developer, Mfr & Whslr
N.A.I.C.S.: 513210
Zvi Slonimsky *(Chm)*
Subsidiaries:

Surf Japan, KK.   (1)
Nihon Sunrise Bldg 3F 1-5-1 Nihonbashi Ningyocho, Chuo-ku, Tokyo, 103-0013, Japan
Tel.: (81) 362062635
Software Development Services
N.A.I.C.S.: 541511

SURFACE MOUNT TECHNOLOGY (HOLDINGS) LIMITED
12 F Wyler Centre Phase 2, 200 Tai Lin Pai Road, Kwai Chung, New Territories, China (Hong Kong)
Tel.: (852) 3757 4000   HK
Web Site: http://www.smthk.com
Year Founded: 1986
Electronic Components Mfr
N.A.I.C.S.: 334419
Kei Biu Chan *(Sr Mng Dir & Founder)*
Subsidiaries:

Dongguan Sizhing Electronic Co., Ltd.   (1)
Ngai Lang Hum Tai Lang Shan, Dongguan, 523833, Guangdong, China
Tel.: (86) 769 8896 0000
Electronic Components Mfr
N.A.I.C.S.: 334419

Dongguan Superior Manufacturing Technology Co. Ltd.   (1)
No 2 2 Hong Ye Road North Tangxia Town, Dongguan, 523710, Guangdon, China
Tel.: (86) 769 8781 0780
Electronic Components Mfr
N.A.I.C.S.: 334419

Sizhing Electronic (Suzhou) Company Limited   (1)
No 37 Nan Hu Road Wuzhong Economic Development Zone, Suzhou, 215128, Jiangsu, China
Tel.: (86) 512 6563 8872
Electronic Products Mfr
N.A.I.C.S.: 334418

Surface Mount Technology (Japan) Company Limited   (1)
4 F Takada Mill Building 6-1-10 Honkomagome, Bunkyo-ku, Tokyo, 113-0021, Japan
Tel.: (81) 3 5848 8777
Web Site: http://www.smthk.com
Sales Range: $25-49.9 Million
Emp.: 2
Electronic Products Mfr
N.A.I.C.S.: 334419

Surface Mount Technology Limited   (1)
12 F Wyler Centre Phase 2 200 Tai Lin Pai Road, Kwai Chung, New Territories, China (Hong Kong)
Tel.: (852) 3757 4000
Web Site: http://www.smthk.com
Electronic Products Mfr
N.A.I.C.S.: 334418

SURFACE TRANSFORMS PLC
Image Business Park Acornfield Road Knowsley Industrial Estate, Liverpool, L33 7UF, United Kingdom
Tel.: (44) 1513562141
Web Site:
    https://www.surfacetransforms.com
SCE—(LSE)
Rev.: $2,650,269
Assets: $11,696,758
Liabilities: $3,987,624
Net Worth: $7,709,134
Earnings: ($3,126,829)
Emp.: 48
Fiscal Year-end: 12/31/20
Carbon Fiber Ceramic Products Mfr
N.A.I.C.S.: 335991
Kevin R. Johnson *(CEO)*

SURFILM SAS
ZI de l'Orignade, 17600, Medis, France
Tel.: (33) 546058044   FR
Web Site: http://www.surfilm.fr
Year Founded: 1985
Sales Range: $10-24.9 Million
Emp.: 50
Plastic Bag & Other Packaging Products Mfr & Distr
N.A.I.C.S.: 326111
Pierre Schoettel *(CEO)*

SURFILTER NETWORK TECHNOLOGY CO., LTD.
Floor 6 Building 2 Software Park Kejizhonger Road, Nanshan District, Shenzhen, 518000, China
Tel.: (86) 75586168366
Web Site: https://www.1218.com.cn
Year Founded: 2000
300311—(CHIN)
Rev.: $102,433,032
Assets: $219,921,156
Liabilities: $99,254,376
Net Worth: $120,666,780
Earnings: ($140,400)
Emp.: 1,000
Fiscal Year-end: 12/31/22
Content & Behavior Monitoring Products Mfr
N.A.I.C.S.: 334118
Jing Xiaojun *(Chm)*

SURFSTITCH GROUP LIMITED
C/ - FTI Consulting Level 15 50 Pitt Street, Sydney, 2000, NSW, Australia
Tel.: (61) 75507 0979   AU
Web Site:
    http://www.surfstitchgroup.com
SRF—(ASX)
Action Sports & Youth Culture Apparel Content Network & Online Retailer
N.A.I.C.S.: 315990
Stephanie Mary Belton *(Sec)*

SURGE BATTERY METALS INC.
1220 - 789 West Pender Street, Vancouver, V6C 1H2, BC, Canada
Tel.: (778) 945-2656   Ca
Web Site:
    http://www.surgeexploration.com
Year Founded: 1987
NILIF—(OTCIQ)
Assets: $4,745,980
Liabilities: $206,116
Net Worth: $4,539,864
Earnings: ($1,684,508)
Fiscal Year-end: 12/31/21
Mineral Exploration Services
N.A.I.C.S.: 213114
Simon Tso *(CFO)*

SURGE COMMUNICATIONS
123 St George Ste 105, London, N6A 3A1, ON, Canada
Tel.: (519) 672-9090
Year Founded: 1999
Sales Range: $25-49.9 Million
Emp.: 35
Advertising Agencies
N.A.I.C.S.: 541810
Grant Beamish *(Acct Dir)*
Subsidiaries:

Sparks Event Marketing   (1)
260 Holiday Inn Dr Ste 27 2nd F, Cambridge, N3C 4E8, ON, Canada
Tel.: (519) 654-9804
Emp.: 10
Advertising Agencies
N.A.I.C.S.: 541810

SURGE COPPER CORP.
888 - 700 West Georgia Street, PO Box 10351, Vancouver, V7Y 1G5, BC, Canada
Tel.: (604) 718-5454   BC
Web Site:
    https://www.surgecopper.com
Year Founded: 1965
SURG—(TSXV)
Rev.: $19,502
Assets: $37,926,508
Liabilities: $3,629,467
Net Worth: $34,297,041
Earnings: ($1,281,376)
Fiscal Year-end: 03/31/24
Mineral Exploration Services
N.A.I.C.S.: 213114
Shane Ebert *(Pres & VP-Exploration)*

SURGE ENERGY INC.
Suite 1200 520 - 3rd Avenue SW, Calgary, T2P 0R3, AB, Canada
Tel.: (403) 930-1010   AB
Web Site:
    https://www.surgeenergy.ca
Year Founded: 1998
ZPTAF—(OTCIQ)
Rev.: $168,832,452
Assets: $553,826,078
Liabilities: $605,625,530
Net Worth: ($51,799,452)
Earnings: ($584,595,497)
Emp.: 71
Fiscal Year-end: 12/31/20
Crude Oil & Natural Gas Exploration, Development & Production Services
N.A.I.C.S.: 211120
Paul Colborne *(Pres & CEO)*

SURGENOR NATIONAL LEASING LTD.
881 St Laurent Blvd, Ottawa, K1K 3B1, ON, Canada
Tel.: (613) 746-9616
Web Site: http://www.snlease.com
Year Founded: 1971
Rev.: $18,432,329
Emp.: 125
Auto Renting & Leasing Services
N.A.I.C.S.: 532490
Andy Conde *(Gen Mgr)*

SURGENOR PONTIAC BUICK LIMITED
939 St Laurent Blvd, Ottawa, K1K 3B1, ON, Canada
Tel.: (613) 741-0741
Web Site: http://www.surgenor.com
Year Founded: 1947
Rev.: $161,431,690
Emp.: 310
New & Used Car Dealers
N.A.I.C.S.: 441110

SURGICAL INNOVATIONS GROUP PLC

SURGICAL INNOVATIONS GROUP PLC
Clayton Wood House 6 Clayton Wood Bank, Leeds, LS16 6QZ, United Kingdom
Tel.: (44) 1132307597
Web Site:
    https://www.sigroupplc.com
SUN—(AIM)
Rev.: $15,289,571
Assets: $18,230,362
Liabilities: $4,888,589
Net Worth: $13,341,774
Earnings: $(649,266)
Fiscal Year-end: 12/31/23
Surgery Devices Mfr
N.A.I.C.S.: 339112
Charmaine Day (Sec & Controller-Fin)

Subsidiaries:

Elemental Healthcare Limited   (1)
Shefford Park Farm, Great Shefford, Hungerford, RG17 7ED, Berkshire, United Kingdom
Tel.: (44) 844 412 0020
Web Site:
    https://www.elementalhealthcare.co.uk
Medical Equipment Distr
N.A.I.C.S.: 423450

Surgical Innovations Limited   (1)
Clayton Wood House 6, Clayton Wood Bank, Leeds, LS16 6QZ, Yorkshire, United Kingdom
Tel.: (44) 1132307597
Web Site: https://www.surginno.com
Sales Range: $25-49.9 Million
Surgical Instrument Mfr
N.A.I.C.S.: 339112
Stavros G. Vizirgianakis (Co-Founder)

SURGICAL SCIENCE SWEDEN AB
Drakegatan 7, 412 50, Gothenburg, Sweden
Tel.: (46) 317416560
Web Site: https://surgicalscience.com
SUS—(OMX)
Rev.: $75,167,421
Assets: $435,486,901
Liabilities: $38,692,855
Net Worth: $396,794,047
Earnings: $17,606,002
Emp.: 243
Fiscal Year-end: 12/31/22
Virtual Reality Simulators for Medical Training
N.A.I.C.S.: 334510
Gisli Hennermark (CEO)

Subsidiaries:

Mimic Technologies Inc.   (1)
811 1st Ave Ste 408, Seattle, WA 98104-3442
Web Site: https://mimicsimulation.com
Computer Terminal & Other Computer Peripheral Equipment Mfr
N.A.I.C.S.: 334118
Jan Ostman (VP-Mktg & Intl Sls)

Simbionix USA Corporation   (1)
7100 Euclid Ave Ste 180, Cleveland, OH 44103
Tel.: (216) 229-2040
Medical Instrument Mfr
N.A.I.C.S.: 334510

Subsidiary (Non-US):

Simbionix Ltd.   (2)
3 Golan, Lod, Airport City, Israel
Tel.: (972) 39114444
Web Site: https://simbionix.com
Medical Instrument Mfr
N.A.I.C.S.: 334510

SURGUTNEFTEGAS OAO
Grigory Kukuyevitsky st 1, Russian Federation Tyumen region Surgut, Surgut, Russia
Tel.: (7) 3462427009   RU
Web Site:
    https://www.surgutneftegas.ru
SGTZY—(MOEX)
Rev.: $25,435,510,228
Assets: $78,680,868,538
Liabilities: $5,469,318,700
Net Worth: $73,211,549,838
Earnings: $6,913,080,054
Fiscal Year-end: 12/31/21
Gas & Oil-Field Construction & Development; Oil, Gas & Petrochemical Products Producer & Marketer
N.A.I.C.S.: 211120
Vladimir Leonidovich Bogdanov (Dir Gen)

Subsidiaries:

Bank SNGB JSC   (1)
19 Kukuyevitskogo Street, Surgut, 628400, Russia
Tel.: (7) 3462 39 88 04
Web Site: http://www.sngb.ru
Securities Brokerage Services
N.A.I.C.S.: 523150
Andrei Vitalyevich Korol (Chm-Mgmt Bd)

Kirishinefteorgsintez Ltd   (1)
Shosse Entuziastov 1, 187110, Kirishi, Leningradskaya, Russia   (100%)
Tel.: (7) 8136891209
Web Site: http://www.kinef.ru
Sales Range: $1-4.9 Billion
Emp.: 6,070
Oil Refining; Production & Export of Petroleum & Petrochemicals
N.A.I.C.S.: 324110

Limited Liability Company KIRISHIAVTOSERVIS   (1)
st Malaya Posadskaya 28/2 building 1 room 1H of 212, 197046, Saint Petersburg, Russia
Tel.: (7) 8123253347
Web Site: http://www.kirishiavtoservis.ru
Sales Range: $150-199.9 Million
Emp.: 400
Petroleum Product Whslr
N.A.I.C.S.: 424710

Limited Liability Company Marketing Association Tverneftteprodukt   (1)
6 ul Novotorzhskaya, Tver, 170100, Russia
Tel.: (7) 4822322131
Web Site: http://www.tverneftteproduct.ru
Petroleum Products Sales
N.A.I.C.S.: 424710

Limited Liability Company Novgorodnefteprodukt   (1)
st Germana 18, Velikiy Novgorod, Russia
Tel.: (7) 8162771010
Web Site: http://www.novnp.ru
Refined Petroleum Products Whslr
N.A.I.C.S.: 424720
Andrey V. Serebrennikov (Deputy Gen Dir-Comml Affairs)

Limited Liability Company Oil Refining and Petrochemical Enterprises Design Institute   (1)
Obvodny Channel Embankment 94, PO Box 567, 196084, Saint Petersburg, Russia
Tel.: (7) 8123162988
Web Site: http://www.lgnch.spb.ru
Sales Range: $100-124.9 Million
Emp.: 400
Petrochemical Plant Construction Services
N.A.I.C.S.: 237120
Fomin Alexandr Stepanovich (Gen Dir)

Pskovnefteprodukt Ltd   (1)
4 Oktyabrsky Prospect, Pskov, Russia
Tel.: (7) 8112663989
Web Site: http://pskovnp.ru
Sales Range: $600-649.9 Million
Emp.: 1,012
Petroleum Product Whslr
N.A.I.C.S.: 424720
Yuri Maleshin (Gen Dir)

SURIA CAPITAL HOLDINGS BERHAD
1st and 2nd Floor Menara Jubili 53 Jalan Gaya, 88000, Kota Kinabalu, Sabah, Malaysia
Tel.: (60) 88257788
Web Site: https://suriagroup.com.my
Year Founded: 1983
SURIA—(KLS)
Rev.: $63,911,111
Assets: $313,041,058
Liabilities: $63,724,233
Net Worth: $249,316,825
Earnings: $12,513,651
Emp.: 1,088
Fiscal Year-end: 12/31/22
Property Development Services
N.A.I.C.S.: 531312
Mariam Mahmun (Head-Corp Affairs & Comm Grp)

Subsidiaries:

S.P. Satria Logistics Sdn. Bhd.   (1)
1st and 2nd Floor Menara Jubili 53 Jalan Gaya, 88000, Kota Kinabalu, Sabah, Malaysia
Tel.: (60) 88 231 026
Web Site: http://www.spslogistics.com.my
Sales Range: $25-49.9 Million
Emp.: 37
Fuel Bunkering Services
N.A.I.C.S.: 457210

S.P. Satria Sdn. Bhd.   (1)
1st & 2nd Floor Menara Jubili No 53 Jalan Gaya, 88000, Kota Kinabalu, Sabah, Malaysia
Tel.: (60) 88483390
Sales Range: $25-49.9 Million
Cargo Handling Services
N.A.I.C.S.: 488320

SCHB Engineering Services Sdn. Bhd.   (1)
4th Floor Wisma Perkasa, Jalan Gaya, 88821, Kota Kinabalu, Sabah, Malaysia
Tel.: (60) 88235787
Web Site: https://schbeng.my
Emp.: 18
Port Construction & Engineering Services
N.A.I.C.S.: 237990
Hiew Kim Fatt (Sr Mgr)

SP Marine Services Sdn. Bhd.   (1)
Wisma SabahPorts Jalan Sapangar Sapangar Bay, PO Box 203, Pos Mini Indah Permai, 88450, Kota Kinabalu, Sabah, Malaysia
Tel.: (60) 88483390
Port Operation Services
N.A.I.C.S.: 488310

Sabah Ports Sdn. Bhd.   (1)
Wisma SabahPorts Jalan Sapangar Sapangar Bay, PO Box 203, Pos Mini Indah Permai, 88450, Kota Kinabalu, Sabah, Malaysia
Tel.: (60) 88483390
Cargo Handling & Berthing Services
N.A.I.C.S.: 488320
Faisyal Yusof Hamdain Diego (Chm-Interim)

Suria Bumiria Sdn. Bhd.   (1)
4th Floor Wisma Perkasa Jalan Gaya, Kota Kinabalu, 88820, Sabah, Malaysia
Tel.: (60) 88235787
Web Site: http://www.suriagroup.com.my
Sales Range: $25-49.9 Million
Emp.: 32
Property Development Services
N.A.I.C.S.: 531210

SURONGO SA
rue du Bois Sauvage 17, 1000, Brussels, Belgium
Tel.: (32) 22275450
Real Estate Investment Services
N.A.I.C.S.: 531210
Bruno Spilliaert (CFO)

SURPLUSGLOBAL, INC.
56 Seochon-ro Namsa-eup, Cheoingu, Yongin, 17118, Gyeonggi-do, Korea (South)
Tel.: (82) 317281400

INTERNATIONAL PUBLIC

Web Site:
    https://www.surplusglobal.com
Year Founded: 2000
140070—(KRS)
Rev: $180,184,589
Assets: $282,524,190
Liabilities: $139,477,172
Net Worth: $143,047,018
Earnings: $19,597,471
Emp.: 55
Fiscal Year-end: 12/31/22
Semiconductor Equipment Distr
N.A.I.C.S.: 423690
Bruce Kim (Founder & CEO)

Subsidiaries:

EQ Bestech Inc.   (1)
2091 Gyeongchung-daero, Bubal-eub, Icheon, Kyounggi-do, Korea (South)
Tel.: (82) 316302995
Web Site: http://www.eqbestech.com
Sales Range: $1-9.9 Million
Semiconductor & Related Equipment Mfr
N.A.I.C.S.: 334413
Jonghyun Nam (CEO)

SURPRO GMBH
Rumflether Strasse 13, 25554, Wilster, Germany
Tel.: (49) 4823770
Web Site: http://www.surpro.de
Year Founded: 1974
Sales Range: $10-24.9 Million
Metal Component Surface Coating Services
N.A.I.C.S.: 332812
Thorsten Schmidt (Mng Dir)

SURREY HONDA
15291 Fraser Highway, Surrey, V3R 3P3, BC, Canada
Tel.: (604) 583-7421
Web Site:
    http://www.surreyhonda.com
Year Founded: 1988
New & Used Car Dealers
N.A.I.C.S.: 441110
Abdul Ahmad (Mgr-Svc)

SURTECO GROUP SE
Johan-Viktor-Bausch-Str 2, 86647, Buttenwiesen, Germany
Tel.: (49) 827499880
Web Site: https://ir.surteco.com
Year Founded: 1999
SUR—(DUS)
Rev: $921,830,798
Assets: $1,150,000,727
Liabilities: $716,588,249
Net Worth: $433,412,478
Earnings: $(13,566,562)
Emp.: 3,756
Fiscal Year-end: 12/31/23
Surface Material Mfr & Distr
N.A.I.C.S.: 337212
Herbert Muller (Chm-Mgmt Bd)

Subsidiaries:

BauschLinnemann North America, Inc.   (1)
1175 Harrelson Blvd, Myrtle Beach, SC 29577
Decorative Surface Foil Mfr & Distr
N.A.I.C.S.: 322220

Chapacinta S.A. de C.V.   (1)
Av Recursos Hidraulicos No 224 Col San Pablo Tultitlan, CP 54930, Mexico, Mexico
Tel.: (52) 58856811
Web Site: https://www.chapacinta.com
Adhesive Material Mfr
N.A.I.C.S.: 325520

Dollken Profiles GmbH   (1)
Industriestrasse 1, 59199, Bonen, Germany
Tel.: (49) 36434170711
Web Site: https://www.doellken-profiles.com
Skirting Board Mfr
N.A.I.C.S.: 321918

AND PRIVATE COMPANIES

Dollken Sp.z o.o. (1)
ul K K Baczyskiego 25E, 41-203, Sosnowiec, Poland
Tel.: (48) 327812090
Web Site: https://www.doellken.pl
Light-Emitting Diode Light Mfr & Distr
N.A.I.C.S.: 334511

Gislaved Folie AB (1)
Abjornsgatan 8, 332 36, Gislaved, Sweden
Tel.: (46) 37183700
Web Site: https://www.gislavedfolie.se
Plastic Foil Mfr & Distr
N.A.I.C.S.: 326199

Nenplas Limited (1)
Blenheim Rd Airfield Industrial Est, Ashbourne, Derby, DE6 1HA, Derbyshire, United Kingdom (85%)
Tel.: (44) 1335 340340
Web Site: http://www.nenplas.co.uk
Plastic Extrusion & Injection Molding
N.A.I.C.S.: 314120

OOO SURTECO (1)
Tel.: (7) 4952801056
Web Site: https://www.surteco.ru
Furniture Decorative Surface Distr
N.A.I.C.S.: 423220
Rashid Ibragimov (Gen Dir)

P.T. Doellken Bintan Edgings & Profiles (1)
Panbil Industrial Estate Type C2 Lot 2 Jalan Ahmad Yani, Muka Kuning-Sungei, Batam, 29433, Indonesia
Tel.: (62) 6562260669
Decorative Surfacing Material Mfr & Distr
N.A.I.C.S.: 321918

Polyplas Extrusions Ltd. (1)
Unit 1 Wilden Industrial Estate Wilden Lane, Stourport-on-Severn, DY13 9JY, United Kingdom
Tel.: (44) 1299827344
Web Site: https://www.polyplasextrusions.co.uk
Plastic Extrusion Mfr & Distr
N.A.I.C.S.: 326199

Proadec Brasil Ltda. (1)
Rua Leozir Ferreira dos Santos 705, Sao Jose dos Pinhais, 83090-590, Parana, Brazil
Tel.: (55) 4132992300
Web Site: https://www.proadec.com.br
Plastics Product Mfr
N.A.I.C.S.: 326199
Alvaro Rodrigues (Mgr-Sls Industry)

Proadec Portugal, S.A. (1)
Mindelo, 4486-851, Vila do Conde, Portugal
Tel.: (351) 229287000
Web Site: https://www.proadec.com
Furniture Thermoplastic Edge Mfr & Distr
N.A.I.C.S.: 337127
Tiago Rocha (Mgr-Sls & Logistics)

Proadec UK Ltd. (1)
Unit 5-6 Quadrant Court Thames Street Crossways Business Park, Greenhithe, DA9 9AY, Kent, United Kingdom
Tel.: (44) 1322382932
Web Site: http://www.proadec.co.uk
Adhesive Material Mfr
N.A.I.C.S.: 325520

SURTECO Art GmbH (1)
Niersweg 80, 47877, Willich, Germany
Tel.: (49) 2156599830
Web Site: https://www.surteco-art.com
Furniture Decorative Surface Mfr
N.A.I.C.S.: 337127

SURTECO Australia Pty. Ltd. (1)
7-11 Penelope Crescent, Arndell Park, 2148, NSW, Australia
Tel.: (61) 294210300
Web Site: https://www.surteco.com
Decorative Surface Foil Mfr
N.A.I.C.S.: 322220
Wayne Crews (CFO)

SURTECO Canada Ltd. (1)
230 Orenda Road, Brampton, L6T 1E9, ON, Canada
Tel.: (905) 759-1074
Web Site: http://www.na.surteco.com
Decorative Surface Foil Mfr & Distr
N.A.I.C.S.: 322220

SURTECO Decorative Material Co. Ltd. (1)
Unit 306 Block 10 LiHe technology Park 99 Taoyuan Road, East Nanhai District, Foshan, 528225, China
Tel.: (86) 75766813008
Wood Product Mfr & Distr
N.A.I.C.S.: 333243

SURTECO Dekor A.S. (1)
Akcaburgaz Cad Akcaburgaz Mah No 89, Esenyurt, 34510, Istanbul, Turkiye
Tel.: (90) 2128869430
Web Site: http://www.surteco.com.tr
Furniture Decorative Surface Distr
N.A.I.C.S.: 423220
Emre Ozbay (Gen Dir)

SURTECO France S.A.S. (1)
2 Rue du Tertre Z I Angers Beaucouze, 49070, Beaucouze, France
Tel.: (33) 241810130
Web Site: https://www.fr.surteco.com
Plastic Product Distr
N.A.I.C.S.: 424610

SURTECO GmbH (1)
Przedstawicielstwo w Polsce ul Slonimskiego 7/11, 80-280, Gdansk, Poland
Tel.: (48) 587101475
Furniture Thermoplastic Edge Mfr & Distr
N.A.I.C.S.: 337127

SURTECO Iberia S.L. (1)
C/ Serrano 93 - 6 C, 28006, Madrid, Spain
Tel.: (34) 915619006
Web Site: http://www.es.surteco.com
Furniture Decorative Surface Distr
N.A.I.C.S.: 423220

SURTECO North America Inc. (1)
1175 Harrelson Blvd, Myrtle Beach, SC 29577
Wood Product Mfr & Distr
N.A.I.C.S.: 333243

SURTECO Pte. Ltd. (1)
25 International Business Park 02-70/71 German Centre, Singapore, 609916, Singapore
Tel.: (65) 62260669
Decorative Surface Foil Mfr
N.A.I.C.S.: 322220
Christoph Koelnsperger (Area Mgr-Sls)

SURTECO UK Ltd. (1)
Widow Hill Road, Burnley, BB10 2TB, Lancashire, United Kingdom
Tel.: (44) 1282686850
Web Site: https://www.surteco.co.uk
Furniture Decorative Surface Distr
N.A.I.C.S.: 423220
Kim Hughes (Mng Dir)

SURTECO USA Inc. (1)
7104 Cessna Dr, Greensboro, NC 27409
Tel.: (336) 668-9555
Decorative Surface Foil Mfr & Distr
N.A.I.C.S.: 322220

SURUGA BANK LTD.
Tel.: (81) 559620080
Web Site: https://www.surugabank.co.jp
Year Founded: 1895
8358—(TKS)
Rev.: $604,464,670
Assets: $23,536,498,010
Liabilities: $21,585,754,810
Net Worth: $1,950,743,200
Earnings: $92,540
Emp.: 1,214
Fiscal Year-end: 03/31/24
Bank Services
N.A.I.C.S.: 522110
Michio Arikuni (Pres)

Subsidiaries:

Suruga Card Co., Ltd. (1)
1-7-1 Nihonbashi Muromachi, Chuo-ku, Tokyo, 103-0022, Japan
Tel.: (81) 559520202
Web Site: https://www.suruga-card.co.jp
Emp.: 27
Credit Card Solution Services
N.A.I.C.S.: 522320

Suruga Computer Service Co., Ltd. (1)
500-12 Hachibundaira Higashino, Nagaizumi-cho Sunto-gun, Shizuoka, 411-0931, Japan
Tel.: (81) 559871121
Web Site: https://www.suruga-csk.co.jp
Software Development Services
N.A.I.C.S.: 541511

SURYA INDIA LTD.
B-1/F-12 Mohan Co-Operative Industrial Estate Mathura Road, New Delhi, 110 044, India
Tel.: (91) 1145204100
Web Site: https://www.suryaindialtd.com
Year Founded: 1956
539253—(BOM)
Rev.: $521,156
Assets: $16,928,446
Liabilities: $1,168,371
Net Worth: $15,760,074
Earnings: $69,648
Emp.: 3
Fiscal Year-end: 03/31/23
Financial Support Services
N.A.I.C.S.: 523999
Jitesh Grover (Officer-Compliance & Sec)

SURYA PHARMACEUTICAL LIMITED
1596 First Floor Bhagirath Place Chandni Chowk, Delhi, 110006, India
Tel.: (91) 195 245350
Web Site: http://www.suryapharma.com
Sales Range: $10-24.9 Million
Emp.: 2,500
Pharmaceuticals Products & Services
N.A.I.C.S.: 524114

SURYA ROSHNI LIMITED
Padma Tower-1 Rajendra Place, New Delhi, 110008, India
Tel.: (91) 1125810093
Web Site: https://www.surya.co.in
Year Founded: 1973
SURYAROSNI—(BOM)
Rev.: $759,771,285
Assets: $401,502,465
Liabilities: $214,868,745
Net Worth: $186,633,720
Earnings: $21,609,315
Emp.: 3,407
Fiscal Year-end: 03/31/21
Lighting Equipment Mfr
N.A.I.C.S.: 335139
Jai Prakash Agarwal (Chm)

Subsidiaries:

Surya Roshni Led Lighting Projects Limited (1)
Padma Tower - 1 Rajendra Place, New Delhi, 110008, India
Tel.: (91) 1147108000
Light Mfr
N.A.I.C.S.: 335132

SURYAAMBA SPINNING MILLS LIMITED
1st Floor Surya Towers 105 Sardar Patel Road, Secunderabad, 500 003, Andhra Pradesh, India
Tel.: (91) 4027813360
Web Site: https://www.suryaamba.com
Year Founded: 2007
533101—(BOM)
Rev.: $30,004,496
Assets: $16,273,821
Liabilities: $9,012,505
Net Worth: $7,261,315
Earnings: $948,241
Emp.: 829
Fiscal Year-end: 03/31/23

Spinning Mill Operator
Virender Kumar Agarwal (Chm & Co-Mng Dir)

SURYACHAKRA POWER CORPORATION LTD
Suryachakra House Plot No 304 L III Road No 78, Jubilee Hills, Hyderabad, 500 096, India
Tel.: (91) 4030823000
Web Site: http://www.suryachakra.in
532874—(BOM)
Sales Range: $10-24.9 Million
Emp.: 29
Power Generation
N.A.I.C.S.: 221112

SURYAJYOTI LIFE INSURANCE COMPANY LTD.
Sano Gaucharan, Kathmandu, Nepal
Tel.: (977) 14545941
Web Site: https://suryajyotilife.com
Year Founded: 2008
SJLIC—(NEP)
Sales Range: $25-49.9 Million
Insurance Services
N.A.I.C.S.: 524298
Keshab Prasad Bhattarai (Chm)

SURYAJYOTI SPINNING MILLS LIMITED
7th Floor Surya Towers S P Road, Secunderabad, 500 003, India
Tel.: (91) 4027810086
Web Site: http://www.suryajyoti.com
Year Founded: 1992
Yarn Mfr
N.A.I.C.S.: 339999
Arun Kumar Agarwal (Exec Dir)

SURYALAKSHMI COTTON MILLS LIMITED
Surya Towers 6th Floor 105 Sardar Patel Road, Secunderabad, 500 003, Telangana, India
Tel.: (91) 4027819856
Web Site: https://www.suryalakshmi.com
Year Founded: 1962
SURYALAXMI—(BOM)
Rev.: $102,786,596
Assets: $78,418,824
Liabilities: $46,882,333
Net Worth: $31,536,491
Earnings: $1,247,060
Emp.: 1,730
Fiscal Year-end: 03/31/23
Yarn Mfr
N.A.I.C.S.: 339999
L. N. Agarwal (Chm & Mng Dir)

Subsidiaries:

Suryakiran International Ltd (1)
Surya Towers 6th Floor 105 Sardar Patel Road, Secunderabad, 500 003, Andhra Pradesh, India
Tel.: (91) 40 27819856
Web Site: http://www.suryakiranintl.com
Sales Range: $25-49.9 Million
Emp.: 15
Denim Garment Mfr
N.A.I.C.S.: 313210

SURYALATA SPINNING MILLS LIMITED
Surya Towers 1st Floor 105 Sardar Patel Road, Secunderabad, 500 003, India
Tel.: (91) 4027774200
Web Site: https://www.suryalata.com
514138—(BOM)
Rev.: $58,427,888
Assets: $41,735,951
Liabilities: $14,268,437
Net Worth: $27,467,514
Earnings: $4,047,623

SURYALATA SPINNING MILLS LIMITED

Suryalata Spinning Mills Limited—(Continued)
Emp.: 445
Fiscal Year-end: 03/31/23
Synthetic Yarn Mfr & Distr
N.A.I.C.S.: 313110
Vithaldas Agarwal (Co-Mng Dir)

SURYAVANSHI SPINNING MILLS LIMITED
Surya Towers 6th Floor 105 Sardar Patel Road, Secunderabad, 500 003, AP, India
Tel.: (91) 40 30512700
Web Site:
http://www.suryavanshi.com
Year Founded: 1978
Sales Range: $1-9.9 Million
Yarn Mfr
N.A.I.C.S.: 313110
B.N. Agarwal (Chm)

SURYO FOODS & INDUSTRIES LIMITED
Dinalipi Bhawan A-54/1 & A-55/1 Nayapalli Baramunda, Bhubaneswar, 751 003, Orissa, India
Tel.: (91) 6742563832
Web Site:
https://www.suryofoods.com
Year Founded: 1989
519604—(BOM)
Rev.: $50,920
Assets: $409,532
Liabilities: $875,283
Net Worth: ($465,751)
Earnings: ($19,231)
Fiscal Year-end: 03/31/23
Frozen Prawn Processing Services
N.A.I.C.S.: 311710
Amarendra Dash (Chm & Mng Dir)

SURYODAY ALLO-METALS POWDERS LIMITED
302 B - Wing Narayan Chambers 555 Narayan Peth, Pune, 411 030, India
Tel.: (91) 20 2543 8635
Web Site:
http://www.suryodayallometals.com
Year Founded: 1993
Sales Range: $10-24.9 Million
Iron & Steel Product Whslr
N.A.I.C.S.: 423510
Sanjay Sonawani (Compliance Officer)

SURYODAY SMALL FINANCE BANK LTD.
Unit No 1101 Sharda Terraces Plot, No 65 Sector 11, Cbd Belapur Navi Mumbai, Mumbai, 400614, India
Tel.: (91) 2240435800
Web Site:
https://www.suryodaybank.com
Year Founded: 2008
543279—(BOM)
Rev.: $119,523,795
Assets: $916,185,993
Liabilities: $901,699,139
Net Worth: $14,486,854
Earnings: $1,618,262
Emp.: 5,131
Fiscal Year-end: 03/31/21
Banking Services
N.A.I.C.S.: 523150
Ramachandran Rajaraman (Chm)

SURYODAYA INVESTMENT & TRADING COMPANY LIMITED
714 Raheja Chambers 213, Nariman Point, Mumbai, 400 021, Maharashtra, India
Tel.: (91) 22 22022621
Web Site:
http://www.suryodayainvest.com
Year Founded: 1975

Investment Services
N.A.I.C.S.: 523999

SURYODAYA WOMI LAGHU-BITTA BITTIYA SANSTHA LTD
Banepa Municipality-1, Kavrepalanchwok, Banepa, Nepal
Tel.: (977) 15912753
Web Site: https://swmfi.com.np
WOMI—(NEP)
Financial Banking Services
N.A.I.C.S.: 522110
Bindiya Shresth Pradhan (Chm)

SUS CO., LTD.
5F Kyoto Mitsui Building 8 Nagatohokocho, Shijo-dori Karasumahigashi-iru Shimogyo-ku, Kyoto, 600-8008, Japan
Tel.: (81) 752296514
Web Site: https://www.sus-g.co.jp
Year Founded: 1999
6554—(TKS)
Rev.: $81,542,090
Assets: $35,506,720
Liabilities: $12,031,730
Net Worth: $23,474,990
Earnings: $3,268,490
Emp.: 363
Fiscal Year-end: 09/30/23
Human Resource Consulting Services
N.A.I.C.S.: 541612
Tomosada Yoshikawa (Exec VP)

Subsidiaries:

SUS(Singapore) Pte. Ltd. (1)
19 Tannery Road, Singapore, Singapore
Tel.: (65) 68424348
Emp.: 14
Unit Equipment Distr
N.A.I.C.S.: 423830

Standard Units Supply (India) Pvt. Ltd. (1)
43/1 Padasalai Street, Ayanambakkam, Chennai, Tamil Nadu, India
Tel.: (91) 4449524482
Emp.: 23
Unit Equipment Distr
N.A.I.C.S.: 423830

Standard Units Supply Philippines Corporation (1)
Building R1-D Lot 13 Phase 1B First Philippine Industrial Park, Batangas Special Economic Zone, Tanauan, Philippines
Tel.: (63) 434300290
Emp.: 37
Unit Equipment Distr
N.A.I.C.S.: 423830

Standard Units Supply Vietnam Company Limited (1)
Workshop X6 Hai Thanh Leasing workshop area, Hai Thanh Ward Duong Kinh District, Haiphong, Vietnam
Tel.: (84) 2253632403
Emp.: 75
Unit Equipment Distr
N.A.I.C.S.: 423830

Stone Free Co., Ltd. (1)
5th floor Kyoto Mitsui Building, 8 Naginatabokocho Karasuma Higashiir Shijo-dori Shimogyo-ku, Kyoto, 600-8008, Japan
Web Site: http://www.stone-free.jp
Emp.: 12
Hand-Knit Product Mfr & Distr
N.A.I.C.S.: 313240

SUSCO PUBLIC COMPANY LIMITED
139 Ratburana Road Bangpakok, Ratburana, Bangkok, 10140, Thailand
Tel.: (66) 24280029 TH
Web Site: https://www.susco.co.th
Year Founded: 1977
SUSCO—(THA)
Rev.: $983,967,340
Assets: $286,997,671
Liabilities: $153,436,527

Net Worth: $133,561,145
Earnings: $35,787,137
Emp.: 2,517
Fiscal Year-end: 12/31/23
Fuel Distribution Services
N.A.I.C.S.: 457210
Mongkol Simaroj (Chm)

SUSGLOBAL ENERGY CORP.
200 Davenport Road, Toronto, M5R 1J2, ON, Canada
Tel.: (416) 223-8500 DE
Web Site:
https://www.susglobalenergy.com
Year Founded: 2014
SNRG—(OTCQB)
Rev.: $610,461
Assets: $11,755,903
Liabilities: $30,823,963
Net Worth: ($19,068,060)
Earnings: ($8,225,334)
Emp.: 5
Fiscal Year-end: 12/31/23
Waste Recycling Services
N.A.I.C.S.: 562920
Marc M. Hazout (Founder, Chm, Pres & CEO)

Subsidiaries:

SusGlobal Energy Belleville Ltd. (1)
704 Phillipston Road, Belleville, K0K 2Y0, ON, Canada
Tel.: (613) 477-2424
Solar Energy Services
N.A.I.C.S.: 221118

SUSI PARTNERS AG
Bahnhofplatz, CH-6300, Zug, Switzerland
Tel.: (41) 582557575
Web Site: https://www.susi-partners.com
Year Founded: 2009
Investment Services
N.A.I.C.S.: 523999
Marius Dorfmeister (Co-CEO & Head-Global Clients)

Subsidiaries:

Encore Redevelopment, LLC (1)
110 Main St 2nd Fl Ste 2E, Burlington, VT 05401
Tel.: (802) 861-3023
Web Site:
http://www.encoreredevelopment.com
Activities Related to Real Estate
N.A.I.C.S.: 531390
Chad Farrell (Founder & CEO)

SUSMED, INC.
MFPR Nihonbashi Honcho Building 10th floor 3-7-2 Nihonbashi Honcho, Chuo-ku, Tokyo, 103-0023, Japan
Web Site: https://www.susmed.co.jp
Year Founded: 2015
4263—(TKS)
Biotechnology Research & Development Services
N.A.I.C.S.: 541714

SUSS MICROTEC SE
Schleissheimer Strasse 90, 85748, Garching, Germany
Tel.: (49) 89320070 De
Web Site: https://www.suss.com
Year Founded: 1960
SMHN—(STU)
Rev.: $328,363,911
Assets: $399,020,073
Liabilities: $208,412,476
Net Worth: $190,607,598
Earnings: $18,708,180
Emp.: 1,345
Fiscal Year-end: 12/31/23
Microstructuring Applications Equipment & Process Solutions Mfr
N.A.I.C.S.: 551112
Burkhardt Frick (CEO)

Subsidiaries:

SUSS MicroTec (Taiwan) Co., Ltd (1)
7F No 7 Li-Hsin 3rd Rd, Hsinchu Science Park, Hsin-chu, 300094, Taiwan (100%)
Tel.: (886) 35169098
Sales Range: $25-49.9 Million
Emp.: 50
Industrial Machinery Mfr
N.A.I.C.S.: 333248

SUSS MicroTec (Singapore) Pte. Ltd. (1)
21 Bukit Batok Crescent, Wcega Tower 05-70, Singapore, 658065, Singapore
Tel.: (65) 62715780
Semiconductor Equipment Mfr
N.A.I.C.S.: 333242

SUSS MicroTec Company Ltd (1)
Room 3703 LL Land Plaza, 580 Nanjing W Rd, Shanghai, 200041, China
Tel.: (86) 2152340432
Sales Range: $25-49.9 Million
Emp.: 20
Testing Laboratories
N.A.I.C.S.: 541380
Li Gong (Mng Dir)

SUSS MicroTec KK (1)
BENEX S-3 5F 3-20-8 Shin-Yokohama, Kohoku-ku, Yokohama, 222-0033, Kanagawa, Japan (100%)
Tel.: (81) 454753556
Web Site: https://www.suss.jp
Sales Range: $25-49.9 Million
Emp.: 45
Industrial Machinery & Equipment Whslr
N.A.I.C.S.: 423830
Hiroyuki Ishida (Mgr-Bus Dev)

SUSS MicroTec Lithography GmbH (1)
Schleissheimer Str 90, D-85748, Garching, Germany
Tel.: (49) 89320070
Web Site: https://www.suss.com
Testing Devices Mfr
N.A.I.C.S.: 334515

SUSS MicroTec Lithography GmbH (1)
Ferdinand-von-Steinbeis-Ring 10, 75447, Sternenfels, Germany (100%)
Tel.: (49) 7045410
Web Site: http://www.suss.com
Sales Range: $10-24.9 Million
Emp.: 80
Photolithographic, Semiconductor & Magnetic Storage Machinery Mfr
N.A.I.C.S.: 333248

Subsidiary (US):

HamaTech USA, Inc. (2)
1826 B Kramer Ln, Austin, TX 78758 (100%)
Tel.: (512) 929-1880
Photolithographic, Semiconductor & Magnetic Storage Machinery Mfr
N.A.I.C.S.: 333248

SUSS MicroTec Ltd. (1)
The Apex 2 Sheriffs Orchard, Coventry, CV1 3PP, United Kingdom (100%)
Tel.: (44) 1606891936
Web Site: https://www.suss.com
Instruments for Measuring & Testing Electricity & Electrical Signals
N.A.I.C.S.: 334515
Rolf Wolf (Mng Dir)

SUSS MicroTec Photomask Equipment GmbH & Co. KG (1)
Ferdinand-von-Steinbeis-Ring 10, 75447, Sternenfels, Germany
Tel.: (49) 7045410
Semiconductor Equipment Mfr
N.A.I.C.S.: 333242

SUSS MicroTec Reman GmbH (1)
Mittenheimerstr 60, 85764, Oberschleissheim, Germany (100%)
Tel.: (49) 8932007563
Web Site: https://www.sussreman.com
Semiconductor & Related Device Mfr
N.A.I.C.S.: 334413
Rolf Wolf (Gen Mgr)

AND PRIVATE COMPANIES — SUUMAYA CORPORATION LTD.

SUSS MicroTec S.a.r.l. (1)
74A Boulevard le I Europe BP 13, 69491,
Pierre-Benite, Cedex, France
Tel.: (33) 966903163
Semiconductor Equipment Mfr
N.A.I.C.S.: 333242

SUSS MicroTec, Inc. (1)
2520 Palisades Dr, Corona, CA 92882
Tel.: (951) 817-3700
Semiconductor Equipment Mfr
N.A.I.C.S.: 333242
Gary Choquette *(Pres & Gen Mgr)*

Suss MicroTec Korea Co. Ltd (1)
41F Gangnam Finance Center 737
Yeoksam-Dong, Gangnam-Gu, Seoul, 135-984, Korea (South)
Tel.: (82) 2 2008 4656
Microelectronics Equipment Mfr & Distr.
N.A.I.C.S.: 334419

Suss MicroTec S.A.S (1)
320 Avenue Berthelot, 69371, Lyon, France
Tel.: (33) 963599025
Web Site: https://www.suss.com
Sales Range: $25-49.9 Million
Emp.: 5
Semiconductor Devices Mfr
N.A.I.C.S.: 334413
Wolf Rolf *(Gen Mgr)*

SUSSEX INSURANCE AGENCY INCORPORATED
136 W 3rd St Upper Level, North
Vancouver, V7M 1E8, BC, Canada
Tel.: (604) 983-6955
Web Site:
 http://www.sussexinsurance.com
Year Founded: 1976
Insurance Agency Services
N.A.I.C.S.: 524210
Ken Armstrong *(Founder, Pres & CEO)*

SUSTAINED INFRASTRUCTURE HOLDING COMPANY SJSC
Saudi Business Center Suite 501 Al
Madinah Road, PO Box 14221, Jeddah, 21424, Saudi Arabia
Tel.: (966) 126619500
Web Site: https://www.sisco.com.sa
Year Founded: 1988
2190—(SAU)
Rev: $264,987,869
Assets: $1,348,708,413
Liabilities: $731,140,118
Net Worth: $617,568,295
Earnings: $14,805,659
Emp.: 4,676
Fiscal Year-end: 12/31/22
Financial Investment Services
N.A.I.C.S.: 523999
Mohammed Al-Mudarres *(CEO)*

Subsidiaries:

Kindasa Water Services Company (1)
Sari Gate Building Tower B Third Floor
Suite 304 Sari Street, Jeddah, 21482,
Saudi Arabia
Tel.: (966) 126067818
Web Site: http://www.kindasa.com
Water Services
N.A.I.C.S.: 221310
Fawzi M. Adel Habhab *(CEO & Mng Dir)*

Red Sea Gateway Terminal Company Limited (1)
PO Box 51327, Jeddah, 21543, Saudi Arabia
Tel.: (966) 126273000
Web Site: http://www.rsgt.com
Logistic Services
N.A.I.C.S.: 541614
Jens O. Floe *(CEO)*

SUTL ENTERPRISE LIMITED
100J Pasir Panjang Road No 05-00,
Singapore, 118525, Singapore
Tel.: (65) 62788555
Web Site:
 https://www.sutlenterprise.com
BHU—(SES)
Rev: $30,380,974
Assets: $96,219,041
Liabilities: $49,246,383
Net Worth: $46,972,658
Earnings: $5,666,894
Emp.: 175
Fiscal Year-end: 12/31/23
Electronic & IT-Related Product Distr.
N.A.I.C.S.: 423430
Arthur Teng Guan Tay *(Chm & CEO)*

Subsidiaries:

Achieva Investments Pte Ltd (1)
240 Macpherson Road, # 02-04 Pines Industrial Bld, 348574, Singapore,
Singapore (100%)
Tel.: (65) 68414898
Sales Range: $50-74.9 Million
Emp.: 55
Miscellaneous Financial Investment Activities
N.A.I.C.S.: 523999

Astone Holdings Pty Ltd (1)
Unit 7-8 5 Dunlop Street Strathfield South,
Sydney, 2136, NSW, Australia (70%)
Tel.: (61) 297423288
Web Site: http://www.astone.com.au
Sales Range: $25-49.9 Million
Emp.: 12
Other Computer Peripheral Equipment Mfr
N.A.I.C.S.: 334118

ONE15 Luxury Yachting Pte. Ltd. (1)
11 Cove Drive 01-01 Sentosa Cove, Singapore, 098497, Singapore
Tel.: (65) 63059676
Web Site:
 https://www.one15luxuryyachting.com
Yacht Rental Services
N.A.I.C.S.: 532284

PT. ATIKOM Mega Pratama (1)
Jl Mangga Dua Abdad Komp, Rukan
Mangga Dua Elok B/16, 10730, Jakarta,
Indonesia
Tel.: (62) 216123612
Other Computer Related Services
N.A.I.C.S.: 541519

Verdure Xchange Tech Inc. (1)
2/F Topy Main Bldg 3 Economia St, Bagumbayan Libis, Quezon City, 1110, Metro Manila, Philippines (100%)
Tel.: (63) 2 636 8069
Web Site: https://verdurexchange.com
Sales Range: $25-49.9 Million
Emp.: 52
Other Computer Peripheral Equipment
Manufacturing
N.A.I.C.S.: 334118

SUTOR TECHNOLOGY GROUP LTD.
No 8 Huaye Road Dongbang Industrial Park, Changshu, 215534, Jiangsu, China
Tel.: (86) 51252680988
Web Site: http://www.sutorcn.com
Sales Range: $400-449.9 Million
Emp.: 537
Mfr of Steel Finishing Fabrication
Products
N.A.I.C.S.: 332111
Lifang Chen *(Chm & CEO)*

Subsidiaries:

ChangShu Huaye Steel Strip Co.,Ltd (1)
No 8 Huaye Rd Dongbang Industrial Park,
Changshu, 215534, Jiangsu, China
Tel.: (86) 51252686877
Web Site: http://www.sutorcn.com
Steel Products Mfr
N.A.I.C.S.: 332312
Charlie Zhang *(Mgr-Sls)*

SUTTON HARBOUR GROUP PLC
Guys Quay Sutton Harbour, Plymouth, PL4 0ES, United Kingdom
Tel.: (44) 1752204186 UK
Web Site:
 https://suttonharbourgroup.com
Year Founded: 1989
SUH—(LSE)
Rev: $9,767,438
Assets: $121,287,843
Liabilities: $44,969,044
Net Worth: $76,318,799
Earnings: ($351,649)
Emp.: 28
Fiscal Year-end: 03/31/22
Holding Company; Marina Owner &
Operator
N.A.I.C.S.: 551112
Mark Brimacombe *(Mgr-Marina)*

Subsidiaries:

Newquay Cornwall International Airport Limited (1)
North Quay House, Plymouth, PL4 0RA,
United Kingdom (100%)
Tel.: (44) 1752204186
Sales Range: $25-49.9 Million
Emp.: 22
Law firm
N.A.I.C.S.: 541110

Plymouth City Airport Limited (1)
Crownhill, Plymouth, PL6 8BW, United
Kingdom
Tel.: (44) 1752204090
Web Site: http://www.plymouthairport.com
Oil Transportation Services
N.A.I.C.S.: 488190

Plymouth Fisheries Limited (1)
N Quay House, Plymouth, PL40 LH, United Kingdom (100%)
Tel.: (44) 1752204186
Web Site: http://www.plymouthfisheries.com
Sales Range: $25-49.9 Million
Emp.: 25
Marine Cargo Handling
N.A.I.C.S.: 488320
Graham Miller *(Chm)*

Sutton Harbour Company (1)
Sutton Harbour Office Guy's Quay Sutton
Harbour, Plymouth, PL4 0ES, United
Kingdom (100%)
Tel.: (44) 1752204186
Web Site: http://www.sutton-harbour.co.uk
Sales Range: $25-49.9 Million
Emp.: 40
Water Transportation Services
N.A.I.C.S.: 488390

Sutton Harbour Development Limited (1)
N Quay House, PL4 0RA, Plymouth, United Kingdom - England (100%)
Tel.: (44) 1752204186
Web Site: http://www.sutton-harbour.co.uk
Sales Range: $25-49.9 Million
Law firm
N.A.I.C.S.: 541199

Sutton Harbour Services Limited (1)
North Quay House, Plymouth, PL4 0RA,
United Kingdom (100%)
Tel.: (44) 1752204186
Web Site: http://www.sutton-harbour.co.uk
Sales Range: $25-49.9 Million
Emp.: 22
Ship Building & Repairing
N.A.I.C.S.: 336611
Michael A. Knight *(Chm)*

SUTTONS CONSUMER PRODUCTS LIMITED
Woodview Road, Paignton, TQ4
7NG, Devon, United Kingdom
Tel.: (44) 8443262200 UK
Web Site: http://www.suttons.co.uk
Year Founded: 1806
Sales Range: $10-24.9 Million
Emp.: 100
Home Garden Seed, Bulb, Shrub &
Tree Production & Distr
N.A.I.C.S.: 111422
David Robinson *(Mng Dir)*

SUTTONS MOTORS
484 Victoria Street, Wetherill Park,
2164, NSW, Australia
Tel.: (61) 287118619
Web Site: http://www.suttons.com.au
Year Founded: 1943
Emp.: 1,300
Automotive Retailer
N.A.I.C.S.: 441110
Nick Petkovski *(Gen Mgr)*

SUTTONS TRANSPORT GROUP LTD.
Gorsey Lane, Widnes, WA8 0GG,
Cheshire, United Kingdom
Tel.: (44) 151 420 20 20
Web Site:
 http://www.suttonsgroup.com
Year Founded: 1926
Emp.: 600
Bulk Transport, Storage & Llogistics
Services
N.A.I.C.S.: 488999
John Sutton *(CEO)*

Subsidiaries:

Suttons International Freight Forwarding (Shanghai) Co., Ltd (1)
Unit D 9/F Long Life Mansion 1566 Yan An
West Road, Shanghai, 200052, China
Tel.: (86) 2152586000
Freight Forwarding Services
N.A.I.C.S.: 488510

Suttons International GmbH (1)
Speyerer Str 56b, 67227, Frankenthal, Germany
Tel.: (49) 62333533152
Transport Support Services
N.A.I.C.S.: 488999

Suttons International Japan KK (1)
Rm 203 Saito Bldg 14-6 Kyobashi 3-chome,
Chuo-ku, Tokyo, 104-0031, Japan
Tel.: (81) 362287486
Transport Support Services
N.A.I.C.S.: 488999

Suttons International N.A. Inc. (1)
6723 Atasca S Ct, Humble, TX 77346
Tel.: (281) 973-9460
Transport Support Services
N.A.I.C.S.: 488999

Suttons International NV (1)
North Trade Building Noorderlaan 133, Antwerp, Belgium
Tel.: (32) 35400033
Transport Support Services
N.A.I.C.S.: 488999
Koen Lauryssen *(Mgr-Ops)*

Suttons International Singapore Pte Ltd (1)
3 Harbour front Place 05-03/04 Harbourfront Tower 2, Singapore, 99254, Singapore
Tel.: (65) 65156720
Transport Support Services
N.A.I.C.S.: 488999
Jinqiang Tan *(Gen Mgr)*

Suttons Malaysia (1)
B30 2nd Floor Lorong Tun Ismail 1, 25000,
Kuantan, Pahang, Malaysia
Tel.: (60) 95171006
Transport Support Services
N.A.I.C.S.: 488999

SUUMAYA CORPORATION LTD.
542 Grand Trunk Road Near Mullick
Fatak Howrah Railway Station, Bally
Jagachha, Howrah, 711101, West
Bengal, India
Tel.: (91) 2269218000
Web Site:
 https://suumayacorporation.com
Year Founded: 2009
543274—(BOM)
Rev: $4,889,395
Assets: $80,358,492
Liabilities: $68,958,696
Net Worth: $11,399,796

SUUMAYA CORPORATION LTD.

Suumaya Corporation Ltd—(Continued)
Earnings: ($4,545,291)
Emp.: 2
Fiscal Year-end: 03/31/23
Textile Products Mfr
N.A.I.C.S.: 313310
Ushik Gala (Chm & Mng Dir)

SUVEN LIFE SCIENCES LTD.
6th Floor SDE Serene Chambers,
Avenue 7 Road No 5 Banjara Hills,
Hyderabad, 500 034, Telangana, India
Tel.: (91) 4023541142
Web Site: https://www.suven.com
Year Founded: 1989
530239—(BOM)
Rev.: $2,898,168
Assets: $17,529,057
Liabilities: $2,786,279
Net Worth: $14,742,778
Earnings: ($9,848,639)
Emp.: 130
Fiscal Year-end: 03/31/21
Pharmaceuticals Product Mfr
N.A.I.C.S.: 325412
Venkateswarlu Jasti (Chm & CEO)

Subsidiaries:

Rising Pharma Holdings, Inc. (1)
Park 80 W Plaza 1 250 Pehle Ave Ste 601,
Saddle Brook, NJ 07663
Tel.: (201) 961-9000
Holding Company
N.A.I.C.S.: 551112

Subsidiary (Domestic):

Rising Pharmaceuticals, LLC (2)
2 Tower Ctr Blvd Ste 1401A, Saddle Brook,
NJ 08816
Tel.: (201) 961-9000
Web Site: https://www.risingpharma.com
Pharmaceuticals Mfr
N.A.I.C.S.: 325412
Eric Schumacher (Sr VP)

Suven Neurosciences Inc. (1)
1100 Cornwall Rd Ste 110, Monmouth
Junction, NJ 08852
Tel.: (732) 718-9024
Web Site: https://www.suvenneuro.com
Biopharmaceutical Research Services
N.A.I.C.S.: 541714

SUVIDHA INFRAESTATE CORPORATION LIMITED
A-305/306 Krishna Complex Opp
DevashishSchool Bodakdev,
Ahmedabad, 380054, Gujarat, India
Tel.: (91) 7926872845
Web Site: https://www.sicl.in
Year Founded: 1992
531640—(BOM)
Rev.: $84
Assets: $322,307
Liabilities: $640,309
Net Worth: ($318,003)
Earnings: ($32,720)
Emp.: 7
Fiscal Year-end: 03/31/23
Real Estate Development Services
N.A.I.C.S.: 531390
Ashok Kumar Goswami (Exec Dir)

SUVIDHAA INFOSERVE LIMITED
Mahakali Caves Road, Andheri East,
Mumbai, 400093, Maharashtra, India
Tel.: (91) 2267765300
Web Site: https://www.suvidhaa.com
Year Founded: 2007
SUVIDHAA—(BOM)
Rev.: $15,931,461
Assets: $17,002,577
Liabilities: $5,901,714
Net Worth: $11,100,863
Earnings: ($549,822)
Emp.: 40

Fiscal Year-end: 03/31/21
Financial Services
N.A.I.C.S.: 522390
Tanuj Paresh Rajde (Chm)

SUWEN ELECTRIC ENERGY TECHNOLOGY CO., LTD.
No 3 Changfan Road, Wujin Economic Development Zone,
Changzhou, 213100, Jiangsu, China
Tel.: (86) 51969897107
Web Site: http://www.swdnkj.com
Year Founded: 2007
300982—(SSE)
Rev.: $330,956,538
Assets: $666,680,218
Liabilities: $238,970,207
Net Worth: $427,710,011
Earnings: $35,962,449
Fiscal Year-end: 12/31/22
Energy Distribution Services
N.A.I.C.S.: 221122
Xiaobo Shi (Chm & Gen Mgr)

SUXIN JOYFUL LIFE SERVICES CO., LTD.
Room 3001 30/F SND International
Commerce Tower 28 Shishan Road,
Gaoxin District, Suzhou, Jiangsu,
China
Tel.: (86) 51268251855 CN
Web Site: https://www.suxinfuwu.com
Year Founded: 1994
2152—(HKG)
Rev.: $100,396,544
Assets: $223,835,982
Liabilities: $111,561,115
Net Worth: $112,274,867
Earnings: $11,093,542
Emp.: 1,647
Fiscal Year-end: 12/31/23
Property Management Services
N.A.I.C.S.: 531311

SUYOG GURBAXANI FUNICULAR ROPEWAYS LTD.
Saptashrungi God Temple Kalwan
Taluka, Mumbai, 400083, Maharashtra, India
Tel.: (91) 25795516
Web Site: https://www.sgfrl.com
543391—(BOM)
Construction Services
N.A.I.C.S.: 236210
Chirag Kalra (Sec)

SUYOG TELEMATICS LIMITED
Suyog House Plot No 30 MIDC Central Road Andheri East, Vikhroli West,
Mumbai, 400093, Maharashtra, India
Tel.: (91) 2225795516
Web Site:
https://www.suyogtelematics.co.in
Year Founded: 1995
537259—(BOM)
Rev.: $18,258,174
Assets: $57,523,710
Liabilities: $29,436,796
Net Worth: $28,086,913
Earnings: $5,551,933
Emp.: 389
Fiscal Year-end: 03/31/23
Poles, Towers & Fiber Optic Cable
Systems Installer
N.A.I.C.S.: 237130
Shivshankar Lature (Mng Dir)

SUZANO HOLDING S.A.
Av Brigadeiro Faria Lima 1355, do 6
ao 8 andar Pinheiros, Sao Paulo,
1452-919, SP, Brazil
Tel.: (55) 1135039320
Web Site: http://www.suzano.com.br
Sales Range: $1-4.9 Billion
Emp.: 3,000
Holding Company

N.A.I.C.S.: 551112

Subsidiaries:

Sun Paper and Board Limited (1)
2 Churchill Court Hortons Way, Westerham,
TN16 1BT, Kent, United Kingdom
Tel.: (44) 1959 568040
Web Site: http://www.sunfinepapers.com
Emp.: 3
Paper Board Mfr & Distr
N.A.I.C.S.: 322211
Seb Douglas (Gen Mgr)

Suzano Pulp and Paper America
Inc. (1)
800 Corporate Dr Ste 320, Fort Lauderdale,
FL 33334
Tel.: (954) 772-7716
Web Site: http://www.susano.com
Pulp & Paper Product Distr
N.A.I.C.S.: 424130
Fernando Silveira (Mgr-Logistics & Customer Svc)

Suzano Pulp and Paper Asia
S.A. (1)
3201 United Plaza n 1 468 Nanjing West
Road, Shanghai, 200040, China
Tel.: (86) 21 6289 2817
Pulp & Paper Product Distr
N.A.I.C.S.: 424130
Jeff Yang (Mng Dir)

Suzano Pulp and Paper Europe
S.A. (1)
En Flechere 5, 1274, Signy, Switzerland
Tel.: (41) 22 596 4646
Web Site: http://www.suzano.com.br
Pulp & Paper Product Distr
N.A.I.C.S.: 424130

Suzano S.A. (1)
Professor Magalhaes Neto Avenue, Salvador, 1752, Bahia, Brazil
Tel.: (55) 1135039000
Web Site: http://www.suzano.com.br
Rev.: $7,928,123,442
Assets: $28,635,561,871
Liabilities: $19,699,416,692
Net Worth: $8,936,145,179
Earnings: $2,813,118,157
Emp.: 20,627
Fiscal Year-end: 12/31/2023
Paper Products Mfr
N.A.I.C.S.: 333243
Walter Schalka (CEO)

Subsidiary (Domestic):

Fibria Celulose S.A. (2)
Rua Fidencio Ramos 302 Villa Olimpia,
04551-010, Sao Paulo, Brazil
Tel.: (55) 11 2138 4565
Web Site: http://www.fibria-institucional-qa.azurewebsites.net
Sales Range: $1-4.9 Billion
Coated & Uncoated Printing Paper, Thermal
& Carbonless Paper & Specialty Paper Producer
N.A.I.C.S.: 322120
Marcelo Castelli (Pres & Member-Exec Bd)

Subsidiary (US):

Fibria Celulose USA Inc. (3)
Aventura Harbour Ctr 18851 NE 29th Ave
Ste 530, Aventura, FL 33180
Tel.: (305) 940-9762
Bleached Eucalyptus Pulp Mfr
N.A.I.C.S.: 322110

Subsidiary (Non-US):

Fibria Innovations Ltd. (3)
4705 Wayburne Dr., Burnaby, V5G 3L1,
BC, Canada
Tel.: (604) 222-9800
Web Site: http://www.lignol.ca
Biorefinery Technology Services
N.A.I.C.S.: 541715
Michael Rushton (COO)

Subsidiary (Domestic):

Lignol Innovations Ltd. (4)
101-4705 Wayburne Dr, Burnaby, V5G 3L1,
BC, Canada
Tel.: (604) 222-9800
Cellulosic Ethanol Mfr
N.A.I.C.S.: 325199

INTERNATIONAL PUBLIC

Subsidiary (Non-US):

FuturaGene Ltd. (2)
2 Pekeris Street 4th Floor, Park Tamar, Rehovot, Israel
Tel.: (972) 89319550
Web Site: http://www.futuragene.com
Sales Range: $10-24.9 Million
Emp.: 40
Biotechnology Research & Development
Services
N.A.I.C.S.: 541714
Stanley Hirsch (Pres & CEO)

SUZHOU ALTON ELECTRICAL & MECHANICAL INDUSTRY CO., LTD.
No 888 Laixiu Road, Fenhu High-tech
Development Zone Wujiang District,
Suzhou, China
Tel.: (86) 51282876660
Web Site:
https://www.altonindustries.cn
Year Founded: 2009
301187—(CHIN)
Rev.: $171,284,661
Assets: $326,960,591
Liabilities: $116,596,929
Net Worth: $210,363,661
Earnings: $24,628,775
Emp.: 200
Fiscal Year-end: 12/31/23
Electrical Component Mfr & Distr
N.A.I.C.S.: 335210
Weidong Lu (Chm)

Subsidiaries:

Alton Industry Ltd. (1)
643 Innovation Dr, West Chicago, IL 60185
Tel.: (630) 389-1030
Web Site: https://www.altonindustries.com
Industrial Fans Mfr
N.A.I.C.S.: 333413

Alton Japan Co., Ltd. (1)
7F Sanwa Building 2-2-3 Kotobashi,
Sumida-ku, Tokyo, 130-0022, Japan
Tel.: (81) 120954565
Web Site: https://www.altonjapan.co.jp
Emp.: 1,000
Industrial Machinery Mfr & Distr
N.A.I.C.S.: 333924

Shenzhen Jiede Innovation Technology Co., Ltd. (1)
Room 1001 Chuanghui Building Bantian
Street, Wuhe Longgang District, Shenzhen,
China
Tel.: (86) 75585229626
Web Site: https://www.jndclean.com
Household Appliance Distr
N.A.I.C.S.: 423620

Suzhou Illinois Medicare Robot Co.,
Ltd. (1)
No 888 Laixiu Road Fenhu Development
Zone, Wujiang District, Suzhou, China
Tel.: (86) 51282876660
Web Site: https://www.ylinuo.com
Aerodynamic Equipment Mfr & Distr
N.A.I.C.S.: 336412

SUZHOU ANJIE TECHNOLOGY CO., LTD.
No 2011 Sunwu Road Suzhou Taihu
National Tourism Vaction Zone, Xiangshan Sub-district, Suzhou,
215159, Jiangsu, China
Tel.: (86) 51266513400
Web Site: https://www.anjiecorp.com
Year Founded: 1999
002635—(SSE)
Rev.: $589,490,207
Assets: $1,091,726,518
Liabilities: $261,171,518
Net Worth: $830,555,000
Earnings: $33,028,272
Emp.: 8,000
Fiscal Year-end: 12/31/22
Functional Device & Glass Product
Mfr
N.A.I.C.S.: 334419

AND PRIVATE COMPANIES — SUZHOU GOLD MANTIS CONSTRUCTION DECORATION CO., LTD.

Wang Chunsheng *(Chm)*

Subsidiaries:

Anjie USA Inc. (1)
19925 Stevens creek Blud Ste 100, Cupertino, CA 95014
Tel.: (510) 366-3482
Metal Stamping Mfr
N.A.I.C.S.: 336370

Anjie Wireless Technology (Suzhou) Co., Ltd. (1)
No 66 Fuju Rd, Guangfu Town wuzhong district, Suzhou, China
Tel.: (86) 51266513400
Web Site: http://www.anjiewl.com
Automobile Transmission Product Mfr
N.A.I.C.S.: 336350
Weidong Chen *(Co-Founder & CEO)*

Chongqing Anjie Electronics Co., Ltd. (1)
No 990 Biqing North Road, Biquan Subdistrict Bishan District, Chongqing, China
Tel.: (86) 2341688612
Insulation Material Mfr
N.A.I.C.S.: 327993

Huizhou Weibo (Weibrass) Precision Technology Co., Ltd. (1)
Weibo Technology Square of Boling Industrial Park, Xiaojin Village Luoyang Town Boluo County, Huizhou, China
Tel.: (86) 7526566222
Construction Machinery Mfr
N.A.I.C.S.: 333120

Seksun Technology Singapore Co., Ltd. (1)
No 35 Marsiling Industrial Estate Road 3 05-04 Woodlands Central, Singapore, 739257, Singapore
Tel.: (65) 64819936
Precision Metal Components Mfr
N.A.I.C.S.: 332721

Seksun Technology Thailand Co., Ltd. (1)
99 Moo 9 Tumbol Thanu, Rojana Ind Park, Uthai, 13210, Ayutthaya, Thailand
Tel.: (66) 35800100
Metal Component Mfr
N.A.I.C.S.: 332999

Shenzhen Anjie Electronic Co., Ltd. (1)
Floor 5 of Building 3 at No 68 Chaoyang Road, Yanchuan Neighbourhood Yanluo Sub-district Bao'an District, Shenzhen, China
Tel.: (86) 755233507850
Insulation Material Mfr
N.A.I.C.S.: 327993

Suzhou Seksun Technology Co., Ltd. (1)
No 16 Tianling Road Wuzhong Economic Development Zone, Suzhou, 215128, Jiangsu, China
Tel.: (86) 51265656111
Electronic Components Mfr
N.A.I.C.S.: 334419

Suzhou WSDS Electronic Technology Co., Ltd. (1)
No 3019 Haizang West Road, Luzhi Town Wuzhong District, Suzhou, China
Tel.: (86) 51288188698
Emp.: 160
Electronic Part Mfr & Distr
N.A.I.C.S.: 334417

Suzhou Weisidongshan Electronic Technology Co., Ltd. (1)
No 3019 Haizang West Road, Luzhi Town Wuzhong District, Suzhou, Jiangsu, China
Tel.: (86) 51288188698
Wireless Communication Equipment Mfr
N.A.I.C.S.: 334290

SUZHOU ASEN SEMICONDUCTORS CO., LTD.
188 Suhong W Rd Yuan Qu Hu Xi, Wuzhong District, Suzhou, 215021, China
Tel.: (86) 51267251788
Emp.: 100
Integrated Device Mfr
N.A.I.C.S.: 334413

SUZHOU BASECARE MEDICAL CORPORATION LIMITED
Unit 101 Building A3 BioBay No 218, Xinghu Street Suzhou Industrial Park, Suzhou, Jiangsu, China
Tel.: (86) 51282782588 CN
Web Site: https://www.basecare.cn
Year Founded: 2010
2170—(HKG)
Rev.: $28,795,968
Assets: $262,805,577
Liabilities: $69,226,434
Net Worth: $193,579,143
Earnings: ($26,770,741)
Emp.: 586
Fiscal Year-end: 12/31/23
Software Development Services
N.A.I.C.S.: 541511
Bo Liang *(Chm)*

SUZHOU CHEERSSON PRECISION METAL FORMING CO., LTD.
No 28 Huchen Road, Huguan Industrial Park High-tech Zone, Suzhou, 215151, Jiangsu, China
Tel.: (86) 51269007888
Web Site: https://www.cheersson.com
Year Founded: 2012
002976—(SSE)
Rev.: $169,346,114
Assets: $268,332,410
Liabilities: $148,945,657
Net Worth: $119,386,753
Earnings: $9,394,922
Emp.: 1,000
Fiscal Year-end: 12/31/22
Metal Parts Mfr & Distr
N.A.I.C.S.: 332119
Xiaomin Chen *(Chm & Gen Mgr)*

SUZHOU CHUNQIU ELECTRONIC TECHNOLOGY CO., LTD.
988 Yide Road, Zhangpu Town, Kunshan, 215321, Jiangsu, China
Tel.: (86) 51282603998
Web Site: https://www.szchunqiu.com
Year Founded: 2011
603890—(SHG)
Rev.: $539,791,836
Assets: $728,794,778
Liabilities: $337,563,804
Net Worth: $391,230,974
Earnings: $22,080,385
Fiscal Year-end: 12/31/22
Mold Product Mfr & Distr
N.A.I.C.S.: 326199

SUZHOU CHUNXING PRECISION MECHANICAL CO., LTD.
No 120 East Jinling Road Weiting Town, Suzhou Industrial Park, Suzhou, Jiangsu, China
Tel.: (86) 51262625333
Web Site: https://www.chunxing-group.com
Year Founded: 2001
002547—(SSE)
Rev.: $363,293,031
Assets: $794,944,309
Liabilities: $720,136,226
Net Worth: $74,808,082
Earnings: ($20,106,066)
Emp.: 5,000
Fiscal Year-end: 12/31/22
Aluminum Structure Parts Mfr for Electronics
N.A.I.C.S.: 331318
Jing Yuan *(Chm)*

SUZHOU CORPORATION
112 Room B2 Bldg No 88 Dongchang RD SIP, Suzhou, China
Tel.: (86) 51262387156 CN
Display Equipment Mfr
N.A.I.C.S.: 337215

SUZHOU DONGSHAN PRECISION MANUFACTURING CO., LTD.
No 68 Nanhu Road Wuzhong Economic Development Zone, Dongshan Industrial Park, Suzhou, Jiangsu, China
Tel.: (86) 51282286000
Web Site: https://www.dsbj.com
Year Founded: 1998
002384—(SSE)
Rev.: $4,433,852,597
Assets: $5,690,603,112
Liabilities: $3,387,151,938
Net Worth: $2,303,451,175
Earnings: $332,399,738
Emp.: 119
Fiscal Year-end: 12/31/22
Precision Metal Products Mfr
N.A.I.C.S.: 332999

Subsidiaries:

Multek Corporation (1)
Xin Qing Science & Tech Ind Park Jing An Town, Doumen, Zhuhai, 519180, Guangdong, China (100%)
Tel.: (86) 7565539888
Web Site: http://www.multek.com
Rigid Flex & Flexible Printed Circuits
N.A.I.C.S.: 334419
Todd Robinson *(CTO)*

Multi-Fineline Electronix, Inc. (1)
Ste 250 101 Academy Dr, Irvine, CA 92617 (100%)
Tel.: (949) 453-6800
Web Site: http://www.mflex.com
Sales Range: $600-649.9 Million
Flexible Printed Circuits & Circuit Assemblies Mfr
N.A.I.C.S.: 334412
Reza A. Meshgin *(CEO)*

Suzhou JDI Electronics Inc. (1)
No 168 Jin Feng Road Suzhou New District, Suzhou, 215011, China
Tel.: (86) 51268257002
Mobile Device Screen Mfr
N.A.I.C.S.: 334419

SUZHOU ELECTRICAL APPARATUS SCIENCE ACADEMY CO., LTD.
No 5 Qianzhu Road, Yuexi Wuzhong District, Suzhou, 215104, China
Tel.: (86) 51269511355
Web Site: https://www.dqjc.com
Year Founded: 1965
300215—(CHIN)
Rev.: $87,471,991
Assets: $404,189,836
Liabilities: $122,173,360
Net Worth: $282,016,476
Earnings: $2,690,390
Emp.: 1,200
Fiscal Year-end: 12/31/23
Electrical Testing Equipment Mfr
N.A.I.C.S.: 334515

Subsidiaries:

Chengdu Sanfang Electrical Application Co. Ltd. (1)
No 24 Hangitan Road, Chengdu, Sichuan, China
Tel.: (86) 84216686
Electrical Testing Instrument Mfr
N.A.I.C.S.: 334515

SUZHOU ETRON TECHNOLOGIES CO., LTD.
No 50 Chunxing Road Xiangcheng Economic Development Zone, Suzhou, 215143, Jiangsu, China
Tel.: (86) 51265466838 CN
Web Site: https://www.etron.cn
Year Founded: 2001
603380—(SHG)
Rev.: $277,048,666
Assets: $283,732,226
Liabilities: $106,875,007
Net Worth: $176,857,219
Earnings: $25,064,334
Fiscal Year-end: 12/31/22
Electronic Components Mfr
N.A.I.C.S.: 334419

SUZHOU FUSHILAI PHARMACEUTICAL CO., LTD.
No 16 Haiwang Road New Material Industrial Park, Changshu, 215500, Jiangsu, China
Tel.: (86) 51252835990
Web Site: https://www.fuslai.com
Year Founded: 2000
301258—(CHIN)
Rev.: $68,914,450
Assets: $298,039,422
Liabilities: $24,007,704
Net Worth: $274,031,717
Earnings: $15,800,253
Emp.: 500
Fiscal Year-end: 12/31/23
Pharmaceutical Product Mfr & Distr
N.A.I.C.S.: 325412
Xiangyun Qian *(Chm)*

SUZHOU GOLD MANTIS CONSTRUCTION DECORATION CO., LTD.
No 888 West Ring Road, Suzhou, 215004, China
Tel.: (86) 51268508000
Web Site: https://www.goldmantis.com
Year Founded: 1993
002081—(SSE)
Rev.: $3,062,586,042
Assets: $5,199,903,357
Liabilities: $3,400,946,771
Net Worth: $1,798,956,586
Earnings: $178,663,549
Emp.: 14,000
Fiscal Year-end: 12/31/22
Interior & Exterior Design Structure Mfr
N.A.I.C.S.: 332323

Subsidiaries:

Agile Intelligent Technology Co., Ltd. (1)
No 66 Wangmi Street High-tech Zone, Suzhou, China
Tel.: (86) 5126 855 2002
Interior Decoration Services
N.A.I.C.S.: 541410

Gold Mantis Art Co., Ltd. (1)
No 99 Jinshang Road, Suzhou Industrial Park, Suzhou, China
Tel.: (86) 5128 227 2088
Interior Decoration Services
N.A.I.C.S.: 541410

Gold Mantis Exhibition Design Company (1)
No 99 Jinshang Road, Suzhou Industrial Park, Suzhou, China
Tel.: (86) 5126 860 1529
Interior Decoration Services
N.A.I.C.S.: 541410

Gold Mantis JosTechnologies Inc. (1)
No 66 Wangmi Street High-tech Zone, Suzhou, China
Tel.: (86) 5126 511 6998
Interior Decoration Services
N.A.I.C.S.: 541410

Gold Mantis Residential Integrated Decoration Co. Ltd. (1)
No 99 Jinshang Road, Suzhou Industrial Park, Suzhou, China
Tel.: (86) 5128 227 2000

SUZHOU GOLD MANTIS CONSTRUCTION DECORATION CO., LTD.

Suzhou Gold Mantis Construction Decoration Co., Ltd.—(Continued)
Interior Decoration Services
N.A.I.C.S.: 541410

HBA Union Hotel Consultants Limited (1)
2nd Floor No 9800 Changde Road, Yanan District, Shanghai, China
Tel.: (86) 216 433 0062
Interior Decoration Services
N.A.I.C.S.: 541410

Hirsch Bedner Associates Inc. (1)
3216 Nebraska Ave, Santa Monica, CA 90404 (70%)
Tel.: (310) 829-9087
Web Site: http://www.hbadesign.com
Emp.: 1,200
Interior Design Services
N.A.I.C.S.: 541410
Michael Bedner (Chm)

Liaoning Gold Mantis Curtain Wall Decoration Co., Ltd. (1)
Shenyang International Software Park F7501 No 860-2m, Shengou Village Dongling District, Shenyang, China
Tel.: (86) 248 377 3131
Interior Decoration Services
N.A.I.C.S.: 541410

Suzhou Gold Mantis Curtain Wall Co. Ltd. (1)
Du Village Industrial Park, Linhu Town Wuzhong District, Suzhou, China
Tel.: (86) 5126 858 2858
Interior Decoration Services
N.A.I.C.S.: 541410

Suzhou Gold Mantis Furniture Design & Manufacturing Co., Ltd. (1)
No 5 Minsheng Road, Private Industrial Zone Suzhou Industrial Park, Suzhou, China
Tel.: (86) 5126 593 6593
Interior Decoration Services
N.A.I.C.S.: 541410

Suzhou Gold Mantis Landscape Co. Ltd. (1)
No 99 Jinshang Road, Suzhou Industrial Park, Suzhou, China
Tel.: (86) 5126 866 9731
Interior Decoration Services
N.A.I.C.S.: 541410

Suzhou Meiruide Building Decoration Co., Ltd. (1)
No 89 Jinshang Road, Suzhou Industrial Park, Suzhou, China
Tel.: (86) 5126 858 2858
Interior Decoration Services
N.A.I.C.S.: 541410

SUZHOU GOLDENGREEN TECHNOLOGIES LTD
No 38 Huoju Road National High-tech Zone, Suzhou, 215011, Jiangsu, China
Tel.: (86) 51282276818
Web Site: https://www.sgt21.com
Year Founded: 2002
002808—(SSE)
Rev.: $23,284,610
Assets: $74,948,749
Liabilities: $20,046,031
Net Worth: $54,902,718
Earnings: ($2,904,581)
Fiscal Year-end: 12/31/22
Printer Mfr & Distr
N.A.I.C.S.: 325992
Rongqing Yu (Chm & Gen Mgr)

SUZHOU GOOD-ARK ELECTRONICS CO., LTD.
No 200 Huajin Road, Tongan Development Zone, Suzhou, 215011, Jiangsu, China
Tel.: (86) 51268188888 CN
Web Site: https://www.goodark.com
Year Founded: 1990
002079—(SSE)
Rev.: $458,855,182
Assets: $479,924,715
Liabilities: $93,262,469
Net Worth: $386,662,246
Earnings: $52,067,888
Emp.: 2,800
Fiscal Year-end: 12/31/22
Semiconductor Mfr & Distr
N.A.I.C.S.: 334413

Subsidiaries:

Good-Ark (H.K.) Electronics Ltd. (1)
Merit Industrial Centre A1 12/F 94 to Kwa Wan Road, Kowloon, China (Hong Kong)
Tel.: (852) 27743886
Semiconductor Product Distr
N.A.I.C.S.: 423690

Good-Ark Semiconductor USA Corp. (1)
90 - 8 13th Ave, Ronkonkoma, NY 11779
Tel.: (631) 319-1858
Web Site: http://www.goodarksemi.com
Semiconductor Product Mfr & Distr
N.A.I.C.S.: 334413
Brett Singer (Mgr-Sls)

Suzhou Good-Ark New Energy Technology Co., Ltd. - Suzhou Factory (1)
No 158 West Shihu Road, Suzhou, China
Tel.: (86) 51267086525
Junction Box Mfr
N.A.I.C.S.: 335932

SUZHOU GYZ ELECTRONIC TECHNOLOGY CO., LTD.
No 269 Songjiagang Road, Zhoushi Town, Kunshan, 215300, Jiangsu, China
Tel.: (86) 51236691876
Web Site: http://www.gyzet.com
Year Founded: 2013
688260—(SHG)
Rev.: $65,013,905
Assets: $186,762,930
Liabilities: $127,998,987
Net Worth: $58,763,943
Earnings: ($9,563,557)
Fiscal Year-end: 12/31/22
Electronic Product Mfr & Distr
N.A.I.C.S.: 334419
Bin Wang (Chm & Gen Mgr)

SUZHOU HAILU HEAVY INDUSTRY CO., LTD.
Southeast 1st Avenue, Zhangjiagang, 215618, Jiangsu, China
Tel.: (86) 51258913200
Web Site: https://www.hailu-boiler.cn
Year Founded: 1956
002255—(SSE)
Rev.: $332,019,015
Assets: $843,115,282
Liabilities: $365,279,340
Net Worth: $477,835,942
Earnings: $47,256,646
Fiscal Year-end: 12/31/22
Heat Boiler Mfr
N.A.I.C.S.: 332410
Yuansheng Xu (Chm & Pres)

Subsidiaries:

Raschka Engineering Ltd. (1)
Dachsweg 12, 4410, Liestal, Switzerland
Tel.: (41) 61 534 9913
Web Site: http://www.raschka-engineering.com
Emp.: 115
Energy Consulting Services
N.A.I.C.S.: 541690

Subsidiary (Non-US)

Raschka Guangzhou Engineering & Consulting Co., Ltd. (2)
Room 401 South Tower Peace Business Centre, No 898 of Guangzhou Avenue South, 510305, Guangzhou, China
Tel.: (86) 2089664189
Energy Consulting Services
N.A.I.C.S.: 541690

SUZHOU HANCHUAN INTELLIGENT TECHNOLOGY CO., LTD.
No 32 Tingtao Road, Suzhou Industrial Park, Suzhou, 215126, Jiangsu, China
Tel.: (86) 4000909665
Web Site: https://www.harmontronics.com
Year Founded: 2012
688022—(SHG)
Rev.: $160,449,710
Assets: $422,009,434
Liabilities: $278,418,633
Net Worth: $143,590,801
Earnings: $10,321,253
Emp.: 1,000
Fiscal Year-end: 12/31/22
Electric Equipment Mfr
N.A.I.C.S.: 335999
Changwei Cai (Chm & Gen Mgr)

SUZHOU HENGMINGDA ELECTRONIC TECHNOLOGY CO., LTD.
1568 Taji Road, Kunshan, Jiangsu, China
Tel.: (86) 51257655916
Web Site: https://www.hengmingda.com
Year Founded: 2011
002947—(SSE)
Rev.: $217,305,392
Assets: $349,622,774
Liabilities: $87,753,791
Net Worth: $261,868,983
Earnings: $27,101,819
Fiscal Year-end: 12/31/22
Electronic Product Mfr & Distr
N.A.I.C.S.: 337126
Jin Tianping (Gen Mgr)

Subsidiaries:

Dongguan aitaji New Material Co., Ltd. (1)
Xi Xi Tian Yuan Jie, Liaobu Town, Dongguan, China
Tel.: (86) 76922230656
Electronic Device Mfr & Distr
N.A.I.C.S.: 334419

Heng shi cheng (Hong Kong) international holding limited (1)
1568 Taji Road, Bacheng Town, Kunshan, China
Tel.: (86) 51257655916
Electronic Device Mfr & Distr
N.A.I.C.S.: 334419

Huizhou hengmingda Electronic Technology Co., Ltd. (1)
Yanhe Road section of Huizhou Huiyang Economic Development Zone, Huizhou, China
Tel.: (86) 7523265537
Electronic Device Mfr & Distr
N.A.I.C.S.: 334419

Shenzhen hengmingda New Technology Research Institute Co., Ltd. (1)
Workshop 201 Of Huayangtong Company Longcheng Street, Zhangbei Community Longgang District, Shenzhen, China
Tel.: (86) 75561881056
Electronic Device Mfr & Distr
N.A.I.C.S.: 334419

Shenzhen huayangtong electromechanical Co., Ltd. (1)
322 Zhangbeiyuanhu Road, Longgang District, Shenzhen, China
Tel.: (86) 75561881056
Electronic Device Mfr & Distr
N.A.I.C.S.: 334419

SUZHOU HESHENG SPECIAL MATERIAL CO., LTD.
Room No 2410 Building 1 Rongsheng Business Center No 135 Wangdun Road, Suzhou Industrial Park, Suzhou, 215000, Jiangsu, China
Tel.: (86) 51265073528
Web Site: http://www.szhssm.com.cn
Year Founded: 2002
002290—(SSE)
Rev.: $299,509,971
Assets: $214,697,883
Liabilities: $128,426,772
Net Worth: $86,271,111
Earnings: $9,256,853
Emp.: 340
Fiscal Year-end: 12/31/22
Pre-Coated Metal (PCM) Sheets, Vinyl Coated Metal (VCM) Sheets & Polyethylene Terephthalate (PET) Materials Mfr
N.A.I.C.S.: 332812
Liang Xu (Chm)

SUZHOU HUAXIN INTERNATIONAL PROPERTY MANAGEMENT CO., LTD
Qingshuiwan Garden No 99 Shihu West Road, Suzhou, 215128, China
Tel.: (86) 51262562551
Property Management Services
N.A.I.C.S.: 531311
Jiang Qiufu (Deputy Gen Mgr)

SUZHOU HUAYA INTELLIGENCE TECHNOLOGY CO., LTD.
No 58 Chunxing Road, Caohu Industrial Park Xiangcheng Economic Development Zone, Suzhou, 215413, Jiangsu, China
Tel.: (86) 51266731800
Web Site: https://www.huaya.net.cn
Year Founded: 1998
003043—(SSE)
Rev.: $86,957,765
Assets: $211,710,213
Liabilities: $59,569,530
Net Worth: $152,140,683
Earnings: $21,093,864
Fiscal Year-end: 12/31/22
Precision Metal Mfr & Distr
N.A.I.C.S.: 332721
Cainan Wang (Chm & Gen Mgr)

SUZHOU HYC TECHNOLOGY CO., LTD.
No 8 Qingqiu Lane Suzhou Industrial Park, Suzhou, China
Tel.: (86) 51288168816
Web Site: https://www.hyc.com
Year Founded: 2005
688001—(SHG)
Rev.: $325,725,936
Assets: $778,815,746
Liabilities: $245,333,556
Net Worth: $533,482,190
Earnings: $46,477,946
Fiscal Year-end: 12/31/22
Electronic Product Mfr & Distr
N.A.I.C.S.: 334419
Wenyuan Chen (Chm & Gen Mgr)

SUZHOU HYCAN HOLDINGS CO., LTD.
No 1948 Taowu Rd Taoyuan, Wujiang District, Suzhou, 215236, Jiangsu, China
Tel.: (86) 51286879060
Web Site: https://www.hycan-pack.com
Year Founded: 1998
Sales Range: $125-149.9 Million
Packaging Products Mfr
N.A.I.C.S.: 332431
Li Zhicong (Chm & Gen Mgr)

SUZHOU INDUSTRIAL PARK HESHUN ELECTRIC CO., LTD.

8 Heshun Road Industrial Park, Suzhou, 215122, China
Tel.: (86) 51262862607
Web Site: https://www.cnheshun.com
300141—(CHIN)
Rev.: $43,608,240
Assets: $139,580,064
Liabilities: $45,085,248
Net Worth: $94,494,816
Earnings: ($1,429,272)
Fiscal Year-end: 12/31/22
Electrical Machinery & Equipment Mfr
N.A.I.C.S.: 335999

SUZHOU INSTITUTE OF BUILDING SCIENCE GROUP CO., LTD.

No 82 Beiguandu Road, Wuzhong District, Suzhou, 215000, Jiangsu, China
Tel.: (86) 51268286356
Web Site: http://www.szjkjt.com
Year Founded: 2001
603183—(SHG)
Rev.: $113,137,156
Assets: $286,225,056
Liabilities: $72,238,903
Net Worth: $213,986,153
Earnings: $14,493,281
Fiscal Year-end: 12/31/22
Building Material Mfr & Distr
N.A.I.C.S.: 327120
Xiaoxiang Wu *(Chm & Gen Mgr)*

SUZHOU IRON TECHNOLOGY CO., LTD.

No 27 Xinfa Road, Suzhou Industrial Park, Suzhou, 215123, Jiangsu, China
Tel.: (86) 51266607092
Web Site: https://www.iron-tech.cn
Year Founded: 2006
688329—(SHG)
Rev.: $67,020,179
Assets: $198,375,793
Liabilities: $79,155,526
Net Worth: $119,220,267
Earnings: $14,376,637
Fiscal Year-end: 12/31/22
Medical Product Mfr & Distr
N.A.I.C.S.: 339112
Yinhua Zhang *(Board of Directors, Chm & Gen Mgr)*

SUZHOU JIN HONG SHUN AUTO PARTS CO., LTD.

No 30 Changxing Road Economic Development Zone, Zhangjiagang, 215600, Jiangsu, China
Tel.: (86) 51255373805
Web Site: http://www.jinhs.com
Year Founded: 2003
603922—(SHG)
Rev.: $72,488,899
Assets: $176,562,491
Liabilities: $30,911,208
Net Worth: $145,651,283
Earnings: ($1,674,635)
Fiscal Year-end: 12/31/22
Auto Parts Mfr & Distr
N.A.I.C.S.: 336370
Jiancang Hong *(Chm, Vice Chm & Pres)*

SUZHOU JINFU TECHNOLOGY CO., LTD.

No 39 Jiangpu Road, Suzhou Industrial Park, Suzhou, 215123, Jiangsu, China
Tel.: (86) 51262820000
Web Site: https://www.jin-fu.cn
Year Founded: 1998
300128—(CHIN)
Rev.: $245,493,944
Assets: $553,689,984
Liabilities: $323,754,669
Net Worth: $229,935,315
Earnings: ($31,551,456)
Emp.: 3,000
Fiscal Year-end: 12/31/23
Photoelectrical Display Thin Film Components Mfr
N.A.I.C.S.: 326199
Peng Xiao *(Chm)*
Subsidiaries:

Jin-fu XinNuo Precision Plastic Col,Ltd (1)
No 1 2-4 F Jinzhou Road, Gao District, Weihai, 264209, Shandong, China
Tel.: (86) 631 5663018
Web Site: http://www.jin-fu.cn
Insulation Products Distr
N.A.I.C.S.: 424690

Suzhou Jiufu Electronic Co.,Ltd (1)
No 46 Minsheng Road Shengpu Area, Suzhou, 215126, Jiangsu, China
Tel.: (86) 51262861511
Photoelectrical Display Mfr
N.A.I.C.S.: 334513

SUZHOU JINHONG GAS CO., LTD.

Anmin Road, Panyang Industrial Park Huangdai Town Xiangcheng, Suzhou, 215152, Jiangsu, China
Tel.: (86) 51265789892
Web Site: http://www.jinhonggroup.com
Year Founded: 1999
688106—(SHG)
Rev.: $276,174,339
Assets: $664,726,103
Liabilities: $242,270,239
Net Worth: $422,455,864
Earnings: $32,168,869
Fiscal Year-end: 12/31/22
Oil & Gas Distribution Services
N.A.I.C.S.: 221210
Xianghua Jin *(Chm & Gen Mgr)*

SUZHOU KEDA TECHNOLOGY CO., LTD.

131 Jinshan Road, New District, Suzhou, 215011, China
Tel.: (86) 51268418188
Web Site: https://www.kedacom.com
Year Founded: 2004
603660—(SHG)
Rev.: $221,386,806
Assets: $466,500,818
Liabilities: $281,308,318
Net Worth: $185,192,500
Earnings: ($81,879,469)
Fiscal Year-end: 12/31/22
Electronic Products Mfr
N.A.I.C.S.: 334419
Chen Dongger *(Chm)*

SUZHOU KELIDA BUILDING & DECORATION CO., LTD.

No 6 Dengwei Road, Hi-tech Zone, Suzhou, 215011, Jiangsu, China
Tel.: (86) 51268257826
Web Site: http://www.kldzs.com
Year Founded: 2000
603828—(SHG)
Rev.: $292,930,462
Assets: $736,563,840
Liabilities: $609,568,446
Net Worth: $126,995,394
Earnings: ($48,146,965)
Fiscal Year-end: 12/31/22
Interior Decoration Services
N.A.I.C.S.: 541410
Zhenhua Sun *(CFO)*

SUZHOU KINGSWOOD EDUCATION TECHNOLOGY CO., LTD.

No 989 Chun Shen Road Pan Yang Industrial Park, Suzhou, 215152, China
Tel.: (86) 51265379085
Web Site: https://www.szkinks.com
300192—(CHIN)
Rev.: $111,568,860
Assets: $154,008,972
Liabilities: $49,837,788
Net Worth: $104,171,184
Earnings: $10,400,832
Fiscal Year-end: 12/31/22
Offset Prinking Ink Mfr
N.A.I.C.S.: 325910

SUZHOU LONGJIE SPECIAL FIBER CO., LTD.

No 19 Zhenxing Road Zhangjiagang Economic Development Zone, Zhangjiagang, 215600, Jiangsu, China
Tel.: (86) 51256979228
Web Site: http://www.jslongjie.com
Year Founded: 2003
603332—(SHG)
Rev.: $149,695,477
Assets: $217,119,825
Liabilities: $38,896,191
Net Worth: $178,223,634
Earnings: ($7,077,087)
Fiscal Year-end: 12/31/22
Textile Products Mfr
N.A.I.C.S.: 314999
Wenjie Xi *(Chm & Pres)*

SUZHOU MAXWELL TECHNOLOGIES CO., LTD.

No 228 Ludang Road, Wujiang District, Suzhou, 215200, Jiangsu, China
Tel.: (86) 51263929889
Web Site: https://www.maxwell-gp.com
Year Founded: 2010
300751—(CHIN)
Rev.: $1,139,272,155
Assets: $3,270,062,082
Liabilities: $2,276,073,308
Net Worth: $993,988,774
Earnings: $128,722,294
Fiscal Year-end: 12/31/23
Precision Product Mfr & Distr
N.A.I.C.S.: 332721
Wang Zhenggen *(Pres & Gen Mgr)*

SUZHOU MINGZHI TECHNOLOGY CO., LTD.

No 1999 West Tongxiao Road, Suzhou, 215216, Jiangsu, China
Tel.: (86) 51263329988
Web Site: https://www.mingzhi-tech.eu
Year Founded: 2003
688355—(SHG)
Rev.: $86,018,096
Assets: $205,341,599
Liabilities: $55,126,179
Net Worth: $150,215,420
Earnings: $5,198,338
Emp.: 800
Fiscal Year-end: 12/31/22
Hardware Product Mfr & Distr
N.A.I.C.S.: 332510
Qinfang Wu *(Chm)*
Subsidiaries:

Mingzhi Technology Leipzig GmbH (1)
Am Glaschen 7, 04420, Markranstadt, Germany
Tel.: (49) 34205893420
Mining Machinery & Equipment Mfr & Distr
N.A.I.C.S.: 333131

SUZHOU NEW DISTRICT HI-TECH INDUSTRIAL CO., LTD.

Suzhou New District Science and Technology City, Jinfeng Road 199 Building A International Business Building 20th Floor, Suzhou, 215163, Jiangsu, China
Tel.: (86) 51267379058
Web Site: https://www.sndnt.com
600736—(SHG)
Rev.: $1,822,454,399
Assets: $9,432,713,776
Liabilities: $7,047,655,404
Net Worth: $2,385,058,373
Earnings: $62,120,527
Fiscal Year-end: 12/31/21
Property Development Services
N.A.I.C.S.: 531110
Wang Xing *(Chm)*

SUZHOU PARSUN POWER MACHINE CO., LTD.

No 567 Lian Gang Road Xushuguan Development Zone, Suzhou, 215151, Jiangsu, China
Tel.: (86) 51266571365 CN
Year Founded: 2001
Outboard Engine & Motor Mfr
N.A.I.C.S.: 333618

SUZHOU SECOTE PRECISION ELECTRONIC CO., LTD.

No 585 of Songjia Road Guoxiang Street, Wuzhong, Suzhou, 215124, Jiangsu, China
Tel.: (86) 51265627778 CN
Web Site: https://www.secote.com
Year Founded: 2002
603283—(SHG)
Rev.: $411,340,621
Assets: $679,817,502
Liabilities: $434,560,071
Net Worth: $245,257,431
Earnings: $43,101,480
Fiscal Year-end: 12/31/22
Industrial Automation Services
N.A.I.C.S.: 541420
Sun Feng *(Chm & Gen Mgr)*

SUZHOU SHIHUA NEW MATERIAL TECHNOLOGY CO., LTD.

No 168 DaGuang Road, Wujiang Economic and Technological Development Zone Wujiang District, Suzhou, 215200, Jiangsu, China
Tel.: (86) 51263199366
Web Site: https://www.szshihua.com.cn
Year Founded: 2010
688093—(SHG)
Rev.: $64,906,106
Assets: $206,683,233
Liabilities: $8,027,328
Net Worth: $198,655,905
Earnings: $26,026,650
Fiscal Year-end: 12/31/22
Electronic Product Mfr & Distr
N.A.I.C.S.: 334419
Zhengqing Gu *(Chm & Gen Mgr)*

SUZHOU SHIJIA SCIENCE & TECHNOLOGY INC

No 439 Jianlin Road, Suzhou, 215129, Jiangsu, China
Tel.: (86) 51266161736
Web Site: http://www.sz-shijia.com
Year Founded: 1990
002796—(SSE)
Rev.: $153,752,208
Assets: $202,722,900
Liabilities: $83,761,924
Net Worth: $118,960,976
Earnings: $4,411,284
Fiscal Year-end: 12/31/22
Cabinet System Mfr & Distr
N.A.I.C.S.: 332510
Juan Wang *(Chm)*

Suzhou Shijia Science & Technology Inc—(Continued)

SUZHOU SHIJING ENVIRONMENTAL TECHNOLOGY CO., LTD.
No 58 Jinrui Road Taiping Street, Xiangcheng, Suzhou, 215137, Jiangsu, China
Tel.: (86) 51265996560
Web Site: https://www.sz-sjef.com
Year Founded: 2005
301030—(CHIN)
Rev.: $484,890,449
Assets: $1,093,626,518
Liabilities: $827,831,533
Net Worth: $265,794,985
Earnings: $30,513,690
Emp.: 160
Fiscal Year-end: 12/31/23
Engineeering Services
N.A.I.C.S.: 541330
Shihong Dong (Chm)

SUZHOU SLAC PRECISION EQUIPMENT COMPANY LIMITED
1028 Sunwu Road Xukou Town, Wuzhong District, Suzhou, 215164, Jiangsu, China
Tel.: (86) 51266939207
Web Site: https://www.slac.com.cn
Year Founded: 2004
300382—(CHIN)
Rev.: $243,077,328
Assets: $574,259,868
Liabilities: $229,103,316
Net Worth: $345,156,552
Earnings: $31,719,168
Emp.: 500
Fiscal Year-end: 12/31/22
High-Speed Easy Open Lid Production Equipment & Precision Molding Mfr
N.A.I.C.S.: 333248

SUZHOU SONAVOX ELECTRONICS CO., LTD.
No 333 Zhongchuang Road, Yuanhe Technology Park Xiangcheng District, Suzhou, 215133, China
Tel.: (86) 51265795888
Web Site: https://www.sonavox-group.com
Year Founded: 1992
688533—(SHG)
Rev.: $248,355,076
Assets: $313,808,265
Liabilities: $158,906,208
Net Worth: $154,902,056
Earnings: $12,238,120
Emp.: 2,400
Fiscal Year-end: 12/31/22
Electronic Product Mfr & Distr
N.A.I.C.S.: 334419
Jianming Zhou (Chm & Gen Mgr)

Subsidiaries:

Detroit Sonavox Inc. (1)
37557 Schoolcraft Rd, Livonia, MI 48150
Tel.: (734) 293-1400
Loudspeaker Distr
N.A.I.C.S.: 423620

Mexico Sonavox Electronics Co. S. de R.L. de C.V. (1)
C Virgin of Charity 19 Interior H2, Industrial Xicohtencatl II, 90500, Mexico, Tlaxcala, Mexico
Tel.: (52) 2476890072
Web Site: https://mexico-sonavox-electronics-co-s-de.negocio.site
Loudspeaker Mfr
N.A.I.C.S.: 334310

Sonavox CZ s.r.o. (1)
Lhotka nad Becvou 93, Lesna, 756 41, Tachov, Czech Republic
Tel.: (420) 556674013

Web Site: https://www.sonavox.cz
Car Speaker Mfr
N.A.I.C.S.: 334310

Sonavox Europe GmbH (1)
Liegnitzer Strasse 6, 82194, Grobenzell, Germany
Tel.: (49) 81424103773
Automobile Electronic Product Mfr & Distr
N.A.I.C.S.: 336320

Sonavox Industria e Comercio de Alto Falantes Ltd.a. (1)
Estrada General Motors 852 Shed 15 and 16, Caldeira Neighborhood Indaiatuba, Sao Paulo, 13347-500, Brazil
Tel.: (55) 1931152200
Automobile Electronic Product Mfr & Distr
N.A.I.C.S.: 336320

SUZHOU SUNMUN TECHNOLOGY CO.,LTD.
No 219 North Huangpujiang Road, Kunshan, 215337, Jiangsu, China
Tel.: (86) 51257665888
Web Site: https://www.smcolor.com.cn
Year Founded: 2001
300522—(CHIN)
Rev.: $96,002,642
Assets: $153,690,520
Liabilities: $38,810,682
Net Worth: $114,879,838
Earnings: $2,536,497
Fiscal Year-end: 12/31/23
Colorant Mfr & Distr
N.A.I.C.S.: 325998
Lu Yong (Chm & Pres)

SUZHOU SUSHI TESTING GROUP CO., LTD.
No 18 Kefeng Road Suzhou Industrial Park, Weiting Town Zhongxin Technology City, Suzhou, 215122, Jiangsu, China
Tel.: (86) 51266658033
Web Site: http://www.chinasti.com
Year Founded: 1956
300416—(SSE)
Rev.: $298,140,505
Assets: $683,073,977
Liabilities: $265,562,097
Net Worth: $417,511,880
Earnings: $44,265,296
Fiscal Year-end: 12/31/23
Vibration & Other Mechanical Environment Test Equipment Mfr
N.A.I.C.S.: 334519
Zhong Qionghua (Chm)

Subsidiaries:

SUSHI Guangbo Environment & Reliability technology (Chongqing) Co., Ltd (1)
No 1 Tongjiaxi Wuxing West Road Beibei District, Chongqing, 400709, China
Tel.: (86) 2368365363
Testing Equipment Mfr
N.A.I.C.S.: 334515

SUSHI Guangbo Environment & Reliability technology (Nanjing) Co., Ltd (1)
No 1 Huqiao East Road Pukou Economic Development Zone, Nanjing, 211800, China
Tel.: (86) 2558465192
Testing Equipment Mfr
N.A.I.C.S.: 334515

SUSHI Zhongbo Environment & Reliability technology (Chongqing) Co., Ltd (1)
Building 1 No 1399 Jiangyue Road, Shanghai, 201114, China
Tel.: (86) 2164206266
Testing Equipment Mfr
N.A.I.C.S.: 334515

SUZHOU TFC OPTICAL COMMUNICATION CO., LTD.
No 695 of Changjiang Road, High-

new District, Suzhou, Jiangsu, China
Tel.: (86) 51266560886
Web Site: https://www.tfcsz.com
300394—(CHIN)
Rev.: $273,051,472
Assets: $549,064,752
Liabilities: $75,356,525
Net Worth: $473,708,227
Earnings: $102,803,513
Fiscal Year-end: 12/31/23
Fiber Optical Component Mfr
N.A.I.C.S.: 327212

Subsidiaries:

Auxora (Shenzhen) Inc. (1)
Floor 1 and 3 Building 5 1 Tangtou Road Shiyan Community, Zhong Yun Tai Industrial Park Bao'an District, Shenzhen, Guangdong, China
Tel.: (86) 75586016789
Web Site: http://www.auxora.com
Optical Component Mfr
N.A.I.C.S.: 333310

Gaoan TFC Photoelectric Technology Co., Ltd. (1)
Chengxi Industrial Park, Gao'an, Jiangxi, China
Tel.: (86) 51266560886
Optical Communication Device Mfr
N.A.I.C.S.: 335921

SUZHOU THVOW TECHNOLOGY CO., LTD.
No 1 Linjiang Road, Changshan Village Jingang Town, Zhangjiagang, 200061, Jiangsu, China
Tel.: (86) 2160290016
Web Site: https://www.thvow.com
Year Founded: 1998
002564—(SSE)
Rev.: $504,130,349
Assets: $3,316,486,497
Liabilities: $3,629,096,603
Net Worth: ($312,610,105)
Earnings: ($362,337,230)
Emp.: 2,220
Fiscal Year-end: 12/31/22
Pressure Vessels & Other Machinery Mfr
N.A.I.C.S.: 333132
Yi Xiaorong (Chm)

SUZHOU TZTEK TECHNOLOGY CO., LTD.
No 188 Wutaishan Road, New District, Suzhou, Jiangsu, China
Tel.: (86) 4008852280
Web Site: https://www.tztek.com
Year Founded: 2009
688003—(SHG)
Rev.: $223,119,103
Assets: $411,106,012
Liabilities: $174,684,697
Net Worth: $236,421,315
Earnings: $21,355,345
Fiscal Year-end: 12/31/22
Measuring Instruments Mfr
N.A.I.C.S.: 334513
Yihua Xu (Chm & Gen Mgr)

SUZHOU UIGREEN MICRO & NANO TECHNOLOGIES CO., LTD.
80 Emeishan Road Suzhou High-tech Zone, Suzhou, Jiangsu, China
Tel.: (86) 51287176308
Web Site: https://www.uigreen.com
Year Founded: 2012
688661—(SHG)
Rev.: $40,497,285
Assets: $188,145,674
Liabilities: $11,560,550
Net Worth: $176,585,124
Earnings: $5,353,424
Emp.: 350
Fiscal Year-end: 12/31/22
Electronic Product Mfr & Distr

N.A.I.C.S.: 334419
Xingshun Luo (Chm & Gen Mgr)

SUZHOU VEICHI ELECTRIC CO., LTD.
No 1000 of Songjia Road Wuzhong, Wuzhong Economic & Technological Development Zone, Suzhou, 518108, China
Tel.: (86) 13828818903
Web Site: https://veichi.com
Year Founded: 2013
688698—(SHG)
Rev.: $127,200,996
Assets: $206,578,537
Liabilities: $69,113,290
Net Worth: $137,465,247
Earnings: $19,640,205
Emp.: 1,000
Fiscal Year-end: 12/31/22
Electrical Equipment Mfr & Distr
N.A.I.C.S.: 335999
Zhiyong Hu (Chm & Gen Mgr)

Subsidiaries:

Veichi Electric (India) Private Limited (1)
A-402 SiddhiVinayak Towers B/H DCP Office Near Kataria Automobiles, Off S G Road Makarba, Ahmedabad, 380 451, Gujarat, India
Tel.: (91) 7948415799
Industrial Automation Control Product Mfr
N.A.I.C.S.: 335314

Veichi Electric (M) Sdn. Bhd. (1)
18-34D Jalan Persiaran Gurney, 10250, Pulau Penang, Malaysia
Tel.: (60) 108090110
Industrial Automation Control Product Mfr
N.A.I.C.S.: 335314

SUZHOU VICTORY PRECISION MANUFACTURE CO., LTD.
55 Xujing RD Xuguan Industry Zone, Suzhou New District, Suzhou, Jiangsu, China
Tel.: (86) 51266167000
Web Site: https://www.vicsz.com
Year Founded: 2003
002426—(SSE)
Rev.: $578,844,419
Assets: $1,200,422,991
Liabilities: $600,669,487
Net Worth: $599,753,503
Earnings: ($34,903,370)
Emp.: 1,000
Fiscal Year-end: 12/31/22
Audio & Video Equipment Mfr
N.A.I.C.S.: 334310

Subsidiaries:

Victory Technology Polska Sp.z o.o. (1)
ul Brzezinska 5 15 92-103, Lodz, Poland
Tel.: (48) 602528835
Web Site: http://www.vicszpl.com
Sales Range: $50-74.9 Million
Emp.: 200
Television Accessories Mfr
N.A.I.C.S.: 334419

SUZHOU WANSHEN FLOUR PRODUCTS CO., LTD.
Renhe Road, Dongshili Circular Economy Park Anhui, Suzhou, China
Tel.: (86) 5573332828
Web Site: http://www.ahwanshen.com
Year Founded: 2003
Sales Range: $100-124.9 Million
Emp.: 700
Flour Product Manufacturing
N.A.I.C.S.: 311211
Bai Ying (Sls Mgr)

SUZHOU WANXIANG TECHNOLOGY CO., LTD.

No 1688 Songjia Road, Wuzhong District, Suzhou, 215000, Jiangsu, China
Tel.: (86) 51266591110
Web Site: https://www.wxtech.com
Year Founded: 1994
301180—(CHIN)
Rev.: $123,019,098
Assets: $231,603,605
Liabilities: $44,881,732
Net Worth: $186,721,873
Earnings: $3,533,028
Emp.: 1,100
Fiscal Year-end: 12/31/23
Electronic Component Mfr & Distr
N.A.I.C.S.: 334419
Jun Huang *(Chm & Gen Mgr)*

Subsidiaries:

Changzhou Micro Battery Technology Co., Ltd. (1)
111 Pinghu Road, Jintan District, Changzhou, China
Tel.: (86) 51982205868
Web Site: https://en.micro-bat.com
Lithium Ion Battery Mfr
N.A.I.C.S.: 335910

SUZHOU WEIZHIXIANG FOOD CO., LTD.
No 1778 Songlu Road, Guoxiang Wuzhong Zone, Suzhou, 215127, Jiangsu, China
Tel.: (86) 51280806931
Web Site: http://www.weizhixiang.com
Year Founded: 2008
605089—(SHG)
Rev.: $112,080,520
Assets: $183,187,434
Liabilities: $12,775,108
Net Worth: $170,412,325
Earnings: $20,102,135
Fiscal Year-end: 12/31/22
Packaged Food Product Mfr & Distr
N.A.I.C.S.: 311991
Jing Xia *(Chm & Gen Mgr)*

SUZHOU XIANGLOU NEW MATERIAL CO., LTD.
No 285 Xueying Road, Wujiang, Suzhou, 215200, Jiangsu, China
Tel.: (86) 51263365777
Web Site: https://www.xl-nm.com
Year Founded: 2005
301160—(SSE)
Rev.: $170,141,901
Assets: $222,224,011
Liabilities: $48,399,362
Net Worth: $173,824,649
Earnings: $19,817,558
Fiscal Year-end: 12/31/22
Steel Product Mfr & Distr
N.A.I.C.S.: 331210
Qian Hesheng *(Chm)*

SUZHOU XINGYE MATERIAL & TECHNOLOGY CO., LTD
No 15 Daoan Road Huguan Industrial Park Hi-tech Zone, Suzhou, 215151, Jiangsu, China
Tel.: (86) 51268836907
Web Site: http://www.chinaxingye.com
Year Founded: 1996
603928—(SHG)
Rev.: $250,941,876
Assets: $282,777,085
Liabilities: $73,560,432
Net Worth: $209,216,653
Earnings: $16,320,349
Emp.: 600
Fiscal Year-end: 12/31/22
Foundry Material Mfr & Distr
N.A.I.C.S.: 333511
Wang Jinxing *(Chm & Gen Mgr)*

SUZHOU YANGTZE NEW MATERIALS CO., LTD.
88 Chunfeng Road Panyang Industrial Park, Xiangcheng District, Suzhou, 215143, Jiangsu, China
Tel.: (86) 51268327201
Web Site: http://www.yzjnm.com
Year Founded: 2002
002652—(SSE)
Rev.: $67,939,981
Assets: $84,124,914
Liabilities: $52,195,623
Net Worth: $31,929,291
Earnings: ($5,084,333)
Fiscal Year-end: 12/31/22
Steel Pole Mfr
N.A.I.C.S.: 332996
Wang Mengbing *(Chm)*

SUZHOU YOURBEST NEW-TYPE MATERIALS CO., LTD.
No 22 Youxiang Road, Yuexi Wuzhong District, Suzhou, 215104, China
Tel.: (86) 51265691360
Web Site: https://en.yourbest.com.cn
Year Founded: 2002
301266—(CHIN)
Rev.: $382,445,641
Assets: $429,837,035
Liabilities: $204,999,543
Net Worth: $224,837,492
Earnings: $20,953,520
Emp.: 250
Fiscal Year-end: 12/31/23
Welding Belt Mfr
N.A.I.C.S.: 332618
Feng Xiao *(Chm)*

SUZHOU ZELGEN BIOPHARMACEUTICALS CO., LTD.
No 209 Chenfeng Road, Yushan Town, Kunshan, 215300, Jiangsu, China
Tel.: (86) 51257011882
Web Site: http://www.zelgen.com
Year Founded: 2009
688266—(SHG)
Rev.: $42,443,636
Assets: $234,230,892
Liabilities: $123,667,816
Net Worth: $110,563,077
Earnings: ($64,271,161)
Fiscal Year-end: 12/31/22
Pharmaceutical Product Mfr & Distr
N.A.I.C.S.: 325412
Sheng Zelin *(Chm & Gen Mgr)*

Subsidiaries:

Shanghai Zelgen Pharma-Tech Co., Ltd. (1)
999 Cailun Road Building 3, Shanghai, 201203, China
Tel.: (86) 2150682838
Medicine Mfr & Distr
N.A.I.C.S.: 325411

Suzhou Zelgen Biosciences Co. Ltd. (1)
No 209 Chenfeng Road, Kunshan, Jiangsu, China
Tel.: (86) 51257018310
Medicine Mfr & Distr
N.A.I.C.S.: 325411

SUZLON ENERGY LTD.
One Earth, Hadapsar, Pune, 411028, India
Tel.: (91) 2067022000
Web Site: https://www.suzlon.com
Year Founded: 1995
SUZLON—(NSE)
Rev.: $718,201,547
Assets: $662,236,077
Liabilities: $530,452,611
Net Worth: $131,783,466
Earnings: $346,177,088
Emp.: 5,706
Fiscal Year-end: 03/31/23
Wind Power Generation Equipment & Services
N.A.I.C.S.: 333611
Tulsi R. Tanti *(Founder, Chm & Mng Dir)*

Subsidiaries:

AE Rotor Holding B.V. (1)
Goudstraat 15, Hengelo, 7554 NG, Overijssel, Netherlands
Tel.: (31) 742552630
Wind Turbine Mfr
N.A.I.C.S.: 333611

SE Composites Limited (1)
One Earth Opp Magarpatta City, Hadapsar, Pune, 411 028, Maharashtra, India
Tel.: (91) 2067022000
Web Site: http://www.suzlon.com
Wind Turbine Mfr
N.A.I.C.S.: 333611

SE Forge Limited (1)
Plot No 1 SEZ Unit in AspenPark Infra, Piparia Waghodia, Vadodara, 391 760, Gujarat, India
Tel.: (91) 2668245086
Web Site: https://www.seforge.com
Steel Forging Products Mfr & Distr
N.A.I.C.S.: 332111

Suzlon Blade Technology B.V. (1)
Jan Tinbergenstraat 290, 7559 ST, Hengelo, Netherlands
Tel.: (31) 742552630
Web Site: http://www.suzlonbladetechnology.nl
Sales Range: $25-49.9 Million
Emp.: 70
Wind Turbine Mfr
N.A.I.C.S.: 333611

Suzlon Energy (Tianjin) Limited (1)
Hi Tech Road No 15 Tianjin Hi Tech Industrial Park, Tianjin, 300384, China
Tel.: (86) 2223706666
Wind Turbine Mfr & Distr
N.A.I.C.S.: 333611

Suzlon Energy A/S (1)
Tel.: (45) 89438943
Sales Range: $50-74.9 Million
Wind Turbine Mfr
N.A.I.C.S.: 333611

Suzlon Energy Australia Pty. Ltd. (1)
1/182-184 Stawell St, Burnley, Melbourne, 3121, VIC, Australia
Tel.: (61) 384158900
Web Site: http://www.suzlon.com
Sales Range: $75-99.9 Million
Wind Power Turbine Distr
N.A.I.C.S.: 423610

Suzlon Energy GmbH (1)
Kurt Dunkelmann Strsse 5 House 245, 18057, Rostock, Germany
Tel.: (49) 381128840
Sales Range: $50-74.9 Million
Emp.: 150
Wind Turbine Construction Services
N.A.I.C.S.: 237130

Suzlon Generators Limited (1)
Gate No 339/3 Plot No 20 A 1 Village Mhalunge, Chakan, Pune, 410501, Maharashtra, India
Tel.: (91) 2135671100
Sales Range: $100-124.9 Million
Emp.: 300
Power Generator Mfr
N.A.I.C.S.: 333611
Sanjay Patil *(Gen Mgr)*

Suzlon Infrastructure Services Limited (1)
303/304 Gunjan Tower Alembic Road, Subhanpura, Baroda, 390 023, India
Tel.: (91) 2656450256
Web Site: http://www.suzlon.com
Sales Range: $400-449.9 Million
Wind Turbine Mfr
N.A.I.C.S.: 333611

Suzlon Power Infrastructure Pvt. Ltd. (1)
3rd Floor Sai Hira Mundhwa Road, Pune, 411036, Maharashtra, India
Tel.: (91) 2040125000
Web Site: http://www.spipl.in
Wind Turbine Mfr
N.A.I.C.S.: 333611

Suzlon Rotor Corporation (1)
1711 S Hwy 75, Pipestone, MN 56164-3205
Tel.: (507) 562-6700
Wind Turbine Mfr
N.A.I.C.S.: 333611

Suzlon Structures Limited (1)
5 Shrimali Society B H Shree Krishna Centre, Navrangpura, Ahmedabad, 380009, Gujarat, India
Tel.: (91) 7926471355
Wind Turbine Mfr
N.A.I.C.S.: 333611

Suzlon Towers and Structures Limited (1)
Suzlon 5 Shrimali Society Near Shri Krishna Complex, Navrangpura, Ahmedabad, 380009, Gujarat, India
Tel.: (91) 7926471100
Sales Range: $25-49.9 Million
Emp.: 100
Wind Turbine Mfr
N.A.I.C.S.: 333611

Suzlon Wind Energy Corporation (1)
8750 W Bryn Mawr Ave Ste 300E, Chicago, IL 60631
Tel.: (773) 328-5077
Web Site: http://www.suzlon.com
Wind Turbine Mfr
N.A.I.C.S.: 333611

Suzlon Wind Energy Espana, S.L (1)
Calle de Rosario Pino 14-16 5 planta, 28020, Madrid, Spain
Tel.: (34) 915794727
Web Site: http://www.suzlon.com
Sales Range: $25-49.9 Million
Wind Turbine Mfr
N.A.I.C.S.: 333611

SUZUDEN CORP.
2-2-2 Yushima, Bunkyo-ku, Tokyo, 113-0034, Japan
Tel.: (81) 369106828
Web Site: https://www.suzuden.co.jp
Year Founded: 1948
7480—(TKS)
Rev.: $336,640,690
Assets: $187,063,000
Liabilities: $64,996,130
Net Worth: $122,066,870
Earnings: $13,821,510
Emp.: 2,210
Fiscal Year-end: 03/31/24
Electrical Equipment Whslr
N.A.I.C.S.: 423610

SUZUKEN CO., LTD.
8 Higashi Kataha-machi, Higashi-ku, Nagoya, 461-8701, Aichi, Japan
Tel.: (81) 529506362 JP
Web Site: https://www.suzuken.co.jp
Year Founded: 1932
9987—(SAP)
Rev.: $15,294,542,451
Assets: $7,572,494,219
Liabilities: $4,853,458,870
Net Worth: $2,719,035,349
Earnings: $134,430,129
Emp.: 13,429
Fiscal Year-end: 03/31/23
Pharmaceutical Product Mfr & Distr
N.A.I.C.S.: 325412
Hiromi Miyata *(Pres & Exec Officer)*

Subsidiaries:

Sanki Wellbe Co., Ltd. (1)
6-1-11 Shoko Center, Nishi-ku, Hiroshima, 733-0833, Japan
Tel.: (81) 822702266
Web Site: https://www.sanki-wellbe.com
Nursing Services
N.A.I.C.S.: 623110

Sanwa Kagaku Kenkyusho Co., Ltd. (1)

SUZUKEN CO., LTD.

Suzuken Co., Ltd.—(Continued)
35 Higashisotobori-cho, Higashi-ku, Nagoya, 461-8631, Aichi, Japan
Tel.: (81) 529518130
Web Site: https://www.skk-net.com
Sales Range: $550-599.9 Million
Emp.: 966
Pharmaceutical Preparation Mfr
N.A.I.C.S.: 325412
Katsumi Hata *(Pres & CEO)*

SUZUKI CO., LTD.

2150-1 Ogawara, Suzaka, 382-8588, Nagano, Japan
Tel.: (81) 262512600
Web Site: https://www.suzukinet.co.jp
6785—(TKS)
Rev.: $172,455,720
Assets: $230,531,860
Liabilities: $68,413,780
Net Worth: $162,118,080
Earnings: $14,100,740
Emp.: 1,073
Fiscal Year-end: 06/30/24
Sub-Micron, Ultra-High Precision Mfr
N.A.I.C.S.: 335999
Katsuto Yokoyama *(Sr Mng Exec Officer)*

Subsidiaries:

P.T. Global Teknindo Berkatama (1)
Kawasan Industri Kiic Ji Harapan VIII Lot LI-16, Karawang, 41361, Jawa Barat, Indonesia
Tel.: (62) 2129569349
Web Site: https://global-teknik.com
Precision Meld & Precision Parts Mfr
N.A.I.C.S.: 333511

SUZUKI MOTOR CORPORATION

300 Takatsuka-cho, Chuo-ku, Hamamatsu, 432-8611, Shizuoka, Japan
Tel.: (81) 534402061
Web Site: https://www.suzuki.co.jp
Year Founded: 1920
SZKMY—(OTCIQ)
Rev.: $33,280,587,480
Assets: $32,822,202,210
Liabilities: $14,835,396,810
Net Worth: $17,986,805,400
Earnings: $1,585,337,190
Emp.: 16,550
Fiscal Year-end: 03/31/23
Automobiles, Trucks, Motorcycles, Outboard Motors, Generators, General Purpose Engines & Other Related Products Mfr & Designer
N.A.I.C.S.: 336110
Toshihiro Suzuki *(Pres & Pres)*

Subsidiaries:

American Suzuki Motor Corporation (1)
3251 E Imperial Hwy, Brea, CA 92821-6722 **(100%)**
Tel.: (714) 996-7040
Web Site: http://www.suzuki.com
Sales Range: $150-199.9 Million
Emp.: 365
Automobiles, Motorcycles & Outboard Motors Distr
N.A.I.C.S.: 423110
Larry Vandiver *(VP-Motorcycle Mktg & Sls)*

CHANGZHOU HAOJUE SUZUKI MOTORCYCLE CO., LTD. (1)
No 888 Huanghe West Road, Changzhou, 213133, Jiangsu, China
Tel.: (86) 51983688999
Automobile Parts Mfr
N.A.I.C.S.: 336390

Enshu Seiko Co., Ltd. (1)
1246-1 Yamahigashi, Tenryu-Ku, Hamamatsu, 431-3303, Shizuoka, Japan
Tel.: (81) 539252111
Automobile Parts Mfr
N.A.I.C.S.: 336390

Hamamatsu Pipe Co., Ltd. (1)
6-2 Minamihiramatsu, Iwata, 438-0221, Shizuoka, Japan
Tel.: (81) 538668866
Automobile Parts Distr
N.A.I.C.S.: 423140

Jiangxi Changhe Suzuki Automobile Co., Ltd. (1)
No 208 Xinchang East Road, Jingdezhen, 333002, Jiangxi, China
Tel.: (86) 4008879988
Web Site: http://www.changhe-suzuki.com
Automobile Mfr & Distr
N.A.I.C.S.: 336110

Magyar Suzuki Corp. (1)
Schweidel Jozsef utca 52/A, 2500, Esztergom, Hungary
Tel.: (36) 12674848
Web Site: https://www.suzuki.hu
Sales Range: $800-899.9 Million
Emp.: 2,700
Motor Vehicles & Passenger Car Bodies
N.A.I.C.S.: 336211

Maruti Suzuki India Limited (1)
1 Nelson Mandela Road Vasant Kunj, New Delhi, 110 070, India **(54.21%)**
Tel.: (91) 1146781000
Web Site: https://www.marutisuzuki.com
Rev.: $10,006,582,950
Assets: $9,730,088,550
Liabilities: $2,563,756,650
Net Worth: $7,166,331,900
Earnings: $599,112,150
Emp.: 16,025
Fiscal Year-end: 03/31/2021
Automobile Mfr
N.A.I.C.S.: 336110
Kenichi Ayukawa *(CEO & Mng Dir)*

Myanmar Suzuki Motor Co., Ltd. (1)
Block No 23 Plot 476C Mogoke St, Industrial Zone 1 Dagon Myo Th, Yangon, Myanmar **(60%)**
Tel.: (95) 1591303
Sales Range: $25-49.9 Million
Emp.: 50
Motor Vehicles Mfr; Owned 70% by Suzuki Motor Corporation & 30% by Myanmar Automobile & Diesel Engine Industries
N.A.I.C.S.: 336211

Pak Suzuki Motor Co., Ltd. (1)
DSU Pakistan Steel Industrial Est Bin Qasim, PO Box 4206, Karachi, Pakistan
Tel.: (92) 201750788
Sales Range: $200-249.9 Million
Emp.: 600
Motor Vehicles & Passenger Car Bodies
N.A.I.C.S.: 336211
Masafumi Harano *(CEO)*

SOLOSON IMPORT C.A. (1)
Avenida Principal Parque Industrial El Marques, Edificio Soloson Oficina Administrativa Zona, Guatire, 1221, Miranda, Venezuela
Tel.: (58) 212 655 1600
Web Site: https://www.solosonimport.com
Automotive Parts Mfr & Distr
N.A.I.C.S.: 336390

Suzuki Akita Auto Parts Manufacturing Co., Ltd. (1)
192-1 East of Hamaikawa Ienohigashi, Ikawa-cho Minamiakita-gun, Akita, 018-1516, Japan
Tel.: (81) 18 874 2321
Web Site: https://www.suzuki-akita.co.jp
Emp.: 427
Automobile Parts Mfr & Distr
N.A.I.C.S.: 336340
Taki Junichi *(Pres)*

Suzuki Assemblers Malaysia Sdn. Bhd. (1)
No 2690 Lorong Perusahaan 6A Kawasan Perusahaan Perai, 13600, Prai, Penang, Malaysia
Tel.: (60) 4 3908231
Web Site: http://www.suzuki.com.my
Emp.: 165
Automotive Spare Parts Assembling Services
N.A.I.C.S.: 561990
Siti Hajar *(Mgr-HR)*

Suzuki Australia Pty. Ltd. (1)
97-105 Cherry Lane, Laverton, 3026, VIC, Australia **(100%)**
Tel.: (61) 1800777088
Web Site: http://www.suzuki.com.au
Sales Range: $50-74.9 Million
Emp.: 100
Import, Sales & Distribution of Automobiles
N.A.I.C.S.: 425120
Mac Kato *(Mng Dir)*

Suzuki Austria Automobil Handels GmbH (1)
Munchner Bundesstrasse 160, 5020, Salzburg, Austria **(100%)**
Tel.: (43) 6 622 1550
Web Site: https://www.suzuki.at
Sales Range: $100-124.9 Million
Emp.: 50
Motor Vehicles & Passenger Car Bodies Mfr
N.A.I.C.S.: 336211

Suzuki Business Co., Ltd. (1)
21339 Shinohara-cho Shinohara Plaza 3F, Nishi-Ku, Hamamatsu, 431-0201, Shizuoka, Japan
Tel.: (81) 53 440 0860
Web Site: https://www.suzuki-business.co.jp
Emp.: 481
Business Support Services
N.A.I.C.S.: 561499

Suzuki Canada, Inc. (1)
360 Saunders Road, Barrie, L4N 9Y2, ON, Canada **(100%)**
Tel.: (705) 999-8600
Web Site: https://www.suzuki.ca
Sales Range: $75-99.9 Million
Emp.: 125
Distribution of Suzuki Automobiles, Motorcycles & Outboard Motors
N.A.I.C.S.: 425120
Keiichi Maruyama *(Pres)*

Suzuki Construction Co., Ltd. (1)
1 of 117 Hattabata, Mishima, 411-8577, Shizuoka, Japan
Tel.: (81) 55 971 3040
Web Site: https://www.szki.co.jp
Emp.: 41
Building Construction Services
N.A.I.C.S.: 531190
Shinji Chiba *(Chm & CEO)*

Suzuki Egypt S.A.E. (1)
11 Oqba Street, Giza, Egypt
Tel.: (20) 237488500
Automobile Parts Mfr
N.A.I.C.S.: 336390

Suzuki Finance Co., Ltd. (1)
300 Takatsuka-cho, Minami-ku, Hamamatsu, 432-8065, Shizuoka, Japan **(95.93%)**
Tel.: (81) 53 445 0700
Web Site: https://www.suzuki-finance.co.jp
Sales Range: $550-599.9 Million
Emp.: 69
Vehicle Leasing Services
N.A.I.C.S.: 525990
Toshiaki Suzuki *(Pres)*

Suzuki France S.A. (1)
8 avenue des freres Lumieres, BP 50136, 78190, Trappes, France
Tel.: (33) 82 500 4063
Web Site: https://www.suzuki-moto.com
Sales Range: $50-74.9 Million
Emp.: 130
Motorcycle Dealers
N.A.I.C.S.: 441227

Suzuki GB PLC (1)
Steinbeck Crescent Snelshall West, Milton Keynes, MK4 4AE, Bucks, United Kingdom
Tel.: (44) 808 501 1959
Web Site: https://www.suzuki.co.uk
Sales Range: $50-74.9 Million
Emp.: 140
Cars, Motorcycles, Marine Engines & ATVs to the UK
N.A.I.C.S.: 441227
Graeme Jenkins *(Head-Fleet)*

Suzuki International Europe GmbH (1)
Suzuki-Allee 7, 64625, Bensheim, Germany
Tel.: (49) 62 515 7000
Web Site: https://www.auto.suzuki.de
Sales Range: $75-99.9 Million
Emp.: 200
Import, Sales & Distribution of Automobiles
N.A.I.C.S.: 425120

INTERNATIONAL PUBLIC

Suzuki Italia S.p.A. (1)
Via Ettore De Sonnaz 19, 10121, Turin, Italy **(100%)**
Tel.: (39) 011 921 3711
Web Site: http://www.suzuki.et
Sales Range: $50-74.9 Million
Emp.: 120
Motor Vehicles & Passenger Car Bodies
N.A.I.C.S.: 336110

Suzuki Kasei Co.,Ltd. (1)
5158-1 Hirakuchi, Hamakita-Ku, Hamamatsu, 434-0041, Shizuoka, Japan
Tel.: (81) 53 585 2111
Web Site: https://www.suzuki-kasei.co.jp
Automobile Parts Mfr
N.A.I.C.S.: 336390

Suzuki Marina, Hamanako, Co., Ltd. (1)
4494-90 Shinjo, Kosai, 431-0421, Shizuoka, Japan **(100%)**
Tel.: (81) 53 578 2452
Web Site: https://www.suzukimarine.co.jp
Sales Range: $25-49.9 Million
Emp.: 30
Mfr of Outboard Engines
N.A.I.C.S.: 333618

Suzuki Marine Co., Ltd. (1)
300 Takatsukacho, Minami-Ku, Hamamatsu, 432-8065, Shizuoka, Japan
Tel.: (81) 534402303
Automobile Parts Distr
N.A.I.C.S.: 423110

Suzuki Motor (Thailand) Co., Ltd. (1)
855 Onnut Road, Prawet Sub-Distrct, Bangkok, 10250, Thailand
Tel.: (66) 2 727 5920
Web Site: https://www.suzuki.co.th
Motorcycle Mfr
N.A.I.C.S.: 336991

Suzuki Motor Corporation (1)
300 Takatsuka, PO Box 1, Hamamatsu, 432 8611, Shizuoka, Japan
Tel.: (81) 534402061
Web Site: http://www.globalsuzuki.com
Sales Range: $1-4.9 Billion
Emp.: 7,995
Transportation of Automobiles
N.A.I.C.S.: 488490
Osamu Suzuki *(CEO & Chm)*

Suzuki Motor Espana, S.A. (1)
Galileo Galilei 771, Poligono Industrial Porceyo, 33392, Gijon, Spain
Tel.: (34) 985307061
Web Site: http://www.suzuki.es
Motor Vehicles & Passenger Car Bodies Mfr
N.A.I.C.S.: 336110

Suzuki Motor Iberica, S.A.U. (1)
C/ Carlos Sainz 35 Poligono Ciudad del Automovil, 28914, Leganes, Madrid, Spain
Tel.: (34) 910783600
Web Site: http://moto.suzuki.es
Sales Range: $25-49.9 Million
Emp.: 35
Car Dealer
N.A.I.C.S.: 441110

Suzuki Motor Poland z.o.o. (1)
ul Polczynska 10, 01-378, Warsaw, Poland **(100%)**
Tel.: (48) 22 899 8898
Web Site: https://www.suzuki.pl
Sales Range: $25-49.9 Million
Emp.: 60
Mfr of Motor Vehicles
N.A.I.C.S.: 336340

Suzuki Motor Sales Kinki Inc. (1)
1-1-5 Shikitsunishi, Naniwa-Ku, Osaka, 556-0015, Japan
Tel.: (81) 666330613
Automotive Distr
N.A.I.C.S.: 423110

Suzuki Motor de Colombia S.A. (1)
KM 15 VIA Cartago, Pereira, 3241, Colombia **(100%)**
Tel.: (57) 3009108092
Web Site: http://www.suzuki.com.co
Sales Range: $125-149.9 Million
Emp.: 300
Motorcycle Mfr & Distr
N.A.I.C.S.: 336991

Suzuki Motorcycle India Private Limited (1)

2nd Floor Plot No 1 Nelson Mandela Road,
Vasant Kunj, New Delhi, 110 070, India
Tel.: (91) 114 312 7000
Web Site:
https://www.suzukimotorcycle.co.in
Emp.: 3,000
Motorcycle & Scooter Mfr
N.A.I.C.S.: 336991
Satoshi Uchida *(Mng Dir)*

Suzuki New Zealand Ltd. (1)
1 Heads Road, Wanganui, 4500, New
Zealand (100%)
Tel.: (64) 6 349 1222
Web Site: https://www.suzuki.co.nz
Sales Range: $25-49.9 Million
Emp.: 40
Import, Sales & Distribution of Automobiles
N.A.I.C.S.: 425120
Tom Peck *(CEO)*

Suzuki Philippines, Inc. (1)
126 Progress Avenue, Carmelray Industrial
Park 1 Carmeltown Canlubang, Calamba,
4028, Laguna, Philippines (100%)
Tel.: (63) 28 462 5000
Web Site: https://www.suzuki.com.ph
Sales Range: $25-49.9 Million
Emp.: 250
Import, Sales & Distribution of Automobiles
N.A.I.C.S.: 425120
Akira Utsumi *(Pres)*

Suzuki Special Products Manufacturing Co., Ltd. (1)
1-2 Utari, Shiratori, Toyokawa, Aichi, Japan
Tel.: (81) 533848820
Mfr of Automotive Parts
N.A.I.C.S.: 336340

Suzuki Toyama Auto Parts Mfg Co.,
Ltd. (1)
3200 Mizushima, Oyabe, 932-0102,
Toyama, Japan
Tel.: (81) 766613511
Automobile Parts Mfr
N.A.I.C.S.: 336390

Thai Suzuki Motor Co., Ltd. (1)
31/1 Rangsit-Ongkharak Road, Bueng Yitho
Subdistrict, Thanyaburi, 12130, Pathum
Thani, Thailand (100%)
Tel.: (66) 25 331 1609
Web Site: https://www.thaisuzuki.co.th
Emp.: 800
Automobile & Motorcycle Mfr
N.A.I.C.S.: 336110

SUZUKI MOTORLU ARACLAR PAZARLAMA A.S.
Acibadem Mahallesi Alidede Sokak
No 2, Kadikoy, 34718, Turkiye
Tel.: (90) 4445795
Web Site: http://www.suzuki.com.tr
SZUKI—(IST)
Car Retailer
N.A.I.C.S.: 441110
Caglar Gogus *(Chm)*

SUZUMO MACHINERY COMPANY LIMITED
2-23-2 Toyotamakita, Nerima-ku, Tokyo, 176-0012, Japan
Tel.: (81) 339931371
Web Site:
https://www.suzumokikou.com
Year Founded: 1955
6405—(TKS)
Rev.: $95,937,540
Assets: $120,308,610
Liabilities: $23,934,810
Net Worth: $96,373,800
Earnings: $7,535,400
Emp.: 485
Fiscal Year-end: 03/31/24
Rice Cooking Machinery Mfr
N.A.I.C.S.: 333241
Minako Suzuki *(Pres)*

Subsidiaries:

Suzumo International
Corporation (1)

1815 W 205th St Ste 101, Torrance, CA
90501
Tel.: (310) 328-0400
Food Processing Machinery Distr
N.A.I.C.S.: 423830

Suzumo Singapore Corporation Pte.
Ltd. (1)
421 Tagore Industrial Avenue Suite 04-11
Tagore 8, Singapore, 787805, Singapore
Tel.: (65) 62542080
Food Processing Machinery Distr
N.A.I.C.S.: 423830

SUZUNUI CORPORATION
1-11-31 Jonan-cho, Hitachi, 317-0077, Ibaraki, Japan
Tel.: (81) 29 4225311
Web Site: http://www.suzunui.co.jp
Year Founded: 1964
Sales Range: $125-149.9 Million
Emp.: 181
Construction Engineering Services
N.A.I.C.S.: 541330
Kazuyoshi Suzuki *(Pres & CEO)*

SUZUYO SHINWART CORPORATION
22nd floor Mita NN Building 4-1-23
Shiba, Minato-ku, Tokyo, Japan
Tel.: (81) 354402800
Web Site: https://www.shinwart.co.jp
Year Founded: 1947
9360—(TKS)
Rev.: $113,427,600
Assets: $70,819,540
Liabilities: $47,155,740
Net Worth: $23,663,800
Earnings: $5,089,700
Emp.: 16,955
Fiscal Year-end: 03/31/24
Software Development Services
N.A.I.C.S.: 541511

SV INVESTMENT CORPORATION
Three IFC 46F 10 Gukjegeumyung-ro, Yeongdeungpo-gu, Seoul, Korea (South)
Tel.: (82) 237751020
Web Site: https://www.svinvest.com
289080—(KRS)
Investment Management Service
N.A.I.C.S.: 523999
Hong Won-Ho *(CEO)*

SV TRADING & AGENCIES LIMITED
Shop No F-227 1st Floor Raghuleela
Mega Mall Road Behind Poisar Depot, Kandivali W, Mumbai, 400 067,
Maharashtra, India
Tel.: (91) 2265027372
Web Site: https://www.svtrading.in
Year Founded: 1980
503622—(BOM)
Rev.: $140,911
Assets: $6,940,675
Liabilities: $2,862
Net Worth: $6,937,813
Earnings: $128,487
Emp.: 3
Fiscal Year-end: 03/31/21
Securities Trading Services
N.A.I.C.S.: 523150
Manoharbhai P. Joshi *(Exec Dir)*

SV VISION LIMITED
Unit 4 12/F 18 King Wah Road, North
Point, China (Hong Kong)
Tel.: (852) 22352880
Web Site: http://www.iciclegroup.com
8429—(HKG)
Rev.: $7,604,865
Assets: $9,780,908
Liabilities: $2,174,258
Net Worth: $7,606,650
Earnings: ($374,723)

Emp.: 42
Fiscal Year-end: 12/31/22
Marketing Services
N.A.I.C.S.: 541870
Bonnie Chan Tak Chi Woo *(Chm & CEO)*

SVA (GROUP) CO., LTD.
3 F 757 Yishan Rd, Shanghai,
200233, China
Tel.: (86) 2154973988
Holding Company; Electronic Components Mfr
N.A.I.C.S.: 551112
Xinhua Fu *(Pres)*

Subsidiaries:

SVA Information Industry Co.,
Ltd. (1)
3800 Jindu Road, Shanghai, 201108,
China (63.94%)
Tel.: (86) 2164189198
Emp.: 6,667
Household Electrical Appliance & Electronic
Information Product Mfr
N.A.I.C.S.: 334419

SVA INDIA LIMITED
162-C Mittal Tower 16th Floor Nariman Point, Mumbai, 400 021, Maharashtra, India
Tel.: (91) 2222886789
Web Site: https://www.svaindia.com
Year Founded: 1981
531885—(BOM)
Rev.: $466,543
Assets: $3,952,940
Liabilities: $2,459,637
Net Worth: $1,493,304
Earnings: ($135,567)
Emp.: 1
Fiscal Year-end: 03/31/23
Chemical Product Whslr
N.A.I.C.S.: 424690
Raghav Vinod Gupta *(Exec Dir)*

SVAM SOFTWARE LIMITED
224 G/F, Swayam Seva Co-Operative
Housing Society Ltd, Jhilmil New
Delhi, Delhi, 110032, India
Tel.: (91) 1140363174
Web Site: http://svamsoftwareltd.in
Year Founded: 1992
523722—(BOM)
Rev.: $281,663
Assets: $2,556,415
Liabilities: $243,557
Net Worth: $2,312,858
Earnings: $17,009
Fiscal Year-end: 03/31/23
Software Development Services
N.A.I.C.S.: 541511
Manisha Agarwal *(Mng Dir)*

SVARAJ TRADING & AGENCIES LIMITED
Office No 30 2nd floor 380/82
Amruteshwar Co-operative Housing
Soc Ltd, Jagannath Sunkersett Road,
Mumbai, 400 002, Maharashtra, India
Tel.: (91) 2222053575
Web Site:
https://www.svarajtrading.in
Year Founded: 1980
503624—(BOM)
Rev.: $33,363
Assets: $6,945,273
Liabilities: $3,887
Net Worth: $6,941,386
Earnings: ($9,854)
Emp.: 6
Fiscal Year-end: 03/31/23
Securities Trading Services
N.A.I.C.S.: 523150
Harendra Kumar Gupta *(Mng Dir)*

SVARNIM TRADE UDYOG LIMITED
3 A Mangoe Lane 1st Ashok Vihar
noormahal road Punjab guest house
st, Nakodar dist, Jalandhar, 144040,
West Bengal, India
Tel.: (91) 9152594408
Web Site: https://www.svarnim.com
Year Founded: 1982
539911—(BOM)
Assets: $6,319
Liabilities: $2,398
Net Worth: $3,921
Earnings: ($37,396)
Fiscal Year-end: 03/31/23
Textile Products Distr
N.A.I.C.S.: 424310
Dhiraj Vinod Sosa *(Chm)*

SVAROG ASSET MANAGEMENT LLC
12D Hospytalna Street, Kiev, Ukraine
Tel.: (380) 44 496 1460
Private Investment Firm
N.A.I.C.S.: 523999

Subsidiaries:

JSSC Ukrrichflot (1)
8 Elektrykiv Str, Kiev, 04071,
Ukraine (97.83%)
Tel.: (380) 44 594 57 88
Web Site: http://www.ukrrichflot.ua
Logistics Consulting Servies
N.A.I.C.S.: 541614
Oleksii Koshelev *(COO)*

SVAS BIOSANA S.P.A.
Via Trentola 7, Somma Vesuviana,
Naples, Italy
Tel.: (39) 0818995411
Web Site: https://www.svas.it
Year Founded: 1972
SVS—(ITA)
Rev.: $91,577,514
Assets: $111,316,639
Liabilities: $168,877,347
Net Worth: ($57,560,708)
Earnings: $3,570,240
Emp.: 390
Fiscal Year-end: 12/31/21
Biotechnology Research & Development Services
N.A.I.C.S.: 541714

SVC INDUSTRIES LIMITED
301 3rd Floor Shubham Centre-1
Near Holy Family Church 491, Cardinal Gracias Road Andheri East,
Mumbai, 400 099, India
Tel.: (91) 2228324296
Web Site:
https://www.svcindustriesltd.com
Year Founded: 1989
524488—(BOM)
Rev.: $87,128
Assets: $61,510,886
Liabilities: $23,706,160
Net Worth: $37,804,726
Earnings: ($661,315)
Fiscal Year-end: 03/31/21
Specialty Chemicals Mfr
N.A.I.C.S.: 325998
Sanjay Agarwal *(CFO & Mgr)*

SVC RESOURCES LTD.
Office No 42 Citi Mall Link Road,
Andheri West, Mumbai, 400053, Maharashtra, India
Tel.: (91) 9867849564
Web Site:
http://www.svcresources.co.in
Sales Range: Less than $1 Million
Iron Ore Mining Services
N.A.I.C.S.: 212210

SVEASKOG AB

SVEASKOG AB

Sveaskog AB—(Continued)
Torsgatan 4, 105 22, Stockholm, Sweden
Tel.: (46) 86559000
Web Site: http://www.sveaskog.se
Rev.: $772,588,530
Assets: $4,452,806,330
Liabilities: $1,926,380,750
Net Worth: $2,526,425,580
Earnings: $166,970,860
Emp.: 682
Fiscal Year-end: 12/31/19
Producer & Seller of Timber & Cartonboard
N.A.I.C.S.: 113110
Eva Farnstrand (Chm)

Subsidiaries:

Sveaskog Baltfor SIA (1)
Brivibas iela 40 - 23, Riga, 1007, Latvia
Tel.: (371) 67240175
Millwork & Timber Distr
N.A.I.C.S.: 423310
Guntars Zvejsalnieks (Mng Dir)

Sveaskog Forvaltnings AB (1)
Torsgatan 4, 105 22, Stockholm, Sweden   **(100%)**
Tel.: (46) 86559000
Web Site: http://www.sveaskog.se
Sales Range: $10-24.9 Million
Emp.: 50
Timber & Cartonboard Mfr
N.A.I.C.S.: 113110

Unit (Domestic):

Segra Group (2)
Pipers Vag 2, SE 105 22, Stockholm, Sweden
Tel.: (46) 87050470
Web Site: http://www.segragroup.se
Mfr of Timber
N.A.I.C.S.: 113110

Svenska Skogsplantor AB (1)
Vibytorp, 694 36, Hallsberg, Sweden
Tel.: (46) 5 82 68 69 70
Web Site: http://www.skogsplantor.se
Forestry Services
N.A.I.C.S.: 115310

SVEDBERGS I DALSTORP AB

Verkstadsvagen 1, 514 63, Dalstorp, Sweden
Tel.: (46) 321533000
Web Site:
https://www.svedbergs.com
Year Founded: 1920
SVED.B—(OMX)
Rev.: $79,276,310
Assets: $82,334,414
Liabilities: $54,564,877
Net Worth: $27,769,538
Earnings: $5,881,814
Emp.: 247
Fiscal Year-end: 12/31/20
Bathroom Interiors Designer & Mfr
N.A.I.C.S.: 541410
Andersson Per-Arne (Pres & CEO)

Subsidiaries:

Orregent AB (1)
Danska Vagen 13, 332 36, Jonkoping, Sweden   **(60%)**
Tel.: (46) 37180219
Sales Range: $25-49.9 Million
Emp.: 13
Plastics Product Mfr
N.A.I.C.S.: 326199

Svedbergs Ceramics AS (1)
Piirimae 14 Tanassilma, Saku Vald, 76401, Harjumaa, Estonia   **(51%)**
Tel.: (372) 6889150
Ceramic Products Mfr
N.A.I.C.S.: 327120

Svedbergs OY (1)
Klovinpellontie 3, 2180, Espoo, Finland   **(100%)**
Tel.: (358) 9584100
Web Site: http://www.svedbergs.sa

Sales Range: $1-9.9 Million
Emp.: 13
Bathroom Interiors Designer & Mfr
N.A.I.C.S.: 541410

SVEJSEMASKINEFABRIKKEN MIGATRONIC A/S

Aggersundvej 33, Fjerritslev, DK-9690, Denmark
Tel.: (45) 96500600
Web Site: http://www.migatronic.com
Year Founded: 1970
MIGA.B—(OMX)
Rev.: $50,948,263
Assets: $38,958,311
Liabilities: $17,115,225
Net Worth: $21,843,086
Earnings: $1,518,738
Emp.: 290
Fiscal Year-end: 12/31/19
Welding Machinery Mfr & Distr
N.A.I.C.S.: 333992
Anders Hoiris (Vice Chm)

Subsidiaries:

Migatronic Cz A.S (1)
Tolsteho 474/2, 415 03, Teplice, Czech Republic
Tel.: (420) 411135600
Welding Equipment Mfr
N.A.I.C.S.: 333992

Migatronic Equipement de Soudure S.A.R.L. (1)
Parc Avenir II 313 Rue Marcel Merieux, 69530, Brignais, France
Tel.: (33) 478506511
Welding Equipment Mfr
N.A.I.C.S.: 333992

Migatronic India Private Ltd. (1)
No 22 and 39/20H Sowri Street, Alandur, 600 016, Chennai, India
Tel.: (91) 22300074
Welding Equipment Mfr
N.A.I.C.S.: 333992

Migatronic Kereskedelmi Kft. (1)
Szent Miklos u 17/a, 6000, Kecskemet, Hungary
Tel.: (36) 76481412
Welding Equipment Mfr
N.A.I.C.S.: 333992

Migatronic Nederland B.V. (1)
Hallenweg 34, 5683 CT, Best, Netherlands
Tel.: (31) 499375000
Welding Equipment Mfr
N.A.I.C.S.: 333992

Migatronic Norge AS (1)
Industriveien 6, 3300, Hokksund, Norway
Tel.: (47) 32256900
Welding Equipment Mfr
N.A.I.C.S.: 333992

Migatronic Oy (1)
PO Box 105, 04301, Tuusula, Finland
Tel.: (358) 102176500
Welding Equipment Mfr
N.A.I.C.S.: 333992

Migatronic S.R.L. (1)
Via Dei Quadri 40, 20059, Vimercate, MB, Italy
Tel.: (39) 0399278093
Welding Equipment Mfr
N.A.I.C.S.: 333992

Migatronic Schweissmaschinen GmbH (1)
Sandusweg 12, 35435, Wettenberg, Germany
Tel.: (49) 641982840
Welding Equipment Mfr
N.A.I.C.S.: 333992

Migatronic Svetsmaskiner AB (1)
Naas Fabriker, Box 5015, Middle Factory Plan 4, 448 50, Tollered, Sweden
Tel.: (46) 31440045
Welding Equipment Mfr
N.A.I.C.S.: 333992

Migatronic Welding Equipment Ltd. (1)
21 Jubilee Drive Belton Park, Loughborough, LE11 5XS, Leicestershire, United Kingdom
Tel.: (44) 1509267499
Welding Equipment Mfr
N.A.I.C.S.: 333992

Suzhou Migatronic Welding Technology Co., Ltd. (1)
4 FengHe Road Industrial Park, Suzhou, China
Tel.: (86) 51287179800
Welding Equipment Mfr
N.A.I.C.S.: 333992

SVENSKA CELLULOSA AKTIEBOLAGET SCA

Skepparplatsen 1, SE-851 88, Sundsvall, Sweden
Tel.: (46) 60193000   SE
Year Founded: 1929
SCA.A—(OMX)
Rev.: $1,794,925
Assets: $14,687,395
Liabilities: $4,334,981
Net Worth: $10,352,413
Earnings: $359,859
Emp.: 3,334
Fiscal Year-end: 12/31/23
Hygiene Products, Packaging & Graphic Papers Mfr
N.A.I.C.S.: 322130
Ulf Larsson (Pres & CEO)

Subsidiaries:

AB SCA Finans (1)
Klarabergsviadukten 63, PO Box 200, SE-101 23, Stockholm, Sweden
Tel.: (46) 87885100
Rev.: $221,725,800
Assets: $9,996,019,632
Liabilities: $2,613,626,836
Net Worth: $7,382,392,796
Earnings: $86,554,421
Emp.: 6
Fiscal Year-end: 12/31/2015
Borrowing, Liquidity, Currency & Risk Management Services
N.A.I.C.S.: 522320
Johan Rydin (Pres)

BSN medical GmbH (1)
Quickbornstrasse 24, D-20253, Hamburg, Germany
Tel.: (49) 404909909
Web Site: http://www.bsnmedical.com
Medical Devices Mfr & Distr
N.A.I.C.S.: 339112
Ann Maitland (Dir-Global Ops)

Subsidiary (US):

BSN medical, Inc. (2)
5825 Carnegie Blvd, Charlotte, NC 28209
Tel.: (704) 554-9933
Web Site: http://www.bsnmedical.com
Orthopaedic Supplies Distr
N.A.I.C.S.: 334510
Todd Healy (Pres-North America)

Subsidiary (Domestic):

BSN-Jobst GmbH (2)
Beiersdorfstrasse 1, D-46446, Emmerich am Rhein, Germany
Tel.: (49) 28226070
Web Site: http://www.bsnmedical.de
Compression Bandages & Garments Mfr
N.A.I.C.S.: 315250

Subsidiary (US):

JoViPak Corporation (2)
19625 62nd Ave S Bldg C Ste 101, Kent, WA 98032
Tel.: (866) 888-5684
Web Site: http://www.jovipak.com
Lymphoedema Garments Mfr
N.A.I.C.S.: 315990

Wright Therapy Products, Inc. (2)
103-B International Dr, Oakdale, PA 15071
Tel.: (800) 631-9535
Web Site: http://www.wrighttherapy.com
Electromedical & Electrotherapeutic Apparatus Mfr
N.A.I.C.S.: 334510

INTERNATIONAL PUBLIC

Oy SCA Hygiene Products Ab (1)
Itsehalintokuja 6, Espoo, 00380, Finland
Tel.: (358) 950 68 81
Sanitary Paper Products Distr
N.A.I.C.S.: 424130
Helena Pettersson (Owner)

SCA Americas Inc. (1)
2929 Arch St Ste 2600, Philadelphia, PA 19104
Tel.: (610) 499-3700
Sales Range: $50-74.9 Million
Emp.: 120
Sanitary Paper Products, Incontinence Products
N.A.I.C.S.: 322291
Victoria Ravin (Mgr-Bus Intelligence)

Subsidiary (Non-US):

SCA Hygiene Products Inc (2)
999 Farrell Drummondville, J2C 5P6, Quebec, QC, Canada
Tel.: (819) 475-4500
Web Site: http://www.sca.com
Sales Range: $25-49.9 Million
Emp.: 200
Personal Care Paper Products Mfr
N.A.I.C.S.: 322299

Subsidiary (Domestic):

SCA Personal Care, Inc (2)
Cira Ctr 2929 Arch St Ste 2600, Philadelphia, PA 19104
Tel.: (610) 499-3700
Sanitary Paper Product Mfr
N.A.I.C.S.: 322291

SCA Tissue North America, LLC (2)
PO Box 2400, Neenah, WI 54957-2400
Tel.: (920) 725-7031
Emp.: 170
Tissue Products Mfr
N.A.I.C.S.: 322120
Joe Fahley (CFO)

Plant (Domestic):

SCA Tissue North America, LLC - Flagstaff (3)
1600 E Butler Ave, Flagstaff, AZ 86001-5909
Tel.: (928) 774-7375
Sales Range: $25-49.9 Million
Emp.: 90
Mfr of Tissue Paper Products
N.A.I.C.S.: 322291
Tim Holman (Mgr-Deinking)

SCA Emballage France SAS (1)
8 Terrasse Bellini, Puteaux, 92800, France
Tel.: (33) 155614411
Packaging Paper Materials Mfr
N.A.I.C.S.: 322220
Mark Shaw (Gen Mgr)

SCA Forest Products AB (1)
Skepparplatsen 1, 852 34, Sundsvall, Sweden   **(100%)**
Tel.: (46) 60193000
Web Site:
http://www.forestproducts.sca.com
Sales Range: $50-74.9 Million
Emp.: 150
N.A.I.C.S.: 315210

Plant (Domestic):

SCA Obbola (2)
Linjevagen 33, Obbola, 91380, Sweden   **(100%)**
Tel.: (46) 90154000
Paper Mills
N.A.I.C.S.: 322130

Subsidiary (Non-US):

SCA Timber France (2)
Bassin No 3, PO Box 90136, Rochefort, FR 173 06, France   **(100%)**
Tel.: (33) 546834949
Web Site: http://www.scatimber.com
Sales Range: $25-49.9 Million
Emp.: 80
Timber Product Sales
N.A.I.C.S.: 423990
Patrick Fournier (Mng Dir)

SCA Forsakrings AB (1)
Klarabergsviadukten 63, PO Box 200,

Stockholm, 101 23, Sweden (100%)
Tel.: (46) 87885243
Sales Range: $25-49.9 Million
Emp.: 4
N.A.I.C.S.: 315210
Charlotte Pillengren (Treas)

SCA GmbH (1)
Adalperostrasse 31, 85737, Ismaning, Germany
Tel.: (49) 89 97006 0
N.A.I.C.S.: 315210
Ulrich Beltz (Dir-Data Mgmt)

SCA Graphic Paper (1)
Skepparplatsen 1, Sundsvall, 85234, Sweden (100%)
Tel.: (46) 60193800
Web Site: http://www.sca.sa
Sales Range: $25-49.9 Million
Emp.: 45
N.A.I.C.S.: 315210
Ulf Larsson (Pres)

SCA Graphic Sundsvall AB (1)
Ortviken Paper Mill, Box 846, 851 23, Sundsvall, Sweden
Tel.: (46) 60 19 40 00
Emp.: 800
Paper Products Mfr & Distr
N.A.I.C.S.: 322120

SCA Hygiene Malaysia Sdn Bhd (1)
No 2A Jalan Pelabur 23/1 Seksyen 23, 40300, Shah Alam, Selangor Darul Ehsan, Malaysia
Tel.: (60) 3 5521 7488
Sales Range: $150-199.9 Million
Emp.: 30
Sanitary Paper Products Mfr & Distr
N.A.I.C.S.: 322291

SCA Hygiene Marketing (M) Sdn Bhd (1)
3 Jalan Gicing Hulu 28/33 HICOM Industrial Estate Sector C, 40400, Shah Alam, Selangor, Malaysia
Tel.: (60) 3 5101 6618
Sanitary Paper Products Distr
N.A.I.C.S.: 424130

SCA Hygiene Products A/S (1)
Grensesvingen 9, PO Box 6227, Etterstad, 0603, Oslo, Norway
Tel.: (47) 22 70 62 00
Sanitary Paper Products Distr
N.A.I.C.S.: 424130
Deon Irose (Mgr)

SCA Hygiene Products AB (1)
Backstensgatan 5 Molndal, Gothenburg, 431 49, Sweden (100%)
Tel.: (46) 317460000
Sales Range: $200-249.9 Million
Emp.: 900
Mfr of Personal Care, Tissue & Forest Products
N.A.I.C.S.: 812990
Milind Pingle (Mng Dir-SCA Hygiene Products India Pvt Ltd)

Plant (Domestic):

SCA Hygiene Products (2)
Backstensgatan 5, SE 405 03, Molndal, Gothenburg, Sweden (100%)
Tel.: (46) 317460000
Web Site: http://www.sca.se
Sales Range: $150-199.9 Million
Emp.: 900
N.A.I.C.S.: 315210
Christina Rydebrinks (VP)

Subsidiary (Non-US):

SCA Hygiene Products (2)
Adalperostr 31, PO Box 241540, Ismaning, 85737, Germany (100%)
Tel.: (49) 89970060
Sales Range: $50-74.9 Million
Emp.: 250
Personal Care Products
N.A.I.C.S.: 322291

SCA Hygiene Products SA (2)
59 Rue De La Vignette, 59126, Linsellers, France (100%)
Tel.: (33) 320693333
Sales Range: $100-124.9 Million
Emp.: 300
Diapers

N.A.I.C.S.: 322291

SCA Hygiene Products AE (1)
17th Km National Rd Athens Lamia, 14234, Athens, Greece
Tel.: (30) 210 270 57 00
Sanitary Paper Product Mfr
N.A.I.C.S.: 322291

SCA Hygiene Products AG (1)
Baarerstrasse 133, 6301, Zug, Switzerland
Tel.: (41) 768 9300
Paper Product Distr
N.A.I.C.S.: 424130

SCA Hygiene Products GmbH (1)
Storchengasse 1, 1150, Vienna, Austria
Tel.: (43) 1 899 01 0
Emp.: 65
Tissue Paper Distr
N.A.I.C.S.: 424130
Thomas Strasser (Country Mgr)

Joint Venture (Domestic):

Bunzl & Biach Ges.m.b.H (2)
Steinheilgasse 5, 1210, Vienna, Austria (49%)
Tel.: (43) 1250610
Web Site: https://www.bunzl-biach.at
Waste Paper Product Distr
N.A.I.C.S.: 424130
Andreas Mang (Mng Dir)

SCA Hygiene Products Kft (1)
Budakeszi Ut 51, PO Box 178, 1525, Budapest, Hungary
Tel.: (36) 1 392 21 00
Sanitary Paper Products Distr
N.A.I.C.S.: 424130

SCA Hygiene Products Nederland B.V. (1)
Arnhemse Bovenweg 120, Zeist, 3708 AH, Netherlands
Tel.: (31) 306984600
Sales Range: $50-74.9 Million
Emp.: 20
Pharmaceuticals Product Mfr
N.A.I.C.S.: 325412
Andre Voogsgeerd (Gen Mgr)

Division (Domestic):

SCA Tissue Nederland (2)
Lange Linden 22, 5433 NC, Katwijk aan Zee, NB, Netherlands
Tel.: (31) 485339339
Sales Range: $125-149.9 Million
Emp.: 300
Holding Company
N.A.I.C.S.: 551112
Jan Fassbender (Mng Dir)

SCA Hygiene Products Russia LLC (1)
Krzhizhanovskogo Str 14/3, Moscow, 117218, Russia
Tel.: (7) 495 967 33 67
Web Site: http://www.sca.ru
Paper Products Mfr
N.A.I.C.S.: 322291
Ingolf Braun (Mgr)

SCA Hygiene Products S.L. (1)
Ctra De Valls a Puigpelat Km 1 6, PO Box 115, 43812, Puigpelat, Tarragona, Spain
Tel.: (34) 977 03 06 00
Web Site: http://www.scaconsumertissue.com
Consumer Tissue Mfr & Distr
N.A.I.C.S.: 322291

Subsidiary (Domestic):

SCA Hygiene Spain, S.Com. p.A. (2)
Poligono Ind Miravete SN, FR 31262, Allo, Spain (100%)
Tel.: (34) 948 548 305
Web Site: http://www.colhogar.com
Sales Range: $100-124.9 Million
Emp.: 350
Paper Products Mfr
N.A.I.C.S.: 322299

SCA Hygiene Products S.p.a (1)
Via S Quasimodo 12, 20025, Legnano, Milan, Italy
Tel.: (39) 0331 443811

Sales Range: $25-49.9 Million
Emp.: 90
Personal Care & Health Care Product Retailer
N.A.I.C.S.: 456199
Mirella Credali (Mgr)

SCA Hygiene Products SA-NV (1)
Rue de la Papeterie 2, 4801, Verviers, Belgium
Tel.: (32) 87306611
Sales Range: $125-149.9 Million
Emp.: 300
Tissue Paper Mfr
N.A.I.C.S.: 322291
Jacky Dechamps (Mgr)

SCA Hygiene Products Sp. z.o.o. (1)
ul 3 Maja 30A, Olawa, 55200, Poland
Tel.: (48) 71 301 3000
Emp.: 500
Personal Care Product Mfr
N.A.I.C.S.: 325620

SCA Hygiene Products UK Limited (1)
Southfields Road, Dunstable, LU6 3EJ, Bedfordshire, United Kingdom
Tel.: (44) 1582 677 400
Emp.: 250
Paper Product Distr
N.A.I.C.S.: 424130
Paul Bailey (Dir-Fin)

Subsidiary (Non-US):

SCA Hygiene Products Manchester Ltd (2)
Trafford Park Road Trafford Park Mill, M17 1EQ, Manchester, United Kingdom - England
Tel.: (44) 161 888 6002
Web Site: http://www.sca.com
Tissue Paper Mfr
N.A.I.C.S.: 322291
Robert Fuhrmann (Mgr-Site)

SCA Skog AB (1)
Skepparplatsen 1, 851 88, Sundsvall, Sweden
Tel.: (46) 60193000
Emp.: 100
Pulp & Newsprint Paper Mfr
N.A.I.C.S.: 322120
Mats Sandgren (Pres)

SCA Timber AB (1)
Skepparplatsen 1, 851 88, Sundsvall, Sweden
Tel.: (46) 601930000
Web Site: http://www.sca.com
Emp.: 150
Wood Products Mfr
N.A.I.C.S.: 321113

Subsidiary (Non-US):

N. A. Sitaras Ltd. (2)
32A Philadelpheos Street, Kifisia, 14562, Athens, Greece
Tel.: (30) 2 10 623 05 66
Web Site: http://www.sca.com
Wood Product Distr
N.A.I.C.S.: 423990

Plant (Domestic):

SCA Timber AB - Bollsta Sawmill (2)
Bruksvagen 15, Bollstabruk, 873 80, Kramfors, Sweden
Tel.: (46) 612 880 73
Web Site: http://www.sca.com
Wood Products Mfr
N.A.I.C.S.: 321113
Katarina Levin (Mgr)

SCA Timber AB - Munksund Sawmill (2)
Masvagen 20, Box 783, Munksund, 941 28, Pitea, Sweden
Tel.: (46) 911 767 91
Web Site: http://www.sca.com
Wood Products Mfr
N.A.I.C.S.: 321113
Anders Nilsson (Mgr)

SCA Timber AB - Rundvik Sawmill (2)
Brogatan 3, Box 3, 914 29, Rundvik, Sweden

Tel.: (46) 930 462 21
Wood Products Mfr
N.A.I.C.S.: 321113
Magnus Karlsson (Mgr)

SCA Timber AB - Tunadal Sawmill (2)
Box 815, 851 23, Sundsvall, Sweden
Tel.: (46) 60 19 39 31
Wood Products Mfr
N.A.I.C.S.: 321113
Ville Huittinen (Mgr)

SCA Timber AB - Vilhelmina Sawmill (2)
Industrivagen 36, Vilhelmina, 15891223, Sweden
Tel.: (46) 940 154 17
Web Site: http://www.sca.com
Sales Range: $25-49.9 Million
Emp.: 46
Wood Products Mfr
N.A.I.C.S.: 321113

Subsidiary (Non-US):

SCA Timber China & S.E. Asia Ltd. (2)
17/F Woon Lee Commercial Building 7-9 Austin Avenue, Tsim Sha Tsui, Kowloon, China (Hong Kong)
Tel.: (852) 2947 0775
Sales Range: $25-49.9 Million
Emp.: 4
Wood Product Distr
N.A.I.C.S.: 423310
Mathias Fridholm (Mng Dir)

SCA Timber Supply Ltd (1)
Etruscan Street Etruria, Stoke-on-Trent, ST1 5PG, Staffordshire, United Kingdom
Tel.: (44) 1782 224 100
Sales Range: $75-99.9 Million
Emp.: 75
Wood Products Mfr & Distr
N.A.I.C.S.: 321999
John Griffiths (Mng Dir)

SCA Tissue France SAS (1)
11 Route Industrielle, 68320, Kunheim, France (100%)
Tel.: (33) 389 722 300
Sales Range: $500-549.9 Million
Emp.: 2,500
Holding Company
N.A.I.C.S.: 551112

Plant (Domestic):

SCA Tissue France SAS (2)
Blvd Industriel Z I, BP 518, 76807, Saint Etienne-du-Rouvray, Cedex, France (100%)
Tel.: (33) 235643939
Sales Range: $125-149.9 Million
Emp.: 350
Paper Product Whslr
N.A.I.C.S.: 424130
Cathy Cloarec (Head-Training)

SCA Wood Hong Kong Ltd. (1)
9/F Oriental Crystal Finance Centre No 107-109 Chatham Road South, Tsimshatsui, Kowloon, China (Hong Kong)
Tel.: (852) 2 947 0775
Wood Product Mfr & Whslr
N.A.I.C.S.: 321999
Hakan Persson (Mng Dir)

SVENSKA HANDELSBANKEN AB

Kungstradgardsgatan 2, 106 70, Stockholm, Sweden
Tel.: (46) 87011000 NL
Web Site:
  https://www.handelsbanken.se
Year Founded: 1871
SVNLY—OTCIQ
Rev: $5,830,359,568
Assets: $331,356,317,963
Liabilities: $312,147,667,350
Net Worth: $19,208,650,613
Earnings: $2,726,872,536
Emp.: 10,902
Fiscal Year-end: 12/31/23
Domestic & International Banking Services

SVENSKA HANDELSBANKEN AB

Svenska Handelsbanken AB—(Continued)
N.A.I.C.S.: 522110
Par Boman *(Chm)*

Subsidiaries:

AB Handel och Industri (1)
Nybrokajen 15, 106 70, Stockholm, Sweden
Tel.: (46) 87014110
Commercial Banking Services
N.A.I.C.S.: 522110

Handelsbanken Asset Management (1)
Kungstradgardsgatan 2, 10670, Stockholm, Sweden (100%)
Tel.: (46) 87011000
Web Site: http://www.handelsbanken.se
Sales Range: $300-349.9 Million
Emp.: 600
Fund & Discretionary Asset Management & Custody Services
N.A.I.C.S.: 531390

Handelsbanken Capital Markets (1)
Blasieholmstorg 11 & 12, 106 70, Stockholm, Sweden (100%)
Tel.: (46) 87011000
Web Site: http://www.handelsbanken.se
Sales Range: $200-249.9 Million
Emp.: 450
Financial Services
N.A.I.C.S.: 523940
Per Beckman *(Mng Dir)*

Handelsbanken Denmark (1)
Havneholmen 29, 1561, Copenhagen, Denmark (100%)
Tel.: (45) 46791200
Web Site: http://www.handelsbanken.dk
Sales Range: $100-124.9 Million
Emp.: 180
Banking Services
N.A.I.C.S.: 522110
Lars Moesgaard *(CEO & Dir-Admin)*

Handelsbanken Finans AB (1)
Torsgatan 12, 106 70, Stockholm, Sweden (100%)
Tel.: (46) 87011000
Web Site: http://www.handelsbanken.se
Sales Range: $200-249.9 Million
Emp.: 300
Factoring, Leasing, Corporate & Consumer Finance & Operation of the Credit Cards
N.A.I.C.S.: 522210
Charlotta Reuterving *(CFO-Acting)*

Subsidiary (Domestic):

Kredit-Inkasso AB (2)
Torsgatan 12-14, 106 35, Stockholm, Sweden
Tel.: (46) 87014700
Web Site: http://www.kredit-inkasso.se
Sales Range: $25-49.9 Million
Emp.: 35
Commercial Banking Services
N.A.I.C.S.: 522110
Pauline Bdsethdrum *(Gen Mgr)*

Subsidiary (Non-US):

Kreditt Inkasso As (2)
Stabbursveien 2, PO Box 435, 1601, Fredrikstad, Norway
Tel.: (47) 69361832
Web Site: http://www.kredittinkasso.no
Sales Range: $50-74.9 Million
Emp.: 5
Commercial Banking Services
N.A.I.C.S.: 522110

Spartacus A/S (2)
Vestergaee 2, 7430, Ikast, Denmark
Tel.: (45) 97725711
Sales Range: $25-49.9 Million
Emp.: 27
Commercial Banking Services
N.A.I.C.S.: 522110

Handelsbanken Finland (1)
Itamerenkatu 11-13, 00180, Helsinki, Finland
Tel.: (358) 1044411
Web Site: http://www.handelsbanken.fi
Sales Range: $350-399.9 Million
Emp.: 640
Banking Services
N.A.I.C.S.: 522110

Handelsbanken Fondbolag Ab (1)
Aleksanterinkatu 11, Helsinki, 00100, Finland
Tel.: (358) 1044411
Web Site: http://www.handelsbanken.fi
Commercial Banking Services
N.A.I.C.S.: 522110
Kristina Marklen *(Mgr-HR)*

Handelsbanken Fonder AB (1)
Blasieholmstorg 12, 106 70, Stockholm, Sweden (100%)
Tel.: (46) 87011000
Web Site: http://www.handelsbanken.se
Sales Range: $1-4.9 Billion
Emp.: 3,500
Investment Fund Management
N.A.I.C.S.: 525910
Daniel Andersson *(Chm)*

Handelsbanken Information Systems Department (1)
Tegeluddsvagen 10, 115 82, Stockholm, Sweden
Tel.: (46) 87011000
Web Site: http://www.handelsbanken.se
Sales Range: $1-4.9 Billion
Emp.: 3,000
N.A.I.C.S.: 522299
Frank Jensen *(Pres)*

Handelsbanken Kapitalforvaltning AS (1)
Tjuvholmen Alle 11, 252, Oslo, Norway
Tel.: (47) 22397000
Commercial Banking Services
N.A.I.C.S.: 522110

Handelsbanken Liv (1)
Kungstradgatan 2, PO Box 1325, 106 70, Stockholm, Sweden (100%)
Tel.: (46) 87011000
Web Site: http://www.handelsbanken.com
Complete Range of Life Insurance Products
N.A.I.C.S.: 524113

Handelsbanken Liv Forsakrings AB (1)
Box 1325, 111 83, Stockholm, Sweden
Tel.: (46) 87017100
Web Site: http://www.handelsbankenliv.se
Emp.: 100
Insurance Agency Services
N.A.I.C.S.: 524210

Handelsbanken Markets Securities, Inc (1)
Tel.: (212) 838-5200
Securities Brokerage Services
N.A.I.C.S.: 523150

Handelsbanken Norway (1)
Tjuvholmen Alle 11, PO Box 1342, Vika, 0113, Oslo, Norway (100%)
Tel.: (47) 22397000
Web Site: http://www.handelsbanken.no
Sales Range: $200-249.9 Million
Emp.: 400
Banking Services
N.A.I.C.S.: 522110

Handelsbanken Wealth & Asset Management Limited (1)
No 1 Kingsway, London, WC2B 6AN, United Kingdom
Tel.: (44) 2070451320
Web Site: https://www.wealthandasset.co.uk
Wealth Management Services
N.A.I.C.S.: 525110

Handelsinvest Investeringsforvaltning A/S (1)
Ostergade 2, 7400, Herning, Denmark
Tel.: (45) 97123355
Web Site: https://www.handelsinvest.dk
Emp.: 5
Investment Management Service
N.A.I.C.S.: 523999

Heartwood Wealth Management Limited (1)
No 1 Kingsway, London, WC2B 6AN, United Kingdom
Tel.: (44) 2070451325
Web Site: http://www.heartwoodgroup.co.uk
Sales Range: $10-24.9 Million
Emp.: 85
Investment Management Service
N.A.I.C.S.: 523940

Noland Carter *(Chief Investment Officer)*

Lokalbolig A/S (1)
Slotsgade 36, 3400, Hillerod, Denmark
Tel.: (45) 48 28 34 00
Property Management Services
N.A.I.C.S.: 531312

Optimix Vermogensbeheer N.V. (1)
Johannes Vermeerstraat 14, 1071 DR, Amsterdam, Netherlands
Tel.: (31) 205703030
Web Site: https://www.optimix.nl
Emp.: 40
Asset Management Services
N.A.I.C.S.: 523940

Subsidiary (Non-US):

Add Value Fund Management BV (2)
Tel.: (31) 205703057
Web Site: https://www.addvaluefund.nl
Fund Management Services
N.A.I.C.S.: 523940
Willem Verschoor *(Chm)*

Stadshypotek AB (1)
Torsgatan 12-14, 103 70, Stockholm, Sweden (100%)
Tel.: (46) 87015400
Web Site: http://www.stadshypotek.se
Sales Range: $50-74.9 Million
Emp.: 6,500
Mortgages for Single-family Homes, Multi-dwellings, Apartments, Commercial Properties & Office Buildings
N.A.I.C.S.: 522292
David Haqvinsson *(CEO)*

Svenska Handelsbanken (1)
875 3rd Ave 4th Fl, New York, NY 10022-4644
Tel.: (212) 326-5100
Web Site: http://www.handelsbanken.se
Sales Range: $50-74.9 Million
Emp.: 80
Banking
N.A.I.C.S.: 523150

Svenska Handelsbanken (1)
8 Avenue Felix Faure, 06000, Nice, France (100%)
Tel.: (33) 492008090
Web Site: http://www.handelsbanken.fr
Sales Range: $50-74.9 Million
Emp.: 20
International Banking
N.A.I.C.S.: 522299

Svenska Handelsbanken France (1)
7 Rue drouot, 75009, Paris, France (100%)
Tel.: (33) 142665898
Web Site: http://www.hendelsbanken.fr
Sales Range: $1-9.9 Million
Emp.: 20
N.A.I.C.S.: 522299
Jorgen Oldensand *(Gen Mgr)*

Svenska Property Nominees Limited (1)
3 Thomas More Street, Shadwell, London, E1W 1WY, United Kingdom
Tel.: (44) 20 7578 8000
Web Site: http://www.handelsbanken.se
Emp.: 25
Property Management Services
N.A.I.C.S.: 531312

XACT Fonder AB (1)
Blasieholmstorg 12, 10670, Stockholm, Sweden
Tel.: (46) 87014000
Web Site: http://www.xact.se
Sales Range: $50-74.9 Million
Emp.: 11
Exchange Traded Funds Manager
N.A.I.C.S.: 522299
Par Nurnberg *(CEO)*

SVENSKA ORIENT LINIEN AB

Klippan 1A, SE-414 51, Gothenburg, Sweden
Tel.: (46) 31 354 40 00
Web Site: http://www.sollines.se
Sales Range: $50-74.9 Million
Water Transportation Services
N.A.I.C.S.: 488510

INTERNATIONAL PUBLIC

Michael Kjellberg *(Chm)*

SVERIGES RIKSBANK

Brunkebergstorg 11, 103 37, Stockholm, Sweden
Tel.: (46) 87870000
Web Site: http://www.riksbank.se
Year Founded: 1668
Sales Range: $800-899.9 Million
Emp.: 336
Banking Services
N.A.I.C.S.: 521110
Tomas Lundberg *(Chief Press Officer)*

SVETOFOR GROUP PJSC

13 Generala Khruleva str room 1N, Saint Petersburg, 197348, Russia
Tel.: (7) 8126400809
Web Site:
https://www.svetoforgroup.ru
Year Founded: 2010
SVET—(MOEX)
Educational Support Services
N.A.I.C.S.: 611710
Turygin Dmitry Vladimirovich *(Chm & CEO)*

SVG GROUP CO., LTD.

No 68 Xinchang Road, Suzhou Industrial Park, Suzhou, 215123, Jiangsu, China
Tel.: (86) 51262868882
Web Site:
https://www.svgoptronics.com
Year Founded: 2001
300331—(CHIN)
Rev.: $240,899,724
Assets: $455,439,348
Liabilities: $200,779,020
Net Worth: $254,660,328
Earnings: ($39,181,428)
Emp.: 100
Fiscal Year-end: 12/31/22
Advanced Laser Based Maskless & Interference Lithography Systems Mfr
N.A.I.C.S.: 333248

SVI PUBLIC CO., LTD.

141-142 Moo 5 Tiwanon Rd Bangkadi, Muang, Pathumthani, 12000, Thailand
Tel.: (66) 21050456
Web Site: https://svi-hq.com
Year Founded: 1985
SVI—(THA)
Rev.: $666,674,002
Assets: $450,832,771
Liabilities: $252,576,254
Net Worth: $198,256,517
Earnings: $26,970,432
Emp.: 3,081
Fiscal Year-end: 12/31/23
Printed Circuit Board Mfr
N.A.I.C.S.: 334412
Pongsak Lothongkam *(CEO)*

Subsidiaries:

SVI (AEC) Company Limited (1)
Phnom Penh Special Economic Zone Kantok Phleung Chheh Roteh, Beong Thum Commune Khan Por Senchey, Phnom Penh, Cambodia
Tel.: (855) 23934777
Electric Equipment Mfr
N.A.I.C.S.: 334416

SVI (HKG) Limited (1)
Room 337 3/F South China CS Building 13-17 Wah Sing Street, Kwai Chung, China (Hong Kong)
Tel.: (852) 23741213
Electric & Electronic Appliances Mfr
N.A.I.C.S.: 335220

SVI Electronic (Tianjin) Limited (1)
6-C-D Zhongxiaoyuan Micro-Electronic Industrial Park Jin Gang Rd, Jin Gang Highway Xiquing Distr, Tianjin, China (100%)
Tel.: (86) 2223885699

Web Site: http://www.svi.com.ch
Sales Range: $25-49.9 Million
Emp.: 80
Motor Vehicle Electrical & Electronic Equipment Mfr
N.A.I.C.S.: 336320

SVI Electronics (USA) LLC (1)
PO Box 770, Webster, NY 14580
Tel.: (330) 360-2514
Electric & Electronic Appliances Mfr
N.A.I.C.S.: 335220

SVI Hungary Kft. (1)
Ipari Park 5749/2 hrsz, 8400, Ajka, Hungary
Tel.: (36) 88511432
Electric & Electronic Appliances Mfr
N.A.I.C.S.: 335220

SVI Public (HK) Limited (1)
ROOM 337 3/F South China C S Building Wah Sing Street, Kwai Chung, China (Hong Kong)
Tel.: (852) 23741213
Electric Equipment Mfr
N.A.I.C.S.: 334419

Subsidiary (Non-US):

SVI (Austria) GmbH (2)
Frauentaler Strasse 100, 8530, Deutschlandsberg, Austria
Tel.: (43) 36344600
Electric Equipment Mfr
N.A.I.C.S.: 334419

Tohoku Solutions Company Limited (1)
Amphur U-thai Phra Nakhon Si, Uthaithaya, 13210, Thailand
Tel.: (66) 35330990
Web Site: https://en.nc-net.com
Emp.: 1,007
Electric & Electronic Appliances Mfr
N.A.I.C.S.: 335220

SVIAZ-BANK
31/7 Novoryazanskaya Street Building 2, Moscow, 105066, Russia
Tel.: (7) 4957 71 32 60
Web Site: http://www.sviaz-bank.ru
Banking Services
N.A.I.C.S.: 522110

SVILOSA AD
Western Industrial Zone, Svishtov, 5250, Bulgaria
Tel.: (359) 631 45277   BG
Web Site: http://www.svilosa.bg
Year Founded: 1966
Sales Range: $75-99.9 Million
Paper Products Mfr
N.A.I.C.S.: 322299
Krasimir Banchev Dachev (Chm)

SVINECOMPLEX NIKOLOVO AD
S Nikolovo, Ruse, 7057, Bulgaria
Tel.: (359) 81183730
SVNK—(BUL)
Sales Range: Less than $1 Million
Pig & Other Animal Farming Services
N.A.I.C.S.: 112210
Delian Dimov (Dir-IR)

SVININ & PARTNERS MANAGEMENT COMPANY
Karelia Business-Hotel Office 1051 27/2 Marshal Tukhachevsky St, litera A, Saint Petersburg, 195067, Russia
Tel.: (7) 8123240524
Web Site: http://www.svinin.com
Year Founded: 2003
Sales Range: Less than $1 Million
Real Estate Manangement Services
N.A.I.C.S.: 531210

SVJETLOST-SARS D.D.
Muhameda Kantardzica br 3, 71 000, Sarajevo, Bosnia & Herzegovina
Tel.: (387) 33644342
SARSR—(SARE)
Rev.: $767,113

Assets: $14,032,596
Liabilities: $11,426,169
Net Worth: $2,606,427
Earnings: $2,027
Emp.: 11
Fiscal Year-end: 12/31/20
Household Appliance Distr
N.A.I.C.S.: 423440

SVJETLOSTKOMERC D.D. SARAJEVO
Ul Muhameda Kantardzica 3, 71000, Sarajevo, Bosnia & Herzegovina
Tel.: (387) 33200840
Web Site: http://www.svjetlostkomerc.ba
SVKOR—(SARE)
Rev.: $4,911,464
Assets: $14,243,583
Liabilities: $5,753,008
Net Worth: $8,490,574
Earnings: $215,806
Emp.: 73
Fiscal Year-end: 12/31/21
Book & Computer Equipment Whslr
N.A.I.C.S.: 238990

SVOA PUBLIC COMPANY LIMITED
1023 MS Siam Tower 31st Floor Rama 3 Road, Chong Nonsi Yannawa, Bangkok, 10120, Thailand
Tel.: (66) 26863000
Web Site: https://www.svoa.co.th
Year Founded: 1981
SVOA—(THA)
Rev.: $269,736,325
Assets: $193,719,324
Liabilities: $119,975,977
Net Worth: $73,743,347
Earnings: $3,193,811
Emp.: 743
Fiscal Year-end: 12/31/23
Computer Equipment Distr
N.A.I.C.S.: 423430
Krit Kulsuppaisarn (Co-COO)

Subsidiaries:

Lease IT Public Company Limited (1)
1023 MS Siam Tower 29th Floor Rama 3 Road Chong Nonsi, Yannawa, Bangkok, 10120, Thailand
Tel.: (66) 21634260
Web Site: https://www.leaseit.co.th
Rev.: $3,214,471
Assets: $41,583,633
Liabilities: $12,659,746
Net Worth: $28,923,887
Earnings: ($3,433,347)
Fiscal Year-end: 12/31/2023
Loan Brokerage Services
N.A.I.C.S.: 522310
Sompon Aketerajit (CEO & Mng Dir)

SVOGL OIL GAS AND ENERGY LIMITED
Tower 1 5th Floor NBCC Plaza Sector V, Pushp Vihar Saket, New Delhi, 110017, India
Tel.: (91) 1129564592   In
Web Site: http://www.shiv-vani.co.in
Year Founded: 1989
SVOGL—(NSE)
Sales Range: $25-49.9 Million
Oil & Gas Exploration
N.A.I.C.S.: 211120

Subsidiaries:

Shiv Vani Oil & Gas Co. LLC. (1)
PO Box 861, 112, Ruwi, Oman
Tel.: (968) 24811578
Sales Range: $100-124.9 Million
Emp.: 240
Oil & Natural Gas Drilling Services
N.A.I.C.S.: 213112

SVOLDER AB

Birger Jarlsgatan 13, 111 45, Stockholm, Sweden
Tel.: (46) 84403770
Web Site: http://www.svolder.se
Year Founded: 1993
SVOL.B—(OMX)
Assets: $493,523,280
Liabilities: $2,013,731
Net Worth: $491,509,549
Earnings: ($49,219,328)
Emp.: 5
Fiscal Year-end: 08/31/23
Financial Services
N.A.I.C.S.: 921130

SVP BUILDERS INDIA LTD.
17 Kiran Enclave near Samrat Hotel, GT Road, Ghaziabad, India
Tel.: (91) 120 4187000
Web Site: http://www.svpgroup.in
Emp.: 700
Residential Housing & Commercial Buildings Construction
N.A.I.C.S.: 236116
Vijay Kumar Jindal (Founder & Chm)

SVP GLOBAL TEXTILES LIMITED
97 and 99 Maker Tower F Cuffe Parade, Mumbai, 400 005, India
Tel.: (91) 2240290011
Web Site: https://www.svpglobal.co.in
Year Founded: 1982
505590—(BOM)
Rev.: $194,157,224
Assets: $527,940,995
Liabilities: $357,564,636
Net Worth: $170,376,359
Earnings: $3,392,050
Emp.: 17
Fiscal Year-end: 03/31/21
Jewelry & Textile Whslr
N.A.I.C.S.: 423940
Chirag Pittie (Exec Dir)

SVS VENTURES LIMITED
1009 Mondeal Heights Nr Panchratan Party Plot S G Highway, Ahmedabad, 380051, Gujarat, India
Tel.: (91) 7940397191   In
Web Site: https://www.svsventures.co.in
543745—(BOM)
Rev.: $796,187
Assets: $4,346,610
Liabilities: $383,766
Net Worth: $3,962,844
Earnings: $83,712
Emp.: 6
Fiscal Year-end: 03/31/23
Real Estate Development Services
N.A.I.C.S.: 531390
Shashikant Vedprakash Sharma (CEO)

SVYAZMONTAZH HOLDING LLP
83a Angarskaya str, 050000, Almaty, Kazakhstan
Tel.: (7) 727 2989479
Sales Range: $1-9.9 Million
Telecommunication Line Construction & Repair Services; Radio Telecommunications Operations
N.A.I.C.S.: 237130

SW UMWELTTECHNIK STOISER & WOLSCHNER AG
Bahnstrasse 89, 9020, Klagenfurt, Austria
Tel.: (43) 46332109700
Web Site: https://www.sw-umwelttechnik.com
Year Founded: 1910
SWUT—(VIE)
Sales Range: $75-99.9 Million

Emp.: 501
Precast Concrete Products Mfr
N.A.I.C.S.: 327390
Klaus Einfalt (Member-Mgmt Bd)

Subsidiaries:

OMS Kornyezetvedelmi Kft. (1)
Bela ut 37 Bacso, 2890, Tata, Hungary
Tel.: (36) 34 487 869
Web Site: http://www.oms.hu
Construction Materials Whslr
N.A.I.C.S.: 423390

SW Umwelttechnik Osterreich GmbH (1)
Bahnstrasse 87-93, 9020, Klagenfurt, Austria
Tel.: (43) 463321090
Web Site: http://www.sw-umwelttechnik.at
Construction Materials Whslr
N.A.I.C.S.: 423390
Werbitsth Reinhart (CEO)

SW Umwelttechnik Romania S.R.L. (1)
Str Zavoiului Nr 1 Sat Izvoru, Comuna Vanatorii Mici, Giurgiu, 87253, Romania
Tel.: (40) 246 207 050
Web Site: http://www.sw-umwelttechnik.ro
Construction Materials Whslr
N.A.I.C.S.: 423320

SWADESHI INDUSTRIES & LEASING LIMITED
C-101 247 Park LBS Marg, Opp Swagat Hall Kasturba Road No.5 Borivali, Mumbai, 400 083, Vikroli, India
Tel.: (91) 2228648850
Web Site: https://www.swadeshiglobal.com
Rev.: $335,417
Assets: $1,648,570
Liabilities: $238,080
Net Worth: $1,410,489
Earnings: ($137,556)
Emp.: 6
Fiscal Year-end: 03/31/19
Plastic Product Mfr & Whslr
N.A.I.C.S.: 326160
Gourav Jain (Chm & Mng Dir)

SWADESHI POLYTEX LIMITED
KJ77 Kavi Nagar, Ghaziabad, 201 002, UP, India
Tel.: (91) 1202701472
Web Site: https://www.splindia.co.in
Year Founded: 1970
503816—(BOM)
Rev.: $21,349
Assets: $2,018,289
Liabilities: $6,656,204
Net Worth: ($4,637,915)
Earnings: ($221,812)
Fiscal Year-end: 03/31/21
Textile Products Mfr
N.A.I.C.S.: 313110
Bhuwan Chaturvedi (CEO)

SWAGTAM TRADING & SERVICES LTD.
R-489 GF-A New Rajinder Nagar, New Delhi, 110 060, India
Tel.: (91) 1142475489
Web Site: https://www.swagtam.com
539406—(BOM)
Rev.: $57,041
Assets: $540,830
Liabilities: $4,951
Net Worth: $535,879
Earnings: $16,862
Fiscal Year-end: 03/31/23
Real Estate Support Services
N.A.I.C.S.: 531390
Lalita Mittal (CFO)

SWAJAS AIR CHARTERS LTD
36G 1st Floor North Parade Road Saint Thomas Mount, St Thomas

SWAJAS AIR CHARTERS LTD

Swajas Air Charters Ltd—(Continued)
Mount, Chennai, 600016, India
Tel.: (91) 44 43519017
Web Site:
  htttp://www.swajasaircharter.com
Year Founded: 1996
Sales Range: $25-49.9 Million
Emp.: 40
Air Charter Operations, Aircraft Management & Emergency Medical Evacuations
N.A.I.C.S.: 481211
Raghunathan Jayakumar *(Mng Dir)*

SWALLOW HOTELS GROUP
1 Queen Charlotte Lane, Edinburgh, EH6 6BL, United Kingdom
Tel.: (44) 8707700777
Web Site: http://www.swallow-hotels.com
Sales Range: $150-199.9 Million
Emp.: 2,255
Hotel Services
N.A.I.C.S.: 721110

SWAN ENERGY LTD.
6 Feltham House 2nd Floor 10 J N Heredia Marg Ballard Estate, Mumbai, 400001, India
Tel.: (91) 2240587300
Web Site: https://www.swan.co.in
503310—(BOM)
Rev.: $44,282,347
Assets: $673,777,964
Liabilities: $482,993,566
Net Worth: $190,784,398
Earnings: ($9,365,852)
Emp.: 110
Fiscal Year-end: 03/31/21
Real Estate Development Services
N.A.I.C.S.: 531390
Navinbhai Chandulal Dave *(Chm)*

Subsidiaries:

Veritas (India) Limited (1)
Veritas House 70 Mint Road Fort, Mumbai, 400 001, India (55%)
Tel.: (91) 2222755555
Web Site: http://www.veritasindia.net
Rev.: $259,932,390
Assets: $494,110,713
Liabilities: $217,907,248
Net Worth: $276,203,465
Earnings: $11,367,736
Emp.: 30
Fiscal Year-end: 03/31/2023
Chemical Products Distr
N.A.I.C.S.: 424690
Rajaram Shanbhag *(CFO)*

SWAN GENERAL LTD.
Swan Centre 10 Intendance Street, Port Louis, Mauritius
Tel.: (230) 2073500
Web Site:
  https://www.swangroup.com
Year Founded: 1855
SWAN—(MAU)
Rev.: $198,146,726
Assets: $1,328,858,110
Liabilities: $1,224,045,667
Net Worth: $104,812,444
Earnings: $18,875,338
Fiscal Year-end: 12/31/20
Insurance Services
N.A.I.C.S.: 524126
Jean Michel Louis Rivalland *(CEO-Grp)*

Subsidiaries:

Swan Life Ltd. (1)
10 Intendance Street, Port Louis, Mauritius (76.5%)
Tel.: (230) 2073500
Web Site: https://www.swanforlife.com
Rev.: $116,417,508
Assets: $1,194,876,401
Liabilities: $1,150,070,402
Net Worth: $44,805,999

Earnings: $13,752,736
Fiscal Year-end: 12/31/2020
Financial Services
N.A.I.C.S.: 523999
Nitish Beni Madhu *(Chief Investment Officer)*

Subsidiary (Domestic):

Anglo-Mauritius Stockbrokers Limited (2)
1st Fl Swan Group Centre 10 Intendance Street, Port Louis, Mauritius
Tel.: (230) 2087010
Web Site: http://www.anglostockbrokers.mu
Sales Range: $50-74.9 Million
Emp.: 12
Securities Brokerage Services
N.A.I.C.S.: 523150
Neeraj Umanee *(Gen Mgr)*

SWAN MILL PAPER COMPANY LTD.
Goldsel Road, Swanley, BR8 8EU, Kent, United Kingdom
Tel.: (44) 1322 665566
Web Site: http://www.swantex.com
Year Founded: 1892
Sales Range: $50-74.9 Million
Emp.: 222
Paper Product Whslr
N.A.I.C.S.: 424130

Subsidiaries:

Firebrand Art Ltd (1)
26 Dodd Ave, Warwick, CV34 6QS, United Kingdom
Tel.: (44) 1926866604
Web Site: http://www.firebrandart.co.uk
Stationery Product Distr
N.A.I.C.S.: 424120

Ling Design Ltd (1)
14-20 Eldon Way Paddock Wood, Kent, TN12 6BE, United Kingdom
Tel.: (44) 1892838574
Web Site: http://www.lingdesign.co.uk
Stationery Product Distr
N.A.I.C.S.: 424120
David Byk *(CEO)*

Swantex Asia Limited (1)
16F Nandao Commercial Building N 359-361 Queen's Road, Central, China (Hong Kong)
Tel.: (852) 27219088
Web Site: http://www.swantexasia.com
Paper Product Mfr & Distr
N.A.I.C.S.: 322299

SWAN REAL ESTATE PLC
8th Floor 58 Waterloo Street, Glasgow, G2 7DA, United Kingdom
Tel.: (44) 1414338290
Web Site:
  http://www.swanholdinggroup.com
Year Founded: 2016
SWAN—(CYP)
Rev.: $5,087,181
Assets: $10,157,369
Liabilities: $8,824,729
Net Worth: $1,332,639
Earnings: $2,466,570
Fiscal Year-end: 01/31/19
Building Construction Services
N.A.I.C.S.: 236116
Philip McGinlay *(Exec Dir)*

SWANCOR ADVANCED MATERIALS CO., LTD.
No 618 Songsheng Road, Songjiang District, Shanghai, 201600, China
Tel.: (86) 2157746183
Web Site: https://swancor.com.cn
Year Founded: 2000
688585—(SHG)
Rev.: $261,110,964
Assets: $256,053,995
Liabilities: $95,088,020
Net Worth: $160,965,975
Earnings: $11,814,084
Fiscal Year-end: 12/31/22

Chemical Product Mfr & Distr
N.A.I.C.S.: 325520
Li Peiyi *(Sec)*

SWANCOR IND. CO., LTD.
No 9 Industry South 6 Road, Nant'ou, 54066, Taiwan
Tel.: (886) 49 2255420
Web Site: http://www.swancor.com
Year Founded: 1992
Chemical & Resin Mfr
N.A.I.C.S.: 325998

Subsidiaries:

Swancor (Tianjin) Wind Blade Materials Co., Ltd. (1)
No 6 Caiyun Street Modern Industrial Park, Tianjin, 300480, China
Tel.: (86) 2259916567
Web Site: https://www.swancor.com
Chemicals Mfr & Distr
N.A.I.C.S.: 325998

SWANG CHAI CHUAN LIMITED
Lot 147-A Kawasan Perindustrian Semambu, Kuantan, 25350, Pahang, Malaysia
Tel.: (60) 95664766
Web Site:
  https://www.sccgroup.com.my
Year Founded: 1982
2321—(HKG)
Rev.: $206,886,735
Assets: $91,351,013
Liabilities: $38,651,580
Net Worth: $52,699,433
Earnings: $6,629,783
Emp.: 779
Fiscal Year-end: 12/31/22
Grocery Retailer
N.A.I.C.S.: 445110
See Beng Soon *(Chm)*

SWANSEA BUILDING SOCIETY
1-4 Portland Street, Swansea, SA1 3DH, United Kingdom
Tel.: (44) 1792 739100
Web Site: http://www.swansea-bs.co.uk
Year Founded: 1923
Rev.: $15,034,871
Assets: $485,760,241
Liabilities: $454,325,124
Net Worth: $31,435,117
Earnings: $2,404,163
Emp.: 39
Fiscal Year-end: 12/31/19
Mortgage Lending & Other Financial Services
N.A.I.C.S.: 522310
Alun Williams *(CEO)*

SWANSWAY GARAGES LTD.
Gateway, Crewe, CW1 6YY, United Kingdom
Tel.: (44) 1270 848980
Web Site:
  http://www.swanswaygarages.com
Year Founded: 2002
Sales Range: $400-449.9 Million
Emp.: 520
New & Used Car Dealer
N.A.I.C.S.: 441110
Michael Smyth *(Chm)*

SWARAJ SUITING LIMITED
F-483 to F-487 RIICO Growth Centre Hamirgarh, Bhilwara, 311025, Rajasthan, India
Tel.: (91) 9509784862
Web Site:
  https://www.swarajsuiting.com
Year Founded: 2003
SWARAJ—(NSE)
Rev.: $26,368,635
Assets: $27,650,716

INTERNATIONAL PUBLIC

Liabilities: $19,680,571
Net Worth: $7,970,146
Earnings: $663,881
Emp.: 308
Fiscal Year-end: 03/31/23
Textile Product Mfr & Distr
N.A.I.C.S.: 314999

SWARCO AG
Blattenwaldweg 8, 6112, Wattens, Austria
Tel.: (43) 522458770 AT
Web Site: http://www.swarco.com
Year Founded: 1969
Sales Range: $150-199.9 Million
Emp.: 1,000
Holding Company; Road Markings
N.A.I.C.S.: 551112
Egbert Tolle *(Vice Chm)*

Subsidiaries:

APT Controls Limited (1)
The Power House Chantry Place Headstone Lane, Harrow, HA3 6NY, Middlesex, United Kingdom
Tel.: (44) 20 8421 2411
Web Site: http://www.aptcontrols.co.uk
Transportation Support Services
N.A.I.C.S.: 488999

DAMBACH Corporate Design Elements GmbH (1)
Adolf-Dambach-Strasse, Postfach 1240, 76571, Gaggenau, Germany
Tel.: (49) 7225 64 01
Advertising Services
N.A.I.C.S.: 541890
Marcus Kramer *(Co-Mng Dir)*

Heoscont Hungaria Kft. (1)
Kulso Veszpremi u 50-B, Gyor, 9028, Hungary
Tel.: (36) 96514840
Sales Range: $25-49.9 Million
Emp.: 50
Advertising Agencies
N.A.I.C.S.: 541810

IMS International Marking Systems, GmbH (1)
PO Box 101951, 45659, Recklinghausen, Germany
Tel.: (49) 5032913273
Web Site: https://www.ims-marking.de
Sales Range: $25-49.9 Million
Emp.: 20
Plastics Materials & Basic Forms & Shapes Whslr
N.A.I.C.S.: 424610

Limburger Lackfabrik GmbH (1)
Robert-Bosch-Str 17, Diez, 65574, Germany
Tel.: (49) 643291840
Web Site: http://www.limburgerlackfabrik.de
Sales Range: $25-49.9 Million
Emp.: 20
Paint & Coating Mfr
N.A.I.C.S.: 325510
Haraod Guder *(Gen Mgr)*

M. Swarovski GmbH (1)
Industriestrasse 10, 3300, Amstetten, Austria
Tel.: (43) 74722020
Web Site: http://www.swarco.com
Sales Range: $25-49.9 Million
Emp.: 50
Amusement & Recreation Industries
N.A.I.C.S.: 713990

Raswa Company Ltd. (1)
PO Box 117, 11383, Riyadh, Saudi Arabia
Tel.: (966) 14981177
Web Site: http://www.swarco.com
Production of Glass Beads for Commercial Technology
N.A.I.C.S.: 327215
Friedrich Peter Hofstadler *(VP-Reg 2)*

SWARCO BULGARIA Ltd. (1)
Louis Ahailler Str 2, 1404, Sofia, Bulgaria
Tel.: (359) 2 958 67 45
Road Safety Services
N.A.I.C.S.: 488490

SWARCO LEA d.o.o. (1)

AND PRIVATE COMPANIES

Finzgarjeva ulica 1a, 4248, Lesce, Slovenia
Tel.: (386) 4 53 53 653
Web Site: http://www.swarco.com
Emp.: 32
Electrical Sign Mfr
N.A.I.C.S.: 339950
Adnan Susic (Mgr-Mktg)

SWARCO Limburger Lackfabrik GmbH (1)
Robert-Bosch-Str 17, 65582, Diez, Germany
Tel.: (49) 6432 9184 0
Road Marking Liquid Material Mfr
N.A.I.C.S.: 325510

SWARCO MEXICO S.A. de C.V. (1)
Homero N 136-Dep 404 Col Sec 5, Del Miguel Hidalgo, Mexico, 11570, Mexico
Tel.: (52) 55 5531 9554
Web Site: http://www.swarco.com
Emp.: 2
Traffic Control Services
N.A.I.C.S.: 561990

SWARCO Mizar S.p.A (1)
Via Nizza 262/57, 10126, Turin, Italy
Tel.: (39) 0116500411
Web Site: http://www.swarco.com
Sales Range: $25-49.9 Million
Emp.: 80
Industrial Machinery Mfr
N.A.I.C.S.: 333248
Gioganni D'Oorazio (Mng Dir)

SWARCO Nederland B.V. (1)
New Yorkstraat 14, 1175 RD, Lijnden, Netherlands
Tel.: (31) 20 4303040
Web Site: http://www.swarco.nl
Traffic Management Services
N.A.I.C.S.: 488490
Freek Van der Valk (Mng Dir)

SWARCO ROMANIA SRL (1)
23 Dr Lister Street, 5th district, 050541, Bucharest, Romania
Tel.: (40) 21 315 57 97
Paint Distr
N.A.I.C.S.: 424950

SWARCO SAUDIA LLC (1)
2nd Floor Cercon Building 6 Mousa Ibn Naseer, 11422, Riyadh, Saudi Arabia
Tel.: (966) 1 464 3914
Traffic Management Services
N.A.I.C.S.: 488490
Arnold Cabading (Project Engr)

SWARCO SERVICE ITALIA s.r.l. (1)
Via Boccalara 36, 35030, Cervarese Santa Croce, Padua, Italy
Tel.: (39) 049 9915577
Road Transportation Support Services
N.A.I.C.S.: 488490

SWARCO TRAFFIC AUSTRIA GmbH (1)
Muhlgasse 86, 2380, Perchtoldsdorf, Austria
Tel.: (43) 1 98 35 763 620
Software Development Services
N.A.I.C.S.: 541511

SWARCO TRAFFIC BRASIL LTDA. (1)
Avenida Pascoal da Rocha Falcao 253, Jardim Santa Helena, 04785-000, Sao Paulo, Brazil
Tel.: (55) 11 5666 4484
Software Development Services
N.A.I.C.S.: 541511

SWARCO TRAFFIC POLSKA Sp. z.o.o. (1)
ul Mineralna 46B, 02-274, Warsaw, Poland
Tel.: (48) 22 675 69 49
Traffic Software Development Services
N.A.I.C.S.: 541511

SWARCO TRAFFIC SYSTEMS GmbH (1)
Kelterstrasse 67, 72669, Unterensingen, Germany
Tel.: (49) 7022 6025 200
Traffic System Integrator Services
N.A.I.C.S.: 541512

SWARCO TRAFFIC Switzerland GmbH (1)
Industriestrasse 23, 5036, Oberentfelden, Switzerland
Tel.: (41) 62 723 9222
Traffic Management Services
N.A.I.C.S.: 488490

SWARCO Traffic Holding AG (1)
Bodenseestrasse 113, 81243, Munich, Germany
Tel.: (49) 89 89699 102
Holding Company
N.A.I.C.S.: 551112

Subsidiary (Non-US):

SWARCO TRAFFIC CZ s.r.o. (2)
Pod Visnovkou 37, 140 00, Prague, Czech Republic
Tel.: (420) 241 441 024
Web Site: http://www.swarco.com
Software Development Services
N.A.I.C.S.: 541511
Frantisek Lusk (Mng Dir)

SWARCO Traffic Limited (1)
7 Mercury Rd Gallowfields Trading Estate, Richmond, DL10 4TQ, North Yorkshire, United Kingdom
Tel.: (44) 1748 824624
Software Development Services
N.A.I.C.S.: 541511
Carl Dyer (Dir-Technical)

SWARCO Ukraine LLC (1)
Horodotska Str 367 B 2, 79040, L'viv, Ukraine
Tel.: (380) 32 2422952
Traffic Software Development Services
N.A.I.C.S.: 541511
Roman Kinder (Coord-Project)

SWARCO V.S.M. GmbH (1)
Blumenstrasse 10, 73779, Deizisau, Germany
Tel.: (49) 71536103390
Web Site: http://www.swarco.com
Sales Range: $25-49.9 Million
Emp.: 100
Traffic Specialists
N.A.I.C.S.: 541614
Reimund Scheulen (Mng Dir)

SWARCO Vestglas GmbH (1)
Rumplerstr 12, 45659, Recklinghausen, Germany
Tel.: (49) 2361 6094 0
Glass Products Mfr
N.A.I.C.S.: 327215
Andreas Beyer (Mgr-Glass Beads & Glass Grit Sls)

Senalamiento Vial de Centro America, S.A. de C.V. (1)
47 Calle 17-45 Zona 12, 01012, Guatemala, Guatemala
Tel.: (502) 24775621
Sales Range: $50-74.9 Million
Emp.: 60
Holding Company
N.A.I.C.S.: 551112

Shanghai Swarco Traffic Management And Equipment Co., Ltd. (1)
Building No 9 3rd F Room No C 3051 He Chuan Rd, 201103, Shanghai, China
Tel.: (86) 2164464466
Sales Range: $50-74.9 Million
Emp.: 10
Industrial Machinery & Equipment Whslr
N.A.I.C.S.: 423830

Signalbau Huber Hellas A.E. (1)
Kifisia Ikarou 5 St, 14564, Athens, Greece
Tel.: (30) 210 8003760
Web Site: http://www.signalbau-huber.gr
Traffic Control Services
N.A.I.C.S.: 561990

Stollreflex GmbH (1)
Industriestrasse 10, 3300, Amstetten, Austria
Tel.: (43) 74722020
Web Site: http://www.stollreflex.com
Sales Range: $25-49.9 Million
Emp.: 1
Paint & Coating Mfr
N.A.I.C.S.: 325510

Swarco Albania Shpk (1)
Str Budi No 115, 00004, Tirana, Albania
Tel.: (355) 4251188

Web Site: http://www.swarco.com
Holding Company
N.A.I.C.S.: 551112

Swarco America Inc. (1)
270 Rutherford Ln, Columbia, TN 38401
Tel.: (931) 388-5900
Web Site: http://www.swarco.com
Sales Range: $50-74.9 Million
Emp.: 100
Mfr of Highway Marking Products
N.A.I.C.S.: 326299

Subsidiary (Domestic):

Ceroglass Technologies Inc. (2)
919 N James Campbell Blvd, Columbia, TN 38401
Tel.: (931) 490-8030
Web Site: http://www.ceroglass.com
Sales Range: $25-49.9 Million
Emp.: 5
Ceramic Wall & Floor Tile Mfr
N.A.I.C.S.: 327120
Teresa Bradley (Mgr-Sls)

Colorado Paint Company (2)
4747 Holly St, Denver, CO 80216
Tel.: (303) 388-9265
Emp.: 20
Paints Mfr
N.A.I.C.S.: 325510
Diana Reyes (Gen Mgr)

McCain, Inc. (2)
2365 Oak Rdg Way, Vista, CA 92081-8348
Tel.: (760) 727-8100
Web Site: http://www.mccain-inc.com
Traffic Control Equipment & Devices Mfr
N.A.I.C.S.: 334290

Swarco Industries Inc (2)
270 Rutherford Ln, Columbia, TN 38401
Tel.: (931) 388-5900
Sales Range: $10-24.9 Million
Emp.: 50
Rubber Tape
N.A.I.C.S.: 326299
Audrey Morris (Controller)

Swarco Reflex Inc. (2)
900 N Denton St, Mexia, TX 76667
Tel.: (254) 562-9879
Web Site: http://www.swarco.com
Sales Range: $25-49.9 Million
Emp.: 56
Purchased Glass Product Mfr
N.A.I.C.S.: 327215

Swarco Traffic Management Inc. (2)
270 Rutherford Ln, Columbia, TN 38402
Tel.: (931) 388-5900
Web Site: http://www.swarco.com
Measuring & Testing Electricity & Electrical Signals Instrument Mfr
N.A.I.C.S.: 334515
John Sproul (Mgr)

Swarco Asia Ltd. (1)
3rd Fl Jonsim Pl, 228 Queens Rd E, Wanchai, China (Hong Kong)
Tel.: (852) 28612222
Air Traffic Control
N.A.I.C.S.: 488111

Swarco Central Services GmbH (1)
Blattenwaldweg 8, 6112, Wattens, Austria
Tel.: (43) 522458770
Web Site: http://www.swarco.com
Sales Range: $25-49.9 Million
Emp.: 35
Management Consulting Services
N.A.I.C.S.: 541618

Swarco Danmark AS (1)
Tonsbakken 16-18, Skovlunde, 2740, Denmark
Tel.: (45) 36888888
Web Site: http://www.swarco.dk
Sales Range: $25-49.9 Million
Emp.: 30
Industrial Machinery & Equipment Whslr
N.A.I.C.S.: 423830

Swarco Finland Oy (1)
Niittylanpolku 16, 00620, Helsinki, Finland
Tel.: (358) 207410301
Electrical Apparatus & Equipment Wiring Supplies & Construction Material Whslr
N.A.I.C.S.: 423610

Swarco Fuelcell Systems GmbH (1)
Blattenwaldweg 8, 6112, Wattens, Austria
Tel.: (43) 522458770
Web Site: http://www.swarco.com
Sales Range: $50-74.9 Million
Emp.: 50
Fossil Fuel Electric Power Generation
N.A.I.C.S.: 221112

Swarco Futurit Verkehrssignalsysteme GesmbH (1)
Manfred-Swarovski-Str 1, Neutal, 7343, Austria
Tel.: (43) 2618200250
Web Site: http://www.swarco.com
Sales Range: $50-74.9 Million
Emp.: 200
Communication Equipment Mfr
N.A.I.C.S.: 334290
Schuch Michael (Mgr)

Swarco Heoscont Strassenmarkierungen GesmbH (1)
Munchendorferstr 33, Guntramsdorf, 2353, Austria
Tel.: (43) 2236537170
Web Site: http://www.swarco.com
Amusement & Recreation Industries
N.A.I.C.S.: 713990

Swarco Mizar AB (1)
Molndalsvagen 93, 412 63, Gothenburg, Sweden
Tel.: (46) 771882288
Web Site: http://www.swarco.com
Sales Range: $25-49.9 Million
Emp.: 11
Engineeering Services
N.A.I.C.S.: 541330

Swarco Norge AS (1)
Brynsveien 12, 667, Oslo, Norway
Tel.: (47) 23170900
Web Site: http://www.swarco.no
Sales Range: $25-49.9 Million
Emp.: 40
Nonresidential Buildings Lessors
N.A.I.C.S.: 531120

Swarco Recycling GmbH (1)
Blattenwaldweg 8, 6112, Wattens, Austria
Tel.: (43) 522458770
Web Site: http://www.swarco.com
Sales Range: $25-49.9 Million
Emp.: 35
Holding Company
N.A.I.C.S.: 551112

Swarco Sverige AB (1)
Heliosgatan 24, 12030, Stockholm, Sweden
Tel.: (46) 855697650
Engineeering Services
N.A.I.C.S.: 541330

Swarco Technology ApS (1)
Klokkestobervej 21, Odense, 5260, Denmark
Tel.: (45) 63152200
Web Site: http://www.swarco.com
Sales Range: $25-49.9 Million
Emp.: 23
Electrical Equipment & Component Mfr
N.A.I.C.S.: 335999
Morten Sondergaard (Gen Mgr)

Swarco Traffic Hungaria Kft. (1)
Gyomroi ut 150, 1103, Budapest, Hungary
Tel.: (36) 1 22 08 751
Software Distr
N.A.I.C.S.: 423430
Tamas Laufer (Dir-Technical)

Swarco Vicas S.A. (1)
Sos Gaesti nr 8, Targoviste, 130087, Romania
Tel.: (40) 245615080
Web Site: http://www.swarco.com
Sales Range: $25-49.9 Million
Emp.: 45
Chemical & Allied Products Whslr
N.A.I.C.S.: 424690
Constanein Balentin (Gen Mgr)

SWARNA SECURITIES LIMITED

2nd Floor Swarnalok Complex Eluru Road Governorpet, Vijayawada, 520002, Andhra Pradesh, India
Tel.: (91) 8662575928   In

SWARNA SECURITIES LIMITED

Swarna Securities Limited—(Continued)
Web Site:
https://www.swarnasecurities.com
Year Founded: 1990
531003—(BOM)
Rev.: $145,194
Assets: $668,260
Liabilities: $63,397
Net Worth: $604,863
Earnings: $85,371
Fiscal Year-end: 03/31/23
Securities Brokerage Services
N.A.I.C.S.: 523150
M. Murali Krishna (Chm & Mng Dir)

SWARNAJYOTHI AGROTECH & POWER LIMITED

A/5 Indian Airline Housing Colony, Opp Police Line Begumpet, Secunderabad, 500 016, Andhra Pradesh, India
Tel.: (91) 40 27902527
Web Site:
http://www.swarnajyothi.com
Sales Range: $1-9.9 Million
Castor Oil Mfr
N.A.I.C.S.: 311224
K. Nagendra Kumar (CFO)

SWARNSARITA JEWELS INDIA LTD.

10 Floor-1st Plot-40/42 Ruby Chambers Dhanji Street, Zaveri Bazar Mumbadevi Mandvi, Mumbai, 400 003, Maharashtra, India
Tel.: (91) 2243590000
Web Site:
https://www.swarnsarita.com
526365—(BOM)
Rev.: $101,079,324
Assets: $29,737,474
Liabilities: $15,615,994
Net Worth: $14,121,480
Earnings: $754,343
Emp.: 47
Fiscal Year-end: 03/31/23
Gold & Diamond Jewellery Mfr & Distr
N.A.I.C.S.: 339910
Mahendra Madanlal Chordia (Mng Dir)

SWAROJGAR LAGHUBITTA BITTIYA SANSTHA LTD

Banepa-05, Kavrepalanchok, Dhulikhel, Nepal
Tel.: (977) 11661060
Web Site: https://www.slbbl.com.np
Year Founded: 2009
SLBBL—(NEP)
Rev.: $7,840,088
Assets: $53,040,769
Liabilities: $46,084,564
Net Worth: $6,956,205
Earnings: $578,216
Emp.: 471
Fiscal Year-end: 07/16/23
Commercial Banking Services
N.A.I.C.S.: 522110
Gynendra Prashad Pandey (Chm)

SWAROVSKI & CO.

Swarovskistrasse 30, Wattens, 6112, Austria
Tel.: (43) 52245000
Web Site: http://www.swarovski.com
Year Founded: 1895
Sales Range: $1-4.9 Billion
Emp.: 25,995
Crystal & Costume Jewelry Mfr
N.A.I.C.S.: 339910
Gernot Langes Swarovski (Chm & CEO)

Subsidiaries:

Swarovski North America Limited Inc. (1)
1 Kenney Dr, Cranston, RI 02920-4468
Tel.: (401) 463-3000
Web Site: http://www.swarovski.com
Sales Range: $200-249.9 Million
Emp.: 785
Glass Products & Jewelry
N.A.I.C.S.: 339910

Affiliate (Domestic):

Signity (2)
Ste 260 110 Wild Basin Rd S, Austin, TX 78746-3348
Tel.: (212) 221-8234
Web Site: http://www.signity.com
Sales Range: $25-49.9 Million
Emp.: 6
Provider of Costume Jewelry
N.A.I.C.S.: 339910

Subsidiary (Domestic):

Swarovski Consumer Goods Ltd. (2)
1 Kenney Dr, Cranston, RI 02920-4403
Tel.: (401) 463-6400
Sales Range: $100-124.9 Million
Emp.: 350
Provider of Costume Jewelry And Consumer Products
N.A.I.C.S.: 339910
Francis Belin (Sr VP-Asia Pacific)

Swarovski Lighting Parts (2)
29 W 57th St, New York, NY 10019 (100%)
Tel.: (212) 935-6110
Web Site: http://www.swavorski.com
Sales Range: $25-49.9 Million
Emp.: 30
Provider of Lighting Parts
N.A.I.C.S.: 334419
Reinhard Mackinger (Mgr)

Swarovski Optik North America Limited (2)
2 Slater Rd, Cranston, RI 02920-4498
Tel.: (401) 734-1800
Web Site: http://www.swarovskioptik.com
Sales Range: $25-49.9 Million
Emp.: 25
Provider of Optical Goods
N.A.I.C.S.: 423490
Albert Wannenmacher (CEO)

Swarovski U.K. Ltd. (1)
Perrywood Bus Pk, Salfords, RH1 5JQ, Surrey, United Kingdom
Tel.: (44) 1737856812
Web Site: http://www.swarovskioptik.com
Sales Range: $25-49.9 Million
Emp.: 4
Binoculars, Telescopes, Laser Rangefinders, Night Observation Telescopes & Rifle Scopes Mfr
N.A.I.C.S.: 333310
Ludwig Pernstich (Dir-Technical)

Tyrolit Schleifmittelwerke Swarovski KG (1)
Swarovskistrasse 33, 6130, Schwaz, Austria
Tel.: (43) 52426060
Web Site: http://www.tyrolit.com
Sales Range: $600-649.9 Million
Emp.: 4,580
Mfr of Drilling & Sawing Tools
N.A.I.C.S.: 333517

Subsidiary (US):

Acme Holding Co. (2)
781 N Glenhurst Dr, Birmingham, MI 48009-1142
Tel.: (586) 759-3332
Web Site: http://www.acmeabrasive.com
Offices of Other Holding Companies
N.A.I.C.S.: 551112
Robert Beebe (Pres)

Radiac Abrasives, Inc. (2)
1015 S College Ave PO Box 1410, Salem, IL 62881-7410
Tel.: (618) 548-4200
Web Site: http://www.radiac.com
Sales Range: $75-99.9 Million
Emp.: 600
Grinding Wheel Mfr
N.A.I.C.S.: 327910
Jim Blair (Engr-Primary Metals Applications)

Tyrolit Wickman Inc. (2)
4636 Regency Dr, Shelby, MI 48316-1533
Tel.: (248) 548-3822
Web Site: http://www.tyrolit.com
Sales Range: $25-49.9 Million
Emp.: 50
Diamond CBN Wheels & Hones
N.A.I.C.S.: 327910

SWARTH GROUP

30 Hasivim Street, Petah Tiqwa, 4959388, Israel
Tel.: (972) 3 926 6555
Privater Equity Firm
N.A.I.C.S.: 523999
Shaul Shani (Founder, Chm & CEO)

SWASTI VINAYAKA ART & HERITAGE CORPORATION LIMITED

303 Tantia Jogani Industrial Estate J R Boricha Marg, Next to Ahura Centre Mahakali Caves Road Andheri East, Mumbai, 400 011, India
Tel.: (91) 2243443555
Web Site:
https://www.swastivinayakaart.co.in
Year Founded: 1985
512257—(BOM)
Rev.: $1,556,226
Assets: $4,387,075
Liabilities: $2,006,786
Net Worth: $2,380,289
Earnings: $351,034
Emp.: 36
Fiscal Year-end: 03/31/23
Jewelry Product Mfr & Distr
N.A.I.C.S.: 339910
Dinesh Poddar (Chm & Mng Dir)

SWASTI VINAYAKA SYNTHETICS LIMITED

306 Tantia Jogani Industrial Estate J R Boricha Marg, Lower Parel, Mumbai, 400 011, Maharastra, India
Tel.: (91) 2243443555
Web Site:
https://www.swastivinayaka.com
Year Founded: 1981
510245—(BOM)
Rev.: $3,246,640
Assets: $4,235,118
Liabilities: $2,004,436
Net Worth: $2,230,682
Earnings: $238,523
Emp.: 18
Fiscal Year-end: 03/31/23
Apparel Product Mfr
N.A.I.C.S.: 315250
Rajesh Kumar Poddar (Chm & Mng Dir)

SWASTIK ENTERPRISES PRIVATE LIMITED

10A Hospital Street 3rd Floor Suite No 303, Kolkata, West Bengal, India
Tel.: (91) 3322152570
Web Site:
http://www.swastikenterprises.net
Year Founded: 1995
Solar Panel Mfr & Installation Services
N.A.I.C.S.: 334413

SWASTIK SAFE DEPOSIT & INVESTMENTS LIMITED

4th Floor Piramal Tower Annexe, Ganpatrao Kadam Marg Lower Parel, Mumbai, 400 013, Maharashtra, India
Tel.: (91) 2230767000
Web Site:
https://www.swastiksafedeposit.in
Year Founded: 1940
501386—(BOM)
Rev.: $93,807
Assets: $76,998,573
Liabilities: $55,201
Net Worth: $76,943,373

INTERNATIONAL PUBLIC

Earnings: $54,217
Fiscal Year-end: 03/31/23
Financial Investment Services
N.A.I.C.S.: 523999
Jitesh K. Agarwal (Compliance Officer & Sec)

SWASTIKA INVESTMART LTD.

Flat No 18 2nd Floor North Wing Madhaveshwar Co-op-Hsg Society Ltd, Madhav Nagar 11/12 S V Road Andheri W, Mumbai, 400058, Maharashtra, India
Tel.: (91) 2226254568
Web Site: https://www.swastika.co.in
530585—(BOM)
Rev.: $10,514,515
Assets: $28,423,540
Liabilities: $23,094,192
Net Worth: $5,329,348
Earnings: $1,537,315
Emp.: 787
Fiscal Year-end: 03/31/21
Investment Management Service
N.A.I.C.S.: 523940
Sunil Nyati (Mng Dir)

SWAZILAND POSTS & TELECOMMUNICATIONS CORPORATION

Phutfumani Building Mahlokohla Street, Mbabane, Eswatini
Tel.: (268) 2405 2000
Web Site: http://www.sptc.co.sz
Year Founded: 1986
Telecommunication & Postal Services
N.A.I.C.S.: 517111
Petros Dlamini (Mng Dir)

Subsidiaries:

Swazi Post (1)
Po Box 125, Warner Street, Mbabane, 8100, Eswatini
Tel.: (268) 4052000
Web Site: http://wwwsttc.co.sz
Postal Service
N.A.I.C.S.: 491110
Petros Dlamini (CEO)

Swazi Telecom (1)
Maflokohla St, Warner Street, Mbabane, Eswatini
Tel.: (268) 4052000
Web Site: http://www.sptc.co.sz
Telecommunication Servicesb
N.A.I.C.S.: 517111
Amon Dlamini (Mng Dir)

SWAZILAND PROPERTY INVESTMENT LIMITED

2nd Floor Development House, Mbabane, Eswatini
Tel.: (268) 4043869
SWP—(ESE)
Rev.: $1,390,278
Assets: $17,076,441
Liabilities: $3,646,057
Net Worth: $13,430,384
Earnings: $230,278
Fiscal Year-end: 06/30/23
Investment Management Service
N.A.I.C.S.: 523940

SWCC CORPORATION

Cube Kawasaki Building 2F 1-14 Nisshin cho, Kawasaki-Ku, Kawasaki, 210-0024, KANAGAWA, Japan
Web Site: http://www.swcc.co.jp
Year Founded: 1936
5805—(TKS)
Rev.: $1,413,905,440
Assets: $1,068,063,630
Liabilities: $558,260,770
Net Worth: $509,802,860
Earnings: $58,419,180
Emp.: 1,500
Fiscal Year-end: 03/31/24

Optical Fiber, Wire & Cables Mfr & Whslr
N.A.I.C.S.: 332618
Takayo Hasegawa *(Chm, Pres, Pres & CEO)*

Subsidiaries:

SWCC SHOWA CABLE SYSTEMS CO.,LTD. (1)
Room 5-5 No 191 Fushing North Road, Taipei, Taiwan
Tel.: (886) 2 2546 8873
Sales Range: $25-49.9 Million
Emp.: 2
Optical Cable Mfr & Whslr
N.A.I.C.S.: 331318

SWCC Showa (H.K.) Co., Ltd. (1)
Unit 701 7/F Greenfield Tower Concordia Plaza 1 Science Museum Rd, Tsim Sha Tsui, Kowloon, China (Hong Kong)
Tel.: (852) 27124141
Web Site: http://www.swcc.co.jp
Electric Cable Whslr
N.A.I.C.S.: 423610

SWCC Showa (S) Pte. Ltd. (1)
64 Sungei Kadut Street 1, Singapore, 729365, Singapore
Tel.: (65) 6 365 4380
Web Site: https://www.swcc.co.jp
Sales Range: $25-49.9 Million
Emp.: 3
Wire Products Mfr & Sales
N.A.I.C.S.: 332618
Makoto Sekine *(Mng Dir)*

Showa-Tbea (Shandong) Cable Accessories Co., Ltd. (1)
No 68 HP Road Xinwen Industrial Park, Xintai, 271219, Shandong, China
Tel.: (86) 5387308118
Web Site: http://www.tbea-swcc.com
Wire & Cable Mfr
N.A.I.C.S.: 335929

Swcc Showa (Shanghai) Co., Ltd. (1)
Room No 2501 ShengGao International Building No 137 Xianxia Road, Changning District, Shanghai, 200051, China
Tel.: (86) 2162419661
Wire & Cable Mfr
N.A.I.C.S.: 335929

SWECO AB
Gjorwellsgatan 22, PO Box 34044, SE-100 26, Stockholm, Sweden
Tel.: (46) 86956000 SE
Web Site: http://www.sweco.se
SWEC—(OMX)
Rev.: $2,546,344,640
Assets: $2,435,251,840
Liabilities: $1,513,792,000
Net Worth: $921,459,840
Earnings: $157,727,360
Emp.: 17,627
Fiscal Year-end: 12/31/20
Engineering & Consulting Services
N.A.I.C.S.: 541330
Johan Nordstrom *(Chm)*

Subsidiaries:

Afvalverwerking Stainkoeln B.V. (1)
Winschoterweg 1, 9723 CG, Groningen, Netherlands
Tel.: (31) 505416633
Web Site: http://www.stainkoeln.nl
Recycling Center Services
N.A.I.C.S.: 562920

Arkkitehtitoimisto Brunow & Maunula Oy (1)
Paelkaeneentie 19B, Helsinki, 510, Finland
Tel.: (358) 9 7744 500
Web Site: http://www.brunowmaunula.fi
Emp.: 19
Architectural Design Services
N.A.I.C.S.: 541310
Ulla Torikka *(Sec)*

Arstiderne Arkitekter AS (1)
Jordeshagen 15C, 3540, Nes, Norway
Tel.: (47) 32076760
Architecture & Planning Services
N.A.I.C.S.: 541310

Axro Holding AB (1)
PO Box 34044, Stockholm, 100 26, Sweden
Tel.: (46) 31428310
Investment Management Service
N.A.I.C.S.: 523940

FMC Laskentapalvelut Oy (1)
Ilmalanportti 2, 00240, Helsinki, Finland
Tel.: (358) 207393900
Web Site: http://www.fmclaskentapalvelut.fi
Bookkeeping Services
N.A.I.C.S.: 541219

Finnmap Consulting Oy (1)
Ratamestarinkatu 7 a, PO Box 88, Helsinki, 00520, Finland
Tel.: (358) 207 393 300
Web Site: http://www.sweco.fi
Sales Range: $100-124.9 Million
Emp.: 260
Structural Engineering Services
N.A.I.C.S.: 541330

Subsidiary (Domestic):

Aaro Kohonen Oy (2)
Kauppakatu 5, Seinajoki, 60100, Finland
Tel.: (358) 207 393 000
Web Site: http://www.aarokohonen.com
Emp.: 80
Civil & Structural Engineering Services
N.A.I.C.S.: 541330
Leif Sebbas *(Mng Dir)*

Air-Ix Tieto Oy (2)
Salhojankatu 42, 33500, Tampere, Finland
Tel.: (358) 10 241 4000
Civil Engineering Services
N.A.I.C.S.: 541330

Airix Talotekniikka Oy (2)
Salhojankatu 42 Pirkanmaa, Tampere, 33500, Finland
Tel.: (358) 102414000
Civil Engineering Services
N.A.I.C.S.: 541330

Contesta Oy (2)
Kilterinkuja 2, PO Box 23, 01600, Vantaa, Finland
Tel.: (358) 9 2525 2424
Web Site: http://www.contesta.fi
Sales Range: $25-49.9 Million
Emp.: 20
Concrete Testing & Research Services
N.A.I.C.S.: 541380

FM Projects Ltd Oy (2)
Ratamestarinkatu 7 A, Helsinki, 00521, Finland
Tel.: (358) 207 393300
Civil Engineering Services
N.A.I.C.S.: 541330

Fennopro-Consulting Oy (2)
Koronakatu 2 Uusimaa, Espoo, 02210, Finland
Tel.: (358) 207393030
Web Site: http://www.aarokohonen.si
Emp.: 6
Civil Engineering Services
N.A.I.C.S.: 541330
Markku Veijalainen *(Gen Mgr)*

Subsidiary (Non-US):

Finnmap Consulting Engineers (India) Pvt. Ltd. (2)
424 Udyog Vihar Phase 4, Gurgaon, 122015, India
Tel.: (91) 124 4209979
Sales Range: $25-49.9 Million
Emp.: 25
Engineering Consulting Services
N.A.I.C.S.: 541330

Subsidiary (Domestic):

Narmaplan Oy (2)
Pitkaemaeenkatu 4a, Turku, 20250, Finland
Tel.: (358) 22739999
Web Site: http://www.narmaplan.fi
Sales Range: $25-49.9 Million
Emp.: 62
Civil Engineering Consulting Services
N.A.I.C.S.: 541330
Meniqo Fren *(Mgr)*

Subsidiary (Non-US):

OOO FM Stroiproject (2)
Vyborgskaya Naberezhnaya 47 Business Center Gredanersky 5th Floor, 195009, Saint Petersburg, Russia
Tel.: (7) 81 2493 3348
Sales Range: $25-49.9 Million
Emp.: 25
Structural Engineering Services
N.A.I.C.S.: 541330

Subsidiary (Domestic):

Rakennushanke H. Lumivirta Oy (2)
Laentinen Pitkaekatu 23E, Turku, 20100, Finland
Tel.: (358) 24690744
Web Site: http://www.korjausasiantuntijat.fi
Sales Range: $25-49.9 Million
Emp.: 5
Civil Engineering Services
N.A.I.C.S.: 541330
Hannu Lumivirta *(Mng Dir)*

GSA Gesellschaft fur Strassenanalyse GmbH (1)
Firmensitz Kaiserslautern Flickerstal 5, D-67657, Kaiserslautern, Germany
Tel.: (49) 631366140
Web Site: https://www.gsa-mbh.de
Software Publishing Services
N.A.I.C.S.: 513210

HYDROCOOP, spol. s r.o. (1)
Dobsinskeho 32, 811 05, Bratislava, Slovakia
Tel.: (421) 2 4564 0927
Web Site: http://www.hydrocoop.sk
Sales Range: $75-99.9 Million
Emp.: 24
Water Consulting & Management Services
N.A.I.C.S.: 221310
Peter Gemeran *(Exec Dir)*

K-konsult Elteknik i Gavle AB (1)
Kyrkogatan 29, Gavle, 80311, Sweden
Tel.: (46) 26 54 32 30
Electrical Engineering Services
N.A.I.C.S.: 541330

Lahden Projektiimi Oy (1)
Ahjokatu 4 B, 15800, Lahti, Finland
Tel.: (358) 3783 2136
Web Site: http://www.projektiimi.fi
Civil Engineering Services
N.A.I.C.S.: 541330

Secundaire Bouwstoffen Unie B.V. (1)
Winschoterweg 1, 9723 CG, Groningen, Netherlands
Tel.: (31) 505416633
Web Site: http://www.sbubv.nl
Building Materials Distr
N.A.I.C.S.: 444180

Stockholms stads Utrednings- och Statistikkontor AB (1)
Kaplansbacken 10, Stockholm, 112 24, Sweden
Tel.: (46) 8 50 83 50 00
Web Site: http://www.statistikomstockholm.se
Geographical Research & Development Services
N.A.I.C.S.: 541720

Sweco Architects A/S (1)
Bygmestervej 5, Copenhagen, 2400, Denmark
Tel.: (45) 39 15 00 60
Web Site: http://www.sweco.dk
Sales Range: $25-49.9 Million
Emp.: 35
Civil Engineering Services
N.A.I.C.S.: 541330
Mads Stenbaek Jakobsen *(Partner & Mng Dir)*

Sweco Central Eastern Europe AB (1)
Gjoerwellsgatan 22, Stockholm, 112 60, Sweden
Tel.: (46) 86 95 60 00
Civil Engineering Services
N.A.I.C.S.: 541330
Bo Carlson *(Gen Mgr)*

Subsidiary (Non-US):

Sweco Architekci Sp. z o.o. (2)
Ul Lelechowska 5, 02-351, Warsaw, Poland
Tel.: (48) 22 2571777
Sales Range: $25-49.9 Million
Emp.: 6
Architectural Design Services
N.A.I.C.S.: 541310
Porzowie Michal *(Mng Dir)*

Sweco Polska sp.z o.o. (2)
street Saska 25 D, 30-720, Krakow, Poland
Tel.: (48) 124112102
Civil Engineering Services
N.A.I.C.S.: 541330
Marek Watroba *(Mgr-IT)*

Sweco Projekt AS (2)
Valukoja 8/1, 11415, Tallinn, Estonia
Tel.: (372) 6744000
Sales Range: $25-49.9 Million
Emp.: 58
Civil Engineering Services
N.A.I.C.S.: 541330

UAB Sweco Hidroprojektas (2)
A Strazdo G 22, 48488, Kaunas, Lithuania
Tel.: (370) 37 221056
Web Site: http://www.hidroprojektas.lt
Sales Range: $100-124.9 Million
Emp.: 80
Hydroelectric Power Generation Services
N.A.I.C.S.: 221111

Vealeidja OU (2)
Veerenni 58a-41, 11314, Tallinn, Estonia
Tel.: (372) 6 799 530
Web Site: http://www.vealeidja.ee
Sales Range: $10-24.9 Million
Emp.: 32
Construction Engineering Services
N.A.I.C.S.: 541330
Riho Koost *(Mng Dir)*

Sweco Connect AB (1)
Gjoerwellsgatan 22, Stockholm, 112 60, Sweden
Tel.: (46) 86956000
Civil Engineering Services
N.A.I.C.S.: 541330

Sweco EST OU (1)
Valukoja 8 1, Tallinn, Estonia
Tel.: (372) 6799530
Engineering Consultancy Services
N.A.I.C.S.: 541330

Sweco Eastern Europe AB (1)
Gjorwellsgatan 22, 112 60, Stockholm, Sweden
Tel.: (46) 86956000
Web Site: http://www.sweco.se
Civil Engineering Services
N.A.I.C.S.: 541330
Thomas Carlsson *(Gen Mgr)*

Sweco Energoproekt JSC (1)
20 Kosta Lulchev Str, Sofia, 1113, Bulgaria
Tel.: (359) 28072600
Web Site: http://www.sweco.bg
Engineering Consultancy Services
N.A.I.C.S.: 541330

Sweco Energuide AB (1)
Gjorwellsgatan 22, PO Box 34044, Stockholm, 100 26, Sweden
Tel.: (46) 86 95 60 00
Web Site: http://www.sweco.se
Power Management Consulting Services
N.A.I.C.S.: 541618
Nygard Pia *(Project Mgr)*

Sweco Environment AB (1)
Gjoerwellsgatan 22, Stockholm, 112 60, Sweden
Tel.: (46) 86956000
Environmental Consulting Services
N.A.I.C.S.: 541620

Sweco EuroFutures AB (1)
Kaplansbacken 10, Stockholm, 10026, Sweden
Tel.: (46) 86130800
Web Site: http://www.sweco.com
Sales Range: $25-49.9 Million
Emp.: 100
Engineering Consulting Services
N.A.I.C.S.: 541618

Sweco Finland Oy (1)
Ilmalantori 4, PO Box 75, 00240, Helsinki, Finland
Tel.: (358) 207393000

SWECO AB

Sweco AB—(Continued)

Web Site: https://www.sweco.fi
Sales Range: $150-199.9 Million
Emp.: 700
Civil Engineering Services
N.A.I.C.S.: 541330

Subsidiary (Non-US):

Sweco Industry AB (2)
Hospitalsgatan 22, Nykoping, 611 32, Sweden
Tel.: (46) 155615000
Industrial Engineering Services
N.A.I.C.S.: 541330

Sweco Hydroprojekt a.s. (1)
Taborska 31, 140 16, Prague, Czech Republic
Tel.: (420) 261102242
Web Site: https://www.sweco.cz
Sales Range: $25-49.9 Million
Emp.: 226
Construction Engineering Services
N.A.I.C.S.: 541330

Sweco Infrastructure AB (1)
Gjoerwellsgatan 22, Stockholm, 10026, Sweden
Tel.: (46) 86956000
Web Site: http://www.swecogroup.com
Emp.: 1,800
Civil Engineering Services
N.A.I.C.S.: 541330

Sweco International AB (1)
Tel.: (46) 86956000
Emp.: 1,600
Civil Engineering Services
N.A.I.C.S.: 541330
Blixt Karin *(Project Mgr)*

Sweco International Export AB (1)
PO Box 34044, 10026, Stockholm, Sweden
Tel.: (46) 8 695 60 00
Web Site: http://www.sweco.se
Emp.: 400
Civil Engineering Services
N.A.I.C.S.: 541330

Sweco Management AB (1)
Gjoerwellsgatan 22, Stockholm, 112 60, Sweden
Tel.: (46) 86956000
Web Site: http://www.sweco.se
Civil Engineering Consulting Services
N.A.I.C.S.: 541618
Elizabeth Philipson *(Gen Mgr)*

Sweco Mec AS (1)
Gismeroyveien 89, 4515, Mandal, Norway
Tel.: (47) 38 27 22 22
Web Site: http://www.mec.no
Construction Engineering Services
N.A.I.C.S.: 541330

Sweco NIPI TRTI (1)
Ul Chugunnaya 36 Lit A, 194044, Saint Petersburg, Russia
Tel.: (7) 812 333 31 70
Web Site: http://www.sweco.ru
Sales Range: $25-49.9 Million
Emp.: 90
Engineering Consulting Services
N.A.I.C.S.: 541330
Valery Myachin *(Gen Dir)*

Sweco Nederland B.V. (1)
De Holle Bilt 22, 3732 HM, De Bilt, Netherlands
Tel.: (31) 888116600
Web Site: https://www.sweco.nl
Environmental, Water, Energy, Transportation & Building Engineering Consulting Services
N.A.I.C.S.: 541330
Tomas Carlsson *(CEO)*

Subsidiary (Non-US):

Sweco Belgium nv (2)
Arenbergstraat 13, PO Box 1, 1000, Brussels, Belgium
Tel.: (32) 23830640
Web Site: https://www.swecobelgium.be
Emp.: 800
Construction Engineering Services
N.A.I.C.S.: 541330
Patrick Callewaert *(Mgr-Bus Dev-Industry Div)*

Sweco Consulting sp. z o.o. (2)
Franklina Roosevelta 22, 60-829, Poznan, Poland
Tel.: (48) 618649300
Web Site: https://www.sweco.pl
Construction Engineering Services
N.A.I.C.S.: 541330
Ina Brandes *(Pres-Central Europe)*

Sweco Danmark A/S (2)
Granskoven 8, 2600, Glostrup, Denmark
Tel.: (45) 72 207 207
Web Site: http://www.sweco.dk
Construction Engineering Services
N.A.I.C.S.: 541330
John Chubb *(Mng Dir)*

Sweco GmbH
Karl-Ferdinand-Braun-Strasse 9, 28359, Bremen, Germany
Tel.: (49) 42120326
Web Site: https://www.sweco-gmbh.de
Sales Range: $50-74.9 Million
Emp.: 800
Construction Engineering Services
N.A.I.C.S.: 541330
Ina Brandes *(Pres)*

Sweco UK Limited (2)
Grove House Mansion Gate Drive, Leeds, LS7 4DN, United Kingdom
Tel.: (44) 1132620000
Web Site: https://www.sweco.co.uk
Engineering Services
N.A.I.C.S.: 541330
Max Joy *(Mng Dir)*

Sweco Norge AS (1)
Drammensveien 260, PO Box 80, Skoyen, 0212, Oslo, Norway
Tel.: (47) 67128000
Web Site: https://www.sweco.no
Sales Range: $75-99.9 Million
Emp.: 500
Civil Engineering Services
N.A.I.C.S.: 541330

Sweco PM Oy (1)
Valimotie 9, PO Box 39, 00381, Helsinki, Finland
Tel.: (358) 207527200
Civil Engineering Services
N.A.I.C.S.: 541330
Juha Rantanen *(Project Mgr)*

Sweco Paatela Architects Oy (1)
Valimotie 9, PO Box 32, 00381, Helsinki, Finland
Tel.: (358) 20 752 7300
Web Site: http://www.sweco.fi
Sales Range: $25-49.9 Million
Emp.: 20
Architectural Design Services
N.A.I.C.S.: 541310
Heikki S. Laherma *(CEO)*

Sweco Position AB (1)
Gjoerwellsgatan 22, Stockholm, 112 60, Sweden
Tel.: (46) 86956000
Web Site: http://www.sweco.se
Emp.: 1,900
Geophysical Consulting Services
N.A.I.C.S.: 541360
Thomas Carlson *(CEO)*

Sweco Russia AB (1)
Gjoerwellsgatan 22, Stockholm, 112 60, Sweden
Tel.: (46) 86 95 60 00
Web Site: http://www.sweco.se
Civil Engineering Services
N.A.I.C.S.: 541330
Jonas Dahlberg *(Mgr)*

Sweco Structures AB (1)
Gjorwellsgatan 22, PO Box 340 44, 10026, Stockholm, Sweden
Tel.: (46) 8 695 60 00
Web Site: http://www.sweco.se
Civil Engineering Services
N.A.I.C.S.: 541330

Top Gaarkeuken B.V. (1)
Hoendiep z z 7a, Oldekerk, 9821 TJ, Groningen, Netherlands
Tel.: (31) 594213544
Biomass Electric Services
N.A.I.C.S.: 221118

UAB Sweco Lietuva (1)
Ozo str 12A-1, LT-08200, Vilnius, Lithuania
Tel.: (370) 61458530
Web Site: https://www.sweco.lt
Engineering Consultancy Services
N.A.I.C.S.: 541330

Vagroen B.V. (1)
Rozenburglaan 11, 9727 DL, Groningen, Netherlands
Tel.: (31) 507440486
Web Site: http://www.vagroen.nl
Biomass Electric Services
N.A.I.C.S.: 221118

SWEDBANK AB

Landsvagen 40, 172 63, Sundbyberg, Sweden
Tel.: (46) 858590000
Web Site: https://www.swedbank.se
Year Founded: 1942
SWDBF—(OTCIQ)
Rev.: $6,842,657,375
Assets: $267,453,332,959
Liabilities: $248,834,284,002
Net Worth: $18,619,048,957
Earnings: $3,196,680,622
Emp.: 3,640
Fiscal Year-end: 12/31/23
Commercial Banking Services
N.A.I.C.S.: 522110
Mikael Bjorknert *(Head-Swedish Banking)*

Subsidiaries:

AB Spintab (1)
Brunkebergstorg 8, SE 105 34, Stockholm, Sweden **(100%)**
Tel.: (46) 858592100
Web Site: http://www.swedbank.se
Sales Range: $200-249.9 Million
Emp.: 330
Mortgage Lending
N.A.I.C.S.: 522210

FIM Oyj (1)
Mikonkatu 9, 00100, Helsinki, Finland **(51%)**
Tel.: (358) 96134600
Web Site: http://www.fim.com
Sales Range: $200-249.9 Million
Commercial Banking Services
N.A.I.C.S.: 522110

Forenings Sparbanken AB (1)
Brunkebergstorg 8, 105 34, Stockholm, Sweden **(100%)**
Tel.: (46) 858590000
Web Site: http://www.swedbank.se
Sales Range: $400-449.9 Million
Emp.: 1,000
Michel Wolf *(Mng Dir)*

ForeningsSparbanken Fastighetsbyra AB (1)
Regeringsgatan 29, Stockholm, 10534, Sweden **(100%)**
Tel.: (46) 87877880
Web Site: http://www.swedbank.se
N.A.I.C.S.: 522210
Jan Liden *(Pres & CEO)*

ForeningsSparbanken Finans AB (1)
Junuhallsdagen 1, SE 112 64, Stockholm, Sweden **(100%)**
Tel.: (46) 858590000
Web Site: http://www.swedbank.se
Sales Range: $75-99.9 Million
Emp.: 160
Finance Company
N.A.I.C.S.: 921130
Hans Karlsson *(Mgr-Mktg)*

ForeningsSparbanken Oland AB (1)
Storgatan 15, PO Box 26, Borgholm, 38721, Sweden **(60%)**
Tel.: (46) 485564500
Web Site: http://www.olandsbank.se
Sales Range: $10-24.9 Million
Emp.: 60
N.A.I.C.S.: 522210

Olands Bank AB (1)
Storgatan 15, 387 31, Borgholm, Sweden
Tel.: (46) 48515000
Web Site: http://www.olandsbank.se
Commercial Banking Services

INTERNATIONAL PUBLIC

N.A.I.C.S.: 522110

Robur Kapitalforvaltning AB (1)
Malmtorgsgatan 8, 10534, Stockholm, Sweden **(100%)**
Tel.: (46) 858592400
Web Site: http://www.swedbankrobur.se
Sales Range: $200-249.9 Million
Emp.: 300
Fund Manager
N.A.I.C.S.: 525910
Thomas Eriksson *(Pres)*

SparFond Livforsakrings AB (1)
Roburab, SE 105 34, Stockholm, Sweden **(100%)**
Tel.: (46) 86572000
Web Site: http://www.robur.se
Sales Range: $50-74.9 Million
Emp.: 25
Provider of Banking Services
N.A.I.C.S.: 522210

Sparia Forsakrings AB (1)
Brunkebergstorg 8, Stockholm, 105 34, Sweden
Tel.: (46) 858590000
Insurance Management Services
N.A.I.C.S.: 524210

Swedbank (Lithuania) AB (1)
Konstitucijos pr 20A, 03502 , Vilnius, Lithuania
Tel.: (370) 5 268 4444
Web Site: http://www.swedbank.lt
Banking Services
N.A.I.C.S.: 522110

Swedbank (Luxembourg) S.A. (1)
65 Boulevard Grande Duchesse Charlotte, 1331, Luxembourg, Luxembourg
Tel.: (352) 4049401
Web Site: http://www.swedbank.lu
Banking Services
N.A.I.C.S.: 522110

Swedbank AS (1)
Liivalaia 8, 15040, Tallinn, Estonia
Tel.: (372) 6310310
Web Site: http://www.swedbank.ee
Commercial Banking Services
N.A.I.C.S.: 522110
Ede Raagmets *(Head-Customer Svc)*

Swedbank Fastighetsbyra AB (1)
Vastra Jarnvagsgatan 7, PO Box 644, 101 32, Stockholm, Sweden
Tel.: (46) 854545500
Web Site: http://www.fastighetsbyran.com
Real Estate Manangement Services
N.A.I.C.S.: 531390

Swedbank Finans AB (1)
Junohallsvagen 1, 105 34, Stockholm, Sweden
Tel.: (46) 8 5859 2200
Web Site: http://www.swedbankfinans.se
Commercial Banking Services
N.A.I.C.S.: 522110

Swedbank First Securities LLC (1)
570 Lexington Ave 35th Fl, New York, NY 10022
Tel.: (212) 906-0820
Web Site: http://www.swedbankfs.com
Sales Range: $50-74.9 Million
Emp.: 15
Securities Brokerage Services
N.A.I.C.S.: 523150
Leonardo Rago *(Head-Ops)*

Swedbank Management Company S.A. (1)
65 Boulevard Grande Duchesse Charlotte, 1331, Luxembourg, Luxembourg **(100%)**
Tel.: (352) 40 49 40 1
Web Site: http://www.swedbank.lu
Sales Range: $50-74.9 Million
Emp.: 50
Investment Management
N.A.I.C.S.: 523150
Ann-Charlotte Lawyer *(Head)*

Swedbank Markets (1)
Sodra Hammgatan 27, 404 80, Gothenburg, Sweden **(100%)**
Tel.: (46) 317397630
Web Site: http://www.swedbank.se
Sales Range: $400-449.9 Million
N.A.I.C.S.: 522210

SWEDEGAS AB

Kilsgatan 4, 411 04, Gothenburg, Sweden
Tel.: (46) 3143 9300　　SE
Web Site: http://www.swedegas.com
Year Founded: 1976
Emp.: 40
Natural Gas Pipeline Operator
N.A.I.C.S.: 486210
Linus Hellman *(Controller-Mktg)*

SWEDEN BUYERSCLUB AB
Charkmastargatan 2, 121 62, Johanneshov, Sweden
Tel.: (46) 20455000
Web Site: https://www.buyersclub.se
Year Founded: 2015
BUY—(OMX)
Rev.: $5,217,702
Assets: $2,378,542
Liabilities: $1,623,087
Net Worth: $755,455
Earnings: ($964,918)
Emp.: 13
Fiscal Year-end: 12/31/23
Online Shopping Services
N.A.I.C.S.: 425120
Andreas Onstorp *(Chm)*

SWEDENCARE AB
Medeon Science Park, 205 12, Malmo, Sweden
Tel.: (46) 4085933
Web Site:
　　https://www.swedencare.com
SECARE—(OMX)
Rev.: $171,350,698
Assets: $937,055,457
Liabilities: $238,273,062
Net Worth: $698,782,395
Earnings: $8,846,366
Emp.: 525
Fiscal Year-end: 12/31/22
Animal Health Product Distr
N.A.I.C.S.: 459999
Hakan Lagerberg *(CEO)*

Subsidiaries:

Animal Pharm Care USA, Inc.　(1)
2600 Lakepointe Pkwy, Odessa, FL 33556
Web Site: https://www.anmpharm.com
Pharmaceutical Product Mfr & Distr
N.A.I.C.S.: 325412

Biovet I.K.E.　(1)
27 Sofouli str, Pylaia, 55535, Thessaloniki, Greece
Tel.: (30) 2310325328
Web Site: https://www.biovet.gr
Veterinarian Equipment Mfr & Distr
N.A.I.C.S.: 339112

Nutravet (UK) Limited　(1)
The Warehouse Shardlane, Hambleton, Poulton-le-Fylde, FY6 9BX, Lancashire, United Kingdom
Tel.: (44) 8456041688
Web Site: https://www.nutravet.co.uk
Pet Food Retailer
N.A.I.C.S.: 459910

Rx Vitamins, Inc.　(1)
150 Clearbrook Rd Ste 149, Elmsford, NY 10523-1140
Tel.: (914) 592-2323
Web Site: https://www.rxvitamins.com
Drugs & Druggists' Sundries Merchant Whslr
N.A.I.C.S.: 424210
Ben Lanza *(VP)*

Swedencare Buccosante SARL　(1)
16 Le Jas Neuf, 83480, Puget-sur-Argens, France
Tel.: (33) 494191546
Web Site: http://www.buccosante.eu
Veterinarian Product Distr
N.A.I.C.S.: 423450

Swedencare Ireland Ltd.　(1)
Unit 8 Ida Industrial Park, Waterford, X91 AX51, Ireland
Tel.: (353) 51304010
Web Site:
　　https://www.swedencareireland.com
Veterinarian Product Distr
N.A.I.C.S.: 423450

Swedencare Spain SLU　(1)
C/Caldes d Estrac 20 1-3, Mataro, 08302, Barcelona, Spain
Tel.: (34) 935394512
Web Site: https://www.swedencare.es
Veterinarian Product Distr
N.A.I.C.S.: 423450

Swedencare UK Ltd.　(1)
1 Great Exhibition Way, Kirkstall, Leeds, LS5 3BF, United Kingdom
Tel.: (44) 1135187004
Web Site: http://www.swedencare.co.uk
Veterinarian Product Distr
N.A.I.C.S.: 423450

Swedencare USA Inc.　(1)
19494 7th Ave NE, Poulsbo, WA 98370
Tel.: (360) 697-3550
Web Site: https://www.swedencareusa.com
Veterinarian Product Distr
N.A.I.C.S.: 423450

The Garmon Corp.　(1)
27461 Via Industria, Temecula, CA 92590
Tel.: (951) 296-6308
Web Site: http://www.naturvet.com
Miscellaneous Mfr
N.A.I.C.S.: 339999
Scott Garmon *(Pres)*

Vetio Animal Health　(1)
2705 Dougherty Ferry Rd Ste 202, Saint Louis, MO 63122
Tel.: (561) 804-7603
Web Site: http://www.vetio.com
Contract Development & Manufacturing Services
N.A.I.C.S.: 424690
John Kane *(CEO)*

SWEDISH LOGISTIC PROPERTY AB
Stromgatan 2, 212 25, Malmo, Sweden
Tel.: (46) 701827830
Web Site: https://www.slproperty.se
Year Founded: 2018
SLP.B—(OMX)
Rev.: $58,073,740
Assets: $1,088,113,267
Liabilities: $574,880,388
Net Worth: $513,232,880
Earnings: $30,575,576
Emp.: 15
Fiscal Year-end: 12/31/23
Real Estate Manangement Services
N.A.I.C.S.: 531210
Peter Strand *(CEO)*

SWEDISH ORPHAN BIOVITRUM AB
Tomtebodavagen 23A Solna, SE-112 76, Stockholm, Sweden
Tel.: (46) 86972000　　SE
Web Site: https://www.sobi.com
Year Founded: 2001
SOBI—(OMX)
Rev.: $2,196,180,076
Assets: $7,348,760,226
Liabilities: $3,986,737,416
Net Worth: $3,362,022,810
Earnings: $239,144,682
Emp.: 1,772
Fiscal Year-end: 12/31/23
Biopharmaceutical Research & Development
N.A.I.C.S.: 325412
Anders Ullman *(Chief Medical Officer & Head-R&D)*

Subsidiaries:

BVBA Swedish Orphan Biovitrum　(1)
Rue Neerveld 101-103, 1200, Saint-Stevens-Woluwe, Belgium
Tel.: (32) 28806119
Pharmaceutical Preparation Mfr
N.A.I.C.S.: 325412

CTI BioPharma Corp.　(1)
3101 Western Ave Ste 800, Seattle, WA 98121
Tel.: (206) 282-7100
Web Site: https://www.ctibiopharma.com
Rev.: $53,948,000
Assets: $125,925,000
Liabilities: $143,502,000
Net Worth: ($17,577,000)
Earnings: ($92,992,000)
Emp.: 127
Fiscal Year-end: 12/31/2022
Cancer Treatments Developer & Marketer
N.A.I.C.S.: 325412
Henrik Stenqvist *(Treas)*

Subsidiary (Domestic):

Aequus BioPharma, Inc.　(2)
11042 Forest Ln NE, Bainbridge Island, WA 98110-1542
Tel.: (206) 855-7802
Web Site: http://www.aequusbiopharma.com
Sales Range: $150-199.9 Million
Biotherapeutics Research, Development & Marketing
N.A.I.C.S.: 541714
Ronald Berenson *(Pres & CEO)*

Dova Pharmaceuticals, Inc.　(1)
240 Leigh Farm Rd Ste 245, Durham, NC 27707
Tel.: (919) 748-5975
Web Site: http://www.dova.com
Rev.: $10,355,000
Assets: $112,169,000
Liabilities: $35,811,000
Net Worth: $76,358,000
Earnings: ($72,282,000)
Emp.: 115
Fiscal Year-end: 12/31/2018
Pharmaceutical Product Mfr & Distr
N.A.I.C.S.: 325412
Lee F. Allen *(Chief Medical Officer)*

OOO Swedish Orphan Biovitrum　(1)
Prechistenka st 40/2 building 1 room 12 floor 5, Moscow, 119034, Russia
Tel.: (7) 4957488479
Web Site: https://sobi-russia.ru
Sales Range: $25-49.9 Million
Emp.: 2
Biopharmaceutical Research & Development
N.A.I.C.S.: 325412

Oy Swedish Orphan Biovitrum AB　(1)
Ayritie 18, 01510, Vantaa, Finland
Tel.: (358) 201558840
Web Site: https://www.sobi.com
Biopharmaceutical Research & Development
N.A.I.C.S.: 325412

SOBI Middle East FZ-LLC　(1)
Office 704 DSC Tower Dubai Studio City, PO Box 392356, Dubai, United Arab Emirates
Tel.: (971) 43616399
Pharmaceutical Preparation Mfr
N.A.I.C.S.: 325412

Sobi Pharma (Shanghai) Company Limited　(1)
Room 121 5 Floor Wework center International Media Port, Longwen Road 69 Xuhui District, Shanghai, China
Tel.: (86) 4001046466
Pharmaceuticals Mfr
N.A.I.C.S.: 325412

Sobi Single Member I.K.E　(1)
56 Ermou Street, 10563, Athens, Greece
Tel.: (30) 2130994031
Pharmaceutical Preparation Mfr
N.A.I.C.S.: 325412

Sobi, Inc.　(1)
77 4th Ave 3rd Fl, Waltham, MA 02451
Tel.: (781) 786-7370
Pharmaceutical Preparation Mfr
N.A.I.C.S.: 325412

Swedish Orphan Biovitrum (SOBI) Canada, Inc.　(1)
1155 North Service Road West Unit 11, Oakville, L6M 3E3, ON, Canada
Tel.: (289) 291-3852
Web Site: https://www.sobi.com
Pharmaceutical Preparation Mfr
N.A.I.C.S.: 325412

Swedish Orphan Biovitrum A/S　(1)
Sorgenfrivej 17, 2800, Kongens Lyngby, Denmark
Tel.: (45) 32966869
Web Site: https://www.sobi.com
Sales Range: $25-49.9 Million
Emp.: 9
Biopharmaceutical Research & Development
N.A.I.C.S.: 325412

Swedish Orphan Biovitrum AG　(1)
Riehenring 182, 6314, Basel, Switzerland
Tel.: (41) 615087213
Web Site: https://www.sobi.com
Pharmaceutical Preparation Mfr
N.A.I.C.S.: 325412

Swedish Orphan Biovitrum AS　(1)
Dronning Eufemias Gate 16, 0191, Oslo, Norway
Tel.: (47) 66823400
Web Site: https://www.sobi.com
Sales Range: $25-49.9 Million
Emp.: 10
Biopharmaceutical Research & Development
N.A.I.C.S.: 325412

Swedish Orphan Biovitrum GmbH　(1)
Fraunhoferstr 9a, 82152, Martinsried, Germany
Tel.: (49) 8955066760
Web Site: https://www.sobi.com
Biopharmaceutical Research & Development
N.A.I.C.S.: 325412

Swedish Orphan Biovitrum International AB　(1)
Tomtebodavagen 23a, 171 65, Solna, Sweden
Tel.: (46) 86972000
Web Site: http://www.sobi.com
Sales Range: $125-149.9 Million
Emp.: 400
Pharmaceuticals Product Mfr
N.A.I.C.S.: 325412

Swedish Orphan Biovitrum Ltd　(1)
Suite 2 Riverside 3 Granta Park, Great Abington, Cambridge, CB21 6AD, Cambridgeshire, United Kingdom
Tel.: (44) 122 389 1854
Web Site: https://sobi-uk.co.uk
Biopharmaceutical Research & Development
N.A.I.C.S.: 325412

Swedish Orphan Biovitrum Manufacturing AB　(1)
Tvistevagen 48, 907 19, Umea, Sweden
Tel.: (46) 90172250
Web Site: http://www.sobi.com
Sales Range: $25-49.9 Million
Emp.: 450
Pharmaceutical Preparation Mfr
N.A.I.C.S.: 325412

Swedish Orphan Biovitrum S.L.　(1)
C/Ramirez de Arellano 29 6 planta, 28043, Madrid, Spain
Tel.: (34) 913913580
Web Site: https://www.sobi.com
Emp.: 23
Biopharmaceutical Research & Development
N.A.I.C.S.: 325412

Swedish Orphan Biovitrum S.R.L.　(1)
Strada Quarta 61 D, 43100, Parma, Italy
Tel.: (39) 0521 19111
Biopharmaceutical Research & Development
N.A.I.C.S.: 325412

Swedish Orphan Biovitrum SARL　(1)
32 Rue Guersant, 75837, Paris, France
Tel.: (33) 1 70 39 53 41
Biopharmaceutical Research & Development
N.A.I.C.S.: 325412

Swedish Orphan Biovitrum Sverige AB　(1)

SWEDISH ORPHAN BIOVITRUM AB

Swedish Orphan Biovitrum AB—(Continued)
Tomtebodavagen 23A, 11276, Solna, Sweden
Tel.: (46) 8 697 2000
Web Site: https://www.sobi.com
Sales Range: $25-49.9 Million
Emp.: 100
Biopharmaceutical Research & Development
N.A.I.C.S.: 325412

Swedish Orphan Biovitrum s.r.o (1)
Na strzi 1702/65, 140 00, Prague, Czech Republic
Tel.: (420) 296183236
Web Site: https://www.sobi.com
Biopharmaceutical Research & Development
N.A.I.C.S.: 325412

SWEET EARTH HOLDINGS CORPORATION
Suite 1300 - 1030 West Georgia Street, Vancouver, V6E 2Y3, BC, Canada
Tel.: (604) 423-4499
Web Site:
http://www.seawayenergy.com
Year Founded: 1998
SE—(OTCIQ)
Rev.: $7,070
Assets: $12,942
Liabilities: $222,892
Net Worth: ($209,950)
Earnings: $133,725
Fiscal Year-end: 06/30/24
Environmental Consulting Services
N.A.I.C.S.: 541620

SWEET NATURAL TRADING CO. LIMITED
41 Lesmil Rd, North York, M3B 2T3, ON, Canada
Tel.: (416) 288-1019   Ca
Web Site:
http://www.sweetnaturaltrading.com
Year Founded: 2004
Rev.: $4,897,235
Assets: $2,698,189
Liabilities: $4,659,097
Net Worth: ($1,960,908)
Earnings: ($3,082,750)
Fiscal Year-end: 12/31/17
Organic Chemical Mfr
N.A.I.C.S.: 325199
Steven Haasz (Pres & CEO)

SWEET POISON SPIRITS INC
Suite 750 - 580 Hornby Street, Vancouver, V6C 3B6, BC, Canada
Tel.: (604) 602-4935
Web Site:
https://www.sweetpoisonspirits.com
HFH—(CNSX)
Assets: $24,542
Liabilities: $386,464
Net Worth: ($361,922)
Earnings: ($1,179,808)
Fiscal Year-end: 04/30/21
Cannabis Product Mfr & Distr
N.A.I.C.S.: 325412
Robert Eadie (CEO)

SWEET PRODUCTS LOGISTICS NV
Industriepark E17/3, Mosten, Lokeren, 9160, Belgium
Tel.: (32) 93 26 82 70
Web Site:
http://www.sweetproductslogic.be
Sales Range: $200-249.9 Million
Emp.: 2,000
Chocolate Product Mfr
N.A.I.C.S.: 311351
Fons Walder (CEO & Owner)

Subsidiaries:

Baronie Chocolates Belgium NV (1)
Ondernemingenstraat 5, 8630, Veurne, Belgium
Tel.: (32) 58 31 01 50
Web Site: http://www.baronie.com
Chocolate Confections Mfr
N.A.I.C.S.: 311352
Jean-Marie van Logtestijn (Gen Mgr)

Subsidiary (Non-US):

Baronie - De Heer B.V. (2)
Galvanistraat 14, 3029 AD, Rotterdam, Netherlands
Tel.: (31) 10 22 14 214
Web Site: http://www.baronie.com
Chocolate Confections Mfr
N.A.I.C.S.: 311352
Jean-Marie van Logtestijn (Gen Mgr)

Division (Domestic):

Continental Chocolate B.V. (3)
Oceanenweg 1, 1047 BA, Amsterdam, Netherlands
Tel.: (31) 20 40 70 500
Web Site: http://www.baronie.com
Chocolate Confections Mfr
N.A.I.C.S.: 311352

Subsidiary (Domestic):

Kathy Chocolaterie N.V. (2)
Pathoekeweg 82, 8000, Brugge, Belgium
Tel.: (32) 50320926
Web Site: http://www.confiseriekathy.be
Sales Range: $25-49.9 Million
Emp.: 4
Chocolate Confections Mfr
N.A.I.C.S.: 311352

Subsidiary (Non-US):

Stollwerck GmbH (2)
Stollwerckstrasse 27-31, Cologne, 51149, Germany (100%)
Tel.: (49) 2203430
Web Site: http://www.stollwerck.de
Sales Range: $700-749.9 Million
Emp.: 250
Chocolate Confectionery Mfr & Distr
N.A.I.C.S.: 311351

Subsidiary (Non-US):

Jacques Chocolaterie SA (3)
Industriestrasse 16, B 4700, Eupen, Belgium (100%)
Tel.: (32) 87592911
Web Site: http://www.chocojacques.be
Sales Range: $75-99.9 Million
Emp.: 130
Chocolate Mfr
N.A.I.C.S.: 311351

Plant (Domestic):

Stollwerck GmbH - Saalfeld (3)
Neumuehle 1, D 07318, Saalfeld, Germany (100%)
Tel.: (49) 36718210
Web Site: http://www.stollwerck.de
Sales Range: $150-199.9 Million
Chocolate Confectionery Mfr
N.A.I.C.S.: 311351
Stefan Kragkei (Mgr-Quality Control)

Subsidiary (Non-US):

Stollwerck Italia S.p.A. (3)
Viale Milano Fiori Strada 1 Palazzo E/2, Assago, 20090, Milan, Italy
Tel.: (39) 0257514487
Sales Range: $25-49.9 Million
Emp.: 30
Confectionery Sales
N.A.I.C.S.: 424450
Massimo Garavaglio (Mgr)

SWEETEN REAL ESTATE DEVELOPMENT CO., LTD.
3F No 201 Sec 2 Rd Wen Hsin, Taichung, Taiwan
Tel.: (886) 422595777
Web Site:
https://www.sweeten.com.tw
5525—(TAI)
Rev.: $164,204,938
Assets: $546,440,314
Liabilities: $378,686,764
Net Worth: $167,753,550
Earnings: $22,231,694
Fiscal Year-end: 12/31/23
Real Estate Development Services
N.A.I.C.S.: 531390
Xingshu Ke (Chm)

SWEETS OF OMAN S.A.O.G
Rusayl Industrial Estate, PO Box 49, 124, Muscat, Oman
Tel.: (968) 24446278   OM
Web Site:
http://www.sweetsofoman.com
Year Founded: 1990
OSCI—(MUS)
Rev.: $27,402,706
Assets: $33,174,569
Liabilities: $21,211,839
Net Worth: $11,962,729
Earnings: $207,932
Emp.: 332
Fiscal Year-end: 12/31/19
Chocolates & Confectionery Mfr
N.A.I.C.S.: 311351

SWELECT ENERGY SYSTEMS LTD.
Swelect House No 5 Sir PS Sivasamy Salai, Mylapore, Chennai, 600 004, Tamil Nadu, India
Tel.: (91) 4424993266
Web Site: https://www.swelectes.com
SWELECTES—(NSE)
Rev.: $38,545,948
Assets: $163,045,578
Liabilities: $60,796,022
Net Worth: $102,249,557
Earnings: $3,553,900
Emp.: 293
Fiscal Year-end: 03/31/21
Uninterrupted Power Supply Systems Mfr & Distr
N.A.I.C.S.: 335999
Chellapan R. (Co-Mng Dir)

Subsidiaries:

Numeric Solar Energy Private Limited (1)
No 5 Sir P S Sivasamy Salai, Mylapore, Chennai, 600 004, India
Tel.: (91) 44 2499 3266
Web Site: http://www.swelectes.com
Sales Range: $25-49.9 Million
Emp.: 5
Solar Power Device Mfr
N.A.I.C.S.: 334413
Ramasamy Chellappan Gounder (Mng Dir)

SWELECT Energy Systems Pte Limited (1)
2 Kallang Pudding Road 02-12 Mactech Industrial Building, Singapore, 349307, Singapore
Tel.: (65) 67462359
Uninterrupted Power Supply Systems Mfr
N.A.I.C.S.: 221118

Swelect HHV Solar Photovoltaics Private Limited (1)
SF No166 & 169, Kuppepalayam Village Sembagounden Pudur Sarkar Samakulam, Coimbatore, 641107, India
Tel.: (91) 4424679651
Solar Photovoltaic Modules Mfr
N.A.I.C.S.: 334413

SWENEX - SWISS ENERGY EXCHANGE LTD.
Nidfeldstrasse, 1 PO Box 2260, Kriens 2, CH-6010, Lucerne, Switzerland
Tel.: (41) 413173838
Web Site: http://www.swenex.ch
Energy Management Solutions
N.A.I.C.S.: 926130
Jannik Bollinger (Ops Mgr)

Subsidiaries:

Tetrag Automation AG (1)
An der Reuss, Gisikon, 6038, Switzerland
Tel.: (41) 41 455 64 60
Web Site: http://www.tretag.ch
Building Automation Installation Services
N.A.I.C.S.: 238210
Markus Koschenz (Gen Mgr)

SWIBER HOLDINGS LIMITED
12 International Business Park Swiber IBP 04-01, Singapore, 609920, Singapore
Tel.: (65) 65050800
Web Site: http://www.swiber.com
Year Founded: 1996
Sales Range: $800-899.9 Million
Emp.: 2,700
Offshore Construction & Marine Services
N.A.I.C.S.: 237990
Jean Pers (Co-Pres & CEO-Engrg)

Subsidiaries:

Equatoriale Pte. Ltd. (1)
12 International Business Park Swiber IBP 04-01, Singapore, 609920, Singapore
Tel.: (65) 6505 0800
Web Site: http://www.Swiber.com
Emp.: 100
Deep Water Drilling Services
N.A.I.C.S.: 213111

PT Swiber Berjaya (1)
Menara Jamsostek Gedung Menara Utara 12th Floor, Jl Jend Gatot Subroto No 38, Jakarta, 12710, Indonesia
Tel.: (62) 21 5296 1960
Emp.: 60
Vessel Chartering Services
N.A.I.C.S.: 483111
Gohboon Keong (Mgr-Mkgt)

PT Swiber Offshore (1)
Menara Jamsostek Gedung Menara Utara 12th Floor, Jl Jend Gatot Subroto No 38, Jakarta, 12710, Indonesia
Tel.: (62) 2152961960
Web Site: http://www.swiber.com
Sales Range: $25-49.9 Million
Emp.: 19
Offshore Engineering Services
N.A.I.C.S.: 541330
Hendrik Eddy Purnomo (Pres)

Swiber Corporate Services Pte Ltd. (1)
12 International Business Park Swiber IBP 04-01, Singapore, 609920, Singapore
Tel.: (65) 6505 0800
Business Support Services
N.A.I.C.S.: 561499

Swiber Engineering Pte Ltd. (1)
12 International Business Park Swiber IBP 04-01, Singapore, 609620, Singapore
Tel.: (65) 6505 0800
Engineeering Services
N.A.I.C.S.: 541330

Swiber Marine Pte Ltd. (1)
12 International Business Park Swiber IBP 04-01, Singapore, 609920, Singapore
Tel.: (65) 6505 0800
Construction Services
N.A.I.C.S.: 237990

Swiber Offshore (B) Sdn Bhd. (1)
No 19 Simpang 94 Jalan Lorong Setia Di-Raja, KA1131, Kuala Belait, Negara, Brunei Darussalam
Tel.: (673) 333 7230
Construction Services
N.A.I.C.S.: 237990

Swiber Offshore (India) Pvt. Ltd. (1)
502 B Wing Delphi Hiranandani Business Park, Powai, Mumbai, 400076, India
Tel.: (91) 22 4243 4400
Web Site: http://www.swiber.com
Emp.: 55
Construction & Marine Services
N.A.I.C.S.: 237990

Swiber Offshore Construction Pte Ltd (1)
12 International Business Park Cyberhub IBP 04-01, Singapore, 609920, Singapore
Tel.: (65) 65050800

Web Site: http://www.swiber.com
Offshore Marine Engineering Services
N.A.I.C.S.: 541330

Swiber Offshore Marine Pte Ltd (1)
12 International Business Park Cyberhub
IBP 04-01, Singapore, 609920, Singapore
Tel.: (65) 65050800
Offshore Engineering Services
N.A.I.C.S.: 541330

**Swiber Offshore Middle East
(FZE)** (1)
Q3-015 SAIF Zone, PO Box 122715,
Sharjah, United Arab Emirates
Tel.: (971) 6 5579 102
Construction & Marine Services
N.A.I.C.S.: 237990

Swiber Offshore Pte Ltd. (1)
12 International Business Park Swiber IBP
04-06, Singapore, 609920, Singapore
Tel.: (65) 6505 0800
Construction Services
N.A.I.C.S.: 237990

SWICORP
King Fahd Road Kingdom Tower 49th
Fl, Riyadh, 11451, Saudi Arabia
Tel.: (966) 112110737 SA
Web Site: http://www.swicorp.com
Year Founded: 1987
Sales Range: $1-4.9 Billion
Emp.: 127
Corporate Finance Advisory, Private
Equity & Principal Investment Firm
N.A.I.C.S.: 523940
Kamel Lazaar *(Founder & Chm)*

Subsidiaries:

Swicorp (UAE) Limited (1)
DIFC Al Fattan Currency House Tower 2
Office 1502, Dubai, United Arab Emirates
Tel.: (971) 4 384 1600
Web Site: http://www.swicorp.com
Investment Banking, Asset Management
Services & Private Equity Firm
N.A.I.C.S.: 523940
Mehdi Charfi *(Exec Dir)*

SWIETELSKY BAUGESELL-
SCHAFT M.B.H.
Edlbacherstrasse 10, 4020, Linz,
Austria
Tel.: (43) 73269717420
Web Site: http://www.swietelsky.at
Sales Range: $1-4.9 Billion
Emp.: 6,887
Railway, Tunnel, Bridge & Roadway
Construction Services
N.A.I.C.S.: 237310
Adolf Scheuchenpflug *(Mng Dir)*

Subsidiaries:

A.S.T. Baugesellschaft m.b.H. (1)
Ruttenenstrasse 25, 6800, Feldkirch, Austria
Tel.: (43) 55 22 72 470
Web Site: http://www.ast-bau.at
Residential Building Construction Services
N.A.I.C.S.: 236115
Franz Schauer *(CEO)*

Bahnbau Petri Hoch- und Tiefbau Gesellschaft m.b.H. (1)
Klein Neusiedler Strasse 27, 2401, Fischamend Dorf, Austria
Tel.: (43) 2230 80270
Construction Engineering Services
N.A.I.C.S.: 541330

BauQ Projekt GmbH (1)
Gewerbepark 7b, 8075, Hart bei Graz, Austria
Tel.: (43) 316 491037
Web Site: http://www.bauq.at
Construction Engineering Services
N.A.I.C.S.: 541330

Baumeister Karl Sedlmayer Gesellschaft mit beschrankter Haftung (1)
Kleiner Worth 26, 3484, Grafenworth, Austria
Tel.: (43) 2738 2377

Web Site: http://www.bm-sedlmayer.at
Construction Engineering Services
N.A.I.C.S.: 541330

C. Peters Baugesellschaft m.b.H. (1)
Sudtirolerstrasse 4, 4020, Linz, Austria
Tel.: (43) 732 657401 0
Web Site: http://www.cpeters.at
Pipeline Construction Services
N.A.I.C.S.: 237990

G.K.S. SWIETELSKY Kft. (1)
Szekesdulo sor, 2120, Dunakeszi, Hungary
Tel.: (36) 27 548 900
Construction Engineering Services
N.A.I.C.S.: 541330

Georg Fessl GmbH. (1)
Rudmanns 90, 3910, Zwettl, Austria
Tel.: (43) 2822 52441 0
Web Site: http://www.fessl.at
Construction Engineering Services
N.A.I.C.S.: 541330

HTB - Hoch-Tief-Bau Srl (1)
Via Vilpiano 36, Nals, 39010, Bolzano, Italy
Tel.: (39) 0471 050435
Web Site: http://www.htb-italia.it
Construction Engineering Services
N.A.I.C.S.: 541330

Hans Held Tiefbau GmbH & Co (1)
Reith 9, 85560, Ebersberg, Germany
Tel.: (49) 8092 8507990
Web Site: http://www.held-tiefbau.de
Construction Engineering Services
N.A.I.C.S.: 541330

Harmathaz Kft. (1)
Harmat utca 129, 1100, Budapest, Hungary
Tel.: (36) 30 2225252
Web Site: http://www.harmathaz.hu
Construction Engineering Services
N.A.I.C.S.: 541330

Hoch-Tief-Bau Imst Gesellschaft m.b.H. (1)
Gewerbepark Pitztal 16 A, 6471, Arzl im Pitztal, Austria
Tel.: (43) 5412 63975 0
Web Site: http://www.htb-imst.at
Construction Engineering Services
N.A.I.C.S.: 541330

Ing. Karl Voitl Gesellschaft m.b.H. (1)
Enenkelstrasse 21/1, 1160, Vienna, Austria
Tel.: (43) 1 4931321
Construction Engineering Services
N.A.I.C.S.: 541330

Jos. Ertl GmbH (1)
Paschinger Strasse 1, 4063, Horsching, Austria
Tel.: (43) 7221 63 114 0
Web Site: http://www.josertl.at
Construction Engineering Services
N.A.I.C.S.: 541330

Kontinentale Baugesellschaft m.b.H. (1)
Brunner Strasse 43, 3830, Waidhofen an der Thaya, Austria
Tel.: (43) 2842 533 84
Web Site: http://www.kontibau.at
Roadway Construction Services
N.A.I.C.S.: 237310

MAVEPCELL Kft. (1)
Nagy Sandor ter 14, 9500, Celldomolk, Hungary
Tel.: (36) 95 420 026
Web Site: http://www.mavepcell.hu
Railway Construction Services
N.A.I.C.S.: 237310

RTS Rail Transport Service GmbH (1)
Puchstrasse 184 a, Graz, 8055, Austria
Tel.: (43) 31621613351
Web Site: http://www.rts-rail.com
Sales Range: $25-49.9 Million
Emp.: 25
Railway Engineering & Construction Services
N.A.I.C.S.: 488210
Rienhart Zeller *(Gen Mgr)*

Subsidiary (Non-US):

RTS Rail Transport Service Germany GmbH (2)

Landsberger Strasse 480, 81241, Munich, Germany
Tel.: (49) 898207523610
Web Site: http://www.rts-germany.com
Sales Range: $25-49.9 Million
Emp.: 15
Railway Engineering & Construction Services
N.A.I.C.S.: 488210

Romberger Fertigteile GmbH (1)
Rombergerstrasse 3, 4942, Gurten, Austria
Tel.: (43) 7757 7030 0
Web Site: http://www.romberger.at
Residential Building Construction Services
N.A.I.C.S.: 236115

S.C. DRUMSERV SA (1)
Str 8 Martie nr 66, Targu Mures, 540229, Romania
Tel.: (40) 265 252 315
Web Site: http://www.drumserv.ro
Emp.: 60
Roadway Construction Services
N.A.I.C.S.: 237310
Targu Cretu *(Exec Dir)*

SWIETELSKY Baugesellschaft mbH. (1)
Falkensteinstrasse 2, 83278, Traunstein, Germany
Tel.: (49) 861 98964 5022
Web Site: http://www.swietelsky.de
Construction Engineering Services
N.A.I.C.S.: 541330

SWIETELSKY Bautrager Ges.m.b.H. (1)
Wiedner Hauptstr 56/7, 1040, Vienna, Austria
Tel.: (43) 1 58021 1717
Construction Engineering Services
N.A.I.C.S.: 541330

SWIETELSKY Constructii SRL (1)
Strasse Constantin Balacescu 14 Sec 1, 10918, Bucharest, Romania
Tel.: (40) 21 4117820
Web Site: http://www.swietelsky.com
Emp.: 200
Construction Engineering Services
N.A.I.C.S.: 541330
Peter Kritsch *(Gen Mgr)*

SWIETELSKY Epito Kft. (1)
kulterulet 0425/9 hrsz, 4075, Gorbehaza, Hungary
Tel.: (36) 52 578 011
Construction Engineering Services
N.A.I.C.S.: 541330

SWIETELSKY Magyarorszag Kft. (1)
Irinyi u 4-20 B ep V em, 1117, Budapest, Hungary
Tel.: (36) 1 889 6300
Web Site: http://www.swietelsky.hu
Railway Construction Services
N.A.I.C.S.: 237310
Kun Edit *(Mgr-Site)*

SWIETELSKY RAIL (AUSTRALIA) PTY LTD (1)
Suite 513 55 Holt Street, Surry Hills, 2010, NSW, Australia
Tel.: (61) 29205 5336
Construction Engineering Services
N.A.I.C.S.: 541330

SWIETELSKY Rail Benelux B.V. (1)
Parklaan 13, 5061 JV, Oisterwijk, Netherlands
Tel.: (31) 13 5299800
Web Site: http://www.swietelsky-rail.nl
Railway Construction Services
N.A.I.C.S.: 237310

SWIETELSKY Rail Norway AS (1)
Hans Kiaersgate 1, 3401, Drammen, Norway
Tel.: (47) 90749096
Web Site: http://www.swietelsky-rail.no
Railway Construction Services
N.A.I.C.S.: 237310

SWIETELSKY Rail Polska Spolka Z o.o. (1)
ul Wielicka 250, 30-663, Krakow, Poland
Tel.: (48) 605 992 744
Construction Engineering Services
N.A.I.C.S.: 541330

SWIETELSKY Rail SRB d.o.o. (1)
Krunska 38, 11000, Belgrade, Serbia
Tel.: (381) 11 301 2460
Construction Engineering Services
N.A.I.C.S.: 541330

SWIETELSKY Slovakia spol. s.r.o. (1)
Mokran zahon 4, 821 04, Bratislava, Slovakia
Tel.: (421) 2 57 10 17 10
Web Site: http://www.swietelsky.sk
Emp.: 70
Construction Engineering Services
N.A.I.C.S.: 541330
Lucia Gilosikova *(CEO)*

SWIETELSKY gradbeno d.o.o. (1)
Linhartova cesta 11A, 1000, Ljubljana, Slovenia
Tel.: (386) 1 4341800
Construction Engineering Services
N.A.I.C.S.: 541330

SWIETELSKY stavebni s.r.o. (1)
Prazska tr 495/58, 370 04, Ceske Budejovice, Czech Republic
Tel.: (420) 387 002 711
Web Site: http://www.swietelsky.cz
Construction Engineering Services
N.A.I.C.S.: 541330

Swietelsky Construction Company Ltd. (1)
63 Castle Street, 47 57 Queens Road, Reading, RG1 7SN, Berks, United Kingdom
Tel.: (44) 1189503380
Web Site: http://www.swietelsky.at
Sales Range: $25-49.9 Million
Emp.: 50
Railway, Bridge & Tunnel Engineering & Construction Services
N.A.I.C.S.: 237310
Georg Skalla *(Mng Dir)*

Swietelsky Spolka Z.o.o (1)
Cisowa 9, 20703, Lublin, Poland
Tel.: (48) 817454250
Web Site: http://www.swietelsky.com
Sales Range: $25-49.9 Million
Emp.: 25
Bridge, Road & Tunnel Engineering & Construction Services
N.A.I.C.S.: 237310

Swietelsky d.o.o (1)
Nova Cesta 192, 10000, Zagreb, Croatia
Tel.: (385) 13689300
Web Site: http://www.swietelsky.hr
Sales Range: $25-49.9 Million
Emp.: 50
Road, Bridge & Tunnel Engineering & Construction Services
N.A.I.C.S.: 237310

Transportbeton und Asphaltgesellschaft m.b.H. (1)
Am Parges 3, 6511, Zams, Austria
Tel.: (43) 5442 64927
Web Site: http://www.tba-zams.at
Industrial Building Construction Services
N.A.I.C.S.: 236210

Wadle Bauunternehmung GmbH (1)
Oskar von Miller Strasse 8, 84051, Landshut, Germany
Tel.: (49) 870393980
Web Site: http://www.wadle.de
Sales Range: $25-49.9 Million
Emp.: 50
Bridge, Road & Tunnel Engineering & Construction
N.A.I.C.S.: 237310

SWIFT CRAFTED LTD
2 Epsom Downs Metro Centre, Waterfield, Tadworth, KT20 5LR, Surrey, United Kingdom
Tel.: (44) 1737362571
Web Site:
http://www.swiftcrafted.co.uk
Year Founded: 1987
Sales Range: $10-24.9 Million
Emp.: 48
Commercial & Residential Construction Services
N.A.I.C.S.: 236220

SWIFT CRAFTED LTD

Swift Crafted Ltd—(Continued)

Simon Hearle *(Mng Dir)*

SWIFT HAULAGE SDN. BHD.
Lot 3 Jalan Sultan Muhammad 5, Kawasan Perindustrian Sultan Sulaiman, 42000, Port Klang, Malaysia
Tel.: (60) 331760162
Web Site:
http://www.swiftlogistics.com.my
Freight Hauling Services
N.A.I.C.S.: 488510

SWIFT NETWORKS GROUP LIMITED
1060 Hay Street, West Perth, 6005, WA, Australia
Tel.: (61) 861037595　　AU
Web Site:
https://www.swiftnetworks.com.au
Year Founded: 1983
SW1—(ASX)
Rev.: $13,490,307
Assets: $11,090,600
Liabilities: $10,833,160
Net Worth: $257,440
Earnings: ($3,651,662)
Fiscal Year-end: 06/30/21
Telecommunication Servicesb
N.A.I.C.S.: 517810
Pippa Leary *(Board of Directors & CEO)*

Subsidiaries:

VOD Pty Ltd　　(1)
Unit 2A 87-89 Moore Street, Leichhardt, 2040, NSW, Australia
Tel.: (61) 295608426
Web Site: http://www.vod.net.au
Television Broadcasting Services
N.A.I.C.S.: 516120

SWIFT TRADE INC.
55 St Clair Ave W, Toronto, M4V 2Y7, ON, Canada
Tel.: (416) 351-0000
Web Site: http://www.swifttrade.com
Year Founded: 1997
Sales Range: $25-49.9 Million
Emp.: 100
Direct Access Electronic Trading
N.A.I.C.S.: 523999
Peter Beck *(Pres)*

SWIFT WORLDWIDE RESOURCES
Innova House Innova Business Park Kinetic Crescent, Enfield, EN3 7XH, Middlesex, United Kingdom
Tel.: (44) 1992 704 900
Web Site:
http://www.swiftworldwide.com
Year Founded: 1984
Sales Range: $500-549.9 Million
Emp.: 309
Human Resource Consulting Services
N.A.I.C.S.: 541612
Samuel Cross *(Mng Dir-North America)*

SWIFTAIR S.A.
C Ingeniero Torres Quevedo 14, 28022, Madrid, Spain
Tel.: (34) 917480760
Web Site: http://www.swiftair.com
Year Founded: 1986
Sales Range: $75-99.9 Million
Emp.: 350
Oil Transportation Services
N.A.I.C.S.: 481111
Neil Ferguson *(Chm)*

SWIFTMERGE ACQUISITION CORP.
100 Park Royal Executive Suite 200, West Vancouver, V7T 1A2, BC, Canada
Tel.: (604) 685-7303　　Ky
Web Site: https://www.swiftmerg.com
Year Founded: 2021
IVCP—(NASDAQ)
Assets: $230,768,608
Liabilities: $238,480,358
Net Worth: ($7,711,750)
Earnings: $1,059,800
Emp.: 4
Fiscal Year-end: 12/31/22
Investment Services
N.A.I.C.S.: 523999
George Jones *(Chm)*

SWIFTNET LIMITED
Olympia House Armitage Road, London, NW11 8RQ, United Kingdom
Tel.: (44) 3445450051　　UK
Web Site: http://www.swiftnet.co.uk
Year Founded: 1987
Sales Range: $10-24.9 Million
Emp.: 16
Telecommunication Servicesb
N.A.I.C.S.: 517111
Abraham Keinan *(Chm)*

SWINGER INTERNATIONAL SPA
Via Festara Vecchia 44, Bussolengo, 37012, Verona, Italy
Tel.: (39) 0456719811
Web Site: http://www.swinger.it
Sales Range: $50-74.9 Million
Emp.: 200
Men's & Women's Clothing & Accessories Including Shoes & Fragrances Mfr & Retailer
N.A.I.C.S.: 315990
Dino Facchini *(Pres)*

SWISS LIFE HOLDING
General-Guisan-Quai 40, PO Box 2831, 8022, Zurich, Switzerland
Tel.: (41) 432843311　　CH
Web Site: https://www.swisslife.com
Year Founded: 1857
SLHN—(SWX)
Rev.: $24,606,308,160
Assets: $269,004,658,860
Liabilities: $249,454,829,250
Net Worth: $19,549,829,610
Earnings: $1,190,225,970
Emp.: 9,823
Fiscal Year-end: 12/31/20
Individual & Group Life Insurance & Pension Services
N.A.I.C.S.: 524292
Rolf Dorig *(Chm)*

Subsidiaries:

ASN AG　　(1)
Tel.: (41) 43 399 8989
Web Site: https://www.asn-insurance.com
Sales Range: $75-99.9 Million
Emp.: 10
N.A.I.C.S.: 524128

AWD - Versicherungsmakler und -beratungs GmbH　　(1)
Swiss Life-Platz 1, 30659, Hannover, Germany
Tel.: (49) 51190200
General Insurance Services
N.A.I.C.S.: 524210

Actuaires et Associes SA　　(1)
Route de Chancy 59 - Building D 1st Floor, PO Box 564, 1213, Petit-Lancy, Switzerland
Tel.: (41) 228797877
Web Site: http://www.actuairesassocies.ch
Commercial Banking Services
N.A.I.C.S.: 522110

Adroit Private Equity AG　　(1)
Tel.: (41) 432843311
General Insurance Services
N.A.I.C.S.: 524210

Aker Drift AS　　(1)
Per Krohgs vei 4 C, Oslo, Norway
Tel.: (47) 22167080
Web Site: https://www.akerpdrift.no
Parking Services
N.A.I.C.S.: 812930

Aker Eiendomsdrift AS　　(1)
Haakon VII's Gate 1, Oslo, Norway
Tel.: (47) 22008181
Web Site: https://www.aker-eiendom.no
Real Estate Services
N.A.I.C.S.: 531390

BEOS AG　　(1)
Kurfurstendamm 188, 10707, Berlin, Germany
Tel.: (49) 302800990
Web Site: https://beos.net
Emp.: 250
Portfolio Management Services
N.A.I.C.S.: 523940
Holger Matheis *(Chm)*

BEREM Property Management GmbH　　(1)
Kurfurstendamm 188, 10707, Berlin, Germany
Tel.: (49) 308871669150
Web Site: https://berem.net
Portfolio Management Services
N.A.I.C.S.: 523940
Pekka Yla-Outinen *(Mng Dir)*

Bizztools GmbH　　(1)
Universitatsallee 17, 28359, Bremen, Germany
Tel.: (49) 421 8002 000
Web Site: http://www.bizztools.de
General Management Consulting Services
N.A.I.C.S.: 541611

CEGEMA S.A.　　(1)
679 Avenue du Docteur Julien Lefebvre, PO Box 679, 06272, Villeneuve-Loubet, France
Tel.: (33) 4 92 02 08 50
General Insurance Services
N.A.I.C.S.: 524210

CORPUS SIREO Projektentwicklung Wohnen GmbH　　(1)
Aachener Strasse 186, 50931, Cologne, Germany
Tel.: (49) 2212025871
Portfolio Management Services
N.A.I.C.S.: 523940

CORPUS SIREO Real Estate GmbH　　(1)
Aachener Strasse 186, 50931, Cologne, Germany
Tel.: (49) 221399000
Web Site: http://www.the-inbetween-frankfurt.de
Real Estate Services
N.A.I.C.S.: 531390

Financial Solutions AG Service & Vermittlung　　(1)
Berliner Str 85, Munich, 80805, Bavaria, Germany
Tel.: (49) 89381090
Financial Management Services
N.A.I.C.S.: 523999

Financiere du Patrimoine SAS　　(1)
50 Rue Leon Desoyer, 78100, Saint Germain-en-Laye, France
Tel.: (33) 13 904 0180
Web Site: https://www.financiere-de-patrimoine.fr
Portfolio Management Services
N.A.I.C.S.: 523940

Garantie Assistance S.A　　(1)
38 Rue La Bruyere, 75009, Paris, France
Tel.: (33) 1 53 21 24 33
General Insurance Services
N.A.I.C.S.: 524210

Horbach Wirtschaftsberatung GmbH　　(1)
Swiss-Life-Platz 1, 30659, Hannover, Germany
Tel.: (49) 51190207700
Web Site: https://www.horbach.de
Financial Advisory Services
N.A.I.C.S.: 523930
Thomas Uchtmann *(Co-CEO)*

INTERNATIONAL PUBLIC

La Suisse Assurances (France)　　(1)
41 Rue Du Chateau Dun, Blvd Usmenn, Paris, 75008, Cedex, France　　(100%)
Tel.: (33) 140823838
Web Site: http://www.swisslife.fr
N.A.I.C.S.: 524128

La Suisse Assurances IARD (France)　　(1)
7 St Belgrand, 92682, Levallois-Perret, France　　(98%)
Tel.: (33) 140823838
Web Site: http://www.lasuisse.com
Sales Range: $800-899.9 Million
Emp.: 2,500
N.A.I.C.S.: 524128

La Suisse Assurances-Vie (France)　　(1)
7 Rue Belgrand, 92300, Levallois-Perret, Cedex, France　　(100%)
Tel.: (33) 146173838
Web Site: http://www.swisslife.fr
Sales Range: $100-124.9 Million
N.A.I.C.S.: 524128

Livit AG　　(1)
Altstetterstrasse 124, 8048, Zurich, Switzerland　　(100%)
Tel.: (41) 583603333
Web Site: https://www.livit.ch
Sales Range: $75-99.9 Million
Emp.: 200
Real Estate Management
N.A.I.C.S.: 531390

Livit FM Services AG　　(1)
Altstetterstrasse 124, 8048, Zurich, Switzerland
Tel.: (41) 58 360 38 38
Web Site: http://www.livit-fm.ch
Sales Range: $75-99.9 Million
Real Estate Manangement Services
N.A.I.C.S.: 531390

MA Sante Facile S.A.　　(1)
3 rue du 127 Eme RI, 59300, Valenciennes, France
Tel.: (33) 327519999
Health Insurance Services
N.A.I.C.S.: 524114

Mayfair Capital Investment Management Limited　　(1)
55 Wells Street, London, W1T 3PT, United Kingdom　　(100%)
Tel.: (44) 2074951929
Web Site: https://uk.swisslife-am.com
Investment Fund Management Services
N.A.I.C.S.: 523999
Stefan Machler *(Exec Dir)*

Holding (Domestic):

Timeweave Limited　　(2)
9th Floor Winchester House 259-269 Old Marylebone Road, London, NW1 5RA, United Kingdom
Tel.: (44) 20 3869 0190
Web Site: http://www.timeweave.com
Holding Company
N.A.I.C.S.: 551112
David Craven *(CEO)*

Pensioen ESC　　(1)
Schottegatweg E 102, PO Box 3326, Willemstad, Curacao　　(100%)
Tel.: (599) 94617366
Web Site: http://www.pensioenesc.com
Sales Range: $25-49.9 Million
Emp.: 6
N.A.I.C.S.: 524128

Placement Direct SAS　　(1)
20 rue Bernadotte, 64000, Pau, France
Tel.: (33) 810 250 360
Online Retail Services
N.A.I.C.S.: 561311

SL Beteiligungs-GmbH & Co. Grundstucksverwaltung KG　　(1)
Tel.: (49) 89381090
Fire Insurance Services
N.A.I.C.S.: 524113

SLPM Schweizer Leben Pensions-Management GmbH　　(1)
Tel.: (49) 89381092000
Web Site: https://www.slpm.de

AND PRIVATE COMPANIES — SWISS LIFE HOLDING

Sales Range: $50-74.9 Million
Fire Insurance Services
N.A.I.C.S.: 524113
Thomas Hubner *(Mng Dir)*

Societe Suisse / Swiss Life (France) (1)
86 Blvd Haussmann, Paris, 75008, France
Tel.: (33) 140823714
Web Site: http://www.swisslife.fr
Sales Range: $75-99.9 Million
Emp.: 75
Individual & Group Life Insurance & Pension
N.A.I.C.S.: 524128
Charles Relecom *(Pres)*

Swiss Life (1)
General-Guisan-Quai 40, PO Box 8022, 8022, Zurich, Switzerland **(100%)**
Tel.: (41) 432843311
Web Site: https://www.swisslife.ch
Sales Range: $700-749.9 Million
Emp.: 2,500
Life Insurance
N.A.I.C.S.: 524113
Patrick Frost *(CEO)*

Swiss Life (Italia) (1)
Corso Di Porta Romana 2, 20122, Milan, Italy **(100%)**
Tel.: (39) 027256671
Sales Range: $50-74.9 Million
Emp.: 23
N.A.I.C.S.: 524128

Swiss Life (Italia) Infortuni E Malattie (1)
Corso Di Porta Romana 2, 20122, Milan, Italy **(100%)**
Tel.: (39) 027256671
N.A.I.C.S.: 524128

Swiss Life (Liechtenstein) AG (1)
Tel.: (423) 3777000
Web Site: https://www.swisslife.com
General Insurance Services
N.A.I.C.S.: 524210

Swiss Life (Liechtenstein) Services AG (1)
In der Specki 3, Schaan, 9494, Liechtenstein
Tel.: (423) 377 70 00
Web Site: http://www.swisslife.com
Emp.: 30
General Insurance Services
N.A.I.C.S.: 524210

Swiss Life (Luxembourg) S.A. (1) **(100%)**
Tel.: (352) 4239591
Sales Range: $75-99.9 Million
Emp.: 70
Insurance Services
N.A.I.C.S.: 524113

Swiss Life (Singapore) Pte. Ltd. (1)
250 North Bridge Road 37-03/04 Raffles City Tower, Singapore, 179101, Singapore
Tel.: (65) 65806680
Sales Range: $50-74.9 Million
Emp.: 30
Fire Insurance Services
N.A.I.C.S.: 524113
Nils Frowein *(Chm)*

Swiss Life Asset Management (France) (1)
86 Boulevard Haussmann, 75008, Paris, France
Tel.: (33) 1 58 36 55 00
Sales Range: $50-74.9 Million
Emp.: 35
Asset Management Services
N.A.I.C.S.: 523940

Joint Venture (Non-US):

Nortegas Energia Distribucion, S.A.U.
Plaza Euskadi 5- Planta 23, 48009, Bilbao, Spain
Tel.: (34) 944035700
Web Site: http://www.nortegas.es
Rev.: $109,384,982
Assets: $3,479,107,707
Liabilities: $2,243,707,972
Net Worth: $1,235,399,735
Earnings: $14,359,946
Emp.: 250
Fiscal Year-end: 12/31/2017
Natural Gas Distribution Services
N.A.I.C.S.: 221210
Alejandro Legarda Zaragueta *(Chm)*

Subsidiary (Domestic):

NED Espana Distribucion Gas, S.A.U. (3)
Calle General Concha 20, 48010, Bilbao, Spain
Tel.: (34) 946 140 020
Web Site: http://www.nortegas.es
Gas Distr
N.A.I.C.S.: 221210

Swiss Life Asset Management AG (1)
General-Guisan-Quai 40, 8022, Zurich, Switzerland
Tel.: (41) 432847709
Portfolio Management Services
N.A.I.C.S.: 523940
Michael Klose *(CEO-Third Party Asset Mgmt)*

Joint Venture (Non-US):

Brisa Auto-Estradas de Portugal, S.A. (2)
Quinta da Torre da Aguilha - Edificio Brisa, 2785-599, Sao Domingos de Rana, Portugal
Tel.: (351) 214448500
Web Site: http://www.brisa.pt
Rev.: $853,839,235
Earnings: $180,718,820
Emp.: 2,344
Fiscal Year-end: 12/31/2018
Highway & Street Construction Services
N.A.I.C.S.: 237310
Vasco De Mello *(Chm)*

Subsidiary (US):

BRISA NORTH AMERICA, INC (3)
1420 Peachtree St N E 220, Atlanta, GA 30309-3049
Tel.: (404) 835-8400
Road & Building Construction Services
N.A.I.C.S.: 237310

Subsidiary (Domestic):

BRISA O&M, S.A. (3)
Quinta Da Torre Da Agulha Edificio Brisa, Sao Domingos de Rana, 2785-599, Portugal
Tel.: (351) 214448500
Civil Engineering Construction Services
N.A.I.C.S.: 237310

Subsidiary (US):

BRISA UNITED STATES, LLC (3)
2755 Nothwoods Pkwy, Norcross, GA 30071
Tel.: (404) 835-8400
Sales Range: $25-49.9 Million
Emp.: 7
Highway & Street Construction Services
N.A.I.C.S.: 237310

Subsidiary (Domestic):

Brisa - Servicos Viarios, SGPS, S.A. (3)
Quinta da Torre Da Aguilha, Edificio Brisa Domingos De Ran, Cascais, 2785-599, Portugal
Tel.: (351) 214448500
Web Site: http://www.brisa.pt
Other Holding Companies Offices
N.A.I.C.S.: 551112

Brisa Assistencia Rodoviaria, S.A. (3)
Quinta Da Aguilha, Quinta Da Torre Da Aguilha, Cascais, 2785599S AO, Portugal
Tel.: (351) 214448500
Web Site: http://www.brisa.com
All Other Support Activities for Transportation
N.A.I.C.S.: 488999
Vasco Mello *(Pres)*

Brisa Internacional, SGPS, S.A. (3)
Edificio Brisa, Quinta Da Torre Da Aguilha, Cascais, Portugal
Tel.: (351) 214449100

Other Holding Companies Offices
N.A.I.C.S.: 551112

CONTROLAUTO - CONTROLO TECNICO AUTOMOVEL, S.A. (3)
Rua Alfredo Lopes Vilaverde 15-B Room 7, 2770-009, Paco d'Arcos, Portugal
Tel.: (351) 21 441 8376
Web Site: https://www.controlauto.pt
Emp.: 40
Automotive Control & Maintenance Services
N.A.I.C.S.: 811121
Zosa Enjra *(Gen Mgr)*

M. CALL, S.A. (3)
Taguspark Edificio Mcall Tecnologia III Corpo 2, 2740-257, Porto Salvo, Portugal
Tel.: (351) 707 50 30 40
Web Site: http://www.mcall.pt
Emp.: 80
Business Process Outsourcing Services
N.A.I.C.S.: 561499
Joel Pereira *(Mng Dir)*

Swiss Life Asset Management GmbH (1)
Zeppelinstrasse 1, Munich, 85748, Garching, Germany
Tel.: (49) 89381091313
Portfolio Management Services
N.A.I.C.S.: 523940

Swiss Life Asset Managers Deutschland GmbH (1)
Clever Strasse 36, 50668, Cologne, Germany
Tel.: (49) 221399000
Web Site: https://de.swisslife-am.com
Emp.: 59
Real Estate Asset Management Services
N.A.I.C.S.: 531390

Swiss Life Asset Managers France S.A.S (1)
Tour la Marseillaise 2 Bis Boulevard Euromediterranee, Quai d Arenc - CS 50575, 13236, Marseille, Cedex 2, France
Tel.: (33) 491166010
Web Site: https://fr.swisslife-am.com
Emp.: 280
Real Estate Asset & Security Services
N.A.I.C.S.: 531190

Swiss Life Asset Managers Luxembourg SA (1)
4a Rue Albert Borschette, 1246, Luxembourg, Luxembourg
Tel.: (352) 2675850
Web Site: https://lu.swisslife-am.com
Emp.: 90
Real Estate Asset Management Services
N.A.I.C.S.: 531390

Swiss Life Asset Managers Nordic AS (1)
Haakon VIIs gt 1, 0161, Oslo, Norway
Tel.: (47) 23116400
Web Site: https://no.swisslife-am.com
Asset Management Services
N.A.I.C.S.: 533110

Swiss Life Assurance Solutions S.A. (1)
23 Route d Arlon, 8009, Strassen, Luxembourg
Tel.: (352) 26 68 97 1
Web Site: http://www.swisslife-solutions.com
Emp.: 6
General Insurance Services
N.A.I.C.S.: 524210
Nicolas Golif *(Gen Mgr)*

Swiss Life Assurance et Patrimoine S.A. (1)
86 Boulevard Haussman, 75008, Paris, France
Tel.: (33) 1 40 82 38 38
Fire Insurance Services
N.A.I.C.S.: 524113

Swiss Life Assurances de Biens S.A. (1)
86 Blvd Hausseman, 75008, Paris, France
Tel.: (33) 1 40 82 30 00
Fire Insurance Services
N.A.I.C.S.: 524113

Swiss Life Banque Privee S.A. (1)
7 Place Vendome, 75001, Paris, France
Tel.: (33) 153291414

Web Site: https://banqueprivee.swisslife.fr
Sales Range: $100-124.9 Million
Emp.: 20
Commercial Banking Services
N.A.I.C.S.: 522110
Tanguy Polet *(Gen Mgr)*

Swiss Life Capital Holding AG (1)
Tel.: (41) 432843311
Emp.: 3,000
Investment Management Service
N.A.I.C.S.: 523999

Swiss Life Deutschland Holding GmbH (1) **(100%)**
Tel.: (49) 51190200
Web Site: http://www.swisslife.de
Sales Range: $75-99.9 Million
Emp.: 100
Insurance Services
N.A.I.C.S.: 524298
Jorg Arnold *(Co-CEO)*

Subsidiary (Domestic):

Swiss Life Beteiligungs GmbH (2)
Berliner Strasse 85, 80717, Munich, Germany
Tel.: (49) 89381090
Web Site: http://www.swisslife.de
Insurance Services
N.A.I.C.S.: 524298

Subsidiary (Domestic):

Swiss Life Deutschland Vertriebsholding AG (3)
AWD Platz 1, 30659, Hannover, Germany
Tel.: (49) 51190205430
Web Site: http://www.awd.de
Investment Advice & Financial Planning Services
N.A.I.C.S.: 523999
Bruno Pfister *(Chm-Supervisory Bd)*

Subsidiary (Domestic):

AWD Deutschland GmbH (4)
AWD-Platz 1, 30659, Hannover, Germany
Tel.: (49) 1801110000
Web Site: http://www.awd.de
Sales Range: $250-299.9 Million
Emp.: 600
Financial Advisory Services
N.A.I.C.S.: 523940

Subsidiary (Domestic):

Horbach Wirtschaftsberatung GmbH (5)
Swiss Life Place 1, 30659, Hannover, Germany
Tel.: (49) 90207700
Web Site: http://www.horbach.de
Sales Range: $125-149.9 Million
Financial Advisory Services
N.A.I.C.S.: 523940

tecis Finanzdienstleistungen AG (5)
Alter Teichweg 17, 22081, Hamburg, Germany
Tel.: (49) 4069696969
Web Site: https://www.tecis.de
Financial Advisory Services
N.A.I.C.S.: 523940

Holding (Non-US):

AWD Hungary (4)
Fehervari ut 50-52, 1117, Budapest, Hungary
Tel.: (36) 12482170
Web Site: http://www.awd.hu
Sales Range: $25-49.9 Million
Emp.: 100
Financial Advice Services
N.A.I.C.S.: 523940

AWD Romania (4)
Str T Vladimirescu Nr 56/A, Tirgu Mures, Romania
Tel.: (40) 265306462
Web Site: http://www.awd-romania.ro
Sales Range: $50-74.9 Million
Emp.: 10
Financial Advisory Services
N.A.I.C.S.: 523940

AWD Switzerland (4)
Zahlerweg 8, Zug, CH 6304, Switzerland

SWISS LIFE HOLDING

Swiss Life Holding—(Continued)
Tel.: (41) 417265100
Web Site: http://www.awd.ch
Sales Range: $150-199.9 Million
Emp.: 400
Financial Advisory Services
N.A.I.C.S.: 523940

AWD d.o.o. (4)
Petrovaradinska 1/VII kat, 10000, Zagreb, Croatia
Tel.: (385) 16312820
Financial Advisory Services
N.A.I.C.S.: 523940

AWD s.r.o. (4)
Stefanovicova 12, Bratislava, 811 04, Slovakia
Tel.: (421) 233002266
Fire Insurance Services
N.A.I.C.S.: 524113

AWD sp. z o.o. (4)
Jana Pawla II 27, 00- 67, Warsaw, Poland
Tel.: (48) 22 695 05 00
Web Site: http://www.awd.pl
Financial Advisory Services
N.A.I.C.S.: 523940

Chase de Vere IFA Group Plc (4)
60 New Broad Street, London, EC2M 1JJ, United Kingdom
Tel.: (44) 3456092002
Web Site: https://chasedevere.co.uk
Sales Range: $250-299.9 Million
Independent Financial Services
N.A.I.C.S.: 523999

Subsidiary (Domestic):

Chase de Vere Financial Solutions Limited (5)
4th Floor 20 Manvers Street, Bath, BA1 1JW, United Kingdom
Tel.: (44) 3453006256
Web Site: http://www.chasedevere.co.uk
Financial Advisory Services
N.A.I.C.S.: 523940

Subsidiary (Non-US):

Chase de Vere Independent Financial Advisers Ltd (5)
Tel.: (44) 3456092002
Web Site: https://www.chasedevere.co.uk
Sales Range: $100-124.9 Million
Emp.: 50
Financial Advisory Services
N.A.I.C.S.: 523940

Subsidiary (Non-US):

DEUTSCHE PROVENTUS AG (4)
Tel.: (49) 511123245050
Web Site: https://www.proventus.de
Financial Management Consulting Services
N.A.I.C.S.: 541618
Ivo Bergmann (Chm-)

Subsidiary (Domestic):

ProVentus Akademie- und Vertriebs GmbH (5)
Universitatsallee 15, 28359, Bremen, Germany
Tel.: (49) 421 20222 0
Financial Management Services
N.A.I.C.S.: 523999

Holding (Non-US):

Swiss Life Select Ceska republika s.r.o. (4)
Prazakova 1024/66a, 639 00, Brno, Czech Republic
Tel.: (420) 515 907 777
Web Site: http://www.swisslifeselect.cz
Sales Range: $25-49.9 Million
Emp.: 14
Financial Advisory Services
N.A.I.C.S.: 523940
Martin Valach (Mng Dir)

Subsidiary (Domestic):

Swiss Life Select Deutschland GmbH (4)
Swizz Life Platz 1, 30659, Hannover, Germany
Tel.: (49) 51190200

Web Site: https://www.swisslife-select-kundenportal.de
Business Management Consulting Services
N.A.I.C.S.: 541611
Stefan Kuehl (Co-CEO)

Swiss Life France S.A. (1)
86 Boulevard Haussmann, 75008, Paris, France
Tel.: (33) 1 40 82 38 38
Fire Insurance Services
N.A.I.C.S.: 524113

Swiss Life Fund Management (Lux) S.A. (1)
4a Rue Albert Borschette, 1246, Luxembourg, Luxembourg
Tel.: (352) 2675850
Portfolio Management Services
N.A.I.C.S.: 523940

Swiss Life Intellectual Property Management AG (1)
General-Guisan-Quai 40, Zurich, 8002, Switzerland
Tel.: (41) 432843311
Web Site: http://www.swisslife.com
Fire Insurance Services
N.A.I.C.S.: 524113

Swiss Life International Holding AG (1)
Tel.: (41) 432843311
Emp.: 3,000
Investment Management Service
N.A.I.C.S.: 523999

Swiss Life Invest GmbH (1)
Zeppelinstrasse 1, Munich, 85748, Garching, Germany
Tel.: (49) 89381092800
Portfolio Management Services
N.A.I.C.S.: 523940

Swiss Life Investment Management Holding AG (1)
Tel.: (41) 432843311
Investment Management Service
N.A.I.C.S.: 523999

Swiss Life Kapitalverwaltungsgesellschaft mbH (1)
Tel.: (49) 692648642123
Portfolio Management Services
N.A.I.C.S.: 523940
Robin van Berkel (Chm-)

Swiss Life Osterreich AG (1)
Land street Hauptstrasse 14, 1030, Vienna, Austria
Tel.: (43) 1 89 00 454 444
Web Site: http://www.swisslife.com
Emp.: 1
Fire Insurance Services
N.A.I.C.S.: 524113

Swiss Life Partner Service- und Finanzvermittlungs GmbH (1)
Tel.: (49) 89381091515
Portfolio Management Services
N.A.I.C.S.: 523940

Swiss Life Pension Services AG (1)
General-Guisan-Quai 40, 8022, Zurich, Switzerland
Tel.: (41) 800002525
Web Site: http://www.swisslife.ch
Pension Fund Management Services
N.A.I.C.S.: 523940

Swiss Life Pensionsfonds AG (1)
Tel.: (49) 89381090
Portfolio Management Services
N.A.I.C.S.: 523940
Daniel von Borries (Chm-)

Swiss Life Pensionskasse AG (1)
Tel.: (49) 89381090
Portfolio Management Services
N.A.I.C.S.: 523940
Daniel von Borries (Chm-)

Swiss Life Portfolio Management (1)
General-guisan-quai-40, 8022, Zurich, Switzerland (100%)
Tel.: (41) 432843311
Web Site: http://www.swisslife.ch
Sales Range: $800-899.9 Million
Emp.: 2,500
Direct Insurance Carrier
N.A.I.C.S.: 524128

Swiss Life Prevoyance et Sante S.A. (1)
86 Blvd Hausseman, 75008, Paris, France
Tel.: (33) 140823838
Fire Insurance Services
N.A.I.C.S.: 524113

Swiss Life Private Equity Partners AG (1)
General Guisan-Quai 40, 8002, Zurich, Switzerland
Tel.: (41) 432843311
Fire Insurance Services
N.A.I.C.S.: 524113

Swiss Life Private Placement (Middle East) Limited (1)
Level 7 Gate Precinct Bldg 6, Dubai, United Arab Emirates
Tel.: (971) 4 363 7746
Sales Range: $25-49.9 Million
Emp.: 5
Human Resource Consulting Services
N.A.I.C.S.: 541612

Swiss Life Property Management AG (1)
General-Guisan-Quai 40, 8022, Zurich, Switzerland
Tel.: (41) 432847709
Web Site: http://www.swisslife.ch
Real Estate Management Services
N.A.I.C.S.: 531390

Swiss Life Select Osterreich GmbH (1)
Wiedner Hauptstrasse 120-124 2nd Floor, 1050, Vienna, Austria
Tel.: (43) 1716990
Web Site: https://www.swisslife-select.at
Sales Range: $50-74.9 Million
Insurance Management Services
N.A.I.C.S.: 524298
Rolf Werner Aeberli (Chm-)

Swiss Life Select Schweiz AG (1)
Zahlerweg 8, CH-6302, Zug, Switzerland
Tel.: (41) 417265100
Web Site: https://www.swisslife-select.ch
Emp.: 140
Portfolio Management Services
N.A.I.C.S.: 523940

Swiss Life Select Slovensko, A.S. (1)
Green Point Offices Blok H Mlynske Nivy 49/II 16920, 821 09, Bratislava, Slovakia
Tel.: (421) 232118760
Web Site: https://www.swisslifeselect.sk
Insurance & Brokerage Services
N.A.I.C.S.: 524210

Swiss Life Service GmbH (1)
Zeppelinstrasse 1, 85748, Munich, Germany (100%)
Tel.: (49) 89381090
Web Site: http://www.swisslife.de
Fire Insurance Services
N.A.I.C.S.: 524113
Markus Leibundgut (CEO-Germany)

SwissFEX AG (1)
Hardturmstrasse 253, 8005, Zurich, Switzerland
Tel.: (41) 442752700
Web Site: https://www.swissfex.ch
Mortgage Services
N.A.I.C.S.: 522310

aXenta AG (1)
Tafernstrasse 5, CH-5405, Baden-Dattwil, Switzerland
Tel.: (41) 564830909
Web Site: https://www.axenta.ch
Emp.: 30
Insurance Services
N.A.I.C.S.: 524210

SWISS PRIME SITE AG

Poststrasse 4a, CH-6300, Zug, Switzerland
Tel.: (41) 583171717 CH
Web Site: https://www.sps.swiss
SPSN—(SWX)
Rev.: $782,716,904
Assets: $16,375,404,159
Liabilities: $8,605,755,920
Net Worth: $7,769,648,239

INTERNATIONAL PUBLIC

Earnings: $103,035,418
Emp.: 570
Fiscal Year-end: 12/31/23
Other Activities Related to Real Estate
N.A.I.C.S.: 531390
Peter Lehmann (CEO-Immobilien AG & Member-Exec Bd)

Subsidiaries:

Jelmoli Holding AG (1)
Bahnhofstrasse, 8021, Zurich, Switzerland
Tel.: (41) 442204411
Web Site: http://www.jelmoli.ch
Sales Range: $550-599.9 Million
Holding Company
N.A.I.C.S.: 551112

Subsidiary (Domestic):

Jelmoli AG (2)
Seidengasse 1, 8001, Zurich, Switzerland (100%)
Tel.: (41) 442204411
Web Site: https://www.jelmoli.ch
Sales Range: $100-124.9 Million
Emp.: 500
Department Stores
N.A.I.C.S.: 455110

Jelmoli Ltd (1)
Seidengasse 1, 8001, Zurich, Switzerland
Tel.: (41) 442204411
Web Site: http://www.jelmoli.ch
Retail Services
N.A.I.C.S.: 455110

Le Manoir AG (1)
Neuenburgstrasse 6, Gampelen, 3236, Bern, Switzerland
Tel.: (41) 323120200
Retirement Home Services
N.A.I.C.S.: 623312

Perlavita Rosenau AG (1)
Rosenbergstrasse 3, 9533, Kirchberg, Saint Gallen, Switzerland
Tel.: (41) 719323131
Retirement Home Services
N.A.I.C.S.: 623312

Residence Joli Automne SA (1)
Chemin des Crets 28, 1024, Ecublens, Switzerland
Tel.: (41) 216951515
Retirement Home Services
N.A.I.C.S.: 623312

Residence le Pacific SA (1)
Route Suisse 6a, 1163, Etoy, Switzerland
Tel.: (41) 218212828
Retirement Home Services
N.A.I.C.S.: 623312

SPS Beteiligungen Alpha AG (1)
C/o Swiss Prime Site Ag Froburgstrasse 1, Olten, 4601, Solothurn, Switzerland
Tel.: (41) 622130606
Web Site: http://www.swiss-prim-site.ch
Emp.: 35
Real Estate Manangement Services
N.A.I.C.S.: 531390

SPS Immobilien AG (1)
C/o Swiss Prime Site Ag Froburgstrasse 1, Olten, 4600, Solothurn, Switzerland
Tel.: (41) 622130606
Web Site: http://www.swiss-prime-site.ch
Sales Range: $50-74.9 Million
Emp.: 2
Real Estate Manangement Services
N.A.I.C.S.: 531190

SPS Immobilien Ltd (1)
Prime Tower Hardstrasse 201, 8005, Zurich, Switzerland
Tel.: (41) 583000000
Property Management Services
N.A.I.C.S.: 531312

Swiss Prime Site Immobilien AG (1)
Prime Tower Hardstrasse 201, 8005, Zurich, Switzerland
Tel.: (41) 583171717
Real Estate Services
N.A.I.C.S.: 531390

Swiss Prime Site Solutions AG (1)

AND PRIVATE COMPANIES — SWISS RE LTD.

Prime Tower Hardstrasse 201, 8005, Zurich, Switzerland
Tel.: (41) 583171717
Asset Management Services
N.A.I.C.S.: 523940
Anastasius Tschopp (CEO)

Tertianum AG (1)
Seminarstrasse 28, 8042, Zurich, Switzerland
Tel.: (41) 43 544 1515
Web Site: http://www.tertianum.ch
Sales Range: $25-49.9 Million
Emp.: 4,700
Senior Care Facilities Operator
N.A.I.C.S.: 623312
Luca Stager (CEO)

Tertianum Romandie Management SA (1)
Chemin des Lentillieres 24, 1023, Crissier, Switzerland
Tel.: (41) 218054900
Residential Property Services
N.A.I.C.S.: 531311
Yves Alin Romerio (Project Mgr)

Wohn- und Pflegezentrum Salmenpark AG (1)
Baslerstrasse 2, 4310, Rheinfelden, Switzerland
Tel.: (41) 615250100
Retirement Home Services
N.A.I.C.S.: 623312

SWISS PROPERTIES INVEST A/S
Schleppegrellsgade 8 kl, 2200, Copenhagen, Denmark
Tel.: (45) 52407152
Web Site: https://www.swisspropertyinvest.dk
Year Founded: 2021
SWISS—(CSE)
Rev.: $2,993,582
Assets: $97,629,258
Liabilities: $60,022,299
Net Worth: $37,606,959
Earnings: $1,969,978
Emp.: 6
Fiscal Year-end: 12/31/23
Real Estate Investment Services
N.A.I.C.S.: 531190
Christian Seidelin (Vice Chm)

SWISS RE LTD.
Mythenquai 50, 8022, Zurich, Switzerland
Tel.: (41) 432852121   CH
Web Site: https://www.swissre.com
Year Founded: 1863
SREN—(OTCIQ)
Rev.: $45,998,000,000
Assets: $170,676,000,000
Liabilities: $157,867,000,000
Net Worth: $12,809,000,000
Earnings: $472,000,000
Emp.: 14,408
Fiscal Year-end: 12/31/22
Holding Company; Reinsurance Products & Services
N.A.I.C.S.: 551112
Jonathan Isherwood (Pres-Americas & CEO-Reinsurance-Americas)

Subsidiaries:

Elips Life AG (1)
Gewerbeweg 15, Vaduz, Liechtenstein
Tel.: (423) 2399555
Web Site: https://www.elipslife.com
Insurance Services
N.A.I.C.S.: 524298

Lumico Life Insurance Company (1)
175 King St, Armonk, NY 10504
Web Site: https://lumico.com
Insurance Services
N.A.I.C.S.: 524298

Swiss Re Asia Pte. Ltd. (1)
Asia Square Tower 2 16-01 12 Marina View, Singapore, 018961, Singapore
Tel.: (65) 65322161
Insurance Services
N.A.I.C.S.: 524298

Swiss Re Brasil Resseguros S.A. (1)
Av Brigadeiro Faria Lima 3064 - 8o andar, Itaim Bibi, Sao Paulo, 01451-000, Brazil
Tel.: (55) 1130738000
Web Site: https://www.swissre.com
Insurance Services
N.A.I.C.S.: 524298

Swiss Re Corporate Solutions Brasil Seguros S.A (1)
Av Brigadeiro Faria Lima 3064 - 8o andar, Itaim Bibi, Sao Paulo, 01451-000, Brazil
Tel.: (55) 8000100123
Web Site: https://corporatesolutions.swissre.com
Insurance Services
N.A.I.C.S.: 524298

Swiss Re Corporate Solutions Insurance China Ltd. (1)
Unit 902 Tower 1 Century Link Building No 1198 Century Avenue, Pudong, Shanghai, 200122, China
Tel.: (86) 2160359188
Web Site: https://www.swissrecorpsolutions.com.cn
Insurance Services
N.A.I.C.S.: 524298

Swiss Re Finance (UK) Plc (1)
11th Floor 200 Aldersgate Street, London, EC1A 4HD, United Kingdom
Tel.: (44) 432852121
Insurance Services
N.A.I.C.S.: 524298

Swiss Re Global Business Solutions India Private Limited (1)
2nd to 5th Floors Fairwinds Building Off Intermediate Ring Road, Embassy Golf Links Business Park Challaghatta Village Varthur Hobli, Bengaluru, 560 071, Karnataka, India
Tel.: (91) 8046167000
Insurance Services
N.A.I.C.S.: 524298

Swiss Re Management Ltd. (1)
Soodring 6, 8134, Adliswil, Switzerland
Tel.: (41) 432852121
Insurance Services
N.A.I.C.S.: 524298

Swiss Reinsurance Company Ltd. (1)
Mythenquai 50, 8002, Zurich, 8022, Switzerland
Tel.: (41) 432852121
Web Site: http://www.swissre.com
Reinsurance Products & Services
N.A.I.C.S.: 524130
Justin Excell (Mng Dir & Head-Internal Investments & Asset Mgmt)

Subsidiary (Non-US):

Algemene Levensherverzekering Maatschappij NV (2)
Prof J H Bavincklaan 2, 1183 AT, Amstelveen, Netherlands
Tel.: (31) 205453000
General Insurance Services
N.A.I.C.S.: 524210

Compania Suiza de Reaseguros Oficina de Representacione (2)
13th Floor Avenida de Chile Torre B Carrera 7 No 71-21, Bogota, Cundinamarca, Colombia (100%)
Tel.: (57) 13251101
Web Site: http://www.swissre.com
Sales Range: $50-74.9 Million
Emp.: 23
Insurance Services
N.A.I.C.S.: 524298

European Finance Reinsurance Company Ltd. (2)
Carleton Court High Street, Bridgetown, Barbados (100%)
Tel.: (246) 4296019
Web Site: http://www.swissre.com
Sales Range: $75-99.9 Million
Emp.: 5
N.A.I.C.S.: 524298

European International Reinsurance Company Ltd. (2)
Carleton Court High Street, Bridgetown, Barbados (100%)
Tel.: (246) 4296019
Sales Range: $75-99.9 Million
Emp.: 5
N.A.I.C.S.: 524298
Adrien Deana (Pres & CFO)

NM Life Group Limited (2)
The Priory Tilehouse Street, Hitchin, SG5 2DX, Hertfordshire, United Kingdom
Tel.: (44) 2079333000
Fire Insurance Services
N.A.I.C.S.: 524113

Subsidiary (Domestic):

Reinsurance Finance Consultants Ltd. (2)
Mythenquai 50/60, Zurich, 8022, Switzerland (50%)
Tel.: (41) 432852121
Web Site: http://www.swissre.com
Emp.: 2,000
Reinsurance Financial Consulting Services
N.A.I.C.S.: 541618

Affiliate (Non-US):

SR Risk Management Services Limited (2)
Asia Square Tower 2 16-01 12 Marina View, Singapore, 018961, Singapore (49%)
Tel.: (65) 64281800
Web Site: http://www.swissre.com
Sales Range: $75-99.9 Million
Emp.: 200
Insurance Services
N.A.I.C.S.: 524298

Subsidiary (Non-US):

Suisse de Reassurances (France) (2)
11-15 Rue Saint-Georges, 75009, Paris, France (100%)
Tel.: (33) 143183360
Web Site: http://www.swissre.com
Sales Range: $50-74.9 Million
Emp.: 50
N.A.I.C.S.: 524298

Suiza Re Mexico, S.A. de C.V. (2)
Insurgentes Sur 1898 piso 8, 01030, Mexico, Mexico (100%)
Tel.: (52) 5553228400
Web Site: http://www.swissre.com
Sales Range: $75-99.9 Million
Emp.: 100
Insurance Activities
N.A.I.C.S.: 524298

Suiza de Reseguros Venezuela C.A. (2)
Paseo Enrique Eraso Torre La Noria Piso 8, Urb Las Mercedes, Caracas, 1060, Venezuela
Tel.: (58) 2129925422
Web Site: http://www.swissre.com
Insurance
N.A.I.C.S.: 524298

Swiss Re (Israel) Ltd. (2)
12 Abba Hillel Silver Street, Ramat-Gan, Tel Aviv, 5250606, Israel (100%)
Tel.: (972) 37140130
Web Site: http://www.swissre.com
Sales Range: $75-99.9 Million
Emp.: 12
Insurance
N.A.I.C.S.: 524298

Subsidiary (US):

Swiss Re America Holding Corp. (2)
175 King St, Armonk, NY 10504-1606 (100%)
Tel.: (914) 828-8000
Web Site: http://www.swissre.com
Sales Range: $1-4.9 Billion
Emp.: 1,000
Fire, Marine & Casualty Insurance
N.A.I.C.S.: 524126

Subsidiary (Domestic):

Swiss Re Atrium Corporation (3)
55 E 52 St, New York, NY 10055 (100%)
Tel.: (212) 317-5400
Web Site: http://www.swissre.com
Sales Range: $150-199.9 Million
Emp.: 500
Provider of Reinsurance Services
N.A.I.C.S.: 524210

Swiss Re Capital Markets Corporation (3)
55 E 52nd St Park Ave Plz, New York, NY 10055 (100%)
Tel.: (212) 317-5400
Web Site: http://www.src.com
Sales Range: $350-399.9 Million
Emp.: 600
Provider of Financial Services
N.A.I.C.S.: 523150
Jamshid Ehsani (Mng Dir & Head-Life Assets)

Swiss Re Financial Products Corporation (3)
Park Ave Plz 55 E 52nd St, New York, NY 10055 (100%)
Tel.: (212) 317-5400
Web Site: http://www.swissre.com
Sales Range: $75-99.9 Million
Emp.: 400
Provider of Financial Services
N.A.I.C.S.: 541618

Swiss Re Solutions Holding Corporation (3)
5200 Metcalf Ave, Overland Park, KS 66202
Tel.: (913) 676-5200
Web Site: http://www.swissre.com
Emp.: 450
Investment Management Service
N.A.I.C.S.: 523999
Michael Mann (Office Mgr)

Swiss Re Treasury (US) Corporation (3)
175 King St, Armonk, NY 10504
Tel.: (914) 828-8000
Web Site: http://www.swissre.com
Emp.: 900
Financial Management Services
N.A.I.C.S.: 523999

Swiss Reinsurance (3)
22th Fl Ste 2200 100 Pine St, San Francisco, CA 94111
Tel.: (415) 834-2200
Web Site: http://www.swissre.com
Sales Range: $50-74.9 Million
Emp.: 15
Reinsurance Services
N.A.I.C.S.: 524130

Division (Domestic):

Swiss Reinsurance America (3)
175 King St, Armonk, NY 10504
Tel.: (914) 828-8000
Web Site: http://www.swissre.com
Sales Range: $350-399.9 Million
Emp.: 1,000
Reinsurance Products & Services
N.A.I.C.S.: 524130
Keith Wolfe (Pres)

Subsidiary (Domestic):

European Reinsurance Corporation of America (4)
55 E 52nd St, New York, NY 10055 (100%)
Tel.: (212) 317-5400
Web Site: http://www.swissre.com
N.A.I.C.S.: 524298

North American Specialty Insurance Company (4)
650 Elm St, Manchester, NH 03101-2596 (100%)
Tel.: (603) 644-6600
Sales Range: $50-74.9 Million
Emp.: 60
N.A.I.C.S.: 524298

Subsidiary (Domestic):

North American Capacity Insurance Company (5)
650 Elm St, Manchester, NH 03101-2596
Tel.: (603) 644-6600
Sales Range: $125-149.9 Million
Specialty Reinsurance
N.A.I.C.S.: 524130

SWISS RE LTD.

Swiss Re Ltd.—(Continued)
Robert Solitro *(Pres)*

Subsidiary (Domestic):

Sterling Re Inc. (4)
509E Hillside Dr Ste 101, Bloomington, IN 47401
Tel.: (812) 333-1966
Web Site: https://sterlingbloomington.com
Real Estate Manangement Services
N.A.I.C.S.: 531390
Trish Sterling *(Gen Mgr)*

Swiss Re Corporate Solutions Premier Insurance Corporation (4)
1450 American Ln, Schaumburg, IL 60173
Tel.: (847) 273-1300
Web Site: http://www.nassurety.com
Sales Range: $25-49.9 Million
Emp.: 50
Insurance Agents, Nec
N.A.I.C.S.: 524126

Swiss Re Life & Health America Holding Company (4)
175 King St, Armonk, NY 10504-1606
Tel.: (914) 828-8000
Web Site: http://www.swissre.com
Sales Range: $25-49.9 Million
Emp.: 60
Holding Company for Insurance Companies
N.A.I.C.S.: 524126

Subsidiary (Domestic):

Swiss Re Life & Health America, Inc. (5)
175 King St, Armonk, NY 10504-1613 (100%)
Tel.: (914) 828-8000
Web Site: http://www.swissre.com
Provider of Insurance Services
N.A.I.C.S.: 524126

Branch (Domestic):

Swiss Reinsurance America (4)
550 52nd St, New York, NY 10006
Tel.: (212) 577-4000
Web Site: http://www.swissre.com
Sales Range: $50-74.9 Million
Emp.: 30
Insurance Services
N.A.I.C.S.: 524298

Swiss Reinsurance America (4)
227 W Monroe St Ste 3850, Chicago, IL 60606-5085 (100%)
Tel.: (312) 553-4220
Sales Range: $25-49.9 Million
Emp.: 24
Insurance Agents Brokers & Service
N.A.I.C.S.: 524126
William Samson *(Branch Mgr)*

Swiss Reinsurance America (4)
1150 Sanctuary Park Ste-425, Alpharetta, GA 30009
Tel.: (770) 569-7100
Sales Range: $25-49.9 Million
Emp.: 40
Insurance Company
N.A.I.C.S.: 524126
Marilea Welhouse *(Sr VP)*

Swiss Reinsurance America (4)
12750 Merit Dr Ste 500, Dallas, TX 75251 (100%)
Tel.: (972) 776-8500
Web Site: http://www.swissre.com
Sales Range: $50-74.9 Million
Emp.: 9
Reinsurance Company
N.A.I.C.S.: 524126

Subsidiary (Domestic):

Swiss-Am Reassurance Company (4)
55 E 52nd St, New York, NY 10055 (100%)
Tel.: (212) 317-5400
Provider of Reinsurance Services
N.A.I.C.S.: 523940

Subsidiary (Non-US):

Swiss Re Australia Ltd. (2)
200 Barangaroo Avenue, International Towers Sydney Tower Two Level 36 Barangaroo, Sydney, 2000, NSW, Australia (100%)
Tel.: (61) 282959500
Web Site: http://www.swissre.com
Sales Range: $75-99.9 Million
Emp.: 100
N.A.I.C.S.: 524298
Michael Renny *(Mgr-Client)*

Swiss Re Brasil Servicos e Participacoes Ltda (2)
Alameda Santos 1940 10 Andar, Conjunto 102, 01418 200, Sao Paulo, SP, Brazil (100%)
Tel.: (55) 1133716570
Web Site: http://www.swissre.com
Sales Range: $50-74.9 Million
Emp.: 30
Insurance Services
N.A.I.C.S.: 524298

Swiss Re Capital Markets Limited (2)
30 Saint Mary Axe, London, EC3A 8EP, United Kingdom
Tel.: (44) 2079334184
Investment Management Service
N.A.I.C.S.: 523999

Swiss Re Denmark Services A/S (2)
Midtermolen 3 4th Floor, 2100, Copenhagen, Denmark
Tel.: (45) 33979593
Web Site: http://www.swissre.com
Emp.: 23
General Insurance Services
N.A.I.C.S.: 524210

Swiss Re Europe S.A. (2)
Prof JH Bavincklaan 2, 1183 AT, Amstelveen, Netherlands (100%)
Tel.: (31) 205453000
Sales Range: $50-74.9 Million
Emp.: 100
Insurance Services
N.A.I.C.S.: 524298

Swiss Re Europe, S.A. (2)
Paseo de la Castellana 95, Torre Europa, 28046, Madrid, Spain (100%)
Tel.: (34) 915981726
Web Site: http://www.swissre.com
Sales Range: $50-74.9 Million
Emp.: 50
Insurance Services
N.A.I.C.S.: 524298

Swiss Re Holdings (Canada) Inc. (2)
150 King Street W Suite 2200, Toronto, M5H 1J9, ON, Canada
Tel.: (416) 408-0272
Web Site: http://www.swissre.com
Emp.: 150
Investment Management Service
N.A.I.C.S.: 523999

Subsidiary (Domestic):

Swiss Reinsurance Company Canada (3)
150 King Street West, Toronto, M5H 1J9, ON, Canada (100%)
Tel.: (416) 408-0272
Web Site: http://www.swissre.com
Sales Range: $125-149.9 Million
Emp.: 150
N.A.I.C.S.: 524298
Monica Ningen *(Head-Canada & English Caribbean)*

Subsidiary (Non-US):

Swiss Re International SE (2)
2A rue Albert Borschette, Luxembourg, 1246, Luxembourg
Tel.: (352) 26 12 16
Holding Company
N.A.I.C.S.: 551112

Subsidiary (Domestic):

Swiss Re Europe Holdings S.A. (3)
2 A Rue Albert Borschette, 1246, Luxembourg, Luxembourg (100%)
Tel.: (352) 26121630
Web Site: http://www.swissre.com
Emp.: 30
Investment Management Service
N.A.I.C.S.: 523999

Swiss Re Finance (Luxembourg) S.A. (3)
Rue Mathias Hardt 8-10, 1717, Luxembourg, Luxembourg
Tel.: (352) 26 12 16
Financial Management Services
N.A.I.C.S.: 523999

Subsidiary (Non-US):

Swiss Re Italia S.p.A. (2)
Via di San Basilio 72, 00187, Rome, Italy (100%)
Tel.: (39) 06323931
Web Site: http://www.swissre.com
Sales Range: $100-124.9 Million
Emp.: 160
Insurance Services
N.A.I.C.S.: 524298

Swiss Re Life & Health Africa Ltd (2)
2nd Floor Beechwood House The Boulevard, Searle Street, 7925, Cape Town, South Africa
Tel.: (27) 214698403
Web Site: http://www.swissre.com
Sales Range: $25-49.9 Million
Emp.: 42
Insurance Products & Financial Services
N.A.I.C.S.: 524298

Swiss Re Life & Health Australia Limited (2)
Level 36 Tower Two International Towers Sydney 200 Barangaroo Avenue, Sydney, 2000, NSW, Australia
Tel.: (61) 282959500
Sales Range: $75-99.9 Million
Emp.: 14
Fire Insurance Services
N.A.I.C.S.: 524113
Rodney Hanratty *(Mgr-HR)*

Swiss Re Treasury (Hungary) Group Financing Limited Liability Company (2)
Andrassy ut 100, Budapest, 1062, Hungary
Tel.: (36) 1 8873789
Financial Management Services
N.A.I.C.S.: 523999

Swiss Reinsurance Company (2)
14 Fitzwilliam Sq, Dublin, 2, Ireland (100%)
Tel.: (353) 16764459
Web Site: http://www.swissre.com
Sales Range: $50-74.9 Million
Emp.: 13
Insurance
N.A.I.C.S.: 524298

Swiss Reinsurance Company (2)
1 Raffles Place Level 47-00, Singapore, 048616, Singapore (100%)
Tel.: (65) 65322161
Web Site: http://www.swissre.com
Sales Range: $50-74.9 Million
Emp.: 80
Insurance Agents
N.A.I.C.S.: 524298

Swiss Reinsurance Company UK Ltd. (2)
30 Saint Mary Axe, London, EC3A 8EP, United Kingdom (100%)
Tel.: (44) 2079333000
Web Site: http://www.swissre.com
Sales Range: $900-999.9 Million
Emp.: 1,200
N.A.I.C.S.: 524298

Subsidiary (Domestic):

SR International Business Insurance Company Ltd. (3)
30 Saint Mary Axe, London, EC3A 8EP, United Kingdom (100%)
Tel.: (44) 2076233456
Web Site: http://www.swissre.com
N.A.I.C.S.: 524298

Subsidiary (Non-US):

SwissRe Advisers Tallinn (2)
Lai Tanav 27, EE0001, Tallinn, Estonia (100%)
Tel.: (372) 498938441354
Web Site: http://www.swissre.com
N.A.I.C.S.: 524298

INTERNATIONAL PUBLIC

SwissRe Finance (Bermuda) Ltd. (2)
Mintflower Place, PO Box HM1767, 8 Par-la-ville Road, Hamilton, HM 08, Bermuda (100%)
Tel.: (441) 2958907
N.A.I.C.S.: 524298

elipsLife EMEA Holding B.V. (1)
Capellalaan 65, 2132 JL, Hoofddorp, Netherlands
Tel.: (31) 207559800
Insurance Services
N.A.I.C.S.: 524298

iptiQ Group Holding Ltd. (1)
Mythenquai 50, 8002, Zurich, Switzerland
Tel.: (41) 432852121
Web Site: https://www.iptiq.com
Insurance Services
N.A.I.C.S.: 524298

SWISS STEEL HOLDING AG

Landenbergstrasse 11, CH-6005, Lucerne, Switzerland
Tel.: (41) 415814000
Year Founded: 1919
STLN—(SWX)
Rev.: $4,372,328,945
Assets: $2,575,005,396
Liabilities: $2,002,050,507
Net Worth: $572,954,889
Earnings: $10,144,615
Emp.: 9,857
Fiscal Year-end: 12/31/22
Specialty Steel Long Products Mfr
N.A.I.C.S.: 331110

Subsidiaries:

A. Finkl & Sons Co. (1)
2011 N Southport Ave, Chicago, IL 60614-4015
Tel.: (773) 975-2510
Web Site: http://www.finkl.com
Rev.: $100,000,000
Emp.: 340
Steel Ingots, Forgings, Die Blocks & Hot Works, Forged Rolls & Open Die Forgings Mfr
N.A.I.C.S.: 331110
Joseph E. Curci *(Pres)*

Subsidiary (Domestic):

Composite Forgings Limited Partnership (2)
2300 W Jefferson Ave, Detroit, MI 48216 (100%)
Tel.: (313) 496-1226
Web Site: https://www.compforge.com
Sales Range: $1-9.9 Million
Emp.: 45
Iron And Steel Forgings, Nsk
N.A.I.C.S.: 332111
Albert Jenkins *(Gen Mgr)*

Subsidiary (Non-US):

Sorel Forge Co. (2)
100 McCarthy, Saint-Joseph-de-Sorel, J3R 3M8, QC, Canada (100%)
Tel.: (450) 746-4030
Web Site: http://www.sorelforge.com
Sales Range: $50-74.9 Million
Emp.: 300
Tool & Die Steel & Custom Forgings
N.A.I.C.S.: 333514
Richard LaHaye *(Pres)*

Asco Industries SAS (1)
Avenue de France, 57300, Hagondange, France
Tel.: (33) 450984188
Web Site: http://www.ascometal.com
Steel Mills & Machine Shops Operator
N.A.I.C.S.: 331110
Pierre Frentzel *(Pres & CEO)*

Boxholm Stal AB (1)
Nordenstens vag 2, Boxholm, 59012, Sweden (100%)
Tel.: (46) 14255100
Web Site: http://www.bxs.se
Sales Range: $25-49.9 Million
Emp.: 65
Steel Processing
N.A.I.C.S.: 331513

AND PRIVATE COMPANIES

Mikael Nissle *(CEO, Mgr-Pur-Steel & Market Comm & Head-Sls)*

DEUTSCHE EDELSTAHLWERKE GmbH (1)
Auestrasse 4, 58452, Witten, Germany
Tel.: (49) 2302290
Web Site: http://www.dew-stahl.com
Sales Range: $200-249.9 Million
Emp.: 1,000
Steel Mfrs
N.A.I.C.S.: 331513
Oliver Bell *(Gen Mgr)*

Dr. William Mertens GmbH (1)
52 Birkbuschstrasse, 12167, Berlin, Germany
Tel.: (49) 307799080
Web Site: http://www.mertens-stahl.de
Sales Range: $25-49.9 Million
Emp.: 25
Steel Product Distr
N.A.I.C.S.: 331513
Heiner Melles *(Mng Dir)*

Schmolz + Bickenbach Distributions GmbH (1)
Eupener Str 70, Dusseldorf, 40549, Germany
Tel.: (49) 2115090
Web Site: http://www.schmolz-bickenbach.de
Sales Range: $200-249.9 Million
Emp.: 900
Specialty Steel Long Products Mfr
N.A.I.C.S.: 331110
Clemens Iller *(CEO)*

Schmolz + Bickenbach USA Inc. (1)
365 Village Dr, Carol Stream, IL 60188-1828
Tel.: (630) 682-3900
Web Site: http://www.schmolz-bickenbach.us
Sales Range: $75-99.9 Million
Emp.: 60
Steel Supplier
N.A.I.C.S.: 423510
John Stocker *(Dir-Sls)*

Steeltec AG (1)
Emmenweidstrasse 90, CH-6020, Emmenbrucke, Switzerland (100%)
Tel.: (41) 412095151
Web Site: https://www.steeltec.ch
Sales Range: $100-124.9 Million
Emp.: 260
Steel Processing
N.A.I.C.S.: 331513
Dirk Ochmann *(Head-Sls)*

Swiss Steel AG (1)
Emmenweidstrasse 90, 6020, Emmenbrucke, Switzerland
Tel.: (41) 412095151
Web Site: https://www.swiss-steel.com
Sales Range: $200-249.9 Million
Emp.: 750
Steel Mfrs
N.A.I.C.S.: 331513
Carlo Mischler *(Dir-Sls)*

Ugitech S.A. (1)
Avenue Paul Girod, CS90100, Ugine, France
Tel.: (33) 479893030
Web Site: https://www.ugitech.com
Rev.: $676,093,600
Emp.: 2,800
Stainless Steel & Alloy Long Products Mfr
N.A.I.C.S.: 332111
Patrick Lamarque d'Arrouzat *(CEO)*

SWISS WATER DECAFFEINATED COFFEE COMPANY, INC.
3131 Lake City Way, Burnaby, V5A 3A3, BC, Canada
Tel.: (604) 420-4050
Web Site: http://www.swisswater.com
Food & Beverage Services
N.A.I.C.S.: 722110
Iain Carswell *(CFO)*

SWISS WATER DECAFFEINATED COFFEE INC.
7750 Beedie Way, Delta, V4G 0A5, BC, Canada
Tel.: (604) 420-4050 BC
Web Site: https://www.swisswater.com
SWP—(TSX)
Rev.: $97,844,453
Assets: $131,614,699
Liabilities: $88,123,842
Net Worth: $43,490,857
Earnings: $388,011
Emp.: 86
Fiscal Year-end: 12/31/21
Decaffeinated Coffee Processing
N.A.I.C.S.: 311920
Frank Dennis *(Pres & CEO)*

Subsidiaries:

Seaforth Supply Chain Solutions Inc. (1)
7167 Progress Way, Delta, V4G 1K8, BC, Canada
Tel.: (604) 420-0065
Web Site: https://www.seaforthscs.ca
Coffee Product Warehousing Services
N.A.I.C.S.: 493110
Suzanne DeSilva *(Coord-Inbound Logistics)*

SWISSBIT AG
Industriestrasse 4, Bronschhofen, 9552, Switzerland
Tel.: (41) 71 913 03 03
Web Site: http://www.swissbit.com
Year Founded: 2001
Storage & Security products Mfr
N.A.I.C.S.: 561621
Silvio Muschter *(CEO)*

Subsidiaries:

Hyperstone GmbH (1)
Line-Eid-Strasse 3, 78467, Konstanz, Germany
Tel.: (49) 753198030
Web Site: http://www.hyperstone.com
Sales Range: $25-49.9 Million
Emp.: 36
Semiconductor & Microprocessor Design Services
N.A.I.C.S.: 334413

Subsidiary (Non-US):

Hyperstone Asia Pacific Ltd. (2)
3F No 501 Sec 2 Tiding Blvd, Neihu District, Taipei, 114, Taiwan
Tel.: (886) 287510203
Web Site: http://www.hyperstone.com
Sales Range: $25-49.9 Million
Emp.: 14
Semiconductor & Microprocessor Design & Mfr
N.A.I.C.S.: 334413

Subsidiary (US):

Hyperstone Inc. (2)
486 N Patterson Ave Ste 301, Winston Salem, NC 27101
Tel.: (336) 744-0724
Web Site: http://www.hyperstone.com
Sales Range: $25-49.9 Million
Emp.: 20
Electronic Design Services
N.A.I.C.S.: 334413

SWISSCO HOLDINGS LIMITED
21 Tuas Road, Singapore, 638489, Singapore
Tel.: (65) 62652855
Web Site: http://www.swissco.net
Sales Range: $50-74.9 Million
Holding Company; Ship Chartering, Repairing & Marine Logistics Services
N.A.I.C.S.: 551112
Fuh Gih Tan *(CEO)*

Subsidiaries:

Scott & English Energy Pte. Ltd. (1)
6 3rd Lok Yang Road, Singapore, 628001, Singapore
Tel.: (65) 6265 5388

Web Site: http://www.sneenergy.com
Generator Mfr
N.A.I.C.S.: 335312
Tan Fuh Gih *(Chm)*

SWISSCOM AG
Alte Tiefenaustrasse 6, Worblaufen, CH-3050, Bern, Switzerland
Tel.: (41) 582219911 CH
Web Site: https://www.swisscom.ch
Year Founded: 1998
SCMN—(OTCIQ)
Rev.: $12,274,944,568
Assets: $27,439,024,390
Liabilities: $14,554,323,725
Net Worth: $12,884,700,665
Earnings: $1,896,895,787
Emp.: 19,729
Fiscal Year-end: 12/31/23
Telecommunication Servicesb
N.A.I.C.S.: 517111
Mario Rossi *(Member-Exec Bd)*

Subsidiaries:

7Layers S.R.L. (1)
Via Tosco Romagnola Sud 1, FL, 50056, Montelupo Fno, Italy
Tel.: (39) 05711738106
Web Site: https://7layers.it
Cyber Security Services
N.A.I.C.S.: 561621

AdUnit Ltd. (1)
Seestrasse 39, 8700, Kusnacht, Switzerland
Tel.: (41) 438182424
Web Site: https://www.adunit.ch
Emp.: 13
Programmatic Advertising Services
N.A.I.C.S.: 541810

Ajila Ltd. (1)
Centralstrasse 8b, 6210, Sursee, Switzerland
Tel.: (41) 419219790
Web Site: https://www.ajila.com
Emp.: 60
Software Development Services
N.A.I.C.S.: 541511

Audio-Video G+M Ltd. (1)
Walenbuchelstrasse 1, 9000, Saint Gallen, Switzerland
Tel.: (41) 712740505
Web Site: https://www.audiovideo-sa.ch
Emp.: 35
Video Surveillance System Distr
N.A.I.C.S.: 423690

Axept Business Software Ltd. (1)
Kemptpark 12, 8310, Kemptthal, Switzerland
Tel.: (41) 588719595
Web Site: https://www.axept.ch
Emp.: 180
Software Development Services
N.A.I.C.S.: 541511

Billag AG (1)
Avenue De Tivoli 3, 1701, Fribourg, Switzerland
Tel.: (41) 844 834 834
Web Site: http://www.billag.com
Collection Agency Services
N.A.I.C.S.: 561440
Ewout Kea *(CEO)*

Blue Entertainment Ltd. (1)
Machinenstrasse 10, 8005, Zurich, Switzerland
Tel.: (41) 582219510
Web Site: https://www.blueplus.ch
Video Streaming Services
N.A.I.C.S.: 512120

Cablex Ltd. (1)
Tannackerstrasse 7, 3073, Gumligen, Switzerland
Tel.: (41) 800222444
Web Site: https://www.cablex.ch
Network Construction Services
N.A.I.C.S.: 541512

Curabill Ltd (1)
Hardturmstrasse 3, 8005, Zurich, Switzerland
Tel.: (41) 58 822 22 00

Health Care Management Services
N.A.I.C.S.: 621999

Easypsim Ltd. (1)
Scharenmoosstrasse 77, 8052, Zurich, Switzerland
Tel.: (41) 433888371
Web Site: https://easypsim.com
Software Development Services
N.A.I.C.S.: 541511

FastWeb S.p.A. (1)
Via Caracciolo 51, 20155, Milan, Italy
Tel.: (39) 0642986411
Web Site: https://www.fastweb.it
Sales Range: $1-4.9 Billion
Emp.: 3,440
Broadband Telecommunication Services
N.A.I.C.S.: 517111
Fabrizio Casati *(Chief Wholesale Officer & Member-Mgmt Bd)*

Subsidiary (Domestic):

E Bismedia S.p.A. (2)
Via Caracciolo 51, 20155, Milan, Italy (100%)
Tel.: (39) 02 45 42 32 31
Web Site: http://www.ebismedia.tv
Sales Range: $50-74.9 Million
Emp.: 250
Video On Demand & IPTV Services
N.A.I.C.S.: 516210
Sergio Scalpelli *(Dir-PR & Pub Affairs)*

HSIA Hospitality Services Netherlands B.V. (1)
Jan Willem Frisolaan 3a, Hague, 2517 JS, Netherlands
Tel.: (31) 703060444
Sales Range: $10-24.9 Million
Emp.: 1
General Hospitality Services
N.A.I.C.S.: 623110

HSIA Hospitality Services Portugal SA (1)
Av da Igreja n 42 9 Andar, 1700-239, Lisbon, Portugal
Tel.: (351) 21 340 33 50
Sales Range: $25-49.9 Million
Emp.: 55
Hospitality Telecommunication Services
N.A.I.C.S.: 517810

Hospitality Networks and Services Espana SA (1)
Calle Mallorca 245 3rf Floor, Barcelona, 8008, Spain
Tel.: (34) 93 544 11 70
Sales Range: $25-49.9 Million
Emp.: 12
Internet Providing Services
N.A.I.C.S.: 517810
Jorge Ramos *(Gen Mgr)*

Hospitality Networks and Services UK Ltd (1)
Elysium Gate 2nd Floor Unit 9 126-128 New Kings Road, London, SW6 4LZ, United Kingdom
Tel.: (44) 207 348 6770
Sales Range: $25-49.9 Million
Emp.: 15
Telecommunication Servicesb
N.A.I.C.S.: 517810
Simon l'Anson *(Mng Dir)*

Hospitality Services Italia S.r.l. (1)
Via Largo La Floppa 1, 20121, Milan, Italy
Tel.: (39) 02 8904 611
Sales Range: $10-24.9 Million
Emp.: 1
General Hospitality Services
N.A.I.C.S.: 622110
Simone Colombo *(Gen Mgr)*

Hospitality Services Plus SA (1)
2 chemin du Pavillon, Case postale 2200, CH-1211, Geneva, Switzerland
Tel.: (41) 795600151
Web Site: http://www.swisscom.com
Sales Range: $25-49.9 Million
Emp.: 60
Hospitality Industry High-Speed Internet Services
N.A.I.C.S.: 517810

Innovative Web Ltd. (1)
Nordstrasse 31, 8006, Zurich, Switzerland

SWISSCOM AG

Swisscom AG—(Continued)
Tel.: (41) 443669090
Web Site: https://www.i-web.ch
Web Application Development Services
N.A.I.C.S.: 541511

ItnetX (Switzerland) Ltd. (1)
Industriestrasse 46, 8152, Glattbrugg, Switzerland
Tel.: (41) 848990000
Web Site: https://www.itnetx.ch
Cloud Service Provider
N.A.I.C.S.: 518210

JLS Digital Ltd. (1)
Libellenrain 17, 6004, Lucerne, Switzerland
Tel.: (41) 412598000
Web Site: https://www.jls.ch
Software Development Services
N.A.I.C.S.: 541511

MTF Solutions Ltd. (1)
Alte Tiefenaustrasse 6, 3048, Worblaufen, Switzerland
Tel.: (41) 622059707
Web Site: https://www.mtf.ch
Emp.: 190
Information Technology Services
N.A.I.C.S.: 541511

Sicap Africa Pty Ltd (1)
Montecasino Office No 64 & 65 1st Floor William Nicol Drive, PO Box 2092, Fourways Witkoppen, Johannesburg, 2068, South Africa
Tel.: (27) 11 510 0337
Telecommunication Servicesb
N.A.I.C.S.: 517810

Sicap Malaysia Sdn Bhd (1)
B-17-03 North Point Office Suite No 1, Medan Syed Putra Utara, Mid Valley City, 59200, Kuala Lumpur, Malaysia
Tel.: (60) 3 2284 6322
Web Site: http://www.sicap.com
Sales Range: $25-49.9 Million
Emp.: 2
Telecommunication Servicesb
N.A.I.C.S.: 517810

Swisscom Ag Innovations (1)
Alte Tiefenaustrasse 6, 3048, Bern, Switzerland
Tel.: (41) 622861212
Web Site: http://www.swisscom.com
Sales Range: $50-74.9 Million
Emp.: 170
Telecommunications Research & Development
N.A.I.C.S.: 517810

Swisscom Belgium N.V. (1)
Belgacom Towers Konig Albert II-laan 27, 1030, Brussels, Belgium
Tel.: (32) 2 202 13 67
Web Site: http://www.swisscom-belgium.be
Telecommunication Servicesb
N.A.I.C.S.: 517810
Ueli Dietiker (Chm)

Swisscom Broadcast Ltd (1) (100%)
Tel.: (41) 800817620
Sales Range: $100-124.9 Million
Emp.: 240
Wireless Telecommunications Transmission Services
N.A.I.C.S.: 517112

Swisscom Cloud Lab Ltd. (1)
675 Forest Ave, Palo Alto, CA 94301
Tel.: (650) 822-4948
Web Site: https://outpost.swisscom.com
Information Technology Services
N.A.I.C.S.: 541519

Swisscom Directories Ltd (1) (69%)
Tel.: (41) 800889977
Web Site: https://www.directoriesdata.ch
Sales Range: $100-124.9 Million
Emp.: 245
Telecommunications & Information Directory Services
N.A.I.C.S.: 513140

Subsidiary (Domestic):

local.ch Ltd (2)
Morgenstrasse 131b, Bumpliz, 3050, Bern, Switzerland
Tel.: (41) 848 86 80 86
Web Site: http://www.local.ch
Online Directory Publishing Services
N.A.I.C.S.: 513140

Swisscom Event & Media Solutions Ltd (1)
Alte Tiefenaustrasse 6, 3050, Bern, Switzerland
Tel.: (41) 800 22 40 40
Sales Range: $25-49.9 Million
Emp.: 45
Web Media Services
N.A.I.C.S.: 541840
Nicole Anhalt (Acct Mgr)

Swisscom Fixnet Ltd (1)
Alte Tiefenaustrasse 6, Worblaufen, 3048, Bern, Switzerland
Tel.: (41) 313421111
Web Site: http://www.swisscom-fixnet.ch
Sales Range: $1-4.9 Billion
Emp.: 7,205
Fixed Network Communications Services
N.A.I.C.S.: 517111

Swisscom IT Services AG (1)
Alte Tiefenaustrasse 6, 3050, Bern, Ostermundigen, Switzerland
Tel.: (41) 582219804
Web Site: http://www.swisscom.com
Sales Range: $650-699.9 Million
Emp.: 100
Telecommunications Information Technology Services
N.A.I.C.S.: 541990

Subsidiary (Domestic):

Sourcag AG (2)
Emil Frey-Strasse 100, 4142, Munchenstein, Switzerland (60%)
Tel.: (41) 614187272
Web Site: http://www.sourcag.ch
Sales Range: $25-49.9 Million
Data Processing & Outsourcing Services; Owned 60% by Swisscom AG, 20% Basellandschaftliche Kantonalbank, 20% Basler Kantonalbank
N.A.I.C.S.: 518210

Swisscom IT Services Enterprise Solutions Ltd (1)
Zurcherstrasse 156, Frauenfeld, 8500, Switzerland
Tel.: (41) 434433200
Sales Range: $75-99.9 Million
Emp.: 430
Information Technology Consulting Services
N.A.I.C.S.: 541512

Swisscom IT Services Finance Ltd (1)
Pflanzschulstrasse 7, 8004, Zurich, Switzerland
Tel.: (41) 58 221 70 70
Web Site: http://finance.swisscom.ch
Financial Information Technology Consulting Services
N.A.I.C.S.: 541512

Swisscom IT Services Sourcing Ltd (1)
Emil Frey-Strasse 100, Munchenstein, 4142, Switzerland
Tel.: (41) 614187272
Information Technology Consulting Services
N.A.I.C.S.: 541512

Swisscom Immobilien Ltd (1)
Alte Tiefenaustrasse 6, 3050, Bern, Switzerland
Tel.: (41) 622861212
Web Site: http://www.swisscom.com
Sales Range: $200-249.9 Million
Emp.: 390
Commercial Real Estate Properties & Telecommunications Facility Management
N.A.I.C.S.: 531390

Swisscom Mobile Ltd (1)
Waldeggstrasse 51, Liebefeld, 3097, Bern, Switzerland (100%)
Tel.: (41) 622861212
Web Site: http://www.swisscom-mobile.ch
Sales Range: $1-4.9 Billion
Emp.: 2,457
Mobile Communications
N.A.I.C.S.: 517112

Swisscom Solutions Ltd (1)
Alte Tiefenaustrasse 6, 3048, Bern, Switzerland
Tel.: (41) 791234567
Web Site: http://www.swisscom.com
Sales Range: $900-999.9 Million
Emp.: 1,929
Commercial Telecommunications Services
N.A.I.C.S.: 517111

Swisscom Trust Services Ltd. (1)
Konradstrasse 12, 8005, Zurich, Switzerland
Tel.: (41) 800724724
Web Site: https://trustservices.swisscom.com
Software Development Services
N.A.I.C.S.: 541511

United Security Provider Ltd. (1)
Stauffacherstrasse 65/15, 3014, Bern, Switzerland
Tel.: (41) 319590202
Web Site: https://www.united-security-providers.ch
Information Technology Security Services
N.A.I.C.S.: 561621

WECO Inkasso AG (1)
Eggbuhlstrasse 25, PO Box 30, 8070, Zurich, Switzerland (100%)
Tel.: (41) 443659520
Web Site: http://www.weco-inkasso.ch
Sales Range: $10-24.9 Million
Emp.: 30
Factoring & Collection Services
N.A.I.C.S.: 561440

Webcall GmbH (1)
Seestrasse 356, 8038, Zurich, Switzerland
Tel.: (41) 44 325 66 33
Web Site: http://www.webcall.ch
Telecommunication Servicesb
N.A.I.C.S.: 517810

Worklink AG (1)
Laupenstrasse 6, 3008, Bern, Switzerland
Tel.: (41) 582237018
Web Site: https://www.worklink.ch
Human Resource Consulting Services
N.A.I.C.S.: 541612
Frederic Bracher (Pres)

SWISSLION INDUSTRIJA ALATA A.D.

Niksicki put 20, 89101, Trebinje, 89101, Bosnia & Herzegovina
Tel.: (387) 59286801
Web Site: http://www.iat-tools.com
IATR-R-A—(BANJ)
Sales Range: Less than $1 Million
Tool Mfr
N.A.I.C.S.: 333517
Slavko Vucurevic (Pres)

SWISSLION MILODUH A.D.

Dusana Urosevica 1, 34000, Kragujevac, Serbia
Tel.: (381) 112069300
Web Site: https://www.swisslion-takovo.com
Year Founded: 1997
SLMH—(BEL)
Rev: $1,733,811
Assets: $2,242,556
Liabilities: $302,855
Net Worth: $1,939,701
Earnings: ($135,506)
Emp.: 45
Fiscal Year-end: 12/31/22
Food Products Mfr
N.A.I.C.S.: 311999
Miloje Simovic (Gen Mgr)

SWISSMED CENTRUM ZDROWIA SA

Ul Wilenska 44, 80-215, Gdansk, Poland
Tel.: (48) 585241500
Web Site: http://www.swissmed.com.pl
SWD—(WAR)

INTERNATIONAL PUBLIC

Health Care Srvices
N.A.I.C.S.: 621999
Roman Walasinski (Chm)

SWISSOIL DEL ECUADOR S.A.

Ciudadela Nueve de Octubre Callejon Noveno entre Av, Domingo Comin y La Ria, Guayaquil, Ecuador
Tel.: (593) 42445340
Web Site: http://www.swissoil.com.ec
Sales Range: $50-74.9 Million
Emp.: 77
Lube Oil Mfr
N.A.I.C.S.: 324191
Hugo de la Torre (Mgr-Fin)

SWISSPOR MANAGEMENT AG

Bahnhofstrasse 50, Steinhausen, 6312, Switzerland
Tel.: (41) 566789898
Web Site: http://www.swisspor-gruppe.com
Year Founded: 1971
Sales Range: $10-24.9 Million
Emp.: 2,000
Holding Company
N.A.I.C.S.: 551112
Bernhard Alpstaeg (Founder)

Subsidiaries:

Aeroflex AG (1)
Juraweg 30, 4852, Rothrist, Switzerland
Tel.: (41) 62 785 57 00
Web Site: http://www.aeroflex.ch
Insulation Material Mfr & Distr
N.A.I.C.S.: 326150

Alporit AG (1)
Industriestrasse, 5623, Boswil, Switzerland
Tel.: (41) 56 678 99 00
Insulation Material Mfr
N.A.I.C.S.: 238290

Eternit (Schweiz) AG (1)
Eternitstrasse 3, CH 8867, Niederurnen, Switzerland
Tel.: (41) 556171111
Web Site: http://www.eternit.ch
Fibre Cement Product Mfr
N.A.I.C.S.: 444180
Anders Holte (CEO)

Subsidiary (Non-US):

Eternit Werke Ludwig Hatschek AG (2)
Eternitstrasse 34, Vocklabruck, 4840, Linz, Austria (80%)
Tel.: (43) 76727070
Web Site: http://www.eternit.at
Sales Range: $150-199.9 Million
Emp.: 460
Roofing Product Mfr
N.A.I.C.S.: 423330

Isosystem Dulliken AG (1)
Im Hardli 11A, 4657, Dulliken, Switzerland
Tel.: (41) 62 285 31 31
Insulation Material Mfr
N.A.I.C.S.: 326140

S.C. Isopor SRL (1)
Calea Baciului 1-3, Cluj-Napoca, Romania
Tel.: (40) 264 435 807
Web Site: http://www.isoporrom.ro
Emp.: 55
Insulation Material Mfr
N.A.I.C.S.: 326140

S.C. swisspor S.A. (1)
Soseaua de Centura Ploiesti Est 2028, Ploiesti, Prahova, Romania
Tel.: (40) 244 518 318
Web Site: http://www.swisspor.ro
Insulation Material Mfr & Distr
N.A.I.C.S.: 326140

Swisshaus AG (1)
Bahnhofstrasse 4, CH-5600, Lenzburg, Switzerland
Tel.: (41) 58 201 11 00
Web Site: http://www.swisshaus.ch
Emp.: 80
Construction Management Services
N.A.I.C.S.: 236115
Andrea Rutishauser (CEO)

Swisspearl Group AG (1)
Eternitstrasse 3, 8867, Niederurnen, Switzerland
Tel.: (41) 55617 1160
Web Site: https://www.swisspearl.com
Building Materials Whslr
N.A.I.C.S.: 444180
Harry Bosshardt (CEO)

Subsidiary (Non-US):

Cembrit Holding A/S (2)
Gasvaerksvej 24 1, PO Box 750, 9000, Aalborg, Denmark
Tel.: (45) 99372222
Web Site: http://www.cembrit.dk
Holding Company; Roof Material Mfr & Whslr
N.A.I.C.S.: 332322
Kent Arentoft (Chm)

Subsidiary (Non-US):

Cembrit Kft. (3)
Becsi Ut 7, 2536, Nyergesujfalu, Hungary
Tel.: (36) 33 887 700
Web Site: http://www.cembrit.hu
Fibre Cement Mfr & Distr
N.A.I.C.S.: 327310

Cembrit Ltd. (3)
57 Kellner Road, London, SE28 0AX, United Kingdom
Tel.: (44) 20 8301 8900
Web Site: http://www.cembrit.co.uk
Emp.: 15
Fibre Cement Slate Mfr
N.A.I.C.S.: 327310
Jacquie Avery (Mgr)

Cembrit S.A. (3)
Gnieznienska 4, 62-240, Trzemeszno, Wielkopolskie, Poland
Tel.: (48) 614154330
Web Site: http://www.cembrit.pl
Cement Mfr & Distr
N.A.I.C.S.: 327310

Cembrit SAS (3)
Rue des Fontainiers ZA Sud, 05100, Briancon, France
Tel.: (33) 4 92 21 24 65
Web Site: http://www.cembrit.fr
Fiber Cement Mfr
N.A.I.C.S.: 327310

Cembrit a.s. (3)
Lidicka 302, 266 38, Beroun, 3, Czech Republic
Tel.: (420) 311744111
Web Site: http://www.cembrit.cz
Cement Mfr & Distr
N.A.I.C.S.: 327310

Vaparoid AG (1)
Beim Bahnhof, 3946, Turtmann, Switzerland
Tel.: (41) 27 933 11 11
Polyurethane Foam Product Mfr
N.A.I.C.S.: 326150

Wannerit AG (1)
Linth-Escherstrasse 23, 8865, Glarus Nord, Switzerland
Tel.: (41) 55 619 64 64
Insulation Material Mfr
N.A.I.C.S.: 326140

swisspor Deutschland GmbH (1)
Kreisstrasse 34 c, Dankerode, 06493, Harzgerode, Germany
Tel.: (49) 39484 7 12 0
Web Site: http://www.swisspor-deutschland.de
Insulation Material Mfr
N.A.I.C.S.: 326140

swisspor Osterreich GmbH & Co. KG (1)
Waidhofner Strasse 5, Gleiss, 3332, Sonntagberg, Austria
Tel.: (43) 7448 400 0
Web Site: http://www.swisspor.at
Insulation Material & System Mfr
N.A.I.C.S.: 327993

swisspor Polska sp. z o.o. (1)
ul Kroczymiech 2, 32-500, Chrzanow, Poland
Tel.: (48) 32 62 57 250
Web Site: http://www.swisspor.pl
Insulation Material Mfr

N.A.I.C.S.: 326140

swisspor Romandie SA (1)
chemin du Bugnon 100, CP 60, 1618, Chatel Saint Denis, Switzerland
Tel.: (41) 21 948 48 48
Insulation Material Mfr & Distr
N.A.I.C.S.: 326140

swisswindows AG (1)
Haltelhusstrasse 14, PO Box 9016, Morschwil, Saint Gallen, Switzerland
Tel.: (41) 71 868 68 68
Web Site: http://www.swisswindows.ch
Window & Door Mfr
N.A.I.C.S.: 332321

Unit (Domestic):

swisswindows AG - Dulliken works (2)
Hardli 11A, 4657, Dulliken, Switzerland
Tel.: (41) 62 788 58 58
Window Mfr
N.A.I.C.S.: 332321

SWISSQUOTE GROUP HOLDING LTD.
Chemin de la Cretaux 33, Case Postale 319, CH-1196, Gland, Switzerland
Tel.: (41) 229999411
Web Site:
    https://www.swissquote.com
Year Founded: 2000
SQN—(SWX)
Rev.: $452,490,542
Assets: $11,328,598,390
Liabilities: $10,506,948,619
Net Worth: $821,649,772
Earnings: $174,494,187
Emp.: 850
Fiscal Year-end: 12/31/22
Online Financial & Trading Services
N.A.I.C.S.: 523150
Markus Dennler (Chm)

Subsidiaries:

Swissquote Asia Ltd. (1)
Suites 3202-4 Level 32/F ICBC Tower 3 Garden Road, Central, China (Hong Kong)
Tel.: (852) 39020000
Web Site: https://en.swissquoteasia.com
Financial Institution Services
N.A.I.C.S.: 522320

Swissquote Bank Europe S.A. (1)
2 rue Edward Steichen, 2958, Luxembourg, Luxembourg
Tel.: (352) 26032003
Web Site: https://www.swissquote.lu
Online Brokerage Services
N.A.I.C.S.: 523150

Swissquote Financial Services (Malta) Ltd. (1)
Palazzo Spinola 46 St Christophers Street, Valletta, VLT 1464, Malta
Tel.: (356) 2 226 5140
Web Site: https://en.swissquote.mt
Financial Institution Services
N.A.I.C.S.: 522320
Andrew Zarb Mizzi (CEO)

Swissquote Ltd. (1)
Boston House 63-64 New Broad Street, London, EC2M 1JJ, United Kingdom
Tel.: (44) 2071862600
Web Site: https://en.swissquote.co.uk
Financial & Trading Services
N.A.I.C.S.: 522320

Swissquote MEA Ltd. (1)
Al Fattan Currency House Level 9 Office 904 Tower 2 DIFC, PO Box 121364, Dubai, United Arab Emirates
Tel.: (971) 44501777
Web Site: https://www.swissquote.com
Financial Institution Services
N.A.I.C.S.: 522320

Swissquote Pte. Ltd. (1)
Office 34-01A One Raffles Quay North Tower, Singapore, 048583, Singapore
Tel.: (65) 69826780
Web Site: https://en.swissquote.sg

Financial Institution Services
N.A.I.C.S.: 522320
Mathias Dalla Valeria (CEO)

SWISSTEK (CEYLON) PLC
No 215 Nawala Road Narhenpita, 5, Colombo, Sri Lanka
Tel.: (94) 114526700
Web Site:
    https://www.swisstekceylon.com
PARQ—(COL)
Rev.: $29,859,272
Assets: $36,321,933
Liabilities: $28,616,484
Net Worth: $7,705,449
Earnings: ($2,339,100)
Emp.: 481
Fiscal Year-end: 03/31/23
Imported Timber Sales & Aluminum Products Mfr
N.A.I.C.S.: 423310
Dayal de Silva (Gen Mgr-Timber Ops)

SWISSVOICE SA
9 Rue Newton, 75116, Paris, France
Tel.: (33) 142930988
Web Site: http://www.swissvoice.net
Rev.: $25,900,000
Emp.: 43
Telephone Communication, Except Radio
N.A.I.C.S.: 517121
Jacques Savary (Chm)

SWITCH CONCEPTS LIMITED
Hounsdown House Hounsdown Business Park, Southampton, SO40 9LX, United Kingdom
Tel.: (44) 333 200 1230
Web Site:
    http://www.switchconcepts.com
Year Founded: 2008
Sales Range: $10-24.9 Million
Emp.: 130
Software Development Services
N.A.I.C.S.: 541511
Tom Barnett (Co-Founder & CEO)

SWITCHING TECHNOLOGIES GUNTHER LIMITED
B9 B10 Special Economic Zone MEPZ, Kadapperi Tambaram, Chennai, 600 045, India
Tel.: (91) 4422622460
Web Site:
    https://www.switchingtechltd.com
517201—(BOM)
Rev.: $1,382,459
Assets: $1,251,532
Liabilities: $1,531,371
Net Worth: ($279,839)
Earnings: $1,359,175
Emp.: 103
Fiscal Year-end: 03/31/23
Reed Switch Mfr
N.A.I.C.S.: 334419
P. Ramesh (Mng Dir)

SWITZERLAND CHEESE MARKETING AG
Brunnmattstrasse 21, 3001, Bern, Switzerland
Tel.: (41) 313852626
Web Site:
    http://www.schweizerkaese.ch
Year Founded: 1914
Sales Range: $25-49.9 Million
Emp.: 50
Cheese Marketing & Sales
N.A.I.C.S.: 424430
Martin Spahr (CMO)

SWITZERLAND GLOBAL ENTERPRISE

Stampfenbachstrasse 85, 8006, Zurich, Switzerland
Tel.: (41) 44 365 5151
Web Site: http://www.s-ge.com
Year Founded: 1927
Sales Range: $25-49.9 Million
Trade Promotion Services
N.A.I.C.S.: 561990
Daniel Kung (CEO)

Subsidiaries:

Switzerland Global Enterprise Lausanne (1)
Avenue dOuchy 47, 1006, Lausanne, Switzerland
Tel.: (41) 21 545 9494
Web Site: http://www.s-ge.com
Trade Promotion Services
N.A.I.C.S.: 926110
Daniel Kung (CEO)

SWMBRD SPORTS INC.
1450789 West Pender, Vancouver, V6C 1H2, BC, Canada
Tel.: (778) 870-1497   BC
Web Site: https://www.swmbrd.com
Year Founded: 2015
SWIM—(CNSX)
Assets: $366,484
Liabilities: $215,063
Net Worth: $151,421
Earnings: $1,607,020
Fiscal Year-end: 02/28/23
Sports Product Mfr & Distr
N.A.I.C.S.: 339920
Justin Schroenn (Pres & Founder)

SWOOP HOLDINGS LIMITED
Level 5 126 Phillip Street, Sydney, 2000, NSW, Australia
Tel.: (61) 0280721400
Web Site: http://www.stemify.com.au
SWP—(ASX)
Rev.: $54,181,885
Assets: $84,045,232
Liabilities: $44,333,782
Net Worth: $39,711,450
Earnings: ($3,556,802)
Fiscal Year-end: 06/30/24
3D Printing Solutions
N.A.I.C.S.: 323120
Tim Grice (Chm)

SWORD GROUP SE
2 rue d Arlon, L8399, Windhof, Luxembourg
Tel.: (352) 26112611   LU
Web Site: https://www.sword-group.com
Year Founded: 2000
9RS—(DEU)
Rev.: $318,057,181
Assets: $276,568,054
Liabilities: $160,208,632
Net Worth: $116,359,422
Earnings: $25,509,438
Emp.: 3,015
Fiscal Year-end: 12/31/23
Holding Company; Information Technology Advisory & Integration Services
N.A.I.C.S.: 551112
Jacques Mottard (Chm)

Subsidiaries:

Aaa Ltd. (1)
Deebridge House 4 Leggart Terrace, Aberdeen, AB12 5US, United Kingdom
Tel.: (44) 1224211211
Information Technology Services
N.A.I.C.S.: 541511

AiM Services SA (1)
Rue du Lievre 2-4, PO Box 379, Les Acacias, 1227, Geneva, Switzerland
Tel.: (41) 22 309 0505
Web Site: https://www.aim-services.ch
Sales Range: $25-49.9 Million
Emp.: 155

SWORD GROUP SE

Sword Group SE—(Continued)
IT Consultancy Outsourcing & Technical Services
N.A.I.C.S.: 541512
Thierry G. Papilloud *(Founder & CEO)*

Cba Sourcing S.A. (1)
Business Park Terre-Bonne Batiment A1
Route de Crassier 7, Eysins, 1262, Nyon, Switzerland
Tel.: (41) 22 748 4880
Web Site: https://www.cba-sourcing.ch
Information Technology Services
N.A.I.C.S.: 541511
Mouhez Kachlef *(Mgr-Sls Dev)*

Data Co & Sword It Solutions Ltd. (1)
4th Floor Johnstone House 50-54 Rose Street, Aberdeen, AB10 1UD, United Kingdom
Tel.: (44) 1224506110
Information Technology Services
N.A.I.C.S.: 541511

Dataco Australia Pty Ltd. (1)
Suite 3 Level 1 Ord Street, West Perth, 6005, WA, Australia
Tel.: (61) 893804490
Information Technology Services
N.A.I.C.S.: 541511

Dataco Global Ltd. (1)
The Mille 1000 Great West Road, London, TW8 9DW, United Kingdom
Tel.: (44) 1224576980
Information Technology Services
N.A.I.C.S.: 541511

Lemonade Software Development S.L. (1)
Carrer de Pau Claris 194-196 7 1a, 08037, Barcelona, Spain
Tel.: (34) 937635249
Web Site: https://www.lemonade.be
Information Technology Services
N.A.I.C.S.: 541511

Magique Galileo Software Ltd. (1)
Birchin Court 20 Birchin Lane, London, EC3V 9DU, United Kingdom
Tel.: (44) 2037134590
Web Site: http://www.magiquegalileo.com
Information Technology Services
N.A.I.C.S.: 541511

Minttulip Ltd. (1)
WeWork 30 Stamford Street, Southbank Central, London, SE1 9LQ, United Kingdom
Tel.: (44) 2039655990
Information Technology Services
N.A.I.C.S.: 541511
Felice Gianneri *(Dir-Customer Solutions)*

Phusion IM Ltd. (1)
16 Earls Nook Belasis Hall Technology Park, Billingham, TS23 4EF, Cleveland, United Kingdom
Tel.: (44) 1642373000
Web Site: https://www.phusionim.com
Technical Consulting Services
N.A.I.C.S.: 541690

Riskonnect Active Risk Group Limited (1)
1 Grenfell Road, Maidenhead, SL6 1HN, Berks, United Kingdom
Tel.: (44) 1628582500
Web Site: https://riskonnect.com
Risk Management & Software Development Services
N.A.I.C.S.: 541511

Sword Charteris Limited (1)
1000 Great West Road, Brentford, London, TW8 9HH, United Kingdom
Tel.: (44) 20 8232 2555
Web Site: http://www.charteris.com
Systems Integration & Other Consulting Services
N.A.I.C.S.: 561499

Sword Connect SAS (1)
37 rue de Lyon, 75012, Paris, France
Tel.: (33) 144672408
Web Site: http://www.sword-connect.com
Information Technology Services
N.A.I.C.S.: 541511

Sword Creation Informatique Ltd. (1)
Waterfall Crescent North Waterfall Park, Vorna Valley, Midrand, 1685, South Africa
Tel.: (27) 112344206
Web Site: http://www.sword-group.com
Sales Range: $25-49.9 Million
Emp.: 20
Custom Computer Systems Design & Sales
N.A.I.C.S.: 541512

Sword Grc Inc. (1)
13221 Woodland Park Rd Ste 440, Herndon, VA 20171
Tel.: (703) 673-9580
Software Development Services
N.A.I.C.S.: 541511

Sword Grc Pty Ltd. (1)
Level 14 333 Collins Street, Melbourne, 3000, VIC, Australia
Tel.: (61) 39 071 1866
Web Site: https://www.sword-grc.com
Software Development Services
N.A.I.C.S.: 541511

Sword Integra SA (1)
Avenue de Tervueren 270, 1150, Brussels, Belgium
Tel.: (32) 22351000
Web Site: https://www.sword-group.com
Emp.: 10
Software Development Services
N.A.I.C.S.: 541511
Jean-Bernard Trussart *(Mng Dir)*

Sword It Solutions Ltd. (1)
1000 Great West Road, Brentford, TW8 9DW, Middlesex, United Kingdom
Tel.: (44) 2082322555
Information Technology Services
N.A.I.C.S.: 541511

Sword Middle East FZ LLC (1)
1st floor Building 2, PO Box 500406, Dubai Internet City, Dubai, United Arab Emirates
Tel.: (971) 43670375
Web Site: https://www.sword-group.com
Information Technology Services
N.A.I.C.S.: 541511

Sword Middle East Software Solutions LLC (1)
Empire Heights 8th Floor Tower B Business Bay, PO Box 413706, Dubai, United Arab Emirates
Tel.: (971) 45656228
Information Technology Services
N.A.I.C.S.: 541511

Sword Services SA (1)
Avenue des Baumettes 19, 1020, Renens, Switzerland
Tel.: (41) 216329000
Web Site: https://www.sword-group.com
Sales Range: $25-49.9 Million
Emp.: 55
Software Development Services
N.A.I.C.S.: 541511

Subsidiary (Non-US):

Sword Lebanon (2)
Berytech Technology & Health, Rue de Damas, Beirut, Lebanon
Tel.: (961) 9611612500
Web Site: http://www.sword-group.com
Custom Computer Systems Design & Sales
N.A.I.C.S.: 541512
Nasser Hammoud *(Mng Dir)*

Sword Solutions Inc. (1)
PO Box 8761, Mesa, AZ 85214
Tel.: (517) 487-8943
Web Site: https://swordsolutions.com
Information Technology Services
N.A.I.C.S.: 541511

Sword Technologies Ltd. (1)
105 Route d'Arlon, 8009, Strassen, Luxembourg
Tel.: (352) 26112611
Sales Range: $25-49.9 Million
Emp.: 40
Custom Computer Systems Design & Sales
N.A.I.C.S.: 541512

Sword Technology Solutions Ltd. (1)
1000 Great West Road, Brentford, TW8 9DW, Mddx, United Kingdom
Tel.: (44) 2082322555
Web Site: http://www.sword-group.com
Sales Range: $25-49.9 Million
Emp.: 20
Information Technology Consultancy Services
N.A.I.C.S.: 541690
Tony Allen *(CEO)*

Subsidiary (Domestic):

Sword General Partners Ltd. (2)
1000 Great West Road, Brentford, TW8 9DW, Middlesex, United Kingdom (100%)
Tel.: (44) 2082322555
Web Site: http://www.sword-group.com
Emp.: 3
Software Development Services
N.A.I.C.S.: 541511

Subsidiary (Non-US):

Sword Global India Pvt. Ltd. (2)
Elnet Software City 3rd Floor TS 140 Block 2 & 9 Rajiv Gandhi Salai, Taramani, Chennai, 600 113, India (100%)
Tel.: (91) 4466363636
Web Site: https://www.sword-group.com
Sales Range: $25-49.9 Million
Custom Computer Systems Design & Sales
N.A.I.C.S.: 541512
Lalitha Balakrishnan *(Mng Dir)*

Sword, Inc. (1)
17 State St 26th Fl, New York, NY 10004 (100%)
Tel.: (212) 279-6734
Web Site: http://www.sword-group.com
Sales Range: $25-49.9 Million
Emp.: 30
Custom Computer Systems Design & Sales
N.A.I.C.S.: 541512

Tipik Communication Agency S.A. (1)
Avenue de Tervueren 270, 1150, Brussels, Belgium
Tel.: (32) 22355670
Web Site: https://www.tipik.eu
Emp.: 49
Information Technology Services
N.A.I.C.S.: 541511
Erik Morren *(Mng Partner)*

Venture Information Management Ltd. (1)
Staines One Station Approach, Staines-upon-Thames, TW18 4LY, United Kingdom
Tel.: (44) 2031410500
Information Technology Services
N.A.I.C.S.: 541511

SWORD SOUTH AFRICA (PTY) LTD.

Waterfall Crescent North Waterfall Park, Vorna Valley, Midrand, 1685, South Africa
Tel.: (27) 112344206 ZA
Web Site: http://www.sword-sa.com
Sales Range: $25-49.9 Million
Information Technology Management & Advisory Services
N.A.I.C.S.: 541512
Kays Mguni *(Mng Dir)*

SWORD-EDGE COMMERCIALS LIMITED

401 4th Floor Solitaire Business Park Near T-2 International Airport, New Mtnl Road Andheri Kurla Road Near Telephone Exchange Andheri East, Mumbai, 400072, Andheri, India
Tel.: (91) 2226204757
512359—(BOM)
Rev.: $55,009
Assets: $4,574,460
Liabilities: $2,004,838
Net Worth: $2,569,623
Earnings: ($145,537)
Fiscal Year-end: 03/31/22
Commercial Trading Services
N.A.I.C.S.: 523150
Sakshi Jhala *(Exec Dir)*

SWORDFISH VENTURES CORPORATION

INTERNATIONAL PUBLIC

Room B3 20th Floor Boldwin Industrial Building, 16-18 Wah Sing Street, Kwai Chung, China (Hong Kong)
Tel.: (852) 69463282 NV
Year Founded: 2009
Investment Services
N.A.I.C.S.: 523999
Gao Hai *(Pres, CEO, CFO, Treas & Sec)*

SWP GROUP LIMITED

Bedford House 1 Regal Lane, Soham, CB7 5BA, Cambs, United Kingdom
Tel.: (44) 1353 723270 UK
Web Site:
http://www.swpgroupplc.com
Sales Range: $10-24.9 Million
Emp.: 148
Holding Company; Industrial Engineered Product Mfr
N.A.I.C.S.: 551112
David J. Pett *(Fin Dir)*

SWS CAPITAL BERHAD

Lot PTD 6001 Jalan Perindustrian 5 Kawasan Perindustrian Bukit Bakri, 84200, Muar, Johor Darul Takzim, Malaysia
Tel.: (60) 69865236
Web Site: https://www.swscap.com
SWSCAP—(KLS)
Rev.: $26,900,506
Assets: $45,999,806
Liabilities: $14,022,781
Net Worth: $31,977,025
Earnings: ($1,385,952)
Fiscal Year-end: 12/31/23
Furniture Mfr
N.A.I.C.S.: 337121
Khoon Hai Tan *(Chm)*

Subsidiaries:

Poh Keong Industries Sdn. Bhd. (1)
Lot 1789 Jalan Raja Mukiam Sungai Raya, Mukim Sungai Raya, 84300, Muar, Johor, Malaysia
Tel.: (60) 6 985 0258
Web Site:
https://www.pohkeongfurniture.com
Sales Range: $25-49.9 Million
Emp.: 150
Furnitures Mfr & Distr
N.A.I.C.S.: 337214
Wee Shang *(Mgr-Mktg)*

Syarikat U.D. Trading Corporation Sdn. Bhd. (1)
PTD 6001 Batu 8 Jalan Perindustrian 5 Kawasan, Perindustrian Bukit Bakri, 84200, Muar, Johor Darul Takzim, Malaysia
Tel.: (60) 69865236
Emp.: 20
Hardware & Fasteners Distr
N.A.I.C.S.: 423710
Lee Yew Chye *(Mng Dir)*

U.D. Industries Sdn. Bhd. (1)
PTD 6001 Batu 8 Kawasan Perindustrian Bukit Bakri, Jalan Perindustrian 5, 84200, Muar, Johor, Malaysia
Tel.: (60) 69865236
Web Site: http://www.udpanelform.com
Emp.: 200
Fasteners & Coil Nails Mfr
N.A.I.C.S.: 339993
Lee Yew Chye *(Mng Dir)*

U.D. Panelform lamination and Sdn. Bhd. (1)
Lot 8800 Jalan Perindustrian 5 Batu 8, Kawasan Perindustrian Bukit Bakri, 84200, Muar, Johor, Malaysia
Tel.: (60) 69868882
Web Site: https://www.udpanelform.com
Premier Veneer Furniture Mfr
N.A.I.C.S.: 321991

SWVL HOLDINGS CORP.

The Offices 4 One Central Dubai World Trade Centre, Dubai, United Arab Emirates

Tel.: (971) 42241293 VG
Web Site: https://www.swvl.com
Year Founded: 2017
SWVL—(NASDAQ)
Rev.: $51,489,952
Assets: $57,462,556
Liabilities: $54,833,363
Net Worth: $2,629,193
Earnings: ($123,579,448)
Emp.: 203
Fiscal Year-end: 12/31/22
Holding Company
N.A.I.C.S.: 551112

SY CO., LTD.
340-2 Jeongjo-ro, Gwonseon-gu, Suwon, Gyeonggi, Korea (South)
Tel.: (82) 15880680
Web Site: https://www.sypanel.com
Year Founded: 1994
109610—(KRS)
Rev.: $412,034,286
Assets: $320,931,809
Liabilities: $175,811,909
Net Worth: $145,119,900
Earnings: $6,213,711
Emp.: 277
Fiscal Year-end: 12/31/22
Sandwich Panel Mfr & Distr
N.A.I.C.S.: 423310
Kim Ok-Ju (CEO)

Subsidiaries:

P.T. Kencana Sr Build (1)
Kencana Tower lt 3 Business Park Kebon Jeruk Jl Meruya Ilir Raya no 88, Jakarta Barat, Indonesia
Tel.: (62) 2129325742
Building Panel Mfr & Distr
N.A.I.C.S.: 332311

SY Coming Co, Ltd. (1)
Geolmae-li 23-120 Injusandan-ro, Inju-Myeon, Asan, Chungcheongnam-do, Korea (South)
Tel.: (82) 415348482
Building Panel Mfr & Distr
N.A.I.C.S.: 332311

SY Panel Nepal Pvt. Ltd. (1)
Tinkune 32, Subidanagar, Kathmandu, Nepal
Tel.: (977) 14111704
Web Site: https://www.synepal.com
Construction Panel Mfr
N.A.I.C.S.: 332311

SY HOLDINGS GROUP LIMITED
18/F 10/F Kerry Plaza Tower 2 1 ZhongXin No 4 Road, Futian District, Shenzhen, China
Tel.: (86) 75561880088 Ky
Web Site: http://www.shengyecapital.com
Year Founded: 2014
6069—(HKG)
Rev.: $112,379,670
Assets: $1,597,535,644
Liabilities: $1,018,569,708
Net Worth: $578,965,936
Earnings: $34,202,563
Emp.: 377
Fiscal Year-end: 12/31/22
Financial Transaction Processing Services
N.A.I.C.S.: 522320
Jeff Chi Fung Tung (Founder, Chm & Compliance Officer)

Subsidiaries:

Sheng Ye Commercial Factoring Limited (1)
Room 3006 30/F TEDA MSD-C3 No 79 1st Avenue TEDA, Tianjin, China
Tel.: (86) 2260122808
Financial Investment Services
N.A.I.C.S.: 522299

SY INNOVATION CO., LTD.
222 Wongsipli Road Sageun-Dong Sungdong-Gu, Seoul, Korea (South)
Tel.: (82) 2 33950601
Web Site: http://www.syin.co.kr
Plastics Product Mfr
N.A.I.C.S.: 326199
Sang-Hee Jeon (Exec Dir)

SYARIKAT KAYU WANGI BERHAD
Batu 6 Jalan Yong Peng/Muar, 83710, Batu Pahat, Johor Darul Ta'zim, Malaysia
Tel.: (60) 74847388
Web Site: http://www.skw.com.my
Year Founded: 1980
Sales Range: $1-9.9 Million
Lumber Distr
N.A.I.C.S.: 423990
Choon Ying Lee (Exec Dir)

Subsidiaries:

SKW Subari Sdn. Bhd. (1)
51 3/4 Jalan Air Hitam, Simpang Renggam, 86200, Keluang, Johor, Malaysia
Tel.: (60) 77541544
Sawn Timber Mfr & Distr
N.A.I.C.S.: 321215

Wangi KMB Bhd. (1)
No 4 Ground Floor Jalan Melaka Raya 15, 75000, Melaka, Penang, Malaysia
Tel.: (60) 62819393
Emp.: 100
Property Development Services
N.A.I.C.S.: 531210
Chan Hwa Lim (Mng Dir)

SYBER
Lieu dit Barbat, 32160, Plaisance, Gers, France
Tel.: (33) 562694048
Sales Range: $10-24.9 Million
Emp.: 24
Grocery Stores
N.A.I.C.S.: 445110
Sylvette Sourzat (Dir-Admin)

SYBLY INDUSTRIES LTD.
Pawan Puri, Muradnagar Distt, Ghaziabad, 201206, Uttar Pradesh, India
Tel.: (91) 1232261765
Web Site: http://www.sybly.com
531499—(BOM)
Rev.: $94,491
Assets: $1,633,163
Liabilities: $1,005,383
Net Worth: $627,780
Earnings: ($266,615)
Emp.: 5
Fiscal Year-end: 03/31/23
Polyester Yarn Mfr
N.A.I.C.S.: 313110
Nishant Mittal (Chm & Mng Dir)

SYCAL VENTURES BERHAD
Lot 4 21 4th Floor Plaza Prima 4 1/2 Miles Old Klang Road, 58200, Kuala Lumpur, Malaysia
Tel.: (60) 379839099
Web Site: https://www.sycalberhad.com
SYCAL—(KLS)
Rev.: $16,399,598
Assets: $114,585,818
Liabilities: $44,984,858
Net Worth: $69,600,960
Earnings: $334,868
Fiscal Year-end: 06/30/22
Construction Services
N.A.I.C.S.: 236220
Kim Koon Koh (Sec)

Subsidiaries:

Sycal Berhad (1)
Lot 4 21 4th Floor Plaza Prima 4 1/2 Miles Old Klang Road, 58200, Kuala Lumpur, Federal Territory, Malaysia
Tel.: (60) 379839099
Property Development Services
N.A.I.C.S.: 236220
Seow Yong Chin (Mng Dir)

Subsidiary (Domestic):

Sycal Kulai Sdn Bhd (2)
No 26 Jalan Enau 15 Taman Teratai, 81300, Skudai, Johor, Malaysia
Tel.: (60) 75217464
Web Site: http://www.sycalberhad.com
Property Development Services
N.A.I.C.S.: 531311

Sycal Properties Sdn. Bhd. (2)
Lot 7 2 40 Jalan 17/144A Taman Bukit Cheras, Kuala Lumpur, 56000, Federal Territory, Malaysia
Tel.: (60) 391010922
Property Managing Services
N.A.I.C.S.: 531311

Sycal Resorts Sdn. Bhd. (2)
Lot 4 21 4th Floor Plaza Prima 4 1/2 Miles Old Klang Road, 58200, Kuala Lumpur, Malaysia
Tel.: (60) 37 980 7777
Web Site: http://www.sycalberhad.com
Emp.: 200
Property Investment & Development Services
N.A.I.C.S.: 525990

Sycalland Development Sdn. Bhd. (2)
No 26 Jalan Enau 15 Taman Teratai, 81300, Johor Bahru, Johor, Malaysia
Tel.: (60) 75217464
Property Management Services
N.A.I.C.S.: 531311

SYCAMORE ENTERTAINMENT GROUP, INC.
Suite 502 4445 Lougheed Highway, Vancouver, V5C 0E4, BC, Canada
Tel.: (310) 773-3485
Web Site:
    http://www.sycamoreentertain.com
SEGI—(OTCIQ)
Sales Range: Less than $1 Million
Motion Picture Distr & Marketer
N.A.I.C.S.: 512120
Edward Sylvan (Co-Founder, Chm & CEO)

SYCAMORE VENTURES PTE. LTD.
1 North Bridge Road 13-03 High Street Centre, Singapore, 179094, Singapore
Tel.: (65) 6535 0112 SG
Web Site:
    http://www.sycamorevc.com
Sales Range: $25-49.9 Million
Emp.: 20
Venture Capital Investment Firm
N.A.I.C.S.: 523999
Charles Law (Mng Partner)

SYDAMI
18 Route Des Sables, La Roche-sur-Yon, 85000, Vendee, France
Tel.: (33) 251625896
Web Site: http://www.bernistrucks.fr
Rev.: $28,900,000
Emp.: 71
New & Used Car Dealers
N.A.I.C.S.: 441110
Laurent Bret (Dir)

SYDBANK A/S
Peberlyk 4, PO Box 1038, DK-6200, Aabenraa, Denmark
Tel.: (45) 74373737
Web Site: https://www.sydbank.com
Year Founded: 1970
SYDB—(OTCIQ)
Rev.: $646,579,190
Assets: $273,686,060,000
Liabilities: $271,627,802,170
Net Worth: $2,058,257,830
Earnings: $131,890,930
Emp.: 2,184
Fiscal Year-end: 12/31/20
Investment & Banking Services
N.A.I.C.S.: 522110
Karen Frosig (CEO)

Subsidiaries:

Ejendomsselskabet af 1. juni 1986 A/S (1)
Peberlyk 4, Aabenraa, Denmark (100%)
Tel.: (45) 74631111
Real Estate Agents & Brokers
N.A.I.C.S.: 531210

Green Team Group A/S (1)
Simmelbrovej 44, Sonder Omme, 7260, Grindsted, Denmark
Tel.: (45) 7 650 4060
Web Site: https://www.greenteam-group.com
Christmas Tree Mfr & Distr
N.A.I.C.S.: 339999
Sune Graae Norsker (CEO)

SoFinans A/S (1)
Storegade 18, 6200, Aabenraa, Denmark (100%)
Tel.: (45) 74364550
Financial Investment Activities
N.A.I.C.S.: 523999

Sydfactoring A/S (1)
Storegade 18, 6200, Aabenraa, Denmark (100%)
Tel.: (45) 74362336
Commercial Banking
N.A.I.C.S.: 522110

Sydleasing A/S (1)
Storegade 18, 6200, Aabenraa, Denmark (100%)
Tel.: (45) 74364545
Web Site: http://www.sydleasing.dk
Financial Investment Activities
N.A.I.C.S.: 523999

SYDEK CORPORATION
5 6 2 Oroshimachi, Wakabayashi-Ku, Sendai, 984 0015, Japan
Tel.: (81) 22 235 2222
Web Site: http://www.sydek.com
Year Founded: 1950
Sales Range: $10-24.9 Million
Emp.: 90
Plastic Trays & Industrial Packaging Mfr
N.A.I.C.S.: 326112
Katsuhiko Shida (Pres)

Subsidiaries:

Sydek Corporation Binan Factory (1)
North Science Avenue Special Export Processing Zone, Laguna Technopark, Binan, 4024, Laguna, Philippines
Tel.: (63) 495410075
Plastics Product Mfr
N.A.I.C.S.: 325211

Sydek Corporation Sendai Factory (1)
3-3-27 Oroshimachi-Higashi, Wakabayashi-ku, Sendai, 984-0002, Japan
Tel.: (81) 222885511
Plastics Product Mfr
N.A.I.C.S.: 325211

Sydek Hang Fung Trading Co., Ltd. (1)
Room 813 8th Fl Tower 1, 1 Hok Cheung St Harbour Ctr, Kowloon, China (Hong Kong)
Tel.: (852) 26359208
Packaging Material Whslr
N.A.I.C.S.: 423840

Subsidiary (Non-US):

Sydek Hang Fung Precise Package (Shanghai) Co., Ltd. (2)
2/F TenMa Pudong Building 438 Fu Te Dong Yi Rd Shanghai Outer Gaoqiao, Free Trade Zone D12-12, Shanghai, 200131, China
Tel.: (86) 21 5866 6009
Web Site: http://www.hangfungint.com

SYDEK CORPORATION

Sydek Corporation—(Continued)
Sales Range: $25-49.9 Million
Emp.: 7
Industrial Packaging Mfr
N.A.I.C.S.: 326112

Sydek Hang Fung Precision (Suzhou) Co., Ltd. (2)
269 He Feng Road Xu Kou Wu Zhong, Suzhou, Jiangsu, China
Tel.: (86) 512 6656 3230
Industrial Packaging Mfr
N.A.I.C.S.: 326112

Sydek Precision (Zhongshan) Co., Ltd. (1)
Shunjing Industrial Zone, Banfutong, Zhongshan, Guangdong, China
Tel.: (86) 76023618666
Electronic Components Mfr
N.A.I.C.S.: 334416

SYDNEY AIRPORT HOLDINGS PTY LTD
The Nigel Love Building 10 Arrivals Court, Locked Bag 5000, Sydney International Airport, Sydney, 2020, NSW, Australia
Tel.: (61) 296679111   AU
Web Site:
    http://www.sydneyairport.com.au
SYD—(ASX)
Rev.: $1,146,719,844
Assets: $8,834,974,236
Liabilities: $9,362,034,540
Net Worth: ($527,060,304)
Earnings: $150,368,850
Emp.: 508
Fiscal Year-end: 12/31/19
Airport Property Management Services
N.A.I.C.S.: 531312
Trevor Gerber (Chm)

Subsidiaries:

Southern Cross Airports Corporation Holdings Limited (1)
10 Arrivals Court Sydney International Airport, Mascot, 2020, NSW, Australia (100%)
Tel.: (61) 2 9667 9111
Web Site: http://www.sydneyairport.com.au
Sales Range: $1-4.9 Billion
Airport Holding Company
N.A.I.C.S.: 551112
Kerrie Mather (CEO & Mng Dir)

Subsidiary (Domestic):

Sydney Airport Corporation Limited (2)
Ulm Bldg 1 Link Road International Terminal, Sydney, 2020, NSW, Australia
Tel.: (61) 296679111
Web Site: http://www.sydneyairport.com.au
Sales Range: $50-74.9 Million
Emp.: 250
Airport Construction Services
N.A.I.C.S.: 488119

Sydney Airport Finance Company Pty. Ltd. (2)
1 Link Rd, Sydney Intl Airport, Sydney, 2020, NSW, Australia
Tel.: (61) 296676451
Web Site: http://www.sydneyairport.com.au
Sales Range: $75-99.9 Million
Emp.: 250
Financial Services
N.A.I.C.S.: 523999

SYDNEY BREAST CLINIC PTY LIMITED
Level 12 97-99 Bathurst Street, Sydney, 2000, NSW, Australia
Tel.: (61) 1300653065
Web Site:
    http://www.sydneybreastclinic.com
Year Founded: 1978
Sales Range: $10-24.9 Million
Emp.: 55
Diagnostic Breast Imaging Services
N.A.I.C.S.: 621512
Ron Phillips (Mng Dir)

SYDNEY FISH MARKET PTY LTD
Bank St, Pyrmont, 2009, NSW, Australia
Tel.: (61) 290041100
Web Site:
    http://www.sydneyfishmarket.com
Sales Range: $50-74.9 Million
Emp.: 55
Fish & Seafood Markets
N.A.I.C.S.: 445250
Bryan Skepper (Gen Mgr)

SYDNEY MARKETS LTD
Level 3 Sydney Markets Plaza Business And Shopping Centre, 250-318 Parramatta Road, Sydney, 2129, NSW, Australia
Tel.: (61) 293256200
Web Site:
    http://www.sydneymarkets.com.au
Sales Range: $25-49.9 Million
Emp.: 80
Retail Markets
N.A.I.C.S.: 459999
Bradley Latham (CEO)

SYDNEY OPERA HOUSE
Bennelong Point, Sydney, 2001, NSW, Australia
Tel.: (61) 292507111
Web Site:
    http://www.sydneyoperahouse.com
Sales Range: $50-74.9 Million
Emp.: 700
Opera Productions
N.A.I.C.S.: 711110
Rachel Healy (Dir-Performing Arts)

SYDSVENSKA HEM AB
Stenhuggaregatan 4, PO Box 7415, 211 41, Malmo, Sweden
Tel.: (46) 707246848
Web Site:
    https://www.sydsvenskahem.se
Real Estate Manangement Services
N.A.I.C.S.: 531390
Johan Askogh (CEO)

SYDVEST ENERGI AMBA
Edison Park 1, 6715, Esbjerg, Denmark
Tel.: (45) 70 11 50 00
Web Site: http://www.se.dk
Sales Range: $200-249.9 Million
Emp.: 1,500
Energy Services & Broadband Fiber Network Services
N.A.I.C.S.: 221122
Niels Duedahl (CEO)

Subsidiaries:

Stofa A/S (1)
Slet Parkvej 5-7, 8310, Tranbjerg, Denmark
Tel.: (45) 88 30 30 30
Web Site: http://www.stofa.dk
Sales Range: $200-249.9 Million
Emp.: 400
Internet, Cable Television & Telephone Services
N.A.I.C.S.: 516210

SYENSQO SA
Rue de la Fusee 98, 1130, Brussels, Belgium
Tel.: (32) 22641900
Web Site: https://www.syensqo.com
Year Founded: 2023
SYENS—(ITA)
Chemical Products Mfr
N.A.I.C.S.: 325199
Ilham Kadri (CEO)

SYGNIA LIMITED
7th Floor The Foundry Cardiff Street, Green Point, Cape Town, 8001, South Africa
Tel.: (27) 214464940   ZA
Web Site: https://www.sygnia.co.za
Year Founded: 2003
SYG—(JSE)
Rev.: $44,565,849
Assets: $7,559,303,066
Liabilities: $7,515,942,500
Net Worth: $43,360,566
Earnings: $15,866,243
Emp.: 316
Fiscal Year-end: 09/30/23
Holding Company
N.A.I.C.S.: 551112
Haroon I. Bhorat (Chm)

SYLA TECHNOLOGIES CO., LTD.
Ebisu Prime Square Tower 7F 1-1-39 Hiroo, Shibuya-ku, Tokyo, 150-0012, Japan
Tel.: (81) 345600650   JP
Web Site: https://www.syla-tech.jp
Year Founded: 2009
SYT—(NASDAQ)
Rev.: $150,270,301
Assets: $264,845,900
Liabilities: $190,972,858
Net Worth: $73,873,043
Earnings: $4,906,634
Emp.: 138
Fiscal Year-end: 12/31/23
Property Management Services
N.A.I.C.S.: 531311
Takahide Watanabe (Chief Strategy Officer)

SYLLA GOLD CORP.
1550 Bedford Highway Suite 802 Sun Tower, Bedford, B4A 1E6, NS, Canada
Tel.: (902) 832-5555
Web Site: https://syllagold.com
Year Founded: 1985
ANL—(TSXV)
Assets: $43,475
Liabilities: $928,286
Net Worth: ($884,810)
Earnings: ($1,064,348)
Fiscal Year-end: 02/29/24
Mineral Exploration Services
N.A.I.C.S.: 213114

Subsidiaries:

Sylla Gold Mining S.A.R.L. (1)

SYLOGIST LTD.
5920 1a St SW, Calgary, T2S 1R8, AB, Canada
Tel.: (403) 266-4808   AB
Web Site: https://www.sylogist.com
Year Founded: 1993
SYZ—(TSXV)
Rev.: $49,470,932
Assets: $72,926,469
Liabilities: $44,536,222
Net Worth: $28,390,247
Earnings: $830,632
Fiscal Year-end: 12/31/23
Enterprise Financial Management Solutions Developer, Installer & Integrater
N.A.I.C.S.: 561499
Barry Foster (Chm)

Subsidiaries:

Epic Data (1)
5 Richard Way SW Suite 102, Calgary, AB, Canada
Tel.: (604) 273-9146
Web Site: http://www.epicdata.com
Integrated Data Capture, Processing & Dissemination Products Mfr
N.A.I.C.S.: 541512

INTERNATIONAL PUBLIC

Subsidiary (Non-US):

Epic Data Limited (2)
Medway House Newbury Business Park, London Road, Newbury, RG14 2PZ, Berkshire, United Kingdom
Tel.: (44) 1635 521140
Web Site: http://www.epicdata.com
Sales Range: $25-49.9 Million
Emp.: 3
Integrated Data Capture, Processing & Dissemination Products Mfr
N.A.I.C.S.: 541512

Information Strategies, Inc. (1)
5101 Wisconsin Ave NW Ste 420, Washington, DC 20016
Tel.: (202) 364-8822
Web Site: https://www.infostrat.com
Custom Computer Programming Services
N.A.I.C.S.: 541511
James Townsend (VP)

Serenic Canada Inc. (1)
15397-117th Avenue Suite 208, Edmonton, T5M 3X4, AB, Canada
Tel.: (780) 489-5756
Web Site: https://www.serenic.com
Financial & Business Management Software Developer, Publisher & Whslr
N.A.I.C.S.: 513210

Serenic Software, Inc. (1)
10354 W Chatfield Ave Ste 200, Littleton, CO 80127
Tel.: (303) 980-6007
Web Site: https://www.serenic.com
Financial & Business Management Software Developer, Publisher & Whslr
N.A.I.C.S.: 513210

SYLPH TECHNOLOGIES LIMITED
G -18A Rajani Bhawan 569/2 M G Road, AB Road, Indore, 452001, MP, India
Tel.: (91) 9904747441
Web Site:
    https://www.sylphtechnologies.com
Year Founded: 1992
511447—(BOM)
Rev.: $155,282
Assets: $2,050,762
Liabilities: $220,802
Net Worth: $1,829,960
Earnings: $45,509
Emp.: 6
Fiscal Year-end: 03/31/22
Software Development Services
N.A.I.C.S.: 541511
Vineet Shrivastava (Exec Dir)

Subsidiaries:

Sakshi Powertech Private Limited (1)
101-A Press House 22 Press Complex A B Road, Indore, 452008, India
Tel.: (91) 731 2571451
Web Site: http://www.sakshipower.com
Electrical Lamp Mfr & Distr
N.A.I.C.S.: 335139

SYLVANIA PLATINUM LIMITED
Clarendon House 2 Church Street, Hamilton, HM 11, Bermuda
Tel.: (441) 892264777
Web Site:
    http://www.sylvaniaplatinum.com
SLP—(AIM)
Rev.: $151,944,273
Assets: $279,437,947
Liabilities: $28,751,615
Net Worth: $250,686,332
Earnings: $56,150,844
Emp.: 628
Fiscal Year-end: 06/30/22
Metal Exploration Services
N.A.I.C.S.: 213114
Jaco J. Prinsloo (Co-CEO & Mng Dir)

Subsidiaries:

Sylvania South Africa (Pty) Ltd. (1)

Constantia Office Park Cycad House Ground Floor Block 17, Cnr 14th Avenue & Hendrik Potgieter Road Weltevreden Park, 1709, Johannaberg, Gauteng, South Africa
Tel.: (27) 116731171
Web Site: http://www.sylvaniaplatinum.com
Sales Range: $50-74.9 Million
Emp.: 30
Metal Mining & Exploration Services
N.A.I.C.S.: 212290
Terry McConnachie (Mng Dir)

SYLVESTRE FRERES INC.
7151 rue Jean Talon Est bureau 608, Montreal, H1M 3N8, QC, Canada
Tel.: (514) 351-6561
Web Site:
  http://www.sylvestrefreres.com
Year Founded: 1927
Rev.: $17,132,731
Emp.: 12
Wine Mfr
N.A.I.C.S.: 312130
Michel Sylvestre (Pres)

SYMAP SAS
ZAC des Fontanelles route de Labege, 31320, Castanet-Tolosan, France
Tel.: (33) 524667979
Sales Range: $25-49.9 Million
Emp.: 60
Miscellaneous General Merchandise Stores,
N.A.I.C.S.: 445110
Sylviane Lebreton (Pres)

SYMAX LIFT (HOLDING) CO. LTD.
2150-11980 Hammersmith Way, Richmond, V7A 0A4, BC, Canada
Tel.: (604) 277-6678   Ca
Web Site: http://www.symax.ca
Year Founded: 2006
Elevator Mfr & Sales
N.A.I.C.S.: 333921
Sabrina Xiaoyan Zhang (Pres & CEO)

SYMBIO PHARMACEUTICALS LIMITED
Toranomon Towers Office 7th floor 4-1-28 Toranomon, Minato-ku, Tokyo, 105-0001, Japan
Tel.: (81) 354721125
Web Site:
  https://www.symbiopharma.com
Year Founded: 2005
4582—(TKS)
Rev.: $39,626,010
Assets: $57,925,300
Liabilities: $6,813,490
Net Worth: $51,111,810
Earnings: ($13,910,580)
Fiscal Year-end: 12/31/23
Pharmaceuticals Mfr
N.A.I.C.S.: 325412
Fuminori Yoshida (Pres & CEO)

SYMBIOSIS PHARMA PVT LTD
Suketi Road, Kala Amb, Nagal Saketi, Himachal, Pradesh, 173030, India
Tel.: (91) 9812317700
Web Site: https://symbiosispharma.in
Pharmaceuticals Mfr
N.A.I.C.S.: 325412

SYMBIOX INVESTMENT & TRADING COMPANY LTD.
221 Rabindra Sarani 3rd Floor Room No 1, Kolkata, 700007, West Bengal, India
Tel.: (91) 3322740090
Web Site:
  https://www.symbioxinvestment.com
Year Founded: 1979

539278—(BOM)
Rev.: $421,450
Assets: $4,538,845
Liabilities: $312,492
Net Worth: $4,226,353
Earnings: $9,472
Fiscal Year-end: 03/31/21
Financial Investment Services
N.A.I.C.S.: 523999
Mahavir Verma (CFO)

SYMCOR INC.
1 Robert Speck Pkwy Ste 400, Mississauga, L4Z 4E7, ON, Canada
Tel.: (905) 273-1000
Web Site: http://www.symcor.com
Year Founded: 1996
Sales Range: $350-399.9 Million
Emp.: 5,000
Business & Management Services
N.A.I.C.S.: 561499
Gary Eisen (Gen Counsel, Sec & Sr VP)

SYMPHONY COMMUNICATION PUBLIC COMPANY LIMITED
123 Suntowers Building B 35th 36th Floor Vibhavadee Rangsit Road, Chomphon Chatuchak, Bangkok, 10900, Thailand
Tel.: (66) 21011111
Web Site:
  https://investor.symphony.net.th
Year Founded: 2005
SYMC—(THA)
Rev.: $58,862,825
Assets: $123,915,549
Liabilities: $39,009,511
Net Worth: $84,906,039
Earnings: $7,724,984
Emp.: 437
Fiscal Year-end: 12/31/23
High Speed Data Communication Circuits
N.A.I.C.S.: 334220
Woodtipong Moleechad (Chm)

SYMPHONY ENVIRONMENTAL TECHNOLOGIES PLC
6 Elstree Gate Elstree Way, Borehamwood, WD6 1JD, Hertfordshire, United Kingdom
Tel.: (44) 2082075900
Web Site:
  https://www.symphonytech.com
SYM—(AIM)
Rev.: $12,438,073
Assets: $8,750,505
Liabilities: $4,036,502
Net Worth: $4,714,004
Earnings: ($1,908,954)
Emp.: 37
Fiscal Year-end: 12/31/21
Plastic Container Developer
N.A.I.C.S.: 326199
Michael Stephen (Deputy Chm & Dir-Comml)

Subsidiaries:

Symphony Energy Limited (1)
6 Elstree Gate Elstree Way, Borehamwood, WD6 1JD, Hertfordshire, United Kingdom
Tel.: (44) 2082075900
Web Site:
  http://www.symphonyenvironmental.com
Sales Range: $25-49.9 Million
Emp.: 24
Polythene Products Distr
N.A.I.C.S.: 424130

Symphony Environmental Limited (1)
6 Elstree Gate Elstree Way, Borehamwood, WD6 1JD, Hertfordshire, United Kingdom
Tel.: (44) 208 207 5900
Web Site:
  https://www.symphonyenvironmental.com

Sales Range: $25-49.9 Million
Emp.: 50
Eco Friendly Polythene Products Distr
N.A.I.C.S.: 424130

SYMPHONY HOLDINGS LIMITED
10/F Island Place Tower No 510 Kings Road, North Point, China (Hong Kong)
Tel.: (852) 29078888   BM
Web Site:
  http://www.symphonyholdings.com
1223—(HKG)
Rev.: $35,592,008
Assets: $655,106,093
Liabilities: $292,292,858
Net Worth: $362,813,235
Earnings: ($11,342,528)
Emp.: 193
Fiscal Year-end: 12/31/22
Casual & Athletic Footwear Mfr
N.A.I.C.S.: 316210
Gary Kar Lee Chan (COO)

Subsidiaries:

China Rise Securities Asset Management Company Limited (1)
10/F Island Place Tower 510 King's Road, North Point, China (Hong Kong)
Tel.: (852) 2 158 9000
Web Site: http://www.chinarisesec.com.hk
Security Trading & Asset Management Services
N.A.I.C.S.: 523150

Liang Shing Industries (HK) Limited (1)
10th Floor Island Place Twr, North Point, China (Hong Kong) (100%)
Tel.: (852) 29078888
Web Site:
  http://www.symphonyholdings.com
Sales Range: $25-49.9 Million
Emp.: 60
Footwear Mfr
N.A.I.C.S.: 316210

Lucky Port Trading Limited (1)
10th Floor Island Place Twr, North Point, China (Hong Kong) (100%)
Tel.: (852) 29078888
Footwear Mfr
N.A.I.C.S.: 316210

Power Plus Limited (1)
The Power House, W Dock St, Hull, HU34HH, United Kingdom (100%)
Tel.: (44) 1482221522
Industrial Building Construction & Mfr
N.A.I.C.S.: 236210

Symphony Resources Limited (1)
10th Floor Island Place Tower 510 Kings Road, North Point, China (Hong Kong)
Tel.: (852) 29078888
Sales Range: $50-74.9 Million
Emp.: 60
Sportswear Distr
N.A.I.C.S.: 424350

SYMPHONY INTERNATIONAL HOLDINGS LIMITED
200 Newton Road 07-01 Newton 200, Singapore, 307983, Singapore
Tel.: (65) 65366177
Web Site:
  https://www.symphonyasia.com
SIHL—(LSE)
Rev.: $12,280,000
Assets: $381,818,000
Liabilities: $425,000
Net Worth: $381,393,000
Earnings: ($102,235,000)
Fiscal Year-end: 12/31/23
Investment Management Service
N.A.I.C.S.: 523999
Pierangelo Bottinelli (Chm)

Subsidiaries:

Eagles Holdings Pte. Ltd. (1)

22 Sin Ming Lane, Singapore, 573969, Singapore
Tel.: (65) 66943020
Web Site: http://www.eaglepetro.com
Oil & Energy Services
N.A.I.C.S.: 213112
Rolin Agnel Dsouza (CEO)

Symphony Asia Holdings Pte Ltd (1)
200 Newton Road 07-01 Newton 200, Singapore, 307983, Singapore
Tel.: (65) 65366177
Web Site: http://www.symphonyasia.com
Emp.: 8
Investment Management Service
N.A.I.C.S.: 523999
Raj Rajkumar (Partner)

Symphony Asia Limited (1)
Rm 1408 2 Exchange Sq 8 Connaught Place, Central, China (Hong Kong)
Tel.: (852) 28016199
Web Site: http://www.symphonyasia.com
Emp.: 12
Investment Consulting Services
N.A.I.C.S.: 523940
Sunil Chandiramani (Co-Partner)

SYMPHONY LIFE BERHAD
01-3 3rd Floor Menara Symphony No 5 Jalan Khoo Kay Kim, Seksyen 13, 46200, Petaling Jaya, Selangor Darul Ehsan, Malaysia
Tel.: (60) 376881888
Web Site:
  https://www.symphonylife.my
Year Founded: 1964
SYML—(KLS)
Rev.: $64,639,328
Assets: $376,215,840
Liabilities: $149,271,210
Net Worth: $226,944,630
Earnings: $13,644,675
Fiscal Year-end: 03/31/21
Property Development & Investment Services
N.A.I.C.S.: 531311
Hazurin Harun (CFO)

SYMPHONY LIMITED
Symphony House Third Floor FP12-TP50 Bodakdev Off SG Highway, Ahmedabad, 380 059, Gujarat, India
Tel.: (91) 7966211111
Web Site:
  https://www.symphonylimited.com
Year Founded: 1988
517385—(BOM)
Rev.: $148,407,170
Assets: $168,260,896
Liabilities: $62,642,527
Net Worth: $105,618,368
Earnings: $13,893,651
Emp.: 462
Fiscal Year-end: 03/31/23
Evaporative Air Cooler & Water Heater Mfr
N.A.I.C.S.: 333415
Achal Bakeri (Founder, Chm & Mng Dir)

Subsidiaries:

Symphony AU Pty. Limited (1)
Level 27 Suite 27 06 1 Farrer Place, Sydney, 2000, NSW, Australia
Tel.: (61) 291398894
Web Site: https://symphonyinfra.com.au
Energy Transition Services
N.A.I.C.S.: 221118

Symphony Limited - SEZ Unit (1)
Plot no 177 178 201 & 202 Surat Special Economic Zone, Sachin Dist, Surat, 394230, Gujarat, India
Tel.: (91) 261 2397038
Web Site: http://www.symphonylimited.com
Air Cooler & Water Heater Mfr
N.A.I.C.S.: 333415

Symphony USA Inc. (1)
1100 N 24th Ave Ste 601, Phoenix, AZ 85029
Tel.: (602) 281-7816

SYMPHONY LIMITED

Symphony Limited—(Continued)
Web Site: https://www.symphony-usa.com
Air Conditioning Equipment Mfr
N.A.I.C.S.: 333415

SYMRISE AG
Muhlenfeldstrasse 1, 37603, Holzminden, Germany
Tel.: (49) 5531900 De
Web Site: http://www.symrise.com
Year Founded: 1874
Rev.: $3,816,319,380
Assets: $6,671,240,071
Liabilities: $3,911,420,131
Net Worth: $2,759,819,939
Earnings: $341,710,721
Emp.: 10,264
Fiscal Year-end: 12/31/19
Fragrance Flavor & Cosmetic Ingredient Mfr
N.A.I.C.S.: 311930
Achim Daub *(Pres-Scent & Care & Member-Exec Bd)*

Subsidiaries:

American Dehydrated Foods, Inc. (1)
3801 E Sunshine St, Springfield, MO 65809
Tel.: (417) 881-7755
Web Site: http://www.adfinc.com
Egg Processing
N.A.I.C.S.: 311999
William H. Darr *(Founder)*

Cobell Limited (1)
The Juice House Unit 1 Leigham Business Units Silverton Road, Exeter, EX2 8HY, United Kingdom
Tel.: (44) 1392825400
Web Site: http://www.cobell.co.uk
Fruit & Vegetable Whslr
N.A.I.C.S.: 424480
Nick Sprague *(Founder)*

DIANA S.A.S. (1)
10 rue de la ferme du Talhouet, 56250, Saint Nolff, Cedex, France
Tel.: (33) 2 9748 4900
Web Site: http://www.diana-symrise.com
Sales Range: $550-599.9 Million
Emp.: 2,000
Organic Ingredients & Concentrates Mfr
N.A.I.C.S.: 325199
Caroline Avier *(Specialist-Comm)*

Subsidiary (US):

DIANA Naturals Inc. (2)
1702 Eska Way, Silverton, OR 97381-1294
Tel.: (503) 873-3600
Web Site: http://www.diana-food.com
Sales Range: $10-24.9 Million
Emp.: 50
Vegetable Extracts & Concentrates Mfr
N.A.I.C.S.: 311930

DianaPlantSciences Inc. (2)
18183 SW Boones Ferry Rd, Portland, OR 97224-7744 (100%)
Tel.: (503) 505-6977
Web Site: http://www.diana-group.com
Sales Range: $10-24.9 Million
Emp.: 12
Fungus & Chemicals Research
N.A.I.C.S.: 541720

Diana Food Canada Inc. (1)
240 Route Ste-Marie, Industrial Site, Saint-Adelphe-de-Champlain, G0X 1C0, QC, Canada
Tel.: (819) 295-1100
Pet Food Mfr
N.A.I.C.S.: 311111

Diana Food Chile SpA (1)
Longitudinal Sur Km 40, PO Box 258, Industrial Site Research & Development Center and Sales Office, Buin, Chile
Tel.: (56) 224107600
Cosmetics Products Mfr
N.A.I.C.S.: 325620
Juliette Silva Guerrero *(Mgr-HR)*

Diana Food Limited (1)
Holbeach Technology Park, Holbeach, King's Lynn, PE12 7PT, Lincolnshire, United Kingdom
Tel.: (44) 3450345340
Pet Food Mfr
N.A.I.C.S.: 311111

Diana Food SAS (1)
5 rue de la Gare, Antrain, 35560, Saint-Ouen-l'Aumone, France
Tel.: (33) 299292030
Web Site: http://www.diana-food.com
Fruit & Vegetable Whslr
N.A.I.C.S.: 424480
Jean-Yves Parisot *(Dir-Publication)*

Diana Pet Food Colombia S.A.S. (1)
Lote 41 Ereda Tibito, Parque Industrial Gran Sabana Tocancipa, 251017, Cundinamarca, Colombia
Tel.: (57) 17024260
Pet Food Mfr
N.A.I.C.S.: 311111

Diana Petfood (Chuzhou) Company Limited (1)
33 Central Avenue Gate 4, Lai An Economic Development Zone Industrial Site, Chuzhou, Anhui, China
Tel.: (86) 5502350079
Pet Food Mfr
N.A.I.C.S.: 311111

DrinkStar GmbH (1)
Aussere Oberaustrasse 36/5, 83026, Rosenheim, Germany
Tel.: (49) 8031 2434 0
Web Site: http://www.drinkstar.de
Emp.: 40
Beverage Product Distr
N.A.I.C.S.: 424820
Roland Bittermann *(Mng Dir)*

Flavors Direct Ltd (1)
12 Cockerell Road, Corby, NN17 5DU, Northamptonshire, United Kingdom
Tel.: (44) 1536 463120
Pickled Fruit Vegetable & Sauce Mfr
N.A.I.C.S.: 311941

International Dehydrated Foods, Inc. (1)
3801 E Sunshine St, Springfield, MO 65809
Tel.: (417) 881-7820
Web Site: http://www.idf.com
Mfr of Meat Powders, Fats & Broths
N.A.I.C.S.: 311615
Debbie Thomas *(Office Mgr)*

OOO Symrise Rogovo (1)
Near Township Rogovo estate 1 Settlement Rogovskoe, 142167, Moscow, Russia
Tel.: (7) 4959262417
Cosmetics Products Mfr
N.A.I.C.S.: 325620

Octopepper SAS (1)
22 Vital Carles Street, 33000, Bordeaux, France
Tel.: (33) 950279074
Web Site: http://www.octopepper.com
Digital Marketing Services
N.A.I.C.S.: 541613

Origines S.a.r.L. (1)
Lot ID 63 Ambohidahy Anosy, Antananarivo, 101, Madagascar
Tel.: (261) 202222297
Cosmetics Products Mfr
N.A.I.C.S.: 325620

P.T. Symrise (1)
Menara Bidakara 20th Fl Jl Jend Gatot Subroto Kav 71-73, Pancoran, Jakarta, 12870, Indonesia
Tel.: (62) 21 8379 3001
Emp.: 40
Specialty Chemicals Distr
N.A.I.C.S.: 424690

Probi AB (1)
Ideongatan 1A, 223 70, Lund, Sweden (72.5%)
Tel.: (46) 462868920
Web Site: https://www.probi.com
Rev.: $57,909,747
Assets: $147,038,692
Liabilities: $14,922,307
Net Worth: $132,116,384
Earnings: $3,804,734
Emp.: 154
Fiscal Year-end: 12/31/2022
Nutritional Products Developer
N.A.I.C.S.: 445298
Jean-Yves Parisot *(Chm)*

Probi Asia-Pacific Pte Ltd. (1)
226 Pandan Loop, Singapore, 128412, Singapore
Tel.: (65) 66351939
Health Care & Food Product Mfr
N.A.I.C.S.: 325411

Probi Food AB (1)
Ideongatan 1A, 223 70, Lund, Sweden
Tel.: (46) 462868920
Web Site: http://www.probi.com
Health Care & Food Product Mfr
N.A.I.C.S.: 325411

Probi US, Inc. (1)
9609 153rd Ave NE, Redmond, WA 98052
Tel.: (425) 883-9518
Health Care & Food Product Mfr
N.A.I.C.S.: 325411
Kimberly Fry *(Mgr-Quality Sys)*

Roseland World Corp. (1)
Roseland World Building Round About 12 Jebel Ali Free Zone, Dubai, United Arab Emirates
Tel.: (971) 48830220
Web Site: http://www.symrise.com
Sales Range: $25-49.9 Million
Emp.: 25
Fruit Juices Mfr
N.A.I.C.S.: 311411
Tamer Abwini *(Mng Dir)*

Scelta Umami B.V. (1)
Pannenberg 3, 5951 DM, Belfeld, Netherlands
Tel.: (31) 778503025
Food Seasoning Mfr
N.A.I.C.S.: 311942
Jan Klerken Jr. *(Exec Dir)*

Specialites Pet Food SA de C.V (1)
Parque Ind Bernardo Quintana Av La Canada No 20, El Marques, 76246, Queretaro, Mexico
Tel.: (52) 4422215762
Pet Food Mfr
N.A.I.C.S.: 311111

Specialites Pet Food SAS (1)
Z A du Gohelis, 56250, Elven, France
Tel.: (33) 297938080
Web Site: http://www.diana-petfood.com
Pet Food Mfr
N.A.I.C.S.: 311111
Bertrand De Launay *(Dir-Publication)*

Specialites Pet Food South Africa (Pty) Ltd. (1)
Old Paarl Road R101 Southern, Paarl, 7646, South Africa
Tel.: (27) 218632886
Cosmetics Products Mfr
N.A.I.C.S.: 325620

Symotion GmbH (1)
Muhlenfeldstr 1, 37603, Holzminden, Germany
Tel.: (49) 5531 90 2929
Web Site: http://www.symotion.com
Logistics Consulting Servies
N.A.I.C.S.: 541614
Reinhard Nowak *(Mng Dir)*

Symrise (1)
13 Rue Jean Jaures, F 92807, Puteaux, France
Tel.: (33) 149065500
Web Site: http://www.symrise.com
Sales Range: $100-124.9 Million
Emp.: 500
Mfr & Sales of Fragrance & Flavors
N.A.I.C.S.: 311930

Symrise (Pty) Ltd (1)
27 Wrench Road, Isando, 1600, South Africa
Tel.: (27) 11 281 3000
Web Site: http://www.symrise.com
Food Products Mfr
N.A.I.C.S.: 311999

Symrise Aromas e Fragrancias Ltda. (1)
Rua Alexandre de Gusmao 568, Bairro Socorro, 04760-020, Sao Paulo, Brazil
Tel.: (55) 1156946000

INTERNATIONAL PUBLIC

Cosmetics Products Mfr
N.A.I.C.S.: 325620

Symrise Asia Pacific Pte Ltd (1)
No 226 Pandan Loop, Singapore, 128412, Singapore
Tel.: (65) 6779 4551
Food Products Ingredient Mfr
N.A.I.C.S.: 325998

Symrise Asia Pacific Pte Ltd. (1)
190 Pandan Loop, Singapore, 128379, Singapore
Tel.: (65) 67794551
Web Site: http://www.symrise.com
Sales Range: $100-124.9 Million
Emp.: 300
Marketing & Distribution of Flavorings & Fragrance Compounds
N.A.I.C.S.: 311930
Mathys Boeren *(Pres-Flavors)*

Symrise B.V. (1)
Stationsplein 3c, 5241 GN, Rosmalen, Netherlands
Tel.: (31) 73 5235151
Sales Range: $25-49.9 Million
Emp.: 12
Cosmetic Ingredient Mfr
N.A.I.C.S.: 325998
Jan Hein Hagenbeek *(Gen Mgr)*

Symrise BioActives GmbH (1)
Porgersing 50, 22113, Hamburg, Germany
Tel.: (49) 407360450
Cosmetics Products Mfr
N.A.I.C.S.: 325620

Symrise C.A. (1)
Av Casanova Entre Calles Villaflor y Union Torre Banco Plaza Piso 9, Ofic 9C Sabana Grande, Caracas, 1050, Venezuela
Tel.: (58) 2127619181
Cosmetics Products Mfr
N.A.I.C.S.: 325620

Symrise GmbH (1)
Anton Jaumann Industrie Pk 9, 86720, Nordlingen, Germany
Tel.: (49) 908180120
Web Site: http://www.symrise.com
Sales Range: $25-49.9 Million
Emp.: 150
Mfr of Flavorings & Fragrances
N.A.I.C.S.: 311930
Carnelia Lichter *(Mgr-Mktg)*

Symrise Holding Pte Ltd (1)
226 Pandan Loop Clementi, Singapore, 128412, Singapore
Tel.: (65) 67794551
Investment Management Service
N.A.I.C.S.: 523999

Symrise Iberica S.L. (1)
Carretera 17 Km 15 Poligono Industrial Con Volart, Apartado De Correos 48, Parets del Valles, 08150, Spain
Tel.: (34) 935735700
Web Site: http://www.symrise.com
Sales Range: $50-74.9 Million
Emp.: 90
Sale of Flavoring Distr
N.A.I.C.S.: 424490

Symrise Inc (1)
18/F Taipan Place F Ortigas Jr Road, Pasig, 1605, Philippines
Tel.: (63) 2 6345961
Web Site: http://www.symrise.com
Sales Range: $25-49.9 Million
Cosmetic & Fragrance Ingredient Chemicals Mfr
N.A.I.C.S.: 325998

Symrise Italy (1)
Viale Certosa 144, 20156, Milan, Italy
Tel.: (39) 02 380 9811
Web Site: https://www.symrise.com
Sales Range: $25-49.9 Million
Emp.: 40
Mfr Flavors
N.A.I.C.S.: 311930
Daniele Sarei *(Mgr)*

Symrise K.K. (1)
3-32-3 Shiba, Minato-ku, Tokyo, 105 0014, Japan
Tel.: (81) 337984261
Mfr & Sales of Fragrances & Flavors
N.A.I.C.S.: 311930

AND PRIVATE COMPANIES

Symrise Kimya Sanayi ve Ticaret Ltd (1)
Ataturk Cad No 82 Sitkibey Plaza D16, Kozyatagi, 34736, Istanbul, Turkiye
Tel.: (90) 216 477 71 90
Chemical Products Distr
N.A.I.C.S.: 424690

Symrise Ltd (1)
11FL BS Tower 6-4 Sunae-Dong Bundang-Gu Seongnam-Si, Bundang-gu, Seongnam, 463-825, Gyeonggi-Do, Korea (South)
Tel.: (82) 31 778 8822
Web Site: http://www.symrise.com
Sales Range: $25-49.9 Million
Emp.: 9
Personal Care Chemicals Mfr
N.A.I.C.S.: 325998
Nick Henry (Gen Mgr)

Symrise Ltd (1)
9th Floor Q House Sathorn Building 11 South Sathorn Road, Tungmahamek Sathorn, Bangkok, 10120, Thailand
Tel.: (66) 2 679 1966
Web Site: http://www.symrise.com
Cosmetics Products Mfr
N.A.I.C.S.: 325620

Symrise Ltd. (1)
Fieldhouse Lane, Marlow, SL7 1TB, Buckinghamshire, United Kingdom
Tel.: (44) 162 864 6017
Web Site: https://www.symrise.com
Sales Range: $50-74.9 Million
Emp.: 80
Sales of Fragrance & Flavor Compounds
N.A.I.C.S.: 424490

Symrise Ltda. (1)
Rua Alexandre De Gusmao 568, Socorro, Sao Paulo, 4779900, Brazil
Tel.: (55) 156946000
Web Site: http://www.symrise.com
Sales Range: $25-49.9 Million
Emp.: 200
Mfr & Sell Flavors & Fragrances
N.A.I.C.S.: 311930

Symrise Ltda. (1)
Carrera 58 No 1080, NIL, Bogota, Colombia
Tel.: (57) 14252200
Web Site: http://www.symrise.com
Sales Range: $25-49.9 Million
Emp.: 100
Mfr & Sales of Flavors & Fragrances
N.A.I.C.S.: 311930
Mauricio Torres (Acct Mgr)

Symrise Middle East Limited (1)
Jebel Ali Free Zone, PO Box 18188, Dubai, United Arab Emirates
Tel.: (971) 4 883 0220
Sales Range: $25-49.9 Million
Emp.: 25
Food Ingredient Distr
N.A.I.C.S.: 424690
Tamer Abwini (Mng Dir)

Symrise Parsian PJS Co. (1)
Flat No 9 - 12th Floor Negar Tower Vanak Square, Tehran, Iran
Tel.: (98) 218864198085
Cosmetics Products Mfr
N.A.I.C.S.: 325620

Symrise Pty. Ltd. (1)
168 S Creek Rd Locked Bag 2, Dee Why, 2099, Nsw, Australia
Tel.: (61) 299827800
Web Site: http://www.symrise.com
Sales Range: $1-9.9 Million
Emp.: 60
Flavoring Product Mfr
N.A.I.C.S.: 311930

Symrise Pvt Ltd (1)
140 Old Mahabalipuram Road, Semmancheri, Chennai, 600 119, India
Tel.: (91) 44 2450 1739
Web Site: http://www.symrise.com
Sales Range: $25-49.9 Million
Cosmetic Ingredient Mfr
N.A.I.C.S.: 325998

Symrise S.A. de C.V. (1)
Calz. Union No. 7, Complejo Industrial Cuamatla, Cuautitlan, 54730, Mexico, Mexico
Tel.: (52) 5558641200

Web Site: http://www.symrise.com
Sales Range: $25-49.9 Million
Emp.: 52
Frangrances & Flavors Mfr & Whslr
N.A.I.C.S.: 311930
Maartha Soto (Mgr)

Symrise S.A.E. (1)
3rd Industrial Zone-New Extension, 6th of October City, Egypt
Tel.: (20) 238341821
Cosmetics Products Mfr
N.A.I.C.S.: 325620

Symrise S.R.L. (1)
Valparaiso 4125, B1667BBQ, Tortuguitas, Buenos Aires, Argentina
Tel.: (54) 3327459508
Cosmetics Products Mfr
N.A.I.C.S.: 325620

Symrise S.a.r.L. (1)
Lot ID 63 Ambohidahy Anosy, Antananarivo, 101, Madagascar
Tel.: (261) 320522164
Cosmetics Products Mfr
N.A.I.C.S.: 325620

Symrise S.r.l. (1)
Viale Certosa 144, 20156, Milan, Italy
Tel.: (39) 023809811
Cosmetics Products Mfr
N.A.I.C.S.: 325620
Giovanna Berti (Acct Mgr)

Symrise SA (1)
Lira 2338, 894 0578, San Joaquin, Santiago, Chile
Tel.: (56) 2 5442422
Sales Range: $25-49.9 Million
Emp.: 3
Beverages Mfr
N.A.I.C.S.: 312111
Natalia Dimitroff Djurovic (Gen Mgr)

Symrise Sdn Bhd (1)
2-3 Level 2 Block B Peremba Square Saujana Resort Seksyen U2, 40150, Shah Alam, Selangor Darul Ehsan, Malaysia
Tel.: (60) 3 7843 0030
Web Site: http://www.symrise.com
Cosmetics Products Mfr
N.A.I.C.S.: 325620

Symrise Shanghai Limited (1)
30 Long Qiao Road Jin Qiao Export Processing Zone, Pudong New Area, Shanghai, 201206, China
Tel.: (86) 2158996218
Food Products Mfr
N.A.I.C.S.: 311999
Cady Zhou (Mktg Mgr)

Symrise Vertriebs GmbH (1)
Heiligenstadter Strasse 31/3, 1190, Vienna, Austria
Tel.: (43) 1 86682
Sales Range: $25-49.9 Million
Emp.: 2
Chemical & Allied Products Whslr
N.A.I.C.S.: 424690
Manuel Franke (Gen Mgr)

Symrise, Inc. (1)
300 N St, Teterboro, NJ 07608
Tel.: (201) 288-3200
Web Site: http://www.symrise.com
Mfr & Sell Flavors, Fragrances & Aroma Chemicals Used in Foods, Perfumery, Cosmetics & Other Consumer Products
N.A.I.C.S.: 325620
Rhona Stokols (VP-Fine Fragrance Sls-North America)

Subsidiary (Domestic):

Symrise Corporation (2)
1636 Bushy Pk Rd, Goose Creek, SC 29445-6326
Tel.: (843) 414-3400
Sales Range: $25-49.9 Million
Emp.: 48
Mfr of Specialty Chemicals
N.A.I.C.S.: 324110

Tesium GmbH (1)
Muehlenfeldstrasse 1, 37603, Holzminden, Germany
Tel.: (49) 5531903333
Web Site: http://www.tesium.com
Industrial Engineering Services

N.A.I.C.S.: 541330

SYMTEK AUTOMATION ASIA CO., LTD.
No 421 Rongmin Road, Zhongli District, Taoyuan, 320, Taiwan
Tel.: (886) 34356870
Web Site: https://www.saa-symtek.com
Year Founded: 1999
6438—(TAI)
Rev.: $180,151,924
Assets: $247,262,202
Liabilities: $131,835,631
Net Worth: $115,426,570
Earnings: $20,833,974
Emp.: 926
Fiscal Year-end: 12/31/22
Solar Equipment Mfr
N.A.I.C.S.: 333414
Chung-Cheng Liang (VP-EBU Bus)

SYN HF
Suourlandsbraut 8, 108, Reykjavik, Iceland
Tel.: (354) 5999000
Web Site: https://www.syn.is
SYN—(ICE)
Rev.: $172,660,972
Assets: $256,950,418
Liabilities: $181,281,150
Net Worth: $75,669,269
Earnings: $15,511,906
Emp.: 458
Fiscal Year-end: 12/31/23
Media Marketing Services
N.A.I.C.S.: 541840
Signy Magnusdottir (CFO)

SYN MUN KONG INSURANCE PUBLIC COMPANY LIMITED
313 Srinakarin Road Huamark Bangkapi, Bangkok, 10240, Thailand
Tel.: (66) 23787000
Web Site: http://www.smk.co.th
Year Founded: 1951
SMK—(THA)
Rev.: $226,584,336
Assets: $199,793,208
Liabilities: $1,038,221,665
Net Worth: ($838,428,458)
Earnings: ($900,888,297)
Emp.: 1,700
Fiscal Year-end: 12/31/22
Insurance Services
N.A.I.C.S.: 524298
Reungvit Dusdeesurapot (Chm)

SYN PROP E TECH SA
Av Brigadeiro Faria Lima, 3600 14 andar Itaim Bibi, 04538-132, Sao Paulo, 04538-132, Brazil
Tel.: (55) 1154127600
Web Site: https://syn.com.br
SYYNY—(OTCIQ)
Rev.: $84,695,982
Assets: $798,577,525
Liabilities: $286,985,941
Net Worth: $511,591,584
Earnings: $1,105,993
Fiscal Year-end: 12/31/23
Commercial Real Estate Investment Services
N.A.I.C.S.: 531390
Pedro Marcio Daltro Dos Santos (CEO)

SYN-TECH CHEM & PHARM CO., LTD.
No 168 Kai Yuan Rd, Hsin Ying, Tainan City, 73055, Taiwan
Tel.: (886) 663621213
Web Site: https://www.syn-tech.com.tw
Year Founded: 1982

1777—(TPE)
Rev.: $30,838,258
Assets: $86,903,199
Liabilities: $18,138,636
Net Worth: $68,764,562
Earnings: $9,232,655
Fiscal Year-end: 12/31/22
Pharmaceuticals Product Mfr
N.A.I.C.S.: 325412
J. M. Hsiao (Chm)

SYNACT PHARMA AB
Scheelevagen 2, 223 63, Lund, Sweden
Tel.: (46) 103001023
Web Site: https://synactpharma.com
Year Founded: 2013
SYNACT—(OMX)
Emp.: 5
Pharmaceutical Products Distr
N.A.I.C.S.: 424210
Henrik Stage (CFO)

SYNAIRGEN PLC
Mailpoint 810 Southampton General Hospital, Tremona Road, Southampton, SO16 6YD, United Kingdom
Tel.: (44) 2380512800 UK
Web Site: https://www.synairgen.com
SNG—(AIM)
Assets: $18,103,055
Liabilities: $1,985,989
Net Worth: $16,117,066
Earnings: ($10,706,519)
Emp.: 34
Fiscal Year-end: 12/31/23
Pharmaceutical Development Services
N.A.I.C.S.: 325412
Phillip Monk (Chief Scientific Officer)

Subsidiaries:

Synairgen Research Limited (1)
Mailpoint 810 Southampton General Hospital Tremona Road, Southampton, SO16 6YD, United Kingdom
Tel.: (44) 2380512800
Web Site: https://www.synairgen.com
Sales Range: $25-49.9 Million
Drug Discovery & Development Services
N.A.I.C.S.: 541715
Richard Marsten (CEO)

SYNALIA
42 Rue D Enghien, 75010, Paris, France
Tel.: (33) 155332300
Web Site: http://synalia.net
Rev.: $21,600,000
Emp.: 50
Jewelers' Cooperative
N.A.I.C.S.: 423940
Alain Regnier (Dir)

SYNBIOTIC SE
Barer Str 7, 80333, Munich, Germany
Web Site: https://www.synbiotic.com
Year Founded: 2015
SBX—(DEU)
Rev.: $4,260,956
Assets: $38,547,301
Liabilities: $21,117,121
Net Worth: $17,430,180
Earnings: ($11,734,187)
Emp.: 55
Fiscal Year-end: 12/31/23
Biotechnology Research & Development Services
N.A.I.C.S.: 541714
Lars Muller (CEO)

SYNCHRO FOOD CO., LTD.
EBIS South 1 1-7-8 Ebisu Minami, Shibuya-ku, Tokyo, 150-0022, Japan
Tel.: (81) 357689522
Web Site: https://www.synchro-food.co.jp

SYNCHRO FOOD CO., LTD.

Synchro Food Co., Ltd.—(Continued)
Year Founded: 2003
3963—(TKS)
Rev.: $23,809,220
Assets: $33,512,700
Liabilities: $5,142,580
Net Worth: $28,370,120
Earnings: $4,653,440
Emp.: 61
Fiscal Year-end: 03/31/24
Online Advertising Services
N.A.I.C.S.: 541810
Shinichi Fujishiro (CEO)

SYNCLAYER INC.
2-21-18 Chiyoda, Naka-ku, Nagoya, 460-0012, Japan
Tel.: (81) 522427871
Web Site: https://synclayer.co.jp
Year Founded: 1962
1724—(TKS)
Rev.: $74,040,870
Assets: $75,763,740
Liabilities: $35,471,270
Net Worth: $40,292,470
Earnings: $3,069,970
Emp.: 168
Fiscal Year-end: 12/31/23
Cable System Integration Services
N.A.I.C.S.: 541512
Masahiro Yamaguchi (Pres & CEO)

Subsidiaries:

Cable System Construction Co., Ltd. (1)
2-21-18 Chiyoda, Naka-ku, Nagoya, 460-0012, Aichi, Japan
Tel.: (81) 522427885
Web Site: https://www.c-sysken.co.jp
Electric Transmission Equipment Services
N.A.I.C.S.: 811310
Shigeyuki Aoyama (Pres)

SYNCMOLD ENTERPRISE CORP.
9F No 168 Jiankang Rd, Zhonghe Dist, New Taipei City, Taiwan
Tel.: (886) 266215888
Web Site:
https://www.syncmold.com.tw
Year Founded: 1979
1582—(TAI)
Rev.: $286,782,977
Assets: $393,910,087
Liabilities: $163,835,371
Net Worth: $230,074,716
Earnings: $20,849,831
Emp.: 94
Fiscal Year-end: 12/31/23
Plastic & Metal Molds Mfr
N.A.I.C.S.: 333511
Po-Sen Chiu (Gen Mgr)

Subsidiaries:

Chongqing Fulfil Tech Co., Ltd. (1)
No 8 Shiyang 1st Rd, Qinggang Town Bishan Dist, Chongqing, China
Tel.: (86) 2341518988
Monitor Assembly Mfr
N.A.I.C.S.: 334418

Dongguan Khuan Huang Precise Mold Plastic Co., Ltd. (1)
Area 3 Jinhe Management Zone, Zhangmutou Town Jinhe Industrial Zone Third District, Dongguan, Guangdong, China
Tel.: (86) 76982127128
Hardware Product Mfr
N.A.I.C.S.: 326199

Fujian Khuan Hua Precise Mold., Ltd. (1)
Hongzhi Road, Hongkuan Industrial Village Yangxia Town, Fuqing, Fujian, China
Tel.: (86) 59185193799
Plastics Product Mfr
N.A.I.C.S.: 326199

Kunshan Fulfil Tech Co., Ltd. (1)
No 257 FUIL Road, Zhang Pu Town, Kunshan, Jiangsu, China
Tel.: (86) 51236696996
Stamping Parts Mfr
N.A.I.C.S.: 334418

Suzhou Fulfil Electronics Co., Ltd. (1)
No 1201 Fuyuan Road, Xiangcheng Economic Development Zone, Suzhou, Jiangsu, China
Tel.: (86) 51265798188
Monitor Assembly Mfr
N.A.I.C.S.: 334418

Zhongshan Fulfil Tech Co., Ltd. (1)
No 18 Shabian Road, Huoju Development Zone, Zhongshan, Guangdong, China
Tel.: (86) 76088580588
Monitor Assembly Mfr
N.A.I.C.S.: 334418

SYNCOM FORMULATIONS (INDIA) LIMITED.
7 Niraj Industrial Estate Off Mahakali Caves Road Andheri East, Mumbai, 400 093, Maharashtra, India
Tel.: (91) 2226877700
Web Site:
https://www.syncomformulation.com
Year Founded: 1955
524470—(BOM)
Rev.: $34,390,645
Assets: $39,810,185
Liabilities: $14,204,969
Net Worth: $25,605,216
Earnings: $3,981,973
Emp.: 740
Fiscal Year-end: 03/31/21
Pharmaceuticals Product Mfr
N.A.I.C.S.: 325412
Kedarmal Shankarlal Bankda (Chm)

SYNCOM HEALTHCARE LIMITED
502 Advent Atria Chincholi Bunder Road, Opp Kingston Complex Malad (West), Mumbai, 400064, MH, India
Tel.: (91) 2228813796
Web Site:
http://www.syncomhealthcare.com
Rev.: $8,224,004
Assets: $7,092,736
Liabilities: $7,222,241
Net Worth: ($129,505)
Earnings: ($1,631,017)
Emp.: 416
Fiscal Year-end: 03/31/19
Pharmaceuticals Mfr
N.A.I.C.S.: 325412
Ajay Shankarlal Bankda (Chm & Mng Dir)

SYNCOMM TECHNOLOGY CORP.
10F-1 No 101 Sec 2 Gongdao 5th Rd, East Dist, Hsinchu, 30070, Taiwan
Tel.: (886) 35169188
Web Site:
https://www.syncomm.com.tw
Year Founded: 1998
3150—(TAI)
Semiconductor Equipment Mfr
N.A.I.C.S.: 333242
Tsai Ling-Chun (Chm)

SYNCONA LTD.
8 Bloomsbury Street, London, WC1B 3SR, United Kingdom
Tel.: (44) 2086393399
Web Site:
https://www.synconaltd.com
Year Founded: 2012
SYNC—(LSE)
Rev.: $24,506,328
Assets: $1,748,340,968
Liabilities: $30,878,760
Net Worth: $1,717,462,208
Earnings: $11,591,008
Fiscal Year-end: 03/31/22
Portfolio Management & Investment Advice
N.A.I.C.S.: 523940
Martin Murphy (CEO)

Subsidiaries:

Applied Genetic Technologies Corporation (1)
14193 NW 119th Ter Ste 10, Alachua, FL 32615
Tel.: (386) 462-2204
Web Site: https://www.agtc.com
Rev.: $325,000
Assets: $66,684,000
Liabilities: $37,207,000
Net Worth: $29,477,000
Earnings: ($68,943,000)
Emp.: 102
Fiscal Year-end: 06/30/2022
Pharmaceutical Preparation Mfr
N.A.I.C.S.: 325412
Stephen W. Potter (Chief Bus Officer)

Blue Earth Diagnostics Limited (1)
The Oxford Science Park Magdalen Centre Robert Robinson Avenue, Oxford, OX4 4GA, United Kingdom
Tel.: (44) 1865784186
Web Site:
http://www.blueearthdiagnostics.com
Diagnostic Services
N.A.I.C.S.: 621512
Jonathan Allis (CEO)

Freeline Therapeutics Limited (1)
Stevenage Bioscience Catalyst Gunnels Wood Road, Stevenage, SG1 2FX, Herts, United Kingdom
Tel.: (44) 1438906870
Web Site: http://www.freeline.life
Clinical Services
N.A.I.C.S.: 621999
Amit Nathwani (Co-Founder)

Quell Therapeutics Limited (1)
84 Wood Lane, London, W12 0BZ, United Kingdom
Tel.: (44) 2070969012
Web Site: http://www.quell-tx.com
Therapy Services
N.A.I.C.S.: 621999
Marc Martinez-Llordella (Founder & VP-Biology)

Syncona Investment Management Limited (1)
2nd Floor 8 Bloomsbury Street, London, WC1B 3SR, United Kingdom
Tel.: (44) 2039817909
Investment Services
N.A.I.C.S.: 523999

Subsidiary (Domestic):

Freeline Therapeutics Holdings plc (2)
Stevenage Bioscience Catalyst Gunnels Wood Road, Stevenage, SG1 2FX, Hertfordshire, United Kingdom (100%)
Tel.: (44) 1438906870
Web Site: http://www.freeline.life
Rev.: $9,843,000
Assets: $86,641,000
Liabilities: $34,227,000
Net Worth: $52,414,000
Earnings: ($88,972,000)
Emp.: 152
Fiscal Year-end: 12/31/2022
Holding Company
N.A.I.C.S.: 551112
David S. Arrington (VP-IR & Corp Comm)

SYNCORDIA TECHNOLOGIES AND HEALTHCARE SOLUTIONS CORP.
245 Carlaw Avenue Suite 500, Toronto, M4M 2S1, ON, Canada
Tel.: (416) 922-9096
Year Founded: 2014
Investment Services
N.A.I.C.S.: 523999
Bartley Heath (CFO)

SYNCORE BIOTECHNOLOGY CO., LTD.
84 Chung Shan Rd, Chung Shan Village Tung-Shan I-Lan, Taipei, 269, Taiwan
Tel.: (886) 39586101
Web Site:
https://www.syncorebio.com
Year Founded: 2008
4192—(TPE)
Rev.: $495,795
Assets: $13,652,503
Liabilities: $5,866,742
Net Worth: $7,785,761
Earnings: ($5,898,946)
Fiscal Year-end: 12/31/22
Health Care Srvices
N.A.I.C.S.: 621999
Muh-Hwan Su (Gen Mgr)

SYNEAR FOOD HOLDINGS LIMITED
Xisha Road East, Jinshui, Zhengzhou, 450008, Henan, China
Tel.: (86) 37165697086
Web Site: http://www.synear.com
Sales Range: $250-299.9 Million
Freeze & Dried Foods Mfr
N.A.I.C.S.: 311423

SYNECTICS PLC
Synectics House 3-4 Broadfield Close, Sheffield, S8 0XN, United Kingdom
Tel.: (44) 1142802828
Web Site:
https://www.synecticsplc.com
SNX—(AIM)
Rev.: $53,108,576
Assets: $71,174,398
Liabilities: $20,936,042
Net Worth: $50,238,355
Earnings: $1,989,060
Emp.: 305
Fiscal Year-end: 11/30/22
Electronic Control Systems for Closed-Circuit Television Security Applications
N.A.I.C.S.: 334419
Paul A. Webb (CEO)

Subsidiaries:

Quadrant Security Group Limited (1)
3 Attenborough Lane, Chilwell, Nottingham, NG9 5JN, United Kingdom
Tel.: (44) 1159252521
Web Site: http://www.qsg.co.uk
Sales Range: $150-199.9 Million
Emp.: 420
Security System Distr
N.A.I.C.S.: 423610

Subsidiary (Domestic):

Quadrant Security Group plc (2)
Axis 6 Rhodes Way Radlett Road, Watford, WD24 4YW, Herts, United Kingdom
Tel.: (44) 1923211550
Web Site: http://www.qsg.co.uk
Sales Range: $75-99.9 Million
Emp.: 130
Electronic Security Devices & Systems
N.A.I.C.S.: 561621

Division (Domestic):

Quadrant SSS (3)
Axis 6 Rhodes Way Radlett Road, Watford, WD24 4YW, Hertfordshire, United Kingdom
Tel.: (44) 1923211550
Web Site: http://www.qsg.co.uk
Sales Range: $10-24.9 Million
Emp.: 40
Security Services
N.A.I.C.S.: 561621

Subsidiary (Domestic):

Synectic Systems Group Limited (2)
3 - 4 Broadfield Close, Sheffield, S8 0XN, South Yorkshire, United Kingdom
Tel.: (44) 1142552509
Web Site: http://www.synx.com

AND PRIVATE COMPANIES

Sales Range: $25-49.9 Million
Emp.: 60
Surveillance Systems Distr
N.A.I.C.S.: 423610

Synectic Systems (Asia) Pte Limited (1)
150 Kampong Ampat 01-01/01-01A, Singapore, 368324, Singapore
Tel.: (65) 6 749 6166
Security & Surveillance Services
N.A.I.C.S.: 561621

Synectic Systems (Macau) Limited (1)
Alameda Dr Carlos D' Assumpcao No 411-417 Edf Dynasty Plaza 6 andar Q, Nape, Macau, China (Macau)
Tel.: (853) 2 855 5178
Security & Surveillance Services
N.A.I.C.S.: 561621

Synectic Systems GmbH (1)
Wilhelmstrasse 118, 10963, Berlin, Germany
Tel.: (49) 89 748 8620
Security & Surveillance Services
N.A.I.C.S.: 561621

Synectic Systems, Inc (1)
6398 Cindy Ln Ste 200, Carpinteria, CA 93013
Tel.: (805) 745-1920
Web Site: http://www.synecticsusa.com
Sales Range: $25-49.9 Million
Emp.: 25
Electronic Parts & Equipment Merchant Whslr
N.A.I.C.S.: 449210

Synectics Industrial Systems Ltd, (1)
The Flarepath Elsham Wold, Brigg, DN20 0SP, North Lincolnshire, United Kingdom
Tel.: (44) 1652688908
Sales Range: $25-49.9 Million
Emp.: 50
Surveillance Systems Distr
N.A.I.C.S.: 423610

Synectics Security Networks Ltd (1)
3 - 4 Broadfield Close, Sheffield, S8 0XNc, South Yorkshire, United Kingdom
Tel.: (44) 1142552509
Emp.: 50
Surveillance Systems Mfr
N.A.I.C.S.: 334419

SYNEKTIK S.A.
ul Jozefa Piusa Dziekonskiego 3, 00-728, Warsaw, Poland
Tel.: (48) 223270900
Web Site:
https://www.synektik.com.pl
Year Founded: 2001
SNT—(WAR)
Rev.: $113,534,443
Assets: $76,198,008
Liabilities: $42,102,223
Net Worth: $34,095,785
Earnings: $13,326,268
Fiscal Year-end: 09/30/23
Medical Equipment Whslr
N.A.I.C.S.: 423450
Artur Mieczyslaw Ostrowski *(Member-Mgmt Bd)*

SYNEL MLL PAYWAY LTD.
Rehov Hamadaa 2 TD 142, Yokneam, 20692, Israel
Tel.: (972) 49596777   II
Web Site: http://www.synel.co.il
Year Founded: 1991
SNEL—(TAE)
Rev.: $27,213,703
Assets: $30,987,981
Liabilities: $13,188,009
Net Worth: $17,799,972
Earnings: $3,853,847
Emp.: 900
Fiscal Year-end: 12/31/23
Offices of Other Holding Companies
N.A.I.C.S.: 551112
Erez Buganim *(Deputy CEO-Acting & VP-Mktg & Strategic Bus Dev-Intl)*

SYNERGETIC AUTO PERFORMANCE PCL
149 Moo 3 Theparak Road Theparak A, Mueang Samut Sakhon, 10270, Samut Prakarn, Thailand
Tel.: (66) 20918000
Web Site:
https://www.asapcarrent.com
ASAP—(THA)
Rev.: $96,997,955
Assets: $199,805,033
Liabilities: $174,608,497
Net Worth: $25,196,536
Earnings: ($8,425,371)
Emp.: 392
Fiscal Year-end: 12/31/23
Car Rental Services
N.A.I.C.S.: 532111
Sirawut Sukantanak *(Chm)*

SYNERGIA ENERGY LTD
Level 1 11 Lucknow Place, West Perth, 6005, WA, Australia
Tel.: (61) 894853200   AU
Web Site: http://www.oilex.com.au
SYN—(AIM)
Rev.: $108,366
Assets: $19,751,189
Liabilities: $8,577,382
Net Worth: $11,173,807
Earnings: ($1,579,826)
Emp.: 45
Fiscal Year-end: 06/30/22
Oil & Gas Producer & Sales
N.A.I.C.S.: 213112
Mark Bolton *(CFO)*

Subsidiaries:

Oilex (JPDA 06-103) Ltd. (1)
Level 3 50 Kings Park Road, West Perth, 6005, WA, Australia
Tel.: (61) 8 9226 5577
Web Site: http://www.oilex.com.au
Oil & Gas Property Development Services
N.A.I.C.S.: 211120

Oilex Oman Limited (1)
133 Alkhuwair, PO Box 1306, Ghallah, Oman
Tel.: (968) 24596336
Web Site: http://www.oilex.com.au
Sales Range: $50-74.9 Million
Emp.: 2
Oilfield Contractors & Services
N.A.I.C.S.: 213112

SYNERGIE CAD GROUP
1st Avenue 2nd Street, PO Box 423, 06515, Carros, France
Tel.: (33) 493082525
Web Site: http://www.synergie-cad.com
Year Founded: 1995
Sales Range: $10-24.9 Million
Emp.: 180
Design of Printed Circuit Board Mfr
N.A.I.C.S.: 335999
Alain Librati *(CEO)*

Subsidiaries:

SYNERGIE CAD Germany GmbH (1)
Fraunhoferstrasse 11, Ismaning, Germany
Tel.: (49) 89 969 9809 41
Web Site: http://www.synergie-cad.com
Printed Circuit Board Mfr & Distr
N.A.I.C.S.: 334419

SYNERGIE CAD Ltd. (1)
Greetwell Place Limeklin Way, Greetwell Road, Lincoln, United Kingdom
Tel.: (44) 1522 520 222
Web Site: http://www.synergie-cad.co.uk
Emp.: 9
Printed Circuit Board Mfr & Distr
N.A.I.C.S.: 334419
Roger Cooke *(Dir-Ops)*

SYNERGIE CAD Marocco (1)
Angle boulevard d Anfa et My Youssef Residence, Bab Abdelaziz 7eme etage, Casablanca, Morocco
Tel.: (212) 522 49 17 40
Printed Circuit Board Mfr & Distr
N.A.I.C.S.: 334419

SYNERGIE CAD PSC (1)
9 rue Marius Terce, Toulouse, France
Tel.: (33) 5 62 74 35 94
Printed Circuit Board Mfr & Distr
N.A.I.C.S.: 334419

SYNERGIE CAD Philippines (1)
Unit 702 common Goal Tower Finance cor, Alabang, Muntinlupa, Philippines
Tel.: (63) 2 842 3013
Printed Circuit Board Mfr & Distr
N.A.I.C.S.: 334419
Adrianne Failoga *(Engr-Design)*

SYNERGIE CAD South Korea (1)
Yatap-dong Bundan-gu, Seongnam, Gyeonggi-do, Korea (South)
Tel.: (82) 31 704 8102
Printed Circuit Board Mfr & Distr
N.A.I.C.S.: 334419

SYNERGIE CAD Test (1)
Parc Sainte Victoire Batiment 12, Meyreuil, 13590, France
Tel.: (33) 4 42 58 62 07
Web Site: http://www.synergie-cad-test.fr
Testing Device Mfr
N.A.I.C.S.: 334419
Thierry Canaud *(Dir-Ops & R&D)*

SYNERGIE CAD USA Inc (1)
555 Republic Dr Ste 305, Plano, TX 75074
Tel.: (972) 422-0271
Web Site: http://www.synergie-cad.us
Printed Circuit Board Mfr & Distr
N.A.I.C.S.: 334419
Malcolm Owens *(Dir-Ops)*

Synergy Board Systems USA, Inc. (1)
3420 E Shea Blvd Ste 143, Phoenix, AZ 85028-3399   (100%)
Tel.: (602) 992-3120
Web Site: http://www.sbsglobal.com
Mfr & Design of Printed Circuit Boards
N.A.I.C.S.: 334413

SYNERGIE SA
11 Avenue du Colonel Bonnet, 75016, Paris, France
Tel.: (33) 144149020
Web Site: https://www.synergie.fr
SDG—(EUR)
Rev.: $3,109,061,590
Assets: $1,461,187,651
Liabilities: $807,856,541
Net Worth: $653,331,109
Earnings: $94,053,767
Emp.: 68,028
Fiscal Year-end: 12/31/22
Human Resource Management Services
N.A.I.C.S.: 541612
Daniel Augereau *(Chm-Mgmt Bd)*

Subsidiaries:

ADR Transportdiensten B.V. (1)
Madame Curieweg 8, 5482 TL, Schijndel, Netherlands
Tel.: (31) 735496216
Web Site: http://www.synergiejobs.nl
Sales Range: $25-49.9 Million
Emp.: 35
Recruitment Services
N.A.I.C.S.: 541612

ADR Uitzendgroep B.V. (1)
Madame Curieweg 8, Schijndel, 5482, Noord-Brabant, Netherlands
Tel.: (31) 735495592
Recruitment Services
N.A.I.C.S.: 541612

Acorn (Synergie) UK Ltd. (1)
Somerton House Hazell Drive Cleppa Park, Newport, NP10 8FY, Gwent, United Kingdom
Tel.: (44) 1633222258
Sales Range: $75-99.9 Million
Emp.: 280
Recruitment Services
N.A.I.C.S.: 541612

SYNERGIE SA

Acorn Global Recruitment Ltd. (1)
Somerton House Hazell Drive Cleppa Park, Newport, NP10 8FY, Gwent, United Kingdom
Tel.: (44) 1270213113
Web Site: http://www.acornpeople.com
Emp.: 20
Recruitment & Outsourcing Services
N.A.I.C.S.: 541612
Andrew Tugwell *(COO)*

Acorn Learning Solutions Ltd. (1)
Somerton House Hazell Dr, Newport, NP10 8FY, United Kingdom
Tel.: (44) 1633664000
Web Site: http://www.acornpeople.com
Sales Range: $25-49.9 Million
Emp.: 150
Professional Training Services
N.A.I.C.S.: 611430

Acorn Recruitment Ltd. (1)
Somerton House Hazell Dr, Newport, NP10 8FY, United Kingdom
Tel.: (44) 1633660000
Web Site: http://www.acornpeople.com
Emp.: 80
Recruitment & Training Services
N.A.I.C.S.: 541612

Aile Medicale SAS (1)
11 Ave du Colonel Bonnet, 75016, Paris, France
Tel.: (33) 144149020
Web Site: http://www.aile-medicale.fr
Emp.: 447
Recruitment Services
N.A.I.C.S.: 541612

Concept Staffing Ltd. (1)
2 Boutport St, Barnstaple, EX31 1RH, Devon, United Kingdom
Tel.: (44) 1271343222
Web Site: http://www.conceptstaffing.co.uk
Sales Range: $25-49.9 Million
Emp.: 4
Recruitment Services
N.A.I.C.S.: 541612

Eurydice Partners SAS (1)
94 rue la Fayette, 75010, Paris, France
Tel.: (33) 147708027
Web Site: http://www.eurydicepartners.fr
Recruitment Services
N.A.I.C.S.: 541612

Gestion Hunt Inc. (1)
666 rue Sherbrooke Ouest bur 2000, Montreal, H3A 1E7, QC, Canada
Tel.: (514) 842-4691
Web Site: https://www.hunt.ca
Sales Range: $25-49.9 Million
Emp.: 25
Recruitment Services
N.A.I.C.S.: 541612

Permanence Europeenne SAS (1)
35 rue de Clichy, Paris, 75009, France
Tel.: (33) 1 53 20 33 10
Web Site: http://www.synergie.fr
Recruitment Services
N.A.I.C.S.: 541612

Skill Search S.L. (1)
Avenida Diagonal 459, Barcelona, 08036, Spain
Tel.: (34) 934265051
Web Site: http://www.synergie.es
Sales Range: $25-49.9 Million
Emp.: 5
Recruitment Services
N.A.I.C.S.: 541612

Synergie Formation S.A.R.L. (1)
28 rue Basfroi, 75011, Paris, France
Tel.: (33) 155343940
Web Site: http://www.synergieformation.com
Education Training Services
N.A.I.C.S.: 611710

Synergie Human Resources B.V. (1)
Madame Curieweg 8, Schijndel, Noord-Brabant, Netherlands
Tel.: (31) 735496216
Sales Range: $25-49.9 Million
Emp.: 15
Recruitment Services
N.A.I.C.S.: 541612

Synergie Slovakia S.r.o. (1)

SYNERGIE SA

Synergie SA—(Continued)

Dunajska 4, 811 08, Bratislava, 811 08, Slovakia
Tel.: (421) 254415522
Web Site: http://www.synergie.sk
Sales Range: $25-49.9 Million
Emp.: 10
Recruitment Services
N.A.I.C.S.: 541612

Synergie TT ETT SA (1)
C/ Enrique Granados 51-53, 08008, Barcelona, Spain
Tel.: (34) 934515656
Web Site: http://www.synergie-ett.com
Sales Range: $25-49.9 Million
Emp.: 25
Recruitment Services
N.A.I.C.S.: 541612

SYNERGIZE CONSULTING LTD.

Worth Corner Business Centre Turners Hill Road, Crawley, RH10 7SL, W Sussex, United Kingdom
Tel.: (44) 1293 887524
Web Site:
http://www.synergizecl.co.uk
Year Founded: 2002
Sales Range: $10-24.9 Million
Emp.: 11
Information Technology Recruitment Services
N.A.I.C.S.: 561311
Chris Earl (Co-Founder & Dir-Client Svcs)

SYNERGO SGR S.P.A.

Via Campo Lodigiano 3, 20122, Milan, Italy
Tel.: (39) 02 859111 IT
Web Site: http://www.synergosgr.it
Year Founded: 2004
Rev.: $1,158,640,000
Emp.: 14
Privater Equity Firm
N.A.I.C.S.: 523999
Alessandra Gavirati (Partner)

SYNERGON HOLDING PLC

2 Solunska Str, 1000, Sofia, Bulgaria
Tel.: (359) 29333599
Web Site: https://www.synergon.bg
Year Founded: 1996
6S7—(BUL)
Rev.: $368,699,209
Assets: $219,812,828
Liabilities: $69,402,943
Net Worth: $150,409,885
Earnings: $4,620,750
Fiscal Year-end: 12/31/21
Financial Holding Services
N.A.I.C.S.: 551112

Subsidiaries:

Balkanceramic Plc. (1)
52 Zavodsko shosse str, Novi Iskar, 1280, Bulgaria
Tel.: (359) 700 144 07
Web Site: http://www.balkanceramic.bg
Concrete Roof Tile Mfr
N.A.I.C.S.: 327390

Belchinski Mineralni Bani Ltd. (1)
2024 The village of Belchinski bani, Samokov, Bulgaria
Tel.: (359) 7124 2284
Rehabilitation Services
N.A.I.C.S.: 624190

Energy-Delta Ltd. (1)
15 Sofia shosse str, 2000, Samokov, Bulgaria
Tel.: (359) 884 030 847
Spa Operator
N.A.I.C.S.: 713940

Lackprom Plc. (1)
16 Sinchets str, Svetovrachene, 1252, Sofia, Bulgaria
Tel.: (359) 2 996 3112
Web Site: http://www.lackprom.com

Paint & Varnish Mfr & Distr
N.A.I.C.S.: 325510

Parasyn Ltd. (1)
7 Alexander Malinov blvd, 1784, Sofia, Bulgaria
Tel.: (359) 2 974 4979
Web Site: http://www.travelsolutions.bg
Travel Agency
N.A.I.C.S.: 561510

Petar Karaminchev Plc. (1)
71 TPP Iztok Str, 7009, Ruse, Bulgaria
Tel.: (359) 82 841 466
Web Site: http://www.pkar.bg
Plastics Product Mfr
N.A.I.C.S.: 325211

Petromel 1 Ltd. (1)
Comoshtitsa, Montana, Bulgaria
Tel.: (359) 971 66 462
Web Site: http://www.petromel.com
Grain Flour Mfr & Distr
N.A.I.C.S.: 311211

Premier PL Plc. (1)
8 Bulgarian Aviation Street, 5800, Pleven, Bulgaria
Tel.: (359) 64823946
Web Site: http://www.premier-bg.com
Furniture Mfr & Whslr
N.A.I.C.S.: 337122

Shamot Plc. (1)
1 Stara Planina str, Elin Pelin, 2109, Sofia, Bulgaria
Tel.: (359) 725 60 421
Refractory Material Mfr
N.A.I.C.S.: 327120

Svetlina Plc (1)
6 Stefan Karadja Blvd, 8800, Sliven, Bulgaria (100%)
Tel.: (359) 44 663 193
Web Site: http://www.svetlina-sliven.com
Lamp Whslr
N.A.I.C.S.: 423220

Synergon Card Service Ltd. (1)
2 Pavlina Unfrieva Street Floor 2, Poduyane, 1510, Sofia, Bulgaria
Tel.: (359) 2936 6192
Web Site: http://www.scs.bg
Emp.: 3
Electronic Payment Services
N.A.I.C.S.: 522320
Christo Blessnokov (Mgr)

Synergon Energy Ltd. (1)
23 Bacho Kiro Street, Sofia, Bulgaria
Tel.: (359) 70080080
Web Site: https://synergonenergy.bg
Renewable Energy Distr
N.A.I.C.S.: 486210

Synergon Hotels Plc. (1)
Zlatyu Boyadzhiev 2, 4003, Plovdiv, Bulgaria
Tel.: (359) 32 934442
Home Management Services
N.A.I.C.S.: 561110
Zlatina Georgieva (Sls Mgr)

Synergon Petroleum Ltd. (1)
Kremikovtsi refinery 24 Markovets Str, Kremikovtsi district, 1870, Sofia, Bulgaria
Tel.: (359) 2 814 5400
Web Site: http://www.sng.bg
Petroleum Storage Services
N.A.I.C.S.: 493190
Venetka Georgieva (Mgr-HR)

Synergon Transport Ltd. (1)
24 Markovets Str, Kremikovtsi District, 1870, Sofia, Bulgaria
Tel.: (359) 28145435
Liquefied Petroleum Gas Transportation Services
N.A.I.C.S.: 213111

Toplivo AD (1)
2 Pavlina Unufrieva Str, 1510, Sofia, 1510, Bulgaria (82.82%)
Tel.: (359) 889715063
Web Site: https://www.toplivo.bg
Sales Range: Less than $1 Million
Liquefied Petroleum Gas Dealers
N.A.I.C.S.: 457210
Bedo Bohos Doganian (Chm)

Subsidiary (Domestic):

Toplivo Gas Ltd. (2)

11 Rezbarska Str, Malashevtsi district, 1510, Sofia, Bulgaria
Tel.: (359) 24475601
Web Site: http://www.toplivogas.com
Gasoline Distr
N.A.I.C.S.: 424720

V-Gas Bulgaria Plc (1)
2 Solunska Str, 1000, Sofia, Bulgaria
Tel.: (359) 28237337
Web Site: https://v-gas.bg
Emp.: 70
Liquefied Petroleum Gas Distr
N.A.I.C.S.: 424720

SYNERGY EMPIRE LIMITED

Lot 1G & 2G No 2 Persiaran Seri Perdana, 62250, Putrajaya, Malaysia
Tel.: (60) 388902968 NV
SHMY—(OTCQB)
Rev.: $5,000
Assets: $44,914
Liabilities: $451,793
Net Worth: ($406,879)
Earnings: $788,254
Emp.; 26
Fiscal Year-end: 03/31/24
Holding Company
N.A.I.C.S.: 551112
Hsien Loong Wong (Pres, Treas & Sec)

SYNERGY FINANCE LIMITED

Kamaladi, Kathmandu, Nepal
Tel.: (977) 1 4442462
Financial Services
N.A.I.C.S.: 523999
Padma Raj Neupane (Chm)

SYNERGY GREEN INDUSTRIES LTD.

392 E Ward Shahupuri, Post Box No 201, Kolhapur, 416001, Maharashtra, India
Tel.: (91) 2312658375
Web Site:
https://www.synergygreenind.com
Year Founded: 2010
541929—(BOM)
Rev.: $27,260,240
Assets: $23,147,340
Liabilities: $16,986,634
Net Worth: $6,160,707
Earnings: $505,656
Emp.: 173
Fiscal Year-end: 03/31/21
Industrial Casting Product Mfr
N.A.I.C.S.: 331529
Nilesh Mohan Mankar (Chief Compliance Officer & Sec)

SYNERGY GRID & DEVELOPMENT PHILIPPINES INC.

1602 16th Floor, Tycoon Center Bldg Condominium Pearl Drive, Pasig, Philippines
Tel.: (63) 25843930
Web Site: https://synergygrid.ph
Year Founded: 1970
SGP—(PHI)
Rev.: $956,933,831
Assets: $8,416,999,045
Liabilities: $5,610,187,347
Net Worth: $2,806,811,697
Earnings: $421,921,635
Emp.: 10
Fiscal Year-end: 12/31/23
Construction Services
N.A.I.C.S.: 541330
Mark Jayson E. Alapoop (Compliance Officer & Treas)

SYNERGY GROUP

Avenida Washington Luis 7059 6th Floor, Santo Amaro, 04627-006, SP, Brazil
Tel.: (55) 1137975003

INTERNATIONAL PUBLIC

Web Site:
http://www.synergygroupcorp.com
Sales Range: $800-899.9 Million
Emp.: 5,000
Holding Company
N.A.I.C.S.: 551112
German Efromovich (Chm & Pres)

Subsidiaries:

Avianca Group International Limited (1)
Arias Fabrega & Fabrega PH ARIFA Floors 9 and 10, West Boulevard Santa Maria Business District, Panama, Panama
Tel.: (507) 2056000
Web Site: http://www.avianca.com
Rev.: $4,771,126,000
Assets: $8,633,047,000
Liabilities: $7,751,815,000
Net Worth: $881,232,000
Earnings: $138,004,000
Emp.: 13,000
Fiscal Year-end: 12/31/2023
Airline Operator
N.A.I.C.S.: 481111
Renato Covelo (Chief People and Legal Officer)

Subsidiary (Non-US):

Aerovias del Continente Americano S.A. (2)
Avenida El Dorado Calle 26 92-30, Bogota, Colombia
Tel.: (57) 14578662
Web Site: http://www.avianca.com
Sales Range: $800-899.9 Million
Emp.: 2,700
Airline Passenger Services
N.A.I.C.S.: 481111
Fabio Ramirez Villegas (Pres & CEO)

Grupo TACA (2)
Paseo General Escalon y 71 Avenida Norte, Centro Comercial Galerias, Local 21, San Salvador, El Salvador
Tel.: (503) 2267 82222
Web Site: http://www.taca.com
Holding Company; Air Transportation
N.A.I.C.S.: 551112
Alfredo Schildknecht (Pres)

Subsidiary (Non-US):

Grupo TACA-Guatemala (3)
Avenida Hincapie 12-22 Zone 13, 0013, Guatemala, Guatemala
Tel.: (502) 2470 8222
Sales Range: $50-74.9 Million
Emp.: 240
Airline Ticketing Services
N.A.I.C.S.: 481111

Subsidiary (Domestic):

Taca International Airlines, S.A. (3)
Paseo General Escalon y 71 Avenida Norte Centro Comercial Galerias, Local 21, 1153, San Salvador, El Salvador
Tel.: (503) 22678222
Web Site: http://www.taca.com
Oil Transportation Services
N.A.I.C.S.: 481111

Division (US):

Taca International Airlines, S.A. (4)
1450 NW 87th Ave Ste 201, Miami, FL 33172
Tel.: (305) 871-1587
Web Site: http://www.taca.com
Oil Transportation Services
N.A.I.C.S.: 481111

OceanAir Linhas Aereas Ltda. (1)
av Washington Luis 7059, Campo Belo, Sao Paulo, 04627006, Brazil
Tel.: (55) 1121761000
Web Site: http://www.avianca.com.br
Airline Operations
N.A.I.C.S.: 481112
Jorge Vianna (Pres)

Unit (Domestic):

OceanAir Taxi Aereo Ltda. (2)
Ganaral Panctaleao Telles 40 Target, Cogonha Airport, Sao Paulo, 04355-040, Brazil

Tel.: (55) 1121761000
Web Site:
　http://www.oceanairtaxiaereo.com.br
Sales Range: $25-49.9 Million
Emp.: 25
Airline Operations
N.A.I.C.S.: 481212

SYNERGY HOUSE BERHAD
Lot 19 A Level 19 Top Glove Tower, No 16 Persiaran Setia Dagang Bandar Setia Alam Seksyen U13, 40170, Shah Alam, Selangor, Malaysia
Tel.: (60) 173663426
Web Site:
　https://www.synergyhouse.com
Year Founded: 1990
SYNERGY—(KLS)
Rev.: $58,809,686
Assets: $47,976,329
Liabilities: $26,030,504
Net Worth: $21,945,824
Earnings: $5,909,471
Emp.: 165
Fiscal Year-end: 12/31/23
Furniture Product Mfr & Distr
N.A.I.C.S.: 337126

SYNERGY INNOVATION CO., LTD.
5F Suntech City II 52 Sagimakgol-ro, Jungwon-Gu, Seongnam, 601-607, Gyeonggi-Do, Korea (South)
Tel.: (82) 317462560
Web Site:
　https://www.synergyinno.com
Year Founded: 1998
048870—(KRS)
Rev.: $23,254,622
Assets: $174,397,271
Liabilities: $42,730,886
Net Worth: $131,666,384
Earnings: $17,499,601
Emp.: 63
Fiscal Year-end: 12/31/22
Semiconductor Product Mfr
N.A.I.C.S.: 334413
Hyung Ja Goo *(Co-CEO)*

Subsidiaries:

NovisBio Co., Ltd. (1)
104 Wonseungdu-Gil, Gongdo-eup, Anseong, 17562, Gyeonggi-do, Korea (South)
Tel.: (82) 316924156
Web Site: https://www.novisbio.co.kr
Emp.: 63
Health Functional Food Mfr
N.A.I.C.S.: 311412

SYNERGY PARTNERS CO., LTD.
13th floor 275 Gangnam-daero, Seocho-gu, Seoul, Korea (South)
Tel.: (82) 25865981
Web Site:
　http://www.synergypartners.kr
Privater Equity Firm
N.A.I.C.S.: 523940

SYNERGY PROJECTS LTD.
120 110 Carleton Drive, Saint Albert, T8N 3Y4, AB, Canada
Tel.: (780) 459-3344
Web Site:
　http://www.synergybuilds.com
Rev.: $15,051,001
Emp.: 30
Design & Construction Services
N.A.I.C.S.: 541490
Tim Varughese *(Pres)*

SYNERGY SCIENTECH CORP.
6F-3 No 9 Prosperity 1st Rd, East Dist Hsinchu Science Park, Hsinchu, 30078, Taiwan
Tel.: (886) 35643700
Web Site: https://www.synst.com.tw

Year Founded: 1997
6558—(TAI)
Rev.: $39,136,040
Assets: $70,480,785
Liabilities: $22,456,587
Net Worth: $48,024,198
Earnings: ($1,460,741)
Emp.: 555
Fiscal Year-end: 12/31/23
Lithium Battery Mfr
N.A.I.C.S.: 335910
Hsueh Kun Hsing *(Chm & Pres)*

SYNERTEC CORPORATION LIMITED
Ground Floor 2-6 Railway Pde, Camberwell, 3124, VIC, Australia
Tel.: (61) 392743000　　　　BM
Web Site:
　https://www.synertec.com.au
Year Founded: 2012
SOP—(ASX)
Rev.: $6,425,032
Assets: $6,304,271
Liabilities: $4,698,002
Net Worth: $1,606,269
Earnings: ($2,567,500)
Fiscal Year-end: 06/30/21
Holding Company; Engineering Consulting Services
N.A.I.C.S.: 551112
Michael Carroll *(Founder, Mng Dir & Principal)*

Subsidiaries:

Synertec Pty. Ltd. (1)
L1 / 57 Stewart St, Richmond, 3121, VIC, Australia
Tel.: (61) 392743000
Engineering Consulting Services
N.A.I.C.S.: 541330

SYNERTONE COMMUNICATION CORPORATION
Room 1012 10/F Tsim Sha Tsui Centre 66 Mody Road, Kowloon, Hong Kong, China (Hong Kong)
Tel.: (852) 2 865 4498
Web Site: http://www.synertone.net
1613—(HKG)
Rev.: $14,725,002
Assets: $35,011,879
Liabilities: $21,412,873
Net Worth: $13,599,006
Earnings: ($14,674,442)
Emp.: 123
Fiscal Year-end: 03/31/22
Communication Equipment Mfr
N.A.I.C.S.: 334290
Weining Han *(CEO)*

SYNEX RENEWABLE ENERGY CORPORATION
4248 Broughton Avenue, Niagara Falls, L2E 3K6, ON, Canada
Tel.: (604) 688-8271
Web Site: https://www.synex.com
Year Founded: 1987
SXI—(TSX)
Rev.: $2,110,144
Assets: $16,512,705
Liabilities: $11,709,970
Net Worth: $4,802,735
Earnings: ($6,050,862)
Emp.: 6
Fiscal Year-end: 06/30/19
Holding Company
N.A.I.C.S.: 551112
Tanya L. DeAngelis *(Chm & Sec)*

Subsidiaries:

Hancock Sigma Sensing Inc (1)
400 -1444 Alberni St, Vancouver, V6G 2Z4, BC, Canada
Tel.: (604) 688-8271
Industrial Control Mfr
N.A.I.C.S.: 334290

Sigma Engineering Ltd. (1)
400 -1444 Alberni St, Vancouver, V6G 2Z4, BC, Canada
Tel.: (604) 688-8271
Web Site: http://www.sigmaengineering.com
Engineeering Services
N.A.I.C.S.: 541330
Greg Sumell *(Pres & Principal)*

Synex Energy Resources Ltd. (1)
4248 Broughton Avenue, Niagara Falls, L2E 3K6, ON, Canada
Tel.: (604) 688-8271
Web Site: http://www.synex.com
Hydroelectric Energy
N.A.I.C.S.: 221111

Subsidiary (Domestic):

Kyuquot Power Ltd. (2)
400 -1444 Alberni St, Vancouver, V6G 2Z4, BC, Canada
Tel.: (604) 688-8271
Powerline Construction Services
N.A.I.C.S.: 237990

SYNGROUP MANAGEMENT CONSULTING GMBH
Kartner Ring 17, 1010, Vienna, Austria
Tel.: (43) 1 503 86 30
Web Site: http://www.syn-group.com
Year Founded: 1995
Sales Range: $25-49.9 Million
Consulting Services
N.A.I.C.S.: 541618
Gerald Judmann *(Partner)*

Subsidiaries:

Bayern Consult Unternehmensberatung Gmbh (1)
Ismaninger Strasse 68, 81675, Munich, Germany
Tel.: (49) 89 414198 0
Web Site: http://www.bayernconsult.de
Sales Range: $10-24.9 Million
Consulting Services
N.A.I.C.S.: 541618
Juergen Kogler *(Mng Dir)*

SYNLAIT MILK LIMITED
1028 Heslerton Rd, Rakaia, 7740, New Zealand
Tel.: (64) 33733000
Web Site: https://www.synlait.com
Year Founded: 2000
SML—(NZX)
Rev.: $789,927,033
Assets: $1,008,139,952
Liabilities: $535,428,230
Net Worth: $472,711,722
Earnings: ($8,459,330)
Emp.: 440
Fiscal Year-end: 07/31/23
Dairy Product Mfr & Distr
N.A.I.C.S.: 311514
Rob Stowell *(Gen Mgr-Supply Chain)*

SYNNEX (THAILAND) PUBLIC CO., LTD.
433 Sukhonthasawat Road Lat Phrao, Bangkok, 10230, Thailand
Tel.: (66) 25538888
Web Site: http://www.synnex.co.th
SYNEX—(THA)
Rev.: $1,066,486,816
Assets: $403,339,057
Liabilities: $284,267,550
Net Worth: $119,071,507
Earnings: $14,955,311
Emp.: 644
Fiscal Year-end: 12/31/23
Computer Equipment & Software Whslr
N.A.I.C.S.: 423430
Supant Mongkolsuthree *(Chm)*

SYNNEX TECHNOLOGY INTERNATIONAL CORPORATION
4F No 75 Sec 3 Minsheng E Rd, Taipei, 104, Taiwan
Tel.: (886) 225063320
Web Site: https://www.synnex.com.tw
2347—(TAI)
Rev.: $12,381,290,967
Assets: $6,698,568,646
Liabilities: $4,369,246,756
Net Worth: $2,329,321,890
Earnings: $246,407,248
Emp.: 4,238
Fiscal Year-end: 12/31/23
Computer Equipment & Software Mfr & Whslr
N.A.I.C.S.: 423430
Matthew Feng-Chiang Miao *(Chm & CEO-Overseas Operation)*

Subsidiaries:

Bestcom Infotech Corp. (1)
103 8th Floor No 243 Section 2 Chongqing North Road, Datong District, Taipei, Taiwan
Tel.: (886) 225570808
Web Site: http://www.bestcom.com.tw
Education Services
N.A.I.C.S.: 611710

PT My Icon Technology (1)
Kompleks Pergudangan BGR Blok I Jalan Boulevard BGR No 1, Perintis Kemerdekaan Kelapa Gading Barat, Jakarta, 14240, Indonesia
Tel.: (62) 2129345615
Web Site:
Electronic Device Distr
N.A.I.C.S.: 449210

PT. Synnex Metrodata Indonesia (1)
APL Tower 42nd Floor Jl Letjen S Parman Kav 28, Jakarta, 11470, Indonesia
Tel.: (62) 2129345800
Web Site:
　https://www.synnexmetrodata.com
Logistic Services
N.A.I.C.S.: 488999

Synnex Australia Pty. Ltd. (1)
92 Carroll Road, Oakleigh South, Melbourne, 3167, VIC, Australia
Tel.: (61) 1300100100
Web Site: https://www.synnex.com.au
Computer Products & Peripherals Distr
N.A.I.C.S.: 423430
Kee Ong *(CEO)*

Synnex Technology International (HK) Ltd (1)
16th Floor Phase 1 Metro Centre 32 Lam Hing Street, Kowloon Bay, Kowloon, China (Hong Kong)
Tel.: (852) 23052228
Web Site: https://www.synnex.com.hk
Computer Hardware, Software & Peripherals Distr
N.A.I.C.S.: 423430
Matthew F. C. Miau *(Chm)*

SYNNOVIA PLC
Room 1 1 London Heliport Bridges Court Road, London, SW11 3BE, United Kingdom
Tel.: (44) 2079780574
Web Site:
　http://www.plasticscapital.com
Year Founded: 2002
Rev.: $103,512,581
Assets: $94,901,148
Liabilities: $52,889,551
Net Worth: $42,011,597
Earnings: $2,451,351
Emp.: 592
Fiscal Year-end: 03/31/18
Plastics Product Mfr
N.A.I.C.S.: 326199
Faisal John Rahmatallah *(Founder & Chm)*

Subsidiaries:

BNL (UK) Limited (1)
Manse Lane, Knaresborough, HG5 8LF, North Yorkshire, United Kingdom
Tel.: (44) 1423 799200
Web Site: http://www.bnl-bearings.com
Emp.: 11

SYNNOVIA PLC

Synnovia Plc—(Continued)
Plastic Bearings Mfr
N.A.I.C.S.: 332991
Derek Mansfield (CEO)

Subsidiary (Non-US):

BNL (Japan) Inc (2)
Yamatane-Hokozaki Bldg 7F Hakozaki-cho 8-1, Nihonbashi Chuo-Ku, Tokyo, 103-0015, Japan
Tel.: (81) 3 5652 5557
Emp.: 7
Plastic Bearings Mfr
N.A.I.C.S.: 332991
Mark Taniguchi (Acct Dir)

BNL (US) Inc
56 Leonard St Unit 5, Foxboro, MA 02035-2939
Tel.: (508) 698-8880
Web Site: http://www.bnl-bearings.com
Sales Range: $50-74.9 Million
Emp.: 6
Plastic Bearing Whslr
N.A.I.C.S.: 423840
Shelagh Ashe (Coord-Customer Svcs)

Bell Plastics Limited (1)
450 Blandford Road, Poole, BH16 5BN, United Kingdom
Tel.: (44) 1202 625596
Web Site: http://www.bellplastics.co.uk
Emp.: 25
Rubber & Plastic Hose Mfr
N.A.I.C.S.: 326220
David Kavanagh (Mng Dir)

C&T Matrix Limited (1)
Sanders Road, Wellingborough, NN8 4NL, Northamptonshire, United Kingdom
Tel.: (44) 1933 273444
Web Site: http://www.candtmatrix.co.uk
Sales Range: $25-49.9 Million
Emp.: 20
Precision Creasing System Mfr
N.A.I.C.S.: 333248
Simon Shenton (Mng Dir)

Palagan Limited (1)
Tavistock Street, Dunstable, LU6 1NE, Bedfordshire, United Kingdom
Tel.: (44) 1582 600234
Web Site: http://www.palagan.co.uk
Emp.: 45
Packaging Plastic Film Mfr
N.A.I.C.S.: 322220
Kevin Pitcher (Mgr-Sls)

SYNOPEX INC.
5442 Dongtan Hana 1gil, Hwaseong, Gyeonggi-do, Korea (South)
Tel.: (82) 313797777
Web Site: https://www.synopex.com
Year Founded: 1991
025320—(KRS)
Rev.: $187,737,987
Assets: $164,801,607
Liabilities: $84,351,086
Net Worth: $80,450,521
Earnings: $6,492,960
Emp.: 164
Fiscal Year-end: 12/31/22
Mobile Phone Component Mfr
N.A.I.C.S.: 334419
Kyoung-Ik Son (CEO)

Subsidiaries:

Hanxing Printec Co., Ltd. (1)
270 Keji Road, Hi-Tech Industries Development Zone, Weihai, Shangdong, China
Tel.: (86) 7074917040
Wireless Device Component Mfr
N.A.I.C.S.: 334419

Synopex Vietnam Co., Ltd. (1)
16 Plot Quang Minh Industrial Park, Me Linh Dist, Hanoi, Vietnam
Tel.: (84) 7074917300
Wireless Device Component Mfr
N.A.I.C.S.: 334419

Tianjin Synopex Co., Ltd. (1)
27-3 1th Building Shehuishan Garden, Zhangjiawo Town Xiqing District, Tianjin, China
Tel.: (86) 7074911220
Wireless Device Component Mfr
N.A.I.C.S.: 334419

SYNOVA CAPITAL LLP
55 Wells Street 1st Floor, London, W1T3PT, United Kingdom
Tel.: (44) 2034757660
Web Site: http://www.synova.pe
Year Founded: 2007
Venture Capital & Private Equity
N.A.I.C.S.: 523940
Alex Bowden (Partner)

Subsidiaries:

Orbis Protect Limited (1)
Beaufort House Cricket Field Rd, Uxbridge, UB8 1QG, Mddx, United Kingdom
Tel.: (44) 1895465500
Web Site: http://www.orbisprotect.com
Vacant Properties & Buildings Security, Cleaning, Clearing & Refurbishment Services Contractor
N.A.I.C.S.: 238990
Guy Other (CEO)

SYNSAM AB
Sankt Eriksgatan 60, 112 34, Stockholm, Sweden
Tel.: (46) 86192860
Web Site: https://www.synsamgroup.com
Year Founded: 1968
SYNSAM—(OMX)
Rev.: $560,566,467
Assets: $752,667,023
Liabilities: $517,107,346
Net Worth: $235,559,677
Earnings: $29,128,851
Emp.: 3,413
Fiscal Year-end: 12/31/23
Optical Product Distr
N.A.I.C.S.: 456130
Hakan Lundstedt (CEO)

Subsidiaries:

Audionomkliniken Sverige AB (1)
Hantverkargatan 2 D, 112 21, Stockholm, Sweden
Tel.: (46) 852520800
Web Site: https://www.audionomkliniken.se
Health Care Services
N.A.I.C.S.: 621340

Profil Optik A/S (1)
Oldenburg Alle 1 2 sal, 2630, Taastrup, Denmark
Tel.: (45) 36888686
Web Site: https://www.profiloptik.dk
Eye Health Care Services
N.A.I.C.S.: 622110

Synsam Group AB (1)
Sankt Eriksgatan 60, 112 34, Stockholm, Sweden
Tel.: (46) 852520800
Eye Health Care Services
N.A.I.C.S.: 622110

Synsam Group Finland Oy (1)
Porkkalankatu 3, 00180, Helsinki, Finland
Tel.: (358) 102372000
Web Site: https://www.synsam.fi
Eye Health Care Services
N.A.I.C.S.: 622110

Synsam Group Norway AS (1)
Karl Johans gate 6B, 0154, Oslo, Norway
Tel.: (47) 22422000
Web Site: https://www.synsam.no
Eye Health Care Services
N.A.I.C.S.: 622110

Synsam Group Sweden AB (1)
Sankt Eriksgatan 60, 112 34, Stockholm, Sweden
Tel.: (46) 86192860
Web Site: https://www.synsam.se
Eye Health Care Services
N.A.I.C.S.: 622110

SYNSTREAM ENERGY CORP.
1404 Memorial Drive NW, Calgary, T2N 3E5, AB, Canada
Tel.: (403) 863-6034
Web Site: http://www.synstreamenergy.com
Year Founded: 2007
SHM—(TSXV)
Sales Range: Less than $1 Million
Oil & Gas Exploration Services
N.A.I.C.S.: 213112
Johannes J. Kingma (CEO)

SYNTAGMA CAPITAL MANAGEMENT SA
Avenue Louise 326, Blue Tower 18th Floor, 1050, Brussels, Belgium
Tel.: (32) 23157012
Web Site: https://syntagmacapital.com
Year Founded: 2009
Investment Management
N.A.I.C.S.: 523999
Sebastien Kiekert Le Moult (Founder & Mng Partner)

Subsidiaries:

Erasteel SAS (1)
10 Boulevard de Grenelle, 33 Avenue du Maine, 75015, Paris, Cedex 15, France
Tel.: (33) 145386300
Web Site: http://www.erasteel.com
Steel Products Mfr
N.A.I.C.S.: 332117
Kerstin Konradsson (CEO)

Subsidiary (Non-US):

ERASTEEL KLOSTER AB (2)
Bruksplan 1, PO Box 100, 815 82, Soderfors, Tierp, Sweden
Tel.: (46) 29354300
Sales Range: $50-74.9 Million
Emp.: 400
Steel Products Mfr
N.A.I.C.S.: 331110
Frank Bjorklund (Gen Mgr)

ERASTEEL STUBS LTD. (2)
Causeway Avenue, Warrington, WA4 6QB, Cheshire, United Kingdom
Tel.: (44) 1925653939
Sales Range: $25-49.9 Million
Emp.: 55
Steel Products Mfr
N.A.I.C.S.: 331110

Plant (Domestic):

Erasteel Champagnole (2)
23 Rue Georges Clemenceau, BP 104, 39300, Champagnole, France
Tel.: (33) 38 452 6444
Web Site: https://www.erasteel.com
Steel Products Mfr
N.A.I.C.S.: 331110

Erasteel SAS- Commentry Plant (2)
1 place Martenot, BP 1, 03600, Commentry, France
Tel.: (33) 47 028 7800
Web Site: https://www.erasteel.com
Steel Products Mfr
N.A.I.C.S.: 331110

SYNTEC BIOFUEL, INC.
Suite 212 1166 Alberni Street, Vancouver, V6E 3Z3, BC, Canada
Tel.: (604) 648-2090
Renewable Energy Consulting Services
N.A.I.C.S.: 541690
Michael Jackson (Chm & CEO)

SYNTEC CONSTRUCTION PUBLIC COMPANY LIMITED
555/7-11 Soi Sukhumvit 63 Ekamai Sukhumvit Rd Klongton Nua Wattana, Bangkok, 10110, Thailand
Tel.: (66) 23816333
Web Site: https://www.synteccon.com
Year Founded: 1988
SYNTEC—(THA)
Rev.: $218,911,329
Assets: $315,342,434
Liabilities: $145,011,339

INTERNATIONAL PUBLIC

Net Worth: $170,331,095
Earnings: $5,233,187
Emp.: 871
Fiscal Year-end: 12/31/23
Engineeering Services
N.A.I.C.S.: 541330
Somchai Sirilertpanich (Vice Chm & CEO)

SYNTEGRA CAPITAL INVESTORS LIMITED
17 Hanover Square, London, W1S 1HU, United Kingdom
Tel.: (44) 207 355 0840
Web Site: http://www.syntegracapital.com
Sales Range: $25-49.9 Million
Emp.: 8
Privater Equity Firm
N.A.I.C.S.: 523999
Philip Percival (Partner)

SYNTEKABIO, INC.
1903 1 Expo-ro, Yuseong-Gu, Daejeon, Korea (South)
Tel.: (82) 7076630958
Web Site: https://www.syntekabio.com
Year Founded: 2009
226330—(KRS)
Rev.: $187,142
Assets: $42,713,251
Liabilities: $18,582,837
Net Worth: $24,130,414
Earnings: ($3,456,429)
Emp.: 57
Fiscal Year-end: 12/31/22
Software Development Services
N.A.I.C.S.: 541511
Jongsun Jung (Pres & CEO)

SYNTELLIX AG
Aegidientorplatz 2a, 30159, Hannover, Germany
Tel.: (49) 51127041350
Web Site: http://www.syntellix.de
Year Founded: 2008
Medical Technology Devices Mfr
N.A.I.C.S.: 339112
Utz Claassen (Chm, CEO & Chief Disruption Officer)

SYNTHESIS ELECTRONIC TECHNOLOGY CO., LTD.
No 699 Shunhua West Road, High-Tech Zone, Jinan, 250101, Shandong, China
Tel.: (86) 53188878969
Web Site: http://www.sdses.com
Year Founded: 2004
300479—(CHIN)
Rev.: $58,395,283
Assets: $187,659,793
Liabilities: $109,858,690
Net Worth: $77,801,103
Earnings: ($9,764,764)
Fiscal Year-end: 12/31/23
Software Development Services
N.A.I.C.S.: 541511
Yan Long (Chm)

SYNTHETIC PRODUCTS ENTERPRISES LIMITED
127-S Quaid-e-Azam Industrial Estate Township, Kot Lakhpat, Lahore, Pakistan
Tel.: (92) 42111005005
Web Site: https://www.spelgroup.com
Year Founded: 1978
SPEL—(PSX)
Rev.: $23,135,424
Assets: $24,638,104
Liabilities: $7,960,655
Net Worth: $16,677,449
Earnings: $1,766,725
Emp.: 550

Fiscal Year-end: 06/30/23
Engineered Plastics & Injection Molding
N.A.I.C.S.: 326199
Zia Hyder Naqi (CEO)

SYNTHETICA AD
Sofia 1407 N Y Vaptsarov No 47,
Varna, Bulgaria
Tel.: (359) 24621299
Web Site: https://www.synthetica.bg
Year Founded: 2010
81P—(DEU)
Holding Company
N.A.I.C.S.: 551112
Lubomir Krasimirov Kolchev (Chm)

SYNTHIKO FOILS LIMITED
84/1 84/2 Jamsar Road, Jawhar,
Thane, 401603, India
Tel.: (91) 2520222360
Web Site:
    https://www.synthikofoilsltd.com
513307—(BOM)
Rev.: $3,076,470
Assets: $1,259,133
Liabilities: $563,132
Net Worth: $696,001
Earnings: $19,867
Emp.: 24
Fiscal Year-end: 03/31/23
Metal Product Whslr
N.A.I.C.S.: 423510
Ramesh Chandra Dadhia (Chm, Mng Dir & CFO)

SYNTHOMER PLC
Central Road Temple Fields, Harlow,
CM20 2BH, Essex, United Kingdom
Tel.: (44) 1279436211   UK
Web Site:
    https://www.synthomer.com
SYNT—(LSE)
Rev.: $2,871,407,550
Assets: $3,670,834,200
Liabilities: $2,271,205,200
Net Worth: $1,399,629,000
Earnings: ($31,196,550)
Fiscal Year-end: 12/31/22
Holding Company; Specialty Chemical Mfr
N.A.I.C.S.: 551112
Lily Liu (CFO)

Subsidiaries:

Indra Sistemas Mexico S.A. de C.V. (1)
Presidente Masarik No 111 PH2 Colonia Chapultepec Morales, Miguel Hidalgo, Mexico, 11570, Mexico
Tel.: (52) 55 91 261 100
Business Software Development Services
N.A.I.C.S.: 541511
Judith Silva Reyes (Mgr-Svc)

Revertex (Malaysia) Sdn. Bhd. (1)
1 1/2 Miles Jalan Batu Pahat, Keluang, 6000, Johor, Malaysia
Tel.: (60) 77731000
Web Site: http://www.revertex.com.my
Latex Compounds Mfr
N.A.I.C.S.: 325212
Ting Ting Sieng (Mng Dir-Polymer Div)

Synthomer (UK) Ltd. (1)
Central Road, Templefields, Harlow, CM20 2BH, United Kingdom   (100%)
Tel.: (44) 1279436211
Web Site: http://www.synthomer.com
Specialty Chemicals Mfr
N.A.I.C.S.: 325998

Synthomer BV (1)
Ijsselstraat 41, 5347, Oss, Noord Brabant, Netherlands
Tel.: (31) 412681700
Web Site: http://www.synthomer.com
Emp.: 40
Synthetic Rubber Compounds Mfr
N.A.I.C.S.: 325212

Synthomer Chemicals (Pty) Ltd (1)
200 Landowne Road, Jacobs, 4052, Kwa-Zulu Natal, South Africa   (100%)
Tel.: (27) 314808100
Emp.: 120
Synthetic Resin & Emulsions Mfr
N.A.I.C.S.: 325211
Gerhard Lategan (Mgr-Natl Sls)

Synthomer Finland Oy (1)
Nuottasaarentie 17, 90400, Oulu, Finland
Tel.: (358) 103879500
Chemical Product & Preparation Mfr
N.A.I.C.S.: 325998

Synthomer GmbH (1)
Gwinnerstrasse 19, 60334, Frankfurt am Main, Germany   (100%)
Tel.: (49) 69941790
Web Site: http://www.synthomer.com
Emp.: 35
Synthetic Resins & Polymers Mfr
N.A.I.C.S.: 325211

Synthomer SA (1)
Boulevard du Textile 1, 7700, Mouscron, Hainaut, Belgium
Tel.: (32) 56852155
Web Site: http://www.synthomer.com
Emp.: 60
Synthetic Polymers Distr
N.A.I.C.S.: 424610

Synthomer Sdn Bhd (1)
16-03 Menara MPPJ Jalan Tengah, 46200, Petaling Jaya, Selangor Darul Ehsan, Malaysia
Tel.: (60) 379563997
Web Site: http://www.synthomer.com
Emp.: 200
Synthetic Rubber Compounds Mfr
N.A.I.C.S.: 325212

Synthomer Vietnam Co. Ltd. (1)
No 8 Road 6 Song Than 1 Industrial Zone, Di An, Binh Duong, Vietnam   (60%)
Tel.: (84) 6503790027
Web Site: http://www.synthomer.com
Emp.: 60
Polymers Mfr
N.A.I.C.S.: 325211

William Blythe Ltd. (1)
Church, Accrington, BB5 4PD, Lancashire, United Kingdom
Tel.: (44) 1254320000
Web Site: http://www.williamblythe.com
Emp.: 80
Inorganic Chemicals Mfr & Distr
N.A.I.C.S.: 325180

Yule Catto Holdings GmbH (1)
Innerstetal 2, Langelsheim, 38685, Langelsheim, Niedersachsen, Germany
Tel.: (49) 69941790
Investment Management Service
N.A.I.C.S.: 523999

SYNTHOS S.A.
ul Chemikow 1, 32-600, Oswiecim, Poland
Tel.: (48) 33 844 18 21   PL
Web Site:
    http://www.synthosgroup.com
Year Founded: 1945
Sales Range: $1-4.9 Billion
Emp.: 2,975
Synthetic Rubber, Latex, Styrene Plastics, Vinyl & Copolymer Dispersions Mfr
N.A.I.C.S.: 325212
Zbigniew Warmuz (Chm-Mgmt Bd)

Subsidiaries:

Bioelektrownia Hydropol-4 Sp. z o.o. (1)
ul Zagnanska 27, 52-528, Kielce, Poland
Tel.: (48) 13631700
Biogas Power Generation
N.A.I.C.S.: 221118

EMPOS Ltd. (1)
ul Nadwislanska 46, Oswiecim, Poland   (76.79%)
Tel.: (48) 338473433
Industrial & Municipal Sewage Treatment Solutions & Services
N.A.I.C.S.: 221320

Energetyka Dwory Sp. z o.o. (1)
ul Chemikow 1, 32 600, Oswiecim, Poland   (100%)
Tel.: (48) 338472770
Web Site: http://www.energetyka.dwory.pl
Energy Generation & Distr
N.A.I.C.S.: 221118

Synthos Dwory 2 Sp. z o.o. (1)
ul Chemikow 1, 32-600, Oswiecim, Poland
Tel.: (48) 33 844 18 21
Chemical Products Mfr
N.A.I.C.S.: 325998

Synthos Dwory Sp. z o.o. (1)
ul Chemikow 1, 32 600, Oswiecim, Poland   (100%)
Tel.: (48) 338441821
Web Site: http://www.synthosgroup.com
Synthetic Rubbers & Latex & Polystyrene Mfr
N.A.I.C.S.: 325212

Synthos Kralupy a.s. (1)
O Wichterleho 810, 278 01, Kralupy nad Vltavou, Czech Republic   (100%)
Tel.: (420) 315711111
Sales Range: $500-549.9 Million
Emp.: 800
Styrene, Polystyrene Plastics & Synthetic Rubber Mfr
N.A.I.C.S.: 325212
Ladislav Varhanik (Dir-Fin)

SYNTONIC LIMITED
Level 26 140 St Georges Terrace,
Perth, 6000, WA, Australia
Tel.: (61) 865580886
Web Site:
    http://www.syntoniclimited.com
SYT—(ASX)
Rev.: $78,421
Assets: $1,791,351
Liabilities: $1,480,849
Net Worth: $310,502
Earnings: ($2,350,312)
Fiscal Year-end: 06/30/20
Investment Services
N.A.I.C.S.: 523999
Gary Greenbaum (Founder)

SYOUNG GROUP CO., LTD.
101-1 Comprehensive Building Building 1 No 390 Guyuan Road, Yuelu District, Changsha, 410000, Hunan, China
Tel.: (86) 73185238868
Web Site: http://www.yujiahui.com
Year Founded: 2012
300740—(CHIN)
Rev.: $632,854,036
Assets: $579,594,919
Liabilities: $287,354,705
Net Worth: $292,240,214
Earnings: $41,437,422
Fiscal Year-end: 12/31/23
Cosmetic Product Whslr
N.A.I.C.S.: 424210
Yuefeng Dai (Chm & Gen Mgr)

SYRAH RESOURCES LIMITED
Level 7 477 Collins Street, Melbourne, 3000, VIC, Australia
Tel.: (61) 396707264   AU
Web Site:
    https://www.syrahresources.com.au
SYR—(OTCIQ)
Rev.: $106,180,000
Assets: $569,970,000
Liabilities: $131,793,000
Net Worth: $438,177,000
Earnings: ($26,845,000)
Emp.: 579
Fiscal Year-end: 12/31/22
Exploration of Mineral Resources
N.A.I.C.S.: 213115
Melanie Leydin (Sec)

Subsidiaries:

Syrah Global DMCC (1)
Office 22F Gold Tower Cluster I Jumeirah Lakes Towers, Dubai, United Arab Emirates
Tel.: (971) 42445955
Graphite Product Mfr & Distr
N.A.I.C.S.: 335991

Twigg Exploration & Mining, Limitada (1)
Av Vladimir Lenine nr 174 Millennium Park Bloco B nivel 5, Maputo, Mozambique
Tel.: (258) 21422814
Web Site: http://www.twigg.co.mz
Graphite Product Distr
N.A.I.C.S.: 424690
Jeffery William (Officer-Logistic)

SYRIA GULF BANK S.A.
29 Ayyar Street, PO Box 373, Damascus, Syria
Tel.: (963) 11 9721
Web Site: http://www.sgbsy.com
Year Founded: 2007
SGB—(DSE)
Sales Range: $1-9.9 Million
Commercial Banking Services
N.A.I.C.S.: 522110
Masaud Hayat (Chm)

SYRIA INTERNATIONAL ISLAMIC BANK
Highway Mezzeh -Villas East, PO Box 35494, Damascus, Syria
Tel.: (963) 11 6630504
Web Site: http://www.siib.sy
Year Founded: 2007
SIIB—(DSE)
Sales Range: Less than $1 Million
Commercial Banking Services
N.A.I.C.S.: 522110
Tayseer Al-Zoubi (Chm)

SYRMA SGS TECHNOLOGY LIMITED
Unit No 601 Floral Deck Plaza 6th Floor MIDC Andheri East, Mumbai, 400093, Maharashtra, India
Tel.: (91) 2240363000
Web Site: https://www.syrmasgs.com
Year Founded: 1978
543573—(BOM)
Rev.: $250,840,717
Assets: $304,676,578
Liabilities: $119,688,508
Net Worth: $184,988,070
Earnings: $14,756,429
Emp.: 1,065
Fiscal Year-end: 03/31/23
Electronic Components Mfr
N.A.I.C.S.: 334419

Subsidiaries:

SGS Solutions GMBH (1)
Friedrich-List-Str 9, 71364, Winnenden, Germany
Tel.: (49) 71959292261
Web Site: https://sgs-solutions.de
Electric Equipment Mfr
N.A.I.C.S.: 334419

SYS HOLDINGS CO., LTD.
2F Daiichifuji Building 35-16 Daikancho, Higashi-ku, Nagoya, 461-0002, Aichi, Japan
Tel.: (81) 52937020923
Web Site: https://www.syshd.co.jp
3988—(TKS)
Rev.: $77,109,340
Assets: $41,114,200
Liabilities: $20,196,340
Net Worth: $20,917,860
Earnings: $2,929,620
Emp.: 1,454
Fiscal Year-end: 07/31/24
Information Technology Services
N.A.I.C.S.: 541512
Hironori Suzuki (Founder, Chm & Pres)

SYS HOLDINGS CO., LTD.

SYS Holdings Co., Ltd.—(Continued)

Subsidiaries:

Global Information Technology Co., Ltd. (1)
Daiichi Fuji Building 2F 35-16 Daikancho, Higashi-ku, Nagoya, 461-0002, Aichi, Japan
Tel.: (81) 529906628
Web Site: https://www.git-sysg.com
Emp.: 59
Business Application Development Services
N.A.I.C.S.: 541511

NETPARK21 Co., Ltd. (1)
5F Sharona Building 1-8-20 Kanayama, Naka-ku, Nagoya, Aichi, Japan
Tel.: (81) 523247400
Web Site: https://www.netpark21.co.jp
Emp.: 70
Web Design & Development Services
N.A.I.C.S.: 541511

PT. SYS Indonesia (1)
Graha Induk KUD Lt 2 Jl Warung Buncit Raya No 18-20, Pejaten Barat-Pasar Minggu, Jakarta Selatan, 12510, Indonesia
Tel.: (62) 2127531516
Web Site: https://www.sysystem.co.jp
Computer System Consulting Services
N.A.I.C.S.: 541512

SYI Co., Ltd. (1)
2F Daiichi Fuji Building 35-16 Daikan-cho, Higashi-ku, Nagoya, 461-0002, Aichi, Japan
Tel.: (81) 529906627
Web Site: https://www.sy-inf.co.jp
Emp.: 22
Computer Software Development Services
N.A.I.C.S.: 541511

SYSystem Co., Ltd. (1)
Dai-ichi Fuji Bldg 2F 35-16 Daikan-cho, Higashi-ku, Nagoya, 461-0002, Aichi, Japan
Tel.: (81) 529370201
Web Site: https://www.sysystem.co.jp
Emp.: 507
Information Providing Services
N.A.I.C.S.: 519290
Hironori Suzuki (Pres)

Thai Software Engineering Co., Ltd. (1)
No 518/3 Maneeya Center North Building 6th Floor Ploenchit Road, Lumpini Patumwan, Bangkok, Thailand
Tel.: (66) 265208112
Web Site: https://www.tse.in.th
Software Development Services
N.A.I.C.S.: 541511

SYSCHEM (INDIA) LIMITED

Vill Bargodam Tehsil Kalka, Panchkula, 133302, India
Tel.: (91) 7082923502
Web Site: https://www.syschem.in
531173—(BOM)
Rev.: $15,661,543
Assets: $11,116,060
Liabilities: $8,441,796
Net Worth: $2,674,264
Earnings: $541,107
Emp.: 82
Fiscal Year-end: 03/31/23
Specialty Chemicals Mfr
N.A.I.C.S.: 325998
Amarjeet Kaur (Compliance Officer & Sec)

SYSCO INDUSTRIES LIMITED

206/7 Rajhans Complex Bs Nirmal Hospital Ring Road, Surat, 395 002, Gujarat, India
Tel.: (91) 2612337750
Web Site: http://www.syscogroup.in
Year Founded: 2009
Packaging Product Mfr & Distr
N.A.I.C.S.: 326112
Bharat Bhushan Jain (Chm)

SYSCOM COMPUTER ENGINEERING COMPANY

6F No 115 Emei Street, Wanhua District, Taipei, 108, Taiwan
Tel.: (886) 221916066
Web Site: http://www.syscom.com.tw
Year Founded: 1975
2453—(TAI)
Rev.: $208,764,831
Assets: $158,483,594
Liabilities: $89,243,137
Net Worth: $69,240,457
Earnings: $9,046,666
Emp.: 1,500
Fiscal Year-end: 12/31/23
Information Technology Consulting Services
N.A.I.C.S.: 541512
Liu Raff (Chm)

Subsidiaries:

Casemaker, Inc. (1)
1680 Civic Center Dr, Santa Clara, CA 95050
Tel.: (408) 261-8265
Web Site: http://www.casemaker.com
Sales Range: $1-9.9 Million
Emp.: 14
Software Publishing Services
N.A.I.C.S.: 513210
Austin Lo (Mgr)

Coach Tech Management Co. (1)
2F No 24 Kangding Road, Wanhua District, Taipei, 108, Taiwan
Tel.: (886) 223128896
Web Site: https://www.coachtm.com.tw
Computer Training Services
N.A.I.C.S.: 611420

DBMaker Japan Inc. (1)
Shinbashi 5-20-3 Shinbashi ST building 3F, Minato-ku, Tokyo, 105-0004, Japan
Tel.: (81) 364359196
Web Site: http://www.dbmaker.co.jp
Software Product Retailer
N.A.I.C.S.: 423430

Syscom Computer(Thailand) Co., Ltd. (1)
52 Thaniya Plaza Tower A Silom Rd, Bangkok, Thailand
Tel.: (66) 263403056
Web Site: http://www.syscom.co.th
Software Development Services
N.A.I.C.S.: 541511

SYSGRATION LTD.

6Fl No 1 Sec 1 Tiding Blvd, Neihu Dist, Taipei, Taiwan
Tel.: (886) 227900088
Web Site: https://www.sysgration.com
Year Founded: 1977
5309—(TPE)
Rev.: $106,442,641
Assets: $111,601,820
Liabilities: $50,857,956
Net Worth: $60,743,864
Earnings: $10,583,716
Emp.: 366
Fiscal Year-end: 12/31/22
Power Supplies Mfr
N.A.I.C.S.: 335999
Chia-Fu Yeh (VP)

SYSGROUP PLC

55 Spring Gardens, Manchester, M2 2BY, United Kingdom
Tel.: (44) 3331019000
Web Site: https://www.sysgroup.com
Year Founded: 2006
SYS—(AIM)
Rev.: $26,869,815
Assets: $48,551,832
Liabilities: $21,955,059
Net Worth: $26,596,773
Earnings: ($12,411)
Fiscal Year-end: 03/31/23
Domain Name Registration & Hosting Services
N.A.I.C.S.: 518210
Martin Richard Audcent (CFO)

SYSMA HOLDINGS LIMITED

2 Balestier Road 03-669, Balestier Hill Shopping Centre, Singapore, 320002, Singapore
Tel.: (65) 6256 2288
Web Site: http://sysma.sg
5UO—(CAT)
Rev.: $42,168,835
Assets: $79,729,150
Liabilities: $35,009,326
Net Worth: $44,719,824
Earnings: $1,998,881
Emp.: 377
Fiscal Year-end: 07/31/21
Residential, Commercial & Industrial Building Construction
N.A.I.C.S.: 236117
Ee Wuen Sin (Deputy CEO)

SYSMEX CORPORATION

1-5-1 Wakinohama-Kaigandori, Chuoku, Kobe, 651-0073, Hyogo, Japan
Tel.: (81) 782650500
Web Site: https://sysmex.co.jp
Year Founded: 1968
SSMXY—(OTCIQ)
Rev.: $2,943,299,340
Assets: $3,807,800,580
Liabilities: $1,023,288,060
Net Worth: $2,784,512,520
Earnings: $327,848,250
Emp.: 10,522
Fiscal Year-end: 03/31/23
Diagnostic Testing Instruments, Reagents, Particle Analyzers & Related Software Developer, Mfr, Sales, Importer & Exporter
N.A.I.C.S.: 339112
Masayo Takahashi (Member-Mgmt Bd)

Subsidiaries:

BNA Inc. (1)
7-7-20 Saito-Asagi, Osaka, 567-0085, Ibaraki, Japan
Tel.: (81) 726467037
Web Site: http://www.bna.jp
Pharmaceutical & Diagnostic Research Services
N.A.I.C.S.: 541714
Kenji Iwakabe (CEO)

Creative Nanosystems Corporation (1)
4-4-4 Takatsukadai, Nishi-ku, Kobe, 651-2271, Hyogo, Japan
Tel.: (81) 78 991 1410
Web Site: https://www.creative-nano.co.jp
Bio Device Product Mfr
N.A.I.C.S.: 339112
Hiroya Kirimura (Pres)

Cytocell Limited (1)
418 Cambridge Science Park Milton Road, Cambridge, CB4 0PZ, United Kingdom
Tel.: (44) 1223294048
Web Site: www.cytocell.com
Pharmaceutical & Diagnostic Research Services
N.A.I.C.S.: 541714
John Murray (Dir-Ops)

HITADO GmbH (1)
Dreihausen 2, 59519, Mohnesee, Germany
Tel.: (49) 29 249 7050
Web Site: https://www.hitado.de
Diagnostic Equipment Whslr
N.A.I.C.S.: 423450

HYPHEN BioMed, SAS (1)
155 Rue d'Eragny, 95000, Neuville-sur-Oise, France
Tel.: (33) 13 440 6510
Web Site: https://www.hyphen-biomed.com
Sales Range: $25-49.9 Million
Emp.: 50
Diagnostic Equipment Whslr
N.A.I.C.S.: 423450
Anne Marie Vissac (Founder)

Jinan Sysmex Medical Electronics Co., Ltd. (1)
7493 Airport Road Yaoqiang Town, Licheng District, Jinan, 250107, Shandong, China

INTERNATIONAL PUBLIC

Tel.: (86) 531 8873 4440
Medical Equipment Distr
N.A.I.C.S.: 423450

Medicaroid, Inc. (1)
3075 N 1st St, San Jose, CA 95134
Tel.: (408) 503-0850
Medical Robotic Device Mfr
N.A.I.C.S.: 339112

Oxford Gene Technology (Operations) Limited (1)
Begbroke Science Park Begbroke Hill Woodstock Road, Begbroke, OX5 1PF, Oxfordshire, United Kingdom
Tel.: (44) 186 585 6800
Web Site: https://www.ogt.com
Genetic Research Services
N.A.I.C.S.: 541714
David Oxlade (Chm)

Oxford Gene Technology Inc. (1)
520 White Plains Rd Ste 500, Tarrytown, NY 10591
Tel.: (914) 467-5285
Genetic Research Services
N.A.I.C.S.: 541714

PT. Sysmex Indonesia (1)
Cyber 2 Tower 5th Floor Unit E Jl HR Rasuna Said Blok X5 No 13, Jakarta, 12950, Indonesia
Tel.: (62) 213 002 6688
Web Site: https://www.sysmex.co.id
In Vitro Diagnostic Systems & Reagents Sales
N.A.I.C.S.: 423450

Riken Genesis Co., Ltd. (1)
Art Village Osaki Central Tower 8F 1-2-2 Osaki, Shinagawa-ku, Tokyo, 141-0032, Japan
Tel.: (81) 35 759 6041
Web Site: https://www.rikengenesis.jp
Contract Genetic Analysis Services
N.A.I.C.S.: 541714
Naoto Kondo (Pres & CEO)

Sysmex (Thailand) Co., Ltd. (1)
18th Floor Tonson Tower 900 Ploenchit Road, Lumpini Pathumwan, Bangkok, 10330, Thailand
Tel.: (66) 2 032 2536
Web Site: https://www.sysmex.co.th
Diagnostic Reagent Distr
N.A.I.C.S.: 424210

Sysmex America, Inc. (1)
577 Aptakisic Rd, Lincolnshire, IL 60069
Tel.: (847) 996-4500
Web Site: www.sysmex.com
In Vitro Diagnostic Medical Analyzers Mfr & Distr
N.A.I.C.S.: 339112
Ralph Taylor (CEO)

Sysmex Asia Pacific Pte. Ltd. (1)
9 Tampines Grande 06-18, Singapore, 528735, Singapore
Tel.: (65) 6 221 3629
Web Site: https://www.sysmex-ap.com
Sales Range: $50-74.9 Million
Emp.: 75
In Vitro Diagnostic Systems & Reagents Sales
N.A.I.C.S.: 423450
Frank Buescher (Pres & CEO)

Subsidiary (Non-US):

Sysmex (Malaysia) Sdn Bhd (2)
No 11A 15 Jalan PJS 7/21 Bdr Sunway, 47500, Subang Jaya, Selangor, Malaysia
Tel.: (60) 35 637 1788
Web Site: https://www.sysmex.com.my
Sales Range: $25-49.9 Million
Emp.: 50
In Vitro Diagnostic Systems & Reagents Sales
N.A.I.C.S.: 423450

Sysmex India Pvt. Ltd. (2)
1002 Damji Shamji Business Galleria 10th Floor LBS Marg, Kanjurmarg West, Mumbai, 400 078, India
Tel.: (91) 226 112 6666
Web Site: https://www.sysmex.co.in
Emp.: 16
Healthcare Information Technology Consulting Services
N.A.I.C.S.: 541512

SYSMEX CORPORATION
AND PRIVATE COMPANIES

Sysmex Philippines Inc. (2)
30th Floor MDC 100 Building E Rodriguez Jr Ave cor Eastwood Ave, Bagumbayan, Quezon City, Philippines
Tel.: (63) 2 621 2460
Web Site: https://www.sysmex.com.ph
Sales Range: $25-49.9 Million
Emp.: 25
Software Development Services
N.A.I.C.S.: 541511
Romeo Joseph Ignacio *(Gen Mgr)*

Sysmex Australia Pty Ltd. (1)
Suite 3 level 5 15 Talavera Road, Macquarie Park, 2113, NSW, Australia
Tel.: (61) 29 016 3040
Web Site: https://www.sysmex.com.au
Medical Device Mfr
N.A.I.C.S.: 339112
James Webster *(CEO)*

Sysmex Austria GmbH (1)
Odoakergasse 34-36, 1160, Vienna, Austria
Tel.: (43) 1 486 16 31
Web Site: http://www.sysmex.at
Vitro Diagnostic Reagent Distr
N.A.I.C.S.: 424210

Sysmex Belgium N.V. (1)
Terhulpsesteenweg 6a Building A, 1560, Hoeilaart, Belgium
Tel.: (32) 2 769 7474
Web Site: https://www.sysmex.nl
Sales Range: $50-74.9 Million
Emp.: 5
Diagnostic Equipment Distr
N.A.I.C.S.: 423450
Christian Frenzel *(Officer-Data Protection)*

Sysmex CNA Co., Ltd. (1)
2-3-7 Hakata Ekimae City 21 Building 8F, Hakata-ku, Fukuoka, 812-0011, Japan
Tel.: (81) 92 476 1121
Web Site: https://www.sysmex-cna.co.jp
Emp.: 204
Diagnostic Information Systems Software Developer & Distr
N.A.I.C.S.: 334610

Sysmex CZ s.r.o. (1)
Elgartova 683/4, 614 00, Brno, Czech Republic
Tel.: (420) 54 821 6855
Web Site: https://www.sysmex.cz
Sales Range: $25-49.9 Million
Emp.: 2
Diagnostic System & Reagent Whslr
N.A.I.C.S.: 423450

Sysmex Canada, Inc. (1)
5700 Explorer Drive Suite 200, Mississauga, L4W 0C6, ON, Canada
Tel.: (905) 366-7900
Web Site: http://www.sysmex.com
Sales Range: $25-49.9 Million
Emp.: 43
Hematology Analyzers Distr
N.A.I.C.S.: 423450
Robert Edward Degnan *(Pres & COO)*

Sysmex Chile SpA (1)
Badajoz 45 Office 1701 Torre B, Las Condes, 7560941, Santiago, Chile
Tel.: (56) 229402369
Vitro Diagnostic Product Mfr
N.A.I.C.S.: 325413

Sysmex Colombia SAS (1)
Calle 90 12-28 Offices 11 and 16, Bogota, Colombia
Tel.: (57) 16581683
Vitro Diagnostic Product Mfr
N.A.I.C.S.: 325413

Sysmex Corporation - Kakogawa Factory (1)
314-2 Kitano Noguchi-cho, Kakogawa, 675-0011, Hyogo, Japan
Tel.: (81) 79 424 1171
Web Site: http://www.sysmex.co.jp
Clinical Laboratory Equipment Mfr
N.A.I.C.S.: 334516

Sysmex Deutschland GmbH (1)
Bornbarch 1, 22848, Norderstedt, Germany
Tel.: (49) 40 534 1020
Web Site: https://www.sysmex.de
Sales Range: $75-99.9 Million
Emp.: 250
In Vitro Diagnostic Systems & Reagents Sales
N.A.I.C.S.: 423450

Sysmex Diagnosticos Mexico, S. de R.L. de C.V. (1)
Paseo de la Reforma 250 esq Niza 8th Floor, Colonia Juarez, Mexico, Mexico
Tel.: (52) 5536007106
Vitro Diagnostic Product Mfr
N.A.I.C.S.: 325413

Sysmex Digitana AG (1)
Todistrasse 50, 8810, Horgen, Switzerland
Tel.: (41) 44 718 38 38
Web Site: http://www.sysmex.ch
Vitro Diagnostic Reagent Whslr
N.A.I.C.S.: 424210
Oliver Herrmann *(Mng Dir & Head-Diagnostics & POC)*

Sysmex Espana S.L. (1)
Frederic Mompou 4B Planta 2, 08960, Sant Just Desvern, Spain
Tel.: (34) 90 209 0552
Web Site: https://www.sysmex.es
Emp.: 50
Medical Equipment Distr
N.A.I.C.S.: 423450

Sysmex Europe GmbH (1)
Bornbarch 1, 22848, Norderstedt, Germany
Tel.: (49) 4 052 7260
Web Site: https://www.sysmex-europe.com
Sales Range: $150-199.9 Million
Emp.: 80
In Vitro Diagnostic Systems & Reagents Mfr & Sales
N.A.I.C.S.: 325413
Alain Baverel *(CEO)*

Subsidiary (Non-US):

Sysmex South Africa (Pty) Ltd. (2)
Fernridge Office Park Block 1, Ferndale, Randburg, 2194, South Africa
Tel.: (27) 11 329 9480
Web Site: https://www.sysmex.co.za
Sales Range: $25-49.9 Million
Emp.: 15
Technical Support Training Services
N.A.I.C.S.: 541990
Samantha Giangregorio *(Dir)*

Sysmex France S.A.R.L. (1)
22 Avenue des Nations, BP 51414, Villepinte, 95944, Roissy-en-France, Cedex, France
Tel.: (33) 14 817 0190
Web Site: https://www.sysmex.fr
Sales Range: $50-74.9 Million
Emp.: 70
Diagnostic Information Systems Software & In Vitro Diagnostic Systems & Reagents Sales
N.A.I.C.S.: 423450

Sysmex Hong Kong Limited (1)
Room 907 9/F Tower One Silvercord 30 Canton Road, Tsim Sha Tsui, Kowloon, China (Hong Kong)
Tel.: (852) 25435123
Web Site: http://www.sysmex.com.hk
Diagnostic Reagent Distr
N.A.I.C.S.: 424210

Sysmex Hungaria Kft. (1)
Forum Offices Obuda Irodahaz Becsi ut 271, 1037, Budapest, Hungary
Tel.: (36) 1 210 96 70
Web Site: http://www.sysmex.hu
Sales Range: $25-49.9 Million
Emp.: 12
Vitro Diagnostic Reagent Whslr
N.A.I.C.S.: 424210

Sysmex Inostics GmbH (1)
Falkenried 88, 20251, Hamburg, Germany
Tel.: (49) 403259070
Web Site: http://www.sysmex-inostics.com
Pharmaceuticals Product Mfr
N.A.I.C.S.: 325412
Bhuwnesh Agrawal *(Mng Dir)*

Sysmex Inostics, Inc. (1)
1812 Ashland Ave Ste 500, Baltimore, MD 21205
Pharmaceuticals Product Mfr
N.A.I.C.S.: 325412

Sysmex International Reagents Co., Ltd (1)
4-3-2 Takatsukadai, Nishi-ku, Kobe, 651-2271, Hyogo, Japan
Tel.: (81) 78 991 2211
Web Site: http://www.sysmex-irc.co.jp
Emp.: 180
Vitro Diagnostic Reagent Mfr & Whslr
N.A.I.C.S.: 325412

Plant (Domestic):

Sysmex International Reagents Co., Ltd. - Ono Factory (2)
17 Takudai, Ono, 675-1322, Hyogo, Japan
Tel.: (81) 794 62 7001
Web Site: http://www.sysmex-irc.co.jp
Vitro Diagnostic Reagent Mfr
N.A.I.C.S.: 325412

Sysmex Logistics Co., Ltd. (1)
17 Takumidai, Ono, Hyogo, 675-1322, Japan
Tel.: (81) 794642326
Web Site: http://www.sysmex.co.jp
Sales Range: $50-74.9 Million
Emp.: 12
In Vitro Diagnostic Systems & Reagents Distr & Logistics
N.A.I.C.S.: 423450

Sysmex Logistics UK Ltd. (1)
Unit 4 IO Centre Fingle Drive, Stonebridge, Milton Keynes, MK13 0AT, United Kingdom
Tel.: (44) 8709029213
Web Site: http://www.sysmex.co.uk
Sales Range: $50-74.9 Million
Emp.: 80
In Vitro Diagnostic Systems & Reagents Distr & Logistics Services
N.A.I.C.S.: 423450
Keith Howes *(Officer-Data Protection)*

Sysmex Medica Co., Ltd. (1)
323-7 Miyaoki Yumesaki-cho, Shikama-gun, Himeji, 671-2121, Hyogo, Japan
Tel.: (81) 79 335 2080
Web Site: https://www.sysmex-medica.co.jp
Disposable Products Mfr; In Vitro Diagnostic Systems Assembler
N.A.I.C.S.: 325413

Sysmex Middle East FZ-LLC (1)
Dubai Healthcare City City Pharmacy Building C/P 72 Office 304, PO Box 505119, Dubai, United Arab Emirates
Tel.: (971) 4 437 0515
Web Site: https://www.sysmex-mea.com
Emp.: 17
Diagnostic Reagent Distr
N.A.I.C.S.: 424210
Saad Kayali *(Mng Dir)*

Sysmex Nederland B.V. (1)
PO Box 251, 4870 AG, Etten-Leur, Netherlands
Tel.: (31) 76 5086000
Web Site: http://www.sysmex.nl
Sales Range: $50-74.9 Million
Emp.: 10
Diagnostic Equipment Whslr
N.A.I.C.S.: 423450
Christian Frenzel *(Officer-Data Protection)*

Sysmex New Zealand Limited (1)
386 Manukau Road, Epsom, Auckland, 1023, New Zealand
Tel.: (64) 96303554
Web Site: http://www.sysmex.co.nz
Sales Range: $25-49.9 Million
Emp.: 50
Diagnostic Information Systems Software Developer & Sales
N.A.I.C.S.: 334610
Arjit Bhana *(CEO)*

Sysmex Nordic ApS (1)
Foreningsgatan 217, 261 51, Landskrona, Sweden
Tel.: (46) 30 056 7202
Web Site: https://www.sysmex.se
Pharmaceuticals Product Mfr
N.A.I.C.S.: 325412
Jerker Rangstrom *(Gen Mgr)*

Sysmex Nordic ApS (1)
Hedegaardsvej 88, 2300, Copenhagen, Denmark
Tel.: (45) 7 020 4501
Web Site: https://www.sysmex.dk
Pharmaceuticals Product Mfr
N.A.I.C.S.: 325412
Ulf S. Skimmeland *(Mng Dir)*

Sysmex Norge AS (1)
Hvamsvingen 24, 2013, Skjetten, Norway
Tel.: (47) 6 384 0160
Web Site: https://www.sysmex.no
Diagnostic Equipment Whslr
N.A.I.C.S.: 423450
Ulf S. Skimmeland *(Mng Dir)*

Sysmex Partec Burkina Faso SARL (1)
BP 1323, Ouagadougou, Burkina Faso
Tel.: (226) 50304559
Medical Device Mfr
N.A.I.C.S.: 339112

Sysmex Partec GmbH (1)
Arndtstrasse 11 a-b, 02826, Goerlitz, Germany
Tel.: (49) 35 818 7460
Web Site: https://www.sysmex-partec.com
Vitro Diagnostic Product Mfr
N.A.I.C.S.: 325413

Sysmex Partec Italia S.R.L (1)
Via Merendi 19, 20007, Cornaredo, Milan, Italy
Tel.: (39) 028 945 0500
Web Site: https://www.sysmex-partec.it
Medical Device Mfr
N.A.I.C.S.: 339112
Tommaso Cardani *(CEO)*

Sysmex Polska S.P.Z O.O (1)
Al Jerozolimskie 176, 02-486, Warsaw, Poland
Tel.: (48) 22 572 8400
Web Site: https://www.sysmex.pl
Sales Range: $50-74.9 Million
Emp.: 25
In Vitro Diagnostic Systems & Reagents Sales
N.A.I.C.S.: 423450
Justyna Kurycyn *(Mng Dir)*

Sysmex R&D Center Europe GmbH (1)
Falkenried 88, 20251, Hamburg, Germany
Tel.: (49) 4032 590 7239
Web Site: https://www.sysmex-rdce.com
Vitro Diagnosis Research & Development Services
N.A.I.C.S.: 541714
Seigo Suzuki *(Pres & Mng Dir)*

Sysmex RA Co., Ltd (1)
1850-3 Hirookanomura, Shiojiri, 399-0702, Nagano, Japan
Tel.: (81) 26 354 2251
Web Site: https://www.sysmex-ra.co.jp
Emp.: 200
Medical Equipment Mfr
N.A.I.C.S.: 334510

Sysmex RUS LLC (1)
1st Magistral Deadlock 11 building 10 Business Center YaRD office 1020, 123290, Moscow, Russia
Tel.: (7) 4957816772
Web Site: http://www.sysmex.ru
Sales Range: $25-49.9 Million
Emp.: 60
Medical Device Mfr & Distr
N.A.I.C.S.: 334510
Elena Aleksandrovna Kozyreva *(CEO & Gen Dir)*

Sysmex Reagents America, Inc. (1)
2 Nelson C White Pkwy, Mundelein, IL 60060
Tel.: (847) 367-2800
Web Site: http://www.sysmex.com
Vitro Diagnostic Reagent Mfr & Distr
N.A.I.C.S.: 325412

Sysmex San Tung Co., Ltd. (1)
1f 11 Lane 6 Hang Chou S Rd Sec 1, Taipei, 10050, Taiwan
Tel.: (886) 223419290
Diagnostic Reagent Whslr
N.A.I.C.S.: 424210

Sysmex Shanghai Ltd. (1)
1366 Lujiazui Ring Road Foxconn Building 6th Floor, Shanghai, 200120, China
Tel.: (86) 2120524666
Web Site: http://www.sysmex.com.cn
Diagnostic Reagent Distr
N.A.I.C.S.: 424210

Sysmex Slovakia s.r.o. (1)

SYSMEX CORPORATION

Sysmex Corporation—(Continued)
Trencianska 47, 821 09, Bratislava, Slovakia
Tel.: (421) 2 6453 2881
Web Site: http://www.sysmex.cz
Diagnostic Reagent Distr
N.A.I.C.S.: 424210

Sysmex TMC Co., Ltd. (1)
1-3-3 Muroya, Nishi-ku, Kobe, 651-2241, Hyogo, Japan
Tel.: (81) 78 992 5883
Web Site: http://www.sysmex-tmc.co.jp
Emp.: 67
Medical Equipment Repair & Maintenance Services
N.A.I.C.S.: 811210

Sysmex Taiwan Co., Ltd. (1)
18th Floor No 156 Section 1 Zhongshan Road, Banqiao District, New Taipei City, Taiwan
Tel.: (886) 22 341 9290
Web Site: https://www.sysmex.com.tw
Medical Device Mfr
N.A.I.C.S.: 339112

Sysmex Transasia Services Pvt. Ltd. (1)
308 ASCOT Centre 3rd Floor Sahar Airport Road, Andheri East, Mumbai, 400 099, India
Tel.: (91) 22 2822 4040
Web Site: http://www.sysmex.com
Emp.: 14
Health Care Srvices
N.A.I.C.S.: 621999
Peter Layr *(Mng Dir)*

Sysmex Turkey Diagnostik Sistemleri Ltd. Sti. (1)
Maslak Office Building Maslak Mh Sumer Sk No 4 Kat 16, Sariyer, 34485, Istanbul, Türkiye
Tel.: (90) 216 681 6600
Web Site: https://www.sysmex.com.tr
Medical Device Mfr
N.A.I.C.S.: 339112
Umut Gokalp *(Mng Dir)*

Sysmex UK Limited (1)
Sysmex House Garamonde Drive, Wymbush, Milton Keynes, Mk8 8DF, United Kingdom
Tel.: (44) 333 320 3460
Web Site: https://www.sysmex.co.uk
Sales Range: $25-49.9 Million
Emp.: 50
In Vitro Diagnostic Systems & Reagents Sales
N.A.I.C.S.: 423450

Sysmex Vietnam Company Limited (1)
Room 802 Centre Point Building 106 Nguyen Van Troi street, ward 08 Phu Nhuan district, Ho Chi Minh City, Vietnam
Tel.: (84) 2839979400
Web Site: http://www.sysmex.com.vn
Sales Range: $25-49.9 Million
Emp.: 11
Diagnostic Equipment Distr
N.A.I.C.S.: 423450

Sysmex West & Central Africa Ltd. (1)
148A Marvel House Giffard Road Burma Camp - Trade Fair Road, East Cantonments, Accra, Ghana
Tel.: (233) 30 279 8867
Web Site: https://www.sysmex-wca.com
Medical Device Mfr
N.A.I.C.S.: 339112

Sysmex Wuxi Co., Ltd. (1)
8-9 No 93 Science Technology Stand-Up Park, New District, Wuxi, 214028, Jiangsu, China
Tel.: (86) 510 8534 5837
Diagnostic Reagent Distr
N.A.I.C.S.: 424210

Sysmex do Brasil Industria e Comercio Ltda. (1)
Joaquim Nabuco Street 615, Cidade Jardim Neighborhood, Sao Jose dos Pinhais, 83040-210, PR, Brazil
Tel.: (55) 4121041314
Vitro Diagnostic Product Mfr

N.A.I.C.S.: 325413

SYSTECH BHD
B-01-08 Tower B The Vertical Business Suite, Bangsar South No 8 Jalan Kerinchi, 59200, Kuala Lumpur, Malaysia
Tel.: (60) 322421833 MY
Web Site: https://www.systech.asia
SYSTECH—(KLS)
Rev.: $3,692,910
Assets: $7,033,862
Liabilities: $2,119,788
Net Worth: $4,914,074
Earnings: $62,011
Emp.: 121
Fiscal Year-end: 03/31/23
Investment Holding Services
N.A.I.C.S.: 551112
Raymond Hock Ann Tan *(CEO-Grp)*

Subsidiaries:

SysArmy Sdn Bhd (1)
Suite 12-11 12th Floor Wisma Zelan Jalan Tasik Permaisuri 2, Bandar Sri Permaisuri, 56000, Kuala Lumpur, Malaysia
Tel.: (60) 391711562
Web Site: https://www.sysarmy.net
Software Development Services
N.A.I.C.S.: 541511

Subsidiary (Non-US):

PT SysArmy Indocyber Security (2)
Synergy Building Unit 11-08 & 09 11th Floor, Jl Jalur Sutera Barat No 17 Alam Sutera Barat - Serpong Tangerang, 15325, Jakarta, Indonesia
Tel.: (62) 2130052323
Software Development Services
N.A.I.C.S.: 541511

SYSTEM AND APPLICATION TECHNOLOGIES INC.
7F SATower 175 LS-ro, Gunpo, Gyeonggi-do, Korea (South)
Tel.: (82) 314501400
Web Site: https://www.satech.co.kr
Year Founded: 1998
060540—(KRS)
Rev.: $133,738,663
Assets: $129,423,391
Liabilities: $50,402,065
Net Worth: $79,021,325
Earnings: $7,011,617
Emp.: 81
Fiscal Year-end: 12/31/22
Software Publishing Services
N.A.I.C.S.: 513210
Sung Won Jung *(Pres & CEO)*

SYSTEM INFORMATION CO., LTD.
1-7-3 Kachidoki San Square 7F, Chuo-ku, Tokyo, 104-0054, Japan
Tel.: (81) 3 5547 5700
Web Site: http://www.sysj.co.jp
3677—(JAS)
Rev.: $125,878,720
Assets: $68,214,960
Liabilities: $21,557,360
Net Worth: $46,657,600
Earnings: $10,599,600
Emp.: 462
Fiscal Year-end: 09/30/21
Software Developer
N.A.I.C.S.: 513210

SYSTEM INTEGRATOR CORP.
2nd Axis Tower 11 Shintoshin 32F, Chuo-ku, Saitama, 330-6032, Saitama, Japan
Tel.: (81) 486003880 JP
Web Site: http://www.sint.co.jp
Year Founded: 1995
3826—(TKS)
Sales Range: $25-49.9 Million
Emp.: 226
Software Development Services

N.A.I.C.S.: 513210
Hiroyuki Umeda *(Pres)*

SYSTEM LOCATION CO., LTD.
SLC Meguro Higashiyama Building 2-6-3 Higashiyama, Meguro-Ku, Tokyo, 153-0043, Japan
Tel.: (81) 364522864
Web Site: https://www.slc.jp
Year Founded: 1968
2480—(TKS)
Rev.: $12,603,360
Assets: $34,848,000
Liabilities: $5,314,320
Net Worth: $29,533,680
Earnings: $4,084,960
Emp.: 38
Fiscal Year-end: 03/31/22
Automobile Financing Services
N.A.I.C.S.: 327910
Takehiko Chimura *(Pres & CEO)*

Subsidiaries:

Every's Co., Ltd. (1)
Minami Ikebukuro M building 303 2-47-13 Minami Ikebukuro, Toshima-ku, Tokyo, 171-0022, Japan
Tel.: (81) 359532425
Financial Services
N.A.I.C.S.: 523999
Takeshi Tamura *(CEO)*

J Core Co., Ltd. (1)
Higashiyama 2-6-3, Meguro-ku, Tokyo, 153-0043, Japan
Tel.: (81) 364522865
Financial Services
N.A.I.C.S.: 523999
Hirokazu Uchimura *(CEO)*

Japan Wheelchair-accessible Vehicle Dealer Co., Ltd. (1)
Minami Ikebukuro 2-47-13, Toshima-ku, Tokyo, 171-0022, Japan
Tel.: (81) 368216717
Financial Services
N.A.I.C.S.: 523999
Takeshi Tamura *(CEO)*

Qian Che Technology Service Beijing Co., Ltd. (1)
509RM 5F Moma Building 199 Chaoyang-Beilu, Chaoyang District, Beijing, 100026, China
Tel.: (86) 1065992088
Financial Services
N.A.I.C.S.: 523999
Sadamu Maeda *(Pres & CEO)*

ValuAble Co., Ltd. (1)
5F Songhyeon Building 116 Myeongdal-ro, Seocho-gu, Seoul, Korea (South)
Tel.: (82) 25879229
Web Site: https://www.vab.co.kr
Automobile Data Integration Solution Services
N.A.I.C.S.: 518210

SYSTEM RESEARCH CO., LTD.
260 Tsurugicho, Nakamura-ku, Nagoya, 453-0842, Aichi, Japan
Tel.: (81) 524136820
Web Site: https://www.sr-net.co.jp
Year Founded: 1981
3771—(TKS)
Rev.: $154,145,200
Assets: $106,718,450
Liabilities: $37,154,810
Net Worth: $69,563,640
Earnings: $13,015,090
Fiscal Year-end: 03/31/24
Software Development Services
N.A.I.C.S.: 541511
Toshiyuki Yamada *(Chm)*

SYSTEM SUPPORT, INC.
1-5-2 Honmachi Ishikawa Rifare 9F, Kanazawa, 920-0853, Ishikawa, Japan
Tel.: (81) 762655151
Web Site: https://www.sts-inc.co.jp

INTERNATIONAL PUBLIC

Year Founded: 1980
4396—(TKS)
Rev.: $137,020,380
Assets: $61,758,380
Liabilities: $30,316,280
Net Worth: $31,442,100
Earnings: $7,613,280
Emp.: 1,260
Fiscal Year-end: 06/30/24
Application Development Services
N.A.I.C.S.: 541511
Kenji Suzuki *(Sr Mng Dir)*

Subsidiaries:

ACROSS Solutions, Inc. (1)
3-6-6 Kitayasue 1F/2F Messeyasuda, Kanazawa, 920-0022, Ishikawa, Japan
Tel.: (81) 76 255 2012
Web Site: https://www.acrossjapan.co.jp
Real Estate Services
N.A.I.C.S.: 531390

STS Medic Inc. (1)
Iwashita Building 3F 1-11-12 Shinjuku, Shinjuku-ku, Tokyo, 160-0022, Japan
Tel.: (81) 35 919 8851
Web Site: https://www.sts-medic.jp
Software Development Services
N.A.I.C.S.: 541511

T4C Co., Ltd. (1)
7-9-2 Nishigotanda KDX Gotanda Building 6F, Shinagawa-ku, Tokyo, 141-0031, Japan
Tel.: (81) 35 435 6191
Web Site: https://www.t4c.co.jp
Information Technology Consulting Services
N.A.I.C.S.: 541618

SYSTEM1 GROUP PLC
26 Hatton Garden, Holborn, London, EC1N 8BR, United Kingdom
Tel.: (44) 2070431000 UK
Web Site: https://www.system1group.com
Year Founded: 1999
SYS1—(AIM)
Rev.: $29,070,538
Assets: $18,603,406
Liabilities: $7,915,233
Net Worth: $10,688,173
Earnings: $501,687
Emp.: 150
Fiscal Year-end: 03/31/23
Online Market Research Services
N.A.I.C.S.: 541910
John Kearon *(Founder, Founder, Pres & Pres)*

Subsidiaries:

System1 Research B.V. (1)
Weena 505, 3013 AL, Rotterdam, Netherlands
Tel.: (31) 102130268
Marketing & Brand Consulting Services
N.A.I.C.S.: 541613
Ellen de Kruijf *(Country Dir)*

System1 Research France Sarl (1)
17 Rue de Turbigo 3rd Floor, 75002, Paris, France
Tel.: (33) 140261440
Marketing & Brand Consulting Services
N.A.I.C.S.: 541613
Laurent Calvayrac *(Country Dir)*

System1 Research GmbH (1)
Axel-Springer-Platz 3, 20355, Hamburg, Germany
Tel.: (49) 1713041755
Marketing & Brand Consulting Services
N.A.I.C.S.: 541613
Kathrin Posnanski *(Country Dir)*

System1 Research Sarl (1)
Avenue Gratta Paille 2, 1018, Lausanne, Switzerland
Tel.: (41) 799472031
Marketing & Brand Consulting Services
N.A.I.C.S.: 541613
Paul Munn *(Country Dir)*

SYSTEMAIR AB

AND PRIVATE COMPANIES — SYSTEMAIR AB

Industrivagen 3, SE-739 30,
Skinnskatteberg, Sweden
Tel.: (46) 22244000 SE
Web Site: https://www.systemair.com
Year Founded: 1974
SYSR—(OMX)
Rev.: $1,129,365,815
Assets: $902,254,442
Liabilities: $408,422,078
Net Worth: $493,832,364
Earnings: $97,848,586
Emp.: 5,947
Fiscal Year-end: 04/30/23
Heating, Ventilation & Cooling Equipment Mfr
N.A.I.C.S.: 333413
Gerald Engstrom (Chm)

Subsidiaries:

Divid AB (1)
Jarnvagsgatan 3, S-553 15, Jonkoping, Sweden
Tel.: (46) 367777220
Web Site: https://www.divid.se
Software Development Services
N.A.I.C.S.: 541511
Stefan Svensson (Co-Founder)

Fantech Inc. (1)
10048 Industrial Blvd, Lenexa, KS 66215
Web Site: https://www.fantech.net
Ventilation Equipment Mfr
N.A.I.C.S.: 333413
Phil Rivas (Pres)

Fantech Ltd.
50 Kanalflakt Way, Bouctouche, E4S 3M5, NB, Canada
Tel.: (506) 743-9500
Web Site: http://www.fantech.net
Emp.: 120
Ventilation Equipment Mfr
N.A.I.C.S.: 333413

Subsidiary (US):

Fantech Systemair Mfg Inc. (2)
10048 Industrial Blvd, Lenexa, KS 66215-1219
Tel.: (913) 752-6000
Web Site: http://www.fantech.net
Sales Range: $10-24.9 Million
Emp.: 150
Ventilation Equipment Mfr
N.A.I.C.S.: 333413

Frico A/S (1)
Thorsvej 106, 7200, Grindsted, Denmark
Tel.: (45) 50802023
Web Site: https://www.frico.net
Ventilating Product Mfr
N.A.I.C.S.: 333413

Frico AB (1)
Industrivagen 41, SE-433 61, Savedalen, Sweden
Tel.: (46) 313368600
Web Site: https://www.frico.net
Emp.: 45
Heating Equipment Mfr
N.A.I.C.S.: 333413
Jonas Valentin (CEO)

Subsidiary (Non-US):

Frico SAS (2)
ZAC Bel Air La Logere 237 allee des Noyers, 69480, Pommiers, France
Tel.: (33) 437552940
Web Site: https://www.frico.net
Ventilation Equipment Mfr & Distr
N.A.I.C.S.: 333413

Frico AS (1)
Brynsveien 12, 0667, Oslo, Norway
Tel.: (47) 23371900
Air Curtain Mfr & Distr
N.A.I.C.S.: 333413

Frico B.V. (1)
Van Leeuwenhoekstraat 2, 3846 CB, Harderwijk, Netherlands
Tel.: (31) 341439100
Web Site: https://www.frico.net
Ventilating Product Mfr
N.A.I.C.S.: 333413

Frico GmbH (1)
Hesslachshof 14/3, DE-74677, Dorzbach, Germany
Tel.: (49) 79382070010
Web Site: https://www.frico.net
Air Curtain Mfr & Distr
N.A.I.C.S.: 333413

Holland Heating B.V. (1)
Zanddonkweg 7a, 5144 NX, Waalwijk, Netherlands
Tel.: (31) 416 685555
Ventilation Equipment Mfr
N.A.I.C.S.: 333413
Wim Kampen (Dir-Sls)

IMOS-Systemair spol. s.r.o. (1)
Hlavna 371, 900 43, Kalinkovo, Slovakia
Tel.: (421) 24 020 3111
Web Site: https://www.systemair.com
Ventilation Equipment Distr
N.A.I.C.S.: 423730
Gabriela Cermakova (Acct Mgr)

LGB GmbH (1)
Albert-Einstein-Strasse 11 Businesspark, Galkhausen Rhld, 40764, Langenfeld, Germany
Tel.: (49) 2173106370
Web Site: https://www.lgb-gmbh.de
Ventilation Product Mfr & Distr
N.A.I.C.S.: 333413

Lautner Enegiespartechnik GmbH (1)
Steinweg 5, Helmstadt, 74921, Wurzburg, Germany
Tel.: (49) 726 340 8220
Web Site: https://www.lautner.eu
Rotary Heat Exchanger Mfr
N.A.I.C.S.: 333414

Menerga AS (1)
Nye Vakasvei 20, 1395, Hvalstad, Norway
Tel.: (47) 67573989
Web Site: https://www.menerga.com
Ventilating Product Mfr
N.A.I.C.S.: 333413

Menerga GmbH (1)
Alexanderstrasse 38, 45472, Mulheim an der Ruhr, Germany
Tel.: (49) 20899810
Web Site: https://www.menerga.com
Emp.: 400
Ventilation & Air Conditioning Mfr
N.A.I.C.S.: 333413

Menerga NV (1)
Nieuwlandlaan 133/ B635, 3200, Aarschot, Belgium
Tel.: (32) 16314200
Web Site: https://www.menerga.be
Air Conditioning & Ventilating Product Distr
N.A.I.C.S.: 423730

Menerga Polska Sp. z o.o. (1)
Al Krakowska 169, Lazy Wolka Kosowska, 05-552, Warsaw, Poland
Tel.: (48) 226700832
Cooling Product Mfr
N.A.I.C.S.: 333415

OOO Systemair (1)
Shabolovka Street 31G, 115162, Moscow, Russia
Tel.: (7) 4952527277
Ventilating Product Mfr
N.A.I.C.S.: 333413

Pacific Ventilation Pty. Ltd. (1)
2/63 Wells Road, Chelsea Heights, 3196, VIC, Australia
Tel.: (61) 397733200
Web Site: https://www.pacificventilation.com
Ventilating Product Mfr
N.A.I.C.S.: 333413
Andrew Twisse (Natl Sls Mgr)

Poly-Rek d.o.o. (1)
Vojvodici 23a, Novaki, 10431, Sveta Nedelja, Croatia
Tel.: (385) 14870658
Web Site: https://www.poly-rek.hr
Ventilating Product Mfr
N.A.I.C.S.: 333413

Recutech s.r.o. (1)
Fablovka 592, 533 52, Pardubice, Czech Republic
Tel.: (420) 467070245
Web Site: https://www.recutech.com

Emp.: 100
Heat Exchanger Mfr
N.A.I.C.S.: 333414
Filip Hazuka (CEO)

Safeair S.L. (1)
Avda San Isidro Nave C-3, Sesena, 45223, Toledo, Spain
Tel.: (34) 918098371
Fire Protection Equipment Mfr
N.A.I.C.S.: 334290

Servicebolaget i Sverige AB (1)
Kastellvagen 19, 824 55, Hudiksvall, Sweden
Tel.: (46) 20222200
Web Site: https://www.servicebolaget.se
Ventilation Product Distr
N.A.I.C.S.: 423730

Systemair (Pty) Ltd (1)
Treger Lane Precinctnr Dormehl and Davidson Streets, Cape Town, 1459, South Africa
Tel.: (27) 878077862
Web Site: https://www.systemair.com
Ventilation Equipment Mfr & Distr
N.A.I.C.S.: 333413

Systemair (SEA) PTE Ltd. (1)
33 Tannery Lane 01-01, Singapore, 347789, Singapore
Tel.: (65) 68420688
Web Site: https://www.systemair.com
Ventilation Equipment Mfr & Distr
N.A.I.C.S.: 333413

Systemair A/S (1)
Ved Milepaelen 7, DK-8361, Hasselager, Denmark
Tel.: (45) 87387500
Web Site: https://www.systemair.com
Emp.: 200
Air Handling Unit Mfr
N.A.I.C.S.: 333413

Systemair AC SAS (1)
Route de Verneuil, 27570, Tillieres-sur-Avre, France
Tel.: (33) 2 32 60 61 00
Web Site: http://www.systemair.com
Sales Range: $50-74.9 Million
Emp.: 200
Ventilation Products Mfr
N.A.I.C.S.: 333415

Systemair AS (1)
Tel.: (372) 6061888
Web Site: https://www.systemair.com
Ventilation Equipment Distr
N.A.I.C.S.: 423730
Aivar Paluvee (Gen Mgr)

Systemair AS (1)
Odborarska 52, 831 02, Bratislava, Slovakia
Tel.: (421) 249205311
Web Site: https://www.systemair.com
Ventilation Equipment Mfr
N.A.I.C.S.: 333413
Eduard Godovic (Chm)

Systemair B.V. (1)
Van Leeuwenhoekstraat 2, 3846 CB, Harderwijk, Netherlands
Tel.: (31) 850066200
Web Site: https://www.exera.asia
Ventilating Product Mfr
N.A.I.C.S.: 333413

Systemair Co. Ltd (1)
247 An Le Rd, Taipei, Taiwan
Tel.: (886) 229477779
Heating Equipment Mfr
N.A.I.C.S.: 333414

Systemair EOOD (1)
11 Panorama Sofia Str Ground floor office 5, 1766, Sofia, Bulgaria
Tel.: (359) 29732693
Web Site: https://www.systemair.com
Ventilation Equipment Mfr
N.A.I.C.S.: 333413

Systemair Fans & Spares Ltd (1)
Unit 28 Gravelly Industrial Park, Birmingham, B24 8HZ, West Midlands, United Kingdom
Tel.: (44) 121 322 0200
Web Site: https://www.systemair.com
Ventilation Equipment Distr
N.A.I.C.S.: 423730
Neil Rapley (Mng Dir)

Systemair GmbH (1)
Seehofer Strasse 45, 97944, Boxberg-Windischbuch, Germany
Tel.: (49) 793092720
Web Site: https://www.systemair.com
Heating, Ventilation & Cooling Equipment Mfr
N.A.I.C.S.: 333413
Kurt Maurer (Mng Dir)

Systemair GmbH (1)
Kolpingstrasse 14, 1230, Vienna, Austria
Tel.: (43) 1 615 38 50 0
Ventilation Equipment Mfr
N.A.I.C.S.: 333413

Systemair HSK (1)
Buyukdere Cd No 121 Ercan Han Kat 7 Esentepe - Sisli, Istanbul, Turkiye
Tel.: (90) 212 356 4060
Web Site: https://www.systemair.com
Ventilation Equipment Mfr
N.A.I.C.S.: 333413

Systemair HSK Hav. Ekip. San. ve Tic. Ltd. (1)
Yapi Kredi Plaza Levent Mah Comert Sok No 1 B Blok Floor 5, Esentepe Sisli, Istanbul, Turkiye
Tel.: (90) 2123564060
Web Site: https://www.systemair.com
Cooling Product Mfr
N.A.I.C.S.: 333415

Systemair HVAC S.L.U. (1)
C/ Montecarlo 14, Fuenlabrada, 28942, Madrid, Spain
Tel.: (34) 916002900
Web Site: https://www.systemair.com
Ventilation Equipment Mfr
N.A.I.C.S.: 333413

Systemair Hav. Ekip. San.ve Tic. Ltd Sti. (1)
Barbaros Mh Sedef Sk No 1/1, Istanbul, Turkiye
Tel.: (90) 216 474 75 35
Ventilation Equipment Mfr
N.A.I.C.S.: 333413

Systemair Hellas S.A. (1)
13 Astrous Str Ilion, PO Box 131-22, 13121, Athens, Greece
Tel.: (30) 2105789766
Web Site: https://www.systemair.com
Ventilation Equipment Mfr & Distr
N.A.I.C.S.: 333413
George Mantesis (Mng Dir)

Systemair Hong Kong Ltd. (1)
Room 505 OfficePlus Prince Edward 794-802 Nathan Road, Kowloon, China (Hong Kong)
Tel.: (852) 21915562
Web Site: https://www.systemair.com
Ventilation Equipment Mfr
N.A.I.C.S.: 333413
Kent Chau (Mng Dir)

Systemair IOOO (1)
Dzerzhinskogo Ave 104-1203, 220116, Minsk, Belarus
Tel.: (375) 173502463
Web Site: https://www.systemair.com
Cooling Product Mfr
N.A.I.C.S.: 333415

Systemair India Pvt. Ltd (1)
Plot No 03 ECOTECH I Sector-31 Site IV KasnaGreater, Noida, 201308, Uttar Pradesh, India
Tel.: (91) 1204763100
Web Site: https://www.systemair.com
Emp.: 400
Ventilation Equipment Mfr
N.A.I.C.S.: 333413

Systemair Italy S.r.l. (1)
Via XXV Aprile 29, 20825, Barlassina, MB, Italy
Tel.: (39) 03621869501
Ventilating Product Mfr
N.A.I.C.S.: 333413

Systemair Ltd (1)
8 Rouse Street, Tillsonburg, N4G 5W8, ON, Canada
Tel.: (519) 688-6363
Web Site: https://www.systemair.com
Ventilation Equipment Mfr

SYSTEMAIR AB

Systemair AB—(Continued)
N.A.I.C.S.: 333413
Rob Thompson (Mng Dir)

Systemair Ltd (1)
Unit 02 Furry Park, Santry, Dublin, D09 A2K0, Ireland
Tel.: (353) 18624544
Web Site: https://www.systemair.com
Ventilation Equipment Mfr & Distr
N.A.I.C.S.: 333413

Systemair Maroc SARL (1)
163 Zone Industrielle Sud-ouest, Mohammedia, Morocco (100%)
Tel.: (212) 523320790
Web Site: https://www.systemair.com
Ventilation Equipment Distr
N.A.I.C.S.: 423730

Systemair Mfg Inc. (1)
10048 Industrial Blvd, Lenexa, KS 66215
Tel.: (519) 688-6363
Cooling Product Mfr
N.A.I.C.S.: 333415

Systemair Middle East LLC (1)
New Souq Al Haraj Near Barwa Village Block 8 Mezzanine Office 4, Al Wakrah, Doha, Qatar
Tel.: (974) 44188744
Ventilation Equipment Distr
N.A.I.C.S.: 423730
Wolfgang W. Schelhorn (Mng Dir)

Systemair NV (1)
Nieuwlandlaan 133 - B635, 3200, Aarschot, Belgium
Tel.: (32) 1 638 7080
Web Site: https://www.systemair.com
Ventilation Equipment Mfr
N.A.I.C.S.: 333413

Systemair OOO (1)
Shabolovka Str 31G, 115162, Moscow, Russia
Tel.: (7) 4952527277
Cooling Product Mfr
N.A.I.C.S.: 333415

Systemair Oy (1)
Tammisto kauppatie 27, 01510, Vantaa, Finland
Tel.: (358) 207920520
Web Site: https://www.systemair.com
Emp.: 15
Ventilation Equipment Distr
N.A.I.C.S.: 423730
Matti-Jussi Partanen (Product Mgr)

Systemair Peru SAC (1)
Tel.: (51) 4641200
Web Site: https://www.systemair.com
Ventilating Product Mfr
N.A.I.C.S.: 333413

Systemair Rt (1)
Becsi ut 267, 1037, Budapest, Hungary
Tel.: (36) 14530161
Web Site: https://www.systemair.com
Ventilation Equipment Mfr & Distr
N.A.I.C.S.: 333413

Systemair S.p.A. (1)
Via XXV Aprile 29, 20825, Barlassina, MonzaBrianza, Italy
Tel.: (39) 03621869501
Web Site: https://www.systemair.com
Ventilation Equipment Mfr & Distr
N.A.I.C.S.: 333413

Systemair SA (1)
Oderska 333/5, 196 00, Prague, Czech Republic
Tel.: (420) 283910900
Web Site: https://www.systemair.com
Ventilation Equipment Mfr
N.A.I.C.S.: 333413

Systemair SA (1)
Al Krakowska 169 Lazy, 05-552, Wolka Kosowska, Poland
Tel.: (48) 227035000
Web Site: https://www.systemair.com
Ventilation Equipment Distr
N.A.I.C.S.: 423730

Systemair SA (1)
Zona Industrial da Maia Sector IX Norte Rua de Joao Veiga Anjos n 18, 4470-439, Moreira, Portugal
Tel.: (351) 22 999 7900
Web Site: https://www.systemair.com
Ventilation Equipment Mfr & Distr
N.A.I.C.S.: 333413

Systemair SAS (1)
ZAC Bel Air La Logere-237 Allee Des Noyers, 69480, Pommiers, France
Tel.: (33) 43 755 2960
Ventilating Product Mfr
N.A.I.C.S.: 333413

Systemair SIA (1)
Balasta dambis 80a, Riga, LV-1048, Latvia
Tel.: (371) 67601841
Web Site: https://www.systemair.com
Ventilation Equipment Mfr & Distr
N.A.I.C.S.: 333413

Systemair Sdn Bhd (1)
Lot 1565 Kampung Jaya Industrial Area Jalan Kusta 13 1/2 Miles, 47000, Sungai Buloh, Selangor, Malaysia
Tel.: (60) 361571177
Web Site: https://www.systemair.com
Ventilation Equipment Mfr
N.A.I.C.S.: 333413

Systemair SpA (1)
Americo Vespucio 1385 Parque empresarial Spacioflex Quilicura, Santiago, Chile
Tel.: (56) 2 257 50 40
Ventilation Equipment Mfr
N.A.I.C.S.: 333413
Marco Godoy Ocares (Acct Mgr)

Systemair Suisse AG (1)
Wueristrasse 41, Buchs, CH-8107, Zurich, Switzerland
Tel.: (41) 434111177
Web Site: https://www.systemair.com
Ventilation Equipment Mfr & Distr
N.A.I.C.S.: 333413

Systemair Sverige AB (1)
Industrivagen 3, 739 30, Skinnskatteberg, Sweden
Tel.: (46) 22244000
Web Site: https://www.systemair.com
Ventilating Product Mfr
N.A.I.C.S.: 333413

Systemair TOO (1)
19A Utepov str, Almaty, Kazakhstan
Tel.: (7) 7273390233
Web Site: https://www.systemair.com
Ventilating Product Mfr
N.A.I.C.S.: 333413

Systemair TOV (1)
Vikentiya Khvoiky Str 21 Office 529, 04080, Kiev, Ukraine
Tel.: (380) 442233434
Cooling Product Mfr
N.A.I.C.S.: 333415

Systemair Trading LLC (1)
The Citadel Tower 2905 Business Bay, Dubai, 391989, United Arab Emirates
Tel.: (971) 43477901
Web Site: https://www.systemair.com
Ventilation Equipment Distr
N.A.I.C.S.: 423730
Brian Suggitt (Mng Dir)

Systemair UAB (1)
Linu g 101, 20174, Ukmerge, Lithuania
Tel.: (370) 34060165
Web Site: https://www.systemair.com
Ventilation Equipment Mfr
N.A.I.C.S.: 333413
Mindaugas Martisius (Mng Dir)

Systemair d.o.o. (1)
Spelina ulica 2, SI-2000, Maribor, Slovenia
Tel.: (386) 24601801
Web Site: https://www.systemair.com
Ventilation Equipment Mfr
N.A.I.C.S.: 333413
Anton Zupancic (Dir)

Systemair d.o.o. (1)
Bulevar Zorana Djindjica 87 III/8, 11070, Belgrade, Serbia
Tel.: (381) 116304987
Ventilation Equipment Distr
N.A.I.C.S.: 423730
Mirjana Sofrenovic (Mng Dir)

Systemair d.o.o. (1)
Svetonedeljska cesta 62b, Kerestinec, 10431, Sveta Nedelja, Croatia
Tel.: (385) 1 644 5445
Web Site: https://www.systemair.com
Ventilation Equipment Mfr & Distr
N.A.I.C.S.: 333413

TEKADOOR GmbH (1)
Albert-Einstein-Str 11, 40764, Langenfeld, Germany
Tel.: (49) 2173207660
Web Site: https://www.tekadoor.de
Emp.: 18
Air Curtain Mfr
N.A.I.C.S.: 333413
Ute Schmelzer (Mng Dir)

TTL GmbH (1)
Fabrikstrasse 5, 73650, Winterbach, Germany
Tel.: (49) 71 814 0090
Web Site: https://www.luftschleier.de
Air Curtain Mfr
N.A.I.C.S.: 333413
Andre Szameitat (Mng Dir)

VEAB Heat Tech AB (1)
Stattenavagen 50, Box 265, S-28133, Hassleholm, Sweden
Tel.: (46) 45148500
Web Site: https://www.veab.com
Sales Range: $10-24.9 Million
Emp.: 90
Heating Equipment Mfr
N.A.I.C.S.: 333414
Bjorn Walther (Mng Dir)

Viking Air Conditioning (1)
Tel.: (27) 11 393 9800
Web Site: https://www.vikingac.co.za
Emp.: 40
Air Conditioning Units & Systems Mfr
N.A.I.C.S.: 333415
John Bennett (Pres)

SYSTEMATIX CORPORATE SERVICES LTD.
206-207 Bansi Trade Centre, 581/5 MG Road, Indore, 452001, Madhya Pradesh, India
Tel.: (91) 7313018111
Web Site:
   https://www.systematixgroup.in
526506—(BOM)
Rev.: $9,444,758
Assets: $21,734,956
Liabilities: $9,853,942
Net Worth: $11,881,014
Earnings: $609,328
Emp.: 18
Fiscal Year-end: 03/31/23
Financial Support Services
N.A.I.C.S.: 523999
Chandra Prakash Khandelwal (Founder & Chm)

SYSTEMATIX SECURITIES LTD.
35 Old Industrial RIICO Area, Chittorgarh, 312001, Rajasthan, India
Tel.: (91) 9414111117
Web Site:
   https://systematixsecurities.in
Year Founded: 1986
Rev.: $66,546
Assets: $1,267,629
Liabilities: $29,839
Net Worth: $1,237,790
Earnings: $2,602
Fiscal Year-end: 03/31/18
Security Brokerage Services
N.A.I.C.S.: 523150
Sudhir Samdani (Mng Dir)

SYSTEMD INC.
603 Karasuma-dori Sanjo Agarubanocho, Nakagyo-ku, Kyoto, 604-8172, Japan
Tel.: (81) 752567777
Web Site: https://www.systemd.co.jp
Year Founded: 1984
3804—(TKS)
Rev.: $33,578,240

INTERNATIONAL PUBLIC

Assets: $44,277,050
Liabilities: $15,257,680
Net Worth: $29,019,370
Earnings: $4,480,880
Emp.: 290
Fiscal Year-end: 10/31/23
Business Consulting Services
N.A.I.C.S.: 541618
Michio Dohyama (Chm)

SYSTEMEXE VIET NAM CO., LTD.
2nd Fl Etown 1 Building 364 Cong Hoa St, Ward 13 Tan Binh, Ho Chi Minh City, Vietnam
Tel.: (84) 2838103385   VN
Web Site: http://www.system-exe.com.vn
Software Development Services
N.A.I.C.S.: 541511

SYSTEMS DESIGN CO., LTD.
6th floor Asahi Life Daitabashi Building 1-22-19 Izumi, Suginami-Ku, Tokyo, 168-0063, Japan
Tel.: (81) 353007800
Web Site: https://www.sdcj.co.jp
Year Founded: 1967
3766—(TKS)
Rev.: $62,517,380
Assets: $41,828,080
Liabilities: $12,354,090
Net Worth: $29,473,990
Earnings: $2,254,010
Emp.: 168
Fiscal Year-end: 03/31/24
System Design Services
N.A.I.C.S.: 541512
Hiroshi Kumamoto (Pres)

SYSTEMS ENGINEERING CONSULTANTS CO., LTD.
Setagaya Business Square 4-10-1 Yoga, Setagaya-ku, Tokyo, 158-0097, Japan
Tel.: (81) 354914770
Web Site: https://www.sec.co.jp
Year Founded: 1970
3741—(TKS)
Rev.: $54,187,860
Earnings: $5,553,780
Emp.: 301
Fiscal Year-end: 03/31/19
Software Development Services
N.A.I.C.S.: 541511
Akira Nakamura (Exec VP)

SYSTEMS LIMITED
Systems Campus E1 - Sehjpal Near DHA Phase-VIII Ex-Air Avenue, Lahore, Pakistan
Tel.: (92) 3015455267
Web Site:
   https://www.systemsltd.com
Year Founded: 1977
SYS—(PSX)
Rev.: $189,781,996
Assets: $179,946,624
Liabilities: $65,117,323
Net Worth: $114,829,302
Earnings: $30,859,548
Emp.: 6,021
Fiscal Year-end: 12/31/23
Software Publisher, IT & BPO Services
N.A.I.C.S.: 513210
Asif Peer (CEO & Mng Dir)

SYSTEMSOFT CORPORATION
12-1 Tenjin Hinode Fukuoka Building 10th floor, Chuo-ku, Fukuoka, 810-8665, Japan
Tel.: (81) 927321515
Web Site:
   https://www.systemsoft.co.jp
Year Founded: 1983

7527—(TKS)
Rev.: $16,077,600
Assets: $36,609,600
Liabilities: $6,215,280
Net Worth: $30,394,320
Earnings: ($10,655,760)
Emp.: 74
Fiscal Year-end: 09/30/24
Application Software Services
N.A.I.C.S.: 541511
Haruki Yoshio (Pres)

SYSTEMTRANSPORT A/S
Transportcenter Alle 19, 7400, Herning, Denmark
Tel.: (45) 97220400
Web Site: http://www.systemtransport.eu
Year Founded: 1979
Freight Transportation Services
N.A.I.C.S.: 488510
Rafal Jabloski (CEO)

Subsidiaries:

System Transport Zoo (1)
ul Bystra 7, Poznan, 61-366, Poland
Tel.: (48) 618731904
Shipping Consulting Services
N.A.I.C.S.: 488510
John Oholt (CEO)

SYSTENA CORPORATION
1-2-20 Kaigan Shiodome Building 14F, Minato-ku, Tokyo, 105-0022, Japan
Tel.: (81) 363673840
Web Site: https://www.systena.co.jp
2317—(TKS)
Rev.: $508,573,400
Assets: $357,191,180
Liabilities: $102,038,570
Net Worth: $255,152,610
Earnings: $47,803,520
Emp.: 290
Fiscal Year-end: 03/31/24
IT Services
N.A.I.C.S.: 541512
Kenji Miura (Pres)

Subsidiaries:

GaYa Co. Ltd. (1)
Yokohama Landmark Tower 38F 2-2-1 Minatomirai, Nishi-ku, Yokohama, Kanagawa, Japan
Tel.: (81) 452276030
Web Site: https://www.gaya-corp.jp
Smartphone Games Development Services
N.A.I.C.S.: 541511

Hokuyo Information System., Ltd (1)
5-6 East 2 North 1, Chuo-ku, Sapporo, 060-0031, Hokkaido, Japan
Tel.: (81) 112106634
Web Site: http://www.hokuyois.co.jp
Sales Range: $50-74.9 Million
Emp.: 223
Software Products Sales & Development Serices
N.A.I.C.S.: 541511

Idy Corporation (1)
2-8-1 Kanda Sakuma-cho Champier Akihabara Building 5F, Chiyoda-ku, Tokyo, Japan
Tel.: (81) 34 400 7970
Web Site: https://www.idy-design.com
Antenna Mfr & Distr
N.A.I.C.S.: 334220

LittleSoft Corporation (1)
8th floor Tact 4 Building 2-32-12 Minamiikebukuro, Toshima-ku, Tokyo, 171-0022, Japan
Tel.: (81) 359543111
Web Site: https://www.littlesoft.jp
Sales Range: $25-49.9 Million
Emp.: 10
Web Application Software Development Services
N.A.I.C.S.: 541511
Toshihiro Nagao (Pres)

One Tech Japan, Inc. (1)
Ami Hall 5F 511 1-1-3 Shibuya, Shibuya-ku, Tokyo, 150-0002, Japan
Tel.: (81) 36 403 0814
Web Site: https://www.onetech.jp
Emp.: 5
Software Development Services
N.A.I.C.S.: 541511

ProVision Co., Ltd. (1)
2-2-1 Minatomirai Yokohama Landmark Tower 40th / 38th / 33rd floor, Nishi-ku, Yokohama, 220-8140, Kanagawa, Japan
Tel.: (81) 458724000
Web Site: https://www.pro-vision.jp
Emp.: 913
Terminal Software Development Services
N.A.I.C.S.: 541511

Systena America Inc. (1)
1825 S Grant St WeWork 9F, San Mateo, CA 94402
Tel.: (650) 346-9774
Web Site: https://www.systena.us
Software Development Services
N.A.I.C.S.: 541511
Katsuhiro Fuchinoue (Pres & CEO)

Tokyoto Business Service Co., Ltd. (1)
Time 24 Building 5F 2-4-32 Aomi, Koto-ku, Tokyo, 135-0064, Qinghai, Japan
Tel.: (81) 364260147
Web Site: https://www.tokyotobs.co.jp
Sales Range: $25-49.9 Million
Emp.: 361
Outsourced Business Support Services
N.A.I.C.S.: 561499

SYSTEX CORPORATION
No 318 Rueiguang Rd, Neihu District, Taipei, Taiwan
Tel.: (886) 277201888
Web Site: https://www.tw.systex.com
Year Founded: 1997
6214—(TAI)
Rev.: $1,150,605,863
Assets: $1,000,579,183
Liabilities: $517,485,902
Net Worth: $483,093,281
Earnings: $51,633,080
Emp.: 4,364
Fiscal Year-end: 12/31/23
Information Technology Services
N.A.I.C.S.: 541512
T. J. Huang (Chm)

Subsidiaries:

Concord System Management Corporation (1)
13th Floor Guangfu South Road, Taipei, 10214, Taiwan
Tel.: (886) 227786161
Web Site: http://www.econcord.com.tw
Business Management Software Development Services
N.A.I.C.S.: 541511

Dawning Technology Inc. (1)
5th Floor No 303 Section 1 Fuxing South Road, Da'an District, Taipei, Taiwan
Tel.: (886) 289785386
Web Site: https://www.dawningtech.com.tw
Software Development Services
N.A.I.C.S.: 541511

Docutek Solution, Inc. (1)
4F-1 No11 Lane 35 KeeHu Rd, Neihu District, Taipei, 11492, Taiwan
Tel.: (886) 226588970
Web Site: https://www.docutek-inc.com
Information Technology Services
N.A.I.C.S.: 541519

Nexsys Corp. (1)
5F-6 No 288 Section 6 Shimin Avenue, Xinyi District, Taipei, 110047, Taiwan
Tel.: (886) 223577711
Web Site: https://www.systexfintech.com
Financial Payment Services
N.A.I.C.S.: 522320

Palsys Digital Technology Corp. (1)
105 3F No 167 Fuxing North Road, Songshan District, Taipei, Taiwan
Tel.: (886) 227187266
Web Site: https://www.palsys.com.tw
Value Added Agency Services
N.A.I.C.S.: 541810

Rainbow Tech Information (HK) Ltd. (1)
13/F TAL Building 49 Austin Road, Kowloon, China (Hong Kong)
Tel.: (852) 3 610 5498
Web Site: https://www.rainbowtech.com.hk
Computer Peripheral Product Distr
N.A.I.C.S.: 449210
Eric Or (Mng Dir)

SYSTEX Information (H.K.) Ltd. (1)
13/F TAL Building 49 Austin Road, Kowloon, China (Hong Kong)
Tel.: (852) 36105400
Web Site: https://www.systex.com.hk
Sales Range: $25-49.9 Million
Computer Related Services
N.A.I.C.S.: 541519

SoftMobile Technology Corp. (1)
7F-4 No 2 Lane 258 Ruiguang Road, Neihu District, Taipei, 114, Taiwan
Tel.: (886) 287525527
Web Site: https://www.softmobile.com.tw
Software Development Services
N.A.I.C.S.: 541511

Systek Information (Shanghai) Ltd. (1)
Floor 8-9 No 396 Cao Xi Road North, Shanghai, 200030, China
Tel.: (86) 2133688777
Business Process Outsourcing Services
N.A.I.C.S.: 561110

Systex Software & Service Corp. (1)
17th Floor No 100 Section 2 Roosevelt Road, Zhongzheng District, Taipei, 10084, Taiwan
Tel.: (886) 223670188
Web Site: https://www.systexsoftware.com.tw
Software Development Services
N.A.I.C.S.: 541511

Sysware (Thailand) Co., Ltd. (1)
17th Floor Unit 1705 One Pacific Place Building 140 Sukhumvit Rd, Klong Toey, Bangkok, 10110, Thailand
Tel.: (66) 2653 1895
Web Site: http://www.systexgroup.com
Sales Range: $25-49.9 Million
Emp.: 12
Business Process Outsourcing Services
N.A.I.C.S.: 561499

Sysware Singapore Pte. Ltd. (1)
237 Alexandra Road 04-18 The Alexcier, Singapore, Singapore
Tel.: (65) 64726066
Sales Range: $25-49.9 Million
Emp.: 14
Business Process Outsourcing Services
N.A.I.C.S.: 561110

Taifon Computer Co., Ltd. (1)
8th Floor No 318 Ruiguang Road, Neihu District, Taipei, 114, Taiwan
Tel.: (886) 287525566
Web Site: https://www.taifon.com.tw
Information Technology Services
N.A.I.C.S.: 541511

TaiwanPay Corporation (1)
6F No 318 Ruiguang Road, Neihu District, Taipei, 114, Taiwan
Tel.: (886) 287986268
Web Site: http://www.taiwanpay.com
Credit Card Processing Services
N.A.I.C.S.: 522320

uniXecure Corp. (1)
8F No 13 Ln 35 Jihu Rd, Neihu Dist, Taipei, 114, Taiwan
Tel.: (886) 287986088
Web Site: https://www.unixecure.com
Information Technology Services
N.A.I.C.S.: 541519

SYSTRA LTD.
3rd Floor 5 Old Bailey, London, United Kingdom
Tel.: (44) 2038550079
Web Site: http://www.systra.co.uk
Trucking Service
N.A.I.C.S.: 484122
Pascal Mercier (Mng Dir-UK)

Subsidiaries:

TSP Projects Limited (1)
Meridian House The Crescent, York, YO24 1AW, United Kingdom
Tel.: (44) 1904 454 600
Web Site: https://www.tspprojects.co.uk
Rail Products & Services
N.A.I.C.S.: 541690
Emily Shaw (Mgr-Programme)

SYSTRAN INTERNATIONAL CO., LTD.
5th Floor STX R&D Center 163 Yangjaecheon-ro, Gangnam-gu, Seoul, Korea (South)
Tel.: (82) 2 557 6826   KR
Web Site: http://www.csli.co.kr
Year Founded: 1992
Language Translation Software Developer, Publisher & Whslr
N.A.I.C.S.: 513210
Ki-hyun Park (CEO)

SYSU INTERNATIONAL, INC.
145 Panay Ave, Quezon City, 1008, Philippines
Tel.: (63) 2 920 5291
Web Site: http://www.sysu.com.ph
Emp.: 850
Food Product Mfr & Distr
N.A.I.C.S.: 311999
Johnny K. Sy (Mng Dir)

Subsidiaries:

Lee Kum Kee Limited (1)
2-4 Dai Fat Street, Tai Po Industrial Estate, Tai Po, China (Hong Kong)
Tel.: (852) 26603600
Web Site: http://www.hk-kitchen.lkk.com
Food Product Mfr & Distr
N.A.I.C.S.: 311919
Pat Poon (Sr Mgr-HR)

Subsidiary (Non-US):

Lee Kum Kee (Europe) Limited (2)
88 Beaufort Court Admirals Way, London, E14 9XL, United Kingdom
Tel.: (44) 2070687888
Web Site: http://www.lkkquality.com
Food Product Mfr & Distr
N.A.I.C.S.: 311919
Belinda Yip (Product Mgr)

Lee Kum Kee (Malaysia) Sdn. Bhd. (2)
No 8 Jalan Halba 16/16, 40200, Shah Alam, Selangor, Malaysia
Tel.: (60) 356232288
Food Products Distr
N.A.I.C.S.: 424490
May Lim (Mng Dir)

Subsidiary (US):

Lee Kum Kee (U.S.A.) Inc. (2)
14841 Don Julian Rd, City of Industry, CA 91746
Tel.: (626) 709-1888
Web Site: http://usa.lkk.com
Sales Range: $1-9.9 Million
Emp.: 49
Grocery & Related Products Merchant Whslr
N.A.I.C.S.: 424490
Shawn Bell (VP-Logistics)

Subsidiary (Domestic):

Lee Kum Kee (USA) Foods Inc. (3)
14455 Don Julian Rd, City of Industry, CA 91746
Tel.: (626) 336-3886
Web Site: http://www.lkk.com
Rev.: $7,500,000
Emp.: 75
Perishable Prepared Food Mfr
N.A.I.C.S.: 311991
David H. Lee (CEO)

Representative Office (Non-US):

Lee Kum Kee Limited - Canada Office (2)
3660 Midland Avenue Suite 309, Scarbor-

SYSU INTERNATIONAL, INC.

SYSU International, Inc.—(Continued)
ough, M1V 0B8, ON, Canada
Tel.: (416) 613-7776
Web Site: http://www.ca.lkk.com
Food Product Mfr & Distr
N.A.I.C.S.: 311919

McCormick Philippines, Inc. (1)
SYSU Centre 145 Panay Avenue, Quezon City, 1103, Philippines
Tel.: (63) 29205291
Web Site: http://www.mccormick.com.ph
Sales Range: $125-149.9 Million
Emp.: 300
Flavorings, Seasonings & Spices
N.A.I.C.S.: 311919
Steven Sy (Gen Mgr)

San Remo Macaroni Company Pty Ltd (1)
4 Boden Court, Windsor, 5087, SA, Australia
Tel.: (61) 883348200
Web Site: http://www.sanremo.com.au
Food Products Mfr
N.A.I.C.S.: 311919
Nicole Peake (Mgr-Comml)

The Folger Coffee Company (1)
1 Strawberry Ln, Orrville, OH 44667-0280
Tel.: (800) 937-9745
Web Site: http://www.folgerscoffee.com
Coffee Product Mfr
N.A.I.C.S.: 311920

SYSWIN INC.
9/F Syswin Building 316 Nan Hu Zhong Yuan, Chaoyang District, Beijing, 100102, China
Tel.: (86) 10 84978088 Ky
Sales Range: $75-99.9 Million
Emp.: 3,855
Real Estate Brokerage & Other Related Services
N.A.I.C.S.: 531210
Xiaoling Hu (Chm)

SYSWORK CO., LTD.
32-13 Techno 7-ro, Yuseong-gu, Daejeon, 34029, Korea (South)
Tel.: (82) 429324800
Web Site: https://www.syswork.co.kr
Year Founded: 2004
269620—(KRS)
Rev.: $22,669,435
Assets: $58,739,454
Liabilities: $30,803,694
Net Worth: $27,935,760
Earnings: ($5,637,292)
Emp.: 58
Fiscal Year-end: 12/31/22
Electric Equipment Mfr
N.A.I.C.S.: 335999
Hyun-Kyu Lee (VP)

SYUPPIN CO., LTD.
Daiwa Nishi-Shinjuku Bldg 3F 14-11 Nishi-Shinjuku 1-chome, Shinjuku-ku, Tokyo, 160-0023, Japan
Tel.: (81) 333420088
Web Site: https://www.syuppin.co.jp
Year Founded: 2005
3179—(TKS)
Rev.: $317,822,572
Assets: $110,121,420
Liabilities: $57,815,750
Net Worth: $52,305,671
Earnings: $10,948,632
Emp.: 160
Fiscal Year-end: 03/31/20
Camera & Photographic Equipment E-Commerce
N.A.I.C.S.: 423410
Kei Suzuki (Chm)

SYZYGY AG
Horexstrasse 28, 61352, Bad Homburg, Germany
Tel.: (49) 61729488252
Web Site: https://www.syzygy.de

Year Founded: 1995
SYZ—(DUS)
Rev.: $79,191,634
Assets: $96,367,851
Liabilities: $52,334,477
Net Worth: $44,033,374
Earnings: ($3,223,300)
Emp.: 615
Fiscal Year-end: 12/31/23
Media Advertising Services
N.A.I.C.S.: 541840
Wilfried Beeck (Chm-Supervisory Bd)

Subsidiaries:

Ars Thanea S.A. (1)
ul Jozefa Piusa Dziekonskiego 3, 00-728, Warsaw, Poland
Tel.: (48) 530000795
Web Site: https://www.arsthanea.com
Production Studio Services
N.A.I.C.S.: 512110
Piotr Jaworowski (CEO)

diffferent GmbH (1)
Schlesische Strasse 38, 10997, Berlin, Germany
Tel.: (49) 306953740
Web Site: https://www.diffferent.de
Marketing & Advertising Services
N.A.I.C.S.: 541810
Jan Pechmann (Mng Dir)

SZAIDEL COSMETIC GMBH
Fabrikstrasse 9, D - 66892, Kaiserslautern, Germany
Tel.: (49) 637291220
Web Site: http://www.szaidel-cosmetic.de
Rev.: $35,981,472
Emp.: 288
Cosmetics Products Mfr
N.A.I.C.S.: 325620
Szaidel Szaidel (Mng Dir)

SZZT ELECTRONICS CO., LTD.
SZZT Industrial Park No 3 Tongguan Rd, Guangming District, Shenzhen, 518132, Guangdong, China
Tel.: (86) 75581728888
Web Site: https://www.szzt.com.cn
Year Founded: 1993
002197—(SSE)
Rev.: $171,971,369
Assets: $840,179,335
Liabilities: $487,683,500
Net Worth: $352,495,836
Earnings: ($75,570,117)
Emp.: 1,800
Fiscal Year-end: 12/31/22
Computer Equipment Mfr
N.A.I.C.S.: 334118

T & I GLOBAL LTD.
11 Jassal House 4A Auckland Square, Kolkata, 700 017, India
Tel.: (91) 3322833613
Web Site: https://tiglobal.com
Year Founded: 1949
522294—(BOM)
Rev.: $18,765,332
Assets: $15,514,951
Liabilities: $6,771,580
Net Worth: $8,743,371
Earnings: $1,010,391
Emp.: 935
Fiscal Year-end: 03/31/23
Tea Processing Machinery Mfr & Distr
N.A.I.C.S.: 333310
Sajjan Bagaria (Chm)

T C H DE ANGELI
Boulevard Jules Durand, 76071, Le Havre, France
Tel.: (33) 235534999 FR
Web Site: http://www.deangeliprodotti.com
Year Founded: 2003
Miscellaneous Fabricated Wire Products

N.A.I.C.S.: 332618
Valerie Merzougui (Pur Mgr-Comml/Specific)

T CAPITAL PARTNERS CO., LTD.
Tokio Marine Nichido Bldg Shinkan 6F 1-2-1 Marunouchi, Chiyoda-ku, Tokyo, 100-0005, Japan
Tel.: (81) 3 5223 3516 JP
Web Site: http://www.tmcap.co.jp
Year Founded: 1991
Privater Equity Firm
N.A.I.C.S.: 523999
Koji Sasaki (Pres)

T D A NOYON
69 Avenue Jean Jaures, 60400, Noyon, Oise, France
Tel.: (33) 344933710
Web Site: http://www.peugeotoccasions-noyon.com
Rev.: $29,400,000
Emp.: 45
New & Used Car Dealers
N.A.I.C.S.: 441110
Richard Tuppin (Pres)

T ENGINEERING CORPORATION PUBLIC COMPANY LIMITED
Rajanakam Building 15th Floor No 3 South Sathorn Road, Yannawa Sathorn District, Bangkok, 10120, Thailand
Tel.: (66) 2 018 7190
Web Site: http://www.t-pcl.com
Year Founded: 1981
Sales Range: $10-24.9 Million
Engineeering Services
N.A.I.C.S.: 541330

T H MARCH & CO. LIMITED
10/12 Ely Place, London, EC1N 6RY, United Kingdom
Tel.: (44) 2074050009
Web Site: http://www.thmarch.co.uk
Year Founded: 1887
Sales Range: $10-24.9 Million
Emp.: 93
Insurance Brokerage Services
N.A.I.C.S.: 524210
Mark Smith (Chm)

T J MORRIS LTD.
Axis Business Park East Lancs Road, Gillmoss, Liverpool, L11 OJA, United Kingdom
Tel.: (44) 1515302920
Web Site: http://www.tjmorris.co.uk
Sales Range: $450-499.9 Million
Emp.: 2,732
N.A.I.C.S.: 455219
Thomas Joseph Morris (Founder)

T PLUS PJSC
Mayakovskovo Street 15, Samara, 443100, Russia
Tel.: (7) 8462796763
Web Site: http://www.tplusgroup.ru
Sales Range: Less than $1 Million
Electric Power Distribution Services
N.A.I.C.S.: 237130
Roman V. Nizhankovsky (Deputy Gen Dir & Exec Dir)

T S FLOUR MILL PUBLIC COMPANY LIMITED
90/9 Moo 1 Poochaosamingphrai Rd Samrongklang, Phapradaeng, Samut Prakan, 10130, Thailand
Tel.: (66) 20179999
Web Site: https://www.tmill.co.th
Year Founded: 2007

TMILL—(THA)
Rev.: $54,602,499
Assets: $50,374,698
Liabilities: $19,407,095
Net Worth: $30,967,603
Earnings: $1,725,110
Emp.: 127
Fiscal Year-end: 12/31/23
Wheat Flour Producer
N.A.I.C.S.: 311211
Pricha Attavipach (Co-Chm)

T SCIENTIFIC CO., LTD
3rd floor Etoday Building 62gil Yeouidaebang-ro, Dongjak-gu, Seoul, Korea (South)
Tel.: (82) 220387585
Web Site: https://tscientific.co.kr
Year Founded: 1998
057680—(KRS)
Rev.: $6,668,553
Assets: $201,366,907
Liabilities: $62,833,935
Net Worth: $138,532,972
Earnings: ($9,057,029)
Emp.: 31
Fiscal Year-end: 12/31/22
Telecommunication Servicesb
N.A.I.C.S.: 517112
Kim Sang Woo (CEO)

Subsidiaries:

Mongol Content LLC (1)
Mars Center 18/1 Sambuu Street 5th Khoroo, Chingeltei District, Ulaanbaatar, 15160, Mongolia
Tel.: (976) 11326590
Web Site: http://www.mongolcontent.mn
Application Software Development Services
N.A.I.C.S.: 541511
G. Gantuya (CEO)

T T R AUTOMOBILES
Val De Murigny 10 Rue Roger Caillois, 51100, Reims, Marne, France
Tel.: (33) 326094242
Rev.: $28,500,000
Emp.: 28
New & Used Car Dealers
N.A.I.C.S.: 441110
Christine Fournier (Mgr-Fin)

T&D HOLDINGS, INC.
2-7-1 Nihonbashi, Chuo-ku, Tokyo, 103-6031, Japan
Tel.: (81) 332726110 JP
Web Site: https://www.td-holdings.co.jp
Year Founded: 2004
8795—(TKS)
Rev.: $21,204,820,510
Assets: $113,738,997,100
Liabilities: $104,419,386,240
Net Worth: $9,319,610,860
Earnings: $231,350
Emp.: 129
Fiscal Year-end: 03/31/24
Holding Company
N.A.I.C.S.: 551112
Tetsuhiro Kida (Chm)

Subsidiaries:

Daido Life Insurance Company (1)
1-2-1 Edobori, Nishi-ku, Osaka, 550-0002, Japan
Tel.: (81) 664476111
Sales Range: $350-399.9 Million
Emp.: 6,912
Term Life Insurance & Other Insurance & Asset Management Products & Services
N.A.I.C.S.: 524128
Tetsuhiro Kida (Chm)

Subsidiary (Domestic):

Daido Life Total Maintenance, Inc. (2)
1 2 1 Edobori, Nishiku, Osaka, 550 0002, Japan
Tel.: (81) 664476111

AND PRIVATE COMPANIES

Nihon System Shuno, Inc. (2)
1-23-23 Esakacho Daido Life Esaka Building, Suita, 564-8523, Osaka, Japan
Tel.: (81) 663860823
Web Site: http://www.nss-jp.com
Sales Range: $50-74.9 Million
Emp.: 60
Collector of Premiums
N.A.I.C.S.: 524298

T&D Confirm Ltd. (2)
Taiyoseimeikanda 2 Bldg 2-4-9 Iwamotocho, Tokyo, 101 0032, Japan
Tel.: (81) 356875805
Provider of Policyholder Confirmation Services
N.A.I.C.S.: 524298

T&D Taiyo Daido Lease Co., Ltd. (2)
Birviahamamatsucho 6F 1-9-10 Hamamatsucho, Tokyo, 105 0013, Japan
Tel.: (81) 354013060
Provider of Leasing Services
N.A.I.C.S.: 533110

Zenkoku Business Centre Co., Ltd. (2)
, Tokyo, Japan
Insurance Services
N.A.I.C.S.: 524298

Daido Management Service Co., Ltd. (1)
6th floor Nihonbashi Koamicho Square Building, 17-10 Nihonbashi Koamicho Chuo-ku, Tokyo, 103-0016, Japan
Tel.: (81) 336678375
Emp.: 40
General Insurance Services
N.A.I.C.S.: 524114

Pet & Family Insurance Co., Ltd. (1)
4-27-3 Higashiueno, Taito-ku, Tokyo, 110-0015, Japan
Tel.: (81) 120584412
General Insurance Services
N.A.I.C.S.: 524114

Pet & Family Small-amount Short-term Insurance Company (1)
4-27-3 Higashiueno, Taito-ku, Tokyo, 110-0015, Japan
Tel.: (81) 120584412
Web Site: https://www.petfamilyins.co.jp
Art Insurance Services
N.A.I.C.S.: 524298

T&D Asset Management Co., Ltd. (1)
Mita Belliu Building 5-36-7 Shiba, Minato-ku, Tokyo, 108-0014, Japan (100%)
Tel.: (81) 334345695
Web Site: https://www.tdasset.co.jp
Emp.: 151
Investment Advisory & Investment Trust Services
N.A.I.C.S.: 523940

T&D Customer Services Co., Ltd. (1)
4-2-18 Harigaya Taiyoseimei Urawa Bldg, Urawa-Ku, Saitama, 330-0075, Japan
Tel.: (81) 488256110
General Insurance Services
N.A.I.C.S.: 524210

T&D Financial Life Insurance Company (1)
1-1-1 Shibaura, Minato-ku, Tokyo, 105-0023, Japan
Tel.: (81) 367456850
Sales Range: $200-249.9 Million
Emp.: 275
Provider of Insurance & Financial Services
N.A.I.C.S.: 524128
Masafumi Itasaka *(Pres)*

T&D Information System Ltd. (1)
Taiyo Life Urawa Building 4-2-18 Harigaya, Urawa-ku, Saitama, 330-0075, Japan
Tel.: (81) 488256101
Emp.: 716
Fire Insurance Services
N.A.I.C.S.: 524113

T&D Lease Co., Ltd (1)
2-16-2 Konan Taiyo Life Shinagawa Building, Minato- ku, Tokyo, 108-0075, Japan
Tel.: (81) 364331160
Web Site: http://www.td-lease.co.jp
Sales Range: $25-49.9 Million
Emp.: 50
Industrial Equipments Leasing Services
N.A.I.C.S.: 532490

T&D United Capital Co., Ltd. (1)
2-7-1 Nihonbashi, Chuo-ku, Tokyo, 103-0027, Japan
Tel.: (81) 332726864
Financial Investment Services
N.A.I.C.S.: 523999
Chikahiro Tsuboi *(Pres)*

Joint Venture (Non-US):

Fortitude Group Holdings, LLC (2)
Chesney House 96 Pits Bay Road 3rd Floor, Pembroke, HM 08, Bermuda (25%)
Web Site: http://www.fortitude-re.com
Holding Company
N.A.I.C.S.: 551111
James Bracken *(CEO)*

Subsidiary (US):

Prudential Annuities Life Assurance Corporation (3)
1 Corporate Dr, Shelton, CT 06484
Tel.: (203) 926-1888
Web Site: http://www.prudential.com
Rev.: $7,488,807,000
Assets: $58,578,130,000
Liabilities: $56,896,403,000
Net Worth: $1,681,727,000
Earnings: $4,965,361,000
Emp.: 12,500
Fiscal Year-end: 12/31/2021
Insurance Annuities Investment Services
N.A.I.C.S.: 523999
Dylan J. Tyson *(Pres & Co-CEO)*

Taiyo Credit Guarantee Co., Ltd (1)
Taiyo Seimei Ikebukuro Building 2-49-4 Minamiikebukuro, Toshima-ku, Tokyo, 171-0022, Japan
Tel.: (81) 359570502
Web Site: https://www.taiyo-sinyo-hosyo.co.jp
Credit Guarantee Services
N.A.I.C.S.: 522390

The Taiyo Life Insurance Company (1)
2-7-1 Nihonbashi, Chuo-ku, Tokyo, 103-6031, Japan (100%)
Tel.: (81) 332726211
Sales Range: $1-4.9 Billion
Emp.: 10,805
Life & Health Insurance
N.A.I.C.S.: 524113

Subsidiary (Non-US):

Mizhuo Trust & Banking (Luxembourg) S. A. (2)
1B Rue Gabriel Lippmann, 5365, Munsbach, Luxembourg (100%)
Tel.: (352) 4216171
Sales Range: $100-124.9 Million
Emp.: 156
Investment Fund Administration Services
N.A.I.C.S.: 523940
Obata Katsunori *(CEO & Mng Dir)*

Toyo Insurance Agency Co., Ltd (1)
Taiyo Seimei Akabane Building 2-17-4 Akabane, Kita-ku, Tokyo, 115-0045, Japan
Tel.: (81) 352494117
Web Site: https://www.sonpo.co.jp
Insurance Management Services
N.A.I.C.S.: 524210

Zenkoku Business Center Co., Ltd (1)
17-10 Nihonbashi Koami-cho, Chuo-ku, Tokyo, 103-0016, Japan (100%)
Tel.: (81) 336678332
Web Site: https://www.zbc-jp.com
Insurance Agency Services
N.A.I.C.S.: 524298
Yasuhiko Oyama *(CEO)*

T&K TOKA CORPORATION
283-1 Chikumazawa, Miyoshi-Machi, Saitama, 354-8577, Iruma-Gun, Japan
Tel.: (81) 492581611
Web Site: http://www.tk-toka.co.jp
4636—(TKS)
Rev.: $422,696,560
Assets: $656,739,600
Liabilities: $181,219,280
Net Worth: $475,520,320
Earnings: $10,715,760
Emp.: 775
Fiscal Year-end: 03/31/23
Printing Ink, Synthetic Resin, Paint & Adhesive Mfr
N.A.I.C.S.: 325910
Akira Yoshimura *(Mng Dir)*

Subsidiaries:

Hangzhou Toka Ink Chemical Co., Ltd. (1)
2 No 5 Avenue South Hangzhou Economic & technical development park, Hangzhou, 310018, China
Tel.: (86) 571 88183204
Web Site: http://www.hhink.com
Emp.: 500
Printing Ink Mfr
N.A.I.C.S.: 325910

PT. Cemani Toka (1)
Jl Landbaw Km 2 5 Desa Sanja, Bogor, 16810, Indonesia
Tel.: (62) 21 876 3333
Web Site: http://www.cemani-toka.co.id
Emp.: 300
Printing Ink Mfr
N.A.I.C.S.: 325910

Toka Ink (Bangladesh) Ltd (1)
2 DIT Avenue Extn Motijheel C/A, Dhaka, 1000, Bangladesh
Tel.: (880) 2223350088
Web Site: https://tokaink.com.bd
Printing Ink Mfr
N.A.I.C.S.: 325910

T&L CO., LTD.
63 Wonam-ro Namsa-eup, Cheoin-Gu, Yongin, 17124, Gyeonggi-do, Korea (South)
Tel.: (82) 313233113
Web Site: https://www.tnl.co.kr
Year Founded: 1998
340570—(KRS)
Rev.: $62,569,859
Assets: $89,736,906
Liabilities: $8,379,367
Net Worth: $81,357,538
Earnings: $16,197,172
Emp.: 151
Fiscal Year-end: 12/31/22
Pharmaceutical & Medicine Mfr & Distr
N.A.I.C.S.: 325412
Yoon-So Choi *(CEO)*

T&M PHAEDRA PUBLIC COMPANY LTD.
4 Markou Botsari Str, Aglantzia, Nicosia, Cyprus
Tel.: (357) 22000881
Web Site: http://www.phaedraltd.com
Real Estate Asset Management Services
N.A.I.C.S.: 531390

Subsidiaries:

ActiveGen SA (1)
Pente Pigadion 30, 26441, Patras, Greece
Tel.: (30) 2610622522
Web Site: http://www.activegen.gr
Health Care Srvices
N.A.I.C.S.: 621610

Devcon S.A. (1)
61 Riga Feraiou str 2nd floor, 26221, Patras, Greece
Tel.: (30) 2610622522
Web Site: http://www.devcon.gr
Real Estate Development Services
N.A.I.C.S.: 531390

Ninety Nine Per Cent Development S.A. (1)
30 Pente Pigadion, 26441, Patras, Greece
Tel.: (30) 2610622522
Web Site: http://www.ninetyninepercent.eu
Cannabis Cultivation Services
N.A.I.C.S.: 111998

T&N TRADING & INVESTMENT COMPANY LIMITED
19 Hang Thiec Street, Hoan Kiem District, Hanoi, Vietnam
Tel.: (84) 2439233172   VN
Analytical Laboratory Instrument Mfr
N.A.I.C.S.: 334516

T&R BIOFAB
96 Mayu-ro, Siheung, 15111, Gyeonggi-do, Korea (South)
Tel.: (82) 314313344
Web Site: https://www.tnrbiofab.com
Year Founded: 2013
246710—(KRS)
Rev.: $4,413,814
Assets: $58,244,336
Liabilities: $28,129,659
Net Worth: $30,114,677
Earnings: ($7,928,519)
Emp.: 88
Fiscal Year-end: 12/31/22
Imprinter Mfr
N.A.I.C.S.: 339112
Yun Wonsoo *(Pres & CEO)*

T&S COMMUNICATIONS CO.,LTD.
T&S Hi-tech Park 8 Jinxiu Middle Road, Pingshan, Shenzhen, 518118, Guangdong, China
Tel.: (86) 75532983688
Web Site: https://www.china-tscom.com
Year Founded: 2000
300570—(CHIN)
Rev.: $124,620,643
Assets: $236,253,522
Liabilities: $42,862,937
Net Worth: $193,390,585
Earnings: $21,844,412
Emp.: 1,500
Fiscal Year-end: 12/31/23
Optical Fiber Cable Mfr & Distr
N.A.I.C.S.: 334417

Subsidiaries:

AuspChip Technologies Co., Ltd. (1)
4F Bldg A Golden Valley Optoelectronics Community, Nanhai, Foshan, 528251, Guangdong, China
Tel.: (86) 75786776169
Web Site: http://www.auspchip.com
Electronic Chip Mfr & Distr
N.A.I.C.S.: 334413

T&S Communications Co., Ltd. - Shenzhen Factory (1)
3/F East Bldg Bantian High Tech Industry Zone Bell Road Longgang Dist, Shenzhen, China
Tel.: (86) 75589397558
Fiber Optic Communication Product Mfr
N.A.I.C.S.: 334417

T&S GROUP INC.
MM Park Building F11 3-6-3 Minatomirai, Nishi-ku, Yokohama, 220-0012, Kanagawa, Japan
Tel.: (81) 452261040
Web Site: https://www.tecsvc.co.jp
Year Founded: 2016
4055—(TKS)
Emp.: 300
Software Development Services
N.A.I.C.S.: 541511
Yoshihiro Takekawa *(Pres & CEO)*

T'WAY AIR CO., LTD.
10th Floor KT Daegu Tower 167 Dongdeok-ro, Jung-Gu, Daegu, Korea (South)

T'WAY AIR CO., LTD.

T'way Air Co., Ltd.—(Continued)
Tel.: (82) 16888686
Web Site: https://www.twayair.com
Year Founded: 2003
091810—(KRS)
Passenger Air Transport Services
N.A.I.C.S.: 481111
Hong-Geun Jeong (CEO)

T-BULL SA
Szczesliwa 33/2B09, 53-445, Wroclaw, Poland
Tel.: (48) 534326597
Web Site: https://www.t-bull.com
TBL—(WAR)
Rev.: $2,655,488
Assets: $2,203,252
Liabilities: $625,254
Net Worth: $1,577,998
Earnings: ($952,998)
Fiscal Year-end: 12/31/23
Mobile Game Development Services
N.A.I.C.S.: 541511
Damian Fijalkowski (Chm & CTO)

T-FLEX TECHVEST PCB CO., LTD.
No 12 Gongye 2nd Rd, Pingzhen Dist, Taoyuan, 324, Taiwan
Tel.: (886) 34698860
3276—(TPE)
Rev.: $41,644,436
Assets: $51,669,981
Liabilities: $22,135,666
Net Worth: $29,534,315
Earnings: $2,231,123
Fiscal Year-end: 12/31/22
Electronic Part & Component Mfr
N.A.I.C.S.: 334419
Hsu Cheng-Min (Chm)

T-GAIA CORP.
Ebisu Neonato 14-18F 4-1-18 Ebisu, Shibuya-ku, Tokyo, 150-8575, Japan
Tel.: (81) 364091111
Web Site: https://www.t-gaia.co.jp
Year Founded: 1997
3738—(TKS)
Rev.: $2,967,585,940
Assets: $1,640,998,600
Liabilities: $1,129,358,160
Net Worth: $511,640,440
Earnings: $46,355,930
Emp.: 5,384
Fiscal Year-end: 03/31/24
Information Technology Services; Mobile Telecommunications, Networking Communications & Electronic Payment Resources
N.A.I.C.S.: 517121
Masato Ishida (Pres, CEO, Chief Strategy Officer & Exec VP)

Subsidiaries:

Career Design Academy (CDA) Co., Ltd. (1)
4-1-18 Ebisu Ebisu Neonat, Shibuya-ku, Tokyo, 150-0013, Japan
Tel.: (81) 35 449 6111
Web Site: https://www.careerdesign-acad.co.jp
Career Design Academy Training Services
N.A.I.C.S.: 611430

Infinity Communication Co., Ltd. (1)
7F Kanda Hiranuma Building 2-6 Kanda Tsukasamachi, Chiyoda-ku, Tokyo, 101-0048, Japan
Tel.: (81) 36 722 0421
Web Site: https://www.infinity-c.co.jp
Network System Consulting Services
N.A.I.C.S.: 541512

Popular-Soft Co., Ltd. (1)
Imassony Building 3F 1-11-9 Ueno, Taito-Ku, Tokyo, 110-0005, Japan
Tel.: (81) 33 831 2144
Web Site: https://www.popular-soft.com
Emp.: 50

Software Development Services
N.A.I.C.S.: 541511
Jubun Sakano (Pres)

QUO Card Co., Ltd. (1)
Nihonbashi Honcho Tokyu Building 2-4-1 Nihonbashi Honcho, Chuo-ku, Tokyo, 103-0023, Japan (100%)
Tel.: (81) 332432223
Web Site: http://www.quocard.com
Emp.: 126
Card Store
N.A.I.C.S.: 522210
Takatoshi Sugimoto (Mng Exec Officer)

T-Gaia (Shanghai) Corporation (1)
Unit 2906-2907 Tower A 100 Zunyi Road, Shanghai, 200051, China
Tel.: (86) 2160730588
Web Site: http://www.t-gaia.cn
Telecommunication Servicesb
N.A.I.C.S.: 517111

V-Growth Co., Ltd. (1)
2-10-1 Shibakoen Sumitomo Real Estate Shibaen Building 8F, Minato-ku, Tokyo, 105-0011, Japan
Tel.: (81) 36 777 5120
Web Site: https://www.v-growth.co.jp
Educational Support Services
N.A.I.C.S.: 611710

T-ROBOTICS CO., LTD.
103-37 Gajangsanupbuk-Ro, Osan, Gyeonggi-do, Korea (South)
Tel.: (82) 317699219
Web Site: https://www.t-robotics.net
Year Founded: 2004
117730—(KRS)
Rev.: $43,511,442
Assets: $67,123,896
Liabilities: $48,609,660
Net Worth: $18,514,236
Earnings: ($1,007,040)
Emp.: 115
Fiscal Year-end: 12/31/22
Semiconductor Machinery Mfr
N.A.I.C.S.: 333242
Jung Hae Yoon (VP)

T-SOLAR GLOBAL S.A.
Calle caballeroa andande 8, 28042, Madrid, Spain
Tel.: (34) 913248900
Web Site: http://www.tsolar.eu
Year Founded: 2007
Sales Range: $150-199.9 Million
Emp.: 50
Solar Power
N.A.I.C.S.: 221118
Marta Martinez (CFO)

T-T ELECTRIC
Vassingerod Bygade 46, 3540, Lynge, Denmark
Tel.: (45) 48175500
Web Site: http://www.ttelectric.dk
Sales Range: $10-24.9 Million
Emp.: 78
DC Electric Motor Mfr
N.A.I.C.S.: 335312
Brian Walker (Mng Dir)

Subsidiaries:

T-T Electric GmbH (1)
Helgolandstr 67, 70439, Stuttgart, Germany
Tel.: (49) 7113804410
Web Site: http://www.t-telectic.de
Industrial D.C. Motors
N.A.I.C.S.: 335312

Thrige Electric S.A. (1)
22 rue du 8 Mai 1945, F 95340, Persan, France
Tel.: (33) 130286201
Web Site: http://www.thrige-electric.fr
Emp.: 80
Industrial DC Motors Production
N.A.I.C.S.: 335312
Mikkel Pedersen (Mgr)

T. C. HARRISON GROUP LIMITED
Milford House Mill Street, Bakewell, DE45 1HH, United Kingdom
Tel.: (44) 16 2981 6000
Web Site: http://www.tch.co.uk
Year Founded: 1931
Sales Range: $300-349.9 Million
Emp.: 509
New & Used Car Dealer
N.A.I.C.S.: 441110
Paul Lowe (Dir-Svc)

T. HASEGAWA CO. LTD.
4-4-14 Nihonbashi-honcho, Chuo-ku, Tokyo, 103-8431, Japan
Tel.: (81) 332411151
Web Site: https://www.t-hasegawa.co.jp
4958—(TKS)
Rev.: $459,956,660
Assets: $986,396,250
Liabilities: $161,694,540
Net Worth: $824,701,710
Earnings: $47,297,390
Emp.: 1,111
Fiscal Year-end: 09/30/23
Fragrances, Food Additives & Food Production & Sales
N.A.I.C.S.: 311942
Yoshiaki Chino (Sr Exec VP)

Subsidiaries:

T. HASEGAWA Co Ltd - Fine Foods Unit (1)
10-1 Oaza Okura Itakura-machi, Oura-gun, Gunma, 374-0131, Japan
Tel.: (81) 276825141
Flavor Mfr
N.A.I.C.S.: 311930

T. HASEGAWA Co Ltd - Itakura Facility (1)
10-3 Oaza Okura Itakura-machi, Oura-gun, Gunma, 374-0131, Japan
Tel.: (81) 276820661
Web Site: http://www.t-hasegawa.co.jp
Flavor Mfr
N.A.I.C.S.: 311930

T. Hasegawa (South East Asia) Co Ltd. (1)
159/39 Serm-Mit Tower 25FL Sukhumvit 21 Road, North Klong Toey Wattana, Bangkok, 10110, Thailand
Tel.: (66) 22585890
Web Site: http://www.t-hasegawa.co.jp
Sales Range: $50-74.9 Million
Emp.: 7
Food Additives Whslr
N.A.I.C.S.: 424490

T. Hasegawa USA Inc. (1)
14017 E 183rd St, Cerritos, CA 90703
Tel.: (714) 522-1900
Web Site: http://www.thasegawa.com
Sales Range: $25-49.9 Million
Emp.: 60
Flavor & Fragrance Mfr
N.A.I.C.S.: 311930

Subsidiary (Domestic):

Abelei, Inc (2)
194 Alder Dr, North Aurora, IL 60542
Tel.: (630) 859-1410
Web Site: http://www.abelei.com
Sales Range: $1-9.9 Million
Emp.: 10
Other Grocery & Related Products Merchant Whslr
N.A.I.C.S.: 424490
Karen R. Criss (Pres)

Flavor Ingredient Holdings, LLC (2)
2026 Cecilia Cir, Corona, CA 92881
Tel.: (951) 479-4682
Web Site: http://www.thasegawa.com
Prepared Sauces Mfr
N.A.I.C.S.: 311941

T. KRUNGTHAI INDUSTRIES PUBLIC COMPANY LIMITED

23 Soi Chan 43 Yak 21 Chan Road Tungwatdon, Sathorn, Bangkok, 10120, Thailand
Tel.: (66) 22112762
Web Site: https://www.tkrungthai.com
Year Founded: 1980
TKT—(THA)
Rev.: $36,928,651
Assets: $34,442,836
Liabilities: $15,675,788
Net Worth: $18,767,048
Earnings: ($809,780)
Emp.: 877
Fiscal Year-end: 12/31/23
Automobile Parts Mfr
N.A.I.C.S.: 336110
Terdsak Marrome (Chm)

T. SPIRITUAL WORLD LIMITED
4 Netaji Subhas Road 1st Floor, Kolkata, 700 001, India
Tel.: (91) 3322315717
Web Site: https://www.tspiritualworld.com
Year Founded: 1986
532444—(BOM)
Rev.: $14,174
Assets: $430,020
Liabilities: $7,799
Net Worth: $422,221
Earnings: ($156,591)
Fiscal Year-end: 03/31/21
Wellness Studio Operating Services
N.A.I.C.S.: 621999
Hanunmanmal Hindumal Singhi (Exec Dir)

T.A.C. CONSUMER PCL
23rd Floor UM Tower building 9231233 Ramkumheng Road, Suanlaung, Bangkok, 10250, Thailand
Tel.: (66) 27172898
Web Site: https://www.tacconsumer.com
Year Founded: 2002
TACC—(THA)
Rev.: $50,406,034
Assets: $32,566,655
Liabilities: $11,615,866
Net Worth: $20,950,788
Earnings: $5,973,916
Emp.: 161
Fiscal Year-end: 12/31/23
Convenience Food Retailer
N.A.I.C.S.: 445131
Apichat Pengsrithong (Chm)

T.C. TOPLU KONUT IDARESI BASKANLIGI
Bilkent Plaza B1 Blok, Bilkent Cankaya, 06800, Ankara, Turkiye
Tel.: (90) 3125652000
Web Site: http://www.toki.gov.tr
TOKI—(IST)
Emp.: 636
Real Estate Development Services
N.A.I.C.S.: 531390
Omer Bulut (Pres)

Subsidiaries:

GEDAS Gayrimenkul Degerleme A.S. (1)
Halkali Atakent Mahallesi 221 Sok No 5, opposite Kanuni Sultan Suleyman Hospital Halkali Kucukcekmece, Istanbul, 34307, Turkiye
Tel.: (90) 212 669 0915
Web Site: https://www.gedas.com.tr
Real Estate Services
N.A.I.C.S.: 531390

TOKI-Buyuksehir Belediyesi Insaat Emlak ve Proje A.S. (1)
TOBAS General Directorate Yesiltepe Mah North Ankara 2nd Stage, Recreation Area Cluster Houses No 9 Kecioren, Ankara, Turkiye
Tel.: (90) 312 340 5858

AND PRIVATE COMPANIES

Web Site: https://www.tobas.com.tr
Housing Construction Services
N.A.I.C.S.: 236115

Vakif G.Y.O. A.S. (1)
Serifali Mah Bayraktar Bulv Nutuk Sok No 4, Umraniye, Istanbul, Turkiye
Tel.: (90) 216 265 4050
Web Site: https://www.vakifgyo.com.tr
Real Estate Investment Services
N.A.I.C.S.: 531390

Vakif Ins. Restorasyon ve Tic. A.S. (1)
Vaccine F N Aat Restriction Tic A ereny Mah Central Mosque Street, Ereny Central No 15/17 Kat 2 D 8 Atasehir, Istanbul, Turkiye
Tel.: (90) 216 577 3963
Web Site: https://www.vakifinsaat.com.tr
Housing Construction Services
N.A.I.C.S.: 236115

T.C. ZIRAAT BANKASI A.S.
Haci Bayram Mahallesi Ataturk Bulvar No 8, Altindag, 06050, Ankara, Turkiye
Tel.: (90) 3125842000
Web Site:
http://www.ziraatbank.com.tr
TCZB—(IST)
Rev.: $16,162,884,783
Assets: $144,081,208,511
Liabilities: $131,788,263,476
Net Worth: $12,292,945,036
Earnings: $3,371,059,715
Emp.: 36,549
Fiscal Year-end: 12/31/23
Commercial Banking Services
N.A.I.C.S.: 522110
Huseyin Aydin *(CEO)*

Subsidiaries:

Ziraat Bank Azerbaycan ASC (1)
Hasan bey Zardabi ave 191, Yasamal district, AZ1122, Baku, Azerbaijan
Tel.: (994) 125055616
Web Site: https://www.ziraatbank.az
Financial Services
N.A.I.C.S.: 541611
Bilgehan Kuru *(Chm)*

Ziraat Bank BH d.d. (1)
Zmaja od Bosne 47c, 71000, Sarajevo, Bosnia & Herzegovina
Tel.: (387) 33955015
Web Site: https://www.ziraatbank.ba
Financial Services
N.A.I.C.S.: 541611
Mehmet Cengiz Gogebakan *(Chm)*

Ziraat Bank Uzbekistan JSC (1)
15 ABV Bunyodkor Avenue, 100043, Tashkent, Uzbekistan
Tel.: (998) 781476767
Web Site: https://www.ziraatbank.uz
Financial Services
N.A.I.C.S.: 541611
Emin Chubikci *(Chm)*

Ziraat Gayrimenkul Yatirim Ortakligi A.S. (1)
Finanskent Mah Finans Cad B Blok No 44/B ic Kapi No 12, Umraniye, 34734, Istanbul, Turkiye
Tel.: (90) 2165901540
Web Site: https://www.ziraatgyo.com.tr
Real Estate Services
N.A.I.C.S.: 531210
Ilker Met *(Chm)*

Ziraat GiriSim Sermayesi Yatirim Ortakligi A.S. (1)
Finanskent Mahallesi Finans Caddesi B Blok No 44B ic Kapi No 14, Umraniye, 34760, Istanbul, Turkiye
Tel.: (90) 2165901500
Web Site: https://www.ziraatgsyo.com.tr
Financial Services
N.A.I.C.S.: 541611
Ahmet Sefa Sen *(Fin Dir)*

Ziraat Teknoloji A.S. (1)
Yildiz Technical University Davutpasa C2 Block, Technology Development Zone Esenler, 34220, Istanbul, Turkiye

Tel.: (90) 2124846000
Web Site: https://www.ziraatteknoloji.com
Information Technology Services
N.A.I.C.S.: 541511
Dilek Emci *(Mgr-Software Dev)*

T.C.J. ASIA PUBLIC COMPANY LIMITED
3/4 Moo 9 Bangna-Trad KM18 Rd Bangchalong, Bang Phli, 10540, Samutprakarn, Thailand
Tel.: (66) 23126699
Web Site: https://www.tcjasia.com
Year Founded: 1980
TCJ—(THA)
Rev.: $38,642,026
Assets: $74,292,275
Liabilities: $37,065,424
Net Worth: $37,226,851
Earnings: ($1,249,347)
Fiscal Year-end: 12/31/23
Construction Machinery Whslr
N.A.I.C.S.: 423810
Somchai Eiamrot *(Sec)*

T.D.I. CO., LTD.
6-8-1 Nishi-Shinjuku, Shinjuku-ku, Osaka, 163-6013, Japan
Tel.: (81) 3 3372 1711
Web Site: http://www.tdi.co.jp
Year Founded: 1968
Sales Range: $200-249.9 Million
Emp.: 1,710
Software Development Services
N.A.I.C.S.: 513210
Noboru Yasunaga *(Chm)*

T.K.S. TECHNOLOGIES PUBLIC COMPANY LIMITED
30/88 Moo 1 Chetsadawithi Road, Khokkam sub-district Muang Samutsakhon, Bangkok, 74000, Thailand
Tel.: (66) 27845888   TH
Web Site: http://www.tks.co.th
Year Founded: 1954
TKS—(THA)
Rev.: $45,040,505
Assets: $148,766,120
Liabilities: $33,169,625
Net Worth: $115,596,494
Earnings: $8,513,728
Emp.: 597
Fiscal Year-end: 12/31/23
Business Forms & Office Paper Mfr & Distr
N.A.I.C.S.: 322120
Jutiphan Mongkolsuthree *(Mng Dir)*

Subsidiaries:

Gofive Co., Ltd. (1)
2525 FYI Center Building 1 5th Floor Unit 1/506 Rama 4 Road, Klong Toei, Bangkok, Thailand
Tel.: (66) 27845855
Web Site: https://www.gofive.co.th
Software Development Services
N.A.I.C.S.: 541511

Plus Tech Innovation Public Company Limited (1)
41/1 Moo 10 Poochaosamingprai Road, Samrong Tai Sub-district Phra Pradaeng District, Bangkok, 10130, Samutprakarn, Thailand
Tel.: (66) 27542650
Web Site: https://www.plustech.co.th
Rev.: $40,485,512
Assets: $60,147,839
Liabilities: $29,005,876
Net Worth: $31,141,962
Earnings: ($547,095)
Emp.: 237
Fiscal Year-end: 12/31/2023
Security Documents Mfr
N.A.I.C.S.: 561621
Santithorn Bunchua *(CEO)*

T.K.S. Technologies Phet Bury Factory (1)
88/8 Moo 3 Phetchakasem Road Huayroang Sub-District, Khaoyoi District, Phet

Buri, 76140, Thailand
Tel.: (66) 324476113
Paper Mills
N.A.I.C.S.: 322120

T.M.C. INDUSTRIAL PUBLIC COMPANY LIMITED
125/10 Moo 5 Bansuan, Muang, Chon Buri, 20000, Thailand
Tel.: (66) 38271933
Web Site: https://www.tmc.co.th
Year Founded: 1972
TMC—(THA)
Rev.: $9,534,416
Assets: $21,480,571
Liabilities: $3,468,359
Net Worth: $18,012,211
Earnings: $430,156
Emp.: 219
Fiscal Year-end: 12/31/23
Hydraulic & Mechanical Press Systems Mfr
N.A.I.C.S.: 333248
Manu Leopairoj *(Chm)*

T.O. HOLDINGS CO., LTD.
3-18-15 Minato-cho, Hakodate, 041-8610, Hokkaido, Japan
Tel.: (81) 138453911   JP
Web Site: https://www.tohd.co.jp
Year Founded: 1955
9812—(TKS)
Rev.: $169,249,050
Assets: $117,856,300
Liabilities: $113,857,250
Net Worth: $3,999,050
Earnings: $733,710
Emp.: 32
Fiscal Year-end: 05/31/24
Holding Company; Wood Flooring Construction Services
N.A.I.C.S.: 551112
Yasumasa Ogasawara *(Pres & CEO)*

T.R. HINAN CONTRACTORS INC.
31 Church Street, Saint Catharines, L2R 3B7, ON, Canada
Tel.: (905) 684-9964
Web Site: http://www.trhinan.com
Year Founded: 1983
Rev.: $14,519,807
Emp.: 50
Building Construction Services
N.A.I.C.S.: 236220

T.RAD CO., LTD.
3-25-3 Yoyogi, Shibuya-ku, Tokyo, 151-0053, Japan
Tel.: (81) 333731101
Web Site: https://www.trad.co.jp
Year Founded: 1936
7236—(TKS)
Rev.: $1,048,735,990
Assets: $681,405,070
Liabilities: $382,064,610
Net Worth: $299,340,460
Earnings: $8,229,450
Emp.: 4,365
Fiscal Year-end: 03/31/24
Automotive Parts Mfr & Whslr
N.A.I.C.S.: 336390
Hiromi Kano *(Chm & CEO)*

Subsidiaries:

PT. T.RAD INDONESIA (1)
Jl Jababeka II kav C-8 Kawasan Industri Jababeka I, Cikarang, Bekasi, 17530, Indonesia
Tel.: (62) 218934010
Automobile Parts Distr
N.A.I.C.S.: 423120

T.RAD (Changshu) Co., Ltd. (1)
No 28 Jinzhou Rd, Changshu, 215557, Jiangsu, China
Tel.: (86) 51282355600
Automobile Parts Distr

T.S. SIMMS & CO., LIMITED

N.A.I.C.S.: 423120

T.RAD (Changshu) R&D Center Co., Ltd. (1)
No 28 Jinzhou Rd, Changshu, Jiangsu, China
Tel.: (86) 5128 235 5600
Heat Exchanger Mfr & Distr
N.A.I.C.S.: 333414

T.RAD (Thailand) Co., Ltd. (1)
150 Moo 5 Tambol Bangsamurk Amphur, Bangpakong, Chachoengsao, 24130, Thailand
Tel.: (66) 38571450
Automobile Parts Distr
N.A.I.C.S.: 423120

T.RAD (Zhongshan) Co., Ltd. (1)
No 14 Shichong Road Zhongshan Torch Hi-Tech, Industrial Development Zone, Zhongshan, 528437, China
Tel.: (86) 76085338036
Automobile Parts Distr
N.A.I.C.S.: 423120

T.RAD Co., Ltd. - Hatano Works (1)
937 Soya, Hadano, 257-0031, Kanagawa, Japan
Tel.: (81) 463811551
Automobile Parts Mfr
N.A.I.C.S.: 336390

T.RAD Co., Ltd. - Nagoya Works (1)
1-7 Ohaza Fujie Aza Orido, Chita-gun, Higashiura, 470-2197, Aichi, Japan
Tel.: (81) 562833141
Automobile Parts Mfr
N.A.I.C.S.: 336390

T.RAD Co., Ltd. - Shiga Works (1)
297 Gochi-cho, Higashi-omi, 527-8508, Shiga, Japan
Tel.: (81) 748224611
Automobile Parts Mfr
N.A.I.C.S.: 336390

T.RAD Connect Co., Ltd. (1)
3-25-3 Yoyogi, Shibuya-ku, Tokyo, 151-0053, Japan
Tel.: (81) 33 373 1101
Web Site: https://www.trad-connect.co.jp
Software Development Services
N.A.I.C.S.: 541511
Tomio Miyazaki *(CEO)*

T.RAD Czech s.r.o. (1)
Lidicka 1044, 273 51, Unhost, Czech Republic
Tel.: (420) 312500715
Web Site: https://www.trad.cz
Heat Exchanger Mfr & Distr
N.A.I.C.S.: 332410

T.RAD North America, Inc. (1)
750 Frank Yost Ln, Hopkinsville, KY 42240
Tel.: (270) 885-9116
Web Site: http://www.tradna.com
Automotive Parts Mfr & Distr
N.A.I.C.S.: 336390
Tetsuya Ide *(Pres)*

Division (Domestic):

T.RAD North America, Inc. - TRA C/B Division (2)
210 Bill Bryan Blvd, Hopkinsville, KY 42240
Tel.: (270) 885-9116
Automobile Parts Mfr
N.A.I.C.S.: 336390

T.RAD Sales Europe GmbH (1)
Konigstrasse 10C, 70173, Stuttgart, Germany
Tel.: (49) 7112 225 4116
Heat Exchanger Mfr & Distr
N.A.I.C.S.: 333414

TRM LLC (1)
Str 20 Novikova-Priboya, 603135, Nizhniy Novgorod, Russia
Tel.: (7) 8312573312
Automobile Parts Distr
N.A.I.C.S.: 423120

T.S. SIMMS & CO., LIMITED
560 Main Street Ste 320, Saint John, E2K 1J5, NB, Canada
Tel.: (506) 635-6330
Web Site: http://www.tssimms.com

T.S. Simms & Co., Limited—(Continued)

Year Founded: 1866
Rev.: $16,822,038
Emp.: 90
Quality Paint Applicator Mfr
N.A.I.C.S.: 339994
Thomas Stockwell Simms III *(CEO)*

T.Y. LIMITED, INC.

Room 4204 Park Axis Aoyama 1-chome Tower, 1-3-1 Minami Aoyama, Minato-ku, Tokyo, 107-0062, Japan
Tel.: (81) 357757816   JP
Year Founded: 1988
Investment Management & Consulting Firm
N.A.I.C.S.: 523940
Tatsumi Yoda *(Founder, Chm & CEO)*

Subsidiaries:

GAGA Corporation   (1)
2-2-18 Minami-Aoyama, Minato-ku, Tokyo, 107-0062, Japan   (55%)
Tel.: (81) 3 5786 7140
Motion Picture & Video Distr
N.A.I.C.S.: 512120
Tatsumi Yoda *(Chm, Pres & CEO)*

T3EX GLOBAL HOLDINGS CORP.

12F No 563 Sec 4 Zhongxiao E Rd, Xinyi District, Taipei, 11072, Taiwan
Tel.: (886) 227532093
Web Site: https://www.t3ex-group.com
Year Founded: 1987
2636—(TAI)
Rev.: $478,146,847
Assets: $540,064,305
Liabilities: $247,144,305
Net Worth: $292,919,999
Earnings: $50,646,978
Emp.: 1,745
Fiscal Year-end: 12/31/23
Freight Transportation Services
N.A.I.C.S.: 541614
David Yen *(Founder, Founder, Chm, Chm, Pres, Pres, Gen Mgr & Gen Mgr)*

Subsidiaries:

Air Tropolis Express (S) Pte. Ltd.   (1)
119 Airport Cargo Road 01-01/02 Changi Cargo Agents Megaplex 1, Singapore, 819454, Singapore
Tel.: (65) 62600888
Web Site: https://t3ex-tecatp.com
Trucking & Warehousing Services
N.A.I.C.S.: 562119

Hiview Logistics Co., Ltd.   (1)
Tel.: (886) 35631733
Logistic Services
N.A.I.C.S.: 541614

T-Cube Global Logistics Co., Ltd.   (1)
803 Chang Hui Mansion No 977 Ying Xiang Road, Shanghai, 201802, China
Tel.: (86) 2151650133
Web Site: http://www.t3ex-tcube.com
Logistic Services
N.A.I.C.S.: 541614

T.H.I. & Maruzen Co., Ltd.   (1)
7F Shinsendo BLDG 2-15-15 Nihonbashi Ningyocho, Chuo-ku, Tokyo, 103-0013, Japan
Tel.: (81) 366610556
Web Site: http://thimaruzen.co.jp
Logistic Services
N.A.I.C.S.: 541614

T.H.I. Group (Cambodia) Co., Ltd.   (1)
Room 3FA Vtrust Office Center St 109 Sangkat Mittapheap Khan 7 Makara, Phnom Penh, Cambodia
Tel.: (855) 239661089
Air & Sea Freight Forwarding Services
N.A.I.C.S.: 541614

T.H.I. Group (Shanghai) Ltd.   (1)
10F Kaikai Mansion 88 Wanhangdu Rd Jingan Dist, Shanghai, 200042, China
Tel.: (86) 2161339533
Web Site: http://www.e-thi.com
Logistic Services
N.A.I.C.S.: 541614

T.H.I. Group Limited   (1)
Rm601-7 Prosperity Millennia Plaza 663 King s Rd, Quarry Bay, China (Hong Kong)
Tel.: (852) 27811818
Web Site: https://www.thi-group.com
Warehousing & Freight Forwarding Services
N.A.I.C.S.: 541614

T.H.I. Group Singapore Pte. Ltd.   (1)
Web Site: http://www.t3ex-group.com
Logistic Services
N.A.I.C.S.: 541614

T.H.I. Group Vietnam Co., Ltd.   (1)
Rm509B 5th Fl TD Business center tower 20A Le Hong Phong str, Haiphong, Vietnam
Tel.: (84) 2253686883
Logistic Services
N.A.I.C.S.: 541614

T.H.I. Japan Co., Ltd.   (1)
Shinsendo Building 7th Floor 2-15-15, Nihonbashi Ningyocho Chuo, Tokyo, 103-0013, Japan
Tel.: (81) 366610556
Web Site: https://www.thijapan.jp
Air & Sea Freight Forwarding Services
N.A.I.C.S.: 541614

T.H.I. Logistics (Hong Kong) Co., Limited   (1)
Rm601-7 Prosperity Millennia Plaza 663 King s Rd, Quarry Bay, China (Hong Kong)
Tel.: (852) 27811818
Air & Sea Freight Forwarding Services
N.A.I.C.S.: 541614

T.H.I. Logistics (Malaysia) Sdn. Bhd.   (1)
13-2 Jalan Mahogani 5/KS7, 41200, Bandar Botanic, Selangor Darul Ehsan, Malaysia
Tel.: (60) 333182200
Air & Sea Freight Forwarding Services
N.A.I.C.S.: 541614

T.H.I. Logistics Philippines Corp.   (1)
Unit 1605 16/F Ayala Tower One Ayala Ave, Makati, 1226, Philippines
Tel.: (63) 22773840
Air & Sea Freight Forwarding Services
N.A.I.C.S.: 541614

TEC Motion Co., Ltd.   (1)
4F-2 No 43 Yi 1st Rd, Zhongzheng Dist, Keelung, Taiwan
Tel.: (886) 224272141
Freight Forwarding Services
N.A.I.C.S.: 541614

Taiwan Express (HK) Co., Ltd.   (1)
Unit 305 3/F Magnet Place Tower 1 77-81 Container Port Road, New Territories, Kwai Chung, China (Hong Kong)
Tel.: (852) 23619298
Freight Forwarding Services
N.A.I.C.S.: 541614

T4F ENTRETENIMENTO S.A.

Avenida das Nacoes Unidas, 17955 Santo Amaro, 04795-100, Sao Paulo, SP, Brazil
Tel.: (55) 1135761200
Web Site: http://www.t4f.com.br
Year Founded: 1983
SHOW3—(BRAZ)
Rev.: $125,269,119
Assets: $89,962,458
Liabilities: $57,729,749
Net Worth: $32,232,709
Earnings: $10,403,461
Fiscal Year-end: 12/31/23
Live Entertainment Programming Services
N.A.I.C.S.: 516120
Luciano Nogueira Neto *(Chm)*

Subsidiaries:

Ticketek Argentina S.A.   (1)
Jose Antonio Cabrera 6061, Buenos Aires, Argentina
Tel.: (54) 11 5237 7200
Movie & Concert Ticketing Services
N.A.I.C.S.: 561599

Ticketmaster Chile S.A.   (1)
la Concepcion 266 Of 503 Piso 6, Santiago, Chile
Tel.: (56) 2 6902320
Web Site: http://www.t4f.cl
Emp.: 2
Event Management Services
N.A.I.C.S.: 711310

Vicar Promocoes Desportivas S.A.   (1)
Antonia Martins Luiz 705, 13347-404, Indaiatuba, Sao Paulo, Brazil
Tel.: (55) 1135761356
Sport Event Organizer
N.A.I.C.S.: 711310

T4G LIMITED

340 King Street East Suite 300, Toronto, M5A1K8, ON, Canada
Tel.: (416) 462-4200
Web Site: http://www.t4g.com
Year Founded: 1996
Rev.: $15,131,600
Emp.: 170
Information Technology Consulting Services
N.A.I.C.S.: 541513
Michael Cottenden *(Mng Partner)*

T7 GLOBAL BERHAD

C-16-01 Level 16 KL Trillion Corporate Tower Block C 338, Jalan Tun Razak, 50400, Kuala Lumpur, Malaysia
Tel.: (60) 327857777   MY
Web Site: https://www.t7global.com.my
Year Founded: 2004
T7GLOBAL—(KLS)
Rev.: $76,819,054
Assets: $218,599,221
Liabilities: $156,803,461
Net Worth: $61,795,760
Earnings: $4,283,379
Emp.: 317
Fiscal Year-end: 12/31/22
Offshore Oilfield Operating Services
N.A.I.C.S.: 213112
Kean Soon Tan *(Deputy Chm)*

Subsidiaries:

Fircroft Tanjung Sdn Bhd   (1)
Lot E Level 5 Tower 1 Etiqa Twins 11 Jalan Pinang, 50450, Kuala Lumpur, Malaysia   (51%)
Tel.: (60) 321617171
Employee Recruitment Services
N.A.I.C.S.: 561311
Russell Marland *(Bus Mgr)*

T7 Gastec Sdn Bhd   (1)
5205A Kawasan Perindustrian Balakong Jaya 2, 43300, Balakong, Selangor, Malaysia
Tel.: (60) 389613390
Integrated Oil & Gas Operation Services
N.A.I.C.S.: 213112

Subsidiary (Domestic):

T7 Wenmax Sdn Bhd   (2)
C-16-01 Level 16 KL Trillion Corporate Tower Block C, 338 Jalan Tun Razak, 50400, Kuala Lumpur, Malaysia
Tel.: (60) 327857777
Integrated Oil & Gas Operation Services
N.A.I.C.S.: 213112

T7 Kilgour Sdn Bhd   (1)
Lot No 29138 Plot 8 Seksyen 20 Mukim Bandar, 48200, Serendah, Selangor, Malaysia
Tel.: (60) 360210777
Integrated Oil & Gas Operation Services
N.A.I.C.S.: 213112

TA ANN HOLDINGS BERHAD

No 6 Jalan Rawang, 96000, Sibu, Sarawak, Malaysia
Tel.: (60) 84320200
Web Site: https://www.taann.com.my
TAANN—(KLS)
Rev.: $365,846,172
Assets: $594,145,372
Liabilities: $157,290,205
Net Worth: $436,855,167
Earnings: $43,926,372
Emp.: 3,681
Fiscal Year-end: 12/31/23
Plywood Mfr
N.A.I.C.S.: 321211
Jan Moi Voon *(Co-Sec)*

Subsidiaries:

Borlin Sendirian Berhad   (1)
No 6 Jalan Rawang, 96000, Sibu, Sarawak, Malaysia
Tel.: (60) 84334366
Emp.: 1,500
Timber Logging Services
N.A.I.C.S.: 113110
Ting Nichras *(Gen Mgr)*

Borneo Tree Seeds & Seedlings Supplies Sendirian Berhad   (1)
1st Floor Sublot 24 Lot 214 Kld Pentaloo Mile 6, Jalan Pintulu Tatau, 97000, Bintulu, Sarawak, Malaysia
Tel.: (60) 84331125
Emp.: 10
Seed Whslr
N.A.I.C.S.: 424910

Hariwood Sdn. Bhd.   (1)
No 6 Jln Rawang Bangunan Ta Ann, 96000, Sibu, Sarawak, Malaysia
Tel.: (60) 84313863
Sales Range: $25-49.9 Million
Emp.: 122
Timber Logging Services
N.A.I.C.S.: 113110
Hie Ping Lau *(Gen Mgr)*

Lik Shen Sawmill Sdn. Bhd.   (1)
No 6 Level 2A Jalan Rawang, PO Box 1489, 96008, Sibu, Sarawak, Malaysia
Tel.: (60) 84320757
Emp.: 200
Timber Logging Services
N.A.I.C.S.: 113110
Charlie Tan *(Gen Mgr)*

Manis Oil Sendirian Berhad   (1)
Level 3A Ta Ann Buting No 6 Jalan Rawang, 96000, Sibu, Sarawak, Malaysia
Tel.: (60) 84 331 328
Palm Oil Mfr
N.A.I.C.S.: 311225

Multi Maximum Sendirian Berhad   (1)
No 6 3B Bangunan Ta Ann Jln Rawang, 96000, Sibu, Sarawak, Malaysia
Tel.: (60) 84347360
Sales Range: $25-49.9 Million
Emp.: 13
Oil Palm Cultivation Services
N.A.I.C.S.: 115112
Dato Wong *(Mng Dir)*

Pasin Sdn. Bhd.   (1)
No 6 Lot 9 Lorong 20A2 Jalan Pedada, PO Box 1489, Sibu, 96000, Sarawak, Malaysia
Tel.: (60) 84312299
Web Site: http://www.taann.com.my
Sales Range: $25-49.9 Million
Emp.: 2
Timber Logging Services
N.A.I.C.S.: 113110

Questate Sdn. Bhd.   (1)
6 Lot 9 Lorong 20A 2 Jalan Pedada, PO Box 1489, 96008, Sibu, Sarawak, Malaysia
Tel.: (60) 84347868
Sales Range: $25-49.9 Million
Emp.: 10
Timber Logging Services
N.A.I.C.S.: 113110

Raplex Sdn. Bhd.   (1)
No 6 Lot 9 Lorong 20A2 Jalan Pedada, Sibu, 96000, Sarawak, Malaysia
Tel.: (60) 84331214
Sales Range: $25-49.9 Million
Emp.: 4
Timber Logging Services

N.A.I.C.S.: 113310
Wong Kuo Hea (Mng Dir)

Ta Ann Plywood Sdn. Bhd. (1)
No 6 Jalan Rawang, 96000, Sibu, Sarawak, Malaysia
Tel.: (60) 84312168
Web Site: http://www.taann.com.my
Plywood Mfr & Sales
N.A.I.C.S.: 321211

Subsidiary (Non-US):

Ta Ann Tasmania Pty. Ltd. (2)
150 Davey Street, Hobart, 7000, TAS, Australia
Tel.: (61) 36 227 5500
Web Site: https://www.taanntas.com.au
Sales Range: $25-49.9 Million
Emp.: 100
Wood Veneer Mfr
N.A.I.C.S.: 321211
Robert Yong (Gen Mgr)

Subsidiary (Domestic):

Tanjong Manis Holdings Sdn Bhd (2)
No 6 Jalan Rawang, 96000, Sibu, Sarawak, Malaysia
Tel.: (60) 84312299
Lumber Product Whslr
N.A.I.C.S.: 423310
Dato Wong (CEO)

Tanahead Sendirian Berhad (1)
6 Jalan Rawang, 96000, Sibu, Sarawak, Malaysia
Tel.: (60) 84 320 200
Web Site: http://www.taann.com.my
Emp.: 12
Property Development Services
N.A.I.C.S.: 531312

Woodley Sdn. Bhd. (1)
No 6 Lot 9 Lorong 20 A2 Jalan Pedada, PO Box 1489, 96008, Sibu, Sarawak, Malaysia
Tel.: (60) 84312299
Sales Range: $25-49.9 Million
Emp.: 3
Timber Logging Services
N.A.I.C.S.: 113110
Ali Mat Dollah (Mng Dir)

TA CHEN STAINLESS PIPE, LTD.
No 125 Hsin Tien 2nd Street Hsin-Tien, Jeng-Ten, T'ainan, Taiwan
Tel.: (886) 62701756 TW
Web Site: http://www.tachen.com.tw
Year Founded: 1986
2027—(TAI)
Rev.: $3,311,311,592
Assets: $4,418,565,254
Liabilities: $1,982,929,485
Net Worth: $2,435,635,769
Earnings: $222,719,636
Fiscal Year-end: 12/31/23
Stainless Steel Pipes & Valves Mfr
N.A.I.C.S.: 331110
Judy Chen (Sr Mgr-Sls-Taipei)

Subsidiaries:

Empire Resources, Inc. (1)
2115 Linwood Ave, Fort Lee, NJ 07024
Tel.: (201) 944-2200
Web Site: http://www.empireresources.com
Rev.: $458,864,000
Assets: $205,550,000
Liabilities: $155,832,000
Net Worth: $49,718,000
Earnings: $3,301,000
Emp.: 60
Fiscal Year-end: 12/31/2016
Semi-Finished Aluminum Products Distr
N.A.I.C.S.: 423510

Subsidiary (Non-US):

Empire Resources Pacific Ltd. (2)
12a/617 Seventeen Mile Rocks Rd, Seventeen Mile Rocks, Brisbane, 4073, QLD, Australia
Tel.: (61) 732797899
Web Site: http://www.empireresources.com
Semi-Finished Aluminum & Steel Products Distr

N.A.I.C.S.: 331318

Primus Pipe & Tube, Inc. (1)
241 W Clarke St, Wildwood, FL 34785
Web Site: https://www.primuspipeandtube.com
Stainless Steel Wire Mfr
N.A.I.C.S.: 331110

Shijiazhuang Ji-Tai Precision Casting Co., Ltd. (1)
No 379 Heping East Road, Shijiazhuang, Hebei, China
Tel.: (86) 31187225850
Aluminum & Nickel Alloy Coil Product Distr
N.A.I.C.S.: 423510

Ta Chen (Boye) Precision Casting Co., Ltd. (1)
Bo Xing Middle Road, Boye, Baoding, 171300, Hebei, China
Tel.: (86) 3128719285
Web Site: http://www.tachen.com
Metal Products Mfr
N.A.I.C.S.: 331511

Ta Chen (Changshu) Machinery Co., Ltd. (1)
Haiyang Road, Haiyu Town, Changshu, 215519, Jiangsu, China
Tel.: (86) 51252565588
Web Site: http://www.tachen.com
Metal Products Mfr
N.A.I.C.S.: 331511

TA CORPORATION LTD.
8 Kaki Bukit Avenue 1 04-08, Singapore, 417941, Singapore
Tel.: (65) 63922988 SG
Web Site: http://www.tiongaik.com.sg
Year Founded: 1995
PA3—(SES)
Rev.: $104,797,394
Assets: $492,844,808
Liabilities: $413,390,896
Net Worth: $79,453,912
Earnings: $23,150,042
Fiscal Year-end: 12/31/23
Residential & Other Property Development, Sales & Construction
N.A.I.C.S.: 237210
Kiam Teck Liong (Founder, Exec Chm & Chm)

Subsidiaries:

Prime Industries Pre-cast Pte. Ltd. (1)
No 1 Jalan Berseh 03-03 New World Centre, Singapore, 209037, Singapore
Tel.: (65) 6 291 5584
Web Site: https://www.primeprecast.com.sg
Construction Pre Cast Component Mfr
N.A.I.C.S.: 332311

Sino Holdings (S'pore) Pte Ltd. (1)
1 Jalan Berseh 03-03 New World Centre, Singapore, 209037, Singapore
Tel.: (65) 63922988
Web Site: http://www.tiongaik.com.sg
Sales Range: $50-74.9 Million
Emp.: 105
Investment Management Service
N.A.I.C.S.: 523940
Kiam Teck Liong (Chm)

Subsidiary (Domestic):

Grovehill Pte. Ltd (2)
1 Jalan Berseh 03-03 New World Centre, Singapore, 209037, Singapore
Tel.: (65) 6392 2988
Web Site: http://www.tiongaik.com.sg
Sales Range: $25-49.9 Million
Emp.: 5
Real Estate Development Services
N.A.I.C.S.: 531390

Sino Tac Resources Pte. Ltd. (1)
24 Pioneer Crescent 02-08 West Park Bizcentral, Singapore, 628557, Singapore
Tel.: (65) 6 298 0988
Web Site: https://www.sinotac.com.sg
Automotive Related Product Distr
N.A.I.C.S.: 423120
Christine Tok (Sr Mgr)

SinoTac Builder's (S) Pte Ltd (1)

1 Jalan Berseh 03-03 New World Centre, Singapore, 209037, Singapore
Tel.: (65) 6392 2988
Web Site: http://www.tiongait.com.sg
Emp.: 10
Real Estate Development Services
N.A.I.C.S.: 531390
Eugene Soon (Gen Mgr)

TA Resources Myanmar Company Limited (1)
No 137 B U Ta Yoke Gyi Street, Hlaing Thar Yar Industrial Zone 4 Hlaing Thar Yar Township, Yangon, Myanmar
Tel.: (95) 168 5806
Web Site: https://www.taresourcesmm.com
Emp.: 100
Shell Lubricant Distr
N.A.I.C.S.: 424720
Captain Win (Founder & CEO)

TK Modular Pte. Ltd. (1)
67A Sungei Kadut Drive TAC Centre 03-01, Singapore, 729575, Singapore
Tel.: (65) 6 362 1658
Web Site: https://www.tkmodular.com.sg
Modular Construction Product Mfr
N.A.I.C.S.: 332311

Tiong Aik Construction Pte Ltd. (1)
1 Jalan Berseh 03-03 New World Centre, Singapore, 209037, Singapore
Tel.: (65) 6392 2988
Web Site: http://www.tiongaik.com.sg
Emp.: 10
Building Construction Services
N.A.I.C.S.: 236220

Subsidiary (Domestic):

Tiong Aik Resources (S) Pte Ltd (2)
1 Jalan Berseh 03-01 New World Centre, Singapore, 209037, Singapore
Tel.: (65) 62953294
Real Estate Management Services
N.A.I.C.S.: 531390

TA ENTERPRISE BERHAD
34th Floor Menara TA One 22 Jalan P Ramlee, 50250, Kuala Lumpur, Malaysia
Tel.: (60) 320721277 MY
Web Site: http://www.ta.com.my
Year Founded: 1990
TA—(KLS)
Rev.: $201,306,353
Assets: $246,134,790
Liabilities: $148,798,980
Net Worth: $97,335,810
Earnings: $3,625,875
Emp.: 1,213
Fiscal Year-end: 12/31/20
Holding Company; Financial Services
N.A.I.C.S.: 551112
Zainab Ahmad (Exec Dir)

Subsidiaries:

Indo Aman Bina Sdn Bhd (1)
34 Floor Menara TA One 22 Jalan P Ramlee, Kuala Lumpur, 50250, Malaysia
Tel.: (60) 3 2072 1277
Web Site: http://www.ta.com.my
Emp.: 400
Property Management Services
N.A.I.C.S.: 531390

Subsidiary (Non-US):

Aava Whistler Hotel Ltd (2)
4005 Whistler Way, Whistler, V8E 1J1, BC, Canada
Tel.: (604) 932-2522
Web Site: http://www.aavawhistlerhotel.com
Emp.: 50
Home Management Services
N.A.I.C.S.: 721110

TA Properties (Canada) Ltd (2)
1111 Georgia Street W Suite 2121, Vancouver, V6E 4M3, BC, Canada
Tel.: (604) 683-1628
Web Site: http://www.ta-managment.com
Property Management Services
N.A.I.C.S.: 531311

TA Asset Management Sdn Bhd (1)
23rd Floor Menara TA One, 22 Jalan P Ramlee, 50250, Kuala Lumpur, Malaysia (100%)
Tel.: (60) 320725358
Emp.: 70
Financial Services
N.A.I.C.S.: 523999

TA Centre Berhad (1)
22 Menara TA One Jln P Ramlee, Kuala Lumpur, 50250, Malaysia
Tel.: (60) 3 2072 1277
Web Site: http://www.ta.com.my
Sales Range: $200-249.9 Million
Emp.: 500
Securities Brokerage Services
N.A.I.C.S.: 523150
Alicia Tiah (Mng Dir)

TA First Credit Sdn. Bhd (1)
14 Floor Menara TA ONE 22 Jalan P Ramlee, Kuala Lumpur, 50250, Malaysia
Tel.: (60) 3 2072 1277
Sales Range: $50-74.9 Million
Emp.: 20
Property Development Services
N.A.I.C.S.: 531390

TA Futures Sdn Bhd (1)
32nd Floor Menara TA One, 22 Jalan P Ramlee, 50250, Kuala Lumpur, Malaysia (70%)
Tel.: (60) 320724831
Emp.: 30
Financial Services
N.A.I.C.S.: 523999
Dayang Ku (Exec Dir-Ops)

TA Global Berhad (1)
34th Floor Menara TA One 22 Jalan P Ramlee, 50250, Kuala Lumpur, Malaysia (100%)
Tel.: (60) 320721277
Web Site: http://www.taglobal.com.my
Rev.: $182,726,425
Assets: $1,324,706,271
Liabilities: $549,988,533
Net Worth: $774,717,737
Earnings: $30,074,557
Fiscal Year-end: 12/31/2019
Commercial Real Estate Investment & Property Development
N.A.I.C.S.: 531390
Kimmy Poh Kim Khoo (Exec Dir)

TA Properties Sdn Bhd (1)
34th Floor Menara TA One, 22 Jalan P Ramlee, 50250, Kuala Lumpur, Malaysia (100%)
Tel.: (60) 321615148
Web Site: http://www.ta.com.my
Sales Range: $100-124.9 Million
Emp.: 200
Financial Services
N.A.I.C.S.: 523999

Subsidiary (Domestic):

TA Capital Sdn Bhd (2)
14th Floor Menara TA One, 22 Jalan P Ramlee, 50250, Kuala Lumpur, Malaysia (100%)
Tel.: (60) 320721277
Sales Range: $50-74.9 Million
Emp.: 10
Financial Services & Short & Medium Term Loans
N.A.I.C.S.: 525990

Subsidiary (Non-US):

TA Management Limited (2)
308-1111 West Georgia Street, Vancouver, V6E 4M3, BC, Canada (100%)
Tel.: (604) 683-1628
Web Site: https://www.ta-management.com
Sales Range: $25-49.9 Million
Emp.: 35
Financial Services
N.A.I.C.S.: 523999

TA Securities Holding Berhad (1)
34th Floor Menara TA 1 22 Jalan P Ramlee, 50250, Kuala Lumpur, Malaysia (100%)
Tel.: (60) 320721277
Web Site: http://www.tasecurities.com.my
Sales Range: $200-249.9 Million
Emp.: 500
Financial Services
N.A.I.C.S.: 523150

Subsidiary (Domestic):

TA Investment Management Berhad (2)

TA ENTERPRISE BERHAD

TA Enterprise Berhad—(Continued)
23rd Fl Menara TA One, 22 Jalan P Ramlee, 50250, Kuala Lumpur, Malaysia
Tel.: (60) 320316603 **(70%)**
Emp.: 55
Financial Services
N.A.I.C.S.: 523999
Mien Wong *(CEO)*

TA JIANG CO., LTD.
6F No 71 Sec 2 Tung Hwa South Road, Taipei, Taiwan
Tel.: (886) 27069999
Web Site: http://www.tajiang.com.tw
1453—(TAI)
Rev.: $6,667,059
Assets: $67,727,392
Liabilities: $20,382,190
Net Worth: $47,345,202
Earnings: $1,987,279
Fiscal Year-end: 12/31/23
Textile Products Mfr
N.A.I.C.S.: 314999
Yi Hsiung Yeh *(Chm & Gen Mgr)*

TA LIANG TECHNOLOGY CO., LTD.
No 68 Toyota Road, Bade District, Taoyuan, Taiwan
Tel.: (886) 33686368
Web Site: https://www.taliang.com
Year Founded: 1980
3167—(TAI)
Rev.: $42,260,242
Assets: $141,452,200
Liabilities: $72,314,363
Net Worth: $69,137,837
Earnings: $383,139
Emp.: 127
Fiscal Year-end: 12/31/23
Electric Machinery & Equipment Mfr
N.A.I.C.S.: 335999
Tso-Ching Wang *(Chm)*

Subsidiaries:

Nanjing Taliang Numeric Control Tech. Co., Ltd. **(1)**
No 1 Shaw Chi Rd, Shung Zhou Industrial Park Rio Ho District, Nanjing, China
Tel.: (86) 2557512518
Drilling Machines Mfr
N.A.I.C.S.: 333132

TA WIN HOLDINGS BERHAD
Unit 26-11 & 26-12 Level 26 Q Sentral Jalan Stesen Sentral 2, 50470, Kuala Lumpur, Malaysia
Tel.: (60) 322766522 **MY**
Web Site: https://www.ta-win.com
TAWIN—(KLS)
Rev.: $134,526,645
Assets: $106,753,680
Liabilities: $32,226,480
Net Worth: $74,527,200
Earnings: ($765,518)
Emp.: 634
Fiscal Year-end: 06/30/22
Silo Mfr
N.A.I.C.S.: 333992
Chin Kiang Yeoh *(Gen Mgr)*

Subsidiaries:

Cyprium Wire Technology Sdn. Bhd. **(1)**
Lot 63-70 Block 3 Jalan Industrial 21 Alor Gajah Industrial Estate, 78000, Melaka, Malaysia
Tel.: (60) 65401080
Web Site: https://www.twcyprium.com.my
Automobile Wire & Cable Mfr
N.A.I.C.S.: 335931

Ta Win Industries (M) Sdn. Bhd. **(1)**
Lot 63-70 Alor Gajah Industrial Estate, Alor Gajah, 78000, Melaka, Malaysia
Tel.: (60) 65564784

Sales Range: $25-49.9 Million
Emp.: 100
Enameled Copper Wires Mfr
N.A.I.C.S.: 331420

Twin Industrial (H.K.) Company Limited **(1)**
5/F Unit 1 Wan Shing Ctr 11-13 Shing Yip St, Kwun Tong, Kowloon, China (Hong Kong)
Tel.: (852) 27933255
Enameled Copper Wires Distr
N.A.I.C.S.: 423610

TA YA ELECTRIC WIRE & CABLE CO., LTD.
No 249 Sec 2 Chung Shan Rd, Kuan Miao Dist, T'ainan, 71847, Taiwan
Tel.: (886) 65953131
Web Site: https://www.taya.com.tw
1609—(TAI)
Rev.: $864,508,944
Assets: $1,520,021,166
Liabilities: $980,543,342
Net Worth: $539,477,824
Earnings: $102,368,942
Emp.: 1,806
Fiscal Year-end: 12/31/23
Electric Wires & Cables Mfr
N.A.I.C.S.: 238210
San-Yi Shen *(Pres)*

Subsidiaries:

CUPRIME Material Co., Ltd. **(1)**
7F No 149 Wu Kung Road Wu Ku Industrial Park, Taipei, 24886, Taiwan
Tel.: (886) 2 22997080
Web Site: http://www.taya.com.tw
Emp.: 65
Copper Wires Mfr
N.A.I.C.S.: 331420

HENG YA Electric (Kunshan) Ltd. **(1)**
No 200 Industrial Park West Lighthouse Rd, Yushan Town, Kunshan, 215300, Jiangsu, China
Tel.: (86) 51257167888
Web Site: http://www.taya.com.tw
Electronic Cable Mfr
N.A.I.C.S.: 335921

Heng Ya Electric (Dongguan) Ltd. **(1)**
No 2 ZhenAn West Road, South Industry-Zone XiaGangVillage ChangAn Town, Dongguan, 523873, GuangDong, China
Tel.: (86) 76985337985
Magnet Wire Mfr
N.A.I.C.S.: 335929

TA AN Precision Co., Ltd. **(1)**
No 29 Nanxing Road, Yongkang, T'ainan, 710, Taiwan
Tel.: (886) 6 2723461
Web Site: http://www.taya.com.tw
Diamond Dies Mfr & Sales
N.A.I.C.S.: 423840

TA HENG Electric Wire & Cable Co., Ltd. **(1)**
No 149 Yilin Road Jen Der Hsiang, T'ainan, 717, Taiwan
Tel.: (886) 62793716
Emp.: 100
Copper Wire & Cable Mfr
N.A.I.C.S.: 331420

TA YA Venture Capital Co., Ltd. **(1)**
3F No 108 Sec 1 Tun Hwa S Road, Da-an District, Taipei, 105, Taiwan
Tel.: (886) 287739996
Web Site: http://www.taya.com.tw
Investment Management Service
N.A.I.C.S.: 523999

TA YI Plastic Co., Ltd **(1)**
No 15-1 Nanxing Road, Nanwan Village Yongkang District, T'ainan, Taiwan
Tel.: (886) 62717052
Plastics Product Mfr
N.A.I.C.S.: 326199

Ta Ya (Vietnam) Electric Wire & Cable Co., Ltd. **(1)**
No 1 1A Road Bien Hoa Industrial Zone II,

Bien Hoa, Dong Nai, Vietnam
Tel.: (84) 613836361
Web Site: http://www.taya.com.tw
Electrical Wires & Cables Mfr
N.A.I.C.S.: 335999

UNITED Electric Industry Co., Ltd. **(1)**
39 Ke Chi 7th Road, Kueishan Hsiang, Gueishan, 33383, Tao Yuan, Taiwan
Tel.: (886) 33960101
Cable Accessories Mfr
N.A.I.C.S.: 332618
Shu-lin Huang *(Pres)*

TA YANG GROUP HOLDINGS LIMITED
Unit 4210 42nd Floor Office Tower Convention Plaza, 1 Harbour Road, Wanchai, China (Hong Kong)
Tel.: (852) 36785088 **Ky**
Web Site: http://www.tayang.com
1991—(HKG)
Rev.: $43,801,478
Assets: $81,793,418
Liabilities: $64,404,968
Net Worth: $17,388,450
Earnings: ($12,610,260)
Emp.: 853
Fiscal Year-end: 12/31/22
Manufacture of Silicone Rubber Input Devices
N.A.I.C.S.: 325212
Qi Shi *(Chm & CEO)*

Subsidiaries:

Ta Yang Group Holdings Limited - Dongguan Factory **(1)**
Xin Guang Road Jin-He Industrial District Zhangmutou Town, Dongguan, Guangdong, China
Tel.: (86) 76987197979
Silicone Rubber Input Device Mfr
N.A.I.C.S.: 334118

Ta Yang Group Holdings Limited - Huzhou Factory **(1)**
389 Cheng Ye Road Southwest Sub-district, Huzhou, 313000, Zhejiang, China
Tel.: (86) 5722120388
Silicone Rubber Input Device Mfr
N.A.I.C.S.: 334118

TA-I TECHNOLOGY CO., LTD.
No 4 Ln 17 Sec 3 Nanshan Rd, Luzhu Dist, Taoyuan, 33860, Taiwan
Tel.: (886) 33246169
Web Site: https://www.tai.com.tw
2478—(TAI)
Rev.: $150,259,355
Assets: $311,759,039
Liabilities: $95,417,342
Net Worth: $216,341,697
Earnings: $12,234,638
Fiscal Year-end: 12/31/23
Electronic Resistor Mfr
N.A.I.C.S.: 334416

Subsidiaries:

PT TAI Electronic Indonesia **(1)**
Blok T1 E F JI Jababeka IV, Cikarang Industrial Estate, Bekasi, 17530, Indonesia
Tel.: (62) 21 89830123
Web Site: http://www.pttai.com
Sales Range: $50-74.9 Million
Emp.: 200
Resistors Mfr
N.A.I.C.S.: 334416

Ta-I Ohmelectronics (M) Sdn.Bhd. **(1)**
Plot 564 D Lorong Perusshaan Baru 2, Kawasan Perindustrian, Prai, 13600, Penang, Malaysia
Tel.: (60) 43900480
Web Site: http://www.taiohm.com.my
Electronic Components Mfr
N.A.I.C.S.: 334416

Ta-I Technology (Suzhou)Co., Ltd. **(1)**
675th N Lu-Xiang Rd, Songling Town, Wuji-

ang, 215200, China
Tel.: (86) 512 6345 7879
Web Site: http://www.ta-i.com.tw
Electronic Components Mfr
N.A.I.C.S.: 334419

Tyee Products Inc. **(1)**
579 S State College Blvd, Fullerton, CA 92831
Tel.: (714) 525-9123
Web Site: http://www.tyeeusa.com
Sales Range: $25-49.9 Million
Electronic Components Mfr
N.A.I.C.S.: 334416

TA-YUAN COGENERATION CO., LTD.
No 286 Huanke Rd 1st Neighborhood Datan Vil, Guanyin Dist, Taoyuan, 32841, Taiwan
Tel.: (886) 34736668
Web Site: https://www.tycc.com.tw
Year Founded: 1993
8931—(TPE)
Rev.: $89,454,022
Assets: $139,300,285
Liabilities: $71,228,965
Net Worth: $68,071,319
Earnings: $11,508,270
Fiscal Year-end: 12/31/22
Electric Power Distribution Services
N.A.I.C.S.: 221122
Shiaw-Tzong Lee *(Chm)*

TAAGEER FINANCE COMPANY SAOG
PO Box 200, 136, Ruwi, Oman
Tel.: (968) 24839999
Web Site: https://www.taageer.com
Year Founded: 2000
TFCI—(MUS)
Rev.: $47,398,503
Assets: $488,869,119
Liabilities: $380,669,956
Net Worth: $108,199,163
Earnings: $9,852,774
Emp.: 150
Fiscal Year-end: 12/31/19
Financial Services
N.A.I.C.S.: 523999
V. V. Suresh Kumar *(Gen Mgr-Mktg & Sls)*

TAAL DISTRIBUTED INFORMATION TECHNOLOGIES INC.
181 Bay Street Unit 4260, Toronto, M5J 2V1, ON, Canada
Tel.: (604) 929-0900 **BC**
Web Site: https://www.taal.com
Year Founded: 2011
TAAL—(CNSX)
Rev.: $6,253,115
Assets: $32,100,250
Liabilities: $21,264,418
Net Worth: $10,835,832
Earnings: ($16,725,273)
Fiscal Year-end: 12/31/20
Gold & Other Metal Mining
N.A.I.C.S.: 212220
Stefan Matthews *(Chm & CEO)*

TAAL ENTERPRISES LTD.
2nd Floor MMPDA Towers 184 Royapettah High Road, Chennai, 600 014, India
Tel.: (91) 4443508393
Web Site: https://www.taalent.co.in
539956—(BOM)
Rev.: $20,030,406
Assets: $18,718,074
Liabilities: $3,831,533
Net Worth: $14,886,542
Earnings: $3,744,008
Emp.: 3
Fiscal Year-end: 03/31/23
Transportation & Charter Flight Services
N.A.I.C.S.: 481211

AND PRIVATE COMPANIES

Salil Taneja *(Exec Dir)*

TAALERI OYJ
Kasarmikatu 21 B, 00130, Helsinki, Finland
Tel.: (358) 931527300
Web Site: https://www.taaleri.com
Year Founded: 2007
TAALA—(HEL)
Rev.: $72,446,186
Assets: $339,895,132
Liabilities: $109,576,112
Net Worth: $230,319,020
Earnings: $31,446,076
Emp.: 118
Fiscal Year-end: 12/31/23
Wealth Management & Private Equity
N.A.I.C.S.: 523940
Juhani Elomaa *(Chm)*

Subsidiaries:

Garantia Insurance Company Ltd. (1)
Tel.: (358) 207479800
Web Site: https://www.garantia.fi
Non-Life Insurance Services
N.A.I.C.S.: 524298
Tuukka Fabritius *(Head-Housing Svcs, Legal & Back Office)*

Isonevan Tuulipuisto Oy (1)
Kasarmikatu 21B, 00130, Helsinki, Finland
Tel.: (358) 503399995
Web Site: https://www.isonevantuulipuisto.fi
Electricity Generation Services
N.A.I.C.S.: 541330

Lainaamo Oy (1)
Ratakatu 1BA 10, 00120, Helsinki, Finland
Tel.: (358) 75 756 8600
Emp.: 15
Financial Investment Services
N.A.I.C.S.: 523999
Jouni Hintikka *(CEO)*

Taaleri Bioindustry Ltd. (1)
Kasarmikatu 21 B 4th Floor, 00130, Helsinki, Finland
Tel.: (358) 931527300
Web Site: https://www.taaleribioteollisuus.fi
Industry Development & Fund Management Services
N.A.I.C.S.: 523910

Taaleri Energia Ltd. (1)
Kasarmikatu 21 B 4th Floor, 00130, Helsinki, Finland
Tel.: (358) 931527300
Web Site: https://www.taalerienergia.com
Turbine Mfr
N.A.I.C.S.: 333611
Kai Rintala *(Mng Dir)*

Taaleri Kapitaali Ltd. (1)
Kasarmikatu 21 B 4 Kerros, 00130, Helsinki, Finland
Tel.: (358) 931527300
Web Site: https://www.taalerikapitaali.fi
Investment Banking Services
N.A.I.C.S.: 523150
Vesa Heikkila *(Partner & Mng Dir)*

Taaleri Portfoy Yonetimi A.S. (1)
Buyukdere Cad Levent Loft Binasi No 201 Daire 62 Levent, 34394, Istanbul, Turkiye
Tel.: (90) 212 909 1270
Web Site: http://www.taaleri.com.tr
Wealth Management Services
N.A.I.C.S.: 523150

Taaleri Real Estate Ltd. (1)
Kasarmikatu 21 B 4 kerros, 00130, Helsinki, Finland
Tel.: (358) 931527300
Web Site: https://www.taalerikiinteistot.com
Real Estate Asset Management Services
N.A.I.C.S.: 531390

Turun Toriparkki Oy (1)
Yliopistonkatu, Turku, Finland
Tel.: (358) 33878222
Web Site: https://www.turuntoriparkki.fi
Parking Garage Services
N.A.I.C.S.: 561612

TAAT GLOBAL ALTERNATIVES INC.
2630-1075 West Georgia Street, Vancouver, V6E 3C9, BC, Canada
Tel.: (604) 687-2038 BC
Web Site: http://www.taatusa.com
Year Founded: 2006
TOBAF—(OTCIQ)
Rev.: $539
Assets: $444,053
Liabilities: $538,391
Net Worth: ($94,339)
Earnings: ($358,858)
Fiscal Year-end: 10/31/19
Oil & Gas Exploration Services
N.A.I.C.S.: 213112
Joel S. Dumaresq *(CFO)*

Subsidiaries:

Puffs Inc. (1)
1851 Gleco Mills Ln, Charlottesville, VA 22903
Tel.: (434) 977-0427
Web Site: https://puffinc.com
Roofing Material Mfr & Distr
N.A.I.C.S.: 327390

TAAVURA HOLDINGS, LTD.
320 Industrial Zone, Ramla, 72102, Israel
Tel.: (972) 89270420 IL
Web Site: http://www.taavura.com
Holding Company; Truck Transportation & Logistics
N.A.I.C.S.: 551112
Zvi Livnat *(CEO-Commerce & Deputy)*

Subsidiaries:

Maman Cargo Terminals & Handling, Ltd. (1)
Ben Gurion Airport, PO Box 58, Tel Aviv, 70100, Israel
Tel.: (972) 39715300
Web Site: http://www.maman.co.il
Sales Range: $75-99.9 Million
Logistics & Cargo Services
N.A.I.C.S.: 481212
Opher Lincheski *(CEO)*

Subsidiary (Domestic):

Archive 2000 Ltd. (2)
Ben Gurion Airport, PO Box 58, 70100, Tel Aviv, Israel
Tel.: (972) 39721733
Web Site: http://www.archive2000.co.il
Archiving & Retrieval Services
N.A.I.C.S.: 493190

Logisticare, Ltd. (2)
5 Pesach Lev St North Industrial Zone, PO Box 58, 71293, Lod, Israel
Tel.: (972) 89271919
Web Site: http://www.logisticare.co.il
Logistic Services
N.A.I.C.S.: 541614
Moti Dodi *(Pres)*

Subsidiary (Domestic):

Logisticare Bonded (3)
5 Pesach Lev St North Industrial Zone Ben Gurion Airport, 70100, Lod, Israel
Tel.: (972) 8 927 1919
Web Site: http://www.en.logisticare.co.il
Emp.: 500
Warehousing Services
N.A.I.C.S.: 493110

Subsidiary (Domestic):

Maman Aviation Ltd. (2)
65 Yigal Alon St., Toyota Tower, 9th floor, Tel Aviv, Israel
Tel.: (972) 35629334
Web Site: http://www.mamanaviation.co.il
Emp.: 15
Air Cargo & Handling Operations
N.A.I.C.S.: 481112

Maman Cargo & Security Ltd. (2)
Ben Gurion Airport, PO Box 58, Tel Aviv, 70100, Israel
Tel.: (972) 39715300
Web Site: http://www.maman.co.il
Emp.: 80
Cargo Security & Logistic Processes
N.A.I.C.S.: 541614
Opher Linchevski *(Gen Mgr)*

Smerling Synchro Energy Engineering Ltd. (1)
3 Havoda St New Industrial Zone, PO Box 762, Ramla, 7210202, Israel
Tel.: (972) 89210080
Web Site: http://www.shmerling.co.il
Sales Range: $25-49.9 Million
Emp.: 18
Diesel Generators & Electrical Panel Design, Production & Marketing
N.A.I.C.S.: 335312
Amos Rettig *(Mng Dir)*

TAAZA INTERNATIONAL LTD.
Plot No 29 Kharkhana Road HACP Colony, Secunderabad, 500009, India
Tel.: (91) 4030228228
Web Site: https://www.taazastores.com
Year Founded: 2001
537392—(BOM)
Rev.: $4,046
Assets: $1,657,811
Liabilities: $319,171
Net Worth: $1,338,640
Earnings: ($54,515)
Emp.: 3
Fiscal Year-end: 03/31/21
Grocery Store Operator
N.A.I.C.S.: 445110
P. Ravinder Rao *(Mng Dir)*

TAB INDIA GRANITES PVT. LTD.
502 Apex Mall Tonk Road, Jaipur, India
Tel.: (91) 1412744200
Web Site: http://www.tabindia.com
Year Founded: 1997
Sales Range: $25-49.9 Million
Emp.: 1,200
Natural Stone Quarrying & Product Mfr & Distr
N.A.I.C.S.: 327991
Sumit Gupta *(Mng Dir)*

Subsidiaries:

Amsum & Ash, Inc. (1)
30 52nd Way NE, Minneapolis, MN 55421
Tel.: (763) 571-8400
Web Site: http://www.amsumash.com
Sales Range: $1-9.9 Million
Emp.: 12
Granite & Natural Stone Products Importer & Distr
N.A.I.C.S.: 327991
Amit Gupta *(Pres)*

Tab India Granites Pvt. Ltd. - NORTH Plant (1)
E-147 Riico Industrial Area Bagru Extension Phase II, Jaipur, 303007, Rajasthan, India
Tel.: (91) 141 2864178
Natural Stone Product Mfr
N.A.I.C.S.: 212313

Tab India Granites Pvt. Ltd. - SOUTH Plant (1)
N H 7 Nallaganakothapally Village Krishnagiri Road, Koneripalli, Hosur, 635117, Tamil Nadu, India
Tel.: (91) 4344 257 400
Emp.: 600
Natural Stone Product Mfr
N.A.I.C.S.: 212313
Sumit Gupta *(Mng Dir)*

TABCORP HOLDINGS LIMITED
Level 19 Tower 2 727 Collins Street, Melbourne, 3008, VIC, Australia
Tel.: (91) 392466010 AU
Web Site: https://www.tabcorp.com.au
Year Founded: 1961
TABCF—(OTCIQ)
Rev.: $4,356,556,340

Assets: $9,093,909,110
Liabilities: $3,963,500,870
Net Worth: $5,130,408,240
Earnings: $206,105,110
Emp.: 5,000
Fiscal Year-end: 06/30/21
Leisure & Entertainment Company; Wagering & Gaming Activities
N.A.I.C.S.: 611620
Ben Simons *(Chief Strategy Officer)*

Subsidiaries:

Luxbet Pty. Ltd. (1)
GPO Box 863, Darwin, 0801, NT, Australia
Tel.: (61) 282405700
Web Site: http://www.luxbet.com
Sales Range: $25-49.9 Million
Emp.: 13
Online Racing & Sports Betting Services
N.A.I.C.S.: 713290
Andrew Vouris *(Gen Mgr)*

Maxgaming NSW Pty Ltd (1)
1 Figtree Dr Sydney Olympic Park, 2127, Sydney, NSW, Australia
Tel.: (61) 1800706221
Web Site: http://www.nsw.maxgaming.com.au
Gaming Machine Monitoring Services
N.A.I.C.S.: 561990
Curt Pahl *(Mgr-State)*

Maxgaming QLD Pty Ltd (1)
87 Ipswich Rd, Woolloongabba, 4102, QLD, Australia
Tel.: (61) 736371309
Web Site: http://qld.maxgaming.com.au
Gaming Machine Monitoring Services
N.A.I.C.S.: 561990
Belinda McBain *(Acct Mgr-Wide Bay)*

Melbourne Cricket Club Foundation Ltd. (1)
Gate 2 Melbourne Cricket Ground, Brunton Ave, 6014, Jolimont, Australia
Tel.: (61) 396578888
Web Site: https://www.mcc.org.au
Cricket Club
N.A.I.C.S.: 713910

eBet Gaming Systems Pty Limited (1)
112-118 Talavera Rd Unit 13118, North Ryde, 2113, NSW, Australia
Tel.: (61) 288174700
Web Site: http://www.ebetgamingsystems.com
Sales Range: $25-49.9 Million
Emp.: 50
Online Gambling Services
N.A.I.C.S.: 713290
Tony Toohey *(Deputy Chm & Exec Dir)*

eBet Inc. (1)
2440 Grand Ave Ste B, Vista, CA 92081-7829
Tel.: (760) 599-6533
Gaming Platform & Software Development Services
N.A.I.C.S.: 513210

eBet Systems Pty Limited (1)
Unit 13 112-118 Talavera Rd, North Ryde, 2113, NSW, Australia
Tel.: (61) 288174700
Web Site: http://www.ebetgroup.com
Sales Range: $25-49.9 Million
Emp.: 80
Online Gambling Services
N.A.I.C.S.: 713290
Ken Carr *(CEO)*

TABIKOBO CO., LTD.
46F Sunshine60 Bldg 3-1-1 Ikebukuro, Toshima-ku, Tokyo, 170-6046, Japan
Tel.: (81) 359562003
Web Site: http://www.tabikobo.com
6548—(TKS)
Rev.: $20,787,240
Assets: $21,925,500
Liabilities: $8,303,700
Net Worth: $13,621,800
Earnings: ($2,195,660)
Emp.: 668

TABIKOBO CO., LTD.

TABIKOBO Co., Ltd.—(Continued)
Fiscal Year-end: 06/30/24
Travel Tour Operator
N.A.I.C.S.: 561520
Yasuhito Takayama (Chm & Pres)

TABIO CORPORATION

16F Namba Parks Parks Tower
2-10-70 Namba-Nakacho, Naniwa-ku,
Osaka, 556-0011, Japan
Tel.: (81) 666321200
Web Site: https://www.tabio.com
Year Founded: 1977
2668—(TKS)
Rev.: $114,999,800
Assets: $54,451,200
Liabilities: $22,751,810
Net Worth: $31,699,390
Earnings: $3,325,210
Fiscal Year-end: 02/29/24
Apparel Distr
N.A.I.C.S.: 424350
Katsuhiro Ochi (Pres)

Subsidiaries:

Tabio Europe Limited (1)
51 Neal Street, London, WC2H 9PQ, United Kingdom
Tel.: (44) 2078363713
Web Site: https://tabiouk.com
Hosiery Distr
N.A.I.C.S.: 424350
Masatoshi Ogiwara (Pres)

Tabio France SAS (1)
32 Rue Saint-Sulpice, 75006, Paris, France
Tel.: (33) 143262812
Hosiery Distr
N.A.I.C.S.: 424350
Masatoshi Ogiwara (Pres & Dir)

Tabio Nara Co., Ltd. (1)
578 Mitsuyoshi Koryo-cho Kita-Katsuragi-gun, Nara, Japan
Tel.: (81) 745555050
Logistics Consulting Servies
N.A.I.C.S.: 541614
Shuji Hirai (Pres)

TABUK AGRICULTURE DEVELOPMENT COMPANY

PO Box 808, Tabuk, 71421, Saudi Arabia
Tel.: (966) 144500000
Web Site: https://www.tadco-agri.com
Year Founded: 1983
6040—(SAU)
Rev.: $35,827,593
Assets: $117,259,020
Liabilities: $41,521,764
Net Worth: $75,737,256
Earnings: ($14,608,312)
Emp.: 613
Fiscal Year-end: 12/31/22
Agricultural Product Mfr
N.A.I.C.S.: 111199
Alwaleed K. Alshathre (Chm)

TABUK CEMENT COMPANY

PO Box 122, Duba, Saudi Arabia
Tel.: (966) 144324100
Web Site: http://www.tcc-sa.com
Year Founded: 1994
3090—(SAU)
Rev.: $70,686,952
Assets: $438,296,545
Liabilities: $92,658,353
Net Worth: $345,638,192
Earnings: $5,264,836
Emp.: 354
Fiscal Year-end: 12/31/23
Cement Mfr
N.A.I.C.S.: 327310
Saud Soleiman Al-Juhni (Deputy Chm)

TAC CO., LTD.

3-2-18 Kanda-Misaki-cho, Chiyoda-ku, Tokyo, 101-8383, Japan
Tel.: (81) 352768911 JP
Web Site: https://www.tac-school.co.jp
Year Founded: 1980
4319—(TKS)
Rev.: $125,596,610
Assets: $137,421,900
Liabilities: $98,607,980
Net Worth: $38,813,920
Earnings: ($1,447,590)
Emp.: 550
Fiscal Year-end: 03/31/24
Professional Training Center Operator
N.A.I.C.S.: 611430

Subsidiaries:

TAC (Dalian) Co., Ltd. (1)
Nami B/D 4F No 416 No 3 Huoju Road Gaoxinyuan District, Dalian, China
Tel.: (86) 41139571358
Web Site: http://www.cn.e-tac.net
Educational Support Services
N.A.I.C.S.: 611710

TAC GOLD CORPORATION

Suite 203 2780 Granville Street, Vancouver, V6H 3J3, BC, Canada
Tel.: (604) 730-0234 BC
Web Site: http://www.tacgold.com
Year Founded: 2005
Gold Mining Services
N.A.I.C.S.: 212220
Gregory M. Thomas (CEO)

TAC HEALTHCARE GROUP LTD.

Wellheads Crescent Dyce, Aberdeen, AB21 7GA, United Kingdom
Tel.: (44) 3330143488
Web Site: https://www.tachealthcaregroup.com
Healtcare Services
N.A.I.C.S.: 621999
Phil Webb (CEO)

Subsidiaries:

International SOS Assistance UK Limited (1)
Chiswick Park Building 4 566 Chiswick High Road, London, W4 5YE, United Kingdom (90%)
Tel.: (44) 2087628000
Web Site: http://www.internationalsos.com
Emergency Response Services
N.A.I.C.S.: 561421
Suzanne Withers (Head-PR & IC)

TACC CONSTRUCTION LTD.

270 Chrislea Road, Woodbridge, L4L 8A8, ON, Canada
Tel.: (905) 856-8500
Web Site: http://www.tacc.com
Year Founded: 1977
Rev.: $13,563,412
Emp.: 200
Construction Services
N.A.I.C.S.: 237110
John DeGasperis (Founder)

TACHAN SECURITIES CO., LTD.

17th Floor No 17 Section 1 Chengde Road, Datong Dist, Taipei, 10351, Taiwan
Tel.: (886) 25551234
Web Site: https://tachan.com.tw
Year Founded: 1977
6020—(TPE)
Rev.: $1,827,158
Assets: $190,919,739
Liabilities: $63,334,709
Net Worth: $127,585,030
Earnings: $8,434,543
Fiscal Year-end: 12/31/22
Financial Security Services
N.A.I.C.S.: 523999
Yu-Ping Li (Chm)

TACHI-S CO., LTD.

1-3-1 Suehiro-cho, Ome-shi, Tokyo, 198-0025, Japan
Tel.: (81) 428331919 JP
Web Site: https://www.tachi-s.co.jp
Year Founded: 1954
7239—(TKS)
Rev.: $1,936,379,670
Assets: $1,195,127,660
Liabilities: $558,597,880
Net Worth: $636,529,780
Earnings: $35,839,420
Emp.: 10,474
Fiscal Year-end: 03/31/24
Seats & Interior Parts Mfr
N.A.I.C.S.: 336360
Taro Nakayama (Chm & CEO)

Subsidiaries:

Nui Tec Corporation (1)
1-7-8 Suehirocho, Ome, 198-0025, Tokyo, Japan
Tel.: (81) 428301933
Web Site: https://www.nuitec.co.jp
Emp.: 15
Automotive Seat Parts Mfr
N.A.I.C.S.: 336360

SETEX Automotive Mexico, S.A. de C.V. (1)
Avenida el Fortin 100, Parque Industrial Amistad Bajio, 38160, Apaseo el Grande, Guanajuato, Mexico
Tel.: (52) 4614784600
Web Site: http://www.setex.mx
Automotive Seat Parts Mfr & Whslr
N.A.I.C.S.: 336360

Setex, Inc. (1)
1111 McKinley Rd, Saint Marys, OH 45885
Tel.: (419) 394-7800
Web Site: http://www.setexinc.com
Automotive Seat Mfr & Distr
N.A.I.C.S.: 336360
Tim Nance (Supvr-Matls)

TF-Metal Co., Ltd. (1)
1558 Uchiyama Arai-cho, Arai-cho, Kosai, 431-0304, Shizuoka, Japan
Tel.: (81) 535941040
Web Site: https://www.tf-metal.jp
Automotive Seat Parts Mfr
N.A.I.C.S.: 336360

TF-Metal Guangzhou Co., Ltd. (1)
East of Dongfeng Avenue Auto Town, Huadu District, Guangzhou, 510800, Guangdong, China
Tel.: (86) 2086733687
Web Site: http://www.tf-metal.jp
Automobile Parts Mfr
N.A.I.C.S.: 336360

TF-Metal Higashi Mikawa Co., Ltd. (1)
11-1 Ogaitsu, Tomisaka, Shinshiro, 441-1632, Aichi, Japan
Tel.: (81) 536321041
Automotive Seat Parts Mfr
N.A.I.C.S.: 336360

TF-Metal Iwata Co., Ltd. (1)
1461 Ebijima, Iwata, 438-0212, Shizuoka, Japan
Tel.: (81) 538667121
Automotive Seat Parts Mfr
N.A.I.C.S.: 336360

TF-Metal Kyushu Co., Ltd. (1)
396-1 Daishinden, Nakatsu, 871-0001, Oita, Japan
Tel.: (81) 979249081
Automotive Seat Parts Mfr
N.A.I.C.S.: 336360

TF-Metal USA LLC (1)
70 Precision Dr, Walton, KY 41094-7464
Tel.: (859) 485-3977
Web Site: http://tfmetalamericas.com
Motor Vehicle Parts Mfr
N.A.I.C.S.: 336390

Tachi-S Automotive Seating (Thailand) Co Ltd. (1)
4/1 Moo1 Bangna Trad Road, T Bangchalong, Bangkok, 10540, Thailand
Tel.: (66) 23372030

Automotive Components Mfr
N.A.I.C.S.: 423110

Tachi-S Brasil Industria de Assentos Automotivos Ltda. (1)
Rodovia Presidente Dutra S/N Km 306 Fazenda da Barra, Resende, Rio de Janeiro, 27537-000, Brazil
Tel.: (55) 2433557401
Web Site: https://www.tachi-s.com.br
Automotive Seat Parts Mfr
N.A.I.C.S.: 336360

Tachi-S Engineering U.S.A., Inc. (1)
23227 Commerce Dr, Farmington Hills, MI 48335
Tel.: (248) 478-5050
Web Site: http://www.tachi-s.com
Automotive Seat Mfr & Distr
N.A.I.C.S.: 336360

Tachi-S H&P Co., Ltd. (1)
2-13-18 Matsubara-cho, Akishima, Tokyo, Japan
Tel.: (81) 425432411
Web Site: http://www.tachi-s-hp.co.jp
Automotive Seat Parts Mfr
N.A.I.C.S.: 336360

Tachi-S Service Co., Ltd. (1)
1-7-8 Suehiro-cho, Ome, 198-0025, Tokyo, Japan
Tel.: (81) 428301929
Facility Operation & Maintenance Services
N.A.I.C.S.: 561210

TACHIA YUNG HO MACHINE INDUSTRY CO., LTD.

No 69 Yu-Shih Road, Dajia District, Taichung, 437, Taiwan
Tel.: (886) 426815496
Web Site: https://www.yhmco-daja.com
Year Founded: 1943
2221—(TPE)
Rev.: $54,551,387
Assets: $55,445,580
Liabilities: $20,007,316
Net Worth: $35,438,264
Earnings: $8,949,160
Emp.: 249
Fiscal Year-end: 12/31/22
Electric Power Distribution Device Mfr
N.A.I.C.S.: 334512
Shih-Feng Huang (Chm)

TACHIBANA ELETECH CO., LTD.

1-13-25 Nishi-honmachi, Nishi-ku, Osaka, 550-8555, Japan
Tel.: (81) 665398800
Web Site: https://www.tachibana.co.jp
Year Founded: 1921
8159—(TKS)
Rev.: $1,527,187,620
Assets: $1,178,437,410
Liabilities: $566,536,490
Net Worth: $611,900,920
Earnings: $55,993,310
Emp.: 1,436
Fiscal Year-end: 03/31/24
N.A.I.C.S.: 335999
Takeo Watanabe (Pres, CEO & COO)

Subsidiaries:

Advanced Logistics Ltd. (1)
10-28 Toyohara-Cho, Ibaraki, 567 0053, Japan
Tel.: (81) 726403575
Electrical Equipment Whslr
N.A.I.C.S.: 334515

DAIDENSHA Co., Ltd (1)
1-6-17 Nipponbashi Nishi, Naniwa-ku, Osaka, 556-0004, Japan
Tel.: (81) 666326111
Web Site: https://www.daidensha.co.jp
Emp.: 103
Electrical Equipments Mfr & Distr
N.A.I.C.S.: 335999
Shimoyoshi Hideyuki (Chm)

AND PRIVATE COMPANIES — TADANO LTD.

KENDEN INDUSTRY Co., LTD. (1)
2-6-23 Goheijima, Nishiyodogawa-ku,
Osaka, 555-0012, Japan
Tel.: (81) 664719451
Web Site: https://kenden.net
Emp.: 18
Electrical Equipment Distr
N.A.I.C.S.: 423440

PT Tachibana Sales (Indonesia) (1)
PLAZA SENTRAL 10th FL JL Jend
Sudirman No 47, Jakarta, 12930, Indonesia
Tel.: (62) 215205620
Web Site: https://www.tachibana.co.jp
Industrial Equipment Whsr
N.A.I.C.S.: 423690

TACHIBANA SALES (S) PTE., LTD (1)
10 Anson Road 05-19B International Plaza,
Singapore, 079903, Singapore
Tel.: (65) 62704567
Web Site: https://www.tachibana.co.jp
Semiconductor Equipment Distr
N.A.I.C.S.: 423690

TACHIBANA SOLUTIONS PLAZA LTD. (1)
1-13-25 Nishi-honmachi, Nishi-ku, Osaka,
550-8555, Japan
Tel.: (81) 6 6539 5155
Web Site:
http://tcplaza.shop29.makeshop.jp
Electronic Goods Retailer
N.A.I.C.S.: 449210

Tachibana Create Ltd (1)
1 13 25 Nishi honmachi, Nishi ku, Osaka,
550 8555, Japan
Tel.: (81) 665393124
Web Site: https://www.tachibana.co.jp
Electric Equipment Mfr
N.A.I.C.S.: 335999

Tachibana Device Component Co., Ltd. (1)
4-18-32 Shibaura, Minato-ku, Tokyo, 108-0023, Japan
Tel.: (81) 354189200
Web Site: https://tachibana-device-component.co.jp
Emp.: 25
Semiconductor Mfr & Distr
N.A.I.C.S.: 334413
Hiroshi Higuchi *(Pres)*

Tachibana ES Ltd (1)
1-13-25 Nishi honmachi, Nishi ku, Osaka,
550-8555, Japan
Tel.: (81) 665392708
Web Site: http://www.tachibana.co.jp
Electric Equipment Mfr
N.A.I.C.S.: 335999

Tachibana Electronic Solutions Co., Ltd. (1)
4-18-32 Shibaura, Minato-ku, Tokyo, 108-0023, Japan
Tel.: (81) 366991870
Web Site: https://tachibana-denshi-solutions.co.jp
Emp.: 83
Electronic Product Whslr
N.A.I.C.S.: 423690

Tachibana Kouwa System Service Co., LTD. (1)
2-5-1 Ohama-cho, Amagasaki, 660-0095,
Hyogo, Japan
Tel.: (81) 664133623
Web Site: http://www.tachibanakouwa.co.jp
Electronic Equipment Distr
N.A.I.C.S.: 423690

Tachibana Management Service Ltd. (1)
1-13-25 Nishi-honmachi, Nishi-ku, Osaka,
5508555, Japan
Tel.: (81) 665395021
Web Site: http://www.tachibana.co.jp
Electrical Equipment Whslr
N.A.I.C.S.: 334515

Tachibana Overseas Holdings Ltd. (1)
Unit 2605 26/F One Kowloon No 1 Wang
Yuen Street, Kowloon Bay, Kowloon, China
(Hong Kong)
Tel.: (852) 28388103
Industrial Equipment Mfr & Whslr
N.A.I.C.S.: 334413

Tachibana Sales (H.K.) Ltd. (1)
Unit 2605 26/F One Kowloon No 1 Wang
Yuen Street, Kowloon Bay, Kowloon, China
(Hong Kong)
Tel.: (852) 28388103
Sales Range: $25-49.9 Million
Emp.: 25
Electric & Electronic Devices Mfr
N.A.I.C.S.: 334513

Tachibana Sales (Korea) Ltd. (1)
C-Dong 3005 Daelin Acrotel 467-6 Dogok-Dong, Gangnam-Gu, Seoul, 135 270, Korea (South)
Tel.: (82) 221877102
Sales Range: $25-49.9 Million
Emp.: 4
Electric & Electronic Devices Mfe
N.A.I.C.S.: 334419

Tachibana Sales (Malaysia) Sdn. Bhd. (1)
First Subang S-14-05 Jalan SS15/4G,
47500, Subang Jaya, Selangor, Malaysia
Tel.: (60) 358886502
Web Site: https://www.tachibana.co.jp
Semiconductor Whslr
N.A.I.C.S.: 423690

Tachibana Sales (Shanghai) Ltd. (1)
Tel.: (86) 2131001700
Sales Range: $25-49.9 Million
Emp.: 18
Electric & Electronic Devices Mfr
N.A.I.C.S.: 334513

Tachibana Sales (Singapore) Pte. Ltd. (1)
10 Anson Road 05 19B International Plaza,
Singapore, 079903, Singapore
Tel.: (65) 62704567
Semiconductor Whslr
N.A.I.C.S.: 423690
Alan Fang *(Mgr-Engrg)*

Tachibana Sales Bangkok Co., Ltd. (1)
62 Thaniya Building 8FL Room No 803- 804
Silom Road, Suriyawong Bangrak, Bangkok, 10500, Thailand
Tel.: (66) 26525191
Web Site: http://www.tachibana.co.jp
Sales Range: $25-49.9 Million
Emp.: 5
Electric & Electronic Devices Sales Services
N.A.I.C.S.: 333242
Satoshi Tamaki *(Mng Dir)*

Tachibana Sales Taiwan Ltd. (1)
Room 507 No 372 Linsen N Rd, PO Box
104, Zhongshan Dist, Taipei, 104, Taiwan
Tel.: (886) 225418177
Web Site: https://www.tachibana.co.jp
Sales Range: $25-49.9 Million
Emp.: 4
Electronic Components Mfr
N.A.I.C.S.: 334419

Taiyo Shokai Co., Ltd (1)
138 Fukaehama-cho, Higashinada-ku,
Kobe, 658-0023, Japan
Tel.: (81) 784411121
Web Site: https://www.taiyo-shokai.jp
Emp.: 95
Electrical Equipment Merchants
N.A.I.C.S.: 423610

Takagi Co., Ltd. (1)
2-2-7 Kitasenzoku, Ota-ku, Tokyo, 145-0062, Japan
Tel.: (81) 337836314
Web Site: https://www.takagishokai.co.jp
Emp.: 204
Control Systems & Information Technology
Electronic Equipment & Parts Designer & Mfr
N.A.I.C.S.: 334419
Hiroyuki Nakayama *(CEO)*

TecNet Inc. (1)
3-8-15 Hinaga-higashi, Yokkaichi, 510 0886,
Japan
Tel.: (81) 593459090
Sales Range: $25-49.9 Million
Emp.: 8
Electric & Electronic Devices Mfr
N.A.I.C.S.: 327110
Norio Inagaki *(Gen Mgr)*

TACHIKARA COMPANY, LTD.
Matasugaya1-13-15, Taito-Ku, Tokyo,
111-0036, Japan
Tel.: (81) 338426811
Web Site: http://www.tachikara.co.jp
Year Founded: 1946
Sales Range: $50-74.9 Million
Emp.: 40
Sales of Sporting Goods
Hirobumi Kaihoko *(CEO)*

Subsidiaries:

Tachikara USA Inc. (1)
958 United Cir, Sparks, NV 89431
Tel.: (775) 352-3500
Web Site: http://www.tachikara.com
Sales Range: $25-49.9 Million
Emp.: 11
Sales of Athletic Goods
N.A.I.C.S.: 423910

TACHIKAWA CORPORATION
1-12 Mita 3-Chome, Minato-ku, Tokyo, 108-8334, Japan
Tel.: (81) 354846250
Web Site: https://www.blind.co.jp
Year Founded: 1938
7989—(TKS)
Rev.: $292,852,450
Assets: $447,676,780
Liabilities: $90,043,000
Net Worth: $357,633,780
Earnings: $19,199,720
Emp.: 1,252
Fiscal Year-end: 12/31/23
Interior Product Mfr & Whslr
N.A.I.C.S.: 337920

Subsidiaries:

Tachikawa Trading Co., Ltd. (1)
1-12 Mita 3-Chome, Minato-ku, Tokyo, 108-8334, Japan
Tel.: (81) 354846250
Blind & Window Covering Product Mfr
N.A.I.C.S.: 337920

TACIRLER YATIRIM MENKUL DEGERLER A.S.
Nispetiye Cad B3 Blok Kat 9 Akmerkez Etiler, Besiktas, 34337, Istanbul, Turkiye
Tel.: (90) 2123552655
Web Site: http://www.tacirler.com.tr
Year Founded: 1991
TCRYT—(IST)
Rev.: $4,240,886,906
Assets: $146,312,069
Liabilities: $114,344,776
Net Worth: $31,967,293
Earnings: $15,256,412
Fiscal Year-end: 12/31/22
Financial Investment Services
N.A.I.C.S.: 523940
Alaettin Tacir *(Chm)*

TACMINA CORPORATION
2-2-14 Awajimachi, Chuo-ku, Osaka,
541-0047, Japan
Tel.: (81) 662083974
Web Site: https://www.tacmina.com
Year Founded: 1956
6322—(TKS)
Rev.: $72,809,150
Assets: $98,535,270
Liabilities: $32,283,240
Net Worth: $66,252,030
Earnings: $7,898,950
Emp.: 366
Fiscal Year-end: 03/31/24
Pumps Mfr
N.A.I.C.S.: 333914
Nobuhiko Yamada *(Chm, Pres & CEO)*

Subsidiaries:

TACMINA USA CORPORATION (1)
105 W Central Rd, Schaumburg, IL 60195
Web Site: http://www.tacminausa.com
Pump Distr
N.A.I.C.S.: 423830

TACTICAL RESOURCES CORP.
2288-1177 West Hastings Street,
Vancouver, V6E 2K3, BC, Canada
Tel.: (778) 588-5483 BC
Web Site:
https://www.tacticalresources.com
Year Founded: 2018
USREF—(OTCIQ)
Rev.: $529
Assets: $1,106,842
Liabilities: $338,317
Net Worth: $768,525
Earnings: ($1,957,400)
Fiscal Year-end: 07/31/23
Mineral Exploration Services
N.A.I.C.S.: 212220
Ranjeet Sundher *(CEO)*

TACTICS GROUP
6 Gasheka Street, 125047, Moscow,
Russia
Tel.: (7) 4952210000
Web Site: http://www.tgrp.ru
Year Founded: 1993
Property Development, Consulting & Real Estate Operations in Commercial Property Market
N.A.I.C.S.: 531390
Pavel Shishkin *(Principal)*

Subsidiaries:

OAO Bolshevik (1)
Leningradski Prospekt 15, Moscow,
125040, Russia
Tel.: (7) 4957779000
Biscuits, Cookies & Chocolate Products Mfr & Marketer
N.A.I.C.S.: 311821

TADANO LTD.
Ko-34 Shinden-cho, Takamatsu, 761-0185, Kagawa, Japan
Tel.: (81) 878395555
Web Site: https://www.tadano.com
6395—(TKS)
Rev.: $1,987,085,940
Assets: $2,589,579,960
Liabilities: $1,303,780,100
Net Worth: $1,285,799,860
Earnings: $55,110,570
Emp.: 1,596
Fiscal Year-end: 12/31/23
Construction Machinery Mfr
N.A.I.C.S.: 333120
Shinichi Iimura *(Mng Exec Officer)*

Subsidiaries:

TADANO MANTIS Corporation (1)
1705 Columbia Ave Ste 200, Franklin, TN 37064
Tel.: (615) 794-4556
Web Site: https://tadanoamericas.com
Sales Range: $25-49.9 Million
Emp.: 30
Crane Mfr
N.A.I.C.S.: 333924
Ed Hisrich *(Officer-Sales-Customer Support & VP)*

Tadano (Beijing) Ltd. (1)
Room 1902 No 302 Huateng Mansion Jinsong 3 District, Chaoyang, Beijing, China
Tel.: (86) 1087769766
Crane Machinery Mfr & Distr
N.A.I.C.S.: 333923

Tadano (Thailand) Co., Ltd. (1)
500/70 Moo 2 T Tasit A, Pluak Daeng, Rayong, 21140, Thailand
Tel.: (66) 33010939
Crane Machinery Mfr & Distr
N.A.I.C.S.: 333923

TADANO LTD.

Tadano Ltd.—(Continued)

Tadano America Corporation (1)
4242 W Greens Rd, Houston, TX 77066
Tel.: (281) 869-0030
Web Site: https://tadanoamericas.com
Sales Range: $25-49.9 Million
Emp.: 55
Crane Mfr
N.A.I.C.S.: 333924
Mark Krajci (Mgr-All Terrain Cranes)

Tadano Asia Pte. Ltd. (1)
11 Tuas View Crescent Multico Building, Singapore, 637643, Singapore
Tel.: (65) 68636901
Web Site: http://asia.tadano.com
Sales Range: $25-49.9 Million
Emp.: 16
Cranes Sales & Marketing Services
N.A.I.C.S.: 423830
Hisashi Miyazaki (Mng Dir)

Tadano Belgium BV (1)
Industrieterrein 2 nr 13 I Z Webbekom 2114, 3290, Diest, Belgium
Tel.: (32) 13351660
Crane Machinery Distr
N.A.I.C.S.: 423810

Tadano Brasil Equipamentos de Elevacao Ltda. (1)
Avenida Angelica 2491-Conjunto 77, Sao Paulo, 01227-200, SP, Brazil
Tel.: (55) 1147720222
Crane Machinery Mfr & Distr
N.A.I.C.S.: 333923

Tadano Chile SpA (1)
San Pio X 2460 Oficina 1110, Providencia, Santiago, Chile
Tel.: (56) 232802077
Crane Machinery Mfr & Distr
N.A.I.C.S.: 333923

Tadano Demag Espana, S.A. (1)
Poligono Industrial Camporroso Bulevar Buenos Aires S/N, 28806, Alcala de Henares, Spain
Tel.: (34) 918720900
Lifting Machineries Mfr
N.A.I.C.S.: 333923

Tadano Demag GmbH (1)
Europaallee 2, 66482, Zweibrucken, Germany
Tel.: (49) 6332830
Mobile Telescopic & Lattice Boom Cranes
N.A.I.C.S.: 333923

Tadano Demag Scandinavia AB (1)
Depagatan 87, 254 64, Helsingborg, Sweden
Tel.: (46) 42179590
Web Site: http://www.tadano.com
Cranes
N.A.I.C.S.: 333923

Tadano Escorts India Pvt. Ltd. (1)
Plot No 219 Sec-58, Ballabgarh Distt, Faridabad, 121004, Haryana, India
Tel.: (91) 129 230 6400
Web Site: http://tei.tadano.com
Crane Machinery Mfr & Distr
N.A.I.C.S.: 333923

Tadano Faun GmbH (1)
Faunberg 2, 91207, Lauf an der Pegnitz, Germany
Tel.: (49) 91231850
Crane Mfr
N.A.I.C.S.: 333924
Alexander Knecht (Pres & CEO)

Subsidiary (Non-US):

Tadano Faun Holland B.V. (2)
Antennestraat 6, 3903 LZ, Veenendaal, Utrecht, Netherlands
Tel.: (31) 318546700
Web Site: http://www.tadano-faun.nl
Sales Range: $25-49.9 Million
Emp.: 6
Crane Mfr
N.A.I.C.S.: 333924

Tadano France SAS (1)
42 Avenue Longchamp, 57500, Saint-Avold, France
Tel.: (33) 675712277
Crane Machinery Mfr & Distr

N.A.I.C.S.: 333923

Subsidiary (Domestic):

Tadano Demag France SA (2)
Rue Saule, PO Box 106, 71300, Montceau-les-Mines, France
Tel.: (33) 385673800
Sales Range: $75-99.9 Million
Cranes
N.A.I.C.S.: 333923

Tadano Imes Ltd. (1)
4-12 Kamezawa 2-chome Tadano Ryogoku Bldg 4F, Sumida-ku, Tokyo, 130-0014, Japan
Tel.: (81) 336217741
Web Site: http://www.tadano-imes.com
Sales Range: $25-49.9 Million
Emp.: 21
Crane Mfr
N.A.I.C.S.: 333923

Tadano Italthai Co., Ltd. (1)
7th Floor 2013 New Petchburi Road, Bangkapi Huay Kwang, Bangkok, 10310, Thailand
Tel.: (66) 23185192
Crane Machinery Mfr & Distr
N.A.I.C.S.: 333923

Tadano Korea Co Ltd (1)
Room B-213 Garden Five Works 52 Chungmin-ro, Songpa-gu, Seoul, 05839, Korea (South)
Tel.: (82) 27141600
Web Site: http://www.tadano.com
Crane Mfr
N.A.I.C.S.: 333924

Tadano ME Lifting Equipment Trading L.L.C (1)
Office No 406 ICON Tower Barsha Heights, PO Box 392674, Dubai, United Arab Emirates
Tel.: (971) 45749700
Crane Machinery Mfr & Distr
N.A.I.C.S.: 333923
Andric Schulz (Mgr-Customer Svc)

Tadano Nederland B.V. (1)
Component 1, 1446 WZ, Purmerend, Netherlands
Tel.: (31) 29 939 0055
Web Site: https://www.tadanoeurope.com
Crane Machinery Distr
N.A.I.C.S.: 423810

Tadano Oceania Pty Ltd (1)
1/146 Lindum Road, Lytton, Brisbane, 4178, QLD, Australia
Tel.: (61) 130 082 3266
Web Site: https://www.tadano.com.au
Crane Machinery Mfr
N.A.I.C.S.: 333923
Anthony Grosser (Mng Dir)

Tadano South China Company Ltd. (1)
Rm 1803 18 F Seaview Comml Bldg, 21-24 Connaught Rd W, Sheung Wan, China (Hong Kong)
Tel.: (852) 25449310
Web Site: http://www.tadano.co.jp
Crane Mfr
N.A.I.C.S.: 333923

Tadano UK Ltd. (1)
14 Hikers Way Crendon Industrial Park, Long Crendon, Aylesbury, HP18 9RW, Bucks, United Kingdom
Tel.: (44) 808 164 2301
Web Site: https://www.tadanoeurope.com
Crane Machinery Mfr & Distr
N.A.I.C.S.: 333923

Subsidiary (Domestic):

Tadano Demag UK Limited (2)
14 Hikers Way, Crendon Industrial Park, Aylesbury, HP18 9RW, Bucks, United Kingdom
Tel.: (44) 1844203700
Construction Machinery Equipment Mfr
N.A.I.C.S.: 333120
Paul Bartlett (Dir-Sls)

Taiwan Tadano Ltd. (1)
4F No 77 Sec 2 Dunhua S Rd, Da'an Dist, Taipei, 10682, Taiwan
Tel.: (886) 227540252

Crane Machinery Mfr & Distr
N.A.I.C.S.: 333923

TADBIK GROUP
4 Baltimore Street, Petach Tikva, 4951015, Israel
Tel.: (972) 3 9278000
Web Site: http://www.tadbik.com
Year Founded: 1983
Sales Range: $75-99.9 Million
Emp.: 950
Labeling & Packaging Products Mfr
N.A.I.C.S.: 326112
Arik Schor (Chm)

Subsidiaries:

Logotech, Inc. (1)
18 Madison Rd, Fairfield, NJ 07004
Tel.: (973) 882-9595
Web Site: http://www.logotech-inc.com
Sales Range: $1-9.9 Million
Emp.: 39
Label Printing Services
N.A.I.C.S.: 561910
Leslie Gurland (Pres)

Tadbik Pack SA (1)
89 Main Reef Rd, Johannesburg, 2092, South Africa
Tel.: (27) 11 830 1437
Packaging Materials Mfr
N.A.I.C.S.: 326112
Clinton Parsons (Mgr)

Subsidiary (Domestic):

Alex White & Co (Pty) Ltd (2)
22 Yaron Avenue, Johannesburg, 1709, Gauteng, South Africa
Tel.: (27) 116741227
Web Site: http://www.awh.co.za
Sales Range: $25-49.9 Million
Emp.: 50
Commercial Printing Services
N.A.I.C.S.: 323111
Andre Smith (Gen Mgr)

TADHAMON INTERNATIONAL ISLAMIC BANK
Zubiri St, Sana'a, Yemen
Tel.: (967) 203270
Web Site: http://www.tiib.com
Year Founded: 1996
Emp.: 700
Banking Services
N.A.I.C.S.: 522110

TADIR-GAN (PRECISION PRODUCTS) 1993 LTD.
Alon Tavor, PO Box 2001, Afula, 1812001, Israel
Tel.: (972) 732267300
Web Site: https://www.ortal.co.il
TGI—(TAE)
Rev.: $49,866,330
Assets: $76,345,914
Liabilities: $43,073,044
Net Worth: $33,272,870
Earnings: $6,658,261
Fiscal Year-end: 06/30/23
Automobile Parts Mfr
N.A.I.C.S.: 336390
Barak Dotan (Chm)

TADIRAN GROUP LTD.
Rabanitzky 9, Petah Tiqwa, 4912502, Israel
Tel.: (972) 39283372
Web Site: https://www.tadiran-international.com
Year Founded: 1989
TDRN—(TAE)
Rev.: $540,003,307
Assets: $419,005,381
Liabilities: $278,044,201
Net Worth: $140,961,180
Earnings: $26,581,848
Emp.: 327
Fiscal Year-end: 12/31/23

Crane Machinery Mfr & Distr
N.A.I.C.S.: 333923

Household Appliances, Electric Housewares & Consumer Electronics Merchant Wholesalers
N.A.I.C.S.: 423620
Moshe Mamrud (CEO)

TADVEST LTD.
7th Floor Tower NeXteracom Cybercity, 72201, Ebene, 72201, Mauritius
Tel.: (230) 4034250
Web Site: https://www.tadvest.com
Year Founded: 2014
TAD.N0000—(MAU)
Rev.: $544,018
Assets: $74,625,728
Liabilities: $51,148
Net Worth: $74,574,580
Earnings: $6,247,535
Fiscal Year-end: 12/31/23
Financial Investment Services
N.A.I.C.S.: 523999
Ian A. Chambers (Exec Dir)

TAE WON MULSAN CO., LTD.
14 Teheran-ro 86-gil, Gangnam-gu, Seoul, Korea (South)
Tel.: (82) 25554301
Web Site: https://www.twms.co.kr
Year Founded: 1955
001420—(KRS)
Rev.: $8,402,217
Assets: $26,805,503
Liabilities: $4,122,603
Net Worth: $22,682,900
Earnings: ($1,043,731)
Emp.: 34
Fiscal Year-end: 12/31/22
Gypsum & Automobile Parts Mfr
N.A.I.C.S.: 327420
Nam Ki-Young (Pres & CEO)

Subsidiaries:

Tae Won Mulsan Co., Ltd. - Incheon Machinery Factory (1)
1385-4 Juan-dong, Incheon, Incheon, Korea (South)
Tel.: (82) 32 873 624
Automobile Parts Mfr
N.A.I.C.S.: 336390

Tae Won Mulsan Co., Ltd. - Ulsan Gypsum Factory (1)
198 Yeocheon-dong, Nam-gu, Ulsan, Korea (South)
Tel.: (82) 52 272 7161
Gypsum Product Mfr
N.A.I.C.S.: 327420

TAEGU BROADCASTING CORPORATION
23 Dongdaeguro, Suseonggu, Daegu, Korea (South)
Tel.: (82) 537601900
Web Site: http://www.tbc.co.kr
Year Founded: 1994
033830—(KRS)
Rev.: $32,584,681
Assets: $98,742,277
Liabilities: $5,481,399
Net Worth: $93,260,879
Earnings: $3,779,601
Emp.: 119
Fiscal Year-end: 12/31/22
Television Broadcasting Services
N.A.I.C.S.: 516120
Jin-Min Choi (Chm & CEO)

TAEKWANG INDUSTRIAL CO., LTD.
162-1 Jangchung-dong 2-ga, Jung-Gu, Seoul, Korea (South)
Tel.: (82) 234060300
Web Site: https://www.taekwang.co.kr
Year Founded: 1950
003240—(KRS)
Rev.: $2,073,853,939
Assets: $3,765,974,158

Liabilities: $538,576,101
Net Worth: $3,227,398,056
Earnings: $262,490,456
Emp.: 1,243
Fiscal Year-end: 12/31/22
Petrochemical Mfr
N.A.I.C.S.: 325110
Hyun Min Hong (CEO)

Subsidiaries:

Daehan Synthetic Fiber Co., Ltd. (1)
310 Dongho-ro, Jung-gu, Seoul, 100-852, Korea (South)
Tel.: (82) 234060300
Web Site: https://www.daehansf.co.kr
Rev.: $115,712,851
Assets: $641,798,396
Liabilities: $94,172,156
Net Worth: $547,626,239
Earnings: $25,647,777
Emp.: 170
Fiscal Year-end: 12/31/2022
Polyester Product Mfr
N.A.I.C.S.: 313110
Hyung-Saeng Kim (CEO)

Taekwang Industrial Co., Ltd. - Baneyo Factory (1)
161 Banyeo 1-dong, Haewundae-gu, Busan, Korea (South)
Tel.: (82) 51 522 4031
Cotton Spun Yarn Mfr
N.A.I.C.S.: 313110

Taekwang Industrial Co., Ltd. - Busan Factory (1)
90 Guseo-dong, Geumjeong, Busan, Korea (South)
Tel.: (82) 51 582 3871
Textile Products Mfr
N.A.I.C.S.: 314999

Taekwang Industrial Co., Ltd. - Daegu Factory (1)
2041-27 Bisan dong, Seo-gu, Daegu, Korea (South)
Tel.: (82) 53 356 0567
Web Site: http://www.taekwang.co.kr
Polyester Fabric Mfr
N.A.I.C.S.: 325220

Taekwang Industrial Co., Ltd. - Gyeongju Factory (1)
1069 Hwangseong-dong, Gyeongju, Gyeongsangbuk-do, Korea (South)
Tel.: (82) 54 776 2511
Web Site: http://www.taekwang.co.kr
Polyester Fabric Mfr
N.A.I.C.S.: 325220

Taekwang Industrial Co., Ltd. - Petrochemical 1 Plant (1)
353-1 Yeocheon-dong, Nam-gu, Ulsan, 680909, Korea (South)
Tel.: (82) 522598718
Web Site: http://www.taekwang.co.kr
Emp.: 150
Terephthalic Acid Mfr
N.A.I.C.S.: 325199

Taekwang Industrial Co., Ltd. - Petrochemical 2 Plant (1)
355-10 Yeocheon dong, Nam-gu, Ulsan, Korea (South)
Tel.: (82) 52 259 8670
Propylene & Hydrogen Peroxide Mfr
N.A.I.C.S.: 325998

Taekwang Industrial Co., Ltd. - Petrochemical 3 Plant (1)
88 Bugok-dong, Nam-gu, Ulsan, Korea (South)
Tel.: (82) 52 259 9612
Petrochemical Products Mfr
N.A.I.C.S.: 325110

Taekwang Industrial Co., Ltd. - Snipyeong Factory (1)
653-4 Sinpyeong-dong, Saha-gu, Busan, Korea (South)
Tel.: (82) 51 202 6011
Fabrics Mfr
N.A.I.C.S.: 314999

Taekwang Industrial Co., Ltd. - Ulsan Plant (1)
221 Seonam-dong, Nam-gu, Ulsan, Korea (South)
Tel.: (82) 52 272 7211
Textile Products Mfr
N.A.I.C.S.: 314999

Taekwang Industrial Co., Ltd. - Ungsang Factory (1)
6 Soju-ri, Ungsang-eup, Yangsan, Gyeongsangnam-do, Korea (South)
Tel.: (82) 55 385 2393
Spun Yarn Mfr
N.A.I.C.S.: 313110

Taekwang Industrial Gaeseong Co., Ltd. (1)
Gaeseong Industrial Complex BL-11-5, Kaesong, Korea (North)
Tel.: (850) 85852365
Synthetic Fiber Mfr & Distr
N.A.I.C.S.: 325220

Taekwang Synthetic Fiber (Changshu) Co., Ltd. (1)
Tel.: (86) 51252339088
Synthetic Fiber Mfr & Distr
N.A.I.C.S.: 325220

TAEKYUNG BK CO., LTD.
467 Gonghang-daero, Gangseo-Gu, Seoul, Korea (South)
Tel.: (82) 236612993
Web Site: https://www.taekyungbk.co.kr
Year Founded: 1980
014580—(KRS)
Rev.: $264,654,280
Assets: $277,071,217
Liabilities: $73,856,639
Net Worth: $203,214,578
Earnings: $22,102,404
Emp.: 286
Fiscal Year-end: 12/31/22
Lime Product Mfr
N.A.I.C.S.: 327410
Kim Min Jeong (CEO)

Subsidiaries:

Baekkwang Mineral Products Co., Ltd. - Danyang 1 Factory (1)
106 Auigok-Ri, Meapo-Eup, Danyang, Chungbuk, Korea (South)
Tel.: (82) 43 420 1142
Lime Product Mfr
N.A.I.C.S.: 327410

Baekkwang Mineral Products Co., Ltd. - Danyang 2 Factory (1)
132 Sangshi-Ri Maepo-Eup, Danyang, Chungbuk, Korea (South)
Tel.: (82) 43 421 4811
Lime Product Mfr
N.A.I.C.S.: 327410

Baekkwang Mineral Products Co., Ltd. - Gyeongju Factory (1)
729 Sindang-Ri, Chonbuk-Myeon, Gyeongju, Gyeongbuk, Korea (South)
Tel.: (82) 54 774 1131
Lime Product Mfr
N.A.I.C.S.: 327410

Taekyung Chemical Co., Ltd. (1)
157841 Songwon Building 467 Gonghang-daero, Gangseo-gu, Seoul, 157-841, Korea (South)
Tel.: (82) 236654251
Web Site: https://www.taekyungchemical.co.kr
Rev.: $45,723,538
Assets: $128,389,586
Liabilities: $15,381,546
Net Worth: $113,008,041
Earnings: $6,697,814
Emp.: 108
Fiscal Year-end: 12/31/2022
Industrial Gas Mfr & Distr
N.A.I.C.S.: 325120
Hwa Sung Nam (Deputy Gen Mgr)

TAEKYUNG INDUSTRIAL CO., LTD.
652-12 Songwon Bldg 4F Dengchon-Dong, Kangseo-Ku, Seoul, Korea (South)
Tel.: (82) 236618011
Web Site: https://www.taekyung.co.kr
Year Founded: 1975
015890—(KRS)
Rev.: $562,505,802
Assets: $479,404,808
Liabilities: $156,622,942
Net Worth: $322,781,866
Earnings: $17,662,839
Emp.: 251
Fiscal Year-end: 12/31/22
Calcium Carbonate Mfr
N.A.I.C.S.: 325998
Hae Ryun Kim (Pres & CEO)

Subsidiaries:

NAMYUNG LIGHTING Co., Ltd. (1)
Songwon Building 467 Gonghang-daero, Gangseo-gu, Seoul, 154030, Korea (South)
Tel.: (82) 236618011
Web Site: https://www.namyung.co.kr
Emp.: 30
Automotive Light & Household Lamp Mfr
N.A.I.C.S.: 335139
S. Y. Jin (Gen Mgr)

TAESAN LCD CO., LTD.
91-2 Samgeo-ri Eumbong-Myeon, Asan, Chungnam, Korea (South)
Tel.: (82) 41 537 7900
Web Site: http://www.taesanlcd.co.kr
Year Founded: 1983
Display Component Mfr
N.A.I.C.S.: 334419
Taehyun Choi (Co-CEO)

TAESUNG CO., LTD.
228 Haeanro, Danwon-gu, Ansan, Gyeonggi-do, Korea (South)
Tel.: (82) 314822240
Web Site: https://www.taesung2000.com
Year Founded: 2000
323280—(KRS)
Printed Circuit Board Mfr & Distr
N.A.I.C.S.: 334412

TAEWOONG CO., LTD.
67 Noksansandan 27-ro, Gangseo-Gu, Busan, Korea (South)
Tel.: (82) 513295000
Web Site: https://www.taewoong.com
Year Founded: 1981
044490—(KRS)
Rev.: $302,095,495
Assets: $582,081,464
Liabilities: $212,851,769
Net Worth: $369,229,696
Earnings: $419,787
Emp.: 436
Fiscal Year-end: 12/31/22
Die Forging Mfr
N.A.I.C.S.: 331110
Jang Hee-Sang (CEO)

Subsidiaries:

TAEWOONG MANUFACTURING & MACHINING DIVISION Co., Ltd. (1)
75 Noksansaneopbuk-ro, Gangseo-gu, Busan, 46751, Korea (South)
Tel.: (82) 51 831 6685
Web Site: http://www.taewoongtech.com
Industrial Machinery Mfr
N.A.I.C.S.: 333517
Jaewon Son (CEO)

TAEWOONG MANUFACTURING & MACHINING DIVISION Co., Ltd. - Factory 2 (1)
24-11 Noksansandan 335-rd, Gangseo-gu, Busan, Korea (South)
Tel.: (82) 51 832 6602
Industrial Machinery Mfr
N.A.I.C.S.: 333517

TAEWOONG STEEL MATERIALS TRADING DIVISION Co., Ltd. (1)
246 Noksansaneopbuk-ro, Gangseo-gu, Busan, Korea (South)
Tel.: (82) 51 831 6002
Web Site: http://www.taewoongsteel.com
Industrial Casting Machinery Mfr
N.A.I.C.S.: 333248
Yongdeok Park (CEO)

Taesang Co. Ltd (1)
30 Dasan-ro 176beon-gil, Saha-gu, Busan, Korea (South)
Tel.: (82) 51 264 5000
Web Site: http://www.taesang.co.kr
Die Forging Mfr & Distr
N.A.I.C.S.: 331110
Sam-Yong Lee (Dir-Sls)

Taewoong P & C (1)
33 Noksansaneopbuk-ro 61beon-gil, Gangseo-gu, Busan, Korea (South)
Tel.: (82) 51 329 5216
Web Site: http://www.taewoongpnc.com
Industrial Equipment Mfr
N.A.I.C.S.: 333517
Yongdeok Park (CEO)

TAEWOONG LOGISTICS CO., LTD.
Taewoong B/D 9F 13-6 Teheran-Ro 37-Gil, Gangnam-Gu, Seoul, Korea (South)
Tel.: (82) 220294300
Web Site: https://www.e-tgl.com
Year Founded: 1996
124560—(KRS)
Rev.: $1,018,735,024
Assets: $287,893,180
Liabilities: $127,229,092
Net Worth: $160,664,088
Earnings: $71,665,671
Emp.: 338
Fiscal Year-end: 12/31/22
Logistic Services
N.A.I.C.S.: 488999
Han Jae Dong (CEO)

Subsidiaries:

FE Taewoong LLC (1)
Taewoong B/D Fidokor Str 7, Mirabad District, 100015, Tashkent, Uzbekistan
Tel.: (998) 712302336
Logistic Services
N.A.I.C.S.: 541614
Joshua Lee (Branch Mgr)

TGL Chile S.A. (1)
Av Luis Thayer Ojeda 166 Office 802, Providencia, Santiago, Chile
Logistic Services
N.A.I.C.S.: 541614

TGL Colombia Ltda (1)
Carrera 16 93-11 Centro Empresarial 93-16 Ofc 702, Bogota, Colombia
Tel.: (57) 6017424857
Web Site: https://www.tglcolombia.com.co
Logistic Services
N.A.I.C.S.: 541614

TGL Hungary kft. (1)
Nagyszombat utca 4 1st floor no 4, 1036, Budapest, Hungary
Tel.: (36) 12757038
Logistic Services
N.A.I.C.S.: 541614
Hawks Kim (Branch Mgr)

TGL Indonesia. PT (1)
Sequis Center 10th JL Jend Sudirman NO 71, Jakarta, 12190, Indonesia
Tel.: (62) 2131182844
Logistic Services
N.A.I.C.S.: 541614
James An (Branch Mgr)

TGL Japan Co., Ltd (1)
3Floor Tekkou Kumiai Building 1-7 Odenmacho, Nihonbashi Chuo-Ku, Tokyo, 103-0011, Japan
Tel.: (81) 356142371
Logistic Services
N.A.I.C.S.: 541614
S. H. Kim (Branch Mgr)

TGL Malaysia Sdn. Bhd. (1)
109-01 Jalan Molek 3/1 Taman Molek, 81100, Johor Bahru, Johor, Malaysia
Tel.: (60) 6073574650
Logistic Services
N.A.I.C.S.: 541614
Tim Kim (Branch Mgr)

TAEWOONG LOGISTICS CO., LTD.

Taewoong Logistics Co., Ltd.—(Continued)

TGL Qingdao Co., Ltd. (1)
Room 708 Bldg 2 No 39 Shiling Road, Qingdao, China
Tel.: (86) 53285779950
Logistic Services
N.A.I.C.S.: 541614
Max Lim (Branch Mgr)

TGL RUS LLC (1)
Office 209 7 Engels Street, Novorossiysk, Krasnodar, Russia
Tel.: (7) 8617303354
Logistic Services
N.A.I.C.S.: 541614
Sasha Han (Branch Mgr)

TGL Shanghai Co., Ltd. (1)
Room 902C A Jingting Mansion 1000 Hongquan RD, Minhang Dist, Shanghai, China
Tel.: (86) 2160907168
Logistic Services
N.A.I.C.S.: 541614
Brad Lee (Branch Mgr)

TGL Shenzhen Co., Ltd. (1)
Room508 Building China Nonferrous NO 6013 Shennan RD, Futian District, Shenzhen, China
Tel.: (86) 75586339908
Logistic Services
N.A.I.C.S.: 541614
Daniel Park (Branch Mgr)

TGL USA Inc. (1)
3237 Satellite Blvd Satellite Pl 300 Ste 475, Duluth, GA 30096
Tel.: (678) 899-1630
Logistic Services
N.A.I.C.S.: 541614
Junghun Seo (Branch Mgr)

TOO TGLI Kaz Logistics (1)
9th F 904 Block 2B Business Center Nurly Tau 19 Al-Farabi Avenue, Almaty, Kazakhstan
Tel.: (7) 727 345 0505
Logistic Services
N.A.I.C.S.: 541614
Simon Lee (Branch Mgr)

TAEYANG CORPORATION

Upseong-dong 485-5, Seobuk-gu, Cheonan, Chungcheongnam-Do, Korea (South)
Tel.: (82) 416219810
Web Site:
https://www.taeyangsun.co.kr
Year Founded: 1989
053620—(KRS)
Rev.: $133,640,296
Assets: $161,977,651
Liabilities: $28,794,802
Net Worth: $133,182,849
Earnings: $5,050,175
Emp.: 257
Fiscal Year-end: 12/31/22
Household Appliances Mfr
N.A.I.C.S.: 335220
Chang-Soo Hyun (CEO)

TAEYANG METAL INDUSTRIAL CO., LTD

212 Haebong-ro, Danwon-gu, Ansan, Gyeonggi-do, Korea (South)
Tel.: (82) 314905500
Web Site:
https://www.taeyangmetal.com
Year Founded: 1954
004100—(KRS)
Rev.: $436,808,624
Assets: $376,587,751
Liabilities: $290,638,655
Net Worth: $85,949,096
Earnings: ($480,350)
Emp.: 513
Fiscal Year-end: 12/31/22
Automobile Parts Mfr
N.A.I.C.S.: 336110
Wu Sam Han (Chm & CEO)

Subsidiaries:

Taeyang Metal (Zhangjiagang) Co., Ltd. (1)
Tangshi Li Xiang Cun, Zhangjiagang, 215 600, Jiangsu, China
Tel.: (86) 512 5899 0751
Automobile Parts Mfr
N.A.I.C.S.: 336390

Yantai Taeyang Metal Co., Ltd. (1)
Automobile Parts Mfr
N.A.I.C.S.: 336390

TAEYOUNG ENGINEERING & CONSTRUCTION CO., LTD.

111 Yeoui Park-ro, Yeougdeunpo-gu, Seoul, 07241, Korea (South)
Tel.: (82) 220902200
Web Site: https://www.taeyoung.com
Year Founded: 1973
009410—(KRS)
Rev.: $1,998,109,194
Assets: $3,315,977,440
Liabilities: $2,747,735,854
Net Worth: $568,241,586
Earnings: $48,179,684
Emp.: 1,784
Fiscal Year-end: 12/31/22
Water, Sewer Line & Related Structures Construction
N.A.I.C.S.: 237110
Suk-Mynn Yoon (Chm)

Subsidiaries:

Blue One Co., Ltd. (1)
391 Bobul-ro, Gyeongju, Gyeongsangbuk-do, Korea (South)
Tel.: (82) 18991888
Web Site: https://www.blueone.com
Hospitality Services
N.A.I.C.S.: 721110

Taeyoung Grain Terminal Corporation (1)
55 Pyeongtaek Hangan-ro, Poseung-eup, Pyeongtaek, Gyeonggi-do, Korea (South)
Tel.: (82) 3180532100
Web Site: https://www.tygt.co.kr
Grain Export-Import Services
N.A.I.C.S.: 424510

TAFI INDUSTRIES BERHAD

PLO 3 Kawasan Perindustrian Bukit Pasir, Mukim Sungai Raya, 84300, Muar, Johor, Malaysia
Tel.: (60) 69859781
Web Site:
https://welcome.tafi.com.my
Year Founded: 2004
TAFI—(KLS)
Rev.: $14,972,750
Assets: $41,861,570
Liabilities: $24,403,497
Net Worth: $17,458,074
Earnings: $159,290
Emp.: 212
Fiscal Year-end: 12/31/23
Furniture Mfr
N.A.I.C.S.: 337121
Eng Guan Saw (Mng Dir)

Subsidiaries:

Home & Office Furniture Sdn. Bhd. (1)
Lot 267 Kawasan Perindustrian Bukit Pasir, Mukim Sungai Raya Bukit Pasir, Muar, 84300, Johor, Malaysia
Tel.: (60) 69859781
Web Site: http://www.tafurniture.com.my
Furniture Distr
N.A.I.C.S.: 423210

T.A. Furniture Industries Sdn. Bhd. (1)
Plot 3 Kawasan Perindustrian Bukit Pasir, Mukim Sungai Raya Bukit Pasir, 84300, Muar, Johor, Malaysia
Tel.: (60) 6 985 9781
Web Site: https://www.tafurniture.com.my
Sales Range: $100-124.9 Million
Emp.: 410
Office Furniture Mfr
N.A.I.C.S.: 337211

Subsidiary (Domestic):

T.A. E-Furnishings Sdn. Bhd. (2)
Plo 3 Kawasan Perindustrian Bukit Pasir Mukim Sg Raya, 84300, Muar, Johor, Malaysia
Tel.: (60) 69859781
Web Site: http://www.tafurniture.com.my
Furniture Distr
N.A.I.C.S.: 423210

T.A. Systems Furniture Industries Sdn. Bhd. (1)
Plot 3 Kawasan Perindustrian Bukit Pasir Mukim Sungai Raya, Bukit Pasir, 84300, Muar, Johor, Malaysia
Tel.: (60) 69859781
Office Furniture Mfr
N.A.I.C.S.: 337214

TAG AVIATION S.A.

20 Chemin des Papillons, PO Box 36, 1215, Geneva, Switzerland
Tel.: (41) 227170000
Web Site: http://www.tagaviation.com
Sales Range: $150-199.9 Million
Emp.: 400
Holding Company; Private Aircraft Acquisition & Sales, Management, Maintenance & Chartering Services
N.A.I.C.S.: 551112
Robert H. Wells (Pres & CEO)

Subsidiaries:

TAG Aviation (UK) Ltd (1)
Farnborough Airport, Farnborough, GU14 6XA, Hampshire, United Kingdom
Tel.: (44) 1252 377 977
Web Site: http://www.tagaviation.uk
Emp.: 60
Aircraft Maintenance Services
N.A.I.C.S.: 488190
Russ Allchorne (VP-Flight Ops-Europe)

TAG Aviation Asia Ltd. (1)
7th Floor Harcourt House 39 Gloucester Road, Wanchai, China (Hong Kong)
Tel.: (852) 3141 2000
Web Site: http://www.tagaviation.com
Emp.: 150
Aircraft Maintenance Services
N.A.I.C.S.: 488190
Jolie Howard (CEO)

TAG Aviation Australia Pty Ltd. (1)
Suite 3-08 Aero 247, 247 Coward Street Mascot, Sydney, 2020, NSW, Australia
Tel.: (61) 420979234
Web Site: http://www.tagaviation.com.au
Aircraft Management, Acquisition & Sales, Maintenance & Flight Chartering Services
N.A.I.C.S.: 488190

TAG Aviation Espana S.L. (1)
C/ Bahia de Pollensa 11, 28042, Madrid, Spain
Tel.: (34) 91 660 0590
Aircraft Maintenance Services
N.A.I.C.S.: 488190
Carlos Gomez (Mng Dir)

TAG Aviation Europe S.A. (1)
20 Chemin des Papillons, PO Box 36, Airport, Geneva, 1215, Switzerland
Tel.: (41) 227170000
Web Site: http://www.tagaviation.com
Sales Range: $150-199.9 Million
Emp.: 350
Aircraft Management, Acquisition & Sales, Maintenance & Flight Chartering Services
N.A.I.C.S.: 488190
Franck Madignier (Pres)

Subsidiary (Non-US):

Farnborough Airport Limited (2)
Farnborough Airport, Farnborough, GU14 6XA, Hampshire, United Kingdom
Tel.: (44) 1252379000
Web Site: http://www.tagfarnborough.com
Airport Operator
N.A.I.C.S.: 488119
Brandon O'Reilly (CEO)

TAG Maintenance Services Farnborough Ltd. (2)
Farnborough Airport, Farnborough, GU14 6XA, Hants, United Kingdom
Tel.: (44) 1252526701
Sales Range: $25-49.9 Million
Emp.: 100
Aircraft Maintenance & Engineering Services
N.A.I.C.S.: 488190

TAG Aviation Middle-East WLL (1)
Office 102 Platinum Tower Building 190 Road 2803 Block 428, Manama, Bahrain
Tel.: (973) 1733 9463
Aircraft Maintenance Services
N.A.I.C.S.: 488190
Kevin Hewitt (Mgr-Security)

TAG Aviation USA, Inc. (1)
1628 John F Kennedy Blvd Ste 950, Philadelphia, PA 19103-2110
Tel.: (650) 425-3848
Web Site: http://www.tagaviation.com
Sales Range: $25-49.9 Million
Aircraft Completion Services, Acquisition & Sales
N.A.I.C.S.: 488190
Arun Daniel (Sr Mgr-IT Ops)

TAG D.D. GORAZDE

Visegradska bb, 73000, Gorazde, Bosnia & Herzegovina
Tel.: (387) 3 822 1797
Web Site: http://www.tagbih.com
TALGRK4—(SARE)
Rev.: $932,008
Assets: $1,621,850
Liabilities: $1,463,446
Net Worth: $158,404
Earnings: ($110,179)
Emp.: 74
Fiscal Year-end: 12/31/20
Machine Tools Mfr
N.A.I.C.S.: 333517

TAG IDEA REVOLUTION

10 Disera Drive Suite 260, Thornhill, L4J 0A7, ON, Canada
Tel.: (905) 940-1948
Web Site: https://tagagency.info
Sales Range: $1-9.9 Million
Emp.: 30
Advetising Agency
N.A.I.C.S.: 541810
Matt Orlando (Pres)

TAG IMMOBILIEN AG

Steckelhorn 5, 20457, Hamburg, Germany
Tel.: (49) 4038032300   De
Web Site: https://www.tag-ag.com
TEG—(STU)
Rev.: $510,305,773
Assets: $8,058,052,766
Liabilities: $4,785,624,242
Net Worth: $3,272,428,525
Earnings: ($453,625,124)
Emp.: 1,816
Fiscal Year-end: 12/31/23
Property Investment
N.A.I.C.S.: 525990
Rolf Elgeti (Chm-Supervisory Bd)

Subsidiaries:

Bau-Verein zu Hamburg Hausverwaltungsgesellschaft mbH (1)
Steckelhorn 5, 20457, Hamburg, Germany (100%)
Tel.: (49) 40380320
Web Site: https://www.bau-verein.de
Residential Property Management Services
N.A.I.C.S.: 531311
Axel Walker (Mng Dir)

Colonia Real Estate AG (1)
Bayenstrasse 65, 50678, Cologne, Germany
Tel.: (49) 2217160710
Web Site: http://www.colonia.ag

Sales Range: $100-124.9 Million
Emp.: 104
Real Estate & Investment Services
N.A.I.C.S.: 531390

Subsidiary (Domestic):

CRE German Office GmbH (2)
Zeppelinstrasse 4-8, 50667, Cologne, Nordrhein-Westfalen, Germany
Tel.: (49) 2217160710
Web Site: http://www.colonia.ag
Real Estate Asset Management Services
N.A.I.C.S.: 531390
Stephan Rind (CEO)

CRE Resolution GmbH (2)
Kantstrasse 13, 10623, Berlin, Germany
Tel.: (49) 3033006390
Web Site: http://www.polares-ream.com
Emp.: 60
Real Estate Asset Management Services
N.A.I.C.S.: 531390
Michael Amann (CEO)

CRE Wohnen GmbH (2)
Zeppelinstr 4-8, 50667, Cologne, Nordrhein-Westfalen, Germany
Tel.: (49) 2217160710
Real Estate Asset Management Services
N.A.I.C.S.: 531390

CRE Wohnen Service GmbH (2)
Marktstrasse 9-10, 14641, Nauen, Brandenburg, Germany
Tel.: (49) 332144540
Web Site: http://www.cre.ag
Real Estate Asset Management Services
N.A.I.C.S.: 531390

TAG Leipzig-Immobilien GmbH (1)
Kreuzstrasse 7c, 04103, Leipzig, Germany
Tel.: (49) 34133967180
Real Estate
N.A.I.C.S.: 531120

TAG Logistik Immobilien GmbH & Co. KG (1)
Steckelhoern 5 & 7, 20457, Hamburg, 20457, Germany
Tel.: (49) 4038032109
Real Estate Property Management Services
N.A.I.C.S.: 531312

TAG Magdeburg-Immobilien GmbH (1)
Schillerstrasse 3, 39108, Magdeburg, Germany
Tel.: (49) 34133967180
Real Estate
N.A.I.C.S.: 531120

TAG Potsdam-Immobilien GmbH (1)
Kurfurstenstrasse 87, 10787, Berlin, Germany
Tel.: (49) 30520054100
Real Estate
N.A.I.C.S.: 531120

TAG Stadthaus am Anger GmbH (1)
Juri-Gagarin-Ring 21, 99084, Erfurt, Germany
Tel.: (49) 36155895180
Real Estate Services
N.A.I.C.S.: 531120

TAG Wohnen & Service GmbH (1)
Steckelhorn 5, 20457, Hamburg, Germany
Tel.: (49) 40380320
Web Site: https://tag-wohnen.de
Sales Range: $75-99.9 Million
Emp.: 150
Real Estate Asset Management Services
N.A.I.C.S.: 531390

Subsidiary (Domestic):

Trinom Business Apartments GmbH (2)
Markgrafenstr 10, 04109, Leipzig, Germany
Tel.: (49) 34121338800
Web Site: https://home.apartment-leipzig.de
Apartments Renting Services
N.A.I.C.S.: 531110

TAG Wohnen & Service GmbH (1)
Steckelhorn 5, 20457, Hamburg, Germany
Tel.: (49) 40380320
Web Site: https://www.tag-wohnen.de
Real Estate Services
N.A.I.C.S.: 531120

TAG Wohnimmobilien Halle GmbH & Co. KG (1)
Zur Saaleaue 2, 06122, Halle, Germany
Tel.: (49) 34133967180
Real Estate Services
N.A.I.C.S.: 531120

TAG Wolfsburg-Immobilien GmbH (1)
Wuppertaler Strasse 9, 38440, Wolfsburg, Germany
Tel.: (49) 53411886180
Real Estate Services
N.A.I.C.S.: 531120

Vantage Development S.A. (1)
CU Office bud B ul Jaworska 11, 53-612, Wroclaw, Poland
Tel.: (48) 717860000
Web Site: https://www.vantage-sa.pl
Real Estate Development
N.A.I.C.S.: 237210
Grzegorz Dzik (Chm-Supervisory Bd)

TAG OIL LTD.
Tel.: (604) 682-6496 BC
Web Site: https://www.tagoil.com
Year Founded: 1990
TAOIF—(OTCQX)
Rev.: $425,966
Assets: $30,628,522
Liabilities: $1,525,570
Net Worth: $29,102,952
Earnings: ($2,240,238)
Emp.: 8
Fiscal Year-end: 03/31/23
Oil & Gas Exploration Services
N.A.I.C.S.: 211120
Giuseppe J. Perone (Gen Counsel & Sec)

Subsidiaries:

LQWD Technologies Corp. (1)
1710 - 1050 West Pender Street, Vancouver, V6E 3S7, BC, Canada
Tel.: (604) 669-0912
Web Site: https://lqwdtech.com
Rev.: $54,386
Assets: $14,069,914
Liabilities: $414,709
Net Worth: $13,655,204
Earnings: ($17,961,110)
Emp.: 9
Fiscal Year-end: 02/28/2022
Metal Mining & Oil & Gas Exploration Services
N.A.I.C.S.: 212290
Giuseppe J. Perone (CEO-Interim)

TAGANROGSKIY KOMB ZAVOD AO
Instrumentalnaya 2, Taganrog, 347923, Russia
Tel.: (7) 8634329308
Farm Machinery Equipment Mfr
N.A.I.C.S.: 333111

TAGMASTER AB
Kronborgsgrand 11, 164 46, Kista, Sweden
Tel.: (46) 86321950 SE
Web Site: https://www.tagmaster.com
Year Founded: 1994
TAGM.B—(OMX)
Rev.: $34,970,182
Assets: $38,962,320
Liabilities: $17,261,624
Net Worth: $21,700,697
Earnings: ($2,486,281)
Emp.: 111
Fiscal Year-end: 12/31/20
Traffic & Rail Information Software
N.A.I.C.S.: 513210
Margaretha Narstrom (CFO)

Subsidiaries:

CA Traffic Ltd. (1)
Suite 64 Midshires House Midshires Business Park, Smeaton Close, Aylesbury, HP19 8HL, Bucks, United Kingdom
Tel.: (44) 1296333499
Web Site: http://www.ca-traffic.com
Traffic Monitoring Equipment Supplier
N.A.I.C.S.: 488999
Thomas Greene (Natl Sls Mgr-Traffic Solutions)

Sensys Networks, Inc. (1)
1608 4th St Ste 200, Berkeley, CA 94710
Tel.: (510) 548-4620
Web Site: https://www.sensysnetworks.com
Wireless Traffic Detection & Integrated Traffic Data Systems
N.A.I.C.S.: 541614
Amine Haoui (Co-Founder & CEO)

TAH HSIN INDUSTRIAL CORPORATION
No51 35th Road Industrial Zone, Taichung, Taiwan
Tel.: (886) 423595511
Web Site: https://www.tahhsin.com.tw
Year Founded: 1958
1315—(TAI)
Rev.: $70,544,914
Assets: $370,934,909
Liabilities: $23,535,399
Net Worth: $347,399,509
Earnings: $11,462,343
Emp.: 343
Fiscal Year-end: 12/31/23
Plastic Products, Apparels, Steel Products & Machinery Mfr
N.A.I.C.S.: 313320
Zi-Cong Wu (Chm)

Subsidiaries:

Have Our Plastic Inc. (1)
2370 Meadowvale Blvd Unit 2, Mississauga, L5N 0H1, ON, Canada
Tel.: (905) 821-7550
Web Site: http://www.hop.ca
Sales Range: $25-49.9 Million
Emp.: 12
Office Stationery Products Mfr & Distr
N.A.I.C.S.: 322230

Myanmar Tah Hsin Industrial Co., Ltd. (1)
No 365 367 2nd Floor Bogyoke Aung San Road, Pabedan Township, Yangon, Myanmar
Tel.: (95) 1377755
Web Site: https://myanmaryellowpages.biz
Advertising Services
N.A.I.C.S.: 541890

Tah Hsin Industrial Corporation - TAICHUNG Plant (1)
No 51 35th Road Taichung Industrial Park, Taichung, Taiwan
Tel.: (886) 4 23595511
Rainwear & Garments Mfr
N.A.I.C.S.: 315250

Tahsin Industrial Corp (1)
685 State Route 10, Randolph, NJ 07869
Tel.: (973) 328-8678
Web Site: http://www.redledge.com
Rainwear Mfr
N.A.I.C.S.: 315250

Tahsin Shoji Co.,Ltd (1)
2-8-2 Imame, Higashiosaka, 578-0903, Japan
Tel.: (81) 72 964 1661
Web Site: http://www.tahsin.co.jp
Apparels Mfr
N.A.I.C.S.: 315990

Tamerica Products Inc. (1)
9157 Rochester Ct, Rancho Cucamonga, CA 91730
Tel.: (909) 476-6033
Web Site: http://www.tamericaproducts.net
Emp.: 15
Binding & Laminating Machinery Mfr
N.A.I.C.S.: 333310
James Lee (Chm)

Yuk Wing Development Ltd. (1)
Unit 3 15th Floor Telford House No 16 Wang Hoi Road, Kowloon Bay, Kowloon, China (Hong Kong)
Tel.: (852) 27517250
Textile & Plastic Products Mfr
N.A.I.C.S.: 326199

TAH KONG CHEMICAL INDUSTRIAL CORP.
7F No778 Sec 4 Bade Rd, Nangang Dist, Taipei, 115, Taiwan
Tel.: (886) 227859081
Web Site: https://www.tkc.com.tw
Year Founded: 1966
4706—(TPE)
Rev.: $38,140,575
Assets: $51,395,085
Liabilities: $4,890,317
Net Worth: $46,504,768
Earnings: $1,589,344
Emp.: 178
Fiscal Year-end: 12/31/22
Pigment Product Mfr
N.A.I.C.S.: 325130
Teng Chia-Hui (Chm)

Subsidiaries:

TKC Fine Chemical (Kun-Shan) Co., Ltd. (1)
126 Qin-feng North Road, Qiandeng Town, Kunshan, China
Tel.: (86) 51257469992
Organic Pigment Power Mfr
N.A.I.C.S.: 325130

Tah Kong Fine Chemical (Kun-Shan) Co., Ltd. (1)
126 Qin-Feng North Road, Qiandeng Town, Kunshan, Jiangsu, China
Tel.: (86) 51257469992
Chemical Products Mfr
N.A.I.C.S.: 325998

TAH TONG TEXTILE CO., LTD.
No 346 3/F Sec 3 Nanking E Rd, Taipei, 10595, Taiwan
Tel.: (886) 227522244
Web Site: https://www.tahtong.com.tw
1441—(TAI)
Rev.: $37,861,047
Assets: $62,585,007
Liabilities: $51,267,338
Net Worth: $11,317,669
Earnings: ($10,885,771)
Emp.: 389
Fiscal Year-end: 12/31/23
Yarn & Fabrics Mfr
N.A.I.C.S.: 313110
Chen Shiou Chung (Chm)

Subsidiaries:

Tah Tong Textile Co., Ltd. - Chungli Mill (1)
No 741 Sec 3 Shinsheng Rd Chungli City, Taoyuan, 32056, Taiwan
Tel.: (886) 34531858
Yarn & Fabric Mfr
N.A.I.C.S.: 313110

Tah Tong Textile Co., Ltd. - Taichung Mill (1)
No 148-1 Jennhsing Rd East District, Taichung, 40152, Taiwan
Tel.: (886) 422113191
Yarn & Fabric Mfr
N.A.I.C.S.: 313110

TAHA SPINNING MILLS LIMITED
406 Commerce Centre Hasrat Mohani Road, Karachi, Pakistan
Tel.: (92) 32638522 PK
Web Site: http://www.hmiml.com
Year Founded: 1984
UNITY—(PSX)
Rev.: $350,020,118
Assets: $269,095,252
Liabilities: $195,157,075
Net Worth: $73,938,177
Earnings: $2,342,566
Emp.: 577
Fiscal Year-end: 06/30/23
Textile Mill Operator
N.A.I.C.S.: 314999

TAHMAR ENTERPRISES LIMITED

Taha Spinning Mills Limited—(Continued)

TAHMAR ENTERPRISES LIMITED
A-70 MIDC Sinnar, Nasik District,
Mumbai, 422103, Maharashtra, India
Tel.: (91) 9321752685
Web Site:
   http://www.sardapapers.com
Year Founded: 1991
516032—(BOM)
Rev.: $819
Assets: $37,606
Liabilities: $49,290
Net Worth: ($11,684)
Earnings: ($11,903)
Fiscal Year-end: 03/31/21
Paper Mfr
N.A.I.C.S.: 322120

TAHOE INVESTMENT GROUP CO., LTD.
No 43 Hudong Road Olympic Building, Fuzhou, 350003, Fujian, China
Tel.: (86) 591 8761 0213   CN
Year Founded: 1996
Investment Holding Company
N.A.I.C.S.: 551112
Qisen Huang *(Founder & Chm)*

Subsidiaries:

Macau Pension Fund Management
Company Limited   (1)
Avenida da Praia Grande No 594 Edf BCM
11th Floor, Macau, China (Macau)
Tel.: (853) 28555078
Web Site: https://www.mpfm.com.mo
Pension Fund & Life Insurance Carriers
N.A.I.C.S.: 524113

Tahoe Group Co., Ltd.   (1)
Floor 20-31 Taihe Ctr Taihe Square East
2nd Ring Road, Jinan District, Fuzhou,
350001, China
Tel.: (86) 59187542888
Web Site: http://www.tahoecn.com
Rev.: $553,782,141
Assets: $33,220,921,114
Liabilities: $30,146,535,713
Net Worth: $3,074,385,401
Earnings: ($765,964,202)
Fiscal Year-end: 12/31/2020
Commercial Real Estate Investment & Development
N.A.I.C.S.: 531390

Subsidiary (Non-US):

Tahoe Life Insurance Co., Ltd.   (2)
4th Floor Dah Sing Financial Centre, PO
Box 141, 108 Gloucester Road, Wanchai,
China (Hong Kong)   (100%)
Tel.: (852) 25078866
Web Site: http://www.tahoelife.com.hk
Insurance Agencies & Brokerages
N.A.I.C.S.: 524210

TAI CHEUNG HOLDINGS LIMITED
20th Floor The Hong Kong Club
Building 3A Chater Road, Central,
China (Hong Kong)
Tel.: (852) 25322688   BM
Web Site: https://www.taicheung.com
Year Founded: 1956
0088—(HKG)
Rev.: $17,012,462
Assets: $899,622,602
Liabilities: $38,513,428
Net Worth: $861,109,174
Earnings: $374,042
Emp.: 150
Fiscal Year-end: 03/31/22
Property Management Services
N.A.I.C.S.: 531312
Wing Sau Li *(Controller-Project Mgmt & Construction Div)*

TAI FOONG INTERNATIONAL LTD.
44 Milner Ave, Scarborough, M1S
3P8, ON, Canada
Tel.: (416) 299-7575
Web Site: http://www.tfifoong.com
Year Founded: 1977
Sales Range: $25-49.9 Million
Emp.: 95
Fish & Seafood Import & Sales
N.A.I.C.S.: 445250
David Lam *(Pres)*

TAI HING GROUP HOLDINGS LIMITED
13/F Chinachem Exchange Square 1
Hoi Wan Street, Quarry Bay, China
(Hong Kong)
Tel.: (852) 22093300   Ky
Web Site: http://www.taihing.com
Year Founded: 1989
6811—(HKG)
Rev.: $341,083,665
Assets: $320,363,768
Liabilities: $198,580,103
Net Worth: $121,783,665
Earnings: ($5,491,935)
Emp.: 6,000
Fiscal Year-end: 12/31/22
Holding Company
N.A.I.C.S.: 551112
Wing On Chan *(Co-Founder & Chm)*

TAI INDUSTRIES LIMITED
53A Mirza Ghalib Street 3rd Floor,
Kolkata, 700016, India
Tel.: (91) 3340416666
Web Site: https://www.taiind.com
Year Founded: 1983
519483—(BOM)
Rev.: $31,198,561
Assets: $9,830,873
Liabilities: $6,628,260
Net Worth: $3,202,614
Earnings: $553,252
Emp.: 68
Fiscal Year-end: 03/31/23
Fruit Product Distr
N.A.I.C.S.: 424480
Rohan Ghosh *(Mng Dir)*

TAI KAM HOLDINGS LIMITED
Wealth Commercial Centre 48 Kwong
Wah Street Mong Kok, Kowloon,
China (Hong Kong)
Tel.: (852) 26631166   Ky
Web Site:
   http://www.taikamholdings.com
8321—(HKG)
Rev.: $12,409,830
Assets: $11,983,725
Liabilities: $2,268,735
Net Worth: $9,714,990
Earnings: ($4,047,998)
Emp.: 23
Fiscal Year-end: 04/30/23
Slope Work Contracting Services
N.A.I.C.S.: 238140
Mabel Tsz Fa Tsui *(CEO, & Officer-Compliance & Chm)*

TAI PING CARPETS INTERNATIONAL LIMITED
Units 1801-1804 18th Floor 909 Cheung Sha Wan Road, Cheung Sha
Wan, Kowloon, China (Hong Kong)
Tel.: (852) 28487668   BM
Web Site:
   http://www.houseoftaiping.com
0146—(HKG)
Rev.: $75,279,951
Assets: $101,637,401
Liabilities: $46,288,084
Net Worth: $55,349,316
Earnings: $3,259,970
Emp.: 72
Fiscal Year-end: 06/30/22

Holding Company; Carpet Designer,
Mfr & Distr; Yarn Mfr & Whslr; Property Investment & Leasing Services
N.A.I.C.S.: 551112
Mark S. Worgan *(CEO)*

Subsidiaries:

Manufacture des Tapis de Cogolin
SAS   (1)
4-6 rue de Montalembert, 75007, Paris,
France
Tel.: (33) 142229654
Floor Covering & Carpet Design Mfr
N.A.I.C.S.: 314110

Tai Ping Carpets (S) Pte. Limited   (1)
315 Alexandra Road Sime Darby Business
Centre 04-13, Singapore, 159944, Singapore
Tel.: (65) 62352477
Web Site: http://www.taipingcarpets.com
Sales Range: $50-74.9 Million
Emp.: 4
Carpet Distr
N.A.I.C.S.: 423220

Tai Ping Carpets Americas, Inc.   (1)
715 Curtis Pkwy SE, Calhoun, GA 30701-3677
Tel.: (706) 625-8905
Sales Range: $10-24.9 Million
Emp.: 50
Carpet & Home Furnishings Whslr
N.A.I.C.S.: 423220
William Palmer *(Dir-Global)*

Subsidiary (Domestic):

Edward Fields, Incorporated   (2)
11th Fl 150 E 58th St, New York, NY 10155
Tel.: (212) 310-0400
Web Site: https://www.edwardfields.com
Sales Range: $25-49.9 Million
Emp.: 9
Carpets & Rugs
N.A.I.C.S.: 314110

Premier Yarn Dyers, Inc.   (2)
128 George St E, Adairsville, GA 30103-2412
Tel.: (770) 773-3695
Web Site: https://premier-yarn-
   dyers.business.site
Fabrics Dyeing & Finishing Services
N.A.I.C.S.: 313310

Tai Ping Carpets Europe SAS   (1)
3 place des Victoires, 75001, Paris, France
Tel.: (33) 142229654
Sales Range: $1-9.9 Million
Emp.: 50
Carpets & Home Furnishings Whslr
N.A.I.C.S.: 423220

Tai Ping Carpets India Private
Limited   (1)
Unit No 208-210 2nd Floor Centrum Plaza
Sector 53 Golf Course Road, Gurgaon,
122001, Haryana, India
Tel.: (91) 1244693900
Web Site: http://www.taipingcarpets.com
Sales Range: $25-49.9 Million
Emp.: 28
Carpet Distr
N.A.I.C.S.: 314110

Tai Ping Carpets Interieur GmbH   (1)
Steinhoft 11, 20459, Hamburg, Germany
Tel.: (49) 4080819490
Web Site: http://www.taipingcarpets.com
Sales Range: $25-49.9 Million
Emp.: 10
Carpet Distr
N.A.I.C.S.: 314110
Catherine Vergez *(Co-Mng Dir)*

Tai Ping Carpets Latin America
S.A.   (1)
Avenida Del Libertador 7270 Piso 7 Oficina
A, Buenos Aires, 1429, Argentina
Tel.: (54) 1147016002
Sales Range: $50-74.9 Million
Emp.: 9
Carpet Distr
N.A.I.C.S.: 423220
Daniel Sergio Kasakoff *(VP)*

Tai Ping Carpets Limited   (1)
213 Prince's Building 10 Chater Road, Cen-

INTERNATIONAL PUBLIC

tral, China (Hong Kong)
Tel.: (852) 25227138
Sales Range: $25-49.9 Million
Emp.: 90
Carpet Mfr
N.A.I.C.S.: 314110
Celia Yeung *(Mng Dir)*

Tai Ping Carpets UK Limited   (1)
Chelsea Harbour 406-407 Design Centre
East, London, SW10 0XF, United Kingdom
Tel.: (44) 2078089650
Web Site:
Floor Covering & Carpet Design Mfr
N.A.I.C.S.: 314110
Tony Ash *(Mng Dir)*

TAI SANG LAND DEVELOPMENT LTD
15/F TS Tower 43 Heung Yip Road,
Wong Chuk Hang, Hong Kong, China
(Hong Kong)
Tel.: (852) 25292936   HK
Web Site: https://www.tsld.com.hk
Year Founded: 1968
0089—(HKG)
Sales Range: $25-49.9 Million
Emp.: 170
Property Investment Management
Services
N.A.I.C.S.: 531312
Katy Ching Man Ma *(Sec)*

Subsidiaries:

Cambella Limited   (1)
11 Fl Tai Sang Bank Bldg 130 Des Voeux
Rd, Central, China (Hong Kong)
Tel.: (852) 25292936
Web Site: http://www.tsld.com
Property Development Services
N.A.I.C.S.: 531311

Central Financial Management Company Inc.   (1)
456 Montgomery St No 180, San Francisco,
CA 94104-1247
Tel.: (415) 398-4568
Emp.: 10
Estate Management Services
N.A.I.C.S.: 531390

Montgomery Enterprises Limited   (1)
11 Fl Tai Sang Bank Bldg 130-132 Des
Voeux Rd, Central, China (Hong
Kong)   (100%)
Tel.: (852) 252 92936
Web Site: http://www.taisangland.com.hk
Property Management Rentals & Sales, Hotel Operations & Investment Holding
N.A.I.C.S.: 531312
Alfred Ma Ching Kuen *(Mng Dir)*

TAI SHAN COMMUNICATIONS, INC.
1366 Zhongtianmen Dajie Xinghuo
Science & Tech Park High-tech Zone,
Tai'an, 271000, Shandong, China
Tel.: (86) 5386052010   VG
Sales Range: $1-9.9 Million
Emp.: 1,700
Telecommunications Outsourcing
Services
N.A.I.C.S.: 561499
Gary Wang *(Chm & CEO)*

TAI SHING ELECTRONICS COMPONENTS CORP.
Rm A 6F No 4 Gongye 6th Rd,
Pingzhen Dist, Taoyuan, 324, Taiwan
Tel.: (886) 34699777
Web Site: https://www.tai-
   shing.com.tw
Year Founded: 1973
3426—(TPE)
Electronic Products Mfr
N.A.I.C.S.: 334419
Li-Lan Lin *(Acct Mgr)*

TAI SHING INTERNATIONAL (HOLDINGS) LIMITED
Malahon Centre 21st Floor 10-12

AND PRIVATE COMPANIES
TAI-TECH ADVANCED ELECTRONICS (S) PTE LTD.

Stanley Street, Central, China (Hong Kong)
Tel.: (852) 31080188
Sales Range: $10-24.9 Million
Emp.: 97
Investment Management Service
N.A.I.C.S.: 523940
Bo Liu *(Chm & Compliance Officer)*

TAI SIN ELECTRIC LIMITED
24 Gul Crescent Jurong Town, Singapore, 629531, Singapore
Tel.: (65) 66729292
Web Site: https://www.taisin.com.sg
500—(SES)
Rev.: $312,505,372
Assets: $223,839,200
Liabilities: $70,630,604
Net Worth: $153,208,596
Earnings: $12,456,465
Emp.: 950
Fiscal Year-end: 06/30/23
Power & Instrumentation Cables Mfr
N.A.I.C.S.: 331491
Bobby Chye huat Lim *(Chm)*

Subsidiaries:

CAST Laboratories Pte. Ltd. (1)
17 Tuas Avenue 8, Singapore, 639232, Singapore
Tel.: (65) 68016000
Web Site: https://www.castlab.com.sg
Laboratory Testing Services
N.A.I.C.S.: 541380
Lim Eng Heng *(CEO)*

Subsidiary (Non-US):

CAST Laboratories (Cambodia) Co. Ltd. (2)
Building No 400 Phnom Penh Hanoi Friendship Blvd 1019, Trapeang Svay Sangkat Kork Kleang Khan SenSok, Phnom Penh, Cambodia
Tel.: (855) 93888213
Web Site: https://www.becl.com.kh
Laboratory Testing Services
N.A.I.C.S.: 621511

Castconsult Sdn. Bhd. (2)
PTD 42928 Jalan Murni 12, Taman Perindustrian Murni, 81400, Senai, Johor, Malaysia
Tel.: (60) 75989767
Web Site: https://www.castlab.com.my
Laboratory Testing & Research Services
N.A.I.C.S.: 541380
Mohd Nizam B. Mohd Yusof *(Dir)*

PT CAST Laboratories Indonesia (2)
Central Sukajadi Block B1 No 3A-5, Batam, 29462, Indonesia
Tel.: (62) 7787367502
Web Site: https://www.castlab.co.id
Laboratory Testing & Research Services
N.A.I.C.S.: 541380

LKH Precicon Pte. Ltd. (1)
63 Hillview Ave 10-21 Lam Soon, Industrial Building, Singapore, 669569, Singapore
Tel.: (65) 66729229
Web Site: https://www.precicon.com.sg
Industrial Automation Product Distr
N.A.I.C.S.: 423830
Joyce Tan *(Gen Mgr)*

LKH Projects Distribution Pte. Ltd. (1)
Lim Kim Hai Building 53 Kallang Place 4th Storey, Singapore, 339177, Singapore
Tel.: (65) 68977078
Web Site: https://www.lkhpd.com.sg
Electrical Products Distr
N.A.I.C.S.: 423610

Lim Kim Hai Electric (VN) Company Limited (1)
78 Hoa Cuc Street, Ward 7 District Phu Nhuan, Ho Chi Minh City, 84, Vietnam
Tel.: (84) 2835171717
Web Site: https://www.limkimhai.com.vn
Sales Range: $25-49.9 Million
Emp.: 30
Power Transmission Equipment Distr
N.A.I.C.S.: 423610
Sin Tuyet Mai *(Gen Dir)*

Lim Kim Hai Electric Co (S) Pte Ltd (1)
Lim Kim Hai Building 53 Kallang Place, Singapore, 339177, Singapore
Tel.: (65) 64905000
Web Site: https://www.limkimhai.com.sg
Sales Range: $75-99.9 Million
Emp.: 140
Electrical Material Distr
N.A.I.C.S.: 423610
Ong Wee Heng *(CEO)*

Subsidiary (Non-US):

LKH Electric Middle East (FZE) (2)
Q4-201 Sharjah Airport International Free Zone, PO Box 121890, Sharjah, United Arab Emirates
Tel.: (971) 6 557 9720
Web Site: http://www.lkhelectric.ae
Sales Range: $25-49.9 Million
Emp.: 3
Power Control Components Mfr
N.A.I.C.S.: 334220

Subsidiary (Domestic):

LKH Precicon Pte Ltd (2)
63 Hillview Avenue 10-21 Lam Soon Industrial Building, Singapore, 669569, Singapore
Tel.: (65) 66729229
Web Site: https://www.precicon.com.sg
Sales Range: $25-49.9 Million
Emp.: 43
Industrial Controls Distr
N.A.I.C.S.: 423610
Chia Heng *(Mng Dir)*

LKH Projects Distribution Pte Ltd (2)
Lim Kim Hai Building 53 Kallang Place 4th Storey, Singapore, 339177, Singapore
Tel.: (65) 68977078
Web Site: https://www.lkhpd.com.sg
Emp.: 8
Electrical Component Distr
N.A.I.C.S.: 423610

Nylect Engineering Pte. Ltd. (1)
1 Woodlands Sector 1 Nylect Industrial Building, Singapore, 738309, Singapore
Tel.: (65) 67596888
Web Site: https://www.nylect.com
Mechanical & Electrical Engineering Services
N.A.I.C.S.: 541330

Nylect Technology (Myanmar) Ltd. (1)
Crystal Tower 6-04 Junction Square Compound Kyun Taw Road, Kamaryut Tsp, Yangon, Myanmar
Tel.: (95) 9971966146
Mechanical & Electrical Engineering Services
N.A.I.C.S.: 541330

PKS Sdn Bhd (1)
Lot B Kawasan Perindustrian Beribi I Jalan Gadong, BE 1118, Bandar Seri Begawan, Brunei Darussalam
Tel.: (673) 2421348
Switchgear Mfr
N.A.I.C.S.: 335313
Tony Ng *(Gen Mgr)*

Shanghai Nylect Engineering Co., Ltd. (1)
No 990 Da Lian Road HiShanghai New City Block 10 Room 403, Shanghai, 200092, China
Tel.: (86) 2151287228
Mechanical & Electrical Design Services
N.A.I.C.S.: 541330

Tai Sin Electric Cables (Malaysia) Sdn Bhd (1)
PTD 37433 37434 and 37444 Off Jalan Perindustrian Senai 3, PO Box 73, Kawasan Perindustrian Senai Fasa 2, 81400, Senai, Johor Darul Takzim, Malaysia
Tel.: (60) 75998888
Web Site: https://www.taisin.com.my
Sales Range: $25-49.9 Million
Emp.: 60
Electric Cables Mfr & Whslr
N.A.I.C.S.: 331420
Y. K. Kuan *(Mgr-Sls)*

Tai Sin Electric Cables (VN) Company Limited (1)
20 VSIP II Street 2 Viet Nam-Singapore Industrial Park 2, Hoa Phu Ward, Thu Dau Mot, Binh Duong, Vietnam
Tel.: (84) 2743635088
Web Site: http://www.taisin.com.vn
Sales Range: $25-49.9 Million
Emp.: 55
Fiber Optic Cable Mfr
N.A.I.C.S.: 335921
Andy Yew Choy Pang *(Mng Dir)*

Tai Sin Power Distribution Pte. Ltd. (1)
27 Gul Avenue, Singapore, 629667, Singapore
Tel.: (65) 68977078
Web Site: https://tspd.com.sg
Power Cable Mfr & Distr
N.A.I.C.S.: 335921

TAI TUNG COMMUNICATION CO., LTD.
No 3 Lane 12 Wuquan 3rd Road, Xinzhuang District, New Taipei City, 24891, Taiwan
Tel.: (886) 222991066
Web Site: https://www.ttcc.com.tw
Year Founded: 1981
8011—(TAI)
Rev.: $66,556,687
Assets: $255,335,449
Liabilities: $132,901,823
Net Worth: $122,433,626
Earnings: $1,205,762
Emp.: 270
Fiscal Year-end: 12/31/23
Optical Cables & Other Communications Cables & Equipment Mfr
N.A.I.C.S.: 335921
Ching Hung Lee *(Pres)*

Subsidiaries:

Tai Tung Communication Co., Ltd. - Anhui Factory (1)
No 88 Ta Shan East Rd, Lai-An county, Chuzhou, An-Hui, China
Tel.: (86) 5505605188
Telecommunication Servicesb
N.A.I.C.S.: 517111

Tai Tung Communication Co., Ltd. - Taoyuan Factory (1)
No 10 Datong 1st Rd Guanyin Shiang, Taoyuan, 328, Taiwan
Tel.: (886) 32729010
Telecommunication Servicesb
N.A.I.C.S.: 517111

TAI TWUN ENTERPRISE CO., LTD.
13F No 880 Chung Cheng Rd, Zhonghe Dist, Xinbei City, 235, Taiwan
Tel.: (886) 232349988
Web Site: https://www.taitwun.com.tw
Year Founded: 1988
3432—(TAI)
Rev.: $541,777
Assets: $10,422,381
Liabilities: $1,800,811
Net Worth: $8,621,570
Earnings: ($706,988)
Emp.: 2,500
Fiscal Year-end: 12/31/23
Electronic Components Mfr
N.A.I.C.S.: 334419
Louis Lin *(Chm)*

TAI UNITED HOLDINGS LIMITED
Room 2902 29th Floor China United Centre 28 Marble Road, North Point, Hong Kong, China (Hong Kong)
Tel.: (852) 25286608 BM
Year Founded: 1995
0718—(HKG)
Rev.: $20,301,443
Assets: $460,353,668
Liabilities: $431,976,248
Net Worth: $28,377,420
Earnings: ($185,563,628)
Emp.: 169
Fiscal Year-end: 12/31/22
Holding Company; Metal-Related & Petrochemical Products Trading
N.A.I.C.S.: 551112
Benny Kai Sing Kwong *(CEO)*

TAI ZI CAPITAL LIMITED
Unit 2204 22nd Floor Convention Plaza Office Tower, No 1 Harbour Road, Wanchai, China (Hong Kong)
Tel.: (852) 3719 7333 Ky
Web Site: http://www.taizicapital.com
Property Investor & Manager
N.A.I.C.S.: 531390
Lawrence Man Kwan Ng *(Sec)*

TAI-I ELECTRIC WIRE & CABLE CO., LTD.
10F No 129 Sec 3 Minsheng E Rd, Songshan District, Taipei, 105, Taiwan
Tel.: (886) 2 2718 7333
Web Site: http://www.tai-i-int.com.tw
Year Founded: 1954
Electric Wire & Cable Mfr & Distr
N.A.I.C.S.: 335921
Shou-Hsin Hsu *(Chm)*

Subsidiaries:

Tai-I Copper (Guangzhou) Co., Ltd. (1)
No 77 Dongpeng Rd Eastern District of Guangzhou Economic, Technological Development District, Guangzhou, 510530, China
Tel.: (86) 2082265950
Wire & Cable Mfr
N.A.I.C.S.: 332618

Tai-I Electric Wire & Cable Co., Ltd. - Guanyin Plant (1)
No 606 Xinfu Rd Vicinity 3 Fuyuan Village Guanyin Dist, Taoyuan, 328, Taiwan
Tel.: (886) 34907711
Wire & Cable Mfr
N.A.I.C.S.: 332618

Tai-I Electric Wire & Cable Co., Ltd. - Hsinchu Plant (1)
No 25 Datong Rd Hsinchu Industrial Park, Hsinchu, 310, Taiwan
Tel.: (886) 35981521
Wire & Cable Mfr
N.A.I.C.S.: 332618

Tai-I Jiang Corp (Guangzhou) Co., Ltd. (1)
No 251 Jun Ye Rd Eastern District of Guangzhou Economic, Technological Development District, Guangzhou, 510530, China
Tel.: (86) 2082265949
Wire & Cable Mfr
N.A.I.C.S.: 332618

TAI-SAW TECHNOLOGY CO., LTD.
No 3 Industrial 2nd Road, Ping-Chen Industrial District, Taoyuan, 324, Taiwan
Tel.: (886) 34690038
Web Site: https://www.taisaw.com
Year Founded: 1997
3221—(TPE)
Rev.: $104,992,965
Assets: $113,910,327
Liabilities: $38,038,208
Net Worth: $75,872,120
Earnings: $10,548,229
Emp.: 386
Fiscal Year-end: 12/31/22
Communication Component Mfr
N.A.I.C.S.: 335999
Huang Yu-Tung *(Chm & CTO)*

TAI-TECH ADVANCED ELECTRONICS (S) PTE LTD.
16 New Industrial Road 06-01 To 08 Hudson Technocentre, Singapore, 536204, Singapore

TAI-TECH ADVANCED ELECTRONICS (S) PTE LTD.

Tai-Tech Advanced Electronics (S) Pte Ltd.—(Continued)
Tel.: (65) 6298 9880
Web Site: http://www.tai-tech.com.sg
Year Founded: 1997
Emp.: 32
Prototype Mfr
N.A.I.C.S.: 336414
Adeline Wong *(Dir-Sls-Overseas Market)*

Subsidiaries:

Superworld Electronics (HK) Limited (1)
Unit 8-9 1/F Hope Sea Industrial Centre 26 Lam Hing Street, Kowloon Bay, Kowloon, China (Hong Kong)
Tel.: (852) 2612 2969
Electronic Component Sales
N.A.I.C.S.: 423690

Superworld Electronics (S) Pte Ltd. (1)
16 New Industrial Road, 06 01-08 Hudson Technocentre, Singapore, 536204, Singapore
Tel.: (65) 6298 2866
Web Site: http://www.superworld.com.sg
Emp.: 35
Electronic Component Sales
N.A.I.C.S.: 423690
Elena Rabinovich *(Mng Dir)*

TAI-TECH ADVANCED ELECTRONICS CO., LTD.

No 1 Yousi Road, Youshi Industrial Zone Yangmei District, Taoyuan, Taiwan
Tel.: (886) 34641148
Web Site: https://www.tai-tech.com.tw
Year Founded: 1992
3357—(TPE)
Rev.: $159,282,602
Assets: $219,674,807
Liabilities: $92,836,313
Net Worth: $126,838,494
Earnings: $26,132,247
Fiscal Year-end: 12/31/20
Electronic Parts Mfr
N.A.I.C.S.: 334419
Ming-Liang Hsieh *(Pres)*

TAIBA INVESTMENTS COMPANY

6575 Abdulla Alsahmi St Al Safarat 3031, PO Box 7777, Riyadh, 12511, Saudi Arabia
Tel.: (966) 114816666 SA
Web Site: https://www.taiba.com.sa
Year Founded: 1988
4090—(SAU)
Rev.: $88,063,966
Assets: $1,158,983,197
Liabilities: $184,012,328
Net Worth: $974,970,869
Earnings: $34,584,612
Emp.: 406
Fiscal Year-end: 12/31/22
Holding Company
N.A.I.C.S.: 551112
Walid Mohammad Alissa *(Chm)*

Subsidiaries:

Al Aqeeq Real Estate Development Company (1)
PO Box 4646, Medina, Saudi Arabia (100%)
Tel.: (966) 48378888
Web Site: https://www.alaqeeq.com.sa
Real Estate & Construction Services
N.A.I.C.S.: 531390

TAICANG BONDEX-NISSHIN LOGISTICS CO., LTD.

No 9 Beihuan Road, Fuqiao town, Taicang, China
Tel.: (86) 2158308477

Logistic Services
N.A.I.C.S.: 541614

TAICERA ENTERPRISE COMPANY

Go Dau Industrial Zone Phuoc Thai, Long Thanh, Dong Nai, Vietnam
Tel.: (84) 38661293
Web Site: https://www.taicera.com
Year Founded: 1994
TCR—(HOSE)
Rev.: $36,756,786
Assets: $38,114,079
Liabilities: $20,566,051
Net Worth: $17,548,028
Earnings: ($304,262)
Fiscal Year-end: 12/31/23
Ceramic Tile Mfr
N.A.I.C.S.: 327120
Chen Cheng Jen *(Exec Dir)*

TAICHUNG COMMERCIAL BANK CO., LTD.

No 87 Mincyuan Rd, West District, Taichung, 40341, Taiwan
Tel.: (886) 422236021
Web Site: http://www.tcbbank.com.tw
2812—(TAI)
Rev.: $694,956,840
Assets: $28,710,806,626
Liabilities: $26,208,599,847
Net Worth: $2,502,206,779
Earnings: $223,075,763
Emp.: 2,919
Fiscal Year-end: 12/31/23
Banking Services
N.A.I.C.S.: 522110
Kai-Yu Lin *(Exec VP)*

TAIDOC TECHNOLOGY CORP.

Tel.: (886) 266258188
Web Site: https://www.taidoc.com
4736—(TPE)
Rev.: $230,965,223
Assets: $374,284,293
Liabilities: $102,722,283
Net Worth: $271,562,011
Earnings: $72,712,550
Fiscal Year-end: 12/31/20
Medical Device Mfr
N.A.I.C.S.: 339112
Chao-Wang Chen *(Chm & Pres)*

TAIER HEAVY INDUSTRY CO., LTD.

669 Chaoshan Road, Economic & Technological Development Zone, Ma'anshan, 243000, Anhui, China
Tel.: (86) 5552202289
Web Site: https://english.taiergroup.com
Year Founded: 2001
002347—(SSE)
Rev.: $152,028,602
Assets: $357,247,730
Liabilities: $180,019,588
Net Worth: $177,228,141
Earnings: ($5,410,089)
Fiscal Year-end: 12/31/22
Mechanical Power Transmission Equipment & Shearing Blades Mfr & Distr
N.A.I.C.S.: 333613

TAIFLEX SCIENTIFIC CO., LTD.

No 1 Huanqu 3rd Rd Kaohsiung Cianjhen Technology Industrial Park, Cianjhen Dist, Kaohsiung, 806, Taiwan
Tel.: (886) 78139989
Web Site: https://www.taiflex.com.tw
Year Founded: 1997
8039—(TAI)
Rev.: $266,539,739
Assets: $426,157,216
Liabilities: $162,295,523

Net Worth: $263,861,693
Earnings: $11,796,428
Emp.: 1,180
Fiscal Year-end: 12/31/23
Flexible Copper Cladded Laminates, Coverlays & Solar Energy Module Backsheets Mfr
N.A.I.C.S.: 322220
Joseph Jaw *(VP-Supply Chain & Information Center)*

Subsidiaries:

Koatech Technology Corporation (1)
No 79 Guangfu Rd Hukou Township, Hsinchu, 303036, Taiwan
Tel.: (886) 35971882
Web Site: https://www.koatech.com.tw
Electronic Component Mfr & Distr
N.A.I.C.S.: 334419

Kun-san Taiflex Electronic Material Co., Ltd. (1)
No 1 TaiHong Road Wu Song Jiang Industry Park, Yushan, Kunshan, Jiangsu, China
Tel.: (86) 512 57561168
Electronic Materials Mfr
N.A.I.C.S.: 334419
Ye Yongmao *(Gen Mgr)*

Kunshan Koatech Technology Corporation (1)
Building F No 19 Taihong Road, Yushan Town, Kunshan, Jiangsu, China
Tel.: (86) 51283519612
Electric Component Whslr
N.A.I.C.S.: 423610

Kunshan Taiflex Electronic Co., Ltd. (1)
Room 321 Yuda Science & Technology Park 6 Leshan Road, Kunshan, Jiangsu, China
Tel.: (86) 51257561168
Semiconductor Component Distr
N.A.I.C.S.: 423690

Rudong Fuzhan Scientific Co., Ltd. (1)
No 88 Jinshan Road High-tech Industrial Development Zone, Rudong County, Nantong, Jiangsu, China
Tel.: (86) 51368971867
Electronic Material Mfr & Distr
N.A.I.C.S.: 334419

Shenzhen Taiflex Electronic Co., Ltd. (1)
Unit 906 Building B No 3 Xinyu Road Xiangshan Community, Xinqiao Subdistrict Baoan District, Shenzhen, Guangdong, China
Tel.: (86) 75527332080
Coating Material Distr
N.A.I.C.S.: 424690

Taichem Materials Co., Ltd. (1)
3F No 8 S 3rd Rd, Qianzhen Dist, Kaohsiung, Taiwan
Tel.: (886) 78231888
Web Site: https://www.taichem.net
Semiconductor Material Mfr & Distr
N.A.I.C.S.: 334413

Taiflex Green Power Co., Ltd. (1)
No 1 Huanqu 3rd Rd, Qianzhen Dist, Kaohsiung, 806011, Taiwan
Tel.: (886) 78139989
Solar Power Plant Design Services
N.A.I.C.S.: 541330

Taiflex Scientific (Thailand) Co., Ltd. (1)
700/816 Moo 10, Phanthong Subdistrict, Phan Thong, 20160, Chonburi, Thailand
Tel.: (66) 33136768
Electronic Component Mfr & Distr
N.A.I.C.S.: 334419

Taiflex Scientific Japan Co., Ltd. (1)
14F Arca Central 1-2-1, Kinshi, Sumida, 130-0013, Tokyo, Japan
Tel.: (81) 368536633
Electronic Material Distr
N.A.I.C.S.: 423690

Taiflex USA Corporation (1)
2033 Gateway Pl Ste 500, San Jose, CA 95110

INTERNATIONAL PUBLIC

Tel.: (408) 961-8795
Electronic Material Distr
N.A.I.C.S.: 423690

TAIGEN BIOPHARMACEUTICALS HOLDINGS LTD.

7F No 138 Xinming Rd, Neihu Dist, Taipei, 11470, Taiwan
Tel.: (886) 281777020
4157—(TPE)
Rev.: $1,132,789
Assets: $32,736,360
Liabilities: $2,406,841
Net Worth: $30,329,519
Earnings: ($7,415,314)
Emp.: 53
Fiscal Year-end: 12/31/22
Pharmaceuticals Product Mfr
N.A.I.C.S.: 325412
Huang Kuo-Lung *(Chm, Pres & CEO)*

TAIHAN CABLE & SOLUTION CO., LTD.

Taihan Smart Tower 317 Simin-daero, Dongan-gu, Anyang, Gyeonggi-do, Korea (South)
Tel.: (82) 23169114
Web Site: https://www.taihan.com
Year Founded: 1955
001440—(KRS)
Rev.: $1,337,076,384
Assets: $1,062,165,351
Liabilities: $793,289,287
Net Worth: $268,876,064
Earnings: ($10,859,847)
Emp.: 863
Fiscal Year-end: 12/31/19
Electrical Wire Mfr
N.A.I.C.S.: 332618
Hyung-Kyun Na *(Pres & CEO)*

Subsidiaries:

Malesela Taihan Electric Cable (Pty) Ltd. (1)
273 General Hertzog Rd, Peacehaven, Vereeniging, 1939, Gauteng, South Africa (49%)
Tel.: (27) 164508200
Web Site: https://www.m-tec.co.za
Non-Ferrou Cable Mfr
N.A.I.C.S.: 335929

Taihan Electric USA, Ltd. (1)
Landmark Bldg 99 Tulip Way Ste 106, Floral Park, NY 11001
Tel.: (516) 355-5600
Web Site: www.taihan.com
Sales Range: $25-49.9 Million
Emp.: 1
Sales
N.A.I.C.S.: 333613

Taihan Electric Wire Co., Ltd. - Dangjin Plant (1)
1110 Janghang-ri Godae-myeon, Dangjin, South Chungcheong, Korea (South)
Tel.: (82) 413609114
Eletric Power Generation Services
N.A.I.C.S.: 221111

TAIHAN FIBEROPTICS CO., LTD.

49 Jangjagol-ro, Danwon-gu, Ansan, Korea (South)
Tel.: (82) 314503968
Web Site: https://www.taihanfiber.com
Year Founded: 1974
010170—(KRS)
Rev.: $145,813,226
Assets: $193,344,234
Liabilities: $112,404,195
Net Worth: $80,940,040
Earnings: ($2,365,483)
Emp.: 272
Fiscal Year-end: 12/31/22
Fiber Optic Electrical Equipment Mfr
N.A.I.C.S.: 335921
Ha-Young Park *(CEO)*

AND PRIVATE COMPANIES / TAIHEIYO CEMENT CORPORATION

Subsidiaries:

Tfo America Inc. (1)
1313 Ave R, Grand Prairie, TX 75050
Web Site: https://tforods.com
Fishing Rod Mfr & Distr
N.A.I.C.S.: 339920

TAIHAN PRECISION TECHNOLOGY CO., LTD.
1F No 568 Section 1 Minsheng North Road, Guishan District, Taoyuan, 248, Taiwan
Tel.: (886) 33112025
Web Site: https://www.thpt.com.tw
Year Founded: 1987
1336—(TPE)
Rev.: $83,455,336
Assets: $86,717,412
Liabilities: $32,828,315
Net Worth: $53,889,097
Earnings: $4,934,090
Emp.: 1,920
Fiscal Year-end: 12/31/22
Plastic Mfr
N.A.I.C.S.: 326199
Chien Ping Yang *(Chm & Pres)*

TAIHAN TEXTILE CO., LTD.
48 Jungnim-ro, Jung-gu, Seoul, Korea (South)
Tel.: (82) 23680114
Web Site: https://www.thtc.co.kr
Year Founded: 1953
001070—(KRS)
Rev.: $146,895,603
Assets: $161,560,541
Liabilities: $57,825,754
Net Worth: $103,734,787
Earnings: ($4,012,081)
Emp.: 359
Fiscal Year-end: 12/31/22
Textile Products Mfr
N.A.I.C.S.: 313310
Snow Beom *(Chm & CEO)*

Subsidiaries:

PT. TAIHAN Indonesia (1)
GD Plaza Pondok Indah III Block E No 3 4 Floor Pondok Pinang, Kebayoran Lama, Jakarta, 12310, Selatan, Indonesia
Tel.: (62) 2129519314
Textile Products Distr
N.A.I.C.S.: 424990

Qingdao Taihan Dyeing & Printing Co., Ltd. (1)
Cuhe Street, Laixi, Qingdao, China
Tel.: (86) 532 8745 8021
Textile Products Mfr
N.A.I.C.S.: 313310

Qingdao Tayuan Textile Ltd. (1)
No 153 Wenhua Street, Jimo, Qingdao, China
Tel.: (86) 532 8859 9621
Textile Products Mfr
N.A.I.C.S.: 313110

Taihan Textile Co., Ltd. - Daegu Plant (1)
26 Yeomsaekgongdon-ro, Seo-gu, Daegu, Korea (South)
Tel.: (82) 53 720 4400
Textile Products Mfr
N.A.I.C.S.: 313310

Taihan Textile Co., Ltd. - Jeonju Plant (1)
220 Yuyeon 151 Hyojadong 3 sam-ga, Wansan-gu, Jeonju, Jeollabuk-do, Korea (South)
Tel.: (82) 63 222 7121
Textile Products Mfr
N.A.I.C.S.: 313110

Taihan Textile(Shanghai)Co., Ltd. (1)
Rm 512 Hyunoon International Bldg Wuzhong Road 1100, Shanghai, 201103, China
Tel.: (86) 2164019276
Textile Products Distr
N.A.I.C.S.: 424990

TAIHEI DENGYO KAISHA LTD.
2-4 Kanda Jimbo-cho, Chiyoda-ku, Tokyo, 101-8416, Japan
Tel.: (81) 352137211
Web Site: https://www.taihei-dengyo.co.jp
Year Founded: 1947
1968—(TKS)
Rev.: $855,089,430
Assets: $1,011,482,030
Liabilities: $346,568,910
Net Worth: $664,913,120
Earnings: $55,490,950
Emp.: 1,532
Fiscal Year-end: 03/31/24
Construction Services
N.A.I.C.S.: 237990
Jo Nojiri *(Pres & CEO)*

Subsidiaries:

Fuji I-Tec Co., Ltd. (1)
Iwanami Shoten Hitotsubashi Bldg 2-5-5 Hitotsubashi, Chiyoda-ku, Tokyo, 101-0003, Japan
Tel.: (81) 332346001
Emp.: 150
Heat & Cold Insulation Services
N.A.I.C.S.: 238390
Toshio Goto *(Chm)*

Tokyo Doryoku Co., Ltd. (1)
11-8 Tsukuno-cho, Tsurumi-ku, Yokohama, 230-0061, Japan
Tel.: (81) 455823181
Power Plant Construction Services
N.A.I.C.S.: 237990

TAIHEI MACHINERY WORKS, LTD.
955-8 Miyamae Irukade-Shinden, Komaki, 485-0084, Aichi, Japan
Tel.: (81) 568736421
Web Site: https://www.taihei-ss.co.jp
Year Founded: 1925
63420—(TKS)
Rev.: $58,427,470
Assets: $79,497,830
Liabilities: $34,218,689
Net Worth: $45,279,142
Earnings: $7,036,668
Emp.: 156
Fiscal Year-end: 03/31/24
Woodworking Machinery Mfr
N.A.I.C.S.: 333243
Takeshi Saito *(Pres)*

Subsidiaries:

Taihei Housing Co., Ltd. (1)
Nino 1979-1, Kani, 509-0232, Gifu, Japan
Tel.: (81) 574621923
Web Site: http://www.taihei-housing.co.jp
Residential Construction Services
N.A.I.C.S.: 236116

Taihei Machinery Works, Ltd. - Osaka Plant (1)
2-3-33 Midori, Suminoe-ku, Osaka, Japan
Tel.: (81) 666859551
Web Site: http://www.taihei-ss-osaka.jp
Emp.: 50
Industrial Machinery Mfr
N.A.I.C.S.: 333248

TAIHEIYO CEMENT CORPORATION
Bunkyo Garden Gate Tower 1-1-1 Koishikawa, Bunkyo-ku, Tokyo, 112-8503, Japan
Tel.: (81) 358010333
Web Site: https://www.taiheiyo-cement.co.jp
Year Founded: 1881
5233—(FKA)
Rev.: $5,804,416,140
Assets: $9,097,740,540
Liabilities: $5,305,835,850
Net Worth: $3,791,904,690
Earnings: ($238,087,020)
Emp.: 1,841
Fiscal Year-end: 03/31/23
Cement, Limestone Products & Building Materials Mfr & Distr
N.A.I.C.S.: 327310
Shuji Fukuda *(Chm)*

Subsidiaries:

Abekawa Kaihatsu Co., Ltd (1)
4-9-37 Toshinden, Suruga-ku, Shizuoka, 421-0112, Japan
Tel.: (81) 542593126
Glass & Ceramic Products Distr
N.A.I.C.S.: 423320

Asano Concrete Co., Ltd. (1)
Higashi Nihonbashi 2-27-8 Asano East Bridge Building, Chuo-ku, Tokyo, 103-0004, Japan
Tel.: (81) 35 823 6168
Web Site: https://www.asano-concrete.co.jp
Ready Mixed Concrete Mfr & Distr
N.A.I.C.S.: 327320

Buko Mining Co., Ltd. (1)
721 Harajuku, Hidaka, 350-1205, Saitama, Japan
Tel.: (81) 42 989 8125
Web Site: http://www.buko-mining.co.jp
Limestone Mining Services
N.A.I.C.S.: 327310

Chichibu Concrete Industry Co., Ltd. (1)
1-5-7 Higashinippori, Arakawa-ku, Tokyo, 116-0014, Japan
Tel.: (81) 358502661
Construction Materials Distr
N.A.I.C.S.: 423390

Chichibu Taiheiyo Cement Corporation (1)
1800 Onohara, Chichibu, 368-0005, Saitama, Japan
Tel.: (81) 494221300
Cement Mfr
N.A.I.C.S.: 327310

DC Co., Ltd. (1)
8 Higashida-cho, Kawasaki-ku, Kawasaki, 210-0005, Kanagawa, Japan
Tel.: (81) 44 223 4759
Web Site: https://www.dccorp.jp
Sales Range: $300-349.9 Million
Emp.: 452
Cement Mfr & Distr
N.A.I.C.S.: 327310
Hideki Kudo *(Pres)*

Dalian Onoda Cement Co., Ltd. (1)
No 5 New Cement Road Ganjingzi District, Dalian, 116035, Liaoning, China
Tel.: (86) 41186425056
Cement Mfr
N.A.I.C.S.: 327310

Ichihara Ecocement Corporation (1)
1-8 Yawatakaigandoori, Chiba, 290-0067, Ichihara, Japan
Tel.: (81) 436428881
Web Site: http://www.ichiharaeco.co.jp
Cement Mfr
N.A.I.C.S.: 327310

Ishizaki Co., Ltd. (1)
130 1 Fujiwarachotozenji, Inabe, 511-0515, Mie, Japan
Tel.: (81) 594462074
Cement Mfr

Joyo Remicon Co., Ltd. (1)
28-5 Kanda Higashimatsushita- cho 3rd Floor of Yoshimoto Building, Chiyoda-ku, Tokyo, 101-0042, Japan
Tel.: (81) 35 577 5466
Web Site: https://www.joyo-remicon.co.jp
Ready Mixed Concrete Mfr & Distr
N.A.I.C.S.: 327320

Kalahari Dry (Thailand) Co., Ltd. (1)
Khwang Silom Khet Bang Rak, Bangkok, 10500, Thailand
Tel.: (66) 22668342
Web Site: http://www.kalaharidry.co.th
Cement Mfr
N.A.I.C.S.: 327310

Kansai Matech Co., Ltd. (1)
11FL KDX Minamihonmachi Building 2-3-8 Minamihonmachi, Chuo-ku, Osaka, 541-0054, Japan
Tel.: (81) 66 260 0170
Web Site: https://www.kansaimatec.co.jp
Aggregate Stably Mfr & Distr
N.A.I.C.S.: 333120
Kunio Umetsu *(Pres)*

Kansai Taiheiyo Minerals Corporation (1)
2-3-18 Minamitsumori Nishinari Ku, Osaka, 557-0063, Japan
Tel.: (81) 666594141
Mineral Mining Services
N.A.I.C.S.: 212390

Kiyosumi Golf Club Co., Ltd. (1)
1875 Oaza Kobe, Higashimatsuyama, 355-0066, Saitama, Japan
Tel.: (81) 49 335 3344
Web Site: https://www.kiyosumi-golf.co.jp
Golf Club Services
N.A.I.C.S.: 713910

Kokusai Kigyo Co., Ltd. (1)
1-38-2 Higashi Kanamachi Ebata Bldg 4/F, Katsushika-ku, Tokyo, 1382, Japan
Tel.: (81) 3 3826 4331
Sales Range: $25-49.9 Million
Emp.: 50
Construction Materials Whslr
N.A.I.C.S.: 423320
Ryo Yokoyama *(Pres)*

Kosyu Saiseki Co., Ltd (1)
5-27-9 Sendagaya Asano Shinjuku Building 4 F, Shibuya-Ku, Tokyo, 151-0051, Japan
Tel.: (81) 333542431
Cement Mfr
N.A.I.C.S.: 327310

Mitsui Wharf Co., Ltd. (1)
9-1 Ogimachi, Kawasaki-ku, Kawasaki, 210-0867, Kanagawa, Japan
Tel.: (81) 443335311
Web Site: http://www.mitsui-wharf.co.jp
Sales Range: $50-74.9 Million
Emp.: 160
Port Transportation; Warehousing; Stevedoring; Freight Forwarding; Customs Brokerage; Shipping Agency; Real Estate Services
N.A.I.C.S.: 483111

Myojyo Cement Co., Ltd. (1)
Uekari 7 chome No 1 winnowing fan mine, Itoigawa, 941-0064, Japan
Tel.: (81) 255522011
Web Site: http://www.myojyo-cement.co.jp
Emp.: 131
Cement Mfr
N.A.I.C.S.: 327310

NACODE Corporation (1)
2-27-8 Higashinihombashi, Chuo-ku, Tokyo, 103-0004, Japan
Tel.: (81) 338613870
Cement Mfr
N.A.I.C.S.: 327310

Ofunato Power Inc. (1)
2025 E Financial Way, Glendora, CA 91741
Web Site: https://www.calportland.com
Construction Materials Mfr
N.A.I.C.S.: 327120

Oita Taiheiyo Mining Corporation (1)
3700 Shimoaoe, Tsukumi, 879-2446, Oita, Japan
Tel.: (81) 972850271
Coal Mining Services
N.A.I.C.S.: 213113

Okutama Kogyo Co., Ltd (1)
1-18-2 Akebono-cho, Tachikawa, Tokyo, 190-0012, Japan
Tel.: (81) 425405670
Web Site: http://www.okutama.co.jp
Sales Range: $100-124.9 Million
Emp.: 200
Limestone Mining Services
N.A.I.C.S.: 212312
Masanori Matsukawa *(Pres)*

Subsidiary (Domestic):

Fukuyama Mizuho Unyu Co., Ltd. (2)
2-23-17 Nishishingaicho, Fukuyama, 721-0958, Japan
Tel.: (81) 849544220
Freight Forwarding Services
N.A.I.C.S.: 488510

TAIHEIYO CEMENT CORPORATION

Taiheiyo Cement Corporation—(Continued)

Mizuho Unyu Co., Ltd (2)
422 Nihongi Mizuhomachi, Nishitama-gun, Tokyo, 190-1201, Japan
Tel.: (81) 425571310
Web Site: http://www.mizuhounyu.com
Freight Forwarding Services
N.A.I.C.S.: 488510

Niigata PCC Co., Ltd. (2)
2-3 Kamiosemachi, Higashi-ku, Niigata, 950-0063, Japan
Tel.: (81) 252709616
Paper Products Mfr
N.A.I.C.S.: 322299

Sankyo Unyu Kogyo Co., Ltd. (2)
420 Nihongi Mizuhomachi, Nishitama-Gun, Tokyo, 190-1201, Japan
Tel.: (81) 425566507
Freight Forwarding Services
N.A.I.C.S.: 488510

Yokohama Kairyodo Center Co., Ltd. (2)
1-6-8 Suehirocho, Tsurumi-Ku, Yokohama, 230-0045, Japan
Tel.: (81) 455023745
Limestone Mining Services
N.A.I.C.S.: 212312

Onoda Chemical Industry Co., Ltd (1)
1-15-1 Kaigan Suzue Baydium 6th floor, Minato-ku, Tokyo, 105-0022, Japan
Tel.: (81) 35 776 8222
Web Site: https://www.onoda-kagaku.co.jp
Sales Range: $150-199.9 Million
Emp.: 301
Chemical Fertilizers Mfr & Sales
N.A.I.C.S.: 325180
Shinji Matsui (Pres & CEO)

Onoda Chemico Co., Ltd. (1)
3-21 Kanda Nishikicho, Chiyoda-ku, Tokyo, 101-0054, Japan
Tel.: (81) 36 386 7030
Web Site: https://www.chemico.co.jp
Emp.: 361
Soil Improvement Services
N.A.I.C.S.: 238910

PNG-Taiheiyo Cement Limited (1)
PO Box 4150, Lae, 411, Morobe, Papua New Guinea
Tel.: (675) 472 7499
Web Site: https://www.pngtaiheiyo.com
Sales Range: $125-149.9 Million
Emp.: 400
Cement Mfr
N.A.I.C.S.: 327310
Hiroyuki Egawa (Mng Dir)

Pacific Systems Corporation (1)
8-4-19 Tajima, Sakura-ku, Saitama, 338-0837, Japan
Tel.: (81) 488452200
Web Site: https://www.pacific-systems.co.jp
Rev.: $72,214,250
Assets: $61,102,840
Liabilities: $20,219,990
Net Worth: $40,882,850
Earnings: $3,833,800
Fiscal Year-end: 03/31/2024
Computer Peripheral Distr
N.A.I.C.S.: 423430
Yasuhiro Watanabe (Pres & CEO)

Sanyo White Cement Co., Ltd. (1)
1-2-1 Itozaki Minami, Mihara, 729-0329, Hiroshima, Japan (100%)
Tel.: (81) 848622131
Web Site: http://www.sanyowhitecement.com
Sales Range: $25-49.9 Million
Emp.: 33
White Cement Mfr
N.A.I.C.S.: 327310
Hiroshi Hanada (Pres)

Shanghai Sanhang Onoda Cement Co., Ltd (1)
No 760 Dongtang Road Pudong New Area, Shanghai, 200137, China
Tel.: (86) 2158674655
Cement Mfr
N.A.I.C.S.: 327310

Taiheiyo Accounting & Financial Services Corporation (1)
2-3-5 Daiba, Minato-ku, Tokyo, 135-8578, Japan
Tel.: (81) 355317325
Web Site: http://www.taiheiyo-cement.co.jp
Financial Support Services
N.A.I.C.S.: 522390

Taiheiyo Cement (China) Investment Co., Ltd
3001 Room 30F Tull Tower No 9 Dongsanhuanzhong Road, Chao Yang District, Beijing, 100020, China
Tel.: (86) 1085911815
Web Site: http://www.taiheiyo-cement.co.jp
Concrete Mfr
N.A.I.C.S.: 327320

Taiheiyo Cement Philippines, Inc. (1)
11th Floor Insular Life Cebu Business Park, Cebu, 6000, Philippines
Tel.: (63) 32 230 7333
Web Site: https://www.taiheiyo-cement.com.ph
Cement Mfr
N.A.I.C.S.: 327310

Taiheiyo Cement U.S.A., Inc. (1)
2025 E Financial Way, Glendora, CA 91741-4692 (100%)
Tel.: (626) 852-6200
Sales Range: $75-99.9 Million
Emp.: 150
Holding Company; Cement Mfr & Distr
N.A.I.C.S.: 327310
Ken Kikuchi (Pres)

Subsidiary (Domestic):

California Portland Cement Company (2)
2025 E Financial Way, Glendora, CA 91741
Tel.: (626) 852-6200
Web Site: https://www.calportland.com
Cement Mfr & Distr
N.A.I.C.S.: 327310

Subsidiary (Domestic):

CalPortland Cement Company (3)
5975 E Marginal Way S, Seattle, WA 98134-2414
Tel.: (206) 764-3000
Web Site: http://www.calportland.com
Sales Range: $250-299.9 Million
Emp.: 650
Ready-Mix Concrete, Building Materials Supplier
N.A.I.C.S.: 327320
Allen Hamblen (Pres & CEO)

Branch (Domestic):

CalPortland Cement Company (3)
4005 Dean Martin Dr, Las Vegas, NV 89103
Tel.: (702) 893-6557
Web Site: http://www.calportland.com
Sales Range: $10-24.9 Million
Emp.: 90
Ready-Mixed Concrete Mfr & Distr
N.A.I.C.S.: 327320
Steven D. Hill (Sr VP)

Division (Domestic):

CalPortland Concrete Products (3)
519 S Benson Ave, Ontario, CA 91762
Tel.: (909) 983-9789
Web Site: https://www.calportland.com
Sales Range: $1-9.9 Million
Emp.: 45
Concrete Manhole Mfr
N.A.I.C.S.: 327332
Allen Hamblen (Pres & CEO)

Plant (Domestic):

California Portland Cement Company-Colton Cement Plant (3)
695 S Rancho Ave, Colton, CA 92324
Tel.: (909) 825-4260
Web Site: http://www.calportland.com
Sales Range: $50-74.9 Million
Emp.: 150
Cement Mfr & Distr
N.A.I.C.S.: 327310
Mike Scobel (Superintendent)

California Portland Cement Company-Mojave Cement Plant (3)
9350 Oak Creek Rd, Mojave, CA 93501
Tel.: (661) 824-2401
Web Site: https://www.calportland.com
Sales Range: $50-74.9 Million
Emp.: 120
Cement Mfr & Distr
N.A.I.C.S.: 327310

California Portland Cement Company-Rillito Cement Plant (3)
11115 Casa Grande Hwy, Rillito, AZ 85654
Tel.: (520) 682-2221
Web Site: https://www.calportland.com
Sales Range: $50-74.9 Million
Emp.: 130
Cement Mfr & Distr
N.A.I.C.S.: 327310

Taiheiyo Engineering Corporation (1)
8-4-6 Nishikasai Street Nishikasai Building 4 F, Edogawa-ku, 134-0088, Tokyo, Japan
Tel.: (81) 356793260
Web Site: http://www.taiheiyo-eng.co.jp
Sales Range: $25-49.9 Million
Emp.: 184
Engineering Consulting Services
N.A.I.C.S.: 541330
Bhaskar Alagala (Mgr-Overseas)

Taiheiyo Materials Corporation (1)
6-1-1 Tabata, Kita-ku, Tokyo, 114-0014, Japan
Tel.: (81) 35 832 5211
Web Site: https://www.taiheiyo-m.co.jp
Emp.: 380
Construction Engineering Services
N.A.I.C.S.: 541330
Toshiro Goto (Pres)

Taiheiyo Precast Concrete Industry Co., Ltd. (1)
5-13-9 Taiheiyo Real Estate Shinjuku Building 4F, Shinjuku-ku, Tokyo, 160-0022, Japan
Tel.: (81) 33 350 0681
Web Site: https://www.t-pc.co.jp
Concrete Products Mfr
N.A.I.C.S.: 327390

Taiheiyo Real Estate Co., Ltd. (1)
5-27-9 Sendagaya Shinjuku Park Building 4 F, Shibuya-ku, Tokyo, 151-0051, Japan
Tel.: (81) 333528582
Web Site: http://www.taiheiyofudofan.co.jp
Sales Range: $25-49.9 Million
Emp.: 30
Real Estate Manangement Services
N.A.I.C.S.: 531390

Taiheiyo Singapore Pte. Ltd. (1)
16 Raffles Quay 41-03 Hong Leong Bldg, Singapore, 048581, Singapore (100%)
Tel.: (65) 62209495
Web Site: http://www.taiheiyo-cement.co.jp
Sales Range: $25-49.9 Million
Emp.: 3
N.A.I.C.S.: 327320
Yoshihiko Kajiki (Mng Dir)

TAIHEIYO KOUHATSU INCORPORATED

6th Floor MATAI BLDG 2-6-7 Motoasakusa, Taito-ku, Tokyo, 111-0041, Japan
Tel.: (81) 358301601
Web Site: https://www.taiheiyo.net
Year Founded: 1920
8835—(TKS)
Rev.: $271,697,440
Assets: $296,471,720
Liabilities: $189,297,180
Net Worth: $107,174,540
Earnings: $4,137,860
Emp.: 240
Fiscal Year-end: 03/31/24
Real Estate Development Services
N.A.I.C.S.: 531390
Yoshinori Itagaki (Pres)

Subsidiaries:

HCC Inc. (1)
pickingHarutori8-chome 2-10, Kushiro, 085-0813, Hokkaido, Japan
Tel.: (81) 154465311
Web Site: https://www.hccnet.co.jp
Emp.: 51

INTERNATIONAL PUBLIC

Software Development Services
N.A.I.C.S.: 541511

Kunneppu Sekkai Kogyo Inc. (1)
86 Omachi Kunneppu-cho, Tokoro-gun, Hokkaido, 099-1436, Japan
Tel.: (81) 157 47 2101
Web Site: http://www.k-sekkai.net
Fertilizer Mfr & Distr
N.A.I.C.S.: 325314

Marimo Koutsu Inc. (1)
5-18-27 Harutori, Kushiro, 085-0813, Hokkaido, Japan
Tel.: (81) 154 46 3123
Taxi Service
N.A.I.C.S.: 485310

Taiheiyo Coal Mining Co., Ltd. (1)
5-2-23 Okotsu, Kushiro, 085-0811, Hokkaido, Japan
Tel.: (81) 154 46 3111
Coal Mining Services
N.A.I.C.S.: 213113

Taiheiyo Coal Service & Transportation Co., Ltd. (1)
3-18 Shirito, Kushiro, 085-0844, Hokkaido, Japan
Tel.: (81) 154 41 9155
Web Site: http://www.youhan.co.jp
Coal Whslr
N.A.I.C.S.: 423520

Taiheiyo Seisakusho Inc. (1)
7-4-1 Kuroganecho, Kushiro, 085-0018, Hokkaido, Japan
Tel.: (81) 154651025
Web Site: https://www.t-fact.co.jp
Emp.: 39
Chemical Products Mfr
N.A.I.C.S.: 325998

Taiheiyo Silver Service Co., Ltd. (1)
2-8-19 Kyonan-cho, Musashino, 180-0023, Tokyo, Japan
Tel.: (81) 422341636
Web Site: https://www.kaiteki.info
Emp.: 341
Real Estate Manangement Services
N.A.I.C.S.: 531390

Taiheiyo Silver Service Hokkaido Co., Ltd. (1)
7-4-1 Kuroganecho, Kushiro, 085-0018, Hokkaido, Japan
Tel.: (81) 154252101
Web Site: https://www.silvercity.jp
Real Estate Manangement Services
N.A.I.C.S.: 531390

Taiheiyo Unyu Inc. (1)
3-7-22 Kaizuka, Kushiro, 085-0816, Hokkaido, Japan
Tel.: (81) 154414471
Web Site: https://www.taiun.net
Emp.: 34
General Freight Trucking Services
N.A.I.C.S.: 484110

TAIHO KOGYO CO., LTD

3-65 Midorigaoka, Toyota, 471-8502, Aichi, Japan
Tel.: (81) 565282225 JP
Web Site: https://www.taihonet.co.jp
Year Founded: 1944
6470—(TKS)
Rev.: $740,610,840
Assets: $789,610,770
Liabilities: $309,810,700
Net Worth: $479,800,070
Earnings: $11,547,670
Emp.: 4,107
Fiscal Year-end: 03/31/24
Motor Vehicle Parts & Accessories Mfr
N.A.I.C.S.: 336340
Koichi Sugihara (Pres)

Subsidiaries:

Nippon Gasket Co., Ltd. (1)
5th floor Shin-Osaka Meiko Building 4-3-12 Miyahara, Yodogawa-ku, Osaka, 532-0003, Japan
Tel.: (81) 648075678
Web Site: https://www.npgkt.co.jp

Sales Range: $25-49.9 Million
Emp.: 695
Automotive Gasket Mfr
N.A.I.C.S.: 339991

PT. Taiho Nusantara (1)
Jl Permata Raya Lot BB-8B Kawasan Industri KIIC, Karawang, 41361, Jawa Barat, Indonesia
Tel.: (62) 2189106545
Web Site: http://www.taihonet.co.jp
Engine Bearings Mfr
N.A.I.C.S.: 336310

Taiho Corporation of America, Inc. (1)
194 Heritage Dr, Tiffin, OH 44883-9503
Tel.: (419) 443-1645
Web Site: https://taihousa.com
Sales Range: $25-49.9 Million
Emp.: 280
Automobile Parts Mfr
N.A.I.C.S.: 336390
Jonna Lewis (Mgr-HR)

Taiho Corporation of Europe Kft. (1)
Japan fasor 7, 2367, Ujhartyan, Pest, Hungary
Tel.: (36) 29572800
Web Site: https://www.taiho.hu
Sales Range: $50-74.9 Million
Emp.: 200
Automotive Components Mfr
N.A.I.C.S.: 332912

Taiho Corporation of Korea (1)
16 Seongseoseo-ro 15-gil, Dalseo-Gu, Daegu, 42718, Korea (South)
Tel.: (82) 535932212
Web Site: http://www.taihonet.co.jp
Sales Range: $25-49.9 Million
Emp.: 60
Engine Bearings Mfr
N.A.I.C.S.: 336310

Taiho Kogyo Co., Ltd - Main Plant (1)
3-65 Midorigaoka, Toyota, 471-8502, Aichi, Japan
Tel.: (81) 565282225
Web Site: http://www.taihonet.co.jp
Powdered Alloy & Aluminum Die Cast Products Mfr
N.A.I.C.S.: 331110

Taiho Kogyo Corporation of Yantai (1)
NO 42 Guang Zhou road, Yantai Eco tech Development Zone, Yantai, 264006, Shandong, China
Tel.: (86) 5356952996
Web Site: http://www.taihonet.co.jp
Sales Range: $100-124.9 Million
Emp.: 400
Engine Bearings Mfr
N.A.I.C.S.: 332991

TAIHO TRANSPORTATION CO., LTD.
5-3-17 Kanayama, Naka, Nagoya, 460-0022, Aichi, Japan
Tel.: (81) 528715831
Web Site: https://www.taiho-gh.com
Year Founded: 1951
9040—(NGO)
Sales Range: $5-14.9 Billion
Transport Services
N.A.I.C.S.: 485999
Kazutoshi Ogasawara (Chm)

TAIJI COMPUTER CORPORATION LIMITED
No 211 Beisihuan Middle Road, Haidian District, Beijing, 100102, China
Tel.: (86) 1057702596
Web Site: http://www.taiji.com.cn
Year Founded: 1987
002368—(SSE)
Rev.: $1,488,356,672
Assets: $2,226,178,946
Liabilities: $1,595,528,696
Net Worth: $630,650,250
Earnings: $53,023,618
Fiscal Year-end: 12/31/22
Computer Systems

N.A.I.C.S.: 541512
Lv Yi (Chm)

TAIKANG INSURANCE GROUP CO., LTD.
156 Fuxingmennei Street, Taikang Life Building, Beijing, 100031, China
Tel.: (86) 10 6642 9988   CN
Web Site: http://www.taikang.com
Year Founded: 1996
Sales Range: Less than $1 Million
Emp.: 700,000
Health & Wealth Management Services
N.A.I.C.S.: 524210
Dongsheng Chen (Chm & CEO)

TAIKISHA LTD.
Sumitomo Fudosan Shinjuku Grand Tower 8-17-1 Nishi-Shinjuku, Shinjuku-ku, Tokyo, 160-6129, Japan
Tel.: (81) 333655320
Web Site: http://www.taikisha.co.jp
Year Founded: 1913
1979—(TKS)
Rev.: $1,940,405,160
Assets: $1,761,525,340
Liabilities: $759,700,520
Net Worth: $1,001,824,820
Earnings: $103,129,220
Emp.: 5,174
Fiscal Year-end: 03/31/24
Air-Conditioning Design, Supervision & Construction
N.A.I.C.S.: 238220
Nagata Masashi (Pres & CEO)

Subsidiaries:

Custom-Ace Ltd. (1)
1-7-10 Shingashi, Itabashi-ku, Tokyo, 175-0081, Japan
Tel.: (81) 339358843
Web Site: http://www.custom.co.jp
Sales Range: $25-49.9 Million
Emp.: 30
Custom Home Building Services
N.A.I.C.S.: 541350

Geico Brasil Ltda. (1)
Francisco Rocha Rd 2113 Bairo Bigorrilho, Curitiba, 80710-540, Parana, Brazil
Tel.: (55) 4130192727
Automated Auto Body Paint Shop Construction Services
N.A.I.C.S.: 811121

Geico Paint Shop India Private Limited (1)
A 4 5th Floor The 5th Avenue Dhole Patil Road, Pune, 411001, Maharashtra, India
Tel.: (91) 9970393892
Automated Auto Body Paint Shop Construction Services
N.A.I.C.S.: 811121

Geico Painting System (Suzhou) Co., Ltd. (1)
Room 1702 Harmony Mansion No 8 wansheng street building 1, Suzhou Industrial Park, Suzhou, 215000, China
Tel.: (86) 51285550256
Automated Auto Body Paint Shop Construction Services
N.A.I.C.S.: 811121

Geico Russia LLC (1)
12 Krasnopresnenskaya Emb Entrance 6 Office 317, 123610, Moscow, Russia
Tel.: (7) 4952490780
Automated Auto Body Paint Shop Construction Services
N.A.I.C.S.: 811121
Mikhail Tikhonov (Gen Dir)

J-Co America Corporation (1)
1945 Boulan Dr, Troy, MI 48084
Tel.: (248) 422-6200
Automated Auto Body Paint Shop Construction Services
N.A.I.C.S.: 811121

J-Co Mexico, S. De R.L. De C.V. (1)
Bosque de Ciruelos 180 - Bosques de Las Lomas, Miguel Hidalgo, 11700, Mexico, Mexico
Tel.: (52) 5522821030
Automated Auto Body Paint Shop Construction Services
N.A.I.C.S.: 811121

J-Pm Systems GmbH (1)
Hewlett Packard Strasse 1 1, 71083, Herrenberg, Germany
Tel.: (49) 70327869928
Automated Auto Body Paint Shop Construction Services
N.A.I.C.S.: 811121
Axel Halbmeyer (Dir-Engrg)

Makiansia Engineering (M) Sdn. Bhd. (1)
No 141 Jalan SS 17/1A, 47500, Subang Jaya, Selangor, Malaysia
Tel.: (60) 356352394
Web Site: http://www.taikisha-group.com
Sales Range: $25-49.9 Million
Emp.: 10
Engineering Consulting Services
N.A.I.C.S.: 541330
Shen Tien (CEO)

Nicomac Clean Rooms Far East LLP (1)
Plot No 116 IDA Bollaram Near Miyapur, Sangareddy District Medak, Hyderabad, 50232, Telangana, India
Tel.: (91) 9515192020
Emp.: 131
Clean Room Panel Mfr
N.A.I.C.S.: 321992
Ramesh Gundala (COO)

Nicomac Taikisha Clean Rooms Private Limited (1)
Plot no 116 IDA Bollaram Jinnaram Mandal Near Miyapur, Sangareddy Dt, Telangana, 502325, India
Tel.: (91) 9515192020
Web Site: https://www.taikisha-cleanrooms.com
Clean Room Constructing Services
N.A.I.C.S.: 541330

Nippon Noise Control Ltd. (1)
Sumitomo Nakano Sakaue Building 13F 1-38-1 Chuo, Nakano-ku, Tokyo, 164-0011, Japan
Tel.: (81) 359376532
Web Site: https://www.noisecontrol.co.jp
Noise Controlling Equipments Mfr
N.A.I.C.S.: 339113

P.T. Taikisha Indonesia Engineering (1)
Menara Bidakara I 13th Floor Jl Jend Gatot Subroto Kav 71-73, Jakarta, 12870, Indonesia
Tel.: (62) 2183793325
Web Site: http://www.taikisha-group.com
Sales Range: $50-74.9 Million
Emp.: 221
Electrical Instrument Mfr
N.A.I.C.S.: 334515

P.T. Taikisha Manufacturing Indonesia (1)
Jl Permata V Lot EE-5, Kawasan Industri KIIC, Karawang, 41361, West Java, Indonesia
Tel.: (62) 21 8911 4831
Web Site: http://www.taikisha-mfg.co.id
Sales Range: $50-74.9 Million
Emp.: 100
Electronic Components Mfr
N.A.I.C.S.: 334419

San Esu Industry Co., Ltd. (1)
3-24 Ikaga Midoricho, Hirakata, 573-0067, Osaka, Japan
Tel.: (81) 728450128
Web Site: https://www.sanesu-ind.co.jp
Sales Range: $50-74.9 Million
Emp.: 130
Construction & Civil Engineering Services
N.A.I.C.S.: 237990

Shanghai Dongbo-Taiki Conveyor System Manufacturing Co., Ltd. (1)
Room 906 Building 1 SCG Business Plaza No 51 Wuzhong Road, Shanghai, 201103, China
Tel.: (86) 2164430780

Web Site: http://www.taikisha-group.com
Sales Range: $25-49.9 Million
Emp.: 55
Conveyor System Mfr
N.A.I.C.S.: 333922
Jui Yogawa (Pres)

TKS Industrial Company (1)
901 Tower Dr Ste 300, Troy, MI 48098-2817
Tel.: (248) 786-5000
Sales Range: $25-49.9 Million
Emp.: 40
Environmental System Services
N.A.I.C.S.: 541620

Subsidiary (Domestic):

Encore Automation LLC (2)
50 Corporate Dr, Auburn Hills, MI 48326
Tel.: (248) 253-0200
Automotive Engineering Services
N.A.I.C.S.: 541330
Gordon Arnold (VP-Business Development-Proposals, Technical Clarifications)

Taikisha Canada Inc. (2)
901 Tower Dr Ste 150, Troy, MI 48098-2817
Tel.: (248) 786-5000
Web Site: http://www.tks-america.com
Sales Range: $25-49.9 Million
Emp.: 30
Environmental Remedial Services
N.A.I.C.S.: 562910

Subsidiary (Non-US):

Taikisha do Brasil Ltda. (2)
Avenida Alexandre Ludke 156 - piso superior, Vila Bandeirantes Municipio de Jundiai, Sao Paulo, 13214-020, Brazil
Tel.: (55) 1140388880
Web Site: http://www.taikisha-group.com
Sales Range: $25-49.9 Million
Emp.: 7
Environmental Research Services
N.A.I.C.S.: 541620

Taikisha (Cambodia) Co., Ltd. (2)
No 37 39 Phnom Penh Special Economic Zone National Road No 4, Trapaingkol Village Sangkat Kantouk Khan Posenchey, Phnom Penh, Cambodia
Tel.: (855) 23729317
Web Site: https://www.taikisha-group.com
Emp.: 10
Peripheral Equipment Mfr & Whslr
N.A.I.C.S.: 333248
Yasuo Fukushima (Pres)

Taikisha (Singapore) Pte. Ltd. (2)
2 International Business Park 11-01 The Strategy Tower 1, Jurong East, Singapore, 609930, Singapore
Tel.: (65) 62239928
Web Site: http://www.taikisha.co.jp
Sales Range: $25-49.9 Million
Emp.: 47
Construction Engineering Services
N.A.I.C.S.: 541330

Taikisha (Taiwan) Ltd. (1)
3F No 6 Taiyuen 1st Street, Tai Yuen Hi-Tech Industrial Park, Zhubei, Hsinchu, Taiwan
Tel.: (886) 35601661
Emp.: 51
Peripheral Equipment Mfr
N.A.I.C.S.: 333248
Shuichi Unagami (Pres)

Taikisha (Thailand) Co., Ltd. (1)
6th Floor 62 silom Road, Thaniya Bldg, Bangkok, 10500, Thailand
Tel.: (66) 22368055
Web Site: https://www.taikisha.co.th
Sales Range: $150-199.9 Million
Emp.: 771
Environmental Pollution Control System Mfr
N.A.I.C.S.: 541620
Shigeru Mikami (Pres)

Subsidiary (Domestic):

TKA Co., Ltd. (2)
Bangplee Factory 445 Bangplee Industrial Estate, Bangsaothong, Bang Phli, 10570, Samut Prakan, Thailand
Tel.: (66) 270583636
Web Site: http://www.tka.co.th

TAIKISHA LTD.

Taikisha Ltd.—(Continued)
Sales Range: $25-49.9 Million
Emp.: 97
Precision Tool Mfr
N.A.I.C.S.: 332721

Division (Domestic):

Taikisha (Thailand) Co., Ltd. - Paint Finishing Division (2)
9th Floor Thaniya Bldg 62 Silom Road, Bangkok, 10500, Thailand
Tel.: (66) 22676400
Web Site: http://www.taikisha.co.jp
Emp.: 1,000
Automotive Painting Services
N.A.I.C.S.: 811121

Subsidiary (Domestic):

Taikisha Trading (Thailand) Co., Ltd. (2)
6th Floor Thaniya Bldg 62 Silom Road, Bangkok, 10500, Thailand
Tel.: (66) 22368055
Sales Range: $25-49.9 Million
Emp.: 16
Trading Services
N.A.I.C.S.: 425120

Thaiken Maintenance & Service Co., Ltd. (2)
445 Bangplee Industrial Estate, Bangsaothong, Bang Phli, 10540, Samut Prakan, Thailand
Tel.: (66) 270587447
Web Site: http://www.tkm.co.th
Sales Range: $10-24.9 Million
Emp.: 50
Electrical Maintenance & Repair Services
N.A.I.C.S.: 811114

Token Interior & Design Co., Ltd. (2)
9th Floor Thaniya Bldg 62 Silom Road, Bangkok, 10500, Thailand
Tel.: (66) 22369103
Web Site: http://www.taikisha-group.com
Sales Range: $25-49.9 Million
Emp.: 89
Household Furniture Whslr
N.A.I.C.S.: 423220

Taikisha Engineering (M) Sdn. Bhd. (1)
Suite W306 3rd Floor West Wing Wisma Consplant 1 No 2 Jalan SS 16/4, 47500, Subang Jaya, Selangor, Malaysia
Tel.: (60) 356237200
Web Site: http://www.taikisha-group.com
Sales Range: $25-49.9 Million
Emp.: 38
Electronic Components Mfr
N.A.I.C.S.: 334419

Taikisha Engineering India Ltd. (1)
Plot No 26 Udyog Vihar Ph IV, Gurgaon, 122015, Haryana, India
Tel.: (91) 1242455215
Web Site: https://www.taikishaindia.com
Sales Range: $25-49.9 Million
Emp.: 300
Automotive Painting Services
N.A.I.C.S.: 811121

Plant (Domestic):

Taikisha Engineering India Pvt. Ltd. - Manufacturing Plant (2)
Plot No 19 Sector-3 IMT, Manesar, Gurgaon, 122050, Haryana, India
Tel.: (91) 1244669000
Web Site: http://www.taikishaindia.com
Sales Range: $10-24.9 Million
Automotive Painting Equipment Mfr
N.A.I.C.S.: 336320

Taikisha Korea Ltd. (1)
6F Geumcheon Lotte Castle GoldPark 4th 315 Siheung-daero, Geumcheon-gu, Seoul, 08608, Korea (South)
Tel.: (82) 27830270
Web Site: http://www.taikisha-group.com
Sales Range: $25-49.9 Million
Emp.: 16
Environmental Control Services
N.A.I.C.S.: 334512
Sanghee Choi (Pres)

Plant (Domestic):

Tuksu Engineering & Construction Ltd. - Asan Factory (2)
329-11 Juksan-ri, Seonjang-myeon, Asan, 336 890, Chungnam, Korea (South)
Tel.: (82) 415415080
Web Site: http://www.tuksu.co.kr
Sales Range: $25-49.9 Million
Environmental Control Services
N.A.I.C.S.: 541620

Taikisha Lao Co., Ltd. (2)
1-2 Room 1st Floor 1st Plant office Plant Area Ruyi road, Located 21 Km Saysettha Saysettha Development Zone Nano Village, Vientiane, Lao People's Democratic Republic
Tel.: (856) 21737066
Web Site: https://www.taikisha-group.com
Emp.: 9
Peripheral Equipment Mfr & Whslr
N.A.I.C.S.: 333248
Yasushi Nakayama (Pres)

Taikisha Myanmar Co., Ltd. (1)
Room No 11J 11th floor Ga Mone Complex Kabaraye Pagoda Road, Mayangone Township, Yangon, Myanmar
Tel.: (95) 1653653
Emp.: 8
Peripheral Equipment Mfr & Whslr
N.A.I.C.S.: 333248
Odamura Shigeo (Pres)

Taikisha Philippines Inc. (1)
5th Floor Golden Rock Bldg No 168 Salcedo St, Legaspi Village, Makati, 1229, Philippines
Tel.: (63) 288181707
Web Site: http://www.taikisha-group.com
Sales Range: $50-74.9 Million
Emp.: 281
Air Conditioners Design & Installation Services
N.A.I.C.S.: 333415
Taichi Nagano (Pres)

Taikisha Vietnam Engineering Inc. (1)
12th Floor Detech Tower No 8 Ton That Thuyet Street, My Dinh 2 Ward Nam Tu Liem District, Hanoi, Vietnam
Tel.: (84) 2435622750
Web Site: http://www.taikishavietnam.com.vn
Sales Range: $50-74.9 Million
Emp.: 170
Electrical Instrument Mfr
N.A.I.C.S.: 335999
Takeyoshi Sasaki (Pres)

Tianjin Dongchun-Taiki Metal Finishing & Conveyor System Manufacturing Co., Ltd. (1)
NO 9 NO 7 Road North area of Economic Development Zone of Jinghai, Jinghai Co, Tianjin, 301617, China
Tel.: (86) 2268645848
Web Site: https://www.taikisha-group.com
Sales Range: $50-74.9 Million
Emp.: 219
Conveyor Product Mfr
N.A.I.C.S.: 333922
Jui Yogawa (Pres)

Tianjin Taikisha Paint Finishing System Ltd. (1)
No7 Road 7 North Side, Economic Development Zone of Jinghai, Tianjin, 301600, China
Tel.: (86) 2268299518
Emp.: 39
Peripheral Equipment Mfr
N.A.I.C.S.: 333248
Satoshi Furuya (Pres)

Token Myanmar Co., Ltd. (1)
Room No 11J 11th floor Ga Mone Complex Kabaraye Pagoda Road, Mayangone Township, Yangon, Myanmar
Tel.: (95) 1653653
Emp.: 8
Peripheral Equipment Mfr & Whslr
N.A.I.C.S.: 333248

Tokyo Taikisha Service Ltd. (1)
4th Fl Nishi-Shinjuku Sato Bldg 7-9-16 Nishi-Shinjuku, Shinjuku-ku, Tokyo, 160-0023, Japan
Tel.: (81) 359253575
Construction & Civil Engineering Services
N.A.I.C.S.: 237990

Wuzhou Taikisha Engineering Co., Ltd. (1)
1110 Beijing Fortune Bldg 5 Dong San Huan Bei Lu, Chaoyang District, Beijing, 100004, China
Tel.: (86) 1065908251
Emp.: 133
Peripheral Equipment Mfr
N.A.I.C.S.: 333248
Hiromi Akagawa (Pres)

TAIKO PHARMACEUTICAL CO., LTD.

1-4-1 Nishi-Honmachi Nishi-ku, Osaka, 550-0005, Japan
Tel.: (81) 643911110
Web Site: http://www.seirogan.co.jp
4574—(TKS)
Rev.: $43,390,800
Assets: $93,729,800
Liabilities: $45,950,290
Net Worth: $47,779,510
Earnings: ($25,601,990)
Emp.: 208
Fiscal Year-end: 12/31/23
Pharmaceuticals Mfr
N.A.I.C.S.: 325412
Hitoshi Shibata (Chm)

Subsidiaries:

Taiko EnvironmentalTechnologies(Shanghai) Co., Ltd. (1)
Room 115 NO 328 HuaShan Road, Shanghai, China
Tel.: (86) 2162196029
Pharmaceutical Mfr & Distr
N.A.I.C.S.: 325411

Taiko Pharmaceutical (Asia Pacific) Co., Ltd. (1)
Office No 2 16/F No 148 Electric Road, North Point, Hong Kong, China (Hong Kong)
Tel.: (852) 29077300
Pharmaceutical Mfr & Distr
N.A.I.C.S.: 325411

Taiko Pharmaceutical (Shenzhen) Co., Ltd. (1)
Room 1217-1218 Shenzhen Kerry Center No 2008 Renmin South Road, Luohu Community Nanhu Street Luohu District, Shenzhen, China
Tel.: (86) 75582219008
Pharmaceutical Mfr & Distr
N.A.I.C.S.: 325411

Taiwan Taiko Pharmaceutical Co., Ltd. (1)
8F No 516 Sec 5 Zhongshan N Rd, Shilin District, Taipei, 111009, Taiwan
Tel.: (886) 228828276
Pharmaceutical Mfr & Distr
N.A.I.C.S.: 325411

TAILAM TECH CONSTRUCTION HOLDINGS LIMITED

31/F Tower Two Times Square 1 Matheson Street, Causeway Bay, China (Hong Kong)
Tel.: (852) 34991499 Ky
Web Site: https://www.tailamgroup.com
Year Founded: 2019
6193—(HKG)
Rev.: $49,971,740
Assets: $61,742,864
Liabilities: $27,154,481
Net Worth: $34,588,383
Earnings: $1,373,374
Emp.: 53
Fiscal Year-end: 12/31/22
Holding Company
N.A.I.C.S.: 551112
Alice Han Yu Wong (CEO)

TAILIM CO,. LTD.

Shihwa Industrial Complex Chungwang-dong 1295-1, Siheung, Kyungki-do, Korea (South)
Tel.: (82) 31 499 3333

INTERNATIONAL PUBLIC

Web Site: http://www.tailim.com
Year Founded: 1962
Sales Range: $200-249.9 Million
Emp.: 493
Paper Packaging Product Mfr
N.A.I.C.S.: 322220

Subsidiaries:

Tailim Co,. Ltd. - Cheongwon Factory (1)
Dureng-ri 15-1 Ochang-myeon, Cheongwon, Chungcheongbuk-do, Korea (South)
Tel.: (82) 43 212 1100
Paper Packaging Product Mfr
N.A.I.C.S.: 322220

Tailim Co,. Ltd. - Gwangju Factory (1)
Jangdeok-dong, Gwangsan-gu, Gwangju, Jeollanam-do, Korea (South)
Tel.: (82) 62 565 5555
Paper Packaging Product Mfr
N.A.I.C.S.: 322220

Tailim Co,. Ltd. - Iksan Factory (1)
Osanmyun Osanli, Iksan, Junla-bukdo, Korea (South)
Tel.: (82) 63 856 7755
Paper Packaging Product Mfr
N.A.I.C.S.: 322220

Tailim Co,. Ltd. - Kumi Factory (1)
Gongdan-dong, Kumi, 300-016, Gyungki-do, Korea (South)
Tel.: (82) 54 465 9999
Paper Packaging Product Mfr
N.A.I.C.S.: 322220

Tailim Co,. Ltd. - Pocheon Factory (1)
Masan-ri Gasan-myeon, Pocheon, Kyungki-do, Korea (South)
Tel.: (82) 31 541 2688
Paper Packaging Product Mfr
N.A.I.C.S.: 322220

Tailim Co,. Ltd. - Yangju Factory (1)
Sangsuri 646-6 Nammun, Yangju, Kyungki-do, Korea (South)
Tel.: (82) 31 868 8051
Paper Packaging Product Mfr
N.A.I.C.S.: 322220

TAILIM PAPER CO., LTD.

492-1 Mongnae-dong, Danwon-gu, Ansan, 15609, Gyeonggi, Korea (South)
Tel.: (82) 31 491 0010
Web Site: http://www.dongilpaper.co.kr
Year Founded: 1986
Sales Range: $350-399.9 Million
Emp.: 270
Corrugated Cardboard Base Paper Mfr
N.A.I.C.S.: 322211
Yeong Sik Kim (Pres & CEO)

TAILWIND ENERGY LTD.

62 Buckingham Gate, London, SW1E 6AJ, United Kingdom
Tel.: (44) 2037149009 UK
Web Site: http://www.tailwind.co.uk
Year Founded: 2016
Oil & Gas Extraction
N.A.I.C.S.: 211120
Steve Edwards (CEO)

TAILYN TECHNOLOGIES, INC.

No 10 Rong-an Road, Luzhu, Taoyuan, 33852, Taiwan
Tel.: (886) 33222201
Web Site: https://www.tailyn.com.tw
Year Founded: 1980
5353—(TPE)
Rev.: $59,790,107
Assets: $62,473,001
Liabilities: $24,485,914
Net Worth: $37,987,087
Earnings: $4,251,415
Emp.: 457
Fiscal Year-end: 12/31/22

Electric Equipment Mfr
N.A.I.C.S.: 334419
Jim Chen *(Pres)*

TAIMED BIOLOGICS INC.
3F No 607 Ruiguang Rd, Nei-Hu Dist, Taipei, 11492, Taiwan
Tel.: (886) 226580058
Web Site:
    https://www.taimedbiologics.com
Year Founded: 2007
4147—(TPE)
Rev.: $17,603,352
Assets: $128,227,871
Liabilities: $43,341,400
Net Worth: $84,886,471
Earnings: ($8,419,754)
Emp.: 70
Fiscal Year-end: 12/31/22
Biotechnology Research & Development Services
N.A.I.C.S.: 541714
James Chang *(Pres & CEO)*

Subsidiaries:

TaiMed Biologics USA Corp.   (1)
4790 Irvine Blvd Ste 105-697, Irvine, CA 92620
Tel.: (949) 331-3225
Research & Development Services
N.A.I.C.S.: 541714

TAIMIDE TECH. INC.
No 127 Sec 3 Wender Rd Shinpu Jen, Hsin-chu, 30541, Taiwan
Tel.: (886) 35896088
Web Site: https://www.taimide.com.tw
Year Founded: 2000
3645—(TAI)
Rev.: $52,641,288
Assets: $158,233,422
Liabilities: $66,125,345
Net Worth: $92,108,077
Earnings: ($5,019,294)
Emp.: 301
Fiscal Year-end: 12/31/23
Electronic Parts & Components Mfr
N.A.I.C.S.: 334419
Claire Tseng *(Assoc Mgr)*

Subsidiaries:

Kunshan Taimide Tech. Inc.   (1)
Room 1312 A Building Modern Square No 18 Weiye Rd Development Area, Kuanshan, Suzhou, 215301, China
Tel.: (86) 51257112658
Electrical Equipment Whslr
N.A.I.C.S.: 423690

Pomiran metalization research Co., Ltd.   (1)
No 671 Zhongfeng Road, Pingzhen District, Taoyuan, 32456, Taiwan
Tel.: (886) 34570368
Web Site: https://www.pmr.com.tw
Copper Clad Laminates Mfr
N.A.I.C.S.: 326130

TAIMING ASSURANCE BROKER CO., LTD.
11F No 49 Guanqian Rd, Taipei, 100, Taiwan
Tel.: (886) 255585988
Web Site: https://tabc.com.tw
Year Founded: 2002
5878—(TPE)
Rev.: $23,072,132
Assets: $24,195,573
Liabilities: $7,493,700
Net Worth: $16,701,873
Earnings: $2,062,064
Fiscal Year-end: 12/31/22
General Insurance Services
N.A.I.C.S.: 524210
Cheng-Chih Li *(Chm)*

TAINAN ENTERPRISES CO., LTD.
15F No 15-1 Sec 1 Han-Chou South Rd, Taipei, Taiwan
Tel.: (886) 223916421
Web Site: https://www.tai-nan.com
Year Founded: 1961
1473—(TAI)
Rev.: $212,835,598
Assets: $177,715,452
Liabilities: $56,754,372
Net Worth: $120,961,080
Earnings: $10,185,715
Emp.: 11,440
Fiscal Year-end: 12/31/23
Apparels Mfr
N.A.I.C.S.: 315250

Subsidiaries:

PT Tainan Enterprises Indonesia   (1)
Jl Irian Blok E No 28 KBN Cakung-Cilincing, Jakarta Utara, Jakarta, 14140, Indonesia
Tel.: (62) 214401178
Sales Range: $350-399.9 Million
Emp.: 1,500
Fashion Apparels Mfr
N.A.I.C.S.: 315210

Tainan Enterprise (Cayman) Co., Ltd.   (1)
1F No 297 Sec 2 Dongmen Rd, East Dist, T'ainan, 701, Taiwan
Tel.: (886) 62006277
Web Site: https://www.tainancayman.com
Rev.: $69,825,302
Assets: $60,583,405
Liabilities: $36,623,204
Net Worth: $23,960,201
Earnings: $3,652,605
Emp.: 436
Fiscal Year-end: 12/31/2023
Holding Company; Apparel Mfr & Distr
N.A.I.C.S.: 551112
Ching-Hon Yang *(Chm)*

Tainan Enterprises Co., Ltd. - Taiwan Factory   (1)
320 Sec3 Chung-San Road, Kuei Jen Hsiang, T'ainan, Taiwan
Tel.: (886) 62307911
Apparels Mfr
N.A.I.C.S.: 315120

TAINAN SPINNING COMPANY LIMITED
10F No 398 Sec 1 Zhonghua E Rd, East District, T'ainan, 701, Taiwan
Tel.: (886) 62376161
Web Site:
    https://www.tainanspin.com.tw
Year Founded: 1955
1440—(TAI)
Rev.: $635,900,823
Assets: $1,695,360,085
Liabilities: $719,790,450
Net Worth: $975,569,635
Earnings: $71,641,647
Emp.: 4,987
Fiscal Year-end: 12/31/23
Textile Mfr
N.A.I.C.S.: 313110
Peng Yu *(Pres)*

Subsidiaries:

Tainan Spinning Co. Ltd.   (1)
NO 9 Road 17A, Bien Hoa Industrial Zone No 2, Bien Hoa, Dong Nai, Vietnam
Tel.: (84) 2513836671
Textile Fiber Mfr
N.A.I.C.S.: 325613

Tainan Spinning Company Limited - Rende Plant & Fiber Plant   (1)
No 45 Ln 862 Sec 2 Zhongzheng Rd Rende Dist, Tainan City, 71743, Taiwan
Tel.: (886) 62792711
Textile Fiber Mfr
N.A.I.C.S.: 325613

Tainan Spinning Company Limited - Sinshih Plant   (1)
No 111 Zhonghua Rd Xinshi Dist, Tainan City, 74448, Taiwan
Tel.: (886) 65982611

Textile Fiber Mfr
N.A.I.C.S.: 325613

Tainan Spinning Company Limited - Taizi Plant   (1)
No 419 Sec 3 Zhongzheng Rd Rende Dist, Tainan City, 71757, Taiwan
Tel.: (886) 62724421
Textile Fiber Mfr
N.A.I.C.S.: 325613

Tainan Textile Co., Ltd.   (1)
Road 7C, Nhon Trach Industrial Zone No 2 NhonTrachDistrict, Nhon Trach, Dong Nai, Vietnam
Tel.: (84) 2513568114
Textile Fiber Mfr
N.A.I.C.S.: 325613

TAINERGY TECH CO., LTD.
3F No 97 Sec 2 Nan-Kang Rd, Taipei, Taiwan
Tel.: (886) 227883798
Web Site:
    https://www.tainergy.com.tw
Year Founded: 2007
4934—(TAI)
Rev.: $70,150,166
Assets: $99,363,873
Liabilities: $24,453,448
Net Worth: $74,910,426
Earnings: ($6,224,795)
Emp.: 500
Fiscal Year-end: 12/31/23
Solar Cell Mfr
N.A.I.C.S.: 334419
Hsieh Ching-Fu *(Chm)*

Subsidiaries:

Tainergy Technology (Kunshan) Co., Ltd   (1)
No 5 Tze-Chiang 1st Rd Chungli Industrial Zone, Chung-li, 320, Taiwan
Tel.: (886) 3 4555807
Solar Cell Mfr
N.A.I.C.S.: 334419

TAINET COMMUNICATION SYSTEM CORP.
3F No 108 Ruiguang Road, Neihu Dist, Taipei, 114, Taiwan
Tel.: (886) 226583000
Web Site: https://www.tainet.net
Year Founded: 1990
4905—(TPE)
Rev.: $2,592,784
Assets: $85,034,299
Liabilities: $1,126,098
Net Worth: $83,908,201
Earnings: ($1,374,168)
Fiscal Year-end: 12/31/22
Telecommunication Servicesb
N.A.I.C.S.: 517810
Jack Huang *(Gen Mgr)*

TAINWALA CHEMICALS AND PLASTICS (INDIA) LIMITED
Tainwala House Road No 18 MIDC, Andheri East, Mumbai, 400 093, Maharashtra, India
Tel.: (91) 2267166100
Web Site: https://www.tainwala.in
Year Founded: 1985
507785—(BOM)
Rev.: $1,709,799
Assets: $12,499,837
Liabilities: $181,013
Net Worth: $12,318,825
Earnings: $50,314
Emp.: 39
Fiscal Year-end: 03/31/22
Plastic Sheets Mfr
N.A.I.C.S.: 326199
Rakesh Tainwala *(Chm & Mng Dir)*

TAIPE TRANCOSO EMPREENDIMENTOS S.A.
Est Municipal Trancoso - Km 18, 45810000, Porto Seguro, BA, Brazil

Tel.: (55) 7335755840
Resort Management Services
N.A.I.C.S.: 721110

TAIPEI EXCHANGE
15F No 100 Sec 2 Roosevelt Road, Taipei, 10084, Taiwan
Tel.: (886) 2 2369 9555
Web Site: http://www.tpex.org.tw
Year Founded: 1994
Rev.: $69,057,711
Assets: $515,284,355
Liabilities: $322,775,466
Net Worth: $192,508,888
Earnings: $15,969,220
Emp.: 304
Fiscal Year-end: 12/31/18
Securities Exchange Operator
N.A.I.C.S.: 523210
Philip Chen *(Chm)*

TAIROUN PRODUCTS CO., LTD.
6th Fl No 206 Nanking E Rd Sec 2, Taipei, Taiwan
Tel.: (886) 225069521
Web Site: https://www.tairoun.com.tw
Year Founded: 1969
1220—(TAI)
Rev.: $107,717,318
Assets: $104,517,083
Liabilities: $21,645,246
Net Worth: $82,871,837
Earnings: $5,160,895
Emp.: 225
Fiscal Year-end: 12/31/23
Feedstuff Product Mfr
N.A.I.C.S.: 311119
Wei-Kung Chen *(Chm)*

TAISEI CORPORATION
1-25-1 Nishi-Shinjuku, Shinjuku-ku, Tokyo, 163-0606, Japan
Tel.: (81) 333481111   JP
Web Site: https://www.taisei.co.jp
Year Founded: 1873
TISCY—(OTCIQ)
Rev.: $11,778,245,040
Assets: $14,459,860,890
Liabilities: $8,480,482,410
Net Worth: $5,979,378,480
Earnings: $337,879,080
Emp.: 8,613
Fiscal Year-end: 03/31/23
Contracting Services
N.A.I.C.S.: 541330
Takashi Yamauchi *(Co-Chm)*

Subsidiaries:

AISEI Myanmar Co., Ltd.   (1)
2nd Floor Tokyo Enterprise Building No 32 Pyay Road 61/2miles, Hlaing Township, Yangon, Myanmar
Tel.: (95) 1654838
Engineering & Construction Services
N.A.I.C.S.: 541330

Ehime Hospital Pertners Co., Ltd.   (1)
12-2 Suehiromachi, Matsuyama, 790-0023, Ehime Prefecture, Japan
Tel.: (81) 899681631
Web Site: http://www.ehime-hp.co.jp
Hospital Services
N.A.I.C.S.: 622110

Hotel Precede Koriyama Co. Ltd.   (1)
12-2 Nakamachi, Koriyama, 963-8004, Fukushima Prefecture, Japan
Tel.: (81) 24 925 3411
Web Site: https://www.precede-k.co.jp
Emp.: 26
Hotel Operator
N.A.I.C.S.: 721110
Koji Eguchi *(CEO)*

J-Fast Co., Ltd.   (1)
1-32-2 Honmachi, Nakano-ku, Tokyo, 164-8721, Japan
Tel.: (81) 333728811
Web Site: https://j-fast.co.jp

TAISEI CORPORATION

Taisei Corporation—(Continued)

Emp.: 583
Construction Management Services
N.A.I.C.S.: 541330

P.T. Indotaisei Indah Development (1)
Kawasan Industri Indotaisei Kota Bukit Indah Sector IA Block B, Karihurip Karawan, Cikampek, Jawa Barat, Indonesia
Tel.: (62) 264351003
Web Site: http://www.kotabukitindah.com
Civil Engineering Construction
N.A.I.C.S.: 237990

P.T. P.P. Taisei Indonesia Construction (1)
Plz PP 1st Fl Db Seema Tupa Banh No 57, Jakarta, 13760, Indonesia
Tel.: (62) 218416037
Sales Range: $25-49.9 Million
Emp.: 50
Engineeering Services
N.A.I.C.S.: 541330
Yukio Matsuno (Pres)

PT Taisei Pulauintan Construction International (1)
L'Avenue Office Tower 28th Floor Jl Raya Pasar Minggu Kav 16, Pancoran, Jakarta Selatan, 12780, Indonesia
Tel.: (62) 2180667321
Engineering & Construction Services
N.A.I.C.S.: 541330

Seiwa Renewal Works Co., Ltd. (1)
6-8-1 Nishishinjuku Sumitomo Fudosan Shinjuku Oak Tower 34f, Shinjuku-Ku, Tokyo, 160-0023, Japan
Tel.: (81) 353260711
Construction Machinery Mfr
N.A.I.C.S.: 333120

Symbol Tower Development Co., Ltd. (1)
Takamatsu Symbol Tower Tower Building 6F Sunport 2-1, Takamatsu, 760-0019, Japan
Tel.: (81) 878221707
Web Site: www.symboltower.com
Real Estate Development Services
N.A.I.C.S.: 531210

Taisei (Deutschland) GmbH (1)
Bohmerstrasse 19, Frankfurt, 6000, AM MAIN 1, Germany
Tel.: (49) 695975004
Engineeering Services
N.A.I.C.S.: 541330

Taisei (Thailand) Co., Ltd. (1)
1550 Thanapoom Tower 9th Floor New Petchaburi Road, Makkasan Rachtavee, Bangkok, 10400, Thailand
Tel.: (66) 2 207 0330
Web Site: https://www.taisei-thailand.co.th
Sales Range: $25-49.9 Million
Emp.: 200
General Contracting
N.A.I.C.S.: 541330

Taisei (West Africa) Ltd. (1)
No 35 Joel Ogunaike Street Gra, Ikeja, Lagos, Nigeria
Tel.: (234) 14977760
Web Site: http://www.taisei.co.jp
Engineering & Rail Services
N.A.I.C.S.: 541330

Taisei Construction Corporation (1)
(100%)
Tel.: (714) 886-1530
Web Site: http://www.taisei.com
Sales Range: $25-49.9 Million
Emp.: 25
Contracting Services
N.A.I.C.S.: 236220

Taisei Corporation (1)
9-3 9th Fl Faber Imperial Court, Jalan Sultan Ismail, 50250, Kuala Lumpur, Malaysia (100%)
Tel.: (60) 320706155
Sales Range: $1-9.9 Million
Emp.: 30
Building Construction, Real Estate Development, Engineering & Civil Engineering Services
N.A.I.C.S.: 541330

Ken Yositomi (Gen Mgr)

Taisei Housing Corporation (1)
19th Floor Shinjuku Park Tower 3-7-1, Nishi-Shinjuku Shinjuku-ku, Tokyo, 163-1019, Japan (100%)
Tel.: (81) 85 339 8051
Web Site: https://palcon.jp
Construction Engineering Services
N.A.I.C.S.: 541330

Taisei Philippine Construction Inc. (1)
23rd Floor Equitable Bank Tower Paseo de Roxas, Makati, 1227, Metro Manila, Philippines
Tel.: (63) 28860670
Sales Range: $25-49.9 Million
Emp.: 45
Civil Engineering Construction
N.A.I.C.S.: 237990
Yukinori Iyoda (Pres)

Taisei Rotec Corporation (1)
8-17-1 Nishi Sumitomo Realty and Development Shinjuku Grand Tower, Shinjuku-ku, Tokyo, 160-6112, Japan (58.3%)
Tel.: (81) 359259431
Web Site: http://www.taiseirotec.co.jp
Sales Range: $900-999.9 Million
Emp.: 1,087
Road Pavers
N.A.I.C.S.: 237310
Yoshinori Nishida (Pres)

Taisei Saudi Arabia Co., Ltd. (1)
Office 1603 16th Floor Sultan Tower Najda Street, PO Box 73898, Abu Dhabi, United Arab Emirates (100%)
Tel.: (971) 26341005
Web Site: http://www.taisei.com
Sales Range: $25-49.9 Million
Emp.: 8
Engineering & Rail Services
N.A.I.C.S.: 541330

Taisei Setsubi Co., Ltd. (1)
6-8-1 Nishishinjuku Shinjuku Oak Tower 10 Floor, Shinjuku-Ku, Tokyo, 160-0023, Japan
Tel.: (81) 363020150
Air Conditioning Equipment Installation Services
N.A.I.C.S.: 238220

Taisei U. Lec Co., Ltd. (1)
3rd TOC Building 7-23-1, Nishigotanda, Tokyo, 141-0031, Japan
Tel.: (81) 334934941
Web Site: http://www.u-lec.com
Sales Range: $250-299.9 Million
Emp.: 441
Engineeering Services
N.A.I.C.S.: 236115
Eiji Hatta (Pres)

Taisei-Yuraku Real Estate Co., Ltd. (1)
3-14-1 Kyobashi, Chuo-Ku, Tokyo, 104-8330, Japan
Tel.: (81) 335679411
Web Site: http://www.taisei-yuraku.co.jp
Emp.: 3,024
Real Estate Leasing, Development & Facilities Management
N.A.I.C.S.: 531311

Tas Plan, Inc. (1)
23rd Floor BDO Equitable Tower 8751 Paseo de Roxas, Salcedo Village, Makati, 1227, Metro Manila, Philippines
Tel.: (63) 28860664
Web Site: http://www.tasplan.net
Sales Range: $50-74.9 Million
Emp.: 170
Civil Engineering Construction
N.A.I.C.S.: 237990

Vinata International Co., Ltd. (1)
3rd level Block C Song Da building Pham Hung, Nam Tu Liem District, Hanoi, Vietnam
Tel.: (84) 2435533839
Web Site: http://www.vinata.com.vn
Civil Industrial Construction Services
N.A.I.C.S.: 237990

Vinata International Joint Venture Ltd., Co. (1)
Taisei Corporation Vietnam Office, 2A 4A 17th Fl Ton Duc Thang Di, Ho Chi Minh City, Vietnam (71%)
Tel.: (84) 88297264
Web Site: http://www.vinata.com.vn
Sales Range: $25-49.9 Million
Emp.: 20
Engineering & Rail Services
N.A.I.C.S.: 541330

Zhong Da Enterprise Corp. (1)
Zhong Da Ofc Bldg 23 Zizhuyuan S Rd, Beijing, 100044, Haidian, China
Tel.: (86) 1068451267
Engineeering Services
N.A.I.C.S.: 541330

TAISEI LAMICK CO., LTD.
873-1 Shimo-osaki, Shiraoka, Saitama, 349-0293, Japan
Tel.: (81) 480970221
Web Site: https://www.lamick.co.jp
Year Founded: 1966
4994—(TKS)
Rev.: $185,271,690
Assets: $216,424,620
Liabilities: $58,088,680
Net Worth: $158,335,940
Earnings: $7,165,240
Emp.: 652
Fiscal Year-end: 03/31/24
Plastic Film Mfr & Whslr
N.A.I.C.S.: 326112
Tadashi Hasebe (Pres)

Subsidiaries:

Taisei Lamick Co., Ltd. - Machine Factory (1)
9-15 Shinkou-cho, Mitsuke, 954-0076, Niigata, Japan
Tel.: (81) 258615008
Plastic Packaging Film Mfr
N.A.I.C.S.: 326112

Taisei Lamick Co., Ltd. - Shiraoka Factory 2 (1)
1-1 Shimo-osaki, Shiraoka, Saitama, 349-0293, Japan
Tel.: (81) 480881001
Plastic Packaging Film Mfr
N.A.I.C.S.: 326112

Taisei Lamick Co., Ltd. - Shiraoka Factory 3 (1)
778-2 Shinozu, Shiraoka, Saitama, 349-0293, Japan
Tel.: (81) 480923773
Plastic Packaging Film Mfr
N.A.I.C.S.: 326112

Taisei Lamick USA, Inc. (1)
2416 Estes Ave, Elk Grove Village, IL 60007
Tel.: (847) 258-3283
Plastic Packaging Film Mfr & Distr
N.A.I.C.S.: 326112

TAISEI ONCHO CO., LTD.
49-10 Oi 1-chome, Shinagawa-ku, Tokyo, 140-8515, Japan
Tel.: (81) 357427320
Web Site: https://www.taisei-oncho.co.jp
Year Founded: 1941
1904—(TKS)
Rev.: $403,580,160
Assets: $302,539,700
Liabilities: $132,570,160
Net Worth: $169,969,540
Earnings: $12,968,820
Emp.: 792
Fiscal Year-end: 03/31/24
Air Conditioning & Plumbing Equipment Installation Services
N.A.I.C.S.: 238220
Kenichi Mizutani (Pres & CEO)

Subsidiaries:

Taisei Oncho (Hong Kong) Co., Ltd (1)
Unit 02 15F 56 Kwai Chuong Rd, Kwai Chung, New Territories, China (Hong Kong)
Tel.: (852) 2564 8423

INTERNATIONAL PUBLIC

Sales Range: $25-49.9 Million
Emp.: 20
Air Conditioning System Installation Services
N.A.I.C.S.: 238220

Taisei Oncho (Shanghai) Co., Ltd (1)
Room No 402 Tongda Chuangye Mansion No 1 Lane 600 Tian Shan Road, Shanghai, 200051, China
Tel.: (86) 2161430993
Web Site: http://www.taisei-oncho.co.jp
Air Conditioning Equipments Mfr & Installation Services
N.A.I.C.S.: 333415

Taisei Oncho Hawaii Inc. (1)
2655 Waiwai Loop, Honolulu, HI 96819
Tel.: (808) 834-1085
Web Site: http://www.alakaimechanical.com
Sales Range: $25-49.9 Million
Emp.: 170
Mechanical Contractor
N.A.I.C.S.: 238220
Ralph Inouye (Pres)

Subsidiary (Domestic):

Alakai Mechanical Corporation (2)
2655 Waiwai Loop, Honolulu, HI 96819
Tel.: (808) 834-1085
Web Site: http://www.alakaimechanical.com
Sales Range: $50-74.9 Million
Emp.: 200
Mechanical Contractor
N.A.I.C.S.: 238220
Sam Kurasawa (Chm)

Taisei Oncho India Pvt., Ltd (1)
Unit No 315 316 317 Third Floor Square 1, Saket District Center, New Delhi, 110 017, India
Tel.: (91) 11 4658 7496
Web Site: http://www.taisei-oncho.co.jp
Air Conditioning & Plumbing Equipment Mfr
N.A.I.C.S.: 333415

TAISHIN FINANCIAL HOLDING CO., LTD.
No 118 Sec 4 Ren-ai Rd, Da-an District, Taipei, Taiwan
Tel.: (886) 223268888
Web Site: https://www.taishinholdings.com.tw
Year Founded: 2002
2887—(TAI)
Rev.: $1,450,513,898
Assets: $86,446,066,567
Liabilities: $80,102,264,797
Net Worth: $6,343,801,770
Earnings: $464,493,418
Emp.: 10,696
Fiscal Year-end: 12/31/22
Holding Company
N.A.I.C.S.: 551112
Steve Sun (CIO)

Subsidiaries:

Prudential Life Insurance Company of Taiwan Inc. (1)
10F 161 Sec 5 Nanjing E Rd, Taipei, 10570, Taiwan
Tel.: (886) 227678866
Web Site: http://www.prulife.com.tw
Financial Management Services
N.A.I.C.S.: 541611

Taishin International Bank Co., Ltd. (1)
No 44 Section 2 Zhongshan N Road, Zhongshan District, Taipei, 104, Taiwan
Tel.: (886) 22 568 3988
Web Site: https://www.taishinbank.com.tw
Sales Range: $1-4.9 Billion
Banking Services
N.A.I.C.S.: 522110
Oliver Shang (Pres)

Taiwan Bills Finance Co., Ltd. (1)
118 Ren-ai Rd, 104, Taipei, Taiwan
Tel.: (886) 223268888
Financial Management & Investment Services
N.A.I.C.S.: 523999

TAISHO PHARMACEUTICAL HOLDINGS CO., LTD

3-24-1 Takada, Toshima-ku, Tokyo, 170-8655, Japan
Tel.: (81) 339852020
Web Site: https://www.taisho-holdings.co.jp
Year Founded: 2011
4581—(TKS)
Rev.: $2,596,205,040
Assets: $8,597,379,120
Liabilities: $1,163,555,360
Net Worth: $7,433,823,760
Earnings: $127,020,960
Emp.: 9,134
Fiscal Year-end: 03/31/22
Holding Company
N.A.I.C.S.: 551112
Akira Uehara *(CEO)*

Subsidiaries:

Biofermin Pharmaceutical Co., Ltd. (1)
1-1-2 Sannomiya-cho 12th Floor Sannomiya Central Building, Chuo-ku, Kobe, 653-0011, Hyogo, Japan **(63.9%)**
Tel.: (81) 78 332 2890
Web Site: http://www.biofermin.co.jp
Sales Range: $75-99.9 Million
Emp.: 220
Pharmaceutical Product Mfr & Whslr
N.A.I.C.S.: 325412
Ken Uehara *(Chm)*

Compania Internacional de Comercio, S.A.P.I. de C.V. (1)
Monzon No 184 Col Cerro de la Estrella, Iztapalapa, 09860, Mexico, Mexico
Tel.: (52) 5550370300
Web Site: https://www.ksk.com.mx
Pharmaceutical Product Mfr & Distr
N.A.I.C.S.: 325412

DHG Pharmaceutical Joint Stock Company (1)
288 Bis Nguyen Van Cu Street, Ninh Kieu District, Can Tho, Vietnam **(50.77%)**
Tel.: (84) 7103891433
Web Site: https://www.dhgpharma.com.vn
Rev.: $501,539,500
Assets: $611,047,400
Liabilities: $125,753,900
Net Worth: $485,293,500
Earnings: $105,066,300
Emp.: 2,485
Fiscal Year-end: 12/31/2023
Pharmaceutical Preparation Mfr
N.A.I.C.S.: 325412

Duoc Hau Giang Pharmaceutical JSC (1)
288 Bis Nguyen Van Cu Street, An Hoa Ward Ninh Kieu District, Can Tho, Vietnam
Tel.: (84) 2923891433
Web Site: https://www.dhgpharma.com.vn
Emp.: 2,485
Pharmaceutical Product Mfr & Distr
N.A.I.C.S.: 325412

Taisho Pharma Co., Ltd. (1)
3-25-1 Takada, Toshima-ku, Tokyo, 170-8635, Japan
Tel.: (81) 36 833 1804
Web Site: https://www.taisho-pharma.co.jp
Pharmaceuticals Product Mfr
N.A.I.C.S.: 325412

Taisho Pharmaceutical Co., Ltd. (1)
3-24-1 Takada, Toshima-ku, Tokyo, 170-8633, Japan
Tel.: (81) 339851111
Web Site: http://www.taisho.co.jp
Sales Range: $1-4.9 Billion
Emp.: 2,885
Pharmaceuticals Product Mfr
N.A.I.C.S.: 325412
Akira Uehara *(Chm)*

Subsidiary (Domestic):

Dr. Program Co., Ltd. (2)
1-34-14 Hatagaya, Shibuya-ku, Tokyo, 151-0072, Japan
Tel.: (81) 120022622
Web Site: http://www.trinityline.com
Cosmetics Mfr
N.A.I.C.S.: 325620
Morioka Susumu *(Pres & CEO)*

Subsidiary (Non-US):

HOEPharma Holdings Sdn Bhd (2)
B 3A 07 Dataran 32 No 2 Jalan 19/1, 46300, Petaling Jaya, Selangor, Malaysia
Tel.: (60) 379581077
Web Site: http://www.hoepharma.com.my
Sales Range: $25-49.9 Million
Emp.: 250
Holding Company
N.A.I.C.S.: 551112

Subsidiary (Domestic):

HOE Pharmaceuticals Sdn. Bhd. (3)
B-3A-07 Dataran 32 No 2 Jalan 19/1, 46300, Petaling Jaya, Selangor Darul Ehsan, Malaysia
Tel.: (60) 379581077
Web Site: https://www.hoepharma.com.my
Sales Range: $50-74.9 Million
Emp.: 118
Pharmaceuticals Product Mfr
N.A.I.C.S.: 325412

Joint Venture (Non-US):

Osotspa Taisho Co., Ltd. (2)
2100 Ramkhamhaeng Rd, Bangkok, 10240, Thailand
Tel.: (66) 23740120
Web Site: http://www.taisho.co.jp
Pharmaceuticals Mfr & Sales; Owned 51% by Osotspa Co., Ltd. & 49% by Taisho Pharmaceutical Co., Ltd.
N.A.I.C.S.: 325412

Subsidiary (Non-US):

PT Taisho Pharmaceutical Indonesia Tbk (2)
Millennium Centennial Center 8th floor Jl Jend Sudirman Kav 25, Jakarta, 12920, Indonesia
Tel.: (62) 2139706720
Web Site: https://taisho.co.id
Rev.: $49,256,561
Assets: $36,745,752
Liabilities: $9,905,219
Net Worth: $26,840,532
Earnings: $15,821,462
Emp.: 155
Fiscal Year-end: 12/31/2019
Pharmaceuticals Mfr
N.A.I.C.S.: 325412
Dyah Eka Budiastuti *(Sec)*

Joint Venture (Domestic):

Sanofi-Synthelabo-Taisho Pharmaceuticals Co., Ltd. (2)
3 23 Kioicho, Chiyoda Ku, Tokyo, 102 0094, Japan
Tel.: (81) 352757139
Pharmaceuticals Mfr; Owned 49% by Taisho Pharmaceutical Co., Ltd. & 51% by Sanofi-Aventis
N.A.I.C.S.: 325412

Subsidiary (Domestic):

Shimoda Central Co., Ltd. (2)
3-26-3 Takada, Toshima-Ku, Tokyo, Japan
Tel.: (81) 3 3987 2823
Home Management Services
N.A.I.C.S.: 721110

TOKUHON Corporation (2)
Davinci Takada 3-Chrome Bldg 6F 3-28-2, Takada Toshima-ku, Tokyo, 171-0033, Japan
Tel.: (81) 3 6907 7800
Web Site: http://www.tokuhon.co.jp
Emp.: 157
Pharmaceutical Product Mfr & Distr
N.A.I.C.S.: 325412
Takao Aketo *(Pres)*

Subsidiary (Non-US):

Taisho (Australia) Pty. Ltd. (2)
Suite 4 102 Alfred St, Sydney, 2061, NSW, Australia
Tel.: (61) 289202455
Web Site: http://www.taisho.co.jp
Provider of Pharmaceuticals
N.A.I.C.S.: 325412

Subsidiary (Domestic):

Taisho Active Health Co., Ltd. (2)
3 24 1 Takada, Toshima-Ku, Tokyo, Japan
Tel.: (81) 486631111
Pharmaceutical Products Distr
N.A.I.C.S.: 424210

Taisho Business Research Institute Co., Ltd. (2)
26 3 Takata 3 Chome, Toshima Ku, Tokyo, 171 0033, Japan **(100%)**
Tel.: (81) 339851140
Provider of Research Services
N.A.I.C.S.: 541715

Subsidiary (Non-US):

Taisho Guan Sheng Yuan Co., Ltd. Shanghai (2)
No 4733 Cao An Rd, 886-2-2896-1635, Shanghai, 201804, China **(85%)**
Tel.: (86) 2159598874
Provider of Pharmaceutical Services
N.A.I.C.S.: 325412

Affiliate (Non-US):

Taisho Hizon Manufacturing, Inc. (2)
Sitio Malanim Barangay Dela Paz, Sumulong Hwy Antipolo City, Pasig, 1870, Philippines **(50%)**
Tel.: (63) 26963857
Web Site: http://www.taisho.co.jp
Mfr of Pharmaceuticals
N.A.I.C.S.: 325412

Subsidiary (Domestic):

Taisho M.T.C. Co., Ltd. (2)
2-2-1 Yaesu, Chuo-ku, Tokyo, 104-0028, Japan **(60%)**
Tel.: (81) 362533859
Web Site: https://www.taisho-mtc.com
Emp.: 30
Manufacture & Sale of Raw Materials for Medicines
N.A.I.C.S.: 325412

Taisho Okinawa Co., Ltd. (2)
19-17 Kume 1-Chome, Naha, 900-0033, Okinawa, Japan **(100%)**
Tel.: (81) 988687809
Web Site: http://www.taisho.co.jp
Pharmaceuticals Mfr & Distr
N.A.I.C.S.: 325412

Subsidiary (Non-US):

Taisho Pharmaceutical (M) Sdn. Bhd. (2)
Lot 9 Jalan P 12 Kawasan Perusahaan Seksyen 10 Bandar Baru Bangi, 43650, Kuala Lumpur, 43650, Malaysia **(100%)**
Tel.: (60) 389261228
Web Site: http://www.taisho.com
Sales Range: $25-49.9 Million
Emp.: 100
Provider of Pharmaceuticals
N.A.I.C.S.: 325412
Kok Chuan Ee *(Mgr-Mktg)*

Taisho Pharmaceutical (Taiwan) Co., Ltd. (2)
4F-1 No 180 Chang'an West Road, Datong District, Taipei, 303, Taiwan **(100%)**
Tel.: (886) 225581208
Sales Range: $25-49.9 Million
Emp.: 45
Pharmaceutical Products Mfr & Distr
N.A.I.C.S.: 325412

Subsidiary (US):

Taisho Pharmaceutical California Inc. (2)
3528 Torrance Blvd Ste 320, Torrance, CA 90503-6707 **(100%)**
Tel.: (310) 543-2035
Web Site: https://lipovitan.com
Sales Range: $25-49.9 Million
Emp.: 12
Mfr of Pharmaceutical Preparations
N.A.I.C.S.: 424210
Jun Kuroda *(Pres)*

Plant (Domestic):

Taisho Pharmaceutical Co., Ltd. - The Hanyu Factory (2)
1-603-27 Komatsudai, Hanyu, 348-8540, Saitama, Japan
Tel.: (81) 48 563 1121
Web Site: http://www.taisho.co.jp
Pharmaceuticals Product Mfr
N.A.I.C.S.: 325412

Taisho Pharmaceutical Co., Ltd. - The Okayama Factory (2)
33-2 Taiheidai Shouou-cho, Katsuta-gun, Okayama, 709-4321, Japan
Tel.: (81) 868 38 6131
Web Site: http://www.taisho.co.jp
Pharmaceuticals Product Mfr
N.A.I.C.S.: 325412

Taisho Pharmaceutical Co., Ltd. - The Omiya Factory (2)
1-403 Yoshino-Cho, Kita-Ku, Saitama, 331-9520, Japan
Tel.: (81) 48 663 1111
Web Site: http://www.taisho.co.jp
Sales Range: $200-249.9 Million
Emp.: 700
Pharmaceuticals Product Mfr
N.A.I.C.S.: 325412

Subsidiary (Domestic):

Taisho Pharmaceutical Logistics Co., Ltd. (2)
3-24-1 Takada, Toshima-ku, Tokyo, 170 8633, Japan **(100%)**
Tel.: (81) 339851111
Management & Operation of Transport Services
N.A.I.C.S.: 541614

Subsidiary (US):

Taisho Pharmaceutical R&D Inc. (2)
350 Mount Kemble Ave, Morristown, NJ 07960 **(100%)**
Tel.: (973) 285-0870
Web Site: http://www.taisho.co.jp
Sales Range: $25-49.9 Million
Emp.: 10
Pharmaceuticals Product Mfr
N.A.I.C.S.: 325412
Shigeru Nakayama *(Pres)*

Subsidiary (Non-US):

Taisho Pharmaceuticals Philippines Inc. (2)
8th Floor Clipp Center Bldg 11th Avenue corner 39th Street, Bonifacio Global City, Taguig, 1225, Metro Manila, Philippines **(100%)**
Tel.: (63) 88979868
Web Site: https://taisho.com.ph
Sales Range: $25-49.9 Million
Emp.: 33
Provider of Pharmaceuticals
N.A.I.C.S.: 325412

Joint Venture (Domestic):

Taisho Toyama Pharmaceutical Co., Ltd. (2)
3 25 1 Takada, Toshima ku, Tokyo, 171 0033, Japan
Tel.: (81) 339858100
Web Site: http://www.toyama-chemical.co.jp
Prescription Pharmaceuticals Distr; Owned 55% by Taisho Pharmaceutical Co., Ltd. & 45% by Toyama Chemical Co., Ltd.
N.A.I.C.S.: 325412

Subsidiary (Non-US):

Taisho Vietnam Co., Ltd. (2)
Phu Nu Towers 20 Nguyen Van Giai Street, Thao Dien Ward Thu Duc City, Ho Chi Minh City, Vietnam **(100%)**
Tel.: (84) 1900571579
Web Site: https://old.lipovitan.vn
Sales Range: $25-49.9 Million
Emp.: 12
Manufacture & Sale of Pharmaceutical Products
N.A.I.C.S.: 325412

UPSA SAS (2)
3 rue Joseph Monier, 92500, Rueil-Malmaison, France
Tel.: (33) 1 5883 8700
Web Site: http://www.upsa.com
Pharmaceutical Mfr & Whslr
N.A.I.C.S.: 325412

TAISHO PHARMACEUTICAL HOLDINGS CO., LTD

Taisho Pharmaceutical Holdings Co., Ltd—(Continued)

Subsidiary (Non-US):

UPSAMEDICA GmbH (3)
Hinterbergstrasse 16, 6330, Cham, Switzerland
Tel.: (41) 417677200
Web Site: http://www.pms.com
Sales Range: $10-24.9 Million
Emp.: 160
Pharmaceuticals Mfr
N.A.I.C.S.: 325412
Michel Lock (Gen Mgr)

Taisho Pharmaceutical Singapore Private Limited
152 Beach Rd The Gateway East 09-06, Singapore, 189721, Singapore
Tel.: (65) 63388177
Emp.: 4
Pharmaceutical Product Mfr & Distr
N.A.I.C.S.: 325412
Seiichi Hattori (Dir)

UPSA Switzerland A.G. (1)
Bahnhofstrasse 29, 6300, Zug, Switzerland
Tel.: (41) 7481900
Pharmaceutical Product Mfr & Distr
N.A.I.C.S.: 325412

Union de Pharmacologie Scientifique Appliquee S.A.S. (1)
3 Rue Joseph Monier, 92500, Rueil-Malmaison, France
Tel.: (33) 171239500
Web Site: https://www.upsa.com
Emp.: 1,500
Pharmaceutical Product Mfr & Distr
N.A.I.C.S.: 325412

TAISOL ELECTRONICS CO., LTD.
3F No 302 Ruiguang Rd, Neihu District, Taipei, 114, Taiwan
Tel.: (886) 226562658 CN
Web Site: https://www.taisol.com
Year Founded: 1994
3338—(TAI)
Rev.: $124,653,352
Assets: $125,438,237
Liabilities: $63,430,816
Net Worth: $62,007,421
Earnings: $7,956,244
Emp.: 1,051
Fiscal Year-end: 12/31/23
Electronics Thermal Cooling & Flash Media Connectors Mfr
N.A.I.C.S.: 334419
Ching-Sung Yu (Chm)

Subsidiaries:

DongGuan TaiSol Electronics Co., Ltd. (1)
Tel.: (86) 76985321851
Electronic Thermal Cooling & Flash Media Connector Mfr
N.A.I.C.S.: 334419

SiYang TaiSol Electronics Co., Ltd. (1)
No 88 Huaihai East Road Economic Development Zone, Siyang County, Suqian, China
Tel.: (86) 52780625666777
Electronic Connector Mfr & Distr
N.A.I.C.S.: 334417

Suzhou TaiSol Electronics Co., Ltd. (1)
No 248 Dongan Rd, Lili Industrial Park, Wujiang, 215212, Jiangsu, China
Electronic Thermal Cooling & Flash Media Connector Mfr
N.A.I.C.S.: 334419

Tai-Shuo Electronics, Inc. (1)
3182 Campus Dr 308, San Mateo, CA 94403
Tel.: (650) 861-9555
Electronic Thermal Cooling & Flash Media Connector Mfr
N.A.I.C.S.: 334419

TaiSol Electronics Japan Co., Ltd. (1)
1-18-20 Yotsuya Meika Building 6th Floor, Shinjuku-ku, Tokyo, Japan
Tel.: (81) 353675369
Electronic Connector Mfr & Distr
N.A.I.C.S.: 334417

Taoyuan TaiSol Electronics Co., Ltd. (1)
3F No 18 Aly 50 Ln 642 Dongwanshou Rd, Guishan Dist, Taoyuan, Taiwan
Tel.: (886) 33592789
Electronic Connector Mfr & Distr
N.A.I.C.S.: 334417

TAISUN ENTERPRISE CO., LTD.
10F No 99 Sec 2 Changan E Rd, Zhongshan Dist, New Taipei City, 104, Taiwan
Tel.: (886) 225064152
Web Site: https://www.taisun.com.tw
1218—(TAI)
Rev.: $367,193,975
Assets: $447,338,483
Liabilities: $52,163,117
Net Worth: $395,175,367
Earnings: $2,636,940
Emp.: 921
Fiscal Year-end: 12/31/23
Food Product Mfr & Whslr
N.A.I.C.S.: 311999
Fred Chan (Gen Mgr)

TAISUN INT'L (HOLDING) CORP
Lot A1-6 N5 Street Tay Bac Cu Chi IZ, Cu Chi District, Ho Chi Minh City, Vietnam
Tel.: (84) 2837908681
Web Site: http://www.taisun.com.vn
Year Founded: 2001
8480—(TAI)
Rev.: $67,409,561
Assets: $106,525,321
Liabilities: $42,794,765
Net Worth: $63,730,556
Earnings: $13,910,716
Emp.: 800
Fiscal Year-end: 12/31/20
Diaper & Sanitary Napkin Mfr & Distr
N.A.I.C.S.: 322291
Tom Lin (Dir-IR)

Subsidiaries:

Winsun (Cambodia) Co., Ltd. (1)
Phnom Penh Special Economic Zone National Road 4 Lot P2-083, Tachet Village Beung Thom Commune Kambol District, Phnom Penh, Cambodia
Tel.: (855) 23 977 8015
Web Site: https://www.winsuncambodia.com
Baby Care Product Mfr & Distr
N.A.I.C.S.: 322291

TAIT ELECTRONICS LTD.
558 Wairakei rd, Christchurch, 8053, New Zealand
Tel.: (64) 33583399
Web Site: http://www.taitradio.com
Year Founded: 1968
Sales Range: $300-349.9 Million
Emp.: 4,000
Radio Communication Equipment Mfr
N.A.I.C.S.: 334220
Trevor Laughton (CTO-Radio Comm)

TAITA CHEMICAL COMPANY LIMITED
12th Floor No 37 Ji Hu Road, Nei-hu District, Taipei, 114, Taiwan
Tel.: (886) 287516888
Web Site: https://www.ttc.com.tw
Year Founded: 1960
1309—(TAI)
Rev.: $497,251,755
Assets: $290,766,626
Liabilities: $73,362,828
Net Worth: $217,403,798
Earnings: ($8,945,256)
Emp.: 489
Fiscal Year-end: 12/31/23
Acrylonitrile Butadiene Styrene Resin Mfr
N.A.I.C.S.: 325211
Quintin Wu (Chm)

Subsidiaries:

Taita Chemical Company Limited - Cubic Printing (1)
571 Min Tsu Rd Toufen, Toufen, Miao-li, Taiwan
Tel.: (886) 37627705
Web Site: http://www.ttc.com.tw
Printing Services
N.A.I.C.S.: 323111

Taita Chemical Company Limited - Toufen Plant (1)
571 Min Tsu Road, Toufen, Miao-li, Taiwan
Tel.: (886) 37627700
Sales Range: $25-49.9 Million
Emp.: 100
Glass Door Mfr
N.A.I.C.S.: 313210
S. P. Chen (Plant Mgr)

TAITIEN ELECTRONICS CO., LTD.
No 5 Shutan Street, Shulin Dist, New Taipei City, 238, Taiwan
Tel.: (886) 226861287
Web Site: https://www.taitien.com
Year Founded: 1976
8289—(TPE)
Rev.: $74,083,701
Assets: $80,353,094
Liabilities: $25,834,881
Net Worth: $54,518,213
Earnings: $11,220,179
Emp.: 359
Fiscal Year-end: 12/31/22
Electronic Equipment Mfr & Distr
N.A.I.C.S.: 336320

Subsidiaries:

Colorado Crystal Corporation (1)
2303 W 8th St, Loveland, CO 80537
Tel.: (970) 667-9248
Web Site: https://coloradocrystal.com
Electronic Products Mfr
N.A.I.C.S.: 334419

Isotemp Research Inc. (1)
1801 Broadway St, Charlottesville, VA 22902
Tel.: (434) 295-3101
Electronic Products Mfr
N.A.I.C.S.: 334419
Renee Pearison (Mgr)

Taitien Electronics (Nanjing) Co., Ltd. (1)
Jiangning Economic Technology Development Zone No 18 Chi-Tian Road, Jiangning Economic & Technology Development Zone, Nanjing, 211100, Jiangsu, China
Tel.: (86) 2552108713
Electronic Products Mfr
N.A.I.C.S.: 334419

Taitien Electronics (Shenzhen) Co., Ltd. (1)
8F Block 7 Nanyou Tian'an Industrial Estate, Nanshan Dist, Shenzhen, 518054, Guangdong, China
Tel.: (86) 75526522955
Electronic Products Mfr
N.A.I.C.S.: 334419

Taitien U.S.A. Inc. (1)
3720 Oceanic Way Ste 210, Oceanside, CA 92056
Tel.: (510) 252-0686
Electronic Products Mfr
N.A.I.C.S.: 334419

Wintron Electronics Co., Ltd. (1)
129 Fifth Street 2 High-Technology Industrial Park, National Economic & Technological Development Area, Zhengzhou, 450016,
Henan, China
Tel.: (86) 37186585690
Electronic Products Mfr
N.A.I.C.S.: 334419

INTERNATIONAL PUBLIC

TAITTINGER SA
9 Place Saint-Nicaise, 51100, Reims, France
Tel.: (33) 3 26 85 45 35 FR
Web Site: http://www.taittinger.com
Year Founded: 1734
Rev.: $99,900,640
Emp.: 220
Producer of Champagne
N.A.I.C.S.: 312130
Pierre-Emmanuel Taittinger (Pres)

Subsidiaries:

Domaine Carneros (1) (75.9%)
1240 Duhig Rd, Napa, CA 94559
Tel.: (707) 257-0101
Web Site: http://www.domainecarneros.com
Sales Range: $25-49.9 Million
Emp.: 100
Winery
N.A.I.C.S.: 312130
Eileen Crane (Pres)

TAIW FRUCTOSE CO., LTD.
5th Floor No 265 Nankan Road, Luzhu District, Taoyuan, 338019, Taiwan
Tel.: (886) 32125889
Web Site: https://fructose.com.tw
Year Founded: 1984
4207—(TPE)
Rev.: $157,722,853
Assets: $176,662,039
Liabilities: $77,736,891
Net Worth: $98,925,148
Earnings: $5,984,242
Emp.: 154
Fiscal Year-end: 12/31/22
Pharmaceutical Product Mfr & Distr
N.A.I.C.S.: 325412
Yung-Ming Kang (Chm)

TAIWAN ADVANCE BIO-PHARMACEUTICAL, INC.
12F No 25 Ln 169 Kangning St, Xizhi Dist, New Taipei City, 22180, Taiwan
Tel.: (886) 226926222
4186—(TAI)
Health Care Srvices
N.A.I.C.S.: 621999
Wen-Lung Su (Chm & Pres)

TAIWAN ALLIED CONTAINER TERMINAL CORP.
No 2 Sanhe Street, Qidu District, Keelung, 206, Taiwan
Tel.: (886) 224515151
Web Site: https://tactc.com.tw
Year Founded: 1962
5601—(TPE)
Rev.: $2,706,063
Assets: $58,597,442
Liabilities: $15,247,100
Net Worth: $43,350,342
Earnings: $896,820
Fiscal Year-end: 12/31/22
Warehousing & Freight Forwarding Services
N.A.I.C.S.: 488510
Tung-Chieh Chien (Chm)

TAIWAN ALPHA ELECTRONIC CO., LTD.
9F No 1221 Zhongzheng Rd, Taoyuan Dist, Taoyuan, 330010, Taiwan
Tel.: (886) 33577799
Web Site: https://www.taiwanalpha.com
Year Founded: 1970
6204—(TPE)
Rev.: $12,374,341

Assets: $15,878,707
Liabilities: $5,388,207
Net Worth: $10,490,500
Earnings: $13,527,028
Emp.: 500
Fiscal Year-end: 12/31/23
Electronic Material Mfr & Distr
N.A.I.C.S.: 334419
Chen Shuo Tsan (Chm)

TAIWAN BIOMATEIRAL CO., LTD.
1F NO 188 Sec 1 Shengyi Rd, Hsinchu County, Zhubei, 302058, Taiwan
Tel.: (886) 36683088
Web Site: https://www.twbm.com.tw
6649—(TPE)
Rev.: $3,980,427
Assets: $22,990,651
Liabilities: $2,779,195
Net Worth: $20,211,456
Earnings: $1,055,404
Fiscal Year-end: 12/31/22
Medical Device Product Mfr
N.A.I.C.S.: 339112
Chun-Jen Liao (CEO)

TAIWAN BUSINESS BANK LTD.
No 30 Ta Cheng St, Taipei, Taiwan
Tel.: (886) 225597171   TW
Web Site: https://www.tbb.com.tw
Year Founded: 1915
2834—(TAI)
Rev.: $1,535,713,129
Assets: $69,093,409,968
Liabilities: $65,337,593,284
Net Worth: $3,755,816,684
Earnings: $330,415,377
Emp.: 5,424
Fiscal Year-end: 12/31/23
Commercial Banking Services
N.A.I.C.S.: 522110
Huang Bor-yi (Chm)

Subsidiaries:

TBB (Cambodia) Microfinance Institution Plc (1)
2E2F Street 315 Sangkat Boeung Kok1, Khan Toul Kork, Phnom Penh, Cambodia
Tel.: (855) 23887171
Web Site: https://tbbmfi.com.kh
Financial Services
N.A.I.C.S.: 541611
Sreyleak Kheng (Officer-Admin)

TAIWAN CEMENT CORPORATION
No 113 Sec 2 Zhongshan North Road, Taipei, Taiwan
Tel.: (886) 225317099
Web Site:
   https://www.taiwancement.com
Year Founded: 1946
1101—(TAI)
Rev.: $3,417,888,722
Assets: $14,677,751,368
Liabilities: $6,739,126,442
Net Worth: $7,938,624,926
Earnings: $312,810,337
Emp.: 12,113
Fiscal Year-end: 12/31/23
Cement Product Mfr
N.A.I.C.S.: 327310
Nelson Chang (Co-Chm)

Subsidiaries:

Cimpor Portugal SGPS S.A. (1)
Rua Alexandre Herculano 35, Lisbon, 1250-009, Portugal (100%)
Tel.: (351) 213118100
Holding Company
N.A.I.C.S.: 551112
Filipa S. Mendes (Head-IR)

Onyx Ta-Ho Environmental Services Co. Ltd. (1)
7F No 16-5 DeHui Street, Taipei, 10461, Taiwan
Tel.: (886) 225860177
Web Site: https://www.tahoho.com.tw
Waste Management Services
N.A.I.C.S.: 562998

TCC Cement Corp. (1)
3/F Legaspi Towers 300, Roxas Boulevard Malate, Manila, 1004, Philippines
Tel.: (63) 2 5249657
Cement Product Distr
N.A.I.C.S.: 423320

TCC International Holdings Limited (1)
16th Floor Hong Kong Diamond Exchange Building 8-10 Duddell Street, Central, China (Hong Kong) (63.05%)
Tel.: (852) 2526 6626
Web Site: http://www.tcchk.com
Sales Range: $1-4.9 Billion
Cement Mfr & Distr
N.A.I.C.S.: 327310
Nelson An-Ping Chang (Chm)

Taiwan Prosperity Chemical Corporation (1)
9F No 113 Section 2 Chung Shan North Road Jhongshan District, Taipei, 104, Taiwan (73.61%)
Tel.: (886) 225633228
Web Site: http://www.tpcc.com.tw
Rev.: $344,812,508
Assets: $284,557,324
Liabilities: $229,859,079
Net Worth: $54,698,245
Earnings: ($66,934,577)
Emp.: 181
Fiscal Year-end: 12/31/2019
Petrochemical Product Mfr & Distr
N.A.I.C.S.: 324110
Tian-Fu Chao (Gen Mgr)

TAIWAN CHELIC CORP. LTD.
No 21 Guifeng St, Taishan District, New Taipei City, 24355, Taiwan
Tel.: (886) 229041235
Web Site: https://www.chelic.com
Year Founded: 1986
4555—(TAI)
Rev.: $45,038,423
Assets: $144,203,827
Liabilities: $49,974,229
Net Worth: $94,229,598
Earnings: ($1,101,181)
Emp.: 790
Fiscal Year-end: 12/31/23
Pneumatic Product Manufacturing
N.A.I.C.S.: 811310
Yu Ping-Cheng (Chm & Pres)

Subsidiaries:

Shenzhen Chelic Pneumatic Corp. (1)
3rd Floor B Block The 12th Building B Street, Shangcun Liantang Industry Gongming Town Guangming New District, Shenzhen, Guangdong, China
Tel.: (86) 75533699188
Automation Component Mfr
N.A.I.C.S.: 332912

TAIWAN CHINSAN ELECTRONIC INDUSTRIAL CO., LTD.
No 1 Aly 11 Ln 68 Sec 1 Guangfu Rd, San Chung District, New Taipei City, 24158, Taiwan
Tel.: (886) 229950535
Web Site: https://www.chinsan.com
Year Founded: 1970
8042—(TPE)
Rev.: $104,434,019
Assets: $264,552,886
Liabilities: $136,754,401
Net Worth: $127,798,484
Earnings: $2,983,126
Emp.: 1,620
Fiscal Year-end: 12/31/23
Electronic Component Mfr & Distr
N.A.I.C.S.: 334419

Chiang Shih Hsin (Chm)

Subsidiaries:

Chinsan Electronic Ind. (Thailand) Co., Ltd. (1)
94/6 Soi Serithai 85 Serthai Rd, Bangchan Industrial Estate Kannayao, Bangkok, 10230, Thailand
Tel.: (66) 2 919 8874
Electric Capacitor Whslr
N.A.I.C.S.: 423610

TAIWAN COGENERATION CORPORATION
6F No 392 Rui Guang Road, Neihu, Taipei, 11492, Taiwan
Tel.: (886) 287982000
Web Site: https://www.cogen.com.tw
Year Founded: 1992
8926—(TAI)
Rev.: $174,904,405
Assets: $855,325,943
Liabilities: $345,575,284
Net Worth: $509,750,659
Earnings: $40,628,698
Emp.: 168
Fiscal Year-end: 12/31/23
Project Planning Services
N.A.I.C.S.: 237110
Ming-Chieh Chang (Chm)

Subsidiaries:

Star Buck Power Corporation (1)
6F 392 Jui Kuang Road, Taipei, 11492, Taiwan
Tel.: (886) 287982366
Sales Range: $75-99.9 Million
Emp.: 10
Eletric Power Generation Services
N.A.I.C.S.: 221112

Ta-Yuan Cogen Co., Ltd. (1)
No 286 Huanke Rd, Guanyin Dist, Taoyuan, 328, Taiwan
Tel.: (886) 34736668
Web Site: http://www.tycc.com.tw
Electric Power & Heat Production & Distribution Services
N.A.I.C.S.: 221112
Shiaw-Tzong Lee (Chm)

Taiwan Cogeneration Corporation - Achem Cogeneration Plant (1)
No 161 Min Fu Road Section 2, Yang Mei Town, Taoyuan, 33324, Taiwan
Tel.: (886) 3 472 2296
Electric Power & Heat Production & Distribution Services
N.A.I.C.S.: 221118

Taiwan Cogeneration Corporation - Kuan-Tien Cogeneration Plant (1)
No 28 Gung-Yeh West Road Kuan Tien Industrial Park, T'ainan, 72041, Taiwan
Tel.: (886) 6 698 9024
Web Site: http://www.cogen.com.tw
Electric Power & Heat Production & Distribution Services
N.A.I.C.S.: 221112

TAIWAN COOPERATIVE FINANCIAL HOLDING CO., LTD.
17 19F Bldg A No 225 Sec 2 Chang'an East Rd, Songshan Dist, Taipei, 105, Taiwan
Tel.: (886) 221738888
Web Site: https://www.tcfhc.com.tw
Year Founded: 2011
5880—(TAI)
Rev.: $2,920,665,197
Assets: $150,195,508,739
Liabilities: $142,510,843,167
Net Worth: $7,684,665,572
Earnings: $558,991,183
Emp.: 9,590
Fiscal Year-end: 12/31/23
Holding Company
N.A.I.C.S.: 551112
Mei-Tsu Chen (Pres)

Subsidiaries:

BNP Paribas Cardif TCB Life Insurance Co., Ltd. (1)
10F No 325 Sec 4 Jhongsiao East Rd, Da'an Dist, Taipei, 106, Taiwan
Tel.: (886) 800033133
Web Site: https://my.tcb-life.com.tw
Holding Company
N.A.I.C.S.: 551112

Co-operative Asset Management Corp. (1)
7th Floor No 325 Section 4 Jhongsiao East Road, Taipei, Taiwan
Tel.: (886) 287720868
Web Site: http://www.coamc.com.tw
Banking Services
N.A.I.C.S.: 522110

Co-operative Assets Management Co., Ltd. (1)
3F No 77 Guangqian Rd, Zhongzheng Dist, Taipei, 100, Taiwan
Tel.: (886) 223820868
Web Site: https://www.coamc.com.tw
Holding Company
N.A.I.C.S.: 551112

Taiwan Cooperative Bank Co., Ltd. (1)
No 77 Guancian Rd, Jhongjheng District, Taipei, 100, Taiwan
Tel.: (886) 223118811
Web Site: http://www.tcb-bank.com.tw
Rev.: $1,596,734,424
Assets: $99,735,478,964
Liabilities: $93,689,196,448
Net Worth: $6,046,282,516
Earnings: $397,982,504
Emp.: 8,273
Fiscal Year-end: 12/31/2016
Banking Services
N.A.I.C.S.: 522110
James Shen-Gang Mai (Mng Dir)

Subsidiary (Domestic):

Cooperative Insurance Brokers Co., Ltd. (2)
5th Floor No 85 Yanping S Road, Taipei, Taiwan
Tel.: (886) 223898811
Insurance Brokerage Services
N.A.I.C.S.: 524126

Subsidiary (Non-US):

United Taiwan Bank (2)
1F Square de Meeus 1, 1000, Brussels, Belgium (100%)
Tel.: (32) 22305359
Web Site: http://www.utb-bank.be
Sales Range: $50-74.9 Million
Emp.: 8
Commericial Banking
N.A.I.C.S.: 522110

Taiwan Cooperative Bills Finance Co., Ltd. (1)
14F No 85 87 Sec 2 Nanjing East Rd, Zhongshan Dist, Taipei, 104, Taiwan
Tel.: (886) 225221656
Holding Company
N.A.I.C.S.: 551112

Taiwan Cooperative Bills Finance Corporation (1)
14th Floor No 85/87 Section 2 Nanjing E Road, Jhongshan District, Taipei, 10407, Taiwan
Tel.: (886) 225221656
Sales Range: $50-74.9 Million
Emp.: 45
Financial Banking Services
N.A.I.C.S.: 522110

Taiwan Cooperative Securities Co., Ltd. (1)
6F Bldg C No 225 Sec 2 Chang'an East Rd, Songshan Dist, Taipei, 105, Taiwan
Tel.: (886) 227528000
Holding Company
N.A.I.C.S.: 551112

Taiwan Cooperative Securities Investment Trust Co., Ltd. (1)
Tel.: (886) 221815999
Web Site: http://www.tcb-am.com.tw

TAIWAN COOPERATIVE FINANCIAL HOLDING CO., LTD.

Taiwan Cooperative Financial Holding Co., Ltd.—(Continued)

Treasury Services
N.A.I.C.S.: 541611

Taiwan Cooperative Venture Capital Co., Ltd. (1)
4-1F No 7 Sec 1 Roosevelt Rd, Zhongzheng Dist, Taipei, 100, Taiwan
Tel.: (886) 223952115
Web Site: https://eng.tcvc.com.tw
Holding Company
N.A.I.C.S.: 551112

TAIWAN ENVIRONMENT SCIENTIFIC CO LTD.
26F-3 No 175 Zhongzheng 2Nd Rd, Lingya Dist, Kaohsiung, 802, Taiwan
Tel.: (886) 72229115
8476—(TAI)
Rev.: $50,475,717
Assets: $92,418,061
Liabilities: $29,061,315
Net Worth: $63,356,746
Earnings: $12,028,614
Fiscal Year-end: 12/31/23
Engineering Consulting Services
N.A.I.C.S.: 541330
Jerry Kuo *(Chm)*

TAIWAN FERTILIZER CO., LTD.
17F No 170 Jingmao 1st Rd, Nangang Dist, Taipei, 11568, Taiwan
Tel.: (886) 225422231
Web Site: https://www.taifer.com.tw
Year Founded: 1946
1722—(TAI)
Rev.: $491,016,300
Assets: $2,666,069,686
Liabilities: $875,962,098
Net Worth: $1,790,107,588
Earnings: $128,161,511
Emp.: 652
Fiscal Year-end: 12/31/23
Fertilizer Mfr
N.A.I.C.S.: 325314
Chin-Sheng Lin *(VP)*

Subsidiaries:

Al-Jubail Fertilizer Co.(SAMAD) (1)
PO Box 10046, Al Jubayl, 31961, Eastern Province, Saudi Arabia
Tel.: (966) 33416488
Chemical Products Mfr
N.A.I.C.S.: 325311

Taiwan Yes Deep Ocean Water Co., Ltd. (1)
No 15 East China, Hualien County, Hualien, Taiwan
Tel.: (886) 38236633
Web Site: https://www.taiwanyes-dow.com.tw
Food & Grocery Whslr
N.A.I.C.S.: 445110

TAIWAN FIRE & MARINE INSURANCE CO., LTD.
8F No 49 Guanqian Rd, Zhongzheng District, Taipei, 100, Taiwan
Tel.: (886) 223821666
Web Site: https://www.tfmi.com.tw
Year Founded: 1946
2832—(TAI)
Rev.: $287,785,692
Assets: $745,943,888
Liabilities: $380,014,473
Net Worth: $365,929,415
Earnings: $31,991,529
Emp.: 912
Fiscal Year-end: 12/31/23
Insurance Services
N.A.I.C.S.: 524298
Steve Tai-Hung Lee *(Chm)*

TAIWAN FU HSING INDUSTRIAL CO., LTD.
No 88 Yucai Road, Gangshan Dist, Kaohsiung, 820, Taiwan
Tel.: (886) 76225151
Web Site: https://www.fuhsing.com.tw
9924—(TAI)
Rev.: $296,721,235
Assets: $315,209,380
Liabilities: $84,984,659
Net Worth: $230,224,721
Earnings: $31,054,742
Emp.: 1,567
Fiscal Year-end: 12/31/23
Door Locks Mfr & Distr
N.A.I.C.S.: 332510
Jui-chang Lin *(Chm)*

Subsidiaries:

ARCTEK Industrial Co., Ltd. (1)
No 1 Sec 1 Sihai Rd, Beidou Township, Chang-Hua, 521, R.O.C., Taiwan
Tel.: (886) 48887771
Web Site: http://www.arctek.com.tw
Door Closures Mfr & Distr
N.A.I.C.S.: 332321

Arctek Security Technologies (Shanghai) Co., Ltd. (1)
Room 905 He Xing Building No 651 Yuengling East Road, Puto District, Shanghai, China
Tel.: (86) 2162216991
Transom Closer Mfr
N.A.I.C.S.: 332510

Formflex Metal Industrial (Changshu) Co., Ltd. (1)
No 120 Huangpujiang Road, Changshu Hi-Tech Industrial Development Area, Jiangsu, China
Tel.: (86) 51252356868
Door Lock Hardware Mfr & Distr
N.A.I.C.S.: 332321

Fortress Door Control Product (Changshu) Co., Ltd. (1)
No 120 Huangpujiang Road Dongnan Economic Development Zone, Changshu, Jiangsu, China
Tel.: (86) 51252356868
Door Lock Hardware Mfr & Distr
N.A.I.C.S.: 332321

Fortress Industrial Co., Ltd. (1)
103 Xingong 1st Rd, Beidou Township, Changhua, 521, Taiwan
Tel.: (886) 48877610
Web Site: https://www.fortress-hardware.com
Door Lock Hardware Mfr
N.A.I.C.S.: 332321

Fu Hsing America, Inc. (1)
1000 Satellite Blvd Ste 101, Suwanee, GA 30024
Tel.: (770) 441-2830
Sales Range: $25-49.9 Million
Emp.: 10
Hardware Retailer
N.A.I.C.S.: 444140
Joseph Chu *(Pres)*

Sunion Technology Co., Ltd. (1)
6F No 69 Section 2 Guangfu Road, Sanchong District, New Taipei City, 241, Taiwan
Tel.: (886) 285121456
Web Site: http://www.sunion.com.tw
Electronic Lock Services
N.A.I.C.S.: 561622

Taiwan Fu Hsing Industrial Co., Ltd. - Changhua Factory (1)
103 Hsin Tang First Road, Chang-Hua, 521, Taiwan
Tel.: (886) 4 8877610
Door Locks Mfr
N.A.I.C.S.: 332510

Techform Industrial Co., Ltd. (1)
No 12 Bengong Rd, Gangshan Dist, Kaohsiung, 820, Taiwan
Tel.: (886) 76225100
Door Lock Hardware Distr
N.A.I.C.S.: 423710

Ziyong Hardware Products (Taicang) Co., Ltd. (1)
204 High Way Chengxiang Town, Taicang, 215411, Jiangsu, China
Tel.: (86) 512 53407588
Die Casting Mfr
N.A.I.C.S.: 331523

TAIWAN GLASS INDUSTRY CORPORATION
No 261 Sec 3 Nanjing E Rd, Songshan District, Taipei, 10550, Taiwan
Tel.: (886) 227130333
Web Site: http://www.taiwanglass.com
Year Founded: 1964
1802—(TAI)
Rev.: $1,491,841,992
Assets: $2,958,823,820
Liabilities: $1,300,477,239
Net Worth: $1,658,346,580
Earnings: $812,616
Emp.: 11,520
Fiscal Year-end: 12/31/23
Glass Mfr
N.A.I.C.S.: 327211
P. F. Lin *(Chm)*

Subsidiaries:

Chang Jiang Float Glass Co., Ltd. (1)
1 Taibo Rd Zhangpu Town, Kunshan, Jiangsu, China (100%)
Tel.: (86) 51257440001
Web Site: http://www.tgglass.com
Sales Range: $125-149.9 Million
Emp.: 400
Float Glass for Buildings, Automobiles & Mirrors
N.A.I.C.S.: 327211

Qingdao Float Glass Co., Ltd. (1)
Technology Development Park Dayao Jianan, Qingdao, 264432, Shandong, China (95%)
Tel.: (86) 5323161177
Web Site: http://www.taiwanglass.com
Sales Range: $450-499.9 Million
Emp.: 1,600
Mfr of Clear Float Glass, Mirror Glass, Tempered Glass & Laminated Glass Products
N.A.I.C.S.: 327211

T.G.U.S. Corp. (1)
9450 SW Commerce Cir Ste 420, Wilsonville, OR 97070 (82%)
Tel.: (503) 682-2255
Web Site: http://www.sanyo.com
Rev.: $1,500,000
Emp.: 10
Mfr of Flat Glass
N.A.I.C.S.: 423390

Subsidiary (Non-US):

Qingdao Rolled Glass Co., Ltd. (2)
Tayao Huangdao District, Shingdong City, Qingdao, 2266400, China (60%)
Tel.: (86) 53283161177
Web Site: http://www.taiwanglass.com
Sales Range: $100-124.9 Million
Rolled Glass
N.A.I.C.S.: 327211

TG Changjiang Glass Co., Ltd. (1)
1 Taibo Rd, Zhangpu Town, Kunshan, 215321, Jiangsu, China
Tel.: (86) 51257440001
Glass Mirror Mfr
N.A.I.C.S.: 327215

TG Donghai Glass Co., Ltd. (1)
238 Gangtie Road Niushan, Donghai, Lianyungang, Jiangsu, China
Tel.: (86) 51887266866
Glass Mirror Mfr
N.A.I.C.S.: 327215

TG Huanan Glass Co., Ltd. (1)
Taiying Industrial Park, Hongmei Town, Dongguan, 523160, Guangdong, China
Tel.: (86) 76988841000
Glass Mirror Mfr
N.A.I.C.S.: 327215

TG Tianjin Glass Co., Ltd. (1)
Tianyu Science Park, Jinghai County, Tianjin, China
Tel.: (86) 2268660077
Glass Mirror Mfr
N.A.I.C.S.: 327215

TG Yueda Solar Mirror Co., Ltd. (1)
88 Nanhuan Road Economic Developing Zone, Yancheng, Jiangsu, China
Tel.: (86) 51589850600
Glass Mirror Mfr
N.A.I.C.S.: 327215

TAIWAN GREEN ENVIRONMENT TECHNOLOGY INC.
3F-1 No 396 Sec 1 Neihu Rd, Nei-Hu Dist, Taipei, Taiwan
Tel.: (886) 226587118
Web Site: https://www.twget.com.tw
5205—(TPE)
Rev.: $425,288
Assets: $3,136,979
Liabilities: $868,086
Net Worth: $2,268,893
Earnings: $333,271
Fiscal Year-end: 12/31/22
Water Supply & Irrigation System Services
N.A.I.C.S.: 221310
Eagle Chan *(CEO)*

TAIWAN HIGH SPEED RAIL CORPORATION
13F No 66 Jingmao 2nd Road, Nangang District, Taipei, 11568, Taiwan
Tel.: (886) 287892000
Web Site: http://www.thsrc.com.tw
Year Founded: 1998
Emp.: 3,756
Rail Transportation Support Services
N.A.I.C.S.: 488210
Victor W. Liu *(Chm)*

TAIWAN HON CHUAN ENTERPRISE CO., LTD.
No 6 2nd Rd Taichung Industrial Park, Xitun Dist, Taichung, Taiwan
Tel.: (886) 423590088
9939—(TAI)
Rev.: $863,638,641
Assets: $1,237,752,169
Liabilities: $699,394,689
Net Worth: $538,357,480
Earnings: $83,717,123
Emp.: 2,840
Fiscal Year-end: 12/31/23
Bottle Caps Mfr
N.A.I.C.S.: 326199
Hsih-Chung Tsao *(Pres & Mng Dir)*

Subsidiaries:

Hon Chuan Enterprise (Changsha) Co., Ltd. (1)
Chuangye Boulevard Economic Development Area, Ningxiang County, Changsha, Hunan, China
Tel.: (86) 73187854999
Emp.: 149
Plastics Product Mfr
N.A.I.C.S.: 326199

Hon Chuan Food Packing (Anyang) Co., Ltd. (1)
Intersection of Gongxing Avenue and Guangming Road, Chengguan town Tangyin County, Anyang, Henan, China
Tel.: (86) 3726299816
Emp.: 10
Plastics Product Mfr
N.A.I.C.S.: 326199

Hon Chuan Food Packing (Chuzhou) Co., Ltd. (1)
No 1 Fu Yang Road, Cheng Bei Industrial Park Economic and Technological Development Zone, Chuzhou, Anhui, China
Tel.: (86) 5503061995
Emp.: 80
Plastics Product Mfr
N.A.I.C.S.: 326199

Hon Chuan Food Packing (Jinan) Co., Ltd. (1)
No 1 Jiwang Road, Mingshui Economic Development Area Zhangqiu City, Jinan, Shandong, China
Tel.: (86) 53183328388
Emp.: 310

AND PRIVATE COMPANIES

Plastics Product Mfr
N.A.I.C.S.: 326199

Hon Chuan Food Packing (Qingxin) Co., Ltd. (1)
No M-05B, Yingfu Industrial Park Taiping Town Qingxin County, Qingyuan, Guangdong, China
Tel.: (86) 7635383698
Emp.: 371
Plastics Product Mfr
N.A.I.C.S.: 326199

Hon Chuan Food Packing (Taiyuan) Co., Ltd. (1)
Residential Area 129, State-level Economic-Technological Development Area, Taiyuan, Shanxi, China
Tel.: (86) 3515694988
Emp.: 245
Plastics Product Mfr
N.A.I.C.S.: 326199

Hon Chuan Food Packing (Xiantao) Co., Ltd. (1)
No 59 West Sec Huangjin Avenue, Xiantao, Hubei, China
Tel.: (86) 7288280516
Emp.: 130
Plastics Product Mfr
N.A.I.C.S.: 326199

Hon Chuan Food Packing (Zhangzhou) Co., Ltd. (1)
Changtai Economic Development Area, Xingtai Industrial Park, Zhangzhou, Fujian, China
Tel.: (86) 5966950666
Emp.: 142
Plastics Product Mfr
N.A.I.C.S.: 326199

Honly Food & Beverage Co., Ltd. (1)
44 Street National Road 4, Tropeangkul Village Kantok Commune Posenchey District, Phnom Penh, Cambodia
Tel.: (855) 86888025
Web Site: http://www.honlyfood.com
Beverage & Yogurt Distr
N.A.I.C.S.: 424430
Khut Veasna (Mgr-Voice Sls)

Taiwan Hon Chuan Enterprise Co., Ltd. - Anhui Chuzhou Plant (1)
No 1 Fu Yang Road Cheng Bei Industrial Park Economic and, Technological Development Zone, Chuzhou, Anhui, China
Tel.: (86) 5503061995
Emp.: 80
Beverage Product Mfr & Distr
N.A.I.C.S.: 312111

Taiwan Hon Chuan Enterprise Co., Ltd. - Anhui Liuan Plant (1)
North of Shouxian Rd East of Zongsih Rd, Economic and Technological Development Zone, Lu'an, Anhui, China
Tel.: (86) 5643228558
Emp.: 24
Beverage Product Mfr & Distr
N.A.I.C.S.: 312111

Taiwan Hon Chuan Enterprise Co., Ltd. - Cambodia Honly Plant (1)
House 4 Street National Road 4 Group 5 Trapeang Kol Village, Kantouk Commune Po Sen Chey, Phnom Penh, Cambodia
Tel.: (855) 23729588
Emp.: 125
Beverage Product Mfr & Distr
N.A.I.C.S.: 312111

Taiwan Hon Chuan Enterprise Co., Ltd. - Henan Anyang Plant (1)
Intersection of GongXing Avenue and GuangMing Road Chengguan Town, Tangyin County, Anyang, Henan, China
Tel.: (86) 3726299816
Emp.: 10
Beverage Product Mfr & Distr
N.A.I.C.S.: 312111

Taiwan Hon Chuan Enterprise Co., Ltd. - Hon Chuan Changsha Plant (1)
Chuangye Boulevard Economic Development Area, Changsha, Ningxiang, China
Tel.: (86) 73187854999

Emp.: 149
Beverage Product Mfr & Distr
N.A.I.C.S.: 312111

Taiwan Hon Chuan Enterprise Co., Ltd. - Hon Chuan Guangdong Plant (1)
No M-05 B Yingfu Industrial Park Qingxin, Qingyuan, Guangdong, China
Tel.: (86) 7635383698
Emp.: 371
Beverage Product Mfr & Distr
N.A.I.C.S.: 312111

Taiwan Hon Chuan Enterprise Co., Ltd. - Hon Chuan Jinan Plant (1)
No 1 Jiwang Road Mingshui Economic Development Area Zhangqiu, Jinan, Shandong, China
Tel.: (86) 53183328388
Emp.: 310
Beverage Product Mfr & Distr
N.A.I.C.S.: 312111

Taiwan Hon Chuan Enterprise Co., Ltd. - Hon Chuan Kunming (Pepsi) Plant (1)
Majinpu Kunming New Hi-Tech Industries Base Chenggong, Kunming, China
Tel.: (86) 87167443553
Emp.: 14
Beverage Product Mfr & Distr
N.A.I.C.S.: 312111

Taiwan Hon Chuan Enterprise Co., Ltd. - Hon Chuan Kunming Plant (1)
Lot I5-1-1 New Hi-Tech Industries Base, Kunming, China
Tel.: (86) 87167443478
Emp.: 32
Beverage Product Mfr & Distr
N.A.I.C.S.: 312111

Taiwan Hon Chuan Enterprise Co., Ltd. - Hon Chuan Suzhou Plant (1)
No 58 Yingbin Rd Luzhi Economic Development Zone Wuzhong Area, Suzhou, China
Tel.: (86) 51265010680
Emp.: 286
Beverage Product Mfr & Distr
N.A.I.C.S.: 312111

Taiwan Hon Chuan Enterprise Co., Ltd. - Hon Chuan Taiyuan Plant (1)
Residential Area 129 State-level Economic, Technological Development Area, Taiyuan, Shanxi, China
Tel.: (86) 3515694988
Emp.: 245
Beverage Product Mfr & Distr
N.A.I.C.S.: 312111

Taiwan Hon Chuan Enterprise Co., Ltd. - Hon Chuan Xian (Coca Cola) Plant (1)
No 20 Fengcheng Second Road, Xi'an, China
Tel.: (86) 2986521101
Emp.: 43
Beverage Product Mfr & Distr
N.A.I.C.S.: 312111

Taiwan Hon Chuan Enterprise Co., Ltd. - Hon Chuan Zhengzhou Plant (1)
West of Shennanduan Gongwen Highway Heluo Town, Gongyi, China
Tel.: (86) 37160265558
Emp.: 27
Beverage Product Mfr & Distr
N.A.I.C.S.: 312111

Taiwan Hon Chuan Enterprise Co., Ltd. - Hon Chuna FD Plant (1)
695/5 Moo 1 Banbung-Bankai Rd Klongkew, Ban Bueng, 20220, Chonburi, Thailand
Tel.: (66) 38202020
Web Site: http://www.honchuan.com.tw
Emp.: 116
Beverage Product Mfr & Distr
N.A.I.C.S.: 312111
Hengkai Chen (Gen Mgr)

Taiwan Hon Chuan Enterprise Co., Ltd. - Hubei Xiantao Plant (1)
No 257 Fuzhou Avenue, Xiantao, Hubei, China
Tel.: (86) 7288280516

Emp.: 130
Beverage Product Mfr & Distr
N.A.I.C.S.: 312111

Taiwan Hon Chuan Enterprise Co., Ltd. - Indonesia (ABC) Plant (1)
Dusun Mangga Besar I RT 09 RW 03 Desa Walahar Kec Klari, Karawang, Jawa Barat, Indonesia
Tel.: (62) 267438489
Emp.: 19
Beverage Product Mfr & Distr
N.A.I.C.S.: 312111

Taiwan Hon Chuan Enterprise Co., Ltd. - Indonesia (Futami) Plant (1)
16730 JI M HE Sukma KM 18 Gang Telkom Ds Pasir Muncang, Kec Caringin Kab, Bogor, Indonesia
Tel.: (62) 2518222767
Emp.: 17
Beverage Product Mfr & Distr
N.A.I.C.S.: 312111

Taiwan Hon Chuan Enterprise Co., Ltd. - Indonesia Plant (1)
Delta Silicon V Jalan Kenari Raya Blok G2 No 1 17 Kawasan Industri, Lippo Cikarang, Indonesia
Tel.: (62) 2129617888
Emp.: 114
Beverage Product Mfr & Distr
N.A.I.C.S.: 312111

Taiwan Hon Chuan Enterprise Co., Ltd. - Indonesia Surabaya Plant (1)
Ngoro Industrial Park block F2-1 JI Raya Ngoro Kecamatan, Ngoro Kabupaten, Mojokerto, 61385, Jawa Timur, Indonesia
Tel.: (62) 3216820888
Emp.: 145
Beverage Product Mfr & Distr
N.A.I.C.S.: 312111

Taiwan Hon Chuan Enterprise Co., Ltd. - Mozambique Shimada Plant (1)
Rua Sofala 173-C, Matola, Mozambique
Tel.: (258) 2149662
Emp.: 63
Beverage Product Mfr & Distr
N.A.I.C.S.: 312111

Taiwan Hon Chuan Enterprise Co., Ltd. - Myanmar (KH) Plant (1)
351/352 11th st Yangon Industrial Zone Mingaladon Garden, Yangon, Myanmar
Tel.: (95) 1637173
Emp.: 5
Beverage Product Mfr & Distr
N.A.I.C.S.: 312111

Taiwan Hon Chuan Enterprise Co., Ltd. - Myanmar (LoiHein) Plant (1)
No 525 Pyay Road Hmawbi Township, Yangon, Myanmar
Tel.: (95) 1229954
Beverage Product Mfr & Distr
N.A.I.C.S.: 312111

Taiwan Hon Chuan Enterprise Co., Ltd. - Myanmar Plant (1)
Plot B-5 Mingaladon Industrial Park Mingaladon Township, Yangon, Myanmar
Tel.: (95) 1639098
Emp.: 100
Beverage Product Mfr & Distr
N.A.I.C.S.: 312111

Taiwan Hon Chuan Enterprise Co., Ltd. - Suzhou Hon Hsing Beverage Plant (1)
No 58A Yingbin Rd Luzhi Economic Development Zone Wuzhong Area, Suzhou, China
Tel.: (86) 51265047855
Emp.: 154
Beverage Product Mfr & Distr
N.A.I.C.S.: 312111

Taiwan Hon Chuan Enterprise Co., Ltd. - Thailand (Foodstar) Plant (1)
58/9 Moo 6 T Taladjinda A, Sam Phran, 73110, Nakhon Pathom, Thailand
Tel.: (66) 34109752
Emp.: 10
Beverage Product Mfr & Distr
N.A.I.C.S.: 312111

TAIWAN LAND DEVELOPMENT CORPORATION

Taiwan Hon Chuan Enterprise Co., Ltd. - Thailand (Uni-President) Plant (1)
502/5 Moo 3 Prapatone-Banpaw Road Tumbol Donyaihom, Amphur Muang, Nakhon Pathom, Thailand
Tel.: (66) 342298003
Emp.: 22
Beverage Product Mfr & Distr
N.A.I.C.S.: 312111

Taiwan Hon Chuan Enterprise Co., Ltd. - Thailand Plant (1)
101/116 Moo 20 Navanakhon Industrial Estate T Klong-Nueng, Khlong Luang, 12120, Pathumthani, Thailand
Tel.: (66) 25293189
Emp.: 317
Beverage Product Mfr & Distr
N.A.I.C.S.: 312111

Taiwan Hon Chuan Enterprise Co., Ltd. - Vietnam (Tribeco) Plant (1)
No 8 Street 11 Vietnam-Singapore Industrial Park, Thuan An, Binh Duong, Vietnam
Tel.: (84) 2743769519
Emp.: 11
Beverage Product Mfr & Distr
N.A.I.C.S.: 312111

Taiwan Hon Chuan Enterprise Co., Ltd. - Vietnam Plant (1)
No 29 VSIP II Street 7 Vietnam Singapore Industrial Park II VSIP II, Hoa Phu Ward, Thu Dau Mot, Binh Duong, Vietnam
Tel.: (84) 2743769516
Emp.: 120
Beverage Product Mfr & Distr
N.A.I.C.S.: 312111

Taiwan Hon Chuan Enterprise Co., Ltd. - Zhangzhou Aseptic-filling Plant (1)
Xingtai Industrial Park Changtai Economic Development Area, Zhangzhou, Fujian, China
Tel.: (86) 5966950666
Emp.: 142
Beverage Product Mfr & Distr
N.A.I.C.S.: 312111

TAIWAN HOPAX CHEMICALS MFG CO., LTD.
No 28 Hua Dong Road Chaoliao, Daliao, Kaohsiung, Taiwan
Tel.: (886) 77887600
Web Site: https://www.hopaxfc.com
6509—(TPE)
Rev.: $170,722,884
Assets: $208,760,373
Liabilities: $97,355,189
Net Worth: $111,405,184
Earnings: $18,739,674
Emp.: 1,400
Fiscal Year-end: 12/31/22
Paper Making & Water Treatment Chemical Mfr
N.A.I.C.S.: 325992
Tsung-Tien Kuo (Chm & Pres)

TAIWAN LAND DEVELOPMENT CORPORATION
14th Floor No 51 Hengyang Road, Taipei, Taiwan
Tel.: (886) 223311234
Web Site: http://www.tldc.com.tw
2841—(TAI)
Rev.: $11,908,978
Assets: $1,286,073,900
Liabilities: $647,050,811
Net Worth: $639,023,089
Earnings: ($65,057,566)
Emp.: 180
Fiscal Year-end: 12/31/20
Land Development & Management Services
N.A.I.C.S.: 924120
Tai-Sheng Lian (Vice Chm)

Subsidiaries:

Wind Lion Plaza Corporation (1)
No 8-8 Zhongshan Road Next to Shangyi

TAIWAN LAND DEVELOPMENT CORPORATION

Taiwan Land Development Corporation—(Continued)
Airport, Kinmen County, Jinhu, Taiwan
Tel.: (886) 800586188
Web Site: http://www.windlion.com
Food & Grocery Product Retailer
N.A.I.C.S.: 455219

TAIWAN LINE TEK ELECTRONIC CO., LTD.
272 Sec 3 Bei Shen Rd, Shen Keng Dist, New Taipei City, 22206, Taiwan
Tel.: (886) 226625600
Web Site: https://www.linetek.com.tw
Year Founded: 1978
2462—(TAI)
Rev.: $128,231,494
Assets: $178,479,963
Liabilities: $78,493,309
Net Worth: $99,986,654
Earnings: $8,810,916
Emp.: 280
Fiscal Year-end: 12/31/23
Power Cords Mfr
N.A.I.C.S.: 334419
Chen Longshui *(Chm)*

Subsidiaries:

Electronic Component Sales Inc. (1)
22525 SE 64th Pl Ste 2247, Issaquah, WA 98027
Tel.: (425) 968-2407
Web Site: http://www.ecsrep.com
Electronic Components Distr
N.A.I.C.S.: 423690

FONGMA TEK(SUZHOU) CO., LTD. (1)
5F No 269 Dong Jin Road Guo Lane, Wu Jhong Area, Suzhou, 215168, Jiangsu, China
Tel.: (86) 51267546711
Power Cords & Cables Mfr
N.A.I.C.S.: 335931

LINETEK JAPAN CO., LTD. (1)
3-16-22 Tsukuda, Nishiyodogawa-ku, Osaka, 555-0001, Japan
Tel.: (81) 664731021
Web Site: http://w3.linetek.com.tw
Sales Range: $25-49.9 Million
Emp.: 3
Power Cords Mfr
N.A.I.C.S.: 335931

MOTION MICRO INC. (1)
1 Lincoln Ctr Ste 525 10300 SW Greenburg Rd, Portland, OR 97223
Tel.: (888) 294-2704
Web Site: http://www.motionmicro.com
Electric Equipment Mfr
N.A.I.C.S.: 334413

SIN LINE TEK ELECTRONIC CO. SDN. BHD. (1)
PT 464 Jalan Kasawari, Kawasan Perusahaan Kebun Baru, 42500, Teluk Panglima Garang, Selangor Darul Ehsan, Malaysia
Tel.: (60) 331231090
Power Cords & Cables Mfr
N.A.I.C.S.: 335931

Solution Korea Company (1)
129-5 Bansong-dong, Hwaseong, 445-160, Gyeonggi-do, Korea (South)
Tel.: (82) 31 8015 3477
Web Site: http://w3.linetek.com.tw
Emp.: 15
Power Cords Distr
N.A.I.C.S.: 423840

TAIWAN LIPOSOME COMPANY, LTD.
11F 1 No 3 Yuanqu Street Nankang, Taipei, 11503, Taiwan
Tel.: (886) 226557377   TW
Web Site: http://www.tlcbio.com
Year Founded: 1997
TLC—(NASDAQ)
Rev.: $3,625,579
Assets: $62,228,328
Liabilities: $31,519,786
Net Worth: $30,708,541
Earnings: ($34,976,301)
Emp.: 112
Fiscal Year-end: 12/31/20
Proprietary Drug Development & Commercialization
N.A.I.C.S.: 541715
Keelung Hong *(Founder, Chm & CEO)*

Subsidiaries:

TLC Biopharmaceuticals, B.V. (1)
J H Oortweg 20, 2333 CH, Leiden, Netherlands
Tel.: (31) 71 3322 340
Pharmaceutical Products Distr
N.A.I.C.S.: 424210

Taiwan Liposome Company - US (1)
432 N Canal St U 20, South San Francisco, CA 94080   (100%)
Tel.: (650) 872-8816
Web Site: http://www.tlcbio.com
Biopharmaceutical Research & Development
N.A.I.C.S.: 541714

TAIWAN MASK CORPORATION
No 11 Innovation Road 1 Science-Based Industrial Park, Hsinchu, Taiwan
Tel.: (886) 35634370
Web Site: http://www.tmcnet.com.tw
2338—(TAI)
Rev.: $235,453,570
Assets: $684,262,344
Liabilities: $519,138,703
Net Worth: $165,123,641
Earnings: $5,372,445
Emp.: 1,346
Fiscal Year-end: 12/31/23
Photomasks Mfr
N.A.I.C.S.: 334413
Sean Chen *(Chm)*

TAIWAN MOBILE CO., LTD.
12F No 88 Yanchang Road, Xinyi Dist, Taipei, 110, Taiwan
Tel.: (886) 266062999   TW
Web Site: https://www.taiwanmobile.com
Year Founded: 1997
3045—(TAI)
Rev.: $5,995,873,576
Assets: $7,945,464,267
Liabilities: $4,891,598,854
Net Worth: $3,053,865,413
Earnings: $468,785,881
Emp.: 10,378
Fiscal Year-end: 12/31/23
Telecommunication Servicesb
N.A.I.C.S.: 517112
Naomi Lee *(VP-Corp Grp)*

Subsidiaries:

Phoenix Cable TV Co., Ltd. (1)
All the way Daliao District, Kaohsiung, 312, Taiwan
Tel.: (886) 77016998
Web Site: http://www.phoenixcatv.com.tw
Cable Television Distribution Services
N.A.I.C.S.: 517111

Taiwan Cellular Co., Ltd. (1)
13 Floor No 88 Yanchang Road Xinyi District, Taipei, 11072, Taiwan
Tel.: (886) 2 6606 2977
Investment Management Service
N.A.I.C.S.: 523940

Subsidiary (Domestic):

Taiwan Fixed Network Co., Ltd. (2)
9th Floor-1 172-1 Keelung Road Section 2, Taipei, 10662, Taiwan
Tel.: (886) 266365168
Fixed Line Providing Services
N.A.I.C.S.: 517111

TAIWAN NAME PLATE CO., LTD.
No 36 Hwa Ya 1St Rd, Kueishan Dist, Taoyuan, 333, Taiwan
Tel.: (886) 33270567
Web Site: https://www.tnp.com.tw
Year Founded: 1970
6593—(TPE)
Rev.: $21,854,246
Assets: $33,016,546
Liabilities: $9,960,332
Net Worth: $23,056,214
Earnings: $1,475,849
Fiscal Year-end: 12/31/23
Credit Card Issuing Services
N.A.I.C.S.: 522210
Hsu Chia Chun *(Chm)*

TAIWAN NAVIGATION CO., LTD.
29 Section 2 Chi Nan Rd, Taipei, 100, Taiwan
Tel.: (886) 223941769
Web Site: https://www.taiwanline.com.tw
2617—(TAI)
Rev.: $130,485,263
Assets: $803,006,085
Liabilities: $280,771,238
Net Worth: $522,234,847
Earnings: $54,380,128
Emp.: 240
Fiscal Year-end: 12/31/23
Shipping Services
N.A.I.C.S.: 483111
Wen-Ching Liu *(Chm)*

TAIWAN OASIS TECHNOLOGY CO., LTD.
27F No 97 Sec 1 Xintai 5th Rd, Xizhi Dist, New Taipei City, 22175, Taiwan
Tel.: (886) 277286688
Web Site: https://www.oasistek.com
Year Founded: 1974
3066—(TPE)
Rev.: $7,013,506
Assets: $50,925,339
Liabilities: $14,460,512
Net Worth: $36,464,827
Earnings: ($4,757,807)
Fiscal Year-end: 12/31/23
LCD Products Mfr
N.A.I.C.S.: 334413
Ming-Shun Lee *(Founder & Chm)*

TAIWAN OPTICAL PLATFORM CO., LTD.
6-6F No 201 Section 2 Wenxin Road, Xitun District, Taichung, 407, Taiwan
Tel.: (886) 437050000
Web Site: https://www.topmso.com.tw
Year Founded: 2006
6464—(TAI)
Rev.: $136,582,650
Assets: $611,023,130
Liabilities: $340,058,066
Net Worth: $270,965,064
Earnings: $24,849,994
Emp.: 311
Fiscal Year-end: 12/31/23
Cable Television & Multimedia Services
N.A.I.C.S.: 516210
Lin Ya'ao *(Vice Chm)*

Subsidiaries:

A-First Technology Co., Ltd. (1)
No 221 Zhonghe St, Zhubei, 302, Hsinchu, Taiwan
Tel.: (886) 35550019
Web Site: https://www.a-first.com.tw
Television Broadcasting Services
N.A.I.C.S.: 516120

CNT CATV Co., Ltd. (1)
320 Daming Road 1/F Jushan Jen, Nant'ou, 557, Taiwan
Tel.: (886) 437050000
Television Broadcasting Services
N.A.I.C.S.: 516120

Da-Tun Cable TV Co., Ltd. (1)
No 68 Section 1 Guoguang Road Dali District, Taichung, Taiwan
Tel.: (886) 440556688
Web Site: http://www.tdtv.com.tw
Television Broadcasting Services
N.A.I.C.S.: 516120

TAIWAN OSTOR CORPORATION
9F No 451 Chongyang Rd, Nangang Dist, Taipei, 115, Taiwan
Tel.: (886) 227820018
Web Site: https://www.ost.com.tw
Year Founded: 1993
8080—(TPE)
Electrolytic Capacitor Mfr & Distr
N.A.I.C.S.: 334416
Huang Shouzuo *(Chm & Gen Mgr)*

TAIWAN PAIHO LIMITED
No 575 Ho Kang Rd Ho Mei Town, Chang-Hua, Taiwan
Tel.: (886) 47565307
Web Site: https://www.paiho.com
9938—(TAI)
Rev.: $406,985,269
Assets: $1,035,789,195
Liabilities: $581,191,874
Net Worth: $454,597,321
Earnings: $9,064,913
Emp.: 5,829
Fiscal Year-end: 12/31/23
Sport Goods & Accessories Mfr
N.A.I.C.S.: 313220
Cheng-We Cheng *(Gen Mgr)*

Subsidiaries:

China Star International Limited (1)
No 6008 Northern Fu-I Road Waigang, Jiading District, Shanghai, China
Tel.: (86) 2169575626
Coating Powder Mfr & Distr
N.A.I.C.S.: 325510

Dongguan Paiho Powder Coating Co., Ltd. (1)
Dajingtou No 2 Industrial Zone, Dalang Town, Dongguan, 523777, Guangdong, China
Tel.: (86) 769 83483361
Web Site: http://www.paiho.com
Textiles & Elastic Tapes Mfr
N.A.I.C.S.: 314999

Dongguan Paiho Textile, Limited (1)
No 11 Paiho Road Hengliu Management, District Shatian Town, Dongguan, Guangdong, China
Tel.: (86) 76988745111
Web Site: http://www.paiho.com
Sewn Products Mfr
N.A.I.C.S.: 316110

Paiho Europe S.A. (1)
Torrent de Can Dansa 1, Gualba, 8448, Barcelona, Spain
Tel.: (34) 938713713
Web Site: http://www.paihoeurope.com
Sales Range: $50-74.9 Million
Emp.: 8
Textile & Elastic Tapes Distr
N.A.I.C.S.: 523920
Domingo Nadal *(Mng Dir)*

Paiho North America Corporation (1)
16051 El Prado Rd, Chino, CA 91708
Tel.: (661) 257-6611
Web Site: http://www.paiho-usa.com
Sales Range: $25-49.9 Million
Emp.: 40
Hooks & Fasteners Mfr
N.A.I.C.S.: 332722
Mark Jacob *(Founder)*

Paiho Shih Holdings Corporation (1)
No 575 Ho Kang Road, Ho Mei Town, Chang-Hua, 508, Taiwan
Tel.: (886) 47561340
Web Site: https://www.kypaiho.com
Rev.: $172,321,946
Assets: $586,777,211
Liabilities: $428,758,184
Net Worth: $158,019,027
Earnings: ($20,514,666)

Emp.: 1,000
Fiscal Year-end: 12/31/2023
Holding Company; Tape & Belting Mfr
N.A.I.C.S.: 551112

Subsidiary (Non-US):

Wuxi Paiho Textiles Co., Ltd. (2)
No 18 Hexin Road Xishan Economic Development Zone, Wuxi, 214101, Jiangsu, China (93.2%)
Tel.: (86) 510 88261688
Web Site: http://www.paiho.cn
Apparels Mfr
N.A.I.C.S.: 315990

Spring Rich Limited (1)
No 575 Hegang Rd, Changhua County, Hemei, 508, Taiwan
Tel.: (886) 47562800
Molded Hook Tape Mfr
N.A.I.C.S.: 322230

Taiwan Paiho Limited - Taiwan Factory (1)
No 49 Lane 616 De Mei Road, Ho Mei Town, Chang-Hua, Taiwan
Tel.: (886) 4 7551566
Web Site: http://www.paiho.com
Textile Tapes Mfr
N.A.I.C.S.: 313220

Thomas Dynamic Material (jiangsu) Co., Ltd. (1)
No 18 Hexin Rd Xishan Economic Development Zone, Wuxi, 214101, Jiangsu, China
Tel.: (86) 51088261688
Touch Fastener Mfr
N.A.I.C.S.: 339993

VietNam Paiho Limited (1)
Lot 30-32-34 Road No 3 Tan Tao Industrial Park, Tan Tao A Ward Binh Tan District, Ho Chi Minh City, Vietnam
Tel.: (84) 837540103
Web Site: https://www.vnpaiho.com
Textile Products Mfr & Distr
N.A.I.C.S.: 313220

Wuxi Paihong Real Estate Co., Ltd. (1)
No 1399 Dongxiang Rd Anzhen St, Xishan District, Wuxi, Jiangsu, China
Tel.: (86) 51088789866
Commercial Property Management Services
N.A.I.C.S.: 531312

Wuxi Paisen Chemical Fibre CO., LTD. (1)
No 18 Hexin Road Dongting Town, Xishan District, Wuxi, 214101, Jiangsu, China
Tel.: (86) 51088266979
Web Site: http://www.paisenfibre.com
Emp.: 100
Chemical Fiber Mfr
N.A.I.C.S.: 325220
Simon Yang (Mgr-Sls)

Wuxi Paisen Commerce Co., Ltd. (1)
No 18 Hexin Rd, Xishan Economic Development District, Wuxi, Jiangsu, China
Tel.: (86) 51088266979
Textile Product Mfr & Distr
N.A.I.C.S.: 313310

Wuxi Paiwei Biotechnology Co., Ltd. (1)
No 18 Hexin Rd, Xishan Enconomic Development District, Wuxi, Jiangsu, China
Tel.: (86) 51088263199
Textile Product Mfr & Distr
N.A.I.C.S.: 313310

TAIWAN PCB TECHVEST CO., LTD.
No 12 Gongye 2nd Rd, Pingzhen Dist, Taoyuan, 324403, Taiwan
Tel.: (886) 34698860
Web Site: https://www.tpt-pcb.com.tw
Year Founded: 1998
8213—(TAI)
Rev.: $619,177,844
Assets: $971,136,887
Liabilities: $467,631,788
Net Worth: $503,505,099
Earnings: $36,990,090
Emp.: 2,292
Fiscal Year-end: 12/31/23
Printed Circuit Boards & Electronic Components Mfr & Sales
N.A.I.C.S.: 334412

TAIWAN PELICAN EXPRESS CO., LTD.
2F No 19-9 Sanchong Road, Nangang District, Taipei, 155, Taiwan
Tel.: (886) 266165500
Web Site: https://www.e-can.com.tw
2642—(TAI)
Rev.: $136,971,806
Assets: $142,173,872
Liabilities: $69,408,644
Net Worth: $72,765,228
Earnings: $3,090,225
Emp.: 1,416
Fiscal Year-end: 12/31/23
Courier Delivery Services
N.A.I.C.S.: 492110
Chwen-Jy Chiu (Chm)

TAIWAN POWER COMPANY
242 Sec 3 Roosevelt Road, Zhongzheng District, Taipei, 10016, Taiwan
Tel.: (886) 223651234   TW
Web Site: http://www.taipower.com.tw
Year Founded: 1946
Sales Range: $15-24.9 Billion
Emp.: 27,261
Electric Power Distr & Generation Services
N.A.I.C.S.: 221122
Jung-Chiou Hwang (Chm)

TAIWAN PULP & PAPER CORPORATION
No 94 Nantzu St, Shin Ying Dist, Taipei, Taiwan
Tel.: (886) 6 656 3811
Web Site: http://www.tppc.com.tw
Rev.: $107,172,288
Assets: $303,243,658
Liabilities: $84,163,546
Net Worth: $219,080,112
Earnings: $14,601,143
Fiscal Year-end: 12/31/18
Pulp & Paper Mfr
N.A.I.C.S.: 322120
Feng Zhihong (Asst VP)

Subsidiaries:

Taiwan Pulp & Paper Corporation - Hsingying mill (1)
94 Nan Tzu Street, Hsinying, T'ainan, Taiwan
Tel.: (886) 66563811
Web Site: http://www.tppc.com.tw
Pulp Mfr
N.A.I.C.S.: 322110

TAIWAN SAKURA CORPORATION
No 436 Sec 4 Yatan Rd, Daya Dist, Taichung, Taiwan
Tel.: (886) 425666106
Web Site: http://www.sakura.com.tw
9911—(TAI)
Rev.: $270,526,004
Assets: $311,793,866
Liabilities: $114,343,401
Net Worth: $197,450,465
Earnings: $34,962,130
Emp.: 949
Fiscal Year-end: 12/31/23
Kitchen Articles Mfr & Distr
N.A.I.C.S.: 327110
Yung-Chieh Chang (Chm)

Subsidiaries:

Sakura Shunde Co. Ltd. (1)
No 2 Ronggui Avenue South Ronggui Road Shunde District, Foshan, 528305, Guangdong, China
Tel.: (86) 75728888338
Solar Equipment Mfr
N.A.I.C.S.: 335220

TAIWAN SANYO ELECTRIC CO., LTD.
10th Floor No 266 Songjiang Road Zhongshan District, Zhongshan District, Taipei, Taiwan
Tel.: (886) 225210251
Web Site: https://sanlux.com.tw
1614—(TAI)
Rev.: $188,219,621
Assets: $226,353,993
Liabilities: $42,832,825
Net Worth: $183,521,168
Earnings: $10,591,549
Fiscal Year-end: 12/31/23
Household Electrical Appliance Mfr
N.A.I.C.S.: 335220
Wen-Feng Li (Chm)

TAIWAN SECOM COMPANY LTD.
No 139 6F Cheng-Chou Rd, Taipei, Taiwan
Tel.: (886) 25575050
Web Site: https://www.secom.com.tw
9917—(TAI)
Rev.: $559,797,879
Assets: $878,393,309
Liabilities: $451,231,089
Net Worth: $427,162,219
Earnings: $85,744,920
Emp.: 9,082
Fiscal Year-end: 12/31/23
Security System Services
N.A.I.C.S.: 561621
Shiaw-Shinn Lin (Chm)

Subsidiaries:

Comlink Fire Systems Inc. (1)
9th Floor N 139 Zhengzhou Road, Datong District, Taipei, 103, Taiwan
Tel.: (886) 225578319
Web Site: https://www.comlinkfire.com
Safety Consulting Services
N.A.I.C.S.: 541690

SIGMU D.P.T. Co., Ltd. (1)
6th Floor No 139 Zhengzhou Road, Datong District, Taipei, Taiwan
Tel.: (886) 277469919
Web Site: http://www.sigmudpt.com.tw
Disaster Prevention Services
N.A.I.C.S.: 624230

TAIWAN SEMICONDUCTOR CO., LTD.
11 Fl No 205 Sec 3 Beishin Rd, Xindian Dist, New Taipei City, 231, Taiwan
Tel.: (886) 289131588   TW
Web Site: https://www.taiwansemi.com
Year Founded: 1979
5425—(TPE)
Rev.: $514,112,716
Assets: $569,578,182
Liabilities: $234,228,684
Net Worth: $335,349,498
Earnings: $68,064,753
Emp.: 654
Fiscal Year-end: 12/31/22
Semiconductor Device Mfr & Distr
N.A.I.C.S.: 334413
Wang Shiu Ting (Chm & CEO)

Subsidiaries:

Taiwan Semiconductor (H.K.) Co., Ltd. (1)
5F Meeco Industrial Building 53 - 55 Au Pui Wan Street Fo Tan Shatin, Hong Kong, China (Hong Kong)
Tel.: (852) 2 790 8881
Semiconductor Product Mfr & Distr
N.A.I.C.S.: 334413

Taiwan Semiconductor Europe GmbH (1)
Georg-Wimmer-Ring 8b, 85604, Zorneding, Germany
Tel.: (49) 8106 996 3660
Semiconductor Product Mfr & Distr
N.A.I.C.S.: 334413

Taiwan Semiconductor Japan Ltd. (1)
Yuasa Bldg 3F 2-13-10 Hongo, Bunkyo-ku, Tokyo, 113-0033, Japan
Tel.: (81) 35 840 6381
Semiconductor Product Mfr & Distr
N.A.I.C.S.: 334413

TAIWAN SEMICONDUCTOR MANUFACTURING COMPANY LTD.
No 8 Li-Hsin Road 6 Hsinchu Science Park, Hsin-chu, Taiwan
Tel.: (886) 35636688   TW
Web Site: http://www.tsmc.com
Year Founded: 1987
TSM—(NYSE)
Rev.: $80,526,613,541
Assets: $176,585,810,187
Liabilities: $72,798,511,719
Net Worth: $103,787,298,468
Earnings: $35,331,492,479
Emp.: 73,090
Fiscal Year-end: 12/31/22
Semiconductor Mfr
N.A.I.C.S.: 334413
Maria Marced (Pres-Europe)

Subsidiaries:

Mutual-Pak Technology Co., Ltd. (1)
No 2 Songjiang N Rd, Jhongli Industrial Park, Taoyuan, 24252, Taiwan
Tel.: (886) 34638332
Web Site: https://www.mutualpak.com
Sales Range: $25-49.9 Million
Emp.: 50
Semiconductor Devices Mfr
N.A.I.C.S.: 334413
Fred Chia (Chm)

TSMC China Company Limited (1)
4000 Wen Xiang Road, Songjiang, Shanghai, 201616, China
Tel.: (86) 2157768000
Integrated Circuit Board Mfr & Distr
N.A.I.C.S.: 334413

TSMC Design Technology Canada Inc. (1)
535 Legget Dr Suite 600, Kanata, K2K 3B8, ON, Canada
Tel.: (613) 576-1990
Industrial Designing Services
N.A.I.C.S.: 541420

TSMC Design Technology Japan, Inc. (1)
10F Minatomirai Grand Central Tower 4-6-2 Minatomirai, Nishi-ku, Yokohama, 220-0012, Kanagawa, Japan
Tel.: (81) 45 664 4500
Semiconductor Product Mfr & Distr
N.A.I.C.S.: 334413

TSMC Europe B.V. (1)
World Trade Center Zuidplein 60, Zuidplein 60, 1077 XV, Amsterdam, Netherlands (100%)
Tel.: (31) 203059900
Sales Range: $25-49.9 Million
Emp.: 45
Semiconductor Marketing & Service
N.A.I.C.S.: 423690
Maria Marced (Pres)

TSMC Japan 3DIC R&D Center, Inc. (1)
2F 7D Bldg West 16-1 Onogawa, Tsukuba, Ibaraki, Japan
Tel.: (81) 298932968
Semiconductor Mfr
N.A.I.C.S.: 334413

TSMC Japan KK (1)
21F Queen's Tower C 2-3-5 Minatomirai, Nishi-ku, Yokohama, 220-6221, Kanagawa, Japan (100%)

TAIWAN SEMICONDUCTOR MANUFACTURING COMPANY LTD.

Taiwan Semiconductor Manufacturing Company Ltd.—(Continued)
Tel.: (81) 456820670
Sales Range: $50-74.9 Million
Emp.: 30
Semiconductor Marketing & Service
N.A.I.C.S.: 423690

TSMC Korea Limited (1)
Rm 2104-2105 West Hanshin Inter Valley 24 Building 322 Teheran-ro, Gangnam-gu, Seoul, 06211, Korea (South)
Tel.: (82) 221831688
Semiconductor Devices Mfr
N.A.I.C.S.: 334413

TSMC Nanjing Company Limited (1)
16 Zifeng Road, Pukou Economic Development Zone, Nanjing, Jiangsu, China
Tel.: (86) 255 766 8000
Semiconductor Product Mfr & Distr
N.A.I.C.S.: 334413

TSMC North America Inc. (1)
2851 Junction Ave, San Jose, CA 95134
Tel.: (408) 382-8000
Sales Range: $50-74.9 Million
Emp.: 80
Electronic Engineering Support & Services
N.A.I.C.S.: 423690
David Keller (Pres & CEO)

Subsidiary (Domestic):

TSMC Technology, Inc. (2)
2851 Junction Ave, San Jose, CA 95134
Tel.: (408) 382-8000
Semiconductor Devices Mfr
N.A.I.C.S.: 334413

VentureTech Alliance Holdings, LLC (2)
2851 Junction Ave, San Jose, CA 95134
Tel.: (408) 382-8086
Web Site: http://www.vtalliance.com
Financial Management Services
N.A.I.C.S.: 523999

WaferTech, LLC (2)
5509 NW Parker St, Camas, WA 98607
Tel.: (360) 817-3000
Web Site: https://www.wafertech.com
Emp.: 1,000
Semiconductor Mfr
N.A.I.C.S.: 334413

TSMC Solar Ltd. (1)
No 9 Li-Hsin Rd 4 Hsinchu Science Park, Hsin-chu, 300-78, Taiwan
Tel.: (886) 3 563 6688
Web Site: http://www.tsmc.com
Sales Range: $100-124.9 Million
Emp.: 300
Semiconductor Devices Mfr
N.A.I.C.S.: 334413

Subsidiary (Non-US):

TSMC Solar Europe GmbH (2)
Tel.: (49) 40808074540
Emp.: 6
Electricity Production Services
N.A.I.C.S.: 334515

VisEra Technologies Company Ltd. (1)
No 12 Dusing Rd 1 Hsinchu Science Park, Hsinchu, 30078, Taiwan
Tel.: (886) 3 666 8788
Web Site: https://www.viseratech.com
Image Sensor Mfr & Distr
N.A.I.C.S.: 333310
Robert Kuan (CEO & Chm)

TAIWAN SHIN KONG SECURITY CO., LTD.
No 128 Xingai Rd, Neihu District, Taipei, Taiwan
Tel.: (886) 277199888
Web Site: https://www.sks.com.tw
9925—(TAI)
Rev.: $252,222,136
Assets: $605,608,499
Liabilities: $205,517,439
Net Worth: $400,091,060
Earnings: $32,957,453
Emp.: 6,428
Fiscal Year-end: 12/31/23
Security System Services
N.A.I.C.S.: 561621
Po-Fong Lin (Chm & CEO)

Subsidiaries:

Beijing Yi Kong Property Management Ltd. (1)
Room 902 Unit 1 Unit A Building 4 Changyi Commercial Plaza, Beijing-Tianjin Highway Beichen District, Tianjin, China
Tel.: (86) 1051096300
Property Management Services
N.A.I.C.S.: 531390

Shin Kong (Myanmar) Consulting Ltd. (1)
0502 5th floor Sakura Tower 339 Bogyoke Aung San Road, Kyauktada Towership, Yangon, Myanmar
Tel.: (95) 1255082
Management Consulting Services
N.A.I.C.S.: 541611

Shinsoft Co., Ltd. (1)
3F No 128 Shi-Hu 2nd Rd Neihu District, Taipei, 114, Taiwan
Tel.: (886) 227968887
Web Site: http://www.shinsoft.com.tw
Security System & Equipment Maintenance Services
N.A.I.C.S.: 561621

Thai-SK Security International Co., Ltd. (1)
25 Soi 8 Seri 7 Rama 9 Khwang Suan Luang, Bangkok, Thailand
Tel.: (66) 27201171
Security System & Equipment Maintainence Services
N.A.I.C.S.: 561621

Xiamen Shin-Po Property Service Co., Ltd. (1)
No 498 Xinglinwan Road Building 702C No 10 Building Jimei District, Xiamen, China
Tel.: (86) 5927115658
Property Management Services
N.A.I.C.S.: 531390

Xiamen Shin-Po Security Equipment Ltd. (1)
No 498 Xinglinwan Road Building 702C No 10 Building Jimei District, Xiamen, China
Tel.: (86) 5927115658
Security Equipment Distr
N.A.I.C.S.: 423610

TAIWAN STOCK EXCHANGE CORPORATION
3F 9-12F No 7 Sec 5 Xinyi Rd, Taipei, 11049, Taiwan
Tel.: (886) 281013101   TW
Web Site: http://www.twse.com.tw
Year Founded: 1961
Sales Range: $650-699.9 Million
Emp.: 500
Stock Exchange
N.A.I.C.S.: 523210
Shie-Jay Yang (Exec VP-Secretarial & Legal Dept)

TAIWAN STYRENE MONOMER CORPORATION
8F-1 No 6 Sec 1 Roosevelt Rd, Taipei, 100, Taiwan
Tel.: (886) 223966007
Web Site: http://www.smct.com.tw
Year Founded: 1979
1310—(TAI)
Rev.: $312,017,451
Assets: $319,278,055
Liabilities: $84,375,908
Net Worth: $234,902,146
Earnings: ($15,064,554)
Emp.: 197
Fiscal Year-end: 12/31/23
Resin Product Mfr
N.A.I.C.S.: 325211
Wen Yuan Lin (Chm)

Subsidiaries:

Taiwan Styrene Monomer Corporation - Kaohsiung Plant (1)
No 7 Industrial 1st Road Lin-Yuan, Kaohsiung, 83203, Taiwan
Tel.: (886) 76414511
Styrene Monomer Product Mfr
N.A.I.C.S.: 325212

Taiwan United Medical Inc. (1)
242 3rd Floor No 1 Lane 8 Lane 188 Min an Road, Xinzhuang District, New Taipei City, Taiwan
Tel.: (886) 222071938
Web Site: http://www.pmtech.com.tw
Chemical Distr
N.A.I.C.S.: 424690

Yung-Fu Co., Ltd. (1)
Civil Aid Service Road 188 Alley 8 Lane 13, New Zhuang District, New Taipei City, Taiwan
Tel.: (886) 222066826
Web Site: http://www.yung-fu.tw
Electrical Machinery Design & Engineering Services
N.A.I.C.S.: 541330

TAIWAN SURFACE MOUNTING TECHNOLOGY CORP.
No 437 Taoying Rd, Taoyuan, 330, Taiwan
Tel.: (886) 32189988
Web Site: https://www.tsmt.com
Year Founded: 1990
6278—(TAI)
Rev.: $1,520,521,052
Assets: $1,590,269,471
Liabilities: $941,511,557
Net Worth: $648,757,914
Earnings: $82,210,207
Emp.: 10,948
Fiscal Year-end: 12/31/23
Printed Circuit Board Mfr
N.A.I.C.S.: 334412
Dysan Lin (VP)

Subsidiaries:

Regent Electron (Chong Qing) Co., Ltd. (1)
No 1 Songshan Mid Road, New North Zone Dazhulin Town, Chongqing, China
Tel.: (86) 2363569688
Printed Circuit Board Mfr
N.A.I.C.S.: 334412

Regent Electron (Dongguan) Co., Ltd. (1)
400 Quantang Section Shida Road, Quantang Area Liaobu town, Dongguan, Guangdong, China
Tel.: (86) 76982395598
Printed Circuit Board Mfr
N.A.I.C.S.: 334412

Regent Electron (He Fei) Co., Ltd. (1)
1551 Penglai Road, Hefei Economic Technological Development Area, Hefei, Anhui, China
Tel.: (86) 55165860000
Printed Circuit Board Mfr
N.A.I.C.S.: 334412

Regent Electron (Ningbo) Co., Ltd. (1)
No 71 Yanshanhe North Road Beilun Zone, Ningbo, 315800, China
Tel.: (86) 57486809136
Printed Circuit Board Mfr
N.A.I.C.S.: 334412

Regent Electron (Suzhou) Co., Ltd. (1)
No 888 Gan Quan Road Tongjin Main Street, Economic Development Zone, Wujiang, Jiangsu, China
Tel.: (86) 51263401633
Printed Circuit Board Mfr
N.A.I.C.S.: 334412

Subsidiary (Domestic):

Regent Electron (Xian Yang) Co., Ltd. (2)
Room 206 Zone A Xianyang High-Tech Zone, South Korea industrial park, Xianyang, shaanxi, China
Tel.: (86) 18013747513

INTERNATIONAL PUBLIC

Printed Circuit Board Mfr
N.A.I.C.S.: 334412

Regent Electron (Xiamen) Co., Ltd. (1)
No 3689 North Ziang an Road Xiang an Branch, Touch high-tech industrial Development Zone, Xiamen, Fujian, China
Tel.: (86) 5927761588
Printed Circuit Board Mfr
N.A.I.C.S.: 334412

TSMT Technology (India) Pvt. Ltd. (1)
No 6 8th Avenue 1st Cross Road Mahindra World City, Chengalpattu, Kanchipuram, 603004, Tamilnadu, India
Tel.: (91) 4467499599
Printed Circuit Board Mfr
N.A.I.C.S.: 334412

Tai Ming Green Power Co., Ltd. (1)
14F-2 No 8 Zihciang S Rd, Hsinchu County, Jhubei, 30264, Taiwan
Tel.: (886) 36205650
Web Site: https://www.tming-green.com
LED Lighting Mfr
N.A.I.C.S.: 335132

Wellight Technology Corp. (1)
4F-12 No 3 Wu Chuan 1st Rd, Hsin Chuang, Taipei, 248-92, Taiwan
Tel.: (886) 277161811
LED Lighting Mfr
N.A.I.C.S.: 335132

TAIWAN TAFFETA FABRIC CO., LTD.
8F No 70-1 Xining N Rd, Datong Dist, Taipei, 103601, Taiwan
Tel.: (886) 225568282
Web Site: https://www.tttfco.com
Year Founded: 1973
1454—(TAI)
Rev.: $49,496,156
Assets: $66,759,506
Liabilities: $14,469,210
Net Worth: $52,290,295
Earnings: $638,902
Fiscal Year-end: 12/31/23
Polyester Fabric Mfr
N.A.I.C.S.: 325220
Chang Yu-Shen (Chm & CEO)

TAIWAN TAXI CO., LTD.
F2 No 162 Sect 2 Chang an East, Zhongshan District, New Taipei City, 241, Taiwan
Tel.: (886) 240588888
Web Site: https://www.taiwantaxi.com.tw
Year Founded: 2005
2640—(TPE)
Rev.: $79,111,872
Assets: $99,651,940
Liabilities: $40,817,935
Net Worth: $58,834,006
Earnings: $10,335,022
Fiscal Year-end: 12/31/22
Transportation Services
N.A.I.C.S.: 485999
Tsun-Tien Lin (Chm)

TAIWAN TEA CORPORATION
15F No 3 Park St, Nangang District, Taipei, 115, Taiwan
Tel.: (886) 36591188
Web Site: https://www.ttch.com.tw
2913—(TAI)
Rev.: $12,410,706
Assets: $705,717,328
Liabilities: $290,226,321
Net Worth: $415,491,008
Earnings: ($9,400,896)
Fiscal Year-end: 12/31/23
Tea Mfr
N.A.I.C.S.: 311920
Ching-Yuan Wu (Chm)

Subsidiaries:

Great Construction System, Inc. (1)

15th Floor No 3 Yuanyuan Street, Nan Kang District, Taipei, 115, Taiwan
Tel.: (886) 226557655
Web Site: http://www.gcsi.com.tw
Curtain Wall Mfr
N.A.I.C.S.: 332323

Tai Lin Investment Company (1)
15F No 3 Park Street, Nankang District, Taipei, 100, Taiwan
Tel.: (886) 233931700
Web Site: http://www.ttch.com.tw
Investment Management Service
N.A.I.C.S.: 523940

Tai-Ling Biotech, Inc. (1)
80 Jiouhbu, Xinying, 730, Tainan, Taiwan
Tel.: (886) 66582000
Web Site: http://www.okis.com.tw
Sales Range: $25-49.9 Million
Emp.: 150
Orchid Plantation Services
N.A.I.C.S.: 111422

TAIWAN THICK-FILM INDUSTRIES CORP.
3F No 7 Ln332 Siyuan Rd, Xinzhuang Dist, New Taipei City, 242, Taiwan
Tel.: (886) 222772828
Web Site: https://www.tai-lon.com
Year Founded: 1982
6246—(TPE)
Rev.: $52,257,594
Assets: $43,437,871
Liabilities: $32,108,114
Net Worth: $11,329,756
Earnings: $467,212
Emp.: 516
Fiscal Year-end: 12/31/20
Capacitor Mfr
N.A.I.C.S.: 334416
Wu Chi-Chih (VP)

TAIWAN TOBACCO & LIQUOR CORPORATION
No 4 Sec 1 Nanchang Rd, Jhongjheng District, Taipei, 100, Taiwan
Tel.: (886) 223214567
Web Site: http://www.ttl.com.tw
Year Founded: 1901
Sales Range: $1-4.9 Billion
Emp.: 6,500
Alcoholic Beverages & Tobacco
N.A.I.C.S.: 312120
Chun-Kai Tseng (Pres)

TAIWAN WAX COMPANY LTD.
No 1 Chung Cheng Rd, Minhsiung Industrial District Hsien, Chiayi, Taiwan
Tel.: (886) 52219180
Web Site: https://www.wax.com.tw
Year Founded: 1987
1742—(TPE)
Rev.: $15,070,881
Assets: $82,062,377
Liabilities: $42,532,252
Net Worth: $39,530,125
Earnings: ($3,865,647)
Fiscal Year-end: 12/31/22
Chemical Product Mfr & Distr
N.A.I.C.S.: 325998
Je-Yin Lin (Chm)

TAIYEN BIOTECH CO., LTD.
No 297 Sec 1 Chien-Kang Rd, South Dist, T'ainan, Taiwan
Tel.: (886) 62160688
Web Site: https://www.tybio.com.tw
1737—(TAI)
Rev.: $111,475,551
Assets: $272,073,733
Liabilities: $57,912,421
Net Worth: $214,161,312
Earnings: $7,106,053
Emp.: 478
Fiscal Year-end: 12/31/23

Beauty Product Mfr
N.A.I.C.S.: 325620
Ya-Chuan Liu (Acting Chm)

TAIYO BUSSAN KAISHA LTD
Shimomoto Bldg 3rd Floor 1-46-3 Hatsudai, Shibuya-ku, Tokyo, 151-0061, Japan
Tel.: (81) 353338080
Web Site: http://www.taiyo-bussan.co.jp
Year Founded: 1941
9941—(TKS)
Emp.: 42
Agricultural Product Whslr
N.A.I.C.S.: 456191
Shigeru Kashiwabara (Chm & Pres)

Subsidiaries:

SHANGHAI TAIYO EIKO CO., LTD. (1)
0 Room 2402 No 1 Lane600 TongDa ChuangYe BuilDing Tianshan Road, Shanghai, 200051, China
Tel.: (86) 21 6116 8466
Food Product Mfr & Distr
N.A.I.C.S.: 311999

TAIYO CO., LTD.
3-14 Nanei, Kagoshima, 891-0195, Japan
Tel.: (81) 99 268 1211
Web Site: http://www.taiyonet.com
Year Founded: 1960
Emp.: 1,230
Supermarket Owner & Operator; Food Mfr & Distr
N.A.I.C.S.: 445110
Kazuhiko Kiyokawa (Pres & Dir)

TAIYO HOLDINGS CO., LTD.
16F Metropolitan Plaza Bldg 1-11-1 Nishi-Ikebukuro, Toshima-ku, Tokyo, 171-0021, Japan
Tel.: (81) 359535200
Web Site: https://www.taiyo-hd.co.jp
Year Founded: 1953
4626—(TKS)
Rev.: $692,562,750
Assets: $1,406,284,110
Liabilities: $742,653,330
Net Worth: $663,630,780
Earnings: $57,202,940
Emp.: 2,210
Fiscal Year-end: 03/31/24
Specialty Chemicals Mfr
N.A.I.C.S.: 325998
Eiji Sato (Pres & CEO)

Subsidiaries:

TAIWAN TAIYO INK CO., LTD. (1)
No 7 Datong 2nd Rd, Guanyin Industry Park Guanyin Dist, Taoyuan, 32849, Taiwan
Tel.: (886) 34833230
Web Site: http://www.taiyoink.com.tw
Sales Range: $50-74.9 Million
Emp.: 133
Specialty Chemicals Mfr
N.A.I.C.S.: 325998
Atsushi Miura (Pres)

TAIYO INK (SUZHOU) CO., LTD. (1)
No 26 Taishan Road, Suzhou New District, Suzhou, Jiangsu, China
Tel.: (86) 51266655550
Web Site: http://www.taiyoink.com.cn
Sales Range: $50-74.9 Million
Emp.: 250
Specialty Chemicals Mfr
N.A.I.C.S.: 325998

TAIYO INK INTERNATIONAL (HK) LTD. (1)
Room 2305 23/F The Metropolis Tower 10 Metropolis Drive, Hunghom, Kowloon, China (Hong Kong)
Tel.: (852) 27350636
Emp.: 3
Specialty Chemicals Mfr
N.A.I.C.S.: 325998

TAIYO INK INTERNATIONAL (SINGAPORE) PTE. LTD. (1)
133 New Bridge Road 09-08 Chinatown Point, No 11-07 08 San Ctr, Singapore, 059413, Singapore
Tel.: (65) 63721141
Web Site: http://www.taiyoink.co.jp
Sales Range: $25-49.9 Million
Emp.: 7
Specialty Chemicals Mfr
N.A.I.C.S.: 325998
Akira Kasagi (Mng Dir)

TAIYO INK MFG. CO., LTD. (1)
900 Hirasawa Arashiyama-cho, Hiki-gun, Saitama, 355-0215, Japan
Tel.: (81) 493612711
Web Site: http://www.taiyoink.co.jp
Emp.: 250
Specialty Chemicals Mfr
N.A.I.C.S.: 325998

TAIYO KAGAKU CO., LTD.
800 Yamadacho, Yokkaichi, 512-111, Mie, Japan
Tel.: (81) 593400800
Web Site: https://www.taiyokagaku.com
Year Founded: 1948
29020—(NGO)
Rev.: $283,911,463
Assets: $387,327,387
Liabilities: $81,466,799
Net Worth: $305,860,588
Earnings: $18,876,776
Emp.: 873
Fiscal Year-end: 03/31/23
Food Products Mfr
N.A.I.C.S.: 311999
Naganori Yamazaki (Exec VP-Overseas Bus)

Subsidiaries:

Jeanavice (Tianjin) Food Co., Ltd. (1)
13 Shuangchen Zhong Road, Beichen Economic Development Area, Tianjin, 300400, China
Tel.: (86) 2226970042
Food Mfr
N.A.I.C.S.: 311999

Kaifeng Taiyo Kinmei Food Co., Ltd. (1)
Jinming Dongjie Zhongduan Kaifaqu, Kaifeng, 475004, Henan, China
Tel.: (86) 3783856804
Food Mfr
N.A.I.C.S.: 311999

Taiyo GmbH (1)
Hagener Str 20, 58285, Gevelsberg, Germany
Tel.: (49) 2332967880
Web Site: https://www.taiyogmbh.com
Food Mfr
N.A.I.C.S.: 311999

Taiyo Green Power Co., Ltd. (1)
No 22 Lihe Road, Shuofang Industry Park Wuxi New District, Wuxi, 214142, Jiangsu, China
Tel.: (86) 51085311586
Web Site: http://www.taiyogreenpower.com
Green Tea Mfr
N.A.I.C.S.: 311920

Taiyo Inter Korea Limited (1)
302 Windstone Hofficetel 79 Nonhyeon-ro, Seocho-gu, Seoul, 06775, Korea (South)
Tel.: (82) 25717588
Food Mfr
N.A.I.C.S.: 311999

Taiyo International, Inc. (1)
1601 Utica Ave S Ste 109, Minneapolis, MN 55416
Tel.: (763) 398-3003
Web Site: https://www.taiyointernational.com
Food Ingredient Product Mfr
N.A.I.C.S.: 311999
Naganori Yamazaki (Pres)

Taiyo Kagaku China Co., Ltd. (1)
Room DE 6F World Plaza, No 855 Pudong South Road Pudong, Shanghai, 200120, China
Tel.: (86) 2168766828
Food Mfr
N.A.I.C.S.: 311999

Taiyo Kagaku India Pvt. Ltd. (1)
M-101 Waluj MIDC, Aurangabad, 431136, Maharastra, India
Tel.: (91) 2402551511
Web Site: https://www.taiyokagakuindia.com
Food Formulation Mfr
N.A.I.C.S.: 311999

TAIYO KISOKOGYO CO., LTD.
2nd Floor Daini Taiyo Building 107 Yanagimori-cho, Nakagawa-ku, Nagoya, 454-0871, Aichi, Japan
Tel.: (81) 523626351
Web Site: https://www.taiyoukiso.co.jp
Year Founded: 1967
1758—(TKS)
Sales Range: Less than $1 Million
Engineeering Services
N.A.I.C.S.: 541330
Yukimasa Kato (Pres)

TAIYO KOGYO CORPORATION
2 33 16 Ikejiri, Setagaya-ku, Tokyo, 154-0001, Japan
Tel.: (81) 337143366 JP
Web Site: http://www.taiyokogyo.com
Year Founded: 1946
Membrane Roofing System & Dome Mfr
N.A.I.C.S.: 326199

Subsidiaries:

Birdair Mexico, S.A.de C.V. (1)
Av Prol Americas 1600 Piso 1 Col Country Club, 44610, Guadalajara, Jalisco, Mexico
Tel.: (52) 33 36789276
Architectural Services
N.A.I.C.S.: 541310
Michiaki Ishii (Gen Mgr)

Birdair, Inc. (1)
65 Lawrence Bell Dr Ste 100, Amherst, NY 14221-7075
Tel.: (716) 633-9500
Web Site: http://www.birdair.com
Architectural Membrane Structures Contractor
N.A.I.C.S.: 236220
Michele Roth (Mgr-Bus Dev & Mktg)

Higashi-Nihon Container Service Co.,Ltd. (1)
343-3 Imazuasayama, Ichihara, 299-0106, Japan
Tel.: (81) 4 3662 6681
Container Transportation Services
N.A.I.C.S.: 488490
Yoko Yamato (Pres)

International Taiyo Trading PTE LTD (1)
111 North Bridge Road 13-03 Peninsula Plaza, Singapore, 179098, Singapore
Tel.: (65) 6223 5442
Roofing Installation Services
N.A.I.C.S.: 238160

Osaka Container Service Co.,Ltd. (1)
3-5 Rinkuminamihama, Sennan, 590-0535, Osaka, Japan
Tel.: (81) 724853355
Logistics Consulting Servies
N.A.I.C.S.: 541614

PT.Taiyo Kogyo Indonesia (1)
Multika Building Lantai 5 Ruang 503 Ji Mampang Prapatan Raya No 71-73, Jakarta, 12790, Selatan, Indonesia
Tel.: (62) 21 797 5127
Web Site: http://www.makmax.com
Architectural Services
N.A.I.C.S.: 541310

Shanghai Helios International Trade Co.,Ltd. (1)
Room 3610 No 2200 Kaixuan Building Kaixuan Rd, Shanghai, 200030, China

TAIYO KOGYO CORPORATION

Taiyo Kogyo Corporation—(Continued)
Tel.: (86) 21 6448 4121
Web Site: http://www.helios-sh.cn
Architectural & Logistics Consulting Services
N.A.I.C.S.: 541310

Shanghai Taiyo Kogyo Co.,Ltd. (1)
Room 3601 No 2200 Kaixuan Rd, Shanghai, 200030, China
Tel.: (86) 21 6448 4126
Web Site: http://www.taiyokogyo.com.cn
Emp.: 80
Roofing Installation Services
Karasawa Tant *(Gen Mgr)*

Taiwan Taiyokogyo Inc. (1)
4th Floor 181 Mincyuan E Road Sec 3, Taipei, Taiwan
Tel.: (886) 2 2713 7177
Web Site: http://www.twtaiyo.com.tw
Roofing Installation Services
N.A.I.C.S.: 238160

Taiyo Birdair do Brasil Ltda. (1)
Av Jabaquara 2958 1 Andar sala 15, Mirandopolis, Sao Paulo, Brazil
Tel.: (55) 11 5070 3832
Roofing Installation Services
N.A.I.C.S.: 238160

Taiyo Europe GmbH (1)
Muhlweg 2, 82054, Sauerlach, Germany
Tel.: (49) 8104 62898 0
Web Site: http://www.taiyo-europe.com
Architectural Services
N.A.I.C.S.: 541310
Frank Horeth *(Dir-Ops)*

Taiyo Kogyo(Thailand) Co.,Ltd. (1)
Rojana Industrial Park 62 Moo 9 Rojana Rd, Thanu U-thai, Ayutthaya, 13210, Thailand
Tel.: (66) 35 226 539
Roofing Installation Services
N.A.I.C.S.: 238160

Taiyo Membrane Corporation Pty Ltd (1)
133 Lavarack Avenue, Eagle Farm, 4009, QLD, Australia
Tel.: (61) 7 3633 5900
Web Site: http://www.makmax.com.au
Architectural Services
N.A.I.C.S.: 541310
Brian VenderVelde *(Project Mgr)*

Taiyo Membrane India Pvt Ltd (1)
311 3rd Floor Square One Saket District Centre, Saket, New Delhi, 110017, India
Tel.: (91) 11 2956 4231
Web Site: http://www.taiyomembrane.in
Roofing Installation Services
N.A.I.C.S.: 238160

Taiyo Middle East LLC (1)
Warehouse No 7 Plot 613-1124 10b St Ras Al Khor Industrial 2, Dubai, United Arab Emirates
Tel.: (971) 4 320 5494
Roofing Installation Services
N.A.I.C.S.: 238160

Thai Taiyo Tent Co.,Ltd. (1)
869 Phattanakan Rd T Suanluang A, Suanluang, Bangkok, 10250, Thailand
Tel.: (66) 2 719 9919
Web Site: http://www.taiyo-tent.co.th
Roofing Installation Services
N.A.I.C.S.: 238160
Chew Visessan *(Mng Dir)*

Transport & Distribution Service, Inc. (1)
550 Village Center Dr, Saint Paul, MN 55127
Tel.: (651) 483-1300
Web Site: http://www.tdsd.com
Logistics Consulting Servies
N.A.I.C.S.: 541614
Skip Krawczyk *(Pres)*

TAIYO KOKO CO LTD
1-1-39 Isobe-dori, Chuo-ku, Kobe, 651-0084, Japan
Tel.: (81) 782313700
Web Site: https://www.taiyokoko.co.jp

All Other Miscellaneous Chemical Product Mfr
N.A.I.C.S.: 325998

Subsidiaries:

Toho Kinzoku Co., Ltd. (1)
2F Nihon Seika Bldg 2-4-9 Bingo-machi, Chuo-ku, Osaka, 541-0051, Japan
Tel.: (81) 662023376
Web Site: http://www.tohokinzoku.co.jp
Sales Range: $25-49.9 Million
Electric & Electronic Product Mfr
N.A.I.C.S.: 335314

TAIYO TECHNOLEX CO.,LTD.
661 Arimoto, Wakayama, 640-8390, Japan
Tel.: (81) 734316311
Web Site: https://www.taiyo-tx.com
Year Founded: 1960
6663—(TKS)
Rev.: $24,183,990
Assets: $32,450,930
Liabilities: $14,449,420
Net Worth: $18,001,510
Earnings: ($893,340)
Emp.: 197
Fiscal Year-end: 12/31/23
Electronic Board Mfr
N.A.I.C.S.: 334412
Yoshinori Hosoe *(Pres)*

Subsidiaries:

MIRAC Co., LTD. - Wakayama Factory (1)
800 Narukami, Wakayama, 640-8303, Japan
Tel.: (81) 734741431
Grinder Machinery Mfr
N.A.I.C.S.: 333991

Taiyo Industrial Co., Ltd. - Kyushu Plant (1)
384-20 Akimachi Shimobaru Kunisaki, Oita, 873-0231, Japan
Tel.: (81) 978673311
Printed Circuit Board Assembly Mfr
N.A.I.C.S.: 334418

Taiyo Technolex (Shanghai) Co., LTD. (1)
Room 2902 Modern Plaza Tower 1369 Xian Xia Road, Shanghai, China
Tel.: (86) 2152080991
Web Site: http://www.taiyo-xelcom.com.cn
Visual Inspection Equipment Distr
N.A.I.C.S.: 423830

Taiyo Technolex (Thailand) Co., LTD. (1)
12th Floor Abdulrahim Place 990 Rama 4 Road silom, Bangrak, Bangkok, 10500, Thailand
Tel.: (66) 2 636 0755
Web Site: https://www.technolex.co.th
Emp.: 6
Industrial Electronic Equipment Distr
N.A.I.C.S.: 423610
Yoshinori Hosoe *(Pres)*

TAIYO YUDEN COMPANY LTD.
Kyobashi East Bldg 2-7-19 Kyobashi, Chuo-ku, Tokyo, 104-0031, Japan
Tel.: (81) 367578310
Web Site: https://www.yuden.co.jp
Year Founded: 1950
6976—(TKS)
Rev.: $2,132,696,670
Assets: $3,831,724,460
Liabilities: $1,649,776,680
Net Worth: $2,181,947,780
Earnings: $54,975,370
Emp.: 21,823
Fiscal Year-end: 03/31/24
Electronic Components Mfr
N.A.I.C.S.: 334419
Shoichi Tosaka *(Pres & CEO-R&D & Engrg)*

Subsidiaries:

Chuki Seiki Co., Ltd. (1)
4026-22 Inanbara Inami-cho, Hidaka-gun, Wakayama, 649-1532, Japan
Tel.: (81) 738440241
Web Site: http://www.chuki-seiki.jp
Sales Range: $50-74.9 Million
Emp.: 200
Electronic Components Mfr
N.A.I.C.S.: 334416

Elna Co., Ltd. (1)
Kyobashi East Buillding 2-7-19 Kyobashi, Chuo-ku, Tokyo, 104-0031, Japan
Tel.: (81) 34224950 **(63.75%)**
Web Site: http://www.elna.co.jp
Sales Range: $200-249.9 Million
Emp.: 1,893
Aluminum & Tantalum Solid-State Electrolytic Capacitors, Electric Double Layer Capacitors, Build-Up PCBs, Multilayer PCBs & Double-Sided PCBs
N.A.I.C.S.: 334416
Akihiko Mochizuki *(Pres)*

Subsidiary (Non-US):

Elna (HK) Co., Ltd. (2)
Unit 11 1-F Mirror Tower 61 Mody Rd, Tsimshatsui East, Kowloon, China (Hong Kong)
Tel.: (852) 27234285
Web Site: http://www.egco.th
Sales Range: $50-74.9 Million
Emp.: 1
Electronic Parts & Equipment Whslr
N.A.I.C.S.: 423690

Elna (Shanghai) Co., Ltd. (2)
Room 6203 Rui Jin Hotel Business Center 118 Rui Jin 2 Road, Shanghai, 200020, China
Tel.: (86) 2164452269
Web Site: http://www.elna.co.jp
Sales Range: $50-74.9 Million
Emp.: 8
Electronic Parts & Equipment Whslr
N.A.I.C.S.: 423690

Subsidiary (US):

Elna America, Inc. (2)
21250 Hawthorne Blvd Ste 500, Torrance, CA 90503
Tel.: (714) 761-8600
Web Site: http://www.elna-america.com
Sales Range: $25-49.9 Million
Emp.: 20
Electronic Capacitor Mfr
N.A.I.C.S.: 334416

Plant (Domestic):

Elna Co., Ltd. - Shiga Factory (2)
30 Ta-cho, Nagahama, 529-0142, Shiga, Japan
Tel.: (81) 749 73 3021
Web Site: http://www.elna.co.jp
Capacitor & Printed Circuit Board Mfr
N.A.I.C.S.: 334416

Elna Co., Ltd. - Shirakawa Factory (2)
9-32 Aza-sugiyama Oaza-yone, Nishigomura Nishishirakawa-gun, Fukushima, 961-8031, Japan
Tel.: (81) 248481654
Capacitor & Printed Circuit Board Mfr
N.A.I.C.S.: 334412

Subsidiary (Domestic):

Elna Components Co., Ltd. (2)
KDX Shin Yokohama Bldg 3-8-11 Shin Yokohama, Kouhoku-ku, Yokohama, Kanagawa, Japan
Tel.: (81) 47 470 7251
Electronic Components Mfr
N.A.I.C.S.: 334419

Subsidiary (Non-US):

Elna Electronics (S) Pte. Ltd. (2)
103 Kallang Avenue, 04-01 AIS Industrial Building, Singapore, 339504, Singapore
Tel.: (65) 62930181
Sales Range: $25-49.9 Million
Emp.: 16
Electronic Parts & Equipment Whslr
N.A.I.C.S.: 423690
Bernard Chang *(Mng Dir)*

Subsidiary (Domestic):

Elna Matsumoto Co., Ltd. (2)
4130-5 Azusagawayamato, Matsumoto, 390-1701, Nagano, Japan
Tel.: (81) 263784631
Web Site: http://www.elna.co.jp
Bare Printed Circuit Board Mfr
N.A.I.C.S.: 334412

Subsidiary (Non-US):

Elna PCB (M) Sdn. Bhd. (2)
Plot 558 Lorong Perusahaan 4 Free Trade Zone, Prai Industrial Estate, 13600, Penang, Malaysia
Tel.: (60) 43973934
Web Site: http://www.elnapcb.com
Sales Range: $200-249.9 Million
Emp.: 600
Bare Printed Circuit Board Mfr
N.A.I.C.S.: 327910

Subsidiary (Domestic):

Elna Tohoku Co., Ltd. (2)
1-349-1 Okonoki, Kuroishi, 036-0357, Aomori, Japan
Tel.: (81) 17 252 4166
Web Site: http://www.elna.co.jp
Electronic Resistor Mfr
N.A.I.C.S.: 334416
Masayuki Hiraiwa *(Mng Dir)*

Subsidiary (Non-US):

Elna-Sonic Sdn. Bhd. (2)
2473 Tingkat Perusahaan 6, Free Trade Zone Prai Industrial Estate, 13600, Penang, Malaysia
Tel.: (60) 43992916
Web Site: http://www.elna.co.jp
Sales Range: $25-49.9 Million
Emp.: 75
Electronic Capacitor Mfr
N.A.I.C.S.: 334416

Tanin Elna Co., Ltd. (2)
2/85 Bangna Complex Office Tower 16th Fl Soi Bangna-Trad 25, Bangna-nua Bangna, Bangkok, 10260, Thailand
Tel.: (66) 27441464
Sales Range: $200-249.9 Million
Electronic Capacitor Mfr
N.A.I.C.S.: 334416

Fukushima Taiyo Yuden Co., Ltd. (1)
1-3 Yanagawa Industrial Park, Yanagawa, Date, 960-0719, Fukushima, Japan **(100%)**
Tel.: (81) 24 577 4105
Web Site: http://www.f-yuden.co.jp
Inductors Mfr
N.A.I.C.S.: 334416
Yuji Arai *(Pres)*

Hong Kong Taiyo Yuden Company Ltd. (1)
Unit 2801-08 The Metropolis Tower 10 Metropolis Drive, Hunghom, Kowloon, China (Hong Kong)
Tel.: (852) 27836001
Web Site: http://www.yuden.co.jp
Electric Component Whslr
N.A.I.C.S.: 423690

Kankyo Assist Co., Ltd. (1)
2925-3 Kuraganomachi, Takasaki, 370-1201, Gunma, Japan
Tel.: (81) 273466114
Web Site: https://www.kankyoassist.com
Sales Range: $25-49.9 Million
Emp.: 14
Environmental Consulting Services
N.A.I.C.S.: 541620

Korea Kyong Nam Taiyo Yuden Co., Ltd (1)
82 Oegukgieop-ro, Sanam-myeon, Sacheon, 52530, Gyeongsangnam, Korea (South)
Tel.: (82) 55 851 5500
Web Site: http://www.yuden.co.jp
Sales Range: $200-249.9 Million
Emp.: 700
Electronic Components Mfr & Whslr
N.A.I.C.S.: 334419

Korea Taiyo Yuden Co., Ltd. (1)
19F T Tower 30 Sowol-ro 2-gil, Jung-gu, Seoul, 04637, Gyeongsangnam-do, Korea (South)
Tel.: (82) 222294200

AND PRIVATE COMPANIES — TAIZHOU SHIMGE MACHINERY & ELECTRONIC CO., LTD.

Electronic Component Mfr & Sales
N.A.I.C.S.: 334416

Korea Tong Yang Yujun Co. Ltd (1)
No 468 Do Nam Dong, Tongyeong, 650-150, Gyeongsangnam-do, Korea (South)
Tel.: (82) 556402700
Web Site: http://www.yuden.co.jp
Electronic Components Mfr
N.A.I.C.S.: 334416

Niigata Taiyo Yuden Co., Ltd. (1)
197-8 Kamiyoshi, Kubiki-ku, Joetsu, 942-0145, Niigata, Japan
Tel.: (81) 255452511
Web Site: https://www.niigata-yuden.com
Electronic Components Mfr
N.A.I.C.S.: 334416

Sun Vertex Co., Ltd. (1)
1-15 Iwaoshimachi, Takasaki, 370-0044, Gunma, Japan (100%)
Tel.: (81) 27 310 8638
Web Site: http://www.sunvertex.co.jp
Employment Placement Services
N.A.I.C.S.: 561311

Taiwan Taiyo Yuden Company Ltd. (1)
12F NO 18 Wenhu St, Neihu District, Taipei, 11445, Taiwan
Tel.: (886) 227972155
Electronic Component Mfr & Sales
N.A.I.C.S.: 334416

Taiyo Yuden (China) Co., Ltd. (1)
Room 804 East Tower China Overseas Fortune Center, No 9 Suzhou West Avenue Suzhou Industrial Park, Suzhou, Jiangsu, China
Tel.: (86) 51262806080
Electric Component Whslr
N.A.I.C.S.: 423690

Taiyo Yuden (Guangdong) Co., Ltd. (1)
No 13 Shijie Keji Dong Road, Shi Jie Town, Dongguan, 523290, China
Tel.: (86) 76986636888
Aluminium Electrolytic Capacitors Mfr & Distr
N.A.I.C.S.: 334416

Taiyo Yuden (Malaysia) Sdn Bhd (1)
Unit 1202 Block B Amcorp Tower Amcorp Trade Centre, 18 Jalan Persiaran Barat, 46050, Petaling Jaya, Selangor, Malaysia
Tel.: (60) 379542613
Web Site: http://www.yuden.co.jp
Sales Range: $25-49.9 Million
Emp.: 7
Electronic Components Mfr & Whslr
N.A.I.C.S.: 334416

Taiyo Yuden (Philippines) Inc. (1)
Mactan Economic Zone, Lapu-Lapu, 6015, Cebu, Philippines
Tel.: (63) 322393800
Electronic Component Mfr & Sales
N.A.I.C.S.: 334416

Taiyo Yuden (Sarawak) Sdn Bhd (1)
Lot 977 Block 12 Sama Jaya Free Industrial Zone, 93450, Kuching, Sarawak, Malaysia
Tel.: (60) 82350700
Sales Range: $900-999.9 Million
Emp.: 3,000
Electronic Components Mfr & Whslr
N.A.I.C.S.: 334416

Taiyo Yuden (Singapore) Pte Ltd (1)
3 International Business Park Nordic European Centre 06-28, Singapore, 609927, Singapore
Tel.: (65) 68614400
Web Site: http://www.ty-top.com
Sales Range: $25-49.9 Million
Emp.: 75
Electronic Component Mfr & Sales
N.A.I.C.S.: 334416

Taiyo Yuden (Suzhou) Co., Ltd. (1)
No 200 Xingpu Rd Suzhou Industrial Park, Suzhou, Jiangsu, China
Tel.: (86) 51262952840
Multilayer Ceramic Capacitors Mfr & Whslr
N.A.I.C.S.: 334416

Taiyo Yuden (Tianjin) Electronics Co., Ltd. (1)
No 10 Fu Sheng Road Zhong Bei Industry Area Xi Qing, Economy Development Zone, Tianjin, China
Tel.: (86) 2287913580
Web Site: http://www.yuden.co.jp
Sales Range: $100-124.9 Million
Emp.: 150
Electronic Components Mfr
N.A.I.C.S.: 334416
Wata Nuki (Mgr)

Taiyo Yuden (U.S.A.), Inc. (1)
440 Stevens Ave Ste 300, Solana Beach, CA 92075
Tel.: (858) 350-6800
Web Site: http://www.t-yuden.com
Sales Range: $50-74.9 Million
Emp.: 80
Power Supply Equipment Sales
N.A.I.C.S.: 423690

Subsidiary (Domestic):

Taiyo Yuden (U.S.A.), Inc. (2)
10 N Martingale Rd Ste 575, Schaumburg, IL 60173-4169
Tel.: (630) 237-2405
Web Site: http://www.t-yuden.com
Sales Range: $25-49.9 Million
Emp.: 25
Sales & Manufacturing of Electronic Parts & Components
N.A.I.C.S.: 423690

Taiyo Yuden (changzhou) Co., Ltd. (1)
No 88 Gongye Road Wujin High-tech Industrial Development Zone, Changzhou, 213161, China
Tel.: (86) 51968216668
Aluminium Electrolytic Capacitors Mfr & Distr
N.A.I.C.S.: 334416

Taiyo Yuden (shanghai) Trading Co., Ltd. (1)
Room 601 New Town Center No 83 Lou Shan Guan Road, Shanghai, 200336, China
Tel.: (86) 2162368999
Aluminium Electrolytic Capacitors Mfr & Distr
N.A.I.C.S.: 334416

Taiyo Yuden (shenzhen) Electronics Trading Co., Ltd. (1)
Room 6802 Ping An Finance Centre 16 Fuhua Si Road, Futian District, Shenzhen, 518046, China
Tel.: (86) 75582900999
Electronic Component Mfr & Distr
N.A.I.C.S.: 334419

Taiyo Yuden Company Ltd. - Anechoic Chamber Test Facility (1)
5607-2 Nakamuroda-machi, Takasaki, 370-3347, Gunma, Japan
Tel.: (81) 273608300
Web Site: http://www.yuden.co.jp
Electronic Components Testing Services
N.A.I.C.S.: 541380

Taiyo Yuden Company Ltd. - Nakanojo Plant (1)
1988 Nakanojo, Nakanojo-machi Agatsuma-gun, Gunma, 377-0424, Japan
Tel.: (81) 279 75 2221
Web Site: http://www.yuden.co.jp
Electronic Components Mfr
N.A.I.C.S.: 334416

Taiyo Yuden Company Ltd. - Yawatabara Plant (1)
43-1 Yawatabara-machi, Takasaki, 370-0024, Gunma, Japan
Tel.: (81) 27 346 1611
Web Site: http://www.yuden.co.jp
Electronic Components Mfr
N.A.I.C.S.: 334416

Taiyo Yuden Energy Device Co., Ltd. (1)
152-1 Tottori-machi, Maebashi, 371-0131, Gunma, Japan
Tel.: (81) 272102188
Web Site: http://ed-yuden.com
Sales Range: $25-49.9 Million
Emp.: 95
Capacitor Mfr
N.A.I.C.S.: 334416

Haruyuki Iijima (Pres)

Taiyo Yuden Europe GmbH (1)
Siemensstrasse 3, 90766, Furth, Germany (100%)
Tel.: (49) 91193640
Web Site: http://www.ty-top.com
Sales Range: $25-49.9 Million
Emp.: 40
Building Materials Distr
N.A.I.C.S.: 444180

Taiyo Yuden Mobile Technology Co., Ltd. (1)
6-16-3 Shin-machi, Ome, 198-0024, Tokyo, Japan
Tel.: (81) 428333600
Sales Range: $50-74.9 Million
Emp.: 150
Mobile Communication Components Mfr
N.A.I.C.S.: 334419
Osamu Ikata (Pres & CEO)

Taiyo Yuden Techno Solutions Co., Ltd. (1)
43-1 Yawatabara-machi, Takasaki, 370-0024, Gunma, Japan
Tel.: (81) 27 346 9903
Web Site: http://www.jtty.jp
Emp.: 150
Printed Circuit Assemblies Mfr
N.A.I.C.S.: 334418
Zhoukou Iijima (Pres)

Tsukiyono Denshi Co., Ltd. (1)
1500 Gokan Minakami-machi, Tone-gun, Gunma, 379-1305, Japan
Tel.: (81) 278 62 2331
Web Site: http://www.yuden.co.jp
Electronic Components Mfr
N.A.I.C.S.: 334416

TAIYUAN HEAVY INDUSTRY CO., LTD.
Hi-tech Industrial Development Zone
No 53 Yuhe Street, Wanbailin,
Taiyuan, 030024, Shanxi, China
Tel.: (86) 3516361155
Web Site: http://www.tyhi.com.cn
Year Founded: 1950
600169—(SHG)
Rev.: $1,128,761,749
Assets: $4,434,716,703
Liabilities: $3,537,623,714
Net Worth: $897,092,988
Earnings: $30,322,609
Emp.: 7,598
Fiscal Year-end: 12/31/22
Heavy Machinery Mfr & Sales
N.A.I.C.S.: 423830
Ji He (CFO)

Subsidiaries:

CEC Crane Engineering & Consulting GmbH (1)
Thundorfer Strasse 17, Freystadt, 92342, Neumarkt, Germany
Tel.: (49) 9179 964 3390
Web Site: https://cec-cranes.de
Emp.: 35
Construction Machinery Mfr
N.A.I.C.S.: 333120

Casting & Smelting Sub-Co. (1)
No 53 Yuhe Street, Wanbailin District, Taiyuan, 030024, Shanxi, China
Tel.: (86) 3516367016
Machinery Equipment Mfr
N.A.I.C.S.: 333242

Chemical Equipment Sub-Co. (1)
No 69 Bohai 50th Road Harbor Economic Park, Binhai New Area, Tianjin, China
Tel.: (86) 2265666510
Machinery Equipment Mfr
N.A.I.C.S.: 333242

Coking Equipment Sub-Co. (1)
No 53 Yuhe Street, Wanbailin District, Taiyuan, 030024, Shanxi, China
Tel.: (86) 3516365602
Machinery Equipment Mfr
N.A.I.C.S.: 333242

Construction Machinery Co., Ltd. (1)
No 58 Shangzhuang Street, Wanbailin District, Taiyuan, Shanxi, China
Tel.: (86) 3516367337
Machinery Equipment Mfr
N.A.I.C.S.: 333242

Crane Sub-Co. (1)
No 53 Yuhe Street, Wanbailin District, Taiyuan, 030024, Shanxi, China
Tel.: (86) 3516365261
Machinery Equipment Mfr
N.A.I.C.S.: 333242

Forging Equipment Sub-Co. (1)
No 69 Bohai 50th Road Harbor Economic Park, Binhai New Area, Tianjin, China
Tel.: (86) 2265666645
Machinery Equipment Mfr
N.A.I.C.S.: 333242

Forging Sub-Co. (1)
No 53 Yuhe Street, Wanbailin District, Taiyuan, 030024, Shanxi, China
Tel.: (86) 3516363414
Heavy Machinery Mfr & Distr
N.A.I.C.S.: 333248

Gears & Transmission Sub-Co. (1)
No 53 Yuhe Street, Wanbailin District, Taiyuan, 030024, Shanxi, China
Tel.: (86) 3516362324
Machinery Equipment Mfr
N.A.I.C.S.: 333242

Mining Equipment Sub-Co. (1)
No 53 Yuhe Street, Wanbailin District, Taiyuan, 030024, Shanxi, China
Tel.: (86) 3516366691
Machinery Equipment Mfr
N.A.I.C.S.: 333242

New Energy Equipment Co., Ltd. (1)
No 17 Dianzi Street Economic-Technical Development Zone, Taiyuan, Shanxi, China
Tel.: (86) 3516362895
Machinery Equipment Mfr
N.A.I.C.S.: 333242

Offshore Engineering Equipment Sub-Co. (1)
No 69 Bohai 50th Road Harbor Economic Park, Binhai New Area, Tianjin, China
Tel.: (86) 2265666831
Machinery Equipment Mfr
N.A.I.C.S.: 333242

Oil Film Bearing Sub-Co. (1)
No 53 Yuhe Street, Wanbailin District, Taiyuan, 030024, Shanxi, China
Tel.: (86) 3516362514
Heavy Machinery Mfr & Distr
N.A.I.C.S.: 333248

Port Machinery Equipment Sub-Co. (1)
No 69 Bohai 50th Road Harbor Economic Park, Binhai New Area, Tianjin, China
Tel.: (86) 2265666786
Machinery Equipment Mfr
N.A.I.C.S.: 333242

Railway Transit Equipment Co., Ltd. (1)
No 17 Dianzi Street Economic-Technical Development Zone, Taiyuan, Shanxi, China
Tel.: (86) 3517651820
Machinery Equipment Mfr
N.A.I.C.S.: 333242

Steel Rolling Equipment Sub-Co. (1)
No 53 Yuhe Street, Wanbailin District, Taiyuan, 030024, Shanxi, China
Tel.: (86) 3516362347
Machinery Equipment Mfr
N.A.I.C.S.: 333242

TAIZHOU SHIMGE MACHINERY & ELECTRONIC CO., LTD.
Dayangcheng Industrial Zone, Wenling, 317525, Zhejiang, China
Tel.: (86) 57686337078
Web Site: http://www.shimge-compressor.com
Year Founded: 2003
Air Compressor & Electrical Component Mfr
N.A.I.C.S.: 333912
Andy King (Sls Mgr)

TAIZHOU WATER GROUP COMPANY LIMTED

Taizhou Water Group Company Limted—(Continued)

TAIZHOU WATER GROUP COMPANY LIMTED
No 308 Yin Quan Road Xicheng Street, Huangyan District, Taizhou, Zhejiang, China
Tel.: (86) 57684236086   **CN**
Web Site: http://www.zjtzwater.com
Year Founded: 1993
1542—(HKG)
Rev.: $76,189,324
Assets: $805,565,779
Liabilities: $641,779,211
Net Worth: $163,786,568
Earnings: $8,108,662
Emp.: 237
Fiscal Year-end: 12/31/22
Water Supply Services
N.A.I.C.S.: 221310
Junzhou Zhang *(Exec Dir)*

TAJGVK HOTELS & RESORTS LTD
Taj Krishna Road no-1 Banjara Hills, Hyderabad, 500034, Telangana, India
Tel.: (91) 4066662323
Web Site: https://www.tajgvk.in
Year Founded: 1995
TAJGVK—(NSE)
Rev.: $49,441,149
Assets: $90,828,236
Liabilities: $35,517,391
Net Worth: $55,310,845
Earnings: $9,570,409
Emp.: 921
Fiscal Year-end: 03/31/23
Hotel Resort
N.A.I.C.S.: 721110
J. Srinivasa Murthy *(CFO, Compliance Officer & Sec)*

TAJIMA INDUSTRIES LTD.
19 22 Shirakabe 3 Chome, Higashi Ku, 461 0011, Nagoya, Japan
Tel.: (81) 0529323444   **JP**
Web Site: http://www.tajima.com
Year Founded: 1970
Sales Range: $100-124.9 Million
Emp.: 1,000
Sales, Importer & Exporter of Multi-Head Electronic Embroidery Machines & Other Related Equipment
N.A.I.C.S.: 313220
Hitoshi Tajima *(Pres)*

Subsidiaries:

Cytrad Co., Ltd. (1)
2F No 2 Kuo Chung Rd, Yung Ho City, Taipei, Taiwan
Tel.: (886) 2 2232 0739
Web Site: http://www.tajima.com.tw
Embroidery Machine Distr
N.A.I.C.S.: 423830
Ko Yuan Tseng *(Pres)*

Huizhou ShenTian Precision Machines Co. Ltd.
No 168 Zhong Kai Road Hui Huan, Hui Cheng District, Huizhou, Guangdong, China
Tel.: (86) 752 265 3808
Textile Machinery Repair & Maintenance Services
N.A.I.C.S.: 811310
Xiaobing Guo *(Mgr-Pur)*

Korea Tajima Co., Ltd. (1)
Yulsan B/D 6F 791-1 Majang-Dong, Sungdong-Gu, Seoul, Korea (South)
Tel.: (82) 2 2295 7771
Web Site: http://www.koreatajima.com
Embroidery Machine Distr
N.A.I.C.S.: 423830
Gen Shinozuka *(Pres)*

PT. Tajima Gunung Mas (1)
Jl Ciedng Barat 47-C, Jakarta, Indonesia
Tel.: (62) 21 633 9969
Web Site: http://www.tajima.co.id
Emp.: 70
Embroidery Machine Distr

N.A.I.C.S.: 423830
Tjong Kok Poo *(Pres)*

STITCH TECHNOLOGIES (THAILAND) CO., LTD. (1)
270/62-63 Soi Phrayamonthadratchasripijit KlongBangbon, Bangbon, Bangkok, 10150, Thailand
Tel.: (86) 2 464 9841 5
Web Site: http://www.tajimastt.com
Embroidery Machine Distr
N.A.I.C.S.: 423830
Kamolchanok Nimtrakul *(Mgr-Sls)*

Shanghai Tajima Embroidery Machinery Co., Ltd. (1)
No 18 Xuanzhong Rd, Nanhui Industrial Zone, Shanghai, 201300, China
Tel.: (86) 2158185858
Embroidery Machine Mfr & Distr
N.A.I.C.S.: 333248
Satoru Yamauchi *(Pres)*

Tajima America Corporation (1)
19925 S Susana Rd, Rancho Dominguez, CA 90221
Tel.: (310) 604-8200
Embroidery Machinery Sales & Maintenance Services
N.A.I.C.S.: 423830
Hitoshi Tajima *(Pres)*

Tajima Asia Pte Ltd. (1)
209 Henderson Road 01-02 03-02, Henderson Industrial Park, Singapore, 159551, Singapore
Tel.: (65) 62703977
Embroidery Machine Distr
N.A.I.C.S.: 423830
Noboru Ito *(Mng Dir)*

Tajima Australia Pty. Ltd. (1)
74 Raglan Street, Preston, 3072, VIC, Australia
Tel.: (61) 3 9484 5898
Web Site: http://www.tajimaaustralia.com.au
Embroidery Machine Distr
N.A.I.C.S.: 423830

Tajima Colombo (Pte) Ltd (1)
No 28 Galle Road, Dehiwala-Mount Lavinia, Sri Lanka
Tel.: (94) 11 2719904
Emp.: 135
Embroidery Machine Distr
N.A.I.C.S.: 423830
M. M. Hassan *(Chm & Mng Dir)*

Tajima Do Brasil (1)
Rua da Graca 597-2nd Fl, Sao Paulo, 01125-001, Brazil
Tel.: (55) 11 3222 9166
Web Site: http://www.tajimadobrasil.com.br
Embroidery Machine Distr
N.A.I.C.S.: 423830
Eduardo Molinero *(Dir-Sls)*

Tajima Embroidery Machines (China) Co. Ltd.
Meiyun Industrial Area, Rongcheng, Jieyang, Guangdong, China
Tel.: (86) 663 8885588
Web Site: http://www.tajima.com.cn
Embroidery Machine Distr
N.A.I.C.S.: 423830

Tajima Embroidery Machines Ltd. (1)
Unit 1701 17/F Tower 2 Enterprise Square, Kowloon, Hong Kong, China (Hong Kong)
Tel.: (852) 27968111
Web Site: http://www.tajima.com.hk
Embroidery Machine Distr
N.A.I.C.S.: 423830

Tajima Europe S.A.R.L (1)
375 avenue du mistral, 13600, La Ciotat, France
Tel.: (33) 9 72 47 46 46
Web Site: http://www.tajimaeurope.com
Embroidery Machine Distr
N.A.I.C.S.: 423830

Tajima Service Ltd. (1)
22 Malinovaya street, Leninskiy Region, 142715, Moscow, Russia
Tel.: (7) 4997071957
Web Site: http://www.tajima-service.ru
Embroidery Machine Distr
N.A.I.C.S.: 423830

Tajima USA, Inc. (1)
550 Commerce St, Franklin Lakes, NJ 07417
Tel.: (201) 405-1201
Sales of Multi-Head Electronic Embroidery Machines & Related Equipment; Joint Venture of Hirsch International Corp. (55%) & Tajima Industries Ltd. (45%)
N.A.I.C.S.: 811210

Tokai Industrial Sewing Machine Co., Ltd. (1)
1800 Ushiyama-cho, Kasugai, 486-0901, Aichi, Japan
Tel.: (81) 568331161
Embroidery Machine Mfr
N.A.I.C.S.: 333248
Hitoshi Tajima *(Pres)*

TAJIRI RESOURCES CORP.
409 Granville St Suite 608, Vancouver, V6C 1T2, BC, Canada
Tel.: (604) 642-0115   **BC**
Web Site: http://tajiriresources.com
Year Founded: 2008
TAJ—(TSXV)
Assets: $2,849,768
Liabilities: $836,233
Net Worth: $2,013,535
Earnings: ($337,303)
Fiscal Year-end: 04/30/24
Minerals Exploration
N.A.I.C.S.: 212290
Graham Keevil *(Pres & CEO)*

TAK LEE MACHINERY HOLDINGS LIMITED
Lot No 117 D D 111 Sheung Che Village Pat Heung Yuen Long N T, PO Box 351, Hong Kong, China (Hong Kong)
Tel.: (852) 2 488 8888   **Ky**
Web Site: http://www.tlmc-hk.com
Year Founded: 2001
2102—(HKG)
Rev.: $62,658,097
Assets: $65,831,392
Liabilities: $10,434,224
Net Worth: $55,397,168
Earnings: $6,782,284
Emp.: 215
Fiscal Year-end: 07/31/21
Heavy Equipment Leasing Services
N.A.I.C.S.: 532412
Luen Fat Chow *(Chm & CEO)*

Subsidiaries:

Tak Lee Machinery Company Limited (1)
DD 111 Lot No 117 Pat Heung, PO Box 351, Sheung Che Village, Yuen Long, New Territories, China (Hong Kong)
Tel.: (852) 24888888
Web Site: https://www.tlmc-hk.com
Heavy Construction Equipment Rental Leasing Services
N.A.I.C.S.: 532412
Luen Fat Chow *(Chm & CEO)*

TAK SHUN TECHNOLOGY GROUP LIMITED
Unit 10 6F One Midtown No 11 Hoi Shing Rd, Tsuen Wan, 351133, China (Hong Kong)
Tel.: (852) 24198831
Web Site: http://www.takshun.com.hk
Year Founded: 2003
Sales Range: $50-74.9 Million
Emp.: 5
Electronic Products Distributor
N.A.I.C.S.: 423690
Sammi Yeung *(Gen Mgr)*

Subsidiaries:

Advance Display Technology Limited (1)
Ste 09 32 F Cable TV Tower 9 Hoi Shing Rd, New Territories, Tsuen Wan, China (Hong Kong)

INTERNATIONAL PUBLIC

Tel.: (852) 24198831
Web Site: http://www.adt.com.hk
Sales Range: $25-49.9 Million
Emp.: 12
Liquid Crystal Display Products Mfr
N.A.I.C.S.: 334419
Sammi Yeung *(Gen Mgr)*

Deji Electronic Co., Ltd. (1)
Shiting Hanjiang Fujian, Putian, 351115, Fujian, China
Tel.: (86) 5943696189
Electronic Products Mfr
N.A.I.C.S.: 334419

Putian Dexing Electronic Co., Ltd (1)
Wuxing Vlg Jiangkou Town, Hanjiang District, Putian, 351115, Fujian, China
Tel.: (86) 5943687030
Electronic Calculators Mfr
N.A.I.C.S.: 334419

TAKA JEWELLERY HOLDINGS LIMITED
3 Kaki Bukit Place Eunos Tech Park, Singapore, 416181, Singapore
Tel.: (65) 67468777   **SG**
Web Site: https://www.takajewelleryholding.com
Year Founded: 1997
42L—(CAT)
Rev.: $108,105,965
Assets: $143,872,545
Liabilities: $55,326,417
Net Worth: $88,546,128
Earnings: $6,595,776
Emp.: 151
Fiscal Year-end: 06/30/23
Investment Holding Services
N.A.I.C.S.: 551112
Michael Boon Leng Teo *(Co-Founder & Mng Dir)*

TAKA-Q CO., LTD.
3-9-7 Itabashi, Itabashi-ku, Tokyo, 173-0004, Japan
Tel.: (81) 0352484100   **JP**
Web Site: https://www.taka-q.com
Year Founded: 1950
8166—(TKS)
Sales Range: $200-249.9 Million
Emp.: 712
Store Operator
N.A.I.C.S.: 458110
Hiroo Hayashi *(Mng Dir & Mng Exec Officer)*

TAKACHIHO CO.,LTD.
5888 Daizushima, Nagano, 381-0022, Japan
Tel.: (81) 262216677
Web Site: https://www.kk-takachiho.jp
Year Founded: 1949
8225—(TKS)
Rev.: $50,790,960
Assets: $35,312,640
Liabilities: $26,503,840
Net Worth: $8,808,800
Earnings: ($1,490,720)
Fiscal Year-end: 03/31/22
Tourism Souvenirs Whslr
N.A.I.C.S.: 459420

TAKACHIHO KOHEKI CO., LTD.
YOTSUYA TOWER 7F 1-6-1 Yotsuya, Shinjuku-ku, Tokyo, 160-0004, Japan
Tel.: (81) 333551111   **JP**
Web Site: https://www.takachiho-kk.co.jp
Year Founded: 1952
2676—(TKS)
Rev.: $166,730,640
Assets: $151,785,430
Liabilities: $40,506,080
Net Worth: $111,279,350
Earnings: $9,498,570

Emp.: 474
Fiscal Year-end: 03/31/24
Technology Systems & Electronics Components Wholesale Trade Distr
N.A.I.C.S.: 425120
Keiichi Obara *(Exec Officer)*

Subsidiaries:

Mighty Card Corporation (1)
Shibuya-Minami Tokyu Bldg 5F 3-12-18, Shibuya-Ku, Tokyo, 150-0002, Japan
Tel.: (81) 3 5466 0510
Web Site: http://www.mightycard.co.jp
Sales Range: $25-49.9 Million
Emp.: 20
Data Carrier System Mfr
N.A.I.C.S.: 334519

S-Cube Inc. (1)
TMM Bldg 1-10-5 Iwamoto-cho, Chiyoda-ku, Tokyo, 101-0032, Japan
Tel.: (81) 3 5820 3151
Web Site: http://www.s-cubekk.co.jp
Security System Mfr & Distr
N.A.I.C.S.: 334290

TAKACHIHO TRADING (SHANGHAI) Co., Ltd. (1)
Room 1507 City Center of Shanghai A No 100 Zunyi Road, Shanghai, 200051, China
Tel.: (86) 2162371035
Semiconductor Product Distr
N.A.I.C.S.: 423690

Takachiho Fire, Security & Services (Thailand) Ltd. (1)
1858/110-111 Interlink Tower Bangna 25Fl Debaratna Rd, Bangna, Bangkok, 10260, Thailand
Tel.: (66) 23669000
Web Site: https://www.tkfs.co.th
Emp.: 123
Fire Prevention Equipment Distr
N.A.I.C.S.: 423850
Masaru Itoga *(Pres)*

Takachiho Koheki (H.K.) Ltd. (1)
Room 505 5/F Lippo Sun Plaza 28 Canton Road, Tsimshatsui, Kowloon, China (Hong Kong)
Tel.: (852) 27303334
Electronic Product Mfr & Distr
N.A.I.C.S.: 334419
Michiaki Itou *(Pres)*

TAKADA CORPORATION
1-1 Tsukiji-machi, Yahatanishi-ku, Kitakyushu, 806-8567, Fukuoka, Japan
Tel.: (81) 936322631
Web Site: https://www.takada.co.jp
Year Founded: 1940
1966—(TKS)
Rev.: $345,418,770
Assets: $248,734,300
Liabilities: $137,098,010
Net Worth: $111,636,290
Earnings: $11,025,480
Emp.: 1,412
Fiscal Year-end: 03/31/24
Plant Engineering Construction Services
N.A.I.C.S.: 237990
Juichiro Takada *(Pres)*

Subsidiaries:

Kikuchi Industry (Thailand) Co., Ltd. (1)
8/1-8/2 Seri 9 Road, Suanluang, Bangkok, 10250, Thailand
Tel.: (66) 27190365
Web Site: http://www.kikuchi-th.com
Pipeline Construction Services
N.A.I.C.S.: 237120
Koichi Hirohashi *(Mng Dir)*

Singapore Takada Industries Pte., Ltd. (1)
51 Gul Road, Singapore, 629352, Singapore
Tel.: (65) 68613666
Web Site: https://www.takada.com.sg
Piping Work Maintenance Services
N.A.I.C.S.: 238220

Sri Takada Industries (Malaysia) Sdn. Bhd. (1)
No 18 Lorong Keluli 1B Seksyen 7, Kawasan Perindustrian Bukit Raja Selatan, 40000, Shah Alam, Selangor, Malaysia
Tel.: (60) 333435948
Web Site: https://www.sritakada.com.my
Civil Engineering & Construction Services
N.A.I.C.S.: 237990

Takada Corporation Asia Ltd. (1)
140 One Pacific Place 16th Floor Unit 1601-03 Sukhumvit Road, Klongtoey District, Bangkok, 10110, Thailand
Tel.: (66) 225476989
Web Site: https://www.thaitakada.co.th
Piping Work Maintenance Services
N.A.I.C.S.: 238220
Shuji Kawakami *(Mng Dir)*

TAKADAKIKO (STEEL CONSTRUCTION) CO., LTD.
2-10-70 Namba-naka, Naniwa-ku, Osaka, 556-0011, Japan
Tel.: (81) 666495100
Web Site: https://www.takadakiko.com
Year Founded: 1932
5923—(TKS)
Sales Range: $25-49.9 Million
Steel Products Mfr
N.A.I.C.S.: 332312
Hiroshi Takahashi *(Pres)*

TAKAFUL EMARAT - INSURANCE (PSC)
8th Floor Al Moosa Tower 2 Sheikh Zayed Road, PO Box 57589, Umm Al Sheif, Dubai, United Arab Emirates
Tel.: (971) 600522550 AE
Web Site: https://www.takafulemarat.com
Year Founded: 2008
TAKAFUL.EM—(DFM)
Rev.: $62,269,931
Assets: $180,808,650
Liabilities: $191,604,773
Net Worth: ($10,796,123)
Earnings: ($3,383,250)
Emp.: 142
Fiscal Year-end: 12/31/23
Insurance Services
N.A.I.C.S.: 524298
Abdulla Bakheet Al Murar *(Chm)*

TAKAFUL ISLAMI INSURANCE LIMITED
Monir Tower 7th 8th 9th Floor1671 DIT Extension Road Motijheel, Dhaka, Bangladesh
Tel.: (880) 241070071
Web Site: https://www.takaful.com.bd
Year Founded: 2002
TAKAFULINS—(DHA)
Rev.: $432,232
Assets: $11,776,496
Liabilities: $4,308,205
Net Worth: $7,468,291
Earnings: $772,703
Emp.: 930
Fiscal Year-end: 12/31/23
Insurance Services
N.A.I.C.S.: 524298
K. A. M. Ferdous *(CEO)*

TAKAFUL OMAN INSURANCE SAOG
Taminat Complex Building No 55/9 Street No 53 6th floor Al Ghubrah St, PO Box 207, 134, Muscat, Oman
Tel.: (968) 22701600
Web Site: https://www.takafuloman.com
Year Founded: 2014
TAOI—(MUS)
Rev.: $31,917,634
Assets: $50,485,467
Liabilities: $7,778,960

Net Worth: $42,706,507
Earnings: ($3,393,550)
Emp.: 81
Fiscal Year-end: 12/31/23
Insurance Management Services
N.A.I.C.S.: 524298
Rashid Saif Al Saadi *(Chm)*

TAKAGI CHOKOKU CO., LTD.
1525 Nakanoshima, Wakayama, 640-8392, Japan
Tel.: (81) 734235205
Web Site: http://www.takagi-chokoku.co.jp
Year Founded: 1921
Emp.: 86
Specialized Machinery Mfr
N.A.I.C.S.: 333998
Hidehito Takagi *(Pres)*

TAKAGI CO., LTD.
2-4-1 Ishida-Minami, Kokura-Minami-Ku, Kitakyushu, Fukuoka, Japan
Tel.: (81) 939620941
Web Site: http://www.takagi.co.jp
Year Founded: 1961
Plastic Products & Water Purifiers Mfr & Sales
N.A.I.C.S.: 326199
Toshio Takagi *(Founder & Pres)*

Subsidiaries:

Takagi Vietnam Co., Ltd. (1)
Plot No C-1 & C-2 Thang Long Industrial Park II, Yen My District, Hanoi, Hung Yen, Vietnam
Tel.: (84) 61 3936496
Web Site: http://www.takagi.co.jp
Emp.: 257
Plastic Mold Injection Product Mfr
N.A.I.C.S.: 326130
Tadashi Kubo *(Gen Dir)*

TAKAGI SEIKO CORPORATION
322-3 Futazuka, Takaoka, 933-8628, Toyama, Japan
Tel.: (81) 766245522
Web Site: https://www.takagi-seiko.co.jp
4242—(TKS)
Rev.: $458,173,760
Assets: $371,160,240
Liabilities: $235,495,040
Net Worth: $135,665,200
Earnings: $9,738,080
Emp.: 827
Fiscal Year-end: 03/31/22
Metal Stamping Product Mfr
N.A.I.C.S.: 332119
Akihiro Takagi *(Pres)*

Subsidiaries:

Dalian Daxian Takagi Mold Co., Ltd. (1)
F T Z Warehouse and Manufacture Zone IC-31, Dalian, 116600, Shandong, China
Tel.: (86) 4117308630
Web Site: https://www.dldaxian.mouldsnet.com
Plastic Product Mfr & Distr
N.A.I.C.S.: 423830

KOHWA PRECISION MOLDING (SHANGHAI) CO., LTD. (1)
No272 Dong Sheng Road, Shanghai Pudong Heqing Industrial Zone, Shanghai, 201201, China
Tel.: (86) 2158972258
Web Site: http://www.johnson.mouldsnet.com
Plastic Product Mfr & Distr
N.A.I.C.S.: 333511

THAI TAKAGI SEIKO CO., LTD. (1)
358-358/1 Moo 17 2nd Floor Office Building Bangphli Industrial Estate, Theaparuk Rd A Bangsaothong, Samut Prakan, 10540, Thailand
Tel.: (66) 27058800

Automotive Part Whslr
N.A.I.C.S.: 423120

Takagi Auto Parts (Foshan) Co., Ltd. (1)
Chuangye Road Songxia Industrial Park Songgang, Nanhai, Foshan, 528234, Guangdong, China
Tel.: (86) 75785235690
Web Site: http://www.tap-foshan.com.cn
Plastic Product Mfr & Distr
N.A.I.C.S.: 424990

Takagi Seiko (H.K.) Limited (1)
Workshop No 1 27/F Mega Trade Centre 1-6 Mei Wan Street Tsuen Wan, New Territories, Kowloon, China (Hong Kong)
Tel.: (852) 2967 9484
Automotive Part Whslr
N.A.I.C.S.: 423120

TAKAHASHI CURTAIN WALL CORPORATION
1-5-4 Nihonbashi Honcho, Chuo-Ku, Tokyo, 103-0023, Japan
Tel.: (81) 332711711
Web Site: https://www.t-cw.co.jp
Year Founded: 1965
1994—(TKS)
Rev.: $51,983,880
Assets: $90,106,810
Liabilities: $14,236,720
Net Worth: $75,870,090
Earnings: $2,141,180
Fiscal Year-end: 12/31/23
Exterior Wall Construction Services
N.A.I.C.S.: 237990
Takeharu Takahashi *(Pres)*

TAKAKITA CO., LTD.
2828 Natsumi, Nabari, 518-0441, Mie, Japan
Tel.: (81) 595633111
Web Site: https://www.takakita-net.co.jp
Year Founded: 1945
6325—(TKS)
Rev.: $77,156,380
Assets: $100,393,160
Liabilities: $34,928,530
Net Worth: $65,464,630
Earnings: $6,547,380
Emp.: 292
Fiscal Year-end: 03/31/20
Agricultural Machine Mfr & Distr
N.A.I.C.S.: 333111
Mitsuo Matsumoto *(Pres)*

TAKAMATSU CONSTRUCTION GROUP CO., LTD.
1-2-3 Shin-kitano, Yodogawa-ku, Osaka, 532-0025, Japan
Tel.: (81) 663038101
Web Site: https://www.takamatsu-cg.co.jp
Year Founded: 1965
1762—(TKS)
Rev.: $2,066,814,800
Assets: $1,620,434,890
Liabilities: $734,238,800
Net Worth: $886,196,090
Earnings: $60,580,650
Emp.: 4,892
Fiscal Year-end: 03/31/24
Construction Engineering Services
N.A.I.C.S.: 541330
Nobuhiko Yoshitake *(Pres)*

Subsidiaries:

Aoki Marine Co., Ltd. (1)
4-6-12 Shiba, Minato-ku, Tokyo, 108-0014, Japan
Tel.: (81) 364539656
Web Site: https://www.aokimarine.co.jp
Emp.: 48
Engineering Construction Services
N.A.I.C.S.: 237990

Asunaro Aoki Construction Co., Ltd. (1)

TAKAMATSU CONSTRUCTION GROUP CO., LTD.

Takamatsu Construction Group Co., Ltd.—(Continued)
4-8-2 Shiba, Minato-ku, Tokyo, 108-0014, Japan **(100%)**
Tel.: (81) 3 54191011
Web Site: http://www.aaconst.co.jp
Rev.: $1,362,431,760
Assets: $965,433,600
Liabilities: $386,191,200
Net Worth: $579,242,400
Earnings: $47,516,880
Emp.: 1,751
Fiscal Year-end: 03/31/2018
Construction Engineering Services
N.A.I.C.S.: 541330
Tomoyasu Nishikawa *(Auditor)*

Subsidiary (Domestic):

Mirai Construction Co., Ltd. **(2)**
No 6-12 Shiba 4-chome, Minato-ku, Tokyo, 108-0014, Japan
Tel.: (81) 364363710
Web Site: https://www.mirai-const.co.jp
Construction Engineering Services
N.A.I.C.S.: 541330

Mibu Corporation Co., Ltd. **(1)**
Ebisu Prime Square Tower 15F 1-1-39 Hiroo, Shibuya-ku, Tokyo, 150-0011, Japan
Tel.: (81) 357783732
Web Site: https://www.mibucorp.co.jp
Emp.: 92
Real Estate Services
N.A.I.C.S.: 531390

Nakamura Shaji Co., Ltd.
7-4-3 Kinosakidori, Ichinomiya, Aichi, Japan
Tel.: (81) 586717821
Web Site: https://nakamurasyaji.co.jp
Temple Construction Services
N.A.I.C.S.: 531390

Niigata Mirai Co., Ltd. **(1)**
224 Yuzawa, Yuzawa-machi Minamiuonuma-gun, Niigata, 949-6101, Japan
Tel.: (81) 257843521
Web Site: http://www.niigata-mirai.co.jp
Paving Material Mfr & Whslr
N.A.I.C.S.: 324121

Taisho Kogyo Corporation
18-1 Kamitanabecho, Takatsuki, 569-0805, Japan
Tel.: (81) 726826881
Web Site: https://www.taisho-ind.co.jp
Emp.: 82
Construction & Renovation Services
N.A.I.C.S.: 236118

Takamatsu Estate Co., Ltd. **(1)**
5F Shiba 4-8-2, Minato-ku, Tokyo, 108-0014, Japan
Tel.: (81) 334557101
Web Site: https://www.takamatsuestate.jp
Emp.: 387
Real Estate Services
N.A.I.C.S.: 531390

Takamatsu House Co., Ltd. **(1)**
Ebisu Prime Square Tower 15F 1-1-39 Hiroo, Shibuya-ku, Tokyo, 150-0012, Japan
Tel.: (81) 334861134
Web Site: https://takamatsu-house.co.jp
Real Estate Services
N.A.I.C.S.: 531390

Takamatsu Techno Service Co., Ltd.
4-8-2 Shiba, Minato-ku, Tokyo, 108-0014, Japan
Tel.: (81) 334549080
Web Site: https://www.takamatsutechno.jp
Emp.: 298
Renovation Services
N.A.I.C.S.: 236118

Tatsumi Planning Co., Ltd. **(1)**
2 3 5 Minatomirai Queens Tower C Building 11F, Nishi-ku, Yokohama, 220-6211, Kanagawa, Japan
Tel.: (81) 456647800
Web Site: http://www.tatsumi-planning.co.jp
Residence Construction Services
N.A.I.C.S.: 531390

Toko Geotech Co., Ltd. **(1)**
7-12-7 Ginza, Chuo-ku, Tokyo, 104-0061, Japan
Tel.: (81) 334568761
Web Site: https://www.toko-geo.co.jp
Road Construction Services
N.A.I.C.S.: 237310

TAKAMATSU MACHINERY CO., LTD.

1-8 Asahigaoka, Hakusan, 924-8558, Ishikawa, Japan
Tel.: (81) 762076155
Web Site: https://www.takamaz.co.jp
Year Founded: 1961
6155—(TKS)
Rev.: $93,756,240
Assets: $147,488,930
Liabilities: $37,643,950
Net Worth: $109,844,980
Earnings: $(3,734,650)
Emp.: 535
Fiscal Year-end: 03/31/24
Machine Tools Mfr
N.A.I.C.S.: 333515
Kiyoshi Takamatsu *(Chm)*

Subsidiaries:

HANGZHOU FEELER TAKAMATSU MACHINERY CO., LTD **(1)**
No 6800 Jiangdong 3rd road Jiangdong Industrial Park, Xiaoshan, Hangzhou, Zhejiang, China
Tel.: (86) 57182153760
Web Site: http://www.takamazfeeler.com
Machine Tool Distr
N.A.I.C.S.: 423830

PT. TAKAMAZ INDONESIA **(1)**
Jl Festival Boulevard Blok AA 11 No 30 31 Grand Wisata Tambun, Bekasi, 17510, Indonesia
Tel.: (62) 2182616431
Web Site: https://www.takamaz.co.id
Machine Tool Distr
N.A.I.C.S.: 423830
Soichiro Takamatsu *(Pres)*

Takamatsu Machinery (Thailand) Co., Ltd.
888/59 Moo 9 Bangpla, Bangplee, Bang Phli, 10540, Samutprakarn, Thailand
Tel.: (66) 21367831
Web Site: https://www.smri.asia
Machine Tool Distr
N.A.I.C.S.: 423830

Takamatsu Machinery U.S.A., Inc. **(1)**
1320 Landmeier Rd, Elk Grove Village, IL 60007
Tel.: (847) 981-8577
Machine Tool Distr
N.A.I.C.S.: 423830
Takahiro Futagami *(Engr-Svc)*

Takamaz Machinery Europe GmbH **(1)**
Im Hulsenfeld 19, 40721, Hilden, Germany
Tel.: (49) 21037894882
Machine Tool Distr
N.A.I.C.S.: 423830

TAKAMISAWA CO., LTD.

1605-14 Midorimachi, Nagano, 380-0813, Japan
Tel.: (81) 262280111
Web Site: https://www.kk-takamisawa.co.jp
Year Founded: 1951
5283—(TKS)
Rev.: $443,915,180
Assets: $244,850,300
Liabilities: $156,433,000
Net Worth: $88,417,300
Earnings: $4,720,980
Emp.: 412
Fiscal Year-end: 06/30/24
Concrete Mfr & Distr
N.A.I.C.S.: 327320
Hideshige Takamisawa *(Pres)*

Subsidiaries:

Jonen Corporation **(1)**
243 Oya, Ueda, 386-0152, Nagano, Japan **(66.6%)**
Tel.: (81) 268351200
Web Site: http://www.jonen.co.jp
Emp.: 150
Petroleum Product Distr
N.A.I.C.S.: 424720
Hideshige Takamisawa *(Pres)*

TAKAMISAWA CYBERNETICS CO., LTD.

2-48-5 Chuo, Nakano-ku, Tokyo, 164-0011, Japan
Tel.: (81) 332273361
Web Site: https://www.tacy.co.jp
Year Founded: 1969
6424—(TKS)
Rev.: $86,260,500
Assets: $116,659,890
Liabilities: $83,127,360
Net Worth: $33,532,530
Earnings: $4,329,550
Fiscal Year-end: 03/31/24
Automatic Ticket Vending Machine Mfr & Distr
N.A.I.C.S.: 333310
Kazuo Takamisawa *(Pres)*

Subsidiaries:

Takamisawa Mex Co., Ltd. **(1)**
525 Kitagawa, Saku, 384-0304, Nagano, Japan
Tel.: (81) 267783181
Web Site: https://www.tamex.co.jp
Precision Equipment Mfr
N.A.I.C.S.: 332721

Takamisawa Service Corporation **(1)**
2-12-3 Nishi-Gotanda Daiichi Shinko Building 5F Main, Shinagawa-ku, Tokyo, 141-0031, Japan
Tel.: (81) 334905321
Web Site: https://www.takamisawa-s.co.jp
Emp.: 168
Temporary Staffing Services
N.A.I.C.S.: 561320

Takamisawa Solutions Co., Ltd. **(1)**
2-48-5 Chuo, Nakano-ku, Tokyo, 164-0011, Japan
Tel.: (81) 353328261
Web Site: https://www.tasol.co.jp
Emp.: 142
Software Development Services
N.A.I.C.S.: 541511

TAKAMIYA CO., LTD.

Grand Front Osaka Tower-B Bldg 27F 3-1, Ofuka-cho Kita-ku, Osaka, 530-0011, Japan
Tel.: (81) 663753900
Web Site: https://www.takamiya.co
Year Founded: 1969
2445—(TKS)
Rev.: $291,679,470
Assets: $455,726,450
Liabilities: $309,268,680
Net Worth: $146,457,770
Earnings: $12,473,070
Emp.: 1,362
Fiscal Year-end: 03/31/24
Construction Machinery Sales & Rental Services
N.A.I.C.S.: 423810
Takahiro Shozaki *(Sr Exec Officer & Gen Mgr-Sls & Mktg Plng Dept-Sls & Mktg Div)*

Subsidiaries:

AOMORI ATOM Co., Ltd. **(1)**
35-135 Yakeyamakawame Odanozawa, Higashitori Village Shimokita, Aomori, 039-4223, Japan
Tel.: (81) 175457750
Web Site: https://www.am-atom.jp
Construction Equipment Rental Services
N.A.I.C.S.: 532412

DIMENSION-ALL INC. **(1)**
Unit 906 One Corporate Center Meralco Avenue Corner Julia Vargas, San Antonio, Pasig, 1605, Philippines
Tel.: (63) 29974001

INTERNATIONAL PUBLIC

Web Site: http://www.dimension-all.com
Equipment Rental Services
N.A.I.C.S.: 532490
Yuki Mukaiyama *(Pres)*

HORY VIETNAM Co., Ltd. **(1)**
Long Duc Industrial Park, Long Duc Ward, Long Thanh, Dong Nai, Vietnam
Tel.: (84) 2513681211
Construction Equipment Mfr
N.A.I.C.S.: 333120
Michio Ashida *(Pres)*

Hory Corporation
Onward Park Bldg 12F 3-10-5 Nihonbashi Chuo-ku, Tokyo, 103-0027, Japan
Tel.: (81) 3 3276 3920
Web Site: http://www.hory.asia
Construction Equipment Mfr & Distr
N.A.I.C.S.: 333120
Yasunori Nishioka *(Pres)*

IWATA Co., Ltd. **(1)**
523-2 Jonodan Chogetsu, Momoyama-cho, Kinokawa, 649-6112, Wakayama, Japan
Tel.: (81) 736663450
Web Site: https://www.iw-iwata.com
Emp.: 25
Construction Equipment Rental Services
N.A.I.C.S.: 532412

Nextech Co., Ltd. **(1)**
Grand Front Tower-B Bldg 27F 3-1 Oofuka-cho Kita-ku, Osaka, 530-0011, Japan
Tel.: (81) 663759200
Web Site: http://www.asahi-kougyou.jp
Timber Products Distr
N.A.I.C.S.: 423990
Shu Yamanashi *(Pres)*

SN Builtech Co., Ltd. **(1)**
Onward Park Bldg 11F 3-10-5 Nihonbashi, Chuo, 103-0027, Tokyo, Japan
Tel.: (81) 332763930
Web Site: http://www.snbt.co.jp
Construction Equipment Rental Services
N.A.I.C.S.: 532412
Hiroyuki Kuroiwa *(Pres)*

TATSUMI Co., Ltd. **(1)**
2000-7 Shimodoshi, Higashiibaraki-gun, Ibaraki, 311-3155, Japan
Tel.: (81) 292972406
Web Site: http://www.kk-tatsumi.jp
Construction Equipment Rental Services
N.A.I.C.S.: 532412

TOTAL TOSHISEIBI Co., Ltd. **(1)**
Onward Park Bldg 11F 3-10-5, Nihonbashi, Nagoya, 103-0027, Japan
Tel.: (81) 332763930
Web Site: http://www.total-toshiseibi.jp
Construction Equipment Rental Services
N.A.I.C.S.: 532412
Hideto Ito *(Pres)*

TAKANASHI MILK PRODUCTS CO., LTD.

5 Honjuku-cho, Asahi-ku, Yokohama, 241-0023, Japan
Tel.: (81) 453381940
Web Site: http://www.takanashi-milk.co.jp
Year Founded: 1946
Dairy Products Mfr
N.A.I.C.S.: 311511
Nobuyoshi Takanashi *(Pres)*

Subsidiaries:

Haagen-Dazs Japan, Inc. **(1)**
2-1-1 Kamimeguro, Meguro-ku, Tokyo, 153-0051, Japan **(10%)**
Tel.: (81) 120190821
Web Site: https://www.haagen-dazs.co.jp
Sales Range: $50-74.9 Million
Ice Cream Producer
N.A.I.C.S.: 311520

Takanashi Milk Oceania Pty.Ltd. **(1)**
Level 19 367 Collins street, Melbourne, 3000, VIC, Australia
Tel.: (61) 396292865
Dairy Products Distr
N.A.I.C.S.: 424490

Takanashi Milk Products Sales Co., Ltd **(1)**
YBP East Tower 13F 134 Godo-cho,

AND PRIVATE COMPANIES — TAKARA BELMONT CORPORATION

Hodogaya-ku, Yokohama, Japan
Tel.: (81) 453381948
Dairy Products Distr
N.A.I.C.S.: 424490

TAKANET SERVICE CO., LTD.
4-4-2 Minatomirai, Nishi-ku Kanagawa 2nd floor of Yokohama Blue Avenue, Yokohama, 220-0012, Japan
Tel.: (81) 452224488
Web Site: http://www.takanet-s.com
Year Founded: 2009
7672—(TKS)
Rev.: $2,111,130,560
Assets: $970,090,880
Liabilities: $716,339,360
Net Worth: $253,751,520
Earnings: $69,386,240
Fiscal Year-end: 05/31/20
Used Truck Distr
N.A.I.C.S.: 423110
Takao Nishiguchi *(CEO)*

TAKANO CO., LTD.
137 Miyada-mura, Kamiina-gun, Nagano, 399-4301, Japan
Tel.: (81) 265853150
Web Site: https://www.takano-net.co.jp
Year Founded: 1941
7885—(TKS)
Rev.: $166,393,530
Assets: $262,278,190
Liabilities: $53,845,060
Net Worth: $208,433,130
Earnings: $3,972,610
Emp.: 593
Fiscal Year-end: 03/31/24
Office Furniture Mfr & Whslr
N.A.I.C.S.: 337211
Tsutomu Takano *(Mng Dir)*

Subsidiaries:

Nikko Co., Ltd. (1)
6634-1 Miyada-mura, Kamiina-gun, Nagano, 399-4301, Japan
Tel.: (81) 265853050
Web Site: http://www.takano-net.co.jp
Furniture Mfr
N.A.I.C.S.: 337211

Takano Co., Ltd. - Ina Factory (1)
5331 Shimogawara Nishiharuchika, Ina, 399-4431, Nagano, Japan
Tel.: (81) 265723147
Office Furniture Mfr
N.A.I.C.S.: 337211

Takano Co., Ltd. - Minamidaira Factory (1)
2053-7 Miyada-mura, Kamiina-gun, Nagano, 399-4301, Japan
Tel.: (81) 265854080
Web Site: http://www.takano.com
Emp.: 300
Office Furniture Mfr
N.A.I.C.S.: 337211
Takano Jun *(Gen Mgr)*

Takano Co., Ltd. - Shimojima Factory (1)
3587-1 Kodaira Nishiharuchika, Ina, 399-4431, Nagano, Japan
Tel.: (81) 265732088
Office Furniture Mfr
N.A.I.C.S.: 337211

Takano Machinery Co., Ltd. (1)
5450-205 Miyada-mura, Kamiina-gun, Nagano, 399-4301, Japan
Tel.: (81) 265853156
Industrial Machinery Mfr
N.A.I.C.S.: 333998

TAKAOKA TOKO CO., LTD.
8F Toyosu Prime Square 5-6-36 Toyosu, Koto-ku, Tokyo, 135-0061, Japan
Tel.: (81) 363715000 JP
Web Site: https://www.tktk.co.jp
Year Founded: 2012
6617—(TKS)
Rev.: $709,768,580
Assets: $770,904,470
Liabilities: $348,928,680
Net Worth: $421,975,790
Earnings: $30,855,480
Emp.: 2,520
Fiscal Year-end: 03/31/24
Holding Company; Electrical Equipment & Components Mfr
N.A.I.C.S.: 551112
Naoshi Nishikawa *(Sr Mng Exec Officer)*

Subsidiaries:

Dexco, Ltd. (1)
203 2F Urban Square Bldg 1-18 Kandasudacho, Chiyoda-ku, Tokyo, 101-0041, Japan
Tel.: (81) 33 251 1231
Electrical Equipment Distr
N.A.I.C.S.: 423610

Fushun Takaoka Switchgear Company Limited (1)
No 58 Shendong 3rd Road, Economic Development Zone, Fushun, 113122, Liaoning, China
Tel.: (86) 245 765 2427
Disconnector Mfr & Distr
N.A.I.C.S.: 335313

Mintwave Co., Ltd. (1)
Central Plaza 6F 1-1 Kaguragashi, Shinjuku-ku, Tokyo, 162-0823, Japan
Tel.: (81) 503 818 0201
Web Site: https://www.mintwave.co.jp
Communication Equipment Mfr & Distr
N.A.I.C.S.: 334290

Tactico, Ltd. (1)
A-406 Asterium Seoul 372 Hangang-daero, Yongsan-gu, Seoul, 04323, Korea (South)
Tel.: (82) 708 240 0511
Web Site: https://www.tactico.co.kr
Electric Equipment Mfr
N.A.I.C.S.: 335999
Hoseok Han *(CEO)*

Takaoka Densetsu Co., Ltd. (1)
38-1 Nakai, Yoshikawa, 342-0015, Saitama, Japan
Tel.: (81) 48 981 5147
Telecommunication Construction Services
N.A.I.C.S.: 237130

Takaoka Electric Mfg. Co., Ltd. (1)
Tokyosu 5636 Kotokoto, Chuo-ku, Tokyo, 1350061, Japan (100%)
Tel.: (81) 363715434
Web Site: http://www.tktkco.jp
Sales Range: $700-749.9 Million
Emp.: 1,472
Electrical Equipment & Components Mfr
N.A.I.C.S.: 335313
Takatsu Hiroaki *(Pres)*

Subsidiary (Domestic):

TAKAOKA CHEMICAL CO., LTD. (2)
80 Nagare Jimokuji, Ama, 490-1111, Aichi, Japan
Web Site: http://www.takaokakasei.co.jp
Emp.: 153
Capacitor Mfr & Distr
N.A.I.C.S.: 334416

Takaoka Engineering Co., Ltd. (2)
3-29 Kandajimbou-cho, Chiyoda-Ku, Tokyo, 101-0051, Japan
Tel.: (81) 5038217773
Web Site: http://www.takaoka-eng.co.jp
Emp.: 35
Engineering Consulting Services
N.A.I.C.S.: 541330
Akihiko Ichikawa *(Pres)*

UQUEST, LTD. (2)
Shoko Chukin Dai-ichi Seimei Ueno Bldg 7F 1-10-12 Ueno, Taito-ku, Tokyo, 110-0005, Japan
Tel.: (81) 358161051
Web Site: http://www.uquest.co.jp
Emp.: 53
Computer Software Distr
N.A.I.C.S.: 423430
Shoji Tanahashi *(Pres & CEO)*

Toko Electric (Suzhou) Co., Ltd. (1)
No 1868 Guangming Road Building H Plainvim Industrial Park, Wujiang Economic and Technological Development Zone, Suzhou, 215200, China
Tel.: (86) 5126 667 0790
Instrument Transformer Mfr & Distr
N.A.I.C.S.: 335311

Toko Electric Corporation (1)
1-7-1 Yuraku-cho, Chiyoda-ku, Tokyo, 100-0006, Japan
Tel.: (81) 3 3214 5281
Web Site: http://www.tokodenki.co.jp
Sales Range: $550-599.9 Million
Emp.: 1,048
Electric Equipment & Component Mfr
N.A.I.C.S.: 334419

Subsidiary (Domestic):

Toshiba Toko Meter Systems Co., Ltd. (2)
3484-1 Kurohama, Hasuda, 349-0192, Saitama, Japan
Tel.: (81) 488773440
Web Site: http://www.t2ms.co.jp
Electrical Product Mfr & Distr
N.A.I.C.S.: 335999
Isao Aoki *(Pres)*

Toko Kizai Corporation (1)
3497 Kurohama, Hasuda, 349-0101, Saitama, Japan
Tel.: (81) 48 765 1188
Web Site: https://www.toukoukizai.co.jp
High Voltage Testing Equipment Mfr
N.A.I.C.S.: 334515

Toko Takaoka Korea Co., Ltd. (1)
81 Ungcheondong-ro 43beon-gil, Jinhae-gu, Changwon, 51618, Gyeongsangnam-do, Korea (South)
Tel.: (82) 55 713 7700
Transformer Mfr & Distr
N.A.I.C.S.: 335311

Watt Line Service Co., Ltd. (1)
3506-3 Sakuragaoka Oaza Kurohama, Hasuda, 349-0101, Saitama, Japan
Tel.: (81) 48 768 7658
Web Site: https://www.wattlineservice.co.jp
Freight Transportation Services
N.A.I.C.S.: 488510

TAKARA & COMPANY LTD.
28-8 Takada 3-chome, Toshima-ku, Tokyo, 171-0033, Japan
Tel.: (81) 339713260
Web Site: https://www.takara-company.co.jp
Year Founded: 1960
7921—(TKS)
Rev.: $193,527,580
Assets: $239,242,340
Liabilities: $54,155,730
Net Worth: $185,086,610
Earnings: $19,922,540
Emp.: 1,193
Fiscal Year-end: 05/31/24
Financial Industry Printing Services
N.A.I.C.S.: 323111
Akira Tsuda *(Exec Officer)*

Subsidiaries:

Disclosure Innovation Inc. (1)
3-23-10 Takada, Toshima-ku, Tokyo, 171-0033, Japan
Tel.: (81) 359850920
Web Site: https://www.di-inc.co.jp
Sales Range: $25-49.9 Million
Emp.: 23
Information Management Services
N.A.I.C.S.: 519290

Simul International, Inc. (1)
G-7 Building 7-16-12 Ginza, Chuo-ku, Tokyo, 104-0061, Japan (100%)
Tel.: (81) 33 524 3100
Web Site: https://www.simul.co.jp
Sales Range: $25-49.9 Million
Emp.: 120
Interpretation, Language Instruction & Translation Services
N.A.I.C.S.: 611630
Junichi Hayashi *(Pres)*

Task Co,. Ltd. (1)
21 10 Soi Ruamrudee 1 Ploenchit Rd, Pathumwan, Bangkok, Thailand
Tel.: (66) 22541777
Web Site: https://www.taskfurniture.com
Sales Range: $25-49.9 Million
Emp.: 240
General Consulting Services
N.A.I.C.S.: 541611

TAKARA BELMONT CORPORATION
2 1 1 Higashi Shinsaibashi, Osaka, 542 0083, Japan
Tel.: (81) 662135945
Web Site: http://www.takarabelmont.co.jp
Year Founded: 1921
Sales Range: $250-299.9 Million
Emp.: 1,200
Commercial & Service Industry Machinery Mfr
N.A.I.C.S.: 333310
Hidetaka Yoshikawa *(Chm & CEO)*

Subsidiaries:

Koken Manufacturing Company, Inc. (1)
1631 Martin Luther King Dr, Saint Louis, MO 63106
Tel.: (314) 231-7383
Web Site: http://www.takarabelmont.com
Sales Range: $25-49.9 Million
Emp.: 92
Barber & Beauty Shop Equipment Mfr
N.A.I.C.S.: 337127

Division (Domestic):

Takara Belmont Corporation Marble Products Div. (2)
2080 S Edwards St, Wichita, KS 67213-1869
Tel.: (316) 942-7600
Web Site: http://www.kokenstl.com
Sales Range: $25-49.9 Million
Emp.: 20
Mfr of Marble Products
N.A.I.C.S.: 327991

TAKARA BELMONT (KOREA) CORPORATION (1)
2F 298 Seokchonhosu-Ro, Songpa-Gu, Seoul, 138849, Korea (South)
Tel.: (82) 2 413 5977
Web Site: http://www.takarabelmont.co.kr
Industrial Machinery Mfr
N.A.I.C.S.: 333248
Junmin Cha *(Mgr)*

TAKARA BELMONT (SHANGHAI) CORPORATION (1)
8A Jinjiang Xiangyang Building 993 Nanjing West Road, Jingan, Shanghai, China
Tel.: (86) 21 6272 8166
Institutional Furniture Mfr
N.A.I.C.S.: 337127

TAKARA BELMONT (TAIWAN) CORP. (1)
1F No 1 Lane 200 Sung Teh Road, Taipei, 11075, Taiwan
Tel.: (886) 2 8789 0809
Web Site: http://www.takara-twn.com
Emp.: 3
Institutional Furniture Mfr
N.A.I.C.S.: 337127

TAKARA BELMONT PARA AMERICA DO SUL INDUSTRIA E COMERCIO DE MOVEIS LTDA. (1)
Rua 13 DE Maio 1315, Bela Vista, Sao Paulo, 01327-001, Brazil
Tel.: (55) 11 3284 9577
Institutional Furniture Mfr
N.A.I.C.S.: 337127

TAKARA BELMONT(U.K.)LTD. (1)
Belmont House One St Andrews Way, Bow, London, E3 3PA, United Kingdom
Tel.: (44) 20 7515 0333
Web Site: http://www.takara.co.uk
Emp.: 35
Institutional Furniture Mfr
N.A.I.C.S.: 337127

TAKARA BELMONT CORPORATION

Takara Belmont Corporation—(Continued)

TAKARA COMPAGNIE PARIS S.A.R.L. (1)
56 rue des Hautes Patures, BP 906, 92009, Nanterre, Cedex, France
Tel.: (33) 1 42 42 66 28
Web Site: http://www.belmont.fr
Institutional Furniture Mfr
N.A.I.C.S.: 337127

TAKARA COMPANY EUROPE GmbH (1)
Berner Strasse 18, 60437, Frankfurt, Germany
Tel.: (49) 69 50 68 78 0
Web Site: http://www.takara-belmont.de
Institutional Furniture Mfr
N.A.I.C.S.: 337127

TAKARA COMPANY, CANADA, LTD. (1)
2455 Meadowvale Blvd, Mississauga, L5N 5S2, ON, Canada
Tel.: (905) 822-2755
Web Site: http://www.takarabelmont.ca
Institutional Furniture Mfr
N.A.I.C.S.: 337127
Masa Ando (Pres)

TS BELMONT (TAIWAN) CO., LTD. (1)
Ts Belmont Taichung Factory East Area Chien Jen St 38, Taichung, Taiwan
Tel.: (886) 4 2283 4059
Institutional Furniture Mfr
N.A.I.C.S.: 337127

Takara Belmont U.S.A., Inc. (1)
17 W 56th St, New York, NY 10019-3902 (100%)
Tel.: (212) 541-6660
Web Site: http://www.takarabelmont.com
Sales Range: $50-74.9 Million
Emp.: 6
Showroom for Furniture for Barber & Beauty Shops
N.A.I.C.S.: 423850

Takara Standard Co., Ltd. (1)
1-2-1 Shigino-higashi, Joto-ku, Osaka, 536-8536, Japan
Tel.: (81) 669621542
Web Site: http://www.takara-standard.co.jp
Rev.: $1,626,052,320
Emp.: 6,067
Fiscal Year-end: 03/31/2017
Enameled Kitchen Equipment, Bathroom Equipment & Water Heaters Mfr
N.A.I.C.S.: 337126
Takeo Watanabe (Pres)

TAKARA HOLDINGS, INC.

20 Naginatabokō-cho Shijo-dori Karasuma Higashi-iru, Shimogyo-ku, Kyoto, 600-8008, Japan
Tel.: (81) 752415130
Web Site: https://www.takara.co.jp
Year Founded: 1925
2531—(TKS)
Rev.: $2,243,248,920
Assets: $2,891,663,480
Liabilities: $1,037,789,830
Net Worth: $1,853,873,650
Earnings: $106,923,360
Fiscal Year-end: 03/31/24
Holding Company; Alcoholic & Non-Alcoholic Drink Producer; Gene Research; Bottle Mfr; Printing; Transportation & Travel Businesses
N.A.I.C.S.: 551112
Minori Mori (Sr Mng Exec Officer)

Subsidiaries:

AGE International, Inc. (1)
W Main St, Frankfort, KY 40602
Tel.: (502) 223-9874
Web Site: http://www.blantonsbourbon.com
Sales Range: $25-49.9 Million
Emp.: 5
Winery
N.A.I.C.S.: 312130

Beijing Takara Shuzo Brewery Co., Ltd. (1)
31 Nanyuan West St, Fengtai District, Beijing, China (72%)
Tel.: (86) 1067991363
Mfr & Sales of Alcohol, Alcoholic Beverages, Raw Alcohol & Seasonings
N.A.I.C.S.: 312130

Cominport Distribucion S.L. (1)
Avda de Andalucia km 10 3 PAE Neisa Sur Edif 1 - c/Marconi, 28021, Madrid, Spain
Tel.: (34) 915413750
Web Site: https://www.cominport.com
Food Product Whslr
N.A.I.C.S.: 424490

FOODEX S.A.R.L. (1)
Rue de Riant-Coteau 11, 1196, Gland, Vaud, Switzerland
Tel.: (41) 229608080
Web Site: https://www.foodex.ch
Sales Range: $25-49.9 Million
Emp.: 9
Beverage Food Product Mfr & Distr
N.A.I.C.S.: 312120

FOODEX S.R.L. (1)
Via Galileo Galilei 12/14, Burago di Molgora, 20875, Monza, Milan, Italy
Tel.: (39) 0396260866
Web Site: https://www.foodex.it
Restaurant Operating Services
N.A.I.C.S.: 722511

FOODEX SUD S.A.R.L. (1)
2 Rue Joseph Fournier Zone Ecopole, Mas de Laurent, 13310, Saint-Martin-de-Crau, France
Tel.: (33) 490960701
Web Site: https://shopsud.foodex.fr
Sales Range: $25-49.9 Million
Emp.: 14
Food Products Mfr & Distr
N.A.I.C.S.: 311999
Remi Benoiton (Mgr-Agency)

Foodex S.A.S. (1)
11 rue Alfred Kastler, 94460, Valenton, France
Tel.: (33) 145102400
Web Site: https://www.foodex.fr
Food Product Whslr
N.A.I.C.S.: 424490

J&W Hardie Ltd. (1)
Tomatin, Inverness, IV13 7YT, United Kingdom
Tel.: (44) 1463248148
Web Site: http://www.tomatin.com
Mfr & Sales of Scotch Whiskey
N.A.I.C.S.: 312130

Kawahigashi Shoji Co., Ltd. (1)
20 Naginataboko-cho Shijo-dori Karasuma Higashi-iru, Shimogyo-ku, Kyoto, 600-8008, Japan
Tel.: (81) 752415198
Web Site: http://www.takara.co.jp
Alcoholic Beverage Distr
N.A.I.C.S.: 424820

Keta Foods, Lda. (1)
Industrial Park Olival das Minas Rua dos Quintanilhas No 2, 2625-577, Vialonga, Portugal
Tel.: (351) 219246688
Web Site: https://www.ketafoods.com
Food Product Whslr
N.A.I.C.S.: 424490

Luc Corporation, Ltd. (1)
Akasaka Noah Building 8F 3-2-12 Akasaka, Minato-ku, Tokyo, 107-0052, Japan (100%)
Tel.: (81) 335867501
Web Site: https://www.luc-corp.co.jp
Emp.: 25
Importer & Sales of Alcoholic Beverages
N.A.I.C.S.: 312130
Kazuhiro Kanai (Pres)

Nippon Food Supplies Company Pty. Ltd. (1)
Unit 8 9 / 63 Campbell Road, Alexandria, 2015, NSW, Australia
Tel.: (61) 280959522
Web Site: https://www.nipponfoodsupplies.com.au
Food Product Whslr
N.A.I.C.S.: 424490

Shanghai Takara Shuzo International Trading Co., Ltd. (1)
Shenergy International Building 18th Floor Room 1808A No 1, FuXing Middle RD Huangpu District, Shanghai, 200021, China
Tel.: (86) 2161526623
Web Site: http://www.takarashuzo.co.jp
Importer & Sales of Alcoholic Beverages & Food
N.A.I.C.S.: 312130

TB Co., Ltd (1)
55-13 osumihama, Kyotanabe, 610-0343, Kyoto, Japan
Tel.: (81) 774653840
Web Site: http://www.takara.co.jp
Transportation Services
N.A.I.C.S.: 488999

Taihei Butsuryu Co., Ltd. (1)
486 Shimohiroya, Kawagoe Shi, Saitama, 350 0804, Japan (60%)
Tel.: (81) 492341171
Provider of Transportation
N.A.I.C.S.: 488490

Taihei Printing Ltd. (1)
1 Butaicho, Fushimi-ku, Kyoto, 803-0821, Tokyo, Japan (99%)
Tel.: (81) 756053330
Web Site: https://www.taihei.co.jp
Sales Range: $125-149.9 Million
Emp.: 99
Printing
N.A.I.C.S.: 323117

Takara Bio, Inc. (1)
Nojihigashi 7-4-38, Kusatsu, Shiga, 525-0058, Japan (100%)
Tel.: (81) 775656920
Web Site: https://www.takara-bio.com
Rev.: $287,568,050
Assets: $801,475,720
Liabilities: $62,583,480
Net Worth: $738,892,240
Earnings: $9,782,800
Emp.: 1,838
Fiscal Year-end: 03/31/2024
Develops, Produces & Markets Biological Products
N.A.I.C.S.: 325414
Hisashi Ohmiya (Chm)

Subsidiary (Non-US):

Takara Bio Europe S.A.S. (2)
34 rue de la Croix de Fer, 78100, Saint Germain-en-Laye, France (100%)
Tel.: (33) 139046880
Web Site: http://www.takaracontact.eu
Emp.: 50
Genetic Engineering Research
N.A.I.C.S.: 541715
Jean-Jacques Farhi (Mng Dir)

Subsidiary (US):

Takara Bio USA Holdings Inc. (2)
1290 Terra Bella Ave, Mountain View, CA 94043
Tel.: (650) 919-7520
Web Site: http://www.clontech.com
Investment Management Service
N.A.I.C.S.: 523999

Subsidiary (Domestic):

Rubicon Genomics, Inc. (3)
4743 Venture Dr, Ann Arbor, MI 48108
Tel.: (734) 677-4845
Web Site: http://www.rubicongenomics.com
Sales Range: $1-9.9 Million
Emp.: 10
Research & Development in Biotechnology
N.A.I.C.S.: 541714
James J. Koziarz (CEO)

Takara Bio USA, Inc. (3)
1290 Terra Bella Ave, Mountain View, CA 94043 (100%)
Tel.: (650) 919-7300
Web Site: http://www.takarabio.com
Sales Range: $25-49.9 Million
Emp.: 120
Genetic Engineering Research
N.A.I.C.S.: 541715
Carol Lou (Pres)

WaferGen Bio-systems, Inc. (3)
34700 Campus Dr, Fremont, CA 94555
Tel.: (510) 651-4450
Web Site: http://www.wafergen.com

INTERNATIONAL PUBLIC

Laboratory Analytical Instruments Mfr, Developer & Marketer
N.A.I.C.S.: 334516
Syed Husain (Sr VP-Engrg)

Subsidiary (Non-US):

Takara Biomedical Technology (Beijing) Co., Ltd. (2)
No 22 Science Park Road, Changping District, Beijing, 102206, China (100%)
Tel.: (86) 1080720980
Web Site: https://www.takarabiomed.com.cn
Sales Range: $25-49.9 Million
Emp.: 34
Develops, Produces & Markets Gene Medicine
N.A.I.C.S.: 325414

Takara Biotechnology (Dalian) Co., Ltd. (2)
No 19 Dongbei 2nd Street Development Zone, Dalian, 116600, China (100%)
Tel.: (86) 41187619944
Web Site: http://www.takara.com.cn
Sales Range: $25-49.9 Million
Emp.: 500
Genetic Engineering Research; Research Reagents Mfr
N.A.I.C.S.: 541715

Takara Korea Biomedical, Inc. (2)
St 601 Newt Castle 108 Gasan Digital 2-ro, Geumcheon-gu, Seoul, 08506, Korea (South) (100%)
Tel.: (82) 220812525
Web Site: https://www.takara.co.kr
Sales Range: $10-24.9 Million
Emp.: 40
Genetic Engineering Research
N.A.I.C.S.: 541715
Lee Dong-Geun (CEO)

Takara Bussan Co., Ltd. (1)
5-487 Shinmachi, Fushimi Ku, Kyoto, 612-8081, Japan (100%)
Tel.: (81) 756016267
Sales Range: $25-49.9 Million
Emp.: 2
Seller of Food & Fodder
N.A.I.C.S.: 311423

Takara Butsuryu System Co., Ltd. (1)
55-13 Osumihama, Kyotanabe, 610-0343, Kyoto, Japan (100%)
Tel.: (81) 774681720
Web Site: http://www.takara-butsuryu.co.jp
Sales Range: $25-49.9 Million
Emp.: 100
Transportation Logistics
N.A.I.C.S.: 541614

Takara Network System Co., Ltd. (1)
20 Naginatahoko-cho Shijo-dori Karasuma Higishi-iru, Shimogyo-ku, Kyoto, 600 8688, Japan (65%)
Tel.: (81) 752415139
Web Site: http://www.takara.co.jp
Computer System Development, Operation & Maintenance
N.A.I.C.S.: 541512

Takara Sake USA Inc. (1)
708 Addison St, Berkeley, CA 94710-1925
Tel.: (510) 540-8250
Web Site: http://www.takarasake.com
Sales Range: $1-9.9 Million
Emp.: 40
Mfr & Seller of Alcoholic Beverages
N.A.I.C.S.: 312140

Takara Shuzo Asia Pacific Pte. Ltd. (1)
81 Anson Road Suite 8 08, Singapore, 079908, Singapore
Tel.: (65) 65006334
Drink Product Distr
N.A.I.C.S.: 493190

Takara Shuzo Co., Ltd (1)
20 Nagatohokocho Shijo-dori Karasuma Higashiiri, Shimogyo-ku, Kyoto, 600-8688, Japan
Tel.: (81) 752415110
Web Site: https://www.takarashuzo.co.jp
Emp.: 20
Alcoholic Beverage & Seasoning Distr
N.A.I.C.S.: 424820

AND PRIVATE COMPANIES

Takara Shuzo Foods Co., Ltd. (1)
No 31 Nanyuan West St, Fengtai District, Beijing, 100076, China
Tel.: (86) 1067915801
Drink Product Mfr & Distr
N.A.I.C.S.: 312111

Takara Shuzo International Co., Ltd. (1)
20 Naginataboko-cho Shijo-dori Karasuma Higashi-iru, Shimogyo-ku, Kyoto, 600-8688, Japan
Tel.: (81) 752125074
Web Site: https://www.takara-intl.co.jp
Food Product Whslr
N.A.I.C.S.: 424490
Minori Mori (Pres)

Subsidiary (US):

Mutual Trading Co., Inc. (2)
431 Crocker St, Los Angeles, CA 90013-2114 **(70.7%)**
Tel.: (213) 626-9458
Web Site: http://www.lamtc.com
Sales Range: $75-99.9 Million
Emp.: 105
Whslr of Japanese Foods
N.A.I.C.S.: 424410
Noritoshi Kanai (Founder, Chm & Pres)

Subsidiary (Domestic):

Arizona Mutual Trading Co., Inc. (3)
5402 W Roosevelt St Ste104, Phoenix, AZ 85043
Tel.: (602) 455-8000
Toy & Hobby Goods Whslr
N.A.I.C.S.: 423920

Las Vegas Mutual Trading Co., Inc. (3)
6580 S Lindell Rd Ste 100, Las Vegas, NV 89118
Tel.: (702) 216-2715
Food Product Whslr
N.A.I.C.S.: 445298

New England Mutual Trading Inc. (3)
460 Totten Pond Rd Ste 220, Waltham, MA 02451
Tel.: (617) 469-8312
Food & Beverage Distr
N.A.I.C.S.: 424490

New York Mutual Trading, Inc. (3)
77 Metro Way Unit 1, Secaucus, NJ 07094
Tel.: (201) 933-9555
Web Site: http://www.nymtc.com
Emp.: 150
Food Product Whslr
N.A.I.C.S.: 445298

San Diego Mutual Trading Co., Inc. (3)
13790 Stowe Dr Ste A, Poway, CA 92064
Tel.: (858) 748-9458
Web Site: http://www.sd-mtc.com
Sales Range: $10-24.9 Million
Emp.: 30
Food Products Distr
N.A.I.C.S.: 238990
Min Lee (Gen Mgr)

The Cherry Company, Ltd. (3)
3375 Koapaka St Ste A 185, Honolulu, HI 96819
Tel.: (808) 422-6555
Web Site: http://www.cherryco.com
Sales Range: $10-24.9 Million
Emp.: 25
Food Products Distr
N.A.I.C.S.: 311999
Teru Kishii (VP)

Yamasho Inc. (3)
750 Touhy Ave, Elk Grove Village, IL 60007-4916
Tel.: (847) 981-9342
Web Site: http://www.yamashoinc.com
Sales Range: $1-9.9 Million
Emp.: 28
Packaged Frozen Food Whslr
N.A.I.C.S.: 424420

Takara Yoki Co., Ltd. (1)
20 Naginataboko-cho Shijo-dori Karasuma Higashi-iru, Shimogyo-ku, Kyoto, 600-8008, Japan
Tel.: (81) 752567760
Glass Bottles Whslr
N.A.I.C.S.: 425120

Tazaki Foods Limited (1)
12 Innova Way, Enfield, EN3 7FL, Middlesex, United Kingdom
Tel.: (44) 2083443000
Web Site: https://www.tazakifoods.com
Food Product Whslr
N.A.I.C.S.: 424490

Tokyo Mutual Trading Co., Ltd. (1)
4-26-4 Taito, Taito-ku, Tokyo, 110-0016, Japan
Tel.: (81) 338358101
Web Site: https://www.tmtc.co.jp
Food Order Distr
N.A.I.C.S.: 424990

Tomatin Distillery Co Ltd (1)
Tomatin, Inverness, IV13 7YT, United Kingdom **(100%)**
Tel.: (44) 1463248148
Web Site: https://www.tomatin.com
Sales Range: $25-49.9 Million
Emp.: 40
Scotch Whiskey Mfr & Sales
N.A.I.C.S.: 312140
Stephen Bremner (Mng Dir)

Total Management Business Co., Ltd. (1)
9F Shijo Karasuma FT Square Higashiiri Shijo Karasuma, Shimogyo-ku, Kyoto, 600-8008, Japan **(100%)**
Tel.: (81) 752415172
Web Site: https://www.total-mb.co.jp
Sales Range: $10-24.9 Million
Emp.: 50
Provider of Advertising, Marketing & Placement Services
N.A.I.C.S.: 561499

USA Takara Holding Company (1)
708 Addison St, Berkeley, CA 94710
Tel.: (510) 540-8250
Web Site: http://www.takarasake.com
Investment Management Service
N.A.I.C.S.: 523999
Masa Ohata (Pres)

TAKARA LEBEN INFRASTRUCTURE FUND, INC.
Otemachi Nomura Bldg 16F 2-1-1 Otemachi, Chiyoda-ku, Tokyo, 100-0004, Japan
Tel.: (81) 362626402
Web Site: http://www.tif9281.co.jp
Year Founded: 2015
9281—(TKS)
Sales Range: Less than $1 Million
Investment Management Service
N.A.I.C.S.: 525990
Masahide Kikuchi (Exec Officer)

TAKARA LEBEN REAL ESTATE INVESTMENT CORPORATION
1-14-15 Akasaka, Minato-ku, Tokyo, 107-0052, Japan
Tel.: (81) 364355264
Web Site: https://www.takara-reit.co.jp
Year Founded: 2017
3492—(TKS)
Real Estate Investment Services
N.A.I.C.S.: 531190
Masayuki Ishihara (Exec Dir)

TAKASAGO INTERNATIONAL CORPORATION
17F Nissay Aroma Square 5-37-1 Kamata, Ota-ku, Tokyo, 144-8721, Japan
Tel.: (81) 357440511
Web Site: https://www.takasago.com
Year Founded: 1920
4914—(TKS)
Rev.: $1,295,163,400
Assets: $1,509,902,470
Liabilities: $644,785,670
Net Worth: $865,116,800
Earnings: $17,833,780
Emp.: 4,041
Fiscal Year-end: 03/31/24
Chemical Product Mfr & Whslr
N.A.I.C.S.: 325998
Hisaya Fujiwara (Sr VP)

Subsidiaries:

Centre Ingredient Technology, Inc. (1)
101 Commerce Pl, Rockingham, NC 28379
Tel.: (910) 895-9277
Web Site: http://www.bioingredients.com
Sales Range: $1-9.9 Million
Spice & Extract Mfr
N.A.I.C.S.: 311942
Mohamad Farbood (Founder)

Dan Kaffe (Malaysia) SDN. BHD (1)
7 Jalan Angkasa Mas 6 Kawasan Perindustrian Tebrau 2, Mukim Tebrau, 81100, Johor Bahru, Johor, Malaysia
Tel.: (60) 73536350
Web Site: https www.dankaffe.com
Emp.: 105
Coffee Mfr & Distr
N.A.I.C.S.: 311920

P.T. Takasago Indonesia (1)
Desa Tambaksogra Kecamatan Sumbang Purwokerto Kabupaten Banyumas, PO Box 11, Jawa Tengah, Purwokerto, 53183, Indonesia
Tel.: (62) 2816842838
Natural Ingredient Mfr
N.A.I.C.S.: 325199

PT. Takasago International Indonesia (1)
Foresta Business Loft 1 Unit 18-19 Jl BSD Raya Utama, Serpong, Tangerang, 15345, Indonesia
Tel.: (62) 2130407324
Personal Care Product Mfr
N.A.I.C.S.: 325620

Shanghai Takasago-Union Fragrances & Flavors Co., Ltd. (1)
516 Xiang Yang South Road, Shanghai, 200031, China
Tel.: (86) 2164374490
Fragrance Mfr & Distr
N.A.I.C.S.: 325620

Plant (Domestic):

Shanghai Takasago-Union Fragrances & Flavors Co., Ltd. - Shanghai Factory (2)
456 Kangyi Road Kangqiao Industrial Zone, Pudong, Shanghai, 201315, China
Tel.: (86) 2158122612
Fragrance Mfr
N.A.I.C.S.: 325620

Ste Cananga Sarl. (1)
Lot B1 N 99, Zone Industrielle Tassila Inezgane, 80650, Agadir, Morocco
Tel.: (212) 528832009
Personal Care Product Mfr
N.A.I.C.S.: 325620

Takasago (U.K.) Ltd. (1)
Scammell House 9 High Street, Ascot, SL5 7JF, Berkshire, United Kingdom
Tel.: (44) 1344874193
Fragrance Distr
N.A.I.C.S.: 424210

Takasago De Centroamerica S.A. (1)
Av Reforma 6-39 Zona 10 centro Coorporativo Guayacan Nivel 12, Officina 1201, 01001, Guatemala, Guatemala
Tel.: (502) 2386 1087
Chemical Products Distr
N.A.I.C.S.: 424690

Takasago De Mexico S.A. De C.V. (1)
16 De Septiembre No 98, 54075, Los Reyes, Tlalnepantla, Mexico
Tel.: (52) 5553900877
Chemical Product Mfr & Distr
N.A.I.C.S.: 325998
Deny Amador (Mgr-Flavour Application)

Takasago Europe G.m.b.H. (1)
Industriestrasse 40, 53909, Zulpich, Germany
Tel.: (49) 22529480
Chemical Product Mfr & Distr
N.A.I.C.S.: 325998
Paul-Henry Bonifay (Dir-Sls)

Takasago Europe G.m.b.H. (1)
12 Trubnaya Street, 107045, Moscow, Russia
Tel.: (7) 4957871797
Personal Care Product Mfr
N.A.I.C.S.: 325620

Takasago Europe Perfumery Laboratory S.A.R.L. (1)
12 Rue Torricelli, 75017, Paris, France
Tel.: (33) 140546500
Chemical Product Mfr & Distr
N.A.I.C.S.: 325998

Plant (Domestic):

Takasago Europe Perfumery Laboratory S.A.R.L. - Saint-Ouen l'Aumone Factory (2)
23-25 Avenue de la Mare, 95310, Saint-Ouen-l'Aumone, France
Tel.: (33) 134324444
Fragrance Mfr
N.A.I.C.S.: 325620

Takasago Europe Perfumery Laboratory S.A.R.L. (1)
2004 Clover Bay Tower Al Abraj Street, PO Box no 87253, Business Bay, Dubai, United Arab Emirates
Tel.: (971) 45512758
Personal Care Product Mfr
N.A.I.C.S.: 325620

Takasago Fragrancias E Aromas Ltda. (1)
Rua Francisco Foga 200 Distrito Indl, Vinhedo, 13288-166, SP, Brazil
Tel.: (55) 1938569500
Fragrance Mfr & Distr
N.A.I.C.S.: 325620

Takasago Import and Export (Thailand) Ltd. (1)
15th Floor Supalai Grand Tower 1011 Rama 3 Road, Chongnonsi Yannawa, Bangkok, 10120, Thailand
Tel.: (66) 26830119
Chemical Products Distr
N.A.I.C.S.: 424690

Takasago International (Deutschland) G.m.b.H. (1)
Industriestrasse 40, 53909, Zulpich, Germany
Tel.: (49) 22529480
Personal Care Product Mfr
N.A.I.C.S.: 325620

Takasago International (Espana) S.R.L. (1)
Rambla de Catalunya 91-93 7o-3a, 08008, Barcelona, Spain
Tel.: (34) 934877444
Fragrance Distr
N.A.I.C.S.: 424210

Takasago International (Guangzhou) Co., Ltd. (1)
57 Hefeng Road Yonghe Economic Zone of the Guangzhou, Economic & Technological Development District, Guangzhou, 511356, China
Tel.: (86) 2082986660
Chemical Products Distr
N.A.I.C.S.: 424690

Takasago International (India) Pvt. Ltd. (1)
198/2 Bye Pass Road, Poonamalle, Chennai, 600 056, Tamil Nadu, India
Tel.: (91) 44 6679 6500
Web Site: http://www.takasago.com
Emp.: 46
Chemical Product Mfr & Distr
N.A.I.C.S.: 325998
Shaheel Ttp (Mng Dir)

Takasago International (Italia) S.R.L. (1)
Via Manzoni 17, 20121, Milan, Italy
Tel.: (39) 024392911

TAKASAGO INTERNATIONAL CORPORATION

Takasago International Corporation—(Continued)

Fragrance Distr
N.A.I.C.S.: 424210

Takasago International (Malaysia) Sdn. Bhd. (1)
No 6 Jalan Kontraktor U1/14, Hicom Glenmarie Industrial Park, 40150, Shah Alam, Selangor, Malaysia
Tel.: (60) 355679505
Personal Care Product Mfr
N.A.I.C.S.: 325620

Takasago International (Philippines), Inc. (1)
4th Floor Tower 1 The Rockwell Business Center Ortigas Avenue, Pasig, 1604, Philippines
Tel.: (63) 284707867
Chemical Products Distr
N.A.I.C.S.: 424690
Joseph Victor Zablan (Asst Mgr-Sls)

Takasago International (Shanghai) Co., Ltd. (1)
516 Xiang Yang South Road, Shanghai, 200031, China
Tel.: (86) 2164374490
Personal Care Product Mfr
N.A.I.C.S.: 325620

Takasago International (Singapore) Pte. Ltd. (1)
5 Sunview Road, Singapore, 627616, Singapore
Tel.: (65) 67791077
Chemical Product Mfr & Distr
N.A.I.C.S.: 325998
Indah Arifin (Mgr-Bus Dev)

Takasago International (Singapore) Pte. Ltd. (1)
4th Floor 39B Truong Son Street Hai Au Building, Ward 4 Tan Binh District, Ho Chi Minh City, Vietnam
Tel.: (84) 2839979808
Personal Care Product Mfr
N.A.I.C.S.: 325620

Takasago International (Singapore) Pte. Ltd. (1)
No 59/A Aung Tagon Condominium Room - PH 9th Floor Top Floor, Aye Yeikthar 1st Street Bahan Township, Yangon, Myanmar
Tel.: (95) 9457494520
Personal Care Product Mfr
N.A.I.C.S.: 325620

Takasago International (Singapore) Pte. Ltd. (1)
Unit12 82-86 Pacific Highway, Saint Leonards, 2065, NSW, Australia
Tel.: (61) 299068801
Personal Care Product Mfr
N.A.I.C.S.: 325620

Takasago International Chemicals (Europe) S.A. (1)
Av De Mazarron N 49, El Palmar, 30120, Murcia, Spain
Tel.: (34) 968889920
Chemical Product Mfr & Distr
N.A.I.C.S.: 325998
Antonio Ruiz Toral (Engr-Process)

Takasago International Corp. (1)
4 Volvo Dr, Rockleigh, NJ 07647-0932
Tel.: (201) 767-9001
Web Site: http://www.takasago.com
Emp.: 250
Chemical Product Mfr & Distr
N.A.I.C.S.: 325998

Plant (Domestic):

Takasago International Corp. - Flavor Factory (2)
100 Green St, Teterboro, NJ 07608
Tel.: (201) 767-4262
Chemical Products Mfr
N.A.I.C.S.: 325998

Takasago International Corp. - Harriman Fragrance Factory (2)
114 Commerce Dr, Harriman, NY 10926
Tel.: (845) 751-0600
Web Site: http://www.takasago.com
Emp.: 100

Fragrance Mfr
N.A.I.C.S.: 325620
Hisaya Fujiwara (Sr VP)

Takasago International Corp. - Northvale Fragrance Factory (2)
114 Commerce Dr S, Harriman, NY 10926
Tel.: (201) 767-9001
Fragrance Mfr
N.A.I.C.S.: 325620

Takasago International Corporation (1)
8F-3 No 22 Nanking West Road, Taipei, 10352, Taiwan
Tel.: (886) 225580935
Personal Care Product Mfr
N.A.I.C.S.: 325620

Takasago International Corporation (1)
A-806 11 Beobwon-ro 11-gil, Songpa-gu, Seoul, 05836, Korea (South)
Tel.: (82) 221445620
Personal Care Product Mfr
N.A.I.C.S.: 325620

Takasago International Corporation South Africa (Pty) Ltd. (1)
Building 6 Upper Floor Thornhill Office Park 94 Bekker road, Vorna Vally, Midrand, 1685, South Africa
Tel.: (27) 113157740
Web Site: http://www.takasago.com
Emp.: 6
Fragrance Distr
N.A.I.C.S.: 424210
Conrad Edwards (Mng Dir)

Takasago International Turkey Esans ve Aroma San. Tic. A.S. (1)
Buyaka-2 Sitesi Kule 2 Kat 17, Umraniye, 34771, Istanbul, Turkiye
Tel.: (90) 2162903606
Web Site: http://www.takasago.com
Fragrance Distr
N.A.I.C.S.: 424210

Takasago Madagascar S.A. (1)
24 Rue Ratsimilaho, Antaninarenina, 101, Antananarivo, Madagascar
Tel.: (261) 202222044
Vanilla Extract Mfr
N.A.I.C.S.: 311942

Takasago Morocco (Societe Cananga S.A.R.L.) (1)
Lot B1 N 99 Zone Industrielle Tassila Inezgane, Dcheira, Agadir, Morocco
Tel.: (212) 528832009
Vanilla Extract Mfr
N.A.I.C.S.: 311942

Xiamen Hua Ri Foods Industrial Co., Ltd. (1)
No 1355 Tongji Middle Road, Xiamen, 361100, China
Tel.: (86) 5927572152
Food Products Distr
N.A.I.C.S.: 424690

TAKASAGO TEKKO K.K.
1-1-1 Shinkawagishi, Itabashi-ku, Tokyo, 175-0081, Japan
Tel.: (81) 353998111
Web Site: https://www.takasago-t.co.jp
Year Founded: 1923
5458—(TKS)
Rev.: $80,516,410
Assets: $63,845,990
Liabilities: $34,722,330
Net Worth: $29,123,660
Earnings: $1,546,740
Emp.: 142
Fiscal Year-end: 03/31/24
Stainless Steel Products Mfr
N.A.I.C.S.: 331221
Masaki Hatada (Mng Dir-Accounting)

Subsidiaries:

TAKASAGO STEEL CO., LTD. (1)
2-3-28 Nishi-zutsumi-hondori-nishi, Higashi, Osaka, 577-0046, Japan
Tel.: (81) 667852100
Stainless Steel Products Mfr

N.A.I.C.S.: 331221

TAKATETSU LIFE CO., LTD. (1)
1-1-1 Shingashi, Itabashi-ku, Tokyo, 175-0081, Japan
Tel.: (81) 425552326
Stainless Steel Products Mfr
N.A.I.C.S.: 331221

TAKASAGO THERMAL ENGINEERING CO., LTD.
6-27-30 Shinjuku, Shinjuku-Ku, Tokyo, 160-0022, Japan
Tel.: (81) 363698212
Web Site: https://www.tte-net.com
Year Founded: 1923
1969—(TKS)
Rev.: $2,401,849,260
Assets: $2,248,100,660
Liabilities: $1,142,703,750
Net Worth: $1,105,396,910
Earnings: $129,635,320
Emp.: 2,230
Fiscal Year-end: 03/31/24
Plumbing, Heating & Air-Conditioning Products Mfr
N.A.I.C.S.: 333415
Susumu Hashimoto (Exec Officer & Gen Mgr-Tohoku Branch)

Subsidiaries:

CEEDI Takasago Engineering & Consulting Co., Ltd. (1)
No 27 Wanshou Road, Haidian District, Beijing, 100840, China
Tel.: (86) 1068207546
Web Site: http://www.tte.co.jp
Sales Range: $25-49.9 Million
Emp.: 15
Engineering Consulting Services
N.A.I.C.S.: 541330

Hucoss Co., Ltd. (1)
Higashi Ote Building 1-1-7 Uchikanda, Chiyoda-ku, Tokyo, 101-0047, Japan
Tel.: (81) 332926680
Web Site: https://hucoss.tte-net.com
Fire Insurance Services
N.A.I.C.S.: 524210

Integrated Cleanroom Technologies Pvt. Ltd. (1)
201 Sri Vensai Towers Varuna Block, Kompally, Hyderabad, 500 014, Telangana, India (56.4%)
Tel.: (91) 4027165311
Web Site: https://www.icleantech.com
Air Conditioning Equipment Mfr
N.A.I.C.S.: 333415
Gopi Katamaneni (Mng Dir)

Ishikari Atsuta Green Energy Co., Ltd. (1)
4-1 Kita 3-Jo Nishi, Chuo-Ku Hokkaido, Sapporo, 060-0003, Japan
Tel.: (81) 112612531
Power Supply Services
N.A.I.C.S.: 532490

Kazusa Environmental Research Center Co., Ltd. (1)
2-12 Shiomi, Kisarazu, 292-0834, Chiba, Japan
Tel.: (81) 438365001
Web Site: https://www.kazusakankyo.co.jp
Emp.: 90
Environmental Consulting Services
N.A.I.C.S.: 541620

Kiyota Kougyo Co., Ltd. (1)
5F Ozawa Building 3-4-14 Higashi Nihonbashi, Chuo-ku, Tokyo, 103-0004, Japan
Tel.: (81) 336623661
Web Site: https://www.kiyota.co.jp
Emp.: 67
Engineeering Services
N.A.I.C.S.: 541330

Nihon Kaihatsu Kosan Co., Ltd. (1)
NK Building 3-6-2 Kanda-Ogawamachi, Chiyoda-ku, Tokyo, 101-0052, Japan
Tel.: (81) 3 3292 6680
Plumbing, Heating & Air-Conditioning Equipment Mfr
N.A.I.C.S.: 333415

INTERNATIONAL PUBLIC

Nihon Setsubi Kogyo Co., Ltd. (1)
Daiwa River Gate 19F 36-2 Nihonbashi Hakozakicho, Chuo-ku, Tokyo, 103-0015, Japan
Tel.: (81) 342134900
Web Site: https://www.nihonsetsubi.co.jp
Emp.: 375
Plumbing, Heating & Air-Conditioning Equipment Mfr
N.A.I.C.S.: 333415

Nippon Development Kosan Co., Ltd. (1)
Higashi Ote Building 1-1-7 Uchikanda, Chiyoda-ku, Tokyo, 101-0047, Japan
Tel.: (81) 332926680
Web Site: https://hucoss.tte-net.com
Temporary Staffing Services
N.A.I.C.S.: 561320

Nippon Floda Co., Ltd. (1)
Yamajin Building 1-1 Kanda-Ogawamachi, Chiyoda-ku, Tokyo, 101-0052, Japan
Tel.: (81) 3 5282 7800
Plumbing, Heating & Air-Conditioning Equipment Mfr
N.A.I.C.S.: 333415

Nippon PMAC Co., Ltd. (1)
Toranomon 37 Mori Bldg 3-5-1 Toranomon, Minato, Tokyo, 105-0001, Japan
Tel.: (81) 354731426
Web Site: https://usa.pmac.co.jp
Plumbing, Heating & Air-Conditioning Equipment Mfr
N.A.I.C.S.: 333415

PT. Takasago Thermal Engineering (1)
Gedung Mugi Griya Jl MT Haryono Kav 10 5th Floor Unit 506, Tebet, Jakarta Selatan, 12810, Indonesia
Tel.: (62) 2183708518
Web Site: https://www.takasago.co.id
Air Conditioning & Ventilation Services
N.A.I.C.S.: 238220

T.T.E. Engineering (Malaysia) Sdn. Bhd. (1)
4th Floor Menara Choy Fook On Jalan Yong Shook Lin, Petaling Jaya, 46050, Selangor, Malaysia (100%)
Tel.: (60) 379555972
Web Site: http://www.ttemalayasia.com.my
Sales Range: $25-49.9 Million
Emp.: 40
Engineeering Services
N.A.I.C.S.: 541330
Keiichi Asano (Mng Dir)

TMES Corporation (1)
4-13-23 Shibaura MS Shibaura Building 8F, Minato-ku, Tokyo, 108-0023, Japan
Tel.: (81) 334553600
Web Site: https://www.tm-es.co.jp
Emp.: 1,404
Building Cleaning Services
N.A.I.C.S.: 561720

Takasago Constructors & Engineers (Beijing) Co., Ltd. (1)
26GHI Oriental Kenzo Plaza 48 Dong Zhimengwai Street, Dongcheng, Beijing, 100027, China
Tel.: (86) 51268092986
Web Site: https://takasago.cn
Sales Range: $25-49.9 Million
Emp.: 190
Engineeering Services
N.A.I.C.S.: 541330
Sun Tiebin (Deputy Mng Dir)

Takasago Constructors and Engineers (China) Co., Ltd. (1)
26GHI Oriental Kenzo Plaza 48 Dong Zhimengwai Street, Dongcheng District, Beijing, China
Tel.: (86) 51268092986
Web Site: https://takasago.cn
Emp.: 190
Construction Engineering Services
N.A.I.C.S.: 541330

Takasago Engineering Mexico, S.A. de C.V. (1)
Anillo Vial II Fray Junipero Serra No 2601 4th F Colonia, Juriquilla Santa fe, 76230, Queretaro, Mexico
Tel.: (52) 14422171054

Web Site: https://www.takasago-mexico.com
Emp.: 45
Engineeering Services
N.A.I.C.S.: 541330
Ayumu Kondo *(Pres)*

Takasago Marusei Engineering Service Co., Ltd. (1)
Sasazuka Center Building 2-1-6 Sasazuka, Shibuya-ku, Tokyo, 151-0073, Japan
Tel.: (81) 3 5308 6511
Plumbing, Heating & Air-Conditioning Equipment Mfr
N.A.I.C.S.: 333415

Takasago Singapore Pte. Ltd. (1)
1 Jalan Kilang Timor 08-01, Pacific Tech Center, Singapore, 159303, Singapore
Tel.: (65) 67373312
Web Site: https://www.takasago.com.sg
Emp.: 96
Highway & Street Construction
N.A.I.C.S.: 237310

Takasago Thermal Engineering (Hong Kong) Co., Ltd. (1)
Unit A 15/F Yardley Commercial Building No 3 Connaught Road West, Hong Kong, China (Hong Kong)
Tel.: (852) 25202403
Web Site: https://www.takasago.com.hk
Sales Range: $25-49.9 Million
Emp.: 20
Plumbing Heating & Air-Conditioning Contractors
N.A.I.C.S.: 238220

Takasago Thermal Engineering Co., Ltd. (1)
Unit 501 & 502 Aurira Business Tower No 40 No 1 Industrial Road, Bahan Township, Yangon, Myanmar
Tel.: (95) 9457598770
Web Site: https://www.takasagomyanmar.com.mm
Air Conditioning & Ventilation Services
N.A.I.C.S.: 238220
Atsushi Ouchi *(Chm & CEO)*

Takasago Vietnam Co., Ltd. (1)
19th Floor IDMC My Dinh Building No 15 Pham Hung Street, My Dinh 2 Ward Nam Tu Liem District, Hanoi, Vietnam
Tel.: (84) 2462751932
Web Site: https://takasago.vn
Air Conditioning & Ventilation Services
N.A.I.C.S.: 238220

Thai Takasago Co., Ltd. (1)
Bangna Towers C 16th Fl 40/14 Moo 12 Bangna-Trad Rd, Bangkaew, Bang Phli, 10540, Samutprakarn, Thailand
Tel.: (66) 275196959
Web Site: https://www.thaitakasago.co.th
Sales Range: $25-49.9 Million
Emp.: 106
Engineeering Services
N.A.I.C.S.: 541330

Tomakomai Heat Supply Co., Ltd. (1)
1-11-25 Taiseicho, Tomakomai, 053-0806, Hokkaido, Japan
Tel.: (81) 144721216
Web Site: https://www.tomanetsu.co.jp
Emp.: 30
Heating Equipment Distr
N.A.I.C.S.: 423720

TAKASE CORPORATION
4-9-17 Tokai, Ota-ku, Tokyo, 143-0001, Japan
Tel.: (81) 337999111
Web Site: https://www.takase.co.jp
Year Founded: 1872
9087—(TKS)
Rev.: $54,135,900
Assets: $65,491,880
Liabilities: $17,734,630
Net Worth: $47,757,250
Earnings: $2,016,050
Emp.: 72
Fiscal Year-end: 03/31/24
Cargo Handling Services
N.A.I.C.S.: 488320
Fumio Daiguji *(Co-Pres)*

Subsidiaries:

ADD SYSTEM CO., LTD. (1)
20F Yue Thai Commercial Bldg 128 Connaught Road, Central, China (Hong Kong)
Tel.: (852) 2547 9653
Logistics Consulting Servies
N.A.I.C.S.: 541614

TAKASE ADD SYSTEM (SHANGHAI) INC. (1)
8th Floor Eastern Tower 689 Beijing Road, Huangpu District, Shanghai, China
Tel.: (86) 21 6360 1751
Logistics Consulting Servies
N.A.I.C.S.: 541614

TAKASE ADD SYSTEM, INC. (1)
1920 Obisco Ave, Long Beach, CA 90804
Tel.: (562) 597-4900
Logistics Consulting Servies
N.A.I.C.S.: 541614
Tom Mullins *(Asst VP)*

TAKASHIMA & CO., LTD.
Ochanomizu Kyoun Bldg 12F 2-2 Kanda Surugadai, Chiyoda-ku, Tokyo, 101-8118, Japan
Tel.: (81) 352177600
Web Site: https://www.tak.co.jp
Year Founded: 1915
8007—(TKS)
Rev.: $595,693,200
Assets: $399,303,490
Liabilities: $243,452,910
Net Worth: $155,850,580
Earnings: $31,939,520
Emp.: 1,162
Fiscal Year-end: 03/31/24
Building Materials Whslr
N.A.I.C.S.: 423390
Koichi Takashima *(Pres)*

Subsidiaries:

Hi-Land Techno Corporation (1)
1544 Yotsukumachi, Nasushiobara, 329-2746, Tochigi, Japan
Tel.: (81) 287374146
Textile Products Distr
N.A.I.C.S.: 424990

Kitasan kowa Co., Ltd. (1)
6-1-6 Nijuyonkensanjo, Nishi-ku, Sapporo, 063-0803, Hokkaido, Japan
Tel.: (81) 11 631 8590
Industrial Fabric Whslr
N.A.I.C.S.: 424310

Ono Sangyo Co., Ltd. (1)
600 Hongo Nishikata-cho, Tochigi, 322-0603, Japan
Tel.: (81) 282 920091
Web Site: http://www.onosg.co.jp
Emp.: 165
Plastics Product Mfr
N.A.I.C.S.: 326199
Tsutomu Miyamoto *(Pres & Dir)*

SUZUKI SOLAR TECHNO Corp. (1)
2-3-10 Mikawa Anjo Higashicho, Anjo, 446-0057, Aichi, Japan
Tel.: (81) 566913880
Web Site: https://powerbase.tak.co.jp
Mounting Clamp Mfr
N.A.I.C.S.: 333515

T Medical Service Inc. (1)
Shintomi191 Bldg 1-9-1 Shintomi, Chuo, 104-0041, Tokyo, Japan
Tel.: (81) 3 3553 0311
Web Site: http://www.tak.co.jp
Medical Equipment Distr
N.A.I.C.S.: 423450

TAK Green Service Co., Ltd. (1)
7-12-14 2F Tsukiji, Chuo, 104-0045, Tokyo, Japan
Tel.: (81) 3 6737 1248
Web Site: http://www.tak-green.co.jp
Electric Component Whslr
N.A.I.C.S.: 423610

TAKASHIMA MITSUGI PF (THAILAND) CO., LTD. (1)
1234 Moo 13 Klong Neung, Klong Luang, Pathumthani, 12120, Thailand
Tel.: (66) 2908 1772

Packaging Material Whslr
N.A.I.C.S.: 423840

Takashima (U.S.A.), Inc. (1)
18010 Sky Park Cir Ste 145, Irvine, CA 92614
Tel.: (949) 825-6126
Web Site: https://www.takashimausa.com
Industrial Supplies Distr
N.A.I.C.S.: 423840
Hiroyuki Ishikawa *(Pres)*

Takashima Home Service Corp. (1)
Ochanomizu kyoun Bldg 2-2 Kandasurugadai, Chiyoda-ku, Tokyo, 101-8118, Japan
Tel.: (81) 3 3295 7232
Real Estate Maintenance Services
N.A.I.C.S.: 531390

iTak (International) Limited (1)
Room 2613 26F North Tower Concordia Plaza No 1 Science Museum Road, TST East, Kowloon, China (Hong Kong)
Tel.: (852) 27826661
Web Site: https://itak.co.jp
Emp.: 27
Electronic Components Distr
N.A.I.C.S.: 423690

iTak International (Shanghai) Limited (1)
Room 1303 Shanghai International Group Mansion No 511, Wei Hai Road, Shanghai, 200041, China
Tel.: (86) 2162555051
Web Site: https://itak.co.jp
Electric Component Whslr
N.A.I.C.S.: 423690

iTak International (Shenzhen) Limited (1)
Room 2003 20F Development Center Bldg 2010 Renmin South Rd, Shenzhen, 518001, China
Tel.: (86) 75582234467
Web Site: https://itak.co.jp
Emp.: 37
Electronic Components Mfr
N.A.I.C.S.: 335999

iTak International (Thailand) Ltd. (1)
Room 1207 BB Building 54 Sukhumvit 21 Asoke Rd, Klongtoey-Nua Wattana, Bangkok, 10110, Thailand
Tel.: (66) 266443902
Emp.: 44
Electric Component Whslr
N.A.I.C.S.: 423690

TAKASHIMAYA COMPANY, LIMITED
5-1-5 Namba, Chuo-ku, Osaka, 542-8510, Japan
Tel.: (81) 666311101 JP
Web Site: https://www.takashimaya.co.jp
Year Founded: 1831
8233—(TKS)
Rev.: $3,304,890,060
Assets: $9,007,667,750
Liabilities: $5,612,961,570
Net Worth: $3,394,706,180
Earnings: $224,185,800
Emp.: 10,768
Fiscal Year-end: 02/29/24
Department Stores
N.A.I.C.S.: 455110
Koji Suzuki *(Chm)*

Subsidiaries:

A.T.A. Co., Ltd. (1)
2-12-10 Nihonbashi Takashimaya Group Headquarters Building 3rd Floor, Chuo-ku, Tokyo, 103-0027, Japan
Tel.: (81) 33 246 6750
Web Site: https://www.ata.co.jp
Advertising Agency Services
N.A.I.C.S.: 541810

Dayeh Takashimaya Department Store, Inc. (1)
11148 No 55 Section 2 Zhongcheng Road, Shilin District, Taipei, Taiwan
Tel.: (886) 28312345
Web Site: http://www.dayeh-takashimaya.com.tw

High-End Department Stores
N.A.I.C.S.: 459999

Good Liive Co., Ltd. (1)
2-12-10 Nihonbashi, Chuo-ku, Tokyo, 103-0027, Japan
Tel.: (81) 35 205 6137
Web Site: https://www.goodlive.co.jp
Alcoholic Beverages Whslr
N.A.I.C.S.: 424820

Taipei Takashimaya International Co., Ltd. (1)
Loyalty Road 55, Taipei, 2, Shihlin District, Taiwan
Tel.: (886) 228312345
Department Stores
N.A.I.C.S.: 455110

Takashimaya (France) S.A. (1)
3 Rue De Castellane, 75008, Paris, France **(100%)**
Tel.: (33) 147421450
Web Site: http://www.takashimaya.com
Sales Range: $50-74.9 Million
Department Store Operations
N.A.I.C.S.: 455110
Ito Satoshi *(Gen Mgr)*

Takashimaya Enterprises, Inc. (Shiro of Japan) (1)
401 Old Country Rd, Carle Place, NY 11514-2122
Tel.: (516) 997-4770
Web Site: http://www.shiroofjapan.com
Department Stores
N.A.I.C.S.: 455110

Takashimaya Financial Partners Co., Ltd. (1)
2-4-1 Nihonbashi, Chuo-ku, Tokyo, Japan
Tel.: (81) 33 668 1700
Web Site: https://www.takashimaya-fp.co.jp
Credit Card Business Services
N.A.I.C.S.: 522320

Takashimaya Hong Kong Enterprises Limited (1)
Room 1804 18th Floor All ledkhaima Building, 138 Glloueesper Road, Wanchai, China (Hong Kong) **(100%)**
Tel.: (852) 28611183
Web Site: http://www.takashimaya.com
Sales Range: $50-74.9 Million
Emp.: 3
Department Store Operations
N.A.I.C.S.: 455110

Takashimaya Service Co., Ltd. (1)
2-12-7 Nihombashikayabacho Koueiikayabacho Bldg 6f, Chuo-ku, Tokyo, 103-0025, Japan
Tel.: (81) 336687370
Department Stores Operation Services
N.A.I.C.S.: 455110

Takashimaya Singapore Ltd. (1)
391A Orchard Road, Singapore, 238873, Singapore **(100%)**
Tel.: (65) 67381111
Web Site: https://www.takashimaya.com.sg
Sales Range: $150-199.9 Million
Department Stores
N.A.I.C.S.: 455110
Masahiro Yoshino *(Gen Mgr)*

Takashimaya Vietnam Ltd. (1)
92-94 Nam Ky Khoi Nghia Street, Ben Nghe Ward District 1, Ho Chi Minh City, Vietnam
Tel.: (84) 2838211819
Web Site: https://takashimaya-vn.com
Shopping Mall Management Services
N.A.I.C.S.: 531120

Toshin Development Co. Ltd. (1)
391b 3023-04-06 Ngee Ann City Orchard Rd 04 20 E, Singapore, 238874, Singapore **(100%)**
Tel.: (65) 67326631
Sales Range: $25-49.9 Million
Emp.: 25
Department Store Operations
N.A.I.C.S.: 455110
Toshikazu Takahashi *(Mgr-Fin)*

TAKASHO CO.,LTD.
20-1 Minamiakasaka, Kainan, 642-0017, Wakayama, Japan

TAKASHO CO., LTD.

Takasho Co., Ltd.—(Continued)
Tel.: (81) 734824128
Web Site: https://takasho.co.jp
Year Founded: 1980
7590—(TKS)
Rev.: $137,623,990
Assets: $164,020,060
Liabilities: $75,402,150
Net Worth: $88,617,910
Earnings: ($531,750)
Emp.: 479
Fiscal Year-end: 01/31/24
Outdoor Product Mfr
N.A.I.C.S.: 339999
Nobuo Takaoka (CEO)

Subsidiaries:

Aoyama Garden Co., Ltd. (1)
Azabu Point 302 4-22-8, Nishiazabu
Minato-ku, Tokyo, Japan
Tel.: (81) 120494128
Web Site: https://aoyama-garden.com
Beauty Product Distr
N.A.I.C.S.: 424120

Nara Garden Create Co. Ltd (1)
527-5 Natsuaki, Nabari, 518-0731, Mie, Japan
Tel.: (81) 595611021
Garden Supplies Whslr
N.A.I.C.S.: 424910

Takasho Australasia Pty Ltd. (1)
32 Mickle street, Dandenong, 3175, VIC, Australia
Tel.: (61) 397064438
Web Site: https://www.takasho.com.au
Garden Supplies Whslr
N.A.I.C.S.: 424910

Takasho Garden Living India Pte. Ltd. (1)
E-17 Siddhi Vinayak business Towers Behind DCP Office Off S G Highway, Makarba, Ahmedabad, Gujarat, India
Tel.: (91) 8401118322
Web Site: https://www.takasho.in
Garden Product Mfr & Distr
N.A.I.C.S.: 333112

VegTrug USA Inc. (1)
1900 Bethlehem Pike Ste 130, Hatfield, PA 19440
Garden Product Mfr & Distr
N.A.I.C.S.: 333112

Wakayama Garden Create Co. Ltd (1)
400 Onoda, Kainan, 642-0014, Wakayama, Japan
Tel.: (81) 734870184
Garden Supplies Whslr
N.A.I.C.S.: 424910

TAKATORI CORPORATION

313-1 Shindo-cho, Kashihara, 634-8580, Nara, Japan
Tel.: (81) 744248580
Web Site: https://www.takatori-g.co.jp
Year Founded: 1950
6338—(TKS)
Rev.: $116,042,030
Assets: $127,910,690
Liabilities: $69,900,310
Net Worth: $58,010,380
Earnings: $13,520,630
Emp.: 240
Fiscal Year-end: 09/30/23
Electric Equipment Mfr
N.A.I.C.S.: 334413

Subsidiaries:

MTC Co., Ltd. (1)
4-705-1 Sakuragichou, Omiya-ku, Saitama, 330-0854, Saitama-ken, Japan
Tel.: (81) 486507510
Web Site: https://www.mtcinfo.co.jp
Semiconductor Machinery Mfr & Distr
N.A.I.C.S.: 333242
Hidekazu Tamaki (Pres)

Plant (Domestic):

MTC Co., Ltd. - Nagaoka Factory (2)
2-2-29 Higashitakami, Nagaoka, Niigata-ken, Japan
Tel.: (81) 258227900
Semiconductor Machinery Mfr & Distr
N.A.I.C.S.: 333242

TAKBO GROUP HOLDINGS LIMITED

35/F EGL Tower 83 Hung To Road Kwun Tong, Kowloon, China (Hong Kong)
Tel.: (852) 26628098   Ky
Web Site: http://www.takbogroup.com
Year Founded: 1994
8436—(HKG)
Rev.: $26,685,750
Assets: $33,584,393
Liabilities: $4,933,358
Net Worth: $28,651,035
Earnings: $128,520
Emp.: 160
Fiscal Year-end: 12/31/22
Beauty Products Mfr & Distr
N.A.I.C.S.: 325620
Naam Or (Founder & CEO)

Subsidiaries:

B&B (H.K.) Limited (1)
83 Tung Wan Road, Cheung Chau, Hong Kong, China (Hong Kong)
Tel.: (852) 29869990
Web Site: https://ibnb.hk
Reservation Services
N.A.I.C.S.: 561599

TAKE AND GIVE. NEEDS CO. LTD.

Seafort Square Center Bldg 17F
2-3-12 Higashi-Shinagawa, Shinagawa-ku, Tokyo, 140-0002, Japan
Tel.: (81) 368331122
Web Site: https://www.tgn.co.jp
Year Founded: 1998
4331—(TKS)
Rev.: $310,802,200
Assets: $359,451,800
Liabilities: $247,326,370
Net Worth: $112,125,430
Earnings: $12,102,910
Emp.: 1,661
Fiscal Year-end: 03/31/24
Wedding Ceremonial Services
N.A.I.C.S.: 812990
Yoshitaka Nojiri (Chm)

Subsidiaries:

And Company Co., Ltd. (1)
17th Floor Seafort Square Center Building
2-3-12 Higashi-Shinagawa, Shinagawa-ku, Tokyo, 140-0002, Japan
Tel.: (81) 33 471 6751
Web Site: https://www.monohoiku.jp
Nursery School Services
N.A.I.C.S.: 624410

Anniversary Travel Co., Ltd. (1)
Seafort Square Center Building 16F 2-3-12 Higashi-Shinagawa, Shinagawa-ku, Tokyo, 140-0002, Japan
Tel.: (81) 357818070
Web Site: https://www.anniversary-t.com
Sales Range: $25-49.9 Million
Emp.: 25
Tour Operator
N.A.I.C.S.: 561520

GOODLUCK Corporation Co., Ltd. (1)
1-1-71 Nakameguro, Meguro-ku, Tokyo, 153-0061, Japan
Tel.: (81) 357251133
Web Site: https://www.goodluck-corp.com
Emp.: 311
Wedding Planner Services
N.A.I.C.S.: 812990

Gentle Co., Ltd. (1)
5-47-6 Jinguma, Shibuya-ku, Tokyo, Japan
Tel.: (81) 36 897 3777
Web Site: https://www.gentle-base.com
Restaurant Operators
N.A.I.C.S.: 722511

Life Angel Co., Ltd. (1)
Sea Fort Square Center Building 16F
2-3-12 Higashi-Shinagawa, Shinagawa-ku, Tokyo, 140-0002, Japan
Tel.: (81) 12 069 8515
Web Site: https://www.lifeangel.jp
Installment Payment Services
N.A.I.C.S.: 522210

Take and Give. Arts Co., Ltd. (1)
5-9-20-101 Roppongi Minato-Ku, Tokyo, 106-0032, Japan
Tel.: (81) 3 5414 3227
Web Site: http://www.t-g-arts.com
Party Planning Services
N.A.I.C.S.: 812990

TAKE OFF S.P.A.

Z I Via Baione 272/D, 70043, Monopoli, BA, Italy
Tel.: (39) 0804176645   IT
Web Site: https://takeoffoutlet.com
Year Founded: 2003
TKF—(EUR)
Rev.: $32,424,265
Assets: $57,286,217
Liabilities: $28,233,262
Net Worth: $29,052,955
Earnings: $6,926,429
Emp.: 219
Fiscal Year-end: 12/31/21
Clothing Accessories Retailer
N.A.I.C.S.: 424350
Aldo Piccarreta (Chm)

TAKE SOLUTIONS LIMITED

No 27 Tank Bund Road Nungambakkam, Chennai, 600034, India
Tel.: (91) 4466110700   In
Web Site: https://www.takesolutions.com
Year Founded: 2000
532890—(BOM)
Rev.: $313,500,320
Assets: $347,655,420
Liabilities: $125,700,820
Net Worth: $221,954,600
Earnings: ($1,531,880)
Emp.: 1,297
Fiscal Year-end: 03/31/20
Business Technology Solutions
N.A.I.C.S.: 541690
Avaneesh Singh (Sec)

Subsidiaries:

APA Engineering Private Ltd. (1)
No E-7 8 9 & 10 Gem & Jewellery Complex Phase- 1 MEPZ - Spl Eco Zone, Tambaram, Chennai, 600 045, Tamil Nadu, India
Tel.: (91) 4466922800
Web Site: http://www.apaengineering.com
Sales Range: $25-49.9 Million
Outsource Consulting Services
N.A.I.C.S.: 541618
K. Vaidyanathan (CEO)

Ecron Acunova Limited (1)
Mobius Towers Sjr -I Park Epip, Whitefield, Bengaluru, 560066, India
Tel.: (91) 8043515700
Web Site: https://www.ecronacunova.com
Clinical Research & Development Services
N.A.I.C.S.: 541715

Navitas Data Sciences Inc. (1)
502 Carnegie Ctr Ste 102, Princeton, NJ 08540
Tel.: (609) 720-1002
Web Site: https://www.navitaslifesciences.com
Research Services
N.A.I.C.S.: 541715
Avaneesh Singh (Chief Legal Officer & Sr VP-Legal)

Navitas LLP (1)
No 56 Ragas Building Dr Radhakrishnan Salai, Mylapore, Chennai, 600004, India
Tel.: (91) 4466110700
Digital Health Care Services
N.A.I.C.S.: 621610

INTERNATIONAL PUBLIC

TAKE Solutions, Inc. (1)
502 Carnegie Ctr Ste 102, Princeton, NJ 08540
Tel.: (609) 720-1002
Web Site: http://www.takesolutions.com
Business Technology Solutions; Life Sciences & Supply Chain Management
N.A.I.C.S.: 541690

TAKE United Sdn Bhd (1)
910 Block F Phileo Damansara 1 9 Jalan 16/11 Off Jalan Damansara, 46350, Petaling Jaya, Selangor Darul Ehsen, Malaysia
Tel.: (60) 376653911
Web Site: http://www.takesupplychain.com
IT Solutions & Services
N.A.I.C.S.: 541511

TOWELL TAKE Solutions LLC (1)
Musandam Building 5th Floor, PO Box 270, 112, Ruwi, Oman
Tel.: (968) 24794550
Web Site: http://www.towelltake.com
Sales Range: $25-49.9 Million
Business Consulting Services
N.A.I.C.S.: 541618

TAKEBISHI CORPORATION

29 Nishikyogoku Mameda cho, Ukyo-ku, Kyoto, 615-8501, Japan
Tel.: (81) 753252111
Web Site: https://www.takebishi.co.jp
Year Founded: 1926
7510—(TKS)
Rev.: $669,956,550
Assets: $430,522,520
Liabilities: $172,197,110
Net Worth: $258,325,410
Earnings: $16,531,610
Emp.: 813
Fiscal Year-end: 03/31/24
Automation Equipment Mfr & Software Developer
N.A.I.C.S.: 333921

Subsidiaries:

First Brain Co., Ltd. (1)
Minami-Shinagawa JN Bld 2F 2-2-13 Minami-Shinagawa, Shinagawa-ku, Tokyo, 140-0004, Japan
Tel.: (81) 364330963
Semiconductor Equipment Mfr
N.A.I.C.S.: 333242

Fuji Telecoms Co., Ltd. (1)
Nagahori Fuji Building 1-11-26 Minamisenba, Chuo-ku, Osaka, 542-0081, Japan
Tel.: (81) 662642224
Web Site: https://www.fujitelecoms.jp
Emp.: 150
Mobile Phone Equipment Whslr
N.A.I.C.S.: 449210

Le Champ (South East Asia) Pte Ltd. (1)
3 Jalan Mesin, Singapore, 368810, Singapore
Tel.: (65) 62728877
Web Site: https://www.lechamp.com.sg
Electronic Equipment Distr
N.A.I.C.S.: 423690

TS Engineering Co., Ltd. (1)
24-1 Daimon-cho Nishi-kyogoku, Ukyo-ku, Kyoto, 615-0812, Japan
Tel.: (81) 753123900
Semiconductor Equipment Mfr
N.A.I.C.S.: 333242

Takebishi (Thailand) Co., Ltd. (1)
28F Sathorn Square Office Tower 98 North Sathorn Road Silom Bangrak, Bangkok, 10500, Thailand
Tel.: (66) 20231588
Web Site: https://www.takebishi.co.jp
Electronic Equipment Distr
N.A.I.C.S.: 423690

Takebishi Electric Sales Hong Kong Limited (1)
2106 21F AIA TOWER 183 Electric Road, Fortress Hill, China (Hong Kong)
Tel.: (852) 25061857
Web Site: https://www.takebishi.co.jp
Electronic Equipment Distr

AND PRIVATE COMPANIES

N.A.I.C.S.: 423690

Takebishi Electric Sales Shanghai Limited (1)
ROOM F 22 Floor Huarun building No 500 Zhangyang Road, Shanghai, 200122, China
Tel.: (86) 2168756680
Web Site: http://www.takebishi.co.jp
Electronic Equipment Distr
N.A.I.C.S.: 423690

Takebishi Europe B.V. (1)
World Trade Center Amsterdam Tower A-12th floor Strawinskylaan 1219, 1077 XX, Amsterdam, Netherlands
Tel.: (31) 207055150
Web Site: http://www.takebishi.nl
Electronic Equipment Distr
N.A.I.C.S.: 423690
Masanori Nishida (Pres)

Takebishi Vietnam Co., Ltd. (1)
Floor 608 Me Linh Point Tower 2 Ngo Duc Ke Street, Ben Nghe Ward District 1, Ho Chi Minh City, Vietnam
Tel.: (84) 2835202793
Electronic Equipment Supplier
N.A.I.C.S.: 423690

Umezawa Musen Denki co.,Ltd. (1)
Ferris Building 4F 2-3-14 Kajicho, Chiyoda-ku, Tokyo, 101-0044, Japan
Tel.: (81) 332564491
Web Site: https://www.umezawa.co.jp
Emp.: 34
Semiconductor Mfr
N.A.I.C.S.: 334515

TAKEDA IP HOLDINGS CO.,LTD.
1-11-10 Shirokane Showa, Nagoya, 466-8512, Japan
Tel.: (81) 528716351
Web Site: https://www.takeda-prn.co.jp
7875—(NGO)
Rev.: $209,243,417
Assets: $208,047,514
Liabilities: $93,168,127
Net Worth: $114,879,386
Earnings: $5,622,727
Fiscal Year-end: 03/31/24
Book Printing & Publishing Services
N.A.I.C.S.: 513130

Subsidiaries:

Dalian Guanghua Software And Technology Co., Ltd. (1)
No 8 Room 608 6th Floor Building A Softscape Center, No1A - 4 Software Park Road Hi-Tech Industrial Zone, Dalian, Liaoning, China
Tel.: (86) 41139737702
Packaging Materials Mfr
N.A.I.C.S.: 322220

Nichiei Printing Co., Ltd. (1)
2-143 Wakabayashi-cho, Yao, 581-0038, Osaka, Japan
Tel.: (81) 729764001
Web Site: http://www.nichiei-prn.com
Emp.: 42
Packaging Materials Mfr
N.A.I.C.S.: 322220

Process Lab. Micron (Suzhou) Co., Ltd. (1)
5A - 02-01 02 A02-01 02 No 5 Xing-Han Street Suzhou Industrial Park, Suzhou, China
Tel.: (86) 51285557188
Mask Mfr
N.A.I.C.S.: 325992

Process Lab. Micron Co., Ltd. (1)
1-103-52 Yoshinodai, Kawagoe, Saitama, Japan
Tel.: (81) 492263111
Web Site: http://www.lab-micron.co.jp
Stencil Mfr & Distr
N.A.I.C.S.: 339940
Ryoji Hattori (Pres & CEO)

Shanghai Takeda Printing Co., Ltd. (1)
No 736 Songsheng RD Songjiang Industrial Zone, Shanghai, 201613, China

Tel.: (86) 2152392546
Packaging Material Distr
N.A.I.C.S.: 423840

Tokyo Process Service Co., Ltd. (1)
2012-4 Endo, Fujisawa, 252-0816, Kanagawa, Japan
Tel.: (81) 466894083
Web Site: https://www.topro.com
Emp.: 152
Photomask Mfr & Distr
N.A.I.C.S.: 325992
Minoru Ota (Pres)

TAKEDA MACHINERY CO., LTD.
132 Nishi Ao-machi, Nomi, 923-1101, Ishikawa, Japan
Tel.: (81) 761588211
Web Site: https://www.takeda-mc.co.jp
Year Founded: 1966
6150—(TKS)
Rev.: $36,117,040
Assets: $52,291,710
Liabilities: $19,248,320
Net Worth: $33,043,390
Earnings: $2,822,470
Emp.: 199
Fiscal Year-end: 05/31/24
Metal Working Machine Mfr & Sales
N.A.I.C.S.: 327999
Yuichi Takeda (Pres)

Subsidiaries:

TAKEDA SEIKI CO., LTD. (1)
Tokkozi Muda 25th place Hinai-cho, Odate, Akita, Japan
Tel.: (81) 18 656 2421
Web Site: https://www.takedaseiki.co.jp
Air Filter Mfr
N.A.I.C.S.: 333413

TAKEDA PHARMACEUTICAL COMPANY LIMITED
1-1 Nihonbashi-Honcho 2-chome, Chuo-ku, Tokyo, 103-8668, Japan
Tel.: (81) 332782111   JP
Web Site: https://www.takeda.com
Year Founded: 1781
TAK—(NYSE)
Rev.: $26,524,181,200
Assets: $93,989,377,625
Liabilities: $48,738,962,582
Net Worth: $45,250,415,043
Earnings: $897,026,465
Emp.: 49,281
Fiscal Year-end: 03/31/24
Pharmaceuticals, Industrial Chemicals, Cosmetics, Food Additives, Enriched Foods & Drinks, Agricultural Chemicals & Fertilizers Mfr & Developer
N.A.I.C.S.: 325412
Teresa Bitetti (Pres-Global Oncology-Takeda)

Subsidiaries:

Amato Pharmaceutical Products Ltd. (1)
2-20-4 Osadano-cho, Kyoto, 620-0853, Japan
Tel.: (81) 773221100
Web Site: https://www.amato.co.jp
Pharmaceuticals Mfr
N.A.I.C.S.: 424210

Millennium Pharmaceuticals, Inc. (1)
40 Landsdowne St, Cambridge, MA 02139-4134
Tel.: (617) 679-7000
Web Site: http://www.millennium.com
Sales Range: $500-549.9 Million
Emp.: 966
Treatments & Diagnostics for Asthma, Stroke, Colitis & Crohn's Disease
N.A.I.C.S.: 325412
Nancy A. Simonian (Pres)

Mitsui Takeda Chemicals, Inc. (1)
1-52-2 Higashi-Shimbashi, Minato-ku, Tokyo, 105-7117, Japan
Tel.: (81) 362534100
Web Site: http://www.takeda.com
Sales Range: $200-249.9 Million
Emp.: 900
Urethane Raw Materials & Derivatives & Organic Acids Mfr & Sales; Owned 51% by Mitsui Chemicals, Inc. & 49% by Takeda Pharmaceutical Company Limited
N.A.I.C.S.: 325199

Joint Venture (Non-US):

Croslene Chemical Industries, Ltd. (2)
11F No 22 Nanjing W Rd, Datong Dist, Taipei, 103, Taiwan
Tel.: (886) 225556661
Web Site: http://www.croslene.com.tw
Synthetic Resins Mfr & Sales; Owned 50% by Mitsui Takeda Chemicals, Inc. & 48% by Lidye Co., Ltd.
N.A.I.C.S.: 325211

Kumho Mitsui Chemicals, Inc. (2)
Floor 11th East Bldg Signature Tower 100 Cheonggyecheon-ro, Joong-gu, Seoul, Korea (South)
Tel.: (82) 269613750
Web Site: https://www.kmci.co.kr
Emp.: 248
MDI Mfr & Sales
N.A.I.C.S.: 325998

Mizusawa Industrial Chemicals, Ltd. (1)
REVZO Nihonbashi Horidomecho 1-10-13 Nihonbashi-horidomecho, Chuo-ku, Tokyo, 103-0012, Japan   (53%)
Tel.: (81) 67002960
Web Site: https://www.mizusawa-chem.co.jp
Sales Range: $100-124.9 Million
Emp.: 300
Sales of Chemical Reagents
N.A.I.C.S.: 424690

Nihon Pharmaceutical Co., Ltd. (1)
8-1 Akashi-cho, Chiyoda-ku, Tokyo, 101-0031, Japan   (87.3%)
Tel.: (81) 338648411
Web Site: http://www.nihon-pharm.co.jp
Sales Range: $25-49.9 Million
Emp.: 80
Pharmaceuticals Research, Development, Manufacturing & Marketing
N.A.I.C.S.: 325412

Shire plc (1)
Block 2 Miesian Plaza 50-58 Baggot Street Lower, Dublin, 2, Ireland   (100%)
Tel.: (353) 1 609 6000
Web Site: http://www.shire.com
Rev.: $15,160,600,000
Assets: $67,756,900,000
Liabilities: $31,580,500,000
Net Worth: $36,176,400,000
Earnings: $4,271,500,000
Emp.: 23,044
Fiscal Year-end: 12/31/2017
Holding Company; Specialty Pharmaceuticals Developer & Mfr
N.A.I.C.S.: 551112
Susan O'Reilly (Sec)

Subsidiary (Non-US):

Fibrotech Therapeutics Pty Ltd (2)
Level 9 278 Collins Street, Wonga Park, Melbourne, 3000, VIC, Australia
Tel.: (61) 392882546
Pharmaceuticals Product Mfr
N.A.I.C.S.: 325412

Subsidiary (Domestic):

NPS Pharma International Limited (2)
Alexandra House The Sweepstakes Ballsbridge, Dublin, Ireland
Tel.: (353) 16319000
Pharmaceuticals Product Mfr
N.A.I.C.S.: 325412

Subsidiary (Non-US):

NPS Pharma Sweden AB (2)
Svardvagen 11 D, 182 33, Danderyd, Sweden
Tel.: (46) 31404009
Advertising Agency Services

N.A.I.C.S.: 541810
Andrea Fransson (Dir-Medical-Nordic)

Premacure AB (2)
Uppsala Science Park, Uppsala, 751 83, Sweden
Tel.: (46) 706502852
Pharmaceuticals Product Mfr
N.A.I.C.S.: 325412
Jan Borg (CEO)

SOLPHARM d.o.o. za trgovinu i usluge (2)
Praska 8, Zagreb, 10000, Croatia
Tel.: (385) 14921914
Business Consulting Services
N.A.I.C.S.: 541330

Shire AG (2)
Business Park Terre Bonne 15, 1262, Eysins, Switzerland
Tel.: (41) 224194000
Web Site: http://www.shire.com
Sales Range: $50-74.9 Million
Emp.: 28
Pharmaceuticals Product Mfr
N.A.I.C.S.: 325412

Shire Australia Pty Limited (2)
Level 6 123 Epping Rd, PO Box 6240, North Ryde, North Ryde, 2113, NSW, Australia
Tel.: (61) 2 8019 4400
Web Site: http://www.shireaustralia.com
Emp.: 5
Pharmaceuticals Product Mfr
N.A.I.C.S.: 325412

Shire Austria GmbH (2)
Industriestrasse 67, 1221, Vienna, Austria
Tel.: (43) 1201000
Pharmaceutical Product Whslr
N.A.I.C.S.: 424210

Shire Belgium BVBA (2)
Rue Montoyer 47, 1000, Brussels, Belgium
Tel.: (32) 27110230
Sales Range: $25-49.9 Million
Emp.: 50
Pharmaceuticals Product Mfr
N.A.I.C.S.: 325412

Subsidiary (Domestic):

Shire Biopharmaceuticals Ireland Limited (2)
50-58 Baggot St Lower Miesian Plaza Blocks 2 & 3, Dublin, Ireland
Tel.: (353) 16096000
Web Site: http://www.shire.com
Pharmaceutical Products Mfr & Distr
N.A.I.C.S.: 325412

Subsidiary (Non-US):

Shire Colombia S.A.S (2)
Calle 116 No 7 -15 Interior 2 Piso 7 Oxocenter Business Center, Bogota, Colombia
Tel.: (57) 5111070
Web Site: http://www.shire.co
Pharmaceuticals Product Mfr
N.A.I.C.S.: 325412

Shire Czech S.R.O. (2)
Narodni 135/14, 110 00, Prague, Czech Republic
Tel.: (420) 225379700
Pharmaceuticals Product Mfr
N.A.I.C.S.: 325412

Shire Deutschland GmbH (2)
Friedrichstrasse 149, 10117, Berlin, Germany   (100%)
Tel.: (49) 302065820
Web Site: http://www.takeda.com
Pharmaceuticals Mfr
N.A.I.C.S.: 325412

Subsidiary (Domestic):

Shire Orphan Therapies GmbH (3)
Friedrichstrasse 149, 10117, Berlin, Germany
Tel.: (49) 302065820
Pharmaceuticals Product Mfr
N.A.I.C.S.: 325412

Subsidiary (Non-US):

Shire Farmaceutica Brasil Ltda (2)
Av das Nacoes Unidas 14 171 5th floor

TAKEDA PHARMACEUTICAL COMPANY LIMITED

Takeda Pharmaceutical Company Limited—(Continued)
Torre Ebony, Sao Paulo, 04794-000, Brazil
Tel.: (55) 1130147300
Web Site: http://www.takeda.com.br
Pharmaceutical Product Whslr
N.A.I.C.S.: 424210

Shire France SA (2)
88 Rue Dome, 92100, Boulogne-Billancourt, France (100%)
Tel.: (33) 146109000
Web Site: http://www.shirefrance.com
Sales Range: $25-49.9 Million
Pharmaceuticals Mfr
N.A.I.C.S.: 325412

Shire Holdings Luxembourg S.a r.l.
7 A Rue Robert Stumper, 2557, Luxembourg, Luxembourg
Tel.: (352) 2649584463
Investment Management Service
N.A.I.C.S.: 523999

Shire Human Genetic Therapies (Canada) Inc. (2)
4120 Yonge Street Suite 404, Toronto, M2P 2B8, ON, Canada
Tel.: (416) 225-6100
Biopharmaceutical Research & Development Services
N.A.I.C.S.: 541715

Shire Human Genetic Therapies AB (2)
Svardvagen 11d, Danderyd, 182 33, Sweden
Tel.: (46) 854496400
Web Site: http://www.shire.com
Sales Range: $50-74.9 Million
Emp.: 2
Pharmaceutical Products Distr
N.A.I.C.S.: 424210

Shire Human Genetic Therapies S.A. (2)
Boulevard Cecilia Grierson 255 Piso 4, C1107CPE, Buenos Aires, Argentina
Tel.: (54) 1137534400
Web Site: http://www.shire.com
Pharmaceutical Products Mfr & Distr
N.A.I.C.S.: 424210

Shire IP Services Corporation (2)
2250 Boul Alfred-Nobel Bureau 500, Ville Saint Laurent, H4S 2C9, QC, Canada
Tel.: (514) 787-2319
Sales Range: $25-49.9 Million
Emp.: 5
Intellectual Property Management Services
N.A.I.C.S.: 541199
Antonio Aveledo (Advisor-Intellectual Property)

Shire Ilac Ticaret Limited Sirketi (2)
Buyukdere Cad Bahar Sok No 13 Kat 24, 34394, Istanbul, Turkiye
Tel.: (90) 2123868900
Pharmaceutical Product Whslr
N.A.I.C.S.: 424210

Subsidiary (US):

Shire Incorporated (2)
300 Shire Way, Lexington, MA 02421
Tel.: (617) 349-0200
Web Site: http://www.shire.com
Holding Company; Regional Managing Office; Pharmaceutical Preparation Mfr
N.A.I.C.S.: 551112

Subsidiary (Non-US):

Shire Pharmaceuticals Mexico SA de CV (3)
Av Paseo de los Tamarindos 90 Torre 1 Piso 7 Col Bosques de las Lomas, Del Cuajimalpa, 05120, Mexico, Mexico
Tel.: (52) 5550810120
Web Site: http://www.shire.com
Sales Range: $25-49.9 Million
Emp.: 3
Pharmaceuticals Product Mfr
N.A.I.C.S.: 325412

Subsidiary (Domestic):

Shire US Inc. (3)

300 Shire Way, Lexington, MA 02421 (100%)
Tel.: (617) 349-0200
Web Site: http://www.shire.com
Pharmaceuticals Marketing & Sales
N.A.I.C.S.: 424210

Subsidiary (Domestic):

Advanced BioHealing, Inc. (4)
36 Church Ln, Westport, CT 06880
Tel.: (203) 682-7222
Web Site: http://www.abh.com
Sales Range: $75-99.9 Million
Emp.: 5
Cell-Based Therapies Developer & Mfr
N.A.I.C.S.: 325414
Kevin L. Rakin (Chm & CEO)

Allelix Neuroscience, Inc. (4)
7 Cedarbrook Dr, Cranbury, NJ 08512
Tel.: (908) 561-0303
Pharmaceutical Preparation Mfr
N.A.I.C.S.: 325412

Baxalta Incorporated (4)
1200 Lakeside Dr, Bannockburn, IL 60015 (100%)
Tel.: (224) 940-2000
Web Site: http://www.baxalta.com
Biopharmaceutical Developer & Mfr
N.A.I.C.S.: 325412

Subsidiary (Non-US):

Baxter Manufacturing S.p.A. (5)
Via Dell'Osmannoro 253, 50019, Florence, Italy
Tel.: (39) 05542951
Emp.: 77
Medical Instrument Mfr
N.A.I.C.S.: 339112

Subsidiary (Domestic):

BearTracks, Inc. (4)
328 Mockingbird Ln, Lexington, KY 40503
Tel.: (859) 421-0522
Business Support Services
N.A.I.C.S.: 561990

Bikam Pharmaceuticals, Inc. (4)
55 Cambridge Pkwy Ste 301, Cambridge, MA 02142
Tel.: (617) 252-4343
Pharmaceutical Product Whslr
N.A.I.C.S.: 424210

FerroKin BioSciences, Inc. (4)
2729 Debbie Court, San Carlos, CA 94070
Tel.: (650) 218-5710
Biotechnology Research & Development Services
N.A.I.C.S.: 541714
Jennifer Peppe (Sr Dir-Clinical Ops)

Foresight Biotherapeutics, Inc (4)
50 W 57th St 15th Fl, New York, NY 10019
Tel.: (646) 747-9100
Pharmaceuticals Product Mfr
N.A.I.C.S.: 325412
Lindsay Birch (VP)

Lotus Tissue Repair Inc (4)
One Mifflin Pl Ste 400, Cambridge, MA 02138
Tel.: (617) 674-7610
Web Site: http://www.lotustissuerepair.com
Outpatient Health Care Services
N.A.I.C.S.: 621340

Lumena Pharmaceuticals, LLC (4)
12531 High Bluff Dr Ste 110, San Diego, CA 92130
Tel.: (858) 461-0694
Emp.: 17
Biopharmaceutical Mfr
N.A.I.C.S.: 325412

Shire Development LLC (4)
300 Shire Way, Lexington, MA 02421
Tel.: (781) 428-9222
Administrative Management Services
N.A.I.C.S.: 561110

Shire Human Genetic Therapies, Inc. (4)
300 Shire Way, Lexington, MA 02421
Tel.: (617) 349-0200
Sales Range: $75-99.9 Million
Emp.: 400
Protein & Cell-Based Therapeutics Mfr

N.A.I.C.S.: 541715
David D. Pendergast (Exec VP)

Shire Pharmaceuticals LLC (4)
725 Chesterbrook Blvd, Wayne, PA 19087
Tel.: (484) 595-8800
Web Site: http://www.shire.com
Pharmaceutical Developer & Mfr
N.A.I.C.S.: 325412

Shire ViroPharma Incorporated (4)
730 Stockton Dr, Exton, PA 19341-1171
Tel.: (610) 458-7300
Web Site: http://www.viropharma.com
Pharmaceuticals Product Developer
N.A.I.C.S.: 325412

Subsidiary (Non-US):

Shire International GmbH (2)
Zahlerweg 10, 6301, Zug, Switzerland
Tel.: (41) 412884000
Biological Product Mfr
N.A.I.C.S.: 325414
Jenny Inglefield (Dir-Global Mktg)

Shire Italia S.p.A (2)
Via Mike Bongiorno 13, 20124, Milan, Italy
Tel.: (39) 0265535001
Web Site: http://www.shireitalia.it
Pharmaceuticals Mfr
N.A.I.C.S.: 325412

Shire Japan KK (2)
21st Floor Building 1-8-2 Marunouchi, Yubinbango Shinjuku-ku Chiyoda-ku, Tokyo, 100-0005, Japan
Tel.: (81) 367370100
Web Site: http://www.shire.co.jp
Biopharmaceutical Product Mfr
N.A.I.C.S.: 325412

Shire Luxembourg Finance S.a r.l.
1 Rue Hildegard von Bingen, L-1282, Luxembourg, Luxembourg
Tel.: (352) 2649584460
Biological Product Mfr
N.A.I.C.S.: 325414

Shire Pharmaceuticals Group Limited (2)
Lime Tree Way Hampshire International Business Park Chineham, Basingstoke, RG24 8EP, United Kingdom
Tel.: (44) 1256 894000
Pharmaceuticals Product Mfr
N.A.I.C.S.: 325412

Subsidiary (Domestic):

Shire Pharmaceuticals Ltd. (3)
Hampshire International Business Park, Chineham, Basingstoke, RG24 8EP, Hants, United Kingdom (100%)
Tel.: (44) 1256894000
Web Site: http://www.shirepharmaceuticals.co.uk
Sales Range: $125-149.9 Million
Emp.: 400
Pharmaceuticals Mfr
N.A.I.C.S.: 325412

Subsidiary (Domestic):

Shire Human Genetic Therapies Limited (4)
Lime Tree Way Hampshire Int Business Park, Basingstoke, Hampshire, United Kingdom
Tel.: (44) 1256894000
Biopharmaceutical Research & Development Services
N.A.I.C.S.: 541715

Shire Pharmaceutical Contracts Limited (4)
Hampshire International Business Park, Chineham, Basingstoke, RG24 8EP, United Kingdom
Tel.: (44) 12 5689 4000
Pharmaceuticals Product Mfr
N.A.I.C.S.: 325412

Shire Pharmaceutical Development Limited (4)
Hampshire International Business Park Chineham, Basingstoke, RG24 8EP, Hampshire, United Kingdom
Tel.: (44) 1256894000

INTERNATIONAL PUBLIC

Biopharmaceutical Research & Development Services
N.A.I.C.S.: 541715

Subsidiary (Non-US):

Shire Pharmaceuticals Iberica S.L. (2)
Avda Partenon 16 18 4, 28042, Madrid, Spain (100%)
Tel.: (34) 915500691
Web Site: http://www.shire.com
Sales Range: $25-49.9 Million
Emp.: 24
Pharmaceuticals Mfr
N.A.I.C.S.: 325412

Subsidiary (Domestic):

Shire Pharmaceuticals Ireland Ltd. (2)
5 River Walk Citywest Business Campus, Dublin, Ireland (100%)
Tel.: (353) 14297700
Web Site: http://www.shire.com
Sales Range: $25-49.9 Million
Emp.: 100
Pharmaceuticals Mfr
N.A.I.C.S.: 325412

Subsidiary (Non-US):

Shire Pharmaceuticals Portugal, Lda (2)
Av da Republica N 50-10, 1069-211, Lisbon, Portugal
Tel.: (351) 217990420
Pharmaceutical Product Mfr & Whslr
N.A.I.C.S.: 325412
Gregorio Lopes (Head-Portugal)

Shire Polska Sp. z. o. o. (2)
Ul Emilii Plater 53, 00-113, Warsaw, Poland
Tel.: (48) 22 528 69 97
Sales Range: $50-74.9 Million
Emp.: 10
Pharmaceutical Products Distr
N.A.I.C.S.: 424210

Shire Services BVBA (2)
Rue Montoyer 47, Brussels, 1000, Belgium
Tel.: (32) 27470971
Biopharmaceutical Product Mfr
N.A.I.C.S.: 325412
Diederik Bries (Mgr-Quality Assurance)

Shire Singapore Pte. Ltd. (2)
8 Marina Boulevard 15-01 Marina Bay Financial Centre Tower 1, Singapore, 18981, Singapore
Tel.: (65) 68123900
Pharmaceutical Product Mfr & Whslr
N.A.I.C.S.: 325412
Por Chin Ang (Mgr-Quality Assurance, Distr & Transportation)

Shire Sweden AB (2)
Svardvagen 11D 4th Floor, Danderyd, 182 33, Sweden
Tel.: (46) 854496400
Web Site: http://www.shire.com
Emp.: 6
Pharmaceutical Products Distr
N.A.I.C.S.: 424210

Shire Switzerland GmbH (2)
Zahlerweg 10, 6301, Zug, Switzerland
Tel.: (41) 412884000
Web Site: http://www.shireswitzerland.ch
Biopharmaceutical Product Mfr
N.A.I.C.S.: 325412

Shire-Movetis NV (2)
Veedijk 58 1004, Turnhout, 2300, Belgium
Tel.: (32) 14404390
Web Site: http://www.movetis.com
Sales Range: $1-9.9 Million
Emp.: 38
Gastrointestinal Pharmaceutical Products Mfr
N.A.I.C.S.: 325412

Solpharm Adriatic d.o.o. Beograd (2)
Uskocka 8/IV, Belgrade, Serbia
Tel.: (381) 114113177
Business Consulting Services
N.A.I.C.S.: 541330
Gordana Radivojevic (Gen Mgr)

Tanaud International BV (2)
Fred Roeskestraat 123-1hg, 1076 EE, Am-

AND PRIVATE COMPANIES — TAKEDA PHARMACEUTICAL COMPANY LIMITED

sterdam, Netherlands
Tel.: (31) 204700555
Pharmaceutical Products Distr
N.A.I.C.S.: 424210

Takeda (China) Holdings Co., Ltd. (1)
29F Wheelock Square No 1717 West Nanjing Rd, Shanghai, 200040, China
Tel.: (86) 212 230 6888
Pharmaceuticals Product Mfr
N.A.I.C.S.: 325412

Takeda AS (1)
Drammensveien 852, 1383, Asker, Norway
Tel.: (47) 6 676 3030
Emp.: 280
Pharmaceutical Product Mfr & Distr
N.A.I.C.S.: 325412

Takeda America Holdings, Inc. (1)
767 3rd Ave, New York, NY 10017-2023 (100%)
Tel.: (212) 421-6950
Web Site: http://www.takeda.com
Holding Company
N.A.I.C.S.: 551112
Asit Parikh *(Sr VP & Head-Gastroenterology Therapeutic Area)*

Subsidiary (Domestic):

Takeda Pharmaceuticals International, Inc. (2)
One Takeda Pkwy, Deerfield, IL 60015
Tel.: (224) 554-6500
Pharmaceuticals Mfr
N.A.I.C.S.: 424210

Takeda Pharmaceuticals U.S.A, Inc. (2)
1 Takeda Pkwy, Deerfield, IL 60015-4832
Tel.: (224) 554-6500
Web Site: http://www.takeda.us
Sales Range: $450-499.9 Million
Pharmaceuticals Mfr
N.A.I.C.S.: 325412
Ramona Sequeira *(Pres-Portfolio Division-Global)*

Takeda San Diego, Inc (2)
10410 Science Ctr Dr, San Diego, CA 92121
Tel.: (858) 622-8528
Web Site: http://www.takedasd.com
Sales Range: $25-49.9 Million
Emp.: 150
Pharmaceutical Products Research & Development Services
N.A.I.C.S.: 541715

Takeda Development Center Asia, Pte. Ltd. (1)
21 Biopolis Road Nucleos North Tower Level 4, Singapore, 138567, Singapore
Tel.: (65) 6 808 9500
Pharmaceuticals Product Mfr
N.A.I.C.S.: 325412

Takeda Development Centre Europe Ltd. (1)
1 Kingdom Street, London, W2 6BD, United Kingdom
Tel.: (44) 333 300 0181
Pharmaceuticals Product Mfr
N.A.I.C.S.: 325412

Takeda Distribuidora Ltda. (1)
Av Das Nacoes Unidas 14 401-Torre Jequitiba-10 11 e 12 Andares, Sao Paulo, 04794-000, Brazil
Tel.: (55) 115 464 9001
Pharmaceutical Product Mfr & Distr
N.A.I.C.S.: 325412

Takeda Italia S.p.A. (1)
Via Elio Vittorini 129, 00144, Rome, Italy
Tel.: (39) 0650 2601
Emp.: 400
Pharmaceuticals Product Mfr
N.A.I.C.S.: 325412

Takeda Pharma A/S (1)
Delta Park 45, 2665, Vallensbaek, Denmark
Tel.: (45) 4 677 1111
Pharmaceutical Product Mfr & Distr
N.A.I.C.S.: 325412

Takeda Pharmaceutical (China) Company Limited (1)
No 836 Yaocheng Road, Taizhou, 225300, Jiangsu, China
Tel.: (86) 108 468 7000
Pharmaceuticals Product Mfr
N.A.I.C.S.: 325412

Takeda Pharmaceutical Co., Ltd. - Hikari Plant (1)
4720 Takeda Mitsui, Hikari, 743-8502, Japan
Tel.: (81) 833711600
Pharmaceuticals Product Mfr
N.A.I.C.S.: 325412

Takeda Pharmaceutical Co., Ltd. - Osaka Plant (1)
17-84 Jusohonmachi 2-chome, Yodogawa-ku, Osaka, 532-8686, Japan
Tel.: (81) 663006111
Web Site: http://www.takeda.com
Pharmaceuticals Product Mfr
N.A.I.C.S.: 325412

Takeda Pharmaceuticals International GmbH (1)
Thurgauerstrasse 130, Glattpark-Opfikon, 8152, Zurich, Switzerland
Tel.: (41) 44 555 1000
Web Site: http://www.tpi.takeda.com
Sales Range: $1-4.9 Billion
Emp.: 12,000
Pharmaceutical Mfr & Distr
N.A.I.C.S.: 325412
Stuart Dollow *(Pres-Takeda Dev Center Americas Inc)*

Subsidiary (Non-US):

Boie-Takeda Chemicals, Inc. (2)
12th Fl Sky Plaza Bldg 6788 Ayala Ave, Makati, Metro Manila, Philippines (50%)
Tel.: (63) 28866954
Web Site: http://www.boie-takeda.com
Sales Range: $50-74.9 Million
Emp.: 125
Sales of Pharmaceuticals
N.A.I.C.S.: 424210

Laboratoires Takeda (2)
15 Quai de Dion Bouton, FR 92816, Puteaux, Cedex, France (100%)
Tel.: (33) 146251616
Web Site: http://www.takeda.com
Sales Range: $25-49.9 Million
Emp.: 100
Retailer of Pharmaceuticals
N.A.I.C.S.: 424210

Subsidiary (Domestic):

IDM Pharma, S.A.S. (3)
11-15 Quai de Dion Bouton, 92816, Puteaux, France
Tel.: (33) 1 4625 1264
Pharmaceuticals Product Mfr
N.A.I.C.S.: 325412

Subsidiary (Non-US):

Oy Leiras Takeda Pharmaceuticals Ab (2)
Paciuksenkatu 21, PO Box 1406, FI-00101, Helsinki, Finland
Tel.: (358) 207465000
Web Site: http://www.leiras.com
Sales Range: $75-99.9 Million
Emp.: 55
Pharmaceuticals Product Mfr
N.A.I.C.S.: 325412

P.T. Takeda Indonesia (2)
Plz DM 15th Fl Jalan Jenderal Sudirman Kav 25, Jakarta, 12920, Indonesia (70%)
Tel.: (62) 215267656
Web Site: http://www.takeda.co.id
Sales Range: $50-74.9 Million
Emp.: 200
Mfr & Sales of Pharmaceuticals
N.A.I.C.S.: 325412

Takeda (Thailand), Ltd. (2)
57 Park Ventures Ecoplex Building 15th Floor Wireless Road Lumpini, Lumpini Patumwan, Bangkok, 10330, Thailand (52%)
Tel.: (66) 26979300
Web Site: https://www.takeda.com
Sales Range: $50-74.9 Million
Emp.: 200
Mfr & Retailer of Pharmaceuticals
N.A.I.C.S.: 325412

Takeda Austria GmbH (2)
St Peterstrasse 25, 4020, Linz, Austria
Tel.: (43) 7326919
Web Site: http://www.takeda.at
Sales Range: $25-49.9 Million
Emp.: 700
Pharmaceuticals Mfr
N.A.I.C.S.: 325412

Takeda Belgium SCA/CVA (2)
Gentsesteenweg 615, 1080, Brussels, Belgium
Tel.: (32) 24640611
Web Site: http://www.takeda.be
Sales Range: $100-124.9 Million
Emp.: 400
Pharmaceuticals Product Mfr
N.A.I.C.S.: 325412

Takeda Bio Development Center Limited (2)
7-12 Marunouchi 1-Chome Chiyoda, Tokyo, 100-0005, Japan
Tel.: (81) 352249050
Pharmaceuticals Mfr
N.A.I.C.S.: 424210

Takeda Cambridge Limited (2)
418 Cambridge Science Park, Cambridge, CB4 0PA, United Kingdom (100%)
Tel.: (44) 1223477910
Web Site: http://www.takedacam.co.uk
Sales Range: $25-49.9 Million
Emp.: 30
Pharmaceutical Research
N.A.I.C.S.: 325412
Mark Carlton *(Pres & Chief Scientific Officer)*

Takeda Canada, Inc. (2)
Bay Adelaide Centre 22 Adelaide Street West Suite 3800, Toronto, M5H 4E3, ON, Canada
Tel.: (647) 798-2200
Web Site: https://www.takeda.com
Pharmaceuticals Mfr
N.A.I.C.S.: 424210

Takeda Chemical Industries (Taiwan), Ltd. (2)
7th Fl Great China Bldg No 217 Sec 3 Nanking E Rd, Taipei, 104, Taiwan (100%)
Tel.: (886) 227121112
Web Site: http://www.takeda.com.tw
Sales Range: $10-24.9 Million
Emp.: 120
Pharmaceuticals Mfr
N.A.I.C.S.: 325412

Takeda Clinical Research Singapore Private Limited (2)
21 Boipolis Rd Nucleos North Tower Level 4, Singapore, 138567, Singapore
Tel.: (65) 65212100
Pharmaceuticals Mfr
N.A.I.C.S.: 424210

Takeda Europe Holdings B.V. (2)
Strawinskylaan 1217, 1077 XX, Amsterdam, Netherlands (100%)
Tel.: (31) 205752830
Sales Range: $25-49.9 Million
Emp.: 2
Holding Company
N.A.I.C.S.: 551112

Takeda Farmaceutica Espana S.A. (2)
Av Europa 19 Planta Tercera B, Pozuelo de Alarcon, Madrid, 28224, Spain
Tel.: (34) 917690900
Pharmaceuticals Mfr
N.A.I.C.S.: 424210

Takeda Farmaceutica Espana S.A.U. (2)
C/ Alsasua 20, Madrid, 28023, Spain
Tel.: (34) 917149900
Web Site: http://www.takeda.es
Emp.: 80
Pharmaceuticals Mfr
N.A.I.C.S.: 325412

Takeda Farmaceuticos Portugal Unipessoal LDA (2)
Av da Torre de Belem 19-1 E, 1400-342, Lisbon, Portugal
Tel.: (351) 211201457
Web Site: http://www.tekada.pt
Emp.: 67
Pharmaceuticals Mfr
N.A.I.C.S.: 424210
Filomena Carichas *(Mgr)*

Takeda France S.A.S. (2)
112 Ave Kleber, 75116, Paris, France
Tel.: (33) 140673300
Web Site: https://www.takeda.com
Sales Range: $50-74.9 Million
Emp.: 250
Pharmaceuticals Mfr
N.A.I.C.S.: 325412

Takeda Global Research & Development Centre Europe Ltd. (2)
61 Aldwych, London, WC2B 4AE, United Kingdom (100%)
Tel.: (44) 2077595000
Web Site: http://www.takeda.com
Sales Range: $50-74.9 Million
Emp.: 200
Pharmaceuticals Research & Development
N.A.I.C.S.: 325412

Takeda GmbH (2)
Byk-Gulden-Strasse 2, 78467, Konstanz, Germany
Tel.: (49) 7531 84 0
Web Site: http://www.takeda.de
Sales Range: $50-74.9 Million
Emp.: 110
Pharmaceuticals Mfr
N.A.I.C.S.: 325412

Unit (Domestic):

Takeda GmbH - Oranienburg (3)
Lehnitzstrasse 70-98, Oranienburg, 16515, Germany
Tel.: (49) 33018180
Sales Range: $125-149.9 Million
Pharmaceuticals Mfr
N.A.I.C.S.: 325412
Micheal Keck *(Gen Mgr)*

Subsidiary (Non-US):

Takeda Healthcare Products Co., Ltd. (2)
21 Osadano-Cho 2-Chome, Fukuchiyama-Shi, Kyoto, 620-0853, Japan
Tel.: (81) 773275421
Web Site: http://www.takeda.com
Pharmaceuticals Mfr
N.A.I.C.S.: 424210

Takeda Ilaclari Tic. Ltd. Sti. (2)
Eski Buyukdere Cad Ayazaga Yolu Giz 2000 Plaza No 7, Kat 4, Istanbul, 34398, Turkiye
Tel.: (90) 2127053400
Web Site: http://www.takeda.com.tr
Pharmaceuticals Mfr
N.A.I.C.S.: 424210

Takeda Ireland Ltd. (2)
Kilruddery Bray Business Park, Wicklow, Ireland (100%)
Tel.: (353) 12050600
Web Site: https://www.takeda.ie
Sales Range: $100-124.9 Million
Emp.: 350
Mfr of Pharmaceuticals
N.A.I.C.S.: 325412

Takeda Italia Farmaceutici S.p.A. (2)
Via Elio Vittorini 129, I 00144, Rome, Italy (76.9%)
Tel.: (39) 06502601
Web Site: http://www.takeda.it
Sales Range: $100-124.9 Million
Emp.: 500
Mfr & Sales of Pharmaceuticals
N.A.I.C.S.: 325412

Takeda Mexico S.A. de C.V. (2)
Av Primero de Mayo No 130 Col Industrial Atoto, 53519, Naucalpan, Mexico
Tel.: (52) 53 87 93 30
Web Site: http://www.takedamexico.com
Sales Range: $100-124.9 Million
Emp.: 500
Pharmaceuticals Mfr
N.A.I.C.S.: 325412

Takeda Nederland bv (2)
Jupiterstraat 250, 2132 HK, Hoofddorp, Netherlands
Tel.: (31) 235668700

TAKEDA PHARMACEUTICAL COMPANY LIMITED

Takeda Pharmaceutical Company Limited—(Continued)
Web Site: http://www.takeda.nl
Sales Range: $25-49.9 Million
Emp.: 100
Pharmaceuticals Mfr
N.A.I.C.S.: 325412

Takeda Nycomed AS (2)
Drammensveien 852, 1383, Asker, Norway
Tel.: (47) 66763030
Web Site: http://www.takedanycomed.no
Sales Range: $100-124.9 Million
Emp.: 280
Pharmaceuticals Mfr
N.A.I.C.S.: 325412
Bjorn Lie (CEO)

Subsidiary (Domestic):

Takeda Pharma AG (2)
Alpenblickstrasse 26, CH 8853, Lachen,
Switzerland (100%)
Tel.: (41) 554515200
Web Site: http://www.takeda.ch
Sales Range: $25-49.9 Million
Emp.: 45
Marketer of Pharmaceuticals
N.A.I.C.S.: 424210

Subsidiary (Non-US):

Takeda Pharma Ges.m.b.H. (2)
Gebeaude F Technologiestrasse 5 A, 1120,
Vienna, Austria (100%)
Tel.: (43) 15244064
Web Site: http://www.takeda.at
Sales Range: $25-49.9 Million
Emp.: 70
Pharmaceutical Products
N.A.I.C.S.: 325412

Takeda Pharma GmbH (2)
Viktoriaallee 325, D 52066, Aachen,
Germany (100%)
Tel.: (49) 2419410
Web Site: http://www.takeda.de
Sales Range: $100-124.9 Million
Emp.: 500
Provider of Pharmaceuticals
N.A.I.C.S.: 325412

Takeda Pharma Ltda. (2)
Rodovia SP 340 N 0 Campinas to Mogi
Mirim KM 133, 5 Nucleo Residencial Dr
Joao Aldo Nassif, Jaguariuna, 13916-072,
SP, Brazil
Tel.: (55) 1938475580
Web Site: https://www.takeda.com
Sales Range: $100-124.9 Million
Emp.: 300
Pharmaceuticals Mfr
N.A.I.C.S.: 325412

Takeda Pharma S.A. (2)
Tronador 4890 Edificio Pan-American Seat,
Capital, C1430DNN, Buenos Aires, Federal,
Argentina (100%)
Tel.: (54) 11 4546 4700
Web Site: http://www.takedaargentina.com
Pharmaceuticals Mfr
N.A.I.C.S.: 325412

Takeda Pharma Sp. z.o.o. (2)
street Prosta 68, 00-838, Warsaw, Poland
Tel.: (48) 226081300
Pharmaceuticals Mfr
N.A.I.C.S.: 325412

Takeda Pharmaceuticals (Philippines), Inc. (2)
12th Fl Sky Plaza Bldg, 6788 Ayala Ave,
Manila, Makati City, Philippines
Tel.: (63) 28866954
Sales Range: $25-49.9 Million
Emp.: 40
Pharmaceuticals Mfr
N.A.I.C.S.: 424210

Takeda Pharmaceuticals Asia Private Limited (2)
10 Marina Boulevard 15-01 Marina Bay Financial Centre Tower 2, Singapore, 018983,
Singapore
Tel.: (65) 68089500
Pharmaceuticals Mfr
N.A.I.C.S.: 424210

Takeda Pharmaceuticals Benelux bvba (2)
A J .Wybranlaan 40, 1070, Brussels, Belgium
Tel.: (32) 25295932
Pharmaceuticals Mfr
N.A.I.C.S.: 424210

Takeda Pharmaceuticals Czech Republic s.r.o. (2)
Skretova 490/12, 120 00, Prague, Czech Republic
Tel.: (420) 234722722
Web Site: https://www.takeda.com
Sales Range: $25-49.9 Million
Emp.: 22
Pharmaceuticals Mfr
N.A.I.C.S.: 325412

Takeda Pharmaceuticals Korea Co., Ltd (2)
12th Floor KT&G Kosmo Daechi Tower
945-10 Daechi-dong, Gangnam-gu, Seoul,
135-280, Korea (South)
Tel.: (82) 234840800
Emp.: 20
Pharmaceutical Product Whslr
N.A.I.C.S.: 424210

Takeda Pharmaceuticals Mexico, S.A. de C.V (2)
Omega Building Campos Eliseos 345 4th
Floor Colony Chapultepec Polanco, Mexico,
11560, Mexico
Tel.: (52) 55 5005 1300
Web Site: http://www.takedamexico.com
Pharmaceutical Product Whslr
N.A.I.C.S.: 424210

Takeda Pharmaceuticals Nordics AB (2)
Bjornstigen 87, 112 46, Stockholm, Sulna,
Sweden
Tel.: (46) 858613580
Web Site: http://www.takeda.se
Emp.: 50
Pharmaceuticals Mfr
N.A.I.C.S.: 325412

Takeda Pharmaceuticals Slovakia s.r.o. (2)
Svatoplukova II 18892/ 2 A, 821 08, Bratislava, Slovakia
Tel.: (421) 220602600
Web Site: https://www.takeda.com
Sales Range: $25-49.9 Million
Emp.: 30
Pharmaceuticals Mfr
N.A.I.C.S.: 325412

Takeda Pharmaceuticals Taiwan (2)
17F No 1 Songgao Road, Xinyi District, Taipei, Taiwan
Tel.: (886) 800008999
Web Site: https://www.takeda.com
Sales Range: $25-49.9 Million
Emp.: 40
Pharmaceuticals Mfr
N.A.I.C.S.: 424210

Takeda UK Limited (2)
1 Kingdom Street, London, W2 6BD, Bucks,
United Kingdom (100%)
Tel.: (44) 3333000181
Web Site: https://www.takeda.com
Sales Range: $10-24.9 Million
Emp.: 60
Sales of Pharmaceuticals
N.A.I.C.S.: 424210

Tianjin Takeda Pharmaceuticals Co., Ltd. (2)
No 11 Xinghua Road, Xiqing District, Tianjin, 300385, China (75%)
Tel.: (86) 2223970011
Web Site: https://www.takeda.com.cn
Pharmaceuticals Mfr & Sales
N.A.I.C.S.: 325412

Joint Venture (Non-US):

Zydus Nycomed Healthcare Private Ltd. (2)
C 4 MIDC Village Pawne, Thane-Belapur
Road, Vashi, 400 705, Navi Mumbai, India
Tel.: (91) 2227682666
Web Site: http://www.zydusnycomed.com
Sales Range: $50-74.9 Million
Emp.: 240
Pharmaceuticals Mfr
N.A.I.C.S.: 325412

Ravi Chandran (Mng Dir)

Takeda Pharmaceuticals Limited Liability Company (1)
st Usacheva House 2 Building 1 Business
Center Fusion Park, 4th and 5th Floor,
119048, Moscow, Russia
Tel.: (7) 4959335511
Web Site: http://www.takeda.com
Pharmaceuticals Product Mfr
N.A.I.C.S.: 325412

TAKEEI CORPORATION
Shiba Park Building A-10F 2-4-1
Shibakouen, Minato-ku, Tokyo, 105-0011, Japan
Tel.: (81) 363616820
Web Site: http://www.takeei.co.jp
Year Founded: 1977
2151—(TKS)
Rev.: $345,828,210
Assets: $735,956,690
Liabilities: $476,720,790
Net Worth: $259,235,900
Earnings: $16,185,050
Emp.: 1,304
Fiscal Year-end: 03/31/20
Waste Recycling Services
N.A.I.C.S.: 562111
Mamoru Mitsumoto (Chm)

Subsidiaries:

FUJI CAR MANUFACTURING Co., Ltd. (1)
13-1 Chishiro-cho, Moriyama, 524-0034,
Shiga, Japan
Tel.: (81) 775831235
Web Site: http://www.fujicar.com
Forging Machine Mfr
N.A.I.C.S.: 333517
Meguru Torii (Pres)

Gypro Co., Ltd. (1)
32 Shinmachi, Yashio, 340-0807, Saitama,
Japan
Tel.: (81) 489332181
Web Site: http://www.gypro.co.jp
Emp.: 22
Industrial Waste Recycling Services
N.A.I.C.S.: 562111

Shinshu Takeei Co., Ltd. (1)
1749 Kamisuwa, Suwa, 392-0009, Nagano,
Japan
Tel.: (81) 266580022
Web Site: http://www.shinshu-takeei.co.jp
Emp.: 64
Waste Disposal Services
N.A.I.C.S.: 562211

TOKAI TECHNO Co., Ltd. (1)
Umaokoshi chome No 4 No 18, Yokkaichi,
510-0023, Mie, Japan
Tel.: (81) 593325122
Web Site: http://www.tokai-techno.com
Emp.: 117
Environmental Consulting Services
N.A.I.C.S.: 541620

Takeei Green Recycling Co., Ltd. (1)
4838 Kamiyoshida, Fujiyoshida, 403-0005,
Japan
Tel.: (81) 555233611
Web Site: http://www.takeeigr.co.jp
Emp.: 43
Waste Disposal Services
N.A.I.C.S.: 562211

Takeei Metal Co., Ltd. (1)
512-8 Chiyo, Aoi-ku, Shizuoka, 421-1212,
Shizuoka, Japan
Tel.: (81) 542770202
Web Site: http://www.takeeimetal.co.jp
Waste Disposal Services
N.A.I.C.S.: 562211

Top Planning Japan Co., Ltd. (1)
3-14 Nihonbashi Koamicho, Chuo-ku, Tokyo, 103-0016, Japan
Tel.: (81) 336607720
Web Site: http://www.tpjp.co.jp
Emp.: 50
Civil Engineering Services
N.A.I.C.S.: 541330

TAKEFUJI CORPORATION

INTERNATIONAL PUBLIC

15-1 Nishi Shinjuku 8-chome,
Shinjuku-ku, Tokyo, 163-8654, Japan
Tel.: (81) 333658000
Web Site: http://www.takefuji.co.jp
Year Founded: 1966
Sales Range: $1-4.9 Billion
Emp.: 2,103
Consumer Financial Services
N.A.I.C.S.: 522210
Taketeru Takei (Exec VP)

Subsidiaries:

TakeOne Co., Ltd. (1)
Otemae Center Building 10F 1-2-15
Otemae, Chuo-ku, Osaka, 540-0008, Japan
Tel.: (81) 669447577
Web Site: http://www.takeone.jp
Sales Range: $50-74.9 Million
Emp.: 102
Multi-Media Production Services
N.A.I.C.S.: 516120
Tame Mori Takashi (Pres)

TAKEMOTO YOHKI CO., LTD.
2-21-5 Matsugaya, Taito-ku, Tokyo,
111-0036, Japan
Tel.: (81) 338456107
Web Site: https://takemotopkg.com
4248—(TKS)
Rev.: $101,507,530
Assets: $127,045,710
Liabilities: $48,984,810
Net Worth: $78,060,900
Earnings: $2,084,460
Emp.: 826
Fiscal Year-end: 12/31/23
Plastic Packaging Container Mfr
N.A.I.C.S.: 326199
Takahiro Fukazawa (Mng Dir)

Subsidiaries:

Shanghai Takemoto Packages Co., Ltd (1)
Room 2508-2512 BHC Center West Tower
2218, Pudong New District, Shanghai,
201204, China
Tel.: (86) 215 812 3999
Web Site: https://www.takemotosh.com
Emp.: 78
Plastic Container Mfr
N.A.I.C.S.: 332999

Plant (Domestic):

Shanghai Takemoto Packages Co., Ltd - Shanghai Factory (2)
No 501 Kangyi Road Kangqiao Industry
Pudong, Shanghai, 201315, China
Tel.: (86) 2158128040
Plastic Container Distr
N.A.I.C.S.: 424910

TAKEMOTO PACKAGING (THAILAND) CO., LTD. (1)
86/ 1 Thai Virawat Building 16th Floor Zone
E Krung Thonburi Road, Bang Lamphu
Lang Khlong Sah, Bangkok, 10600, Thailand
Tel.: (66) 21182723
Web Site: https://www.takemototh.com
Plastic Container Distr
N.A.I.C.S.: 424910

Takemoto Netherlands B.V. (1)
Grasbeemd 1, 5705 DE, Helmond, Netherlands
Tel.: (31) 638454812
Plastic Container Distr
N.A.I.C.S.: 424910

Takemoto Yohki (Kunshan) Co., Ltd (1)
No 433 Taji Road, Shipai Industrial Zone,
Kunshan, 215312, Jiangsu, China
Tel.: (86) 51257688333
Emp.: 450
Plastic Container Distr
N.A.I.C.S.: 424910

TAKENAKA CORPORATION
1-13 Hommachi 4-chome Chuo-ku,
Osaka, 541 0053, Japan
Tel.: (81) 662521201

AND PRIVATE COMPANIES

Web Site: http://www.takenaka.co.jp
Sales Range: $5-14.9 Billion
Emp.: 7,570
Architecture, Engineering & Construction
N.A.I.C.S.: 541310
Toichi Takenaka *(Chm)*

Subsidiaries:

Asahi Facilities Inc. (1)
2-5-14 Minamisuna, Koto-ku, Tokyo, 136-0076, Japan **(100%)**
Tel.: (81) 356831181
Web Site: http://www.asahifm.com
Emp.: 1,278
Insurance, Building Maintenance & Real Estate Services
N.A.I.C.S.: 531390
Yoshiyuki Hirano *(Exec Mng Officer)*

Chang Cheng-Takenaka Construction Co., Ltd. (1)
Fanila Daxia Room 405, Dong Cheng District, Beijing, China **(100%)**
Tel.: (86) 1065882177
Sales Range: $25-49.9 Million
Emp.: 165
Design Services
N.A.I.C.S.: 541310

P.T. Takenaka Indonesia (1)
MidPlaza 1 18th Floor Jl Jend Sudirman Kav 10-11, Jakarta, 10220, Indonesia **(100%)**
Tel.: (62) 21 5735660
Web Site: http://www.takenaka.com
Sales Range: $25-49.9 Million
Emp.: 180
Design Services
N.A.I.C.S.: 541310

Tak Development, Inc. (1)
70 E 55th St, New York, NY 10019-2220
Tel.: (212) 489-6001
Web Site: http://www.takenaka.com
Sales Range: $25-49.9 Million
Emp.: 3
Engineering & Design Services
N.A.I.C.S.: 541310
Akhiro Tachibana *(Pres)*

Tak Engineering Osaka, Inc. (1)
1-13-4 Chome Honmachi Chuo-ku, Osaka, 541 0053, Japan **(100%)**
Tel.: (81) 662521201
Web Site: http://www.takenaka.co.jp
Sales Range: $1-4.9 Billion
Design & Construction Services
N.A.I.C.S.: 541310

Tak Hawaii, Inc. (1)
745 Fort St Ste 1608, Honolulu, HI 96813-4112
Tel.: (808) 523-5899
Web Site: http://www.takenaka.co.jp
Design Services
N.A.I.C.S.: 541310

Tak Systems Corporation (1)
1-13 4-Chome Hommachi, Chuo-ku, Osaka, 541-0053, Japan
Tel.: (81) 663738231
Web Site: http://www.tak-s.co.jp
Design & Engineering Services
N.A.I.C.S.: 541310

Takenaka (China) Construction Co.,Ltd. (1)
Middle Yincheng Rd 488 Taiping Finance Tower, Shanghai, 200120, China
Tel.: (86) 2168591201
Sales Range: $25-49.9 Million
Emp.: 170
Engineeering Services
N.A.I.C.S.: 541330

Takenaka (Malaysia) Sdn. Bhd. (1)
Lot 2 01 Level 2 Menara Manulife No 6 Jalan Gelenggang, Damansara Heights, 50490, Kuala Lumpur, Malaysia **(100%)**
Tel.: (60) 320951000
Web Site: http://www.takenaka.com
Sales Range: $25-49.9 Million
Emp.: 50
Architectural & Design Services
N.A.I.C.S.: 541310

Takenaka (U.K.) Ltd. (1)
Tavistock House S Tavistock Sq, London,
WC1H 9HR, United Kingdom
Tel.: (44) 2072554060
Web Site: http://www.takenaka.co.uk
Sales Range: $25-49.9 Million
Emp.: 9
Architectural Services
N.A.I.C.S.: 541310
Kuniyasu Shimizu *(Gen Mgr)*

Takenaka Civil Engineering & Construction Co., Ltd. (1)
1-1-1 Shinsuna, Koto-ku, Tokyo, 136 0075, Japan **(100%)**
Tel.: (81) 3 6810 5000
Web Site: http://www.takenaka-doboku.co.jp
Sales Range: $400-449.9 Million
Emp.: 1,600
Engineering & Construction Services
N.A.I.C.S.: 237990

Takenaka Corporation (1)
167 Jalan Bukit Merah 16-10 Tower 5, Singapore, 150167, Singapore **(100%)**
Tel.: (65) 6899 8989
Web Site: http://www.takenaka.co.jp
Sales Range: $25-49.9 Million
Emp.: 200
Environmental Architectural Services
N.A.I.C.S.: 541310

Takenaka Corporation USA (1)
555 W Pierce Rd Ste 190, Itasca, IL 60143-2628
Tel.: (630) 250-3400
Web Site: http://www.takenakausa.com
Sales Range: $25-49.9 Million
Emp.: 8
General Contractors
N.A.I.C.S.: 541310

Division (Domestic):

Takenaka Corporation USA (2)
56 S Park Blvd, Greenwood, IN 46143-8836 **(100%)**
Tel.: (317) 881-1610
Sales Range: $25-49.9 Million
Design & Architectural Services
N.A.I.C.S.: 541310

Takenaka Europe (1)
Kabelweg 21, 1014 BA, Amsterdam, Netherlands **(100%)**
Tel.: (31) 206866101
Sales Range: $25-49.9 Million
Emp.: 15
Architecture, Engineering & Construction Services
N.A.I.C.S.: 541310

Takenaka Europe GmbH (1)
Oststrasse 10, 40211, Dusseldorf, Germany **(100%)**
Tel.: (49) 211167940
Web Site: http://www.takenaka.eu
Sales Range: $25-49.9 Million
Emp.: 100
Architectural Services
N.A.I.C.S.: 541310
Masayuki Takinami *(Pres & Mng Dir)*

Branch (Domestic):

Takenaka Europe GmbH, Frankfurt (2)
Friedrich-Ebert-Anlage 56, Frankfurt, 60325, Germany **(100%)**
Tel.: (49) 69748059
Web Site: http://www.takenaka-eu.com
Construction & Architectural Services
N.A.I.C.S.: 541310
Beom-Yong Sung *(Office Mgr)*

Branch (Non-US):

Takenaka Europe GmbH, Italy (2)
Via San Maurilio 13 14, 20145, Milan, Italy
Tel.: (39) 028056532
Web Site: http://www.takenaka.it
Sales Range: $25-49.9 Million
Emp.: 3
Design & Architectural Services
N.A.I.C.S.: 541310

Takenaka Europe GmbH, Spain (2)
Plaza Doctor Letamendi 37 4-4, 08007, Barcelona, Spain **(100%)**
Tel.: (34) 934097273
Web Site: http://www.takenaka-eu.com
Sales Range: $10-24.9 Million
Emp.: 6
Design & Architectural Services
N.A.I.C.S.: 541310

Takenaka Europe GmbH, Belgium (1)
Airport Business Park Berkenlaan 1, 1831, Diegem, Belgium **(100%)**
Tel.: (32) 27145110
Web Site: http://www.takenaka-eu.com
Sales Range: $25-49.9 Million
Emp.: 16
Engineering & Construction Services
N.A.I.C.S.: 236210
M. Takinami *(Gen Mgr)*

Takenaka Hungaria kft (1)
Varmegye utca 3-5, Budapest, 1052, Hungary
Tel.: (36) 1 486 2360
Web Site: http://www.takenaka.com
Emp.: 40
R&D Laboratory Construction Services
N.A.I.C.S.: 541310
Kitori Idaki *(Gen Mgr)*

Takenaka India Private Limited (1)
805 8th Floor Vatika City point Mehrauli Gurgaon Road, Gurgaon, 122 002, Haryana, India
Tel.: (91) 1244835900
Web Site: http://www.takenaka.com
Emp.: 150
Commercial Building Construction Services
N.A.I.C.S.: 237990
Minuru Maekawa *(Pres)*

Takenaka Research & Development Institute (1)
5-1 1-chome Otsuka, Inzai, 270-1395, Chiba, Japan
Tel.: (81) 476471700
Web Site: http://www.takenaka.co.jp
Research, Engineering & Design Services
N.A.I.C.S.: 541715

Thai Takenaka International Ltd. (1)
Silom Complex 26 Fl 191 Silom Rd, Bangrak, Bangkok, 10500, Thailand **(100%)**
Tel.: (66) 22662800
Web Site: http://www.takenaka.com
Sales Range: $75-99.9 Million
Emp.: 400
Design Services
N.A.I.C.S.: 541310

TAKEUCHI MFG. CO., LTD.
205 Uwandaira Sakaki-machi, Hanishina-gun, Nagano, 389-0605, Japan
Tel.: (81) 268811100
Web Site: http://www.takeuchi-mfg.co.jp
Year Founded: 1963
Sales Range: $350-399.9 Million
Emp.: 450
Construction Machinery
N.A.I.C.S.: 333120
Akio Takeuchi *(Chm)*

Subsidiaries:

TAKEUCHI QINGDAO MFG. CO., LTD. (1)
2238 South Kunlunshan Road Huangdao Zone, Qingdao, China
Tel.: (86) 53286837266
Web Site: http://www.takeuchi-china.com
Construction Equipment Mfr
N.A.I.C.S.: 333120
Akio Takeuchi *(Chm)*

Takeuchi France S.A.S. (1)
Zone Industrielle les Bethunes 3 Avenue de la Mare, 95310, Saint-Ouen-l'Aumone, France
Tel.: (33) 134643030
Web Site: http://www.takeuchi-france.com
Sales Range: $25-49.9 Million
Emp.: 18
Professional Equipment & Supplies Whslr
N.A.I.C.S.: 423490
Takashi Mamba *(Mng Dir)*

Takeuchi Mfg. (U.K.) Ltd. (1)
Units East - 2B John Boyd Dunlop Drive, Kingsway Business Park, Rochdale, OL16 4NG, United Kingdom
Tel.: (44) 1706657722
Web Site: http://www.takeuchi-mfg.co.uk
Sales Range: $25-49.9 Million
Emp.: 21
Construction Machinery Mfr
N.A.I.C.S.: 333120
T. Tamru *(Gen Mgr)*

Takeuchi Mfg. (U.S.), Ltd. (1)
519 Bonnie Valentine Way, Pendergrass, GA 30567
Tel.: (706) 693-3600
Web Site: http://www.takeuchi-us.com
Sales Range: $25-49.9 Million
Emp.: 50
Construction Machinery Mfr
N.A.I.C.S.: 333120
Jeff Stewart *(VP & Gen Mgr)*

Takeuchi Mfg. Co., Ltd. - Togura Plant (1)
174 Uchikawa, Chikuma-shi, Nagano, 389-0802, Japan
Tel.: (81) 262765577
Construction Equipment Mfr
N.A.I.C.S.: 333120

TAKI CHEMICAL CO., LTD.
2 Midoromachi Befu-cho, Kakogawa, 675-0124, Hyogo, Japan
Tel.: (81) 794376002
Web Site: http://www.takichem.co.jp
Year Founded: 1885
4025—(TKS)
Rev.: $247,100,680
Assets: $363,709,910
Liabilities: $123,366,000
Net Worth: $240,343,910
Earnings: $9,614,040
Emp.: 474
Fiscal Year-end: 12/31/23
Chemical Fertilizer Mfr & Whslr
N.A.I.C.S.: 325312
Takamoto Taki *(Pres)*

TAKIHYO CO., LTD.
23F 24F Nagoya Lucent Tower 6-1 Ushijima-cho, Nishi-ku, Nagoya, 451-8688, Aichi, Japan
Tel.: (81) 525877111   JP
Web Site: https://www.takihyo.co.jp
Year Founded: 1751
9982—(TKS)
Rev.: $409,348,240
Assets: $344,254,950
Liabilities: $129,534,300
Net Worth: $214,720,650
Earnings: $5,452,210
Emp.: 537
Fiscal Year-end: 02/29/24
Textile Mfr & Sales
N.A.I.C.S.: 424990
Kazuo Taki *(CEO)*

Subsidiaries:

Takihyo (H.K.) Co., Ltd. (1)
Room504/505 East Ocean Centre 98 Granville Road T S T, Kowloon, China (Hong Kong)
Tel.: (852) 23662599
Web Site: http://www.takihyo.co.jp
Sales Range: $50-74.9 Million
Emp.: 5
Clothing & Furnishings Whslr
N.A.I.C.S.: 424350

Takihyo Kemica Co., Ltd. (1)
Th No2 Building 2-11-27, Nishiki Naka-Ku, Nagoya, 4600003, Japan
Tel.: (81) 522221170
Chemical Product Whslr
N.A.I.C.S.: 424690

Takihyo Operation Plaza Co., Ltd. (1)
2094-3 Shimoi, Shimoicho, Owariasahi, Japan
Tel.: (81) 561547013
Non-Durable Goods Whslr
N.A.I.C.S.: 424990

TAKIZAWA HAM CO., LTD.

TAKIZAWA HAM CO., LTD.

TAKIZAWA HAM CO., LTD.—(Continued)
556 Izumigawamachi, Tochigi, 328-8586, Japan
Tel.: (81) 282235640
Web Site: http://www.takizawaham.co.jp
Year Founded: 1950
2293—(TKS)
Rev.: $285,337,360
Assets: $130,525,120
Liabilities: $93,392,640
Net Worth: $37,132,480
Earnings: $1,684,320
Emp.: 692
Fiscal Year-end: 03/31/22
Meat Product Mfr & Distr
N.A.I.C.S.: 311612
Taro Takizawa *(Pres & CEO)*

TAKOR GROUP LTD
Unit 28 12 Cowcher Place, Belmont, 6104, WA, Australia
Tel.: (61) 69136358337
Web Site: http://www.takor.com.au
Year Founded: 2009
Geospatial Technology Services
N.A.I.C.S.: 541370

TAKORADI LIMITED
Level 9 10 Loftus Street, Sydney, 2000, NSW, Australia
Tel.: (61) 29 252 6844
Web Site: http://www.takoradi.com.au
Exploration of Minerals
N.A.I.C.S.: 213115
Brendan Jones *(Sec)*

TAKOVO A.D.
ul Vaska Pope br 4, Belgrade, Serbia
Tel.: (381) 11 20 69 300
Web Site: http://www.swisslion-takovo.com
Year Founded: 1997
Sales Range: $10-24.9 Million
Ice Cream Mfr
N.A.I.C.S.: 311520

TAKOVO OSIGURANJE A.D.
Dr Zorana Dindica 15a, 34000, Kragujevac, Serbia
Tel.: (381) 34 303 000
Web Site: http://www.takovo-osiguranje.rs
Year Founded: 1992
Sales Range: $25-49.9 Million
Insurance Agency Services
N.A.I.C.S.: 524210
Snezana Zivkovic *(Gen Dir)*

TAKOVO TRANSPORT A.D.
Pancevacki put 20, Belgrade, Serbia
Tel.: (381) 112993484
Year Founded: 1998
TATR—(BEL)
Rev.: $23,898
Assets: $111,013
Liabilities: $134,087
Net Worth: ($23,074)
Earnings: $696
Emp.: 1
Fiscal Year-end: 12/31/23
Food Transportation Services
N.A.I.C.S.: 484121
Dragan Dokic *(CEO & Exec Dir)*

TAKSHEEL SOLUTIONS LTD
Lanco Hills Technology Park Pvt Ltd (SEZ), Survey 201 Manikonda, Rajendra Nagar Mandal, Hyderabad, 500089, Andhra Pradesh, India
Tel.: (91) 4040215915
Web Site: http://www.taksheel.com
Year Founded: 1999
Sales Range: $300-349.9 Million
Emp.: 65
IT Services & Software
N.A.I.C.S.: 541519
Pavan Kumar Kuchana *(Chm & Mng Dir)*

TAKUMA CO., LTD.
2-2-33 Kinrakuji-cho, Amagasaki, 660-0806, Hyogo, Japan
Tel.: (81) 664832630
Web Site: https://www.takuma.co.jp
Year Founded: 1938
6013—(TKS)
Rev.: $985,987,260
Assets: $1,263,699,800
Liabilities: $529,989,800
Net Worth: $733,710,000
Earnings: $57,863,940
Emp.: 4,278
Fiscal Year-end: 03/31/24
N.A.I.C.S.: 334512
Takaaki Kato *(Chm)*

Subsidiaries:

Anan High Trust Co., Ltd. (1)
1-5 Kokatsu Tachibana-cho, Anan, 779-1631, Tokushima, Japan
Tel.: (81) 88 449 5823
Web Site: https://www.ecopark-anan.com
Waste Water Treatment Services
N.A.I.C.S.: 221320

Biopower Katsuta Co., Ltd. (1)
1974-1 Koya, Hitachinaka, Ibaraki, 312-0002, Japan
Tel.: (81) 29 270 3341
Web Site: http://www.takuma.co.jp
Eletric Power Generation Services
N.A.I.C.S.: 221118

Campo Recycle Plaza Co., Ltd. (1)
Takaya Nishiya Sonobe-cho, Nantan, 622-0032, Kyoto, Japan
Tel.: (81) 771 68 3636
Web Site: http://www.c-rp.co.jp
Emp.: 60
Industrial Wastes Treatment Services
N.A.I.C.S.: 562219

Dan-Takuma Technologies Inc. (1)
LIVMO Rising Bldg 3-19-1 Shinyokohama, Kohoku-ku, Yokohama, 222-0033, Kanagawa, Japan
Tel.: (81) 454711101
Sales Range: $50-74.9 Million
Emp.: 81
Industrial Machinery & Equipment Merchant Whslr
N.A.I.C.S.: 423830

Ecos Yonezawa Co., Ltd. (1)
7028-1 Yanazawa, Yonezawa, 992-0077, Yamagata, Japan
Tel.: (81) 238394050
Web Site: https://www.ecos-y.co.jp
Industrial Wastes Treatment Services
N.A.I.C.S.: 562219

Energy Mate Co., Ltd. (1)
JRE Midosuji Daiwa Building 12F 3-6-8 Kyutaromachi, Chuo-ku, Osaka, 541-0056, Japan
Tel.: (81) 662416200
Sales Range: $75-99.9 Million
Emp.: 10
Steam & Air-Conditioning Supply
N.A.I.C.S.: 221330

Fujisawa High Trust Co., Ltd. (1)
2168 Ishikawa, Fujisawa, 252-0815, Kanagawa, Japan
Tel.: (81) 466455411
Industrial Machinery & Equipment Merchant Whslr
N.A.I.C.S.: 423830
Mitsunobu Masuda *(Gen Mgr)*

Hitachinaka-Tokai High Trust Co., Ltd. (1)
103-2 Shinkocho, Hitachinaka, 312-0005, Ibaraki, Japan
Tel.: (81) 29 265 5371
Web Site: https://www.hitachinaka-tokai-ht.com
Facility Management Services
N.A.I.C.S.: 561210

Hokkaido Sanitary Maintenance Co., Ltd. (1)
In Daigo Building 5-11 Odori Nishi, Chuo-ku, Sapporo, 060-0042, Japan
Tel.: (81) 112218398
Web Site: https://tsukurimo.jp
Emp.: 55
Hazardous Waste Treatment & Disposal & Facility Maintenance Services
N.A.I.C.S.: 562211

Hokutan High Trust Co., Ltd. (1)
943 Takenocho Booka, Toyooka, 669-6331, Hyogo, Japan
Tel.: (81) 79 621 9111
Web Site: https://www.hokutan-ht.com
Waste Disposal Services
N.A.I.C.S.: 562211

Ichihara New Energy Co., Ltd. (1)
733 Mandano, Ichihara, 290-0549, Chiba, Japan
Tel.: (81) 436508300
Industrial Wastes Treatment Services
N.A.I.C.S.: 562219

Imabari High Trust Co., Ltd. (1)
394 Machiyakou, Imabari, 799-1514, Ehime, Japan
Tel.: (81) 89 835 5181
Boiler Mfr
N.A.I.C.S.: 332410

Iwate-Kenpoku Clean Co., Ltd. (1)
48-34 Esashiya 20, Kunohe, 028-6505, Iwate, Japan
Tel.: (81) 195424085
Emp.: 45
Industrial Wastes Treatment Services
N.A.I.C.S.: 562219

Kankyo Sol-Tech Co., Ltd. (1)
1-2-1 Shinhama Arai-cho, Takasago, 676-0008, Hyogo, Japan
Tel.: (81) 794436508
Sales Range: $10-24.9 Million
Emp.: 48
Temporary Help Service
N.A.I.C.S.: 561320

Kashihara High Trust Co., Ltd. (1)
1038-2 Kawanishi-cho, Kashihara, 634-0826, Nara, Japan
Tel.: (81) 74 426 6227
Boiler Mfr
N.A.I.C.S.: 332410

Katsuta Co., Ltd. (1)
1968-2 Takano, Hitachinaka, 312-0002, Ibaraki, Japan
Tel.: (81) 292703711
Web Site: https://eco-katsuta.com
Sales Range: $25-49.9 Million
Emp.: 57
Waste Collection & Environment Management Services
N.A.I.C.S.: 562998

Kurume High Trust Co., Ltd. (1)
2225 Hatchojima Miyanojinmachi, Kurume, 839-0805, Fukuoka, Japan
Tel.: (81) 94 227 7490
Web Site: https://www.kurume-ht.com
Waste Treatment Facility Services
N.A.I.C.S.: 562998

Kyoritsu Setsubi Co., Ltd. (1)
No 38 Yurikahara 5 -chome, Kita-ku, Sapporo, 002-8081, Japan
Tel.: (81) 117702811
Web Site: https://kyouritu-s.co.jp
Installing Building Equipment Installation Services
N.A.I.C.S.: 238290

Midac Fujinomiya Co., Ltd. (1)
3507-20 Yamamiya, Fujinomiya, Shizuoka, 418-0111, Japan
Tel.: (81) 544585858
Web Site: http://www.midacfujinomiya.jp
Sales Range: $25-49.9 Million
Emp.: 100
Waste Treatment & Disposal
N.A.I.C.S.: 562211

Nagaizumi High Trust Co., Ltd. (1)
374-12 Higashino, Nagaizumi-machi Suntogun, Shizuoka, 411-0931, Japan
Tel.: (81) 559892268
Industrial Machinery & Equipment Merchant Whslr
N.A.I.C.S.: 423830

Nippon Thermoener Co., Ltd. (1)
Shirokanedai Bldg 3-2-10 Shirokanedai, Minato-ku, Tokyo, 108-0071, Japan
Tel.: (81) 364088251
Web Site: https://www.n-thermo.com
Sales Range: $50-74.9 Million
Emp.: 100
Industrial Machinery & Equipment Merchant Whslr
N.A.I.C.S.: 423830

R.B.N. Co., Ltd. (1)
3059-20 Nakajima, Shikama-ku, 672-8035, Hyogo, Himeji, Japan
Tel.: (81) 792431200
Sales Range: $25-49.9 Million
Emp.: 30
Commercial & Service Industry Machinery Mfr
N.A.I.C.S.: 333310

Siam Takuma Co., Ltd (1)
77/53 Sinn Sathorn Tower 15th Floor Krungthonburi Road, Klongtonsai Klongsarn, Bangkok, 10600, Thailand
Tel.: (66) 24385616
Sales Range: $25-49.9 Million
Emp.: 13
Electronic Parts & Equipment Merchant Whslr
N.A.I.C.S.: 423690

Sun Plant Co., Ltd. (1)
1-1-7 Higashi -Nihonbashi, Higashi-Nihonbashi Chuo-ku, Tokyo, 103-0004, Japan
Tel.: (81) 358250921
Web Site: https://sunplant.co.jp
Emp.: 107
Electric Equipment Mfr
N.A.I.C.S.: 335999

Suwako High Trust Co., Ltd. (1)
4769-14 Azauchiyama, Okaya, 394-0055, Nagano, Japan
Tel.: (81) 26 678 1590
Web Site: https://www.suwako-ht.jp
Hazardous Waste Treatment Services
N.A.I.C.S.: 562211

Taiden Environtech Co., Ltd. (1)
7F No 16 Lane 35 Jihu Rd, Neihu District, Taipei, 114-92, Taiwan
Tel.: (886) 226597137
Sales Range: $25-49.9 Million
Emp.: 12
Heavy & Civil Engineering Construction
N.A.I.C.S.: 237990

Takuma Co., Ltd. - Harima Factory (1)
1-2-1 Shinhama, Arai-cho, Takasago, 676-8540, Hyogo, Japan
Tel.: (81) 794436511
Cooling Equipment Mfr
N.A.I.C.S.: 333415

Takuma Energy Co., Ltd. (1)
Takuma Bldg 2-2-33 Kinrakuji-cho, Amagasaki, 660-0806, Hyogo, Japan
Tel.: (81) 66 487 4870
Electric Power Distribution Services
N.A.I.C.S.: 221122

Takuma Engineering Co., Ltd. (1)
Takuma Building 2-2-33, Kinrakuji-cho, Amagasaki, 660-0806, Japan
Tel.: (81) 664874820
Sales Range: $25-49.9 Million
Emp.: 60
Engineeering Services
N.A.I.C.S.: 541330

Takuma Plant Co., Ltd. (1)
2-2-33 Kinrakuji-cho, Amagasaki, 660-0806, Hyogo, Japan
Tel.: (81) 66 488 8434
Web Site: https://www.takuma-plant.co.jp
Water Treatment Equipment & Parts Distr
N.A.I.C.S.: 423720

Takuma Plant Service Co., Ltd. (1)
2-2-27 Kinrakuji-cho, Amagasaki, 660-0806, Hyogo, Japan
Tel.: (81) 6 6488 8434
Web Site: http://www.takuma-ps.com
Boiler Plant Construction Services
N.A.I.C.S.: 237990

Takuma System Control Co., Ltd. (1)
Takuma Building 2-2-33, Kinrakuji-cho,

Amagasaki, 660-0806, Hyogo, Japan
Tel.: (81) 664874830
Custom Computer Programming Services
N.A.I.C.S.: 541511

Takuma Technos Co., Ltd. (1)
Shibaura Rene Site Tower 3-9-1 Shibaura, Minato-ku, Tokyo, 108-0023, Japan
Tel.: (81) 354394171
Emp.: 1,990
Waste Treatment Services
N.A.I.C.S.: 562211

Takuma Technos Hokkaido Co., Ltd. (1)
Daigo Bldg 5-11 Ohdori Nishi, Chuo-ku, Sapporo, 060-0042, Japan
Tel.: (81) 112214128
Waste Management Services
N.A.I.C.S.: 562998

Techno Links Inc. (1)
1270-14 Hagisono, Chigasaki, 253-0071, Kanagawa, Japan
Tel.: (81) 46 783 6225
Web Site: https://www.techno-l.co.jp
Pneumatic Conveying Equipment Mfr & Distr
N.A.I.C.S.: 333922

Tochigi High Trust Co., Ltd. (1)
18-3 Kinugaoka, Moka, 321-4367, Tochigi, Japan
Tel.: (81) 285833966
Emp.: 51
Industrial Machinery & Equipment Merchant Whslr
N.A.I.C.S.: 423830

TAKUNG ART CO., LTD.
Room 709 Tower 2 Admiralty Centre 18 Harcourt Road Admiralty, Hong Kong, China (Hong Kong)
Tel.: (852) 31580977 DE
Web Site: http://www.takungae.com
Year Founded: 2009
MI—(NYSEAMEX)
Rev.: $2,153,515
Assets: $73,692,097
Liabilities: $12,888,459
Net Worth: $60,803,638
Earnings: $5,203,564
Emp.: 27
Fiscal Year-end: 12/31/23
Online Art Retailer
N.A.I.C.S.: 459920
Yaobin Wang *(CFO)*

Subsidiaries:

Hong Kong Takung Art Company Limited (1)
Ste 2003 Hutchison House 10 Harcourt Road, Central, China (Hong Kong)
Tel.: (852) 39035777
Web Site: http://www.en.takungae.com
Art Dealer Services
N.A.I.C.S.: 459920

TAKUNI GROUP PUBLIC COMPANY LIMITED
140/1 Takuni Building Nawincharoenthap Alley Kanchanaphisek Road, Bang Khae Subdistrict Bang Khae District, Bangkok, 10160, Thailand
Tel.: (66) 24552888
Web Site: https://www.takunigroup.com
Year Founded: 1995
TAKUNI—(THA)
Rev.: $114,463,065
Assets: $90,549,461
Liabilities: $42,211,771
Net Worth: $48,337,690
Earnings: $4,250,362
Emp.: 4,527
Fiscal Year-end: 12/31/23
Liquefied Petroleum Gas
N.A.I.C.S.: 213112
Chatchai Payuhanawichai *(Chm)*

Subsidiaries:

CAZ (Thailand) Company Limited (1)
239 Huaypong-Nongbon Rd, T Huaypong A Muangrayong, Rayong, 21150, Thailand
Tel.: (66) 3 860 6242
Web Site: https://www.caz.co.th
Engineering & Construction Services
N.A.I.C.S.: 541330

G Gas Logistics Company Limited (1)
140/1 Soi Nawee Charoensap Kanchanaphisek Road, Bang Khae Subdistrict Bang Khae District, Bangkok, 10160, Thailand
Tel.: (66) 28028621
Web Site: https://www.ggaslogistics.com
Natural Gas Pipeline Distr
N.A.I.C.S.: 486210

Rajchapluek Engineering Company Limited (1)
140/1 Soi Navee Charoen Sap Kanchanaphisek Road, Bang Khae District, Bangkok, 10160, Thailand
Tel.: (66) 24552888
Web Site: http://www.rajchapleuk.com
Engineering Testing & Inspection Services
N.A.I.C.S.: 541330
Bunjob Chansathep *(Ops Mgr)*

Takuni (Thailand) Company Limited (1)
140/1 Takuni Building Nawincharoenthap Alley Kanchanaphisek Road, Bang Khae Subdistrict Bang Khae District, Bangkok, 10160, Thailand
Tel.: (66) 24552888
Web Site: https://www.takuni.com
Liquid Petroleum Gas Distr
N.A.I.C.S.: 424720

TAKWEEN ADVANCED INDUSTRIES
16th Floor Al Othman Office Towers King Saud Road, PO Box 2500, Al Khobar, 31952, Saudi Arabia
Tel.: (966) 138534355
Web Site: https://www.takweenai.com
Year Founded: 1993
1201—(SAU)
Rev.: $278,735,902
Assets: $440,382,882
Liabilities: $324,498,067
Net Worth: $115,884,815
Earnings: ($42,371,950)
Fiscal Year-end: 12/31/22
Plastics Product Mfr
N.A.I.C.S.: 326199
Abdulmohsen Mohammed Al-Othman *(Mng Dir)*

Subsidiaries:

Saudi Plastic Packaging System Company (1)
PO Box 34495, Jeddah, 21468, Saudi Arabia (100%)
Tel.: (966) 12 6380660
Web Site: http://www.plastico.com.sa
Coated & Laminated Paper Mfr
N.A.I.C.S.: 322220

Ultrapak Manufacturing Company Limited (1)
Warehouse City, PO Box 18092, Khomra District, Jeddah, 21415, Saudi Arabia
Tel.: (966) 12 636 0030
Web Site: http://www.ultrapakpet.com
Plastic Bottle Mfr & Distr
N.A.I.C.S.: 326160
Hani Aljamal *(Gen Mgr)*

TAL EDUCATION GROUP
5/F Tower B Heying Center Xiaoying west street, Haidian District, Beijing, 100085, China
Tel.: (86) 1052926692 Ky
Web Site: https://www.100tal.com
TAL—(NYSE)
Rev.: $4,390,907,000
Assets: $5,082,528,000
Liabilities: $1,080,266,000
Net Worth: $4,002,262,000
Earnings: ($1,136,115,000)
Emp.: 16,200
Fiscal Year-end: 02/28/22
K-12 Afterschool Tutoring Services
N.A.I.C.S.: 611691
Bangxin Zhang *(Founder & CEO)*

TAL LANKA HOTELS PLC
Tel.: (94) 112446622
Year Founded: 1980
TAJ.N0000—(COL)
Rev.: $12,410,233
Assets: $16,649,109
Liabilities: $21,281,050
Net Worth: ($4,631,941)
Earnings: $319,737
Fiscal Year-end: 03/31/24
Hotel & Restaurant Operator
N.A.I.C.S.: 721110
P. Verma *(Chm)*

TALAAT MOUSTAFA GROUP HOLDING COMPANY
34/36 Mussadak St, Cairo, Egypt
Tel.: (20) 233016701
Web Site: https://www.talaatmoustafa.com
Year Founded: 2007
Rev.: $507,274,210
Assets: $6,464,529,230
Liabilities: $4,458,797,533
Net Worth: $2,005,731,697
Earnings: $121,223,682
Fiscal Year-end: 12/31/19
Real Estate Development Services
N.A.I.C.S.: 531390
Tarek Talaat Moustafa *(Chm & Chm)*

TALAM TRANSFORM BERHAD
Unit 17 01 Level 17 Menara Maxisegar Jalan Pandan Indah 4/2, Pandan Indah, 55100, Kuala Lumpur, Malaysia
Tel.: (60) 342962000 MY
Web Site: https://www.ttransform.com.my
Year Founded: 1920
TALAMT—(KLS)
Rev.: $12,995,767
Assets: $137,920,212
Liabilities: $82,354,709
Net Worth: $55,565,503
Earnings: ($3,287,619)
Emp.: 84
Fiscal Year-end: 03/31/23
Property Development Services
N.A.I.C.S.: 531312
Kim Lan Chua *(Exec Dir)*

Subsidiaries:

Abra Development Sdn. Bhd. (1)
Menara Maxisegar Jalan Pandan Indah 4/2, Pandan Indah, 55100, Kuala Lumpur, Malaysia
Tel.: (60) 342971375
Property Development Services
N.A.I.C.S.: 237210

TALANT OPTRONICS (SUZHOU) CO., LTD.
2990 Taidong Road, Huangbu Town Xiangcheng District, Suzhou, 215143, Jiangsu, China
Tel.: (86) 8651266833338
Web Site: https://www.sz-talant.com
Year Founded: 2010
301045—(CHIN)
Rev.: $84,002,507
Assets: $166,793,211
Liabilities: $28,621,690
Net Worth: $138,171,521
Earnings: $1,244,676
Emp.: 600
Fiscal Year-end: 12/31/23
Electronic Component Mfr & Distr
N.A.I.C.S.: 334419
Tan Mei *(Chm)*

Subsidiaries:

Guangzhou Jinghao Photoelectric Technology Co., Ltd. (1)
No 88 Lianlin Road, Shiji Town Panyu District, Guangzhou, China
Tel.: (86) 2031179005
Backlight Product Mfr & Distr
N.A.I.C.S.: 334413

Suzhou Talant Optronlics Technology Co., Ltd. (1)
2990 Taidong Road, Huangbu Town Xiangcheng District, Suzhou, Jiangsu, China
Tel.: (86) 51266833338
Photoelectric Light Guide Plate Mfr & Distr
N.A.I.C.S.: 334413

TALANX AG
HDI-Platz 1, 30659, Hannover, Germany
Tel.: (49) 51137470 De
Web Site: https://www.talanx.com
Year Founded: 1996
TLX—(MUN)
Rev.: $50,486,805,200
Assets: $222,356,884,880
Liabilities: $201,324,503,120
Net Worth: $21,032,381,760
Earnings: $826,605,520
Emp.: 23,527
Fiscal Year-end: 12/31/20
Financial Investment Services
N.A.I.C.S.: 551112
Herbert K. Haas *(Chm-Supervisory Bd)*

Subsidiaries:

Argenta Underwriting Asia Pte. Ltd. (1)
138 Market Street CapitaGreen 04-03, Singapore, Singapore
Tel.: (65) 65366375
Transportation Insurance Services
N.A.I.C.S.: 524298

Commercial & Industrial Acceptances (Pty.) Ltd. (1)
13E Riley Road, Bedfordview, South Africa
Tel.: (27) 861242777
Web Site: https://cia.co.za
Building Insurance Services
N.A.I.C.S.: 531120

ERGO SIGORTA A.S. (1)
Saray Mah Dr Adnan Buyukdeniz Caddesi No 4 Akkom Ofis Park 2, Blok Kat 10-1 Umraniye, Istanbul, Turkiye
Tel.: (90) 216 666 71 00
Web Site: http://www.ergoturkiye.com
Reinsurance Services
N.A.I.C.S.: 524130

Firedart Engineering Underwriting Managers (Pty.) Ltd. (1)
Level 1 1 Bompas 1 Bompas Road, Dunkeld, Johannesburg, South Africa
Tel.: (27) 118331400
Web Site: https://firedart.co.za
Construction & Engineering Insurance Services
N.A.I.C.S.: 524113

Glencar Underwriting Managers, Inc. (1)
500 Park Blvd Ste 825, Itasca, IL 60143
Tel.: (630) 361-9400
Web Site: https://glencarum.com
Commercial Property Insurance Services
N.A.I.C.S.: 531312

HDI Deutschland AG (1)
HDI-Platz 1, 30659, Hannover, Germany
Tel.: (49) 5116450
Life & Health Insurance Services
N.A.I.C.S.: 524113

HDI Global Insurance Company (1)
161 N Clark St 48th Fl, Chicago, IL 60601
Tel.: (312) 580-1900
Insurance Services
N.A.I.C.S.: 524113

HDI Global Insurance Limited Liability Company (1)
5A building 1 17th floor Beregovoy proezd

TALANX AG

Talanx AG—(Continued)

ili Grad Business Center, Moscow, 121087, Russia
Tel.: (7) 4959679265
International Insurance Services
N.A.I.C.S.: 524113

HDI Global SA Ltd. (1)
20 Baker Street 3rd Floor, Rosebank, Johannesburg, South Africa
Tel.: (27) 113400100
Insurance & Risk Management Services
N.A.I.C.S.: 524210

HDI Global SE (1)
HDI-Platz 1, 30659, Hannover, Germany
Tel.: (49) 5116450
Web Site: https://www.hdi.global
Emp.: 4,500
Insurance & Risk Management Services
N.A.I.C.S.: 524210

Subsidiary (US):

Indiana Lumbermens Mutual Insurance Co. (2)
8888 Keystone Croosing Ste 250, Indianapolis, IN 46240
Tel.: (317) 875-3600
Web Site: http://www.plmilm.com
Rev.: $54,995,329
Emp.: 95
Property Damage Insurance
N.A.I.C.S.: 524126
John Wolf (Pres & CEO)

HDI Global Specialty SE (1)
HDI-Platz 1, 30659, Hannover, Germany
Tel.: (49) 51156042909
Insurance & Risk Management Services
N.A.I.C.S.: 524210

HDI Italia, S.p.A. (1)
Viale Certosa 222, 20156, Milan, Italy
Tel.: (39) 0230761
Web Site: https://www.hditalia.it
Fire Insurance Services
N.A.I.C.S.: 524113

HDI Seguros S.A. (1)
Tte Gral Juan D Peron 650 5 Piso, C1038AAN, Buenos Aires, Argentina
Tel.: (54) 115 300 3300
Web Site: https://www.hdi.com.ar
Insurance Services
N.A.I.C.S.: 524128

HDI Seguros S.A. (1)
Avenida Eng Luis Carlos Berrini 901-5 andar, Brooklin Novo, 04571-010, Sao Paulo, SP, Brazil
Tel.: (55) 11 5508 1300
Web Site: http://www.hdi.com.br
Sales Range: $75-99.9 Million
Emp.: 100
Insurance; Joint Venture of Gerling Insurance & Sul America
N.A.I.C.S.: 524298
Murilo Riedel (Pres)

HDI-Gerling Industrie Versicherung AG (1)
Riethorst 2, 30659, Hannover, Germany (100%)
Tel.: (49) 5116450
Web Site: http://www.hdi-gerling.de
Sales Range: $300-349.9 Million
Emp.: 1,000
Reinsurance Services
N.A.I.C.S.: 524130

Branch (Non-US):

HDI Versicherung AG - Slovakia Office (2)
Obchodna 2, 81106, Bratislava, Slovakia
Tel.: (421) 257108611
Web Site: http://www.hdi.sk
Insurance Services
N.A.I.C.S.: 524298

HDI Versicherung AG, organizacni slozka (2)
Jugoslavska 29, 120 00, Prague, 2, Czech Republic
Tel.: (420) 220 190 210
Web Site: http://www.hdiczech.cz
Industrial & Commercial Insurance Services
N.A.I.C.S.: 524298

Subsidiary (US):

HDI-Gerling America Insurance Company (2)
161 N Clark St 48th Fl, Chicago, IL 60601
Tel.: (312) 580-1900
Web Site: http://www.hdi.global.com
Sales Range: $75-99.9 Million
Emp.: 40
Property & Casualty Insurance Services
N.A.I.C.S.: 524128
Patricia Ryan (Gen Counsel, Corp Sec & Sr VP)

Branch (Domestic):

HDI-Gerling America Insurance Company (3)
700 N Brand Blvd Ste 400, Glendale, CA 91203
Tel.: (818) 637-6000
Sales Range: $75-99.9 Million
Emp.: 7
Property & Casualty Insurance Services
N.A.I.C.S.: 524128
John Thomson (Branch Mgr)

Branch (Non-US):

HDI-Gerling Industrie Versicherung AG - France Office (2)
Tour Opus 12 - La Defense 9 77 Esplanade du General de Gaul, 75116, Paris, France
Tel.: (33) 144055600
Web Site: http://www.hdi-gerling.fr
Sales Range: $75-99.9 Million
Emp.: 105
Insurance Services
N.A.I.C.S.: 524298

HDI-Gerling Industrie Versicherung AG - Norway Office (2)
CJ Hambros plass 2D, 0164, Oslo, Norway
Tel.: (47) 23213650
Web Site: http://www.hdi-gerling.com
Marine Insurance Services
N.A.I.C.S.: 524298

HDI-Gerling Industrie Versicherung AG - Switzerland Office (2)
Dufourstrasse 46, Zurich, 8008, Switzerland
Tel.: (41) 442654747
Web Site: http://www.hdi-gerling.ch
Sales Range: $75-99.9 Million
Emp.: 70
Insurance Services
N.A.I.C.S.: 524298
Hans Mazenauer (CEO)

Subsidiary (Non-US):

HDI-Gerling Insurance of South Africa Limited (2)
20 Baker St, Rosebank, 2197, South Africa
Tel.: (27) 113400100
Web Site: http://www.gerling.com
Sales Range: $75-99.9 Million
Emp.: 12
Insurance Services
N.A.I.C.S.: 524298

HDI-Gerling de Mexico Seguros, S.A. (2)
Av Paseo de las Palmas N 239-104, Col Lomas de Chapultepec, 11000, Mexico, Mexico
Tel.: (52) 5552027534
Web Site: http://www.hdi-gerling.com.mx
Sales Range: $75-99.9 Million
Emp.: 15
Insurance Services
N.A.I.C.S.: 524298

Hannover Re (Ireland) Designated Activity Company (1)
Number 3 Dublin Landings 6th Floor North Wall Quay 1, Dublin, Ireland
Tel.: (353) 16338800
Life & Health Insurance Services
N.A.I.C.S.: 524113

Hannover Ruck SE (1)
Karl Wiechert Allee 50, 30625, Hannover, Germany (50.2%)
Tel.: (49) 51156040
Web Site: https://www.hannover-re.com
Assets: $73,393,335,851
Liabilities: $62,214,665,135
Net Worth: $11,178,670,716

Earnings: $2,014,341,976
Emp.: 3,626
Fiscal Year-end: 12/31/2023
Reinsurance Products & Services
N.A.I.C.S.: 524130
Herbert K. Haas (Chm-Supervisory Bd)

Subsidiary (Non-US):

HR Hannover Re, Correduria de Reaseguros, S.A. (2)
Paseo Del General Martinez Campos 46, 28010, Madrid, Spain
Tel.: (34) 91 319 0049
Web Site: https://www.hannover-re.com
Sales Range: $50-74.9 Million
Emp.: 7
Reinsurance Broker
N.A.I.C.S.: 524298

Hannover Life Re of Australasia Ltd. (2)
Level 7 70 Phillip St, Sydney, 2000, NSW, Australia
Tel.: (61) 292516911
Web Site: http://www.hannoverre.com
Sales Range: $50-74.9 Million
Emp.: 90
Life & Disability Reinsurance
N.A.I.C.S.: 524130

Hannover Life Reassurance (Ireland) Ltd (2)
No 4 Custom House Plz IFSC, Dublin, 1, Ireland
Tel.: (353) 16125716
Web Site: http://www.hannoverlifere.com
Sales Range: $250-299.9 Million
Emp.: 12
Financial Reinsurance
N.A.I.C.S.: 524130

Hannover Life Reassurance (UK) Ltd. (2)
Hannover House 1 Station Pride, Virginia Water, GU25 4AA, Surrey, United Kingdom
Tel.: (44) 1344845282
Web Site: http://www.hannover-re.com
Sales Range: $50-74.9 Million
Emp.: 60
Life & Health Reinsurance
N.A.I.C.S.: 524130

Subsidiary (Domestic):

Hannover Services (UK) Ltd. (3)
Hannover House, Virginia Water, GU25 4AA, Surrey, United Kingdom
Tel.: (44) 344845282
Web Site: http://www.hannoverlifere.co.uk
Sales Range: $50-74.9 Million
Emp.: 4
Direct Life Insurance Company
N.A.I.C.S.: 524113
Stuart Hill (Mng Dir)

Subsidiary (US):

Hannover Life Reassurance Company of America (2)
200 S Orange Ave Ste 1900, Orlando, FL 32801
Tel.: (407) 649-8411
Web Site: https://www.hannover-re.com
Sales Range: $10-24.9 Million
Emp.: 36
Life & Health Reinsurance
N.A.I.C.S.: 524130
Jeff Burt (Pres)

Subsidiary (Non-US):

Hannover Re (Bermuda) Ltd. (2)
50 Parliament Street 2nd Floor, Hamilton, HM 12, Bermuda
Tel.: (441) 1 294 31 10
Reinsurance Carriers
N.A.I.C.S.: 524130

Hannover Re (Ireland) Limited (2)
Number 3 Dublin Landings 6th Floor North Wall Quay, Dublin, D01 C4E0, Ireland
Tel.: (353) 1 633 8800
Web Site: https://www.hannover-re.com
Sales Range: $250-299.9 Million
Emp.: 25
Life Reinsurance
N.A.I.C.S.: 524130
Debbie O'Hare (CEO)

Hannover Re Services Italy S.r.l. (2)

INTERNATIONAL PUBLIC

Via Dogana 1, 20123, Milan, Italy
Tel.: (39) 028 068 1311
Web Site: https://www.hannover-re.com
Sales Range: $50-74.9 Million
Emp.: 20
Reinsurance Services
N.A.I.C.S.: 524130

Hannover Re Services Japan KK (2)
Hakuyo Building 7th Floor 3 - 10 Nibancho, Chiyoda-ku, Tokyo, 102-0084, Japan
Tel.: (81) 35 214 1101
Web Site: https://www.hannover-re.com
Sales Range: $50-74.9 Million
Emp.: 10
Reinsurance Services
N.A.I.C.S.: 524298

Hannover Reinsurance Group Africa (Pty) Limited (2)
Hillside House, Cnr Hillside and Empire Rd, Parktown, 2193, South Africa
Tel.: (27) 114816500
Web Site: http://www.hannover-re.co.za
Sales Range: $250-299.9 Million
Emp.: 200
Holding Company; Life Insurance & Reinsurance Products & Services
N.A.I.C.S.: 551112
Achim Klennert (Mng Dir-Grp)

Subsidiary (Domestic):

Compass Insurance Company Ltd. (3)
5th floor 90 Rivonia Rd, Sandton, Johannesburg, 2196, South Africa
Tel.: (27) 117458333
Web Site: https://www.compass.co.za
Sales Range: $50-74.9 Million
Emp.: 36
Reinsurance Carriers
N.A.I.C.S.: 524130

Hannover Life Reassurance Africa Ltd. (3)
17 Corona Empire Hillside House, Cnr Hillside & Empire Roads, Johannesburg, 2193, Parktown, South Africa
Tel.: (27) 114816500
Web Site: http://www.hannover-re.co.za
Sales Range: $50-74.9 Million
Emp.: 100
Life Reinsurance
N.A.I.C.S.: 524130
Achim Klannerchi (Mng Dir)

Hannover Reinsurance Africa Ltd. (3)
Corner Hillside House No 17 Empire Rd Corner, Hillside, Parktown, 2193, South Africa
Tel.: (27) 114816500
Web Site: http://www.hannover-re.co.za
Sales Range: $75-99.9 Million
Emp.: 130
Non-Life Reinsurance
N.A.I.C.S.: 524130
Achim Klennert (Mng Dir)

Subsidiary (Non-US):

Hannover Services Mexico S.A. de C.V. (2)
German Centre Oficina 4-4-28 Av Santa Fe No 170, Col Lomas De Santa Fe, 01210, Mexico, DF, Mexico
Tel.: (52) 5591400800
Web Site: http://www.hannover-ra.com
Sales Range: $50-74.9 Million
Emp.: 6
Reinsurance Services
N.A.I.C.S.: 524130
Guadalute Covarruvias (Mng Dir)

International Insurance Company of Hannover Ltd. (2)
10 Fenchurch Street, Bracknell, EC3M 3BE, Berkshire, United Kingdom
Tel.: (44) 1344397600
Web Site: http://www.inter-hannover.com
Emp.: 150
Reinsurance Carriers
N.A.I.C.S.: 524130

Branch (Domestic):

International Insurance Company of Hannover Ltd.-London (3)

AND PRIVATE COMPANIES

10 Fenchurch Street, London, EC3M 4AD, United Kingdom
Tel.: (44) 2070154000
Sales Range: $75-99.9 Million
Emp.: 200
Reinsurance Carriers
N.A.I.C.S.: 524130
Nick Parr *(Mng Dir)*

Branch (Non-US):

International Insurance Company of Hannover Ltd.-Stockholm (3)
Hantverkargatan 25, PO Box 22085, Stockholm, 104 22, Sweden
Tel.: (46) 86175400
Web Site: http://www.hannover-re.com
Sales Range: $50-74.9 Million
Emp.: 70
Reinsurance Carriers
N.A.I.C.S.: 524130

Subsidiary (Domestic):

London & European Title Insurance Services Limited (3)
118-119 Fenchurch Street 2nd Floor, London, EC3M 5BA, United Kingdom
Tel.: (44) 2079297650
Web Site: http://www.titlesolv.com
Sales Range: $50-74.9 Million
Emp.: 13
Title Insurance
N.A.I.C.S.: 524210
Christopher Taylor *(CEO)*

Joint Venture (Non-US):

Skandia Leben AG (2)
Birmensdorferstrasse 108, Postfach 8418, Zurich, 8036, Switzerland
Tel.: (41) 848 33 66 99
Web Site: http://www.skandia.ch
Life Insurance Products & Services
N.A.I.C.S.: 524113
Armin Holzmuller *(Chm & Pres-Admin Council)*

Joint Venture (Domestic):

Viridium Holding AG (2)
Dornhofstrasse 36, 63263, Neu-Isenburg, Germany
Tel.: (49) 61 025 9950
Web Site: https://www.viridium-gruppe.com
Holding Company; Insurance Services
N.A.I.C.S.: 551112
Heinz-Peter Ross *(CEO)*

Holding (Domestic):

Generali Lebensversicherung AG (3)
Oeder Weg 151, 60318, Frankfurt am Main, Germany **(89.9%)**
Tel.: (49) 6915022000
Web Site: http://www.generali.de
Sales Range: $100-124.9 Million
Emp.: 250
Insurance Services
N.A.I.C.S.: 524128

Subsidiary (US):

Beacon Capital Strategic L.P. (4)
200 State St 5th Fl, Boston, MA 02109
Tel.: (617) 457-0400
Real Estate Manangement Services
N.A.I.C.S.: 531390

Subsidiary (Domestic):

GLL Real Estate Partners GmbH (GLL) (4)
Lindwurmstrasse 76, 80337, Munich, Germany
Tel.: (49) 89 726 103 930
Web Site: http://www.gll-partners.com
Real Estate Fund Manager Investments
N.A.I.C.S.: 523999
Rainer Gobel *(Co-Founder & Mng Dir)*

Generali Partner GmbH (4)
Adenauerring 7, 81737, Munich, Germany
Tel.: (49) 89 51210
General Insurance Services
N.A.I.C.S.: 524210

Generali Pensionsmanagement GmbH (4)
Besenbinderhof 43, 20097, Hamburg, Germany
Tel.: (49) 4028654050
Pension Fund Services
N.A.I.C.S.: 525110

Generali Properties Fund I GmbH & Co. KG (4)
Lindwurmstr 76, 80337, Munich, Germany
Tel.: (49) 89 726103930
Web Site: http://www.gll-partners.com
Sales Range: $25-49.9 Million
Emp.: 70
Property Management Services
N.A.I.C.S.: 531311

Thuringia Generali 1. Immobilien AG & Co. KG (4)
Adenauerring 7, 81737, Munich, Germany
Tel.: (49) 8951210
Real Estate Rental Services
N.A.I.C.S.: 531390

Thuringia Generali 2. Immobilien AG & Co. KG (4)
Sonnenstrasse 31, 80331, Munich, Germany
Tel.: (49) 892103760
General Insurance Services
N.A.I.C.S.: 524210

Volksfursorge 1. Immobilien AG & Co. KG (4)
Besenbinderhof 43, 20097, Hamburg, Germany
Tel.: (49) 40 2865 0
Financial Management Services
N.A.I.C.S.: 523999

Volksfursorge Fixed Asset GmbH (4)
Besenbinderhof 43, 20097, Hamburg, Germany
Tel.: (49) 40 380781454
Asset Management Services
N.A.I.C.S.: 523940

Holding (Domestic):

Heidelberger Lebensversicherung AG (3)
Dornhofstrasse 36, 63263, Neu-Isenburg, Germany
Tel.: (49) 4021 995 6900
Web Site: https://www.heidelberger-leben.de
Sales Range: $75-99.9 Million
Life Insurance Products & Services
N.A.I.C.S.: 524113
Michael Sattler *(Member-Exec Bd & CFO)*

Subsidiary (Domestic):

Skandia Retail Europe Holding GmbH (4)
Kaiserin Augusta Allee 108, Berlin, 10553, Germany
Tel.: (49) 30310070
Web Site: http://www.skandia.de
Holding Company; Life Insurance Products & Services
N.A.I.C.S.: 551112
Rolf-Peter Hoenen *(Chm-Supervisory Bd)*

Subsidiary (Non-US):

Skandia Lebensversicherung AG (5)
Tel.: (49) 6102 833 9910
Web Site: https://www.ska-lv.de
Life Insurance Products & Services
N.A.I.C.S.: 524113
Michael Sattler *(Chm)*

Subsidiary (Domestic):

Skandia Versicherung Management & Service GmbH (5)
Kaiserin Augusta Allee, Berlin, 10553, Germany
Tel.: (49) 30310072835
Web Site: http://www.skandia.de
Insurance & Investment Products Services
N.A.I.C.S.: 524113
Heinz-Peter Ross *(Mng Dir)*

InLinea S.p.A. (1)
Piazza Guglielmo Marconi 25, 00144, Rome, Italy
Tel.: (39) 068537881
Web Site: https://www.inlineaspa.it
Insurance Services
N.A.I.C.S.: 524113

Inchiaro Life Designated Activity Company (1)
Pembroke Hall 38/39 Baggot Street Lower 2, Dublin, D02T938, Ireland
Tel.: (353) 16788700
Web Site: https://www.inchiarolife.com
Fire Insurance Services
N.A.I.C.S.: 524113

Landmark Underwriting Agency (Pty.) Ltd. (1)
53 Second Avenue, Westdene, Bloemfontein, South Africa
Tel.: (27) 514303371
Web Site: https://landmark-ua.co.za
Agricultural Insurance Services
N.A.I.C.S.: 524126

Lifestyle Protection AG (1)
Proactiv-Platz 1, 40721, Hilden, Germany
Tel.: (49) 2103347700
Risk Managemeng Srvices
N.A.I.C.S.: 524210

Lifestyle Protection Lebensversicherung AG (1)
Proactiv-Platz 1, 40721, Hilden, Germany
Tel.: (49) 2103347700
Risk Managemeng Srvices
N.A.I.C.S.: 524210

MUA Insurance Acceptances (Pty.) Ltd. (1)
Office 0009 Second Floor Tijgerpark 5 Willie Van Schoor Drive, Bellville, South Africa
Tel.: (27) 861682467
Web Site: https://mua.co.za
Insurance Services
N.A.I.C.S.: 524113

Markham Real Estate Partners (KSW) Pty. Limited (1)
Level 9 Challis House 4 Martin Place, Sydney, NSW, Australia
Tel.: (61) 292258300
Web Site: https://markham.com.au
Real Estate Agency Services
N.A.I.C.S.: 531211

Neue Leben Holding AG (1)
Sachsenstrasse 8, 20097, Hamburg, Germany
Tel.: (49) 40238910
Fire Insurance Services
N.A.I.C.S.: 524113

Neue Leben Unfallversicherung AG (1)
Sachsenstrasse 8, 20097, Hamburg, Germany
Tel.: (49) 40238910
Accident & Life Insurance Services
N.A.I.C.S.: 524113

Svedea AB (1)
Box 3489, 10369, Stockholm, Sweden
Tel.: (46) 771160190
Web Site: https://www.svedea.se
Motorcycle & Snowmobiles Insurance Services
N.A.I.C.S.: 524126

Talanx Deutschland AG (1)
HDI-Platz 1, 30659, Hannover, Germany
Tel.: (49) 511 645 0
Web Site: http://www.hdi.de
Holding Company; Insurance Products & Services
N.A.I.C.S.: 551112
Jan Wicke *(Chm-Mgmt Bd)*

Subsidiary (Domestic):

HDI Lebensversicherung AG (2)
Charles-de-Gaulle-Platz 1, 50679, Cologne, Germany
Tel.: (49) 221 144 5599
Web Site: https://www.hdi.de
Life Insurance & Pension Products & Services
N.A.I.C.S.: 524113

Branch (Non-US):

HDI Lebensversicherung AG - Austria (3)
Dresdner strasse 91 BIG BIZ C2 3rd floor, 3 OG/BIG BIZ C, 1200, Vienna, Austria
Tel.: (43) 120 7090
Web Site: https://www.hdi-leben.at

Fire Insurance Services
N.A.I.C.S.: 524298

Subsidiary (Domestic):

HDI Versicherung AG (2)
HDI-Platz 1, 30659, Hannover, Germany
Tel.: (49) 5113 806 3806
Web Site: https://www.hdi.de
General Insurance Products & Services
N.A.I.C.S.: 524126

Talanx Reinsurance Broker GmbH (1)
HDI-Platz 1, 30659, Hannover, Germany
Tel.: (49) 51154223000
Web Site: https://trb.talanx.com
Reinsurance Consultancy Services
N.A.I.C.S.: 524298

Towarzystwo Ubezpieczen Europa S.A. (1)
ul Gwiazdzista 62, 53-413, Wroclaw, Poland **(50%)**
Tel.: (48) 713692887
Web Site: http://www.tueuropa.pl
Rev.: $156,106,078
Assets: $604,241,726
Liabilities: $401,888,313
Net Worth: $202,353,413
Earnings: $36,693,247
Fiscal Year-end: 12/31/2014
Insurance Products & Services
N.A.I.C.S.: 524298
Jacek Podoba *(Chm-Mgmt Bd)*

Towarzystwo Ubezpieczen i Reasekuracji Warta S.A. (1)
roundabout I Daszynskiego 1, 00-843, Warsaw, Poland **(75.74%)**
Tel.: (48) 50 230 8308
Web Site: https://www.warta.pl
Insurance Products & Services
N.A.I.C.S.: 524298
Jaroslaw Parkot *(Chm-Mgmt Bd)*

Towarzystwo Ubezpieczen na Zycie Europa S.A. (1)
Ul Gen Wladyslawa Sikorskiego 26, 53-659, Wroclaw, Poland
Tel.: (48) 713692887
Web Site: https://tueuropa.pl
Life & Property Insurance Services
N.A.I.C.S.: 524113

Transit Underwriting Managers (Pty.) Ltd. (1)
32 O Connor Road Dawncliffe, Westville, 3629, South Africa
Tel.: (27) 861113597
Web Site: https://transitum.co.za
Innovative Insurance Services
N.A.I.C.S.: 524126

TALAWAKELLE TEA ESTATES PLC

Tel.: (94) 112627000
Web Site:
https://www.talawakelleteas.com
TPL—(COL)
Rev.: $27,293,875
Assets: $30,443,194
Liabilities: $9,914,051
Net Worth: $20,529,144
Earnings: $8,584,222
Emp.: 4,803
Fiscal Year-end: 03/31/23
Black Tea Mfr
N.A.I.C.S.: 111998
Dilantha S. Seneviratne *(Co-CEO & Co-CFO)*

TALBROS AUTOMOTIVE COMPONENTS LIMITED

14/1 Mathura Road Faridabad, Delhi, 121003, Haryana, India
Tel.: (91) 1292251400
Web Site: https://www.talbros.com
Year Founded: 1956
TALBROAUTO—(NSE)
Rev.: $61,855,166
Assets: $72,191,192
Liabilities: $38,403,988
Net Worth: $33,787,203
Earnings: $5,341,341

TALBROS AUTOMOTIVE COMPONENTS LIMITED

Talbros Automotive Components Limited—(Continued)
Emp.: 546
Fiscal Year-end: 03/31/21
Automotive Components Mfr
N.A.I.C.S.: 339999
Umesh Talwar *(Vice Chm & Co-Mng Dir)*

Subsidiaries:

Talbros Automotive Components Limited - GASKET DIVISION (1)
14/1 Mathura Road, Faridabad, 121 003, Haryana, India
Tel.: (91) 1292251400
Web Site: http://www.talbros.com
Industrial Gasket Mfr
N.A.I.C.S.: 339991

TALBROS ENGINEERING LIMITED
Plot 74-76 Sector-6, Faridabad, 121 006, Haryana, India
Tel.: (91) 1294284300
Web Site:
https://www.talbrosaxles.com
Year Founded: 1980
538987—(BOM)
Rev.: $32,673,909
Assets: $25,634,755
Liabilities: $15,907,123
Net Worth: $9,727,632
Earnings: $1,454,189
Emp.: 198
Fiscal Year-end: 03/31/21
Industrial Machinery Parts Mfr
N.A.I.C.S.: 333248
Tarun Talwar *(COO)*

TALDE GESTION, S.G.E.I.C., S.A
C/ Elcano 9 4ª planta, 48008, Bilbao, Spain
Tel.: (34) 944355040
Web Site: https://www.talde.com
Year Founded: 1976
Emp.: 100
Private Equity
N.A.I.C.S.: 523940

Subsidiaries:

Plymouth Rubber Europa, S.A. (1)
Ctra Salceda km 1 5, 36400, Porrino, Spain
Tel.: (34) 986344148
Web Site: http://www.plymouthrubber.com
Sales Range: $50-74.9 Million
Emp.: 75
PVC Adhesive Tape Mfr
N.A.I.C.S.: 322220
Jaime Santiago Souto *(Dir-Ops)*

TALDOR COMPUTER SYSTEMS (1986) LTD.
Kiryat Aryeh, PO Box 7070, Petach Tikva, 49170, Israel
Tel.: (972) 39298255
Web Site: http://www.taldor.co.il
TALD—(TAE)
Rev.: $234,682,230
Assets: $178,646,721
Liabilities: $131,860,169
Net Worth: $46,786,552
Earnings: $3,565,036
Fiscal Year-end: 12/31/19
Information Technology Services
N.A.I.C.S.: 541519
Nati Avrahami *(CEO)*

TALEA GROUP S.P.A.
Via Marco Polo 190, 55049, Viareggio, Italy
Tel.: (39) 05841660450
Web Site:
https://www.taleagroupspa.com
Year Founded: 2012
TALEA—(EUR)
Emp.: 242

Personal Care Product Distr
N.A.I.C.S.: 456199
Alberto Maglione *(Deputy Chm)*

TALEB GROUP
Taleb Trading Building Taleb Signal C Ring Road, PO Box 8055, Doha, Qatar
Tel.: (974) 4660041
Web Site:
http://www.talebgroup.com.qa
Year Founded: 1955
Rev.: $46,724,500
Emp.: 5,000
Holding Company
N.A.I.C.S.: 551112
Taleb Mohammed Al Khouri *(Chm)*

Subsidiaries:

Al Adekhar Real Estate Co. W.L.L (1)
PO Box 300, Doha, Qatar
Tel.: (974) 4466 0042
Web Site: http://www.talebgroup.qa
Emp.: 80
Real Estate Manangement Services
N.A.I.C.S.: 531390
Mohamed Taleb *(Gen Mgr)*

Al Jazeera Technical Laboratories Company LLC (1)
Street No 43 Gate No 50 Industrial Area - 2, PO Box 300, Doha, Qatar
Tel.: (974) 4460 4941
Sales Range: $10-24.9 Million
Emp.: 15
Laboratory Testing Services
N.A.I.C.S.: 621512

Al Khoory Building Materials & Trading Co. (1)
Building No 1 Shop No 9 & 11 Barwa Village, PO Box 2355, Barwa Village Al-Wakra, Al Wakra, 2355, Qatar
Tel.: (974) 4415 1049
Web Site: http://www.talebgroup.com.qa
Building Material Dealers
N.A.I.C.S.: 444180

Doha Modern Carpentary Co. W.L.L (1)
industrial area st 14 gate 92, PO Box 2355, Doha, 2355, Qatar
Tel.: (974) 4460 0722
Web Site: http://www.talebgroup.com.qa
Sales Range: $25-49.9 Million
Emp.: 43
Construction Engineering Services
N.A.I.C.S.: 541330
Ali Taleb Al-Khori *(Gen Mgr)*

Networth Systems Co. W.L.L (1)
C-Ring Road New Salata, PO Box 300, Doha, Qatar
Tel.: (974) 44637456
Software Development Services
N.A.I.C.S.: 541511

Qatar Industrial Gases Co. W.L.L (1)
PO Box 8055, Doha, Qatar
Tel.: (974) 4460 2353
Industrial Gas Mfr
N.A.I.C.S.: 325120

Spartan Readymix & Tiles Co. W.L.L (1)
348 industrial area, PO Box 4851, Doha, Qatar
Tel.: (974) 4460 1109
Web Site: http://www.talebgroup.com.qa
Ready Mix Concrete Mfr & Distr
N.A.I.C.S.: 327320
Amir Zafar *(Mgr-Quality Assurance & Quality Control)*

Taleb Medical Company (1)
PO Box 8055, Ad Dawhah, Doha, Qatar
Tel.: (974) 44660041
Medical Equipment Distr
N.A.I.C.S.: 423450

Taleb Trading Co. W.L.L (1)
PO Box 8055, Doha, 8055, Qatar
Tel.: (974) 44660041
Web Site: http://www.talebgroup.com.qa
Emp.: 30
Automobile Accessories Whslr

N.A.I.C.S.: 423120
Arun Chandy *(Mgr-Svc)*

TALENCE GESTION SAS
38 Avenue Hoche, 75008, Paris, France
Tel.: (33) 1 40 73 89 60
Web Site:
http://www.talencegestion.fr
Emp.: 25
Asset Management Firm
N.A.I.C.S.: 523999
Cathy Gessrey *(Mgr)*

TALENOM OY
Nuottasaarentie 5, 90400, Oulu, Finland
Tel.: (358) 207 525 000
Web Site: http://www.talenom.fi
Sales Range: $25-49.9 Million
Emp.: 530
Accounting Services
N.A.I.C.S.: 541219
Harri Tahkola *(CEO)*

TALENT PROPERTY GROUP LIMITED
No 281 and The 21 Storey Commercial Building Lin and Road, Tianhe District, Guangzhou, 510000, China
Tel.: (86) 2038790760 BM
Web Site: http://www.760hk.com
0760—(HKG)
Rev.: $38,766,265
Assets: $565,898,065
Liabilities: $331,410,971
Net Worth: $234,487,094
Earnings: ($5,496,379)
Emp.: 199
Fiscal Year-end: 12/31/22
Electronic Products Mfr
N.A.I.C.S.: 334419
Zhangguan Luo *(Gen Mgr-Fin)*

Subsidiaries:

Sure Win Inc. Limited (1)
China Aerospace Tower Tsim Sha Tsui East Yau Tsim Mong, Hong Kong, China (Hong Kong)
Tel.: (852) 26206028
Web Site: http://www.760hk.com
Emp.: 4
Property Investment Services
N.A.I.C.S.: 531210
Lee Wai Keen Lee *(Mgr)*

TALENTHOUSE AG
Zugerstrasse 8a, CH-6340, Baar, Switzerland
Tel.: (41) 433443838
Web Site:
https://business.talenthouse.com
NEWN—(BER)
Sales Range: Less than $1 Million
Investment Services
N.A.I.C.S.: 523999
Roman Scharf *(Chm & Pres)*

TALEX S.A.
ul Karpia 27d, 61-619, Poznan, Poland
Tel.: (48) 618275500
Web Site: https://www.talex.pl
TLX—(WAR)
Rev.: $20,505,451
Assets: $19,105,914
Liabilities: $6,272,421
Net Worth: $12,833,492
Earnings: $439,130
Emp.: 269
Fiscal Year-end: 12/31/22
Information Technology Services & Solutions
N.A.I.C.S.: 513210
Radoslaw Wesolowski *(Member-Mgmt Bd)*

INTERNATIONAL PUBLIC

TALGA GROUP LTD
Suite 3 03 Level 3 46 Colin Street, West Perth, 6005, WA, Australia
Tel.: (61) 894816667
Web Site:
https://www.talgagroup.com
TLG—(ASX)
Rev.: $907,817
Assets: $30,779,919
Liabilities: $3,917,775
Net Worth: $26,862,144
Earnings: ($25,545,228)
Emp.: 71
Fiscal Year-end: 06/30/24
Iron Ore Mining
N.A.I.C.S.: 212210
Mark Thompson *(Mng Dir)*

Subsidiaries:

Talga Advanced Materials GmbH (1)
Prof Hermann-Klare-Str 25, 07407, Rudolstadt, Germany
Tel.: (49) 36724766930
Mineral Resource Services
N.A.I.C.S.: 212390

TALGO S.A.
Paseo Del Tren Talgo 2, Las Matas, 28290, Madrid, Spain
Tel.: (34) 916313800
Web Site: http://www.talgo.com
Year Founded: 1942
TLGO—(MAD)
Rev.: $449,842,163
Assets: $988,721,034
Liabilities: $662,028,756
Net Worth: $326,692,278
Earnings: $43,076,535
Emp.: 2,597
Fiscal Year-end: 12/31/19
Passenger Train Parts Mfr
N.A.I.C.S.: 336350
Carlos De Palacio Oriol *(Chm)*

Subsidiaries:

Talgo UK Ltd. (1)
Barrow Hill Roundhouse Railway Centre Campbell Drive, Barrow Hill, Chesterfield, S43 2PR, Derbyshire, United Kingdom
Tel.: (44) 1246472450
Railway Maintenance Equipment Mfr
N.A.I.C.S.: 336510

TALI DIGITAL LIMITED
Suite 201 697 Burke Road, Camberwell, 3124, VIC, Australia
Tel.: (61) 1300082013
Web Site: https://talidigital.com
TD1—(ASX)
Rev.: $116,570
Assets: $1,463,596
Liabilities: $27,782
Net Worth: $1,435,815
Earnings: ($2,081,357)
Fiscal Year-end: 06/30/24
Childhood Attention Difficulty Treatment Products
N.A.I.C.S.: 325412
John Osborne *(Sec)*

TALIS CAPITAL LIMITED
Suite 4 Rowan Court 56 High Street, Wimbledon, London, SW19 5EE, United Kingdom
Tel.: (44) 20 3542 6260
Web Site: http://www.taliscapital.com
Newspaper Publishers
N.A.I.C.S.: 541810
Kirill Tasilov *(Partner)*

Subsidiaries:

SMS Passcode A/S (1)
Park Alle 350D, 2605, Brondby, Denmark
Tel.: (45) 70 22 55 33
Web Site: http://www.smspasscode.com
Emp.: 11
Security Software Development Services
N.A.I.C.S.: 541511

AND PRIVATE COMPANIES

Claus Kotasek *(CEO)*

TALISKER CORPORATION
145 Adelaide Street West Suite 500, Toronto, M5H 4E5, ON, Canada
Tel.: (416) 864-0213
Sales Range: $10-24.9 Million
Emp.: 20
Real Estate Development & Investment
N.A.I.C.S.: 531390
Jack Bistricer *(Chm & CEO)*

Subsidiaries:

The Canyons Resort (1)
4000 The Canyons Resort Dr, Park City, UT 84098
Tel.: (435) 649-5400
Web Site: http://www.canyonsresort.com
Year-Round Resort Featuring Skiing & Summer Activities
N.A.I.C.S.: 713920
Mike Goar *(Mng Dir)*

TALISKER RESOURCES LTD.
365 Bay Street Suite 400, Toronto, M5H 2V1, ON, Canada
Tel.: (416) 361-2808 Ca
Web Site: http://www.eurocontrol.ca
TSKFF—(OTCQX)
Rev.: $20,662
Assets: $47,515,492
Liabilities: $29,764,048
Net Worth: $17,751,444
Earnings: ($29,487,183)
Emp.: 66
Fiscal Year-end: 12/31/21
Oil Products Mfr
N.A.I.C.S.: 324199
Andres Tinajero *(CFO)*

Subsidiaries:

New Carolin Gold Corp. (1)
250 - 1199 West Hastings Street, Vancouver, V6E 3T5, BC, Canada
Tel.: (416) 471-3366
Gold Mine Development
N.A.I.C.S.: 212220

TALISMAN MINING LIMITED
Suite 1 Ground Floor 33 Colin Street, West Perth, 6005, WA, Australia
Tel.: (61) 893804230 AU
Web Site: https://www.talismanmining.com.au
TLM—(ASX)
Rev.: $168,269
Assets: $6,294,070
Liabilities: $976,896
Net Worth: $5,317,174
Earnings: ($1,947,115)
Fiscal Year-end: 06/30/24
Mineral Exploration Services
N.A.I.C.S.: 213115
Alexander Neuling *(Sec)*

TALIUS GROUP LIMITED
Suite 2/17 Cairns Street, Loganholme, 4129, QLD, Australia
Tel.: (61) 1300889838 AU
Web Site: https://www.talius.com.au
TAL—(ASX)
Rev.: $5,455,015
Assets: $5,412,317
Liabilities: $2,630,587
Net Worth: $2,781,730
Earnings: ($1,243,630)
Fiscal Year-end: 12/31/22
Oil & Gas Exploration Services
N.A.I.C.S.: 213112
Graham Russell *(Mng Dir)*

TALIWORKS CORPORATION BERHAD
Level 19 Menara LGB No 1 Jalan Wan Kadir Taman Tun Dr Ismail, 60000, Kuala Lumpur, Malaysia
Tel.: (60) 327889100 MY
Web Site: https://www.taliworks.com.my
TALIWRK—(KLS)
Rev.: $71,473,439
Assets: $392,446,561
Liabilities: $170,679,153
Net Worth: $221,767,407
Earnings: $14,059,259
Emp.: 8,881
Fiscal Year-end: 12/31/22
Water Plant Management & Maintenance Services
N.A.I.C.S.: 221310
Yew Boon Lim *(Exec Dir)*

Subsidiaries:

Air Kedah Sdn. Bhd. (1)
28 Jalan Wan Kadir 1 Tamantun Dr Ismail, 60000, Kuala Lumpur, Federal Territory, Malaysia
Tel.: (60) 377257110
Water Supply Systems Design & Construction Services
N.A.I.C.S.: 237110

Grand Saga Sdn. Bhd. (1)
Wisma Grand Saga KM 16 Lebuhraya Cheras-Kajang, 43200, Cheras, Selangor Darul Ehsan, Malaysia
Tel.: (60) 390865555
Web Site: https://www.grandsaga.com.my
Highway Construction Services
N.A.I.C.S.: 237310

Puresino (Guanghan) Water Co. Ltd. (1)
No 5 Yuelong Village, Dongnan, 618300, Guanghan, Sichuan, China
Tel.: (86) 8385103279
Sales Range: $10-24.9 Million
Emp.: 27
Waste Water Treatment Services
N.A.I.C.S.: 562998

Sungai Harmoni Sdn. Bhd. (1)
Logi Pembersih Air Sungai Selangor Fasa 1, Beg Berkunci 216, Bestari Jaya, 45600, Selangor, Malaysia
Tel.: (60) 332791616
Web Site: https://www.taliworks.com.my
Sales Range: $25-49.9 Million
Emp.: 90
Water Treatment Plants Operation & Maintenance Services
N.A.I.C.S.: 562219

Taliworks (Langkawi) Sdn. Bhd. (1)
Loji Penapisan Air Jln Kuala Sungai Baru, 02700, Simpang Empat, Perlis, Malaysia
Tel.: (60) 49809071
Sales Range: $75-99.9 Million
Emp.: 22
Water Supply & Distribution Facilities Operation & Maintenance Services
N.A.I.C.S.: 221310

TALKH CHIKHER JSC
Talkh Chikher JSC Building 29th khoroo, Songinokhairkhan district, Ulaanbaatar, Mongolia
Tel.: (976) 98111955
Web Site: http://www.talkhchikher.mn
Year Founded: 1984
TCK—(MONG)
Rev.: $23,960,624
Assets: $27,743,472
Liabilities: $7,780,139
Net Worth: $19,963,333
Earnings: $1,153,663
Fiscal Year-end: 12/31/20
Food Mfr
N.A.I.C.S.: 311999
Myagmar Bazar-Uugan *(CEO)*

TALKMED GROUP LIMITED
101 Thomson Road 0902 United Square, Singapore, 307591, Singapore
Tel.: (65) 62586918
Web Site: https://www.talkmed.com.sg

5G3—(SES)
Rev.: $63,464,364
Assets: $87,696,736
Liabilities: $24,030,902
Net Worth: $63,665,833
Earnings: $22,232,068
Emp.: 232
Fiscal Year-end: 12/31/23
Medical Oncology Services
N.A.I.C.S.: 339112
Peng Tiam Ang *(CEO)*

Subsidiaries:

CellVec Pte. Ltd. (1)
100 Pasir Panjang Road 04-02, Singapore, 118518, Singapore
Tel.: (65) 68738818
Web Site: https://www.cellvec.com
Laboratory Services
N.A.I.C.S.: 621511
Lim Zyi *(Co-Founder)*

Stem Med Pte. Ltd. (1)
100 Pasir Panjang Road 03-05, Singapore, 118518, Singapore
Tel.: (65) 6 369 9191
Web Site: https://www.stem-med.sg
Stem Cell Bank Services
N.A.I.C.S.: 621991
Khoo Kei Siong *(Chm)*

TALKPOOL AG
Gauggelistrasse 7, 7000, Chur, Switzerland
Tel.: (41) 812502020
Web Site: https://www.talkpool.com
Year Founded: 2000
TALK—(OMX)
Rev.: $27,517,420
Assets: $8,748,677
Liabilities: $9,996,395
Net Worth: ($1,247,719)
Earnings: $1,338,374
Emp.: 250
Fiscal Year-end: 12/31/22
Telecommunication Servicesb
N.A.I.C.S.: 517112
Erika Loretz *(CFO)*

Subsidiaries:

Camouflage B.V. (1)
Mijlstraat 45b, 5281 LJ, Boxtel, Netherlands
Tel.: (31) 411849230
Web Site: https://www.camouflage.nl
Wireless Network Services
N.A.I.C.S.: 517112

TP Management SA (1)
3eme etage Bld Digicel 151 Angle Ave Jean Paul II Et Impasse Duverger, Port-au-Prince, Haiti
Tel.: (509) 37012005
Information Technology Consulting Services
N.A.I.C.S.: 541512

Talkpool NV (1)
Woluwelaan 145, 1831, Diegem, Belgium
Tel.: (32) 27095390
Web Site: http://www.talkpool.be
Electronic Repair & Configuration Services
N.A.I.C.S.: 811210

TALKWEB INFORMATION SYSTEM INC.
No 298 Tongzipo West Road, Yuelu District, Changsha, 410205, Hunan, China
Tel.: (86) 73188799888
Web Site: http://www.talkweb.com.cn
Year Founded: 2001
002261—(SSE)
Rev.: $314,027,275
Assets: $630,803,974
Liabilities: $259,952,973
Net Worth: $370,851,002
Earnings: ($142,210,781)
Emp.: 3,000
Fiscal Year-end: 12/31/22
Online Education Services
N.A.I.C.S.: 611710
Xinyu Li *(Chm & Gen Mgr)*

TALLINNA KAUBAMAJA AS

TALLER GMBH
Im Ermlisgrund 11, 76337, Waldbrunn, Germany
Tel.: (49) 724360030
Web Site: http://www.taller.de
Year Founded: 1978
Rev.: $73,301,316
Emp.: 154
Electrical Supplies Distr
N.A.I.C.S.: 423610
Michael Schone *(Mng Dir)*

Subsidiaries:

INSERT Ltd. (1)
Dudullu OSB Mahallesi Des-1 Cadde Des Sanayi Sitesi Ticaret Merkez, Binasi No 3/20 Umraniye, 34775, Istanbul, Turkiye
Tel.: (90) 2163148358
Electrical Component Distr
N.A.I.C.S.: 423610

TALLER Dongguan Electronics Components Ltd (1)
1/f Building A, Pingqian Industria, Dongguan, 523840, China
Tel.: (86) 76985359
Electrical Component Distr
N.A.I.C.S.: 423610

TALLINNA KAUBAMAJA AS
Kaubamaja 1, 10143, Tallinn, Estonia
Tel.: (372) 6673200
Web Site: https://www.tkmgroup.ee
Year Founded: 1960
TKM1T—(TAL)
Rev.: $1,045,652,942
Assets: $763,338,117
Liabilities: $472,604,040
Net Worth: $290,734,077
Earnings: $41,311,403
Emp.: 4,700
Fiscal Year-end: 12/31/23
Offices of Other Holding Companies
N.A.I.C.S.: 551112
Raul Puusepp *(Chm-Exec Bd)*

Subsidiaries:

KIA Auto AS (1)
Tel.: (372) 6050150
Web Site: https://www.kia.ee
Car Distr
N.A.I.C.S.: 441120

Kaubamaja AS (1)
Tel.: (372) 6673100
Web Site: https://www.kaubamaja.ee
Consumer Product Services
N.A.I.C.S.: 532289
Erkki Laugus *(CEO)*

Kulinaaria OU (1)
Taevakivi 7, Tallinn, Estonia
Tel.: (372) 53003775
Web Site: https://www.kulinaariatoit.ee
Emp.: 300
Catering & Food Services
N.A.I.C.S.: 722320

OU Tartu Kaubamaja Kinnisvara (1)
Riia 1, 51004, Tartu, Estonia
Tel.: (372) 7314800
Web Site: http://www.tartukaubamaja.ee
Online Accessory Distr
N.A.I.C.S.: 458110

SIA Forum Auto (1)
Karla Ulmana Gatve 101, Marupe, LV-2167, Latvia
Tel.: (371) 67320044
Web Site: http://www.kia.forumauto.lv
Car Distr
N.A.I.C.S.: 441110

SIA Verte Auto (1)
Bikernieku Street 125, Riga, LV-1021, Latvia
Tel.: (371) 67304050
Web Site: http://www.verteauto.lv
Car Distr
N.A.I.C.S.: 441120

Selver AS (1)
Tel.: (372) 6026800
Web Site: https://www.selver.ee
Consumer Product Services

TALLINNA KAUBAMAJA AS

Tallinna Kaubamaja AS—(Continued)
N.A.I.C.S.: 532289

UAB KIA Auto (1)
Perkunkiemio st 2, 12126, Vilnius, Lithuania
Tel.: (370) 52125123
Web Site: https://www.kiavilnius.lt
Car Distr
N.A.I.C.S.: 441120
Daiva Kacinauskiene (Sls Mgr)

Verte Auto SIA (1)
Bikernieku Iela 125, Riga, 1021, Latvia
Tel.: (371) 67304050
Web Site: https://www.verteauto.lv
Automotive Services
N.A.I.C.S.: 811111

Viking Motors AS (1)
Tammsaare tee 51, 13415, Tallinn, Estonia
Tel.: (372) 6652600
Web Site: https://www.vikingmotors.ee
Car Dealer
N.A.I.C.S.: 441110

Viking Security AS (1)
Parnu mnt 186, 11314, Tallinn, Estonia
Tel.: (372) 6711080
Web Site: https://www.vikingsecurity.ee
Emp.: 700
Security Alarm Services
N.A.I.C.S.: 561612

TALLINNA SADAM AS
Sadama 25, 15051, Tallinn, Estonia
Tel.: (372) 6318555
Web Site: https://www.ts.ee
TSM1T—(TAL)
Rev.: $128,762,557
Assets: $669,129,043
Liabilities: $252,240,865
Net Worth: $416,888,178
Earnings: $17,531,736
Emp.: 461
Fiscal Year-end: 12/31/23
Other Support Activities for Water Transportation
N.A.I.C.S.: 488390
Valdo Kalm (Chm & CEO)

Subsidiaries:

TS Shipping OU (1)
Sadama 25/3, 10111, Tallinn, Estonia
Tel.: (372) 5200270
Web Site: https://www.ts-shipping.com
Freight Forwarding & Shipping Services
N.A.I.C.S.: 488510

TALLWOODS INTERNATIONAL GOLF RESORT PTY. LIMITED
The Boulevard, PO Box 155, Tallwoods Village, Hallidays Point, 2430, NSW, Australia
Tel.: (61) 265933228 AU
Web Site: http://tallwoods.com.au
Golf Course & Resort Operator
N.A.I.C.S.: 713910
Linda Cooke (Gen Mgr)

TALLY LTD.
29 Finsbury Circus, London, United Kingdom
Tel.: (44) 2080650215 GY
Web Site: http://www.lionsgold.com
Assets: $5,444,367
Liabilities: $104,724
Net Worth: $5,339,643
Earnings: $1,163,287
Fiscal Year-end: 06/30/17
Gold Mining Services
N.A.I.C.S.: 212220
Cameron John Parry (CEO)

Subsidiaries:

Kolar Gold Pty Ltd. (1)
9 Buchanan St, West End, 4101, QLD, Australia
Tel.: (61) 738460211
Gold Mining Services
N.A.I.C.S.: 212220

TALMA TRAVEL AND TOURS LTD.
BSR Tower 4 7 Mezada Street, Bnei Braq, Israel
Tel.: (972) 37541717
Web Site: https://www.talma.com
Year Founded: 1987
Emp.: 550
Tourism Services & Business Travel
N.A.I.C.S.: 561599

Subsidiaries:

Brickell Travel Management, LLC (1)
175 SW 7th St, Miami, FL 33130
Tel.: (305) 856-8889
Web Site: http://www.brickelltravel.com
Scheduled Passenger Air Transportation
N.A.I.C.S.: 481111
Michael Rodriguez (Mgr)

TALMORA DIAMOND INC.
6 Willowood Court, Toronto, M2J 2M3, ON, Canada
Tel.: (416) 491-6771 ON
Web Site: https://www.talmoradiamond.com
Year Founded: 1997
TAI—(CNSX)
Rev.: $2
Assets: $15,365
Net Worth: $15,365
Earnings: ($62,064)
Fiscal Year-end: 12/31/22
Diamond Mining Services
N.A.I.C.S.: 212311
Richard M. Hogarth (Chm)

TALON METALS CORP.
Craigmuir Chambers, PO Box 71, Road Town, Tortola, Virgin Islands (British)
Tel.: (284) 4163619636
Web Site: https://talonmetals.com
TLOFF—(OTCIQ)
Rev.: $715,460
Assets: $175,124,370
Liabilities: $4,278,332
Net Worth: $170,846,038
Earnings: ($1,734,887)
Emp.: 94
Fiscal Year-end: 12/31/23
Minerals Exploration
N.A.I.C.S.: 213115
Warren E. Newfield (Chm)

Subsidiaries:

Brazilian Resources Mineracao Ltda (1)
Av Jornalista Ricardo Marinho No 360 salas 111-113 Ed Cosmopolitan, Barra Da Tijuca, CEP 22631-350, Rio de Janeiro, RJ, Brazil
Tel.: (55) 2121327440
Web Site: http://www.talonmetals.com
Mineral Exploration Services
N.A.I.C.S.: 213115

TALPA HOLDING B.V.
Familie de Mollaan 1, 1217 ZB, Hilversum, Netherlands
Tel.: (31) 35 5333 111 NI
Web Site: http://www.talpaholding.nl
Year Founded: 2005
Holding Company; Television Broadcasting, Programming Production & Content Distribution; Radio Broadcastion Stations
N.A.I.C.S.: 551112
John de Mol (Founder)

Subsidiaries:

Talpa Radio B.V. (1)
Bergweg 70, 1217 SC, Hilversum, Netherlands
Tel.: (31) 35 625 2727
Web Site: http://www.talparadio.nl
Radio Broadcasting Stations Operator
N.A.I.C.S.: 516110
Menno Koningsberger (Mng Dir)

Talpa TV (1)
Rietlandpark 333, 1019 DW, Amsterdam, Netherlands
Tel.: (31) 208007000
Web Site: http://tv.talpanetwork.com
Television Broadcasting
N.A.I.C.S.: 516120
Andre Kreuzen (CEO)

Unit (Domestic):

NET 5 (2)
Rietlandpark 333, 1019 DW, Amsterdam, Netherlands
Tel.: (31) 20 800 7000
Web Site: http://tv.talpanetwork.com
Television Broadcasting Network
N.A.I.C.S.: 517111

SBS 6 (2)
Rietlandpark 333, 1019 DW, Amsterdam, Netherlands
Tel.: (31) 208007000
Web Site: http://tv.talpanetwork.com
Television Broadcasting Network
N.A.I.C.S.: 517111

Veronica (Televisie) (2)
Rietlandpark 333, 1019 DW, Amsterdam, Netherlands (100%)
Tel.: (31) 20 800 7000
Web Site: http://www.veronicatv.nl
Television Broadcasting Network
N.A.I.C.S.: 517111

TALWALKARS BETTER VALUE FITNESS LIMITED
801-813 Mahalaxmi Chambers 22 Bhulabhai Desai Road, Mumbai, 400 026, India
Tel.: (91) 2266126300
Web Site: http://www.talwalkars.net
Year Founded: 1932
533200—(BOM)
Rev.: $9,037,870
Assets: $70,066,058
Liabilities: $37,803,487
Net Worth: $32,262,571
Earnings: $1,365,390
Emp.: 9
Fiscal Year-end: 03/31/18
Health & Fitness Club Owner & Operator
N.A.I.C.S.: 713940
Madhukar Vishnu Talwalkar (Exec Dir)

TAM DEVELOPMENT COMPANY
King Fahd Branch Road Grand Tower 10th Floor, Riyadh, Saudi Arabia
Tel.: (966) 556007482
Web Site: https://www.tam.sa
Year Founded: 2012
9570—(SAU)
Rev.: $50,239,495
Assets: $50,339,329
Liabilities: $21,071,009
Net Worth: $29,268,320
Earnings: $10,826,901
Emp.: 83
Fiscal Year-end: 12/31/23
Management Consulting Services
N.A.I.C.S.: 541611
Abdullah A. Yousef (Founder)

TAM FAKTORING A.S.
Cemal Sahir Sokak 26/28 Profilo Plaza A Blok Kat 2 Mecidiyekoy, Sisli, 34340, Istanbul, Turkiye
Tel.: (90) 2123554200
Web Site: http://www.tamfaktoring.com.tr
TAMFA—(IST)
Sales Range: Less than $1 Million
Financial Investment Services
N.A.I.C.S.: 523940
Isak Antika (Chm)

TAMA CHEMICALS CO., LTD.

INTERNATIONAL PUBLIC

6-1 Higashidacho, Kawasaki-ku, Kawasaki, 210-0005, Kanagawa, Japan
Tel.: (81) 442001700 JP
Web Site: http://www.tama-chem.co.jp
Year Founded: 1949
Sales Range: $10-24.9 Million
Emp.: 240
Sales of Chemicals Mfr
N.A.I.C.S.: 325998
Toshitsura Cho (Pres)

Subsidiaries:

Moses Lake Industries, Inc. (1)
8248 Randolph Rd NE, Moses Lake, WA 98837-9328
Tel.: (509) 762-5336
Web Site: http://www.mlindustries.com
Sales Range: $1-9.9 Million
Emp.: 115
Mfr of High Purity Chemicals
N.A.I.C.S.: 325199

TAMA HOME CO., LTD.
3-22-9 Tama Home Headquarters Takanawa Minato-ku, Tokyo, 108-0074, Japan
Tel.: (81) 364081200 JP
Web Site: http://www.tamahome.jp
Year Founded: 1998
1419—(TKS)
Rev.: $1,637,515,130
Assets: $592,170,070
Liabilities: $338,828,600
Net Worth: $253,341,470
Earnings: $57,850,720
Emp.: 3,420
Fiscal Year-end: 05/31/24
Construction, Architectural Design, Real Estate & Insurance Services
N.A.I.C.S.: 236115
Yasuhiro Tamaki (Chm & Chm)

Subsidiaries:

Japan Wood Co., Ltd. (1)
5-11 Hakataeki Chuogai, Hakata-ku, Fukuoka, Japan
Tel.: (81) 924760280
Web Site: https://japan-wood.co.jp
Wood Product Mfr & Distr
N.A.I.C.S.: 321113

Tama AD.Co., Ltd. (1)
3-19-26 Takanawa SOC Takanawa Building 3rd floor, Minato-ku, Tokyo, 108-0074, Japan
Tel.: (81) 35 475 6652
Web Site: https://www.tama-ad.jp
Emp.: 5
Advertisement & Promotion Services
N.A.I.C.S.: 541890

Tama Finance Co., Ltd. (1)
No 19-26 3-chome SOC Takanawa 3rd floor, Takanawa Minato-ku, Tokyo, 108-0074, Japan
Tel.: (81) 36 408 1203
Web Site: https://www.tamafinance.jp
Mortgage Loan Services
N.A.I.C.S.: 522310

Tama Home (Cambodia) Ltd. (1)
09 Street 242 Sangkat Chaktmuk, Khan Daun Penh, Phnom Penh, 12207, Cambodia
Tel.: (855) 23 992 560
Web Site: http://www.tamahomecambodia.jp
Emp.: 10
Real Estate Development Services
N.A.I.C.S.: 531390
Takenori Ueda (Gen Mgr)

Tama Living Co., Ltd. (1)
3-3-8 Tama Woody Gate Mita 3rd Floor, Mita Minato-ku, Tokyo, 108-0073, Japan
Tel.: (81) 354395601
Web Site: http://www.tamahome-living.jp
Furniture Whslr
N.A.I.C.S.: 423210

TAMAGAWA HOLDINGS CO., LTD.
11th floor Shiba 2-chome Building

28-8 Shiba, Minato-ku, Tokyo, 105-0014, Japan
Tel.: (81) 364356933
Web Site: https://www.tmex.co.jp
Year Founded: 1968
6838—(TKS)
Rev.: $60,364,480
Assets: $80,915,120
Liabilities: $28,236,560
Net Worth: $52,678,560
Earnings: $1,432,640
Emp.: 245
Fiscal Year-end: 03/31/22
Holding Company
N.A.I.C.S.: 551112
Toru Masuzawa (Pres & CEO)

Subsidiaries:

Tamagawa Electronics Co., Ltd. (1)
3-11-23 Kamitsutidana-naka, Ayase, 252-1113, Kanagawa, Japan
Tel.: (81) 467762293
Web Site: https://www.tmele.jp
Emp.: 117
Electronic Equipment Mfr & Distr
N.A.I.C.S.: 334515
Masanori Kobayashi (Pres)

TAMAI STEAMSHIP CO., LTD.
A-PLACE Tamachi East 5F 2-16 Shibaura 3-Chome, Minato-Ku, Tokyo, 108-0023, Japan
Tel.: (81) 354390260
Web Site: https://www.tamaiship.co.jp
Year Founded: 1929
9127—(TKS)
Rev.: $41,107,590
Assets: $78,116,980
Liabilities: $29,381,450
Net Worth: $48,735,530
Earnings: $4,831,910
Fiscal Year-end: 03/31/24
Marine Freight Transportation Services
N.A.I.C.S.: 488510
Mitsuyoshi Goto (Auditor)

TAMAR PETROLEUM LTD.
Galgaeli Haplada 11 St, Herzliya Pituach, Israel
Tel.: (972) 747044779
Web Site: https://www.tamarpetroleum.co.il
Year Founded: 2017
TMRP—(TAE)
Rev.: $234,019,000
Assets: $1,222,168,000
Liabilities: $829,396,000
Net Worth: $392,772,000
Earnings: $49,510,000
Emp.: 7
Fiscal Year-end: 12/31/23
All Other Petroleum & Coal Products Manufacturing
N.A.I.C.S.: 324199
Liami Vaisman (CEO)

TAMARACK VALLEY ENERGY LTD.
Tel.: (403) 263-4440 AB
Web Site: http://www.tamarackvalley.ca
Year Founded: 2002
9TA1—(DEU)
Rev.: $1,096,977,171
Assets: $3,177,641,615
Liabilities: $1,535,306,964
Net Worth: $1,642,334,652
Earnings: $71,129,284
Emp.: 98
Fiscal Year-end: 12/31/23
Oil & Natural Gas Exploration & Extraction Services
N.A.I.C.S.: 211120
Brian Schmidt (Pres & CEO)

TAMARES GROUP
Zollstrasse 32/34, Vaduz, 9490, Liechtenstein
Tel.: (423) 2312030
Web Site: http://www.tamares.com
Rev.: $200,000,000
Private Equity Firm
N.A.I.C.S.: 523999
Poju Zabludowicz (Chm & CEO)

Subsidiaries:

Plaza Hotel & Casino (1)
1 S Main St, Las Vegas, NV 89101
Tel.: (702) 386-2110
Web Site: http://www.plazahotelcasino.com
Sales Range: $200-249.9 Million
Emp.: 1,500
Casino Hotels
N.A.I.C.S.: 721120
Tony Santo (Pres & CEO)

TAMARIND MANAGEMENT SDN. BHD.
Level 26 PETRONAS Tower 3, Kuala Lumpur City Centre, 50088, Kuala Lumpur, Malaysia
Tel.: (60) 3 2303 6007 MY
Web Site: http://www.tamarindresources.com
Year Founded: 2014
Upstream Energy Investment Firm
N.A.I.C.S.: 523999
Michael Arnett (Exec Dir)

Subsidiaries:

Tamarind New Zealand Pty. Limited (1)
Level 8 33 Gill Street, New Plymouth, 4310, New Zealand
Tel.: (64) 67592173
Web Site: http://www.tamarindresources.com
Oil & Gas Exploration Services
N.A.I.C.S.: 213111

Tamarind Taranaki Limited (1)
Level 8 33 Gill Street, PO Box 8156, New Plymouth, 4310, New Zealand
Tel.: (64) 67592173
Web Site: http://www.tamarindresources.com
Oil & Gas Field Exploration Services
N.A.I.C.S.: 211120

TAMAWOOD LIMITED
1821 Ipswich Road, PO Box 16, Sherwood, Rocklea, 4075, QLD, Australia
Tel.: (61) 732740761 AU
Web Site: https://www.tamawood.com.au
TWD—(ASX)
Rev.: $56,820,245
Assets: $32,149,439
Liabilities: $9,971,287
Net Worth: $22,178,152
Earnings: $3,697,249
Fiscal Year-end: 06/30/24
Home Contract Construction Services
N.A.I.C.S.: 236116
Timothy Bartholomaeus (Mng Dir)

Subsidiaries:

AstiVita Limited (1)
81 Shettleston Street, Rocklea, 4106, QLD, Australia
Tel.: (61) 737262000
Web Site: http://www.astivita.com.au
Sales Range: $25-49.9 Million
Emp.: 23
Bathroom & Kitchen Products Whslr
N.A.I.C.S.: 327110
Scott Ison (Gen Mgr)

Dixon Homes (1)
1821 Ipswich Rd, Rocklea, 4106, QLD, Australia
Tel.: (61) 130 010 1010
Web Site: https://www.dixonhomes.com.au
Sales Range: $50-74.9 Million
Emp.: 200
Residential Building Construction Services
N.A.I.C.S.: 236116

Dixon Systems Pty Ltd (1)
1821 Ipswich Rd, Rocklea, 4106, QLD, Australia
Tel.: (61) 732740773
Web Site: http://www.dixonhomes.com.au
Sales Range: $25-49.9 Million
Emp.: 30
Building Products Supplier
N.A.I.C.S.: 423390
Angela Gibson (Mgr)

Tamawood Realty Pty Ltd. (1)
1821 Ipswich Rd, Rocklea, 4106, Queensland, Australia
Tel.: (61) 7 32770000
Web Site: http://www.dixonhomes.com.au
Real Estate Agencies
N.A.I.C.S.: 531210
Tim Bartholoneaus (Gen Mgr)

TAMBLA LIMITED
Level 16 132 Arthur Street, North Sydney, 2060, NSW, Australia
Tel.: (61) 2 9122 6200
Web Site: http://www.tambla.com.au
Rev.: $6,839,709
Assets: $3,389,141
Liabilities: $3,333,000
Net Worth: $56,141
Earnings: ($245,379)
Emp.: 100
Fiscal Year-end: 12/31/18
Software Devolepment
N.A.I.C.S.: 513210
Christopher Brooke (CFO & Sec)

Subsidiaries:

E-tivity Corporation (APAC) Pty. Ltd. (1)
Level 16 132 Arthur Street, North Sydney, 2060, NSW, Australia
Tel.: (61) 2 9923 8000
Web Site: http://www.etivitycorp.com
Software Development Services
N.A.I.C.S.: 541511

TAMBOLI INDUSTRIES LIMITED
Mahavir Palace 8-A Kalubha Road, Bhavnagar, 364002, Gujarat, India
Tel.: (91) 2786541222
Web Site: https://tamboliindustries.com
533170—(BOM)
Rev.: $10,254,325
Assets: $14,278,209
Liabilities: $1,883,676
Net Worth: $12,394,533
Earnings: $1,265,176
Emp.: 3
Fiscal Year-end: 03/31/23
Investment Management Service
N.A.I.C.S.: 523999
Priyanka Dineshkumar Jasani (Sec)

Subsidiaries:

Tamboli Castings Limited (1)
Sidsar Road, Vartej, Bhavnagar, 364060, Gujarat, India
Tel.: (91) 2782541000
Web Site: https://www.tcl.in
Sales Range: $50-74.9 Million
Emp.: 510
Precision & Investment Casting Mfr
N.A.I.C.S.: 331512
Vaibhav B. Tamboli (Exec Dir)

TAMBORAN RESOURCES LIMITED
Tower One International Towers Suite 1 Level 39 100 Barangaroo Avenue, Barangaroo, 2000, NSW, Australia
Tel.: (61) 283300626 AU
Web Site: https://www.tamboran.com
Year Founded: 2009
TBN—(ASX)
Rev.: $192,740
Assets: $166,562,563
Liabilities: $22,575,722
Net Worth: $143,986,841
Earnings: ($28,199,613)
Fiscal Year-end: 06/30/23
Exploration & Mining Services
N.A.I.C.S.: 213115
Richard K. Stoneburner (Chm)

TAMBOURAH METALS LTD.
Unit 2 Level 2/10 Ord St, West Perth, 6005, WA, Australia
Tel.: (61) 894818669 AU
Web Site: https://www.tambourahmetals.com
Year Founded: 2020
TMB—(ASX)
Rev.: $1,532
Assets: $6,010,980
Liabilities: $127,355
Net Worth: $5,883,625
Earnings: ($360,309)
Fiscal Year-end: 06/30/22
Metal Exploration Services
N.A.I.C.S.: 213114
Graeme Smith (Sec)

TAMBOV ENERGOSBYT COMPANY
Sovetskaya st 104/14, Tambov, 392000, Russia
Tel.: (7) 4752559988
Web Site: https://tesk.su
TASB—(MOEX)
Sales Range: Less than $1 Million
Electric Power Distribution Services
N.A.I.C.S.: 221122

TAMBUN INDAH LAND BERHAD
12-01 Penthouse Wisma Pantai Jalan Wisma Pantai, Kampung Gajah, 12200, Butterworth, Penang, Malaysia
Tel.: (60) 43240088 MY
Web Site: https://www.tambunindah.com
Year Founded: 1993
TAMBUN—(KLS)
Rev.: $48,145,528
Assets: $187,281,758
Liabilities: $30,836,591
Net Worth: $156,445,167
Earnings: $12,723,436
Emp.: 79
Fiscal Year-end: 12/31/22
Residential Property Developer
N.A.I.C.S.: 236117
Kiak Seng Teh (Deputy Chm)

Subsidiaries:

Cenderaman Development Sdn Bhd (1)
12-01 Penthouse Wisma Pantai, Jalan Wisma Pantai, Butterworth, 12200, Penang, Malaysia
Tel.: (60) 43240088
Web Site: https://www.tambunindah.com
Emp.: 80
Property Development Services
N.A.I.C.S.: 236210
Theng Theng Teh (Dir)

Denmas Sdn Bhd (1)
12-01 Penthouse Wisma Pantai Jalan , Butterworth, 12200, Penang, Malaysia
Tel.: (60) 43240088
Web Site: https://www.tambunindah.com
Sales Range: $25-49.9 Million
Emp.: 30
Property Development Services
N.A.I.C.S.: 236210
Irine Ngiam (Mgr-HR)

Intanasia Development Sdn Bhd (1)
12-01 Penthouse Wisma Pantai Jalan Kampung Gajah, Butterworth, 12200, Penang, Malaysia
Tel.: (60) 43240088
Web Site: https://www.tambunindah.com.my
Sales Range: $25-49.9 Million
Property Development Services
N.A.I.C.S.: 236210

TAMBUN INDAH LAND BERHAD

Tambun Indah Land Berhad—(Continued)

Theng Theng Teh *(Mgr)*

Jasnia Sdn Bhd (1)
12-01 Penthouse Wisma Jalan Pantai, Kampung Gajah, Butterworth, 12200, Penang, Malaysia
Tel.: (60) 43240088
Web Site: https://www.tambunindah.com
Sales Range: $25-49.9 Million
Property Development Services
N.A.I.C.S.: 236210

Juru Heights Sdn Bhd (1)
12-01 Penthouse Wisma Jalan Pantai, Kampung Gajah, Butterworth, 12200, Penang, Malaysia
Tel.: (60) 45084008
Property Development Services
N.A.I.C.S.: 236210

Tokoh Edaran Sdn Bhd (1)
12-01 Penthouse Wisma Pantai Jalan Kampung Gajah, Butterworth, 12200, Penang, Malaysia
Tel.: (60) 43240093
Property Development Services
N.A.I.C.S.: 236210
Theng Theng Teh *(Gen Mgr)*

Zipac Development Sdn Bhd (1)
12-01 Penthouse Wisma Jalan Pantai Wisma Pantai, Kampung Gajah, Butterworth, 12200, Penang, Malaysia
Tel.: (60) 43240088
Web Site: https://www.tambunindah.com
Sales Range: $25-49.9 Million
Property Development Services
N.A.I.C.S.: 236210

TAMBURI INVESTMENT PARTNERS S.P.A

Via Pontaccio 10, 20121, Milan, Italy
Tel.: (39) 028858801
Web Site: https://www.tipspa.it
Year Founded: 2000
TIP—(ITA)
Sales Range: $1-9.9 Million
Emp.: 15
Investment Management Service
N.A.I.C.S.: 523940
Cesare d'Amico *(Vice Chm)*

Subsidiaries:

Be Shaping the Future S.p.A (1)
Via dell'Esperanto 71, 00144, Rome, Italy
Tel.: (39) 0654248624
Web Site: http://www.be-tse.it
Sales Range: $125-149.9 Million
Emp.: 1,167
Global Outsourcing Solutions & Outsourcing of Back-Office Administration & Management
N.A.I.C.S.: 561499
Stefano Achermann *(Mng Dir)*

Subsidiary (Non-US):

Be Poland Think, Solve & Execute sp z.o.o (2)
Al Jana Pawla II 22 Q22 28th Floor, 00-133, Warsaw, Poland
Tel.: (48) 222218052
Web Site: http://www.be-tse.pl
Financial Services
N.A.I.C.S.: 523999
Marco Bosco *(CEO)*

Be Shaping the Future - Financial Industry Solutions AG (2)
Fruhlingstrasse 2, 84034, Landshut, Germany
Tel.: (49) 87127660
Web Site: http://www.be-stf.de
Financial Investment Services
N.A.I.C.S.: 523999
Stefan Reither *(Chm-Exec Bd)*

Fimas GmbH (2)
Mergenthalerallee 45-47, 65760, Eschborn, Germany
Tel.: (49) 61965249111
Web Site: http://www.fimas-consulting.com
Financial Services
N.A.I.C.S.: 523999

Subsidiary (Domestic):

Confinity GmbH (3)
Wittenberger Strasse 21, 39106, Magdeburg, Germany
Tel.: (49) 3916208690
Web Site: http://www.confinity.de
Software Development Services
N.A.I.C.S.: 541511
Christian Konig *(Co-Mng Dir)*

Subsidiary (Domestic):

Iquii S.r.l. (2)
Viale dell Esperanto 71, 00144, Rome, Italy
Tel.: (39) 067215125
Web Site: http://www.iquii.com
Laboratory Services
N.A.I.C.S.: 541380
Mirko Lalli *(CEO)*

Juniper Extensible Solutions S.r.l. (2)
Via ai Canzocoi 4, Predazzo, 38037, Trento, Italy
Tel.: (39) 046223546
Web Site: http://www.juniper-xs.it
Mobile Application Services
N.A.I.C.S.: 541511

Subsidiary (Non-US):

Targit GmbH (2)
Brucknerstrasse 2 Tur 3, 1040, Vienna, Austria
Tel.: (43) 189011980
Web Site: http://www.targit.at
Financial Services
N.A.I.C.S.: 523999
Rudiger Borsutzki *(Mng Dir)*

Subsidiary (Domestic):

Tesla Consulting S.r.l. (2)
Via Enrico Mattei 88, 40138, Bologna, Italy
Tel.: (39) 0510548633
Web Site: http://www.teslaconsulting.it
Network Security Services
N.A.I.C.S.: 561621

TAMDEEN REAL ESTATE COMPANY K.S.C.C.

360 Mall 6th Ring Road South Surra Al Zhara Area, PO Box 21816, Tamdeen Group Offices 4th & 5th Floor Safat, 13079, Kuwait, 13079, Kuwait
Tel.: (965) 25362330
Web Site: https://www.tamdeen.com
TAM—(KUW)
Rev.: $76,928,077
Assets: $1,915,635,867
Liabilities: $695,245,214
Net Worth: $1,220,390,653
Earnings: $69,674,023
Emp.: 96
Fiscal Year-end: 12/31/22
Real Estate Investment & Other Related Services
N.A.I.C.S.: 523999
Mohammed Jassim K. Al Marzouq *(Chm)*

Subsidiaries:

Al-Tamdeen Investment Company K.S.C.C. (1)
Al-Zahraa - 360 Complex - 4th Floor, PO Box 22509, Safat, Kuwait, 13066, Kuwait (51.37%)
Tel.: (965) 25362330
Web Site: http://www.tamdeeninvestment.com
Rev.: $57,361,695
Assets: $1,145,705,402
Liabilities: $74,503,396
Net Worth: $1,071,202,005
Earnings: $41,503,341
Emp.: 50
Fiscal Year-end: 12/31/2022
Investment Banking & Portfolio Management Services
N.A.I.C.S.: 523150
Nawaf Ahmad Al-Marzouq *(Chm)*

TAMENY INC.

1-20-3 Imasu Osaki Building 3rd floor Osaki, Shinagawa-ku, Tokyo, 141-0032, Japan
Tel.: (81) 357592700
Web Site: https://www.tameny.jp
Year Founded: 2004
6181—(TKS)
Rev.: $42,310,200
Assets: $37,870,800
Liabilities: $36,738,300
Net Worth: $1,132,500
Earnings: ($1,789,350)
Emp.: 290
Fiscal Year-end: 03/31/23
Marriage Information Service
N.A.I.C.S.: 812990
Shigeru Sato *(Chm & Pres)*

TAMEX OBIEKTY SPORTOWE SA

ul Idzikowskiego 16, 00-710, Warsaw, Poland
Tel.: (48) 225562423
Web Site: https://www.tamex.pl
Sports Club Facility Operator
N.A.I.C.S.: 713940
Edyta Sobecka *(Pres)*

TAMIL NADU INDUSTRIAL DEVELOPMENT CORPORATION LTD.

19 A Rukmini Lakshmipathy Road, Egmore, Chennai, 600 008, India
Tel.: (91) 4428554479
Web Site: http://www.tidco.com
Year Founded: 1965
Sales Range: $25-49.9 Million
Emp.: 60
Investment Holding Company
N.A.I.C.S.: 551112
B. Elangovan *(Sr Gen Mgr-Projects)*

Subsidiaries:

Tanfac Industries Limited (1)
14 Sipcot Inustrial Complex, SAV District, Cuddalore, 607 005, India
Tel.: (91) 4142239001
Web Site: http://www.tanfac.com
Sales Range: $25-49.9 Million
Emp.: 50
Fluorine Chemicals Mfr
N.A.I.C.S.: 325998
T. C. Kalyankumar *(Sr Mgr-Mktg)*

TAMIL NADU NEWSPRINT & PAPERS LTD

67 Mount Road, Guindy, Chennai, 600 032, Tamil Nadu, India
Tel.: (91) 4422301094
Web Site: https://www.tnpl.com
Year Founded: 1979
TNPL—(NSE)
Rev.: $626,510,557
Assets: $734,137,582
Liabilities: $501,045,285
Net Worth: $233,092,297
Earnings: $46,504,406
Emp.: 2,427
Fiscal Year-end: 03/31/23
Newspaper Print & Publisher
N.A.I.C.S.: 513110
A. Balasubramanian *(Gen Mgr-Comml & E&I)*

TAMILNADU JAI BHARATH MILLS LIMITED

504 Avinashi Road, Coimbatore, 641 004, India
Tel.: (91) 422 4310200
Web Site: http://www.tnjb.net.in
Year Founded: 1993
Rev.: $11,116,696
Assets: $8,052,128
Liabilities: $11,657,683
Net Worth: ($3,605,554)
Earnings: ($3,190,374)
Fiscal Year-end: 03/31/19

INTERNATIONAL PUBLIC

Yarn Mfr & Whslr
N.A.I.C.S.: 313110
T. R. Dhinakaran *(Chm & Mng Dir)*

TAMILNADU PETROPRODUCTS LIMITED

Manali Express Highway Manali, Chennai, 600068, India
Tel.: (91) 4425945588
Web Site: https://www.tnpetro.com
Year Founded: 1984
500777—(BOM)
Rev.: $260,788,586
Assets: $132,704,059
Liabilities: $33,735,711
Net Worth: $98,968,347
Earnings: $11,292,417
Emp.: 381
Fiscal Year-end: 03/31/23
Petrochemical Mfr
N.A.I.C.S.: 325110
Ashwin C. Muthiah *(Vice Chm)*

TAMILNADU STEEL TUBES LIMITED

Mercury Apartments 1st Floor 65 Pantheon Road Egmore, Chennai, 600 008, Tamil Nadu, India
Tel.: (91) 4428555653
Web Site: https://tntpipes.com
Year Founded: 1979
513540—(BOM)
Rev.: $11,114,789
Assets: $3,906,936
Liabilities: $2,797,578
Net Worth: $1,109,358
Earnings: $67,826
Emp.: 133
Fiscal Year-end: 03/31/23
Steel Tube Mfr
N.A.I.C.S.: 331210
M. T. Elumalai *(Exec Dir)*

TAMILNADU TELECOMMUNICATION LIMITED

No 16 1st Floor Aziz Mulk 3rd Street, Thousandlights, Chennai, 600006, India
Tel.: (91) 4428292653
Web Site: https://www.ttlofc.in
Year Founded: 1988
523419—(BOM)
Rev.: $21,963
Assets: $2,156,000
Liabilities: $20,016,433
Net Worth: ($17,860,433)
Earnings: ($1,434,727)
Emp.: 63
Fiscal Year-end: 03/31/23
Optical Fiber Mfr
N.A.I.C.S.: 335921
J. Ramesh Kannan *(CFO)*

TAMIN PETROLEUM & PETROCHEMICAL INVESTMENT CO.

Number 101 West Hoveize St North Sohrevardi St, Tehran, Iran
Tel.: (98) 2142575000
Web Site: https://www.tappico.com
Year Founded: 2002
PTAP1—(THE)
Sales Range: Less than $1 Million
Emp.: 16,800
Petrochemical Products Mfr
N.A.I.C.S.: 325110
Mahmood Makhdoomi *(Mng Dir)*

TAMINO MINERALS, INC.

Bulevard Hidalgo 67, 83260, Hermosillo, Sonora, Mexico
Tel.: (52) 4166024892
Web Site: https://www.taminominerals.ca
TINO—(OTGIQ)
Sales Range: Less than $1 Million
Mineral Exploration Services

AND PRIVATE COMPANIES

N.A.I.C.S.: 213114
Pedro Villagran-Garcia *(CEO)*

TAMKEEN HOLDING CO
Qebla-Ali Al Salem Street-Al Jawhara Tower-8th floor Safat, PO Box 22816, Kuwait, Kuwait
Tel.: (965) 22255929
Web Site:
 http://www.tamkeenholding.com
Holding Company
N.A.I.C.S.: 551112

TAMNAVAPUT A.D.
Ulica Prvog maja broj 126, 14210, Ub, Serbia
Tel.: (381) 14 414 237
Web Site:
 http://www.tamnavaput.co.rs
Year Founded: 1980
Sales Range: $1-9.9 Million
Emp.: 40
Road Construction & Maintenance Services
N.A.I.C.S.: 237310

TAMRON CO. LTD.
1385 Hasunuma, Minuma-ku, Saitama, 337-8556, Japan
Tel.: (81) 486849111
Web Site: https://tamron.com
7740—(TKS)
Rev.: $506,410,340
Assets: $617,269,580
Liabilities: $115,779,700
Net Worth: $501,489,880
Earnings: $76,657,080
Emp.: 4,604
Fiscal Year-end: 12/31/23
Photographic Lenses & Optical Components Mfr
N.A.I.C.S.: 333310
Shiro Ajisaka *(Pres & CEO)*
Subsidiaries:

Tamron (Russia) LLC (1)
Unikon Business Center 2F No 4 Plekhanova Street 4a, Moscow, 111123, Russia
Tel.: (7) 4959700112
Web Site: https://www.tamron.ru
Lens Distr
N.A.I.C.S.: 423460

Tamron Co. Ltd. - Namioka Plant (1)
64-1 Shimoshimada Kitanakano Namioka, Aomori, 038-1325, Japan
Tel.: (81) 172629555
Lens Mfr
N.A.I.C.S.: 339115

Tamron Co., Ltd. - Hirosaki Plant (1)
3-2 Shimizu 3-chome Hirosaki-shi, Aomori, 036-8254, Japan
Tel.: (81) 172341144
Web Site: http://www.tamron.com
Lenses Mfr & Sales
N.A.I.C.S.: 333310

Tamron Co., Ltd. - Owani Plant (1)
31-1 Maeda Owani-cho, Minamitsugaru-gun, Aomori, 038-0243, Japan
Tel.: (81) 172476713
Web Site: http://www.tamron.co.jp
Sales Range: $25-49.9 Million
Lens Mfr
N.A.I.C.S.: 333310

Tamron Europe GmbH (1)
Robert-bosch-strasse 9, 50769, Cologne, Germany
Tel.: (49) 2216695440
Web Site: http://www.tamron.de
Sales Range: $25-49.9 Million
Lens Mfr
N.A.I.C.S.: 333310
Michael Dickel *(Mng Dir)*

Tamron France EURL (1)
5 av Georges Bataille, PO Box 31, 60330, Le Plessis-Belleville, France
Tel.: (33) 344607300
Web Site: http://www.tamron.eu

Sales Range: $25-49.9 Million
Lens Mfr
N.A.I.C.S.: 333310

Tamron India Private Limited (1)
Unit No 805-807 8th Floor Vatika City Point MG Road, Gurgaon, 122001, Haryana, India
Tel.: (91) 1244116812
Web Site: https://www.tamron.in
Lens Distr
N.A.I.C.S.: 423460
Nitin Goyal *(Pres & CEO)*

Tamron Industries (Hong Kong) Limited (1)
Unit 908 9/F Elite Centre 22 Hung To Road, Kwun Tong, Kowloon, China (Hong Kong)
Tel.: (852) 27217388
Web Site: http://www.tamron.com.hk
Sales Range: $25-49.9 Million
Lens Mfr
N.A.I.C.S.: 333310

Tamron Optical (Foshan) Co., Ltd. (1)
No 76 West of Langbao Road, Chancheng District, Foshan, Guangdong, China
Tel.: (86) 75782982222
Lens Mfr
N.A.I.C.S.: 339115

Tamron Optical (Shanghai) Co., Ltd. (1)
Room 1707 Ruijin Building No 205 Maoming South Road, Shanghai, 200020, China
Tel.: (86) 2151028880
Web Site: http://www.tamron.com.cn
Sales Range: $25-49.9 Million
Camera Lenses Mfr
N.A.I.C.S.: 333310

Tamron Optical (Vietnam) Co., Ltd. (1)
Plot No 69B and 70A Noi Bai Industrial Zone, Mai Dinh Commune Soc Son District, Hanoi, Vietnam
Tel.: (84) 2437621759
Lens Mfr
N.A.I.C.S.: 339115

Tamron USA Inc. (1)
10 Austin Blvd, Commack, NY 11725
Tel.: (631) 858-8400
Web Site: http://www.tamron-usa.com
Sales Range: $25-49.9 Million
Digital Camera Lenses Mfr
N.A.I.C.S.: 333310

TAMTRON GROUP OYJ
Vestonkatu 11, PO Box 15, 33561, Tampere, Finland
Tel.: (358) 331435000
Web Site:
 https://www.tamtrongroup.com
Year Founded: 1972
TAMTRON—(HEL)
Rev.: $33,215,654
Assets: $32,413,780
Liabilities: $28,201,118
Net Worth: $4,212,662
Earnings: $169,410
Emp.: 269
Fiscal Year-end: 12/31/21
Logistic Services
N.A.I.C.S.: 541614
Juho Koskinen *(Mng Dir)*

TAMURA CORPORATION
1-19-43 Higashi-Oizumi, Nerima-ku, Tokyo, 178-8511, Japan
Tel.: (81) 339782111   JP
Web Site:
 https://www.tamuracorp.com
Year Founded: 1924
6768—(TKS)
Rev.: $704,771,420
Assets: $759,112,230
Liabilities: $377,080,670
Net Worth: $382,031,560
Earnings: $14,806,400
Emp.: 4,410
Fiscal Year-end: 03/31/24
Electronic Components Mfr

N.A.I.C.S.: 334419
Naoki Tamura *(Chm)*
Subsidiaries:

Aizu Tamura Corporation (1)
27-2 Kamimurakita, Onuma-gun aizumisato, Fukushima, 969-6103, Japan
Tel.: (81) 242562911
Web Site: https://www.aizutamura.co.jp
Sales Range: $25-49.9 Million
Emp.: 100
Electronic Components Mfr
N.A.I.C.S.: 334416

Earth Tamura Electronic (Myanmar) Co., Ltd. (1)
No 475 / Ka Yauk Kaw Street Block No 23, Industrial Zone 1 South Dagon Township, Yangon, Myanmar
Tel.: (95) 159 5217
Electronic Component Mfr & Distr
N.A.I.C.S.: 334419

Hefei Ecriee-Tamura Electric Co., Ltd. (1)
No 41 Tianzhi Road, High and New Technology Development Zone, Hefei, 230088, Anhui, China
Tel.: (86) 551 627 2499
Electronic Component Mfr & Distr
N.A.I.C.S.: 334419

Indusul Industria De Transformadores Ltda. (1)
Avenida Francisco Andrade Ribeiro 543 Bloco 4, Bairro Familia Andrade, Santa Rita do Sapucai, 37540-000, Minas Gerais, Brazil
Electronic Components Mfr
N.A.I.C.S.: 334419

Koha Co., Ltd. (1)
1-19-43 Higashi-Oizumi, Nerima-ku, Tokyo, 178-8511, Japan
Tel.: (81) 33 978 2110
Web Site: http://www.koha.co.jp
Vending Machine Mfr & Distr
N.A.I.C.S.: 333310
Norihiko Nanjo *(Pres)*

Op-Seed Co., (BD) Ltd. (1)
Plot 29-32 and 56-59 Sector 7 Chattogram Export Processing Zone, Halishahar, Chittagong, Bangladesh
Tel.: (880) 317 406 4142
Web Site: https://www.opseed.com.bd
Emp.: 750
Electronic Components Mfr
N.A.I.C.S.: 334419
Hiroshi Kato *(Mng Dir)*

Shanghai Xiangle Tamura Electro Chemical Industry Co., Ltd. (1)
555 Xiangjiang Road Nanxiang, Jiading, Shanghai, China
Tel.: (86) 2139199231
Electronic Chemicals Mfr
N.A.I.C.S.: 325180

Taiwan Tamura Technology Co., Ltd. (1)
13F No 866 Chung-Cheng Road, Chung-Ho District, New Taipei City, 23586, Taiwan
Tel.: (886) 28 228 2001
Electronic Component Mfr & Distr
N.A.I.C.S.: 334419

Tamura Chemical Korea Co., Ltd. (1)
98-22 Gongdan 1-ro, Anseong, 17575, Gyeonggi, Korea (South)
Tel.: (82) 316721154
Sales Range: $25-49.9 Million
Emp.: 34
Electronic Components Mfr & Whslr
N.A.I.C.S.: 334416

Tamura Corporation - Iruma Factory (1)
16-2 Sayamagahara, Iruma, 358-8501, Saitama, Japan
Tel.: (81) 429346134
Web Site: http://www.tamura-ss.co.jp
Sales Range: $50-74.9 Million
Emp.: 250
Electrochemicals Mfr
N.A.I.C.S.: 325411

Tamura Corporation - Kodama Factory (1)

TAMURA CORPORATION

200-2 Motohara, Kamikawa-cho, Kodama, 367-0241, Saitama, Japan
Tel.: (81) 495773611
Sales Range: $25-49.9 Million
Emp.: 50
Electronic Chemicals Mfr
N.A.I.C.S.: 325998

Tamura Corporation - Sakado Factory (1)
5-5-30 Chiyoda, Sakado, 350-0214, Saitama, Japan
Tel.: (81) 492845711
Electronic Components Mfr
N.A.I.C.S.: 334419

Tamura Corporation - Sayama Factory (1)
2-3-1 Hirosedai, Sayama, 350-1328, Saitama, Japan
Tel.: (81) 429553111
Electronic Components Mfr
N.A.I.C.S.: 334416

Tamura Corporation Singapore Pte. Ltd. (1)
1 Maritime Square 09-30 HarbourFront Centre, Singapore, 099253, Singapore
Tel.: (65) 65697077
Web Site: http://www.tamura.com.sg
Sales Range: $25-49.9 Million
Emp.: 23
Electronic Component Mfr & Distr
N.A.I.C.S.: 334416

Tamura Corporation Vietnam Co., Ltd. (1)
9th Floor TTC Tower Lot B1A Industrial Handicraft and Small Industry, Complex Cau Giay District Dich Vong Hau Ward, 100000, Hanoi, Vietnam
Tel.: (84) 243 795 5962
Electronic Chemical Product Mfr
N.A.I.C.S.: 325998

Tamura Corporation of America (1)
1040 S Andreasen Dr Ste 100, Escondido, CA 92029
Tel.: (760) 871-2009
Web Site: http://www.tamuracorp.com
Sales Range: $25-49.9 Million
Emp.: 15
Mfr of Power Supplies & Transformers
N.A.I.C.S.: 423690

Subsidiary (Domestic):

Tamura Kaken Corporation U.S.A. (2)
2001 Gateway Pl Ste 740 W, San Jose, CA 95110
Tel.: (408) 246-1708
Electronic Chemicals Whslr
N.A.I.C.S.: 424690

Tamura Corporation of China Limited (1)
13F Block A International Shopping Centre Shanghai, No 527 Huaihai Zhong Road, Shanghai, 200020, China
Tel.: (86) 216 387 9388
Electronic Component Mfr & Distr
N.A.I.C.S.: 334419

Tamura Corporation of Hong Kong Limited (1)
Unit 2 2/F Hong Kong Worsted Mills Industrial Bldg, No 31-39 Wo Tong Tsui Street, Kwai Chung, New Territories, China (Hong Kong)
Tel.: (852) 24207666
Electronic Components Mfr
N.A.I.C.S.: 334419

Tamura Corporation of Korea (1)
513 Hyundai I-Valley 31 Galmachi-ro 244 beon-gil, Jungwon-gu, Seongnam, 13212, Gyeonggi, Korea (South)
Tel.: (82) 24895354
Web Site: http://www.tamurakorea.co.kr
Electronic Component Mfr & Whslr
N.A.I.C.S.: 334416

Tamura Elcomponics Technologies Private Limited (1)
C-24 Phase -II, Noida, 201 305, Uttar Pradesh, India
Tel.: (91) 120 474 3300
Web Site: https://www.tetpl.in
Power Generation Component Mfr & Distr

TAMURA CORPORATION

Tamura Corporation—(Continued)
N.A.I.C.S.: 335312

Tamura Electronic Material (Tianjin) Co., Ltd. (1)
No 199 Binhai High-tech 2nd Rd Binhai New Area, Tianjin, 300301, China
Tel.: (86) 225 853 2956
Electronic Component Mfr & Distr
N.A.I.C.S.: 334419

Tamura Electronics (H.K.) Co., Ltd. (1)
Unit 2 2F HK Worsted Mills Industrial Bldg, No 31-39 Wo Tong Tsui Street, Kwai Chung, New Teritories, China (Hong Kong)
Tel.: (852) 23894321
Electric Component Whslr
N.A.I.C.S.: 423690

Tamura Electronics (Hui Zhou) Co., Ltd. (1)
ZhouJi Industry Park, XiaLang Village LuoYang Town BoLuo County, Huizhou, 516100, Guangdong, China
Tel.: (86) 7526207338
Electric Component Whslr
N.A.I.C.S.: 423690

Tamura Electronics (M) Sdn. Bhd. (1)
Lot No 2 Jalan Halba 16/16 Seksyen 16, 40200, Shah Alam, Selangor, Malaysia
Tel.: (60) 355256000
Web Site: http://www.tamura.com.my
Electronic Component Mfr & Distr
N.A.I.C.S.: 334416

Tamura Electronics (S.Z.) Co., Ltd. (1)
101 No 30-6 Rhine Road Xinsheng Community Longgang Street, Longgang District, Shenzhen, 518116, China
Tel.: (86) 7558 950 2707
Electronic Component Mfr & Distr
N.A.I.C.S.: 334419

Tamura Electronics (Shanghai) Co., Ltd. (1)
819 Room Interchina Commercial Building 33 Dengshikou Street, Dong Cheng District, Beijing, China
Tel.: (86) 1065229967
Web Site: http://www.tamura-ss.co.jp
Electric Component Whslr
N.A.I.C.S.: 423690

Tamura Electronics (Suzhou) Co., Ltd. (1)
No 46 Hucundang Road Caohu Street, Suzhou, 215144, Jiangsu, China
Tel.: (86) 5126 939 0818
Electronic Component Mfr & Distr
N.A.I.C.S.: 334419

Tamura Electronics (Thailand) Co., Ltd. (1)
27 Soi Bangna-Trad 34 Bangna, Bangkok, 10260, Thailand
Tel.: (66) 2361 1756
Web Site: http://www.tamura-ss.co.jp
Sales Range: $50-74.9 Million
Emp.: 10
Electronic Components Distr
N.A.I.C.S.: 423690

Tamura Elsold GmbH (1)
Huttenstrasse 1, 38871, Ilsenburg, Germany
Tel.: (49) 394 524 8790
Web Site: https://www.tamura-elsold.de
Electronic Component Mfr & Distr
N.A.I.C.S.: 334419

Tamura Europe Limited (1)
Clark Avenue Porte Marsh Industrial Estate, Calne, SN11 9BS, Wiltshire, United Kingdom
Tel.: (44) 1380731700
Web Site: http://www.tamura-europe.co.uk
Emp.: 20
Electronic Components Distr
N.A.I.C.S.: 423690

Tamura Fa System (Suzhou) Co., Ltd. (1)
No 18 Tonghe Street, WeiTing, Suzhou, 215121, Jiangsu, China
Tel.: (86) 51282157666

Web Site: http://www.tfz-tamura.com
Sales Range: $50-74.9 Million
Emp.: 200
Reflow Soldering Equipment Mfr
N.A.I.C.S.: 333992

Tamura Kaken (Dongguan) Ltd. (1)
The Scientific and Technologic Industry Zone, Shijie Town, Dongguan, 523290, Guangdong, China
Tel.: (86) 7698 630 5888
Electronic Component Mfr & Distr
N.A.I.C.S.: 334419

Tamura Kaken (M) Sdn. Bhd. (1)
No 3A-20 IOI Business Park 1 Persiaran Puchong Jaya Selatan, Bandar Puchong Jaya, 47100, Puchong, Selangor, Malaysia
Tel.: (60) 380709951
Sales Range: $50-74.9 Million
Emp.: 4
Electronic Component Mfr & Whslr
N.A.I.C.S.: 334416

Tamura Kaken (U.K.) Ltd. (1)
Caswell Road, Brackmills, Northampton, NN4 7PW, Northamptonshire, United Kingdom
Tel.: (44) 1604768888
Sales Range: $25-49.9 Million
Emp.: 7
Electrochemicals Mfr
N.A.I.C.S.: 325992

Tamura Kaken Tech Co., Ltd. (1)
5F-3 No181 Fusing N Rd, Songshan District, Taipei, 105, Taiwan
Tel.: (886) 287126023
Electronic Component Mfr & Whslr
N.A.I.C.S.: 334416

Tamura Machinery (Thailand) Co., Ltd. (1)
169 Soi Phayasuren 30 Phayasuren Road Bangchan, Khlong Sam Wa, Bangkok, 10510, Thailand
Tel.: (66) 2919 1418
Web Site: http://www.tamura-ss.co.jp
Electronic Component Mfr & Sales
N.A.I.C.S.: 334416

Tamura Magnetic Engineering S.R.L. (1)
Via Ponchielli 6, Ellera Corciano, 06073, Perugia, Italy
Tel.: (39) 075 518 3611
Electronic Components Mfr
N.A.I.C.S.: 334419

Tamura Power Technologies De Mexico, S.A. de C.V. (1)
Avenida Pacifico 14633, Parque Industrial Pacifico, 22643, Tijuana, Baja California, Mexico
Tel.: (52) 664 626 5490
Electronic Components Mfr
N.A.I.C.S.: 334419

Tamura Power Technology Co., Ltd (1)
13F No 866 Chung Cheng Road, Chungho, Taipei, 23586, Taiwan
Tel.: (886) 282282001
Electrical Equipment Mfr & Whslr
N.A.I.C.S.: 334416

Tamura Thermal Device Corporation (1)
Sayama Technopark Device Block 2-3-1 Hirosedai, Sayama, 350-1328, Saitama, Japan
Tel.: (81) 429000039
Web Site: http://www.tamurathermaldevice.co.jp
Sales Range: $25-49.9 Million
Emp.: 32
Thermal Links Mfr & Whslr
N.A.I.C.S.: 334513
Takeo Munetaka (Mgr-Sls)

Subsidiary (Non-US):

Anzen Dengu (Hui Zhou) Co., Ltd. (2)
The Sixth Team Yangjin Road Jimadi Village Luoyang Town, Boluo County, Huizhou, Guangdong, China
Tel.: (86) 7526209263
Electric Component Whslr
N.A.I.C.S.: 423690

Tamura Thermal Device (H.K.) Co., Ltd. (1)
Unit 2 2F HK Worsted Mills Industrial Building, No 31-39 Wo Tong Tsui Street, Kwai Chung, New Teritories, China (Hong Kong)
Tel.: (852) 23894546
Web Site: http://www.tamura-ss.co.jp
Thermal Link Whslr
N.A.I.C.S.: 423610

Telepart Tamura Industria e Comercio Ltda (1)
Rua Waldomiro Anselmo 179-Jardim Marcondes, Jacarei, 12305-090, Sao Paulo, Brazil
Tel.: (55) 1239586060
Web Site: http://www.tamura-ss.co.jp
Transformer Mfr
N.A.I.C.S.: 334416

Toyota Boshoku Gateway (Thailand) CO., LTD. (1)
182 Moo 7 Gateway City Industrial Estate, Hua-Samrong Plangyao, Chachoengsao, 24190, Thailand
Tel.: (66) 38575236
Sales Range: $200-249.9 Million
Emp.: 716
Automotive Parts Mfr & Distr
N.A.I.C.S.: 336360

Wakayanagi Tamura Corporation (1)
40-1 Azakawaminami kamizutumi Wakayanagi, Kurihara, 989-5502, Miyagi, Japan
Tel.: (81) 228322211
Sales Range: $25-49.9 Million
Emp.: 100
Electronic Components Mfr
N.A.I.C.S.: 334416
Naoki Tamura (Pres)

TAMWEEL MORTGAGE FINANCE COMPANY S.A.E.
World Trade Ctr 12th Fl, Corniche El Ni, 1191, Cairo, Egypt
Tel.: (20) 225785844
Web Site: http://www.tamweeleg.com
Sales Range: $50-74.9 Million
Emp.: 60
Mortgage Services
N.A.I.C.S.: 522310

TAN BINH IMPORT-EXPORT JOINT STOCK CORPORATION
89 Ly Thuong Kiet Phuong 9, Quan Tan Binh, Ho Chi Minh City, Vietnam
Tel.: (84) 838686377
Web Site: http://www.tanimex.com.vn
TIX—(HOSE)
Rev.: $8,620,441
Assets: $50,008,931
Liabilities: $15,269,668
Net Worth: $34,739,263
Earnings: $4,344,087
Emp.: 100
Fiscal Year-end: 09/30/23
Real Estate Investment Services
N.A.I.C.S.: 531390
Tran Quang Truong (Exec Dir)

TAN CANG LOGISTICS AND STEVEDORING JOINT STOCK COMPANY
470 Dong Van Cong, Thanh My Loi Ward, Ho Chi Minh City, Vietnam
Tel.: (84) 2837423560
Web Site: https://tancanglogistics.com
Year Founded: 2007
TCL—(HOSE)
Rev.: $63,011,939
Assets: $38,747,858
Liabilities: $14,074,785
Net Worth: $24,673,073
Earnings: $5,538,145
Fiscal Year-end: 12/31/23
Logistic Services
N.A.I.C.S.: 541614
Le Van Cuong (Chm & CEO)

INTERNATIONAL PUBLIC

TAN CHONG INTERNATIONAL LIMITED
Unit 3001-3003 30/F Shui On Centre 6-8 Harbour Road, Wanchai, China (Hong Kong)
Tel.: (852) 28244473
Web Site: https://www.tanchong.com
0693—(HKG)
Rev.: $1,718,530,043
Assets: $2,802,223,178
Liabilities: $1,286,684,228
Net Worth: $1,515,538,950
Earnings: $65,109,660
Emp.: 4,034
Fiscal Year-end: 12/31/22
Motor Vehicle Distribution
N.A.I.C.S.: 333310
Chiew Sng (Fin Dir)

Subsidiaries:

Advance Pacific Holdings Limited (1)
Unit 3001 30 F Shui On Ctr 6-8 Harbour Rd, Wanchai, China (Hong Kong)
Tel.: (852) 28244473
Emp.: 3
Investment Holding & Administrative Services
N.A.I.C.S.: 551112

Subsidiary (Non-US):

Autolution Industrial Pte Ltd (2)
19 Ubi Road 4, Singapore, 408623, Singapore
Tel.: (65) 6 490 9766
Web Site: https://autolution.com.sg
Automotive Repair & Maintenance Services
N.A.I.C.S.: 811111

Subsidiary (Domestic):

Motor Image (HK) Limited (2)
G/F Continental Electric Industrial Building 17 Wang Chiu Road, Kowloon Bay, Kowloon, 000020, China (Hong Kong)
Tel.: (852) 28282488
Web Site: http://www.motorimage.net
Sales Range: $25-49.9 Million
Automotive Distr
N.A.I.C.S.: 423110

Motor Image China Limited (2)
Rm 3001 30 F Shui On Ctr 6-8 Harbour Rd, Wanchai, China (Hong Kong)
Tel.: (852) 28244473
Automobile Mfr & Sales
N.A.I.C.S.: 336211
Jason Tan (Gen Mgr)

Subsidiary (Non-US):

Motor Image (Cambodia) Ltd. (3)
No 175-177 Russian Blvd, Phnom Penh, Cambodia
Tel.: (855) 23994628
Web Site: http://www.subaru.asia
Sales Range: $50-74.9 Million
Emp.: 6
Automotive Distr
N.A.I.C.S.: 423110

Subsidiary (Domestic):

Motor Image Kowloon Limited (3)
Shop 4 G/F Billion Centre No 1 Wang Kwong Road, Kowloon Bay, Hong Kong, China (Hong Kong)
Tel.: (852) 28282488
Automotive Parts Accessory Services
N.A.I.C.S.: 811111

Subsidiary (Non-US):

Motor Image Vietnam Co., Ltd (3)
Unit 05 Centre Point Building 106 Nguyen Van Troi Street, Ward 8 Phu Nhuan District, Ho Chi Minh City, Vietnam
Tel.: (84) 838462888
Web Site: http://www.motorimage.net
Sales Range: $25-49.9 Million
Emp.: 20
Automotive Distr
N.A.I.C.S.: 423110

Auto Business Pte. Ltd. (1)

911 Bukit Timah Road, Singapore, 589622, Singapore
Tel.: (65) 64667711
Automobile Spare Parts Services
N.A.I.C.S.: 811111

Downtown Travel Services Pte Ltd
19 Lorong 8 Toa Payoh Subaru Hub, Subaru Hub Showroom, Singapore, 319255, Singapore
Tel.: (65) 6 334 1700
Web Site: https://www.dts.com.sg
Sales Range: $50-74.9 Million
Emp.: 100
Car Rental Services
N.A.I.C.S.: 532111

ETHOZ Group Ltd. (1)
30 Bukit Batok Crescent, Singapore, 658075, Singapore
Tel.: (65) 6 319 8000
Web Site: https://www.ethozgroup.com
Sales Range: $75-99.9 Million
Emp.: 200
Car Rental Services
N.A.I.C.S.: 532111

Foton Truck (Thailand) Co., Ltd. (1)
59 Moo 1 Rangsit-Pathumthani Road, Ban Klang Subdistrict Mueang District, Ayutthaya, 12000, Pathum Thani, Thailand
Tel.: (66) 2 567 2882
Web Site: https://www.foton.co.th
Commercial Truck Mfr & Distr
N.A.I.C.S.: 336120
Natthapoom Puranachaikiree (Gen Mgr)

MAN Commercial Vehicles (Thailand) Co., Ltd. (1)
8/8 Moo 1 Rangsit-Pathumthani Road T Ban Klang, A Muang District, Ayutthaya, 12000, Phathum Thani, Thailand
Tel.: (66) 256700705
Web Site: http://www.man-cv.co.th
Man Truck & Bus Vehicle Distr
N.A.I.C.S.: 423110

Metaquip TC Industrial Pte. Ltd. (1)
23 Jalan Buroh, Singapore, 619479, Singapore
Tel.: (65) 6 265 3666
Web Site: https://www.metaquip.com
Automobile Spare Parts & Services
N.A.I.C.S.: 811111

Motor Image Enterprises Pte Ltd (1)
25 Leng Kee Road, Singapore, 159097, Singapore
Tel.: (65) 67038163
Web Site: https://www.subaru.asia
Automotive Distr
N.A.I.C.S.: 423110

Motor Image Malaysia Sdn Bhd (1)
No 10 Jalan 51A / 223 Petaling Jaya, 46100, Kuala Selangor, Malaysia
Tel.: (60) 379526116
Automotive Parts Accessory Services
N.A.I.C.S.: 811111

Motor Image Pilipinas, Inc. (1)
187 EDSA Greenhills San Juan, Manila, 1503, Philippines
Tel.: (63) 53226600
Web Site: http://www.motorimage.net
Sales Range: $25-49.9 Million
Emp.: 40
Automotive Distr
N.A.I.C.S.: 423110

Motor Image Subaru (Thailand) Co. Ltd. (1)
12/17 Moo 2 Serithai Road, Khlongkum Sub-District Buengkum District, Bangkok, 10240, Thailand
Tel.: (66) 27251888
Web Site: http://www.motorimage.net
Sales Range: $50-74.9 Million
Emp.: 60
Automobiles Maintenance Services & Distr
N.A.I.C.S.: 423110

Nissan Diesel (Thailand) Co., Ltd. (1)
59 Moo 1 Rangsit-Pathumthani Rd, Ban Klang Muang Dist, Pathumthani, 12000, Thailand
Tel.: (66) 25672882
Web Site: http://www.nissandiesel.co.th

Sales Range: $75-99.9 Million
Emp.: 150
Trucks Distr
N.A.I.C.S.: 423830
Chua Tong Guan (Dir-Fin & Acctg)

PT TC Subaru (1)
Jl Sultan Iskandar Muda Arteri Pondok Indah No 55 Blok Q Kav No 3, Jakarta, 12240, Indonesia
Tel.: (62) 21 723 8999
Web Site: http://www.motorimage.net
Automobile Distribution & Maintenance Services
N.A.I.C.S.: 423110

Singapore Automotive Industries Pte. Ltd. (1)
No 1 Sixth Lok Yang Road TC Nissan Hub, Singapore, 628099, Singapore
Tel.: (65) 6 703 8412
Web Site: https://www.saiauto.com.sg
Automotive Electrical Parts & Accessory Mfr
N.A.I.C.S.: 336390

TC Autoclinic Pte Ltd (1)
No 1 Sixth Lok Yang Road, Singapore, 628099, Singapore
Tel.: (65) 6 262 2212
Web Site: http://www.tanchong.com
Automotives Repair & Maintenance Services
N.A.I.C.S.: 811111

TC Autohub (Thailand) Co., Ltd. (1)
59 Moo 1 Rangsit-Pathumthani Road, BanKlang Sub-District Muang District, Ayutthaya, 12000, Pathum Thani, Thailand
Tel.: (66) 2 567 2882
Web Site: https://www.tcautohub.co.th
Commercial Vehicle & Industrial Equipment Services
N.A.I.C.S.: 811310

Taiwan Motor Image Co., Ltd (1)
33 Ln 250 Hsin Hu 2nd Rd, Neihu Dist, Taipei, 11494, Taiwan
Tel.: (886) 227932288
Sales Range: $50-74.9 Million
Emp.: 100
Automobile Maintenance Services & Distr
N.A.I.C.S.: 423110
Seetoh Kwok Meng (Gen Mgr)

Tan Chong & Sons Motor Co (S) Pte Ltd (1)
911 Bukit Timah Road, Singapore, 589622, Singapore
Tel.: (65) 64667711
Web Site: https://www.tanchong.com
Automobile Sales & Maintenance Services
N.A.I.C.S.: 423110

Subsidiary (Domestic):

T8 Gallery Pte. Ltd. (2)
25 Leng Kee Road, Singapore, 159097, Singapore
Tel.: (65) 67038954
Web Site: https://www.t8gallery.com.sg
Vehicle Equipment Spare Parts & Services
N.A.I.C.S.: 811310

Waste Management Pte Ltd (2)
913 Bukit Timah Road, Singapore, 589623, Singapore
Tel.: (65) 64686559
Web Site: https://www.wastemanagement.com.sg
Waste Collection & Disposal Equipment Distr
N.A.I.C.S.: 423730
Gohleng Kwang (Mng Dir)

Tan Chong (Vietnam) Industrial Machinery Co., Ltd. (1)
No 10 Road No 8 VSIP 1, Hiep Phu Ward Dist 9, Thuan An, Binh Duong, Vietnam
Tel.: (84) 6503763214
Web Site: https://www.tcim.com.vn
Forklift Trucks Sales & Maintenance Services
N.A.I.C.S.: 423830

Tan Chong Credit Pte Ltd (1)
911 Bukit Timah Rd, Singapore, 589622, Singapore
Tel.: (65) 64667711
Web Site: https://www.tanchong.com
Emp.: 6

Hire Purchase Financing & Vehicle Insurance Services
N.A.I.C.S.: 522220
Christina Tan (Mgr-Hire Purchase & Road Tax)

Tan Chong Industrial Machinery (Pte) Ltd (1)
23 Jalan Buroh, Singapore, 619479, Singapore
Tel.: (65) 67038766
Web Site: https://www.tcim.com.sg
Sales Range: $25-49.9 Million
Emp.: 40
Industrial Equipment & Trucks Distr
N.A.I.C.S.: 423120

Subsidiary (Non-US):

Tan Chong Industrial Trading (Shanghai) Ltd (2)
No 176 Shanghai Mei Fu Rd, Shanghai, 200000, China
Tel.: (86) 2154376333
Web Site: http://www.tcim.com.cn
Forklift Trucks Maintenance Services
N.A.I.C.S.: 423830

Tan Chong Land Company Pte Ltd (1)
911 Bukit Timah Road, Singapore, 589622, Singapore
Tel.: (65) 64667711
Web Site: http://www.tanchong.com
Property Development Services
N.A.I.C.S.: 531210

Tan Chong Motor Sales (1)
911 Bukit Timah Road, Singapore, 589622, Singapore
Tel.: (65) 6 466 7711
Web Site: https://www.nissan.com.sg
Nissan Automotive Sales & Services
N.A.I.C.S.: 336110

Tan Chong Motor Sales Pte Ltd (1)
911 Bukit Timah Road, Singapore, 589622, Singapore
Tel.: (65) 6 466 7711
Web Site: http://www.tcil.com
Sales Range: $150-199.9 Million
Emp.: 300
Automobiles & Spare Parts Distr
N.A.I.C.S.: 423110

Tan Chong Realty (Private) Limited (1)
15 Queen Street 05-00, Singapore, 188537, Singapore
Tel.: (65) 63381422
Web Site: https://www.tanchong.com
Sales Range: $25-49.9 Million
Emp.: 30
Real Estate Development Services
N.A.I.C.S.: 531312

Wilby Estate International Pte. Ltd. (1)
15 Queen Street 01-01, Singapore, 188537, Singapore
Tel.: (65) 6 868 1888
Web Site: https://www.wilbyestate.com
Real Estate Services
N.A.I.C.S.: 531390

Wuxi Chengchang Seats Manufacturing Co Ltd (1)
10 NanHuan Rd, QingYang Town, Jiangyin, 214401, Jiangsu, China
Tel.: (86) 51086501398
Web Site: http://www.tanchong.com
Automobile Seats Mfr
N.A.I.C.S.: 336360

TAN CHONG MOTOR HOLDINGS BERHAD
62-68 Jalan Sultan Azlan Shah, 51200, Kuala Lumpur, Malaysia
Tel.: (60) 340478888
Web Site: https://www.tanchonggroup.com
Year Founded: 1972
TCHONG—(KLS)
Rev.: $691,646,000
Assets: $1,141,709,000
Liabilities: $495,963,000
Net Worth: $645,746,000

Earnings: ($12,432,000)
Emp.: 6,379
Fiscal Year-end: 12/31/22
Motor Vehicle Distr
N.A.I.C.S.: 236210
Heng Chew Tan (Pres)

Subsidiaries:

Auto Research and Development Sdn. Bhd. (1)
No 4185 Jln Segambut, Kuala Lumpur, Kuala Lumpur, Malaysia
Tel.: (60) 3 6257 2750
Web Site: http://www.arad.com.my
Sales Range: $25-49.9 Million
Emp.: 20
Automobile Research & Development Services
N.A.I.C.S.: 541720

ETCM (Labuan) Pty. Ltd. (1)
SU 3140 Jalan Tg Kubong, Labuan, 87000, Wilayah Persekutuan, Malaysia
Tel.: (60) 87422382
New Car Dealers
N.A.I.C.S.: 441110

ETCM (Myanmar) Company Limited (1)
YuZaNa Hi Way Complex Room 001 Building C-1 Ground Floor HninSi Street, 6th Quarter Kamaryut Township, Yangon, Myanmar
Tel.: (95) 1539977
Web Site: https://www.etcmyanmar.com
Construction Services
N.A.I.C.S.: 236220

Edaran Tan Chong Motor Sdn. Bhd. (1)
21 Jalan Ipoh Kecil, 50350, Kuala Lumpur, Federal Territory, Malaysia
Tel.: (60) 340478788
New Car Dealers
N.A.I.C.S.: 441110
Dheo Ang (CEO)

Nissan Vietnam Co. Ltd. (1)
Discovery 302 Dich Vong Street, Cau Giay County, Hanoi, Vietnam
Tel.: (84) 19001189
Web Site: https://www.nissanvietnam.vn
Automotive Vehicle Mfr & Distr
N.A.I.C.S.: 336110

Pemasaran Alat Ganti Sdn. Bhd. (1)
Lot 8 Jalan Perusahaan Dua, 68100, Batu Caves, Selangor, Malaysia
Tel.: (60) 361842212
Web Site: http://www.pagtc.com
Sales Range: $25-49.9 Million
Emp.: 30
Automobile Parts Distr
N.A.I.C.S.: 441330

TC Auto Tooling Sdn. Bhd. (1)
249 Jalan Segambut, 51200, Kuala Lumpur, Wilayah Persekutuan, Malaysia
Tel.: (60) 362585266
Web Site: https://www.tcat.com.my
Sales Range: $25-49.9 Million
Car Alarm & Navigation Systems Mfr
N.A.I.C.S.: 334511

TC Capital Resources Sdn. Bhd. (1)
No 8 Jalan Ipoh Kecil Off Jalan Ipoh, Wilayah Persekutuan, 50350, Kuala Lumpur, Malaysia
Tel.: (60) 340478888
Web Site: https://www.tccr.com.my
Hire Purchase Financing Services
N.A.I.C.S.: 522220

TC Contact Centre Services Sdn. Bhd. (1)
Level 2 Block C Wisma Tan Chong No 62-68 Jalan Sultan Azlan Shah, 50350, Kuala Lumpur, Malaysia
Tel.: (60) 327883107
Web Site: https://www.tccs.my
Road Assistance Services
N.A.I.C.S.: 561421
Kong Chooi Kheng (Mgr)

TC Euro Cars Sdn. Bhd. (1)
Lot 1A Jalan Kemajuan, Seksyen 13, 46200, Petaling Jaya, Selangor, Malaysia
Tel.: (60) 800188663

TAN CHONG MOTOR HOLDINGS BERHAD

Tan Chong Motor Holdings Berhad—(Continued)
Web Site: https://www.renault.com.my
Sales Range: $25-49.9 Million
New Car Dealers
N.A.I.C.S.: 441110

TC Motor Vietnam Co. Ltd. (1)
Lot X1-X4 Road No 10B and 12B Lot U12-U15 Road No 10BND 12B and 14B, Hoa Khanh Industrial Zone Hoa Khanh Bac ward Lien Chieu district, Da Nang, Vietnam
Tel.: (84) 2363676688
Web Site: https://www.kinglong.com.vn
Motor Vehicle Distr
N.A.I.C.S.: 423110

TC Motors (Sarawak) Sdn. Bhd. (1)
Lot 869 Section 66 Jalan Kemajuan Pending Indus Estate, 93450, Kuching, Sarawak, Malaysia
Tel.: (60) 82488811
Web Site: https://www.tanchongmotorssarawa.com
Emp.: 30
New Car Dealers
N.A.I.C.S.: 441110
Allan Chong (Reg Mgr)

TC iTech Sdn. Bhd. (1)
62-68 Jalan Sultan Azlan Shah Chow Kit, Wilayah Persekutuan, 51200, Kuala Lumpur, Malaysia
Tel.: (60) 340478888
Web Site: https://www.tc-itech.com
Automobile Maintenance Services
N.A.I.C.S.: 811111
Nicholas Tan Chye Seng (Exec VP)

TCIE Vietnam Pte. Ltd. (1)
No 10 Road 8, Vietnam Singapore Industrial Park, Thuan An, Binh Duong, Vietnam
Tel.: (84) 2743763214
Web Site: https://www.tcie.com.vn
Automobile Mfr
N.A.I.C.S.: 336110

TCM Stamping Products Sdn. Bhd. (1)
Lot 4185 Jalan Segambut, 51200, Kuala Lumpur, Federal Territory, Malaysia
Tel.: (60) 362574106
Web Site: https://www.tcmstamping.com
Sales Range: $25-49.9 Million
Emp.: 300
Motor Vehicle Parts Mfr
N.A.I.C.S.: 336390

Tan Chong & Sons Motor Company Sdn. Bhd. (1)
3rd Floor Tan Chong Building 62-68 Jalan Ipoh, 51200, Kuala Lumpur, Federal Territory, Malaysia
Tel.: (60) 340478888
Sales Range: $25-49.9 Million
New Car Dealers
N.A.I.C.S.: 441110
Dato Tan Hang Chew (Grp Pres)

Tan Chong Education Services Sdn. Bhd. (1)
Lot 9 2nd Floor Jalan Kemajuan 12/18, 46200, Petaling Jaya, Selangor Darul Ehsan, Malaysia
Tel.: (60) 379541628
Web Site: https://www.tcedu.com.my
Emp.: 400
Education Services
N.A.I.C.S.: 611710

Tan Chong Ekspres Auto Servis Sdn. Bhd. (1)
Lot 9 Jalan Kemajuan 12/18, 46200, Petaling Jaya, Selangor, Malaysia
Tel.: (60) 1800883838
Web Site: https://www.tceas.com
Automotive Repair Services
N.A.I.C.S.: 811111
Alex Yap (Mgr)

Tan Chong Industrial Equipment (Sabah) Sdn. Bhd. (1)
Mile 5 1/4 Jalan Tuaran, 88300, Kota Kinabalu, Sabah, Malaysia
Tel.: (60) 88425688
Web Site: https://tciesabah.com.my
Sales Range: $50-74.9 Million
Motor Vehicle Whslr
N.A.I.C.S.: 423110

Tan Chong Industrial Equipment Sdn. Bhd. (1)

Lot 3 Jalan Perusahaan Satu, 68100, Batu Caves, Selangor Darul Ehsan, Malaysia
Tel.: (60) 361899832
Web Site: https://www.tcie.com.my
Buses & Trucks Distr
N.A.I.C.S.: 423110

Tan Chong Trading (Malaysia) Sdn. Bhd. (1)
62-68 Jalan Ipoh, 51200, Kuala Lumpur, Federal Territory, Malaysia
Tel.: (60) 60340478888
Web Site: https://www.tctrading.com.my
Sales Range: $25-49.9 Million
Emp.: 8
Online Shopping Services
N.A.I.C.S.: 423110

Truckquip Sdn. Bhd. (1)
Lot 1 and Lot 3 Jalan 6/3, Kawasan Perusahaan, 43300, Seri Kembangan, Selangor Darul Ehsan, Malaysia
Tel.: (60) 382105288
Web Site: https://www.truckquip.com.my
Automobile Mfr & Distr
N.A.I.C.S.: 336110

TAN DAI HUNG PLASTIC J.S CO.
414 Luy Ban Bich Street Hoa Thanh Ward, Tan Phu District, 70000, Ho Chi Minh City, Vietnam
Tel.: (84) 839737277
Web Site: https://tandaihungplastic.com
Year Founded: 1984
TPC—(HOSE)
Rev.: $23,362,295
Assets: $19,030,733
Liabilities: $7,199,824
Net Worth: $11,830,910
Earnings: ($2,009,571)
Emp.: 439
Fiscal Year-end: 12/31/23
Plastics Product Mfr
N.A.I.C.S.: 326199
Pham Trung Cang (Vice Chm)

TAN KY CONSTRUCTION REAL ESTATE TRADING CORPORATION
63 Ung Van Khiem, Ward 25 Binh Thanh District, Ho Chi Minh City, Vietnam
Tel.: (84) 2838409437
Web Site: http://www.tanky.com.vn
Year Founded: 1999
TKC—(HNX)
Rev.: $24,262,233
Assets: $60,776,055
Liabilities: $54,027,385
Net Worth: $6,748,670
Earnings: $129,347
Fiscal Year-end: 12/31/21
Real Estate Trading & Investment Services
N.A.I.C.S.: 531390
Tran Trong Dung (Chm)

TAN PHU VIET NAM JSC
314 Luy Ban Bich Str Hoa Thanh Ward, Tan Phu District, Ho Chi Minh City, Vietnam
Tel.: (84) 2838609003
Web Site: https://tanphuvietnam.vn
Year Founded: 1977
TPP—(HNX)
Rev.: $54,809,764
Assets: $49,765,346
Liabilities: $36,586,381
Net Worth: $13,178,965
Earnings: $329,564
Fiscal Year-end: 12/31/21
Plastics Product Mfr
N.A.I.C.S.: 326160

TAN TIEN PLASTIC PACKAGING JOINT STOCK COMPANY
Lot II Grp 4 Rd 13 Tan Binh Industrial Zone, Tay Tanh Ward Tan Phu District, Ho Chi Minh City, Vietnam
Tel.: (84) 8 3816 0777
Web Site: http://www.tapack.com
Year Founded: 1966
Sales Range: $50-74.9 Million
Plastic Packaging Products Mfr
N.A.I.C.S.: 326112
Minh Cuong Le (Chm-Exec Bd & Gen Dir)

TANA RESOURCES CORP.
Suite 830-1100 Melville St, Vancouver, V6E 4A6, BC, Canada
Tel.: (778) 855-3394
Web Site: https://www.tanaresources.ca
TANA—(CNSX)
Metal Exploration & Mining Services
N.A.I.C.S.: 213113
Vartan Korajian (Pres & CEO)

TANABE CONSULTING GROUP CO., LTD.
3-3-41 Miyahara, Yodogawa-ku, Osaka, 532-0003, Japan
Tel.: (81) 671774000 JP
Web Site: https://www.tanabeconsulting.co.jp
Year Founded: 1963
9644—(TKS)
Rev.: $84,204,790
Assets: $93,458,790
Liabilities: $18,739,350
Net Worth: $74,719,440
Earnings: $4,237,010
Emp.: 813
Fiscal Year-end: 03/31/24
Holding Company; Consulting & Sales Promotion Services
N.A.I.C.S.: 551112
Takahiko Wakamatsu (Pres & CEO)

Subsidiaries:

Tanabe Consulting Co., Ltd. (1)
3-3-41 Miyahara, Yodogawa-ku, Osaka, 532-0003, Japan
Tel.: (81) 671774000
Web Site: https://review.tanabeconsulting.co.jp
Management Consulting Services
N.A.I.C.S.: 541611
Jiro Tanable (Chm)

Subsidiary (Domestic):

Growin' Partners Inc. (2)
14F Kioi Tower Tokyo Garden Terace Kioicho 1 - 3 Kioicho, Chiyoda-ku, Tokyo, 102-0094, Japan
Tel.: (81) 362724707
Emp.: 84
Financial Advisory Services
N.A.I.C.S.: 523940
Tetsuya Sano (CEO)

Leading Solutions Co., Ltd. (2)
4th floor Shin Kokusai Building 3-4-1 Marunouchi, Chiyoda-ku, Tokyo, 100-0005, Japan
Tel.: (81) 358603601
Software Development Services
N.A.I.C.S.: 541511

TANABE ENGINEERING CORPORATION
20 Fukuda, Niigata Prefecture, Joetsu, 942-0032, Niigata, Japan
Tel.: (81) 255456500
Web Site: https://www.tanabe-ind.co.jp
Year Founded: 1969
1828—(TKS)
Rev.: $342,675,620
Assets: $305,639,790
Liabilities: $156,035,660
Net Worth: $149,604,130
Earnings: $12,525,950
Emp.: 380

INTERNATIONAL PUBLIC

Fiscal Year-end: 03/31/24
Construction Engineering Services
N.A.I.C.S.: 541330
Yoshio Watanuki (Pres)

Subsidiaries:

Tanabe Engineering Singapore Pte. Ltd. (1)
31 Tuas Avenue 11 Level 4, Singapore, 639105, Singapore
Tel.: (65) 62679140
Emp.: 10
Construction Engineering Services
N.A.I.C.S.: 541330
Tetsuya Ono (Mng Dir)

TANAC AUTOMATION CO., LTD.
No 398 Xinjing Road Yaozhuang Town Industrial Park, Jiashan, 314117, Zhejiang, China
Tel.: (86) 57389118800
Web Site: https://www.tanac.cn
Year Founded: 2003
300461—(CHIN)
Rev.: $26,751,816
Assets: $130,637,988
Liabilities: $37,041,732
Net Worth: $93,596,256
Earnings: ($8,911,188)
Fiscal Year-end: 12/31/22
Computer Numerical Control (CNC) Automatic Winding Equipment & Accessories Mfr
N.A.I.C.S.: 333519
Xiao Yongfu (Chm & Gen Mgr)

Subsidiaries:

Tanack Seiki (Malaysia) SDN. BHD (1)
No 34 Jalan Puteri 5/16 Bandar Puter, 47100, Puchong, Selangor, Malaysia
Tel.: (60) 380682819
Grinding Machine Mfr
N.A.I.C.S.: 333519

TANACHIRA GROUP
Room MH3401 34th floor The Offices at Central World building 999/9, Bangkok, 10330, Thailand
Tel.: (66) 226450801
Web Site: http://www.tanachira.co.th
Bags & Jewelries Store
N.A.I.C.S.: 458310
Tanapong Chirapanidchakul (CEO)

Subsidiaries:

Cath Kidston Ltd. (1)
125-135 Freston Road 2nd Floor Frestonia, London, W10 6TH, United Kingdom
Tel.: (44) 8450262440
Web Site: http://www.cathkidston.co.uk
Sales Range: $25-49.9 Million
Designs, Distributes & Retails Clothing, Housewares, Accessories & Outdoor Products
N.A.I.C.S.: 424350
Cath Kidston (Founder)

TANAKA CO., LTD.
3-2-2 Minamioi, Shinagawa-ku, Tokyo, 140-8543, Japan
Tel.: (81) 337655211
Web Site: https://www.tanakashoji.co.jp
Year Founded: 1962
7619—(TKS)
Rev.: $276,139,360
Assets: $205,544,560
Liabilities: $111,761,880
Net Worth: $93,782,680
Earnings: $7,779,970
Emp.: 414
Fiscal Year-end: 03/31/24
Electrical Equipment Whslr
N.A.I.C.S.: 423610

TANAKA CO., LTD.

AND PRIVATE COMPANIES

TANAKA HOLDINGS CO., LTD.

5-26 Meizen-cho, Mizuho-ku, Nagoya, Aichi, Japan
Tel.: (81) 52 811 8511   JP
Web Site: http://www.tanakacorp.com
Year Founded: 2007
Sales Range: $1-9.9 Million
Emp.: 4
Foundry Equipment Designer, Mfr, Retrofitter, Remodeller & Repairer
N.A.I.C.S.: 811310
Makoto Tanaka *(CEO)*

TANAKA HOLDINGS CO., LTD.
Tokyo Building 7-3 Marunouchi 2-chome, Chiyoda-ku, Tokyo, 100-6422, Japan
Tel.: (81) 3 6311 5511   JP
Web Site: http://www.tanaka.co.jp
Year Founded: 1885
Rev.: $8,382,837,480
Assets: $5,027,919,480
Liabilities: $2,976,644,880
Net Worth: $2,051,274,600
Earnings: $107,370,060
Emp.: 5,123
Fiscal Year-end: 03/31/19
Holding Company
N.A.I.C.S.: 551112
Koichiro Tanaka *(CEO)*

Subsidiaries:

Electroplating Engineers of Japan Ltd. (1)
5-50 Shinmachi, Hiratsuka, 254-0076, Kanagawa, Japan
Tel.: (81) 463328131
Web Site: http://www.eeja.com
Sales Range: $50-74.9 Million
Emp.: 109
Wafer Plating Equipment
N.A.I.C.S.: 334419
Kazumasa Naito *(Pres & CEO)*

Subsidiary (US):

EEJA America Inc. (2)
235 Vineyard Ct Ste 150, Morgan Hill, CA 95037
Tel.: (408) 778-3217
Web Site: http://www.eeja.com
Sales Range: $25-49.9 Million
Emp.: 2
Metal Plating Solutions
N.A.I.C.S.: 332999

Gimel Trading Co., Ltd. (1)
36-2 Okuike-cho, Ashiya, 659-0003, Hyogo, Japan
Tel.: (81) 797220850
Web Site: https://gimelgimel.com
Fragrant Product Retailer
N.A.I.C.S.: 456120

LT Metal Co., Ltd. (1)
20 Magokjungang 8-ro, Gangseo-gu, Seoul, Korea (South)
Tel.: (82) 27577181
Web Site: https://www.ltmetal.co.kr
Precious Metal Product Mfr & Distr
N.A.I.C.S.: 339910

Metalor Technologies SA (1)
Route des Perveuils 8, CH-2074, Marin, Switzerland
Tel.: (41) 327206111
Web Site: http://www.metalor.com
Sales Range: $1-9.9 Million
Holding Company; Precious Metal Refiner, Coater & Specialty Product Mfr
N.A.I.C.S.: 551112

Subsidiary (Non-US):

Metalor Technologies (Deutschland) GmbH (2)
Kronacher Strasse 66, D-96257, Redwitz an der Rodach, Germany (100%)
Tel.: (49) 9574 624 0
Web Site: http://www.metalor.com
Precious Metal Coater & Specialty Product Mfr
N.A.I.C.S.: 335931

Metalor Technologies (France) S.A.S. (2)

Rue des Aquees, PO Box 29, 28190, Courville-sur-Eure, France (100%)
Tel.: (33) 237237844
Web Site: http://www.metalor.com
Precious Metal Coater & Specialty Product Mfr
N.A.I.C.S.: 335931

Metalor Technologies (Hong Kong) Ltd. (2)
Ste 1705-9 The Metropolis Tower 10 Metropolis Dr, Hung Hom, Kowloon, China (Hong Kong) (100%)
Tel.: (852) 25214131
Web Site: http://www.metalor.com
Sales Range: $50-74.9 Million
Emp.: 60
Precious Metal Refining & Coating Services
N.A.I.C.S.: 331410
Kenneth W. Beilstein *(Gen Mgr)*

Metalor Technologies (Iberica) SA (2)
Espronceda 183 - 1 1 andar, ES-08018, Barcelona, Spain (100%)
Tel.: (34) 933030112
Web Site: http://www.metalor.com
Precious Metal Refining & Coating Services
N.A.I.C.S.: 331410

Metalor Technologies (Italia) S.R.L. (2)
Via G Di Vittorio 28, Peschiera Borromeo, IT-20068, Milan, Italy (100%)
Tel.: (39) 025165181
Web Site: http://www.metalor.com
Precious Metal Coating Services
N.A.I.C.S.: 332812

Metalor Technologies (Singapore) Pte. Ltd. (2)
8 Buroh Street #01-06, Singapore, 627563, Singapore (100%)
Tel.: (65) 68631600
Web Site: http://www.metalor.com
Sales Range: $25-49.9 Million
Emp.: 60
Precious Metal Coating Services
N.A.I.C.S.: 332812
Kenneth Soo *(Mng Dir)*

Metalor Technologies (Suzhou) Ltd. (2)
Building B 48 Dongfu Road, Suzhou Industrial Park, Suzhou, 215123, Jiangsu, China (100%)
Tel.: (86) 51265936181
Web Site: http://www.metalor.com
Sales Range: $75-99.9 Million
Emp.: 100
Precious Metal Refiner, Coater & Specialty Product Mfr
N.A.I.C.S.: 331410
Kenneth W. Beilstein *(Gen Mgr)*

Metalor Technologies (Sweden) AB (2)
Sagagatan 22, 50635, Boras, Sweden (100%)
Tel.: (46) 33444250
Web Site: http://www.metalor.com
Precious Metal Coating Services
N.A.I.C.S.: 332812

Metalor Technologies (UK) Ltd. (2)
74 Warstone Lane, Birmingham, B18 6NG, United Kingdom (100%)
Tel.: (44) 1212363241
Web Site: http://www.metalor.com
Sales Range: $25-49.9 Million
Emp.: 34
Precious Metal Coater & Specialty Product Mfr
N.A.I.C.S.: 335931
Stephanie Burling *(Mng Dir)*

Subsidiary (Domestic):

Metalor Technologies SA (2)
Avenue du Vignoble, PO Box 9, CH-2009, Neuchatel, Switzerland (100%)
Tel.: (41) 327206111
Web Site: http://www.metalor.com
Sales Range: $150-199.9 Million
Precious Metal Refiner, Coater & Specialty Product Mfr
N.A.I.C.S.: 331410

Subsidiary (Domestic):

Metalor Finance SA (3)

Avenue du Vignoble, PO Box 9, CH-2009, Neuchatel, Switzerland (100%)
Tel.: (41) 327206111
Web Site: http://www.metalor.com
Sales Range: $50-74.9 Million
International Trade Financing Services
N.A.I.C.S.: 522299

Branch (Domestic):

Metalor Technologies - Marin (3)
Rue des Perveuils 8, 2074, Marin, Switzerland
Tel.: (41) 327206111
Web Site: http://www.metalor.com
Sales Range: $125-149.9 Million
Precious Metal Refining & Coating Services
N.A.I.C.S.: 331410

Subsidiary (US):

Metalor Technologies USA Corporation (2)
255 John L Dietsch Blvd, North Attleboro, MA 02761 (100%)
Tel.: (508) 699-8800
Web Site: http://www.metalor.com
Precious Metal Refiner, Coater & Specialty Product Mfr
N.A.I.C.S.: 332812
Laurence Drummond *(Gen Mgr)*

Subsidiary (Domestic):

Metalor Electrotechnics (U.S.A.) Corp. (3)
1003 Corporate Ln, Export, PA 15632
Tel.: (724) 733-8332
Web Site: http://www.metalor.com
Sales Range: $50-74.9 Million
Electrical Contact Products Mfr
N.A.I.C.S.: 335931

Subsidiary (Domestic):

Metalor Electrotechnics (Puerto Rico) LLC (4)
KM 3 Hwy 992, Luquillo, PR 00773
Tel.: (787) 889-2400
Web Site: http://www.metalor.com
Sales Range: $25-49.9 Million
Electrical Contact Products Mfr
N.A.I.C.S.: 335931

Subsidiary (Domestic):

Metalor USA Refining Corporation (3)
255 John L Dietsch Blvd, North Attleboro, MA 02763 (100%)
Tel.: (508) 699-8800
Web Site: http://www.metalor.com
Precious Metals Refining Services
N.A.I.C.S.: 331410

Plant (Non-US):

Metalor USA Refining Corporation Succursal del Peru (4)
Avenida Produccion Nacional 268 Edif Hermes Urb, LaVilla Chorillos, Lima, 09, Peru
Tel.: (51) 12515456
Web Site: http://www.metalor.com
Sales Range: $25-49.9 Million
Emp.: 4
Precious Metals Refining Services
N.A.I.C.S.: 331410
Gonzalo De Cossio *(Gen Mgr)*

Mitomo Semicon Engineering Co., Ltd. (1)
5842 Sakatemachi, Joso, 303-0042, Ibaraki, Japan
Tel.: (81) 297218180
Web Site: https://mitomo-semicon-eng.co.jp
Metal Plating Mfr & Distr
N.A.I.C.S.: 332813

Nippon PGM Co., Ltd. (1)
22F Akihabara UDX Bldg 4-14-1 Sotokanda, Chiyoda-Ku, Tokyo, 101-0021, Japan
Tel.: (81) 368471205
Web Site: https://www.nipponpgm.dowa.co.jp
Emp.: 300
Collection & Smelting of Spent Automobile & Petrochemical Catalyst for Recovery of Platinum Group Metals

N.A.I.C.S.: 331410
Masao Yamada *(Mng Dir)*

Subsidiary (US):

Nippon PGM America Inc. (2)
500 Richards Run, Burlington, NJ 08016
Tel.: (609) 747-9994
Web Site: http://www.dowa.co.jp
Catalyst Smelting
N.A.I.C.S.: 332999

Taiwan Tanaka Kikinzoku Kogyo Co., Ltd. (1)
Room C 9F No 146 Songjiang Rd Zhongshan District, Taipei, 10458, Taiwan
Tel.: (886) 225715870
Web Site: http://www.tanaka.co.jp
Fabricated Wire Materials
N.A.I.C.S.: 332618

Tanaka Denshi Kogyo K.K. (1)
2303-15 Oaza-yoshida Yoshinogari-cho, Kanzaki-gun, Saga, 842 0031, Japan
Tel.: (81) 952 53 2345
Web Site: http://www.tanaka-bondingwire.com
Bonding Wire & Other Electronics Manufacturing
N.A.I.C.S.: 332618

Subsidiary (Non-US):

Tanaka Electronics (Hangzhou) Co., Ltd. (2)
F1 Area West No19 Street North No10 Street, Hangzhou Development Zone, Hangzhou, China
Tel.: (86) 57186714400
Sales Range: $50-74.9 Million
Bonding Wire Support & Services
N.A.I.C.S.: 423840

Tanaka Electronics Malaysia Sdn. Bhd. (2)
Plot 11 Phase IV Bayan Lepas Free Industrial Zone, Penang, 11900, Malaysia
Tel.: (60) 46429950
Web Site: http://www.tanaka.co.jp
Bonding Wire Mfr
N.A.I.C.S.: 332618

Tanaka Electronics Singapore Pte. Ltd. (2)
29 Pardon Crescent, Singapore, 128473, Singapore
Tel.: (65) 67784411
Web Site: http://www.tanaka.co.jp
Gold Bonding Wire & Semiconductor Materials
N.A.I.C.S.: 332618

Tanaka Kikinzoku (Suzhou) Co., Ltd. (1)
100 Tongsheng Road Suzhou Industrial Park, Suzhou, 215106, Jiangsu, China
Tel.: (86) 51262815111
Web Site: http://www.tanaka.co.jp
Glass Melting Equipment
N.A.I.C.S.: 423830

Tanaka Kikinzoku Hanbai K.K. (1)
Tokyo Building 7-3 Marunouchi 2-Chome Chiyoda-ku, Tokyo, 100-6422, Japan
Tel.: (81) 352221300
Industrial Precious Metals Sales
N.A.I.C.S.: 423840

Tanaka Kikinzoku International K.K. (1)
Tokyo Bldg 7-3 Marunouchi 2-chome, Chiyoda-ku, Tokyo, 100 6422, Japan
Tel.: (81) 352221380
Web Site: http://www.tanaka.co.jp
Sales Range: $1-4.9 Billion
Industrial Precious Metals Sales
N.A.I.C.S.: 423840

Subsidiary (US):

Tanaka Kikinzoku International (America) Inc. (2)
6505E 82nd St Ste 209, Indianapolis, IN 46250
Tel.: (317) 598-0796
Web Site: http://www.tanaka.co.jp
Sales Range: $25-49.9 Million
Emp.: 4
Industrial Precious Metals
N.A.I.C.S.: 423840

TANAKA HOLDINGS CO., LTD.

Tanaka Holdings Co., Ltd.—(Continued)

Subsidiary (Non-US):

Tanaka Kikinzoku International (Europe) GmbH (2)
Friedensstrasse 7, Frankfurt, 60311, Germany
Tel.: (49) 692193870
Web Site: http://www.tanaka.co.jp
Sales Range: $25-49.9 Million
Emp.: 6
Industrial Precious Metals
N.A.I.C.S.: 423840

Tanaka Kikinzoku International (Shanghai) Co.,Ltd. (2)
RmNo2806 2 Grand Gateway3 Hong Qiao Rd, Xuhui District, Shanghai, 200030, China
Tel.: (86) 2164485988
Web Site: http://www.tanaka-precious.com
Sales Range: $25-49.9 Million
Emp.: 36
Industrial Precious Metals
N.A.I.C.S.: 423840

Tanaka Kikinzoku International (Thailand)Co.,Ltd. (2)
14th Fl Ramaland Bldg 952 Rama IV Road, Bang Rak, Bangkok, 10500, Thailand
Tel.: (66) 026525180
Industrial Precious Metals
N.A.I.C.S.: 423840

Tanaka Kikinzoku Jewelry K.K. (1)
177 Ginza 1-chome Chuo-ku, Tokyo, 104 0061, Japan
Tel.: (81) 335610491
Web Site: http://www.ginzatanaka.co.jp
Sales Range: $50-74.9 Million
Emp.: 170
Precious Metals Jewelry Sores
N.A.I.C.S.: 458310

Tanaka Kikinzoku Kogyo K.K. (1)
Tokyo Building 7-3 Marunouchi 2-chome Chiyoda-ku, Chiyoda-ku, Tokyo, 100-6422, Japan
Tel.: (81) 363115511
Web Site: http://www.gold.tanaka.co.jp
Sales Range: $5-14.9 Billion
Precious Metals
N.A.I.C.S.: 423940

TANAKA SEIMITSU KOGYO CO., LTD.

328 Shimada Funauchi-cho, Toyama, 939-0071, Japan
Tel.: (81) 764699107
Web Site: https://www.tanasei.co.jp
Year Founded: 1957
7218—(TKS)
Rev.: $281,222,450
Assets: $282,114,800
Liabilities: $82,849,740
Net Worth: $199,265,060
Earnings: $14,660,980
Emp.: 1,309
Fiscal Year-end: 03/31/24
Automotive Parts Mfr & Distr
N.A.I.C.S.: 336390

Subsidiaries:

Asian Tanaka Bangkok Co., Ltd. (1)
589/134 Central City Tower 1 24th Floor Bangna-Trade Road KM 3 Bangna, Bangkok, 10230, Thailand
Tel.: (66) 23993115
Business Management Services
N.A.I.C.S.: 561110

FT Precision Inc. (1)
9731 Mt Gilead Rd, Fredericktown, OH 43019
Tel.: (740) 694-1500
Precision Parts Mfr & Distr
N.A.I.C.S.: 332721

Tanaka Engineering Co., Ltd. (1)
Tel.: (81) 764515600
Automobile Parts Mfr
N.A.I.C.S.: 336390
Tomohide Nakanishi (Pres)

Tanaka Precision (Thailand) Co., Ltd. (1)
Northern Region Industrial Estate 122 Mootee 4 Tambon Ban-Klang, Amphur Muang, 51000, Lamphun, Thailand
Tel.: (66) 53581224
Car Parts Mfr
N.A.I.C.S.: 336390

Tanaka Precision Vietnam Co., Ltd. (1)
Plot No E-3, Thang Long Industrial Park 2 Lieu Xa, Yen My, Hung Yen, Vietnam
Tel.: (84) 3213589990
Automotive Parts Mfr & Distr
N.A.I.C.S.: 336390

Tanaka Seimitsu Kogyo Co., Ltd. - Fuchu Factory (1)
328 Shimada Fuchu-machi, Toyama, 939-2617, Toyama, Japan
Tel.: (81) 764693585
Car Parts Mfr
N.A.I.C.S.: 336390

Tanaka Seimitsu Kogyo Co., Ltd. - Kureha Factory (1)
2508 Takagi, Toyama, 930-0106, Toyama, Japan
Tel.: (81) 764346256
Car Parts Mfr
N.A.I.C.S.: 336390

Tanaka Seimitsu Kogyo Co., Ltd. - Namerikawa Factory (1)
8500 Kamijima, Namerikawa, 936-0852, Toyama, Japan
Tel.: (81) 764752023
Car Parts Mfr
N.A.I.C.S.: 336390

Tanaka Seimitsu Kogyo Co., Ltd. - Nyuzen Factory (1)
1117 Aoki Nyuzen-machi Shimoniikawa-gun, Toyama, 939-0643, Japan
Tel.: (81) 765720673
Car Parts Mfr
N.A.I.C.S.: 336390

TANAKEN KK

4-24-11 Shinbashi, Minato-Ku, Tokyo, 105-0004, Japan
Tel.: (81) 334336401
Web Site: http://www.tanaken-1982.co.jp
Year Founded: 1982
1450—(TKS)
Building Construction Services
N.A.I.C.S.: 236220
Kazuyoshi Unezawa (Chm & Pres)

TANAMI GOLD NL

Unit 202 Level 2 39 Mends Street, South Perth, 6151, WA, Australia
Tel.: (61) 863735130
Web Site: https://www.tanami.com.au
TAM—(ASX)
Rev.: $1,071,715
Assets: $34,541,266
Liabilities: $3,577,724
Net Worth: $30,963,542
Earnings: ($4,104,567)
Fiscal Year-end: 06/30/24
Gold Mining & Mineral Exploration
N.A.I.C.S.: 212220
Pauline Collinson (Sec)

Subsidiaries:

Tanami Exploration NL (1)
Level 4 50 Colin St, West Perth, 6005, Western Australia, Australia
Tel.: (61) 892125999
Web Site: http://www.tanami.com.au
Sales Range: $50-74.9 Million
Emp.: 20
Gold Ore Exploration & Mining Services
N.A.I.C.S.: 212220

TANBRIDGE CORPORATION

1601Church Avenue, Winnipeg, R2X 1G9, MB, Canada
Tel.: (204) 633-7042
Rev.: $71,150,042
Emp.: 290
Tanning Operation & Services
N.A.I.C.S.: 316110
Alasdair Grant (Pres)

TANCO HOLDINGS BERHAD

No 1 Jalan Bandar 1 Pusat Bandar Puchong, 47160, Puchong, Selangor Darul Ehsan, Malaysia
Tel.: (60) 380708288
Web Site:
https://www.tancoholdings.com
TANCO—(KLS)
Rev.: $19,862,434
Assets: $88,668,783
Liabilities: $37,352,593
Net Worth: $51,316,190
Earnings: $4,427,937
Fiscal Year-end: 06/30/23
Property Development Services
N.A.I.C.S.: 531312
Siew Fun Choi (Sec)

Subsidiaries:

Herbitec (M) Sdn. Bhd. (1)
No 1 Jalan Bandar 1 Pusat Bandar, 47160, Puchong, Selangor, Malaysia
Tel.: (60) 173844120
Web Site: https://www.herbitec.com
Pharmaceutical Product Whslr
N.A.I.C.S.: 424210

Palm Springs Resort (MM2H) Sdn. Bhd. (1)
No 1 Jalan Bandar 1 Pusat Bandar, 47160, Puchong, Selangor, Malaysia
Tel.: (60) 380708288
Resort Services
N.A.I.C.S.: 721110

Palm Springs Resort Berhad (1)
13th Mile Jalan Pantai Mukim Pasir Panjang, Port Dickson, Malaysia
Tel.: (60) 66619599
Web Site:
https://www.palmspringsresortcity.com
Resort Services
N.A.I.C.S.: 721110

Tanco Resorts Berhad (1)
No 1 Persiaran Ledang Off Jalan Duta, 54080, Kuala Lumpur, Malaysia
Tel.: (60) 320933030
Web Site: http://www.tancoresorts.com
Resort Operators Services
N.A.I.C.S.: 721110

TANDE CO., LTD.

Room 12701 Digital Building Gaoxin International Business Center, No 33 Keji Road Gaoxin District, Xi'an, 710075, Shaanxi, China
Tel.: (86) 2988325003
Web Site: https://www.tande.cn
Year Founded: 1992
600665—(SHG)
Rev.: $1,063,576,160
Assets: $6,323,676,870
Liabilities: $5,627,404,832
Net Worth: $696,272,038
Earnings: $57,731,060
Fiscal Year-end: 12/31/21
Housing Construction Services
N.A.I.C.S.: 236116
Wangjia Yuan (Chm)

TANDEM GROUP PLC

35 Tameside Drive, Castle Bromwich, Birmingham, B35 7AG, United Kingdom
Tel.: (44) 1217488075
Web Site:
https://tandemgroupplc.co.uk
TND—(LSE)
Rev.: $50,311,672
Assets: $44,024,071
Liabilities: $21,475,057
Net Worth: $22,549,014
Earnings: $4,694,996
Emp.: 76
Fiscal Year-end: 12/31/20
Transportation Industry
N.A.I.C.S.: 336991

INTERNATIONAL PUBLIC

Jim C. Shears (CEO & Sec)

Subsidiaries:

Claud Butler Limited (1)
Bridge Street, PO Box 3, Brigg, DN20 8PB, North Lincolnshire, United Kingdom
Tel.: (44) 1652656000
Web Site: http://www.claudbutler.co.uk
Sales Range: $25-49.9 Million
Emp.: 20
Bicycles & Bicycle Parts Mfr
N.A.I.C.S.: 336991

Dawes Cycles Limited (1)
35 Tameside Dr, Castle Bromwich, Birmingham, B35 7AG, West Midlands, United Kingdom
Tel.: (44) 1217488050
Web Site: http://www.dawescycles.com
Sales Range: $25-49.9 Million
Emp.: 30
Bicycles Online Sales & Distr
N.A.I.C.S.: 423910
John Bellamy (Dir-Ops)

Expressco Direct Limited (1)
Unit 1 Redbourn Park Liliput Road Brackmills, Northampton, NN4 7DT, United Kingdom
Tel.: (44) 1604813428
Bicycle & Part Mfr
N.A.I.C.S.: 336991

M.V. Sports (Hong Kong) Limited (1)
Austin Tower Room 1001-3 1005-7 10th Floor 152 Austin Road, Tsim Sha Tsui, Kowloon, China (Hong Kong)
Tel.: (852) 2 736 6902
Web Site: http://www.mvsports.com
Sales Range: $25-49.9 Million
Emp.: 9
Toys Mfr & Sales
N.A.I.C.S.: 339930

MV Sports & Leisure Limited (1)
35 Tameside Drive, Castle Bromwich, Birmingham, B35 7AG, United Kingdom
Tel.: (44) 121 748 8000
Web Site: https://www.mvsports.co.uk
Sport & Leisure Product Distr
N.A.I.C.S.: 423910

Subsidiary (Domestic):

Ben Sayers Limited (2)
35 Tameside Drive Castle Bromwich, Birmingham, B35 7AG, United Kingdom
Tel.: (44) 1217488044
Web Site: http://www.bensayers.co.uk
Golf Equipment Mfr & Distr
N.A.I.C.S.: 339920

Tandem Group Cycles Limited (1)
35 Tameside Drive Castle Bromwich, Birmingham, B35 7AG, United Kingdom
Tel.: (44) 1217488050
Bicycle & Part Mfr
N.A.I.C.S.: 336991

TANDET MANAGEMENT INC.

1351 Speers Road, Oakville, L6L 2X5, ON, Canada
Tel.: (905) 827-4200
Web Site: http://www.tandet.com
Year Founded: 1978
Trucking & Logistics Services
N.A.I.C.S.: 541614
Scott Tilley (Co-Pres)

Subsidiaries:

Tandet Industrial Inc. (1)
244 Dalton Avenue Unit 160, Kingston, K7K 6C3, ON, Canada
Tel.: (613) 887-2644
Web Site: http://www.tandetindustrial.com
Power Generator Repair Services
N.A.I.C.S.: 811310

TANDLIANWALA SUGAR MILLS LTD.

66-L Gulberg-II, Lahore, 54660, Pakistan
Tel.: (92) 4235754701
Web Site: https://www.tsmlgroup.com
TSML—(PSX)
Rev.: $15,185,379

Assets: $110,829,298
Liabilities: $65,507,450
Net Worth: $45,321,848
Earnings: $5,429,414
Emp.: 3,452
Fiscal Year-end: 09/30/23
Sugar Mfr
N.A.I.C.S.: 311314
Akbar Khan (CEO)

TANDOM METALLURGICAL GROUP LTD.
Radnor Park Industrial Estate, Congleton, CW12 4XE, Cheshire, United Kingdom
Tel.: (44) 1260 271122
Web Site: http://www.tandom.co.uk
Year Founded: 2008
Sales Range: $50-74.9 Million
Emp.: 54
Steel Products Mfr
N.A.I.C.S.: 331110
Tom Muir (Mng Dir)

Subsidiaries:

Tandom Metallurgical (Midlands) Ltd (1)
79 Eyre St, Birmingham, B18 7AD, United Kingdom
Tel.: (44) 1216474240
Metal Product Distr
N.A.I.C.S.: 423510

TANEHASHI KIKAI CO., LTD.
2-23-3 Sengoku Bunkyo-ku, Tokyo, 112-0011, Japan
Tel.: (81) 339443581
Web Site: http://www.tanehashi.co.jp
Semiconductor Assembly & Packaging Products
N.A.I.C.S.: 326199
Shigeo Tanehashi (Pres)

TANEJA AEROSPACE & AVIATION LIMITED
Belagondapalli Village Thally Road Denkanikottai Taluk, Belagondapalli, Hosur, 635114, Tamil Nadu, India
Tel.: (91) 4347233508
Web Site: https://www.taal.co.in
Year Founded: 1994
522229—(BOM)
Rev.: $4,752,248
Assets: $17,258,937
Liabilities: $2,985,678
Net Worth: $14,273,259
Earnings: $848,825
Emp.: 146
Fiscal Year-end: 03/31/21
Aerospace Engineering Services & Aircraft Mfr
N.A.I.C.S.: 541330
Mahendra Nalluri (CFO)

TANFIELD GROUP PLC
1 St James Gate, Newcastle upon Tyne, NE99 1YQ, Tyne & Wear, United Kingdom
Tel.: (44) 8451557755   UK
Web Site:
  https://www.tanfieldgroup.com
Year Founded: 2000
TAN—(AIM)
Assets: $26,551,341
Liabilities: $2,384,367
Net Worth: $24,166,974
Earnings: ($687,021)
Fiscal Year-end: 12/31/21
Holding Company; Aerial Work Platforms Mfr
N.A.I.C.S.: 551112
Daryn Ashley Robinson (Chm & Sec)

Subsidiaries:

Snorkel International Holdings, LLC (1)

2009 Roseport Rd, Elwood, KS 66024   (49%)
Tel.: (785) 989-3000
Web Site: https://www.snorkellifts.com
Emp.: 200
Holding Company; Aerial Work Platforms Mfr & Whslr
N.A.I.C.S.: 551112
Don F. Ahern (Owner)

Subsidiary (Non-US):

Snorkel Europe Limited (2)
Vigo Centre Birtley Road, Washington, NE38 9DA, Tyne & Wear, United Kingdom
Tel.: (44) 8451550057
Web Site: https://www.snorkellifts.com
Aerial Work Platforms Mfr & Whslr
N.A.I.C.S.: 333923
Amelia Pearce (Mktg Dir-Global)

Subsidiary (Non-US):

Ahern Australia Pty. Ltd. (3)
8-10 McIlwraith Street, Wetherill Park, 2164, NSW, Australia
Tel.: (61) 29 609 8500
Web Site:
  https://www.ahernaustralia.com.au
Aerial Work Platforms Mfr & Whslr
N.A.I.C.S.: 333923
Bruce MacLean (Gen Mgr-Asia Pacific)

Subsidiary (Non-US):

Snorkel New Zealand Limited (4)
36 Bruce Rd, Horowhenua, Levin, 5510, New Zealand
Tel.: (64) 80 076 6753
Web Site: https://www.snorkellifts.com
Aerial Work Platforms Whslr
N.A.I.C.S.: 423830
Rob Theunissen (Pres)

Subsidiary (US):

Snorkel International, LLC (3)
2009 Roseport Rd, Elwood, KS 66024
Tel.: (785) 989-3000
Web Site: http://www.snorkellifts.com
Aerial Work Platforms Mfr & Whslr
N.A.I.C.S.: 333923
Don Ahern (Owner)

Subsidiary (Non-US):

Snorkel Japan Co., Ltd. (3)
3F Yamamoto Building 3-15-2 Shibaura, Minato-ku, Tokyo, 108-0023, Japan
Tel.: (81) 3 5765 6841
Web Site: http://www.snorkeljp.com
Emp.: 1,200
Aerial Work Platforms Whslr
N.A.I.C.S.: 423830

Tanfield Engineering Systems (US), Inc. (1)
2686 S Maple Ave, Fresno, CA 93725
Tel.: (559) 443-6600
Web Site: http://www.upright.com
Engineeering Services
N.A.I.C.S.: 541330

Tanfield Engineering Systems Ltd. (1)
Tanfield Lea Industrial Estate North, Stanley, DH9 9NX, Durham, United Kingdom
Tel.: (44) 1207521111
Web Site:
  http://www.tanfieldengineering.com
Engineeering Services
N.A.I.C.S.: 541330
Tony Parry (Mgr)

TANG PALACE (CHINA) HOLDINGS LTD.
Unit 3 10th Floor Greenfield Tower Concordia Plaza, No 1 Science Museum Road, Kowloon, China (Hong Kong)
Tel.: (852) 21807055
Web Site: http://www.tanggong.cn
1181—(HKG)
Rev.: $132,251,746
Assets: $105,735,942
Liabilities: $71,234,467
Net Worth: $34,501,475
Earnings: ($21,385,307)

Emp.: 3,000
Fiscal Year-end: 12/31/22
Restaurant Owner & Operator
N.A.I.C.S.: 722511
Shu Ming Yip (Co-Founder & Chm)

Subsidiaries:

Vital Pepper (Beijing) Management Co., Ltd. (1)
Rm B631 6f Building B No 2 Dongjiaomin Lane, Dongcheng, Beijing, 100005, China
Tel.: (86) 1065265600
Food Products Mfr
N.A.I.C.S.: 311423

TANGEL CULTURE CO., LTD.
Building 6 Malanshan Information Port No 71 Puyuan Road, Kaifu District, Changsha, 410013, Hunan, China
Tel.: (86) 73188834956
Web Site: http://www.t-angel.com
Year Founded: 2003
300148—(CHIN)
Rev.: $63,084,828
Assets: $207,615,125
Liabilities: $51,890,253
Net Worth: $155,724,873
Earnings: ($8,426,520)
Fiscal Year-end: 12/31/23
Children's & Young Adult Book Publisher & Distr
N.A.I.C.S.: 513130
Zhihong Xiao (Chm)

TANGELO GAMES CORP.
65 Queen Street West Suite 815, Toronto, M5H 2M5, ON, Canada
Tel.: (416) 861-2267   BC
Web Site:
  http://www.tangelogames.com
Year Founded: 2011
Rev.: $28,287,186
Assets: $56,255,496
Liabilities: $85,371,539
Net Worth: ($29,116,043)
Earnings: ($34,786,046)
Fiscal Year-end: 12/31/17
Social Gaming Software
N.A.I.C.S.: 513210
Vicenc Marti (CEO)

TANGENT COMMUNICATIONS PLC
Threeways House 40-44 Clipstone Street, London, W1W 5DW, United Kingdom
Tel.: (44) 2074626100   UK
Web Site: http://www.tangent.co.uk
Sales Range: $25-49.9 Million
Emp.: 270
Holding Company; Online Printing & Digital Marketing Services
N.A.I.C.S.: 551112
Timothy Green (CEO)

Subsidiaries:

Tangent On Demand (1)
84-86 Great Portland Street, London, W1N 7NR, United Kingdom
Tel.: (44) 2076318660
Web Site: http://www.toduk.com
Sales Range: $1-9.9 Million
Emp.: 20
Digital Printing Services
N.A.I.C.S.: 323111
Timothy Green (CEO)

Tangent Snowball (1)
Threeways House 40-44 Clipstone Street, London, W1W 5DW, United Kingdom
Tel.: (44) 2074626100
Web Site: http://www.tangentsnowball.com
Sales Range: $1-9.9 Million
Emp.: 70
Online Marketing Services
N.A.I.C.S.: 541613

TANGENT INTERNATIONAL GROUP PLC
11 Woodbrook Crescent, Billericay, CM12 0EQ, Essex, United Kingdom
Tel.: (44) 1277 635800
Web Site: http://www.tanint.com
Year Founded: 1987
Employee Recruitment Services
N.A.I.C.S.: 561311
Simon Dear (CEO)

Subsidiaries:

Tangent Germany (1)
Postfach 25 03 22, 40092, Dusseldorf, Germany
Tel.: (49) 15730299004
Employee Recruitment Services
N.A.I.C.S.: 561311

Tangent Innovation (1)
Office Suite 1513 Grosvenor Business Tower TECOM, PO Box 71521, Dubai, United Arab Emirates
Tel.: (971) 44473680
Employee Recruitment Services
N.A.I.C.S.: 561311

Tangent International Limited (1)
Ave 2 Poniente Ext 323 Int A Col Centro, 72000, Puebla, Mexico
Tel.: (52) 15527551603
Employee Recruitment Services
N.A.I.C.S.: 561311

Tangent International Limited (1)
Pallazo Towers West Monte Casino, William Nicol Drive Fourways, Johannesburg, South Africa
Tel.: (27) 115100113
Employee Recruitment Services
N.A.I.C.S.: 561311

Tangent International Pty Limited (1)
Level 10 10 Spring Street, Sydney, 2000, NSW, Australia
Tel.: (61) 299299001
Employee Recruitment Services
N.A.I.C.S.: 561311

Tanintco Inc. (1)
5700 Granite Pkwy Ste 200, Plano, TX 75024
Tel.: (214) 387-6005
Employee Recruitment Services
N.A.I.C.S.: 561311

TANGERINE BEACH HOTELS PLC
236 Galle Road, PO Box 195, 3, Colombo, 03, Sri Lanka
Tel.: (94) 112422518
Web Site:
  https://www.tangerinehotels.com
TANG—(COL)
Rev.: $1,894,708
Assets: $12,693,745
Liabilities: $3,056,416
Net Worth: $9,637,329
Earnings: ($668,292)
Emp.: 306
Fiscal Year-end: 03/31/23
Home Management Services
N.A.I.C.S.: 721110
Lakal Hemendra Jayasinghe (Gen Mgr)

TANGIAMO TOUCH TECHNOLOGY AB
Lindholmspiren 7, 417 56, Gothenburg, Sweden
Tel.: (46) 31515730
Web Site: https://www.tangiamo.com
Year Founded: 2004
TANGI—(OMX)
Rev.: $677,946
Assets: $3,055,145
Liabilities: $1,022,404
Net Worth: $2,032,741
Earnings: ($1,574,195)
Emp.: 10
Fiscal Year-end: 12/31/21
Software Development Services

Tangiamo Touch Technology AB—(Continued)
N.A.I.C.S.: 541511
Christopher Steele (CEO)

TANGIERS GROUP PLC
54 Melita Street, Valletta, VLT 1122, Malta
Tel.: (356) 2247 9700 Mt
Web Site: http://www.tangiersgroup.com
Year Founded: 2006
Medical Case Management, Emergency Services, Insurance Underwriting & Security Risk Intelligence Services
N.A.I.C.S.: 524298
Chris Catrambone (CEO)

Subsidiaries:

Osprey Insurance Brokers Co. Ltd. (1)
54 Melita Street, Valletta, VLT1122, Malta
Tel.: (356) 22781197
Web Site: http://www.ospreybrokers.com
Insurance Brokers
N.A.I.C.S.: 524126
Charlot Bartolo (Mng Dir)

TANGRENSHEN GROUP CO., LTD.
Liyu Industrial Park National High-tech Development Zone, Zhuzhou, 412007, Hunan, China
Tel.: (86) 73128591298
Web Site: https://www.trsgroup.com.cn
Year Founded: 1988
002567—(SSE)
Rev.: $3,726,016,660
Assets: $2,587,858,893
Liabilities: $1,544,571,499
Net Worth: $1,043,287,395
Earnings: $18,963,603
Emp.: 3,700
Fiscal Year-end: 12/31/22
Animal Feeds, Meats & Boars
N.A.I.C.S.: 311119
Tao Yishan (Chm)

Subsidiaries:

AnHui Hefei XiangDa Camel Feed Co., Ltd (1)
No 1 Tongda Road Longgang Economic Development Zone, Hefei, Anhui, China
Tel.: (86) 5514329800
Animal Feed Mfr
N.A.I.C.S.: 311119

Beijing TangRenShen Meat Product Co., Ltd (1)
No 50 Gucheng South Street Shijingshan District, Beijing, China
Tel.: (86) 1086007560
Animal Feed Mfr
N.A.I.C.S.: 311119

ChangDe XiangDa Camel Feed Co., Ltd (1)
Taolin Road Deshan Development zone, Changde, Hunan, China
Tel.: (86) 7367320669
Animal Feed Mfr
N.A.I.C.S.: 311119

Changsha TangRenShen XiangDa Camel feed Co., Ltd (1)
No 6 Renhe Road Wangcheng Agricultural technology park, Changsha, Hunan, China
Tel.: (86) 73188051828
Animal Feed Mfr
N.A.I.C.S.: 311119

ChenZhou XiangDa Camel Feed Co., Ltd (1)
Shigaitang Industrial Park Beihu District, Chenzhou, Hunan, China
Tel.: (86) 7352130008
Animal Feed Mfr
N.A.I.C.S.: 311119

ChengDu XiangDa Camel Feed Co., Ltd (1)
No 518 Xihanggang Road Southwest Airport Economic Development Zone, Shuangliu, Chengdu, Sichuan, China
Tel.: (86) 2885726118
Animal Feed Mfr
N.A.I.C.S.: 311119

FuJian XiangDa Camel Feed Co., Ltd (1)
Yangguang No 117 Fengming village Dongyuan Town, Longhai, Fujian, China
Tel.: (86) 5966708578
Animal Feed Mfr
N.A.I.C.S.: 311119

GuangDong XiangDa Camel Feed Co., Ltd (1)
Shiwan Technology Industrial Park Shiwan Town, Huizhou, Boluo Guangdong, China
Tel.: (86) 7526573595
Animal Feed Mfr
N.A.I.C.S.: 311119

GuiZhou XiangDa Camel Feed Co., Ltd (1)
Xixiu New District Industrial Park, Anshun, Guizhou, China
Tel.: (86) 8533529366
Animal Feed Mfr
N.A.I.C.S.: 311119

HengYang XiangDa Camel Feed Co., Ltd (1)
No 40 Banbian Street Renmin Village Dongyangdu Town Zhuhui District, Hengyang, Hunan, China
Tel.: (86) 7343139808
Animal Feed Mfr
N.A.I.C.S.: 311119

HuaiHua XiangDa Camel Feed Co., Ltd (1)
Zhijiang Ecological Industrial Park, Huaihua, Hunan, China
Tel.: (86) 7456931618
Animal Feed Mfr
N.A.I.C.S.: 311119

JingZhou XiangDa Camel Feed Co., Ltd (1)
Dongfang Street Jingzhou Hi-tech Development Park, Jingzhou, Hubei, China
Tel.: (86) 7168353899
Animal Feed Mfr
N.A.I.C.S.: 311119

NanNing XiangDa Camel Feed Co., Ltd (1)
Chengnan Industrial Park Yiling Industrial District, Nanning, Guangxi, China
Tel.: (86) 7716020998
Animal Feed Mfr
N.A.I.C.S.: 311119

SanHe XiangDa Camel Feed Co., Ltd (1)
No 12 Yanchang Road Yangjiao Economic Development Zone, Langfang, Hebei, China
Tel.: (86) 3163311855
Animal Feed Mfr
N.A.I.C.S.: 311119

ShanXi XiangDa Camel Feed Co., Ltd (1)
Shenlong Road East Yangling Hi-tech Demonstration District, Yangling, Shanxi, China
Tel.: (86) 2987035589
Animal Feed Mfr
N.A.I.C.S.: 311119

Shanghai TangRenShen Meat Product Co., Ltd (1)
No 69 Lane 280 Xiujiang Road Zhujing Town Jinshan District, Shanghai, China
Tel.: (86) 2157319303
Animal Feed Mfr
N.A.I.C.S.: 311119

Shanghai Xinyang Veterinary Drugs Co., Ltd (1)
No 3060 Zhennan Road, Shanghai, China
Tel.: (86) 2166954486
Animal Feed Mfr
N.A.I.C.S.: 311119

ShaoYang XiangDa Camel Feed Co., Ltd (1)

Baoqing Science & Technology Park, Shaoyang, Hunan, China
Tel.: (86) 7395282577
Animal Feed Mfr
N.A.I.C.S.: 311119

ShenYang Camel XiangDa Pasture Co., Ltd (1)
No 138 Huishan Road, Shenyang, Liaoning, China
Tel.: (86) 2429874008
Animal Feed Mfr
N.A.I.C.S.: 311119

WuHan XiangDa Camel Feed Co., Ltd (1)
No 168 Xinandu Road Xihu District, Wuhan, Hubei, China
Tel.: (86) 2783064772
Animal Feed Mfr
N.A.I.C.S.: 311119

XuZhou XiangDa Camel Feed Co., Ltd (1)
No 1 Guangming Road Pizhou, Jiangsu, China
Tel.: (86) 51686289408
Animal Feed Mfr
N.A.I.C.S.: 311119

YongZhou XiangDa Camel Feed Co., Ltd (1)
No 992 Lingling South Road Shuitan District, Yongzhou, Hunan, China
Tel.: (86) 7468412596
Animal Feed Mfr
N.A.I.C.S.: 311119

YueYang Camel Feed Co., Ltd (1)
Yueyang ecological Industrial park, Yueyang, Hunan, China
Tel.: (86) 7307603108
Animal Feed Mfr
N.A.I.C.S.: 311119

ZhongYuan XiangDa Camel Feed Co., Ltd (1)
No 7 Dangui Road South Development Zone, Zhumadian, Henan, China
Tel.: (86) 3962958366
Animal Feed Mfr
N.A.I.C.S.: 311119

ZhouKou XiangDa Camel Feed Co., Ltd (1)
No 6 Nanhuan Road Zhoukou Economic & Technological Development Zone, Zhoukou, Henan, China
Tel.: (86) 3948311955
Animal Feed Mfr
N.A.I.C.S.: 311119

TANGSHAN JIA YUAN REAL ESTATE DEVELOPMENT CO., LTD.
, Lubei District, Tangshan, China
Tel.: (86) 315 235 1500 CN
Web Site: http://www.jiayuangroup.com
Year Founded: 2000
Real Estate Investment & Development
N.A.I.C.S.: 531390
Yuxing Shen (Chm)

TANGSHAN JIDONG CEMENT CO., LTD.
No 233 Linyin Road, Fengrun District, Tangshan, 064000, Hebei, China
Tel.: (86) 1059512082
Web Site: http://www.jdsn.com.cn
Year Founded: 1994
000401—(SSE)
Rev.: $4,849,927,632
Assets: $8,707,456,368
Liabilities: $4,130,007,299
Net Worth: $4,577,449,069
Earnings: $190,619,592
Emp.: 9,000
Fiscal Year-end: 12/31/22
Construction Material Mfr & Distr
N.A.I.C.S.: 327310
Qianjin Ren (CFO, Sec & Deputy Gen Mgr)

Subsidiaries:

Jidong Cement Luanxian Co., Ltd. (1)
Yangliu Village, Luan County, Tangshan, Hebei, China
Tel.: (86) 3157520627
Cement Mfr
N.A.I.C.S.: 327310

Laishui Jidong Cement Co., Ltd. (1)
No 88 Jiancai Road, Congxi Village Yongyang County Laishui County, Baoding, Hebei, China
Tel.: (86) 3125848666
Cement Mfr
N.A.I.C.S.: 327310

Shenzhou Jidong Cement Co., Ltd. (1)
255 West of Taoyuan Street North of Changjiangdong Ave Shenzhou City, Hengshui, Hebei, China
Tel.: (86) 3183213211
Cement Mfr
N.A.I.C.S.: 327310

Tangxian Jidong Cement Co., Ltd. (1)
Baihe Village, Tang County, Baoding, Hebei, China
Tel.: (86) 3127496000
Cement Mfr
N.A.I.C.S.: 327310

TANGSHAN JIDONG EQUIPMENT EQUIPMENT CO., LTD.
Jinyu Jidong Technology Building Tongdao Road, Caofeidian District, Tangshan, 063200, Hebei, China
Tel.: (86) 3158860671
Web Site: http://www.jdzbgc.com
Year Founded: 1998
000856—(SSE)
Rev.: $449,215,542
Assets: $307,732,904
Liabilities: $249,005,606
Net Worth: $58,727,298
Earnings: $1,927,509
Fiscal Year-end: 12/31/22
Mechanical Equipment Mfr
N.A.I.C.S.: 335312
Jiao Liujun (Chm)

TANGSHAN PORT GROUP CO., LTD.
Haigang Economic Development Zone, Tangshan, 063611, Hebei, China
Tel.: (86) 3152916417
Web Site: http://www.jtport.com.cn
Year Founded: 2003
601000—(SHG)
Rev.: $789,040,152
Assets: $3,276,224,720
Liabilities: $392,762,865
Net Worth: $2,883,461,855
Earnings: $237,229,289
Fiscal Year-end: 12/31/22
Cargo Transportation Services
N.A.I.C.S.: 488320
Ma Xiping (Chm)

TANGSHAN SANYOU CHEMICAL INDUSTRIES CO., LTD.
Nanbao Development Zone, Tangshan, 063305, Hebei, China
Tel.: (86) 3158511642
Web Site: https://www.sanyou-chem.com.cn
Year Founded: 1999
600409—(SHG)
Rev.: $3,551,752,523
Assets: $3,981,808,396
Liabilities: $1,872,091,375
Net Worth: $2,109,717,021
Earnings: $256,015,442
Emp.: 20,000
Fiscal Year-end: 12/31/21
Chemical Products Mfr

N.A.I.C.S.: 325199
Wang Chunsheng *(Chm)*

TANGSHAN SUNFAR SILICON INDUSTRIES CO., LTD.
No 512 Hope Road, Nanpu Development Zone, Tangshan, 063305, Hebei, China
Tel.: (86) 3155658261 CN
Web Site: https://www.tssunfar.com
Year Founded: 2006
603938—(SHG)
Rev.: $371,824,268
Assets: $468,397,847
Liabilities: $145,587,724
Net Worth: $322,810,123
Earnings: $104,995,304
Fiscal Year-end: 12/31/22
Chemical Product Mfr & Distr
N.A.I.C.S.: 325180
Sun Renjing *(Chm)*

TANHAY CO., LTD.
165 Magokjoongang-ro Unit 1201, Gangseo-ku, Seoul, Korea (South)
Tel.: (82) 226918888 KR
Web Site: http://www.tanhay.com
Year Founded: 1973
Pneumatic Equipment Distr
N.A.I.C.S.: 423840

TANICO INC.
387 Whitby Shores Greenway, Whitby, L1N 9R6, ON, Canada
Tel.: (775) 404-0333 NV
Year Founded: 2021
Assets: $9,611
Liabilities: $41,928
Net Worth: ($32,317)
Earnings: ($20,967)
Fiscal Year-end: 09/30/24
Household Equipment Mfr
N.A.I.C.S.: 332215
Anton Mikhalev *(Pres & CEO)*

TANJONG PLC
Level 30 Menara Maxis Kuala Lumpur City Ctr, Kuala Lumpur, 50088, Malaysia
Tel.: (60) 323813388
Web Site: http://www.tanjongplc.com
Sales Range: $1-4.9 Billion
Emp.: 1,660
Holding Company; Power Generation, Leisure & Property Investment
N.A.I.C.S.: 551112
Gerard Nathan *(CFO)*

Subsidiaries:

Pan Malaysian Pools Sdn Bhd (1)
Level 29 Menara Maxis, Kuala Lumpur City Ctr, 50088, Kuala Lumpur, Malaysia
Tel.: (60) 3813388
Web Site: http://www.pmp.com.my
Sales Range: $100-124.9 Million
Emp.: 400
Totalisators Management Services
N.A.I.C.S.: 334514

Suez Gulf Power S.A.E. (1)
El Ahram St, Cairo, Egypt
Tel.: (20) 224142985
Sales Range: $50-74.9 Million
Emp.: 27
Power Generation Services
N.A.I.C.S.: 221122
Anbarasan Sellabban *(Mng Dir)*

TGV Cinemas Sdn Bhd (1)
Level 6 Menara Maxis, Kuala Lumpur City Ctr, Kuala Lumpur, 50088, Malaysia
Tel.: (60) 323813535
Web Site: http://www.tgv.com.my
Entertainment Provider
N.A.I.C.S.: 512131

Tanjong Management Services Sdn Bhd. (1)
Level 29 Menara Maxis Wilayah Persekutuan, Kuala Lumpur City Ctr, Kuala Lumpur, 50088, Malaysia
Tel.: (60) 323813388
Web Site: http://www.tanjong.com
Sales Range: $150-199.9 Million
Emp.: 300
Property Management Services
N.A.I.C.S.: 531312
Jered Nathan *(CFO)*

TANKE BIOSCIENCES CORPORATION
Room 2801 East Tower of Hui Hao Building No 519 Machang Road, Pearl River New City, Guangzhou, 510627, China
Tel.: (86) 38859025 NV
Web Site: https://www.tanke-bio.com
Year Founded: 1989
TNBI—(OTCIQ)
Sales Range: $25-49.9 Million
Emp.: 130
Animal Nutrition & Feed Additives Mfr
N.A.I.C.S.: 311119

TANKERSKA NEXT GENERATION D.D
Bozidara Petranovica 4, 23000, Zadar, Croatia
Tel.: (385) 23202135
Web Site: http://www.tng.hr
Year Founded: 2014
TPNG—(ZAG)
Rev.: $36,997,445
Assets: $159,995,939
Liabilities: $82,193,730
Net Worth: $77,802,209
Earnings: ($12,343,739)
Emp.: 3
Fiscal Year-end: 12/31/21
Seaborne Transportation Services
N.A.I.C.S.: 483111
John Karavanic *(CEO)*

TANKERSKA PLOVIDBA D.D
Bozidara Petranovica 4, 23000, Zadar, Hrvatska, Croatia
Tel.: (385) 23202202
Web Site: https://www.tankerska.hr
Year Founded: 1955
Emp.: 216
Maritime Transportation
N.A.I.C.S.: 713930

Subsidiaries:

Atlantska plovidba d.d. (1)
Dr Ante Starcevica 24, PO Box 192, 20000, Dubrovnik, Hrvatska, Croatia (64.11%)
Tel.: (385) 20352333
Web Site: https://www.atlant.hr
Sales Range: Less than $1 Million
Fleet & Cargo Handling Services
N.A.I.C.S.: 488320
Marko Domijan *(CEO)*

TANKSHIPS INVESTMENT HOLDINGS INC.
109 Kifisias Avenue & Sina Street, Marousi, 151 24, Athens, Greece
Tel.: (30) 210 809 0570 MH
Year Founded: 2010
Crude Oil Petroleum Transportation
N.A.I.C.S.: 483111
George Economou *(Chm, Pres & CEO)*

TANLA PLATFORMS LIMITED
Tanla Technology Centre HiTech City Road, Madhapur, Hyderabad, 500081, Telangana, India
Tel.: (91) 4040099999
Web Site: https://www.tanla.com
532790—(BOM)
Rev.: $322,604,141
Assets: $220,120,924
Liabilities: $98,212,473
Net Worth: $121,908,450
Earnings: $48,612,769
Emp.: 162
Fiscal Year-end: 03/31/21
Telecom Services
N.A.I.C.S.: 517112
Seshanuradha Chava *(Officer-Compliance, Sec & VP-Legal & Secretarial)*

Subsidiaries:

Tanla Mobile Asia Pacific Pte Ltd. (1)
111 North Bridge Rd, 05-32 Peninsula Plz, Singapore, 179098, Singapore
Tel.: (65) 31505603
Telecommunication Servicesb
N.A.I.C.S.: 517810

Subsidiary (Non-US):

Tanla Mobile South Africa Proprietary Ltd (2)
2nd Fl West Tower Nelson Mandela Sq, Maude St, Sandton, 2196, Johannesburg, South Africa
Tel.: (27) 110224817
Web Site: http://www.tanla.com
Sales Range: $25-49.9 Million
Emp.: 2
Telecommunication Servicesb
N.A.I.C.S.: 517810

Tanla Solutions (UK) Ltd (1)
39-41 Charing Cross Rd, London, WC2H 0AR, United Kingdom
Tel.: (44) 2074945600
Telecommunication Servicesb
N.A.I.C.S.: 517810

Subsidiary (Domestic):

Tanla Mobile (UK) Ltd. (2)
5th Fl 39 Chraling Cross Rd, WC2H OAR, London, United Kingdom
Tel.: (44) 2074945600
Telecommunication Servicesb
N.A.I.C.S.: 517810

ValueFirst Digital Media Pvt Ltd (1)
B-18 Sector-34 InfoCity, Gurgaon, 122001, India (100%)
Tel.: (91) 01244632000
Web Site: http://www.vfirst.com
Communication Software & Products
N.A.I.C.S.: 334220
Vish Bajaj *(CEO)*

TANNENHOF SCHWARZWALDER FLEISCHWAREN GMBH & CO. KG
Gewerbestr 4, Niedereschach, 78078, Germany
Tel.: (49) 772892630
Web Site: http://www.tannenhof-schinken.de
Year Founded: 1975
Rev.: $25,518,155
Emp.: 120
Organic Ham Mfr
N.A.I.C.S.: 311119
Claudia Schnekenburger *(Mgr-Mktg)*

TANNERIE REMY CARRIAT
225 Itsasuko Errebidea, BP 1, 64250, Espelette, Pyrenees Atlantiques, France
Tel.: (33) 559939088
Web Site: http://www.carriat.com
Year Founded: 1927
Sales Range: $1-4.9 Billion
Emp.: 62
Leather Mfr
N.A.I.C.S.: 316110
Marie Hiriart *(Pres)*

TANNERIES DUPIRE SA
Route De Juvardeil, 49330, Chateauneuf-sur-Sarthe, France
Tel.: (33) 241694435 FR
Web Site: http://www.tanneriesdupire.com
Year Founded: 1863
Sales Range: $1-9.9 Million
Emp.: 60
Luxury Leather Goods Mfr
N.A.I.C.S.: 316110
Cyril Ponsignon *(Dir Gen)*

TANSEISHA CO. LTD.
Shinagawa Season Terrace 19F 1-2-70 Konan, Minato-ku, Tokyo, 108-8220, Japan
Tel.: (81) 364558100
Web Site: https://www.tanseisha.co.jp
Year Founded: 1946
9743—(TKS)
Rev.: $575,708,000
Assets: $359,115,590
Liabilities: $134,887,250
Net Worth: $224,228,340
Earnings: $19,646,390
Emp.: 1,434
Fiscal Year-end: 01/31/24
Planning & Construction Services
N.A.I.C.S.: 523940
Yoshimitsu Aota *(Chm)*

Subsidiaries:

T&T Co., Ltd. (1)
5 2 1 Tanseisha Bekkan Bldg 3F, Ueno Taito-ku, Tokyo, 110-0005, Japan
Tel.: (81) 338368600
Web Site: http://www.tx-tansei.co.jp
Sales Range: $25-49.9 Million
Emp.: 10
Business Support Services
N.A.I.C.S.: 541611

Tansei Business Co., Ltd. (1)
Shibaura Crystal Shinagawa 10F 1-6-41, Minato-ku, Tokyo, 108-0075, Japan
Tel.: (81) 364558250
Web Site: https://www.tansei.biz
Sales Range: Less than $1 Million
Business Support Services
N.A.I.C.S.: 561499

Tansei Co., Ltd. (1)
Shanghai Lingling Road International Plaza, No 899 18th Floor Block A, Shanghai, 200030, China
Tel.: (86) 2164861817
Web Site: http://www.tansei.cn
Interior Design Services
N.A.I.C.S.: 541410

Tansei Creative Design Consulting Co., Ltd. (1)
Room 903 Dobe Bund WE, 501 Jiujiang Rd, Shanghai, 200001, China
Tel.: (86) 2164861817
Web Site: http://www.tansei.cn
Sales Range: $25-49.9 Million
Building, Consulting & Designing Services
N.A.I.C.S.: 541310

Tansei Display Co., Ltd. (1)
Shibuya Hashimoto Building 4F 5-5 Maruyamacho, Shibuya-ku, Tokyo, 150-0044, Japan
Tel.: (81) 337706851
Web Site: https://www.tanseidisplay.co.jp
Business Support Services
N.A.I.C.S.: 561499

Tansei Humanet Co., Ltd. (1)
BIZ SMART Kanda 9F 1-10-6, Kajicho Chiyoda-ku, Tokyo, 101-0044, Japan (100%)
Tel.: (81) 368688758
Web Site: https://www.tansei-hnt.com
Emp.: 163
Human Resouce Services
N.A.I.C.S.: 541612

Tansei Institute Co., Ltd. (1)
Shibaura Crystal Shinagawa 10F 1-6-41, Konan, Minato-ku, Tokyo, 108-0075, Japan
Tel.: (81) 364558280
Business Support Services
N.A.I.C.S.: 561499
Naoyuki Sawada *(Pres)*

Tansei TDC Co., Ltd. (1)
4-16-23 Shibaura AQUACITY Shibaura 2F, Minato-ku, Tokyo, 108-0023, Japan
Tel.: (81) 364538758
Web Site: http://www.tanseitdc.com

TANSEISHA CO. LTD.

TANSEISHA CO. LTD.—(Continued)
Sales Range: Less than $1 Million
Business Support Services
N.A.I.C.S.: 561110

TANSUN TECHNOLOGY CO., LTD.
Room 608 Building A Tibet Xixin Trading Co Ltd No 7, Linqionggang E 1st Rd Lhasa Economic & Technological Development Zone, Lhasa, 850000, China
Tel.: (86) 8916401153
Web Site: https://www.tansun.com.cn
Year Founded: 2003
300872—(SSE)
Rev.: $277,352,015
Assets: $443,297,893
Liabilities: $123,243,232
Net Worth: $320,054,661
Earnings: $8,528,079
Emp.: 8,500
Fiscal Year-end: 12/31/22
Information Technology Services
N.A.I.C.S.: 541512
Jianping Ouyang *(Chm, Pres & Gen Mgr)*

TANTAL PJSC
Str 50 years of October 110, Saratov, 410040, Russia
Tel.: (7) 8452670461
Web Site: http://www.oao-tantal.ru
Year Founded: 1949
Holding Company
N.A.I.C.S.: 551112
Alexander Aleksandrovich Solopov *(Chm-Mgmt Bd & Pres)*

TANTALEX LITHIUM RESOURCES CORPORATION
1410 -120 Adelaide St W, PO Box 964, Toronto, M5H 1T1, ON, Canada
Tel.: (416) 417-9176   BC
Web Site: https://tantalexlithium.com
Year Founded: 2009
TTX—(DEU)
Assets: $4,656,774
Liabilities: $16,711,205
Net Worth: ($12,054,432)
Earnings: ($11,912,821)
Fiscal Year-end: 02/28/22
Metal Mining Services
N.A.I.C.S.: 212290
Kyle Appleby *(CFO)*

Subsidiaries:

Tantalex SAU S.A.R.L. (1)

TANTALIZERS PLC.
Makay Plaza 1 Close 21 Road Festac Town, Lagos, Nigeria
Tel.: (234) 014707383
Web Site:
  http://www.tantalizersnig.com
Year Founded: 1997
TANTALIZER—(NIGE)
Rev.: $1,796,570
Assets: $1,883,847
Liabilities: $1,400,221
Net Worth: $483,626
Earnings: ($195,480)
Emp.: 276
Fiscal Year-end: 12/31/22
Restaurant Operating Services
N.A.I.C.S.: 722511
Jaiye Oyedotun *(Chm)*

TANTALUM CORPORATION LIMITED
2FA 2 Finsbury Avenue, London, EC2M 2PP, United Kingdom
Tel.: (44) 20039681444
Web Site:
  http://www.tantalumcorporation.com

Year Founded: 1997
Automotive Technology & Innovation in Connected Services
N.A.I.C.S.: 811198
Erik Ramberg *(CEO)*

Subsidiaries:

Lysanda Ltd. (1)
Tintagel House, London Road, Kelvedon, CO5 9BP, Essex, United Kingdom
Tel.: (44) 1376 574 400
Web Site: http://www.lysanda.com
Emp.: 100
Telematics & Iinfomatics Software Mfr
N.A.I.C.S.: 423430
Hugh Wolley *(CFO)*

Subsidiary (Domestic):

TRACKER Network (UK) Ltd (2)
Otter House Cowley Business Park High Street, Cowley, UB8 2AD, Middlesex, United Kingdom
Tel.: (44) 845 602 2356
Web Site: http://www.tracker.co.uk
Stolen Vehicle Tracking Services
N.A.I.C.S.: 517810
David Wilson *(Dir-Sls & Svcs)*

TANTALUS RARE EARTHS AG
Kronstadter Strasse 4, 81677, Munich, Germany
Tel.: (49) 89 693 960 66
Web Site: http://www.tre-ag.com
Year Founded: 2008
Sales Range: Less than $1 Million
Minerals Mining & Exploration Services
N.A.I.C.S.: 212390
Ulrich Krauskopf *(Chm-Supervisory Bd)*

TANTALUS SYSTEMS HOLDING INC.
Suite 2900 550 Burrard Street, Vancouver, V6C 0A3, BC, Canada
Tel.: (778) 381-6322
Web Site:
  http://www.risetechcapital.com
TNTLF—(OTCIQ)
Rev.: $42,146,982
Assets: $34,798,593
Liabilities: $32,479,871
Net Worth: $2,318,722
Earnings: ($1,685,197)
Emp.: 130
Fiscal Year-end: 12/31/23
Asset Management Services
N.A.I.C.S.: 523940
Shahrzad Rafati *(Founder)*

Subsidiaries:

Tantalus Systems Corp. (1)
3555 Gilmore Way Suite 200, Burnaby, V5G 0B3, BC, Canada
Tel.: (604) 299-0458
Web Site: http://www.tantalus.com
Smart Grid Communications Technology for Electric, Gas & Water Utilities
N.A.I.C.S.: 334290
Peter A. Londa *(Pres & CEO)*

Subsidiary (US):

Tantalus Systems Inc. (2)
1121 Situs Ct Ste 190, Raleigh, NC 27606
Tel.: (919) 900-8970
Web Site: http://www.tantalus.com
Smart Grid Communications Technology for Electric, Gas & Water Utilities
N.A.I.C.S.: 334290
Pete Londa *(Pres, Pres, COO, Exec VP, VP, VP, VP & VP)*

TANTECH HOLDINGS LTD.
No 10 Cen Shan Road Shuige Industrial Zone, Lishui, 323000, Zhejiang, China
Tel.: (86) 5782262305   VG
Web Site: https://www.tantech.cn

TANH—(NASDAQ)
Rev.: $47,318,420
Assets: $141,686,597
Liabilities: $18,681,365
Net Worth: $123,005,232
Earnings: $5,017,546
Emp.: 86
Fiscal Year-end: 12/31/23
Bamboo Charcoal Products Mfr
N.A.I.C.S.: 325180
Wangfeng Yan *(CEO)*

TANTIA CONSTRUCTIONS LTD.
DD-30 7th floor sector 1 Saltlake City, Kolkata, 700064, India
Tel.: (91) 3340190000
Web Site: http://www.tantiagroup.com
TCLCONS—(NSE)
Rev.: $36,328,956
Assets: $193,990,086
Liabilities: $203,097,420
Net Worth: ($9,107,334)
Earnings: ($27,174,300)
Emp.: 250
Fiscal Year-end: 03/31/19
Infrastructure Construction Services
N.A.I.C.S.: 237990
Rahul Tantia *(CFO & Dir-Ops)*

Subsidiaries:

Nigolice Trading Private Limited (1)
DD-30 Sector 1, Saltlake City, Kolkata, 700064, India
Tel.: (91) 3340190000
Holding Company
N.A.I.C.S.: 551112

TANVI FOODS (INDIA) LIMITED
Flat No 101 Alekhya Homes Temple trees Raghavendra Colony, Kondapur, Hyderabad, 500084, Telangana, India
Tel.: (91) 9246369900
Web Site: https://tanvifoods.com
Year Founded: 2007
540332—(BOM)
Rev.: $9,804,928
Assets: $9,512,128
Liabilities: $5,965,122
Net Worth: $3,547,006
Earnings: $80,079
Emp.: 217
Fiscal Year-end: 03/31/23
Food Product Mfr & Distr
N.A.I.C.S.: 311230
Adusumilli Sarat Chandra Babu *(Chm)*

Subsidiaries:

Squarepeg Distribution Services Pvt. Ltd. (1)
D No 7-2-4/D/A Old Canteen Building Ground Floor Industrial Estate, Sanathnagar, Hyderabad, 500 018, India
Tel.: (91) 4023817299
Web Site: https://www.frozenkings.in
Cold Storage Services
N.A.I.C.S.: 493120

TANYUAN TECHNOLOGY CO LTD
No 7 Lanxiang Road Wujin Economic Development Zone, Changzhou, 213145, Jiangsu, China
Tel.: (86) 51981581152
Web Site:
  http://www.tanyuantech.com
603133—(SHG)
Rev.: $49,514,408
Assets: $105,080,611
Liabilities: $49,048,649
Net Worth: $56,031,961
Earnings: ($70,380,078)
Fiscal Year-end: 12/31/21
Graphite Product Mfr & Distr
N.A.I.C.S.: 335991

INTERNATIONAL PUBLIC

Shizhong Xu *(Chm & Pres)*

TANZANIA MINERALS CORP.
Unit 450-800 West Pender Street, PO Box 6, Vancouver, V6C 2V6, BC, Canada
Tel.: (604) 576-0388   BC
Year Founded: 2007
Gold Ore Mining Services
N.A.I.C.S.: 212220

TAO HEUNG HOLDINGS LIMITED
No 18 Dai Fat Street Tai Po Industrial Estate, Tai Po, New Territories, China (Hong Kong)
Tel.: (852) 39606111
Web Site:
  http://www.taoheung.com.hk
0573—(HKG)
Rev.: $306,235,748
Assets: $289,804,695
Liabilities: $131,306,640
Net Worth: $158,498,055
Earnings: ($17,469,923)
Emp.: 5,221
Fiscal Year-end: 12/31/22
Restaurant Operators
N.A.I.C.S.: 813910
Yuen Wah Ho *(Exec Dir)*

TAOKAENOI FOOD & MARKETING PUBLIC COMPANY LIMITED
337 Bond Street, Bangphut Pak, Nonthaburi, 11120, Thailand
Tel.: (66) 29840666
Web Site:
  https://th.taokaenoiglobal.com
TKN—(THA)
Rev.: $156,305,013
Assets: $94,406,691
Liabilities: $29,219,740
Net Worth: $65,186,951
Earnings: $21,820,014
Emp.: 2,778
Fiscal Year-end: 12/31/23
Processed Food Manufacturing
N.A.I.C.S.: 311710
Yuth Worachattarn *(Chm)*

Subsidiaries:

Tao Kae Noi Care Company Limited (1)
469 Bond Street Road, Bang Phut, Pak Kret, Nonthaburi, Thailand
Tel.: (66) 29601999
Supplement Whslr
N.A.I.C.S.: 456191

Tao Kae Noi Restaurant & Franchise Company Limited (1)
469 Bond Street, Bang Phut, Pak Kret, Nonthaburi, Thailand
Tel.: (66) 29601477
Seaweed Snack Product Distr
N.A.I.C.S.: 445298

Taokaenoi USA Inc. (1)
18173 Pioneer Blvd Ste R, Artesia, CA 90701
Tel.: (562) 402-0005
Web Site: https://www.taokaenoiusa.com
Seaweed Snack Distr
N.A.I.C.S.: 445298

TAOMEE HOLDINGS LIMITED
12-16F Building No A-2 No 1528 Gumei Road, Xuhui District, Shanghai, 200233, China
Tel.: (86) 2161280056
Web Site: http://www.taomee.com
Year Founded: 2007
Holding Company; Children's Entertainment Books, Magazines & Online Media Publisher; Children's Television & Film Media Production Services
N.A.I.C.S.: 551112
Jason Liqing Zeng *(Chm)*

AND PRIVATE COMPANIES

TARATRANS A.D.

Subsidiaries:

Taiwan Taomee Co., Ltd. (1)
1F No 99-10 Sec 2 Nangang Rd, Nangang,
Taipei, 11578, Taiwan
Tel.: (886) 2 22856611
Event Operating Services
N.A.I.C.S.: 711320

TAOPING INC.
21st Floor Everbright Bank Building
Zhuzilin, Futian District, Shenzhen,
518040, China
Tel.: (86) 75588319888 VG
Web Site: http://en.taop.com
TAOP—(NASDAQ)
Rev.: $24,233,463
Assets: $29,208,815
Liabilities: $19,592,123
Net Worth: $9,616,692
Earnings: ($7,081,647)
Emp.: 63
Fiscal Year-end: 12/31/22
Information Technology Software &
Equipment Mfr
N.A.I.C.S.: 513210
Zhiqiang Zhao *(Pres & Interim CFO)*

Subsidiaries:

Wuda Geoinformatics Co., Ltd. (1)
Whu S&T Park East Lake Development
Zone, 430223, Wuhan, China
Tel.: (86) 2787196368
Sales Range: $200-249.9 Million
Emp.: 515
Prepackaged Software Services
N.A.I.C.S.: 513210

TAP OIL LIMITED
Level 2 190 St Georges Terrace,
Perth, 6000, WA, Australia
Tel.: (61) 8 9485 1000 AU
Web Site: http://www.tapoil.com.au
Year Founded: 1995
Rev.: $41,906,000
Assets: $83,957,000
Liabilities: $35,722,000
Net Worth: $48,235,000
Earnings: $34,318,000
Emp.: 7
Fiscal Year-end: 12/31/19
Oil & Gas Exploration Services
N.A.I.C.S.: 213112
Christopher Basil Newton *(Chm)*

TAP-TRANSPORTES AEREOS PORTUGUESES, SGPS, S.A.
Aeropuerto de Lisboa, 1704-801, Lisbon, Portugal
Tel.: (351) 218 415 000 PT
Web Site: http://www.tapportugal.com
Year Founded: 1945
Rev.: $3,694,142,124
Assets: $5,770,415,610
Liabilities: $5,619,753,092
Net Worth: $150,662,519
Earnings: ($107,100,536)
Emp.: 9,006
Fiscal Year-end: 12/31/19
Holding Company; Air Transportation Services
N.A.I.C.S.: 551112
Miguel Jorge Reis Antunes Frasquilho *(Chm)*

Subsidiaries:

Cateringpor - Catering Portugal, S. A. (1)
Aeroporto de Lisboa Rua C Edificio 59,
1749-036, Lisbon, Portugal
Tel.: (351) 21 854 71 00
Web Site: http://www.cateringpor.pt
Catering Services
N.A.I.C.S.: 722320
Carlos Branca *(Mgr-Ops)*

TAP-Manutencao e Engenharia Brasil, S.A. (1)
Estrada das Canarias 1862, Rio de Janeiro,

21941-480, Brazil
Tel.: (55) 21 3383 2782
Web Site: http://www.tapme.com.br
Emp.: 2,650
Aircraft Maintenance & Engineering Services
N.A.I.C.S.: 488190
Anderson Fenocchio *(Gen Mgr-Sls)*

Transportes Aereos Portugueses, S.A. (1)
Aeroporto de Lisboa Edificio 25-8 rua C,
Lisbon, 1704-801, Portugal (100%)
Tel.: (351) 218415000
Web Site: http://www.flytap.com
Emp.: 3,000
Passenger & Freight Air Transportation Services
N.A.I.C.S.: 481111
Michael Anthony Conolly *(Exec Dir)*

Branch (US):

TAP Portugal - US Representative Office (2)
263 Lafayette St 3rd Flr, Newark, NJ 07105
Tel.: (973) 854-6800
Web Site: http://www.flytap.com
Rev.: $50,000,000
Emp.: 47
Oil Transportation Services
N.A.I.C.S.: 481111

U.C.S.-Cuidados Integrados de Saude, S.A (1)
Aeroporto de Lisboa Edificio 35 Apartado
8426, 1804-001, Lisbon, Portugal
Tel.: (351) 21 843 63 00
Web Site: http://www.ucs.pt
Health Care Srvices
N.A.I.C.S.: 621999

TAPACO PUBLIC COMPANY LIMITED
789/40 M 1 Tambon Nongkham Sriracha, Bangkok, 20230, Chonburi, Thailand
Tel.: (66) 38296339
Web Site: https://www.tapaco.com
Year Founded: 2000
TAPAC—(THA)
Rev.: $52,419,437
Assets: $53,341,027
Liabilities: $28,140,475
Net Worth: $25,200,552
Earnings: ($2,238,148)
Fiscal Year-end: 10/31/23
Engineering Plastic Parts Mfr
N.A.I.C.S.: 326199
Nuttapong Panjaworayan *(Chm)*

Subsidiaries:

C4 Global Co., Ltd. (1)
173/21 Asia Centre Building 20th Fl South
Sathorn Road Thung Maha Mek, Sathorn,
Bangkok, 10120, Thailand
Tel.: (66) 21636451
Web Site: http://www.c4global.net
Cosmetic Product Distr
N.A.I.C.S.: 424210

C4 Hus AB (1)
Bjorkhemsvagen 17, 291 54, Kristianstad, Sweden
Tel.: (46) 445909980
Web Site: http://www.c4hus.se
Residential Construction Services
N.A.I.C.S.: 236116

TAPARIA TOOLS LIMITED
52 & 52-B MIDC Satpur, Nasik,
422007, India
Tel.: (91) 2532350317
Web Site: https://www.tapariatools.com
Year Founded: 1969
505685—(BOM)
Rev.: $92,185,780
Assets: $41,855,464
Liabilities: $9,436,952
Net Worth: $32,418,512
Earnings: $8,670,979
Emp.: 292

Fiscal Year-end: 03/31/23
Hand Tool Mfr & Distr
N.A.I.C.S.: 332216
H. N. Taparia *(Chm & Mng Dir)*

TAPEX INC.
812 Ace Gwanggyo Tower 17 Daehak
4-ro, Yeongtong-gu, Suwon,
Gyeonggi-do, Korea (South)
Tel.: (82) 3180474100
Web Site: https://tapex.co.kr
Year Founded: 1994
055490—(KRS)
Rev.: $139,794,202
Assets: $151,547,588
Liabilities: $38,056,945
Net Worth: $113,490,644
Earnings: $14,521,666
Emp.: 396
Fiscal Year-end: 12/31/22
Plastics Product Mfr
N.A.I.C.S.: 326199
Kim Sang-goo *(CEO)*

TAPLEN COMMERCIAL CONSTRUCTION INC.
1505 Laperriere Avenue, Ottawa, K1Z 7T1, ON, Canada
Tel.: (613) 521-2550
Web Site: http://www.taplenconstruction.com
Year Founded: 1961
Building Construction Services
N.A.I.C.S.: 236220
Michael Assal *(Pres)*

TAQA MOROCCO SA
Sidi Bouzid, PO Box 99, El Jadida, Morocco
Tel.: (212) 523389000
Web Site: https://www.taqamorocco.ma
Year Founded: 1997
TQM—(CAS)
Rev.: $1,351,731,934
Assets: $2,234,606,956
Liabilities: $1,485,606,053
Net Worth: $749,000,902
Earnings: $166,301,405
Emp.: 462
Fiscal Year-end: 12/31/22
Electric Power Distribution Services
N.A.I.C.S.: 221118
Khaleefa Ali Mohamed Abdulla Alqamzi *(Vice Chm-Supervisory Bd)*

Subsidiaries:

Jorf Lasfar Energy Company 5&6 S.A. (1)
Tel.: (212) 522977380
Eletric Power Generation Services
N.A.I.C.S.: 221118

TAQUIPNEU
590 Avenue De Paris, 82000, Montauban, Tarn Et Garonne, France
Tel.: (33) 563200230
Rev.: $28,900,000
Emp.: 31
Apartment Building Operator
N.A.I.C.S.: 441330
Julien Taqui *(Gen Mgr)*

TARA CHAND LOGISTIC SOLUTIONS LTD.
342 Industrial Area Phase 1, Chandigarh, 160002, India
Tel.: (91) 8511135071
Web Site: https://www.tarachandindia.in
Year Founded: 1980
TARACHAND—(NSE)
Rev.: $15,357,321
Assets: $29,882,918
Liabilities: $22,381,876
Net Worth: $7,501,041
Earnings: $350,027

Emp.: 884
Fiscal Year-end: 03/31/21
Industrial Equipment Distr
N.A.I.C.S.: 423830
Himanshu Aggarwal *(Exec Dir)*

TARA HEALTH FOODS LTD.
Jitwal Kalan Tehsil - Malerkotla, Sangrur, 148023, Punjab, India
Tel.: (91) 1675274302
Web Site: http://www.tarahealthfoods.co.in
Year Founded: 1977
Sales Range: $10-24.9 Million
Emp.: 200
Edible Oil & Cattle Feed Mfr
N.A.I.C.S.: 311225
Jaswant Singh *(Chm)*

TARACHI GOLD CORP
700 - 1090 West Georgia Street,
Vancouver, V6E 3V7, BC, Canada
Tel.: (604) 838-4327
Web Site: https://tarachigold.com
Year Founded: 2016
TRG—(CNSX)
Rev.: $8,434
Assets: $2,582,571
Liabilities: $43,139
Net Worth: $2,539,432
Earnings: ($13,289,633)
Fiscal Year-end: 07/31/23
Mineral Exploration Services
N.A.I.C.S.: 213115
Cameron Tymstra *(Pres)*

TARAI FOODS LIMITED
13 Hanuman Road Connaught Place,
New Delhi, 110001, India
Tel.: (91) 1132629838
Web Site: https://www.taraifoods.in
Year Founded: 1990
519285—(BOM)
Rev.: $402,071
Assets: $448,498
Liabilities: $628,261
Net Worth: ($179,763)
Earnings: ($32,319)
Emp.: 12
Fiscal Year-end: 03/31/21
Frozen Fruit & Vegetable Mfr
N.A.I.C.S.: 311411
Gurprit Singh Sandhu *(Mng Dir)*

Subsidiaries:

TARAI FOODS LIMITED - RUDRAPUR FACTORY (1)
Sandhu Farms, PO Box 18, Distt Udham
Singh Nagar, Rudrapur, 263 153, Uttaranchal, India
Tel.: (91) 594 424 4304
Web Site: https://www.taraifoods.com
Vegetable Processing Services
N.A.I.C.S.: 311411

TARANIS RESOURCES INC.
1177 W Hastings Street Suite 1710,
Vancouver, V6E 2L3, BC, Canada
Tel.: (606) 640-6360 BC
Web Site: https://www.jjgmining.com
Year Founded: 2001
TNREF—(OTCQB)
Rev.: $25,313
Assets: $4,209,573
Liabilities: $769,926
Net Worth: $3,439,647
Earnings: ($96,256)
Fiscal Year-end: 12/31/19
Metal Mining Exploration Service
N.A.I.C.S.: 213114
John Gardiner *(Pres & CEO)*

TARATRANS A.D.
Milenka Topalovica 76, Bajina Basta, Serbia
Tel.: (381) 31865263
Year Founded: 1964

TARATRANS A.D.

Taratrans a.d.—(Continued)
TRTN—(BEL)
Rev.: $31,302
Assets: $326,304
Liabilities: $130,536
Net Worth: $195,768
Earnings: ($61,314)
Emp.: 5
Fiscal Year-end: 12/31/22
Freight Transportation Services
N.A.I.C.S.: 484121

TARC LIMITED
2Nd Floor C-3 Qutab Institutional Area, Katwaria Sarai, New Delhi, 110016, India
Tel.: (91) 1141244300
Web Site: https://www.tarc.in
Year Founded: 2016
543249—(BOM)
Rev.: $44,921,036
Assets: $378,550,602
Liabilities: $216,449,829
Net Worth: $162,100,773
Earnings: $2,441,185
Emp.: 177
Fiscal Year-end: 03/31/23
Real Estate Services
N.A.I.C.S.: 531390
Anil Sarin (Founder & Chm)

Subsidiaries:

Capital Buildcon Pvt. Ltd. (1)
Opp Dunda primary School Old Dhamtari Road, Dunda, Raipur, India
Tel.: (91) 9165514000
Web Site:
  https://www.capitalbuildconpvtltd.com
Construction Services
N.A.I.C.S.: 236220

Krishna Buildtech Pvt. Ltd. (1)
253 Okhla Industrial Estate Phase - III, New Delhi, 110020, India
Tel.: (91) 1146019800
Web Site: https://www.kbe.co.in
Construction Services
N.A.I.C.S.: 236220

TARCZYNSKI S.A.
Ujezdziec Maly 80, 55-100, Trzebnica, Poland
Tel.: (48) 713121283 PL
Web Site: https://www.tarczynski.pl
TAR—(WAR)
Rev.: $486,899,389
Assets: $387,421,239
Liabilities: $245,147,103
Net Worth: $142,274,136
Earnings: $33,758,638
Fiscal Year-end: 12/31/23
Jerky & Other Dried Meat Snacks Mfr & Whslr
N.A.I.C.S.: 311612
Radoslaw Chmurak (Vice Chm-Mgmt Bd, Sls Dir & Mktg Dir)

TARGA EXPLORATION CORP.
Suite 700-1090 West Pender Street, Vancouver, V6E 3V7, BC, Canada
Tel.: (604) 687-0544
Web Site:
  https://www.targaexploration.com
Year Founded: 2017
TRGEF—(OTCQB)
Rev.: $114,059
Assets: $1,788,952
Liabilities: $1,019,418
Net Worth: $769,534
Earnings: ($7,294,634)
Emp.: 2
Fiscal Year-end: 03/31/24
Mineral Exploration Services
N.A.I.C.S.: 213115

TARGET ADVERTISING AGENCY LIMITED
9th Fl No 1 Fu Hsing N Rd, Taipei, 10559, Taiwan
Tel.: (886) 227411136 TW
Year Founded: 1983
Rev.: $265,000,000
Emp.: 20
N.A.I.C.S.: 541810
Sherman S.Y. Yeh (Chm)

TARGET ENERGY LIMITED
Suite 5 6 Richardson Street, West Perth, 6005, WA, Australia
Tel.: (61) 89 476 9000 AU
Web Site:
  http://www.targetenergy.com.au
TEX—(ASX)
Sales Range: Less than $1 Million
Oil & Gas Exploration
N.A.I.C.S.: 211120

TARGET GROUP, INC.
20 Hempstead Drive, Hamilton, L8W 2E7, ON, Canada
Tel.: (905) 541-3833 DE
Web Site:
  https://www.targetgroupinc.ca
Year Founded: 2013
CBDY—(OTCIQ)
Rev.: $811,464
Assets: $7,565,634
Liabilities: $14,125,459
Net Worth: ($6,559,825)
Earnings: ($4,520,064)
Emp.: 56
Fiscal Year-end: 12/31/22
Herbal MedicineMfr
N.A.I.C.S.: 524114
Anthony Carlo Zarcone (Pres & CEO)

TARGET HEALTHCARE REIT PLC
1st Floor Glendevon House Castle Business Park, Stirling, FK9 4TZ, United Kingdom
Tel.: (44) 1786845912 UK
Web Site:
  https://www.targethealthcarereit.uk
Year Founded: 2013
THRL—(LSE)
Rev.: $85,518,808
Assets: $1,146,500,884
Liabilities: $319,931,835
Net Worth: $826,569,048
Earnings: ($8,295,885)
Fiscal Year-end: 06/30/23
Real Estate Development Services
N.A.I.C.S.: 531190
Donald Cameron (Sec)

TARGET INSURANCE (HOLDINGS) LIMITED
5/F Low Block Grand Millennium Plaza 181 Queens Road, Central, China (Hong Kong)
Tel.: (852) 2 390 1868
Web Site:
  http://www.targetinsholdings.com
Rev.: $56,817,059
Assets: $257,720,026
Liabilities: $218,442,489
Net Worth: $39,277,537
Earnings: ($25,491,953)
Emp.: 72
Fiscal Year-end: 12/31/19
Automobile Insurance
N.A.I.C.S.: 524126
Haywood Cheung (Chm)

Subsidiaries:

Target Insurance Company, Limited (1)
5/F Low Block Grand Millennium Plaza 181 Queens Road, Central, China (Hong Kong)
Tel.: (852) 29262926
Web Site: http://www.6161.com.hk
Insurance Providing Services
N.A.I.C.S.: 524126

TARGET MARKETING COMMUNICATIONS
Brandon House 62 Painswick Rd, Cheltenham, GL50 2EU, Glos, United Kingdom
Tel.: (44) 1242 633 100 UK
Web Site:
  http://www.targetgroup.co.uk
Year Founded: 1977
Rev.: $20,857,320
Emp.: 15
N.A.I.C.S.: 541810
David Dare (Mgr-Media)

TARGETED MICROWAVE SOLUTIONS, INC.
1066 West Hastings Street Suite 2300, Vancouver, V6E 3L2, BC, Canada
Tel.: (778) 995-5833
Year Founded: 2015
Pollution Control Equipment Mfr
N.A.I.C.S.: 334512
Gurminder Sangha (CEO)

TARGRAY TECHNOLOGY INTERNATIONAL INC.
18105 Transcanadienne, Kirkland, H9J 3Z4, QC, Canada
Tel.: (514) 695-8095
Web Site: http://www.targray.com
Year Founded: 1989
Rev.: $97,213,606
Emp.: 30
Optical Media Products Mfr
N.A.I.C.S.: 334610
Andrew Richardson (Pres)

TARIM KREDI HOLDING A.S.
Buyaka A Blok Poligon Caddesi FSM Mahallesi Buyaka 2 Sitesi Blok 1, No 8 Kat 11, 34771, Istanbul, Turkiye
Tel.: (90) 2163505062
TKHOL—(IST)
Holding Company
N.A.I.C.S.: 551112
Onur Aydin (Head-Grp HR)

TARINI INTERNATIONAL LTD
D2 Amar Colony Lajpat Nagar IV, New Delhi, 110024, Delhi, India
Tel.: (91) 1126479995
Web Site: https://www.tariniinfra.com
Year Founded: 1999
538496—(BOM)
Rev.: $278,425
Assets: $4,904,790
Liabilities: $1,498,148
Net Worth: $3,406,642
Earnings: ($47,827)
Emp.: 30
Fiscal Year-end: 03/31/23
Engineering, Construction & Consulting
N.A.I.C.S.: 237990
Vakamulla Chandrashekhar (Mng Dir)

TARIQ CORPORATION LIMITED
28-C Block E-1 Gulberg-III, Lahore, Pakistan
Tel.: (92) 42111111476 PK
Web Site: https://tariqcorp.com
Year Founded: 1966
HSM—(LAH)
Rev.: $36,808,288
Assets: $29,888,023
Liabilities: $17,276,604
Net Worth: $12,611,420
Earnings: $1,890,415
Emp.: 576
Fiscal Year-end: 09/30/19
Sugar Mfr
N.A.I.C.S.: 311314
Khalid Mahmood (Sec)

INTERNATIONAL PUBLIC

TARIQ GLASS INDUSTRIES LTD
128-J Model Town, Lahore, Pakistan
Tel.: (92) 42111343434
Web Site: https://www.tariqglass.com
TGL—(PSX)
Rev.: $102,266,143
Assets: $82,021,877
Liabilities: $26,865,090
Net Worth: $55,156,786
Earnings: $9,062,584
Emp.: 1,211
Fiscal Year-end: 06/30/23
Glass Mfr
N.A.I.C.S.: 327212
Omer Baig (CEO & Mng Dir)

TARKETT S.A.
1 Terrasse Bellini Tour Initiale La Defense, 92919, Paris, France
Tel.: (33) 1 41 20 40 98 FR
Web Site: http://www.tarkett.com
TKTT—(EUR)
Sales Range: $1-4.9 Billion
Emp.: 12,000
Flooring & Sports Surface Products Mfr & Distr
N.A.I.C.S.: 326199
Fabrice Barthelemy (CEO & Member-Mgmt Bd)

Subsidiaries:

AO Tarkett (1)
Andropova Avenue 18 Building 7 7th Floor, 115432, Moscow, Russia
Tel.: (7) 4957753737
Web Site: http://www.tarkett.ru
Building Material Mfr & Distr
N.A.I.C.S.: 327120

Desso Czech Republic s.r.o. (1)
Pod Klapici 123, Radotin, Prague, Czech Republic
Tel.: (420) 257216304
Web Site: http://www.desso.cz
Building Material Mfr & Distr
N.A.I.C.S.: 327120

Desso Group B.V. (1)
Taxandriaweg 15, 5142 PA, Waalwijk, Netherlands
Tel.: (31) 416684100
Web Site: http://www.desso.com
Carpet Mfr & Distr
N.A.I.C.S.: 314110

Desso USA Inc. (2)
10 Corbin Dr 2nd Fl, Darien, CT 06820
Tel.: (888) 337-7687
Web Site: http://www.desso.com
Woven Carpet Distr
N.A.I.C.S.: 314110
John Reader (Gen Mgr)

Fieldturf Australia Pty Ltd (1)
Unit 8 1 1A Hale Street, Portair Industrial Estate, Botany, 2019, NSW, Australia
Tel.: (61) 293167244
Web Site: http://www.fieldturf.com.au
Sports Product Mfr
N.A.I.C.S.: 339920
Adam Laraghy (Sls Mgr)

Johnsonite Canada Inc. (1)
560 Weber St N, Waterloo, N2L 5C6, ON, Canada
Tel.: (519) 886-0222
Building Material Mfr & Distr
N.A.I.C.S.: 327120

M.E.T GmbH (1)
Hattinger Strasse 607, 44879, Bochum, Germany
Tel.: (49) 234592246
Web Site: http://www.met-gmbh.de
Electrical Installation Services
N.A.I.C.S.: 238210

Tarkett A/S (1)
Lunikvej 2, 2670, Greve, Denmark
Tel.: (45) 43906011
Web Site: http://www.tarkett.dk

AND PRIVATE COMPANIES   TARMAT LTD.

Sales Range: $25-49.9 Million
Emp.: 30
Flooring
N.A.I.C.S.: 326199

Tarkett AB (1)
Hammarbacken 12, Box 4538, 191 24, Sollentuna, Sweden
Tel.: (46) 771251900
Web Site: http://www.proffs.tarkett.se
Building Material Mfr & Distr
N.A.I.C.S.: 327120

Tarkett AS (1)
Omstedgata 2, Box 500, Brakeroya, 3002, Drammen, Norway
Tel.: (47) 32209200
Web Site: http://www.tarkett.no
Sales Range: $25-49.9 Million
Emp.: 22
Flooring
N.A.I.C.S.: 326199
Pers Oaxspte *(Gen Mgr)*

Tarkett Asia Pacific (Shanghai) Management Co. Ltd.
Rm 1521-1549 15F MTR City Plaza No 1518 Jinshajiang Road, Shanghai, 200333, China
Tel.: (86) 2160956838
Web Site: http://www.home.tarkett.cn
Building Material Mfr & Distr
N.A.I.C.S.: 327120
Richard Li *(Reg Sls Mgr)*

Tarkett Asia Pacific Ltd. (1)
10/F Easey Commercial Building, Wanchai, China (Hong Kong)
Tel.: (852) 25118716
Web Site: http://www.tarkett-commercial.com
Sales Range: $25-49.9 Million
Emp.: 25
Flooring Product Distr
N.A.I.C.S.: 423310

Tarkett Asia Pacific Ltd. (1)
5 Lorong Bakar Batu 05 02, Singapore, 348742, Singapore
Tel.: (65) 67435384
Web Site: http://www.tarkett-commercial.com
Flooring Product Distr
N.A.I.C.S.: 423310

Tarkett Aspen Zemin AS (1)
Zemin Kaplamalari Tic A S Leylak Sokak Murat is Merkezi B Blok, Kat 6 Daire 23 Mecidiyekoy-Sisli, 34387, Istanbul, Turkiye
Tel.: (90) 2122136580
Web Site: http://www.ticari.tarkett.com.tr
Building Material Mfr & Distr
N.A.I.C.S.: 327120
Cumhur Dincer *(Gen Mgr)*

Tarkett Australia Pty. Ltd. (1)
16 Anella Ave, Castle Hill, 2154, NSW, Australia
Tel.: (61) 288531200
Flooring
N.A.I.C.S.: 326199

Tarkett BV (1)
Taxandriaweg 15, 5142 PA, Waalwijk, Netherlands
Tel.: (31) 416684100
Web Site: http://www.vloeren.projecten.tarkett.nl
Building Material Mfr & Distr
N.A.I.C.S.: 327120
Nico Littooij *(District Mgr)*

Tarkett Benelux B.V. (1)
Denarius Straat 21, 4903 RC, Oosterhout, Brabant, Netherlands
Tel.: (31) 765780700
Web Site: http://www.tarkett.com
Sales Range: $25-49.9 Million
Emp.: 50
Flooring
N.A.I.C.S.: 326199
Ernst van der Weerde *(Mng Dir)*

Tarkett Brasil Revestimentos Ltda (1)
Avenida Getulio Vargas 2185 - Jardim Marcondes, Jacarei, 12305-010, SP, Brazil
Tel.: (55) 1299221560
Web Site: http://www.tarkettlatam.com
Building Material Mfr & Distr

N.A.I.C.S.: 327120
Valerio Faria *(Mgr-Acctg & Tax)*

Tarkett Flooring India Private Ltd. (1)
460 Krishna Temple Road Off Cmh Road Indiranagar, Bengaluru, 560038, India
Tel.: (91) 8041303793
Building Material Mfr & Distr
N.A.I.C.S.: 327120

Tarkett Floors S.L. (1)
Avenida del Llano Castellano 13, 28034, Madrid, Spain
Tel.: (34) 914951400
Web Site: http://www.tarkett.com
Sales Range: $25-49.9 Million
Emp.: 50
Flooring
N.A.I.C.S.: 326199

Tarkett France SAS (1)
1 Terrasse Bellini Tour Initiale, 92919, Paris, France
Tel.: (33) 141204040
Web Site: http://www.professionnels.tarkett.fr
Building Material Mfr & Distr
N.A.I.C.S.: 327120

Tarkett Ges.m.b.H. (1)
Herbeckstrasse 5, 1180, Vienna, Austria
Tel.: (43) 14788062
Web Site: http://www.tarkett.at
Sales Range: $25-49.9 Million
Emp.: 5
Flooring
N.A.I.C.S.: 326199

Tarkett Holding GmbH (1)
Rheinallee 13, 67061, Ludwigshafen, Germany
Tel.: (49) 62168172300
Web Site: http://www.tarkett.de
Emp.: 150
Holding Company; Flooring Mfr & Distr
N.A.I.C.S.: 551112

Tarkett Hong Kong Ltd. (1)
601B Empire Centre 68 Mody Road TSTE, Kowloon, China (Hong Kong)
Tel.: (852) 25118716
Building Material Mfr & Distr
N.A.I.C.S.: 327120
Sally Pun *(Mgr-HR & Admin)*

Tarkett Limited (1)
Dickley Lane Lenham, Maidstone, ME17 2QX, Kent, United Kingdom
Tel.: (44) 1622854000
Web Site: http://www.tarkett.com
Sales Range: $50-74.9 Million
Emp.: 100
Flooring
N.A.I.C.S.: 326199
Jason Crump *(Mng Dir)*

Tarkett Middle East (1)
FreeWay Center 5th floor, PO Box 90 1407, Sin El Fil, Beirut, Lebanon
Tel.: (961) 1513363
Sales Range: $25-49.9 Million
Emp.: 7
Flooring
N.A.I.C.S.: 326199

Tarkett Monoprosopi Ltd. (1)
Perikli Stavrou 1, Nea Filothei, 11524, Athens, Greece
Tel.: (30) 2106745340
Web Site: http://www.professionals.tarkett.gr
Building Material Mfr & Distr
N.A.I.C.S.: 327120

Tarkett NV (1)
Robert Ramlotstraat 89, 9200, Dendermonde, Belgium
Tel.: (32) 52262411
Web Site: http://particuliers.tarkett.be
Building Material Mfr & Distr
N.A.I.C.S.: 327120
Philippe Roels *(Mgr-Customer Svcs)*

Tarkett Oy (1)
Saterinkatu 6, 02600, Espoo, Finland
Tel.: (358) 942579000
Web Site: http://www.kuluttajamyyntilattiat.tarkett.fi
Sales Range: $25-49.9 Million
Emp.: 30
Flooring
N.A.I.C.S.: 326199

Tarkett Polska Sp.z.o.o. (1)
Ul Miloslawska 13A Orzechowo, 62-322, Warsaw, Poland
Tel.: (48) 221609231
Web Site: http://www.obiektowe.tarkett.pl
Building Material Mfr & Distr
N.A.I.C.S.: 327120
Monika Dominik *(Reg Sls Mgr)*

Tarkett S.p.A. (1)
Via S Anna 6, 05035, Narni, TR, Italy
Tel.: (39) 0744755258
Web Site: http://www.tarkett-floors.com
Flooring
N.A.I.C.S.: 326199

Tarkett Sp. z o.o. (1)
ul Smolenskiego 2, PL03, Warsaw, Poland
Tel.: (48) 226393171
Web Site: http://www.tarkett.pl
Sales Range: $25-49.9 Million
Emp.: 25
Flooring
N.A.I.C.S.: 326199

Tarkett Sports S.A. (1)
2 Rue de l'Egalite, Nanterre, 92748, France
Tel.: (33) 141204040
Web Site: http://www.tarkett-sports.com
Sales Range: $250-299.9 Million
Sports Surfacing Mfr & Distr
N.A.I.C.S.: 321918
Eric Daliere *(Pres)*

Subsidiary (US):

Beynon Sports Surfaces, Inc. (2)
16 Alt Rd, Cockeysville, MD 21030
Tel.: (410) 771-9473
Web Site: http://www.beynonsports.com
Flooring Contractors
N.A.I.C.S.: 238330
John Beynon *(Pres)*

Subsidiary (Non-US):

FieldTurf, Inc. (2)
7445 Cote de Liesse Rd Ste 200, Montreal, H4T 1G2, QC, Canada
Tel.: (514) 340-9311
Web Site: http://www.fieldturf.com
Sales Range: $50-74.9 Million
Emp.: 75
Synthetic Grass & Field Mfr
N.A.I.C.S.: 237110
Darren Gill *(Dir-Mktg)*

Subsidiary (US):

EasyTurf (3)
2750 La Mirada Dr, Vista, CA 92081-8401
Web Site: http://www.easyturf.com
Installation & Distribution of Artificial Grass
N.A.I.C.S.: 326199
David Hartman *(Pres)*

Tarkett Sverige AB (1)
Hammarbacken 12, PO Box 4538, Sollentuna, 191 49, Sweden
Tel.: (46) 771251900
Web Site: http://www.tarkett.se
Sales Range: $25-49.9 Million
Emp.: 40
Flooring
N.A.I.C.S.: 326199
Son Taryon *(Coord-Mktg)*

Tarkett, Inc. (1)
2728 Summer St, Houston, TX 77007
Web Site: http://www.tarkettna.com
Holding Company; Flooring Products Mfr & Distr
N.A.I.C.S.: 551112
Eric Daliere *(Pres-North America & Sports)*

Subsidiary (Non-US):

Tarkett Inc. (2)
1001 Yamaska Street East, Farnham, J2N 1J7, QC, Canada
Tel.: (450) 293-3173
Sales Range: $125-149.9 Million
Emp.: 450
Resilient Flooring Products Mfr & Distr
N.A.I.C.S.: 326199

Subsidiary (Domestic):

Tarkett USA Inc. (2)
1139 Lehigh Ave Ste 300, Whitehall, PA 18052-5515

Tel.: (610) 266-5500
Web Site: http://www.tarkettna.com
Sales Range: $25-49.9 Million
Flooring Product Distr
N.A.I.C.S.: 423310

Subsidiary (Domestic):

Diamond W Supply Co. (3)
19321 E Walnut Dr N, City of Industry, CA 91748   **(100%)**
Tel.: (909) 859-8939
Web Site: http://www.diamondw.com
Sales Range: $10-24.9 Million
Emp.: 40
Floor Coverings
N.A.I.C.S.: 423220
Dan Erickson *(CFO)*

Johnsonite Inc. (3)
16910 Munn Rd, Chagrin Falls, OH 44023
Tel.: (440) 543-8916
Web Site: http://www.johnsonite.com
Sales Range: $25-49.9 Million
Resilient Flooring Products Mfr
N.A.I.C.S.: 326199
Sharon Folliard *(VP-Design & Dev)*

Lexmark Carpet Mills, Inc. (3)
285 Kraft Dr, Dalton, GA 30721-5094
Web Site: http://www.lexmarkcarpet.com
Carpet & Rug Mills
N.A.I.C.S.: 314110
Todd White *(Pres)*

Subsidiary (Domestic):

Northwest Carpet Inc. (4)
3399 Carpet Capital Dr, Dalton, GA 30720
Tel.: (706) 259-9486
Web Site: http://www.northwestcarpets.net
Rev.: $20,869,754
Emp.: 68
Fiscal Year-end: 12/31/2014
Carpets, Hand & Machine Made
N.A.I.C.S.: 314110
Randall L. Coker *(Pres)*

Subsidiary (Domestic):

Tandus Group, Inc. (3)
311 Smith Industrial Blvd, Dalton, GA 30722
Tel.: (706) 259-3034
Web Site: http://www.tandus-centiva.com
Holding Company
N.A.I.C.S.: 551112
James T. Harley *(Sr VP-Mfg)*

TARKU RESOURCES LTD.
Suite 1730 - 800 boul Rene-Levesque W, Montreal, H3B 1X9, QC, Canada
Tel.: (514) 618-7287   BC
Web Site:
https://www.tarkuresources.com
Year Founded: 2011
TRKUF—(OTCQB)
Assets: $1,467,774
Liabilities: $137,447
Net Worth: $1,330,327
Earnings: ($2,034,258)
Fiscal Year-end: 09/30/21
Investment Services
N.A.I.C.S.: 523999
Julien Davy *(Pres & CEO)*

TARMAT LTD.
A K General Vaidya Marg Film City Road, Goregaon East, Mumbai, 400063, India
Tel.: (91) 2228402130
Web Site: https://www.tarmat.in
Year Founded: 1986
532869—(NSE)
Rev.: $26,912,381
Assets: $31,742,147
Liabilities: $23,375,721
Net Worth: $8,366,426
Earnings: $702,497
Emp.: 83
Fiscal Year-end: 03/31/21
Airport Runway, Port, Highway & Road Construction
N.A.I.C.S.: 237990

TARMAT LTD.

Tarmat Ltd.—(Continued)

Shivatosh Chakraborty *(CFO, Officer-Compliance & Sec)*

TARNAISE DES PANNEAUX SAS
10 Boulevard Pasteur, Labruguiere, 81290, France
Tel.: (33) 563733313
Web Site: http://www.tarnaisepanneaux.fr
Sales Range: $25-49.9 Million
Wood Products Mfr
N.A.I.C.S.: 321999
Pierre Chaignon *(Mgr-DP)*

TARO PLAST S.P.A.
Strada Diolo 57, 43019, Soragna, Parma, Italy
Tel.: (39) 0524596711
Web Site: http://www.taroplast.com
Sales Range: $25-49.9 Million
Emp.: 70
Plastic Materials Mfr
N.A.I.C.S.: 325211
Giuseppe Squeri *(Owner)*

TAROKO CO., LTD.
No 186 Section 4 Fuxing Road, East District, Taichung, 40144, Taiwan
Tel.: (886) 436118888   TW
Web Site: https://www.taroko.com.tw
Year Founded: 1973
1432—(TAI)
Rev.: $43,322,278
Assets: $159,311,319
Liabilities: $133,504,164
Net Worth: $25,807,154
Earnings: $1,797,966
Emp.: 532
Fiscal Year-end: 12/31/23
Textile Products Mfr
N.A.I.C.S.: 325220
Man Li Lin *(Chm)*

Subsidiaries:

P.T. Indonesia Taroko Corporation (1)
Desa Kembang Kuning Kec Jatiluhur, Purwakarta, 41361, Jawa Barat, Indonesia
Tel.: (62) 264206481
Fabric Weaving & Dyeing Services
N.A.I.C.S.: 313210

Taroko (Hong Kong) Ltd. (1)
Unit C15F Silvercorp International Tower 707-713 Nathan Road, Mongkok, Kowloon, China (Hong Kong)
Tel.: (852) 23965063
Fabric Distr
N.A.I.C.S.: 424310

TAROLIT A.D.
Savska 26, Lathe, 11251, Belgrade, Serbia
Tel.: (381) 118070998
Web Site: http://www.tarolit.co.rs
Year Founded: 1989
TRLT—(BEL)
Sales Range: $1-9.9 Million
Concrete Products Mfr
N.A.I.C.S.: 327390
Radmila Pavlovic *(Exec Dir & Dir)*

TAROS CAPITAL NETHERLANDS B.V.
Vinoly Tower 21st Floor, 1082 MD, Amsterdam, Netherlands
Tel.: (31) 204041221
Web Site: http://www.taroscapital.com
Sales Range: $50-74.9 Million
Emp.: 2
Privater Equity Firm
N.A.I.C.S.: 551112
Paul Lamers *(Mng Partner)*

Subsidiaries:

Taros Capital GmbH (1)
Friedrich Ebert Anlage 54, 60325, Frankfurt am Main, Germany
Tel.: (49) 699720830
Privater Equity Firm
N.A.I.C.S.: 523999

TARPON INVESTIMENTOS S.A.
Av Brigadeiro Faria Lima 3355, 23 Andar - Itaim Bibi, 04538-133, Sao Paulo, SP, Brazil
Tel.: (55) 11 3074 5800
Web Site: http://www.tarponinvest.com.br
Year Founded: 2002
Rev.: $14,207,428
Assets: $19,449,255
Liabilities: $3,524,323
Net Worth: $15,924,932
Earnings: $2,845,408
Fiscal Year-end: 12/31/17
Investment Management Service
N.A.I.C.S.: 523940
Marcelo Guimaraes Lopo Lima *(CEO & Dir-IR)*

TARSONS PRODUCTS LIMITED
902 Martin Burn Business Park Saltlake Sector-V, PO Box BP-3, Kolkata, 700091, India
Tel.: (91) 3335220300
Web Site: https://www.tarsons.com
543399—(BOM)
Plastic Mfr
N.A.I.C.S.: 326199
Sanjive Sehgal *(Chm & Mng Dir)*

Subsidiaries:

Nerbe plus GmbH & Co. KG (1)
Porschestrasse 25, Luhe, 21423, Winsen, Germany
Tel.: (49) 417178490
Web Site: https://www.nerbe-plus.de
Laboratory Equipment Mfr & Distr
N.A.I.C.S.: 339114

TARTISAN NICKEL CORP.
B17F No 127 Wunong 2nd Rd, Wugu Dist, 24888, New Taipei City, Taiwan
Tel.: (886) 266258188
Web Site: http://www.taidoc.com
Year Founded: 1998
Personal Care Product Distr
N.A.I.C.S.: 456199
Chao-Wang Chen *(Chm & Pres)*

TARTISAN NICKEL CORP.
Suite 1102 44 Victoria Street, Toronto, M5C 1Y2, ON, Canada
Tel.: (416) 804-0280   ON
Web Site: https://tartisannickel.com
Year Founded: 2008
8TA—(DEU)
Assets: $11,139,976
Liabilities: $318,101
Net Worth: $10,821,875
Earnings: ($4,430,621)
Fiscal Year-end: 03/31/23
Gold, Silver, Copper & Zinc Exploration & Mine Development
N.A.I.C.S.: 213114
D. Mark Appleby *(Pres & CEO)*

Subsidiaries:

Minera Tartisan Peru S.A.C. (1)
Botoneros 278, Santiago de Surco, Lima, Peru
Tel.: (51) 98 665 1325
Web Site: http://www.tartisanresources.com
Gold & Silver Mining
N.A.I.C.S.: 212220

TARUGA MINERALS LIMITED
Level 8 99 St Georges Tce, Perth, 6000, WA, Australia
Tel.: (61) 894864036
Web Site: https://www.tarugaminerals.com.au
Year Founded: 2012
TAR—(ASX)
Rev.: $55,239
Assets: $1,769,076
Liabilities: $158,855
Net Worth: $1,610,221
Earnings: ($6,876,720)
Fiscal Year-end: 06/30/24
Gold Mining
N.A.I.C.S.: 212220
Thomas Line *(CEO)*

TAS GROUP LLC
30 Symona Petlury Str, Kiev, 01032, Ukraine
Tel.: (380) 44 593 73 01
Web Site: http://www.tas.ua
Year Founded: 1998
Financial & Industrial Services
N.A.I.C.S.: 523999
Sergiy Popenko *(CEO)*

Subsidiaries:

Universal Bank PJSC (1)
st Avtozavodskaya 54/19, 04114, Kiev, Ukraine
Tel.: (380) 800 300 200
Web Site: http://www.universalbank.com.ua
Commercial Banking Services
N.A.I.C.S.: 522110
Oleksandr Mischyshyn *(Mgr-IT)*

TAS OFFSHORE BERHAD
Lot 199 Jalan Sungai Maaw Sungai Bidut, PO Box 920, 96000, Sibu, Sarawak, Malaysia
Tel.: (60) 84310211   MY
Web Site: https://www.tasoffshore.com
Year Founded: 2002
TAS—(KLS)
Rev.: $7,645,664
Assets: $32,261,884
Liabilities: $12,109,706
Net Worth: $20,152,177
Earnings: $3,233,050
Emp.: 60
Fiscal Year-end: 05/31/23
Ship Building & Repairing Services
N.A.I.C.S.: 336611
Nai Hoh Lau *(Founder & Mng Dir)*

Subsidiaries:

Tuong Aik Shipyard Sdn. Bhd. (1)
Lot 199 Jalan Sg Ma'aw Sungai Bidut, PO Box 920, 96000, Sibu, Sarawak, Malaysia
Tel.: (60) 84310211
Web Site: https://www.tuongaik.com.my
Offshore Vessel Product Distr
N.A.I.C.S.: 423860
Lau Nai Hoh *(Mng Dir)*

TAS TECNOLOGIA AVANZATA DEI SISTEMI SPA
Via Cristoforo Colombo 149, 00142, Rome, Italy
Tel.: (39) 0672 9141
Web Site: http://www.tasgroup.it
Year Founded: 1982
TAQ—(DEU)
Rev.: $75,726
Assets: $129,556
Liabilities: $82,132
Net Worth: $47,424
Earnings: $10,866
Emp.: 560
Fiscal Year-end: 12/31/20
Financial Software Development Services
N.A.I.C.S.: 541511
Valentino Bravi *(CEO)*

INTERNATIONAL PUBLIC

Subsidiaries:

Infraxis AG (1)
Via Serafino Balestra 22B, 6900, Lugano, Switzerland
Tel.: (41) 919854060
Web Site: https://www.infraxis.com
Credit Card Issuing Services
N.A.I.C.S.: 522210

Mitobit S.R.L. (1)
Via V Monti 32, 20123, Milan, Italy
Tel.: (39) 0287177652
Web Site: https://www.mitobit.com
Software Solutions Services
N.A.I.C.S.: 541511

Nemos S.R.L. (1)
Via Ugolani Dati 6, 26100, Cremona, Italy
Tel.: (39) 0372807950
Web Site: https://www.nemosweb.it
Software Solutions Services
N.A.I.C.S.: 541511

TAS Americas Ltd. (1)
4476 E Washington Bvld, Commerce, CA 90023
Tel.: (818) 246-9330
Web Site: http://www.tasamerica.com
Screen Printing Machinery Mfr
N.A.I.C.S.: 323113
Luis Cruz *(Co-Owner)*

TAS France Sasu (1)
15 traverse des Brucs, Sophia Antipolis, 06560, Valbonne, France
Tel.: (33) 825563400
Web Site: http://www.tasgroup.fr
Cloud Computing Services
N.A.I.C.S.: 541512

TAS Iberia SLU (1)
C/Juan Camarillo 47 B304-B306, 28037, Madrid, Spain
Tel.: (34) 918040625
Web Site: http://www.tasgroup.es
Cloud Computing Services
N.A.I.C.S.: 541512

TAS International SA (1)
Via Serafino Balestra 22A, 6900, Lugano, Switzerland
Tel.: (41) 919854060
Web Site: http://www.tasgroup.eu
Cloud Computing Services
N.A.I.C.S.: 541512

TASCO BERHAD
Lot No 1A Persiaran Jubli Perak Jalan 22/1 Seksyen 22, 40300, Shah Alam, Selangor, Malaysia
Tel.: (60) 351018888
Web Site: https://www.tasco.com.my
TASCO—(KLS)
Rev.: $340,070,586
Assets: $181,616,745
Liabilities: $85,936,368
Net Worth: $95,680,377
Earnings: $19,525,766
Emp.: 2,300
Fiscal Year-end: 03/31/23
Transportation Services
N.A.I.C.S.: 483111
Lai Ling Loh *(Co-Sec)*

TASCO INLAND AUSTRALIA PTY LTD
220 Tenth Street, Mildura, 3500, VIC, Australia
Tel.: (61) 350511700
Web Site: http://www.tasco-inland.com.au
Year Founded: 1995
Sales Range: $25-49.9 Million
Emp.: 140
Petroleum & Petroleum Products Distr
N.A.I.C.S.: 424720
Ross G. Lake *(Gen Mgr)*

TASCO JSC
Tasco Building Pham Hung, Nam Tu Liem, Hanoi, Vietnam
Tel.: (84) 437738558

Web Site: https://tasco.com.vn
HUT—(HNX)
Rev.: $107,316,100
Assets: $1,163,237,200
Liabilities: $775,890,500
Net Worth: $387,346,700
Earnings: $14,456,500
Emp.: 154
Fiscal Year-end: 12/31/22
Construction Contracting Services
N.A.I.C.S.: 236220
Pham Quang Dung (Chm-Mgmt Bd)

Subsidiaries:

Tasco Insurance Company Limited (1)
Toa nha Tasco Duong Pham Hung, Quan Nam Tu Liem, Hanoi, Vietnam
Tel.: (84) 19001562
Web Site: https://www.baohiemtasco.vn
Fire Insurance Services
N.A.I.C.S.: 524210

TASECO AIR SERVICES JSC

NO2-T1 Building Doan Ngoai Giao Xuan Tao Street, Bac Tu Liem District, Hanoi, Vietnam
Tel.: (84) 928556688
Web Site: https://www.tasecoairs.vn
Year Founded: 2005
Rev.: $45,639,748
Assets: $34,948,361
Liabilities: $9,185,541
Net Worth: $25,762,821
Earnings: $7,634,351
Emp.: 1,424
Fiscal Year-end: 12/31/19
Oil Transportation Services
N.A.I.C.S.: 481112
Pham Ngoc Thanh (Chm)

TASEKO MINES LIMITED

12th Floor1040 West Georgia Street, Vancouver, V6E 4H1, BC, Canada
Tel.: (778) 373-4533   BC
Web Site:
  https://www.tasekomines.com
TGB—(NYSEAMEX)
Rev.: $306,347,889
Assets: $1,000,288,920
Liabilities: $721,477,287
Net Worth: $278,811,633
Earnings: ($20,316,594)
Emp.: 244
Fiscal Year-end: 12/31/22
Copper & Gold Mining Services
N.A.I.C.S.: 212230
Ronald William Thiessen (Chm)

Subsidiaries:

Gibraltar Mines Ltd. (1)
10251 Gibraltar Mine Rd, Ottawa, V0L 1P0, QC, Canada
Tel.: (250) 297-6211
Copper Mining & Exploration Services
N.A.I.C.S.: 212230

Yellowhead Mining Inc. (1)
Suite 730-800 West Pender Street, Vancouver, V6C 2V6, BC, Canada
Tel.: (604) 681-1709
Web Site: http://www.yellowheadmining.com
Rev.: $1,504
Assets: $2,600,803
Liabilities: $402,044
Net Worth: $2,198,759
Earnings: ($831,657)
Emp.: 1
Fiscal Year-end: 12/31/2017
Mineral Exploration Services
N.A.I.C.S.: 213114
Frank David Wheatley (CEO)

Subsidiary (Domestic):

Harper Creek Mining Corporation (2)
245 24 Ave E, Vancouver, V5V 1Z7, BC, Canada
Tel.: (604) 417-6375
Copper & Nickel Mining Services
N.A.I.C.S.: 212230

TASFOODS LIMITED

Level 2 89-93 Cimitiere Street, PO Box 425, Launceston, 7250, TAS, Australia
Tel.: (61) 363316983   AU
Web Site:
  https://www.tasfoods.com.au
TFL—(ASX)
Rev.: $32,566,583
Assets: $23,979,974
Liabilities: $12,008,719
Net Worth: $11,971,255
Earnings: ($3,437,777)
Fiscal Year-end: 12/31/23
Loyalty Card, Reward Card & Payment Solutions
N.A.I.C.S.: 561499
John Murphy (Deputy Chm)

Subsidiaries:

OnCard Ltd. (1)
744-746 Kings Rd 2nd Fl Rm 208, Stanhope House, Quarry Bay, China (Hong Kong)
Tel.: (852) 22140099
Web Site: http://www.oncard.com
Dining Cards Creation & Marketing Services
N.A.I.C.S.: 541910

TASHEEL HOLDING GROUP

Tasheel Commercial Plaza Suwaid Bin Sakher St, Al Mohammadiyah Dsitrict 1, Jeddah, Saudi Arabia
Tel.: (966) 12 215 7911
Web Site: https://www.tasheel.com
Emp.: 100
Holding Company
N.A.I.C.S.: 551112

TASHI INDIA LIMITED

Imambada Road, Nagpur, 440 018, Maharashtra, India
Tel.: (91) 7122720071
Web Site: https://www.tashiindia.com
Year Founded: 1985
512271—(BOM)
Rev.: $122,738
Assets: $1,756,405
Liabilities: $26,150
Net Worth: $1,730,256
Earnings: $20,670
Fiscal Year-end: 03/31/23
Financial Investment Management Services
N.A.I.C.S.: 523940
Aarti Batra (CFO & Sec)

TASHIN HOLDING BERHAD

Plot 40 Lorong Perusahaan Maju 7 Kawasan Perusahaan 4, Prai, 13600, Penang, Malaysia
Tel.: (60) 45090888   MY
Web Site: https://www.tashin.com.my
Year Founded: 2017
TASHIN—(KLS)
Rev.: $91,915,896
Assets: $79,907,026
Liabilities: $25,121,489
Net Worth: $54,785,537
Earnings: $2,777,726
Fiscal Year-end: 12/31/22
Holding Company
N.A.I.C.S.: 551112
Lim Choon Teik (Mng Dir)

TASK GROUP HOLDINGS LIMITED

Level 2 2 Graham Street, Auckland, 1010, New Zealand
Tel.: (64) 93581500
Web Site: https://www.plexure.com
Year Founded: 2000
TSK—(ASX)
Rev.: $39,102,273
Assets: $104,008,971
Liabilities: $23,717,105
Net Worth: $80,291,866
Earnings: $218,301
Emp.: 172
Fiscal Year-end: 03/31/23
Software Development Services
N.A.I.C.S.: 541511

TASLY PHARMACEUTICAL GROUP CO., LTD.

Tasly Modern Chinese Medicine City No 2 Pujihe East Road, Beichen District, Tianjin, 300410, China
Tel.: (86) 2226736999
Web Site: http://www.tasly.com
Year Founded: 1998
600535—(SHG)
Rev.: $1,206,485,252
Assets: $2,306,809,290
Liabilities: $527,973,695
Net Worth: $1,778,835,596
Earnings: ($36,014,566)
Fiscal Year-end: 12/31/22
Pharmaceutical Product Mfr & Distr
N.A.I.C.S.: 325412
Yan Kaijing (Chm)

Subsidiaries:

Jiangsu Tasly Diyi Pharmaceutical Co., Ltd. (1)
No 168 Chaoyang Road, Qingpu Industrial Park, Huai'an, 223003, Jiangsu, China
Tel.: (86) 5178 088 9680
Web Site: https://www.taslydiyi.com
Chemical Products Mfr
N.A.I.C.S.: 325998

PT. Tasly Indonesia (1)
Kirana Two Office Tower LT 11 Unit F Jl Boulevard Timur Kav, 88 Pegangsaan Dua Kelapa Gading, Jakarta Utara, 14250, Indonesia
Tel.: (62) 2129629666
Web Site: http://ina.taslyint.com
Pharmaceutical Products Distr
N.A.I.C.S.: 424210

Tasly (Malaysia) Sdn. Bhd. (1)
No 16G-16-3 Jalan Metro Pudu 2 Fraser Business Park Off Jalan Yew, 55100, Kuala Lumpur, Malaysia
Tel.: (60) 392223811
Web Site: http://www.tasly.com.my
Health Food & Related Product Whslr
N.A.I.C.S.: 424490
Liang Liu (Gen Mgr)

Tasly Europe Co., Ltd. (1)
Rue des Deux-Ponts 14, 1205, Geneva, Switzerland
Tel.: (41) 52141222
Pharmaceutical Products Distr
N.A.I.C.S.: 424210

Tasly International Vietnam Co., Ltd. (1)
Room A7 3rd Floor Horison Hotel 40 Cat Linh, Hanoi, Vietnam
Tel.: (84) 437366832
Pharmaceutical Products Distr
N.A.I.C.S.: 424210

Tasly Japan Co., Ltd. (1)
TOC Ariake West Tower 9th Floor 3-5-7, Ariake Koto-ku, Tokyo, 135-0063, Japan
Tel.: (81) 335290101
Web Site: http://www.tasly.jp
Frozen Food Whslr
N.A.I.C.S.: 424420

Tasly Pharmaceutical International Co., Ltd. (1)
Tasly TCM Garden No 2 Pujihe East Road, Beichen district, Tianjin, 300410, China
Tel.: (86) 2226736617
Web Site: http://www.taslyint.com
Pharmaceutical Product Mfr
N.A.I.C.S.: 325412
Yan Xijun (Chm)

Tasly Pharmaceuticals, Inc. (1)
One Research Ct Ste 450-54, Rockville, MD 20850
Tel.: (301) 216-3838
Pharmaceutical Products Distr
N.A.I.C.S.: 424210

Tasly South Africa (Pty) Ltd. (1)
15-17 Humber Street Woodmead, 2157, Sandton, South Africa
Tel.: (27) 112341549
Web Site: http://sa.taslyint.com
Pharmaceutical Products Distr
N.A.I.C.S.: 424210

Tasly World (Russia) Co. Ltd. (1)
No 3 Ural street, Yekaterinburg, Russia
Tel.: (7) 89221632691
Pharmaceutical Products Distr
N.A.I.C.S.: 424210

Taslyhealthpac Integrative Medicine Pty. Ltd. (1)
Shop 28 Lemongrove Shopping Center 431 Victoria Ave Chatswood, Sydney, Australia
Tel.: (61) 294103172
Pharmaceutical Products Distr
N.A.I.C.S.: 424210

Tri-gen Pharma Int'l (Pvt) Ltd. (1)
301-B 3rd Floor Lakson Square Building No 3 Sarwar Shaheed Road, Karachi, 74200, Pakistan
Tel.: (92) 215655582
Pharmaceutical Products Distr
N.A.I.C.S.: 424210

TASMAN CAPITAL PARTNERS PTY. LIMITED

Level 10 50 Pitt Street, Sydney, 2000, NSW, Australia
Tel.: (61) 282262200   AU
Web Site:
  http://www.tasmancapital.com.au
Year Founded: 2006
Sales Range: $50-74.9 Million
Emp.: 9
Equity Investment & Management Services
N.A.I.C.S.: 523999
Gene Lorenz (Co-Founder & Mng Dir)

TASMAN RESOURCES LIMITED

Level 15 197 St George's Terrace, Perth, 6000, WA, Australia
Tel.: (61) 892825889   AU
Web Site:
  https://www.tasmanresources.com
Year Founded: 1987
TAS—(ASX)
Rev.: $1,346,581
Assets: $15,690,174
Liabilities: $11,337,288
Net Worth: $4,352,886
Earnings: ($12,246,755)
Fiscal Year-end: 06/30/24
Mineral Exploration Services
N.A.I.C.S.: 212290
Gregory Howard Solomon (Chm)

TASMANIA MINES LIMITED

C/- Kanji Group Pty Ltd Level 33 ABN AMRO Tower 88 Phillip Street, Sydney, 2000, NSW, Australia
Tel.: (61) 2 9251 4244   AU
Web Site:
  http://www.tasmines.com.au
Scheelite & Magnetite Mining Services
N.A.I.C.S.: 212290
Kenneth J. Broadfoot (Co-Sec)

Subsidiaries:

Kara Industrial Minerals Pty Ltd (1)
11 Stroud St, Allworth, 2425, NSW, Australia
Tel.: (61) 2 49949343
Metal Mining Services
N.A.I.C.S.: 212290

TASSAL GROUP LIMITED

Level 9 1 Franklin Wharf, Hobart, 7000, TAS, Australia
Tel.: (61) 3 6244 9035
Web Site: http://www.tassal.com.au
Year Founded: 1986

TASSAL GROUP LIMITED

Tassal Group Limited—(Continued)
TGR—(ASX)
Rev.: $455,143,677
Assets: $1,262,188,460
Liabilities: $648,818,120
Net Worth: $613,370,340
Earnings: $26,525,498
Emp.: 450
Fiscal Year-end: 06/30/21
Salmon & Trout Farming, Processing & Marketing
N.A.I.C.S.: 112519
Mark Ryan *(CEO & Mng Dir)*

Subsidiaries:

Aquatas Pty Ltd (1)
10 Marina Dr, Margate, 7054, Tasmania, Australia (100%)
Tel.: (61) 362676767
Sales Range: $10-24.9 Million
Emp.: 50
Finfish Farming & Fish Hatcheries
N.A.I.C.S.: 112511

Tassal Operations Pty Ltd (1)
2 Salamanca Square, Battery Point, Hobart, 7004, TAS, Australia (100%)
Tel.: (61) 362449025
Web Site: http://www.tassal.com.au
Marketing Consulting Services
N.A.I.C.S.: 541613

TASTE GOURMET GROUP LIMITED
Unit B 24th Floor Crawford Tower 99 Jervois Street, Sheung Wan, China (Hong Kong)
Tel.: (852) 28580778   Ky
Web Site: http://www.tastegourmet.com.hk
Year Founded: 2007
8371—(HKG)
Rev.: $95,308,418
Assets: $87,789,998
Liabilities: $63,570,480
Net Worth: $24,219,518
Earnings: $8,863,928
Emp.: 1,130
Fiscal Year-end: 03/31/23
Hotel & Restaurant Management Services
N.A.I.C.S.: 722511
Ngai Shan Wong *(Chm)*

TASTY CONCEPTS HOLDING LTD.
6/F Goldsland Building 22-26 Minden Avenue Tsim Sha Tsui, Kowloon, China (Hong Kong)   Ky
Year Founded: 2010
8096—(HKG)
Rev.: $5,402,507
Assets: $3,716,436
Liabilities: $3,495,214
Net Worth: $221,223
Earnings: ($1,244,648)
Emp.: 78
Fiscal Year-end: 03/31/23
Holding Company
N.A.I.C.S.: 551112
Chun Ho Chandle Tang *(Founder)*

TASTY DAIRY SPECIALITIES LTD.
D-3 Upsidc, Industrial Area Jainpur Kanpur Dehat, Kanpur, 209311, Uttar Pradesh, India
Tel.: (91) 5124003999
Web Site: https://www.tastydairy.com
Year Founded: 1992
540955—(BOM)
Rev.: $13,484,024
Assets: $12,293,196
Liabilities: $8,561,405
Net Worth: $3,731,791
Earnings: ($10,971)
Fiscal Year-end: 03/31/23

Milk Dairy Product Mfr & Distr
N.A.I.C.S.: 311511
Atul Mehra *(Chm)*

TASTY PLC
32 Charlotte Street, London, W1T 2NQ, United Kingdom
Tel.: (44) 2039498800
TAST—(AIM)
Rev.: $59,719,714
Assets: $55,085,739
Liabilities: $76,104,125
Net Worth: ($21,018,386)
Earnings: ($18,421,323)
Fiscal Year-end: 12/31/23
Restaurant Operating Services
N.A.I.C.S.: 722511
Daniel Jonny Plant *(Co-CEO)*

TASUKI CORPORATION
2-7-9 Kita-Aoyama, Minato-Ku, Tokyo, 107-0061, Japan
Tel.: (81) 368129330
Web Site: http://www.tasukicorp.co.jp
Year Founded: 2013
2987—(TKS)
Investment Management Service
N.A.I.C.S.: 523999
Koji Murata *(Pres)*

TAT HONG TRAINING SERVICES PTE. LTD.
No 19 Sungei Kadut Avenue, Singapore, 729654, Singapore
Tel.: (65) 62695269   SG
Web Site: http://www.tathongtraining.com
Year Founded: 1999
Sales Range: $1-9.9 Million
Industrial Equipment Training Services
N.A.I.C.S.: 611519
Tony Sun Ho Ng *(Owner & Mng Dir)*

TAT SERVICES SASU
25 Rue de la Milletiere, 37000, Tours, France
Tel.: (33) 247850000   FR
Web Site: http://www.tat.com
Year Founded: 1968
Sales Range: $400-449.9 Million
Emp.: 2,400
Aircraft Maintenance Services
N.A.I.C.S.: 488190
Rodolphe Marchais *(Chm & CEO)*

Subsidiaries:

EADS Sogerma Services (1)
20 Rue Georges Barres, PO Box BP 2, Rue Marcel Essartier, 33701, Merignac, Cedex, France
Tel.: (33) 556554000
Web Site: http://www.sogerma.eads.net
Sales Range: $750-799.9 Million
Emp.: 900
Aviation Engineering Services
N.A.I.C.S.: 541330

Sabena technics (1)
Tour Maine Montparnasse 33 avenue du Maine BP47, 75 755, Paris, Cedex 15, France (100%)
Tel.: (33) 1 56 54 42 30
Web Site: http://www.sabenatechnics.com
Sales Range: $350-399.9 Million
Emp.: 2,700
Aircraft Maintenance Services
N.A.I.C.S.: 488190
Jean-Marc Schaefer *(CFO)*

TAT THE ASTONISHING TRIBE AB
Torggatan 2, 211 40, Malmo, Sweden
Tel.: (46) 40109700
Web Site: http://www.tat.se
Sales Range: $10-24.9 Million
Emp.: 152
Mobile Phone Developer
N.A.I.C.S.: 334220

Ola Larsen *(VP-Mktg)*

TATA AUTOCOMP SYSTEMS LIMITED
TACO House Damle Path, Off Law College Road, Pune, 411 004, India
Tel.: (91) 20 6608 5000
Web Site: http://www.tacogroup.com
Sales Range: $150-199.9 Million
Emp.: 10,000
Motor Vehicle Parts Mfr
N.A.I.C.S.: 336211
Shvetal Diwanji *(VP-Grp Mktg Corp Comm & Sustainability)*

Subsidiaries:

Automotive Stampings & Assemblies Limited (1)
TACO House Plot No- 20/B FPN085 V G Damle Path Off Law College Road, Erandwane, Pune, 411004, Maharashtra, India (75%)
Tel.: (91) 2066314300
Web Site: https://www.autostampings.com
Rev.: $83,252,920
Assets: $24,692,195
Liabilities: $29,567,183
Net Worth: ($4,874,988)
Earnings: $7,140,424
Emp.: 409
Fiscal Year-end: 03/31/2022
Motor Vehicle Parts Mfr
N.A.I.C.S.: 336370

TATA ELXSI LIMITED
ITPB Road Whitefield, Bengaluru, 560 048, India
Tel.: (91) 8022979123
Web Site: https://www.tataelxsi.com
Year Founded: 1989
500408—(BOM)
Rev.: $343,342,804
Assets: $296,092,155
Liabilities: $77,568,910
Net Worth: $218,523,246
Earnings: $75,030,160
Emp.: 9,376
Fiscal Year-end: 03/31/22
Information Technology Services
N.A.I.C.S.: 519290
Madhukar Dev *(CEO & Mng Dir)*

Subsidiaries:

Tata Elxsi Incorporated (1)
PO Box 1582, Mount Edgecombe, Durban, 4301, South Africa
Tel.: (27) 315665585
Software Development Services
N.A.I.C.S.: 541511

TATA GROUP OF COMPANIES LTD.
8 8th Fl Textile Plaza M A Jinnah Road, Karachi, Pakistan
Tel.: (92) 21 242 676124
Web Site: http://www.tatatex.com
Sales Range: $50-74.9 Million
Emp.: 200
Holding Company
N.A.I.C.S.: 551112
Anwar Ahmed Tata *(Chm)*

Subsidiaries:

Island Textile Mills Ltd. (1)
6th Floor Textile Plaza M A Jinnah Road, Karachi, 74000, Pakistan
Tel.: (92) 2132426740
Web Site: http://www.tatapakistan.com
Rev.: $54,261,008
Assets: $71,011,195
Liabilities: $39,758,934
Net Worth: $31,252,261
Earnings: $1,326,355
Emp.: 1,087
Fiscal Year-end: 06/30/2019
Textile Mfr
N.A.I.C.S.: 314999
Anwar Ahmed Tata *(Chm)*

Tata Textile Mills Limited (1)

INTERNATIONAL PUBLIC

6th Floor Textile Plaza M A Jinnah Road Karachi, Karachi, Pakistan
Tel.: (92) 32412955
Web Site: http://www.tatapakistan.com
Rev.: $125,591,162
Assets: $166,211,102
Liabilities: $89,299,293
Net Worth: $76,911,809
Earnings: $937,240
Emp.: 3,135
Fiscal Year-end: 06/30/2023
Textile Mill
N.A.I.C.S.: 314999

TATA HEALTH INTERNATIONAL HOLDINGS LTD.
Flat F-J 11th Floor Block 2 Kwai Tak Industrial Centre, 15-33 Kwai Tak Street, Kwai Chung, NT, China (Hong Kong)
Tel.: (852) 26120003
Web Site: https://www.s-culture.com
Year Founded: 1996
1255—(HKG)
Rev.: $18,437,265
Assets: $22,446,630
Liabilities: $20,032,163
Net Worth: $2,414,468
Earnings: $408,765
Emp.: 156
Fiscal Year-end: 12/31/22
Footwear Retailer & Distr
N.A.I.C.S.: 458210
Jun Yang *(Chm)*

TATA METALIKS LTD
Tata Centre 10th Floor 43 Jawaharlal Nehru Road, Kolkata, 700071, West Bengal, India
Tel.: (91) 336 613 4200
Web Site: http://www.tatametaliks.com
513434—(NSE)
Rev.: $377,038,730
Assets: $320,663,316
Liabilities: $112,464,288
Net Worth: $208,199,027
Earnings: $32,411,734
Emp.: 1,453
Fiscal Year-end: 03/31/22
Pig Iron Mfr
N.A.I.C.S.: 331110
Debasish Mishra *(VP-Operations-PI)*

TATA MOTORS LIMITED
24 Bombay House Homi Mody Street, Mumbai, 400 001, India
Tel.: (91) 2266658282   In
Web Site: https://www.tatamotors.com
Year Founded: 1945
500570—(BOM)
Rev.: $53,219,559,010
Assets: $44,441,459,746
Liabilities: $33,279,786,130
Net Worth: $11,161,673,616
Earnings: $3,813,530,724
Emp.: 91,496
Fiscal Year-end: 03/31/24
Commercial Vehicle & Passenger Automobile Mfr
N.A.I.C.S.: 336110
Girish Wagh *(Exec Dir)*

Subsidiaries:

Bowler Motors Limited (1)
Leonard House Queen Street, Belper, DE56 1NR, Derbyshire, United Kingdom
Tel.: (44) 1773827111
Web Site: https://www.bowlermotors.com
Car Dealer
N.A.I.C.S.: 441110

Brabo Robotics & Automation Limited (1)
Floor-3 4 Plot-18 Nanavati Mahalaya Mudhana Shetty Marg BSE Fort, Mumbai, 400001, India
Tel.: (91) 2066135549
Web Site: http://braboautomation.com

AND PRIVATE COMPANIES — TATA MOTORS LIMITED

Industrial Robots Mfr
N.A.I.C.S.: 334513
Amit Bhingurde *(CEO)*

Jaguar Cars Overseas Holdings Ltd (1)
Abbey Road Whitley, Coventry, CV3 4LF, United Kingdom
Tel.: (44) 2476303080
Web Site: http://www.jaguarlandrovercovenrty.com
Investment Management Service
N.A.I.C.S.: 523940

Jaguar Hispania SL (1)
Paseo Castellana 130 Planta 8, 28046, Madrid, Spain
Tel.: (34) 915786200
Web Site: http://www.jaguar.com
Sales Range: $25-49.9 Million
Emp.: 40
Automotive Distr
N.A.I.C.S.: 423110

Jaguar Land Rover (South Africa) (Pty) Ltd (1)
28 Victoria Link Route 21 Corporate Park Nellmapius Drive Irene X30, Tshwane, Centurion, Gauteng, South Africa
Tel.: (27) 110230462
Web Site: https://www.landrover.co.za
Car Distr
N.A.I.C.S.: 423120

Jaguar Land Rover Australia Pty Ltd (1)
L 1 U 2 65 Epping Rd, North Ryde, Sydney, 2113, NSW, Australia
Tel.: (61) 290201515
Automobile Whslr
N.A.I.C.S.: 423110

Jaguar Land Rover Austria GmbH (1)
Furbergstrasse 35, 5020, Salzburg, Austria
Tel.: (43) 66221210
Web Site: http://www.landrover.com
Emp.: 50
Automotive Spare Parts Whslr
N.A.I.C.S.: 423120
Alexander Wortberg *(COO-Slovakia)*

Jaguar Land Rover Belux NV (1)
Generaal Lemanstraat 47, 2018, Antwerp, Belgium
Tel.: (32) 24007624
Web Site: https://www.jaguar.be
Car Mfr
N.A.I.C.S.: 336999

Jaguar Land Rover Canada ULC (1)
75 Courtneypark Drive West Unit 3, Mississauga, L5W 0E3, ON, Canada
Tel.: (905) 792-1121
Web Site: https://www.landrover.ca
Automobile Whslr
N.A.I.C.S.: 423110

Jaguar Land Rover Deutschland GmbH (1)
Am Kronberger Hang 2a, Schwalbach, 65824, Germany
Tel.: (49) 619695210
Web Site: http://www.landrover.com
Sales Range: $25-49.9 Million
Emp.: 50
Automotive Distr
N.A.I.C.S.: 423110

Jaguar Land Rover France, SAS (1)
34 rue de la Croix de Fer, 78105, Saint Germain-en-Laye, France
Tel.: (33) 161016700
Automobile Whslr
N.A.I.C.S.: 423110

Jaguar Land Rover Italia SpA (1)
V le Marchetti 105, 00148, Rome, Italy
Tel.: (39) 06658531
Web Site: https://www.landrover.it
Sales Range: $25-49.9 Million
Emp.: 40
Automotive Distr
N.A.I.C.S.: 423110

Jaguar Land Rover Japan Ltd (1)
Kamiyacho Central Place 6F, Minato-ku, Tokyo, 105-0001, Japan
Tel.: (81) 3 5470 4242
Automobile Mfr
N.A.I.C.S.: 336110

Jaguar Land Rover Korea Co. Ltd (1)
25th Flr W Tower Mirae Asset Center 1 Bldg 26 Suhadong, Jung-gu, 100-210, Seoul, Korea (South)
Tel.: (82) 2 2071 7000
Web Site: http://www.jaguarkorea.co.kr
Sales Range: $25-49.9 Million
Emp.: 25
Automobile Mfr
N.A.I.C.S.: 336110
David McIntyre *(Mng Dir)*

Jaguar Land Rover Nederland BV (1)
Stationsweg 8, 4153 RD, Beesd, Netherlands
Tel.: (31) 345 688 800
Web Site: http://www.jaguar.com
Automobile Mfr
N.A.I.C.S.: 336110

Jaguar Land Rover North America LLC (1)
100 Jaguar Land Rover Way, Mahwah, NJ 07430
Tel.: (201) 818-8500
Web Site: https://www.landroverusa.com
Automobile Whslr
N.A.I.C.S.: 423110
Jeff Curry *(VP-Brands)*

Jaguar Land Rover Plc (1)
Banbury Rd Lighthorne Heath, Gaydon, CV35 0BJ, Warwickshire, United Kingdom
Tel.: (44) 1926641111
Web Site: http://www.jaguarlandrover.com
Sales Range: $15-24.9 Billion
Emp.: 15,000
Automobile Mfr
N.A.I.C.S.: 336110
Natarajan Chandrasekaran *(Chm)*

Subsidiary (Domestic):

Jaguar Cars Limited (2)
Browns Lane Allesley, Coventry, CV5 9DR, W Midlands, United Kingdom
Tel.: (44) 2476402121
Web Site: http://www.jaguar.com
Sales Range: $1-4.9 Billion
Emp.: 8,000
Luxury Sportscar Mfr
N.A.I.C.S.: 336110

Subsidiary (Non-US):

Jaguar Canada Inc. (3)
50 Coachworks Cres, Brampton, L6R 3Y2, ON, Canada
Tel.: (905) 500-2005
Web Site: http://www.jaguar.ca
Automobile Marketer & Distr
N.A.I.C.S.: 423110

Subsidiary (Non-US):

Jaguar Hong Kong (2)
Shop2 56 Gloucester Road, Wanchai, China (Hong Kong)
Tel.: (852) 2520 0989
Automotive Distr
N.A.I.C.S.: 423110

Jaguar Motors (Macau) Limited (2)
Avenida Olimpica No 675 r/c Loja F Edif Kingsville, Taipa, China (Macau)
Tel.: (853) 2852 1212
Automobile Whslr
N.A.I.C.S.: 423110

Subsidiary (Domestic):

Land Rover (2)
Banbury Rd, Gaydon, CV35 0RR, Warwickshire, United Kingdom
Tel.: (44) 926641111
Web Site: http://www.landrover.com
Sales Range: $700-749.9 Million
Emp.: 4,005
Sport Utility Vehicle Mfr
N.A.I.C.S.: 336110

Land Rover Belux SA/NV (1)
Hunderenveldlaan 10, 1082, Brussels, Belgium
Tel.: (32) 2 709 79 79
Web Site: http://www.landrover.be

Sales Range: $25-49.9 Million
Emp.: 46
Automotive Distr
N.A.I.C.S.: 423110

Land Rover Espana SL (1)
Paseo Castellana 130, 28046, Madrid, Spain
Tel.: (34) 915786100
Web Site: http://www.landrover.com
Sales Range: $50-74.9 Million
Emp.: 80
Automotive Distr
N.A.I.C.S.: 423110

Land Rover Ireland Ltd (1)
Clonlara Avenue Baldonnell Business Park, Dublin, Ireland
Tel.: (353) 14893790
Web Site: https://www.landrover.ie
Automotive Distr
N.A.I.C.S.: 423110

PT Tata Motors Indonesia (1)
Tel.: (62) 2129328041
Web Site: https://www.tatamotors.co.id
Automobile Mfr
N.A.I.C.S.: 335910

Spark44 Communicacions SL (1)
Prim 19, 28004, Madrid, Spain
Tel.: (34) 91 308 6090
Advertising Services
N.A.I.C.S.: 541810

Tata Daewoo Commercial Vehicle Co. Ltd. (1)
172 Dongjangsan-ro, Gunsan, 573-715, Jeollabuk, Korea (South)
Tel.: (82) 221063600
Web Site: https://www.tata-daewoo.com
Sales Range: $450-499.9 Million
Emp.: 1,300
Truck Mfr & Distr
N.A.I.C.S.: 336120

Subsidiary (Non-US):

Tata Advanced Materials Ltd (2)
10 Jigani Industrial Area Jigani, Bengaluru, India
Tel.: (91) 8066955500
Web Site: http://www.tamlindia.com
Aerospace & Defense Composite Product Mfr
N.A.I.C.S.: 334511

Tata Africa Holdings (SA) Pty. Ltd. (2)
39 Ferguson Road, c/r Rivonia & Ferguson Roads, Illovo, Gauteng, South Africa
Tel.: (27) 114591700
Sales Range: $25-49.9 Million
Emp.: 35
Investment Management Service
N.A.I.C.S.: 523940
Len Brand *(Mng Dir)*

Tata Ceramics Limited (2)
Cochin Special Economic Zone Plot No 26, Kakanad, Kochi, 682 037, India
Tel.: (91) 4846604100
Web Site: https://tclceramics.com
Emp.: 3,000
Ceramic Products Mfr
N.A.I.C.S.: 327120
Govind Raj *(Mng Dir)*

Tata Chemicals Magadi Ltd (2)
PO Box 1, 00205, Magadi, 00205, Kenya
Tel.: (254) 20 6999000
Web Site: http://www.tatachemicals.com
Sales Range: $200-249.9 Million
Emp.: 1,000
Soda Ash Mfr
N.A.I.C.S.: 325180
Subodh Srivastav *(CEO & Mng Dir)*

Subsidiary (US):

Tata Chemicals North America Inc. (2)
111 E Sego Lily Dr Ste 200, Sandy, UT 84070
Tel.: (801) 406-7022
Web Site: https://www.tatachemicals.com
Soda Ash Mfr
N.A.I.C.S.: 325180
H. Scott Ellis *(Mng Dir)*

Tata Hispano Motors Carrocera S.A. (1)
Pol Empresarium Ctra Castellon Km 230 5 La Cartuja Baja, 50720, Zaragoza, Spain
Tel.: (34) 976720500
Web Site: http://www.tatahispano.com
Bus Mfr & Distr
N.A.I.C.S.: 336110

Tata Marcopolo Motors Ltd. (1)
Belur Industrial Area Mummigatti Post, Hubli-Dharwad, 580 007, Karnataka, India
Sales Range: $150-199.9 Million
Emp.: 3,500
Bus Mfr
N.A.I.C.S.: 336110

Tata Motors European Technical Centre PLC (1)
Tel.: (44) 2476524717
Web Site: https://www.tmetc.com
Automotive Engineering Consulting Services
N.A.I.C.S.: 541330

Tata Motors Finance Ltd. (1)
I-Think Techno Campus A-Wing 2nd Floor Pokhran Road, No 2 Off Express Highway Thane West, Thane, 400 601, India
Tel.: (91) 2261815400
Web Site: https://www.tmf.co.in
Sales Range: $200-249.9 Million
Emp.: 300
Automobile Financing Services
N.A.I.C.S.: 522220
Nasser Munjee *(Chm)*

Tata Motors Insurance Broking and Advisory Services Ltd. (1)
1st Floor AFL House Lok Bharati Complex Marol Maroshi Road, Andheri East, Mumbai, 400 059, India
Tel.: (91) 2266207900
Web Site: https://www.tatamotorsinsurance.com
Sales Range: $50-74.9 Million
Emp.: 60
Insurance Brokerage & Advisory Services
N.A.I.C.S.: 524298

Tata Technologies GmbH (1)
Ohmstrasse 4, 85080, Gaimersheim, Germany
Tel.: (49) 71149039659
Engineering & Digital Services
N.A.I.C.S.: 541330

Tata Technologies Ltd. (1)
Plot No 25 Rajiv Gandhi Infotech Park, Hinjawadi, Pune, 411057, India
Tel.: (91) 2066529299
Web Site: https://www.tatatechnologies.com
Information Technology Services
N.A.I.C.S.: 541512
Anand Bhade *(Pres-Sls-APAC & Head-Tech Solutions-Global)*

Subsidiary (Non-US):

Tata Technologies Coventry (2)
Enterprise Centre Coventry University Technology Park Puma Way, Coventry, CV1 2TT, United Kingdom
Tel.: (44) 8443759685
Information Technology Consulting Services
N.A.I.C.S.: 541512
Richard Welford *(Pres-Sls-Europe)*

Tata Technologies Pte. Ltd (2)
8 Shenton Way 19-05 AXA Tower, Singapore, 068811, Singapore
Tel.: (65) 67794733
Web Site: http://www.tatatechnologies.com
Engineeering Services
N.A.I.C.S.: 541330

Tata Technologies de Mexico, S.A. de C.V. (2)
Calle Parral No 16 Planta Alta Col Condesa, Mexico, 06140, Mexico
Tel.: (52) 55 5211 2297
Software Development Services
N.A.I.C.S.: 541511

Subsidiary (US):

Tata Technologies, Inc. (2)
41050 W Eleven Mile Rd, Novi, MI 48375-1302
Tel.: (248) 426-1482

TATA MOTORS LIMITED

Tata Motors Limited—(Continued)
Web Site: http://www.tatatechnologies.com
Computer Integrated Systems Design Services
N.A.I.C.S.: 541611
Warren Harris (CEO & Mng Dir)

The Jaguar Collection Ltd (1)
Unipart House Garsington Road, Oxford, OX4 2PG, United Kingdom
Tel.: (44) 1865383297
Web Site: http://www.jaguarcollection.com
Electronic Equipment Whslr
N.A.I.C.S.: 423690

Trilix S.r.l. (1)
Via Teano 3/5, 10042, Nichelino, Italy
Tel.: (39) 0114062401
Sales Range: $25-49.9 Million
Emp.: 50
Automotive Design & Engineering Services
N.A.I.C.S.: 541330
Alberto Pasino (Project Mgr)

TATA PETRODYNE LTD.
3rd Floor West Wing Metropolitan Building Bandra Kurla Complex, Bandra E, Mumbai, 400 051, India
Tel.: (91) 22 67338484
Web Site: http://www.tatapetrodyne.in
Year Founded: 1993
Crude Oil & Gas Exploration & Production Services
N.A.I.C.S.: 211120
Atanu Guha (VP-Fin)

TATA POWER COMPANY LIMITED
Bombay House 24 Homi Mody Street, Mumbai, 400 001, India
Tel.: (91) 2266658282   In
Web Site: https://www.tatapower.com
Year Founded: 1919
TATAPOWER—(NSE)
Rev.: $7,604,042,109
Assets: $16,771,482,607
Liabilities: $12,164,665,641
Net Worth: $4,606,816,965
Earnings: $514,380,706
Emp.: 22,372
Fiscal Year-end: 03/31/24
Electricity Generation
N.A.I.C.S.: 334515
Hanoz M. Mistry (Sec)

Subsidiaries:

Bhira Investments Ltd. (1)
Tel.: (230) 4673000
Investment Management Service
N.A.I.C.S.: 523940

Bhivpuri Investments Ltd. (1)
IFS Court Twenty Eight Cybercity, Ebene, 1721-04, Mauritius
Tel.: (230) 4673000
Solar Electric Power Generation Services
N.A.I.C.S.: 221114

OTP Geothermal Power (1)
ampoerna Strategic Square North Tower 24th Floor, Jl Jend Sudirman Kav 45-46, 12930, Jakarta, Indonesia
Tel.: (62) 21 57851080
Geothermal Energy Production
N.A.I.C.S.: 221116

TP Solar Ltd. (1)
34 Sant Tukaram Road Carnac Bunder, Mumbai, 400009, Maharashtra, India
Tel.: (91) 2267171000
Web Site: https://www.tpsolarltd.com
Solar & Wind Power Structure Installation Services
N.A.I.C.S.: 238220

Tata Power Delhi Distribution Ltd. (1)
NDPL House Hudson Lines Kingsway Camp, Delhi, 110 009, India
Tel.: (91) 1166112222
Web Site: https://www.tatapower-ddl.com
Power Distribution Services
N.A.I.C.S.: 221122
Suranjit Mishra (CFO)

Tata Power International Pte. Ltd. (1)
Tel.: (65) 62209718
Solar Electric Power Generation Services
N.A.I.C.S.: 221114

Tata Power Renewable Energy Ltd. (1)
Corporate Centre A-Block 34 Sant Tukaram Road Carnac Bunder, Mumbai, 400 009, India
Tel.: (91) 2267171231
Web Site: https://www.tatapowerrenewables.com
Solar Electric Power Generation Services
N.A.I.C.S.: 221114
Jeraz Mahernosh (Sec)

Tata Power Solar Systems Limited (1)
78 Electronics City Phase I Hosur Road, Bengaluru, 560 100, India
Tel.: (91) 8067772000
Web Site: https://www.tatapowersolar.com
Emp.: 300
Solar Photovoltaic & Thermal Product Mfr & Distr
N.A.I.C.S.: 335999
Praveer Sinha (Chm)

Tata Power Trading Co. Ltd. (1)
B-12/13 2nd Floor Shatabdi Bhavan Sector-04, Noida, 201 301, Uttar Pradesh, India
Tel.: (91) 1206102000
Web Site: https://tatapowertrading.com
Electric Power Distribution Services
N.A.I.C.S.: 221122

TATA SONS LIMITED
Bombay House 24 Homi Mody Street, Mumbai, 400 001, India
Tel.: (91) 2266658282   In
Web Site: http://www.tata.com
Year Founded: 1868
Sales Range: $75-99.9 Billion
Emp.: 722,281
Holding Company
N.A.I.C.S.: 551112
Natarajan Chandrasekaran (Chm)

Subsidiaries:

Advinus Therapeutics Ltd. (1)
Quantum Towers Plot No 9 Rajiv Gandhi Infotech Park, Phase I Hinjewadi, Pune, 411057, India
Tel.: (91) 20 66539600
Web Site: http://www.advinus.com
Sales Range: $10-24.9 Million
Pharmaceuticals Mfr
N.A.I.C.S.: 325412
R. Gopalakrishnan (Chm)

Associated Building Company (1)
Bombay House 24 Homi Mody Street, Mumbai, 400 001, India
Tel.: (91) 22 6665 7156
Web Site: http://www.tata.com
Emp.: 28
Electrical Contracting Services
N.A.I.C.S.: 238210
Freddy P. Talati (CEO)

Best Bar Pty. Ltd. (1)
367 Mandurah Road, Rockingham, 6168, WA, Australia
Tel.: (61) 8 9411 9300
Web Site: http://www.bestbar.com.au
Emp.: 300
Steel Bar Mfr
N.A.I.C.S.: 331221
Brad Johnston (Grp Dir-Production)

Cambric Corporation (1)
555 E Broadway Ste 300, Salt Lake City, UT 84102
Tel.: (801) 415-7300
Web Site: http://www.cambric.com
Information Technology Consulting Services
N.A.I.C.S.: 541512
Brian Horwath (VP)

Dhaanya Seeds Limited (1)
Plot No 3 KIADB 4th Phase Bommasandra, Bengaluru, 560099, Karnataka, India
Tel.: (91) 8110 420500
Web Site: http://www.dhaanya.com
Seed Processing Services

N.A.I.C.S.: 111191
S. Ravi Krishna (CEO)

Dutch Lanka Trailers Manufactures LLC (1)
PC 217 CR 1036351, PO Box 453, Salalah, Oman
Tel.: (968) 23213010
Truck Trailer Mfr
N.A.I.C.S.: 336212

Ecofirst Services Private Limited (1)
Unit No NB 1502 SB -1501 15th Floor Empire Tower Cloud City Campus, GUT NO 31 Village Elthan Kalwa Industrial Estate, Navi Mumbai, 400708, India
Tel.: (91) 22 61148181
Web Site: http://www.ecofirst.in
Emp.: 30
Engineering Consulting Services
N.A.I.C.S.: 541330
Amit Sharma (Chm)

Subsidiary (Domestic):

Benares Hotels Limited (2)
Taj Palace Hotel Sardar Patel Marg, New Delhi, 110 021, India
Tel.: (91) 1166503704
Web Site: https://www.benareshotelslimited.com
Rev.: $3,386,401
Assets: $12,407,099
Liabilities: $2,547,076
Net Worth: $9,860,023
Earnings: ($713,704)
Emp.: 145
Fiscal Year-end: 03/31/2021
Home Management Services
N.A.I.C.S.: 721110
Anant Narain Singh (Chm)

Unit (US):

The Pierre Hotel (2)
2 E 61st St 5th Ave, New York, NY 10065
Tel.: (212) 838-8000
Web Site: http://www.tajhotels.com
Sales Range: $100-124.9 Million
Hotel Services
N.A.I.C.S.: 721110
Heiko Kuenstle (Gen Mgr)

Infiniti Retail Limited (1)
701 7th Floor Kaledonia Sahar Road Andheri East, Andheri, Mumbai, 400 069, India
Tel.: (91) 22 6761 3600
Electronic Equipment Distr
N.A.I.C.S.: 423690
Avijit Mitra (CEO)

MGDC S.C. (1)
Av Tizoc 97, 45050, Zapopan, Jalisco, Mexico
Tel.: (52) 33 3003 8200
Information Technology Consulting Services
N.A.I.C.S.: 541512

NOVA Integrated Systems Limited (1)
3rd Floor Eastern Wing Thapar House 124 Janpath, New Delhi, 110001, India
Tel.: (91) 11 6603 3990
Web Site: http://www.novaintegrated.com
Missile & Radar System Mfr
N.A.I.C.S.: 334511

TATA Housing Development Co. Ltd (1)
12th floor Times Tower Kamala Mills Compound Lower Parel, Senapati Bapat Marg, Mumbai, 400 013, India
Tel.: (91) 22 6661 4444
Web Site: http://www.tatahousing.com
Emp.: 700
Real Estate Development Services
N.A.I.C.S.: 531390
K. Venkataraman (VP & Head-Fin)

TCE QSTP-LLC (1)
Qatar Science & Technology Park, PO Box 5825, Doha, Qatar
Tel.: (974) 491 3386 90
Civil Engineering Services
N.A.I.C.S.: 541330
Aditya K. Mishra (Gen Mgr)

TRL Krosaki Refractories Limited (1)
Tata Center 11th Floor 43 J L Nehru Road, Kolkata, 700 071, West Bengal, India

INTERNATIONAL PUBLIC

Tel.: (91) 33 64990527
Web Site: http://www.tataref.com
Refractory Mfr & Distr
N.A.I.C.S.: 327120
Priyabrata Panda (Mng Dir)

Subsidiary (Non-US):

TRL China Limited (2)
Metallurgical and Chemical Industrial Park Bayuquan, Yingkou, 115212, Liaoning, China
Tel.: (86) 417 7233803
Refractory Mfr
N.A.I.C.S.: 327120

Subsidiary (Domestic):

Tata Teleservices (Maharashtra) Ltd. (2)
D-26 TTC Industrial Area MIDC Sanpada P O Turbhe, Navi Mumbai, 400703, India
Tel.: (91) 2266551515
Web Site: https://www.tatateleservices.com
Rev.: $152,367,600
Assets: $239,989,400
Liabilities: $2,687,071,800
Net Worth: ($2,447,082,400)
Earnings: ($519,975,400)
Emp.: 368
Fiscal Year-end: 03/31/2020
Cellular Telecommunications Services
N.A.I.C.S.: 517112

TSN Wires Co. Ltd (1)
199 Moo 11 T Nonglalok Bankai, Rayong, 21120, Thailand
Tel.: (66) 38 924 178
Web Site: http://www.tsnwires.co.th
Galvanized Wire Mfr
N.A.I.C.S.: 331110

Tata Asset Management Company Ltd. (1)
9th Floor Mafatlal Centre Nariman Point, Mumbai, 400 021, Maharashtra, India
Tel.: (91) 22 6657 8282
Web Site: http://www.tatamutualfund.com
Financial Management Services
N.A.I.C.S.: 523999
F. N. Subedar (Chm)

Tata BP Solar India Limited (1)
Plot No 78 Electronic City, Hosur Road, Bengaluru, 560 100, India
Tel.: (91) 8056601300
Web Site: http://www.tatabpsolar.com
Sales Range: $250-299.9 Million
Emp.: 500
Solar Cells, Solar PV Modules & Systems & Solar Thermal Systems Mfr
N.A.I.C.S.: 221121

Tata Capital Limited (1)
One Forbes 1st Fl, Dr VB Gandhi Marg, Mumbai, 400 001, India
Tel.: (91) 22 6745 9000
Web Site: http://www.tatacapital.com
Investment Services
N.A.I.C.S.: 523999
Padmanabh Sinha (Mng Partner-Tata Opportunities Fund)

Tata Chemicals Limited (1)
Bombay House 24 Homi Mody Street, Fort, Mumbai, 400 001, Maharashtra, India
Tel.: (91) 2266658282
Web Site: https://www.tatachemicals.com
Rev.: $1,424,271,030
Assets: $3,868,027,800
Liabilities: $1,801,066,995
Net Worth: $2,066,960,805
Earnings: $59,544,030
Emp.: 1,699
Fiscal Year-end: 03/31/2021
Fertilizer, Food Additive & Inorganic Chemical Mfr
N.A.I.C.S.: 325180
R. Mukundan (CEO & Mng Dir)

Subsidiary (Non-US):

Brunner Mond Group Limited (2)
Mond House, PO Box 4, Northwich, CW8 4DT, United Kingdom
Tel.: (44) 16 0672 4000
Web Site: http://www.tatachemicals.co.uk
Emp.: 350
Chemical Products Mfr
N.A.I.C.S.: 325998

AND PRIVATE COMPANIES — TATA SONS LIMITED

Martin Ashcrost *(Gen Mgr)*

Subsidiary (Domestic):

British Salt Ltd. (3)
Cledford Lane, Middlewich, CW10 OJP, Cheshire, United Kingdom
Tel.: (44) 1606839250
Web Site: http://www.british-salt.co.uk
Sales Range: $25-49.9 Million
Emp.: 100
Salt Mfr
N.A.I.C.S.: 325998
Tim Brown *(Bus Mgr)*

Brunner Mond Generation Company Limited (3)
Winnington Lane, Northwich, CW8 4DT, United Kingdom
Tel.: (44) 1606724000
Web Site: http://www.tatachemicals.com
Emp.: 200
Chemical Products Mfr
N.A.I.C.S.: 325998
Martin Ashcroft *(CEO)*

Subsidiary (US):

General Chemical Industrial Products Inc. (2)
100 Enterprise Dr 7th Fl Ste 701, Brooklyn, NJ 07866
Tel.: (973) 599-5500
Web Site: http://www.tatachemicals.com
Sales Range: $300-349.9 Million
Emp.: 736
Sodium Ash Mfr
N.A.I.C.S.: 325180

Tata Chemicals (Soda Ash) Partners, Inc. (2)
20 MilesWof Green River, Green River, WY 82935
Tel.: (307) 875-3350
Soda Ash Mfr
N.A.I.C.S.: 325180

Subsidiary (Non-US):

Tata Chemicals Europe (2)
Winnington Lane Mond House, Northwich, CW8 4DT, Cheshire, United Kingdom
Tel.: (44) 1606 724000
Web Site: http://www.tatachemicals.com
Emp.: 300
Mfr of Household, Industrial Chemicals & Agricultural Products.
N.A.I.C.S.: 325998
Martin Ashcroft *(Mng Dir)*

Plant (Non-US):

Tata Chemicals Limited - Magadi Plant (2)
PO Box 1, 00205, Magadi, Kenya
Tel.: (254) 20 699 9000
Soda Ash Mfr
N.A.I.C.S.: 325180
Charles Theuri *(Plant Mgr)*

Plant (US):

Tata Chemicals Limited - Tata Chemicals North America Plant (2)
100 Enterprise Dr Ste 701, Rockaway, NJ 07866
Tel.: (973) 599-5500
Soda Ash Mfr
N.A.I.C.S.: 325180

Subsidiary (Non-US):

Tata Chemicals South Africa (Proprietary) Limited (2)
39 Ferguson Road Corner of Rivonia and Ferguson Roads, Illovo, 2196, Johannesburg, South Africa
Tel.: (27) 11 459 1700
Soda Ash Mfr
N.A.I.C.S.: 325180
Lebo Motsisi *(Head-Corp Comm)*

Tata Communications Limited (1)
VSB Mahatma Gandhi Road Fort, Mumbai, 400 001, India (50.03%)
Tel.: (91) 2266591968
Web Site: https://www.tatacommunications.com
Rev.: $2,355,561,390
Assets: $2,912,010,465
Liabilities: $2,892,404,970
Net Worth: $19,605,495
Earnings: $170,832,480
Emp.: 5,999
Fiscal Year-end: 03/31/2021
Telecommunication Servicesb
N.A.I.C.S.: 517111
Tri Pham *(Chief Strategy Officer)*

Subsidiary (Domestic):

Direct Internet Limited (2)
274 Capt Gaur Marg, Sriniwaspuri, 110065, New Delhi, India (100%)
Tel.: (91) 1166179797
Sales Range: $25-49.9 Million
Emp.: 50
Telecommunications Resellers
N.A.I.C.S.: 517121

Subsidiary (Non-US):

Tata Communications Deutschland GmbH (2)
Bettinastrasse 30, 60325, Frankfurt, Germany (100%)
Tel.: (49) 6997461121
Web Site: http://www.tatacommunications.com
Sales Range: $25-49.9 Million
Emp.: 20
Telecommunications Resellers
N.A.I.C.S.: 517121

Tata Communications France SAS (2)
131 Avenue Charles de Gaulle, Neuilly-sur-Seine, 92200, France (100%)
Tel.: (33) 141434200
Web Site: http://www.tatacommunication.com
Sales Range: $25-49.9 Million
Emp.: 50
Telecommunications Resellers
N.A.I.C.S.: 517121
Claude Sassoulas *(Mng Dir)*

Tata Communications Hong Kong Ltd. (2)
2402 Bank of America Tower, 12 Harcourt Rd, Central, China (Hong Kong) (100%)
Tel.: (852) 36938888
Web Site: http://www.tatacommunications.com
Sales Range: $25-49.9 Million
Emp.: 50
Telecommunications
N.A.I.C.S.: 517810

Tata Communications International Pte. Ltd. (2)
35 Tai Seng Street #06-01, Singapore, 534103, Singapore
Tel.: (65) 66326700
Web Site: http://www.tatacommunication.com
Sales Range: $25-49.9 Million
Emp.: 100
Telecommunication Servicesb
N.A.I.C.S.: 517112
Amur Swaminathan Lakshminarayanan *(CEO & Mng Dir)*

Subsidiary (Non-US):

Tata Communications Ltd (3)
1441 Rue Carrie-Derick, Montreal, H3C 4S9, QC, Canada
Tel.: (514) 868-7272
Web Site: http://www.vsnlinternational.com
Holding Company
N.A.I.C.S.: 551112

Division (US):

Tata Communications (America) Inc. (4)
2355 Dulles Corner Blvd 7th Fl, Herndon, VA 20171
Tel.: (703) 547-5900
Web Site: http://www.tatacommunications.com
Sales Range: $350-399.9 Million
Emp.: 2,082
Data Communication Products & Services; Long-Distance Telecommunications Services
N.A.I.C.S.: 518210

Subsidiary (US):

The Switch Enterprises, LLC (2)
60 Hudson St Ste 201, New York, NY 10013
Tel.: (212) 227-9191
Web Site: https://www.theswitch.tv
Video Switching Services
N.A.I.C.S.: 512199
James Eric Cooney *(Pres & CEO)*

Subsidiary (Domestic):

Pacific Television Center (3)
3440 Motor Ave, Los Angeles, CA 90034
Tel.: (310) 287-3800
Web Site: http://www.pactv.com
Sales Range: $1-9.9 Million
Emp.: 200
Teleproduction & Other Postproduction Services
N.A.I.C.S.: 512191
Scott Beers *(CEO)*

Tata Consultancy Services Ltd. (1)
TCS House Raveline Street, Fort, Mumbai, 400 001, India
Tel.: (91) 2267789595
Web Site: http://www.tcs.com
Rev.: $27,651,965,600
Assets: $17,353,040,800
Liabilities: $6,335,356,000
Net Worth: $11,017,684,800
Earnings: $5,110,202,400
Emp.: 614,795
Fiscal Year-end: 03/31/2023
Information Technology & Business Process Outsourcing Consulting Services
N.A.I.C.S.: 541611
Venkataraman Ramakrishnan *(CFO)*

Subsidiary (Non-US):

Cambric Consulting SRL (2)
Str Branduselor No 84, Brasov, 500397, Romania
Tel.: (40) 268 546 063
Information Technology Consulting Services
N.A.I.C.S.: 541512

Subsidiary (Domestic):

Computational Research Laboratories Limited (2)
3rd floor Taco House Damle Path Off Law College Road, Near Indsearch Building, Pune, 411004, India
Tel.: (91) 20 6620 9861
Web Site: http://www.crlindia.com
Information Technology Consulting Services
N.A.I.C.S.: 541512
Seetha Rama Krishna *(Head-Ops)*

Subsidiary (Non-US):

Diligenta Limited (2)
Lynch Wood Park, Peterborough, PE2 6FY, United Kingdom
Tel.: (44) 8458826747
Web Site: http://www.diligenta.co.uk
Sales Range: $200-249.9 Million
Emp.: 1,000
Business Process Outsourcing Consulting Services
N.A.I.C.S.: 541611
Shalini Pandita *(Dir-Governance)*

TATASOLUTION CENTER S.A (2)
Francisco Salazar E10-61, Quito, Pichincha, Ecuador
Tel.: (593) 22902888
Business Process Outsourcing Services
N.A.I.C.S.: 561499

TCS Uruguay S. A. (2)
Ruta 8 Km17 500 600 Building Zonamerica, 91600, Montevideo, Uruguay
Tel.: (598) 2 518 5600
Information Technology Consulting Services
N.A.I.C.S.: 541512

Subsidiary (US):

TCS e-Serve America, Inc. (2)
4270 Ivy Pointe Blvd, Cincinnati, OH 45245
Tel.: (513) 553-8300
Business Process Outsourcing Services
N.A.I.C.S.: 561499
George Verghese *(Gen Mgr)*

Tata America International Corporation (2)
101 Park Ave 26th Fl, New York, NY 10178
Tel.: (212) 557-8038
Web Site: http://www.tcs.com
Sales Range: $25-49.9 Million
Emp.: 50
Information Technology & Business Process Outsourcing Consulting Services
N.A.I.C.S.: 541611

Unit (Domestic):

TCS America (3)
2825 Palmer St, Missoula, MT 59808
Tel.: (952) 921-3974
Rev.: $10,000,000
Emp.: 12
Information Technology & Business Process Outsourcing Consultancy Services
N.A.I.C.S.: 541611

Subsidiary (Non-US):

Tata Consultancy Services (Philippines) Inc. (2)
10th floor Ascendas Accralaw Tower 2nd Ave Corner 30th St E-Square, Crescent Park West Bonifacio, Taguig, Philippines
Tel.: (63) 2 667 8000
Information Technology Consulting Services
N.A.I.C.S.: 541512
Virgilio Calapatan *(Mgr-IT-Delivery)*

Tata Consultancy Services (South Africa) (PTY) Ltd. (2)
Regus Century City First Floor Foyer 3 Colosseum Building Century Wall, Century City, Cape Town, South Africa
Tel.: (27) 21 659 4848
Information Technology Consulting Services
N.A.I.C.S.: 541512

Tata Consultancy Services Argentina S.A. (2)
Uspallata 3046 - Parque Patricios, C1437JCJ, Buenos Aires, Argentina
Tel.: (54) 11 5091 6000
Web Site: http://www.tcs.com
Information Technology Consulting Services
N.A.I.C.S.: 541512

Tata Consultancy Services Asia Pacific Pte Ltd. (2)
60 Anson Road 18-01 Mapletree Anson, Singapore, 079914, Singapore
Tel.: (65) 6372 4822
Web Site: http://www.tcs.com
Information Technology Consulting Services
N.A.I.C.S.: 541512
Girish S. *(Dir-HR)*

Subsidiary (Non-US):

PT Tata Consultancy Services Indonesia (3)
Level 16-F Menara Prima Building Jl Lingkar Mega Kuningan Block 6 2, Jakarta, 12950, Indonesia
Tel.: (62) 21 5794 7951
Business Process Outsourcing Services
N.A.I.C.S.: 561499

Tata Consultancy Services (China) Co., Ltd. (3)
Tower D 3rd Block Zhongguancun Software Park Building 8, Dongbeiwang West Road Haidian, Beijing, 100094, China
Tel.: (86) 10 58950000
Business Process Outsourcing Services
N.A.I.C.S.: 561499

Tata Consultancy Services (Thailand) Limited (3)
32/46 18th Floor Unit B2 Sino -Thai Tower Sukhumvit 21 Road, Soi Asoke Klongtoey Wattana, Bangkok, 10110, Thailand
Tel.: (66) 2259 5878
Web Site: http://www.tcs.com
Emp.: 40
Financial Management Services
N.A.I.C.S.: 523999
Rajesh Singh *(Country Mgr)*

Tata Consultancy Services Malaysia Sdn Bhd (3)
Level 21 Suite 21-16 G Tower No 199 Jalan Tun Razak, Kuala Lumpur, 50400, Malaysia
Tel.: (60) 3 2171 1031

TATA SONS LIMITED

Tata Sons Limited—(Continued)
Information Technology Consulting Services
N.A.I.C.S.: 541512
Narendra Redkar *(Program Dir)*

Subsidiary (Non-US):

Tata Consultancy Services Belgium S.A. (2)
Lenneke Marelaan 4, 1932, Saint-Stevens-Woluwe, Belgium
Tel.: (32) 2 2821920
Web Site: http://www.tcs.com
Information Technology Consulting Services
N.A.I.C.S.: 541512

Tata Consultancy Services Chile S.A (2)
Curico 18 Piso 3, Santiago, Chile
Tel.: (56) 2 250 5500
Information Technology Consulting Services
N.A.I.C.S.: 541512
Teresa Valeta *(CFO)*

Tata Consultancy Services De Mexico S.A., De C.V (2)
Insurgentes Sur No 664 Piso 2, Federal, Mexico, 03100, Mexico
Tel.: (52) 5591578282
Information Technology Consulting Services
N.A.I.C.S.: 541512

Tata Consultancy Services Deutschland GmbH (2)
Friedrich-Ebert-Anlage 49, 60308, Frankfurt, Germany
Tel.: (49) 69787020
Web Site: http://www.tcs.com
Sales Range: $25-49.9 Million
Emp.: 50
Information Technology & Business Process Outsourcing Consulting Services
N.A.I.C.S.: 541611
Sapthagiri Chapalapalli *(Dir-Central Europe)*

Tata Consultancy Services Do Brasil Ltda (2)
Avenida Aruana 70 Tambore, Barueri, 06460-010, Sao Paulo, Brazil
Tel.: (55) 11 3306 7000
Information Technology Consulting Services
N.A.I.C.S.: 541512

Tata Consultancy Services Japan Ltd (2)
4-1-4 Shibakoen, Minato, Tokyo, 105-8551, Japan (66%)
Tel.: (81) 3 6736 7000
Information Technology Consulting Services
N.A.I.C.S.: 541512

Tata Consultancy Services Netherlands BV (2)
Symphony Offices 20th Floor Gustav Mahlerplein 85-91, Amsterdam, 1082 MS, Netherlands
Tel.: (31) 20 715 5400
Information Technology Consulting Services
N.A.I.C.S.: 541512

Subsidiary (Non-US):

TCS Italia SRL (3)
Via Castagna 3 trav 1, Casoria, Italy
Tel.: (39) 0823 1684637
Web Site: http://www.tcsitalia.com
Information Technology Consulting Services
N.A.I.C.S.: 541512

Tata Consultancy Services De Espana S.A. (3)
Ps Castellana 135, Madrid, 28046, Spain
Tel.: (34) 91 310 6570
Information Technology Consulting Services
N.A.I.C.S.: 541512

Tata Consultancy Services France SAS (3)
ServicesTour Franklin 19th floor - La Defense 8, 100-101 Quartier Boieldieu, 2800, Puteaux, France
Tel.: (33) 1 77 68 30 30
Information Technology Consulting Services
N.A.I.C.S.: 541512
John Gaynor *(Program Mgr)*

Tata Consultancy Services Luxembourg S.A. (3)
89 Rue Pafebruch, 8308, Mamer, Luxembourg
Tel.: (352) 26 101 1
Information Technology Consulting Services
N.A.I.C.S.: 541512

Tata Consultancy Services Portugal Unipessoal Limitada (3)
Edificio Atlas IV Av Jose Gomes Ferreira 15 Piso 7- U, Miraflores, 1495-139, Alges, Portugal
Tel.: (351) 21 4122710
Web Site: http://www.tcs.com
Emp.: 15
Information Technology Consulting Services
N.A.I.C.S.: 541512
Ana Almeida *(Country Mgr)*

Tata Consultancy Services Switzerland Ltd. (3)
Regus Business Center Terre Bonne Route de Crassier 7 Eysins, 1262, Nyon, Switzerland
Tel.: (41) 22 595 67 67
Information Technology Consulting Services
N.A.I.C.S.: 541512

Subsidiary (Non-US):

Tata Consultancy Services Sverige AB (2)
Master Samuelsgatan 42, 111 57, Stockholm, Sweden
Tel.: (46) 8 503 88 400
Web Site: http://www.tcs.com
Information Technology Consulting Services
N.A.I.C.S.: 541512

Subsidiary (Domestic):

WTI Advanced Technology Limited (2)
98 Peters Road, Chennai, 600 086, India
Tel.: (91) 44 2835 0442
Web Site: http://www.wtiatl.com
Information Technology Consulting Services
N.A.I.C.S.: 541512
F. C. Kohli *(Chm)*

Tata Consumer Products Limited (1)
1 Bishop Lefroy Road, Kolkata, 700 020, India
Tel.: (91) 3322813891
Web Site: https://www.tataconsumer.com
Rev.: $1,600,245,465
Assets: $2,764,926,255
Liabilities: $631,835,295
Net Worth: $2,133,090,960
Earnings: $127,007,790
Emp.: 2,852
Fiscal Year-end: 03/31/2021
Tea & Coffee Mfr
N.A.I.C.S.: 311920
L. Krishnakumar *(CFO)*

Subsidiary (US):

Good Earth Teas, Inc. (2)
831 Almar Ave, Santa Cruz, CA 95060
Tel.: (831) 423-7913
Sales Range: $1-9.9 Million
Emp.: 70
Tea Mfr
N.A.I.C.S.: 311920

Subsidiary (Non-US):

Joekels Tea Packers (Proprietary) Ltd (2)
23-33 Hagart Road, PO Box 10455, Pinetown, 3610, South Africa
Tel.: (27) 31 709 1409
Web Site: http://www.joekels.co.za
Tea & Coffee Product Mfr
N.A.I.C.S.: 311920
Joe Swart *(Co-Founder)*

Subsidiary (Domestic):

Tata Coffee (2)
57 Railway Parallel Road, Kumara Park West, Bengaluru, 560 020, India
Tel.: (91) 8023560695
Web Site: http://www.tatacoffee.com
Sales Range: $25-49.9 Million
Emp.: 100
Coffee Mfr.
N.A.I.C.S.: 311920
Harish Bhat *(Chm)*

Subsidiary (US):

Eight O'Clock Coffee (3)
155 Chestnut Rdg, Montvale, NJ 07645
Tel.: (201) 571-0300
Web Site: http://www.eightoclock.com
Sales Range: $25-49.9 Million
Coffee Mfr
N.A.I.C.S.: 311920
David Allen *(VP-Mktg)*

Branch (Non-US):

Tata Global Beverages (2)
325 Oldfield Lane North, Greenford, UB6 0AZ, Middlesex, United Kingdom
Tel.: (44) 2083384000
Web Site: http://www.tataglobalbeverages.com
Sales Range: $450-499.9 Million
Emp.: 200
Tea Processor & Distr
N.A.I.C.S.: 311920
Ajoy K. Misra *(CEO & Mng Dir)*

Subsidiary (US):

Southern Tea LLC (3)
1267 Cobb Industrial Dr, Marietta, GA 30066-6616
Tel.: (770) 428-5555
Sales Range: $25-49.9 Million
Emp.: 200
Mfr of Tea Bags
N.A.I.C.S.: 311920
Sandy Milton *(Dir-HR)*

Tetley USA Inc. (3)
155 Chestnutridge Rd Fl 2, Montvale, NJ 07645
Tel.: (203) 929-9200
Web Site: http://www.tetleyusa.com
Sales Range: $25-49.9 Million
Emp.: 100
Producer & Retailer of Tea
N.A.I.C.S.: 311920

Subsidiary (Non-US):

Tata Global Beverages Australia Pty Ltd (2)
Level 2 620 Church Street, Richmond, 3121, VIC, Australia
Tel.: (61) 3 9825 3300
Tea & Coffee Product Distr
N.A.I.C.S.: 424490
L. Krishna Kumar *(CFO)*

Tata Global Beverages Canada Inc (2)
10 Carlson Court Suite 700, Etobicoke, M9W 6L2, ON, Canada
Tel.: (416) 798-1224
Web Site: http://www.tataglobalbeverages.com
Emp.: 15
Tea & Coffee Product Distr
N.A.I.C.S.: 424490
Steve Rice *(Pres)*

Tata Global Beverages GB Ltd (2)
Durham Lane Industrial Park, Eaglescliffe, Stockton-on-Tees, TS16 0RB, United Kingdom
Tel.: (44) 1642 705000
Web Site: http://www.tgbl.com
Emp.: 500
Tea & Coffee Product Distr
N.A.I.C.S.: 424490

Tata Global Beverages Polska sp.zo.o (2)
UL Zolny 33, 02-815, Warsaw, Poland
Tel.: (48) 22 546 9000
Tea & Coffee Product Distr
N.A.I.C.S.: 424490

Teapigs Ltd (2)
1 The Old Pumping Station Pump Alley, Brentford, TW8 0AP, United Kingdom
Tel.: (44) 203 141 8495
Web Site: http://www.teapigs.co.uk
Emp.: 18
Tea Whslr
N.A.I.C.S.: 424490
Valerie Corrigall *(Head-Intl Sls & Dev)*

Tata Inc. (1)
101 Park Ave Rm 2603, New York, NY 10178-2604

INTERNATIONAL PUBLIC

Tel.: (212) 213-5553
Web Site: http://www.tatasteel.com
Sales Range: $50-74.9 Million
Emp.: 10
Distribution of Iron & Steel Products
N.A.I.C.S.: 423510
B. Muthuraman *(Mng Dir)*

Tata Industrial Services Limited (1)
Shailendra Technopark 3rd floor Front Wing 1st Stage, Whitefield, Bengaluru, 560 066, India
Tel.: (91) 80 67160000
Web Site: http://www.tisl.in
Supply Chain Management Services
N.A.I.C.S.: 541614

Tata Interactive Systems Limited (1)
Leela Business Park Andheri-Kurla Road, Andheri E, Mumbai, 400 059, India
Tel.: (91) 22 6643 8000
Web Site: http://www.tatainteractive.com
Information Technology Consulting Services
N.A.I.C.S.: 541512
Rajesh Jumani *(Exec VP)*

Tata International Limited (1)
7th Floor Trent House G-Block Bandra Kurla Complex, Bandra E, Mumbai, 400 051, India
Tel.: (91) 22 66652200
Web Site: http://www.tatainternational.com
Emp.: 10,000
Steel Product Mfr & Distr
N.A.I.C.S.: 331513
Noel N. Tata *(Mng Dir)*

Subsidiary (Non-US):

Blackwood Hodge (Zimbabwe) Private Limited (2)
Stand 4917 Corner Hobbs Road & Simon Mazorodze Road Southerton, PO Box 1978, Harare, Zimbabwe
Tel.: (263) 4 620 951 3
Automobile Parts Distr
N.A.I.C.S.: 423120

TSI (NA) Limited (2)
Ave Morones Prieto 2805 Pt Edificio Torre GIA 2do Piso, Monterrey, 64710, Mexico
Tel.: (52) 81 83990096
Commercial & Industrial Vehicle Distr
N.A.I.C.S.: 423110

Tata Africa (Senegal) SARL (2)
Villa No 9434 Bis Sacre Coeur - 3 VDN, BP 16612, Dakar, Senegal
Tel.: (221) 33 867 36 46
Motor Vehicle Whslr
N.A.I.C.S.: 423110

Tata Africa Holdings (Ghana) Limited (2)
Plot no IND/A/71/15 New Industrial Layout, Kpone, Tema, Ghana
Tel.: (233) 54 4335046
Web Site: http://www.tatamotors.com.gh
Holding Company
N.A.I.C.S.: 551112
Udaysingh Ingle *(Mgr-Healthcare Div)*

Tata Africa Holdings (Kenya) Limited (2)
Tata Africa House Mombassa Road, Nairobi, Kenya
Tel.: (254) 20 260 3428
Holding Company
N.A.I.C.S.: 551112
Chandrajit Gupta *(Head-Sls & Mktg)*

Tata Africa Holdings (Tanzania) Limited (2)
Plot No 1 and 2 Vingunguti Industrial Area Nyerere Road, PO Box 40207, Dar es Salaam, Tanzania
Tel.: (255) 22 2865 177
Web Site: http://www.tatainternational.com
Holding Company
N.A.I.C.S.: 551112
Suraj Rao *(Controller-Fin)*

Tata Africa Services (Nigeria) Limited (2)
Plot C89 Amuwo Odofin Industrial Layout Apapa Oshodi Expressway, Lagos, Nigeria
Tel.: (234) 800 3560 8188
Web Site: http://www.tata-nigeria.com
Motor Vehicle Whslr
N.A.I.C.S.: 423110

AND PRIVATE COMPANIES   TATA SONS LIMITED

Dominic Kiki Ebube *(Head-HR & Admin)*

Tata Holdings Mocambique Limitada (2)
Avenue De Mozambique no 235, Maputo, Mozambique
Tel.: (258) 21 275 000
Metal Product Distr
N.A.I.C.S.: 423510

Tata International AG (2)
Gotthardstrasse 3, 6300, Zug, Switzerland
Tel.: (41) 41 710 0141
Information Technology Consulting Services
N.A.I.C.S.: 541512

Tata International Metals (Asia) Limited (2)
Unit 2106-10 Devon House 979 King's Road, Quarry Bay, China (Hong Kong)
Tel.: (852) 22725401
Metal Product Distr
N.A.I.C.S.: 423510

Tata International Singapore PTE Limited (2)
22 Tanjong Kling Road, Singapore, Singapore
Tel.: (65) 66605503
Metal Product Distr
N.A.I.C.S.: 423510

Tata International Trading Brazil Limitada (2)
Av Brigadeiro Faria Lima 1685 cj 5J, Pinheiros, 01452, Sao Paulo, Brazil
Tel.: (55) 847 5852564
Metal Product Distr
N.A.I.C.S.: 423510

Tata South-East Asia (Cambodia) Limited (2)
77-E2 iCon Professional Bldg 216 Norodom Blvd Sangkat Tonle Bassac, Khan Chamkarmorn, Phnom Penh, Cambodia
Tel.: (855) 23 432 250
Metal Product Distr
N.A.I.C.S.: 423510

Tata South-East Asia Ltd (2)
Shanghai Rep Room 2506 K Wah Centre 1010 Huai Hai Road, Xuhui 200 03, Shanghai, China
Tel.: (86) 21 54051616
Metal Product Distr
N.A.I.C.S.: 423510

Tata Uganda Limited (2)
Plot 52 Lugogo By Pass Road Lugogo, Kampala, 7153, Uganda
Tel.: (256) 754777704
Web Site: http://www.tatauganda.com
Automotive Distr
N.A.I.C.S.: 423110
Ruchir Bhatnagar *(Gen Mgr)*

Tata West Asia FZE (2)
ZB07 R/A 08 Blue Shed Area Jebel Ali Free Zone, PO Box 16980, Dubai, United Arab Emirates
Tel.: (971) 4 8837967
Steel Product Distr
N.A.I.C.S.: 423510

Tata Zambia Limited (2)
Plot 3025 Airport Road, 71516, Ndola, Zambia
Tel.: (260) 212 610377
Automotive Distr
N.A.I.C.S.: 423110

Tata International Metals Americas (1)
111 SW Columbia St Suite 725, Portland, OR 97201
Tel.: (503) 222-2102
Web Site: http://totemsteel.com
Rev.: $6,900,000
Emp.: 115
Trading & Distribution of Flat Rolled Steel & Forestry Products
N.A.I.C.S.: 331221
James L. Kotchik *(CFO & Exec VP)*

Tata Investment Corporation Limited (1)
Elphinstone Building 2nd Floor 10 Nariman Road, Mumbai, 400 001, India
Tel.: (91) 2266657186

Web Site: https://www.tatainvestment.com
Rev.: $34,670,904
Assets: $2,865,145,429
Liabilities: $179,130,110
Net Worth: $2,686,015,318
Earnings: $29,274,691
Emp.: 22
Fiscal Year-end: 03/31/2022
Financial Management Services
N.A.I.C.S.: 523999
N. N. Tata *(Chm)*

Tata Limited (1)
18 Grosvenor Place, London, SW 1X 7HS, United Kingdom
Tel.: (44) 2072358281
Web Site: http://www.tata.com.uk
Sales Range: $25-49.9 Million
Emp.: 21
Holding Company
N.A.I.C.S.: 551112
Alexander Ehmann *(Head-Pub Affairs)*

Tata Quality Management Services (1)
TMTC Campus 1 Mangaldas Road, Pune, 411 001, India
Tel.: (91) 20 65238076
Web Site: http://www.tataquality.com
Business Management & Training Services
N.A.I.C.S.: 561499
Prasad R. Menon *(Chm)*

Tata Realty and Infrastructure Limited (1)
Elphinstone Building 2nd floor 10 Veer Nariman Road, Fort, Mumbai, 400 001, India
Tel.: (91) 22 6629 4000
Web Site: http://www.tata-realty.com
Construction Engineering Services
N.A.I.C.S.: 541330

Tata Steel Limited (1)
Tel.: (91) 8001088282
Web Site: https://www.tatasteel.com
Rev.: $29,301,621,006
Assets: $34,532,910,497
Liabilities: $21,922,730,052
Net Worth: $12,610,180,445
Earnings: $968,209,340
Emp.: 36,151
Fiscal Year-end: 03/31/2023
Steel Products Mfr
N.A.I.C.S.: 331221
Natarajan Chandrasekaran *(Chm)*

Subsidiary (Domestic):

Hooghly Met Coke & Power Co. Ltd. (2)
16th floor Tata Centre 43 Jawarharlal Nehru Road, Kolkata, 700 071, India
Tel.: (91) 33 2288 5463
Metallurgical Coke Distr
N.A.I.C.S.: 423520

Jamshedpur Utilities & Services Company Limited (2)
Sakchi Boulevard Road, Northern Town Bistupur, Jamshedpur, 831 001, Jharkhand, India
Tel.: (91) 657 6646000
Web Site: http://www.juscoltd.com
Construction Engineering Services
N.A.I.C.S.: 541330
Ashish Mathur *(Mng Dir)*

Rohit Ferro-Tech Limited (2)
132A S P Mukherjee Road, Kolkata, 700 026, India
Tel.: (91) 3322119805
Web Site: https://www.rohitferrotech.com
Rev.: $86,860,533
Assets: $155,051,619
Liabilities: $434,220,614
Net Worth: ($279,168,995)
Earnings: ($9,468,213)
Emp.: 379
Fiscal Year-end: 03/31/2021
Ferro Alloy Mfr
N.A.I.C.S.: 331110

T S Alloys Limited (2)
N3/24 IRC Village Nayapalli, Bhubaneswar, Odisha, India
Tel.: (91) 92 38 106222
Web Site: http://www.tsalloys.com
Ferro Alloy Mfr
N.A.I.C.S.: 331110
Rajeev Singhal *(Chm)*

Affiliate (Domestic):

Tata Ryerson Ltd. (2)
43 Chowringhee Rd Tata Ctr Bldg, Kolkata, 700 071, India
Tel.: (91) 3366130600
Web Site: http://www.tataryerson.com
Sales Range: $25-49.9 Million
Emp.: 35
Metal Fabrication, Processing & Distr
N.A.I.C.S.: 332999
Sandipan Chakravortty *(Mng Dir)*

Subsidiary (Non-US):

Tata Steel (Thailand) Public Co., Ltd. (2)
Rasa Tower 2 20th Floor 555 Phaholyothin Road, Chatuchak, Bangkok, 10900, Thailand
Tel.: (66) 29371000
Web Site: http://www.tatasteelthailand.com
Rev.: $678,953,765
Assets: $420,684,555
Liabilities: $73,594,688
Net Worth: $347,089,866
Earnings: $2,648,338
Emp.: 1,081
Fiscal Year-end: 03/31/2024
Metal Products Mfr & Distr
N.A.I.C.S.: 331221
Rajiv Mangal *(Bd of Dirs, Pres & CEO)*

Subsidiary (Domestic):

Tata Steel BSL Ltd. (2)
Ground Floor Mira Corporate Suites Plot No 1 and 2 Ishwar Nagar, Mathura Road, New Delhi, 110065, India **(72.65%)**
Tel.: (91) 11 3919 4000
Web Site: http://www.tatasteelbsl.co.in
Rev.: $2,936,155,049
Assets: $5,066,299,111
Liabilities: $2,199,227,285
Net Worth: $2,867,071,826
Earnings: $343,729,632
Emp.: 5,707
Fiscal Year-end: 03/31/2021
Steel Tube Mfr
N.A.I.C.S.: 331221
Davra O. P. *(Co-Sec)*

Subsidiary (Non-US):

Bowen Energy Ltd. (3)
Level 7 10 Barrack Street, Sydney, 2000, NSW, Australia
Tel.: (61) 292767766
Coal & Mineral Exploration & Development
N.A.I.C.S.: 423520

Subsidiary (Non-US):

Tata Steel Europe Limited (2)
30 Millbank, London, SW1P 4WY, United Kingdom
Tel.: (44) 20 7717 4444
Web Site: http://www.tatasteeleurope.com
Holding Company; Regional Managing Office
N.A.I.C.S.: 551112
N. K. Misra *(Exec Dir-Fin)*

Subsidiary (Non-US):

Blume Stahlservice GmbH (3)
Umschlag 10, 45478, Mulheim an der Ruhr, Germany
Tel.: (49) 208 58003 0
Web Site: http://www.blume-stahlservice.de
Rolled Steel Mfr
N.A.I.C.S.: 331221
Holger Lisiecki *(Mgr-Depot)*

Blume Stahlservice Polska Sp.Z.O.O (3)
ul Grota Roweckiego 155, 41-214, Sosnowiec, Poland
Tel.: (48) 32 294 84 47
Rolled Steel Mfr
N.A.I.C.S.: 331221

Catnic GmbH (3)
Am Leitzelbach 16, 74889, Sinsheim, Germany
Tel.: (49) 7261 9297 0
Web Site: http://www.catnic.de
Emp.: 20
Building Materials Mfr
N.A.I.C.S.: 339999

Cbs Investissements SAS (3)
14 av Saria, 77700, Serris, France
Tel.: (33) 1 60 43 57 10
Steel Products Mfr
N.A.I.C.S.: 331513

Subsidiary (Domestic):

Cogent Power Ltd. (3)
Stephenson Street, PO Box 30, Newport, NP19 0RB, United Kingdom
Tel.: (44) 1633290033
Web Site: http://www.cogent-power.com
Sales Range: $100-124.9 Million
Emp.: 450
Electrometallurgical Product Mfr
N.A.I.C.S.: 331110

Subsidiary (Non-US):

Cogent Power, Inc. (4)
845 Laurentian Drive, Burlington, L7N 3W7, ON, Canada
Tel.: (905) 637-3033
Web Site: https://jfeshojipower.com
Rev.: $21,234,400
Emp.: 225
Electrometallurgical Product Mfr
N.A.I.C.S.: 331110

Subsidiary (Domestic):

Orb Electrical Steels Ltd (4)
Stephenson Street, PO Box 30, Newport, NP19 0RB, United Kingdom
Tel.: (44) 1633290033
Web Site: http://www.cogent-power.com
Sales Range: $75-99.9 Million
Emp.: 400
Electrical Steel Mfr
N.A.I.C.S.: 331210

Subsidiary (Non-US):

Surahammars Bruks AB (4)
Elektroplatvagen, PO Box 201, 735 351, Surahammar, Sweden
Tel.: (46) 22034671
Web Site: http://www.sura.se
Sales Range: $25-49.9 Million
Emp.: 170
Electrical Steel Mfr
N.A.I.C.S.: 331210
Mark Cichuta *(Mng Dir)*

Subsidiary (Domestic):

Color Steels Limited (3)
Corus Colorsteels North Blackvein Industrial Estat, Newport, NP11 7YD, Gwent, United Kingdom
Tel.: (44) 1495 279 100
Steel Sheet Mfr
N.A.I.C.S.: 331221

Subsidiary (Non-US):

Corus Building Systems Bulgaria AD (3)
1 Grivishko shose str, Pleven, 5800, Bulgaria
Tel.: (359) 64 822772
Web Site: http://www.corusbsb.bg
Steel Products Mfr
N.A.I.C.S.: 331513

Corus Building Systems SAS (3)
Batiment Saria B Serris, Serris, 77700, Seine Et Marne, France
Tel.: (33) 160435710
Web Site: http://www.kalzip.com
Emp.: 4
Steel Products Mfr
N.A.I.C.S.: 331513

Subsidiary (Domestic):

Corus Group Limited (3)
30 Millbank, London, SW1P 4WY, United Kingdom
Tel.: (44) 2077174444
Web Site: http://www.corusgroup.com
Holding Company; Metal Products Mfr & Distr
N.A.I.C.S.: 551112

Subsidiary (Non-US):

Degels GmbH (3)
Konigsberger Strasse 25, 41460, Neuss, Germany

TATA SONS LIMITED

Tata Sons Limited—(Continued)
Tel.: (49) 2131 74950 0
Web Site: http://www.degels.de
Steel Products Mfr
N.A.I.C.S.: 331513

Subsidiary (Domestic):

Dsrm Group Plc (3)
9 Whessoe Road, Darlington, DL3 0QP,
Durham, United Kingdom
Tel.: (44) 1325 380 014
Steel Products Mfr
N.A.I.C.S.: 331513

Subsidiary (Non-US):

Fischer Profil GmbH (3)
Waldstrasse 67, 57250, Netphen, Germany
Tel.: (49) 27 37 5 08 0
Web Site: http://www.fischerprofil.com
Sheet Metal Mfr
N.A.I.C.S.: 332322

Hille & Muller GmbH (3)
AM Tripplesbert 48, 40589, Dusseldorf,
Germany
Tel.: (49) 211 7950 471
Web Site: http://www.corusgroup.com
Sales Range: $100-124.9 Million
Emp.: 450
Steel Processing
N.A.I.C.S.: 331110

Layde Steel S.L. (3)
B Eguzkitza 11 Ctra Durango-Elorrio Km 1,
48200, Durango, Biscay, Spain
Tel.: (34) 94 621 78 50
Web Site: http://www.layde.es
Steel Products Mfr
N.A.I.C.S.: 331513
Ramon Uria (Mgr-Fin)

Montana Bausysteme AG (3)
Durisolstrasse 11, 5612, Villmergen, Switzerland
Tel.: (41) 56 619 8585
Web Site: http://www.montana-ag.ch
Metal Building Components Mfr
N.A.I.C.S.: 332311
Marcel Kamm (Mng Dir)

NatSteel (Xiamen) Ltd. (3)
Haicang Port Industrial Zone Built Road,
Xiamen, 361026, Fujiang, China
Tel.: (86) 592 6082602
Web Site: http://www.natsteelxiamen.com.cn
Steel Products Mfr
N.A.I.C.S.: 331513

NatSteel Australia Pty. Ltd. (3)
Nexus Industry Park Building 2 43-47 Lyn
Parade, Preston, 2170, NSW, Australia
Tel.: (61) 2 9607 1555
Web Site: http://www.natsteel.com.au
Emp.: 3,500
Steel Bar Mfr & Distr
N.A.I.C.S.: 331221
Lonesh Govind (Mgr-Production)

Joint Venture (Non-US):

Norsk Staal Tynnplater AS (3)
Harborveien 60, Fredrikstad,
Norway (50%)
Tel.: (47) 69358400
Web Site: http://www.tynnplater.com
Steel Sheets, Plates & Stainless Steel
Products Distr
N.A.I.C.S.: 423510

Subsidiary (Non-US):

S A B Profil GmbH (3)
Industriestrasse 13, 36272, Niederaula,
Germany
Tel.: (49) 6625 9218 0
Web Site: http://www.sabprofil.de
Emp.: 34
Roofing Product Whslr
N.A.I.C.S.: 423330

SIA Corus Building Systems (3)
Darzciema iela 60, Riga, 1073, Latvia
Tel.: (371) 671 38 858
Iron & Steel Product Distr
N.A.I.C.S.: 423390

Service Center Gelsenkirchen GmbH (3)
Grimbergstrasse 75, 45889, Gelsenkirchen,
Germany
Tel.: (49) 209 98460
Steel Products Whslr
N.A.I.C.S.: 423510

Societe Europeenne De Galvanisation (Segal) Sa (3)
50 Chaussee de Ramioul, 4400, Ivoz-Ramet, Belgium
Tel.: (32) 4 273 73 83
Web Site: http://www.segal.be
Steel Products Mfr
N.A.I.C.S.: 331110

Surahammar Bruks AB (3)
Elektroplatvagen, 735 31, Surahammar,
Sweden
Tel.: (46) 220 34500
Web Site: http://www.sura.se
Emp.: 125
Steel Products Mfr
N.A.I.C.S.: 332322
Mark Cichuta (Mng Dir)

Tata Steel (KZN) (Pty) Ltd (3)
Bronze Bar, PO Box 9690, Alton North,
Richards Bay, 3900, South Africa
Tel.: (27) 35 788 0710
Metal Product Distr
N.A.I.C.S.: 423510

Tata Steel Asia (Hong Kong) Ltd. (3)
Units 6-8 25th Floor Enterprise Square Two
3 SheungYuet Road, Kowloon Bay, Kowloon, China (Hong Kong)
Tel.: (852) 27070273
Steel Products Mfr
N.A.I.C.S.: 331513

Tata Steel Belgium Packaging Steels N.V. (3)
Walemstraat 38 Duffel, Antwerp, 2570, Belgium
Tel.: (32) 15745020
Emp.: 36
Steel Products Mfr
N.A.I.C.S.: 331513
Chris Western (Gen Mgr)

Tata Steel Belgium Services N.V. (3)
Coremansstraat 34, 2600, Berchem, Belgium
Tel.: (32) 3 280 80 20
Web Site: http://www.tatasteeleurope.com
Steel Products Mfr
N.A.I.C.S.: 331513

Tata Steel Denmark Byggsystemer A/S (3)
Kaarsbergvej 2, Syddjurs, 8400, Ebeltoft,
Denmark
Tel.: (45) 89532000
Steel Products Mfr
N.A.I.C.S.: 331513

Tata Steel France Batiment et Systemes SAS (3)
Rue Geo Lufbery, BP 103, Chauny, 02300,
France
Tel.: (33) 323406666
Emp.: 40
Steel Products Mfr
N.A.I.C.S.: 331513
Laurent Stehly (Gen Mgr)

Tata Steel France Rail SA (3)
3 Allee des Barbanniers, 92632, Gennevilliers, Cedex, France
Tel.: (33) 141473329
Web Site: http://www.tatasteelrail.com
Steel Product Distr
N.A.I.C.S.: 423510
Gerre Glas (Mng Dir)

Tata Steel International (Benelux) BV (3)
Ankerkade 71, 6222NL, Maastricht, Netherlands
Tel.: (31) 43 4079 219
Emp.: 7
Steel Products Whslr
N.A.I.C.S.: 423510
Peter Galla (Head-Office)

Tata Steel International (Denmark) A/S (3)
Frederiksborgvej 23, 3520, Farum, Denmark
Tel.: (45) 39960900
Emp.: 5
Steel Products Whslr
N.A.I.C.S.: 423510

Tata Steel International (Finland) OY (3)
Hitsaajankatu 22, Uusimaa, Helsinki, 00810,
Finland
Tel.: (358) 94542450
Web Site: http://www.tatasteel.com
Emp.: 4
Steel Products Whslr
N.A.I.C.S.: 423510
Raimo Jarvela (Mng Dir)

Tata Steel International (Italia) S.r.l. (3)
Via Winckelmann No 2, Milan, 20146, Italy
Tel.: (39) 02 422 5541
Web Site: http://www.tatasteel.com
Sales Range: $25-49.9 Million
Emp.: 24
Metal Product Whslr
N.A.I.C.S.: 423510

Tata Steel International (Poland) sp Z.O.O. (3)
ul Piastowska 7, 40-005, Katowice, Poland
Tel.: (48) 32 6083510
Steel Products Whslr
N.A.I.C.S.: 423510

Tata Steel International (Sweden) AB (3)
Barlastgatan 2, Gothenburg, 414 63, Sweden
Tel.: (46) 317793200
Steel Products Whslr
N.A.I.C.S.: 423510
Johan Magelsen (Acct Mgr)

Tata Steel Istanbul Metal Sanayi ve Ticaret AS (3)
Hamli Beldesi Sakarya 1 Organize Sanayi
Bolgesi, Adapazari, Sakarya, 54060, Turkiye
Tel.: (90) 264 2914202
Steel Products Whslr
N.A.I.C.S.: 423510

Tata Steel Nederland B.V. (3)
Dudok Huis 3H-18 Wenckebachstraat 1,
1951 JZ, Velsen, Netherlands
Tel.: (31) 251499111
Web Site: http://www.tatasteel.nl
Sales Range: $1-4.9 Billion
Emp.: 10,000
Steel & Aluminum Mfr
N.A.I.C.S.: 331513
Karl-Ulrich Kohler (Grp CEO & Mng Dir)

Subsidiary (Domestic):

Corus Primary Aluminium B.V. (4)
Wenckebachstraat 1, Postbus 10000, 1970
CA, IJmuiden, Netherlands
Tel.: (31) 251 499108
Web Site: http://www.tatasteel.nl
Sales Range: $1-4.9 Billion
Emp.: 6,700
Aluminum Foundry
N.A.I.C.S.: 331524

Joint Venture (Domestic):

Danieli Corus Technical Services BV (4)
Rooswijkweg 291, Noord, 1951 ME, Velsen,
Netherlands
Tel.: (31) 251500500
Web Site: https://www.danieli-corus.com
Emp.: 250
Engineering Services
N.A.I.C.S.: 541330
Peter Zonneveld (Mng Dir)

Subsidiary (US):

Danieli Corus, Inc. (5)
8300 Mississippi Street, Merrillville, IN
46410
Tel.: (219) 650-5500
Web Site: http://www.danieli-corus.com
Metals Industry Equipment Mfr
N.A.I.C.S.: 541330

Subsidiary (Domestic):

Namascor B.V. (4)
Industrieterrein Moerdijk, 4782 PZ, Moer-

INTERNATIONAL PUBLIC

dijk, Netherlands
Tel.: (31) 168 393 400
Web Site: http://www.namascor.com
Hot-Rolled Steel Products Mfr & Distr
N.A.I.C.S.: 331221

S.A.B.-Profiel B.V. (4)
Produktieweg 2, 3401 MG, IJsselstein,
Netherlands
Tel.: (31) 306879700
Web Site: http://www.sabprofiel.com
Sales Range: $25-49.9 Million
Emp.: 100
Steel Building Systems Mfr
N.A.I.C.S.: 332311

Service Centre Maastricht B.V. (4)
Fregatweg 42, 6222 NZ, Maastricht, Netherlands
Tel.: (31) 43 368 8444
Web Site:
http://www.servicecentremaastricht.com
Emp.: 200
Metal Service Center & Fabrication Services
N.A.I.C.S.: 423510
Jens Lauber (Gen Mgr)

Tata Steel IJmuiden B.V. (4)
Wenckebachstraat 1, Postbus 10000,
IJmuiden, 1951, Netherlands
Tel.: (31) 251493186
Web Site: http://www.tatasteeleurope.com
Sales Range: $1-4.9 Billion
Emp.: 10,000
Cold-Rolled Packaging Steel Mfr
N.A.I.C.S.: 331221
Luc Brantjes (Comml Dir-Packaging)

Division (Domestic):

Tata Steel Strip Products IJmuiden (4)
Wenckebachstraat 1, Postbus 10000, NL
1970 CA, IJmuiden, Netherlands
Tel.: (31) 251496126
Web Site: http://www.tatasteel.com
Rolled & Coated Steel Strip Mfr
N.A.I.C.S.: 331221

Subsidiary (Non-US):

Tata Steel Netherlands Holdings B.V (3)
Wenckebachstraat 1, 1951 JZ, Velsen,
Netherlands
Tel.: (31) 251 499111
Holding Company
N.A.I.C.S.: 551112

Unit (Domestic):

Tata Steel Tubes Europe (3)
Weldon Road, PO Box 101, Corby, NN17
5UA, Northants, United Kingdom
Tel.: (44) 1536 402 121
Web Site: http://www.tatasteeleurope.com
Sales Range: $150-199.9 Million
Emp.: 500
Steel Tubing Mfr & Distr
N.A.I.C.S.: 331210
Remco Blaauw (Mng Dir)

Subsidiary (Non-US):

Tata Steel Nederland Tubes B.V. (4)
Souvereinstrat 27-35, 4903RH, Oosterhout, Netherlands
Tel.: (31) 162482000
Web Site: http://www.tatasteel.com
Sales Range: $75-99.9 Million
Emp.: 300
Steel Tube Mfr
N.A.I.C.S.: 331210

Plant (Domestic):

Tata Steel Nederland Tubes B.V. - Arnhem Plant (5)
Westervoortsedijk 65, Postbus 5030, 6827
AT, Arnhem, Netherlands
Tel.: (31) 263689111
Web Site: http://www.corustubes.com
Sales Range: $100-124.9 Million
Emp.: 250
Steel Precision Tubes Mfr
N.A.I.C.S.: 331210

Subsidiary (Domestic):

Tata Steel UK Limited (3)

AND PRIVATE COMPANIES

30 Millbank, London, SW1P 4WY, United Kingdom
Tel.: (44) 20 7717 4444
Web Site: http://www.tatasteel.com
Metal Products Mfr
N.A.I.C.S.: 332111
Karl Koehler *(Mng Dir)*

Unit (Domestic):

Tata Steel - Distribution UK & Ireland, Steelpark (4)
The Steelpark Steelpark Way, Wednesfield, Wolverhampton, WV11 3SR, W Midlands, United Kingdom
Tel.: (44) 1902 631 163
Web Site:
 http://www.tatasteelservicecentres.com
Emp.: 525
Steel Product Distr
N.A.I.C.S.: 423510
Paul Steele *(Gen Mgr)*

Subsidiary (US):

Tata Steel USA Inc. (3)
475 N Martingale Rd Ste 400, Schaumburg, IL 60173-2257
Tel.: (847) 619-0400
Web Site: http://www.tatasteelamericas.com
Holding Company; Metal Products Mfr & Distr
N.A.I.C.S.: 551112

Subsidiary (Domestic):

Apollo Metals, Ltd. (4)
1001 14th Ave, Bethlehem, PA 18018-0045
Tel.: (610) 867-5826
Steel Strip Electroplating Services
N.A.I.C.S.: 332813

Hille & Muller (U.S.A.), Inc (4)
Delaware Ave NW, Warren, OH 44485
Tel.: (330) 841-6262
Web Site: http://www.tatasteeleurope.com
Steel Products Mfr
N.A.I.C.S.: 331513

Oremco, Inc. (4)
60 E 42 St Ste 2028, New York, NY 10165
Tel.: (212) 867-4400
Sales Range: $25-49.9 Million
Emp.: 6
Coal Distr
N.A.I.C.S.: 541611
Michael Grim *(VP)*

Tata Steel International (Americas) Inc. (4)
475 N Martingale Rd, Schaumburg, IL 60173-2405
Tel.: (847) 619-0400
Web Site: http://www.tatasteelamericas.com
Sales Range: $250-299.9 Million
Metal Product Whslr
N.A.I.C.S.: 423510
Terrence Schaefer *(VP-Fin & IT)*

Thomas Steel Strip Corp. (4)
Delaware Ave NW, Warren, OH 44485
Tel.: (330) 841-6429
Sales Range: $150-199.9 Million
Emp.: 300
Electroplated Cold-Rolled Steel Strip Mfr
N.A.I.C.S.: 331221
William Boyd *(Gen Mgr-Plating-North America)*

Subsidiary (Non-US):

Trierer Walzwerk GmbH (3)
Bruhlstrasse 14-15, 54295, Trier, Germany
Tel.: (49) 651 203 0
Copper, Brass & Zinc-Plated Cold-Rolled Strip Products Mfr
N.A.I.C.S.: 331420

Unitol SAS (3)
1 rue Fernand Raynaud, ZA de l'Apport Paris, F-91814, Corbeil-Essonnes, Cedex, France
Tel.: (33) 1 6088 7777
Sales Range: $50-74.9 Million
Emp.: 130
Metals Service Center
N.A.I.C.S.: 423510

Subsidiary (Non-US):

Tata Steel Holdings Pte. Ltd. (2)

NatSteel Holdings 22 Tanjong Kling Road, Singapore, 628048, Singapore
Tel.: (65) 6265 1233
Holding Company
N.A.I.C.S.: 551112

Tata Steel International (Japan) Ltd. (2)
Burex Kojimachi 3-5-2 Kojimachi, Chiyoda-ku, Tokyo, 102-0083, Japan
Tel.: (81) 3 5215 0445
Web Site:
 http://www.tatasteelinternational.com
Metal Product Whslr
N.A.I.C.S.: 423510

Tata Steel Logistics & Shipping B.V. (2)
2E Rijksbinnenhaven 39, Postbus 512, 1951 JN, Velsen, Netherlands
Tel.: (31) 251495500
Web Site: http://www.nebam.nl
Sales Range: $25-49.9 Million
Emp.: 12
Freight Shipping Agency
N.A.I.C.S.: 488510

Subsidiary (Domestic):

Tinplate Company of India Ltd (2)
4 Bankshall Street, Kolkata, 700001, India (74.96%)
Tel.: (91) 3322435401
Web Site: http://www.tatatinplate.com
Rev.: $585,522,101
Assets: $270,373,685
Liabilities: $110,536,308
Net Worth: $159,837,378
Earnings: $48,172,679
Emp.: 1,388
Fiscal Year-end: 03/31/2022
Tin Mfr
N.A.I.C.S.: 331110
Koushik Chatterjee *(Chm)*

Joint Venture (Domestic):

mjunction Services Limited (2)
Godrej Waterside 3rd Floor Tower 1 Plot V Block DP Sector V, Salt Lake, Kolkata, 700091, India
Tel.: (91) 3366106100
Web Site: http://www.mjunction.in
Emp.: 900
Procurement & Selling Services
N.A.I.C.S.: 561499
Vinaya Varma *(CEO & Mng Dir)*

Tata Strategic Management Group (1)
B-1001 Marathon Futurex N M Joshi Marg Lower Parel E, Mumbai, 400013, India
Tel.: (91) 22 66376789
Web Site: http://www.tsmg.com
Business Management Consulting Services
N.A.I.C.S.: 541611

Tata Teleservices Limited (1)
A E & F Blocks Voltas Premises TB Kadam Marg, Chinchpokli, Mumbai, 400033, India
Tel.: (91) 22 66671414
Web Site: http://www.tataindicom.com
Telecommunication Servicesb
N.A.I.C.S.: 517112
Anuraag Srivastava *(CFO)*

Tayo Rolls Ltd. (1)
XLRI Campus Circuit House Area E, Jamshedpur, 831001, Jharkhand, India
Tel.: (91) 6572225643
Web Site: http://www.tayorolls.com
Sales Range: $200-249.9 Million
Emp.: 650
Mfr of Steel Ingot & Roll; Joint Venture of Sojitz Corporation & The Tata Group
N.A.I.C.S.: 331110
Suresh Padmanabhan *(Deputy CFO)*

The Indian Hotels Company Limited (1)
Mandlik House Mandlik Road, Mumbai, 400 001, Maharashtra, India
Tel.: (91) 2266395515
Web Site: http://www.tajhotels.com
Rev.: $438,353,370
Assets: $1,786,733,130
Liabilities: $741,790,140
Net Worth: $1,044,942,990
Earnings: ($36,168,405)
Emp.: 15,135

Fiscal Year-end: 03/31/2022
Hotels Owner & Operator
N.A.I.C.S.: 721110
Beejal Desai *(Sec & Sr VP-Corp Affairs)*

The Siam Industrial Wire Company Ltd. (1)
Rasa Tower 14th Floor 555 Phaholyothin Road, Bangkok, 10900, Chatuchak, Thailand
Tel.: (66) 2 9370060 67
Web Site: http://www.siw.co.th
Steel Products Mfr
N.A.I.C.S.: 331513
Pek Hoong Chong *(Mng Dir)*

Voltas Limited (1)
Voltas House A Block 4th Fl Dr Babasaheb Ambedkar Road, Chinchpokli, Mumbai, 400 033, India (100%)
Tel.: (91) 2266656666
Web Site: http://www.voltas.com
Sales Range: $350-399.9 Million
Emp.: 700
Engineering & Air-Conditioning Services
N.A.I.C.S.: 541330
V. P. Malhotra *(Sec & VP-Taxation & Legal)*

Subsidiary (Domestic):

Auto Aircon (India) Limited (2)
5/4 Nagar Road, Pune, 411 014, India
Tel.: (91) 20 27011665
Auto Parts & Equipment Mfr
N.A.I.C.S.: 336390

Rohini Industrial Electricals Limited (2)
Voltas Premises T B Kadam Marg, Chinchpokli, Mumbai, 400 033, India
Tel.: (91) 22 66481500
Web Site: http://www.rohinielectricals.com
Electrical Contracting Services
N.A.I.C.S.: 238210

Universal Comfort Products Limited (2)
277/4 School Falia Dadra Demni Road, Dadra, 396 191, India
Tel.: (91) 260 2668373
Air Conditioning System Mfr
N.A.I.C.S.: 333415

Subsidiary (Non-US):

Voltas Netherlands B.V (2)
Herikerbergweg 238 Luna ArenA, Zuidoost, 1101 CM, Amsterdam, Netherlands
Tel.: (31) 20 5755600
Air Conditioning System Mfr
N.A.I.C.S.: 333415

Voltas Oman LLC (2)
ORIS 3817-A Ground Floor Way No 4451 Behind Al Meera Hypermarket, PO Box 2263, Azaiba, Ruwi, 112, Oman
Tel.: (968) 24490521
Emp.: 400
Air Conditioning System Mfr
N.A.I.C.S.: 333415
Dilip K. Sharma *(Gen Mgr)*

Weathermaker Limited (2)
Jebel Ali Free Zone, PO Box 17127, Dubai, United Arab Emirates
Tel.: (971) 48816752
Web Site: http://www.weathermakeruae.com
Steel Duct Mfr
N.A.I.C.S.: 331110
Urmeez Nanda *(Gen Mgr)*

TATA STEEL LONG PRODUCTS LTD.

PO Joda Dist, Keonjhar, 758 034, Orissa, India
Tel.: (91) 676 727 8122
Web Site: http://www.tatasponge.com
Year Founded: 1982
TATASTLLP—(BOM)
Rev.: $659,042,475
Assets: $806,540,280
Liabilities: $452,441,535
Net Worth: $354,098,745
Earnings: $78,079,365
Emp.: 2,395
Fiscal Year-end: 03/31/21
Iron Mfr

TATE & LYLE PLC

N.A.I.C.S.: 331110
Partha Chattopadhyay *(COO-Sponge Bus)*

TATE & LYLE PLC

Mold Business Park Maes Gwern, Mold, CH7 1XW, Flintshire, United Kingdom
Tel.: (44) 1352705500 UK
Web Site:
 https://www.tateandlyle.com
Year Founded: 1859
TATE—(LSE)
Rev.: $2,173,166,100
Assets: $3,111,437,700
Liabilities: $1,634,528,700
Net Worth: $1,476,909,000
Earnings: $157,619,700
Fiscal Year-end: 03/31/23
Cane Sugar Refining; Molasses Trading; Animal Nutrition; Cereal Sweetener; Starch Production; Beet Sugar Processing, Sugar By-Products & Trading
N.A.I.C.S.: 311314
Rowan Adams *(Exec VP-Corp Affairs)*

Subsidiaries:

Charles E. Ford, Limited (1)
Avonmouth Old Dock, Bristol, BS11 9BE, Glos, United Kingdom
Tel.: (44) 1179825001
Sugar Refining
N.A.I.C.S.: 311314

Eastern Sugar BV (1)
Zwanebloem 31, 4823 MV, Breda, Netherlands
Tel.: (31) 765424994
Holding Company
N.A.I.C.S.: 551112

G.C. Hahn & Cie. S.A.R.L. (1)
Croissy III Bat 3 113 Chem De Ronde 7, 78290, Croissy-sur-Seine, France
Tel.: (33) 130150101
Food Products Ingredient Mfr
N.A.I.C.S.: 311999

G.C. Hahn & Co. Limited (1)
Mold Business Park Maes Gwern, Mold, CH7 1XW, Flintshire, United Kingdom
Tel.: (44) 1352 705500
Web Site: http://www.yoursfoodsystems.com
Sales Range: $25-49.9 Million
Emp.: 6
Food Ingredient Chemicals Mfr
N.A.I.C.S.: 325998

G.C. Hahn & Co. Stabilisierungstechnik GmbH (1)
Roggenstrasse 31, 23556, Lubeck, Germany
Tel.: (49) 45116040
Web Site: https://www.tateandlyle.com
Food Stabilizer System Mfr
N.A.I.C.S.: 333241
Michael Auschra *(Gen Mgr)*

G.C. Hahn & Co. Stabilizacni technika s.r.o. (1)
Ostravska 169, Klatovy, 33901, Czech Republic
Tel.: (420) 376317555
Web Site: http://www.tateandlyle.com
Food Ingredient Chemicals Mfr
N.A.I.C.S.: 325998

G.C. Hahn & Co. Technika stabilizowania sp. z.o.o. (1)
Bagienna 1, Gmina Mniow, 62-081, Chyby, Poland
Tel.: (48) 618162069
Sales Range: $25-49.9 Million
Emp.: 9
Food Ingredient Mfr
N.A.I.C.S.: 311352
Marisu Gmerec *(Mgr-Sls)*

G.C. Hahn Estabilizantes y Tecnologia para Alimentos SL (1)
Calle Inmaculada 20, Casinos, 46171, Valencia, Spain
Tel.: (34) 961647243
Specialty Chemicals Mfr

TATE & LYLE PLC

Tate & Lyle PLC—(Continued)
N.A.I.C.S.: 325998

Nederlandse Glucose Industrie BV (1)
Lagedijk 5, 1541 KA, Koog aan de Zaan, Netherlands
Tel.: (31) 756532111
Web Site: https://www.tateandlyle.com
Flavoring Syrup Mfr.
N.A.I.C.S.: 311930
Tom Reitsma (Mng Dir)

Sweet Green Fields Co., Limited (1)
Health Medicine Industry Garden, Anji Economic Development Zone, Huzhou, Zhejiang, China
Tel.: (86) 572 588 6168
Food & Beverage Mfr & Distr
N.A.I.C.S.: 311999

Sweet Green Fields USA LLC (1)
11 Bellwether Way Ste 305, Bellingham, WA 98225
Tel.: (360) 483-4555
Web Site: https://sweetgreenfields.com
Food & Beverage Mfr
N.A.I.C.S.: 311999
Jack Shi (Chm)

Tate & Lyle (1)
2200 E Eldorado St, Decatur, IL 62521-1578 (100%)
Tel.: (217) 423-4411
Web Site: http://www.tateandlyle.com
Sales Range: $25-49.9 Million
Emp.: 200
Cereal Sweeteners Mfr
N.A.I.C.S.: 311230
Catherine McClurkin (Dir-Global Quality)

Group (Domestic):

Tate & Lyle LLC (2)
2200 E Eldorado St, Decatur, IL 62521-1578 (100%)
Tel.: (217) 423-4411
Web Site: http://www.tlna.com
Corn Processing, Production of Sweeteners, Starches & Chemicals
N.A.I.C.S.: 325998

Tate & Lyle ANZ Pty Limited (1)
180 Albert Road Ground Floor, South Melbourne, 3205, VIC, Australia
Tel.: (61) 399263400
Specialty Chemical Whslr
N.A.I.C.S.: 424690

Tate & Lyle Acucares Portugal (1)
Quinta Do Ferral Apartado 1711, 2690 364, Santa Iria de Azoia, Portugal (100%)
Tel.: (351) 219405500
Web Site: http://www.sidul.pt
Sales Range: $25-49.9 Million
Emp.: 250
Cane Sugar Refining
N.A.I.C.S.: 311314

Tate & Lyle Custom Ingredients LLC (1)
1631 S Prairie Dr, Sycamore, IL 60178
Tel.: (815) 895-6300
Web Site: http://www.tateandlyle.com
Emp.: 100
Food Ingredients Mfr & Distr
N.A.I.C.S.: 311351
Brian Walker (Gen Mgr)

Tate & Lyle Europe (1)
Thames Refinery, Silvertown, London, E16 2EW, United Kingdom (100%)
Tel.: (44) 7074455
Web Site: http://www.tateandlyle.co.uk
Sales Range: $25-49.9 Million
Emp.: 100
Sugar Refinery
N.A.I.C.S.: 311314

Tate & Lyle Holdings Limited (1)
Sugar Quay, London, EC3DQ 6DQ, United Kingdom
Tel.: (44) 20 7626 6525
Cane Sugar Refining Services
N.A.I.C.S.: 311214

Tate & Lyle Industries Limited (1)
Sugar Quay Lower Thames St, London, EC3R 6DQ, United Kingdom (100%)
Tel.: (44) 2076266525

Web Site: http://www.tateandlyle.com
Sales Range: $50-74.9 Million
Emp.: 70
Holding Company
N.A.I.C.S.: 551112

Tate & Lyle Ingredients Americas, LLC (1)
2200 E Eldorado St, Decatur, IL 62521
Tel.: (217) 423-4411
Web Site: http://www.tayteandlyle.com
Food Ingredient Mfr
N.A.I.C.S.: 311351
John Schnake (CFO)

Tate & Lyle Ingredients France S.A.S. (1)
9 Allee de la Laiterie, 59650, Villeneuve d'Ascq, France
Tel.: (33) 32 877 7000
Food & Beverage Mfr
N.A.I.C.S.: 312111

Tate & Lyle Insurance (Gilbraltar) Limited (1)
Suite 913 Europort, Gibraltar, GX111AA, Gibraltar
Tel.: (350) 20043882
Web Site: http://www.tateandlyle.com
Insurance Management Services
N.A.I.C.S.: 524298

Tate & Lyle International Finance Limited (1)
Sugar Quay Lower Thames St, London, EC3R 6DQ, United Kingdom (100%)
Tel.: (44) 2076266525
Web Site: http://www.tateandlyle.com
Sales Range: $50-74.9 Million
Emp.: 80
Financial Services
N.A.I.C.S.: 522320

Tate & Lyle Investments Limited (1)
Sugar Quay Lower Thames St, London, EC3R 6DQ, United Kingdom (100%)
Tel.: (44) 2076266525
Web Site: http://www.tateandlyle.com
Sales Range: $50-74.9 Million
Emp.: 60
Holding Company
N.A.I.C.S.: 551112

Tate & Lyle Ltd (1)
Sugar Quay Lower Thames St, London, EC3R 6DQ, United Kingdom (100%)
Tel.: (44) 2076266525
Web Site: http://www.tateandlyle.com
Sales Range: $25-49.9 Million
Emp.: 100
Feed Blocks Mfr
N.A.I.C.S.: 445298

Tate & Lyle Management & Finance Ltd (1)
33 35 Reid St, Hamilton, HM 12, Bermuda (100%)
Tel.: (441) 2959911
Web Site: http://www.tateandlyle.com
Financial Services
N.A.I.C.S.: 522320

Tate & Lyle Netherlands BV (1)
Lagedijk 5, Koog aan de Zaan, 1541 KA, Netherlands
Tel.: (31) 756532111
Sales Range: $25-49.9 Million
Emp.: 21
Flavoring Syrup & Concentrate Mfr
N.A.I.C.S.: 311930
Tom Reitsma (Gen Mgr)

Tate & Lyle Reinsurance Ltd. (1)
Jardin House 33-35 Reid St, PO Box HM 337, Hamilton, HM BX, Bermuda (100%)
Tel.: (441) 2959911
Web Site: http://www.tateandlyle.co.uk
Reinsurance
N.A.I.C.S.: 524298

Tate & Lyle Services Belgium NV (1)
Industrielaan 4, 9320, Aalst, Belgium
Tel.: (32) 53857370
Investment Management Service
N.A.I.C.S.: 523999

Tate & Lyle Singapore Pte Ltd (1)
3 Biopolis Drive 05-11 Synapse, Singapore, 138623, Singapore
Tel.: (65) 6335 7700

Sugar Mfr
N.A.I.C.S.: 311314
Karsten Ries (Mgr-Sls)

Tate & Lyle South Africa (Pty) Limited (1)
1 Gravel Drive Kya Sand Business, Johannesburg, 2169, Gauteng, South Africa
Tel.: (27) 117089100
Emp.: 35
Flavoring Syrup & Concentrate Mfr
N.A.I.C.S.: 311930
Kennedy Desmond (Mgr-Fin)

Tate & Lyle Sucralose LLC (1)
Industrial Rd, McIntosh, AL 36553
Tel.: (251) 944-3700
Flavoring Syrup & Concentrate Mfr
N.A.I.C.S.: 311930

Tate & Lyle Sugar Quay Investments Ltd (1)
Sugar Quay Lowr Thames St, London, EC3R 6DQ, United Kingdom (100%)
Tel.: (44) 2076266525
Web Site: http://www.tateandlyle.com
Sales Range: $25-49.9 Million
Emp.: 50
Holding Company
N.A.I.C.S.: 551112

Tate & Lyle Trading (Shanghai) Limited (1)
24/F Technology Plaza Xingyuan No 418 Guiping Road, Xuhui District, Shanghai, 200233, China
Tel.: (86) 2151763100
Food Ingredient Chemicals Whslr
N.A.I.C.S.: 424690

Tate & Lyle do Brasil Servicos e Participacoes Ltda. (1)
10th Floor Sigma Tower Avenue Nacoes Unidas 17007, Sao Paulo, 0473-0090, Brazil (100%)
Tel.: (55) 1150903950
Web Site: http://www.tateandlyle.com
Emp.: 80
Sales & Marketing of Molasses
N.A.I.C.S.: 424490
Oswaldo Nardinelli (Gen Mgr)

ZSR Corporation Ltd. (1)
Douglas Rd, Workington, Harare, Zimbabwe (100%)
Tel.: (263) 4668901
Web Site: http://www.zsr.com
Sugar Refining
N.A.I.C.S.: 311314

TATIA GLOBAL VENTURE LTD.

New No 29 Old No 12 Second Floor Mookathal Street, Purasawalkam, Chennai, 600 007, India
Tel.: (91) 4448676773
Web Site: https://www.tatia.co.in
521228—(BOM)
Rev.: $588,562
Assets: $3,850,021
Liabilities: $792,255
Net Worth: $3,057,766
Earnings: $526,719
Emp.: 5
Fiscal Year-end: 03/31/23
Textile Products Mfr
N.A.I.C.S.: 314999
S. P. Bharat Jain Tatia (Chm & Mng Dir)

TATRA HOLDINGS S.R.O.

Areal Tatry 1450 1, Koprivnice, 742 21, Czech Republic
Tel.: (420) 556491111   CZ
Web Site: http://www.tatra.cz
Sales Range: $350-399.9 Million
Emp.: 2,000
Holding Company
N.A.I.C.S.: 551112
Ronald A. Adams (Founder & Chm)

TATRA, A.S.

Areal Tatry 1450/1, 742 21, Koprivnice, Czech Republic

INTERNATIONAL PUBLIC

Tel.: (420) 556491111   CZ
Web Site: http://www.tatratrucks.com
Sales Range: $200-249.9 Million
Emp.: 1,000
Heavy Duty Military & Commercial Truck Mfr
N.A.I.C.S.: 336120
Rene Matera (Chm-Supervisory Bd)

Subsidiaries:

Tafonco a.s. (1)
Areal Tatry 1448-5, Koprivnice, 742 21, Czech Republic
Tel.: (420) 556492519
Web Site: http://www.tatra.cz
Sales Range: $125-149.9 Million
Emp.: 400
Ferrous & Non-Ferrous Castings
N.A.I.C.S.: 332112

Taforge a.s. (1)
Stefanikova 1163, Koprivnice, 742 21, Czech Republic
Tel.: (420) 556493652
Web Site: http://www.taforge.cz
Emp.: 300
Die Forging, Metal Pressing & Heat Treatment Services
N.A.I.C.S.: 332111
Vaclav Petras (CEO)

TATRY MOUNTAIN RESORTS A.S.

Demanovska Dolina 72, 3101, Liptovsky Mikulas, Slovakia
Tel.: (421) 903960099
Web Site: https://www.tmr.sk
TMR—(PRA)
Rev.: $144,205,698
Assets: $620,188,863
Liabilities: $584,567,235
Net Worth: $35,621,627
Earnings: ($12,893,374)
Emp.: 1,359
Fiscal Year-end: 10/31/22
Resort Owner & Operator
N.A.I.C.S.: 721110
Bohus Hlavaty (Chm-Supervisory Bd)

Subsidiaries:

Slaskie Wesole Miasteczko Sp. z o.o. (1)
Plac Atrakcji 1, Katowice, 40-102, Poland
Tel.: (48) 666031196
Web Site: http://www.wesole-miasteczko.pl
Hotel Operator
N.A.I.C.S.: 721110
Pawel Cebula (Dir-Ops)

TATTARANG PTY. LTD.

PO Box 3155 Broadway, Nedlands, 6009, WA, Australia
Tel.: (61) 864604949
Web Site: http://www.tattarang.com
Privater Equity Firm
N.A.I.C.S.: 523999
Andrew Hagger (CEO)

Subsidiaries:

Squadron Energy Pty. Ltd. (1)
171-173 Mounts Bay Road, Perth, WA, Australia
Tel.: (61) 8664604949
Web Site: http://www.squadronenergy.com
Solar Energy, Natural Gas & Wind Energy Distr
N.A.I.C.S.: 221210
Stuart Johnston (CEO)

Subsidiary (Domestic):

Windlab Limited (2)
L4 60 Marcus Clarke Street, PO Box 361, Canberra, 2601, ACT, Australia (75%)
Tel.: (61) 261754600
Web Site: http://www.windlab.com
Rev.: $2,453,236
Assets: $42,993,093
Liabilities: $7,563,223
Net Worth: $35,429,871
Earnings: ($2,691,911)
Fiscal Year-end: 12/31/2018

Renewable Energy Development Services
N.A.I.C.S.: 221115
Roger Price (CEO)

Wyloo Metals Pty. Ltd. (1)
PO Box 3155, Boadway, Nedlands, 6009, WA, Australia
Tel.: (61) 864604949
Web Site: http://www.wyloometals.com
Nickel Mining
N.A.I.C.S.: 212230
Luca Giacovazzi (Head)

Subsidiary (Domestic):

Mincor Resources NL (2)
Ground Floor 9 Havelock Street, West Perth, 6005, WA, Australia (92.71%)
Tel.: (61) 894767200
Web Site: http://www.mincor.com.au
Rev.: $24,804,635
Assets: $172,036,472
Liabilities: $93,931,829
Net Worth: $78,104,642
Earnings: ($11,267,590)
Emp.: 60
Fiscal Year-end: 06/30/2022
Nickel Mining Services
N.A.I.C.S.: 212230
Robert J. Hartley (Gen Mgr-Exploration)

Subsidiary (Domestic):

Goldfields Mine Management Pty Ltd (3)
Otter Juan Minesite Kalgoorlie-Kambalda Hwy, Kambalda, 6442, WA, Australia
Tel.: (61) 890278704
Web Site: http://www.mincor.com.au
Emp.: 50
Copper Ore & Nickel Ore Mining Services
N.A.I.C.S.: 212230

Mincor Operations Pty Limited (3)
PO Box 342, Kambalda, 6444, WA, Australia
Tel.: (61) 890208642
Web Site: http://www.mincor.co.au
Emp.: 70
Copper & Nickel Ore Mining Services
N.A.I.C.S.: 212230

Subsidiary (Non-US):

Noront Resources Ltd. (2)
212 King Street West Suite 501, Toronto, M5H 1K5, ON, Canada
Tel.: (416) 367-1444
Web Site: http://www.norontresources.com
Rev.: $132,649
Assets: $22,313,414
Liabilities: $52,348,754
Net Worth: ($30,035,340)
Earnings: ($10,900,814)
Emp.: 9
Fiscal Year-end: 12/31/2020
Metal Exploration & Mining Services
N.A.I.C.S.: 212230

TATTELEKOM
N Yershova 57, 420061, Kazan, Russia
Tel.: (7) 8432222222
Web Site: http://www.tattelecom.ru
TTLK—(MOEX)
Sales Range: Less than $1 Million
Telecommunication Related Services
N.A.I.C.S.: 517810

TATTON ASSET MANAGEMENT PLC
Paradigm House Brooke Court, Wilmslow, SK9 3ND, Cheshire, United Kingdom
Tel.: (44) 1614863441 UK
Web Site: https://www.tattonassetmanage.com
Year Founded: 2007
TAM—(AIM)
Rev.: $39,857,228
Assets: $56,137,649
Liabilities: $13,988,589
Net Worth: $42,149,060
Earnings: $12,548,048
Emp.: 95
Fiscal Year-end: 03/31/22

Portfolio Management & Investment Advice
N.A.I.C.S.: 523940
Paul Hogarth (CEO)

Subsidiaries:

Paradigm Partners Limited (1)
Paradigm House Brooke Court, Handforth, Wilmslow, SK9 3ND, Cheshire, United Kingdom
Tel.: (44) 1614864890
Web Site: http://www.consultparadigm.co.uk
Financial Management Services
N.A.I.C.S.: 541611

Sinfonia Asset Management Limited (1)
17 St Swithin's Lane, London, EC4N 8AL, United Kingdom
Tel.: (44) 2071391473
Web Site: http://www.sinfonia.com
Asset Management Services
N.A.I.C.S.: 523940
Paul Hogarth (CEO)

Tatton Investment Management Limited (1)
17 St Swithin's Lane, London, EC4N 8AL, United Kingdom
Tel.: (44) 2071391470
Web Site: http://www.tattoninvestments.com
Investment Management Service
N.A.I.C.S.: 523940
Lothar Mentel (Founder, CEO & Chief Investment Officer)

TATUNG COMPANY
No 22 Sec 3 Zhongshan N Roa, Zhongshan Dist, Taipei, 104427, Taiwan
Tel.: (886) 225925252 TW
Web Site: https://www.tatung.com
Year Founded: 1918
2371—(TAI)
Rev.: $1,646,591,324
Assets: $4,489,288,264
Liabilities: $2,342,131,047
Net Worth: $2,147,157,216
Earnings: $92,214,621
Emp.: 2,474
Fiscal Year-end: 12/31/23
Digital, Electronic & Household Consumer Products Mfr
N.A.I.C.S.: 334290
Wkang-Hsiang Wang (Chm)

Subsidiaries:

Central Research Technology Co. (1)
11 Lane 41 Fushuen St, Taipei, 104, Taiwan
Tel.: (886) 2 25984542
Web Site: http://www.crc-lab.com
Technical Testing & Certification Services
N.A.I.C.S.: 541380

Chunghwa Picture Tubes, Ltd. (1)
No 1 Huaying Road Longtan District, Taoyuan, 325, Taiwan
Tel.: (886) 34805678
Web Site: http://www.cptt.com.tw
Emp.: 9,500
Display Devices & Picture Tubes Mfr
N.A.I.C.S.: 334419
J.L. Tsay (Chm)

Subsidiary (Non-US):

Chunghwa Picture Tubes (Malaysia) Sdn. Bhd. (2)
Lot 1 Subang Hi-Tech Industrial Park Batu Tiga, 40000, Shah Alam, Selangor Darul Ehsan, Malaysia
Tel.: (60) 356355055
Web Site: http://www.chunghwapicture.com
Sales Range: $350-399.9 Million
Emp.: 2,000
Display & Color Picture Tube Mfr
N.A.I.C.S.: 334419

Chunghwa Picture Tubes SDN. BHD. (2)
Lot 1 Subang Hi-tech Industrial Park, Batu Tiga, 40000, Shah Alam, Selangor, Malaysia (100%)

Tel.: (60) 56355055
Web Site: http://www.streamy.com
Sales Range: $25-49.9 Million
Emp.: 1,300
Mfr of Display & Color Tubes
N.A.I.C.S.: 335999

Dongguan Tongli Trading Co., Ltd. (1)
No 5 Lane 3, Xianfeng Village New District Shatian Town, Dongguan, Guangdong, China
Tel.: (86) 76981522235
Electronic Equipment Mfr & Distr
N.A.I.C.S.: 335313

FDK Tatung (Thailand) Co., Ltd. (1)
700/50, 52, 54 Moo 6 T Nongmaidang, A Muang, Chon Buri, 20000, Thailand
Tel.: (66) 38 213080 5
Web Site: http://www.tatung.com
Sales Range: $100-124.9 Million
Emp.: 300
Mfr of Ferrite Cores for Deflection Yokes, Generators, Rotary Transformer Core
N.A.I.C.S.: 335999

Makolin Electronics Sdn. Bhd. (1)
Lot 181723 Taman Baru Industrial Zone Mukim Kampar District Of Kinta, Perak, 31900, Darul Ridzuan State, Malaysia (42%)
Tel.: (60) 54665780
Sales Range: $10-24.9 Million
Emp.: 400
Mfr of Deflection Yokes for Color Tubes
N.A.I.C.S.: 335999
Henry Chen (Mng Dir)

Shan Chih Asset Development Co., Ltd. (1)
No 22 Sec 3 ChungShan N Rd, Taipei, 00104, Taiwan
Tel.: (886) 225925252
Web Site: http://www.shangchih.com.tw
Emp.: 65
Asset Management Services
N.A.I.C.S.: 523940

Tatung (Shanghai) Co., Ltd. (1)
Room 508 building 9W-ark 185Jiangtian East Road, Songjiang District, Shanghai, 201613, China
Tel.: (86) 2157605299
Web Site: https://www.tatungsh.com
Motor & Generator Mfr & Whslr
N.A.I.C.S.: 335312

Tatung (Thailand) Co., Ltd. (1)
Estatebangna-Trad Road Km 57 700/50 52 54 Moo 6, Amata City Chonburi Industrial Nongmaidang Muang, Chon Buri, 20000, Thailand
Tel.: (66) 38213080
Web Site: https://www.tatung.co.th
Electronic Computer Mfr
N.A.I.C.S.: 334111

Tatung CZECH s.r.o (1)
On Joy 184/59, 155 21, Prague, Czech Republic
Tel.: (420) 234720357
Web Site: http://www.tatung.cz
Digital Equipments Mfr
N.A.I.C.S.: 334419

Tatung Coatings (Kunshan) Co., Ltd. (1)
NO 333 Lianhe Road, Qianderng Town, Kunshan, 215341, Jiangsu, China
Tel.: (86) 51257663208
Electronic Equipment Mfr & Distr
N.A.I.C.S.: 335313

Tatung Company - Tatung Heavy Electric Business Unit (1)
22 Changshan N Rd 3rd Sec, Taipei, 104, Taiwan
Tel.: (886) 2 2592 5252
Emp.: 500
Transformer & Switchgear Mfr
N.A.I.C.S.: 334416
Wy Lin (Gen Mgr)

Tatung Company of America (1)
2850 El Presidio St, Long Beach, CA 90810-1119
Tel.: (310) 637-2105
Web Site: http://www.tatungusa.com

Sales Range: $50-74.9 Million
Emp.: 200
Electronic Computer Mfr
N.A.I.C.S.: 334111

Tatung Consumer Products (Taiwan) Co. Ltd. (1)
No 22 Sec 3 ChungShan N Rd, Taipei, 00104, Taiwan
Tel.: (886) 225925252
Web Site: http://tcpc.tatung.com
Consumer Products Whslr
N.A.I.C.S.: 424990

Tatung DIE Casting Co., Ltd. (1)
No 352 Xidong Rd, Sanxia Dist, New Taipei City, 273, Taiwan
Tel.: (886) 286766888
Electronic Equipment Mfr & Distr
N.A.I.C.S.: 335313

Tatung Electric Co. of America, Inc. (1)
14381 Chambers Rd, Tustin, CA 92780-6911 (100%)
Tel.: (714) 838-3293
Web Site: http://tatungelectric.com
Sales Range: $25-49.9 Million
Emp.: 15
Motor & Diesel Generator Set Mfr
N.A.I.C.S.: 333611
Bernard Chen (Pres)

Tatung Electronics (Singapore) Pte. Ltd. (1)
8 Boon Lay Way 02-14 TradeHub 21, Singapore, 609964, Singapore (100%)
Tel.: (65) 62656526
Web Site: http://www.tatung.com
Sales Range: $25-49.9 Million
Emp.: 5
Sales & Purchasing of Electronic Equipment
N.A.I.C.S.: 449210

Tatung Information (Singapore) Pte. Ltd. (1)
10 Collyer 19 - 08, Ocean Building, Singapore, 049315, Singapore
Tel.: (65) 65365355
Electronic Equipment Mfr & Distr
N.A.I.C.S.: 335313

Tatung Information Technology (Jiangsu) Co., Ltd. (1)
No 123 Jiang - Ling N Rd, Song-ling Town, Wujiang, Jiangsu, China
Tel.: (86) 51263401328
Electronic Component Mfr & Whslr
N.A.I.C.S.: 423620

Tatung Medical Healthcare Technologies Co., Ltd. (1)
No 22 Sec 3 Zhongshan N Rd, Zhongshan Dist, Taipei, 104427, Taiwan
Tel.: (886) 227002737
Web Site: https://www.tmhtc.net
Medical Equipment Mfr
N.A.I.C.S.: 339112

Tatung Telecom Corp. (1)
A 2660 Marine Way, Mountain View, CA 94043-1126
Tel.: (408) 486-9898
Web Site: http://www.tatung.com
Sales Range: $25-49.9 Million
Emp.: 20
Distr of Telephone Products
N.A.I.C.S.: 334210

Tatung UK Ltd. (1)
Stafford Park 10, Telford, TF3 3AB, Salop, United Kingdom (100%)
Tel.: (44) 1952290111
Sales Range: $25-49.9 Million
Emp.: 30
Marketing, Service & Products for Consumer & IT Electronic Products
N.A.I.C.S.: 423620

Tatung Wire and Cable (Thailand) Co., Ltd. (1)
700 50 52 54 Moo 6 T Nongmaidang, A Muang, Chon Buri, 20000, Thailand (100%)
Tel.: (66) 38743411
Web Site: http://www.cable.tatung.com.tw
Sales Range: $25-49.9 Million
Emp.: 45
Mfr of Color TV Sets & Computer Monitors
N.A.I.C.S.: 334310

TATUNG COMPANY

Tatung Company—(Continued)

Tatung Wire and Cable (Wujiang) Co., Ltd. (1)
Fenhu Main Rd Eastside, Luxu Town, Wujiang, Jiangsu, China
Tel.: (86) 512 63262125
Electric Wire & Cable Mfr & Whslr
N.A.I.C.S.: 335929

Tatung of Japan, Inc. (1)
Sanko Building Honkan 2F 10 5 Ginza 4 Chome Chuo Ku, Tokyo, 104 0061, Japan (100%)
Tel.: (81) 335452969
Web Site: http://www.tatung.co.jp
Sales Range: $25-49.9 Million
Emp.: 22
Sales & Purchasing of Electronic Equipment
N.A.I.C.S.: 449210

Tatung-Fanuc Robotics Company (1)
22 Sec 3 Chungshan N Rd, Taipei, 104, Taiwan
Tel.: (886) 225925252
Web Site: http://www.tatungfanuc.com.tw
Sales Range: $200-249.9 Million
Emp.: 1,000
Robot Sales & Services
N.A.I.C.S.: 335314

TATUNG FINE CHEMICALS CO., LTD.
247-1 16 Ling, Tsaotah Village Kuanyin, Taoyuan, Taiwan
Tel.: (886) 34830321
Web Site: https://en.twtfc.com
Year Founded: 1980
Coating Product Mfr
N.A.I.C.S.: 325510
Yung -Tsung Wu *(Pres)*

TATUNG SYSTEM TECHNOLOGIES, INC.
22 Sec 3 Chung-Shan North Road, Taipei, Taiwan
Tel.: (886) 225915266
Computer Peripheral Equipment Distr
N.A.I.C.S.: 423430
Liu Ying-Hsiu *(Pres)*

TATVA CHINTAN PHARMA CHEM LIMITED
Plot No 353 G I D C Makarpura, Vadodara, 390010, Gujarat, India
Tel.: (91) 7574848533
Web Site: https://www.tatvachintan.com
Year Founded: 1996
TATVA—(NSE)
Rev.: $51,478,449
Assets: $90,678,017
Liabilities: $28,956,178
Net Worth: $61,721,839
Earnings: $5,453,750
Emp.: 608
Fiscal Year-end: 03/31/23
Chemicals Mfr
N.A.I.C.S.: 325199
Chintan Nitinkumar Shah *(Mng Dir)*

TATWAH SMARTECH CO., LTD.
Building No 17 Area G Fuzhou Software Park No 89 Ruanjian Avenue, Gulou District, Fuzhou, 350003, Fujian, China
Tel.: (86) 59187510387
Web Site: http://www.twh.com.cn
Year Founded: 1993
002512—(SSE)
Rev.: $244,639,545
Assets: $681,554,025
Liabilities: $472,955,512
Net Worth: $208,598,514
Earnings: ($45,872,022)
Emp.: 940
Fiscal Year-end: 12/31/22

Radio Frequency Identification Products Including Contactless Smart Cards, Tags, Labels, Reading Modules & Readers Mfr
N.A.I.C.S.: 334220
Xiaoru Cai *(Chm)*

TAU CAPITAL PLC
IOMA House Hope Street, Douglas, IM1 1AP, Isle of Man
Tel.: (44) 1624 681 250 IM
Web Site: http://www.taucapitalplc.com
Year Founded: 2007
Rev.: $12
Assets: $7,704,480
Liabilities: $544,400
Net Worth: $7,160,080
Earnings: ($601,460)
Fiscal Year-end: 12/31/16
Investment Management Service
N.A.I.C.S.: 523999
Philip Scales *(Sec)*

TAUBATKOMPANIET AS
Strandveien 43, 7067, Trondheim, Norway
Tel.: (47) 73991199
Web Site: http://www.boa.no
Rev.: $108,901,538
Assets: $370,263,419
Liabilities: $416,685,995
Net Worth: ($46,422,576)
Earnings: ($33,277,503)
Emp.: 281
Fiscal Year-end: 12/31/18
Holding Company; Harbour Towage & General Service Operators
N.A.I.C.S.: 551112
Ole Bjornevik *(Chm)*

Subsidiaries:

Boa Offshore AS (1)
Strandveien 43, 7067, Trondheim, Norway
Tel.: (47) 73991199
Web Site: http://www.boa.no
Rev.: $111,315,563
Assets: $310,603,307
Liabilities: $381,921,110
Net Worth: ($71,317,803)
Earnings: ($22,570,901)
Fiscal Year-end: 12/31/2019
Harbour Towage & General Service Operators
N.A.I.C.S.: 483211
Ole T. Bjornevik *(Owner)*

TAUNG GOLD INTERNATIONAL LIMITED
Unit 1901 19/F Nina Tower 8 Yeung Uk Road, Tsuen Wan, China (Hong Kong)
Tel.: (852) 3 907 0330 BM
Web Site: http://www.taunggold.com
0621—(HKG)
Rev.: $240,290
Assets: $427,160,865
Liabilities: $2,918,688
Net Worth: $424,242,177
Earnings: ($85,819,423)
Emp.: 30
Fiscal Year-end: 03/31/21
Gold Mining Services
N.A.I.C.S.: 212220
Pak Sum Cheung *(Co-Chm)*

Subsidiaries:

Taung Gold Limited (1)
Corner House Office Park 1st Floor, PO Box 463, Leslie Avenue East Fourways, Sandton, South Africa
Tel.: (27) 11 548 9801
Gold Exploration Services
N.A.I.C.S.: 212220

TAURISSON S.A.
1 Allee Des Chataigniers, 19360, Malemort-sur-Correze, France

Tel.: (33) 555177979 FR
Sales Range: $10-24.9 Million
Emp.: 13
New Car Dealers
N.A.I.C.S.: 441110
Jean-Max Taurisson *(Co-Pres)*

TAURON POLSKA ENERGIA S.A.
ul ks Piotra Sciegiennego 3, 40-114, Katowice, Poland
Tel.: (48) 327742405
Web Site: https://www.tauron.pl
TNPGY—(OTCIQ)
Rev.: $10,837,652,411
Assets: $12,651,930,862
Liabilities: $8,090,701,199
Net Worth: $4,561,229,663
Earnings: $426,321,137
Emp.: 18,946
Fiscal Year-end: 12/31/23
Holding Company; Power Operations
N.A.I.C.S.: 551112
Teresa Famulska *(Vice Chm-Supervisory Bd)*

Subsidiaries:

Bioeko Grupa Tauron Sp. z o.o. (1)
Ul Energetykow 13, 37-450, Stalowa Wola, Poland
Tel.: (48) 158776485
Web Site: https://bioeko.tauron.pl
Eletric Power Generation Services
N.A.I.C.S.: 221118

Nowe Jaworzno Grupa Tauron Sp. z o.o. (1)
Ul Dobrej Energii 11, 43-603, Jaworzno, Poland
Tel.: (48) 32 715 5970
Web Site: https://www.nowejaworzno-grupatauron.pl
Electric Power Generation Services
N.A.I.C.S.: 221118

Polska Energia Pierwsza Kompania Handlowa Sp. z o.o (1)
ul Zlota 59, 00-120, Warsaw, Poland
Tel.: (48) 32 744 26 55
Web Site: http://www.polskaenergia.pl
Electric Power Distr
N.A.I.C.S.: 221122

TAURON Cieplo S.A. (1)
ul Grazynskiego 49, 40-126, Katowice, Poland
Tel.: (48) 326638399
Web Site: http://www.tauron-cieplo.pl
Power Generation & Transmission Services
N.A.I.C.S.: 221118

TAURON Czech Energy s.r.o. (1)
Na Rovince 879, Hrabova, 720 00, Ostrava, Czech Republic
Tel.: (420) 552302530
Web Site: https://www.tauronenergy.cz
Electric Power & Natural Gas Distr
N.A.I.C.S.: 221122

TAURON EKOENERGIA sp. z o.o. (1)
ul Obroncow Pokoju 2B, 58-500, Jelenia Gora, Poland
Tel.: (48) 757546800
Web Site: https://ekoenergia.tauron.pl
Power Generation Services
N.A.I.C.S.: 221118

TAURON Serwis GZE sp. z o.o. (1)
44-100 Mysliwska 6, Gliwice, Poland
Tel.: (48) 32 303 80 01
Electrical Equipment Distr
N.A.I.C.S.: 423830

TAURON Wytwarzanie S.A. (1)
ul Promienna 51, 43-603, Jaworzno, Poland
Tel.: (48) 327153301
Web Site: https://www.tauron.pl
Power Generation & Transmission Services
N.A.I.C.S.: 221122

Tauron Dystrybucja Pomiary Sp. z o.o. (1)
Ul Krysztalowa 1/3, 33-100, Tarnow, Poland
Tel.: (48) 146311305

INTERNATIONAL PUBLIC

Web Site: https://pomiary.tauron-dystrybucja.pl
Eletric Power Generation Services
N.A.I.C.S.: 221118

TAURUS ARMAS S.A.
Avenida Sao Borja 2181 Predio A - Fazenda Sao Borja, 93035-411, Sao Leopoldo, 93035-411, RS, Brazil
Tel.: (55) 5130213000
Web Site: https://www.taurus.com.br
Year Founded: 1939
TASA4—(BRAZ)
Rev.: $318,529,692
Assets: $385,023,675
Liabilities: $189,852,876
Net Worth: $195,170,800
Earnings: $27,312,704
Fiscal Year-end: 12/31/23
Firearms, Helmets & Plastic Mfr & Whslr
N.A.I.C.S.: 332994
Salesio Nuhs *(CEO)*

TAURUS ENERGY AB
Sven Hultins gata 9C, 412 58, Gothenburg, Sweden
Tel.: (46) 704547469
Web Site: https://taurusenergy.eu
Year Founded: 1990
8LU—(DEU)
Ethanol Product Mfr
N.A.I.C.S.: 325193
Fredrik Weschke *(CEO)*

TAURUS GOLD CORP.
239 9768-170th Street, Edmonton, T5T 5L4, AB, Canada
Tel.: (587) 608-5035
Web Site: https://www.taurusgold.ca
Year Founded: 2019
TAUR—(CNSX)
Assets: $1,253,099
Liabilities: $240,230
Net Worth: $1,012,869
Earnings: ($108,429)
Fiscal Year-end: 07/31/22
Mineral Exploration Services
N.A.I.C.S.: 213114

TAURUS GROUP
Av Barcelona s/n, Oliana, Lleida, Spain
Tel.: (34) 973470550
Web Site: http://www.group-taurus.com
Year Founded: 1962
Small Electric Appliances Mfr
N.A.I.C.S.: 335210
Enric Tria Benito *(Mng Dir-Europe)*

Subsidiaries:

Electrodomesticos Taurus SL (1)
Avenida Barcelona s/n 25790, Oliana, Lleida, Spain
Tel.: (34) 900 800 291
Web Site: http://www.taurusprofessional.com
Household Appliances, Electric Housewares & Consumer Electronics Merchant Whslr
N.A.I.C.S.: 423620

Subsidiary (Non-US):

SUPRA SA (2)
28 Rue du General Leclerc, 67210, Obernai, France
Tel.: (33) 388951200
Web Site: http://www.supra.fr
Biomass Wood Heating Solution Mfr
N.A.I.C.S.: 333414
Alberto Morgando *(Chm)*

TAUW GROUP B.V.
Handelskade 37 Deventer, Zwolle, 7400 AC, Overijssel, Netherlands
Tel.: (31) 57 069 9911
Web Site: http://www.tauw.nl
Year Founded: 1928

Consultancy & Engineering Agency; Water Management & Other Environmental Services
N.A.I.C.S.: 541618
Rob Salman (Dir-Staff Svcs)

TAV HAVALIMANLARI HOLDING A.S.
Vadistanbul Bulvar Ayazaga Mahallesi Azerbaycan Caddesi 2C Blok No 3L, Sariyer, 34485, Istanbul, Turkiye
Tel.: (90) 2124633000
Web Site:
  https://www.tavhavalimanlari.com.tr
Year Founded: 1997
TAVHL—(IST)
Holding Company
N.A.I.C.S.: 551112
Edward Rodolphe Paul Arkwright (Chm)

Subsidiaries:

Almaty International Airport JSC (1)
Ul Maylina 2, 050039, Almaty, Kazakhstan (85%)
Tel.: (7) 7272703131
Web Site: http://www.alaport.com
Rev.: $1,445,730,213
Assets: $5,246,824,154
Liabilities: $3,672,213,269
Net Worth: $1,574,610,884
Earnings: $285,609,891
Emp.: 18,929
Fiscal Year-end: 12/31/2023
Airport Operations
N.A.I.C.S.: 488119
Alp Er Tunga Ersoy (Pres & CEO)

Batumi Airport LLC (1)
Batumi International Airport, Batumi, Georgia
Tel.: (995) 422235100
Web Site: https://www.batumiairport.com
Airport Operator & Maintenance Services
N.A.I.C.S.: 488119

Gestio I Servies Trade Center S.A. (1)
Moll de Barcelona s/n Edifici Este 1a Planta, 08039, Barcelona, Spain
Tel.: (34) 935088125
Web Site: https://www.premium-traveller.com
Airport Travel Arrangements Services
N.A.I.C.S.: 561510

TAV Akademi Egitim ve Danismanlik Hizmetleri A.S. (1)
109L 2C Blok Sariyer Ayazaga Mahallesi Cendere Caddesi, Vadistanbul Bulvar, 34485, Istanbul, Turkiye
Tel.: (90) 2124633000
Airport Consultancy Services
N.A.I.C.S.: 488190

TAV JCS
Peace Avenue 18th khoroo, Songinokhairkhan District, Ulaanbaatar, Mongolia
Tel.: (976) 70172741
TAV—(MONG)
Sales Range: Less than $1 Million
Truck Transportation Services
N.A.I.C.S.: 488490

TAVERNIER RESOURCES LTD.
Plot No 42 CTS No 1 PT Village Deonar, Near Mahesh Pharma Ancillary Ind Estate Govandi, Mumbai, 400 043, India
Tel.: (91) 8879382912
Web Site: https://www.tavernier.com
Year Founded: 1994
531190—(BOM)
Rev.: $408,201
Assets: $1,072,945
Liabilities: $411,990
Net Worth: $660,956
Earnings: ($14,112)
Emp.: 3

Fiscal Year-end: 03/31/23
Mineral Exploration Services
N.A.I.C.S.: 212311
Sudhir Milapchand Naheta (Mng Dir)

TAVISTOCK INVESTMENTS PLC
1 Queen's Square Lyndhurst Road, Ascot Business Park, Ascot, SL5 9FE, Berkshire, United Kingdom
Tel.: (44) 1753867000
Web Site:
  https://www.tavistockinvest.com
TAVI—(AIM)
Rev.: $42,164,077
Assets: $75,143,802
Liabilities: $23,272,574
Net Worth: $51,871,228
Earnings: ($1,732,311)
Emp.: 161
Fiscal Year-end: 03/31/23
Investment Services
N.A.I.C.S.: 523999
Oliver Cooke (Chm)

Subsidiaries:

Duchy Independent Financial Advisers Limited (1)
Chy Jenner Newham Quay, Truro, TR1 2DP, United Kingdom
Tel.: (44) 1872240368
Web Site: https://www.duchyifa.co.uk
Financial Planning Services
N.A.I.C.S.: 523940

King Financial Planning LLP (1)
Causeway House 1 Dane Street, Bishop's Stortford, CM23 3BT, Herts, United Kingdom
Tel.: (44) 1279598710
Web Site: https://www.kingfp.co.uk
Financial Advisory Services
N.A.I.C.S.: 523940

Price Bailey Financial Services Limited (1)
Causeway House 1 Dane Street, Bishop's Stortford, CM23 3BT, Hertfordshire, United Kingdom
Tel.: (44) 1279755888
Web Site: https://www.pricebailey.co.uk
Accounting & Auditing Services
N.A.I.C.S.: 541211
Martin Clapson (Mng Dir)

Tavistock Partners (UK) Ltd. (1)
Kemble House 36-39 Broad Street, Hereford, HR4 9AR, United Kingdom
Tel.: (44) 1432343322
Web Site:
  https://www.tavistockpartnersuk.com
Financial Planning Services
N.A.I.C.S.: 523940

Tavistock Private Client Limited (1)
The Barn Downing Park Station Rd, Swaffham Bulbeck, Cambridge, CB25 0NW, United Kingdom
Tel.: (44) 1223869030
Web Site:
  https://www.tavistockprivateclient.com
Financial Planning Services
N.A.I.C.S.: 523940
Mark Evans (Mng Dir)

The Tavistock Partnership Limited (1)
2 The Cornerstone Market Place, Kegworth, Derby, DE74 2EE, United Kingdom
Tel.: (44) 1509674335
Web Site:
  https://www.tavistockpartnership.com
Financial Advisory Services
N.A.I.C.S.: 523940

TAWOOS LLC
PO Box 1676, Muttrah, 114, Oman
Tel.: (968) 24796636   OM
Web Site: http://www.tawoos.com
Year Founded: 1982
Sales Range: $75-99.9 Million
Emp.: 1,500
Diverse Holding & Trading Company
N.A.I.C.S.: 551112

Samir J. Fancy (Chm)

Subsidiaries:

Al Oloum Bookshop LLC (1)
PO Box 474, Ruwi, 112, Oman
Tel.: (968) 571 536
Web Site: http://www.tawoos.com
Retailer & Sales of Books, Magazines & Stationery
N.A.I.C.S.: 459210

Amani Financial Services SAOC (1)
PO Box 1676, Muttrah, 114, Oman
Tel.: (968) 24796636
Web Site: http://www.tawoos.com
Sales Range: $50-74.9 Million
Emp.: 3
Financial Advisory Services
N.A.I.C.S.: 523940

Oman Expo (1)
1st Floor SABCO Building, Wattayah, Muscat, Oman
Tel.: (968) 24660124
Web Site: http://www.omanexpo.com
Sales Range: $25-49.9 Million
Emp.: 20
Exhibition & Event Management Services
N.A.I.C.S.: 561920

TAWOOS AGRICULTURE (UAE) LLC (1)
PO Box 294255, Aweer, Dubai, United Arab Emirates
Tel.: (971) 4 3336070
Fruit & Vegetable Distr
N.A.I.C.S.: 424480

Tawoos Agricultural Systems LLC (1)
PO Box 121, Barka, 320, Oman
Tel.: (968) 26796235
Web Site: http://www.tawoos.com
Sales Range: $50-74.9 Million
Emp.: 250
Exporter & Farming of Produce
N.A.I.C.S.: 444240
Babu Samuel (Gen Mgr)

Tawoos Descon Engineering LLC (1)
PO Box 1676, Muttrah, 114, Oman
Tel.: (968) 24796636
Web Site: http://www.tawoos.com
Engineering & Construction Services
N.A.I.C.S.: 541330

Tawoos LLC (1)
Bldg No 488 Way No 2708 Mbd area, Muttrah, 114, Oman (100%)
Tel.: (968) 24701607
Web Site: http://www.tawoos.com
Sales Range: $25-49.9 Million
Emp.: 4
Provider of Computer Applications & Software Development Services
N.A.I.C.S.: 541512

Tawoos Oilfield Supply Company LLC (1)
PO Box 1676, Muttrah, 114, Oman
Tel.: (968) 590385
Web Site: http://www.tawoos.com
Provider of Oil & Gas Services
N.A.I.C.S.: 221210

Tawoos Power & Telecommunications LLC (1)
Salalah Bldg 7th Fl, PO Box 1676, Muttrah, 116, Oman
Tel.: (968) 24791484
Web Site: http://www.tawoos.com
Sales Range: $25-49.9 Million
Emp.: 4
Provider of Power & Telecommunications Services
N.A.I.C.S.: 517111
Ahmed Imtiaz (Asst Gen Mgr)

TAY NGUYEN ELECTRICITY INVESTMENT JOINT STOCK COMPANY
114 Truong Chinh, Pleiku, Gia Lai, Vietnam
Tel.: (84) 592222170
Web Site: http://www.ticcom.com.vn
TIC—(HOSE)

Sales Range: Less than $1 Million
Eletric Power Generation Services
N.A.I.C.S.: 221118
Huynh Doan (Exec Dir)

TAY NINH CABLE CAR TOUR JOINT-STOCK COMPANY
Ninh Son Ward, Tay Ninh, Vietnam
Tel.: (84) 2763823448   VN
Web Site: https://www.catour.com.vn
Year Founded: 1998
TCT—(HOSE)
Rev.: $1,776,338
Assets: $14,901,051
Liabilities: $1,254,458
Net Worth: $13,646,594
Earnings: $755,938
Emp.: 31
Fiscal Year-end: 12/31/23
Ropeway & Slideway Passenger Transportation Services
N.A.I.C.S.: 487990

TAY NINH RUBBER JOINT STOCK COMPANY
National Highway 22B Da Hang Hamlet, Hiep Thanh Commune, Go Dau Ha, Tay Ninh, Vietnam
Tel.: (84) 66853606
Web Site: https://www.taniruco.com
TRC—(HOSE)
Rev.: $23,182,375
Assets: $82,245,994
Liabilities: $14,236,701
Net Worth: $68,009,293
Earnings: $2,784,749
Emp.: 1,325
Fiscal Year-end: 12/31/23
Rubber Products Mfr
N.A.I.C.S.: 326299
Le Van Chanh (Exec Dir)

TAY NINH TOURIST-TRADING JOINT STOCK COMPANY
No 1253 Cach Mang Thang Tam Street Ninh Phuoc Quarter, Ninh Thanh Ward, Tay Ninh, Tay Ninh, Vietnam
Tel.: (84) 663822376
TTT—(HNX)
Rev.: $14,158,800
Assets: $48,209,600
Liabilities: $5,058,500
Net Worth: $43,151,100
Earnings: $2,440,900
Fiscal Year-end: 12/31/23
Travel Agency & Services
N.A.I.C.S.: 561510
Tran Thi Hien (Gen Mgr)

TAY PAPER RECYCLING PTE. LTD
48 Gul Avenue, Singapore, 629681, Singapore
Tel.: (65) 6863 3230
Web Site: http://taypaper.com
Sales Range: Less than $1 Million
Paper Recycling Services
N.A.I.C.S.: 562920
Jimmy Tay (Gen Mgr)

TAY TWO CO., LTD.
650-111 Imamura, Kita-ku, Okayama, 700-0974, Japan
Tel.: (81) 862438600
Web Site: http://www.tay2.co.jp
Year Founded: 1990
7610—(TKS)
Rev.: $259,888,640
Assets: $90,653,200
Liabilities: $43,308,320
Net Worth: $47,344,880
Earnings: $14,510,320
Emp.: 283
Fiscal Year-end: 02/28/22
Video Game Software Distr

TAY TWO CO., LTD.

TAY TWO CO., LTD.—(Continued)
N.A.I.C.S.: 513210
Katsuji Fujiwara *(Pres & CEO)*

TAYA (VIETNAM) ELECTRIC WIRE & CABLE JOINT STOCK COMPANY
So 1 duong 1A Khu cong nghiep Bien Hoa II, Dong Nai, Vietnam
Tel.: (84) 613836361
Web Site: https://www.taya.com.tw
TYA—(HOSE)
Rev.: $60,472,989
Assets: $39,360,132
Liabilities: $19,595,050
Net Worth: $19,765,082
Earnings: $39,593
Emp.: 336
Fiscal Year-end: 12/31/23
Electric Wire & Cable Mfr
N.A.I.C.S.: 335999
Wang Ting Shu *(Exec Dir)*

TAYA CO. LTD.
5-23-13 Sendagaya, Shibuya-ku, Tokyo, Japan
Tel.: (81) 363842221
Web Site: https://www.taya.co.jp
Year Founded: 1961
4679—(TKS)
Sales Range: $150-199.9 Million
Emp.: 1,039
Beauty Salons
N.A.I.C.S.: 812112
Hisashi Tashiro *(Corp Officer, Exec VP & Gen Mgr-Corp Plng Promotion Office)*

TAYA INVESTMENT COMPANY LTD.
14 Ha'haroshet St, Ra'anana, 52681, Israel
Tel.: (972) 37549944
Web Site: http://www.taya.co.il
Year Founded: 1935
TAYA—(TAE)
Rev.: $22,186,213
Assets: $81,597,457
Liabilities: $10,287,056
Net Worth: $71,310,401
Earnings: $29,076,391
Emp.: 100
Fiscal Year-end: 12/31/23
Teleproduction & Other Postproduction Services
N.A.I.C.S.: 512191

TAYBURN LTD.
15 Kittle Yards, Causewayside, Edinburgh, EH9 1PJ, United Kingdom
Tel.: (44) 131-662 0662   UK
Web Site: http://www.tayburn.co.uk
Sales Range: $1-9.9 Million
Emp.: 40
Advetising Agency
N.A.I.C.S.: 541810
Malcolm Stewart *(Partner & Creative Dir)*

TAYCA CORPORATION
4-11-6 Tanimachi, Chuo-ku, Osaka, 540-0012, Japan
Tel.: (81) 669436401
Web Site: https://www.tayca.co.jp
Year Founded: 1919
4027—(TKS)
Rev.: $350,283,730
Assets: $546,706,490
Liabilities: $164,886,450
Net Worth: $381,820,040
Earnings: $12,334,260
Emp.: 815
Fiscal Year-end: 03/31/24
Chemical Product Mfr & Distr
N.A.I.C.S.: 325180
Shunji Idei *(Pres & Exec Officer)*

Subsidiaries:
TRS Technologies, Inc.   (1)
2820 E College Ave Ste J, State College, PA 16801-7548
Tel.: (814) 238-7539
Web Site: http://www.trstechnologies.com
Electrical Equipment & Component Mfr
N.A.I.C.S.: 335999
Thomas R. Shrout *(Founder)*

TAYIH KENMOS AUTO PARTS CO.
No 4-12 Shalun, Anding Dist, T'ainan, Taiwan
Tel.: (886) 65934786
Web Site: https://www.kenmos.com.tw
8107—(TPE)
Rev.: $25,445,299
Assets: $94,909,077
Liabilities: $47,920,083
Net Worth: $46,988,994
Earnings: $1,029,547
Fiscal Year-end: 12/31/22
Automobile Parts Mfr
N.A.I.C.S.: 336340

TAYLOR ENGINEERING & PLASTICS LIMITED
Molesworth Street, Rochdale, OL16 2BD, Lancashire, United Kingdom
Tel.: (44) 1706 714700
Web Site: http://www.tep.co.uk
Year Founded: 1949
Sales Range: $25-49.9 Million
Emp.: 205
Industrial Mold Mfr
N.A.I.C.S.: 333511
Rodney Taylor *(Chm)*

TAYLOR FORD SALES LTD
10 Lewisville Road, Moncton, E1C AM7, NB, Canada
Tel.: (506) 857-2300
Web Site: http://www.taylorford.ca
Year Founded: 1980
Rev.: $53,210,309
Emp.: 106
New & Used Car Dealers
N.A.I.C.S.: 441110
Paul Leblanc *(CFO)*

TAYLOR MARITIME INVESTMENTS LIMITED
1 Royal Plaza Royal Avenue, Saint Peter Port, GY1 2H, Guernsey
Tel.: (44) 2038380530   UK
Web Site: https://www.taylormaritime.com
Year Founded: 2014
TMI—(LSE)
Rev.: $31,079,140
Assets: $488,408,076
Liabilities: $3,401,669
Net Worth: $485,006,407
Earnings: ($53,482,934)
Emp.: 12
Fiscal Year-end: 03/31/24
Investment Management Service
N.A.I.C.S.: 523999
Alexander Slee *(Deputy CEO)*

TAYLOR SMITH GROUP
Taylor Smith House Old Quay D Road, Port Louis, 11615, Mauritius
Tel.: (230) 2063333
Web Site: http://www.taylorsmith.com
Year Founded: 1908
Sales Range: $10-24.9 Million
Emp.: 700
Logistics & Distribution Services
N.A.I.C.S.: 488330
Colin Taylor *(CEO)*

Subsidiaries:
AEL DDS Ltd   (1)
34-35 Tamariniers street, Port Louis, Mauritius
Tel.: (230) 2302402881
Petroleum Product Transportation Services
N.A.I.C.S.: 486910
Robert Desvaux *(Gen Mgr)*

Bourbon Vanilla Ltd   (1)
Rogers Industrial Park 1, Riche Terre, Mauritius
Tel.: (230) 2302492620
Web Site: http://www.vaynilla.mu
Grocery Product Distr
N.A.I.C.S.: 424490
Dominique Vaudin *(Gen Mgr)*

Geotechnical Services Ltd   (1)
Trunk Road St Jean, Port Louis, Mauritius
Tel.: (230) 2304667526
Web Site: http://www.gets.mu
Geotechnical laboratory Services
N.A.I.C.S.: 541380

Mauritius Molasses Company Ltd   (1)
Harbour Area Quay D, Port Louis, Mauritius
Tel.: (230) 2302427318
Fuel Storage Services
N.A.I.C.S.: 493190
Jean-Claude Ng *(Mgr-Fin & Admin)*

Sofap Ltd.   (1)
DBM Industrial Zone, Coromandel, Port Louis, Mauritius
Tel.: (230) 2332530
Web Site: http://www.sofapltd.com
Paints & Coatings Distr
N.A.I.C.S.: 424950

TAYLOR STEEL INC.
477 Arvin Avenue, PO Box 3366, Stoney Creek, L8E 2N1, ON, Canada
Tel.: (905) 662-4925
Web Site: http://www.taylorsteel.com
Year Founded: 1967
Rev.: $221,033,384
Emp.: 450
Flat Rolled Steel Mfr
N.A.I.C.S.: 331221
Michael W. Taylor *(Owner & Chm)*

Subsidiaries:
Taylor Steel Inc.   (1)
2260 Industrial Trace, Lordstown, OH 44481
Tel.: (330) 824-8600
Flat Rolled Steel Mfr
N.A.I.C.S.: 331221

TAYLOR WIMPEY PLC
Gate House Turnpike Road, High Wycombe, HP12 3NR, Buckinghamshire, United Kingdom
Tel.: (44) 1494558323   UK
Web Site: https://www.taylorwimpey.co.uk
Year Founded: 1921
TW—(LSE)
Rev.: $4,441,986,847
Assets: $7,903,943,363
Liabilities: $2,186,804,849
Net Worth: $5,717,138,514
Earnings: $441,102,123
Emp.: 4,618
Fiscal Year-end: 12/31/23
Housing & Development Company
N.A.I.C.S.: 236118
James Jordan *(Co-Sec & Dir-Legal Grp)*

Subsidiaries:
Los Arqueros Golf & Country Club S.A.   (1)
Ronda Road A-397 Km 44 5, Benahavis, 29679, Malaga, Spain
Tel.: (34) 95 278 4600
Web Site: https://www.losarquerosgolf.com
Golf Course Services
N.A.I.C.S.: 713910

Taylor (Insurance Brokers) Limited   (1)
2 Princes Way, Solihull, B91 3ES, West Midlands, United Kingdom   (100%)
Tel.: (44) 216008000
Sales Range: $350-399.9 Million
Emp.: 600
Insurance Brokerage
N.A.I.C.S.: 524210

Taylor Wimpey (Solihull) Limited   (1)
Second Floor Fore 2 Fore Business Park Huskisson Way, Shirley, Solihull, B90 4SS, United Kingdom
Tel.: (44) 1217033300
Residential Remodeling Services
N.A.I.C.S.: 236118
Roger Northam *(Mng Dir)*

Taylor Wimpey Logistics   (1)
St Leger Drive, Newmarket Business Park, Newmarket, CB8 7DT, Suffolk, United Kingdom
Tel.: (44) 163 866 6006
Web Site: https://www.taylorwimpey.co.uk
Sales Range: $25-49.9 Million
Emp.: 40
Residential Construction
N.A.I.C.S.: 236117

Taylor Wimpey UK Limited   (1)
Gates House Turnpike Road, High Wycombe, HP12 3NR, Bucks, United Kingdom
Tel.: (44) 1494558323
Sales Range: $650-699.9 Million
Emp.: 80
Administrative, Financial, Legal & Technical Services
N.A.I.C.S.: 561499

Taylor Wimpey de Espana S.A.U   (1)
C/Arago 223-223 A, 07008, Palma de Mallorca, Spain
Tel.: (34) 971706972
Web Site: http://taylorwimpeyspain.com
Residential Construction
N.A.I.C.S.: 236117
Marc Pritchard *(Dir-Sls & Mktg)*

Wainhomes (Northern) Limited   (1)
Kelburn Court Daten Park, Birchwood, Warrington, WA3 6UT, United Kingdom
Tel.: (44) 1925885400
Housing Development Services
N.A.I.C.S.: 624229

Wainhomes (Southern) Limited   (1)
Unit 2 Exeter International Office Park Exeter, Clyst Honiton, Devon, EX5 2HL, United Kingdom
Tel.: (44) 1392448900
Housing Development Services
N.A.I.C.S.: 624229

Wimpey Overseas Holdings Limited   (1)
Gate House Turnpike Road, High Wycombe, HP12 3NR, Buckinghamshire, United Kingdom
Tel.: (44) 1494558323
Web Site: http://www.taylorwimpey.com
Residential Construction
N.A.I.C.S.: 236117

TAYLORMADE RENEWABLES LTD.
1201 to 1215 12th Floor Solitaire Connect, Nr BMW Showroom SG Highway Makarba, Ahmedabad, 380051, Gujarat, India
Tel.: (91) 7940040888
Web Site: https://www.trlindia.com
541228—(BOM)
Rev.: $59,432
Assets: $3,039,418
Liabilities: $582,759
Net Worth: $2,456,659
Earnings: ($247,311)
Fiscal Year-end: 03/31/21
Cook Stoves Mfr
N.A.I.C.S.: 335220
Samir Patel *(Head-Technical)*

TAZE KURU GIDA SANAYI VE TICARET A.S.
Yarbasi Sk No 6, Akcay Mh Kizilcahamam, Ankara, Turkiye
Tel.: (90) 2165454126
Web Site: https://www.tazekuru.com

AND PRIVATE COMPANIES — TBG TREUHAND PARTNER AG

Year Founded: 2009
TETMT—(IST)
Rev.: $1,674,941
Assets: $3,763,375
Liabilities: $1,546,413
Net Worth: $2,216,962
Earnings: $1,571,603
Fiscal Year-end: 12/31/23
Dried Food Product Mfr
N.A.I.C.S.: 311423

TAZMO CO., LTD.
5311 Haga, Kita-ku, Okayama, 701-1221, Japan
Tel.: (81) 862395000
Web Site: https://www.tazmo.co.jp
6266—(TKS)
Rev.: $199,661,490
Assets: $336,264,520
Liabilities: $193,790,970
Net Worth: $142,473,550
Earnings: $16,704,040
Emp.: 1,156
Fiscal Year-end: 12/31/23
Liquid Crystal Display Equipment & Semiconductor Device Mfr; Precision Molding Dies & Plastic Molding
N.A.I.C.S.: 334419
Toshio Ikeda (Pres)

Subsidiaries:

Apprecia Technology, Inc. (1)
1st 29-29 Takadanobaba Shinjuku-ku, Tokyo, 169-0075, Japan **(100%)**
Tel.: (81) 362339150
Web Site: http://www.appreciatech.jp
Sales Range: $10-24.9 Million
Emp.: 90
Special Industry Machinery
N.A.I.C.S.: 333310
Toshio Ikeda (Pres)

PRETEC Co., Ltd. (1)
2750 Kinoko-cho, Ibara, 715-0004, Okayama, Japan
Tel.: (81) 86 662 0770
Web Site: https://pretec.jp
Emp.: 85
Molded Plastic Product Mfr
N.A.I.C.S.: 326199

Shanghai TAZMO Precision Machinery Co., Ltd.
No 661-2 ChenJing Road, Sijing Town Songjiang District, Shanghai, 201601, China
Tel.: (86) 215 763 3107
Web Site: http://www.tazmo.co.jp
Molded Plastic Products Mfr & Distr
N.A.I.C.S.: 333511

TAZMO Vietnam Co., Ltd. (1)
Lot H 09 Road 1, Long Hau Industrial Park Long Hau Commune Can Giuoc District, Ho Chi Minh City, Long An Province, Vietnam
Tel.: (84) 283 873 4192
Web Site: https://tazmo-vn.com
Emp.: 349
Semiconductor Machinery Mfr
N.A.I.C.S.: 333242

Tazmo Co., Ltd. - Plant No.2 (1)
6186 Kinoko-cho, Ibara, 715-8603, Okayama, Japan
Tel.: (81) 866620923
Web Site: http://www.tazmo.co.jp
Sales Range: $100-124.9 Million
Semiconductor Wafers Mfr
N.A.I.C.S.: 334413

Tazmo Co., Ltd. - Plant No.3 (1)
2751-1 Kinoko-cho, Ibara, 715-8603, Okayama, Japan
Tel.: (81) 866630760
Sales Range: $125-149.9 Million
Injection Molding Machine Mfr
N.A.I.C.S.: 326199
Masahiro Sekido (Mgr-Sls & Mktg)

Tazmo Co., Ltd. - Plant No.5 (1)
6831-7 Kinoko-cho, Ibara, 715-8603, Okayama, Japan
Tel.: (81) 866622214
Molded Dies Mfr
N.A.I.C.S.: 333514

Tazmo Co., Ltd. - Tamashima Plant (1)
8230 Otoshima Tamashima, Kurashiki, 713-8063, Okayama, Japan
Tel.: (81) 86 525 2111
Web Site: http://www.tazmo.co.jp
Semiconductor Machinery Mfr
N.A.I.C.S.: 333242

Tazmo Inc. (1)
42840 Christy St Ste 103, Fremont, CA 94538
Tel.: (510) 438-4890
Web Site: https://www.tazmoinc.com
Sales Range: $25-49.9 Million
Emp.: 5
Semiconductor Equipment Distr
N.A.I.C.S.: 334413
Toshio Ikeda (Pres)

TB GROUP INC.
NREG Hongo 3-chome Building 3-26-6 Hongo, Bunkyo-ku, Tokyo, 113-0033, Japan
Tel.: (81) 356842321
Web Site: https://www.tb-group.co.jp
Year Founded: 1946
6775—(TKS)
Rev.: $15,229,440
Assets: $10,377,700
Liabilities: $5,102,920
Net Worth: $5,274,780
Earnings: ($1,612,840)
Emp.: 130
Fiscal Year-end: 03/31/24
Electric Device Mfr
N.A.I.C.S.: 334419
Saburo Murata (Chm & Pres)

TB SA ACQUISITION CORP.
Boundary Hall Cricket Square, PO Box 1093, Grand Cayman, Georgetown, KY1-1102, Cayman Islands
Tel.: (345) 814 5771   Ky
Year Founded: 2021
TBSAU—(NASDAQ)
Investment Services
N.A.I.C.S.: 523999
Andrew Rolfe (CEO)

TBC BANK GROUP PLC
7 Marjanishvili Street, 102, Tbilisi, Georgia
Tel.: (995) 322272727   UK
Web Site: https://www.tbcbankgroup.com
Year Founded: 1992
TBCG—(LSE)
Rev.: $1,206,468,588
Assets: $12,266,895,158
Liabilities: $10,473,205,562
Net Worth: $1,793,689,596
Earnings: $424,208,318
Emp.: 4,221
Fiscal Year-end: 12/31/23
Commercial Banking Services
N.A.I.C.S.: 522110
Arne Berggren (Chm)

Subsidiaries:

JSC TBC Insurance (1)
Tel.: (995) 2422222
Web Site: https://www.tbcinsurance.ge
Emp.: 300
Property Insurance Services
N.A.I.C.S.: 524126

TBC Capital LLC (1)
Tel.: (995) 322272797
Web Site: https://www.tbccapital.ge
Financial Advisory Services
N.A.I.C.S.: 523940
Tornike Kordzaia (Head-Res)

TBC Kredit LLC (1)
28 May str 71-77, Baku, Azerbaijan
Tel.: (994) 2277
Web Site: https://www.tbckredit.az
Commercial Banking Services
N.A.I.C.S.: 522110
Tetrashvili Nukri (CEO)

TBC Leasing JSC (1)
St Tbilisi I Chavchavadze 76 M St Batumi 55, Chavchavadze st Tbilisi d Agmashenebeli alley 0131, 0162, Tbilisi, Georgia
Tel.: (995) 322122777
Web Site: https://www.tbcleasing.ge
Emp.: 150
Financial Lending Services
N.A.I.C.S.: 523999

TBEA CO., LTD.
No 189 Beijing South Road, Changji, 831100, Xinjiang, China
Tel.: (86) 9946508000
Web Site: https://www.tbea.com
600089—(SHG)
Rev.: $13,597,480,007
Assets: $26,569,882,061
Liabilities: $14,422,690,269
Net Worth: $12,147,191,792
Earnings: $1,481,877,312
Emp.: 24,000
Fiscal Year-end: 12/31/23
Electric Power Transmission & Transformation Equipment Mfr
N.A.I.C.S.: 335999
Xin Zhang (Chm)

Subsidiaries:

TBEA Energy (India) Pvt. Ltd. (1)
National Highway No 8 Village Miyagam, Karjan, Vadodara, 391440, India
Tel.: (91) 2666660000
Web Site: https://www.tbeaindia.com
Electric Equipment Mfr
N.A.I.C.S.: 335999

TBEA Hengyang Transformer Co., Ltd. (1)
Bai Sha Zhou, Hengyang, 421007, Hunan, China
Tel.: (86) 7348498115
Electric Equipment Mfr
N.A.I.C.S.: 335999

TBEA Shandong Luneng Taishan Cable Co., Ltd. (1)
No 6 Zhailiang Road, Xintai, Shandong, China
Tel.: (86) 5387309801
Web Site: http://www.tbeacable.diytrade.com
Electric Equipment Mfr
N.A.I.C.S.: 335999

TBEA Shenyang Transformer Group Co., Ltd. (1)
No 18 Middle Bei Er Zhong Road, Tiexi district, Shenyang, 110025, Liaoning, China
Tel.: (86) 2425698216
Electric Equipment Mfr
N.A.I.C.S.: 335999

TBEA Tianjin Transformer Co., Ltd. (1)
No 3 North Complex Nan Ni Wan Road Huang He Dao, Nankai i District, Tianjin, 300112, China
Tel.: (86) 2227514532
Electric Equipment Mfr
N.A.I.C.S.: 335999

TBEA Xian Electric Technology Co.,Ltd. (1)
70 TBEA Xian Industrial Park Shanglinyuan 4 Road High-Tech Zone, Xi'an, 710119, Shaanxi, China
Tel.: (86) 2968760666
Web Site: http://en.sunoasis.com.cn
Photovoltaic Product Mfr
N.A.I.C.S.: 334413

TBEA Xinjiang Cable Co., Ltd. (1)
No 52 South Yanan Road, Xinjiang, 831100, Changji, China
Tel.: (86) 9946553133
Web Site: http://www.en.tbea-dl.com.cn
Electric Equipment Mfr
N.A.I.C.S.: 335999

TBEA Xinjiang Sunoasis Co., Ltd. (1)
No 399 South Changchun Road Urumqi High-tech Zone, Xinjiang, China
Tel.: (86) 9913673257
Web Site: http://www.en.tbeaenergy.com

Wind Power Energy Development Services
N.A.I.C.S.: 221115

Xinte Energy Co., Ltd. (1)
No 2499 Mianguangdong Street, Ganquanpu Industrial Park State of High-tech Level Development Zone, Urumqi, Xinjiang, China **(60.25%)**
Tel.: (86) 9916392099
Web Site: http://www.xtnysolar.com
Rev.: $4,257,836,137
Assets: $11,897,631,918
Liabilities: $6,188,745,542
Net Worth: $5,708,886,377
Earnings: $708,562,758
Emp.: 8,586
Fiscal Year-end: 12/31/2023
Solar Grade Polysilicon Products Mfr
N.A.I.C.S.: 335131
Jianxin Zhang (Chm)

TBG DIAGNOSTICS LIMITED
Level 18 101 Collins St, Melbourne, 3000, VIC, Australia
Tel.: (61) 7 3088 7926   AU
Web Site: http://www.tbgbio.com
Rev.: $2,339,874
Assets: $10,518,413
Liabilities: $1,526,803
Net Worth: $8,991,610
Earnings: $433,718
Fiscal Year-end: 12/31/19
Cancer Therapeutics Developer
N.A.I.C.S.: 325412
Jitto Arulampalam (Chm)

TBG HOLDINGS NV
1 Avenue des Citronniers, BP 89, 98000, Monte Carlo, Monaco
Tel.: (377) 93155100
Year Founded: 1918
Sales Range: $1-4.9 Billion
Emp.: 7,000
Holding Company
N.A.I.C.S.: 551112
Georg Heinrich Thyssen-Bornemisza (Chm & CEO)

Subsidiaries:

Sterling SIHI GmbH (1)
Lindenstrasse 170, PO Box 1941, 25524, Itzehoe, Germany **(100%)**
Tel.: (49) 482177101
Web Site: http://www.sterlingsihi.com
Sales Range: $300-349.9 Million
Emp.: 1,500
Self-Priming Centrifugal Pumps, Branch Channel Pumps, Oil & Fuel Pumps
N.A.I.C.S.: 333996
Hans-Peter Rix (Chm-Mgmt Bd)

Subsidiary (US):

SIHI Pumps, Inc. (2)
303 Industrial Blvd, Grand Island, NY 14072-0460 **(100%)**
Tel.: (716) 773-6450
Web Site: http://www.sihi-pumps.com
Sales Range: $25-49.9 Million
Emp.: 50
Mfr of Liquid Ring Vaccuum Pumps, Oil Free Compressors & Centrifugal Pumps
N.A.I.C.S.: 333914
Mike Pastore (VP)

Subsidiary (Non-US):

Sterling Fluid Systems (UK) Limited (2)
Europa House Second Ave Trafford Park, Manchester, M17 1EE, United Kingdom **(100%)**
Tel.: (44) 1619286371
Web Site: http://www.sterlingsihi.com
Sales Range: $600-649.9 Million
Emp.: 25
Mfr of Pumps, Valves, Vacuum Technology & Water Treatment Systems
N.A.I.C.S.: 333996
Gary Leatherbarrow (Gen Mgr)

TBG TREUHAND PARTNER AG

TBG TREUHAND PARTNER AG

TBG Treuhand Partner AG—(Continued)
Kohlrainstrasse 10, 8700, Kusnacht,
Switzerland
Tel.: (41) 44 914 70 10
Web Site: http://www.tbg.ch
Privater Equity Firm
N.A.I.C.S.: 523999
Alain Scherrer (Controller)

Subsidiaries:

Telvent GIT, S.A. (1)
Calle Valgrande 6, 28108, Alcobendas,
Spain
Tel.: (34) 917147000
Information Technology Services
N.A.I.C.S.: 541511

Subsidiary (Non-US):

Telvent Australia Pty. Limited (2)
78 Waterloo Road, Macquarie Park, Macquarie Park, 2113, NSW, Australia
Tel.: (61) 8 92 44 2346
Meteorological & Monitoring Products Mfr
N.A.I.C.S.: 334519

Subsidiary (US):

Telvent USA Inc. (1)
7000 Hollister Dr, Houston, TX 77040-5337
Tel.: (713) 939-9399
Remote Control Systems Mfr
N.A.I.C.S.: 541511

Subsidiary (Domestic):

DTN, LLC (3)
11400 Rupp Dr, Burnsville, MN 55337
Tel.: (402) 390-2328
Web Site: http://www.dtn.com
Subscription-based Services (Real-time
Weather, Agricultural, Energy & Commodity
Market Information)
N.A.I.C.S.: 519290
Ron Sznaider (Vice Chm)

Subsidiary (Domestic):

ClearAg, Inc. (4)
4324 University Ave Ste B, Grand Forks,
ND 58203
Tel.: (701) 792-1800
Software Publishing Services
N.A.I.C.S.: 513210
Joe Bergera (Pres & CEO)

Subsidiary (Non-US):

The Weather Company (4)
L 5 8 West St, Sydney, 2060, NSW, Australia
Tel.: (61) 299659200
Web Site: http://www.weatherzone.com
Professional Scientific & Technical Services
N.A.I.C.S.: 541990

Subsidiary (Domestic):

Weather Decision Technologies,
Inc. (4)
201 David L Boren Blvd Ste 270, Norman,
OK 73072
Tel.: (405) 579-7675
Web Site: http://www.wdtinc.com
Rev.: $5,500,000
Emp.: 55
Business Products & Services
N.A.I.C.S.: 513199
Bill Conway (Sr VP-Intl Sys)

Wilkens Weather Technologies,
L.P. (4)
2925 Briarpark Dr Ste 550, Houston, TX
77042-3720
Tel.: (713) 568-7800
Web Site: http://www.wilkensweather.com
Weather Support Services
N.A.I.C.S.: 541620
Steve Krcek (Sls Mgr & Meteorologist)

TBH GLOBAL CO., LTD.
147-9 Garak-dong, Songpa-gu,
Seoul, 05824, Korea (South)
Tel.: (82) 220583800
Web Site: https://tbhglobal.co.kr
Year Founded: 2000

084870—(KRS)
Rev.: $155,771,197
Assets: $86,155,294
Liabilities: $39,995,337
Net Worth: $46,159,956
Earnings: $3,779,240
Emp.: 268
Fiscal Year-end: 12/31/22
Apparel Mfr & Whslr
N.A.I.C.S.: 315990
Jong Wan Woo (CEO)

Subsidiaries:

TBH Hongkong Limited (1)
Level 19 Two Chinachem Central 26 Des
Voeux Road, Central, Hong Kong, China
(Hong Kong)
Tel.: (852) 21588424
Risk Managemeng Srvices
N.A.I.C.S.: 541618

The Basic House(Shanghai) Co.,
Ltd. (1)
2F Suite A NO 2163 Wanyuan Rd, Shanghai, China
Tel.: (86) 2164656516
Underwear Distr
N.A.I.C.S.: 423610

TBI MOTION TECHNOLOGY CO., LTD.
No 123 Sanduo Rd, Shulin Dist, New
Taipei City, 23876, Taiwan
Tel.: (886) 226892689
Web Site:
https://www.tbimotion.com.tw
Year Founded: 1986
4540—(TAI)
Rev.: $84,083,649
Assets: $253,802,306
Liabilities: $147,211,610
Net Worth: $106,590,695
Earnings: ($3,388,338)
Fiscal Year-end: 12/31/23
Linear Motion Product Mfr
N.A.I.C.S.: 332991
Ching-Kun Li (Chm)

Subsidiaries:

TBI Motion Intelligence Co., Ltd. (1)
4F No 123 Sanduo Rd, Shulin District, New
Taipei City, 23876, Taiwan
Tel.: (886) 226892696
Ball Screw Mfr & Distr
N.A.I.C.S.: 332722

TBI Motion Techonology (Suzhou)
Co., Ltd. (1)
No 3 Fuyang Industrial Workshop Fuyuan
Road Chengyang Street, Xiangcheng Economic and Technological Development
Zone, Suzhou, China
Tel.: (86) 51262930178
Ball Screw Mfr & Distr
N.A.I.C.S.: 332722

Tbi Motion Technology (Suzhou) Co.,
Ltd. (1)
2008 Office Building C Suzhou Center, Suzhou Industrial Park, Suzhou, China
Tel.: (86) 51262930178
Linear Motion Product Mfr
N.A.I.C.S.: 332991

TBILVINO JOINT STOCK COMPANY
2 Sarajishvili Avenue, Tbilisi, 0153,
Georgia
Tel.: (995) 32 2 651 625
Web Site: http://www.tbilvino.com.ge
Year Founded: 1962
Wine Mfr & Distr
N.A.I.C.S.: 312130

TBK & SONS HOLDINGS LIMITED
Lot 333 Kampung Paya Batu 2 Jalan
Seremban, Port Dickson, Negeri
Sembilan, Malaysia

Web Site:
https://www.tbksholdings.com
Year Founded: 2018
1960—(HKG)
Rev.: $204,412,230
Assets: $59,741,055
Liabilities: $21,913,403
Net Worth: $37,827,653
Earnings: $2,608,650
Emp.: 298
Fiscal Year-end: 06/30/22
Holding Company
N.A.I.C.S.: 551112
Wing Tai Lam (Sec)

TBK CO. LTD.
4-21-1 Minami Naruse Machida, Tokyo, 194-0045, Japan
Tel.: (81) 427391471
Web Site: https://www.tbk-jp.com
7277—(TKS)
Rev.: $374,515,990
Assets: $373,702,960
Liabilities: $179,646,580
Net Worth: $194,056,380
Earnings: $2,194,520
Fiscal Year-end: 03/31/24
Brakes Mfr
N.A.I.C.S.: 335314
Masahiko Kuramura (Exec Officer &
Gen Mgr-Bus Plng Div)

Subsidiaries:

Chang'an TBK Co., Ltd. (1)
No 3 Industrial Zone Xinghua Rd Jiangbei
Wusha Village Chang'an Town, Dongguan,
523859, Guangdong, China
Tel.: (86) 769 8541 1030
Web Site: http://www.tbk-jp.com
Brake Linings & Other Automotive Products
Mfr & Marketing Services
N.A.I.C.S.: 336340

Changchun TBK Shili Auto Parts Co.,
Ltd. (1)
No 1899 Huaguang Street High-tech Development Zone, Gaoxin District, Changchun,
130012, Jilin, China
Tel.: (86) 43187053183
Web Site: https://www.cctbk.com
Brake Linings Mfr & Marketing Services
N.A.I.C.S.: 336340

Hangzhou TBK-APG Auto Brakes
Co., Ltd. (1)
Yatai Rd Shushan St, Xiaoshan Dist,
Hangzhou, 311203, Zhejiang, China
Tel.: (86) 57182765065
Web Site: http://www.apg-tbk.com
Automobile Brakes & Parts Mfr
N.A.I.C.S.: 336340

Qiaotou TBK Co., Ltd. (1)
NO 229 Heshi Road, Qiaotou Town, Dongguan, 523527, Guangdong, China
Tel.: (86) 76983439662
Brake Lining Mfr & Distr
N.A.I.C.S.: 336340

Suntec Corporation (1)
2-2-7 Honcho, Funabashi, 273-0005, Chiba,
Japan
Tel.: (81) 47 433 4511
Real Estate & Building Maintenance Services
N.A.I.C.S.: 561790

TBK America Inc. (1)
3700 W Industries Rd, Richmond, IN
47374-1386
Tel.: (765) 962-0147
Sales Range: $25-49.9 Million
Emp.: 45
Engine Components & Pumps Marketing &
Mfr
N.A.I.C.S.: 333914
Kaoru Ogata (Pres)

TBK China Co., Ltd. (1)
NO 229 Heshi Road, Qiaotou Town, Dongguan, 523527, Guangdong, China
Tel.: (86) 76983439662
Web Site: http://www.tbk-jp.com
Brakes & Pumps Marketing Services
N.A.I.C.S.: 333914

INTERNATIONAL PUBLIC

TBK Co. Ltd. - Fukushima No. 1
Plant (1)
304-7 Miyanomae Kawabe Tamakawa,
Ishikawa, Fukushima, 963-6313, Japan
Tel.: (81) 247574911
Web Site: http://www.tbk-jp.com
Disc Brakes & Drum Brakes Mfr
N.A.I.C.S.: 336340

TBK Co. Ltd. - Fukushima No. 2
Plant (1)
304-11 Miyanomae Kawabe Tamakawa-
mura, Ishikawa, Fukushima, 963-6313, Japan
Tel.: (81) 247574911
Web Site: http://www.tbk-jp.com
Automobile Water Pumps Mfr
N.A.I.C.S.: 333914

TBK India Private Ltd. (1)
Gat No 103/264/658/666 to
719/721/749/773/774/784, Village-Mhavashi
Tal-Khandara Dist-Satara, Satara, 412 802,
Maharashtra, India
Tel.: (91) 9850968149
Emp.: 100
Pump Mfr & Distr
N.A.I.C.S.: 336310
Ujjwal Kirloskar (Mng Dir)

TBK Sales Co., Ltd. (1)
4-19-3 Minami-Naruse, Machida, 194-0045,
Tokyo, Japan
Tel.: (81) 427241555
Web Site: http://www.tbk-jp.com
Construction Machinery & Vehicle Parts
Marketing & Service
N.A.I.C.S.: 238290

TBKK (Thailand) Co., Ltd (1)
Amata Nakorn Ind Estate 700/1017 Moo 9,
Mabpong Panthong, Chon Buri, 20160,
Thailand
Tel.: (66) 38109360
Pump Mfr & Distr
N.A.I.C.S.: 336310
Pachara Manpian (Suprv-Sls & Mktg)

TBR Co., Ltd. (1)
1-11-16 Takarada, Tsuruoka, 997-0011,
Yamagata, Japan
Tel.: (81) 235239551
Brake Shoes & Oil Pumps Mfr
N.A.I.C.S.: 333914

Tokyo Seiko Co., Ltd. (1)
393-1 Miyanomae Oaza Kawabe
Tamakawa-mura, Ishikawa-gun, Fukushima,
963-6313, Japan
Tel.: (81) 247573181
Web Site: http://www.tbk-jp.com
Water Pumps, Oil Pumps, Gears & Various
Types of Engine Components Mfr
N.A.I.C.S.: 333914

TBP ELECTRONICS BV
Vlakbodem 10, 3247 CP, Dirksland,
Netherlands
Tel.: (31) 187602744
Web Site: http://www.tbp.nl
Year Founded: 1976
Sales Range: $75-99.9 Million
Emp.: 140
Printed Circuit Assembly & Electronic
Components Mfr Services
N.A.I.C.S.: 334419
Ton Plooy (Founder)

Subsidiaries:

tbp electronics Belgium (1)
Bell Telephonelaan 3, B-2440, Geel, Belgium
Tel.: (32) 014572000
Sales Range: $100-124.9 Million
Emp.: 300
Development & Manufacture of Telecommunications & Electronics Equipment
N.A.I.C.S.: 335999

TBS HOLDINGS, INC.
5-3-6 Akasaka, Minato-ku, Tokyo,
107-8006, Japan
Tel.: (81) 337461111
Web Site:
https://www.tbsholdings.co.jp
Year Founded: 1951

9401—(TKS)
Rev.: $2,606,382,490
Assets: $10,361,201,440
Liabilities: $2,760,051,770
Net Worth: $7,601,149,670
Earnings: $252,012,860
Emp.: 254
Fiscal Year-end: 03/31/24
Holding Company; Television & Radio Broadcasting Services
N.A.I.C.S.: 551112
Hiroyuki Aiko *(Sr Exec Officer)*

Subsidiaries:

AKasaka Heat Supply Co Ltd (1)
5-4-8 Akasaka Clair Taiyo Bldg 4 F, Minato-ku, Tokyo, 107-0052, Japan
Tel.: (81) 335057567
Sales Range: $25-49.9 Million
Emp.: 20
Television Network Broadcasting Services
N.A.I.C.S.: 516120

Akasaka Graphics Art Inc (1)
2-6-24 Akasaka Akasaka Mizuno Building 4F, Minato-ku, Tokyo, 107-0052, Japan
Tel.: (81) 335057252
Web Site: http://www.aga.co.jp
Graphic Design Services
N.A.I.C.S.: 541430

Art Communication System, Inc (1)
2-14-5 Akasaka Daiwa Akasaka Building 2F, Minato-ku, Tokyo, 107-0052, Japan
Tel.: (81) 335831160
Web Site: http://www.acs-art.co.jp
Emp.: 144
Art Design Support Services
N.A.I.C.S.: 711510

Dreamax Telivision Inc (1)
2-14-5 Daiwa Akasaka Building 7th floor, Minato-ku, Tokyo, 107-0052, Japan
Tel.: (81) 335880981
Web Site: http://www.dreamax.co.jp
Sales Range: $25-49.9 Million
Emp.: 72
Television Network Broadcasting Services
N.A.I.C.S.: 516120
Mizutome Akira *(Pres)*

FF Toho Inc (1)
5-3-6 TBS Broadcasting Center 15F Akasaka, Minato-ku, Tokyo, 107-0052, Japan
Tel.: (81) 335057364
Web Site: http://www.fftoho.co.jp
Sales Range: $75-99.9 Million
Emp.: 349
Television Production Services
N.A.I.C.S.: 516120
Kamiya Satoshi *(Pres)*

Midoriyama Studio City, Inc (1)
Midoriyama Studio City 2100 Midoriyama, Aoba-ku, Yokohama, 227-0037, Kanagawa, Japan
Tel.: (81) 459636018
Web Site: https://www.midoriyama.co.jp
Open Studio Leasing & Maintenance Services
N.A.I.C.S.: 531120

NICHION, INC (1)
Sumitomo Fudosan Shin-Akasaka Bldg 7F 4-2-6 Akasaka, Minato-ku, Tokyo, 107-8380, Japan
Tel.: (81) 355623880
Web Site: https://www.nichion.co.jp
Sales Range: $25-49.9 Million
Emp.: 92
Music Publishing Services
N.A.I.C.S.: 512230

OXYBOT, Inc (1)
7-6-38 Akasaka Alphabet Seven 1 F, Minato-Ku, Tokyo, 107-0052, Japan
Tel.: (81) 335054355
Web Site: http://www.oxybot.com
Sales Range: $25-49.9 Million
Emp.: 30
Motion Picture & Video Production Services
N.A.I.C.S.: 512110
Sumyhiao Sori *(Mgr)*

Rg Marketing Co Ltd (1)
12-13 Fl 5-9-11 Kitashinagawa, Shinagawa-ku, Tokyo, 141-0001, Japan
Tel.: (81) 334419161
Web Site: http://www.rg-mark.co.jp
Cosmetic Product Whslr
N.A.I.C.S.: 424210

StylingLife Holdings Inc. (1)
Shinjuku Front Tower 2-21-1 Kita-Shinjuku, Shinjuku-ku, Tokyo, 169-0074, Japan
Tel.: (81) 368725000
Web Site: https://www.stylinglife.co.jp
Holding Company; Retail Store Operator
N.A.I.C.S.: 551112

Subsidiary (Domestic):

CP Cosmetics Inc. (2)
2-21-1 Kita-Shinjuku, Shinjuku-ku, Tokyo, 169-0074, Japan
Tel.: (81) 368725200
Web Site: https://www.cp-cosmetics.com
Sales Range: $25-49.9 Million
Emp.: 82
Cosmetics & Beauty Products Developer, Mfr & Marketer
N.A.I.C.S.: 325620

LightUp Shopping Club Inc. (2)
Shinjuku Front Tower 2-21-1 Kita Shinjuku, Shinjuku-ku, Tokyo, 169-8228, Japan
Tel.: (81) 368725300
Web Site: https://www.lusc.co.jp
Sales Range: $25-49.9 Million
Emp.: 177
General Merchandise Retailer
N.A.I.C.S.: 459999

Plazastyle Corporation (2)
2-12-2 Kita-Aoyama, Minato-ku, Tokyo, 107-0061, Japan
Tel.: (81) 354138711
Web Site: http://www.plazastyle.co.jp
Sales Range: $350-399.9 Million
General Merchandise Retailer
N.A.I.C.S.: 459999

TC Entertainment, Inc. (1)
2-14-5 Akasaka Daiwa Akasaka Building 6th floor, Minato-Ku, Tokyo, 107-0052, Japan
Tel.: (81) 367340035
Web Site: http://www.tc-ent.co.jp
Animation Production & Software Services
N.A.I.C.S.: 334610
Kodama Shigehiko *(Pres)*

Telecom Sound Inc (1)
8170 Beverly Blvd, Los Angeles, CA 90048-4524
Tel.: (310) 689-2344
Music Production & Distribution Services
N.A.I.C.S.: 512110

Tlc Co Ltd (1)
2-1-1 Ojima, Koto-ku, Tokyo, 136-0072, Japan
Tel.: (81) 336388241
Television Network Broadcasting Services
N.A.I.C.S.: 516120

Tokyo Broadcasting System Television, Inc.
5-3-6 Akasaka, Minato-ku, Tokyo, 107-8066, Japan **(100%)**
Tel.: (81) 337461111
Web Site: https://www.tbs.co.jp
Television Programming & Broadcasting Services
N.A.I.C.S.: 516120

Subsidiary (Domestic):

TBS Kikaku Co., Ltd. (2)
6-4-19 Akasaka Akasakatsc Building 4 F, Minato-ku, Tokyo, 107-0052, Japan
Tel.: (81) 335057273
Emp.: 5
Car Parking & Insurance Agencies Management Services
N.A.I.C.S.: 812930
Kazuto Yokota *(Mgr)*

TBS Media Research Institute Inc. (2)
7th Seiko Building 7F 5-5-9 Akasaka, Minato-ku, Tokyo, 107-0052, Japan
Tel.: (81) 335866003
Web Site: https://www.tbs-mri.co.jp
Marketing Research Service
N.A.I.C.S.: 541910

TBS Radio & Communications, Inc (2)
5-3-6 Akasaka, Minato-ku, Tokyo, 107-0052, Japan
Tel.: (81) 337461111
Web Site: https://tbsradio.co.jp
Emp.: 68
Radio Broadcasting Services
N.A.I.C.S.: 516110

TBS Service, Inc (2)
TBS Broadcast Center 18 F 5-3-6 Akasaka, Minato-ku, Tokyo, 107-8482, Japan
Tel.: (81) 335057216
Web Site: http://www.tbss.co.jp
Emp.: 150
Television Network Broadcasting Services
N.A.I.C.S.: 516120

TBS Sunwork, Inc (2)
THE HEXAGON 4F No 4-7 Akasaka 5-chome, Minato-ku, Tokyo, 107-0052, Japan
Tel.: (81) 335057530
Web Site: https://www.tbssw.co.jp
Emp.: 281
Commercial Building Operation & Management Services
N.A.I.C.S.: 236220

TBS Vision, Inc (2)
5-3-6 Akasaka Tbs Hoso Ctr 18 F, Minato-Ku, Tokyo, 107-8471, Japan
Tel.: (81) 355715020
Web Site: http://www.tbs-v.co.jp
Sales Range: $50-74.9 Million
Emp.: 111
Television Network Broadcasting Services
N.A.I.C.S.: 516120
Suyuhao Tahiro *(Pres)*

TSB Trimedia Inc (2)
Akasaka Iinuma Bldg 1F, Minato, Tokyo, 107-0052, Japan
Tel.: (81) 335057305
Video Production Services
N.A.I.C.S.: 512110

Subsidiary (US):

Tokyo Broadcasting System International, Inc. (2)
733 3rd Ave Ste 1700-14, New York, NY 10017
Tel.: (212) 652-0006
Web Site: https://www.tbsi-us.com
Television Network Broadcasting Services
N.A.I.C.S.: 516120

Tomo-Digi Corporation (1)
Kokusai Shin Akasaka East Building 13 F 2-14-27 Akasaka, Minato-ku, Tokyo, 107-0052, Japan
Tel.: (81) 355492495
Web Site: http://www.tomo-digi.co.jp
Data Broadcasting Service
N.A.I.C.S.: 518210
Kunio Ogawa *(Auditor)*

Totsu Inc (1)
5-2-20 Akasaka, Minato-ku, Tokyo, 107-6109, Japan
Tel.: (81) 335866158
Web Site: http://www.totsu.co.jp
Emp.: 313
Television Network Broadcasting Services
N.A.I.C.S.: 516120

YARUKI Switch Career Co., Ltd. (1)
Hatchobori 2-24-2 Hatchobori Dailchi Seimei Bldg, Chuo, Tokyo, 104-0032, Japan
Tel.: (81) 368581287
Web Site: https://www.ys-career.jp
Educational Support Services
N.A.I.C.S.: 611710

YPSwitch Co., Ltd. (1)
Hatchobori Dai-ichi Life Building 2-24-2 Hatchobori, Chuo-ku, Tokyo, 104-0032, Japan
Tel.: (81) 368451235
Web Site: https://ypswitch.jp
Educational Institution Services
N.A.I.C.S.: 611710

TBS INTERNATIONAL PLC
Block A1 EastPoint Business Park, Fairview, Dublin, 3, Ireland
Tel.: (353) 1 2400 222 IE
Web Site: http://www.tbsship.com
Year Founded: 1993
Sales Range: $400-449.9 Million
Emp.: 170
Ocean transportation Services & Cargo Logistics
N.A.I.C.S.: 483111
Gregg L. McNelis *(Pres & CEO)*

Subsidiaries:

Compass Chartering Corp. (1)
612 E Grassy Sprain Rd, Yonkers, NY 10710
Tel.: (914) 713-3330
Sales Range: $25-49.9 Million
Emp.: 50
Marine Cargo Handling
N.A.I.C.S.: 488320
Stephen J. Dilorenzo *(Pres)*

Roymar Ship Management Inc. (1)
Scarsdale Plz 455 Ctr Park Ave, Scarsdale, NY 10583-1060
Tel.: (914) 337-0714
Web Site: http://www.tbsship.com
Sales Range: $25-49.9 Million
Emp.: 75
Navigational Services to Shipping
N.A.I.C.S.: 488330
Ajoy Choudhury *(Mgr-Fleet Tech)*

TBS Shipping Services, Inc. (1)
612 E Grassy Sprain Rd, Yonkers, NY 10710
Tel.: (914) 961-1000
Web Site: http://www.tbsship.com
Sales Range: $1-9.9 Million
Emp.: 65
Freight Transportation Arrangement Local Trucking Operator
N.A.I.C.S.: 488510

Transworld Cargo Carriers, S.A. (1)
C-o The Alexander Corporate Group, Nassau, Bahamas
Tel.: (242) 3222511
Holding Company
N.A.I.C.S.: 551112

TBWA/HAKUHODO
1-13-10 Shibaura, Tokyo, 105-0023, Minato-ku, Japan
Tel.: (81) 3 3545 3523 JP
Web Site: http://www.tbwahakuhodo.co.jp
Year Founded: 1955
Sales Range: $50-74.9 Million
Emp.: 295
Advetising Agency
N.A.I.C.S.: 541810
Ichiro Zama *(Exec VP)*

TC BALKANA A.D.
Balkana Bb, 70260, Mrkonjic Grad, Bosnia & Herzegovina
Tel.: (387) 50212505
BKMG-R-A—(BANJ)
Rev.: $231,335
Assets: $370,846
Liabilities: $217,137
Net Worth: $153,709
Earnings: ($72,212)
Emp.: 7
Fiscal Year-end: 12/31/12
Home Management Services
N.A.I.C.S.: 721110
Miroslav Jaslar *(Chm-Mgmt Bd)*

TC BEFEKTETESI NYILVA-NOSAN MUKODO RESZVE-NYTARSASAG
1123 Budapest Alkotas utca 50, HU-1123, Budapest, Hungary
Tel.: (36) 14892200 HU
Web Site: http://www.tcnyrt.hu
Emp.: 100
Investment Services
N.A.I.C.S.: 523999
Vever Monika *(Chm)*

TC BIOPHARM (HOLDINGS) PLC

TC BIOPHARM (HOLDINGS) PLC

TC Biopharm (Holdings) plc—(Continued)

Maxim 1 2 Parklands Way, Holytown, Motherwell, ML1 4WR, United Kingdom UK
Tel.: (44) 1414337557
Web Site: https://tcbiopharm.com
Year Founded: 2021
TCBP—(NASDAQ)
Rev.: $5,219,798
Assets: $14,867,917
Liabilities: $14,902,779
Net Worth: ($34,862)
Earnings: ($1,886,832)
Emp.: 77
Fiscal Year-end: 12/31/22
Holding Company
N.A.I.C.S.: 551112
Michael Leek *(Co-Founder & CTO)*

TC ENERGY CORPORATION

450 - 1 Street S W, Calgary, T2P 5H1, AB, Canada Ca
Tel.: (403) 920-2000
Web Site: https://www.tcenergy.com
Year Founded: 1951
TRP—(NYSE)
Rev.: $11,869,785,459
Assets: $93,142,133,492
Liabilities: $64,083,730,632
Net Worth: $29,058,402,861
Earnings: $2,107,419,547
Emp.: 7,415
Fiscal Year-end: 12/31/23
Holding Company; Energy Resource Pipeline Transmission & Power Generation
N.A.I.C.S.: 551112
Siim A. Vanaselja *(Chm)*

Subsidiaries:

Columbia Pipeline Group, Inc. (1)
5151 San Felipe St Ste 2500, Houston, TX 77056
Tel.: (713) 386-3701
Web Site: http://www.columbiapipelinegroup.com
Rev.: $1,382,000,000
Assets: $10,537,700,000
Liabilities: $5,148,300,000
Net Worth: $5,389,400,000
Earnings: $116,800,000
Emp.: 1,782
Fiscal Year-end: 12/31/2016
Holding Company; Natural Gas Pipeline Transportation & Transmission Services
N.A.I.C.S.: 551112

Subsidiary (Domestic):

Columbia Energy Group (2)
5151 San Felipe St Ste 2500, Houston, TX 77056 (100%)
Tel.: (713) 386-3701
Holding Company
N.A.I.C.S.: 551112

Subsidiary (Domestic):

Columbia Pipeline Partners LP (3)
5151 San Felipe St Ste 2500, Houston, TX 77056 (100%)
Tel.: (713) 386-3701
Sales Range: $1-4.9 Billion
Holding Company; Natural Gas Transportation Pipelines & Related Energy Infrastructure Assets Operator
N.A.I.C.S.: 551112
Glen L. Kettering *(Pres)*

Subsidiary (Domestic):

Columbia Gas Transmission, LLC (4)
700 Louisiana St, Houston, TX 77002
Tel.: (832) 320-7000
Web Site: http://www.columbiagastrans.com
Natural Gas Pipeline Transportation & Transmission Services
N.A.I.C.S.: 486210

Branch (Domestic):

Columbia Gas Transmission, LLC - West Virginia Office (5)

1700 MacCorkle Ave SE, Charleston, WV 25314-1518
Tel.: (304) 357-2000
Natural Gas Pipeline Transportation & Transmission Services
N.A.I.C.S.: 486210

Subsidiary (Domestic):

Columbia Gulf Transmission, LLC (4)
5151 San Felipe St Ste 2500, Houston, TX 77056
Tel.: (713) 386-3701
Natural Gas Pipeline Transportation & Transmission Services
N.A.I.C.S.: 486210

Subsidiary (Domestic):

Columbia Pipeline Group Services Company (2)
5151 San Felipe St Ste 2500, Houston, TX 77056
Tel.: (713) 386-3701
Natural Gas Pipeline Transportation Support & Storage Services
N.A.I.C.S.: 213112

CrossAlta Gas Storage & Services Ltd. (1)
Firt Canadian Air Centre, 3500 350 7th Avenue SW, Calgary, T2P 3N9, AB, Canada (100%)
Tel.: (403) 298-3575
Web Site: http://www.crossalta.com
Natural Gas Transmission & Power Services
N.A.I.C.S.: 221210

TC PipeLines, LP (1)
700 Louisiana St Ste 700, Houston, TX 77002-2761 (100%)
Web Site: http://www.tcpipeslp.com
Rev.: $403,000,000
Assets: $2,853,000,000
Liabilities: $2,093,000,000
Net Worth: $760,000,000
Earnings: $280,000,000
Fiscal Year-end: 12/31/2019
Natural Gas Pipelines Management
N.A.I.C.S.: 486210
Jack A. Dobson *(Sec)*

Subsidiary (Domestic):

Bison Pipeline LLC (2)
717 Texas St, Houston, TX 77002-2761 (100%)
Tel.: (832) 320-5000
Web Site: http://www.bisonpipelinellc.com
Natural Gas Pipeline Transportation Services
N.A.I.C.S.: 486210

Gas Transmission Northwest LLC (2)
700 Louisiana St Ste 1300, Houston, TX 77002-2761 (100%)
Tel.: (832) 320-5000
Web Site: https://www.tcplus.com
Natural Gas Pipeline Transportation Services
N.A.I.C.S.: 486210
Russ Mahan *(VP)*

Joint Venture (Domestic):

Iroquois Gas Transmission System, LP (2)
1 Corporate Dr Ste 600, Shelton, CT 06484-6209 (49.3%)
Tel.: (203) 925-7200
Web Site: http://www.iroquois.com
Sales Range: $25-49.9 Million
Emp.: 109
Natural Gas Pipelines
N.A.I.C.S.: 486210
Jeffrey A. Bruner *(Pres)*

Subsidiary (Domestic):

North Baja Pipeline, LLC (2)
700 Louisiana St, Houston, TX 77002-2761
Tel.: (832) 320-5675
Web Site: http://www.northbajapipeline.com
Natural Gas Pipeline Transportation Services
N.A.I.C.S.: 486210

Tuscarora Gas Transmission Company (2)
1140 Financial Blvd Ste 900, Reno, NV 89502
Tel.: (775) 336-3200
Gas Transmission & Pipeline Company
N.A.I.C.S.: 486210

Trans Quebec & Maritimes Pipeline Inc. (1)
1 Place Ville-Marie 39th floor, Montreal, H2B 4M7, QC, Canada
Tel.: (450) 462-5300
Web Site: http://www.gazoductqm.com
Sales Range: $75-99.9 Million
Emp.: 4
Natural Gas Distr
N.A.I.C.S.: 486210
David Marchand *(CFO)*

TransCanada Energy Ltd. (1)
450 1st St SW, Calgary, T2P 5H1, AB, Canada (100%)
Tel.: (403) 920-2000
Web Site: http://www.transcanada.com
Energy Marketing Services
N.A.I.C.S.: 221122

TransCanada International Ltd. (1)
450 1st St SW, Calgary, T2P 5H1, AB, Canada (100%)
Tel.: (403) 920-2000
Web Site: http://www.transcanada.com
Sales Range: $1-4.9 Billion
Emp.: 3,000
N.A.I.C.S.: 486210

TransCanada PipeLines Limited (1)
TC Energy Tower 450 1 Street SW, Calgary, T2P 5H1, AB, Canada (100%)
Tel.: (403) 920-2000
Web Site: http://www.transcanada.com
Oil & Natural Gas Pipeline Distr
N.A.I.C.S.: 221210

Subsidiary (US):

TransCanada PipeLine USA Ltd. (2)
717 Texas St, Houston, TX 77002-2761
Tel.: (403) 920-2153
Sales Range: $25-49.9 Million
Emp.: 15
Petroleum Bulk Station Operating Services
N.A.I.C.S.: 424710
Mary Catharine Davis *(VP-Law)*

Subsidiary (Domestic):

ANR Pipeline Company (3)
700 Louisiana St Bank of America, Houston, TX 77002
Tel.: (832) 320-5000
Web Site: http://www.anrpl.com
Natural Gas Pipelines
N.A.I.C.S.: 486210
Dean Ferguson *(Pres-US)*

Subsidiary (Domestic):

ANR Storage Company (4)
700 Louisiana St, Houston, TX 77002
Tel.: (832) 320-5000
Web Site: http://www.latec.com
Sales Range: $25-49.9 Million
Emp.: 75
Gas Storage
N.A.I.C.S.: 493190

Subsidiary (Domestic):

Great Lakes Gas Transmission Company (3)
5250 Corporate Dr, Troy, MI 48098
Tel.: (248) 205-7400
Sales Range: $50-74.9 Million
Natural Gas Transmission
N.A.I.C.S.: 486210

TransCanada GTN System (3)
1 Sw Columbia St Ste 475, Portland, OR 97258-2015
Tel.: (503) 833-4000
Web Site: http://www.gastransmissionnw.com
Natural Gas Transmission Services
N.A.I.C.S.: 486210

TransCanada Keystone PipeLine, LP (3)
7509 NW Tiffany Springs Pkwy Northpointe

INTERNATIONAL PUBLIC

Cir II Ste 200, Kansas City, MO 64153
Tel.: (866) 717-7473
Crude Oil Transportation Services
N.A.I.C.S.: 486110
Russell K. Girling *(Pres & CEO)*

TransCanada Power L.P. (1)
450 1 St SW, Calgary, T2P 5H1, AB, Canada (30%)
Tel.: (403) 920-2000
Web Site: http://www.transcanada.com
Sales Range: $1-4.9 Billion
Emp.: 4,800
Provider of Electric Energy Services
N.A.I.C.S.: 926130

TransGas de Occidente S.A. (1)
Calle 110 #9-25 Oficina 1014, Bogota, Colombia (44%)
Tel.: (57) 1 657 7070
Sales Range: $25-49.9 Million
Emp.: 25
Operational Gas Pipelines
N.A.I.C.S.: 486210

TC SIGLO 21 S.A.A.

Jorge Basadre Avenue No 910, San Isidro, Peru
Tel.: (51) 3300267
Year Founded: 1989
TELCAAC1—(LIM)
Sales Range: Less than $1 Million
Cable Television Broadcasting Services
N.A.I.C.S.: 516120

TC SISTEMA SERVIZI SPA

Viale Forlanini 36, Garbagnate Milenese, 20024, Milan, Italy
Tel.: (39) 02995141
Web Site: http://www.tcsistema.com
Sales Range: $10-24.9 Million
Emp.: 100
Information Technology Systems
N.A.I.C.S.: 541512
Leonardo Marone *(Pres)*

TC UNTERHALTUNG-SELEKTRONIK AG

Im Kimmelberg 2-4, 56072, Koblenz, Germany
Tel.: (49) 261984360
Web Site: http://www.telecontrol.de
TCU—(DEU)
Rev.: $496,439
Assets: $2,007,339
Liabilities: $1,899,417
Net Worth: $107,921
Earnings: ($10,792)
Emp.: 4
Fiscal Year-end: 12/31/23
Broadcasting Equipment Mfr
N.A.I.C.S.: 334220
Thomas Nachtigahl *(Chm-Supervisory Bd)*

TCB-ARROW LTD

Watchmoor House Watchmoor Road, Camberley, GU15 3AQ, Surrey, United Kingdom
Tel.: (44) 1276 679394
Web Site: http://www.tcb-arrow.co.uk
Sales Range: $1-9.9 Million
Emp.: 30
Industrial Mold Mfr
N.A.I.C.S.: 333511
Murray Humphries *(Mng Dir)*

Subsidiaries:

Global Components Inc. (1)
17th St E, Palmetto, FL 34221
Tel.: (941) 723-9820
Web Site: http://www.globalcomponentsinc.com
Industrial Mold Mfr
N.A.I.C.S.: 333511

TCB-Arrow Ltd - Cable Plant (1)
Unit 1 Firsdale Ind Est Nangreave Street, Lancs, Leigh, WN7 4TN, United Kingdom
Tel.: (44) 1942 681659

Plastics Product Mfr
N.A.I.C.S.: 325211

TCC ASSETS (THAILAND) COMPANY LIMITED
19th Floor Park Ventures Ecoplex 57 Wireless Road, Bangkok, 10330, Thailand
Tel.: (66) 2 643 7392   TH
Web Site: http://www.tccassets.com
Year Founded: 2013
Investment Holding & Real Estate Company
N.A.I.C.S.: 551112
Panote Sirivadhanabhakdi *(CEO)*

TCC CONCEPTS LTD
5th Floor VB Capitol Building Range Hill Road Opp Hotel Symphony, Bhoslenagar Shivajinagar, Pune, 411007, Gujarat, India
Tel.: (91) 8669663441
Web Site: https://tccltd.in
512038—(BOM)
Sales Range: Less than $1 Million
Textile Product Whslr
N.A.I.C.S.: 424990
Vishal Omprakash Sharma *(CFO)*

Subsidiaries:

Brantford Limited (1)
9th Floor VB Capitol Range Hill Rd Bhoslenagar, Shivajinagar, Pune, 411007, Maharashtra, India
Tel.: (91) 9168621591
Web Site: https://www.brantfordindia.com
Commercial Real Estate Services
N.A.I.C.S.: 531210

TCC STEEL CORP.
9th floor 29 Eulji-ro, Jung-gu, Seoul, 04523, Korea (South)
Tel.: (82) 226333311
Web Site: https://www.tccsteel.com
Year Founded: 1959
002710—(KRS)
Rev.: $524,946,022
Assets: $389,238,937
Liabilities: $229,085,517
Net Worth: $160,153,420
Earnings: $22,677,719
Emp.: 275
Fiscal Year-end: 12/31/22
Steel Plate Mfr & Whslr
N.A.I.C.S.: 331110
B. R. Sohn *(Chm)*

Subsidiaries:

One Alloy Corporation (1)
165 Namdong-daero 86B/3L, Namdong-gu, Incheon, Korea (South)
Tel.: (82) 328169676
Alloy Product Mfr
N.A.I.C.S.: 331491

TCC America Corp. (1)
3510 Torrance Blvd Ste 217, Torrance, CA 90503
Tel.: (310) 781-9730
Steel Raw Material Distr
N.A.I.C.S.: 423510

TCC Engineering Corporation (1)
513 Cheolgang-ro, Nam-gu, Pohang, Gyeongsangbuk-do, Korea (South)
Tel.: (82) 542401133
Steel Mfr & Distr
N.A.I.C.S.: 332312

TCC Hanjin Corporation (1)
6045 Donghaean-ro, Nam-gu, Pohang, Gyeongsangbuk, Korea (South)
Tel.: (82) 542937501
Steel Material Mfr
N.A.I.C.S.: 332312

TCC INS Corporation (1)
18F Dongyang Tower 543 Gukhoe-daero, Yeongdeungpo-gu, Seoul, Korea (South)
Tel.: (82) 226391756
Information Technology Services
N.A.I.C.S.: 541512

TCC Logis Corporation (1)
42 Seoman-ro, Nam-gu, Pohang, Gyeongsangbuk-do, Korea (South)
Tel.: (82) 542862653
Warehouse Storage Services
N.A.I.C.S.: 531130

TCC Metal Corporation (1)
35 Jangheung-ro 197beon-gil, Nam-gu, Pohang, Gyeongsangbuk-do, Korea (South)
Tel.: (82) 542785921
Steel Product Mfr & Distr
N.A.I.C.S.: 331221

TCC Trading Corporation (1)
5th floor 29 Eulji-ro, Jung-gu, Seoul, 04523, Korea (South)
Tel.: (82) 226720637
Web Site: https://www.tcctr.com
Steel Product Distr
N.A.I.C.S.: 423510

TCECUR SWEDEN AB
Kungsgatan 9, 111 43, Stockholm, Sweden
Tel.: (46) 195001000
Web Site: https://tcecur.com
Electrical Equipment Distr
N.A.I.C.S.: 423610
Ole Oftedal *(Chm)*

TCFC FINANCE LTD
501 Raheja Chambers, Nariman Point, Mumbai, 400021, India
Tel.: (91) 2222844701
Web Site: https://www.tcfcfinance.com
532284—(BOM)
Rev.: $257,487
Assets: $12,214,850
Liabilities: $536,720
Net Worth: $11,678,130
Earnings: $71,987
Emp.: 8
Fiscal Year-end: 03/31/23
Finance Company
N.A.I.C.S.: 522291
Venkatesh Kamath *(CFO)*

TCG MERCHANT GROUP, INC.
Calle 56 y 57 Oficina 19JK Sortis Business Tower, Panama, Panama
Tel.: (507) 397 3579
Web Site: http://www.firstfactoringinc.com
FFAC—(PAN)
Sales Range: Less than $1 Million
Financial Services
N.A.I.C.S.: 523999

TCHAIKAPHARMA HIGHQUALITY MEDICINES AD
1 G M Dimitrov Blvd, 1172, Sofia, Bulgaria
Tel.: (359) 29625454
Web Site: https://www.tchaikapharma.com
Year Founded: 1999
7TH—(BUL)
Rev.: $19,882,268
Assets: $67,495,730
Liabilities: $12,217,139
Net Worth: $55,278,591
Earnings: $1,470,385
Fiscal Year-end: 12/31/19
Pharmaceuticals Product Mfr
N.A.I.C.S.: 325412
Pavel Manolov *(Mgr-Sls)*

TCHUGUNOLEENE JSC
3B - 4B Industialen put Str, 2050, Ihtiman, Bulgaria
Tel.: (359) 724 810 10
Web Site: http://www.tchugunoleene.com
Year Founded: 1975
Iron Moulds & Castings Mfr
N.A.I.C.S.: 331523
Emil Sharankov *(CEO & Mng Dir)*

TCI EXPRESS LIMITED
TCI House 69 Institutional Area Sector - 32, Gurgaon, 122001, Haryana, India
Tel.: (91) 1242384090
Web Site: https://www.tciexpress.in
Year Founded: 1996
TCIEXP—(NSE)
Rev.: $116,248,860
Assets: $74,209,590
Liabilities: $14,986,335
Net Worth: $59,223,255
Earnings: $13,731,900
Emp.: 2,709
Fiscal Year-end: 03/31/21
Transportation Services
N.A.I.C.S.: 541614
Chander Agarwal *(Mng Dir)*

TCI FINANCE LTD.
Plot no 20 Survey no 12 4th Floor Kothaguda Kondapur, Hyderabad, 500081, India
Tel.: (91) 4071204284
Web Site: https://www.tcifl.in
TCIFINANCE—(NSE)
Rev.: $580,739
Assets: $11,390,311
Liabilities: $15,466,501
Net Worth: ($4,076,190)
Earnings: ($1,060,264)
Emp.: 3
Fiscal Year-end: 03/31/21
Financial Management Services
N.A.I.C.S.: 523999
Dhanpat Ram Agarwal *(Chm)*

Subsidiaries:

ITAG Business Solutions Ltd. (1)
1-7-293 Mahatma Gandhi Road, Secunderabad, 500 003, Andhra Pradesh, India
Tel.: (91) 402 784 4284
Web Site: https://www.itagbs.com
Knowledge Process Outsourcing Services
N.A.I.C.S.: 561499
Dhanpat Ram Agarwal *(Dir-)*

TCI INDUSTRIES LTD
N A Sawant Marg, Near Colaba Fire Brigade, Mumbai, 400 005, Colaba, India
Tel.: (91) 2222822340
Web Site: https://www.tciil.in
532262—(BOM)
Rev.: $267,118
Assets: $1,551,166
Liabilities: $247,995
Net Worth: $1,303,171
Earnings: $79,528
Emp.: 5
Fiscal Year-end: 03/31/23
Logistic Solution Provider
N.A.I.C.S.: 541614
Dharmpal Agarwal *(Mng Dir & Vice Chm)*

TCL TECHNOLOGY GROUP CORP.
TCL Technology Building, No 17 Huifeng 3rd Road Zhongkai Hi-tech Development District, Huizhou, 516001, Guangdong, China
Tel.: (86) 7533311666
Web Site: http://www.tcl.com
Year Founded: 1981
000100—(SSE)
Rev.: $23,395,153,298
Assets: $50,543,470,973
Liabilities: $31,991,190,052
Net Worth: $18,552,280,921
Earnings: $36,689,188
Emp.: 75,000
Fiscal Year-end: 12/31/22
Cell Phone, Television & Household Appliance Mfr & Retailer
N.A.I.C.S.: 335220
Tomson Dong Sheng Li *(Founder)*

Subsidiaries:

TCL China Star Optoelectronics Technology Co., Ltd. (1)
No 9-2 TangMing Avenue, GuangMing New District, Shenzhen, 518132, China   (91.56%)
Tel.: (86) 755 8690 8888
Web Site: http://en.szcsot.com
Holding Company; Semiconductor & Liquid Crystal Display Technologies Developer, Mfr & Whslr
N.A.I.C.S.: 551112
Jun Zhao *(Sr VP & Gen Mgr-Wuhan)*

Holding (Non-US):

China Display Optoelectronics Technology Holdings Limited (2)
8/F Building 22E Phase Three Hong Kong Science Park, Pak Shek Kok, Hong Kong, New Territories, China (Hong Kong)   (65.05%)
Tel.: (852) 24377610
Web Site: https://www.cdoth8.com
Rev.: $590,852,340
Assets: $362,257,412
Liabilities: $221,834,246
Net Worth: $140,423,166
Earnings: $23,731,110
Emp.: 2,061
Fiscal Year-end: 12/31/2022
Holding Company; Liquid Crystal Display Mfr & Distr
N.A.I.C.S.: 551112
Feng Zhang *(Exec Dir)*

Subsidiary (Non-US):

China Display Optoelectronics Technology (Huizhou) Co., Ltd. (3)
No 23 ZhongKai High Tech Development Zone, Huizhou, 516006, Guangdong, China   (100%)
Tel.: (86) 752 580 8888
Web Site: http://www.cdoth8.com
LCD Module Mfr
N.A.I.C.S.: 334419

Subsidiary (Domestic):

Shenzhen Huaxing Optoelectronic Technology Co., Ltd. (2)
No 9-2 TangMing Avenue, GuangMing New District, Shenzhen, China
Tel.: (86) 755 8690 8888
Web Site: http://www.szcsot.com
Electronic Display Panels Mfr
N.A.I.C.S.: 334419
Cho Lan Wu *(Chief HR Officer)*

TCL Electronics Holdings Limited (1)
7th Floor Building 22E 22 Science Park East Avenue, Hong Kong Science Park New Territories, Sha Tin, China (Hong Kong)
Tel.: (852) 24377300
Web Site: http://www.electronics.tcl.com
Rev.: $9,097,305,413
Assets: $7,025,944,493
Liabilities: $4,874,043,353
Net Worth: $2,151,901,140
Earnings: $70,625,310
Emp.: 24,694
Fiscal Year-end: 12/31/2022
Mfr, Designer & Sales of Multi-media Consumer Electronics, Information Technology & Mobile Communication Equipment
N.A.I.C.S.: 449210
Dong Sheng Li *(Founder & Chm)*

Subsidiary (US):

Lotus Pacific Inc. (2)
Ste 740 1350 Bayshore Hwy, Burlingame, CA 94010-1816
Tel.: (949) 475-1880
Sales Range: $50-74.9 Million
Emp.: 150
Mfr of Audio & Video Equipment
N.A.I.C.S.: 334310

Subsidiary (Domestic):

Opta Systems, LLC (3)
7835 E McClain Dr, Scottsdale, AZ 85260-1732
Tel.: (650) 579-3610
Web Site: http://www.govideo.com

TCL TECHNOLOGY GROUP CORP.

TCL Technology Group Corp.—(Continued)

Sales Range: $25-49.9 Million
Emp.: 55
Developer & Marketer of Consumer Electronic Products & Home Theater
N.A.I.C.S.: 423620

Subsidiary (Non-US):

TCL Communication Technology Holdings Limited (2)
Block F4 TCL Communication Technology Building, TCL International E City Zhong Shan Yuan Road Nanshan District, Shenzhen, 518052, Guangdong, China **(100%)**
Tel.: (86) 755 3331 3000
Web Site: http://www.tclcom.com
Sales Range: $1-4.9 Billion
Emp.: 12,000
Holding Company; Mobile Handsets Designer, Mfr & Marketer
N.A.I.C.S.: 551112

Subsidiary (Non-US):

TCL Mobile Communication (HK) Company Limited (3)
19th F Tower 3 China Hong Kong City 33 Canton Rd, Tsim Sha Tsui, Kowloon, China (Hong Kong)
Tel.: (852) 31802888
Sales Range: $25-49.9 Million
Emp.: 12
Mobile Phone Apparatus Mfr
N.A.I.C.S.: 334220
Fei Liu (CEO)

Subsidiary (Domestic):

TCL Mobile Communication (Hohhot) Co., Ltd. (3)
Tengfei Avenue Ruyi District, Economic Technology, Development Zone, Huhehaote, 010010, China
Tel.: (86) 47 1461 0538
Mobile Phone Apparatus Mfr
N.A.I.C.S.: 334220

Subsidiary (Non-US):

TCL Moka Manufacturing S.A. de C.V. (2)
Calle 4 No 55 Ciudad Industrial, Tijuana, 22500, Baja California, Mexico
Tel.: (52) 6646233944
Electronic Consumer Products Mfr & Distr
N.A.I.C.S.: 335220
Fernando Cababa (Mgr-HR)

Tonly Electronics Holdings Limited (1)
Section 37 Zhongkai Hi-Tech Development Zone, Huizhou, 516006, Guangdong, China **(100%)**
Tel.: (86) 85224377460
Web Site: http://www.tonlyele.com
Rev.: $1,165,784,327
Assets: $803,983,739
Liabilities: $539,065,857
Net Worth: $264,917,882
Earnings: $38,810,580
Emp.: 9,247
Fiscal Year-end: 12/31/2019
Holding Company; Audio & Video Electronic Products Mfr
N.A.I.C.S.: 551112
Xiaofeng Wang (CMO & Sr VP)

Subsidiary (Domestic):

Tonly Electronics Ltd. (2)
19 Zhongkai Hi-Tech Zone, Huizhou, 516006, Guangdong, China
Tel.: (86) 75 2263 9180
Web Site: http://www.tonlyele.com
Audio & Video Electronic Products Mfr
N.A.I.C.S.: 334310
Guanghui Yu (CEO)

TCL ZHONGHUAN RENEWABLE ENERGY TECHNOLOGY CO.,LTD.
No 12 Haitai East Road Huayuan Industrial Zone, New Technology Industrial Park, Tianjin, 300384, China
Tel.: (86) 2223789787   In
Web Site: https://www.tjsemi.com

Year Founded: 1958
002129—(SSE)
Rev.: $8,189,308,706
Assets: $17,315,995,140
Liabilities: $8,975,677,226
Net Worth: $8,340,317,914
Earnings: $472,981,142
Emp.: 17,000
Fiscal Year-end: 12/31/23
Semiconductor Material Mfr
N.A.I.C.S.: 334413

Subsidiaries:

Inner Mongolia Zhonghuan Solar Material Co., Ltd. (1)
No 15 Baolir Street Saihan District, Hohhot, Inner Mongolia, China
Tel.: (86) 4713252350
Web Site: http://www.zhonghuansolar.com
Solar Material Mfr
N.A.I.C.S.: 334413

Sichuan Zhonghuan Energy Co., Ltd. (1)
No 1604 Block B Zhonghai International Center Jiaozi Road 117, Hi-tech north Zone, Chengdu, China
Tel.: (86) 2886026268
Solar Power Generation Services
N.A.I.C.S.: 221114

Tianjin HuanOu International Silicon Materials Co., Ltd. (1)
Unit 2001 20th Floor World Financial Center No 2 North Dagu Road, Heping District, Tianjin, China
Tel.: (86) 2223786026
Semiconductor Material Distr
N.A.I.C.S.: 423690

TCM BIOTECH INTERNATIONAL CORP.
24F-8 No 97 Sec 1 Xintai 5th Rd, Xizhi Dist, New Taipei City, 221416, Taiwan
Tel.: (886) 226972628
Web Site: https://www.tcmbio.com
Year Founded: 1998
4169—(TAI)
Biotechnology Research & Development Services
N.A.I.C.S.: 541714
Shining Hsu (Chm)

TCM CORPORATION PUBLIC COMPANY LIMITED
2054 New Petchburi Road, Bangkapi Huaykwang, Bangkok, 10310, Thailand
Tel.: (66) 23183960   TH
Web Site: https://www.tcm-corporation.com
Year Founded: 1967
TCMC—(THA)
Rev.: $234,476,221
Assets: $226,619,876
Liabilities: $148,962,063
Net Worth: $77,657,813
Earnings: $2,382,574
Emp.: 1,186
Fiscal Year-end: 12/31/23
Carpet Mfr
N.A.I.C.S.: 314110
Pimol Srivikorn (Chm)

Subsidiaries:

Carpets International Thailand Public Company Limited (1)
2054 Petchburi New Road, Bangkapi Huai Khwang, Bangkok, 10310, Thailand **(99.3%)**
Tel.: (66) 23145402
Web Site: https://carpetsinter.com
Carpet Whslr
N.A.I.C.S.: 423220

United Carpet Manufacturing Co., Ltd. (1)
1/4 Moo 3 Ladsawai, Lam Luk Ka, Pathumthani, 12150, Thailand
Tel.: (66) 2 199 2091 4

Web Site: http://www.unitedcarpet.co.th
Carpet & Rug Mfr
N.A.I.C.S.: 314110
Kanawi R. Decha (Mgr-Export Sls)

TCM GROUP A/S
Skautrupvej 16 Tvis, 7500, Holstebro, Denmark
Tel.: (45) 97435200
Web Site: https://www.tcmgroup.dk
Year Founded: 1952
TCM—(CSE)
Rev.: $160,805,950
Assets: $173,760,038
Liabilities: $97,122,021
Net Worth: $76,638,017
Earnings: $3,114,121
Emp.: 500
Fiscal Year-end: 12/31/23
Kitchen & Bathroom Furnishing Mfr
N.A.I.C.S.: 337110
Sanna Suvanto-Harsaae (Chm)

Subsidiaries:

AUBO Production A/S (1)
Weavervej 19-23, 7490, Aulum, Denmark
Tel.: (45) 97473500
Web Site: https://aubo.dk
Kitchen Interior Mfr & Distr
N.A.I.C.S.: 337127

Nettoline A/S (1)
Vaevervej 33-35, Aulum, 7490, Holstebro, Denmark
Tel.: (45) 96410100
Web Site: http://www.nettoline.dk
Household Appliance Whslr
N.A.I.C.S.: 423620

TCM LIMITED
House No 28/2917 Aiswarya Ponneth Temple Road, Shanthi Nagar Kadavanthra, Cochin, 682 020, Kerala, India
Tel.: (91) 4842316771   In
Web Site: https://www.tcmlimited.in
Year Founded: 1943
524156—(BOM)
Rev.: $883,568
Assets: $8,250,441
Liabilities: $4,655,692
Net Worth: $3,594,749
Earnings: ($512,152)
Emp.: 37
Fiscal Year-end: 03/31/23
Chemical Products Mfr
N.A.I.C.S.: 325180
Joseph Varghese (Mng Dir)

Subsidiaries:

Ispark Learning Solutions Pvt Ltd (1)
53/10 Soundarya Colony Anna Nagar West Extension, Chennai, 600101, Tamil Nadu, India
Tel.: (91) 4442127570
Web Site: https://www.isparklearning.com
Educational Support Services
N.A.I.C.S.: 611710
Joseph Varghese (Co-Founder & Chm)

TCM Healthcare Private Limited (1)
Aiswarya H/No 28/2917 Ponneth Temple Rd Shanthi Nagar, Kadavanthra, Kochi, 682020, Kerala, India
Tel.: (91) 6282017736
Web Site: https://www.tcmhealthcare.in
Healthcare Product Distr
N.A.I.C.S.: 423450

TCM Solar Private Limited (1)
Aiswarya 28/2917 Ponneth Temple Rd, Shanthi Nagar Kadavanthra, Kochi, 682020, Kerala, India
Tel.: (91) 7012339221
Web Site: https://www.tcmsolar.com
Solar Installation Services
N.A.I.C.S.: 221114

TCNS CLOTHING CO., LTD.
119 and 127 W-House Neelagagan Towers Mandi Rd, Mehrauli, Sultanpur, 110030, India

INTERNATIONAL PUBLIC

Tel.: (91) 1142193193
Web Site: https://www.tcnsclothing.com
541700—(BOM)
Rev.: $145,986,212
Assets: $178,200,108
Liabilities: $104,858,821
Net Worth: $73,341,286
Earnings: ($2,103,831)
Emp.: 4,056
Fiscal Year-end: 03/31/23
Textile Products Mfr
N.A.I.C.S.: 314999
Onkar Singh Pasricha (Chm)

TCO HOLDINGS JOINT STOCK COMPANY
189 Dinh Vu St, Dong Hai 2 Ward Hai An Dist, Haiphong, Vietnam
Tel.: (84) 2253978895
Web Site: http://www.tasaduyenhai.com
Year Founded: 1995
Sales Range: $100-124.9 Million
Emp.: 290
Holding Company Shipping Container Transportation Arrangement & Warehousing Services
N.A.I.C.S.: 551112

Subsidiaries:

Duyen Hai Hanoi Multimodal Transport Co., LTD (1)
Room 212 N3A Le Van Luong St Trung Hoa Urban zone-Nhan Chinh, Thanh Xuan, Hanoi, Vietnam
Tel.: (84) 435561814
Shipping Support Services
N.A.I.C.S.: 488510

Duyen Hai Manufacturing & Trading Co., Ltd. (1)
189 Dinh Vu St, Dong Hai 2 Ward Hai An Dist, Haiphong, Vietnam
Tel.: (84) 31 3614017
Wholesale Trade Broker
N.A.I.C.S.: 425120
Khanh Toan Le (Mgr)

Duyen Hai Phu Tho Transport Co., LTD (1)
Thuy Van Industrial Zone, Viet Tri, Phu Th, Vietnam
Tel.: (84) 210395232
Shipping Support Services
N.A.I.C.S.: 488510

Duyen Hai Phu Tho Transport Co., Ltd. (1)
Thuy Van Industrial Zon, Viet Tri, Phu Tho, Vietnam
Tel.: (84) 210 395232
Freight Transportation Arrangement & Storage Services
N.A.I.C.S.: 488510
Thi Hue Trinh (Mgr)

Duyen Hai Road Transport Co., LTD (1)
189 Dinh Vu St Dong Hai 2 ward, Haiphong, Hai An, Vietnam
Tel.: (84) 313614221
Shipping Support Services
N.A.I.C.S.: 488510
Luu Thi Hue (Accountant)

Duyen Hai Road Transport Co., Ltd. (1)
189 Dinh Vu St, Dong Hai 2 Ward Hai An Distr, Haiphong, Vietnam
Tel.: (84) 31 3614221
Freight Transportation Arrangement Services
N.A.I.C.S.: 488510
Anh Van Tran (Mgr)

Duyen Hai Transport Co., LTD (1)
Km 104 200 Nguyen Binh Khiem Dong Hai 2 ward, Haiphong, Hai An, Vietnam
Tel.: (84) 31382512
Shipping Support Services
N.A.I.C.S.: 488510
Nguyen Thu Hoan (Accountant)

Duyen Hai Transport Co., Ltd. (1)

Km 104 200 Nguyek Binh Khiem, Dong Hai 2 ward Hai An District, Haiphong, Vietnam
Tel.: (84) 31 3825120
Freight Transportation Arrangement & Storage Services
N.A.I.C.S.: 488510
Thi Bich Thuy Nguyen *(Mgr)*

Minh Thanh Container Company Limited (1)
No 189 Dinh Vu Road, Dong Hai 2 Ward Hai An District, Haiphong, Vietnam
Tel.: (84) 313 614 500
Shipping Container Handling Services Firm
N.A.I.C.S.: 488320
Khanh Toan Le *(Mgr)*

TCP LIMITED
Sapthagiri Bhavan New No 4 Old No 10, Karpagambal Nagar Mylapore, Chennai, 600 004, Tamil Nadu, India
Tel.: (91) 4424991518
Web Site: http://www.tcpindia.com
Year Founded: 1971
Sales Range: $50-74.9 Million
Chemical Product Mfr & Whslr
N.A.I.C.S.: 325180
V. R. Venkataachalam *(Chm & Mng Dir)*

TCP-TERMINAL DE CONTEINERES DE PARANAGUA S.A.
Av Portuaria S/N-Porto D Pedro II, Paranagua, Parana, 83221-570, Brazil
Tel.: (55) 4121525800
Web Site: http://www.tcp.com.br
Year Founded: 1998
Emp.: 100
Container Transportation Services
N.A.I.C.S.: 484110
Haisheng Shi *(CEO)*

TCPL PACKAGING LIMITED
Empire Mills Complex 414 Senapati Bapat Marg, Lower Parel, Mumbai, 400013, Maharashtra, India
Tel.: (91) 2261646000
Web Site: https://www.tcpl.in
Year Founded: 1990
523301—(BOM)
Rev.: $123,719,096
Assets: $114,413,672
Liabilities: $73,402,179
Net Worth: $41,011,493
Earnings: $4,569,228
Emp.: 1,908
Fiscal Year-end: 03/31/21
Printed Folding Carton Mfr
N.A.I.C.S.: 322212
Saket Kanoria *(Mng Dir)*

Subsidiaries:

TCPL PACKAGING LIMITED - Goa Factory (1)
Shed no 1 & 2 Plot no 124 & 127A, Kundaim Industrial Estate Kundaim, Ponda, 403115, Goa, India
Tel.: (91) 832 2395235
Printed Folding Carton Mfr
N.A.I.C.S.: 322212

TCPL PACKAGING LIMITED - Haridwar Plant (1)
Plot 1 & 2 Sector 6A Integrated Industrial Estate SIDCUL, Haridwar, 249 403, Uttarakhand, India
Tel.: (91) 133 423 9176
Web Site: https://www.tcpl.in
Printed Folding Carton Mfr
N.A.I.C.S.: 322212

TCPL PACKAGING LIMITED - Silvassa Factory (1)
18/22 Govt Ind Estate, Masat, Silvassa, 396 230, Dadra and Nagar Have, India
Tel.: (91) 260 2640259
Printed Folding Carton Mfr
N.A.I.C.S.: 322212

TCR CAPITAL SAS
3 Avenue Victor Hugo, 75116, Paris, France
Tel.: (33) 1 5381 7781   FR
Web Site: http://www.tcrcapital.com
Rev.: $412,035,000
Investment Management Service
N.A.I.C.S.: 523940
Marc Demicheli *(Mng Partner)*

Subsidiaries:

Locatel S.A. (1)
Parc d'affaires SILIC Immeuble Axe Seine 1 rue du 1er Mai, 92000, Nanterre, France
Tel.: (33) 826 46 46 46
Web Site: http://www.locatel.net
Emp.: 300
Televisions & Information Technology Equipment Leasing Services for Hotels & Hospitals
N.A.I.C.S.: 532210
Pierre Lestage *(CEO)*

TCS GROUP HOLDING BERHAD
No 1 & 3 Bangunan TCS Jln SP 1/1 Bandar Saujana Putra, Jenjarom, 42610, Kuala Selangor, Malaysia
Tel.: (60) 351038888   MY
Web Site: http://www.tcsgroup.com.my
Year Founded: 1999
TCS—(KLS)
Rev.: $55,363,134
Assets: $47,870,442
Liabilities: $30,240,646
Net Worth: $17,629,796
Earnings: ($718,853)
Fiscal Year-end: 12/31/22
Holding Company
N.A.I.C.S.: 551112
Yap Choo Cheng *(CFO)*

TCS GROUP HOLDING PLC
Berengaria 25 25 Spyrou Araouzou 4th Floor, 3036, Limassol, Cyprus
Tel.: (357) 25050668   CY
Web Site: http://www.tcsgh.com.cy
TCS—(LSE)
Rev.: $254,247,709,496
Assets: $2,505,573,463,205
Liabilities: $2,192,166,906,146
Net Worth: $313,406,557,059
Earnings: $89,338,779,127
Emp.: 70,414
Fiscal Year-end: 12/31/23
Holding Company
N.A.I.C.S.: 551112
Constantinos Economides *(Chm)*

TCS HOLDINGS CO., LTD.
Tokyo Tatemono Daisan Muromachi Bldg 4-8-14 Nihonbashi-Honcho, Chuo-ku, Tokyo, 103-0023, Japan
Tel.: (81) 3 3245 2411   JP
Web Site: http://www.tcs-hd.jp
Year Founded: 1974
Emp.: 30
Investment Holding Company
N.A.I.C.S.: 551112
Masanori Takayama *(Pres & CEO)*

Subsidiaries:

AIREX INC. (1)
Mutoh Ikejiri Bldg 3-1-3 Ikejiri, Setagaya-Ku, Tokyo, 154-0001, Japan
Tel.: (81) 3 34195111
Web Site: http://www.airex.co.jp
Rev.: $29,481,600
Assets: $19,882,320
Liabilities: $10,016,640
Net Worth: $9,865,680
Earnings: $1,962,480
Fiscal Year-end: 03/31/2018
Communication Development Services
N.A.I.C.S.: 541512
Joji Takahashi *(Pres)*

ANDOR Co., Ltd. (1)
Tokyo Tatemono Daisan Muromachi Bldg 4-8-14, Nihombashi Hon-cho Chuo, Tokyo, 103-0023, Japan (100%)
Tel.: (81) 332431711
Web Site: http://www.andor.co.jp
Rev.: $25,213,980
Assets: $24,697,560
Liabilities: $6,523,200
Net Worth: $18,174,360
Earnings: $1,839,180
Emp.: 320
Fiscal Year-end: 03/31/2019
Software Publishing Services
N.A.I.C.S.: 513210
Takaaki Kuribara *(Chm & Pres)*

Technol Seven Co., Ltd. (1)
Mutoh Ikejiri 3-1-3 Ikejiri Bldg, Setagaya-Ku, Tokyo, 154-0001, Japan (100%)
Tel.: (81) 3 34194411
Web Site: http://www.techno7.co.jp
Rev.: $27,234,360
Assets: $35,170,920
Liabilities: $10,038,480
Net Worth: $25,132,440
Earnings: $1,793,880
Emp.: 330
Fiscal Year-end: 03/31/2019
Office Equipment Mfr & Whslr
N.A.I.C.S.: 423420
Masashi Saito *(Pres)*

TCS MEDIA NORTH
Camellia House, 76 Water Ln, Wilmslow, SK9 5BB, Cheshire, United Kingdom
Tel.: (44) 1625 536795   UK
Web Site: http://www.tcsnorth.com
Year Founded: 1982
Rev.: $43,450,000
Emp.: 9
Media Buying Services, Planning & Consultation
N.A.I.C.S.: 541830
Steve Evans *(Mng Dir)*

TCS SASU
3 rue Joseph Bonnet, Bordeaux, France
Tel.: (33) 557541010
Web Site: http://www.tcs.fr
Logistic Services
N.A.I.C.S.: 541614
Jocelyne Lebret *(Dir-HR)*

Subsidiaries:

Novea SAS (1)
Chaban, 79180, Chauray, France
Tel.: (33) 8 20 82 06 76
Insurance Services
N.A.I.C.S.: 524210

TCS TURCONTROLSYSTEME AG
Geschwister Scholl Str 7, Genthin, 39307, Germany
Tel.: (49) 3933879910
Web Site: http://www.tcsag.de
Year Founded: 1995
Rev.: $12,808,609
Emp.: 300
Security Alarm Services
N.A.I.C.S.: 561621
Otto Duffner *(Chm-Exec Bd)*

Subsidiaries:

ARTIS LTD CO. (1)
Vyborgskaya Bank 61 Office 312, 197342, Saint Petersburg, Russia
Tel.: (7) 8127031055
Web Site: http://www.artislight.ru
Electrical Equipment Distr
N.A.I.C.S.: 423610

Automated Building Company (1)
Prince Naser bin Abdulaziz St, PO Box 102078, Alrawdah Suburb, Riyadh, 11657, Saudi Arabia
Tel.: (966) 14961671
Web Site: http://www.abc.sa
Building Automation Control System Distr
N.A.I.C.S.: 423610

Caribou Group (1)
Home Ideas Centre 66 Merivale St, Brisbane, 4101, QLD, Australia
Tel.: (61) 733939605
Web Site: http://www.caribou.com.au
Lighting Product Distr
N.A.I.C.S.: 423220
Karen Beaton *(Coord-Projects)*

Echonova S.r.l. (1)
Handwerkerzone Auf der Hort 2, Tramin, 39040, Bolzano, Italy
Tel.: (39) 0471860428
Web Site: http://www.echonova.it
Electronic Security System Distr
N.A.I.C.S.: 423610
Philly Wallin *(Head-Quality)*

Electromatik FZCO (1)
Saeed Tower 1 Suite 2603 Sheikh Zayed Road, PO Box 191601, Dubai, United Arab Emirates
Tel.: (971) 43325886
Web Site: http://www.electromatik.net
Building Automation Control System Distr
N.A.I.C.S.: 423610

Energija SK (1)
Kaschirskoe Chaussee 53-3-199, 115211, Moscow, Russia
Tel.: (7) 4953449420
Web Site: http://www.energiask.ru
Electronic Components Distr
N.A.I.C.S.: 423690

Gasper Janic ENERGA d.o.o. (1)
Gotovlje 62 d, 3310, Zalec, Slovenia
Tel.: (386) 35101130
Integrated Security Services
N.A.I.C.S.: 561621

Housecomp Ingatlanstudio (1)
Szolgaltato Beteti Tarasag Haros u 115B, 1222, Budapest, Hungary
Tel.: (36) 205814305
Integrated Security Services
N.A.I.C.S.: 561621

Internetdom LLC (1)
ul Tallinskaja d 26, 123458, Moscow, Russia
Tel.: (7) 4959214046
Web Site: http://www.i-dom.ru
Electronic Components Distr
N.A.I.C.S.: 423690

Iskraft hf (1)
Smidjuvegur 5, 200, Kopavogur, Iceland
Tel.: (354) 5351200
Electrical Equipment Distr
N.A.I.C.S.: 423610

JSYL SOLUTION PTE LTD (1)
61 Kaki Bukit Avenue 1 05-36 Shun Li Industrial Park, Singapore, 417943, Singapore
Tel.: (65) 67477668
Web Site: http://www.jsyl-solution.com
Electronic Security System Distr
N.A.I.C.S.: 423690

KROBEL PROMET d.o.o. (1)
Zagrebacka cesta 145a, 10000, Zagreb, Croatia
Tel.: (385) 13041041
Web Site: http://www.krobel.hr
Electronic Security System Distr
N.A.I.C.S.: 423690
Boris Belosevic *(Mgr-IT)*

OPTOSAT s.r.o. (1)
Brezova 23, 182 00, Prague, Czech Republic
Tel.: (420) 286882277
Web Site: http://www.optosat.cz
Integrated Security Services
N.A.I.C.S.: 561621

Paha Mehr Persian Co. (1)
Unit B/72 No 62 Karimkhan St, 1584854681, Tehran, Iran
Tel.: (98) 2188861684
Integrated Security Services
N.A.I.C.S.: 561621

Progress Engineering & Trading Enterprise (1)
Pharaon bldg facing EDL 53 Papinien Str Rmeil, PO Box 11-1111, Beirut, Lebanon
Tel.: (961) 1 444664
Building Automation Control System Distr
N.A.I.C.S.: 423610

TCS TurControlSysteme AG—(Continued)

Qualitronic Odd Jubal-Andersen & Co AS (1)
Tvetenveien 157, 0671, Oslo, Norway
Tel.: (47) 22757460
Web Site: http://www.qualitronic.no
Integrated Security Services
N.A.I.C.S.: 561621

Rohatec s.a.r.l (1)
5 rue d'Arlon, 8399, Windhof, Luxembourg
Tel.: (352) 450146
Web Site: http://www.rohatec.lu
Integrated Security Services
N.A.I.C.S.: 561621

S. C. Gamma International S.R.L (1)
Jud Nures Str Horia Teculescu 65, 545400, Sighisoara, Romania
Tel.: (40) 265771140
Integrated Security Services
N.A.I.C.S.: 561621
Nicholas Munns (Partner)

Scantron A/S (1)
Gammelso 2, 5000, Odense, Denmark
Tel.: (45) 66139966
Web Site: http://www.scantron.dk
Electronic Security System Distr
N.A.I.C.S.: 423690

TCS (Asia) Co. Ltd. (1)
138 Gloucheter Road Room 2304 23/F Allied Kajima Building, Wanchai, China (Hong Kong)
Tel.: (852) 25988818
Integrated Security Services
N.A.I.C.S.: 561621

TCS Intelligent Building Technology (Shanghai) Co. Ltd. (1)
Room 1510 15/F Building A 85 Loushanghuan Rd, Orient International Plaza, Shanghai, 200336, China
Tel.: (86) 2162097829
Building Automation Control System Distr
N.A.I.C.S.: 423610

TCS Kapi iletisim ve Bina Otomatizasyon Tic. Ltd. Sti (1)
Atasehir Ataturk Mahallesi Turgut Ozal Bulvari Gardenya Plaza 7/1, Atasehir, 34756, Istanbul, Turkiye
Tel.: (90) 2164567848
Integrated Security Services
N.A.I.C.S.: 561621

TCS PACIFIC Pty Ltd. (1)
28 Hazelmere Crescent, Ormeau, 4208, QLD, Australia
Tel.: (61) 438092606
Integrated Security Services
N.A.I.C.S.: 561621

TCS TurControlSysteme GmbH (1)
Gewerbepark 21, 2821, Lanzenkirchen, Austria
Tel.: (43) 2627452660
Web Site: http://www.tcs-austria.at
Integrated Security Services
N.A.I.C.S.: 561621

TCST Building Solutions India Pvt. Ltd. (1)
Suite 52 7th Floor Wing-B Vatika Business Centre Supreme Business Park, Powai, Mumbai, 400076, India
Tel.: (91) 2242019148
Building Automation Control System Distr
N.A.I.C.S.: 423610
Rohit Lore (Project Engr)

TENART (1)
ul Zarechnaya d 9 of 502, 121087, Moscow, Russia
Tel.: (7) 4955653718
Web Site: http://www.tenart.su
Integrated Security Services
N.A.I.C.S.: 561621
Valentin Druzhinin (Dir-Comml)

Technomat S.A. (1)
Sindos industrial area, Thessaloniki, Greece
Tel.: (30) 2310777040
Web Site: http://www.technomat-shop.com
Electrical Equipment Distr
N.A.I.C.S.: 423610
Tiflioris Polideykis (Co-Founder & Mng Dir)

d.o.o. TCS S.E. Europe (1)
Vase Pelagica St 22, 26300, Vrsac, Serbia
Tel.: (381) 113807211
Integrated Security Services
N.A.I.C.S.: 561621
Milan Djukic (Gen Mgr)

TCTM KIDS IT EDUCATION INC.
6/F No 1 Andingmenwai Street Litchi Tower, Chaoyang District, Beijing, 100011, China
Tel.: (86) 1062135687 Ky
Web Site: https://ir.tctm.cn
Year Founded: 2002
TCTM—(NASDAQ)
Rev.: $190,406,513
Assets: $140,984,022
Liabilities: $348,858,136
Net Worth: $(207,874,114)
Earnings: $1,433,595
Emp.: 7,024
Fiscal Year-end: 12/31/23
Professional Education Services
N.A.I.C.S.: 611710
Shaoyun Han (Founder & Chm)

TD MAKOSPED AD
ul Makedonija br 19, Skopje, North Macedonia
Tel.: (389) 23171011
Web Site: http://www.makosped.com.mk
Year Founded: 1946
MKSD—(MAC)
Rev.: $875,017
Assets: $17,747,883
Liabilities: $79,128
Net Worth: $17,668,755
Earnings: $168,813
Fiscal Year-end: 12/31/23
Transport & Warehousing Services
N.A.I.C.S.: 483113
Marija Karanfilovikj (Exec Dir)

TD POWER SYSTEMS LIMITED
27 28 and 29 KIADB Industrial Area Dobbaspet, Nelamangala Taluk Bengaluru Rural District, Bengaluru, 562111, India
Tel.: (91) 8022995700
Web Site: https://www.tdps.co.in
TDPOWERSYS—(NSE)
Rev.: $82,296,778
Assets: $107,135,820
Liabilities: $42,888,491
Net Worth: $64,247,329
Earnings: $6,170,401
Emp.: 659
Fiscal Year-end: 03/31/21
Turbines & Engines Mfr
N.A.I.C.S.: 333611
N. Srivatsa (Officer-Compliance & Sec)

Subsidiaries:

DF Power Systems Private Limited (1)
RMJ Mandoth Towers 37 7th Cross Vasanth Nagar, Bengaluru, 560 052, India
Tel.: (91) 8022017800
Web Site: https://www.dfps.in
Sales Range: $500-549.9 Million
Emp.: 800
Thermal Power Generation Services
N.A.I.C.S.: 221118

TD SPLIT INC.
66 Wellington Street West 9th Floor TD Tower, Toronto, M5K 1A2, ON, Canada
Tel.: (416) 982-2680
Web Site: http://www.tdsecurities.com
Year Founded: 2000
Emp.: 3,500
Financial Investment Services
N.A.I.C.S.: 523999

Joe Beamer (Mng Dir)

TDA
Victoria House St James Sq, Cheltenham, GL50 3PR, Gloucestershire, United Kingdom
Tel.: (44) 1242 633111
Sales Range: $10-24.9 Million
Emp.: 14
Financial
N.A.I.C.S.: 541810
Heather Westgate (CEO)

TDB AUTOMOBILES SA
14 rue des Prunus, 22100, Dinan, France
Tel.: (33) 2 96 87 69 69
Web Site: http://www.tdb-peugeot-dinan.fr
Automotive Retailer
N.A.I.C.S.: 441110
Thierry du Boishamon (Mng Dir)

TDC SOFT INC.
Shinjuku Bunka Quinto Building 7F 3-22-7 Yoyogi, Shibuya-ku, Tokyo, 151-0053, Japan
Tel.: (81) 36730811
Web Site: https://www.tdc.co.jp
Year Founded: 1962
4687—(TKS)
Rev.: $262,403,780
Assets: $168,588,050
Liabilities: $46,455,080
Net Worth: $122,132,970
Earnings: $20,418,290
Emp.: 2,335
Fiscal Year-end: 03/31/24
System Software Development Services
N.A.I.C.S.: 541512
Fumio Hashimoto (Chm)

TDCX INC.
750D Chai Chee Rd 06-01/06 ESR BizPark Chai Chee, Singapore, 469004, Singapore
Tel.: (65) 63091688 Ky
Web Site: https://www.tdcx.com
Year Founded: 2020
TDCX—(NYSE)
Rev.: $501,390,676
Assets: $511,718,666
Liabilities: $87,537,262
Net Worth: $424,181,404
Earnings: $79,225,042
Emp.: 17,883
Fiscal Year-end: 12/31/22
Holding Company
N.A.I.C.S.: 551112
Laurent Junique (Chm & CEO)

Subsidiaries:

Agorae Information Consulting (Beijing) Co., Ltd. (1)
103 1F Building 3 Rong Hui Park Airport, Shunyi District, Beijing, China
Tel.: (86) 1080458888
Software Development Services
N.A.I.C.S.: 541511

TDCX Information Consulting (Shanghai) Co., Ltd. (1)
Room 1008 No 386 Guoan Road, Yangpu District, Shanghai, China
Tel.: (86) 2160572020
Business Process Outsourcing Services
N.A.I.C.S.: 541611

TDCX Japan KK (1)
24th Floor DIA Building 1-7 Kinko-cho, Kanagawa-ku, Yokohama, Kanagawa, Japan
Tel.: (81) 5017459596
Business Process Outsourcing Services
N.A.I.C.S.: 541611

Teledirect Hong Kong Limited (1)
RM 1001 10/F Block A Sea View Estate 2-8 Watson Road North Point, Hong Kong, China (Hong Kong)
Tel.: (852) 25393888
Software Development Services
N.A.I.C.S.: 541511

Teledirect Telecommerce (Thailand) Limited (1)
15th - 16th Fl Spring Tower Building 188 Phayathai Road, Thung Phayathai Ratchathewi, Bangkok, Thailand
Tel.: (66) 22688000
Software Development Services
N.A.I.C.S.: 541511

TDE - TRANS DATA ELEKTRONIK GMBH
Im Defdahl 233, Dortmund, 44141, Germany
Tel.: (49) 2319143127
Web Site: http://www.tde.de
Year Founded: 1991
Rev.: $13,794,000
Emp.: 21
Copper & Fibre Optic Cable Products Mfr
N.A.I.C.S.: 335921
Andre Engel (Mng Dir)

TDG HOLDING CO., LTD.
No 129 Shuanglian Road, Haining, 314400, Zhejiang, China
Tel.: (86) 57380701391
Web Site: https://www.tdgcore.com
Year Founded: 1984
600330—(SHG)
Rev.: $632,883,439
Assets: $1,528,542,073
Liabilities: $428,896,967
Net Worth: $1,099,645,106
Earnings: $93,987,396
Fiscal Year-end: 12/31/22
Holding Company
N.A.I.C.S.: 551112
Zheng Xiaobin (Chm)

TDH HOLDINGS, INC.
2521 Tiejueshan Road, Huangdao District, Qingdao, Shandong, China
Tel.: (86) 53286157918 VG
Web Site: http://www.tiandihui.com
Year Founded: 2015
PETZ—(NASDAQ)
Rev.: $3,098,733
Assets: $36,513,397
Liabilities: $15,359,494
Net Worth: $21,153,903
Earnings: $803,700
Emp.: 51
Fiscal Year-end: 12/31/22
Pet Food Mfr
N.A.I.C.S.: 311111
Rongfeng Cui (Founder & Chm)

Subsidiaries:

Qingdao Tiandihui Foodstuffs Co., Ltd. (1)
Rm 7221 BD B World Trade Center No 6 Hongkong Middle Rd, Qingdao, 266071, China
Tel.: (86) 53285919267
Web Site: http://www.tdhpetfood.com
Emp.: 2,500
Pet Food Mfr
N.A.I.C.S.: 311111

TDJ S.A.
ul Armii Krajowej 51, 40-698, Katowice, Poland
Tel.: (48) 359 63 01
Web Site: http://www.tdjsa.pl
Year Founded: 1977
Privater Equity Firm
N.A.I.C.S.: 523999
Radosaw Toporek (Dir-HR)

Subsidiaries:

Grenevia SA (1)

AND PRIVATE COMPANIES

TDK CORPORATION

ul Armii Krajowej 51, 40-698, Katowice, Poland
Tel.: (48) 323596300 **(71.28%)**
Web Site: https://grenevia.com
Rev.: $325,579,058
Assets: $921,971,562
Liabilities: $395,668,995
Net Worth: $526,302,567
Earnings: $30,146,209
Emp.: 2,453
Fiscal Year-end: 12/31/2022
Mining Machinery Mfr
N.A.I.C.S.: 333131
Beata Zawiszowska *(CFO, Member-Mgmt Bd & VP)*

Subsidiary (Domestic):

Kopex S.A. (2)
Grabowa 1, 40-172, Katowice, Poland
Tel.: (48) 326047000
Web Site: http://kopex.com.pl
Mining & Construction Services
N.A.I.C.S.: 541330
Beata Zawiszowska *(Pres-Mgmt Bd)*

PGO S.A. (1)
Tysiaclecia 101, 40-875, Katowice, Poland
Tel.: (48) 328321800
Web Site: https://pgosa.pl
Rev.: $103,533,715
Assets: $111,470,286
Liabilities: $37,303,093
Net Worth: $74,167,193
Earnings: $6,245,003
Fiscal Year-end: 12/31/2019
Iron Alloy Castings
N.A.I.C.S.: 331511
Jacek Leonkiewicz *(Chm-Supervisory Bd)*

TDK CORPORATION

Nihonbashi Takashimaya Mitsui Building 2-5-1, Chuo-ku, Tokyo, 103-6128, Japan
Tel.: (81) 367781000 JP
Web Site: https://www.tdk.com
Year Founded: 1935
TTDKF—(OTCIQ)
Rev.: $15,636,457,890
Assets: $22,564,183,590
Liabilities: $12,075,427,200
Net Worth: $10,488,756,390
Earnings: $818,720,790
Emp.: 102,908
Fiscal Year-end: 03/31/23
Magnetic Recording Tapes & Electronic Materials & Components Mfr
N.A.I.C.S.: 334610
Joachim Thiele *(Deputy Gen Mgr-Electronic Components Sls & Mktg Grp)*

Subsidiaries:

AFI Technologies (Changan) Limited (1)
Conrad Hi-Tech Park Zhen An Road, Changan Town, Dongguan, 523870, Guangdong, China
Tel.: (86) 7698 541 5668
Electrical & Electronic Product Mfr
N.A.I.C.S.: 335999

Acrathon Precision Technologies (Dongguan) Co., Ltd. (1)
No 61 Zhenan East Road, Changan Town, Dongguan, 523852, Guangdong, China
Tel.: (86) 7698 531 2169
Web Site: https://www.acrathon.tdk.com.cn
Suspension Component Mfr
N.A.I.C.S.: 336330
Koji Inada *(Gen Mgr)*

Becromal S.p.A. (1)
Via E Ch Rosenthal 5, Milan, 20089, Italy
Tel.: (39) 02 892131
Web Site: http://www.becromal.eu
Rev.: $124,590,400
Emp.: 350
Aluminum Foil Mfr
N.A.I.C.S.: 331315

CoreSolid Storage Corporation (1)
Zhonghe Dist, Zhonghe Dist, Taipei, 23553, Taiwan
Tel.: (886) 2 66206168
Web Site: http://www.coresolid-storage.com
Flash Memory Device Mfr
N.A.I.C.S.: 334118

Dongguan Amperex Electronics Technology Co., Ltd. (1)
1 West Industrial Road, North Zone of SongShan Lake S and T Industry Park, Dongguan, 523808, Guangdong, China
Tel.: (86) 7698 898 9338
Appliances, Electrical & Electronics Mfr
N.A.I.C.S.: 335999

Dongguan NVT Technology Co., Ltd. (1)
No 8 Xingguo Road, Jiaoshe Dongkeng Town, Dongguan, China
Tel.: (86) 7693 882 6188
Web Site: https://www.nvtpower.com
Storage Battery Mfr
N.A.I.C.S.: 335910

EPCOS AG (1)
Saint Martin Strasse 53, 81669, Munich, Germany
Tel.: (49) 89540200
Web Site: http://www.epcos.com
Sales Range: $1-4.9 Billion
Emp.: 23,619
Passive Electronic Components Mfr
N.A.I.C.S.: 334419
Norbert Hess *(Member-Mgmt Bd)*

Subsidiary (Non-US):

EPCOS (Xiaogan) Co., Ltd (2)
257-1 Changzheng Road, Xiaogan, 432104, Hubei, China
Tel.: (86) 712 210 5833
Web Site: http://en.tdk.eu
Electronic Components Mfr
N.A.I.C.S.: 334419
Eric Liu *(Gen Mgr)*

EPCOS (Zhuhai FTZ) Co., Ltd. (2)
Lian Feng Road Zhuhai Free Trade Zone, Wanzai, Zhuhai, 519030, Guangdong, China
Tel.: (86) 756 886 30 00
Electronic Components Mfr
N.A.I.C.S.: 334419

EPCOS Electronic Components S.A. (2)
Avenida de Jose Ortega y Gasset 173, 29006, Malaga, Spain
Tel.: (34) 95 204 92 34
Sales Range: $100-124.9 Million
Emp.: 350
Electronic Components Mfr
N.A.I.C.S.: 334419

EPCOS Elektronikai Alkatresz Kft. (2)
Csaba utca 30, Szombathely, 9700, Hungary
Tel.: (36) 94 52 21 01
Web Site: http://www.globalck.com
Electronic Component Mfr & Whslr
N.A.I.C.S.: 334419
Koch Bernhard *(CEO)*

EPCOS Limited (2)
1/F SAE Technology Centre 6 Science Park East Avenue, Hong Kong Science Park, Sha Tin, New Territories, China (Hong Kong)
Tel.: (852) 36 69 82 00
Electronic Components Distr
N.A.I.C.S.: 423690

EPCOS OHG (2)
Siemensstrasse 43, PO Box 90, 8530, Deutschlandsberg, Austria
Tel.: (43) 34 62 800 000
Web Site: http://www.epcos.com
Emp.: 700
Electronic Components Mfr
N.A.I.C.S.: 334419
Ernst Kern *(Head-HR & PR)*

EPCOS Pte Ltd (2)
166 Kallang Way, Singapore, 349249, Singapore
Tel.: (65) 6841 2011
Web Site: http://www.epcos.com.sg
Sales Range: $200-249.9 Million
Emp.: 700
Electronic Components Distr
N.A.I.C.S.: 423690

EPCOS Technology (Wuxi) Co., Ltd. (2)
Wuxi Singapore Industrial Park No 2 Xin Du Road, Wuxi, 214028, Jiangsu, China
Tel.: (86) 510 8528 1222
Sales Range: $75-99.9 Million
Emp.: 50
Surface Acoustic Wave Component Mfr
N.A.I.C.S.: 334419
Sherry Chou *(Gen Mgr)*

EPCOS do Brasil Ltda. (2)
e-business Park Predio 11 / Torre A Cj 32A Rua Werner Von Siemens 111, 05069-010, Sao Paulo, Brazil
Tel.: (55) 1132899599
Web Site: http://en.tdk.eu
Electronic Components Distr
N.A.I.C.S.: 423610

EPCOS s.r.o. (2)
Feritova Street 1, 78715, Sumperk, Czech Republic
Tel.: (420) 583 360 111
Sales Range: $400-449.9 Million
Emp.: 1,500
Electronic Components Mfr
N.A.I.C.S.: 334419

Subsidiary (US):

EPCOS, Inc. (2)
485 B Route 1 S Ste 200, Iselin, NJ 08830
Tel.: (732) 906-4300
Electronic Components Mfr
N.A.I.C.S.: 334419

Subsidiary (Domestic):

Crystal Technology Inc. (3)
1040 E Meadow Cir, Palo Alto, CA 94303-4230
Tel.: (650) 856-7911
Web Site: http://www.crystaltechnology.com
Sales Range: $25-49.9 Million
Emp.: 150
Single Oxide Crystals Mfr for Production of Optical Components
N.A.I.C.S.: 334419

Subsidiary (Domestic):

TDK-EPC AG & Co. KG (2)
Ruhlsdorfer Strasse 95 Gebaude 4, 14532, Stahnsdorf, Germany
Tel.: (49) 89540200
Web Site: http://en.tdk.eu
Piezoelectric Pressure Sensors Mfr
N.A.I.C.S.: 334419

Guangdong TDK Rising Rare Earth High Technology Material Co., Ltd. (1)
No 1 Road Gaoxin II Meizhou High-tech Industrial Park, SheJiang Town Meixian District, Meizhou, 514000, Guangdong, China
Tel.: (86) 753 275 6268
Appliances, Electrical & Electronics Mfr
N.A.I.C.S.: 335999

ICsense NV (1)
Gaston Geenslaan 14, 3001, Leuven, Belgium
Tel.: (32) 1 658 9700
Web Site: https://www.icsense.com
Semiconductor Mfr
N.A.I.C.S.: 334413
Bram De Muer *(CEO)*

Korea TDK Co. Ltd. (1)
670 Gasan-Dong, Geumcheon-Gu, Seoul, 153 803, Korea (South) **(100%)**
Tel.: (82) 232825000
Web Site: http://www.tdkkorea.co.kr
Sales Range: $10-24.9 Million
Emp.: 340
Production & Sale of Electronic Materials & Components
N.A.I.C.S.: 334220

Magnecomp Precision Technology Public Company Limited (1)
162 M 5 Phaholyothin Road, Ayutthaya, 13170, Thailand
Tel.: (66) 3 521 5225
Web Site: https://www.magnecomp.tdk.com
Emp.: 6,000
Computer Hard Drive Component Mfr
N.A.I.C.S.: 334112

Media Technology Corporation (1)
801 Nakadate, Chuo, 409-3801, Yamanashi, Japan
Tel.; (81) 55 273 0771
Magnetic Application Product Mfr
N.A.I.C.S.: 334610

NVT Battery Design Solution Co. Ltd. (1)
7/F No 155 Xinhu 1st Road, Neihu District, Taipei, 114, Taiwan
Tel.: (886) 22 790 3332
Appliances, Electrical & Electronics Mfr
N.A.I.C.S.: 335999

Navitasys Technology Limited (1)
3503 Wharf Cable TV Tower 9 Hoi Shing Road, Tsuen Wan, Hong Kong, China (Hong Kong)
Tel.: (852) 2 498 0908
Appliances, Electrical & Electronics Mfr
N.A.I.C.S.: 335999

Ningde Amperex Technology Limited (1)
No 1 Xingang Road, Zhangwan Town Jiaocheng District, Ningde, Fujian, China
Tel.: (86) 593 258 3888
Electrical Equipment & Component Mfr
N.A.I.C.S.: 335999

PT. TDK Electronics Indonesia (1)
Jalan EPCOS Jaya Blok B1-10 Kawasan Industri Panbil, Kawasan Industri Panbil Muka Kuning, Pulau Batam, 29433, Indonesia
Tel.: (62) 778 404 0100
Appliances, Electrical & Electronics Mfr
N.A.I.C.S.: 335999

Poweramp Technology Limited (1)
No 1 Xinghui Road Songshan Lake industrial park, Dongguan, 523450, Guangdong, China
Tel.: (86) 7698 991 2222
Appliances, Electrical & Electronics Mfr
N.A.I.C.S.: 335999

Qingdao TDK Electronics Co., Ltd. (1)
No 16 Tonghe Road, Pingdu, Qingdao, 266706, Shandong, China
Tel.: (86) 5328 060 7000
Appliances, Electrical & Electronics Mfr
N.A.I.C.S.: 335999

SAE Components (Changan) Ltd. (1)
Conrad Hi-Tech Park Zhen An Road, Changan Town, Dongguan, 523870, Guangdong, China
Tel.: (86) 7698 547 3980
Appliances, Electrical & Electronics Mfr
N.A.I.C.S.: 335999

SAE Technologies Development (Dongguan) Co., Ltd. (1)
Winnerway Industrial Area, Nancheng, Dongguan, 523087, Guangdong, China
Tel.: (86) 7692 281 0033
Electronic Components Mfr
N.A.I.C.S.: 334419

SolidGear Corporation (1)
Shinyokohama kaneko Bldg 8F 2-3-9, Shinyokohama Kohoku-ku, Yokohama, 222-0033, Japan
Tel.: (81) 45 470 4511
Web Site: https://www.solidgear.tdk.com
Electronic Components Mfr
N.A.I.C.S.: 334419
Tsuyoshi Oyaizu *(Pres & CEO)*

TDK (Malaysia) Sdn. Bhd. (1)
PT 1164 Nilai Industrial Estate, Nilai, 71800, Nilai, Negeri Sembilan, Malaysia **(100%)**
Tel.: (60) 6 797 8800
Web Site: http://www.tdk.com
Sales Range: $150-199.9 Million
Emp.: 720
Production & Sale of Electronic Materials & Components
N.A.I.C.S.: 811310

TDK (Shanghai) Investment Ltd. (1)
Shanghai International Trade Centre Room 3305 33/F, No 2201 Yan An Road West, Shanghai, 200336, China
Tel.: (86) 212 219 1500
Appliances, Electrical & Electronics Mfr

TDK CORPORATION

TDK Corporation—(Continued)
N.A.I.C.S.: 335999

TDK (Suzhou) Co., Ltd. (1)
No 226 Xin Hai Street Suzhou Industrial Park, Suzhou, 215021, Jiangsu, China
Tel.: (86) 512 6256 8660
Electronic Capacitor Mfr
N.A.I.C.S.: 334416

TDK (Thailand) Co., Ltd. (1)
1550 Thanapoom Tower 19th floor Zone A D E New Petchburi Road, Makkasan Rachatewi, Bangkok, 10400, Thailand **(100%)**
Tel.: (66) 2 033 5441
Web Site: http://www.tdk.co.jp
Sales Range: $25-49.9 Million
Emp.: 13
Mfr & Sales of Magnetic Recording Tapes & Electronic Material & Components
N.A.I.C.S.: 334610

TDK (Xiamen) Electronics Co., Ltd. (1)
No 413-419 Tongji Nan Road, Jimei, Xiamen, 361021, Fujian, China
Tel.: (86) 592 360 2800
Appliances, Electrical & Electronics Mfr
N.A.I.C.S.: 335999

TDK (Xiaogan) Co., Ltd. (1)
257-1 Changzheng Road, Xiaogan, 432000, Hubei, China
Tel.: (86) 712 210 5989
Appliances, Electrical & Electronics Mfr
N.A.I.C.S.: 335999

TDK (Zhuhai FTZ) Co., Ltd. (1)
No 4 Lianfeng Road, Xiangzhou District, Zhuhai, 519030, China
Tel.: (86) 756 886 3000
Appliances, Electrical & Electronics Mfr
N.A.I.C.S.: 335999

TDK Austria GesmbH (1)
Griefinggasse 2, 1210, Vienna, Austria
Tel.: (43) 12563 630 5639
Appliances, Electrical & Electronics Mfr
N.A.I.C.S.: 335999

TDK CIS LLC (1)
Leningradsky Prospect 74A, 125315, Moscow, Russia
Tel.: (7) 4956632100
Appliances, Electrical & Electronics Mfr
N.A.I.C.S.: 335999

TDK China Co., Ltd. (1)
Room 1907 Shanghai International Trade Centre 2201 Yan An Rd W, Changning District, Shanghai, 200336, China
Tel.: (86) 216 196 2345
Web Site: http://www.tdkchina.com
Sales Range: $25-49.9 Million
Emp.: 27
Electronic Components Mfr
N.A.I.C.S.: 334419
Toshihide Asanuma *(Pres & CEO)*

Subsidiary (Domestic):

Foshan Nanhai Pingzhou Electronic Factory Co., Ltd. (2)
No 3 Nangang Road Pingzhou, Nanhai, Foshan, Guangdong, China
Tel.: (86) 757 8677 7899
Electronic Components Mfr
N.A.I.C.S.: 334419

TDK (Guangzhou) Co., Ltd. (2)
Room 2602 Goldlion Digital Network Center, 138 Tiyu Rd East, Guangzhou, 510620, China **(100%)**
Tel.: (86) 2038781088
Web Site: http://www.tdkchina.com
Sales Range: $25-49.9 Million
Emp.: 100
Mfr & Sales of Magnetic Recording Tapes & Electronic Material & Components
N.A.I.C.S.: 334610

TDK (Shanghai) International Trading Co., Ltd. (2)
Room 3201 Shanghai International Trade Centre 2201 Yan An Rd W, Changning District, Shanghai, 200336, China **(100%)**
Tel.: (86) 216 196 2345
Web Site: https://www.tdk.com

Sales Range: $25-49.9 Million
Emp.: 60
Mfr & Sales of Magnetic Recording Tapes & Electronic Material & Components
N.A.I.C.S.: 334610

TDK Dalian Corporation (2)
No 68 West Huaihe Road, Dalian Economic Technical Development Zone, Dalian, 116600, Liaoning Province, China **(100%)**
Tel.: (86) 4118 731 4455
Web Site: https://www.china.tdk.com
Production of Electronic Materials & Components
N.A.I.C.S.: 811310

Wuxi TDK-Lambda Electronics Co., Ltd. (2)
No 6 Xing Chuang Er Lu Wuxi-Singapore Industrial Park, Wuxi, 214028, Jiangsu, China
Tel.: (86) 510 85281029
Power Supplies Mfr & Distr
N.A.I.C.S.: 335999

TDK Components Pte. Ltd. (1)
11 North Buona Vista Drive 13-08 The Metropolis Tower 2, Singapore, 138589, Singapore
Tel.: (65) 6 597 0628
Appliances, Electrical & Electronics Mfr
N.A.I.C.S.: 335999

TDK Components Taiwan Co., Ltd. (1)
Room 700 -702 7F No 66 San Chong Road, Nangang District, Taipei, 115, Taiwan
Tel.: (886) 22 655 7676
Appliances, Electrical & Electronics Mfr
N.A.I.C.S.: 335999

TDK Czech s.r.o. (1)
Bucharova 14, 158 00, Prague, Czech Republic
Tel.: (420) 23 303 2281
Appliances, Electrical & Electronics Mfr
N.A.I.C.S.: 335999

TDK Design Inc. (1)
5F Kato Building 2-1-14 Nihonbashi, Chuoku, Tokyo, 103-0027, Japan
Tel.: (81) 33 278 2520
Web Site: https://www.design.tdk.com
Emp.: 50
Media Streaming Services
N.A.I.C.S.: 518210

TDK Electronics AG (1)
Rosenheimer Strasse 141 e, 81671, Munich, Germany
Tel.: (49) 8 954 0200
Appliances, Electrical & Electronics Mfr
N.A.I.C.S.: 335999

TDK Electronics Europe GmbH (1)
Wanheimer Strasse 57, D 40472, Dusseldorf, Germany **(100%)**
Tel.: (49) 21190770
Web Site: http://www.tdk.co.jp
Sales Range: $25-49.9 Million
Emp.: 70
Mfr & Sale of Electronic Components & Recording Media
N.A.I.C.S.: 449210
Andreas Keller *(Mgr)*

TDK Electronics France (1)
3 rue de Brennus, Saint-Denis, 93210, La Plaine Saint-Denis, France **(100%)**
Tel.: (33) 14 946 6789
Web Site: http://www.tdk.de
Sales Range: $25-49.9 Million
Emp.: 26
Mfr & Sales of Magnetic Recording Tapes & Electronic Material & Components
N.A.I.C.S.: 334610

TDK Electronics Italy (1)
Centro Commerciale Milano E Scala H 1 Piano Via Tolstoi 86, 20098, San Giuliano Milanese, Italy **(100%)**
Tel.: (39) 029822271
Web Site: http://www.tdk.eu
Sales Range: $25-49.9 Million
Emp.: 10
Mfr & Sales of Magnetic Recording Tapes & Electronic Material & Components
N.A.I.C.S.: 334610
Moriggi Massimo *(Gen Mgr)*

TDK Electronics Korea Corporation (1)

Seocho-Dong 8F Songnam Building 273, Gangnam-Daero Seocho-Gu, Seoul, 06730, Korea (South)
Tel.: (82) 23 019 4300
Appliances, Electrical & Electronics Mfr
N.A.I.C.S.: 335999

TDK Electronics Nordic (1)
Anton Tamms Vag 3, S 19429, Upplands Vasby, Sweden **(100%)**
Tel.: (46) 859099100
Web Site: http://www.tdk.de
Sales Range: $25-49.9 Million
Emp.: 15
Mfr & Sales of Magnetic Recording Tapes & Electronic Material & Components
N.A.I.C.S.: 334610

TDK Electronics Philippines Corporation (1)
119 East Science Avenue, Special Export Processing Zone Laguna Technopark, Binan, 4024, Laguna, Philippines
Tel.: (63) 49 541 3141
Web Site: http://www.tdk.co.jp
Electronic Components Mfr
N.A.I.C.S.: 334419

TDK Electronics do Brasil Ltda. (1)
Rua Bernardo Joaquim Ferreira 624 Parque dos Anjos, Gravatai, 94000-970, Rio Grande do Sul, Brazil
Tel.: (55) 513 484 7000
Appliances, Electrical & Electronics Mfr
N.A.I.C.S.: 335999

TDK Electronics s.r.o. (1)
Feritova 1, 787 01, Sumperk, Czech Republic
Tel.: (420) 58 336 0111
Appliances, Electrical & Electronics Mfr
N.A.I.C.S.: 335999

TDK Europe S.A. (1)
rue de l Industrie 20, Windhof Grand, 8399, Windhof, Luxembourg
Tel.: (352) 505011
Web Site: http://www.global.tdk.com
Emp.: 4
Electronic Components Mfr
N.A.I.C.S.: 334419

TDK Foil Iceland ehf. (1)
Krossanes 4, 600, Akureyri, Iceland
Tel.: (354) 522 4800
Web Site: https://foil.tdk-electronics.tdk.com
Appliances, Electrical & Electronics Mfr
N.A.I.C.S.: 335999

TDK Hong Kong Co., Ltd. (1)
1/F SAE Technology Center 6 Science Park East Ave, Hong Kong Science Park, Sha Tin, New Territories, China (Hong Kong)
Tel.: (852) 27362238
Sales Range: $25-49.9 Million
Emp.: 80
Passive Component Mfr & Distr
N.A.I.C.S.: 334419

Subsidiary (Domestic):

SAE Magnetics (H.K.) Ltd. (2)
SAE Technology Center 6 Science Park East Avenue, Hong Kong Science Park, Sha Tin, New Territories, China (Hong Kong)
Tel.: (852) 2 612 8882
Web Site: https://www.sae.tdk.com
Magnetic Application Product Mfr
N.A.I.C.S.: 334610

TDK Italy S.r.l. (1)
Via Mecenate 90, 20138, Milan, Italy
Tel.: (39) 025 099 5425
Appliances, Electrical & Electronics Mfr
N.A.I.C.S.: 335999

TDK Kofu Corporation (1)
160 Miyazawa, Minami-Alps, 400-0495, Yamanashi, Japan
Tel.: (81) 55 284 3111
Web Site: http://www.global.tdk.com
Magnetic Application Product Mfr
N.A.I.C.S.: 334610

TDK Management Services GmbH (1)
Rosenheimer Strasse 116b, 81671, Munich, Germany
Tel.: (49) 8 954 0200
Electrical & Electronics Mfr

INTERNATIONAL PUBLIC

N.A.I.C.S.: 335999

TDK Philippines Corporation (1)
119 East Science Avenue Special Export Processing Zone, Laguna Technopark, Binan, Laguna, Philippines
Tel.: (63) 2 584 4380
Electronic Component Mfr & Distr
N.A.I.C.S.: 334419

TDK Precision Tool Corporation (1)
191 Okumacho, Tsuzuki-ku, Yokohama, 224-0042, Kanagawa, Japan
Tel.: (81) 45 471 5360
Magnetic Application Product Mfr
N.A.I.C.S.: 334610

TDK Service Corporation (1)
2-5-1 Nihonbashi Nihonbashi Takashimaya Mitsui Building 28F, Chuo-ku, Tokyo, 103-6128, Chiba, Japan
Tel.: (81) 36 778 1120
Web Site: http://www.service.tdk.co.jp
Insurance Management Services
N.A.I.C.S.: 524298

TDK Singapore (Pte.) Ltd. (1)
11 North Buona Vista Drive 13-08 The Metropolis Tower 2, Singapore, 138589, Singapore **(100%)**
Tel.: (65) 6 273 5022
Web Site: http://www.tdk.com.sg
Sales Range: $25-49.9 Million
Emp.: 80
Sale of Electronic Components & Materials
N.A.I.C.S.: 449210

TDK Taiwan Corporation (1)
7th Floor 66 San Chong Road, Taipei, 11560, Nangang, Taiwan **(80.95%)**
Tel.: (886) 2 2789 1117
Sales Range: $25-49.9 Million
Emp.: 80
Production & Sale of Electronic Materials & Components
N.A.I.C.S.: 334419

TDK Techno Corporation (1)
2-15-7 Higashiowada, Ichikawa, 272-0026, Chiba, Japan
Tel.: (81) 47 378 9185
Electronic Components Mfr
N.A.I.C.S.: 334419

TDK U.S.A. Corporation (1)
455 RXR Plz, Uniondale, NY 11556
Tel.: (516) 535-2600
Web Site: http://www.us.tdk.com
Sales Range: $25-49.9 Million
Emp.: 20
Finance & Administration for TDK Affiliates in the U.S.
N.A.I.C.S.: 561110

Subsidiary (Domestic):

Headway Technologies Inc. (2)
682 S Hillview Dr, Milpitas, CA 95035-5457 **(100%)**
Tel.: (408) 934-5300
Web Site: https://www.headway.tdk.com
Sales Range: $200-249.9 Million
Emp.: 800
Mfr of Recording Heads for Hard Disk Drives
N.A.I.C.S.: 334112
Wenjie Chen *(Pres)*

Subsidiary (Domestic):

Hutchinson Technology Incorporated (3)
40 W Highland Park Dr NE, Hutchinson, MN 55350
Tel.: (320) 587-3797
Web Site: http://www.htch.com
Disk Drive Suspension Assemblies Mfr
N.A.I.C.S.: 334419
Connie L. Pautz *(VP-HR)*

Plant (Domestic):

Hutchinson Technology Inc. - Eau Claire (4)
2435 Alpine Rd, Eau Claire, WI 54703-9562
Tel.: (715) 838-9800
Web Site: https://www.hutchinson.tdk.com
Computer Device Stamping & Assembly Operations
N.A.I.C.S.: 334112

AND PRIVATE COMPANIES

Subsidiary (Non-US):

Hutchinson Technology Operations (Thailand) Co., Ltd. (4)
50 Moo 4 Rojana Industrial Park Phase 8, Ayutthaya, 13210, Thailand
Tel.: (66) 35334800
Web Site: http://www.htch.com
Precision Turned Product Mfr
N.A.I.C.S.: 332721

Subsidiary (Domestic):

InvenSense, Inc. (2)
1745 Technology Dr, San Jose, CA 95110
Tel.: (408) 501-2200
Web Site: https://invensense.tdk.com
Sales Range: $1-9.9 Million
Integrated Motion Processing Device Mfr
N.A.I.C.S.: 334413
Daniel Goehl (VP-Worldwide Sls)

Subsidiary (Non-US):

InvenSense Japan G.K. (3)
9F Yusen Shinyokohama Building 3-17-2 Shinyokohama, Kohoku-Ku, Yokohama, 222-0033, Japan
Tel.: (81) 45 308 9721
Web Site: http://www.invensense.com
Semiconductor & Related Device Mfr
N.A.I.C.S.: 334413

InvenSense Korea Ltd. (3)
5F Songnam Building 273 Gangnam-Daero, Seocho-Gu, Seoul, 06730, Korea (South)
Tel.: (82) 2 541 2900
Web Site: http://www.invensense.com
Semiconductor & Related Device Mfr
N.A.I.C.S.: 334413
Jaewook Jung (Sr Mgr-Customer Quality)

InvenSense Taiwan Co., Ltd. (3)
1F 9 Prosperity 1st Road, Hsinchu Science Park, Hsin-chu, 30078, Taiwan
Tel.: (886) 3 668 6999
Web Site: http://www.invensense.com
Semiconductor & Related Device Mfr
N.A.I.C.S.: 334413
Eric Huang (Gen Mgr)

InvenSense Taiwan Sales Co., Ltd. (3)
7F-6 No 65 Gaotie 7th Road, Hsinchu County, Zhubei, 30273, Taiwan
Tel.: (886) 3 658 5222
Web Site: http://www.invensense.com
Semiconductor & Related Device Mfr
N.A.I.C.S.: 334413

Movea SAS (3)
22 Avenue Doyen Louis Weil, Le Doyen 8e etage, 38000, Grenoble, France
Tel.: (33) 438211931
Web Site: http://www.movea.com
Motion Sensing Technology Developer
N.A.I.C.S.: 334419

Trusted Positioning, Inc (3)
405 1000 Veterans Place NW, Calgary, T3B 4M1, AB, Canada
Tel.: (587) 393-0510
Web Site: https://www.trustedpositioning.tdk.com
Software Development Services
N.A.I.C.S.: 541511
Chris Goodall (Mng Dir)

Subsidiary (Domestic):

Magic Technologies, Inc. (2)
463 S Milpitas Blvd, Milpitas, CA 95035
Tel.: (408) 935-1300
Magnetic Application Products Mfr & Distr
N.A.I.C.S.: 334610

TDK Components U.S.A., Inc (2)
1 TDK Blvd, Peachtree City, GA 30269-2047
Tel.: (770) 631-0410
Web Site: http://www.tdk.com
Sales Range: $50-74.9 Million
Emp.: 145
Electronic Capacitor Mfr
N.A.I.C.S.: 334416

TDK Corporation of America (2)
475 Half Day Rd Ste 300, Lincolnshire, IL 60069-2934 (100%)
Tel.: (847) 699-2299
Web Site: https://www.us.tdk.com
Sales Range: $50-74.9 Million
Sale of Electronic Materials & Components
N.A.I.C.S.: 423120
Sara M. Lambeth (Mgr-Mktg)

TDK Ferrites Corporation (2)
5900 N Harrison St, Shawnee, OK 74804
Tel.: (405) 275-2100
Web Site: http://www.tdk.com
Ceramic Magnet Mfr
N.A.I.C.S.: 327110
Charlene Norvell (Pres & CEO)

TDK Innoveta Inc. (2)
3320 Matrix Dr Ste 100, Richardson, TX 75082
Tel.: (214) 239-3100
Web Site: http://www.tdkinnoveta.com
Power Supplies Mfr
N.A.I.C.S.: 335999
Curt Lankford (Mgr-Info Sys)

TDK RF Solutions Inc. (2)
1101 Cypress Creek Rd, Cedar Park, TX 78613
Tel.: (512) 258-9478
Web Site: https://www.tdkrfsolutions.tdk.com
Electromagnetic Equipment Mfr
N.A.I.C.S.: 334513

TDK UK Limited (1)
Bridge House Brants Bridge, Bracknell, RG12 9BG, United Kingdom
Tel.: (44) 134 48 1510
Appliances, Electrical & Electronics Mfr
N.A.I.C.S.: 335999

TDK Ugo Corporation (1)
146-1 Haraikawa Ohuchi-Sankawa, Yurihonjo, 018-0731, Akita, Japan
Tel.: (81) 184 65 2197
Electronic Components Mfr
N.A.I.C.S.: 334419

TDK Ujo Corporation (1)
50 Kamota Ushiroseki, Showa-Midarehashi, Katagami, 018-1402, Akita, Japan
Tel.: (81) 18 877 3311
Electronic Components Mfr
N.A.I.C.S.: 334419

TDK Yurihonjo Corporation (1)
16-57 Yamanokami Ishiwaki, Yurihonjo, 015-0014, Akita, Japan
Tel.: (81) 184 23 4117
Web Site: http://www.global.tdk.com
Electronic Components Mfr
N.A.I.C.S.: 334419

TDK da Amazonia Importacao e Comercio Ltda. (1)
Praca Nossa Senhora Auxiliadora 04, Loja A Cento, 69025 090, Manaus, AM, Brazil
Tel.: (55) 926221697
Web Site: http://www.tdk.co.jp
Mfr & Sales of Magnetic Recording Tapes & Electronic Material & Components
N.A.I.C.S.: 334610

TDK do Brasil Electronic Components Ltda. (1)
Av Marques de Sao Vicente Avenue 2219 - Cj 1707 and 1708 17 Floor, Building Office Time Agua Branca, Sao Paulo, 05036-040, Brazil
Tel.: (55) 113 289 9599
Appliances, Electrical & Electronics Mfr
N.A.I.C.S.: 335999

TDK do Brasil Ind. e Com. Ltda. (1)
Rua 7 de Abril 230 Bloco A 9o Andar CJ 91 Sala A, 01044-000, Sao Paulo, Brazil
Tel.: (55) 11 3289 9599
Sales Range: $25-49.9 Million
Emp.: 11
Electronic Components Distr
N.A.I.C.S.: 423690

TDK-EPC Corporation (1)
1-13-1 Nihonbashi, Chuo-ku, Tokyo, 103-0027, Japan
Tel.: (81) 3 3278 5111
Electronic Component Mfr & Distr
N.A.I.C.S.: 334419

TDK-EPC Hong Kong Ltd. (1)
SAE Technology Center 6 Science Park East Ave Hong Kong Science Park, Sha Tin, New Territories, China (Hong Kong)
Tel.: (852) 2736 2238
Electronic Components Mfr
N.A.I.C.S.: 334419

TDK-Lambda Corporation (1)
Nihonbashi Takashimaya Mitsui Bldg 2-5-1 Nihonbashi, Chuo-ku, Tokyo, 103-6128, Japan (100%)
Tel.: (81) 36 778 1111
Web Site: https://www.jp.lambda.tdk.com
Sales Range: $300-349.9 Million
Emp.: 656
Standard Switching & Linear Electronic Power Supplies Mfr
N.A.I.C.S.: 335313

Subsidiary (Non-US):

Nemic Lambda Ltd. (2)
Karmiel Industrial Zone, PO Box 500, Karmiel, 21614, Israel
Tel.: (972) 49887491
Web Site: http://www.nemic.co.il
Sales Range: $25-49.9 Million
Emp.: 150
Electronic Power Supplies & Power Supply Systems Mfr
N.A.I.C.S.: 335999
Ariel Yerushalmi (Controller)

Subsidiary (US):

TDK-Lambda Americas Inc. (2)
401 Mile of Cars Way Ste 325, National City, CA 91950
Tel.: (619) 575-4400
Web Site: https://www.us.lambda.tdk.com
Sales Range: $25-49.9 Million
Emp.: 64
Standard Switching & Linear Electronic Power Supplies Mfr
N.A.I.C.S.: 335313

Branch (Non-US):

TDK-Lambda Americas (Canada) (3)
4 Lake Road, Dollard Des Ormeaux, H9B 3H9, QC, Canada
Tel.: (514) 620-7042
Web Site: http://www.lambdapower.com
Rev: $50,000,000
Emp.: 1
Measuring, Medical & Controlling Devices Mfr
N.A.I.C.S.: 334519

Branch (Domestic):

TDK-Lambda Americas Inc. (3)
145 Marcus Blvd Ste 3, Hauppauge, NY 11788
Tel.: (631) 967-3000
Web Site: https://www.us.lambda.tdk.com
Standard Switching & Linear Power Supplies, DC-DC Converters, Power Systems, Military Power Supplies & Systems
N.A.I.C.S.: 423690

Division (Domestic):

TDK-Lambda High Power Division (3)
405 Essex Rd, Neptune, NJ 07753-7701
Tel.: (732) 922-9300
Sales Range: $10-24.9 Million
Mfr & Designers of Standard & Custom High Power Switchmode DC & Capacitor Changing Power Supplies
N.A.I.C.S.: 335999
Brad Canfield (Reg Mgr)

Subsidiary (Non-US):

TDK-Lambda France SAS (2)
3 Avenue du Canada Parc Technopolis-Batiment Sigma, 91940, Les Ulis, France
Tel.: (33) 16 012 7165
Web Site: https://www.emea.lambda.tdk.com
Sales Range: $25-49.9 Million
Emp.: 15
Marketing & Sales of Electronic Equipment & Supplies
N.A.I.C.S.: 334419

TDK-Lambda Germany GmbH (2)
Karl-Bold-Strasse 40, 77855, Achern, Germany
Tel.: (49) 7 841 6660
Web Site: https://www.emea.lambda.tdk.com
Sales Range: $25-49.9 Million
Emp.: 114

TDM BERHAD

Marketing & Sales of Electronic Power Supplies
N.A.I.C.S.: 449210
Gustav Erl (Mng Dir)

TDK-Lambda Malaysia Sdn. Bhd. (2)
Ste 4-3 Level 4 Menara Merais No 1 Jalan 19/3, Section 19/3, 46300, Petaling Jaya, Selangor Darul Ehsan, Malaysia
Tel.: (60) 3 7957 8800
Sales Range: $200-249.9 Million
Emp.: 400
Electronic Power Supplies Mfr
N.A.I.C.S.: 221118

Plant (Domestic):

TDK-Lambda Malaysia Sdn. Bhd. - Kuantan Factory (3)
Lots 2&3 Kawasan Perindustrian Bandar Baru Jaya Gading Kuantan, Kuantan, 26070, Pahang, Malaysia
Tel.: (60) 9 5382255
Electronic Components Mfr
N.A.I.C.S.: 334419

TDK-Lambda Malaysia Sdn. Bhd. - Senai Factory (3)
PLO 33 Kawasan Perindustrian Senai, Locked Bag No 110, 81400, Senai, Johor, Malaysia
Tel.: (60) 75993901
Electronic Components Mfr
N.A.I.C.S.: 334419
Kei Suke Minami (Pres)

Subsidiary (Non-US):

TDK-Lambda UK Ltd. (2)
Kingsley Avenue, Ilfracombe, EX34 8ES, Devon, United Kingdom
Tel.: (44) 127 185 6600
Web Site: https://www.emea.lambda.tdk.com
Sales Range: $100-124.9 Million
Emp.: 280
Standard Switching & Linear Electronic Power Supplies Mfr
N.A.I.C.S.: 335313
Geoff Wilby (Mng Dir)

TDK-MCC Corporation (1)
151 Maeda Hirasawa, Nikaho, 018-0402, Akita, Japan
Tel.: (81) 184 35 5705
Electronic Components Mfr
N.A.I.C.S.: 334419

TDK-Micronas GmbH (1)
Hans-Bunte-Strasse 19, PO Box 840, 79008, Freiburg, Germany
Tel.: (49) 761 5170
Web Site: https://www.micronas.tdk.com
Semiconductor Devices Mfr
N.A.I.C.S.: 334413

TDK-Micronas K.K. (1)
9F Yusen Shin-Yokohama Building 3-17-2, Shin-Yokohama Kohoku-Ku, Yokohama, 222-0033, Japan
Tel.: (81) 45 478 0580
Appliances, Electrical & Electronics Mfr
N.A.I.C.S.: 335999

Tronics Microsystems S.A. (1)
98 rue du Pre de l'Horme, 38926, Crolles, Cedex, France (74.58%)
Tel.: (33) 476972950
Web Site: https://www.tronicsgroup.com
Sales Range: $1-9.9 Million
Micro-Electromechanical Components Mfr
N.A.I.C.S.: 334413
Julien Bon (CEO)

TDM BERHAD
Wisma TDM 443D Jalan Kama, 20400, Kuala Terengganu, Terengganu, Malaysia
Tel.: (60) 96204800 MY
Web Site: https://www.tdmberhad.com.my
2054—(KLS)
Rev.: $130,025,820
Assets: $352,476,402
Liabilities: $213,452,063
Net Worth: $139,024,339
Earnings: ($6,291,852)

TDM BERHAD

TDM Berhad—(Continued)

Emp.: 4,308
Fiscal Year-end: 12/31/22
Oil Mfr
N.A.I.C.S.: 211120
Mohammad Mardi Ismail *(Head-HR, Risk Mgmt, Integrity, Compliance & Sustainability)*

Subsidiaries:

Kumpulan Medic Iman Sdn. Bhd. (1)
25th Floor Menara KH Jalan Sultan Ismail, Wilayah Persekutuan, 50250, Kuala Lumpur, Malaysia
Tel.: (60) 327790573
Web Site: http://www.kmihealthcare.com
Health Care Srvices
N.A.I.C.S.: 621999
Rayney Azmi Ali *(CEO)*

Subsidiary (Domestic):

Kelana Jaya Medical Centre Sdn. Bhd. (2)
No 1 FAS Business Avenue Jalan Perbandaran SS 7, Kelana Jaya, 47301, Petaling Jaya, Selangor, Malaysia
Tel.: (60) 378052111
Health Care Srvices
N.A.I.C.S.: 621999

Kuala Terengganu Specialist Hospital Sdn. Bhd. (2)
Lot 3963 Jalan Sultan Mahmud Kg Batu Buruk Mukim, 20400, Kuala Terengganu, Terengganu, Malaysia
Tel.: (60) 96378888
Health Care Srvices
N.A.I.C.S.: 621999
Abel Ahing *(Gen Mgr)*

Kuantan Medical Centre Sdn. Bhd. (2)
Jalan Tun Razak Bandar Indera Mahkota, 25200, Kuantan, Pahang, Malaysia
Tel.: (60) 95902828
Health Care Srvices
N.A.I.C.S.: 621999
Abdul Hadi Sadan *(Mgr-HR)*

TDR CAPITAL LLP

20 Bentinck St, London, W1U 2EU, United Kingdom
Tel.: (44) 2073994200 UK
Web Site: http://www.tdrcapital.com
Year Founded: 2002
Privater Equity Firm
N.A.I.C.S.: 523999
Manjit Dale *(Co-Founder & Partner)*

Subsidiaries:

ASDA Group Limited (1)
Asda House Southbank Great Wilson St, Leeds, LS11 5AD, United Kingdom (67.5%)
Tel.: (44) 1132435435
Web Site: http://www.asda.co.uk
Sales Range: $25-49.9 Billion
Emp.: 500
Grocery & Apparel Retailer
N.A.I.C.S.: 445110
Roger Burnley *(CEO)*

Aggreko plc (1)
8th Floor 120 Bothwell Street, Glasgow, G2 7JS, Scotland, United Kingdom
Tel.: (44) 141 225 5900
Web Site: http://www.aggreko.com
Rev.: $2,115,610,800
Assets: $3,293,427,600
Liabilities: $1,510,963,200
Net Worth: $1,782,464,400
Earnings: $169,196,400
Emp.: 6,456
Fiscal Year-end: 12/31/2019
Power Generators, Temperature Control Equipment & Compressed Air Systems Mfr
N.A.I.C.S.: 335312
Bruce Pool *(Pres-Rental Solutions)*

Subsidiary (Non-US):

Aggreko (NZ) Limited (2)
1048-1050 Great South Road, Mt Wellington, Auckland, 1060, New Zealand
Tel.: (64) 92597000
Motor & Generator Mfr
N.A.I.C.S.: 335312

Aggreko (Thailand) Limited (2)
AIA Capital Center Building 7th Floor Unit 707 89 Ratchadaphisek Road, Din Daeng, Bangkok, 10400, Thailand
Tel.: (66) 20263628
Motor & Generator Mfr
N.A.I.C.S.: 335312

Aggreko Angola Lda. (2)
Edificio Bengo n 210, Belas, Luanda, Angola
Tel.: (244) 23482331
Motor & Generator Mfr
N.A.I.C.S.: 335312

Aggreko Canada Inc. (2)
22-3500 Saprae Creek Trail, Fort McMurray, T9H 0H6, AB, Canada
Web Site: https://www.aggreko.com
Motor & Generator Mfr
N.A.I.C.S.: 335312

Aggreko Chile Limitada (2)
Industrial Park Buenaventura, Quilicura, Santiago, Chile
Tel.: (56) 24723902
Motor & Generator Mfr
N.A.I.C.S.: 335312

Aggreko Energy Rental Solutions Inc. (2)
Unit 1101 Picadilly Star Building 4th Avenue Corner 27th Street, Bonifacio Global City, Taguig, 1634, Philippines
Tel.: (63) 29898425
Motor & Generator Mfr
N.A.I.C.S.: 335312

Aggreko Energy Rental South Africa (Proprietary) Limited (2)
7 Stanley Street Richmond Hill, Port Elizabeth, South Africa
Tel.: (27) 861244735
Motor & Generator Mfr
N.A.I.C.S.: 335312

Aggreko Energy Rentals Panama SA (2)
Panama Pacifico Howard Boulevard De Las Americas Panamerica, PO Box 0823-03612, Corregimiento de Veracruz, Panama, Panama
Tel.: (507) 8000520526
Motor & Generator Mfr
N.A.I.C.S.: 335312

Aggreko Eurasia LLC (2)
16 Tverskaya St Bld 3 Office 10, Tyumen, 625014, Russia
Tel.: (7) 4956461782
Motor & Generator Mfr
N.A.I.C.S.: 335312

Aggreko Finland Oy (2)
Mannerheimintie 12 B, Helsinki, Finland
Tel.: (358) 102866320
Motor & Generator Mfr
N.A.I.C.S.: 335312

Aggreko Generator Rentals (PNG) Limited (2)
Gabaka Street, PO Box 107, Boroko, Port Moresby, Papua New Guinea
Tel.: (675) 3253825
Motor & Generator Mfr
N.A.I.C.S.: 335312

Subsidiary (Domestic):

Aggreko Holdings Ltd. (2)
121 W Regent St, Glasgow, G2 5D, United Kingdom
Tel.: (44) 412255900
Sales Range: $25-49.9 Million
Emp.: 30
Holding Company
N.A.I.C.S.: 551112

Subsidiary (Domestic):

Aggreko UK Ltd. (3)
121 W Rigent St, Glasgow, G2 5D, United Kingdom
Tel.: (44) 412255900
Supplier of Temporary Power, Temperature Control & Oil Free Compressed Air
N.A.I.C.S.: 334513

Subsidiary (US):

Aggreko Holdings, Inc. (2)
15600 JFK Blvd Ste 900, Houston, TX 77032
Web Site: http://www.aggreko.com
Holding Company; Regional Managing Office
N.A.I.C.S.: 551112
Bruce Pool *(Mng Dir-North America)*

Subsidiary (Domestic):

Aggreko, LLC (3)
15600 John F Kennedy Blvd Ste 600, Houston, TX 77032
Web Site: http://www.aggreko.com
Supplier of Temporary Power, Temperature Control & Oil Free Compressed Air
N.A.I.C.S.: 532490

Subsidiary (Domestic):

A Contact Electric Rentals, L.P. (4)
2217 Aldine Bender Rd, Houston, TX 77032
Tel.: (281) 442-7253
Web Site: http://www.acontact.net
Consumer Electronics & Appliances Rental
N.A.I.C.S.: 532210
Clay Jones *(CEO)*

DRYCO LLC (4)
5400 Janes Ave, Downers Grove, IL 60515
Tel.: (866) 672-4628
Web Site: http://www.drycogroup.com
Climate Control Equipment Rental Services
N.A.I.C.S.: 238220
Joe Schroeder *(Founder & Pres)*

Tuco Industrial Products, Inc. (4)
5223 180th St SW #4A-1, Lynnwood, WA 98037
Tel.: (425) 743-9533
Web Site: http://www.tucoheat.com
Warm Air Heating & Air-Conditioning Equipment & Supplies Merchant Whslr
N.A.I.C.S.: 423730

Subsidiary (Non-US):

Aggreko Iberia SA (2)
Pol Ind Can Salvatella Avgda Torre Mateu 35-37, Barbera Del Valles, Barcelona, 08210, Spain
Tel.: (34) 902221101
Motor & Generator Mfr
N.A.I.C.S.: 335312

Aggreko Italia S.R.L. (2)
Via A Einstein 29, 20090, Assago, MI, Italy
Tel.: (39) 024840491
Motor & Generator Mfr
N.A.I.C.S.: 335312

Aggreko Japan Limited (2)
1004 Aios Ginza 8-17-5 Ginza, Chuo-ku, Tokyo, 104-0061, Japan
Tel.: (81) 368108340
Motor & Generator Mfr
N.A.I.C.S.: 335312

Aggreko Kenya Energy Rentals Limited (2)
First Freight Lane JKIA Freight Terminal, Nairobi, Kenya
Tel.: (254) 707000888
Motor & Generator Mfr
N.A.I.C.S.: 335312

Aggreko Myanmar Co. Limited (2)
42 / A Pantra Street, Dagon Township, Yangon, 11191, Myanmar
Tel.: (95) 1378975
Motor & Generator Mfr
N.A.I.C.S.: 335312

Aggreko Namibia Energy Rentals (Pty) Ltd. (2)
Harbor Park Office no 7 B Second Street East, PO Box 5200, Walvis Bay, Namibia
Tel.: (264) 64227451
Motor & Generator Mfr
N.A.I.C.S.: 335312

Aggreko Norway AS (2)
Sorlandsveien 318, Egersund, 4379, Norway
Tel.: (47) 81000333
Motor & Generator Mfr
N.A.I.C.S.: 335312

INTERNATIONAL PUBLIC

Aggreko Polska Spolka Zorganiczana (2)
Ul Fort Ordona 6, Nowy Kazun, 05-152, Czosnow, Poland
Tel.: (48) 608608419
Motor & Generator Mfr
N.A.I.C.S.: 335312

Aggreko South East Europe S.R.L. (2)
36 Al I Cuza Tunari, Ilfov, 077180, Bucharest, Romania
Tel.: (40) 743151516
Motor & Generator Mfr
N.A.I.C.S.: 335312

Aggreko South Korea Limited (2)
101/2504 109 Mapo-Daero, Mapo-gu, Seoul, 04146, Korea (South)
Tel.: (82) 553430350
Motor & Generator Mfr
N.A.I.C.S.: 335312

Aggreko de Venezuela C.A. (2)
Av Venezuela Torre Lamaletto Piso 5, Oficina Unica Urbanizacion El Rosal, Caracas, 1060, Venezuela
Tel.: (58) 1148467403
Motor & Generator Mfr
N.A.I.C.S.: 335312

Subsidiary (Domestic):

Golden Triangle Generators Limited (2)
2 Voyager Drive Orbital Retail Center, Cannock, WS11 8XP, United Kingdom
Tel.: (44) 3458247365
Motor & Generator Mfr
N.A.I.C.S.: 335312

Subsidiary (Non-US):

Younicos GmbH (2)
Am Studio 16, 12489, Berlin, Germany
Tel.: (49) 30 818 79 9010
Energy Solutions; Mobile & Modular Power
N.A.I.C.S.: 457210

Algeco Scotsman, Inc. (1)
901 S Bond St Ste 600, Baltimore, MD 21231-5997
Tel.: (410) 931-6000
Web Site: http://www.algecoscotsman.com
Mobile & Modular Construction
N.A.I.C.S.: 332311
Jon Veldman *(Exec VP-Global Lean Ops)*

Applus Services, S.A. (1)
Campus UAB Ronda de la Font del Carme s/n Bellaterra, 8193, Barcelona, Spain
Tel.: (34) 900103067
Web Site: https://www.applus.com
Rev.: $2,209,012,453
Assets: $2,619,887,292
Liabilities: $1,987,546,158
Net Worth: $632,341,134
Earnings: $42,348,648
Emp.: 26,770
Fiscal Year-end: 12/31/2023
Testing, Inspection, Certification & Technological Services
N.A.I.C.S.: 541990
Christopher Cole *(Chm)*

Subsidiary (Non-US):

3C Test Limited (2)
Unit 3 - Silverstone Technology Park, Silverstone Circuit, Northampton, NN12 8GX, Northamptonshire, United Kingdom
Tel.: (44) 1327857500
Web Site: https://www.3ctest.co.uk
Material Testing Services
N.A.I.C.S.: 541380
James Gordon *(Founder)*

A2M Industries, SAS (2)
ZA du Parc Secteur Gampille, 42490, Fraisses, France
Tel.: (33) 477401430
Web Site: https://www.a2m-industrie.fr
Material Testing Services
N.A.I.C.S.: 541380

Subsidiary (Domestic):

AC6 Metrologia, S.L. (2)
Poligono Comarca I Edificio Pasarela, 31160, Orkoien, Navarre, Spain
Tel.: (34) 948355300

AND PRIVATE COMPANIES — TDR CAPITAL LLP

Web Site: https://www.ac6m.com
Measurement Equipment Calibration Services
N.A.I.C.S.: 811210

Alpe Metrologia Industrial, S.L.U. (2)
Plz Donantes de Navarra 8 - trasera, Berriozar, 31013, Navarra, Spain
Tel.: (34) 948215858
Web Site: https://www.alpemetrologia.com
Industrial Calibration Services
N.A.I.C.S.: 541380

Subsidiary (Non-US):

Applus (Shangai) Quality inspection Co, Ltd. (2)
3999 Xiu Pu Rd - Building 23, Jucheng Industrial Park, Shanghai, 201315, Pudong, China
Tel.: (86) 2152370776
Testing Lab Services
N.A.I.C.S.: 541380

Applus Argentina, S.A. (2)
Reconquista 661 Piso 2, C1003ABM, Buenos Aires, Argentina
Tel.: (54) 1148931333
Automotive Inspection Services
N.A.I.C.S.: 811198

Applus Car Testing Service, Ltd. (2)
Lakedrive 3026 Citywest Business Campus Naas Road, Dublin, D24 RCRV, Ireland
Tel.: (353) 14135900
Web Site: https://www.ncts.ie
Automotive Inspection Services
N.A.I.C.S.: 811198

Applus Chile, S.A. (2)
Av Departamental 390, San Joaquin, Santiago, Chile
Tel.: (56) 232393670
Web Site: https://www.applusprt.cl
Automotive Inspection Services
N.A.I.C.S.: 811198

Applus Costa Rica, S.A. (2)
Paseo Ruben Dario s/n Panamerican Hwy Piso 2 San Pedro, Edificio Centro Hispanico, San Jose, Costa Rica
Tel.: (506) 2806890
Product Certification Services
N.A.I.C.S.: 541380

Applus Czech Republic, s.r.o. (2)
U Stadionu 89, 530 02, Pardubice, Czech Republic
Tel.: (420) 466530858
Web Site: https://www.applus.com
Testing Lab Services
N.A.I.C.S.: 541380

Applus Danmark, A/S (2)
Hoje Taastrup Boulevard 23 2 th, 2630, Taastrup, Denmark
Tel.: (45) 70131212
Web Site: https://www.applusbilsyn.dk
Automotive Inspection Services
N.A.I.C.S.: 811198

Applus Fomento de Control, S.A. (2)
1 Bd Chefchaouni Angle Avec Ancienne Routre De Rabat, Yassmine Business Center Etage 3 Bureau 26 Ain Sebaa, 21000, Casablanca, Morocco
Tel.: (212) 808625218
Web Site: https://www.applusfomentocontrole.com
Material Testing Services
N.A.I.C.S.: 541380

Applus II Meio Ambiente Portugal, Lda. (2)
Complexo Petroquimico Monte Feio Apartado 227-E C, Sines, 7521-903, Portugal
Tel.: (351) 269634325
Management Consulting Services
N.A.I.C.S.: 541611

Applus India Private Limited (2)
H No 1-11-254/255 Flat No 402 Vijaysri Nivas Street No 1 Prakash Nagar, Begumpet, Hyderabad, 500016, Telangana, India
Tel.: (91) 4029709499
Automotive Inspection Services
N.A.I.C.S.: 811198

Applus Ingenieria y Consultoria, SAS (2)
Calle 17 No 69-46, Montevideo industrial area, Bogota, Colombia
Tel.: (57) 17441133
Automotive Inspection Services
N.A.I.C.S.: 811198

Applus Italy, S.R.L. (2)
Via Cinquentenario 8, 24044, Dalmine, BG, Italy
Tel.: (39) 0351991131
Business Consulting Services
N.A.I.C.S.: 541611

Subsidiary (Domestic):

Applus Iteuve Galicia, S.L.U. (2)
Carretera Nacional VI Km 582, Sada, 15168, A Coruna, Spain
Tel.: (34) 981014500
Automotive Inspection Services
N.A.I.C.S.: 811198

Subsidiary (Non-US):

Applus Japan KK. (2)
Yamauchi Building 3F 3-24-8 Nishi Shimbashi, Minato-ku, Tokyo, 105-0003, Japan
Tel.: (81) 345773514
Automotive Inspection Services
N.A.I.C.S.: 811198

Subsidiary (US):

Applus K2 America, LLC (2)
7337 Empire Central Dr, Houston, TX 77301
Tel.: (281) 617-4021.
Material Testing Services
N.A.I.C.S.: 541380

Subsidiary (Non-US):

Applus Kazakhstan LLC (2)
14 Kirov Square, 060000, Atyrau, Kazakhstan
Tel.: (7) 7017734141
Automotive Inspection Services
N.A.I.C.S.: 811198

Applus Laboratories, AS (2)
Tidemans gate 2, 3616, Kongsberg, Norway
Tel.: (47) 97471515
Testing Lab Services
N.A.I.C.S.: 541380

Applus Mexico, S.A. de C.V. (2)
Blvd Manuel Avila Camacho 184 Piso 4-B, 11650, Mexico, Mexico
Tel.: (52) 5591383838
Web Site: https://www.applus.com
Automotive Inspection Services
N.A.I.C.S.: 811198

Applus Mongolia, LLC (2)
The Landmark 7th Floor Chinggis Avenue - 13, Sukhbaatar District, Ulaanbaatar, Mongolia
Tel.: (976) 70119700
Web Site: http://applus-mongolia-llc.business.site
Automotive Inspection Services
N.A.I.C.S.: 811198

Applus Norcontrol Guatemala, S.A. (2)
Carretera a El Salvador Km 22 Ecoplaza 403 Oficina Applus, Guatemala, Guatemala
Tel.: (502) 30447507
Web Site: https://www.applus.com
Automotive Inspection Services
N.A.I.C.S.: 811198

Applus Norcontrol Peru, S.A.C. (2)
Av El Derby 254 Oficina 901 Edificio Lima Central Tower, Santiago de Surco, 15023, Lima, Peru
Tel.: (51) 12003830
Web Site: https://www.applus.com
Testing Lab Services
N.A.I.C.S.: 541380

Applus Norcontrol Republica Dominicana, S.R.L. (2)
Plaza El Avellano Calle Dr Jacinto Ignacio Manon No 5 Local No 08, Primer Piso, Santo Domingo, Dominican Republic
Tel.: (809) 2271285
Inspection and Technical Assistance Services
N.A.I.C.S.: 541990

Subsidiary (Domestic):

Applus Norcontrol, S.L. (2)
Carretera Nacional VI Km 582, Sada, 15168, A Coruna, Spain
Tel.: (34) 981014500
Laboratory Testing Services
N.A.I.C.S.: 541380

Subsidiary (Non-US):

Applus PNG Limited (2)
Unit 11 Section 53 Allotment 15 and 16 Ume Street 121, National Capital District, Port Moresby, Papua New Guinea
Tel.: (675) 79998700
Web Site: https://www.applus.com
Automotive Inspection Services
N.A.I.C.S.: 811198

Applus PTY, Ltd. (2)
94 Discovery Drive, Bibra Lake, 6163, WA, Australia
Tel.: (61) 894109300
Testing Lab Services
N.A.I.C.S.: 541380

Applus Panama, S.A. (2)
Calle Jacinto Palacios Cobos Edificio No 223 piso 3 local Ay C, Ciudad del Saber, 0843-03081, Panama, Panama
Tel.: (507) 2654150
Automotive Inspection Services
N.A.I.C.S.: 811198

Applus Portugal, Lda. (2)
Rua Joao de Rianho 33, Vila do Conde, 4480-195, Porto, Portugal
Tel.: (351) 252065227
Web Site: https://www.applus.com
Laboratory Testing Services
N.A.I.C.S.: 541380

Applus Qualitec Servicos de Engenharia, Ltda. (2)
Av Marechal Floriano 45 - 10a Andar-Centro, Rio de Janeiro, 20080-003, RJ, Brazil
Tel.: (55) 213553183738
Web Site: https://www.applus.com
Laboratory Testing Services
N.A.I.C.S.: 541380

Applus RTD (2)
Delftweg 144, 3046 NC, Rotterdam, Netherlands
Tel.: (31) 107166000
Web Site: http://www.applus.com
Sales Range: $500-549.9 Million
Construction Inspection & Certification Services
N.A.I.C.S.: 541350

Subsidiary (Non-US):

Applus UK Ltd (3)
Unit s 2c 2d West Mains Industrial Estate, Grangemouth, Falkirk, FK3 8YE, United Kingdom
Tel.: (44) 1324489785
Web Site: https://applustraining.co.uk
Construction Inspection & Certification Services
N.A.I.C.S.: 541350

Subsidiary (US):

JanX Integrity Group, Inc. (3)
17 Kennedy Blvd, East Brunswick, NJ 08816-1250
Tel.: (732) 748-0220
Web Site: http://www.janx.net
Sales Range: $1-9.9 Million
Emp.: 50
Testing Laboratory
N.A.I.C.S.: 541715
Daniel Williams *(Gen Mgr)*

Quality Inspection Services, Inc. (3)
80 Lawrence Bill Dr, Williamsville, NY 14221
Tel.: (716) 853-2611
Web Site: http://www.applusrtd.com
Sales Range: $25-49.9 Million
Emp.: 15
Inspection, Testing & Engineering Services
N.A.I.C.S.: 541350
Greg Rossmiller *(Pres & CEO)*

Subsidiary (Non-US):

Applus RTD Deutschland inspektionsGesellschaft, Gmbh (2)
Industriestrasse 34B, 44894, Bochum, Germany
Tel.: (49) 234927980
Web Site: https://www.applus.com
Automotive Inspection Services
N.A.I.C.S.: 811198

Applus RTD PTE, Ltd. (2)
521 Bukit Batok St 23 Unit 05-E, Singapore, 659544, Singapore
Tel.: (65) 65457646
Automotive Inspection Services
N.A.I.C.S.: 811198

Subsidiary (US):

Applus RTD USA, Inc. (2)
3 Sugar Creek Ctr Blvd Ste 600, Sugar Land, TX 77478
Tel.: (832) 295-5023
Automotive Inspection Services
N.A.I.C.S.: 811198

Subsidiary (Non-US):

Applus Singapore PTE Ltd. (2)
1 Corporation Drive 04-10, Singapore, 619775, Singapore
Tel.: (65) 65457646
Web Site: https://www.applus.com
Material Testing Services
N.A.I.C.S.: 541380

Applus Steel Test (Pty.) Ltd. (2)
28 Senator Rood Road, Vereeniging, 1939, South Africa
Tel.: (27) 164224930
Laboratory Testing Services
N.A.I.C.S.: 541380

Applus Turkey Gozetim Hizmetleri Limited Sirketi (2)
1042 Cadde 1319 Sokak No 9/5, Ovecler, Ankara, Turkiye
Tel.: (90) 3124787992
Automotive Inspection Services
N.A.I.C.S.: 811198

Applus Uruguay, S.A. (2)
Br Artigas 220-Of 801, 11300, Montevideo, Uruguay
Tel.: (598) 8001884
Web Site: https://www.applusitv.uy
Automotive Inspection Services
N.A.I.C.S.: 811198

Applus Velosi SA (Pty) Ltd. (2)
28 Senator Rood Road, Vereeniging, 1939, Gauteng, South Africa
Tel.: (27) 164224930
Automotive Inspection Services
N.A.I.C.S.: 811198

BK WerstofftechnikPrufstelle FUr Werkstoffe, Gmbh (2)
Zur Aumundswiese 2, 28279, Bremen, Germany
Tel.: (49) 421438280
Web Site: https://www.bk-werkstofftechnik.com
Material Testing Services
N.A.I.C.S.: 541380

Subsidiary (Domestic):

CTAG-Idiada Safety Technology, S.L. (2)
Poligono A Granxa parcela 249 - 250, 36410, Porrino, Spain
Tel.: (34) 986900300
Automotive Engineering Services
N.A.I.C.S.: 541330

Subsidiary (Non-US):

Emilab, SRL. (2)
Via F lii Solari 5/A, 33020, Amaro, UD, Italy
Tel.: (39) 0433468625
Web Site: http://en.emilab.it
Automotive Inspection Services
N.A.I.C.S.: 811198

Enertis Chile, SpA (2)
Nueva de Lyon 145 Oficina 503, Providencia, Santiago, Chile
Tel.: (56) 224029642
Web Site: https://www.enertisapplus.com
Testing & Inspection Services
N.A.I.C.S.: 541350

Enertis Colombia S.A.S. (2)

TDR Capital LLP—(Continued)

Calle 93A no 13 - 24 Piso 5, 110221, Bogota, Colombia
Tel.: (57) 16672590
Engineering Consulting Services
N.A.I.C.S.: 541330

Subsidiary (Domestic):

Enertis Solar, S.L.U. (2)
C/Campezo 1 Parque Empresarial Las Mercedes, 28022, Madrid, Spain
Tel.: (34) 916517021
Web Site: https://www.enertisapplus.com
Information Technology Services
N.A.I.C.S.: 541511

Subsidiary (Non-US):

Enertis UK Limited (2)
51 Eastcheap, London, EC3M 1DT, United Kingdom
Tel.: (44) 1928508858
Engineering Consulting Services
N.A.I.C.S.: 541330

Subsidiary (Domestic):

IDIADA Automotive Technology, S.A. (2)
PO Box 20, Santa Oliva L'Albornar, 43710, Tarragona, Spain
Tel.: (34) 977166000
Web Site: http://www.applusidiada.com
Emp.: 2,450
Automotive Engineering Services
N.A.I.C.S.: 541330

Subsidiary (Non-US):

IDIADA CZ, A.S. (2)
Prazska trida 320/8, 500 04, Hradec Kralove, Czech Republic
Tel.: (420) 493654811
Web Site: https://www.idiada.cz
Emp.: 200
Automotive Engineering Services
N.A.I.C.S.: 541330

IDIADA Fahrzeugtechnik, GmbH (2)
Manchinger Str 97, 85053, Ingolstadt, Germany
Tel.: (49) 841885380
Web Site: https://www.applusidiada.com
Automotive Testing Services
N.A.I.C.S.: 811198

IMA Materialforschung und Anwendungstechnik GmbH
Wilhelmine-Reichard-Ring 4, 01109, Dresden, Germany
Tel.: (49) 35188370
Web Site: https://www.ima-dresden.de
Emp.: 200
Software Product Development Services
N.A.I.C.S.: 541511

Idiada Automotive Technology India Pvt. Ltd.
Unit No 304 B wing 3rd floor Sai Radhe Building, 100-101 Raja Bahadur Mill Road, Pune, 411 001, India
Tel.: (91) 2066056800
Automotive Testing Services
N.A.I.C.S.: 811198

Idiada Automotive Technology Mexico S de RL de CV. (2)
Carretera Lateral Mexico Puebla 7534, 72110, Puebla, Mexico
Tel.: (52) 12221078463
Automotive Testing Services
N.A.I.C.S.: 811198

Idiada Automotive Technology Rus, LLC (2)
Lenina av 115 office 301, 603004, Nizhniy Novgorod, Russia
Tel.: (7) 8312199183
Automotive Testing Services
N.A.I.C.S.: 811198

Idiada Automotive Technology UK, Ltd. (2)
St Georges Way, Bermuda Industrial Estate, Nuneaton, CV10 7JS, United Kingdom
Tel.: (44) 2476328083
Automotive Testing Services
N.A.I.C.S.: 811198

Subsidiary (Domestic):

Indoor Climate Management S.L. (2)
Av Via Augusta 15-25 Ed Sant Cugat Business Park, 08174, Sant Cugat del Valles, Spain
Tel.: (34) 931514559
Web Site: https://www.indoorclima.com
Air Conditioning Management Services
N.A.I.C.S.: 811412

Subsidiary (Non-US):

Inspeccio Tecnica de vehicles i serveis, S.A. (2)
Carretera de Bixessarri s/n, Aixovall, AD600, Sant Julia de Loria, Andorra
Tel.: (376) 741350
Web Site: http://www.itvserveis.ad
Automotive Inspection Services
N.A.I.C.S.: 811198

Subsidiary (Domestic):

Iteuve Canarias, S.L. (2)
Camino San Lazaro Los Rodeos, San Cristobal de La Laguna, 38206, Santa Cruz de Tenerife, Spain
Tel.: (34) 922100180
Web Site: https://www.iteuvecanarias.com
Automotive Engineering Services
N.A.I.C.S.: 541330

Subsidiary (Non-US):

K1 Kasastajat, OY (2)
Rieskalahteentie 76, 20300, Turku, Finland
Tel.: (358) 306100900
Web Site: http://www.k1katsastus.fi
Automotive Inspection Services
N.A.I.C.S.: 811198

Subsidiary (US):

Kiefner & Associates Inc. (2)
4480 Bridgeway Ave Ste D, Columbus, OH 43219
Tel.: (614) 888-8220
Web Site: http://www.kiefner.com
Sales Range: $1-9.9 Million
Emp.: 15
Engineering Consulting Services
N.A.I.C.S.: 541330

Subsidiary (Non-US):

LGAI Chile, S.A. (2)
Agustinas 640 piso 9 Santiago Centro, Providencia Metropolitana de Santiago, Santiago, Chile
Tel.: (56) 228187000
Testing Lab Services
N.A.I.C.S.: 541380

Subsidiary (Domestic):

LGAI Technological, Center, S.A. (2)
Campus UAB - Ronda de la Font del Carme s/n, Bellaterra, 08193, Barcelona, Spain
Tel.: (34) 935672000
Testing Lab Services
N.A.I.C.S.: 541380

Laboratorio de Ensayos Metrologicos, S.L.
Avenida Can Sucarrats 110 nave 11, 08191, Rubi, Spain
Tel.: (34) 935862680
Web Site: http://www.lem-sl.com
Testing Lab Services
N.A.I.C.S.: 541380

Subsidiary (US):

Lightship Security USA, Inc. (2)
3600 O Donnell St Ste 2, Baltimore, MD 21224
Tel.: (512) 362-6594
Cyber Security Testing Services
N.A.I.C.S.: 541690

Subsidiary (Non-US):

Lightship Security, Inc. (2)
1101 - 150 Isabella Street, Ottawa, K1S 1V7, ON, Canada
Tel.: (613) 512-1070
Web Site: https://lightshipsec.com
Cyber Security Testing Services
N.A.I.C.S.: 541690

Liuzhou Reliable Auto Analysis Testing Ltd. (2)
No 12 Building 7 4th Floor Suite 417 Fuxin Road, Liuzhou, 545000, China
Tel.: (86) 7723605991
Testing Lab Services
N.A.I.C.S.: 541380

Subsidiary (US):

Matereality, LLC (2)
23 Dutch Mill Rd, Ithaca, NY 14850
Tel.: (607) 257-1784
Web Site: https://www.matereality.com
Software Development Services
N.A.I.C.S.: 541511

Subsidiary (Non-US):

NRAY Services, Inc. (2)
56A Head Street, Dundas, L9H 3H7, ON, Canada
Tel.: (905) 627-1302
Web Site: http://www.nray.ca
Radiographic Inspection Services
N.A.I.C.S.: 541380

Norcontrol Chile, S.A. (2)
Agustinas 640 Piso 9, Santiago Centro, Santiago, Chile
Tel.: (56) 225629000
Automotive Inspection Services
N.A.I.C.S.: 811198

Norcontrol Nicaragua, S.A. (2)
Colonia Los Robles Septima Etapa Casa 45, Managua, Nicaragua
Tel.: (505) 22935410
Automotive Inspection Services
N.A.I.C.S.: 811198

Subsidiary (Domestic):

Novotec Consultores, S.A., Sociedad Unipersonal (2)
Calle Campezo 1 edificio 3 Parque Empresarial Las Mercedes, 28022, Madrid, Spain
Tel.: (34) 912107900
Web Site: http://www.novotec.es
Consulting Services
N.A.I.C.S.: 541613

Subsidiary (US):

QPS America, Inc. (2)
Crown Ctr 5005 Rockside Rd Ste 600, Independence, OH 44131-6827
Tel.: (216) 377-3191
Web Site: http://www.qpsamerica.com
Product Testing & Certification Services
N.A.I.C.S.: 541380

Subsidiary (Non-US):

QPS Europe B.V. (2)
Berg en Dalseweg 122, 6522 BW, Nijmegen, Netherlands
Tel.: (31) 850030144
Web Site: http://www.qpscertification.eu
Product Certification Services
N.A.I.C.S.: 541380
Maurice Hoendervangers *(Dir-Area)*

QPS Evaluation Services Inc. (2)
81 Kelfield St Unit 8, Toronto, M9W 5A3, ON, Canada
Tel.: (416) 241-8857
Web Site: http://www.qps.ca
Product Testing & Certification Services
N.A.I.C.S.: 541380

RITEVE SyC, S.A. (2)
Avenida Central Calles 8 y 10 puerta metalica segunda planta, Post Mail 65-3006, frente a MundoMagico, Alajuela, Costa Rica
Tel.: (506) 8007880000
Web Site: http://www.rtv.co.cr
Automotive Inspection Services
N.A.I.C.S.: 811198
Andres Muruais *(Country Mgr)*

RTD Quality Services Nigeria Ltd. (2)
3A Alabi Street Off Toyin Street, Ikeja, Nigeria
Tel.: (234) 8033367195
Laboratory Testing Services
N.A.I.C.S.: 541380

Reliable Analysis (Shanghai) Inc. (2)
No 19 Lane 1365 Kang Qiao Road East, Shanghai, China
Tel.: (86) 2168183293
Web Site: https://ralab.com.cn
Automotive Raw Material Testing Services
N.A.I.C.S.: 541380

Revisiones Tecnicas Applus del Ecuador Applusiteuve, S.A. (2)
Avda Patria n E4-41 Interseccion Avda Amazonas edificio Patria, Piso 10 Oficina 01, Quito, Pichincha, Ecuador
Tel.: (593) 45005005
Web Site: http://www.applusrtv.ec
Automotive Inspection Services
N.A.I.C.S.: 811198

Rontgen Technische Dienst B.V. (2)
Delftweg 144, 3046 NC, Rotterdam, Netherlands
Tel.: (31) 107166505
Web Site: https://www.applus.com
Certification Services
N.A.I.C.S.: 541990

SKC Engineering Ltd. (2)
19165 94th Avenue, Surrey, V4N 3S4, BC, Canada
Tel.: (604) 882-1889
Web Site: https://www.skceng.com
Mfr Consultation Services
N.A.I.C.S.: 541614
Mathew Smith *(Dir-Professional Svcs)*

Shangai IDIADA Automotive Technology Services Co., Ltd. (2)
Jucheng Pioneer Park Building 23 3999 Xiu Pu Road, Nan Hui Pudong District, Shanghai, 201315, China
Tel.: (86) 2162100894
Automotive Testing Services
N.A.I.C.S.: 811198

Shanghai IDIADA Automotive Technology Services Co., Ltd. (2)
Jucheng Pioneer Park Building 23 3999 Xiu Pu Road Nan Hui, Kangqiao Town Pudong District, Shanghai, 201315, China
Tel.: (86) 2162100894
Laboratory Testing Services
N.A.I.C.S.: 541380

Subsidiary (US):

Talon Test Laboratories (Phoenix) Inc. (2)
5700 Crooks Rd Ste 450, Troy, MI 48089
Tel.: (602) 454-2500
Testing Lab Services
N.A.I.C.S.: 541380

Talon Test Laboratories Incorporated (2)
5700 Crooks Rd Ste 450, Troy, MI 48089
Tel.: (805) 987-7755
Web Site: http://www.talontestlabs.com
Testing Lab Services
N.A.I.C.S.: 541380

Subsidiary (Domestic):

Tunnel Safety Testing, S.A. (2)
Centro experimental San Pedro de Anes, 33189, Siero, Asturias, Spain
Tel.: (34) 985741645
Web Site: http://www.tunneltest.com
Ventilation Fan Testing Services
N.A.I.C.S.: 238220

Subsidiary (Non-US):

Velosi Bahrain WLL. (2)
Flat 11 Bldg 1033 Road 3721 Block 337, PO Box 5652, Umm al Hassam, Manama, Bahrain
Tel.: (973) 17180245
Automotive Inspection Services
N.A.I.C.S.: 811198

Velosi Engineering Management Consultancy (Shangai) Ltd Co. (2)
Room 1304 ShengKang LiaoShi Building No 738 Shang Cheng Rd, Pudong District, Shanghai, 200135, China
Tel.: (86) 2161650588
Business Management Consulting Services
N.A.I.C.S.: 541611

Velosi LLC (2)
Azadlyg Pr house 189 apt 61, Binagadi District, AZ1130, Baku, Azerbaijan

Velosi Limited (2)
Walker House PO Box 72, 28-34 Hill Street, Saint Helier, JE4 8PN, Jersey
Tel.: (994) 124048998
Web Site: http://www.velosi.com
Sales Range: $150-199.9 Million
Inspection, Quality Assurance, Certification & Testing Services
N.A.I.C.S.: 561499

Subsidiary (Non-US):

Applus+ Velosi (3)
Eli France Cafe Bldg Ramada Junction, PO Box 3408, Doha, Qatar
Tel.: (974) 4352850
Web Site: http://www.velosi.com
Sales Range: $200-249.9 Million
Emp.: 700
Inspection & Legislative Certification Services
N.A.I.C.S.: 926150

Kurtec Inspection Services Sdn Bhd (3)
No 46 Jalan PJS 11/20 Bandar Sunway, 46150, Petaling Jaya, Selangor Darul Ehsan, Malaysia
Tel.: (60) 356388689
Web Site: http://www.kurtec.com
Sales Range: $10-24.9 Million
Emp.: 16
Visual Inspection Services
N.A.I.C.S.: 926150

Plant Design Engineers Sdn Bhd (3)
C-17-5 Block C No 12 Megan Avenue II Jalan Yap Kwan Seng, 50450, Kuala Lumpur, Malaysia
Tel.: (60) 3 2168 8832
Sales Range: $25-49.9 Million
Emp.: 15
Software Solutions & 3D Laser Scanning Imaging for Oil & Gas Industries
N.A.I.C.S.: 334610

QA Management Services Pty Ltd. (3)
Ste 5 202 Hampden Rd, Nedlands, 6009, WA, Australia
Tel.: (61) 893865555
Web Site: http://www.qamanage.com.au
Sales Range: $200-249.9 Million
Emp.: 900
Quality Management Consulting & Inspection Services
N.A.I.C.S.: 541611
Philip Wilton (Mng Dir)

Steel Test (Proprietary) Ltd. (3)
28 Senator Rood Road Ext 1, Duncanville, Vereeniging, 1939, Gauteng, South Africa
Tel.: (27) 164224930
Web Site: http://www.steeltest.co.za
Sales Range: $50-74.9 Million
Emp.: 74
Pipe & Steel Testing Services
N.A.I.C.S.: 213112
Willie Maritz (Mgr-HR)

VCS Quality Services Pvt. Ltd (3)
505 5th Fl 360 Degree Bus Pk Next to R-Mall, LBS Marg Mulund West, Mumbai, 400080, Maharashtra, India
Tel.: (91) 2221649720
Web Site: https://www.vcsprojects.com
Sales Range: $75-99.9 Million
Emp.: 450
Certification Services
N.A.I.C.S.: 523150

Velosi (Ghana) Ltd. (3)
2nd Fl Design House Ring Rd E, PO Box OS 0854, Osu Dist, Accra, Ghana
Tel.: (233) 21 786828
Sales Range: $25-49.9 Million
Emp.: 10
Engineering Projects Inspection & Consulting Services
N.A.I.C.S.: 541330

Velosi (Vietnam) Co Ltd. (3)
Rm 250 Petro Tower 8 Hoang Dieu St Ward 1, Vung Tau, Ba Ria-Vung Tau, Vietnam
Tel.: (84) 646253222
Web Site: http://www.velosi.com
Sales Range: $25-49.9 Million
Emp.: 6
Project Inspection & Verification Services
N.A.I.C.S.: 541990
Chandra Shekhar (Reg Mgr)

Subsidiary (US):

Velosi America LLC (3)
222 Pennbright Dr Ste 230, Houston, TX 77090-5907
Tel.: (281) 872-3600
Emp.: 50
Quality Assurance & Inspection Services
N.A.I.C.S.: 926150

Subsidiary (Non-US):

Velosi Angola LDA (3)
Rua Marien Ngouabi N37 No 53, Maianga, Luanda, Angola
Tel.: (244) 923337622
Inspection & Manpower Supply Services
N.A.I.C.S.: 561320

Velosi CBL (M) Sdn Bhd (3)
No 2119 1st Fl Jln Yakin, 98000, Miri, Sarawak, Malaysia
Tel.: (60) 85425885
Web Site: http://www.vcbl.com.my
Sales Range: $25-49.9 Million
Emp.: 6
Third Party Survey & Certification Services
N.A.I.C.S.: 541380

Velosi Certification Bureau Limited (3)
Unit 18 Dawkins Road, Poole, BH15 4JY, Berkshire, United Kingdom
Tel.: (44) 1189207030
Sales Range: $10-24.9 Million
Emp.: 20
Inspection Services
N.A.I.C.S.: 926150
Martin Coles (Sec)

Velosi Certification Services L.L.C (3)
No 201 & 205 Block B Abu Dhabi Bus Hub ICAD-1, PO Box 427, Mussafah, Abu Dhabi, 114182, United Arab Emirates
Tel.: (971) 25502600
Web Site: http://www.velosi.com
Sales Range: $50-74.9 Million
Emp.: 200
Certification & Inspection Services
N.A.I.C.S.: 541380
Brian Dawes (Reg Mgr)

Velosi Certification W.L.L (3)
28 Bubyan Complex 1st Fl Dhajij, PO Box 1589, Farwaniya Salmiya Dist, 22016, Kuwait, Kuwait
Tel.: (965) 24346738
Web Site: http://www.velosi.com
Sales Range: $25-49.9 Million
Emp.: 15
Inspection & Certification Services
N.A.I.C.S.: 561110

Velosi Europe Limited (3)
Unit 18 Dawkins Road, Poole, BH15 4JY, Berkshire, United Kingdom
Tel.: (44) 1189207030
Web Site: http://www.velosi.com
Sales Range: $10-24.9 Million
Emp.: 30
Quality Assurance & Inspection Services
N.A.I.C.S.: 813910
Ben Upton (Mgr-Ops)

Velosi Industries Sdn Bhd (3)
No 152-3-18A Kompleks Malur, Jalan Jejaka Taman Maluri, 55100, Kuala Lumpur, Selangor, Malaysia
Tel.: (60) 60351914020
Web Site: http://www.velosi.com.my
Sales Range: $25-49.9 Million
Emp.: 20
Metal Wastes & Scrap Processing Services
N.A.I.C.S.: 331492

Velosi International Italy Srl (3)
Via Cinquantenario 8, 23807, Dalmine, Lecco, Italy
Tel.: (39) 0395983436
Web Site: http://www.applus.com
Sales Range: $10-24.9 Million
Emp.: 6
Certification & Inspection Services

N.A.I.C.S.: 926150

Velosi Quality Management International L.L.C. (3)
No 201 & 205 Block B Abu Dhabi Bus Hub ICAD-1 Mussafah, PO Box 427, Abu Dhabi, United Arab Emirates
Tel.: (971) 25502600
Sales Range: $25-49.9 Million
Emp.: 4
Certification & Inspection Services
N.A.I.C.S.: 523150
Hakim Genavdalla (Country Mgr)

Velosi Saudi Arabia Co Ltd. (3)
Buld No-7031 Additional No-2958 Sub of Amir Mohammed Bin Fahd Rd, PO Box 7114, Al-Qusur Dist, Dhahran, 34247, Saudi Arabia
Tel.: (966) 38315950
Sales Range: $25-49.9 Million
Emp.: 15
Engineering Projects Inspection & Consulting Services
N.A.I.C.S.: 541330

Velosi Thai Co., Ltd. (3)
217/27 Moo 12 Tumbol, Thungsukhla Amphoe, Si Racha, 20230, Chon Buri, Thailand
Tel.: (66) 38351660
Sales Range: $25-49.9 Million
Emp.: 2
Quality Assurance & Manpower & Inspection Services
N.A.I.C.S.: 561320

Subsidiary (Non-US):

Velosi PromService LLC (2)
Staropetrovsky passage Building 19 Office 7 7-a, 125130, Moscow, 125130, Russia
Tel.: (7) 4991108973
Corrosion Control Services
N.A.I.C.S.: 237120

Velosi Uganda Ltd. (2)
3rd Floor Rewenzori House 1 Lumumba Avenue, Kampala, Uganda
Tel.: (256) 417701000
Automotive Inspection Services
N.A.I.C.S.: 811198

WIAM GmbH (2)
Hermann-Reichelt-Str 3, 01109, Dresden, Germany
Tel.: (49) 35188376343
Web Site: https://www.wiam.de
Software Product Development Services
N.A.I.C.S.: 541511

Subsidiary (Domestic):

ZYX Metrology S.L.U. (2)
Avenida Torre de en Mateo no 29, Ripollet, 08291, Barcelona, Spain
Tel.: (34) 936917837
Web Site: http://www.zyx.es
Automotive Inspection Services
N.A.I.C.S.: 811198

Arrow Holdings S.a.r.l. (1)
20 Rue Eugene Ruppert, L-2453, Luxembourg, Luxembourg
Tel.: (352) 26493298
Investment Services
N.A.I.C.S.: 523999

Subsidiary (US):

Target Hospitality Corp. (2)
9320 Lakeside Blvd Ste 300, The Woodlands, TX 77381 (64%)
Tel.: (281) 362-5397
Web Site: https://www.targethospitality.com
Rev.: $501,985,000
Assets: $771,727,000
Liabilities: $570,880,000
Net Worth: $200,847,000
Earnings: $73,939,000
Emp.: 921
Fiscal Year-end: 12/31/2022
Investment Services
N.A.I.C.S.: 523999
James Brad Archer (Pres, CEO & COO)

Subsidiary (Domestic):

Target Logistics Management LLC (3)
500 Lincoln St, Boston, MA 02111

Tel.: (617) 586-1100
Web Site: http://www.targetlogistics.net
Sales Range: $25-49.9 Million
Temporary Housing Services
N.A.I.C.S.: 624221

BCA Marketplace plc (1)
20 Buckingham Street, London, WC2N 6EF, United Kingdom
Tel.: (44) 20 7389 6873
Web Site: http://www.bcamarketplaceplc.com
Holding Company; Automobile Auction Services
N.A.I.C.S.: 551112
Tim Lampert (CFO)

Subsidiary (Domestic):

British Car Auctions Limited (2)
Headway House Crosby Way, Farnham, GU9 7XG, Surrey, United Kingdom
Tel.: (44) 1252721200
Web Site: http://www.british-car-auctions.co.uk
Automobile Auction Services
N.A.I.C.S.: 441120
Tim Naylor (Mgr-PR)

Division (Domestic):

BCA Logistics Limited (3)
Unit 3700 Solihull Parkway, Birmingham Business Park, Birmingham, B37 7YT, United Kingdom
Tel.: (44) 8447420744
Web Site: http://www.bca-logistics.co.uk
Vehicle Remarketing Logistics Services
N.A.I.C.S.: 541614

BPP Holdings Limited (1)
BPP House Aldine Place 142-144 Uxbridge Road, London, W12 8AA, United Kingdom
Tel.: (44) 330 060 3100
Web Site: http://www.bpp.com
Holding Company; Legal & Financial Industries Vocational Education & Training Services
N.A.I.C.S.: 551112
Graham Gaddes (CEO)

Subsidiary (Non-US):

BPP (CI) Limited (2)
Whiteley Chambers 39 Don Street, Saint Helier, JE2 4TR, Jersey
Tel.: (44) 1534 711800
Web Site: http://www.bppci.com
Education Training Services
N.A.I.C.S.: 611710
Chris Usher (Mng Dir)

Subsidiary (Domestic):

BPP Actuarial Education Ltd. (2)
First Floor McTimoney House 1 Kimber Road, Abingdon, OX14 1BZ, Oxfordshire, United Kingdom
Tel.: (44) 1235 550005
Web Site: http://www.bppacted.com
Educational Support Services
N.A.I.C.S.: 611710

Subsidiary (Domestic):

Actuarial Education Company Limited (3)
First Floor McTimoney House 1 Kimber Road, Abingdon, OX14 1BZ, United Kingdom
Tel.: (44) 1235550005
Web Site: http://www.acted.co.uk
Education Training Services
N.A.I.C.S.: 611710
Darrell Chainey (Mng Dir)

Subsidiary (Domestic):

BPP Learning Media Limited (2)
BPP House Aldine Place 142-144 Uxbridge Road, London, W12 8AA, United Kingdom
Tel.: (44) 3300 603 100
Web Site: http://www.bpp.com
All Other Business Support Services
N.A.I.C.S.: 561499

Subsidiary (Non-US):

BPP Nederland BV (2)
Paasheuvelweg 35, Amsterdam, 1105BG, Netherlands

TDR CAPITAL LLP

TDR Capital LLP—(Continued)
Tel.: (31) 205677888
Colleges Universities & Professional Schools
N.A.I.C.S.: 611310

Subsidiary (Domestic):

BPP Professional Education Limited (2)
BPP House Aldine Place 142-144 Uxbridge Road, London, W12 8AW, United Kingdom
Tel.: (44) 3300 603 100
Web Site: http://www.bpp.com
Business Education Colleges
N.A.I.C.S.: 923110

Subsidiary (Non-US):

BPP Professional Education SP Z.O.O. (2)
ul Chalubinskiego 8, 00-613, Warsaw, Poland
Tel.: (48) 226562700
Web Site: http://www.bpp.pl
Education Training Services
N.A.I.C.S.: 611710

Subsidiary (Domestic):

BPP University Limited (2)
BPP House Aldine Place 142-144 Uxbridge Road, London, W12 8AA, United Kingdom
Tel.: (44) 3300603100
Web Site: http://www.bpp.com
Education Training Services
N.A.I.C.S.: 611710

David Lloyd Leisure Ltd. (1)
The Hangar Mosquito Way, Hatfield Business Park, Hatfield, AL10 9AX, Hertfordshire, United Kingdom
Tel.: (44) 1707283500
Web Site: http://www.davidlloydleisure.co.uk
Sales Range: $450-499.9 Million
Leisure & Fitness Club Operator
N.A.I.C.S.: 713940
Scott Lloyd *(Deputy Chm)*

Euro Garages Ltd. (1)
Euro House Beehive Trading Park Haslingen Road, Blackburn, BB1 2EE, Lancashire, United Kingdom
Tel.: (44) 1254 582111
Web Site: http://www.eurogarages.com
Convenience Store Owner & Operator
N.A.I.C.S.: 445131
Zuber Issa *(Co-Founder & Co-CEO)*

Subsidiary (US):

Cumberland Farms, Inc. (2)
165 Flanders Rd, Westborough, MA 01581
Tel.: (508) 270-1400
Web Site: http://www.cumberlandfarms.com
Sales Range: Less than $1 Million
Emp.: 6,000
Convenience Store & Gas Station Operator
N.A.I.C.S.: 445131
Ari Haseotes *(Pres & CEO)*

Junior Food Stores of West Florida, Inc. (2)
619 8th Ave, Crestview, FL 32536-2101 (100%)
Tel.: (850) 682-6171
Web Site: http://www.tomthumbcstores.com
Convenience Store
N.A.I.C.S.: 445131

Kwik Shop Inc. (2)
734 E Fort Ave, Hutchinson, KS 67501
Tel.: (620) 669-8504
Web Site: http://www.kwikshop.com
Chain Convenience Stores
N.A.I.C.S.: 445131

Mini Mart, Inc. (2)
442 Keeler Pkwy, Pueblo, CO 81001
Tel.: (719) 948-3071
Web Site: http://www.loafnjug.com
Convenience Store Owner & Operator
N.A.I.C.S.: 445131

Subsidiary (Domestic):

Mini Mart, Inc. - Wyoming (3)
395 W Broadway Ave, Jackson, WY 83001
Tel.: (307) 733-7947
Web Site: http://www.loafnjug.com

Grocery Store Operator
N.A.I.C.S.: 445110

Subsidiary (US):

Quik Stop Markets, Inc. (2)
4567 Enterprise St, Fremont, CA 94538-7605
Tel.: (510) 657-8500
Web Site: http://www.quikstop.com
Supermarket Operator
N.A.I.C.S.: 533110

Hurtigruten AS (1)
Fredrik Langes gate 14, PO Box 6144, 9291, Tromso, Norway (90%)
Tel.: (47) 77597045
Web Site: http://www.hurtigruten.no
Sales Range: $500-549.9 Million
Marine Freight Transportation, Passenger Ferry & Bus Transportation Services; Operator of Cruise Ships, Travel Agencies & Hotels
N.A.I.C.S.: 483211
Asta Lassesen *(CEO-Expeditions)*

Subsidiary (US):

Hurtigruten Inc. (2)
320 120th Ave NE Ste 199, Bellevue, WA 98005
Tel.: (866) 522-0371
Web Site: http://www.hurtigruten.com
Cruise & Vacation Planning Services
N.A.I.C.S.: 561520
Monika Tillman *(Mng Dir)*

Subsidiary (Domestic):

Kleven Maritime A/S (2)
Klubbenesvegen 39, 6065, Ulsteinvik, Norway
Tel.: (47) 70019100
Ship Building Services
N.A.I.C.S.: 336611
Kjersti Kleven *(Chm)*

Subsidiary (Domestic):

Kleven Maritime Technology AS (3)
Strandgata 72, 6060, Hareid, Norway
Tel.: (47) 97 05 80 62
Web Site: http://www.kleven.no
Emp.: 5
Ship Building Services
N.A.I.C.S.: 336611
Trond Liavaag *(Mng Dir)*

Kleven Verft AS (3)
N 6065, Ulsteinvik, Norway (100%)
Tel.: (47) 70019100
Web Site: http://www.kleven.no
Sales Range: $50-74.9 Million
Emp.: 290
Specialized Ships & Related Services Supplier
N.A.I.C.S.: 488510
Ole Kristensen *(Mgr-Sls & Tech)*

TE CHANG CONSTRUCTION CO., LTD.
1F No 401-1 Wuquan Rd, North Dist, Taichung, 404, Taiwan
Tel.: (886) 422013611
Web Site: https://tccon.com.tw
Year Founded: 1986
5511—(TPE)
Rev.: $265,264,609
Assets: $404,544,227
Liabilities: $247,755,495
Net Worth: $156,788,732
Earnings: $16,991,402
Fiscal Year-end: 12/31/22
Construction Management Services
N.A.I.C.S.: 236220
Cheng-Yung Huang *(Chm)*

TE CONNECTIVITY LTD.
Muhlenstrasse 26, 8200, Schaffhausen, Switzerland
Tel.: (41) 526336677   CH
Web Site: https://www.te.com
Year Founded: 1941
TEL—(NYSE)
Rev.: $16,034,000,000
Assets: $21,712,000,000

Liabilities: $10,161,000,000
Net Worth: $11,551,000,000
Earnings: $1,910,000,000
Emp.: 90,000
Fiscal Year-end: 09/29/23
Electric Equipment Mfr
N.A.I.C.S.: 551112
Terrence R. Curtin *(CEO)*

Subsidiaries:

AMP Limited (1)
Buyukdere Cad Yapi Kredi Plz B Blok, Tr Kat 10 Levent, 34330, Istanbul, Turkiye
Tel.: (90) 2122818181
Emp.: 20
Distr of Electronic Connectors
N.A.I.C.S.: 423690

Subsidiary (Non-US):

AMP Amermex, S.A. de C.V. (2)
Av Obrero Mundial No 9, Hermosillo, 83200, Mexico
Tel.: (52) 6622897200
Electronic Components Mfr
N.A.I.C.S.: 335999

AMP Hungary Trading Co. Ltd. (2)
Grassalkovich ut 255, H-1239, Budapest, Hungary
Tel.: (36) 012891000
Sales Range: $25-49.9 Million
Electronic & Telecommunication Products
N.A.I.C.S.: 423690
Genos Teller *(Mgr-Distr & Sls)*

AMP Products Pacific Limited (2)
Canton Road Room 1301 Ocean Centre, Tsim Sha Tsui, Kowloon, China (Hong Kong)
Tel.: (852) 27351628
Electronic Components Mfr
N.A.I.C.S.: 334419

American Sensor Technologies, Inc. (1)
450 Clark Dr, Mount Olive, NJ 07828
Tel.: (973) 448-1901
Web Site: http://www.te.com
Sales Range: $10-24.9 Million
Emp.: 65
Pressure Sensors, Pressure Transducers & Pressure Transmitters Mfr
N.A.I.C.S.: 334519

Cima de Acuna S.A. de C.V. (1)
Av Antonio J Bermudez No 1950, Ciudad Juarez, 32470, Mexico
Tel.: (52) 6562296700
Relay & Industrial Control Mfr
N.A.I.C.S.: 335314

Compagnie Deutsch S.A.S. (1)
8 rue Paul Heroult, 92500, Rueil-Malmaison, France
Tel.: (33) 155472550
Web Site: http://www.deutsch.net
Sales Range: $650-699.9 Million
Emp.: 3,500
Holding Company; Electronic Connectors & Relay Equipment Mfr
N.A.I.C.S.: 551112

Subsidiary (Non-US):

Deutsch Engineered Connecting Devices (2)
Tel.: (951) 765-2250
Web Site: http://www.deutschecd.com
Sales Range: $75-99.9 Million
Emp.: 350
Electronic Connector Mfr
N.A.I.C.S.: 334417

Division (Non-US):

Deutsch Industrial Products Division (3)
Tel.: (951) 765-2250
Web Site: http://www.deutsch.net
Sales Range: $25-49.9 Million
Emp.: 100
Truck, Bus & Off-Highway Vehicle Electronic Connector & Wire Terminating Devices Mfr
N.A.I.C.S.: 334417

Connecteurs Electriques Deutsch SAS (1)

INTERNATIONAL PUBLIC

17 Rue Lavoisier, Evreux, 27091, France
Tel.: (33) 232235700
Web Site: http://www.deutsch.net
Sales Range: $250-299.9 Million
Emp.: 540
Electronic Components Distr
N.A.I.C.S.: 423690

Creganna Medical Group (1)
Parkmore West, Galway, Ireland
Tel.: (353) 91757801
Web Site: http://www.creganna.com
Medical Device Mfr
N.A.I.C.S.: 339112

Subsidiary (US):

Creganna Medical - Minnesota (2)
5905 Trenton Ln N, Plymouth, MN 55442
Tel.: (763) 559-6002
Web Site: http://www.creganna.com
Custom Design, Development & Disposable Medical Devices, Primarily Catheters Mfr
N.A.I.C.S.: 339112

Creganna Medical - Oregon (2)
10230 SW Spokane Ct, Tualatin, OR 97062
Tel.: (503) 691-2027
Web Site: http://www.creganna.com
Wire & Coil Mfr
N.A.I.C.S.: 335999

DRI Relays Inc. (1)
55 Engineers Rd, Hauppauge, NY 11788
Tel.: (631) 342-1700
Web Site: http://www.drirelays.net
Sales Range: $50-74.9 Million
Emp.: 100
Electro-Mechanical Relays, Time Delay Devices & Mating Sockets Designer & Mfr
N.A.I.C.S.: 335314
Helen Barbarito *(Mgr-Inside Sls)*

Deutsch India Power Connectors (Pvt.) Ltd. (1)
104 Prestige Omega EPIP Zone, White Field Road, Bengaluru, 560066, Karnataka, India
Tel.: (91) 8040466500
Sales Range: $50-74.9 Million
Emp.: 200
Electronic Components Mfr
N.A.I.C.S.: 334419

Deutsch Israel Ltd. (1)
31 Hutzot Hayotzer Street Southern Industrial Zone, PO Box 5082, Ashkelon, 78150, Israel
Tel.: (972) 86719020
Web Site: http://www.te.com
Electronic Components Distr
N.A.I.C.S.: 334419

Deutsch Japan Limited (1)
4-3-28 Nishidai Itabashi-ku, Tokyo, 175-0045, Japan
Tel.: (81) 359221345
Web Site: http://www.nihon-deutsch.co.jp
Sales Range: $25-49.9 Million
Emp.: 30
Electronic Connectors Distr
N.A.I.C.S.: 334417

Dongguan Transpower Electric Products Co., Ltd. (1)
Jinxing Industrial Zone Jinmei Management Zone, Changping Town, Dongguan, 523579, Guangdong, China
Tel.: (86) 76983335747
Electronic Components Mfr
N.A.I.C.S.: 334419

Elo Touch Systems Argentina S.A. (1)
Saavedra 2950 El Talar de Pacheco, B1618ACP, Buenos Aires, Argentina
Tel.: (54) 11 47332200
Electronic Components Mfr
N.A.I.C.S.: 334419

Fayser S.R.L. (1)
Escobar Industrial Plaza Pan-American Highway Km 57 5, Escobar East Collector Branch, Buenos Aires, Argentina
Tel.: (54) 1160916186
Web Site: https://fayser.com.ar
Fabricated Metal Products Mfr
N.A.I.C.S.: 332311

Harger Inc. (1)
301 Ziegler Dr, Grayslake, IL 60030

AND PRIVATE COMPANIES
TE CONNECTIVITY LTD.

Tel.: (847) 548-8700
Web Site: https://www.harger.com
Sales Range: $10-24.9 Million
Emp.: 42
Provider of Solutions to the Lightning Protection & Grounding Industries
N.A.I.C.S.: 335931
Mark Harger *(Pres)*

Hong Kong Sensors Technologies Limited (1)
Unit No 2 on 24/F Perfect Industrial Building, No 31 Tai Yau Street San Po Kong, Kowloon, China (Hong Kong)
Tel.: (852) 22425048
Web Site: http://www.hkstsensors.com
Sensor & Scanning System Mfr
N.A.I.C.S.: 334413

Hong Kong Sensors Technologies Limited (1)
Unit No 2 on 24/F Perfect Industrial Building No 31 Tai Yau Street, San Po Kong, Hong Kong, China (Hong Kong)
Tel.: (852) 22425048
Web Site: http://www.hkstsensors.com
Connectivity & Sensor Equipment Mfr
N.A.I.C.S.: 334413

L. L. Rowe Company (1)
66 Holton St, Woburn, MA 01801
Tel.: (781) 729-7860
Web Site: http://www.llrowe.com
Connectivity & Sensor Equipment Mfr
N.A.I.C.S.: 334413

LGC Wireless Communication (Shenzhen) Co. Ltd. (1)
Unit B 11f Evoc Technology Bldg No 31 High Tech Park, 518057, Shenzhen, China
Tel.: (86) 75526062028
Wireless Telecommunication Services
N.A.I.C.S.: 517112

LSA, LLC (1)
9521 5th Pl, Lorton, VA 22079
Tel.: (703) 967-9730
Web Site: http://www.lsallc.net
Business Consulting Services
N.A.I.C.S.: 541611
Leslie Smith *(CEO)*

MEAS Ireland (Betatherm) Limited (1)
Ballybrit Business Park, Galway, Ireland
Tel.: (353) 91753238
NTC Thermostat Mfr
N.A.I.C.S.: 334416

MEAS Norway AS (1)
Sandviksveien 26, 1363, Sandvika, Akershus, Norway
Tel.: (47) 24131500
Surveillance & Communication System Mfr
N.A.I.C.S.: 334511

Measurement Specialties, Inc. (1)
1000 Lucas Way, Hampton, VA 23666
Tel.: (757) 766-1500
Sales Range: $400-449.9 Million
Emp.: 3,721
Sensors & Pressure Transmitters Mfr
N.A.I.C.S.: 334514
Mario Calastri *(Treas & VP)*

Subsidiary (Non-US):

MEAS Asia Limited (2)
Unit 1508 15/F Winfield Commercial Building 6-8 Prat Avenue, Tsim Tsa Tsui, China (Hong Kong)
Tel.: (852) 24209088
Sales Range: $10-24.9 Million
Emp.: 2
Sensor & Pressure Transmitter Mfr
N.A.I.C.S.: 334513
Peggy Lam *(Mgr)*

MEAS France SAS (2)
Impasse Jeanne Benozzi CS 83 163, 31027, Toulouse, France
Tel.: (33) 582082200
Sensor & Pressure Transmitter Mfr
N.A.I.C.S.: 334513

MEAS Switzerland S.a.r.l. (2)
Chemin des Chapons-des-Pres 11, 2022, Bevaix, Switzerland
Tel.: (41) 328479550
Sales Range: $25-49.9 Million
Emp.: 85
Sensor & Pressure Transmitter Mfr
N.A.I.C.S.: 334513
Frederic Piaget *(Controller & Mgr-HR)*

Measurement Specialties (China) Ltd. (2)
No 26 Langshan Road Shenzhen High-Tech Park North, Nanshan District, Shenzhen, 518057, China (100%)
Tel.: (86) 755 33305088
Sales Range: $250-299.9 Million
Emp.: 1,400
Measurement Instruments
N.A.I.C.S.: 334513

Unit (Domestic):

Measurement Specialties - Advanced Thermal Products Operations (2)
1711 139th Ln NW, Andover, MN 55304
Tel.: (763) 689-4870
Web Site: http://precisionsensors.measspec.com
Emp.: 40
Thermal Detection Sensory Equipment Mfr
N.A.I.C.S.: 334511

Measurement Specialties - Precision Inertial Products Operations (2)
2236 N Cleveland-Massllion Rd, Akron, OH 44333-1255
Tel.: (330) 659-3312
Web Site: http://www.te.com
Emp.: 14
Precision Inertial Sensors & Measuring Systems Mfr
N.A.I.C.S.: 334513

Subsidiary (Domestic):

Silicon Microstructures Inc. (2)
1701 McCarthy Blvd, Milpitas, CA 95035 (100%)
Tel.: (408) 577-0100
Web Site: http://www.si-micro.com
Sales Range: $25-49.9 Million
Emp.: 80
Relay & Industrial Control Mfr
N.A.I.C.S.: 335314
Omar Abed *(Pres & CEO)*

Plant (Domestic):

TE Connectivity - Measurement Specialties - Chatsworth (2)
20630 Plummer St, Chatsworth, CA 91311
Tel.: (818) 701-2750
Web Site: http://www.celesco.com
Sales Range: $10-24.9 Million
Emp.: 55
Linear & Rotary Measurement Transducers Designer & Mfr
N.A.I.C.S.: 334513

TE Connectivity - Sensor Solutions - Fremont (2)
45738 N Port Loop W, Fremont, CA 94538
Tel.: (408) 934-2090
Sales Range: $25-49.9 Million
Emp.: 50
Designer & Mfr of Pressure Transmitters & Sensors
N.A.I.C.S.: 334513
Dave Wagner *(Dir-Engrg & Product Mgr-Pressure Products)*

MicroGroup, Inc. (1)
7 Industrial Park Rd, Medway, MA 02053
Tel.: (508) 533-4925
Web Site: http://www.microgroup.com
Metal Stock & Custom Tubing
N.A.I.C.S.: 331210

PT KRONE Indonesia (1)
Gedung TIFA Level 9 Jl Kuningan Barat No 26, Jakarta, 12710, Indonesia
Tel.: (62) 215200231
Telecommunication Equipment Distr
N.A.I.C.S.: 423690

PT. Tyco Precision Electronics (1)
The City Tower Building 11th Floor Jl, M H Thamrin No 81, Jakarta, 10310, Indonesia
Tel.: (62) 2129293800
Sales Range: $25-49.9 Million
Emp.: 13
Electronic Components Distr
N.A.I.C.S.: 334419

Potter & Brumfield de Mexico, S.A. de C.V. (1)
Av Antonio J Bermudez 1950, Ciudad Juarez, 32470, Chihuahua, Mexico
Tel.: (52) 6566296700
Relay & Industrial Control Mfr
N.A.I.C.S.: 335314

Precision Subsea AS (1)
Merdeveien 1, 3676, Notodden, Norway
Tel.: (47) 35019811
Optical Instrument Repair & Maintenance Service
N.A.I.C.S.: 811210
Stine K. Larsen *(Mgr-Fin & HR)*

Raychem Electronics (Shanghai) Ltd. (1)
307 Qinjiang Road Caohejing Hi-Tech Development Park, Shanghai, 200233, China
Tel.: (86) 2161067000
Switchgear & Switchboard Apparatus Mfr
N.A.I.C.S.: 335999

Raychem Juarez, S.A. de C.V. (1)
Santiago Troncoso No 331, Ciudad Juarez, 32599, Chihuahua, Mexico
Tel.: (52) 6566495100
Electronic Components Mfr
N.A.I.C.S.: 334419

Raychem Limited (1)
35 Efal Street, 49511, Petah Tiqwa, Israel
Tel.: (972) 39290990
Electronic Component Mfr & Distr
N.A.I.C.S.: 334419

Raychem Shanghai Cable Accessories Ltd (1)
287 Qinjiang Road Caohejing Hi- Tech Development Park, Shanghai, 200233, China
Tel.: (86) 2164853288
Electronic Components Mfr
N.A.I.C.S.: 334419

Rayenergo (1)
Leningrad avenue 72 house 72 office 807, 125315, Moscow, Russia
Tel.: (7) 84957907902
Web Site: http://www.rayenergo.ru
Industrial Electronic Systems Sales & Maintenance Services
N.A.I.C.S.: 423690
Igor Markelov *(Exec Dir)*

SEACON Advanced Products LLC (1)
1321 Nelius Rd, Bellville, TX 77418
Tel.: (979) 865-8846
Connectivity & Sensor Equipment Mfr
N.A.I.C.S.: 334413
Ryan Huff *(Coord-R&D)*

Schaffner Holding AG (1)
Nordstrasse 11e, 4542, Luterbach, Switzerland (98.7%)
Tel.: (41) 326816626
Web Site: http://www.schaffner.com
Rev.: $175,371,397
Assets: $133,952,328
Liabilities: $56,508,869
Net Worth: $77,443,459
Earnings: $13,988,914
Emp.: 1,826
Fiscal Year-end: 09/30/2022
Holding Company
N.A.I.C.S.: 551112
Guido Schlegelmilch *(Exec VP-EMC Div)*

Subsidiary (Non-US):

Schaffner Deutschland GmbH (2)
Schoemperlenstrasse 12B, 76185, Karlsruhe, Germany
Tel.: (49) 72156910
Emp.: 4
Electronic Device Distr
N.A.I.C.S.: 423690
Ulrich Sticksel *(Gen Mgr)*

Schaffner EMC AB (2)
Ostermalmstrorg 1, 114 42, Stockholm, Sweden
Tel.: (46) 850502425
Electronic Device Mfr & Distr
N.A.I.C.S.: 334419

Schaffner EMC Co., Ltd. (2)
Northern Region Industrial Estate 67 Moo 4 Tambon Ban Klang, PO Box 14, Amphur Mueang, Lamphun, 51000, Thailand (100%)
Tel.: (66) 53581104
Sales Range: $400-449.9 Million
Emp.: 1,500
Electronic Components Mfr
N.A.I.C.S.: 334419
Michael Arnold *(Mng Dir)*

Subsidiary (US):

Schaffner EMC Inc. (2)
52 Mayfield Ave, Edison, NJ 08837-3821
Tel.: (732) 225-9533
Web Site: http://www.schaffnerusa.com
Sales Range: $25-49.9 Million
Emp.: 20
Electronic Components Distr
N.A.I.C.S.: 423690

Subsidiary (Non-US):

Schaffner EMC K.K. (2)
ISM Sangenjaya 7F 1-32-12 Kamiuma, Setagaya-Ku, Tokyo, 154-0011, Japan (100%)
Tel.: (81) 357123650
Web Site: http://www.schaffner.jp
Electronic Components Distr
N.A.I.C.S.: 423690

Schaffner EMC Pte. Ltd. (2)
Blk 3015A Ubi Road 1 05-09 Kampong Ubi Industrial Estate, Singapore, 408705, Singapore (95%)
Tel.: (65) 63773283
Web Site: http://www.schaffner.com
Sales Range: $50-74.9 Million
Emp.: 10
Electronic Components Distr
N.A.I.C.S.: 423690
Stesan Krattiger *(Mng Dir)*

Schaffner EMC S.A.S. (2)
16-20 Rue Louis Rameau, 95875, Bezons, France (100%)
Tel.: (33) 134343060
Web Site: http://www.schaffner.com
Sales Range: $50-74.9 Million
Emp.: 7
Electronic Parts & Equipment Whslr
N.A.I.C.S.: 423690

Schaffner EMC S.r.l. (2)
Via Ticino 30, 20900, Monza, MB, Italy (100%)
Tel.: (39) 0392141070
Web Site: http://www.schaffner.com
Sales Range: $50-74.9 Million
Emp.: 2
Electronic Components Distr
N.A.I.C.S.: 423690

Subsidiary (Domestic):

Schaffner EMV AG (2)
Nordstrasse 11e, 4542, Luterbach, Switzerland (100%)
Tel.: (41) 326816626
Web Site: http://www.schaffner.com
Sales Range: $25-49.9 Million
Emp.: 105
Cable & Subscription Programming
N.A.I.C.S.: 516210

Subsidiary (Non-US):

Schaffner EMV Hungary Kft. (2)
Trafo u 4, 6000, Kecskemet, Hungary (100%)
Tel.: (36) 76500540
Web Site: http://www.schaffner.com
Sales Range: $50-74.9 Million
Emp.: 200
Fiber Optic Cable Mfr
N.A.I.C.S.: 335921

Schaffner Ltd (2)
1 Oakmede Place, Binfield, Bracknell, RG42 4JF, United Kingdom (100%)
Tel.: (44) 1189770070
Web Site: http://www.schaffner.uk.com
Sales Range: $25-49.9 Million
Emp.: 7
Electronic Components Mfr
N.A.I.C.S.: 334419

Schaffner Oy (2)
Lohjanharjuntie 1109, 08500, Lohja, Finland (100%)
Tel.: (358) 504687284

TE CONNECTIVITY LTD.

TE Connectivity Ltd.---(Continued)
Web Site: http://www.schaffner.com
Sales Range: $25-49.9 Million
Emp.: 15
Management Consulting Services
N.A.I.C.S.: 541618

Seacon (Europe) Limited (1)
Seacon House Hewett Road, Gapton Hall Industrial Estate, Great Yarmouth, NR31 0RB, Norfolk, United Kingdom
Tel.: (44) 1493652733
Connector & Electric Wire Mfr
N.A.I.C.S.: 334417
Gary Kelly *(Mgr-Sls)*

Seacon Produtos e Servicos Opticos e Eletricos Ltda. (1)
R Conde de Bonfim, 120-Room 212 Tijuca, Rio de Janeiro, 20520-053, Brazil
Tel.: (55) 2125691600
Electronic Connector & Peripheral Mfr
N.A.I.C.S.: 334417

Shenzhen Century Man Communication Equipment Co., Ltd. (1)
Bldg B Zone 5 Honghualing Industrial Area Xili Town, Nanshan District, Shenzhen, 518055, China
Tel.: (86) 755 33962288
Web Site: http://www.centuryman.com.cn
Sales Range: $200-249.9 Million
Emp.: 1,000
Network Monitoring System Mfr & Whslr
N.A.I.C.S.: 334511

Skyline Technologies, Inc. (1)
1400 Lombardi Ave, Green Bay, WI 54304
Tel.: (920) 437-1360
Web Site:
  http://www.skylinetechnologies.com
Sales Range: $1-9.9 Million
Emp.: 65
Custom Computer Programming Services
N.A.I.C.S.: 541511
Daniel P. Hoffmann *(VP-Client Relationships)*

TE Connectivity (Denmark) ApS (1)
Smedeland 13 1, 2600, Glostrup, Denmark
Tel.: (45) 63154300
Connectivity & Sensor Equipment Mfr
N.A.I.C.S.: 334413

TE Connectivity (Wuxi) Company Limited (1)
No 88 Qiming Rd B Dist Of Export Processing Zone, Suzhou, 215121, Jiangsu, China
Tel.: (86) 51287176188
Communication Equipment Mfr
N.A.I.C.S.: 334290

TE Connectivity AMP Espana S.L.U. (1)
Enterprise Networks Department Tordera 6 Pol Ind Pla den Coll, Montcada, 8110, Valles Occidental, Spain
Tel.: (34) 932910634
Electronic Connector Mfr
N.A.I.C.S.: 335999

TE Connectivity AMP Italia S.r.l. (1)
Corso Fratelli Cervi 15, 10093, Collegno, Italy
Tel.: (39) 0114012111
Web Site: http://www.ampnetconnect.it
Sales Range: $100-124.9 Million
Emp.: 500
Electronic Connector Mfr
N.A.I.C.S.: 334417

TE Connectivity Colombia S.A.S. (1)
Calle 74 11-81 Piso 6, Bogota, Colombia
Tel.: (57) 13198999
Sensor & Scanning System Mfr
N.A.I.C.S.: 334413

TE Connectivity Germany GmbH (1)
Amperestrasse 12-14, 64625, Bensheim, Germany
Tel.: (49) 61516071999
Optical Component Mfr & Distr
N.A.I.C.S.: 334413

TE Connectivity HK Limited (1)
Rm 1301 13/F Ocean Center, Tsim Sha Tsui, Kowloon, China (Hong Kong)
Tel.: (852) 27388731
Electronic Connector Mfr
N.A.I.C.S.: 334417

TE Connectivity India Private Limited (1)
No 22 B TE Park Phase 2 Whitefield Main Rd, Doddanakundi Industrial Area 2 EPIP Zone, Bengaluru, 560048, Karnataka, India
Tel.: (91) 80399722200
Emp.: 800
Electronic Components Distr
N.A.I.C.S.: 423690
Arun Kakatkar *(Mng Dir & VP-HR-Asia Pacific)*

TE Connectivity Limerick (1)
International Science Park University of Limerick Castletroy, Limerick, Ireland
Tel.: (353) 61470800
Emp.: 15
Electronic Components Mfr
N.A.I.C.S.: 334419
Joe Lane *(Mgr)*

TE Connectivity Nederland B.V. (1)
Rietveldenweg 32, 5222 AR, 's-Hertogenbosch, Netherlands
Tel.: (31) 736246333
Electronic Connector & Peripheral Mfr
N.A.I.C.S.: 334417
Bianca Van Zon *(Mng Dir & Mgr-HR)*

TE Connectivity Nederland B.V. (1)
Rietveldenweg 32, 5222 AR, 's-Hertogenbosch, Netherlands
Tel.: (31) 736246246
Emp.: 30
Connectivity & Sensor Equipment Mfr
N.A.I.C.S.: 334413
Eric Leijtens *(Mng Dir)*

TE Connectivity Phoenix Optix Inc. (1)
15 Gray Ln Ste 109, Ashaway, RI 02804
Tel.: (401) 637-4600
Web Site: http://www.phoenixoptix.com
Connectivity & Sensor Equipment Mfr
N.A.I.C.S.: 334413

TE Connectivity Sensors Germany GmbH (1)
Hauert 13, Dortmund, 44227, Germany
Tel.: (49) 231 97400
Electrical & Electronic Mfr
N.A.I.C.S.: 334417

Subsidiary (Domestic):

First Sensor AG (2)
Peter-Behrens-Strasse 15, 12459, Berlin, Germany (71.9%)
Tel.: (49) 3063992399
Web Site: https://www.first-sensor.com
Rev.: $148,591,941
Assets: $186,542,991
Liabilities: $46,528,120
Net Worth: $140,014,871
Earnings: $4,514,828
Emp.: 674
Fiscal Year-end: 09/30/2023
Sensor Mfr
N.A.I.C.S.: 334511
Peter McCarthy *(Deputy Chm-Supervisory Bd)*

Subsidiary (Non-US):

First Sensor Corp. (3)
1980 Sherbrooke St West Suite 220, Montreal, H3H 1E8, QC, Canada
Tel.: (514) 938-8089
Electronic Parts Whslr
N.A.I.C.S.: 423690

First Sensor France S.A.S. (3)
5 rue du Havre, 75008, Paris, France
Tel.: (33) 186950233
Electronic Parts Whslr
N.A.I.C.S.: 423690

Subsidiary (US):

First Sensor Inc. (3)
5700 Corsa Ave Ste 105, Westlake Village, CA 91362-4056
Tel.: (818) 706-3400
Web Site: http://www.first-sensor.com
Sales Range: $25-49.9 Million
Emp.: 15
Silicon Photodiodes Mfr
N.A.I.C.S.: 334413

Subsidiary (Domestic):

First Sensor Lewicki GmbH (3)
Allee 35, 89610, Oberdischingen, Germany
Tel.: (49) 730596020
Electronic Parts Whslr
N.A.I.C.S.: 423690
Bernhard Gierl *(CEO)*

First Sensor Microelectronic Packaging GmbH (3)
Grenzstrasse 22, 01109, Dresden, Germany
Tel.: (49) 3512136100
Electronic Parts Whslr
N.A.I.C.S.: 423690
Matthias Peschke *(CEO)*

First Sensor Mobility GmbH (3)
Konigsbrucker Strasse 96, 01099, Dresden, Germany
Tel.: (49) 3513177620
Electronic Parts Whslr
N.A.I.C.S.: 423690
Marcus Resch *(Co-CEO)*

Subsidiary (Non-US):

First Sensor Technics Ltd. (3)
Unit B3 First Floor Illuma Park Gelders Hall Road, Gelders Hall Ind Est, Shepshed, LE12 9NH, Leicestershire, United Kingdom
Tel.: (44) 1509503451
Electronic Parts Whslr
N.A.I.C.S.: 423690

Klay Instruments B. V. (3)
Nijverheidsweg 5, Dwingeloo, 7991 CZ, Meppel, Netherlands
Tel.: (31) 521591550
Web Site: http://www.klay-instruments.com
Stainless Steel Mfr
N.A.I.C.S.: 331110

Subsidiary (Domestic):

Lewicki microelectronic GmbH (3)
Allee 35, 89610, Oberdischingen, Baden-WurttembergWur, Germany
Tel.: (49) 730596020
Web Site: http://www.lewicki-gmbh.de
Electronic Components Mfr & Distr
N.A.I.C.S.: 334416

Sensortechnics GmbH (3)
Boschstrasse 10, Puchheim, 82178, Germany
Tel.: (49) 89800830
Web Site: http://www.sensortechnics.com
Sales Range: $25-49.9 Million
Emp.: 80
Piezoresistive Pressure Transducer & Transmitter Mfr
N.A.I.C.S.: 334513

TE Connectivity Services India Private Limited (1)
88 Sahasra Shree 1st Floor, EPIP Zone Whitefield, Bengaluru, 560066, Karnataka, India
Tel.: (91) 180030003888
Connectivity & Sensor Equipment Mfr
N.A.I.C.S.: 334413

TE Connectivity Solutions GmbH (1)
Werk Axicom Wohlen Industriestrasse 14, Wohlen, 5610, Switzerland
Tel.: (41) 566188700
Web Site: http://www.te.com
Emp.: 200
Electronic Components Mfr
N.A.I.C.S.: 334419

TE Connectivity Spain, S.A.U. (1)
Northern Highway 1, 28108, Alcobendas, Madrid, Spain
Tel.: (34) 916630400
Fiber Optic Cable Mfr
N.A.I.C.S.: 334417
Juan Olivares *(Mng Dir)*

TE Connectivity UK Limited (1)
Merrion Avenue Terminal House, Stanmore, HA7 4RS, Middlesex, United Kingdom
Tel.: (44) 1793528171
Web Site: http://www.te.com
Sales Range: $25-49.9 Million
Emp.: 100
Electrical & Electronic Components Mfr
N.A.I.C.S.: 334417

Subsidiary (Domestic):

Tyco Electronics Precision Engineering Ltd. (2)

INTERNATIONAL PUBLIC

29-31 Chartwell Drive, Wigston, LE18 2FL, Leicestershire, United Kingdom
Tel.: (44) 116 257 0704
Web Site: http://www.subcom.com
Sales Range: $25-49.9 Million
Emp.: 34
Electronic Connector Mfr
N.A.I.C.S.: 334417

Tyco Electronics UK Infrastructure Limited (2)
Heriot House Heriot Road, Chertsey, KT16 9DT, Surrey, United Kingdom
Tel.: (44) 1932575900
Sales Range: $25-49.9 Million
Emp.: 40
Electronic Components Mfr
N.A.I.C.S.: 334417

Tyco Electronics UK Ltd. (2)
Freebournes Rd, Witham, CM8 3AH, Essex, United Kingdom
Tel.: (44) 1376509509
Web Site: http://www.tycoelectronics.com
Sales Range: $25-49.9 Million
Emp.: 200
Analogue Switchboard & Panel Meters, Telemetry Transducers, Power Projection Units, Digital Panel Meters, Shunts & Current Transformers Mfr
N.A.I.C.S.: 335313

Subsidiary (Domestic):

Dorman Smith Switchgear Limited (3)
1 Nile Close Nelson Court Business Centre, Ashton on Ribble, Preston, PR2 2XU, Lancashire, United Kingdom
Tel.: (44) 1772325380
Low-Voltage Electrical Distribution & Circuit Protection Switchgear Mfr
N.A.I.C.S.: 335313

Subsidiary (Non-US):

Dorman Smith Switchgear LLC (4)
Al Quoz 3 Industrial Area Street 6A, PO Box 12872, Sheikh Zayed Road, Dubai, United Arab Emirates
Tel.: (971) 43470226
Web Site:
  http://www.dormansmithswitchgear.com
Sales Range: $25-49.9 Million
Emp.: 52
Low-Voltage Electrical Distribution & Circuit Protection Switchgear Mfr
N.A.I.C.S.: 335313

TE Connectivity UK Ltd (1)
Shannon Way Tewkesbury Business Park, Tewkesbury, GL20 8GB, United Kingdom
Tel.: (44) 1684 857966
Web Site: http://www.te.com
Sales Range: $25-49.9 Million
Emp.: 40
Electronic Components Mfr
N.A.I.C.S.: 334419

TE Connectivity ULC (1)
20 Esna Park Drive, Markham, L3R 1E1, ON, Canada
Tel.: (905) 475-6222
Electronic Connector & Peripheral Mfr
N.A.I.C.S.: 334417

TechDevice LLC (1)
650 Pleasant St, Watertown, MA 02472
Tel.: (617) 972-5800
Web Site: http://www.techdevice.com
Surgical & Medical Instrument Mfr
N.A.I.C.S.: 339112

Subsidiary (Domestic):

MP&E, LLC (2)
6271 Bury Dr, Eden Prairie, MN 55346
Tel.: (952) 835-1468
Web Site: http://www.mp-einc.com
Sales Range: $1-9.9 Million
Emp.: 53
Catheter Assemblies Mfr
N.A.I.C.S.: 339112

Touch Panel Systems K.K. (1)
Sun Hamada Building 2F Shin-Yokohama 1-19-20, Kohoku-ku, Yokohama, 222-0033, Kanagawa, Japan
Tel.: (81) 454782161
Web Site: http://www.tps.co.jp

AND PRIVATE COMPANIES

Sales Range: $25-49.9 Million
Emp.: 30
Touch Screen Monitor Mfr
N.A.I.C.S.: 334118

Tyco Electronics (Gibraltar) Holding Limited (1)
5-9 Main Street, Gibraltar, Gibraltar
Tel.: (350) 20078777
Holding Company
N.A.I.C.S.: 551112

Tyco Electronics (M) Sdn. Bhd. (1)
Wisma Goodyear 13 Fl Block B Kealana Centre Point 3 Jalan SS/19 K, 47301, Petaling Jaya, Selangor, Malaysia
Tel.: (60) 378053055
Web Site: http://www.tycoelectronics.com
Sales Range: $25-49.9 Million
Emp.: 45
Electronic Connectors Distr
N.A.I.C.S.: 423690

Tyco Electronics (Qingdao) Ltd. (1)
No 21 Deshun North Road Economic And Technologies Development Zone, Huanhai, Qingdao, 266108, China
Tel.: (86) 53266795057
Sales Range: $400-449.9 Million
Emp.: 2,000
Electronic Connector Mfr
N.A.I.C.S.: 334417
Gerry Shi (Gen Mgr)

Tyco Electronics (Schweiz) AG (1)
Amperestrasse 3, 9323, Steinach, Switzerland
Tel.: (41) 714470447
Web Site: http://www.tycoelectronics.ch
Sales Range: $125-149.9 Million
Emp.: 400
Electronic Connectors Distr
N.A.I.C.S.: 423690

Tyco Electronics (Shanghai) Co., Ltd (1)
Room 904 Floor 9 Building 12 Panjiayuan Nanli, Chaoyang, Beijing, 100022, China
Tel.: (86) 1058280863
Web Site: http://www.cccme.com.cn
Electric Equipment Mfr
N.A.I.C.S.: 335999

Tyco Electronics (Suzhou) Ltd. (1)
No 88 Qiming Road Area B Export Processing Zone Industrial P, Suzhou, 215121, Jiangsu, China
Tel.: (86) 51287176188
Motor Vehicle Parts Mfr
N.A.I.C.S.: 336390

Tyco Electronics (Thailand) Limited (1)
Fl 5 Eetatao Tower 323 M6 Vibhaevaedi Sitad Tunt Sont, Bangkok, 10120, Thailand
Tel.: (66) 29550500
Web Site: http://www.tycoelectronics.com
Sales Range: $50-74.9 Million
Emp.: 56
Electronic Connectors Distr
N.A.I.C.S.: 423690

Tyco Electronics (Wuxi) Ltd (1)
No 99 Xiqing Road Yanqiao Town, Huishan, Wuxi, 214171, China
Tel.: (86) 51083750971
Fiber Optic Cable Mfr
N.A.I.C.S.: 335921

Tyco Electronics (Zhuhai) Ltd (1)
Building 10 Diheng Industrial Park No 5 Free Trade Zone, Zhuhai, 519030, Guangdong, China
Tel.: (86) 7563888688
Electronic Connector Mfr
N.A.I.C.S.: 334417

Tyco Electronics (Zibo) Co., Ltd. (1)
South Suwang Village Dakunlun Chengnan, Zichuan Dist, Zibo, 255129, Shandong, China
Tel.: (86) 5335781048
Sales Range: $75-99.9 Million
Emp.: 110
Electronic Equipment Distr
N.A.I.C.S.: 423690

Tyco Electronics AMP Espana, S.A. (1)
Tordera 6 Montcada, E-08110, Barcelona, Spain
Tel.: (34) 932910330
Web Site: http://www.te.com
Sales Range: $150-199.9 Million
Emp.: 400
Electronic Connectors Distr
N.A.I.C.S.: 423690

Tyco Electronics AMP K.K. (1)
3 5 8 Hisamoto Takatsu-ku, Kawasaki, 213-8535, Japan
Tel.: (81) 448448111
Web Site: http://www.te.com
Sales Range: $150-199.9 Million
Emp.: 400
Electronic Connectors Distr
N.A.I.C.S.: 423690
Shu Ebe (Pres)

Tyco Electronics AMP Korea Limited (1)
5th Fl Seocho Bldg 1365-10, Seocho-Dong Seocho-Ku, Seoul, Korea (South)
Tel.: (82) 234154550
Web Site: http://www.tycoelectronics.com
Sales Range: $150-199.9 Million
Emp.: 500
Electronic Connectors Distr
N.A.I.C.S.: 423690

Tyco Electronics AMP Qingdao Ltd. (1)
No 21 Deshun North Road Huanhai Economic & Technologies, Development Zone, Qingdao, 266108, Shandong, China
Tel.: (86) 53266795057
Electronic Connector Mfr
N.A.I.C.S.: 334417

Tyco Electronics AMP Shanghai Ltd. (1)
No 688 Gui Ping Road, Shanghai, 200233, China
Tel.: (86) 2124071057
Electric Equipment Mfr
N.A.I.C.S.: 335999

Tyco Electronics Argentina S.A. (1)
Saavedra 2950 El Talar De Pacheco, 1617, Buenos Aires, Vuenos Ailes, Argentina
Tel.: (54) 1147332200
Web Site: http://www.tycoelectronics.com
Sales Range: $50-74.9 Million
Emp.: 60
Electronic Connectors Distr
N.A.I.C.S.: 423690

Tyco Electronics Austria GmbH (1)
Pilzgasse 33, 1210, Vienna, Austria
Tel.: (43) 1905600
Web Site: http://www.tycoelectronics.at
Sales Range: $50-74.9 Million
Emp.: 40
Electronic Connectors Distr
N.A.I.C.S.: 423690

Tyco Electronics Belgium EC BVBA (1)
Siemenslaan 14, 8020, Oostkamp, Belgium
Tel.: (32) 50 83 22 25
Web Site: http://www.te.be.com
Sales Range: $200-249.9 Million
Emp.: 650
Electronic Components Mfr
N.A.I.C.S.: 334419
Vera Zanoose (Mgr-HR)

Tyco Electronics Brasil S.A. (1)
Rua Ado Benatti 53, Sao Paulo, 05037-010, SP, Brazil
Tel.: (55) 1121036000
Web Site: http://www.tycoelectronics.com
Sales Range: $450-499.9 Million
Emp.: 1,200
Electronic Connectors Mfr & Distr
N.A.I.C.S.: 334417

Tyco Electronics Canada ULC (1)
20 Esna Park Drive, Markham, L3R 1E1, ON, Canada
Tel.: (905) 475-6222
Web Site: http://www.tycoelectronics.com
Sales Range: $75-99.9 Million
Emp.: 175
Electrical Cables & Connectors Mfr
N.A.I.C.S.: 335931

Tyco Electronics Colombia Ltda. (1)
Cl 74 No 11-81 P 6, Bogota, Colombia
Tel.: (57) 13198999

Sales Range: $25-49.9 Million
Emp.: 25
Electronic Components Distr
N.A.I.C.S.: 423690

Tyco Electronics Componentes Electromecanicos Lda. (1)
Parque Industrial Rua J 16, 7002-505, Evora, Portugal
Tel.: (351) 266740200
Sales Range: $550-599.9 Million
Emp.: 1,500
Electronic Components Distr
N.A.I.C.S.: 423690
Jorge Garcia (Mng Dir)

Tyco Electronics Corporation (1)
1050 Westlakes Dr, Berwyn, PA 19312
Tel.: (610) 893-9800
Emp.: 29,000
Solderless Terminals, Connectors, Relays, Wireless Components, Touch Screens, Circuit Protection Devices, Sealing Systems, Electronic Modules, Wire, Cable & Fiberoptic Components Mfr
N.A.I.C.S.: 334417

Subsidiary (Domestic):

Image Scan LLC (2)
390 S Fair Oaks Ave, Pasadena, CA 91105-2540
Tel.: (626) 844-2050
Electronic Products Mfr
N.A.I.C.S.: 334417

LADD Industries, LLC (2)
4849 Hempstead Station Dr, Kettering, OH 45429
Tel.: (937) 438-2646
Web Site: http://www.laddinc.com
Sales Range: $50-74.9 Million
Emp.: 80
Electrical Connector & Accessories Distr
N.A.I.C.S.: 423610

Subsidiary (Domestic):

LADD Distribution LLC (3)
4849 Hempstead Station Dr, Kettering, OH 45429
Tel.: (937) 438-2646
Web Site: http://www.laddinc.com
Industrial Electrical Connector Distr
N.A.I.C.S.: 334419

Subsidiary (Domestic):

Precision Interconnect LLC (2)
10025 SW Freeman Dr, Wilsonville, OR 97070
Tel.: (503) 685-9300
Cable Assembly Mfr & Distr
N.A.I.C.S.: 334417

Princeton Optics, Inc. (2)
101 Walters Ave, Ewing, NJ 08638
Tel.: (609) 771-8562
Optical Instrument Mfr
N.A.I.C.S.: 333310

Rochester Corporation (2)
751 Old Brandy Rd, Culpeper, VA 22701-2866
Tel.: (540) 825-2111
Web Site: http://www.rochestercables.com
Rev: $41,000,000
Emp.: 275
Cables & Wires
N.A.I.C.S.: 335921
Paul D. Moore (Officer-Credit)

SEA CON Brantner & Associates Inc. (2)
1700 Gillespie Way, El Cajon, CA 92020-1081
Tel.: (619) 562-7070
Web Site: http://www.seacon-usa.com
Rev: $25,000,000
Emp.: 240
Mfr of Electronic Connectors
N.A.I.C.S.: 334417

Sigma Circuits, Inc. (2)
393 Mathew St, Santa Clara, CA 95050
Tel.: (408) 727-9169
Electronic Interconnect Product Mfr
N.A.I.C.S.: 334417

TE Connectivity Inc. (2)

TE CONNECTIVITY LTD.

607 14th St NW Ste 250, Washington, DC 20005
Tel.: (202) 471-3400
Electronic Components Mfr
N.A.I.C.S.: 334419

Branch (Domestic):

Tyco Connectivity (3)
1396 Charlotte Hwy, Fairview, NC 28730-0520
Tel.: (828) 338-1000
Web Site: http://www.te.net
Emp.: 300
High Performance Relay Products & Specialized Industrial Products Mfr
N.A.I.C.S.: 334417

Subsidiary (Domestic):

TE Connectivity Networks, Inc. (2)
1050 Westlakes Dr, Berwyn, PA 19312
Tel.: (610) 893-9800
Communication Equipment Mfr
N.A.I.C.S.: 334290

The Whitaker Corporation (2)
4550 New Linden Hill Rd Ste 140, Wilmington, DE 19808-2952
Tel.: (302) 633-2740
Sales Range: $25-49.9 Million
Emp.: 10
Patent Services
N.A.I.C.S.: 541199

Subsidiary (Domestic):

The Whitaker LLC (3)
4550 New Linden Hill Rd Ste 140, Wilmington, DE 19808-2952
Tel.: (302) 633-2740
Electronic Components Mfr
N.A.I.C.S.: 334419

Unit (Domestic):

Tyco Electronics (2)
1050 Westlakes Dr, Berwyn, PA 19312
Tel.: (717) 564-0100
Web Site: http://www.te.com
Sales Range: $100-124.9 Million
Emp.: 300
Electronic Components
N.A.I.C.S.: 334417

Tyco Electronics (2)
2245 Brighton Henrietta Town Line Rd, Rochester, NY 14623-2705
Tel.: (585) 272-3100
Sales Range: $25-49.9 Million
Emp.: 54
Electronic Parts Mfr
N.A.I.C.S.: 334419

Tyco Electronics (2)
300 Constitution Dr, Menlo Park, CA 94025-1140
Tel.: (650) 361-3333
Web Site: http://www.tycoelectronics.com
Sales Range: $25-49.9 Million
Emp.: 100
Heat-Shrinkable Products, Cable Connector Systems, Wire & Cable & Fiber-Optics Mfr
N.A.I.C.S.: 335921

Tyco Electronics (2)
5037 Ruffner St, San Diego, CA 92111-1107
Tel.: (858) 279-7872
Sales Range: $25-49.9 Million
Emp.: 50
Microwave Stripline Circuit Boards Mfr
N.A.I.C.S.: 334412

Tyco Electronics (2)
10025 SW Freeman Dr, Wilsonville, OR 97070-9289
Tel.: (503) 685-9300
Sales Range: $75-99.9 Million
Emp.: 500
Electronic Wiring Devices Mfr
N.A.I.C.S.: 335931
Sean Schwelm (Engr-Sls)

Tyco Electronics - Corcom (2)
620 S Butterfield Rd, Mundelein, IL 60060-9457
Tel.: (847) 680-7400
Web Site: http://www.corcom.com
Sales Range: $125-149.9 Million
Emp.: 500
Radio Frequency Interference Filters Mfr

TE CONNECTIVITY LTD.

TE Connectivity Ltd.—(Continued)
N.A.I.C.S.: 334416

Tyco Electronics - Crompton Instruments (2)
1610 Cobb International Blvd NW Ste 4,
Kennesaw, GA 30152-4362
Tel.: (800) 425-8903
Web Site: http://www.cromptonusa.com
Sales Range: $25-49.9 Million
Emp.: 20
Registering Consumption Meters
N.A.I.C.S.: 423830

Subsidiary (Non-US):

Crompton Technologies (3)
7538 Bath Road, Mississauga, L4T 1L2,
ON, Canada
Tel.: (905) 671-2304
Web Site: https://www.cromptoncanada.com
Sales Range: $25-49.9 Million
Emp.: 5
Industrial Machinery & Equipment Mfr
N.A.I.C.S.: 333248

Unit (Domestic):

Tyco Electronics - Kilovac (2)
550 Linden Ave, Carpinteria, CA 93013-2038
Tel.: (805) 220-2020
Web Site: http://www.ciitech.com
Sales Range: $25-49.9 Million
Emp.: 100
High Voltage & Radio Frequency Relays Mfr
N.A.I.C.S.: 335314

Subsidiary (Domestic):

Tyco Electronics Integrated Cable Systems LLC (2)
100 Piscataqua Dr, Newington, NH 03801
Tel.: (603) 436-6100
Fiber Optic Cable Mfr
N.A.I.C.S.: 335921
Bill Suydam *(Dir-Sls & Project Mgmt)*

Tyco Electronics Subsea Communications LLC (2)
250 Industrial Way W, Eatontown, NJ 07724
Tel.: (732) 578-7000
Web Site: http://www.subcom.com
Undersea Communications Systems & Services
N.A.I.C.S.: 517810

Unit (Domestic):

Tyco Electronics Telecom OSP (2)
8000 Purfoy Rd, Fuquay Varina, NC 27526-8938
Tel.: (919) 557-8900
Web Site: http://www.telecomosp.com
Sales Range: $25-49.9 Million
Emp.: 200
Electrical Products Mfr
N.A.I.C.S.: 335999

Subsidiary (Domestic):

Tyco Telecommunications (US) Inc. (2)
60 Columbia Rd, Morristown, NJ 07960
Tel.: (973) 656-8000
Web Site: http://www.tycotelecom.com
Sales Range: $50-74.9 Million
Emp.: 150
Global Broadband Communication Services
N.A.I.C.S.: 517810

Tyco Electronics Corporation India Pvt Limited (1)
Mobius Tower 1 Ground Floor SJR iPark
Opp Sathya Sai Hospital EPIP, Industrial
Area Whitefield, Bengaluru, 560066, India
Tel.: (91) 8040115000
Sales Range: $25-49.9 Million
Emp.: 32
Electronic Components Mfr
N.A.I.C.S.: 334419
Vikram Audipudi *(Mgr-Sls)*

Tyco Electronics Czech s.r.o. (1)
K Amp 1293, 664 34, Kurim, Czech Republic
Tel.: (420) 541162108
Web Site: http://www.tycoelectronics.cz
Sales Range: $400-449.9 Million
Emp.: 2,000
Electronic Products
N.A.I.C.S.: 334419

Tyco Electronics Denmark A/S (1)
Naverland 8, 2600, Glostrup, Denmark
Tel.: (45) 43480411
Web Site: http://www.tycoelectronics.com
Sales Range: $25-49.9 Million
Emp.: 25
Electronic Connectors Distr
N.A.I.C.S.: 423690

Tyco Electronics EC Trutnov s.r.o. (1)
Komenskeho 821, Trutnov, 54101, Czech Republic
Tel.: (420) 499 909 111
Web Site: http://www.tycoelectronics-trutnov.cz
Sales Range: $400-449.9 Million
Emp.: 1,200
Relay & Industrial Control Mfr
N.A.I.C.S.: 335314

Tyco Electronics Energy Pty Ltd (1)
Unit 1 4 Reaghs Farm Rd, Minto, 2566, NSW, Australia
Tel.: (61) 1300656090
Sales Range: $25-49.9 Million
Emp.: 10
Electronic Components Mfr
N.A.I.C.S.: 334419

Tyco Electronics Finland Oy (1)
Konalantie 47, PO Box 100, 00391, Helsinki, Finland
Tel.: (358) 95123420
Sales Range: $25-49.9 Million
Emp.: 19
Electronic Connectors Sales & Distr
N.A.I.C.S.: 423690
Perdag Gundersen *(Mng Dir)*

Tyco Electronics France (1)
29 Chausse Jules-Cesar, BP 30039, 95300, Pontoise, France
Tel.: (33) 134208888
Web Site: http://www.te.com
Sales Range: $100-124.9 Million
Emp.: 450
Electronics & Electronic Connectors Mfr, Sales & Distr
N.A.I.C.S.: 334417

Tyco Electronics France (1)
Route Nationale 90, F 38530, Chapareillan, France
Tel.: (33) 476453434
Sales Range: $100-124.9 Million
Emp.: 260
Electronic Connectors
N.A.I.C.S.: 334417

Tyco Electronics Germany Holdings GmbH (1)
Pfnorstr 1, 64293, Darmstadt, Hessen, Germany
Tel.: (49) 62511330
Investment Management Service
N.A.I.C.S.: 523940

Subsidiary (Domestic):

Tyco Electronics AMP GmbH (2)
Amperestrasse 12-14, Bensheim, 64625, Germany
Tel.: (49) 62511330
Web Site: http://www.tycoelectronics.com
Sales Range: $200-249.9 Million
Emp.: 600
Electronic Products
N.A.I.C.S.: 335931

Tyco Electronics Group S.A. (1)
17 Boulevard Grande Duchesse Charlotte, Luxembourg, 1331, Luxembourg
Tel.: (352) 464 340 1
Electronic Components Mfr
N.A.I.C.S.: 334419

Tyco Electronics H.K. Limited (1)
Rm 1301 Ocean Centre 5 Canton Road, Tsim Sha Tsui, Kowloon, China (Hong Kong)
Tel.: (852) 27351628
Web Site: http://www.ampchina.com
Sales Range: $400-449.9 Million
Emp.: 1,200

Passive Electronics Components Mfr & Distr
N.A.I.C.S.: 335999

Tyco Electronics Hellas MEPE (1)
223 Syngrou Avenue, 171 21, Athens, Greece
Tel.: (30) 210 93 70 396
Electronic Components Mfr
N.A.I.C.S.: 334419

Tyco Electronics Hungary Termelo Kft (1)
Ipartelep Street 2, Esztergom, Hungary
Tel.: (36) 33 540 100
Automotive Electronic Equipment Mfr
N.A.I.C.S.: 336320

Tyco Electronics Idento sas (1)
1 Rue du Port, 38120, Saint Egreve, France
Tel.: (33) 456591200
Sales Range: $10-24.9 Million
Emp.: 50
Bar Code Labeling Services
N.A.I.C.S.: 561910
William Montclair *(Gen Mgr)*

Tyco Electronics Industrial Y Comercial Chile Limitada (1)
Calle Veintiuno de Mayo 921 Of 42, Antofagasta, Chile
Tel.: (56) 55269790
Electronic Equipment Whslr
N.A.I.C.S.: 423690

Tyco Electronics Ireland Ltd. (1)
Shannon Industrial Estate, Shannon, Ireland
Tel.: (353) 61472855
Sales Range: $25-49.9 Million
Emp.: 15
Electronic Connectors Distr
N.A.I.C.S.: 423690

Tyco Electronics Israel Ltd. (1)
35 Efal, Petah Tiqwa, Israel
Tel.: (972) 39290999
Electronic Components Mfr
N.A.I.C.S.: 334419

Tyco Electronics Italia Holding S.r.l. (1)
Corso Fratelli Cervi 15, 10093, Collegno, Italy
Tel.: (39) 011 4012 111
Investment Management Service
N.A.I.C.S.: 523940

Tyco Electronics Japan G.K. (1)
3-5-8 Hisamoto, Takatsu-ku, Kawasaki, 213-8535, Kanagawa, Japan
Tel.: (81) 448448111
Web Site: http://www.te.com
Electronic Components Mfr
N.A.I.C.S.: 334419

Tyco Electronics Logistics AG (1)
Via della Posta, 6934, Bioggio, Switzerland
Tel.: (41) 916100700
Logistics Consulting Servies
N.A.I.C.S.: 541614

Tyco Electronics Mexico, S. de R.L. de C.V. (1)
Via Gustavo Baz No 2160 Edif 4 PB, Tlalnepantla, 54060, La Loma, Mexico
Tel.: (52) 5511060900
Electronic Component Mfr & Distr
N.A.I.C.S.: 335999

Tyco Electronics Middle East FZE (1)
Free Zone Area, Jebel Ali, Dubai, United Arab Emirates
Tel.: (971) 48871577
Electronic Equipment & Appliance Mfr
N.A.I.C.S.: 334419
Leo Benedict *(Gen Mgr)*

Tyco Electronics NZ Limited (1)
57 Mahunga Dr Mangere, Auckland, 2022, New Zealand
Tel.: (64) 96344580
Web Site: http://www.te.com
Sales Range: $25-49.9 Million
Emp.: 35
Electronic Parts & Products Distr
N.A.I.C.S.: 423690

Tyco Electronics Nederland B.V. (1)

INTERNATIONAL PUBLIC

Rietveldenweg 32, PO Box 288, 5222 AR, 's-Hertogenbosch, Netherlands
Tel.: (31) 736246246
Web Site: http://www.teconnectivity.com
Sales Range: $75-99.9 Million
Emp.: 350
Electronic Connectors Mfr & Distr
N.A.I.C.S.: 334417

Tyco Electronics Netherlands (India) Cooperatief U.A. (1)
Rietveldenweg 32, 5222 AR, 's-Hertogenbosch, Netherlands
Tel.: (31) 736246246
Sales Range: $150-199.9 Million
Emp.: 400
Electronic Equipment Distr
N.A.I.C.S.: 423690

Tyco Electronics Norge AS (1)
PO Box 74, NL 1378, Nesbru, Norway
Tel.: (47) 66778899
Web Site: http://www.tyco.com
Sales Range: $25-49.9 Million
Emp.: 17
Electronic Connectors Distr
N.A.I.C.S.: 423690

Tyco Electronics Philippines, Inc. (1)
Unit 24 E 24th Fl Citibank Tower Balero St, Makati, 1226, Philippines
Tel.: (63) 28480171
Web Site: http://www.tycoelectronics.com
Sales Range: $25-49.9 Million
Emp.: 25
Electronic Connectors Distr
N.A.I.C.S.: 423690

Tyco Electronics Polska Sp z o.o. (1)
Cybernetyki 19, 02 676, Warsaw, Poland
Tel.: (48) 224576700
Web Site: http://www.tycoelectronics.com
Sales Range: $25-49.9 Million
Emp.: 25
Electronic Connector Systems & Application Tooling Equipment Sales & Distr
N.A.I.C.S.: 423690

Tyco Electronics Pty Limited (1)
Level 1 15 Bourke Road, Mascot, 2020, NSW, Australia
Tel.: (61) 295542600
Web Site: http://www.tycoelectronics.com.au
Sales Range: $50-74.9 Million
Emp.: 41
Electronic Parts & Products Distr
N.A.I.C.S.: 423690

Tyco Electronics Raychem GmbH (1)
Werk Ottobrunn, Finsinger Field 1, 85505, Ottobrunn, Germany
Tel.: (49) 8960890
Web Site: http://energy.tycoelectronics.com
Sales Range: $200-249.9 Million
Emp.: 600
Electrical Power Products & Systems
N.A.I.C.S.: 335999

Tyco Electronics Raychem Korea Limited (1)
5F Seocho Bldg 1365-10 Seocho-Dong, Seocho-ku, Seoul, 137-863, Korea (South)
Tel.: (82) 234154657
Web Site: http://www.te.com
Emp.: 200
Touch Screen Monitor Distr
N.A.I.C.S.: 423430

Tyco Electronics Raychem N.V. (1)
Diestsesteenweg 692, 3010, Kessel-Lo, Belgium
Tel.: (32) 016351011
Web Site: http://www.telecomosp.com
Sales Range: $200-249.9 Million
Emp.: 700
Electronic Component Products
N.A.I.C.S.: 334417

Tyco Electronics Rus OOO (1)
Khutorskaya str 38A bld 8, Moscow, 127287, Russia
Tel.: (7) 495 790 7902
Emp.: 50
Electronic Components Mfr
N.A.I.C.S.: 334419
Konstantin Dmitriev *(Gen Mgr)*

Tyco Electronics SIMEL SAS (1)

1 Rue Paul Martin, 21220, Gevrey-Chambertin, France
Tel.: (33) 134208993
Electronic Connector Mfr
N.A.I.C.S.: 334417

Tyco Electronics Saudi Arabia Limited (1)
Khaleej Building King Fahad Road Riyadh Golf Center Area Office 207, 57372, Riyadh, Saudi Arabia
Tel.: (966) 14633303
Sales Range: $25-49.9 Million
Emp.: 5
Electronic Components Mfr
N.A.I.C.S.: 334419

Tyco Electronics Services GmbH (1)
Rheinstrasse 20, 8200, Schaffhausen, Switzerland
Tel.: (41) 526336600
Electronic Component Mfr & Distr
N.A.I.C.S.: 335999

Tyco Electronics Servicios de Mexico, S. de R. L. de C. V. (1)
Via Dr Gustavo Baz Prada No 2160 Edif 4 P B, Tlalnepantla, 54060, Mexico
Tel.: (52) 5511060900
Sales Range: $25-49.9 Million
Emp.: 6
Electronic Components Mfr
N.A.I.C.S.: 334419

Tyco Electronics Singapore Pte Ltd (1)
83 Clemenceau Avenue 06-01 UE Square, Singapore, 239920, Singapore
Tel.: (65) 65905386
Sales Range: $100-124.9 Million
Emp.: 500
Electronic Connector Mfr
N.A.I.C.S.: 334417

Tyco Electronics South Africa (Proprietary) Limited (1)
Office Block B Aero Park, Port Elizabeth, 6070, Eastern Cape, South Africa
Tel.: (27) 415034500
Web Site: http://www.tycoelectronics.com
Emp.: 9
Electronic Components Mfr
N.A.I.C.S.: 335999

Tyco Electronics Svenska AB (1)
Kanalvagen 10C 7 Tr, PO Box 619, Upplands Vasby, 19461, Sweden
Tel.: (46) 850725000
Web Site: http://www.tycoelectronics.com
Sales Range: $25-49.9 Million
Emp.: 40
Electronic Connectors Sales & Distr
N.A.I.C.S.: 423690

Tyco Electronics Svenska Holdings AB (1)
Bruttovagen 7, PO Box 598, Jarfalla, 17526, Stockholm, Sweden
Tel.: (46) 850725000
Emp.: 100
Holding Company
N.A.I.C.S.: 551112
Malim Trank (Mgr)

Tyco Electronics Systems India Pvt Ltd (1)
27th K M Bellary Road Doddajala Post, Bengaluru, 562 157, India
Tel.: (91) 80 2854 0800
Electric Equipment Mfr
N.A.I.C.S.: 335999

Tyco Electronics Taiwan Co., Ltd. (1)
3rd Fl 45 Dong-Sing Road, Taipei, 11070, Taiwan
Tel.: (886) 287682788
Web Site: http://www.te.com
Sales Range: $75-99.9 Million
Emp.: 218
Electronic Connectors Distr
N.A.I.C.S.: 423690

Tyco Electronics Technology (Kunshan) Co., Ltd. (1)
No 389 Zhongyang Av Area B Export Processing Zone, Kunshan, 215312, Jiangsu, China
Tel.: (86) 51257032234

Electric Equipment Mfr
N.A.I.C.S.: 335999

Tyco Electronics Tecnologias S. de R.L. de C.V. (1)
Ave Produccion No 20 Parque Industrial Internacional Tijuana, Tijuana, 22424, Baja California, Mexico
Tel.: (52) 6646474513
Electronic Components Mfr
N.A.I.C.S.: 335999

Tyco Electronics Ukraine Limited (1)
3 Markovetska Street, Khryplyn, 76495, Ukraine
Tel.: (380) 342717159
Sales Range: $200-249.9 Million
Emp.: 600
Electronic Components Mfr
N.A.I.C.S.: 334419
Goetz Alexander (CEO)

Tyco Electronics Vermogensverwaltungs GmbH & Co KG (1)
Amperestr 12-14, Bensheim, 64625, Germany
Tel.: (49) 62511330
Emp.: 750
Real Estate Development Services
N.A.I.C.S.: 531390

Tyco Elektronik AMP Ticaret Limited (1)
Buyukdere Cad Yapi Kredi Plaza B Blok Kat 10 No 26/A, Besiktas, 34100, Istanbul, Turkiye
Tel.: (90) 2122355172
Communication Equipment Mfr
N.A.I.C.S.: 334290

Tyco Marine, S.A. (1)
Silva 1, 28013, Madrid, Spain
Tel.: (34) 915 40 15 00
Marine Transportation Services
N.A.I.C.S.: 488390

Tyco Networks (Netherlands) B.V. (1)
Rietveldenweg 32, 's-Hertogenbosch, 5222 AR, Netherlands
Tel.: (31) 73 624 6246
Electronic Components Mfr
N.A.I.C.S.: 334419

Tyco Networks Iberica, S.L. (1)
Plaza Callao 5 - Piso 7, Madrid, 28013, Spain
Tel.: (34) 915401590
Communication Equipment Mfr
N.A.I.C.S.: 334290

Wema Americas LLC (1)
4183 Eagle Hill Dr Ste 101, High Point, NC 27265
Tel.: (336) 393-0222
Electronic Component Mfr & Distr
N.A.I.C.S.: 423690
Carson Spencer (Pres)

Wema Automotive System Private Limited (1)
No 41 & 42 Koduvalli Karanai, Thiruvallur High Road Redhills, Chennai, 600055, India
Tel.: (91) 9841960646
Agricultural Machinery & Equipment Mfr
N.A.I.C.S.: 333922

Wema Environmental Technologies (Shanghai) Co., Ltd. (1)
Unit 1106 Zizhu Building, No 1088 Fangdian Road Pudong, Shanghai, 201204, China
Tel.: (86) 2160897688
Sensor & Scanning System Mfr
N.A.I.C.S.: 334413
Hengdi Li (Gen Mgr)

Wema Environmental Technologies Ltd. (1)
999/18 Bangkok Free Trade Zone, Moo 15 Bangna-Trad KM 23 Road, Samut Prakan, Samutprakarn, Thailand
Tel.: (66) 21825291
Sensor & Scanning System Mfr
N.A.I.C.S.: 334413
Arne Kaland Svren (Gen Mgr)

Wema System AG (1)
Riedstrasse 1, 6343, Rotkreuz, Switzerland
Tel.: (41) 412113700

Sensor & Scanning System Mfr
N.A.I.C.S.: 334413
Rupert Paris (CEO)

Wema System AS (1)
Lonningsflaten 21, Bergen, 5258, Norway
Tel.: (47) 55603700
Commercial Vehicles Sensor Mfr
N.A.I.C.S.: 334512

XOL Technologies Private Limited (1)
Survey No 166/3 Gut No 95 Kesnand Village Wagholi-Rahu Road, Pune, 412207, Maharashtra, India
Tel.: (91) 2066405303
Electronic Components Mfr
N.A.I.C.S.: 334419

TE-MAPOL POLIMER PLASTIK VE INSAAT TICARET SANAYI A.S.
Mimarsinan Org San Bol 5 Cd No 9, 38260, Kayseri, Turkiye
Tel.: (90) 3523212066
Web Site: https://www.temapol.com.tr
Year Founded: 2007
TMPOL—(IST)
Rev.: $25,688,886
Assets: $44,317,988
Liabilities: $28,549,068
Net Worth: $15,768,920
Earnings: $653,696
Fiscal Year-end: 12/31/23
Plastics Product Mfr
N.A.I.C.S.: 326199
Ibrahim Ahmet Samanci (Chm)

TE-TO AD
Gazi Baba 515 Str No 8, 1000, Skopje, North Macedonia
Tel.: (389) 23203800
Web Site: http://www.te-to.com.mk
Year Founded: 2005
Hydroelectric Power Generation Services
N.A.I.C.S.: 221118

TEA LIFE CO., LTD.
118 Ushio, Shimada, 428-8651, Shizuoka, Japan
Tel.: (81) 547463459
Web Site: https://www.tealifeir.com
Year Founded: 1983
3172—(TKS)
Rev.: $80,866,220
Assets: $55,886,700
Liabilities: $16,787,780
Net Worth: $39,098,920
Earnings: $1,984,180
Emp.: 167
Fiscal Year-end: 07/31/24
Tea, Food & Cosmetics Mail Order Sales
N.A.I.C.S.: 424490
Nobuji Ueda (Chm)

Subsidiaries:

Lifeit Co., Ltd. (1)
3-10-1 Aobadai Vort Aobadai II 4th Floor, Meguro-ku, Tokyo, 153-0042, Japan
Tel.: (81) 368235900
Web Site: https://www.lifeit.co.jp
Online Marketing Services
N.A.I.C.S.: 541613

TEA REGION PARISIENNE
Z I Des Ciroliers Rue Clement Ader, 91700, Fleury Merogis, Essonne, France
Tel.: (33) 169467676
Sales Range: $10-24.9 Million
Emp.: 131
Transportation Services
N.A.I.C.S.: 484121
Jean-Louis Cherel (Pres)

TEA SMALLHOLDER FACTORIES PLC

No 186 Vauxhall Street, 02, Colombo, Sri Lanka
Tel.: (94) 779191603
Web Site: https://tsfl-keells.com
Year Founded: 1991
Tea Leaf Mfr
N.A.I.C.S.: 311920
Riza Ahamed (Mgr-Fin)

TEA TIME LIMITED
84/1A Topsia Road South Trinity Plaza 3rd Floor, Kolkata, 700 046, India
Tel.: (91) 3340556800
Web Site: http://www.teatimeltd.co.in
Year Founded: 1979
Rev.: $143,425
Assets: $3,997,161
Liabilities: $2,960
Net Worth: $3,994,201
Earnings: ($932,086)
Fiscal Year-end: 03/31/17
Cultivation Services
N.A.I.C.S.: 111998
V. N. Agarwal (Pres)

TEACHERS BUILDING SOCIETY
Allenview House Hanham Road, Wimborne, BH21 1AG, Dorset, United Kingdom
Tel.: (44) 1202 843500
Web Site: http://www.teachersbs.co.uk
Year Founded: 1966
Rev.: $10,390,495
Assets: $388,978,589
Liabilities: $360,884,117
Net Worth: $28,094,472
Earnings: $263,632
Emp.: 46
Fiscal Year-end: 12/31/19
Mortgage Lending & Other Financial Services
N.A.I.C.S.: 522310
Patrick E. Jarman (Sec & Dir-Legal)

TEAK HOLZ INTERNATIONAL AG
Stallburggasse 4, Vienna, 1010, Austria
Tel.: (43) 73290890990
Web Site: http://www.teak-ag.com
Year Founded: 1998
Teak Wood Producer
N.A.I.C.S.: 321999
Reinhard Schanda (Chm-Supervisory Bd)

Subsidiaries:

Teak Holz Handels- und Verarbeitungs GmbH (1)
blumruerstrasse 74, 4040, Linz, Austria
Tel.: (43) 709089090
Web Site: http://www.teak-austria.com
Teak Wood Trees Distr
N.A.I.C.S.: 423310

TEAL AD
Str Braca Miladinovi bb, 1200, Tetovo, North Macedonia
Tel.: (389) 44335291
Web Site: https://www.teal.mk
Year Founded: 1979
TEAL—(MAC)
Rev.: $3,175,964
Assets: $4,048,697
Liabilities: $92,490
Net Worth: $3,956,207
Earnings: ($372,749)
Emp.: 40
Fiscal Year-end: 12/31/23
Aluminum Alloy Mfr
N.A.I.C.S.: 331524
Vasil Corbadziev (Exec Dir)

TEAM CONSULTING ENGI-

TEAM CONSULTING ENGINEERING & MANAGEMENT PCL (CONTINUED)

151 Nuan Chan Road Nuan Chan, Bueng Kum, Bangkok, 10230, Thailand
Tel.: (66) 25099000
Web Site: https://www.teamgroup.co.th
TEAMG—(THA)
Rev.: $49,197,691
Assets: $71,004,892
Liabilities: $36,404,073
Net Worth: $34,600,818
Earnings: $3,773,639
Emp.: 1,211
Fiscal Year-end: 12/31/23
Engineeering Services
N.A.I.C.S.: 541330
Sanit Rangnoi *(Chm)*

Subsidiaries:

ATT Consultants Company Limited (1)
151 Moo 12 5-6th Floor Team Building Nuan Chan Road, Nuan Chan Bung Kum, Bangkok, 10230, Thailand
Tel.: (66) 250990506
Web Site: https://www.attconsult.com
Engineering & Architectural Services
N.A.I.C.S.: 541310

TEAM Construction Management Company Limited (1)
TEAM Building 151 Nuan Chan Road, Nuan Chan Bueng Kum, Bangkok, 10230, Thailand
Tel.: (66) 236249001
Web Site: https://www.teamcm.co.th
Construction Services
N.A.I.C.S.: 236220
Nakorn Sanyasiri *(Exec Dir)*

TEAM INDIA MANAGERS LTD.

35-B 2nd Floor Khatau Building Alkesh Dinesh Modi Marg Fort, Mumbai, India
Tel.: (91) 2267495501
Web Site: https://timl.in
Business Support Services
N.A.I.C.S.: 561499
Hemang Bhatt *(Dir)*

Subsidiaries:

TIMES GUARANTY LTD. (1)
5th Floor Times Towers Kamala Mills Compound Senapati Bapat Marg, Lower Parel, Mumbai, 400013, India **(70.39%)**
Tel.: (91) 2267534000
Web Site: https://www.timesguarantylimited.com
Rev.: $371,389
Assets: $5,839,675
Liabilities: $10,087
Net Worth: $5,829,587
Earnings: $213,663
Emp.: 2
Fiscal Year-end: 03/31/2022
Financial Advisory Services
N.A.I.C.S.: 523940
Shweta Chaturvedi *(Officer-Compliance & Sec)*

TEAM INTERNET GROUP PLC

4th Floor Saddlers House 44 Gutter Lane, London, EC2V 6BR, United Kingdom
Tel.: (44) 2033880600
Web Site: https://teaminternet.com
TIG—(AIM)
Rev.: $728,237,000
Assets: $558,712,000
Liabilities: $391,581,000
Net Worth: $167,131,000
Earnings: ($9,581,000)
Emp.: 823
Fiscal Year-end: 12/31/22
Domain Name Registrar Services
N.A.I.C.S.: 518210
Benjamin Crawford *(CEO)*

Subsidiaries:

1API GmbH (1)
Kaiserstrasse 172-174, 66386, Saint Ingbert, Germany
Tel.: (49) 68949396760
Web Site: https://www.1api.net
Domain Name Registrar Services
N.A.I.C.S.: 518210
Oliver Fries *(Co-CEO & Head-)*

Brandshelter Inc. (1)
222 Catoctin Cir Site 225, Leesburg, VA 20175
Tel.: (703) 574-3831
Web Site: https://www.brandshelter.com
Monitoring Services
N.A.I.C.S.: 561621

CentralNic Australia Pty. Ltd. (1)
Level 2/222-225 Beach Road, Mordialloc, 3001, VIC, Australia
Tel.: (61) 397831800
Web Site: https://www.centralnicdomains.com
Domain Name Provider
N.A.I.C.S.: 518210

CentralNic Poland Sp. z o.o. (1)
Ul Lubicz 17G, 31-503, Krakow, Poland
Tel.: (48) 72 106 7878
Information Technology Services
N.A.I.C.S.: 541511

CentralNic USA Ltd. (1)
885 Harrison St SE, Leesburg, VA 20175
Tel.: (703) 574-3831
Information Technology Development Services
N.A.I.C.S.: 541511

Commerce Media Tech Sp. z o.o. (1)
Lubicz 17G, 31-503, Krakow, Poland
Tel.: (48) 721067878
Web Site: https://cm.tech
Software Development Services
N.A.I.C.S.: 541511

GFDK Gesellschaft fur digitale Kaufberatung GmbH (1)
Seestrasse 85-87, 15755, Schwerin, Germany
Tel.: (49) 33766439816
Web Site: https://www.digitale-kaufberatung.de
Information Technology Services
N.A.I.C.S.: 541519

InterNexum GmbH (1)
Blumenstrasse 54, 02826, Gorlitz, Germany
Tel.: (49) 35817230000
Web Site: https://www.internexum.de
Information Technology Services
N.A.I.C.S.: 541519

Key-Systems GmbH (1)
Kaiserstrasse 172-174, 66386, Saint Ingbert, Germany
Tel.: (49) 68949396850
Web Site: https://www.key-systems.net
Internet Consulting Services
N.A.I.C.S.: 541512

PTS GmbH (1)
Plauener Str 160, 13053, Berlin, Germany
Tel.: (49) 3054 906 5280
Web Site: https://www.pts.space
Domain Name Registrar Services
N.A.I.C.S.: 518210

RegistryGate GmbH (1)
Wilhelm-Wagenfeld-Str 16, 80807, Munich, Germany
Tel.: (49) 180 573 4437
Web Site: https://www.registrygate.com
Domain Name Registrar Services
N.A.I.C.S.: 518210

Safebrands S.A.S. (1)
Pole Media Belle de Mai 37 Rue Guibal, 13356, Marseille, Cedex 3, France
Tel.: (33) 488662222
Web Site: https://safebrands.com
Information Technology Services
N.A.I.C.S.: 541519

Sublime Technology (France) S.A.R.L. (1)
170 Boulevard de la Villette, 75019, Paris, France
Tel.: (33) 184791460
Web Site: https://www.sublime.xyz
Emp.: 120
Software Development Services
N.A.I.C.S.: 541511

Traffic.club IT GmbH (1)
Kaiserstrasse 172-174 St, 66386, Saint Ingbert, Germany
Tel.: (49) 68949396560
Web Site: https://traffic.club
Digital Marketing Services
N.A.I.C.S.: 541613

VGL Publishing AG (1)
Oranienstrasse 6, 10997, Berlin, Germany
Tel.: (49) 3012064292
Web Site: https://www.vergleich.org
Book & Periodical Publisher
N.A.I.C.S.: 513120

TEAM KALORIK GROUP NV

Middenhutlaan 1, 1640, Saint Genesius-Rode, Flemish Brabant, Belgium
Tel.: (32) 23599510
Web Site: http://www.kalorikshop.be
Household Appliance Distr
N.A.I.C.S.: 423220
Michael Stolle *(CEO)*

TEAM PRECISION PUBLIC COMPANY LIMITED

198 Moo 13 Suwansorn Rd Dong-Khee-Lek, Muang Prachinburi, Bangkok, 25000, Thailand
Tel.: (66) 37403340
Web Site: https://www.teampcba.com
Year Founded: 1996
TEAM—(THA)
Rev.: $94,513,749
Assets: $58,203,862
Liabilities: $21,035,827
Net Worth: $37,168,035
Earnings: $8,321,027
Emp.: 993
Fiscal Year-end: 12/31/23
Electronics Circuit Board Mfr
N.A.I.C.S.: 334418
Chakkaphant Manutsathit *(Chm & CEO)*

Subsidiaries:

Team Precision Public Company Limited - Prachinburi Factory (1)
198 Moo 13 Suwansorn Rd Dong-Khee-Lek, Muang Prachinburi, 25000, Pathumthani, Prachin Buri, Thailand
Tel.: (66) 37403340
Electric Equipment Mfr
N.A.I.C.S.: 336320

Team Precision Public Company Limited - Rangsit Factory (1)
152/8 Moo 3 Rangsit, Tanyaburi, Pathumthani, 12110, Thailand
Tel.: (66) 25772350
Electric Equipment Mfr
N.A.I.C.S.: 336320

TEAM RELOCATIONS

Drury Way, London, NW10 0TJ, United Kingdom
Tel.: (44) 2087840100
Web Site: http://www.teamrelocations.com
Sales Range: $150-199.9 Million
Emp.: 850
Corporate Moving Services
N.A.I.C.S.: 484210
Donald Trump *(Pres)*

TEAM TELECOMMUNICATIONS GROUP LTD.

Field House Uttoxeter Old Road, Derby, DE1 1NH, United Kingdom
Tel.: (44) 1332 375596
Web Site: http://www.teamtelecomgroup.com
Telecommunication Servicesb
N.A.I.C.S.: 517810

Peter Burridge *(Chm)*

Subsidiaries:

Affini Technology Ltd. (1)
Belvedere House, Basing View, Basingstoke, RG21 4HG, United Kingdom
Tel.: (44) 1256 660000
Web Site: http://www.affini.co.uk
Information Technology Consulting Services
N.A.I.C.S.: 541690
Jason Colombo *(CEO)*

Simoco Australasia Pty. Ltd. (1)
1270 Ferntree Gully Road, Scoresby, 3179, VIC, Australia
Tel.: (61) 3 9730 3999
Web Site: https://www.simocogroup.com
Communications Systems Solutions
N.A.I.C.S.: 517810
Robert Meachem *(Gen Mgr)*

Simoco EMEA Ltd. (1)
Field House, Uttoxeter Old Road, Derby, DE1 1NH, United Kingdom
Tel.: (44) 1332 375 500
Web Site: http://www.simocogroup.com
Sales Range: $25-49.9 Million
Mobile Radio Communications Services & Products
N.A.I.C.S.: 517112
Ian Carr *(Mng Dir & CEO)*

TEAM YOUN BIO MEDICINE INTERNATIONAL CORP. LIMITED

Flat/Room 1006 10/F Hang Seng Tsim Sha Tsui Bldg 18 Carnarvon Road, Tsim Sha Tsui, Kowloon, China (Hong Kong)
Tel.: (852) 9738 1833
Medical Devices
N.A.I.C.S.: 339112
Wei-Tao Wang *(Pres/CEO-Eternity Healthcare)*

Subsidiaries:

Eternity Healthcare Inc. (1)
Hang Seng Tsim Sha Tsui Bldg 18 Carnarvon Road Flat/Rm 1006 10/F, Tsim Sha Tsui, Kowloon, China (Hong Kong) **(76.04%)**
Tel.: (852) 1369 188 4662
Web Site: http://www.eternityhealthcare.com
Emp.: 1
Holding Company; In-Home Medical Diagnostic Kits Mfr & Distr
N.A.I.C.S.: 551112
Wei-Tao Wang *(Pres, CEO & CFO)*

TEAM17 GROUP PLC

3 Red Hall Avenue Paragon Business Park, Wakefield, WF1 2UL, West Yorkshire, United Kingdom
Tel.: (44) 1924267776   UK
Web Site: https://www.team17groupplc.com
Year Founded: 1990
TM17—(AIM)
Rev.: $173,496,592
Assets: $413,693,512
Liabilities: $95,011,361
Net Worth: $318,682,151
Earnings: $29,636,455
Emp.: 362
Fiscal Year-end: 12/31/22
Gaming Software Development Services
N.A.I.C.S.: 541511
Debbie Bestwick *(CEO)*

Subsidiaries:

Astragon Entertainment GmbH (1)
Am Wehrhahn 33, 40211, Dusseldorf, Germany
Tel.: (49) 2115405150
Web Site: https://www.astragon.com
Video Game Development Services
N.A.I.C.S.: 518210

StoryToys Limited (1)
Exchequer Chambers Exchequer St, Dublin 2, Dublin, Ireland
Tel.: (353) 871323892

Web Site: https://storytoys.com
Edutainment App Development Services
N.A.I.C.S.: 541511

TEAMAX SMART CITY TECHNOLOGY CORPORATION LIMITED
No 137 Xinxing Er Road, Wuzhou, 543002, Guangxi, China
Tel.: (86) 774 3863686
Year Founded: 1995
000662—(SSE)
Rev.: $2,287,539
Assets: $460,837,294
Liabilities: $364,759,782
Net Worth: $96,077,512
Earnings: ($725,984,722)
Emp.: 409
Fiscal Year-end: 12/31/19
Cosmetics & Pharmaceuticals Mfr
N.A.I.C.S.: 325620
Jiantong Xia *(Chm & Pres)*

TEAMINVEST PRIVATE GROUP LIMITED
Ground Floor Suite 2 23 Ryde Road, Pymble, 2073, NSW, Australia
Tel.: (61) 299559540   AU
Web Site:
  https://www.tipgroup.com.au
Year Founded: 2012
TIP—(ASX)
Rev.: $71,000,848
Assets: $80,635,718
Liabilities: $24,026,863
Net Worth: $56,608,854
Earnings: $2,608,724
Fiscal Year-end: 06/30/23
Asset Management Services
N.A.I.C.S.: 523999
Dean Robinson *(Co-Sec)*

Subsidiaries:

Automation Group Limited   (1)
Level 2 318 Lambton Quay, Wellington, 6011, New Zealand
Tel.: (64) 1300724743
Automation Engineering Services
N.A.I.C.S.: 541330

East Coast Traffic Controllers Pty. Ltd.   (1)
3/30 Maud Street, Maroochydore, 4558, QLD, Australia
Tel.: (61) 1300011203
Web Site:
  https://www.eastcoasttrafficcontrol.com.au
Traffic Management Services
N.A.I.C.S.: 541370

Icon Metal Pty. Ltd.   (1)
81 Egerton Street, Silverwater, 2128, NSW, Australia
Tel.: (61) 296372102
Web Site: https://www.iconmetal.com
Emp.: 50
Building Construction Services
N.A.I.C.S.: 532412

TIP Group (UK) Pty. Ltd.   (1)
Trafford Point Twining Road Trafford Park, Manchester, M17 1SH, United Kingdom
Tel.: (44) 1618682600
Web Site: https://www.tip-group.com
Trailer Rental Services
N.A.I.C.S.: 532120

Teaminvest Pty. Ltd.   (1)
Ground Floor 23 Ryde Road, Pymble, 2073, NSW, Australia
Tel.: (61) 294165954
Web Site: https://www.teaminvest.com.au
Financial Consulting Services
N.A.I.C.S.: 522320

TEAMLEASE SERVICES LTD.
315 Work Avenue Campus Ascent Building 77, Koramangala Industrial Layout Jyothi Nivas College Road Koramangala, Bengaluru, 560 095, Karnataka, India
Tel.: (91) 8068243000

Web Site:
  https://www.teamlease.com
Year Founded: 2002
TEAMLEASE—(NSE)
Rev.: $671,057,928
Assets: $178,923,231
Liabilities: $89,375,286
Net Worth: $89,547,945
Earnings: $10,711,797
Emp.: 976
Fiscal Year-end: 03/31/21
Human Resource Consulting Services
N.A.I.C.S.: 541612
Manish Mahendra Sabharwal *(Co-Founder & Chm)*

Subsidiaries:

I.M.S.I Staffing Private Limited   (1)
Doon Express Business Park Suite 2410 Opp Transport Nagar, Subhash Nagar, Dehradun, 248001, Uttarakhand, India
Tel.: (91) 1356677449
Web Site: https://www.imsistaffing.com
Recruitment Services
N.A.I.C.S.: 561311

TeamLease E-Hire Private Limited   (1)
Commercial Complex Nilayam 8th Floor BMTC 80 Feet Rd, Koramangala, Bengaluru, 560095, Karnataka, India
Tel.: (91) 8095811114
Web Site: http://www.teamleaseehire.com
Recruitment Services
N.A.I.C.S.: 561311
Kaushik Banerjee *(VP & Head-Bus)*

TeamLease Edtech Limited   (1)
B-903 Western Edge II Borivali East, Mumbai, 400066, India
Tel.: (91) 2248968005
Web Site:
  https://www.teamleaseedtech.com
Software Development Services
N.A.I.C.S.: 541511

TeamLease RegTech Private Limited   (1)
Opposite Commissioner Office 1 Church Road Camp, Pune, 411001, Maharashtra, India
Tel.: (91) 9899245318
Web Site:
  https://www.teamleaseregtech.com
Software Development Services
N.A.I.C.S.: 541511

TEAMSPIRIT, INC.
19F Hibiya Park Front 2-1-6 Uchisaiwai-cho, Chiyoda-ku, Tokyo, 100-0011, Japan
Tel.: (81) 345777510
Web Site: https://www.teamspirit.com
Year Founded: 1996
4397—(TKS)
Rev.: $27,498,620
Assets: $22,964,240
Liabilities: $15,319,860
Net Worth: $7,644,380
Earnings: ($1,119,600)
Fiscal Year-end: 08/31/24
Software Development Services
N.A.I.C.S.: 541511
Koji Ogishima *(Founder, Chm, Pres & CEO)*

TEAMWAY INTERNATIONAL GROUP HOLDINGS LIMITED
Suites 2005-2006 20/F Tower 6 The Gateway Harbour City, 9 Canton Road Tsim Sha Tsui, Kowloon, China (Hong Kong)
Tel.: (852) 21167600   Ky
Web Site:
  http://www.teamwaygroup.com
Year Founded: 2011
1239—(HKG)
Rev.: $54,076,885
Assets: $49,005,076
Liabilities: $69,408,706

Net Worth: ($20,403,630)
Earnings: ($6,963,980)
Emp.: 598
Fiscal Year-end: 12/31/22
Holding Company; Packaging Products & Structural Components Mfr
N.A.I.C.S.: 551112
Mei Ngai *(Exec Dir)*

Subsidiaries:

Chongqing Guangjing Packaging Materials Co. Ltd   (1)
Pengqiao Economic Development Zone Guangxing Town Jiangjin District, Chongqing, China
Tel.: (86) 2348606111
Packaging Product Mfr & Distr
N.A.I.C.S.: 326140
Xian Geng Jiang *(Deputy Gen Mgr)*

Chuzhou Chuangce Packaging Materials Company Limited   (1)
No 919 Zhong Du Avenue Chuzhou Economic Development Zone, Chuzhou, Anhui, China
Tel.: (86) 5503211785
Packaging Product Mfr & Distr
N.A.I.C.S.: 326140

Sichuan Jinghong Packaging Co. Ltd   (1)
No 35 East Mianxing Road High Technology Industrial Development Zone, Mianyang, Sichuan, China
Tel.: (86) 8162410272
Packaging Product Mfr & Distr
N.A.I.C.S.: 326140
Hui Sheng Xia *(Gen Mgr)*

Teamway Finance Limited   (1)
Unit 832 8/F Rykadan Capital Tower No 135 Hoi Bun Road, Kwun Tong, Kowloon, China (Hong Kong)
Tel.: (852) 29116466
Packaging Product Mfr & Whslr
N.A.I.C.S.: 561910

TEAMYOUNG TECHNOLOGY CO., LTD.
18F No 400 Huanbei Rd, Zhongli Dist, Taoyuan, 320, Taiwan
Tel.: (886) 32805160
Web Site:
  https://www.teamyoung.com
5345—(TAI)
Rev.: $205,203
Assets: $2,645,937
Liabilities: $981,709
Net Worth: $1,664,228
Earnings: ($1,840,290)
Fiscal Year-end: 12/31/22
Power Control System Mfr
N.A.I.C.S.: 335931
Wang Dy-Cheng *(Chm & CEO)*

TEAR CORP.
35-1 Kurokawa Hondori, Kita-ku, Nagoya, 462-0841, Japan
Tel.: (81) 529188200
Web Site: https://www.tear.co.jp
Year Founded: 1997
2485—(NGO)
Rev.: $99,744,793
Assets: $109,018,761
Liabilities: $53,155,154
Net Worth: $55,863,607
Earnings: $5,594,160
Fiscal Year-end: 09/30/23
Funeral Services & Funeral Parlor Operator
N.A.I.C.S.: 812210
Tomiyasu Tokuhisa *(Pres & CEO)*

TEARLACH RESOURCES LIMITED
Suite 610 - 700 West Pender St, Vancouver, V6C 1G8, BC, Canada
Tel.: (604) 688-5007
Web Site: https://www.tearlach.ca

V44—(DEU)
Rev.: $28,831
Assets: $3,280,028
Liabilities: $344,308
Net Worth: $2,935,719
Earnings: $4,912,674
Fiscal Year-end: 09/30/23
Oil & Gas Exploration Service
N.A.I.C.S.: 213112
Charles E. Ross *(CFO)*

TEC BUILDING SERVICES (NORTH WEST) CO., LTD.
The Meadows Victoria Avenue East, Manchester, M9 6HE, Lancashire, United Kingdom
Tel.: (44) 161 7412424
Web Site:
  http://www.tecbuildingservices.co.uk
Sales Range: $10-24.9 Million
Emp.: 60
Property Repairs & Building Maintenance
N.A.I.C.S.: 561790
Terry Connor *(Mng Dir)*

TEC MARITSA 3 AD
Promishlena zona, Dimitrovgrad, 6400, Bulgaria
Tel.: (359) 39161250
Web Site: http://www.tec-marica3.com
6TMA—(BUL)
Sales Range: Less than $1 Million
Eletric Power Generation Services
N.A.I.C.S.: 221111
Ilian Dimitrov Pavlov *(CEO)*

TECAN GROUP AG
Seestrasse 103, 8708, Mannedorf, Switzerland
Tel.: (41) 449228111   CH
Web Site: https://www.tecan.com
Year Founded: 1980
Rev.: $1,072,022,149
Assets: $2,260,619,627
Liabilities: $873,462,786
Net Worth: $1,387,156,841
Earnings: $137,775,168
Emp.: 215,545
Fiscal Year-end: 12/31/21
Automation & Detection Solutions For Life Science Lab
N.A.I.C.S.: 541715
Andreas Wilhelm *(Gen Counsel & Exec VP)*

Subsidiaries:

Paramit Corporation   (1)
18735 Madrone Pkwy, Morgan Hill, CA 95037
Tel.: (408) 782-5600
Web Site: http://www.paramit.com
Outsourced Medical Device Engineering, Mfr & Post-Manufacturing Services
N.A.I.C.S.: 334510
Francesco Grieco *(VP-Ops)*

Subsidiary (Domestic):

Emphysys, Inc.   (2)
2x Gill St, Woburn, MA 01801-1721
Tel.: (339) 227-6475
Web Site: http://www.emphysys.com
Professional, Scientific & Technical Services
N.A.I.C.S.: 541990
Donna Tinsley *(VP)*

Lathrop Engineering, Inc.   (2)
1101 S Winchester Blvd B-110, San Jose, CA 95128
Tel.: (408) 260-2111
Web Site:
  http://www.lathropengineering.com
Sales Range: $1-9.9 Million
Emp.: 50
Design & Manufacturing of Diagnostic & Analytical Life-Science Instrumentation
N.A.I.C.S.: 334516
Brian M. Jarvis *(VP-Bus Dev)*

TECAN GROUP AG

Tecan Group AG—(Continued)

Subsidiary (Non-US):

Paramit Malaysia Sdn. Bhd. (2)
Phase 2 Bayan Lepas Free Industrial Zone, Penang, 11900, Malaysia
Tel.: (60) 46191000
Web Site: http://www.paramit.com.my
Sales Range: $50-74.9 Million
Outsourced Medical Device Engineering, Mfr & Post-Manufacturing Services
N.A.I.C.S.: 334510
Siew Peng Yew *(CFO)*

Paramit Malysia Sdn. Bhd. (1)
Plot 372 Penang Science Park Lorong Perindustrian Bukit Minyak 21, Taman Perindustrian Bukit Minyak Seberang Perai Tengah, 14100, Simpang Empat, Penang, Malaysia
Tel.: (60) 45407000
Web Site:
Sales Range:
Electronic Medical Device Mfr & Distr
N.A.I.C.S.: 334510

Tecan (Shanghai) Laboratory Equipment Co., Ltd. (1)
12F Tianan Financial Building 1529 Guozhan Road, Pudong New District, Shanghai, 200122, China
Tel.: (86) 4008213888
Electronic Medical Device Mfr & Distr
N.A.I.C.S.: 334510

Tecan (Shanghai) Trading Co., Ltd. (1)
Room 205 No 388 Fushan Road, Pudong New Area, Shanghai, 200122, China
Tel.: (86) 2122063206
Web Site: http://www.tecan.com
Sales Range: $25-49.9 Million
Laboratory Instruments Distr
N.A.I.C.S.: 423450

Tecan Asia (Pte.) Ltd. (1)
18 Boon Lay Way No Unit 10-106 Trade-Hub 21, Singapore, 609966, Singapore
Tel.: (65) 64441886
Web Site: http://www.tecan.com
Sales Range: $50-74.9 Million
Emp.: 6
Laboratory Instruments Distr
N.A.I.C.S.: 423450

Tecan Australia Pty Ltd (1)
Unit 21 / 3 Westside Avenue, Port Melbourne, 3207, VIC, Australia
Tel.: (61) 39 647 4100
Laboratory Instrument Mfr
N.A.I.C.S.: 334516

Tecan Austria GmbH (1)
Untersbergstrasse 1a, 5082, Grodig, Salzburg, Austria
Tel.: (43) 6246 8933 0
Web Site: http://www.tecan.com
Laboratory Instrument Mfr
N.A.I.C.S.: 333110

Tecan Benelux B.V.B.A. (1)
Mechelen Campus Schalienhoevedreef 20A, 2800, Mechelen, Belgium
Tel.: (32) 1 570 9054
Laboratory Instrument Mfr
N.A.I.C.S.: 334516

Tecan Deutschland GmbH (1)
Werner-von-Siemens-Strasse 23, 74564, Crailsheim, Germany
Tel.: (49) 79 51 94 170
Web Site: http://www.tecan.com
Laboratory Instruments Distr
N.A.I.C.S.: 423450

Tecan Genomics, Inc. (1)
900 Chesapeake Dr, Redwood, CA 94063
Tel.: (888) 654-5444
Web Site: https://www.tecan.com
Sales Range: $1-9.9 Million
Convention & Trade Show Organizers
N.A.I.C.S.: 561920

Tecan Iberica Instrumentacion S.L.U (1)
Sabino Arana 32, 08028, Barcelona, Spain
Tel.: (34) 93 490 01 74
Laboratory Instruments Distr
N.A.I.C.S.: 423450

Tecan Italia S.r.l. (1)
Via Brescia 39, 20063, Cernusco sul Naviglio, Cernusco sul Navigli, Italy
Tel.: (39) 029244790
Sales Range: $25-49.9 Million
Emp.: 11
Laboratory Instruments Distr
N.A.I.C.S.: 423450

Tecan Japan Co., Ltd. (1)
Kawasaki-Tech Ctr Bldg 17F 580-16 Horikawa-cho, Saiwai-ku, Kawasaki, 212-0013, Kanagawa, Japan
Tel.: (81) 445567311
Web Site: http://www.tecan.co.jp
Sales Range: $25-49.9 Million
Emp.: 30
Laboratory Instruments Distr
N.A.I.C.S.: 423450

Tecan Korea Ltd. (1)
149 Gasan digital 1-ro, Geumcheon-gu, Seoul, Korea (South)
Tel.: (82) 28183300
Electronic Medical Device Mfr & Distr
N.A.I.C.S.: 334510

Tecan Nordic AB (1)
Sveavagen 159 1tr, 113 46, Stockholm, Sweden
Tel.: (46) 87503940
Web Site: http://www.tecan.se
Sales Range: $25-49.9 Million
Emp.: 16
Laboratory Instruments Distr
N.A.I.C.S.: 423450

Tecan SP, Inc. (1)
14180 Live Oak Ave, Baldwin Park, CA 91706 (100%)
Tel.: (626) 962-0010
Web Site: http://www.spewarecorporation.com
Emp.: 60
Advanced Sample Preparation Solutions to Laboratories
N.A.I.C.S.: 541380
Phil Dimson *(Founder & CEO)*

Tecan Sales Austria GmbH (1)
Untersbergstrasse 1 A, Grodig, 5082, Salzburg, Austria
Tel.: (43) 624689330
Sales Range: $75-99.9 Million
Emp.: 160
Laboratory Instruments Distr
N.A.I.C.S.: 423450
Rudolf Eugster *(Mng Dir)*

Tecan Sales Switzerland AG (1)
Seestrasse 103, 8708, Mannedorf, Switzerland
Tel.: (41) 449228922
Web Site: http://www.tecan.com
Laboratory Instruments Distr
N.A.I.C.S.: 423450

Tecan Schweiz AG (1)
Seestrasse 103, 8708, Mannedorf, Switzerland
Tel.: (41) 449228282
Web Site: http://www.tecan.com
Laboratory Instrument Mfr
N.A.I.C.S.: 333310

Tecan Software Competence Center GmbH (1)
Peter-Sander Street 41a, Mainz-Kastel, Mainz-Kastel, 55252, Hesse, Germany
Tel.: (49) 613418140
Sales Range: $25-49.9 Million
Emp.: 35
Customized Software Development Services
N.A.I.C.S.: 541511
Christoph Eckerskorn *(Mng Dir)*

Tecan Trading AG (1)
Seestrasse 103, 8708, Mannedorf, Switzerland
Tel.: (41) 449228585
Web Site: http://www.tecan.com
Emp.: 500
Laboratory Instruments Distr
N.A.I.C.S.: 423450

Tecan UK Ltd. (1)
Theale Ct 11-13 High St, Theale, Reading, RG7 5AH, Berkshire, United Kingdom
Tel.: (44) 1189300300
Web Site: http://www.tecan.com
Sales Range: $25-49.9 Million
Emp.: 25
Laboratory Instruments Distr
N.A.I.C.S.: 423450

Tecan US, Inc. (1)
9401 Globe Center road Ste 140, Durham, NC 27560
Tel.: (919) 361-5200
Sales Range: $50-74.9 Million
Emp.: 80
Laboratory Instruments Distr
N.A.I.C.S.: 423450
Ray Szafranski *(CFO)*

Subsidiary (Domestic):

Tecan Systems, Inc. (2)
2450 Zanker Rd, San Jose, CA 95131
Tel.: (408) 953-3100
Web Site: http://www.tecan.com
Sales Range: $25-49.9 Million
Laboratory Technical Support Services
N.A.I.C.S.: 811210

TECBLU TECELAGEM BLUMENAU S.A.

Rua Padre Carapuceiro 968 Edf Empresarial Janete Costa Sala 101, Boa Viagem, Recife, 51020-280, PE, Brazil
Tel.: (55) 8138781200
Web Site:
https://tecblutecelagemblumen.com
Year Founded: 1969
Textile Products Mfr
N.A.I.C.S.: 314120

TECH MECHANICAL SYSTEMS LTD

105-455 Banga Pl, Victoria, V8Z 6X5, BC, Canada
Tel.: (250) 475-1011
Year Founded: 1980
Rev.: $10,923,947
Emp.: 45
Plumbing Contractor
N.A.I.C.S.: 238220
Russ Hepworth *(Owner)*

TECH PRO TECHNOLOGY DEVELOPMENT LIMITED

Unit 1402 14/F Grand Millennium Plaza 181 Queens Road, Central, China (Hong Kong)
Tel.: (852) 3908 1238
Web Site: http://www.techprotd.com
Year Founded: 2007
3823—(HKG)
Sales Range: $25-49.9 Million
Aluminum Electrolytic Capacitor Mfr & Distr
N.A.I.C.S.: 335999
Wing Sang Li *(Chm)*

Subsidiaries:

Jiangxi Lantian Wei Guang Technology Company Limited (1)
Shiyan Street Third Industrial Zone Nangang Tangtou 5 4-6F, Baoan District, Shenzhen, China
Tel.: (86) 755 29510249
Web Site: http://www.lt-wgled.com
Packaging Services
N.A.I.C.S.: 561910

LEDUS Lighting Technology Limited (1)
Unit 1402 14/F Grand Millennium Plaza 181 Queens Road, Central, China (Hong Kong)
Tel.: (852) 390 81212
Web Site: http://www.ledus.com
Holding Company
N.A.I.C.S.: 551112

TECH SEMICONDUCTORS CO., LTD.

No 162 Shengli Avenue, Xiangcheng District, Xiangyang, 441021, Hubei, China
Tel.: (86) 7103506236
Web Site: http://www.tech-sem.com
Year Founded: 1966

INTERNATIONAL PUBLIC

300046—(CHIN)
Rev.: $45,034,337
Assets: $171,177,597
Liabilities: $15,108,839
Net Worth: $156,068,758
Earnings: $4,386,027
Fiscal Year-end: 12/31/23
Semiconductor Mfr
N.A.I.C.S.: 334413
Xing Yan *(Chm & Gen Mgr)*

TECH-BANK FOOD CO., LTD.

Room 1805 Building A Yangguang Guoji, Yuyao, 200233, Zhejiang, China
Tel.: (86) 2154484407
Web Site: https://www.tianbang.com
Year Founded: 1996
002124—(SSE)
Rev.: $1,343,760,271
Assets: $2,745,035,093
Liabilities: $2,185,457,765
Net Worth: $559,577,327
Earnings: $68,718,963
Emp.: 10,000
Fiscal Year-end: 12/31/22
Aquatic & Livestock Feed Distr
N.A.I.C.S.: 112112
Banghui Zhang *(Co-Founder, Chm & CEO)*

TECH-LINK STORAGE ENGINEERING PTE LTD.

2 Loyang Way 1, Singapore, 508703, Singapore
Tel.: (65) 6545 5454
Web Site:
http://www.techlinkengineering.com
Storage Solutions
N.A.I.C.S.: 493190

Subsidiaries:

Dexion (Australia) Pty. Ltd. (1)
23 Tattersall Road, Kings Park, 2148, NSW, Australia
Tel.: (61) 288751111
Web Site: http://www.dexion.com.au
Sales Range: $75-99.9 Million
Warehousing Storage Services
N.A.I.C.S.: 493110
Peter Farmakis *(CEO)*

Subsidiary (Non-US):

Dexion (New Zealand) Limited (2)
423 East Tamaki Road, Auckland, New Zealand
Tel.: (64) 92730488
Web Site: http://www.dexion.co.nz
Storage Systems Mfr
N.A.I.C.S.: 493190
Craig Landon *(Reg Gen Mgr)*

Dexion Asia Sdn. Bhd. (2)
MR2-01-01 Sri Acappella Commercial Annex Jalan Lopmat Tinggi 13/33, Seksyen 13, 40100, Shah Alam, Selangor, Malaysia
Tel.: (60) 3 5520 6000
Web Site: http://www.dexion.biz
Industrial & Commercial Storage Handling Systems
N.A.I.C.S.: 531130

Dexion China (2)
Room 1102 Block A, Phase 1 Zhangjiang Jidian Port, Shanghai, 201203, China
Tel.: (86) 21 6879 4410
Web Site: http://www.dexion-china.com
Racks & Shelves Mfr
N.A.I.C.S.: 493190

Subsidiary (Domestic):

Dexion Integrated Systems Pty Limited (2)
Building E 22 Powers Road, Seven Hills, 2147, NWS, Australia
Tel.: (61) 298305000
Software Publisher
N.A.I.C.S.: 513210

TECH-VALUE S.P.A.
Via Generale Gustavo Fara 35, 20124, Milan, Italy
Tel.: (39) 02 83242006
Web Site: http://www.tech-value.com
Year Founded: 1997
Sales Range: $1-9.9 Million
Emp.: 70
Technology Outsourcing
N.A.I.C.S.: 541519
Elio Radice *(Chm & CEO)*

TECH21 LIMITED
Syd's Quay Eel Pie Island, Twickenham, TW1 3DY, United Kingdom
Tel.: (44) 20 3301 7690
Web Site: http://www.tech21.uk.com
Year Founded: 2005
Sales Range: $25-49.9 Million
Emp.: 35
Plastic Bag & Pouch Mfr
N.A.I.C.S.: 326111
Lindsey Virdee *(Head-Ops)*

TECHBASE INDUSTRIES BERHAD
Tel.: (60) 42108833
Web Site:
https://www.techbaseindustries.com
TECHBASE—(KLS)
Rev.: $47,243,810
Assets: $88,228,148
Liabilities: $18,059,683
Net Worth: $70,168,466
Earnings: $4,215,450
Emp.: 2,000
Fiscal Year-end: 07/31/23
Garments Mfr
N.A.I.C.S.: 315120
Peng Loon Lee *(Co-Sec)*

Subsidiaries:

Honsin Apparel Sdn. Bhd. (1)
531 Batu 2 Jalan Kluang, 83000, Batu Pahat, Johor, Malaysia
Tel.: (60) 74318388
Apparel & Fabric Face Mask Mfr
N.A.I.C.S.: 315990

Plas Industries Sdn. Bhd. (1)
6944 Jalan Mak Mandin Kawasan Perusahaan, Mak Mandin, 13400, Butterworth, Penang, Malaysia
Tel.: (60) 43319608
Provision Apparel Mfr
N.A.I.C.S.: 315990

Trans Pacific Textile (M) Sdn. Bhd. (1)
Batu 6 Jalan Mersing, 86000, Kluang, Johor, Malaysia
Tel.: (60) 77010369
Fabrics Mfr
N.A.I.C.S.: 313310

TECHBOND GROUP BERHAD
No 36 Jalan Anggerik Mokara 31/59 Seksyen 31 Kota Kemuning, 40460, Shah Alam, Selangor, Malaysia
Tel.: (60) 351223333 MY
Web Site:
https://www.techbond.com.my
TECHBND—(KLS)
Rev.: $23,057,566
Assets: $46,475,556
Liabilities: $10,438,730
Net Worth: $36,036,825
Earnings: $2,329,735
Emp.: 100
Fiscal Year-end: 06/30/23
Chemical Product Mfr & Distr
N.A.I.C.S.: 325520
Lee Seng Thye *(Mng Dir)*

Subsidiaries:

Techbond (Sabah) Sdn. Bhd. (1)
2nd Floor Shoplot No 5 Taman Fortuna Phase II Jalan Penampang, 88200, Kota Kinabalu, Sabah, Malaysia
Tel.: (60) 88266380
Industrial Adhesive Distr
N.A.I.C.S.: 424690

Techbond (Vietnam) Co. Ltd. (1)
Quarter 4, An Phu Ward, Thuan An, Binh Duong, Vietnam
Tel.: (84) 2743770717
Industrial Adhesive Mfr & Distr
N.A.I.C.S.: 325520

Techbond MFG (Vietnam) Co., Ltd. (1)
No 18 VSIP II - A Street 23 Vietnam, Singapore Industrial Park Vinh Tan Ward, Tan Uyen, Binh Duong, Vietnam
Tel.: (84) 2743803959
Industrial Adhesives Mfr
N.A.I.C.S.: 325520

Techbond Manufacturing Sdn. Bhd. (1)
No 36 Jalan Anggerik Mokara 31/59 Seksyen 31, Kota Kemuning, 40460, Shah Alam, Selangor, Malaysia
Tel.: (60) 351223333
Industrial Adhesive Mfr & Distr
N.A.I.C.S.: 325520

TECHCENTIAL INTERNATIONAL LTD.
PTD 4093 Kawasan Perindustrian Parit Jamil, Parit Jawa, 84150, Muar, Malaysia
Tel.: (60) 69873999
Web Site: https://www.techcential-international.com
Year Founded: 2001
6616—(TPE)
Rev.: $36,094,644
Assets: $24,335,710
Liabilities: $11,041,303
Net Worth: $13,294,406
Earnings: $844,105
Emp.: 580
Fiscal Year-end: 12/31/22
Furniture Product Mfr
N.A.I.C.S.: 337127

TECHCOM VIETNAM REIT FUND
10th Floor 191 Ba Trieu Street, Hai Ba Trung, Hanoi, Vietnam
Tel.: (84) 2439446368
Real Estate Investment Services
N.A.I.C.S.: 531190

TECHCOM, INC.
Jl Gaharu No 2B Graha Harmoni Building 5th Floor, Medan, 20235, Sumatera Utara, Indonesia
Tel.: (62) 6180512888 DE
Year Founded: 2000
TCRI—(OTCIQ)
Liabilities: $201,931
Net Worth: ($201,931)
Earnings: ($77,324)
Emp.: 2
Fiscal Year-end: 12/31/23
Business Management Services
N.A.I.C.S.: 561110
Simon Wajcenberg *(CFO & Sec)*

TECHCONN HOLDING GROUP CO., LTD.
17F Block B Hui Hai Plaza 1st Chuangye Road, Long Hua District, Shenzhen, China
Tel.: (86) 755 61883366
Web Site:
http://www.techconn.com.cn
Intelligent Mfr & Techonlgy Services
N.A.I.C.S.: 513210
Raymond Ma *(Deputy General Mgr-AI Div)*

TECHEDGE S.P.A.
Via Caldera 21 Building B2, 20153, Milan, Italy
Tel.: (39) 0287311
Web Site:
http://www.techedgegroup.com
Year Founded: 2004
Information Technology Support Services
N.A.I.C.S.: 541512
Domenico Restuccia *(Chm & Mng Dir)*

TECHEM ENERGY METERING SERVICE GMBH & CO. KG
Hauptstrasse 89, 65760, Eschborn, Germany
Tel.: (49) 61 96 5 22 0
Web Site: http://www.techem.com
Holding Company Energy Billing & Energy Management Services
N.A.I.C.S.: 551112

TECHEN CO., LTD.
99 Gukgasandan-Daero 50-Gil Eung-Am-Ri Guji-Myeon, Guji-Myeon Dalseong-Gun, Daegu, Korea (South)
Tel.: (82) 535935678
Web Site: https://www.techen.co.kr
Year Founded: 2009
308700—(KRS)
Lighting Fixture Mfr & Distr
N.A.I.C.S.: 335132
Young-Seb Lee *(CEO)*

TECHFINANCIALS, INC.
City House 6 Karaiskakis, Limassol, CY-3032, Cyprus
Tel.: (357) 25503164 VG
Web Site:
http://www.techfinancials.com
Year Founded: 2009
Rev.: $7,764,000
Assets: $8,089,000
Liabilities: $1,622,000
Net Worth: $6,467,000
Earnings: ($5,075,000)
Fiscal Year-end: 12/31/18
Software Development Services
N.A.I.C.S.: 541511
Asaf Lahav *(Founder & CEO)*

TECHFIRM HOLDINGS, INC.
1-32-12 Higashi Shibuya-ku, Tokyo, 150-0011, Japan
Tel.: (81) 354682778
Web Site: http://www.techfirm.co.jp
Year Founded: 1991
3625—(TKS)
Rev.: $31,547,840
Assets: $25,284,300
Liabilities: $11,133,800
Net Worth: $14,150,500
Earnings: $964,100
Emp.: 254
Fiscal Year-end: 06/30/24
Computer Programming Services
N.A.I.C.S.: 541511
Yuichiro Tsutsui *(Chm)*

TECHINDIA NIRMAN LIMITED
Nath House Nath Road, PO Box No 318, Aurangabad, 431005, Maharashtra, India
Tel.: (91) 2403502421
Web Site:
https://www.techindianirman.com
Year Founded: 1980
TECHIN—(NSE)
Rev.: $328
Assets: $9,685,931
Liabilities: $7,985,086
Net Worth: $1,700,845
Earnings: ($71,758)
Emp.: 2
Fiscal Year-end: 03/31/22
Seed Farming & Processing
N.A.I.C.S.: 111191
Satish Kagliwal *(Mng Dir)*

TECHINT S.P.A.
Via Monte Rosa 93, 20149, Milan, Italy
Tel.: (39) 0243841 IT
Web Site:
http://www.techintgroup.com
Year Founded: 1945
Sales Range: $25-49.9 Billion
Emp.: 55,383
Holding Company
N.A.I.C.S.: 551112
Gianfelice Mario Rocca *(Chm)*

Subsidiaries:

Alcatel-Lucent Techint S.A (1)
San Martin 344 22-29 Floors, 1004, Buenos Aires, Argentina
Tel.: (54) 1143437500
Telecommunication Infrastructure Services
N.A.I.C.S.: 517112

Clinche Gavazzeni spa (1)
Via Mauro Gavazzeni 21, 24125, Bergamo, Italy
Tel.: (39) 0354204111
Web Site: http://www.gavazzeni.it
Hospital Management Services
N.A.I.C.S.: 622110

Confab servicos Tubulares Ltda. (1)
Av Gastao Vidigal Neto 475 - Cidade Nova, Pindamonhangaba, Sao Paulo, 12414-900, Brazil
Tel.: (55) 123 644 9001
Steel Tube Mfr
N.A.I.C.S.: 331210

Edelap S.A. (1)
Calle 45 entre 3 y 4, 1900, La Plata, Buenos Aires, Argentina
Tel.: (54) 11 21 29 2200
Electric Power Distr
N.A.I.C.S.: 221122

Humanitas Foundation for Research (1)
Via Manzoni 113, 20089, Milan, Rozzano, Italy
Tel.: (39) 02 8224 2448
Web Site: http://www.humanitas.it
Clinical Research
N.A.I.C.S.: 541720

Humanitas Mater Domini - Castellanza (1)
Via Gerenzano 2, 21053, Castellanza, Italy
Tel.: (39) 0331476111
Web Site: http://www.materdomini.it
Hospital Management Services
N.A.I.C.S.: 622110

Impripost Tecnologias S.A (1)
Av de los Constituyentes 3702 ex Ruta 9 - Km 355, Buenos Aires, B1617AGS, Argentina (50%)
Tel.: (54) 3327451467
Web Site: http://www.impripost.com.ar
Sales Range: $25-49.9 Million
Printing Services
N.A.I.C.S.: 323111

Kazakhstan Pipe Threaders Limited Liability Partnership (1)
SEZ Morport Aktau Subzone 1 ABK 1, Aktau, Kazakhstan
Tel.: (7) 729 229 0345
Steel Pipe Mfr & Distr
N.A.I.C.S.: 331210

LOSA - Ladrillos Olavarria S.A. (1)
Hipolito Bouchard 557 15 Fl, 1006, Buenos Aires, Argentina (100%)
Tel.: (54) 1140182100
Web Site: http://www.losa.com
Sales Range: $25-49.9 Million
Emp.: 20
Terrazzo Tiles Mfr
N.A.I.C.S.: 238340

Saudi Techint Ltd (1)
Al Khobar Highway, PO Box 12780, 31483, Dammam, Saudi Arabia
Tel.: (966) 3 868 1570
Industrial Building Construction Services
N.A.I.C.S.: 236210
Jaleel Seyyed *(Mgr-Logistics)*

Socominter S.A. (1)

TECHINT S.P.A.   INTERNATIONAL PUBLIC

Techint S.p.A.—(Continued)

Av La Estancia Edificio La General 9th Floor, Chuao, 1061, Caracas, Venezuela
Tel.: (58) 212 918 3199
Steel Pipe Mfr & Distr
N.A.I.C.S.: 331210

Sudprogetti S.p.A. (1)
Via Stentinello Ctr Targia 1, 96100, Siracusa, Italy
Tel.: (39) 0931409211
Web Site: http://www.sudprogettigroup.it
Design & Construction of Petrochemical Plants
N.A.I.C.S.: 325110

Tagliaferri Electric Arc Furnaces (1)
Via Monte Rosa 93, 20149, Milan, Italy
Tel.: (39) 0000243841
Web Site: http://www.techint-technologies.com
Furnace Mfr
N.A.I.C.S.: 333994

Techint - Compagnia Tecnica Internazionale S.p.A. (1)
Via Monte Rosa 93, Milan, 20120, Italy
Tel.: (39) 0243841
Web Site: http://www.engineering.techint.com
Sales Range: $200-249.9 Million
Emp.: 600
Engineering & Construction Services
N.A.I.C.S.: 237990
Pablo Videla *(Gen Dir)*

Techint Chile S.A. (1)
Cerro El Plomo 5420 Piso 16, Las Condes, 7561185, Santiago, Chile
Tel.: (56) 2 2363 3200
Web Site: http://www.techint-ingenieria.com
Building Construction & Civil Engineering Services
N.A.I.C.S.: 541330
Grover Segales *(Mgr-Project & Procurement)*

Techint Cimimontubi Nigeria Ltd (1)
Kajola House 4tj floor 62/64 Campbell Street, Lagos Island, Lagos, Nigeria
Tel.: (234) 8135184896
Web Site: http://www.techint-ingenieria.com
Building Construction & Civil Engineering Services
N.A.I.C.S.: 541330

Techint Engenharia e Construcao S/A (1)
Rua Tabapua 41 Piso 14, Itaim Bibi, 04533-010, Sao Paulo, Brazil
Tel.: (55) 1121376000
Web Site: http://www.techint-ingenieria.com
Oil & Gas Pipeline Construction Services
N.A.I.C.S.: 237120

Techint Iberia, S.L. (1)
Calle Garcia de Paredes 94 1 A, 28010, Madrid, Spain
Tel.: (34) 917022955
Oil & Gas Pipeline Construction Services
N.A.I.C.S.: 237120

Techint India Pvt.Ltd. (1)
5th Floor iThink Techno Campus Pokhran Road No 2, Off Eastern Express Highway Near TCS Yantra Park, Thane, 400 601, Maharashtra, India
Tel.: (91) 2261133500
Oil & Gas Pipeline Construction Services
N.A.I.C.S.: 237120
Prashant Chaudhari *(Gen Mgr-Instrumentation)*

Techint Industrial Technologies (Beijing) Co. Ltd. (1)
1700 Air China Plaza 36 xiaoyun Lu, 100027, Beijing, China
Tel.: (86) 1084475656
Mining Machinery Mfr
N.A.I.C.S.: 333131

Techint S.A. de C.V. (1)
Edificio Plaza del Parque Guillermo Gonzalez Camarena 1200 Piso 7, Colonia Centro de Ciudad Santa Fe, Delegacion Alvaro Obregon, 01210, Mexico, DF, Mexico
Tel.: (52) 558525700 7199
Mining Machinery Mfr
N.A.I.C.S.: 333131

Techint S.A.C. (1)
Av Ricardo Rivera Navarrete 495 Piso12, San Isidro, Lima, Peru
Tel.: (51) 2135555
Web Site: http://www.techint-ingenieria.com
Oil & Gas Pipeline Construction Services
N.A.I.C.S.: 237120
Grover Segales *(Mgr-Project & Procurement)*

Techint-Italimpianti (1)
Torre Shipping Via Aldareto 31, 16149, Genoa, Italy
Tel.: (39) 01060541
Web Site: http://www.techintgroup.com
Sales Range: $50-74.9 Million
Emp.: 250
Industrial Furnace Manufacturing
N.A.I.C.S.: 333994

Tecpetrol S.A. (1)
Carlos Maria Della Paolera 299 20 th Fl, C1001ADA, Buenos Aires, Argentina
Tel.: (54) 43185900
Web Site: http://www.tecpetrol.com
Emp.: 4,100
Petroleum & Mining Services
N.A.I.C.S.: 324110
Juan Andres Thurburn *(Mgr-HR)*

Subsidiary (Non-US):

Tecpetrol International S.A. (2)
La Cumparsita 1373 Floor 3 office 302, 11200, Montevideo, Uruguay
Tel.: (598) 29032956
Web Site: http://www.tecpetrol.com
Oil & Gas Pipeline Construction Services
N.A.I.C.S.: 237120

Subsidiary (Non-US):

Alpha Lithium Corporation (3)
Suite 400 725 Granville Street, Vancouver, V7Y 1G5, BC, Canada (100%)
Tel.: (604) 681-1568
Web Site: http://www.alphalithium.com
Assets: $1,604,085
Liabilities: $797,348
Net Worth: $806,737
Earnings: ($1,194,075)
Fiscal Year-end: 12/31/2019
Mineral Exploration Services
N.A.I.C.S.: 212390

Subsidiary (Non-US):

Tecpetrol de Venezuela S.A. (2)
Torre Empresarial Claret Av 3 E and 78 floor 5 office 57, 4001, Maracaibo, Estado Zulia, Venezuela
Tel.: (58) 261 793 6435
Web Site: http://www.tecpetrol.com
Renewable Energy Consulting Services
N.A.I.C.S.: 541690

Tecpetrol del Peru (2)
Av Victor Andres Belaunde 147 Via Principal 155 Torre Real Tres, Office 501, San Isidro, Peru
Tel.: (51) 16177777
Web Site: http://www.tecpetrol.com
Renewable Energy Consulting Services
N.A.I.C.S.: 541690

Tenaris Global Services Far East Pte. Ltd. (1)
200 Cantonment Road 04-01 Southpoint, Singapore, Singapore
Tel.: (65) 6 395 9000
Steel Pipe Mfr & Distr
N.A.I.C.S.: 331210

Tenaris Global Services Nigeria Ltd. (1)
Oil and Gas Freezone Federal Lighter Terminal Onne, Port Harcourt, Rivers, Nigeria
Tel.: (234) 809 366 0200
Steel Pipe Mfr & Distr
N.A.I.C.S.: 331210

Tenaris Global Services de Bolivia S.R.L. (1)
Torre ALAS piso 7 Av Las Ramblas esquina Tropical, Santa Cruz, Bolivia
Tel.: (591) 3 388 8891
Steel Tube Mfr
N.A.I.C.S.: 331210

Tenaris Nigeria Ltd. (1)
King's Court Building 6th Floor Keystone Bank Crescent, Victoria Island, Lagos, Nigeria
Tel.: (234) 809 366 0300
Steel Pipe Mfr & Distr
N.A.I.C.S.: 331210

Tenaris S.A. (1)
26 Boulevard Royal-4th Floor, L-2449, Luxembourg, Luxembourg (60.4%)
Tel.: (352) 26478978
Web Site: http://www.tenaris.com
Rev.: $14,868,860,000
Assets: $21,081,895,000
Liabilities: $4,051,458,000
Net Worth: $17,030,437,000
Earnings: $3,957,833,000
Emp.: 29,134
Fiscal Year-end: 12/31/2023
Steel Pipe Products Mfr & Distr
N.A.I.C.S.: 331210
Paolo Rocca *(Chm & CEO)*

Subsidiary (Non-US):

Confab Industrial S.A. (2)
Av Dr Gastao Vidigal Neto 475 Cidade Nova, Pindamonhangaba, 12414-020, Sao Paulo, Brazil
Tel.: (55) 1236449000
Web Site: http://www.tenaris.com
Sales Range: $600-649.9 Million
Welded Steel Pipe Mfr
N.A.I.C.S.: 331210

Dalmine S.p.A. (2)
Piazza Caduti Luglio 1, Dalmine, 24044, Bergamo, Italy (99%)
Tel.: (39) 035560111
Web Site: http://www.tenaris.com
Sales Range: $400-449.9 Million
Emp.: 2,500
Steel Pole Mfr
N.A.I.C.S.: 331210
Paolo Rocca *(CEO)*

Subsidiary (Domestic):

Dalmine Energie S.p.A. (3)
Piazza Caduti 6 Luglio 1944 1, 24044, Dalmine, Bergamo, Italy
Tel.: (39) 0355609174
Energy Industry Steel Pipe Mfr
N.A.I.C.S.: 331210

Subsidiary (US):

IPSCO Tubulars Inc. (2)
2650 Warrenville Rd Ste 700, Downers Grove, IL 60515
Tel.: (630) 874-0078
Welded & Seamless Steel Pipes Production
N.A.I.C.S.: 331210

Subsidiary (Domestic):

IPSCO Koppel Tubulars Corporation (3)
6403 6th Ave, Koppel, PA 16136
Tel.: (724) 843-7100
Steel Works, Electric Furnace, Rolling Mill, Tube Mill & Bar Mill
N.A.I.C.S.: 331110

IPSCO Tubulars (Kentucky) Inc. (3)
100 Steel Plant Rd, Wilder, KY 41071-1317
Tel.: (859) 292-6060
Tubular Welded Pipe, Coil & Steel Products Mfr
N.A.I.C.S.: 331210

Subsidiary (Non-US):

PT Seamless Pipe Indonesia Jaya (2)
Unit No 211A 11 floor Sentral Senayan II, Building Jl Asia-Afrika N 8, Gelora Bung Karno, 10270, Jakarta, Senayan, Indonesia
Tel.: (62) 2129966300
Web Site: http://www.tenaris.com
Sales Range: $125-149.9 Million
Emp.: 500
Industrial Pipe Mfr
N.A.I.C.S.: 331210
Lucio Costarrosa *(Country Mgr)*

Siat S.A. (2)
Guatemala 3400, B1822AXZ, Alsina, Argentina (82%)
Tel.: (54) 11 4365 9500
Web Site: http://www.siat.com.ar

Welded Steel Pipe Mfr
N.A.I.C.S.: 331210

Siderca S.A.I.C. (2)
Dr Jorge Simini 250, B2804MHA, Campana, Buenos Aires, Argentina
Tel.: (54) 3489433100
Web Site: http://www.tenaris.com
Rev.: $1,511,500,000
Emp.: 2,681
Seamless Steel Pipe Mfr
N.A.I.C.S.: 331210

Socotherm Brasil S.A. (2)
Av Doutor Gastao Vidigal Neto 745, Pindamonhangaba, Brazil
Tel.: (55) 1236449245
Web Site: http://www.socothermbrasil.com.br
Sales Range: $50-74.9 Million
Emp.: 200
Metal Coating Engraving & Allied Mfr
N.A.I.C.S.: 332812
Giovanni Pelagatti *(Mng Dir)*

Subsidiary (US):

Tenaris Global Services (U.S.A.) Corporation (2)
2200 W Loop S Ste 800, Houston, TX 77027 (100%)
Tel.: (713) 767-4400
Web Site: http://www.tenaris.com
Sales Range: $1-4.9 Billion
Mfr & Distr of Steel Pipe Products
N.A.I.C.S.: 331210
Paola Mazzoleni *(Dir-HR)*

Subsidiary (Domestic):

Precision Tube Technology Inc. (3)
8615 E Sam Houston Pkwy N, Houston, TX 77044
Tel.: (281) 458-2883
Web Site: http://www.tenaris.com
Sales Range: $100-124.9 Million
Emp.: 300
Mfr of Coiled Steel Pipes & Tubes
N.A.I.C.S.: 331210

SeaCAT L.P. (3)
8762 Clay Rd, Houston, TX 77080-1859
Tel.: (713) 460-1500
Web Site: http://www.tenaris.com
Sales Range: $10-24.9 Million
Emp.: 35
Mfr of Subsea Umbilical Tubing
N.A.I.C.S.: 331210

Subsidiary (Non-US):

Tubos de Acero de Mexico, S.A. (2)
Via Xalapa Km 4337, 91697, Veracruz, Mexico, Mexico
Tel.: (52) 2299891100
Sales Range: $700-749.9 Million
Emp.: 2,700
Producer & Supplier of Seamless Steel Castings, Tubings & Line Pipes Used in Various Phases of Oil & Gas Production & Transportation
N.A.I.C.S.: 331210

Tenova Re Energy GmbH (1)
Graf Adolf Platz 6, 40213, Dusseldorf, Germany
Tel.: (49) 211 5409 760
Web Site: http://www.techint.com
Supplier of Advanced Technological Solutions for the Metals & Mining Industries
N.A.I.C.S.: 212290

Tenova S.p.A. (1)
Via Gerenzano 58, 21053, Castellanza, Italy
Tel.: (39) 0331 444 111
Web Site: http://www.tenova.com
Emp.: 3,000
Steel Manufacturing Equipment Mfr
N.A.I.C.S.: 333994
Andrea Lovato *(CEO)*

Subsidiary (Non-US):

TAKRAF GmbH (2)
Torgauer Strasse 336, 04347, Leipzig, Germany
Tel.: (49) 3412423500
Web Site: http://www.takraf.tenova.com
Surface Mining Equipment Mfr
N.A.I.C.S.: 333131
Frank Hubrich *(CEO-Mining)*

AND PRIVATE COMPANIES

Subsidiary (Non-US):

TAKRAF Tenova Mining Technologies (Beijing) Co. Ltd. (3)
Room 802-806 8th floor T5 Building Hans Plaza No 2 Yard, Ronghua South Road YiZhuang Beijing Economic & Tech Development Zone, 100176, Beijing, China
Tel.: (86) 1084475656
Mining Equipment Distr
N.A.I.C.S.: 423810

Unit (US):

TAKRAF USA Inc. (3)
2750 Morris Rd Ste A120, Lansdale, PA 19446
Tel.: (215) 855-4300
Web Site: http://www.techint.com
Mining Equipment & Sytems, Bulk Material Handling, Minerals Processing, Beneficiation & Air Environmental Industries Products & Services
N.A.I.C.S.: 333131
Eric Jackson *(Sls Dir)*

Subsidiary (Non-US):

Tenova Australia Pty. Ltd. (3)
L10 Ann Street 410, 4000, Brisbane, QLD, Australia
Tel.: (61) 731249080
Mining Machinery Mfr
N.A.I.C.S.: 333131
Sudhirkumar Surendran *(Sr Project Mgr)*

Tenova Chile S.p.A (3)
5420 Cerro el Plomo 3rd floor Offices 302A-303-304A, Las Condes, 7550647, Santiago, Chile
Tel.: (56) 223983000
Winding Machinery Distr
N.A.I.C.S.: 333131

Tenova East Europe LLC (3)
Lane Elektricheskiy house 3/10 bld 4, 123557, Moscow, Russia
Tel.: (7) 4959959507
Mining Equipment & Machinery Mfr
N.A.I.C.S.: 333131

Tenova Goodfellow Inc. (3)
6711 Mississauga Road Suite 200, Mississauga, L5N 2W3, ON, Canada
Tel.: (905) 567-3030
Mining Equipment Distr
N.A.I.C.S.: 423810

Tenova Hypertherm Pvt Ltd (3)
601 6th Floor Boomerang B2 Wing Chandivli, Andheri, 400072, Mumbai, India
Tel.: (91) 2261045700
Mining Equipment Distr
N.A.I.C.S.: 423810
Narayan Raut *(Sr Mgr)*

Tenova Industrial Technology Co., Ltd (3)
Shanghai Branch Room 1604 Hai Tong Securities Tower B, 689 Guangdong Road, 200001, Shanghai, China
Tel.: (86) 2162483170
Mining Equipment Distr
N.A.I.C.S.: 423810

Tenova Minerals (Pty) Ltd (3)
58 Emerald Parkway Road Greenstone Hill Extension 21, 1609, Johannesburg, South Africa
Tel.: (27) 118999111
Mining Equipment Distr
N.A.I.C.S.: 423810

Unit (US):

Tenova Mining & Minerals USA Inc (3)
Regency Plz 4643 S Ulster St, Denver, CO 80237
Tel.: (303) 770-8161
Mining Equipment Distr
N.A.I.C.S.: 423810
Mark Erickson Sr. *(Program Mgr)*

Subsidiary (Non-US):

Tenova do Brasil Ltda (3)
Rua Andaluzita 131 10 Andar, 030310-030, Belo Horizonte, Brazil
Tel.: (55) 3132983000
Steel Products Mfr
N.A.I.C.S.: 332111

Subsidiary (US):

Tenova Inc. (2)
100 Corp Ctr Dr, Coraopolis, PA 15108-3185
Tel.: (412) 262-2240
Web Site: http://www.tenovacore.com
Mining Machinery & Equipment Mfr
N.A.I.C.S.: 333131
Jared Kaufman *(VP-Technical Svcs)*

Subsidiary (Domestic):

Tenova Pomini (2)
Via Gerenzano 58, 21053, Castellanza, Italy
Tel.: (39) 0331 444111
Web Site: http://www.tenova.com
Supplier of Advanced Technologies for Metals & Mining Industries
N.A.I.C.S.: 332999

Ternium S.A. (1)
26 Boulevard Royal 4th Floor, L-2449, Luxembourg, Luxembourg **(62.02%)**
Tel.: (352) 26683152
Web Site: https://www.ternium.com
Rev.: $17,610,092,000
Assets: $24,179,104,000
Liabilities: $7,367,245,000
Net Worth: $16,811,859,000
Earnings: $986,374,000
Emp.: 34,458
Fiscal Year-end: 12/31/2023
Steel Products Mfr
N.A.I.C.S.: 551112
Paolo Rocca *(Chm)*

Subsidiary (Non-US):

Ternium Brasil Ltda. (2)
Av Joao XXIII s/n - Santa Cruz, Industrial District, Rio de Janeiro, Brazil
Tel.: (55) 21 2141 2550
Iron & Steel Mfr
N.A.I.C.S.: 331110
Marcelo Chara *(Pres)*

Ternium Hylsa S.A. de C.V. (2)
Munich Ave 101, San Nicolas, 66452, NL, Mexico
Tel.: (52) 8188651240
Web Site: http://www.hylsamex.com.mx
Production & Distribution of Steel Products
N.A.I.C.S.: 331221
Paolo Rocca *(Chm)*

Subsidiary (Domestic):

Acerex S.A. (3)
Nogalar Ave 330, Col Cuauhtemoc, 66452, San Nicolas, NL, Mexico
Tel.: (52) 8188651900
Web Site: http://www.acerex.com.mx
Production & Distribution of Steel Products
N.A.I.C.S.: 331221

Hylsa S.A. de C.V.-Technology Division (3)
Eugenio Clariony 101, 66452, San Nicolas, NL, Mexico
Tel.: (52) 8188652000
Web Site: http://www.hylsamex.com.mx
Sales Range: $1-9.9 Million
Emp.: 210
Production & Distribution of Steel Products
N.A.I.C.S.: 331221

Hylsa S.A.-Bar & Rod Division (3)
Av De Las Industrias No 7319 Esq Con Juan Escutia Col Nombre de Dios, CP 31105, Chihuahua, Mexico
Tel.: (52) 614 419 6064
Web Site: http://www.ternium.mx
Sales Range: $100-124.9 Million
Emp.: 10
Production & Distribution of Steel Products
N.A.I.C.S.: 331221
Carlos Mendiola *(Gen Mgr)*

Hylsa S.A.-Flat Steel Division (3)
Los Angeles Ave 325 Ote, 66452, San Nicolas, NL, Mexico
Tel.: (52) 8188652241
Web Site: http://www.Ternium.com.mx
Sales Range: $350-399.9 Million
Emp.: 2,000
Production & Distribution of Steel Products
N.A.I.C.S.: 331221
Gulean Egoren *(Mng Dir)*

Subsidiary (Non-US):

Ternium Mexico S.A. de C.V. (2)
Av Universidad 992 Nte Colonia Cuauhtemoc, San Nicolas De Los Garcia, 66450, Nuevo Leon, Mexico
Tel.: (52) 8188652828
Web Site: http://mx.ternium.com
Steel Products Mfr
N.A.I.C.S.: 331110

Usinas Siderurgicas de Minas Gerais S.A. (2)
Rua Prof Jose Vieira De Mondonca 3011, Belo Horizonte, 31310-260, Minas Gerais, Brazil **(51.5%)**
Tel.: (55) 3134998000
Web Site: https://www.usiminas.com
Rev.: $4,940,624,455
Assets: $7,179,304,970
Liabilities: $2,433,333,984
Net Worth: $4,745,970,986
Earnings: $293,231,790
Emp.: 19,308
Fiscal Year-end: 12/31/2023
Steel Mfr & Distr
N.A.I.C.S.: 331110
Sergio Leite de Andrade *(CEO & Member-Exec Bd)*

Subsidiary (Domestic):

Automotiva Usiminas S.A. (3)
Gil Pimentel Moura S/n, Pouso Alegre, 37550-000, Minas Gerais, Brazil
Tel.: (55) 3534499400
Web Site: http://www.automotivausiminas.com
Automotive Bodies Mfr
N.A.I.C.S.: 336110

FASAL (3)
Av Dr Angelo Teixeira da Costa 602, 33045 170, Santa Luzia, Brazil
Tel.: (55) 3136493200
Sales Range: $50-74.9 Million
Emp.: 150
Iron & Steel Products Processing & Distr
N.A.I.C.S.: 331110

Solucoes em Aco Usiminas S.A. (3)
Avenida Monteiro Lobato 2805 Vila Mirian Guarulhos, 03126-001, Sao Paulo, Brazil
Tel.: (55) 11 2464 3622
Steel Plates Mfr & Distr
N.A.I.C.S.: 331110

Usiminas Mecanica SA (3)
Rua Professor Jose Vieira de Mendonca 3011, Bairro Engenho Nogueira, 31310-260, Belo Horizonte, Brazil
Tel.: (55) 3134999607
Web Site: http://www.usiminasmecanica.com.br
Equipment & Steel Structure Fabrication
N.A.I.C.S.: 332111

TECHLANTIC LTD.
2415 Dunwin Drive Units 15 16, Mississauga, L5L 4L9, ON, Canada
Tel.: (905) 465-1062
Web Site: http://www.techlantic.com
Rev.: $18,049,061
Emp.: 4
Automobile Whslr
N.A.I.C.S.: 423110
Tom Van Essen *(Founder)*

TECHMAGIC
41 Devonshire Street, London, W1G 7AJ, United Kingdom
Tel.: (44) 20 7097 8871
Web Site: https://www.techmagic.co
Year Founded: 2014
Emp.: 200
Software Devolepment
N.A.I.C.S.: 513210
Oleg Dats *(CEO)*

Subsidiaries:

Dynamo Development, Inc. (1)
420 Lexington Ave, New York, NY 10170
Tel.: (212) 385-1552
Web Site: http://www.dynamo-ny.com
Rev.: $2,990,900
Emp.: 20

Custom Computer Programming Services
N.A.I.C.S.: 541511
Dmitry Grinberg *(Pres)*

TECHMATION ELECTRIC & CONTROLS LTD.
117 Kingsview Road SE, Airdrie, T4A 0A8, AB, Canada
Tel.: (403) 243-0990
Web Site: https://www.techmationelectric.com
Year Founded: 1995
Emp.: 1,200
Electrical & Instrumentation Construction & Maintenance Services
N.A.I.C.S.: 238210
Derek Polsfut *(Pres)*

TECHMATRIX CORPORATION
SHINAGAWA SEASON TERRACE 24F 2-70 Konan 1-chome, Minato-ku, Tokyo, 108-8588, Japan
Tel.: (81) 344057800
Web Site: https://www.techmatrix.co.jp
Year Founded: 1984
3762—(TKS)
Rev.: $352,332,830
Assets: $566,847,160
Liabilities: $388,092,930
Net Worth: $178,754,230
Earnings: $23,399,400
Emp.: 1,595
Fiscal Year-end: 03/31/24
IT Business & Consulting Services
N.A.I.C.S.: 541690
Takashi Yuri *(Pres & CEO)*

Subsidiaries:

CASAREAL, inc. (1)
24th floor Shinagawa Season Terrace 1-2-70 Konan, Minato-ku, Tokyo, 108-0075, Japan
Tel.: (81) 344057865
Web Site: https://www.casareal.co.jp
Emp.: 84
Information Technology Consulting Services
N.A.I.C.S.: 541512

CROSS HEAD KK (1)
Shinagawa Season Terrace 24F 2-70 Konan 1-chome, Minato-ku, Tokyo, 108-0075, Japan **(100%)**
Tel.: (81) 344057911
Web Site: https://www.crosshead.co.jp
Sales Range: $75-99.9 Million
Emp.: 390
Information Technology Consulting Services
N.A.I.C.S.: 541512

Subsidiary (Domestic):

NCL Communications K.K. (2)
Akasaka Twin Tower Main Bldg 10 Fl 2-17-22 Akasaka, Minato-ku, Tokyo, 107-0052, Japan
Tel.: (81) 362298711
Web Site: http://www.nclc.co.jp
Sales Range: $10-24.9 Million
Emp.: 30
Information Technology Consulting Services
N.A.I.C.S.: 541512
Takashi Sekine *(Pres & CEO)*

Ichigo llc (1)
25th floor Shinagawa Season Terrace 1-2-70 Konan, Minato-ku, Tokyo, 108-0075, Japan
Tel.: (81) 344057862
Web Site: https://www.ichigo-llc.co.jp
Information Technology Consulting Services
N.A.I.C.S.: 541512

OCH Co., Ltd. (1)
3rd Floor Kahuna Asahibashi Block B Building 1-9 Asahimachi, Naha, 900-0029, Okinawa, Japan
Tel.: (81) 988600203
Web Site: https://www.och.co.jp
Building Construction Services
N.A.I.C.S.: 541330

Okinawa Cross Head Co., Ltd. (1)
9-9 Kahuna Asahibashi B Block Building 3F,

TECHMATRIX CORPORATION

TECHMATRIX CORPORATION—(Continued)
Asahi-Cho, Naha, 900-0029, Okinawa, Japan
Tel.: (81) 988600203
Web Site: http://www.och.co.jp
Information Technology Consulting Services
N.A.I.C.S.: 541512

TECHNA-X BERHAD
Level 7 Menara Milenium Jalan Damanlela Pusat Bandar Damansara, Damansara Heights, 50490, Kuala Lumpur, Malaysia
Tel.: (60) 327158688
Web Site: https://www.techna-x.com
Year Founded: 1976
TECHNAX—(KLS)
Rev.: $15,710,265
Assets: $45,652,910
Liabilities: $36,798,519
Net Worth: $8,854,392
Earnings: $53,783,280
Emp.: 1,000
Fiscal Year-end: 12/31/22
Coke Mfr
N.A.I.C.S.: 324110
Guodong Liu *(Mng Dir)*

Subsidiaries:

Linyi Yehua Coking Co., Ltd. (1)
Shenquan Village Industrial Park, Luozhuang District, Linyi, Shandong, China
Tel.: (86) 5397100015
Metallurgical Coke Mfr & Whslr
N.A.I.C.S.: 324199

TECHNICAL ADHESIVES LIMITED
3035 Jarrow Ave, Mississauga, L4X 2C6, ON, Canada
Tel.: (905) 625-1284
Web Site: http://www.technicaladhesives.ca
Year Founded: 1961
Rev.: $10,259,504
Emp.: 40
Adhesive Mfr
N.A.I.C.S.: 325520
Conrad Maziarczyk *(Pres)*

TECHNICAL INSPECTION & CORROSION CONTROL CO
No 11 Block 18 St kooh-e-noor St Motahari, Tehran, Iran
Tel.: (98) 2188529728
Web Site: http://www.en.techinco.net
TKIN1—(THE)
Sales Range: Less than $1 Million
Emp.: 681
Technical Inspection Services
N.A.I.C.S.: 541350

TECHNICAL OLYMPIC SA
20 Solomou St, Alimos, 174 56, Athens, Greece
Tel.: (30) 2109977000
Web Site: https://www.techol.gr
Year Founded: 1965
OLYMP—(ATH)
Rev.: $18,008,382
Assets: $245,593,726
Liabilities: $41,050,874
Net Worth: $204,542,851
Earnings: $6,577,564
Emp.: 64
Fiscal Year-end: 12/31/23
Construction Services
N.A.I.C.S.: 236220
Andreas Stengos *(Vice Chm & Gen Mgr)*

Subsidiaries:

DELOS MARINAS S.A. (1)
20 Solomou Street, Alimos, 174 56, Athens, Greece
Tel.: (30) 2109977000
Web Site: http://www.delosmarinas.gr

Emp.: 70
Marina Operation Services
N.A.I.C.S.: 713930
Constantine Stengos *(CEO)*

Domain Porto Carras S.A. (1)
20 Solomou Street, Alimos, Athens, 17456, Greece
Tel.: (30) 210 9949809
Web Site: http://www.portocarraswines.gr
Emp.: 40
Vineyard Cultivation & Wines Mfr
N.A.I.C.S.: 115112

MELTEMI KASTRI S.A. (1)
20 Solomou Street, Alimos, 174 56, Athens, Greece
Tel.: (30) 2109977000
Web Site: http://www.techol.gr
Emp.: 50
Wind Park Construction Services
N.A.I.C.S.: 237130

Mapiva Porto Carras S.A. (1)
Porto Carras, Sithonia, 630 81, Chalkidiki, Greece
Tel.: (30) 2375077000
Web Site: http://www.portocarras.com
Emp.: 600
Resort Operating Services
N.A.I.C.S.: 721120

Marina Porto Carras SA (1)
Porto Carras, 63081, Neos Marmaras, Chalkidiki, Greece
Tel.: (30) 2375071381
Home Management Services
N.A.I.C.S.: 721110

Porto Carras S.A. (1)
Central Office 20 Solomou Street, Alimos, 174 56, Athens, Greece
Tel.: (30) 2109949809
Web Site: http://www.portocarras.com
Tourist Resorts Operation Services
N.A.I.C.S.: 721110

Subsidiary (Domestic):

Golf Porto Carras S.A. (2)
Porto Carras, Sithonia, Chalkidiki, 63081, Greece
Tel.: (30) 2375077300
Web Site: http://www.portocarras.com
Golf Course Operation Services
N.A.I.C.S.: 713910
Christos Zikos *(Gen Mgr)*

TOUSA, Inc. (1)
4000 Hollywood Blvd Ste 400 N, Hollywood, FL 33021-1220
Tel.: (954) 364-4000
Holding Company; Home Construction Services
N.A.I.C.S.: 551112

TECHNICHE LIMITED
Ground Floor 143 Coronation Drive, Milton, 4064, QLD, Australia
Tel.: (61) 1300556673 AU
Web Site: http://www.technichegroup.com
Rev.: $6,856,626
Assets: $12,060,732
Liabilities: $4,240,457
Net Worth: $7,820,275
Earnings: ($874,516)
Fiscal Year-end: 06/30/19
Financial Investment Services
N.A.I.C.S.: 523999
Karl Phillip Jacoby *(Chm & CEO)*

Subsidiaries:

ERST Technology GmbH (1)
Frankenstrasse 5, 20097, Hamburg, Germany
Tel.: (49) 3947610300
Web Site: http://www.erst-technology.com
Software Development Services
N.A.I.C.S.: 541511
Thomas Huben *(Mng Dir)*

Urgent Technology Ltd (1)
Power House Harrison Close, Milton Keynes, MK5 8PA, Buckinghamshire, United Kingdom
Tel.: (44) 1908 391160
Web Site: http://urgent.technichegroup.com

Emp.: 20
Software Development Services
N.A.I.C.S.: 541511

TECHNICO INDUSTRIES LTD.
118-119 1st Floor Suncity Success Tower, Main Golf Course Extension Road Sec-65, Gurgaon, 122005, Haryana, India
Tel.: (91) 1242841300
Web Site:
    http://www.technicoindustries.com
Year Founded: 1972
Automotive Components Mfr
N.A.I.C.S.: 336390
Arun Gupta *(Co-Mng Dir)*

Subsidiaries:

Technico Industries Ltd. - Bawal Works (1)
Plot No 19-21 36-38 Sector-6 Industrial Estate, Rewari, Bawal, 123501, India
Tel.: (91) 1244341111
Automotive Components Mfr
N.A.I.C.S.: 336390

TECHNICS OIL & GAS LIMITED
8 Wilkie Road 03-01 Wilkie Edge, Singapore, 228095, Singapore
Tel.: (65) 6533 7600
Year Founded: 1990
5CQ—(SES)
Sales Range: Less than $1 Million
Oil & Gas Engineering Services
N.A.I.C.S.: 541330
Nathan Elumalay *(Chm)*

Subsidiaries:

Norr Systems Korea Co., Ltd (1)
154-1 Busan Gijang-Gun, Busan, 619-906, Korea (South)
Tel.: (82) 70 7432 6952
Web Site: http://www.norrsystems.com
Sales Range: $25-49.9 Million
Emp.: 6
Offshore Engineering Equipments Mfr
N.A.I.C.S.: 333132

Norr Systems Pte. Ltd. (1)
37A Tampines Street 92 08-00, Singapore, 528886, Singapore
Tel.: (65) 67850500
Web Site: http://www.norrsystems.com
Marine Engineering System Mfr & Distr
N.A.I.C.S.: 334290

PT Technics Offshore Jaya (1)
Sekupang Logistics Base Block G No 1, Jl RE Marthadinata Sekupang, Batam, 29422, Indonesia
Tel.: (62) 778327091
Web Site: http://www.technicsgrp.com
Sales Range: $75-99.9 Million
Emp.: 50
Engineeering Services
N.A.I.C.S.: 541330
Fong Ing Lim *(Gen Mgr)*

Petro Process System Pte. Ltd. (1)
72 Loyang Way 04-29 Changi International Logistics Ctr, Singapore, 508724, Singapore
Tel.: (65) 65459968
Sales Range: $25-49.9 Million
Emp.: 100
Engineering Services
N.A.I.C.S.: 541330

Technics Offshore Engineering Pte Ltd (1)
72 Loyang Way, Singapore, 508762, Singapore
Tel.: (65) 65459968
Sales Range: $25-49.9 Million
Emp.: 100
Offshore Engineering Services
N.A.I.C.S.: 541330

Vina Offshore Engineering Co., Ltd. (1)
Road #5 Dong Xuyen Industrial Zone Rach Dua Ward, Vung Tau, Vietnam
Tel.: (84) 64 3832 888

INTERNATIONAL PUBLIC

Web Site: http://www.technicsgrp.com
Oil & Gas Production
N.A.I.C.S.: 213112

Wecom Engineering Pte Ltd (1)
19 Tuas South Street 1, Singapore, 638066, Singapore
Tel.: (65) 65587639
Web Site: http://www.wecom-engrg.com
Emp.: 100
Industrial Valve Repair & Maintenance Services
N.A.I.C.S.: 811310
Daniel Wong *(Mng Dir)*

TECHNILINE SA
135 rue du Fosse Blanc, 92622, Gennevilliers, Cedex, France
Tel.: (33) 140105555
Sales Range: $50-74.9 Million
Emp.: 70
Photography, Audiovisual & Film Equipment Importer & Distr
N.A.I.C.S.: 423410
Zakaria Chtioui *(Chm & CEO)*

TECHNIP ENERGIES N.V.
2126 boulevard de la Defense CS 10266, 92741, Nanterre, France
Tel.: (33) 147782121
Web Site: https://www.ten.com
Year Founded: 2021
THNPY—(OTCIQ)
Rev.: $6,627,221,549
Assets: $9,570,040,845
Liabilities: $7,416,160,725
Net Worth: $2,153,880,120
Earnings: $379,291,313
Emp.: 15,498
Fiscal Year-end: 12/31/23
Construction Engineering Services
N.A.I.C.S.: 541330
Bruno Vibert *(CFO)*

Subsidiaries:

Cyxplus S.A.S. (1)
20 Avenue Lamartine ZA de l'Agavon, 13170, Les Pennes-Mirabeau, France
Tel.: (33) 140901000
Web Site: https://www.cyxplus.fr
Automobile Parts Mfr & Distr
N.A.I.C.S.: 326211

Genesis Energies Consultants Ltd. (1)
One St Pauls Churchyard, London, EC4M 8AP, United Kingdom
Tel.: (44) 2075856000
Oil & Gas Engineering Services
N.A.I.C.S.: 811191

Inocean AB (1)
Gardatorget 1, SE-412 50, Gothenburg, Sweden
Tel.: (46) 31169820
Marine & Offshore Engineering Services
N.A.I.C.S.: 541330

Inocean AS (1)
Bryggegata 9, 0250, Oslo, Norway
Tel.: (47) 22331131
Web Site: https://www.inocean.no
Marine & Offshore Engineering Services
N.A.I.C.S.: 541330

Inocean Poland Sp. Z o.o. (1)
Dubois 20, PO Box 73, 71-610, Szczecin, Poland
Tel.: (48) 914315357
Engineering & Construction Services
N.A.I.C.S.: 541330

T.EN Australia and New Zealand Pty. Ltd. (1)
One William Street, Perth, 6000, WA, Australia
Tel.: (61) 863719100
Engineering & Construction Services
N.A.I.C.S.: 541330

T.EN Colombia S.A. (1)
Calle 38 8-62 Piso 3, 110111, Bogota, Colombia
Tel.: (57) 6013320200
Web Site: https://www.tipiel.com.co

AND PRIVATE COMPANIES — TECHNIPFMC PLC

Real Estate & Construction Services
N.A.I.C.S.: 236220

T.EN E&C Limited (1)
170 Midsummer Boulevard, Milton Keynes, MK9 1BP, United Kingdom
Tel.: (44) 1908203300
Engineering & Construction Services
N.A.I.C.S.: 541330

T.EN Ingenierie Regionale pour Industries S.A.S. (1)
14 rue Linus Carl Pauling Parc d Activite de la Vatine, 76130, Mont-Saint-Aignau, France
Tel.: (33) 235592510
Web Site: https://www.technip-normandie.fr
Engineering Services
N.A.I.C.S.: 541330

T.EN Loading Systems S.A.S. (1)
Route des Clerimois, CS10705, 89109, Sens, France
Tel.: (33) 386958700
Onshore & Offshore Logistics Services
N.A.I.C.S.: 541614

T.EN Netherlands B.V. (1)
Afrikaweg 30, 2713 AW, Zoetermeer, Netherlands
Tel.: (31) 793293600
Onshore & Offshore Logistics Services
N.A.I.C.S.: 541614

T.EN Process Technology, Inc. (1)
1 Financial Ctr, Boston, MA 02111
Tel.: (617) 748-7100
Engineering & Construction Services
N.A.I.C.S.: 541330

T.EN Zimmer GmbH (1)
Friesstrasse 20, 60388, Frankfurt am Main, Germany
Tel.: (49) 69667784500
Web Site: https://www.zimmer-polymers.com
Engineering Consulting Services
N.A.I.C.S.: 541330

Technip Energies India Limited (1)
Technip Centre No 19 Velachery Main Road, Guindy, Chennai, 600 032, India
Tel.: (91) 4422303100
Engineering & Construction Services
N.A.I.C.S.: 541330

TECHNIPFMC PLC
One St.Paul s Churchyard, London, EC4M 8AP, United Kingdom
Tel.: (44) 2034293950 UK
Web Site: http://www.technipfmc.com
Year Founded: 2015
FTI—(NYSE)
Rev.: $9,097,267,088
Assets: $12,822,714,996
Liabilities: $8,373,873,872
Net Worth: $4,448,841,124
Earnings: ($145,547,584)
Emp.: 23,346
Fiscal Year-end: 12/31/22
Holding Company; Oil & Gas Industry Engineering, Technologies & Support Services
N.A.I.C.S.: 551112
Douglas J. Pferdehirt *(Chm & CEO)*

Subsidiaries:

F.A. Sening GmbH (1)
Regentstrasse 1, 25474, Ellerbek, Germany
Tel.: (49) 41013040
Oil & Gas Technology Services
N.A.I.C.S.: 213112

FMC Technologies Algeria SARL (1)
9 Rue Naama Sebti Ex Paul Langevin, El Mouradia, Algiers, Algeria
Tel.: (213) 21602128
Oil & Gas Technology Services
N.A.I.C.S.: 213112

FMC Technologies Cameroon SARL (1)
Zone Portuaire Place De L'Udeac BP, Bonanjo, 12804, Douala, Cameroon
Tel.: (237) 650787228
Oil & Gas Technology Services
N.A.I.C.S.: 213112

FMC Technologies Egypt LLC (1)
2nd Floor Building n A2 Block 14B01 Southern Wing Administrative, District Cairo Festival City Project, New Cairo, Egypt
Tel.: (20) 22804407
Oil & Gas Field Services
N.A.I.C.S.: 213112

FMC Technologies Gabon S.A.R.L. (1)
Base DPS SPIE O and G, PO Box 3021, Port-Gentil, Gabon
Tel.: (241) 65303720
Oil & Gas Field Services
N.A.I.C.S.: 213112

FMC Technologies India Private Limited (1)
A-4 Sector 1 Institutional Area, Noida, Uttar Pradesh, India
Tel.: (91) 1204301000
Oil & Gas Technology Services
N.A.I.C.S.: 213112

FMC Technologies Overseas, S.A.S. (1)
Batiment C Zone ECOParc Rue Nelson Mandela, 89100, Sens, France
Tel.: (33) 371360267
Oil & Gas Field Services
N.A.I.C.S.: 213112

FMC Technologies Service SARL (1)
Rue du Lac Tanganyica Immeuble Junior Les Berges Du Lac, 1053, Tunis, Tunisia
Tel.: (216) 71963679
Oil & Gas Technology Services
N.A.I.C.S.: 213112

FMC Technologies Servicios Corporativos, S. de R.L de C.V. (1)
Calle Laurel Lt 41 Mz 19 Col Bruno Pagliai, 91697, Veracruz, Mexico
Tel.: (52) 2299231470
Oil & Gas Technology Services
N.A.I.C.S.: 213112

FMC Technologies, Inc. (1)
11740 Katy Fwy, Houston, TX 77079
Tel.: (281) 591-4000
Web Site: http://www.technipfmc.com
Technology Solutions for Energy Industry & Industrial Markets
N.A.I.C.S.: 333132

Subsidiary (Domestic):

Control Systems International, Inc. (2)
8040 Nieman Rd, Lenexa, KS 66214-1523
Tel.: (913) 599-5010
Software Mfr
N.A.I.C.S.: 513210

Direct Drive Systems, Inc. (2)
621 Burning Tree Rd, Fullerton, CA 92833-1447
Tel.: (714) 872-5500
Web Site: http://www.technipfmc.com
Motors & Generators Mfr
N.A.I.C.S.: 335312

Unit (Domestic):

FMC Fluid Control (2)
2825 W Washington St, Stephenville, TX 76401
Tel.: (254) 968-2181
Web Site: http://www.technipfmc.com
Supplier of Flowline Products, Pumps & Manifold Systems for High-Pressure Oilfield Applications
N.A.I.C.S.: 325180

Subsidiary (Non-US):

FMC Kongsberg Holding AS (2)
Kirkegaardsveien 45, Kongsberg, 3601, Norway
Tel.: (47) 32286700
Web Site: http://www.technipfmc.com
Investment Management Service
N.A.I.C.S.: 523999

Subsidiary (Domestic):

FMC Kongsberg Subsea AS (3)
Kirkegaardveien 45, 3616, Kongsberg, Norway (100%)
Tel.: (47) 32286700
Supplier of Turnkey Subsea Production & Completion Systems
N.A.I.C.S.: 333132
Audun Oksavik *(Mgr-Mktg Comm)*

Subsidiary (Non-US):

FMC Kongsberg Services Limited (4)
One St Pauls Chruchyard, London, EC4M 8AP, United Kingdom (100%)
Tel.: (44) 2034293950
Web Site: http://www.technipfmc.com
Mfr & Distribution of Industrial Chemicals
N.A.I.C.S.: 325998

Subsidiary (Non-US):

FMC Technologies AG (2)
1 Sheikh Zayed, Dubai, United Arab Emirates
Tel.: (971) 4 883 0303
Energy Industry Equipment Whslr
N.A.I.C.S.: 423830

FMC Technologies Argentina S.R.L. (2)
World Trade Center Lola Mora 421 18th Floor Office 1802, C1107BGA, Buenos Aires, Argentina
Tel.: (54) 11 6009 1140
Web Site: http://www.technipfmc.com
Energy Industry Equipment Whslr
N.A.I.C.S.: 423830

FMC Technologies Company Ltd. (2)
144 4 Ave SW, Calgary, T2P 3N4, AB, Canada
Tel.: (403) 262-4000
Web Site: http://www.technipfmc.com
Oil & Gas Field Machinery & Equipment Mfr
N.A.I.C.S.: 333132

Unit (Domestic):

FMC Technologies Canada Co. (3)
6703 68 Ave, Edmonton, T6B 3E3, AB, Canada
Tel.: (780) 468-9231
Web Site: http://www.technipfmc.com
Energy Industry Equipment Distr
N.A.I.C.S.: 423830
Curtis Holmes *(Mgr-Branch)*

Subsidiary (Non-US):

FMC Technologies Ltd. (2)
Hadrian House Wincomblee Road, Newcastle upon Tyne, NE6 3PL, United Kingdom (100%)
Tel.: (44) 1483227380
Supplier & Business Developer of Equipment for the Oil & Gas Industry
N.A.I.C.S.: 333132
Mathew Cole *(Sr Engr-Field Dev)*

Subsidiary (Domestic):

FMC Technologies Measurement Solutions, Inc. (2)
1602 Wagner Ave, Erie, PA 16510
Tel.: (814) 898-5000
Web Site: http://www.technipfmc.com
Provider of Liquid & Gas Custody Transfer Solutions
N.A.I.C.S.: 325180

Branch (Domestic):

FMC Technologies Measurement Solutions (3)
1602 Wagner Ave, Erie, PA 16510
Tel.: (814) 898-5000
Web Site: http://www.technipfmc.com
Fluid Meters & Counting Devices
N.A.I.C.S.: 334514

Subsidiary (Non-US):

FMC Technolocgies SA (2)
Batiment C Zone ECOParc Rue Nelson Mandela, PO Box 705, 89100, Sens, France
Tel.: (33) 371360267
Mfr of Industrial Inorganic Chemicals
N.A.I.C.S.: 325180
Graham Horn *(Gen Mgr)*

FMC Technologies Singapore Pte. Ltd. (2)
149 Gul Circle, Singapore, 629605, Singapore
Tel.: (65) 68613011
Web Site: http://www.fmctechnologies.com
Fluid Control Systems
N.A.I.C.S.: 334519

Unit (Domestic):

FMC Technologies Surface Wellhead (2)
475 17th #850, Denver, CO 80202
Tel.: (303) 382-1010
Web Site: http://www.technipfmc.com
Construction Equipment Mfr
N.A.I.C.S.: 423810

Subsidiary (Non-US):

FMC Technologies de Mexico S.A. de C.V. (2)
Tel.: (52) 2299231470
Web Site: http://www.technipfmc.com
Energy Industry Equipment Mfr & Distr
N.A.I.C.S.: 423830
Miguel Flores *(Mgr-Sls)*

P.T. FMC Santana Petroleum Equipment Indonesia (2)
Jalan Cakung Cilincing Raya Km 2 5 Semper Barat Cilincing, RT4/RW3 Semper Tim Jakarta Utara Kota Jkt Utara Daerah Khusus Ibukota, Jakarta, 14130, Indonesia
Tel.: (62) 2129806100
Drilling Machinery & Equipment Mfr
N.A.I.C.S.: 333132

Kanfa AS (1)
Philip Pedersens vei 7, 1366, Lysaker, Norway (100%)
Tel.: (47) 64001800
Oil Gas Off Shore Contract Services
N.A.I.C.S.: 213112

Magma Global Ltd. (1)
Magma House Trafalgar Wharf Hamilton Road, Portsmouth, Hampshire, United Kingdom
Tel.: (44) 2393872800
Web Site: https://www.magmaglobal.com
Carbon Fiber Mfr
N.A.I.C.S.: 335991

Technip S.A. (1)
89 avenue de la Grande Armee, 75773, Paris, Cedex 16, France
Tel.: (33) 147782400
Web Site: http://www.technipfmc.com
Holding Company; Oil & Gas Industry Engineering, Technologies & Project Management Services
N.A.I.C.S.: 551112

Subsidiary (Non-US):

Angoflex Limitada (2)
14th floor Rua Rei Katyavala n 43-45, Po Box 5364, Caix Postal 5364, Luanda, Angola (70%)
Tel.: (244) 226424800
Umbilical Cabling & Pipe Mfr
N.A.I.C.S.: 332996

Asiaflex Products Sdn Bhd (2)
Tanjung Langsat Industrial Complex, 81700, Pasir Gudang, Johor Darul Takzim, Malaysia
Tel.: (60) 72548000
Web Site: http://technip.fr
Flexible Pipe Mfr
N.A.I.C.S.: 332919

Brasflex Tubos Flexiveis Ltda. (2)
Rua da Gloria 178 Gloria, Rio de Janeiro, CEP-20241-180, Brazil (100%)
Tel.: (55) 2732221615
Mfr of Flexible Pipeline Equipment
N.A.I.C.S.: 332996

Cybernetix S.A. (2)
Web Site: http://www.cybernetix.fr
Robotics Equipment Mfr
N.A.I.C.S.: 333248
Samuel Rocher *(CEO)*

Flexibras Vitoria (2)
Rua Jurema Barroso 35, Ilha do Principe, Vitoria, ES, Brazil (100%)
Tel.: (55) 27 2123 9444

TECHNIPFMC PLC

TechnipFMC plc—(Continued)
Web Site: http://technip.fr
Mfr of Pipeline Equipment
N.A.I.C.S.: 332996

Genesis Oil & Gas Consultants (2)
1120 Hay Street, West Perth, 6005, WA, Australia **(100%)**
Tel.: (61) 893200100
Web Site: http://www.genesisoilandgas.com
Oil & Gas Industry Engineering Consultants
N.A.I.C.S.: 541620

Genesis Oil & Gas Consultants Ltd (2)
One St Pauls Churchyard, London, EC4M 8AP, United Kingdom
Tel.: (44) 2076115555
Web Site: http://www.genesisoilandgas.com
Oil & Gas Exploration Services
N.A.I.C.S.: 213112

Genesis Oil & Gas Consultants Ltd. (2)
One St Paul's Churchyard, London, EC4M 8AP, United Kingdom **(100%)**
Tel.: (44) 2075856000
Sales Range: $25-49.9 Million
Emp.: 200
Oil & Gas Industry Engineering Consultants
N.A.I.C.S.: 541330

Genesis Oil & Gas Pty. Ltd. (2)
1 William Street, PO Box 7292, Perth, 6000, WA, Australia **(100%)**
Tel.: (61) 893200100
Undersea Engineering & Construction
N.A.I.C.S.: 541330

PT Technip Indonesia **(100%)**
Tel.: (62) 2157990888
Web Site: http://www.technip.fr
Engineeering Services
N.A.I.C.S.: 541330
Justin Vaughan *(Mng Dir)*

Subsidiary (Domestic):

Seal Engineering SA (2)
19 Avenue Feucheres, 30 000, Nimes, France
Tel.: (33) 466369061
Web Site: https://sealengineering.fr
Oil & Gas Field Engineering Services
N.A.I.C.S.: 541330
Ange Luppi *(Founder)*

Technip (2)
Technip tower 6/8 Alle L'arche, 92873, Courbevoie, Cedex, France **(100%)**
Tel.: (33) 147782121
Web Site: http://www.technip.pic
Sales Range: $900-999.9 Million
Emp.: 4,000
Undersea Petroleum; Robotics, Telecommunications, Construction & Maintenance
N.A.I.C.S.: 236220

Subsidiary (Domestic):

Flexi France (3)
132 Rue Jean Hure, PO Box 7, 76580, Le Trait, France **(100%)**
Tel.: (33) 235055000
Flexible Pipeline Mfr
N.A.I.C.S.: 332996

Subsidiary (Non-US):

Technip Abu Dhabi (2)
FMC Technologies GMBH GASOS plot ICAD III Mussafah, PO Box 6203, Abu Dhabi, United Arab Emirates **(100%)**
Tel.: (971) 28853777
Petrochemical Engineering Services
N.A.I.C.S.: 541330

Technip Beijing (2)
Room 906 Hyundai Motor Tower No 38 Xiaoyun Road, Chaoyang District, Beijing, 100027, China **(100%)**
Tel.: (86) 10 8453 9880
Web Site: http://www.technip.com
Engineering & Construction
N.A.I.C.S.: 541330

Technip Benelux B.V. (2)
Afrikaweg 30, 2713AW, Zoetermeer, Netherlands **(100%)**

Tel.: (31) 793293600
Web Site: http://www.technip.fr
Engineering & Construction
N.A.I.C.S.: 541330
Frans Jeunink *(Sr Project Mgr)*

Technip Brazil (2)
Rua Dom Marcos Barbosa n2, Cidade Nova, Rio de Janeiro, 20211-178, Brazil
Tel.: (55) 21 2139 7000
Web Site: http://www.technip.fr
Sales Range: $700-749.9 Million
Emp.: 270
Offshore Engineering Services
N.A.I.C.S.: 541330

Technip Canada Limited (2)
131 Kelsey Drive, Saint John's, A1B 0L2, NL, Canada
Tel.: (403) 262-4000
Web Site: http://www.technip.fr
Oil & Gas Field Engineering Services
N.A.I.C.S.: 213112

Technip E&C Limited (2)
1 St Pauls, Churchyard, London, EC4M 8AP, United Kingdom **(100%)**
Tel.: (44) 2075855555
Web Site: http://www.genesisoilandgas.com
Engineering, Design, Construction & Consulting Services for Power, Industrial & Civil Works Projects, Oil & Gas Exploration & Production
N.A.I.C.S.: 541330

Technip Engineering (B) Sdn Bhd (2)
Unit 1 2nd Floor TCY Building Lot 118, Kuala Belait, Negara, KA2331, Brunei Darussalam
Tel.: (673) 33472209
Engineering Consultancy Services
N.A.I.C.S.: 541330

Technip Engineering Consultant (Shanghai) Co. Ltd. (2)
10th Floor Yunhai Mansion 1329 Huai Hai Middle Road, Shanghai, 200031, China
Tel.: (86) 21 6415 4525
Web Site: http://www.technip.fr
Engineeering Services
N.A.I.C.S.: 541330

Subsidiary (Domestic):

Technip Eurocash SNC (2)
89 Avenue De La Grande Armee Cedex, Paris, 75016, France
Tel.: (33) 589803261
Construction Engineering Services
N.A.I.C.S.: 541330

Technip France (2)
6-8 Allee de l'Arche, Faubourg de lArche ZAC Danton, 92400, Courbevoie, France **(100%)**
Tel.: (33) 147782121
Web Site: http://technip.fr
Engineering & Construction
N.A.I.C.S.: 541330

Subsidiary (Non-US):

Technip Holding Benelux BV (2)
Afrikaweg 30, Zoetermeer, 2713 AW, Netherlands
Tel.: (31) 793293600
Web Site: http://www.technip.com
Emp.: 100
Investment Management Service
N.A.I.C.S.: 523999

Technip Iberia (2)
Plaza Pau SN World Trade Center-Almeba Park Tornella Llobrega, 08940, Barcelona, Spain **(100%)**
Tel.: (34) 933309800
Web Site: http://www.technip.fr
Engineering Services
N.A.I.C.S.: 541330
Jeronimo Farnos *(Gen Dir)*

Technip India Ltd (2)
Gr 1st 5th Floor Prima Bay Tower B Gate No 5 Saki Vihar Road, Powai Andheri East, Mumbai, 400072, Maharashtra, India **(100%)**
Tel.: (91) 226702000
Engineering Services
N.A.I.C.S.: 541330
Bhaskar Patel *(Mng Dir)*

Subsidiary (Domestic):

Technip KT India Ltd. (3)
Technip Tower A-4 Sector-1, Noida, 201 301, India
Tel.: (91) 120 4301 000
Web Site: http://www.technip.com
Environmental Consulting Services
N.A.I.C.S.: 541620
Ram Kishore Iruvanti *(Mng Dir)*

Subsidiary (Non-US):

Technip Italy S.p.A. (2)
68 Viale Castello Della Magliana, 00148, Rome, Italy **(100%)**
Tel.: (39) 0665981
Web Site: http://www.technip.com
Sales Range: $1-4.9 Billion
Emp.: 100
Engineeering Services
N.A.I.C.S.: 541330

Technip Malaysia (2) **(100%)**
Web Site: http://www.technip.com
Engineering & Construction
N.A.I.C.S.: 541330

Technip Maritime UK Ltd (2)
Hadrian House Wincomblee Road, Newcastle upon Tyne, NE6 3PL, United Kingdom
Tel.: (44) 2076115555
Oil & Gas Exploration Services
N.A.I.C.S.: 213112

Technip Norge AS (2)
Philip Pedersens Vei 7, PO Box 400, Lysaker, 1366, Norway
Tel.: (47) 67 58 85 00
Web Site: http://www.technip.fr
Marine Engineering Services
N.A.I.C.S.: 541330

Technip Oceania Pty Ltd (2)
1120 Hay St, West Perth, Perth, 6005, WA, Australia
Tel.: (61) 894632500
Construction Engineering Services
N.A.I.C.S.: 541330

Technip Offshore International S.A. (2)
Tel.: (33) 147782121
Web Site: http://www.technipfmc.com
Water Pipeline Construction Services
N.A.I.C.S.: 237110

Subsidiary (Non-US):

Technip Norge AS (3)
Philip Pedersens vei 7, PO Box 400, 1366, Lysaker, Norway **(100%)**
Tel.: (47) 67588500
Undersea Pipeline Engineering Services
N.A.I.C.S.: 541330

Branch (Domestic):

Technip Norge AS-Orkanger Spoolbase (4)
Gronora Industriomrade, Gronora Industriomade, 7301, Orkanger, Norway **(100%)**
Tel.: (47) 675885006
Web Site: http://technip.fr
Undersea Pipeline Engineering Services
N.A.I.C.S.: 541330

Subsidiary (Non-US):

Technip Offshore Finland Oy (3) **(100%)**
Tel.: (358) 102322000
Offshore Drilling Platform Construction & Pipeline Installation Services
N.A.I.C.S.: 237120

Subsidiary (Non-US):

Technip Oil and Gas B.V. (2)
Afrikaweg 30, 2713 AW, Zoetermeer, Netherlands
Tel.: (31) 793293600
Engineeering Services
N.A.I.C.S.: 541330

Technip Polska Sp. z o.o. (2)
Al Jana Pawla II 43B, 31-864, Krakow, Poland
Tel.: (48) 228390520

INTERNATIONAL PUBLIC

Oil & Gas Pipeline Construction Services
N.A.I.C.S.: 237120

Technip Russia (2)
266 litera O Ligovsky prospekt St, Saint Petersburg, Russia **(100%)**
Tel.: (7) 8124954870
Web Site: http://www.technip.fr
Engineering & Construction Services
N.A.I.C.S.: 541330

Technip Servicios de Mexico (2)
Av Vasco de Quiroga No 3000 Conjunto Calakmul Col, Sta Fe, Mexico, 01210, Alvaro Obregon, Mexico **(100%)**
Tel.: (52) 8182456700
Web Site: http://www.echnip.fr
Engineering Services
N.A.I.C.S.: 541330

Technip Ships (Netherlands) B.V. (2)
Zuidplein 126 WTC Tower H 15th Fl, 1077XV, Amsterdam, Netherlands
Tel.: (31) 793293600
Marine Transportation Services
N.A.I.C.S.: 483112

Technip Singapore Pte Ltd (2) **(100%)**
Tel.: (65) 55053500
Web Site: http://www.technipfmc.com
Engineeering Services
N.A.I.C.S.: 541330

Technip South Africa Limited (2)
34 Monkor Road Randpark, Randburg, 2194, South Africa
Web Site: http://technip.co.za
Construction Engineering Services
N.A.I.C.S.: 541330

Technip Thailand (2)
20th Floor Suntowers Building A 123 Vibhavadee-Rangsit Road Jomphon, Jatujak, Bangkok, 10900, Thailand
Tel.: (66) 26177939
Web Site: http://www.tpthailand.com
Engineeering Services
N.A.I.C.S.: 541330
Jean Francois Redon *(Exec VP-Projects)*

Technip Tianchen Chemical Engineering (Tianjin) Co., Ltd. (2)
10th Floor Yunhai Mansion 1329 Middle Huaihai Road, Shanghai, 200 031, China **(100%)**
Tel.: (86) 21 6415 2600
Web Site: http://www.technip.com
Petrochemical Engineering Services
N.A.I.C.S.: 541330

Technip UK Limited (2)
Enterprise Dr, Westhill Industrial Estate, Aberdeen, AB32 6TQ, Aberdeenshire, United Kingdom **(100%)**
Tel.: (44) 1224271000
Web Site: http://www.technip.com
Undersea Pipeline Engineering Services
N.A.I.C.S.: 541330

Subsidiary (US):

Technip USA, Inc. (2)
11700 Katy Fwy Ste 100, Houston, TX 77079
Tel.: (281) 591-4000
Oil & Gas Construction & Engineering Services
N.A.I.C.S.: 541330

Subsidiary (Domestic):

Duco Inc. (3)
16661 Jacintoport Blvd, Houston, TX 77015 **(100%)**
Tel.: (281) 249-2800
Web Site: http://www.technip.com
Flexible Pipe Equipment Mfr
N.A.I.C.S.: 237120
Kim Lopez *(Reg Sls Mgr-North America & Canada)*

Genesis Oil & Gas Consultants Inc. (3)
11740 Katy Fwy Ste 100, Houston, TX 77079
Tel.: (281) 249-3300
Web Site: http://www.genesisoilandgas.com
Engineeering Services
N.A.I.C.S.: 541330

AND PRIVATE COMPANIES

Technip Offshore, Inc. (3)
11700 Old Katy Rd Ste 150, Houston, TX 77079-1297
Tel.: (281) 870-1111
Web Site: http://www.technip.com
Undersea Engineering; Oil & Gas Platform Construction; Pipeline Construction
N.A.I.C.S.: 541330

Subsidiary (Non-US):

Technip-EPG B.V. (2)
Fascinatio Boulevard 522, Capelle aan de Ijssel, 2909 VA, Rotterdam, 290964, Netherlands
Tel.: (31) 102207070
Engineeering Services
N.A.I.C.S.: 541330
Hans Barendrecht *(Mgr-Ops)*

Technipfmc Umbilicals Ltd (2)
One St. Pauls Churchyard, Newcastle, EC4M 8AP, United Kingdom (100%)
Tel.: (44) 2034293950
Web Site: http://www.technipfmc.com
Mfr of Undersea Control Cabling
N.A.I.C.S.: 331318

TechnipFMC Canada Limited (1)
131 Kelsey Drive, Saint John's, NL, Canada
Tel.: (403) 262-4000
Oil & Gas Technology Services
N.A.I.C.S.: 213112

TechnipFMC Guyana INC. (1)
175 Middle Street North Cummingsburg, Georgetown, Guyana
Tel.: (592) 2235592
Oil & Gas Field Services
N.A.I.C.S.: 213112

TechnipFMC Nigeria Limited (1)
22a Gerrard Road Ikoyi, Lagos, Nigeria
Tel.: (234) 9062873875
Oil & Gas Technology Services
N.A.I.C.S.: 213112

TECHNIS INTERNATIONAL PLC
5 St John's Lane, London, EC1M 4BH, United Kingdom
Tel.: (44) 2075493666
Year Founded: 2007
Sales Range: Less than $1 Million
Technology Developer
N.A.I.C.S.: 334118
Bernard Hulme *(Chm)*

TECHNIWELD CORPORATION
2300 Winston Park Drive, Oakville, L6H 7T7, ON, Canada
Tel.: (905) 829-8780
Web Site: http://www.techniweld.com
Year Founded: 1983
Sales Range: $10-24.9 Million
Welding Equipment & Safety Products Whslr
N.A.I.C.S.: 423840
John Metcalf *(Pres)*

TECHNO ALPHA CO., LTD.
Meiji Yasuda Seimei Gotanda Bldg 2-27-4 Nishi Gotanda, Shinagawa-Ku, Tokyo, 141-0031, Japan
Tel.: (81) 334927421
Web Site:
  https://www.technoalpha.co.jp
Year Founded: 1989
3089—(TKS)
Rev.: $30,976,210
Assets: $21,078,570
Liabilities: $8,302,390
Net Worth: $12,776,180
Earnings: $1,176,940
Emp.: 70
Fiscal Year-end: 11/30/23
Chip-Making Equipment & Electronic Materials Distr
N.A.I.C.S.: 423690
Junichi Tamai *(Auditor)*

Subsidiaries:

Peritec Corporation (1)

1-17-2 Kataoka, Takasaki, 370-0862, Gunma, Japan
Tel.: (81) 273286970
Web Site: http://www.peritec.co.jp
Emp.: 30
Electrical Circuit Design Mfr
N.A.I.C.S.: 334515
Toshihiro Izawa *(CEO)*

TECHNO ELECTRIC & ENGINEERING COMPANY LTD.
1B & C Park Plaza 71 Park Street, Nehru Place, Kolkata, 700016, India
Tel.: (91) 3340513000
Web Site: https://www.techno.co.in
Year Founded: 1963
TECHNOE—(NSE)
Rev.: $108,403,873
Assets: $331,980,373
Liabilities: $100,555,135
Net Worth: $231,425,238
Earnings: $22,403,669
Emp.: 360
Fiscal Year-end: 03/31/23
Engineering, Procurement & Construction Services
N.A.I.C.S.: 541330
P. P. Gupta *(Chm & Mng Dir)*

Subsidiaries:

Techno Electric & Engineering Company Ltd. - Power Plant & Electric Division (1)
3F Park Plz N Block, 71 Park St, Kolkata, 700 016, West Bengal, India
Tel.: (91) 3330213000
Web Site: http://www.techno.co.in
Sales Range: $150-199.9 Million
Electrical Engineering & Construction Services
N.A.I.C.S.: 541330
Manoj Sood *(Pres-HR)*

TECHNO HORIZON CO., LTD.
1131 Chikamatori, Minami-ku, Nagoya, 457-0071, Aichi, Japan
Tel.: (81) 528238551
Web Site:
  https://www.technohorizon.co.jp
Year Founded: 2010
6629—(TKS)
Rev.: $321,398,030
Assets: $238,568,120
Liabilities: $173,704,190
Net Worth: $64,863,930
Earnings: $6,616,610
Fiscal Year-end: 03/31/24
Holding Company
N.A.I.C.S.: 551111
Hironobu Nomura *(Pres)*

TECHNO MATHEMATICAL CO., LTD.
7F Gotanda NN Building 2-12-19 Nishigotanda, Shinagawa-ku, Tokyo, 141-0031, Japan
Tel.: (81) 334923633
Web Site: https://www.tmath.co.jp
Year Founded: 2000
3787—(TKS)
Sales Range: Less than $1 Million
Software Development Services
N.A.I.C.S.: 541511
Masafumi Tanaka *(Pres & CEO)*

TECHNO MEDICA CO., LTD.
5-5-1 Nakamachidai, Tsuduki-ku, Yokohama, 224-0041, Kanagawa, Japan
Tel.: (81) 459481967
Web Site:
  https://www.technomedica.co.jp
Year Founded: 1987
6678—(TKS)
Sales Range: $50-74.9 Million
Emp.: 225
Medical Equipment Mfr & Whslr
N.A.I.C.S.: 334510

TECHNO MEDICAL PCL
29 Ladprao 92 Phlabphla, Wangthonglang, Bangkok, 10310, Thailand
Tel.: (66) 29336112
Web Site: https://technomedical.co.th
Year Founded: 2002
TM—(THA)
Rev.: $20,347,095
Assets: $28,705,632
Liabilities: $16,687,298
Net Worth: $12,018,334
Earnings: ($131,072)
Fiscal Year-end: 12/31/23
Medical Equipment Distr
N.A.I.C.S.: 423450
Supapong Chanlongbutra *(Chm & CEO)*

TECHNO RYOWA LTD.
26-20 Minamiotsuka 2-chome, Toshima-ku, Tokyo, 170-0005, Japan
Tel.: (81) 359782541
Web Site: https://www.techno-ryowa.co.jp
Year Founded: 1949
1965—(TKS)
Rev.: $487,077,680
Assets: $503,867,080
Liabilities: $178,747,620
Net Worth: $325,119,460
Earnings: $29,784,660
Emp.: 806
Fiscal Year-end: 03/31/24
Air Conditioning Equipment Mfr & Distr
N.A.I.C.S.: 333415
Hidehiko Kuroda *(Pres)*

TECHNO SMART CORP.
2nd Floor Kyutaromachi Tsunewa Building 2528 Kyutaromachi, Chuoku, Osaka, 541-0056, Japan
Tel.: (81) 662537200
Web Site:
  https://www.technosmart.co.jp
Year Founded: 1912
6246—(TKS)
Sales Range: $75-99.9 Million
Emp.: 253
Device Mfr
N.A.I.C.S.: 334413
Susumu Takahashi *(Pres)*

Subsidiaries:

Techno Smart Corp. - Shiga Factory (1)
No 3200 Ooshinohara, Yasu, 520-2313, Shiga, Japan
Tel.: (81) 775872022
Film Device Mfr
N.A.I.C.S.: 333310

TECHNO TAR ENGINEERING COMPANY
No 20 7th Fath, Fath Highway Old Karaj Road, Tehran, Iran
Tel.: (98) 21 66812668
Web Site: http://www.technotar.com
TKNO1—(THE)
Sales Range: Less than $1 Million
Refueling Equipment Design & Production
N.A.I.C.S.: 457210

TECHNO-AGRICULTURAL SUPPLYING JOINT STOCK COMPANY
1D Pham Ngu Lao st, Ninh Kieu Dist, Can Tho, Vietnam
Tel.: (84) 2432001155
Web Site:
  https://www.tsccantho.com.vn
Year Founded: 2003
TSC—(HOSE)
Rev.: $19,566,127
Assets: $122,553,026

TECHNOALPIN S.P.A.

Liabilities: $20,114,952
Net Worth: $102,438,073
Earnings: ($461,440)
Fiscal Year-end: 12/31/23
Agricultural Chemical Mfr
N.A.I.C.S.: 325320
Phan Minh Sang *(Vice Chm & Gen Dir)*

Subsidiaries:

Westfood Company (1)
Cai Son Hang Bang Industrial Zone, An Binh Ward Ninh Kieu District, Can Tho, Vietnam
Tel.: (84) 2923893893
Web Site: http://www.westfood.vn
Canned Agricultural Product Whslr
N.A.I.C.S.: 424590
Vu Nguyen *(Sls Dir)*

TECHNOALPIN S.P.A.
Via P Agostini 2, 39100, Bolzano, Italy
Tel.: (39) 0471 550 550   IT
Web Site:
  http://www.technoalpin.com
Year Founded: 1990
Sales Range: $125-149.9 Million
Emp.: 270
Snow-Making Equipment Designer, Mfr & Distr
N.A.I.C.S.: 333415
Walter Rieder *(Mng Dir)*

Subsidiaries:

TechnoAlpin Austria GmbH (1)
Stadlweg 25, 6020, Innsbruck, Austria
Tel.: (43) 512341501
Snow Making Machinery Distr
N.A.I.C.S.: 423740

TechnoAlpin Deutschland GmbH (1)
Unterfeldring 3a, 85256, Vierkirchen, Germany
Tel.: (49) 8139995225
Snow Making Machinery Distr
N.A.I.C.S.: 423740

TechnoAlpin East Europe s.r.o. (1)
Priemyselna 2, 01004, Zilina, Slovakia
Tel.: (421) 417002644
Snow Making Machinery Distr
N.A.I.C.S.: 423740

TechnoAlpin France SAS (1)
3 Chemin du Jubin bat 2, Mini Parc de Dardilly, 69570, Dardilly, France
Tel.: (33) 4 7220 9160
Web Site: http://www.technoalpin.fr
Snow-Making Equipment Designer, Mfr & Distr
N.A.I.C.S.: 333415
Marc Lanaspeze *(Commi Dir)*

Branch (Domestic):

MYNEIGE S.A.S. - Sainte-Luce-sur-Loire (2)
2 Rue Alexandro Volta, 44984, Carquefou, France
Tel.: (33) 2 4018 4600
Web Site: http://www.myneige.com
Sales Range: $25-49.9 Million
Emp.: 35
Snow-Making Equipment Mfr & Distr
N.A.I.C.S.: 333415
Laurent Travers *(Gen Mgr)*

Subsidiary (Non-US):

MYNEIGE S.r.l. (2)
Via dell Industria 4, Erbusco, 25030, Brescia, BS, Italy
Tel.: (39) 0307242285
Web Site: http://www.myneige.it
Snow-Making Equipment Mfr & Distr
N.A.I.C.S.: 333415

TechnoAlpin Nordic AB (1)
Sundgatan 11, 68633, Sunne, Sweden
Tel.: (46) 56510303
Snow Making Machinery Distr
N.A.I.C.S.: 423740

TechnoAlpin Romania Srl (1)

TECHNOALPIN S.P.A.

TechnoAlpin S.p.A.—(Continued)
Calea Fagarasului 8 A, 500053, Brasov, Romania
Tel.: (40) 268411364
Snow Making Machinery Distr
N.A.I.C.S.: 423740

TechnoAlpin Schweiz A.G. (1)
Aschoren, PF 43, 6454, Fluelen, Switzerland
Tel.: (41) 418745000
Snow Making Machinery Distr
N.A.I.C.S.: 423740

TechnoAlpin USA, Inc. (1)
7257 S Revere Pkwy, Centennial, CO 80112
Tel.: (720) 895-2340
Snow-Making Equipment Mfr & Distr
N.A.I.C.S.: 333415

Technoalpin Snow Making Equipment (Sanhe) Co., Ltd. (1)
Yanchang Road 235 Yanjiao Development Zone, 065201, Sanhe, Hebei, China
Tel.: (86) 18680397629
Snow Making Machinery Distr
N.A.I.C.S.: 423740

TECHNOCRAFT INDUSTRIES INDIA LIMITED

A-3 Road No 03, Andheri East, Mumbai, 400093, Maharashtra, India
Tel.: (91) 2240982222
Web Site:
  https://www.technocraftgroup.com
Year Founded: 1972
TIIL—(NSE)
Rev.: $184,594,192
Assets: $242,441,690
Liabilities: $94,419,261
Net Worth: $148,022,429
Earnings: $18,309,018
Emp.: 1,539
Fiscal Year-end: 03/31/21
Drum Closures, Pipes & Tubes Mfr
N.A.I.C.S.: 332322
Ashish Kumar Saraf *(CFO)*

Subsidiaries:

Technocraft (Hungary) KFT (1)
Hunyadi Utca 6, 1191, Budapest, Hungary
Tel.: (36) 12808236
Web Site: http://www.technocraft.hu
Sales Range: $25-49.9 Million
Emp.: 3
Galvanized Steel Tubes Mfr
N.A.I.C.S.: 331210

Technocraft Australia Pty ltd (1)
1/211 Newton Road, Wetherill Park, 2164, NSW, Australia
Tel.: (61) 297565425
Web Site: http://technocraftgroup.com.au
Sales Range: $25-49.9 Million
Emp.: 3
Drum Closures Mfr
N.A.I.C.S.: 322219

Technocraft International Ltd (1)
Unit 2 Hammond Court Hammond Avenue Whitehill Industrial Estate, Stockport, SK4 1PQ, Cheshire, United Kingdom
Tel.: (44) 1614806888
Sales Range: $25-49.9 Million
Emp.: 20
Engineeering Services
N.A.I.C.S.: 541330

Technocraft NZ Limited (1)
59 Lady Ruby Drive, East Tamaki, Auckland, 2013, New Zealand
Tel.: (64) 223747050
Web Site: https://technocraftgroup.co.nz
Software Development Services
N.A.I.C.S.: 541511

Technocraft Trading Spolka z o.o. (1)
Ul Pilsudzkiego 133m, 92-318, Lodz, Poland
Tel.: (48) 601602325
Web Site: https://technocraft.pl
Drum Closure Mfr & Distr
N.A.I.C.S.: 332439

Technosoft Engineering Inc. (1)
200 S Executive Dr Ste 101, Brookfield, WI 53005
Tel.: (919) 337-0866
Digital Engineering & Consulting Services
N.A.I.C.S.: 541330

Technosoft Engineering Projects Limited (1)
A-25 MIDC Road No 3 Andheri East, Mumbai, 400 093, Maharashtra, India
Tel.: (91) 2240982222
Web Site: https://technosofteng.com
Emp.: 800
Digital Engineering & Consulting Services
N.A.I.C.S.: 541330

Technosoft Engineering UK Limited (1)
Manchester Business Park 3000 Aviator Way, Manchester, M22 5TG, United Kingdom
Tel.: (44) 1617910768
Digital Engineering & Consulting Services
N.A.I.C.S.: 541330

Technosoft GmbH (1)
Kaiserstr 61, 44135, Dortmund, Germany
Tel.: (49) 23158699717
Web Site: https://www.technosoft.de
Software Development Services
N.A.I.C.S.: 541511

Technosoft Information Technologies (India) Ltd. (1)
A25 Rd No 03 Marol Industrial Area MIDC Andheri E, Mumbai, 400 093, Maharashtra, India
Tel.: (91) 2266916159
Sales Range: $25-49.9 Million
Emp.: 220
Information & Software Development
N.A.I.C.S.: 541330
Laxmi Kant Ladha *(Mgr-Fin)*

Technosoft Services Inc. (1)
200 S Executive Dr Ste 101, Brookfield, WI 53005
Tel.: (919) 317-0866
Web Site: https://www.technosoftsrv.com
Information Technology Services
N.A.I.C.S.: 541519

TECHNODEX BERHAD

Unit E-07-03 Menara Suezcap 2 KL Gateway No 2 Jalan Kerinchi, 59200, Kuala Lumpur, Malaysia
Tel.: (60) 379320111 MY
Web Site:
  https://www.technodex.com
Year Founded: 2001
TDEX—(KLS)
Rev.: $11,874,797
Assets: $5,942,397
Liabilities: $1,635,766
Net Worth: $4,306,631
Earnings: ($1,677,216)
Fiscal Year-end: 06/30/23
Information Technology Services
N.A.I.C.S.: 541512
Sze Chong Tan *(Mng Dir-Grp)*

Subsidiaries:

Grayscale Technologies Sdn. Bhd. (1)
Unit E-07-03 Menara Suezcap 2 KL Gateway No 2 Jalan Kerinchi, Off Jalan Chan Sow Lin, 59200, Kuala Lumpur, Malaysia
Tel.: (60) 79320111
Web Site: https://grayscale.my
Application Development Services
N.A.I.C.S.: 541511
Daisie Gan *(Mgr-Acct)*

Idealseed Resources Sdn. Bhd. (1)
19-1 Jalan Radin Anum Bandar Baru Sri Petaling, 57000, Kuala Lumpur, Malaysia
Tel.: (60) 3 9056 2206
Web Site: http://idealseed.com
Recruitment Services
N.A.I.C.S.: 561311
Wah Choy Tan *(CEO)*

TECHNOFAB ENGINEERING LIMITED

913 Hemkunt Chambers 89 Nehru Place, New Delhi, 110 019, India
Tel.: (91) 1126411931
Web Site:
  https://www.technofabengineer.com
Rev.: $53,591,205
Assets: $92,368,617
Liabilities: $55,513,678
Net Worth: $36,854,939
Earnings: ($3,678,068)
Emp.: 432
Fiscal Year-end: 03/31/19
Engineering & Construction Services
N.A.I.C.S.: 541330
Vijay Nagarajan *(Dir-Subsidiary)*

TECHNOFIRST SA

Parc de Napollon 48 avenue des Templiers, 13400, Aubagne, France
Tel.: (33) 442187187
Web Site: http://www.technofirst.com
Noise Control Device Mfr
N.A.I.C.S.: 339113
Christian Carme *(Founder)*

TECHNOFLEX CORPORATION

1-5-1 Kuramae, Taito-ku, Tokyo, 111-0051, Japan
Tel.: (81) 358223211
Web Site:
  https://www.technoflex.co.jp
Year Founded: 1977
3449—(TKS)
Rev.: $150,605,780
Assets: $230,077,590
Liabilities: $70,977,990
Net Worth: $159,099,600
Earnings: $6,848,940
Emp.: 368
Fiscal Year-end: 12/31/23
Semiconductor Product Mfr
N.A.I.C.S.: 334413
Gaku Maejima *(Pres)*

Subsidiaries:

Technoflex (Shanghai) Inc. (1)
315 Chunguang Road, Xinzhuang Industrial Park, Shanghai, China
Tel.: (86) 2154427750
Web Site: http://en.tfshanghai.com
Welding Assembly Product Mfr & Distr
N.A.I.C.S.: 333992

TECHNOFLEX SA

ZA de Bassilour, 64210, Bidart, France
Tel.: (33) 5 59 54 66 66
Web Site: http://www.technoflex.net
Year Founded: 1986
Sales Range: $50-74.9 Million
Emp.: 300
Plastics Bag Mfr
N.A.I.C.S.: 326111

TECHNOGYM SPA

Via Calcinaro 2861, 47521, Cesena, FC, Italy
Tel.: (39) 054756047
Web Site:
  https://www.technogym.com
Year Founded: 1983
TGYM—(ITA)
Rev.: $892,031,129
Assets: $903,310,520
Liabilities: $501,818,082
Net Worth: $401,492,439
Earnings: $85,183,795
Emp.: 2,285
Fiscal Year-end: 12/31/23
Fitness Equipment Mfr
N.A.I.C.S.: 339920
Nerio Alessandri *(Co-Founder, Chm & CEO)*

Subsidiaries:

Sidea S.r.l. (1)
Via de Gasperi 90, 47035, Bologna, Gambettola, Italy
Tel.: (39) 0547313298
Web Site: http://www.sideaita.net
Fitness Training Services
N.A.I.C.S.: 812990

Technogym Asia Ltd. (1)
Unit 303-304 3/F NEO 123 Hoi Bun Road, Kwun Tong, Kowloon, China (Hong Kong)
Tel.: (852) 31162622
Web Site: https://www.technogym.com
Fitness Training Services
N.A.I.C.S.: 812990

Technogym France SAS (1)
15 Av de Friedland, Issy les Moulineaux, 75008, Paris, France
Tel.: (33) 145299000
Web Site: https://www.technogym.com
Fitness Training Services
N.A.I.C.S.: 812990

Technogym Germany GmbH (1)
Frankfurter Str 211 Eingang Du-Pont-Strasse, 63263, Neu-Isenburg, Germany
Tel.: (49) 6102822380
Web Site: https://www.technogym.com
Fitness Training Services
N.A.I.C.S.: 812990

Technogym Japan Ltd. (1)
2 Chome-3-12 Seafort Square Center Building 18th floor, Shinagawa City Higashishinagawa, Tokyo, 140-0002, Japan
Tel.: (81) 120576876
Web Site: https://www.technogym.com
Fitness Machine Whslr
N.A.I.C.S.: 423910

Technogym Shanghai Int. Trading Co. Ltd. (1)
4th Floor Building 1 No 881 Wuding Road, Jingan District, Shanghai, 200040, China
Tel.: (86) 2158886355
Web Site: https://www.technogym.com
Fitness Training Services
N.A.I.C.S.: 812990

Technogym ZAO (1)
Vereiskaya street 29 bld 154 BC Vereiskaya Plaza-1 office 42, 121357, Moscow, Russia
Tel.: (7) 4959333834
Web Site: http://www.technogym.ru
Fitness Training Services
N.A.I.C.S.: 812990

Wellness Partners Ltd. (1)
5th Floor-Aldemary House 10/15 Queen Street, London, EC4N 1TX, United Kingdom
Tel.: (44) 7186792613
Web Site:
  http://www.wellnessconsulting.com
Advisory Firm Services
N.A.I.C.S.: 541611

Wellness Partners USA Inc. (1)
705 E Bidwell Ste 2-150, Folsom, CA 95630
Web Site: http://www.wellnesspartners.com
Pharmaceuticals Product Mfr
N.A.I.C.S.: 325412

TECHNOJET CONSULTANTS LIMITED

Neville House J N Heredia Marg Ballard Estate, Mumbai, 400 001, India
Tel.: (91) 2222618071
Web Site: https://www.technojet.in
Year Founded: 1982
509917—(BOM)
Rev.: $4,017
Assets: $84,276
Liabilities: $516
Net Worth: $83,760
Earnings: ($6,007)
Emp.: 1
Fiscal Year-end: 03/31/23
Electronic Equipment Mfr & Distr
N.A.I.C.S.: 334510
Chandukumar Parmar *(CFO & Sec)*

TECHNOLEASING LLP

VP-1 11 Turan ave, Nur-Sultan, 010000, Kazakhstan
Tel.: (7) 172688282
Web Site: http://www.tnl.kz
THLZ—(KAZ)
Rev.: $2,106,523

AND PRIVATE COMPANIES

Assets: $39,792,099
Liabilities: $30,672,775
Net Worth: $9,119,324
Earnings: $1,371,372
Fiscal Year-end: 12/31/19
Commercial Banking Services
N.A.I.C.S.: 522110
Dmitri Kogai (Mng Dir)

TECHNOLOGICAL DEVELOPMENT & AUTOMATION LTD.
Business Park 85 Medinat Hayehudim Street, Herzliya Pituach, 46766, Israel
Tel.: (972) 99602010
Web Site: http://www.tedea.com
TEDE—(TAE)
Rev.: $167,150
Assets: $9,841,138
Liabilities: $4,886,586
Net Worth: $4,954,552
Earnings: ($2,113,828)
Emp.: 57
Fiscal Year-end: 12/31/23
Holding Company
N.A.I.C.S.: 551112

TECHNOLOGIES AND INNOVATIONS CORPORATION SAEDINENIE PLC
27A Hristo Botev Blvd, Central district, 4000, Plovdiv, Bulgaria
Tel.: (359) 32585886
Web Site: https://www.saedinenie.com
Year Founded: 1992
Information Solution Services
N.A.I.C.S.: 519290

TECHNOLOGY & TELECOMMUNICATION ACQUISITION CORPORATION
C3-2-23A Jalan 1/152 Taman OUG Parklane Off Jalan Kelang Lama, 58200, Kuala Lumpur, Malaysia
Tel.: (60) 123348193   Ky
Web Site: https://tete-acquisition.com
Year Founded: 2021
TETE—(NASDAQ)
Rev.: $1,326,997
Assets: $118,543,290
Liabilities: $4,129,848
Net Worth: $114,413,442
Earnings: $826,045
Emp.: 2
Fiscal Year-end: 11/30/22
Investment Services
N.A.I.C.S.: 523999
Tek Che Ng (CEO & Chm)

TECHNOLOGY MINERALS PLC
18 Savile Row, London, W1S 3PW, United Kingdom
Tel.: (44) 2038859209   UK
Web Site: https://www.technologyminerals.uk
Year Founded: 2021
TM1—(LSE)
Rev.: $59,328
Assets: $30,176,723
Liabilities: $2,808,634
Net Worth: $27,368,089
Earnings: ($4,948,245)
Emp.: 5
Fiscal Year-end: 06/30/23
Mineral Exploration Services
N.A.I.C.S.: 213115
Alex Stanbury (CEO)

TECHNOLOGYONE LIMITED
Level 11 TechnologyOne HQ 540 Wickham Street, PO Box 96, Fortitude Valley, 4006, QLD, Australia
Tel.: (61) 731677300   AU
Web Site: https://www.technologyonecorp.com
Year Founded: 1987
TNE—(ASX)
Rev.: $300,635,515
Assets: $433,715,006
Liabilities: $225,278,251
Net Worth: $208,436,755
Earnings: $70,074,246
Emp.: 1,200
Fiscal Year-end: 09/30/23
Software Developer & Publisher
N.A.I.C.S.: 513210
Adrian Di Marco (Founder & Chm)

Subsidiaries:

Technology One Corporation Sdn. Bhd.   (1)
36th Floor Menara Maxis Kuala Lumpur City Centre, Kuala Lumpur, 50088, Malaysia
Tel.: (60) 326150106
Web Site: http://www.technologyonecorp.com
Sales Range: $25-49.9 Million
Emp.: 4
Business Software Solution Services
N.A.I.C.S.: 513210

Technology One Limited   (1)
Level 11 TechnologyOne HQ 540 Wickham Street, PO Box 96, Fortitude Valley, 4006, QLD, Australia
Tel.: (61) 731677300
Web Site: http://www.technologyonecorp.com
Sales Range: $100-124.9 Million
Emp.: 500
Data Processing Services
N.A.I.C.S.: 518210

Technology One New Zealand Ltd.   (1)
Level 14 1-3 Albert Street, Auckland, 1010, New Zealand
Tel.: (64) 99159300
Web Site: http://www.technologyonecorp.com
Sales Range: $25-49.9 Million
Emp.: 25
Business Software Solution Services
N.A.I.C.S.: 541511

TECHNOMECA AEROSPACE SA
Mendelu Kalea 53, Hondarribia, 20280, Manresa, Spain
Tel.: (34) 662313494
Web Site: https://tecnomecagroup.com
Year Founded: 2013
TQT—(MAD)
Sales Range: Less than $1 Million
Automotive Tool & Spare Part Mfr
N.A.I.C.S.: 336390

TECHNOPACK POLYMERS LIMITED
M/s Gokul Industries Rafaleshvar Industrial Estate, Nr Rafaleshvar Rlw Track Morb Jambudiya, Rajkot, 363642, Gujarat, India
Tel.: (91) 9099070066
Web Site: https://www.technopackltd.com
Year Founded: 2010
543656—(BOM)
Rev.: $1,368,918
Assets: $1,264,386
Liabilities: $854,381
Net Worth: $410,005
Earnings: $287,783
Fiscal Year-end: 03/31/22
Packaging Materials Mfr
N.A.I.C.S.: 322220

TECHNOPLUS INDUSTRIES SAS
ZAC de l'Agavon 5 ave Lamartine, BP 113, 13752, Les Pennes-Mirabeau, cedex, France
Tel.: (33) 442106310
Web Site: http://www.technoplus-industries.com
Machinery Mfr
N.A.I.C.S.: 333998

TECHNOPLUS VENTURES LTD.
Three Azrieli Center 132 Menachem Begin St Triangle Tower, Tel Aviv, 67023, Israel
Tel.: (972) 36074200
Web Site: http://www.technoplusvc.com
Year Founded: 1997
TNPV—(TAE)
Rev.: $66,000
Assets: $5,647,000
Liabilities: $373,000
Net Worth: $5,274,000
Earnings: $35,000
Fiscal Year-end: 12/31/23
Miscellaneous Financial Investment Activities
N.A.I.C.S.: 523999
Tomer Cheifetz (CEO)

Subsidiaries:

RapiDx Ltd.   (1)
132 Menachem Begin St Azrieli Triangle Tower, Tel Aviv, Israel
Tel.: (972) 36074205
Web Site: http://www.rapidx.co.il
Blood Testing Device Mfr
N.A.I.C.S.: 339113

TECHNOPOLIS PLC
Elektroniikkatie 8, 90590, Oulu, Finland
Tel.: (358) 46 7120000   FI
Web Site: http://www.technopolis.fi
Year Founded: 1982
Rev.: $215,269,816
Assets: $2,060,067,649
Liabilities: $1,143,844,899
Net Worth: $916,222,750
Earnings: $102,101,993
Emp.: 224
Fiscal Year-end: 12/31/17
Real Estate Services
N.A.I.C.S.: 531390
Kari Kokkonen (Chief Real Estate Officer)

TECHNOPROBE S.P.A.
Via Cavalieri di Vittorio Veneto 2, 23870, Cernusco Lombardone, LC, Italy
Tel.: (39) 02272540135   IT
Web Site: https://www.technoprobe.com
Year Founded: 1995
TPRO—(ITA)
Rev.: $592,412,044
Assets: $935,482,409
Liabilities: $140,128,427
Net Worth: $795,353,982
Earnings: $159,955,752
Emp.: 2,120
Fiscal Year-end: 12/31/22
Semiconductor Devices Mfr
N.A.I.C.S.: 334413
Giuseppe Crippa (Founder)

Subsidiaries:

Harbor Electronics, Inc.   (1)
3021 Kenneth St, Santa Clara, CA 95054
Tel.: (408) 988-6544
Web Site: https://www.harbor-electronics.com
Electric Equipment Mfr
N.A.I.C.S.: 334419

Technoprobe Asia Pte. Ltd.   (1)
9 Raffles Place 26-01 Republic Plaza, Singapore, 048619, Singapore
Tel.: (65) 64558324
Electric Equipment Mfr
N.A.I.C.S.: 334419

Technoprobe France S.A.S.   (1)
Rousset Parc Club 467 avenue Francis Perrin, 13106, Rousset, France
Tel.: (33) 442538545
Electric Equipment Mfr
N.A.I.C.S.: 334419

Technoprobe Germany GmbH   (1)
Werner-von-Siemens-Str 5, 78166, Donaueschingen, Germany
Tel.: (49) 39999251
Electric Equipment Mfr
N.A.I.C.S.: 334419

Technoprobe Korea Co. Ltd.   (1)
302 TECHTREE Building 55 Sinwon-ro, Yeongtong-gu, Suwon, 16677, Gyeonggi-do, Korea (South)
Tel.: (82) 312843636
Electric Equipment Mfr
N.A.I.C.S.: 334419

Technoprobe US Holding LLC   (1)
2526 Qume Dr Unit 27, San Jose, CA 95131
Tel.: (408) 573-9911
Electric Equipment Mfr
N.A.I.C.S.: 334419

Technoprobe Wuxi Co. Ltd.   (1)
No 6 Building Export Processing Zones, Xinwu District, Wuxi, 214028, JianSu, China
Tel.: (86) 51088780697
Electric Equipment Mfr
N.A.I.C.S.: 334419

TECHNOS S.A.
Avenida das Americas n 4200 6 pavimento bloco 05, Rio de Janeiro, 22640102, Brazil
Tel.: (55) 2121318950
Web Site: https://www.grupotechnos.com.br
Year Founded: 1900
TECN3—(BRAZ)
Rev.: $68,271,413
Assets: $132,738,060
Liabilities: $52,435,138
Net Worth: $80,302,922
Earnings: $11,210,091
Fiscal Year-end: 12/31/23
Apparel Store Operator
N.A.I.C.S.: 315990

Subsidiaries:

Technos da Amazonia Industria e Comercio S.A.   (1)
Rua Mogno 600 Distrito Industrial, Manaus, 69075-170, Amazonas, Brazil
Tel.: (55) 9221262903
Watch Mfr & Distr
N.A.I.C.S.: 316990

TECHNOTRANS AG
Robert Linnemann Strasse 17, 48336, Sassenberg, Germany
Tel.: (49) 25833011000   De
Web Site: https://www.technotrans.com
Sales Range: $125-149.9 Million
Emp.: 600
Printing Trades Machinery Mfr
N.A.I.C.S.: 333248
Dirk Engel (Member-Mgmt Bd-Fin)

Subsidiaries:

KLH Kaltetechnik GmbH   (1)
Am Waldrand 10, 18209, Bad Doberan, Germany
Tel.: (49) 38203960
Web Site: http://www.klh-kaeltetechnik.de
Cooling Equipment Mfr
N.A.I.C.S.: 333415

Taicang KLH Cooling Systems Co. Ltd.   (1)
No 8 North Loujiang Road, Taicang, 215400, Jiangsu, China
Tel.: (86) 51253378736
Printing Machinery & Equipment Mfr

TECHNOTRANS AG

Technotrans AG—(Continued)
N.A.I.C.S.: 333248

Technotrans America Inc. (1)
1441 East Business Ctr Dr, Mount Prospect, IL 60090 **(100%)**
Tel.: (847) 227-9200
Web Site: http://www.technotrans.com
Sales Range: $25-49.9 Million
Emp.: 50
Printing Trades Machinery Mfr
N.A.I.C.S.: 333248
Hubert Oberscheidt (Mgr-Svc)

Technotrans America Latina Ltda (1)
Rua Marechal Hastimphilo de Moura, 179
Morumbi, 05641-000, Sao Paulo,
Brazil **(100%)**
Tel.: (55) 1137475050
Web Site: http://www.technotrans.com
Communication Equipment Mfr
N.A.I.C.S.: 334290

Technotrans China Ltd. (1)
Unit 20 15/F Tuen Mun Central Square 22
Hoi Wing Road, 22 Hoi Wing Road, Tuen
Mun, China (Hong Kong) **(100%)**
Tel.: (852) 23702900
Web Site: http://www.technotrans.com
Sales Range: $25-49.9 Million
Emp.: 10
Communication Equipment Mfr
N.A.I.C.S.: 334290
Alan Yau (Gen Mgr)

Technotrans France S.a.r.l. (1)
Zaet Les Haies Rue Albert Einstein, 60740,
Toulon, Cedex, France **(100%)**
Tel.: (33) 344240053
Web Site: http://www.technotrans.com
Sales Range: $25-49.9 Million
Emp.: 17
Communication Equipment Mfr
N.A.I.C.S.: 334290

Technotrans Graphics Limited (1)
Axis 1 Brunel Way Severalls Business Pk,
Colchester, CO4 9QX, United
Kingdom **(100%)**
Tel.: (44) 1206224200
Web Site: http://www.technotrans.co.uk
Sales Range: $25-49.9 Million
Emp.: 20
Communication Equipment Mfr
N.A.I.C.S.: 334290
Peter Benton (Mng Dir)

Technotrans Italia S.r.l. (1)
Via Spallanzani 18, Legnano, Italy **(100%)**
Tel.: (39) 0331455609
Web Site: http://www.technotrans.it
Communication Equipment Mfr
N.A.I.C.S.: 334290

Technotrans Japan K.K. (1)
Technotrans Bldg, 1-4-6 Shin-Yokohama
Kohoku-ku, Yokohama, Japan **(100%)**
Tel.: (81) 454707712
Communication Equipment Mfr
N.A.I.C.S.: 334290

Technotrans Printing Equipment (Beijing) Company Ltd. (1)
Xincheng Industrial Park B1-4 No 9 Kechuang Er Jie, Eastern Area BDA, 100023,
Beijing, China **(100%)**
Tel.: (86) 1058086300
Web Site: http://www.technotrans.de
Communication Equipment Mfr
N.A.I.C.S.: 334290

Technotrans Scandinavia AB (1)
PO Box 1100, Taby, Sweden **(100%)**
Tel.: (46) 854444500
Web Site: http://www.technotrans.se
Communication Equipment Mfr
N.A.I.C.S.: 334290

Technotrans Technologies Pte. Ltd. (1)
66 Kallang Pudding Road 04-03 Hor Kew
Business Centre, Singapore, 349324,
Singapore **(100%)**
Tel.: (65) 65086800
Emp.: 7
Communication Equipment Mfr
N.A.I.C.S.: 334290
Thomas Lengowski (Mng Dir)

Termotek GmbH (1)
Im Rollfeld 6, 76532, Baden-Baden, Germany
Tel.: (49) 722197110
Web Site: http://www.termotek-ag.com
Heating & Cooling Equipment Mfr
N.A.I.C.S.: 333415
Peter Hirsch (Mng Dir)

gds GmbH (1)
Mansfelder Strasse 56, 06108, Halle, Germany
Tel.: (49) 25833013063
Web Site: http://www.gds.eu
Software Development & Consulting Services
N.A.I.C.S.: 541511
Ulrich Pelster (Mng Dir)

gds-Sprachenwelt GmbH (1)
Kaiserstrasse 1, 36088, Hunfeld, Germany
Tel.: (49) 6652911440
Web Site: http://www.gds.eu
Computer Software Consulting Services
N.A.I.C.S.: 541512
Ulrich Pelster (Mng Dir)

technotrans india pvt ltd (1)
24 Eden Plaza Second Floor Mount Poonamallee High Road, Nandambakkam, Chennai, Tamil Nadu, India
Tel.: (91) 4465659349
Printing Machinery & Equipment Mfr
N.A.I.C.S.: 333248
Matthew S. T. Sunil (Gen Mgr)

technotrans middle east FZ-LLC (1)
Circular Building Block D IMPZ Second
Floor Office 208, PO Box 485010, Dubai,
United Arab Emirates
Tel.: (971) 44484225
Printing Machinery & Equipment Mfr
N.A.I.C.S.: 333248

TECHNOVATIVE GROUP, INC.
Unit 701 7/F Tower 2 Silvercord, 30
Canton Rd Tsim Sha Tsui Kowloon,
Hong Kong, China (Hong Kong)
Tel.: (852) 2162 7529 DE
Web Site: http://www.technovative.co
Year Founded: 2010
TEHG—(OTCQX)
Sales Range: Less than $1 Million
Emp.: 25
Application Software Development Services
N.A.I.C.S.: 541511
Nicolas Kuan Liang Lin (Pres, CEO, Treas & Sec)

TECHNOVATOR INTERNATIONAL LIMITED
66 Tannery Lane N0 04-10/10A Sindo
Building, Singapore, 347805, Singapore
Tel.: (65) 68411788
Web Site: https://www.technovator.com.sg
Year Founded: 2005
1206—(HKG)
Rev.: $258,874,647
Assets: $781,454,364
Liabilities: $373,210,281
Net Worth: $408,244,083
Earnings: ($14,077,042)
Emp.: 665
Fiscal Year-end: 12/31/23
Integrated Building Automation & Energy Management Systems
N.A.I.C.S.: 541512
Xiaobo Zhao (CEO)

Subsidiaries:

Tongfang Technovator Int (Beijing) Co., Ltd. (1)
No 1 Wang Zhuang Road A22F Tsinghua
Tongfang Hi-Tech Plaza, Hai Dian District,
Beijing, 100083, China
Tel.: (86) 1082399521
Energy Management Services
N.A.I.C.S.: 541690
Yuan Cao (Mgr-Project)

TECHNVISION VENTURES LIMITED
1486 12-13- 522 Lane No 13 Street
No 14, Tarnaka, Secunderabad,
500017, Telangana, India
Tel.: (91) 4027170822
Web Site: https://www.technvision.com
501421—(BOM)
Rev.: $18,177,663
Assets: $2,270,775
Liabilities: $427,085
Net Worth: $1,843,690
Earnings: $26,126
Emp.: 77
Fiscal Year-end: 03/31/23
Data Management Services
N.A.I.C.S.: 541513
Veena Gundavelli (Mng Dir)

Subsidiaries:

Solix Technologies, Inc. (1)
4701 Patrick Henry Dr Bldg 20, Santa
Clara, CA 95054
Tel.: (408) 654-6400
Web Site: https://www.solix.com
Sales Range: $25-49.9 Million
Emp.: 25
Enterprise Data Management Services
N.A.I.C.S.: 561110
Sai Gundavelli (Founder & CEO)

TECHSHINE ELECTRONICS CO., LTD.
18th Floor Building 1 Qianhai Kexing
Science Park Xixiang Street, Baoan
District, Shenzhen, 518101, Guangdong, China
Tel.: (86) 75527449672
Web Site: https://www.techshine.com.cn
Year Founded: 2005
301379—(SSE)
Rev.: $173,160,936
Assets: $234,518,544
Liabilities: $58,935,708
Net Worth: $175,582,836
Earnings: $16,612,128
Emp.: 1,700
Fiscal Year-end: 12/31/22
Electronic Component Mfr & Distr
N.A.I.C.S.: 334419
Siwei Wang (Chm & Gen Mgr)

TECHSTAR ACQUISITION CORPORATION
Unit No 1506B of Level 15th International Commerce Centre No 1, Austin
Road West, Kowloon, China (Hong Kong)
Tel.: (852) 21878118 Ky
Web Site: https://www.techstaracq.com
Year Founded: 2022
7855—(HKG)
Investment Management Service
N.A.I.C.S.: 523999
Zhengdong Ni (Chm)

TECHSTEP ASA
Brynsalleen 4, 0667, Oslo, Norway
Tel.: (47) 91523337
Web Site: https://www.techstep.io
Year Founded: 1996
TECH—(OSL)
Rev.: $122,217,439
Assets: $122,233,512
Liabilities: $69,442,084
Net Worth: $52,791,428
Earnings: ($6,337,890)
Emp.: 312
Fiscal Year-end: 12/31/22
Software Developer & Marketer
N.A.I.C.S.: 513210
Borge Astrup (CEO)

INTERNATIONAL PUBLIC

Subsidiaries:

Birdstep Technology Ltd (1)
3rd Floor, 52 Burleigh Street, Cambridge,
CB1 1DJ, United Kingdom **(100%)**
Tel.: (44) 1223 461 656
Software Publisher
N.A.I.C.S.: 513210

TECHTRAN OPHTHALMICS PVT LTD.
220 Sadodaya Plaza Central Avenue
Road, Nagpur, 440008, India
Tel.: (91) 71 2273 6311
Ophthalmic Lens Mfr
N.A.I.C.S.: 339115

Subsidiaries:

Techtran Lenses Inc. (1)
601 Heritage Dr Ste 118, Jupiter, FL 33458
Tel.: (561) 623-5490
Ophthalmic Lens Mfr
N.A.I.C.S.: 339115

TECHTRONIC INDUSTRIES CO., LTD.
29/F Tower 2 Kowloon Commerce
Centre, 51 Kwai Cheong Road New
Territories, Kwai Chung, China (Hong
Kong)
Tel.: (852) 24026888
Web Site: https://www.ttigroup.com
Year Founded: 1985
0669—(HKG)
Rev.: $13,253,917,000
Assets: $13,315,598,000
Liabilities: $8,110,117,000
Net Worth: $5,205,481,000
Earnings: $1,077,150,000
Emp.: 44,705
Fiscal Year-end: 12/31/22
Investment Holding Company; Electrical & Electronic Products Mfr
N.A.I.C.S.: 333991
Horst Julius Pudwill (Chm)

Subsidiaries:

Hart Consumer Products, Inc. (1)
100 Innovation Way, Anderson, SC 29621
Web Site: https://www.harttools.com
Outdoor Power Equipment Product Distr
N.A.I.C.S.: 423610

LLC A&M Electroinstrumenti (1)
Tsentralnaya str 20B, 141014, Mytishchi,
Moscow, Russia
Tel.: (7) 4957754606
Power Tool Mfr & Distr
N.A.I.C.S.: 333517

Marco Polo Industries Merchandising Company Limited (1)
29 F Tower 2 KCC 51 kwai chung Road,
Kwai Chung, New Territories, China (Hong Kong)
Tel.: (852) 24026888
Web Site: http://www.ttigroup.com
Electrical & Electronic Components Mfr
N.A.I.C.S.: 334419

Sang Tech Industries Limited (1)
29 F Tower 2 51 Kwai Cheong Road, Tsuen
Wan, New Territories, China (Hong Kong)
Tel.: (852) 24026888
Electronic Products Mfr
N.A.I.C.S.: 334419
Joe Galli (CEO)

Santo Industries Limited (1)
29 F Tower 2 KCC 51 kwai chung Road,
Kwai Chung, New Territories, China (Hong Kong)
Tel.: (852) 24026888
Web Site: http://www.ttigroup.com
Industrial Machinery Mfr
N.A.I.C.S.: 333248

Solar Wide Industrial Limited (1)
18/F CDW Building 388 Castle Peak Road,
Tsuen Wan, New Territories, China (Hong Kong)
Tel.: (852) 24800888
Web Site: http://www.solarwide.com.hk
Electronic Components Mfr

AND PRIVATE COMPANIES — TECHWING INC.

N.A.I.C.S.: 334419

South Asian Pacific Co., Ltd. (1)
Unit D 18/F CDW Building 388 Castle Peak Road, Tsuen Wan, New Territories, China (Hong Kong)
Tel.: (852) 2492 2181
Web Site: http://www.sap.com.hk
Electrical Home Appliances Mfr & Distr
N.A.I.C.S.: 335999

Techtronic Cordless GP (1)
100 Innovation Way, Anderson, SC 29621
Tel.: (864) 226-6511
Outdoor Power Equipment Mfr
N.A.I.C.S.: 333112

Techtronic Industries (Dongguan) Co. Ltd (1)
No 2 Hujing Road, Houjie Town, Dongguan, 523945, Guangdong, China
Tel.: (86) 76982728888
Web Site: https://www.ttigroup.com
Electronic Products Mfr
N.A.I.C.S.: 334419

Techtronic Industries (Suzhou) Co., Ltd. (1)
13/F Block 1 XinTuo Mansion 308 SuYa Road Suzhou Industrial Park, Jiangsu, China
Tel.: (86) 51268181570
Power Tool Mfr & Distr
N.A.I.C.S.: 333517

Techtronic Industries (Taiwan) Co. Ltd (1)
10 f-3 122-19 Tai Chung Kang Road Sector 2, Taichung, 40757, Taiwan
Tel.: (886) 427068052
Electronic Components Mfr
N.A.I.C.S.: 334419

Techtronic Industries (UK) Ltd (1)
Medina House Fieldhouse Lane, Marlow, SL7 1TB, Bucks, United Kingdom (100%)
Tel.: (44) 1628894400
Power Tools Whslr
N.A.I.C.S.: 423710

Techtronic Industries Argentina, S.R.L. (1)
Tres Aarroyos 3762 1 er Piso A CABA, 1407, Buenos Aires, Argentina
Tel.: (54) 1145820145
Power Tool Mfr & Distr
N.A.I.C.S.: 333517

Techtronic Industries Australia Pty. Limited (1)
Tel.: (61) 1300361505
Electronic Products Mfr
N.A.I.C.S.: 334419

Techtronic Industries Central Europe B.E. (1)
Jan Valsterweg 83, 3315 LG, Dordrecht, Netherlands
Tel.: (31) 786524150
Power Tool Mfr & Distr
N.A.I.C.S.: 333517

Techtronic Industries Com Ferram do Brasil Ltda. (1)
Rua Arandu 57 Conj 104, 09861-730, Sao Paulo, Brazil
Tel.: (55) 1123113334
Power Tool Mfr & Distr
N.A.I.C.S.: 333517

Techtronic Industries France SAS (1)
Le Grand Roissy Z A du Gue 35 Rue de Guivry, 77990, Le Mesnil-Amelot, France
Tel.: (33) 160946970
Emp.: 150
Power Equipment Products Whslr
N.A.I.C.S.: 423830

Techtronic Industries Germany Holding GmbH (1)
Max-Eyth-Str 10, Winnenden, 71364, Baden-Wurttemberg, Germany
Tel.: (49) 7195120
Electric Equipment Mfr
N.A.I.C.S.: 336320

Subsidiary (Domestic):

DreBo Werkzeugfabrik GmbH (2)
Ulrichstrasse 22 Max-Eyth-Strasse, 88361, Altshausen, Germany
Tel.: (49) 758429000
Web Site: https://www.drebo.de
Sales Range: $25-49.9 Million
Emp.: 400
Industrial Drilling Equipment Mfr
N.A.I.C.S.: 333517

Subsidiary (US):

DreBo America, Inc. (3)
500 Technology Dr, Coal Center, PA 15423
Tel.: (724) 938-0690
Emp.: 35
Industrial Drilling Equipment Mfr
N.A.I.C.S.: 333248
Wayne Chappell (Gen Mgr)

Subsidiary (Domestic):

Royal Appliance International GmbH (2)
Jagenbergstr 19, 41468, Neuss, Germany
Tel.: (49) 213160900
Web Site: http://www.dirt-devil.de
Vacuum Cleaner Mfr
N.A.I.C.S.: 335210

Subsidiary (Non-US):

Techtronic Industries Central Europe GmbH (2)
Tel.: (49) 21039600
Web Site: https://de.ryobitools.eu
Electronic Product Distr
N.A.I.C.S.: 423690

Techtronic Industries ELC GmbH (2)
Tel.: (49) 7195120
Electronic Products Mfr
N.A.I.C.S.: 334419

Subsidiary (Domestic):

Techtronic Industries GmbH (2)
Otto-Hahn-Str 10, D-71665, Vaihingen an der Enz, Germany (100%)
Tel.: (49) 7195120
Sales Range: $150-199.9 Million
Emp.: 150
Power Tool Mfr
N.A.I.C.S.: 333991

Techtronic Industries N.Z. Limited (1)
Unit C 70 Business Parade South, East Tamaki, Auckland, 2013, New Zealand
Tel.: (64) 800279624
Web Site: https://www.ttigroup.com
Sales Range: $25-49.9 Million
Emp.: 25
Industrial Machinery Mfr
N.A.I.C.S.: 333248

Techtronic Industries Nordic A/S (1)
Stamholmen 147 4, 2650, Hvidovre, Denmark
Tel.: (45) 43 56 55 55
Sales Range: $25-49.9 Million
Emp.: 20
Electrical Appliances Distr
N.A.I.C.S.: 423620

Techtronic Industries North America, Inc. (1)
Tel.: (864) 226-6511
Web Site: http://www.ttigroupna.com
Holding Company; Regional Managing Office
N.A.I.C.S.: 551112

Subsidiary (Domestic):

Homelite Consumer Products, Inc (2)
100 Innovation Way, Anderson, SC 29621
Tel.: (864) 226-6511
Web Site: http://www.homelite.com
Sales Range: $75-99.9 Million
Emp.: 500
Gardening Tools & Equipment Mfr
N.A.I.C.S.: 333111
Lee Sowell (Pres)

Imperial Blades LLC (2)
450 Progress Way, Sun Prairie, WI 53590
Web Site: http://www.imperialblades.com
Electrical & Electronic Product Mfr
N.A.I.C.S.: 333991

Milwaukee Electric Tool Corp. (2)
13135 W Lisbon Rd, Brookfield, WI 53005-2550
Tel.: (262) 781-3600
Web Site: https://www.milwaukeetool.com
Sales Range: $100-124.9 Million
Emp.: 2,000
Portable Electric Power Tools Mfr
N.A.I.C.S.: 333991
Steven P. Richman (Pres)

Subsidiary (Domestic):

Empire Level Manufacturing Corp. (3)
929 Empire Dr, Mukwonago, WI 53149
Tel.: (262) 368-2000
Web Site: http://www.empirelevel.com
Sales Range: $25-49.9 Million
Emp.: 200
Levels, Squares & Tape Measures Mfr
N.A.I.C.S.: 332216

Subsidiary (Non-US):

Milwaukee Electric Tool (Canada) Ltd. (3)
7303 Warden Ave Suite 202, Markham, L3R 5Y6, ON, Canada
Tel.: (416) 439-4181
Web Site: http://www.milwaukeetool.ca
Emp.: 40
Sales & Services Heavy-Duty Electric Tools
N.A.I.C.S.: 811210

Subsidiary (Domestic):

One World Technologies, Inc. (2)
255 Pumpkintown Hwy, Pickens, SC 29671 (100%)
Tel.: (864) 878-6331
Sales Range: $250-299.9 Million
Emp.: 800
Holding Company; Power Tools Mfr & Distr
N.A.I.C.S.: 551112
Austin Knapik (Mgr-Windows Sys)

Subsidiary (Domestic):

OWT Industries, Inc. (3)
225 Pumkintown Hwy, Pickens, SC 29671-0035
Tel.: (864) 878-6331
Sales Range: $50-74.9 Million
Emp.: 200
Power Tools Mfr & Distr
N.A.I.C.S.: 333991

Subsidiary (Domestic):

Royal Appliance Mfg. Co. (2)
8405 IBM Dr, Charlotte, NC 28262
Tel.: (440) 996-2000
Web Site: http://www.ttifloorcare.com
Sales Range: $350-399.9 Million
Emp.: 150
Appliance Mfr
N.A.I.C.S.: 335210

Subsidiary (Domestic):

Oreck Corporation (3)
1400 Salem Rd, Cookeville, TN 38506
Tel.: (931) 646-7876
Web Site: http://www.oreck.com
Sales Range: $350-399.9 Million
Emp.: 645
Holding Company; Vacuum Cleaners, Air Purifiers & Steam Mops Mfr, Distr & Retailer
N.A.I.C.S.: 551112

Subsidiary (Domestic):

Oreck Floor Care Centers, Ltd. (4)
13231 Champion Forest Dr Ste 404, Houston, TX 77069-2649
Tel.: (281) 866-0027
Web Site: http://www.myoreckstore.com
Sales Range: $75-99.9 Million
Emp.: 325
Vacuum Cleaner Retail Stores Operator
N.A.I.C.S.: 449210
Thomas A. Oreck (Pres)

Oreck Manufacturing Company (4)
1400 Salem Rd, Cookeville, TN 38506
Tel.: (931) 646-7876
Web Site: http://www.oreck.com
Sales Range: $25-49.9 Million
Emp.: 250

Vacuum Cleaners, Air Purifiers & Steam Mops Mfr
N.A.I.C.S.: 335210

Subsidiary (Domestic):

Stiletto Tool Company (2)
6061 N Winton Way, Winton, CA 95388
Web Site: http://www.stiletto.com
Cutting Tool Mfr
N.A.I.C.S.: 333515
Mark Martinez (Owner)

Subsidiary (Non-US):

Techtronic Industries Canada, Inc (2)
7303 Warden Avenue Suite 202, Markham, L3R 5Y6, ON, Canada
Tel.: (905) 479-4355
Web Site: http://www.ttigroup.com
Sales Range: $25-49.9 Million
Emp.: 50
Industrial Machinery Mfr
N.A.I.C.S.: 333248

Techtronic Industries do Brasil Ltda (1)
Travessa Claudio Armando No 171 Bloco 2 Galpao 21, Sao Bernardo do Campo, 09861-730, Sao Paulo, Brazil
Tel.: (55) 1123113334
Industrial Machinery Mfr
N.A.I.C.S.: 333248

Techtronic Power Tools Technology Limited (1)
Trident Chambers, Road Town, Tortola, Virgin Islands (British)
Tel.: (284) 494 2434
Power Tool Mfr
N.A.I.C.S.: 333997

Techtronic Trading Limited (1)
29 F Tower 2 KCC 51 kwai chung Road, Kwai Chung, China (Hong Kong)
Tel.: (852) 24026888
Web Site: http://www.ttigroup.com
Electronic Components Mfr
N.A.I.C.S.: 334419

Vax Limited (1)
Pointon Way, Stonebridge Cross Business Park Hampton Lovett, Droitwich, WR9 0LW, Worcestershire, United Kingdom
Tel.: (44) 1905795959
Web Site: https://www.vax.co.uk
Floor Cleaner Products Mfr
N.A.I.C.S.: 333310

TECHTUIT HOLDINGS CO., LTD.
Techtuit Bldg 1-10-10 Kinshi-cho, Sumida-ku, Tokyo, 130 0013, Japan
Tel.: (81) 345822525 JP
Web Site: http://www.techtuit.com
Year Founded: 2008
Holding Company
N.A.I.C.S.: 551112

Subsidiaries:

Techtuit Co., Ltd. (1)
Techtuit Bldg 1-10-10 Kinshi-cho, Sumida-ku, Tokyo, 130 0013, Japan
Tel.: (81) 3 5611 2525
Electronic Parts Mfr & Distr
N.A.I.C.S.: 423620
Yoshikazu Matsumoto (Pres)

TECHWING INC.
37 Dongtan Sandan 6-gil, Dongtan-myeon, Hwaseong, Gyeonggi-do, Korea (South)
Tel.: (82) 313798000 KR
Web Site: https://www.techwing.co.kr
Year Founded: 2002
089030—(KRS)
Rev.: $205,165,667
Assets: $374,489,557
Liabilities: $186,146,889
Net Worth: $188,342,668
Earnings: $25,493,439
Emp.: 219
Fiscal Year-end: 12/31/22

TECHWING INC.

Techwing Inc.—(Continued)

Semiconductor Machinery & Equipment Mfr
N.A.I.C.S.: 333242
Nam Jang *(Co-CEO)*

Subsidiaries:

ENC Technology Co., Ltd. (1)
47 Dongtan Sandan 8-gil Dongtan-myeon, Hwaseong, Gyeonggi, Korea (South)
Tel.: (82) 312121034
Automobile Equipment Mfr
N.A.I.C.S.: 333248

FAS Inc. (1)
129 Gieonpdanji-ro Wongok-myeon, Anseong, Gyeonggi, Korea (South)
Tel.: (82) 313797871
Automotive Machinery & Equipment Mfr
N.A.I.C.S.: 333248

Truetech Co., Ltd. (1)
86-25 3gongdon 6-ro, Seobuk-gu, Cheonan, Chungcheongnam, Korea (South)
Tel.: (82) 416211741
Automobile Equipment Mfr
N.A.I.C.S.: 333248

TECITY GROUP

1 Wallich Street 15-01 Guoco Tower, Singapore, 078881, Singapore
Tel.: (65) 6876 9900
Web Site: http://www.tecity.com.sg
Investment Holding Company
N.A.I.C.S.: 551112
David Goh *(Chief Investment Officer & Chief Strategist)*

Subsidiaries:

The Straits Trading Company Limited (1)
1 Wallich Street 15-01 Guoco Tower, Singapore, 078881, Singapore
Tel.: (65) 64224288
Web Site: https://www.straitstrading.com.sg
Rev.: $372,384,306
Assets: $2,605,126,106
Liabilities: $1,395,203,362
Net Worth: $1,209,922,744
Earnings: $(9,198,667)
Emp.: 127
Fiscal Year-end: 12/31/2023
Tin Smelting & Tin Products Mfr
N.A.I.C.S.: 331410
Gek Khim Chew *(Chm)*

Holding (Non-US):

Malaysia Smelting Corporation Berhad (2)
Lot 6 8 and 9 Jalan Perigi Nanas 6/1, Pulau Indah Industrial Park West Port Port Klang, 42920, Pulau Indah, Selangor, Malaysia **(54.8%)**
Tel.: (60) 331023083
Web Site: https://www.msmelt.com
Rev.: $318,220,317
Assets: $276,371,217
Liabilities: $111,821,799
Net Worth: $164,549,418
Earnings: $21,469,630
Emp.: 1,281
Fiscal Year-end: 12/31/2022
Tin Metal Production & Mining Services
N.A.I.C.S.: 331410
Madzlan Zam *(Sr Gen Mgr-Rahman Hydraulic Tin Sdn Bhd)*

TECK CONSTRUCTION LLP

5197 - 216 Street, Langley, V3A 2N4, BC, Canada
Tel.: (604) 534-7917
Web Site: https://www.teck.ca
Year Founded: 1957
Rev.: $10,031,515
Emp.: 30
Building Construction Services
N.A.I.C.S.: 236220
Al R. Tecklenborg *(Founder)*

TECK GUAN PERDANA BERHAD

Teck Guan Regency 318 Jln St Patrick Off Jln Belunu, 91000, Tawau, Sabah, Malaysia
Tel.: (60) 89779955
Web Site: https://www.teckguan.com
Year Founded: 1994
TECGUAN—(KLS)
Rev.: $124,370,968
Assets: $54,206,002
Liabilities: $34,756,642
Net Worth: $19,449,361
Earnings: $4,883,339
Emp.: 5,000
Fiscal Year-end: 01/31/22
Cocoa Butter & Cocoa Powder Mfr
N.A.I.C.S.: 311351
Vui Vun Tham *(Chm)*

Subsidiaries:

Majulah Koko Tawau Sdn. Bhd. (1)
318 Teck Guan Regency Jalan Belunu off Jalan St Patrick, 91007, Tawau, Sabah, Malaysia
Tel.: (60) 89779955
Cacao Beans Mfr
N.A.I.C.S.: 311351

TECK RESOURCES LIMITED

Ste 3300-550 Burrard Street, Vancouver, V6C 0B3, BC, Canada
Tel.: (604) 699-4000
Web Site: https://www.teck.com
Year Founded: 1906
TECK—(NYSE)
Rev.: $11,088,867,548
Assets: $41,510,674,448
Liabilities: $20,610,918,224
Net Worth: $20,899,756,224
Earnings: $1,704,956,785
Emp.: 12,600
Fiscal Year-end: 12/31/23
Mineral Mining Services
N.A.I.C.S.: 212290
Real Foley *(Sr VP-Mktg & Logistics)*

Subsidiaries:

Canada Tungsten (Cayman) Inc. (1)
Willow House II Fl Cricket Sq, Georgetown, KY1-1103, Cayman Islands
Tel.: (345) 949 7555
Mineral Exploration Services
N.A.I.C.S.: 213115

Subsidiary (Non-US):

Compania Minera Teck Carmen de Andacollo S.A. (2)
Camino a Chepiquilla s/n Coquimbo Region, Andacollo, Chile
Tel.: (56) 51431589
Copper & Gold Mining Services
N.A.I.C.S.: 212230

Elkview Mine Limited Partnership (1)
R R 1 Highway 3, Sparwood, V0B 2G1, BC, Canada
Tel.: (250) 425-8325
Steel Mfrs
N.A.I.C.S.: 331110

Teck American Incorporated (1)
501 N Riverpoint Blvd Ste 300, Spokane, WA 99202 **(100%)**
Tel.: (509) 747-6111
Web Site: http://www.teck.com
Sales Range: $50-74.9 Million
Emp.: 30
Metals Exploration & Processing
N.A.I.C.S.: 212230

Subsidiary (Domestic):

Teck Advanced Materials Incorporated (2)
13670 Danielson St Ste H I, Poway, CA 92064
Tel.: (858) 391-2935
Metal Mining Services
N.A.I.C.S.: 213114

Subsidiary (Non-US):

Teck Alaska Incorporated (2)
(100%)
Web Site: http://www.teck.com

Zinc Mining Services
N.A.I.C.S.: 212230

Teck Australia Pty Ltd. (1)
Level 2 35 Ventnor Avenue, West Perth, 6005, WA, Australia
Tel.: (61) 893214936
Sales Range: $50-74.9 Million
Emp.: 25
Mineral Exploration Services
N.A.I.C.S.: 213115
Ian Sandl *(Gen Mgr-Exploration)*

Teck Base Metals Ltd. (1)
550 Burrard St Suite 3300, Vancouver, V6C 0B3, BC, Canada
Tel.: (604) 699-4000
Metal Mining Services
N.A.I.C.S.: 213114

Teck Coal Limited (1)
Suite 1400 500 Center St S E, Calgary, T2G 1A6, AB, Canada
Tel.: (604) 699-4000
Web Site: http://www.teck.com
Sales Range: $50-74.9 Million
Emp.: 100
Coal Mining
N.A.I.C.S.: 212115

Teck Highland Valley Copper Partnership (1)
Hwy 97C, PO Box 1500, Logan Lake, V0K 1W0, BC, Canada
Tel.: (250) 523-2443
Web Site: http://www.teck.com
Sales Range: $250-299.9 Million
Emp.: 1,100
Copper Mining
N.A.I.C.S.: 212230

Teck Ireland Ltd. (1)
Arklow Business Enterprise Centre Kilbride Industrial Estate, Arklow, Wicklow, Y14 T440, Ireland
Tel.: (353) 40464676
Sales Range: $50-74.9 Million
Emp.: 6
Mineral Exploration Services
N.A.I.C.S.: 213115
Bill Sheppard *(Country Mgr)*

Teck Madencilik Sanayi Ticaret A.S. (1)
Turan Gunes Bulv No 86/4, 06550, Cankaya, Ankara, Turkiye
Tel.: (90) 3124406441
Sales Range: $50-74.9 Million
Emp.: 70
Mineral Exploration Services
N.A.I.C.S.: 213115
Ugur Kiziltepe *(Mgr-Exploration)*

Teck Metals Ltd. (1)
100 Wellington Street West Suite 600, PO Box 125, Toronto, M5K 1H1, ON, Canada
Tel.: (647) 788-3000
Web Site: http://www.teck.com
Sales Range: $25-49.9 Million
Emp.: 40
Metal Products Sales
N.A.I.C.S.: 423510

Unit (Non-US):

Teck Metals Ltd. - Applied Research Technology (2)
Tel.: (250) 364-4432
Smelting & Refining of Zinc, Gold, Lead, Silver, Indium & Germanium
N.A.I.C.S.: 331410

Unit (Domestic):

Teck Metals Ltd. - Trail Operations (2)
25 Aldridge Ave, PO Box 1000, Trail, V1R 4L8, BC, Canada
Tel.: (250) 364-4222
Web Site: http://www.teck.com
Sales Range: $1-4.9 Billion
Earnings: $205,000,000
Zinc & Lead Smelting & Refining Services
N.A.I.C.S.: 331410
Thompson Hickey *(Gen Mgr)*

Teck Namibia Limited (1)
10 Bismarck Street, PO Box 28156, Windhoek, Namibia
Tel.: (264) 61377380

Copper Exploration Services
N.A.I.C.S.: 213114
Nuri Ceyhan *(Mgr-Exploration)*

Teck Peru S.A. (1)
Pasaje Los elfines 159 4to Piso Las Gardenias, Surco, 33, Lima, Peru
Tel.: (51) 16172600
Emp.: 20
Mineral Exploration Services
N.A.I.C.S.: 213115

Teck Resources Chile Limitada (1)
Alonso de Cordova 4580 Piso 10, Las Condes, Santiago, Chile
Tel.: (56) 224645700
Copper Mining Services
N.A.I.C.S.: 212230
David R. Baril *(VP)*

Subsidiary (Domestic):

Compania Minera Quebrada Blanca S.A. (2)
Esmeralda 340 Piso 10, Region de Tarapaca, Iquique, Chile
Tel.: (56) 57528100
Copper Mining Services
N.A.I.C.S.: 212230

TECKENTRUP GMBH & CO. KG

Industriestrasse 50, Gutersloh, 33415, Germany
Tel.: (49) 52465040
Web Site: http://www.teckentrup.biz
Year Founded: 1932
Rev.: $204,347,316
Emp.: 200
Door Mfr
N.A.I.C.S.: 238290
Kai Teckentrup *(Owner & CEO)*

Subsidiaries:

SC Teckentrup Romania SRL (1)
Str Otetelsanu Ion Nr 3A et.1 Ap 2 Interfon 1, 10143, Bucharest, Romania
Tel.: (40) 725354222
Web Site: http://www.ro.teckentrup.biz
Door Distr
N.A.I.C.S.: 423310

Teckentrup B.V. (1)
Elektrostraat 12, 7483 PG, Haaksbergen, Netherlands
Tel.: (31) 535739020
Web Site: http://www.teckentrup.nl
Door Distr
N.A.I.C.S.: 423310

Teckentrup France SAS (1)
Le Valparc Quasar 1 16 rue Frederic Japy, 25200, Montbeliard, France
Tel.: (33) 384565846
Web Site: http://www.teckentrup.fr
Door Distr
N.A.I.C.S.: 423310

Teckentrup GmbH & Co. KG Grosszoberitz Plant (1)
Teckentrupstrasse 1, 6780, Zorbig, Germany
Tel.: (49) 34956650
Door Mfr
N.A.I.C.S.: 332999

Teckentrup Scandinavia AB (1)
Taljstensvagen 2, 443 61, Lerum, Sweden
Tel.: (46) 302609500
Web Site: http://www.dk.teckentrup.biz
Door Distr
N.A.I.C.S.: 423310

Teckentrup Schweiz AG (1)
Otelfingerstr 42, 5430, Wettingen, Switzerland
Tel.: (41) 564370808
Web Site: http://www.teckentrup.ch
Door Distr
N.A.I.C.S.: 423310

Teckentrup Sp. z o.o. (1)
Wieclaw 18, 74-400, Debno, Poland
Tel.: (48) 957600013
Door Mfr
N.A.I.C.S.: 332999

Teckentrup UK Ltd. (1)

AND PRIVATE COMPANIES

Unit 7-9 Gemini Trade Park Europa Boulevard, Westbrook, Warrington, WA5 7YF, United Kingdom
Tel.: (44) 1925924050
Web Site: http://www.teckentrup.co.uk
Door Distr
N.A.I.C.S.: 423310
Nick Morson (Project Mgr-Technical)

TECKWAH INDUSTRIAL CORPORATION LTD
51 Tai Seng Avenue 05-01 Pixel Red, Singapore, 533941, Singapore
Tel.: (65) 68728181
Web Site: http://www.teckwah.com.sg
Rev.: $130,459,169
Assets: $168,079,435
Liabilities: $48,535,776
Net Worth: $119,543,659
Earnings: $8,076,944
Emp.: 1,576
Fiscal Year-end: 12/31/19
Plain Paper Products Mfr
N.A.I.C.S.: 322120
Michelle Swee Oi Lo (Co-Sec)

Subsidiaries:

PT Teckwah Trading Indonesia (1)
Jl Raya Pekapuran No 1 RT 005/RW 002, Kel Curug Kec Cimanggis, Depok, 16453, Jawa Barat, Indonesia
Tel.: (62) 2180451510
Logistic Services
N.A.I.C.S.: 541614

Profoto Digital Services Pte Ltd (1)
Blk 12 Lorong Bakar Batu 07-07/08, Kolam Ayer Industrial Estate, Singapore, 348745, Singapore
Tel.: (65) 62943456
Web Site: http://www.profoto.com.sg
Emp.: 120
Printing Machinery Services
N.A.I.C.S.: 811310
Andrew Kok (Dir-Bus Dev)

Techwave Media Services Pte Ltd (1)
51 Tai Seng Avenue 05-01 Pixel Red, Singapore, 533941, Singapore
Tel.: (65) 68728181
Sales Range: $150-199.9 Million
Emp.: 600
Value Chain Management Services
N.A.I.C.S.: 541611

Subsidiary (Non-US):

Teckwah Packaging Systems (Shanghai) Co Ltd (2)
15 5th Floor Block C No 69 Xi Ya Road Waigaoqiao, Free Trade Zone Pudong, Shanghai, 200131, China
Tel.: (86) 21 5046 1515
Packaging Products Mfr
N.A.I.C.S.: 322120

Teckwah Value Chain (Shanghai) Co., Ltd. (2)
Building D2 No 33 Forward Road, Jiading, Shanghai, 201807, China
Tel.: (86) 2159900909
Web Site: http://www.teckwah.com
Emp.: 100
Value Chain Management Services
N.A.I.C.S.: 541611
Doreen Wang (Gen Mgr)

Teckwah Logistics (India) Private Limited (1)
91-92 Kiran Garden Main Matiyala Road, New Delhi, 110059, India
Tel.: (91) 1125333924
Logistic Services
N.A.I.C.S.: 541614
Ajay Gupta (Mgr-IT)

Subsidiary (Non-US):

Teckwah Value Chain Sdn. Bhd. (2)
11-1 Jalan Suria Puchong 4 Pusat Perniagaan Surai, 47110, Puchong, Selangor, Malaysia
Tel.: (60) 382111131
Logistic Services
N.A.I.C.S.: 541614

Teckwah Logistics Pte Ltd (1)
51 Tai Seng Avenue 05-01 Pixel Red, Singapore, 533941, Singapore
Tel.: (65) 68728181
Web Site: http://www.teckwah.com.sg
Emp.: 600
Logistics Consulting Servies
N.A.I.C.S.: 541614

Subsidiary (Domestic):

JNE Logistics Singapore Pte Ltd (2)
25 Pandan Crescent 05-15 TIC Tech Ctr, Singapore, 128477, Singapore
Tel.: (65) 62820475
Web Site: http://www.jnelogistics.com
Emp.: 40
Logistics Consulting Servies
N.A.I.C.S.: 541614

Subsidiary (Non-US):

Teckwah Trading (Shanghai) Co., Ltd. (2)
Bldg No 5 255 Beihe Rd, Jia Ding, Shanghai, China
Tel.: (86) 2159167580
Sales Range: $25-49.9 Million
Emp.: 25
Logistics Consulting Servies
N.A.I.C.S.: 541614

Teckwah Value Chain Pte Ltd (1)
51- Ave Unit 05-01 Pixel reg, Singapore, 533941, Singapore
Tel.: (65) 68728181
Web Site: http://www.teckwah.com.sg
Emp.: 600
Business Process Outsourcing Services
N.A.I.C.S.: 561439

Subsidiary (Non-US):

PT Teckwah Paper Products Indonesia (2)
Batamindo Industrial Park Jalan Beringin, Lot 268-269 & 318 Mukakuning, Batam, 29433, Riau Islands, Indonesia
Tel.: (62) 770612042
Sales Range: $50-74.9 Million
Emp.: 200
Corrugated Paper Products Mfr & Whslr
N.A.I.C.S.: 322211
Kee Hing Kew (Mgr-Fin)

Subsidiary (Domestic):

Singapore Print Media Hub Pte Ltd (2)
61 Tai Seng Avenue 05-13 UE Print Media Hub, Singapore, 534167, Singapore
Tel.: (65) 6593 9788
Paper Products Mfr
N.A.I.C.S.: 322130

Subsidiary (Non-US):

Teckwah Value Chain (Japan) Co Ltd (2)
3-6-1 Heiwajima Tokyo Danchi Souko A-1 Tou 2nd Fl, Ota-ku, Tokyo, 143-0006, Japan
Tel.: (81) 357678686
Web Site: http://www.teckwahvaluechain.com
Sales Range: $25-49.9 Million
Emp.: 8
Value Chain Management Services
N.A.I.C.S.: 541611

Teckwah Value Chain (Thailand) Co Ltd (2)
10th Floor Unit B Thanapoom Tower 1550 New Petchburi Road, Makasan Rajathevi, Bangkok, 10400, Thailand
Tel.: (66) 2 6526866
Web Site: http://www.teckwah.com.sg
Sales Range: $25-49.9 Million
Emp.: 8
Value Chain Management Services
N.A.I.C.S.: 541611

Teckwah Value Chain Pty Ltd (2)
Unit 3/314 Horsley Rd, Milperra, 2214, NSW, Australia
Tel.: (61) 287238900
Sales Range: $25-49.9 Million
Emp.: 17
Value Chain Management Services
N.A.I.C.S.: 541611

TECMA SOLUTIONS S.P.A.
Via Roberto Bracco 6, Milan, Italy
Tel.: (39) 0266809409
Web Site: https://www.tecmasolutions.com
Year Founded: 2012
TCM—(ITA)
Rev.: $13,558,892
Assets: $10,279,280
Liabilities: $3,741,031
Net Worth: $6,538,249
Earnings: ($8,498,731)
Emp.: 180
Fiscal Year-end: 12/31/23
Architectural Services
N.A.I.C.S.: 541310

TECMAT SERVICE
22 Rue Monseigneur Ancel, 69800, Saint Priest, Rhone, France
Tel.: (33) 472900650
Web Site: http://www.groupehbi.fr
Rev.: $22,100,000
Emp.: 43
Construction Equipment Supplier
N.A.I.C.S.: 423490
Xavier Lucand (Dir)

TECNAU SRL
Via Torino 603 10015, Ivrea, Italy
Tel.: (39) 035996711
Web Site: http://www.tecnau.com
Year Founded: 1988
Digital Printing Services
N.A.I.C.S.: 323120

Subsidiaries:

Tecnau AB (1)
Langgatan 21, S 341 32, Ljungby, Sweden (100%)
Tel.: (46) 37225600
Web Site: http://www.tecnau.com
Sales Range: $50-74.9 Million
Emp.: 225
Automated Paper Handling, Monitoring & Processing Equipment Mfr
N.A.I.C.S.: 333243
AnnaPia Johansson (CFO)

Subsidiary (US):

Tecnau Inc. (2)
4 Suburban Park Dr, Billerica, MA 01821
Tel.: (978) 608-0500
Web Site: http://www.tecnau.com
Sales Range: $25-49.9 Million
Emp.: 175
Paper Idustry Machinery Mfr
N.A.I.C.S.: 333243

Tecnau Ltd. (1)
Room 200 North Bldg 223 XiKang Road, Jing An District, 200040, Shanghai, China
Tel.: (86) 15900710147
Industrial Machinery & Equipment Distr
N.A.I.C.S.: 423830

Tecnau Pte Ltd (1)
Block 829 Jurong West Street 81 03-314, Singapore, 640829, Singapore
Tel.: (65) 67939478
Industrial Machinery & Equipment Distr
N.A.I.C.S.: 423830

TECNICA Y PROYECTOS S.A.
Gomera 9, San Sebastian de los Reyes, 28703, Madrid, Spain
Tel.: (34) 91 722 73 00
Web Site: http://www.typsa.com
Year Founded: 1966
Emp.: 1,800
Engineeering Services
N.A.I.C.S.: 541330
Carlos del Alamo Jimenez (Deputy Chm)

Subsidiaries:

Engecorps Engenharia S.A. (1)
Alameda Tocantins 125 4th floor, Barueri, Brazil
Tel.: (55) 1121355252
Web Site: http://www.engecorps.com

TECNICAS REUNIDAS, S.A.

Engineering Consulting Services
N.A.I.C.S.: 541330

MEXTYPSA (1)
Avenida Homero, 11540, Mexico, Mexico
Tel.: (52) 5555804935
Web Site: http://www.mextypsa.mx
Engineeering Services
N.A.I.C.S.: 541330

SA Agrer NV (1)
Avenue Louise 251 b23, 1050, Brussels, Belgium (100%)
Tel.: (32) 26406310
Web Site: http://www.agrer.com
Sales Range: $25-49.9 Million
Emp.: 25
Engineeering Services
N.A.I.C.S.: 541330
Robert Couturier (Mng Dir)

TECNOFISIL, Consultores de Engenharia, S.A. (1)
Av Luis Biivar n 85 A, 1050-143, Lisbon, Portugal
Tel.: (351) 213504480
Web Site: http://www.tecnofisil.pt
Engineeering Services
N.A.I.C.S.: 541330

TECNICAS REUNIDAS, S.A.
Parque Empresarial Adequa Edificio 6 Avenida de Burgos 89, 28015, Madrid, Spain
Tel.: (34) 915920300
Web Site: https://www.tecnicasreunidas.es
Year Founded: 1959
TRE—(MAD)
Rev.: $4,564,689,260
Assets: $4,968,445,745
Liabilities: $4,610,219,672
Net Worth: $358,226,074
Earnings: $65,934,430
Emp.: 7,984
Fiscal Year-end: 12/31/23
Engineering & Construction Services
N.A.I.C.S.: 237990

Subsidiaries:

Eurocontrol, S.A. (1)
Zurbano 48, 28010, Madrid, Spain
Tel.: (34) 902 01 05 62
Web Site: http://www.eurocontrol.es
Administrative Management Services
N.A.I.C.S.: 541611

Heymo Ingenieria, S. A. (1)
Burgos Avenue No 89 Building 5 1st floor, ADEQUA Business Park, 28050, Madrid, Spain
Tel.: (34) 913822300
Web Site: https://www.heymo.com
Engineering & Consulting Services
N.A.I.C.S.: 541330

Layar Real Reserva, S.A. (1)
Avenida de Burgos 89 Edificio 6, Parque empresarial Adequa, 28050, Madrid, Spain
Tel.: (34) 914460500
Environmental Engineering Services
N.A.I.C.S.: 541330

TR Canada Inc. (1)
Suit 500 - 500 4th Avenue SW, Calgary, T2P 2V6, AB, Canada
Tel.: (403) 234-0051
Web Site: http://www.trcanada.ca
Emp.: 50
Environmental Engineering Services
N.A.I.C.S.: 541330

TR Sagemis International Srl (1)
Via Italia 50, 20900, Monza, Italy
Tel.: (39) 0395167815
Engineering & Construction Services
N.A.I.C.S.: 541330

Tecnicas Reunidas Chile Ltda. (1)
Badajoz N 45 Oficina 1901 Edificio Fundadores, Las Condes, Santiago, Chile
Tel.: (56) 25914500
Environmental Engineering Services
N.A.I.C.S.: 541330
Iglazio Darniude (Gen Mgr)

Tecnicas Reunidas Gulf Ltd. (1)

TECNICAS REUNIDAS, S.A.

Tecnicas Reunidas, S.A.—(Continued)
PO Box 39561, Dhahran, 31942, Saudi Arabia
Tel.: (966) 38692461
Construction Engineering Services
N.A.I.C.S.: 541330
Carlos Nazar (CEO)

Tecnicas Reunidas Mexico Ingenieria y Construccion de R.L. de C.V. (1)
Polanco Chapultepec, Miguel Hidalgo, 11560, Mexico, Mexico
Tel.: (52) 96892504
Engineering & Construction Services
N.A.I.C.S.: 541330

Tecnicas Reunidas Oman LLC (1)
Safe Way Building Building n 68 Way n Dohah-Al Abad Street, Al Khuwair, 3305, Muscat, Oman
Tel.: (968) 24604420
Environmental Engineering Services
N.A.I.C.S.: 541330

Tecnicas Reunidas Peru Ingenieria y Construccion, S.A.C. (1)
Jorge Chavez 184-Oficina 403, Miraflores, Lima, Peru
Tel.: (51) 7066601
Engineering & Construction Services
N.A.I.C.S.: 541330

Tecnicas Reunidas Tec Ltda. (1)
Edificio el Cubo II 2 Piso Avenida las Ramblas, Zona Empresarial Equipetrol Norte, Santa Cruz, Bolivia
Tel.: (591) 33111730
Environmental Engineering Services
N.A.I.C.S.: 541330
Jesus Bengoechea Fernandez-Castano (CFO)

Tecnicas Reunidas de Construcao Unip. LDA (1)
Edificio Zils-s 512/6, Monte Feio-Sines, Sines, 7520-064, Portugal
Tel.: (351) 269 634 282
Construction Engineering Services
N.A.I.C.S.: 541330

Tecnicas Reunidas, S.A. - Madrid Plant (1)
C/ Maria de Portugal 9-11, 28050, Madrid, Spain
Tel.: (34) 911581000
Engineering & Construction Services
N.A.I.C.S.: 541330

Tecnicas Reunidas, S.A. - Woodlands Branch (1)
1790 Hughes Landing Blv Ste 390, The Woodlands, TX 77380
Tel.: (832) 823-7800
Power Plant Construction Services
N.A.I.C.S.: 541330

TECNISA S.A.
Brigadeiro Faria Lima Avenue 3144 - 2nd and 3rd floor, Sao Paulo, 01452-000, Brazil
Tel.: (55) 1137081000
Web Site: https://www.tecnisa.com.br
Year Founded: 1977
TCSA3—(BRAZ)
Rev.: $78,139,466
Assets: $272,986,175
Liabilities: $177,257,820
Net Worth: $95,728,354
Earnings: ($9,879,516)
Emp.: 3,476
Fiscal Year-end: 12/31/23
Real Estate Development Services
N.A.I.C.S.: 531390
Joseph Meyer Nigri (Deputy CEO & Member-Exec Bd)

TECNISCO LTD.
2-2-15 Minami Shinagawa, Shinagawa-ku, Tokyo, 140-0004, Japan
Tel.: (81) 334584561
Web Site: http://www.tecnisco.co.jp
Year Founded: 1970
Sales Range: $50-74.9 Million
Emp.: 320
Electronic Components Mfr
N.A.I.C.S.: 334419
Keizo Sekiya (Chm & CEO)

TECNO FAST SA
La Montana 692 Lampa, Santiago, Chile
Tel.: (56) 934695135
Web Site: http://tecnofast.cl
Year Founded: 1995
Modular Space Design Mfr & Sales
N.A.I.C.S.: 532490
Christian Goldberg Valenzuela (Pres)

Subsidiaries:

Triumph Modular, Inc. (1)
194 Ayer Rd, Littleton, MA 01460-1103
Web Site: http://www.triumphmodular.com
Commercial & Institutional Building Construction
N.A.I.C.S.: 236220
Cliff Cort (Pres)

TECNOCAP S.P.A.
Via Starza, Cava de Tirreni, 84013, Italy
Tel.: (39) 08 944 1522
Web Site: https://www.tecnocapclosures.com
Year Founded: 1993
Sales Range: $150-199.9 Million
Emp.: 700
Metal Cap & Closure Mfr
N.A.I.C.S.: 332119
Michelangelo Morlicchio (Founder & Mng Dir)

Subsidiaries:

Tecnocap Eurl (1)
Moulin de Laborie, 24140, Saint-Jean-d'Estissac, France
Tel.: (33) 553823433
Metal Cap & Closure Distr
N.A.I.C.S.: 423840

Tecnocap GmbH (1)
Bodensee str 19, 81241, Munich, Germany
Tel.: (49) 896092053
Metal Cap & Closure Distr
N.A.I.C.S.: 423840
Raik Trobner (Area Mgr-Sls)

Tecnocap LLC (1)
1701 Wheeling Ave, Glen Dale, WV 26038
Tel.: (304) 845-3402
Web Site: http://www.penn-wheeling.com
Sales Range: $50-74.9 Million
Emp.: 110
Metal Cap & Closure Mfr
N.A.I.C.S.: 332119
Lou S. Comadena (Pres)

Tecnocap UA (1)
Str Vokzalna 18, Zhovkva, 80356, Lviv, Ukraine
Tel.: (380) 325261939
Metal Cap & Closure Distr
N.A.I.C.S.: 423840

Tecnocap s.r.o. (1)
Strizovice 67, Strmilov, Jindrichuv Hradec, 378 53, Czech Republic
Tel.: (420) 384373111
Web Site: http://www.tecnocapclosures.com
Food Products Mfr
N.A.I.C.S.: 311919

Tecnocap-Met S.l. (1)
Calle B- Nave 27 Pol Ind San Jorge, Las Torres de Cotillas, 30565, Murcia, Spain
Tel.: (34) 968389448
Metal Cap & Closure Distr
N.A.I.C.S.: 423840

TECNOGLASS INC.
Avenida Circunvalar a 100 mts de la Via 40, Barrio Las Flores, Barranquilla, Colombia
Tel.: (57) 53734000 Ky
Web Site: https://www.tecnoglass.com
Year Founded: 2011

TGLS—(NYSE)
Rev.: $833,265,000
Assets: $962,717,000
Liabilities: $414,697,000
Net Worth: $548,020,000
Earnings: $182,882,000
Emp.: 8,531
Fiscal Year-end: 12/31/23
Hi-Spec, Architectural Glass & Windows Mfr
N.A.I.C.S.: 327211
Jose M. Daes (CEO)

Subsidiaries:

C.I. Energia Solar S.A. (1)
Avenida Circunvalar a 100 mts de la via 40, Barrio Las Flores, Barranquilla, Colombia
Tel.: (57) 5 3664600
Web Site: http://www.energiasolarsa.com
Windows & Doors Mfr
N.A.I.C.S.: 332321

TECNOLAMA S.A.
Ctra Constanti Km 3, 43204, Reus, Spain
Tel.: (34) 977 774 065
Web Site: http://www.fermator.com
Year Founded: 1977
Sales Range: $25-49.9 Million
Emp.: 200
Automatic Elevator Door Mfr
N.A.I.C.S.: 333921
Josep Vila Gomis (CEO)

Subsidiaries:

Doors Movement Technology S.L. (1)
Poligon Industrial Sort dels Capellans, Parcel la 19, 43730, Falset, Tarragona, Spain
Tel.: (34) 977 831 901
Web Site: http://www.fermator.com
Emp.: 14
Elevator Doors Mfr
N.A.I.C.S.: 333921
David Blasco Mercade (CEO)

Enginova Sp. z o.o. (1)
ul Wschodnia 11, 99 300, Kutno, Poland (100%)
Tel.: (48) 24 357 54 00
Web Site: http://www.fermator.com
Emp.: 4
Elevator Doors Mfr
N.A.I.C.S.: 333921
Eduardo Gomis Edea (Mng Dir)

Etablessements Henri Peignen S.A. (1)
3 Rue de la Borne Blanche - ZAC Parisud VI, 77380, Combs-la-Ville, France (100%)
Tel.: (33) 160 566 100
Web Site: http://www.fermator.com
Sales Range: $25-49.9 Million
Emp.: 90
Development & Production of Elevator Door Mfr
N.A.I.C.S.: 333921

Fermator Nordic AB (1)
Reprovagen 7, 183 77, Taby, Sweden
Tel.: (46) 858627200
Web Site: http://www.fermatornordic.se
Automatic Door Mfr
N.A.I.C.S.: 332321

Kiefer A.E. (1)
Kilkis Industrial Area, Stavroxori, 61100, Kilkis, Greece
Tel.: (30) 23410 75 730
Web Site: http://www.fermator.com
Elevator Doors Mfr
N.A.I.C.S.: 333921

Ningbo Arttec Co. Ltd. (1)
Ningbo European Industrial Park First Seashore Road, Hangzhou Bay New Zone, Cixi, 315336, Zhejiang, China
Tel.: (86) 574 63079260
Web Site: http://www.fermator.com
Emp.: 88
Elevator Doors Mfr
N.A.I.C.S.: 333921

Tecnidoors S.p.A. (1)
Via M Ferrari 5 / 7, 28012, Cressa, Novara, Italy
Tel.: (39) 0322 86 26 98
Web Site: http://www.fermator.com
Elevator Doors Mfr
N.A.I.C.S.: 333921
Verruto Roberto (Gen Mgr)

Tecno Doors Pvt. Ltd. (1)
Plot No. L-1 SIPCOT Ind Park Sriperumbudur Mambakkam & Pondur 'A', Kanchipuram Dist, Sriperumbudur, Tamil Nadu, India
Tel.: (91) 44 6713 9541
Web Site: http://www.fermator.com
Elevator Doors Mfr
N.A.I.C.S.: 333921

Tecnoamerica Ind. e Comercio Ltda. (1)
Av Joao Oswaldo Cardoso 1200, Taubate, 12042 050, SP, Brazil
Tel.: (55) 12 3627 8700
Web Site: http://www.fermator.com
Elevator Doors Mfr
N.A.I.C.S.: 333921

Tecnolama, S.A. (1)
Akasya Kent Kule A Blok Kat 30 No 190, 34660, Istanbul, Turkiye
Tel.: (90) 2165041230
Automatic Door Mfr
N.A.I.C.S.: 332321

TECNOLINES OU
Lootsa tn 8a, Lasnamae District, 15176, Tallinn, Estonia
Tel.: (372) 5186237 EE
Power & Communication Networks Design, Construction & Maintenance Services
N.A.I.C.S.: 237130

Subsidiaries:

Eltel Networks AS (1)
Tuisu 19, 11314, Tallinn, Estonia
Tel.: (372) 6063100
Web Site: http://www.eltelnetworks.com
Electrical & Telecommunications Network Maintenance & Transmission Services
N.A.I.C.S.: 237130

TECNOMAGNETE SPA
Via Nerviano 31, 20020, Lainate, Italy
Tel.: (39) 02 937591
Web Site: http://www.tecnomagnete.com
Year Founded: 1974
Sales Range: $25-49.9 Million
Emp.: 200
Electro Magnetic Technology Mfr
N.A.I.C.S.: 333248
Nico Marchiante (Mgr-Mktg)

Subsidiaries:

Tecmag Japan Co. (1)
1F Saito bdg 2-34-6 Nihonbashi Hamacho, Chuo-ku, Tokyo, 103-0007, Japan
Tel.: (81) 356457991
Electro Magnetic System Mfr
N.A.I.C.S.: 327110

Tecnomagnete GmbH (1)
Ohmstrasse 4, 63225, Langen, Germany
Tel.: (49) 6103750730
Electro Magnetic System Mfr
N.A.I.C.S.: 327110

Tecnomagnete SARL (1)
52 avenue Saint-Exupery, 01200, Bellegarde-sur-Valserine, France
Tel.: (33) 450560600
Electro Magnetic System Mfr
N.A.I.C.S.: 327110

Tecnomagnete, Inc. (1)
6655 Allar Dr, Sterling Heights, MI 48312
Tel.: (586) 276-6001
Web Site: http://www.tecnomagnete.com
Sales Range: $25-49.9 Million
Emp.: 11
Electro Magnetic Technology Mfr
N.A.I.C.S.: 423830
Pete Moorhead (Mgr-Sls)

TECNON ELECTRONICS CO., LTD.
Wuzhai Park Jiaojiang Road, Taiwanese Investment Zone Jiaomei Town, Zhangzhou, 363107, Fujian, China
Tel.: (86) 4008885806
Web Site: https://www.tecnon.net
Year Founded: 2002
300650—(SSE)
Rev.: $454,243,603
Assets: $297,297,112
Liabilities: $137,874,106
Net Worth: $159,423,007
Earnings: $7,660,631
Fiscal Year-end: 12/31/22
Lighting Equipment Mfr & Distr
N.A.I.C.S.: 335139

Subsidiaries:

Guangdong Tecnon KeYi Lighting Technology Co., Ltd. (1)
Room 206 building 15 No 644 Shibei industrial road Dashi Street, Innovation Industry Park Panyu District, Guangzhou, China
Tel.: (86) 13318863330
Lighting Fixture Mfr & Distr
N.A.I.C.S.: 335132

Re-sense Lighting Technology (Shanghai) Co., Ltd. (1)
Room 301-302 building B3 suning Tianyu International Plaza No 99, Danba Road Putuo district, Shanghai, China
Tel.: (86) 13717959088
Lighting Fixture Mfr & Distr
N.A.I.C.S.: 335132

Shanghai Tnhg Lighting Technology Co., Ltd. (1)
Room 301-302 building B3 suning Tianyu International Plaza No 99, Danba Road Putuo district, Shanghai, China
Tel.: (86) 2162252310
Lighting Fixture Mfr & Distr
N.A.I.C.S.: 335132

Shenzhen Tecnon EXCO-Vision Technology Co., Ltd. (1)
3rd Floor Building 1 CIMC Zhoushi Road Shiyan Street, Chuanggu Industrial Park Baoan District, Shenzhen, China
Tel.: (86) 18675593055
Lighting Fixture Mfr & Distr
N.A.I.C.S.: 335132

Shenzhen Tecnon Lighting Technology Co., Ltd. (1)
Building 1 CIMC Zhoushi Road Shiyan Street, Chuanggu Industrial Park Baoan District, Shenzhen, China
Tel.: (86) 13502835562
Lighting Fixture Mfr & Distr
N.A.I.C.S.: 335132

Shiyuan (Xiamen) Lighting Technology Co., Ltd. (1)
Room 705 Building 1 Golden Bay Wealth Center No 999 Anling Road, Huli District, Xiamen, China
Tel.: (86) 13599690143
Lighting Fixture Mfr & Distr
N.A.I.C.S.: 335132

TECNON (Xiamen) Lighting Appliance Sales Service Co., Ltd. (1)
Unit 811 34 Pingshan South Lane, Haicang District, Xiamen, China
Tel.: (86) 13385923888
Lighting Fixture Mfr & Distr
N.A.I.C.S.: 335132

Tecnon (Guangdong) Lighting Technology Co., Ltd. (1)
2505 zhongying bulding Poly Clover Plaza No 9 Huaqiang Road, Tianhe District, Guangzhou, China
Tel.: (86) 2037887581
Lighting Fixture Mfr & Distr
N.A.I.C.S.: 335132

Tecnon Smart Display Technology (Shenzhen) Co., Ltd. (1)
Floor 1 Floor 2 Building A Floor 1 Building C CIMC Zhoushi Road, Chuanggu Industrial Park Shiyan Street Baoan District, Shenzhen, China
Tel.: (86) 13570856793
Lighting Fixture Mfr & Distr
N.A.I.C.S.: 335132

TECNOS DATA SCIENCE ENGINEERING, INC.
3-20-2 Nishishinjuku, Shinjuku-Ku, Tokyo, 163-1427, Japan
Tel.: (81) 363833261
Web Site: https://www.tdse.jp
Year Founded: 2013
7046—(TKS)
Sales Range: $10-24.9 Million
Software Development Services
N.A.I.C.S.: 541511
Naohiko Shirotani *(Chm)*

TECNOS JAPAN INC.
Tokyo Opera City Tower 14th Floor Nishi Shinjuku 3-20-2, Shinjuku-ku, Tokyo, 163-1414, Japan
Tel.: (81) 333741212
Web Site: https://www.tecnos.co.jp
Year Founded: 1994
3666—(TKS)
Rev.: $83,545,747
Assets: $65,424,359
Liabilities: $17,179,562
Net Worth: $48,244,797
Earnings: $9,166,616
Emp.: 864
Fiscal Year-end: 03/31/24
Computer Consulting Services
N.A.I.C.S.: 541519
Takashi Yoshioka *(Pres)*

Subsidiaries:

Brainsellers.com Corp. (1)
8F Hulic Kudan Building 1-13-5 Kudankita, Chiyoda-ku, Tokyo, 102-0073, Japan
Tel.: (81) 332340671
Web Site: https://www.brainsellers.com
Business Software Development Services
N.A.I.C.S.: 541511

Dainihon Jochugiku Co., Ltd. (1)
1-4-11 Tosabori, Nishi-ku, Osaka, 550-0001, Japan
Tel.: (81) 664410451
Web Site: https://www.kincho.co.jp
Emp.: 493
Household Insecticides Mfr & Distr
N.A.I.C.S.: 325320

Eneos Nuc Corporation (1)
10 F RiverK Building 12-1 Ekimae-honcho, Kawasaki-ku, Kawasaki, 210-0007, kanagawa-ken, Japan
Tel.: (81) 442211610
Web Site: https://www.eneos-nuc.co.jp
Emp.: 392
Polyethylene Product Mfr & Distr
N.A.I.C.S.: 325211
Tsutomu Iwasaki *(Pres)*

Isehan Co., Ltd. (1)
6-11 Yonbancho, Chiyoda-ku, Tokyo, 102-8370, Japan
Tel.: (81) 332623111
Web Site: https://www.isehan.co.jp
Emp.: 340
Cosmetics Product Mfr & Distr
N.A.I.C.S.: 325620

Okinawa Tecnos Co. (1)
1-3-1 Kumoji Kumoji Central Building 7F, Naha, 900-0015, Japan
Tel.: (81) 988607837
Application Software Development Services
N.A.I.C.S.: 541511

Tecnos Global Company Of America, Inc. (1)
1525 McCarthy Blvd Ste 228, Milpitas, CA 95035
Tel.: (408) 906-0382
Information Technology Services
N.A.I.C.S.: 541512

Subsidiary (Domestic):

Lirik, Inc. (2)
1525 McCarthy Blvd Ste 228, Milpitas, CA 95035 (100%)
Tel.: (408) 906-0382
Web Site: https://lirik.io
Information Technology Consulting Services
N.A.I.C.S.: 541512

TECNOSOLO ENGENHARIA SA
R Conego Felipe 219, 22713010, Rio de Janeiro, Brazil
Tel.: (55) 21 3513 9906
Web Site: http://tecnosolo.com.br
Year Founded: 1957
TCNO3—(BRAZ)
Emp.: 616
Civil Engineering Services
N.A.I.C.S.: 541330

TECNOTREE CORPORATION
Tekniikantie 14, 02150, Espoo, Finland
Tel.: (358) 9804781
Web Site: https://www.tecnotree.com
Year Founded: 1978
TEM1V—(HEL)
Rev.: $78,878,801
Assets: $97,538,223
Liabilities: $14,424,451
Net Worth: $83,113,773
Earnings: $22,443,630
Emp.: 750
Fiscal Year-end: 12/31/21
Value-Added Service Systems for Telecommunications
N.A.I.C.S.: 517112
Padma Ravichander *(CEO)*

Subsidiaries:

Tecnomen GmbH (1)
Am Lachengraben 7, D-63303, Dreieich, Germany (100%)
Tel.: (49) 610350850
Value-Added Service Systems for Telecommunications Providers
N.A.I.C.S.: 517112

Tecnomen Russia (1)
FRCC Pokrovski bulvar 4/17 korp 4B, 101000, Moscow, Russia
Tel.: (7) 4956259047
Value-Added Service Systems for Telecommunications Providers
N.A.I.C.S.: 517112

Tecnotree (M) Sdn Bhd (1)
8 Avenue Business Centre A-3-9 Jalan 8/1 Seksyen 8, 46050, Petaling Jaya, Selangor, Malaysia (100%)
Tel.: (60) 12 296 2930
Web Site: https://www.tecnotree.com
Telecommunications Value-Added Service Systems
N.A.I.C.S.: 334220

Tecnotree B.V. (1)
Zandrak 101, NL-2924 BC, Krimpen aan de Ijssel, Netherlands
Tel.: (31) 180580465
Web Site: http://www.tecnotree.com
Sales Range: $100-124.9 Million
Emp.: 400
Value-Added Telecommunications Service Systems
N.A.I.C.S.: 517112

Tecnotree Convergence Private Limited (1)
6th Floor No 184 Aveda Meta Building Old Madras Road Indiranagara, Bagmane Tech Park C V Raman Nagar Byrasandra, Bengaluru, 560038, India
Tel.: (91) 8040140600
Telecommunication Services[b]
N.A.I.C.S.: 517810

Tecnotree Latin America (1)
Ave Eng Carlos Berrini 1500 cj 72, Brooklin Novo, Sao Paulo, 04571-000, Brazil (100%)
Tel.: (55) 1155059774
Web Site: http://www.tecnotree.com
Sales Range: $25-49.9 Million
Emp.: 80
Value-Added Service Systems for Telecommunications
N.A.I.C.S.: 517112

Tecnotree Ltd. (1)
Shannon Industrial Estate, Shannon, Clare, Ireland
Tel.: (353) 61 702 200
Web Site: http://www.tecnotree.com
Sales Range: $25-49.9 Million
Emp.: 61
Telecommunication Services[b]
N.A.I.C.S.: 517810

Tecnotree MEA (1)
Unit 901 Swiss Tower Jumerah Lake Towers, PO Box 500815, Alpha Building, Dubai, 309114, United Arab Emirates
Tel.: (971) 44331580
Web Site: http://www.tecnotree.com
Sales Range: $25-49.9 Million
Emp.: 12
Value-Added Service Systems for Telecommunications
N.A.I.C.S.: 517112

Tecnotree Sistemas de Telecommunicacao Ltda (1)
Rua Vitorino de Morais 139 Sala Ricardo Boechat Chacara Santo Antonio, Sao Paulo, CEP 04714-020, Brazil
Tel.: (55) 11992120677
Sales Range: $25-49.9 Million
Telecommunication Services[b]
N.A.I.C.S.: 517810

Tecnotree Spain S.L. (1)
Calle Real 6-1, Colmenar Viejo, 28770, Madrid, Spain
Tel.: (34) 918486208
Web Site: http://www.tecnotree.com
Value-Added Service Systems for Telecommunications
N.A.I.C.S.: 517112

TECO 2030 ASA
Lysaker Torg 45, 1366, Lysaker, Norway
Tel.: (47) 67200300
Web Site: https://teco2030.no
Year Founded: 2019
TE9—(DEU)
Rev.: $1,134,309
Assets: $32,158,690
Liabilities: $22,947,461
Net Worth: $9,211,229
Earnings: ($8,399,477)
Emp.: 40
Fiscal Year-end: 12/31/22
Engineeering Services
N.A.I.C.S.: 541330
Pal Christian Johnsen *(CFO)*

Subsidiaries:

TECO 2030 Pte. Ltd. (1)
8 Boon Lay Way 07-01 Tradehub 21, Singapore, 609964, Singapore
Tel.: (65) 84816132
Electronic Appliance Mfr & Distr
N.A.I.C.S.: 335210

TECO ELECTRIC & MACHINERY CO., LTD.
5F No 19-9 San Chong Road Nan-Kang, Taipei, 11501, Taiwan
Tel.: (886) 226553333
Web Site: https://www.teco.com.tw
Year Founded: 1956
1504—(TAI)
Rev.: $1,942,302,193
Assets: $4,163,438,477
Liabilities: $1,336,571,126
Net Worth: $2,826,867,351
Earnings: $207,071,250
Emp.: 13,139
Fiscal Year-end: 12/31/23
Electric & Motor Machinery Mfr
N.A.I.C.S.: 333310
Sophia Chwen-Jy Chiu *(Chm)*

Subsidiaries:

Ejoy Australia Pty. Ltd. (1)
Shop 37 342 McCullough St SunnyPark Shopping Centre, Sunnybank, Brisbane, 4109, QLD, Australia
Tel.: (61) 73 345 5668

TECO ELECTRIC & MACHINERY CO., LTD.

Teco Electric & Machinery Co., Ltd.—(Continued)
Web Site: https://www.ejoy.com.au
Home Appliance Distr
N.A.I.C.S.: 449210

Eurasia Food Service Co., Ltd. (1)
Unit 39 Paices Hill, Youngs Industrial Estate
Aldermaston, Reading, RG7 4PW, Berkshire, United Kingdom
Tel.: (44) 1189811117
Web Site: https://www.eurasiafoods.co.uk
Restaurant Operators
N.A.I.C.S.: 722513
Mohammed Abul (Founder)

Fujian Teco Precision Co., Ltd. (1)
Xiayang Jiazhao Saiqi Development Zone, Zhanggang Village, Ningde, Fujian, China
Tel.: (86) 593 633 0300
Motor Mfr & Distr
N.A.I.C.S.: 336110

Information Technology Total Services Co., Ltd. (1)
B1 No 96 Section 1 Jianguo North Road, Taipei, Taiwan
Tel.: (886) 225048125
Web Site: https://www.itts.com.tw
Information Technology Services
N.A.I.C.S.: 541512

Jiangxi Teco Electric & Machinery Co., Ltd. (1)
189 Dongyuan Rd Hi-Tech Zone, Nanchang, Jiangxi, China
Tel.: (86) 798 819 5999
Motor Mfr & Distr
N.A.I.C.S.: 336110

Motovario Gear Solution Private Ltd. (1)
B2-12/15 Budge Budge Trunk Road, Mahestala, Kolkata, 700 143, West Bengal, India
Tel.: (91) 332 950 0524
Motor Mfr & Distr
N.A.I.C.S.: 336110

Motovario International Trading Co. Ltd. (1)
No 1018 Xikang Road Floor 11 room 1110, Putuo District, Shanghai, 200060, China
Tel.: (86) 215 760 9755
Motor Mfr & Distr
N.A.I.C.S.: 336110

Motovario S.P.A. (1)
Via Quattro Passi 1/3, 41043, Formigine, MO, Italy
Tel.: (39) 059579700
Web Site: http://www.motovario.it
Emp.: 600
Gear Reducer, Motors & Power-Transmission Products Mfr
N.A.I.C.S.: 333612

Subsidiary (US):

Motovario Corporation (2)
1440 Bluegrass Lakes Pkwy, Alpharetta, GA 30004
Tel.: (770) 752-0911
Web Site: http://www.motovario.com
Gear Reducer, Motors & Power-Transmission Products Mfr & Distr
N.A.I.C.S.: 333612
James Y. Suh (CEO, CFO & Sec)

P.T Teco Multiguna Electro (1)
Jl Mayor Oking Km 2 7, Gunung Putri Citeureup, 16961, Bogor, Indonesia
Tel.: (62) 21 875 3401
Motor Mfr & Distr
N.A.I.C.S.: 336110

Qingdao Teco Precision Mechatronics Co., Ltd. (1)
No 666 Beijing Road, Qingdao Lingang Economic Development Zone, Jiaonan, 266431, Shandong, China
Tel.: (86) 5328 905 8888
Motor Mfr & Distr
N.A.I.C.S.: 336110

Shanghai Teco Electric & Machinery Co., Ltd. (1)
Room 325 3rd Floor No 6 Alley 1279 West Zhongshan Road, Shanghai, China
Tel.: (86) 215 116 8255

Motor Mfr & Distr
N.A.I.C.S.: 336110

Tai-An Technology (Wuxi) Co., Ltd. (1)
29 Gaolang East Road, New District, Wuxi, 214028, Jiangsu, China
Tel.: (86) 5108 522 7555
Web Site: https://www.taian-technology.com
Electrical Appliance Mfr & Distr
N.A.I.C.S.: 335999

Taian (Subic) Electric Co., Inc. (1)
SBGP1 Argonaut Highway Corner Braveheart Street, Subic Bay Freeport Zone, Subic, 2222, Zambales, Philippines
Tel.: (63) 472521665
Web Site: https://www.taiansubic.com
Motor Mfr & Distr
N.A.I.C.S.: 336110

Taian-Jaya Electric Sdn. Bhd. (1)
No 7861 7863 Jalan Teluk Batu 1 Batu 4 1/2 Jalan Kebun Seksyen 36, 40470, Shah Alam, Selangor, Malaysia
Tel.: (60) 351611129
Web Site: https://www.taianjaya.com
Electrical Product Mfr & Distr
N.A.I.C.S.: 335999

Tecnos International Consultant Co., Ltd. (1)
6th Floor No 125 Songjiang Road, Taipei, Taiwan
Tel.: (886) 225612571
Web Site: https://www.tecnos.com.tw
Staffing Services
N.A.I.C.S.: 561320

Teco (New Zealand) Limited (1)
Unit 3 477 Great South Road, Penrose, New Zealand
Tel.: (64) 9 526 8480
Electric Motor Mfr & Distr
N.A.I.C.S.: 335312

Teco (Thai) Co. (1)
128/1 Soi Watsrivareenoi Moo 7 Bangna-Trad Rd Km 18, Bangchalong, Bang Phli, 10540, Samut Prakan, Thailand
Tel.: (66) 233 713 1120
Motor Mfr & Distr
N.A.I.C.S.: 336110

Teco (Vietnam) Electric & Machinery Company Ltd. (1)
Lot A 7B, My Phuoc 3 Industrial Zone Thoi Hoa Ward, Ben Cat, Binh Duong, Vietnam
Tel.: (84) 90 337 7844
Motor Mfr & Distr
N.A.I.C.S.: 336110

Teco Electric Europe Limited (1)
7 Dakota Avenue, Salford, M50 2PU, United Kingdom
Tel.: (44) 161 877 8025
Motor Mfr & Distr
N.A.I.C.S.: 336110

Teco Electro Devices Co., Ltd. (1)
11-1 An-Tung Rd, Chung-Li Industrial District, Taoyuan, 320, Taiwan
Tel.: (886) 34525031
Web Site: https://www.tedmotors.com
Motor Mfr & Distr
N.A.I.C.S.: 336110

Teco Elektrik Turkey A.S. (1)
Yesilkoy Mah Ataturk Cad IDTM Is Bloklari A3 Blok 10/2 D 307-314, Bakirkoy, 34149, Istanbul, Turkey
Tel.: (90) 212 465 4590
Web Site: https://www.tecoturkey.com
Motor Mfr & Distr
N.A.I.C.S.: 336110

Teco Smart Technologies Co., Ltd. (1)
5F No 19-8 Sanchong Rd, Nangang Dist, Taipei, 115, Taiwan
Tel.: (886) 226550676
Web Site: https://www.tecosmart.com
Card Mfr
N.A.I.C.S.: 326199
Eric Kao (Chm)

Teco Technology & Marketing Center Co., Ltd. (1)
29th Floor Hamamatsucho Building 1-1-1, Shibaura Minato-ku, Tokyo, 105-0023, Japan

Tel.: (81) 36 809 3883
Investment Services
N.A.I.C.S.: 523999

Teco Technology (Vietnam) Co., Ltd. (1)
136-138 No 7A, Binh Tri Dong B Ward Binh Tan District, Ho Chi Minh City, Vietnam
Tel.: (84) 283 751 9149
Web Site: https://en.teco.com.vn
Motor Mfr & Distr
N.A.I.C.S.: 336110

Teco Westinghouse Motor Company (1)
5100 N IH-35, Round Rock, TX 78681
Tel.: (512) 255-4141
Web Site: http://www.tecowestinghouse.com
Sales Range: $125-149.9 Million
Emp.: 500
Mfr of Motor Generator Sets
N.A.I.C.S.: 335312

Wuhan Tecom Co., Ltd. (1)
9th Floor Gaoke Building Wuhan East Lake Development Zone Garden Road, Wuhan, China
Tel.: (86) 278 761 7326
Telecommunications Equipment Mfr
N.A.I.C.S.: 334210

Wuxi Teco Electric & Machinery Co., Ltd. (1)
No 9 Changjiang S Rd, Wuxi, 214028, JiangSu, China
Tel.: (86) 510 534 2005
Motor Mfr & Distr
N.A.I.C.S.: 336110

Wuxi Teco Precision Industry Co., Ltd. (1)
No 17 Changjiang East Road New District, Wuxi, 214028, JiangSu, China
Tel.: (86) 5108 899 0311
Motor Mfr & Distr
N.A.I.C.S.: 336110

Yatec Engineering (VN) Company Limited (1)
4th Floor No 136-138 Road 7A, Binh Tri Dong B Ward Binh Tan District, Ho Chi Minh City, Vietnam
Tel.: (84) 283 620 9851
Electric Appliance Development & Maintenance Services
N.A.I.C.S.: 811412

Yatec Engineering Corporation (1)
2F No 19-8 Sanchong Rd, Nangang Dist, Taipei, 115601, Taiwan
Tel.: (886) 226551333
Web Site: https://www.yatec.com.tw
Electric Appliance Maintenance Services
N.A.I.C.S.: 811210

TECO GROUP AS

Lysaker Torg 12, 1327, Lysaker, Norway
Tel.: (47) 6720 0300 NO
Web Site: http://www.tecomaritimegroup.no
Holding Company
N.A.I.C.S.: 551112
Henrik Badin (CEO)

Subsidiaries:

TECO Maritime ASA (1)
Lysaker Torg 8, 1366, Lysaker, Norway
Tel.: (47) 67200300
Web Site: http://www.tecomaritime.com
Sales Range: $25-49.9 Million
Emp.: 71
Voyage Repair & Maintenance Services to the Maritime Industry
N.A.I.C.S.: 336611

Subsidiary (Domestic):

TECO Coating Services AS (2)
Lysaker Torg 8, No-1366, Lysaker, Norway (100%)
Tel.: (47) 67200300
Web Site: http://www.tecomaritime.nl
Marine Coating Services
N.A.I.C.S.: 325510

TECO Electronics AS (2)

INTERNATIONAL PUBLIC

Tormod Gjesclansveg, 3908, Porsgrunn, Norway (100%)
Tel.: (47) 35 56 03 00
Web Site: http://www.tecomaritime.no
Sales Range: $25-49.9 Million
Emp.: 17
Marine Electronic Products Sales & Services
N.A.I.C.S.: 423690

TECO Maritime AS (2)
Tollbodalmenningen 1B, 5004, Bergen, Norway
Tel.: (47) 55212150
Web Site: http://www.teco.no
Sales Range: $25-49.9 Million
Emp.: 8
Tank Cleaning Services
N.A.I.C.S.: 562998

TECO Maritime Holding AS (2)
Lysaker Torg 8, 1366, Lysaker, Norway (100%)
Tel.: (47) 67200300
Web Site: http://www.teco.no
Sales Range: $25-49.9 Million
Emp.: 20
Holding Company
N.A.I.C.S.: 551112

Subsidiary (Non-US):

TECO Maritime Benelux B.V. (3)
Puntweg 3, Spijkenisse, 3208 LD, Netherlands (100%)
Tel.: (31) 181600780
Web Site: http://www.teco.no
Sales Range: $25-49.9 Million
Emp.: 4
Marine Electronic Products Mfr
N.A.I.C.S.: 335910
Gerrit Kempers (Gen Mgr)

TECO Maritime Far East Pte Ltd. (3)
8 Boon Lay Way 07-01 Trade Hub21, Singapore, 609964, Singapore (100%)
Tel.: (65) 67777052
Web Site: http://www.teco.no
Sales Range: $25-49.9 Million
Emp.: 6
Ship Repair & Maintenance Services
N.A.I.C.S.: 336611
Tore Enger (Pres)

TECO Maritime Houston, Inc. (1)
5750 N Sam Houston Pkwy E Ste 816, Houston, TX 77032
Tel.: (832) 622-2255
Ship Building & Repair Services
N.A.I.C.S.: 336611
Ashley Stephens (Mgr-Ops)

Teco Maritime Poland Sp. z o.o. (1)
ul Szkolna 10/9, 81-363, Gdynia, Poland
Tel.: (48) 512 313 936
Ship Building & Repair Services
N.A.I.C.S.: 336611

TECOFI SAS

83 Rue Marcel Merieux, 69690, Chassieu, Rhone, France
Tel.: (33) 472790579
Web Site: http://www.tecofi.fr
Year Founded: 1985
Emp.: 200
N.A.I.C.S.: 423720
Jean-Claude Renard (Pres)

TECOM CO., LTD.

23 R&D Rd II, Hsinchu Science-Based Industrial Park, Hsin-chu, 300, Taiwan
Tel.: (886) 35775141
Web Site: https://www.tecom.com.tw
Year Founded: 1980
2321—(TAI)
Rev.: $26,293,599
Assets: $45,790,704
Liabilities: $30,595,048
Net Worth: $15,195,657
Earnings: ($660,290)
Fiscal Year-end: 12/31/23
Wireless Communication Services
N.A.I.C.S.: 517112
Chao-Kai Liu (Chm)

AND PRIVATE COMPANIES — TEE INTERNATIONAL LIMITED

Subsidiaries:

Baycom Opto-Electronics Technology Co., Ltd. (1)
23 R and D Road 2 Hsinchu Science Park, Hsin-chu, 300, Taiwan
Tel.: (886) 35786178
Web Site: http://www.baycom.com.tw
Sales Range: $50-74.9 Million
Emp.: 70
Optical Telecom Products Mfr
N.A.I.C.S.: 334220

TECON BIOLOGY CO., LTD.
Tian Kang Enterprise Building High-Tech Zone, No 528 Changchun South Road, Urumqi, 830011, Xinjiang, China
Tel.: (86) 9916679236
Web Site: https://www.tcsw.com.cn
Year Founded: 1993
002100—(SSE)
Rev.: $2,349,117,707
Assets: $2,718,283,684
Liabilities: $1,361,321,784
Net Worth: $1,356,961,900
Earnings: $42,337,437
Emp.: 2,393
Fiscal Year-end: 12/31/22
Animal Feed Mfr
N.A.I.C.S.: 311119

TECPRO SYSTEMS LIMITED
Tecpro House Plot No 78 Sector-34 NH-8, Gurgaon, 122 001, Haryana, India
Tel.: (91) 124 4880 100
Web Site: http://www.tecprosystems.com
Sales Range: $125-149.9 Million
Emp.: 1,540
Bulk Material Handling Machinery Mfr
N.A.I.C.S.: 333922
Pankaj Tandon (Sec & Compliance Officer)

TECSIS GMBH
Carl-Legien-Strasse 40 - 44, 63073, Offenbach, Germany
Tel.: (49) 6958060
Web Site: http://www.tecsis.de
Year Founded: 2001
Sales Range: $10-24.9 Million
Emp.: 189
Sensor Mfr
N.A.I.C.S.: 334513
Reinhol Ost (Mng Dir)

Subsidiaries:

tecsis (Shanghai) Industrial Measurement Technology Co., Ltd. (1)
German Center Room 710 Tower 1 88 Ke Yuan Road, Shanghai, 201203, China
Tel.: (86) 2128986343
Electronic Components Distr
N.A.I.C.S.: 423690

tecsis (Shenzhen) Sensors Co., Ltd. (1)
HaiNengDaScience and Technology Park No 3 BaoLongSi Road, Longgang District, Shenzhen, 518172, China
Tel.: (86) 75525576988
Electronic Components Distr
N.A.I.C.S.: 423690

tecsis Far East Pte. Ltd. (1)
51 Goldhill Plaza 21-01, Singapore, 308900, Singapore
Tel.: (65) 63526310
Electronic Components Distr
N.A.I.C.S.: 423690

tecsis Instruments (India) Pvt. Ltd. (1)
209 Plot 12-13-97 Tara Tycoon Opposite Aradhana Theatre, Tarnaka, 500017, Secunderabad, India
Tel.: (91) 4027006201
Electronic Components Distr
N.A.I.C.S.: 423690

tecsis LP (1)
771-F Dearborn Park Ln, Worthington, OH 43085
Tel.: (614) 430-0683
Web Site: http://www.tecsis.us
Electronic Components Mfr
N.A.I.C.S.: 334419

TECSTAR TECHNOLOGY CO., LTD.
326 No 32 Ln 863 Gaoshi Rd, Yangmei, Taoyuan, Taiwan
Tel.: (886) 34962286
Web Site: https://www.tecstar.com.tw
3117—(TPE)
Rev.: $16,245,219
Assets: $27,679,661
Liabilities: $20,509,664
Net Worth: $7,169,997
Earnings: ($7,469,014)
Fiscal Year-end: 12/31/19
Electronic Equipment Distr
N.A.I.C.S.: 423690
Lucky Hsueh (Pres)

TECSYS, INC.
1 Place Alexis Nihon Suite 800, Montreal, H3Z 3B8, QC, Canada
Tel.: (514) 866-0001
Web Site: https://infohub.tecsys.com
TCS—(TSX)
Rev.: $107,328,816
Assets: $98,445,244
Liabilities: $44,715,907
Net Worth: $53,729,337
Earnings: $3,503,050
Emp.: 719
Fiscal Year-end: 04/30/22
Developer, Marketer & Seller of Wide-Chain Management Software
N.A.I.C.S.: 334118
Peter Brereton (Pres & CEO)

Subsidiaries:

TECSYS US Inc. (1)
Ste 330 1515 E Woodfield Rd, Schaumburg, IL 60173-5445 (100%)
Tel.: (847) 969-8800
Web Site: http://www.tecsys.com
Sales Range: $25-49.9 Million
Emp.: 10
Developer, Marketer & Seller of Wide-Chain Management Software
N.A.I.C.S.: 513210

Tecsys A/S (1)
Station Park 25, 2600, Glostrup, Denmark
Tel.: (45) 43432929
Web Site: https://tecsys.dk
Emp.: 700
Logistics Consulting Services
N.A.I.C.S.: 541614

TECT HOLDINGS LIMITED
The Kollective 145 17th Avenue, Tauranga, New Zealand
Tel.: (64) 075785094
Web Site: https://www.tect.org.nz
Emp.: 100
Holding Company; Investment Services
N.A.I.C.S.: 551112

TECTONA LTD
Raul Whallenberg 20, Tel Aviv, Israel
Tel.: (972) 733976815
Web Site: https://tectona.io
Year Founded: 1981
TECT—(TAE)
Rev.: $4,043,000
Assets: $12,502,000
Liabilities: $1,239,000
Net Worth: $11,263,000
Earnings: $699,000
Emp.: 25
Fiscal Year-end: 12/31/23
Custom Computer Programming Services
N.A.I.C.S.: 541511

TECTONIC GOLD PLC
Level 15 50 Pitt Street, Sydney, 2000, NSW, Australia
Tel.: (61) 292417665
Web Site: https://www.tectonicgold.com
Year Founded: 2004
TTAU—(AQSE)
Assets: $4,667,552
Liabilities: $677,378
Net Worth: $3,990,174
Earnings: ($661,848)
Fiscal Year-end: 06/30/23
Gold Exploration Services
N.A.I.C.S.: 212220
Anne Adaley (CFO)

TECTONIC METALS, INC.
312-744 West Hastings Street, Vancouver, V6C 1A5, BC, Canada
Web Site: https://www.tectonicmetals.com
Year Founded: 2017
TECT—(OTCIQ)
Assets: $3,248,854
Liabilities: $239,098
Net Worth: $3,009,756
Earnings: ($4,210,541)
Fiscal Year-end: 12/31/20
Metal Exploration Services
N.A.I.C.S.: 213115
Tony Reda (Co-Founder, Pres & CEO)

TED'S CAMERA STORES (VIC) PTY LTD
387 City Rd, South Melbourne, Melbourne, 3205, VIC, Australia
Tel.: (61) 396000711
Web Site: http://www.teds.com.au
Sales Range: $25-49.9 Million
Emp.: 200
Camera & Photographic Supplies Retailer
N.A.I.C.S.: 449210

TEDERIC MACHINERY CO., LTD.
No 245 North Wenze Road, Jianggan District, Hangzhou, 311224, Zhejiang, China
Tel.: (86) 57186733387   CN
Web Site: https://www.tedericglobal.com
Year Founded: 2003
603289—(SHG)
Rev.: $168,161,764
Assets: $289,338,617
Liabilities: $85,409,979
Net Worth: $203,928,638
Earnings: $21,787,994
Emp.: 1,000
Fiscal Year-end: 12/31/21
Injection Molding Machinery Mfr & Distr
N.A.I.C.S.: 333248
Jianguo Zheng (Chm & Gen Mgr)

TEE HONG KONG LIMITED
Room 1511 15/F Olympia Plaza 255 Kings Road, North Point, Hong Kong, China (Hong Kong)
Tel.: (852) 25668178
Engineeering Services
N.A.I.C.S.: 541330

TEE INTERNATIONAL LIMITED
TEE Building 25 Bukit Batok Street 22, Singapore, 659591, Singapore
Tel.: (65) 65611066
Web Site: http://www.teeintl.com
M1Z—(SES)
Rev.: $21,602,075
Assets: $35,486,476
Liabilities: $138,349,759
Net Worth: ($102,863,283)
Earnings: ($190,441)
Emp.: 198
Fiscal Year-end: 09/30/23
Engineering & Real Estate Services
N.A.I.C.S.: 541330
Boon Kin Phua (Mng Dir)

Subsidiaries:

Amcorp Global Limited (1)
11 Sam Leong Road 03-06, Singapore, 207903, Singapore
Tel.: (65) 63516628
Web Site: https://www.amcorpglobal.com
Rev.: $62,658,233
Assets: $142,155,931
Liabilities: $82,523,018
Net Worth: $59,632,913
Earnings: $3,067,586
Emp.: 22
Fiscal Year-end: 03/31/2023
Property Developer
N.A.I.C.S.: 237210
Cher Chew Phua (CEO)

Development 83 Pte. Ltd. (1)
Block 2024 Bukit Batok Street 23 03-26, Singapore, 659529, Singapore
Tel.: (65) 65689914
Web Site: http://www.teeintl.com
Sales Range: $50-74.9 Million
Emp.: 15
Property Development Services
N.A.I.C.S.: 531210
Jonathan Phuan (Exec Dir)

Oscar Estate Management Co., Ltd. (1)
121 Soi Kheharomklao 1/2, Kwaeng Klong Song Ton Nun Khet Latkrabang, Bangkok, 10520, Thailand
Tel.: (66) 254308445
Web Site: https://www.oem.co.th
Real Estate Manangement Services
N.A.I.C.S.: 531210

PBT Engineering Pte Ltd (1)
25 Bukit Batok Street 22 Tee Building, Singapore, 659591, Singapore
Tel.: (65) 65611066
Web Site: http://www.teeintl.com
Facilities Management Services
N.A.I.C.S.: 561210

PBT Engineering Sdn Bhd (1)
Unit No 1 2nd Floor Blk A Hassanin Complex Lot 4879 Spg 42 Jalan Muara, Kg Delima Satu, BB4713, Bandar Seri Begawan, Brunei Darussalam
Tel.: (673) 233 7093
Construction Engineering Services
N.A.I.C.S.: 541330

Security Pro-Telco Pte Ltd. (1)
Block 2 Bukit Batok Street 24, #09-13 Skytech Building, Singapore, 659480, Singapore
Tel.: (65) 6665 0606
Sales Range: $25-49.9 Million
Emp.: 20
Security Consulting Services
N.A.I.C.S.: 561621

TEE Development Pte Ltd (1)
25 Bukit Batok Street 22, PO Box 659591, Singapore, Singapore
Tel.: (65) 65611066
Emp.: 13
Civil Engineering Services
N.A.I.C.S.: 541330

TEE E&C (Malaysia) Sdn. Bhd. (1)
Lot 1 39 First Floor Kompleks Wilayah No 2 Jalan Munshi Abdullah, 50100, Kuala Lumpur, Malaysia
Tel.: (60) 326936991
Mechanical Engineering Services
N.A.I.C.S.: 541330

TEE Management Pte Ltd (1)
Block 2024 Bukit Batok Street 23 03-48, Singapore, 659529, Singapore
Tel.: (65) 611066
Web Site: http://www.teeintl.com
Sales Range: $75-99.9 Million
Emp.: 250
Real Estate Manangement Services
N.A.I.C.S.: 531311

TEE Property Pte. Ltd. (1)

TEE INTERNATIONAL LIMITED

TEE International Limited—(Continued)
Block 2024 Bukit Batok Street 23 03-48, Singapore, 659529, Singapore
Tel.: (65) 68991428
Sales Range: $25-49.9 Million
Emp.: 30
Real Estate Manangement Services
N.A.I.C.S.: 531210
Jonathan Phua *(CEO & Exec Dir)*

TEE Realty Pte Ltd **(1)**
Block 2024 Bukit Batok Street 23 03-48, Singapore, 659529, Singapore
Tel.: (65) 65611066
Web Site: http://www.teeintl.com
Emp.: 100
Real Estate Development & Management Services
N.A.I.C.S.: 531210

Trans Equatorial Engineering Pte Ltd **(1)**
25 Bukit Batok Street 32, Singapore, 659591, Singapore
Tel.: (65) 65611066
Sales Range: $75-99.9 Million
Emp.: 300
Electrical Engineering Services
N.A.I.C.S.: 541330
Loh Chooi Leng *(Mgr-HR)*

Workotel Limited **(1)**
17-19 Main South Road, Riccarton, 8042, Christchurch, New Zealand
Tel.: (64) 33485690
Web Site: http://www.workotelnz.co.nz
Hotel Services
N.A.I.C.S.: 721110

TEEJAY LANKA PLC
Tel.: (94) 364279500
Web Site: https://www.teejay.com
Year Founded: 2000
TJL—(COL)
Rev.: $279,741,440
Assets: $199,920,832
Liabilities: $93,255,434
Net Worth: $106,665,397
Earnings: $7,079,428
Emp.: 3,195
Fiscal Year-end: 03/31/23
Weft Knit Mfr
N.A.I.C.S.: 313240
Salman Nishtar *(CFO)*

Subsidiaries:

Ocean Mauritius Limited **(1)**
56 Nalletamby Avenue, Phoenix, Mauritius
Tel.: (230) 6977985
Web Site: https://www.oceanmauritius.com
Business Services
N.A.I.C.S.: 561499

Teejay India (Private) Limited **(1)**
Plot No 15 BIAC SEZ Pudimadaka Road, Atchuthapuram, Visakhapatnam, 531011, Andhra Pradesh, India
Tel.: (91) 8924237010
Textile Products Mfr
N.A.I.C.S.: 314999
Krishna Diwakar *(Mgr-IT)*

Teejay Lanka Prints (Private) Limited **(1)**
Block D3, Seethawaka Export Processing Zone Avissawella, Colombo, Sri Lanka
Tel.: (94) 364279500
Textile Products Mfr
N.A.I.C.S.: 314999
Kavinda Abeyrathna *(Sr Engr-Sys)*

TEEKANNE GMBH
Kevelaerer Str 21 - 23, 40549, Dusseldorf, Germany
Tel.: (49) 21150850
Web Site: http://www.teekanne.com
Year Founded: 1882
Sales Range: $50-74.9 Million
Emp.: 600
Tea Bags & Other Tea Product Mfr
N.A.I.C.S.: 311920

Subsidiaries:

Redco Foods, Inc. **(1)**
1 Hansen, Little Falls, NY 13365
Tel.: (315) 823-1300
Web Site: http://www.redcofoods.com
Sales Range: $25-49.9 Million
Emp.: 45
Mfr of Teas & Desserts
N.A.I.C.S.: 311920
Gordon Boggis *(CEO)*

TEEKAY CORPORATION
Fourth Floor Belvedere Building 69 Pitts Bay Road, Hamilton, HM 08, Bermuda
Tel.: (441) 2982530 **BS**
Web Site: https://www.teekay.com
Year Founded: 1973
TK—(NYSE)
Rev.: $1,190,184,000
Assets: $2,164,846,000
Liabilities: $795,240,000
Net Worth: $1,369,606,000
Earnings: $78,407,000
Emp.: 2,470
Fiscal Year-end: 12/31/22
International Crude Oil & Petroleum Product Transportation
N.A.I.C.S.: 483111
Arthur Bensler *(Gen Counsel, Sec & Exec VP)*

Subsidiaries:

TEEKAY NAVION OFFSHORE LOADING PTE LTD. **(1)**
8 Shenton Way 41-01 AXA Tower, Singapore, 68811, Singapore
Tel.: (65) 65596800
Marine Shipping Services
N.A.I.C.S.: 488510

Teekay Netherlands European Holdings B.V. **(1)**
Unit 2 02 De Geelvinck Singel 540, 1017 AZ, Amsterdam, Netherlands
Tel.: (31) 205141010
Web Site: http://www.teekay.com
Sales Range: $50-74.9 Million
Emp.: 3
Oil & Gas Storage Vessel Mfr
N.A.I.C.S.: 213112

Teekay Petrojarl Producao Petroliferado Brasil Ltda. **(1)**
Estr Sao Joao e Imboassica s/n 1000 Sala 201 Edificio G1, PO Box 120824, Macae, 27925 540, Rio de Janeiro, Brazil
Tel.: (55) 2221236100
Web Site: http://www.teekay.com
Oil Exploration Services
N.A.I.C.S.: 213112

Teekay Shipping (Australia) Pty. Ltd. **(1)**
1753-1765 Botany Rd Bayview Tower Level 6, Banksmeadow, 2019, NSW, Australia **(100%)**
Tel.: (61) 293161000
Web Site: http://www.teekay.com
Sales Range: $25-49.9 Million
Emp.: 50
International Crude Oil & Petroleum Product Transportation
N.A.I.C.S.: 483111

Teekay Shipping (Canada) Ltd. **(1)**
Suite 2100 Bentall 5 550 Burrard Street, Vancouver, V6C 2K2, BC, Canada **(100%)**
Tel.: (604) 683-3529
Web Site: http://www.teekay.com
Sales Range: $50-74.9 Million
Emp.: 240
International Crude Oil & Petroleum Product Transportation
N.A.I.C.S.: 483111

Teekay Shipping (Glasgow) Ltd. **(1)**
144 Elliot Street, Glasgow, G3 8EX, United Kingdom **(100%)**
Tel.: (44) 1412229000
Sales Range: $50-74.9 Million
Emp.: 130
International Crude Oil & Petroleum Product Transportation
N.A.I.C.S.: 483111

Teekay Shipping (India) Pvt. Ltd. **(1)**
Metro House 4th Floor Mahatma Ghandi Road, Mumbai, 400 020, India
Tel.: (91) 2267468800
Sales Range: $25-49.9 Million
Emp.: 2
Marine Transporting Services
N.A.I.C.S.: 488320

Teekay Shipping (Japan) Ltd. **(1)**
5F Shibiya Kokusai Bldg Uchisawaicho, Tokyo, 100 0011, Japan
Tel.: (81) 352518031
Sales Range: $25-49.9 Million
Emp.: 10
International Crude Oil & Petroleum Product Transportation
N.A.I.C.S.: 483111

Teekay Shipping (Latvia) **(1)**
4 Torna St C 102, Riga, LV 1050, Latvia
Tel.: (371) 7508092
Sales Range: $25-49.9 Million
Emp.: 1
International Crude Oil & Petroleum Product Transportation
N.A.I.C.S.: 483111

Teekay Shipping (Singapore) Pte, Ltd. **(1)**
1 George Street Level 10, Singapore, 049145, Singapore **(100%)**
Tel.: (65) 62217988
Sales Range: $25-49.9 Million
Emp.: 50
International Crude Oil & Petroleum Product Transportation
N.A.I.C.S.: 483111

Teekay Shipping (UK) Ltd. **(1)**
Thomas House 4th Floor 84 Eccleston Square, London, SW1V 1PX, United Kingdom **(100%)**
Tel.: (44) 2073891400
Sales Range: $25-49.9 Million
Emp.: 15
International Crude Oil & Petroleum Product Transportation
N.A.I.C.S.: 483111

Teekay Shipping (USA), Inc. **(1)**
825 Town and Country Ln Ste 350, Houston, TX 77024 **(100%)**
Tel.: (713) 735-8490
Sales Range: $25-49.9 Million
Emp.: 4
International Crude Oil & Petroleum Product Transportation
N.A.I.C.S.: 483111

Teekay Shipping Norway AS **(1)**
Verven 4, N 4068, Stavanger, Norway
Tel.: (47) 51442700
Sales Range: $25-49.9 Million
Emp.: 100
International Crude Oil & Petroleum Product Transportation
N.A.I.C.S.: 483111
Axel Wiedenmann *(Mgr-Comm)*

Teekay Shipping Philippines, Inc. **(1)**
3rd Floor 4th Floor CYA Land Properties Inc 110 Rada Street, Legaspi Village, Makati, 1229, Metro Manila, Philippines
Tel.: (63) 287848484
Sales Range: $25-49.9 Million
Emp.: 17
International Crude Oil & Petroleum Product Transportation
N.A.I.C.S.: 483111

Teekay Shipping Spain, S.L. **(1)**
C/Musgo no 5-2aPlanta, 28023, Madrid, Spain
Tel.: (34) 913077329
Web Site: http://www.teekay.com
Goods Transporting Services
N.A.I.C.S.: 488490

Teekay Tankers Ltd. **(1)**
Fourth Floor Belvedere Building 69 Pitts Bay Road, Hamilton, HM 08, Bermuda
Tel.: (441) 2982530
Web Site: https://www.teekay.com
Rev.: $1,364,452,000
Assets: $1,873,494,000
Liabilities: $347,709,000
Net Worth: $1,525,785,000
Earnings: $513,671,000
Emp.: 1,590
Fiscal Year-end: 12/31/2023
Oil Tanker Operator

INTERNATIONAL PUBLIC

N.A.I.C.S.: 483111
Kenneth Hvid *(Chm)*

TEERA-MONGKOL INDUSTRY CO., LTD.
260/2 Charoen Nakhon Road, Samrae, Bangkok, 10120, Thailand
Tel.: (66) 2 877 9510
Web Site: http://www.thaiballast.com
Emp.: 100
Household Lighting Equipment Mfr
N.A.I.C.S.: 335131
Prawit Prasitratanaphorn *(Chm)*

TEESTA AGRO INDUSTRIES LIMITED
Maza Bari Rajgang, Jalpaiguri, 735134, West Bengal, India
Tel.: (91) 3561254284
Web Site: https://teestaagro.in
Year Founded: 1986
Rev.: $13,392,492
Assets: $18,966,084
Liabilities: $5,407,100
Net Worth: $13,558,984
Earnings: $164,936
Fiscal Year-end: 03/31/18
Fertilizer Mfr
N.A.I.C.S.: 325314
Hardev Singh *(Founder, Chm & Mng Dir)*

TEEVER ACHLAL JOINT STOCK COMPANY
4th Khoroo, 2nd khoroolol, Ulaanbaatar, Mongolia
Tel.: (976) 70045107
ACL—(MONG)
Rev.: $1,126,753
Assets: $6,692,348
Liabilities: $4,225,262
Net Worth: $2,467,087
Earnings: $(544,751)
Fiscal Year-end: 12/31/20
Transportation Services
N.A.I.C.S.: 488999

TEFRON LTD.
Center Misgav, PO Box 1365, Misgav, 20179, Israel
Tel.: (972) 49900805 **Il**
Web Site: https://www.tefron.com
Year Founded: 1977
TFRFF—(OTCIQ)
Rev.: $180,000,000
Assets: $108,201,000
Liabilities: $80,812,000
Net Worth: $27,389,000
Earnings: $4,560,000
Fiscal Year-end: 12/31/20
Men's Underwear & Women's Intimate Apparel & Swimsuit Designer, Developer, Mfr & Marketer
N.A.I.C.S.: 315210
Ben Lieberman *(CEO)*

Subsidiaries:

Hi-Tex Founded By Tefron Ltd. **(1)**
Teradyon Industrial Zone, PO Box 1365, Misgav, 20179, Israel
Tel.: (972) 49900000
Womens Childrens & Infants Clothing & Accessories Whslr
N.A.I.C.S.: 424350

Tefron Canada Inc. **(1)**
55 Rue Louvain Suite 201, Montreal, QC, Canada
Tel.: (514) 383-1951
Seamless Garment Mfr
N.A.I.C.S.: 331110

Tefron Trading (Shanghai) Company Limited **(1)**
Room 1119 JH Plaza No 2008 Hu Qing Ping Road, Shanghai, China
Tel.: (86) 215971946800
Active Wear Textile Product Mfr & Distr
N.A.I.C.S.: 314999

AND PRIVATE COMPANIES

Tefron USA, Inc. (1)
201 St Germain Ave SW, Valdese, NC 28690-2744
Tel.: (828) 879-6500
Sales Range: $25-49.9 Million
Emp.: 30
Knit Underwear & Women's Hosiery Mfr
N.A.I.C.S.: 315120

TEGA INDUSTRIES LIMITED
Godrej Waterside Tower-Ii Office No 807 8th Floor, Block Dp-5 Salt Lake Sector V Bidhannagar, Kolkata, 700091, West Bengal, India
Tel.: (91) 3340939000
Web Site:
  https://www.tegaindustries.com
Year Founded: 1976
543413—(BOM)
Mining & Metal Services
N.A.I.C.S.: 212290
Madan Mohanka *(Chm)*

Subsidiaries:

Edoctum Peru S.A.C. (1)
Calle Bajada Balta N 131, Miraflores, Lima, Peru
Tel.: (51) 1 743 4950
Mining Equipment Mfr
N.A.I.C.S.: 333131
Delbi Molina *(Pres)*

Edoctum S.A. (1)
Rosario Sur 91 Of 703, Las Condes, Santiago, Chile
Tel.: (56) 22 656 4175
Web Site: https://www.edoctum.cl
Metal Mining Services
N.A.I.C.S.: 213114
Rodrigo Madrid *(Pres)*

Losugen Pty Ltd (1)
Unit 2/26 Biscayne Way, Jandakot, 6164, WA, Australia
Tel.: (61) 89 414 7922
Rubber Products Mfr
N.A.I.C.S.: 326291

McNally Sayaji Engineering Limited (1)
Ecospace Business Park Campus-2B 4th Floor 11F/12 Rajarhat New Town, Kolkata, 700 160, India
Tel.: (91) 3330141213
Web Site: http://mcnallysayaji.com
Heavy Construction Equipment & Mining Machinery Mfr
N.A.I.C.S.: 333120
Pradip Kumar Tibdewal *(CEO)*

Tega Industries Africa Proprietary Limited (1)
Tel.: (27) 10 595 7853
Web Site: https://www.tegaindustries.co.za
Rubber Products Mfr
N.A.I.C.S.: 326291

Tega Industries Australia Pty. Ltd. (1)
Unit 6/57 Kent Street, Cannington, 6107, WA, Australia
Tel.: (61) 89 358 0844
Web Site:
  https://www.tegaindustries.com.au
Rubber Products Mfr
N.A.I.C.S.: 326291

Tega Industries Peru SAC (1)

TEGMA GESTAO LOGISTICA S.A.
Avenida Nicola Demarchi n 2000, Sao Bernardo do Campo, 09820-655, Sao Paulo, Brazil   BR
Web Site: http://www.tegma.com.br
TGMA3—(BRAZ)
Rev.: $283,060,360
Assets: $214,460,050
Liabilities: $64,919,467
Net Worth: $149,540,583
Earnings: $32,518,545
Fiscal Year-end: 12/31/23
Transportation & Logistics Services
N.A.I.C.S.: 484220

Gennaro Oddone *(CEO & Officer-IR)*

Subsidiaries:

Tegma Cargas Especiais Ltda. (1)
Av Bandeirantes 625, Alemoa, Santos, 11095-300, Sao Paulo, Brazil
Tel.: (55) 1332965909
General Freight Trucking Services
N.A.I.C.S.: 484110

TEGNER HERMANSSON AB
Dirgerg Garlsgagam 55, 111 45, Stockholm, Sweden
Tel.: (46) 0858741080
Year Founded: 1880
Sales Range: $10-24.9 Million
Emp.: 6
Wines & Spirits Mfr
N.A.I.C.S.: 312130
Jeanette Hermansson *(Owner)*

TEGO SCIENCE INC.
93 Magok Jung-ang 8-ro, Gangseo-gu, Seoul, Korea (South)
Tel.: (82) 28182900
Web Site:
  https://www.tegoscience.com
Year Founded: 2001
191420—(KRS)
Rev.: $5,889,322
Assets: $39,395,294
Liabilities: $2,211,881
Net Worth: $37,183,413
Earnings: $202,881
Emp.: 45
Fiscal Year-end: 12/31/22
Skin Cell Therapy Products
N.A.I.C.S.: 325414
Saewha Jeon *(CEO-Cutigen Laboratories)*

TEGOMETALL INTERNATIONAL SALES GMBH
Industriestrasse 7, 8574, Lengwil-Oberhofen, Switzerland
Tel.: (41) 716869300
Web Site: http://www.tegometall.com
Metal Shelving Systems Mfr
N.A.I.C.S.: 332999

Subsidiaries:

Tegometall France Sarl (1)
1 Rue Jules Verne, 57600, Forbach, France
Tel.: (33) 387888770
Web Site: http://www.tegometall.fr
Metal Product Distr
N.A.I.C.S.: 423310

Tegometall Inzeniring d.o.o. (1)
Cesta Kozjanskega odreda 29, 3230, Sentjur pri Celju, Slovenia
Tel.: (386) 37463244
Web Site: http://www.tegometall-inzeniring.si
Metal Products Mfr
N.A.I.C.S.: 337215

Tegometall Limited (1)
Tegometall House 10 Meadowbank Way, Eastwood, Nottingham, NG16 3SB, United Kingdom
Tel.: (44) 1773711322
Web Site: http://www.tegometall.co.uk
Metal Product Distr
N.A.I.C.S.: 423310
Peter Moore *(Head-Sls)*

Tegometall Oprema, d.o.o. (1)
Cesta Leona Dobrotinska 29, Sentjur pri Celju, 3230, Slovenia
Tel.: (386) 3 7466 820
Web Site: http://www.Tegometall-inganiring.com
Emp.: 160
Steel Pole Mfr
N.A.I.C.S.: 332322

Tegometall Polczerkezet Gjarto Kft. (1)
Berenyi ut 134, 5600, Bekescsaba, Hungary
Tel.: (36) 66441286
Web Site: http://www.tegometall.hu

Metal Product Distr
N.A.I.C.S.: 423310

Tegometall Wyposazenie Sklepow Pniewy Sp. z o.o. (1)
ul Koninska 26, 62-045, Pniewy, Poland
Tel.: (48) 612910597
Web Site: http://www.tegometall.pl
Metal Product Distr
N.A.I.C.S.: 423310

TEHMAG FOODS CORP.
No 31 Wuquan 5th Rd, Wugu Dist, New Taipei City, 24888, Taiwan
Tel.: (886) 222981347
Web Site:
  https://www.tehmag.com.tw
Year Founded: 1989
1264—(TPE)
Rev.: $166,994,841
Assets: $147,159,960
Liabilities: $33,310,978
Net Worth: $113,848,982
Earnings: $22,860,957
Fiscal Year-end: 12/31/22
Bakery Products Mfr
N.A.I.C.S.: 311812
Hsueh-Chiao Lin *(Chm)*

Subsidiaries:

Tehmag Foods Corporation Sdn. Bhd. (1)
5 and 7 Jalan Sepadu 25 123A Sec 25, 40400, Shah Alam, Malaysia
Tel.: (60) 355258879
Web Site: https://www.tehmagfoods.com.my
Dairy Products Mfr
N.A.I.C.S.: 311512

Zoom Foods (H.K.) Co., Ltd. (1)
Blk A 2/F Houtex Ind Bldg 16 Hung To Rd, Chi Shing Industrial Building, Kwun Tong, China (Hong Kong)
Tel.: (852) 23426586
Web Site: https://www.zoomfoods.com.hk
Food & Beverage Product Mfr
N.A.I.C.S.: 311999

TEHNICKI REMONTNI ZAVOD HADZICI D.D.
ul 6 mart bb, 71240, Hadzici, Bosnia & Herzegovina
Tel.: (387) 3 342 0324
Web Site: http://www.trz.ba
TRZHR—(SARE)
Rev.: $499,085
Assets: $5,375,177
Liabilities: $2,939,707
Net Worth: $2,435,470
Earnings: ($269,180)
Emp.: 42
Fiscal Year-end: 12/31/20
Military Combat Equipment Mfr
N.A.I.C.S.: 336992

TEHNIKA A.D.
Dositejeva 11, Vrsac, Serbia
Tel.: (381) 13 832 855
Year Founded: 1977
Sales Range: $1-9.9 Million
Emp.: 61
Electrical Installation Services
N.A.I.C.S.: 238210

TEHNIKA D.D.
Ulica grada Vukovara 274, 10 000, Zagreb, Croatia
Tel.: (385) 16301111
Web Site: https://www.tehnika.hr
Year Founded: 1947
THNK—(ZAG)
Sales Range: Less than $1 Million
Real Estate Manangement Services
N.A.I.C.S.: 531210

TEHNOGRADNJA A.D.
Petra Drapsina 1, Zrenjanin, Serbia
Tel.: (381) 23545457

TEHNORADIONICA A.D.

Web Site:
  http://www.tehnogradnja.biz
Year Founded: 1998
THGRZ—(BEL)
Sales Range: Less than $1 Million
Emp.: 3
Building Construction Services
N.A.I.C.S.: 236115
Stevan Cukilo *(Dir)*

TEHNOHEMIJA A.D.
Tel.: (381) 112751122
Web Site:
  https://www.tehnohemija.com
Year Founded: 1997
THHM—(BEL)
Rev.: $4,145,885
Assets: $17,983,321
Liabilities: $5,566,873
Net Worth: $12,416,447
Earnings: $16,859
Emp.: 45
Fiscal Year-end: 12/31/22
Chemical Product Mfr & Whslr
N.A.I.C.S.: 325998
Goran Radovanovic *(Gen Mgr)*

TEHNOHEMIJA A.D.
Svetog Save 17, Sremska Mitrovica, Serbia
Tel.: (381) 112750422
Web Site:
  https://www.tehnohemija.com
Year Founded: 2000
THSM—(BEL)
Rev.: $30,552
Assets: $997,007
Liabilities: $243,783
Net Worth: $753,224
Earnings: ($32,428)
Emp.: 1
Fiscal Year-end: 12/31/23
Hardware Product Whslr
N.A.I.C.S.: 444140
Ivan Artukov *(Gen Mgr)*

TEHNOMETAL-VARDAR AD SKOPJE
5 Gjuro Strugat Str, 1000, Skopje, North Macedonia
Tel.: (389) 2 3165 007
Web Site: http://www.tehnometal-vardar.com.mk
Year Founded: 1947
Rev.: $1,558,134
Assets: $19,030,843
Liabilities: $13,928,768
Net Worth: $5,102,076
Earnings: $1,703
Emp.: 400
Fiscal Year-end: 12/31/15
Metal Processor & Distr
N.A.I.C.S.: 423510

TEHNOPROMET A.D.
Zorza Klemansoa 19, Belgrade, Serbia
Tel.: (381) 63282007
Year Founded: 1946
THPT—(BEL)
Rev.: $11,770
Assets: $4,778,036
Liabilities: $568,577
Net Worth: $4,209,460
Earnings: ($295,633)
Emp.: 4
Fiscal Year-end: 12/31/21
Hardware Product Whslr
N.A.I.C.S.: 423710

TEHNORADIONICA A.D.
Petra Drapshina 1, 23000, Zrenjanin, Serbia
Tel.: (381) 23544598
Web Site:
  https://www.tehnoradionica.rs
Year Founded: 1911

TEHNORADIONICA A.D.

Tehnoradionica a.d.—(Continued)
THNRZ—(BEL)
Rev.: $899,430
Assets: $868,136
Liabilities: $431,780
Net Worth: $436,356
Earnings: ($64,444)
Emp.: 20
Fiscal Year-end: 12/31/23
Industrial Machinery & Equipment Mfr
N.A.I.C.S.: 333998
Marko Stanivukovic *(Exec Dir)*

TEHNOSERVIS A.D.
Brankova 13-15, Belgrade, Serbia
Tel.: (381) 112851679
Year Founded: 1952
THNSE—(BEL)
Sales Range: Less than $1 Million
Emp.: 2
Real Estate Manangement Services
N.A.I.C.S.: 531390
Marina Bakovic *(Board of Directors & Exec Dir)*

TEHNOUNION D.O.O.
Alipasina 8, Sarajevo, 71000, Bosnia & Herzegovina
Tel.: (387) 33 205 944
Web Site: http://www.tehnounion.ba
Year Founded: 1991
Holding Company; Import/Export Services; Technical Services; Metrology Laboratory Services; Design Consulting Services; Adult Education
N.A.I.C.S.: 551112
Kirlic Tarik *(Dir)*

TEHO INTERNATIONAL INC. LTD.
No1 Commonwealth Lane One Commonwealth 09-23, Singapore, 149544, Singapore
Tel.: (65) 67448777
Web Site: https://www.teho.com.sg
5OQ—(CAT)
Rev.: $52,402,860
Assets: $42,289,221
Liabilities: $25,188,701
Net Worth: $17,100,520
Earnings: $2,104,478
Emp.: 87
Fiscal Year-end: 06/30/23
Steel Wire Rope, Synthetic Fibre Sling & Chain
N.A.I.C.S.: 331222
See Hoe Lim *(Chm & CEO)*

Subsidiaries:

TEHO (Shanghai) Co., Ltd. (1)
Suite 2210A 22/F Tomson Commercial Building 710 Dongfang Road, Pudong, Shanghai, 200122, China
Tel.: (86) 18616273590
Marine Equipment Distr
N.A.I.C.S.: 423860

TEHO Development Pte. Ltd. (1)
1 Commonwealth Lane 09-23 One Commonwealth, Singapore, 149544, Singapore
Tel.: (65) 67448777
Web Site: http://www.tehoproperty.com.sg
Real Estate Services
N.A.I.C.S.: 531390
Cheng Boon Phua *(Dir-Ops)*

TEHO Engineering Pte. Ltd. (1)
1 Commonwealth Lane 09-23 One Commonwealth, Singapore, 149544, Singapore
Tel.: (65) 67448777
Web Site: http://www.tehoengineering.com.sg
Marine Equipment Distr
N.A.I.C.S.: 423860

TEHO Europe B.V. (1)
Nikkelstraat 19, 2984 AM, Ridderkerk, Netherlands
Tel.: (31) 180820995
Web Site: https://www.tehoropes.nl

Marine Equipment Distr
N.A.I.C.S.: 423860

TEHO International (USA), LLC (1)
9260 Bryant St, Houston, TX 77075
Tel.: (281) 485-5368
Web Site: https://www.tehoropes.com
Marine Equipment Distr
N.A.I.C.S.: 423860

TEHO Ropes Korea Co., Ltd. (1)
47 Mieumgukje 4-ro, Gangseo-gu, Busan, Korea (South)
Tel.: (82) 518316678
Wire & Synthetic Rope Product Distr
N.A.I.C.S.: 423510

TEHO Water & Envirotec Pte. Ltd. (1)
No 1 Tuas Lane, Singapore, 638610, Singapore
Tel.: (65) 67660397
Web Site: https://www.tehowater.com.sg
Marine Equipment Distr
N.A.I.C.S.: 423860

Teho Ropes & Supplies Pte. Ltd. (1)
1 Commonwealth Lane 09-23 One Commonwealth, Singapore, 149544, Singapore
Tel.: (65) 67448777
Web Site: https://www.tehoropes.com.sg
Emp.: 35
Rigging & Mooring Equipment Supplier
N.A.I.C.S.: 238290

TEHRAN CEMENT COMPANY
No 5 Shahid Anoshirvani St Ferdowsi St Shahid Tagvi St, PO Box 657-11365, 1145687813, Tehran, Iran
Tel.: (98) 66708391
Web Site: https://tehrancement.co.ir
Year Founded: 1954
Emp.: 3,022
Cement Mfr
N.A.I.C.S.: 327310

Subsidiaries:

Hegmatan Cement Co. (1)
Koushek Street End of the Block Anoushirvan No 6, Ferdowsi Square Ferdowsi St, Tehran, Iran
Tel.: (98) 02166716585
Web Site: https://www.hegmatancement.com
Sales Range: Less than $1 Million
Emp.: 635
Cement & Gypsum Product Mfr
N.A.I.C.S.: 327420

TEHRAN CHEMIE PHARMACEUTICAL COMPANY
No 12 - Nick Raye Alley -North Shams Tabrizi Street, Mirdamad, Tehran, Iran
Tel.: (98) 21 22220318
Web Site: http://www.tehranchemie.co
Year Founded: 1961
Emp.: 850
Pharmaceutical Preparation Mfr
N.A.I.C.S.: 325412

TEHRAN DAROU PHARMACUTICAL CO.
Melat Bank Karaj Road Special Route 7th Kilometer, Tehran, 13445-465, Iran
Tel.: (98) 21 44504841
Pharmaceutical Preparation Mfr
N.A.I.C.S.: 325412
Amir Hossein Ayatollahi *(CEO)*

TEHRAN STOCK EXCHANGE
Saadat Abad Qaisar Aminpour Boulevard Bors Building, 1998896551, Tehran, Iran
Tel.: (98) 64076000
Web Site: https://tse.ir
Trade Contracting Services
N.A.I.C.S.: 238990
Ali Sahraee *(Pres & CEO)*

TEIJIN LIMITED
Kasumigaseki Common Gate West Tower 2-1 Kasumigaseki 3-chome, Chiyoda-ku, Tokyo, 100-8585, Japan
Tel.: (81) 335064529 JP
Web Site: https://www.teijin.com
Year Founded: 1918
3401—(TKS)
Rev.: $6,826,629,530
Assets: $8,269,248,810
Liabilities: $5,083,671,680
Net Worth: $3,185,577,130
Earnings: $70,059,390
Emp.: 21,834
Fiscal Year-end: 03/31/24
Fibers, Chemicals, Plastics, Pharmaceuticals & Medical Products Mfr, Developer & Marketer
N.A.I.C.S.: 325220
Jun Suzuki *(Co-Pres & CEO)*

Subsidiaries:

Dupont Teijin Films China Ltd. (1)
Units 1B-3A 37/F 148 Electric Road, North Point, China (Hong Kong)
Tel.: (852) 27345345
Web Site: https://www.dupontteijinfilms.com
Polyester Film Mfr & Distr
N.A.I.C.S.: 326113
Tim Leung *(Pres)*

Infocom Corporation (1)
2-34-17 Jingumae, Shibuya-ku, Tokyo, 150-0001, Japan (50.1%)
Tel.: (81) 368663000
Web Site: http://www.infocom.co.jp
Sales Range: $350-399.9 Million
Emp.: 1,196
IT Services
N.A.I.C.S.: 541519
Toshihiro Satomi *(Mng Dir)*

Subsidiary (US):

Infocom America, Inc. (2)
1900 S Norfolk St Ste 350, San Mateo, CA 94403
Tel.: (650) 931-2592
Web Site: http://www.infocomamerica.com
Sales Range: $25-49.9 Million
Emp.: 2
Computer Services
N.A.I.C.S.: 541519

N.I. TEIJIN SHOJI (Shangai) CO., LTD (1)
Room 2901 Shanghai International Trading Center, Changning District, Shanghai, 200336, China
Tel.: (86) 2162750400
Web Site: http://www.ni-teijinshoji.co.th
Textile Products Import & Distr
N.A.I.C.S.: 423990

N.I. TEIJIN SHOJI (USA) Inc (1)
1412 Broadway Ste 1100, New York, NY 10018
Tel.: (212) 840-6900
Sales Range: $25-49.9 Million
Emp.: 38
Synthetics Fiber Products Mfr
N.A.I.C.S.: 325199
Sharon Kan *(Coord-Traffic)*

N.I. Teijin Airbag Fabric (Nantong) Co., Ltd. (1)
19 Zhongyang Road Nantong Economic & Technological Development Zone, Nantong, 226009, Jiangsu, China
Tel.: (86) 51385929399
Emp.: 156
Textile Product Mfr & Distr
N.A.I.C.S.: 313210

Nantong Teijin Co Ltd (1)
19 Zhong Rd Nantong Economical and Technological Development Zone, Nantong, 226009, Jiangsu, China
Tel.: (86) 51383599888
Web Site: https://www.teijin.com.cn
Pharmaceuticals Product Mfr
N.A.I.C.S.: 325412

Shenzhen Teijin Kasei Trading Co., Ltd. (1)

INTERNATIONAL PUBLIC

Room 3112-13 ShunHing Square DiWang Commercial Center, 5002 Shennan Road East, Shenzhen, China
Tel.: (86) 75588832100
Chemical Products Distr
N.A.I.C.S.: 424690

Teijin (China) Investment Co., Ltd (1)
Unit 4015 40F Raffles City Changning Office, Tower 1 No 1133 Changning Road, Shanghai, 200051, China
Tel.: (86) 2162193866
Web Site: http://www.teijin.co.jp
Carbon Fiber Products Mfr
N.A.I.C.S.: 335991

Teijin America, Inc. (1)
600 Lexington Ave 27th Fl, New York, NY 10022-6831 (100%)
Tel.: (212) 308-8744
Web Site: http://www.teijin.com
Emp.: 25
Marketing & Sales of Polyester Film
N.A.I.C.S.: 424310

Teijin Aramid B.V (1)
Tivolilaan 50, 6824 BW, Arnhem, Netherlands
Tel.: (31) 882688888
Web Site: http://www.teijinaramid.com
Sales Range: $125-149.9 Million
Emp.: 400
Timber Product Mfr
N.A.I.C.S.: 322219

Subsidiary (Non-US):

Teijin Aramid Asia Co Ltd (2)
Room 1003 Shanghai International Trade Center, Shanghai, 200336, China
Tel.: (86) 21 6219 5365
Sales Range: $25-49.9 Million
Emp.: 20
Chemical Products Mfr
N.A.I.C.S.: 325180

Teijin Aramid Gmbh (2)
Kasinostrasse 19-21, PO Box 100149, 42103, Wuppertal, Germany
Tel.: (49) 202324422
Aramid Fiber Product Mfr
N.A.I.C.S.: 325220

Subsidiary (US):

Teijin Aramid USA Inc. (2)
801-F Blacklawn Rd, Conyers, GA 30012-5187
Tel.: (770) 929-0781
Web Site: http://www.teijinaramid.com
Sales Range: $25-49.9 Million
Emp.: 21
Timber Product Mfr
N.A.I.C.S.: 322219
David Carlson *(Pres)*

Teijin Automotive Technologies NA Holdings Corp. (1)
255 Rex Blvd, Auburn Hills, MI 48326
Tel.: (248) 237-7800
Composite Mfr & Distr
N.A.I.C.S.: 321211

Teijin Automotive Technologies, Inc. (1)
255 Rex Blvd, Auburn Hills, MI 48326 (100%)
Tel.: (248) 237-7800
Web Site: https://www.teijinautomotive.com
Emp.: 4,200
Automotive Thermoset Plastic Composites Mfr
N.A.I.C.S.: 326199
John Hiovich *(CEO, Chief Sls Officer, CTO, Chief HR Officer, Chief HR Officer & VP)*

Plant (Domestic):

Continental Structural Plastics, Inc. - Carey Plant (2)
2915 County Rd 96, Carey, OH 43316
Tel.: (419) 396-1980
Web Site: http://www.cspplastics.com
Automotive Thermoset Plastic Composites Mfr
N.A.I.C.S.: 326199

Continental Structural Plastics, Inc. - Conneaut Plant (2)

AND PRIVATE COMPANIES — TEIJIN LIMITED

333 Gore Rd, Conneaut, OH 44030
Tel.: (440) 945-4800
Web Site: http://www.cspplastics.com
Emp.: 250
Automotive Thermoset Plastic Composites Mfr
N.A.I.C.S.: 326199

Continental Structural Plastics, Inc. - North Baltimore Plant
100 S Poe Rd, North Baltimore, OH 45872
Tel.: (419) 257-2231
Web Site: http://www.cspplastics.com
Automotive Thermoset Plastic Composites Mfr
N.A.I.C.S.: 326199
Rob Turner *(Dir-Ops)*

Plant (Non-US):

Continental Structural Plastics, Inc. - Pouance Plant (2)
Zone Industrielle de la Pidaie, 49420, Pouance, France
Tel.: (33) 2 85 35 61 85
Web Site: http://www.cspplastics.com
Automotive Thermoset Plastic Composites Mfr
N.A.I.C.S.: 326199

Plant (Domestic):

Continental Structural Plastics, Inc. - Sarepta Plant (2)
26755 Hwy 371, Sarepta, LA 71071
Tel.: (318) 299-5299
Web Site: http://www.cspplastics.com
Automotive Thermoset Plastic Composites Mfr
N.A.I.C.S.: 326199

Plant (Non-US):

Continental Structural Plastics, Inc. - Tijuana Plant (2)
Boulevard Insurgentes 20383 Parque Industrial El Florido, 22244, Tijuana, BC, Mexico
Tel.: (52) 664 660 2600
Web Site: http://www.cspplastics.com
Automotive Thermoset Plastic Composites Mfr
N.A.I.C.S.: 326199

Plant (Domestic):

Continental Structural Plastics, Inc. - Van Wert Plant (2)
1276 Industrial, Van Wert, OH 45891
Tel.: (419) 238-4332
Web Site: http://www.cspplastics.com
Emp.: 70
Automotive Thermoset Plastic Composites Mfr
N.A.I.C.S.: 326199

Teijin Automotive Technologies (2)
255 Rex Blvd, Auburn Hills, MI 48326
Tel.: (248) 237-7800
Web Site: https://www.teijinautomotive.com
Automotive Thermoset Plastic Composites Mfr
N.A.I.C.S.: 326199

Teijin Carbon Shanghai Co., Ltd. (1)
Rm 3604 Bldg B New Caohejing International Business Center, 391 Guiping Road Xuhui District, Shanghai, 200233, China
Tel.: (86) 2162362356
Carbon Fiber Product Distr
N.A.I.C.S.: 424130

Teijin Creative Staff Co Ltd (1)
1-6-7 Minamihommachi, Chuo-ku, Osaka, 541-8587, Japan
Tel.: (81) 662683211
Web Site: http://www.teijin.co.jp
Sales Range: $25-49.9 Million
Emp.: 250
Administrative Management Consulting Services
N.A.I.C.S.: 541611
Naoto Takano *(Mng Dir)*

Teijin DuPont Films Japan Limited (1)
Kasumigaseki Common Gate West Tower 3-2-1 Kasumigaseki, Chiyoda-ku, Tokyo, 100-8585, Japan (60%)
Tel.: (81) 3 3506 4243
Polyester Film Mfr & Whslr
N.A.I.C.S.: 326113

Teijin Engineering Limited (1)
Higo-bashi Shimizu Bldg 3-7 Tosabori 1-chome, Nishi-ku, Osaka, 550-8587, Japan (100%)
Tel.: (81) 664595200
Web Site: https://www.teijin-eng.co.jp
Emp.: 255
Chemical Products Mfr
N.A.I.C.S.: 325180
Tsuboi Tadashi *(Pres)*

Teijin Entech Co Ltd (1)
1-6-7 Minami-hommachi 1-chome Chuo-ku, Osaka, 541-8587, Japan
Tel.: (81) 662682220
Web Site: http://www.teijin.co.jp
Emp.: 8,000
Electric Power Generation Services
N.A.I.C.S.: 221118

Teijin Frontier (Shanghai) Co., Ltd. (1)
Room 2901 Shanghai International Trade Center 2201 Yan-an Road West, Shanghai, 200336, China
Tel.: (86) 2162754221
Emp.: 174
Textile & Clothing Product Distr
N.A.I.C.S.: 424310

Teijin Frontier (U.S.A.), Inc. (1)
1412 Broadway Ste 1500, New York, NY 10018
Tel.: (212) 840-6900
Web Site: https://www.teijin-frontier-usa.com
Emp.: 13
Textile Product Mfr & Distr
N.A.I.C.S.: 313210

Teijin Frontier Co., Ltd. (1)
Nakanoshima Festival Tower West 2-4 Nakanoshima 3-chome, Kita-ku, Osaka, 530-8605, Japan (100%)
Tel.: (81) 662332600
Web Site: https://www2.teijin-frontier.com
Emp.: 849
Yarns, Textile Materials & Clothing Products Mfr & Distr
N.A.I.C.S.: 313110
Tetsushi Suzuki *(Exec VP)*

Subsidiary (Non-US):

Teijin Frontier (Thailand) Co., Ltd. (2)
44 Srijulsup Tower Fl 17 Rama 1 Road Rongmuang, Pathumwan, Bangkok, 10330, Thailand (100%)
Tel.: (66) 22195000
Web Site: https://www.teijin-frontier.co.th
Emp.: 67
Textile, Apparel & Industrial Material Equipments Mfr & Distr
N.A.I.C.S.: 314999
Yutaka Kanda *(Pres)*

Teijin Frontier Europe GmbH (2)
Max-Brauer-Allee 50, 22765, Hamburg, Germany (100%)
Tel.: (49) 403696660
Web Site: http://www.teijin-frontier-europe.com
Emp.: 31
Textile, Apparel & Industrial Material Equipments Mfr & Distr
N.A.I.C.S.: 314999
Yudo Hashiguchi *(Mng Dir)*

Teijin Group China Management Limited (1)
Room 2708 Shanghai International Trade Center 2201 Yan An Road West, Shanghai, 200336, China
Tel.: (86) 21 6219 3866
Web Site: http://www.teijin-china.com
Timber Product Mfr
N.A.I.C.S.: 325220

Teijin Holdings Netherlands B.V (1)
World Trade Center Tower B-9th floor Strawinskylaan 925, 1077 XX, Amsterdam, Netherlands
Tel.: (31) 205776057
Sales Range: $25-49.9 Million
Emp.: 5
Biomethanol Mfr
N.A.I.C.S.: 325199

K. Kataoka *(Pres)*

Teijin Holdings USA Inc (1)
1 Harbor Dr Ste 200, Sausalito, CA 94965
Tel.: (415) 887-9742
Web Site: https://www.teijin.com
Fiber Products Whslr
N.A.I.C.S.: 424130

Subsidiary (Domestic):

Renegade Materials Corporation (2)
3363 S Tech Blvd, Miamisburg, OH 45342
Tel.: (937) 350-5274
Web Site: http://www.renegadematerials.com
Research & Development in the Physical, Engineering & Life Sciences
N.A.I.C.S.: 541715

Teijin Home Healthcare Co Ltd (1)
Kasumigaseki Common Gate West Tower 2-1 Kasumigaseki 3-chome, Chiyoda-ku, Tokyo, 100-8585, Japan
Tel.: (81) 335064488
Women Healthcare Services
N.A.I.C.S.: 621610
Jun Suzuki *(CEO)*

Teijin India Private Limited (1)
304-A Tower B Global Business Park Mehrauli Gurgaon road, Gurgaon, 122002, India
Tel.: (91) 1244814999
Sales Range: $25-49.9 Million
Emp.: 20
Rayon Staple Fibers Mfr
N.A.I.C.S.: 322219

Teijin Intellectual Property Center Limited (1)
3-2-1 Kasumigaseki, Chiyoda-Ku, 100-0013, Tokyo, Japan
Tel.: (81) 335064463
Web Site: http://www.teijin.co.jp
Intellectual Property & Legal Support Services
N.A.I.C.S.: 541199
Hiroyuki Umetani *(Mgr)*

Teijin Kasei America, Inc (1)
1200 Harmon Rd, Auburn Hills, MI 48326
Tel.: (248) 724-3570
Web Site: http://www.teijinkasei.com
Sales Range: $25-49.9 Million
Emp.: 6
Polycarbonate Alloys Mfr
N.A.I.C.S.: 331110
Akira Shimizu *(Pres)*

Teijin Kasei Europe B.V (1)
Celsiusweg 32-58, 5928 PR, Venlo, Netherlands
Tel.: (31) 774658950
Web Site: http://www.teijin.nl
Sales Range: $25-49.9 Million
Emp.: 8
Polycarbonate Resin Mfr
N.A.I.C.S.: 325211

Teijin Kasei Malaysia Sdn. Bhd. (1)
Menara Dion 35-02 27 Jalan Sultan Ismail, 50250, Kuala Lumpur, Malaysia
Tel.: (60) 320781288
Chemical Products Distr
N.A.I.C.S.: 424690

Teijin Kasei Taiwan Co., Ltd. (1)
RM B 5F-3 No 88 Dunhua N Rd, Taipei, 10551, Taiwan
Tel.: (886) 287122576
Chemical Products Distr
N.A.I.C.S.: 424690

Teijin Limited - Iwakuni Factory (1)
2-1 Hinodemachi, Iwakuni, 740-8511, Yamaguchi, Japan
Tel.: (81) 827246500
Web Site: http://www.teijin.co.jp
Synthetics Fiber Products Mfr
N.A.I.C.S.: 325199

Teijin Limited - Matsuyama Factory (1)
77 Kitayoshidamachi, Matsuyama, 791-8530, Ehime, Japan
Tel.: (81) 899711000
Web Site: http://www.teijin.co.jp
Sales Range: $250-299.9 Million
Synthetic Fiber & Plastic Products Mfr
N.A.I.C.S.: 326199

Teijin Limited - Tokyo Headquarters (1)
Kasumigaseki Common Gate West Tower 2-1 Kasumigaseki 3-chome, Chiyoda-ku, Tokyo, 100-8585, Japan
Tel.: (81) 335064529
Web Site: https://www.teijin.co.jp
Emp.: 9,583
Executive Office
N.A.I.C.S.: 921110

Teijin Logistics Co Ltd (1)
Higobashi Shimizu Building 1-3-7 Tosabori, Nishi-ku, Osaka, 550-8587, Japan
Tel.: (81) 664595150
Web Site: https://www.teijinbutsuryu.co.jp
Emp.: 190
Synthetics Fiber Products Mfr
N.A.I.C.S.: 314999

Teijin Pharma (Shanghai) Consulting Co., Ltd (1)
10F Shanghai Times Square Office 93 Huai Hai Zhong Road, Shanghai, 200020, China
Tel.: (86) 2163918307
Web Site: http://www.teijin-pharma.co.jp
Emp.: 20
Pharmaceuticals Product Mfr
N.A.I.C.S.: 325412
Kondo Noriaki *(Gen Mgr)*

Teijin Pharma Limited (1)
Kasumigaseki Common Gate West Tower 2-1 Kasumigaseki 3-chome, Chiyoda-ku, Tokyo, 100-8585, Japan
Tel.: (81) 335064077
Web Site: https://www.teijin-pharma.co.jp
Sales Range: $450-499.9 Million
Emp.: 1,864
Pharmaceuticals Mfr
N.A.I.C.S.: 325412
Hiiorruno Runo *(Gen Mgr)*

Teijin Polycarbonate China Ltd (1)
No 888 Yashan West Road Zhapu Economic Development Zone, Jiaxing, 314201, Zhejiang, China
Tel.: (86) 57385583333
Sales Range: $50-74.9 Million
Emp.: 170
Polycarbonate Resin Mfr
N.A.I.C.S.: 325211

Teijin Polycarbonate Singapore Pte Ltd (1)
111 Sakra Avenue 01-01, Singapore, 627881, Singapore
Tel.: (65) 62682811
Web Site: http://www.teijin.co.jp
Sales Range: $50-74.9 Million
Emp.: 180
Polycarbonate Resin Mfr
N.A.I.C.S.: 325211
Tomoyuki Hanai *(Mgr-Fin)*

Teijin Product Development China Co., Ltd. (1)
19 Zhongyang Road Nantong Economic & Technological Development Zone, Nantong, 226009, Jiangsu, China
Tel.: (86) 51355072888
Emp.: 53
Textile Product Mfr & Distr
N.A.I.C.S.: 313210

Teijin Techno Products Limited (1)
6-7 Minami-Hommachi 1 Chome, Chuo-ku, Osaka, 541-8587, Japan
Tel.: (81) 662682635
Web Site: http://www.teijin-technoproducts.co.jp
Sales Range: $150-199.9 Million
Emp.: 300
Aramid Fibers Mfr & Sales
N.A.I.C.S.: 325220

Toho Tenax Co., Ltd. (1)
Kasumigaseki Common Gate West Tower 321 Kasumigaseki, Chiyoda ku, Tokyo, 100-8585, Japan
Tel.: (81) 335066506
Web Site: http://www.tohotenax.com
Sales Range: $300-349.9 Million
Emp.: 1,289
Fiber & Textile Mfr
N.A.I.C.S.: 314999

Subsidiary (US):

Toho Tenax America, Inc. (2)

TEIJIN LIMITED

Teijin Limited—(Continued)
121 Cardiff Valley Rd, Rockwood, TN 37854
Tel.: (865) 354-8408
Web Site: http://www.tohotenaxamerica.com
Sales Range: $50-74.9 Million
Emp.: 150
Carbon Fiber Mfr
N.A.I.C.S.: 325220
Greg Olson (VP-Sls)

Subsidiary (Non-US):

Toho Tenax Europe Gmbh (2)
Kasinostrasse 19-21, 42103, Wuppertal, Germany
Tel.: (49) 2452977050
Web Site: https://www.teijincarbon.com
Sales Range: $100-124.9 Million
Emp.: 400
Synthetic Fiber Mfr
N.A.I.C.S.: 325220
Eckhard Scholten (Mng Dir)

WinTech Polymer Ltd. (1)
JR Shinagawa East Building 18-1 Konan 2-chome, Minato-ku, Tokyo, 108 8380, Japan (40%)
Tel.: (81) 367118610
Web Site: http://www.wintechpolymer.co.jp
Sales Range: $50-74.9 Million
Emp.: 150
Polymer Plastic Products Distr & Mfr
N.A.I.C.S.: 326199

Yuyu Teijin Medicare Inc (1)
4F Building A Jongha Building 27 Dongho-ro 15-gil, Jung-gu, Seoul, 04598, Korea (South)
Tel.: (82) 222540285
Web Site: https://www.yuyuteijin.co.kr
Sales Range: $10-24.9 Million
Emp.: 40
Women Healthcare Services
N.A.I.C.S.: 621610

TEIJIN POLYESTER (THAILAND) LIMITED

19th Floor Ploenchit Tower 898 Ploenchit Road, Bangkok, 10330, Thailand
Tel.: (66) 22630700
Web Site: http://www.teijin.co.th
Sales Range: $350-399.9 Million
Emp.: 1,030
Polyester Fibers Mfr & Sales
N.A.I.C.S.: 325220
Masaya Endo (Pres)

TEIKOKU DATABANK, LTD.

2-5-20 Minami Aoyama, Minato-ku, Tokyo, 107-8680, Japan
Tel.: (81) 357753117
Web Site: http://www.tdb.co.jp
Year Founded: 1900
Sales Range: $500-549.9 Million
Emp.: 3,250
Corporate Credit & Market Research Services
N.A.I.C.S.: 541910
Nobuo Goto (Pres)

Subsidiaries:

TDB Credit Information Korea, Ltd. (1)
4-5th Floor Inho IP Bldg 720, Yeoksam-dong Gangnam-gu, Seoul, Korea (South)
Tel.: (82) 2 2194 5230
Web Site: http://www.tdbkc.co.kr
Credit Research Services
N.A.I.C.S.: 561450

TDB FUSION CORP. (1)
Kita-Aoyama Bldg 7th Fl 1-4-4 Kita-Aoyama, Minato-ku, Tokyo, 107-0061, Japan
Tel.: (81) 3 3470 3291
Web Site: http://www.tdb-fusion.com
Credit Research Services
N.A.I.C.S.: 561450
Chris Hinton (Mgr-Quality Assurance)

TEIKOKU DATABANK AXIS, Ltd., (1)
Annecy Aoyama Bldg 4th Fl 2-6-12 Minami Aoyama, Minato-ku, Tokyo, Japan

Tel.: (81) 3 3470 0620
Software Development Services
N.A.I.C.S.: 541511

Teikoku Databank America, Inc. (1)
Tel.: (212) 421-9805
Web Site: http://www.teikoku.com
Sales Range: $25-49.9 Million
Emp.: 8
Corporate Credit & Market Research Services; Electronic Commerce Support Services; Database & Directory Publisher
N.A.I.C.S.: 561450
Takeo Goto (Pres & CEO)

Teikoku Databank Business Services, Ltd. (1)
1-12-2 shintomi, chuo-ku, Tokyo, 104-8685, Japan
Tel.: (81) 3 5540 1400
Web Site: http://www.tdbbs.co.jp
Data Processing Services
N.A.I.C.S.: 518210

TEIKOKU ELECTRIC MFG. CO., LTD.

60 Hirano Shingu-cho, Tatsuno, 679-4395, Hyogo, Japan
Tel.: (81) 791750411 JP
Web Site: https://www.teikokudenki.co.jp
Year Founded: 1939
6333—(TKS)
Rev.: $193,124,370
Assets: $277,884,400
Liabilities: $63,284,140
Net Worth: $214,600,260
Earnings: $20,656,250
Emp.: 1,252
Fiscal Year-end: 03/31/24
Pumps & Pumping Equipment Mfr
N.A.I.C.S.: 333914
Kiyoshi Murata (Pres, CEO, Mng Dir, Mng Dir, Exec Officer & Exec Officer)

Subsidiaries:

Dalian Teikoku Canned Motor Pump Co.,Ltd. (1)
Sanjianpu Science Technology Industry Area, Dalian, China
Tel.: (86) 41186269333
Web Site: https://www.teikoku-china.com
Pump & Pumping Equipment Mfr
N.A.I.C.S.: 333914

Hirafuku Electric Mfg.Co.,Ltd. (1)
745-1 Fukuchi Taishi-Cho, Ibo-Gun, Hyogo, 671-1534, Japan
Tel.: (81) 792774094
Web Site: https://www.hirafuku-denki.co.jp
Motor Pump & Electronic Equipment Mfr
N.A.I.C.S.: 333914

Kozuki Denso Co., Ltd. (1)
3-29-1 Koto, Shingu-cho, Tatsuno, 679-5165, Hyogo, Japan
Tel.: (81) 791582025
Web Site: https://www.kozukidenso.co.jp
Sales Range: $25-49.9 Million
Emp.: 50
Industrial Pump Mfr
N.A.I.C.S.: 333914

Kyowa Electric Mfg. Co., Ltd. (1)
12 Natsume, Oya-cho, Yabu, 667-0305, Hyogo, Japan
Tel.: (81) 796690022
Web Site: https://www.kyowa-electric.co.jp
Pumps & Pumping Equipment Mfr
N.A.I.C.S.: 333914

Taiwan Teikoku Pump Co.,Ltd. (1)
104 Floor 1 9th Floor No 5 Jinzhou Street, Zhongshan District, Taipei, 104, Taiwan
Tel.: (886) 225679800
Web Site: https://www.teikoku.tw
Fluid Power Pump & Motor Mfr
N.A.I.C.S.: 333996

Teikoku Electric GmbH (1)
Mundelheimer Weg 50, 40472, Dusseldorf, Germany
Tel.: (49) 2117006778
Web Site: https://www.teikokupump.de
Pump & Pumping Equipment Mfr

Teikoku Korea Co.,Ltd (1)
5F HB Tower 25 Nonhyun-ro 87 Gil, Gangnam-gu, Seoul, 06236, Korea (South) (100%)
Tel.: (82) 27907012
Web Site: http://www.teikokukorea.co.kr
Sales Range: $50-74.9 Million
Emp.: 5
Industrial Machinery & Equipment Whslr
N.A.I.C.S.: 423830
Gusun Kang (Pres)

Teikoku South Asia Pte Ltd. (1)
No 15 Joo Koon Crescent, Singapore, 629015, Singapore (100%)
Tel.: (65) 68614121
Web Site: http://www.teikokudenki.co.jp
Emp.: 8
Industrial Machinery & Equipment Whslr
N.A.I.C.S.: 423830
Hisachi Wada (Mng Dir)

Teikoku USA, Inc. (1)
5880 Bingle Rd, Houston, TX 77092-2113
Tel.: (713) 983-9901
Web Site: http://www.chempump.com
Sales Range: $50-74.9 Million
Emp.: 20
Pumps & Pumping Equipment Mfr
N.A.I.C.S.: 423830
Brian Chambers (Product Mgr)

Division (Domestic):

Chempump (2)
959 Mearns Rd, Warminster, PA 18974 (100%)
Tel.: (215) 343-6000
Web Site: http://www.chempump.com
Sales Range: $25-49.9 Million
Fluid Power Pump & Motor Mfr
N.A.I.C.S.: 333996
Thomas Conroy (Pres)

Teishin Electric Mfg. Co., Ltd. (1)
440 Yoshima, Shingu-cho, Tatsuno, 679-4305, Hyogo, Japan
Tel.: (81) 791750315
Web Site: https://www.teishin-electric.co.jp
Emp.: 50
Pumps & Pumping Equipment Mfr
N.A.I.C.S.: 333914

Teiwa Engineering Co., Ltd. (1)
60 Hirano Shingu-cho, Tatsuno, Hyogo, Japan
Tel.: (81) 791754162
Industrial Pump Mfr
N.A.I.C.S.: 333914

TEIKOKU SEN-I CO., LTD.

5-1Nihonbashi 2-Chome, Chuo-Ku, Tokyo, Japan
Tel.: (81) 332813026
Web Site: https://www.teisen.co.jp
3302—(TKS)
Rev.: $198,746,880
Assets: $561,556,360
Liabilities: $100,876,520
Net Worth: $460,679,840
Earnings: $17,335,050
Emp.: 340
Fiscal Year-end: 12/31/23
Disaster Prevention & Preparedness Services
N.A.I.C.S.: 922160
Tsuyoshi Shiraiwa (Pres & CEO)

Subsidiaries:

Teisen Techno Co., Ltd. (1)
2-1 Sayado, Kamimikawa- cho Kawachi-gun, Tochigi, 329-0526, Japan
Tel.: (81) 285510550
Fire Fighting Equipment Mfr & Distr
N.A.I.C.S.: 339113

TEIKOKU TSUSHIN KOGYO CO., LTD.

45-1 Kariyado, Nakahara-ku, Kawasaki, 211-8530, Kanagawa, Japan
Tel.: (81) 444223171
Web Site: https://www.noble-j.co.jp
Year Founded: 1944
6763—(TKS)
Rev.: $100,624,030

INTERNATIONAL PUBLIC

Assets: $212,081,850
Liabilities: $30,901,750
Net Worth: $181,180,100
Earnings: $9,002,820
Emp.: 1,571
Fiscal Year-end: 03/31/24
Electronic Component Mfr & Distr
N.A.I.C.S.: 334416
Masuo Hanyu (Pres)

Subsidiaries:

Ecolopac Co., Ltd. (1)
45-1 Kariyado, Nakahara-ku, Kawasaki, 211-8530, Kanagawa, Japan
Tel.: (81) 444332065
Electric Equipment Mfr
N.A.I.C.S.: 334416

Noble Electronics (Thailand) Co., Ltd. (1)
36 Moo 1 Hi-Tech Industrial Estate Tambol Banpo, Amphur Bang Pa-In, Ayutthaya, 13160, Thailand
Tel.: (66) 35351831
Electronic Component Mfr & Distr
N.A.I.C.S.: 334416

Noble Trading (Bangkok) Co., Ltd. (1)
36 Moo 1 Hi-Tech Industrial Estate Tambol Banpo, Amphur Bang Pa-In, Ayutthaya, 13160, Thailand
Tel.: (66) 35351839
Electronic Component Mfr & Distr
N.A.I.C.S.: 334416

Noble Trading (Shanghai) Co., Ltd. (1)
The Place Unit 2702-3 Tower B 100Zunyi Road, Shanghai, 200051, China
Tel.: (86) 2168869788
Electronic Component Mfr & Distr
N.A.I.C.S.: 334416

Singapore Noble Electronics Pte., Ltd. (1)
2 Toh Guan Road East 03-02, Singapore, 608837, Singapore
Tel.: (65) 67769377
Electronic Component Mfr & Distr
N.A.I.C.S.: 334416

Sunshine Co., Ltd. (1)
45-1 Kariyado, Nakahara-ku, Kawasaki, 211-8530, Kanagawa, Japan
Tel.: (81) 444223171
Emp.: 80
Logistics Transportation Services
N.A.I.C.S.: 541614

Taiwan Noble Electronic Co., Ltd. (1)
No 158 Shanying Road, Guishan Dist, Taoyuan, 33341, Taiwan
Tel.: (886) 33207174
Electronic Component Mfr & Distr
N.A.I.C.S.: 334416

Teitsu Denshi Kenkyusho Co., Ltd. (1)
2-6-31 Kamishinjo, Nakahara-ku, Kawasaki, 211-0045, Kanagawa, Japan
Tel.: (81) 447664411
Web Site: http://www.teitsu-d.co.jp
Electric Equipment Mfr
N.A.I.C.S.: 334416

Teitsu Engineering Co., Ltd. (1)
45-1 Kariyado, Nakahara-ku, Kawasaki, 211-8530, Kanagawa, Japan
Tel.: (81) 444114454
Emp.: 32
Industrial Machinery & Equipment Mfr & Distr
N.A.I.C.S.: 333519

TEIMO CO., LTD.

3-4-10 Imazu-Minami, Tsurumi-ku, Osaka, 538-0043, Japan
Tel.: (81) 6 6961 5171
Web Site: http://www.teimo.co.jp
Year Founded: 1937
Rev.: $19,800,000
Emp.: 33
Container Mfr & Whslr
N.A.I.C.S.: 332439

AND PRIVATE COMPANIES — TEJNAKSH HEALTHCARE LIMITED

Kota Ojima *(Pres)*

TEIN, INC.
3515-4 Kamiyabe-cho, Totsuka-ku, Yokohama, 245-0053, Kanagawa, Japan
Tel.: (81) 458105511
Web Site: https://www.tein.co.jp
Year Founded: 1985
7217—(TKS)
Rev.: $32,157,650
Assets: $55,894,160
Liabilities: $13,775,240
Net Worth: $42,118,920
Earnings: $3,093,480
Emp.: 368
Fiscal Year-end: 03/31/24
Automobile Part Mfr & Distr
N.A.I.C.S.: 336110
Masashi Hara *(Auditor)*

Subsidiaries:

TEIN FAR EAST INTERNATIONAL TRADE COMPANY OF CHINA (1)
Building 1 Floor 7 Room 706 No 168 Beiyuan Road, Chaoyang, Beijing, 100101, China
Tel.: (86) 2028606990
Automobile Parts Mfr
N.A.I.C.S.: 336390

TEIN HONG KONG LIMITED (1)
Unit A G/F Worldwide Centre 123 Tung Chau Street Tai Kok Tsui, Kowloon, China (Hong Kong)
Tel.: (852) 23930899
Automobile Parts Mfr
N.A.I.C.S.: 336390

TEIN U.S.A., INC. (1)
9798 Firestone Blvd, Downey, CA 90241
Tel.: (562) 861-9161
Automotive Part Whslr
N.A.I.C.S.: 423120
Hakaru Ichino *(Pres)*

TEIN UK LIMITED (1)
Unit 7 Avant Business Centre, Denbigh West Industrial Estate, Milton Keynes, MK1 1DL, United Kingdom
Tel.: (44) 1908632861
Automobile Parts Mfr
N.A.I.C.S.: 336390

TEIXEIRA DUARTE SA
Lagoas Park Edificio 2, 2740-265, Porto Salvo, Oeiras, Portugal
Tel.: (351) 217912300
Web Site: https://www.teixeiraduarte.pt
TDSA—(EUR)
Rev.: $876,978,354
Assets: $1,941,486,709
Liabilities: $1,652,304,479
Net Worth: $289,182,230
Earnings: $3,581,629
Emp.: 9,600
Fiscal Year-end: 12/31/20
Commercial & Residential Construction Services
N.A.I.C.S.: 236220
Jose Luciano Vaz Marcos *(Chm)*

Subsidiaries:

Global Net Distrib. (Pty) Ltd. (1)
Office 08-09 15th Floor The Forum Sandton Maude Street, Sandton, Johannesburg, 2196, South Africa
Tel.: (27) 711615033
Construction Services
N.A.I.C.S.: 236220

Hotel Tropico, S.A. (1)
Avenida Pedro de Castro Van-Dunem Loy Bairro Morro Bento Maxipark, Edificio Teixeira Duarte 387, Luanda, Angola
Tel.: (244) 222670100
Hospital Management Services
N.A.I.C.S.: 622110

Quinta De Cravel, S.A. (1)
Lagoas Park Edificio 2, Oeiras, 2740-265, Porto Salvo, Portugal
Tel.: (351) 220922626
Web Site: https://www.quintadecravel.pt
Real Estate Development Services
N.A.I.C.S.: 531390

Recolte, S.A.U. (1)
Av Alberto Alcocer 24 Planta 7a, 28036, Madrid, Spain
Tel.: (34) 915550903
Web Site: http://www.recolte.es
Emp.: 600
Maintenance Services
N.A.I.C.S.: 811310
Joao Machado *(Engr-Mechanical)*

Smotors, S.A. (1)
Avenida Marechal Gomes da Costa 29, 1800-255, Lisbon, Portugal
Tel.: (351) 215996080
Web Site: http://www.smotors.pt
Car Maintenance Services
N.A.I.C.S.: 811310

Somafel, S.A. (1)
Lagoas Park Edificio 2 Piso 2, 2740-265, Porto Salvo, Portugal
Tel.: (351) 217990330
Web Site: http://www.somafel.pt
Emp.: 500
Construction Services
N.A.I.C.S.: 236220
Paulo Serradas *(CEO)*

Subsidiary (Non-US):

Somafel, S.A. (2)
Av das Nacoes Unida N 12 901 ES N 201 - Sala 04 Torre Norte Bloco A, Brooklin Novo, Sao Paulo, 04578-910, Brazil
Tel.: (55) 1135850800
Construction Services
N.A.I.C.S.: 236220

Somafel, S.A. (2)
Angle BD Anfa et Rue Clos de Province N 2 6 eme Etage Apt 6B, 20050, Casablanca, Morocco
Tel.: (212) 22362890
Construction Services
N.A.I.C.S.: 236220

Somafel, S.A. (2)
08 Route de Ben Aknoun, El Biar, Algiers, Algeria
Tel.: (213) 23239580
Construction Services
N.A.I.C.S.: 236220

Somafel, S.A. (2)
Davidson House Forbury Square, Reading, RG1 3EU, United Kingdom
Tel.: (44) 1189001440
Construction Services
N.A.I.C.S.: 236220

TDGI, Ltda. (1)
Av das Nacoes Unidas n 12 901 2 Andar Torre Norte, Brooklin, Sao Paulo, 04578-910, Brazil
Tel.: (55) 1135850800
Technical Maintenance Services
N.A.I.C.S.: 811310
Paulo Lopes *(Country Dir)*

TDGI, S.A. (1)
Avenue Jean Monnet 1, 1348, Louvain-la-Neuve, Belgium
Tel.: (32) 23183804
Technical Maintenance Services
N.A.I.C.S.: 811310
Alexandre Seica *(Country Mgr)*

TDGI, SL (1)
C Caleruega 76 plta 1 of 1, 28033, Madrid, Spain
Tel.: (34) 915550903
Technical Maintenance Services
N.A.I.C.S.: 811310
Raul Garcia Monje *(Mgr-Bus Dev)*

Tdgi, S.A. (1)
Lagoas Park Edificio 2, 2740-265, Porto Salvo, Portugal
Tel.: (351) 210050920
Web Site: https://www.tdgiworld.com
Technical Maintenance Services
N.A.I.C.S.: 811310
Ricardo Cunha *(Mgr-Contracts)*

Tdre Investments, LLC (1)
16800 Dallas Pkwy Ste 240, Dallas, TX 75248-1991
Tel.: (469) 655-5845
Real Estate Development Services
N.A.I.C.S.: 531390

Teixeira Duarte - Engenharia E Construcoes, S.A. (1)
Lagoas Park Edificio 2, 2740-265, Porto Salvo, Portugal
Tel.: (351) 217912300
Web Site: http://www.teixeiraduarteconstrucao.com
Construction Services
N.A.I.C.S.: 236220
Miguel Rocha *(Mgr-Construction)*

Subsidiary (Non-US):

Empa S.A. (2)
Av Paulo Ferreira da Costa 553 Vista Alegre, Lagoa Santa, 33400-000, Minas Gerais, Brazil
Tel.: (55) 3133114788
Web Site: http://www.empa.com.br
Construction Services
N.A.I.C.S.: 236220
Ronaldo Borges *(Mgr-Contracts)*

Subsidiary (Domestic):

Epos, S.A. (2)
Lagoas Park Edificio 2, 2740-265, Porto Salvo, Portugal
Tel.: (351) 213138180
Web Site: http://www.epos.pt
Construction Services
N.A.I.C.S.: 236220
Rui Santos Silva *(Comml Dir-Intl)*

Subsidiary (US):

TD Construction Services, LLC (2)
1048 O Malley Dr, Lake Zurich, IL 60047
Tel.: (847) 512-7415
Web Site: http://www.tdconstructionservices.com
Construction Services
N.A.I.C.S.: 236220
Tom Tomsovic *(Principal)*

Subsidiary (Non-US):

TD-EC, S.A. (2)
Avenida Alberto Alcocer n 24 - 7 C, 28036, Madrid, Spain
Tel.: (34) 915550903
Construction Services
N.A.I.C.S.: 236220

TD-EC, S.A. (2)
Av das Nacoes Unidas 12 901 2 andar cj 201 Torre Norte, Brooklin Novo, Sao Paulo, Brazil
Tel.: (55) 1135850800
Web Site: http://www.teixeiraduarteconstrucao.com
Construction Services
N.A.I.C.S.: 236220

TD-EC, S.A. (2)
Avenida Pedro de Castro Van-Dunem Loy Baixo Morro Bento Maxipark, Edificio Teixeira Duarte 387, Luanda, Angola
Tel.: (244) 222641500
Construction Services
N.A.I.C.S.: 236220

TD-EC, S.A. (2)
Avenida Julyus Nyerere 4 - R/C, Maputo, Mozambique
Tel.: (258) 21491401
Construction Services
N.A.I.C.S.: 236220
Gerson Fernandes *(Project Mgr)*

TD-EC, S.A. (2)
Carrera 11 94-02 - Oficina 201 Edificio Centro de Negocios Manhatan, Bogota, Colombia
Tel.: (57) 16754530
Construction Services
N.A.I.C.S.: 236220

TD-EC, S.A. (2)
Av Venezuela del Rosal con Calle Mohedano Torre JWM frente al, BOD piso 5 El Rosal, 1060, Caracas, Venezuela
Tel.: (58) 2129512012
Construction Services
N.A.I.C.S.: 236220

Tivoli Beira, Lda. (1)
Av Bagamoio 363, Beira, Mozambique
Tel.: (258) 23320300
Hospital Management Services
N.A.I.C.S.: 622110

TEJAS NETWORKS LIMITED
Plot No 25 JP Software Park 2nd 3rd 4th 5th Floor, Electronics City Phase-1 Hosur Road, Bengaluru, 560 100, India
Tel.: (91) 8041794600
Web Site: https://www.tejasnetworks.com
Year Founded: 2000
TEJASNET—(NSE)
Rev.: $75,272,925
Assets: $179,071,620
Liabilities: $24,253,320
Net Worth: $154,818,300
Earnings: $5,124,210
Emp.: 785
Fiscal Year-end: 03/31/21
Telecommunication Servicesb
N.A.I.C.S.: 517112
Sanjay Nayak *(CEO & Mng Dir)*

Subsidiaries:

Tejas Communication (Nigeria) Limited (1)
5th Floor Mulliner Towers Former NNPC Building 39 Alfred Rewane Road, Ikoyi, Lagos, Nigeria
Tel.: (234) 7034042952
Telecommunication Products Mfr
N.A.I.C.S.: 334290

Tejas Communication Pte. Ltd. (1)
77 Robinson Road 13-00 Robinson, Singapore, 068896, Singapore
Tel.: (65) 93808020
Telecommunication Products Mfr
N.A.I.C.S.: 334290

Tejas Communication Pte. Ltd. (1)
Birchwood Court 43 Montrose Street, Vorna Valley Midrand, Johannesburg, 1686, South Africa
Tel.: (27) 829973938
Telecommunication Products Mfr
N.A.I.C.S.: 334290

Tejas Communication Pte. Ltd. (1)
Level 16 1 Sentral Jalan Stesen Sentral 5, 50470, Kuala Lumpur, Malaysia
Tel.: (60) 320929200
Telecommunication Products Mfr
N.A.I.C.S.: 334290

Tejas Networks Ltd. (1)
1050 State House Road, PO Box 102-00510, Nairobi, Kenya
Tel.: (254) 739200103
Telecommunication Products Mfr
N.A.I.C.S.: 334290

Tejas Networks Ltd. (1)
68-72 Church St Ste 6, Northbridge, MA 01588
Telecommunication Products Mfr
N.A.I.C.S.: 334290

Tejas Networks Ltd. (1)
Office No 414 Builing 11 Dubai Internet City, PO Box 73030, Dubai, United Arab Emirates
Tel.: (971) 503461224
Telecommunication Products Mfr
N.A.I.C.S.: 334290

TEJNAKSH HEALTHCARE LIMITED
Sakri Road, Dhule, 424 001, Maharashtra, India
Tel.: (91) 9422285213
Web Site: https://www.tejnaksh.com
Year Founded: 2003
539428—(BOM)
Rev.: $1,442,863
Assets: $3,743,864
Liabilities: $1,056,376
Net Worth: $2,687,489
Earnings: $214,771
Emp.: 38

Tejnaksh Healthcare Limited—(Continued)
Fiscal Year-end: 03/31/23
Health Care Srvices
N.A.I.C.S.: 621111
Ashish Vishwas Rawandale *(Mng Dir)*

TEK SENG HOLDINGS BERHAD
Plot 159 MK13 Jalan Perindustrian Bukit Minyak 7, Bukit Minyak Industrial Park, 14000, Bukit Mertajam, Penang, Malaysia
Tel.: (60) 45075805
Web Site: https://www.tekseng.com.my
TEKSENG—(KLS)
Rev.: $38,652,794
Assets: $67,024,244
Liabilities: $10,521,786
Net Worth: $56,502,458
Earnings: $2,214,568
Emp.: 400
Fiscal Year-end: 12/31/22
Leather Mfr
N.A.I.C.S.: 316110
Chiew Keem P'ng *(Co-Sec)*

Subsidiaries:

Double Grade Non-Woven Industries Sdn. Bhd. (1)
Plot 159 MK13 Jalan Perindustrian Bukit Minyak 7, Bukit Minyak Industrial Park, 14000, Bukit Mertajam, Penang, Malaysia
Tel.: (60) 45075808
Web Site: https://www.doublegrade.com.my
Nonwoven Fabrics Export & Mfr
N.A.I.C.S.: 313230

TS Solartech Sdn. Bhd. (1)
Plot 320 Jalan Perindustrian Bukit Minyak 8, Penang Science Park Bukit Minyak MK13, 14100, Seberang Perai Tengah, Pulau Pinang, Malaysia
Tel.: (60) 45015545
Web Site: https://www.ts-solartech.com
Sell Photovoltaic Product Mfr
N.A.I.C.S.: 334413

Tek Seng Sdn. Bhd. (1)
Plot 159 MK 13 Jalan Perindustrian Bkt Minyak 7 Bukit, PO Box 339, Minyak Industrial Park, Bukit Mertajam, 14000, Penang, Malaysia
Tel.: (60) 45075808
Web Site: https://www.tekseng.com.my
Sales Range: $50-74.9 Million
Emp.: 200
Polyvinyl Chloride Products Mfr
N.A.I.C.S.: 326199

Wangsaga Industries Sdn. Bhd. (1)
Plot 159 MK 13 Jln Perusahaan Bukit Minyak 7, Bukit Minyak Industrial Park, 14000, Bukit Mertajam, Penang, Malaysia
Tel.: (60) 45075808
Web Site: https://www.wangsaga.com.my
Sales Range: $150-199.9 Million
Emp.: 300
Polyvinyl Chloride Products Export & Mfr
N.A.I.C.S.: 325211

TEK-ART INSAAT TICARET TURIZM SANAYI VE YATIRIMLAR A.S.
Sefakoy Halkali Caddesi No 245-12, Kucukcekmece, 34295, Istanbul, Turkiye
Tel.: (90) 902124716119
Web Site: https://www.tek-artinsaat.com
TEKTU—(IST)
Rev.: $5,574,920
Assets: $267,184,916
Liabilities: $107,970,233
Net Worth: $159,214,683
Earnings: ($12,905,450)
Fiscal Year-end: 12/31/21
Hotel & Resort Management Services
N.A.I.C.S.: 721110
Soner Yilmaz *(Chm)*

TEKA - TECELAGEM KUEHNRICH S.A.
Paulo Kuehnrich Street No 68 Itoupava North, Blumenau, 89052-900, SC, Brazil
Tel.: (55) 4733215012
Web Site: http://www.teka.com.br
Year Founded: 1926
TEKA4—(BRAZ)
Rev.: $61,339,516
Assets: $242,388,253
Liabilities: $668,962,595
Net Worth: ($426,574,342)
Earnings: ($31,230,294)
Emp.: 2,180
Fiscal Year-end: 12/31/23
Textile Product Mfr & Whslr
N.A.I.C.S.: 313210
Rui Otte *(Mgr-Judicial)*

TEKALA CORPORATION BERHAD
Wisma Tekala Lot 2 Lorong Indah Jaya 29 Taman Indah Jaya, Jalan Lintas Selatan, 90000, Sandakan, Sabah, Malaysia
Tel.: (60) 89212177   MY
Web Site: http://www.tekala.com.my
Year Founded: 1996
Investment Holding Company; Timber & Plywood Mfr
N.A.I.C.S.: 321211
Chen Vui Chung *(Co-Sec)*

Subsidiaries:

Kalabakan Plywood Sdn. Bhd. (1)
Sungai Imam, PO Box 983, Pasir Putih, 91008, Tawau, Sabah, Malaysia
Tel.: (60) 168262035
Web Site: http://www.kalabakan-plywood.com.my
Sales Range: $200-249.9 Million
Emp.: 700
Plywood Products Mfr
N.A.I.C.S.: 321211
Axel Seah *(Exec Dir)*

TEKCAPITAL PLC
12 New Fetter Lane, London, EC4A 1JP, United Kingdom
Tel.: (44) 2087207171
Web Site: https://www.tekcapital.com
TEK—(AIM)
Rev.: $615,214
Assets: $58,153,738
Liabilities: $388,608
Net Worth: $57,765,130
Earnings: ($12,745,508)
Emp.: 6
Fiscal Year-end: 12/31/22
Innovation Pipeline Services
N.A.I.C.S.: 561499
Clifford M. Gross *(CEO)*

Subsidiaries:

Guident Corp. (1)
901 NW 35th St Ste 101E, Boca Raton, FL 33431
Tel.:
Web Site: https://www.guident.co
Software Development Services
N.A.I.C.S.: 541511

Tekcapital LLC
66 W Flagler St Ste 900, Miami, FL 33130
Tel.: (305) 200-3450
Investment Transfer Services
N.A.I.C.S.: 523999

TEKCHEM, S.A.B. DE C.V.
Tel.: (52) 014646478000
Year Founded: 1991
TEKCHEM—(MEX)
Sales Range: Less than $1 Million
Chemical Product Mfr & Whslr
N.A.I.C.S.: 325998
Ignacio Rivero Darancou *(Chm, Dir Gen & Mng Dir)*

TEKCORE CO., LTD.
No 18 Tzu-Chung 3rd Road, Nan-Kung Industrial Zone, Nantou, 540, Taiwan
Tel.: (886) 492261626
Web Site: https://www.tekcore.com.tw
3339—(TPE)
Rev.: $18,952,225
Assets: $32,401,151
Liabilities: $13,289,841
Net Worth: $19,111,309
Earnings: ($761,842)
Fiscal Year-end: 12/31/22
LCD Products Mfr
N.A.I.C.S.: 334413
Yin-Fu Ye *(Chm)*

TEKFEN HOLDING A.S.
Kultur Mahallesi Tekfen Sitesi Budak Sokak A Blok No 7, Ulus-Besiktas, 34340, Istanbul, Turkiye
Tel.: (90) 2123593300
Web Site: https://www.tekfen.com.tr
Year Founded: 1956
TKFEN—(IST)
Rev.: $947,274,698
Assets: $994,188,970
Liabilities: $667,083,597
Net Worth: $327,105,373
Earnings: $106,512,394
Emp.: 11,950
Fiscal Year-end: 12/31/22
Holding Company; Construction, Engineering & Real Estate Development & Investment Services
N.A.I.C.S.: 551112
Ali Nihat Gokyigit *(Founder)*

Subsidiaries:

Alanar Meyve ve Gida Uretim Pazarlama Sanayi ve Tic. A.S. (1)
Kultur Mahallesi Budak Sokak Tekfen Sitesi D Blok No 2 Ulus, Besiktas, 34340, Istanbul, Turkiye
Tel.: (90) 2123593300
Web Site: https://www.alanar.com.tr
Organic Fruit Mfr & Distr
N.A.I.C.S.: 311423

Antalya Free Trade Zone Operating Co., Inc. (1)
PK 002 Free Zone, Liman, 07070, Antalya, Turkiye
Tel.: (90) 242 259 0930
Web Site: https://www.asbas.com.tr
General Warehousing Services
N.A.I.C.S.: 493110

Cenup Tikinti Servis (1)
Sabail Rayonu Cenub Koprusu, AZ1003, Baku, Azerbaijan
Tel.: (994) 412 4474130
Construction Engineering Services
N.A.I.C.S.: 541330

Hallesche Mitteldeutsche Bau - A.G. (1)
Magdeburger Str 27, 06112, Halle, Germany
Tel.: (49) 345 511 6833
Web Site: https://www.hmb-ag.de
Construction Engineering Services
N.A.I.C.S.: 541330

OOO Rusfen (1)
Usacheva street 35 Building 1 Floor 4 Office II Room 8, Moscow, 119048, Russia
Tel.: (7) 4951856707
Web Site: https://www.rusfen.ru
Gas Pipeline Construction Services
N.A.I.C.S.: 237120

Papfen Joint Stock Company (1)
Yakkasarayskiy Rayon Ul Vasit Vahidov No 41, Tashkent, Uzbekistan
Tel.: (998) 871 1204082
Real Estate Manangement Services
N.A.I.C.S.: 531390

Tekfen Construction & Installation Co., Inc. (1)
Tekfen Tower Buyukdere Cad No 209 4 Levent, 34394, Istanbul, Turkiye
Tel.: (90) 212 359 3500
Web Site: https://www.tekfeninsaat.com.tr
Construction Engineering Services
N.A.I.C.S.: 541330

Tekfen Emlak Gelistirme Yatirim ve Ticaret A.S. (1)
Buyukdere Cad No 209 Tekfen Tower 4 Levent, Sisli, 34394, Istanbul, Turkiye
Tel.: (90) 2123593700
Web Site: http://www.tekfengayrimenkul.com
Emp.: 2,000
Heavy Construction Services
N.A.I.C.S.: 237990

Tekfen Endustri ve Ticaret A.S. (1)
Kultur Mahallesi Aydinlik Sokak Tekfen Sitesi D Blok No 2, Ulus besiktas, Istanbul, Turkiye
Tel.: (90) 2123593780
Web Site: https://www.tekfenendustri.com.tr
Lamp Bulb Mfr
N.A.I.C.S.: 335139

Tekfen Engineering Co., Inc. (1)
Premier Kampus Ofis Gursel Mahallesi Imrahor Caddesi B Blok No 29, Kat 3 Kagithane, 34400, Istanbul, Turkiye
Tel.: (90) 212 357 0303
Web Site: https://www.tekfen.com.tr
Emp.: 500
Construction Engineering Services
N.A.I.C.S.: 541330

Tekfen Gayrimenkul Yatirim A.S. (1)
Buyukdere Cad No 209 Tekfen Tower 4, Levent Sisli, 34394, Istanbul, Turkiye
Tel.: (90) 2123593700
Web Site: http://www.tekfengayrimenkul.com
Real Estate Services
N.A.I.C.S.: 531390

Tekfen Industry & Trade Co., Inc. (1)
Kultur Mahallesi Aydinlik Budak Sokak Tekfen SitesiD Blok No 2, Ulus-Besiktas, 34340, Istanbul, Turkiye
Tel.: (90) 212 3593780
Web Site: http://www.tekfenendustri.com.tr
Lighting Fixture Mfr
N.A.I.C.S.: 335139

Tekfen Insurance Brokerage Services Co., Inc. (1)
Tekfen Tower Esentepe Mah Buyukdere Cad 209 Zemin Kat No 6 4 Levent, Sisli, 34394, Istanbul, Turkiye
Tel.: (90) 212 963 0223
Web Site: https://www.tekfensigorta.com.tr
Insurance Brokerage Services
N.A.I.C.S.: 524210

Tekfen Sigorta Aracilik Hizmetleri A.S. (1)
Tekfen Sigorta Tekfen Tower Esentepe Mah Buyukdere Cad, 209 Zemin Kat No 6 4 Levent Sisli, 34394, Istanbul, Turkiye
Tel.: (90) 2129630223
Web Site: https://www.tekfensigorta.com.tr
Life & Health Insurance Services
N.A.I.C.S.: 524210

Tekfen Tarimsal Arastirma Uretim ve Pazarlama A.S. (1)
Kultur Mahallesi Budak Sokak Tekfen Sitesi D Blok No 2 Ulus Besiktas, 34340, Istanbul, Turkiye
Tel.: (90) 2123593300
Web Site: http://www.tekfentarim.com
Fruit & Vegetable Production Services
N.A.I.C.S.: 311411

Tekfen Turizm ve Isletmecilik A.S. (1)
Tekfen Tower Esentepe Mah Buyukdere Caddesi No 209 4 Levent, Sisli, 34394, Istanbul, Turkiye
Tel.: (90) 2123570000
Web Site: https://www.tekfenservices.com
Real Estate Services
N.A.I.C.S.: 531390

Tekfen Ventures L.P. (1)
50 W 23rd St 7th Fl, New York, NY 10010
Tel.: (646) 849-0900
Web Site: https://www.tekfenventures.com
Heavy Construction Services
N.A.I.C.S.: 237990

Kris Kemeny *(Mng Dir)*

Toros Tarim (1)
Esentepe Mah Buyukdere Cad No 209
Tekfen Tower Floors 19 and 20 Sisli, 34394,
Istanbul, Turkiye
Tel.: (90) 212 357 0202
Web Site: https://www.toros.com.tr
Fertilizer Mfr
N.A.I.C.S.: 325314

Subsidiary (Domestic):

**TAYSEB - Toros Adana Yumurtalik
Free Trade Zone Founder and Operating Co., Inc.** (2)
Sarimazi Mah 1 Bulvar No 6 PK 10, Ceyhan, 01920, Adana, Turkiye
Tel.: (90) 322 634 2080
Web Site: https://www.tayseb.com
General Warehousing Services
N.A.I.C.S.: 493110

Toros Tarim Sanayi ve Ticaret A.S. (1)
Esentepe Mah Buyukdere Cad Tekfen Blok
No 209 Ic Kapi No 27, Sisli, Istanbul, Turkiye
Tel.: (90) 2123570202
Web Site: https://www.toros.com.tr
Agricultural Fertilizer Mfr & Distr
N.A.I.C.S.: 325320

TEKI SOLUTIONS AS
Tvetenveien 6, 0661, Oslo, Norway
Tel.: (47) 2317 2350   NO
Year Founded: 2012
Holding Company; Franchise Mobile
Communications Products Whslr
N.A.I.C.S.: 551112
Haakon Dyrnes *(CEO)*

Subsidiaries:

Nordialog Oslo AS (1)
Tvetenveien 6, 0661, Oslo, Norway
Tel.: (47) 2317 2350
Web Site: http://www.nordialog.no
Franchise Mobile Communications Products
Whslr
N.A.I.C.S.: 423690
Cedric Guttormsen *(Gen Mgr)*

TEKKEN CORPORATION
2-5-3 Kanda-Misakicho, Chiyoda-ku,
Tokyo, 101-8366, Japan
Tel.: (81) 332212152   JP
Web Site: https://www.tekken.co.jp
Year Founded: 1944
1815—(TKS)
Rev.: $1,213,503,460
Assets: $1,396,501,310
Liabilities: $919,715,400
Net Worth: $476,785,910
Earnings: $28,158,600
Emp.: 1,766
Fiscal Year-end: 03/31/24
General Construction, Real Estate &
Sports Facilities Management Services
N.A.I.C.S.: 236220
Yasuo Hayashi *(Chm, Chief Risk Officer, Head, Head, Head & Exec Dir)*

Subsidiaries:

Towa Kensetsu Co., Ltd. (1)
12 5 Lidabashi 1 Chome, Chiyoda Ku, Tokyo, 102 0072, Japan
Tel.: (81) 332302207
Web Site: http://www.towa-kensetsu.co.jp
Provider of Construction Services
N.A.I.C.S.: 541330

TEKMAR GROUP PLC
Unit N791 Grindon Way, Newton Aycliffe, DL5 6SH, United Kingdom
Tel.: (44) 1912497442   UK
Web Site:
  https://investors.tekmar.co.uk
Year Founded: 2018
TGP—(AIM)
Rev.: $34,181,118
Assets: $64,467,468

Liabilities: $20,073,906
Net Worth: $44,393,562
Earnings: ($5,808,186)
Fiscal Year-end: 09/30/22
Other Heavy & Civil Engineering
Construction
N.A.I.C.S.: 237990
Alasdair MacDonald *(CEO)*

Subsidiaries:

AgileTek Engineering Limited (1)
Runway East London Bridge 20 St Thomas
Street, London, SE1 9RS, United Kingdom
Tel.: (44) 2037358155
Web Site: https://www.agiletek.co.uk
Offshore & Subsea Engineering Consulting
Services
N.A.I.C.S.: 541330
Fraser Gibson *(Mng Dir)*

Pipeshield International Limited (1)
No 4 Quay View Business Park Barnards
Way, Lowestoft, NR32 2HD, United Kingdom
Tel.: (44) 1502560900
Web Site: https://www.pipeshield.com
Oil & Gas Machinery & Equipment Mfr
N.A.I.C.S.: 333132

Ryder Geotechnical Limited (1)
Suite 2B 2 Collingwood Street, Newcastle
upon Tyne, NE1 1JF, United
Kingdom   (80%)
Tel.: (44) 1916918480
Web Site: http://www.rydergeotechnical.com
Geotechnical Design & Consulting Services
N.A.I.C.S.: 541330

Tekmar Energy Limited (1)
Innovation House Centurion Way, Darlington, DL3 0UP, United Kingdom
Tel.: (44) 1325379520
Web Site: https://www.tekmar.co.uk
Oil & Gas Machinery & Equipment Mfr
N.A.I.C.S.: 333132
Russell Edmondson *(Mng Dir)*

Tekmar GmbH (1)
Mollneyer Ufer 17, kupferdreh, 45257, Essen, Germany
Tel.: (49) 201486110
Web Site: http://www.tekmar.de
Electric Energy Storage Heater Mfr
N.A.I.C.S.: 333414

TEKNION CORPORATION
1150 Flint Road, Toronto, M3J 2J5,
ON, Canada
Tel.: (416) 661-3370
Web Site: http://www.teknion.com
Sales Range: $600-649.9 Million
Emp.: 3,800
Office Furniture Mfr
N.A.I.C.S.: 337215

Subsidiaries:

Teknion Europe Limited (1)
6985 Tabernacle St, London, EC2A 4BD,
United Kingdom   (100%)
Tel.: (44) 2074902101
Web Site: http://www.teknion.com
Sales Range: $25-49.9 Million
Emp.: 16
Office Furniture
N.A.I.C.S.: 337215
Graham Simmons *(Controller-Fin)*

**Teknion Furniture Systems
Limited** (1)
1150 Flint Rd, Toronto, M3J 2J5, ON,
Canada   (100%)
Tel.: (416) 661-3370
Sales Range: $50-74.9 Million
Emp.: 250
Office Furniture
N.A.I.C.S.: 337215
Gordon Carvelho *(VP)*

Teknion International (1)
1150 Flint Rd, Toronto, M3J 2J5, ON,
Canada   (100%)
Tel.: (416) 661-3370
Web Site: http://www.teknion.com
Sales Range: $25-49.9 Million
Emp.: 10
Office Furniture

N.A.I.C.S.: 337215
Chris Kovac *(Dir-Corp)*

Teknion LLC (1)
350 Fellowship Rd Ste 100, Mount Laurel,
NJ 08054-4323
Tel.: (856) 596-7608
Web Site: http://www.teknion.com
Sales Range: $75-99.9 Million
Emp.: 180
Office Furniture
N.A.I.C.S.: 423210
John Cuellar *(Mgr-Architecture & Design
Market)*

**TEKNO S.A. - INDUSTRIA E
COMERCIO**
R Alfredo Mario Pizzotti 51, Sao
Paulo, 02060-040, SP, Brazil
Tel.: (55) 1129036000
Web Site: https://www.tekno.com.br
Year Founded: 1939
TKNO4—(BRAZ)
Rev.: $49,667,148
Assets: $63,557,496
Liabilities: $12,188,555
Net Worth: $51,368,941
Earnings: $6,581,219
Emp.: 400
Fiscal Year-end: 12/31/23
Sheet Metal Mfr
N.A.I.C.S.: 332322
Valter Takeo Sassaki *(Dir-IR)*

TEKNO-TIP ANALITIK SISTEMLER LTD. STI.
Alacaatli Mahallesi 3346 Cad 3341
Sokak No 35/154 Yesil Baris Sitesi,
Cankaya, Ankara, 06810, Turkiye
Tel.: (90) 3122364207   TR
Web Site: http://www.teknotip.com.tr
Laboratory Equipment Mfr
N.A.I.C.S.: 334516

TEKNOMINING PLC
6 Northbrook Road, Dublin, 6, Ireland
Tel.: (353) 87 2491022   IE
Web Site:
  http://www.teknomining.com
Year Founded: 2010
Copper & Iron Mining Services
N.A.I.C.S.: 212230
Matthew Farrell *(CEO)*

TEKNOS GROUP OY
Takkatie 3, PO Box 107, 00371, Helsinki, Finland
Tel.: (358) 9506091   FI
Year Founded: 1948
Sales Range: $300-349.9 Million
Emp.: 1,700
Industrial Coating & Paint Mfr & Distr
N.A.I.C.S.: 325510
Paula Salastie *(Owner & CEO)*

Subsidiaries:

Teknos (UK) Limited (1)
Unit E1 Heath Farm Banbury Road, Oxford,
OX7 4BN, United Kingdom
Tel.: (44) 1608 683 494
Web Site: http://www.teknos.co.uk
Emp.: 20
Paint & Coating Distr
N.A.I.C.S.: 424950
Michelle Alcock *(Mng Dir)*

Teknos A/S (1)
Industrivej 19, 6580, Vamdrup, Denmark
Tel.: (45) 7693 9400
Web Site: http://www.teknos.dk
Emp.: 170
Paint & Coating Distr
N.A.I.C.S.: 424950
Soren Juhl Hansen *(Mgr-Mktg)*

Teknos AB (1)
Limmaredsv 2, PO Box 211, 514 24,
Tranemo, Sweden
Tel.: (46) 325 61 95 00
Web Site: http://www.teknos.se
Paint & Coating Distr

N.A.I.C.S.: 424950

**Teknos Coatings Trading (Shanghai)
Co., Ltd** (1)
1388 Shaanxi North Road Silver Centre Rm
405a, Putuo District, Shanghai, 200060,
China
Tel.: (86) 21 6149 8582
Web Site: http://www.teknos.cn
Paint & Coating Distr
N.A.I.C.S.: 424950

Teknos Deutschland GmbH (1)
Edelzeller Strasse 62, 36043, Fulda, Germany
Tel.: (49) 661 108 0
Web Site: http://www.teknos.de
Paint & Coating Distr
N.A.I.C.S.: 424950
Matthias Berndt *(Mgr-IT)*

Teknos Ireland Limited (1)
Unit 1 Fortwilliam Industrial Estate Dargan
Crescent, Belfast, BT3 9JP, United Kingdom
Tel.: (44) 2890 960 670
Web Site: http://www.teknosonline.co.uk
Industrial Coating & Paint Distr
N.A.I.C.S.: 424950

Teknos LLC (1)
50 Artema Str Office 5B, 4053, Kiev,
Ukraine
Tel.: (380) 44 359 03 33
Web Site: http://www.teknos.ua
Paint & Coating Distr
N.A.I.C.S.: 424950

Teknos Norge AS (1)
Industriveien 28, 3430, Spikkestad, Norway
Tel.: (47) 3129 4900
Web Site: http://www.teknos.no
Emp.: 19
Paint & Coating Distr
N.A.I.C.S.: 424950
Inger-Toril Odegaard *(Acct Mgr)*

Teknos OOO (1)
Butyrskij Val 68/70 bl 4 of 211, 127055,
Moscow, Russia
Tel.: (7) 495 967 19 61
Web Site: http://www.teknos.ru
Paint & Coating Distr
N.A.I.C.S.: 424950
Andrey Kazakov *(Mgr-Technical Support)*

Teknos Ohtek OOO (1)
Ul Boksitogorskaya 9 lit Z, 195248, Saint
Petersburg, Russia
Tel.: (7) 812 320 76 28
Paint & Coating Mfr
N.A.I.C.S.: 325510

Teknos Oliva Sp. z o.o. (1)
ul Chwaszczynska 129-149, 81-571, Gdynia, Poland
Tel.: (48) 58 629 91 62
Web Site: http://www.oliva.com.pl
Paint & Coating Distr
N.A.I.C.S.: 424950

Teknos Scotland Limited (1)
Nettlehill Road, Houstoun Industrial Estate,
Livingston, EH54 5DL, United Kingdom
Tel.: (44) 1506 436 222
Industrial Coating & Paint Distr
N.A.I.C.S.: 424950

Teknos Sp. z o.o. (1)
ul Ksiecia Ziemowita 59, 03-885, Warsaw,
Poland
Tel.: (48) 22 678 70 04
Web Site: http://www.teknos.pl
Paint & Coating Distr
N.A.I.C.S.: 424950

Teknos d.o.o. (1)
Kidriceva cesta 94, 4220, Skofja Loka, Slovenia
Tel.: (386) 4 236 58 78
Web Site: http://www.teknos.si
Paint & Coating Distr
N.A.I.C.S.: 424950
Milan Bertoncelj *(Mgr-Technical Sls)*

TEKOM A.D.
Kralja Petra I Bb, Republika Srpska,
74270, Teslic, Bosnia & Herzegovina
Tel.: (387) 53410390
Web Site: https://tekom.ba

TEKOM A.D.

Tekom a.d.—(Continued)
Year Founded: 2001
TEKM—(BANJ)
Sales Range: $1-9.9 Million
Emp.: 32
Agricultural Product Whslr
N.A.I.C.S.: 424590
Milan Popovic *(Pres)*

TEKOM TECHNOLOGIES, INC.
10F-1 No 114 Chenggong Rd, North District, Tainan City, 704, Taiwan
Tel.: (886) 62258899 6294—(TPE)
Rev.: $30,714,098
Assets: $45,822,124
Liabilities: $23,150,955
Net Worth: $22,671,169
Earnings: $7,660,945
Fiscal Year-end: 12/31/22
Digital Camera Mfr
N.A.I.C.S.: 333310
Qiu Shi Rong *(Chm & Pres)*

TEKSTIL A.D.
Svetog Stefana 13, Sremska Mitrovica, Serbia
Tel.: (381) 22 622 506
Year Founded: 1999
Sales Range: Less than $1 Million
Emp.: 4
Real Estate Manangement Services
N.A.I.C.S.: 531390
Zeljko Ninkovic *(Exec Dir)*

TEKSTIL A.D.
Stojana Ljubica 4, Leskovac, Serbia
Tel.: (381) 16237395
Year Founded: 1989
TKLE—(BEL)
Rev.: $155,230
Assets: $1,104,332
Liabilities: $28,941
Net Worth: $1,075,391
Earnings: ($924)
Fiscal Year-end: 12/31/22
Textile Product Retailer
N.A.I.C.S.: 458110

TEKSTILPROMET D.D
Ulica grada Gospica 1/A, 10000, Zagreb, Croatia
Tel.: (385) 12700297
Web Site: https://www.tekstilpromet.hr
Year Founded: 1949
TKPR—(ZAG)
Sales Range: Less than $1 Million
Textile Distr
N.A.I.C.S.: 458110

Subsidiaries:

Grateks Ltd. (1)
Kundurdziluk 14, Sarajevo, 71000, Bosnia & Herzegovina
Tel.: (387) 33271360
Web Site: http://www.grateks.ba
Clothing Products Distr
N.A.I.C.S.: 458110

Lauris Moda Ltd. (1)
Grada Gospica Street 1a, 10 000, Zagreb, Croatia
Tel.: (385) 12700701
Clothing Products Distr
N.A.I.C.S.: 458110

TEKSTINA TEKSTILNA INDUSTRIJA D.O.O.
Tovarniska Cesta 15, 5270, Ajdovscina, Slovenia
Tel.: (386) 53692000
Web Site: http://www.tekstina.si
Year Founded: 1828
Technical & Protective Fabrics Mfr
N.A.I.C.S.: 313210
Simeon Spruk *(CEO)*

TEKSTURE CORAP SAN. VE TIC. A.S.
Çevizlibag Yilanli Ayazma Yolu No 20, Topkapi, 34020, Istanbul, Turkiye
Tel.: (90) 2124821033 TR
Real Estate Development Services
N.A.I.C.S.: 531390

TEL AVIV STOCK EXCHANGE LTD.
54 Ahad Ha'am Street, Tel Aviv, 65202, Israel
Tel.: (972) 35677411
Web Site: http://www.tase.co.il
Sales Range: $50-74.9 Million
Emp.: 180
Stock Exchange Services
N.A.I.C.S.: 523210
Amnon Neubach *(Chm)*

TELCOBRIDGES INC.
91 de la Barre Suite 01, Boucherville, J4B 2X6, QC, Canada
Tel.: (450) 655-8993
Web Site: http://www.telcobridges.com
Year Founded: 2002
Sales Range: $10-24.9 Million
Emp.: 39
Telecommunications Hardware & Software Developer & Mfr
N.A.I.C.S.: 334220
Luc Morissette *(Dir-Technical Support)*

TELCON RF PHARMACEUTICAL, INC.
54 Gongse-ro, Giheung-gu, Yongin, Gyeonggi-do, Korea (South)
Tel.: (82) 313718500
Web Site: https://www.telcon.co.kr 200230—(KRS)
Rev.: $21,345,609
Assets: $91,468,518
Liabilities: $26,936,733
Net Worth: $64,531,785
Earnings: ($32,278,697)
Emp.: 135
Fiscal Year-end: 12/31/22
Wireless Communication Component Mfr
N.A.I.C.S.: 334220
Kim Ji-Hoon *(CEO)*

TELCOWARE CO LTD
Telcoware Building 20-7 Beobwon-ro 3-gil Seocho-gu, Seoul, Korea (South)
Tel.: (82) 221059800
Web Site: http://www.telcoware.com 078000—(KRS)
Rev.: $32,650,373
Assets: $101,300,636
Liabilities: $15,764,003
Net Worth: $85,536,633
Earnings: $2,967,597
Emp.: 196
Fiscal Year-end: 12/31/22
Mobile Communication Solutions
N.A.I.C.S.: 334220
Kim Taek-Jin *(Mng Dir)*

TELDOR CABLES & SYSTEMS LTD.
Kibbutz Ein-Dor, Ein Dor, 1933500, Israel
Tel.: (972) 46770555
Web Site: http://www.teldor.com
Sales Range: $75-99.9 Million
Emp.: 325
Communication Equipment Mfr
N.A.I.C.S.: 334220
Izhar Dekel *(CEO)*

TELE GREENLAND A/S
Farip Aqq 8, PO Box 1002, Nuuk, 3900, Greenland
Tel.: (299) 341255 GL
Web Site: http://www.telepost.gl
Year Founded: 1925
Sales Range: $125-149.9 Million
Emp.: 600
Telecommunications Company
N.A.I.C.S.: 517111
Brian Buus Pedersen *(Mng Dir)*

Subsidiaries:

TELE Greenland International A/S (1)
Stensmosevej 24A, 2620, Albertslund, NV, Denmark (100%)
Tel.: (45) 38388300
Web Site: http://www.tgi.gl
Sales Range: $25-49.9 Million
Emp.: 13
Developer of Telecommunications Projects & Operator of Telecommunications Systems
N.A.I.C.S.: 517111
Jorn Jespersen *(Mng Dir)*

TELE MUNCHEN FERNSEH GMBH + CO. PRODUKTIONSGESELLSCHAFT
Kaufingerstr 24, 80331, Munich, Germany
Tel.: (49) 89 29093 0
Web Site: http://www.tmg.de
Year Founded: 1970
Film & Television Production Services
N.A.I.C.S.: 512110
Herbert L. Kloiber *(Mng Dir)*

Subsidiaries:

Odeon Film AG (1)
Hofmannstrasse 21-23, 80807, Munich, Germany (90.82%)
Tel.: (49) 089999513500
Web Site: http://en.odeonfilm.de
Rev.: $70,132,504
Assets: $43,356,872
Liabilities: $32,302,712
Net Worth: $11,054,160
Earnings: ($3,807,544)
Emp.: 300
Fiscal Year-end: 12/30/2020
Motion Picture Production Services
N.A.I.C.S.: 512110
Mischa Hofmann *(CEO & Member-Mgmt Bd)*

TELE PLASTIC, C.A.
Avenida San Felipe Coimasa, Caracas, Venezuela
Tel.: (58) 212 2632455 VE
Plastics Product Mfr
N.A.I.C.S.: 326199
Francisco Mazzarella *(Pres)*

Subsidiaries:

Operaciones al Sur del Orinoco, C.A. (1)
Apartado 497, 8050, Puerto Ordaz, Bolivar, Venezuela (100%)
Tel.: (58) 2869231033
Sales Range: $25-49.9 Million
Emp.: 15
Hot Briquetted Iron Products Mfr & Distr
N.A.I.C.S.: 332999
Masao Tezuka *(Pres)*

TELE-FONIKA KABLE SP. Z O.O. S.K.A.
ul Hipolita Cegielskiego 1, 32-400, Myslenice, Poland
Tel.: (48) 126525000
Web Site: http://www.tfkable.com
Year Founded: 1992
Sales Range: $650-699.9 Million
Emp.: 3,500
Cable & Wire Mfr & Distr
N.A.I.C.S.: 335921
Bartlomiej Zgryzek *(VP-Treasury, M&A & IR)*

INTERNATIONAL PUBLIC

Subsidiaries:

Copper Cable Company Ltd. (1)
Unit 3 Crointee Rd Hilltop Ind Estate Bardon Hill, Coalville, LE67 1TX, Leicestershire, United Kingdom
Tel.: (44) 1530278810
Web Site: http://www.copper-cable.co.uk
Sales Range: $150-199.9 Million
Emp.: 70
Copper Wiring Supplier & Exporter
N.A.I.C.S.: 423610
Mary Walker *(Sec & Controller)*

Ferromontane Distribution S.A. (1)
4 rue Louis-Neel, 21 600, Longvic, France
Tel.: (33) 3 80652510
Sales Range: $50-74.9 Million
Emp.: 7
Electric Cables & Wiring Supplies Distr
N.A.I.C.S.: 423610

TELE-FONIKA Cable Americas Corporation (1)
1160 Pierson Dr, Batavia, IL 60510 (100%)
Tel.: (630) 876-3606
Web Site: http://www.tfcable.com
Sales Range: $25-49.9 Million
Emp.: 20
Cable & Wire Product Distr
N.A.I.C.S.: 423610

TELE-FONIKA France SA (1)
3 rue Gustave Eiffel Bat B, 21700, Nuits-St-Georges, France
Tel.: (33) 3 80650157
Cable & Wire Distr
N.A.I.C.S.: 423610
Jacek Jabonski *(Gen Mgr)*

TELE-FONIKA Kabely CZ s.r.o. (1)
Obornik 2131/31 a, 789 01, Prague, Czech Republic
Tel.: (420) 583 480 725
Cable & Wire Distr
N.A.I.C.S.: 423610
Milan Obrslik *(CEO & Mng Dir)*

TELE-FONIKA Kable GmbH (1)
Kleinhuelsen 29, Hilden, 40721, Germany
Tel.: (49) 21035840
Sales Range: $25-49.9 Million
Emp.: 28
Cable & Wire Product Sales & Distr
N.A.I.C.S.: 423610

TELE-FONIKA Kable Handel S.A. (1)
ul Skladowa 2, 41-902, Bytom, Poland (100%)
Tel.: (48) 126525000
Web Site: http://www.tfkable.pl
Cable Product Distr
N.A.I.C.S.: 423610

TF Cable JSC (1)
Obolonska Quay 3 No 2, Kiev, 04210, Ukraine
Tel.: (380) 445376525
Web Site: http://www.tf-cable.com
Sales Range: $25-49.9 Million
Emp.: 25
Cable & Wire Product Distr
N.A.I.C.S.: 423610

TF Kabel Limited liability company (1)
7 Obolonska Naberezhna st korp 2-A ok, 04210, Kiev, Ukraine
Tel.: (380) 445376525
Web Site: http://www.tfkable.com
Wire & Cable Mfr
N.A.I.C.S.: 335929
Ievgen Kurganov *(CEO)*

Tele Fonika Kable S.A. - Bydgoszcz Factory (1)
ul Fordonska 152, 85-957, Bydgoszcz, Poland
Tel.: (48) 52 364 3210
Cable & Wire Mfr
N.A.I.C.S.: 335921

Tele Fonika Kable S.A. - Chernihiv Factory (1)
3 Kiltseva St, 14007, Chernigov, Ukraine
Tel.: (380) 462 679 597
Cable & Wire Mfr
N.A.I.C.S.: 335921

AND PRIVATE COMPANIES

Hubert Irzenski *(CEO)*

Tele Fonika Kable S.A. - Krakow-Biezanow Factory (1)
ul Nad Drwina 20, 30-741, Krakow, Poland
Tel.: (48) 12 651 40 00
Emp.: 300
Cable & Wire Mfr
N.A.I.C.S.: 335921

Tele Fonika Kable S.A. - Krakow-Wielicka Factory (1)
ul Wielicka 114, Krakow, Krakow, Poland
Tel.: (48) 12 652 50 00
Cable & Wire Mfr
N.A.I.C.S.: 335921

Tele Fonika Kable S.A. - Myslenice Factory (1)
ul H Cegielskiego 1, 32-400, Myslenice, Poland
Tel.: (48) 12 372 71 00
Cable & Wire Mfr
N.A.I.C.S.: 335921

Tele Fonika Kable S.A. - TOW TF Kabel Ukraine Plant (1)
Kilceva 3, 14007, Chernigov, Ukraine
Tel.: (380) 462 679 597
Cable & Wire Mfr
N.A.I.C.S.: 335921

Tele Fonika Kable S.A. - Zajecar Factory (1)
Negotinski put b b, 19000, Zajecar, Serbia
Tel.: (381) 19 444 333
Cable & Wire Mfr
N.A.I.C.S.: 335921

UAB Tele-Fonika Baltic (1)
R Kalantos st 59, 52304, Kaunas, Lithuania
Tel.: (370) 37 328620
Cable & Wire Distr
N.A.I.C.S.: 423610

TELE2 AB
Torshamnsgatan 17, 164 40, Kista, Sweden
Tel.: (46) 856200060   SE
Web Site: http://www.tele2.com
TEL2—(OTCIQ)
Rev.: $2,888,697,014
Assets: $6,557,766,110
Liabilities: $4,296,364,757
Net Worth: $2,261,401,353
Earnings: $370,381,407
Emp.: 4,300
Fiscal Year-end: 12/31/23
Holding Company; Mobile & Fixed Telecommunications, Internet, Data & Cable TV Services
N.A.I.C.S.: 551112
Andrew Barron *(Chm)*

Subsidiaries:

SIA Tele2 (1)
Delu iela 5, Riga, LV-1004, Latvia
Tel.: (371) 29560600
Web Site: https://www.tele2.lv
Sales Range: $50-74.9 Million
Emp.: 200
Wireless Telecommunication Services
N.A.I.C.S.: 517112
Valdis Vancovics *(Chm)*

Tele2 A/S (1)
Frederiksaj, DK 1780, Copenhagen, Denmark   (100%)
Tel.: (45) 77301001
Web Site: http://www.tele2.dk
Sales Range: $25-49.9 Million
Emp.: 100
Mobile & Fixed Telephony, Internet Services, Data Communications & Cable TV Services
N.A.I.C.S.: 517111

Tele2 Finance Belgium SA (1)
Henri Van Heurckstraat 15, Antwerp, 2000, Belgium
Tel.: (32) 32322349
Sales Range: $25-49.9 Million
Emp.: 2
Telecommunication Servicesb
N.A.I.C.S.: 517112

Tele2 Holding AS (1)
Joe 2, Tallinn, 10151, Estonia
Tel.: (372) 6 866 866
Telecommunication Servicesb
N.A.I.C.S.: 517810

Subsidiary (Domestic):

Tele2 Eesti AS (2)
Suur Sojamae 4, 11415, Tallinn, Estonia   (100%)
Tel.: (372) 6866866
Web Site: https://www.tele2.ee
Mobile & Fixed Telecommunications, Internet, Data & Cable TV Services
N.A.I.C.S.: 517111

Subsidiary (Domestic):

Televorgu AS (3)
Kadaka tee 42, Tallinn, 12915, Estonia   (100%)
Tel.: (372) 71 51 266
Web Site: http://www.televork.ee
Sales Range: $10-24.9 Million
Emp.: 250
Telecommunication Servicesb
N.A.I.C.S.: 517810

Tele2 Netherlands Holding B.V. (1)
Wisselwerking 58, NL-1112 XS, Diemen, Netherlands   (100%)
Tel.: (31) 207501000
Web Site: http://www.tele2corporate.nl
Sales Range: $450-499.9 Million
Emp.: 850
Holding Company; Fixed & Mobile Telecommunications, Data, Internet & Cable Television Services
N.A.I.C.S.: 551112
Jeff Dodds *(CEO & Exec VP)*

Tele2 Sverige AB (1)
Borgarfjordsgatan 16, Box 62, 164 94, Kista, Sweden   (100%)
Tel.: (46) 90222
Web Site: https://www.tele2.se
Holding Company; Mobile & Fixed Telecommunications, Internet, Data & Cable TV Services
N.A.I.C.S.: 551112

Subsidiary (Domestic):

Datametrix Integration AB (2)
Borgarfjordsgatan 16, Kista, 164 40, Sweden
Tel.: (46) 852223500
Telecommunication Servicesb
N.A.I.C.S.: 517810

Procure IT Right AB (2)
Karlavagen 108, PO Box 24142, 104 51, Stockholm, Sweden
Tel.: (46) 8 5990 8100
Web Site: http://www.procureitright.com
Sales Range: $25-49.9 Million
Emp.: 50
Telecom & Media Services
N.A.I.C.S.: 517810
Johan Wieslander *(Chm)*

Spring Mobil AB (2)
Box 540 64, 104 30, Stockholm, Sweden
Tel.: (46) 8 674 50 00
Web Site: http://www.springmobil.se
Wireless Telecommunication Services
N.A.I.C.S.: 517112

Swefour GSM AB (2)
Hudiksvallsgatan 4, Stockholm, 113 30, Sweden
Tel.: (46) 856262478
Telecommunication Servicesb
N.A.I.C.S.: 517810

Tele2 Sweden SA (2)
Borgarfjordsgatan 16, PO Box 62, Kista, 164 40, Sweden   (100%)
Tel.: (46) 856264000
Web Site: http://www.tele2.com
Sales Range: $250-299.9 Million
Emp.: 800
Mobile & Fixed Telecommunications, Internet & Data Services
N.A.I.C.S.: 517111

Division (Domestic):

Tele2vision AB (3)
Borgarfjordsgatan 16, PO Box 62, Kista, 16440, Sweden   (100%)
Tel.: (46) 856264352
Web Site: http://www.tele2.com
Sales Range: $50-74.9 Million
Emp.: 200
Cable TV Operator
N.A.I.C.S.: 516210

Subsidiary (Domestic):

Tele2Butikerna AB (2)
Borgarfjordsgatan 16, Kista, 164 40, Sweden
Tel.: (46) 856264000
Web Site: http://www.tele2.com
Telecommunication Servicesb
N.A.I.C.S.: 517810

Tele2 Treasury AB (1)
Tel.: (46) 856262478
Telecommunication Servicesb
N.A.I.C.S.: 517810

iTUX Communication AB (1)
Torshamnsgatan 17, 164 40, Kista, Sweden
Tel.: (46) 771407077
Web Site: https://www.itux.se
Telecommunication Servicesb
N.A.I.C.S.: 517810

TELEC BRASILEIRAS S.A. TELEBRAS
Quadra 04 Lots 075 083 125 and 175 Bloco A Salas 201 202 214 a-224, Edificio Capital Financial Center, 70610-440, Brasilia, DF, Brazil
Tel.: (55) 6120071000
Web Site: http://www.telebras.com.br
TELB3—(BRAZ)
Rev.: $74,514,218
Assets: $715,680,251
Liabilities: $460,831,221
Net Worth: $254,849,031
Earnings: ($22,766,307)
Fiscal Year-end: 12/31/23
Software Publishing Services
N.A.I.C.S.: 513210
Andre Mueller Borges *(Chm)*

TELECANOR GLOBAL LIMITED
504 Lingapur House 3-6-237, Near Minerva Coffe Shop Himayath N Anandnagar, Hyderabad, 500 029, India
Tel.: (91) 4040040737
Web Site: https://www.telecanor.com
Year Founded: 1991
530595—(BOM)
Assets: $1,770,268
Liabilities: $2,427,112
Net Worth: ($656,844)
Earnings: ($386,833)
Emp.: 2
Fiscal Year-end: 03/31/23
Telecommunication Software Development Services
N.A.I.C.S.: 541511

TELECARD LIMITED
1st Floor 75 East Blue Area Fazal ul Haq Road, Islamabad, 44000, Pakistan
Tel.: (92) 21111222123
Web Site: https://www.telecard.com.pk
TELE—(KAR)
Rev.: $7,834,680
Assets: $32,080,111
Liabilities: $16,595,292
Net Worth: $15,484,819
Earnings: ($434,167)
Emp.: 540
Fiscal Year-end: 06/30/19
Telecommunication Servicesb
N.A.I.C.S.: 517112
Sultan ul Arfeen *(Chm)*

Subsidiaries:

Hallmark Company Limited (1)
4th Floor Tower B World Trade Center

TELECHIPS INC.

Khayaban-e-Roomi Block 05 Clifton, Karachi, Pakistan   (62.84%)
Tel.: (92) 2138330000
Web Site: https://www.hiclpk.com
Rev: $6,498
Assets: $6,136
Liabilities: $3,905
Net Worth: $2,231
Earnings: ($10,216)
Emp.: 3
Fiscal Year-end: 06/30/2023
Insurance Services
N.A.I.C.S.: 524298
Kishwar Parveen *(Sec)*

Supernet E-Solutions (Pvt.) Limited (1)
World Trade Centre Tower B 3rd Floor Khayabn-e-Roomi, Clifton, Karachi, Pakistan
Tel.: (92) 111222124
Web Site: https://www.supernetesolutions.com.pk
Software Development Services
N.A.I.C.S.: 541511

Supernet Infrastructure Solutions (Pvt.) Ltd. (1)
9th Floor Tower B World Trade Center, 10 Khayaban e Roomi Block 5 Clifton, Karachi, Pakistan   (81.18%)
Tel.: (92) 2138550000
Web Site: https://superinfra.pk
Information Technology Services
N.A.I.C.S.: 541519

Supernet Limited (1)
9th Floor Tower B World Trade Center 10, Khayaban-e-Roomi Block 5, Clifton, Karachi, 75600, Sindh, Pakistan
Tel.: (92) 2138550000
Web Site: https://www.super.net.pk
Emp.: 300
Broadband Internet Access & Network System Integration Services
N.A.I.C.S.: 517810
Jamal Nasir Khan *(CEO)*

TELECEL GROUP LTD.
5A Wellington Street,, Rose-Hill, Mauritius
Tel.: (230) 2038075773
Web Site: https://telecelgroup.com
International Telecom Company
N.A.I.C.S.: 517810

TELECHIPS INC.
Telechips Pangyo Building 27 Geumto-ro 80beon-gil, Sujeong-gu, Seongnam, 05510, Gyeonggi-do, Korea (South)
Tel.: (82) 230175301
Web Site: https://www.telechips.com
Year Founded: 1999
054450—(KRS)
Rev.: $115,360,107
Assets: $237,902,273
Liabilities: $107,765,432
Net Worth: $130,136,841
Earnings: $35,203,323
Emp.: 331
Fiscal Year-end: 12/31/22
Integrated Circuits Mfr
N.A.I.C.S.: 334413
Leanne Lee *(Head-Product Strategy Ping Grp)*

Subsidiaries:

Telechips Shanghai Co., Ltd. (1)
Room 701 F7 No 1699 Gubei Road, Minhang Dist, Shanghai, 201103, China
Tel.: (86) 2164790501
Semiconductor & Related Device Mfr
N.A.I.C.S.: 334413

Telechips ShenZhen Co., Ltd. (1)
Rm 4105-4106 LANDMARK 4028 Jintian Rd, Futian District, Shenzhen, 518035, China
Tel.: (86) 75582789550
Semiconductor & Related Device Mfr
N.A.I.C.S.: 334413

Telechips USA Inc. (1)

TELECHIPS INC.

Telechips Inc.—(Continued)
200 Spectrum Center Dr Ste 1500, Irvine, CA 92618
Tel.: (858) 784-1201
Semiconductor & Related Device Mfr
N.A.I.C.S.: 334413

TELECOISE
9 B Avenue Blaise Pascal, 60000, Beauvais, Oise, France
Tel.: (33) 344143535
Web Site: http://www.telecoise.fr
Rev.: $22,200,000
Emp.: 195
Electrical Contractor
N.A.I.C.S.: 238210
Gerard Ries (Dir)

TELECOLUMBUS GMBH
Kaiserin-Augusta-Allee 108, 10553, Berlin, Germany
Tel.: (49) 3025777777
Web Site: http://www.telecolumbus.com
Sales Range: $75-99.9 Million
Emp.: 470
Cable Television Services
N.A.I.C.S.: 516210
Olay Zeddelmann (Dir-IT)

TELECOM DESIGN
22 Avenue Leonard de Vinci, 33600, Pessac, France
Tel.: (33) 5 57 35 63 70
Web Site: http://www.telecom-design.com
Sales Range: $1-9.9 Million
Communication Equipment Mfr
N.A.I.C.S.: 334210

TELECOM DIGITAL HOLDINGS LIMITED
19/F YHC Tower No 1 Sheung Yuet Road, Kowloon, China (Hong Kong)
Tel.: (852) 7 777 7777
Web Site: http://www.telecomdigital.cc
6033—(HKG)
Rev.: $194,125,089
Assets: $109,763,399
Liabilities: $56,842,518
Net Worth: $52,920,881
Earnings: $14,582,350
Emp.: 616
Fiscal Year-end: 03/31/22
Interactive Mobile Data Services
N.A.I.C.S.: 517810
King Shek Cheung (Chm)

TELECOM EGYPT
B7 Smart Village, K28 Cairo-Alexandria Road, Cairo, Egypt
Tel.: (20) 1555000111
Web Site: https://www.te.eg
Year Founded: 1854
ETEL—(EGX)
Rev.: $2,352,489,493
Assets: $5,752,107,813
Liabilities: $2,940,283,822
Net Worth: $2,811,823,991
Earnings: $534,118,531
Fiscal Year-end: 12/31/21
Internet & Telecommunications Services
N.A.I.C.S.: 517111
Mohamed Hassan Shamroukh (CFO & Sr VP-Fin Affairs)

Subsidiaries:

Centra Technologies S.A.E. (1)
7 Mosaddak Street, Dokki, Giza, 12311, Egypt
Tel.: (20) 221280000
Web Site: https://www.centra.com.eg
Sales Range: $50-74.9 Million
Emp.: 150
Computer Mfr

N.A.I.C.S.: 334111

TE Data S.A.E. (1)
94 Tahrir Street, Dokki, Giza, 12311, Egypt
Tel.: (20) 2 3332 0700
Web Site: http://www.tedata.net
Internet Service Provider
N.A.I.C.S.: 517810

Subsidiary (Non-US):

TE Data Jordan SAE (2)
91 Abdallah Ghosheh St, Amman, 11953, Jordan
Tel.: (962) 65800333
Web Site: http://www.tedata.net.jo
Emp.: 25
Internet Service Provider
N.A.I.C.S.: 517810
Ahmed Fares (Mgr-Fin)

Xceed Customer Care Maroc (1)
1100 Boulevard Al Quods Sidi Maarouf, 20190, Casablanca, Morocco
Tel.: (212) 529 01 03 00
Customer Care Services
N.A.I.C.S.: 561421

TELECOM LIECHTENSTEIN AG
Schaanerstrasse 1, 9490, Vaduz, Liechtenstein
Tel.: (423) 237 74 00   LI
Web Site: http://www.fl1.li
Internet & Telephone Services
N.A.I.C.S.: 517112
Mathias Maierhofer (CEO)

TELECOM PLUS PLC
508 Edgware Road the Hyde, London, NW9 5AB, United Kingdom
Tel.: (44) 2089555000   UK
Web Site: https://telecomplus.co.uk
TEP—(LSE)
Rev.: $1,313,503,133
Assets: $632,405,610
Liabilities: $353,295,037
Net Worth: $279,110,574
Earnings: $47,524,273
Emp.: 1,987
Fiscal Year-end: 03/31/22
Telecommunications Resellers
N.A.I.C.S.: 517121
Charles Wigoder (Chm)

Subsidiaries:

Cofield Limited (1)
Unit 5 20 Airfield Way, Christchurch, BH23 3PE, Dorset, United Kingdom
Tel.: (44) 3332413209
Web Site: http://plumbbox.co.uk
Plumbing & Heating Equipment Distr
N.A.I.C.S.: 423720

Glow Green Limited (1)
Avalon Floor 5 26-32 Oxford Road, Bournemouth, BH8 8EZ, Dorset, United Kingdom
Tel.: (44) 3301139488
Web Site: https://www.glowgreenltd.com
Heating Equipment Distr
N.A.I.C.S.: 423720

Telecommunications Management Limited (1)
Dryden House The Edge Business Centre, Humber Rd, London, NW2 6EW, United Kingdom
Tel.: (44) 2089555444
Web Site: http://www.tmleurope.com
Sales Range: $25-49.9 Million
Emp.: 75
Mobile & Data Networking Services
N.A.I.C.S.: 518210

TELECOM SERVICE ONE HOLDINGS LIMITED
Unit 2 2/F Shun Fat Industrial Building No 17 Wang Hoi Road, Kowloon Bay, Kowloon, China (Hong Kong)
Tel.: (852) 7 333 6000
Web Site: http://www.tso.cc
Year Founded: 1987

3997—(HKG)
Rev.: $4,482,958
Assets: $12,517,122
Liabilities: $1,255,233
Net Worth: $11,261,889
Earnings: ($129,883)
Emp.: 75
Fiscal Year-end: 03/31/22
Telecommunications Products Repair & Refurbishment
N.A.I.C.S.: 811210
Sunny King Fung Cheung (CEO)

TELECOMMUNICATION TECHNICAL SERVICE JOINT STOCK COMPANY
No 4A 4B 4C Vuong Thua Vu Str Khuong Trung ward, Thanh Xuan District, Hanoi, Vietnam
Tel.: (84) 2437366986
Web Site: https://www.tst.com.vn
TST—(HNX)
Rev.: $3,803,635
Assets: $11,447,376
Liabilities: $7,208,011
Net Worth: $4,239,365
Earnings: ($9,819)
Fiscal Year-end: 12/31/21
Telecommunication Servicesb
N.A.I.C.S.: 517810
Dang Duc Khoi (Chm-Mgmt Bd)

TELECOMMUNICATIONS SERVICES OF TRINIDAD & TOBAGO LIMITED
TSTT House 1 Edward Street, PO Box 3, Port of Spain, Trinidad & Tobago
Tel.: (868) 824 8788   TT
Web Site: http://www.tstt.co.tt
Year Founded: 1991
Telecommunication Servicesb
N.A.I.C.S.: 517111
Rakesh Goswami (Exec VP-Strategic Alliance-Enterprise & Tobago Ops)

TELECOMUNICACOES BRASILEIRAS S.A.
SCN Quadra 4 Block B Sala 903, Centro Empresarial VARIG, CEP 70714 900, Brasilia, DF, Brazil
Tel.: (55) 6134152800
Web Site: http://www.telebras.com.br
Emp.: 300
Telecommunications
N.A.I.C.S.: 517111
Lorival Silva (Head-Investor Rels)

TELECONTROL AG
Unterholzstrasse 10, 4566, Kriegstetten, Switzerland
Tel.: (41) 326744300
Web Site: http://www.telecontrol.ch
Sales Range: $1-9.9 Million
Emp.: 30
Media Monitoring Services
N.A.I.C.S.: 519290
Tanja Hackenbruch (Mng Dir)

TELEDATA MARINE SOLUTIONS LTD
18 Kambar Street Shanthi Colony, Pallikaranai, Chennai, 600 100, India
Tel.: (91) 4465552589
Web Site: http://www.teledatamarine.com
Sales Range: $100-124.9 Million
Emp.: 400
Logistics Management Software & Services
N.A.I.C.S.: 513210
K. Padmanabhan (Mng Dir)

Subsidiaries:

ECM Maritime Services, LLC (1)

INTERNATIONAL PUBLIC

1 Selleck St 1st Fl - Ste 1C, Norwalk, CT 06855
Tel.: (203) 857-0444
Web Site: http://www.ecmmaritime.com
Marine Consulting Services
N.A.I.C.S.: 488390
Ryan Brunelle (Mgr-Non-Tank Plan Dept)

Subsidiary (Non-US):

ECM EUROPE S.r.l. (2)
Porto Turistico di Roma Lungomare Duca degli Abruzzi 84, Box 872, 121, Rome, Italy
Tel.: (39) 06 9760 6135
Web Site: http://www.ecmeurope.net
Marine Consulting Services
N.A.I.C.S.: 488390

TELEDIGITAL D.D.
Semizovac bb, Vogosca, 71 320, Sarajevo, Bosnia & Herzegovina
Tel.: (387) 33911022
Web Site: http://www.teledigital.ba
TTRSR—(SARE)
Rev.: $410,396
Assets: $11,400,763
Liabilities: $5,466,902
Net Worth: $5,933,861
Earnings: $127
Emp.: 7
Fiscal Year-end: 12/31/20
Wireless Internet Services
N.A.I.C.S.: 517112

TELEFIELD INC.
214-1 Galmachi-ro 4th floor, Jungwon-gu, Seongnam, Gyeonggi-do, Korea (South)
Tel.: (82) 317399800
Web Site: https://www.hanwoolms.com
Year Founded: 2000
091440—(KRS)
Rev.: $17,676,110
Assets: $34,333,850
Liabilities: $21,410,977
Net Worth: $12,922,873
Earnings: ($11,443,589)
Emp.: 115
Fiscal Year-end: 12/31/22
Telecommunications Equipment Mfr
N.A.I.C.S.: 334290
Ha Jun-Ho (CEO)

Subsidiaries:

TELEFIELD Inc. - Seongnam Factory (1)
Meta-Networks 2F 55 Galmachi-ro 281beon-gil, Jungwon-gu, Seongnam, Gyeonggi-do, Korea (South)
Tel.: (82) 317399800
Wireless Communication Equipment Mfr
N.A.I.C.S.: 334220

TELEFONAKTIEBOLAGET LM ERICSSON
Torshamnsgatan 21, Kista, 164 83, Stockholm, Sweden
Tel.: (46) 107190000   SE
Web Site: https://www.ericsson.com
Year Founded: 1876
ERIC—(NASDAQ)
Rev.: $28,370,171,200
Assets: $33,148,382,400
Liabilities: $22,749,974,240
Net Worth: $10,398,408,160
Earnings: $2,151,415,840
Emp.: 100,824
Fiscal Year-end: 12/31/20
Mobile & Fixed Network Telecommunications Products & Services
N.A.I.C.S.: 517111
Arun Bansal (Sr VP & Head-Market Area-Europe & Latin America)

Subsidiaries:

Compania Ericsson S.A. (1)
Av Javier Prabo W 203 6th Floor, San Isidro, L27, Lima, Peru

AND PRIVATE COMPANIES

TELEFONAKTIEBOLAGET LM ERICSSON

Tel.: (51) 12156100
Business Communications & Telecommunications Systems Mfr
N.A.I.C.S.: 334290

Compania Ericsson S.A.C.I. (1)
Guemes 676 Piso 1 Vincente Lopez,
B1638CJF, Buenos Aires,
Argentina (100%)
Tel.: (54) 01143195500
Web Site: http://www.ericsson.com
Sales Range: $50-74.9 Million
Emp.: 200
Business Communications & Telecommunications Systems
N.A.I.C.S.: 334290

Compania Ericsson Uruguay S.A. (1)
1200 Lima St, CP 11800, Montevideo,
Uruguay (100%)
Tel.: (598) 29246060
Web Site: http://www.ericsson.com
Sales Range: $25-49.9 Million
Emp.: 75
Telecommunications Equipment Mfr
N.A.I.C.S.: 334418

CradlePoint, Inc. (1)
1111 W Jefferson St, Boise, ID 83702-5389
Tel.: (208) 424-5054
Web Site: http://www.cradlepoint.com
Sales Range: $10-24.9 Million
Emp.: 40
Designer & Mfr of Docking Cradles, Cellular Routers & Software Platforms
N.A.I.C.S.: 513210
Ryan Adamson (Founder & Sr VP-America Sls)

Subsidiary (Domestic):

Pertino, Inc. (2)
973 University Ave, Los Gatos, CA 95032
Tel.: (408) 354-3900
Web Site: http://www.pertino.com
Computer Software Program Mfr
N.A.I.C.S.: 541511
Andrew Mastracci (Founder)

ERICSSON AB LIBYA (1)
Ghaser Benghashir, Tripoli, Libya
Tel.: (218) 21 3615000
Web Site: http://www.ericsson.com
Emp.: 17
Telecommunication Servicesb
N.A.I.C.S.: 517810

ERICSSON CAMEROON (1)
First Floor Immeuble Gicam Rue Vallee des Ministress, Douala, Cameroon
Tel.: (237) 334 23670
Web Site: http://www.ericsson.com
Telecommunication Servicesb
N.A.I.C.S.: 517810

ERICSSON DE BOLIVIA TELECOMUNICACIONES S.A. (1)
Nicolas Ortiz N 323 Barrio Equipetrol, Santa Cruz, Bolivia
Tel.: (591) 3 3426060
Communication Service
N.A.I.C.S.: 517810

ERICSSON DE HONDURAS S.A. (1)
Col Lomas del Guijarro Sur Boulevar Juan Pablo II Torre Alianza II, Piso No 8, Tegucigalpa, Honduras
Tel.: (504) 2 240 3000
Web Site: http://www.ericsson.com
Sales Range: $25-49.9 Million
Emp.: 70
Communication Service
N.A.I.C.S.: 517810

ERICSSON EGYPT LTD (1)
KM28 Smart Village Alex Road B86, Cairo, 12577, Egypt
Tel.: (20) 3536 9100
Telecommunication Servicesb
N.A.I.C.S.: 517810

ERICSSON HAITI (1)
Rue Lamarre 20 Petion Ville, Port-au-Prince, Haiti
Tel.: (509) 7011 063
Web Site: http://www.ericsson.com
Telecommunication Servicesb
N.A.I.C.S.: 517810

ERICSSON LEBANON COMMUNICATIONS SARL (1)
Dolphin Building Daoud Amoun Street, Sin El Fil Jisr Wati, Beirut, 55334, Lebanon
Tel.: (961) 1 517700
Web Site: http://www.ericsson.com
Emp.: 270
Mobile Communications Services

ERICSSON NV/SA (1)
Lozenberg 20, Zaventem, 1932, Belgium
Tel.: (32) 2 745 12 11
Web Site: http://www.ericsson.com
Mobile Communications Services
N.A.I.C.S.: 517112

ERICSSON REPUBLICA DOMINICANA (1)
Avenida Winston Churchill Esquina Victor Garrido Puello, Santo Domingo, Dominican Republic
Tel.: (809) 683 7701
Web Site: http://www.ericsson.com
Telecommunication Servicesb
N.A.I.C.S.: 517810

ERICSSON SLOVAKIA spol. s.r.o (1)
Roznavska 24, 821 04, Bratislava, Slovakia
Tel.: (421) 2 49 499 111
Web Site: http://www.ericsson.com
Sales Range: $50-74.9 Million
Emp.: 150
Mobile Communications Services
N.A.I.C.S.: 517112

ERICSSON TURKIYE (1)
Uso Center No 61 Kat 1-4-5-6-7-10, Maslak, Istanbul, 34398, Turkiye
Tel.: (90) 212 286 86 86
Web Site: http://www.ericsson.com
Communication Service
N.A.I.C.S.: 517810

ERICSSON VIETNAM COMPANY LTD (1)
Level 15 Keangnam Hanoi Landmark Tower Building Plot 6, Tu Liem District, Hanoi, 844, Vietnam
Tel.: (84) 4 3838 0100
Web Site: http://www.ericsson.com
Emp.: 200
Mobile Communications Services
N.A.I.C.S.: 517112

ERICSSON spol. s r o. (1)
Sokolovska 79, CP 192, Prague, 186 00, Czech Republic
Tel.: (420) 2 2400 0111
Web Site: http://www.ericsson.com
Sales Range: $25-49.9 Million
Emp.: 70
Mobile Communications Services
N.A.I.C.S.: 517112

Ericsson (China) Communication Co., Ltd. (1)
No 5 Lize East Street Ericsson Building, 100102, Beijing, Chaoyang, China
Tel.: (86) 10 8476 9000
Web Site: http://www.ericsson.com
Telecommunications Equipment Mfr
N.A.I.C.S.: 334418

Ericsson (China) Company Ltd. (1)
Beijing Lize Ericsson Building 5 East Street, Beijing, 100102, Chaoyang District, China
Tel.: (86) 10 8476 9000
Web Site: http://www.ericsson.com
Telecommunications Equipment Mfr
N.A.I.C.S.: 334418

Ericsson (Malaysia) Sdn. Bhd. (1)
3420 Persiaran Sepang, Cyberjaya, 63000, Selangor Darul Ehsan, Malaysia
Tel.: (60) 3 8314 6000
Web Site: http://www.ericsson.com
Mobile Communications Services
N.A.I.C.S.: 517112

Ericsson A/S (1)
Televeien 1, Serviceboks 504, Grimstad, 4898, Norway (100%)
Tel.: (47) 37293000
Web Site: http://www.ericsson.com
Sales Range: $50-74.9 Million
Emp.: 200
Telecommunications Equipment Mfr
N.A.I.C.S.: 334418

Ericsson A/S (1)
Rolfsbuktveien 4, PO Box 164, Fornebu, 1324, Norway
Tel.: (47) 67250000
Web Site: http://www.ericsson.com
Sales Range: $125-149.9 Million
Emp.: 50
Telecommunications Equipment Mfr
N.A.I.C.S.: 334418

Ericsson AB (1)
Gotalandswagen 230, 12625, Stockholm, Sweden (51%)
Tel.: (46) 87190000
Web Site: http://www.ericsson.com
Telecommunications Equipment Mfr
N.A.I.C.S.: 334418

Branch (Domestic):

Ericsson AB (2)
Torshamnsgatan 21, S 164 83, Stockholm, Sweden
Tel.: (46) 107190000
Web Site: http://www.ericsson.com
Sales Range: $700-749.9 Million
Emp.: 4,780
Mobile Telephones & Paging Systems Mfr
N.A.I.C.S.: 334210

Ericsson AB (2)
Datalinjen 4, PO Box 1248, SE 581 12, Linkoping, Sweden
Tel.: (46) 0013287300
Web Site: http://www.ericsson.com
Sales Range: $150-199.9 Million
Emp.: 1,000
Radio Systems Mfr
N.A.I.C.S.: 334220

Ericsson AB (2)
Torshamngatan 48, SE 16480, Kista, Sweden
Tel.: (46) 87571500
Web Site: http://www.ericsson.se
Telecommunications Equipment Mfr
N.A.I.C.S.: 334418

Ericsson AB (2)
Skolgangen 17, PO Box 6206, SE 800 06, Gavle, Sweden
Tel.: (46) 26156000
Web Site: http://www.ericsson.se
Telecommunications Equipment Mfr
N.A.I.C.S.: 334418

Ericsson AB (2)
Montorgatan 2, 62933, Kumla, Sweden
Tel.: (46) 19584100
Web Site: http://www.ericsson.se
Telecommunications Equipment Mfr
N.A.I.C.S.: 334418

Ericsson AB (2)
Industrivagen 4, SE 149 80, Nynashamn, Sweden
Tel.: (46) 852062000
Web Site: http://www.ericsson.se
Telecommunications Equipment Mfr
N.A.I.C.S.: 334418

Ericsson AB Branch Office-Dhaka (1)
33 Banani Commercial Area SMC Tower Second Fl, Banani, Dhaka, 1213, Bangladesh
Tel.: (880) 29886641
Sales Range: $200-249.9 Million
Emp.: 800
Telecommunications Equipment Mfr
N.A.I.C.S.: 334418

Ericsson AG (1)
Freiburgstrasse 251, 3018, Bern, Switzerland
Tel.: (41) 31 998 35 00
Web Site: http://www.ericsson.com
Mobile Communications Services
N.A.I.C.S.: 517112

Ericsson Antilles (1)
Kaya Jombi Mensing 14 Zeelandia Office Park ING Boulevard 1st floor, PO Box 3304, Zeelandia, Willemstad, Curacao (100%)
Tel.: (599) 94610844
Telecommunications Equipment Mfr
N.A.I.C.S.: 334418

Ericsson Australia Pty. Ltd. (1)
8/818 Bourke St, Docklands, Melbourne, 3008, VIC, Australia (100%)
Tel.: (61) 393011000
Web Site: http://www.ericsson.com.au
Sales Range: $125-149.9 Million
Emp.: 500
Telecommunications Equipment Mfr
N.A.I.C.S.: 334418

Ericsson Australia Pty. Ltd.-Treasury (1)
Bldg C 11 Calavera Rd, North Ryde, 2113, VIC, Australia (100%)
Tel.: (61) 393011000
Web Site: http://www.ericsson.com.au
Sales Range: $25-49.9 Million
Emp.: 65
Telecommunications Equipment Mfr
N.A.I.C.S.: 334418

Ericsson Austria GmbH (1)
Ernst-melchior-Gasse 24, 1020, Vienna, Austria (100%)
Tel.: (43) 1811000
Sales Range: $25-49.9 Million
Emp.: 84
Telecommunications Equipment Mfr
N.A.I.C.S.: 334418
Gottfried Madl (Office Mgr)

Ericsson Business Communications NV/SA (1)
Lozenberg 20, Zaventem, 1932, Belgium (100%)
Tel.: (32) 27451211
Web Site: http://www.ericsson.com
Sales Range: $100-124.9 Million
Emp.: 400
Telecommunications Systems Mfr
N.A.I.C.S.: 334290

Ericsson Business Consulting (M) Sdn. Bhd. (1)
3420 Persiaran Sepang 63000, Cyberjaya, 63000, Selangor Darul Ehsan, Malaysia
Tel.: (60) 383146000
Sales Range: $125-149.9 Million
Emp.: 300
Telecommunications Equipment Mfr
N.A.I.C.S.: 334418

Ericsson Business Consulting Espana, S.A. (1)
Retama 1, 28045, Madrid, Spain (100%)
Tel.: (34) 913391000
Web Site: http://www.ericsson.es
Sales Range: $450-499.9 Million
Emp.: 1,700
Telecommunications Equipment Mfr
N.A.I.C.S.: 334418

Ericsson Business Mobile Networks (1)
Ericssonstraat 2, PO Box 5121, Rijen, 5121 ML, Netherlands
Tel.: (31) 161249911
Web Site: http://www.ericsson.com
Sales Range: $200-249.9 Million
Emp.: 500
Telecommunications Equipment Mfr
N.A.I.C.S.: 334418

Ericsson Business Systems AB (PRS) (1)
Torshamnsgatan 23 Kista, 164 83, Stockholm, Sweden
Tel.: (46) 107190000
Web Site: http://www.ericsson.se
Sales Range: $200-249.9 Million
Emp.: 1,000
Telecommunications Equipment Mfr
N.A.I.C.S.: 334418

Ericsson Canada Incorporated (1)
8275 route Transcanadienne, Ville Saint Laurent, H4S 0B6, QC, Canada (100%)
Tel.: (514) 738-8300
Web Site: http://www.ericsson.ca
Sales Range: $450-499.9 Million
Emp.: 1,500
Telecommunications Equipment Mfr
N.A.I.C.S.: 334418

Ericsson Canada, Inc. (1)
200-2425 Matheson Blvd E, Mississauga, L4W 5K4, ON, Canada
Tel.: (905) 268-2005
Web Site: http://www.ericsson.com
Sales Range: $50-74.9 Million
Emp.: 150
Mobile Phone Mfr

TELEFONAKTIEBOLAGET LM ERICSSON

Telefonaktiebolaget LM Ericsson—(Continued)
N.A.I.C.S.: 334210

Ericsson Chile S.A. (1)
Avda Vitacura 2939 17th Fl, Las Condas,
Santiago, 6763268, Chile **(100%)**
Tel.: (56) 23725000
Web Site: http://www.ericsson.com
Sales Range: $50-74.9 Million
Emp.: 120
Telecommunications Equipment Mfr
N.A.I.C.S.: 334418

Ericsson Communication Solutions Pte Ltd. (1)
510 Thomson Road, Singapore, 298135, Singapore
Tel.: (65) 6880 86 00
Web Site: http://www.ericsson.com
Telecommunication Servicesb
N.A.I.C.S.: 517810

Ericsson Communications (1)
Level 2 2 Owens Road Epsom, Auckland, 1023, New Zealand **(100%)**
Tel.: (64) 96329200
Web Site: http://www.ericsson.com
Sales Range: $25-49.9 Million
Emp.: 40
Telecommunications Equipment Mfr
N.A.I.C.S.: 334418

Ericsson Company for Electronics (1)
Fra Andjela Zvizdovica 1, Unis-Tower A/9, 71000, Sarajevo, Bosnia & Herzegovina
Tel.: (387) 33209414
Web Site: http://www.ericsson.com
Telecommunications Equipment Mfr
N.A.I.C.S.: 334418

Ericsson Corporatia AO (1)
12 8th March St 12, 128083, Moscow, Russia **(100%)**
Tel.: (7) 0952476211
Web Site: http://www.ericsson.ru
Telecommunications Equipment Mfr
N.A.I.C.S.: 334418

Ericsson Credit AB (1)
Torshamnsgatan 21-23, Kista, Stockholm, 164 80, Sweden
Tel.: (46) 107190000
Web Site: http://www.ericsson.com
Financial Management Services
N.A.I.C.S.: 523999

Ericsson Danmark A/S (1)
Arne Jacobsens Alle 17, Copenhagen, 2300, Denmark
Tel.: (45) 33 88 33 88
Web Site: http://www.ericsson.com
Mobile Communications Services
N.A.I.C.S.: 517112

Ericsson De El Salvador S.A. De C.V. (1)
89 Ave Norte y Calle El Mirador World Trade Center Torre II 2a, Planta Ofic 201 Colonia Escal, San Salvador, El Salvador **(100%)**
Tel.: (503) 2271 0123
Web Site: http://www.ericsson.com
Sales Range: $25-49.9 Million
Emp.: 40
Telecommunications Systems
N.A.I.C.S.: 517111

Ericsson De Panama S.A. (1)
PH Torres De Las Americas C Tower 21 Fl, 0823-05332, Panama, Panama
Tel.: (507) 2065100
Sales Range: $50-74.9 Million
Emp.: 200
Telecommunications Equipment Mfr
N.A.I.C.S.: 334418
Jorge Faa *(Gen Mgr)*

Ericsson Defense Systems Pty. Ltd. (1)
Level 8 818 Bourke St, PO Box 256 C, Melbourne, 3008, VIC, Australia
Tel.: (61) 393011000
Web Site: http://www.ericsson.com.au
Sales Range: $400-449.9 Million
Emp.: 1,500
Defense Communications Systems Mfr
N.A.I.C.S.: 334290

Ericsson Diax A/S (1)
Faelledvej 17, DK 7600, Struer, Denmark **(100%)**
Tel.: (45) 9786 9022
Web Site: http://www.ericsson.com
Sales Range: $25-49.9 Million
Emp.: 230
Telecommunications Systems Mfr
N.A.I.C.S.: 517111

Ericsson Eesti AS (1)
Jarvevana Tee 9, PO Box 3542, 11314, Tallinn, Estonia **(100%)**
Tel.: (372) 6500900
Web Site: http://www.ericsson.com
Sales Range: $50-74.9 Million
Emp.: 128
Telecommunications Equipment Mfr
N.A.I.C.S.: 334418

Ericsson Electronic Services (1)
Lensmannslia 4, PO Box 164, N-1371, Asker, Norway
Tel.: (47) 67250000
Web Site: http://www.ericsson.no
Telecommunications Equipment Mfr
N.A.I.C.S.: 334418

Ericsson Erisoft AB (1)
Skelleftehamnsvagen 206, Ursviken, 93283, Umea, Sweden **(100%)**
Tel.: (46) 910731000
Web Site: http://www.ericsson.se
Sales Range: $50-74.9 Million
Emp.: 180
Telecommunications Equipment Mfr
N.A.I.C.S.: 334418

Ericsson Espana S.A. (1)
Calle Retama 1 Bldg Torre Sueccia, 28045, Madrid, Spain **(100%)**
Tel.: (34) 913391000
Web Site: http://www.ericsson.es
Sales Range: $50-74.9 Million
Emp.: 150
Telecommunications Equipment Mfr
N.A.I.C.S.: 334418

Ericsson Eurolab Deutschland GmbH (1)
Ericsson Allee 1, 52134, Herzogenrath, Germany **(100%)**
Tel.: (49) 24075750
Web Site: http://www.ericsson.de
Sales Range: $200-249.9 Million
Emp.: 800
Telecommunications Systems Mfr
N.A.I.C.S.: 517111

Ericsson Finanz AG (1)
Ruchstuckstrasse 21, 8306, Bruttisellen, Switzerland
Tel.: (41) 18072222
Financial Services
N.A.I.C.S.: 522320

Ericsson France S.A. (1)
6-8 Rue Ampere, Massy, 91348, France
Tel.: (33) 169937000
Web Site: http://www.ericsson.fr
Sales Range: $200-249.9 Million
Emp.: 695
Telecommunications Equipment Mfr
N.A.I.C.S.: 334418

Ericsson GmbH (1)
Prinzenallee 21, D-40549, Dusseldorf, Germany
Tel.: (49) 2115340
Sales Range: $125-149.9 Million
Emp.: 500
Telecommunications Equipment Mfr
N.A.I.C.S.: 334418

Ericsson Hellas S.A. (1)
Attiki Odos Km 40 2, Athens, 190 02, Paiania, Greece
Tel.: (30) 2106695100
Web Site: http://www.ericssonhellas.com
Sales Range: $25-49.9 Million
Emp.: 200
Telecommunications Equipment Mfr
N.A.I.C.S.: 517111
Marie Large *(Pres)*

Ericsson Holding International B.V. (1)
Ericssonstraat 2, PO Box 8, 5120 AA, Rijen, Netherlands **(100%)**
Tel.: (31) 161249911
Web Site: http://www.ericsson.com
Sales Range: $25-49.9 Million
Emp.: 45
Holding Company; Telecommunications
N.A.I.C.S.: 551112

Ericsson Holding Ltd. (1)
Midleton Gate Guildford Business Park, Guildford, GU2 8SG, United Kingdom
Tel.: (44) 14 8330 3666
Telecommunication Servicesb
N.A.I.C.S.: 517810

Ericsson Hungary Ltd. (1)
PO Box 107, H 1300, Budapest, Hungary
Tel.: (36) 14377100
Web Site: http://www.ericsson.com
Sales Range: $450-499.9 Million
Emp.: 6,000
Telecommunications Equipment Mfr
N.A.I.C.S.: 334418

Ericsson Inc. (1)
6300 Legacy Dr, Plano, TX 75024-3607
Tel.: (972) 583-0000
Web Site: http://www.ericsson.com
Sales Range: $1-4.9 Billion
Emp.: 7,000
Mobile Telephone & Personal Paging Systems Engineer & Marketer
N.A.I.C.S.: 334220

Subsidiary (Domestic):

Ericsson Caribbean, Inc. (2)
City View Plz Ste 6010, Guaynabo, PR 00968 **(100%)**
Tel.: (787) 771-1700
Web Site: http://www.ericsson.com
Sales Range: $25-49.9 Million
Emp.: 25
Telecommunications Equipment Mfr
N.A.I.C.S.: 334418

Branch (Domestic):

Ericsson Inc. - New York Office (2)
1114 Avenue of the Americas Ste 3410, New York, NY 10036-5537
Tel.: (212) 685-4030
Web Site: http://www.ericsson.com
Sales Range: $25-49.9 Million
Emp.: 20
Telecommunications Equipment Mfr
N.A.I.C.S.: 334418

Subsidiary (Domestic):

Ericsson TEMS (2)
1943 Isaac Newton Sq E, Reston, VA 20190-5012
Tel.: (571) 203-4500
Sales Range: $50-74.9 Million
Emp.: 130
Telecommunications Equipment Mfr
N.A.I.C.S.: 334418

Redback Networks Inc. (1)
100 Headquarters Dr, San Jose, CA 95134-1362
Tel.: (408) 750-5000
Web Site: http://www.redback.com
Sales Range: $250-299.9 Million
Emp.: 724
Broadband Telecommunications Networking Equipment Designer, Mfr & Marketer
N.A.I.C.S.: 334118

Ericsson India (Pvt) Ltd. (1)
Ericsson Forum, DLF-Cyberciti Sector-25A, Gurgaon, 122 002, India
Tel.: (91) 2560808
Web Site: http://www.ericsson.co.in
Sales Range: $25-49.9 Million
Emp.: 100
Telecommunications Systems
N.A.I.C.S.: 517111

Ericsson Invention Ltd. (1)
Cornamaddy, Athlone, Westmeath, Ireland
Tel.: (353) 906474602
Web Site: http://www.ericsson.ie
Sales Range: $125-149.9 Million
Emp.: 300
Printed Circuit Assembly & Telephone Apparatus Mfr
N.A.I.C.S.: 334418

Ericsson Japan K.K. (1)
Yokohama Blue Avenue 4-4-2 Minato Mirai, Nishi-ku, Yokohama, 220-0012, Kanagawa, Japan

INTERNATIONAL PUBLIC

Tel.: (81) 3 6721 3300
Web Site: http://www.ericsson.com
Mobile Communications Services
N.A.I.C.S.: 517112

Ericsson K.f.t. (1)
1037 Budapest Laborc Utca 1, PO Box 107, H 1300, Budapest, Hungary **(100%)**
Tel.: (36) 014377100
Web Site: http://www.ericsson.hu
Sales Range: $200-249.9 Million
Emp.: 800
Telecommunications Equipment Mfr
N.A.I.C.S.: 334418

Ericsson Korea Ltd. (1)
18th Floor ASEM Tower, Samsung dong Gangnam gu, Seoul, 135 798, Korea (South) **(100%)**
Tel.: (82) 234580000
Web Site: http://www.ericsson.com
Sales Range: $25-49.9 Million
Emp.: 31
Telecommunications Equipment Mfr
N.A.I.C.S.: 334418

Ericsson Lebanon S.A.R.L. (1)
Sin El Fil 82, PO Box 55334, Beirut, Lebanon **(100%)**
Tel.: (961) 1517700
Sales Range: $25-49.9 Million
Emp.: 60
Telecommunications Equipment Mfr
N.A.I.C.S.: 334418

Ericsson Limited (1)
12th Fl Stephen House 979 Kings Rd, Quarry Bay, China (Hong Kong) **(100%)**
Tel.: (852) 025902388
Sales Range: $50-74.9 Million
Emp.: 150
Wireless Telecommunication & Communication Equipment Mfr
N.A.I.C.S.: 517112

Ericsson Ltd. (1)
Unit 4 Midleton Gate, Guildford, GU2 8SG, United Kingdom
Tel.: (44) 1483 303 666
Web Site: http://www.ericsson.com
Mobile Communications Services
N.A.I.C.S.: 517112

Subsidiary (Domestic):

Ericsson Television Ltd. (2)
Strategic Park Comines Way, Hedge End, Southampton, SO30 4DA, United Kingdom
Tel.: (44) 2380484000
Sales Range: $250-299.9 Million
Emp.: 500
Television Broadcasting Products & Support Services
N.A.I.C.S.: 334220

Subsidiary (Non-US):

Ericsson Limited (3)
12/F Devon House Taikoo Place 979 King's Road, Quarry Bay, China (Hong Kong)
Tel.: (852) 2590 2388
Web Site: http://www.ericsson.com
Emp.: 115
Television Broadcasting Products & Support Services
N.A.I.C.S.: 334220

Subsidiary (Non-US):

TANDBERG Television Japan (4)
AIOS Gotanda Bldg 609, Higashi Gotanda 1 10 7, Shinagawa ku, Tokyo, Japan
Tel.: (81) 3 5809 5900
Web Site: http://www.tandbergtv.com
Television Broadcasting Products & Support Services
N.A.I.C.S.: 334220

Subsidiary (US):

SkyStream Networks, Inc. (3)
455 DeGuigne Dr, Sunnyvale, CA 94085-3890
Tel.: (408) 616-3300
Sales Range: $25-49.9 Million
Emp.: 100
IP Video Delivery Services
N.A.I.C.S.: 541519

Ericsson Manufacturing Co., Ltd. (1)
Suntowers Bldg B 20th Fl, 123 Vibhavadee-

AND PRIVATE COMPANIES — TELEFONAKTIEBOLAGET LM ERICSSON

Rangsit Road, Bangkok, 10900, Thailand **(100%)**
Tel.: (66) 22997000
Web Site: http://www.Ericsson.com
Sales Range: $200-249.9 Million
Emp.: 600
Telecommunications Equipment Mfr
N.A.I.C.S.: 334418

Ericsson Microwave Systems AB (1)
Torshamnsgatan 39, PO Box 42, SE 164 93, Stockholm, Sweden **(100%)**
Tel.: (46) 317470000
Telecommunications Equipment Mfr
N.A.I.C.S.: 334418

Plant (Domestic):

Ericsson Microwave Systems AB - Boras (2)
Sandlidsgatan 3, PO Box 22150, SE 504 12, Boras, Sweden
Tel.: (46) 107190000
Web Site: http://www.ericsson.se
Sales Range: $400-449.9 Million
Emp.: 1,100
Telecommunications Equipment Mfr
N.A.I.C.S.: 334418

Ericsson Microwave Systems AB - Gothenburg (2)
Solhusgatan 4, 41276, Gothenburg, Sweden
Tel.: (46) 856860000
Web Site: http://www.ericsson.se
Sales Range: $400-449.9 Million
Emp.: 1,200
Telecommunications Equipment System
N.A.I.C.S.: 334418

Ericsson Microwave Systems AB - Kista (2)
Torshamnsgatan 39, SE 164 80, Kista, Sweden
Tel.: (46) 87570000
Web Site: http://www.ericsson.se
Telecommunications Equipment Mfr
N.A.I.C.S.: 334418

Ericsson Mobile Communications (1)
Arne Jacobsons Alle 17, 2300, Copenhagen, Denmark
Tel.: (45) 33883388
Web Site: http://www.ericsson.com
Sales Range: $50-74.9 Million
Emp.: 100
Telecommunications Equipment Mfr
N.A.I.C.S.: 334418

Ericsson Mobile Communications AB (1)
Solvegatan 53, 221 83, Lund, Sweden
Tel.: (46) 107190000
Web Site: http://www.ericsson.com
Sales Range: $100-124.9 Million
Emp.: 400
Wireless Telecommunications
N.A.I.C.S.: 517112

Ericsson Mobile Communications Norway (1)
Vollsveien 4, PO Box 164, Fornebu, 1330, Norway
Tel.: (47) 67250000
Web Site: http://www.ericsson.no
Sales Range: $25-49.9 Million
Emp.: 47
Telecommunications Equipment Mfr
N.A.I.C.S.: 334418

Ericsson Morocco S.A.R.L. (1)
Ctr Daffaires Aile Sud De, 10100, Rabat, Morocco **(100%)**
Tel.: (212) 5 37 56 31 15
Sales Range: $25-49.9 Million
Emp.: 80
Telecommunications Equipment Mfr
N.A.I.C.S.: 334418

Ericsson Nederland B.V. (1)
Ericssonstraat 2, Rijen, 5121 ML, Netherlands
Tel.: (31) 161249911
Web Site: http://www.ericsson.com
Emp.: 300
Communication Equipment Mfr & Distr
N.A.I.C.S.: 334290

Ericsson Network Technologies AB (1)

Kabelvagen 1, SE 824 82, Hudiksvall, Sweden
Tel.: (46) 6503 6844
Specialty Cables Mfr
N.A.I.C.S.: 335929

Ericsson New Zealand (1)
Level 2 2 Owens Road Epsom, Auckland, 1023, New Zealand
Tel.: (64) 9 632 9200
Web Site: http://www.ericsson.com
Telecommunication Servicesb
N.A.I.C.S.: 517810

Ericsson Nikola Tesla D.D. (1)
Krapinska 45, Zagreb, 10000, Croatia
Tel.: (385) 13653535
Web Site: http://www.ericsson.com
Sales Range: $450-499.9 Million
Emp.: 1,700
Telecommunications Equipment Mfr
N.A.I.C.S.: 334418

Ericsson OMC Ltd (1)
Maplewood, Chineham Business Park, Crookwood Ln, Basingstoke, RG24 8YB, Hants, United Kingdom
Tel.: (44) 1256707874
Web Site: http://www.ericsson.co.uk
Telecommunications Equipment Mfr
N.A.I.C.S.: 334418

Ericsson Project Services (Pty) Ltd. (1)
PO Box 730, ZA-2121, Johannesburg, South Africa
Tel.: (27) 118442000
Web Site: http://www.ericsson.com
Sales Range: $200-249.9 Million
Emp.: 800
Telecommunications Equipment Mfr
N.A.I.C.S.: 334418

Ericsson Radio Systems AB (1)
Forsta Avenyen 14 C, 28132, Hassleholm, Sweden **(100%)**
Tel.: (46) 45143400
Web Site: http://www.ericsson.se
Sales Range: $25-49.9 Million
Emp.: 100
Telecommunications Equipment Mfr
N.A.I.C.S.: 334418

Ericsson S.A. (1)
RETAMA 1, 28045, Madrid, Spain
Tel.: (34) 913391000
Web Site: http://www.ericsson.com
Telecommunications Equipment & Services
N.A.I.C.S.: 334418

Ericsson S.p.A. (1)
Via Anagnina 203 CP 4197, Morena, 00118, Rome, Italy **(100%)**
Tel.: (39) 0672581
Web Site: http://www.ericsson.com
Sales Range: $800-899.9 Million
Emp.: 3,000
Telecommunications Equipment Mfr
N.A.I.C.S.: 334210

Ericsson Saudi Arabia (1)
Olaya King Fahd Rd, PO Box 6121, Abraj Atta Awuneya Bldg, Riyadh, 11442, Saudi Arabia
Tel.: (966) 12180444
Sales Range: $25-49.9 Million
Emp.: 50
Business Communications & Telecommunications Systems
N.A.I.C.S.: 334290

Ericsson Senegal SARL (1)
Km 8 Route de Ouakam, BP 8815, Dakar, Senegal
Tel.: (221) 33 829 30 00
Communication Service
N.A.I.C.S.: 517810

Ericsson Slovenia d.o.o. (1)
Dunajska 63, SI 1000, Ljubljana, Slovenia **(100%)**
Tel.: (386) 12363010
Web Site: http://www.ericsson.com
Sales Range: $25-49.9 Million
Emp.: 29
Telecommunications Equipment Mfr
N.A.I.C.S.: 334418

Ericsson South Africa (Pty) Ltd. (1)
148 Kelvin Drive Woodmead - Parklands,

Parklands, ZA-2121, Johannesburg, South Africa
Tel.: (27) 118442000
Web Site: http://www.ericsson.com
Sales Range: $200-249.9 Million
Emp.: 800
Telecommunications Equipment Mfr
N.A.I.C.S.: 334418

Ericsson Sp. z.o.o. (1)
EPO Brama Zachodina, Al Jerozolimskie 92, 00-807, Warsaw, Poland
Tel.: (48) 226916000
Web Site: http://www.ericsson.com
Sales Range: $100-124.9 Million
Emp.: 300
Business Communications Systems
N.A.I.C.S.: 334290

Ericsson Support Centre Sdn. Bhd. (1)
3420 Persiaran Sepang Cyberjala, Petaling Jaya, 63000, Selangor Darul Ehsan, Malaysia
Tel.: (60) 383146000
Web Site: http://www.ericsson.com
Sales Range: $1-4.9 Billion
Emp.: 500
Telecommunications Equipment Mfr
N.A.I.C.S.: 334418

Ericsson Sverige AB (1)
Lm Ericssons Vag 8, 12625, Stockholm, Sweden **(100%)**
Tel.: (46) 857918000
Web Site: http://www.ericsson.se
Sales Range: $50-74.9 Million
Emp.: 175
Telecommunications Equipment Mfr
N.A.I.C.S.: 334418

Ericsson Taiwan Ltd. (1)
4th Floor No 33 Lane 11, Kuang-Fu North Road, Taipei, Taiwan
Tel.: (886) 227695500
Web Site: http://www.ericsson.com.tw
Sales Range: $50-74.9 Million
Emp.: 200
Business Communications & Telecommunications Systems
N.A.I.C.S.: 334290

Ericsson Telecom AB (1)
Torshamnsgatan 23, 164 83, Stockholm, Sweden **(100%)**
Tel.: (46) 10 719 00 00
Web Site: http://www.ericsson.com
Communication Equipment Mfr
N.A.I.C.S.: 334290

Ericsson Telecom S.A. De C.V. (1)
Prolongacion Paseo de la Reforma 1015 5th Floor, Mexico, 80210, Mexico
Tel.: (52) 5511030000
Web Site: http://www.ericsson.com
Sales Range: $200-249.9 Million
Emp.: 1,000
Business Communications & Telecommunications Systems
N.A.I.C.S.: 334290

Ericsson Telecomm. Lanka (PVT) Ltd. (1)
240 High Level Rd Kirillapone, Colombo, 6, Sri Lanka **(100%)**
Tel.: (94) 112828431
Web Site: http://www.ericsson.lk
Sales Range: $25-49.9 Million
Emp.: 30
Telecommunications Equipment Mfr
N.A.I.C.S.: 334418

Ericsson Telecomminicacoes, Lda. (1)
Social Headquarters Edificio Infante D Henrique Paco De Arcos Quinta D, Lisbon, 2770 192, Portugal **(100%)**
Tel.: (351) 214466000
Web Site: http://www.ericsson.pt
Sales Range: $50-74.9 Million
Emp.: 200
Telecommunications Equipment Mfr
N.A.I.C.S.: 334418

Ericsson Telecommunicacues S.A. (1)
Rua Maria Prestes Maia 300, 02096 970, Sao Paulo, Brazil **(100%)**
Tel.: (55) 1162242000
Web Site: http://www.ericsson.com.br

Sales Range: $200-249.9 Million
Emp.: 1,000
Telecommunications Equipment Mfr
N.A.I.C.S.: 334418

Ericsson Telecommunicatie B.V. (1)
Ericssonstraat 2, PO Box 8, NL 5120 AA, Rijen, Netherlands **(100%)**
Tel.: (31) 161249911
Web Site: http://www.ericsson.nl
Sales Range: $200-249.9 Million
Emp.: 700
Telecommunications Equipment Mfr
N.A.I.C.S.: 334418

Ericsson Telecommunications Inc. (1)
7th Fl Octagon Bldg San Miguel Ave, 7 B Ortigas Ctr, Pasig, Philippines **(100%)**
Tel.: (63) 26371600
Web Site: http://www.ericsson.com.ph
Sales Range: $50-74.9 Million
Emp.: 200
Business Communications & Telecommunications Systems
N.A.I.C.S.: 334290

Ericsson Telecommunications Pte, Ltd. (1)
1 Changi Business Park Central 1 One Changi City Level 6-101, Singapore, 486036, Singapore **(100%)**
Tel.: (65) 68808600
Sales Range: $25-49.9 Million
Emp.: 100
Communication Service
N.A.I.C.S.: 517112

Ericsson Telecommunications Romania S.A.R.L. (1)
Gara Herastrau n 4C sector 2 Green Court B Building 10th Floor, 020334, Bucharest, Romania
Tel.: (40) 21 40 10 319
Web Site: http://www.ericsson.com
Telecommunications Equipment Mfr
N.A.I.C.S.: 334418

Ericsson Telecommunications, Bulgaria Eood (1)
55 Nikola vaptsarov expo 2000, 1407, Sofia, Bulgaria **(100%)**
Tel.: (359) 29651888
Web Site: http://www.ericsson.com
Sales Range: $25-49.9 Million
Emp.: 100
Telecommunications Equipment Mfr
N.A.I.C.S.: 334418

Ericsson Telecomunicazioni (1)
Via Cadorna 73 Vainodrone, 20090, Milan, Segrate, Italy **(100%)**
Tel.: (39) 02265941
Telecommunications Equipment Mfr
N.A.I.C.S.: 334418

Ericsson Telecomunicazioni S.p.A. (1)
Via Anagnina 203, CP 4235, Rome, 00118, Italy
Tel.: (39) 0672581
Web Site: http://www.ericsson.com
Telecommunications Equipment Mfr
N.A.I.C.S.: 334418

Ericsson Telekommunikation GmbH & Co. KG (1)
Herriotstrasse 1, Frankfurt, 60528, Hessen, Germany
Tel.: (49) 69 23833100
Sales Range: $200-249.9 Million
Emp.: 600
Mobile Communications Services
N.A.I.C.S.: 517112
Fenghua Li (Engr-Software Test)

Ericsson Tems AB (1)
Skelleftehamnsvaagen 206, PO Box 2003, 930 30, Ursviken, Sweden
Tel.: (46) 910731000
Defense Communications Systems Mfr
N.A.I.C.S.: 334290

Ericsson Thailand Ltd. (1)
Suntowers Bldg B 20th Fl 123 Vibhavadee Rangsit Rd, Khet Chatuchak, Bangkok, 10900, Thailand **(100%)**
Tel.: (66) 22997000
Sales Range: $25-49.9 Million
Emp.: 100
Electrical Related Services

TELEFONAKTIEBOLAGET LM ERICSSON

Telefonaktiebolaget LM Ericsson—(Continued)
N.A.I.C.S.: 561990

Ericsson Tunisia (1)
Bureaux Techniques De Tunsie, BP 398, 44 Avenue Khereddine Pacha, TN-1080, Tunis, Cedex, Tunisia
Tel.: (216) 71962345
Sales Range: $25-49.9 Million
Emp.: 70
Business Communications & Telecommunications Systems
N.A.I.C.S.: 334290

Ericsson d.o.o. (1)
Milentija Popovica 5a/V, Belgrade, 11070, Serbia
Tel.: (381) 11 2013700
Web Site: http://www.ericsson.com
Mobile Communications Services
N.A.I.C.S.: 517112

Ericsson de Colombia S.A. (1)
Calle 93 B No 16-47 Piso 13, Apartado Aereo 4052, Bogota, 814, Colombia (92%)
Tel.: (57) 16239000
Web Site: http://www.ericsson.com
Sales Range: $50-74.9 Million
Emp.: 200
Telecommunications Equipment Mfr
N.A.I.C.S.: 334290

Ericsson de Ecuador C.A. (1)
Av Amazonas y Pasaje Piso 9, Quito, Ecuador
Tel.: (593) 22457077
Telecommunications
N.A.I.C.S.: 517111

Ericsson del Paraguay (1)
Mcal Lopez 965, Codigo Postal, 1532, Asuncion, Paraguay (100%)
Tel.: (595) 21228820
Sales Range: $25-49.9 Million
Emp.: 14
Telecommunications Equipment Mfr
N.A.I.C.S.: 334418

Ericsson, Bahrain (1)
1st Floor HSBC Building Building 2505 Road 2832 Block 428, Seef District, Manama, Bahrain
Tel.: (973) 17584500
Web Site: http://www.ericsson.com
Telecommunications Equipment Mfr
N.A.I.C.S.: 334418

Erisud S.p.A. (1)
Via Madonna Di Fatima 2, 84016, Pagani, Italy (100%)
Tel.: (39) 0815147111
Web Site: http://www.ericsson.com
Sales Range: $50-74.9 Million
Emp.: 200
Telecommunications Equipment Mfr
N.A.I.C.S.: 334418

Izatco Trading Company (Pvt) Ltd. (1)
PO Box 406, Addis Ababa, Ethiopia
Tel.: (251) 654319
Web Site: http://www.airmauritius.com
Telecommunications Equipment Mfr
N.A.I.C.S.: 334418

Johan Ronning HF (1)
Klettagartar 25, IS-104, Reykjavik, Iceland
Tel.: (354) 5200800
Web Site: http://www.ronning.is
Sales Range: $25-49.9 Million
Emp.: 50
Telecommunications Equipment Mfr
N.A.I.C.S.: 334418

LM Ericsson (1)
Al Kawther Center West Dummar, 1st Block New Cham Suburbs, Damascus, Syria
Tel.: (963) 113190000
Sales Range: $25-49.9 Million
Emp.: 70
Telecommunications Equipment Mfr
N.A.I.C.S.: 334418

LM Ericsson (Nigeria) Ltd. (1)
17 Walter Carrington Crescent, PO Box 2512, Victoria Island, GPO, Lagos, Nigeria
Tel.: (234) 4616000
Mfr of Business Communications & Telecommunications Systems
N.A.I.C.S.: 334290

LM Ericsson Bangladesh Limited (1)
Grand Delvistaa Level 3 Plot 1A Road 113, Gulshan-2, Dhaka, 1212, Bangladesh
Tel.: (880) 2 882 3864
Web Site: http://www.ericsson.com
Mobile Communications Services
N.A.I.C.S.: 517112

LM Ericsson Egypt (1)
KM 28 Smart Village Cairo Alex Road, B86 Ericsson, PO Box 27 12577, Cairo, 11511, Egypt (100%)
Tel.: (20) 25229000
Sales Range: $25-49.9 Million
Emp.: 100
Telecommunications Equipment Mfr
N.A.I.C.S.: 334418

LM Ericsson Holdings Ltd. (1)
Beech Hill, Clonskeagh, Dublin, 4, Ireland (100%)
Tel.: (353) 12072000
Web Site: http://www.ericsson.ie
Sales Range: $100-124.9 Million
Emp.: 400
Telecommunications
N.A.I.C.S.: 517112

LM Ericsson International AB (1)
Acropolis Athalassas Avenue No.91 3rd Floor, PO Box 24522, 1300, Nicosia, Cyprus
Tel.: (357) 22453300
Web Site: http://www.ericsson.com
Emp.: 5
Telecommunications Equipment Mfr
N.A.I.C.S.: 334418

LM Ericsson International AB (1)
Plot 24B Akii-Bua Road Naka, 7448, Kampala, Uganda
Tel.: (256) 312 21 5000
Web Site: http://www.ericsson.com
Communication Service
N.A.I.C.S.: 517810

LM Ericsson International AB (1)
13 Pymonenko St Korpus 7 Office No 7B 21, Kiev, 4050, Ukraine (100%)
Tel.: (380) 445374000
Web Site: http://www.ericsson.com.ua
Sales Range: $50-74.9 Million
Emp.: 200
Telecommunications Equipment Mfr
N.A.I.C.S.: 334418

LM Ericsson International AB (1)
43 Dostyk Ave 5th Fl, 480021, Almaty, Kazakhstan
Tel.: (7) 3272581700
Web Site: http://www.ericsson.kz
Sales Range: $25-49.9 Million
Emp.: 30
Telecommunications Equipment Mfr
N.A.I.C.S.: 334418

LM Ericsson Israel Ltd. (1)
13 Amal Street, Rosh Ha'Ayin, 66 184, Israel
Tel.: (972) 39006000
Web Site: http://www.ericsson.com
Emp.: 17
Telecommunications Equipment Mfr
N.A.I.C.S.: 334418

LM Ericsson Ltd. (1)
Beech Hill, Clonskeagh, Dublin, 4, Ireland (100%)
Tel.: (353) 12072000
Web Site: http://www.ericsson.com
Sales Range: $400-449.9 Million
Emp.: 1,650
Business Communications Systems Mfr
N.A.I.C.S.: 334290
Traoloch Collins *(Gen Mgr)*

Nippon Ericsson K.K. (1)
Koraku Mori Bldg 1 4 14 Koraku, Tokyo, 112-0004, Japan
Tel.: (81) 338302200
Telecommunications Equipment Mfr
N.A.I.C.S.: 334418

Opcom Cables Sdn. Bhd. (1)
11 Jalan Utas 15/7, Shah Alam Industrial Estate, Shah Alam, 40200, Selangor Darul Ehsan, Malaysia
Tel.: (60) 355195599
Web Site: http://www.opcom.com.my
Emp.: 120
Fiber Optic Cables & Systems Mfr; Owned 70% by Opcom Holdings Berhad & 30% by Telefonaktiebolaget LM Ericsson
N.A.I.C.S.: 335921
Yusree Putra Alias *(COO)*

Oy LM Ericsson AB (1)
Hirsalan Tie 11, SF 02420, Jorvas, Finland (100%)
Tel.: (358) 92991
Web Site: http://www.ericsson.com
Sales Range: $200-249.9 Million
Emp.: 950
Telecommunications Systems Mfr
N.A.I.C.S.: 334290

P.T. Ericsson Indonesia (1)
Wisma Pondok Indah 2nd Fl Jl Sultan Iskandar Muda Sultan Iskandar Muda, Jakarta, 12310, Indonesia
Tel.: (62) 217692222
Web Site: http://www.ericsson.co.id
Sales Range: $450-499.9 Million
Emp.: 1,500
Telecommunications Equipment Mfr
N.A.I.C.S.: 334418

Perwira Ericsson Sdn. Bhd. (1)
Cyber Jaya, PO Box 7159, 40704, Shah Alam, Selangor, Malaysia (40%)
Tel.: (60) 383146000
Telecommunications Systems
N.A.I.C.S.: 334290

Red Bee Media Limited (1)
Broadcast Center 201 Wood Lane, London, W12 7TP, United Kingdom
Tel.: (44) 20 8495 5000
Web Site: http://www.redbeemedia.com
Mobile Marketing, Promotions & TV & Web Advertising
N.A.I.C.S.: 541810
Andrew D. Bryant *(Dir-Creative)*

Saudi Ericsson Communications Co. (1)
Dammam Tower, PO Box 450, Dammam, 31411, Saudi Arabia
Tel.: (966) 38262222
Web Site: http://www.ericsson.com
Sales Range: $50-74.9 Million
Emp.: 200
Telecommunications Equipment Mfr
N.A.I.C.S.: 334418

Scancables AB (SCS)
Kabelgatan 5, 434 37, Kungsbacka, Sweden
Tel.: (46) 30014510
Sales Range: $25-49.9 Million
Emp.: 2
Cable Mfr
N.A.I.C.S.: 335921

Sielte Italia (1)
Via Verza 4, 95027, San Gregorio Magno, Italy
Tel.: (39) 095724111
Web Site: http://www.sielte.com
Sales Range: $25-49.9 Million
Emp.: 100
Electronic Components & Communications Systems Mfr
N.A.I.C.S.: 334419

Telefon AB LM Ericsson (1)
Torshamns Gatam 23, 16483, Stockholm, Sweden (100%)
Tel.: (46) 87190000
Web Site: http://www.ericsson.com
Development & Supply of Telecommunications Equipment
N.A.I.C.S.: 334418

Telefon AB LM Ericsson (1)
Technical Office UAE Office S 404 Al Ferdous Tower, PO Box 3704, Salem St, Abu Dhabi, United Arab Emirates
Tel.: (971) 26968600
Sales Range: $25-49.9 Million
Emp.: 40
Telecommunications Equipment Mfr
N.A.I.C.S.: 334418

Telefon AB LM Ericsson Libya Branch (1)
Quaser Benghashir, PO Box 5307, Tripoli, Libya
Tel.: (218) 2230800
Sales Range: $50-74.9 Million
Emp.: 190
Telecommunications Systems

INTERNATIONAL PUBLIC

N.A.I.C.S.: 517111

UAB ERICSSON LIETUVA (1)
Vokieciu St 26, Vilnius, 2001, Lithuania
Tel.: (370) 5 27 38800
Web Site: http://www.ericsson.com
Sales Range: $25-49.9 Million
Emp.: 22
Mobile Communications Services
N.A.I.C.S.: 517112

Vonage Holdings Corporation (1)
101 Crawfords Corner Rd, Ste 2416, Holmdel, NJ 07733
Tel.: (732) 528-2600
Web Site: http://www.vonage.com
Rev.: $1,409,015,000
Assets: $1,388,144,000
Liabilities: $770,423,000
Net Worth: $617,721,000
Earnings: $(24,497,000)
Emp.: 2,082
Fiscal Year-end: 12/31/2021
Local & Long Distance Telephone Connection Services; Broadband Internet Access Services
N.A.I.C.S.: 517111
David Levi *(Chief Acctg Officer, Sr VP & Controller)*

Subsidiary (Non-US):

NewVoiceMedia Germany GmbH (2)
Landsberger Strasse 155, 80687, Munich, Germany
Tel.: (49) 89673043030
Software Development Services
N.A.I.C.S.: 513210
Korbinian Heydler *(Sr Acct Mgr-Major Accts)*

NewVoiceMedia Pty. Ltd. (2)
Level 21 Tower 2 Darling Park 201 Sussex St, Sydney, 2000, NSW, Australia
Tel.: (61) 285993444
Software Development Services
N.A.I.C.S.: 513210
Vishaal Gokal *(Mgr-Customer Success)*

NewVoiceMedia Sp. z o.o. (2)
Ul Marszalka Jozefa Pilsudskiego nr 69 Stare Miasto, Wroclaw, Poland
Tel.: (48) 713820733
Software Development Services
N.A.I.C.S.: 513210

Nexmo Asia Pacific Limited (2)
Wework Tower 535 20/F 535 Jaffe Road, Causeway Bay, China (Hong Kong)
Tel.: (852) 75521607589
Software Publisher
N.A.I.C.S.: 513210

Subsidiary (Domestic):

Telesphere Networks Ltd. (2)
9237 E Via de Ventura Ste 250, Scottsdale, AZ 85258
Tel.: (480) 385-7000
Call Center Services
N.A.I.C.S.: 561422

Vonage America Inc. (2)
23 Main St, Holmdel, NJ 07733
Tel.: (732) 444-2892
Web Site: https://www.vonage.com
Sales Range: $200-249.9 Million
Emp.: 300
Telecommunication Servicesb
N.A.I.C.S.: 517810
Rodolpho Cardenuto *(Pres-Applications Grp)*

Vonage Business Solutions, Inc. (2)
3200 Windy Hill Rd Ste 200, Atlanta, GA 30339
Tel.: (404) 492-5575
Web Site: http://www.vonagebusiness.com
Sales Range: $50-74.9 Million
Emp.: 50
Wired Telecommunications Carriers
N.A.I.C.S.: 517111

Vonage International Inc. (2)
23 Main St, Holmdel, NJ 07733
Tel.: (732) 528-2600
Web Site: http://www.vonage.com
Sales Range: $200-249.9 Million
Telecommunication Servicesb
N.A.I.C.S.: 517810

AND PRIVATE COMPANIES — TELEFONICA, S.A.

Subsidiary (Non-US):

Vonage Limited (2)
15 Bonhill Street 3rd Floor, London, EC2A 4DN, United Kingdom
Tel.: (44) 2079939000
Web Site: http://www.vonage.co.uk
Internet Telephone Service Provider
N.A.I.C.S.: 517810

Subsidiary (Domestic):

Vonage Marketing LLC (2)
23 Main St, Holmdel, NJ 07733
Tel.: (732) 528-2600
Web Site: http://www.vonage.com
Sales Range: $200-249.9 Million
Telecommunications Marketing Services
N.A.I.C.S.: 517810

Vonage Network LLC (2)
23 Main St, Holmdel, NJ 07733
Tel.: (732) 528-2600
Web Site: http://www.vonage.com
Sales Range: $200-249.9 Million
Telecommunication Servicesb
N.A.I.C.S.: 517810

Vonage Worldwide Inc. (2)
23 Main St, Holmdel, NJ 07733
Tel.: (732) 528-2600
Web Site: http://www.vonage.com
Sales Range: $200-249.9 Million
Emp.: 14
Telecommunication Servicesb
N.A.I.C.S.: 517810

TELEFONICA, S.A.
Ronda de la Comunicacion s/n, 28050, Madrid, Spain
Tel.: (34) 914823733 ES
Web Site: https://www.telefonica.com
Year Founded: 1924
TEF—(NYSE)
Rev.: $43,872,221,023
Assets: $112,587,955,968
Liabilities: $83,345,564,429
Net Worth: $29,242,391,539
Earnings: ($962,659,184)
Emp.: 3,420
Fiscal Year-end: 12/31/23
Telecommunication Servicesb
N.A.I.C.S.: 551112
Jose Maria Abril Perez (Vice Chm)

Subsidiaries:

Acens Technologies, S.L. (1)
Acens Building C/San Rafael 14, Alcobendas, 28108, Madrid, Spain
Tel.: (34) 91 141 8500
Web Site: https://www.acens.com
Web Hosting Services
N.A.I.C.S.: 518210

Altostratus Solutions, S.L. (1)
Avda Diagonal 452 3A Planta, 08006, Barcelona, Spain
Tel.: (34) 936031900
Web Site: https://www.altostratus.es
Information Technology Services
N.A.I.C.S.: 541519

Atento Colombia, S.A. (1)
Cra 69 Ste 98a - 11, Bogota, Colombia
Tel.: (57) 15940000
Web Site: https://atento.com
Telecommunication Servicesb
N.A.I.C.S.: 517810

BE-terna Business Solutions GmbH (1)
Nussdorfer Strasse 4, Uberlingen, Germany
Tel.: (49) 755194700
Software Development Services
N.A.I.C.S.: 541511

BE-terna Enhancement GmbH (1)
Bornaer Strasse 19, Leipzig, Germany
Tel.: (49) 342976480
Web Site: https://www.be-terna.com
Emp.: 1,110
Software Development Services
N.A.I.C.S.: 541511

BE-terna Industry Solutions GmbH (1)
Am Buchental 3, Sindelfingen, Germany
Tel.: (49) 7031204170
Software Development Services
N.A.I.C.S.: 541511

Fonditel Entidad Gestora de Fondos de Pensiones, S.A. (1)
C Pedro Texeira 7 3, 28020, Madrid, Spain (77%)
Tel.: (34) 915569980
Web Site: http://www.fonditel.es
Sales Range: $50-74.9 Million
Emp.: 75
Administrator of Pension Funds
N.A.I.C.S.: 524292

Geprom Software Engineering S.A. de C.V. (1)
Laguna de San Cristobal No 226A Departamento 204, Delegacion Miguel Hidalgo, 11320, Mexico, Mexico
Tel.: (52) 2229126151
Information Technology Services
N.A.I.C.S.: 541519

Geprom Software Engineering S.L. (1)
Ronda de Can Rabada 2 5-5 Edificio Logic, Castelldefels, 08860, Barcelona, Spain
Tel.: (34) 933284328
Web Site: https://www.geprom.com
Information Technology Services
N.A.I.C.S.: 541519

Gloway Broadcast Services, S.L. (1)
Fernando Rey 8 Ciudad de la Image, Pozuelo de Alarcon, Madrid, 28223, Spain
Tel.: (34) 916 32 48 00
Web Site: http://www.gloway.es
Sales Range: $50-74.9 Million
Emp.: 200
Television Broadcasting Services
N.A.I.C.S.: 334220

Govertis Advisory Services Peru S.A.C. (1)
Av Jose Pardo 434 Oficina 1004, Miraflores, 15074, Lima, Peru
Tel.: (51) 99 991 5801
Technical Consulting Services
N.A.I.C.S.: 541690

Govertis Advisory Services S.L. (1)
Marina De Valencia-Ed Innsomnia C/Travessia s/n-Base 2 Moll Ponent, 46024, Valencia, Spain
Tel.: (34) 90 290 0231
Web Site: https://www.govertis.com
Technical Consulting Services
N.A.I.C.S.: 541690
Eduard Chaveli Donet (Dir, CEO & Gen Mgr)

Iberbanda, S.A. (1)
Via Dos Castillas 7 Edificio Parquesol, Pozuelo de Alarcon, Madrid, 28224, Spain
Tel.: (34) 911 02 10 00
Web Site: http://www.iberbanda.es
Emp.: 5
Broadband Communication Services
N.A.I.C.S.: 517111

Internet Para Todos S.A.C. (1)
Manuel Olguin Avenue 327 12th Floor, Lima, Peru
Tel.: (51) 99 641 4489
Web Site: https://www.ipt.pe
Telecommunication Servicesb
N.A.I.C.S.: 517810
Teresa Gomes de Almeida (CEO)

Media Networks Latin America, S.A.C. (1)
Jr Nazca 704, Jesus Maria, Lima, Peru
Tel.: (51) 1 205 7400
Web Site: https://www.medianetworks.net
Audiovisual Content & Production Services
N.A.I.C.S.: 512110

Pipol A/S (1)
Christianshusvej 193, Hoersholm, Fredensborg, Denmark
Tel.: (45) 70444370
Web Site: https://www.pipol.com
Information Technology Services
N.A.I.C.S.: 541519

Telcel, C.A. (1)
Av Francisco De Miranda Torre Parque Canaima Piso 14, Caracas, Venezuela
Tel.: (58) 2122002117

Wireless Mobile Communication Services
N.A.I.C.S.: 517112

Telefonica Brasil S.A. (1)
Avenida Engenheiro Luis Carlos Berrini 1376 32 andar, 04571-936, Sao Paulo, 04571-936, SP, Brazil (73.68%)
Tel.: (55) 1134303687
Web Site: https://www.telefonica.com.br
Rev.: $10,389,899,491
Assets: $24,077,770,466
Liabilities: $10,192,573,537
Net Worth: $13,885,196,929
Earnings: $1,005,080,666
Emp.: 35,039
Fiscal Year-end: 12/31/2023
Telecommunication Servicesb
N.A.I.C.S.: 517112
David Melcon Sanchez-Friera (Chief Fin & IR Officer)

Subsidiary (Domestic):

Telefonica Engenharia de Seguranca (2)
Haddock Lobo 337 An 2 Cj 21 Cerqueira Cesar, Sao Paulo, 01414-001, Brazil
Tel.: (55) 1131207434
Web Site: http://www.tesb.com.br
Sales Range: $250-299.9 Million
Emp.: 2,000
Security Software Development Services
N.A.I.C.S.: 561621

Telefonica Servicos Empresariais do BRASIL, Ltda. (2)
Av Marques De Sao Vicente 288, Sao Paulo, 01139-000, Brazil
Tel.: (55) 1136185194
Sales Range: $150-199.9 Million
Emp.: 700
Telecommunication Servicesb
N.A.I.C.S.: 517111
Clovis Travassos (Mng Dir)

Subsidiary (Non-US):

Terra Networks Brasil, S.A. (2)
Web Site: http://www.terra.com.br
Internet Service Provider
N.A.I.C.S.: 517810

Telefonica Chile S.A. (1)
Avenida Providencia N111, Santiago, Chile (97.89%)
Tel.: (56) 26912020
Web Site: http://www.telefonicachile.cl
Sales Range: $1-4.9 Billion
Emp.: 4,513
Telecommunication Servicesb
N.A.I.C.S.: 517111
Roberto Munoz Laporte (CEO & Gen Mgr)

Subsidiary (Domestic):

Telefonica Moviles Soluciones y Aplicaciones, S.A. (2)
Avda del Condor 720 4, Huechuraba, Santiago, Chile
Tel.: (56) 2 731 1000
Telecommunication Network Services
N.A.I.C.S.: 517112

Telefonica Deutschland Holding AG (1)
Georg-Brauchle-Ring 50, 80992, Munich, Germany (71.81%)
Tel.: (49) 8924420
Web Site: https://www.telefonica.de
Rev.: $9,296,352,256
Assets: $16,670,623,786
Liabilities: $10,697,172,458
Net Worth: $5,973,451,327
Earnings: $294,625,513
Emp.: 7,268
Fiscal Year-end: 12/31/2023
Telecommunications
N.A.I.C.S.: 517810
Markus Haas (Chm-Mgmt Bd & CEO)

Subsidiary (Domestic):

E-plus Mobilfunk GmbH & Co. KG (2)
E-Plus-Strasse 1, 40472, Dusseldorf, Germany
Tel.: (49) 2114480
Web Site: https://www.telefonica.de
Mobile Telecommunications Services
N.A.I.C.S.: 517112

Alfons Losing (Member-Mgmt Bd)

Telefonica Germany GmbH & Co. OHG (2)
Georg-Brauchle-Ring 50, 80992, Munich, Germany
Tel.: (49) 89787979400
Web Site: https://www.o2online.de
Sales Range: $750-799.9 Million
Emp.: 4,035
Wireless Communication Services
N.A.I.C.S.: 517112

Subsidiary (Domestic):

HanseNet Telekommunikation GmbH (3)
Uberseering 33a, 22297, Hamburg, Germany
Tel.: (49) 40237260
Web Site: http://www.hansenet.de
Sales Range: $1-4.9 Billion
Emp.: 639
Telecommunication Servicesb
N.A.I.C.S.: 517112

Telefonica Digital Limited (1)
260 Bath Rd, Slough, SL1 4DX, United Kingdom
Tel.: (44) 1132722000
Web Site: https://www.telefonica.com
Holding Company; Digital Software, Internet Content & Technologies Development
N.A.I.C.S.: 551112

Telefonica Europe plc (1)
Wellington Street, Slough, SL1 1YP, Berks, United Kingdom (100%)
Tel.: (44) 1132722000
Web Site: http://www.o2.com
Mobile Communications Services
N.A.I.C.S.: 517112

Subsidiary (Non-US):

O2 Slovakia, s.r.o. (2)
Einsteinova 24, 851 01, Bratislava, Slovakia
Web Site: http://www.o2.sk
Fixed & Wireless Telecommunication Services
N.A.I.C.S.: 517111
Igor Toth (CEO)

TCG Holdings, S.A. (2)
28 Rue De Bombanville, Thaon-les-Vosges, 14610, France
Tel.: (33) 2 31 80 05 05
Transportation & Cold Storage Services
N.A.I.C.S.: 488999

Telefonica Europe, B.V. (2)
Zuidplein 112 H Tower 13th Floor, 1077 XX, Amsterdam, Netherlands
Tel.: (31) 205753370
Wireless Telecommunication Services
N.A.I.C.S.: 517112
David Maroto (Mng Dir)

Subsidiary (Domestic):

Telfisa Global, B.V. (3)
Strawinskylaan 665, Amsterdam, 1077 XX, Netherlands
Tel.: (31) 205752200
Sales Range: $25-49.9 Million
Emp.: 15
Telecommunication Servicesb
N.A.I.C.S.: 517810

Subsidiary (Non-US):

Telefonica Insurance S.A. (2)
23 Av Monterey, L-2163, Luxembourg, Luxembourg
Tel.: (352) 297952
Web Site: http://www.telefonicainsurance.es
Reinsurance Services
N.A.I.C.S.: 524130

Subsidiary (Non-US):

Pleyade Peninsular Correduria de Seguros del Grupo Telefonica, S.A. (3)
Avenida General Peron 38 Master II 17, 28020, Madrid, Spain (83.33%)
Tel.: (34) 914177701
Sales Range: $50-74.9 Million
Distr, Promoter & Underwriter of Insurance Policies
N.A.I.C.S.: 524298

TELEFONICA, S.A.

Telefonica, S.A.—(Continued)

Telefonica Finanzas, S.A.U. (1)
Ronda De La Comunicacion Central Building Floor2, Madrid, 28050, Spain
Tel.: (34) 914823147
Emp.: 6
Financial Management Services
N.A.I.C.S.: 327910
Francisco Moretta Sanchez (Mgr)

Telefonica Internacional Internacional S.A.U. (1)
Mayor CL 31, 28013, Madrid, Spain (76.22%)
Tel.: (34) 913 546 231
Web Site: http://www.telefonica.es
Investor in Foreign Telecommunications
N.A.I.C.S.: 517810

Subsidiary (Non-US):

Telefonica Holding de Argentina S.A. (2)
Ave Ingeniero Huergo 723, C1107AOH, Buenos Aires, Argentina
Tel.: (54) 1143322066
Web Site: http://www.telefonica.com.ar
Sales Range: $1-4.9 Billion
Emp.: 8,898
Telecommunications Services; Holding Company
N.A.I.C.S.: 517111
Mario Eduardo Vazquez (Vice Chm & Pres)

Subsidiary (Domestic):

Telefonica de Argentina S.A. (3)
Avenida Ingeniero Huergo 723, C1107AOH, Buenos Aires, Argentina
Tel.: (54) 1143329200
Web Site: http://www.telefonica.com.ar
Telecommunication Servicesb
N.A.I.C.S.: 517111

Telefonica International Wholesale Services America, S.A. (1)
Av Dr Luis A de Herrera 1248 V Torre 1 4 Piso, Edificio World Trade Center, 11300, Montevideo, Uruguay
Tel.: (598) 2628 0020
Telecommunication Servicesb
N.A.I.C.S.: 517810

Subsidiary (Non-US):

Telefonica International Wholesale Services Argentina, S.A. (2)
Av Corrientes 330 1 Piso Edificio Lipsia, C1043AAQ, Buenos Aires, Argentina
Tel.: (54) 11 4344 0902
Telecommunication Servicesb
N.A.I.C.S.: 517112

Telefonica International Wholesale Services Brasil Participacoes, Ltd
Av Brigadeiro Faria Lima 1188 8 Andar JD Paulistano, Sao Paulo, 01451-001, Brazil
Tel.: (55) 11 3038 7488
Telecommunication Servicesb
N.A.I.C.S.: 517112

Telefonica International Wholesale Services Peru, S.A.C. (2)
Av Camino Real 155 4 piso, San Isidro, Lima, Peru
Tel.: (51) 1 422 1979
Telecommunication Servicesb
N.A.I.C.S.: 517112
Guido Arata (Mgr-Comml)

Subsidiary (US):

Telefonica International Wholesale Services USA, Inc. (2)
1111 Brickell Ave Ste 1800, Miami, FL 33131
Tel.: (305) 925-5305
Telecommunication Servicesb
N.A.I.C.S.: 517112
Reinaldo Rivas (Gen Mgr)

Telefonica Investigacion y Desarrollo, S.A. (1)
Emilio Vargas 6, 28043, Madrid, Spain (100%)
Tel.: (34) 913374000
Web Site: http://www.tid.es

Sales Range: $350-399.9 Million
Emp.: 1,500
Research & Development of Products, Exploration, Applied Investigations & Technological Reports in the Telecommunications Field
N.A.I.C.S.: 541715

Telefonica Learning Services, S.L. (1)
Distrito C/Ronda de la comunicacion s/n Building North 1 - Floor 7th, Las Tablas, 28050, Madrid, Spain
Tel.: (34) 91 483 0200
Sales Range: $25-49.9 Million
Emp.: 200
Professional Training Services
N.A.I.C.S.: 611430

Telefonica Moviles Mexico, S.A. de C.V. (1)
Calle Prolongacion Paseo de la Reforma 1200 piso 15, Colonia Cruz Manca, Mexico, 05349, Mexico
Tel.: (52) 1 616 5000
Web Site: http://www.telefonica.com.mx
Telecommunication Servicesb
N.A.I.C.S.: 517112

Telefonica Moviles Panama, S.A. (1)
Urb Costa Del Este Business Park Edif Este, Panama, Panama
Tel.: (507) 3787000
Wireless Telecommunication Services
N.A.I.C.S.: 517112
Eduardo Caride (CEO-HispanoAmerica)

Telefonica Servicios Audiovisuales, S.A.U. (1)
Avenida de los Artesanos 6, Tres Cantos, 28060, Madrid, Spain
Tel.: (34) 914839131
Web Site: https://www.telefonicaserviciosaudio.com
Sales Range: $25-49.9 Million
Emp.: 90
Television & Digital Radio Signal Transmission Services
N.A.I.C.S.: 516120

Telefonica Soluciones Sectoriales, S.A.U. (1)
Calle Doctor Esquerdo 61 Plt Cuarta, Madrid, 28007, Spain
Tel.: (34) 915847233
Management Consulting Services
N.A.I.C.S.: 541618

Telefonica Tech S.L.U. (1)
C/ Gran Via 28, 28013, Madrid, Spain
Tel.: (34) 914823800
Telecommunication Servicesb
N.A.I.C.S.: 517810

Subsidiary (Non-US):

CANCOM Ltd. (2)
Genesis House Merrow Ln, Guildford, GU4 7BN, Surrey, United Kingdom
Tel.: (44) 1483500500
Web Site: http://www.cancomuk.com
Information Technology Solutions
N.A.I.C.S.: 541511

Subsidiary (Domestic):

CANCOM UK Limited (3)
Trinity Building 39 Tabernacle Street, Shoreditch, London, EC2A 4AA, United Kingdom
Tel.: (44) 8456052100
Web Site: http://www.cancom.co.uk
Information Technology Services
N.A.I.C.S.: 513210
Mark Skelton (CTO)

Subsidiary (Non-US):

Novosco Limited (2)
Ormond Quay Upper Ormond Building 31-36, D07 N5YH, Dublin, Ireland
Tel.: (353) 14198000
Information Technology Services

Subsidiary (Domestic):

Novosco Ltd. (3)
Concourse Building 3 Queens Road, Belfast, BT3 9DT, United Kingdom
Tel.: (44) 2890454433

Web Site: http://www.novosco.com
Information Technology Services
N.A.I.C.S.: 513210
John Lennon (Mng Dir)

Telefonica Tech UK Limited (1)
East House New Pound Common, Wisborough Green, Billingshurst, West Sussex, United Kingdom
Tel.: (44) 8456052100
Web Site: https://telefonicatech.uk
Emp.: 992
Information Technology Services
N.A.I.C.S.: 541511

Telefonica Telecomunicaciones Publicas, S.A.U. (1)
Ronda De La Comunicacion s/n Edificio Oeste 1 Planta 6, Madrid, 28050, Spain
Tel.: (34) 901 12 71 27
Wireless Telecommunication Services
N.A.I.C.S.: 517112

Telefonica USA Inc. (1)
1111 Brickell Ave 10th Fl, Miami, FL 33131-3112
Tel.: (305) 925-5471
Web Site: http://www.us.telefonica.com
Sales Range: $25-49.9 Million
Emp.: 100
Telecommunication Network Services
N.A.I.C.S.: 517810

Telefonica de Espana, S.A.U. (1)
Distrito Telefonica - Edificio Central Pl 2 andar, C/ Ronda de la Comunicacion, 28050, Madrid, Spain
Fixed Line Telecommunications, Internet & Broadband Multimedia Data Services
N.A.I.C.S.: 517111

Group (Domestic):

Telefonica de Espana, S.A.U. - Terra Networks Group (2)
Via Dos Castillas 33 Atica Edifictio 1, 28224, Madrid, Spain
Tel.: (34) 914523000
Web Site: http://www.terra.es
Sales Range: $700-749.9 Million
Emp.: 1,606
Internet Service Provider
N.A.I.C.S.: 517810

Telefonica del Peru S.A.A. (1)
Avenida Arequipa 1155, Lima, Peru
Tel.: (51) 12657555
Sales Range: $1-4.9 Billion
Emp.: 5,342
Telephone Services
N.A.I.C.S.: 517111

Subsidiary (Domestic):

Teleatento del Peru, S.A.C. (2)
Av La Molina 190, Lima, Peru
Tel.: (51) 13116400
Web Site: http://www.atento.com
Telecommunication Servicesb
N.A.I.C.S.: 517810

Teleinformatica y Comunicaciones, S.A. (1)
Donarramon Deallcruz 82, 28006, Madrid, Spain (100%)
Tel.: (34) 913956000
Web Site: http://www.telefonica.es
Sales Range: $25-49.9 Million
Emp.: 100
Promotion, Distribution & Marketing of Telephonic & Telematic Equipment & Services
N.A.I.C.S.: 449210

Telxius Telecom SA (1)
Ronda de la Comunicacion S/N Distrito Telefonica, 28050, Madrid, Spain (50.01%)
Tel.: (34) 649916187
Web Site: http://telxius.com
Emp.: 500
Telecommunication Servicesb
N.A.I.C.S.: 517810
Luiz Andrade (Sr Project Mgr-IT)

Tempotel, Empresa de Trabajo Temporal, S.A. (1)
Distrito Telefonica Ronda de la Comunicacion s/n, 28050, Madrid, Spain
Tel.: (34) 915989000
Web Site: https://www.tempotel.es
Human Resource Consulting Services

INTERNATIONAL PUBLIC

N.A.I.C.S.: 541612

Terra Networks Argentina, S.A. (1)
Juana Manso 555 Piso 4 D, 1107, Buenos Aires, Argentina
Tel.: (54) 1157765000
Sales Range: $25-49.9 Million
Emp.: 35
Television Broadcasting Services
N.A.I.C.S.: 516120

Terra Networks Mexico, S.A. de C.V. (1)
Paseo de la Reforma 2620 Lomas Altas Seccion Miguel Hidalgo, Mexico, 11950, Mexico
Tel.: (52) 5530675000
Web Site: http://www.terra.com.mx
Sales Range: $50-74.9 Million
Emp.: 200
Internet Publishing & Broadcasting Services
N.A.I.C.S.: 516210

Terra Networks Peru, S.A. (1)
Calle Los Sauces 374 Of 902 Torre Roja, San Isidro, Lima, Peru
Tel.: (51) 14111260
Internet Service Provider
N.A.I.C.S.: 517810

Torre de Collserola, S.A. (1)
Crta Vallvidrera a Tibidabo s/n, 08017, Barcelona, Spain (30.4%)
Tel.: (34) 934069354
Web Site: https://www.torredecollserola.com
Sales Range: $1-9.9 Million
Emp.: 6
Construction of Telecommunications Towers
N.A.I.C.S.: 517410

Tuenti Technologies, S.L. (1)
Gran Via no 28 6 Floor, 28014, Madrid, Spain (100%)
Tel.: (34) 91 429 40 39
Web Site: http://www.tuenti.com
Emp.: 180
Social Networking Services
N.A.I.C.S.: 541519

VMED O2 UK Limited (1)
Griffin House 161 Hammersmith Road, London, W6 8BS, United Kingdom (50%)
Tel.: (44) 1753565656
Web Site: https://news.virginmedia02.co.uk
Holding Company
N.A.I.C.S.: 551112
Lutz Schuler (CEO)

Subsidiary (Domestic):

Telefonica UK Limited (2)
260 Bath Road, Slough, SL1 4DX, United Kingdom
Tel.: (44) 1132722000
Web Site: http://www.o2.co.uk
Sales Range: $1-4.9 Billion
Emp.: 6,116
Mobile Communications Services
N.A.I.C.S.: 517112
Mark Evans (CEO)

Virgin Media Ltd. (2)
Bartley Wood Business Park Bartley Way, Hook, RG27 9UP, Hampshire, United Kingdom
Tel.: (44) 8453026999
Web Site: http://www.virginmedia.com
Internet, Cable Television & Telecommunications Services
N.A.I.C.S.: 517810
Vani Bassi (Head-Investor Relations)

Subsidiary (Domestic):

Central Cable Limited (3)
Small Heath Business Park Talbot Way, Birmingham, B10 0HJ, United Kingdom
Tel.: (44) 1216281234
Cable Subscription Programming Services
N.A.I.C.S.: 516210

Subsidiary (Non-US):

TV3 Television Network Limited (3)
Westgate Business Park, Ballymount, Dublin, 24, Ireland
Tel.: (353) 14193333
Web Site: https://www.virginmediatelevision.ie
Television Station
N.A.I.C.S.: 516120

Subsidiary (Domestic):

Virgin Media Business Ltd. (3)
10-14 Bartley Way, Hook, RG27 9UP, United Kingdom
Tel.: (44) 8453026999
Web Site: http://www.virginmediabusiness.co.uk
Sales Range: $25-49.9 Million
Telecommunication & Internet Business Services
N.A.I.C.S.: 517111

Branch (Domestic):

Virgin Media Business Ltd. (4)
Communications House 5 Factory Ln, Croydon, CR9 3RA, United Kingdom
Tel.: (44) 2082515151
Web Site: http://www.virginmediabusiness.co.uk
Internet Services
N.A.I.C.S.: 517810

Vivo Participacoes S.A. (1)
Av Doutor Chucri Zaidan 860, 04583 110, Sao Paulo, Brazil
Tel.: (55) 11 5105 1172
Web Site: http://www.vivo.com.br
Sales Range: $5-14.9 Billion
Emp.: 13,419
Wireless Telecommunication Services
N.A.I.C.S.: 517112

TELEFONKABL A.D.
Bulevar Kralja Aleksandra 219, 11000, Belgrade, Serbia
Tel.: (381) 11 3040 200 RS
Web Site: http://www.tkb.rs
Year Founded: 1954
TLKB—(BEL)
Sales Range: $1-9.9 Million
Emp.: 89
Telephone Equipment Installation Services
N.A.I.C.S.: 238210
Bosko Bandic (Mng Dir)

TELEKOM MALAYSIA BERHAD
Level 51 North Wing Menara TM, Jalan Pantai Baharu, 50672, Kuala Lumpur, Malaysia
Tel.: (60) 322401221 MY
Web Site: https://www.tm.com.my
Year Founded: 1984
TM—(KLS)
Rev.: $2,853,427,500
Assets: $5,650,697,250
Liabilities: $3,837,042,000
Net Worth: $1,813,655,250
Earnings: $217,280,250
Emp.: 20,912
Fiscal Year-end: 12/31/21
Telecommunication Servicesb
N.A.I.C.S.: 517112
Imri Mokhtar (CEO & Mng Dir)

Subsidiaries:

Fiberail Sdn. Bhd. (1)
7th Floor Wisma TM Jalan Desa Utama Pusat Bandar Taman Desa, 58100, Kuala Lumpur, Malaysia
Tel.: (60) 37 980 9696
Web Site: https://www.fiberail.com.my
Telecommunication Servicesb
N.A.I.C.S.: 517810
Kamaruzzaman Mohamad Sharif (Head-Reg Ops)

Fibrecomm Network (M) Sdn. Bhd. (1)
Level 35 North Wing Menara TM Off Jalan Pantai Baharu, 59200, Kuala Lumpur, Malaysia
Tel.: (60) 322401533
Web Site: https://www.fibrecomm.net.my
Telecommunication Servicesb
N.A.I.C.S.: 517810
Nazmi Othman (Chm)

GITN Sdn Berhad (1)
Level 12 TM Damansara No1 Jalan Damansara, 60000, Kuala Lumpur, Malaysia
Tel.: (60) 378592525
Web Site: https://www.gitn.com.my
Sales Range: $25-49.9 Million
Emp.: 200
Software Development Services
N.A.I.C.S.: 541511
Muhamad Mat Zain (Head-Human Capital Mgmt)

Inneonusa Sdn. Bhd. (1)
Medini 6 Jalan Medini Sentral 5 Bandar Johor, Medini Iskandar Malaysia, 79250, Iskandar Puteri, Malaysia
Tel.: (60) 300800606
Web Site: https://www.inneonusa.com
Telecommunication Servicesb
N.A.I.C.S.: 517810
Akram Mackeen (CEO)

MMU Creativista Sdn Bhd (1)
Suite 3004 2nd Floor Faculty of Creative Multimedia, Multimedia University, 63100, Cyberjaya, Selangor Darul Ehsan, Malaysia
Tel.: (60) 3 83125827
Web Site: http://www.creativista.com.my
Sales Range: $10-24.9 Million
Emp.: 6
Multimedia Educational Services
N.A.I.C.S.: 611710

Menara Kuala Lumpur Sdn. Bhd. (1)
No 2 Jalan Punchak Off Jalan P Ramlee, 50250, Kuala Lumpur, Malaysia
Tel.: (60) 320205444
Web Site: http://www.menarakl.com.my
Sales Range: $75-99.9 Million
Emp.: 180
Property Holding & Management Company
N.A.I.C.S.: 531210

Multimedia College Sdn. Bhd. (1)
Multimedia University Persiaran Multimedia, 63100, Cyberjaya, Selangor, Malaysia
Tel.: (60) 383125498
Web Site: http://www.mmc.mmu.edu.my
Telecommunication Servicesb
N.A.I.C.S.: 517810

Multimedia University (1)
Multimedia University Jalan Ayer Keroh Lama, Melaka, 75450, Malaysia
Tel.: (60) 62523401
Web Site: http://www.mmu.edu.my
Sales Range: $300-349.9 Million
Emp.: 2,000
University Management Services
N.A.I.C.S.: 611310

Subsidiary (Domestic):

MMU Cnergy Sdn Bhd (2)
Ground Floor FIT Building Multimedia Univeristy Persiaran Multimedia, Cyberjaya, 63100, Selangor, Malaysia
Tel.: (60) 3 8312 5178
Web Site: http://www.mmu-cnergy.com
Sales Range: $25-49.9 Million
Emp.: 500
Multimedia Educational Services
N.A.I.C.S.: 611710
Farah Wahidah Rusdi (Head-Bus Ops)

TM Global Incorporated (1)
Level 51 North Wing Menara TM, Jalan Pantai Baharu, 50672, Kuala Lumpur, Malaysia
Tel.: (60) 322401221
Telecommunication Servicesb
N.A.I.C.S.: 517810

TM Info-Media Sdn Bhd (1)
Ground Floor Block E Mines Waterfromt Business Park No 3 Jalan, Tasik Mines Resort City, 43300, Seri Kembangan, Selangor, Malaysia (100%)
Tel.: (60) 389498228
Web Site: http://www.yellowpages.com.my
Sales Range: $100-124.9 Million
Emp.: 260
Publication & Distribution of Telephone Directories & Information
N.A.I.C.S.: 513140

TMF Autolease Sdn Bhd (1)
Kompleks Telekom Shah Alam Lot 1 Persiaran Jubli Perak Seksyen 17, 40200, Shah Alam, Malaysia
Tel.: (60) 355489888
Fleet Management Services
N.A.I.C.S.: 561990

Mohd Radzi Shamsudin (Gen Mgr)

Telekom Applied Business Sdn. Bhd. (1)
Level 2 Left Wing TM IT Complex 3300 Lingkaran Usahawan 1 Timur, 63000, Cyberjaya, Selangor, Malaysia (100%)
Tel.: (60) 383181709
Web Site: https://www.tab.com.my
Sales Range: $25-49.9 Million
Emp.: 60
Provider of Software Development & Sale of Related Products
N.A.I.C.S.: 541511
Michiel Buitelaar (CEO)

Telekom International (L) Ltd. (1)
Lot 2 3 Level 3 Wisma Labuan, 87000, Labuan, Malaysia
Tel.: (60) 87414073
Sales Range: $25-49.9 Million
Emp.: 11
Telecommunication Servicesb
N.A.I.C.S.: 517112

Telekom Malaysia (Australia) Pty. Ltd. (1)
Suite 1A Level 2 802 Pacific Highway, Gordon, 2072, NSW, Australia
Tel.: (61) 408885752
Telecommunication Servicesb
N.A.I.C.S.: 517810

Telekom Malaysia (Hong Kong) Limited (1)
Unit 03 19/F OfficePlus Wan Chai No 303 Hennessy Road, Wanchai, China (Hong Kong)
Tel.: (852) 29920190
Web Site: https://www.tm.com.my
Sales Range: $25-49.9 Million
Emp.: 10
Telecommunication Servicesb
N.A.I.C.S.: 517810
Yoong Hing Siew (Mng Dir)

Telekom Malaysia (S) Pte Ltd (1)
175A Bencoolen Street 07 - 9212 Burlington Square, Singapore, 189650, Singapore
Tel.: (65) 6532 6369
Web Site: http://www.tmro.com.sg
Telecommunication Servicesb
N.A.I.C.S.: 517810
Lima Wang (Gen Mgr)

Telekom Malaysia (UK) Limited (1)
6 Snow Hill, London, EC1A 2AY, United Kingdom
Tel.: (44) 2070027830
Telecommunication Servicesb
N.A.I.C.S.: 517810

Telekom Malaysia (USA) Inc (1)
7925 Jones Branch Dr Ste LL100, McLean, VA 22102
Tel.: (703) 467-5962
Web Site: https://global.tm.com.my
Sales Range: $25-49.9 Million
Emp.: 7
Telecommunication Servicesb
N.A.I.C.S.: 517810

Telekom Malaysia DMCC (1)
PO Box 728, Dubai, United Arab Emirates
Tel.: (971) 60133245771
Telecommunication Servicesb
N.A.I.C.S.: 517810

Telekom Networks Malawi Limited (1)
5th Floor Livingstone Towers Glyn Jones Road, PO Box 3039, Blantyre, Malawi (70%)
Tel.: (265) 88 880 0800
Web Site: https://www.tnm.co.mw
Telecommunication Servicesb
N.A.I.C.S.: 517112
Christina Mwansa (Chief Legal & Regulatory Officer)

Telekom Research and Development Sdn Bhd (1)
TM Innovation Centre Linkaran Teknokrat Timur, 63000, Cyberjaya, Selangor, Malaysia (100%)
Tel.: (60) 388839595
Web Site: https://www.tmrnd.com.my
Emp.: 300
Research & Development Activities in Information & Communication Technology
N.A.I.C.S.: 541715

Telekom Sales & Services Sdn. Bhd. (1)
Level 12 TM Annexe 1 Jalan Pantai Jaya, Jalan Liku off Riong Bangsar, 59200, Kuala Lumpur, Malaysia
Tel.: (60) 322403000
Web Site: https://www.tsssb.com
Sales Range: $100-124.9 Million
Emp.: 400
Provider of Telecommunications Services
N.A.I.C.S.: 517112

Telesafe Sdn. Bhd. (1)
Ground Floor Bangunan Telekom, Jalan Raja Chulan, 50200, Kuala Lumpur, Malaysia
Tel.: (60) 2081033
Provider of Telecommunications Services
N.A.I.C.S.: 517112

The Network Connections Sdn. Bhd. (1)
41 Jalan USJ 10/1, Taman Seafield Jaya, 47620, Petaling Jaya, Selangor Darul Ehsan, Malaysia
Tel.: (60) 3 5637 0843
Telecommunication Servicesb
N.A.I.C.S.: 517112

UniCLIQ Sdn Bhd (1)
45-8 Level 3 Block C Plaza Damansara Jalan Medan Setia 1, Bukit Damansara, 50490, Kuala Lumpur, Malaysia
Tel.: (60) 320925252
Web Site: http://www.unicliq.com
Online Education & Training Portal; Educational Software & Associated Hardware
N.A.I.C.S.: 513210
Analiz Alias (COO)

VADS Berhad (1)
TM Damansara No 1 Jalan Damansara, 60000, Kuala Lumpur, Malaysia (70%)
Tel.: (60) 378592222
Web Site: https://www.vads.com
Sales Range: $100-124.9 Million
E-Infrastructure & E-Application Services
N.A.I.C.S.: 541512
Mohd Shah Sarpin (CFO)

Subsidiary (Domestic):

VADS Business Process Sdn Bhd (2)
15Th Floor Plaza Vads No 1 Jalan Tun Mohd Fuad Taman Tun Dr Ismail, Ampang, 60000, Selangor, Malaysia
Tel.: (60) 377128888
Business Process Outsourcing Services
N.A.I.C.S.: 561499

Subsidiary (Non-US):

PT VADS Indonesia (3)
Jl Mampang Prapatan No 39, Setiabudi, Jakarta Selatan, 12790, Indonesia
Tel.: (62) 217991445
Web Site: https://www.vads.co.id
Business Process Outsourcing Services
N.A.I.C.S.: 561499
Deddy S. Hermansyah (Chief Mktg Officer)

Subsidiary (Domestic):

VADS Solutions Sdn Bhd (2)
15th Floor Plaza Vads Jalan Tun Mohd Fuad, Kuala Lumpur, 60000, Malaysia
Tel.: (60) 3 7712 8888
System Integration Services
N.A.I.C.S.: 541512

VADS Lyfe Sdn. Bhd. (1)
Level 20 TM Damansara 73 Jalan Damansara, 60000, Kuala Lumpur, Malaysia
Tel.: (60) 300222482
Web Site: https://www.vads.com
Real Estate Services
N.A.I.C.S.: 531390

TELEKOM SLOVENIJE, D.D.
Cigaletova ulica 15, 1000, Ljubljana, Slovenia
Tel.: (386) 12341000 SI
Web Site: https://www.telekom.si
Year Founded: 1998
TLSG—(LJU)
Rev.: $767,096,810

TELEKOM SLOVENIJE, D.D.

Telekom Slovenije, d.d.—(Continued)
Assets: $1,454,758,804
Liabilities: $727,705,045
Net Worth: $727,053,759
Earnings: $51,953,858
Emp.: 3,192
Fiscal Year-end: 12/31/23
Telecommunication Servicesb
N.A.I.C.S.: 517111
Spela Fortin *(Member-Mgmt Bd & Dir-Worker)*

Subsidiaries:

Avtenta.si, d.o.o. (1)
Smartinska 106, Ljubljana, 1000, Slovenia
Tel.: (386) 15836800
Web Site: http://www.avtenta.si
Emp.: 50
Develops & Designs Solutions for Business Communications; Integrates & Maintains Teleinformation Infrastructure for Domestic Companies
N.A.I.C.S.: 517810

GVO, d.o.o. (1)
Cigaletova 10, 1000, Ljubljana, Slovenia
Tel.: (386) 12341950
Web Site: http://www.gvo.si
Sales Range: $25-49.9 Million
Emp.: 100
Construction & Maintenance of Telecommunication Cable Network
N.A.I.C.S.: 516210

Gibtelecom (1)
15/21 John Mackintosh Square, PO Box 929, Gibraltar, GX11 1AA, Gibraltar
Tel.: (350) 200 52200
Web Site: http://www.gibtele.com
Sales Range: $50-74.9 Million
Emp.: 150
Telecommunications; Joint Venture of Telekom Slovenije, d.d. (50%) & the Government of Gibraltar (50%)
N.A.I.C.S.: 517111
Adrian Moreno *(COO)*

MEGANET d. o. o. (1)
10 Narof, 1411, Izlake, Slovenia
Tel.: (386) 35679110
Web Site: http://www.meganet.si
Web Portal Services
N.A.I.C.S.: 519290

Mobitel, d.d. (1)
Vilharjeva 23, 1537, Ljubljana, Slovenia
Tel.: (386) 14722200
Web Site: http://www.mobitel.si
Sales Range: $400-449.9 Million
Emp.: 1,000
Mobile Telecommunication Operator
N.A.I.C.S.: 517112

Subsidiary (Domestic):

Planet 9 (2)
Vojkova 78, 1000, Ljubljana, Slovenia
Tel.: (386) 14730300
Web Site: http://www.planet.si
Sales Range: $25-49.9 Million
Emp.: 100
Management of Mobile Telecommunications Contents & Services
N.A.I.C.S.: 517112

Soline Pridelava Soli d.o.o. (2)
Seca 115, Portorose, 6320, Portoroz, Slovenia
Tel.: (386) 56721330
Web Site: https://www.soline.si
Sales Range: $25-49.9 Million
Emp.: 86
Production & Sale of Salt & Other Products from the Salt-Pans; Management of Secovlje Salina Nature Park & Development of Tourism
N.A.I.C.S.: 327999

On.net (1)
Partizanski Odredi 70/5, PO Box 205, 1000, Skopje, North Macedonia **(83%)**
Tel.: (389) 23100800
Web Site: http://www.on.net.mk
Sales Range: $25-49.9 Million
Emp.: 60
Internet Services
N.A.I.C.S.: 517810

TSinpo, d.o.o. (1)
Litostrojska Cesta 58A, 1000, Ljubljana, Slovenia
Tel.: (386) 15006060
Web Site: https://www.tsinpo.si
Cardboard Mfr
N.A.I.C.S.: 322130

TELEKOM SRBIJA AD

Takovska 2, 11000, Belgrade, Serbia
Tel.: (381) 0800100100
Web Site: http://www.mts.rs
Wireless Telecommuncations
N.A.I.C.S.: 517810
Predrag Culibrk *(Chm & CEO)*

Subsidiaries:

MTS Banka A.D. (1)
Bulevar Fransa d Eperea 88, 11000, Belgrade, Serbia **(97.1%)**
Tel.: (381) 800103103
Web Site: http://www.mtsbanka.rs
Commercial Banking Services
N.A.I.C.S.: 522110

TELEKOM SRPSKE A.D.

Vuka Karadzica 2, 78000, Banja Luka, Bosnia & Herzegovina
Tel.: (387) 51240101
Web Site: https://www.mtel.ba
TLKM-R-A—(BANJ)
Sales Range: Less than $1 Million
Wired Telecommunication Operator
N.A.I.C.S.: 517121
Predrag Culibrk *(Chm-Mgmt Bd)*

TELEKOMUNIKACIJE REPUBLIKE SRPSKE A.D.

93 Kralja Petra I Karadordevica, 78 000, Banja Luka, Bosnia & Herzegovina
Tel.: (387) 51240110
Web Site: https://www.mtel.ba
TLKM.R.A—(BANJ)
Rev.: $284,134,562
Assets: $965,097,135
Liabilities: $397,777,412
Net Worth: $567,319,723
Earnings: $194,528,592
Emp.: 2,621
Fiscal Year-end: 12/31/23
Telecommunication Servicesb
N.A.I.C.S.: 517112
Predrag Culibrk *(Pres & Member-Mgmt Bd)*

Subsidiaries:

Blicnet d.o.o. (1)
Majke Jugovica 25, 78000, Banja Luka, Bosnia & Herzegovina
Tel.: (387) 51921000
Web Site: http://www.blic.net
Broadband Internet Services
N.A.I.C.S.: 517111

Elta-Kabel d.o.o. (1)
Dobojske brigade bb and Celjska bb, 74000, Doboj, Bosnia & Herzegovina
Tel.: (387) 70310312
Web Site: http://www.elta-kabel.com
Cable Internet Services
N.A.I.C.S.: 517111

GO4YU d.o.o. (1)
Franse d'Eperea 88, 11000, Belgrade, Serbia
Tel.: (381) 116558030
Web Site: http://www.go4yu.com
Telecommunication Servicesb
N.A.I.C.S.: 517810

Logosoft d.o.o. (1)
Grbavicka 4, Sarajevo, Bosnia & Herzegovina
Tel.: (387) 33931900
Web Site: https://www.logosoft.ba
Broadband Internet Services
Emp.: 90
N.A.I.C.S.: 517111

Telrad Net d.o.o. (1)
Nusiceva BB, 76300, Bijeljina, Bosnia & Herzegovina
Tel.: (387) 55415415
Web Site: http://www.telrad.net
Cable Internet Services
N.A.I.C.S.: 517111

TELEMA S.P.A

Via Salvoni 60, Frazione Quarto, 29122, Piacenza, Italy
Tel.: (39) 0523557226   IT
Web Site: http://www.telemait.com
Year Founded: 1975
Sales Range: $25-49.9 Million
Emp.: 120
Railways & Industrial Applications Power Resistors Design & Mfr
N.A.I.C.S.: 334416
Mario Fornari *(Owner & Mng Dir)*

Subsidiaries:

Cressall Resistors Limited (1)
Evington Valley Road, Leicester, LE5 5LZ, Leicestershire, United Kingdom **(100%)**
Tel.: (44) 1162733633
Web Site: http://www.cressall.com
Sales Range: $25-49.9 Million
Emp.: 90
High Power Electrical Resistors
N.A.I.C.S.: 334416
Martin Nicholls *(Dir-Sls)*

I-Gard Corporation (1)
7686 Bath Road, Mississauga, L4T 1L2, ON, Canada **(100%)**
Tel.: (905) 673-1553
Web Site: http://www.i-gard.com
Sales Range: $25-49.9 Million
Emp.: 40
Ground Fault Protection & Power Resistor-based Solutions
N.A.I.C.S.: 334416
Edmundo Perich *(VP)*

Mosebach Manufacturing Company, Inc. (1)
1417 McLaughlin Run Rd, Pittsburgh, PA 15241-3103 **(100%)**
Tel.: (412) 220-0200
Web Site: http://www.mosebachresistors.com
Sales Range: $25-49.9 Million
Emp.: 52
High Power Electrical Resistors Mfr
N.A.I.C.S.: 335314

Post Glover Resistors Inc. (1)
4750 Olympic Blvd, Erlanger, KY 41018-3141 **(100%)**
Tel.: (859) 283-0778
Web Site: http://www.postglover.com
High Power Electrical Resistors Mfr
N.A.I.C.S.: 334416
Scott Fuller *(VP-Sls & Mktg)*

Telema & Berger Resistors, Inc. (1)
1002 Ford Cir, Milford, OH 45150
Tel.: (513) 831-7300
Web Site: http://www.tbresistors.com
Sales Range: $1-9.9 Million
Emp.: 25
Mfg Electronic Resistors
N.A.I.C.S.: 334416
Robert Berger *(Pres)*

TELEMASTERS HOLDINGS LIMITED

90 Regency Drive Route 21 Corporate Office Park, Irene, South Africa
Tel.: (27) 879450000   ZA
Web Site: http://www.telemasters.co.za
TLM—(JSE)
Rev.: $3,388,475
Assets: $2,943,980
Liabilities: $968,102
Net Worth: $1,975,878
Earnings: $21,969
Emp.: 47
Fiscal Year-end: 06/30/23
Telecommunication Servicesb
N.A.I.C.S.: 517810
Jaco-Muller Voigt *(CEO)*

INTERNATIONAL PUBLIC

TELEMETRY LTD.

4th Fl Crown House 1432147 Regent St, London, W1B4NR, United Kingdom
Tel.: (44) 20 7148 7777
Web Site: http://www.telemetry.com
Year Founded: 2001
Sales Range: $25-49.9 Million
Emp.: 55
Digital Advertising Analysis & Auditing Services
N.A.I.C.S.: 541613
Anthony Rushton *(CEO)*

Subsidiaries:

Telemetry Inc (1)
7 World Trade Ctr, New York, NY 10007
Tel.: (212) 380-6666
Online Advertising Services
N.A.I.C.S.: 541810

TELEMOS CAPITAL

10 Stratton Street, London, W1J 8LG, United Kingdom
Tel.: (44) 203 906 6820
Web Site: http://telemoscapital.com
Privater Equity Firm
N.A.I.C.S.: 523940
Phillipe Jacobs *(Exec Chm)*

TELENOR ASA

Snaroyveien 30, N-1360, Fornebu, Norway
Tel.: (47) 81077000   NO
Web Site: https://www.telenor.com
Year Founded: 1855
TEL—(OSL)
Rev.: $14,330,815,590
Assets: $29,934,369,010
Liabilities: $24,809,577,590
Net Worth: $5,124,791,420
Earnings: $2,457,374,710
Emp.: 19,000
Fiscal Year-end: 12/31/20
Fixed Line & Mobile Telecommunication, Satellite, Television & Internet Services
N.A.I.C.S.: 517111
Ruza Sabanovic *(CTO & Exec VP)*

Subsidiaries:

B2 Bredband AB (1)
Katarinavagen 15, 11688, Stockholm, Sweden
Tel.: (46) 850698300
Web Site: http://www.telenor.sc
Sales Range: $50-74.9 Million
Emp.: 155
Internet Services
N.A.I.C.S.: 517810
Martin Petersem *(Dir-Customer Svc)*

Canal Digital AS (1)
Snaroyveien 30, 1331, Fornebu, Norway
Tel.: (47) 67 89 00 00
Web Site: http://www.canaldigital.com
Rev.: $726,349,680
Emp.: 290
Television & Radio Broadcasting Services
N.A.I.C.S.: 516120
Kristin Muri Moller *(CFO)*

DNA Oy (1)
Lakkisepantie 21, 00620, Helsinki, Finland
Tel.: (358) 4 414 4044
Web Site: http://www.dna.fi
Emp.: 1,604
Mobile Telecommunications Services
N.A.I.C.S.: 517112
Jukka Leinonen *(Chm)*

Subsidiary (Domestic):

Huuked Labs Oy (2)
PL 41, 1740, Vantaa, Finland
Tel.: (358) 440440
Web Site: http://www.huuked.com
Software Development Services
N.A.I.C.S.: 541511

Datametrix AS (1)
Grenseveien 95, PO Box 6528, Etterstad, 0606, Oslo, Norway

Tel.: (47) 23035900
Web Site: http://www.datametrix.no
Sales Range: $75-99.9 Million
Emp.: 234
Electronic Security Devices Whslr
N.A.I.C.S.: 423690
Jostein Kirkerod *(Dir-Sls)*

Grameenphone Ltd. (1)
GP House Basundhara Baridhara, Gulshan, Dhaka, 1229, Bangladesh **(62%)**
Tel.: (880) 179 988 2990
Web Site: https://www.grameenphone.com
Sales Range: $800-899.9 Million
Emp.: 5,000
Telecommunication Servicesb
N.A.I.C.S.: 517112
Yasir Azman *(CEO)*

Kjedehuset AS (1)
Gjerdrumsvei 19, 0484, Oslo, Norway **(49%)**
Tel.: (47) 9581 6000
Web Site: http://www.kjedehuset.no
Mobile Communications Products Distribution Network Franchisor
N.A.I.C.S.: 533110
Andre Lovestam *(CEO)*

Maritime Communications Partner AS (1)
Nygaten 4, 4838, Arendal, Norway
Tel.: (47) 3709 0000
Web Site: http://www.mcp.com
Emp.: 5
Wireless Telecommunication Services
N.A.I.C.S.: 517112

Norkring AS (1)
Snaroyveien 30 Bygg M, 1360, Fornebu, Norway
Tel.: (47) 67 89 20 00
Web Site: http://www.norkring.no
Television Broadcasting Services
N.A.I.C.S.: 516120
Torbjorn Odegard Teigen *(CEO)*

TELWAY AS (1)
Ingvald Ludvigsens Gate 21, 3027, Drammen, Norway
Tel.: (47) 9 021 7200
Web Site: https://www.telway.no
Sales Range: $25-49.9 Million
Emp.: 15
Multimedia & Broadband Products Distr
N.A.I.C.S.: 423690

Telenor AB (1)
Tatarinavagen 15, PO Box 4247, 10265, Stockholm, Sweden
Tel.: (46) 858787000
Web Site: http://www.telenor.se
Sales Range: $800-899.9 Million
Emp.: 3,000
Mobile Telecommunications Services
N.A.I.C.S.: 517112
Moniqa Lofstedt *(Mgr-HR-Bus Consumer)*

Subsidiary (Domestic):

Telenor Sverige AB (2)
Garvis Carlssons Gata 3, 169 03, Solna, Sweden
Tel.: (46) 20222222
Web Site: http://www.telenor.se
Mobile Telecommunications Services
N.A.I.C.S.: 517112

Telenor Broadcast Holding AS (1)
Snaroyveien 30, Fornebu, 1360, Norway
Tel.: (47) 67890000
Investment Management Service
N.A.I.C.S.: 523999

Subsidiary (Non-US):

Telenor UK Ltd. (2)
40 Bernard Street, London, WC1N 1LE, United Kingdom
Tel.: (44) 207 923 6500
Emp.: 25
Mobile Telecommunications Services
N.A.I.C.S.: 517112
Julian Crudge *(Mng Dir)*

Telenor Connexion AB (1)
Garvis Carlssons gata 3, 169 51, Solna, Sweden
Tel.: (46) 84 103 3800
Web Site:
  https://www.telenorconnexion.com

Wireless Telecommunication Services
N.A.I.C.S.: 517112
Johan Larsson *(Mgr-Bid)*

Telenor Denmark Holding A/S (1)
Frederikskaj 8, 1780, Copenhagen, Denmark **(53.5%)**
Tel.: (45) 6 050 4000
Web Site: https://www.telenor.dk
Sales Range: $400-449.9 Million
Emp.: 1,304
Operation of GSM & Mobile Telephony; Marketing of Mobile Telephony Services & Mobile Phones
N.A.I.C.S.: 517112
Jesper Hansen *(Mng Dir)*

Telenor Eiendom Fornebu Kvartal 3 AS (1)
Snaroyveien 30, Snaroya, 1360, Norway
Tel.: (47) 67890000
Web Site: http://www.telenor.com
Wireless Telecommunication Services
N.A.I.C.S.: 517112

Telenor International AS (1)
Snaroyveien 30, N-1331, Fornebu, Norway
Tel.: (47) 810 77 000
Web Site: http://www.international.telenor.no
Sales Range: $1-4.9 Billion
Emp.: 10,000
N.A.I.C.S.: 517111
Jon Fredrik Baksaas *(Pres & CEO)*

Telenor Kapitalforvaltning ASA (1)
Snaroyveien 30, Fornebu, 1360, Norway
Tel.: (47) 67890000
Web Site: http://www.telenor.com
Sales Range: $25-49.9 Million
Emp.: 2
Telecommunication Servicesb
N.A.I.C.S.: 517111

Telenor Linx AS (1)
Snaroyveien 30, 1360, Fornebu, Norway
Tel.: (47) 81077000
Web Site: https://www.telenorlinx.com
Emp.: 200
Telecommunication Servicesb
N.A.I.C.S.: 517112

Telenor Maritime AS (1)
Kystveien 2D, N-4841, Arendal, Norway
Tel.: (47) 37090000
Web Site: https://telenormaritime.com
Emp.: 120
Ship Mobile Services
N.A.I.C.S.: 517410

Telenor Mobil AS (1)
Snaroyveien 30, 1331, Fornebu, Norway **(100%)**
Tel.: (47) 67890000
Web Site: http://www.telenor.no
Sales Range: $1-4.9 Billion
Emp.: 10,000
Mobile Telecommunications
N.A.I.C.S.: 517111
Jon Fredrik Baksaas *(Pres & CEO)*

Telenor Nett AS (1)
Snaroyveien 30, N 1331, Fornebu, Norway **(100%)**
Tel.: (47) 67890000
Web Site: http://www.telenor.no
Sales Range: $125-149.9 Million
Emp.: 400
Communication Service
N.A.I.C.S.: 517111

Telenor Objects AS (1)
Snaroyveien 30, 1331, Fornebu, Norway
Tel.: (47) 67890000
Web Site: http://www.telenor.com
Telecommunication Servicesb
N.A.I.C.S.: 517810

Telenor Plus AS (1)
Teatergt 9, PO Box 6701, Saint Olavs Plass, N-0130, Oslo, Norway **(100%)**
Tel.: (47) 95833735
Communications Solutions for Residential Customers
N.A.I.C.S.: 517111
Prasoon Sinha *(VP & Head-Dynamic Performance Mgmt Project)*

Telenor Programvare AS (1)
Snaroyveien 30, N 1331, Fornebu, Norway **(100%)**
Tel.: (47) 81077000

Web Site: http://www.telenor.com
Sales Range: $25-49.9 Million
Emp.: 25
Communication Service
N.A.I.C.S.: 517111

Telenor Satellite (1)
Snaroyveien 30 C7c, 1360, Fornebu, Norway
Tel.: (47) 67890000
Web Site: http://www.telenorsat.com
Satellite Communication Services
N.A.I.C.S.: 517410
Martin Foss *(CFO)*

Telenor Traxion AB (1)
Campus Grasvik 12, 371 80, Karlskrona, Sweden
Tel.: (46) 455 619130
Web Site: http://www.telenortraxion.com
Sales Range: $25-49.9 Million
Emp.: 1
Rail Wagon & Container Monitoring Services
N.A.I.C.S.: 561621

Telenor Venture VI AS (1)
Snaroyveien 30, 1331, Fornebu, Norway
Tel.: (47) 22 77 99 10
Financial Management Services
N.A.I.C.S.: 523999

Telenor Venture VII AS (1)
Tollbugata 24, Oslo, 0157, Norway
Tel.: (47) 22779910
Financial Management Services
N.A.I.C.S.: 523999

Subsidiary (Domestic):

TelCage AS (2)
Otto Nielsensvei 12, Trondheim, 7004, Norway
Tel.: (47) 95895010
Web Site: http://www.telcage.com
Sales Range: $25-49.9 Million
Emp.: 6
Aquaculture Industry Remote Operating & Monitoring Services
N.A.I.C.S.: 112519

TELENT LIMITED
Point 3 Haywood Road, Warwick, CV34 5AH, United Kingdom
Tel.: (44) 1926693000
Web Site: http://www.telent.com
Sales Range: $600-649.9 Million
Emp.: 2,172
Holding Company; Communications & High Technology Products
N.A.I.C.S.: 517111
Paul Lester *(Chm)*

Subsidiaries:

GEC Brunei Sdn. Bhd. (1)
Unit No. 313 Kompleks Mohommed Yussof, Mile 1, Jalan Tutong, Bandar Seri Begawan, Brunei Darussalam
Tel.: (673) 2 651089
N.A.I.C.S.: 335313

Marconi (1)
1112 Rock Creek Elementary School Dr, O'Fallon, MO 63366-7577
Tel.: (636) 281-2446
Sales Range: $25-49.9 Million
Emp.: 25
Telphone & Equipment Installation
N.A.I.C.S.: 238210

Marconi Communications Holdings (1)
69 Meadowbrook Industrial Park, Toccoa, GA 30577
Tel.: (706) 779-3323
Web Site: http://www.marconi.com
Sales Range: $25-49.9 Million
Emp.: 190
Telephone &Telegraph Holdings
N.A.I.C.S.: 541690

Marconi Communications Inc. (1)
1122 F St, Lorain, OH 44052-2255
Tel.: (954) 659-3900
Sales Range: $25-49.9 Million
Emp.: 30
Telecommunications
N.A.I.C.S.: 334210

Marconi Communications Inc. (1)
777 108th Ave NE Ste 1250, Bellevue, WA 98004-4375
Tel.: (425) 990-7970
Electronic Parts And Equipment
N.A.I.C.S.: 423690

Marconi Corp. (1)
3000 Marconi Dr, Warrendale, PA 15086-7502
Tel.: (724) 742-4444
Web Site: http://www.marconi.com
Sales Range: $200-249.9 Million
Emp.: 900
Broadband Routing & Switching Services
N.A.I.C.S.: 334118

Marconi Wireless (1)
1755 N Collins Blvd Ste 400, Richardson, TX 75080-3562
Tel.: (972) 669-6300
Web Site: http://www.marconi.com
Sales Range: $50-74.9 Million
Emp.: 200
Cellular Telephone Services
N.A.I.C.S.: 541690

Talent (1)
Pensions Office The Hollies Newport Rd, Stafford, ST16 1BY, United Kingdom **(100%)**
Tel.: (44) 1785785400
Web Site: http://www.telent.co.uk
Sales Range: $50-74.9 Million
Emp.: 40
Trustee of the GEC Plan & Selected Benefit Scheme; Admin of GEC UK Group Retirement Benefit Plans
N.A.I.C.S.: 524292

TELEPERFORMANCE SE
21-25 Rue Balzac, 75 008, Paris, France
Tel.: (33) 153835900 FR
Web Site:
  https://www.teleperformance.com
Year Founded: 1978
TEP—(OTCIQ)
Rev.: $9,006,043,600
Assets: $12,685,085,258
Liabilities: $8,112,454,133
Net Worth: $4,572,631,125
Earnings: $649,687,028
Emp.: 490,000
Fiscal Year-end: 12/31/23
Management Consulting Services
N.A.I.C.S.: 551112
Olivier Rigaudy *(Deputy CEO & CFO-Grp)*

Subsidiaries:

Albania Marketing Service Sh.p.K. (1)
Rruga Abdyl Frasher Hekla Center, Tirana, Albania
Tel.: (355) 42258261
Customer Care Services
N.A.I.C.S.: 561422
Digo Pisa *(Gen Mgr)*

All by Phone + Net Dialogmarketing & Consulting GmbH (1)
Wendenstrasse 375-377, 20537, Hamburg, Germany
Tel.: (49) 40809070
Sales Range: $75-99.9 Million
Emp.: 300
Telemarketing Services
N.A.I.C.S.: 561422

AllianceOne Limited (1)
365 Bloor St E Ste 200, Toronto, M4W3L4, ON, Canada
Tel.: (416) 447-8899
Web Site: http://www.Allianceone.com
Accounting Services
N.A.I.C.S.: 541219

AllianceOne Receivables Management Inc (1)
1160 Ctr Pointe Dr Ste 202, Mendota Heights, MN 55120
Tel.: (651) 255-2040
Online Payment Services
N.A.I.C.S.: 522320

TELEPERFORMANCE SE

Teleperformance SE—(Continued)

Michael Hollerich *(Chief Compliance & Quality Officer)*

BPS Associates Ltd. (1)
Pinnacle House 17 Hartfield Road, London, SW19 3SE, United Kingdom
Tel.: (44) 20 8296 1000
Customer Care Services
N.A.I.C.S.: 541613

CityTech S.A. (1)
Carlos Pellegrini 887 Piso 11, Buenos Aires, C1009ABQ, Argentina
Tel.: (54) 11 5555 3000
Telemarketing Services
N.A.I.C.S.: 561422

Dutch Contact Centers B.V. (1)
Orfeoschouw 70, Zoetermeer, 2726, South Holland, Netherlands
Tel.: (31) 793429800
Web Site: http://www.teleperformance.nl
Sales Range: $400-449.9 Million
Emp.: 2,000
Customer Care Services
N.A.I.C.S.: 541613

Full Sale Teleperformance SA (1)
Carlos Pellegrini 887 3rd Fl, Buenos Aires, C1009ABQ, Argentina
Tel.: (54) 11 5555 3000
Telemarketing Services
N.A.I.C.S.: 561422
Sales Range: $50-74.9 Million
Emp.:
Agustin Grisanti *(CEO)*

Subsidiary (Non-US):

TP Chili (Chile) (2)
Teatinos 950 17th Floor, 8340084, Santiago, Chile
Tel.: (56) 22002200
Customer Care & Back Office Management Services
N.A.I.C.S.: 561499

GN Research France (1)
3 rue Henri Rol Tanguy, 93 100, Montreuil, France
Tel.: (33) 1 45 30 72 03
Web Site: http://www.gnresearch.com
Marketing Research Service
N.A.I.C.S.: 541613

GN Research Germany GmbH (1)
Opitzstrasse 12, 40470, Dusseldorf, Nordrhein-Westfalen, Germany
Tel.: (49) 211478470
Marketing Research Service
N.A.I.C.S.: 541910

Health Advocate, Inc. (1)
3043 Walton Rd Ste 150, Plymouth Meeting, PA 19462
Tel.: (610) 825-1222
Web Site: http://www.healthadvocate.com
Sales Range: $75-99.9 Million
Health Advocacy & Assistance Services
N.A.I.C.S.: 813319
Arthur N. Leibowitz *(Chief Medical Officer)*

Iberphone SAU (1)
Av de Burgos 8 A, 28036, Madrid, Spain
Tel.: (34) 915906000
Customer Care Services
N.A.I.C.S.: 541613

In & out SPA (1)
Viale Bramante 29, Fiumicino, 00054, Rome, Italy
Tel.: (39) 06865191
Web Site: http://www.teleperformanceitalia.it
Customer Care Services
N.A.I.C.S.: 541613

Intelenet Global Services Private Limited (1)
Intelenet Towers Plot CST No 1406 A/28, Mindspace Malad West, Mumbai, 400 090, Maharashtra, India
Tel.: (91) 22 6677 6000
Web Site: http://www.intelenetglobal.com
Emp.: 55,000
Business Process Outsourcing Services
N.A.I.C.S.: 561499
Susir M. Kumar *(Chm)*

Subsidiary (Non-US):

Intelenet Global (UK) Limited (2)
Suite 410/ 1 Northumberland Avenue, Trafalgar Square, London, WC2N 5BW, United Kingdom
Tel.: (44) 845 420 4646
Business Process Outsourcing Services
N.A.I.C.S.: 561499
Steve Morgan *(Mng Dir)*

Language Line Services UK Ltd. (1)
25th Floor 40 Bank Street, Canary Wharf, London, E14 5NR, United Kingdom
Tel.: (44) 8001692879
Web Site: https://www.languageline.com
Translation & Interpretation Services
N.A.I.C.S.: 541930
Scott W. Klein *(Pres & CEO)*

LanguageLine Solutions (1)
1 Lowr Ragsdale Dr Bldg 2, Monterey, CA 93940
Tel.: (44) 8001692879
Web Site: https://www.languageline.com
Over-the-Phone Language Interpretation & Document Translation Services
N.A.I.C.S.: 541930
Scott W. Klein *(Pres & CEO)*

Lion Teleservices CZ AS (1)
Erno Kostala 870, 530 12, Pardubice, Czech Republic
Tel.: (420) 466 029 111
Web Site: http://www.teleperformance.cz
Sales Range: $75-99.9 Million
Emp.: 260
Telemarketing Services
N.A.I.C.S.: 561422

Subsidiary (Non-US):

Lion Teleservices SK (2)
Bytcicka 72, Zilina, 01001, Slovakia
Tel.: (421) 41 5005 005
Web Site: http://www.teleperformance.com
Sales Range: $25-49.9 Million
Emp.: 70
Customer Care Services
N.A.I.C.S.: 541613

Luxembourg Contact Centers SARL (1)
Rue Jean-Pierre Brasseur 32, 1258, Luxembourg, Luxembourg
Tel.: (352) 26 38 36 23
Web Site: http://www.teleperformance.com
Sales Range: $25-49.9 Million
Emp.: 1
Telemarketing Services
N.A.I.C.S.: 561422

MM Teleperformance Holdings Ltd (1)
St James House, Bristol, BS2 8QY, United Kingdom
Tel.: (44) 1179168000
Web Site: http://www.teleperformance.com
Emp.: 450
Customer Care Services
N.A.I.C.S.: 561422

Subsidiary (Non-US):

BPS Contact Centre Services (2)
Pinnacle House 3rd Floor 17-25 Hartfield Road, Wimbledon, sw19 3se, London, United Kingdom - England
Tel.: (44) 2082961000
Web Site: http://www.bpscontact.co.uk
Sales Range: $25-49.9 Million
Emp.: 100
Customer Care & Telemarketing Services
N.A.I.C.S.: 541613

Metis Bilgisayar Sistemliri Sanayi ve Ticaret A.S (1)
Flatofis Otakcilar Caddesi No 78 Kat 4, Eyup, 34050, Istanbul, Turkiye
Tel.: (90) 2123366900
Web Site: http://tr.www.teleperformance.com
Contact Center Services
N.A.I.C.S.: 561422
Barbaros Baysal *(Supvr-Customer Svc)*

North Asia Ltd CRM Technologies (1)
302 Satellite Tower 63 Zhichun Road, HaiDian District, Beijing, 100190, China
Tel.: (86) 1059936000
Customer Care Services
N.A.I.C.S.: 541613

P.T. Telemarketing Indonesia (1)
18th Floor Menara Jamsostek Jl Jend Gatot Subroto kav 38, Jakarta, 12710, Indonesia
Tel.: (62) 2125508111
Telemarketing Services
N.A.I.C.S.: 561422

PGS Progisoftware (1)
37bis rue du General Leclerc, 92130, Issy-les-Moulineaux, France
Tel.: (33) 155958000
Web Site: http://www.pgs.fr
Sales Range: $25-49.9 Million
Software Development & Customer Care Services
N.A.I.C.S.: 541511

Perfect Call (Netherlands) BV (1)
Orfeoschouw 70-76, Zoetermeer, 2726 JH, South Holland, Netherlands
Tel.: (31) 793429800
Web Site: http://www.teleperformance.nl
Sales Range: $100-124.9 Million
Emp.: 500
Customer Care Services
N.A.I.C.S.: 541613

Photel Inc. (1)
Berzenczey utca 9, 1094, Budapest, Hungary
Tel.: (36) 14535300
Web Site: http://photel.hu
Sales Range: $50-74.9 Million
Emp.: 250
Customer Care Services
N.A.I.C.S.: 541613

Plurimarketing (Portugal) (1)
Rua Alexandra Braga 25 B, 1150-003, Lisbon, Portugal
Tel.: (351) 21 311 39 00
Web Site: http://www.teleperformance.pt
Telemarketing Services
N.A.I.C.S.: 541613

Service 800 Teleperformance SA (1)
Thisseos 330, 176 75, Athens, Greece
Tel.: (30) 210 94 90 500
Web Site: http://www.teleperformance.gr
Sales Range: $300-349.9 Million
Emp.: 2,000
Customer Care Services
N.A.I.C.S.: 541422

Subsidiary (Domestic):

Direct Response Service SA (2)
385 Acharnon, 111 43, Athens, Greece
Tel.: (30) 2102013500
Customer Care Services
N.A.I.C.S.: 561422

Mantel SA (2)
Ionias 166, 11144, Athens, Greece
Tel.: (30) 210 20 10 490
Customer Care Services
N.A.I.C.S.: 541421

Subsidiary (Non-US):

TP Romania services 800 CSP (2)
88 Sebastian Street District 5, Bucharest, Romania
Tel.: (40) 214010800
Customer Care & Telemarketing Services
N.A.I.C.S.: 561422

Subsidiary (Domestic):

Teleperformance Debtors Information services (2)
Isminis 59, Athens, Greece
Tel.: (30) 210 9490 500
Customer Care & Telemarketing Services
N.A.I.C.S.: 561422

Subsidiary (Non-US):

Teleperformance Lebanon SAL (2)
Beirut Echocard Street Agility Building, PO Box 11-731, Sin El Fil, Beirut, Lebanon
Tel.: (961) 1511422
Customer Care Services
N.A.I.C.S.: 541613
Wadad Karam *(Mgr)*

Sistemas de Localizacion S.A. de C.V. (1)
Cuauhtemoc No 400 Sur Centro, 64000, Monterrey, Nuevo Leon, Mexico
Tel.: (52) 8181500000
Business Support Services
N.A.I.C.S.: 561499

INTERNATIONAL PUBLIC

Telemarketing Asia (Singapore) Pte Ltd (1)
29 Tai Seng Avenue Natural Cool Lifestyle Hub 06-01, Singapore, 534119, Singapore
Tel.: (65) 63387833
Telemarketing Services
N.A.I.C.S.: 561422

Teleperformance CRM SA (1)
Werner Siemens 111, Lapa, Sao Paulo, 05069-010, Brazil
Tel.: (55) 1121633415
Sales Range: $1-4.9 Billion
Emp.: 14,000
Customer Care Services
N.A.I.C.S.: 541613

Teleperformance CZ, a. s. (1)
Sukova Trida 1556, Zelene Predmesti, 530 02, Pardubice, Czech Republic
Tel.: (420) 800123444
Web Site: http://www.teleperformance.cz
Contact Center Services
N.A.I.C.S.: 561422
Valeriy Svetlov *(Gen Mgr)*

Teleperformance Danemark AS (1)
Di Gebez No 140, 2300, Copenhagen, Denmark
Tel.: (45) 33 36 94 94
Web Site: http://www.teleperformance.dk
Sales Range: $25-49.9 Million
Emp.: 130
Telemarketing Services
N.A.I.C.S.: 561422

Teleperformance Denmark A/S (1)
Hedegaardsvej 88 2, 2300, Copenhagen, Denmark
Tel.: (45) 70219494
Web Site: https://www.teleperformance.dk
Contact Center Services
N.A.I.C.S.: 561422
Jens Skyman *(Dir-Bus Dev & Sls-Nordics)*

Teleperformance EMEA (1)
6/8 Rue Firmin Gillot, 75737, Paris, France
Tel.: (33) 155764080
Telemarketing Services
N.A.I.C.S.: 561422

Teleperformance Finland Oy (1)
Rautatienkatu 21 B, 33100, Tampere, Finland
Tel.: (358) 3411411
Web Site: http://www.teleperformance.fi
Telemarketing Services
N.A.I.C.S.: 561422

Teleperformance France SAS (1)
12/14/16 Rue Sarah Bernhardt, 75737, Asnieres-sur-Seine, France
Tel.: (33) 155764030
Web Site: http://www.teleperformance.fr
Telemarketing Services
N.A.I.C.S.: 561422

Teleperformance Group Inc. (1)
1601 Washington Ave Ste 400, Miami Beach, FL 33139
Tel.: (786) 437-3300
Web Site: http://www.teleperformance.com
Sales Range: $25-49.9 Million
Emp.: 12
Customer Care Services
N.A.I.C.S.: 541613

Teleperformance Nordic AB (1)
Sankt Eriksgatan 115, Box 6777, 113 85, Stockholm, Sweden
Tel.: (46) 86102200
Web Site: http://www.tpnordic.se
Emp.: 615
Customer Care & Telemarketing Services
N.A.I.C.S.: 561422

Teleperformance Norge AS (1)
Grubbegata 14, PO Box 98, 0179, Oslo, Norway
Tel.: (47) 35 02 20 00
Customer Care Services
N.A.I.C.S.: 541613

Teleperformance Polska (1)
ul Domaniewska 50, 02-672, Warsaw, Poland
Tel.: (48) 22 468 7000
Web Site: http://www.teleperformancepolska.pl
Emp.: 450
Customer Care Services

AND PRIVATE COMPANIES

N.A.I.C.S.: 541613

Teleperformance Russia (1)
Preobrazhenskaya sq 8 Bus Ctr PREO 8
Blc B16th Fl, Moscow, 107061, Russia
Tel.: (7) 4957874000
Web Site: http://www.teleperformance.ru
Sales Range: $200-249.9 Million
Emp.: 1,000
Call Center Services
N.A.I.C.S.: 519290

Teleperformance UK Ltd (1)
Spectrum House Bond Street, Bristol, BS1
3LG, United Kingdom
Tel.: (44) 1179168000
Web Site: http://www.teleperformance.com
Emp.: 8,000
Customer Care Services
N.A.I.C.S.: 541613

Teleperformance USA (1)
1991 South 4650 W, Salt Lake City, UT
84104
Tel.: (801) 257-5800
Web Site: http://www.teleperformance.com
Rev.: $53,000,000
Emp.: 80
Telemarketing Services
N.A.I.C.S.: 517810
Brad Hansen (CFO)

Subsidiary (Domestic):

Americall Group, Inc. (2)
550 E Diehl Rd, Naperville, IL 60563-1354
Tel.: (630) 955-9100
Web Site: http://www.americallgroup.com
Sales Range: $1-4.9 Billion
Call Center Services
N.A.I.C.S.: 561422

Subsidiary (Non-US):

CRM Services India Pvt. Ltd. (2)
Plot No 398 Udyog Vihar III Phase III, Gurgaon, 122016, India
Tel.: (91) 124 243 9955
Customer Care Services
N.A.I.C.S.: 561499
Sanjay Metha (Mng Dir)

Subsidiary (Domestic):

The Answer Group Inc. (2)
7562 Southgate Blvd, North Lauderdale, FL
33068-1362
Tel.: (954) 720-4002
Customer Care & Telemarketing Services
N.A.I.C.S.: 561422

Teleperformance Unternehmungsbeatung GmbH (1)
Braeuhausgasse 7-9, 1050, Vienna, Austria
Tel.: (43) 1 54 555 54
Customer Care Services
N.A.I.C.S.: 541613

gnresearch ITALIA (1)
Via di Priscilla 101, 00199, Rome, Italy
Tel.: (39) 06865171
Web Site: http://www.gnresearch.com
Marketing Research Service
N.A.I.C.S.: 541910

TELEPHONE CABLES LTD.
SCO 68 - 70 Sector 17 - C, PO Box
7, Chandigarh, 160017, Punjab, India
Tel.: (91) 1722702720
517159—(BOM)
Cable Mfr
N.A.I.C.S.: 332618
G. L. Tuteja (Sec)

TELEPIZZA GROUP SA
Avenida PQ Empre la Marina 7, Madrid, 28703, Spain
Tel.: (34) 1919221221
Rev.: $430,430,509
Assets: $1,270,951,511
Liabilities: $802,817,555
Net Worth: $468,133,956
Earnings: $(62,718,879)
Emp.: 6,103
Fiscal Year-end: 12/31/19
Restaurant Operators
N.A.I.C.S.: 722511

Emilio Tovar Lazaro (CIO)

TELEPOOL GMBH
Sonnenstrasse 2 1, 80331, Munich,
Germany
Tel.: (49) 89 55 87 60 De
Web Site: http://www.telepool.de
Year Founded: 1963
Film & Television Licensing
N.A.I.C.S.: 533110
Thomas Weymar (CEO)

Subsidiaries:

EuroVideo Bildprogramm GmbH (1)
Oskar-Messter-Str 15, Ismaning, 85737,
Germany
Tel.: (49) 899624440
Web Site: http://www.eurovideo.de
Sales Range: $25-49.9 Million
Emp.: 45
Prerecorded Compact Disc & Tape & Record Reproducing
N.A.I.C.S.: 334610
Ulich Raum (Gen Mgr)

Netleih GmbH & Co.KG (1)
Johann-Zincken-Str 6, 38723, Seesen, Germany
Tel.: (49) 538174929898
Web Site: http://www.videobuster.de
Electronic Parts Distr
N.A.I.C.S.: 423990

TELESAT CORPORATION
160 Elgin Street Suite 2100, Ottawa,
K2P 2P7, ON, Canada
Tel.: (613) 748-0123 BC
Web Site: https://policies.google.com
Year Founded: 2020
TSAT—(NASDAQ)
Holding Company; Satellite Systems
Mfr & Communications Services
N.A.I.C.S.: 551112
Daniel S. Goldberg (Pres & CEO)

Subsidiaries:

Telesat Partnership LP (1)
160 Elgin St Ste 2100, Ottawa, K2P 2P7,
ON, Canada (100%)
Tel.: (613) 748-8700
Holding Company
N.A.I.C.S.: 551112
Daniel S. Goldberg (Pres & CEO)

Subsidiary (US):

Loral Space & Communications Inc. (2)
600 5th Ave, New York, NY 10020 (100%)
Tel.: (212) 697-1105
Rev.: $122,570,000
Assets: $254,469,000
Liabilities: $44,936,000
Net Worth: $209,533,000
Earnings: $93,093,000
Emp.: 441
Fiscal Year-end: 12/31/2020
Holding Company; Commercial & Military Telecommunications Satellites & Satellite Systems Designer, Mfr & Operator
N.A.I.C.S.: 551112
Avi Katz (Pres)

Subsidiary (Non-US):

Telesat Canada (3)
160 Elgin Street Suite 2100, Ottawa, K2P
2P7, ON, Canada (100%)
Tel.: (613) 748-8700
Web Site: http://www.telesat.com
Rev.: $641,835,707
Assets: $4,366,055,660
Liabilities: $3,223,976,926
Net Worth: $1,142,078,734
Earnings: $192,110,758
Emp.: 429
Fiscal Year-end: 12/31/2020
Satellite Telecommunication Services
N.A.I.C.S.: 517410
Daniel S. Goldberg (Pres & CEO)

TELESENSORY (S) PTE. LTD.
71 Bukit Batok Crescent #05-10,
Prestige Ctr, Singapore, 658071,
Singapore
Tel.: (65) 63165372
Web Site:
http://www.telesensory.com
Mfr & Distr of Products for the Vision
Impaired
N.A.I.C.S.: 334118
S. S. Ng (Mng Dir)

Subsidiaries:

Telesensory Corporation (1)
4545 Stockdale Hwy Ste F, Bakersfield, CA
93309
Tel.: (650) 743-9515
Web Site: http://www.telesensory.com
Sales Range: $50-74.9 Million
Emp.: 4
Sales & Repairs of Electronic Products for the Blind & Visually Impaired
N.A.I.C.S.: 423430

Subsidiary (Non-US):

Telesensory Europe Ltd. (2)
Sherwood, The Quarry, Calne, SN11 0BX,
Wiltshire, United Kingdom
Tel.: (44) 1249 814309
Supplier of Electronic Magnification Systems for Visually Impaired
N.A.I.C.S.: 423430

TELESITES, S.A.B. DE C.V.
Av Paseo de las Palmas No 781 Piso
7 Oficina 703, Colonia Lomas de
Chapultepec III Seccion, DF 11000,
Mexico, Mexico
Tel.: (52) 55 5125 0200
Web Site:
http://www.telesites.com.mx
SITES—(MEX)
Sales Range: Less than $1 Million
Telecommunication Servicesb
N.A.I.C.S.: 517112
Gerardo Kuri Kaufmann (CEO)

TELESOFT TECHNOLOGIES LIMITED
Observatory House, Dorset, DT11
9LQ, Blandford, United Kingdom
Tel.: (44) 1258480880
Web Site: http://www.telesoft-technologies.com
Year Founded: 1989
Telecommunications, Monitoring,
Homeland Defense & Intelligence Solutions Services
N.A.I.C.S.: 517810
Robert Downham (Chm)

Subsidiaries:

Telesoft Technologies Inc. (1)
125 Townpark Dr Ste 300, Kennesaw, GA
30144
Tel.: (770) 454-6001
Telecommunication Servicesb
N.A.I.C.S.: 517810

Telesoft Technologies Ltd (1)
Building FC-24 Sector 16A, Noida, 201301,
Uttar Pradesh, India
Tel.: (91) 120 466 0300
Telecommunication Servicesb
N.A.I.C.S.: 517810

TELESTE CORPORATION
Telestenkatu 1, 20660, Littoinen, Finland
Tel.: (358) 22605611
Web Site: https://www.teleste.com
TLT1V—(HEL)
Rev.: $183,222,702
Assets: $166,087,526
Liabilities: $81,351,248
Net Worth: $84,736,278
Earnings: $8,511,703
Emp.: 847
Fiscal Year-end: 12/31/21
Broadband Access & Video Surveillance Services & Products

N.A.I.C.S.: 517112
Jukka Rinnevaara (Pres & CEO)

Subsidiaries:

Cableway AG (1)
Technologiepark Haus 56 Friedrich-Ebert-Str 75, 51429, Bergisch Gladbach, Germany
Tel.: (49) 22044760000
Web Site: http://www.cable-way.de
Cable Broadcasting Network Services
N.A.I.C.S.: 516210

Cableway Cyber Optic GmbH & Co. KG (1)
Friedrich-ebert-strasse 1, Bergisch Gladbach, 51429, Germany
Tel.: (49) 2204845600
Cable Network Services
N.A.I.C.S.: 516210

Cableway Mitte GmbH (1)
Amtsteich 16, 03046, Cottbus, Germany
Tel.: (49) 355 3816621
Cable Network Services
N.A.I.C.S.: 516210

Cableway Nord GmbH (1)
Friedrich-ebert-strabe Tbg, Bergisch Gladbach, 51429, Germany
Tel.: (49) 2204845600
Cable Network Services
N.A.I.C.S.: 516210

Cableway Sud GmbH (1)
Franz Josef Delonge Str 1, 81249, Munich,
Germany
Tel.: (49) 89 540444 0
Telecommunication Cable Installation Services
N.A.I.C.S.: 517810

DINH TechniCom S.A (1)
Rue D Abhooz 22, Herstal, 4040, Belgium
Tel.: (32) 42403535
Web Site: http://www.dinh.be
Sales Range: $25-49.9 Million
Emp.: 20
Telecommunications Equipment Mfr
N.A.I.C.S.: 334220

DINH TeleCom S.A (1)
Rue D Abhooz 22, Herstal, 4040, Belgium
Tel.: (32) 42403535
Web Site: http://www.dinh.be
Sales Range: $25-49.9 Million
Emp.: 20
Telecommunications Equipment Mfr
N.A.I.C.S.: 334290

Flomatik A/S (1)
Tormod Gjestlands Veg 21, Porsgrunn,
3936, Norway (100%)
Tel.: (47) 35560500
Web Site: http://www.flomatik.no
Sales Range: $25-49.9 Million
Emp.: 20
Miscellaneous Retail Stores
N.A.I.C.S.: 339999

Flomatik Network Services Ltd, (1)
9 The Gardens, Fareham, PO16 8SS,
Hampshire, United Kingdom
Tel.: (44) 1489604066
Web Site: http://www.flomatik.co.uk
Sales Range: $25-49.9 Million
Telecommunication Servicesb
N.A.I.C.S.: 517810
Steve Slater (Head-Resourcing)

Satlan Sp. z o o (1)
Ostrowskiego 30, 53-238, Wroclaw, Poland
Tel.: (48) 717900653
Web Site: http://www.satlan.pl
Emp.: 40
Cable Network Services
N.A.I.C.S.: 516210

Suomen Turvakamera Oy (1)
Olarinluoma 14 A, 02200, Espoo,
Finland (100%)
Tel.: (358) 94778140
Web Site: http://www.turvakamera.fi
Sales Range: $25-49.9 Million
Emp.: 8
Armored Car Services
N.A.I.C.S.: 561613

Teleste GmbH (1)

TELESTE CORPORATION

Teleste Corporation—(Continued)
Daimlerring 13, D-31135, Hildesheim, Germany **(100%)**
Tel.: (49) 5121750980
Sales Range: $25-49.9 Million
Emp.: 6
Other Telecommunications
N.A.I.C.S.: 517810

Teleste Intercept, LLC (1)
440 Forsgate Dr, Cranbury, NJ 08512
Tel.: (609) 395-9400
Web Site: https://www.telesteintercept.com
Telecommunication Contractor Services
N.A.I.C.S.: 517810

Teleste LLC (1)
3508 Far West Blvd Ste 320, Austin, TX 78731 **(100%)**
Tel.: (512) 868-2009
Web Site: www.teleste.com
Sales Range: $25-49.9 Million
Emp.: 5
Other Telecommunications
N.A.I.C.S.: 517810
Jukka Rinnavara *(CEO)*

Teleste Networks Services S.A. (1)
Chaussee De Treycovagnes 10D, 1400, Yverdon-les-Bains, Switzerland
Tel.: (41) 24 441 5830
Web Site: https://www.teleste-ns.ch
Emp.: 42
Telecommunication Contractor Services
N.A.I.C.S.: 517810
Jerome Engler *(Production Mgr)*

Teleste Networks Sp. z o.o. (1)
Ul Ostrowskiego 30, 53-238, Wroclaw, Poland
Tel.: (48) 717900653
Web Site: https://www.vsp.teleste.pl
Telecommunication Contractor Services
N.A.I.C.S.: 517810

Teleste Norge A/S (1)
Tormod Gjestlandsveg 16, N-3936, Porsgrunn, Norway
Tel.: (47) 35560500
Web Site: https://www.teleste.no
Telecommunication Contractor Services
N.A.I.C.S.: 517810

Teleste Oyj (1)
Telestenkatu 1, PO Box 323, Turku, Littoinen, 20101, Finland **(100%)**
Tel.: (358) 22605611
Web Site: http://www.teleste.com
Sales Range: $200-249.9 Million
Emp.: 400
Audio & Video Equipment Mfr
N.A.I.C.S.: 334310

Teleste Services GmbH (1)
Daimlerring 13, 31135, Hildesheim, Germany
Tel.: (49) 5121750980
Web Site: http://www.teleste.com
Cable Network Services
N.A.I.C.S.: 516210

Teleste Sp. z o.o. (1)
Ul Ostrowskiego 30, 53-238, Wroclaw, Poland
Tel.: (48) 71 793 7751
Web Site: https://www.teleste.pl
Telecommunication Equipment Distr
N.A.I.C.S.: 423690

Teleste Sweden AB (1)
Ellipsvagen 5, Kungens Kurva, 14175, Sweden **(100%)**
Tel.: (46) 87102190
Sales Range: $50-74.9 Million
Emp.: 10
Computer & Computer Peripheral Equipment & Software Whslr
N.A.I.C.S.: 423430
Kurt Nielsen *(Dir-Sls)*

Teleste Systems GmbH (1)
Lister Strasse 6, 30163, Hannover, Germany
Tel.: (49) 51151510910
Telecommunication Contractor Services
N.A.I.C.S.: 517810

Teleste UK Ltd (1)
Ste 17 8 Kings Ct, Willie Snaith Rd Suffolk, CB87SG, Newmarket, United Kingdom **(100%)**
Tel.: (44) 1638604204
Sales Range: $25-49.9 Million
Emp.: 4
Other Telecommunications
N.A.I.C.S.: 517810

Teleste Video Networks Sp. z o.o. (1)
ul Slusarska 9, 30-710, Krakow, Poland
Tel.: (48) 126267440
Web Site: https://www.telestevn.pl
Telecommunication Contractor Services
N.A.I.C.S.: 517810
Adam Zajkowski *(Reg Dir-Sales)*

Teleste d.o.o. (1)
Cezanjevci 50, Ljutomer, 9240, Ljutomer, Slovenia **(100%)**
Tel.: (386) 2 580 9100
Web Site: https://www.teleste.com
Sales Range: $50-74.9 Million
Emp.: 3
Other Electronic Parts & Equipment Whslr
N.A.I.C.S.: 423690

Teleste s.r.o. (1)
Sabinovska 12, 82102, Bratislava, Slovakia **(100%)**
Tel.: (421) 248208525
Web Site: http://www.teleste.com
Sales Range: $25-49.9 Million
Emp.: 2
Miscellaneous Retail Stores
N.A.I.C.S.: 339999

TELESTONE TECHNOLOGIES CORPORATION
Floor 10 Ruida Plaza No 74 Lugu Road, Shijingshan District, Beijing, 100040, China
Tel.: (86) 10 6860 8335
Web Site: http://www.telestone.com
Year Founded: 1987
Sales Range: $100-124.9 Million
Emp.: 1,200
Holding Company; Wireless Telecommunication Solutions & Services
N.A.I.C.S.: 551112
Guobin Pan *(Pres)*

Subsidiaries:

Beijing Telestone Technology Company Limited (1)
Beijing Telestone Technology Company Limited, Fengtai Technology Park, Beijing, 100070, China
Tel.: (86) 1083670505
Web Site: http://www.telestone.com
Sales Range: $50-74.9 Million
Emp.: 200
Telecommunication Servicesb
N.A.I.C.S.: 517112

Beijing Telestone Wireless Telecommunication Co., Ltd. (1)
Floor 6 Saiou Plaza No 5 Haiying Road, Fengtai Technology Park, Beijing, 100070, China
Tel.: (86) 1083670505
Web Site: http://www.telestone.com
Telecommunication Servicesb
N.A.I.C.S.: 517112

Subsidiary (Domestic):

Beijing Telestone Communication Technology Co., Ltd. (2)
Floor 6 Saiou Plaza No5 Haiying Road, Fengtai Technology Park, Beijing, 100070, China
Tel.: (86) 1083670505
Telecommunication Servicesb
N.A.I.C.S.: 517112

Shandong Guolian Telecommunication Technology Limited (2)
Floor 6 Saiou Plaza No5 Haiying Road, Fengtai Technology Park, Beijing, 100040, China
Tel.: (86) 1083670505
Web Site: http://www.telestone.com
Telecommunication Servicesb
N.A.I.C.S.: 517112

Subsidiary (Domestic):

Pan-Pacific Telecommunication Company Limited (3)
Floor 6 Saiou Plaza No 5 Haiying Road, Fengtai Technology Park, Beijing, 100070, China
Tel.: (86) 1083670505
Telecommunication Servicesb
N.A.I.C.S.: 517112

TELETALK BANGLADESH LIMITED
House 41 Road 27 Block A, Banani, Dhaka, 1213, Bangladesh
Tel.: (880) 28851060
Web Site: http://www.teletalk.com.bd
Year Founded: 2004
Mobile Telecommunications Services
N.A.I.C.S.: 517112
Shyam Sunder Sikder *(Chm)*

TELETYPOS S.A.
4 Rousou Mesogeion Ave, 11526, Athens, Greece
Tel.: (30) 2106903312
Web Site: https://www.megatv.com
Year Founded: 1989
TELET—(ATH)
Television Broadcasting Services
N.A.I.C.S.: 516120
Roussi Stella *(IR Officer)*

TELEVERBIER SA
Televerbier SA, PO Box 419, CH-1936, Verbier, Valais, Switzerland
Tel.: (41) 277752511 **CH**
Web Site: https://verbier4vallees.ch
Year Founded: 1950
TVRB—(EUR)
Sales Range: $50-74.9 Million
Ski Lift Provider & Operator
N.A.I.C.S.: 713920
Jean-Albert Ferrez *(Pres)*

TELEVISION BROADCASTS LIMITED
TVB City 77 Chun Choi Street Tseung Kwan O Industrial Estate, Tseung Kwan O, Kowloon, China (Hong Kong)
Tel.: (852) 23352288 **HK**
Web Site: https://www.tvb.com
Year Founded: 1967
TVBCF—(OTCIQ)
Rev: $351,367,316
Assets: $1,268,104,919
Liabilities: $584,766,944
Net Worth: $683,337,975
Earnings: ($33,161,790)
Emp.: 3,644
Fiscal Year-end: 12/31/20
Television Broadcasting Services
N.A.I.C.S.: 516120
Desmond Shu Hung Chan *(Deputy Gen Mgr-Legal & Intl Ops)*

Subsidiaries:

TVB (Australia) Pty. Ltd. (1)
Level 18 233 Castlereagh St, Sydney, 2000, NSW, Australia
Tel.: (61) 282816898
Web Site: http://www.tvb.com.au
Television Broadcasting Services
N.A.I.C.S.: 516120

TVB (USA) Inc. (1)
39 Dorman Ave, San Francisco, CA 94124
Tel.: (415) 282-8228
Web Site: http://www.tvbusa.com
Television Broadcasting Services
N.A.I.C.S.: 516120

Ztore HK Limited (1)
22/F Hang Seng Tower Telford Plaza 33 Wai Yip Street, Kowloon Bay, Kowloon, China (Hong Kong)
Tel.: (852) 21543800
Web Site: https://www.ztore.com
Ecommerce Services
N.A.I.C.S.: 459999

TELEVISION FRANCAISE 1 S.A.
1 Quai du Point du Jour, 92656, Boulogne-Cedex, France
Tel.: (33) 14141234 **FR**
Web Site: https://www.groupe-tf1.fr
Year Founded: 1987
Television Channel
N.A.I.C.S.: 516120
Philippe Denery *(Exec VP-Fin & Procurement)*

Subsidiaries:

17 Juin Media SA (1)
205 rue Jean-Jacques Rousseau, 92130, Issy-les-Moulineaux, France
Tel.: (33) 158888410
Web Site: http://www.17juin.fr
Multimedia Production Services
N.A.I.C.S.: 512110

Aufeminin S.A. (1)
8 rue Saint-Fiacre, 75002, Paris, France
Tel.: (33) 153577900
Web Site: http://www.aufeminin.com
Rev: $135,957,110
Assets: $226,395,540
Liabilities: $61,090,860
Net Worth: $165,304,680
Earnings: $13,535,818
Fiscal Year-end: 12/31/2017
Cosmetics Whslr
N.A.I.C.S.: 456120
Christophe Decker *(COO)*

Subsidiary (Non-US):

gofeminin.de Gmbh (2)
Im Zollhafen 5/Halle 11, 50678, Cologne, Germany
Tel.: (49) 221283250
Online Advertising & Marketing Services for Women's Health
N.A.I.C.S.: 541810
Tatjana Biallas *(Mng Dir)*

Column Film Nederland BV (1)
Moermanskkade 111, 1013 BC, Amsterdam, Netherlands
Tel.: (31) 205722700
Web Site: http://www.columnfilm.com
Media Production Services
N.A.I.C.S.: 512110
Chantal Van der Horst *(Mng Dir)*

DOCTISSIMO SAS (1)
8 rue Barthelemy Danjou, 92100, Boulogne-Billancourt, France
Tel.: (33) 145195800
Web Site: https://www.doctissimo.fr
Television Broadcasting Services
N.A.I.C.S.: 516120
Fabien Sfez *(Pres)*

De Mensen NV (1)
Wezembeekstraat 3, 1930, Zaventem, Belgium
Tel.: (32) 27097000
Web Site: http://www.demensen.be
Media Production Services
N.A.I.C.S.: 512110

E-Tf1 S.A.S (1)
1 Quai du Point du Jour, 92100, Boulogne-Billancourt, Hauts-de-Seine, France
Tel.: (33) 141411234
Television Program Production Services
N.A.I.C.S.: 516120

Gamned SAS (1)
9 Quai Rive Neuve, 13001, Marseille, France
Tel.: (33) 185091350
Web Site: http://www.gamned.com
Advertising Agency Services
N.A.I.C.S.: 541810
Olivier Goulon *(Co-Founder & CEO)*

La Chaine Info (1)
1 Quai Du Point Du Jour, Boulogne-Billancourt, 92100, France
Tel.: (33) 141412345
Television Broadcasting Services
N.A.I.C.S.: 516120

MDA Conseil SA (1)

AND PRIVATE COMPANIES

6 Impasse de Couzinet, 31500, Toulouse,
France
Tel.: (33) 647030631
Web Site: http://www.mda-conseils.fr
HR Consulting Services
N.A.I.C.S.: 541612

My Little Paris SAS (1)
13 boulevard de Rochechouart, 75009,
Paris, France
Tel.: (33) 982332655
Web Site: http://www.mylittleparis.com
Online Media Services
N.A.I.C.S.: 512110

Newen Studios (1)
123 Boulevard de Grenelle, Paris, 75015,
France
Tel.: (33) 1 53 78 24 00
Web Site: https://www.newenstudios.com
Media Production; Audiovisual Content Producer
N.A.I.C.S.: 516120
Leonor Grandsire (Deputy Mng Dir)

Subsidiary (Non-US):

Reel One Entertainment (2)
486 Sainte-Catherine Suite 100, Montreal,
H3B 1A6, QC, Canada
Tel.: (514) 866-8379
Web Site: http://www.reeloneent.com
Motion Picture & Video Production
N.A.I.C.S.: 512110
Tom Berry (CEO)

Premiere Bobine Inc. (1)
486 Ste-Catherine W Suite 100, Montreal,
H3B 1A6, QC, Canada
Tel.: (514) 866-8379
Web Site: http://www.reeloneent.com
Television Broadcasting Services
N.A.I.C.S.: 516120
Tom Berry (CEO)

Pupkin Film B.V. (1)
Weesperzijde 4, 1091 EA, Amsterdam,
Netherlands
Tel.: (31) 204895088
Web Site: http://www.pupkin.com
Media Production Services
N.A.I.C.S.: 512110

Reel One Entertainment, Inc. (1)
1801 Century Pk E Ste 1820, Los Angeles,
CA 90067
Tel.: (310) 888-2244
Television Broadcasting Services
N.A.I.C.S.: 516120
Laurence Braun (VP-Scripted Content)

Reel One International Limited (1)
Shakespeare House 168 Lavender Hill,
London, SW11 5TG, United Kingdom
Tel.: (44) 2078016263
Television Broadcasting Services
N.A.I.C.S.: 516120
Louisa Cadywould (Sr VP & Head-Distr-Intl)

SCI TF1 Events (1)
1 quai du point du jour, 92100, Boulogne-
Billancourt, France
Tel.: (33) 141413156
Web Site: http://www.tf1events.fr
Event Operation Services
N.A.I.C.S.: 561920

Serie Club SA (1)
120 Ave Charles De Gaulle, Neuilly-sur-
Seine, 92522, France (50%)
Tel.: (33) 00155626666
Web Site: http://www.site.serieclub.m6.fr
Sales Range: $25-49.9 Million
Emp.: 20
Television Station Operator
N.A.I.C.S.: 516120
Guillaume Thouret (Mng Dir)

Skyline Entertainment NV (1)
Wezenbeekstraat 3, 1930, Zaventem, Belgium
Tel.: (32) 22407777
Web Site: http://www.skyline-entertainment.be
Film Production Services
N.A.I.C.S.: 512110

Studio Blue Spirit Canada Inc. (1)
103-3575 bd Saint-Laurent, Montreal, H2X
2T7, QC, Canada
Tel.: (514) 849-8936

Movie Studio Services
N.A.I.C.S.: 512110

TF1 Droits Audiovisuels S.A.S. (1)
1 Quai du Point du Jour, 92100, Boulogne-
Billancourt, Hauts-de-Seine, France
Tel.: (33) 141413030
Motion Picture & Audio Distr
N.A.I.C.S.: 512120

TF1 Films Production S.A.S. (1)
Atrium 6 Place Abel Gance, 92100,
Boulogne-Billancourt, Hauts-de-Seine,
France
Tel.: (33) 141411234
Motion Picture Production Services
N.A.I.C.S.: 512110

TF1 Publicite SAS (1)
1 Quai du Point du Jour, 92100, Boulogne-
Billancourt, Hauts-de-Seine, France
Tel.: (33) 141413251
Web Site: http://www.tf1pub.fr
Sales Range: $700-749.9 Million
Media Advertising Services
N.A.I.C.S.: 541840
Paolini Nonce (CEO)

TV Breizh SA (1)
Quai du Peristyle, 56324, Lorient, Morbihan,
France
Tel.: (33) 297350100
Web Site: http://www.tvbreizh.fr
Sales Range: $25-49.9 Million
Emp.: 40
Television Broadcasting Services
N.A.I.C.S.: 516120

Tuvalu Media BV (1)
Moermanskkade 111, 1013 BC, Amsterdam,
Netherlands
Tel.: (31) 207630063
Web Site: http://www.tuvalu.nl
Media Production Services
N.A.I.C.S.: 512110
Emiel Neervoort (Mng Dir)

Ushuaia TV (1)
1 quai du Point du Jour, 92656, Boulogne,
Cedex, France
Tel.: (33) 141411234
Web Site: http://www.ushuaiatv.fr
Television Broadcasting Services
N.A.I.C.S.: 516120

Vertical Station SAS (1)
174 quai de Jemmapes, 75010, Paris,
France
Tel.: (33) 176410538
Web Site: http://www.verticalstation.com
Marketing & Advertising Services
N.A.I.C.S.: 541810

alFemminile.com s.r.l (1)
Via Torino 61, 20123, Milan, Italy
Tel.: (39) 028725141
Web Site: http://www.alfemminile.com
Media Production Services
N.A.I.C.S.: 512110

TELEVIZIJA LESKOVAC A.D.
Bulevar oslobodenja 92, Leskovac,
Serbia
Tel.: (381) 16 242 155
Web Site: http://www.tvl.rs
Year Founded: 1994
Sales Range: Less than $1 Million
Emp.: 37
Television Broadcasting Services
N.A.I.C.S.: 516120

TELEWARE PLC
Teleware House York Road, Thirsk,
YO7 3BX, North Yorkshire, United
Kingdom
Tel.: (44) 1845526830
Web Site: http://www.teleware.com
Sales Range: $10-24.9 Million
Emp.: 500
Telephony Software Developer
N.A.I.C.S.: 513210
Geoff Haworth (Founder)

TELEWIG
4 A Rue de l'Industrie, Hoerdt, 67720,
Strasbourg, France

Tel.: (33) 388682244
Web Site: http://www.telewig.com
Rev.: $27,000,000
Emp.: 19
Industrial Mach & Equipment
N.A.I.C.S.: 423830
Marc Roth (Gen Mgr)

TELFORCEONE S.A.
ul Krakowska 119, 50-428, Wroclaw,
Poland
Tel.: (48) 71 327 20 00   PL
Web Site: http://www.telforceone.com
Year Founded: 2001
Mobile Accessories Mfr
N.A.I.C.S.: 334220

TELIA COMPANY AB
Stjarntorget 1, 169 94, Solna, Sweden
Tel.: (46) 771990100   SE
Web Site:
  https://www.teliacompany.com
Year Founded: 1853
TLSNF—(OTCIQ)
Rev.: $8,150,463,000
Assets: $20,789,762,400
Liabilities: $15,557,713,200
Net Worth: $5,232,049,200
Earnings: $550,800
Emp.: 18,644
Fiscal Year-end: 12/31/23
Mobile & Broadband Products Mfr
N.A.I.C.S.: 334210
Cecilia Lundin (Sr VP & Head-People & Brand)

Subsidiaries:

AO Telia Carrier Russia (1)
6 Yakimanskiy Lane, 119049, Moscow,
Russia
Tel.: (7) 4957830260
Telecommunication Servicesb
N.A.I.C.S.: 517112

Assembly Organizing Oy (1)
Elimaenkatu 2, 00510, Helsinki, Finland
Tel.: (358) 931574170
Web Site: http://www.assembly.org
Event Organizing Services
N.A.I.C.S.: 561920
Pekka Aakko (Founder & CEO)

Bonnier Entertainment AB (1)
Kungsgatan 49, SE-113 90, Stockholm,
Sweden (100%)
Tel.: (46) 87364000
Web Site: http://www.bonnier.se
Sales Range: $550-599.9 Million
Emp.: 49
Holding Company; Music Publishing; Radio,
Television & Motion Picture Production &
Broadcasting Services
N.A.I.C.S.: 551112

C-Sam AB (1)
Bangatan 6, 151 32, Sodertalje, Sweden
Tel.: (46) 85 503 8730
Web Site: https://www.c-sam.se
Television Services
N.A.I.C.S.: 516120

Cygate AB (1)
(98.66%)
Tel.: (46) 108787000
Web Site: http://www.cygategroup.se
Sales Range: $150-199.9 Million
Emp.: 650
Custom Computer Programming Services
N.A.I.C.S.: 541511

Eesti Telekom (1)
Valge 16, 19095, Tallinn, Estonia
Tel.: (372) 6 111 470
Web Site: http://www.telekom.ee
Sales Range: $450-499.9 Million
Emp.: 2,341
Holding Company: Telecommunications
N.A.I.C.S.: 551112

Subsidiary (Domestic):

AS Elion Esindus (2)
Endla, 15033, Tallinn, Estonia (100%)
Tel.: (372) 6507015

TELIA COMPANY AB

Sales Range: $300-349.9 Million
Emp.: 1,500
Computer Programming Services
N.A.I.C.S.: 541511

AS Mobile Wholesale (2)
Tourie Street 5 11313, Tallinn,
Estonia (100%)
Tel.: (372) 6512730
Sales Range: $25-49.9 Million
Emp.: 40
Electronic Parts & Equipment Whslr
N.A.I.C.S.: 423690
Hanno Eerme (Mng Dir)

AS Sertifitseerimiskeskus (2)
141 Parnu Mnt, Tallinn, Estonia
Tel.: (372) 6101880
Web Site: http://www.sk.ee
Sales Range: $25-49.9 Million
Emp.: 32
Computer Programming Services
N.A.I.C.S.: 541511

EMT Esindused AS (2)
Valge 16, 19095, Tallinn, Estonia (100%)
Tel.: (372) 6397130
Web Site: http://www.emt.ee
Cellular & Other Wireless Telecommunications
N.A.I.C.S.: 517112

Elion Enterprises AS (2)
16 Endla Str, Tallinn, 15033, Estonia
Tel.: (372) 6397213
Web Site: http://www.elion.ee
Sales Range: $250-299.9 Million
Emp.: 1,454
National Phone Network Operator for Local
& Long-Distance; Internet Access & Fixed-
Wireless Networks; Telecommunications
Network Construction & Maintenance Services
N.A.I.C.S.: 517111

MicroLink Estonia (2)
Lootsa 8, Tallinn, 11415, Estonia (100%)
Tel.: (372) 650 1700
Sales Range: $25-49.9 Million
Emp.: 250
Computer System Design Services
N.A.I.C.S.: 541512

Viru Net OU (2)
Uus 2, Johvi, Estonia (100%)
Tel.: (372) 3370146
Sales Range: $25-49.9 Million
Emp.: 50
Telecommunications Resellers
N.A.I.C.S.: 517121

Falt Communications AB (1)
Vasagatan 23, 903 29, Umea, Sweden
Tel.: (46) 90183900
Cloud & Platform Development Services
N.A.I.C.S.: 518210

Fello AB (1)
Vera Sandbergs Alle 5C, 411 33, Gothenburg, Sweden
Tel.: (46) 770332222
Web Site: https://www.fello.se
Mobile Subscription Services
N.A.I.C.S.: 517810

Phonero AS (1)
Tollbodgt 14 5 etasje, 4611, Kristiansand,
Norway (100%)
Tel.: (47) 940 04 500
Web Site: http://www.phonero.no
Telecommunication Servicesb
N.A.I.C.S.: 517810

Ratt Internet Kapacitet i Sverige AB (1)
Formvagen 5, 906 21, Umea, Sweden
Tel.: (46) 770339933
Web Site: http://www.riksnet.se
Broadband Services
N.A.I.C.S.: 519290

Romelebygdens Kabel-TV AB (1)
Norra Jarnvagsgatan 23, Veberod, 247 64,
Lund, Sweden
Tel.: (46) 81155
Web Site: http://www.romele.com
Broadband Services
N.A.I.C.S.: 519290

Subsidiary (Non-US):

Cygate Oy (2)

TELIA COMPANY AB

Telia Company AB—(Continued)
Perkiontie 2, 620, Helsinki, Finland
Tel.: (358) 96138911
Web Site: http://www.cygate.fi
Sales Range: $25-49.9 Million
Emp.: 14
Network Integration Services
N.A.I.C.S.: 541512
Markus Kalalahti (CEO)

SIA Sergel (1)
Lielvardes Street 8a, 1006, Riga, Latvia
Tel.: (371) 67630303
Web Site: http://www.sergel-sia.informacionnajastranica.zl.lv
Sales Range: $50-74.9 Million
Emp.: 1
Financial Management Services
N.A.I.C.S.: 523999

SIA Telia Latvija (1)
Lielvardes 8a, Riga, LV-1006, Latvia
Tel.: (371) 6 708 2100
Web Site: https://www.telia.lv
Telecommunication Servicesb
N.A.I.C.S.: 517112
Liga Kursite (Head-Mktg)

Svensk Filmindustri, AB (1)
Greta Garbosvag 11-13, 169 86, Stockholm, Sweden
Tel.: (46) 84 091 8800
Web Site: https://sfstudios.se
Multimedia Production Services
N.A.I.C.S.: 512110
Anita Simovic (Head-Intl Sls)

Subsidiary (Non-US):

SF Film Finland Oy (2)
Runeberginkitu 5, 100, Helsingfors, Finland
Tel.: (358) 207 300 460
Web Site: http://www.sffilm.fi
Emp.: 50
Multimedia Production Services
N.A.I.C.S.: 512110
Lars Warelius (Country Mgr)

SF Norge AS (2)
Dronningens gt 8a, Oslo, Norway
Tel.: (47) 22007800
Web Site: http://www.sf-film.no
Multimedia Production Services
N.A.I.C.S.: 512110
Allan Spelmann (VP-Sls & Distr)

Svenska Stadsnat AB (1)
Scheelevagen 17 Ideon Beta 6, 223 70, Lund, Sweden
Tel.: (46) 20100095
Web Site: http://svenskastadsnat.se
Network Connection Services
N.A.I.C.S.: 517810

Svenska Stadsnat Perspektiv AB (1)
Isbergsgata 2, 205 21, Malmo, Sweden
Tel.: (46) 755550000
Web Site: http://www.perspektivbredband.se
Telecommunication Servicesb
N.A.I.C.S.: 517112

TDC AS (1)
Sandakerveien 130, 0484, Oslo, Norway
Tel.: (47) 2150 2100
Web Site: http://www.tdc.no
Emp.: 200
Telecommunications & Data Services
N.A.I.C.S.: 517121
Ketil Kivedahl (Mng Dir)

Subsidiary (Domestic):

Get AS (2)
Maridalsveien 323, 0872, Oslo, Norway
Tel.: (47) 21900000
Web Site: http://www.get.no
Emp.: 840
Cable Television Network
N.A.I.C.S.: 516210
Gunnar Evensen (CEO)

TV4 AB (1)
Tegeluddsvagen 3-5, 115 79, Stockholm, Sweden (100%)
Tel.: (46) 84594100
Web Site: http://www.tv4.se
Sales Range: $100-124.9 Million
Television Broadcast Services
N.A.I.C.S.: 516120

Subsidiary (Domestic):

C More Entertainment AB (2)
Tegeluddsvagen 7, SE-115 84, Stockholm, Sweden (65%)
Tel.: (46) 84592800
Web Site: http://www.cmore.se
Sales Range: $25-49.9 Million
Emp.: 50
Television Broadcasting Network
N.A.I.C.S.: 516210
Johan Kleberg (Mng Dir)

TV4 Stockholm AB (2)
Tegeluddsvagen 3-5, 115 79, Stockholm, Sweden
Tel.: (46) 8 459 4000
Web Site: https://www.tv4play.se
Television Broadcasting Network
N.A.I.C.S.: 516120

Tele2 Norge AS (1)
Innspurten 15, 0663, Oslo, Norway (100%)
Tel.: (47) 21319000
Web Site: http://www.tele2.no
Sales Range: $25-49.9 Million
Emp.: 55
Mobile & Fixed Telephony, Internet Services, Data Communications & Cable TV Services
N.A.I.C.S.: 517111

Telia A/S (1)
Holmbladsgade 139, 2300, Copenhagen, Denmark (100%)
Tel.: (45) 80404030
Web Site: http://www.telia.dk
Sales Range: $200-249.9 Million
Mobile Telecommunications
N.A.I.C.S.: 517112

Telia Carrier Czech Republic a.s. (1)
Centrum Nagano IV K Cervenemu Dvoru 25A, 130 00, Prague, Czech Republic
Tel.: (420) 222512711
Telecommunication Servicesb
N.A.I.C.S.: 517112

Telia Carrier Denmark A/S (1)
Holmbladsgade 139, 2300, Copenhagen, Denmark
Tel.: (45) 88313131
Telecommunication Servicesb
N.A.I.C.S.: 517112

Telia Carrier Germany GmbH (1)
Herriotstrasse 1, 60528, Frankfurt, Germany
Tel.: (49) 69907340
Telecommunication Servicesb
N.A.I.C.S.: 517112

Telia Carrier Hungary Kft (1)
Vaci ut 22-24, 1132, Budapest, Hungary
Tel.: (36) 14122700
Telecommunication Servicesb
N.A.I.C.S.: 517112

Telia Carrier Italy S.p.A. (1)
Via Vincenzo Monti 8, 20123, Milan, Italy
Tel.: (39) 0246712370
Telecommunication Servicesb
N.A.I.C.S.: 517112

Telia Carrier Netherlands B.V. (1)
De Entree 236 II B 10de Etage, Amsterdam Zuidoost, 1101 EE, Amsterdam, Netherlands
Tel.: (31) 651754571
Telecommunication Servicesb
N.A.I.C.S.: 517112
Bernd Hoogkamp (Mgr-Products)

Telia Carrier Poland Sp.z.o.o. (1)
ul Nowogrodzka 47 a, 00-695, Warsaw, Poland
Tel.: (48) 224580400
Telecommunication Servicesb
N.A.I.C.S.: 517112
Karolina Mazurek (Mgr)

Telia Carrier U.S. Inc. (1)
2325 Dulles Corner Blvd Ste 550 Herndon, Washington, DC 20171
Tel.: (703) 546-4000
Telecommunication Servicesb
N.A.I.C.S.: 517112

Telia Cygate Oy (1)
Pasila Asema-aukio 1, PO Box 106, 00051, Helsinki, Finland
Tel.: (358) 20401

Information Technology Services
N.A.I.C.S.: 541511

Telia International Holdings AB (1)
Sturegatan 1, 114 35, Stockholm, Sweden
Tel.: (46) 8 456 16 00
Investment Management Service
N.A.I.C.S.: 523999

Telia Nattjanster Norden AB (1)
Marbackagatan 11, Farsta, 123 43, Sweden
Tel.: (46) 705898021
Wired Telecommunication Services
N.A.I.C.S.: 517111

Telia Norge AS (1)
Lorenfaret 1, 0585, Oslo, Norway
Tel.: (47) 23888000
Web Site: https://www.telia.no
Mobile Network Access & Telecommunication Services
N.A.I.C.S.: 517112

Telia Telecommunications International B.V (1)
Rodezand 34k, Rotterdam, 3011 AN, Netherlands
Tel.: (31) 104479366
Telecommunication Servicesb
N.A.I.C.S.: 517810

TeliaSonera Asset Finance AB (1)
Vitsandsgatan 9hu, Farsta, 123 42, Sweden
Tel.: (46) 8 90 100
Financial Management Services
N.A.I.C.S.: 523999

TeliaSonera Chess Holding AS (1)
Moellendals 1, Bergen, 5068, Norway
Tel.: (47) 55 20 46 00
Web Site: http://www.chess.no
Mobile Telecommunications & Information Technology Services
N.A.I.C.S.: 517112
Tibor Alexander Maehlum (Head-Sls & Online Bus)

TeliaSonera Danmark A/S (1)
Holmbladsgade 139, 2300, Copenhagen, Denmark
Tel.: (45) 82 33 70 00
Web Site: http://www.telia.dk
Sales Range: $200-249.9 Million
Emp.: 900
Telecommunication Broadband Services
N.A.I.C.S.: 517111
Michael Hansen (Mgr-Sls-Fixed Voice & Mobility)

TeliaSonera Finans AB (1)
Vitsandsgatan 9D 7th Floor, Farsta, 123 86, Sweden
Tel.: (46) 771 88 30 50
Web Site: http://www.teliasonerafinans.com
Rev: $103,691,000
Emp.: 80
Financial Management Services
N.A.I.C.S.: 523999
Sverker Hannervall (Sr VP)

TeliaSonera Finland (1)
Pasilan asema-aukio 1, PO Box 106, 00051, Helsinki, Finland (100%)
Tel.: (358) 20401
Web Site: http://www.telia.fi
Sales Range: $800-899.9 Million
Mobile Communications
N.A.I.C.S.: 517112

TeliaSonera Forsakring AB (1)
Stureplan 8, Stockholm, 114 35, Sweden
Tel.: (46) 850452988
General Insurance Services
N.A.I.C.S.: 524210

TeliaSonera International Carrier Austria GmbH (1)
Schlosshoferstrasse 4 Stiege 4 Top 22, 1210, Vienna, Austria
Tel.: (43) 1 205 305
Web Site: http://www.teliasoneraic.com
Telecommunication Servicesb
N.A.I.C.S.: 517810

TeliaSonera International Carrier Finland Oy (1)
Sturenkatu 16 A, 00510, Helsinki, Finland
Tel.: (358) 20401
Web Site: http://www.teliasoneraic.com
Telecommunication Servicesb
N.A.I.C.S.: 517810

INTERNATIONAL PUBLIC

TeliaSonera International Carrier France S.A.S. (1)
28 rue de Berri, 75008, Paris, France
Tel.: (33) 1 53 93 00 00
Web Site: http://www.teliasoneraic.com
Sales Range: $25-49.9 Million
Telecommunication Servicesb
N.A.I.C.S.: 517121

TeliaSonera International Carrier Germany GmbH (1)
Kleyerstrasse 88, 60326, Frankfurt am Main, Germany
Tel.: (49) 69 90 73 40
Emp.: 36
Mobile Telecommunications Services
N.A.I.C.S.: 517112
Gerard Harmel (Dir-Fin)

TeliaSonera International Carrier Hungaria Tavkozlesi Kft. (1)
Vaci ut 22 - 24, 1132, Budapest, Hungary
Tel.: (36) 1 412 27 00
Web Site: http://www.teliasoneraic.com
Sales Range: $25-49.9 Million
Telecommunication Servicesb
N.A.I.C.S.: 517810

TeliaSonera International Carrier Italy S.p.A (1)
Via Vincenzo Monti 8, 20123, Milan, Italy
Tel.: (39) 0246712370
Web Site: http://www.teliasoneraic.com
Mobile Telecommunications Services
N.A.I.C.S.: 517112

TeliaSonera International Carrier Latvia SIA (1)
10 Kronvalda Bulvaris, Riga, 1010, Latvia
Tel.: (371) 67321000
Telecommunication Servicesb
N.A.I.C.S.: 517810

TeliaSonera International Carrier Netherlands B.V. (1)
De Entree II 236B 6de Etage 1101, 1101 EE, Amsterdam, Netherlands
Tel.: (31) 20 752 54 00
Mobile Telecommunications Services
N.A.I.C.S.: 517112

TeliaSonera International Carrier Poland Sp. z.o.o. (1)
ul Nowogrodzka 47 a, 00-695, Warsaw, Poland
Tel.: (48) 22 458 04 00
Web Site: http://www.teliasoneraic.com
Sales Range: $25-49.9 Million
Telecommunication Servicesb
N.A.I.C.S.: 517810

TeliaSonera International Carrier, Inc. (1)
2201 Cooperative Way Ste 302, Herndon, VA 20171
Tel.: (703) 546-4000
Web Site: http://www.teliasoneraic.com
Mobile Telecommunications Services
N.A.I.C.S.: 517112

TeliaSonera Mobile Networks AB (1)
Marbackagatan 11, Farsta, 123 43, Sweden
Tel.: (46) 8 90100
Web Site: http://www.teliasonera.com
Mobile Telecommunications Services
N.A.I.C.S.: 517112

TeliaSonera Network Sales AB (1)
Vitsandsgatan 9, Farsta, 123 42, Sweden
Tel.: (46) 771 990100
Wired & Wireless Telecommunication Services
N.A.I.C.S.: 517112
Erik Hallberg (Gen Mgr)

TeliaSonera Skanova Access AB (1)
Vitsandsgatan 9E, 123 42, Farsta, Sweden
Tel.: (46) 86040490
Web Site: http://www.skanova.com
Network Services Sales
N.A.I.C.S.: 517121

TeliaSonera Skanova Access AB (1)
Vitsandsgatan 9E, Farsta, 123 86, Sweden
Tel.: (46) 86 04 04 90
Telecommunication Structure & Fiber Cable Installation Services
N.A.I.C.S.: 517810

TeliaSonera Sverige AB (1)

stjarntorget 1, 169 94, Solna, Sweden
Tel.: (46) 771990100
Web Site: http://www.teliacompany.com
Telecommunication Servicesb
N.A.I.C.S.: 517810

**TeliaSonera Sverige Net Fastigheter
AB** (1)
Marbackagatan 11, Farsta, 123 43, Sweden
Tel.: (46) 850455000
Property Leasing Services
N.A.I.C.S.: 531190

TeliaSonera Sweden (1)
Marbackagatan 11, 123 86, Farsta,
Sweden **(100%)**
Tel.: (46) 87136413
Web Site: http://www.telia.se
Sales Range: $1-4.9 Billion
Telecommunication Servicesb
N.A.I.C.S.: 517810

UAB Sergel (1)
Smolensko Str 10, 3202, Vilnius, Lithuania
Tel.: (370) 5 2310621
Financial Management Services
N.A.I.C.S.: 523999

**ZAO TeliaSonera International Carrier
Russia** (1)
6 Yakimanskiy Lane, 119049, Moscow,
Russia
Tel.: (7) 495 783 02 60
Web Site: http://www.teliasoneraic.com
Telecommunication Servicesb
N.A.I.C.S.: 517810

isMobile AB (1)
Sandviksgatan 81, PO Box 58, 971 03, Lu-
lea, Sweden
Tel.: (46) 92060340
Web Site: https://www.ismobile.com
Facilities Support Services
N.A.I.C.S.: 561210

TELINVEST S.A.
R Iguatemi 354 - Cj 301, 1451010,
Sao Paulo, Brazil
Tel.: (55) 21 3231 8200
Year Founded: 1998
Assets: $122,087
Liabilities: $70,292
Net Worth: $51,794
Fiscal Year-end: 12/31/15
Financial Investment Services
N.A.I.C.S.: 523999
Adriana Maria Mammocci *(CFO &
CTO)*

TELIPHONE CORP.
300-1550 Alberni, Vancouver, V4G
1A5, BC, Canada
Tel.: (514) 313-6000 NV
Web Site: http://www.teliphone.ca
Year Founded: 1999
Sales Range: $1-9.9 Million
Telecommunication Servicesb
N.A.I.C.S.: 517121
Benoit Laliberte *(Pres & CEO)*

TELITI INTERNATIONAL LTD
Suite 703 7th Floor Block A4 Leisure
Commerce Square, Pusat Dagang
Setia Jaya, 9 Jalan PJS 8/9, Petaling
Jaya, 46150, Selangor Darul Ehsan,
Malaysia
Tel.: (60) 3 7873 7733 Ky
Web Site: http://www.teliti.com
Sales Range: $10-24.9 Million
Emp.: 200
IT Services
N.A.I.C.S.: 541519
Ithnin Yacob *(Chm)*

TELIX PHARMACEUTICALS
LIMITED
Level 4 55 Flemington Road, North
Melbourne, 3051, VIC, Australia
Tel.: (61) 330933897 AU
Web Site:
https://www.telixpharma.com
Year Founded: 2017

TLX—(ASX)
Rev.: $3,994,148
Assets: $120,920,872
Liabilities: $60,379,603
Net Worth: $60,541,269
Earnings: ($34,391,971)
Fiscal Year-end: 12/31/20
Biotechnology Research & Develop-
ment Services
N.A.I.C.S.: 541715
Christian P. Behrenbruch *(CEO &
Mng Dir)*

Subsidiaries:

Therapeia GmbH & Co.KG (1)
Veilchenweg 38, 01326, Dresden, Germany
Tel.: (49) 351418800000
Web Site: https://www.therapeia.info
Diagnostic & Therapeutic Services
N.A.I.C.S.: 621340

TELKOM SA SOC LIMITED
61 Oak Avenue The Hub Highveld
Techno Park, Centurion, Johannes-
burg, 157, South Africa
Tel.: (27) 861100948 ZA
Web Site: https://www.telkom.co.za
Year Founded: 1991
TKG—(JSE)
Rev.: $5,881,289,540
Assets: $4,504,339,910
Liabilities: $2,181,517,790
Net Worth: $2,322,822,120
Earnings: $179,513,130
Fiscal Year-end: 03/31/22
Telecommunications & Wireless Ser-
vices
N.A.I.C.S.: 334210
Sipho Nkosinathi Maseko *(CEO-Grp)*

TELKOOR TELECOM LTD.
5 Giborey Israel Street, 42293, Net-
anya, Israel
Tel.: (972) 98632333 II
Web Site: http://www.telkoor.com
Sales Range: $10-24.9 Million
Emp.: 140
Power Supplies Designer, Mfr &
Sales to Communications, Industrial,
Defense & Aerospace Markets
N.A.I.C.S.: 334419
Uri Friedlander *(CFO)*

Subsidiaries:

Telkoor Power Supplies Ltd. (1)
5 Giborey St, Netanya, 42504,
Israel **(100%)**
Tel.: (972) 98632333
Web Site: http://www.telkoor.com
Power Supplies & Products Designer, Mfr &
Whslr
N.A.I.C.S.: 334419
Ben-Zion Diamant *(Chm)*

TELLA, INC.
1F Mitsuihanagiri Bldg 7-22-36 Nish-
ishinjuku, Shinjuku-ku, Tokyo, 160-
0023, Japan
Tel.: (81) 3 5937 2111
Web Site: http://www.tella.jp
Year Founded: 2004
2191—(JAS)
Rev.: $735,680
Assets: $12,506,560
Liabilities: $1,694,000
Net Worth: $10,812,560
Earnings: $10,328,560)
Emp.: 17
Fiscal Year-end: 12/31/20
Medical Research Services
N.A.I.C.S.: 541715
Tomoyuki Taira *(Pres)*

TELLGEN CORPORATION
Building 1 No 115 Lane 572 Bibo
Road Free Trade Zone, Pudong Dis-
trict, Shanghai, 201203, China
Tel.: (86) 2150273499

Web Site: https://www.tellgen.com
Year Founded: 2003
300642—(CHIN)
Rev.: $100,522,188
Assets: $233,726,688
Liabilities: $25,843,428
Net Worth: $207,883,260
Earnings: $17,516,304
Fiscal Year-end: 12/31/22
Diagnostic Product Mfr & Distr
N.A.I.C.S.: 334510
Yao Jianer *(Chm & Gen Mgr)*

TELLHOW GROUP CO., LTD.
Tellhow Information Building 590
Gaoxin Avenue, Qingshanhu District,
Nanchang, 330096, Jiangxi, China
Tel.: (86) 791 8810 5588
Web Site: http://www.tellhow.cn
Holding Company; Power Transmis-
sion & Power System Management
Services
N.A.I.C.S.: 551112

Subsidiaries:

Tellhow Sci-Tech Co., Ltd. (1)
Tellhow Infromation Building No 590 Gaoxin
Road, Qingshanhu District, Nanchang,
330096, Jiangxi, China
Tel.: (86) 79188105588
Web Site: https://www.tellhow.com
Rev.: $869,154,062
Assets: $1,964,954,806
Liabilities: $1,345,891,782
Net Worth: $619,063,024
Earnings: $10,862,299
Emp.: 3,200
Fiscal Year-end: 12/31/2022
Electric Power Product & Air-Conditioner
Mfr
N.A.I.C.S.: 335999
Yang Jian *(Chm)*

Subsidiary (Domestic):

**Longyan Haidexin Automobile Co.,
Ltd** (2)
No 6 Jinlong Road High-Tech Zone
Longzhou Industrial Park, Xinluo District,
Longyan, Fujian, China
Tel.: (86) 5973295658
Web Site: http://www.hyde-sinaean.com
Emp.: 300
Automotive Vehicle Repair & Maintenance
Services
N.A.I.C.S.: 811111

TELLING TELECOM HOLDING
CO., LTD.
Block D Desheng Shangcheng No
117 Dewai Street, Xicheng District,
Beijing, 100088, China
Tel.: (86) 1058300000
Web Site:
https://www.chinatelling.com
000829—(SSE)
Rev.: $10,730,343,162
Assets: $3,007,303,935
Liabilities: $2,638,939,011
Net Worth: $368,364,925
Earnings: $15,426,085
Fiscal Year-end: 12/31/22
Holding Company
N.A.I.C.S.: 551112
Shaowen Huang *(Chm)*

TELO GENOMICS CORP.
MaRS Centre South Tower, 101 Col-
lege Street Suite 200, Toronto, M5G
1L7, ON, Canada
Tel.: (416) 673-8487 Ca
Web Site:
https://www.3dsignatures.com
Year Founded: 2011
3D0A—(DEU)
Assets: $3,003,340
Liabilities: $120,202
Net Worth: $2,883,138
Earnings: ($837,011)
Fiscal Year-end: 06/30/22

Investment Services
N.A.I.C.S.: 523999
Sabine Mai *(Founder)*

TELOGICA LIMITED
Empire Square Plot No 233-A 234 &
235, 3rd Fl Rd No 36 Jubilee Hills,
Hyderabad, 500 033, Telangana, In-
dia
Tel.: (91) 4027531324
Web Site:
http://www.aishwaryatechtele.com
532975—(BOM)
Rev.: $1,160,634
Assets: $3,584,109
Liabilities: $3,878,499
Net Worth: ($294,390)
Earnings: ($383,142)
Emp.: 40
Fiscal Year-end: 03/31/22
Fiber Optic Test Equipment & Cable
Fault Locators Mfr
N.A.I.C.S.: 335999
Gangavaram Rama Manohar Reddy
(Exec Dir)

TELSTRA GROUP LIMITED
Level 41 242 Exhibition Street, Mel-
bourne, 3000, VIC, Australia
Tel.: (61) 1300886677 AU
Web Site: https://www.telstra.com.au
TLS—(ASX)
Rev.: $15,156,158,310
Assets: $29,359,718,328
Liabilities: $17,743,365,717
Net Worth: $11,616,352,611
Earnings: $1,337,288,909
Emp.: 31,000
Fiscal Year-end: 06/30/23
Telecommunication Servicesb
N.A.I.C.S.: 517112
John Patrick Mullen *(Chm)*

Subsidiaries:

**FOXTEL Cable Television Pty.
Limited** (1)
5 Thomas Holt Dr, North Ryde, 2113, NSW,
Australia **(50%)**
Tel.: (61) 298136000
Web Site: http://www.foxtel.com.au
Cable Television Programming & Distribu-
tion
N.A.I.C.S.: 516210

Subsidiary (Domestic):

FOXTEL Management Pty. Ltd. (2)
5 Thomas Holt Drive, North Ryde, 2113,
NSW, Australia **(65%)**
Tel.: (61) 298136000
Web Site: https://www.foxtel.com.au
Media & Broadcasting Services
N.A.I.C.S.: 516120
Keiren Cooney *(Chief Mktg & Sls Officer)*

Ooyala, Inc. (1)
4750 Patrick Henry Dr, Santa Clara, CA
95054
Tel.: (650) 965-8920
Web Site: http://www.ooyala.com
Online Video Management Solutions
N.A.I.C.S.: 513210
Sean Knapp *(Co-Founder)*

Subsidiary (Non-US):

Ooyala Limited (2)
125 Shaftesbury Avenue, London, WC2H
8HR, United Kingdom
Tel.: (44) 20 7494 6200
Online Video Management Solutions
N.A.I.C.S.: 513210
Rags Gupta *(Gen Mgr)*

Ooyala Mexico (2)
Av Real Acueducto 240 Piso 19, Zapopan,
45116, Mexico
Tel.: (52) 33 3817 3644
Web Site: http://www.ooyala.com
Online Video Management Solutions
N.A.I.C.S.: 513210

Pacnet Limited (1)

TELSTRA GROUP LIMITED INTERNATIONAL PUBLIC

Telstra Group Limited—(Continued)

110 Paya Lebar Road Level 8 OneTen
Paya Lebar, Singapore, 409009, Singapore
Tel.: (65) 67229800
Web Site: http://www.telstraglobal.com
Internet Communications Service Supplier
N.A.I.C.S.: 517810

Subsidiary (Non-US):

Pacnet Thailand (2)
140 10th Floor Unit 1007-1008 One Pacific Place Sukhumvit Road, Klongtoey, Bangkok, 10110, Thailand
Tel.: (66) 26872687
Web Site: http://www.telstraglobal.com
Integrated Telecommunications & IP Based Products & Services
N.A.I.C.S.: 517810

Telstra Broadcast Services Pty. Ltd. (1)
L4 Shop 437 Macquarie Centre Cnr Herring Nth Waterloo Rds, Macquarie Park, 2113, NSW, Australia
Tel.: (61) 800724534
Web Site: https://www.telstra.com.au
Satellite Broadcast Delivery Content Management & Transmission Services
N.A.I.C.S.: 517410
Trevor Boal *(Head-Broadcast Svcs)*

Telstra International Limited (1)
10 13 19/F Telecom House 3 Gloucester Road, Wanchai, China (Hong Kong)
Tel.: (852) 28270066
Web Site: http://www.telstraglobal.com
Communications & Information Services
N.A.I.C.S.: 517111

Subsidiary (Non-US):

Telstra International Philippines, Inc. (2)
15f Zuellig Building Paseo De Roxas Cor Makati Ave, Makati, 1226, Philippines
Tel.: (63) 28871591
Web Site: http://www.telstraglobal.com
Telecommunications & Information Services
N.A.I.C.S.: 517111
Ralph Brambles *(Gen Mgr)*

Telstra Super Financial Planning Pty Ltd. (1)
Level 8 215 Spring Street, PO Box 14309, Melbourne, 3000, VIC, Australia
Tel.: (61) 300033166
Web Site: https://www.telstrasuper.com.au
Sales Range: $25-49.9 Million
Emp.: 103
Financial Planning Services
N.A.I.C.S.: 561499
Paul Curtin *(CFO & Exec Gen Mgr-Strategy, PMO, and Investment Ops)*

TELSYS LTD.
5 Granit Street, Petach Tikva, 4951404, Israel
Tel.: (972) 37657666
Web Site: https://www.telsys.co.il
Year Founded: 1963
TLSY—(TAE)
Rev.: $151,628,399
Assets: $120,769,718
Liabilities: $39,205,967
Net Worth: $81,563,751
Earnings: $48,503,936
Emp.: 70
Fiscal Year-end: 12/31/23
Other Electronic Parts & Equipment Merchant Wholesalers
N.A.I.C.S.: 423690
Boaz Finkelstein *(CFO)*

Subsidiaries:

Variscite Ltd. (1)
Tel.: (972) 99562910
Web Site: https://www.variscite.com
System Module Mfr
N.A.I.C.S.: 334419
Oren Rokach *(Founder)*

TELUS CORPORATION
510 West Georgia 8th floor, Vancouver, V6B 0M3, BC, Canada
Tel.: (604) 697-8044 BC
Web Site: https://www.telus.com
Year Founded: 1998
TU—(NYSE)
Rev.: $27,003,718,400
Assets: $75,356,966,400
Liabilities: $52,130,761,600
Net Worth: $23,226,204,800
Earnings: $1,163,860,800
Emp.: 106,400
Fiscal Year-end: 12/31/23
Telecommunications & Internet Services
N.A.I.C.S.: 517111
François Gratton *(Co-Pres & Exec VP)*

Subsidiaries:

ADT Security Services Canada, Inc.
2815 Matheson Blvd, Mississauga, L4Z 1X1, ON, Canada
Tel.: (877) 627-0504
Web Site: http://www.adt.ca
Security System Services
N.A.I.C.S.: 561621

AGT Advanced Communications (1)
#1920 Phipps McKinnon Building, 10020 - 101 A Avenue, Edmonton, T5J 3G2, AB, Canada
Tel.: (403) 498-7309
Telecommunications & Data Communications Services
N.A.I.C.S.: 517810

AGT Mobility Inc. (1)
3030 2nd Avenue SE, T2A5N7, Calgary, Alberta, Canada
Tel.: (403) 530-5300
Telecommunications & Data Communications Services
N.A.I.C.S.: 517810
Darren Entwistle *(Pres & CEO)*

Alta Telecom International Ltd. (1)
4830 River Green Pkwy, Duluth, GA 30096-9409
Tel.: (770) 662-0540
Web Site: http://www.altatelecom.com
Telecommunications & Data Communications Services
N.A.I.C.S.: 517810

Blacksmith Applications, Inc (1)
60 Island St, Lawrence, MA 01840
Tel.: (978) 557-7565
Web Site: http://www.blacksmithapps.com
Sales Range: $1-9.9 Million
Business Management Software Publisher
N.A.I.C.S.: 513210
Paul Wietecha *(Founder, Pres & CEO)*

Subsidiary (Domestic):

TABS Analytics, Inc. (2)
6 Corporate Dr Ste 422, Shelton, CT 06484
Tel.: (203) 925-9162
Web Site: http://www.tabsanalytics.com
Outsourced Sales & Marketing Analytics Services
N.A.I.C.S.: 541910

Subsidiary (Domestic):

Decision Insight, Inc. (3)
201 Main St Ste 200, Kansas, MO 64105
Tel.: (816) 221-0445
Web Site: http://www.decisioninsight.com
Rev.: $4,200,000
Emp.: 21
Fiscal Year-end: 12/31/2009
Marketing Research & Public Opinion Polling
N.A.I.C.S.: 541910

Emergis Inc. (1)
630 Boul Rene-Levesque Ouest 22nd Floor, Montreal, J4K 5B1, QC, Canada (100%)
Tel.: (450) 928-6000
Web Site: http://www.telushealth.com
Sales Range: $150-199.9 Million
Emp.: 185
Information Technology Services for the Health Care & Financial Industries
N.A.I.C.S.: 541512
Sudhakar Kosaraju *(Pres)*

TELUS CORPORATION - TELUS Business Solutions Division (1)
2237 Queen St E, Toronto, M4E 1G1, ON, Canada
Tel.: (866) 468-3587
Telecommunication Services b
N.A.I.C.S.: 517810

TELUS Communications (Quebec) Inc. (1)
6 Rue Jules-A-Brillant Dept R0630, Rimouski, G5L 7E4, QC, Canada
Tel.: (418) 722-5331
Telecommunication Services b
N.A.I.C.S.: 517810

TELUS Communications Company (1)
100 Shepperd Ave E Fl 6, Toronto, M2N 6N5, ON, Canada (100%)
Tel.: (416) 228-3400
Web Site: http://www.businessobjects.com
Sales Range: $25-49.9 Million
Emp.: 100
Telecommunication & Internet Services
N.A.I.C.S.: 517810

TELUS Integrated Communications (1)
25 York St, Toronto, M5J 2Z5, ON, Canada (100%)
Tel.: (416) 507-7400
Sales Range: $450-499.9 Million
Emp.: 2,000
N.A.I.C.S.: 517111
Darren Entwistle *(Pres)*

TELUS International (CDA) Inc. (1)
510 West Georgia Street Floor 7, Vancouver, V6B 0M3, BC, Canada (65%)
Tel.: (604) 695-3455
Web Site: http://www.telusinternational.com
Rev.: $2,708,000,000
Assets: $4,823,000,000
Liabilities: $2,786,000,000
Net Worth: $2,037,000,000
Earnings: $54,000,000
Emp.: 75,347
Fiscal Year-end: 12/31/2023
Holding Company
N.A.I.C.S.: 551112
Jeffrey Puritt *(Pres & CEO)*

Subsidiary (US):

WillowTree, LLC (2)
107 5th St SE Ste B, Charlottesville, VA 22902
Tel.: (888) 329-9875
Web Site: http://www.willowtreeapps.com
Mobile Software Development Services
N.A.I.C.S.: 513210
Tobias A. Dengel *(CEO)*

Xavient Information Systems, Inc. (2)
2125 B Madera Rd Ste B, Simi Valley, CA 93065
Tel.: (805) 955-4111
Web Site: http://www.xavient.com
Software Systems Integrator
N.A.I.C.S.: 449210

TELUS International Philippines, Inc. (1)
31st Floor Discovery Centre 25 ADB Avenue, Ortigas Center, Pasig, 1605, Philippines
Tel.: (63) 26389440
Web Site: http://www.telusinternational.com.ph
Sales Range: $650-699.9 Million
Emp.: 3,000
In-Bound & Out-Bound Call Services
N.A.I.C.S.: 561499

TELUS Mobility (1)
200 Consilium Pl Ste 1600, Scarborough, M1H 3J3, ON, Canada (100%)
Tel.: (416) 279-9000
Web Site: http://www.telusmobility.com
Sales Range: $1-4.9 Billion
Emp.: 7,000
Sales of Digital Wireless Phones & Services
N.A.I.C.S.: 517112

TELUS Quebec, Inc. (1)
6 Rue Jules A Brillant, Rimouski, G5L 7E4, QC, Canada (100%)
Tel.: (418) 723-2271

Web Site: http://www.telusquebec.com
Sales Range: $250-299.9 Million
Emp.: 2,200
Telephone Communications; Operating Company
N.A.I.C.S.: 517810
François Gratton *(CEO)*

TELUS Services Inc. (1)
10020-100 Street NW Suite 100 31st Floor, Edmonton, T5J 0N5, AB, Canada
Tel.: (780) 493-7282
Business Process Outsourcing Services
N.A.I.C.S.: 561499

TEM HOLDINGS LIMITED
Suite 1706 Tower 1 China Hong Kong City 33 Canton Road, Tsim Sha Tsui, Hong Kong, China (Hong Kong)
Tel.: (852) 31682070 Ky
Web Site: http://www.tem-group.com
Rev.: $12,279,053
Assets: $18,036,468
Liabilities: $1,948,294
Net Worth: $16,088,174
Earnings: ($1,374,327)
Emp.: 437
Fiscal Year-end: 06/30/19
Electronic Product Mfr & Distr
N.A.I.C.S.: 334417
Man Tak Lau *(Exec Dir)*

Subsidiaries:

SEAP Trading Pte. Ltd. (1)
16 New Industrial Road 05-02 Hudson Technocentre, Singapore, 536204, Singapore
Tel.: (65) 63451788
Electrical Equipment Distr
N.A.I.C.S.: 423610

TEM Electronics (Jiangmen) Co Ltd (1)
No 173 Jianshe 3rd Road Unit 9 Sha Chong Wei M and N Building, Jiangmen, Guangdong, China
Tel.: (86) 7503213118
Wire & Cable Mfr
N.A.I.C.S.: 332618
Wai Yin Lee *(Gen Mgr)*

TEMAIRAZU, INC.
7F Ebisu NR Bldg 1-21-3 Ebisu, Shibuya-ku, Tokyo, 150-0013, Japan
Tel.: (81) 354476690
Web Site:
https://www.temairazu.co.jp
Year Founded: 2003
2477—(TKS)
Sales Range: $1-9.9 Million
Internet Advertising Services
N.A.I.C.S.: 541810
Tetsuo Watanabe *(Pres & CEO)*

TEMAS RESOURCES CORP.
309 - 2912 West Broadway, Vancouver, V6K 0E9, BC, Canada
Tel.: (604) 428-9480 Ca
Web Site:
https://www.temasresources.com
TMASF—(OTCQB)
Assets: $6,494,028
Liabilities: $1,219,239
Net Worth: $5,274,789
Earnings: ($2,972,899)
Fiscal Year-end: 12/31/22
Metal Mining & Exploration Services
N.A.I.C.S.: 213114
Michael Dehn *(Pres & CEO)*

TEMASEK HOLDINGS (PRIVATE) LIMITED
60B Orchard Rd No 06-18 The Atrium At Orchard Tower 2, Singapore, 238891, Singapore
Tel.: (65) 68286828 SG
Web Site:
http://www.temasek.com.sg
Year Founded: 1974
Investment Holding Company

AND PRIVATE COMPANIES

N.A.I.C.S.: 551112
John W. Marren *(Sr Mng Dir-North America)*

Subsidiaries:

Certis CISCO Security Pte. Ltd. (1)
Certis CISCO Centre 20 Jalan Afifi, Singapore, 409179, Singapore **(100%)**
Tel.: (65) 67472888
Web Site: http://www.certissecurity.com.sg
Sales Range: $150-199.9 Million
Emp.: 9,000
Physical, Information Technology & Data Security Services
N.A.I.C.S.: 561612
Paul Chong *(CEO)*

Constellar Holdings Pte. Ltd. (1)
1 Expo Drive #02-01, Singapore, 486150, Singapore **(60%)**
Tel.: (65) 64032160
Web Site: https://www.constellar.co
Holding Company; Convention & Trade Show Organizer
N.A.I.C.S.: 551112
Robin Hu *(Chm)*

Subsidiary (Domestic):

Sphere Exhibits Pte Ltd (2)
1000 Toa Payoh North News Centre Annexe Block Level 6, Singapore, 318994, Singapore
Tel.: (65) 63194020
Web Site: http://www.sphereexhibits.com.sg
Consumer Segment Event Organizing Services
N.A.I.C.S.: 711310

Subsidiary (Domestic):

Exhibits Inc Pte Ltd (3)
1000 Toa Payoh North News Centre Podium Block Level 3 Mezzanine Floor, Singapore, 318994, Singapore
Tel.: (65) 63193373
Web Site: http://www.exhibitsinc.com.sg
Sales Range: $25-49.9 Million
Emp.: 8
Exhibition Organizing Services
N.A.I.C.S.: 561920

Eastdil Secured, LLC (1)
40 W 57th St 22nd Fl, New York, NY 10019-4001
Tel.: (212) 315-7200
Web Site: http://www.eastdilsecured.com
Real Estate Investment Banking
N.A.I.C.S.: 531390
Benjamin V. Lambert *(Chm)*

Element Materials Technology Ltd. (1)
10 Lower Grosvenor Place, London, SW1W 0EN, United Kingdom
Tel.: (44) 8082341667
Web Site: https://www.element.com
Testing, Inspection & Certification Services
N.A.I.C.S.: 334515
Jo Wetz *(CEO)*

Subsidiary (Non-US):

Element Materials Technology B.V. (2)
Zekeringstraat 33, Amsterdam, 1014 BV, Netherlands
Tel.: (31) 205563555
Web Site: http://www.element.com
Material Testing & Analysis Services
N.A.I.C.S.: 541380

Subsidiary (US):

Element Cleveland (3)
5405 E Schaaf Rd, Cleveland, OH 44131
Tel.: (216) 524-1450
Web Site: http://www.element.com
Specialized Metals Testing
N.A.I.C.S.: 541380

Element Materials Technology - Cincinnati (3)
3701 Port Union Rd, Fairfield, OH 45014
Tel.: (513) 984-4112
Web Site: http://www.element.com
Testing Laboratory Services
N.A.I.C.S.: 541380
Charles Noall *(CEO)*

Subsidiary (Non-US):

Element Materials Technology AB (3)
Studsvik 3, Tystberga, SE-611 99, Nykoping, Sweden
Tel.: (46) 10 279 4700
Web Site: http://www.element.com
Material Testing Services
N.A.I.C.S.: 541380

Element Materials Technology AB - Karlskoga
Artilleriplan 2, PO Box 3, Karlskoga, SE-691 50, Sweden
Tel.: (46) 10 279 47 00
Web Site: http://www.element.com
Material Testing Services
N.A.I.C.S.: 541380

Element Materials Technology Warwick Ltd (3)
Rothwell Road, Warwick, CV34 5JX, Warks, United Kingdom
Tel.: (44) 1926478478
Web Site: http://www.element.com
Telecoms, EMC & Safety Testing Services & Accreditation
N.A.I.C.S.: 541380
Mark Heaven *(Dir-Global Aerospace Product Qualitfication Testing)*

Subsidiary (US):

Element Rancho Dominguez (3)
18100 S Wilmington Ave, Rancho Dominguez, CA 90220
Tel.: (310) 632-8500
Web Site: http://www.element.com
Material Testing & Analysis Services
N.A.I.C.S.: 541380

Subsidiary (Non-US):

Exova Group Limited (3)
10 Lower Grosvenor Place, London, SW1W 0EN, United Kingdom
Tel.: (44) 203 540 1820
Holding Company; Scientific Testing, Calibration & Consulting Services
N.A.I.C.S.: 551112

Subsidiary (Non-US):

Element Metech AB (4)
Broderna Ugglas Gata Hus 103G, SE-581 88, Linkoping, Sweden
Tel.: (46) 10 603 6262
Web Site: http://www.elementmetech.com
Calibration & Metrology Services
N.A.I.C.S.: 541380

Subsidiary (Non-US):

Element Metech A/S (5)
Flyvestation Karup Herningvej 30, 7470, Karup, Denmark
Tel.: (45) 96625000
Web Site: http://www.elementmetech.com
Calibration & Metrology Services
N.A.I.C.S.: 541380
Bendix Christensen *(Gen Mgr)*

Subsidiary (Domestic):

Element Metech AB (5)
Rattvagen 1, 732 48, Arboga, Sweden
Tel.: (46) 10 603 62 12
Web Site: http://www.elementmetech.com
Calibration & Metrology Services
N.A.I.C.S.: 541380

Subsidiary (Non-US):

Element Metech GmbH (5)
Hans-Bockler-Ring 9, Norderstedt, 22851, Germany
Tel.: (49) 405295610
Web Site: http://elementmetech.com
Calibration & Metrology Services
N.A.I.C.S.: 541380
Thomas Etzold *(Mng Dir)*

Element Metech Oy (5)
Kuormakuja 1, Nummela, 358, Finland
Tel.: (358) 400356050
Web Site: http://www.elementmetech.com
Calibration & Metrology Services
N.A.I.C.S.: 541380
Rami Heikkila *(Ops Mgr)*

Subsidiary (US):

Exova Inc. (4)
4949 SE Johnson Creek Blvd, Portland, OR 97222
Tel.: (503) 777-7458
Web Site: http://www.element.com
Laboratory Testing Services
N.A.I.C.S.: 541380

Subsidiary (Domestic):

Element Materials Technology Laboratory Solutions UK Limited (2)
Holm Street Strathaven, Lanark, ML10 6NB, United Kingdom
Tel.: (44) 1357522961
Web Site: http://www.crawfordscientific.com
Analytical Laboratory Instrument Mfr
N.A.I.C.S.: 334516

Subsidiary (US):

Validation Resources LLC (3)
63020 NE Lower Meadow Dr Ste 3, Bend, OR 97701
Tel.: (541) 388-1253
Web Site: https://www.vranalytical.com
Research & Development in Biotechnology
N.A.I.C.S.: 541714

Subsidiary (US):

PCTEST Engineering Laboratory, Inc. (2)
7185 Oakland Mills Rd, Columbia, MD 21046
Tel.: (410) 290-6652
Web Site: http://www.pctestlab.com
Testing Laboratories
N.A.I.C.S.: 541380
Randy Ortanez *(CEO)*

Food & Allied Support Services Corporation Pte. Ltd. (1)
279 Fdawu Tower 03-01 River Valley Road, Singapore, 238320, Singapore
Tel.: (65) 62351296
Web Site: http://www.fasscointernational.com
Facility Management Services
N.A.I.C.S.: 624190

Subsidiary (Non-US):

FASSCO Catering Services L.L.C. (2)
Office No 2407 24th Floor Tamouh Tower A2 Building No 12 Marina Square, PO Box 6360, Al Reem Island, Abu Dhabi, United Arab Emirates
Tel.: (971) 26783331
Catering Services
N.A.I.C.S.: 722320

Global Healthcare Exchange, LLC (1)
1315 W Century Dr Ste 100, Louisville, CO 80027
Tel.: (720) 887-7000
Web Site: http://www.ghx.com
Healthcare Supply Chain Management Services
N.A.I.C.S.: 425120
Bruce Johnson *(Pres & CEO)*

Subsidiary (Non-US):

GHX UK Ltd. (2)
Platinum Building St John's Innovation Park Cowley Road, Milton, Cambridge, CB4 0DS, United Kingdom
Tel.: (44) 845 620 2222
Web Site: http://www.ghxeurope.com
Healthcare Supply Chain Services
N.A.I.C.S.: 541990
Nedzad Fajic *(Pres)*

Subsidiary (Domestic):

Vendormate, Inc. (2)
3445 Peachtree Rd NE Ste 300, Atlanta, GA 30326
Tel.: (877) 483-6368
Web Site: http://www.ghx.com
Hospital Supply Chain & Credentialing Compliance Monitoring Solutions
N.A.I.C.S.: 513210

TEMASEK HOLDINGS (PRIVATE) LIMITED

Heliconia Capital Management Pte. Ltd. (1)
9 Temasek Boulevard 24-03 Suntec Tower Two, Singapore, 038989, Singapore
Tel.: (65) 6828 23322
Web Site: http://www.heliconiacapital.com
Privater Equity Firm
N.A.I.C.S.: 523999
Derek Lau *(CEO)*

Homeplus Co., Limited (1)
398 Hwagokoro, Gangseo-gu, Seoul, 135-080, Korea (South)
Tel.: (82) 234598000
Web Site: http://www.homeplus.co.kr
Hypermarkets, Supermarkets & Convenience Stores Operator & Franchisor
N.A.I.C.S.: 445110
Sang Hyun Kim *(CEO)*

InTouch Plc (1)
SJ INFINITE ONE BUSINESS COMPLEX 29th and 30th Floors 349 Vibhavadi, Rangsit road Chompol Chatuchak, Bangkok, 10900, Thailand **(49.6%)**
Tel.: (66) 21186900
Web Site: http://www.intouchcompany.com
Rev.: $344,300,804
Assets: $1,182,597,155
Liabilities: $2,822,434
Net Worth: $1,179,774,720
Earnings: $423,293,712
Emp.: 21
Fiscal Year-end: 12/31/2023
Telecommunication Servicesb
N.A.I.C.S.: 551112
Virach Aphimeteetamrong *(Chm)*

Innoven Capital India Private Limited (1)
12th Floor Express Towers Nariman Point, Nariman Point, Mumbai, 400 021, India
Tel.: (91) 2267446500
Web Site: http://www.svb.com
Investment Management Service
N.A.I.C.S.: 523940
Anshu Prasher *(Assoc Dir)*

Innoven Capital Singapore Pte. Ltd. (1)
138 Market Street CapitaGreen 27-01, Singapore, 48946, Singapore
Tel.: (65) 65322416
Web Site: http://www.innovencapital.com
Investment Management Service.
N.A.I.C.S.: 523940
Darren Chuah *(Dir-Governance Risk & Compliance)*

Keywords Studios Plc (1)
Whelan House South County Business Park, Dublin, 18, Ireland
Tel.: (353) 19022730
Web Site: https://www.keywordsstudios.com
Rev.: $745,432,765
Assets: $870,610,835
Liabilities: $269,390,244
Net Worth: $601,220,591
Earnings: $51,122,383
Emp.: 12,000
Fiscal Year-end: 12/31/2022
Video Game Technical Services
N.A.I.C.S.: 541990
Ross Graham *(Chm)*

Subsidiary (Non-US):

AMC RO Studios S.R.L. (2)
36 Stirbei Voda St 1st Floor DOMUS I Building, 1st District, 010113, Bucharest, Romania
Tel.: (40) 752219585
Web Site: https://amcstudio.ro
Digital Art Design Services
N.A.I.C.S.: 541430

Babel Media India Private Limited (2)
D-32 Infocity 2 Sector-33, Gurgaon, 122001, Haryana, India
Tel.: (91) 1244410482
Web Site: https://www.babelmedia.com
Outsourced Services
N.A.I.C.S.: 541214

Babel Media Limited (2)
4th Floor 110 High Holborn, London, WC1V 6JS, United Kingdom
Tel.: (44) 1273764100
Web Site: https://www.babelmedia.com

TEMASEK HOLDINGS (PRIVATE) LIMITED

Temasek Holdings (Private) Limited—(Continued)
Video Game Technical Services
N.A.I.C.S.: 541990

Binari Sonori S.r.l. (2)
Viale Fulvio Testi 11, Cinisello Balsamo, 20092, Milan, Italy
Tel.: (39) 0261866310
Web Site: https://binarisonori.info
Audio Production Services
N.A.I.C.S.: 512240

Subsidiary (US):

Binari Sonori America Inc. (3)
350 N Glenoaks Blvd, Burbank, CA 91502
Tel.: (818) 729-8508
Video Game Technical Services
N.A.I.C.S.: 541990
Kirk Lambert *(Pres & Mgr-Ops)*

Subsidiary (US):

Blindlight LLC (2)
8335 Sunset Blvd, West Hollywood, CA 90069
Tel.: (323) 337-9090
Web Site: http://www.blindlight.com
Motion Picture Services
N.A.I.C.S.: 512110

Subsidiary (Non-US):

Cord Worldwide Ltd. (2)
4th Floor 110 High Holborn, London, WC1V 6JS, United Kingdom
Tel.: (44) 2035975350
Web Site: https://www.cordww.com
Musical Troop Services
N.A.I.C.S.: 711130

Descriptive Video Works Inc. (2)
147 W 3rd Avenue, Vancouver, V5Y 1E6, BC, Canada
Tel.: (604) 648-7575
Web Site: https://descriptivevideoworks.com
Entertainment & Studio Services
N.A.I.C.S.: 512110

Subsidiary (US):

GameSim, Inc. (2)
13501 Ingenuity Dr, Orlando, FL 32826
Tel.: (407) 688-0587
Web Site: http://www.gamesim.com
Game Development & Terrain Databases
N.A.I.C.S.: 513210
Derek Minton *(CTO)*

Heavy Iron Studios, Inc. (2)
1600 Rosecrans Ave Bldg 7 Ste 300, Manhattan Beach, CA 90266
Tel.: (310) 216-7703
Web Site: http://www.heavyiron.games
Motion Picture & Video Production
N.A.I.C.S.: 512110
Lyle Hall *(VP)*

High Voltage Software, Inc. (2)
2345 Pembroke Ave, Hoffman Estates, IL 60169
Tel.: (847) 490-9567
Web Site: https://www.high-voltage.com
Entertainment & Studio Services
N.A.I.C.S.: 512110

Subsidiary (Non-US):

Indigo Pearl Limited (2)
Indigo Pearl Keywords Studios 4th Floor 110 High Holborn, London, WC1V 6JS, United Kingdom
Tel.: (44) 2089644545
Web Site: https://www.indigopearl.com
Entertainment & Studio Services
N.A.I.C.S.: 512110

Jinglebell S.r.l. (2)
Via Marco d Oggiono 12, 20123, Milan, Italy
Tel.: (39) 028331141
Web Site: https://jinglebell.com
Entertainment & Studio Services
N.A.I.C.S.: 512110

Keywords International Co. Limited (2)
2F Toshin Building 4-33-10 Yoyogi, Shibuya-ku, Tokyo, 151-0053, Japan
Tel.: (81) 3 4588 6760
Video Game Technical Services
N.A.I.C.S.: 541990

Keywords International Corporation Inc. (2)
410 St-Nicolas Suite 600, Montreal, H2Y 2P5, QC, Canada
Tel.: (514) 789-0404
Video Game Technical Services
N.A.I.C.S.: 541990

Subsidiary (US):

Keywords International Inc. (2)
Plz Ctr 10900 NE 8th St Ste 1000 Bellevue, Seattle, WA 98004
Tel.: (425) 633-3226
Video Game Technical Services
N.A.I.C.S.: 541990

Subsidiary (Non-US):

Keywords International Pte. Limited (2)
20 Kallang Avenue 06-6A Lobby B Pico Creative Centre, Singapore, 339411, Singapore
Tel.: (65) 67098680
Emp.: 50
Video Game Technical Services
N.A.I.C.S.: 541990

Keywords Italia Srl (2)
Viale delle Province 2, 00162, Rome, Italy
Tel.: (39) 06 44 20 25 21
Web Site: http://www.keywordsintl.it
Video Game Technical Services
N.A.I.C.S.: 541990

Subsidiary (US):

Liquid Development LLC (2)
4200 Montrose Blvd 300, Houston, TX 77006
Tel.: (713) 521-9574
Web Site: http://www.liquiddev.com
Computer System Design Services
N.A.I.C.S.: 541512

Subsidiary (Non-US):

Liquid Violet Limited (2)
1st Floor 39 Earlham Street, London, WC2H 9LT, United Kingdom
Tel.: (44) 2039590770
Web Site: https://www.liquidviolet.co.uk
Audio Production Services
N.A.I.C.S.: 512240

Maverick Media Limited (2)
110 High Holborn, London, WC1V 6JS, United Kingdom
Tel.: (44) 2072913450
Web Site: https://maverickmedia.co.uk
Emp.: 12,000
Video Games Design & Development Services
N.A.I.C.S.: 512110

SPOV Ltd. (2)
4th Floor 110 High Holborn, London, WC1V 6JS, United Kingdom
Tel.: (44) 2077395862
Motion Picture Services
N.A.I.C.S.: 512110

Snowed In Studios, Inc. (2)
250 City Centre Ave, Ottawa, K1R 6K7, ON, Canada
Tel.: (613) 656-3372
Web Site: https://www.snowedin.ca
Video Game Design Services
N.A.I.C.S.: 532282

TV+SYNCHRON Berlin GmbH (2)
Moriz Seeler Str 5-7 Franz Ehrlich Haus, 12489, Berlin, Germany
Tel.: (49) 30677749415
Web Site: https://tv-synchron.de
Recording Studio Services
N.A.I.C.S.: 512240

Tantalus Media Pty. Limited (2)
12 Spring Street, Fitzroy, 3065, VIC, Australia
Tel.: (61) 396940900
Web Site: https://www.tantalus.com.au
Video Games Design & Development Services
N.A.I.C.S.: 512110

The TrailerFarm Limited (2)
Lees Housethird Floor West 22 - 33 Dyke Road, Brighton, BN1 3FE, United Kingdom
Tel.: (44) 1273329727
Web Site: https://thetrailerfarm.com
Video Game Design Services
N.A.I.C.S.: 532282

Subsidiary (US):

VMC Consulting Corporation (2)
11601 Willows Rd NE, Redmond, WA 98052 (100%)
Tel.: (425) 558-7700
Web Site: http://www.vmc.com
Quality Assurance, Localization & Support Services
N.A.I.C.S.: 541614

Subsidiary (Non-US):

Wizcorp Inc. (2)
Higashi-Nihonbashi 3-10-14 Sunrise Tachibana 6F, Chuo-ku, Tokyo, 103-0004, Japan
Tel.: (81) 34 550 1448
Web Site: https://www.wizcorp.jp
Sales Range: $1-9.9 Million
Emp.: 35
Mobile Application Development Services
N.A.I.C.S.: 541511
Guillaume Hansali *(Founder & CEO)*

d3t Ltd. (2)
Daresbury Point Greenwood Drive, Manor Park, Runcorn, WA7 1UG, Cheshire, United Kingdom
Tel.: (44) 1928575742
Web Site: https://www.d3tltd.com
Scientific & Technical Services
N.A.I.C.S.: 541990

Lentor Investments Pte. Ltd. (1)
60B Orchard Rd 6-18 Tower 2, The Atrium at Orchard, Singapore, 238891, Singapore
Tel.: (65) 68286828
Holding Company
N.A.I.C.S.: 551112

Manipal Health Enterprises Private Limited (1)
98 HAL Old Airport Road Kodihalli, Bengaluru, 560017, Karnataka, India (51%)
Tel.: (91) 8022221111
Web Site: http://www.manipalhospitals.com
Multi Specialty Healthcare Provider
N.A.I.C.S.: 621999
Dilip Jose *(CEO & Mng Dir)*

Mapletree Investments Pte. Ltd. (1)
10 Pasir Panjang Rd 13-01 Mapletree Business city, Singapore, 117438, Singapore
Tel.: (65) 63776111
Web Site: http://www.mapletree.com.sg
Investment Services
N.A.I.C.S.: 523999
Edmund Cheng Wai Wing *(Chm)*

Subsidiary (US):

Oakwood Worldwide, Inc. (2)
2222 Corinth Ave, Los Angeles, CA 90064-1602
Tel.: (310) 478-1021
Web Site: http://www.oakwood.com
Sales Range: $500-549.9 Million
Emp.: 1,500
Furnished Apartments & Extended-Stay Lodging
N.A.I.C.S.: 531210
Rebecca Tann *(Sr VP-Sls & Mktg)*

MediaCorp Private Ltd (1)
Caldecott Broadcast Centre, Andrew Rd, Singapore, 299939, Singapore
Tel.: (65) 63333888
Web Site: http://www.mediacorp.sg
Sales Range: $750-799.9 Million
Emp.: 2,600
Television & Radio Broadcasting Services; Newspaper Publisher
N.A.I.C.S.: 516120
Chitra Rajaram *(Head-Community Segment)*

Subsidiary (Domestic):

Media Research Consultants Pte Ltd (2)
Caldecott Broadcast Centre, Andrew Road, Singapore, 299939, Singapore
Tel.: (65) 63503963
Web Site: http://www.mrconsultants.sg

INTERNATIONAL PUBLIC

Sales Range: $25-49.9 Million
Emp.: 25
Media Research & Consulting Services
N.A.I.C.S.: 541910
Sandra Lim *(Gen Mgr)*

MediaCorp Press Ltd (2)
24 Raffles Place 28-01 06 Clifford Centre, Singapore, 48621, Singapore
Tel.: (65) 62364886
Web Site: http://www.mediacorppress.sg
Sales Range: $50-74.9 Million
Emp.: 140
News Services
N.A.I.C.S.: 516210
Tham Loke Kheng *(CEO)*

MediaCorp Publishing Pte Ltd (2)
Caldecott Broadcast Centre, 299939, Singapore, Singapore (100%)
Tel.: (65) 63333888
Web Site: http://www.mediacorp.com.sg
Sales Range: $50-74.9 Million
Emp.: 200
Magazine Publisher
N.A.I.C.S.: 513120
Sharon Lin *(Editor-in-Chief)*

MediaCorp Radio Singapore Pte Ltd (2)
Caldecott Broadcast Centre, Andrew Road, Singapore, 299939, Singapore
Tel.: (65) 63333888
Web Site: http://www.mediacorp.com.sg
Radio Broadcasting Services
N.A.I.C.S.: 516110

MediaCorp Raintree Pictures Pte Ltd (2)
Caldecott Broadcast Centre, Andrew Road, Singapore, 299939, Singapore
Tel.: (65) 63503119
Web Site: http://www.mediacorpraintree.com
Sales Range: $25-49.9 Million
Emp.: 4
Movie Production Services
N.A.I.C.S.: 512110

MediaCorp Studios Pte Ltd (2)
Caldecott Broadcast Ctr, Andrew Rd, Singapore, 299939, Singapore
Tel.: (65) 63503000
Web Site: http://www.mediacorpstudios.sg
Production Studio; Artist Management Services
N.A.I.C.S.: 512110
Teo Lian Huay *(Sr Mgr)*

MediaCorp TV Singapore Pte Ltd (2)
Caldecott Broadcast Centre, Andrew Road, Singapore, 299939, Singapore
Tel.: (65) 63333888
Web Site: http://www.mediacorp.sg
Television Broadcasting Services
N.A.I.C.S.: 516120
Shaun Seow *(CEO)*

MediaCorp TV12 Singapore Pte Ltd (2)
Caldecott Center Andrew Rd, Singapore, 299939, Singapore
Tel.: (65) 63333888
Web Site: http://www.mediacorptv12.sg
Sales Range: $25-49.9 Million
Emp.: 35
Television Broadcasting Services
N.A.I.C.S.: 516120
Lim Suat Jien *(Co-CEO)*

MediaCorp Technologies Pte Ltd (2)
Caldecott Broadcast Centre, Andrew Road, Singapore, 299939, Singapore
Tel.: (65) 63333888
Web Site: http://www.mediacorp.sg
Sales Range: $50-74.9 Million
Emp.: 200
Microwave Network & International Shortwave Radio Transmission Manager & Operator
N.A.I.C.S.: 516210
Lau Hing Tong *(Sr VP-Tech Svcs)*

Singapore Media Academy Pte. Ltd. (2)
30 Merchant Road Riverside Point 04-13, Singapore, 058282, Singapore
Tel.: (65) 64356000
Web Site: http://www.esma.sg

AND PRIVATE COMPANIES

Sales Range: $50-74.9 Million
Emp.: 30
Media Educational Services
N.A.I.C.S.: 923110
Pauline Chew *(VP)*

Olam International Limited (1)
7 Straits View Marina One East Tower 20-01, Singapore, 018936, Singapore **(53.5%)**
Tel.: (65) 63394100
Web Site: https://www.olamgroup.com
Rev.: $35,485,062,946
Assets: $24,204,875,739
Liabilities: $19,087,177,964
Net Worth: $5,117,697,775
Earnings: $455,104,221
Emp.: 82,300
Fiscal Year-end: 12/31/2021
Holding Company; Food & Industrial Raw Materials Distr
N.A.I.C.S.: 551112
Joydeep Bose *(Mng Dir & Head-HR-Global)*

Subsidiary (US):

Brooks Peanut Company, Inc. (2)
402 E Main St, Samson, AL 36477
Tel.: (334) 898-7194
Sales Range: $1-9.9 Million
Farm Product Raw Material Merchant Whslr
N.A.I.C.S.: 424590

Subsidiary (Non-US):

LLC Russian Dairy Company (2)
Sverdlova Str 2 floor 3, 440052, Penza, Russia
Tel.: (7) 8412205215
Web Site: http://www.rusmolco.com
Dairy Products Mfr
N.A.I.C.S.: 311511
Harjot Singh *(VP)*

NZ Farming Systems Uruguay Limited (2)
Av Bolivia 1332 CP, 11500, Montevideo, Uruguay **(100%)**
Tel.: (598) 26041595
Web Site: http://www.nzfsu.com.uy
Dairy Farm Operations
N.A.I.C.S.: 112120
Vivek Verma *(Chm)*

Olam Agro Peru S.A.C. (2)
Av VActor Andres Belaunde No 147 Centro Empresarial Real VAa, Principal 155 Edif Oficina 1401, San Isidro, Lima, 27, Peru
Tel.: (51) 17160720
Web Site: http://www.olamgroup.com
Emp.: 151
Coffee, Oregano & Paprika Processing Services
N.A.I.C.S.: 115114
Prashant Jalan *(Gen Mgr & Country Head-Peru)*

Subsidiary (US):

Olam Americas, Inc. (2)
205 E River Park Pl Ste 310, Fresno, CA 93720
Tel.: (559) 447-1390
Web Site: http://www.olamgroup.com
Emp.: 3,576
Farming & Food Processing Services Food & Raw Ingredient Whslr
N.A.I.C.S.: 424590
Greg Estep *(Mng Dir & CEO-Spices)*

Subsidiary (Domestic):

McCleskey Mills, Inc. (3)
197 Rhodes St, Smithville, GA 31787
Tel.: (229) 846-2003
Web Site: http://www.mccleskeymills.com
Emp.: 100
Processor & Marketer of Agricultural Products & Food Ingredients
N.A.I.C.S.: 424590
Keith Chandler *(Pres)*

Unit (Domestic):

Olam Tomato Processors (3)
1175 S 19th Ave, Lemoore, CA 93245-9747
Tel.: (559) 924-6500
Sales Range: $25-49.9 Million
Emp.: 70
Processor of Tomatoes
N.A.I.C.S.: 311421
Colusa Canning *(Gen Mgr)*

Subsidiary (Domestic):

Universal Blanchers, LLC (3)
2077 Convention Center Concourse Ste 150, Atlanta, GA 30337-4204
Tel.: (770) 487-1230
Web Site: http://www.universalblanchers.com
Sales Range: $25-49.9 Million
Emp.: 25
Peanut Processing Services
N.A.I.C.S.: 111992
Larry Hughes *(Gen Mgr)*

Subsidiary (Non-US):

Olam Argentina S.A. (2)
Leandro N Alem 492 6th Fl, 1001, Buenos Aires, Capital Federal, Argentina
Tel.: (54) 3584644886
Sales Range: $25-49.9 Million
Emp.: 200
Peanut Whslr
N.A.I.C.S.: 111992

Olam Brasil Ltda. (2)
1356 7 andar cj 72 Vila Olimpia, Sao Paulo, 04547005, SP, Brazil
Tel.: (55) 1138496888
Web Site: http://www.olamgroup.com
Emp.: 449
Food & Beverages Mfr
N.A.I.C.S.: 311421
M. Sathyamurthy *(Reg Pres-Argentina, Brazil & Uruguay)*

Olam Burkina S.A.R.L. (2)
PO Box 2064, Bobo-Dioulasso, Burkina Faso
Tel.: (226) 20972572
Sales Range: $25-49.9 Million
Emp.: 11
Agricultural Product Mfr
N.A.I.C.S.: 115115

Olam Dairy B.V. (2)
Tramsingel 16, 4814 AB, Breda, Netherlands
Tel.: (31) 765241500
Sales Range: $50-74.9 Million
Emp.: 6
Dairy Product Whslr
N.A.I.C.S.: 424430

Olam Egypt LLC (2)
Ste 1 Bldg 60 Rd 200, Degla Maadi, Cairo, Egypt
Tel.: (20) 2 27546967
Sales Range: $25-49.9 Million
Emp.: 20
Agricultural Product Mfr
N.A.I.C.S.: 115115

Subsidiary (US):

Agri Commodities LLC (3)
533 Bradford St W, Des Moines, IA 52175
Tel.: (641) 315-2050
Agricultural Product Mfr
N.A.I.C.S.: 115115

Subsidiary (Non-US):

Olam Europe B.V. (2)
Conradstraat 38-D2 109, PO Box 29051, Rotterdam, 3013AP, Netherlands
Tel.: (31) 104044011
Web Site: http://www.Olam.com
Sales Range: $25-49.9 Million
Emp.: 26
Cashew Processing Services
N.A.I.C.S.: 111335
Brijesh Krishnaswamy *(Gen Mgr)*

Olam Europe Ltd (2)
New Zealand House, 80 Haymarket, London, SW1Y 4TQ, United Kingdom
Tel.: (44) 2073896464
Web Site: http://www.olamonline.com
Sales Range: $25-49.9 Million
Emp.: 40
Agricultural Product Mfr
N.A.I.C.S.: 115115
Gerry Manley *(Mng Dir)*

Olam Export (India) Limited (2)
III Fl Express Bldg, 9-10 Baahadurshah Zafar Marg, New Delhi, 110002, India
Tel.: (91) 11 43669999

Sales Range: $50-74.9 Million
Emp.: 224
Seeds & Nuts Mfr
N.A.I.C.S.: 445292

Olam France S.A.R.L. (2)
163 165 Ave Charles De Gaulle, 92200, Neuilly-sur-Seine, France
Tel.: (33) 1 41 430244
Sales Range: $25-49.9 Million
Emp.: 4
Agricultural Product Mfr
N.A.I.C.S.: 115115

Olam Information Services Pte Ltd (2)
Zenith Bldg International Tech Park Ascendas CSIR Road, Taramani, Chennai, 600113, Tamil Nadu, India
Tel.: (91) 4442223700
Sales Range: $150-199.9 Million
Emp.: 500
Computer Software Services
N.A.I.C.S.: 423430
Manikandan Thiagarajan *(CTO)*

Olam Ivoire S.A.R.L. (2)
Abidjan 15 En Face Tri Postal Bld de Vridi, PO Box 200, Zone Portuaire, Abidjan, Cote d'Ivoire
Tel.: (225) 21218989
Web Site: http://www.olam.ci
Sales Range: $150-199.9 Million
Emp.: 336
Grain & Field Bean Whslr
N.A.I.C.S.: 424510

Olam Kazakhstan Co Limited (2)
10A Baytursunova St, Shymkent, 160021, Kazakhstan
Tel.: (7) 7252301122
Sales Range: $25-49.9 Million
Emp.: 6
Agricultural Product Mfr
N.A.I.C.S.: 115115

Olam Middle East LLC (2)
608 Sheikha Mariam Bldg, PO Box 44656, P114 Maktoum St, Deira, United Arab Emirates
Tel.: (971) 42289020
Sales Range: $50-74.9 Million
Emp.: 7
Sugar Whslr
N.A.I.C.S.: 424490

Olam Mozambique Limitada (2)
No 217 Predio Pala 1st Fl, Av Karl Marx, Maputo, 284, Mozambique
Tel.: (258) 21315471
Web Site: http://www.e-olam.com
Sales Range: $25-49.9 Million
Emp.: 17
Agricultural Product Mfr
N.A.I.C.S.: 115115

Olam Nigeria (2)
Plot 5 & 6 Abebe Village Road opp FBN Regional Office Iganmu, Lagos, Nigeria
Tel.: (234) 1 791 2194
Web Site: http://www.olamgroup.com
Sales Range: $10-24.9 Million
Emp.: 1,380
Branded Packaged Food Products
N.A.I.C.S.: 333993
Mukul Mathur *(Country Head)*

Olam Polska Sp. z.o.o. (2)
Al Jerozolimskie 123A, Millennium Plz, 02 017, Warsaw, Poland
Tel.: (48) 22 529 57 99
Web Site: http://www.olam.pl
Sales Range: $10-24.9 Million
Emp.: 26
Agricultural Product Mfr
N.A.I.C.S.: 115115
Pawel Redzisz *(Gen Mgr)*

Olam Shandong Limited (2)
598 E Lanzhou Rd, Jiaozhou, Qingdao, 266300, Shandong, China
Tel.: (86) 53287293988
Food Processing Services
N.A.I.C.S.: 311423

Olam Shanghai Limited (2)
2401-05 King Tower No 28 Xinjinqiao Rd, Pudong, Shanghai, 201206, China
Tel.: (86) 2138651588
Sales Range: $25-49.9 Million
Emp.: 50
Food & Beverage Mfr

TEMASEK HOLDINGS (PRIVATE) LIMITED

N.A.I.C.S.: 311421

Olam South Africa (Proprietary) Limited (2)
5 Sinembe Crescent 1st Fl Sinembe Ofc Park, La Lucia Ridge, 4051, Durban, South Africa
Tel.: (27) 315665499
Web Site: http://www.olamonline.net
Agricultural Product Mfr
N.A.I.C.S.: 115115

Olam Ukraine LLC (2)
22 Rybalska St, 01011, Kiev, Ukraine
Tel.: (380) 444991670
Web Site: http://www.olam.pl
Sales Range: $25-49.9 Million
Emp.: 16
Agricultural Product Whslr
N.A.I.C.S.: 115115

Subsidiary (US):

Olde Thompson, LLC (2)
3250 Camino Del Sol, Oxnard, CA 93030
Tel.: (805) 983-0388
Web Site: http://oldethompson.com
Home Furnishing Merchant Whslr
N.A.I.C.S.: 423220
Lilly Laws *(Mgr-Tech)*

Subsidiary (Domestic):

Gel Spice Company Inc. (3)
48 Hook Rd, Bayonne, NJ 07002
Tel.: (201) 339-0700
Web Site: http://www.gelspice.com
Spice Production Services
N.A.I.C.S.: 311942

Subsidiary (Non-US):

Qingdao Key Foods Co Ltd (2)
Jiaoxi Town, Jiaozhao, Qingdao, 266328, China
Tel.: (86) 53285226608
Sales Range: $75-99.9 Million
Emp.: 257
Agriculture Product Distr
N.A.I.C.S.: 115115

Seda Outspan Iberia S.L. (2)
Padre Faustino Calvo s/n, 34005, Palencia, Spain
Tel.: (34) 979716100
Web Site: http://www.sedaoutspan.com
Restaurant Services
N.A.I.C.S.: 722511

PSA International Pte Ltd (1)
38th Floor PSA Building, 460 Alexandra Road, Singapore, 119963, Singapore
Tel.: (65) 62747111
Web Site: http://www.globalpsa.com
Rev.: $2,988,411,015
Assets: $14,804,078,279
Liabilities: $5,994,761,801
Net Worth: $8,809,316,478
Earnings: $914,730,818
Fiscal Year-end: 12/31/2018
Investment Holding Company
N.A.I.C.S.: 551112
Peter Robert Voser *(Chm)*

Subsidiary (Non-US):

Halterm Limited (2)
577 Marginal Road, Halifax, B3H 4P6, NS, Canada
Tel.: (902) 421-1778
Marine Transportation Services
N.A.I.C.S.: 488320
Andrew Snelgrove *(CFO)*

Subsidiary (US):

Penn Terminals Inc. (2)
1 Saville Ave, Eddystone, PA 19022
Tel.: (610) 499-3000
Web Site: http://www.pennterminals.com
Sales Range: $10-24.9 Million
Emp.: 142
Provider of Marine Terminal & Stevedoring Services
N.A.I.C.S.: 488320
Brian Gallen *(COO & Exec VP)*

Rivulis Irrigation Ltd. (1)
Gvat 3657900, Tel Aviv, Israel **(85%)**
Tel.: (972) 73 7800 444
Web Site: http://www.rivulis.com

TEMASEK HOLDINGS (PRIVATE) LIMITED

Temasek Holdings (Private) Limited—(Continued)

Emp.: 3,000
Drip Irrigation Plastic Pipe & Pipe Fittings Designer, Mfr & Whslr
N.A.I.C.S.: 326122
Gregory Lynn Curl (Chm)

Subsidiary (Non-US):

Eurodrip A.V.E.G.E. (2)
55th km National Road Athens - Lamia, 320 11, Inofyta, Viotia, Greece
Tel.: (30) 22620 54800
Web Site: http://www.eurodrip.com
Drip Irrigation Plastic Pipe & Fittings Mfr & Distr
N.A.I.C.S.: 326122
Vassilis Kykrilis (Grp Gen Mgr-Eastern Europe & Middle East Reg)

Jain International Trading BV (2)
Claude Debussylaan 24, Amsterdam, 1082 MD, North Holland, Netherlands
Tel.: (31) 205222555
Irrigation Systems Mfr & Distr
N.A.I.C.S.: 332322

Subsidiary (US):

Rivulis Irrigation, Inc. (2)
7545 Carroll Rd, San Diego, CA 92121
Tel.: (858) 578-1860
Web Site: http://www.rivulisusa.com
Sales Range: $25-49.9 Million
Emp.: 100
Plastic Micro & Drip Irrigation Products Mfr
N.A.I.C.S.: 221310
Fabien Kelbert (Pres)

SMRT Corporation Ltd. (1)
251 North Bridge Road, Singapore, 179102, Singapore (100%)
Tel.: (65) 6331 1000
Web Site: http://www.smrt.com.sg
Sales Range: $900-999.9 Million
Holding Company; Multi-Modal Public Transportation Services
N.A.I.C.S.: 551112
Mario Favaits (Mng Dir-Singapore Rail Engrg)

Subsidiary (Domestic):

SMRT Capital Pte. Ltd. (2)
251 North Bridge Road, Singapore, 179102, Singapore (100%)
Tel.: (65) 6331 1000
Web Site: http://www.smrt.com.sg
Depository & Financing Services
N.A.I.C.S.: 525990
Destmond Kuek (Pres & CEO)

SMRT Engineering Pte. Ltd. (2)
300 Bishan Road, Singapore, 579828, Singapore (100%)
Tel.: (65) 6554 8535
Engineeering Services
N.A.I.C.S.: 541330
Mario Favaits (Mng Dir-Singapore Rail Engineering)

SMRT Far East Pte. Ltd. (2)
251 North Bridge Road, Singapore, 179102, Singapore (100%)
Tel.: (65) 6331 1000
Web Site: http://www.smrt.com.sg
Holding Company
N.A.I.C.S.: 551112

SMRT Institute Pte. Ltd. (2)
300 Bishan Road, Singapore, 579828, Singapore (100%)
Tel.: (65) 6554 8110
Web Site: http://www.smrtinstitute.com.sg
Transportation Industry Education & Training Services
N.A.I.C.S.: 611699
Madelene Lee (Deputy Dir)

SMRT International Pte. Ltd. (2)
300 Bishan Road, Singapore, 579828, Singapore (100%)
Tel.: (65) 6554 8535
Engineering Services
N.A.I.C.S.: 541330

SMRT Investments Pte. Ltd. (2)
251 North Bridge Road, Singapore, 179102, Singapore (100%)
Tel.: (65) 6331 1000

Holding Company; Commercial Property Leasing & Outdoor Advertising Services
N.A.I.C.S.: 551112
Dawn Kar Mun Low (VP-Comml Bus)

SMRT Road Holdings Ltd. (2)
6 Ang Mo Kio Street 62, Singapore, 569140, Singapore (100%)
Tel.: (65) 6482 3888
Holding Company; Road Transportation Services
N.A.I.C.S.: 551112

Subsidiary (Domestic):

SMRT Automotive Services Pte. Ltd. (3)
6 Ang Mo Kio Street 62, Singapore, 569140, Singapore (100%)
Tel.: (65) 6556 3479
Automotive Repair & Maintenance Services
N.A.I.C.S.: 811198

SMRT Buses Ltd. (3)
6 Ang Mo Kio St 62, Singapore, 569140, Singapore (100%)
Tel.: (65) 64823888
Web Site: http://www.smrtbuses.com.sg
Bus Transit Systems Operator
N.A.I.C.S.: 485113

SMRT Taxis Pte. Ltd. (3)
60 Woodlands Industrial Park E4, Singapore, 757705, Singapore (100%)
Tel.: (65) 6369 0111
Taxi Service
N.A.I.C.S.: 485310

Subsidiary (Domestic):

SMRT Trains Ltd. (3)
251 North Bridge Road, Singapore, 179102, Singapore (100%)
Tel.: (65) 6331 1000
Emp.: 7,000
Holding Company; Train Transit Systems Operator
N.A.I.C.S.: 551112

Subsidiary (Domestic):

SMRT Light Rail Pte. Ltd. (3)
1 Woodlands Road 03-01 Ten Mile Junction, Singapore, 677899, Singapore (100%)
Tel.: (65) 6893 6456
Light Rapid Transit System Operator
N.A.I.C.S.: 485112
Lee Ling Wee (Mng Dir)

Subsidiary (Domestic):

Bus-Plus Services Pte. Ltd. (4)
6 Ang Mo Kio Street 62, Singapore, 569140, Singapore (50%)
Tel.: (65) 6481 0166
Web Site: http://www.smrt.com.sg
Luxury Bus Transit Systems
N.A.I.C.S.: 485113

Singapore Airlines Limited (1)
25 Airline Road Airline House, Singapore, 819829, Singapore (55.59%)
Tel.: (65) 91848888
Web Site: https://www.singaporeair.com
Rev.: $2,880,890,023
Assets: $28,372,754,061
Liabilities: $16,083,276,904
Net Worth: $12,289,477,157
Earnings: ($3,224,250,379)
Emp.: 25,547
Fiscal Year-end: 03/31/2021
Airline Services
N.A.I.C.S.: 561599
Swee Wah Mak (Exec VP-Comml)

Subsidiary (Domestic):

SATS Ltd. (2)
20 Airport Boulevard, SATS Inflight Catering Center 1, Singapore, 819659, Singapore (100%)
Tel.: (65) 65425555
Web Site: http://www.sats.com.sg
Rev.: $3,815,931,822
Assets: $6,283,808,811
Liabilities: $4,387,180,432
Net Worth: $1,896,628,379
Earnings: $44,831,419
Emp.: 49,218
Fiscal Year-end: 03/31/2024

Holding Company
N.A.I.C.S.: 551112
Chuan Lye Tan (Chm-Food Solutions & Member-Mgmt Bd)

Subsidiary (Domestic):

Aerolog Express Pte Ltd. (3)
Level 5 Core M 30 Airline Road, PO Box 3, Unit 270 107 Airport Cargo Rd, Singapore, 918141, Singapore (70%)
Tel.: (65) 65456820
Web Site: http://www.aerologexpress.com
Emp.: 20
Cargo Delivery & Management Services; Owned 70% by Singapore Airport Terminal Services Ltd. & 30% by YCH Group Ltd.
N.A.I.C.S.: 488510
Ramanathan Rajesmani (Gen Mgr)

Country Foods Pte. Ltd. (3)
22 Senoko Way, Singapore, 758044, Singapore
Tel.: (65) 67534188
Web Site: http://www.sats.com.sg
Sales Range: $50-74.9 Million
Emp.: 250
Chilled & Frozen Food Products Mfr & Distr
N.A.I.C.S.: 311411

SATS Airport Services Pte.Ltd. (3)
30 Airline Road Singapore Changi Airport, Singapore, 819830, Singapore
Tel.: (65) 65450532
Airport Cargo Handling Services
N.A.I.C.S.: 488119

Joint Venture (Non-US):

SATS HK Limited (3)
Room 6T028 Passenger Terminal Building Hong Kong International Airport, Hong Kong, Lantau, China (Hong Kong) (49%)
Tel.: (852) 21168787
Web Site: http://www.sats.com.sg
Sales Range: $200-249.9 Million
Emp.: 800
Passenger & Ramp Handling Services Including Baggage Handling, Load Control & Flight Operations
N.A.I.C.S.: 488119
Joanne Cheung (Sr Mgr-Mktg)

Subsidiary (Domestic):

Sats Aero Laundry Pte. Ltd. (3)
16 Loyang Crescent, Singapore, 509011, Singapore
Tel.: (65) 82608783
Web Site: http://www.sats.com.sg
Emp.: 130
Laundry Services
N.A.I.C.S.: 812320

Singapore Food Industries Ltd. (3)
234 Pandan Loop, Singapore, 128422, Singapore
Tel.: (65) 67784466
Web Site: http://www.sfi.com.sg
Sales Range: $350-399.9 Million
Emp.: 2,000
Food Distribution, Preparation, Mfr, Processing & Hog Auction
N.A.I.C.S.: 311999

Subsidiary (Non-US):

Cresset Limited (4)
Little Island Industrial Estate, Cork, Ireland (100%)
Tel.: (353) 214354288
Holding Company
N.A.I.C.S.: 551112

Subsidiary (Domestic):

Primary Industries Pte. Ltd. (4)
2 Buroh Ln, Singapore, 618492, Singapore
Tel.: (65) 62670600
Web Site: http://www.sfi.com.sg
Sales Range: $25-49.9 Million
Emp.: 120
Food Processing
N.A.I.C.S.: 311999
Tan Peng Chiok (VP-HR)

Subsidiary (Non-US):

Primary Industries (Qld) Pty. Ltd. (5)
Canoona Rd, Rockhampton, 4700, QLD, Australia (100%)

INTERNATIONAL PUBLIC

Tel.: (61) 749228022
Sales Range: $100-124.9 Million
Emp.: 27
Logistics Solutions & Investments
N.A.I.C.S.: 523999

Subsidiary (Domestic):

SFI Food Pte. Ltd. (4)
2 Buroh Ln, 618492, Singapore, Singapore (100%)
Tel.: (65) 67739348
Web Site: http://www.sfi.com.sg
Food Logistics & Catering Supplier
N.A.I.C.S.: 722320

Subsidiary (Non-US):

Shanghai ST Food Industries Co., Ltd. (4)
3199 Jin Sha Jiang Rd, Jia Ding District, Shanghai, China (100%)
Tel.: (86) 39101337
Web Site: http://www.sstfi.com
Frozen Specialty Food Mfr
N.A.I.C.S.: 311412

Swissco Manufacturing Limited (4)
Little Island Industrial Estate, Cork, Ireland (100%)
Tel.: (353) 214354288
Prepared Frozen Food Distr
N.A.I.C.S.: 424420

Urangan Fisheries Pty. Ltd. (4)
Lot 1 Boat Harbour Dr, PO Box 7146, Hervey Bay, 4655, QLD, Australia (51%)
Tel.: (61) 741251077
Web Site: http://www.uranganfisheries.com.au
Sales Range: $25-49.9 Million
Emp.: 100
Fish & Seafood Whslr
N.A.I.C.S.: 424460
Paul Hodson (Mgr-Sls)

Subsidiary (Domestic):

Schulz Fisheries Pty. Ltd. (5)
Lot 1 Boat Harbour Dr, PO Box 7146, 4655, Hervey Bay, QLD, Australia (50%)
Tel.: (61) 741251077
Web Site: http://www.uranganfisheries.com.au
Fish Processing & Exporting
N.A.I.C.S.: 424460

Subsidiary (Non-US):

TFK Corp. (3)
Narita International Airport, 141 Furugome, Narita, 282-0011, Chiba, Japan (50.7%)
Tel.: (81) 476 21 1234
Web Site: http://www.tfk.co.jp
Sales Range: $250-299.9 Million
Emp.: 1,000
Catering Services
N.A.I.C.S.: 722320
Tsutomo Nomaguchi (Pres)

Subsidiary (Domestic):

Narita Dry Ice Co., Ltd. (4)
67-4 Osato Shibayamamachi, Sambu-Gun, Chiba, 289-1603, Japan
Tel.: (81) 479780391
Sales Range: $1-9.9 Million
Emp.: 23
Industrial Gas Mfr
N.A.I.C.S.: 325120
Tsutomu Nomaguchi (Pres)

Subsidiary (US):

Worldwide Flight Services, Inc. (3)
Rm 361 B151 Hangar Rd Cargo Area A JFK International Airport, Jamaica, NY 11430
Tel.: (718) 244-0900
Web Site: http://www.wfs.aero
Air Cargo & Technical & Ground Handling Services
N.A.I.C.S.: 488119
Michael A. Duffy (Exec VP-Innovation)

Subsidiary (Domestic):

Consolidated Aviation Services LLC (4)
Cargo Building 151 JFK International Airport Cargo Bldg 261, Jamaica, NY 11430

AND PRIVATE COMPANIES

Tel.: (718) 244-0900
Web Site: http://www.casusa.com
Cargo Handling Solutions & Security Screenings
N.A.I.C.S.: 481112
Michael Duffy (CEO)

Subsidiary (Domestic):

SIA Engineering Company Limited (2)
31 Airline Road, Singapore, 819831, Singapore (85.37%)
Tel.: (65) 65415152
Web Site: https://www.siaec.com.sg
Rev.: $590,211,755
Assets: $1,470,674,787
Liabilities: $227,373,560
Net Worth: $1,243,301,227
Earnings: $49,343,118
Emp.: 5,515
Fiscal Year-end: 03/31/2023
Aircraft Maintenance, Repair & Overhaul Services
N.A.I.C.S.: 336411
Chin Hwee Ng (CEO)

Subsidiary (Domestic):

Aerospace Component Engineering Services Pte. Limited (3)
45 Changi North Crescent, Singapore, 499622, Singapore
Tel.: (65) 65461885
Aerospace Hydro Component Mfr
N.A.I.C.S.: 336411
Brian Hunter (Gen Mgr)

Heavy Maintenance Singapore Services Pte. Ltd. (3)
39 Airline Road, Singapore, 819838, Singapore (100%)
Tel.: (65) 65481144
Aviation Support Services
N.A.I.C.S.: 488119
Peter Lundberg (Chief Comml Officer)

JAMCO Aero Design & Engineering Pte Ltd. (3)
Viva Business Park Block 750 04-05 Chai Chee Road, Singapore, 469000, Singapore (55%)
Tel.: (65) 65425212
Web Site: http://www.jamco-jade.com
Aircraft Engineering Services
N.A.I.C.S.: 488190
Seng Weng Gan (Mgr-Engrg)

Subsidiary (Non-US):

SIA Engineering (Philippines) Corporation (3)
Bldg N7691 A Bonifacio Avenue Civil Aviation Complex, Clark Freeport Zone Clarkfield, Mabalacat, 2023, Pampanga, Philippines (100%)
Tel.: (63) 454998862
Web Site: http://www.siaep.com
Aviation Support Services
N.A.I.C.S.: 488119
Ang Song Chiang (Gen Mgr)

Subsidiary (US):

SIA Engineering (USA), Inc. (3)
7001 W Imperial Hwy, Los Angeles, CA 90045
Tel.: (310) 665-9015
Aviation Support Services
N.A.I.C.S.: 488119
Chandra Nair (Gen Mgr)

Subsidiary (Non-US):

SIA Engineering Japan Corporation (3)
2F South Airline Building 1 Senshu-Kuko Naka, Tajiri-cho Sennan-gun, Osaka, 549-0011, Japan
Tel.: (81) 724566282
Aviation Support Services
N.A.I.C.S.: 488119
Poon Keng Hua (Gen Mgr)

Subsidiary (Domestic):

Singapore Aero Support Services Pte. Ltd. (3)
9 Loyang Way Krislite Building 04-01, Singapore, 508722, Singapore
Tel.: (65) 67186550
Web Site: http://www.singaporeaerosupport.com
Aviation Support Services
N.A.I.C.S.: 488119
Krystine Ow (Fin Mgr)

Subsidiary (Domestic):

SilkAir (Singapore) Pte. Ltd. (2)
05-F Airline House, 25 Airline Road, Singapore, 819829, Singapore (100%)
Tel.: (65) 428111
Web Site: http://www.silkair.com
Sales Range: $100-124.9 Million
Emp.: 463
Regional International Asian Airline Services
N.A.I.C.S.: 481111
Chai Woo Foo (CEO)

Representative Office (US):

Singapore Airlines Ltd. - US Representative Office (2)
222 N Pacific Coast Hwy Ste 1600, El Segundo, CA 90245-5615
Tel.: (310) 647-1922
Web Site: http://www.singaporeair.com
Oil Transportation Services
N.A.I.C.S.: 481112

Subsidiary (Domestic):

Tradewinds Tours & Travel Pte Ltd. (2)
3 Tampines Central 1 #02-03 Abacus Plaza, Singapore, 529540, Singapore
Tel.: (65) 64388822
Web Site: http://www.tradewindstours.com
Tour Operator
N.A.I.C.S.: 561520

Singapore Power Ltd. (1)
2 Kallang Sector, Singapore, 349277, Singapore (100%)
Tel.: (65) 6916 8888
Web Site: http://www.spgroup.com.sg
Rev.: $3,051,516,150
Assets: $14,347,793,790
Liabilities: $6,628,500,090
Net Worth: $7,719,293,700
Earnings: $623,906,154
Emp.: 3,500
Fiscal Year-end: 03/31/2019
Electricity & Gas Distr
N.A.I.C.S.: 221122
Jimmy Khoo (CEO-Singapore District Cooling)

Subsidiary (Domestic):

SP Telecommunications Pte. Ltd. (2)
10 Pasir Panjang Road #03-01, Mapletree Business City, Singapore, 117438, Singapore
Tel.: (65) 6378 8282
Web Site: http://www.sptel.com
Telecommunications Network Infrastructure Construction & Maintenance Services
N.A.I.C.S.: 237130
Mui Hoon Poh (CEO)

Singapore Power International Pte. Ltd. (2)
111 Somerset Road No 04-01 Singapore Power Building, Singapore, 238164, Singapore (100%)
Tel.: (65) 6823 8171
Investment Holding Company
N.A.I.C.S.: 551112

Joint Venture (Non-US):

SGSP (Australia) Assets Pty. Ltd. (3)
Level 16 567 Collins Street, Melbourne, 3000, VIC, Australia (40%)
Tel.: (61) 3 9173 7000
Holding Company; Energy & Water Transportation Assets
N.A.I.C.S.: 551112
Paul Adams (Mng Dir-Jemena)

Subsidiary (Domestic):

Jemena Limited (4)
Level 16 567 Collins Street, Melbourne, 3000, VIC, Australia
Tel.: (61) 3 9173 7000
Web Site: http://www.jemena.com.au

TEMASEK HOLDINGS (PRIVATE) LIMITED

Energy Infrastructure Asset Management Services
N.A.I.C.S.: 523940
Shaun Reardon (Exec Gen Mgr-Strategy, Regulation & Markets)

Singapore Technologies Engineering Limited (1)
ST Engineering Hub 1 Ang Mo Kio Electronics Park Road 07-01, Singapore, 567710, Singapore (50.35%)
Tel.: (65) 67221818
Web Site: https://www.stengg.com
Rev: $6,695,148,574
Assets: $11,088,540,200
Liabilities: $9,122,735,087
Net Worth: $1,965,805,113
Earnings: $402,619,489
Emp.: 25,000
Fiscal Year-end: 12/31/2022
Engineering Services Specializing in Aerospace, Electronics, Land Defense Systems & Marine
N.A.I.C.S.: 541330
Chong Seng Kwa (Chm)

Subsidiary (Domestic):

SDDA Pte. Ltd. (2)
16 Benoi Crescent, Singapore, 629979, Singapore (100%)
Tel.: (65) 62655222
Web Site: http://www.sdda.com
Sales Range: $10-24.9 Million
Emp.: 50
Sales & After-Sales for Heavy Duty Engines & Allison Transmissions
N.A.I.C.S.: 811114
Kok Wah Huan (VP & Gen Mgr)

ST Aerospace Engineering Pte Ltd. (2)
540 Airport Rd, Paya Lebar, 539938, Singapore
Tel.: (65) 62871111
Web Site: http://www.staero.aero
Sales Range: $75-99.9 Million
Emp.: 300
Aeronautical Technology
N.A.I.C.S.: 334511
Lim Serh Ghee (CEO)

Subsidiary (Non-US):

ST PAE Holdings Pty Ltd. (3)
Raaf Base Pearce, PO Box 213, Bullsbrook, Perth, 6084, WA, Australia
Tel.: (61) 895716170
Aeronautical Technology
N.A.I.C.S.: 334511

Subsidiary (Domestic):

ST Aerospace Engines Pte Ltd. (2)
501 Airport Rd, Paya Lebar, 539931, Singapore
Tel.: (65) 62851111
Web Site: http://www.staengines.com
Sales Range: $75-99.9 Million
Emp.: 500
Aeronautical Technology
N.A.I.C.S.: 334511

Subsidiary (Non-US):

ST Aerospace Solutions (Europe) A/S (2)
Amager Strandvej 392, DK 2770, Kastrup, Denmark (100%)
Tel.: (45) 2322 4281
Web Site: http://www.staero.aero
Aircraft Component Repair
N.A.I.C.S.: 811210

Subsidiary (Non-US):

Airline Rotables Limited (3)
Building 6002 Taylors End, Stansted Airport, Stansted, CM24 1RL, Essex, United Kingdom
Tel.: (44) 1279681770
Web Site: http://www.airline-rotables.com
Aircraft Repair
N.A.I.C.S.: 811210
Andy Gui (Gen Mgr)

Subsidiary (Domestic):

ST Aerospace Supplies Pte Ltd. (2)
540 Airport Rd, Paya Lebar, 539938, Singapore

Tel.: (65) 63806282
Web Site: http://www.stengg.com
Sales Range: $75-99.9 Million
Emp.: 300
Aeronautical Technology
N.A.I.C.S.: 334511
Ambrose Willen (Gen Mgr)

ST Aerospace Systems Pte Ltd. (2)
505 A Airport Rd, Paya Lebar, 539934, Singapore
Tel.: (65) 62872222
Web Site: http://www.stengg.com
Sales Range: $75-99.9 Million
Emp.: 300
Aeronautical Technology
N.A.I.C.S.: 334511

ST Automotive Industrial Pte Ltd. (2)
51/53 Senoko Road, Singapore, 758133, Singapore
Tel.: (65) 67582222
Web Site: http://www.scauto.com.sg
Sales Range: $25-49.9 Million
Emp.: 100
Automotive Services
N.A.I.C.S.: 441330

ST Automotive Inspection Pte Ltd. (2)
2E Ayer Rajah Crescent, West, 139958, Singapore, Singapore
Tel.: (65) 64760988
Web Site: http://www.stengg.com
Sales Range: $25-49.9 Million
Emp.: 13
Automotive Services
N.A.I.C.S.: 811122

ST Automotive Inspection Pte. Ltd. (2)
302 Sin Ming Road, Singapore, 575627, Singapore
Tel.: (65) 64521398
Web Site: http://www.stengg.com
Sales Range: $25-49.9 Million
Emp.: 40
Automotive Accessories & Services
N.A.I.C.S.: 811122

STATS ChipPAC Pte. Ltd. (2)
10 Ang Mo Kio Street 65 04-08/09 Techpoint, Singapore, 569059, Singapore
Tel.: (65) 68247777
Web Site: http://www.statschippac.com
Sales Range: $1-4.9 Billion
Semiconductor Packaging Assembly, Testing & Distr
N.A.I.C.S.: 334413
Hal Lasky (Chief Sls Officer & Exec VP)

Subsidiary (US):

STATS ChipPAC Inc. (3)
46429 Landing Pkwy, Fremont, CA 94538
Tel.: (510) 979-8000
Web Site: http://www.statschippac.com
Semiconductor & Related Device Mfr
N.A.I.C.S.: 334413

Subsidiary (Non-US):

STATS ChipPAC Korea Ltd. (3)
180-63 Duckee-ro, Majang-myeon, Incheon, 17385, Korea (South)
Tel.: (82) 31 639 1700
Web Site: http://www.statschippac.com
Semiconductor Packaging Assembly, Testing & Distr
N.A.I.C.S.: 334413

STATS ChipPAC Shanghai Co., Ltd (3)
188 Hua Xu Road Xujin County, Qingpu District, Shanghai, 201702, China
Tel.: (86) 2159765858
Web Site: http://www.statschippac.com
Semiconductor Packing & Testing Services
N.A.I.C.S.: 541380

Subsidiary (Non-US):

Singapore Aerospace Kabushiki Kaisha (2)
Level 21 Shiodome Shibarikyu Building, 1-2-3 Kaigan Minato-ku, Tokyo, 105-0022, Japan
Tel.: (81) 354036430
Aeronautical Technology
N.A.I.C.S.: 927110

TEMASEK HOLDINGS (PRIVATE) LIMITED

Temasek Holdings (Private) Limited—(Continued)
Tsuneo Furukawa *(Dir-Representation)*

Subsidiary (Domestic):

Singapore Technologies Aerospace Ltd. (2)
540 Airport Rd, Paya Lebar, 539938, Singapore
Tel.: (65) 62871111
Web Site: http://www.staero.aero
Sales Range: $75-99.9 Million
Emp.: 3,000
Aeronautical Technology
N.A.I.C.S.: 334511
Serh Ghee Lim *(Pres)*

Subsidiary (Non-US):

Elbe-Flugzeugwerke GmbH (3)
Grenstrasse 1, 01109, Dresden, Germany (55%)
Tel.: (49) 35188390
Web Site: http://www.elbeflugzeugwerke.com
Aircraft Part Mfr
N.A.I.C.S.: 336413
Andreas Sperl *(Pres & CEO)*

Subsidiary (Domestic):

ST Aviation Services Co. Pte Ltd. (3)
8 Changi North Way, Singapore, 499611, Singapore
Tel.: (65) 65405608
Web Site: http://www.staero.aero
Aircraft Maintenance & Repair Services
N.A.I.C.S.: 488190

Subsidiary (Domestic):

Singapore Technologies Electronics Limited (2)
24 Ang Mo Kio Street 65, Singapore, 569061, Singapore
Tel.: (65) 6481 8888
Web Site: http://www.stee.stengg.com
Holding Company; Information Communications Technologies Mfr
N.A.I.C.S.: 551112
Kok Leng Soo *(Chm)*

Subsidiary (Domestic):

ST Electronics (Info-Comm Systems) Pte. Ltd. (3)
100 Jurong E St 21, Singapore, 609602, Singapore (100%)
Tel.: (65) 65676769
Sales Range: $100-124.9 Million
Emp.: 600
Electronic Parts & Information Systems Equipment Mfr
N.A.I.C.S.: 334419
Andrew Chow *(Pres)*

ST Electronics (Info-Software Systems) Pte. Ltd. (3)
24 Ang Mo Kio St 65, 5th Fl New Bldg, Singapore, 569061, Singapore (100%)
Tel.: (65) 64818888
Sales Range: $100-124.9 Million
Emp.: 500
N.A.I.C.S.: 449210

ST Electronics (Training & Simulation Systems) Pte. Ltd. (3)
24 Ang Mo Kio Street 65 4th Fl Block D, Singapore, 569061, Singapore (100%)
Tel.: (65) 6413 1307
Web Site: http://www.stee.stengg.com
Simulation Systems Designer & Training Applications
N.A.I.C.S.: 541512

Subsidiary (Non-US):

Singapore Technologies Engineering (Europe) Ltd. (2)
Marquis House 68 Jermyn St, London, SW1Y 6NY, United Kingdom
Tel.: (44) 2079308989
Web Site: http://www.stengg.com
Emp.: 50
Aeronautical Technology
N.A.I.C.S.: 927110
Tan Pheng Hock *(Pres & CEO)*

Singapore Technologies Engineering (Middle East) Ltd. (2)
Office M10 Emirates Islamic Bank Building Mezzanine Floor Al Qusa, PO Box 231789, Dubai, United Arab Emirates
Tel.: (971) 42618999
Web Site: http://www.stengg.com
Aeronautical Technology
N.A.I.C.S.: 927110

Subsidiary (Domestic):

Singapore Technologies Kinetics Ltd. (2)
5 Portsdown Rd, Singapore, 139296, Singapore
Tel.: (65) 64736311
Web Site: http://www.stengg.com
N.A.I.C.S.: 441330
Ravinder Singh *(Pres)*

Subsidiary (Non-US):

Kinetics Drive Solutions Inc. (3)
27489 - 56th Avenue, Langley, V4W 3X1, BC, Canada
Tel.: (604) 607-8877
Web Site: http://www.kineticsdrive.com
Emp.: 75
Power Transmission Equipment Mfr
N.A.I.C.S.: 333613
Gordon Osborn *(Dir-Mktg)*

Subsidiary (Domestic):

Singapore Technologies Marine Ltd. (2)
7 Benoi Road, Singapore, 629882, Singapore
Tel.: (65) 68612244
Web Site: http://www.stengg.com
Sales Range: $150-199.9 Million
Emp.: 1,000
Paper & Wood Pulp Whslr
N.A.I.C.S.: 424110
Sing Chan Ng *(Pres)*

Subsidiary (Domestic):

STSE Technologies Marine Ltd (3)
7 Benoi Rd, Singapore, 629882, Singapore
Tel.: (65) 68612244
Web Site: http://www.stengg.com
Marine Engineering Services
N.A.I.C.S.: 541330

Subsidiary (US):

Vision Technologies Systems, Inc. (2)
99 Canal Ctr Plz Ste 220, Alexandria, VA 22314
Tel.: (703) 739-2610
Web Site: http://www.stengg.us
Technology, Defense & Engineering Services
N.A.I.C.S.: 541330
Tom Vecchiolla *(Chm & CEO)*

Subsidiary (Domestic):

Aethon Inc. (3)
200 Business Ctr Dr, Pittsburgh, PA 15205
Tel.: (412) 322-2975
Web Site: http://www.aethon.com
Robotic Hospital Delivery System Distr
N.A.I.C.S.: 423450
Robert Reilly *(CFO)*

DRB Aviation Consultants Inc. (3)
27326 US Hwy 281 N, San Antonio, TX 78260
Tel.: (210) 888-9430
Web Site: http://www.drbaviation.aero
Sales Range: $25-49.9 Million
Emp.: 35
Aircraft Interior Design Services
N.A.I.C.S.: 336413
Don Bell *(Pres)*

Hackney USA (3)
911 W 5th St, Washington, NC 27889-4726
Tel.: (252) 946-6521
Web Site: http://www.hackneyusa.com
Sales Range: $75-99.9 Million
Emp.: 520
Specialty Truck Bodies & Trailers Mfr
N.A.I.C.S.: 336211

Division (Domestic):

Hackney (4)
400 Hackney Ave, Washington, NC 27889
Tel.: (252) 946-6521
Web Site: http://www.hackneyusa.com
Side-Loader, Overhead Door Truck Bodies Mfr
N.A.I.C.S.: 336211

Division (Domestic):

Hackney International (5)
400 Hackney Ave, Washington, NC 27889-4726
Tel.: (252) 946-6521
Web Site: http://www.hackneyinternational.com
Sales Range: $200-249.9 Million
Emp.: 500
Truck Bodies & Trailers for the Beverage Industry Mfr, Emergency Services & Other Applications
N.A.I.C.S.: 336211
Leandro Rodriguez *(Dir-InterNatl Sls)*

Division (Domestic):

Kidron, Inc. (4)
13442 Emerson Rd, Kidron, OH 44636
Tel.: (800) 321-5421
Web Site: http://www.kidron.com
Sales Range: $75-99.9 Million
Emp.: 500
Refrigerated Truck Bodies & Trailers, Refrigeration Systems & Ice Cream & Food Vending Carts Mfr
N.A.I.C.S.: 493120
David Parker *(District Mgr-Sls)*

Subsidiary (Domestic):

MAK Technologies Inc. (3)
150 Cambridge Park Dr 3rd Fl, Cambridge, MA 02140
Tel.: (617) 876-8085
Web Site: http://www.mak.com
Emp.: 56
Simulation Software Developer
N.A.I.C.S.: 513210
Kathy Pratt *(CFO)*

MRA Systems Inc. (3)
103 Chesapeake Park Plz, Baltimore, MD 21220
Tel.: (410) 682-1500
Web Site: http://www.mras-usa.com
Designer & Mfr of Aircraft Aerostructures & Nacelle Systems
N.A.I.C.S.: 336413
King Thompson *(Mgr-Sr Sls & Customer Support-Maintenance, Repair & Overhaul)*

Miltope Group, Inc. (3)
3800 Richardson Rd S, Hope Hull, AL 36043
Tel.: (334) 284-8665
Web Site: http://www.miltope.com
Sales Range: $25-49.9 Million
Emp.: 200
Microcomputers & Computer Peripheral Equipment, Work Stations, Handheld, Portable & Laptop Computers, Printers, Mass Storage Devices, Terminals & Disk Drives Designer & Mfr
N.A.I.C.S.: 334112
Ed Crowell *(VP-Admin)*

Subsidiary (Domestic):

VT Kinetics, Inc. (4)
3800 Richardson Rd S, Hope Hull, AL 36043-4022 (100%)
Tel.: (334) 284-8665
Web Site: http://www.stengg.com
Computer & Network Peripherals
N.A.I.C.S.: 541519

Subsidiary (Domestic):

ST Aerospace Mobile, Inc. (3)
2100 9th St Brookley Complex, Mobile, AL 36615-1229
Tel.: (251) 438-8888
Web Site: http://www.stmae.com
Sales Range: $500-549.9 Million
Emp.: 1,300
Aircraft Maintenance & Modification Services
N.A.I.C.S.: 488190

INTERNATIONAL PUBLIC

Joseph Ng *(Pres)*

VT LeeBoy (3)
500 Lincoln County Pkwy Ext, Lincolnton, NC 28092
Tel.: (704) 966-3300
Web Site: http://www.leeboy.com
Sales Range: $50-74.9 Million
Emp.: 250
Construction Equipment Mfr
N.A.I.C.S.: 333120
Rob Grail *(VP-Ops)*

VT iDirect, Inc. (3)
13865 Sunrise Vly Dr, Herndon, VA 20171
Tel.: (703) 648-8000
Web Site: http://www.idirect.net
Sales Range: $450-499.9 Million
Emp.: 600
IP-Based Satellite Communications Solutions
N.A.I.C.S.: 334220
David Bettinger *(CTO & Sr VP-Engrg)*

Subsidiary (Domestic):

iDirect Government, LLC (4)
13921 Park Ctr Rd Ste 600, Herndon, VA 20171-4661
Tel.: (703) 648-8118
Web Site: https://www.idirectgov.com
Wireless Communication Equipment Mfr
N.A.I.C.S.: 334220
Tim Winter *(Pres)*

Subsidiary (Domestic):

Volant Aerospace, LLC (3)
11817 Westar Ln, Burlington, WA 98233
Tel.: (360) 757-2376
Web Site: http://www.volant.aero
Sales Range: $25-49.9 Million
Emp.: 60
Aircraft Interior Equipment Mfr
N.A.I.C.S.: 336413
Misty Barnett *(Dir-Ops)*

Subsidiary (Domestic):

Visiontech Engineering Pte., Ltd. (2)
540 Airport Rd, Paya Lebar, Singapore, 539938, Singapore
Tel.: (65) 62871111
Web Site: http://www.stengg.com
Sales Range: $25-49.9 Million
Emp.: 25
Medical Engineering
N.A.I.C.S.: 541330
Tan Jiak Kwang *(Gen Mgr)*

Singapore Technologies Telemedia Pte. Ltd. (1)
1 Temasek Avenue 33-01 Millenia Tower, StarHub Ctr, Singapore, 229469, Singapore
Tel.: (65) 67238777
Web Site: http://www.sttelemedia.com
Information Communications & Entertainment Services
N.A.I.C.S.: 517112
Theng Kiat Lee *(Pres & CEO)*

Singapore Telecommunications Limited (1)
31 Exeter Road Comcentre 19-00, Singapore, 239732, Singapore (52.5%)
Tel.: (65) 68383388
Web Site: https://www.singtel.com
Rev.: $10,843,992,600
Assets: $34,501,995,000
Liabilities: $15,212,391,550
Net Worth: $19,289,603,450
Earnings: $1,656,140,250
Emp.: 24,070
Fiscal Year-end: 03/31/2023
Telecommunication Servicesb
N.A.I.C.S.: 517111
Simon Claude Israel *(Chm)*

Subsidiary (Non-US):

Amobee EMEA Limited (2)
Noah's Yard 10 York Way, London, N1 9AA, United Kingdom
Tel.: (44) 2036088700
Internet Advertising Services
N.A.I.C.S.: 541810

Amobee Ltd (2)
125 Menachem Begin Rd 36th Floor, Tel Aviv, 6701201, Israel
Tel.: (972) 74733346

AND PRIVATE COMPANIES

Internet Advertising Services
N.A.I.C.S.: 541810

Ensyst Pty Limited (2)
111 Elizabeth Street, Sydney, 2000, NSW, Australia
Tel.: (61) 282367600
Web Site: http://www.ensyst.com.au
Computer System Design Services
N.A.I.C.S.: 541512

Hivint Pty Limited (2)
Level 4 405 Collins St, Melbourne, 3000, VIC, Australia
Tel.: (61) 1300733940
Web Site: http://hivint.com
Security System Services
N.A.I.C.S.: 561621
Craig Searle (Co-Founder)

Lanka Communication Services (Pvt) Limited (2)
65 C Dharmapala Mawatha, Colombo, Sri Lanka
Tel.: (94) 112437545
Web Site: http://www.lankacom.net
Telecommunication Servicesb
N.A.I.C.S.: 517810

NCS Information Technology (Suzhou) Co., Ltd. (2)
8F and 9F B11 Phase V 328 Xinghu Street, Suzhou International Science Park Suzhou Industrial Park, Suzhou, 215021, Jiangsu, China
Tel.: (86) 51262886969
Telecommunication Servicesb
N.A.I.C.S.: 517810

Subsidiary (Domestic):

NCS Pte. Ltd. (2)
5 Ang Mo Kio St 62 NCS Hub, Singapore, 569141, Singapore
Tel.: (65) 65568000
Web Site: http://www.ncs.com.sg
Sales Range: $800-899.9 Million
Emp.: 7,000
IT & Communications Engineering Solutions
N.A.I.C.S.: 517111
Chia Wee Boon (CEO)

Subsidiary (Non-US):

Kompakar Inc Bhd. (3)
12 Jalan Bersatu 13 4, 46200, Petaling Jaya, Malaysia
Tel.: (60) 379565800
Web Site: http://www.kompakar.com.my
Sales Range: $100-124.9 Million
Emp.: 300
Supplier of Computer-Aided Engineering (CAE) Software & Comprehensive Finite Element Analysis (FEA) Program
N.A.I.C.S.: 334610

Subsidiary (Domestic):

NCS Communications Engineering Pte. Ltd. (3)
5 Ang Mo Kio Street 62 NCS Hub, Singapore, 569141, Singapore
Tel.: (65) 65568000
Web Site: http://www.ncs.com.sg
Communications Engineering Services
N.A.I.C.S.: 541330

Co-Headquarters (Domestic):

NCS Pte. Ltd - Bedok (3)
7 Bedok South Road, Singapore, 469272, Singapore
Tel.: (65) 68278888
Web Site: http://www.ncs.com.sg
Sales Range: $25-49.9 Million
Emp.: 14
Provider of Information & Communications Technology
N.A.I.C.S.: 541512

Subsidiary (Non-US):

PT SCS Astragraphia Technologies (3)
22nd Fl Wisma Standard Chartered Bank, Jl Jend Sudirman Kav 33A, 10220, Jakarta, Indonesia (51%)
Tel.: (62) 215721177
Web Site: http://www.ag-it.com
Computer System Design Services

N.A.I.C.S.: 541512

SCS Information Technology Sdn. Bhd. (3)
Lot 1 Little Soho Batu Bersurat, BE3719, Bandar Seri Begawan, Negara, Brunei Darussalam (100%)
Tel.: (673) 2237615
Emp.: 7
Computer Related Services
N.A.I.C.S.: 541519

Subsidiary (Non-US):

NCSI (Chengdu) Co., Ltd. (2)
4F Block B2 Tianfu Software Park, Tianfu Avenue High-Tech Zone, Chengdu, 610041, Sichuan, China
Tel.: (86) 2885030088
Telecommunication Servicesb
N.A.I.C.S.: 517810

NCSI (HK) Limited (2)
Units 701-2 7 / F Kerry Centre No 683 Kings Road, Quarry Bay, China (Hong Kong)
Tel.: (852) 22946000
Telecommunication Servicesb
N.A.I.C.S.: 517810

NCSI (Malaysia) Sdn. Bhd. (2)
602B Level 6 Tower B Uptown 5 Jalan SS21 / 39, Damansara Uptown, 47400, Petaling Jaya, Selangor, Malaysia
Tel.: (60) 377256878
Telecommunication Servicesb
N.A.I.C.S.: 517810

NCSI (Shanghai) Co. Ltd. (2)
10F Building 2 Ruili Innovation Center 51 Zhengxue Road, Yangpu District, Shanghai, 200433, China
Tel.: (86) 2161415511
Web Site: http://www.ncsi.com.cn
Telecommunication Servicesb
N.A.I.C.S.: 517810

Prepaid Services Pty Limited (2)
PO Box 888, North Ryde, 1670, NSW, Australia
Tel.: (61) 1300307979
Web Site: http://www.prepaidservices.com.au
Wireless Broadband Services
N.A.I.C.S.: 517112

Subsidiary (Domestic):

SingNet Pte. Ltd. (2)
20 Pickering St 04 00 Pickering Operations Complex, Singapore, 048658, Singapore (100%)
Tel.: (65) 68383899
Web Site: http://www.singnet.com.sg
Internet Services
N.A.I.C.S.: 517810

Subsidiary (Non-US):

SingTel Optus Pty. Ltd. (2)
1 Lyon Park Road Macquarie Park, 2113, Sydney, NSW, Australia
Tel.: (61) 392334000
Web Site: http://www.optus.com.au
Sales Range: $1-4.9 Billion
Emp.: 10,000
Holding Company; Telecommunications Services
N.A.I.C.S.: 551112
John Paitaridis (Mng Dir-Bus)

Subsidiary (Domestic):

Optus Mobile Pty. Ltd. (3)
1 Line Park Road Macquarie Park, Sydney, 2113, NSW, Australia
Tel.: (61) 293427800
Web Site: http://www.optus.com.au
Sales Range: $1-4.9 Billion
Emp.: 8,000
Mobile Telecommunications Services
N.A.I.C.S.: 517112
Ben White (Mng Dir-Mktg & Product-Consumer Bus)

Subsidiary (Domestic):

Vividwireless Pty. Limited (4)
Media City 8 Central Avenue, Eveleigh, Sydney, 2015, NSW, Australia (100%)
Tel.: (61) 292316055

Web Site: http://www.vividwireless.com.au
Wireless Broadband Services
N.A.I.C.S.: 517810
Ryan Kerry Stokes (Chm)

Subsidiary (Domestic):

SIMplus Mobile Pty Ltd (3)
1 Lyon Park Road Macquarie Park, North Ryde, 2113, NSW, Australia
Tel.: (61) 293427800
Web Site: http://www.simplus.com.au
Sales Range: $5-14.9 Billion
Emp.: 180
Mobile Telecommunications Services
N.A.I.C.S.: 517112
Paul Gerard O'Brien (Sec)

Uecomm Ltd (3)
Building 8 658 Church Street, Richmond, 3121, VIC, Australia
Tel.: (61) 392214100
Web Site: http://www.uecomm.com.au
Sales Range: $25-49.9 Million
Emp.: 150
Broadband Services
N.A.I.C.S.: 517112

Subsidiary (Domestic):

Singapore Telecom International Pte. Ltd. (2)
31 Exeter Rd, Comcentre, Singapore, 239732, Singapore
Tel.: (65) 68333388
Web Site: http://info.singtel.com
Holding Company
N.A.I.C.S.: 551112
Chuan Poh Lim (CEO)

Branch (Non-US):

SingTel Taiwan Limited (3)
2nd Fl 290 Chung Hsiao East Rd, Taipei, 106, Taiwan
Tel.: (886) 227411688
Web Site: http://www.singtel.com
Sales Range: $25-49.9 Million
Emp.: 17
Provider of Telecommunications
N.A.I.C.S.: 517111
Tim Chan (Gen Mgr)

SingTel Vietnam (3)
No 30 Nguyen Du Street Unit 502 Hanoi, Hanoi, Vietnam
Tel.: (84) 49432161
Web Site: http://www.singtel.com
Sales Range: $25-49.9 Million
Emp.: 3
Provider of Telecommunications
N.A.I.C.S.: 517111

Singapore Telecom (India-New Delhi) (3)
Express Towers 12th Fl 14 Stateman House, Mumbai, India
Tel.: (91) 2256545500
Sales Range: $25-49.9 Million
Emp.: 15
Provider of Telecommunications
N.A.I.C.S.: 517111

Singapore Telecom (Indonesia) (3)
Plz Lippo 15th Fl Ste 1505 Jalan Jenderal, Sudirman Kavling 25, Jakarta, 12920, Indonesia
Tel.: (62) 215267937
Web Site: http://www.singtel.com
Sales Range: $25-49.9 Million
Emp.: 5
Provider of Telecommunications
N.A.I.C.S.: 517111

Singapore Telecom (Korea) (3)
11th Fl Hansol Bldg, 736 1 Yeoksam Dong Kangnam Ku, Seoul, 135983, Korea (South)
Tel.: (82) 232877576
Web Site: http://www.singtel.co.kr
Sales Range: $25-49.9 Million
Emp.: 14
Provider of Telecommunications
N.A.I.C.S.: 517111

Singapore Telecom (Malaysia) (3)
602 B Level 6 Tower B Uptown 5 Jalan SS 21/39, Damansara Uptown, 47400, Petaling Jaya, Selangor Darul Ehsan, Malaysia
Tel.: (60) 377282813

TEMASEK HOLDINGS (PRIVATE) LIMITED

Web Site: http://www.singtel.com
Sales Range: $25-49.9 Million
Emp.: 80
Provider of Telecommunications
N.A.I.C.S.: 517111

Singapore Telecom (Philippines) (3)
Unit 1504 Liberty Center 104 H V de la Costa Street, Salcedo Village, Makati, 1227, Metro Manila, Philippines
Tel.: (63) 28872791
Web Site: http://www.singtel.com
Sales Range: Less than $1 Million
Emp.: 5
Provider of Telecommunications
N.A.I.C.S.: 517111
Garry Gonalis (Gen Mgr)

Singapore Telecom (Thailand) (3)
9th Fl Ste 6 500 Amarin Tower Ploenchit Rd, Lumpini Pathumwan, Bangkok, 10330, Thailand
Tel.: (66) 22569875
Web Site: http://www.singatel.com
Sales Range: $25-49.9 Million
Emp.: 5
Provider of Telecommunications
N.A.I.C.S.: 517111
Detanan Maneenam (Mgr-Sls)

Singapore Telecom China (3)
Unit 1503 Beijing Silver Tower 2 Dong San Huan Bie Road, Chaoyang District, Beijing, 100027, China
Tel.: (86) 1064106193
Web Site: http://info.singtel.com
Sales Range: $25-49.9 Million
Emp.: 10
Provider of Telecommunications
N.A.I.C.S.: 517111

Singapore Telecom China (3)
Unit 1108 Tower B Wanda Plaza, 36 Guobin Road, Shanghai, 200433, China
Tel.: (86) 2133620388
Web Site: http://www.home.singtel.com
Sales Range: $25-49.9 Million
Emp.: 13
Provider of Telecommunications
N.A.I.C.S.: 517111

Singapore Telecom Europe (3)
201 203 City Rd, London, EC1V 1JN, United Kingdom
Tel.: (44) 79888000
Sales Range: $25-49.9 Million
Emp.: 55
Provider of Telecommunications
N.A.I.C.S.: 517111

Singapore Telecom Hong Kong Limited (3)
120026 Tower 6 The Gateway 9 Canton Rd, Tsimshatsui, Kowloon, China (Hong Kong)
Tel.: (852) 28771500
Web Site: http://www.singtel.com
Sales Range: $25-49.9 Million
Emp.: 25
Provider of Telecommunications
N.A.I.C.S.: 517111
Jenny Fong (Mng Dir)

Singapore Telecom India (3)
Sahar Plz 111 Bonanza Wing B, Mathuradas Vasanji Rd Andheri, Mumbai, 400059, India
Tel.: (91) 2228244999
Web Site: http://www.singtel.com
Sales Range: $25-49.9 Million
Emp.: 10
Telecommunication Servicesb
N.A.I.C.S.: 517111

Singapore Telecom Japan (3)
Arco Tower 5F 1-8-1 Shimomeguro, Meguro-ku, Tokyo, 153 0064, Japan
Tel.: (81) 354377033
Web Site: http://www.singtel.com
Sales Range: $25-49.9 Million
Emp.: 30
Provider of Telecommunications
N.A.I.C.S.: 517111

Subsidiary (US):

Singapore Telecom USA, Inc. (3)
1 Landmark Sq Ste 300, Stamford, CT 06901
Tel.: (203) 323-9690

TEMASEK HOLDINGS (PRIVATE) LIMITED

Temasek Holdings (Private) Limited—Continued

Web Site: http://www.singtel.com
Provider of Telecommunications
N.A.I.C.S.: 541690

Division (Domestic):

Singtel Telecom USA, Inc. - Northwest & Southwest Region (4)
203 Redwood Shores Pkwy Ste 100, Redwood City, CA 94065
Tel.: (650) 558-3950
Web Site: http://www.singtel.com
Sales Range: $25-49.9 Million
Emp.: 25
Provider of Telecommunications
N.A.I.C.S.: 523150

Subsidiary (Domestic):

Singapore Telecom Mobile Pte. Ltd. (2)
31 Exeter Road, Comcentre 19-00, Singapore, 239732, Singapore
Tel.: (65) 68383388
N.A.I.C.S.: 517111

Singtel Innov8 Ventures Pte. Ltd. (2)
71 Ayer Rajah Crescent 02-22, Singapore, 139951, Singapore
Tel.: (65) 68384686
Web Site: http://innov8.singtel.com
Investment Banking Services
N.A.I.C.S.: 523150
Edgar Hardless (CEO)

Telecom Equipment Pte Ltd (2)
31 Exeter Road, Singapore, 239732, Singapore
Tel.: (65) 68383388
Web Site: http://www.singtel.com.sg
N.A.I.C.S.: 517111
Allen Lew (CEO-Singapore)

Subsidiary (Non-US):

Trustwave Canada, Inc. (2)
609 Kumpf Drive Suite 202, Waterloo, N2V 1K8, ON, Canada
Tel.: (519) 620-7227
Security System Services
N.A.I.C.S.: 561621

Trustwave Limited (2)
Westminster Tower, 3 Albert Embankment, London, SE1 7SP, United Kingdom
Tel.: (44) 8454569611
Security System Services
N.A.I.C.S.: 561621

Surbana Jurong Private Limited (1)
168 Jalan Bukit Merah 01-01 Connection One, Singapore, 150168, Singapore (51%)
Tel.: (65) 6248 1288
Web Site: http://www.surbanajurong.com
Emp.: 9,800
Urban & Infrastructure Development Consultancy Services
N.A.I.C.S.: 541690
Heang Fine Wong (CEO)

Subsidiary (Non-US):

SMEC Holdings Limited (2)
Level 10 71 Queens Road, Melbourne, 3004, VIC, Australia
Tel.: (61) 395141500
Web Site: http://www.smec.com
Holding Company; Urban & Infrastructure Development Consultancy Services
N.A.I.C.S.: 551112
Alastair McKendrick (CFO)

TH Inversiones Mexico, S.A. de C.V. (1)
Ruben Dario 281-1303 Bosque de Chapultepec, Mexico, 11580, Mexico
Tel.: (52) 55 4335 3050
Investment Banking Services
N.A.I.C.S.: 523150

TeleChoice International Limited (1)
6 Serangoon North Avenue 5 0316, Singapore, 554910, Singapore
Tel.: (65) 68263600
Web Site: https://telechoice.listedcompany.com
Rev.: $180,329,470

Assets: $95,975,915
Liabilities: $72,220,707
Net Worth: $23,755,207
Earnings: ($8,712,414)
Emp.: 296
Fiscal Year-end: 12/31/2023
Mobile Phone Accessories Distr
N.A.I.C.S.: 334220
Song Puay Goh (VP-HR)

Temasek Brasil Consultoria E Participacoes Ltda. (1)
Rua Iguatemi 151 / 18 andar, 01451-011, Sao Paulo, Itaim Bibi, Brazil
Tel.: (55) 11 3636 7575
Investment Management Service
N.A.I.C.S.: 523940

Temasek Holdings (HK) Limited (1)
TThree Pacific Place Level 3 1 Queen's Road East Room 31, Central, China (Hong Kong)
Tel.: (852) 2588 3507
Holding Company
N.A.I.C.S.: 551112

Temasek Holdings Advisors (Beijing) Co., Ltd (1)
F707/F705 Winland International Finance Center No 7 Financial Street, Xicheng District, Beijing, 100033, China
Tel.: (86) 10 5930 4900
Holding Company
N.A.I.C.S.: 551112

Temasek Holdings Advisors India Pvt. Ltd (1)
12 3 North Avenue Maker Maxity Bandra Kurla Complex, Bandra, Mumbai, 400 051, India
Tel.: (91) 22 6654 5500
Emp.: 20
Holding Company
N.A.I.C.S.: 551112
Khushnam Polishwala (Sec)

Temasek Holdings Consulting (Shanghai) Company Limited (1)
Unit 2201 Tower 1 Plaza 66 1266 Nan Jing Xi Road, Shanghai, 200040, China
Tel.: (86) 21 6133 1900
Holding Company
N.A.I.C.S.: 551112

Temasek International (Europe) Limited (1)
23 King Street, London, SW1Y 6QY, United Kingdom
Tel.: (44) 20 7747 5040
Investment Management Service
N.A.I.C.S.: 523940
Lee Theng Kiat (CEO)

Temasek International (USA) LLC (1)
375 Park Ave 14th Fl, New York, NY 10152
Tel.: (212) 593-8880
Web Site: http://www.temasek.com.sg
Investment Management Service
N.A.I.C.S.: 523940
Martin Fichtner (Mng Dir-TMT)

Temasek Life Sciences Laboratory Limited (1)
1 Research Link National University of Singapore, Singapore, 117604, Singapore
Tel.: (65) 6872 7000
Web Site: http://www.tll.org.sg
Biotechnology Research & Development Services
N.A.I.C.S.: 541714
Teo Ming Kian (Chm)

TEMBO GLOBAL INDUSTRIES LTD.
Plot No PAP D 146/ 147 TTC MIDC, Turbhe Sanpada Road Opp Balmer Lawrie Van Leer Co Turbhe, Navi Mumbai, 400 705, Maharashtra, India
Tel.: (91) 2562239080
Web Site: https://www.tembo.in
Year Founded: 2010
TEMBO—(NSE)
Rev.: $21,330,388
Assets: $10,976,009
Liabilities: $7,973,910
Net Worth: $3,002,098

Earnings: $378,083
Fiscal Year-end: 03/31/22
Steel Products Mfr
N.A.I.C.S.: 331513
Sanjay J. Patel (Mng Dir)

TEMBO GOLD CORP.
Suite 1305 1090 West Georgia Street, Vancouver, V6E 3V7, BC, Canada
Tel.: (604) 685-9316
Web Site: https://www.tembogold.com
Year Founded: 1937
TEM—(OTCIQ)
Assets: $4,815,484
Liabilities: $2,231,461
Net Worth: $2,584,023
Earnings: ($396,332)
Fiscal Year-end: 12/31/19
Gold Exploration Services
N.A.I.C.S.: 212220
David Scott (Pres & CEO)

Subsidiaries:

Tembo Gold (T) Ltd. (1)

TEMBR-BANK JSC
10 Per 1-I Volkonski, Moscow, 127473, Russia
Tel.: (7) 4953634499
Web Site: http://www.tembr.ru
Year Founded: 1994
Sales Range: Less than $1 Million
Commercial Banking Services
N.A.I.C.S.: 522110
Elena Dmitrievna Suchilina (Chm-Mgmt Bd)

TEMC CO., LTD.
3750148 Namburo Samseungmyeon, 28923, Boeun, 28923, Chungbuk, Korea (South)
Tel.: (82) 432983333
Web Site: https://www.temc.co.kr
Year Founded: 2015
425040—(KRS)
Industrial Gas Mfr
N.A.I.C.S.: 325120

TEMENOS AG
Esplanade de Pont-Rouge 9C Grand-Lancy, 1212, Geneva, Switzerland
Tel.: (41) 227081150
Web Site: https://www.temenos.com
Year Founded: 1993
TEMN—(SWX)
Rev.: $1,000,224,000
Assets: $2,326,841,000
Liabilities: $1,644,861,000
Net Worth: $681,980,000
Earnings: $134,677,000
Emp.: 6,558
Fiscal Year-end: 12/31/23
Software Publisher
N.A.I.C.S.: 513210
Andreas Andreades (Chm)

Subsidiaries:

ACTIS BSP Germany GmbH (1)
Einsteinstrasse 2, Grosswallstadt, 63868, Bavaria, Germany
Tel.: (49) 69665370
Web Site: http://www.actisbsp.com
Sales Range: $25-49.9 Million
Emp.: 50
Banking Software Development Services
N.A.I.C.S.: 541511

Avoka Technologies Pty Limited (1)
Level 2 1a Rialto Lane, Manly, 2095, NSW, Australia
Tel.: (61) 299764500
Software Development Services
N.A.I.C.S.: 541511

Fairs Limited (1)
Bede House All Saints Business Centre, Newcastle upon Tyne, NE1 2ES, Tyne &

INTERNATIONAL PUBLIC

Wear, United Kingdom
Tel.: (44) 1912452000
Web Site: http://www.temenos.com
Sales Range: $25-49.9 Million
Emp.: 8
Banking Software Development Services
N.A.I.C.S.: 541511

Genisys Technology Limited (1)
Office Suite 16 Enterprise House Kingsway, Team Valley, Gateshead, NE11 0SR, Tyne & Wear, United Kingdom
Tel.: (44) 1912452000
Web Site: https://www.genisystech.co.uk
Emp.: 9
Document Management Software Development & Sales
N.A.I.C.S.: 541511

Igefi Ireland Limited (1)
Level 1 No 2 Custom House Plaza Harbourmaster Place, Dublin, 1, Ireland
Tel.: (353) 15187400
Software Development Services
N.A.I.C.S.: 541511

Kony India Private Limited (1)
SEZ Unit II Level 7 Building No H06 Hitech City 2, Phoenix Infocity Pvt Ltd SEZ Madhapur, Hyderabad, 500 081, India
Tel.: (91) 4044991000
Software Development Services
N.A.I.C.S.: 541511

Kony, Inc. (1)
9225 Bee Cave Rd Bldg A Ste 300, Austin, TX 78733
Tel.: (512) 792-2900
Web Site: https://www.kony.com
Software Development Services
N.A.I.C.S.: 541511

Odyssey Financial Technologies S.A. (1)
Avenue des Baumettes 23, CH-1020, Renens, Switzerland
Tel.: (41) 213100000
Web Site: http://www.odyssey-group.com
Sales Range: $75-99.9 Million
Emp.: 600
Financial Software Developer
N.A.I.C.S.: 513210
Ben Robinson (VP-Mktg & Product Mgmt)

Rubik Financial Technology Pty Ltd (1)
Lvl 21 321 Kent St, Macquarie Park, Sydney, 2000, NSW, Australia
Tel.: (61) 294884000
Sales Range: $25-49.9 Million
Emp.: 53
Automated Data Processing Equipment Mfr
N.A.I.C.S.: 518210

TEMENOS (Thailand) Co. Limited (1)
319 Chamchuri Square Building 24th Floor Unit no 85 Phayathai Road, Pathumwan, Bangkok, 10330, Thailand
Tel.: (66) 200721312
Sales Range: $25-49.9 Million
Emp.: 40
Software Support Services
N.A.I.C.S.: 513210
Sudchai Sriburanasorn (Mgr-Bus Dev)

TEMENOS Africa (Pty) Limited (1)
2nd Floor 313 Rivonia Road, Morningside, 2198, Johannesburg, Gauteng, South Africa
Tel.: (27) 117071900
Sales Range: $25-49.9 Million
Emp.: 40
Software Support Services
N.A.I.C.S.: 513210

TEMENOS Australia Pty Limited (1)
Level 20 Tower 2 201 Sussex Street, Sydney, 2000, NSW, Australia
Tel.: (61) 290063314
Web Site: http://www.temenos.com
Software Support Services
N.A.I.C.S.: 513210

TEMENOS Deutschland GmbH (1)
Walther-von-Cronberg-Platz 2 Colosseo, 60594, Frankfurt am Main, Germany
Tel.: (49) 69665370
Software Support Services
N.A.I.C.S.: 541511

TEMENOS Ecuador SA (1)

AND PRIVATE COMPANIES — TEMENOS AG

Orellana Building 500 Floors 6 and 7 Orellana Avenue E4-430 1349, Amazonas Avenue Benalcazar, Quito, CP 170518, Pichincha, Ecuador
Tel.: (593) 24008400
Web Site: https://www.temenos.com
Banking Software Development Services
N.A.I.C.S.: 541511

TEMENOS Egypt LLC (1)
Office Number L4-D26 L4-409 Properties numbers 423 422, 3rd sector 5th Compound St 90 N-New Cairo Trivium Bus Complex project, Cairo, Egypt
Tel.: (20) 223067356
Sales Range: $25-49.9 Million
Emp.: 6
Banking Software Support Services
N.A.I.C.S.: 541511

TEMENOS France SAS (1)
112 Avenue Kleber, 75116, Paris, France
Tel.: (33) 144095500
Emp.: 60
Software Support Services
N.A.I.C.S.: 541511

TEMENOS Headquarters SA (1)
2 Rue de l'Ecole-de-Chimie, 1205, Geneva, Switzerland
Tel.: (41) 22 708 1150
Web Site: https://www.temenos.com
Sales Range: $25-49.9 Million
Emp.: 65
Banking Software Development Services
N.A.I.C.S.: 541511

TEMENOS Hellas SA (1)
24B Kifissias Avenue, Maroussi, 151 25, Athens, Greece
Tel.: (30) 2111094600
Sales Range: $25-49.9 Million
Emp.: 30
Banking Software Development Services
N.A.I.C.S.: 541511

TEMENOS Hispania SA (1)
C Doctor Esquerdo N 138 Planta 5 Izquierda, 28007, Madrid, Spain
Tel.: (34) 913432099
Sales Range: $25-49.9 Million
Emp.: 10
Banking Software Support Services
N.A.I.C.S.: 541511

TEMENOS Holdings France SAS (1)
29 Rue Saint Augustin, 75002, Paris, France
Tel.: (33) 144774343
Investment Management Service
N.A.I.C.S.: 523940

TEMENOS Holland BV (1)
Westermarkt 2, 1016 DK, Amsterdam, North Holland, Netherlands
Tel.: (31) 33144095501
Sales Range: $25-49.9 Million
Emp.: 10
Banking Software Development Services
N.A.I.C.S.: 541511

TEMENOS Hong Kong Limited (1)
Unit No 5504 55th Floor Central Plaza 18 Harbour Road, Wanchai, China (Hong Kong)
Tel.: (852) 28662562
Sales Range: $25-49.9 Million
Emp.: 13
Software Development Services
N.A.I.C.S.: 541511

TEMENOS Japan KK (1)
21F Marunouchi Nijyubashi Building 3-2-3 Marunouchi, Chiyoda-ku, Tokyo, 100-0005, Japan
Tel.: (81) 352190655
Banking Software Support Services
N.A.I.C.S.: 541511

TEMENOS Kazakhstan LLP (1)
Office 703 7th Fl Business Ctr Old Sq 98 Panfilov St, 050000, Almaty, Kazakhstan
Tel.: (7) 7272446921
Software Support Services
N.A.I.C.S.: 513210

TEMENOS Korea Limited (1)
21 F Seoul Finance Ctr 84 Taepyungro 1-ga, Jung Gu, Seoul, 100-768, Korea (South)
Tel.: (82) 237824677
Sales Range: $25-49.9 Million
Emp.: 10
Software Support Services
N.A.I.C.S.: 541511
Martarat Yee *(Mgr)*

TEMENOS Luxembourg SA (1)
39 rue du Puits Romain, 8070, Bertrange, Luxembourg
Tel.: (352) 220351
Sales Range: $25-49.9 Million
Emp.: 40
Software Support Services
N.A.I.C.S.: 513210

TEMENOS Malaysia Sdn Bhd (1)
Level 33 ILHAM Tower No.8 Jalan Binjai, Kuala Lumpur, 50450, Malaysia
Tel.: (60) 3 2117 5335
Web Site: http://www.temenos.com
Sales Range: $25-49.9 Million
Emp.: 5
Banking Software Development Services
N.A.I.C.S.: 541511

TEMENOS Mexico SA de CV (1)
Tel.: (52) 5536014400
Banking Software Development Services
N.A.I.C.S.: 541511

TEMENOS Middle East Limited (1)
DIC Building 4 1st floor Office 102 Dubai Internet City, PO Box 500060, 500060, Dubai, United Arab Emirates
Tel.: (971) 43913100
Sales Range: $25-49.9 Million
Emp.: 126
Banking Software Development Services
N.A.I.C.S.: 541511

TEMENOS North Africa LLC (1)
Twin Center Tour Ouest 6th floor, 20100, Casablanca, Morocco
Tel.: (212) 520505604
Sales Range: $25-49.9 Million
Emp.: 40
Software Support Services
N.A.I.C.S.: 518210

TEMENOS Polska Sp. Zo.o (1)
Al Bora-Komorowskiego 25B 13th floor, 31-476, Warsaw, Poland
Tel.: (48) 123966223
Sales Range: $25-49.9 Million
Emp.: 11
Software Support Services
N.A.I.C.S.: 513210

TEMENOS Singapore Pte Limited (1)
5 Shenton Way 18-01 UIC Building, Singapore, 068808, Singapore
Tel.: (65) 65116388
Web Site: https://www.temenos.com
Sales Range: $25-49.9 Million
Emp.: 100
Banking Software Development Services
N.A.I.C.S.: 541511
Martin Frick *(Mng Dir)*

TEMENOS Software Canada Limited (1)
1176 Pl Phillips, Montreal, H3B 3C8, QC, Canada
Tel.: (514) 395-9550
Web Site: http://www.temenos.com
Banking Software Development Services
N.A.I.C.S.: 541511

TEMENOS Software Shanghai Co Limited (1)
Yue Xiu Tower 10th floor Room 1008 No 388 Fushan Road, Pudong New District, Shanghai, 200122, China
Tel.: (86) 2160871380
Web Site: https://www.temenos.com
Banking Software Development Services
N.A.I.C.S.: 541511

Temenos Australia Financial Pty Ltd. (1)
Level 10 85 Castlereagh St, Sydney, 2000, NSW, Australia (100%)
Tel.: (61) 2 9488 4000
Web Site: http://www.temenos.com
Sales Range: $25-49.9 Million
Banking Services
N.A.I.C.S.: 523150
Tom Bentley *(Head-Sls)*

Subsidiary (Domestic):

Clinitec Pty Limited (2)
Suite 15 29 Bertram Street, Macquarie Park, Chatswood, 2067, NSW, Australia
Tel.: (61) 28 889 3660
Web Site: https://www.clinitec.com.au
Clinical Trial Management Software & Services
N.A.I.C.S.: 541511

Temenos Australia Services Pty Limited (1)
Office 317-319 Level 3-Spaces Two Melbourne Quarter 697 Collins Street, Docklands, 3008, VIC, Australia
Tel.: (61) 29 488 4000
Software Development Services
N.A.I.C.S.: 541511

Temenos Belgium SA (1)
Parc du Nysdam Avenue Reine Astrid 92, 1310, La Hulpe, Belgium
Tel.: (32) 27252599
Web Site: https://www.temenos.com
Emp.: 25
Banking Application Software Support Services
N.A.I.C.S.: 541511

Temenos Canada Inc. (1)
2425 Matheson Blvd East Suite 400, Mississauga, L4W 5K4, ON, Canada
Tel.: (905) 214-7600
Emp.: 40
Financial Software Development Services
N.A.I.C.S.: 541511

Temenos Colombia S.A.S. (1)
Regus Parque 93 Calle 93 A 13-24 5th Floor QBO Building, 110221, Bogota, DC, Colombia
Tel.: (57) 16672500
Information Technology Services
N.A.I.C.S.: 541511

Temenos Denmark ApS (1)
Kampmannsgade 2, 1604, Copenhagen, Denmark
Tel.: (45) 89881321
Software Development Services
N.A.I.C.S.: 541511

Temenos East Africa Limited (1)
Coffee 9 7th Floor 9 West Parklands Road, Westlands, 00623, Nairobi, Kenya
Tel.: (254) 703041760
Information Technology Services
N.A.I.C.S.: 541511

Temenos India Private Limited (1)
146 Sterling Road, Nungambakkam, Chennai, 600 034, India
Tel.: (91) 4471331000
Information Technology Services
N.A.I.C.S.: 541511

Temenos Israel Limited (1)
Rothschild Boulevard 22 11th Floor, Tel Aviv, 6688218, Israel
Tel.: (972) 732844500
Information Technology Services
N.A.I.C.S.: 541511

Temenos Philippines, Inc. (1)
27th Floor Tower 2 Room 2715 The Enterprise Centre 6766 Ayala Avenue, Corner Paseo de Roxas, Makati, 1226, Philippines
Tel.: (63) 28858441
Information Technology Services
N.A.I.C.S.: 541511

Temenos Romania SRL (1)
319G Splaiul Independentei Atrium House Ground Floor & 2nd Floor, 6th District, 060044, Bucharest, Romania
Tel.: (40) 317102264
Information Technology Services
N.A.I.C.S.: 541511

Temenos Singapore FT Pte Limited (1)
5 Shenton Way 18-01 UIC Building, Singapore, 068808, Singapore
Tel.: (65) 65116388
Information Technology Services
N.A.I.C.S.: 541511

Temenos Software Brasil Limitada (1)
Av Brig Faria Lima 3144-3ro Andar, Sao Paulo, 01451-001, SP, Brazil
Tel.: (55) 1135682549
Information Technology Services
N.A.I.C.S.: 541511

Temenos Software Luxembourg SA (1)
21 rue du Puits Romain, 8070, Bertrange, Luxembourg
Tel.: (352) 4260801
Information Technology Services
N.A.I.C.S.: 541511

Temenos UK Ltd (1)
71 Fenchurch Street 5th Floor, London, EC3M 4TD, United Kingdom
Tel.: (44) 207 423 3700
Web Site: http://www.temenos.com
Sales Range: $25-49.9 Million
Emp.: 50
Software Publisher
N.A.I.C.S.: 513210

Subsidiary (Non-US):

Financial Objects Limited (2)
45 Monmouth Str 7 Dials Village, WC2H 9DG, London, United Kingdom - England
Tel.: (44) 2078363010
Web Site: http://www.finobj.com
Sales Range: $25-49.9 Million
Software Publisher
N.A.I.C.S.: 513210

Subsidiary (Domestic):

Financial Objects (UK) Limited (3)
Seven Dials Village 45 Monmouth Street Covent Garden, London, WC2H 9DG, United Kingdom
Tel.: (44) 2078363010
Financial Software Retailer
N.A.I.C.S.: 423430

Financial Objects International Limited (3)
Seven Dials Village 45 Monmouth Street Covent Garden, London, WC2H 9DG, United Kingdom
Tel.: (44) 2078363010
Sales Range: $25-49.9 Million
Emp.: 150
Financial Software Development Services
N.A.I.C.S.: 541511

Subsidiary (US):

Financial Objects Inc. (4)
1500 City West Blvd Ste 525, Houston, TX 77042
Tel.: (713) 520-5770
Sales Range: $25-49.9 Million
Emp.: 15
Financial Software Development Services
N.A.I.C.S.: 541511
Debbie Brackett *(COO)*

Temenos USA, Inc. (1)
200 Colonial Center Pkwy Ste 340, Lake Mary, FL 32746
Tel.: (407) 732-5200
Sales Range: $25-49.9 Million
Emp.: 84
Banking Software Developer
N.A.I.C.S.: 513210
Robert Rawlins *(Mgr-Operations)*

Temenos Vietnam Company Limited (1)
9th Floor Vinaconex Tower 34 Lang Ha Street, Dong Da District, Hanoi, Vietnam
Tel.: (84) 437724328
Information Technology Services
N.A.I.C.S.: 541511

Viveo Group SA (1)
15-17 Rue Giyam, 75017, Paris, France
Tel.: (33) 144095500
Application Software Support Services
N.A.I.C.S.: 541511

Subsidiary (Domestic):

Viveo France SAS (2)
251 Boulevard Pereire, 75017, Paris, France
Tel.: (33) 144095500
Sales Range: $25-49.9 Million
Emp.: 100
Software Suport Services
N.A.I.C.S.: 334610

TEMENOS AG

Temenos AG—(Continued)

Subsidiary (Non-US):

Viveo Romania SRL (2)
319 Splaiul Independentei Sema Park Building Courtyard 1 Aripa C, Parter Bucuresti Sectorul 6, 060044, Bucharest, Romania
Tel.: (40) 317102264
Sales Range: $25-49.9 Million
Emp.: 100
Banking Software Development Services
N.A.I.C.S.: 541511

TEMET OY
Asentajankatu 3, 00880, Helsinki, Finland
Tel.: (358) 20 757 9510
Web Site: http://www.temet.com
Year Founded: 1953
Sales Range: $25-49.9 Million
Emp.: 60
Blast Protection, CBRN Filtration & Ventilation Technology of Shelters & Protective Structures
N.A.I.C.S.: 624221
Jyrki Ronkainen *(CEO)*

Subsidiaries:

Temet USA LLC (1)
21162 Mill Branch Dr, Leesburg, VA 20175
Tel.: (703) 759-6000
Web Site: http://www.temetusa.com
Sales Range: $25-49.9 Million
Emp.: 5
Custom Building Services
N.A.I.C.S.: 236220

TEMIR CORP.
Suite 1802-03 18th Floor Strand 50 50 Bonham Strand, Sheung Wan, Hong Kong, China (Hong Kong)
Tel.: (852) 28527388 NV
Year Founded: 2016
Rev.: $219,702
Assets: $51,909
Liabilities: $562,957
Net Worth: ($511,048)
Earnings: ($266,862)
Emp.: 5
Fiscal Year-end: 08/31/21
Tourism Operator
N.A.I.C.S.: 561520
Roy Kong Hoi Chan *(Chm & Pres)*

TEMIRTAU ELECTROMETALLURGY PLANT JSC
2 Privokzalnaya st, Karagandy Region, Temirtau, 101400, Kazakhstan
Tel.: (7) 213935629
Web Site: http://www.temk.kz
TEMK—(KAZ)
Rev.: $9,483,226
Assets: $26,179,775
Liabilities: $19,383,512
Net Worth: $6,796,263
Earnings: $518,315
Fiscal Year-end: 12/31/19
Mineral Mining Services
N.A.I.C.S.: 212390
Zhumabek Zhanykulov *(Chm-Mgmt Bd)*

TEMONA, INC.
Token International Building Main Building 9F 2-12-19 Shibuya, Shibuya-ku, Tokyo, 150-0002, Japan
Tel.: (81) 366356452
Web Site: https://www.temona.co.jp
3985—(TKS)
Rev.: $16,597,690
Assets: $15,980,860
Liabilities: $8,245,670
Net Worth: $7,735,190
Earnings: ($900,430)
Fiscal Year-end: 09/30/23
Software Development Services
N.A.I.C.S.: 541511

Hayato Sagawa *(Founder & Pres)*

TEMPEST MINERALS LIMITED
Level 2 Suite 9 389 Oxford Street, Mount Hawthorn, Hawthorn, 6016, WA, Australia
Tel.: (61) 892000435
Web Site: https://tempestminerals.com
TEM—(ASX)
Rev.: $19,711
Assets: $2,344,187
Liabilities: $67,780
Net Worth: $2,276,406
Earnings: ($578,328)
Fiscal Year-end: 06/30/21
Other Nonmetallic Mineral Mining & Quarrying
N.A.I.C.S.: 212390
Shanthar Pathmanathan *(CEO)*

TEMPLE & WEBSTER PTY LTD.
2/1-7 Unwins Bridge Rd, Saint Peters, 2044, NSW, Australia
Tel.: (61) 10302904935 AU
Web Site: https://www.templeandwebster.com
Year Founded: 2011
TPW—(ASX)
Rev.: $135,111,477
Assets: $51,571,483
Liabilities: $28,598,042
Net Worth: $22,973,441
Earnings: $10,656,937
Fiscal Year-end: 06/30/20
Home Furnishing Mfr
N.A.I.C.S.: 423220
Brian Shanahan *(Co-Founder)*

TEMPLE BAR INVESTMENT TRUST PLC
25 Southampton Buildings, London, WC2A 1AL, United Kingdom
Tel.: (44) 2072276000 UK
Web Site: https://www.templebarinvest.co.uk
Year Founded: 1926
TMPL—(LSE)
Assets: $967,370,085
Liabilities: $92,481,510
Net Worth: $874,888,575
Earnings: ($19,235,865)
Fiscal Year-end: 12/31/22
Investment Management Service
N.A.I.C.S.: 523940
Arthur Copple *(Chm)*

TEMPLETON AND PARTNERS LTD
Templeton House 33-34 Chiswell Street, London, EC1Y 4SF, United Kingdom
Tel.: (44) 20 7074 6000
Web Site: http://www.templeton-recruitment.com
Sales Range: $25-49.9 Million
Emp.: 20
IT Recruitment
N.A.I.C.S.: 561311

Subsidiaries:

Templeton and Partners B.V. (1)
Dam 5, 1012 JS, Amsterdam, Netherlands
Tel.: (31) 20 30 30 000
Web Site: http://www.templeton.nl
IT Recruitment Services
N.A.I.C.S.: 561311

TEMPLETON EMERGING MARKETS FUND
8A rue Albert Borschette, L-1246, Luxembourg, Luxembourg
Tel.: (352) 4666671
EMF—(STU)
Sales Range: Less than $1 Million

Fund Management Services
N.A.I.C.S.: 523940
Chetan Sehgal *(Mgr-Fund)*

TEMPLETON EMERGING MARKETS INVESTMENT TRUST PLC
5 Morrison Street, Edinburgh, EH3 8BH, United Kingdom
Tel.: (44) 2072087040
Web Site: http://www.temit.co.uk
Investment Management Service
N.A.I.C.S.: 523999
Andrew Ness *(Mgr-Fund)*

TEMPO BEVERAGES LTD.
Giboray Israel 2 Poleg Industrial Area, Netanya, Israel
Tel.: (972) 98630530
Web Site: http://www.tempo.co.il
Year Founded: 1954
TMBV.B2—(TAE)
Rev.: $550,905,089
Assets: $584,095,308
Liabilities: $357,143,523
Net Worth: $226,951,785
Earnings: $19,556,016
Emp.: 1,300
Fiscal Year-end: 12/31/23
Wine & Distilled Alcoholic Distr
N.A.I.C.S.: 424820
Jacques Beer *(Chm & CEO)*

Subsidiaries:

Shapiro Brewery Ltd. (1)
Industrial Area Sorek Nacham, Beit Shemesh, 99052, Israel
Tel.: (972) 25612622
Web Site: https://en.shapirobeer.co.il
Beer & Wine Distr
N.A.I.C.S.: 424810

Tempo Beverages Cyprus Ltd. (1)
Emboriou Ave 7-11, Aradippou, 7105, Larnaca, Cyprus
Tel.: (357) 25053300
Web Site: https://tempocyprus.com.cy
Heineken Beer & Wine Distr
N.A.I.C.S.: 424810

TEMPO INTERNATIONAL GROUP LTD.
1208 Kylin Building No 1539 Tiantong North Road, Ningbo, 315100, Zhejiang, China
Tel.: (86) 57487130927 CN
Web Site: http://www.tempo.net.cn
Sales Range: $10-24.9 Million
Emp.: 400
Mfr & Distr of Conveyor Belts, Power Transmission Belts & Pulleys & Related Products
N.A.I.C.S.: 333922
Tianbao Zhou *(Chm)*

Subsidiaries:

Summitech Engineering, Inc. (1)
47440 Michigan Ave Ste 100, Canton, MI 48188
Tel.: (734) 448-2222
Web Site: http://www.summitechinc.com
Rev.: $2,000,000
Emp.: 20
Designs, Engineers & Develops Chassis Components & Systems
N.A.I.C.S.: 336390

TEMPO INTI MEDIA TBK
Gedung Tempo Jalan Palmerah Barat No 8, Jakarta, 12210, Indonesia
Tel.: (62) 217255625
Web Site: https://www.tempo.id
Year Founded: 1971
TMPO—(INDO)
Rev.: $14,076,694
Assets: $27,353,179
Liabilities: $13,743,494
Net Worth: $13,609,685
Earnings: $80,255

Emp.: 474
Fiscal Year-end: 12/31/23
Magazine & Newspaper Publishing Services
N.A.I.C.S.: 513110

Subsidiaries:

P.T. Matair Rumah Kreatif (1)
Gedung Tempo Jl Palmerah Barat No 8, Jakarta, 12210, Indonesia
Tel.: (62) 215482132
Visual Communication Services
N.A.I.C.S.: 541430

P.T. Temprint Inti Niaga (1)
Gedung Grup Tempo Media Jl Palmerah Barat No 8 Lantai Mezanine, Kemanggisan Palmerah DKI Jakarta, Jakarta Barat, Indonesia
Tel.: (62) 215482132
Web Site: https://www.tiniaga.com
Light Weight Coated Paper Distr
N.A.I.C.S.: 424110

TEMPO SCAN PACIFIC TBK
Tempo Scan Tower 16th Floor Jl HR Rasuna Said Kav 3-4, Jakarta, 12950, Indonesia
Tel.: (62) 2129218888
Web Site: https://www.temposcangroup.com
Year Founded: 1970
TSPC—(INDO)
Rev.: $851,998,809
Assets: $734,843,560
Liabilities: $211,061,107
Net Worth: $523,782,453
Earnings: $81,191,102
Emp.: 4,540
Fiscal Year-end: 12/31/23
Pharmaceutical Product Mfr & Distr
N.A.I.C.S.: 325412
Dian Paramita Tamzil *(Pres & Commissioner)*

Subsidiaries:

PT Perusahaan Dagang Tempo (1)
Tempo Scan Tower Jalan HR Rasuna Said Kav 3-4, Jakarta, 12950, Indonesia
Tel.: (62) 2129218888
Web Site: https://www.pttempo.com
Household Product Delivery Services
N.A.I.C.S.: 492210

TEMPTATION FOODS LTD
4 Unity House Mama Parmanand Marg, Opera House, 400004, Mumbai, Maharashtra, India
Tel.: (91) 2242461444
Sales Range: $150-199.9 Million
Emp.: 256
Fruit & Vegetable Processor
N.A.I.C.S.: 115114
Vinit Kumar *(Mng Dir)*

TEMPUS CAPITAL, INC.
Suite 200 3310 South Service Road, Burlington, L7N 3M6, ON, Canada
Tel.: (905) 681-1925
Web Site: https://tempuscapital.ca
TEMP—(CNSX)
Rev.: $839,520
Assets: $11,170,665
Liabilities: $7,182,294
Net Worth: $3,988,371
Earnings: ($146,602)
Fiscal Year-end: 12/31/22
Real Estate Management Services
N.A.I.C.S.: 531311
Russell Tanz *(CEO)*

TEMPUS GLOBAL BUSINESS SERVICE GROUP HOLDING LTD.
Tempus Group Building No 9 Taohua Road Futian Bonded Area, Shenzhen, 518038, China
Tel.: (86) 7558 348 5999

Web Site: http://www.tempus.cn
Year Founded: 1998
300178—(SSE)
Rev.: $83,511,707
Assets: $734,260,457
Liabilities: $710,209,551
Net Worth: $24,050,906
Earnings: ($160,705,033)
Emp.: 81,000
Fiscal Year-end: 12/31/20
Airline Transportation Management Services
N.A.I.C.S.: 561599
Baisheng Zhong (Chm)

TEMPUS HOLDINGS LIMITED
28/F No 9 Des Voeux Road West Sheung Wan, Hong Kong, China (Hong Kong)
Tel.: (852) 4000188199
Web Site: http://ir.oto.com.hk
6880—(HKG)
Rev.: $58,736,955
Assets: $42,349,508
Liabilities: $39,313,478
Net Worth: $3,036,030
Earnings: ($9,515,963)
Emp.: 629
Fiscal Year-end: 12/31/21
Health & Wellness Products Mfr & Distr
N.A.I.C.S.: 325620
Charlie Chee Lai Yip (VP)

TEN ALLIED CO., LTD.
4F K Bldg 2-16-18 Takaban, Meguro-ku, Tokyo, 152-0004, Japan
Tel.: (81) 357687470
Web Site: https://www.teng.co.jp
Year Founded: 1969
8207—(TKS)
Rev.: $91,853,520
Assets: $73,064,640
Liabilities: $56,153,680
Net Worth: $16,910,960
Earnings: ($11,102,960)
Emp.: 348
Fiscal Year-end: 03/31/23
Restaurant Operators
N.A.I.C.S.: 722511
Eita Iida (Pres)

TEN LIFESTYLE GROUP PLC
2nd Floor Fitzroy House 355 Euston Road, London, NW1 3AL, United Kingdom
Tel.: (44) 2033016300   UK
Web Site:
https://www.tenlifestylegroup.com
Year Founded: 1998
TENG—(AIM)
Rev.: $82,778,388
Assets: $53,223,548
Liabilities: $34,397,860
Net Worth: $18,825,688
Earnings: $5,650,190
Emp.: 1,101
Fiscal Year-end: 08/31/23
Travel Agencies
N.A.I.C.S.: 561510
Alex Cheatle (Co-Founder & CEO)

Subsidiaries:

Ten Group (RUS) LLC   (1)
Office 612 Smolenskaya Square 3, 121099, Moscow, Russia
Tel.: (7) 4996091389
Travel & Lifestyle Concierge Services
N.A.I.C.S.: 561599

Ten Group Australia Pty. Limited   (1)
65 Wentworth Place, Banyo, Brisbane, 4014, QLD, Australia
Tel.: (61) 419743194
Web Site: https://www.tengroup.com.au
Construction Tool & Equipment Mfr & Distr
N.A.I.C.S.: 333120

Ten Group Belgium BVBA   (1)
Brussels Airport Corporate Village Leonardo Da Vinciiaan 9, 1935, Zaventem, Belgium
Tel.: (32) 23138731
Travel & Lifestyle Concierge Services

Ten Group Japan K.K.   (1)
7F Sumitomo Sasazuka Taiyo Building 1-48-3, Sasazuka Shibuya-ku, Tokyo, 151-0073, Japan
Tel.: (81) 357905690
Travel & Lifestyle Concierge Services
N.A.I.C.S.: 561599

Ten Group Singapore Pte. Limited   (1)
36 Robinson Road City House 02-127, Singapore, 068877, Singapore
Tel.: (65) 31585000
Travel & Lifestyle Concierge Services
N.A.I.C.S.: 561599

Ten Lifestyle Management (Asia) Limited   (1)
Unit 20-125 WeWork City Plaza Phase 3, Taikoo Shing, China (Hong Kong)
Tel.: (852) 230513673
Travel & Lifestyle Concierge Services
N.A.I.C.S.: 561599

Ten Lifestyle Management (Canada) ULC   (1)
1200 Bay Street Suite 202, Toronto, M5R 2A5, ON, Canada
Tel.: (437) 370-1817
Travel & Lifestyle Concierge Services
N.A.I.C.S.: 561599

Ten Lifestyle Management Africa (Pty.) Limited   (1)
7th Floor 19 Louis Gradner Street Foreshore, Cape Town, 8001, South Africa
Tel.: (27) 212000247
Travel & Lifestyle Concierge Services
N.A.I.C.S.: 561599

Ten Lifestyle Management Limited   (1)
2nd Floor Fitzroy House 355 Euston Road, London, NW1 3AL, United Kingdom
Tel.: (44) 2033016300
Travel & Lifestyle Concierge Services
N.A.I.C.S.: 561599

Ten Lifestyle Management Limited S DE RL DE CV   (1)
Reforma 296 piso 14 Col Juarez Suite 1445, Cuauhtemoc, 06600, Ciudad Juarez, Mexico
Tel.: (52) 5550055720
Travel & Lifestyle Concierge Services
N.A.I.C.S.: 561599

Ten Lifestyle Management Switzerland GmbH   (1)
Red Tower Floor F0 Limmatstrasse 250, 8005, Zurich, Switzerland
Tel.: (41) 443855700
Travel & Lifestyle Concierge Services
N.A.I.C.S.: 561599

Ten Lifestyle Management USA Inc.   (1)
149 New Montgomery St Ste 352 4th Fl, San Francisco, CA 94105
Tel.: (415) 871-2456
Travel & Lifestyle Concierge Services
N.A.I.C.S.: 561599

Ten Servicos de Concierge do Brasil Limited   (1)
Rua Gomes de Carvalho 911 3 andar, Vila Olimpia, Sao Paulo, 04551-000, Brazil
Tel.: (55) 1149493405
Travel & Lifestyle Concierge Services
N.A.I.C.S.: 561599

TEN PAO GROUP HOLDINGS LIMITED
Room 10-12 6th/F Kwong Sang Hong Centre 151-153 Hoi Bun Road Kwun Tong, Kowloon, China (Hong Kong)
Tel.: (852) 27905566   Ky
Web Site: https://www.tenpao.com
Year Founded: 1979
1979—(HKG)
Rev.: $698,872,763
Assets: $496,029,060
Liabilities: $315,857,280
Net Worth: $180,171,780
Earnings: $37,807,703
Emp.: 7,300
Fiscal Year-end: 12/31/22
Electronic Equipment Mfr & Distr
N.A.I.C.S.: 335999
Kwong Yee Hung (Founder, Chm, CEO & Exec Dir)

Subsidiaries:

Ten Pao International Co., Ltd.   (1)
171 Simin-Daero Dongan-Gu, Anyang, 14048, Gyeonggi, Korea (South)
Tel.: (82) 313440258
Power Supply Device Distr
N.A.I.C.S.: 423610

TEN REN TEA CO., LTD.
6F No 107 Sec 4 Chung Hsiao East Road, Taipei, Taiwan
Tel.: (886) 227765580
Web Site: https://www.tenren.com.tw
Year Founded: 1953
1233—(TAI)
Rev.: $69,012,653
Assets: $77,634,812
Liabilities: $28,921,285
Net Worth: $48,713,527
Earnings: $3,135,125
Emp.: 1,404
Fiscal Year-end: 12/31/23
Tea Mfr
N.A.I.C.S.: 311920
Rie-Ho Lee (Pres)

TEN SIXTY FOUR LIMITED
Level 1 Suite 3 1209 Hay Street, West Perth, 6005, WA, Australia
Tel.: (61) 894741330   AU
Web Site: https://www.x64.gold
X64—(ASX)
Rev.: $115,110,000
Assets: $185,207,000
Liabilities: $8,020,000
Net Worth: $177,187,000
Earnings: ($16,993,000)
Emp.: 481
Fiscal Year-end: 06/30/23
Gold Mining Services
N.A.I.C.S.: 212220
James Pingul Llorca (Gen Mgr-Geology & Resources)

TEN SQUARE GAMES SA
ul Traugutta 45, 50-416, Wroclaw, Poland
Tel.: (48) 516089279
Web Site:
https://www.tensquaregames.com
Year Founded: 2017
TEN—(WAR)
Rev.: $110,791,762
Assets: $116,388,032
Liabilities: $42,452,327
Net Worth: $73,935,705
Earnings: $3,863,603
Emp.: 222
Fiscal Year-end: 12/31/23
Mobile Game Software Services
N.A.I.C.S.: 513210
Maciej Zuzalek (Pres)

TENA A.D.
Krajiska Bb, 74270, Teslic, Bosnia & Herzegovina
Tel.: (387) 53430981
Year Founded: 2001
TENA-R-A—(BANJ)
Rev.: $33,715
Assets: $1,172,996
Liabilities: $358,915
Net Worth: $814,081
Earnings: $315
Emp.: 1
Fiscal Year-end: 12/31/12
Textile Products Mfr
N.A.I.C.S.: 314110
Nenad Tomovic (Chm-Mgmt Bd)

TENAGA NASIONAL BERHAD
No 129 Jalan Bangsar, 59200, Kuala Lumpur, Malaysia
Tel.: (60) 322965566
Web Site: http://www.tnb.com.my
TENAGA—(KLS)
Rev.: $13,025,801,250
Assets: $45,193,648,500
Liabilities: $30,741,529,500
Net Worth: $14,452,119,000
Earnings: $956,513,250
Emp.: 34,938
Fiscal Year-end: 12/31/21
Electric Power Utility
N.A.I.C.S.: 221122
Fazlur Rahman Zainuddin (Chief Strategy & Regulatory Officer)

Subsidiaries:

Allo Technology Sdn. Bhd.   (1)
Cyberview Garden Villas Persiaran Multimedia Cyber 7, 63000, Cyberjaya, Selangor, Malaysia
Tel.: (60) 130 038 8000
Web Site: https://www.allo.my
Broadband Services
N.A.I.C.S.: 517111

GSPARX Sdn. Bhd.   (1)
Annexe Building 129 Jalan Bangsar, 59200, Kuala Lumpur, Malaysia
Tel.: (60) 130 080 7828
Web Site: https://www.gsparx.com
Solar Energy Services
N.A.I.C.S.: 221114
Elmie Fairul Mashuri (Mng Dir)

Integrax Berhad   (1)
36 01 Level 36 Menera AIA Cap Square No 10 Jalan Manushi Abdullah, No 10 Jalan Munshi Abdullah, 50100, Kuala Lumpur, Malaysia   (100%)
Tel.: (60) 32 693 7728
Web Site: https://www.integrax.com.my
Holding Company; Port Operations & Marine Services
N.A.I.C.S.: 551112
Theresa Kong (CFO)

Kapar Energy Ventures Sdn. Bhd.   (1)
Jalan Tok Muda Batu 12 Jalan, 42200, Kapar, Selangor, Malaysia
Tel.: (60) 33 250 8801
Web Site: https://www.kaparenergy.com.my
Sales Range: $100-124.9 Million
Motors & Generators Mfr
N.A.I.C.S.: 335312

Lekir Bulk Terminal Sdn. Bhd.   (1)
Lot 1 Jalan Kg Acheh, Lumut Port Industrial Park, 32000, Sitiawan, Perak Darul Ridzuan, Malaysia
Tel.: (60) 5 698 3333
Web Site: https://www.lumutport.com
Port Operation Services
N.A.I.C.S.: 488310
Mubarak Ali Gulam Rasul (CEO)

Malaysia Transformer Manufacturing Sdn. Bhd.   (1)
Lot 22 Jalan AU 3/1, Ulu Klang, 54200, Kuala Lumpur, Selangor Darul Ehsan, Malaysia   (100%)
Tel.: (60) 34 259 6200
Web Site: https://www.mtmsb.com
Sales Range: $125-149.9 Million
Emp.: 300
Transformers & Switchgears Mfr & Sales
N.A.I.C.S.: 335311

Sabah Electricity Sdn. Bhd.   (1)
Wisma SESB Jalan Tunku Abdul Rahman, 88673, Kota Kinabalu, Sabah, Malaysia   (100%)
Tel.: (60) 8 851 5000
Web Site: https://www.sesb.com.my
Emp.: 700
Metering Facilities, Systems & Services
N.A.I.C.S.: 221122
Lisa Wan Siew Han (Gen Mgr-Fin)

TNB Capital (L) Ltd.   (1)

TENAGA NASIONAL BERHAD

Tenaga Nasional Berhad—(Continued)
Unit Level 13 E Main Office Tower, Financial Park Labuan, Labuan, 87000, Malaysia
Tel.: (60) 87451688
Holding Company
N.A.I.C.S.: 551112

TNB Engineering & Cooperation Sdn Bhd (TNEC) (1)
1701 Level 17 Block B Menara Amcorp 18 Persiaran Barat Jalan Sultan, 46000, Petaling Jaya, Selangor Darul Ehsan, Malaysia (100%)
Tel.: (60) 379582121
Web Site: http://www.tnb.com.my
Sales Range: $25-49.9 Million
Engineeering Services
N.A.I.C.S.: 221122

TNB Engineering Corporation Sdn. Bhd. (1)
1701 Block B Menara Amcorp 18 Persiaran Barat Jalan Sultan, 46000, Petaling Jaya, Selangor, Malaysia
Tel.: (60) 37 958 2121
Web Site: https://www.tnec.com.my
Turnkey Contracting Services
N.A.I.C.S.: 236220

TNB Engineers Sdn Bhd (1)
129 Jalan Bangsar, PO Box 11003, 50732, Kuala Lumpur, Malaysia (100%)
Tel.: (60) 322965566
Sales Range: $25-49.9 Million
Emp.: 230
Engineeering Services
N.A.I.C.S.: 541330
Ibrahim Adham Salleh *(Sr Mgr)*

TNB Fuel Services Sdn. Bhd. (1)
Level 4 Crystal Plz Jalan 51A 223, 46100, Petaling Jaya, Selangor Darul Ehsan, Malaysia (100%)
Tel.: (60) 379568349
Rev.: $100,000,000
Emp.: 48
Fuel Supply & Services
N.A.I.C.S.: 424690

TNB Generation Sdn Bhd (1)
129 Jalan Bangsar, 59200, Kuala Lumpur, Malaysia (100%)
Tel.: (60) 322965566
Web Site: http://www.tnb.com.my
Sales Range: $75-99.9 Million
Emp.: 60
Generation & Sale of Energy; Operation & Maintenance of the Power Station
N.A.I.C.S.: 221122

TNB Integrated Learning Solution Sdn Bhd (1)
Jalan Ikram-Uniten, 43650, Bandar Baru Bangi, Selangor, Malaysia
Tel.: (60) 389227222
Web Site: http://www.tnbilsas.com.my
Technical Training Services
N.A.I.C.S.: 611710

TNB Janamanjung Sdn. Bhd. (1)
Stesen Janakuasa Sultan Azlan Shah Jalan Semarak Api Teluk Rubiah, 32040, Seri Manjung, Perak, Malaysia (100%)
Tel.: (60) 56898000
Web Site: http://www.tnbj.com.my
Development of Power Stations; Generation & Sale of Electricity
N.A.I.C.S.: 221122

TNB Labs Sdn. Bhd. (1)
No 1 Lorong Ayer Hitam Kawasan Institusi Penyelidikan, 43000, Kajang, Selangor, Malaysia
Tel.: (60) 38 922 5000
Web Site: https://www.tnblabs.com.my
Testing Laboratory Services
N.A.I.C.S.: 541380
Mohd Hariffin Boosroh *(Exec Dir)*

TNB Power Daharki Ltd. (1)
3rd Floor Li Wan Po Building, PO Box 1130, 12 Remy Ollier Street, Port Louis, Mauritius (100%)
Tel.: (230) 2088000
Investment Holding Company
N.A.I.C.S.: 551112

TNB Remaco Pakistan (Private) Limited (1)

1223 MW Combined Cycle Power Plant Wahadin, Distt Kasoor Pattoki, Kasur, Pakistan
Tel.: (92) 315 839 0000
Web Site: https://www.tnbremaco.com.pk
Electric Utility Repair Services
N.A.I.C.S.: 811310

TNB Repair & Maintenance Sdn Bhd. (1)
Level 23 PJX HM Shah Tower 16A Persiaran Barat, 46050, Petaling Jaya, Selangor, Malaysia (100%)
Tel.: (60) 379642600
Sales Range: $75-99.9 Million
Emp.: 300
Repair, Maintenance & Test Services
N.A.I.C.S.: 811310

TNB Research Sdn. Bhd. (1)
No 1 Lorong Ayer Itam Kawasan Institusi Penyelidikan, 43000, Kajang, Selangor, Malaysia
Tel.: (60) 38 922 5000
Web Site: https://www.tnbr.com.my
Sales Range: $25-49.9 Million
Emp.: 50
Consultancy, Research & Development Services
N.A.I.C.S.: 541715

TNB Ventures Sdn. Bhd. (1)
129 Jalan Bangsar, Kuala Lumpur, 59200, Malaysia
Tel.: (60) 322856236
Holding Company
N.A.I.C.S.: 551112
Md Sidek Ahmad *(CEO)*

Subsidiary (Domestic):

Tenaga Cable Industries Sdn. Bhd. (2)
Lot 2 Jalan P 12 Section 10, Bangi Industrial Estate Bandar Baru, 43650, Bangi, Selangor, Malaysia
Tel.: (60) 389222678
Web Site: https://www.tcisb.com.my
Sales Range: $100-124.9 Million
Emp.: 200
Steel Wire & Related Products Mfr
N.A.I.C.S.: 331222
Mohd Muzammir Husin *(Mng Dir)*

TNB Workshop Services Sdn. Bhd. (1)
Bangunan Ibu Pejabat 129 Jalan Bangsar Peti Surat, 50732, Kuala Lumpur, Malaysia (100%)
Tel.: (60) 322965566
Web Site: http://www.tnbw.com.my
Sales Range: $125-149.9 Million
Emp.: 150
Repair & Maintenance & Related Services
N.A.I.C.S.: 221122

Tenaga Switchgear Sdn Bhd (TSG) (1)
Lot 3 Jalan Teknologi 3/6 Seksyen 3 Taman Sains Selangor 1, Kota Damansara, 47810, Petaling Jaya, Selangor, Malaysia
Tel.: (60) 36 140 6520
Web Site: https://www.mytsg.com.my
Sales Range: $25-49.9 Million
Emp.: 98
Mfr of Switchgears
N.A.I.C.S.: 335313

Universiti Tenaga Nasional Sdn Bhd (UNITEN) (1)
Putra Jaya Campus Jalan Ikram-uniten, 43000, Kajang, Selangor, Malaysia
Tel.: (60) 389212020
Web Site: http://www.uniten.edu.my
Sales Range: $650-699.9 Million
University Academic Programs & Engineering Technology Training
N.A.I.C.S.: 923110
Bahisham Yunus *(COO-Acting)*

Universiti Tenaga Nasional Sdn. Bhd. (1)
Putrajaya Campus Jalan Ikram-Uniten, 43000, Kajang, Selangor, Malaysia
Tel.: (60) 38 921 2020
Web Site: https://www.uniten.edu.my
Educational Support Services
N.A.I.C.S.: 611710
Effy Shafinaz Zainodin *(Mgr-Marketing-Corporate Communications)*

TENAX INTERNATIONAL BV
Via Le Stefeno Franscini 19, 6900, Lugano, Switzerland
Tel.: (41) 919233412
Year Founded: 1960
Plastic Nets & Meshes Mfr
N.A.I.C.S.: 326199
Bordonali Fabio *(Mgr-Team)*

Subsidiaries:

Agritenx SRL (1)
Loc. Pezza Grande Area P.I.P., 84025, Salerno, Italy
Tel.: (39) 0828 332978
Plastic Nets & Meshes Mfr
N.A.I.C.S.: 326199

Tenax Corporation (1)
4800 E Monument St, Baltimore, MD 21205
Tel.: (410) 522-7000
Web Site: http://www.tenaxus.com
Plastic Nets & Meshes Mfr
N.A.I.C.S.: 326199

Tenax Kunststoffe GMBH (1)
Schlostrasse 13, Lindau, 88131, Germany
Tel.: (49) 838293040
Plastic Nets & Meshes Mfr
N.A.I.C.S.: 326199

Tenax Manufacturing Alabama (1)
200 Miller Sellers Dr, Evergreen, AL 36401
Tel.: (251) 578-9003
Web Site: http://www.tenax.net
Sales Range: $50-74.9 Million
Provider of Piece Goods & Notions
N.A.I.C.S.: 326199

Tenax SARL (1)
11 Rue Auguste Lacroix, 69003, Lyon, France
Tel.: (33) 437484933
Web Site: http://www.tenax.net
Sales Range: $25-49.9 Million
Emp.: 2
Plastic Nets & Meshes Mfr
N.A.I.C.S.: 326199

Tenax SPA (1)
Via dell Industria 3, 23897, Lecco, Italy
Tel.: (39) 039 92191
Web Site: http://www.tenax.net
Plastic Nets & Meshes Mfr
N.A.I.C.S.: 326199

Tenax UK Ltd. (1)
Unit 10 Ash Rd N Wrexham Ind Est, Wrexham, LL13 6JT, United Kingdom
Tel.: (44) 1978664667
Web Site: http://www.tenax.co.uk
Emp.: 25
Plastic Nets & Meshes Mfr
N.A.I.C.S.: 326199
Marco Abbiati *(Mng Dir)*

Tianjin Tenax Industrial Plastics Co., Ltd (1)
No 2 8th Xinghua Branch Road, Xiqing Economic Development, 300385, Tianjin, China
Tel.: (86) 22 23963728
Plastic Nets & Meshes Mfr
N.A.I.C.S.: 326199

TENAX INTERNATIONAL S.P.A.
Via Balduina 3, Rio Saliceto, 42010, Reggio Emilia, Italy
Tel.: (39) 0522699421
Web Site:
https://www.tenaxinternational.com
Year Founded: 2016
TNX—(EUR)
Polymer Product Mfr & Distr
N.A.I.C.S.: 325211
Alessandro Simonazzi *(CFO)*

TENAYA GROUP INC.
7420 Bathurst Street Suite 1104, Thornhill, L4J 6X4, ON, Canada
Tel.: (323) 472-7922 NV
Web Site:
http://www.tenayagroupinc.com
Year Founded: 2017
Assets: $53

INTERNATIONAL PUBLIC

Liabilities: $27,585
Net Worth: ($27,532)
Earnings: ($53,168)
Emp.: 1
Fiscal Year-end: 12/31/18
Television Broadcasting Services
N.A.I.C.S.: 516120
Jordan Shefsky *(Treas & Sec)*

TENAZ ENERGY CORP.
605 5th Avenue SW Suite 700, Calgary, T2P 3H5, AB, Canada
Tel.: (403) 984-5197 AB
Web Site:
https://www.tenazenergy.com
Year Founded: 2007
TNZ—(TSX)
Rev.: $10,006,926
Assets: $58,984,694
Liabilities: $7,890,076
Net Worth: $51,094,618
Earnings: $6,523,433
Emp.: 10
Fiscal Year-end: 12/31/20
Investment Services
N.A.I.C.S.: 523999
David Burghardt *(Pres & CEO)*

TENCENT HOLDINGS LIMITED
Tencent Binhai Building No 33 Haitian Second Road, Nanshan District, Shenzhen, 518054, China
Tel.: (86) 75586013388 CN
Web Site: https://www.tencent.com
Year Founded: 1998
TCEHY—(OTCIQ)
Rev.: $39,815,712,229
Assets: $218,505,067,568
Liabilities: $110,111,735,711
Net Worth: $108,393,381,856
Earnings: $26,128,295,304
Emp.: 108,436
Fiscal Year-end: 12/31/22
Holding Company
N.A.I.C.S.: 551112
Martin Chiping Lau *(Pres)*

Subsidiaries:

Funcom SE (1)
Prins Mauritslaan 37-39, Badhoevedorp, 1171LP, Netherlands
Tel.: (31) 122 925900
Web Site: http://www.funcom.com
Multiplayer Online Game Developer & Operator
N.A.I.C.S.: 339930
Alain Tascan *(Vice Chm-Supervisory Bd)*

Subsidiary (US):

Funcom Inc (2)
5826 Fayetteville Rd 201, Durham, NC 27713-8684
Tel.: (919) 806-0707
Web Site: http://www.funcom.com
Computer Game Development & Publishing Services
N.A.I.C.S.: 541511

Subsidiary (Non-US):

Funcom Oslo AS (2)
Drammensveien 167, 0277, Oslo, Norway
Tel.: (47) 22925900
Sales Range: $25-49.9 Million
Emp.: 30
Online Game Development & Publishing Services
N.A.I.C.S.: 541511

HUYA, Inc. (1)
Building A3 E-Park 280 Hanxi Road, Panyu District, Guangzhou, 511446, China (62.7%)
Tel.: (86) 2022907888
Web Site: https://www.huya.com
Rev.: $1,412,666,983
Assets: $2,014,252,942
Liabilities: $352,939,918
Net Worth: $1,661,313,024
Earnings: ($74,560,566)
Emp.: 1,521
Fiscal Year-end: 12/31/2022

AND PRIVATE COMPANIES

Online Streaming Media Services
N.A.I.C.S.: 518210
Rongjie Dong *(CEO)*

Leyou Technologies Holdings Limited (1)
Suite 3201 Tower Two Lippo Centre 89 Queensway, Admiralty, Hong Kong, China (Hong Kong)
Tel.: (852) 25113863
Web Site: http://www.le-you.hk
Rev.: $214,235,000
Assets: $322,848,000
Liabilities: $71,042,000
Net Worth: $251,806,000
Earnings: ($6,489,000)
Emp.: 1,046
Fiscal Year-end: 12/31/2019
Video Games Developer
N.A.I.C.S.: 513210

Riot Games, Inc. (1)
12333 W Olympic Blvd, Los Angeles, CA 90064 **(100%)**
Tel.: (310) 734-6619
Web Site: http://www.riotgames.com
Videogame Developer & Publisher
N.A.I.C.S.: 513210
Brandon Beck *(Co-Founder)*

Shenzhen Tencent Computer System Ltd (1)
3rd-Floor-10th-Foor Feiyada High Technology Mansion, Gaoxin Nanyi Road Hi, Shenzhen, Guangdong, China **(100%)**
Tel.: (86) 75583764818
Computers Equipment & Software
N.A.I.C.S.: 423430

Sogou Inc. (1)
Level 15 Sohu com Internet Plaza No 1 Unit Zhongguancun East Road, Haidian District, Beijing, 100084, China **(100%)**
Tel.: (86) 10 5689 9999
Web Site: http://www.sogou.com
Rev.: $924,664,000
Assets: $1,395,132,000
Liabilities: $417,000,000
Net Worth: $978,132,000
Earnings: ($108,221,000)
Emp.: 2,544
Fiscal Year-end: 12/31/2020
Software Development Services
N.A.I.C.S.: 541511
Xiaochuan Wang *(CEO)*

Tencent Limited (1)
Tencent Binhai Building No 33 Haitian Second Road, Nanshan District, Shenzhen, 518054, Guangdong, China **(100%)**
Tel.: (86) 7558 601 3388
Web Site: https://www.tencent.com
Telecommunications Resellers
N.A.I.C.S.: 517121

Tencent Technology (Beijing) Company Limited (1)
Floor 16 Yinke Building 38 Haidian St, Haidian District, Beijing, China **(100%)**
Tel.: (86) 1062671188
Web Site: http://www.qq.com
Computer Programming Services
N.A.I.C.S.: 541511

Tencent Technology (Shenzhen) Co , Ltd (1)
Tencent Building Kejizhongyi Avenue Hi-tech Park, Nanshan District, Shenzhen, 518057, Guangdong, China **(100%)**
Tel.: (86) 75586013388
Web Site: http://www.tencent.com
Computer Programming Services
N.A.I.C.S.: 541511

eLong, Inc. (1)
3rd Floor Tower B Xingke Building 10 Middle Jiuxianqiao Road, Chaoyang District, Beijing, 100015, China
Tel.: (86) 10 64367570
Web Site: http://www.elong.net
Rev.: $165,465,654
Assets: $341,720,791
Liabilities: $187,306,250
Net Worth: $154,414,541
Earnings: ($161,400,078)
Emp.: 4,222
Fiscal Year-end: 12/31/2015
Online Travel Services
N.A.I.C.S.: 561599

Branch (Domestic):

eLong, Inc. - Chengdu (2)
Unit 5-6 9F Huamin Empire Plaza No 1 Fuxing Street, Chengdu, 610016, China
Tel.: (86) 2886703358
Web Site: http://www.elong.net
Online Travel Services
N.A.I.C.S.: 481212

eLong, Inc. - Guangzhou (2)
Rm 1305-1306 Block B No 242 Fengxing Plaza Tianhe Road, Tianhe District, Guangzhou, China
Tel.: (86) 2085509255
Online Travel Services
N.A.I.C.S.: 481212

eLong, Inc. - Hangzhou (2)
10F Block E&F Zhijun Mansion 96 Fengqi Road, Hangzhou, China
Tel.: (86) 57185802110
Web Site: http://www.elong.net
Online Travel Services
N.A.I.C.S.: 481212

eLong, Inc. - Nanjing (2)
Room 403 Building No 2 Junlin International Building, 5 Guangzhou Road, Nanjing, China
Tel.: (86) 2552481038
Online Travel Services
N.A.I.C.S.: 561599

eLong, Inc. - Shanghai Office (2)
2F No 10 Multimedia Valley Lane 777, Guangzhong West Road, Shanghai, China
Tel.: (86) 2161071417
Online Travel Services
N.A.I.C.S.: 481212

eLong, Inc. - Shenzhen (2)
News Building No 1002 Shennan Middle Road, Shenzhen, China
Tel.: (86) 75588263290
Online Travel Services
N.A.I.C.S.: 481212

eLong, Inc. - Wuhan (2)
Room 4101 World Trade Center Jiefang Avenue 686, Jianghan District, Wuhan, Jianghan, China
Tel.: (86) 2785449265
Web Site: http://www.elong.net
Online Travel Services
N.A.I.C.S.: 481212

TENCENT MUSIC ENTERTAINMENT GROUP
17/F Matsunichi Building Kejizhongyi Road, Midwest District of Hi-tech Park Nanshan District, Shenzhen, 518057, China
Tel.: (86) 75586013388 Ky
Web Site: http://www.tencentmusic.com
Year Founded: 2016
TME—(NYSE)
Rev.: $4,341,818,190
Assets: $10,266,448,890
Liabilities: $2,739,701,220
Net Worth: $7,526,747,670
Earnings: $588,173,190
Emp.: 5,805
Fiscal Year-end: 12/31/22
Oonline Music Entertainment Services
N.A.I.C.S.: 516210
Cussion Kar Shun Pang *(Exec Chm)*

TENDA CO., LTD.
WeWork Shibuya Scramble Square 22412 Shibuya, Shibuya-ku, Tokyo, 150-6139, Japan
Tel.: (81) 335904110
Web Site: https://www.tenda.co.jp
Year Founded: 1995
4198—(TKS)
Rev.: $34,206,750
Assets: $25,812,050
Liabilities: $8,797,910
Net Worth: $17,014,140
Earnings: $2,254,010
Emp.: 387
Fiscal Year-end: 05/31/24
Information Technology Services
N.A.I.C.S.: 541512

TENDANCES ECO GROUP SA
3642 Rue De La Teillaie, 72000, Le Mans, France
Tel.: (33) 243725099
Web Site: http://www.tendanceseco.fr
Sales Range: $50-74.9 Million
Emp.: 20
Solar Photovoltaic & Thermal Products Installation & Sales
N.A.I.C.S.: 238220
Dimitri Bellanger *(Pres)*

TENEDORA DE EMPRESAS SA DE CV
Poniente 134 No 719 Colonia Industrial Vallejo, Mexico, 02300, Mexico
Tel.: (52) 55 5728 5300
Web Site: http://www.nacobre.com.mx
Electronic Components Mfr & Distr
N.A.I.C.S.: 334419

TENEO AI AB
Stureplan 15 2nd Floor, 111 45, Stockholm, Sweden
Tel.: (46) 86635450 SE
Web Site: https://www.teneo.ai
Year Founded: 2011
ASAI—(OMX)
Rev.: $6,059,738
Assets: $8,303,596
Liabilities: $30,188,167
Net Worth: ($21,884,571)
Earnings: ($7,995,167)
Emp.: 68
Fiscal Year-end: 12/31/22
Software Publisher
N.A.I.C.S.: 513210
Asa Hedin *(Chm)*

Subsidiaries:

Artificial Solutions Holding ASH AB (1)
Master Samuelsgatan 60 8th Floor, 111 21, Stockholm, Sweden
Tel.: (46) 8 663 54 50
Web Site: http://www.artificial-solutions.com
Sales Range: $25-49.9 Million
Emp.: 200
Language Interaction Software Development
N.A.I.C.S.: 513210
Lawrence Flynn *(CEO)*

Subsidiary (Non-US):

Artificial Solutions BV (2)
Kingsfordweg 103, 1043 GP, Amsterdam, Netherlands
Tel.: (31) 308991897
Web Site: http://www.artificial-solutions.nl
Software Development Services
N.A.I.C.S.: 541511

Artificial Solutions Germany GmbH (2)
Poststrasse 33, 20354, Hamburg, Germany
Tel.: (49) 403508539
Web Site: http://www.artificial-solutions.de
Software Development Services
N.A.I.C.S.: 541511

Artificial Solutions Iberia, S. L. (2)
Calabria 169 5a Plta, 08015, Barcelona, Spain
Tel.: (34) 932451301
Web Site: http://www.artificial-solutions.com
Software Development Services
N.A.I.C.S.: 541511

Subsidiary (US):

Artificial Solutions Inc (2)
800 W El Camino Real Ste 180, Mountain View, CA 94040
Tel.: (650) 943-2325
Software Development Services
N.A.I.C.S.: 541511

TENET COMPUTER GROUP INC.
2820 14th Avenue Suite 101, Markham, L3R0S9, ON, Canada
Tel.: (416) 665-3069
Web Site: http://wwwtenet.com
Year Founded: 1984
Sales Range: $25-49.9 Million
Emp.: 32
IT Value Added Reseller & Solutions
N.A.I.C.S.: 423430
Carlos Paz-Soldan *(Pres)*

TENET FINTECH GROUP INC
111 Robert-Bourassa Blvd Suite 1500, West Tower Suite 265, Montreal, H3C 2M1, QC, Canada
Tel.: (514) 340-7775
Web Site: https://www.tenetfintech.com
Year Founded: 2008
P0T—(DEU)
Rev.: $81,169,029
Assets: $104,356,554
Liabilities: $17,477,727
Net Worth: $86,878,827
Earnings: ($39,161,694)
Emp.: 86
Fiscal Year-end: 12/31/22
Information Technology Solutions Services
N.A.I.C.S.: 541513
Charles-Andre Tessier *(Chm)*

TENFU (CAYMAN) HOLDINGS COMPANY LIMITED
2901 Building C Xinjing Commerce Center No 25 Jiahe Road, Xiamen, Fujian, China
Tel.: (86) 5923389334 Ky
Web Site: http://www.tenfu.com
6868—(HKG)
Rev.: $240,842,160
Assets: $440,784,677
Liabilities: $192,267,410
Net Worth: $248,517,266
Earnings: $28,985,861
Emp.: 3,643
Fiscal Year-end: 12/31/22
Holding Company
N.A.I.C.S.: 551112
Rie-Ho Lee *(Chm)*

TENGDA CONSTRUCTION GROUP CO., LTD.
No 1 Luqiao Avenue East, Luqiao District, Taizhou, 318050, Zhejiang, China
Tel.: (86) 57682522526
Web Site: https://www.tengdajs.com
Year Founded: 1995
600512—(SHG)
Rev.: $1,061,003,764
Assets: $1,771,521,267
Liabilities: $864,711,112
Net Worth: $906,810,155
Earnings: $125,691,952
Fiscal Year-end: 12/31/21
Construction Engineering Services
N.A.I.C.S.: 237310
Ye Lijun *(Chm)*

TENGELMANN WARENHANDELSGESELLSCHAFT KG
Wissollstrasse 5-43, 45478, Mullheim, Germany
Tel.: (49) 20858060
Web Site: http://www.tengelmann.de
Year Founded: 1867
Sales Range: $25-49.9 Billion
Emp.: 184,000
Supermarkets, Chain
N.A.I.C.S.: 445110
Karl-Erivan W. Haub *(Co-CEO & Mng Partner)*

Subsidiaries:

Baby-Markt.de GmbH (1)

TENGELMANN WARENHANDELSGESELLSCHAFT KG

Tengelmann Warenhandelsgesellschaft KG—(Continued)
Wulfshofstrasse 22, 44149, Dortmund, Germany
Tel.: (49) 231 53471100
Web Site: http://www.baby-markt.de
Online Shopping Services
N.A.I.C.S.: 455219

Emil Capital Partners LLC (1)
67 Mason St, Greenwich, CT 06830
Tel.: (203) 428-4400
Web Site: http://www.emilcapital.org
Investment Management Service
N.A.I.C.S.: 523940
Andreas Guldin *(CEO)*

Hermans Groep B.V. (75%)
Verlengde Lageweg 19, PO Box 249, 1628 PM, Hoorn, Netherlands
Tel.: (31) 229294000
Web Site: http://www.hermansgroup.nl
Sales Range: $25-49.9 Million
Emp.: 100
Grocery Stores
N.A.I.C.S.: 445110

KiK Textil Sp. z o. o. (1)
ul Modrzewskiego 15/17, 50-156, Wroclaw, Poland
Tel.: (48) 71 377 44 00
Web Site: http://www.kik-textilni.pl
Clothing Apparel Retailer
N.A.I.C.S.: 458110

KiK Textil es Non-Food Kft. (1)
Hengermalom ut 19-21, 1117, Budapest, Hungary
Tel.: (36) 29 551 740
Web Site: http://www.kik-textilien.hu
Clothing Apparel Retailer
N.A.I.C.S.: 458110

KiK Textilien und Non-Food GmbH (1)
Siemensstrasse 21, 59199, Bonen, Germany (100%)
Tel.: (49) 23839540
Web Site: http://www.kik-textilien.com
Sales Range: $200-249.9 Million
Emp.: 700
Family Clothing Stores
N.A.I.C.S.: 458110
Patrick Zahn *(Co-CEO)*

KiK textil a Non-Food spol. s r. o. (1)
K Hrusovu 293/2, 10203, Prague, Czech Republic
Tel.: (420) 272089702
Web Site: http://www.kik-textilien.cz
Clothing Apparel Retailer
N.A.I.C.S.: 458110

Kik Textilien und Non-Food d.o.o. (1)
Ruska ulica 6, 2000, Maribor, Slovenia
Tel.: (386) 2 46 00 380
Web Site: http://www.kik-textilien.si
Clothing Apparel Retailer
N.A.I.C.S.: 458110

OBI B.B.C. S.r.l. (1)
Via A Volta nr 16 Expansion Italy, Cologno Monzese, 20093, Italy
Tel.: (39) 0225166216
Web Site: http://www.obi-italia.it
Home Furnishings Retailer
N.A.I.C.S.: 449129

OBI Bau-und Heimwerkermaerkte GmbH & Co. KG (1)
Albert Einstein Strasse 7 9, D 42929, Wermelskirchen, Germany
Tel.: (49) 2196761509
Web Site: http://www.obi.de
Sales Range: $1-4.9 Billion
Emp.: 23,000
Retailer of Tools, Fittings, Materials & Accessories for Domestic Installations by Do-It-Yourselfers
N.A.I.C.S.: 444140

Subsidiary (Domestic):

Emil Lux GmbH & Co. KG (2)
Emil Lux Strasse 1, 42929, Wermelskirchen, Germany
Tel.: (49) 96764000
Web Site: http://www.luxtools.de

Sales Range: $75-99.9 Million
Emp.: 450
Importer & Exporter of Hardware & Small Machines
N.A.I.C.S.: 444140

Subsidiary (Non-US):

OBI Bau-Und Heimwerkermarkte Systemzentrale GmbH (1)
Litfabstrabe 8, Vienna, 1030, Austria
Tel.: (43) 1415150
Web Site: http://www.obi.at
Sales Range: $50-74.9 Million
Emp.: 200
Retailer of Tools, Fittings, Materials & Accessories for Domestic Installations by Do-It-Yourselfers
N.A.I.C.S.: 444140

OBI Centrala Systemowa Sp zoo (2)
Al Krakowska 102, Warsaw, 02-180, Poland (100%)
Tel.: (48) 225195000
Web Site: http://www.obi.pl
Sales Range: $25-49.9 Million
Emp.: 150
Provider of Household Goods & Materials for Do-It-Yourselfers
N.A.I.C.S.: 449210
Andrea Gross *(Mng Dir)*

OBI Hungary Retail Kft (2)
Book Kalman krt 12-14, 1097, Budapest, Hungary (100%)
Tel.: (36) 14555100
Web Site: http://www.obi.hu
Sales Range: $25-49.9 Million
Emp.: 2,100
Home Improvement Store Distr
N.A.I.C.S.: 444140

OBI Systemova centrala spol. s.r.o. (2)
Hanusova 18, 140 00, Prague, Czech Republic
Tel.: (420) 296608111
Web Site: http://www.obi.cz
Sales Range: $50-74.9 Million
Emp.: 150
Retailer of Tools, Fittings, Materials & Accessories for Domestic Installations by Do-It-Yourselfers
N.A.I.C.S.: 449210

OBI Systemzentrale S.r.l. (2)
Via Traversa Fiorentina 6, 59100, Prato, Italy (100%)
Tel.: (39) 057451841
Web Site: http://www.obi-italia.it
Sales Range: $25-49.9 Million
Emp.: 63
Retailer of Tools, Fittings, Materials & Accessories for Domestic Installations by Do-It-Yourselfers
N.A.I.C.S.: 444140

Subsidiary (Domestic):

OBI-Systemzentrale (2)
Albert-Einstein-Strasse 7-9, 42929, Wermelskirchen, Germany (100%)
Tel.: (49) 21969062000
Web Site: http://www.obi.de
Sales Range: $150-199.9 Million
Emp.: 600
Household Appliance Retailer
N.A.I.C.S.: 449129
Sergio Giroldi *(CEO)*

OBI Ceska republika s.r.o. (1)
Budejovicka 3a, 140 00, Prague, Czech Republic
Tel.: (420) 277001004
Web Site: http://www.obi.cz
Home Furnishing Distr
N.A.I.C.S.: 449129

OBI Franchise Center OOO (1)
Ulitsa Aviakonstruktora Mikoyana 12 Block B BC Linkor Floor 7-9, 125252, Moscow, Russia
Tel.: (7) 4959334680
Web Site: http://www.obi.ru
Home Furnishings Retailer
N.A.I.C.S.: 449129
Ian Strickland *(Gen Dir)*

OBI Romania SRL (1)
Cladirea CUBIC Center Blvd Pipera nr 1B

et 5, Voluntari, Jud Ilfov, Romania
Tel.: (40) 372 060 000
Web Site: http://www.obi.ro
Home Furnishings Retailer
N.A.I.C.S.: 449129
Adrian Anghel *(Mgr-Pur Category)*

OBI Ukraine Franchise Centre LLC (1)
26 Moskovskyi Prospect 1st block, 04073, Kiev, Ukraine
Tel.: (380) 44499 49 70
Web Site: http://www.obi.ua
Home Furnishings Retailer
N.A.I.C.S.: 449129

Subrenta Immobilienverwaltungsgesellschaft mbH (1)
Wissollstrasse 5-43, 45478, Mulheim an der Ruhr, Germany
Tel.: (49) 2 08 58 06 66 78
Web Site: http://www.subrenta.de
Property Management Services
N.A.I.C.S.: 531312

TREI Real Estate Austria GmbH (1)
Prinz-Eugen-Strasse 72, 1040, Vienna, Austria
Tel.: (43) 1 504 81 80
Real Estate Manangement Services
N.A.I.C.S.: 531210

TREI Real Estate Czech Republic s.r.o. (1)
Rohanske nabrezi 670/17, 186 00, Prague, Czech Republic
Tel.: (420) 286 001 080
Web Site: http://www.treirealestate.com
Real Estate Manangement Services
N.A.I.C.S.: 531210
Hana Johnova *(Dir-Construction & Admin)*

TREI Real Estate Hungary Kft. (1)
Nepstadion koz 5 I em 2-3, 1143, Budapest, Hungary
Tel.: (36) 1 422 43 80
Real Estate Manangement Services
N.A.I.C.S.: 531210
Gyorgyi Federer *(Dir-Admin & Fin)*

TREI Real Estate Poland Sp. z o.o. (1)
ul Wspolna 47/49, 00-684, Warsaw, Poland
Tel.: (48) 224276301
Real Estate Manangement Services
N.A.I.C.S.: 531210
Krzysztof Kolomyjski *(Dir-Project Dev & Leasing)*

TREI Real Estate Portugal, Lda. (1)
Loja RS 14 I Avenida Euro 2004, 2890-154, Alcochete, Portugal
Tel.: (351) 21 23 48 100
Real Estate Manangement Services
N.A.I.C.S.: 531210
Cristina Ferreira Gomes *(Dir-Real Estate)*

TENIX GROUP PTY LTD.

Level 18/40 Mount Street, North Sydney, 2060, NSW, Australia
Tel.: (61) 299639600
Web Site: http://www.tenix.com
Year Founded: 1997
Sales Range: $800-899.9 Million
Emp.: 100
Holding Company; Defense Contractor & Mfr
N.A.I.C.S.: 551112
Paul Salteri *(Chm)*

Subsidiaries:

Tenix Australia Pty Ltd. (1)
Level 5 600 Saint Kilda Rd, Melbourne, 3004, VIC, Australia (100%)
Tel.: (61) 385179011
Sales Range: $150-199.9 Million
Emp.: 1,000
Defense Contractor & Mfr
N.A.I.C.S.: 541330
Neil Williams *(Mgr-Trng)*

Tenix Solutions Pty Ltd (1)
Level 5 277 William Street, Melbourne, 3000, VIC, Australia
Tel.: (61) 390586500
Web Site: http://www.tenixsolutions.com.au

Sales Range: $75-99.9 Million
Traffic & Parking Management Solution Services
N.A.I.C.S.: 541330
Ryan Brisbane *(CEO)*

TENMA CORPORATION

1-63-6 Akabane, Kita-ku, Tokyo, 115-0045, Japan
Tel.: (81) 335985511
Web Site:
 https://www.tenmacorp.co.jp
Year Founded: 1949
7958—(TKS)
Rev.: $614,273,910
Assets: $673,697,810
Liabilities: $137,871,380
Net Worth: $535,826,430
Earnings: $20,431,510
Emp.: 7,868
Fiscal Year-end: 03/31/24
Plastic Product Mfr & Whslr
N.A.I.C.S.: 326199
Yasuichi Kaneda *(Chm)*

Subsidiaries:

PT. TENMA CIKARANG INDONESIA (1)
Delta Silicon Industrial Park Jl Kruing 3 Blok L8-5A Sukaresmi, Cikarang Selatan, Bekasi, 17550, Indonesia
Tel.: (62) 2189905855
Industrial Supplies Whslr
N.A.I.C.S.: 423840

PT. TENMA INDONESIA (1)
Kawasan Industri MM2100 Blok I NO3-4 Gandamekar Cikarang Barat, Bekasi, 17520, Indonesia
Tel.: (62) 218980905
Industrial Supplies Whslr
N.A.I.C.S.: 423840
Ronny Simanjuntak *(Mgr-HRD)*

Shanghai Tenma Platech & Housewares Co., Ltd. (1)
No 556 Rongle East Road, Songjiang District, Shanghai, China
Tel.: (86) 215 774 2451
Household Item Mfr
N.A.I.C.S.: 326199

TENMA (THAILAND) CO., LTD. (1)
7/119 Moo 4 Amata City Rayong Industrial Estate T Mapyangporn, A Pluakdaeng, Rayong, 21140, Thailand
Tel.: (66) 38650114
Automotive Part Whslr
N.A.I.C.S.: 423120

Plant (Domestic):

TENMA (THAILAND) CO., LTD. - Prachinburi Factory (2)
128 Moo 6 304 Industrial park7 T Srimahaphote, Prachin Buri, 25140, Thailand
Tel.: (66) 37218743
Industrial Equipment Mfr
N.A.I.C.S.: 333998

TENMA Vietnam Co., Ltd. (1)
LotE1 Que Vo Industrial Zone, Phuong Lieu Commune, Bac Ninh, Vietnam
Tel.: (84) 2413617740
Industrial Supplies Whslr
N.A.I.C.S.: 423840

Plant (Domestic):

TENMA Vietnam Co., Ltd. - Ha Noi Factory (2)
Viet Hung Commune, Dong Anh District, Hanoi, Vietnam
Tel.: (84) 43 883 6149
Industrial Equipment Mfr
N.A.I.C.S.: 333998

TENMA Vietnam Co., Ltd. - HoChiMinh Factory (2)
No 10 Road 9A Bien Hoa Industrial Zone, Ho Chi Minh City, Dong Nai, Vietnam
Tel.: (84) 61 383 6280
Industrial Equipment Mfr
N.A.I.C.S.: 333998

Tacmic Co., Ltd. (1)
3277-14 Tana, Chuo-ku, Sagamihara, 252-

0244, Kanagawa, Japan
Tel.: (81) 427133661
Web Site: https://www.tacmic.com
Emp.: 27
Plastics Product Mfr
N.A.I.C.S.: 326199

Tenma Corporation - Hachinohe
Factory (1)
1-2 Ashonai Nango Oaza Shimamori,
Nango-ku, Hachinohe, 031-0202, Aomori,
Japan
Tel.: (81) 178823210
Industrial Equipment Mfr
N.A.I.C.S.: 333998

Tenma Corporation - Hirosaki
Factory (1)
5-1-8 Kanda, Hirosaki, 036-8061, Aomori,
Japan
Tel.: (81) 172802211
Industrial Equipment Mfr
N.A.I.C.S.: 333998

Tenma Corporation - Noda
Factory (1)
2345 Osaki, Noda, 270-0235, Chiba, Japan
Tel.: (81) 471272721
Industrial Equipment Mfr
N.A.I.C.S.: 333998

Tenma Corporation - Shiga
Factory (1)
1456 Ryuboshi, Konan-cho, Koka, 520-
3311, Shiga, Japan
Tel.: (81) 748863111
Industrial Equipment Mfr
N.A.I.C.S.: 333998

Tenma Corporation - Shin-Shirakawa
Factory (1)
1-2 Omotegokomatsu Ushiroyama,
Shirakawa-shi, Fukushima, 961-0405, Ja-
pan
Tel.: (81) 248324321
Household Products Mfr
N.A.I.C.S.: 335220

Tenma Corporation - Yamaguchi
Factory (1)
1173 Yamanoi, Sanyo-Onoda, 757-0003,
Yamaguchi-ken, Japan
Tel.: (81) 836732131
Industrial Equipment Mfr
N.A.I.C.S.: 333998

Tenma Plastic Mexico, SA de CV (1)
Av Cucapah 5315 Fracc El Lago, CP.
22210, Tijuana, BC, Mexico
Tel.: (52) 16641344662
Plastic Product Mfr & Distr
N.A.I.C.S.: 326199

Tenma Precision (Shenzhen) Co.,
Ltd. (1)
No 1301-19 55 Guangguang Road Dabuxi-
ang Community, Longhua District, Shen-
zhen, China
Tel.: (86) 7558 330 8459
Office Automation Equipment Parts Mfr
N.A.I.C.S.: 333998

Tenma Precision (Zhongshan) Co.,
Ltd. (1)
No 8 Minyuan Road, Torch Kaiyu District,
Zhongshan, Dongdong, China
Tel.: (86) 7608 528 0400
Office Automation Equipment Parts Mfr
N.A.I.C.S.: 333998

TENMAYA STORE CO., LTD.
13-16 Okamachi, Kita-ku, Okayama,
700-8502, Japan
Tel.: (81) 862327265
Web Site: https://www.tenmaya-
store.co.jp
Year Founded: 1969
9846—(TKS)
Rev.: $415,240,030
Assets: $303,111,680
Liabilities: $126,932,270
Net Worth: $176,179,410
Earnings: $8,458,370
Emp.: 2,127
Fiscal Year-end: 02/29/24
Supermarket Store Operator
N.A.I.C.S.: 445110

Katsumi Kizumi (Chm)

TENNANT GROUP LTD.
The Midway, Nottingham, NG7 2TS,
Notts, United Kingdom
Tel.: (44) 1159881300 UK
Web Site:
http://www.tennantgroup.co.uk
Year Founded: 1955
Sales Range: $25-49.9 Million
Emp.: 45
Whslr of Industrial Supplies
N.A.I.C.S.: 423840
Richard W. Tennant (Owner & Mng
Dir)

Subsidiaries:

Tennant Holdings (1)
Ruspidge Rd, Cinderford, GL14 3AS,
United Kingdom (100%)
Tel.: (44) 594822375
Rev.: $21,401,399
Emp.: 10
Coatings
N.A.I.C.S.: 325510

TENNANT MINERALS NL
TMS—(ASX)
Rev.: $24,129
Assets: $3,126,693
Liabilities: $337,714
Net Worth: $2,788,979
Earnings: ($2,618,184)
Fiscal Year-end: 06/30/24
Mineral Exploration Services
N.A.I.C.S.: 327999
Vincent Algar (CEO)

TENNOR HOLDING BV
World Trade Center Schiphol, Boule-
vard 127 G4.02, Amsterdam, 1118,
Netherlands
Tel.: (31) 20 201 49 04
Web Site: http://tennor.com
Year Founded: 2009
Private Investment Firm
N.A.I.C.S.: 523999
Lars Windhorst (Founder)

Subsidiaries:

La Perla Fashion Holding N.V. (1)
Schiphol Boulevard 127 G4 02, 1118 BG,
Schiphol, Netherlands (90%)
Tel.: (31) 202014904
Web Site: https://laperlafashionholding.com
Rev.: $74,566,156
Assets: $91,214,116
Liabilities: $457,879,344
Net Worth: ($366,665,228)
Earnings: ($53,352,040)
Emp.: 971
Fiscal Year-end: 12/31/2022
Clothing Accessory Mfr & Distr
N.A.I.C.S.: 315120
Imran Khan (Member-Mgmt Bd)

Subsidiary (Non-US):

Gruppo La Perla Fashion SA (2)
Via Enrico Mattei 10, 40138, Bologna, Italy
Tel.: (39) 051537411
Web Site: http://www.laperla.com
Women's Clothing, Lingerie, Underwear,
Swimwear, Sportswear, Shoes, Eyewear,
Perfume; Men's Underwear & Sportswear;
Children's Underwear & Swimwear
N.A.I.C.S.: 458110

Subsidiary (Non-US):

La Perla Group France S.A.R.L. (3)
Rue Du Faubourg St Honore 20, 75008,
Paris, France
Tel.: (33) 143123350
Web Site: http://www.laperla.com
Fashion Apparel & Accessories
N.A.I.C.S.: 315990

Subsidiary (US):

La Perla North America Inc. (3)
32 E 57th St 6th Fl, New York, NY 10021
Tel.: (212) 459-2775

Web Site: http://www.laperla.com
Fashion Apparel & Accessories
N.A.I.C.S.: 424350

**TENO.HOLDINGS COMPANY
LIMITED.**
5F Gofukumachi Business Center,
Kamigofuku-cho hakata-ku, Fukuoka,
812-0036, Japan
Tel.: (81) 922633550
Web Site: https://www.teno.co.jp
Year Founded: 2015
7037—(TKS)
Rev.: $103,209,130
Assets: $67,546,430
Liabilities: $51,650,650
Net Worth: $15,895,780
Earnings: $709,000
Fiscal Year-end: 12/31/23
Holding Company
N.A.I.C.S.: 551112
Hiroko Ikeuchi (Pres)

TENOX CO., LTD.
5F Hulic Mita Building 25-11 Shiba
5-chome, Minato-Ku, Tokyo, 108-
8380, Japan
Tel.: (81) 334557790
Web Site: https://www.tenox.co.jp
Year Founded: 1970
1905—(TKS)
Rev.: $133,568,270
Assets: $126,026,260
Liabilities: $42,151,970
Net Worth: $83,874,290
Earnings: $2,564,680
Emp.: 366
Fiscal Year-end: 03/31/24
Construction Engineering Services
N.A.I.C.S.: 237990
Masayuki Sato (Pres)

Subsidiaries:

Hiroshimagumi Co., Ltd. (1)
4-12-3 Sakuragawa, Naniwa-ku, Osaka,
556-0022, Japan
Tel.: (81) 665623001
Web Site: https://www.hiroshimagumi.net
Emp.: 30
Civil Engineering & Construction Services
N.A.I.C.S.: 541330

Integrated Geotechnology Institute.,
Ltd. (1)
Kyouritsuyotsuya Bldg 1-23-6 Yotsuya,
Shinjuku-Ku, Tokyo, 160-0004, Japan
Tel.: (81) 353684101
Civil Engineering & Construction Services
N.A.I.C.S.: 541330

Ohmishima Bussan Co., Ltd. (1)
2-4-7 Tokukura, Mishima, 411-0044, Japan
Tel.: (81) 559871990
Web Site: https://www.ohmishima.co.jp
Emp.: 13
Civil Engineering & Construction Services
N.A.I.C.S.: 541330

Tenox Asia Company Limited (1)
15th Floor LMak Long Tower 101-103
Nguyen Cuu Van St, Binh Thanh District
Ward 17, Ho Chi Minh City, Vietnam
Tel.: (84) 2835210061
Web Site: https://www.tenoxasia.com
Civil Engineering & Construction Services
N.A.I.C.S.: 541330

Tenox Giken Co., Ltd. (1)
2459-1 Komurocho, Funabashi, 270-1471,
Japan
Tel.: (81) 474570121
Civil Engineering & Construction Services
N.A.I.C.S.: 541330

TENPOS HOLDINGS, INC.
7F Sanyu Higashikamata Building
2-30-17 Higashikamata, Ota-Ku, Tokyo, 144-0031, Japan
Tel.: (81) 337360319
Web Site: https://www.tenpos.co.jp
Year Founded: 1997
27510—(TKS)

Sales Range: $200-249.9 Million
Kitchen Equipment Mfr & Distr
N.A.I.C.S.: 449210
Kazumitsu Morishita (Dir)

Subsidiaries:

Sunwave Kitchen Techno Corp. (1)
31-4 Wakamatsucho Wakamatsucho Bldg,
Shinjuku-Ku, Tokyo, 162-0056, Japan
Tel.: (81) 352853335
Sales Range: $50-74.9 Million
Kitchen Ware Equipment Mfr
N.A.I.C.S.: 332215

TENRYU SAW MFG. CO., LTD.
3711 Asaba, Fukuroi, 437-1195, Shi-
zuoka, Japan
Tel.: (81) 538236111
Web Site: https://www.tenryu-
saw.com
Year Founded: 1909
5945—(TKS)
Rev.: $78,890,350
Assets: $248,740,910
Liabilities: $22,368,240
Net Worth: $226,372,670
Earnings: $8,103,860
Emp.: 200
Fiscal Year-end: 03/31/24
Machine Tools Mfr
N.A.I.C.S.: 333517
Takaaki Oishi (Pres)

Subsidiaries:

Tenryu (China) Saw Mfg. Co.,
Ltd. (1)
No11 Jinyuan East Road, Langfang Eco-
nomic and Technical Development Zone,
Hebei, 065001, China
Tel.: (86) 3166089022
Web Site: https://www.tenryu.cn
Emp.: 528
Saw Blade Mfr & Distr
N.A.I.C.S.: 332216

Tenryu America, Inc. (1)
3601 Hargrave Dr, Hebron, KY 41048
Tel.: (859) 282-8158
Web Site: http://www.tenryu.com
Emp.: 12
Saw Blade Mfr & Distr
N.A.I.C.S.: 332216
Barry Fladeland (Office Mgr)

Tenryu Europe GmbH (1)
Ulmer Strasse 130, 73431, Aalen, Germany
Tel.: (49) 7361890840
Web Site: http://www.tenryu.de
Saw Blade Distr
N.A.I.C.S.: 423710
Ezio Macor (Mgr-Sls)

Tenryu Saw (Thailand) Co., Ltd. (1)
Amata City Rayong Industrial Estate 7/327
Moo 6, Mabyangphon Sub-district, Pluak
Daeng, 21140, Rayong, Thailand
Tel.: (66) 380363758
Emp.: 200
Saw Blade Distr
N.A.I.C.S.: 423710

Tenryu Saw India Private Limited (1)
plot no 205 122051 Sector 7 IMT Manesar,
Gurgaon, 122052, Haryana, India
Tel.: (91) 1244148205
Web Site: https://www.tenryuindia.com
Saw Blade Distr
N.A.I.C.S.: 423710
Pardeep Arora (Mgr-Sls)

Tenryu Saw Mfg. Co., Ltd. - Giken
Factory (1)
545-15 Tenryugawa, Hamamatsu, 435-
0013, Shizuoka, Japan
Tel.: (81) 534211181
Saw Blades Mfr
N.A.I.C.S.: 332216

Tenryu Saw de Mexico, S.A. de
C.V. (1)
Circuito Logistic Aeropuerto No 22 Lote11
San Antonio Texas, 36270, Silao, Guana-
juato, Mexico
Tel.: (52) 4727489004
Saw Blade Distr

TENRYU SAW MFG. CO., LTD.

Tenryu Saw Mfg. Co., Ltd.—(Continued)
N.A.I.C.S.: 423710

TENSATOR LTD.
Danbury Court, Linford Wood, Milton Keynes, MK14 6TS, Bucks, United Kingdom
Tel.: (44) 1908 684600
Web Site:
 http://www.tensatorgroup.com
Year Founded: 1881
Emp.: 200
Queue Management Solutions & Products Mfr
N.A.I.C.S.: 541618
Gordon Lorimer (Dir-Healthcare Bus)

Subsidiaries:

Tensator Inc. (1)
260 Spur Dr S, Bay Shore, NY 11706-3917
Tel.: (631) 666-0300
Web Site: http://www.tensatorgroup.com
Sales Range: $50-74.9 Million
Emp.: 110
Pedestrian Traffic Control Products Whslr
N.A.I.C.S.: 423440
Kathleen McLaughlin Byrne (Mgr-Sls Ops)

TENSHO ELECTRIC INDUSTRIES CO., LTD.
Tenko Bld 1T 3-65 Minami Machida 5-chome, Machida, 194-0005, Tokyo, Japan
Tel.: (81) 427881555
Web Site: https://www.tensho-plastic.co.jp
Year Founded: 1936
6776—(TKS)
Rev.: $177,842,050
Assets: $184,756,110
Liabilities: $112,508,810
Net Worth: $72,247,300
Earnings: $6,266,280
Emp.: 500
Fiscal Year-end: 03/31/24
Plastic Molding Product Mfr
N.A.I.C.S.: 325211
Tadahiko Ishikawa (Pres)

Subsidiaries:

RYUMAI Plastic Co., Ltd. (1)
535 Ryumaicho, Ota, 373-0806, Gunma, Japan
Tel.: (81) 276451651
Web Site: https://www.ryupla.co.jp
Emp.: 71
Plastic Injection Mold Mfr & Distr
N.A.I.C.S.: 333511

Sanko America Corporation (1)
2320 Paseo de las Americas Ste 106, San Diego, CA 92154
Tel.: (619) 591-0000
Web Site: https://sankousmx.com
Plastic Injection Mold Mfr & Distr
N.A.I.C.S.: 333511

Sanko Plastics Mexico Corporation S.A. de C.V. (1)
Calle Emiliano Zapata 376 Col Reforma, Playas de, CP 22704, Rosarito, Baja California, Mexico
Tel.: (52) 6616139188
Plastic Injection Mold Mfr & Distr
N.A.I.C.S.: 333511

Tensho America Corporation (1)
2320 Paseo de las Americas Ste 106, San Diego, CA 92154
Tel.: (619) 591-0000
Injection Molded Plastic Product Distr
N.A.I.C.S.: 423840

Tensho Electric Industries Co., Ltd. - Fukushima Plant (1)
1 Kakoidan Shibukawa, Nihonmatsu, 969-1403, Fukushima, Japan
Tel.: (81) 243532311
Plastic Molding Product Mfr
N.A.I.C.S.: 325211

Tensho Electric Industries Co., Ltd. - Gunma Plant (1)
278-1 Uekino, Ota, 373-0014, Gunma, Japan
Tel.: (81) 276260151
Plastic Molding Product Mfr
N.A.I.C.S.: 325211

Tensho Electric Industries Co., Ltd. - Mie Plant (1)
3633 Kitafukuzawa Hatta, Iga, 518-1155, Mie, Japan
Tel.: (81) 595201040
Plastic Molding Product Mfr
N.A.I.C.S.: 325211

Tensho Electric Industries Co., Ltd. - Saitama Plant (1)
315 Kamioyashiki, Kawajima Hiki, Saitama, 350-0142, Japan
Tel.: (81) 492993335
Plastic Molding Product Mfr
N.A.I.C.S.: 325211

Tensho Electric Industries Co., Ltd. - Yabuki Plant (1)
203-6 Botandaira Yabuki, Nishishirakawa, Fukushima, 969-0237, Japan
Tel.: (81) 248422100
Plastic Molding Product Mfr
N.A.I.C.S.: 325211

Tensho Mexico Corporation S.A. de C.V. (1)
Calle Emiliano Zapata 376 Col Reforma, 22704, Rosarito, Mexico
Tel.: (52) 6616139188
Injection Molded Plastic Product Distr
N.A.I.C.S.: 423840

Tensho Plastic (Changzhou) Co., Ltd. (1)
No 8-2 Dutou Street, Daitou Industry District, Liyang, 213311, Jiangsu, China
Tel.: (86) 51987368000
Industrial Machinery Mfr
N.A.I.C.S.: 423830

Tensho Poland Corporation Sp. z o.o. (1)
Ostaszewo 57 F, 87-148, Lysomice, Poland
Tel.: (48) 2188686
Web Site: https://bap.boryszew.eu
Injection Molded Plastic Products Mfr
N.A.I.C.S.: 326130
Joanna Falkowska (Mgr-HR)

TENTH AVENUE PETROLEUM CORP.
2003 188 15th Ave S W, Calgary, T2R 1S4, AB, Canada
Tel.: (403) 585-9875
Web Site:
 https://www.tenthavenuepetro.com
Year Founded: 1999
TPC—(TSXV)
Rev.: $2,608,715
Assets: $4,467,978
Liabilities: $3,209,465
Net Worth: $1,258,512
Earnings: ($1,065,372)
Fiscal Year-end: 12/31/23
Gas & Oil Exploration & Production
N.A.I.C.S.: 211120
Gregory J. Leia (Pres & CEO)

TENTHOREY S.A.
ZI La Plaine, 88510, Eloyes, Vosges, France
Tel.: (33) 329643200
Web Site: http://www.sac-citoyen.com
Year Founded: 1906
Broadwoven Fabric Mills
N.A.I.C.S.: 313210
Yves Dubief (Pres)

TENTIWALA METAL PRODUCTS LIMITED
Delhi-Masani Road Radhey Shyam Colony, Mathura, 281 003, Uttar Pradesh, India
Tel.: (91) 565 2530032
Web Site:
 http://www.tentiwalametal.com
Year Founded: 1994
Emp.: 60
Wire & Cable Products Mfr
N.A.I.C.S.: 332618
Radha Pad Tentiwala (Chm & Mng Dir)

TENWOW INTERNATIONAL HOLDINGS LIMITED
Room 3306-12 33F Shui On Centre, 6-8 Harbour Road, Wanchai, China (Hong Kong)
Tel.: (852) 2808 1972
Web Site: http://ir.tenwow.com.hk
Sales Range: $650-699.9 Million
Holding Company
N.A.I.C.S.: 551112
Yue Ming Yeung (VP)

Subsidiaries:

Nanpu Fine Wine & Spirits International Company Limited (1)
1-3/F Block A 52-62 Tsing Yi Road, Hong Kong, China (Hong Kong)
Tel.: (852) 24363369
Web Site: http://www.nanpufinewine.com
Wine Distr
N.A.I.C.S.: 424820

Shanghai Tenwow Foods (Group) Co., Ltd. (1)
No 1300 Jiugan Road Sijing Industrial Zone Songjiang District, Shanghai, 201601, China
Tel.: (86) 2161923333
Web Site: http://www.tenwowfood.com
Emp.: 3,000
Food & Beverage Mfr & Distr
N.A.I.C.S.: 311421

Shenzhen Nanpu Industrial Co., Ltd. (1)
A F 33/F Nuode Financial Center No 1006 Fuzhong No 3 Rd Futian, Shenzhen, 518026, Guangdong, China
Tel.: (86) 75533988011
Food & Beverage Distr
N.A.I.C.S.: 424490

TENZING PRIVATE EQUITY LLP
Heddon House 149-151 Regent Street, London, W1B 4JD, United Kingdom
Tel.: (44) 2032827560
Web Site: https://tenzing.pe
Year Founded: 2015
Privater Equity Firm
N.A.I.C.S.: 523940
Guy Gillon (Co-Founder & CEO)

TEO FOODS INC.
Blvd Insurgentes 19801 Unit 4-D, Tijuana, 22225, BC, Mexico
Tel.: (52) 6197581973 NV
Web Site: http://www.teofoods.com
Year Founded: 2012
TEOF—(OTCQB)
Rev.: $85,759
Assets: $107,725
Liabilities: $1,575,505
Net Worth: ($1,467,780)
Earnings: ($347,309)
Emp.: 2
Fiscal Year-end: 12/31/22
Frozen Food Product Mfr & Distr
N.A.I.C.S.: 311412
Jeffrey Mackay (Pres & CEO)

TEO GUAN LEE CORPORATION BERHAD
Plot 28 Lorong Perusahaan Maju 4 Prai Industrial Estate, 13600, Perai, Penang, Malaysia
Tel.: (60) 45076228
Web Site:
 https://www.tglcorp.com.my

INTERNATIONAL PUBLIC

TGL—(KLS)
Rev.: $32,088,361
Assets: $35,425,915
Liabilities: $8,337,534
Net Worth: $27,088,381
Earnings: $4,200,535
Emp.: 690
Fiscal Year-end: 06/30/22
Garments Mfr
N.A.I.C.S.: 313320
Kian Beng Toh (Mng Dir-Grp)

Subsidiaries:

P.P.A.C. (M) Sdn. Bhd. (1)
Plot 28 Lorong Perusahaan Maju 4, Prai Industrial Estate, Prai, 13600, Penang, Malaysia
Tel.: (60) 45076228
Web Site: http://www.tm.net.my
Sales Range: $25-49.9 Million
Emp.: 60
Garments Whslr
N.A.I.C.S.: 315210
Alex Yeoh (Mgr)

Syarikat Perniagaan Bingel (M) Sdn. Bhd. (1)
No 38 2nd Floor Jln Bunga Tanjung 8 Taman Putra, Ampang, 68000, Selangor, Malaysia
Tel.: (60) 342945911
Apparels Mfr
N.A.I.C.S.: 315990
Kee Lik Kang (Mng Dir)

Teo Guan Lee (K.L.) Sdn. Bhd. (1)
10-12 Jalan 6/91 Batu 3-1/2 Taman Shamelin Perkasa, Cheras, 56100, Kuala Lumpur, Federal Territory, Malaysia
Tel.: (60) 392831422
Sales Range: $25-49.9 Million
Emp.: 200
Apparels Mfr
N.A.I.C.S.: 315990

Subsidiary (Domestic):

JC Garments (M) Sdn. Bhd. (2)
No 1 Jalan Jelita Satu Taman Jelita Off Jalan Reko, Kajang, 43000, Selangor, Malaysia
Tel.: (60) 387333008
Garments Mfr & Sales
N.A.I.C.S.: 315250

TEOLLISUUDEN VOIMA OYJ
Olkiluoto, Eurajoki, 27160, Finland
Tel.: (358) 283811
Web Site: http://www.tvo.fi
Sales Range: $300-349.9 Million
Emp.: 813
Nuclear Electric Power Generation
N.A.I.C.S.: 221113
Mikko Kosonen (Sr VP-Safety)

TEQNION AB
Evenemangsgatan 31A, 169 79, Solna, Sweden
Tel.: (46) 86551200
Web Site: https://www.teqnion.se
Year Founded: 2006
TEQ—(OMX)
Rev.: $124,083,284
Assets: $100,293,162
Liabilities: $58,800,940
Net Worth: $41,492,221
Earnings: $10,330,907
Emp.: 500
Fiscal Year-end: 12/31/22
Industrial Equipment Distr
N.A.I.C.S.: 423830

TEQUILA COMMUNICATION & MARKETING INC.
3556 boul Saint Laurent Bureau Ste 200, Montreal, H2X 2V1, QC, Canada
Tel.: (514) 849-8005
Web Site: http://www.tequila.ca
Sales Range: $10-24.9 Million
Emp.: 22
N.A.I.C.S.: 541810

Bernard Berthiaume *(Pres)*

TEQUITY AB
Sundsliden 13, SE-254 81, Helsingborg, Sweden
Tel.: (46) 709 172902
Web Site: http://www.tequity.se
Investment Services
N.A.I.C.S.: 523999
Nicolas Hassbjer *(Chm)*

TER ALP
Route D Argent, 38510, Morestel, Isere, France
Tel.: (33) 474804050
Web Site: http://www.teralp.com
Sales Range: $1-4.9 Billion
Emp.: 50
Farm Produce Supplies Distribution Manager
N.A.I.C.S.: 424410
David Terrier *(Pres)*

TERA AUTOTECH CORP.
No 1 Gongqi Road Rinanli, Dajia District, Taichung, Taiwan
Tel.: (886) 426822168
Web Site: https://teraauto.com.tw
Year Founded: 1982
6234—(TPE)
Rev.: $41,746,178
Assets: $134,696,620
Liabilities: $50,596,286
Net Worth: $84,100,335
Earnings: $5,741,644
Fiscal Year-end: 12/31/22
Household Appliance Distr
N.A.I.C.S.: 423620
I-Lung Li *(Chm & Pres)*

TERA SCIENCE CO., LTD.
78 Changwon-daero 1144 beon-gil, Seongsan-gu, Changwon, Gyeongsangnam-do, Korea (South)
Tel.: (82) 552137000
Web Site: https://www.tera-science.com
Year Founded: 1977
073640—(KRS)
Rev.: $17,494,559
Assets: $83,201,201
Liabilities: $21,875,928
Net Worth: $61,325,273
Earnings: $22,042,814
Emp.: 45
Fiscal Year-end: 12/31/22
Hydraulic Fitting Mfr
N.A.I.C.S.: 332919
Jong Seok Lee *(CEO)*

Subsidiaries:

S-Tech Japan Co., Ltd. (1)
16-1 Sanbancho, Atsuta-ku, Nagoya, 456-0056, Aichi-ken, Japan
Tel.: (81) 526652451
Web Site: https://s-tech-j.com
Emp.: 22
Hydraulic Hose Fitting Product Distr
N.A.I.C.S.: 423840

Samwon USA Inc. (1)
1261 Wiley Rd Unit J, Schaumburg, IL 60173
Tel.: (630) 635-2647
Web Site: http://samwonusa.com
Hydraulic Fitting Product Distr
N.A.I.C.S.: 423830

TERA SOFTWARE LTD.
8-2-293/82/A/1107 Plot No 1107 Road No-55, Jubilee Hills, Hyderabad, 500 033, India
Tel.: (91) 4023540446
Web Site: https://www.terasoftware.com
TERASOFT—(NSE)
Rev.: $22,377,182
Assets: $40,737,347
Liabilities: $25,906,731
Net Worth: $14,830,616
Earnings: $115,070
Emp.: 610
Fiscal Year-end: 03/31/21
Software Development Services
N.A.I.C.S.: 541511
T. Gopichand *(Vice Chm & Mng Dir)*

TERA YATIRIM MENKUL DEGERLER A.S.
Eski Buyukdere cad No 9 Iz Plaza Giz No 9k 11, Maslak, 34398, Istanbul, Turkiye
Tel.: (90) 2123651000
Year Founded: 1990
TERA—(IST)
Rev.: $148,707,418
Assets: $86,841,278
Liabilities: $66,386,688
Net Worth: $20,454,591
Earnings: $8,846,656
Fiscal Year-end: 12/31/23
Investment Management Service
N.A.I.C.S.: 523940
Oguz Tezmen *(Chm)*

TERACT SA
83 avenue de la Grande Armee a, 75016, Paris, France
Tel.: (33) 889017018
Web Site: https://www.teract.com
Year Founded: 2014
TRACT—(EUR)
Rev.: $964,164,480
Assets: $1,265,245,440
Liabilities: $902,815,360
Net Worth: $362,430,080
Earnings: ($114,254,720)
Emp.: 5,400
Fiscal Year-end: 06/30/23
Agriculture Product Distr
N.A.I.C.S.: 424910
Guillaume Darrasse *(Deputy CEO)*

TERAGO INC.
55 Commerce Valley Drive West Suite 800, Thornhill, L3T 7V9, ON, Canada
Tel.: (905) 482-6512 Ca
Web Site: https://www.terago.ca
TGO—(TSX)
Rev.: $33,875,071
Assets: $72,931,964
Liabilities: $41,435,807
Net Worth: $31,496,157
Earnings: ($11,868,752)
Emp.: 140
Fiscal Year-end: 12/31/21
Wireless Broadband Data Communications Services
N.A.I.C.S.: 517112
David Charron *(Pres-Interim, CEO & CFO)*

TERAI TEA COMPANY LIMITED.
10 Government Place East, Kolkata, 700 069, West Bengal, India
Tel.: (91) 3340214412
Web Site: https://www.teraigroup.com
Year Founded: 1973
530533—(BOM)
Rev.: $12,093,054
Assets: $22,628,752
Liabilities: $4,423,132
Net Worth: $18,205,619
Earnings: $584,889
Emp.: 309
Fiscal Year-end: 03/31/21
Tea Mfr
N.A.I.C.S.: 311920
Ajit Kumar Agarwala *(Chm & Mng Dir)*

TERAJOULE ENERGY GMBH
Stephanstrasse 1, 60313, Frankfurt am Main, Germany
Tel.: (49) 69 98 97 240 00
Web Site: http://www.terajoule.de
Energy Services
N.A.I.C.S.: 221118
Johannes Peschko *(Mng Dir)*

TERALIGHT LTD.
Abba Hillel Silver 12, Ramat Gan, Israel
Tel.: (972) 33733234
Web Site: https://www.teralight.co.il
Year Founded: 2016
TRLT—(TAE)
Rev.: $21,639,011
Assets: $316,974,134
Liabilities: $202,003,687
Net Worth: $114,970,446
Earnings: ($3,094,463)
Fiscal Year-end: 06/30/23
Telecommunication Servicesb
N.A.I.C.S.: 517810
Rani Lifshitz *(CEO)*

TERAOKA SEIKO CO., LTD.
13-12 Kugahara 5-chome, Ohta-Ku, Tokyo, 146-0085, Japan
Tel.: (81) 3 3752 2131
Web Site: http://www.teraokaseiko.com
Year Founded: 1934
Rev.: $466,400,000
Emp.: 1,071
Industrial Machinery Mfr
N.A.I.C.S.: 333998
Kazuharu Teraoka *(Pres)*

TERAOKA SEISAKUSHO CO LTD
1-4-22 Hiromachi Shinagawa-ward, Tokyo, 140-8711, Japan
Tel.: (81) 334911141
Web Site: http://www.teraokatape.co.jp
4987—(TKS)
Rev.: $186,988,560
Assets: $315,858,400
Liabilities: $67,004,960
Net Worth: $248,853,440
Earnings: ($34,915,760)
Emp.: 700
Fiscal Year-end: 03/31/23
Paper Products Producer
N.A.I.C.S.: 322120
Keishiro Teraoka *(Chm)*

Subsidiaries:

Shin-ei Shoji Co., Ltd. (1)
3F Shimbashi 27 MT Building 2-12-11 Shimbashi, Minato Ku, Tokyo, 105-0004, Hyogo, Japan
Tel.: (81) 351572821
Web Site: https://www.shin-ei-shoji.co.jp
Footwear Whslr
N.A.I.C.S.: 424340

Teraoka Seisakusho (Hong Kong) Co., Ltd. (1)
Room 1708 Ever Gain Plaza Tower 2 No 88 Container Port Rd, Kwai Chung, Hong Kong, New Territories, China (Hong Kong)
Tel.: (852) 23699313
Web Site: http://www.teraokatape.co.jp
Sales Range: $25-49.9 Million
Emp.: 14
Adhesive Tape Mfr
N.A.I.C.S.: 325520

Teraoka Seisakusho (Shanghai) Co., Ltd. (1)
Site G 2nd Floor No 185 Taigu Rd Waigaoqiao Free Trade Zone, Shanghai, 200137, China
Tel.: (86) 2158682951
Web Site: http://www.teraokatape.co.jp
Sales Range: $25-49.9 Million
Emp.: 20
Adhesive Tape Mfr
N.A.I.C.S.: 325520

Teraoka Seisakusho Co., Ltd. - Ibaraki Factory (1)
644-16 Hidana Nakagou-cho, Kitaibaraki, 319-1556, Ibaraki, Japan
Tel.: (81) 293424918
Web Site: http://www.teraokatape.co.jp
Sales Range: $200-249.9 Million
Emp.: 800
Electrical Insulation Tapes Mfr
N.A.I.C.S.: 335999

Teraoka Seisakusho Co., Ltd. - Sano Factory (1)
1-1 Sakae-cho Sano, Tochigi, 327-0816, Japan
Tel.: (81) 283231221
Electrical Insulation Tapes Mfr
N.A.I.C.S.: 335999

TERAPLAST S.A.
DN 15A Saratel Village Sieu Magherus Km 45 500, 427301, Bistrita, Bistrita-Nasaud, Romania
Tel.: (40) 263238202
Web Site: https://www.teraplast.ro
Year Founded: 1896
TRP—(BUC)
Rev.: $122,871,611
Assets: $131,554,798
Liabilities: $57,641,195
Net Worth: $73,913,603
Earnings: $5,482,130
Emp.: 528
Fiscal Year-end: 12/31/23
Plastic Pipes & Fittings Mfr
N.A.I.C.S.: 326122
Dorel Goia *(Chm)*

Subsidiaries:

Politub SA (1)
Comuna Sieu Magherus Sat Saratel DN15A km 54 500, Nasaud judetul, Bistrita, Romania
Tel.: (40) 263235901
Web Site: http://www.politub.ro
Metal Pipe Mfr
N.A.I.C.S.: 332996

Teraglass Bistrita SRL (1)
Tarpiului 27A, Jud Bistrita-Nasaud, 420062, Bistrita, Romania
Tel.: (40) 374057057
Web Site: https://www.teraglass.ro
PVC Window & Door Mfr
N.A.I.C.S.: 332321
Simona Giurgiu *(Mgr-Brand)*

Terasteel S.A. (1)
DN 15A km 45 500, Saratel village sieu-Magherus commune Nasaud county, Bistrita, Romania
Tel.: (40) 74 150 4030
Web Site: https://www.terasteel.ro
Construction Services
N.A.I.C.S.: 236220
Cosmin Patroiu *(Gen Mgr)*

TERAS RESOURCES INC.
High Street SE, Calgary, T2Z 3W3, AB, Canada
Tel.: (403) 852-0644 AB
Web Site: https://www.teras.ca
Year Founded: 1994
TRARF—(OTCEM)
Assets: $20,869,095
Liabilities: $782,435
Net Worth: $20,086,660
Earnings: ($480,872)
Fiscal Year-end: 05/31/21
Gold & Other Metal Mining Services
N.A.I.C.S.: 212220
Kuldip C. Baid *(CFO)*

TERASAKI ELECTRIC CO.,LTD
6-13-47 Kamihigashi, Hirano ku, Osaka, 547-0002, Japan
Tel.: (81) 6667912701
Web Site: https://www.terasaki.co.jp
Year Founded: 1923
6637—(TKS)
Rev.: $344,149,650
Assets: $449,764,230

TERASAKI ELECTRIC CO.,LTD

TERASAKI ELECTRIC CO.,LTD—(Continued)
Liabilities: $140,475,720
Net Worth: $309,288,510
Earnings: $26,532,540
Emp.: 2,115
Fiscal Year-end: 03/31/24
Power Distribution Services
N.A.I.C.S.: 221122
Taizo Terasaki *(Pres)*

Subsidiaries:

Denki Taiwan Co., Ltd. (1)
11th Floor Suite 1102B No 18 Section 1
Chang An East Road, Taipei, 104, Taiwan
Tel.: (886) 225618335
Engineering & Lifecycle Services
N.A.I.C.S.: 541330

NHP Electrical Engineering Products (NZ) Ltd. (1)
118a Carbine Road Mt Wellington, Auckland, 1060, New Zealand
Tel.: (64) 800647647
Web Site: https://nhpnz.co.nz
Emp.: 800
Electrical Product Mfr & Distr
N.A.I.C.S.: 335999

TERAMECS CO., LTD. (1)
354 Nakagawara-chou Takeda, Fushimi-ku, Kyoto, 612-8412, Japan
Tel.: (81) 756062800
Web Site: https://www.teramecs.com
Emp.: 53
Medical Equipment Mfr
N.A.I.C.S.: 339112

TERASAKI CIRCUIT BREAKERS (S) PTE. LTD. (1)
17 Tuas Street, Singapore, 638454, Singapore
Tel.: (65) 67449752
Web Site: http://www.terasaki.co.jp
Circuit Breaker Mfr
N.A.I.C.S.: 423610

TERASAKI DO BRASIL LTDA. (1)
Rua Olof Palme No 765 Sala 322 Barra da, Rio de Janeiro, 22783-119, Brazil
Tel.: (55) 2133019898
Web Site: https://www.terasaki.com.br
Electrical Equipment Mfr & Distr
N.A.I.C.S.: 335999

TERASAKI ELECTRIC (CHINA) LTD. (1)
72 Pacific Industrial Park, Xintang Zengcheng, Guangzhou, 511340, China
Tel.: (86) 2082708556
Web Site: http://www.terasaki.cn
Electrical Equipment Distr
N.A.I.C.S.: 423610

TERASAKI ELECTRIC (EUROPE) LTD. (1)
80 Beardmore Way, Clydebank Industrial Estate, Glasgow, G81 4HT, United Kingdom
Tel.: (44) 1419411940
Web Site: https://www.terasaki.co.uk
Electrical Equipment Distr
N.A.I.C.S.: 423610
Kevin Donnachie *(Gen Mgr)*

TERASAKI ELECTRIC (M) SDN. BHD. (1)
Lot3 Jalan Jemuju Empat 16/13D, 40000, Shah Alam, Selangor Darul Ehsan, Malaysia
Tel.: (60) 355493820
Web Site: https://www.terasaki.com.my
Circuit Breaker Mfr & Distr
N.A.I.C.S.: 335313

TERASAKI ELECTRIC (SHANGHAI) CO., LTD. (1)
Building 5 7 No 399 Xuanzhong Rd Nanhui Industrial Zone, Pudong, Shanghai, 201314, China
Tel.: (86) 2158186340
Web Site: https://www.terasaki.com.cn
Electrical Equipment Distr
N.A.I.C.S.: 423610

TERASAKI SKANDINAVISKA AB. (1)
Frasarvagen 32 Skarpnak, Box 2082, 142 50, Skogas, Sweden

Tel.: (46) 8 556 282 30
Web Site: http://www.terasaki.se
Electrical Equipment Mfr & Distr
N.A.I.C.S.: 335313

TERATEC LTD. (1)
7-2-10 Kamihigashi, Hirano-ku, Osaka, 547-0002, Japan
Tel.: (81) 676347531
Web Site: http://www.teratec.co.jp
Emp.: 144
Power Distribution Services
N.A.I.C.S.: 221122
Shunji Okada *(Pres)*

Subsidiary (US):

TERATEC (USA) INC. (2)
21151 S Western Ave Ste 214, Torrance, CA 90501
Tel.: (310) 755-2517
Web Site: http://www.teratec.co.jp
Electrical Equipment Maintenance Services
N.A.I.C.S.: 811310

Terasaki Electric Co. Far East Pte. Ltd. (1)
17 Tuas Street, Singapore, 638454, Singapore
Tel.: (65) 611165
Web Site: https://www.terasaki.com.sg
Electrical Switchboard Mfr & Distr
N.A.I.C.S.: 335313

Terasaki Electric Trading & Services (M) Sdn. Bhd. (1)
No 20 & 22 Jalan Rajawali 2, Bandar Puchong Jaya, 47100, Puchong, Selangor, Malaysia
Tel.: (60) 380702486
Low Voltage Circuit Breaker Mfr
N.A.I.C.S.: 335313

TERATECH CO., LTD.
529 Yongdu-Ri Gongdo-Eup, Anseong, 456-821, Kyounggi-Do, Korea (South)
Tel.: (82) 316538360
Web Site: http://www.semitera.com
Year Founded: 2000
Sales Range: $25-49.9 Million
Emp.: 140
Semiconductor Equipment & Parts Mfr
N.A.I.C.S.: 334413
Byoung-Chun Choi *(CEO)*

TERAVIEW LTD.
Platinum Building St John's Innovation Park, Cowley Road, Cambridge, CB4 0DS, United Kingdom
Tel.: (44) 1223 435380
Web Site: http://www.teraview.com
Year Founded: 2001
3-D Imaging & Spectroscopic Systems Developer
N.A.I.C.S.: 339112
Don Arnone *(CEO)*

TERAXION, INC.
360 Franquet St Unit 40, Quebec, G1T4S8, QC, Canada
Tel.: (418) 658-9500
Web Site: http://www.teraxion.com
Sales Range: $25-49.9 Million
Emp.: 160
Optical Signal Conditioning Equipment Mfr
N.A.I.C.S.: 333310
Chantal Desaulniers *(VP)*

TERENGGANU INCORPORATED SDN. BHD.
Wisma TI Chendering, 21080, Kuala Terengganu, Terengganu, Malaysia
Tel.: (60) 96177771 MY
Web Site: http://www.terengganu-inc.com
Year Founded: 2006
Sales Range: $25-49.9 Million
Emp.: 29
Investment Holding Company

N.A.I.C.S.: 551112
Wan Ahmad Rudirman Wan Razak *(Grp CEO)*

Subsidiaries:

Eastern Pacific Industrial Corporation Berhad (1)
Annex Building Kemaman Supply Base, 24007, Kemaman, Terengganu, Malaysia (100%)
Tel.: (60) 98631566
Web Site: http://www.epicgroup.com.my
Sales Range: $75-99.9 Million
Emp.: 400
Investment Holding Company; Petroleum Supply Bases, Tubular Threading, Fabrication, Port Services & Sludge Management Services
N.A.I.C.S.: 551112
Ahmad Samsuri Mokhtar *(Chm)*

Subsidiary (Domestic):

EPIC Mushtari Engineering Sdn Bhd (2)
Lot 4000 Kawasan Perindustrian Telok Kalong, Kemaman, 24007, Terengganu, Malaysia (100%)
Tel.: (60) 9 863 1564
Web Site: http://www.epicgroup.com.my
Oil & Gas Upstream & Downstream Related Fabrications & Maintenance Services
N.A.I.C.S.: 213112
En Asharl Mohammad *(Gen Mgr)*

Konsortium Pelabuhan Kemaman Sdn. Bhd. (2)
Peti Surat 62, Kemaman, 24007, Terengganu, Malaysia (61%)
Tel.: (60) 9 863 1590
Web Site: http://www.epicgroup.com.my
Port Terminal Operations
N.A.I.C.S.: 488310
Noor Fatzin *(Mng Dir)*

Pangkalan Bekalan Kemaman Sdn Bhd (2)
PO Box 64, Kemaman, 24007, Terengganu, Malaysia (99.07%)
Tel.: (60) 9 863 1566
Web Site: http://www.epicgroup.com.my
Owner & Operator of Petroleum Supply Base
N.A.I.C.S.: 213112

Tubex Sdn. Bhd. (2)
Kawasan Perindustrian Baru KSB, Phase 2 Kemaman Supply Base, Kemaman, 24007, Terengganu, Malaysia (100%)
Tel.: (60) 9 8631640
Web Site: http://www.epicgroup.com.my
Tubular Threading
N.A.I.C.S.: 332999
Wen Mehusain *(Mng Dir)*

Syarikat Air Terengganu Sdn Bhd (1)
Jalan Air Jernih, 20200, Kuala Terengganu, Terengganu, Malaysia
Tel.: (60) 9 620 1111
Web Site: http://www.satuwater.com.my
Water Distr
N.A.I.C.S.: 424490

TEREOS
11 rue Pasteur, 02390, Origny-Sainte-Benoit, France
Tel.: (33) 328387930
Web Site: http://www.tereos.com
Year Founded: 2003
Rev.: $5,076,483,157
Assets: $7,684,667,494
Liabilities: $5,122,921,031
Net Worth: $2,561,746,463
Earnings: ($277,140,317)
Emp.: 26,003
Fiscal Year-end: 03/31/19
Sugar, Starch & Alcohol Products Mfr
N.A.I.C.S.: 311313
Jean-Charles Lefebvre *(Vice Chm-Supervisory Bd)*

Subsidiaries:

Acor & Tereos Iberia SA (1)
Avda Salvador Allende 76 78, 50100, Zaragoza, Spain

INTERNATIONAL PUBLIC

Tel.: (34) 976738100
Sugar Farming Services
N.A.I.C.S.: 111930
Carles Baleta Jover *(Acct Mgr)*

Beghin-Meiji (1)
11 PRV de Rotterdam, 59777, Lille, Cedex, France
Tel.: (33) 388586060
Web Site: https://profeed.beghin-meiji.com
Confectionery Products; Joint Venture of Montedison S.p.A. & Meiji Seiki Kaisha, Ltd.
N.A.I.C.S.: 445292

Bois Rouge (1)
BP 1017, Saint Denis, Cambuston, France
Tel.: (33) 0262 58 83 30
Sugar Mfr
N.A.I.C.S.: 311313

Hubau (1)
43 bd Cordier, Saint-Quentin, 02100, France
Tel.: (33) 3 23 68 67 17
Cereal Mfr
N.A.I.C.S.: 311230

SYRAL s.a.s. (1)
Z I et Portuaire, BP 32, F-67 390, Marckolsheim, France
Tel.: (33) 388586060
Web Site: http://www.tereossyral.com
Rev.: $269,730,000
Emp.: 300
Starch, Starch Sweeteners, Alcohol & Proteins Mfr
N.A.I.C.S.: 311999

Plant (Non-US):

SYRAL Belgium N.V. (2)
Burchstraat 10, B 9300, Aalst, Belgium
Tel.: (32) 53733333
Web Site: http://www.syral.com
Sales Range: $100-124.9 Million
Cereal Sweetener & Starch Productions
N.A.I.C.S.: 311314
Leo Paternot *(Gen Mgr)*

Sodes (1)
12 rue Blaise Pascal, 92200, Lille, France
Tel.: (33) 146371319
Synthesis Alcohol Mfr
N.A.I.C.S.: 325193

TTD (1)
Palackeho Namesti 1, Mlada Boleslav, 294 41, Czech Republic
Tel.: (420) 326 398408
Methanol Mfr
N.A.I.C.S.: 325193

Tereos International (1)
Av Brigadeiro Faria Lima 201 11th floor, Sao Paulo, 05426-100, Brazil
Tel.: (55) 11 3544 4900
Web Site: http://www.tereosinternacional.com
Cane Sugar Mfr
N.A.I.C.S.: 311314
Jacyrc da Silva Costa Filho *(Gen Dir)*

Subsidiary (Non-US):

Tereos UK Ltd (2)
Blois Meadow Business Centre, Haverhill, CB9 7BN, Suffolk, United Kingdom
Tel.: (44) 1440730751
Sugar Cane Distr
N.A.I.C.S.: 424490

Tereos Starch & Sweeteners Europe SAS (1)
Z I et Portuaire BP 32, 67 390, Marckolsheim, France
Tel.: (33) 388586060
Sugar Farming Services
N.A.I.C.S.: 111930
Jean Francois Delanoue *(Mgr-Supply Chain)*

Tereos Sucre France SE (1)
11 rue Pasteur, 02390, Origny-Sainte-Benoit, France
Tel.: (33) 323093232
Sugar Farming Services
N.A.I.C.S.: 111930

TERETNI TRANSPORT BOR U RESTRUKTURIRANJU A.D.

Nade Dimic 99, 19210, Bor, Serbia
Tel.: (381) 30 431 777
Web Site: http://www.teretnitransport-bor.co.rs
Year Founded: 1957
Sales Range: $1-9.9 Million
Emp.: 93
Food Transportation Services
N.A.I.C.S.: 484121

TERILOGY CO., LTD.
Hulic Kudan Bldg 4F 1-13-5 Kudankita, Chiyoda-ku, Tokyo, 102-0073, Japan
Tel.: (81) 332373291
Web Site: http://www.terilogy.com
Year Founded: 1989
3356—(TKS)
Rev.: $50,558,640
Assets: $57,992,880
Liabilities: $34,383,360
Net Worth: $23,609,520
Earnings: $2,642,640
Emp.: 221
Fiscal Year-end: 03/31/22
Computer Network Hardware Distr
N.A.I.C.S.: 423710
Takao Tsubuki (Chm)

Subsidiaries:

Creseed Corp. (1)
1-34-9 Asakusabashi, Taito-ku, Tokyo, 111-0053, Japan
Tel.: (81) 338611311
Web Site: https://www.creseed.jp
Emp.: 55
Information Technology Management Services
N.A.I.C.S.: 541512

Terilogy Serviceware Corporation (1)
Green Oak 9th Floor 1-11-5, Kudankita Chiyoda-ku, Tokyo, 102-0073, Japan
Tel.: (81) 345500555
Web Site: https://terilogy-sw.com
Emp.: 31
Telecommunication Servicesb
N.A.I.C.S.: 517810

Terilogy Worx Corporation (1)
2nd Floor Kudan Industrial Building 1-10-1, Kudankita Chiyoda-ku, Tokyo, 102-0073, Japan
Tel.: (81) 352135533
Web Site: https://www.twx-threatintel.com
Cyber Security Services
N.A.I.C.S.: 541519

TERLINDEN TEXTILPFLEGE AG
Seestrasse 39, 8700, Kusnacht, Switzerland
Tel.: (41) 443803555
Web Site: http://www.terlinden.ch
Sales Range: $10-24.9 Million
Emp.: 120
Dry Cleaner Operator
N.A.I.C.S.: 812320
Peter Muller (CEO)

TERMAS DE PUYEHUE SA
Ruta Internacional 215 K M 76, Puyehue, Osorno, Chile
Tel.: (56) 6002936000
Web Site: http://www.puyehue.cl
Resort & Spa Services
N.A.I.C.S.: 721110
Raimundo Garcia Rioseco (Chm)

TERMBRAY INDUSTRIES INTERNATIONAL (HOLDINGS) LIMITED
Flat B 8/F Waylee Industrial Centre 30-38 Tsuen King Circuit, Tsuen Wan, New Territories, China (Hong Kong)
Tel.: (852) 24875211
Web Site: http://www.termbray.com.hk
0093—(HKG)
Rev.: $20,765,925
Assets: $162,015,015
Liabilities: $22,771,373
Net Worth: $139,243,643
Earnings: $1,936,598
Emp.: 51
Fiscal Year-end: 12/31/22
Property Investment & Development; Oilfield Engineering & Consultancy Services
N.A.I.C.S.: 531390
Tommy Lee (Vice Chm & CEO)

TERME CATEZ, D.D.
Topliska cesta 35, Brezice, 8250, Ljubljana, Slovenia
Tel.: (386) 74936700 SI
Web Site: https://www.terme-catez.si
Year Founded: 1963
TCRG—(LJU)
Rev.: $37,179,600
Assets: $161,415,167
Liabilities: $54,783,089
Net Worth: $106,632,079
Earnings: $2,298,267
Emp.: 371
Fiscal Year-end: 12/31/23
Health Resort & Tourist Services
N.A.I.C.S.: 721110
Blaz De Costa (Asst Gen Mgr-Investments)

Subsidiaries:

Delikatesa D.D. Ljubljana (1)
Krivec 5, 1000, Ljubljana, Slovenia
Tel.: (386) 15133200
Web Site: http://www.delikatesa.si
Sales Range: $10-24.9 Million
Emp.: 50
Restaurant Services
N.A.I.C.S.: 722511

Marina Portoroz d.d. (1)
Cesta Solinarjev 8, SI-6320, Portoroz, Slovenia
Tel.: (386) 56761100
Web Site: http://www.marinap.si
Sales Range: $10-24.9 Million
Emp.: 80
Marina Operations with Living Accommodations, Fitness Facilities & Boat Repairing
N.A.I.C.S.: 713930

TERME DOBRNA D.D.
Dobrna 50, 3204, Dobrna, Slovenia
Tel.: (386) 3 78 08 110
Web Site: http://www.terme-dobrna.si
Year Founded: 1403
Spa & Fitness Center Operator
N.A.I.C.S.: 812112
Leon Tomasic (Pres-Supvry Bd)

TERMIKA A.D.
Pozeska 4 str, 23000, Zrenjanin, Serbia
Tel.: (381) 23 543 020
Web Site: http://www.termika.rs
Year Founded: 1957
Sales Range: Less than $1 Million
Emp.: 23
Non Metallic Mineral Mfr
N.A.I.C.S.: 488999
Milan Boskovic (CEO)

TERMIKA A.D.
Kraljevica Marka 2, Belgrade, Serbia
Tel.: (381) 112623161
Web Site: https://www.termika-beograd.rs
Year Founded: 1970
TRBG—(BEL)
Rev.: $3,524,185
Assets: $3,457,398
Liabilities: $619,191
Net Worth: $2,838,207
Earnings: $95,262
Emp.: 21
Fiscal Year-end: 12/31/23

Construction Engineering Services
N.A.I.C.S.: 541330
Gorcilo Knezevic (Mng Dir)

TERMINAL FOREST PRODUCTS LTD.
12180 Mitchell Road, Richmond, V6V 1M8, BC, Canada
Tel.: (604) 717-1200 BC
Web Site: http://www.terminalforest.com
Year Founded: 1962
Sawmills
N.A.I.C.S.: 321113
Asa Johal (Founder & Chm)

Subsidiaries:

South Everson Lumber Co., Inc. (1)
7205 Mission Rd, Everson, WA 98247
Tel.: (360) 966-2188
Web Site: http://www.terminalforest.com
Sales Range: $10-24.9 Million
Emp.: 180
Sawmills
N.A.I.C.S.: 321113
Kelly O. Toole (Controller)

Terminal Forest Products - Langdale Division (1)
2230 Twin Creeks Road, Gibsons, V0N 1V6, BC, Canada
Tel.: (604) 886-7033
Wood Processing Services
N.A.I.C.S.: 321113

Terminal Forest Products - Mainland Division (1)
8708 Yukon Street, Vancouver, V5X 2Y9, BC, Canada
Tel.: (604) 327-6344
Wood Processing Services
N.A.I.C.S.: 321113

TERMINAL GARAGEM MENEZES CORTES S.A.
Rua Sao Jose 35 - Center, Rio de Janeiro, 20020-010, RJ, Brazil
Tel.: (55) 2125446667
Web Site: https://menezescortes.rio.br
Year Founded: 1998
MNZC3—(BRAZ)
Rev.: $4,153,529
Assets: $15,898,815
Liabilities: $1,216,280
Net Worth: $14,682,535
Earnings: ($8,024,729)
Fiscal Year-end: 12/31/23
Parking Lot Maintenance Services
N.A.I.C.S.: 812930

TERMINAL X ONLINE LTD.
Ben Gurion Road 59, Ramat Gan, Israel
Tel.: (972) 37130000 Il
Web Site: https://www.terminalx.com
TRX—(TAE)
Rev.: $117,058,984
Assets: $148,756,179
Liabilities: $82,384,858
Net Worth: $66,371,321
Earnings: ($96,422)
Fiscal Year-end: 12/31/23
Ecommerce Retailer
N.A.I.C.S.: 459999

TERMINALCARE SUPPORT INSTITUTE, INC.
75-4 Katsuraminamitatsumi-Cho, Nishikyo-Ku, Kyoto, 615-8074, Japan
Tel.: (81) 753937177
Web Site: https://www.t-s-i.jp
Year Founded: 2010
7362—(TKS)
Rev.: $30,153,770
Assets: $29,019,370
Liabilities: $20,575,180
Net Worth: $8,444,190
Earnings: $893,340

Emp.: 418
Fiscal Year-end: 12/31/23
Home Care Support Services
N.A.I.C.S.: 621610
Tadao Kitayama (Founder, Chm, Pres & Dir-Rep)

TERMO-REX S.A.
ul Wojska Polskiego 2i, 43-603, Jaworzno, Poland
Tel.: (48) 326140056
Web Site: https://www.termo-rex.pl
Year Founded: 2011
TRR—(WAR)
Rev.: $12,345,528
Assets: $10,046,240
Liabilities: $2,335,112
Net Worth: $7,711,128
Earnings: $286,585
Fiscal Year-end: 12/31/23
Welding, Thermal & Heat Treatment Equipment Mf
N.A.I.C.S.: 333992
Tomasz Kaminski (Chm-Supervisory Bd)

TERMOMONTAZA AD BANJA LUKA
Karadordeva 2, 78000, Banja Luka, Bosnia & Herzegovina
Tel.: (387) 51316980
Web Site: https://www.termomontaza.com
Year Founded: 1948
TRMN—(BANJ)
Sales Range: $1-9.9 Million
Emp.: 154
Thermo-energetic Services
N.A.I.C.S.: 238220

TERMOVENT SC D.O.O.
Industrijska zona bb, 21235, Temerin, Serbia
Tel.: (381) 21842505
Web Site: https://www.termoventsc.rs
Year Founded: 1963
TLVC—(BEL)
Rev.: $10,154,579
Assets: $5,199,529
Liabilities: $3,182,688
Net Worth: $2,016,841
Earnings: $98,914
Emp.: 157
Fiscal Year-end: 12/31/23
Industrial Products Mfr
N.A.I.C.S.: 333248
Aleksandar Crnogorac (Owner & CEO)

TERN PLC
27/28 Eastcastle Street, London, W1W 8DH, United Kingdom
Tel.: (44) 2038070222
Web Site: https://www.ternplc.com
TERN—(AIM)
Assets: $30,329,310
Liabilities: $397,485
Net Worth: $29,931,825
Earnings: ($12,587,025)
Fiscal Year-end: 12/31/22
Investment Services
N.A.I.C.S.: 523999
Angus Forrest (Founder)

Subsidiaries:

Talking Medicines Limited (1)
25 Blythswood Square, Glasgow, United Kingdom
Tel.: (44) 1414880836
Web Site: https://talkingmedicines.com
Pharmaceutical Research Services
N.A.I.C.S.: 541714

TERN PROPERTIES COMPANY LIMITED
Tel.: (852) 25841200 HK
Web Site: https://tern.com.hk

TERN PROPERTIES COMPANY LIMITED

Tern Properties Company Limited—(Continued)
Year Founded: 1987
0277—(HKG)
Rev.: $7,368,369
Assets: $365,837,969
Liabilities: $14,134,144
Net Worth: $351,703,825
Earnings: ($7,104,605)
Emp.: 17
Fiscal Year-end: 03/31/22
Real Estate Investment Services
N.A.I.C.S.: 531390
Andrew Yan Tin Chan *(Exec Dir)*

Subsidiaries:

High Spark Properties Limited (1)
26 Fl Tern Ctr Block 1 237 Queens Rd,
Sheung Wan, China (Hong Kong)
Tel.: (852) 25455889
Web Site: http://www.tern.hk
Emp.: 20
Real Estate Property Investment Services
N.A.I.C.S.: 531110

TERNA ENERGY SOCIETE ANONYME INDUSTRIAL COMMERCIAL TECHNICAL COMPANY S.A.
85 Mesogion, 11526, Athens, Greece
Tel.: (30) 2106968300
Web Site: https://www.terna-energy.com
Year Founded: 1949
TENERGY—(ATH)
Rev.: $351,901,031
Assets: $2,231,464,149
Liabilities: $1,688,091,456
Net Worth: $543,372,692
Earnings: $66,644,483
Emp.: 446
Fiscal Year-end: 12/31/23
Eletric Power Generation Services
N.A.I.C.S.: 221115
Georgios Peristeris *(Chm)*

Subsidiaries:

Iweco Chonos Lasithiou Crete SA (1)
85 Messogion Ave, 115 26, Athens, Greece
Tel.: (30) 2106968525
Web Site: http://www.w-iwecochonos.gr
Electrical Power Mfr
N.A.I.C.S.: 335311

Terna Energy Finance S.A. (1)
85 Messogion Ave, 115 26, Athens, Greece
Tel.: (30) 2106968000
Web Site: https://www.ternaenergy-finance.com
Electrical Power Mfr
N.A.I.C.S.: 335311

Terna Iliaki Peloponnisou S.A. (1)
124 Kifisias Ave, 115 26, Athens, Greece
Tel.: (30) 2106968525
Web Site: http://www.ph-peloponnisou.gr
Electrical Power Mfr
N.A.I.C.S.: 335311

TERNA S.P.A. - RETE ELETTRICA NAZIONALE
Viale Egidio Galbani 70, 00156,
Rome, Italy
Tel.: (39) 0683138111   IT
Web Site: https://www.terna.it
Year Founded: 1999
TRN—(LUX)
Rev.: $3,199,330,887
Assets: $24,609,216,490
Liabilities: $17,951,435,355
Net Worth: $6,657,781,135
Earnings: $925,642,293
Emp.: 4,047
Fiscal Year-end: 12/31/22
Electricity Distribution Services
N.A.I.C.S.: 221114
Catia Bastioli *(Co-Chm)*

Subsidiaries:

Rete S.r.l. (1)
Via Stelvio 174, Morbegno, 23017, Sondrio,
Italy
Tel.: (39) 0342612610
Web Site: http://www.retesrl.it
Telecommunication Servicesb
N.A.I.C.S.: 517810

Terna Energy Solutions S.r.l. (1)
Viale Egidio Galbani 70, 00156, Rome, Italy
Tel.: (39) 0683138111
High Voltage Transmission Services
N.A.I.C.S.: 221121

Subsidiary (Domestic):

Tamini Trasformatori S.r.l. (2)
Viale Cadorna 56/A, Legnano, 20025, Milan, Italy
Tel.: (39) 02982051
Web Site: http://www.tamini.it
Specialty Transformer Mfr
N.A.I.C.S.: 335311
Danilo Dosi *(Dir-Sls)*

Terna Plus S.r.l. (1)
Viale Egidio Galbani 70, 00156, Rome, Italy
Tel.: (39) 0683138111
Web Site: http://ternaplus.terna.it
Electricity Grid Operation & Maintenance Services
N.A.I.C.S.: 221122
Manlio Coviello *(Chm)*

Subsidiary (Non-US):

SPE Santa Lucia Transmissora de Energia S.A. (2)
Rio Branco Avenue 1 Room 607, Downtown, Rio de Janeiro, 20090-003, Brazil
Tel.: (55) 2122833600
Web Site: http://www.santaluciate.com.br
Electricity Transmission Services
N.A.I.C.S.: 221121
Joao Gabriel Ratton *(CFO)*

SPE Santa Maria Transmissora de Energia S.A. (2)
Avenida Rio Branco 1 Room 607 Part, Downtown, Rio de Janeiro, 20090-003, Brazil
Tel.: (55) 2122833600
Web Site: http://www.santamariate.com.br
Electricity Transmission Services
N.A.I.C.S.: 221121
Joao Gabriel Ratton *(CFO)*

Terna S.p.A. - Cagliari (1)
Piazza Deffenu 1, 9125, Cagliari, Italy
Tel.: (39) 070 35 22 162
Electricity Transmission Grid Operation Services
N.A.I.C.S.: 541330

Terna S.p.A. - Torino (1)
Corso Regina Margherita 267, 10143, Turin, Italy
Tel.: (39) 011 20 65 501
Electricity Transmission Grid Operation Services
N.A.I.C.S.: 237130

TERNIENERGIA S.P.A.
Strada dello Stabilimento 1, 05035,
Narni, Terni, Italy
Tel.: (39) 07447581   IT
Web Site: https://www.ternienergia.com
Year Founded: 2005
TER—(ITA)
Holding Company; Solar Energy, Industrial Reclamation, Waste Treatment & Incineration Services
N.A.I.C.S.: 551112
Stefano Neri *(Chm)*

Subsidiaries:

TerniGreen S.p.A. (1)
Strada dello Stabilimento 1, 05035, Narni, Terni, Italy
Tel.: (39) 07447581
Recycling & Waste Treatment
N.A.I.C.S.: 562219
Stefano Neri *(Chm, Pres & CEO)*

TERPAC PLASTICS INTERNATIONAL INC.
11600 Albert Hudon, Montreal, H1G
3K2, QC, Canada
Tel.: (514) 328-4230
Web Site: http://www.terpac.com
Rev.: $49,600,000
Emp.: 120
Hangers Suppliers
N.A.I.C.S.: 326199
Robert Giustini *(Pres)*

TERRA BALCANICA RESOURCES CORPORATION
250-200 Burrard Street, Vancouver,
V6C 3L6, BC, Canada
Tel.: (604) 999-4136
Web Site: https://www.terrabresources.com
Year Founded: 2020
TERA—(CNSX)
Metal Exploration & Mining Services
N.A.I.C.S.: 213113
Aleksandar Miskovic *(Co-Founder, Co-Pres, Co-CEO, CTO, Head-Sales & Marketing & Exec Dir)*

Subsidiaries:

Drina Resources D.O.O. (1)
Marsala Tita bb, 75430, Srebrenica, Bosnia & Herzegovina
Tel.: (387) 381116902652
Lithological & Structural Mapping Services
N.A.I.C.S.: 541360

Tera Balkanika d.o.o. (1)

TERRA CAPITAL PLC
Millennium House 46 Athol Street,
Douglas, IM1 1JB, Isle of Man
Tel.: (44) 1624692600
Web Site: http://www.terracapitalplc.com
Rev.: $10,883,000
Assets: $71,999,000
Liabilities: $1,401,000
Net Worth: $70,598,000
Earnings: $7,914,000
Fiscal Year-end: 12/31/17
Real Estate Investment Services
N.A.I.C.S.: 525990

TERRA ESTIVAL 2002 S.A.
Hotel Caraiman, Neptun, Constanta,
Romania
Tel.: (40) 241701471
TERA—(BUC)
Assets: $2,692,294
Liabilities: $15,761
Net Worth: $2,676,534
Earnings: ($14,597)
Fiscal Year-end: 12/31/23
Restaurant & Hotel Operator
N.A.I.C.S.: 722511
Calin-Silviu Vere *(Pres)*

TERRA FIRMA CAPITAL PARTNERS LTD.
2 More London Riverside, London,
SE1 2AP, United Kingdom
Tel.: (44) 2070159500   UK
Web Site: http://www.terrafirma.com
Year Founded: 1994
Sales Range: $25-49.9 Million
Emp.: 100
Privater Equity Firm
N.A.I.C.S.: 523999
Guy Hands *(Co-Founder, Chm & Chief Investment Officer)*

Subsidiaries:

AWAS (1)
Block B Riverside IV Sir John Rogersons Quay, Sir John Rogerson's Quay, Dublin, Ireland
Tel.: (353) 16355000
Web Site: http://www.awas.com

INTERNATIONAL PUBLIC

Sales Range: $100-124.9 Million
Aircraft Leasing Services
N.A.I.C.S.: 532411
Jenny Moulton *(Sr VP-Sls-EMEA)*

Branch (US):

AWAS - Miami (2)
801 Brickell Ave Ste 800, Miami, FL 33131
Tel.: (305) 530-3800
Web Site: http://www.awas.com
Aircraft Leasing Services
N.A.I.C.S.: 532411
Walter Valarezo *(Mng Dir)*

Apollo S.r.l. (1)
Via Radici In Monte 232, 42014, Castellarano, Italy
Tel.: (39) 0536 851616
Web Site: http://www.apollosrl.com
Machine Tools Mfr
N.A.I.C.S.: 333517

Consolidated Pastoral Company Pty. Ltd. (1)
Newcastle Waters Station, Newcastle Waters, 0862, NT, Australia (90%)
Tel.: (61) 889644527
Web Site: http://www.pastoral.com
Sales Range: $10-24.9 Million
Cattle Ranching & Farming
N.A.I.C.S.: 112111
Jacqui Cannon *(Dir-Corp Dev)*

EverPower Wind Holdings Inc (1)
1251 Waterfront Pl 3rd Fl, Pittsburgh, PA 15222
Tel.: (412) 253-9400
Web Site: http://www.everpower.com
Wind Electric Power Generation Services
N.A.I.C.S.: 221115
James Spencer *(Pres & CEO)*

Four Seasons Health Care Limited (1)
Norcliffe House Station Road, Alderley Road, Wilmslow, SK9 1BU, Cheshire, United Kingdom
Tel.: (44) 1625417800
Web Site: http://www.fshc.co.uk
Sales Range: $5-14.9 Billion
Emp.: 21,000
Healtcare Services
N.A.I.C.S.: 551112
Tim Hammond *(CEO)*

ODEON Cinemas Ltd. (1)
54 Witcomb St, London, WC2H 7DN, United Kingdom
Tel.: (44) 2073210404
Web Site: http://www.odeon.co.uk
Sales Range: $25-49.9 Million
Emp.: 50
Cinema Operator
N.A.I.C.S.: 512131
Mark Connar *(Mgr)*

Rete Rinnovabile S.r.l. (1)
Viale Regina Margherita 279, 00198, Rome, Italy
Tel.: (39) 06 6489 3200
Web Site: http://www.rtrenergy.it
Solar Electric Power Generation Services
N.A.I.C.S.: 221114
Ingmar Wilhelm *(Chm)*

Terra Firma Capital Management Limited (1)
4th Floor Royal Chambers Saint Julians Avenue, Saint Peter Port, GY1 3RE, Guernsey
Tel.: (44) 1481 231100
Financial Management Services
N.A.I.C.S.: 523999

Terrafirma GmbH (1)
Garden Towers Neue Mainzer Strasse 46 50, 60311, Frankfurt, Germany
Tel.: (49) 69380756000
Sales Range: $50-74.9 Million
Emp.: 3
Private Equity Investments
N.A.I.C.S.: 523999
Tim Pryce *(CEO)*

Welcome Hotels GmbH (1)
Kuhwaldstrasse 46, 60486, Frankfurt, Germany
Tel.: (49) 69 870025 555
Web Site: http://www.welcome-hotels.com

AND PRIVATE COMPANIES

Hotel Administrator & Operator
N.A.I.C.S.: 561110
Abdul Ghaffar *(Supvr-Front Office)*

Wyevale Garden Centres Limited (1)
Syon Park, Slough, TW8 8JF, Middlesex, United Kingdom
Tel.: (44) 8448008428
Web Site:
http://www.thegardencentregroup.co.uk
Sales Range: $350-399.9 Million
Garden Center Operator
N.A.I.C.S.: 444240
Andrew West *(Head-Garden Care)*

TERRA MAURICIA LIMITED
Beau Plan Business Park, 21001, Port Louis, 21001, Mauritius
Tel.: (230) 2040808
Web Site: https://www.terra.co.mu
Year Founded: 1838
TERA—(MAU)
Rev.: $149,942,580
Assets: $568,666,780
Liabilities: $181,545,520
Net Worth: $387,121,260
Earnings: $22,541,100
Emp.: 1,178
Fiscal Year-end: 12/31/22
Holding Company
N.A.I.C.S.: 551112
Alexis Harel *(Exec Dir)*

Subsidiaries:

Sugarworld Limited (1)
Beau Plan, Pamplemousses, Port Louis, 21001, Mauritius
Tel.: (230) 243 7900
Web Site: https://www.aventuredusucre.com
Sugar Cane Mfr
N.A.I.C.S.: 311314

Terra Brands Ltd. (1)
5 Hawkins Avenue Gunners Circle Epping, 7460, Cape Town, South Africa
Tel.: (27) 872300166
Web Site: http://www.terrabrands.co.za
Promotional Product & Gift Distr
N.A.I.C.S.: 424990
Adam Closenberg *(Mng Dir)*

Subsidiary (Non-US):

Grays Distilling Ltd. (2)
Tel.: (230) 2433734
Alcohol Mfr
N.A.I.C.S.: 312140
Cindy Leung *(Mgr-Supply Chain)*

Grays Inc. Ltd. (2)
Beau Plan, Pamplemousses, Port Louis, 21001, Mauritius
Tel.: (230) 209 3000
Web Site: https://www.grays.mu
Wine & Spirit Mfr
N.A.I.C.S.: 312140

Terragri Ltd. (1)
Belle Vue Mauricia, Mapou, 31806, Mauritius
Tel.: (230) 2668485
Sugar Cane Mfr
N.A.I.C.S.: 311314
Jean Marc Jauffret *(Mgr-Agricultural)*

Subsidiary (Domestic):

Beau Plan Development Ltd. (2)
Beau Plan Smart City, Pamplemousses, Port Louis, 21001, Mauritius
Tel.: (230) 204 0808
Web Site: https://www.beauplan.mu
Residential Property Development Services
N.A.I.C.S.: 531110

Subsidiary (Non-US):

Terragen Ltd. (2)
Tel.: (230) 2661226
Emp.: 50
Thermal Power Generation Services
N.A.I.C.S.: 221118
Jean-Marc Iweins *(Mgr-Power Plant)*

TERRA MEDITERRANEA D.D.
Mletacka 12, 52100, Pula, Croatia
Tel.: (385) 989477369
Web Site:
http://www.terramediterranea.hr
Year Founded: 2005
Investment Management Service
N.A.I.C.S.: 523940

TERRA NOVA MOTORS LTD.
595 Kenmount Road, Saint John's, A1B 3B9, NL, Canada
Tel.: (709) 364-4130
Web Site:
http://www.terranovamotors.com
Year Founded: 1930
New & Used Car Dealers
N.A.I.C.S.: 441110
Alex Traverse *(VP)*

TERRA NOVA STEEL & IRON INC.
3595 Hawkestone Road, Mississauga, L5C 2V1, ON, Canada
Tel.: (905) 273-3872
Web Site:
https://www.terranovasteel.ca
Iron & Bronze Bars Distr
N.A.I.C.S.: 331511
Mario Zitella *(Pres)*

Subsidiaries:

Terra Nova Steel & Iron Inc. - Alberta Plant (1)
4156 - 78th Avenue, Edmonton, T6B 3M8, AB, Canada
Tel.: (780) 454-1141
Iron Distr & Warehousing Services
N.A.I.C.S.: 423510

TERRA URANIUM LIMITED
Level 4 100 Albert Road, South Melbourne, 3205, VIC, Australia
Tel.: (61) 402912198   AU
Web Site: https://www.t92.com.au
Year Founded: 2021
T92—(ASX)
Rev.: $134,022
Assets: $6,047,433
Liabilities: $799,383
Net Worth: $5,248,050
Earnings: ($1,194,966)
Fiscal Year-end: 06/30/23
Mineral Exploration Services
N.A.I.C.S.: 212390
Andrew J. Vigar *(Chm)*

TERRABIOGEN TECHNOLOGIES INC.
8536 Baxter Place, Burnaby, V5A 4T8, BC, Canada
Tel.: (604) 444-1023   BC
Web Site:
https://www.terrabiogen.com
Year Founded: 1993
Rev.: $796
Assets: $190,389
Liabilities: $429,580
Net Worth: ($239,191)
Earnings: ($723,858)
Emp.: 10
Fiscal Year-end: 06/30/18
Waste Conversion Services
N.A.I.C.S.: 562119
Bob Nowell *(CFO & Sec)*

TERRACE FORD LINCOLN SALES INC
900 Walkers Line, Burlington, L7N 2G2, ON, Canada
Tel.: (905) 632-6252
Web Site:
http://www.terracefordlincoln.com
New & Used Car Dealers
N.A.I.C.S.: 441110
David McDermott *(Sls Mgr)*

TERRACE GLOBAL, INC.
365 Bay Street Suite 800, Toronto, M5H 2V1, ON, Canada
Tel.: (416) 361-4783
Web Site: http://www.terraceglobal.ca
TRCE—(TSXV)
Assets: $15,304,164
Liabilities: $2,388,200
Net Worth: $12,915,964
Earnings: ($6,498,919)
Cannabis Product Mfr
N.A.I.C.S.: 325411
Francisco Ortiz *(Co-Founder & CEO)*

TERRACE TOTEM FORD SALES LTD.
4631 Keith Avenue, Terrace, V8G1K3, BC, Canada
Tel.: (250) 635-4984
Web Site:
http://www.terracetotemford.ca
Year Founded: 1973
Rev.: $14,909,351
Emp.: 40
New & Used Car Dealers
N.A.I.C.S.: 441110

TERRACOM LIMITED
Blair Athol Mine Access Road, PO Box 131, Claremont, 4721, QLD, Australia
Tel.: (61) 749832038   AU
Web Site:
https://www.terracomresources.com
TER—(ASX)
Rev.: $173,038,861
Assets: $209,948,584
Liabilities: $97,870,593
Net Worth: $112,077,991
Earnings: $16,719,418
Fiscal Year-end: 06/30/24
Coal Mining Services
N.A.I.C.S.: 212115
Craig Wallace *(Deputy Chm)*

Subsidiaries:

Universal Coal Development VIII (Pty.) Ltd. (1)
467 Fehrsen Street, Brooklyn, Pretoria, South Africa
Tel.: (27) 124600805
Coal Mining Services
N.A.I.C.S.: 213113

Universal Coal Plc (1)
6th Floor 60 Gracechurch Street, London, EC3V 0HR, United Kingdom
Tel.: (44) 2072644444
Web Site: http://www.universalcoal.com
Rev.: $305,753,024
Assets: $267,969,716
Liabilities: $130,288,382
Net Worth: $137,681,334
Earnings: $49,499,656
Emp.: 168
Fiscal Year-end: 06/30/2019
Coal Mining Services
N.A.I.C.S.: 212115
Minah Moabi *(Dir-Corp Affairs)*

TERRAFAME GROUP OY
Aleksanterinkatu 17, PL 800, 00100, Helsinki, Finland
Tel.: (358) 20 7130 800
Web Site: http://www.terrafame.com
Sales Range: $250-299.9 Million
Emp.: 650
Metal Mining Services
N.A.I.C.S.: 212220
Kankanen Janne *(Chm)*

Subsidiaries:

Terrafame Oy (1)
Talvivaarantie 66, Tuhkakyla, Sotkamo, 88120, Finland   (84.2%)
Tel.: (358) 20 7130 800
Web Site: http://www.terrafame.fi
Metal Mining Services
N.A.I.C.S.: 212290
Ratia Lauri *(Chm)*

TERRASCEND CORP.

TERRAGEN HOLDINGS LIMITED
Unit 6 41 Access Crescent, Coolum Beach, 4573, QLD, Australia
Tel.: (61) 1300837724   AU
Web Site:
https://www.terragen.com.au
Year Founded: 1996
TGH—(ASX)
Rev.: $2,209,692
Assets: $4,138,201
Liabilities: $828,438
Net Worth: $3,309,763
Earnings: ($2,108,573)
Fiscal Year-end: 06/30/23
Holding Company
N.A.I.C.S.: 551112

TERRAIN MINERALS LTD
Suite 2 28 Outram Street, West Perth, 6005, WA, Australia
Tel.: (61) 893815558
Web Site:
https://www.terrainminerals.com.au
TMX—(ASX)
Rev.: $3,647
Assets: $2,456,248
Liabilities: $106,130
Net Worth: $2,350,118
Earnings: ($1,012,020)
Fiscal Year-end: 06/30/24
Gold & Mineral Exploration Services
N.A.I.C.S.: 213115
Justin Virgin *(Exec Dir)*

TERRAMIN AUSTRALIA LIMITED
2115 Callington Road, Fullarton, Strathalbyn, 5255, SA, Australia
Tel.: (61) 85365950
Web Site:
https://www.terramin.com.au
TZN—(ASX)
Rev.: $72,202
Assets: $44,444,520
Liabilities: $36,336,081
Net Worth: $8,108,439
Earnings: ($4,328,043)
Emp.: 24
Fiscal Year-end: 12/31/23
Mining & Development Services
N.A.I.C.S.: 213114
Michael H. Kennedy *(Deputy Chm)*

TERRANET AB
Mobilvagen 10, 223 62, Lund, Sweden
Tel.: (46) 462863490
Web Site: https://www.terranet.se
Year Founded: 2004
TERRNT.B—(OMX)
Rev.: $101,326
Assets: $7,421,243
Liabilities: $2,060,710
Net Worth: $5,360,533
Earnings: ($4,259,371)
Emp.: 15
Fiscal Year-end: 05/31/20
Software Development Services
N.A.I.C.S.: 541511
Magnus Andersson *(CEO)*

TERRANOVA PARTNERS, L.P.
2 Bloor Street West Suite 3400, Toronto, M4W 3E2, ON, Canada
Tel.: (416) 644-6000
Web Site:
http://www.terranovapartners.com
Private Equity Investment Firm
N.A.I.C.S.: 523940
Vahan Kololian *(Chm)*

TERRASCEND CORP.
77 City Centre Drive Suite 501 East Tower, Mississauga, L5B 1M5, ON, Canada

TERRASCEND CORP.

TerrAscend Corp.—(Continued)
Web Site:
https://www.terrascend.com
TED—(STU)
Rev.: $249,258,000
Assets: $701,587,000
Liabilities: $380,416,000
Net Worth: $321,171,000
Earnings: ($325,351,000)
Emp.: 972
Fiscal Year-end: 12/31/22
Pharmaceuticals Product Mfr
N.A.I.C.S.: 325412
Keith Stauffer *(CFO)*

TERRASEM CO., LTD.
Gwahaksaneop 5-ro Ohchang-Eup,
Cheongwon-Gu, Cheongju, 363-885,
ChungBuk, Korea (South)
Tel.: (82) 432408100
Web Site: http://www.terrasem.com
182690—(KRS)
Rev.: $4,041,632
Assets: $39,581,569
Liabilities: $25,008,329
Net Worth: $14,573,240
Earnings: ($5,899,317)
Emp.: 15
Fiscal Year-end: 12/31/21
Semiconductors & Electronic Devices Mfr
N.A.I.C.S.: 334413

TERRASKY CO., LTD.
15th to 17th floors Taiyo Life Nihonbashi Building 2-11-2 Nihonbashi,
Chuo-ku, Tokyo, 103-0027, Japan
Tel.: (81) 352553410
Web Site: https://www.terrasky.co.jp
3915—(TKS)
Rev.: $135,681,330
Assets: $130,782,140
Liabilities: $41,781,370
Net Worth: $89,000,770
Earnings: $2,127,000
Fiscal Year-end: 02/29/24
Software Developer
N.A.I.C.S.: 513210
Hideya Sato *(Pres)*

Subsidiaries:

Kitalive Inc. (1)
Kita 7 Nishi 1-chome address 1 5 Maruzo building No 18 9 floor, Kita-ku, Sapporo, 060-0807, Hokkaido, Japan
Tel.: (81) 117273351
Web Site: http://www.kitalive.co.jp
Emp.: 43
Information Technology Consulting Services
N.A.I.C.S.: 541512

TerraSky Inc. (1)
1370 Willow Rd, Menlo Park, CA 94025
Tel.: (408) 675-5198
Web Site: http://www.terrasky.com
Information Technology Consulting Services
N.A.I.C.S.: 541512

TERRASSEMENTS ET CANALISATIONS
3 et 5 Rue Lavoisier, 77400, Lagny, Seine Et Marne, France
Tel.: (33) 160075605
Web Site: http://www.terca.fr
Sales Range: $10-24.9 Million
Emp.: 137
Professional Public Works
N.A.I.C.S.: 237110
Jean Marc Dransart *(Sls Mgr)*

TERRATEC AS
Vaekeroveien 3, 0281, Oslo, Norway
Tel.: (47) 454 66 300   NO
Web Site: http://www.terratec.no
Year Founded: 2004
Emp.: 100
Geophysical Surveying & Mapping Services
N.A.I.C.S.: 541360

Subsidiaries:

Terratec Sweden AB (1)
Hammarbacken 6B, 191 49, Sollentuna, Sweden
Tel.: (46) 857824700
Web Site: http://www.terratec.se
Emp.: 14
Geophysical Surveying & Mapping Services
N.A.I.C.S.: 541360
Jonas Lind *(CEO)*

TERRATEC ELECTRONIC GMBH
Herrenpfad 38, D-41334, Nettetal, Germany
Tel.: (49) 215781790
Web Site: http://www.terratec.net
Year Founded: 1994
Rev.: $28,004,436
Emp.: 60
Sound Cards Mfr
N.A.I.C.S.: 334310
Walter Grieger *(Co-Founder)*

TERRAVEST INDUSTRIES, INC.
6205 - 60th Street, Vegreville, T9C 1S3, AB, Canada
Tel.: (780) 632-2040
Web Site:
https://www.terravestindustries.com
TVK—(TSX)
Rev.: $240,522,156
Assets: $317,870,091
Liabilities: $214,562,976
Net Worth: $103,307,115
Earnings: $28,645,529
Emp.: 1,257
Fiscal Year-end: 09/30/21
Investment Holding Company
N.A.I.C.S.: 551112
Charles Pellerin *(Chm)*

Subsidiaries:

Countryside Tank Company (1)
1525 E Eddy Saylor Pkwy, Osceola, IA 50213
Web Site: https://countrysidetank.com
Transport Trailers Mfr & Distr
N.A.I.C.S.: 336212

ECR International, Inc. (1)
2201 Dwyer Ave, Utica, NY 13501
Tel.: (315) 797-1310
Web Site: https://www.ecrinternational.com
Design & Marketing of Hydronic & HVAC Equipment Mfr
N.A.I.C.S.: 333414
Michael Klas *(Dir-Sls & Mktg)*

Unit (Domestic):

Argo Technology, Inc. - USA (2)
2201 Dwyer Ave, Utica, NY 13501
Web Site: https://argocontrols.com
Industrial Supplies Whslr
N.A.I.C.S.: 423840

Olsen/Airco Heating & Cooling Products - US (2)
2201 Dwyer Ave, Utica, NY 13504
Tel.: (315) 797-1310
Air Conditioning & Heating Equipment Mfr
N.A.I.C.S.: 333415

Utica Boilers (2)
2201Dwyer, Utica, NY 13501
Tel.: (315) 797-1310
Web Site: https://www.uticaboilers.com
Cast Iron Heating Boilers
N.A.I.C.S.: 333414

EnviroVault L.P. (1)
4017 - 60th Ave, Box 6280, Innisfail, AB, Canada
Tel.: (403) 263-4433
Web Site: https://envirovault.com
Oil & Gas Storage Tanks Mfr
N.A.I.C.S.: 336390

MTankCo Supply, LLC (1)
7074 302 Industrial Dr, Southaven, MS 38671
Web Site: https://mtankco.com
Liquefied Petroleum Gas Industry Equipment Distr
N.A.I.C.S.: 484230

Mississippi Tank & Manufacturing Co., Inc. (1)
3000 W 7th St, Hattiesburg, MS 39401-5617
Tel.: (601) 264-1800
Web Site: http://www.mstank.com
Sales Range: $10-24.9 Million
Emp.: 89
Metal Tank Mfr
N.A.I.C.S.: 332420
Mike Pitts *(VP-Sls)*

Mississippi Tank Company (1)
3000 W 7th St, Hattiesburg, MS 39401
Tel.: (601) 264-1800
Web Site: https://www.mstank.com
Tank Trailers Repair Services
N.A.I.C.S.: 721211

Platinum Energy Services Ltd. (1)
400 333-11 Ave SW, Calgary, T2R 1L9, AB, Canada
Tel.: (403) 264-6688
Web Site:
http://www.platinumenergycanada.com
Oil Field Equipment Mfr
N.A.I.C.S.: 333132

Signature Truck Systems LLC (1)
13460 N Saginaw Rd, Clio, MI 48420
Tel.: (810) 564-2294
Web Site: https://signaturetruckllc.com
Propane Delivery Truck Mfr
N.A.I.C.S.: 336211
Randy Hacker *(Mgr-Sls)*

TERREIS
11 avenue Paul Langevin, Le Plessis Robinson, 92350, Paris, France
Tel.: (33) 1 82 00 95 40
Web Site: http://www.terreis.fr
Sales Range: $75-99.9 Million
Real Estate Manangement Services
N.A.I.C.S.: 531390
Jacky Lorenzetti *(Chm)*

TERRENO RESOURCES CORP.
44 Victoria Street Suite 1102, Toronto, M5C 1Y2, ON, Canada
Tel.: (905) 467-1109
Web Site:
http://www.terrenoresources.com
Year Founded: 1995
TNO—(TSXV)
Assets: $126,760
Liabilities: $403,433
Net Worth: ($276,673)
Earnings: ($417,904)
Fiscal Year-end: 03/31/23
Mineral Exploration Services
N.A.I.C.S.: 213114
George A. Brown *(CEO)*

TERRITORIAL GENERATING CO NO 1 PJSC
16 Dobrolyubova Pr Corp 2 Litera A Arena Hall Business Centre, Saint Petersburg, 197198, Russia
Tel.: (7) 8126883606
Web Site: http://www.tgc1.ru
Year Founded: 2005
TLGNL—(OTCIQ)
Sales Range: Less than $1 Million
Eletric Power Generation Services
N.A.I.C.S.: 221118
Antonina Maksimova *(Sec & Head-Corp Affairs Directorate)*

TERRITORIAL GENERATING CO NO.14 OAO
Profsoyuznaya Street House 23, Chita, 672000, Russia
Tel.: (7) 3022384666

INTERNATIONAL PUBLIC

Web Site: https://www.tgk-14.com
Year Founded: 2004
TGKN—(MOEX)
Sales Range: Less than $1 Million
Electric Power Generation & Transmission Services
N.A.I.C.S.: 221116
Alexey Lizunov *(Gen Dir)*

TERROIRS DISTILLERS
5 chemin du Chateau, 21190, Chassagne-Montrachet, France
Tel.: (33) 3 8021 9861   FR
Web Site:
http://www.terroirsdistillers.com
Distilled Alcoholic Beverage Mfr & Whslr
N.A.I.C.S.: 312140
Gabriel Picard *(Dir-Publication)*

Subsidiaries:

Louis Royer SAS (1)
27-29 rue du chail, Jarnac, 16200, France
Tel.: (33) 5 4581 0272
Web Site: http://www.louis-royer.com
Distilled Spirits Mfr & Whslr
N.A.I.C.S.: 312140

TERRUZZI FERCALX SPA
Viale Lombardia 7-Zona Industriale 2, Spirano, 24050, Italy
Tel.: (39) 035 4879811
Web Site:
http://www.terruzzifercalxgroup.co.uk
Emp.: 20
Industrial Machinery Engineering & Manufacturing Services
N.A.I.C.S.: 333248
Astorre Terruzzi *(Pres)*

Subsidiaries:

TERRUZZI FERCALX ENERGY SRL (1)
Viale Lombardia 7 Zona Industriale 2, 24050, Spirano, Italy
Tel.: (39) 0354879811
Industrial Machinery Mfr
N.A.I.C.S.: 333248

Terruzzi Fercalx Engineering Pvt Ltd (1)
953/A 2nd Floor 2nd Main Road 4th Block, Rajajinagar, 560010, Bengaluru, India
Tel.: (91) 8023403320
Industrial Machinery Mfr
N.A.I.C.S.: 333248
Srisha Banderaya *(Mng Dir)*

Terruzzi Fercalx India Ltd. (1)
104 105 & 106 Trade Centre C Wing North Main Road Koregaon Park, Pune, 411 001, India (57.69%)
Tel.: (91) 2066450800
Web Site: http://www.vulcanengineers.com
Sales Range: $1-9.9 Million
Industrial Machinery & Equipment Mfr
N.A.I.C.S.: 333248

TERRY SHIELDS PTY. LTD.
10 Church Street, Parramatta, 2150, NSW, Australia
Tel.: (61) 292046444
Web Site:
http://www.terryshieldstoyota.com.au
Year Founded: 1973
Automobile Parts & Services
N.A.I.C.S.: 423140
Rodney Smith *(Principal)*

TERTIARY MINERALS PLC
Silk Point Queens Avenue, Macclesfield, SK10 2BB, Cheshire, United Kingdom
Tel.: (44) 1625838679   UK
Web Site:
https://www.tertiaryminerals.com
Year Founded: 1999
TYM—(AIM)
Rev.: $192,474
Assets: $1,018,980

Liabilities: $101,898
Net Worth: $917,082
Earnings: ($1,335,996)
Fiscal Year-end: 09/30/22
Other Nonmetallic Mineral Mining & Quarrying
N.A.I.C.S.: 212390
Patrick L. Cheetham *(Chm)*

Subsidiaries:

Tertiary Gold Limited (1)
Sunrise House Hulley Road, Macclesfield, SK10 2LP, Cheshire, United Kingdom
Tel.: (44) 1625626203
Gold Mining Services
N.A.I.C.S.: 212220

TERTRE ROUGE ASSETS PLC
48 Chancery Lane, London, WC2A 1JF, United Kingdom
Tel.: (44) 7917715533 UK
Web Site:
  https://www.tertrerougeassets.com
Year Founded: 2020
TRA—(LSE)
Asset Management Services
N.A.I.C.S.: 523999
Simon Holden *(Sec)*

TERUMO CORPORATION
2-44-1 Hatagaya, Shibuya-ku, Tokyo, 151-0072, Japan
Tel.: (81) 333748111 JP
Web Site: https://www.terumo.com
Year Founded: 1921
TRUMF—(OTCIQ)
Rev.: $5,880,898,530
Assets: $11,487,953,250
Liabilities: $3,521,631,540
Net Worth: $7,966,321,710
Earnings: $640,460,250
Emp.: 30,207
Fiscal Year-end: 03/31/23
Medical Devices & Pharmaceuticals Mfr
N.A.I.C.S.: 339112
Takayoshi Mimura *(Chm)*

Subsidiaries:

Bolton Medical, Inc. (1)
799 International Pkwy, Sunrise, FL 33325
Tel.: (954) 838-9699
Web Site: https://www.terumoaortic.com
Surgical & Medical Instrument Mfr
N.A.I.C.S.: 339112
Donna Bean *(VP-Human Resources)*

Changchun Terumo Medical Products Co. Ltd. (1)
4 Huoju Road, Changchun New Technology Development Zone, Changchun, 130012, China (100%)
Tel.: (86) 431 517 9785
Medical Devices & Pharmaceuticals Mfr
N.A.I.C.S.: 325412

Essen Technology (Beijing) Co., Ltd. (1)
Building 1 No A12 Tianzhu West Road, Tianzhu Airport Industrial Zone A Shunyi District, Beijing, 101318, China
Tel.: (86) 106 060 8836
Medical Device Mfr & Distr
N.A.I.C.S.: 339112

Harvest Technologies Corp. (1)
40 Grissom Rd Ste 100, Plymouth, MA 02360
Tel.: (508) 732-7500
Web Site: http://www.harvesttech.com
Sales Range: $25-49.9 Million
Emp.: 61
Electromedical & Electrotherapeutic Apparatus Mfr
N.A.I.C.S.: 334510
J. Patrick Elliott *(Pres & CEO)*

Ikiken Co., Ltd. (1)
2-12-27 Shinsayama, Sayama, 350-1331, Saitama, Japan
Tel.: (81) 42 955 6202
Web Site: https://www.ikiken.co.jp
Emp.: 57
Medical Equipment Mfr & Distr
N.A.I.C.S.: 339112

Laboratoires Terumo France S.A. (1)
Batiment Renaissance 3 Rond-Point des Saules, 78280, Guyancourt, Cedex, France (100%)
Tel.: (33) 130961300
Web Site: http://www.terumo-europe.com
Sales Range: $25-49.9 Million
Emp.: 8
Sales of Pharmaceuticals & Medical Equipment
N.A.I.C.S.: 541380

MicroVention Deutschland G.m.b.H. (1)
Hildebrandtstr 4S, 40212, Dusseldorf, Germany
Tel.: (49) 211 210 7980
Emp.: 3
Surgical & Medical Instruments Distr
N.A.I.C.S.: 423450
Markus Huber *(Gen Mgr)*

MicroVention Europe (1)
30 bis rue du Vieil Abreuvoir, 78100, Saint Germain-en-Laye, France
Tel.: (33) 13 921 7746
Web Site: http://www.microvention.com
Sales Range: $50-74.9 Million
Emp.: 10
Medical & Surgical Supplies Distr
N.A.I.C.S.: 423450

MicroVention UK Ltd. (1)
Suite 3 The Barracks Building 10 Cliffords Fort, North Shields, NE30 1JE, Tyne & Wear, United Kingdom
Tel.: (44) 191 258 6777
Web Site: http://www.microvention.com
Health Care Srvices
N.A.I.C.S.: 621999

MicroVention, Inc. (1)
1311 Valencia Ave, Tustin, CA 92780
Tel.: (714) 247-8000
Web Site: https://www.microvention.com
Surgical & Medical Instruments Mfr
N.A.I.C.S.: 339112
William R. Hughes *(COO & Treas)*

Subsidiary (Domestic):

Terumo Sequent (2)
35 Enterprise, Aliso Viejo, CA 92656 (100%)
Tel.: (714) 247-8000
Web Site:
  https://microvention.herokuapp.com
Surgical Appliance & Supplies Mfr
N.A.I.C.S.: 339113
Carsten Schroeder *(Pres)*

P.T. Terumo Indonesia (1)
Wisma KEIAI 5th Floor JL Jend Sudirman KAV 3, Jl Jend Sudirman Kav 3, Jakarta, 10220, Indonesia (100%)
Tel.: (62) 21 572 4071
Web Site: https://www.terumo.com
Surgical Products
N.A.I.C.S.: 339113

TCVS-Ashland Plant (1)
28 Howe St, Ashland, MA 01721-1305
Tel.: (508) 231-2400
Web Site: http://www.terumo-cvs.com
Sales Range: $50-74.9 Million
Emp.: 150
Medical Devices & Pharmaceuticals Mfr
N.A.I.C.S.: 325412

Terumo (China) Holding Co., Ltd. (1)
Room 805 PICC Building 2 Jianguomenwai Street, Chaoyang District, Beijing, 100022, China
Tel.: (86) 106 409 6685
Medical Device Mfr & Distr
N.A.I.C.S.: 339112

Terumo (Deutschland) G.m.b.H. (1)
Ludwig-Erhard-Strasse 6, 65760, Eschborn, Germany
Tel.: (49) 619680230
Web Site: http://www.terumo-europe.com
Sales Range: $25-49.9 Million
Emp.: 150
Sales of Pharmaceuticals & Medical Equipment
N.A.I.C.S.: 424210

Terumo (Philippines) Corporation (1)
124 East Main Avenue Laguna Technopark, Binan, 4024, Laguna, Philippines (100%)
Tel.: (63) 49 541 2111
Web Site: http://www.terumo.com
Sales Range: $450-499.9 Million
Emp.: 2,000
Medical Devices & Pharmaceuticals Mfr
N.A.I.C.S.: 325412

Terumo (Thailand) Co., Ltd. (1)
No 88 The PARQ Building Unit 8W9-16 8th Floor Ratchadaphisek Road, Klongtoey Subdistrict Klongtoey District, Bangkok, 10110, Thailand (100%)
Tel.: (66) 2 105 6199
Web Site: https://terumo-th.com
Sales Range: $25-49.9 Million
Emp.: 70
Provider of Surgical Products
N.A.I.C.S.: 339112

Terumo Americas Holding, Inc. (1)
265 Davidson Ave Ste 320, Somerset, NJ 08873-1277
Tel.: (732) 302-4900
Web Site: https://www.terumo.com
Surgical & Medical Instrument Mfr
N.A.I.C.S.: 339112

Terumo Asia Holdings Pte. Ltd. (1)
300 Beach Road 33-03 The Concourse, Singapore, 199555, Singapore
Tel.: (65) 6 295 1792
Medical Device Mfr & Distr
N.A.I.C.S.: 339112

Terumo Australia Pty Limited (1)
Level 4 Building A 5 Talavera Road, Macquarie Park, 2113, NSW, Australia
Tel.: (61) 29 878 5122
Medical Device Mfr & Distr
N.A.I.C.S.: 339112

Terumo BCT (Canada), Inc. (1)
4 Robert Speck Pkwy Ste 1500, Mississauga, L4Z 1S1, ON, Canada
Medical Device Mfr & Distr
N.A.I.C.S.: 339112

Terumo BCT Asia Pte. Ltd. (1)
89 Science Park Drive 04-25 Lobby B The Rutherford, Singapore, 118261, Singapore
Tel.: (65) 6 715 3778
Medical Device Mfr & Distr
N.A.I.C.S.: 339112

Terumo BCT Australia Pty. Ltd. (1)
Suite 4 02 Level 4 15 Orion Road, Lane Cove, 2066, NSW, Australia
Tel.: (61) 29 429 3600
Medical Device Mfr & Distr
N.A.I.C.S.: 339112

Terumo BCT Chile S.A. (1)
Apoquindo 2929 piso 16 y 17, Las Condes, Santiago, Chile
Tel.: (56) 22 480 9600
Web Site: https://www.terumoconosur.com
Medical Device Mfr & Distr
N.A.I.C.S.: 339112

Terumo BCT Colombia S.A. (1)
Cra 15 88-64 Edificio Zimma Of 701, Bogota, Colombia
Tel.: (57) 1 744 1311
Medical Device Mfr & Distr
N.A.I.C.S.: 339112

Terumo BCT Japan, Inc. (1)
Nishi Chome No 20 No 2 Tokyo Opera City Tower 49th Floor, Shinjuku-ku, Tokyo, 163-1450, Japan
Tel.: (81) 12 012 8195
Web Site: https://www.terumobct.com
Medical Device Distr
N.A.I.C.S.: 423450

Terumo BCT Latin America S.A. (1)
La Pampa 1517-12th Floor, C1428DZE, Buenos Aires, Argentina
Tel.: (54) 115 530 5200
Medical Device Mfr & Distr
N.A.I.C.S.: 339112

Terumo BCT Medical Product Trading (Shanghai) Ltd. (1)
Unit 603 SCG PARKSIDE No 868 Yinghua Road, Pudong New District, Shanghai, 201204, China
Tel.: (86) 215 162 8710

Medical Device Mfr & Distr
N.A.I.C.S.: 339112

Terumo BCT Mexico S.A. de C.V. (1)
Av Insurgentes Sur 1431 Piso 11, Colonia Insurgentes Mixcoac Benito Juarez, 03920, Mexico, Mexico
Tel.: (52) 555 363 4770
Medical Device Mfr & Distr
N.A.I.C.S.: 339112

Terumo BCT Peru S.A.C. (1)
Av Elmer Faucett N 1798, Urb San Jose distrito de Bellavista, Lima, Callao, Peru
Medical Device Mfr & Distr
N.A.I.C.S.: 339112

Terumo BCT Tecnologia Medica Ltda. (1)
Rua do Rocio 220-4 Conjunto 41, Vila Olimpia, Sao Paulo, 04552-000, Brazil
Tel.: (55) 112 899 2600
Medical Device Mfr & Distr
N.A.I.C.S.: 339112

Terumo BCT Uruguay S.A. (1)
Br Artigas 1443 Apt 1008 Torre De Los Caudillos, 11300, Montevideo, Uruguay
Tel.: (598) 2 400 5632
Medical Device Mfr & Distr
N.A.I.C.S.: 339112

Terumo BCT Venezuela, C.A. (1)
Torre EXA 9th Floor-Off 921 end of Av Libertador With Calle Alameda, Urb El Retiro Chacao, Caracas, Venezuela
Medical Device Mfr & Distr
N.A.I.C.S.: 339112

Terumo BCT Vietnam Co., Ltd. (1)
A6 Long Duc Industrial Park, Long Thanh, Dong Nai, Vietnam
Tel.: (84) 61 368 1235
Medical Device Mfr & Distr
N.A.I.C.S.: 339112

Terumo BCT, Inc. (1)
10810 W Collins Ave, Lakewood, CO 80215-4440
Tel.: (303) 231-4357
Web Site: https://www.terumobct.com
Automated Blood Collection, Therapeutic Apheresis, Cell Therapy, Blood Component Separation & Purification Technologies Developer & Mfr
N.A.I.C.S.: 334510
Scott Larson *(Gen Counsel & Sr VP-Legal)*

Subsidiary (Non-US):

CaridianBCT Tecnologia Medica Ltda. (2)
220 do Rocio St, 4th Fl, BR 04552 000, Sao Paulo, SP, Brazil
Tel.: (55) 1128992600
Web Site: http://www.caridianbct.com
Sales Range: $25-49.9 Million
Emp.: 30
Automated Blood Collection, Therapeutic Apheresis, Cell Therapy, Blood Component Separation & Purification Technologies Sales & Services
N.A.I.C.S.: 423450

Division (Non-US):

Terumo BCT (Hong Kong) Ltd. (2)
Rm 3903-3903A 39/F New York Life Tower Windsor House, 311 Gloucester Road, Causeway Bay, China (Hong Kong)
Tel.: (852) 2283 0700
Web Site: http://www.terumobct.com
Automated Blood Collection, Therapeutic Apheresis, Cell Therapy, Blood Component Separation & Purification Technologies Developer & Mfr
N.A.I.C.S.: 334510

Terumo BCT Europe N.V. (2)
Ikaroslaan 41, 1930, Zaventem, Belgium
Tel.: (32) 27150590
Web Site: http://www.terumobct.com
Automated Blood Collection, Therapeutic Apheresis, Cell Therapy, Blood Component Separation & Purification Technologies Developer & Mfr
N.A.I.C.S.: 334510

Subsidiary (Non-US):

Terumo BCT Europe N.V. (3)

TERUMO CORPORATION
INTERNATIONAL PUBLIC

Terumo Corporation—(Continued)

Sucursal Espana Calle Arago 264 3 2,
08007, Barcelona, Spain
Tel.: (34) 93 214 2288
Web Site: https://www.terumobct.com
Sales Range: $50-74.9 Million
Emp.: 10
Automated Blood Collection, Therapeutic Apheresis, Cell Therapy, Blood Component Separation & Purification Technologies Whslr
N.A.I.C.S.: 423450

Terumo BCT, Ltd. (1)
Old Belfast Road, Millbrook, Larne, BT40 2SH, United Kingdom
Tel.: (44) 145 272 9292
Medical Device Mfr & Distr
N.A.I.C.S.: 339112

Terumo Business Support Corp. (1)
2-44-1 Hatagaya, Shibuya-Ku, Tokyo, 151-0072, Japan
Tel.: (81) 333748136
General Insurance Services
N.A.I.C.S.: 524210

Terumo Cardiovascular Systems Corporation (1)
6200 Jackson Rd, Ann Arbor, MI 48103-9300
Tel.: (734) 663-4145
Web Site: https://www.terumo-cvs.com
Sales Range: $125-149.9 Million
Emp.: 280
Mfr of Equipment for Open Heart Surgery
N.A.I.C.S.: 339112
Robert DeRyke *(Pres & CEO)*

Terumo Cardiovascular Systems Europe, GmbH (1)
Ludwig Erhad Strasse 6, 65760, Eschborn, Germany (100%)
Tel.: (49) 61968023209
Web Site: http://www.terumo-europe.com
Sales Range: $25-49.9 Million
Emp.: 25
Mfr of Surgical Devices
N.A.I.C.S.: 339112

Terumo Chile Ltda. (1)
Carmencita 25 Oficina 22 Edificio Central Park, Las Condes, SantiagoLas Condes, Chile
Tel.: (56) 2 4809600
Health Care Srvices
N.A.I.C.S.: 621999

Terumo China (Hong Kong) Ltd. (1)
5/F 80 Gloucester Road, Wanchai, China (Hong Kong)
Tel.: (852) 2 866 0811
Web Site: http://www.terumo.co.jp
Surgical & Medical Equipment Mfr & Distr
N.A.I.C.S.: 339112

Terumo Clinical Supply Co., Ltd. (1)
3 Kawashima Takehayamachi, Kakamigahara, 501-6024, Gifu, Japan
Tel.: (81) 58 689 2711
Web Site: https://www.terumoclinicalsupply.co.jp
Surgical & Medical Device Distr
N.A.I.C.S.: 423450

Terumo Colombia Andina S.A.S. (1)
Calle 100 No 23 -10 Piso 2, Bogota, Colombia
Tel.: (57) 1 256 8400
Web Site: https://www.terumocolombia.com.co
Surgical & Medical Instrument Distr
N.A.I.C.S.: 423450

Terumo Corporation Beijing Office (1)
Rm 411 Building B Jin Ru Commercial Plaza, 13 Eastern Beiyingfang Fu Wai Street Xi Cheng District, Beijing, 100037, China (100%)
Tel.: (86) 106 836 0571
Web Site: http://www.terumo.co.jp
Sales Range: $25-49.9 Million
Emp.: 10
Medical Devices & Pharmaceuticals Mfr
N.A.I.C.S.: 325412

Terumo Corporation Guangzhou Office (1)
Room 13 F Zhong Qiao Building 74 Xian Lie Zhong Road, Guangzhou, 510070, China
Tel.: (86) 208 732 0721
Web Site: http://www.terumo.com
Sales Range: $25-49.9 Million
Emp.: 20
Medical Devices & Pharmaceuticals Mfr
N.A.I.C.S.: 325412

Terumo Corporation Shanghai Office (1)
Rm 901 Zhongshan Expo Plaza 666 Huaihai Road West, City Center # 100, Changning, Shanghai, 200052, China (100%)
Tel.: (86) 2162371155
Web Site: http://www.terumo.co.jp
Sales Range: $1-4.9 Billion
Emp.: 9,624
Medical Devices & Pharmaceuticals Mfr
N.A.I.C.S.: 325412

Terumo Corporation-Australia (1)
Level 4 Building A 5 Talavera Road, Macquarie Park, 2113, NSW, Australia (100%)
Tel.: (61) 298785122
Web Site: http://www.terumo.com
Mfr & Sales of Medical Equipment
N.A.I.C.S.: 334510

Terumo Europe Espana SL (1)
Avda Juan Carlos I N 13 7a Planta Ed Torre La Garena, 28806, Alcala de Henares, Spain
Tel.: (34) 902 10 12 98
Surgical & Medical Instruments Mfr
N.A.I.C.S.: 339112

Terumo Europe N.V. (1)
Interleuvenlaan 40, 3001, Leuven, Belgium (100%)
Tel.: (32) 16381211
Web Site: http://www.terumo-europe.com
Sales Range: $200-249.9 Million
Emp.: 1,433
Mfr & Sales of Medical Devices
N.A.I.C.S.: 334510

Division (Domestic):

Terumo Europe N.V. Benelux Sales Division (2)
Interleuvenlaan 40, 3001, Leuven, Belgium (100%)
Tel.: (32) 1 638 1211
Web Site: https://www.terumo-europe.com
Medical Devices & Pharmaceuticals Mfr
N.A.I.C.S.: 325412

Terumo France S.A.S. (1)
Batiment Renaissance 3 Rond-Point des Saules, 78280, Guyancourt, France
Tel.: (33) 13 096 1300
Medical Device Mfr & Distr
N.A.I.C.S.: 339112

Terumo Heart, Inc. (1)
6190 Jackson Rd, Ann Arbor, MI 48103
Tel.: (734) 663-4145
Web Site: https://www.terumomedical.com
Heart Care Surgical Instrument Mfr
N.A.I.C.S.: 339112
Kari Olds *(Dir-HR & Org Dev)*

Terumo Human Create Corp. (1)
Hatagaya 2-44-1, Shibuya-Ku, Tokyo, 151-0072, Yubinbango, Japan
Tel.: (81) 33 374 8962
Web Site: https://www.terumohumancreate.co.jp
Emp.: 276
Temporary Staffing Services
N.A.I.C.S.: 561320

Terumo India Private Limited (1)
1601 and 1602 Unitech Cyber Park Tower B 16th Floor Sector-39, Gurgaon, 122 001, India
Tel.: (91) 124 471 8700
Web Site: https://www.terumoindia.com
Medical Device Mfr & Distr
N.A.I.C.S.: 339112
Shishir Agarwal *(Mng Dir)*

Terumo Italia SRL (1)
Via Paolo di Dono 73, 00142, Rome, Italy
Tel.: (39) 069 480 2800
Web Site: http://www.terumoitalia.it
Medical & Surgical Instruments Mfr

Terumo Korea Corp. (1)
23rd Fl GT Tower 411 Seocho-daero, Seocho-gu, Seoul, 06615, Korea (South)
Tel.: (82) 2 565 9225
Web Site: http://www.terumo.co.kr
Surgical & Medical Instruments Mfr & Distr
N.A.I.C.S.: 339112

Terumo Latin America Corp. (1)
Doral Corporate Ctr I 6th Fl 8750 NW 36th St, Miami, FL 33178
Tel.: (305) 477-4822
Medical Equipment Distr
N.A.I.C.S.: 423450

Terumo Lease Co., Ltd. (1)
1-8-2 Marunouchi Daiichitekko Bldg 7f, Chiyoda-Ku, Tokyo, 100-0005, Japan
Tel.: (81) 332176920
Surgical & Medical Equipment Leasing Services
N.A.I.C.S.: 532490

Terumo Malaysia Sdn. Bhd. (1)
Suite C405 4th Floor Centre Tower Wisma Consplant 1 No 2 Jalan SS 16/4, 47500, Subang Jaya, Selangor, Malaysia
Tel.: (60) 35 880 8898
Medical Device Mfr & Distr
N.A.I.C.S.: 339112

Terumo Marketing Philippines, Inc (1)
Unit W-1010 The Philippines Stock Exchange Centre, West Tower Exchange Road Ortigas Centre, Pasig, Philippines
Tel.: (63) 2 633 3307
Web Site: http://www.terumo.co.jp
Sales Range: $25-49.9 Million
Emp.: 16
Medical Devices & Pharmaceuticals Mfr
N.A.I.C.S.: 325412

Terumo Medical (Shanghai) Co., Ltd. (1)
Rm 901 Zhongshan Expo Plaza 666 Huaihai Road West, Changning, Shanghai, 200052, China
Tel.: (86) 21 6237 1155
Medical & Surgical Instruments Distr
N.A.I.C.S.: 423450

Terumo Medical Canada Inc. (1)
10911 Keele Street Units 2-4, Vaughan, L6A 5A6, ON, Canada
Tel.: (647) 715-5973
Web Site: https://www.terumocanada.ca
Medical Device Mfr & Distr
N.A.I.C.S.: 339112

Terumo Medical Corporation (1)
265 Davidson Ave, Somerset, NJ 08873 (100%)
Tel.: (732) 302-4900
Web Site: https://www.terumomedical.com
Sales Range: $200-249.9 Million
Emp.: 1,000
Mfr of Medical Products
N.A.I.C.S.: 339112
J. Cynthia *(Sr Mgr)*

Subsidiary (Domestic):

Onset Medical, Corp. (2)
13900 Alton Pkwy Ste 120, Irvine, CA 92618
Tel.: (949) 716-1100
Web Site: http://www.onsetmedical.com
Sales Range: $1-9.9 Million
Emp.: 20
Surgical & Medical Instrument Mfr
N.A.I.C.S.: 339112

Branch (Domestic):

Terumo Medical Corporation (2)
950 Elkton Blvd, Elkton, MD 21921-1257
Tel.: (410) 398-8500
Web Site: https://www.terumomedical.com
Sales Range: $100-124.9 Million
Emp.: 1,000
Medicinal Product Mfr
N.A.I.C.S.: 325412

Terumo Medical Corporation do Brasil Ltda. (1)
Rua Gomes de Carvalho 1507 - 15 Andar CJS 151/152, Vila Olimpia, Sao Paulo, 04547-005, Brazil (100%)
Tel.: (55) 113 594 3800

Web Site: https://www.terumomedical.com
Sales Range: Less than $1 Million
Emp.: 10
Medical Devices & Pharmaceuticals Mfr
N.A.I.C.S.: 325412

Terumo Medical De Mexico S.A. De C.V. (1)
Av Insurgentes Sur 1647 Piso 11 Col San Jose Insurgentes, Alc Benito Juarez, 03900, Mexico, Mexico
Tel.: (52) 551 085 0770
Web Site: https://www.terumomexico.com
Sales Range: $25-49.9 Million
Emp.: 30
Supplier of Surgical Products
N.A.I.C.S.: 423450

Terumo Medical Phoenix Distribution Center (1)
4550 West Vemburen St B 103, Phoenix, AZ 85043-2905 (100%)
Tel.: (602) 484-7842
Web Site: http://www.terumomedical.com
Sales Range: $50-74.9 Million
Emp.: 6
Medical Supplies Distr
N.A.I.C.S.: 423450

Terumo Medical Products (Hangzhou) Co., Ltd. (1)
M4-9-5 Economic & Technological Development Zone, M4 9 5, Hangzhou, 310018, China (100%)
Tel.: (86) 5718 691 0212
Web Site: https://www.terumomedical.com
Sales Range: $150-199.9 Million
Emp.: 500
Supplier of Surgical Products
N.A.I.C.S.: 423450

Terumo Medical do Brasil Ltda. (1)
Praca Gen Gentil Falcao 108 9th floor- Cidade Moncoes, Sao Paulo, 04571-150, Brazil
Tel.: (55) 11 3594 3800
Web Site: http://www.terumo.com.br
Medical Apparatus & Device Distr
N.A.I.C.S.: 423450

Terumo Medical-Toronto (1)
1165 Credit Stone Road, Vaughan, L4K 4N7, ON, Canada
Tel.: (905) 760-1210
Web Site: http://www.terumomedical.com
Pharmaceuticals Mfr
N.A.I.C.S.: 325412

Terumo Middle East FZE (1)
Building 8WB-Office 317 Dubai Airport Free Zone, PO Box 54614, Dubai, United Arab Emirates
Tel.: (971) 4 292 0200
Medical Device Mfr & Distr
N.A.I.C.S.: 339112

Terumo Penpol Limited (1)
Terumo Penpol Ltd Jawahar Nagar I-2, P B No 6105, I-2 Jawahar Nagar, Thiruvananthapuram, 695 003, India
Tel.: (91) 471 301 5500
Web Site: https://www.terumopenpol.com
Sales Range: $200-249.9 Million
Emp.: 650
Medical Devices & Pharmaceuticals Mfr
N.A.I.C.S.: 325412
C. Padmakumar *(Chm & Mng Dir)*

Terumo Puerto Rico LLC (1)
Innovacion St Lot 21 Calle B Caguas West Industrial Park, Caguas, PR 00725
Tel.: (787) 945-2309
Medical Device Mfr & Distr
N.A.I.C.S.: 339112

Terumo Russia LLC (1)
BC Northern Tower 13th Floor 10 Testovskaya Street, 123112, Moscow, Russia
Tel.: (7) 4959884740
Medical Device Mfr & Distr
N.A.I.C.S.: 339112

Terumo Singapore Pte. Ltd. (1)
300 Beach Road 33-03 The Concourse, Singapore, 199555, Singapore
Tel.: (65) 6 291 3603
Medical Device Mfr & Distr
N.A.I.C.S.: 339112

Terumo Sweden AB (1)

AND PRIVATE COMPANIES — TESCO PLC

Sven Kallfets gata 18, 426 71, Vastra Frolunda, Sweden
Tel.: (46) 317485880
Web Site: https://www.terumo-europe.com
Sales Range: $25-49.9 Million
Emp.: 20
Medical Devices & Pharmaceuticals Mfr
N.A.I.C.S.: 325412

Terumo Taiwan Medical Co., Ltd. (1)
8th Floor No 4 Sec1 Zhongxiao W Rd,
Zhongzheng Dist, Taipei, 100405, Taiwan
Tel.: (886) 22 361 5123
Medical Device Mfr & Distr
N.A.I.C.S.: 339112

Terumo UK Ltd. (1)
Otium House 2 Freemantle Road, Bagshot, GU19 5LL, Surrey, United Kingdom (100%)
Tel.: (44) 127 648 0440
Web Site: https://www.terumo-europe.com
Sales Range: $25-49.9 Million
Emp.: 37
Medical Devices & Pharmaceuticals Mfr
N.A.I.C.S.: 325412

Terumo Vietnam Co., Ltd. (1)
Lot 44A-44B-44C, Quang Minh Industrial Zone Chi Dong Me Linh, Hanoi, Vietnam
Tel.: (84) 243 586 0110
Web Site: https://www.terumo.com.vn
Sales Range: $200-249.9 Million
Emp.: 900
Surgical & Medical Instrument Mfr
N.A.I.C.S.: 339112

Terumo Vietnam Medical Equipment Co., Ltd. (1)
14th and 16th Floor Geleximco Building 36 Hoang Cau Street, O Cho Dua Ward Dong Da District, Hanoi, Vietnam
Tel.: (84) 243 936 1643
Web Site: https://www.terumo.com.vn
Medical Device Distr
N.A.I.C.S.: 423450

Terumo Yamaguchi Corporation (1)
3-22 Sayama, Yamaguchi, 754-0894, Japan
Tel.: (81) 83 988 3210
Web Site: https://www.terumoyamaguchi.co.jp
Medical Device Mfr
N.A.I.C.S.: 339112

Terumo Yamaguchi D&D Corporation (1)
3-22 Sayama, Yamaguchi, 754-0894, Japan
Tel.: (81) 83 988 3456
Medical Device Mfr & Distr
N.A.I.C.S.: 339112

Vascutek Deutschland G.m.b.H. (1)
Luruper Chaussee 125 / House 8 - Middle, PO Box 520152, 22761, Hamburg, Germany
Tel.: (49) 408971330
Web Site: http://www.vascutek.de
Surgical & Medical Instruments Mfr
N.A.I.C.S.: 339112

Vascutek Ltd. (1)
Newmains Avenue, Inchinnan, PA4 9RR, Renfrewshire, United Kingdom
Tel.: (44) 141 812 5555
Web Site: http://www.vascutek.co.uk
Sales Range: $100-124.9 Million
Emp.: 500
Surgical & Medical Instruments Mfr
N.A.I.C.S.: 339112

Wego Terumo (Weihai) Medical Products Co., Ltd. (1)
3F Gate 2 20 Xingshan Road, Torch Hi-Tech Science Park, Weihai, 264310, Shandong, China
Tel.: (86) 631 571 6596
Medical Device Mfr & Distr
N.A.I.C.S.: 339112

TERVEYSTALO PLC
Jaakonkatu 3 B 3rd floor, 00100, Helsinki, Finland
Tel.: (358) 3063311
Web Site: https://www.terveystalo.com
Year Founded: 2001
TTALO—(HEL)
Rev.: $1,154,239,702
Assets: $1,522,225,698
Liabilities: $916,045,480
Net Worth: $606,180,218
Earnings: $60,584,426
Emp.: 13,000
Fiscal Year-end: 12/31/19
Healthcare Services
N.A.I.C.S.: 621610
Ville Ito (Pres & CEO)

Subsidiaries:

Evalua International Ltd. Oy (1)
Jaakonkatu 3b 3 floor, 00100, Helsinki, Finland
Tel.: (358) 207289080
Web Site: http://www.evalua.fi
Personnel Survey Services
N.A.I.C.S.: 541370
Simo Taimela (Founder & CEO)

Evalua Nederland B.V. (1)
Nieuwe Leliestraat 113, 1015 SM, Amsterdam, Netherlands
Tel.: (31) 655147374
Personnel Survey Services
N.A.I.C.S.: 541370

Hierojakoulu Relaxi Oy (1)
Shopping center Tullintori ground floor Tullikatu 6, 33100, Tampere, Finland
Tel.: (358) 449727051
Web Site: http://www.opiskelehierojaksi.fi
Massage Services
N.A.I.C.S.: 812199

Rela-hierojat Oy (1)
Kuortaneenkatu 7 B, 00520, Helsinki, Finland
Tel.: (358) 60013811
Web Site: http://www.relahierojat.fi
Massage Services
N.A.I.C.S.: 812199

TES CO., LTD.
2374-36 Jungbu-Daero Yangji-Myun, Cheoin-gu, Yongin, 17162, Gyeonggi-do, Korea (South)
Tel.: (82) 313232552
Web Site: https://www.hites.co.kr
Year Founded: 2002
095610—(KRS)
Rev.: $274,579,621
Assets: $258,109,426
Liabilities: $22,893,378
Net Worth: $235,216,048
Earnings: $35,870,038
Emp.: 416
Fiscal Year-end: 12/31/22
Semiconductor Devices Mfr
N.A.I.C.S.: 334413
Ju Shoong Ehl (Chm, Pres & CEO)

TES TOUCH EMBEDDED SOLUTIONS (XIAMEN) CO., LTD.
No 60 South Xinglin Rd, Jimei District, Xiamen, 361022, Fujian, China
Tel.: (86) 5926681616
Web Site: https://www.tes-tec.com
Year Founded: 2015
003019—(SSE)
Rev.: $254,393,835
Assets: $259,842,675
Liabilities: $46,245,556
Net Worth: $213,597,119
Earnings: $36,612,150
Fiscal Year-end: 12/31/22
Software Development Services
N.A.I.C.S.: 541511
Daming Sun (Chm)

TESC CONTRACTING COMPANY LTD.
874 Lapointe St, Sudbury, P3A 5N8, ON, Canada
Tel.: (705) 566-5702
Web Site: http://www.tesc.com
Rev.: $14,780,590
Emp.: 70
Construction Services
N.A.I.C.S.: 236220
Dario Zulich (Pres & CEO)

TESCO PLC
Payroll Team Tesco House Ground Floor Smile Shire Park Kestrel Way, Welwyn, AL7 1GA, United Kingdom
Tel.: (44) 800505555 UK
Web Site: https://www.tescoplc.com
Year Founded: 1919
TSCO—(LSE)
Rev.: $86,181,749,088
Assets: $59,452,729,924
Liabilities: $44,709,302,246
Net Worth: $14,743,427,678
Earnings: $2,229,524,769
Emp.: 336,712
Fiscal Year-end: 02/24/24
Household Product Distr
N.A.I.C.S.: 445110
Alan J. H. Stewart (CFO)

Subsidiaries:

Booker Group Limited (1)
Equity House Irthlingborough Road, Wellingborough, NN8 1LT, Northamptonshire, United Kingdom
Tel.: (44) 1933371000
Web Site: http://www.booker.co.uk
Holding Company; Consumer Goods Whslr & Distr
N.A.I.C.S.: 551112
Charles A. Wilson (CEO)

Subsidiary (Domestic):

Booker Limited (2)
Irthlingborough Road, Irthlingborough Rd, Wellingborough, NN8 1LT, Northants, United Kingdom
Tel.: (44) 1933371000
Web Site: http://www.booker.co.uk
Food Products Retailer & Distr
N.A.I.C.S.: 424490
Lee Jones (Branch Mgr)

Subsidiary (Domestic):

Booker Cash & Carry Ltd. (3)
Equity House Irthlingborough Road, Wellingborough, NN8 1LT, Northamptonshire, United Kingdom
Tel.: (44) 1905454336
Web Site: http://www.booker.co.uk
Cash & Carry Whslr
N.A.I.C.S.: 423990

Booker Direct Limited (3)
Equity House Irthlingborough Road, Wellingborough, NN8 1LT, Northants, United Kingdom
Tel.: (44) 1933371000
Web Site: http://www.booker.co.uk
Food & Beverages Whslr
N.A.I.C.S.: 424490

Subsidiary (Domestic):

Makro Self Service Wholesalers Ltd. (2)
Equity House Irthlingborough Road, Eccles, Manchester, NN8 1LT, Northamptonshire, United Kingdom
Tel.: (44) 1617888448
Web Site: http://www.makro.co.uk
Self-Service Wholesale Stores
N.A.I.C.S.: 445110

Booker Retail Partners (GB) Limited (1)
Support Centre - High Wycombe Cressex Industrial Estate Halifax Road, High Wycombe, HP12 3ST, Buckinghamshire, United Kingdom
Tel.: (44) 8700500158
Web Site: https://www.budgens.co.uk
Grocery Product Distr
N.A.I.C.S.: 445110

Crest Ostrava A.S. (1)
Ostrovni 126/30, 110 00, Prague, Czech Republic
Tel.: (420) 73 161 3608
Web Site: https://www.crestcom.cz
Emp.: 27

Public Relations Services
N.A.I.C.S.: 541820

Dunnhumby (Korea) Limited (1)
3F-5F 23 Jongno 12-gi, Jongno-gu, Seoul, 03190, Korea (South)
Tel.: (82) 269494142
Data Processing Services
N.A.I.C.S.: 518210

Dunnhumby (Thailand) Limited (1)
No 319 Chamchuri Square Building 24th Floor Office no 24116, Phayathai road Pathumwan sub district Pathumwan District, Bangkok, 10330, Thailand
Tel.: (66) 24915222
Emp.: 80
Data Processing Services
N.A.I.C.S.: 518210

Dunnhumby Australia Pty Limited (1)
401 Collins Street, Melbourne, 3000, VIC, Australia
Tel.: (61) 290178322
Data Processing Services
N.A.I.C.S.: 518210

Dunnhumby Brasil Consultora Ltda (1)
Av Brigadeiro Luis Antonio 3530-3 Andar, Jardim Paulista, Sao Paulo, 01402-000, Brazil
Tel.: (55) 113 181 6339
Data Processing Services
N.A.I.C.S.: 518210

Dunnhumby Chile SpA (1)
Av Apoquindo 5950, 7550000, Las Condes, Santiago, Chile
Tel.: (56) 998903541
Web Site: https://www.dunnhumby.com
Emp.: 20
Data Processing Services
N.A.I.C.S.: 518210

Dunnhumby Consulting Services India Private Limited (1)
4th Floor Tower B Paras Twin Towers Sector 54, Gurgaon, 122002, Haryana, India
Tel.: (91) 1244763000
Web Site: https://www.dunnhumby.com
Emp.: 700
Data Processing Services
N.A.I.C.S.: 518210

Dunnhumby Ireland Limited (1)
Floor 3 Building 2 Harbour Square Crofton Road, Dun Laoghaire, Dublin, Ireland
Tel.: (353) 2033868109
Web Site: https://www.dunnhumby.com
Emp.: 50
Data Processing Services
N.A.I.C.S.: 518210

Dunnhumby New Zealand Limited (1)
35 Landing Drive, Mangere, Auckland, 2022, New Zealand
Tel.: (64) 273624453
Web Site: https://www.dunnhumby.com
Emp.: 20
Data Processing Services
N.A.I.C.S.: 518210

Dunnhumby Spain S.L. (1)
Paseo de la Castellana 43 5th floor Office 109, 28046, Madrid, Spain
Tel.: (34) 915654230
Web Site: https://www.dunnhumby.com
Marketing Services
N.A.I.C.S.: 541613

Merrion Shopping Centre Limited (1)
Ballsbridge, Dublin, 4, Ireland
Tel.: (353) 12096959
Web Site: https://themerrioncentre.ie
Shopping Mall Operator
N.A.I.C.S.: 455219

One Stop Stores Limited (1)
Apex Road, Brownhills, Walsall, WS8 7HU, West Midlands, United Kingdom
Tel.: (44) 1543363133
Web Site: https://www.onestop.co.uk
Sales Range: $1-4.9 Billion
Emp.: 7,000
Grocery Stores
N.A.I.C.S.: 445110
Sunil Kumar (Mgr-Business Development-Franchise)

TESCO PLC

Tesco PLC—(Continued)

Shopping Mall Eden s.r.o. (1)
Vrsovicka 1527/68b, 100 00, Prague, 10, Czech Republic
Tel.: (420) 272011711
Web Site: https://www.noeden.cz
Shopping Mall Operator
N.A.I.C.S.: 455219

Tesco Akademia Kepzesi es Fejlesztesi Koratolt Felelossegu Tarsasag (1)
Kinizsi ut 1-3, 2040, Budaors, Hungary
Tel.: (36) 6208211118
Web Site: https://www.tescoakademia.hu
Management Training & Development Services
N.A.I.C.S.: 611430

Tesco Bengaluru Private Limited (1)
Tesco Bengaluru Main Campus 81 and 82 EPIP Area Whitefield, Bengaluru, 560066, Karnataka, India
Tel.: (91) 8066588000
Web Site: http://www.tescobengaluru.com
Computer System Design Services
N.A.I.C.S.: 541512
Sumit Mitra (CEO)

Tesco Insurance Ltd. (1)
Tesco House Delamare Rd, Cheshunt, EN8 9SL, United Kingdom (100%)
Tel.: (44) 01992632222
Web Site: http://www.tesco.com
Sales Range: $50-74.9 Million
Emp.: 70
Insurance Agents
N.A.I.C.S.: 524298

Tesco International Sourcing Limited (1)
2604-2605 AXA Tower Landmark East No 100 How Ming Street, Kwun Tong, Kowloon, China (Hong Kong)
Tel.: (852) 27225960
Web Site: http://suppliermanual.tescois.com
Apparel Retailer
N.A.I.C.S.: 458110

Tesco Ireland Limited (1)
Gresham House Marine Road, Dublin, Dun Laoghaire, Ireland
Tel.: (353) 12152000
Web Site: https://tescoireland.ie
Sales Range: $1-4.9 Billion
Emp.: 13,000
Grocery & General Merchandise Retailer
N.A.I.C.S.: 424410
Geoff Byrne (COO)

Tesco Mobile Ireland Limited (1)
Gresham House Marine Road, Dublin, Dun Laoghaire, Ireland
Tel.: (353) 894200000
Web Site: https://www.tescomobile.ie
Ecommerce Services
N.A.I.C.S.: 517122

Tesco Personal Finance Limited (1)
George House 4th Floor, 36 North Hanover Street, Glasgow, G1 2YG, United Kingdom
Tel.: (44) 8457104010
Financial & Insurance Services; Owned 50% by The Royal Bank of Scotland Group plc & 50% by Tesco plc
N.A.I.C.S.: 522210
Andrew Thomas Higginson (Chm)

Tesco Property Holdings Ltd. (1)
Tesco House Shire Park, Kestrel Way, Welwyn Garden City, AL7 1GA, United Kingdom (100%)
Tel.: (44) 1992632222
Web Site: http://www.tesco.com
Sales Range: $350-399.9 Million
Emp.: 1,000
Property Investment
N.A.I.C.S.: 525990
Philip Clarke (CEO)

Tesco Stores (Malaysia) Sdn Bhd (1)
Level 3 No 3 Jalan 7A/62A, Bandar Menjalara, 52200, Kuala Lumpur, Malaysia
Tel.: (60) 362876000
Web Site: http://www.tesco.com.my
Sales Range: $200-249.9 Million
Emp.: 900
Supermarket & Grocery Stores
N.A.I.C.S.: 445110

Tesco Stores Ltd. (1)
ShirePark Falcon Way, Welwyn Garden City, AL7 1TW, United Kingdom (100%)
Tel.: (44) 8003234050
Web Site: http://www.tesco.com
Food Retailer
N.A.I.C.S.: 424490

Tesco Stores SR, A.S. (1)
Cesta na Senec 2, 821 04, Bratislava, Slovakia
Tel.: (421) 800222333
Web Site: https://tesco.sk
Grocery Product Distr
N.A.I.C.S.: 445110

dunnhumby Limited (1)
184 Shepherds Bush Road Brook Green, London, W6 7NL, United Kingdom (100%)
Tel.: (44) 2039865499
Web Site: https://www.dunnhumby.com
Sales Range: $200-249.9 Million
Emp.: 1,900
Database Marketing & Analytics Services
N.A.I.C.S.: 541613
Marc Fischli (Chief Client Officer)

Subsidiary (Domestic):

KSS Retail Limited (2)
City Tower Piccadilly Plaza 19th Floor, Manchester, M1 4BT, United Kingdom
Tel.: (44) 1612421500
Web Site: http://www.kssretail.com
Price Modeling, Optimization & Customer Insights Solutions
N.A.I.C.S.: 541910

TESEC CORPORATION
3-391 Kamikitadai Higashiyamato, Tokyo, 207-0023, Japan
Tel.: (81) 425661111
Web Site: https://www.tesec.co.jp
Year Founded: 1969
6337—(TKS)
Rev.: $56,971,590
Assets: $106,824,210
Liabilities: $11,131,240
Net Worth: $95,692,970
Earnings: $10,014,150
Emp.: 212
Fiscal Year-end: 03/31/24
Semiconductor Equipment Mfr
N.A.I.C.S.: 334413
Kenji Tanaka (Pres)

Subsidiaries:

TESEC (M) SDN. BHD. (1)
Suite A C Level 5 Annexe AMODA 22 Jalan Imbi, 55100, Kuala Lumpur, Malaysia
Tel.: (60) 321410400
Semiconductor Equipment Mfr
N.A.I.C.S.: 334413
Ooi Teong Cheau (Mng Dir)

TESEC CHINA (Shanghai) CO., LTD. (1)
Unit A 2/F Bulding 4 Block A New CaoYang Industry Park Lane, 1340 JinShaJiang Road, Shanghai, 200023, China
Tel.: (86) 2164438520
Semiconductor Equipment Mfr
N.A.I.C.S.: 334413

TESEC, INC. (1)
1225 W 190th St Ste 350, Gardena, CA 90248
Tel.: (310) 817-4904
Semiconductor Equipment Mfr
N.A.I.C.S.: 334413
Makoto Koshimaru (Pres)

TESGAS S.A.
ul Batorowska 9, Dabrowa, 62-070, Dopiewo, Poland
Tel.: (48) 618901600
Web Site: https://www.tesgas.pl
Year Founded: 2009
TSG—(WAR)
Rev.: $35,671,748
Assets: $31,893,547
Liabilities: $9,390,244
Net Worth: $22,503,303
Earnings: $1,097,561
Fiscal Year-end: 12/31/23
Gas Facilities Maintenance, Construction & Design Services
N.A.I.C.S.: 237990
Wlodzimierz Kocik (CEO)

Subsidiaries:

Przedsiebiorstwo InZynierskie Cwiertnia Sp. z o.o. (1)
ul Zi bicka 35 Zobacz jak dojecha, 60-164, Poznan, Poland
Tel.: (48) 61 868 00 08
Web Site: http://www.cwiertnia.com.pl
Construction Engineering Services
N.A.I.C.S.: 541330

SEGUS Sp. z o.o. (1)
ul Debogorska 22, 71-717, Szczecin, Poland
Tel.: (48) 91 421 4210
Web Site: http://www.segus.pl
Gas Transportation Facility Management Services
N.A.I.C.S.: 486210

Stal Warsztat Sp. z o.o. (1)
ul Golezycka 95, 61-357, Poznan, Poland
Tel.: (48) 61 653 10 50
Web Site: http://www.stalwarsztat.pl
Metalworking Machines Mfr
N.A.I.C.S.: 333248

TESLIC PREVOZ A.D.
Krajiska BB, 74270, Teslic, Bosnia & Herzegovina
Tel.: (387) 53431550
Land Transport & Via Pipeline Services
N.A.I.C.S.: 485999

TESMEC S.P.A.
Via Zanica 17/O, 24050, Grassobbio, BG, Italy
Tel.: (39) 0354232911
Web Site: https://www.tesmec.com
Year Founded: 1951
TES—(ITA)
Rev.: $209,605,297
Assets: $445,788,480
Liabilities: $360,489,668
Net Worth: $85,298,812
Earnings: ($8,365,543)
Emp.: 878
Fiscal Year-end: 12/31/20
Construction Machinery Mfr
N.A.I.C.S.: 333120
Ambrogio Caccia Dominioni (Chm & Mng Dir)

Subsidiaries:

4 Service S.R.L. (1)
Via Anna Frank 3, 22076, Mozzate, Italy
Tel.: (39) 0331363540
Web Site: https://www.4service.it
Recycling Machinery Distr
N.A.I.C.S.: 423830

East Trenchers S.r.l. (1)
Via Zanica 17/O, 24050, Grassobbio, BG, Italy
Tel.: (39) 03669205135
Construction Equipment Retailer
N.A.I.C.S.: 423810

Group Marais SAS (1)
Zone d'activite Les portes de l'Anjou 1 rue Pierre et Marie Curie, 49430, Durtal, France
Tel.: (33) 241961690
Web Site: https://www.samarais.com
Emp.: 1,000
Construction Equipment Mfr & Retailer
N.A.I.C.S.: 333120

Subsidiary (Non-US):

Marais Cote d'Ivoire SARL (2)
Residence Begonia - Rue Louis Lumiere Zone 4, BP 432, Marcory-Bietry, 06, Abidjan, Cote d'Ivoire
Tel.: (225) 88808274
Mechanical Laying & Telecommunication Network Services
N.A.I.C.S.: 237130

INTERNATIONAL PUBLIC

Marais Guinee SARLU (2)
Cite Chemin de Fer Immeuble Mamou, Kaloum, Conakry, Guinea
Tel.: (224) 625215133
Transport Material Distr
N.A.I.C.S.: 423860

OOO Tesmec RUS (1)
Tel.: (7) 4957873356
Web Site: http://www.tesmecrus.ru
Construction Equipment Mfr & Retailer
N.A.I.C.S.: 333120

Tesmec Australia (Pty) Ltd. (1)
120 Kurrajong Avenue, Mount Druitt, 2770, NSW, Australia
Tel.: (61) 296250056
Web Site: http://www.tesmec.com.au
Construction Services
N.A.I.C.S.: 236220

Tesmec Automation S.r.l. (1)
Via Zanica 17/O, 24050, Grassobbio, BG, Italy
Tel.: (39) 0354232832
Electric Device Mfr
N.A.I.C.S.: 334419

Tesmec Guinee SARLU (1)
Camayenne C/Dixinn Residence de la Corail 2eme etage Bloc, Conakry, Guinea
Tel.: (224) 625215133
Trencher Sale & Rental Services
N.A.I.C.S.: 532111

Tesmec New Technology Beijing Ltd. (1)
Tel.: (86) 1082604186
Construction Equipment Mfr & Retailer
N.A.I.C.S.: 333120

Tesmec Rail S.r.l. (1)
Via Fogazzaro 51, 70043, Monopoli, BA, Italy
Tel.: (39) 0809374002
Construction Installation Services
N.A.I.C.S.: 238210

Tesmec SA (Pty) Ltd. (1)
Unit B 87 7th Avenue, Edenvale, 1609, South Africa
Tel.: (27) 113972386
Construction Equipment Mfr & Retailer
N.A.I.C.S.: 333120

Tesmec Saudi Arabia LLC (1)
Anas Bin Malek Street Al Hadlag Building First Floor, Riyadh, Saudi Arabia
Tel.: (966) 112331110
Construction Machinery Distr
N.A.I.C.S.: 423810

Tesmec USA, Inc. (1)
12520 E Fm 917, Alvarado, TX 76009
Tel.: (817) 473-2233
Construction Equipment Mfr & Retailer
N.A.I.C.S.: 333120

TESORO GOLD LTD
Level 48 152-158 St Georges Terrace, Perth, 6000, WA, Australia
Tel.: (61) 63119160
Web Site: https://www.tesororesources.com.au
TSORF—(OTCQB)
Rev.: $11,654
Assets: $25,161,270
Liabilities: $463,969
Net Worth: $24,697,301
Earnings: ($193,238)
Fiscal Year-end: 06/30/24
Financial Services
N.A.I.C.S.: 523999
Zeffron Reeves (Mng Dir)

TESORO MINERALS CORP.
1005-409 Granville St, Vancouver, V6C 1T2, BC, Canada
Tel.: (604) 983-8848
Web Site: https://tesorominerals.com
TES—(TSXV)
Assets: $95,338
Liabilities: $29,788
Net Worth: $65,550
Earnings: ($179,984)
Fiscal Year-end: 10/31/23

AND PRIVATE COMPANIES

Mineral Exploration Services
N.A.I.C.S.: 213114
Cyrus H. Driver *(CFO)*

Subsidiaries:

White Gold Corporation (1)
595 Howe St Suite 600, Vancouver, V6C 2T5, BC, Canada
Tel.: (604) 484-7118
Web Site: http://www.whitegoldcorp.com
Gold Ore Mining Services
N.A.I.C.S.: 212220
David D'Onofrio *(CEO)*

TESS AGRO PLC
No 87 New Nuge Road, Kelaniya, Sri Lanka
Tel.: (94) 112910859
Web Site: https://www.tess.lk
Year Founded: 1992
Rev.: $2,015,830
Assets: $3,643,095
Liabilities: $2,461,495
Net Worth: $1,181,601
Earnings: ($323,983)
Fiscal Year-end: 03/31/18
Fruits & Vegetables Exports Services
N.A.I.C.S.: 424480

Subsidiaries:

Tropic Fishery (Pvt) Ltd (1)
16/1 Thamita Rd, Negombo, Western Province, Sri Lanka
Tel.: (94) 312222959
Web Site: http://www.tropicfish.lk
Fishing Services
N.A.I.C.S.: 114111

Tropic Frozen Foods Ltd. (1)
16/1 Tamitta Road, Negombo, 11500, Western Province, Sri Lanka
Tel.: (94) 312222959
Web Site: http://www.tropicsrilanka.com
Emp.: 100
Processed Seafood Distr
N.A.I.C.S.: 424460
Roshan Fernando *(CEO)*

TESS HOLDINGS CO., LTD.
Shin-Osaka Prime Tower 6-1-1 Nishinakajima, Yodogawa, Osaka, 532-0011, Japan
Tel.: (81) 663082794
Web Site: https://www.tess-hd.co.jp
Year Founded: 2009
5074—(TKS)
Rev.: $190,599,460
Assets: $740,976,160
Liabilities: $481,005,040
Net Worth: $259,971,120
Earnings: $7,370,700
Fiscal Year-end: 06/30/24
Holding Company
N.A.I.C.S.: 551112

Subsidiaries:

P.T. International Green Energy (1)
SOHO CAPITAL Podomoro City 41st Floor Suite SC-4109, Jl Letjen S Parman kav 28 Tanjung Duren Selatan Grogol Petamburan, Jakarta Barat, 11470, Indonesia
Tel.: (62) 2150217214
Web Site: https://www.igeid.com
Renewable Energy Services
N.A.I.C.S.: 221117

Prime Solar LLC (1)
15159 N Scottsdale Rd 340, Scottsdale, AZ 85254
Tel.: (602) 561-5156
Web Site: https://www.primesolarusa.com
Solar Energy Development Services
N.A.I.C.S.: 221114

TESS Engineering Co., Ltd. (1)
17th Fl Shin-Osaka Prime Tower 6-1-1 Nishinakajima, Yodogawa-ku, Osaka, 532-0011, Japan
Tel.: (81) 663082073
Web Site: https://www.tess-eng.co.jp
Construction Engineering Services
N.A.I.C.S.: 541330

TESSENDERLO GROUP NV
Troonstraat 130 rue du Trone, BE-1050, Brussels, Belgium
Tel.: (32) 26391811   BE
Web Site: https://www.tessenderlo.com
Year Founded: 1892
TESB—(EUR)
Rev.: $2,792,467,084
Assets: $2,483,164,256
Liabilities: $968,810,706
Net Worth: $1,514,353,551
Earnings: $244,765,810
Emp.: 4,956
Fiscal Year-end: 12/31/22
Holding Company; Chemical Products & Plastic Pipe Mfr & Distr
N.A.I.C.S.: 551112
John Van Essche *(Compliance Officer)*

Subsidiaries:

Akiolis Group S.A.S. (1)
72 Avenue Olivier Messiaen, 72000, Le Mans, France
Tel.: (33) 244815010
Web Site: http://www.akiolis.com
Sales Range: $25-49.9 Million
Emp.: 1,000
Animal By-products Collection & Processing Services
N.A.I.C.S.: 112990

Subsidiary (Domestic):

Atemax Nord-Est S.A.S. (2)
Route d'Etreux, 02510, Venerolles, Aisne, France
Tel.: (33) 323606002
Hazardous Waste Treatment Services
N.A.I.C.S.: 562211

Soleval Nord-Est S.A.S. (2)
Lieu Dit Montmoret, Luyeres, 10150, Aube, France
Tel.: (33) 325812509
Waste Management Services
N.A.I.C.S.: 562998

Soleval Ouest S.A.S. (2)
Route D Alencon Saint-Langis-les-Mortagne, 61400, Saint-Langis-les-Mortagne, Orne, France
Tel.: (33) 233851795
Sales Range: $10-24.9 Million
Emp.: 26
Waste Management Services
N.A.I.C.S.: 562998

Soleval Sud Est S.A.S. (2)
44 Avenue Montmartin, 69960, Corbas, Rhone, France
Tel.: (33) 478214090
Web Site: http://www.akeoles.com
Emp.: 40
Animal Oil & Fats Rendering Services
N.A.I.C.S.: 311225

Soleval Sud Ouest S.A.S. (2)
Route De Boos, 40370, Rion-des-Landes, France
Tel.: (33) 558570300
Sales Range: $25-49.9 Million
Emp.: 13
Animal Byproducts Collection & Processing Services
N.A.I.C.S.: 311611

BT Nyloplast GmbH (1)
Oberbernbacher Weg 24, 86551, Aichach, Germany
Tel.: (49) 825189950
Pipe Fitting & Injection Molding Mfr
N.A.I.C.S.: 332996

BT Nyloplast Kft (1)
Kassai Str 35-37, 3636, Vadna, Hungary
Tel.: (36) 48505040
Pipe Fitting & Injection Molding Mfr
N.A.I.C.S.: 332996

Chemilyl S.A.S. (1)
Rue Clemenceau, 59120, Loos, Nord, France
Tel.: (33) 320225858
Sales Range: $50-74.9 Million
Emp.: 133
Chemicals Mfr

N.A.I.C.S.: 325180

DYKA S.R.L. (1)
46 Grigore Cobalcescu Street ap 9, Sector 1, 010193, Bucharest, Romania
Tel.: (40) 364262803
Plastic Tank Mfr
N.A.I.C.S.: 326122

DYKA SK s.r.o. (1)
Nejedleho 49/9, Bratislava, 841 02, Slovakia
Tel.: (421) 918 973 286
Plastic Pipe Systems Mfr
N.A.I.C.S.: 326122

DYKA Tube S.A. (1)
Avenue De l Europe, 18570, La Chapelle-Saint-Ursin, France
Tel.: (33) 321865900
Rainwater Management Services
N.A.I.C.S.: 221310

Dyka B.V. (1)
Produktieweg 7, 8331 LJ, Steenwijk, Overijssel, Netherlands
Tel.: (31) 521534911
Web Site: http://www.dyka.com
Sales Range: $125-149.9 Million
Emp.: 500
Plastic Tank Mfr
N.A.I.C.S.: 326122

Dyka GmbH (1)
Birkenweg 5, 14552, Wilhelmshorst, Brandenburg, Germany
Tel.: (49) 3320524250
Plastic Tank Mfr
N.A.I.C.S.: 326122

Dyka Plastics N.V. (1)
Nolimpark Industrial Area Stuifzandstraat 47, 4004, Overpelt, Belgium
Tel.: (32) 11800430
Web Site: http://www.dyka-international.com
Plastic Pipes Mfr & Distr
N.A.I.C.S.: 326122

Dyka Polska Sp.z.o.o. (1)
ul Belgijska 5, 55-221, Jelcz-Laskowice, Lower Silesian, Poland
Tel.: (48) 713010000
Web Site: http://www.dyka.pl
Sales Range: $50-74.9 Million
Plastic Tank Mfr
N.A.I.C.S.: 326122

Dyka SAS (1)
25 Route de Brevillers, 62140, Sainte-Austreberthe, France
Tel.: (33) 321865900
Plastic Pipe & Pipe Fitting Mfr
N.A.I.C.S.: 326122

Dyka s.r.o (1)
Unhostska 505, 273 61, Velka Dobra, Czech Republic
Tel.: (420) 312666011
Web Site: http://www.dyka.cz
Sales Range: $25-49.9 Million
Plastic Tank Mfr
N.A.I.C.S.: 326122

ISPAC S.A. (1)
Zone Industrielle, 64130, Mauleon, Pyrenees-Atlantiques, France
Tel.: (33) 5 59 28 27 31
Meat & Fish Whslr
N.A.I.C.S.: 424470

John Davidson Pipes Ltd. (1)
Townfoot, Longtown, Carlisle, CA6 5LY, Cumbria, United Kingdom
Tel.: (44) 1228792391
Web Site: http://www.jdpipes.co.uk
Sales Range: $25-49.9 Million
Water Management Systems Distr
N.A.I.C.S.: 423440

Kuhlmann France S.A.S. (1)
Rue Clemenceau, 59120, Loos, France
Tel.: (33) 320225858
Crop Protection Product Mfr & Distr
N.A.I.C.S.: 325320

LVM Limburg B.V. (1)
Koolwaterstofweg 1, 6161 RA, Geleen, Limburg, Netherlands
Tel.: (31) 464 76 81 48
Web Site: http://www.tessenderlo.com

TESSENDERLO GROUP NV

Sales Range: $25-49.9 Million
Emp.: 100
Polyvinyl Chloride Mfr
N.A.I.C.S.: 325998

Plant (Non-US):

LVM N.V. (2)
H Hartlaan Industrieterrein Schoonhees 2030, 3980, Tessenderlo, Limburg, Belgium
Tel.: (32) 13610211
Chemicals Mfr
N.A.I.C.S.: 325199

Labrousse S.A. (1)
Le Bourg, 46120, Anglars, Lot, France
Tel.: (33) 5 65 40 80 13
Industrial Chemical Whslr
N.A.I.C.S.: 424690

Lianyungang Taile Chemical Industry Co. Ltd. (1)
188 Xinhai Road, Lianyungang, Jiangsu, China
Tel.: (86) 51885255567
Web Site: http://www.tailechem.com
Sales Range: $25-49.9 Million
Emp.: 30
Organic Chemical Mfr
N.A.I.C.S.: 325199
Howard Want *(Chm)*

Nyloplast Europe B.V. (1)
Mijlweg 45, Postbus 5113, 's-Gravendeel, 3295 SG, South Holland, Netherlands
Tel.: (31) 786732044
Web Site: http://www.nyloplast.nl
Sales Range: $25-49.9 Million
Emp.: 100
Synthetic Connectors Mfr
N.A.I.C.S.: 334417

PB Gelatins (Pingyang) Co. Ltd. (1)
Wubanqiao Industrial Zone Aojiang Town, Pingyang County, Wenzhou, Zhejiang, China
Tel.: (86) 57763668005
Web Site: http://www.china-gelatin.com
Sales Range: $50-74.9 Million
Emp.: 200
Gelatin Mfr
N.A.I.C.S.: 339999

PB Gelatins GmbH (1)
Grosse Drakenburgerstrasse 43, 31582, Nienburg, Lower Saxony, Germany
Tel.: (49) 502160100
Web Site: http://www.pbgelatins.com
Sales Range: $25-49.9 Million
Emp.: 80
Gelatin Mfr
N.A.I.C.S.: 325998

PB Leiner Argentina S.A. (1)
Parque Industrial Sauce Viejo Ruta 11 - KM 455, PO BOX 108, 3017, Sauce Viejo, Santa Fe, Argentina
Tel.: (54) 3424501101
Web Site: http://www.pbleiner.com
Gelatin Mfr
N.A.I.C.S.: 325998

Picanol NV (1)
Steverlyncklaan 15, BE-8900, Ieper, West-Vlaanderen, Belgium (100%)
Tel.: (32) 57222111
Web Site: http://www.picanolgroup.com
Rev.: $3,367,465,608
Assets: $3,724,023,680
Liabilities: $1,650,263,264
Net Worth: $2,073,760,416
Earnings: $197,378,168
Emp.: 7,000
Fiscal Year-end: 12/31/2021
Textile Weaving Machinery Mfr & Distr
N.A.I.C.S.: 333248
Luc Tack *(CEO)*

Subsidiary (Domestic):

Melotte NV (2)
Industrieweg 2019, 3520, Zonhoven, Belgium
Tel.: (32) 1 153 9940
Web Site: https://www.melotte.be
Printing Machinery Mfr
N.A.I.C.S.: 333248
Bram Grandjean *(Sls Mgr)*

Subsidiary (Non-US):

PT Picanol Indonesia (2)

TESSENDERLO GROUP NV

Tessenderlo Group NV—(Continued)

Jl Moh Toha Km 5 3 No 56, Jakarta, Jawa Barat, Indonesia
Tel.: (62) 225211865
Industrial Machinery Mfr
N.A.I.C.S.: 333248

Picanol (Suzhou Ind. Park) Textile Machinery Co. Ltd. (2)
Fengting Avenue/Songzhuang Rd 2, Suzhou, China
Tel.: (86) 51268227726
Industrial Machinery Mfr
N.A.I.C.S.: 333248

Picanol India Private Limited (2)
Office No 102 Sunshine Building, Coimbatore, India
Tel.: (91) 4224392878
Industrial Machinery Mfr
N.A.I.C.S.: 333248

Picanol Tekstil Makinalari Ticaret Limited Sirket (2)
Merkez MAH Yenibosna, Istanbul, Turkiye
Tel.: (90) 2124658808
Industrial Machinery Mfr
N.A.I.C.S.: 333248

Picanol de Mexico SA DE CV (2)
Avena 475, Iztacalco, Mexico, Mexico
Tel.: (52) 5556571740
Industrial Machinery Mfr
N.A.I.C.S.: 333248

Picanol do Brasil Ltda (2)
Rua Treze De Maio 164-JD, Sao Domingos, Americana, 13471-050, Sao Paulo, Brazil
Tel.: (55) 1934758989
Industrial Machinery Mfr
N.A.I.C.S.: 333248

Subsidiary (US):

Picanol of America Inc. (2)
65 Kitty Hawk Rd, Greenville, SC 29605
Tel.: (864) 288-5475
Industrial Machinery Mfr
N.A.I.C.S.: 333248

Subsidiary (Domestic):

PsiControl NV (2)
Steverlyncklaan 15, 8900, Ypres, Belgium
Tel.: (32) 5 740 9696
Web Site: https://www.psicontrol.com
Emp.: 380
Electronics Mfr
N.A.I.C.S.: 334419

Subsidiary (Non-US):

PsiControl Srl (2)
Campului Street 1, Rasnov, 505400, Brasov, Romania
Tel.: (40) 268230081
Electronics Mfr
N.A.I.C.S.: 334419

Produits Chimiques de Loos S.A.S. (1)
22 Rue Georges Clemenceau, PO Box 39, 59374, Loos, France
Tel.: (33) 320225858
Web Site: http://www.tessenderlogroup.com
Sales Range: $50-74.9 Million
Emp.: 180
Chemical Products Mfr
N.A.I.C.S.: 325180
Savard Dominique (Dir-Admin)

S8 Engineering Inc. (1)
4600 E Washington St Ste 430, Phoenix, AZ 85008
Tel.: (602) 344-4533
Web Site: http://www.s8engineering.com
Construction Services
N.A.I.C.S.: 236220
Stan Power (Pres)

SAV SAS Plant Mazingarbe (1)
Chemin des Soldats, BP 49, 62160, Bully-les-Mines, Bully-les-Mines, France
Tel.: (33) 321 72 85 06
Plastic Tank Mfr
N.A.I.C.S.: 326122

SR Collecte S.A.S. (1)
1 route de Selestat, Neubois, 67220, Bas-Rhin, France
Tel.: (33) 388576410
Sales Range: $25-49.9 Million
Emp.: 52
Recycling Services
N.A.I.C.S.: 561990

Sotra-Seperef S.A.S. (1)
25 Route de Brevillers, 62140, Sainte-Austreberthe, Pas De Calais, France
Tel.: (33) 321865900
Web Site: http://www.sotra-seperef.com
Sales Range: $50-74.9 Million
Emp.: 200
Plastic Tank Mfr
N.A.I.C.S.: 326122
Thibaud Heilig (Mgr-Export)

Tessenderlo Agrochem Tarim Ve Kimya San. Ve Tic. Ltd. (1)
Kemalpasa OSB Mah Izmir Ankara Yolu Ansizca Mezra Alti No 312, Kemalpasa, 35730, Izmir, Turkiye
Tel.: (90) 2328780093
Web Site: http://www.tessenderlo-agrochem.com
Sales Range: $25-49.9 Million
Emp.: 50
Fertilizers Import & Distr
N.A.I.C.S.: 424910
Ugurtan Cop (Mng Dir)

Tessenderlo Chemie Rotterdam B.V. (1)
Zevenmanshaven 139, 3133 CA, Vlaardingen, South Holland, Netherlands
Tel.: (31) 104452777
Web Site: http://www.tessenderlo.com
Feed Phosphates Mfr
N.A.I.C.S.: 325312

Tessenderlo Finance N.V. (1)
Troonstraat 130, Brussels, 1050, Belgium
Tel.: (32) 26391811
Web Site: http://www.tessenderlogroup.com
Sales Range: $100-124.9 Million
Emp.: 120
Financial Support Services
N.A.I.C.S.: 523999

Tessenderlo Holding UK Ltd. (1)
Unit A6 Severn Road Treforest Industrial Estate, Pontypridd, CF37 5SQ, Mid Glamorgan, United Kingdom
Tel.: (44) 1443 849300
Investment Management Service
N.A.I.C.S.: 523940

Subsidiary (Domestic):

Eurocell Plc (2)
Fairbrook House Clover Nook Road, Alfreton, DE55 4RF, Derbyshire, United Kingdom
Tel.: (44) 1773842100
Web Site: http://www.eurocell.co.uk
Emp.: 500
Conservatory Roofs & Windows Mfr & Distr
N.A.I.C.S.: 321911
Mark Kelly (CEO)

Subsidiary (Domestic):

Eurocell Building Plastics Ltd. (3)
Unit 3 Trowers Way Centre Trowers Way, Redhill, RH1 2LH, Surrey, United Kingdom
Tel.: (44) 3330323200
Web Site: http://www.eurocell.co.uk
Building Plastic Products Mfr
N.A.I.C.S.: 326199

Eurocell Profiles Ltd. (3)
Cotes Park Lane, Somercotes, Alfreton, DE55 4NJ, Derbyshire, United Kingdom
Tel.: (44) 1773842400
Web Site: http://www.eurocell.co.uk
Sales Range: $25-49.9 Million
Emp.: 70
Windows & Doors Mfr
N.A.I.C.S.: 321911

Subsidiary (Domestic):

Merritt Plastics Ltd. (4)
Manners Ave Manners Industrial Estate, Ilkeston, DE7 8EF, Derbyshire, United Kingdom
Tel.: (44) 1159447661
Web Site: http://www.merrittplastics.com
Sales Range: $25-49.9 Million
Emp.: 40
Plastics Product Mfr
N.A.I.C.S.: 326199

Subsidiary (Domestic):

Vista Panels Ltd. (3)
Unit H1 Prenton Way North Cheshire Trading Estate, Wirral, CH43 3DU, United Kingdom (100%)
Tel.: (44) 1516081423
Web Site: https://www.vistapanels.co.uk
Emp.: 200
Door, Glass & Hardware Mfr
N.A.I.C.S.: 321911
Keith Sadler (Mng Dir)

Subsidiary (Domestic):

PB Gelatins UK Ltd. (2)
Building A6 Severn Road Treforest Industrial Estate, Pontypridd, CF37 5SQ, Mid Glamorgan, United Kingdom
Tel.: (44) 1443849300
Emp.: 70
Gelatin Mfr
N.A.I.C.S.: 325998
Carlos Mandolesi (Plant Mgr)

Tessenderlo Fine Chemicals Ltd. (2)
Macclesfield Road, Leek, ST13 8LD, Staffordshire, United Kingdom
Tel.: (44) 1 538 39 91 00
Web Site: http://www.tessenderlofinechemicals.com
Chemical Products Mfr
N.A.I.C.S.: 325998

Tessenderlo Kerley Mexico S.A. de C.V. (1)
Blvd Rodolfo Elias Calles 515-2 Colonia Centro, 85000, Ciudad Obregon, Sonora, Mexico
Tel.: (52) 16444170615
Plastic Pipe & Pipe Fitting Mfr
N.A.I.C.S.: 326122

Tessenderlo NL Holding B.V. (1)
Nijverheidsweg 4, 4854 MT, Bavel, Noord-Brabant, Netherlands
Tel.: (31) 161433450
Investment Management Service
N.A.I.C.S.: 523940

Tessenderlo Schweiz AG (1)
Ostzelg 340, Rekingen, 5332, Bad Zurzach, Aargau, Switzerland
Tel.: (41) 562490969
Web Site: http://www.tessenderlo.ch
Sales Range: $50-74.9 Million
Emp.: 4
Water Treatment Chemicals Whslr
N.A.I.C.S.: 424690

Tessenderlo Trading Shanghai Co.,Ltd. (1)
Room 2201 Shanghai Times Square Office Tower, Huai Hai Zhong Road No 93, 200021, Shanghai, China
Tel.: (86) 2163918066
Sales Range: $50-74.9 Million
Emp.: 8
Chemicals & Pharmaceuticals Whslr
N.A.I.C.S.: 424210

Tessenderlo U.S.A. Inc. (1)
2255 N 44th St Ste 300, Phoenix, AZ 85008-3279
Tel.: (602) 889-8300
Fertilizers & Pesticides Distr
N.A.I.C.S.: 424910

Subsidiary (Domestic):

PB Leiner USA (2)
7001 N Brady St, Davenport, IA 52806 (100%)
Tel.: (563) 386-8040
Web Site: http://www.gelatin.com
Sales Range: $50-74.9 Million
Emp.: 150
Gelatin Mfr & Retailer
N.A.I.C.S.: 325998

Tessenderlo Kerley, Inc. (2)
2910 N 44th St Ste 100, Phoenix, AZ 85018-7272
Tel.: (602) 889-8300
Web Site: http://www.tkinet.com
Sales Range: $100-124.9 Million
Emp.: 200
Sulfur-Based Fertilizer & Soil Amendment Product Mfr
N.A.I.C.S.: 325311

Subsidiary (Non-US):

Tessenderlo Kerley Latinoamericana S.A. (3)
Andres de Fuenzalida 133 Of A Providencia, Santiago, Chile
Tel.: (56) 2 334 6571
Sales Range: $25-49.9 Million
Emp.: 5
Liquid Fertilizers Mfr & Distr
N.A.I.C.S.: 325314
Enrique Alliende (Gen Mgr)

INTERNATIONAL PUBLIC

TESSI S.A.
177 cours de la Liberation, FR-38029, Grenoble, Cedex 2, France
Tel.: (33) 4 76 70 59 10
Web Site: http://www.tessi.fr
Year Founded: 1971
TES—(EUR)
Rev.: $506,154,323
Assets: $852,986,163
Liabilities: $643,859,028
Net Worth: $209,127,136
Earnings: $39,532,178
Emp.: 13,049
Fiscal Year-end: 12/31/19
Information Technology Services
N.A.I.C.S.: 541512
Vincent Menez (Chm-Supervisory Bd)

Subsidiaries:

Asp One.fr SAS (1)
116 rue de Silly, 92100, Boulogne-Billancourt, France
Tel.: (33) 141315230
Web Site: http://www.aspone.fr
Software Services
N.A.I.C.S.: 541511

Dhimyotis SAS (1)
20 Allee de la Raperie, 59650, Villeneuve d'Ascq, France
Tel.: (33) 806115115
Web Site: http://www.dhimyotis.com
Internet Authentication & Electronic Signature Services
N.A.I.C.S.: 541511

GI Qualitas Limitada (1)
Jaime Guzman Errazuriz, Providencia, 3300, Santiago, Chile
Tel.: (56) 223545164
Web Site: http://www.qualitas.cl
Accreditation Agency Services
N.A.I.C.S.: 813920

Hipotecarios Atacas SL (1)
Varela Silvari 11 Bajo, 15001, A Coruna, Spain
Tel.: (34) 902365820
Web Site: http://www.atacas.com
Law firm
N.A.I.C.S.: 541199

T.D.I SAS (1)
21 rue Jean Moulin, Pont-Remy, 80580, Hauts-de-Seine, France
Tel.: (33) 322273027
Web Site: http://www.tdi.fr
Home & Office Product Whslr
N.A.I.C.S.: 424120

Tessi Document Solutions Switzerland GmbH (1)
In der Luberzen 17, Urdorf, 8902, Zurich, Switzerland
Tel.: (41) 447353311
Software Services
N.A.I.C.S.: 541511

Subsidiary (Non-US):

Tessi Document Solutions (Germany) GmbH (2)
Konigsallee 60 f, 40212, Dusseldorf, Germany
Tel.: (49) 21153819710
Web Site: http://www.tessi-solutions.de
Invoice Scanning & Processing Services
N.A.I.C.S.: 518210

Tessi Gestiona SAS (1)
Transv 93 No 51-98 Int 22, Bogota, Colombia

AND PRIVATE COMPANIES

Tel.: (57) 18418815
Web Site: http://www.tessi.co
Data Processing & Related Services
N.A.I.C.S.: 518210

Valdeolmillos Gestores SLU (1)
Plaza de San Lazaro 1, 34001, Palencia, Spain
Tel.: (34) 979702150
Web Site: http://www.valdeolmillos.net
Administrative Management Services
N.A.I.C.S.: 561110

TESSILFORM S.P.A.
Via Gobetti 7/9, Capalle, 50010, Florence, Italy
Tel.: (39) 055 87 444 777   IT
Web Site:
  http://www.patriziapepe.com
Year Founded: 1993
Women's & Men's Clothing Designer, Mfr & Retailer
N.A.I.C.S.: 315250
Claudio Orrea (CEO)

TESSIN NORDIC HOLDING AB
Klara Norra Kyrkogata 29, 111 22, Stockholm, Sweden
Tel.: (46) 841056070
Web Site: https://tessin.com
Year Founded: 2014
TESSIN—(OMX)
Rev.: $4,746,785
Assets: $24,267,798
Liabilities: $23,426,714
Net Worth: $841,084
Earnings: ($4,182,004)
Emp.: 14
Fiscal Year-end: 12/31/22
Technology Management Consulting; Software
N.A.I.C.S.: 541690
Hans Runesten (Chm)

Subsidiaries:

Effnet AB (1)
Stationsgatan 69, 972 34, Lulea, Sweden
Tel.: (46) 92060918
Web Site: http://www.effnet.com
IP Based Networking Services
N.A.I.C.S.: 517810

TESSON HOLDINGS LIMITED
Room 1007 Tsim Sha Tsu Centre West Wing, 66 Mody Road Tsim Sha Tsui, Kowloon, China (Hong Kong)
Tel.: (852) 35203000
Web Site:
  http://www.tessonholdings.com
1201—(HKG)
Rev.: $12,035,873
Assets: $88,848,885
Liabilities: $45,426,848
Net Worth: $43,422,038
Earnings: ($29,071,913)
Emp.: 342
Fiscal Year-end: 12/31/22
Packaging Products Mfr
N.A.I.C.S.: 541430
Hung Mui Cheng (Exec Dir)

Subsidiaries:

Anhui Qiaofeng Package Printing Co., Ltd. (1)
109 Jingsan Road Chengdong Industrial Zone, Chuzhou, 239000, Anhui, China
Tel.: (86) 5502172799
Web Site: http://www.ahqf.cn
Emp.: 180
Graphic Design Services
N.A.I.C.S.: 541430

Harbin Gaomei Printing Co., Ltd. (1)
Dalian First Road Haping Road, Centralized Industrial Area Harbin Development Zone, Harbin, 150060, Heilongjiang, China
Tel.: (86) 45186812607
Package Printing Services
N.A.I.C.S.: 323113
Dekun Chen (Chm)

Yunnan Qiaotong Package Printing Co., Ltd. (1)
6 Suite Qiaotong Road, Zhaoyang District, Zhaotong, 657000, Yunnan, China
Tel.: (86) 8702229174
Web Site: http://www.qtprinting.com
Graphic Design Services
N.A.I.C.S.: 541430

TEST RESEARCH INC.
7F No 45 Dexing W Rd, Shilin Dist, Taipei, 11158, Taiwan
Tel.: (886) 228328918
Web Site: https://www.tri.com.tw
Year Founded: 1989
3030—(TAI)
Rev.: $145,037,471
Assets: $291,241,985
Liabilities: $56,257,855
Net Worth: $234,984,131
Earnings: $32,743,189
Emp.: 923
Fiscal Year-end: 12/31/23
Semiconductor Testing Equipment Mfr
N.A.I.C.S.: 334413
Jason Chieh-Yuan Chen (Chm & Pres)

Subsidiaries:

TRI Test Research Europe Gmbh (1)
O Brien Strasse 14, 91126, Schwabach, Germany
Tel.: (49) 91226312127
Web Site: http://www.tri.com.tw
Emp.: 7
Machinery Equipment Distr
N.A.I.C.S.: 423830

Test Research Innovation Thailand Company Limited (1)
846/9 Summer Lasalle Room No B2 1 3-B2 1 4 1st Floor Lasalle Road, Bang Na Tai Sub-district Bang Na District, Bangkok, Thailand
Tel.: (66) 20015558
Inspection & Testing Equipment Mfr & Distr
N.A.I.C.S.: 339992

Test Research USA Inc. (1)
832 Jury Ct Ste 4, San Jose, CA 95112
Tel.: (408) 567-9898
Web Site: http://www.tri.com.tw
Machinery Equipment Distr
N.A.I.C.S.: 423830

TEST-RITE INTERNATIONAL CO., LTD.
6F No 23 Xinhu 3rd Road, Neihu District, Taipei, 114518, Taiwan
Tel.: (886) 287915888
Web Site:
  https://www.testritegroup.com
Year Founded: 1978
2908—(TAI)
Rev.: $1,158,003,455
Assets: $1,196,595,658
Liabilities: $974,424,732
Net Worth: $222,170,926
Earnings: $9,186,958
Fiscal Year-end: 12/31/23
Hand Tools, Auto Parts, Machinery, Furniture & Home Appliance Importer & Exporter
N.A.I.C.S.: 441330
Tony Ho (Founder, Founder & Co/Co-Pres)

Subsidiaries:

B&S Link Co., Ltd. (1)
5F No 23 Hsin Hu 3rd Road, Neihu, Taipei, 114, Taiwan
Tel.: (886) 287916060
Web Site: http://www.bnslink.com
Sales Range: $25-49.9 Million
Emp.: 65
Electronic Shopping Services
N.A.I.C.S.: 561499

Chung Cin Enterprise Co., Ltd. (1)
5th Fl 23 Hsin Hu 3rd Rd Neihu, Taipei, 114, Taiwan
Tel.: (886) 287915168
Web Site: http://www.testritegroup.com
Household Products Retailer
N.A.I.C.S.: 449210

Fusion International Distribution, Inc. (1)
6F 23 Hsin Hu 3rd Road, Taipei, 11494, Taiwan
Tel.: (886) 287915888
Household Appliance Distr
N.A.I.C.S.: 423620

Test Rite Business Development Corporation (China) Co., Ltd. (1)
No 21 Lane 456 Taihong Road, Minhang District, Shanghai, 201100, China
Tel.: (86) 2124082888
Web Site: http://www.testritegroup.com
Household Products Retailer
N.A.I.C.S.: 449210

Test Rite Int'l (Germany) GmbH (1)
Merkurring 82, 22143, Hamburg, Germany
Tel.: (49) 406068700
Web Site: http://www.testrite.de
Sales Range: $25-49.9 Million
Household Products Retailer
N.A.I.C.S.: 449210

Test Rite Int'l (U.K.) Ltd. (1)
Caledonia House Winnall Manor Road, Winchester, SO23 0RF, Hampshire, United Kingdom (100%)
Tel.: (44) 1962 853 555
Household Products Retailer
N.A.I.C.S.: 449210

Test Rite Intl (Australia) Pty. Ltd. (1)
Suite 3 01 14 Lexington Drive, Bella Vista, 2153, NSW, Australia (100%)
Tel.: (61) 288057777
Web Site: http://www.testritegroup.com
Home Furnishings Retailer
N.A.I.C.S.: 423220

Test Rite Products (Hong Kong) Ltd. (1)
Unit 701 7/F New Bright Building 11 Sheung Yuet Road, Kowloon Bay, Kowloon, China (Hong Kong)
Tel.: (852) 27517789
Sales Range: $25-49.9 Million
Emp.: 10
Household Appliance Retailer
N.A.I.C.S.: 449210

Test Rite Pte. Ltd. (1)
342-31-2 Vista Damai Condominium Jalan Tun Razak, 50400, Kuala Lumpur, Malaysia
Tel.: (60) 321711399
Web Site: http://www.testritegroup.com
Sales Range: $25-49.9 Million
Emp.: 5
Household Products Retailer
N.A.I.C.S.: 449210
Maggy Chen (VP)

Test Rite Retail Co., Ltd. (1)
5F No 23 Hsin Hu 3rd Road, Taipei, 114, Taiwan
Tel.: (886) 287916668
Web Site: http://www.testritegroup.com
Household Products Retailer
N.A.I.C.S.: 449210

Test-Rite (UK) Ltd. (1)
Unit E The Foundry London Road, Kings Worthy, Winchester, SO23 7QN, Hampshire, United Kingdom
Tel.: (44) 1962677663
Automobile Parts Distr
N.A.I.C.S.: 441330

Test-Rite Int'l. (Canada) Ltd. (1)
19 Waterman Ave Suite 208, Toronto, M4B 1Y2, ON, Canada
Tel.: (416) 288-8015
Automobile Parts Distr
N.A.I.C.S.: 441330

Test-Rite Products Corp. (1)
1900 S Burgundy Pl, Ontario, CA 91761 (100%)
Tel.: (909) 605-9899
Web Site: http://www.testrite.com.tw
Rev.: $13,600,000
Emp.: 45
Automotive Tools & Equipment Distr

N.A.I.C.S.: 423710
Chester Lee (Pres)

Test-Rite Pte. Ltd. (1)
138 CECIL Street 13-02 CECIL Court, Singapore, 069538, Singapore
Tel.: (65) 63256538
Web Site: http://www.testritegroup.com
Household Products Retailer
N.A.I.C.S.: 449210

Test-Rite Vietnam Co., Ltd. (1)
Capital Tower 6th floor 6 Nguyen Khac Vien, Tan Phu Ward Dist, Ho Chi Minh City, Vietnam
Tel.: (84) 854122911
Sales Range: $25-49.9 Million
Emp.: 10
Household Products Retailer
N.A.I.C.S.: 449210

Testrite International Co, Ltd. (1)
Batiment B Micro Park Paris Nord 233 rue des Chardonnerets, BP 51266, 95957, Tremblay, Seine-Saint-Denis, France
Tel.: (33) 149389898
Household Products Retailer
N.A.I.C.S.: 449210

Viet Han Co., Ltd. (1)
751 Nguyen Khoai Street, Hoang Mai District, Hanoi, Vietnam
Tel.: (84) 436432498
Hand Tools & Hydraulic Equipments Distr
N.A.I.C.S.: 423710

TETEKS AD
B Miladinovi No 1, Tetovo, North Macedonia
Tel.: (389) 44355000   MK
Web Site: https://www.teteks.com.mk
Year Founded: 1951
TETE—(MAC)
Rev.: $1,843,064
Assets: $30,621,885
Liabilities: $870,377
Net Worth: $29,751,508
Earnings: $1,535,362
Fiscal Year-end: 12/31/23
Textile Products Mfr
N.A.I.C.S.: 314999
Borislav Trpovski (Pres)

TETHYAN RESOURCES PLC
15th Floor 125 Old Broad Street, London, EC2N 1AR, United Kingdom
Tel.: (44) 2073409970
TETH—(AIM)
Sales Range: Less than $1 Million
Emp.: 1
Gold Exploration & Mining Services
N.A.I.C.S.: 212220
John Graham Proust (Chm)

TETHYS INVEST SAS
27-29 Rue des Poissonniers, 92200, Neuilly, France
Tel.: (33) 141439960
Web Site: http://www.tethys-invest.fr
Holding Company
N.A.I.C.S.: 551112
Alexandre Benais (CEO)

Subsidiaries:

Sebia SA (1)
Parc Technologique Leonard de Vinci, Lisses, 91008, France
Tel.: (33) 69 89 80 80
Web Site: http://www.sebia.com
Sales Range: $125-149.9 Million
Emp.: 400
Medical Diagnostic Equipment Mfr
N.A.I.C.S.: 339112
Benoit Adelus (Chm & CEO)

Subsidiary (Non-US):

ORGENTEC Diagnostika GmbH (2)
Carl-Zeiss-Strasse 49-51, 55129, Mainz, Germany
Tel.: (49) 6131 9258 0
Web Site: http://www.orgentec.com
Emp.: 120
Diagnostic Services

TETHYS INVEST SAS

Tethys Invest SAS—(Continued)
N.A.I.C.S.: 621511
Ralf Wehen *(Mng Dir)*

Subsidiary (US):

Corgenix Medical Corporation (3)
11575 Main St Ste 400, Broomfield, CO 80020
Tel.: (303) 457-4345
Web Site: http://www.corgenix.com
Sales Range: $10-24.9 Million
Specialized Diagnostic Test Kits Developer & Marketer for Vascular Diseases & Immunological Disorders
N.A.I.C.S.: 325413
James F. Widergren *(Pres)*

Subsidiary (US):

Sebia, Inc. (2)
1705 Corporate Dr, Norcross, GA 30093
Tel.: (770) 446-3707
Web Site: http://www.sebia-usa.com
Rev.: $3,300,000
Emp.: 22
Medical Diagnostic Equipment Mfr
N.A.I.C.S.: 339112
Theresa Heslin *(CEO)*

Zeus Scientific, Inc. (2)
199 & 200 Evans Way, 08876, Branchburg, NJ
Tel.: (908) 526-3744
Web Site: http://www.zeusscientific.com
Surgical & Medical Instrument Mfr
N.A.I.C.S.: 339112
Mark Kopnitsky *(VP-Science & Quality)*

TETHYS OIL AB

Hovslagargatan 5B 1 tr, SE-111 48, Stockholm, Sweden
Tel.: (46) 850594700
Web Site: https://www.tethysoil.com
Year Founded: 2001
TETY—(OMX)
Rev.: $138,200,000
Assets: $291,100,000
Liabilities: $32,800,000
Net Worth: $258,300,000
Earnings: ($16,500,000)
Emp.: 8
Fiscal Year-end: 12/31/23
Oil & Gas Exploration & Production
N.A.I.C.S.: 211120
Magnus Nordin *(Mng Dir)*

Subsidiaries:

Tethys Oil Middle East North Africa BV (1)
PO Box 9211, Dubai, United Arab Emirates
Tel.: (971) 8 505 947 00
Oil Exploration Services
N.A.I.C.S.: 213112

TETRA BIO-PHARMA INC.

2316 St Joseph Blvd, Orleans, K1C 1E8, ON, Canada
Tel.: (343) 780-2020
Web Site: https://tetrabiopharma.com
Year Founded: 2007
TBP—(TSX)
Assets: $5,907,186
Liabilities: $5,712,137
Net Worth: $195,049
Earnings: $40,815,495
Emp.: 33
Fiscal Year-end: 11/30/21
Cannabis Mfr
N.A.I.C.S.: 325411
Guy Chamberland *(CEO & Chief Regulatory Officer)*

TETRA LAVAL INTERNATIONAL S.A.

70 Avenue General Guisan, PO Box 446, 1009, Pully, Switzerland
Tel.: (41) 217292211 CH
Web Site: http://www.tetralaval.com
Holding Company; Food Packaging, Environmental Protection & Energy Utilization Production & Distr
N.A.I.C.S.: 551112
Jorgen Haglind *(Officer-Grp Comm)*

Subsidiaries:

DeLaval International AB (1)
Gustaf de Lavals vag 15, PO Box 39, 147 41, Tumba, Sweden
Tel.: (46) 855029400
Web Site: http://www.delaval.com
Sales Range: $800-899.9 Million
Emp.: 4,400
Mfr & Marketer of Milk Processing Systems & Animal Husbandry Equipment
N.A.I.C.S.: 311511
Joakim Rosengren *(Pres & CEO)*

Subsidiary (US):

DeLaval Inc. (2)
11100 N Congress Ave, Kansas City, MO 64153
Tel.: (816) 891-7700
Web Site: http://www.delaval-us.com
Sales Range: $25-49.9 Million
Emp.: 160
Mfr & Marketer of Milk Processing Systems & Animal Husbandry Equipment
N.A.I.C.S.: 311511
Marlene Cline *(Mgr-Customer Svc)*

Subsidiary (Domestic):

Delaval Manufacturing Inc. (3)
11100 N Congress Ave, Kansas City, MO 64153-1222
Tel.: (816) 891-1600
Web Site: http://www.delaval.com
Sales Range: $50-74.9 Million
Emp.: 150
Mfr of Teat Dips, Detergents, Acids & Sanitizers for Dairy Industry
N.A.I.C.S.: 325320
Tom List *(VP-Sls)*

Groupe Sidel (1)
Ave De La Patrouille De France Octeville Sur Mer, 76053, Le Havre, France (99%)
Tel.: (33) 232858687
Web Site: http://www.sidel.com
Sales Range: $150-199.9 Million
Emp.: 1,000
Engineering Services; Packaging Machines
N.A.I.C.S.: 541330
Mart Tiismann *(Pres & CEO)*

Subsidiary (Non-US):

Gebo Cermex Canada Inc. (2)
1045 Highway 13 North, Laval, H7W 4V3, QC, Canada
Tel.: (450) 973-3337
Web Site: http://www.gebocermex.com
Filling, Capping & Conveyor Machines Mfr & Whslr
N.A.I.C.S.: 333993
Stephane Banvelli *(VP)*

Subsidiary (Domestic):

Sidel Canada, Inc. (2)
1045 Hwy 13 North, Laval, H7W 4V3, QC, Canada (100%)
Tel.: (450) 680-5224
Web Site: http://www.sidel.com
Sales Range: $25-49.9 Million
Emp.: 250
Food Processing & Packaging Systems Solutions
N.A.I.C.S.: 561910
Stephane Hacpille *(Mng Dir)*

Subsidiary (Non-US):

Sidel Chile SA (3)
Ojos Del Salado 0800, Quilicura, Santiago, CP 873-0609, Chile (100%)
Tel.: (56) 26540400
Web Site: http://www.sidel.com
Sales Range: $25-49.9 Million
Emp.: 55
Machinery & Equipment Sales & Distribution
N.A.I.C.S.: 333248

Sidel UK Ltd. (3)
Unit 2 The IO Cdentre Hearle Way Hatfield Business Park, Hatfield, AL10 9EW, Herts, United Kingdom (100%)
Tel.: (44) 1707 275200
Web Site: http://www.sidel.com
Sales Range: $25-49.9 Million
Emp.: 10
Food Processing & Packaging Systems Solutions
N.A.I.C.S.: 326160

Sidel do Brasil Ltda. (3)
Rua Fideancio Ramos 302 Block B 10th Floor, Vila Olimpia, Sao Paulo, 04551-010, SP, Brazil (100%)
Tel.: (55) 11 4668 7000
Web Site: http://www.sidel.com
Sales Range: $25-49.9 Million
Emp.: 100
Machinery & Equipment Sales & Distribution
N.A.I.C.S.: 333120
Claudia Delavega *(Mgr)*

Sideo GmbH (3)
Dina-Weibmann-Allee 6, Viernheim, 68519, Germany (100%)
Tel.: (49) 620496590
Web Site: http://www.sidel.com
Sales Range: $10-24.9 Million
Emp.: 35
Provider of Engineering Services
N.A.I.C.S.: 541330

Subsidiary (Domestic):

Sidel (2)
Rue Du Commerce, PO Box 73445, Reichstett, 67116, Mundolsheim, France (100%)
Tel.: (33) 388183850
Web Site: http://www.sidel.com
Sales Range: $75-99.9 Million
Emp.: 300
Provider of Engineering Services
N.A.I.C.S.: 541330
Marc Aury *(Gen Mgr)*

Subsidiary (Non-US):

Sidel Argentina (2)
Manuela Saenz 323 Of 506 Puerto Madero Ciudad Autonoma de Bs As, Buenos Aires, C1107DCA, Argentina (100%)
Tel.: (54) 11 5775 0165
Web Site: http://www.sidel.com
Sales Range: $25-49.9 Million
Emp.: 6
Machinery & Equipment Sales
N.A.I.C.S.: 423830
Claudia Delavega *(Mgr-Comm)*

Subsidiary (Domestic):

Sidel Filling Aseptic S.A. (2)
Ave De La Patrouille De France, PO Box 76930, 76 053, Le Havre, Cedex, France (100%)
Tel.: (33) 232859700
Web Site: http://www.sidel.com
Sales Range: $100-124.9 Million
Emp.: 160
Mfr, Designer & Marketer of Filling Machines
N.A.I.C.S.: 333993

Subsidiary (Non-US):

Sidel GmbH (2)
Dina-Wiessmann-Allee 6, Viernheim, 68519, Germany (100%)
Tel.: (49) 620496590
Web Site: http://www.sidel.com
Sales Range: $1-9.9 Million
Emp.: 32
Mfr, Designer & Marketer of Filling Machines
N.A.I.C.S.: 333993

Sidel Greater China (2)
No 8 Jian'an Jie Bejing Economic & Technological Development Area, 100176, Beijing, China (100%)
Tel.: (86) 10 8722 3960
Web Site: http://www.sidel.com
Sales Range: $25-49.9 Million
Emp.: 22
Food Processing & Packaging Systems Supplier
N.A.I.C.S.: 561910

Subsidiary (US):

Sidel Inc. (2)

INTERNATIONAL PUBLIC

5600 Sun Ct, Norcross, GA 30092 (100%)
Tel.: (770) 449-8058
Web Site: http://www.sidelsystems.com
Sales Range: $50-74.9 Million
Emp.: 200
Packaging Equipment Mfr
N.A.I.C.S.: 423830
Richard Persaud *(Dir-Ops & Engrg Field)*

Division (Domestic):

Gebo Cermex USA Inc. (3)
4845 S Old Peachtree Rd, Norcross, GA 30091
Tel.: (678) 221-3500
Web Site: http://www.gebocermex.com
Sales Range: $25-49.9 Million
Emp.: 20
Packaging Machinery
N.A.I.C.S.: 333993
Stephane Cerle *(Mgr-Svc)*

Subsidiary (Non-US):

Sidel India Pvt. Ltd. (2)
609/610 Corporate Avenue Sonawala Road, Goregaon East, Mumbai, 400063, Maharashtra, India
Tel.: (91) 2266839700
Web Site: http://www.sidel.com
Sales Range: $1-9.9 Million
Emp.: 91
Packaging Machinery, Water Treatment Services & Chemicals
N.A.I.C.S.: 333248

Sidel Italia SrL (2)
Corso Sempioni 39, 20145, Milan, Italy (100%)
Tel.: (39) 0234538306
Web Site: http://www.sidel.com
Sales Range: Less than $1 Million
Emp.: 6
Provider of Engineering Services
N.A.I.C.S.: 541330

Subsidiary (Domestic):

Sidel Packaging Solutions S.A.S. (2)
87 Route De Seurre, 21190, Corelles-les-Citeaux, France (100%)
Tel.: (33) 380707100
Overwrapping-Palletization Sector
N.A.I.C.S.: 926150

Subsidiary (Non-US):

Cermex U.K. Ltd. (3)
Huntingdon Business Ctr Blackstone Rd Stukely Meadows Industrial Est, PO Box 12, Huntingdon, PE29 6EF, Cambs, United Kingdom (100%)
Tel.: (44) 1480455919
Web Site: http://www.gebocermex.com
Sales Range: $25-49.9 Million
Emp.: 6
Sales of Packaging Machinery
N.A.I.C.S.: 333993
Mike Lane *(Mgr-Admin)*

Subsidiary (Domestic):

Sidel SA (2)
Avenue De La Patrouille De France, 76930, Octeville-sur-Mer, France (100%)
Tel.: (33) 232858687
Packaging Containers for the Food & Beverage Industries Mfr
N.A.I.C.S.: 327213

Subsidiary (Non-US):

Sidel South Asia-Pacific Ltd. (2)
IYARA Tower 9th Floor 2/22 Chan Road Thungwatdon, Sathorn, Bangkok, 10120, Thailand
Tel.: (66) 26785300
Web Site: http://www.sidel.com
Sales Range: $25-49.9 Million
Emp.: 30
Packaging Machinery Sales
N.A.I.C.S.: 423830

Sidel de Mexico S.A. de C.V. (2)
4920-A Colonia Guadalajara Technology Park, Km 13 Carr Guadalajara-Nogales, 45010, Zapopan, Jalisco, Mexico (100%)
Tel.: (52) 3337773730
Web Site: http://www.sidel.com

AND PRIVATE COMPANIES — TETRA LAVAL INTERNATIONAL S.A.

Sales Range: $25-49.9 Million
Emp.: 100
Glass, Cans & Plastic Bottles Mfr
N.A.I.C.S.: 326160
Claudia Vega (Office Mgr)

Sidel de Mexico, S.A. de C.V (2)
Inglaterra 4920 Guadalajara Technology Pk, Km 13 Carr Guad Nogales, CP 45010, Zapopan, Jalisco, Mexico
Tel.: (52) 3337773730
Sales Range: $25-49.9 Million
Emp.: 100
Plastic Containers & Bottles Mfr for the Beverage Industry
N.A.I.C.S.: 326160

SIDEL GROUP (1)
Bosch 67, PO Box 658, 6331, Hunenberg, Switzerland
Tel.: (41) 41 785 23 60
Web Site: http://www.sidel.com
Emp.: 3,200
Plastics Bottle Mfr
N.A.I.C.S.: 326199
Pavel Shevchuk (VP-Europe & Central Asia)

Subsidiary (Non-US):

Sidel Distribution (Malaysia) Sdn Bhd (2)
28-E 4th Floor Jalan USJ 10/A, 47620, Subang Jaya, Selangor, Malaysia
Tel.: (60) 3 8022 9200
Web Site: http://www.sidel.com
Emp.: 8
Plastic Bottle Distr
N.A.I.C.S.: 423840

Sidel GMEA (2)
PO Box 478835, Studio City, Dubai, United Arab Emirates
Tel.: (971) 4 429 1800
Plastic Bottle Distr
N.A.I.C.S.: 423840

Sidel Iberica, S.L.U. (2)
Pollgono Industrial Palou C/ Mollet 14-16 Nave 3, Granollers, 08401, Barcelona, 08401, Spain
Tel.: (34) 902 20 53 00
Plastic Bottle Distr
N.A.I.C.S.: 423840
Fernando Samaniego (Gen Mgr)

Sidel Packaging Systems South Africa (Pty) Ltd (2)
15 Monza Close Kyalami Business Park, Kyalami, South Africa
Tel.: (27) 11 466 2230
Plastic Bottle Distr
N.A.I.C.S.: 423840

Sidel Panama Corp. (2)
El Carmen Ave 6a C Norte Edificio Mercansa, Panama, Panama
Tel.: (507) 3929313
Plastic Bottle Distr
N.A.I.C.S.: 423840

Sidel Sales and Conveyor Industries Philippines, Inc. (2)
Units 1&2 CRI Bldg 6 Lot 5 Block 7 Phase 3 East Science Ave SEZ, Brgy Malamig, Binan, 4024, Laguna, Philippines
Tel.: (63) 49 502 9261
Plastic Bottle Distr
N.A.I.C.S.: 423840

Tetra Pak International S.A. (1)
70 Ave Generale Guisan, PO Box 446, Pully, 1009, Lausanne, Switzerland
Tel.: (41) 217292111
Web Site: http://www.tetrapak.com
Sales Range: $75-99.9 Million
Emp.: 400
Food Packaging Systems Mfr
N.A.I.C.S.: 322219
Oshiokamele Aruna (Mng Dir-West Africa)

Subsidiary (Non-US):

AB Tetra Pak (2)
Ruben Rausings Gata, 221 86, Lund, Sweden
Tel.: (46) 46 36 10 00
Web Site: http://www.tetrapak.com
Emp.: 4,000

Food Processing & Packaging Systems Supplier
N.A.I.C.S.: 322212

Danice Services A/S (2)
Soren Nymarks Vej 11, Hojbjerg, 8270, Denmark
Tel.: (45) 89393989
Web Site: http://www.danice.com
Sales Range: $10-24.9 Million
Emp.: 10
N.A.I.C.S.: 322212

Affiliate (Non-US):

Huaxin Tetra Pak (Foshan) Packaging Co., Ltd. (2)
No 13 Gangkou Road, High Technology, Development Zone, Foshan, 528041, Guangdong, China
Tel.: (86) 757 3831626
Web Site: http://www.fshxp.com
Sales Range: $50-74.9 Million
Emp.: 200
Laminated Packaging Material Mfr
N.A.I.C.S.: 322220

Subsidiary (Non-US):

Nihon Tetra Pak K.K. (2)
Kioicho 6-12 Fukuda House Bldg 4F, Chiyoda-ku, Tokyo, 102 8544, Japan
Tel.: (81) 352112111
Web Site: http://www.tetrapak.co.jp
Sales Range: $50-74.9 Million
Emp.: 177
Flexible Packaging Products Mfr
N.A.I.C.S.: 322212

Novembal (2)
5 route du Perollier, PO Box 29, 69480, Dardilly, France
Tel.: (33) 472549600
Web Site: http://www.novembal.com
Sales Range: $50-74.9 Million
Emp.: 110
N.A.I.C.S.: 322212

SIG Simonazzi S.p.A. (2)
Via la Spezia 241A, 43040, Parma, Italy
Tel.: (39) 0005219991
Web Site: http://www.sigsimonazzi.com
Plastic Containers & Bottles Mfr for the Beverage Industry
N.A.I.C.S.: 326160

Subsidiary (Non-US):

SIG (China) Beverages Machinery Co. Ltd. (3)
Unit 1403 Yi An Plz, N 33 Jian She Liu Rd, 510060, Guangzhou, China
Tel.: (86) 2083633272
Web Site: http://www.sigsimonazzi.com
Sales Range: $50-74.9 Million
Emp.: 70
Plastic Containers & Bottles Mfr for the Beverage Industry
N.A.I.C.S.: 326160

SIG Beverages Brasil Ltda. (3)
Chedid Jafet 222ck 42 Power B, Itapeceria Da Serra, 4551065, Sao Paulo, Brazil
Tel.: (55) 146687000
Sales Range: $50-74.9 Million
Emp.: 20
Plastic Containers & Bottles Mfr for the Beverage Industry
N.A.I.C.S.: 326160

Subsidiary (Non-US):

Sidal, Inc. (2)
Plz Globus Bldg 1st Fl Samuel Lewis Ave, 55 Saint OBarrio, Panama, Panama (100%)
Tel.: (507) 2639566
Web Site: http://www.tetrapak.com
Sales Range: $25-49.9 Million
Emp.: 60
Sanitary Food Container Mfr
N.A.I.C.S.: 322219

Simonazzi Iberica (2)
Provenza 385, E 08025, Barcelona, Spain
Tel.: (34) 934761818
Sales Range: $25-49.9 Million
Emp.: 9

Sales of Machines, Complete Bottling & Canning Lines, Turnkey Systems for the Beverage Industry; Technical Service & Spare Parts; Line Engineering & Consulting
N.A.I.C.S.: 423830

Tetra Pak (Thailand) Ltd. (2)
1042 Soi Sukhumvit 66/1 Sukhumvit Road Bangchak, Bangkok, 10260, Thailand (100%)
Tel.: (66) 2 704 3000
Web Site: http://www.tetrapak.com
Sales Range: $25-49.9 Million
Emp.: 100
Food Processing & Packaging Solutions
N.A.I.C.S.: 322212

Tetra Pak A/O (2)
Wilhelm Pieck St 8, Moscow, 129226, Russia (100%)
Tel.: (7) 4957878000
Web Site: http://www.tetrapak.com
Sales Range: $100-124.9 Million
Emp.: 400
Paperboard Mfr
N.A.I.C.S.: 322212
Maria Krasilowez (Gen Mgr-Southeast Europe)

Tetra Pak A/S (2)
Vollsveien 2b, N 1327, Lysaker, Norway (100%)
Tel.: (47) 67833000
Web Site: http://www.tetrapak.com
Sales Range: $25-49.9 Million
Emp.: 23
Paperboard Box Manufacturing
N.A.I.C.S.: 322212

Tetra Pak America Latina (2)
Plz Globus Bldg 7th Fl Ave Samuel Lewis y calle 55, Obarrio, Panama, 083401714, Panama (100%)
Tel.: (507) 2085800
Sales Range: $25-49.9 Million
Emp.: 75
Trading & Finance
N.A.I.C.S.: 326199

Tetra Pak B.V. (2)
Oostelijke Randweg 48, 4782 PZ, Moerdijk, Netherlands (100%)
Tel.: (31) 168386500
Web Site: http://www.tetrapak.com
Sales Range: $100-124.9 Million
Emp.: 300
Packaging, Marketing & Converting Mfr
N.A.I.C.S.: 322212
Stephanie Sangerang (Gen Mgr)

Tetra Pak Baltic States (2)
K Ulmana Gatve 86F, LV 1046, Riga, Latvia (100%)
Tel.: (371) 7602000
Web Site: http://www.tetrapak.com
Sales Range: $25-49.9 Million
Emp.: 20
Packaging Systems Supplier
N.A.I.C.S.: 322212

Tetra Pak CIA. Ltda (2)
Av Eloy Alfaro N35-09 & Portugal Edificio Millenium Plaza, Piso 5 to of 505, 170135, Quito, Ecuador
Tel.: (593) 2 398 1800
Web Site: http://www.tetrapak.com
Packaging Mfr
N.A.I.C.S.: 322212

Tetra Pak China Ltd. (2)
29th Floor Citic Square 1168, Nanjing Road West, Shanghai, 200041, China (100%)
Tel.: (86) 2132174688
Web Site: http://www.tetrapak.com
Sales Range: $25-49.9 Million
Emp.: 40
Packaging & Box Mfr
N.A.I.C.S.: 322212

Tetra Pak Dairy & Beverage AB (2)
Soren Nymarksvej 13, Hojbjerg, 227 36, Denmark
Tel.: (45) 89393939
Web Site: http://www.tetrapak.com
Sales Range: $100-124.9 Million
Emp.: 300
Provider of Packaging Products
N.A.I.C.S.: 326199
Steen Thomsen (Gen Mgr)

Tetra Pak Danmark A/S (2)
Soren Nymarks Vej 13, 8270, Hojbjerg, Denmark
Tel.: (45) 89393939
Web Site: http://www.tetrapak.com
Sales Range: $75-99.9 Million
Emp.: 350
Dairy & Food Packaging Marketing Services
N.A.I.C.S.: 561910
Steen Thomsen (Pres)

Subsidiary (Domestic):

Tetra Pak Export SA (2)
70 Ave General Guisan, PO Box 446, Pully, CH 1009, Lausanne, Switzerland (100%)
Tel.: (41) 217292111
Web Site: http://www.tetrapak.com
Box Manufacturing for the Food Service Industry
N.A.I.C.S.: 322212

Subsidiary (Non-US):

Tetra Pak France (2)
Campus Equilibre 56-58 avenue Jean Jaures, 92707, Colombes, France
Tel.: (33) 1 56 47 50 00
Web Site: http://www.tetrapak.com
Packaging & Processing Services
N.A.I.C.S.: 561910

Tetra Pak GmbH & Co. KG. (2)
Frankfurter Strasse 85, 65239, Hochheim, Germany (100%)
Tel.: (49) 6146590
Web Site: http://www.tetrapak.com
Sales Range: $50-74.9 Million
Emp.: 120
Food Packaging Mfr
N.A.I.C.S.: 322212

Tetra Pak Hungary Ltd. (2)
PO Box 200, 2041, Budaors, Hungary (100%)
Tel.: (36) 23885200
Web Site: http://www.tetrapak.com
Sales Range: $50-74.9 Million
Emp.: 200
Paperboard Mfr
N.A.I.C.S.: 322212

Tetra Pak Imports PTY Ltd (2)
2A Hill Road, Homebush Bay, 2127, NSW, Australia (100%)
Tel.: (61) 2 8719 7300
Web Site: http://www.tetrapak.com
Sales Range: $50-74.9 Million
Emp.: 200
Paperboard Mfr
N.A.I.C.S.: 322212
Craig Salkeld (Gen Mgr)

Subsidiary (US):

Tetra Pak Inc. (2)
3300 Airport Rd 900B, Denton, TX 76207-2110
Tel.: (940) 384-2000
Web Site: http://www.tetrapak.com
Sales Range: $25-49.9 Million
Emp.: 100
Packaging Food Products
N.A.I.C.S.: 322220

Branch (Domestic):

Tetra Pak Inc. - Vernon Hills Office (3)
600 Bunker Ct, Vernon Hills, IL 60061
Tel.: (847) 955-6000
Web Site: http://www.tetrapak.com
Processing Equipment Whslr
N.A.I.C.S.: 423830

Subsidiary (Domestic):

Tetra Pak Processing Equipment Inc. (3)
801 Kingsley St, Winsted, MN 55395
Tel.: (320) 485-4401
Web Site: http://www.tetrapak.com
Food Processing Equipment Mfr & Whslr
N.A.I.C.S.: 333261

Subsidiary (Domestic):

Johnson Industries International, Inc. (4)
6391 Lk Rd, Windsor, WI 53598
Tel.: (608) 846-4499
Web Site: http://www.johnsonindint.com

TETRA LAVAL INTERNATIONAL S.A.

Tetra Laval International S.A.—(Continued)
Food Product Machinery Mfr
N.A.I.C.S.: 333241

Subsidiary (Non-US):

Tetra Pak Iran (2)
1st Floor Khorshid Building, PO Box 1435674173, No 1264 Vali Asr Ave, Tehran, 19395-6395, Iran
Tel.: (98) 2182139000
Web Site: http://www.tetrapak.com
Packaging Products Mfr & Distr
N.A.I.C.S.: 333993

Tetra Pak Ireland Ltd. (2)
5th Floor 1 Tuansgate Belgard Square E, Dublin, Ireland (100%)
Tel.: (353) 1 4678000
Web Site: http://www.tetrapak.com
Sales Range: $25-49.9 Million
Emp.: 56
Food Processing & Packaging Systems Supplier
N.A.I.C.S.: 322212
John Foster (Mgr-Media)

Tetra Pak Italiana S.p.A. (2)
Viale Della Resistenza 56 A, Rubiera, I 42048, RE, Italy (100%)
Tel.: (39) 0522263411
Web Site: http://www.tetrapak.com
Sales Range: $50-74.9 Million
Emp.: 150
Paperboard Boxes
N.A.I.C.S.: 322212

Tetra Pak Ltd. (2)
Enterprise/Likoni Road Junction Industrial Area, PO Box 78340, Nairobi, 00507, Kenya (100%)
Tel.: (254) 71 102 1000
Web Site: http://www.tetrapak.com
Sales Range: $25-49.9 Million
Emp.: 80
Food Processing & Packaging Systems Supplier
N.A.I.C.S.: 322212

Tetra Pak Ltda. (2)
World Trade Center Calle 100 No 8A-55, Torre C Oficina 209, Bogota, 110111, Colombia (100%)
Tel.: (57) 16283630
Web Site: http://www.tetrapak.com.co
Sales Range: $25-49.9 Million
Emp.: 100
Food Processing & Packaging Systems Supplier
N.A.I.C.S.: 322212

Tetra Pak Malaysia Sdn Bhd (2)
1201 Level 12 Damansara Uptown 2 No 2 Jalan SS 21/37, Petaling Jaya, 47400, Selangor, Malaysia
Tel.: (60) 3 7724 7000
Web Site: http://www.tetratech.com
Emp.: 100
Food Processing Packaging Solutions
N.A.I.C.S.: 322212
Brian May (Mng Dir)

Subsidiary (Non-US):

Tetra Pak Philippines, Inc. (3)
7th Fl Net One Ctr 26th St, Fort Bonifacio, Taguig, 1634, Philippines
Tel.: (63) 279763400
Web Site: http://www.tetrapak.com
Sales Range: $25-49.9 Million
Emp.: 45
Industrial Machinery & Equipment Merchant Wholesalers
N.A.I.C.S.: 423830

Tetra Pak South East Asia Pte Ltd (3)
19 Gul Lane, Singapore, 629414, Singapore (100%)
Tel.: (65) 68902000
Web Site: http://www.tetrapak.com
Sales Range: $125-149.9 Million
Packaging Systems Solutions
N.A.I.C.S.: 322212

Subsidiary (Non-US):

Tetra Pak Manufacturing Limited (2)
Northern Ring Rd between Exit 6 & 7 Demyat St, PO Box 54380, Al-Taawun District,
11514, Riyadh, Saudi Arabia (100%)
Tel.: (966) 14433488
Web Site: http://www.tetrapak.com
Sales Range: $25-49.9 Million
Emp.: 25
Food Packaging Containers & Paperboard Mfr
N.A.I.C.S.: 322212

Tetra Pak Manufacturing Ltd (2)
Lot No 88-103 Phase 3 JCCI Warehouse City, PO Box 9454, Jeddah, 21413, Saudi Arabia (100%)
Tel.: (966) 122688000
Web Site: http://www.tetrapak.com
Sales Range: $100-124.9 Million
Emp.: 300
Food Processing & Packaging Systems Supplier
N.A.I.C.S.: 322212

Tetra Pak Moulding Packaging Systems Ltd. (2)
Bedwell Road Cross Lanes, Wrexham, LL13 0UT, United Kingdom (100%)
Tel.: (44) 8704426600
Web Site: http://www.tetrapak.com
Sales Range: $25-49.9 Million
Emp.: 100
Folding Paperboard Boxes
N.A.I.C.S.: 322212

Tetra Pak New Zealand Limited (2)
Waikato Innovation Park Ruakura Lane, 3214, Hamilton, New Zealand (100%)
Tel.: (64) 7 859 1442
Web Site: http://www.tetrapak.com
Sales Range: $25-49.9 Million
Emp.: 10
Food Packaging Systems Mfr
N.A.I.C.S.: 322212
Chris Morgan (Mng Dir)

Tetra Pak Oy (2)
Meijeritie 2, 370, Helsinki, Finland (100%)
Tel.: (358) 207633600
Web Site: http://www.tetrapak.com
Sales Range: $25-49.9 Million
Emp.: 50
Food Processing & Packaging Solutions
N.A.I.C.S.: 322212
Sari Hassi (Office Mgr)

Tetra Pak Processing GmbH (2)
Semefelder Ring 27, D 21465, Reinbek, Germany
Tel.: (49) 40600910
Web Site: http://www.tetrapak-processing.com
Sales Range: $25-49.9 Million
Emp.: 90
Dairy & Food Product Packaging
N.A.I.C.S.: 561910
Bengt Norrgren (Pres)

Tetra Pak Processing SNC (2)
Zone industrielle B P 35 3 Rue de Romelet, Longvic, 21601, France (100%)
Tel.: (33) 3 80 73 71 71
Web Site: http://www.tetrapak.com
Food Processing & Packaging Solutions
N.A.I.C.S.: 322212
Le Jousse (Gen Mgr)

Tetra Pak Research GmbH (2)
Untere Waldplatze 27D, 70569, Stuttgart, Germany (100%)
Tel.: (49) 711 687 049 0
Web Site: http://www.tetrapak.com
Sales Range: $50-74.9 Million
Emp.: 25
Food Processing Research & Development
N.A.I.C.S.: 541715
Stephan Karl (Mng Dir)

Tetra Pak S.A. (2)
Edificio Plaza Globus Piso 7 Ave Samuel Lewis y Calle 55 Obarrio, Panama, Panama (100%)
Tel.: (507) 2085800
Web Site: http://www.tetrapak.com
Sales Range: $25-49.9 Million
Emp.: 75
N.A.I.C.S.: 322212
Manuel Calderon (Mng Dir)

Tetra Pak Scanima A/S (2)
Gugvej 152B, 9210, Aalborg, Denmark
Tel.: (45) 96331000
Web Site: http://www.tetrapakscanima.com
Emp.: 70
Mixing Equipment Mfr
N.A.I.C.S.: 333310
Kresten Hjortsballe (Mng Dir)

Subsidiary (Domestic):

Tetra Pak Schweiz AG (2)
Europastrasse 30, Glattbrugg, 8152, Switzerland (100%)
Tel.: (41) 448046600
Web Site: http://www.tetrapak.com
Sales Range: $25-49.9 Million
Emp.: 50
N.A.I.C.S.: 322212

Subsidiary (Non-US):

Tetra Pak Taiwan Ltd (2)
4 Wen Ming 3rd St Lin Kou Industrial Park 3, Taoyuan, 33383, Taiwan (100%)
Tel.: (886) 33283111
Web Site: http://www.tetrapak.com
Sales Range: $50-74.9 Million
Emp.: 200
Food Processing & Packaging Solutions
N.A.I.C.S.: 322212

Tetra Pak a.s. (2)
Buyukdere Caddesi Nurol Plaza No 255 A Blok Kat 10, 343398, Istanbul, Maslak, Turkiye
Tel.: (90) 212 444 6878
Web Site: http://www.tetrapak.com
Sales Range: $25-49.9 Million
Emp.: 100
Packaging Solutions
N.A.I.C.S.: 322212
Hendrik Auggjaard (Mgr)

Tetra Pak de Chile Comercial Ltda. (2)
Av Apoquindo 5400 Piso 4, Las Condes, Santiago, Chile
Tel.: (56) 2 940 7000
Web Site: http://www.tetrapak.com
Commercial Packaging Mfr
N.A.I.C.S.: 322212

TETRAGON FINANCIAL GROUP LIMITED

Mill Court La Charrotterie, GY1 1EJ, Saint Peter Port, GY1 1EJ, Guernsey
Tel.: (44) 2079018328
Web Site:
https://www.tetragoninv.com
TFG—(OTCIQ)
Rev.: $306,600,000
Assets: $2,668,500,000
Liabilities: $194,100,000
Net Worth: $2,474,400,000
Earnings: $171,100,000
Emp.: 380
Fiscal Year-end: 12/31/20
Financial & Investment Services
N.A.I.C.S.: 523999
Patrick Giles Gauntlet Dear (Co-Founder & Mgr-Investments)

TETRIS

100 Esplainade Du General Gegaulle, Paris, 92932, France
Tel.: (33) 149003250
Web Site: http://www.tetris.fr
Rev.: $26,700,000
Emp.: 60
Engineeering Services
N.A.I.C.S.: 541330
Franck Eburderie (Pres)

TETRIS MEDIA LIMITED

Unit 1110 Prosperity Millennia Plaza 663 King's Road, Quarry Bay, China (Hong Kong)
Tel.: (852) 21806117   HK
Web Site: https://www.tetris-media.com
Year Founded: 2008
Emp.: 100
Online Gambling Services
N.A.I.C.S.: 713120

TETROSYL LTD.

INTERNATIONAL PUBLIC

Newgate House Newgate, Lancashire, London, OL16 1AT, United Kingdom
Tel.: (44) 1617645981
Web Site: http://www.tetrosyl.com
Car Care Products Mfr
N.A.I.C.S.: 339999
Peter Schofield (Chm)

Subsidiaries:

James Briggs Ltd. (1)
Salmon Fields, Royton, Oldham, OL2 6HZ, United Kingdom
Tel.: (44) 1616270101
Web Site: http://www.jamesbriggs.co.uk
Chemicals Mfr
N.A.I.C.S.: 325998
James Briggs (CEO)

TETRYS S.A.

Chaussee de Louvain 431 Bat F, B-1380, Lasne, Belgium
Tel.: (32) 23573300
Residential Real Estate Developer & Promoter
N.A.I.C.S.: 236115
Vincent Schobbens (Mng Dir)

TETSUJIN INC.

Tetsujinka Keikaku Bidg 1-4-6 Yakumo, Meguro-ku, Tokyo, 152-0023, Japan
Tel.: (81) 357268500
Web Site: http://www.tetsujin.ne.jp
Year Founded: 1999
2404—(TKS)
Rev.: $43,969,180
Assets: $26,907,720
Liabilities: $25,520,660
Net Worth: $1,387,060
Earnings: $24,880
Emp.: 292
Fiscal Year-end: 08/31/24
Amusement & Entertainment Services
N.A.I.C.S.: 713990

TEUTON RESOURCES CORP.

2130 Crescent Road, Victoria, V8S 2H3, BC, Canada
Tel.: (778) 430-5680
Web Site: https://www.teuton.com
Year Founded: 1982
TUO—(OTCIQ)
Rev.: $4,446,988
Assets: $18,310,756
Liabilities: $62,594
Net Worth: $18,248,162
Earnings: $3,081,532
Fiscal Year-end: 12/31/20
Mineral Exploration Services
N.A.I.C.S.: 213114
Dino Cremonese (Pres & CEO)

TEUZA-A FAIRCHILD TECHNOLOGY VENTURE LTD.

49 Histadrut Avenue, PO Box 25266, Haifa, 31250, Israel
Tel.: (972) 48728788
Web Site: https://teuzafund.com
Year Founded: 1992
TUZA—(TAE)
Assets: $17,251,000
Liabilities: $282,000
Net Worth: $16,969,000
Earnings: ($1,980,000)
Fiscal Year-end: 12/31/23
Financial Management Services
N.A.I.C.S.: 522320
Avi Kerbs (Founder, Pres, CEO & CEO-Teuza Mgmt)

TEVA PHARMACEUTICAL INDUSTRIES, LTD.

124 Deborah Hanaviya, PO 3190, Tel Aviv, 6944020, Israel
Tel.: (972) 39267267   IL
Web Site: https://www.teva.co.il

TEVA PHARMACEUTICAL INDUSTRIES, LTD.

Year Founded: 1901
TEVA—(NYSE)
Rev.: $14,925,000,000
Assets: $44,006,000,000
Liabilities: $35,315,000,000
Net Worth: $8,691,000,000
Earnings: ($2,353,000,000)
Emp.: 34,004
Fiscal Year-end: 12/31/22
Holding Company; Pharmaceuticals Mfr
N.A.I.C.S.: 551112
Nir Baron (Sr VP)

Subsidiaries:

Actavis Group PTC ehf (1)
Reykjavikurvegi 76-78, 220, Hafnarfirdi, Iceland
Tel.: (354) 5503300
Pharmaceutical Products Distr
N.A.I.C.S.: 424210

Actavis d.o.o. Belgrade (1)
Dorda Stanojevica 12, 11070, Belgrade, Serbia
Tel.: (381) 112099300
Pharmaceutical Mfr & Distr
N.A.I.C.S.: 424210
Pavle Marjanovic (Gen Mgr)

CT- Arzneimittel GmbH (1)
Graf-Arco-Str 3, Ulm, 89079, Germany
Tel.: (49) 731 402 02
Web Site: http://www.ct-arzneimittel.de
Generic Drug Mfr & Whslr
N.A.I.C.S.: 325412

IVAX Argentina (1)
Juan Jose Castelli 6701, Villa Adelina, B1652ACM, Buenos Aires, Argentina
Tel.: (54) 1147218100
Pharmaceuticals Product Mfr
N.A.I.C.S.: 325412

Laboratorio Chile S.A. (1)
Av Marathon 1315, Nunoa, Chile **(99.96%)**
Tel.: (56) 223655000
Sales Range: $200-249.9 Million
Emp.: 1,000
Pharmaceuticals Mfr
N.A.I.C.S.: 325412

Medis ehf. (1)
Dalshraun 1, 220, Hafnarfjordur, Iceland
Tel.: (354) 5503200
Web Site: https://www.medis.is
Emp.: 652
Generic Pharmaceutical Mfr
N.A.I.C.S.: 325412
Jo Kim (VP-Comml & Supply Chain & Head)

Subsidiary (Non-US):

Medis Pharma Pty Ltd (2)
Suite 1002 53 Walker St, North Sydney, 2060, NSW, Australia
Tel.: (61) 2 9251 1088
Web Site: http://www.medis.is
Pharmaceuticals Distr
N.A.I.C.S.: 424210

Mepha Pharma AG (1)
Kirschgartenstrasse 14, PO Box 4010, 4010, Basel, Switzerland
Tel.: (41) 617054343
Web Site: https://www.mepha.ch
Sales Range: $125-149.9 Million
Emp.: 500
Generic Pharmaceuticals Marketer & Distr
N.A.I.C.S.: 424210
Andreas Bosshard (Gen Mgr)

PLIVA d.d. (1)
Prilaz Baruna Filipovica 25, 10000, Zagreb, Croatia
Tel.: (385) 13720000
Web Site: https://www.pliva.hr
Sales Range: $1-4.9 Billion
Emp.: 6,137
Mfr, Marketer & Distr of Generic Pharmaceuticals
N.A.I.C.S.: 325412

Subsidiary (Domestic):

PLIVA Croatia Ltd. (2)
Prilaz baruna Filipovica 25, 10000, Zagreb, Croatia
Tel.: (385) 1 37 20 000
Web Site: http://www.pliva.com
Sales Range: $450-499.9 Million
Emp.: 2,000
Pharmaceuticals Product Mfr
N.A.I.C.S.: 325412

Subsidiary (US):

PLIVA, Inc. (2)
72 Eagle Rock Ave, East Hanover, NJ 07936-3151
Tel.: (973) 386-5566
Sales Range: $150-199.9 Million
Emp.: 500
Mfr & Marketer of Generic Pharmaceutical Products
N.A.I.C.S.: 325412

Subsidiary (Domestic):

Pliva Hrvatska d.o.o. (2)
Prilaz Baruna Filipovica 25, 10000, Zagreb, Croatia
Tel.: (385) 13720000
Web Site: https://www.pliva.hr
Sales Range: $1-4.9 Billion
Emp.: 3,000
Pharmaceutical Products Mfr & Whslr
N.A.I.C.S.: 325412
Nikolina Dizdar Cehulic (CFO & Member-Mgmt Bd)

Pliva Ljubljana d.o.o. (1)
Pot k sejmiscu 35, 1231, Ljubljana, Slovenia
Tel.: (386) 15890390
Web Site: https://www.tevasi.si
Pharmaceutical Products Mfr
N.A.I.C.S.: 325412

Ratiopharm Kazakhstan LLP (1)
Al-Farabi Avenue building 17/1 block 5B 6th floor, Bostandyk district, 050059, Almaty, Kazakhstan
Tel.: (7) 273251615
Web Site: https://www.kaz.teva
Pharmaceutical Mfr & Distr
N.A.I.C.S.: 325412

Regent Drugs Limited (1)
Plot No 2G 2H 2I, Udyog Vihar, 201308, Noida, India
Tel.: (91) 120235134046
Pharmaceutical Company
N.A.I.C.S.: 325412

Salomon, Levin and Elstein Ltd. (1)
12 Hatrufa Street, PO Box 8077, Netanya, 42504, Israel **(50%)**
Tel.: (972) 98927878
Web Site: http://www.sle.co.il
Sales Range: $50-74.9 Million
Emp.: 100
Distr of Pharmaceutical Products
N.A.I.C.S.: 424210

Sicor (Societa Italiana Corticosteroidi) S.r.l (1)
Via Messina 38, Milan, 20154, Italy
Tel.: (39) 02 931971
Pharmaceuticals Product Mfr
N.A.I.C.S.: 325412
Stefano Lombardi (Gen Mgr)

Silom Medical Co., Ltd. (1)
689 Bhiraj Tower 21st Fl Sukhumvit Road, Klongton Nua Wattana, Bangkok, 10110, Thailand
Tel.: (66) 2 302 3200
Generic Pharmaceutical Mfr
N.A.I.C.S.: 325412

Specifar S.A. (1)
1 28 Octovriou Str Ag Varvara, 123 51, Athens, Greece
Tel.: (30) 2105401500
Web Site: http://www.specifar.gr
Generic Pharmaceutical Mfr
N.A.I.C.S.: 325412

TEVA Serbia Ltd. (1)
Makenzijeva 24, 11000, Belgrade, Serbia
Tel.: (381) 11 24 00 491
Emp.: 22
Pharmaceuticals Product Mfr
N.A.I.C.S.: 325412
Tatjana Sokolovic (Gen Mgr)

Taisho Pharmaceutical Industries, Ltd. (1)
3 Ohara Ichiba Koka-chou, Koka, 520-3433, Japan
Tel.: (81) 748883366
Web Site: http://www.taishoyakuhin.co.jp
Sales Range: $150-199.9 Million
Emp.: 400
Pharmaceutical Products Mfr & Distr
N.A.I.C.S.: 325412
Ichiro Kikushige (Pres)

Teva API B.V (1)
Computerweg 10, 3542 DR, Utrecht, Netherlands
Tel.: (31) 346 290 222
Web Site: http://www.tapi.com
Pharmaceuticals Product Mfr
N.A.I.C.S.: 325412

Teva Canada Limited (1)
30 Novopharm Ct, Toronto, M1B 2K9, ON, Canada **(100%)**
Web Site: https://www.tevacanada.com
Sales Range: $125-149.9 Million
Emp.: 1,500
Pharmaceuticals Mfr
N.A.I.C.S.: 325412

Teva Czech Industries s.r.o. (1)
Ostravska 29, Komarov, 747 70, Opava, Czech Republic
Tel.: (420) 553641111
Pharmaceuticals Product Mfr
N.A.I.C.S.: 325412

Teva Denmark A/S (1)
Parallelvej 12, 2800, Lyngby, Denmark
Tel.: (45) 4498 5511
Web Site: http://www.tevapharm.dk
Sales Range: $25-49.9 Million
Emp.: 25
Pharmaceuticals Product Mfr
N.A.I.C.S.: 325412

Teva Europe B.V. (1)
Computerweg 10, Utrecht, 3542 DR, Netherlands
Tel.: (31) 346290200
Generic Drug Mfr
N.A.I.C.S.: 325412

Teva Farmaceutica Ltda. (1)
Rua James Joule 92 - 9th floor Cidade Moncoes, Sao Paulo, 04576-080, Brazil
Tel.: (55) 8007778382
Web Site: https://www.tevabrasil.com.br
Pharmaceuticals Product Mfr
N.A.I.C.S.: 325412

Teva Ilaclari Sanayi ve Ticaret A.S. (1)
Fatih Sultan Mehmet Mah Poligon Cad Buyaka 2 Sitesi 2 Blok, No 8b IC Kapi No 18 Kat 5 Umraniye, 34771, Istanbul, Turkiye
Tel.: (90) 2166566700
Web Site: https://www.teva.com.tr
Pharmaceuticals Mfr
N.A.I.C.S.: 325412

Teva India Pvt Ltd. (1)
Teva House 76 Makwana Road Marol Andheri East Maharashtra, Mumbai, 400 059, India
Tel.: (91) 2266762525
Pharmaceutical Product Mfr
N.A.I.C.S.: 325412

Teva Limited Liability Company (1)
Ul Valovaya 35 BC Wall st, 115054, Moscow, Russia
Tel.: (7) 495 644 22 34
Web Site: http://teva.ru
Sales Range: $125-149.9 Million
Emp.: 260
Pharmaceuticals Product Mfr
N.A.I.C.S.: 325412

Teva Nederland B.V. (1)
Swensweg 3 5, 2031 GA, Haarlem, Netherlands
Tel.: (31) 8000228400
Web Site: https://www.teva.nl
Pharmaceuticals Product Mfr
N.A.I.C.S.: 325412

Teva Norway AS (1)
Hagalokkveien 13, 1371, Asker, Norway
Tel.: (47) 66775590
Web Site: http://www.tevapharm.no

Sales Range: $25-49.9 Million
Emp.: 14
Pharmaceuticals Product Mfr
N.A.I.C.S.: 325412

Teva Operations Poland sp. z o.o. (1)
ul Mogilska 80, 31-546, Krakow, Poland
Tel.: (48) 126178000
Pharmaceuticals Product Mfr
N.A.I.C.S.: 325412

Teva Peru S.A. (1)
Av Paseo de la Republica 5895 Piso 11 - Edificio Leuro, Miraflores, Lima, Peru
Tel.: (51) 4150500
Web Site: https://www.teva.com.pe
Pharmaceuticals Mfr
N.A.I.C.S.: 325412

Teva Pharma (New Zealand) Limited (1)
33a Normanby Road, Mount Eden, 1024, Auckland, New Zealand
Tel.: (64) 800800097
Pharmaceuticals Mfr
N.A.I.C.S.: 325412
Nick Cox (Bus Dir)

Teva Pharma - Produtos Farmaceuticos, Lda (1)
Urbinazacao Lagoas Park Edificio 5 piso 2, 2740-245, Porto Salvo, Portugal
Tel.: (351) 21 423 5910
Emp.: 50
Pharmaceuticals Product Mfr
N.A.I.C.S.: 325412

Teva Pharma AG (1)
Kirschgartenstrasse 14, 4010, Basel, Switzerland
Tel.: (41) 617054343
Pharmaceuticals Sales & Marketing
N.A.I.C.S.: 424210
Andreas Bosshard (Gen Mgr)

Teva Pharma Australia Pty. Ltd. (1)
37 Epping Road, Macquarie Park, NSW, Australia
Tel.: (61) 1800288382
Web Site: https://www.tevapharma.com.au
Emp.: 100
Medicine Mfr & Distr
N.A.I.C.S.: 325412

Teva Pharma Belgium N.V. (1)
Laarstraat 16, 2610, Wilrijk, Belgium
Tel.: (32) 38207373
Web Site: https://www.tevabelgium.be
Sales Range: $25-49.9 Million
Emp.: 40
Pharmaceutical Ingredient Mfr
N.A.I.C.S.: 325412

Teva Pharma Israel (1)
12 Trufa St, PO Box 8077, Netanya, 42504, Israel **(100%)**
Tel.: (972) 98639777
Web Site: http://www.tevapharma.com
Sales Range: $200-249.9 Million
Emp.: 600
Mfr of Pharmaceutical & Medical Products
N.A.I.C.S.: 325412

Teva Pharma Japan Inc. (1)
1-24-11 Taiko, Nakamura-ku, Nagoya, 453-0801, Aichi, Japan
Tel.: (81) 5 2459 2001
Web Site: http://www.teva-seiyaku.com
Emp.: 2,000
Mfr of Pharmaceutical Products, Sales & Research & Development
N.A.I.C.S.: 325412

Teva Pharma, S.L.U. (1)
Tel.: (34) 915359180
Web Site: http://www.tevafarmacia.es
Sales Range: $50-74.9 Million
Emp.: 998
Pharmaceuticals Product Mfr
N.A.I.C.S.: 325412

Teva Pharmaceutical Hong Kong Limited (1)
Unit 2303 23/F Mira Place Tower A 132 Nathan Road, Tsim Sha Tsui, Hong Kong, China (Hong Kong)
Tel.: (852) 31884288
Web Site: https://www.tevapharm.hk
Medicine Mfr & Distr

TEVA PHARMACEUTICAL INDUSTRIES, LTD.

Teva Pharmaceutical Industries, Ltd.—(Continued)
N.A.I.C.S.: 325412

Teva Pharmaceutical Information Consulting (Shanghai) Co., Ltd. (1)
No 1717 Nanjing West Road Room 5703 Wheelock International Plaza, Shanghai, China
Tel.: (86) 2160919500
Web Site: https://www.teva.cn
Medicine Mfr & Distr
N.A.I.C.S.: 325412

Teva Pharmaceutical Investments Singapore Pte. Ltd. (1)
20 Anson Road 05-03 Twenty Anson, Singapore, Singapore
Tel.: (65) 65090403
Web Site: https://www.tevapharm.sg
Pharmaceuticals Product Mfr
N.A.I.C.S.: 325412

Teva Pharmaceutical KK (1)
5-1-5 Toranomon 4-chome, Tokyo, 105-0001, Minato-ku, Japan
Tel.: (81) 355428980
Web Site: http://www.tevapharm.com
Sales Range: $25-49.9 Million
Emp.: 13
Pharmaceuticals Product Mfr
N.A.I.C.S.: 325412

Teva Pharmaceutical Ltd. (1)
Unit 1803 Tower 2 Jing An Kerry Center 1539 Nanjing Road West, Shanghai, 200040, China
Tel.: (86) 2160919500
Sales Range: $25-49.9 Million
Emp.: 13
Pharmaceuticals Product Mfr
N.A.I.C.S.: 325412
Afal Refhal *(Country Mgr)*

Teva Pharmaceutical Pte Ltd (1)
20 Anson Road 05-03 Twenty Anson, Singapore, 079912, Singapore
Tel.: (65) 65090403
Pharmaceuticals Product Mfr
N.A.I.C.S.: 325412

Teva Pharmaceuticals (Pty) Ltd (1)
Suite 1 Building 4 Ruimsig Office Park Hole In One Road, Ruimsig, Roodepoort, 1590, Gauteng, South Africa
Tel.: (27) 119562168
Web Site: http://www.tevapharm.com
Sales Range: $25-49.9 Million
Emp.: 30
Pharmaceuticals Product Mfr
N.A.I.C.S.: 325412

Teva Pharmaceuticals CR s.r.o. (1)
Ostravska 29, Opava, 747 70, Komarov, Czech Republic
Tel.: (420) 553 641 111
Web Site: http://www.tevapharm.cz
Sales Range: $200-249.9 Million
Emp.: 800
Pharmaceuticals Product Mfr
N.A.I.C.S.: 325412

Teva Pharmaceuticals Curacao NV (1)
Schotegatweg Oost 29 D, Willemstad, Curacao
Tel.: (599) 7366066
Pharmaceuticals Product Mfr
N.A.I.C.S.: 325412

Teva Pharmaceuticals Europe B.V. (1)
Computerweg 10, 3542 DR, Utrecht, Netherlands (100%)
Tel.: (31) 346290200
Web Site: http://www.tevapharm.com
Sales Range: $25-49.9 Million
Emp.: 50
Holding Company; Regional Managing Office
N.A.I.C.S.: 551112

Subsidiary (Domestic):

Pharmachemie B.V. (2)
Swensweg 5, PO Box 552, 2031 GA, Haarlem, Netherlands (100%)
Tel.: (31) 235147147
Web Site: http://www.pharmachemie.com
Emp.: 1,000
Mfr of Pharmaceuticals

Subsidiary (Non-US):

Plus Chemicals S.A (2)
Via San Salvatore 7 CP 815, Paradiso, Lugano, 6902, Switzerland
Tel.: (41) 919949464
Pharmaceuticals Product Mfr
N.A.I.C.S.: 325412

Teva API International Spain (2)
Cl Pau Claris Num172 P1 PTA1B, 8037, Barcelona, Spain
Tel.: (34) 934877335
Pharmaceuticals Product Mfr
N.A.I.C.S.: 325412

Teva Belgium SA/NV (2)
Laarstraat 16, 2610, Wilrijk, Belgium (100%)
Tel.: (32) 38207373
Web Site: https://www.tevabelgium.be
Sales Range: $25-49.9 Million
Emp.: 50
Pharmaceutical Products Distr
N.A.I.C.S.: 424210

Teva Bulgaria d.o.o. (2)
Sales Range: $25-49.9 Million
Emp.: 30
Pharmaceuticals Product Mfr
N.A.I.C.S.: 325412

Teva Classics France (2)
Immeuble le Palatin 1 1 cours du Triangle de l Arche Puteaux, La Defense, 92936, Paris, France (100%)
Tel.: (33) 155917800
Web Site: http://www.teva.com
Sales Range: $50-74.9 Million
Emp.: 120
Mfr of Pharmaceuticals
N.A.I.C.S.: 325412

Teva Generics Spain (2)
Anabel Segura No 11 B 1st Fl, 28108, Madrid, Spain
Tel.: (34) 915359180
Sales Range: $50-74.9 Million
Pharmaceuticals Product Mfr
N.A.I.C.S.: 325412

Teva GmbH (2)
Graf-Arco-Strasse 3, 89079, Ulm, Germany
Tel.: (49) 73140202
Web Site: https://www.teva.de
Pharmaceuticals Product Mfr
N.A.I.C.S.: 325412

Teva Hungary Ltd. (2)
Rakoczky ut 70-72, 1072, Budapest, Hungary (100%)
Tel.: (36) 12886400
Web Site: http://www.teva.hu
Sales Range: $50-74.9 Million
Mfr of Pharmaceuticals
N.A.I.C.S.: 325412

Teva Italia S.r.l. (2)
Viale del Mulino 1 Palazzo U10, Assago, 20057, Milan, Milanofiori Nord, Italy (100%)
Tel.: (39) 028917981
Web Site: https://www.tevaitalia.it
Sales Range: $25-49.9 Million
Emp.: 20
Pharmaceuticals Sales & Marketing
N.A.I.C.S.: 424210

Subsidiary (Domestic):

Dorom srl (3)
Via Robert Koch 1 2, 20152, Milan, Italy
Tel.: (39) 0248381
Pharmaceuticals Product Mfr
N.A.I.C.S.: 325412

Prosintex Industrie Chimiche Italiane srl (3)
Via Enrico Fermi 20 26, 20019, Settimo Milanese, MI, Italy
Tel.: (39) 02335571
Sales Range: $25-49.9 Million
Pharmaceuticals Product Mfr
N.A.I.C.S.: 325412

Teva Pharmaceutical Fine Chemicals srl (3)
Strada Statale Briantea 83, Bulciago LC,
23892, Seregno, Italy
Tel.: (39) 0318721
Sales Range: $50-74.9 Million
Pharmaceuticals Product Mfr
N.A.I.C.S.: 325412

Unit (Non-US):

Teva Moscow (2)
Bus-Centre Concord 3rd Fl, 10 Shabolovka Str, Moscow, 119049, Russia
Tel.: (7) 4956442234
Sales Range: $50-74.9 Million
Emp.: 200
Pharmaceuticals Product Mfr
N.A.I.C.S.: 325412

Subsidiary (Non-US):

Teva Pharma Portugal Ltd. (2)
Edificio Cyprium, Avenyda 25 Deadril Abril 15 2F, 2795-195, Linda-a-Velha, Portugal
Tel.: (351) 214235910
Sales Range: $25-49.9 Million
Emp.: 30
Pharmaceuticals Product Mfr
N.A.I.C.S.: 325412
Carlos Teixeira *(Gen Mgr)*

Teva Pharmacetials CR sro (2)
Business park Futurama Sokolovska 651/136A, 180 00, Prague, 8, Czech Republic
Tel.: (420) 251007111
Sales Range: $50-74.9 Million
Pharmaceuticals Product Mfr
N.A.I.C.S.: 325412

Teva Pharmaceutical Slovakia sro (2)
ROSUM Bajkalska 19B, 821 01, Bratislava, Slovakia
Tel.: (421) 257267911
Web Site: https://www.teva.sk
Sales Range: $50-74.9 Million
Pharmaceuticals Product Mfr
N.A.I.C.S.: 325412

Teva Pharmaceutical Works Ltd. (2) (100%)
Tel.: (36) 52515100
Web Site: http://www.teva.hu
Mfr of Pharmaceutical Ingredients
N.A.I.C.S.: 325412

Teva Polska Sp. z o.o. (2)
ul Emilii Plater 53, 00-113, Warsaw, Poland
Tel.: (48) 223459300
Pharmaceuticals Product Mfr
N.A.I.C.S.: 325412

Teva Romania srl (2)
Str Domnita Ruxandra nr 12, Bucharest, Romania
Tel.: (40) 212120916
Pharmaceuticals Product Mfr
N.A.I.C.S.: 325412

Teva Sweden AB (2)
Kungstorget 8, Box 1070, 251 10, Helsingborg, Sweden
Tel.: (46) 42121100
Web Site: https://www.teva.se
Sales Range: $25-49.9 Million
Emp.: 20
Pharmaceuticals Sales & Marketing
N.A.I.C.S.: 424210

Teva UK Ltd. (2)
Ridings Point, Whistler Drive, Castleford, WF10 5HX, West Yorkshire, United Kingdom (100%)
Tel.: (44) 2075407117
Web Site: https://www.tevauk.com
Mfr of Pharmaceuticals
N.A.I.C.S.: 325412
Kim Innes *(Gen Mgr-UK & Ireland)*

Unit (Domestic):

Teva Runcorn (3)
Aston Lane North Preston Brook, Runcorn, WA7 3FA, United Kingdom
Tel.: (44) 1928707800
Web Site: http://www.tevapharm.com
Pharmaceuticals Product Mfr
N.A.I.C.S.: 325412

Teva Pharmaceuticals Hellas S.A. (1)

INTERNATIONAL PUBLIC

44 Leoforos Kifisias, 15125, Maroussi, Greece
Tel.: (30) 2118805000
Sales Range: $25-49.9 Million
Emp.: 40
Pharmaceutical Products Distr
N.A.I.C.S.: 325412
Kostas Fitsoros *(Gen Mgr)*

Teva Pharmaceuticals International GmbH (1)
Schlusselstrasse 12, 8645, Jona, Switzerland
Tel.: (41) 552201515
Web Site: https://www.tevapharm.ch
Pharmaceuticals Product Mfr
N.A.I.C.S.: 325412

Teva Pharmaceuticals Ireland (1)
Unit 27-35 Waterford Industrial Estate, Waterford, Ireland
Tel.: (353) 51331331
Sales Range: $200-249.9 Million
Emp.: 710
Pharmaceuticals Mfr
N.A.I.C.S.: 325412
Dipankar Bhattacharjee *(Pres-Generics & CEO-Generics-Europe)*

Teva Pharmaceuticals Mexico (1)
Camino a Santa Teresa no 1040 5th floor, Alvaro Obregon, 14210, Mexico, Mexico
Tel.: (52) 5554499900
Web Site: https://www.tevamexico.com.mx
Sales Range: $50-74.9 Million
Emp.: 180
Pharmaceuticals Product Mfr
N.A.I.C.S.: 325412

Teva Pharmaceuticals Mexico (1)
Ave San Rafael 35 Parque Industrial, Lerma, Mexico (100%)
Tel.: (52) 5559500200
Web Site: http://www.tevagroup.com
Sales Range: $50-74.9 Million
Emp.: 135
Pharmaceuticals Product Mfr
N.A.I.C.S.: 325412

Teva Pharmaceuticals Polska sp. z o.o. (1)
Ul Mogilska 80, 31-546, Krakow, Poland
Tel.: (48) 12 617 80 00
Web Site: http://www.teva.pl
Pharmaceuticals Product Mfr
N.A.I.C.S.: 325412

Teva Pharmaceuticals Romania s.r.l (1)
Tel.: (40) 212306524
Web Site: http://www.tevapharm.ro
Sales Range: $25-49.9 Million
Emp.: 30
Pharmaceuticals Product Mfr
N.A.I.C.S.: 325412

Teva Pharmaceuticals USA, Inc. (1)
1090 Horsham Rd, North Wales, PA 19454
Tel.: (215) 591-3000
Web Site: http://www.tevausa.com
Sales Range: $1-4.9 Billion
Generic Pharmaceuticals Mfr & Distr
N.A.I.C.S.: 325412

Subsidiary (Domestic):

Anda, Inc. (2)
2915 Weston Rd, Weston, FL 33331
Tel.: (954) 217-4500
Web Site: https://www.andanet.com
Emp.: 200
Generic Pharmaceuticals Distr
N.A.I.C.S.: 424210

Subsidiary (Domestic):

Anda Pharmaceuticals, Inc. (3)
8644 Polk Ln, Olive Branch, MS 38654
Tel.: (662) 892-9700
Pharmaceutical Products Distr
N.A.I.C.S.: 424210

Subsidiary (Domestic):

CIMA Labs Inc. (2)
1090 Horshan Rd, North Wales, PA 19454
Tel.: (763) 488-4700
Oral Drug Delivery Systems Mfr & Developer
N.A.I.C.S.: 325412
Jeffrey Thompson *(Sr Dir-Project Mgmt)*

AND PRIVATE COMPANIES

NuPathe Inc. (2)
227 Washington St Ste 200, Conshohocken, PA 19428
Tel.: (484) 567-0130
Web Site: http://www.nupathe.com
Rev.: $23,000
Assets: $30,607,000
Liabilities: $27,594,000
Net Worth: $3,013,000
Earnings: ($24,534,000)
Emp.: 14
Fiscal Year-end: 12/31/2012
Pharmaceuticals Mfr
N.A.I.C.S.: 325412

Teva API, Inc. (2)
400 Interpace Pkwy Morris Corporate Ctr III, Parsippany, NJ 07054
Tel.: (973) 265-3600
Web Site: http://www.tapi.com
Sales Range: $25-49.9 Million
Emp.: 50
Pharmaceuticals Product Mfr
N.A.I.C.S.: 325412

Teva Biopharmaceuticals USA (2)
9410 Key West Ave, Rockville, MD 20850
Tel.: (240) 821-9000
Sales Range: $25-49.9 Million
Emp.: 77
Biopharmaceutical Research & Development Services
N.A.I.C.S.: 325412

Branch (Domestic):

Teva Pharmaceuticals USA, Inc. - Salt Lake City (2)
4745 W Wiley Post Way, Salt Lake City, UT 84116
Tel.: (801) 595-1405
Sales Range: $125-149.9 Million
Emp.: 19
Develops Oral Transmucosal Pharmaceutical Products
N.A.I.C.S.: 325412

Subsidiary (Domestic):

Teva Women's Health, Inc. (2)
400 Chestnut Ridge Rd, Woodcliff Lake, NJ 07677
Tel.: (201) 930-3300
Sales Range: $150-199.9 Million
Emp.: 400
Women's Healthcare Product Mfr
N.A.I.C.S.: 325412

Unit (Domestic):

Teva Women's Health, Inc. - Cincinnati (3)
5040 Duramed Dr, Cincinnati, OH 45213
Tel.: (513) 731-9900
Sales Range: $100-124.9 Million
Emp.: 400
Developer, Mfr & Marketer of Proprietary Pharmaceutical Products
N.A.I.C.S.: 325412
Dereld Miller (Controller)

Teva Pharmachemie B.V. (1)
Swensweg May, 2031 GA, Haarlem, Netherlands
Tel.: (31) 235147147
Web Site: http://www.tevapharmachemie.com
Pharmaceuticals Product Mfr
N.A.I.C.S.: 325412

Teva Sante SAS (1)
100-110 Esplanade du General de Gaulle, La Defense, 92931, Paris, France
Tel.: (33) 155917800
Web Site: https://www.teva-sante.fr
Pharmaceuticals Product Mfr
N.A.I.C.S.: 325412
Erick Roche (Pres)

Teva Takeda Pharma Ltd. (1)
18th Floor Ebisu Garden Place Tower 4-20-3 Ebisu, Shibuya-ku, Tokyo, Japan
Tel.: (81) 364593066
Web Site: https://www.takeda-teva.com
Pharmaceutical Mfr & Distr
N.A.I.C.S.: 325412

Teva Ukraine LLC (1)
Tel.: (380) 445947080
Web Site: http://www.teva.ua

Emp.: 400
Pharmaceuticals Product Mfr
N.A.I.C.S.: 325412

Teva Uruguay S.A. (1)
Av Uruguay 1227 33, 11100, Montevideo, Uruguay
Tel.: (598) 29022668
Web Site: https://www.teva.com.uy
Sales Range: $25-49.9 Million
Emp.: 100
Pharmaceutical Product Whslr
N.A.I.C.S.: 424210

Teva-Handok Pharma Co., Ltd. (1)
3rd floor Handok Building 132 Teheran ro, Gangnam-gu, Seoul, Korea (South)
Tel.: (82) 25275566
Web Site: https://www.teva-handok.co.kr
Pharmaceuticals Mfr
N.A.I.C.S.: 325412

Teva-Tuteur S.A.C.I.F.A. (1)
Av Juan De Garay 842, C1153ABT, Buenos Aires, Argentina
Tel.: (54) 1143076110
Web Site: http://web.tuteur.com.ar
Sales Range: $25-49.9 Million
Emp.: 70
Mfr of Pharmaceuticals
N.A.I.C.S.: 325412

ratiopharm GmbH (1)
Graf-Arco-Str 3, 89079, Ulm, Germany
Tel.: (49) 73140202
Web Site: https://www.ratiopharm.de
Emp.: 5,584
Pharmaceutical Preparation Mfr
N.A.I.C.S.: 325412
Andreas Burkhardt (Mng Dir)

Subsidiary (Non-US):

ratiopharm A/S (2)
Slotsnarken 12 st.tv., Horsholm, 2970, Denmark
Tel.: (45) 45460660
Web Site: http://www2.ratiopharm.com
Pharmaceuticals Mfr
N.A.I.C.S.: 325412

ratiopharm Arzneimittel Vertriebs-GmbH (2)
Donau-City-Strasse 11 Ares Tower Top 13, 1220, Vienna, Austria (75%)
Tel.: (43) 1970070
Web Site: https://www.ratiopharm.at
Sales Range: $25-49.9 Million
Emp.: 125
Pharmaceuticals Mfr
N.A.I.C.S.: 325412

ratiopharm CZ s.r.o. (2)
Belehradska 347/54, 120 00, Prague, Czech Republic (100%)
Tel.: (420) 251021122
Web Site: http://www.ratiopharm.cz
Pharmaceuticals Mfr
N.A.I.C.S.: 325412

ratiopharm Inc. (2)
6755 Mississauga Rd 4th Fl, Mississauga, L5N 7Y2, ON, Canada (100%)
Tel.: (905) 858-9612
Sales Range: $100-124.9 Million
Emp.: 400
Pharmaceuticals Mfr
N.A.I.C.S.: 325412

ratiopharm Oy (2)
Keilaranta 10 E, 7 krs, 02150, Espoo, Finland (100%)
Tel.: (358) 201805900
Web Site: https://www.tevafinland.fi
Sales Range: $25-49.9 Million
Emp.: 30
Pharmaceuticals Mfr
N.A.I.C.S.: 325412

TEVANO SYSTEMS HOLDINGS INC.
1390 320 Granville Street, Vancouver, V6B 0G5, BC, Canada
Tel.: (778) 819-3958   BC
Web Site: https://www.tevano.ca
Year Founded: 2000
TEVNF—(OTCIQ)
Rev.: $8,836
Assets: $55,856

Liabilities: $755,924
Net Worth: ($700,068)
Earnings: ($3,310,678)
Fiscal Year-end: 06/30/22
Holding Company
N.A.I.C.S.: 551112
Eugene Hodgson (CFO)

TEVO OY
Hiientie 17, 92160, Saloinen, Finland
Tel.: (358) 8 265 8800
Web Site: http://www.tevo.fi
Year Founded: 1974
Emp.: 135
Machine Engineering Services
N.A.I.C.S.: 332710
Teuvo Joensuu (Mng Dir)

Subsidiaries:

Tevo Lokomo Oy (1)
Lokomonkatu 3, PO Box 306, 33101, Tampere, Finland
Tel.: (358) 400730433
Mechanical Engineering Services
N.A.I.C.S.: 541330
Timo Norvasto (Mgr-Sls)

TEVVA MOTORS LIMITED
Unit 1, London Distribution Park Windrush Road, Tilbury, RM18 7EW, United Kingdom
Tel.: (44) 3304609460
Web Site: https://www.tevva.com
Year Founded: 2013
Trucks Mfr
N.A.I.C.S.: 336212

TEWOO GROUP CO., LTD.
Yingkou Road, Heping District IV, Tianjin, 300041, China
Tel.: (86) 22 2303 0779   CN
Web Site: http://www.tewoo.com
Sales Range: $1-4.9 Billion
Emp.: 6,000
Holding Company; Wholesale Commodities Trading, Logistics, Real Estate Development, Financial Services & Vocational Education
N.A.I.C.S.: 551112
Jie Yan (Dir Gen-Enterprise Mgmt Div)

Subsidiaries:

Palabora Mining Co. Ltd. (1)
1 Copper Road, Phalaborwa, 1389, South Africa (14.9%)
Tel.: (27) 15 780 2911
Web Site: http://www.palabora.com
Sales Range: $1-4.9 Billion
Emp.: 1,800
Copper Mining
N.A.I.C.S.: 212230
Jinghua Han (Chm & CEO)

Subsidiary (Non-US):

Palabora Asia Pte Limited (2)
101 Thomson Rd, 21 04 United Sq, Singapore, 307591, Singapore
Tel.: (65) 62514744
Web Site: http://www.palabora.com
Sales Range: $25-49.9 Million
Emp.: 9
Metal Whslr
N.A.I.C.S.: 423510

Palabora Europe Limited (2)
3000 Cathedral Hil, Guildford, GU2 7YB, Surrey, United Kingdom
Tel.: (44) 1483 246636
Web Site: http://www.palabora.com
Sales Range: $25-49.9 Million
Emp.: 5
Metal Whslr
N.A.I.C.S.: 423510
Richard Knight (Bus Mgr)

Subsidiary (US):

Palabora US (2)
1000 Cobb Pl Ste 100, Kennesaw, GA 30144

Tel.: (770) 590-7970
Web Site: http://www.palabora.us
Sales Range: $25-49.9 Million
Emp.: 5
Ore Mining
N.A.I.C.S.: 423520
Sandra Delarm (Gen Mgr)

TEWOO Metals International Trade Co., Ltd. (1)
147 Changjiang Road Nankai District, Nankai District, Tianjin, 300193, China
Tel.: (86) 22 2702 0368
Web Site: http://www.tewoo-metals.com
Sales Range: $25-49.9 Million
Metal Wholesale Trade Distr
N.A.I.C.S.: 425120

TIANJIN MATERIALS & EQUIPMENT MERCHANT CO., LTD (1)
No 84 Chengdu Road, Heping Dist, Tianjin, 300051, China
Tel.: (86) 22 28370896
Web Site: http://www.tewoo-tmem.com
Chemical Products Distr
N.A.I.C.S.: 424690

Tewoo International Trade Co., LTD. (1)
14/15 F Block C Wanda Plaza No 59 Jinbin Avenue, Hedong District, Tianjin, 300160, China
Tel.: (86) 22 58156555
Web Site: http://www.tewoointernational.com
Steel Product Distr
N.A.I.C.S.: 423510

Subsidiary (Non-US):

TEWOO (H.K) Limited (2)
Room 1204 12/F Emperor Group Centre, Wanchai, China (Hong Kong)
Tel.: (852) 2877 0428
Steel Product Distr
N.A.I.C.S.: 423510

Subsidiary (US):

TEWOO USA, INC (2)
116 Vermillion, Irvine, CA 92603
Tel.: (949) 336-8630
Steel Product Distr
N.A.I.C.S.: 423510

Tianjin Hoperay Mineral Limited Company (1)
12th and 13th Floor No 59 Block C Wanda Plaza Jinbin Avenue, Hedong, Tianjin, 300161, China
Tel.: (86) 22 58905958
Web Site: http://www.en.hoperay.cn
Chemical Product Mfr & Distr
N.A.I.C.S.: 325180

Subsidiary (Non-US):

TEWOO HOPERAY (SINGAPORE) PTE. LTD. (2)
8 Eu Tong Sen Street, Singapore, 59818, Singapore
Tel.: (65) 62259186
Emp.: 5
Chemical Products Distr
N.A.I.C.S.: 424690
Wenkai Zhao (Mng Dir)

Tianjin Hopetone Co. Ltd. (1)
No 4 Yingkou Road, Heping District, Tianjin, 300041, China
Tel.: (86) 22 23300753
Web Site: http://www.hopetone.com
Chemical Products Distr
N.A.I.C.S.: 424690

Tianjin Materials Industry & International Energy Development Co., Ltd (1)
No 22 Pukou Rd, Hexi Dist, Tianjin, 300203, China
Tel.: (86) 22 23063183
Web Site: http://www.tewooie.com
Coal Product Distr
N.A.I.C.S.: 423520

Tianjin Products & Energy Resources Development Co., Ltd (1)
Bld 2 Shuiyunhuating No 8 Shuishang Park East Road, Nankai District, Tianjin, 300381, China

TEWOO GROUP CO., LTD.

Tewoo Group Co., Ltd.—(Continued)
Tel.: (86) 22 58896087
Web Site: http://www.tewoo-erdc.com
Steel Product Distr
N.A.I.C.S.: 423510

Tianjin Wuhua Mining Industry Co., Ltd (1)
1901-1904 Building A Future Plaza No 103 Weidi Dao, Hexi District, Tianjin, 300201, China
Tel.: (86) 22 23392712
Metal Ore Mining Services
N.A.I.C.S.: 212290

TEX CYCLE TECHNOLOGY (M) BERHAD

Lot 8942 Jalan Telok Gong, 42000, Port Klang, Selangor Darul Ehsan, Malaysia
Tel.: (60) 31341984 **MY**
Web Site: https://www.texcycle.com.my
TEXCYCL—(KLS)
Rev.: $7,638,413
Assets: $38,936,790
Liabilities: $8,429,033
Net Worth: $30,507,758
Earnings: $3,426,567
Emp.: 100
Fiscal Year-end: 12/31/23
Waste Recycling Services
N.A.I.C.S.: 562920
Siew Choong Ho (Exec Dir)

Subsidiaries:

Tex Cycle (P2) Sdn. Bhd. (1)
Lot 8942 Jalan Telok Gong, 42000, Port Klang, Selangor, Malaysia
Tel.: (60) 331341984
Waste Recycling Services
N.A.I.C.S.: 562920

TEX HOLDINGS PLC

Claydon Office Claydon Business Park Gipping Road Great Blakenham, Ipswich, IP6 0NL, Suffolk, United Kingdom
Tel.: (44) 1473830144
Web Site: http://www.tex-holdings.co.uk
Rev.: $55,995,226
Assets: $33,413,655
Liabilities: $19,060,367
Net Worth: $14,353,288
Earnings: $984,858
Emp.: 457
Fiscal Year-end: 12/31/17
Industrial Boring & Construction Equipment Mfr
N.A.I.C.S.: 333120
C. A. Parker (Sec)

Subsidiaries:

ADR Sales Ltd. (1)
Claydon Business Park Gipping Road, Great Blakenham, Ipswich, IP60NL, Suffolk, United Kingdom **(100%)**
Tel.: (44) 1473830144
Web Site: http://www.tex-holdings.co.uk
Sales Range: $25-49.9 Million
Emp.: 100
Supplier of Airfield Damage Repair Systems
N.A.I.C.S.: 333120

BSP International Foundations Limited (1)
Claydon Business Park Gipping Road, Great Blakenham, Ipswich, IP6 0NL, Suffolk, United Kingdom **(100%)**
Tel.: (44) 1473830431
Web Site: http://www.bsp-if.com
Sales Range: $25-49.9 Million
Emp.: 100
Construction Machinery Mfr
N.A.I.C.S.: 333120
Richard Melton (Mng Dir)

Eurotex International Limited (1)
Unit 20 Shipyard Industrial Estate, Brightlingsea Essex, Colchester, CO7 0AR, United Kingdom **(100%)**
Tel.: (44) 1206304063
Web Site: http://www.eurotex-intl.com
Sales Range: $25-49.9 Million
Emp.: 30
Construction Machinery Mfr
N.A.I.C.S.: 333120
Stephen Codd (Mng Dir)

QK Honeycomb Products Limited (1)
Creeting Road, Stowmarket, IP14 5AS, Suffolk, United Kingdom
Tel.: (44) 1449 612145
Web Site: http://www.qkhoneycomb.co.uk
Lightweight Panel Mfr
N.A.I.C.S.: 337214

Quinton & Kaines (Holdings) Ltd. (1)
Creeting Road, Stowmarket, IP14 5AS, Suffolk, United Kingdom
Tel.: (44) 1449612145
Web Site: http://www.quintonkaines.com
Sales Range: $550-599.9 Million
Honeycomb Board & Panel Products Mfr
N.A.I.C.S.: 423390

Tex A.T.C. Limited (1)
Claydon Business Park Gipping Road, Great Blakenham, Ipswich, IP60NL, Suffolk, United Kingdom **(100%)**
Tel.: (44) 1473830144
Web Site: http://www.tex-atc.co.uk
Sales Range: $25-49.9 Million
Emp.: 10
Construction Machinery Mfr
N.A.I.C.S.: 333120
Damian Lummis (Mgr-Design Office)

Tex Engineering Limited (1)
Claydon Business Park Gipping Road, Great Blakenham, Ipswich, IP6 0NL, Suffolk, United Kingdom **(100%)**
Tel.: (44) 1473830144
Web Site: http://www.tex-engineering.co.uk
Sales Range: $25-49.9 Million
Emp.: 30
Construction Machinery Mfr
N.A.I.C.S.: 333120
Wayne Luckie (Sls Mgr)

Tex Industrial Plastics Limited (1)
Wetherby Road, Derby, DE24 8HL, Derbyshire, United Kingdom
Tel.: (44) 1332363249
Web Site: http://www.tex-plastics.co.uk
Sales Range: $50-74.9 Million
Emp.: 124
Plastics Product Mfr
N.A.I.C.S.: 326199

Tex Industrialised Construction Systems Limited (1)
Claydon Business Park Gipping Road, Great Blakenham, Ipswich, IP60NL, Suffolk, United Kingdom **(100%)**
Tel.: (44) 1473830144
Web Site: http://www.tex-ics.co.uk
Sales Range: $100-124.9 Million
Construction Machinery Mfr
N.A.I.C.S.: 333120
Chris Parker (Mng Dir)

Tex Plastic Products Limited (1)
Aviemore Industrial Estate, Barnstaple N, Devon, EX312EU, United Kingdom **(100%)**
Tel.: (44) 1271378528
Web Site: http://www.tex-plastics.co.uk
Sales Range: $25-49.9 Million
Emp.: 100
Construction Machinery Mfr
N.A.I.C.S.: 333120
Christopher Varley (Chm)

Tex Special Projects Limited (1)
Claydon Business Park Gipping Road, Great Blakenham, Ipswich, IP6 0NL, Suffolk, United Kingdom
Tel.: (44) 1473 830144
Web Site: http://www.tex-holdings.co.uk
Plastic Injection Molding Mfr
N.A.I.C.S.: 333248

TEX YEAR INDUSTRIES INC.

No 9 Wuquan 6th Rd New Taipei Industrial Park, New Taipei City, 24889, Taiwan
Tel.: (886) 222992121
Web Site: https://www.texyear.com
4720—(TAI)
Rev.: $109,329,241
Assets: $98,396,249
Liabilities: $49,756,628
Net Worth: $48,639,620
Earnings: $2,012,885
Emp.: 700
Fiscal Year-end: 12/31/23
Adhesive & Chemical Mfr
N.A.I.C.S.: 325520
Shih-Kuang Lue (Founder)

Subsidiaries:

Jiangsu C&M Filtration Solutions Limited (1)
No 29 North Shenfeng Road, Dafeng District, Yancheng, 224100, Jiangsu, China
Tel.: (86) 51583615859
Hot Melt Glue Mfr
N.A.I.C.S.: 325520

Shanghai C&M Filtration Solutions Limited (1)
13J Kaikai Plaza No 888 Wanhangdu Road, Shanghai, 200042, China
Tel.: (86) 2162030560
Web Site: http://www.cmfiltration.com
Hot Melt Glue Mfr
N.A.I.C.S.: 325520

Tex Year (Hong Kong) Ltd. (1)
RM F1 5/F 20 Wang Hoi Rd, Yeung Yiu Chung No 8 Industrial Bldg Kowloon Way, Kowloon, China (Hong Kong)
Tel.: (852) 23312287
Hot Melt Adhesive Mfr
N.A.I.C.S.: 325520

Tex Year Europe Sp. z o. o. (1)
Ul H Cegielskiego 3, 62-200, Gniezno, Poland
Tel.: (48) 611023956
Web Site: https://www.texyear.pl
Hot Melt Adhesive Mfr
N.A.I.C.S.: 325520

Tex Year Fine Chemical Co., Ltd. (1)
No 6 Canghai 2nd Road Yonghe Economic Development Zone, Huangpu District, Guangzhou, Guangdong, China
Tel.: (86) 2032222288
Web Site: https://www.texyear.com.cn
Hot Melt Adhesive Mfr
N.A.I.C.S.: 325520

Tex Year Industrial Adhesives Pvt. Ltd. (1)
704 D Square Building Dadabhai Road, Vile Parle West, Mumbai, 400056, Maharashtra, India
Tel.: (91) 8048077783
Web Site: http://www.hotmelt-adhesive.net
Emp.: 50
Hot Melt Adhesive Mfr
N.A.I.C.S.: 325520
Pranav Mehta (CEO)

Tex Year Minima Technology Inc. (1)
Ul H Cegielskiego 3, 62-200, Gniezno, Poland
Tel.: (48) 611023956
Web Site: https://www.texyear-minima.com
Poly Lactic Acid Mfr & Distr
N.A.I.C.S.: 315990

Tex Year Technology (Jiangsu) Co., Ltd. (1)
No 29 Shenfeng North Rd Dafeng Economic Development Zone, Yancheng, Jiangsu, China
Tel.: (86) 51583890008
Hot Melt Adhesive Mfr
N.A.I.C.S.: 325520

Tex Year Vietnam Co., Ltd. (1)
No 8 Street, Song Than 1 Industrial Zone, Di An, Binh Duong, Vietnam
Tel.: (84) 2743737492
Hot Melt Adhesive Mfr
N.A.I.C.S.: 325520

Wuxi More Tex Technology Co., Ltd. (1)
No 28 Changjiang Road, Wuxi, Jiangsu, China
Tel.: (86) 51085226252
Web Site: http://www.moretex.cn

Hot Melt Adhesive Mfr
N.A.I.C.S.: 325520

Wuxi Tex Year International Trading Co., Ltd. (1)
No 28 Chang Jiang Rd, Wuxi, Jiangsu, China
Tel.: (86) 51085227545
Hot Melt Adhesive Mfr
N.A.I.C.S.: 325520

TEX-RAY INDUSTRIAL CO., LTD.

2F No 426 Linsen N Rd, Taipei, 10451, Taiwan
Tel.: (886) 225215155
Web Site: https://www.texray.com
Year Founded: 1978
1467—(TAI)
Rev.: $148,969,908
Assets: $131,949,634
Liabilities: $37,029,659
Net Worth: $94,919,974
Earnings: ($5,404,068)
Fiscal Year-end: 12/31/23
Textile Products Mfr
N.A.I.C.S.: 313310
Lin Zui-Yeh (Chm)

Subsidiaries:

AiQ Smart Clothing Inc. (1)
8F No 426 Linsen N Road, Taipei, 10451, Taiwan
Tel.: (886) 225215155
Web Site: https://www.aiqsmartclothing.com
Garments Mfr
N.A.I.C.S.: 315250

King's Metal Fiber Technologies Co., Ltd. (1)
8F No 426 Linsen N Rd, Zhongshan Dist, Taipei, 10467, Taiwan
Tel.: (886) 225210298
Web Site: https://www.kingsmetalfiber.com
Garments Mfr
N.A.I.C.S.: 315250

Taiwan Supercritical Technology Co., Ltd. (1)
No 346 Sec 1 Yuan-Tsao Rd Fenyuan, Chang-Hua, Taiwan
Tel.: (886) 492511939
Web Site: http://www.tst.tw
Garments Mfr
N.A.I.C.S.: 315250

TEXAF SA

Avenue Louise 130a, PO Box 6, 1050, Brussels, Belgium
Tel.: (32) 26392000
Web Site: https://www.texaf.be
Year Founded: 1925
TEXF—(EUR)
Rev.: $32,363,396
Assets: $184,022,519
Liabilities: $59,891,820
Net Worth: $124,130,699
Earnings: $12,864,555
Emp.: 194
Fiscal Year-end: 12/31/23
Financial Investment Services
N.A.I.C.S.: 523940
Dominique Moorkens (Vice Chm)

Subsidiaries:

Anagest SA (1)
Route de Moncor 2, 1752, Villars-sur-Glane, Switzerland
Tel.: (41) 26 407 7610
Web Site: https://www.anagest.ch
Portfolio Management Services
N.A.I.C.S.: 523940

Carrigres S.A.R.L. (1)
Avenue de l'ecole 5 II, Kinshasa, Congo, Democratic Republic of
Tel.: (243) 815133005
Web Site: https://www.carrigres.com
Emp.: 40
Crushed Stone & Basement Rubble Distr
N.A.I.C.S.: 423320
Jean-Philippe Waterschoot (Mng Dir)

AND PRIVATE COMPANIES — TEXHONG TEXTILE GROUP LIMITED

TEXAS DE FRANCE
Z I Les Milles 220 Rue Gustave Eiffel, 13290, Aix-en-Provence, Bouches Du Rhone, France
Tel.: (33) 442394696
Sales Range: $25-49.9 Million
Emp.: 49
Electrical Appliances, Television & Rad
N.A.I.C.S.: 423620
Simon Haddad *(Pres)*

TEXAS HOLDINGS LTD.
Barton Hall St Eccles, Manchester, M30 7NB, United Kingdom
Tel.: (44) 1617876800   UK
Web Site:
http://www.texasgroup.co.uk
Sales Range: $25-49.9 Million
Emp.: 12
Holding Company
N.A.I.C.S.: 551112
Laurie Turnbull *(CEO)*

Subsidiaries:

Texas Group plc (1)
Barton Hall Estate Hardy Street, Eccles, M30 7NB, Manchester, United Kingdom
Tel.: (44) 161 787 6800
Web Site: http://www.texasgroup.co.uk
Emp.: 10
Commercial & Residential Property Development Services
N.A.I.C.S.: 531390
Robart Mcdonald *(Mgr)*

TEXCHEM RESOURCES BHD.
Level 18 Menara Boustead Penang 39 Jalan Sultan Ahmad Shah, 10050, Penang, Malaysia
Tel.: (60) 42296000   MY
Web Site:
https://www.texchemgroup.com
TEXCHEM—(KLS)
Rev.: $216,265,783
Assets: $160,730,954
Liabilities: $117,280,366
Net Worth: $43,450,588
Earnings: ($2,369,613)
Emp.: 3,500
Fiscal Year-end: 12/31/23
Electrical Mfr
N.A.I.C.S.: 238210
Fumihiko Konishi *(Chm)*

Subsidiaries:

Fumakilla Malaysia Berhad (1)
Plot No 256 Tingkat Perusahaan 5 Kawasan Perindustrian Perai 2, 13600, Perai, Pulau Pinang, Malaysia
Tel.: (60) 43883777
Web Site:
http://www.texchemfamilycare.com
Household Insecticides Mfr
N.A.I.C.S.: 325320
Li-lian Foo *(Mgr-Sls & Mktg)*

Subsidiary (Non-US):

Technopia (Thailand) Ltd. (2)
323 Moo 6 Ratchasima-Chokchai Rd Nong Rawiang Muang, 30000, Nakhon Ratchasima, Thailand
Tel.: (66) 44212990
Web Site:
http://www.texchemfamilycare.com
Mosquito Coils & Insecticides Mfr
N.A.I.C.S.: 325320

Kokubu Food Logistics Malaysia Sdn. Bhd. (1)
Lot 22204 Jalan 33/52 Seksyen 33, 40400, Shah Alam, Selangor, Malaysia
Tel.: (60) 35 131 3636
Web Site: https://www.kokubu-foodlogistics.com.my
Food Logistics Services
N.A.I.C.S.: 541614

Lifeon Asia Sdn. Bhd. (1)
Lot 3 Jalan P/6 Kawasan Perindustrian Bangi, 43650, Bandar Baru Bangi, Selangor, Malaysia
Tel.: (60) 389250370
Industrial Raw Material Distr
N.A.I.C.S.: 424590

New Material (Malaysia) Sdn. Bhd. (1)
Lot 808 and 809 Jalan Subang 5 Taman Perindustrian Subang, 47610, Subang Jaya, Selangor, Malaysia
Tel.: (60) 380221368
Industrial Raw Material Distr
N.A.I.C.S.: 424590

Sushi King Sdn. Bhd. (1)
Wisma Texchem Lot 808 and 809 Jalan Subang 5, Taman Perindustrian Subang, 47610, Subang Jaya, Selangor, Malaysia (70%)
Tel.: (60) 35 622 5339
Web Site: https://sushi-king.com
Restaurant Management & Catering Services
N.A.I.C.S.: 722511

Technopia Vietnam Pte. Ltd. (1)
7 Road 15A Bien Hoa Industrial Zone 2, Bien Hoa, Dong Nai, Vietnam
Tel.: (84) 613836499
Web Site:
http://www.texchemfamilycare.com
Mosquito Coils & Household Insecticides Mfr
N.A.I.C.S.: 325320

Texchem Corporation Sdn. Bhd. (1)
Level 18 Menara Boustead Penang 39 Jalan Sultan Ahmad Shah, 10050, Penang, Malaysia
Tel.: (60) 4 229 6000
Web Site: https://www.texchemcorp.com
Human Resource Management Services
N.A.I.C.S.: 541612

Subsidiary (Domestic):

Texchem Risk Management Sdn. Bhd. (2)
Level 19 Menara Boustead Penang 39 Jalan Sultan Ahmad Shah, 10050, Penang, Malaysia
Tel.: (60) 43700304
Web Site: https://www.texchemrisk.com
General Insurance Services
N.A.I.C.S.: 524210

Texchem Food Materials (Vietnam) Co. Ltd. (1)
43 Ngan Long Villas Area Nguyen Huu Tho Street Hamlet 5, Phuoc Kien Commune Nha Be District, Ho Chi Minh City, Vietnam
Tel.: (84) 2836365221
Industrial Raw Material Distr
N.A.I.C.S.: 424590

Texchem Materials Sdn. Bhd. (1)
Lot 808 809 Jalan Subang 5 Taman Perindustrian Subang, 47610, Subang Jaya, Selangor, Malaysia
Tel.: (60) 356342630
Web Site: http://www.texmat.com
Rev.: $183,462,000
Emp.: 160
Industrial Chemicals & Materials Distr
N.A.I.C.S.: 424690

Subsidiary (Non-US):

New Material Hong Kong Limited (2)
Unit 1803 18/F 168 Sai Yeung Choi St, Mongkok, Kowloon, China (Hong Kong)
Tel.: (852) 23971118
Web Site: http://www.texchemgroup.com
Logistics Consulting Servies
N.A.I.C.S.: 541614

PT Texchem Indonesia (2)
Menara Hijau Lantai 11 Wing Selatan Ruang 1103 JI MT Haryono Kav 33, Jakarta Selatan, 12770, Indonesia
Tel.: (62) 217 919 9515
Web Site: http://www.texchemgroup.com
Sales Range: $25-49.9 Million
Emp.: 13
Industrial Chemical Whslr
N.A.I.C.S.: 424690

Subsidiary (Domestic):

Texchem Malaysia Sdn. Berhad (2)
Plot 256 Lorong Perusahaan 10, Perai Industrial Estate, 13600, Perai, Penang, Malaysia
Tel.: (60) 4 390 7951
Web Site: http://www.texmat.com
Sales Range: $25-49.9 Million
Emp.: 20
Industrial Chemical Whslr
N.A.I.C.S.: 424690

Subsidiary (Non-US):

Texchem Materials (Thailand) Ltd. (2)
170/29 170/31 11th Floor Ocean Tower 1 Building New Ratchadapisek Road, Klongtoey, Bangkok, 10110, Thailand
Tel.: (66) 2 661 8303
Web Site: http://www.texmat.com
Sales Range: $25-49.9 Million
Emp.: 20
Chemicals & Resins Whslr
N.A.I.C.S.: 424690

Texchem Materials (Vietnam) Co., Ltd. (2)
4th Floor Vietnam Paper Corporation Building 142 Doi Can Street, Ba Dinh District, Hanoi, Vietnam
Tel.: (84) 437366595
Sales Range: $25-49.9 Million
Emp.: 7
Industrial Chemicals & Polymers Whslr
N.A.I.C.S.: 424690

Texchem Singapore Private Limited (2)
31 International Business Park 02-12 Creative Resource, Singapore, 609921, Singapore
Tel.: (65) 6 265 5211
Web Site: http://www.txnat.com
Sales Range: $25-49.9 Million
Emp.: 20
Chemicals & Resins Whslr
N.A.I.C.S.: 424690
Yeo Seah Heng *(Mgr-Sls)*

Texchem Polymer Engineering Sdn. Bhd. (1)
Part of Lot 1241 Phase III Bayan Lepas, Free Industrial Zone, 11900, Bayan Lepas, Penang, Malaysia
Tel.: (60) 4 643 8661
Web Site: https://www.texchem-pack.com
Plastic Parts Mfr
N.A.I.C.S.: 326199
Chun Yinn The *(Mgr-Fin)*

Subsidiary (Domestic):

Eye Graphic Sdn. Bhd. (2)
5 Lorong Perusahaan Maju 11 Taman Perusahaan Pelangi, 13600, Prai, Penang, Malaysia
Tel.: (60) 4 507 4300
Web Site: https://www.eyegraph.com
Flexo Printing Plate Mfr
N.A.I.C.S.: 323120

Subsidiary (Non-US):

PT. Eye Graphic Indonesia (3)
JI Kenari Raya Blok G6-01 Kav 7E Delta Silicon 6 Lippo Cikarang, Desa Jayamukti Kecamatan Cikarang Pusat Kabupaten, Bekasi, 17530, Indonesia
Tel.: (62) 2189918676
Flexo Photopolymer Printing Plate Mfr
N.A.I.C.S.: 333248
Kengo Yoshida *(Gen Mgr)*

Subsidiary (Domestic):

Texchem Life Sciences Sdn. Bhd. (2)
Lot 3 Jalan P/6 Kawasan Perindustrian Bangi, 43650, Bandar Baru Bangi, Selangor, Malaysia
Tel.: (60) 389250370
Precision Injection Moulded Product Mfr
N.A.I.C.S.: 326199

Texchem-Pack (Johor) Sdn. Bhd. (2)
No 3 Jalan Mutiara 7 Taman Perindustrian Plentong, 81750, Masai, Johor, Malaysia
Tel.: (60) 73578868
Precision Injection Moulded Product Mfr
N.A.I.C.S.: 326199

Texchem-Pack (M) Sdn. Bhd. (2)
No 1465 Mukim 11 Lorong Perusahaan Maju 6, Perai Industrial Estate Phase 4, 13600, Perai, Penang, Malaysia
Tel.: (60) 45079753
Precision Injection Moulded Product Mfr
N.A.I.C.S.: 326199

Subsidiary (Non-US):

Texchem-Pack (Thailand) Co., Ltd. (2)
234 Moo 2 Bangpa-in Industrial Estate Klong-Jig, Bangpa-in, Ayutthaya, 13160, Thailand
Tel.: (66) 35258428
Precision Injection Moulded Product Mfr
N.A.I.C.S.: 326199

Texchem-Pack (Vietnam) Co., Ltd. (2)
No 26 Road 3A Bien Hoa Industrial Zone II, An Binh Ward, Bien Hoa, Dong Nai, Vietnam
Tel.: (84) 2513835661
Precision Injection Moulded Product Mfr
N.A.I.C.S.: 326199

Texchem Polymers Sdn. Bhd. (1)
No 1465 Mukim 11 Lorong Perusahaan Maju 6, Prai Industrial Estate Phase 4, 13600, Prai, Penang, Malaysia
Tel.: (60) 45079753
Web Site: https://www.texchem-polymers.com
Electronic & Semiconductor Material Mfr
N.A.I.C.S.: 335999

TEXEL INDUSTRIES LIMITED
Block No 2106 Nr, Village Santej Tal Kalol Ng, Gandhinagar, 382 721, Gujarat, India
Tel.: (91) 8980026110
Web Site:
https://www.geotexelin.com
526638—(BOM)
Rev.: $12,011,187
Assets: $12,921,141
Liabilities: $10,181,149
Net Worth: $2,739,992
Earnings: ($1,340,373)
Emp.: 210
Fiscal Year-end: 03/31/23
Textile Products Mfr
N.A.I.C.S.: 313310
Shailesh R. Mehta *(Mng Dir)*

TEXHONG TEXTILE GROUP LIMITED
Unit 3 37/F Cable TV Tower 9 Hoi Shing Road, Tsuen Wan, Hong Kong, China (Hong Kong)
Tel.: (852) 28770225   Ky
Web Site: http://www.texhong.com
Year Founded: 1997
2678—(HKG)
Rev.: $3,342,271,702
Assets: $3,671,642,380
Liabilities: $2,253,395,149
Net Worth: $1,418,247,230
Earnings: $28,246,514
Emp.: 30,206
Fiscal Year-end: 12/31/22
Textile Mfr
N.A.I.C.S.: 314999
Tianzhu Hong *(Founder & Chm)*

Subsidiaries:

Changzhou Texhong Textile Co., Ltd. (1)
No 2 Nanyang Street Changqi Road, Changzhou, Jiangsu, China
Tel.: (86) 51988770350
Textile Products Mfr
N.A.I.C.S.: 314999

Nantong Century Texhong Textile Co., Ltd. (1)
No 2 West Jianghai Road, Shuangdian Town Rudong County, Nantong, Jiangsu, China
Tel.: (86) 51384611671
Emp.: 964
Textile Products Mfr

TEXHONG TEXTILE GROUP LIMITED

Texhong Textile Group Limited—(Continued)
N.A.I.C.S.: 314999

Sunray Macao Commercial Offshore Limited (1)
11 / N Macao Sq 43 Avenida Do Infante D Henrique, Macau, China (Macau)
Tel.: (853) 2871 7345
Yarn Products Distr
N.A.I.C.S.: 424990

Texhong (China) Investment Co., Ltd. (1)
4/F Tianhong Bldg 80 Xianxia Road, Shanghai, 200336, China
Tel.: (86) 21 62958155
Web Site: http://www.texhong.com
Cotton Textile Products Distr
N.A.I.C.S.: 424990

Twin Dragon Marketing, Inc. (1)
14600 S Broadway, Gardena, CA 90248
Tel.: (310) 715-7070
Textile Products Mfr
N.A.I.C.S.: 314999

Winnitex Limited (1)
Unit 3601-3605 Cable TV Tower 9 Hoi Shing Road, Tsuen Wan, Hong Kong, China (Hong Kong)
Tel.: (852) 24376200
Web Site: https://www.winnitex.com
Emp.: 50
Woven Fabric Mfr & Distr
N.A.I.C.S.: 313310

Xuzhou Texhong Yinfeng Textile Co., Ltd. (1)
No 43 West Erhuan Road, Quanshan District, Xuzhou, Jiangsu, China
Tel.: (86) 51685611718
Textile Products Mfr
N.A.I.C.S.: 314999

Zhejiang Texhong Textile Co., Ltd. (1)
No 85 Hengchang Avenue, Pujiang County, Jinhua, Zhejiang, China
Tel.: (86) 5754115666
Textile Products Mfr
N.A.I.C.S.: 314999

TEXIM BANK AD
bul Todor Aleksandrov 117, Sofia, Bulgaria
Tel.: (359) 29035505
Web Site: https://www.teximbank.bg
Year Founded: 1992
TXIM—(BUL)
Rev.: $6,635,440
Assets: $337,040,635
Liabilities: $314,140,522
Net Worth: $22,900,113
Earnings: $177,765
Emp.: 273
Fiscal Year-end: 12/31/23
Investment Banking Services
N.A.I.C.S.: 523150
Maria Vidolova *(Member-Mgmt Bd & Exec Dir)*

TEXMO PIPES AND PRODUCTS LIMITED
98 Bahadarpur Road, Post Box No 35, Burhanpur, 450 331, MP, India
Tel.: (91) 7325255122
Web Site: https://www.texmopipe.com
Year Founded: 2008
TEXMOPIPES—(NSE)
Rev.: $57,675,659
Assets: $45,831,377
Liabilities: $14,916,119
Net Worth: $30,915,257
Earnings: $1,478,882
Emp.: 458
Fiscal Year-end: 03/31/21
Plastic Tank Mfr
N.A.I.C.S.: 326122
Sanjay Kumar Agrawal *(Mng Dir)*

TEXPA MASCHINENBAU
Mittelweg 9, Saal an der Saale, 97633, Germany
Tel.: (49) 976279100
Web Site: http://www.texpa.de
Rev.: $17,000,000
Emp.: 150
Sewing machines Mfr
N.A.I.C.S.: 339999
Johannes Graf von Westphalen *(CEO)*

TEXSA SYSTEMS, SL.U.
Ferro 7 Poligono Industrial Can Pelegri, Castellbisbal, 08755, Barcelona, Spain
Tel.: (34) 936351400 ES
Web Site: http://www.texsa.com
Emp.: 6,892
Waterproofing & Insulation Products Mfr
N.A.I.C.S.: 326140

Subsidiaries:

Texsa Ltd. (1)
Unit 6 North Orbital Commercial Park Napsbury Lane, Saint Albans, AL1 1XB, Herts, United Kingdom
Tel.: (44) 1727575475
Auxiliary Materials Mfr
N.A.I.C.S.: 336413

Texsa Portugal S.A. (1)
Zona Industrial de Alpiarca Rua A Lote 4 B, 2090-242, Alpiarca, Portugal
Tel.: (351) 243240020
Auxiliary Materials Mfr
N.A.I.C.S.: 336413

Texsa S.A.S. (1)
Chez AE2C Actiparc Bat 4 131 Tra De La Penne Aux Camoins, La Penne Sur Huveaune, 13821, Marseille, France
Tel.: (33) 145421733
Auxiliary Materials Mfr
N.A.I.C.S.: 336413

TEXT S.A.
ul Zwycieska 47, 53-033, Wroclaw, Poland
Tel.: (48) 713454057
Web Site: https://text.com
Year Founded: 2002
TXT—(WAR)
Rev.: $79,315,179
Assets: $49,573,180
Liabilities: $5,581,068
Net Worth: $43,992,112
Earnings: $43,299,251
Emp.: 282
Fiscal Year-end: 03/31/23
Software Publisher
N.A.I.C.S.: 513210
Mariusz Cieply *(Co-Founder, Chm-Mgmt Bd & CEO)*

Subsidiaries:

LiveChat, Inc. (1)
405 North St, Chapel Hill, NC 27514
Tel.: (919) 636-4677
Web Site: http://www.livechatinc.com
Emp.: 70
Software Publisher
N.A.I.C.S.: 513210
Mariusz Cieply *(CEO)*

TEXTBOOK PRINTING JSC IN HOCHIMINH CITY
No 240 Tran Binh Trong Street Ward 4, District 5, Ho Chi Minh City, Vietnam
Tel.: (84) 838353171
Web Site: https://www.sapco.com.vn
Year Founded: 1977
SAP—(HNX)
Rev.: $365,691
Assets: $465,890
Liabilities: $181,033
Net Worth: $284,857
Earnings: $7,540
Fiscal Year-end: 12/31/23

Books Publishing Services
N.A.I.C.S.: 513130

TEXTIL MANUEL GONCALVES, SGPS, S.A.
Apartado 14 S Cosme do Vale, 4764-952, Vila Nova de Famalicao, Portugal
Tel.: (351) 252 300 400 PT
Web Site: http://www.tmg.pt
Year Founded: 1937
Holding Company; Textiles Mfr & Distr
N.A.I.C.S.: 551112
Manuel Antonio Carvalho Goncalves *(Founder)*

TEXTIL RENAUXVIEW S.A.
Centennial 215, CX postal 15, Brusque, 88351-025, Santa Catarina, Brazil
Tel.: (55) 4732551000
Web Site: https://www.renauxview.com
Year Founded: 1925
TXRX4—(BRAZ)
Rev.: $23,723,387
Assets: $35,148,995
Liabilities: $91,292,967
Net Worth: ($56,143,972)
Earnings: $2,993,332
Fiscal Year-end: 12/31/23
Textile Products Mfr
N.A.I.C.S.: 314999
Marcio Luiz Bertoldi *(Dir-Fin)*

TEXTON PROPERTY FUND LTD.
Block D Vunani Office Park 151 Katherine Street, Sandton, 2031, South Africa
Tel.: (27) 117311980
Web Site: https://texton.co.za
Year Founded: 2005
TEX—(JSE)
Rev.: $15,773,825
Assets: $165,924,651
Liabilities: $55,181,297
Net Worth: $110,743,354
Earnings: ($747,367)
Emp.: 20
Fiscal Year-end: 06/30/23
Investment Management Service
N.A.I.C.S.: 525990
Marcel Golding *(Chm)*

TEXWINCA HOLDINGS LIMITED
16th Floor Metroplaza Tower II 223 Hing Fong Road, Kwai Chung, China (Hong Kong)
Tel.: (852) 24818018
Web Site: http://www.texwinca.com
Year Founded: 1975
0321—(HKG)
Rev.: $772,491,263
Assets: $885,694,305
Liabilities: $246,210,023
Net Worth: $639,484,283
Earnings: $8,045,378
Emp.: 9,784
Fiscal Year-end: 03/31/23
Knitted Fabric & Yarn Producer, Dyer & Seller; Casual Apparel & Accessories Retailer & Distr; Franchise Services
N.A.I.C.S.: 313110
Bun Chak Poon *(Founder & Chm)*

Subsidiaries:

Baleno Kingdom Limited (1)
10F LMK Development Estate 10-16 Kwai Ting Road, Kwai Chung, New Territories, China (Hong Kong)
Tel.: (852) 31259888
Web Site: http://www.baleno.com.hk
Casual Apparel & Accessories Retailer

INTERNATIONAL PUBLIC

N.A.I.C.S.: 458110

Creative Textile Technology Company (Guangdong) Limited (1)
Texwinca Industrial Town Ou Chong Cun Ma Chong Zhen, Dongguan, 523138, Guangdong, China
Tel.: (86) 7698 882 1738
Fabric Mfr & Distr
N.A.I.C.S.: 313310

Dongguan Texwinca Textile & Garment Ltd (1)
Texwinca Industrial Town, Ou Chong Guan Li Qu Ma Chong Z, 523138, Dongguan, China
Tel.: (86) 76988821738
Textile Product Mills
N.A.I.C.S.: 314999

Guangzhou Friendship Baleno Company Limited (1)
4F Tower C Bei Ke Qiao Tang Tang Xia Section Zhongshan Avenue, Guangzhou, 510665, Guangdong, China
Tel.: (86) 2085107888
Casual Apparels Mfr & Distr
N.A.I.C.S.: 458110

Megawell Group Co. Ltd. (1)
2nd Floor Wai Cheong Industrial Centre No 5 Shek Pai Tau Road, Tuen Mun, New Territories, China (Hong Kong)
Tel.: (852) 24691112
Web Site: http://www.texwinca.com
Sales Range: $25-49.9 Million
Emp.: 30
Textile Product Mills
N.A.I.C.S.: 314999

Nice Dyeing Factory (Macao Commercial Offshore) Limited (1)
Avenida Do Infante D Henrique No 43 Macau Square, 9 Andar H-J, Macau, China (Macau)
Tel.: (853) 28389129
Textile Dyeing
N.A.I.C.S.: 325130

Texwinca Enterprises Limited (1)
16th Floor Metroplaza Tower II 223 Hing Fong Road, Kwai Chung, China (Hong Kong)
Tel.: (852) 24818018
Web Site: http://www.texwinca.com
Fabric Dyeing & Finishing
N.A.I.C.S.: 325130

Winca Trading Limited (1)
16th Fl Metroplaza Tower II, 223 Hing Fong Rd, Kwai Chung, China (Hong Kong)
Tel.: (852) 24818018
Industrial Machinery & Equipment Merchant Whslr
N.A.I.C.S.: 423830
Poon Bun Chak *(Chm & Mng Dir)*

TEYI PHARMACEUTICAL GROUP CO., LTD.
No 9 11 Changxing Road, Taicheng, Taishan, 529200, China
Tel.: (86) 7505627588
Web Site: https://tczy.com.cn
Year Founded: 2003
002728—(SSE)
Rev.: $124,474,554
Assets: $357,402,900
Liabilities: $160,402,128
Net Worth: $197,000,772
Earnings: $25,019,856
Fiscal Year-end: 12/31/22
Biotechnology Research & Development Services
N.A.I.C.S.: 541714
Danqing Xu *(Chm, Pres & Gen Mgr)*

TEYLOR AG
Zwicky Platz 3 Wallisellen, 8304, Zurich, Switzerland
Tel.: (49) 75315848130
Web Site: https://www.teylor.com
Year Founded: 2018
Financial Services
N.A.I.C.S.: 523999

AND PRIVATE COMPANIES   TFI INTERNATIONAL INC.

Subsidiaries:

creditshelf Aktiengesellschaft (1)
Mainzer Landstrasse 33a, 60329, Frankfurt, Germany
Tel.: (49) 6934877240
Web Site: https://www.creditshelf.com
Rev: $51,116,010
Assets: $146,146,209
Liabilities: $51,298,547
Net Worth: $94,847,663
Earnings: ($55,629,046)
Fiscal Year-end: 12/31/2019
Financial Banking Services
N.A.I.C.S.: 522110

TEYS AUSTRALIA PTY LTD.
Building 3 Freeway Office Park 2728 Logan Road, Eight Mile Plains, 4113, QLD, Australia
Tel.: (61) 7 3198 9000   AU
Web Site: http://www.teysaust.com.au
Year Founded: 1946
Emp.: 5,000
Meat Processing Services
N.A.I.C.S.: 311611
Brad Teys (CEO)

Subsidiaries:

Charlton Feedlot Pty. Ltd. (1)
Seven Mile Road, Yeungroon, 3525, VIC, Australia
Tel.: (61) 354916266
Web Site: http://www.teys.com.au
Sales Range: $10-24.9 Million
Emp.: 35
Cattle Feedlot Operation Services
N.A.I.C.S.: 112112
Ashley Sheahan (Mgr)

Teys (USA) Inc. (1)
770 N Halsted St Ste 202, Chicago, IL 60642
Tel.: (312) 492-7163
Emp.: 12
Beef Whslr
N.A.I.C.S.: 424470
Stacy Elmore (Gen Mgr)

TF BANK AB
Lilla Brogatan 6, PO Box 947, 501 10, Boras, Sweden
Tel.: (46) 337223500   SE
Web Site: https://group.tfbank.se
Year Founded: 1987
TFBANK—(OMX)
Rev.: $235,165,688
Assets: $2,377,226,995
Liabilities: $2,162,710,145
Net Worth: $214,516,850
Earnings: $39,380,945
Emp.: 380
Fiscal Year-end: 12/31/23
Investment Banking Services
N.A.I.C.S.: 523150
Mattias Carlsson (CEO)

Subsidiaries:

Avarda AB (1)
Norrlandsgatan 7-9, 111 43, Stockholm, Sweden
Tel.: (46) 101613350
Web Site: http://www.avarda.com
Ecommerce Services
N.A.I.C.S.: 524210

Subsidiary (Non-US):

Avarda Oy (2)
Keskuskatu 6 b, 00100, Helsinki, Finland
Tel.: (358) 925327100
Web Site: http://www.avarda.com
Ecommerce Services
N.A.I.C.S.: 513210

BB Bank ASA (1)
Markeveien 1 A, 5012, Bergen, Norway
Tel.: (47) 56999200
Web Site: http://www.bbf.no
Banking Services
N.A.I.C.S.: 522110

TF VARLIK KIRALAMA A.S.
Saray Mahallesi Sokullu Caddesi No 6 17 Kat Ofis No 42, Umraniye, 34768, Istanbul, Turkiye
Tel.: (90) 2166762845
Web Site: http://www.tfvarlikkiralama.com.tr
TFNVK—(IST)
Sales Range: Less than $1 Million
Banking & Investment Services
N.A.I.C.S.: 523150
Mete Mehmet Kanat (Chm)

TFE CO., LTD.
50-8 Banwol-gil 320-13 Banwol-dong, Hwaseong, 18384, Gyeonggi-do, Korea (South)
Tel.: (82) 312060541
Web Site: https://tfe.co.kr
Year Founded: 2003
425420—(KRS)
Electronic Components Mfr
N.A.I.C.S.: 334419
Moon Joo (CEO)

TFG INTERNATIONAL GROUP LIMITED
Flat 403 and 405 4th Floor Kowloon City Plaza 128 Carpenter Road, Kowloon, China (Hong Kong)
Tel.: (852) 31889228   Ky
Web Site: http://www.tfginternationalgroup.com
0542—(HKG)
Rev.: $2,883,993
Assets: $517,332,718
Liabilities: $490,573,624
Net Worth: $26,759,094
Earnings: ($27,957,060)
Emp.: 126
Fiscal Year-end: 12/31/20
Real Estate Development Services
N.A.I.C.S.: 531390
Danny Kui Shing Wong (CEO)

TFI INTERNATIONAL INC.
8801 Trans-Canada Highway Suite 500, Montreal, H4S 1Z6, QC, Canada
Tel.: (514) 331-4000   Ca
Web Site: http://www.tfiintl.com
TFII—(NYSE)
Rev.: $7,521,167,000
Assets: $6,283,620,000
Liabilities: $3,692,210,000
Net Worth: $2,591,410,000
Earnings: $504,877,000
Emp.: 25,123
Fiscal Year-end: 12/31/23
Transportation, Logistics & Warehousing Services
N.A.I.C.S.: 488999
Josiane-M. Langlois (Sec & VP-Legal Affairs)

Subsidiaries:

ATS Retail Solutions (1)
96 Disco Road, Etobicoke, M9W 0A3, ON, Canada
Tel.: (416) 679-7979
Web Site: http://www.atsretailsolutions.ca
General Freight Trucking Services
N.A.I.C.S.: 484121

Bulk Transport Company West, Inc. (1)
305 9th Ave, Scottsbluff, NE 69361
Tel.: (308) 220-4000
Web Site: https://btcbulkwest.com
Specialized Freight Trucking; Long-Distance
N.A.I.C.S.: 484230
Kevin Fulk (VP-Ops)

CK Logistics Inc. (1)
10395 Avenue Ryan Suite 100, Dorval, H9P 1A2, QC, Canada
Tel.: (514) 856-7580
Web Site: http://www.cklogistics.ca
Sales Range: $25-49.9 Million
Warehousing & Logistics Services
N.A.I.C.S.: 493110

Camionnage G.H.L. Inc (1)
7887 rue Grenache suite 102, Anjou, H1J 1C4, QC, Canada
Tel.: (514) 353-2025
Web Site: http://www.camionnageghl.com
Sales Range: $25-49.9 Million
General Freight Trucking Services
N.A.I.C.S.: 484110

Canadian Freightways Ltd. (1)
234040 Wrangler Road SE RR 5 Building A, Rocky View, Calgary, T1X 0K2, AB, Canada
Tel.: (403) 287-1090
Web Site: http://www.canadianfreightways.com
Sales Range: $450-499.9 Million
Emp.: 2,500
Freight & Parcel Trucking Services
N.A.I.C.S.: 484122

Centre de Mecanique Henri-Bourassa Inc. (1)
7887 Grenache, Montreal, H1G 1C4, QC, Canada
Tel.: (514) 353-2025
Sales Range: $25-49.9 Million
Emp.: 28
Truck Repair & Maintenance Services
N.A.I.C.S.: 811310
Sylvain Frank (Mgr)

Clarke Transport Inc. (1)
201 WestCreek Blvd Suite 200, PO Box 32, Brampton, L6T 5S6, ON, Canada
Tel.: (905) 291-3000
Web Site: http://www.clarkelink.com
Sales Range: $75-99.9 Million
Truckload & LTL Freight Transportation Services
N.A.I.C.S.: 484121

Concord Transportation Inc. (1)
96 Disco Road, Etobicoke, M9W 0A3, ON, Canada
Tel.: (416) 679-7400
Web Site: http://www.concordtransportation.com
Sales Range: $25-49.9 Million
Emp.: 12
Expedited Freight Transportation & Logistics Services
N.A.I.C.S.: 484121

Contrans Group Inc. (1)
1179 Ridgeway Road, Woodstock, N4V 1E3, ON, Canada
Tel.: (519) 421-4600
Web Site: http://www.contrans.ca
Rev.: $514,725,885
Assets: $350,508,172
Liabilities: $171,145,406
Net Worth: $179,362,767
Earnings: $26,468,770
Emp.: 1,434
Fiscal Year-end: 12/31/2013
Holding Company; Freight Transportation Services
N.A.I.C.S.: 551112
James S. Clark (CFO & VP-Fin)

Subsidiary (Domestic):

Brookville Carriers Flatbed LP (2)
79 Parkway Drive, Truro, B2N 5A9, NS, Canada
Tel.: (902) 893-8805
Web Site: http://www.contransflatbedgroup.com
Sales Range: $25-49.9 Million
Emp.: 25
Offers Legal & Over-Dimensional Cargo & Freight Hauls in Canada & U.S.
N.A.I.C.S.: 488510
Mark Greenwood (Mgr-Ops)

Brookville Carriers Van LP (2)
65 Alloy Drive Spruce Lake Industrial Park, Saint John, E2M 7S9, NB, Canada (100%)
Tel.: (506) 633-7555
Web Site: http://www.contransflatbedgroup.com
Sales Range: $25-49.9 Million
Emp.: 9
Flatbed Freight Transportation Arrangement
N.A.I.C.S.: 488510

Contrans Corp (2)
1179 Ridgeway Rd, PO Box 1669, Woodstock, N4S 0A9, ON, Canada
Tel.: (519) 421-4600
Web Site: http://www.contrans.ca
Emp.: 2,000
Specialized Transportation & Logistics Services
N.A.I.C.S.: 488390

Contrans Flatbed Group LP (2)
80 3rd Line, Hagersville, N0A 1H0, ON, Canada
Tel.: (519) 539-9222
Web Site: http://www.contransflatbedgroup.com
Sales Range: $50-74.9 Million
Transportation & Logistics Services
N.A.I.C.S.: 488999

Division (Domestic):

Contrans Flatbed Group (3)
2278 Lakeshore Road West, Mississauga, L5J 1K2, ON, Canada
Web Site: http://contransflatbedgroup.com
Sales Range: $25-49.9 Million
Emp.: 53
General Freight Trucking, Local
N.A.I.C.S.: 484110

Subsidiary (Domestic):

Cornerstone Logistics LP (2)
2180 Buckingham Rd Unit 204, Oakville, L6H 6H1, ON, Canada
Tel.: (905) 339-1456
Web Site: http://cornerstonelogistics.com
Sales Range: $25-49.9 Million
Emp.: 200
Freight Transportation & Logistics
N.A.I.C.S.: 488510

Subsidiary (US):

Cornerstone Logistics USA LP (2)
85 Northpointe Pkwy Ste 6, Amherst, NY 14228   (100%)
Tel.: (716) 565-9900
Web Site: http://cornerstonelogistics.com
Sales Range: $25-49.9 Million
Emp.: 30
Port Services, Logistics & Freight Transportation Services
N.A.I.C.S.: 488510

Cornerstone Logistics USA LP (2)
18301 Broadwick St, Rancho Dominguez, CA 90220   (100%)
Tel.: (310) 627-4970
Web Site: http://www.cornerstonelogistics.com
Emp.: 5
Solutions & Services to Freight & Shipping Challenges
N.A.I.C.S.: 484230

Subsidiary (Domestic):

Glen Tay Transportation LP (2)
42 Lanark Rd, Perth, K7H 3K5, ON, Canada   (100%)
Tel.: (613) 267-2007
Web Site: http://www.contrans.ca
Sales Range: $25-49.9 Million
Emp.: 100
Pneumatic Bulk & Liquid Tank Carriers
N.A.I.C.S.: 424710

Laidlaw Carriers Bulk LP (2)
3135 Bernard Pilon, Saint-Mathieu-de-Beloeil, J3G 4S5, QC, Canada
Tel.: (519) 539-0471
Web Site: http://www.contrans.com
Sales Range: $25-49.9 Million
Emp.: 480
Waste Transportation from Transfer Stations to Landfill Sites within Ontario & Quebec
N.A.I.C.S.: 562111

Laidlaw Carriers Tank (2)
605 Athlone Avenue, PO Box 1571, Woodstock, N5S 0A7, ON, Canada
Tel.: (519) 539-6103
Web Site: http://www.laidlawcarrierstank.ca
Emp.: 100
Tank Truck Carriers
N.A.I.C.S.: 484121

Laidlaw Carriers Van LP (2)

TFI INTERNATIONAL INC.

TFI International Inc.—(Continued)
21 Kerr Crescent, Puslinch, N0B 2J0, ON, Canada
Tel.: (519) 766-0660
Web Site: https://www.laidlawvan.ca
Sales Range: $25-49.9 Million
Emp.: 35
Freight Management, Hazardous Transportation Solutions & Logistics
N.A.I.C.S.: 562211

Peter Hodge Transport Limited (2)
100 Market Drive, Milton, L9T 3H5, ON, Canada (100%)
Tel.: (905) 693-8088
Web Site: http://www.peterhodgetransport.com
Sales Range: $25-49.9 Million
Emp.: 600
Bulk Product Deliveries Including Scrap Metal, Agricultural Products & Specialized Sands & Gravels
N.A.I.C.S.: 484230

Tri-Line Carriers LP (2)
235185 Ryan Road SE, Rocky View, Calgary, T1X 0K1, AB, Canada (100%)
Tel.: (403) 279-7070
Web Site: http://www.triline.ca
Sales Range: $25-49.9 Million
Emp.: 200
Transportation Specialists in Long Haul/Regional Flatdeck, Dry Bulk, Hazardous Waste & Waste Transfer
N.A.I.C.S.: 562112

Tripar Transportation LP (2)
2180 Buckingham Road, Oakville, L6H 6H1, ON, Canada (100%)
Tel.: (905) 829-8500
Web Site: https://tripartrans.com
Sales Range: $25-49.9 Million
Emp.: 30
Less-than-Truckload Carrier Specializing in Next-Day Freight Deliveries
N.A.I.C.S.: 484121

D&D Sexton Inc. (1)
1154 N Garrison Ave, Carthage, MO 64836
Tel.: (417) 358-8727
Web Site: http://www.ddsextoninc.com
Sales Range: $10-24.9 Million
Emp.: 122
Provider of Trucking Services
N.A.I.C.S.: 484121
David Dean Sexton (Pres)

Dahlsten Truck Line, Inc. (1)
101 W Edgar St, Clay Center, NE 68933-1427
Tel.: (402) 762-3511
Web Site: https://www.dahlsten.com
Sales Range: $75-99.9 Million
Emp.: 130
Provider of Trucking Services
N.A.I.C.S.: 484121

Dynamex Inc. (1)
5429 LBJ Fwy Ste 900, Dallas, TX 75240
Tel.: (214) 560-9000
Sales Range: $400-449.9 Million
Emp.: 1,500
Freight Transportation & Courier Services
N.A.I.C.S.: 484121
Scott Leveridge (Pres-US)

Subsidiary (Non-US):

Dynamex Canada Corp. (2)
2630 Skymark Ave Ste 610, Mississauga, L4W 5A4, ON, Canada
Tel.: (905) 238-6414
Sales Range: $400-449.9 Million
Emp.: 64
Courier Service
N.A.I.C.S.: 492110

Subsidiary (Domestic):

Dynamex Operations East, Inc. (2)
5429 LBJ Fwy Ste 1000, Dallas, TX 75240
Tel.: (214) 560-9000
Sales Range: $400-449.9 Million
Emp.: 50
Holding Company; Courier & Freight Transportation Services
N.A.I.C.S.: 551112

Hot-Line Freight System, Inc. (1)
N4690 Bangor Pkwy, West Salem, WI 54669
Tel.: (608) 486-1600
Web Site: http://www.hotlinefreight.com
Rev.: $1,057,000
Emp.: 7
General Freight Trucking, Long-Distance Services
N.A.I.C.S.: 484121
William Swinehart (Mgr)

Information Communication Services Inc. (1)
1243 Islington Ave, Toronto, M8X 1Y9, ON, Canada
Tel.: (416) 233-5558
Web Site: http://www.ics-canada.net
Courier Service
N.A.I.C.S.: 492110

JHT Holdings, Inc (1)
10801 Corporate Dr, Pleasant Prairie, WI 53158
Tel.: (877) 327-7743
Web Site: http://www.jhtholdings.com
Sales Range: $450-499.9 Million
Emp.: 40
Holding Company; Long-Distance Trucking
N.A.I.C.S.: 484121
John Harrington (Pres & CEO)

Subsidiary (Domestic):

ATC Leasing Company (2)
10801 Corporate Dr, Pleasant Prairie, WI 53158
Tel.: (262) 564-7954
Equipment & Real Estate Leasing & Administrative Support Services to Companies Engaged in Transportation, Distribution, Warehousing, Brokerage & Logistics
N.A.I.C.S.: 532490

Active Truck Transportation Company LLC (2)
10801 Corporate Dr, Pleasant Prairie, WI 53158-1603 (100%)
Tel.: (262) 564-7954
Web Site: http://www.activetransport.com
Sales Range: $300-349.9 Million
Trucking Service
N.A.I.C.S.: 484121
Bruce Jackson (Pres)

Subsidiary (Domestic):

Active Acquisition Corp. (3)
10801 Corporate Dr, Pleasant Prairie, WI 53158
Tel.: (262) 564-7404
Web Site: http://www.activetransport.com
Rev.: $85,700,000
Emp.: 1
Trucking Service
N.A.I.C.S.: 484230

Subsidiary (Domestic):

Active USA Inc. (4)
10801 Corporate Dr, Pleasant Prairie, WI 53158-1603
Tel.: (262) 564-7954
Web Site: http://www.activetransport.com
Trucking & Office Personnel Recruiting
N.A.I.C.S.: 561311

Subsidiary (Non-US):

Active Canada Inc. (3)
325 Keil Drive South, Chatham, N7M 6J5, ON, Canada
Tel.: (262) 564-7270
Emp.: 15
Truck Transport Services
N.A.I.C.S.: 484121
Mahlon Gragen (Dir-Compliance & Safety)

Subsidiary (Domestic):

Auto Truck Transport USA, LLC (2)
PO Box 581045, Pleasant Prairie, WI 53158
Tel.: (888) 770-0001
Web Site: https://www.autotrucktransport.com
Sales Range: $25-49.9 Million
Transportation of Trucks & Truck Chassis from & to Assembly Plants, Ports, Railway Distribution Points, Auctions & Dealerships
N.A.I.C.S.: 484230
Keith Rentzel (Pres)

Subsidiary (Domestic):

Auto Truck Transport Corporation (3)
Terminal 543 320 Bear Poplar Rd, Cleveland, NC 27013
Tel.: (704) 278-0635
Web Site: http://www.autotrucktransport.com
Sales Range: $25-49.9 Million
Trucking & Specialized Freight Distr
N.A.I.C.S.: 484121

Subsidiary (Non-US):

Mexicana Logistics, S.A. de C.V. (3)
Avenida Republica de Ecuador 998 Int A, 21218, Mexicali, Baja California, Mexico
Tel.: (52) 6865636634
Web Site: http://www.mexicanalogistics.com
Truck Transport Services
N.A.I.C.S.: 484121

Subsidiary (Domestic):

Unimark Truck Transport LLC (2)
2900 S Davis Blvd, Joplin, MO 64804
Tel.: (866) 254-2890
Web Site: http://www.unimarktransport.com
Truck Transport Services
N.A.I.C.S.: 484121
Milton Mike (VP-Ops)

Keith Hall & Sons Transport Ltd. (1)
297 Bishopsgate Rd, Burford, N0E 1A0, ON, Canada
Tel.: (519) 449-2401
Web Site: http://www.keithhalltransport.com
Sales Range: $10-24.9 Million
Emp.: 100
Transportation Services
N.A.I.C.S.: 484110
Brian Hall (Pres)

Kingsway Transport (1)
5425 Dixie Rd Bldg 2, Mississauga, L4W 1E6, ON, Canada
Tel.: (905) 238-5477
Web Site: http://www.kingswaytransport.com
Sales Range: $75-99.9 Million
Emp.: 200
N.A.I.C.S.: 484122

La Crete Transport 79 Ltd. (1)
9706 99 St, La Crete, T0H 2H0, AB, Canada
Tel.: (780) 928-3989
Web Site: http://www.latrans.ca
Sales Range: $25-49.9 Million
General Freight Trucking Services
N.A.I.C.S.: 484121

Lafleche Environmental Inc. (1)
17125 Lafleche Rd, Moose Creek, K0C 1W0, ON, Canada
Tel.: (613) 538-2776
Web Site: http://www.leic.com
Waste Management Services
N.A.I.C.S.: 562998
Brian King (Dir-Ops-Compost)

Loomis Express (1)
201 Westcreek Blvd, Brampton, L6T 5S6, ON, Canada
Tel.: (905) 460-2530
Web Site: https://www.loomis-express.com
Sales Range: $25-49.9 Million
Express Mail Services
N.A.I.C.S.: 492110

McMurray Serv-U Expediting Ltd. (1)
320 Macdonald Crescent, Fort McMurray, T9H 4B6, AB, Canada
Tel.: (780) 791-3530
Web Site: https://www.mcmurrayservu.com
General Freight Trucking Services
N.A.I.C.S.: 484121
Elvis Penton (Gen Mgr)

Papineau International L.P. (1)
851 Boulevard Roland-Godard, Saint-Jerome, J7Y 4C2, QC, Canada
Tel.: (450) 432-7555
Web Site: https://papineauintl.com
Transportation Services
N.A.I.C.S.: 484121

Patriot Freight Services Inc. (1)
10325 Ryan Avenue, Dorval, H9P 1A2, QC, Canada
Tel.: (514) 631-2900
Web Site: http://www.patriotfreight.com

INTERNATIONAL PUBLIC

Sales Range: $25-49.9 Million
Freight Forwarding Services
N.A.I.C.S.: 488510

Roland Thibault Inc. (1)
702-137th Rd, Sainte-Cecile-de-Milton, J0E 2C0, QC, Canada
Tel.: (450) 372-2399
Web Site: http://www.transforce.com
Sales Range: $25-49.9 Million
Emp.: 10
Waste Collection Services
N.A.I.C.S.: 562119

SGT 2000 Inc. (1)
354 Chemin Yamaska, Saint Germain, Montreal, J0C1K0, QC, Canada
Tel.: (819) 395-4213
Web Site: https://www.sgt2000.com
Emp.: 253
Freight Services
N.A.I.C.S.: 484121
Denis Coderre (Pres)

Schilli Corporation (1)
900 S Hwy Dr Ste 304, Fenton, MO 63026-2017
Tel.: (636) 343-1877
Web Site: http://schillicorp.com
Sales Range: $25-49.9 Million
Emp.: 300
Provider of Trucking Services
N.A.I.C.S.: 484121

Subsidiary (Domestic):

Bulk Transport Company (2)
20 Research Park Dr, Saint Charles, MO 63304
Tel.: (314) 576-8410
Emp.: 3
Truck Transportation Services
N.A.I.C.S.: 484230
Mike Henson (Gen Mgr)

Contractors Cartage Inc. (2)
2280 Cassens Dr, Fenton, MO 63026-2521
Tel.: (636) 343-1877
Web Site: http://www.schillicorp.com
Sales Range: $10-24.9 Million
Emp.: 100
Provider of Trucking Services
N.A.I.C.S.: 484121
Bob Schilli (Pres)

Material Delivery Service Inc. (2)
887 Bolger Ct, Fenton, MO 63026-2521 (100%)
Tel.: (636) 343-1877
Web Site: http://www.schillicorp.com
Sales Range: $10-24.9 Million
Emp.: 20
Provider of Trucking Services
N.A.I.C.S.: 484121

Southwest Missouri Truck Center Inc. (2)
2527 N Eastgate Ave, Springfield, MO 65803
Tel.: (417) 869-0566
Web Site: https://www.swtrucks.com
Rev.: $23,603,038
Emp.: 40
Automobile & Other Motor Vehicle Distr
N.A.I.C.S.: 541618

TST Expedited Services Inc. (1)
710 Sprucewood Ave, Windsor, N9C 0B2, ON, Canada
Tel.: (519) 972-8111
Web Site: http://tst911.com
Sales Range: $25-49.9 Million
General Freight Trucking Services
N.A.I.C.S.: 484110
Jeff Laforet (VP & Gen Mgr)

Transport Corporation of America, Inc. (1)
1715 Yankee Doodle Rd, Eagan, MN 55121
Tel.: (651) 686-2500
Web Site: http://www.transportamerica.com
Sales Range: $350-399.9 Million
Emp.: 2,132
Freight Trucking & Logistics Services
N.A.I.C.S.: 484121

Transport Couture & Fils Ltee (1)
99 Rte 271 Sud, Saint-Ephrem-de-Beauce, G0M 1R0, QC, Canada
Tel.: (581) 813-1400
Web Site: http://www.tcfl.com

Sales Range: $50-74.9 Million
General Freight Trucking Services
N.A.I.C.S.: 484121
Serge Poulin (Gen Mgr)

Transport Kobelt Inc. (1)
276 Rue Queen, Sherbrooke, J1M 1K6,
QC, Canada
Tel.: (819) 566-0116
Web Site:
http://www.kobelttransportation.com
Sales Range: $25-49.9 Million
Emp.: 11
Transportation Services
N.A.I.C.S.: 484110

Transport Thibodeau Inc. (1)
128 2e Ave, Portneuf, G0A 2Y0, QC,
Canada
Tel.: (418) 286-3311
General Freight Trucking Services
N.A.I.C.S.: 484121

Transport Watson Montreal Ltee (1)
3126 Bernard-Pilon, Saint-Mathieu-de-Beloeil, J3G 4S5, QC, Canada
Tel.: (450) 467-7352
Web Site: http://www.transportwatson.com
Sales Range: $25-49.9 Million
General Freight Trucking Services
N.A.I.C.S.: 484121

UPS Ground Freight, Inc. (1)
1000 Semmes Ave, Richmond, VA 23224-2246
Tel.: (804) 231-8555
Web Site: http://www.upsfreight.com
Less-Than-Truckload & Long-Distance
Freight Transportation Services
N.A.I.C.S.: 484122
Rich McArdle (Pres)

Branch (Domestic):

UPS Ground Freight, Inc. - Western
Regional Office (2)
2900 California Ave, North Salt Lake, UT 84104
Web Site: http://www.upsfreight.com
Sales Range: $150-199.9 Million
Less-Than-Truckload Transportation &
Long-Haul Regional & Interregional Services
N.A.I.C.S.: 484121

Vitran Corporation Inc. (1)
185 The West Mall Suite 701, Toronto, M9C 5L5, ON, Canada
Tel.: (416) 596-7664
Web Site: http://www.vitran.com
Sales Range: Less than $1 Million
Holding Company; Less-than-Truckload
Freight Transportation Services
N.A.I.C.S.: 551112

Subsidiary (Domestic):

Vitran Express Canada, Inc. (2)
1201 Creditstone Road, Concord, L4K 0C2, ON, Canada (100%)
Tel.: (416) 798-4965
Web Site: http://www.vitran.com
Sales Range: $75-99.9 Million
Less-than-Truckload Freight Transportation Services
N.A.I.C.S.: 484122

Westfreight Systems Inc. (1)
8716 - 48th Street SE, Rocky View, Calgary, T2C 2P9, AB, Canada
Tel.: (403) 279-8388
Web Site: http://www.westfreight.com
Sales Range: $25-49.9 Million
General Freight Trucking Services
N.A.I.C.S.: 484121

Subsidiary (US):

Westfreight Holdings (U.S.A.) Inc (2)
3001 N Pole Rd, Moore, OK 73160
Tel.: (405) 672-4273
General Freight Trucking Services
N.A.I.C.S.: 484121

TFI TAB GIDA YATIRIMLARI A.S.
Dikilitas Mahallesi Cad A Blok No 109
Besiktas, Istanbul, Turkiye
Tel.: (90) 212 310 48 99 TR
Web Site: http://www.tabfoods.com
Year Founded: 1995
Sales Range: $1-4.9 Billion
Emp.: 33,432
Restaurant Operators
N.A.I.C.S.: 722511
Erhan Kurdoglu (Chm)

TFP SOLUTIONS BERHAD
Wisma LMS No 6 Jalan Abd Rahman
Idris, Off Jalan Raja Muda Abdul
Aziz, 50300, Kuala Lumpur, Malaysia
Tel.: (60) 392130688
Web Site: https://www.tfp.com.my
0145—(KLS)
Rev.: $4,785,660
Assets: $5,414,558
Liabilities: $1,452,330
Net Worth: $3,962,228
Earnings: ($909,067)
Emp.: 46
Fiscal Year-end: 12/31/20
Holding Company; Technology, Business & Human Resource Management Consulting Services
N.A.I.C.S.: 551112
Rizal A. Rahman (Mng Dir)

Subsidiaries:

Comm Zed Sdn. Bhd. (1)
Block 4801-03-10 Level 3 CBD Perdana 1
Jalan Perdana, 63000, Cyberjaya, Selangor, Malaysia
Tel.: (60) 3 8318 8881
Web Site: http://www.commzed.com.my
Information Technology Consulting Services
N.A.I.C.S.: 541512

MBP Solutions Sdn. Bhd. (1)
No 6-1 Jalan Puteri 4/2, Bandar Puteri, Puchong, 47100, Selangor, Malaysia
Tel.: (60) 380600808
Web Site: https://www.tfp.com.my
Emp.: 80
Software Solutions Provider
N.A.I.C.S.: 513210

O2U Solutions Sdn. Bhd. (1)
No 8-2 Jalan Puteri 4/2 Bandar Puteri,
47100, Puchong, Selangor, Malaysia
Tel.: (60) 380600088
Web Site: http://www.tfp.com.my
Software Development Services
N.A.I.C.S.: 541511

Onecent Sdn. Bhd. (1)
Laman Informasi Nasihat dan Khidmat LINK
Ground Floor D Block, Jalan Dato Onn,
50480, Kuala Lumpur, Malaysia
Tel.: (60) 321741717
Web Site: https://onecent.my
Digital Payment Services
N.A.I.C.S.: 522320

ProDserv Sdn. Bhd. (1)
6-2 Jalan Puteri 4/2 Bandar Puteri, 47100,
Puchong, Selangor, Malaysia
Tel.: (60) 380600808
Web Site: http://www.tfp.com.my
Software Development Services
N.A.I.C.S.: 541511

SBOne Solutions Sdn. Bhd. (1)
Wisma LMS No 6 Jalan Abd Rahman Idris
Off Jalan Raja Muda Aziz, 50300, Kuala
Lumpur, Malaysia
Tel.: (60) 392130688
Web Site: https://www.tfp.co.my
Emp.: 20
Software Solutions Provider
N.A.I.C.S.: 513210
Tan Man Siang (Gen Mgr)

SoftFac Technology Sdn. Bhd. (1)
Bandar Puteri, 47100, Puchong, Malaysia
Tel.: (60) 3 8064 6388
Software Consulting Services
N.A.I.C.S.: 449210

Tech3 Solutions Sdn. Bhd. (1)
No 6-1 Jalan Puteri 4/2 Bandar Puteri Darul
Ehsan, 47100, Puchong, Selangor, Malaysia
Tel.: (60) 380600808
Web Site: http://www.tech3.tfp.com.my
Education Sector Services

N.A.I.C.S.: 611110
Chee Yan Sun (Dir-Consulting)

TG HOLDING AG
Gersthofer 29-31, Vienna, 1180, Austria
Tel.: (43) 14796858
Web Site: http://www.tg-holding.at
Investment Holding Company
N.A.I.C.S.: 551112
Josef Ehn (Chm-Supervisory Bd)

TG METALS LIMITED
Tel.: (61) 862115099
Web Site:
https://www.tgmetals.com.au
Year Founded: 2020
TG6—(ASX)
Assets: $3,440,220
Liabilities: $118,372
Net Worth: $3,321,848
Earnings: ($791,146)
Fiscal Year-end: 06/30/23
Metal Exploration Services
N.A.I.C.S.: 213114
David Selfe (CEO)

TG RESIDENTIAL VALUE PROPERTIES LTD.
Suite 123 - 119 West Pender Street,
Vancouver, V6B 1S5, BC, Canada
Tel.: (604) 558-2500 BC
Web Site: http://www.tgrez.com
Year Founded: 2011
Investment Services
N.A.I.C.S.: 523999
Douglas Thiessen (Pres & CEO)

TGA CO., LTD
604-605 Lattice Aoyama 1-2-6 Minami Aoyama, Minato-ku, Tokyo, Japan
Tel.: (81) 3 5772 1663
Web Site: http://www.tga-net.com
Year Founded: 2002
Rev.: $400,000,000
Emp.: 10
Information Technology Consulting Services
N.A.I.C.S.: 541618
Eijiro Imafuku (Pres)

TGB BANQUETS & HOTELS LIMITED
Plot No 380 S G Road Bodakdev,
Ahmedabad, 380054, Gujarat, India
Tel.: (91) 7926841000
Web Site:
https://www.thegrandbhagwati.com
TGBHOTELS—(NSE)
Rev.: $2,219,913
Assets: $22,332,697
Liabilities: $9,180,321
Net Worth: $13,152,376
Earnings: ($1,125,497)
Emp.: 77
Fiscal Year-end: 03/31/21
Restaurant & Hotel Operator
N.A.I.C.S.: 722511
Devanand Gurmukhdas Somani
(Exec Dir)

Subsidiaries:

Bhagwati Autocast Ltd. (1)
Survey No 816 Village Rajoda Near Bavla,
Ahmedabad, 382 220, India
Tel.: (91) 2714232283
Web Site: https://www.bhagwati.com
Rev.: $18,514,585
Assets: $8,164,391
Liabilities: $4,037,204
Net Worth: $4,127,187
Earnings: $925,712
Emp.: 70
Fiscal Year-end: 03/31/2023
Machine Casting & Molding Services
N.A.I.C.S.: 331523
Dinesh K. Sheth (CFO)

TGK-2
st Pyatnitskaya 6, Yaroslavl Region,
150003, Yaroslavl, 150003, Russia
Tel.: (7) 4852797977
Web Site: https://www.tgc-2.ru
Year Founded: 2005
TGKB—(MOEX)
Sales Range: Less than $1 Million
Eletric Power Generation Services
N.A.I.C.S.: 221118
Nadezhda Ivanovna Pinigina (Chm-Mgmt Bd, CEO, Gen Dir & Exec Dir)

TGLT S.A.
Miones Office Campus Minones,
CABA, 2177, Buenos Aires, Argentina
Tel.: (54) 1152525050
Web Site: https://www.tglt.com
Year Founded: 2004
Sales Range: $50-74.9 Million
Emp.: 65
Real Estate Development Services
N.A.I.C.S.: 531390
Alejandro Belio (COO)

TGS ASA
Askekroken 11, 277, Oslo, 0277, Norway
Tel.: (47) 22550400 NO
Web Site: https://www.tgs.com
Year Founded: 1998
TGSNF—(OTCQX)
Rev.: $794,297,000
Assets: $1,956,414,000
Liabilities: $680,838,000
Net Worth: $1,275,576,000
Earnings: $21,646,000
Emp.: 867
Fiscal Year-end: 12/31/23
Seismographic & Mapping Technologies
N.A.I.C.S.: 541360
Kristian Kuvaas Johansen (CEO)

Subsidiaries:

4C Offshore Ltd. (1)
Orbis Energy Centre Wilde Street,
Lowestoft, United Kingdom
Tel.: (44) 1502307037
Web Site: https://www.4coffshore.com
Renewable Energy Services
N.A.I.C.S.: 221114

Magseis Fairfield ASA (1)
Strandveien 50, N-1366, Lysaker,
Norway (75.4%)
Tel.: (47) 23368020
Web Site: http://www.magseisfairfield.com
Rev.: $193,391,000
Assets: $344,602,000
Liabilities: $152,129,000
Net Worth: $192,473,000
Earnings: ($19,650,000)
Emp.: 370
Fiscal Year-end: 12/31/2020
Geological Surveying
N.A.I.C.S.: 541360
Jan B. Gateman (Founder)

Subsidiary (Domestic):

Magseis Fairfield ASA (2)
Strandveien 50, 1366, Lysaker, Norway
Tel.: (47) 23368020
Web Site: http://www.magseisfairfield.com
Marine Acquisition Services
N.A.I.C.S.: 488330
Carel Hooijkaas (CEO)

Prediktor AS (1)
Habornveien 48b, Gamle, 1630, Fredrikstad, Norway
Tel.: (47) 95408000
Web Site: https://www.prediktor.com
Asset Management Services
N.A.I.C.S.: 523999

Spectrum ASA (1)
Karenlyst Alle 11, NO-0278, Oslo, Norway
Tel.: (47) 23014960
Web Site: http://www.spectrumasa.com
Rev.: $138,793,000
Assets: $312,357,000

TGS ASA

TGS ASA—(Continued)
Liabilities: $146,622,000
Net Worth: $165,735,000
Earnings: $18,905,000
Emp.: 158
Fiscal Year-end: 12/31/2018
Seismic Imaging
N.A.I.C.S.: 541360
Rune Eng *(Pres & CEO)*

Subsidiary (Non-US):

Spectrum ASB Pty limited (2)
105 St Georges Terrace, Perth, 6000, WA, Australia
Tel.: (61) 8 9322 3700
Web Site: http://www.spectrum.com
Emp.: 8
Seismic Geophysical Surveying Services
N.A.I.C.S.: 541360

Spectrum Geo Ltd (2)
Dukes Court Duke Street, Woking, GU21 5BH, Surrey, United Kingdom
Tel.: (44) 1483730201
Emp.: 70
Seismic Geophysical Surveying Services
N.A.I.C.S.: 541360

Subsidiary (US):

Spectrum Geo Inc (3)
16225 Park Ten Pl Ste 300, Houston, TX 77084
Tel.: (281) 647-0602
Emp.: 60
Seismic Geophysical Surveying Services
N.A.I.C.S.: 541360
Eddie Pharr *(VP-Bus Dev-North America)*

Subsidiary (Non-US):

Spectrum Geo Pte Ltd (2)
152 Beach Road Level 28 Gateway East, Singapore, 189721, Singapore
Tel.: (65) 6827 9773
Emp.: 1
Seismic Geophysical Surveying Services
N.A.I.C.S.: 541360
Deborah Lew *(VP)*

Spectrum Geo do Brasil Servicos Geofisicos LTDA (2)
Av Rio Branco 181 Sala 1802 Parte, 20040-007, Rio de Janeiro, Brazil
Tel.: (55) 21 9142 4822
Seismic Geophysical Surveying Services
N.A.I.C.S.: 541360

TGS AP Investments AS (1)
Lensmannslia 4, PO Box 154, Asker, 1386, Norway
Tel.: (47) 66769900
Web Site: http://www.tgs.com
Sales Range: $50-74.9 Million
Emp.: 40
Investment Management Service
N.A.I.C.S.: 523999

TGS Canada Corp. (1)
Suite 720 335 8th Ave SW, Calgary, T2P 1C9, AB, Canada
Tel.: (403) 781-1700
Surveying Services
N.A.I.C.S.: 541370

TGS do Brasil Ltda. (1)
Av Presidente Wilson No 23114o, Andar Sala 1404 Centro, Rio de Janeiro, 20030-021, Brazil
Tel.: (55) 2139953328
Surveying Services
N.A.I.C.S.: 541370

TGS-NOPEC Geophysical Company (UK) Limited (1)
Dukes Court Duke Street, Woking, GU21 5BH, United Kingdom (100%)
Tel.: (44) 1483762620
Web Site: http://www.tgs.com
Sales Range: $25-49.9 Million
Provider of Seismographic & Mapping Technologies for Oil Exploration
N.A.I.C.S.: 541360

TGS-NOPEC Geophysical Company L.P. (1)
10451 Clay Rd, Houston, TX 77041 (100%)
Tel.: (713) 860-2100
Web Site: http://www.tgs.com
Sales Range: $100-124.9 Million
Provider of Seismographic & Mapping Technologies for Oil Exploration
N.A.I.C.S.: 213112

Branch (Domestic):

TGS-NOPEC Geophysical Company (2)
10451 Clay Rd, Houston, TX 77041 (100%)
Tel.: (281) 319-4944
Web Site: http://www.tgsnopec.com
Sales Range: $100-124.9 Million
Emp.: 200
Provider of Seismographic & Mapping Technologies for Oil Exploration
N.A.I.C.S.: 518210

TGS-NOPEC Geophysical Company (2)
1010 Common St Ste 2040, New Orleans, LA 70112 (100%)
Tel.: (504) 524-3450
Web Site: http://www.a2d.com
Sales Range: $25-49.9 Million
Emp.: 9
Provider of Seismographic & Mapping Technologies for Oil Exploration
N.A.I.C.S.: 518210

TGS-NOPEC Geophysical Company Pty. Ltd. (1)
Level 9 220 St George's Terrace, 1100 Hay St, Perth, 6000, WA, Australia (100%)
Tel.: (61) 894800000
Web Site: http://www.tgsnopec.com
Sales Range: $25-49.9 Million
Emp.: 25
Provider of Seismographic & Mapping Technologies for Oil Exploration
N.A.I.C.S.: 541360

TGS DIS TICARET A.S.
Baglar mah Osmanpasa cad No 95 II Istanbul 34 Plaza A Blok Kat 9, Gunesli - Bagcilar, Istanbul, 34209, Turkiye
Tel.: (90) 212 644 58 58
Web Site: http://www.tgsas.com
Sales Range: $700-749.9 Million
Textile & Confectionary Exporter
N.A.I.C.S.: 424350
Cemil Evciman *(Mgr-Export)*

TGS ESPORTS, INC.
4211 No 3 Road, Richmond, V6X 2C3, BC, Canada
Tel.: (604) 562-0606
Web Site: https://tgsesports.gg
TGS—(TSXV)
Sales Range: Less than $1 Million
Sports Club Operator
N.A.I.C.S.: 711211
Spiro Khouri *(CEO)*

TGS INTERNATIONAL LTD.
Room 20 8/F Woon Lee Commercial Building 7-9 Austin Ave Tsim Sha Tsui, Kowloon, China (Hong Kong)
Tel.: (852) 2116 3863 NV
Year Founded: 2016
TGSI—(OTCIQ)
Rev.: $753,694
Assets: $5,049,767
Liabilities: $4,486,389
Net Worth: $563,378
Earnings: ($1,218,463)
Emp.: 40
Fiscal Year-end: 12/31/20
Plastic Product Mfr & Distr
N.A.I.C.S.: 325211
Chi Kin Loo *(Chm & Pres)*

TGV SRAAC LIMITED
40-304 2nd Floor Krishna Jyothsna Complex Bhagyanagar, Kurnool, 518004, AP, India
Tel.: (91) 8518289602
Web Site: https://www.tgvgroup.com
Year Founded: 1981
507753—(BOM)
Rev.: $139,038,258
Assets: $198,320,946
Liabilities: $115,027,062
Net Worth: $83,293,883
Earnings: $3,952,003
Emp.: 1,033
Fiscal Year-end: 03/31/21
Alkalies Chemical Products Mfr
N.A.I.C.S.: 325998
T. G. Venkateeh *(Co-Chm)*

Subsidiaries:

Brilliant Bio Pharma Private Limited (1)
6-2-1012 TGV Mansion 5th Floor, Khairatabad, Hyderabad, 500 004, India
Tel.: (91) 4066667464
Web Site: https://brilliantbiopharma.com
Animal Health Products Mfr
N.A.I.C.S.: 325412

Gowri Gopal Hospitals Private Ltd. (1)
46/87 Woodland Complex Budhawarpet, Kurnool, 518 002, Andhra Pradesh, India
Tel.: (91) 255499
Web Site: https://gghospitals.in
Health Care Srvices
N.A.I.C.S.: 621610

Lakshmi Venkatesh TG College of Nursing (1)
H No 43-267 New Sankal Bagh Behind Venkateshwara Swamy Temple, Kurnool, 518004, Andhra Pradesh, India
Tel.: (91) 9848994526
Web Site: https://lvtgnursing.com
Nursing College Services
N.A.I.C.S.: 611310

Lakshmi Venkatesh TG College of Physiotherapy (1)
H No 43-267 New Sankal Bagh Behind Venkateshwara Swamy Temple, Kurnool, 518004, Andhra Pradesh, India
Tel.: (91) 8518278224
Web Site: https://lvtgphysiotherapy.com
Physiotherapy College Services
N.A.I.C.S.: 611310

Nectar Laboratories Private Limited (1)
No 6-2-1012 3rd Floor TGV Mansion, Khairatabad, Hyderabad, 500 004, India
Tel.: (91) 9515819736
Web Site: https://www.nectarlabs.in
Pharmaceuticals Product Mfr
N.A.I.C.S.: 325412

Sree Maruthi Marine Industries Ltd. (1)
No 1/220 Kamaraj Street Kelambakkam, Kancheepuram Dist, Chennai, 603103, Tamil Nadu, India
Tel.: (91) 9940668365
Web Site: https://www.sreemaruthimarine.com
Marine Transportation Services
N.A.I.C.S.: 114119

Sree Rayalseema Galaxy Projects Private Ltd. (1)
40-304 2nd Floor Krishna Jyothsna Complex, Bhagyanagar, Kurnool, 518004, Andhra Pradesh, India
Tel.: (91) 8518289602
Non Ferric Aluminium Mfr
N.A.I.C.S.: 325211

TGW TRANSPORTGERATE GMBH
Collmannstrasse 2, 4600, Wels, 4600, Austria
Tel.: (43) 72424860 AT
Web Site: http://www.tgw.at
Sales Range: $150-199.9 Million
Emp.: 1,200
Logistics & Transportation Services
N.A.I.C.S.: 541614
Georg Kirchmayr *(Pres)*

Subsidiaries:

TGW Iberica Sistemas Logisticos S.L. (1)
Calle Frederic Mompou 5 7a Planta, E-08960, Barcelona, Sant Just Desvern, Spain
Tel.: (34) 93 480 93 89
Web Site: http://www.tgw-group.com
Industrial Machinery & Equipment Whslr
N.A.I.C.S.: 423830

TGW Italia Srl (1)
Stradello del Mulino 5, San Donnino, I-41100, Modena, Italy
Tel.: (39) 059783497
Web Site: http://www.tgw-italia.it
Engineeering Services
N.A.I.C.S.: 541330

TGW-Ermanco, Inc. (1)
6870 Grand Haven Rd, Spring Lake, MI 49456-9616
Tel.: (231) 798-4547
Web Site: http://www.tgw-group.com
Sales Range: $50-74.9 Million
Emp.: 200
Material Handling Systems & Equipment
N.A.I.C.S.: 333922
Tom Bergy *(Controller)*

TH HEAVY ENGINEERING BHD
Level 26 Menara Bank Islam No 22 Jalan Perak, 50450, Kuala Lumpur, Malaysia
Tel.: (60) 327879000
Web Site: http://www.thhe.com.my
7206—(KLS)
Rev.: $15,324,984
Assets: $66,942,940
Liabilities: $113,704,602
Net Worth: ($46,761,662)
Earnings: ($14,937,643)
Emp.: 108
Fiscal Year-end: 12/31/20
Engineeering Services
N.A.I.C.S.: 541330
Aziz Fadzir *(Chm)*

TH INTERNATIONAL LIMITED
2501 Central Plz 227 Huangpi N Rd, Shanghai, 200003, China
Tel.: (86) 021613666 Ky
Web Site: https://ir.timschina.com
THCH—(NASDAQ)
Holding Company
N.A.I.C.S.: 551112
Yongchen Lu *(CEO)*

TH. WITT KALTEMASCHINEN-FABRIK GMBH
Lukasstr 32, 52070, Aachen, Germany
Tel.: (49) 241182080 De
Web Site: http://www.th-witt.de
Year Founded: 1896
Sales Range: $10-24.9 Million
Refrigeration Components Mfr
N.A.I.C.S.: 333415
Monika Witt *(Co-Mng Dir & Head-Tech & Sls)*

THACHANG GREEN ENERGY PUBLIC COMPANY LIMITED
159 Moo 3, Tambon Tha Chang Amphoe Tha Chang, Surat Thani, 84150, Thailand
Tel.: (66) 77277790 TH
Web Site: https://www.tge.co.th
Year Founded: 2011
TGE—(THA)
Rev.: $26,443,314
Assets: $98,513,455
Liabilities: $30,506,030
Net Worth: $68,007,425
Earnings: $7,005,104
Emp.: 149
Fiscal Year-end: 12/31/23
Biomass Power Generation Services
N.A.I.C.S.: 221117
Patchara Tongprapi *(CFO)*

AND PRIVATE COMPANIES

THACKER & COMPANY LIMITED
Jatia Chambers 60 Dr V B Gandhi Marg Fort, Mumbai, 400 001, Maharashtra, India
Tel.: (91) 2230213333
Web Site: https://www.thacker.co.in
Year Founded: 1878
509945—(BOM)
Rev.: $760,962
Assets: $13,770,254
Liabilities: $141,382
Net Worth: $13,628,871
Earnings: $1,499,766
Emp.: 2
Fiscal Year-end: 03/31/23
Financial Investment Services
N.A.I.C.S.: 523999
Arun Kumar Jatia (Chm)

Subsidiaries:

Fujisan Technologies Limited (1)
Jatia Chambers 60 Dr V B GandhiMarg, Fort, Mumbai, 400001, MH, India
Tel.: (91) 9987567010
Web Site: https://www.fujisan.co.in
Printing Material Distr
N.A.I.C.S.: 424110

THAI AIRWAYS INTERNATIONAL PUBLIC COMPANY LIMITED
89 Vibhavadi Rangsit Road Chattuchak, Bangkok, 10900, Thailand
Tel.: (66) 25453691
Web Site: https://www.thaiairways.com
Year Founded: 1960
TAWNF—(OTCEM)
Rev.: $2,893,389,116
Assets: $5,449,982,654
Liabilities: $7,403,194,336
Net Worth: ($1,953,211,683)
Earnings: ($6,919,418)
Emp.: 21,367
Fiscal Year-end: 12/31/22
Commercial Airlines; Airport Restaurants & Hotels; Fueling Services
N.A.I.C.S.: 481111
Suvimol Bualerd (Exec VP-HR, Legal Mgmt & Gen Admin-Acting)

Subsidiaries:

THAI-Amadeus Southeast Asia Co., Ltd. (1)
No 89 Building 6 2nd Floor Vibhavadi Rangsit Road, Chomphon Sub-district Chatuchak District, Bangkok, 10900, Thailand (55%)
Tel.: (66) 2 207 9090
Web Site: https://www.thaiamadeus.com
Sales Range: $100-124.9 Million
Ticketing & Travel Services
N.A.I.C.S.: 561599

Thai Airways International Ltd. (1)
222 N Sepulveda Blvd Ste 1950, El Segundo, CA 90245
Tel.: (310) 640-0097
Web Site: http://www.thaiair.com
Sales Range: $25-49.9 Million
Emp.: 60
Airline Passenger & Freight Services
N.A.I.C.S.: 561599

Thai Smile Airways Co., Ltd. (1)
89 Vibhavadi Rangsit Road Jompol, Bangkok, 10900, Thailand
Tel.: (66) 21178824
Passenger & Cargo Air Transport Services
N.A.I.C.S.: 481211

THAI BEVERAGE PUBLIC COMPANY LIMITED
14 Vibhavadi Rangsit Road, Chomphon Sub-District Chatuchak District, Bangkok, 10900, Thailand
Tel.: (66) 27855555   TH
Web Site: https://www.thaibev.com
Year Founded: 2003
Y92—(OTCIQ)
Rev.: $7,771,368,286
Assets: $13,600,340,951
Liabilities: $6,958,363,859
Net Worth: $6,641,977,092
Earnings: $845,013,228
Fiscal Year-end: 09/30/23
Alcoholic Beverages Mfr
N.A.I.C.S.: 312120
Thapana Sirivadhanabhakdi (Vice Chm & Grp CEO)

Subsidiaries:

ASM Management Co., Ltd. (1)
14 Sangsom Building Vibhavadi Rangsit Road, Chomphon Sub-district Chatuchak District, Bangkok, 10900, Thailand
Tel.: (66) 27855555
Asset Management Services
N.A.I.C.S.: 523940

Asiaeuro International Beverage (Hong Kong) Limited (1)
7/F Hecny Tower 9 Chatham Road South, Tsim Sha Tsui, Kowloon, China (Hong Kong)
Tel.: (852) 39960332
Web Site: https://www.aibev.com.hk
Spirits Distr
N.A.I.C.S.: 424820

Bangkok Art Biennale Management Co., Ltd. (1)
57 Park Ventures Ecoplex Wireless Road, Lumpini Patumwan, Bangkok, 10330, Thailand
Tel.: (66) 27855555
Web Site: https://www.bkkartbiennale.com
Contemporary Art Services
N.A.I.C.S.: 712110
Apinan Poshyananda (CEO & Dir-)

Beer Chang Co., Ltd. (1)
15 Moo 14 Vibhavadi Rangsit Road, Chomphon Sub-district Chatuchak District, Bangkok, 10900, Thailand
Tel.: (66) 20785991
Beer Concentrate Mfr
N.A.I.C.S.: 312120

Beer Thai (1991) PCL (1)
15 Moo 14 Vibhavadi Rangsit Road, Chomphon Sub-District Chatuchak District, Bangkok, 10900, Thailand
Tel.: (66) 27855555
Web Site: http://www.thaibev.com
Beer Mfr
N.A.I.C.S.: 312120

Beer Thip Brewery (1991) Co., Ltd. (1)
15 Moo 14 Vibhavadi Rangsit Road, Chomphon Sub-District Chatuchak District, Bangkok, 10900, Thailand
Tel.: (66) 27855555
Web Site: http://www.thaibev.com
Beer Mfr
N.A.I.C.S.: 312120

BeerCo Limited (1)
Room 901-2 Silvercord Tower 1 30 Canton Road, Tsim Sha Tsui, Kowloon, China (Hong Kong)
Tel.: (852) 23756648
Alcoholic Beverage Mfr & Distr
N.A.I.C.S.: 312140

Best Spirits Company Limited (1)
Room 901-2 Silvercord Tower 1 30 Canton Road, Kowloon, China (Hong Kong)
Tel.: (852) 23756648
Web Site: https://www.bestspirits.com
Sales Range: $25-49.9 Million
Emp.: 25
Alcoholic Beverage Distr
N.A.I.C.S.: 424820

BevCo Limited (1)
14 Sangsom Building Vibhavadi Rangsit Road, Chomphon Sub-district Chatuchak District, Bangkok, 10900, Thailand
Tel.: (66) 27839100
Beverage Mfr & Distr
N.A.I.C.S.: 312120

BevTech Co., Ltd. (1)
14 Sangsom Building Vibhavadi Rangsit Road, Chomphon Sub-district Chatuchak District, Bangkok, 10900, Thailand
Tel.: (66) 27855555
Plastic Packaging Products Mfr
N.A.I.C.S.: 326112
Pisanu Vichiensanth (Vice Chm & Mng Dir)

Bistro Asia Co., Ltd. (1)
14 Sangsom Building Vibhavadi Rangsit Road, Chomphon Sub-district Chatuchak District, Bangkok, 10900, Thailand
Tel.: (66) 27855555
Restaurant Operators
N.A.I.C.S.: 722310

Blairmhor Limited (1)
Moffat Distillery, Airdrie, ML6 8PL, United Kingdom
Tel.: (44) 1236769377
Beverage Mfr & Distr
N.A.I.C.S.: 312120

Cash Van Management Co., Ltd. (1)
1 East Water Building 17th Floor Soi Vibhavadi Rangsit 5 Vibhavadi, Rangsit Road Chomphon Sub-district Chatuchak District, Bangkok, 10900, Thailand
Tel.: (66) 27855555
Beverage Distr
N.A.I.C.S.: 424810

Certu Systems Inc. (1)
251 Little Falls Dr New Castle County, Wilmington, DE 19808
Tel.: (412) 720-7414
Data Logistics Analytics Services
N.A.I.C.S.: 541614

Chang Corporation Company Limited (1)
14 Sangsom Building Vibhavadi Rangsit Road, Chomphon Sub-district Chatuchak District, Bangkok, 10900, Thailand
Tel.: (66) 20785991
Beverage Mfr & Distr
N.A.I.C.S.: 312120

Chang International Co., Ltd. (1)
62 8th 9th Floor Ratchadaphisek Road, Klongtoey Sub-District, Bangkok, 10110, Thailand
Tel.: (66) 20785991
Advertising & Marketing Promotion Services
N.A.I.C.S.: 541810

Charun Business 52 Co., Ltd. (1)
15 Soi Ya Sup 1 Vibhavadi Rangsit Road, Chomphon Sub-district Chatuchak District, Bangkok, 10900, Thailand
Tel.: (66) 27857151
Bricks Mfr
N.A.I.C.S.: 327331

Cosmos Brewery (Thailand) Co., Ltd. (1)
15 Moo 14 Vibhavadi Rangsit Road, Chomphon Sub-district Chatuchak District, Bangkok, 10900, Thailand
Tel.: (66) 27855555
Drinking Water Mfr
N.A.I.C.S.: 312112
Kanoknart Rangsithienchai (Chm)

D2C Services Co., Ltd. (1)
90 CW Tower Ratchadaphisek Road, Huai Khwang Sub-district, Bangkok, 10310, Thailand
Tel.: (66) 27688665
Ecommerce Services
N.A.I.C.S.: 541618

Dhospaak Co., Ltd. (1)
90 CW Tower 15th Floor Units B 1501-2 and 20th Floor Units B 2001-2, Ratchadaphisek Road Huai Khwang Sub-district, Bangkok, 10310, Thailand
Tel.: (66) 20182100
Advertising Agency Services
N.A.I.C.S.: 541810

Dongguan LiTeng Foods Co., Ltd. (1)
49G Level 3 Qingping Road, Qinghutou Tangxia Town, Dongguan, 523726, Guangdong, China
Tel.: (86) 76982099688
Coffee Product Distr
N.A.I.C.S.: 424490

Feed Addition Co., Ltd. (1)
15 Moo 14 Vibhavadi Rangsit Road, Chomphon Sub-district Chatuchak District, Bangkok, 10900, Thailand
Tel.: (66) 278571516
Feed & Fertilizer Distr
N.A.I.C.S.: 424910

Fraser & Neave Limited (1)
438 Alexandra Road 20-00 Alexandra Point, Singapore, 119958, Singapore (70.08%)
Tel.: (65) 63189393
Web Site: https://www.fraserandneave.com
Rev.: $1,555,467,210
Assets: $3,795,406,447
Liabilities: $1,274,022,971
Net Worth: $2,521,383,475
Earnings: $152,012,597
Emp.: 7,200
Fiscal Year-end: 09/30/2023
Holding Company
N.A.I.C.S.: 551112
Charoen Sirivadhanabhakdi (Chm)

Subsidiary (Domestic):

Alliance Graphics Pte. Ltd. (2)
438 Ang Mo Kio 03-02, Industrial Park 1, Singapore, 569619, Singapore
Tel.: (65) 63830814
Web Site: https://www.alliancegraphics.com.sg
Printing Services
N.A.I.C.S.: 323120
Lawrence Loh (Mng Dir)

Subsidiary (Non-US):

Everbest Printing Investment Limited (2)
10/F Block C Seaview Estate 2-8 Watson Road, North Point, China (Hong Kong)
Tel.: (852) 27274433
Web Site: https://www.everbest.com
Printing Services
N.A.I.C.S.: 323120
James Chung (Founder)

Subsidiary (Domestic):

F&N Creameries (S) Pte. Ltd. (2)
51 Quality Road, Singapore, 618813, Singapore
Tel.: (65) 62613133
Web Site: https://www.fnncreameries.com
Ice Cream Mfr
N.A.I.C.S.: 311520
Yeau Yin Lee (Gen Mgr)

F&N Foods Pte Ltd (2)
2 Tuas Link 3, Singapore, 639468, Singapore
Tel.: (65) 62108261
Web Site: https://www.fnnfoods.com
Emp.: 500
Beverage Mfr & Distr
N.A.I.C.S.: 312120
Jennifer See (Gen Mgr)

F&N Interflavine Pte Ltd (2)
214 Pandan Loop, Singapore, 128405, Singapore
Tel.: (65) 62760135
Beverages Mfr
N.A.I.C.S.: 312120

F&N Investments Pte Ltd (2)
438 Alexandra Road 20-00 Alexandra Point Queenstown, Singapore, 119958, Singapore
Tel.: (65) 63189393
Investment Management Service
N.A.I.C.S.: 523999

Subsidiary (Non-US):

Fraser & Neave Holdings Bhd (2)
No 1 Jalan Bukit Belimbing 26/38 Persiaran Kuala Selangor, Section 26, 40400, Shah Alam, Selangor, Malaysia (56.7%)
Tel.: (60) 351014288
Web Site: https://www.fn.com.my
Rev.: $1,088,670,229
Assets: $1,112,672,406
Liabilities: $383,111,888
Net Worth: $729,560,519
Earnings: $117,986,070
Emp.: 3,800
Fiscal Year-end: 09/30/2023
Soft Drinks Mfr
N.A.I.C.S.: 312111
Bendahara Perlis Badarudin Jamalullail (Chm)

THAI BEVERAGE PUBLIC COMPANY LIMITED

Thai Beverage Public Company Limited—(Continued)

Subsidiary (Non-US):

F&N Dairies (Thailand) Limited (3)
Park Building Room No 8W01-08 8th Floor No 88 Ratchadaphisek Road, Khlong Toei Subdistrict Khlong Toei District, Bangkok, 10110, Thailand
Tel.: (66) 28216988
Food & Beverage Product Mfr
N.A.I.C.S.: 311999
Suchit Riewcharoon *(Mng Dir)*

Subsidiary (Non-US):

Marshall Cavendish Education Chile SpA (2)
Los Militares 5001 of 1301, Las Condes, Santiago, Chile
Tel.: (56) 229295531
Web Site: https://www.mceducation.cl
Educational Support Services
N.A.I.C.S.: 611710
Viviana Lopez *(Project Mgr)*

Subsidiary (Domestic):

Marshall Cavendish Education Pte. Ltd. (2)
No 1 New Industrial Road, Singapore, 536196, Singapore
Tel.: (65) 62139688
Web Site: https://www.mceducation.com
Educational Support Services
N.A.I.C.S.: 611710
Joy Tan *(Gen Mgr)*

Print Lab Pte. Ltd. (2)
438 Ang Mo Kio 03-02, Industrial Park 1, Singapore, 569619, Singapore
Tel.: (65) 67490526
Web Site: https://www.printlab.com.sg
Emp.: 100
Printing Services
N.A.I.C.S.: 323120
Muralikrishnan Rangan *(Founder & CEO)*

Times Publishing Limited (2)
1 New Industrial Road, Singapore, 536196, Singapore
(100%)
Tel.: (65) 62139288
Web Site: https://www.timespublishing.sg
Emp.: 2,000
Publishing, Printing, Retailing, Distribution, Education, Conferences & Exhibitions
N.A.I.C.S.: 513130

Subsidiary (Non-US):

Everbest Printing (Guangzhou) Co. Ltd (3)
334 Huanshi South Road, Nansha Panyu, Guangzhou, 511458, Guangdong, China
Tel.: (86) 2084981812
Commercial Printing Services
N.A.I.C.S.: 323111

Everbest Printing Holdings Limited (3)
Rm 5 10/F Ko Fai Indl Bldg Blk C 7 Ko Fai Rd Yau Tong, Kowloon, China (Hong Kong)
Tel.: (852) 27274433
Sales Range: $25-49.9 Million
Emp.: 40
Commercial Printing Services
N.A.I.C.S.: 323111

Far East Publications Ltd (3)
253 Asoke Building 16th Floor No 253 Sukhumvit 21 Road, Khlong Toei Nuea Sub-district Watthana District, Bangkok, 10110, Thailand
Tel.: (66) 2261190811
Web Site: https://www.fareastpublications.co.th
Reference Books Distr
N.A.I.C.S.: 424920

Subsidiary (Domestic):

JCS Digital Solutions Pte Ltd (3)
Times Centre 1 New Industrial Road, Singapore, 536196, Singapore
Tel.: (65) 62139611
Web Site: http://www.jcs.com.sg
Digital Printing Services
N.A.I.C.S.: 323111
Jason Chia *(Gen Mgr)*

MC Online Pte Ltd (3)
1 New Industrial Road, Times Centre, Singapore, 536196, Singapore
Tel.: (65) 6285 8616
Web Site: http://www.lead.com.sg
Educational Support Services
N.A.I.C.S.: 611710

Subsidiary (Non-US):

Marshall Cavendish (Malaysia) Sdn Bhd (3)
Lot 46 Subang Hi-Tech Industrial Park, Batu Tiga, 40000, Shah Alam, Selangor Darul Ehsan, Malaysia
(100%)
Tel.: (60) 356286888
Sales Range: $100-124.9 Million
Emp.: 300
Book Publishers
N.A.I.C.S.: 513130

Marshall Cavendish Business Information (Hong Kong) Limited (3)
10/F Block C Seaview Estate 2-8 Watson Road, North Point, China (Hong Kong)
Tel.: (852) 39657800
Business Support Services
N.A.I.C.S.: 561499

Subsidiary (US):

Marshall Cavendish Corporation (3)
99 White Plains Rd, Tarrytown, NY 10591-9001
(100%)
Tel.: (914) 332-8888
Web Site: http://www.marshallcavendish.us
Sales Range: $25-49.9 Million
Emp.: 30
Book & Magazine Publisher
N.A.I.C.S.: 513130

Subsidiary (Domestic):

Marshall Cavendish International (S) Pte Ltd (3)
1 New Industrial Road Times Centre, Singapore, 536196, Singapore
(100%)
Tel.: (65) 62139300
Sales Range: $150-199.9 Million
Emp.: 550
Books & Magazine Publisher
N.A.I.C.S.: 513140

Subsidiary (Non-US):

Musicway Corporation Ltd. (3)
Unit 8 29 Business Park Dr, Nottinghill, Melbourne, 3168, VIC, Australia
(100%)
Tel.: (61) 395589666
Web Site: http://www.musicway.com.au
Sales Range: $25-49.9 Million
Emp.: 15
Electronics Distr
N.A.I.C.S.: 513130
Ryan Connolly *(Gen Mgr)*

Subsidiary (Domestic):

Pansing Distribution Pte Ltd (3)
438 Ang Mo Kio Industrial Park 1 Level 1, Singapore, 569619, Singapore
(100%)
Tel.: (65) 67157300
Web Site: https://www.pansingmag.com.sg
Sales Range: $25-49.9 Million
Emp.: 50
Book Distr
N.A.I.C.S.: 333248

Subsidiary (Non-US):

Pansing Marketing Sdn Bhd (3)
Lot 557A & B Jalan Subang 3 Subang Jaya Industrial Estate, 47610, Subang Jaya, Selangor, Malaysia
Tel.: (60) 356310794
Emp.: 13
Book Distr
N.A.I.C.S.: 424920
Bala Rajoo *(Sr Mgr)*

STP Distributors (M) Sdn Bhd (3)
Lot 46 Subang Hi-Tech Industrial Park, Batu Tiga, Shah Alam, 40000, Selangor Darul Ehsan, Malaysia
(30%)
Tel.: (60) 356286888
Sales Range: $25-49.9 Million
Emp.: 2
Book Distr
N.A.I.C.S.: 513130
Vivian Cheng *(Gen Mgr)*

Subsidiary (Domestic):

Times Educational Services Pte Ltd (3)
11 Unity St, 02-14 15 Robertson Walk, Singapore, 237995, Singapore
(100%)
Tel.: (65) 68350355
Web Site: http://www.tes.edu.sg
Sales Range: $25-49.9 Million
Emp.: 20
Educational Publisher
N.A.I.C.S.: 513130

Subsidiary (Non-US):

Times Offset (Malaysia) Sdn Bhd (3)
Times Subang Bangunan Times Publishing Lot 46, Subang Hi-Tech Industrial Park Batu Tiga, 40000, Shah Alam, Selangor Darul Ehsan, Malaysia
(100%)
Tel.: (60) 356286888
Sales Range: $50-74.9 Million
Emp.: 170
Printing Services
N.A.I.C.S.: 513130

Subsidiary (Domestic):

Times Printers Pte Ltd (3)
18 Tuas Avenue 5, Singapore, 639342, Singapore
(100%)
Tel.: (65) 63112888
Sales Range: $75-99.9 Million
Emp.: 1,400
Magazines, Periodicals, Directories & Show Dailies Printing Services
N.A.I.C.S.: 333248

Subsidiary (Non-US):

Times Publishing (Hong Kong) Limited (3)
9/F Block C Seaview Estate 2-8 Watson Road North Point, Hong Kong, China (Hong Kong)
Tel.: (852) 24811930
Web Site: http://www.tpl.hk
Publishing, Retail & Distribution Services
N.A.I.C.S.: 513130

Subsidiary (Domestic):

Times The Bookshop Pte Ltd (3)
438 Ang Mo Kio Industrial Park 1 #02-02 Ang Mo Kio Avenue 10, Singapore, 569619, Singapore
Tel.: (65) 64591355
Web Site: http://www.timesbookstores.com.sg
Book Retailer
N.A.I.C.S.: 459210

Subsidiary (Non-US):

Warburg Vending Malaysia Sdn. Bhd. (2)
2nd Floor Wisma Texchem Lots 808 & 809 Jalan Subang 5, Taman Perindustrian Subang, 47610, Subang Jaya, Selangor, Malaysia
Tel.: (60) 128904123
Web Site: https://warburgvending.com.my
Welding Machine Distr
N.A.I.C.S.: 445132

Subsidiary (Domestic):

Warburg Vending Pte. Ltd. (2)
2 Tuas Link 3, Singapore, 639468, Singapore
Tel.: (65) 65657895
Web Site: https://www.warburgvending.com.sg
Welding Machine Distr
N.A.I.C.S.: 445132
Keng Yuen Chew *(Bus Mgr)*

Subsidiary (Non-US):

Yoke Food Industries Sdn. Bhd. (2)
PLO 183 Jalan Cyber 9, Taman Perindustrian Senai IV, 81400, Senai, Johor, Malaysia
Tel.: (60) 72881331
Web Site: https://www.yokefood.com
Food Products Mfr
N.A.I.C.S.: 311999
Wei Tung Lim *(Head-Fin)*

Fuengfuanant Co., Ltd. (1)
333 Moo 1 Tambon Tha Toom, Amphoe Si

INTERNATIONAL PUBLIC

Maha Phot, Prachin Buri, 25140, Thailand
Tel.: (66) 37285016
Web Site: http://www.thaibev.com
Alcoholic Beverages Mfr
N.A.I.C.S.: 312140

Grand Royal Group International Company Limited (1)
No 33 Pyay Road 6 1/2 miles 11 Quarter, Hlaing Township, Yangon, MYANMAR
Tel.: (95) 1654938
Web Site: https://www.grandroyal-group.com
Beverage Mfr & Distr
N.A.I.C.S.: 312120
Ueychai Tantha-Obhas *(Co-Chm)*

Great Brands Limited (1)
Room 90-12 Silvercord Tower 1 30 Canton Road, Tsim Sha Tsui, Kowloon, China (Hong Kong)
Tel.: (852) 23756648
Brand Management Services
N.A.I.C.S.: 541613

Havi Food Distribution (Thailand) Co., Ltd. (1)
363 Moo 17 Bangna-Trad Road km 23, Tambon Bangsaothong, Bang Sao Thong, 10570, Samut Prakan, Thailand
Tel.: (66) 20238989
Public Cold Storage Services
N.A.I.C.S.: 493120

Horeca Management Co., Ltd. (1)
15 Moo 14 Vibhavadi Rangsit Road, Chomphon Sub-district Chatuchak District, Bangkok, 10900, Thailand
Tel.: (66) 27855555
Beverage Distr
N.A.I.C.S.: 424810

InterBev (Cambodia) Co., Ltd (1)
No 01 Street 484 Corner 97 Sangkat Psar Deum Tkov, Khan Chamkamon, Phnom Penh, Cambodia
Tel.: (855) 23727424
Beverages Mfr
N.A.I.C.S.: 312140

InterBev (Singapore) Limited (1)
No 438 Alexandra Road 05-01 Alexandra point, Singapore, 119958, Singapore
Tel.: (65) 64352880
Web Site: http://www.interbevgroup.com
Emp.: 30
Alcoholic Beverage Distr
N.A.I.C.S.: 424820

InterBev Malaysia Sdn. Bhd. (1)
Unit 30-01 Level 30 Tower A Vertical Business Suite Avenue 3, Bangsar South No 8 Jalan Kerinchi, 59200, Kuala Lumpur, Selangor, Malaysia
Tel.: (60) 386017181
Beverage Mfr & Distr
N.A.I.C.S.: 312120

International Beverage Holdings (China) Limited (1)
Room 901-2 Silvercord Tower 30 Canton Road, Tsim Tsa Tsui, Kowloon, China (Hong Kong)
Tel.: (852) 23756648
Web Site: http://www.thaibev.com
Sales Range: $50-74.9 Million
Emp.: 11
Investment Management Service
N.A.I.C.S.: 523999

Subsidiary (Non-US):

InterBev Trading (China) Limited (2)
Room 01-03 Level 1 No 63 Kunluo Road, Shuangjiang Town Eshan County, Yuxi, 653200, Yunnan, China
Tel.: (86) 8774010319
Web Site: http://www.thaibev.com
Alcoholic Beverage Distr
N.A.I.C.S.: 325193

International Beverage Holdings (Singapore) Pte Limited (1)
438 Alexandra Road 05-01 Alexandra Point, Singapore, 119958, Singapore
Tel.: (65) 64352880
Beverage Mfr & Distr
N.A.I.C.S.: 312120

International Beverage Holdings (UK) Limited (1)

7590

AND PRIVATE COMPANIES — THAI BEVERAGE PUBLIC COMPANY LIMITED

Moffat Distillery, Airdrie, ML6 8PL, Lanarkshire, United Kingdom
Tel.: (44) 1236769377
Web Site: https://www.interbevgroup.com
Sales Range: $50-74.9 Million
Emp.: 184
Alcoholic Beverages Mfr
N.A.I.C.S.: 325193

Subsidiary (Domestic):

Inver House Distillers Limited (2)
Moffat Distillery, Airdrie, ML6 8FU, Lanarkshire, United Kingdom
Tel.: (44) 1236769377
Web Site: http://www.inverhouse.com
Sales Range: $50-74.9 Million
Emp.: 150
Alcoholic Beverages Mfr
N.A.I.C.S.: 325193

International Beverage Holdings Limited USA, Inc. (1)
309 4th Ave Ste 200, San Francisco, CA 94118
Tel.: (415) 292-4770
Web Site: http://www.interbevgroup.com
Sales Range: $50-74.9 Million
Emp.: 7
Alcoholic Beverage Distr
N.A.I.C.S.: 424820

International Beverage Vietnam Company Limited (1)
11th Floor IDMC My Dinh Building No 15 Pham Hung Street, My Dinh 2 Ward Nam Tu Liem District, Hanoi, Vietnam
Tel.: (84) 2471089898
Beverage Distr
N.A.I.C.S.: 424820

Inver House Distillers (ROI) Ltd. (1)
Moffat Distillery Roughrigg Rd, Airdrie, ML6 8FU, Lanarkshire, United Kingdom
Tel.: (44) 123 676 9377
Beverage Mfr & Distr
N.A.I.C.S.: 312120

Kanchanasingkorn Co., Ltd. (1)
14 Vibhavadi Rangsit Road, Chomphon Sub-district Chatuchak District, Bangkok, 10900, Thailand
Tel.: (66) 22784321
Beverage Distr
N.A.I.C.S.: 424810

Luckchai Liquor Trading Co., Ltd. (1)
46 Moo 1 Tambon Nong Klang Na, Muang District, Ratchaburi, 70000, Thailand
Tel.: (66) 32313611
Alcoholic Beverage Distr
N.A.I.C.S.: 424820

Max Asia Co., Ltd. (1)
14 Sangsom Building Vibhavadi Rangsit Road, Chomphon Sub-district Chatuchak District, Bangkok, 10900, Thailand
Tel.: (66) 27855555
Bakery Products Mfr
N.A.I.C.S.: 311812

Mekhong Distillery Limited (1)
14 Vibhavadi Rangsit Road, Chomphon Sub-district Chatuchak District, Bangkok, 10900, Thailand
Tel.: (66) 22784321
Thai Spiced Rum Mfr
N.A.I.C.S.: 311942

Modern Trade Management Co., Ltd. (1)
333 Lao Peng Nguan Tower 1 26th Floor Soi Choei Phuang Vibhavadi, Rangsit Road Chomphon Sub-district Chatuchak District, Bangkok, 10900, Thailand
Tel.: (66) 27857878
Beverage Distr
N.A.I.C.S.: 424810

Mongkolsamai Co., Ltd. (1)
14 Vibhavadi Rangsit Road, Chomphon Sub-District Chatuchak District, Bangkok, 10900, Thailand
Tel.: (66) 22784321
Alcoholic Beverages Mfr
N.A.I.C.S.: 312120

Myanmar Supply Chain & Marketing Services Co., Ltd. (1)
33 61/2 Miles Pyay Road 11 Quarter, Hlaing Township, Yangon, Myanmar
Tel.: (95) 1654938
Logistic Services
N.A.I.C.S.: 541614
Ueychai Tantha-Obhas (Chm)

Nam Kijjakarn Co., Ltd. (1)
383 Moo 8 Tambon Banpo, Amphoe Muang, Nakhon Ratchasima, 30310, Thailand
Tel.: (66) 449551003
Web Site: http://www.thaibev.com
Alcoholic Beverage Distr
N.A.I.C.S.: 424820

Nam Muang Co., Ltd. (1)
16/2 Moo 1 U Thong Road Tambon Tha Wasukri, Amphoe Phra Nakhon, Ayutthaya, 13000, Thailand
Tel.: (66) 35242691
Web Site: http://www.thaibev.com
Alcoholic Beverage Distr
N.A.I.C.S.: 424820

Nam Palang Co., Ltd. (1)
22/1 Soi 2 Paprao Paprao Road Tambon Padad, Amphoe Muang, Chiang Mai, 50100, Chiangmai, Thailand
Tel.: (66) 53275211
Web Site: http://www.thaibev.com
Alcoholic Beverage Distr
N.A.I.C.S.: 424820

Nam Thurakij Co., Ltd. (1)
50/40-41 Moo 3 Sukhumvit Road Tambon Ban Suan, Amphoe Muang, Chon Buri, 20000, Thailand
Tel.: (66) 38287268
Alcoholic Beverage Distr
N.A.I.C.S.: 424820

Namjai ThaiBev (Social Enterprise) Co., Ltd. (1)
14 Sangsom Building Vibhavadi Rangsit Road, Chomphon Sub-district Chatuchak District, Bangkok, 10900, Thailand
Tel.: (66) 27855555
Social Enterprise Services
N.A.I.C.S.: 813410

Nateechai Co., Ltd. (1)
14 Vibhavadi Rangsit Road, Chomphon Sub-District Chatuchak District, Bangkok, 10900, Thailand
Tel.: (66) 22784321
Web Site: http://www.thaibev.com
Alcoholic Beverages Mfr
N.A.I.C.S.: 312140

Num Kijjakarn Co., Ltd. (1)
383 Moo 8, Tambon Ban Pho Amphoe Muang, Nakhon Ratchasima, 30310, Thailand
Tel.: (66) 449551003
Beverage Distr
N.A.I.C.S.: 424810

Num Muang Co., Ltd. (1)
16/2 Moo 1 U Thong Road, Tambon Tha Wasukri Amphoe, Phra Nakhon Si Ayutthaya, 13000, Thailand
Tel.: (66) 35241678
Beverage Distr
N.A.I.C.S.: 424810

Num Nakorn Co., Ltd. (1)
149/3 Chulachomklao Road Tambon Tha Kham, Amphoe Phun Phin, Surat Thani, 84130, Thailand
Tel.: (66) 77914242
Web Site: http://www.thaibev.com
Alcoholic Beverage Distr
N.A.I.C.S.: 424820

Num Palang Co., Ltd. (1)
22/1 Soi 2 Paprao Paprao Road, Tambon Padad Amphoe Muang Chiangma, Chiang Mai, 50100, Thailand
Tel.: (66) 532049534
Beverage Distr
N.A.I.C.S.: 424810

Num Thurakij Co., Ltd. (1)
123/23 Moo 2, Tambon Ban Suan Amphoe Muang, Chon Buri, 20000, Thailand
Tel.: (66) 382872689
Beverage Distr
N.A.I.C.S.: 424810

Num Yuk Co., Ltd. (1)
40/53 Moo 3, Talad Bangkhen Sub-district Laksi District, Bangkok, 10210, Thailand
Tel.: (66) 27857443
Beverage Distr
N.A.I.C.S.: 424810

Numrungrod Co., Ltd. (1)
439 Moo 11 Tambon Muang Kao, Amphoe Muang, Khon Kaen, 40000, Thailand
Tel.: (66) 43224222
Web Site: http://www.thaibev.com
Alcoholic Beverage Distr
N.A.I.C.S.: 424820

Numthip Co., Ltd. (1)
85/33 85/34 Petchakasem Road Tambon Na-Muang, Amphoe Muang, Ratchaburi, 70000, Thailand
Tel.: (66) 32312772
Web Site: http://www.thaibev.com
Alcoholic Beverage Distr
N.A.I.C.S.: 424820

Oishi F&B (Singapore) Pte. Ltd. (1)
438 Alexandra Road 05-01 Alexandra Point, Singapore, 119958, Singapore
Tel.: (65) 64352880
Brand Management Services
N.A.I.C.S.: 541613

Oishi Food Services Co., Ltd. (1)
Unit B3601 36th Floor No 90 CW Tower Ratchadapisek Road, Huai Khwang Sub-district Huai Khwang District, Bangkok, 10310, Thailand
Tel.: (66) 27688888
Food Products Distr
N.A.I.C.S.: 424490

Oishi Group Public Company Limited (1)
36th Floor CW Tower Ratchadapisek Road, Huai Khwang, Bangkok, 10310, Thailand **(98.5%)**
Tel.: (66) 27688888
Web Site: http://www.oishigroup.com
Rev.: $426,578,123
Assets: $350,811,599
Liabilities: $85,336,022
Net Worth: $265,475,577
Earnings: $39,941,022
Emp.: 6,458
Fiscal Year-end: 09/30/2022
Restaurant Operators
N.A.I.C.S.: 721110
Nongnuch Buranasetkul (Pres & CEO)

Oishi Trading Co., Ltd. (1)
Unit B3601 36th Floor No 90 CW Tower Ratchadapisek Road, Huai Khwang Sub-district Huai Khwang District, Bangkok, 10310, Thailand
Tel.: (66) 27688888
Beverage Mfr & Distr
N.A.I.C.S.: 312120

Pan International (Thailand) Co., Ltd. (1)
15 Moo 14 Vibhavadi Rangsit Road, Chomphon Sub-District Chatuchak District, Bangkok, 10900, Thailand
Tel.: (66) 27857000
Industrial Equipment Distr
N.A.I.C.S.: 423830

PomKlung Co., Ltd. (1)
22/1 Soi 2 Paprao Paprao Road Tambon Padad, Amphoe Muang, Chiang Mai, 50100, Thailand
Tel.: (66) 53275211
Web Site: http://www.thaibev.com
Beer Mfr
N.A.I.C.S.: 312120

Pomburapa Co., Ltd. (1)
51/42 Moo 3 Sukhumvit Road Tambon Ban Suan, Amphoe Muang, Chon Buri, 20000, Thailand
Tel.: (66) 38287268
Web Site: http://www.thaibev.com
Beer Mfr
N.A.I.C.S.: 312120

Pomcharoen Co., Ltd. (1)
135/3 Moo 4 Kanchanavithi Road Tambon Bang Kung, Amphoe Muang, Surat Thani, 84000, Thailand
Tel.: (66) 77914242
Web Site: http://www.thaibev.com
Beer Mfr
N.A.I.C.S.: 312120

Pomchok Co., Ltd. (1)
16/1 Moo 1 U Thong Road Tambon Tha Wasukri, Amphoe Phra Nakhon, Ayutthaya, 13000, Thailand
Tel.: (66) 35241032
Web Site: http://www.thaibev.com
Beer Mfr
N.A.I.C.S.: 312120

Pomkit Co., Ltd. (1)
383 Moo 8 Tambon Banpo, Amphoe Muang, Nakhon Ratchasima, 30310, Thailand
Tel.: (66) 44955101
Web Site: http://www.thaibev.com
Beer Mfr
N.A.I.C.S.: 312120

Pomnakorn Co., Ltd. (1)
85/35 85/36 Petchakasem Road Tambon Na-Muang, Amphoe Muang, Ratchaburi, 70000, Thailand
Tel.: (66) 323127724
Beer Mfr
N.A.I.C.S.: 312120

Pompalang Co., Ltd. (1)
6 Moo 15 Tambon Sila, Amphoe Muang, Khon Kaen, 40000, Khon Kaen, Thailand
Tel.: (66) 43407081
Soda Water Distr
N.A.I.C.S.: 424490

Pomthip (2012) Co., Ltd. (1)
40/53 Moo 3, Talad Bangkhen Sub-district Laksi District, Bangkok, 10210, Thailand
Tel.: (66) 27857441
Soda Water Distr
N.A.I.C.S.: 424490

S.S. Karnsura Co., Ltd. (1)
101 Moo 8 Tambon Kaeng Dom, Amphoe Sawang Wirawong, Ubon Ratchathani, 34190, Thailand
Tel.: (66) 45426532
Web Site: http://www.thaibev.com
Alcoholic Beverages Mfr
N.A.I.C.S.: 325193

SPM Foods and Beverages Co., Ltd. (1)
79 Moo 3 Tambon Lumlookbua, Amphoe Dontoom, Nakhon Pathom, 73150, Thailand
Tel.: (66) 34993355
Food & Beverage Whslr
N.A.I.C.S.: 424420
Karn Jitrawimon (Mng Dir)

Sangsom Co., Ltd. (1)
14 Vibhavadi Rangsit Road, Chomphon Sub-District Chatuchak District, Bangkok, 10900, Thailand
Tel.: (66) 22784321
Web Site: http://www.thaibev.com
Alcoholic Beverages Mfr
N.A.I.C.S.: 312140

Sermsuk Beverage Co., Ltd. (1)
No 90 CW Tower 31st-32nd Floor Ratchadapisek Road, Huai Khwang Sub-district Huai Khwang District, Bangkok, 10310, Thailand
Tel.: (66) 27839000
Beverage Mfr & Distr
N.A.I.C.S.: 312120

Sermsuk Training Co., Ltd. (1)
90 CW Tower 31st-32nd Floor Ratchadapisek Road, Huai Khwang Sub-district Huai Khwang District, Bangkok, 10310, Thailand
Tel.: (66) 27839000
Human Resource Development Services
N.A.I.C.S.: 541612

Simathurakij Co., Ltd. (1)
1 Moo 6 Tambon Ban Daen, Amphoe Banphot Phisai, Nakhon Sawan, 60180, Thailand
Tel.: (66) 56279088
Web Site: http://www.thaibev.com
Alcoholic Beverages Mfr
N.A.I.C.S.: 325193

So Water Co., Ltd. (1)
14 Sangsom Building Vibhavadi Rangsit Road, Chomphon Sub-district Chatuchak District, Bangkok, 10900, Thailand
Tel.: (66) 27839100
Alcoholic Beverage Mfr & Distr
N.A.I.C.S.: 312140

THAI BEVERAGE PUBLIC COMPANY LIMITED

Thai Beverage Public Company Limited—(Continued)

Subsidiary (Domestic):

SermSuk Public Company Limited (2)
No 90 CW Tower 31st - 32nd Floor Ratchadapisek Road Huai Khwang Sub-District, Huai Khwang District, Bangkok, 10310, Thailand (99.19%)
Tel.: (66) 27839000
Web Site: http://www.sermsukplc.com
Emp.: 100
Beverage Mfr & Distr
N.A.I.C.S.: 312111

Sub Permpoon 8 Co., Ltd. (1)
15 Moo 14 Vibhavadi Rangsit Road, Chomphon Sub-district Chatuchak District, Bangkok, 10900, Thailand
Tel.: (66) 22784321
Property Development Services
N.A.I.C.S.: 531390

Sura Piset Thipparat Co., Ltd. (1)
14 Sangsom Building Soi Yasoob 1 Vibhavadi Rangsit Road, Chomphon Sub-district Chatuchak District, Bangkok, 10900, Thailand
Tel.: (66) 22784321
Beverage Distr
N.A.I.C.S.: 424810

Thai Beverage Brands Co., Ltd. (1)
15 Moo 14 Vibhavadi Rangsit Road, Chomphon Sub-district Chatuchak District, Bangkok, 10900, Thailand
Tel.: (66) 27855555
Trademark Licensing Services
N.A.I.C.S.: 533110

Thai Beverage Energy Co., Ltd. (1)
15 Moo 14 Vibhavadi Rangsit Road, Chomphon Sub-district Chatuchak District, Bangkok, 10900, Thailand
Tel.: (66) 27857000
Biogas Mfr
N.A.I.C.S.: 325120

Thai Beverage Marketing Co., Ltd. (1)
15 Moo 14 Vibhavadi Rangsit Road, Chomphon Sub-district Chatuchak District, Bangkok, 10900, Thailand
Tel.: (66) 27855555
Advertising & Marketing Promotion Services
N.A.I.C.S.: 541810

Thai Beverage Recycle Co., Ltd. (1)
15 Moo 14 Vibhavadi Rangsit Road, Chomphon Sub-District Chatuchak District, Bangkok, 10900, Thailand
Tel.: (66) 27857030
Web Site: http://www.thaibev.com
Bottles Whslr
N.A.I.C.S.: 423840

Thai Beverage Training Co., Ltd. (1)
14 Vibhavadi Rangsit Road, Chomphon Sub-district Chatuchak District, Bangkok, 10900, Thailand
Tel.: (66) 20785995
Alcoholic Beverage Mfr & Distr
N.A.I.C.S.: 312140

Thai Cooperage Co., Ltd. (1)
15 Moo 14 Vibhavadi Rangsit Road, Chomphon Sub-district Chatuchak District, Bangkok, 10900, Thailand
Tel.: (66) 27855555
Oak Barrel Mfr
N.A.I.C.S.: 332439

Thai Drinks Co., Ltd. (1)
14 Sangsom Building Vibhavadi Rangsit Road, Chomphon Sub-district Chatuchak District, Bangkok, 10900, Thailand
Tel.: (66) 27839100
Beverage Distr
N.A.I.C.S.: 424820

Thai Molasses Co., Ltd. (1)
14 Vibhavadi Rangsit Road, Chomphon Sub-District Chatuchak District, Bangkok, 10900, Thailand
Tel.: (66) 27857140
Web Site: http://www.thaibev.com
Molasses Whslr
N.A.I.C.S.: 424490

Thai Thum Distillery Co., Ltd. (1)
14 Vibhavadi Rangsit Road, Chomphon Sub-district Chatuchak District, Bangkok, 10900, Thailand
Tel.: (66) 22784321
Spirit Mfr & Distr
N.A.I.C.S.: 312140

Thanapakdi Co., Ltd. (1)
315 Moo 4 Tambon Mae Faek, Amphoe San Sai, Chiang Mai, 50290, Thailand
Tel.: (66) 53849550
Web Site: http://www.thaibev.com
Alcoholic Beverages Mfr
N.A.I.C.S.: 312140

The Serm Suk Public Company Limited
No 90 CW Tower 31st 32nd Floor Ratchadapisek Road Huai Khwang Sub-district, Huai Khwang District, Bangkok, 10310, Thailand (64.7%)
Tel.: (66) 27839000
Web Site: https://www.sermsukplc.com
Rev.: $367,605,037
Assets: $411,032,222
Liabilities: $132,149,426
Net Worth: $278,882,796
Earnings: $7,239,627
Emp.: 5,329
Fiscal Year-end: 09/30/2023
Carbonated Soft Drinks Mfr & Distr
N.A.I.C.S.: 312111
Thapana Sirivadhanabhakdi (Vice Chm)

Thipchalothorn Co., Ltd. (1)
62 ThaiBev Quarter Building 9th Floor Ratchadapisek Road, Khlong Toei Sub-district Khlong Toei District, Bangkok, 10110, Thailand
Tel.: (66) 20785887
Non Alcoholic Beverage Distr
N.A.I.C.S.: 424820

Traditional Trade Management Co., Ltd. (1)
14 Vibhavadi Rangsit Road, Chomphon Sub-district Chatuchak District, Bangkok, 10900, Thailand
Tel.: (66) 27857878
Non Alcoholic Beverage Distr
N.A.I.C.S.: 424820

United Products Co., Ltd. (1)
56 Sukhaphiban Road Tambon Nakhon Chai Si, Amphoe Nakhon Chai Si, Nakhon Pathom, 73120, Thailand
Tel.: (66) 34331157
Web Site: http://www.thaibev.com
Alcoholic Beverages Mfr
N.A.I.C.S.: 325193

Vietnam Beverage Company Limited (1)
Room 502A 5/F HCO Building 44B Ly Thuong Kiet, Tran Hung Dao ward Hoan Kiem District, Hanoi, Vietnam
Tel.: (84) 913806820
Beverage Mfr & Distr
N.A.I.C.S.: 312120

Vietnam F&B Alliance Investment Joint Stock Company (1)
Room 502B 5/F HCO Building 44B Ly Thuong Kiet, Tran Hung Dao ward Hoan Kiem District, Hanoi, Vietnam
Tel.: (84) 913806820
Beverage Mfr & Distr
N.A.I.C.S.: 312120

Vietnam Logistics & Supply Chain Company Limited (1)
6F & 7F Me Linh Point Tower No 2 Ngo Duc Ke Street, Ben Nghe Ward District 1, Ho Chi Minh City, Vietnam
Tel.: (84) 2835202903
Transportation Services
N.A.I.C.S.: 541614

Wrangyer Beverage (2008) Co., Ltd. (1)
No 90 CW Tower 31st-32nd Floor Ratchadapisek Road, Huai Khwang Sub-district Huai Khwang District, Bangkok, 10310, Thailand
Tel.: (66) 27839000
Energy Drink Mfr & Distr
N.A.I.C.S.: 312111

Yunnan Yulinquan Liquor Co., Ltd. (1)
Yulin Village, Shuangjiang Town Eshan County, Yuxi, 653200, Yunnan, China
Tel.: (86) 8774022068
Spirit Mfr & Distr
N.A.I.C.S.: 312140

THAI BINH CEMENT JSC
Tien Phong Ward, Thai Binh, Vietnam
Tel.: (84) 2273647505
Web Site: https://www.ximangthaibinh.vn
Year Founded: 1979
TBX—(HNX)
Rev.: $723,343
Assets: $997,682
Liabilities: $196,556
Net Worth: $801,126
Earnings: $4,499
Fiscal Year-end: 12/31/21
Cement Product Mfr
N.A.I.C.S.: 327310
Hanh Thi Nguyen Bui (Chm-Mgmt Bd)

THAI CAPITAL CORPORATION PUBLIC COMPANY LIMITED
87/2 CRC Tower 45th Floor All Seasons Place Wireless Rd, Lumpini Pathumwan, Bangkok, 10330, Thailand
Tel.: (66) 26853600
Web Site: https://www.thaicapital.co.th
Year Founded: 1972
TCC—(THA)
Rev.: $45,911,963
Assets: $46,975,426
Liabilities: $14,541,396
Net Worth: $32,434,030
Earnings: $1,617,527
Fiscal Year-end: 12/31/23
Coal Trading Services
N.A.I.C.S.: 423520
Boon-anant Srikhao (Mng Dir)

THAI CENTRAL CHEMICAL PUBLIC COMPANY LIMITED
Room 801-806 809-810 8th Floor Mitrtown Office Tower 944 Rama 4 Road, Wangmai Pathumwan, Bangkok, 10330, Thailand
Tel.: (66) 26398888
Web Site: http://www.tcccthai.com
TCCC—(THA)
Rev.: $350,878,025
Assets: $381,633,689
Liabilities: $48,505,681
Net Worth: $333,128,008
Earnings: $31,784,845
Fiscal Year-end: 12/31/23
Fertilizer & Other Agricultural Chemicals Mfr
N.A.I.C.S.: 325314
Ko Tojima (Exec Officer & Member-Exec Bd)

Subsidiaries:

Central Pacific (Thailand) Corporation Ltd. (1)
180-184 Metro Building Rajawongse Road, Chakrawad Sampanthawongse, Bangkok, 10100, Thailand
Tel.: (66) 22250200
Web Site: http://www.mcic.co.th
Fertilizers, Agro-Chemicals & Minerals Importer & Distr
N.A.I.C.S.: 424690

MC Agro-Chemicals Co., Ltd. (1)
Bangrak 581 Moo 4 Bangpoo Phraeksa Sub District Muang, Industries Estate Soi 12, Bangkok, 10100, Thailand
Tel.: (66) 22250200
Web Site: http://www.mcic.co.th
Pesticides & Non-Pesticides Marketer, Formulator & Repackager
N.A.I.C.S.: 424690

MC Industrial Chemical Co., Ltd. (1)
180-184 Rajawongse Road, Sampanthawong, Bangkok, 10100, Thailand

INTERNATIONAL PUBLIC

Tel.: (66) 22250200
Web Site: http://www.mcic.co.th
Sales Range: $200-249.9 Million
Emp.: 300
Chemical Products Importer & Exporter; Plastic Bags & Containers Mfr & Distr
N.A.I.C.S.: 424690

N.I.M. Co., Ltd. (1)
284 Moo 1 Susawat Road, Pakklong Bangplakod Sub-district Prasamutjedi District, Bangkok, 10290, Samut Prakan, Thailand
Tel.: (66) 24633689
Web Site: https://www.nim.co.th
Sales Range: $25-49.9 Million
Chemical Storage Services
N.A.I.C.S.: 493110

TCC Agrochemical Co., Ltd (1)
180-184 Metro Building Rajawongse Rd, Chakrawad Sampanthawongse, Bangkok, 10100, Thailand
Tel.: (66) 22250200
Web Site: http://www.mcic.co.th
Chemical & Plastic Products Marketer
N.A.I.C.S.: 424690

Thai Central Chemical Public Company Limited - Nakhon Luang Plant (1)
50 Moo 5 Nakhon Luang Pachee Road Khlong Sa-Kae Sub-district, Nakhon Luang District, Phra Nakhon Si Ayutthaya, 13260, Thailand
Tel.: (66) 35359011
Agricultural Chemical Mfr
N.A.I.C.S.: 325320

Thai Central Chemical Public Company Limited - Phrapradaeng Plant Site (1)
284 Km 17 5 Suksawad Road Pakklong Bang Plakod, Phra Samut Jedee, Samut Prakan, 10290, Thailand
Tel.: (66) 24625904
Fertilizer & Chemical Products Mfr & Distr
N.A.I.C.S.: 325320

THAI COATING INDUSTRIAL PUBLIC COMPANY LIMITED
99/9 Moo 8 304 Road Nongphrong, Ban Srimahapo, 25140, Prachinburi, Thailand
Tel.: (66) 24643260
Year Founded: 1978
TCOAT—(THA)
Rev.: $20,213,104
Assets: $18,404,077
Liabilities: $3,146,019
Net Worth: $15,258,059
Earnings: $93,122
Fiscal Year-end: 12/31/23
Plastic Product Mfr & Whslr
N.A.I.C.S.: 326199
Porntip Charoenapornwatana (Chm)

THAI EASTERN GROUP HOLDINGS PUBLIC COMPANY LIMITED
171 Moo 2 Chonburi-Klaeng Road, Khao Sok Subdistrict Nong Yai District, Chon Buri, 20190, Thailand
Tel.: (66) 3816855558
Web Site: https://www.thaieasterngroup.com
Year Founded: 2018
TEGH—(THA)
Rev.: $355,413,969
Assets: $216,298,100
Liabilities: $123,473,523
Net Worth: $92,824,577
Earnings: $6,275,568
Emp.: 1,279
Fiscal Year-end: 12/31/23
Holding Company
N.A.I.C.S.: 551112
Sineenuch Kokanutaporn (Mng Dir)

THAI ENGER HOLDING PCL
88 Moo 4 Bangkruay-Sainoi Road Bangsong Thong, Bang Kruai, Nonthaburi, 11130, Thailand

Tel.: (66) 28867608
Web Site: https://thaienger.com
Year Founded: 2002
TIGER—(THA)
Rev.: $27,736,166
Assets: $28,141,643
Liabilities: $10,981,143
Net Worth: $17,160,500
Earnings: $114,141
Fiscal Year-end: 12/31/23
Residential Property Management Services
N.A.I.C.S.: 531311
Chaturong Srikulruangroj (CEO)

THAI FUTURE INCORPORATION PUBLIC COMPANY LIMITED
73/3 Moo 4 Bangna-Trad Rd Km 13 Bangchaloang, Bang Phli, 10540, Samutprakan, Thailand
Tel.: (66) 27501350
Web Site: https://thaifutureinc.com
Year Founded: 1983
TFI—(THA)
Rev.: $11,092,406
Assets: $78,475,152
Liabilities: $19,493,773
Net Worth: $58,981,379
Earnings: ($10,884,339)
Fiscal Year-end: 12/31/23
Plastics & Paper Products Mfr
N.A.I.C.S.: 326112
Suvimol Mahagitsiri (Deputy Chm)

Subsidiaries:

Thai Film Industries Public Company Limited - Rayong Factory (1)
327 Moo 8 Mabkha, Nikhompattana, Rayong, 21180, Thailand
Tel.: (66) 38 636 094 7
Packaging Film Mfr & Distr
N.A.I.C.S.: 326112

THAI GROUP HOLDINGS PUBLIC COMPANY LIMITED
315 Thai Group Building 12th Floor Silom Road, Silom Bangrak, Bangkok, 10500, Thailand
Tel.: (66) 26321224   TH
Web Site: http://www.segroup.co.th
Year Founded: 2018
TGH—(THA)
Rev.: $521,290,945
Assets: $2,512,987,899
Liabilities: $2,252,387,548
Net Worth: $260,600,351
Earnings: $3,039,560
Emp.: 1,808
Fiscal Year-end: 12/31/23
Holding Company
N.A.I.C.S.: 551112
Charoen Sirivadhanabhakdi (Chm)

THAI HA PUBLIC COMPANY LIMITED
140 Village No 5, Sam Phran, Bangkok, 73210, Nakhon Pathom, Thailand
Tel.: (66) 617402888   TH
Web Site: https://www.kasetbrand.co.th
Year Founded: 1993
KASET—(THA)
Rev.: $14,111,283
Assets: $20,517,959
Liabilities: $11,455,349
Net Worth: $9,062,611
Earnings: ($2,351,060)
Emp.: 134
Fiscal Year-end: 12/31/23
Agricultural Product Mfr
N.A.I.C.S.: 493130
Pattama Tangpiroonthum (Chm)

THAI HOA VIET NAM GROUP JOINT STOCK COMPANY
D21 Phuong Mai, Hanoi, Vietnam
Tel.: (84) 435740348
Web Site: http://www.thaihoacoffee.com
Year Founded: 1996
Emp.: 1,000
Coffee Mfr
N.A.I.C.S.: 311920
An Van Nguyen (Chm)

THAI HUNG TRADING JSC
Group 14, Thai Nguyen, Vietnam
Tel.: (84) 2083855 276
Web Site: http://thaihung.vn
Year Founded: 1993
Construction Steel, Steel Billets & Metal Scrap Mfr
N.A.I.C.S.: 332999
Thi Vinh Nguyen (Vice Chm & Gen Dir)

THAI HYGIENIC PRODUCTS CO., LTD.
71 Narathiwatratchanakharin Rd Silom, Bangrak, Bangkok, 10500, Thailand
Tel.: (66) 22333495
Web Site: http://www.thaihygienic.thailand.com
Year Founded: 1965
Sales Range: $100-124.9 Million
Emp.: 150
Personal Care Product Mfr
N.A.I.C.S.: 812199
Chulin Narupakorn (Mng Dir)

THAI LIFE INSURANCE PUBLIC COMPANY LIMITED
123 Ratchadaphisek Road, Din Daeng, Bangkok, 10400, Thailand
Tel.: (66) 22470247
Web Site: https://www.thailife.com
Year Founded: 1942
TLI—(THA)
Rev.: $3,174,881,467
Assets: $16,720,958,524
Liabilities: $13,668,080,926
Net Worth: $3,052,877,598
Earnings: $283,356,382
Emp.: 4,483
Fiscal Year-end: 12/31/23
Fire Insurance Services
N.A.I.C.S.: 524113
Kean Hin Lim (Pres)

THAI METAL DRUM MFG. PUBLIC CO., LTD.
Lake-rajada Bldg Floor 35c 193/142 Rajadapisek Road, Khlong Toei, Bangkok, 10110, Thailand
Tel.: (66) 22640817
Web Site: http://www.thaimetaldrum.com
Year Founded: 1958
TMD—(THA)
Rev.: $52,163,801
Assets: $106,290,599
Liabilities: $7,513,490
Net Worth: $98,777,109
Earnings: $9,558,081
Emp.: 160
Fiscal Year-end: 12/31/23
Steel Drums Mfr
N.A.I.C.S.: 331221
Suchin Wanglee (Chm)

Subsidiaries:

Eastplast Co., Ltd. (1)
23/4 Moo 2 Patumthani-Lad Lum Kaow Road, Tambol Banchang Amphur Muang, Pathumthani, 12000, Thailand
Tel.: (66) 2 5817950
Web Site: http://www.thepetco.com
Emp.: 300
Plastic Bottle Mfr & Distr
N.A.I.C.S.: 326160

Thai Metal Drum Mfg. Public Co., Ltd. - Chachoengsao Plant (1)
179 Moo 9 Wellgrow Industrial Estate Tampol Bangbua, Amphur Bangpakong, Chachoengsao, 24180, Thailand
Tel.: (66) 3857198082
Metal Drum Mfr
N.A.I.C.S.: 332439

THAI MUI CORPORATION PUBLIC COMPANY LIMITED
1620/4 Song Wat Road, Samphanthawong Subdistrict, Bangkok, 10100, Thailand
Tel.: (66) 22352940   TH
Web Site: https://www.thaimui.co.th
Year Founded: 1950
THMUI—(THA)
Rev.: $12,009,967
Assets: $20,453,997
Liabilities: $9,431,744
Net Worth: $11,022,252
Earnings: $16,167
Emp.: 187
Fiscal Year-end: 12/31/23
Industrial Equipment Mfr & Distr
N.A.I.C.S.: 333415
Tchakorn Leelaprachakul (CEO)

THAI NAKARIN HOSPITAL PCL
345 Bangna-Trad Highway KM 3 5 Rd, Bang Na, Bangkok, 10260, Thailand
Tel.: (66) 23612727
Web Site: https://www.thainakarin.co.th
Year Founded: 1993
TNH—(THA)
Rev.: $66,538,942
Assets: $87,483,055
Liabilities: $12,279,338
Net Worth: $75,203,717
Earnings: $9,640,736
Emp.: 1,157
Fiscal Year-end: 07/31/23
Health Care Srvices
N.A.I.C.S.: 621610
Jatuporn Sinathatkathakun (Chm)

THAI NAM PLASTIC (PUBLIC) COMPANY LIMITED
40 Moo 7 Phetkasem Road Km 23 Omnoi Kratumban, Samut Sakhon, 74130, Thailand
Tel.: (66) 21193200
Web Site: https://www.thainam.com
Year Founded: 1970
TNPC—(THA)
Rev.: $46,754,054
Assets: $37,562,883
Liabilities: $21,796,318
Net Worth: $15,766,565
Earnings: $875,220
Emp.: 554
Fiscal Year-end: 12/31/23
Plastics Sheets Supplier
N.A.I.C.S.: 326130
Siriphorn Mangkornkarn (Chm & Mng Dir)

THAI NGUYEN IRON AND STEEL CORPORATION
Phuong Cam Gia, Thai Nguyen, Vietnam
Tel.: (84) 2083832236
Web Site: http://www.tisco.com.vn
Year Founded: 1959
Sales Range: $1-4.9 Billion
Emp.: 6,000
Iron & Steel Mfr
N.A.I.C.S.: 331110

Subsidiaries:

Thai Nguyen Iron and Steel Corporation - Phan Me Coal Mine Factory (1)
Giang Tien Town, Phu Luong District, Thai Nguyen, Vietnam
Tel.: (84) 280 877 121
Coal Mining Services
N.A.I.C.S.: 212114

Thai Nguyen Iron and Steel Corporation - TRAI CAU IRON ORE MINE FACTORY (1)
Trai Cau Towns, Dong Hy Dist, Thai Nguyen, Vietnam
Tel.: (84) 280 821 128
Iron Product Mfr
N.A.I.C.S.: 331110

THAI NONDESTRUCTIVE TESTING PUBLIC COMPANY LIMITED
19 Soi Suanson 8 Ramkhamhaeng Rd Huamark Bangkapi, Bangkok, 10240, Thailand
Tel.: (66) 27350801
Web Site: https://www.tndt.co.th
Year Founded: 1982
TNDT—(THA)
Rev.: $9,174,782
Assets: $20,904,546
Liabilities: $18,307,386
Net Worth: $2,597,160
Earnings: ($11,339,570)
Emp.: 245
Fiscal Year-end: 12/31/23
Engineering & Technical Consulting Services
N.A.I.C.S.: 541690
Suwat Dangpibulskul (Chm, Pres & Member-Exec Bd)

Subsidiaries:

PT. Thai NDT Indonesia (1)
Komplek Ruko Permata Niaga Block C No 5 Sukajadi, Batam, 29462, Indonesia
Tel.: (62) 77 842 7394
Web Site: http://www.tndt.co.id
Engineering Inspection Services
N.A.I.C.S.: 541330
Ahmad Zamroni (Mng Dir)

THAI O PP PCL
1741 Chan Road Thungmahamek, Sathorn, Bangkok, 10120, Thailand
Tel.: (66) 267810515
Web Site: http://www.topp.co.th
Year Founded: 1893
TOPP-F—(THA)
Rev.: $53,230,575
Assets: $49,821,925
Liabilities: $5,570,739
Net Worth: $44,251,186
Earnings: $3,777,031
Fiscal Year-end: 12/31/19
Plastic Polypropylene Mfr & Distr
N.A.I.C.S.: 325211
Suthee Limatibul (Vice Chm & Mng Dir)

THAI O.P.P. PUBLIC COMPANY LIMITED
1741 Chan Road Thungmahamek, Sathorn, Bangkok, 10120, Thailand
Tel.: (66) 2 678 1051
Web Site: http://www.topp.co.th
Year Founded: 1983
TOPP—(THA)
Rev.: $53,411,546
Assets: $58,657,988
Liabilities: $9,078,727
Net Worth: $49,579,261
Earnings: $2,933,442
Fiscal Year-end: 12/31/21
Plastics Films Mfr
N.A.I.C.S.: 322220
Arin Jira (Chm)

THAI OIL PUBLIC COMPANY LIMITED

THAI OIL PUBLIC COMPANY LIMITED

Thai Oil Public Company Limited—(Continued)

555/1 Energy Complex Building A
11th Floor Vibhavadi Rangsit Road,
Chatuchak, Bangkok, 10900, Thailand
Tel.: (66) 27972999 TH
Web Site:
  http://www.thaioilgroup.com
TOP—(OTCIQ)
Sales Range: $5-14.9 Billion
Petroleum Refiner & Distr
N.A.I.C.S.: 324110
Nitas Krongvanitchayakul (Sr VP)

Subsidiaries:

TOP Ventures Hong Kong
Limited (1)
18th Floor One Exchange Square 8 Connaught Place, Central, China (Hong Kong)
Tel.: (852) 25822912
Investment Services
N.A.I.C.S.: 523940

Thai Lube Base Public Co., Ltd. (1)
555/1 Energy Complex Building A 11th Floor Vibhavadi Rangsit Road, Chatuchak, Bangkok, 10900, Thailand
Tel.: (66) 2 299 0000
Web Site: http://www.thaioil.co.th
Sales Range: $50-74.9 Million
Emp.: 133
Lubricating Oil Mfr
N.A.I.C.S.: 324191

Thai Paraxylene Co., Ltd (1)
105/12 Moo 2 Sukhumvit Road, Tungsukla, Si Racha, 20230, Chon Buri, Thailand
Tel.: (66) 38351317
Sales Range: $25-49.9 Million
Emp.: 67
Petrochemical Mfr
N.A.I.C.S.: 325110

Thaioil Energy Co., Ltd. (1)
123 Suntowers Bldg B 16th Fl Vibhavadi Rangsit Rd, Chomphon Chatuchak, Bangkok, 10900, Thailand
Tel.: (66) 2617 8300
Energy Consulting Services
N.A.I.C.S.: 541690

Subsidiary (Domestic):

Independent Power Co., Ltd. (2)
123 Suntowers Bldg B 16th Fl Vibhavadi Rangsit Rd, Chomphon Chatuchak, Bangkok, Thailand
Tel.: (66) 2299 0000
Sales Range: $50-74.9 Million
Emp.: 44
Power Generation Services
N.A.I.C.S.: 221118

Thaioil Energy Solutions Co., Ltd (1)
555/1 Energy Complex Building Vibhavadi Ransit, Chatuchak, Bangkok, 10900, Thailand
Tel.: (66) 22990000
Web Site: http://www.thaioilgroup.com
Emp.: 110
Petroleum Product Distr
N.A.I.C.S.: 424720

Thaioil Ethanol Co., Ltd. (1)
555/1 Energy Complex Building A 11th Floor Vibhavadi Rangsit Road, Chatuchak, Bangkok, 10900, Thailand
Tel.: (66) 2 299 0000
Web Site: http://www.thaioilgroup.com
Methanol Mfr
N.A.I.C.S.: 325193

Thaioil Power Co., Ltd. (1)
555/1 Energy Complex Building A 11th Floor Vibhavadi Rangsit Road, Chatuchak, Bangkok, 10900, Thailand (55%)
Tel.: (66) 22990000
Web Site: http://www.ipt.co.th
Sales Range: $50-74.9 Million
Power Generation Services
N.A.I.C.S.: 221118

Thaioil Solvent Company Limited (1)
555/1 Energy Complex Building A 11th Floor Vibhavadi Rangsit Road, Chatuchak, Bangkok, 10900, Thailand
Tel.: (66) 22990000

Business Investment Services
N.A.I.C.S.: 541611

Subsidiary (Domestic):

TOP Solvent Company Limited (2)
555/1 Energy Complex Building A 11th Floor Vibhavadi Rangsit Road, Chatuchak, Bangkok, 10900, Thailand
Tel.: (66) 2 797 2993
Web Site: http://www.topsolvent.com
Solvent & Chemical Product Mfr & Distr
N.A.I.C.S.: 325998
Acharee Tiyabhorn (Mng Dir)

Subsidiary (Domestic):

Sak Chaisidhi Company Limited (3)
4 I-3A Road Map Ta Phud Industrial Estate, Rayong, 21150, Thailand
Tel.: (66) 38683090
Hydrocarbon Solvent Mfr & Distr
N.A.I.C.S.: 325110

THAI OPTICAL GROUP PUBLIC COMPANY LIMITED

15/5 Moo 6 Bangbuathong-Suphanburi Road, Laharn Sub-district Bangbuathong District, Nonthaburi, 11110, Thailand
Tel.: (66) 21941145 TH
Web Site:
  https://www.thaiopticalgroup.com
Year Founded: 1991
TOG—(THA)
Rev.: $88,023,887
Assets: $118,137,425
Liabilities: $52,812,176
Net Worth: $65,325,249
Earnings: $12,426,069
Fiscal Year-end: 12/31/23
Optical Lens Mfr
N.A.I.C.S.: 333310
Sawang Pracharktam (Chm & Vice Chm)

Subsidiaries:

Thai Optical Company Limited (1)
83 Moo 2 Ngarmwongwarn Road, Bang Khen, Nonthaburi, 11000, Thailand
Tel.: (66) 29526429
Optical Lens Mfr & Distr
N.A.I.C.S.: 333310
Kuekul Jutiviwat (Mgr-IT Infrastructure)

THAI PACKAGING & PRINTING PUBLIC COMPANY LIMITED

9/9 Moo 6 King-Kaew Rd Rachatheva, Bang Phli, 10540, Samutprakarn, Thailand
Tel.: (66) 21752201
Web Site: https://www.tpppack.com
Year Founded: 1983
TPP—(THA)
Rev.: $6,403,842
Assets: $30,941,737
Liabilities: $4,000,759
Net Worth: $26,940,977
Earnings: $350,012
Emp.: 300
Fiscal Year-end: 12/31/23
Packaging Products Mfr
N.A.I.C.S.: 322211
Pongsathust Asvinvichit (Mng Dir)

THAI PLASPAC PUBLIC COMPANY LIMITED

77 Soi Thain Thaley 30 Bang Khun Thian-Chay Thaley Rd Tha Kham, Bang Khun Thian, Bangkok, 10150, Thailand
Tel.: (66) 28972250
Web Site: https://tpacpackaging.com
Year Founded: 1983
TPAC—(THA)
Rev.: $201,389,573
Assets: $218,476,240
Liabilities: $137,833,760
Net Worth: $80,642,481
Earnings: $15,821,371

Emp.: 753
Fiscal Year-end: 12/31/23
Plastic Packaging Products Mfr
N.A.I.C.S.: 322220
Theerawit Busayapoka (Mng Dir)

Subsidiaries:

Combi-Pack Sdn Bhd (1)
No 277 Jalan Haruan 1, Oakland Industrial Park, 70300, Seremban, Negeri Sembilan, Malaysia
Tel.: (60) 67611268
Web Site: https://www.combi-pack.com.my
Food Packaging Machinery Mfr
N.A.I.C.S.: 333993

THAI PLASTIC INDUSTRIAL (1994) PCL

53/1 Moo 4 Bang MaeNang, Bangyai, Nonthaburi, 11140, Thailand
Tel.: (66) 2191828889
Web Site: https://www.tpic.co.th
Year Founded: 1994
TPLAS—(THA)
Rev.: $15,189,860
Assets: $10,578,083
Liabilities: $1,506,000
Net Worth: $9,072,083
Earnings: $367,433
Emp.: 58
Fiscal Year-end: 12/31/23
Plastic Bag Distr
N.A.I.C.S.: 424130
Teerachai Teerarujinon (Mng Dir)

THAI POLYCONS PUBLIC COMPANY LIMITED

2 4 Soi Prasert Manukitch 29 Yak 8 Prasert Manukitch Rd, Chorakhebua Ladprao, Bangkok, 10230, Thailand
Tel.: (66) 29426491
Web Site:
  https://www.thaipolycons.co.th
TPOLY—(THA)
Rev.: $175,176,815
Assets: $299,980,012
Liabilities: $203,343,867
Net Worth: $96,636,145
Earnings: $2,424,369
Fiscal Year-end: 12/31/23
Industrial, Commercial & Housing Construction Services
N.A.I.C.S.: 236210
Kanoktip Chanpalangsri (Chm-Exec Bd)

Subsidiaries:

Green Power Plant Co., Ltd. (1)
764 Vangili Complex Salem Road, Namakkal, 637 001, Tamilnadu, India
Tel.: (91) 9944558893
Web Site: http://www.greenpowerplant.in
Solar Product Mfr
N.A.I.C.S.: 334413

TPC Asset Company Limited (1)
2 4 Soi Prasert-Manukitch 29 Yak 8 Prasert Manukit Road, Chorakhe Bua Subdistrict Lat Phrao District, Bangkok, 10230, Thailand
Tel.: (66) 291788545
Web Site: http://www.tpcasset.co.th
Real Estate Services
N.A.I.C.S.: 531390

TPC Bangkok Supply Company Limited (1)
2 4 Soi Prasert-Manukitch 29 Yak 8 Prasert-Manukitch Road Chorakhebua, Ladprao, Bangkok, 10230, Thailand
Tel.: (66) 632084809
Foreign Goods Trading Services
N.A.I.C.S.: 425120

THAI PRESIDENT FOODS PUBLIC COMPANY LIMITED

304 TF Bldg Srinakarin Road Huamark Bangkapi, Bangkok, 10240, Thailand
Tel.: (66) 23744730

INTERNATIONAL PUBLIC

Web Site: http://www.mama.co.th
Year Founded: 1972
TFMAMA—(THA)
Rev.: $815,713,009
Assets: $1,335,967,916
Liabilities: $134,938,447
Net Worth: $1,201,029,469
Earnings: $146,439,835
Emp.: 6,200
Fiscal Year-end: 12/31/23
Foods & Beverages Mfr
N.A.I.C.S.: 311999
Boonsithi Chokwatana (Chm)

Subsidiaries:

Dai-ichi Packaging Co., Ltd. (1)
139 Moo 5 Bangna-Trad Road 36th Km, Bang-Samak, Bang Pakong, 24130, Chachoengsao, Thailand
Tel.: (66) 38545888
Web Site: https://www.dai-ichipack.com
Sales Range: $125-149.9 Million
Emp.: 400
Packaging Materials Mfr
N.A.I.C.S.: 326199

President Bakery Public Company Limited (1)
121/84 85 RS Tower Building 29th Floor Ratchadapisek Road, Dindaeng, Bangkok, 10400, Thailand (51.99%)
Tel.: (66) 22093000
Web Site: https://www.farmhouse.co.th
Rev.: $221,791,222
Assets: $377,055,382
Liabilities: $34,292,632
Net Worth: $342,762,750
Earnings: $49,853,187
Emp.: 4,775
Fiscal Year-end: 12/31/2023
Bakery Products Mfr
N.A.I.C.S.: 311919
Pipat Paniangvait (Chm)

Plant (Domestic):

President Bakery Public Company Limited - Bangchan Factory (2)
1 1/1 Soi Serithai 87 Serithai Road, Bangchan Industrial Estate Minburi, Bangkok, 10510, Thailand
Tel.: (66) 25481200
Snack Food Mfr
N.A.I.C.S.: 311919

President Bakery Public Company Limited - Lardkrabang Factory (2)
91 Mu 4 Lardkrabang Industrial Estate Chalong Krung Road, Lam Pla Thio Lardkrabang, Bangkok, 10520, Thailand
Tel.: (66) 23265400
Snack Food Mfr
N.A.I.C.S.: 311919

President Kourakuen Co., Ltd. (1)
304 TF Bldg Srinakarin Rd Huamark, Bangkapi, Bangkok, 10240, Thailand
Tel.: (66) 23744730
Web Site: https://www.kourakuen.co.th
Food Processing Services
N.A.I.C.S.: 236210
Tsukasa Niida (Founder)

Thai Anbao Paper Products Co., Ltd. (1)
11 Soi Ma Charoen 1 Yaek 3-2, Nong Khang Phlu Nong Khaem, Bangkok, 10240, Thailand
Tel.: (66) 24209184
Web Site: https://www.thaianbao.com
Sales Range: $50-74.9 Million
Paper Products Mfr
N.A.I.C.S.: 322120

Thai President Foods Public Company Limited - Lumphun Factory (1)
Sahapat Group Industrial Park 99/9 Moo 5, Phasuk, 51000, Lumphun, Thailand
Tel.: (66) 53584088
Sales Range: $150-199.9 Million
Emp.: 700
Noodles Mfr
N.A.I.C.S.: 311999

Thai President Foods Public Company Limited - Rayong Factory (1)
43/244 Moo 4 Huayprab-Pluakdaeng Maby-

angporn, Pluakdaeng, Rayong, 21140, Thailand
Tel.: (66) 3 310 1500
Web Site: http://www.mama.co.th
Cookies & Wafers Mfr
N.A.I.C.S.: 311821

Thai President Foods Public Company Limited - Sri Racha Factory (1)
Saha Group Industrial Park 601 Sukapiban 8 Road, Nongkarm, Si Racha, 20230, Cholburi, Thailand
Tel.: (66) 3 848 0502
Web Site: http://www.mama.co.th
Sales Range: $150-199.9 Million
Noodles & Biscuits Mfr
N.A.I.C.S.: 311999

Thai Sun Foods Co., Ltd. (1)
304 TF Building Srinakarin Rd, Huamark Bangkapi, Bangkok, 10240, Thailand
Tel.: (66) 27317250
Web Site: https://www.thaisunfoods.com
Sales Range: $25-49.9 Million
Emp.: 250
Fruit Juices Mfr & Distr
N.A.I.C.S.: 311411

THAI PROPERTY PUBLIC COMPANY LIMITED
2922/305-306 Charnisara Tower 2, 29th Floor New Phetchaburi Road Huay-kwang, Bangkok, 10310, Thailand
Tel.: (66) 23082708
Web Site:
  http://www.thaiproperty.co.th
Year Founded: 1985
Sales Range: $25-49.9 Million
Construction Services
N.A.I.C.S.: 236210
Vitavas Vibhagool *(Mng Dir)*

Subsidiaries:

Pacific Estate Development Limited (1)
29thFloor CharnIssara Tower 2 2922/305 Petchaburi Road, Bang Kapi HuayKwang, Bangkok, 10110, Thailand
Tel.: (66) 22545720
Web Site: http://www.thaiproperty.co.th
Real Estate Development Services
N.A.I.C.S.: 531390

THAI REINSURANCE PUBLIC CO., LTD.
100/3-4 Sathorn Nakorn Tower 3rd - 4th Floor North Sathorn Road Silom, Bang Rak, Bangkok, 10500, Thailand
Tel.: (66) 26606111
Web Site: https://www.thaire.co.th
Year Founded: 1984
THRE—(THA)
Rev.: $146,563,517
Assets: $228,076,276
Liabilities: $117,107,315
Net Worth: $110,968,960
Earnings: $6,754,691
Emp.: 468
Fiscal Year-end: 12/31/23
Reinsurance Services
N.A.I.C.S.: 524130
Chamroen Phusit *(Sr VP-Investment)*

Subsidiaries:

EMCS Thai Co. Ltd. (1)
48/21 Soi Rajchadapisek 20 Rajchadapisek Road, Samsennok Huai Khwang, Bangkok, 10310, Thailand **(57.75%)**
Tel.: (66) 20118600
Web Site: http://www.emcsthai.com
Sales Range: $25-49.9 Million
Emp.: 29
Other Motor Vehicle Electrical & Electronic Equipment Mfr
N.A.I.C.S.: 336320

Firstech Solutions Co. Ltd. (1)
Reget House 14th Floor, 183 Rajadamri Road Lumpini Pat, 10330, Bangkok, Thailand **(80%)**
Tel.: (66) 225564204
Sales Range: $50-74.9 Million
Emp.: 4
All Other Insurance Related Activities
N.A.I.C.S.: 524298

Thaire Life Assurance Public Company Limited (1)
48/15 Soi Rajchadapisek 20 Rajchadapisek Road, Samsennok Huaykwang, Bangkok, 10310, Thailand
Tel.: (66) 26669000
Web Site: https://www.thairelife.co.th
Rev.: $100,866,468
Assets: $79,903,067
Liabilities: $39,972,004
Net Worth: $39,931,063
Earnings: $1,813,202
Emp.: 55
Fiscal Year-end: 12/31/2023
Reinsurance Carriers
N.A.I.C.S.: 524130
Suchin Wanglee *(Chm)*

Thaire Services Co. Ltd. (1)
Reget House 14th Floor, 183 Rajadamri Road Lumpini Pat, 10330, Bangkok, Thailand **(100%)**
Tel.: (66) 225564256
Web Site: http://www.thaireservices.com
Sales Range: $50-74.9 Million
Emp.: 4
Claims Adjusting
N.A.I.C.S.: 524291

THAI RUBBER LATEX GROUP PUBLIC COMPANY LIMITED
99/1-3 Moo 13 Soi Bangna Trad 45 Bangna Trad Road KM 7, Bang Kaeo, Bangkok, 10540, Samutprakan, Thailand
Tel.: (66) 20332333
Web Site: https://www.thaitex.com
Year Founded: 1985
TRUBB—(THA)
Rev.: $194,204,501
Assets: $255,781,819
Liabilities: $151,093,902
Net Worth: $104,687,917
Earnings: $(13,275,712)
Emp.: 678
Fiscal Year-end: 12/31/23
Rubber Products Mfr
N.A.I.C.S.: 326299
Pattrapol Wongsasuthikul *(CEO)*

Subsidiaries:

Agrowealth Co., Ltd. (1)
30 Bangna Complex Soi Bangna-Trad 25 Bangna-Trad Rd Km 3, Bang Na, Bangkok, 10260, Thailand
Tel.: (66) 2 744 0888
Web Site: http://www.agrowealth.com
Securities Brokerage Services
N.A.I.C.S.: 523150

Shanghai Runmao International Trading Co., Ltd. (1)
Shanghai Greentown Room 601 Unit 1 Lane 99 Jinhe Road, Pudong, Shanghai, 200127, China
Tel.: (86) 2138762472
Rubber Product Distr
N.A.I.C.S.: 424690

Thai Rubber Land And Plantation Co., Ltd. (1)
561 Moo 10 Ban Du, Mae Chan District, Chiang Rai, 57100, Thailand
Tel.: (66) 52100979
Rubber Mfr
N.A.I.C.S.: 326299

Thaitex CBD SmartFarmCo., Ltd. (1)
273 Moo 9 Ki Lek, Mae Taeng District, Chiang Mai, Thailand
Tel.: (66) 20332391
Web Site: https://www.thaitexcbd.co.th
Hemp & Cannabin Mfr
N.A.I.C.S.: 313210

THAI RUNG UNION CAR PUBLIC COMPANY LIMITED
304 Ma Charoen Road, Nong Khaem Subdistrict Nong Khaem District, Bangkok, 10160, Thailand
Tel.: (66) 28145034
Web Site: https://www.thairung.co.th
Year Founded: 1967
TRU—(THA)
Rev.: $74,332,973
Assets: $127,468,780
Liabilities: $21,049,746
Net Worth: $106,419,035
Earnings: $5,348,845
Fiscal Year-end: 12/31/23
Motor Vehicle Body Mfr
N.A.I.C.S.: 336110
Pranee Phaoenchoke *(Chm & Pres)*

Subsidiaries:

Thai Auto Pressparts Co., Ltd. (1)
7/122 Moo 4 Amata City Industrial Estate, Pluak Daeng, 21140, Rayong, Thailand
Tel.: (66) 38956156
Sales Range: $100-124.9 Million
Emp.: 30
Automobile Parts Mfr
N.A.I.C.S.: 336390

Thai Ultimate Car Co. Ltd. (1)
304 Majareon Road, Nongkhamphlu Subdistrict Nongkhaem District, Bangkok, 10160, Thailand **(99.53%)**
Tel.: (66) 24310071
Web Site: http://www.thaiultimatecar.com
Auto Dealership & Services
N.A.I.C.S.: 441110

Thai V.P. Auto Service Co., Ltd. (1)
151 Majareon Road, Nongkhamphlu Subdistrict Nongkhaem District, Bangkok, 10160, Thailand
Tel.: (66) 24206708
Automobile Repair & Maintenance Services
N.A.I.C.S.: 811111

THAI SOLAR ENERGY PUBLIC COMPANY LIMITED
725 Metropolis Building 19th FL Sukhumvit Road Klongton Nua, Wattana, Bangkok, 10110, Thailand
Tel.: (66) 22584530
Web Site:
  https://www.thaisolarenergy.com
TSE—(THA)
Rev.: $36,797,214
Assets: $299,504,961
Liabilities: $193,784,417
Net Worth: $105,720,544
Earnings: $(30,225,246)
Emp.: 286
Fiscal Year-end: 12/31/23
Solar Energy
N.A.I.C.S.: 221114
Cathleen Maleenont *(Chm & CFO-Acting)*

Subsidiaries:

Soilcrete Technology Co., Ltd. (1)
112/5 Moo 9 Thepharak Road, Bang Pla Bang Phli, Samut Prakan, 10540, Thailand
Tel.: (66) 27064575
Web Site: https://www.soilcrete.co.th
Soil Remediation Services
N.A.I.C.S.: 562910

THAI STANLEY ELECTRIC PUBLIC COMPANY LIMITED
29/3 Moo 1 Bangpoon-Rungsit Rd, Banklang Muang, Bangkok, 12000, Pathumthanee, Thailand
Tel.: (66) 25815462
Web Site: http://www.thaistanley.com
Year Founded: 1980
STANLY—(THA)
Rev.: $395,454,911
Assets: $681,402,081
Liabilities: $84,584,220
Net Worth: $596,817,861
Earnings: $48,316,133
Emp.: 2,726
Fiscal Year-end: 03/31/24
Automotive Equipment & Lighting Mfr
N.A.I.C.S.: 336320
Apichart Leeissaranukul *(Chm)*

Subsidiaries:

Sirivit Stanley Co., Ltd. (1)
182 Moo 6 Mittraprap Road Kokkraud Muang, Nakhon Ratchasima, 30280, Nakhon Ratchasima, Thailand
Tel.: (66) 44291411
Electronic Components Mfr
N.A.I.C.S.: 334419
Shuji Kajiya *(Mng Dir)*

Sum Hitechs Co., Ltd. (1)
60-63 Phaholyothin Road, Klong 1 Khlong Luang, 12120, Pathumthani, Thailand
Tel.: (66) 25290928
Sales Range: $50-74.9 Million
Emp.: 250
Paint & Coating Mfr
N.A.I.C.S.: 325510

THAI STEEL CABLE PUBLIC COMPANY LIMITED
700 737 Moo 1 Tambol Panthong Amphur Panthong, Chon Buri, 20160, Thailand
Tel.: (66) 38447200
Web Site:
  http://www.thaisteelcable.com
Year Founded: 1978
TSC—(THA)
Rev.: $79,934,741
Assets: $62,953,744
Liabilities: $20,075,269
Net Worth: $42,878,475
Earnings: $7,661,607
Emp.: 743
Fiscal Year-end: 09/30/23
Automobile Control Cables & Steel Cables Mfrs
N.A.I.C.S.: 331221
Thaveechat Jurangkool *(CEO)*

THAI SUGAR TERMINAL PUBLIC COMPANY LIMITED
No 90 Moo 1 Poochaosamingpai Road Samrong klang, Phra Pradaeng, 10130, Samut Prakarn, Thailand
Tel.: (66) 21834567
Web Site: https://www.tstegroup.com
Year Founded: 1976
TSTE—(THA)
Rev.: $78,650,373
Assets: $165,963,361
Liabilities: $56,038,159
Net Worth: $109,925,202
Earnings: $4,256,147
Emp.: 217
Fiscal Year-end: 12/31/23
Sugar Mfr
N.A.I.C.S.: 311314
Amornrat Hattakam *(CFO)*

THAI TEXTILE INDUSTRY PUBLIC COMPANY LIMITED
385 Soi Bang Make Khao Sukhumvit Km 30 5Taiban, Amphur Muang, Samut Prakan, 10280, Thailand
Tel.: (66) 27038484
Web Site: https://www.tti.co.th
Year Founded: 1970
TTI—(THA)
Rev.: $63,798,709
Assets: $103,325,350
Liabilities: $29,074,390
Net Worth: $74,250,960
Earnings: $(3,641,503)
Emp.: 227
Fiscal Year-end: 12/31/23
Textile Products Mfr
N.A.I.C.S.: 314999
Mongkol Mungkornkanok *(Chm & Exec Dir)*

Subsidiaries:

Thai Rung Textile Co., Ltd. (1)

THAI TEXTILE INDUSTRY PUBLIC COMPANY LIMITED

Thai Textile Industry Public Company Limited—(Continued)
62 Soi Vilalai Bangna-Trad Rd Km 20,
Bangchalong, Bang Phli, 10540, Samut
Prakan, Thailand
Tel.: (66) 233723256
Textile Products Mfr
N.A.I.C.S.: 314999

THAI THEPAROS FOOD PRODUCTS PUBLIC COMPANY LIMITED

208 Village No 6 Taiban Road, Taiban
Subdistrict Mueang District, Samut
Prakan, 10280, Thailand
Tel.: (66) 27034444
Web Site: https://www.goldenmountain.com
Sales Range: $25-49.9 Million
Emp.: 750
Mayonnaise, Dressing & Other Prepared Vegetable & Fruit Sauces Mfr
N.A.I.C.S.: 311941
Parinya Winyarat *(Mng Dir & CEO)*

THAI UNION GROUP PUBLIC COMPANY LIMITED

72/1 Moo 7 Sethakit 1 Road Tambon,
Tarsrai Mueang, Samut Sakhon,
74000, Thailand
Tel.: (66) 34816500   TH
Web Site: https://www.thaiunion.com
Year Founded: 1977
TU—(THA)
Rev.: $3,974,565,913
Assets: $4,829,820,778
Liabilities: $2,902,647,605
Net Worth: $1,927,173,173
Earnings: ($385,342,440)
Emp.: 13,030
Fiscal Year-end: 12/31/23
Frozen & Canned Seafood Producer & Exporter
N.A.I.C.S.: 424460
Kraisorn Chansiri *(Co-Chm)*

Subsidiaries:

AMG-Thai Union Feedmill (Private) Limited (1)
416- J EME Society Multan Road Second Floor, Lahore, 54000, Punjab, Pakistan
Tel.: (92) 4232176710
Web Site: https://amg-thaiunion.com
Animal Feed Mfr & Distr
N.A.I.C.S.: 311119

Artur Heymann GmbH (1)
Mecklenburger Strasse 140, 23568,
Lubeck, Germany
Tel.: (49) 45169350
Seafood Distr
N.A.I.C.S.: 424460

Asian-Pacific Can Co Ltd. (1)
38/70 Moo 8 Sethakit 1 Road, Tumbol
Thasai, Amphur Muang, 74000, Samut Sakhon, Thailand
Tel.: (66) 344234016
Web Site: http://www.asiancan.co.th
Steel Can Mfr & Distr
N.A.I.C.S.: 332431

Dalpromryba LLC (1)
BC BERTA HOUSE Staropimenovsky lane 18, Moscow, Russia
Tel.: (7) 4959505354
Web Site: https://www.dalpromryba.ru
Emp.: 150
Sea Food Mfr & Distr
N.A.I.C.S.: 311710

EHS Training & Services Co., Ltd. (1)
106/10 Moo 7 Sethakit 1 Road, Tarsrai Subdistrict Mueang Samut Sakhon District, Samut Sakhon, 74000, Thailand
Tel.: (66) 34419999
Web Site: http://www.ehs-ts.com
Training & Management Services
N.A.I.C.S.: 611430

I-Tail Corporation PCL (1)
979/92-94 29 th Floor S M Tower Phaholyothin Road, Phayathai Sub-district Phayathai District, Bangkok, 10400, Thailand
Tel.: (66) 22980029
Web Site: https://www.i-tail.com
Pet Food Mfr & Distr
N.A.I.C.S.: 311111

King Oscar AS (1)
Nostegaten 58, PB 400, 5805, Bergen, Norway
Tel.: (47) 48293000
Web Site: https://www.kingoscar.no
Processed Seafood Producer & Distr
N.A.I.C.S.: 311710

King Oscar Inc. (1)
3838 Camino Del Rio N, San Diego, CA 92108
Tel.: (619) 578-2040
Canned Seafood Mfr & Distr
N.A.I.C.S.: 311710

MWBrands SAS (1)
104 Avenue Du President Kennedy, 75016, Paris, France
Tel.: (33) 153753353
Sales Range: $550-599.9 Million
Tuna Canning
N.A.I.C.S.: 311710

Subsidiary (Domestic):

Paul Paulet S.A.S. (2)
Zone Industrielle de Pouldavid, 29177, Douarnenez, France
Tel.: (33) 29 874 4000
Web Site: http://www.petitnavire.fr
Emp.: 300
Tuna Fish Canning Operations
N.A.I.C.S.: 311710

Meekrone Fisch-Feinkost GmbH (1)
Mecklenburger Strasse 140, 23568, Lubeck, Germany
Tel.: (49) 45169350
Canned Seafood Product Mfr & Distr
N.A.I.C.S.: 311710

Norway Foods Europe NV (1)
Laarstraat 16 Bus 14, Antwerp, Belgium
Tel.: (32) 32304364
Seafood Distr
N.A.I.C.S.: 424460

Ostsee Fisch GmbH (1)
Hansestrasse 12, Bentwisch b, D-18182, Rostock, Germany
Tel.: (49) 38166628210
Web Site: https://www.ostseefisch.de
Sea Food Mfr & Distr
N.A.I.C.S.: 311710

PT Thai Union Kharisma Lestari (1)
Jl Margomulyo No 4E Tandes Kidul Tandes Kota, Surabaya, 60186, Jawa Timur, Indonesia
Tel.: (62) 317491000
Animal Feed Mfr & Distr
N.A.I.C.S.: 311119

Pakfood Plc (1)
979/91 979/95 SM Tower Floor 29 Phahonyothin Road, Phayathai, Bangkok, 10400, Thailand (74.64%)
Tel.: (66) 22980780
Fiscal Year-end: 12/31/2013
Frozen Food Mfr & Distr
N.A.I.C.S.: 311412
Rittirong Boonmechote *(Chm)*

Subsidiary (Domestic):

Okeanos Food Co., Ltd. (2)
47/29 Moo 4, Khok Kham Sub-district Mueang District, Samut Sakhon, 74000, Thailand
Tel.: (66) 34834483
Frozen Food Mfr & Distr
N.A.I.C.S.: 311412
Rittirong Boonmechote *(Pres)*

Seafood International One FZCO (1)
PO Box 263846, Dubai, United Arab Emirates
Tel.: (971) 48808318
Food Products Distr
N.A.I.C.S.: 424490

Songkla Canning PCL (1)
979/9-10 12th Floor S M Tower Phaholyothin Road, Samsennai Phayathai, Bangkok, 10400, Thailand (100%)
Tel.: (66) 22980029
Web Site: http://www.thaiuniongroup.com
Processor & Exporter of Canned Seafood
N.A.I.C.S.: 311710

T-Holding Co Ltd (1)
7-11 Moo 5 Kanjanapisek Rd Bangbon Bangbon, 10150, Bangkok, Thailand (100%)
Tel.: (66) 28988200
Web Site: http://www.fisho.com
Sales Range: $25-49.9 Million
Emp.: 100
Fresh & Frozen Seafood Processing
N.A.I.C.S.: 311710

TCM Fishery Co., Ltd. (1)
89/1 Moo 2 Rama II Road, Kalong, Mueang Samut Sakhon, 74000, Thailand
Tel.: (66) 344172613
Shrimp Farming Services
N.A.I.C.S.: 112511

TMK Farm Co., Ltd. (1)
89/1 Moo 2 Rama II Road, Kalong, Mueang Samut Sakhon, 74000, Thailand
Tel.: (66) 344172613
Shrimp Farming Services
N.A.I.C.S.: 112511

Thai Marine Development Products Co Ltd (1)
89-1 Moo 2 Rama II Rd Tambon Kalong Amphur, Muangsamutsakorn Samutsakorn, 74000, Bangkok, Thailand
Tel.: (66) 34418094
Web Site: http://www.thaiunion.group.com
Fresh & Frozen Seafood Processing
N.A.I.C.S.: 311710

Thai Union China Co., Ltd. (1)
Room A1810 No 596 of Mid Longhua Rd, Xuhui District, Shanghai, China
Tel.: (86) 2131779766
Food Products Mfr
N.A.I.C.S.: 424490
Cheng Niruttinanon *(Exec Dir)*

Subsidiary (Non-US):

John West Foods Ltd. (2)
No 1 Mann Island, Liverpool, L3 1BP, United Kingdom
Tel.: (44) 1512436200
Web Site: https://www.john-west.co.uk
Sales Range: $50-74.9 Million
Emp.: 75
Canned Tuna & Fish
N.A.I.C.S.: 424460
Paul Stephenson *(Mng Dir)*

Thai Union Europ SAS (1)
104 Avenue du President Kennedy, 75016, Paris, France
Tel.: (33) 298744047
Headquarter Activity Services
N.A.I.C.S.: 561499

Subsidiary (Domestic):

Etablissements Paul Paulet SAS (2)
Zl de Pouldavid, 29100, Douarnenez, France
Tel.: (33) 298744000
Web Site: https://www.petitnavire.fr
Canned Seafood Mfr
N.A.I.C.S.: 311710

Subsidiary (Non-US):

Pioneer Food Cannery Limited (3)
Plot No 10/11 Fishing Harbour, PO Box 40, Tema, Ghana
Tel.: (233) 303205051
Canned Tuna Mfr
N.A.I.C.S.: 311710

Subsidiary (Non-US):

European Seafood Investment Portugal S.A. (2)
Avenida Monsenhor Manuel Bastos Rodrigues de Sousa, Peniche, Leiria, Portugal
Tel.: (351) 262780600
Canned Sardine Mfr & Distr
N.A.I.C.S.: 311422

INTERNATIONAL PUBLIC

Subsidiary (Domestic):

Europeenne De la Mer SAS (2)
55 Avenue de Keradennec, 29556, Quimper, Cedex 9, France
Tel.: (33) 298647272
Holding Company
N.A.I.C.S.: 551112

Subsidiary (Domestic):

Imsaum SCI (3)
55 Avenue de Keradennec, 29556, Quimper, Cedex 9, France
Tel.: (33) 298647272
Property Rental Services
N.A.I.C.S.: 531390

Meralliance Armoric SAS (3)
55 Avenue de Keradennec, 29556, Quimper, Cedex 9, France
Tel.: (33) 298647272
Emp.: 450
Smoked Salmon Mfr
N.A.I.C.S.: 311710

Subsidiary (Non-US):

Meralliance Poland Sp. z.o.o (3)
Targowa 34, Dabrowa Chelminska, 86-070, Bydgoszcz, Poland
Tel.: (48) 523816958
Chilled Salmon Mfr
N.A.I.C.S.: 311710

Subsidiary (Domestic):

Meralliance SAS (3)
55 Avenue de Keradernec, 29156, Quimper, Cedex 9, France
Tel.: (33) 298647272
Web Site: https://www.meralliance.com
Smoked Salmon Distr
N.A.I.C.S.: 424460

Subsidiary (Non-US):

Naco Trading AS (3)
Skutevikboder 1-2, 5053, Bergen, Norway
Tel.: (47) 55961272
Salmon Distr
N.A.I.C.S.: 424460

Subsidiary (Non-US):

Indian Ocean Tuna Limited (2)
Fishing Port, PO Box 676, Victoria, Mahe, Seychelles
Tel.: (248) 4282500
Canned Tuna Mfr & Distr
N.A.I.C.S.: 311710
Medor Paul *(Mgr-IT)*

Irish Seafood Investments Limited (2)
Unit 14 Classon House Dundrum Business Park, Dublin, Ireland
Tel.: (353) 12147345
Canned Seafood Mfr & Distr
N.A.I.C.S.: 311710

Subsidiary (Non-US):

John West Holland BV (3)
Tel.: (31) 302567470
Web Site: https://www.john-west.nl
Canned Seafood Mfr & Distr
N.A.I.C.S.: 311710

Subsidiary (Non-US):

MW Brands Seychelles Limited (2)
Fishing Port, Victoria, Mahe, Seychelles
Tel.: (248) 4282500
Canned Tuna Distr
N.A.I.C.S.: 424460

Mareblu SRL (2)
Via dei Missaglia 97 ed B2, 20142, Milan, Italy
Tel.: (39) 0257420001
Web Site: https://mareblu.it
Canned Seafood Mfr & Distr
N.A.I.C.S.: 311710
Cristiano Giovanelli *(Gen Mgr)*

UK Seafood Investments Limited (2)
No 1 Mann Island, Liverpool, L3 1BP, United Kingdom
Tel.: (44) 1512436200
Holding Company
N.A.I.C.S.: 551112

AND PRIVATE COMPANIES

Thai Union Europe S.A.S. (1)
104 Avenue du President Kennedy, 75016,
Paris, France
Tel.: (33) 153775353
Sea Food Mfr & Distr
N.A.I.C.S.: 311710

Thai Union Feedmill Co Ltd. (1)
89/1 Moo 2 Rama 2 Road, Kalong Sub-
district, Mueang Samut Sakhon, 74000,
Samut Sakhon, Thailand
Tel.: (66) 34417222
Web Site: https://www.thaiunionfeedmill.com
Sales Range: $100-124.9 Million
Animal Feed Mfr
N.A.I.C.S.: 311119

Subsidiary (Domestic):

Thai Union Hatchery Co., Ltd (2)
89/1 Moo 2 Rama II Road, Kalong Sub-
district, Mueang Samut Sakhon, 74000,
Samut Sakhon, Thailand
Tel.: (66) 344172613
Web Site: http://www.thaiunionfeedmill.com
Seafood Processing Services
N.A.I.C.S.: 311710

Thai Union Germany GmbH (1)
Strasse der Jugend 10, 18546, Sassnitz,
Germany
Tel.: (49) 38392600
Holding Company
N.A.I.C.S.: 551112

Subsidiary (Domestic):

Rugen Fisch AG (2)
Strasse der Jugend 10, 18546, Sassnitz,
Germany   (51%)
Tel.: (49) 38392600
Web Site: https://www.ruegenfisch.de
Seafood Mfr & Distr
N.A.I.C.S.: 311710
Madleine Burr *(Mgr-HR)*

Thai Union Graphic Co Ltd (1)
255 Samaedam Road Samaedam, Bangk-
huntien, Bangkok, 10150, Thailand
Tel.: (66) 289558656
Web Site: https://www.thaiuniongraphic.com
Books Printing
N.A.I.C.S.: 323117

Thai Union Investment Holding Co., Ltd. (1)
11th Floor Medine Mews La Chaussee
Street, Port Louis, Mauritius
Tel.: (230) 4057721
Holding Company
N.A.I.C.S.: 551112

Thai Union Manufacturing Company Limited (1)
979/12 M Floor S M Tower Phaholyothin
Road, Phayathai, 10400, Bangkok, Thailand
Tel.: (66) 22980024
Web Site: http://www.thaiuniongroup.com
Sales Range: $100-124.9 Million
Emp.: 300
Seafood Canning
N.A.I.C.S.: 311710

Subsidiary (Domestic):

Phang-nga Fishing Co., Ltd (2)
979/13-16 MFloor S M Tower Phaholyothin
Road, Samsennai, Bangkok, 10400, Thai-
land
Tel.: (66) 2298 0025
Seafood Processing Services
N.A.I.C.S.: 311710

Songkla Fishing Co., Ltd (2)
979/3-4 11th Floor SM Tower Phaholyothin
Road, Samsennai, Bangkok, 10400, Thai-
land
Tel.: (66) 22980025
Sales Range: $75-99.9 Million
Emp.: 300
Seafood Processing Services
N.A.I.C.S.: 311710

Thai Union North America, Inc. (1)
2150 E Grand Ave, El Segundo, CA 90245
Tel.: (424) 397-8600
Holding Company
N.A.I.C.S.: 551112

Subsidiary (Domestic):

Tri-Union Frozen Products, Inc. (2)
2150 E Grand Ave, El Segundo, CA 90245
Tel.: (310) 469-7030
Frozen Seafood Distr
N.A.I.C.S.: 424460

Subsidiary (Domestic):

Tri-Union Frozen Products North America, LLC (3)
2150 E Grand Ave, El Segundo, CA 90245
Tel.: (310) 469-7031
Holding Company
N.A.I.C.S.: 551112

Subsidiary (Domestic):

US Pet Nutrition, LLC (2)
2150 E Grand Ave, El Segundo, CA 90245
Tel.: (424) 397-8600
Pet Food Mfr & Distr
N.A.I.C.S.: 311111

Thai Union Online Shop Co., Ltd. (1)
979/79 26th Floor S M Tower Phaholyothin
Road, Phaya Thai, Bangkok, 10400, Thai-
land
Tel.: (66) 22980024
Ecommerce Services
N.A.I.C.S.: 423620

Thai Union Poland S.p. z o.o. (1)
Strzebielinko 22, Gniewino, 84-250,
Gniewkowo, Poland
Tel.: (48) 586706519
Canned Seafood Mfr & Distr
N.A.I.C.S.: 311710
Piotr Sadowski *(Dir-Plant)*

Thai Union Seafood Co Ltd (1)
979-8 12th Floor S M Tower Phaholyothin
Rd, Samsennai Phayathai, 10400, Bang-
kok, Thailand
Tel.: (66) 22980024
Fresh & Frozen Seafood Processing
N.A.I.C.S.: 311710

Thai Union Trading Europe B.V. (1)
Europalaan 101, 3526KR, Utrecht, Nether-
lands
Tel.: (31) 307100955
Seafood Distr
N.A.I.C.S.: 424460

Thammachart Seafood Retail Co., Ltd. (1)
58 58/1-5 5th Floor Soi Sukhumvit 63,
Phrakhanong Nua Wattana, Bangkok,
10110, Thailand
Tel.: (66) 27141322
Web Site:
https://www.thammachartseafood.com
Seafood Product Whslr
N.A.I.C.S.: 424460

Tri-Union Seafoods LLC (1)
9330 Scranton Rd Ste 500, San Diego, CA
92121
Tel.: (858) 558-9662
Web Site: http://www.chickenofthesea.com
Sales Range: $25-49.9 Million
Emp.: 95
Packager of Tuna Fish
N.A.I.C.S.: 311710

Yueh Chyang Canned Food Co., Ltd. (1)
1 AP Nhut Chanh, Nhut Chanh Commune
Ben Luc District, Ben Luc, Long An, Viet-
nam
Tel.: (84) 723872377
Canned Seafood Mfr & Distr
N.A.I.C.S.: 311710

Subsidiary (Non-US):

Hawesta-Feinkost Hans Westphal GmbH & Co. KG (2)
Mecklenburger Str 140-142, 23568, Lubeck,
Germany
Tel.: (49) 45169350
Seafood Mfr & Distr
N.A.I.C.S.: 311710

Thai Union Marine Nutrients GmbH (2)
Mecklenburger Str 140-142, 23568, Lubeck,
Germany
Tel.: (49) 45169350
Tuna Oil Refinery Mfr
N.A.I.C.S.: 311225

Subsidiary (Domestic):

Arthur Heymann GmbH & Co, KG (3)
Mecklenburger Strasse 140, 23568,
Lubeck, Germany
Tel.: (49) 45169350
Seafood Distr
N.A.I.C.S.: 424460

Meerkrone Fisch-Feinkost GmbH (3)
Mecklenburger Strasse 140, 23568,
Lubeck, Germany
Tel.: (49) 45169350
Property Rental Services
N.A.I.C.S.: 531390

Sassnitz Fisch GmbH (3)
Gewerbepark 13b, 18546, Sassnitz, Ger-
many
Tel.: (49) 39250804
Seafood Mfr & Distr
N.A.I.C.S.: 311710

THAI UNIQUE COIL CENTER PUBLIC COMPANY LIMITED
809 Moo 4 Soi 14 Phattana 1 Road,
Prakasa Muang, Muang District,
Bangkok, 10280, Samutprakarn,
Thailand
Tel.: (66) 2 7093034
Web Site: http://www.tuccplc.com
Year Founded: 1989
Sales Range: $10-24.9 Million
Emp.: 160
Stainless Steel Wire Mfr
N.A.I.C.S.: 331210

THAI USUI CO., LTD.
Hitech Industrial Estate 131 Moo 1
Tambol Banwah, Bangpain, Ayut-
thaya, 13160, Thailand
Tel.: (66) 35 350 042
Web Site: http://www.tuc.co.th
Year Founded: 1990
Sales Range: $10-24.9 Million
Emp.: 328
Precision Plastic Component Mfr
N.A.I.C.S.: 326199
Masato Usui *(Pres)*

THAI VEGETABLE OIL PUBLIC COMPANY LIMITED
149 Ratchadaphisek Road Tha Phra-
Taksin, Bukkhalo Subdistrict Thonburi
District, Bangkok, 10600, Thailand
Tel.: (66) 24779020
Web Site: https://www.tvothai.com
Year Founded: 1985
TVO—(THA)
Rev.: $1,008,188,201
Assets: $381,716,381
Liabilities: $76,129,188
Net Worth: $305,587,193
Earnings: $21,872,085
Emp.: 1,214
Fiscal Year-end: 12/31/23
Soybean Oil Mfr
N.A.I.C.S.: 311224
Sompol Kiatphaibool *(Chm)*

Subsidiaries:

Thai Vegetable Oil Public Company Limited - Nakorn Chaisri Factory (1)
81/7 Moo 1 Tambon Thaiyawas, Nakorn
Chaisri District, Nakhon Pathom, 73120,
Thailand
Tel.: (66) 3426562029
Vegetable Oil Mfr
N.A.I.C.S.: 311225

THAI VILLAGE RESTAURANT LTD.
Block 1002 Tai Seng Avenue 01-
2536, Singapore, 534409, Singapore
Tel.: (65) 64402292
Web Site:
https://www.villagerestaurant.com

596—(SES)
Rev.: $13,600,697
Assets: $47,081,724
Liabilities: $5,630,539
Net Worth: $41,451,185
Earnings: ($3,559,040)
Emp.: 81
Fiscal Year-end: 12/31/23
Restaurant Management Services
N.A.I.C.S.: 721110
John Seow Phun Chen *(Chm)*

Subsidiaries:

Thai Village Restaurant Pte. Ltd. (1)
22 Scotts Road Goodwood Park Hotel, Sin-
gapore, 228221, Singapore
Tel.: (65) 64408251
Web Site:
https://thaivillagerestaurant.com.sg
Restaurant Operating Services
N.A.I.C.S.: 722511

Thai Village Sharksfin Restaurant (Yunnan) Co., Ltd. (1)
19 Yung Ho Road, Singapore, 618592, Sin-
gapore
Tel.: (65) 62683885
Web Site:
http://www.thaivillagerestaurant.com
Restaurant Operating Services
N.A.I.C.S.: 722511
Anthony Soh *(Mgr)*

THAI VIRAWAT CO., LTD.
11th-12th Floors Thai Virawat Build-
ing 86/1 Krungthonburi Road,
Banglamphu-Lang Klongsan, Bang-
kok, 10600, Thailand
Tel.: (66) 28607777   TH
Web Site: http://www.thaivirawat.com
Electrical Equipment Distr
N.A.I.C.S.: 423610

THAI WAH PUBLIC COMPANY LIMITED
21/11 21/13 Thai Wah Tower 1 6th
Floor South Sathorn Road Tungma-
hamek, Sathorn, Bangkok, 10120,
Thailand
Tel.: (66) 22850040
Web Site: https://www.thaiwah.com
Year Founded: 1947
Food Products Mfr
N.A.I.C.S.: 311999
Ho Kwonping *(Chm)*

THAI WAH STARCH PUBLIC COMPANY LIMITED
21/63 21st Floor Thai Wah Tower
21st Floor, S Sathorn Road Thung-
mahamek Sathorn, Bangkok, 10120,
Thailand
Tel.: (66) 2 285 0040
Web Site: http://www.thaiwah.com
Year Founded: 1947
Sales Range: $100-124.9 Million
Food Products Mfr
N.A.I.C.S.: 311999

THAI WIRE PRODUCTS PUBLIC COMPANY LIMITED
101/88 Village No 20 Nawanakorn
Industrial Estate, Khlong Luang,
Bangkok, 12120, Pathumthani, Thai-
land
Tel.: (66) 2520385564
Web Site:
https://www.thaiwireproducts.com
Year Founded: 1985
TWP—(THA)
Rev.: $49,980,475
Assets: $50,641,586
Liabilities: $12,594,395
Net Worth: $38,047,191
Earnings: ($3,064,654)
Fiscal Year-end: 12/31/23
Concrete Wire Mfr
N.A.I.C.S.: 332618

Thai Wire Products Public Company Limited—(Continued)

Suri Buakhom *(Chm)*

Subsidiaries:

Thai Wire Products Public Company Limited - Map Ta Phut Plant (1)
4 I-5 Rd Maptaphud Industrial Estate, Maptaphut Muang Rayong, Rayong, 21150, Thailand
Tel.: (66) 386846103
Concrete Wire Mfr
N.A.I.C.S.: 332618

THAI-GERMAN CERAMIC INDUSTRY PUBLIC COMPANY LIMITED
444 Olympia Thai Tower Fl 10th Ratchadaphisek Road Samsennok, Huaykwang, Bangkok, 10310, Thailand
Tel.: (66) 2 790 9898
Web Site:
   http://www.campanatiles.com
Year Founded: 1969
Rev.: $60,346,483
Assets: $118,298,409
Liabilities: $11,607,079
Net Worth: $106,691,330
Earnings: $5,811,954
Fiscal Year-end: 12/31/17
Ceramic Mfr
N.A.I.C.S.: 327120
Kajohndet Sangsuban *(Chm)*

THAI-GERMAN PRODUCTS PUBLIC COMPANY LIMITED
170/25-28 Ocean Tower 1 10th Floor Soi Sukhumvit 16, Ratchadaphisaek Road Klongtoey, Bangkok, 10110, Thailand
Tel.: (66) 22619955   TH
Web Site:
   https://btovmed.makewebeasy.co
Year Founded: 1973
TGPRO—(THA)
Rev.: $45,675,216
Assets: $81,661,033
Liabilities: $26,596,804
Net Worth: $55,064,229
Earnings: ($7,951,309)
Fiscal Year-end: 12/31/23
Steel Products Mfr
N.A.I.C.S.: 331221
Rachata Leelaprakul *(Mng Dir)*

Subsidiaries:

Thai-German Products Public Company Limited - Rayong Factory (1)
99 Huay Pong-Nongbon Road Huay Pong Amphur, Muang, Rayong, 21150, Thailand
Tel.: (66) 38606061
Stainless Steel Pipe Tube Sheet Mfr & Distr
N.A.I.C.S.: 331210

THAIFOODS GROUP PUBLIC COMPANY LIMITED
1010 Shinawatra Tower 3 12th Fl Viphavadi-Rangsit Road, Chatuchak Subdistrict Chatuchak District, Bangkok, 10900, Thailand
Tel.: (66) 25138989
Web Site: http://www.tfg.co.th
TFG—(THA)
Rev.: $1,650,565,157
Assets: $1,376,275,247
Liabilities: $976,468,215
Net Worth: $399,807,032
Earnings: ($23,818,867)
Emp.: 4,205
Fiscal Year-end: 12/31/23
Chicken Production & Sales
N.A.I.C.S.: 311999
Weerasak Ungkajornkul *(Chm)*

Subsidiaries:

Thai Viet Swine Line Joint Stock Company Limited (1)
Floor 02 666 Ngo Quyen, Da Nang, Vietnam
Tel.: (84) 2363895777
Web Site: http://www.tvsl.com.vn
Live Pig Whslr
N.A.I.C.S.: 424520

THAILAND IRON WORKS PUBLIC COMPANY LIMITED
86 Moo 1 Suksawad Road Tambol Laemphapa, Phrasamutjedee District, Bangkok, 10290, Samutprakarn, Thailand
Tel.: (66) 24250011
Web Site: http://www.tiw.co.th
Year Founded: 1958
NOVA—(THA)
Rev.: $1,631,608
Assets: $161,307,412
Liabilities: $90,134,925
Net Worth: $71,172,487
Earnings: ($1,988,568)
Fiscal Year-end: 12/31/23
Iron Sheet Mfr
N.A.I.C.S.: 331110
Yasuyuki Nakashima *(Asst Mng Dir)*

THAILAND PRIME PROPERTY FREEHOLD & LEASEHOLD REAL ESTATE INVESTMENT TRUST
No 388 39th Floor Room 3903 Exchange Tower Building Sukhumvit Road, Khlong Toei, Bangkok, 10110, Thailand
Tel.: (66) 22584515
Web Site: https://www.tprimereit.com
TPRIME—(THA)
Rev.: $23,427,899
Assets: $278,797,395
Liabilities: $79,442,242
Net Worth: $199,355,154
Earnings: $10,632,494
Fiscal Year-end: 12/31/23
Real Estate Investment Trust Services
N.A.I.C.S.: 531110
Chaiwat Mahatdetkul *(CEO)*

THAIVIVAT INSURANCE PUBLIC COMPANY LIMITED
PACIFIC INSURANCE BLDG 71 DINDAENG RD, PHAYA THAI, Bangkok, 10400, Thailand
Tel.: (66) 22480900   TH
Web Site: http://www.thaivivat.co.th
Year Founded: 1951
TVI—(THA)
Rev.: $156,392,212
Assets: $261,405,377
Liabilities: $216,564,695
Net Worth: $44,840,682
Earnings: $2,587,948
Fiscal Year-end: 12/31/20
General Insurance Services
N.A.I.C.S.: 524210
Jiraphant Asvatanakul *(Pres & CEO)*

THAKKERS DEVELOPERS LIMITED
7 Thakkers Near Nehru Garden, Nashik, 422 005, India
Tel.: (91) 2532598925
Web Site:
   https://www.thakkersdeveloper.com
Year Founded: 1987
526654—(BOM)
Rev.: $7,087,105
Assets: $27,324,249
Liabilities: $9,916,935
Net Worth: $17,407,314
Earnings: $1,911,276
Emp.: 108

Fiscal Year-end: 03/31/23
Real Estate Development Services
N.A.I.C.S.: 531390
Abhishek Narendra Thakker *(CFO)*

THAKRAL CORP. LTD.
20 Upper Circular Road 03-06 The Riverwalk, Singapore, 058416, Singapore
Tel.: (65) 63368966   SG
Web Site:
   https://www.thakralcorp.com
AWI—(SES)
Rev.: $160,773,309
Assets: $249,174,430
Liabilities: $97,124,896
Net Worth: $152,049,534
Earnings: $13,971,067
Emp.: 207
Fiscal Year-end: 12/31/23
Investment Holding Company; Consumer Electronic Products Distr & Equity Investment Services
N.A.I.C.S.: 551112
Lai Yin Chan *(Co-Sec)*

Subsidiaries:

TCAP Pte Ltd (1)
20 Upper Circular Road 03-06 The Riverwalk, Singapore, 058416, Singapore
Tel.: (65) 63368966
Real Estate Investment Services
N.A.I.C.S.: 531390

Thakral (Indo-China) Pte. Ltd (1)
20 Upper Circular Rd 03-06 The Riverwalk, Singapore, 058416, Singapore
Tel.: (65) 63397001
Web Site: http://www.nll.laopdr.com
Financial Management Consulting Services
N.A.I.C.S.: 541611

Thakral Brothers Limited (1)
Thakral Building 2-4-1 Minami Honmachi, Chuo-ku, Osaka, 541-0054, Japan
Tel.: (81) 662646226
Consumer Electronic Products Distr
N.A.I.C.S.: 423620

Thakral Brothers Pte Ltd (1)
20 Upper Circular Rd 03-06 The Riverwalk, Singapore, 058416, Singapore
Tel.: (65) 63374292
Web Site: http://www.thakral.com
Sales Range: $25-49.9 Million
Emp.: 100
Logistics Consulting Management Services
N.A.I.C.S.: 541614
Gurmukh Singh *(Chm)*

Thakral Capital Australia Pty Ltd (1)
Level 3 20 Bond Street, Sydney, 2000, NSW, Australia
Tel.: (61) 28 073 7888
Web Site: https://www.tcap.com.sg
Investment Services
N.A.I.C.S.: 523999
Greggory Piercy *(Mng Dir)*

Thakral China Ltd. (1)
Suite 2101 Caohejing Kehui Plaza 1188 Qinzhou Road North, Shanghai, 200233, China
Tel.: (86) 216 191 7722
Web Site: http://www.thakralchina.com
Real Estate Investment Services
N.A.I.C.S.: 531390

Thakral Corporation (HK) Limited (1)
Units G 1/F Kaiser Estate Phase 2 47-53 Man Yue Street, Hung Hom, Kowloon, China (Hong Kong)
Tel.: (852) 27227752
Web Site: https://thakral.com.hk
Sales Range: $50-74.9 Million
Emp.: 100
Consumer Electronics Distr
N.A.I.C.S.: 423620

Thakral Electronics (Shanghai) Ltd. (1)
Suite 310-315 Huana Hotel Office Tower 1733 Lianhua Road, Shanghai, 201103, China
Tel.: (86) 2161917722
Consumer Electronics Distr

N.A.I.C.S.: 423620

Thakral Lifestyle Pte Ltd (1)
20 Upper Circular Road 03-06 The Riverwalk, Singapore, 058416, Singapore
Tel.: (65) 65330315
Real Estate Investment Services
N.A.I.C.S.: 531390

Wujiang Dafa Real Estate Development Co., Ltd. (1)
2nd Floor C2 Building 15 No 2315 Jiao Tong South Road, Wujiang, 215200, Jiangsu, China
Tel.: (86) 51263483700
Real Estate Property Development Services
N.A.I.C.S.: 531390

THAKRAL SERVICES INDIA LIMITED
Floor Shree Rajarajeshwari Arcade No 23/50/1A/514/2/1-1, Outer Ring Road Near Courtyard Marriot Hotel Veerannapalya Flyover, Bengaluru, 560045, India
Tel.: (91) 8025593891
Web Site: https://www.thakral-india.co.in
Year Founded: 1995
509015—(BOM)
Rev.: $2,342,143
Assets: $2,325,319
Liabilities: $2,298,811
Net Worth: $26,508
Earnings: ($254,619)
Emp.: 15,000
Fiscal Year-end: 03/31/21
Audio & Video Equipment Mfr
N.A.I.C.S.: 334310
Joseph Sequeira *(Chm)*

THALASSO N 1
20 Rue De La Banque, 75002, Paris, France
Tel.: (33) 800220966
Web Site: http://www.thalasso-to.com
Rev.: $29,100,000
Emp.: 10
Travel Agencies
N.A.I.C.S.: 561510
Samia Ben Slimane *(Mng Partner)*

THALES S.A.
31 place des Corolles, 92098, Paris, Cedex, France
Tel.: (33) 157778000   FR
Web Site:
   https://www.thalesgroup.com
Year Founded: 1918
HO—(EUR)
Rev.: $19,887,662,080
Assets: $40,336,384,192
Liabilities: $32,077,084,312
Net Worth: $8,259,299,880
Earnings: $1,393,315,456
Emp.: 80,500
Fiscal Year-end: 12/31/21
Holding Company; Electronics & Defense Systems
N.A.I.C.S.: 334511
Patrice Durand *(Sr VP-Fin & Admin)*

Subsidiaries:

EUROSAM (1)
Centre d'affaires de la Boursidiere Batiment Kerguelen, Le Plessis-Robinson, 92357, France
Tel.: (33) 1 4187 1416
Web Site: http://www.eurosam.com
Emp.: 70
Missile Defense Systems Mfr
N.A.I.C.S.: 336414
Michelle Vigneras *(Mng Dir)*

Eisys S.p.A. (1)
Via Morolo 92, 00131, Rome, Italy
Tel.: (39) 0641235128
Web Site: http://www.eisys.it
Sales Range: $25-49.9 Million
Emp.: 25
Software Development for Military Systems

AND PRIVATE COMPANIES — THALES S.A.

Gemalto N.V. (1)
Joop Geesinkweg 541-542, 1096-AX, Amsterdam, Netherlands
Tel.: (31) 205620680
Web Site: http://www.gemalto.com
Rev.: $3,395,562,510
Assets: $4,869,386,252
Liabilities: $2,268,052,073
Net Worth: $2,601,334,179
Earnings: $68,213,348
Emp.: 12
Fiscal Year-end: 12/31/2018
Holding Company; Digital Security Solutions
N.A.I.C.S.: 551112

Subsidiary (Non-US):

Axalto Participations S.A.S. (2)
6 rue Verrerie, 92190, Meudon, France
Tel.: (33) 1 55 01 50 00
Smartcard Mfr
N.A.I.C.S.: 339999
Olivier Piou (CEO)

Gemalto (Thailand) Ltd (2)
Rasa Tower 23rd Floor 555 Phaholyothin Road, Chatuchak, Bangkok, 10900, Thailand
Tel.: (66) 2 937 1030
Web Site: http://www.gemalto.com
Digital Security Services
N.A.I.C.S.: 561621

Gemalto AB (2)
Vastberga Alle 36 C, Box 42133, 126 15, Stockholm, Sweden
Tel.: (46) 8 709 2 500
Web Site: http://www.gemalto.com
Sales Range: $25-49.9 Million
Emp.: 45
Digital Security Software Development Services
N.A.I.C.S.: 541512

Gemalto Argentina S.A (2)
Av Eduardo Madero No 900-Piso 21, C1106ACV, Buenos Aires, Argentina
Tel.: (54) 11 4850 5200
Web Site: http://www.gemalto.com
Sales Range: $25-49.9 Million
Emp.: 95
Digital Security Software Development Services
N.A.I.C.S.: 541511

Subsidiary (Domestic):

Gemalto B.V. (2)
Barbara Strozzilaan 382, Amsterdam, 1083HN, Netherlands
Tel.: (31) 20 562 06 80
Web Site: http://www.gemalto.com
Sales Range: $25-49.9 Million
Emp.: 25
Digital Security Services
N.A.I.C.S.: 561621

Subsidiary (Non-US):

Gemalto Canada Inc. (2)
780 Brewster Ste 03-300, Montreal, H4C 2K1, QC, Canada
Tel.: (514) 732-2300
Sales Range: $50-74.9 Million
Emp.: 123
Electrical Equipment & Component Mfr
N.A.I.C.S.: 335999
Francois Rebel (Pres)

Gemalto Card International Espana S.A. (2)
Gemalto Avenida Europa 19, Alcobendas, 28108, Spain (98%)
Tel.: (34) 918374450
Web Site: http://www.gemalto.com
Emp.: 100
Plastics Product Mfr
N.A.I.C.S.: 326199

Gemalto Cards Ltd. (2)
Concorde Way, Segensworth North, Fareham, PO15 5RX, Hampshire, United Kingdom (100%)
Tel.: (44) 1489889600
Web Site: http://www.gemalto.com
Sales Range: $200-249.9 Million
Emp.: 600
Plastics Product Mfr
N.A.I.C.S.: 326199

Gemalto Colombia S.A. (2)
Av Cra 9 No 113-52 of 1704, Bogota, Colombia
Tel.: (57) 1 637 98 99
Web Site: http://www.gemalto.com
Digital Security Software Development Services
N.A.I.C.S.: 541511

Gemalto Danmark A/S (2)
Borupvang 1B, PO Box 53, 2750, Ballerup, Denmark (98%)
Tel.: (45) 44827400
Web Site: http://www.setec.dk
Sales Range: $25-49.9 Million
Emp.: 20
Support Services
N.A.I.C.S.: 561990

Gemalto Digital Security Ltd (2)
802 Hallmark Business Plaza Opp Guru Nanak Hospital Sant Dnyaneshwar, Marg Bandra East, Mumbai, 400 051, India
Tel.: (91) 22 30690000
Digital Security Services
N.A.I.C.S.: 561621

Gemalto GmbH (2)
Mercedesstrasse 13, 70794, Filderstadt, Germany
Tel.: (49) 71581850
Web Site: http://www.gemalto.com
Sales Range: $25-49.9 Million
Emp.: 150
Custom Computer Programming Services
N.A.I.C.S.: 541511

Gemalto Holding Pte Ltd (2)
12 Ayer Rajah Crescent, Singapore, 139941, Singapore
Tel.: (65) 67761989
Investment Management Service
N.A.I.C.S.: 523999

Gemalto Hungary Commercial and Services Ltd. (2)
Austria Ofc Bldg, 3-5 Varmegye Str, Budapest, 1052, Hungary (100%)
Tel.: (36) 14111603
Web Site: http://www.gemalto.com
Sales Range: $25-49.9 Million
Management Consulting Services
N.A.I.C.S.: 541618

Subsidiary (US):

Gemalto Inc. (2)
101 Park Dr, Montgomeryville, PA 18936
Tel.: (215) 390-2000
Web Site: http://www.gemalto.com
Sales Range: $150-199.9 Million
Emp.: 400
Identification Cards, Plastics
N.A.I.C.S.: 326199

Subsidiary (Domestic):

Gemalto Cogent, Inc. (3)
639 N Rosemead Blvd, Pasadena, CA 91107
Tel.: (626) 325-9600
Web Site: http://www.gemalto.com
Automated Fingerprint Identification Systems & Other Fingerprint Biometrics Solutions
N.A.I.C.S.: 561621

SafeNet, Inc. (3)
4690 Millennium Dr Ste 400, Belcamp, MD 21017-1526
Tel.: (410) 931-7500
Web Site: http://www.safenet-inc.com
Network Security Products
N.A.I.C.S.: 541512
Jim Summers (Sr VP & Gen Mgr-Data Protection)

Subsidiary (Non-US):

SafeNet (Australia) Pty. Ltd. (4)
Level 14 100 Millar St, North Sydney, 2060, NSW, Australia
Tel.: (61) 299062988
Sales Range: $10-24.9 Million
Emp.: 10
Software Protection Devices
N.A.I.C.S.: 541511

SafeNet Asia Limited (4)
904-906A Core D Cyberport 3 100 Cyberport Rd, NIL, Hong Kong, China (Hong Kong)
Tel.: (852) 31577111
Web Site: http://www.safenet-inc.com
Sales Range: $10-24.9 Million
Emp.: 35
Software Protection Devices
N.A.I.C.S.: 541511

Subsidiary (Non-US):

SafeNet China Ltd. (5)
Room 1603 Jinyu Plaza No 100 Xisanhuan North Road, Haidian District, Beijing, 100048, China
Tel.: (86) 1088519191
Web Site: http://www.cn.safenet-inc.com
Sales Range: $10-24.9 Million
Emp.: 60
Security Electronic Products
N.A.I.C.S.: 541511

Subsidiary (Non-US):

SafeNet India Pvt. Ltd. (4)
Pride Tower Floor 1 Plot No 12-A Sector 125, Noida, 201301, India
Tel.: (91) 120 4020555
Web Site: http://safenet.gemalto.com
Software Monetization & Data Protection Solutions
N.A.I.C.S.: 541511

SafeNet UK Limited (4)
River Ct 3 Meadows Business Park, Station Approach Blackwater, Camberley, GU17 9AB, Surrey, United Kingdom
Tel.: (44) 1276608000
Web Site: http://www.safenet-inc.com
Sales Range: $25-49.9 Million
Emp.: 100
Software Protection Devices
N.A.I.C.S.: 541511

Branch (Domestic):

SafeNet, Inc. (4)
2200 Bridge Pkwy Ste 103, Redwood City, CA 94065
Tel.: (650) 261-2400
Web Site: http://www.safenet.gemalto.com
Emp.: 20
Computer Hardware & Software Piracy Security Products Marketer
N.A.I.C.S.: 334118
Mike Cook (Dir-Facilities)

Subsidiary (Domestic):

SensorLogic, Inc. (3)
2701 Dallas Pkwy Ste 180, Plano, TX 75093
Tel.: (972) 934-7375
Web Site: http://www.sensorlogic.com
Sales Range: $10-24.9 Million
Machine-to-Machine Service Delivery Software Developer
N.A.I.C.S.: 513210

Subsidiary (Non-US):

Gemalto Industrial S.A. de C.V. (2)
Calle 9 Este No 192, Cd Ind Valle de Cuernavaca, 62500, Veracruz, Mexico
Tel.: (52) 7773293900
Plastics Product Mfr
N.A.I.C.S.: 326199

Gemalto International S.A.S. (2)
6 rue de la Verrerie, 92190, Meudon, France
Tel.: (33) 155015000
Digital Security Services
N.A.I.C.S.: 541512

Gemalto Kart ve Terminaller Ltd Sirketi (2)
Dereboyu Cad Meydan Sok No 1 Beybi Giz Plaza K 17, Maslak, Istanbul, 34398, Turkiye
Tel.: (90) 212 359 1700
Web Site: http://www.gemalto.com
Emp.: 14
Digital Security Services
N.A.I.C.S.: 561621

Gemalto LLC (2)
Godovikova Street 9 Building-31 1st Floor, 129085, Moscow, Russia
Tel.: (7) 495 933 05 40
Emp.: 20

Digital Security Services
N.A.I.C.S.: 561621
Alexander Smirnov (Gen Mgr)

Gemalto Middle East (2)
Level 1 Commercial Building C, PO Box 500400, Dubai, United Arab Emirates (98%)
Tel.: (971) 43900150
Web Site: http://www.gemalto.com
Sales Range: $25-49.9 Million
Emp.: 65
Marketing Consulting Services
N.A.I.C.S.: 541613

Gemalto Norge AS (2)
Hoffsveien 70C, 0028, Oslo, Norway (98%)
Tel.: (47) 22417770
Web Site: http://www.gemalto.com
Emp.: 6
Support Services
N.A.I.C.S.: 561990

Gemalto Oy (2)
Myllynkivenkuja 4, PO Box 31, Vantaa, 1620, Finland
Tel.: (358) 9 89 411
Web Site: http://www.gemalto.fi
Sales Range: $125-149.9 Million
Emp.: 400
Digital Security Identity Card Mfr
N.A.I.C.S.: 326199
Tommi Nordberg (CEO)

Gemalto Philippines Inc. (2)
22/F The Enterprise Center Tower 1 6766 Ayala Ave Cor Paseo de Roxasx, Makati, 1200, Philippines
Tel.: (63) 2 884 8971
Web Site: http://www.gemalto.com
Sales Range: $25-49.9 Million
Emp.: 7
Digital Security Services
N.A.I.C.S.: 561621

Gemalto Pte Ltd. (2)
12 Ayer Rajah Crescent, Singapore, 139941, Singapore
Tel.: (65) 63173333
Web Site: http://www.gemalto.com
Sales Range: $250-299.9 Million
Emp.: 700
Electronic Parts & Equipment Whslr
N.A.I.C.S.: 423690

Gemalto Pty Ltd (2)
Level 11 Suite 3 470 Collins Street, Melbourne, 3000, VIC, Australia
Tel.: (61) 3 9910 9600
Digital Security Services
N.A.I.C.S.: 561621

Gemalto S.A. (2)
14 Route du Saint Laurent, 37171, Chambray les Tours, Cedex, France (100%)
Tel.: (33) 247748686
Web Site: http://www.gemalto.com
Sales Range: $25-49.9 Million
Emp.: 100
Support Services
N.A.I.C.S.: 561990

Subsidiary (Domestic):

Gemalto Participations S.A.S. (3)
6 Rue De La Verrerie, Meudon, 92190, France (100%)
Tel.: (33) 155015000
Web Site: http://www.gemalto.com
Open-End Investment Funds
N.A.I.C.S.: 525910

Gemalto S.A.S. (3)
Avenue du Pic de Bertagne, BP 100, 13881, Gemenos, France (98%)
Tel.: (33) 442365000
Web Site: http://www.gemalto.com
New Housing Operative Builders
N.A.I.C.S.: 236117

Subsidiary (Non-US):

Gemalto S.R.O. (2)
BBC Villas Zeletavska 1448/7, Prague, 140 00, Czech Republic
Tel.: (420) 241 051 555
Digital Security Software Consulting Services
N.A.I.C.S.: 541512
Petr Skvaril (CEO)

THALES S.A.

Thales S.A.—(Continued)

Gemalto SP S.A. (2)
Calle Llevant Pg Ind Levante 12, Parets Del Valles, Barcelona, 8150, Spain (100%)
Tel.: (34) 934628300
Web Site: http://www.gemalto.com
Sales Range: $50-74.9 Million
Emp.: 200
Plastics Product Mfr
N.A.I.C.S.: 326199

Gemalto SPA (2)
Business Center HIBISCUS Building A - 7th floor Via Mentore Maggini 50, 143, Rome, Italy
Tel.: (39) 06 977 4771
Sales Range: $25-49.9 Million
Emp.: 5
Digital Security Consulting Services
N.A.I.C.S.: 541512

Gemalto Sdn Bhd (2)
Suite 0201-0204 Level 2 Plaza See Hoy Chan, Jalan Raja Chulan, 50200, Kuala Lumpur, Malaysia (98%)
Tel.: (60) 320352888
Web Site: http://www.gemalto.com
Sales Range: $25-49.9 Million
Emp.: 60
Data Processing Services
N.A.I.C.S.: 518210

Gemalto Southern Africa Pty. Ltd. (2)
13 Friesland Drive Longmeadow Business Estate, Modderfontein, Johannesburg, 1609, South Africa (98%)
Tel.: (27) 110888500
Web Site: http://www.gemalto.com
Sales Range: $25-49.9 Million
Emp.: 58
Data Processing Services
N.A.I.C.S.: 518210

Gemalto Sp. z.o.o (2)
ul Kruczkowskiego 8 Nordic Park Building 4th Floor, Warsaw, 00380, Poland
Tel.: (48) 22 620 00 81
Digital Security Services
N.A.I.C.S.: 561621

Gemalto Sverige AB (2)
Vastberga Alle 36 C, 126 30, Hagersten, Sweden
Tel.: (46) 8 709 25 00
Digital Security Software Development Services
N.A.I.C.S.: 541511

Gemalto Taiwan Co. Ltd (2)
B1 No 192 Lien Chien Road, Chung-Ho City, Taipei, 235, Taiwan
Tel.: (886) 2 2240 7890
Digital Security Services
N.A.I.C.S.: 561621

Gemalto Technologies Asia Ltd (2)
Suite 3103 31F Citicorp Centre, 18 Whitfield Road, Causeway Bay, China (Hong Kong)
Tel.: (852) 2306 3688
Web Site: http://www.gemalto.com
Sales Range: $25-49.9 Million
Emp.: 20
Digital Security Services
N.A.I.C.S.: 561621
Clement Lam *(Office Mgr)*

Gemalto Terminals India Private Ltd (2)
802 Hallmark Business Plaza Opp Guru Nanak Hospital Sant Dnyaneshwar, Marg Bandra East, Mumbai, 400 051, India
Tel.: (91) 22 30690000
Digital Security Services
N.A.I.C.S.: 561621

Gemalto Terminals Ltd. (2)
Concorde Way, Fareham, PO15 5RX, United Kingdom (100%)
Tel.: (44) 1489889606
Sales Range: $25-49.9 Million
Emp.: 60
Measuring & Testing Electricity & Electrical Signals Instrument Mfr
N.A.I.C.S.: 334515
Andrew Bruce *(Mng Dir)*

Gemalto de Mexico S.A. de C.V. (2)
Trigo No 150 Col Granjas Esmeralda, 98100, Mexico, Mexico (100%)
Tel.: (52) 5552498800
Web Site: http://www.gemalto.com
Electrical Equipment & Component Mfr
N.A.I.C.S.: 335999

Gemalto do Brazil Cartoes e Terminais Ltda (2)
Ave Eng Luis Carlos Berrini 1 645-3 Andar, 04571-011, Sao Paulo, Brazil (100%)
Tel.: (55) 1151057600
Sales Range: $50-74.9 Million
Emp.: 127
Wired Telecommunications Carriers
N.A.I.C.S.: 517111

Gemalto eBanking (2)
Fiskhamnsgatan 2, Gothenburg, 414 58, Sweden
Tel.: (46) 3 17 75 88 00
Web Site: http://www.gemalto.com
Sales Range: $25-49.9 Million
Emp.: 46
Banking Security Software Development Services
N.A.I.C.S.: 541511

Gemplus (Tianjin) New Technologies Co. Ltd (2)
No 22 Kaihua Rd Huayuan Industrial Zone, Nankai Dist, Tianjin, 300384, China
Tel.: (86) 2283710322
Digital Security Services
N.A.I.C.S.: 561621

Subsidiary (Domestic):

Gemplus B.V. (2)
Barbara Strozzilaan 382, Amsterdam, 1083 HN, Netherlands
Tel.: (31) 20 562 0690
Sales Range: $25-49.9 Million
Emp.: 100
Digital Security Services
N.A.I.C.S.: 561621

Subsidiary (Non-US):

Goldpac Datacard Solutions Co. Ltd. (2)
Rm 1205-6 12th Floor Cigna Twr, Causeway Bay, China (Hong Kong) (65%)
Tel.: (852) 28386202
Web Site: http://www.goldpac.com
Sales Range: $25-49.9 Million
Emp.: 11
Data Processing Hosting & Related Services
N.A.I.C.S.: 518210

Goldpac International (Holding) Limited (2)
1205-06 Cigna Tower 482 Jaffe Road, Causeway Bay, China (Hong Kong)
Tel.: (852) 28386202
Investment Management Service
N.A.I.C.S.: 523940

Goldpac Secure-Card Zhuhai Ltd (2)
Jinbangda Industrial Park Fuxi, Qianshan, Zhuhai, 519070, China
Tel.: (86) 7568660888
Web Site: http://www.goldpac.com
Magnetic Stripe Card Mfr
N.A.I.C.S.: 335999

Multos International Pte Ltd (2)
No 12 Ayerajh Cresent, Singapore, 139941, Singapore
Tel.: (65) 63173333
Web Site: http://www.multosinternational.com
Smartcard Mfr
N.A.I.C.S.: 326199
Graeme Bradford *(VP-Mktg)*

Multos International Pty Ltd (2)
Level 14 Tower B Zenith Centre 821 Pacific Highway, Chatswood, 2067, NSW, Australia
Tel.: (61) 2 8622 9900
Web Site: http://www.multosinternational.com
Smartcard Operating System Mfr
N.A.I.C.S.: 333248

O3SIS Information Technologies AG (2)
Olper Strasse 33-35, Overath, 51491, Germany
Tel.: (49) 2204 7470
Web Site: http://www.o3sis.com
Sales Range: $25-49.9 Million
Emp.: 6
Wireless Communication Services
N.A.I.C.S.: 517112

PT Gemalto Indonesia (2)
Mulia Business Park Building E No 105&106 JI M T Haryono Kav C 58-60, Jakarta, 12780, Indonesia
Tel.: (62) 21 797 4978
Web Site: http://www.gemalto.com
Digital Security Services
N.A.I.C.S.: 561621

Plastikkart Akilli Kart Iletisim Sistemleri Sanayi ve Ticaret A.S. (2)
Mimar Sinan Mahallesi Trablusgarp Bulvari Blok No 5, Silivri, 34570, Istanbul, Turkiye
Tel.: (90) 2127361200
Web Site: https://www.plastkart.com.tr
Rev.: $29,618,396
Assets: $12,051,282
Liabilities: $7,262,603
Net Worth: $4,788,678
Earnings: $1,261,677
Emp.: 167
Fiscal Year-end: 12/31/2022
Card Mfr
N.A.I.C.S.: 326199
Nassir Ghrous *(Member-Mgmt Bd)*

Step Nexus Ltd (2)
St Andrews House Kelvin Close The Links Birchwood, Warrington, WA3 7PB, United Kingdom
Tel.: (44) 1925 882050
Web Site: http://www.stepnexus.com
Sales Range: $25-49.9 Million
Emp.: 2
Security Software Development Services
N.A.I.C.S.: 541511

Todos Qingdao Co. Ltd (2)
Eastern Zone 9F G2 Building Software Park No 288 Ningxia Road, Shinan District, Qingdao, 266071, China
Tel.: (86) 532 88900790
Sales Range: $25-49.9 Million
Digital Security Services
N.A.I.C.S.: 561621

Trivnet Ltd (2)
Elrod House Hamelacha 45, Netanya, 42504, Israel
Tel.: (972) 9 960 2500
Web Site: http://www.trivnet.com
Mobile Financial Transaction Services
N.A.I.C.S.: 522320

Trusted Logic Africa (Pty) Ltd (2)
Block O Greenford Office Estate Punters Way, Kenilworth, Cape Town, 7700, South Africa
Tel.: (27) 21 671 1175
Sales Range: $25-49.9 Million
Emp.: 1
Smartcard Software Development Services
N.A.I.C.S.: 541511

Trusted Logic Asia (Pte) Ltd (2)
2nd Level 12 Aver Rajah Crescent, Singapore, 139941, Singapore
Tel.: (65) 65 60 66 12
Web Site: http://www.trusted-logic.com
Software Development Services
N.A.I.C.S.: 541511

Trusted Logic S.A. (2)
6 rue de la Verrerie, 92197, Meudon, France
Tel.: (33) 1 78467600
Web Site: http://www.trusted-logic.com
Sales Range: $25-49.9 Million
Emp.: 10
Secure Software Development Services
N.A.I.C.S.: 541511

Subsidiary (Domestic):

Trusted Labs S.A.S.U. (3)
6 rue de la Verrerie, 78000, Meudon, France
Tel.: (33) 130972620
Web Site: http://www.trusted-labs.com
Sales Range: $25-49.9 Million
Secure Software Development Services
N.A.I.C.S.: 541511
Brigitte D'Heygere *(Pres)*

Subsidiary (Non-US):

Valimo Wireless Oy (2)

INTERNATIONAL PUBLIC

Turvalaaksonkaari 2, 1620, Vantaa, Finland
Tel.: (358) 9 89 411
Web Site: http://www.valimo.com
Mobile Communications Services
N.A.I.C.S.: 517112

Zhuhai Goldpac SecurCard Co. Ltd (2)
Goldpac Building Fuxi, Qianshan District, Zhuhai, 519070, Guangdong, China
Tel.: (86) 756 8660888
Magnetic Stripe Card Mfr
N.A.I.C.S.: 326199
David Lu *(Gen Mgr)*

Imperva, Inc. (1)
3400 Bridge Pkwy, Redwood Shores, CA 94065
Tel.: (650) 345-9000
Web Site: http://www.imperva.com
Sales Range: $300-349.9 Million
Emp.: 1,020
Computer Data Security Solutions & Services
N.A.I.C.S.: 513210
Terry Ray *(Sr VP)*

Subsidiary (Non-US):

Imperva Australia Pty. Ltd. (2)
1 Pacific Highway Level 12, North Sydney, 2060, NSW, Australia
Tel.: (61) 299599645
Web Site: http://www.imperva.com
Computer Data Security Solutions
N.A.I.C.S.: 513210

Imperva B.V. (2)
Sloterdijk Teleport Towers Kingsfordweg 151, 1043 GR, Amsterdam, Netherlands
Tel.: (31) 204919970
Web Site: http://www.imperva.com
Computer Data Security Solutions
N.A.I.C.S.: 513210
Haiko Wolberink *(Reg Dir)*

Imperva France SARL (2)
4 Place De La Defense Defense 4, La Defense 4, 94974, Paris, France
Tel.: (33) 1 70 15 07 99
Computer Data Security Solutions
N.A.I.C.S.: 513210

Imperva Italy SRL (2)
Regus Business Center, Via Senigallia 18/2 Torre A, 20161, Milan, Italy
Tel.: (39) 06503459000
Web Site: http://www.imperva.com
Emp.: 2
Computer Data Security Solutions
N.A.I.C.S.: 513210
Elena Accarvi *(Dir-Sls)*

Imperva Japan K.K. (2)
Yusen Shibuya 3 Chome Building 9F 3 16 1 Shibuya, Shibuya ku, Tokyo, 150-0002, Japan
Tel.: (81) 3 5464 8131
Web Site: http://www.imperva.jp
Emp.: 8
Computer Data Security Solutions
N.A.I.C.S.: 513210
Yoshihiro Nagasaka *(Dir-Sls)*

Imperva Ltd. (2)
125 Menachem Begin Street, Tel Aviv, 67010, Israel
Tel.: (972) 3 6840100
Computer Data Security Solutions
N.A.I.C.S.: 513210

Imperva Singapore Pte. (2)
7 Temasek Boulevard Suntec Tower 1 Suite 15-01, Singapore, 038987, Singapore
Tel.: (65) 68357104
Web Site: http://www.imperva.com
Emp.: 10
Computer Data Security Solutions
N.A.I.C.S.: 513210
George Lee *(Reg VP-Asia Pacific & Japan)*

Imperva UK Ltd. (2)
Venture House Arlington Square Downshire Way, Bracknell, RG12 1WA, United Kingdom
Tel.: (44) 2039615000
Web Site: http://www.imperva.com
Computer Data Security Solutions
N.A.I.C.S.: 513210

Subsidiary (Domestic):

Incapsula, Inc. (2)

AND PRIVATE COMPANIES
THALES S.A.

3400 Bridge Pkwy Ste 200, Redwood
Shores, CA 94065 **(82%)**
Tel.: (650) 523-9980
Web Site: http://www.incapsula.com
Cloud-Based Security Solutions
N.A.I.C.S.: 513210

Stesa (1)
PO Box 5463, Riyadh, 11422, Saudi Arabia
Tel.: (966) 1 419 7771
Web Site: http://www.stesa.com
Sales Range: $100-124.9 Million
Emp.: 400
Sales of Electronic Equipment
N.A.I.C.S.: 449210

TDA Armements S.A.S. (1)
Route D Ardon, 45240, La Ferte-Saint-Aubin, France
Tel.: (33) 238516363
Web Site: http://www.tda-arm.com
Military Weapon Systems & Ammunition Developer & Mfr
N.A.I.C.S.: 332993
Pierre Benard *(Chm)*

THALES - SECURITY SOLUTIONS & SERVICES Spa (1)
Via Pio Emanuelli 1/B, 00143, Rome, Italy
Tel.: (39) 0651561
Defence Software Development Services
N.A.I.C.S.: 541511

THALES INTERNATIONAL (1)
Prime Centre 16th Fl - 53 Quang Trung Street, Hanoi, Vietnam
Tel.: (84) 4 943 3027
Web Site: http://www.thalesgroup.com
Military Equipment Mfr
N.A.I.C.S.: 336413

THALES MISSIONS & CONSEIL (1)
67 rue Charles-de-Gaulle, 78350, Jouy-en-Josas, France
Tel.: (33) 1 39 56 72 00
Business Management Services
N.A.I.C.S.: 561110

THALES SECURITY SOLUTIONS & SERVICES SAS (1)
Centre du Bois des Bordes ZAC la chataigneraie, 91229, Bretigny-sur-Orge, France
Tel.: (33) 1 69 88 52 00
Defence Software Development Services
N.A.I.C.S.: 541511

THALES VP (1)
12 Rue Emile Baudot, 91873, Palaiseau, France
Tel.: (33) 1 69 19 62 00
Defence Software Development Services
N.A.I.C.S.: 541511

Thales (China) Enterprises Management Co. Ltd. (1)
Area A N27 Tianzhu Rd Tianzhu Airport Industrial Zone Shunyi, Beijing, 100125, China
Tel.: (86) 10 64573492
Web Site: http://www.thalesgroup.com
Defence Software Development Services
N.A.I.C.S.: 541511
Sophie Chen *(Gen Mgr)*

Thales (Tianjin) Radar Technologies Co., Ltd (1)
No 12 Qiangwei Road Tianjin Port Free Trade Zone Airport, Airport Industrial Park, Tianjin, 300308, China
Tel.: (86) 22 5867 9388
Web Site: http://www.thalesgroup.com
Defence Security Software Development Services
N.A.I.C.S.: 541511

Thales ATM S.A. (1)
19 Rue De La Fontaine, 92221, Bagneux, Cedex, France **(100%)**
Tel.: (33) 140843000
Mfr of Navigation Equipment, ILS Instrument Landing System, VOR VHF Omnirange, DME Distance Measuring Equipment, Differential Global Positioning Systems, Wide Area Augmentation Systems
N.A.I.C.S.: 334511

Subsidiary (Non-US):

Thales ATM GmbH (2)

Robert Bosch Str 25, 63225, Langen, Germany **(100%)**
Tel.: (49) 610391160
Sales Range: $25-49.9 Million
Emp.: 50
Mfr of Navigation Equipment, ILS Instrument Landing System, VOR VHF Omnirange, DME Distance Measuring Equipment, Differential Global Positioning Systems, Wide Area Augmentation Systems
N.A.I.C.S.: 334511

Thales ATM Ltd (2)
Compass Hamp Davis Rd, Chessington, KT9 1TB, United Kingdom **(100%)**
Tel.: (44) 2083916100
Mfr of Navigation Equipment, ILS Instrument Landing System, VOR VHF Omnirange, DME Distance Measuring Equipment, Differential Global Positioning Systems, Wide Area Augmentation Systems
N.A.I.C.S.: 334511

Thales ATM Pty Ltd. (2)
WTC North Bank Wharf Concourse Level Siddeley Street, Melbourne, 3005, Australia **(100%)**
Tel.: (61) 394257400
Sales Range: $25-49.9 Million
Emp.: 250
Mfr of Navigation Equipment, ILS Instrument Landing System, VOR VHF Omnirange, DME Distance Measuring Equipment, Differential Global Positioning Systems, Wide Area Augmentation Systems
N.A.I.C.S.: 334511
Adam Burford *(Pres)*

Thales AVS France SAS (1)
60 Rue du Pommarin, 38340, Moirans, France
Tel.: (33) 476574000
Stationery Product Distr
N.A.I.C.S.: 424120
Adrien Panzuti *(Product Mgr-Engrg)*

Thales Aerospace Asia Pte Ltd (1)
21 Changi North Rise, 498788, 498788, Singapore
Tel.: (65) 6424 7100
Web Site: http://www.thalesgroup.com
Sales Range: $200-249.9 Million
Emp.: 60
Aircraft Systems Mfr
N.A.I.C.S.: 336411

Thales Air Defence (1)
Ctr De Bagneux 7 9 Rue Des Mathurins, 92221, Bagneux, Cedex, France **(100%)**
Tel.: (33) 140844000
Web Site: http://www.thales-airdefence.com
Sales Range: $50-74.9 Million
Emp.: 120
N.A.I.C.S.: 334511

Subsidiary (Non-US):

Forges De Zeebrugge (2)
Rue En Bois 63, 4040, Herstal, Belgium **(100%)**
Tel.: (32) 42482077
Web Site: http://www.fz.be
Sales Range: $25-49.9 Million
Emp.: 54
Mfr of Air-to-Ground Rocket Systems
N.A.I.C.S.: 336414
Brigitte Piette *(Mgr-Fin)*

Affiliate (Non-US):

Stesa (2)
PO Box 5463, Riyadh, 11422, Saudi Arabia **(49%)**
Tel.: (966) 1 291 2000
Web Site: http://www.stesa.com
Electronic Defence & Communications Systems Mfr
N.A.I.C.S.: 541512

Subsidiary (Non-US):

Thales Air Defence Ltd (2)
Alanbrooke Road, Castlereagh, Belfast, BT6 9HB, United Kingdom **(100%)**
Tel.: (44) 890465200
Mfr of Ground-to-Air Missile Systems
N.A.I.C.S.: 336414

Subsidiary (Domestic):

Thales-Raytheon Systems Company SAS (2)

1 Avenue Carnot, 91883, Massy, Cedex, France **(100%)**
Tel.: (33) 169755000
Web Site: http://www.thalesraytheon.com
Air Command, Control & Defense Systems Developer & Mfr
N.A.I.C.S.: 334511
Philippe Duhamel *(CEO-French Ops)*

Subsidiary (Domestic):

Air Command Systems International (3)
1 Ave Carnot, 91883, Massy, Cedex, France
Tel.: (33) 169756000
Web Site: http://www.thalesraytheon.com
Sales Range: $50-74.9 Million
Emp.: 200
Radar Sys
N.A.I.C.S.: 334511
Michel Irle *(Mng Dir)*

Thales Air Systems (1)
21 Changi North Rise, Singapore, 498788, Singapore
Tel.: (65) 6424 7100
Aircraft Parts Whslr
N.A.I.C.S.: 423860

Thales Air Systems GmbH (1)
Thales Plat 1, Ditzingen, 71254, Germany
Tel.: (49) 711860320
Defence Security & Aerospace Electronic Devices Mfr
N.A.I.C.S.: 811310

Thales Air Systems Ltd (1)
Alanbrooke Road, Castlereagh, Belfast, BT6 9HB, United Kingdom
Tel.: (44) 2890 465 200
Web Site: http://www.thalesgroup.com
Sales Range: $100-124.9 Million
Emp.: 477
Aircraft Equipment Mfr
N.A.I.C.S.: 336413
David Peattie *(Gen Mgr)*

Thales Air Systems SA (1)
105 Avenue du General Eisenhower, 31037, Toulouse, France
Tel.: (33) 5 61 19 65 00
Aviation Software Development Services
N.A.I.C.S.: 541511

Subsidiary (US):

Thales Rail Signaling Solutions (2)
5700 Corporate Dr Ste 750, Pittsburgh, PA 15237
Tel.: (412) 366-8814
Sales Range: $25-49.9 Million
Emp.: 30
Train Control & Signalling Equipment Mfr
N.A.I.C.S.: 238210

Thales Airborne Systems Canada (1)
1 Chrysalis Way, Nepean, K2G 5X3, ON, Canada
Tel.: (613) 723-7000
Aeronautical System Mfr
N.A.I.C.S.: 334511

Thales Alenia Space SAS (1)
100 Boulevard du Midi, La Bocca, 06150, Cannes, France **(67%)**
Tel.: (33) 492923310
Web Site: https://www.thalesgroup.com
Sales Range: $1-4.9 Billion
Emp.: 7,500
Holding Company; Satellite & Orbital Infrastructure Mfr
N.A.I.C.S.: 551112
Martin Van Schaik *(Sr VP-Sls)*

Subsidiary (Non-US):

Thales Alenia Space (2)
Berkenrodelei 33, 2660, Hoboken, Belgium
Tel.: (32) 38295111
Web Site: http://www.thalesgroup.com
Sales Range: $25-49.9 Million
Emp.: 45
Provider of Satellite Communications & Control Solutions
N.A.I.C.S.: 517410
Ina Maller *(CEO)*

Thales Alenia Space Espana (2)
Einstein 7, 28760, Madrid, Spain

Tel.: (34) 918077900
Web Site: http://www.thalesalenia.com
Sales Range: $50-74.9 Million
Emp.: 200
Mfr & Developer of Space-Based Communication Systems Hardware;
N.A.I.C.S.: 927110
Eduardo Bellido *(CEO)*

Subsidiary (Domestic):

Thales Alenia Space France SAS (2)
26 Avenue Jean Francois Champollion, 31100, Toulouse, France
Tel.: (33) 534353637
Web Site: https://www.thalesalenia.com
Sales Range: $25-49.9 Million
Emp.: 130
Satellite Communications Systems Mfr
N.A.I.C.S.: 334290
Nathalie Smirnov *(Exec VP-Telecom Bus Line)*

Subsidiary (US):

Thales Alenia Space North America, Inc. (2)
20400 Stevens Creek Blvd, Cupertino, CA 95014
Tel.: (408) 973-9845
Web Site: http://www.thalesgroup.com
Satellite Communications Systems Mfr
N.A.I.C.S.: 334290
Eddie Kato *(CEO)*

Thales Asia Pte Ltd (1)
21 Changi North Rise, 498788, Singapore, 498788, Singapore
Tel.: (65) 6594 6870
Sales Range: $150-199,9 Million
Emp.: 55
Logistics & Transportation Services
N.A.I.C.S.: 541614

Thales Australia Pty. Ltd. (1)
7 Murray Rose Ave, Sydney, 2011, NSW, Australia
Tel.: (61) 280376000
Web Site: https://www.thalesgroup.com.au
Sales Range: $550-599.9 Million
Emp.: 2,500
Defence Engineering Contractor
N.A.I.C.S.: 237990
Paul McClintock *(Chm)*

Subsidiary (Domestic):

Tesserent Limited (2)
Level 5 990 Whitehorse Road, Box Hill, 3128, VIC, Australia
Tel.: (61) 398805555
Web Site: http://www.tesserent.com
Rev.: $52,371,385
Assets: $138,779,995
Liabilities: $71,636,466
Net Worth: $67,143,528
Earnings: ($3,473,139)
Emp.: 85
Fiscal Year-end: 06/30/2021
Internet Security Services
N.A.I.C.S.: 561621
Oliver Carton *(Sec)*

Subsidiary (Domestic):

Loop Secure Pty. Ltd. (3)
Suite 7 03 Level 7 25 Bligh Street, Sydney, NSW, Australia
Tel.: (61) 1300884218
Web Site: https://www.loopsec.com.au
Emp.: 45
Cyber Security Services
N.A.I.C.S.: 541690

Secure Logic Pty. Ltd. (3)
Level 23 International Tower 3 300 Barangaroo Avenue, Sydney, NSW, Australia
Tel.: (61) 290072111
Web Site: https://securelogicgroup.com
Cyber Security Services
N.A.I.C.S.: 561612

Division (Domestic):

Thales Australia - Civil (2)
274 Victoria Road, Rydalmere, 2116, NSW, Australia
Tel.: (61) 298483500
Web Site: http://www.thalesgroup.com.au
Security Systems

THALES S.A.

Thales S.A.—(Continued)
N.A.I.C.S.: 561621
Ian Mcelroy *(VP)*

Thales Australia - Defence Services & Aerospace (2)
Garden island 2011, Sydney, 2011, NSW, Australia
Tel.: (61) 295623333
Web Site: http://www.thalesgroup.com.au
Sales Range: $25-49.9 Million
Emp.: 100
Aerospace Defense
N.A.I.C.S.: 488190
Miller Crawford *(Mng Dir)*

Thales Australia - Land (2)
Level 18 607 Bourke Street, Melbourne, 3000, VIC, Australia
Tel.: (61) 3 8614 2222
Web Site: http://www.thalesgroup.com
Small Arms & Explosive Mfr
N.A.I.C.S.: 332999
Darryl Page *(VP)*

Thales Australia Centre-Air Operations (2)
WTC Northbank Wharf Atrium Lobby Level, Siddeley Street, Melbourne, 3005, VIC, Australia
Tel.: (61) 394257400
Web Site: http://www.thalesgroup.com
Air Traffic Control Management
N.A.I.C.S.: 488111
Chris Jenkins *(CEO)*

Thales Australia Ltd. - Armaments Division (2)
Level 3 Building 51, Garden Island, Sydney, 2011, NSW, Australia
Tel.: (61) 2 9562 3333
Weapon & Ammunition System Mfr
N.A.I.C.S.: 336992
Chris Jenkins *(Mng Dir)*

Thales Australia Ltd. - Maritime & Aerospace Division (2)
274 Victoria Rd, Locked Bag 3000, Garden Island Potts Point, Rydalmere, 2116, NSW, Australia
Tel.: (61) 2 9562 3333
Maritime & Aerospace Software Development Services
N.A.I.C.S.: 541511

Thales Australia Ltd. - National Security & C4I Division (2)
Equinox 3 70 Kent Street, PO Box 158, Deakin West, Deakin, 2600, ACT, Australia
Tel.: (61) 2 6234 6000
Web Site: http://www.thalesgroup.com
Defence Software Development Services
N.A.I.C.S.: 541511

Thales Australia Ltd. - Protected Vehicles Division (2)
Level 1 Building 314, Garden Island, Sydney, 2011, NSW, Australia
Tel.: (61) 2 9562 3333
Protected Vehicle Mfr
N.A.I.C.S.: 336992

Thales Australia Ltd. - Transport Division (2)
Level 2 Building 314, Locked Bag 3000, Garden Island Potts Point, Sydney, 2011, NSW, Australia
Tel.: (61) 2 9562 3333
Web Site: http://www.thalesgroup.com
Maritime Software Development Services
N.A.I.C.S.: 541511

Thales Austria GmbH (1)
Handelskai 92, 1210, Vienna, Austria
Tel.: (43) 1277210
Web Site: http://www.thalesgroup.com
Emp.: 350
Defence Software Development Services
N.A.I.C.S.: 541511
Alfred Veider *(CEO)*

Thales Avionics SA (1)
1 avenue Carnot, 91883, Massy, Cedex, France (100%)
Tel.: (33) 69755000
Web Site: http://www.thalesgroup.com
Sales Range: $900-999.9 Million
Emp.: 3,892

Cockpit Avionics, Utilities & Inflight Entertainment Sys
N.A.I.C.S.: 336413

Joint Venture (US):

Aviation Communication & Surveillance Systems, LLC (2)
19810 N 7th Ave, Phoenix, AZ 85027-4400
Tel.: (623) 445-7000
Web Site: http://www.acss.com
Sales Range: $100-124.9 Million
Emp.: 300
Safety Avionics Systems Mfr
N.A.I.C.S.: 334111
Kris Ganase *(Pres)*

Joint Venture (Non-US):

Diehl Aerospace GmbH (2)
Alte Nussdorfer Strasse 23, D 88662, Uberlingen, Germany
Tel.: (49) 75518902
Web Site: http://www.diehl-aerospace.de
Sales Range: $125-149.9 Million
Emp.: 425
Development of Missiles, Flight Training Systems & Munitions
N.A.I.C.S.: 336414

Subsidiary (Domestic):

Diehl Aerospace GmbH (3)
An der Sanelmuhle 13, 60439, Frankfurt, Germany
Tel.: (49) 6958050
Web Site: http://www.diehl-aerospace.de
Sales Range: $100-124.9 Million
Emp.: 400
Development of Missiles, Flight Training Systems & Munitions
N.A.I.C.S.: 336414
Gerardo Walle *(Pres & Mng Dir)*

Subsidiary (US):

Thales Avionics (2)
58 Discovery, Irvine, CA 92618 (100%)
Tel.: (949) 660-7722
Web Site: http://www.thalesgroup.com
Sales Range: $200-249.9 Million
Emp.: 900
Inflight Entertainment Systems Mfr
N.A.I.C.S.: 336413
Minhhai Nguyen *(Engr-Sys Network Software)*

Branch (Domestic):

Thales Avionics (3)
2811 102th St SW, Seattle, WA 98168-3407
Tel.: (206) 575-0920
Web Site: http://www.thalesgroup.com
Sales Range: $25-49.9 Million
Emp.: 63
Cockpit Avionics, Utilities & Inflight Entertainment Systems
N.A.I.C.S.: 423860

Thales Avionics, Inc. (3)
3920 Park Ave, Edison, NJ 08820-3002 (60%)
Tel.: (732) 494-1010
Sales Range: $50-74.9 Million
Emp.: 160
Aircraft Equipment & Supplies Mfr
N.A.I.C.S.: 336999

Subsidiary (Non-US):

Thales Avionics Asia Pte Ltd (2)
4 Loyang Ln 06 01, Singapore, 508914, Singapore
Tel.: (65) 65422533
Web Site: http://www.thalesgroup.com
Cockpit Avionics, Utilities & Inflight Entertainment Sys
N.A.I.C.S.: 336413

Thales Avionics Canada, Inc. (2)
2800 Marie-Curie, Saint Laurent, H4S 2C2, QC, Canada (100%)
Tel.: (514) 832-0900
Web Site: http://www.thalescanada.com
Sales Range: $25-49.9 Million
Emp.: 160
Aviation Engineering Development Services
N.A.I.C.S.: 541330

Thales Avionics Ltd

88 Bushey Rd, London, SW20 0JW, United Kingdom (100%)
Tel.: (44) 89468011
Web Site: http://www.thalesgroup.com
Sales Range: $75-99.9 Million
Emp.: 380
Mfr of Helicopter Avionics Sys
N.A.I.C.S.: 336413

Subsidiary (Domestic):

Thales Avionics S.A (2)
Tour caro diem 31 CS 20001, La Defense, 92526, Paris, France (100%)
Tel.: (33) 157778000
Web Site: http://www.thalesgroup.com
Sales Range: $150-199.9 Million
Emp.: 1,000
Cockpit Avionics, Utilities & Inflight Entertainment Sys
N.A.I.C.S.: 336413

Thales Avionics S.A (2)
Rue Toussaint Catros, 33187, Le Haillan, Cedex, France (100%)
Tel.: (33) 556135000
Web Site: http://www.thalesgroup.com
Sales Range: $150-199.9 Million
Emp.: 1,000
Mfr of Military Avionics
N.A.I.C.S.: 336413
Dominique Ginnoni *(Mng Dir)*

Thales Avionics SA (2)
25 Rue Jules Vedrines, 26027, Valence, Cedex, France (100%)
Tel.: (33) 475798511
Web Site: http://www.thalesgroup.com
Sales Range: $25-49.9 Million
Emp.: 800
Mfr of Helicopter Avionics Sys
N.A.I.C.S.: 336413

Subsidiary (Non-US):

Thales Avionics SpA (2)
Via Sempione 26 L, 21029, Vergiate, Italy (100%)
Tel.: (39) 0331946123
Web Site: http://www.thalesgroup.com
Cockpit Avionics, Utilities & Inflight Entertainment Sys
N.A.I.C.S.: 336413

Thales Canada, Systems Division (1)
1 Chrysalas Way, Ottawa, K2G 6P9, ON, Canada (100%)
Tel.: (613) 723-7000
Web Site: http://www.thales-systems.ca
Sales Range: $50-74.9 Million
Emp.: 150
Defence Systems Integration
N.A.I.C.S.: 334511

Thales Communications S.A (1)
160 Blvd De Valmy, PO Box 82, 92704, Colombes, Cedex, France (100%)
Tel.: (33) 0141303000
Web Site: http://www.thales-communications.com
Sales Range: $800-899.9 Million
Emp.: 4,100
Mfr & Supplier of Airborne & Naval Communications Systems
N.A.I.C.S.: 334511

Subsidiary (Domestic):

Thales Communications & Security SA (2)
20-22 Rue Grange Dame Rose, 78141, Velizy-Villacoublay, France
Tel.: (33) 1 73 32 00 00
Communications & Security Services
N.A.I.C.S.: 517810

Subsidiary (Non-US):

Thales Communications B,V (2)
Bestevaer 46, 1271 ZA, Huizen, Netherlands (100%)
Tel.: (31) 355248248
Web Site: http://www.thales-communications.nl
Sales Range: $25-49.9 Million
Emp.: 240
Defense & Civil Communications Systems
N.A.I.C.S.: 334290

Thales Communications Belgium S.A (2)

28 Rue Des Freres Taymans, Tubize, 1480, Belgium (100%)
Tel.: (32) 23912211
Web Site: http://www.thales-communications.com
Sales Range: $25-49.9 Million
Emp.: 150
Mfr of Military & Civilian Communications Systems
N.A.I.C.S.: 334290
Alain Quezrien *(Mng Dir)*

Thales Communications S.pA (2)
Via Vincenzo Bellini, 24, 00198, Rome, Italy
Tel.: (39) 06 841 22 08
Web Site: http://www.thales-communications.com
Sales Range: $25-49.9 Million
Emp.: 100
Holding Company; Electronics & Defense Systems
N.A.I.C.S.: 551112

Thales Communications UK Ltd (2)
Manor Royal, Crawley, RH10 9HA, West Sussex, United Kingdom (100%)
Tel.: (44) 1293580000
Sales Range: $350-399.9 Million
Emp.: 2,000
Mfr & Supplier of Civil & Military Communications Systems
N.A.I.C.S.: 334290

Subsidiary (Domestic):

Thales E-Security Ltd (3)
Meadow View House, Long Credon, Aylesbury, HP18 9EQ, Buckinghamshire, United Kingdom
Tel.: (44) 844201800
Web Site: http://www.thales-esecurity.com
Supplier of Cryptographic Security Products & Solutions
N.A.I.C.S.: 561621

Subsidiary (Domestic):

Thales E-Security Ltd (4)
Manor Royal, Crawley, RH10 9HA, West Sussex, United Kingdom (100%)
Tel.: (44) 1844201800
Web Site: http://www.thales-esecurity.com
Sales Range: $10-24.9 Million
Emp.: 50
Supplier of Cryptographic Security Products & Solutions
N.A.I.C.S.: 561621

Subsidiary (US):

Thales E-Security, Inc. (4)
900 South Pine Island Rd Ste 710, Plantation, FL 33324 (100%)
Tel.: (954) 888-6200
Web Site: http://www.thalesesecurity.com
Sales Range: $10-24.9 Million
Emp.: 117
Supplier of Cryptographic Security Products & Solutions
N.A.I.C.S.: 334419
Cindy Provin *(Pres)*

Subsidiary (Domestic):

Vormetric, Inc. (5)
2545 N 1st St, San Jose, CA 95131
Tel.: (408) 433-6000
Web Site: http://www.vormetric.com
Sales Range: $1-9.9 Million
Emp.: 90
Computer Related Services
N.A.I.C.S.: 541519
Tina Stewart *(VP-Mktg)*

Branch (Domestic):

Thales Communications-Massy (2)
3 rue Ampere, F-91349, Massy, Cedex, France (100%)
Tel.: (33) 69 75 50 00
Web Site: http://www.thalesgroup.com
Sales Range: $25-49.9 Million
Emp.: 315
Design & Development of Defense Information Systems
N.A.I.C.S.: 541511

Subsidiary (Non-US):

Thales Electronic Systems GmbH (2)

INTERNATIONAL PUBLIC

AND PRIVATE COMPANIES — THALES S.A.

Ostendstrasse 3, D-75175, Pforzheim, Germany
Tel.: (49) 7231150
Web Site: http://www.thales.com
Sales Range: $75-99.9 Million
Emp.: 400
Military & Civil Communications Systems Mfr
N.A.I.C.S.: 334290
Peter Obermark (Pres)

Thales Norway A/S (2)
Nidre Vollh 11, Okern Nringspark, Etterstad, 0580, Oslo, Norway **(100%)**
Tel.: (47) 22638300
Web Site: http://www.thalesgroup.com
Sales Range: $50-74.9 Million
Emp.: 150
Sale of Communications Equipment
N.A.I.C.S.: 423690
Tom Tuhus (CEO)

Thales e-Security (Asia) Ltd. (2)
Units 4101 45 th floor 248 Queens Row, Ast East, Hong Kong, China (Hong Kong) **(100%)**
Tel.: (852) 28158633
Web Site: http://www.thales-esecurity.com
Sales Range: $10-24.9 Million
Emp.: 15
Supplier of Cryptographic Security Products & Services
N.A.I.C.S.: 561621
Richard Mallett (Mng Dir)

Thales Computers France (1)
19-21 Avenue Morane Saulnier, 92366, Velizy-Villacoublay, France
Tel.: (33) 139455976
Computer Peripheral Equipment Mfr
N.A.I.C.S.: 334118

Thales Consulting & Engineering (1)
Mountbatten House Basing View, Basingstoke, RG21 4HJ, United Kingdom
Tel.: (44) 1256 376600
Engineeering Services
N.A.I.C.S.: 541330

Thales Corporate Services Ltd (1)
2 Dashwood Lang Road The Bourne Business Park, Weybridge, Addlestone, KT15 2NX, United Kingdom
Tel.: (44) 1932 824 800
Emp.: 100
Transportation Services
N.A.I.C.S.: 488999

Thales Corporate Ventures (1)
Tour Carpe Diem 31 Place des Corolles, CS 20001, La Defense, 92098, Paris, France **(100%)**
Tel.: (33) 157778000
Web Site: http://www.ventures.thalesgroup.com
Rev.: $250,000,000
Holding Company; Venture Capital Investments
N.A.I.C.S.: 551112

Thales Critical Information Systems (1)
Casp 17-2, 8010, Barcelona, Spain
Tel.: (34) 912737200
Information System Services
N.A.I.C.S.: 519290
Laurent Maury (VP-Critical Info Sys & Cybersecurity)

Thales Deutschland GmbH (1)
Lorenzstrasse 10, 70435, Stuttgart, Germany
Tel.: (49) 7 11 86 90
Web Site: http://www.thalesgroup.com
Sales Range: $150-199.9 Million
Emp.: 900
Aerospace Defence & Security Services
N.A.I.C.S.: 561621
Peter Obermark (CEO)

Subsidiary (Domestic):

Thales Defence & Security Systems GmbH (2)
Ostendstrasse 3, Pforzheim, 75175, Germany
Tel.: (49) 7231150
Defence Software Development Services
N.A.I.C.S.: 541511
Peter Obermark (Gen Mgr)

Thales Defence Deutschland (2)
Edison Str 3 7051, Kiel, 24145, Germany **(100%)**
Tel.: (49) 4317109245
Web Site: http://www.thales-naval.de
Sales Range: $50-74.9 Million
Emp.: 170
Mfr & Supplier of Naval Combat & Communications Systems
N.A.I.C.S.: 334290
Peter Obermark (Gen Mgr)

Thales Defence Deutschland GmbH (2)
Hermann New Blohm Str No 3, D 20457, Hamburg, Germany **(100%)**
Tel.: (49) 31993070
Web Site: http://www.thales-naval.de
Sales Range: $25-49.9 Million
Emp.: 40
Mfr & Supplier of Naval Combat & Communications Systems
N.A.I.C.S.: 334290

Thales Naval GmbH (2)
Kurt-Schumacher-Strasse 241, D-26356, Wilhelmshaven, Germany **(100%)**
Tel.: (49) 4421755970
Web Site: http://www.thales-naval.de
Mfr & Supplier of Naval Combat & Communications Systems
N.A.I.C.S.: 334290

Thales Electron Devices S.A (1)
2 Rue Marcel Dassault, 78140, Velizy-Villacoublay, France **(100%)**
Tel.: (33) 130703500
Sales Range: $200-249.9 Million
Emp.: 1,000
Mfr of Electronic Devices
N.A.I.C.S.: 334419

Subsidiary (Non-US):

Shanghai Thales Electron Tubes Ltd (2)
205 Yuanxin Rd Baoshan City Industrial Pk, Shanghai, 200444, China
Tel.: (86) 2136160302
Web Site: http://www.shthales.com
Sales Range: $25-49.9 Million
Emp.: 100
Supplier of Digital X-Ray Detection Equipment
N.A.I.C.S.: 334517
Mingkang Wu (Gen Mgr)

Thales Electron Devices (2)
Mountbatten House, Basing View, Basingstoke, RG21 4HJ, Hampshire, United Kingdom **(100%)**
Tel.: (44) 1256387800
Web Site: http://www.thalesgroup.com
Sales Range: $10-24.9 Million
Emp.: 3
Mfr of Electronic Devices
N.A.I.C.S.: 334419

Thales Electron Devices GmbH (2)
Soeflinger Strasse 100, 89077, Ulm, Germany **(100%)**
Tel.: (49) 7319331940
Sales Range: $75-99.9 Million
Emp.: 400
Mfr of Electronic Devices
N.A.I.C.S.: 334413

Unit (Domestic):

Thales Electron Devices S.A. - RF & Microwave Sources (2)
2 avenue ZI de Vongy, BP 84, 74200, Thonon-les-Bains, France
Tel.: (33) 4 50 26 8300
Electron Tube Mfr
N.A.I.C.S.: 334419

Thales Electron Devices S.A. - XRIS (2)
460 Rue Du Pommarin ZA Centr Alp, Moirans, 38146, France
Tel.: (33) 4 76 57 4000
Web Site: http://www.thalesgroup.com
Emp.: 200
Electric Device Mfr
N.A.I.C.S.: 334419
Didier Gallet (Gen Mgr)

Subsidiary (Non-US):

Thales Italia SpA - Components Division (2)
Via Tiburtina 1072, 00151, Rome, Italy
Tel.: (39) 066390248
Web Site: http://www.thalesgroup.com
Supplier of Electronic Devices
N.A.I.C.S.: 334517

Thales Suisse SA (2)
Binzstrasse 18, CH-8045, Zurich, Switzerland **(100%)**
Tel.: (41) 444571717
Web Site: https://www.thalesgroup.com
Sales Range: $25-49.9 Million
Emp.: 800
Mfr of Electronic Devices
N.A.I.C.S.: 334419
Bruno Giger (CEO)

Subsidiary (Domestic):

Trixell (2)
460 Rue Du Pommarin, 38430, Moirans, France **(100%)**
Tel.: (33) 476574100
Web Site: https://www.trixcell.com
Sales Range: $75-99.9 Million
Emp.: 400
Mfr of Digital X-Ray Detection Equipment
N.A.I.C.S.: 334517

Thales Electronic Systems S.A. (1)
48 Konstantinoupoleos Str, 194 00, Koropi, Greece **(100%)**
Tel.: (30) 2106684200
Web Site: http://www.thalesgroup.com
Sales Range: $25-49.9 Million
Emp.: 100
Electronic Components Mfr
N.A.I.C.S.: 334417

Thales Espana GRP, SAU (1)
C/De la Mora n 39 Poligono Industrial Badalona Sur, Parque Empresarial Grand Land, 08918, Barcelona, Spain
Tel.: (34) 93 356 82 20
Web Site: http://www.thalesgroup.com
Defence Security System Services
N.A.I.C.S.: 541511

Subsidiary (Domestic):

Amper Programas de Electronica y Comunicaciones S.A (2)
Avenida Leonardo da Vinci 15 Getafe, 28906, Madrid, Spain
Tel.: (34) 914532400
Military Communications & Electronic Systems Mfr
N.A.I.C.S.: 517112
Rafael Posada (Dir Gen)

Thales Holdings UK PLC (1)
2 Dashwood Lang Rd, The Bourne Business Park, Addlestone, KT12 2NX, Surrey, United Kingdom
Tel.: (44) 2074848070
Web Site: http://www.thalesgroup.com
Holding Company
N.A.I.C.S.: 551112

Subsidiary (Domestic):

Thales UK Ltd (2)
2 Dashwood Lang Road The Boune Business Park, Addlestone, KT12 2NX, Surrey, United Kingdom
Tel.: (44) 1293 528287
Aerospace & Defensive Information Systems Mfr
N.A.I.C.S.: 513210

Subsidiary (Domestic):

Thales Naval Ltd (3)
Building 550 Bristol Business Park, Bristol, BS16 1EJ, United Kingdom
Tel.: (44) 117 314 6000
Sales Range: $50-74.9 Million
Emp.: 15
Security System Mfr
N.A.I.C.S.: 332992

Thales Training & Simulation Ltd (3)
Manor Royal, Crawley, RH10 9HA, West Sussex, United Kingdom
Tel.: (44) 1293 580 000
Web Site: http://www.thalesgroup.com
Emp.: 3,000
Aircraft Training Services
N.A.I.C.S.: 611430

Thales Transport & Security Ltd (3)
Poseidon House Ashurst Drive Bird Hall Lane Cheadle Heath, Stockport, SK3 0XB, United Kingdom
Tel.: (44) 161 491 4001
Web Site: http://www.thales.com
Defence Security & Aerospace Application Mfr
N.A.I.C.S.: 336992

Thales Underwater Systems Ltd (3)
Ocean House Troop Road, Templecombe, BA11 2TA, United Kingdom
Tel.: (44) 1963 370551
Web Site: http://www.thales.co.uk
Emp.: 75
Defence Security & Aerospace Technology Services
N.A.I.C.S.: 541690

Thales Identification Systems (1)
41 Blvd De La Republique, PO Box 53, 78401, Chatou, France **(100%)**
Tel.: (33) 134807674
Sales Range: $25-49.9 Million
Emp.: 200
Identification Cards Mfr
N.A.I.C.S.: 561621

Subsidiary (US):

Thales Identification Systems (2)
675 N Washington St, Alexandria, VA 22202-2054 **(100%)**
Tel.: (703) 838-9685
Web Site: http://www.thales.com
Sales Range: $10-24.9 Million
Emp.: 50
Provider of Security Services in the Form of Identification Cards
N.A.I.C.S.: 561621

Thales India Pvt Ltd (1)
Statesman House - 11th Floor B-148 Barakhamba Road, New Delhi, 110001, India
Tel.: (91) 11 43531800
Web Site: http://www.thalesgroup.com
Sales Range: $50-74.9 Million
Emp.: 215
Aircraft Machinery Mfr
N.A.I.C.S.: 336411

Thales India Pvt. Ltd. (1)
201 A Sarjan Plaza 2nd Floor 100 Dr Annie Basant Rd, Mumbai, 400018, Worli, India **(75%)**
Tel.: (91) 22 611 77000
Emp.: 300
Management & Support Technology Services for Civil & Military Programs
N.A.I.C.S.: 541519

Thales Insurance & Risk Management S.A. (1)
45 Rue De Villiers, 92526, Neuilly-sur-Seine, France
Tel.: (33) 1 57 77 80 00
Insurance & Risk Management Services
N.A.I.C.S.: 524298

Thales Intellectual Property (1)
31-33 Ave Aristide Briand, 94110, Arcueil, Cedex, France **(100%)**
Tel.: (33) 141484500
Web Site: http://www.marks.com
Sales Range: $25-49.9 Million
Emp.: 5
Provider of Licensing Agreements, Technology Transfers, Consulting & Development Services
N.A.I.C.S.: 541611
Cristian Nguem (Gen Mgr)

Thales International (1)
Redec Plaza Building, PO Box 60125, Riyadh, 11545, Saudi Arabia **(100%)**
Tel.: (966) 14792880
Sales of Electronic Equipment
N.A.I.C.S.: 449210

Thales International (1)
7th Floor Graha Niaga Jalan 26, Jenderal Sudirnam Kav 58, Jakarta, 12190, Indonesia **(100%)**
Tel.: (62) 212526768
Sales Range: $50-74.9 Million
Emp.: 200
Electronic Equipment & Systems
N.A.I.C.S.: 449210
Leonard Greindl (Country Dir)

Thales International (1)

THALES S.A.   INTERNATIONAL PUBLIC

Thales S.A.—(Continued)
20 rue Aicha El Taymouria El Zahra Twr, Garden City 5th Fl, Cairo, Egypt **(100%)**
Tel.: (20) 227924611
Web Site: http://www.thalesgroup.com
Sales Range: $50-74.9 Million
Emp.: 7
Electronic Defense Systems
N.A.I.C.S.: 334220

Thales International (1)
4-17 Pokrovsky Blvd, Batiment 3 Appart 4-6, 101000, Moscow, Russia **(100%)**
Tel.: (7) 4959377078
Web Site: http://www.thalesgroup.com
Sales Range: $50-74.9 Million
Emp.: 10
Provider of Electronic Defense Systems
N.A.I.C.S.: 334220
Alla Kuznetsova *(Head-Representative Office)*

Thales International (1)
Al-Selam Tower 18th Floor Fhad Al-Selam Street, PO Box 22514, Kuwait, 13086, Kuwait
Tel.: (965) 2240 6536
Sales Range: $25-49.9 Million
Emp.: 3
Defence Software Development Services
N.A.I.C.S.: 541511

Thales International (1)
Way 3017 Hinse 1345, Shatti Al Qurum, Muscat, Oman
Tel.: (968) 2469 9257
Web Site: http://www.thalesgroup.com
Emp.: 4
Software Development Services
N.A.I.C.S.: 541511
Michael Smith *(Gen Mgr)*

Thales International - China (1)
Unit 1300 Beijing Sunflower Tower, Chaoyang District, Beijing, 100026, China **(100%)**
Tel.: (86) 65003392
Web Site: http://www.thalesgroup.com.cn
Sales Range: $25-49.9 Million
Emp.: 20
Electronic Equipment & Systems
N.A.I.C.S.: 449210

Thales International BV (1)
Avenue de Cortenbergh 60, 1000, Brussels, Belgium
Tel.: (32) 2 627 03 10
Defence Software Development Services
N.A.I.C.S.: 541511
Marc Cathelineau *(Gen Mgr)*

Thales International Brasil Ltda (1)
Av Presidente Antonio Carlos 58 10 Floor, 20030 021, Rio de Janeiro, Brazil
Tel.: (55) 21 22 72 32 00
Web Site: http://www.thalesgroup.com
Sales Range: $25-49.9 Million
Emp.: 2
Defence & Security Application Mfr
N.A.I.C.S.: 336992

Thales International Chile Ltda (1)
Isidora Goyenechea 3250 Fl 3, Las Condes, Santiago, Chile **(100%)**
Tel.: (56) 26798700
Web Site: http://www.thalesgroup.com
Sales Range: $25-49.9 Million
Emp.: 29
Provider of Electronic Defense Systems
N.A.I.C.S.: 334511

Thales International Deutschland GmbH (1)
Godesberger Allee 90, D 53175, Bonn, Germany **(100%)**
Tel.: (49) 228819940
Web Site: http://www.thalesgroup.com
Sales Range: $25-49.9 Million
Emp.: 5
Sales of Electronic Systems
N.A.I.C.S.: 238210

Thales International Europe B.V. (1)
WTC Amsterdam Airport Schiphol Blvd 143, 1118 BG, Schiphol, Netherlands
Tel.: (31) 20 4055300
Sales Range: $25-49.9 Million
Emp.: 15
Security System Services
N.A.I.C.S.: 561621
Bertrand Saurel *(CEO)*

Thales International Greece S.A. (1)
48 Konstantinoupoleos, 19400, Koropi, Greece
Tel.: (30) 210 66 84 200
Emp.: 35
Defence Software Development Services
N.A.I.C.S.: 541511

Thales International Japan KK (1)
Akasaka MK Bldg Akasaka 4 9 9, Minato Ku, Tokyo, 107-0052, Japan **(100%)**
Tel.: (81) 357851800
Electronic Equipment & Systems
N.A.I.C.S.: 449210

Thales International Middle East FZE (1)
Dubai Airport Free Zone 5th fl Bldg 5A, PO Box 54339, West Wing, Dubai, United Arab Emirates
Tel.: (971) 4 299 28 08
Web Site: http://www.thalesgroup.com
Emp.: 50
Electrical & Electronic Equipment Distr
N.A.I.C.S.: 423610
Mark Duslot *(Mng Dir)*

Thales International Nederland B.V. (1)
Haakdbrer St 49, PO Box 42, 7554 PA, Hengelo, Netherlands **(100%)**
Tel.: (31) 742488111
Web Site: http://www.thales-nederland.nl
Sales Range: $550-599.9 Million
Emp.: 2,000
Electronic Equipment & Systems
N.A.I.C.S.: 423690
Adryan Smyts *(Dir-Mktg)*

Thales International Offsets SAS (1)
45 Rue De Villiers, 92200, Neuilly-sur-Seine, France
Tel.: (33) 157778717
Web Site: http://www.thalesgroup.com
Emp.: 40
Business Support Services
N.A.I.C.S.: 561499
Daniel Geistodt-Kiener *(Gen Mgr)*

Thales International Pacific Holdings (1)
2nd Fl ACIL House 103-105 Northbourne Ave, Turner, 2612, ACT, Australia **(100%)**
Tel.: (61) 295623333
Electronic Equipment & Systems
N.A.I.C.S.: 449210

Thales International Polska Sp. z o.o. (1)
Centrum Finansowe Pulawska Ul Pulawska 15, 02515, Warsaw, Poland **(100%)**
Tel.: (48) 227567092
Web Site: http://www.thalesgroup.com
Provider of Electronic Defense Systems
N.A.I.C.S.: 334220

Thales International Pvt Ltd. (1)
11 Fl Statesman House Barakhamba Rd B 148, New Delhi, 110001, India **(100%)**
Tel.: (91) 11 4353 1800
Web Site: http://www.thalesgroup.com
Sales Range: $25-49.9 Million
Emp.: 15
Computerized Equipment & Systems
N.A.I.C.S.: 513210

Thales International S.A.S. (1)
31 Place des Corolles La Defense, 92526, Paris, France
Tel.: (33) 157778000
Defence Software Development Services
N.A.I.C.S.: 541511

Thales International Sverige AB (1)
Tejnernunden 3, 11821, Stockholm, Sweden **(100%)**
Tel.: (46) 84626450
Web Site: http://www.thalesgroup.com
Electronic Components
N.A.I.C.S.: 541512

Thales International Taiwan Company Limited (1)
Tunnan Twr 9th Fl 97, Sec 2, Taipei, 106, Taiwan **(100%)**
Tel.: (886) 227050533
Web Site: http://www.thalesgroup.com

Provider of Electronic Equipment & Systems
N.A.I.C.S.: 449210

Thales International Turkiye (1)
Karyagdi SOkak 13/14, Cankaya, 06680, Ankara, Turkiye **(100%)**
Tel.: (90) 3124404904
Web Site: http://www.thalesgroup.com
Sales Range: $25-49.9 Million
Emp.: 4
Sales of Electronic Equipment
N.A.I.C.S.: 449210
Jean-Bernard Levy *(CEO)*

Thales International Venezuela (1)
Centro Gerencial Mohedano Piso 5 Oficina C Av Mohedano La Castellana, Caracas, 1060, Venezuela **(100%)**
Tel.: (58) 2122614201
Web Site: http://www.thales.com
Sales Range: $25-49.9 Million
Emp.: 5
Provider of Defense Electronic Systems
N.A.I.C.S.: 334511

Thales Italia SpA - Air Operations Division (1)
Via Enrico Mattei 1, 20064, Gorgonzola, Milan, Italy
Tel.: (39) 0295095450
Sales Range: $25-49.9 Million
Emp.: 100
Airline Transportation Services
N.A.I.C.S.: 488190

Thales Italia SpA - Avionics Division (1)
Via Sempione 26, Vergiate, 21029, Varese, Italy
Tel.: (39) 0331946123
Web Site: http://www.thalesgroup.com
Sales Range: $25-49.9 Million
Emp.: 8
Defence Security Software Development Services
N.A.I.C.S.: 541511
Pietro Roveta *(Dir-Site)*

Thales Japan K.K. (1)
Akasaka Tameike Tower 8F Akasaka 2-17-7, Minato-ku, Tokyo, 107-0052, Japan
Tel.: (81) 3 57 85 18 00
Web Site: http://www.thalesgroup.com
Sales Range: $25-49.9 Million
Emp.: 50
Defence Security Software Development Services
N.A.I.C.S.: 541511

Thales Korea Ltd (1)
6/F 36 1 Hannan 1 Dong, Yongsan-Ku, Seoul, 140-885, Korea (South)
Tel.: (82) 232788200
Military Electronic Equipment Mfr
N.A.I.C.S.: 335999

Thales Land & Joint Systems UK (1)
Mountbatten House Basing View, Basingstoke, RG21 4HJ, Hants, United Kingdom
Tel.: (44) 1256 387200
Sales Range: $200-249.9 Million
Emp.: 800
Defence Security & Aerospace Application Mfr
N.A.I.C.S.: 336992

Thales Ltd (1)
EmpireTower 44th Floor River Wing West 4407 195 South Sathorn Road, Yannawa, Bangkok, 10120, Thailand
Tel.: (66) 2 670 1120
Sales Range: $25-49.9 Million
Emp.: 1
Defence Security Software Development Services
N.A.I.C.S.: 541511

Thales Malaysia Sdn Bhd (1)
15th Fl Wisma Genting Jalan Sultan Ismail, 50540, Kuala Lumpur, Malaysia
Tel.: (60) 3 2178 3800
Defence Software Development Services
N.A.I.C.S.: 541511

Thales Microelectronics S.A (1)
Zide Bellevue 6, PO Box 50386, Rennes, 35221, Chaceaubourg, France **(100%)**
Tel.: (33) 299009400
Web Site: http://www.thales-microelectronics.com

Sales Range: $200-249.9 Million
Emp.: 700
Mfr of Microwave Modules for Electronic Warfare Applications
N.A.I.C.S.: 334511

Thales Microwave S.A (1)
173 Blvd Hausmann, 75415, Paris, Cedex, France **(100%)**
Tel.: (33) 163934141
Web Site: http://www.thales-microelectronics.com
Mfr of Microwave Modules for Electronic Warfare Applications
N.A.I.C.S.: 334511

Thales Missile Electronics Ltd (1)
Mountbatten House Basing View, Basingstoke, RG21 4HJ, United Kingdom
Tel.: (44) 1256 387 200
Emp.: 60
Missile Electronic Component Mfr
N.A.I.C.S.: 336419

Thales Naval SA (1)
7 9 Rue Des Mathurins, 92221, Bagneux, Cedex, France **(100%)**
Tel.: (33) 140844000
Web Site: http://www.thales-naval.com
Sales Range: $100-124.9 Million
Emp.: 300
Provider of Systems Engineering & Integration Systems to the Naval Defense Industry
N.A.I.C.S.: 334511

Thales Nederland B.V. (1)
(100%)
Tel.: (31) 742488111
Web Site: https://www.thales-nederland.nl
Sales Range: $400-449.9 Million
Emp.: 2,000
Mfr of Naval & Ground-Based Defence Systems
N.A.I.C.S.: 332994
Gerben Edelijn *(Chm & CEO)*

Subsidiary (Domestic):

Thales Cryogenics B.V (2)
Hooge Zijde 14, PO Box 6034, 5600 HA, Eindhoven, Netherlands **(100%)**
Tel.: (31) 402503603
Web Site: http://www.thales-cryogenics.com
Sales Range: $25-49.9 Million
Emp.: 75
Mfr & Supplier of Cryocoolers for Infrared, Superconductor, X-Ray, Telecommunications & Laser Technologies
N.A.I.C.S.: 334220
Tonny Benschop *(Mng Dir)*

Thales Munitronics BV (2)
Hooge Zijde 14, PO Box 6034, Eindhoven, 6034, Netherlands **(100%)**
Tel.: (31) 402503603
Web Site: http://www.thales-munitronics.nl
Sales Range: $25-49.9 Million
Emp.: 70
Mfr of Batteries
N.A.I.C.S.: 335910

Thales Nederland Tranportation (1)
Bestevaer 46, 3991 CL, Huizen, Netherlands
Tel.: (31) 88 499 99 00
Sales Range: $350-399.9 Million
Emp.: 50
Defence & Security Software Development Services
N.A.I.C.S.: 541511

Thales New Zealand Limited (1)
Level 1 ASB House 101 The Terrace, PO Box 10-672, Wellington, 6143, New Zealand
Tel.: (64) 4 473 7508
Web Site: http://www.thalesgroup.co.nz
Sales Range: $25-49.9 Million
Emp.: 24
Air Traffic Management Software Development Services
N.A.I.C.S.: 541511
Millar Crawford *(Exec VP-Ground Transportation Sys)*

Thales Norway AS (1)
Nedre Vollgate 11, 0158, Oslo, 0158, Norway
Tel.: (47) 22 63 83 00
Web Site: http://www.thales.no
Sales Range: $25-49.9 Million
Emp.: 190
Defence Software Development Services

AND PRIVATE COMPANIES

THALES S.A.

N.A.I.C.S.: 541511
Glenn Pedersen *(CEO)*

Thales Optronique SA (1)
2 Ave Gay Lussac, 78996, Guyancourt, Cedex, France **(100%)**
Tel.: (33) 130967000
Web Site: http://www.fr.thalesgroup.com
Sales Range: $200-249.9 Million
Emp.: 987
Mfr of Airborne, Naval & Terrestrial Optronics Systems
N.A.I.C.S.: 334511
Jean-Jacques Guittard *(Gen Mgr)*

Subsidiary (Non-US):

Arab International Optronics (2)
PO Box 8182, Nasr City, Cairo, 11371, Egypt
Tel.: (20) 22806076
Mfr of Optical Systems
N.A.I.C.S.: 333310

Joint Venture (Domestic):

Sofradir SAS (2)
43 47 Rue Camille Pelletan, 92290, Chatenay-Malabry, France **(50%)**
Tel.: (33) 0141134530
Web Site: http://www.sofradir.com
Sales Range: $150-199.9 Million
Emp.: 550
Infrared Detection Equipment Mfr; Owned 50% by Thales S.A. & 50% by Safran S.A.
N.A.I.C.S.: 334511
Philippe Bensussan *(CEO)*

Subsidiary (Non-US):

Thales AFV Systems Ltd (2)
Linthouse Rd, G51 4BZ, Glasgow, United Kingdom - Scotland
Tel.: (44) 414404000
Web Site: http://www.thalesgroup.com
Sales Range: $150-199.9 Million
Emp.: 700
Terrestrial Optronics Systems Mfr
N.A.I.C.S.: 334511

Subsidiary (Domestic):

Thales Angenieux SA (2)
Blvd Ravel de Malral, 42570, Saint-Heand, France **(100%)**
Tel.: (33) 477907800
Web Site: http://www.angenieux.com
Sales Range: $25-49.9 Million
Emp.: 200
Zoom & Wide Angle Lenses for Photo & Television Cameras Mfr
N.A.I.C.S.: 333310
Philippe Parain *(CEO)*

Subsidiary (Non-US):

Thales Canada Inc.-Optometric Division (2)
4868 Levy St, Saint Laurent, H4R 2P1, QC, Canada **(100%)**
Tel.: (514) 337-7878
Sales Range: $25-49.9 Million
Emp.: 35
Mfr of Airborne, Naval & Terrestrial Optronics Systems
N.A.I.C.S.: 334511

Subsidiary (Domestic):

Thales Cryogenie S.A (2)
4 Rue Marcel Doret, PO Box 70022, 31701, Blagnac, France **(100%)**
Tel.: (33) 562745800
Web Site: http://www.thales-cryogenics.com
Sales Range: $25-49.9 Million
Emp.: 100
Mfr & Supplier of Cryocoolers for Infrared, Superconductor, X-Ray, Telecommunications & Laser Technologies
N.A.I.C.S.: 334220
Marc Komorniczak *(Gen Mgr)*

Subsidiary (Non-US):

Thales Electro Optics Pte. Ltd. (2)
14 Fifth Lok Yang Rd, Jurong Town, Singapore, 629763, Singapore **(100%)**
Tel.: (65) 62655122
Web Site: http://www.thales-eo.com.sg
Sales Range: $150-199.9 Million
Emp.: 600
Mfr, Developer, Designer & Servicer of Advanced Precision Optics & Sighting Systems
N.A.I.C.S.: 333310

Thales Laser K.K (2)
Sunrise Bldg 2 16 4 Omori kita Ohta-ku, Tokyo, 143 0016, Japan **(100%)**
Tel.: (81) 357534541
Web Site: http://www.thaleslaser.co.jp
Sales Range: $25-49.9 Million
Emp.: 9
Mfr of Laser Diodes
N.A.I.C.S.: 334413

Thales Optronics (Glasgow) Ltd (2)
1 Linthouse Rd, Glasgow, G51 4BZ, Lanark Shir, United Kingdom **(100%)**
Tel.: (44) 414404000
Sales Range: $75-99.9 Million
Emp.: 500
Mfr of Airborne, Naval & Terrestrial Optronics Systems
N.A.I.C.S.: 334511

Thales Optronics (Staines) Ltd (2)
Mount Batten House Basing View, Basing Stock, Hampshire, RG21 4HJ, United Kingdom **(100%)**
Tel.: (44) 01256387200
Sales Range: $25-49.9 Million
Emp.: 100
Mfr of Airborne, Naval & Terrestrial Optronics Systems
N.A.I.C.S.: 334511

Thales Optronics (Taunton) Ltd (2)
Lisieux Way, Taunton, United Kingdom
Tel.: (44) 823331071
Mfr of Airborne, Naval & Terrestrial Optronics Systems
N.A.I.C.S.: 334511

Thales Optronics (Vinten) Ltd (2)
Vicon House Western Way, Western Way, Bury Saint Edmunds, IP33 3SP, United Kingdom
Tel.: (44) 284750599
Sales Range: $25-49.9 Million
Emp.: 180
Mfr of Airborne, Naval & Terrestrial Optronics Systems
N.A.I.C.S.: 334511

Thales Optronics BV (2)
Bestevaer 46, PO Box 88, Huizen, 1271AB, Netherlands **(100%)**
Tel.: (31) 355248248
Web Site: http://www.thales-optronics.nl
Sales Range: $25-49.9 Million
Emp.: 225
Mfr of Airborne, Naval & Terrestrial Optronics Systems
N.A.I.C.S.: 334511
Marcel Grisnigt *(CEO)*

Thales Optronique Italia Srl (2)
Via Guiseppe Armellini 37, 143, Rome, Italy **(100%)**
Tel.: (39) 0651956200
Mfr of Airborne, Naval & Terrestrial Optronics Systems
N.A.I.C.S.: 334511

Thales Parking Systems SA (1)
150 D2 Rue Walcourt, 1070, Brussels, Belgium
Tel.: (32) 2 349 10 40
Emp.: 4
Parking System Software Development Services
N.A.I.C.S.: 541511
Marcel Gresnigt *(Mgr-Ops)*

Thales Polska sp. z o.o. (1)
Ul Zachodnia 15, 60-701, Poznan, Poland
Tel.: (48) 61 88 64 401
Defence Software Development Services
N.A.I.C.S.: 541511

Thales Portugal S.A. (1)
Edificio Cristal Rua Calvet Magalhaes 245, Paco De Arcos, 2774-153, Lisbon, Portugal
Tel.: (351) 212484848
Sales Range: $75-99.9 Million
Emp.: 40
Defence Software Development Services
N.A.I.C.S.: 541511
Joao Araujo *(Gen Mgr)*

Thales Properties Ltd (1)
2 Dashwood Lang Road The Bourne Business Park Addlestone, Weybridge, KT15 2NX, United Kingdom
Tel.: (44) 1932 824 800
Emp.: 80
Property Management Services
N.A.I.C.S.: 531312

Thales Rail Signalling Solutions AG (1)
Friesenbergstrasse 75, Postfach 8301, 8036, Zürich, Switzerland
Tel.: (41) 44 465 48 11
Sales Range: $25-49.9 Million
Emp.: 10
Defence Security System Software Development Services
N.A.I.C.S.: 541511
Veronika Pjetri *(Sec)*

Thales Research & Technology (1)
Route Departementale 128, 91767, Palaiseau, France
Tel.: (33) 1 69 41 55 00
Web Site: http://www.thalesgroup.com
Software Research & Development Services
N.A.I.C.S.: 541715
Christian Breant *(VP & Dir-Advanced Studies & Bus Intelligence)*

Thales Research & Technology UK Ltd (1)
Worton Drive Worton Grange Business Park, Reading, RG2 0SB, United Kingdom
Tel.: (44) 1189 868601
Aircraft Research & Developement Services
N.A.I.C.S.: 541715

Thales SAIC Transport (1)
Bldg 28 1000 Jinhai Road, Pudong, Shanghai, 200129, China
Tel.: (86) 21 6105 5522
Web Site: http://www.thalessaic.com.cn
Emp.: 20
Transport System Software Development Services
N.A.I.C.S.: 541511
Werner Paech *(CEO)*

Thales Safare (1)
525 Route des Dolines, 08901, Sophia-Antipolis, Cedex, France **(100%)**
Tel.: (33) 492963000
Web Site: http://www.thalesgroup.com
Sales Range: Less than $1 Million
Emp.: 130
Underwater Communications & On Shore Communications Equipment Research, Development & Mfr
N.A.I.C.S.: 334290

Thales Security Asia Pte Ltd (1)
21 Changi North Rise, 498788, Singapore, Singapore
Tel.: (65) 6424 8135
Web Site: http://www.thalesgroup.com
Defence Software Development Services
N.A.I.C.S.: 541511

Thales Security Solutions & Services Company (1)
Thales Building King Abdulaziz Old Airport Street Al Arkane Area, Riyadh, 11422, Saudi Arabia
Tel.: (966) 1 291 2000
Telecommunication Equipment Whslr
N.A.I.C.S.: 517810

Thales Security Solutions & Services S.A. de C.V. (1)
Jaime Balmes N 11 - Colonia Los Morales Torre A 1 Piso, 11510, Mexico, Mexico
Tel.: (52) 55 2122 2890
Sales Range: $75-99.9 Million
Emp.: 30
Defence Security & Aerospace Technology Services
N.A.I.C.S.: 541690
Antonio Quintanilla *(Gen Dir)*

Thales Security Solutions And Services (Pty) Ltd (1)
55 Richards Road Halfway House, Midrand, 1685, Gauteng, South Africa
Tel.: (27) 11 313 9123
Web Site: http://www.thalesgroup.com
Sales Range: $25-49.9 Million
Emp.: 60

Defence Security Software Development Services
N.A.I.C.S.: 541511

Thales Security Solutions and Services Co. (1)
Malaz, PO Box 5463, Riyadh, 11422, Saudi Arabia
Tel.: (966) 1291 2000
Defence Software Development Services
N.A.I.C.S.: 541511

Thales Security Systems SAS (1)
1921 Ave Morane Saulnier 78140 Verlizy Villacoublay, 92360, Meudon, Cedex, France **(100%)**
Tel.: (33) 140832335
Web Site: http://www.thales-security.com
Sales Range: $25-49.9 Million
Emp.: 80
Provider of Security Services
N.A.I.C.S.: 561621

Thales Services (1)
Zuidelidke Havnweg 40, 7554 RR, Hengelo, Netherlands
Tel.: (31) 74 248 3485
Defence Software Development Services
N.A.I.C.S.: 541511

Thales Services Industrie S.A (1)
31 33 Ave Aristide Briand, 94117, Arcueil, Cedex, France **(100%)**
Tel.: (33) 0141484000
Sales Range: $75-99.9 Million
Emp.: 221
Supplier of Electronics & IT Systems Integration & Services
N.A.I.C.S.: 423690

Branch (Domestic):

Thales Industrial Services SA (2)
1 ave Aristide Briand, 94117, Arcueil, Cedex, France
Tel.: (33) 141484000
Web Site: http://www.thales-industrialservices.com
Information Technology Consultancy Services
N.A.I.C.S.: 541512

Subsidiary (Domestic):

Thales Industrial Services S.A (3)
1 Ave Aristide Briand, 01630, Arcueil, Cedex, France
Tel.: (33) 141484000
Web Site: http://www.thales-industrialservices.com
Information Technology Consultancy Services
N.A.I.C.S.: 541512

Subsidiary (Non-US):

Thales Services Industrie (2)
Z.I Fare UTE, BP 2366, Papeete, French Polynesia
Tel.: (689) 425962
Web Site: http://www.thales-industrialservices.com
Supplier of Electronics & IT Systems Integration & Services
N.A.I.C.S.: 811310

Thales Services Ltd. (1)
Ashurst Drive Bird Hall Lane, Cheadle Heath, Stockport, SK3 0XB, United Kingdom
Tel.: (44) 161 491 4001
Defence Security & Aerospace Technology Services
N.A.I.C.S.: 541690

Thales Services S.A.S. (1)
66-68 Ave Pierre Brossolette, F-92240, Malakoff, Cedex, France **(100%)**
Tel.: (33) 0141480000
Rev.: $16,820,656
Emp.: 2,500
IT Consulting, Outsourcing & Technical Services
N.A.I.C.S.: 541512

Subsidiary (Non-US):

Thales Field Services International Limited (TFSI Ltd) (2)
Ste 8 La Tourgand House, Lowr Pollet, Saint Peter Port, Guernsey

THALES S.A.

Thales S.A.—(Continued)
Tel.: (44) 481729298
Web Site: http://www.tfsi-ltd.com
Project Managment & Recruitment Services
N.A.I.C.S.: 561110

Thales Information Systems (2)
Unit 909 9th Floor New Kowloon Plaza, 38
Tai Kok Tsui Road, Kowloon, China (Hong
Kong) (100%)
Tel.: (852) 23890022
Sales Range: $25-49.9 Million
Emp.: 100
Provider of IT Consultancy, Outsourcing &
Technical Svcs
N.A.I.C.S.: 541512

Thales Information Systems (2)
Carretera de Berroa Km1, Centro de Negocios Of 41, Apartado de correos 6965, Zona Franca, Havana, Cuba
Tel.: (53) 7959846
Provider of IT Consultancy, Outsourcing &
Technical Services
N.A.I.C.S.: 541512

Thales Information Systems (2)
Centro Plaza - Torre A, Piso 14, Of. 14E
Los Palos Grandes, Avenida Francesco de
Miranda, Caracas, Venezuela
Tel.: (58) 2129525051
Sales Range: $25-49.9 Million
Emp.: 14
Provider of IT Consultancy, Outsourcing &
Technical Services
N.A.I.C.S.: 541512

Thales Information Systems SA/NV (2)
Ave De Torg 86, 1000, Brussels,
Belgium (100%)
Tel.: (32) 26747370
Sales Range: $25-49.9 Million
Emp.: 80
Provider of IT Consultancy, Outsourcing &
Technical Svcs
N.A.I.C.S.: 541512

Thales Information Systems SpA (2)
Via Mattei 1, 20064, Gorgonzola,
Italy (100%)
Tel.: (39) 029509951
Sales Range: $25-49.9 Million
Emp.: 150
Provider of IT Consultancy, Outsourcing &
Technical Services
N.A.I.C.S.: 541512

Subsidiary (Domestic):

Thales Training & Simulation SAS (2)
1 Rue Du General De Gaulle, BP 226,
95523, Cergy-Pontoise, France
Tel.: (33) 1 34 22 82 00
Web Site: http://www.thalesgroup.com
Defence Training & Simulation Services
N.A.I.C.S.: 611430

Thales Services SA (1)
Avenida Del Valle 725 Oficina 101-N, Huechuraba, Santiago, Chile
Tel.: (56) 2 738 47 16
Defence Software Development Services
N.A.I.C.S.: 541511

Thales Singapore Pte Ltd (1)
21 Changi North Rise, Singapore, 498788, Singapore
Tel.: (65) 6594 6861
Sales Range: $100-124.9 Million
Emp.: 500
Air Traffic Control System Mfr
N.A.I.C.S.: 334511

Thales Six GTS France SAS (1)
83/85 rue Emile Brault, 53005, Laval,
France
Tel.: (33) 243684000
Information Technology Services
N.A.I.C.S.: 541511
Estelle Yven (Production Mgr)

Thales South Africa Pty Ltd (1)
55 Richards Road Halfway House, Midrand, 1685, Gauteng, South Africa
Tel.: (27) 11 313 9123
Defence Electronic System Distr
N.A.I.C.S.: 423690
Geon Barnard (Mgr-Mktg)

Thales Sverige AB (1)
Tegnerlunden 3, 111 61, Stockholm, Sweden
Tel.: (46) 8 462 64 50
Emp.: 4
Aerospace Defence Security System Services
N.A.I.C.S.: 561621
Hacan Alhstrom (Mgr)

Thales Systems Aeroportes S.A (1)
Centre Charles Nungesser, 2 Ave Gay Lussac, 78851, Elancourt, Cedex,
France (100%)
Tel.: (33) 34816000
Web Site: http://www.thalesgroup.com
Sales Range: $1-4.9 Billion
Emp.: 5,234
Mfr of Electronic Navigation & Guidance Systems
N.A.I.C.S.: 334511

Subsidiary (Non-US):

Thales Aerospace Division (2)
Manor Royal, Crawley, RH10 9PZ, W Sussex, United Kingdom (100%)
Tel.: (44) 93528787
Sales Range: $150-199.9 Million
Emp.: 600
Mfr of Electronic Navigation & Guidance Systems
N.A.I.C.S.: 334511

Thales Canada Systems (2)
1 Chrysalis Way, Ottawa, K2G 6P9, ON,
Canada (100%)
Tel.: (613) 723-7000
Sales Range: $25-49.9 Million
Emp.: 150
Mfr of Electronic Navigation & Guidance Systems
N.A.I.C.S.: 334511

Thales Systems Canada, Inc. (1)
1 Chrysalis Way, Ottawa, K2G 6P9, ON,
Canada
Tel.: (613) 723-7000
Sales Range: $25-49.9 Million
Emp.: 20
Defence Software Development Services
N.A.I.C.S.: 541511

Thales Systems Romania (1)
319G Splaiul Independentei River View
House 13th Fl 6th District, 60044, Bucharest, Romania
Tel.: (40) 213 033 400
Web Site: http://www.thalesgroup.com
Emp.: 20
Rail Signalling Software Development Services
N.A.I.C.S.: 541511
Silviu Agapi (Gen Mgr)

Thales Technologies & Services (1)
13 ave du President Salvador Allende,
94117, Arcueil, Cedex, France
Tel.: (33) 141484115
Web Site: http://www.thales-technologies.com
Sales Range: $25-49.9 Million
Emp.: 173
Defence & Communications Technologies Consultancy Services
N.A.I.C.S.: 541611

Thales Transport & Security (HK) Ltd (1)
248 Queen's Road East, Wanchai, China (Hong Kong)
Tel.: (852) 2815 8633
Sales Range: $25-49.9 Million
Emp.: 2
Security System Services
N.A.I.C.S.: 561621

Thales Transport Signalling & Security Solutions, S.A.U. (1)
Serrano Galvache 56 - C E Parque Norte Building Alamo, Edificio Alamo, 28033, Madrid, Spain
Tel.: (34) 91 273 72 00
Web Site: http://www.thalesgroup.com
Transport Signalling Software Development Services
N.A.I.C.S.: 541511
Jesus Sanchez Bargos (Mgr)

Thales Transportation Systems (1)
Centre Du Bois Des Bordes, PO Box 57, 91229, Bretigny-sur-Orge, France (100%)
Tel.: (33) 169885200
Web Site: http://www.thales-transportservices.com
Sales Range: $150-199.9 Million
Emp.: 600
Joint Venture of Thomson S.A. & Alcatel S.A.
N.A.I.C.S.: 561110
Geanmarc Gargin (CEO)

Thales Transportation Systems GmbH (1)
Lorenzstr 10, Stuttgart, 70435, Baden-Württemberg, Germany
Tel.: (49) 711 8690
Web Site: http://www.thalesgroup.com
Rail Transportation Signalling Software Development Services
N.A.I.C.S.: 541511
Volker Schenk (Gen Mgr)

Thales USA, Inc. (1)
2733 S Crystal Dr Ste 1200, Arlington, VA 22202 (100%)
Tel.: (703) 838-9685
Sales Range: $25-49.9 Million
Emp.: 2,900
Holding Company; Regional Managing Office
N.A.I.C.S.: 551112
Alan Pellegrini (Pres & CEO)

Subsidiary (Domestic):

Guavus, Inc. (2)
2125 Zanker Rd, San Jose, CA 95131
Tel.: (650) 243-3400
Web Site: http://www.guavus.com
Data Analysis Solutions
N.A.I.C.S.: 518210
Anukool Lakhina (Founder & Pres)

Subsidiary (Domestic):

SQLstream, Inc. (3)
1540 Market St Ste 400, San Francisco, CA 94102
Tel.: (877) 571-5775
Web Site: http://www.sqlstream.com
Computer Related Services
N.A.I.C.S.: 541519

Subsidiary (Domestic):

LiveTV, LLC (2)
700 S Babcock St, Melbourne, FL 32901
Tel.: (321) 308-3900
Web Site: http://www.livetv.net
Sales Range: $50-74.9 Million
Emp.: 150
In-Flight Entertainment Systems
N.A.I.C.S.: 488190
Mike Moeller (VP-Sls & Mktg)

Thales Components Corp (2)
40 G Commerce Way, Totowa, NJ
07511-0540 (100%)
Tel.: (973) 812-9000
Web Site: http://www.thalescomponents-us.com
Sales Range: $25-49.9 Million
Emp.: 42
Marketing & Sales of Electron Tubes
N.A.I.C.S.: 423690

Thales Defense & Security, Inc. (2)
22605 Gateway Ctr Dr, Clarksburg, MD 20871-2001 (100%)
Tel.: (240) 864-7000
Web Site: https://www.thalesdsi.com
Sales Range: $75-99.9 Million
Emp.: 350
Secure, Tactical Radio Communications Equipment Mfr
N.A.I.C.S.: 334220
Steve Nichols (Mgr-Pub Safety Mktg)

Subsidiary (Domestic):

Tampa Microwave, Inc. (3)
11200 Dr Martin Luther King St N Ste 103, Petersburg, FL 33626
Tel.: (813) 855-2251
Web Site: http://www.tampamicrowave.com
Sales Range: $1-9.9 Million
Emp.: 52
Radio & Television Broadcasting & Wireless Communications Equipment Mfr

N.A.I.C.S.: 334220
Erick Guerrazzi (Pres)

Subsidiary (Domestic):

Thales Mackay Radio, Inc (2)
22605 Gateway Center Dr, Clarksburg, MD 20871-2001
Tel.: (919) 431-8979
Web Site: http://www.thalesmackayradio.com
Mfr of High Frequency Communications Systems
N.A.I.C.S.: 334220

Thales Transport & Security, Inc. (2)
5700 Corporate Dr Ste 750, Pittsburgh, PA 15237
Tel.: (412) 366-8814
Web Site: http://www.thalesgroup.com
Defence Security & Aerospace Application Mfr
N.A.I.C.S.: 336992
John Brohm (Pres & CEO)

Thales Underwater Systems SAS (1)
525 Route Des Dolines, 06903, Sophia-Antipolis, France
Tel.: (33) 492963000
Submarine Sonar System Mfr
N.A.I.C.S.: 332994
Gallier Patricia (Sec)

Thales Underwater Systems Singapore (1)
21 Changi North Rise, Singapore, 498788, Singapore
Tel.: (65) 6424 7100
Naval Securitry Systems Mfr
N.A.I.C.S.: 332992

Thales Universite Ltd (1)
Mountbatten House Basing View, Basingstoke, RG21 4HJ, Hants, United Kingdom
Tel.: (44) 1256 387200
Web Site: http://www.thalesgroup.com
Sales Range: $50-74.9 Million
Emp.: 500
Aircraft Training Services
N.A.I.C.S.: 611430

Thales Universite S.A. (1)
67 rue Charles-de-Gaulle, Jouy-en-Josas, 78350, France
Tel.: (33) 1 30 84 64 00
Web Site: http://www.thalesgroup.com
Professional Development Training Services
N.A.I.C.S.: 611430

THALIA BUCHER GMBH

Batheyer Strasse 115-117, 58099,
Hagen, Germany
Tel.: (49) 2515309330
Web Site: http://www.thalia.de
Book Retailer & Distr
N.A.I.C.S.: 424920
Silvia Lubitz (Head-HR)

Subsidiaries:

Buch & Medien GmbH (1)
Am Bahndamm 6, 17039, Neubrandenburg, Wulkenzin, Germany
Tel.: (49) 3954212362
School Furniture, Equipment, Books & Teaching Aids for Educational Institutions Supplier
N.A.I.C.S.: 424920

Buch und Kunst GmbH & Co. KG (1)
Peschelstrasse 31, 01139, Dresden, Germany
Tel.: (49) 351402060
Book Store Operating Services
N.A.I.C.S.: 459210

Buecher.de GmbH & Co. KG (1)
Steinerne Furt 65 A, 86167, Augsburg, Germany
Tel.: (49) 82145020
Web Site: http://www.buecher.de
Sales Range: $50-74.9 Million
Emp.: 25
Internet Book Retailer
N.A.I.C.S.: 424920
Gerd Robertz (Mng Dir)

AND PRIVATE COMPANIES

Reinhold Gondrom GmbH & Co. KG (1)
Kerststrasse 9, Kaiserslautern, 67655, Germany
Tel.: (49) 631362190
Web Site: http://www.thalia.de
Book Stores
N.A.I.C.S.: 459210

Thalia Buch & Medien GmbH (1)
Highway 41, 4020, Linz, Austria
Tel.: (43) 732 761565102
Web Site: http://www.thalia.at
Book Stores
N.A.I.C.S.: 459210

Thalia Bucher AG (1)
Freie Strasse 32, 4001, Basel, Switzerland (75%)
Tel.: (41) 612642626
Holding Company; Book Distr & Retailer
N.A.I.C.S.: 551112

Joint Venture (Domestic):

Orell Fussli Thalia AG (2)
Dietzingerstrasse 3, 8036, Zurich, Switzerland
Tel.: (41) 848 849848
Web Site: http://www.orellfuessli.ch
Books Retailing
N.A.I.C.S.: 459210
Pascal Schneebeli *(CEO)*

Unit (Domestic):

buch.ch (3)
Industriestrasse 26, 8404, Winterthur, Switzerland
Tel.: (41) 8 48 28 24 24
Online Retailer of Books, CDs, DVDs, Software & Games
N.A.I.C.S.: 459210

Thalia Medienservice GmbH (1)
Otto-von-Guericke-Ring 10, 65205, Wiesbaden, Germany
Tel.: (49) 61225076100
Cosmetics & Perfumes Distr
N.A.I.C.S.: 424210

Thalia Universitatsbuchhandlung GmbH (1)
Kabeler Strasse 4, 58099, Hagen, Germany
Tel.: (49) 23316900
Web Site: http://www.thalia.de
News Dealers & Newsstands
N.A.I.C.S.: 459210

THAMES & HUDSON LTD
181A High Holbornn, London, WC1V 7QX, United Kingdom
Tel.: (44) 20 7845 5000
Web Site:
   http://www.thamesandhudson.com
Year Founded: 1949
Book Publishers
N.A.I.C.S.: 513130
Rolf Grisebach *(CEO)*

Subsidiaries:

Asia Books Company Ltd (1)
5 Sukhumvit Road, Soi 61 Klongtan Nua Wattana, Bangkok, 10110, Thailand
Tel.: (66) 2715 9000
Book Publishers
N.A.I.C.S.: 513130

Bas van der Zee (1)
President Kennedylaan 66 huis, Amsterdam, 1079 NG, Netherlands
Tel.: (31) 623137695
Book Publishers
N.A.I.C.S.: 513130

Interart S.A.R.L (1)
1 rue de l Est, Paris, 75020, France
Tel.: (33) 1 43 49 36 60
Web Site: http://www.interart.fr
Emp.: 15
Book Publishers
N.A.I.C.S.: 513130
Tierre Samoyault *(Gen Mgr)*

Levant Distributors (1)
Sin El Fil Al Qalaa Area, Sector No 5 Building 31 53rd Street, Beirut, Lebanon
Tel.: (961) 1 488 444

Book Publishers
N.A.I.C.S.: 513130

Per Burell (1)
Idalavagen 1, 182 78, Stocksund, Sweden
Tel.: (46) 885 6475
Book Publishers
N.A.I.C.S.: 513130

Peter Hyde Associates (1)
Corner Nelson & Speke Roads, Observatory, Cape Town, 8000, South Africa
Tel.: (27) 21 447 5300
Book Publishers
N.A.I.C.S.: 513130

Thames & Hudson (Australia) Pty Ltd (1)
11 Central Blvd, Portside Business Park, Fishermans Bend, 3207, VC, Australia
Tel.: (61) 3 9646 7788
Web Site: http://www.thameshudson.co.au
Emp.: 12
Book Publishers
N.A.I.C.S.: 513130
Ganieo Watts *(Mng Dir)*

Thames & Hudson (S) Private Ltd (1)
52 Genting Lane, 06-05 Hiang Kie Complex 1, Singapore, 349560, Singapore
Tel.: (65) 6749 3551
Book Publishers
N.A.I.C.S.: 513130

Thames & Hudson China Ltd (1)
Units B&D 17/F Gee Chang Hong Centre, 65 Wong Chuk Hang Road, Aberdeen, China (Hong Kong)
Tel.: (852) 2553 9289
Book Publishers
N.A.I.C.S.: 513130

Thames and Hudson (S) Private Ltd (1)
Nos. 24 & 26 Jalan SS3/41, 47300, Petaling Jaya, Malaysia
Tel.: (60) 3 7877 6063
Book Publishers
N.A.I.C.S.: 513130

Zeenat Book Supply Ltd (1)
190 Dhaka New Market, Dhaka, 1205, Bangladesh
Tel.: (880) 2 861 7005
Book Publishers
N.A.I.C.S.: 513130

THAMES VENTURES VCT 2 PLC
St Magnus House 3 Lower Thames Street, London, EC3R 6HD, United Kingdom
Tel.: (44) 2074167780 UK
Web Site: https://www.downing.co.uk
Year Founded: 2016
D467—(LSE)
Rev.: $63,116
Assets: $51,757,235
Liabilities: $776,321
Net Worth: $50,980,914
Earnings: ($12,818,758)
Fiscal Year-end: 03/31/24
Investment Brokerage Services
N.A.I.C.S.: 523150
Anne Sanders *(Partner & CFO)*

THAMESIDE INVESTMENT GROUP PLC
Finsgate 5-7 Cranwood Street, London, United Kingdom
Tel.: (44) 8000639955
Investment Services
N.A.I.C.S.: 523999

THANACHART CAPITAL PCL
16th-17th Floor MBK Tower 444 Phayathai Rd, Wangmai Pathumwan, Bangkok, 10330, Thailand
Tel.: (66) 22178000
Web Site:
   https://www.thanachart.co.th
TCPTF—(OTCIQ)
Rev.: $624,111,456

Assets: $4,689,977,725
Liabilities: $2,265,342,834
Net Worth: $2,424,634,891
Earnings: $261,503,423
Emp.: 1,864
Fiscal Year-end: 12/31/20
Investment Management & Financial Services
N.A.I.C.S.: 523999
Somjate Moosirilert *(CEO)*

Subsidiaries:

Eastern Sea Laem Chabang Terminal Co., Ltd. (1)
Laem Chabang Port B3 Toong Sukhla, Sriracha, Chon Buri, 20230, Thailand (100%)
Tel.: (66) 3 300 5678
Web Site: https://www.esco.co.th
Sales Range: $50-74.9 Million
Emp.: 200
Deep-Sea Port Management
N.A.I.C.S.: 488390

MAX Asset Management Company Limited (1)
444 Phayatai Road, Pathum Wan, Bangkok, 10330, Thailand
Tel.: (66) 26119533
Asset Management Services
N.A.I.C.S.: 541618

MBK Life Assurance Plc (1)
No 231 MBK Life Building Ratchadamri Road, Lumpini Subdistrict Pathumwan District, Bangkok, 10330, Thailand
Tel.: (66) 22525070
Web Site: http://www.mbklife.co.th
Fire Insurance Services
N.A.I.C.S.: 524113
Kanokwan Nokwichien *(Sr VP)*

MT Service 2016 Co., Ltd. (1)
231 MBK Life Building 10 11th Floor Ratchadamri Road, Lumpini Pathumwan, Bangkok, 10330, Thailand
Tel.: (66) 22544166
Financial Banking Services
N.A.I.C.S.: 522110

NFS Asset Management Co., Ltd. (1)
444 MBK Tower 17th Floor Phayathai Road, Wangmai Pathumwan, Bangkok, 10330, Thailand
Tel.: (66) 22178000
Asset Management Services
N.A.I.C.S.: 523940

Piboon Concrete Co., Ltd. (1)
263 1 Moo 10 Chiangmai Prao Road, Maefark Sunsai, Chiang Mai, 50290, Thailand (100%)
Tel.: (66) 53849435
Web Site: http://www.pcc-concrete.co.th
Sales Range: $1-9.9 Million
Emp.: 500
Concrete-Pile Manufacturing
N.A.I.C.S.: 333120

RTN Insurance Broker Co., Ltd. (1)
77/20 Sinsathorn Tower 2nd Floor Krungthonburi Road, Khlongtonsai Khlongsan, Bangkok, 10600, Thailand
Tel.: (66) 24319500
Web Site: https://rtnbroker.com
Insurance Broker Services
N.A.I.C.S.: 524210

Sahakol Chassis Co., Ltd. (1)
1418/6-8 Setapaisarn Building 1 Phaholyothin Road, Lardyao, Jatujak, Bangkok, 10900, Thailand
Tel.: (66) 29394439
Produce & Assemble Chassis, Body & Parts for Trucks, Buses & Other Vehicles
N.A.I.C.S.: 336340

Security Scib Services Co., Ltd. (1)
1091/230 Petchburitatmai Road, Makkasan Ratchathew, Bangkok, 10400, Thailand
Tel.: (66) 220850612
Business Support Services
N.A.I.C.S.: 561499

Siam City Credit Finance & Securities Co., Ltd. (1)

THANACHART CAPITAL PCL

16th Floor Maneeya Center Building, 518/5Phlown Chit Road, Lumphini Pathum Wan, Bangkok, 10330, Thailand (46.81%)
Tel.: (66) 2 2548 309
Finance & Securities
N.A.I.C.S.: 921130

Strong Pack Co., Ltd. (1)
91 Moo 13 Kingkaew Road, Bangplee, Samut Prakan, 10540, Thailand
Packaging Industry
N.A.I.C.S.: 322220

T Broker Co., Ltd. (1)
59/5 Paradise Place Building 4th Floor Srinakarin Road, Nong Bon Prawet, Bangkok, 10250, Thailand
Tel.: (66) 20263541
Web Site: https://www.tbroker.co.th
Procurement Insurance Services
N.A.I.C.S.: 524210

T Life Assurance PLC (1)
59/5 Paradise Place Building 4th Floor Srinagarindra Road Nong Bon, Prawet, Bangkok, 10250, Thailand
Tel.: (66) 21110055
General Insurance Services
N.A.I.C.S.: 524210

TM Broker Co., Ltd. (1)
231 MBK Life Building 8th Floor Ratchadamri Road, Lumpini Pathumwan, Bangkok, 10330, Thailand
Tel.: (66) 20263541
Fire Insurance Services
N.A.I.C.S.: 524113

TS Asset Management Co., Ltd. (1)
1101 Petchburi Building 9th Floor Petchburitatmai Road, Makkasan Ratchathewi, Bangkok, 10400, Thailand
Tel.: (66) 22085000
Asset Management Services
N.A.I.C.S.: 523940

Thanachart Broker Co., Ltd. (1)
999/3 999/4 The Nine Tower Rama 9 Road, Suan Luang, Bangkok, 10250, Thailand
Tel.: (66) 27830200
Insurance Broker Services
N.A.I.C.S.: 524210

Thanachart Fund Management Company Limited (1)
231 MBK Life Building 5th-7th Floor Rajdamri Road, Lumpini Pathumwan, Bangkok, 10330, Thailand
Tel.: (66) 21268300
Web Site: http://www.thanachartfund.com
Mutual Investment Fund Services
N.A.I.C.S.: 525910
Amphon Kositapom *(VP)*

Thanachart Group Leasing Co., Ltd. (1)
444 MBK Tower 19th Floor Phayathai Road, Wangmai Pathumwan, Bangkok, 10330, Thailand
Tel.: (66) 22178000
Hire Purchase Services
N.A.I.C.S.: 532490

Thanachart Insurance Public Company Limited (1)
999/1 The Nine Tower Rama 9 Road Phatthanakan, Suan Luang, Bangkok, 10250, Thailand
Tel.: (66) 26668899
Web Site:
   https://www.thanachartinsurance.co.th
Online Insurance Services
N.A.I.C.S.: 524128

Thanachart Management & Services Co., Ltd. (1)
2 Thanachart Suanmali Office Building 2nd Floor Chaloemkhet 4 Road, Wat Thep Sirin Pom Prap Sattru Phai, Bangkok, 10100, Thailand
Tel.: (66) 22202222
Staffing Support Services
N.A.I.C.S.: 561320

Thanachart Plus Co., Ltd. (1)
Thanachart Plus 444 MBK Tower 16th Fl Phaya Thai Rd, Pathum Wan, Bangkok, 10330, Thailand
Tel.: (66) 22178000
Web Site: https://www.thanachartplus.co.th

7607

THANACHART CAPITAL PCL

Thanachart Capital PCL—(Continued)
Financial Services
N.A.I.C.S.: 523999

Thanachart SPV 01 Company Limited (1)
444 MBK Tower 11th Floor Phayathai Road Wangmai, Pathum Wan, Bangkok, 10330, Thailand
Tel.: (66) 22178160
Banking & Securities Broking Services
N.A.I.C.S.: 522110

Thanachart SPV 2 Co., Ltd. (1)
444 MBK Tower 17th Floor Phayathai Road, Wangmai Pathumwan, Bangkok, 10330, Thailand
Tel.: (66) 22178000
Insurance Services
N.A.I.C.S.: 524210

Thanachart Securities Public Company Limited (1)
444 MBK Tower Building 18th Floor Phayathai Road, Wang Mai Subdistrict Pathumwan District, Bangkok, 10330, Thailand
Tel.: (66) 27799000
Web Site: https://www.thanachartsec.com
Sales Range: $200-249.9 Million
Securities Brokerage & Trading Services
N.A.I.C.S.: 523150

Thanachart Training & Development Co., Ltd. (1)
2 Thanachart Suanmali Office Building M Floor Chaloemkhet 4 Road, Wat Thep Sirin Pom Prap Sattru Phai, Bangkok, 10100, Thailand
Tel.: (66) 22202222
Professional Training Services
N.A.I.C.S.: 611430

THANAPIRIYA PUBLIC COMPANY LIMITED
No 329 Village No 8, Ban Du Subdistrict Mueang Chiang Rai District, Chiang Rai, 57100, Thailand
Tel.: (66) 53776144   TH
Web Site: https://www.thanapiriya.co.th
Year Founded: 2000
TNP—(THA)
Rev.: $76,290,222
Assets: $41,062,752
Liabilities: $9,569,075
Net Worth: $31,493,677
Earnings: $4,540,087
Emp.: 617
Fiscal Year-end: 12/31/23
Food Products Distr
N.A.I.C.S.: 456191
Thawatchai Phutthiphiriya *(Mng Dir)*

THANASIRI GROUP PUBLIC COMPANY LIMITED
No 650 652 Boromratchonnanee Road, Bang Bamru Subdistrict Bang Phlat District, Bangkok, 10700, Thailand
Tel.: (66) 28864888
Web Site: https://www.thanasiri.com
THANA—(THA)
Rev.: $15,571,289
Assets: $41,363,854
Liabilities: $25,162,602
Net Worth: $16,201,251
Earnings: $1,193,076
Fiscal Year-end: 12/31/23
Property Developer
N.A.I.C.S.: 531390
Sutthirak Sateanraphap-a-yut *(Mng Dir)*

THANG LONG WINE JSC
No 3-89 Lac Long Quan Nghia Do ward, Cau Giay district, Hanoi, Vietnam
Tel.: (84) 2437533428
Web Site: http://www.vangthanglong.com.vn
VTL—(HNX)
Rev.: $7,986,300
Assets: $10,305,300
Liabilities: $11,533,500
Net Worth: ($1,228,200)
Earnings: ($3,572,600)
Fiscal Year-end: 12/31/22
Alcoholic Beverages Mfr
N.A.I.C.S.: 312130
Lien Tran *(Chief Acctg Officer)*

THANGAMAYIL JEWELLERY LIMITED
Palami Center 2nd and 3rd Floor Near Ramakrishna Mutt, 25/6 New Natham Road Narayanapuram, Madurai, 625014, Tamil Nadu, India
Tel.: (91) 4522565553
Web Site: https://www.thangamayil.com
Year Founded: 2000
THANGAMAYL—(NSE)
Rev.: $299,583,157
Assets: $123,546,751
Liabilities: $79,284,728
Net Worth: $44,262,022
Earnings: $5,261,160
Emp.: 1,688
Fiscal Year-end: 03/31/22
Jewelry Retailer & Distr
N.A.I.C.S.: 458310
Balarama Govinda Das *(Founder, Chm & Co-Mng Dir)*

Subsidiaries:

Balusamy Silvears Jewellery Private Limited (1)
No 347 N Masi St, Madurai, 625 001, Tamil Nadu, India
Tel.: (91) 4522345143
Diamond & Jewelry Retailer
N.A.I.C.S.: 458310

Thangamayil Gold & Diamond Private Limited (1)
No 147 N Masi Street, Madurai, 625 001, Tamil Nadu, India
Tel.: (91) 4522345553
Web Site: http://www.thangamayilinfo.com
Sales Range: $400-449.9 Million
Emp.: 1,700
Diamond & Jewelry Retailer
N.A.I.C.S.: 458310
Ba Ramesh *(Mng Dir)*

THANGLONG INVESTMENT GROUP JOINT STOCK COMPANY
8F Tower B of Song Da Building Pham Hung Street My Dinh I Ward, Nam Tu Liem District, Hanoi, Vietnam
Tel.: (84) 462588555
Web Site: https://www.thanglonginvest.vn
Year Founded: 2001
TIG—(HNX)
Rev.: $94,353,700
Assets: $431,572,300
Liabilities: $181,527,300
Net Worth: $250,045,000
Earnings: $22,722,200
Emp.: 70
Fiscal Year-end: 12/31/22
Investment Holding Company; Real Estate Services
N.A.I.C.S.: 551112
Nguyen Phuc Long *(Chm-Mgmt Bd)*

Subsidiaries:

Thang Long Invest Land JSC (1)
Floor 1 N 6 E Building Nguyen Thi Thap Street Trung Hoa Ward, Cau Giay District, Hanoi, Vietnam
Tel.: (84) 437735721
Real Estate Management Services
N.A.I.C.S.: 531390

Thang Long Phutho Investment Joint Stock Company (1)
King Garden Trung Thinh Commune, Thanh Thuy district, Ho Chi Minh City, PhuTho, Vietnam
Tel.: (84) 2103878464
Real Estate Investment Services
N.A.I.C.S.: 531110

THANH CONG TEXTILE GARMENT INVESTMENT TRADING JOINT STOCK COMPANY
36 Tay Thanh Street Tay Thanh Ward, Tan Phu District, Ho Chi Minh City, Vietnam
Tel.: (84) 838153962
Web Site: https://www.thanhcong.com.vn
TCM—(HOSE)
Rev.: $433,738,900
Assets: $347,706,700
Liabilities: $149,821,000
Net Worth: $197,885,700
Earnings: $27,934,500
Emp.: 6,625
Fiscal Year-end: 12/31/22
Textile Products Mfr
N.A.I.C.S.: 314999
Tran Nhu Tung *(Vice Chm, Member-Mgmt Bd & Deputy Gen Dir)*

Subsidiaries:

Thanh Cong Medical Center Joint Stock Company (1)
36 Tay Thanh Road CN4, Tan Binh Industrial Park Tay Thanh Ward Tan Phu District, Ho Chi Minh City, Vietnam
Tel.: (84) 283 815 9435
Web Site: https://www.thanhcongclinic.com
Women Healthcare Services
N.A.I.C.S.: 621610

THANH NAM FURNITURE & ARCHITECTURE JOINT STOCK COMPANY
Cotana Group Building Lot CC5A Linh Dam Peninsula, Hoang Liet Hoang Mai, Hanoi, Vietnam
Tel.: (84) 462512504   VN
Web Site: http://www.thanhnamdecor.vn
Furniture Mfr
N.A.I.C.S.: 337121

THANH THAI GROUP JOINT STOCK COMPANY
No 6 Nguyen Trai May To Ward, Ngo Quyen district, Haiphong, Vietnam
Tel.: (84) 2253826832
Web Site: https://thanhthaigroup.com.vn
KKC—(HNX)
Rev.: $22,633,800
Assets: $6,894,200
Liabilities: $2,771,900
Net Worth: $4,122,300
Earnings: ($32,301,000)
Fiscal Year-end: 12/31/22
Steel Products Mfr
N.A.I.C.S.: 331110

THANH THANH CONG - BIEN HOA JOINT STOCK COMPANY
Tan Hung Village - Tan Chau District, Ho Chi Minh City, Tay Ninh, Vietnam
Tel.: (84) 3757250   VN
Web Site: https://ttcagris.com.vn
Year Founded: 1995
SBT—(HOSE)
Rev.: $1,045,643,955
Assets: $1,265,022,926
Liabilities: $821,138,973
Net Worth: $443,883,953
Earnings: $25,552,298
Emp.: 2,635
Fiscal Year-end: 12/31/22
Sugar Mfr
N.A.I.C.S.: 311314
Thanh Ngu Nguyen *(Gen Dir)*

INTERNATIONAL PUBLIC

THANH THANH JOINT STOCK COMPANY
Bien Hoa I Industrial Zone, Dong Nai, Vietnam
Tel.: (84) 2513836066
Web Site: https://www.thanhthanhceramic.com
TTC—(HNX)
Rev.: $31,314,700
Assets: $18,333,900
Liabilities: $6,083,000
Net Worth: $12,250,900
Earnings: $1,150,700
Emp.: 650
Fiscal Year-end: 12/31/22
Tile Mfr & Distr
N.A.I.C.S.: 327120
Thanh Tuan Pham *(Chm)*

THANTAWAN INDUSTRY PUBLIC COMPANY LIMITED
32nd Floor Suntowers Building A 123 Vibhavadi-Rangsit Rd Jatuchak, Bangkok, 10900, Thailand
Tel.: (66) 22738333
Web Site: https://www.thantawan.com
Year Founded: 1978
THIP—(THA)
Rev.: $101,629,997
Assets: $92,413,239
Liabilities: $15,250,394
Net Worth: $77,162,845
Earnings: $8,422,222
Emp.: 1,838
Fiscal Year-end: 12/31/23
Plastics Product Mfr
N.A.I.C.S.: 325211
Teerachai Siritunyanont *(Asst Mng Dir & Sec)*

THANULUX PUBLIC COMPANY LIMITED
1291 Chong Nonsi Road, Yannawa, Bangkok, 10120, Thailand
Tel.: (66) 22950911
Web Site: https://www.tnl.co.th
Year Founded: 1975
TNL—(THA)
Rev.: $83,779,439
Assets: $391,768,631
Liabilities: $85,443,116
Net Worth: $306,325,515
Earnings: $14,986,622
Emp.: 1,920
Fiscal Year-end: 12/31/23
Clothing Mfr
N.A.I.C.S.: 315990
Varindr Leelanuwatana *(Chm)*

Subsidiaries:

S. Apparel Co., Ltd. (1)
4 2 Moo 8 Bangna Trad Rd KM 18 Tambol Bangchalong Amphur, Bangplee Samutprakarn, Bangkok, Thailand **(100%)**
Tel.: (66) 27406271
Sales Range: $25-49.9 Million
Emp.: 20
Ladies Apparels Mfr
N.A.I.C.S.: 315210

T-Chamber Co., Ltd. (1)
129 1 Chongnonthri Rd Kwaeng Chongnonthri, Khet Yannawa, Bangkok, Thailand
Tel.: (66) 22840118
Sales Range: $350-399.9 Million
Emp.: 2,000
Garments Retailing Services
N.A.I.C.S.: 315250

THARISA PLC
Office 108-110 S Pittokopides Bus Ctr 17, Neophytou Nicolaides & Kilkis Street, 8011, Paphos, Cyprus
Tel.: (357) 26257052   CY
Web Site: https://www.tharisa.com
Year Founded: 2006

AND PRIVATE COMPANIES

THA—(JSE)
Rev.: $596,345,000
Assets: $703,397,000
Liabilities: $252,123,000
Net Worth: $451,274,000
Earnings: $131,541,000
Emp.: 1,831
Fiscal Year-end: 09/30/21
Metallurgical & Mineral Mining Services
N.A.I.C.S.: 213115
Loucas Pouroulis *(Chm)*

Subsidiaries:

MetQ Proprietary Limited (1)
209 Van Eden Crescent Rosslyn East, Pretoria, 0200, South Africa
Tel.: (27) 125412010
Web Site: https://www.metq.co.za
Polyurethane Hydro Cyclone Mfr
N.A.I.C.S.: 325510

THATTA CEMENT COMPANY LIMITED

CL/5-4 State Life Building 10 Abdullah Haroon Road, Karachi, Pakistan
Tel.: (92) 21111842882
Web Site:
 https://www.thattacement.com
Year Founded: 1980
THCCL—(PSX)
Rev.: $19,883,862
Assets: $27,634,278
Liabilities: $9,316,543
Net Worth: $18,317,735
Earnings: $1,114,025
Emp.: 493
Fiscal Year-end: 06/30/23
Cement Mfr
N.A.I.C.S.: 339114
Muhammad Aslam *(CEO)*

Subsidiaries:

Thatta Power (Private) Limited (1)
CL/5-4 State Life Building 10 Abdullah Haroon Road, Karachi, Pakistan
Tel.: (92) 21111842882
Web Site: https://thattapower.com
Power Plant Maintenance Services
N.A.I.C.S.: 561730

THC BIOMED INTERNATIONAL LTD.

Tel.: (250) 870-2512 **BC**
Web Site:
 https://www.thcbiomed.com
THC—(CNSX)
Rev.: $2,952,576
Assets: $13,608,888
Liabilities: $5,955,523
Net Worth: $7,653,365
Earnings: ($4,974,717)
Emp.: 45
Fiscal Year-end: 07/31/21
Medical Marijuana
N.A.I.C.S.: 325411

Subsidiaries:

Clone Shipper LLC. (1)
13794 W Waddell Rd Ste 203, Surprise, AZ 85374
Web Site: https://www.cloneshipper.com
Plant Shipping Container Mfr & Distr
N.A.I.C.S.: 322211
Larry Fenner *(Founder)*

THE 600 GROUP PLC

Lowfields Way Lowfield Business Park, Elland, HX5 9DA, West Yorkshire, United Kingdom
Tel.: (407) 818-1123 **UK**
Web Site: http://www.600group.com
Year Founded: 1834
SIXH—(LSE)
Rev.: $43,392,731
Assets: $91,093,508
Liabilities: ($52,181,253)
Net Worth: $38,912,255
Earnings: $1,722,947
Emp.: 123
Fiscal Year-end: 03/31/22
Machine Tools & Accessories, Lasers & other Engineering Products Mfr & Distr
N.A.I.C.S.: 333515
Paul Dupee *(Chm)*

Subsidiaries:

600 International Ltd (1)
Baranova 33, 130 00, Prague, Czech Republic (100%)
Tel.: (420) 22240133
Web Site: http://www.the600group.com
Machine Tool Whslr
N.A.I.C.S.: 423830

600 Machine Tools Pty Ltd (1)
27 Foundry Road Seven Hills, Newington, 2147, NSW, Australia (100%)
Tel.: (61) 297481964
Web Site: http://www.600machinery.com.au
Sales Range: $25-49.9 Million
Emp.: 50
Machine Tool Whslr
N.A.I.C.S.: 423830

Branch (Domestic):

600 Machine Tools New South Wales (2)
27 Foundry Road, PO Box 678, Newington Business Park, Seven Hills, 2147, NSW, Australia (100%)
Tel.: (61) 29 674 4738
Web Site:
 https://www.600machinetools.com.au
Sales Range: $25-49.9 Million
Emp.: 12
Machine Tool Whslr
N.A.I.C.S.: 423830

Branch (Non-US):

600 Machine Tools New Zealand (2)
42 Allens Rd E Tamaki, Tamaki, Auckland, New Zealand (100%)
Tel.: (64) 92623025
Web Site: http://www.machines.co.nz
Sales Range: $1-9.9 Million
Emp.: 5
Machine Tool Whslr
N.A.I.C.S.: 423830
Simon Lucas *(Gen Mgr)*

Branch (Domestic):

600 Machine Tools Queensland (2)
292 Evans Road, PO Box 66, Salisbury, 4107, QLD, Australia (100%)
Tel.: (61) 73 277 4844
Web Site:
 https://www.600machinetools.com.au
Sales Range: $25-49.9 Million
Emp.: 5
Machine Tool Whslr
N.A.I.C.S.: 423830

600 Machine Tools Victoria (2)
24 Wadhurst Dr, Boronia, 3155, VIC, Australia (100%)
Tel.: (61) 398003322
Web Site: http://www.600machinery.com.au
Sales Range: $25-49.9 Million
Emp.: 4
Machine Tool Whslr
N.A.I.C.S.: 423830

Ambassador Machine Tools (2)
Suite 2 17 Prowse Street, West Perth, 6005, WA, Australia (100%)
Tel.: (61) 89 321 3611
Web Site: https://www.machinetools.com.au
Machine Tool Whslr
N.A.I.C.S.: 423830

600 Machinery International Ltd (1)
20 Grange Way Business Park Grange Way, Colchester, CO2 8HF, United Kingdom (100%)
Tel.: (44) 1206 796 600
Web Site: http://www.600mac.co.uk
Sales Range: $25-49.9 Million
Emp.: 10
Machine Tools Mfr
N.A.I.C.S.: 333517
Tony Sweeten *(Chm)*

Clausing Industrial Inc (1)
3963 Emerald Dr, Kalamazoo, MI 49001 (100%)
Tel.: (269) 345-7155
Web Site: https://www.clausing-industrial.com
Sales Range: $25-49.9 Million
Emp.: 40
Cutting Tools Mgr
N.A.I.C.S.: 423830
Don Haseltin *(Pres)*

Subsidiary (Non-US):

600 Machine Tools (1)
5220 General Rd, Mississauga, L4W 1G8, ON, Canada (100%)
Tel.: (519) 250-5588
Web Site: http://www.600machinetools.com
Sales Range: $25-49.9 Million
Emp.: 25
Machine Tool Whslr
N.A.I.C.S.: 423830

Subsidiary (Domestic):

Erickson Machine Tools Inc. (2)
409 Market Ave PO Box 320, Story City, IA 50248
Tel.: (515) 733-4361
Web Site: http://www.ericksonmachine.com
Machine Tool Whslr
N.A.I.C.S.: 423830
Dave Lockhart *(Mgr-Svc)*

Lakeshore Machine Tools (2)
2015 N Pitcher St, Kalamazoo, MI 49007 (100%)
Tel.: (269) 349-6000
Web Site: http://www.clausing-industrial.com
Sales Range: $25-49.9 Million
Emp.: 3
Machine Tool Whslr
N.A.I.C.S.: 423830

Colchester Lathe Company Ltd (1)
PO Box 20, Union St, Heckmondwike, WF16 0HN, W Yorkshire, United Kingdom (100%)
Tel.: (44) 1924415005
Web Site: http://www.600uk.com
Sales Range: $25-49.9 Million
Emp.: 200
Lathes Mfr
N.A.I.C.S.: 333517

Electrox Laser Limited (1)
Ave One The Business Park, Letchworth, SG6 2HB, Herts, United Kingdom (100%)
Tel.: (44) 1462 472400
Web Site: http://www.electrox.com
Laser Mfr
N.A.I.C.S.: 333517
Paul Mincher *(Mng Dir)*

Subsidiary (US):

TYKMA, Inc. (2)
370 Gateway Dr, Chillicothe, OH 45601 (80%)
Tel.: (740) 779-9918
Web Site:
 https://www.permanentmarking.com
Sales Range: $1-9.9 Million
Emp.: 34
Laser Marking Systems Mfr
N.A.I.C.S.: 333248
David Grimes *(CEO)*

FMT Colchester z.o.o. (1)
Ul Jana Kochanowskiego 30, Tarnow, 33-100, Poland
Tel.: (48) 14 63 06 355
Web Site: http://www.fmt-colchester.pl
Lathes & Grinding Machines Mfr
N.A.I.C.S.: 333248

Gamet Bearings Ltd (1)
Hythe Station Road, Hythe, Colchester, CO2 8LD, Essex, United Kingdom (100%)
Tel.: (44) 1206862121
Web Site: http://www.gamet-bearings.co.uk
Sales Range: $25-49.9 Million
Emp.: 30
Bearing Mfr
N.A.I.C.S.: 332991
Tony Tankard *(Gen Mgr)*

Pratt Burnerd International Limited (1)

THE 77 BANK, LTD.

Uniworks 1 union street Heckmondwike WF16 0HL, Halifax, HX1 5JH, West Yorkshire, United Kingdom (100%)
Tel.: (44) 1422366371
Web Site: http://www.pratt-burnerd.co.uk
Sales Range: $25-49.9 Million
Emp.: 55
Hand Tool Mfr
N.A.I.C.S.: 333991

The 600 Group (Overseas) Limited (1)
600 House 3 Landmark Court, Leeds, LS11 8JT, West Yorkshire, United Kingdom
Tel.: (44) 113 277 6100
Machine Tools Mfr
N.A.I.C.S.: 333517

The 600 UK Ltd. (1)
Lowfields Way Lowfields Business Park, Elland, HX5 9DA, West Yorkshire, United Kingdom (100%)
Tel.: (44) 1924 415000
Web Site: http://www.colchester.co.uk
Sales Range: $25-49.9 Million
Emp.: 90
Lathes Mfr
N.A.I.C.S.: 333517

THE 77 BANK, LTD.

3-20 Chuo 3-chome, Aoba-ku, Sendai, 980-8777, Miyagi, Japan
Tel.: (81) 222671111
Year Founded: 1878
8341—(TKS)
Rev.: $995,148,720
Assets: $69,412,257,780
Liabilities: $65,435,020,780
Net Worth: $3,977,237,000
Earnings: $446,175
Emp.: 2,536
Fiscal Year-end: 03/31/24
Commercial Banking Services
N.A.I.C.S.: 522110
Makoto Igarashi *(Sr Mng Dir)*

Subsidiaries:

77 Business Services Co., Ltd. (1)
2-chome No 1, Aoba-ku, Sendai, Miyagi, Japan (100%)
Tel.: (81) 22 267 3677
Web Site: http://www.77bank.co.jp
Sales Range: $1-4.9 Billion
Emp.: 2,690
Commercial Banking Services
N.A.I.C.S.: 522110
Hiroshi Kamata *(Chm)*

77 Computer Services Co., Ltd. (1)
1-10 Akedori Izumi-ku, Sendai, Miyagi, Japan (100%)
Tel.: (81) 22 377 8872
Web Site: http://www.77bank.co.jp
Computer-Based Financial Contract Services
N.A.I.C.S.: 518210

77 Lease Co., Ltd. (1)
12th floor Lunar Sendai 2-15-1 Honmachi, Aoba-ku, Sendai, 980-0014, Miyagi, Japan (100%)
Tel.: (81) 222624341
Web Site: https://www.77lease.co.jp
Equipment Finance Leasing Services
N.A.I.C.S.: 561990
Toshinori Hayasaka *(Pres & CEO)*

77 Shin-Yo Hosyo Co., Ltd. (1)
1-12 Kimachidori chome Aoba-ku, Sendai, 980-8777, Miyagi, Japan (100%)
Tel.: (81) 227233685
Web Site: http://www.77bank.co.jp
Guaranty & Credit Investigation Services
N.A.I.C.S.: 522390

The 77 Bank Ltd. - Treasury Administration & International Division (1)
3-20 Chuo 3-chome, Aoba-ku, Sendai, 980-8777, Miyagi, Japan
Tel.: (81) 222119914
Web Site: http://www.77bank.co.jp
Sales Range: $50-74.9 Million
Emp.: 40
Cash Management & Settlement Services
N.A.I.C.S.: 522110
Atsushi Shitoh *(Gen Mgr)*

THE 77 BANK, LTD.

The 77 Bank, Ltd.—(Continued)

The 77 Card Co., Ltd. (1)
3rd floor Sendai Higashiguchi Building
2-4-22 Tsutsugaoka, Miyagino-ku, Sendai,
983-0852, Miyagi, Japan (100%)
Tel.: (81) 222981877
Web Site: https://www.77card.co.jp
Emp.: 61
Credit Card Processing Services
N.A.I.C.S.: 522320

THE A2 MILK COMPANY LIMITED

Level 10 51 Shortland Street, Newmarket, Auckland, 1010, New Zealand
Tel.: (64) 99729802
Web Site:
https://thea2milkcompany.com
Year Founded: 2000
ATM—(NZX)
Rev.: $951,607,656
Assets: $963,943,780
Liabilities: $276,443,182
Net Worth: $687,500,598
Earnings: $86,627,392
Emp.: 286
Fiscal Year-end: 06/30/23
Milk Production
N.A.I.C.S.: 112120
David Hearn (Chm)

THE ACADEMY

1 Hardwick Street, London, EC1R 4RB, United Kingdom
Tel.: (44) 2071007100
Web Site:
http://www.theacademypr.com
Year Founded: 2014
Public Relation Agency Services
N.A.I.C.S.: 541820
Rachel Bell (Chm)

Subsidiaries:

Shine Communications Limited (1)
1 Hardwick St, London, EC1R 4RB, United Kingdom
Tel.: (44) 207 100 7100
Web Site: http://www.shinecom.com
Public Relations
N.A.I.C.S.: 541820
Rachel Bell (Founder)

THE ADITYA BIRLA GROUP

Aditya Birla Centre S K Ahire Marg
Worli, Mumbai, 400030, India
Tel.: (91) 2266525000 In
Web Site:
https://www.adityabirla.com
Year Founded: 1857
Sales Range: $25-49.9 Billion
Emp.: 133,000
Holding Company
N.A.I.C.S.: 551112
Santrupt B. Misra (CEO-Chemical Bus & Dir-HR)

Subsidiaries:

Aditya Birla Capital Advisors Private Limited (1)
Elphinstone Road One India Bulls Centre Tower 1 841, Senapati Bapat Marg, Mumbai, 400 013, India
Tel.: (91) 22 4356 7400
Web Site: http://www.adityabirla-pe.com
Financial Management Services
N.A.I.C.S.: 523999
Piyush Shah (Chief Compliance Officer)

Aditya Birla Fashion & Retail Limited (1)
Piramal Agastya Corporate Park Building A 4th and 5th Floor, Unit No 401 403 501 502 L BS Road Kurla, Mumbai, 400 070, India
Tel.: (91) 8652905000
Web Site: https://www.abfrl.com
Rev.: $726,496,680
Assets: $1,388,405,655
Liabilities: $1,023,094,800
Net Worth: $365,310,855

Earnings: ($1,004,640)
Emp.: 22,351
Fiscal Year-end: 03/31/2021
Clothing Whslr
N.A.I.C.S.: 458110
Chandrashekhar Chavan (Chief HR Officer)

Aditya Birla Finance Limited (1)
802 Samudra Annexe Off C G Road Near Hotel Classic Gold, Navrangpura, Ahmedabad, 380 009, India
Tel.: (91) 79 66636690
Web Site: http://www.adityabirlafinance.com
Financial Management Services
N.A.I.C.S.: 523999
M. S. Sekhar (Head-Risk & Compliance)

Aditya Birla Management Corporation Limited (1)
Aditya Birla Centre 3rd Floor SK Ahire Marg, Worli, Mumbai, 400 025, India (100%)
Tel.: (91) 225 652 5000
Web Site: http://www.adityabirla.com
Sales Range: $25-49.9 Million
Emp.: 50
Management Services & Various Manufacturing Operations
N.A.I.C.S.: 541618
Kumar Mangalam Birla (Chm)

Birla Carbon Company Limited (1)
Aditya Birla Centre S K Ahire Marg, Worli, Mumbai, 400 030, India
Tel.: (91) 22 6652 5000
Carbon Black Mfr
N.A.I.C.S.: 335991
Santrupt Misra (CEO)

Subsidiary (Non-US):

Birla Carbon Alexandria Carbon Black Co. SAE (2)
El Nahda Road, Amreya, Alexandria, 23511, Egypt
Tel.: (20) 3 4770 102 07
Carbon Black Mfr
N.A.I.C.S.: 325180

Birla Carbon Columbian Carbon Europa Srl. (2)
Via S Cassiano 140, San Martino, 28069, Trecate, NO, Italy
Tel.: (39) 0321798266
Web Site: http://www.birlacarbon.com
Emp.: 84
Carbon Black Mfr
N.A.I.C.S.: 325180
Giuseppe Zanotti Fargonare (Mgr)

Birla Carbon Columbian Carbon Spain S.L. (2)
Cantabria Apartado 283 Carretera Gajano-Pontejos, Gajano-Pontejos, 39792, Gajano, Spain
Tel.: (34) 9425 03030
Carbon Black Mfr
N.A.I.C.S.: 325180

Birla Carbon Columbian Chemicals Brazil Ltda (2)
Via Fontal Km 1 s/n, Polo Petroquimico, 42810-320, Camacari, Brazil
Tel.: (55) 71 3616 1100
Web Site: http://www.birlacarbon.com
Carbon Black Mfr
N.A.I.C.S.: 325180

Birla Carbon Columbian Chemicals Deutschland GmbH (2)
Kreis Strasse 20, Misburg, 30629, Hannover, Germany
Tel.: (49) 511 959 350
Carbon Black Mfr
N.A.I.C.S.: 325180

Birla Carbon Columbian Chemicals Korea Co. Ltd. (2)
46-101 Yeosusandan 2-ro, Yeosu, 555-290, Jeonnam, Korea (South)
Tel.: (82) 61 688 3382
Carbon Black Mfr
N.A.I.C.S.: 325180

Birla Carbon Columbian Chemicals Weifang Co. Ltd. (2)
Binhai Economic Development Zone, Weifang, Shandong, China
Tel.: (86) 536 5302 700
Carbon Black Mfr

N.A.I.C.S.: 325180

Birla Carbon Columbian Tiszai Carbon LLC (2)
PO Box 61, Tiszaujvaros, Hungary
Tel.: (36) 495 44000
Carbon Black Mfr
N.A.I.C.S.: 325180

Unit (Domestic):

Birla Carbon Company Limited - Birla Carbon Hi-Tech Carbon India Unit (2)
K-16 Phase II SIPCOT Industrial Complex, Thiruvallur, Gummidipoondi, 601 201, India
Tel.: (91) 44 2798 9233
Carbon Black Mfr
N.A.I.C.S.: 325180
Srathi Rathi (Mng Dir)

Subsidiary (US):

Birla Carbon U.S.A., Inc. (2)
1800 W Oak Commons Ct, Marietta, GA 30062-2253
Tel.: (770) 792-9400
Web Site:
http://www.columbianchemicals.com
Sales Range: $800-899.9 Million
Emp.: 1,300
Carbon Black & Synthetic Iron Oxide Mfr
N.A.I.C.S.: 325180

Subsidiary (Domestic):

Birla Carbon Columbian Chemicals Co. (3)
3500 S Road South, Ulysses, KS 67880
Tel.: (620) 356-3151
Carbon Black Mfr
N.A.I.C.S.: 325180

Subsidiary (Non-US):

Columbian Chemicals Brasil, Ltda. (3)
Avenida Rua do Cafe 277 4th Floor Block B, Jabaquara, Sao Paulo, 04311900, SP, Brazil
Tel.: (55) 11 3598 3800
Web Site: http://www.birlacarbon.com
Emp.: 260
Carbon Black Sales & Mfr
N.A.I.C.S.: 325180
Adilsom Trevisan (Gen Mgr)

Columbian Chemicals Canada Ltd. (3)
755 Parkdale Avenue North, Hamilton, L8H 7M2, ON, Canada
Tel.: (905) 544-3343
Web Site:
http://www.columbianchemicals.com
Carbon Black Mfr
N.A.I.C.S.: 325180
George Zolis (Gen Mgr)

Columbian Chemicals Europa GmbH (3)
Podbielski Strasse 160, Hannover, 30177, Germany
Tel.: (49) 511 63089 0
Web Site: http://www.birlacarbon.com
Emp.: 26
Carbon Black Sales
N.A.I.C.S.: 424690
Lena Theophil (Office Mgr)

Columbian Chemicals Korea Co., Ltd. (3)
7th Floor Tae-woo Building 1357-10, Seocho-Dong Seocho-Gu, Seoul, 137 070, Korea (South)
Tel.: (82) 2 775 1674
Carbon Black Sales
N.A.I.C.S.: 424690

Nanocyl SA (3)
Rue de l Essor 4, 5060, Sambreville, Belgium
Tel.: (32) 71750380
Web Site: http://www.nanocyl.com
Nano Technology Services
N.A.I.C.S.: 541713
Jean Stephenne (Chm)

Subsidiary (Non-US):

Liaoning Birla Carbon Co., Ltd. (2)

INTERNATIONAL PUBLIC

No 22 West Surround Road, Dashiqiao, 115100, Dashiqiao, China
Tel.: (86) 417 3186 666
Carbon Black Mfr
N.A.I.C.S.: 325180

Century Enka Ltd. (1)
Plot No 72 & 72-A MIDC, Bhosari, Pune, 411 026, Maharashtra, India
Tel.: (91) 2066127300
Web Site: http://www.centuryenka.com
Rev.: $169,917,930
Assets: $182,830,830
Liabilities: $34,197,345
Net Worth: $148,633,485
Earnings: $9,680,580
Emp.: 1,656
Fiscal Year-end: 03/31/2021
Synthetic Fiber Mfr
N.A.I.C.S.: 314999
B. K. Birla (Chm)

Domsjo Fabriker AB (1)
Ornskoldsvik, 891 86, Ornskoldsvik, Sweden
Tel.: (46) 660 756 00
Web Site: http://www.domsjoe.com
Emp.: 25
Chemical Products Mfr
N.A.I.C.S.: 325998
Bjorn Edstrom (Mgr-Engrg Unit)

Grasim Industries Limited (1)
Birlagram, Nagda, 456 331, Madhya Pradesh, India
Tel.: (91) 7366246760
Web Site: https://www.grasim.com
Rev.: $14,536,194,473
Assets: $40,429,833,943
Liabilities: $25,692,969,246
Net Worth: $14,736,864,696
Earnings: $1,328,241,712
Emp.: 24,455
Fiscal Year-end: 03/31/2023
Building Materials Mfr
N.A.I.C.S.: 327310
Thomas Varghese (Head-Textiles)

Holding (Non-US):

AV Cell Inc. (2)
175 Mill Ch, Atholville, E3N 4S7, NB, Canada (45%)
Tel.: (506) 789-4491
Web Site: http://www.adityabirla.com
Sales Range: $100-124.9 Million
Emp.: 300
Specialty Cellulose Mill
N.A.I.C.S.: 325199
Vishnu Sharma (VP)

Subsidiary (Non-US):

Aditya Birla Chemicals (Thailand) Ltd., Epoxy Division (2)
888 167 Mahatun Plaza Bldg 16th Floor Ploenchit Rd, Bangkok, 10330, Thailand
Tel.: (66) 2 253 5031
Web Site: http://www.epotec.info
Sales Range: $50-74.9 Million
Emp.: 200
Adhesive Chemical Products Mfr
N.A.I.C.S.: 325520
H. Agarwal (Pres)

Subsidiary (Domestic):

Aditya Birla Nuvo Limited (2)
Birlagram Madhya Pradesh, Nagda, 456 331, India (100%)
Tel.: (91) 07366246760
Web Site: http://www.grasim.com
Rayon Yarn Mfr
N.A.I.C.S.: 313110
Sushil Agarwal (CFO)

Subsidiary (Domestic):

Aditya Birla Money Limited (3)
Ali Centre No 53 Greams Road, Chennai, 600006, India
Tel.: (91) 444 949 0000
Web Site: http://www.adityabirlamoney.com
Rev.: $31,930,872
Assets: $172,923,182
Liabilities: $162,763,078
Net Worth: $10,160,105
Earnings: $3,567,127
Emp.: 616
Fiscal Year-end: 03/31/2022
Asset Management Services

AND PRIVATE COMPANIES

THE ADITYA BIRLA GROUP

N.A.I.C.S.: 523940
Saurabh Shukla (Head-Bus Broking & Distr)

Subsidiary (Domestic):

Aditya Birla Commodities Broking Limited (4)
Ali Centre No 53 Greams Road, Chennai, 600 006, India
Tel.: (91) 44 3919 0002
Commodity Contracts Brokerage Services
N.A.I.C.S.: 523160

Aditya Birla Money Mart Limited (4)
1 Indiabulls Centre Tower 1 14th Floor 841 SB Marg, Elphinstone Road, Mumbai, 400 013, India
Tel.: (91) 2243568300
Web Site: http://www.adityabirlamoney.com
Financial Services
N.A.I.C.S.: 523999
Sudhakar Ramasubramanian (CEO)

Unit (Domestic):

Aditya Birla Nuvo Ltd - Jaya Shree Textiles unit (3)
Rishra Prabasnagar, Dist Hooghly, Kolkata, 712 249, India
Tel.: (91) 33 2600 1351
Web Site: http://www.jayashree-abnl.com
Linen Fabric & Yarn Mfr
N.A.I.C.S.: 313110
B. D. Daga (Sr VP-MSD)

Subsidiary (Domestic):

Indo Gulf Fertilisers Limited (3)
Jagdishpur Industrial Area, Jagdishpur, Sultanpur, 227 817, Uttar Pradesh, India
Tel.: (91) 5361270032
Web Site: http://www.indo-gulf.com
Nitrogenous Fertilizer
N.A.I.C.S.: 325311
Jayant Dua (CEO)

Madura Garments Lifestyle Retail Company Limited (3)
Plot no 5B Regent Gateway KIADB Industrial Area ITPL Road, Doddanakundi Village, Bengaluru, 560 048, India
Tel.: (91) 80 6727 1600
Web Site: http://www.maduragarments.com
Apparel Mfr & Distr
N.A.I.C.S.: 315250
Anurag Srivastava (Head-Corp)

Unit (Domestic):

Grasim Industries Limited - Vikram Woollens Unit (2)
GH I to IV Ghironghi, Malanpur, Bhind, 477 117, Madhya Pradesh, India
Tel.: (91) 7539 283602
Wool & Polyester Mfr
N.A.I.C.S.: 313210
Asitabha Bandopadhyay (Head-PPC & Quality Control)

Joint Venture (Domestic):

Tanfac Industries Limited (2)
14 Sipcot Inustrial Complex, SAV District, Cuddalore, 607 005, India
Tel.: (91) 4142239001
Web Site: http://www.tanfac.com
Sales Range: $25-49.9 Million
Emp.: 50
Fluorine Chemicals Mfr
N.A.I.C.S.: 325998
T. C. Kalyankumar (Sr Mgr-Mktg)

Subsidiary (Domestic):

UltraTech Cement Ltd. (2)
B Wing 2nd Floor Ahura Centre Mahakali Caves Road Andheri East, Mumbai, 400 093, India (57.28%)
Tel.: (91) 2266917800
Web Site: https://www.ultratechcement.com
Rev.: $7,249,056,360
Assets: $11,442,493,335
Liabilities: $4,558,496,670
Net Worth: $6,883,996,665
Earnings: $1,002,498,315
Emp.: 21,921
Fiscal Year-end: 03/31/2022
Cement Mfr
N.A.I.C.S.: 327310
S. K. Chatterjee (Officer-Compliance & Sec)

Subsidiary (Domestic):

Binani Cement Limited (3)
Mercantile Chambers 12 JN Heredia Marg, Ballard Estate, Mumbai, 400001, India
Tel.: (91) 2230263000
Cement Production & Sales
N.A.I.C.S.: 327120
Braj Binani (Chm)

Plant (Domestic):

Gujarat Cement Plant (3)
Abdasa, Sewagram Kutchh, Bhuj, 370 511, Gujarat, India
Tel.: (91) 2831 279299
Cement Mfr
N.A.I.C.S.: 327310

Subsidiary (Domestic):

Narmada Cement Company Limited (3)
Dumas Road Magdalla, Surat, 395007, Gujarat, India
Tel.: (91) 261 272 0160
Cement Mfr & Contracting Services
N.A.I.C.S.: 327310

Subsidiary (Non-US):

Ras Al Khaimah Company for White Cement & Construction Materials PSC (3)
P O Box 2499, Khor Khwair, Ras al Khaimah, United Arab Emirates (65.94%)
Tel.: (971) 72660111
Web Site: https://www.rakcc.ae
Rev.: $69,683,314
Assets: $240,407,805
Liabilities: $23,585,739
Net Worth: $216,822,066
Earnings: $5,594,183
Emp.: 240
Fiscal Year-end: 12/31/2023
Cement & Lime Products Mfr
N.A.I.C.S.: 327310
Mohamed M. Mohamed Alqadi (Vice Chm)

Unit (Domestic):

Wanakbori Cement Grinding Unit (3)
Near Wanakbori Thermal Power Station Sonipur, Sangol, Kheda, 388 245, Gujarat, India
Tel.: (91) 2699 232000
Cement Mfr
N.A.I.C.S.: 327310

Subsidiary (Domestic):

Hindalco Industries Ltd. (1)
21st Floor One Unity Center Senapati Bapat Marg, Prabhadevi, Mumbai, 400013, India (32.08%)
Tel.: (91) 2269477000
Web Site: https://www.hindalco.com
Rev.: $26,072,540,080
Assets: $27,804,930,388
Liabilities: $15,077,035,175
Net Worth: $12,727,895,213
Earnings: $1,217,553,020
Emp.: 22,851
Fiscal Year-end: 03/31/2024
Aluminum & Copper Products Mfr
N.A.I.C.S.: 331524
Satish Pai (Mng Dir)

Subsidiary (Domestic):

Hindalco-Almex Aerospace Limited (2)
AL-1 MIDC Shendra, Aurangabad, 431 007, India
Tel.: (91) 240 2622034
Web Site: http://www.hindalcoalmex.com
Aluminum Alloy Mfr
N.A.I.C.S.: 331314
Abhey Agarwal (Head-Unit)

Subsidiary (US):

HAAL USA Inc (3)
21 Tony Ann Pl, Canfield, OH 44406
Tel.: (330) 286-5256
Aluminum Rolled Product Distr
N.A.I.C.S.: 423510

Subsidiary (US):

Novelis Inc. (2)
3550 Peachtree Rd Ste 1100, Atlanta, GA 30326
Tel.: (404) 760-4000
Web Site: https://www.novelis.com
Rev.: $17,149,000,000
Assets: $15,096,000,000
Liabilities: $12,587,000,000
Net Worth: $2,509,000,000
Earnings: $954,000,000
Emp.: 12,690
Fiscal Year-end: 03/31/2022
Aluminum Rolled Semi-Finished Products Mfr
N.A.I.C.S.: 331318
Steven R. Fisher (Pres & CEO)

Subsidiary (Domestic):

Aleris Corporation (3)
25825 Science Park Dr Ste 400, Cleveland, OH 44122-7392
Tel.: (216) 910-3400
Web Site: http://www.aleris.com
Rev.: $3,375,900,000
Assets: $2,712,200,000
Liabilities: $2,773,400,000
Net Worth: ($61,200,000)
Earnings: ($11,800,000)
Emp.: 5,600
Fiscal Year-end: 12/31/2019
Holding Company; Aluminum Rolled & Extruded Products
N.A.I.C.S.: 551112
Christopher R. Clegg (Gen Counsel, Sec & Exec VP)

Subsidiary (Domestic):

Aleris International, Inc. (4)
25825 Science Park Dr Ste 400, Cleveland, OH 44122
Tel.: (216) 910-3400
Web Site: http://www.aleris.com
Sales Range: Less than $1 Million
Emp.: 7,000
Aluminum Recycler & Common-Alloy Sheet Mfr
N.A.I.C.S.: 331314

Subsidiary (Non-US):

Aleris Aluminum Koblenz GmbH (5)
Carl-spaeter-strasse 10, Koblenz, 56070, Germany
Tel.: (49) 2618910
Sales Range: $200-249.9 Million
Emp.: 1,350
Aluminium Products Mfr
N.A.I.C.S.: 331315

Subsidiary (Domestic):

Aleris Aluminium Vogt GmbH (6)
Bergstrasse 17, Vogt, 88267, Germany
Tel.: (49) 75299990
Web Site: http://www.aluprofil.de
Sales Range: $50-74.9 Million
Emp.: 300
Aluminum Profile Shape Mfr
N.A.I.C.S.: 331318

Subsidiary (Domestic):

Aleris Aluminum Bitterfeld GmbH (6)
Devillestrasse 2, PO Box 11 53, Bitterfeld, 06749, Germany
Tel.: (49) 349372251
Web Site: http://www.aluprofil.de
Sales Range: $25-49.9 Million
Emp.: 150
Aluminum Profile Shape Mfr
N.A.I.C.S.: 331318

Division (Domestic):

Aleris Rolled Products North America (5)
25825 Science Park Dr Ste 400, Cleveland, OH 44122
Tel.: (216) 910-3400
Web Site: http://www.aleris.com
Sales Range: $1-4.9 Billion
Aluminum Rolled Products Mfr
N.A.I.C.S.: 331318

Unit (Domestic):

Aleris Rolled Products, Inc. (6)
1372 State Rte 1957, Lewisport, KY 42351
Tel.: (270) 295-5228
Web Site: http://www.aleris.com
Sales Range: $150-199.9 Million
Emp.: 850
Recycled Metals
N.A.I.C.S.: 331318

Subsidiary (Domestic):

Aleris Specialty Products, Inc. (5)
6340 Indianapolis Blvd, Hammond, IN 46320
Tel.: (219) 931-1927
Web Site: http://drupal.aleris.net
Sales Range: $25-49.9 Million
Emp.: 25
Aluminum Smelting & Refining
N.A.I.C.S.: 331314

Subsidiary (Non-US):

Aluminum Company of Malaysia Berhad (3)
3 Persiaran Waji Kawasan Perindustrian Bukit, Kelang, 41050, Selangor Darul Eshan, Malaysia
Tel.: (60) 333466262
Web Site: http://www.novelis.com
Sales Range: $50-74.9 Million
Emp.: 360
Aluminum Rolling & Processing
N.A.I.C.S.: 331315

Novelis AG (3)
Sternenfeldstrasse 19, Kusnacht, Zurich, 8700, Switzerland
Tel.: (41) 44 386 21 50
Aluminum Rolled Product Distr
N.A.I.C.S.: 423510

Subsidiary (Domestic):

Novelis Corporation (3)
3560 Lenox Rd Ste 2000, Atlanta, GA 30326-4271
Tel.: (404) 760-4000
Web Site: http://www.novelis.com
Sales Range: $50-74.9 Million
Emp.: 200
Aluminium Products Mfr
N.A.I.C.S.: 331315

Unit (Domestic):

Novelis Industrial Products Group (4)
6060 Parkland Blvd, Mayfield Heights, OH 44124-4185
Tel.: (440) 423-6600
Goods & Services to Users of Aluminum Products
N.A.I.C.S.: 331318

Novelis Light Gauge Products (4)
6060 Parkland Blvd, Mayfield Heights, OH 44124
Tel.: (440) 423-6600
Light Gauge Aluminum Products Mfr
N.A.I.C.S.: 331318

Subsidiary (Non-US):

Novelis Italia SpA (3)
Via Vittorio Veneto 106, I 20091, Milan, Italy
Tel.: (39) 02614541
Web Site: http://www.novelis-painted.com
Sales Range: $125-149.9 Million
Emp.: 500
Aluminum Coil & Sheet Mfr
N.A.I.C.S.: 331318

Novelis Korea Limited (3)
Yonseijaedan Severance Building 23rd Floor, 84-11 5-ga Namdaemun-ro, Seoul, 100-753, Jung-gu, Korea (South)
Tel.: (82) 222591600
Web Site: http://www.novelis.co.kr
Sales Range: $350-399.9 Million
Emp.: 1,200
Rolled Aluminum
N.A.I.C.S.: 331318

Novelis Madeira, Unipessoal, Limited (3)
Calcada De Sao Lourenco 3 1 g, Funchal, 9000-061, Portugal
Tel.: (351) 291209600
Aluminum Rolled Product Distr
N.A.I.C.S.: 423510

Novelis Services Limited (3)
Castle Works, Rogerstone, Newport, NP10 9YD, United Kingdom
Tel.: (44) 13 7272 3802
Aluminum Rolled Product Distr
N.A.I.C.S.: 423510

Novelis Switzerland SA (3)

THE ADITYA BIRLA GROUP

The Aditya Birla Group—(Continued)

Routes Des Laminoirs 15, Sierre, 3960, Switzerland
Tel.: (41) 27 457 7111
Aluminum Rolled Product Mfr
N.A.I.C.S.: 331315

Novelis do Brasil Ltda. (3)
Av Nacoes Unidas 12551 15th Floor, Sao Paulo, 04578 000, Brazil
Tel.: (55) 1155030722
Web Site: http://www.novelis.com.br
Sales Range: $50-74.9 Million
Emp.: 60
Bauxite Mining, Alumina, Primary Aluminum, Plate, Sheet, Plain & Converted Foil & Foil Containers
N.A.I.C.S.: 212290
Padeu Nardocci *(Pres)*

Subsidiary (Non-US):

Novelis MEA Limited (2)
Office No 902 Level 9 Al Fattan Currency House Tower International Fin, Dubai, 780, United Arab Emirates
Tel.: (971) 43760700
Web Site: http://www.novelis.com
Aluminum Rolled Product Distr
N.A.I.C.S.: 423510

Novelis Sheet Ingot GmbH (2)
Hannoversche Str 1, Gottingen, 37075, Niedersachsen, Germany
Tel.: (49) 551 3040
Aluminum Recycling Services
N.A.I.C.S.: 562920

Subsidiary (Domestic):

Tubed Coal Mines Limited (2)
M 10 Near Bjp Office Harmu Housing Colony, Ranchi, 834 002, India
Tel.: (91) 651 2247342
Aluminum Rolled Product Mfr
N.A.I.C.S.: 331315

Utkal Alumina International Limited (2)
Guest house 2 Lakshman Nayak St New colony, Rayagada, 765 001, India
Tel.: (91) 68 5622 4192
Metal Mining Services
N.A.I.C.S.: 212290

Indo Thai Synthetics Company Limited (1)
Mahatun Plaza 16th Floor 888/164-165 Ploenchit Road, Bangkok, Thailand
Tel.: (66) 22536745 54
Web Site: http://www.indo-thai.com
Synthetic Textile Mfr
N.A.I.C.S.: 314999
Nirmal K. Maheshwari *(Pres)*

Plant (Domestic):

Indo Thai Synthetics Company Limited - ITS Factory (2)
No 25 Udom Sorayuth Road Bang Pa-In, Chiang Rak Noi, Thailand
Tel.: (66) 35 742222 5
Synthetic Dye Mfr
N.A.I.C.S.: 325130

PT Elegant Textile Industry (1)
Desa Ubrug Jatiluhur, Purwakarta, 41152, Jawa Bharat, Indonesia
Tel.: (62) 264202151
Web Site: http://www.adityabirla-yarn.com
Sales Range: $400-449.9 Million
Emp.: 1,800
Spun Rayon Mfr
N.A.I.C.S.: 313110

PT. Sunrise Bumi Textiles (1)
Jl Raya Bekasi Km 28, Desa Harapan Jaya, Bekasi, 17133, Indonesia
Tel.: (62) 21 8843488
Yarn & Sewing Thread Mfr
N.A.I.C.S.: 313110

Pan Century Surfactants Inc. (1)
Barangay Osmena, Jose Panganiban, Caramines Norte, Philippines
Tel.: (63) 54 731 1004
Basic Organic Chemical Mfr
N.A.I.C.S.: 325199

Swiss Singapore Overseas Enterprises Pte Limited (1)
65 Chulia Street OCBC Centre 48-05/08, Singapore, 049513, Singapore
Tel.: (65) 62218455
Web Site: http://www.swiss-singapore.com
Emp.: 200
Polyester & Yarn Mfr
N.A.I.C.S.: 314999
Jagdish Bajaj *(CFO)*

Subsidiary (Non-US):

PT Swiss Niaga International (2)
Menara Batavia 16th Floor K H Mas Mansyur Kav 126, Jakarta, 10220, Indonesia
Tel.: (62) 21 5722450
Petroleum Product Distr
N.A.I.C.S.: 424720

SSOE Kenya Limited (2)
2nd floor Tea Trade Centre Nyerere Avenue, Mombasa, Kenya
Tel.: (254) 41 2220251
Petroleum Product Distr
N.A.I.C.S.: 424720

Swiss Singapore Canada Pte. Ltd. (2)
Unit-206 12788 76A Avenue, Surrey, V3W 1S9, BC, Canada
Tel.: (778) 590-1776
Web Site: https://www.swiss-singapore.com
Petroleum Product Distr
N.A.I.C.S.: 424720

Thai Rayon Public Company Limited (1)
888/160-1 Mahatun Plaza Building 16th Floor Ploenchit Road Lumpini, Pathumwan, Bangkok, 10330, Thailand
Tel.: (66) 22536745
Web Site: http://www.thairayon.com
Rev.: $240,303,618
Assets: $938,069,778
Liabilities: $83,098,606
Net Worth: $854,971,172
Earnings: $19,619,993
Emp.: 869
Fiscal Year-end: 03/31/2023
Viscose Rayon Staple Fibre Mfr
N.A.I.C.S.: 325220
Suwanna Chalermwat *(Sec)*

Subsidiary (Non-US):

AV Nackawic Inc (2)
103 Pinder Road, Nackawic, E6G 1W4, NB, Canada
Tel.: (506) 575-3200
Web Site: http://www.av-group.ca
Emp.: 325
Pulp Mfr
N.A.I.C.S.: 322110

AV Terrace Bay Inc. (2)
21 Mill Road, Terrace Bay, P0T 2W0, ON, Canada
Tel.: (807) 825-1075
Pulp Product Mfr
N.A.I.C.S.: 322110

Affiliate (Domestic):

Birla Carbon (Thailand) Public Company Limited (2)
888/122 888/128 Mahatun Plaza 12th Floor Ploenchit Road Lumpini, Pratumwan, Bangkok, 10330, Thailand (24.98%)
Tel.: (66) 22536745
Web Site: http://www.birlacarbon.com
Rev.: $405,915,732
Assets: $889,396,977
Liabilities: $80,771,587
Net Worth: $808,625,390
Earnings: $116,372,247
Emp.: 218
Fiscal Year-end: 03/31/2023
Carbon Black Mfr
N.A.I.C.S.: 325180
Sanjeev Sood *(Pres)*

Thai Acrylic Fibre Company Limited (2)
Mahatun Plaza Bldg 16th Floor, Ploenchit Road, Bangkok, Thailand (30%)
Tel.: (66) 22536740
Web Site: http://www.thaiacrylic.com
Sales Range: $25-49.9 Million
Emp.: 400
Acrylic Fiber Mfr

N.A.I.C.S.: 314999
Biswajit Chaudhuri *(CMO)*

THE ADOLFSEN GROUP
Radhusgata 23, 0158, Oslo, Norway
Tel.: (47) 22 98 97 40   NO
Web Site: http://www.adolfsen.com
Emp.: 23,000
Holding Company
N.A.I.C.S.: 551112
John Bjornsen *(Partner-Pioneer Investor)*

Subsidiaries:

Norlandia Care Group AS (1)
Ovre Vollgate 13, 0158, Oslo, Norway
Tel.: (47) 99716617
Web Site: http://www.norlandia.no
Healtcare Services
N.A.I.C.S.: 621491
Hilde Britt Mellbye *(CEO)*

Personalhuset Staffing Group (1)
Dronning Mauds gate 10, 0250, Oslo, Norway
Tel.: (47) 81581340
Web Site: http://www.personalhuset.no
Recruitment Services
N.A.I.C.S.: 561311
Carl-Fredrik Bjor *(CEO)*

THE AFRICAN LAKES CORPORATION PLC
Chenil House 181-183 Kings Road, Chelsea, London, SW3 5EB, United Kingdom
Tel.: (44) 2073514815
Year Founded: 1877
Sales Range: $10-24.9 Million
Emp.: 300
Information Technology & Internet Services Specializing in Trade, Transportation & Motor Vehicles
N.A.I.C.S.: 541512
David Montgomery *(Chm)*

Subsidiaries:

Africa Online Egypt Ltd. (1)
67 El Sewesry B, Nasr City, Cairo, Egypt
Tel.: (20) 24125651
Internet Services
N.A.I.C.S.: 517810

Africa Online Ghana Limited (1)
Kwame Nkrumah Cir 5th Fl GCB Twr, PO Box STC 84, Kaneshie, Accra, Ghana (96%)
Tel.: (233) 212460659
Internet Services
N.A.I.C.S.: 541512

Africa Online Kenya Limited (1)
15th Floor Rahimtulla Tower, Upper Hill Road, Upper Hill, Nairobi, Kenya
Tel.: (254) 202792000
Web Site: http://www.africaonline.co.ke
Internet Services
N.A.I.C.S.: 541512

Africa Online Namibia (Pty) Limited (1)
NUA Building Robert Mugabe Avenue, Windhoek, Namibia (100%)
Tel.: (264) 612058111
Web Site: http://www.africaonline.com.na
Internet Services
N.A.I.C.S.: 541512

Africa Online Swaziland (Pty) Limited (1)
Embassy House Msakato Street, PO Box 5833, Mbabane, H100, Eswatini
Tel.: (268) 4044705
Web Site: http://www.africaonline.com
Internet Services
N.A.I.C.S.: 327910

Africa Online Tanzania Limited (1)
3rd Floor ANC Building, PO Box 2721, 50 Mirambo Street, Dar es Salaam, Tanzania (95%)
Tel.: (255) 222116090
Web Site: http://www.africaonline.co.tz
Internet Services
N.A.I.C.S.: 541512

INTERNATIONAL PUBLIC

Africa Online Uganda Limited (1)
5th Floor Commercial Plaza 7 Kampala Road, PO Box 29331, Kampala, Uganda (100%)
Tel.: (256) 41258143
Web Site: http://www.africaonline.co.ug
Internet Services
N.A.I.C.S.: 541512

Africa Online Zimbabwe (Pvt) Limited (1)
2h Floor Goldbridge South Eastgate Centre 2nd St, PO Box A1571, Harare, Zimbabwe (70%)
Tel.: (263) 4702202
Web Site: http://www.africaonline.co.zw
Internet Services
N.A.I.C.S.: 541512

THE AGENCY GROUP AUSTRALIA LIMITED
68 Milligan Street, Perth, 6000, WA, Australia
Tel.: (61) 892047955
Web Site: http://www.namibiancopper.com.au
Year Founded: 2006
AU1—(ASX)
Sales Range: Less than $1 Million
Mineral Development & Exploration Services
N.A.I.C.S.: 213115
Andrew Jensen *(Chm & COO)*

THE AKITA BANK, LTD.
2-1 Sanno 3-chome, Akita, 010-8655, Japan
Tel.: (81) 188631212
Web Site: https://www.akita-bank.co.jp
Year Founded: 1879
8343—(TKS)
Rev.: $282,471,740
Assets: $23,691,495,900
Liabilities: $22,549,334,170
Net Worth: $1,142,161,730
Earnings: $297,450
Emp.: 1,214
Fiscal Year-end: 03/31/24
Banking Services
N.A.I.C.S.: 522110
Takao Minatoya *(Chm)*

THE AL FADL GROUP OF COMPANIES
Al Hamra Street, PO Box 15, 21411, Jeddah, Saudi Arabia
Tel.: (966) 26603996
Web Site: http://www.alfadlgroup.com
Year Founded: 1947
Sales Range: $100-124.9 Million
Emp.: 350
Holding Company
N.A.I.C.S.: 551112
Abdul Kader Al Fadl *(Chm)*

Subsidiaries:

Al Fadl BRC (Saudia) Ltd. (1)
Industrial Area Phase 1, PO Box 5489, Jeddah, Saudi Arabia
Tel.: (966) 26364724
Web Site: http://www.brc.com.sa
Sales Range: $50-74.9 Million
Emp.: 200
Welded Wire Mesh Mfr
N.A.I.C.S.: 332618

Aldewan Fastfood Company Ltd. (1)
PO Box 15, Jeddah, Saudi Arabia
Tel.: (966) 26672653
Sales Range: $25-49.9 Million
Emp.: 220
Fast Food Restaurant Operator
N.A.I.C.S.: 722513

Alpha Trading & Shipping Agencies Ltd. (1)
Al Mahmal Tower 14th Fl Ste 1401, King Abdul Aziz St, Jeddah, 21411, Saudi Arabia
Tel.: (966) 26440808
Web Site: http://www.alpha-trading.com

Sales Range: $250-299.9 Million
Emp.: 20
Foodstuffs & Related Commodities Marketing Services
N.A.I.C.S.: 424480
Abdul Kader Al Fadl *(Chm)*

Rabya Trading and Agriculture Company Ltd. (1)
Palestine Street, PO Box 5536, 21432, Jeddah, Saudi Arabia
Tel.: (966) 26602856
Web Site: http://www.rabya.com
Landscaping & Garden Services
N.A.I.C.S.: 444240
Mohammed Al Fadl *(Pres)*

Sahara Building Contractors Ltd. (1)
Childerns Hospital Street Al Hamrah Dist, PO Box 11852, Jeddah, 21463, Saudi Arabia
Tel.: (966) 26615050
Web Site: http://www.saharabuilding.com
Industrial Contracting Services
N.A.I.C.S.: 238120

THE ALDO GROUP INC.
2300 Emile-Belanger, Montreal, H4R 3J4, QC, Canada
Tel.: (514) 747-2536
Web Site: http://www.aldogroup.com
Sales Range: $25-49.9 Million
Emp.: 100
Footwear Mfr & Distr
N.A.I.C.S.: 424340
Norman Jaskolka *(Deputy Chm & Pres)*

THE ALUMASC GROUP PLC
Station Road Burton Latimer, Kettering, NN15 5JP, Northamptonshire, United Kingdom
Tel.: (44) 1536383844
Web Site: https://www.alumasc.co.uk
ALU—(AIM)
Rev.: $127,305,359
Assets: $104,162,032
Liabilities: $61,773,256
Net Worth: $42,388,776
Earnings: $11,056,623
Emp.: 470
Fiscal Year-end: 06/30/24
Engineering & Building Products Mfr & Sales
N.A.I.C.S.: 236220
John S. McCall *(Chm)*

Subsidiaries:

Alumasc Exterior Building Products Limited (1)
White House Works Bold Road, Sutton, Saint Helens, WA9 4JG, Merseyside, United Kingdom **(100%)**
Tel.: (44) 3335771500
Web Site: http://www.alumasc-exteriors.co.uk
Sales Range: $50-74.9 Million
Emp.: 120
Asphalt Shingle & Coating Materials Mfr
N.A.I.C.S.: 324122
Paul Hetherington *(Mng Dir)*

Alumasc Precision Components (1)
Burton Latimer, Kettering, NN15 5JP, Northants, United Kingdom **(100%)**
Tel.: (44) 1536383849
Web Site: http://www.alumasc-precision.co.uk
Sales Range: $25-49.9 Million
Emp.: 200
Engineeering Services
N.A.I.C.S.: 541330
Paul Hooper *(Mng Dir)*

Alumasc Precision Limited (1)
APC Kettering Burton Latimer, Kettering, NN15 5JP, United Kingdom
Tel.: (44) 1536383849
Web Site: http://www.alumasc-precision.co.uk
Sales Range: $50-74.9 Million
Emp.: 120
Precision Machining Tools Mfr
N.A.I.C.S.: 333248

Blackdown Horticultural Consultants Limited (1)
Street Ash Nursery Combe St Nicholas Chard, Somerset, TA20 3HZ, United Kingdom
Tel.: (44) 1460 234582
Web Site: http://www.blackdown.co.uk
Sales Range: $25-49.9 Million
Emp.: 10
Green Roofing System Installation Services
N.A.I.C.S.: 238160

Dyson Diecasting (1)
Second Ave, Bletchley, Milton Keynes, MK1 1EA, United Kingdom **(100%)**
Tel.: (44) 190 827 9200
Web Site: https://www.dysondiecastings.co.uk
Sales Range: $25-49.9 Million
Emp.: 90
Aluminum Die-Casting Foundries
N.A.I.C.S.: 331523

Elkington China Limited (1)
Unit 2 16/F Cheung Tat Centre 18 Cheung Lee Street, Chai Wan, China (Hong Kong)
Tel.: (852) 23050100
Construction Materials Distr
N.A.I.C.S.: 423390

Elkington Gatic (1)
Gatic Poulton Close, Holmestone Rd Poulton Close, Dover, CT17 0UF, Kent, United Kingdom **(100%)**
Tel.: (44) 1304203545
Web Site: http://www.gatic.com
Sales Range: $25-49.9 Million
Emp.: 50
Specialty Trade Contractors
N.A.I.C.S.: 236220
Pete Burnat *(Mng Dir)*

Roof-Pro (1)
Polwell Lane Off Station Road, Burton Latimer, Kettering, NN15 5PS, Northamptonshire, United Kingdom **(100%)**
Tel.: (44) 333 577 1500
Web Site: https://www.roof-pro.co.uk
Sales Range: $25-49.9 Million
Emp.: 9
Roofing Siding & Insulation Material Merchant Whslr
N.A.I.C.S.: 423330
Gilbert Jackson *(Mng Dir)*

Scaffold & Construction Products (1)
Swarn House Meadow Lane, Coseley, Wolverhampton, WV14 9NQ, WMD, United Kingdom
Tel.: (44) 1543467800
Web Site: https://www.scpgroup.co.uk
Sales Range: $25-49.9 Million
Emp.: 4
Specialty Trade Contractors
N.A.I.C.S.: 236220

TP Manufacturing Ltd. (1)
Halesfield 19, Telford, TF7 4QT, Shropshire, United Kingdom
Tel.: (44) 195 258 0590
Web Site: https://www.pendock.co.uk
Bespoke Pipe Boxing, Ducting, Casings & Cubicles Mfr
N.A.I.C.S.: 331210

Timloc Building Products Ltd. (1)
Timloc House Ozone Park Howden, Goole, DN14 7SD, E Yorkshire, United Kingdom **(100%)**
Tel.: (44) 140 576 5567
Web Site: https://www.timloc.co.uk
Sales Range: $25-49.9 Million
Emp.: 60
Building Products Services
N.A.I.C.S.: 561621
Liam Cooley *(Mgr-Sls-North West)*

THE AMBASSADOR HOTEL, LTD.
188 Section 2 Zhonghua Road, Hsinchu, 30060, Taiwan
Tel.: (886) 35151111
Web Site: https://www.ambassador-hotels.com
Year Founded: 1962
2704—(TAI)
Rev.: $41,824,420
Assets: $839,985,612
Liabilities: $193,187,998
Net Worth: $646,797,614
Earnings: $16,137,970
Fiscal Year-end: 12/31/23
Hotel Operator
N.A.I.C.S.: 722511

THE ANDHRA PETROCHEMICALS LIMITED
Venkatarayapuram, West Godavari Distrist, Tanuku, 534 215, Andhra Pradesh, India
Tel.: (91) 8819224075
Web Site:
https://theandhrapetrochemical.com
500012—(BOM)
Rev.: $84,126,983
Assets: $76,309,178
Liabilities: $15,733,853
Net Worth: $60,575,325
Earnings: $2,446,856
Emp.: 303
Fiscal Year-end: 03/31/23
Petrochemical Products Mfr
N.A.I.C.S.: 325110
P. Narendranath Chowdary *(Mng Dir)*

THE ANDHRA SUGARS LIMITED
Venkatarayapuram, West Godavari District, Tanuku, 534215, AP, India
Tel.: (91) 8819224911
Web Site:
https://www.theandhrasugars.com
ANDHRSUGAR—(NSE)
Rev.: $209,540,959
Assets: $256,461,742
Liabilities: $66,962,709
Net Worth: $189,499,032
Earnings: $19,285,785
Emp.: 2,051
Fiscal Year-end: 03/31/21
Sugar Mfr & Distr
N.A.I.C.S.: 311313
P. Narendranath Chowdary *(Chm & Co-Mng Dir)*

Subsidiaries:

Jocil Limited (1)
Dokiparru Medikondur Mandal, Guntur, 522 438, Andhra Pradesh, India
Tel.: (91) 8632290190
Web Site: http://www.jocil.in
Rev.: $110,505,114
Assets: $30,406,930
Liabilities: $5,660,524
Net Worth: $24,746,406
Earnings: $1,198,417
Emp.: 794
Fiscal Year-end: 03/31/2023
Basic Organic Chemical Product Mfr
N.A.I.C.S.: 325199
K. Raghuram *(CFO, Compliance Officer, Sec & Asst Gen Mgr-Fin)*

THE AOMORI BANK, LTD.
9-30 Hashimoto 1-chome, Aomori, 030-0823, Japan
Tel.: (81) 177771111
Web Site: http://www.a-bank.jp
Year Founded: 1879
8342—(TKS)
Rev.: $400,268,000
Assets: $35,636,348,880
Liabilities: $34,485,087,120
Net Worth: $1,151,261,760
Earnings: $21,789,680
Emp.: 1,313
Fiscal Year-end: 03/31/21
Commercial Banking Services
N.A.I.C.S.: 522110
Susumu Narita *(Pres)*

Subsidiaries:

Aogin Business Service Co., Ltd. (1)
1-5-18 Hashimoto, Aomori, Japan
Tel.: (81) 177732479
Business Support Services
N.A.I.C.S.: 561499

Aogin Credit Card Co., Ltd. (1)
1-16-16 Furukawa, Aomori, Japan
Tel.: (81) 177736511
Credit Card Issuing
N.A.I.C.S.: 522210

Aogin Lease Co., Ltd. (1)
Aoginfurukawa Bldg, Aomori, Japan
Tel.: (81) 177231665
Commercial & Industrial Machinery & Equipment Rental & Leasing
N.A.I.C.S.: 532490

THE ARAB ASSURERS INSURANCE CO. PSC
Queen Rania Al Abdullah Street Building No 32, Amman, Jordan
Tel.: (962) 65100081
Web Site:
https://www.arabassurers.jo
Year Founded: 1996
ARAS—(AMM)
Rev.: $18,431,702
Assets: $22,414,160
Liabilities: $17,588,061
Net Worth: $4,826,099
Earnings: ($2,130,250)
Emp.: 70
Fiscal Year-end: 12/31/22
Insurance Services
N.A.I.C.S.: 524210
Haitham Al Khatatneh *(Gen Mgr)*

THE ARAB DAIRY PRODUCTS CO.
Piece 29/1 - Industrial Zone Katameya, Cairo, Egypt
Tel.: (20) 106882067
Web Site: https://www.arabdairy.com
Year Founded: 1985
ADPC.CA—(EGX)
Sales Range: Less than $1 Million
Cheese Mfr
N.A.I.C.S.: 311513
Hany Ibrahim Megahed *(Mgr-Investor Relations)*

THE ARAB FINANCIAL INVESTMENT CO.
PO Box 922634, Amman, 11192, Jordan
Tel.: (962) 65002000
Web Site:
http://www.arabinvestco.com
AFIN—(AMM)
Sales Range: $1-9.9 Million
Emp.: 16
Portfolio Management & Brokerage Services
N.A.I.C.S.: 523940
Tareq Mohammad Khater *(CEO)*

THE ARAB HOTELS COMPANY
Movenpick Hotel-Al Masyoon, PO Box 3852, Alberah, Ramallah, Palestine
Tel.: (970) 22965240
Web Site: http://www.ahc-pal.com
Year Founded: 1996
AHC—(PAL)
Rev.: $13,923,914
Assets: $89,940,147
Liabilities: $19,508,030
Net Worth: $70,432,117
Earnings: $1,244,739
Fiscal Year-end: 12/31/23
Home Management Services
N.A.I.C.S.: 721110
Jamal Fuad Jubran Haddad *(Chm)*

THE ARAB PESTICIDES & VETERINARY DRUGS MFG. CO.
AL-Husseini Complex Zahran Street,

THE ARAB PESTICIDES & VETERINARY DRUGS MFG. CO.

The Arab Pesticides & Veterinary Drugs Mfg. Co.—(Continued)
PO Box 930103, 11193, Amman, 11193, Jordan
Tel.: (962) 65354191
Web Site: https://www.mobedco.com
Year Founded: 1991
MBED—(AMM)
Rev.: $31,824,694
Assets: $48,372,955
Liabilities: $10,352,037
Net Worth: $38,020,918
Earnings: $6,190,399
Emp.: 193
Fiscal Year-end: 12/31/20
Pesticides & Veterinary Drugs Marketing & Mfr
N.A.I.C.S.: 325998

Subsidiaries:

The Arab Pesticides & Veterinary Drugs Mfg. Co. - Irbid Factory (1)
El-Hassan Industrial Estate, Irbid, Jordan
Tel.: (962) 27395195
Agrochemical & Veterinary Product Mfr
N.A.I.C.S.: 325320

THE ARDONAGH GROUP LIMITED
2 Minster Court, Mincing Lane, London, EC3R 7PD, United Kingdom
Tel.: (44) 2073982100
Web Site: http://www.ardonagh.com
Year Founded: 2015
Holding Company; Manpower & Investment Services
N.A.I.C.S.: 523999
David Ross (CEO)

Subsidiaries:

Swinton Group Ltd. (1)
101 Cathedral Approach, Salford, M3 7FB, United Kingdom
Tel.: (44) 800 840 5218
Web Site: http://www.swinton.co.uk
Insurance Services
N.A.I.C.S.: 524126
Gill Galassi (Head & Dir-Comm)

Subsidiary (Domestic):

Equity Insurance Group Ltd. (2)
Library House New Road, Brentwood, CM14 4GD, Essex, United Kingdom
Tel.: (44) 01277200100
Web Site: http://www.equitygroup.co.uk
Sales Range: $700-749.9 Million
Emp.: 1,200
Insurance Services
N.A.I.C.S.: 524298
Nick Potts (Mng Dir-Equity Insurance Brokers)

THE ART SHOPPE LTD.
2131 Yonge Street, Toronto, M4S 2A7, ON, Canada
Tel.: (416) 487-3211
Web Site: http://www.theartshoppe.com
Year Founded: 1934
Rev.: $10,626,605
Emp.: 75
Furniture Mfr
N.A.I.C.S.: 337211
Martin Offman (Pres & CEO)

THE ARTISANAL SPIRITS COMPANY PLC
The Vaults 87 Giles Street, Edinburgh, EH6 6BZ, United Kingdom
Tel.: (44) 1315556588 UK
Web Site: https://artisanal-spirits.com
Year Founded: 1983
ART—(AIM)
Rev.: $27,494,320
Assets: $59,787,932
Liabilities: $31,996,970
Net Worth: $27,790,962
Earnings: ($2,162,333)

Emp.: 100
Fiscal Year-end: 12/31/22
Beverage Product Mfr & Distr
N.A.I.C.S.: 312111

Subsidiaries:

The Scotch Malt Whisky Society Limited (1)
A19 17/F Prince Industrial Building 706 Prince Edward Road East, Kowloon, China (Hong Kong)
Tel.: (852) 97244189
Web Site: https://www.smws.hk
Wine Distr
N.A.I.C.S.: 424820

THE ASAHI SHIMBUN COMPANY
5-3-2 Tsukiji Chuo ward, Tokyo, 104-8011, Japan
Tel.: (81) 3 5540 7641 JP
Web Site: http://www.asahi.com
Year Founded: 1879
Sales Range: $900-999.9 Million
Emp.: 4,640
Newspaper Publisher, Commercial Printing, Advertising, Television Broadcasting & Travel Services
N.A.I.C.S.: 513110
Michiko Murayama (Co-Owner)

Subsidiaries:

Asahi Airport Service Co., Ltd. (1)
3-2-7 Minowa Toyonaka, Osaka, 560-0035, Japan
Tel.: (81) 668565002
Web Site: http://www.aas.co.jp
Sales Range: $25-49.9 Million
Emp.: 100
Newsstands Operator
N.A.I.C.S.: 459210
Toshiyaki Takatsu (Pres)

Asahi Building Co., Ltd. (1)
Nakanoshima No 2chome 3 No 18, Kita-ku, Osaka, 530-0005, Japan
Tel.: (81) 662317501
Web Site: http://www.asahibuilding.co.jp
Emp.: 110
Real Estate Brokerage
N.A.I.C.S.: 531390
Keisuke Abe (Pres)

Asahi Culture Center K.K. (1)
Shinjuku Sumitomo Bldg 3F 2-6-1 Nishi-Shinjuku, Tokyo, 163-0204, Japan
Tel.: (81) 3 3344 1941
Web Site: http://www.asahiculture.jp
Sales Range: $25-49.9 Million
Emp.: 10
Courses on Traditional Japanese Culture, Literature, Arts & Foreign Languages
N.A.I.C.S.: 923110
Ishii Tsutomu (Pres)

Asahi Gakusei Shimbun Publishing Company K.K. (1)
Nakagawa Tukiji Building 7F 3-5-4 Tsukiji, Chuo-ku, Tokyo, 104-0045, Japan
Tel.: (81) 335455221
Web Site: http://www.asagaku.com
Newspaper Publishers
N.A.I.C.S.: 513110
H. Yamamoto (Pres)

Asahi Orikomi Inc. (1)
5-3-2 Tukiji, Chuo-ku, Tokyo, 104-8011, Japan
Tel.: (81) 3 3544 7621
Newspaper Advertising Services
N.A.I.C.S.: 541870

Subsidiary (Domestic):

Asahi Orikomi Osaka Inc. (2)
Osaka Nakanoshima 2-3-18 19th Fl Kita-ku Nakanoshima Festival Tower, Osaka, 530-0005, Japan
Tel.: (81) 662261290
Web Site: http://www.ao-osaka.co.jp
Sales Range: $250-299.9 Million
Emp.: 155
Advertising Services
N.A.I.C.S.: 541810
Fujio Shimizu (Dir-Sls & Delivery)

Asahi Shimbun America, Inc. (1)
620 8th Ave, New York, NY 10018-1618
Tel.: (212) 317-3000
News Services
N.A.I.C.S.: 516210

Branch (Domestic):

Asahi Shimbun America, Inc. (2)
529 14th St NW Ste 1022, Washington, DC 20045
Tel.: (202) 783-0523
Web Site: http://www.asahi.com
News Services
N.A.I.C.S.: 516210

Asahi Shimbun International Ltd. (1)
6th Floor Halton House, 20 23 Holborn, London, EC1N 2JD, United Kingdom
Tel.: (44) 20 78311114
News Services
N.A.I.C.S.: 516210

Asahi Tatemono Kanri K.K. (1)
2-chome No 3 No 18 Nakanoshima, Kita-ku, Osaka, 530-0005, Japan
Tel.: (81) 662030521
Web Site: http://www.asahitatemonokanri.co.jp
Emp.: 1,081
Building Maintenance Services
N.A.I.C.S.: 561720
Shinji Onishi (Pres & CEO)

Hokkaido Nikkan Sports Shimbunsha K.K. (1)
3-1-30 Kita Johigashi, Chuo-ku, Hokkaido, 060-0033, Japan
Tel.: (81) 112423900
Web Site: http://www.nikkansports.com
Sales Range: $25-49.9 Million
Emp.: 46
Newspaper Publishers
N.A.I.C.S.: 513110

Nikkan Sports Newspaper (1)
3-5-10 Tsukiji, Chuo-ku, Tokyo, 104-0045, Japan
Tel.: (81) 355508888
Web Site: http://www.nikkansports.com
Newspaper Publishers
N.A.I.C.S.: 513110

THE ASI SOLUTIONS
8 Lord Street, Botany, 2019, NSW, Australia
Tel.: (61) 293848000
Web Site: http://www.asi.com.au
Year Founded: 1985
Emp.: 120
Information Technology Consulting Services
N.A.I.C.S.: 541512
Nathan Lowe (Mng Dir)

THE ASIA BUSINESS DAILY CO., LTD.
10-11th floor Asia Media Tower 29 Chungmuro, Jung-gu, Seoul, Korea (South)
Tel.: (82) 222002114
Web Site: https://www.asiae.co.kr
Year Founded: 2005
127710—(KRS)
Rev.: $65,380,980
Assets: $552,329,518
Liabilities: $406,560,511
Net Worth: $145,769,007
Earnings: $13,397,432
Emp.: 260
Fiscal Year-end: 12/31/22
Business News Publishing Services
N.A.I.C.S.: 513110
Sangsun Hyun (Pres)

THE ASIA-PACIFIC CENTRE FOR RESEARCH, INC.
Rm 425 Cityland Pasong Tamo Tower 2210 Pasong Tamo Street, Makati, 1231, Philippines
Tel.: (63) 27572136 PH
Web Site: http://www.acreinc.net
Year Founded: 1989

INTERNATIONAL PUBLIC

Sales Range: $25-49.9 Million
Emp.: 75
Technology Research & Consulting Services; Software Distr
N.A.I.C.S.: 541715
Nick B. Fontanilla (Pres)

THE AUSTRALIAN REINFORCING COMPANY
380 Docklands Drive, Docklands, 3008, VIC, Australia
Tel.: (61) 399036200
Web Site: http://www.arcreo.com.au
Year Founded: 1920
Steel Reinforcing Mfr & Distr
N.A.I.C.S.: 332312
Sean Mannering (Gen Mgr)

THE AUTODROME PLC
Tel.: (94) 112326181
Web Site: https://www.autodrome.lk
AUTO—(COL)
Rev.: $773,217
Assets: $8,505,642
Liabilities: $2,181,828
Net Worth: $6,323,814
Earnings: $103,212
Emp.: 41
Fiscal Year-end: 03/31/23
Automobile Parts Distr
N.A.I.C.S.: 441340
Asha Peiris Nishantha (Mgr-Sls)

Subsidiaries:

Tourama (Pvt) Ltd. (1)
3/1 304 Union Place, 2, Colombo, Western Province, Sri Lanka
Tel.: (94) 112326181
Web Site: https://www.tourama.net
Sales Range: $25-49.9 Million
Emp.: 25
Travel & Tour Operating Agencies
N.A.I.C.S.: 561520
Rajeev Aloysius (Mng Dir)

THE AUTOPLANET GROUP INC.
30 Van Kirk Drive, Brampton, L7A 2Y4, ON, Canada
Tel.: (905) 454-1434
Web Site: http://www.bramptonautomall.ca
Car Dealership Operator
N.A.I.C.S.: 441110
Glen Alizadeh (Pres)

Subsidiaries:

Classic Honda (1)
30 Van Kirk Drive, Brampton, L7A 2Y4, ON, Canada
Tel.: (905) 454-1434
Web Site: http://www.classichonda.ca
Sales Range: $50-74.9 Million
Emp.: 103
Car Dealership
N.A.I.C.S.: 441110
Firas Alrifai (Mgr-Fin Svc)

THE AWA BANK, LTD.
24-1 Nishisemba-cho 2-chome, Tokushima, 770-8601, Japan
Tel.: (81) 886233131
Web Site: https://www.awabank.co.jp
Year Founded: 1896
8388—(TKS)
Rev.: $503,067,270
Assets: $25,928,121,600
Liabilities: $23,729,490,180
Net Worth: $2,198,631,420
Earnings: $264,400
Fiscal Year-end: 03/31/24
Banking Services
N.A.I.C.S.: 522110

THE AZUR SELECTION S.A.
19 Stratarchou Alexandrou Papagou Str, 16673, Voula, Greece
Tel.: (30) 2109615810

Web Site:
https://www.azurselection.com
MLAZR—(EUR)
Rev.: $5,479,043
Assets: $45,608,975
Liabilities: $31,596,688
Net Worth: $14,012,286
Earnings: $7,615,878
Fiscal Year-end: 12/31/23
Lessors of Other Real Estate Property
N.A.I.C.S.: 531190

THE BANK OF EAST ASIA, LIMITED
10 Des Voeux Road, Central, China (Hong Kong)
Tel.: (852) 36083608 HK
Web Site: https://www.hkbea.com
Year Founded: 1918
00023—(HKG)
Rev.: $5,071,759,940
Assets: $109,954,503,048
Liabilities: $96,110,394,009
Net Worth: $13,844,109,039
Earnings: $528,582,565
Emp.: 8,140
Fiscal Year-end: 12/31/23
Commercial Banking Services
N.A.I.C.S.: 522110
Samson Kai-Cheong Li *(Co-Deputy CEO & Chief Investment Officer)*

Subsidiaries:

BEA Union Investment Management Limited (1)
5/F The Bank of East Asia Building 10 Des Voeux Road, Central, China (Hong Kong)
Tel.: (852) 2/6 08 0306
Web Site: https://bea-union-investment.com
Investment Management Service
N.A.I.C.S.: 523940

Blue Cross (Asia-Pacific) Insurance Limited (1)
29/F BEA Towe Millennium City 5 418 Kwun Tong Road, Kwun Tong, Hong Kong, Kowloon, China (Hong Kong) (100%)
Tel.: (852) 36082988
Web Site: http://www.bluecross.com.hk
Sales Range: $100-124.9 Million
Emp.: 200
Healthcare, General & Life Insurance Services
N.A.I.C.S.: 524113

Credit Gain Finance Company Limited (1)
33/F Millennium City 5 Bea Tower 418 Kwun Tong Road, Kwun Tong, China (Hong Kong)
Tel.: (852) 36081904
Web Site: http://www.creditgain.com.hk
Commercial Banking Services
N.A.I.C.S.: 522110

East Asia Property Agency Co., Ltd. (1)
35th floor PEA Tower Millennium City 5 418 Kwun Kong Road, Nathan Rd Mongkoa, Kowloon, China (Hong Kong) (100%)
Tel.: (852) 36083228
Property Sale & Leasing Services
N.A.I.C.S.: 531210

East Asia Securities Company Limited (1)
9/F The Bank of East Asia Building 10 Des Voeux Road, Central, China (Hong Kong) (100%)
Tel.: (852) 36088077
Web Site: http://www.easecurities.com.hk
Sales Range: $50-74.9 Million
Emp.: 80
Brokerage Services
N.A.I.C.S.: 523150

East Asia Strategic Holdings Limited (1)
11/F 8 Queens Road C, Central, China (Hong Kong)
Tel.: (852) 22838000
Commercial Banking Services
N.A.I.C.S.: 522110

The Bank of East Asia (BVI) Limited (1)
3/F Commerce House Wickhams Cay 1 Road, Tortola, Virgin Islands (British)
Tel.: (284) 3942400
Web Site: http://www.hkbea.com
Banking Services
N.A.I.C.S.: 522110

The Bank of East Asia (China) Limited (1)
29/F BEA Finance Tower 66 Hua Yuan Shi Qiao Road, Pilot Free Trade Zone, Shanghai, 200120, China (100%)
Tel.: (86) 2138663866
Web Site: http://eng.hkbea.com.cn
Banking Services
N.A.I.C.S.: 522110

Tricor Holdings Pte. Ltd. (1)
80 Robinson Rd Unit 02-00, Singapore, 68898, Singapore
Tel.: (65) 62363333
Emp.: 200
Commercial Banking Services
N.A.I.C.S.: 522110
Holon Gee *(Mng Dir)*

Tricor Services Limited (1)
Level 15 International Trade Tower 348 Kwun Tong Road, Kowloon, China (Hong Kong) (100%)
Tel.: (852) 29801888
Web Site: http://www.tricorglobal.com
Sales Range: $50-74.9 Million
Emp.: 700
Integrated Business, Corporate & Investor Services
N.A.I.C.S.: 561499
John Poon *(Dir-China Consultancy Svcs)*

Subsidiary (Non-US):

PT Amalgamated Tricor (2)
31st Floor Wisma GKBI Jl Jend Sudirman, No 28 RT 14/RW 1 Bendungan Hilir Tanah Abang Daerah Khusus Ibukota, Jakarta, 10210, Indonesia
Tel.: (62) 21 574 1177
Web Site: http://www.id.tricorglobal.com
Business Management Consulting Services
N.A.I.C.S.: 541611

Tricor (B) Sdn Bhd (2)
Room 308B 3rd Floor Wisma Jaya, Jalan Pemancha, Bandar Seri Begawan, BS8811, Brunei Darussalam
Tel.: (673) 2232780
Web Site: http://www.bn.tricorglobal.com
Business Management Consulting Services
N.A.I.C.S.: 541611

Tricor Caribbean Limited (2)
One Welches Welches, St Thomas, Christ Church, BB22025, Barbados
Tel.: (246) 430 8400
Web Site: http://www.bb.tricorglobal.com
Emp.: 16
Business Management Consulting Services
N.A.I.C.S.: 541611
Connie Smith *(Mng Dir)*

Tricor Consultancy (Beijing) Limited (2)
Suite 1803 18/F Tower 1 Prosper Center No 5 Guanghua Road, Chaoyang District, Beijing, 100020, China
Tel.: (86) 1085876818
Web Site: http://cn.tricorglobal.com
Business Support Services
N.A.I.C.S.: 561499

Subsidiary (Domestic):

Tricor Japan Limited (2)
Level 28 Three Pacific Place 1 Queens Road East, Hong Kong, China (Hong Kong)
Tel.: (852) 3485 5120
Web Site: http://www.jp.tricorglobal.com
Sales Range: $25-49.9 Million
Emp.: 25
Business Management Consulting Services
N.A.I.C.S.: 541611

Subsidiary (Non-US):

Tricor K.K. (2)
Oak Minami Azabu Building 2F 3-19-23 Minami Azabu, Minato-Ku, Tokyo, 106-0047, Japan

Tel.: (81) 3 4580 2700
Web Site: http://www.tricor.co.jp
Emp.: 80
Business Management Consulting Services
N.A.I.C.S.: 541611

Tricor Praesidium Limited (2)
Office104 Level 1 Tower 1 Al Fattan Currency House, PO Box 506676, Dubai, United Arab Emirates
Tel.: (971) 43587715
Web Site: http://www.tricor.com.hk
Sales Range: $25-49.9 Million
Emp.: 8
Business Management Consulting Services
N.A.I.C.S.: 541611

Tricor Services (Macau) Limited (2)
Avenida da Praia Grande Nr 417-429, Edif Praia Grande Commerce Centre 17 Andar E, Macau, China (Macau)
Tel.: (853) 2878 8022
Web Site: http://www.cn.tricorglobal.com
Business Management Consulting Services
N.A.I.C.S.: 541611

Tricor Services (Malaysia) Sdn. Bhd (2)
Unit 30-01 Level 30 Tower A Vertical Business Suite Avenue 3, Bangsar South No8 Jalan Kerinchi, 59200, Kuala Lumpur, Malaysia
Tel.: (60) 327839299
Web Site: http://www.my.tricorglobal.com
Business Management Consulting Services
N.A.I.C.S.: 541611

Tricor Services Europe LLP (2)
4th Floor 50 Mark Lane, London, EC3R 7QR, United Kingdom
Tel.: (44) 2032162000
Web Site: http://www.uk.tricorglobal.com
Emp.: 20
Business Management Consulting Services
N.A.I.C.S.: 541611

Tricor Singapore Pte Ltd (2)
80 Robinson Road Unit 02-00, Singapore, 068898, Singapore
Tel.: (65) 62363333
Web Site: http://www.sg.tricorglobal.com
Business Management Consulting Services
N.A.I.C.S.: 541611

Tricor Trustco (Labuan) Ltd (2)
Level 15 A1 Main Office Tower, Financial Park Labuan Jalan Merdeka, 87000, Labuan, Malaysia
Tel.: (60) 87453288
Web Site: http://www.tricor.com.hk
Sales Range: $25-49.9 Million
Emp.: 13
Business Management Consulting Services
N.A.I.C.S.: 541611

THE BANK OF ISRAEL
PO Box 780, 91007, Jerusalem, Israel
Tel.: (972) 26552211
Web Site: http://www.bankisrael.gov.il
Sales Range: $1-4.9 Billion
Banking Services
N.A.I.C.S.: 521110
Stanley Fischer *(Governor)*

THE BANK OF IWATE, LTD.
2-3 Chuodori 1-chome, Morioka, 020-8688, Iwate, Japan
Tel.: (81) 196231111 JP
Web Site:
https://www.iwatebank.co.jp
Year Founded: 1932
8345—(TKS)
Rev.: $290,086,460
Assets: $25,974,622,950
Liabilities: $24,656,350,990
Net Worth: $1,318,271,960
Earnings: $264,400
Emp.: 1,340
Fiscal Year-end: 03/31/24
Commercial Banking Services
N.A.I.C.S.: 522110
Masahiro Takahashi *(Chm)*

THE BANK OF KOCHI LTD.
2-24 Sakaimachi, Kochi, 780-0834, Japan
Web Site: https://www.kochi-bank.co.jp
Year Founded: 1930
8416—(TKS)
Rev.: $151,963,900
Assets: $7,550,655,880
Liabilities: $7,141,093,670
Net Worth: $409,562,210
Earnings: $99,150
Emp.: 715
Fiscal Year-end: 03/31/24
Banking Services
N.A.I.C.S.: 522110
Katsuhiko Morishita *(Chm)*

THE BANK OF KOREA
67 Sejong-daero, Jung-gu, Seoul, 04514, Korea (South)
Tel.: (82) 27594114 KR
Web Site: http://www.bok.or.kr
Year Founded: 1950
Rev.: $14,088,512,260
Assets: $423,614,294,460
Liabilities: $407,683,130,720
Net Worth: $15,931,163,740
Earnings: $4,569,260,840
Emp.: 2,456
Fiscal Year-end: 12/31/19
Banking Services
N.A.I.C.S.: 521110

THE BANK OF KYOTO, LTD.
700 Yakushi-mae-cho Karasuma-dori Matsubara Umaru, Shimogyo-ku, Kyoto, 600-8652, Japan
Tel.: (81) 753612211 JP
Web Site:
https://www.kyotobank.co.jp
Year Founded: 1941
8369—(TKS)
Rev.: $823,475,388
Assets: $72,927,723,819
Liabilities: $66,370,888,669
Net Worth: $6,556,835,150
Earnings: $179,801,784
Emp.: 3,353
Fiscal Year-end: 03/31/23
Commercial Banking Services
N.A.I.C.S.: 522110
Nobuhiro Doi *(Pres)*

Subsidiaries:

Karasuma Shoji Co., Ltd. (1)
9 Umetadacho, Sanjodori-Karasumahigashiiru N, Kyoto, Japan
Tel.: (81) 752550114
Web Site: http://www.karasumashoji.co.jp
Nonresidential Buildings Lessors
N.A.I.C.S.: 531120

Kyogin Business Service Co., Ltd. (1)
700 Yakushimae-cho Karasuma-dori Matsubara-Agaru Shimogyo-ku, Kyoto, 600-8652, Japan
Tel.: (81) 75 361 2211
Web Site: http://www.kyotobank.co.jp
Sales Range: $25-49.9 Million
Emp.: 200
Centralized Processing of Clerical Banking Operations
N.A.I.C.S.: 561499
Hideya Naka *(Office Mgr)*

Kyogin Card Service Co., Ltd. (1)
731 Higashishiokojicho Karasuma-dori Nanajo, Shimogyo-ku Kyoto Bank Kyoto Ekimae Building, Kyoto, 600-8216, Japan
Tel.: (81) 753442211
Web Site: https://www.kyotojcb.jp
Sales Range: $50-74.9 Million
Emp.: 25
Nondepository Credit Intermediation
N.A.I.C.S.: 522299

Kyogin Lease & Capital Co., Ltd. (1)
731 Higashi-Shiokoji-cho, Shimogyo-ku, Kyoto, 600-8216, Japan (100%)
Tel.: (81) 753613232

THE BANK OF KYOTO, LTD.

The Bank of Kyoto, Ltd.—(Continued)
Web Site: https://www.kyotoklc.co.jp
Emp.: 48
Machinery & Equipment Rental & Leasing
N.A.I.C.S.: 532420

Kyoto Credit Service Co., Ltd. (1)
731 Higashi-Shiokoji-cho Karasuma-dori
Kyoto Ekimae Building, Shimogyo-ku,
Kyoto, 600-8216, Japan
Tel.: (81) 753415500
Web Site: https://www.kyotodc.co.jp
Sales Range: $50-74.9 Million
Emp.: 30
Nondepository Credit Intermediation
N.A.I.C.S.: 522299
Takasi Otuki *(Pres)*

Kyoto Guaranty Service Co., Ltd. (1)
9 Umetada-cho Sanjo-dori Karasuma
Higashi-Iru, Nakagyo-ku, Kyoto, 600-8652,
Japan
Tel.: (81) 753612211
Web Site: http://www.kyotobank.co.jp
Credit Guarantee Services
N.A.I.C.S.: 522299

Kyoto Research Institute, Inc. (1)
700 Yakushimaecho, Karasumadori-
Matsubaraagaru Sh, Kyoto, Japan
Tel.: (81) 753612377
General Economic Programs Administration
N.A.I.C.S.: 926110

The Bank of Kyoto, Ltd. - Treasury & Investment Division (1)
2-3-14 Yaesu, Chuo-ku, Tokyo, 104-0028,
Japan
Tel.: (81) 332811212
Commercial Banking Services
N.A.I.C.S.: 522110

THE BANK OF MAHARASHTRA LIMITED

Lokmangal 1501 Shivajinagar, Pune,
411 005, India
Tel.: (91) 2025514501   In
Web Site:
https://www.bankofmaharashtra.in
Year Founded: 1935
MAHABANK—(NSE)
Rev.: $2,823,432,498
Assets: $36,934,678,800
Liabilities: $34,546,635,493
Net Worth: $2,388,043,308
Earnings: $489,344,880
Emp.: 13,499
Fiscal Year-end: 03/31/24
Commercial Banking Services
N.A.I.C.S.: 522110
P. N. Deshpande *(Gen Mgr)*

Subsidiaries:

The Maharashtra Executor & Trustee Co. Pvt. Ltd. (1)
568 First Floor Kesari Wada Near Bank of
Maharashtra, Narayan Peth, Pune, 411030,
India
Tel.: (91) 9404051994
Web Site: https://metcoservices.in
Trust Management Services
N.A.I.C.S.: 523940

THE BANK OF MONGOLIA

Baga Toiruu 9, Ulaanbaatar, 46, Mongolia
Tel.: (976) 11310413
Web Site: http://www.mongolbank.mn
Sales Range: $150-199.9 Million
Emp.: 321
Banking Services
N.A.I.C.S.: 522110
D. Boldbaatar *(Dir Gen-Monetary Policy Dept)*

THE BANK OF N.T. BUTTERFIELD & SON LIMITED

65 Front Street, Hamilton, HM 12,
Bermuda
Tel.: (441) 2951111
Web Site:
https://www.butterfieldgroup.com
Year Founded: 1858
NTB—(NYSE)
Rev.: $757,966,000
Assets: $13,374,020,000
Liabilities: $12,370,423,000
Net Worth: $1,003,597,000
Earnings: $225,492,000
Emp.: 1,334
Fiscal Year-end: 12/31/23
Banking Services
N.A.I.C.S.: 522110
Shaun Morris *(Grp Chief Legal Officer & Gen Counsel)*

Subsidiaries:

Butterfield Asset Management Limited (1)
Dwayne Outerbridge 65 Front Street, Hamilton, HM 12, Bermuda
Tel.: (441) 299 3817
Asset Management Services
N.A.I.C.S.: 523940

Butterfield Bank (Cayman) Limited (1)
Tel.: (345) 9497055
Banking & Securities Services
N.A.I.C.S.: 522110
Michael McWatt *(Mng Dir)*

Butterfield Bank (Guernsey) Ltd. (1)
Regency Court Glategny Esplanade, PO
Box 25, Saint Peter Port, GY1 3AP,
Guernsey   (100%)
Tel.: (44) 1481711521
Banking Services
N.A.I.C.S.: 522110

Subsidiary (Domestic):

Butterfield Trust (Guernsey) Limited (2)
Regency Court Glategny Esplanade, PO
Box 25, Saint Peter Port, GY1 3AP, Guernsey
Tel.: (44) 1481711521
Emp.: 20
Trust & Fiduciary Services
N.A.I.C.S.: 523991
Lindsay Ozanne *(Deputy Mng Dir)*

Butterfield Bank (Jersey) Limited (1)
St Pauls Gate New Street, PO Box 250,
Saint Helier, JE4 5PU, Jersey
Tel.: (44) 153 484 3333
Custody Activities Services
N.A.I.C.S.: 523991
Noel McLaughlin *(Mng Dir)*

Butterfield Holdings (UK) Limited (1)
Sun Court 66 - 67 Cornhill, London, EC3V
3NB, United Kingdom   (100%)
Tel.: (44) 2038716900
Sales Range: $50-74.9 Million
Emp.: 34
Financial Services Holding Company
N.A.I.C.S.: 551112

Subsidiary (Domestic):

Butterfield Mortgages Limited (2)
Sun Court 66 - 67 Cornhill, London, EC3V
3NB, United Kingdom
Tel.: (44) 2038716900
Web Site: https://www.butterfieldgroup.com
Sales Range: $50-74.9 Million
Emp.: 100
Mortgage Services
N.A.I.C.S.: 522310
Stephen Murrell *(Mgr-Bus Dev)*

Butterfield Securities (Bermuda) Limited (1)
65 Front Street, Hamilton, Bermuda
Tel.: (441) 299 3972
Securities Brokerage Services
N.A.I.C.S.: 523150

Butterfield Trust (Asia) Limited (1)
14 02-04 6 Battery Road, Singapore,
049909, Singapore
Tel.: (65) 6 916 3636
Fiduciary Services
N.A.I.C.S.: 523991
Mark Florance *(Mng Dir & Chm)*

Butterfield Trust (Bahamas) Limited (1)
3rd Floor Montague Sterling Centre, PO
Box N-3242, Nassau, Bahamas
Tel.: (242) 3938622
Web Site:
http://www.bs.butterfieldgroup.com
Emp.: 33
Trust & Fiduciary Services
N.A.I.C.S.: 523991
Craig Barley *(Mng Dir & Head-Reg)*

Butterfield Trust (Bermuda) Limited (1)
30 Victoria Street, PO Box HM 1369, Hamilton, HM FX, Bermuda
Tel.: (441) 2927212
Sales Range: $50-74.9 Million
Emp.: 5
Trust & Fiduciary Services
N.A.I.C.S.: 523991
Martin Pollock *(Mng Dir)*

Subsidiary (Domestic):

Bermuda Trust Company Ltd (2)
6 Front St, Hamilton, HM DX, Bermuda
Tel.: (441) 2954000
Personal & Corporate Trust & Personal &
Financial Estate Planning & Administration
N.A.I.C.S.: 523991
Philip M. Butterfield *(Chm)*

Butterfield Trust (Cayman) Limited (1)
Butterfield Place 12 Albert Panton Street,
PO Box 705, Georgetown, KY1-1107, Cayman Islands
Tel.: (345) 949 7055
Banking Services
N.A.I.C.S.: 522110
Michael McWatt *(Mng Dir)*

Butterfield Trust (Switzerland) Limited (1)
Boulevard des Tranchees 16, 1206, Geneva, Switzerland
Tel.: (41) 228390000
Web Site:
http://www.ch.butterfieldgroup.com
Sales Range: $50-74.9 Million
Emp.: 6
Banking Services
N.A.I.C.S.: 523150

Grosvenor Trust Company Limited (1)
2nd Floor Butterfield Bank 65 Front Street,
Hamilton, HM 12, Bermuda
Tel.: (441) 2927474
Investment Trust Management Services
N.A.I.C.S.: 523999

THE BANK OF NAGOYA, LTD.

19-17 Nishiki 3-chome, Naka ku, Nagoya, 460-0003, Japan
Tel.: (81) 529629520   JP
Web Site: https://www.meigin.com
Year Founded: 1949
8522—(NGO)
Rev.: $571,915,050
Assets: $36,554,416,650
Liabilities: $34,795,407,720
Net Worth: $1,759,008,930
Earnings: $60,063,090
Fiscal Year-end: 03/31/23
Banking Services
N.A.I.C.S.: 522110
Kazumaro Kato *(Chm)*

Subsidiaries:

Nagoya Lease Co., Ltd. (1)
2-4-5 Kamimaezu 3rd floor Kamimaezu
Building, Naka-ku, Nagoya, 460-0013, Japan
Tel.: (81) 523227531
Web Site: http://www.nagoyalease.co.jp
Emp.: 67
Bank Leasing Services
N.A.I.C.S.: 532490

THE BANK OF NEVIS LTD.

Main Street, PO Box 450, Charlestown, Saint Kitts & Nevis
Tel.: (869) 4695564

INTERNATIONAL PUBLIC

Web Site:
http://www.thebankofnevis.com
BON—(ECA)
Rev.: $9,740,854
Assets: $336,660,793
Liabilities: $296,583,832
Net Worth: $40,076,960
Earnings: $9,556,388
Emp.: 132
Fiscal Year-end: 06/30/21
Banking Services
N.A.I.C.S.: 522110
L. Everette Martin *(Gen Mgr)*

Subsidiaries:

The International Bank of Nevis (1)
Main Street, PO Box 450, Charlestown,
Saint Kitts & Nevis
Tel.: (869) 469 0800
International Banking Services
N.A.I.C.S.: 522110

THE BANK OF NOVA SCOTIA

40 Temperance Street, Toronto, M5H
0B4, ON, Canada
Tel.: (416) 775-0798   Ca
Web Site:
https://www.scotiabank.com
Year Founded: 1832
BNS—(NYSE)
Rev.: $24,101,022,000
Assets: $1,052,448,594,000
Liabilities: $993,763,012,000
Net Worth: $58,685,582,000
Earnings: $5,527,860,000
Emp.: 89,483
Fiscal Year-end: 10/31/23
International Banking Services
N.A.I.C.S.: 522110
Barbara F. Mason *(Chief HR Officer & Head-Grp)*

Subsidiaries:

1832 Asset Management L.P. (1)
48th Floor 40 King St W, Toronto, M5H
1H1, ON, Canada
Tel.: (416) 365-5605
Web Site: https://www.generationalwealth.ca
Building Insurance Services
N.A.I.C.S.: 524210
Donald B. MacDonald *(Sr VP & Portfolio Mgr)*

BNS Asia Limited (1)
1 Raffles Quay 20-01 North Tower One
Raffles Quay, Singapore, 048583, Singapore
Tel.: (65) 6 305 8388
Financial Services
N.A.I.C.S.: 522320

BNS Investments Inc. (1)
Scotia Plz 44 King St W, Toronto, M5H
1H1, ON, Canada
Tel.: (416) 866-6161
Web Site: http://www.scotiabank.com
Sales Range: $250-299.9 Million
Emp.: 10,000
Holding Company
N.A.I.C.S.: 551112

DundeeWealth Inc. (1)
1 Adelaide Street East, Toronto, M5C 2V9,
ON, Canada   (100%)
Tel.: (416) 350-3250
Web Site: http://www.dundeewealth.com
Sales Range: $750-799.9 Million
Emp.: 800
Investment Management, Securities Brokerage, Financial Planning & Investment Advisory Services
N.A.I.C.S.: 523999

Subsidiary (Domestic):

Dundee Insurance Agency Ltd (2)
1 Adelaide St E 27th Fl, Toronto, M5C 2V9,
ON, Canada   (100%)
Tel.: (416) 350-3250
Web Site: http://www.dundeewealth.com
Sales Range: $600-649.9 Million
Insurance Agencies & Brokerages
N.A.I.C.S.: 524210

AND PRIVATE COMPANIES — THE BANK OF NOVA SCOTIA

Grupo BNS de Costa Rica, S.A. (1)
Fte A La Esq Nor-Este De, San Jose, Costa Rica
Tel.: (506) 22104000
Commercial Banking Services
N.A.I.C.S.: 522110

Grupo Financiero Scotiabank Inverlat, S.A. de C.V. (1)
Blvd Manuel Avila Camacho 1 Piso 19, Mexico, CP-11009, DF, Mexico (97%)
Tel.: (52) 5552292310
Web Site: http://www.scotiabank.com.mx
Sales Range: $200-249.9 Million
Emp.: 6,700
Banking Services
N.A.I.C.S.: 522110

Division (Domestic):

Scotia Inverlat Casa de Bolsa (2)
Bosque de Ciruelos 120, Col Bosque de las Lomas, CP 11700, Mexico, Mexico
Tel.: (52) 5553253000
Web Site: http://www.scotiabankinverlat.com
Banking Services
N.A.I.C.S.: 522299

ING Bank of Canada (1)
111 Gordon Baker Rd Ste 110, Toronto, M2H 3R1, ON, Canada (100%)
Tel.: (416) 756-2424
Web Site: http://www.ingdirect.ca
Sales Range: $1-4.9 Billion
Emp.: 1,100
Commercial Banking, Mortgages & Financial Services
N.A.I.C.S.: 522110
Peter R. Aceto (Pres & CEO)

Jarislowsky, Fraser Limited (1)
1010 Sherbrooke Street W 20th Floor, Montreal, H3A 2R7, QC, Canada
Tel.: (514) 842-2727
Web Site: https://www.jflglobal.com
Investment Services
N.A.I.C.S.: 523150
Maxime Menard (Pres & CEO)

MD Financial Management Inc. (1)
1870 Alta Vista Dr, Ottawa, K1G 6R7, ON, Canada
Tel.: (613) 731-4552
Web Site: https://www.mdm.ca
Financial Services
N.A.I.C.S.: 522320
Daniel Labonte (Pres & CEO)

Roynat Inc. (1)
Scotia Plz 40 King St W 26th Fl, Toronto, M5H 1H1, ON, Canada (100%)
Tel.: (416) 933-2730
Web Site: http://www.roynat.com
Sales Range: $50-74.9 Million
Emp.: 45
Holding Company; Equity Investment, Asset & Lease Finance Services
N.A.I.C.S.: 551112

Subsidiary (Domestic):

Roynat Capital Inc. (2)
Scotia Plaza 40 King Street West 26th Floor, Toronto, M5H 1H1, ON, Canada (100%)
Tel.: (416) 933-2730
Web Site: http://www.roynat.ca
Privater Equity Firm
N.A.I.C.S.: 523999

Joint Venture (Domestic):

Pineridge Foods Inc. (3)
91 Delta Park Blvd Unit 2, Brampton, L6T 5E7, ON, Canada
Tel.: (905) 458-8696
Web Site: http://www.pineridgefoods.com
Prepared Frozen Dessert Mfr
N.A.I.C.S.: 311412

Subsidiary (Domestic):

Gourmet Baker, Inc. (4)
502 4190 Lougheed Hwy, Burnaby, V5C 6A8, BC, Canada
Tel.: (604) 298-2652
Web Site: https://www.aspirebakeries.ca
Sales Range: $10-24.9 Million
Frozen Bakery Products
N.A.I.C.S.: 311813

Scotia Capital (Europe) Limited (1)
201 Bishopsgate, London, EC2M 3NS, United Kingdom
Tel.: (44) 2076385644
Web Site: http://www.scotiabank.com
Sales Range: $100-124.9 Million
Emp.: 250
Banking Services
N.A.I.C.S.: 522299

Scotia Capital Inc. (1)
Scotia Plaza 40 King Street West, PO Box 4085, Toronto, M5W 2X6, ON, Canada (100%)
Tel.: (416) 863-7411
Sales Range: $10-24.9 Million
Emp.: 1,900
Banking & Financial Services
N.A.I.C.S.: 522299
Anne Marie O'Donovan (Chief Admin Officer & Exec VP)

Subsidiary (Domestic):

Scotia Asset Management L.P. (2)
40 King St W, Toronto, M5H 1H1, ON, Canada
Tel.: (416) 866-6430
Asset Management Services
N.A.I.C.S.: 523940

Subsidiary (US):

Scotia Capital (USA) Inc. (2)
250 Besty St, New York, NY 10281 (100%)
Tel.: (212) 225-5000
Sales Range: $150-199.9 Million
Emp.: 350
Commodity Trading & Investment Services
N.A.I.C.S.: 523150

Branch (Domestic):

Scotia Capital (USA) Inc. - Houston (3)
711 Louisiana St Ste 1400, Houston, TX 77002-5216
Tel.: (713) 752-0900
Sales Range: $50-74.9 Million
Emp.: 16
Corporate & Investment Banking Services
N.A.I.C.S.: 522299
Mark Ammerman (Mng Dir)

Scotia Capital (USA) Inc. - San Francisco (3)
580 California St Ste 2100, San Francisco, CA 94104-1042
Tel.: (415) 986-1100
Sales Range: $50-74.9 Million
Emp.: 30
Corporate & Investment Banking Services
N.A.I.C.S.: 523991

Subsidiary (Domestic):

Scotia Managed Companies Administration Inc. (2)
Scotia Plaza 26th Floor 40 King Street West, PO Box 4085, Station A, Toronto, M5W 2X6, ON, Canada
Tel.: (416) 945-4800
Web Site: http://www.scotiamanagedcompanies.com
Investment Fund Administration Services
N.A.I.C.S.: 523940

Affiliate (Domestic):

Advantaged Canadian High Yield Bond Fund (3)
Station A, PO Box 4085, Toronto, M5W 2X6, ON, Canada
Tel.: (416) 945-5353
Rev.: $587,202
Assets: $18,950,779
Liabilities: $430,678
Net Worth: $18,520,101
Earnings: $100,060
Fiscal Year-end: 12/31/2018
Closed-End Investment Fund
N.A.I.C.S.: 525990

Allbanc Split Corp. (3)
150 King Street West 18th Floor, Toronto, M5H 1J9, ON, Canada
Tel.: (416) 863-5930
Web Site: http://www.scotiamanagedcompanies.com
Rev.: $12,420,308
Assets: $34,744,129
Liabilities: $11,465,507
Net Worth: $23,278,622
Earnings: $11,456,354
Emp.: 80
Fiscal Year-end: 02/28/2017
Closed-End Investment Fund
N.A.I.C.S.: 525990
Brian D. McChesney (Pres & CEO)

Allbanc Split Corp. II (3)
40 King Street West Scotia Plaza 26th Floor Station A, PO Box 4085, Toronto, M5W 2X6, ON, Canada
Tel.: (416) 863-5930
Web Site: http://www.scotiamanagedcompanies.com
Rev.: $2,692,254
Assets: $34,916,953
Liabilities: $11,122,205
Net Worth: $23,794,749
Earnings: $1,759,834
Fiscal Year-end: 02/28/2018
Closed-End Investment Fund
N.A.I.C.S.: 525990
Brian D. McChesney (Pres & CEO)

Moneda LatAm Corporate Bond Fund (3)
18th Floor 150 King Street West Station A, PO Box 4085, Toronto, M5W 2X6, ON, Canada
Tel.: (416) 945-4262
Web Site: http://www.scotiamanagedcompanies.com
Rev.: $342,976
Assets: $25,869,454
Liabilities: $4,361,872
Net Worth: $21,507,582
Earnings: ($2,905,896)
Fiscal Year-end: 12/31/2018
Closed-End Investment Fund
N.A.I.C.S.: 525990
Brian D. McChesney (Pres & CEO)

NewGrowth Corp. (3)
Scotia Plaza 26th Floor 40 King Street West, PO Box 4085, Station A, Toronto, M5W 2X6, ON, Canada
Tel.: (416) 862-3931
Web Site: http://www.scotiamanagedcompanies.com
Sales Range: $1-9.9 Million
Emp.: 8
Closed-End Investment Fund
N.A.I.C.S.: 525990
Brian D. McChesney (Pres & CEO)

SCITI ROCS Trust (3)
Scotia Plaza 26th Floor 40 King Street West Station A, Box 4085, Toronto, M5W 2X6, ON, Canada
Tel.: (416) 863-7251
Web Site: http://www.scotiamanagedcompanies.com
Rev.: $4,921
Assets: $30,352,453
Liabilities: $303,950
Net Worth: $30,048,504
Earnings: ($5,021,377)
Fiscal Year-end: 12/31/2014
Closed-End Investment Fund
N.A.I.C.S.: 525990

SCITI Trust (3)
Scotia Plaza 26th Floor 40 King Street West Station A, PO Box 4085, Toronto, M5W 2X6, ON, Canada
Tel.: (416) 945-4394
Web Site: http://www.scotiamanagedcompanies.com
Rev.: $9,393,584
Assets: $147,661,573
Liabilities: $30,564,246
Net Worth: $117,097,326
Earnings: $7,815,973
Fiscal Year-end: 12/31/2017
Closed-End Investment Fund
N.A.I.C.S.: 525990
Robert C. Williams (Sr VP-Intl Corp & Comml Banking-Latin America & Caribbean)

Top 20 Europe Dividend Trust (3)
40 King Street West 26th Floor, PO Box 4085, Station A, Toronto, M5W 2X6, ON, Canada
Tel.: (416) 945-4160
Sales Range: $1-9.9 Million
Closed-End Investment Fund
N.A.I.C.S.: 525990
Brian D. McChesney (Pres & CEO)

Top 20 U.S. Dividend Trust (3)
150 King Street West 18th Floor, PO Box 4085, Toronto, M5W 2X6, ON, Canada
Tel.: (416) 945-4173
Web Site: http://www.scotiamanagedcompanies.com
Rev.: $2,380,261
Assets: $19,672,362
Liabilities: $4,530,861
Net Worth: $15,141,502
Earnings: $1,986,637
Fiscal Year-end: 12/31/2019
Closed-End Investment Fund
N.A.I.C.S.: 525990
Brian D. McChesney (Pres & CEO)

Utility Corp. (3)
40 King Street West Scotia Plaza, PO Box 4085, station A, Toronto, M5W 2X6, ON, Canada
Tel.: (416) 863-7411
Web Site: http://www.scotiamanagedcompanies.com
Rev.: $7,449,697
Assets: $43,044,832
Liabilities: $6,491,810
Net Worth: $36,553,022
Earnings: $7,076,799
Emp.: 100
Fiscal Year-end: 05/21/2017
Closed-End Investment Fund
N.A.I.C.S.: 525990

Division (Domestic):

Scotia Waterous (2)
Ste 1800 Scotia Centre 700 2nd Street SW, Calgary, T2P 2W1, AB, Canada
Tel.: (403) 265-8077
Web Site: http://www.scotiawaterous.com
Emp.: 60
Investments in Oil & Gas
N.A.I.C.S.: 523999

Division (US):

Scotia Waterous USA Inc. (3)
Pennzoil Pl S Tower 711 Louisiana Ste 1400, Houston, TX 77002-2716
Tel.: (713) 222-0546
Web Site: http://www.scotiawaterous.com
Emp.: 50
Investments in Oil & Gas
N.A.I.C.S.: 523999

Holding (Domestic):

Summit Gas Resources, Inc. (4)
1 E Alger St, Sheridan, WY 82801
Tel.: (307) 673-9710
Web Site: http://www.summitgas.com
Sales Range: $10-24.9 Million
Emp.: 38
Gas & Oil Exploration Services
N.A.I.C.S.: 211120
Peter G. Schoonmaker (Pres & CEO)

Scotia Dealer Advantage Inc. (1)
4190 Lougheed Highway Suite 300, Burnaby, V5C6A8, BC, Canada
Tel.: (877) 375-2771
Sales Range: $200-249.9 Million
Emp.: 300
Automotive Financial Leasing Services
N.A.I.C.S.: 522220

Scotia El Salvador, S.A. (1)
25 Avenida Norte y 23 Calle Poniente, San Salvador, El Salvador
Tel.: (503) 22344577
Web Site: http://www.scotiabank.com.sv
Banking Services
N.A.I.C.S.: 522299

Scotia Group Jamaica Ltd. (1)
Scotiabank Centre Corner Duke & Port Royal Streets, PO Box 709, Kingston, Jamaica (70%)
Tel.: (876) 9221000
Web Site: https://www.scotiabank.com.jm
Rev.: $344,285,335
Assets: $4,312,534,220
Liabilities: $3,491,543,382
Net Worth: $820,990,838
Earnings: $111,772,109

THE BANK OF NOVA SCOTIA — INTERNATIONAL PUBLIC

The Bank of Nova Scotia—(Continued)

Emp.: 1,485
Fiscal Year-end: 10/31/2023
Banking Services
N.A.I.C.S.: 522299
Audrey Tugwell Henry (Pres & CEO)

Subsidiary (Domestic):

Scotia Jamaica Building Society (2)
95 Harbour Street, PO Box 8463, Kingston,
Jamaica **(100%)**
Tel.: (876) 9223600
Web Site: http://www.scotiabank.com.jm
Sales Range: $50-74.9 Million
Emp.: 25
International Banking
N.A.I.C.S.: 522299

Scotia Jamaica Financial Services Limited (2)
Scotiabank Centre Duke & Port Streets, PO Box 709, Kingston, Jamaica
Tel.: (876) 922 1000
Web Site: http://www.scotiabank.com.jm
International Banking
N.A.I.C.S.: 522299

Scotia Jamaica General Insurance Brokers Limited (2)
5th Floor Scotiabank Centre Duke & Port Royal Streets, PO Box 709, Kingston, Jamaica **(100%)**
Tel.: (876) 9484447
Web Site: http://www.scotiabank.com.jm
Insurance Services
N.A.I.C.S.: 522299

Scotia Jamaica Investment Management Limited (2)
4th Floor Scotiabank Centre Duke Street & Port Royal Street, PO Box 627, Kingston, Jamaica **(100%)**
Tel.: (876) 922 1000
Web Site: http://www.scotiabank.com.jm
Investment Banking Services
N.A.I.C.S.: 522299

Scotia Jamaica Life Insurance Company Limited (2)
5th Fl Scotiabank Ctr, Corner Duke & Port Royal Sts, Kingston, Jamaica
Tel.: (876) 948 4453
Web Site: http://www.scotiajamaicainsurance.com
Fire Insurance Services
N.A.I.C.S.: 524128

Scotia Holdings (US) Inc. (2)
600 Peachtree St NE Ste 2700, Atlanta, GA 30308-2223 **(100%)**
Tel.: (404) 877-1500
Sales Range: $75-99.9 Million
Emp.: 60
Holding Company
N.A.I.C.S.: 551111

Subsidiary (Domestic):

Howard Weil, Inc. (2)
1100 Poydras St Ste 3500, New Orleans, LA 70163
Tel.: (504) 582-2500
Web Site: http://www.howardweil.com
Sales Range: $150-199.9 Million
Emp.: 55
Securities, Futures & Commodities Dealers
N.A.I.C.S.: 523150
Mary Alice Allen (Coord-Conferences)

Branch (Domestic):

Howard Weil, Inc. (3)
3200 Southwest Fwy Ste 1490, Houston, TX 77027-7557
Tel.: (713) 393-4500
Web Site: http://www.howardweil.com
Brokers Security
N.A.I.C.S.: 523150

Subsidiary (Domestic):

ScotiaMocatta Depository Corporation (2)
230 59 International Airport Central Blvd Bldg C Ste 120, Jamaica, NY 11343
Tel.: (212) 912-8531
Sales Range: $50-74.9 Million
Emp.: 100
Banking Services

N.A.I.C.S.: 522110

Scotiabanc Inc. (2)
711 Louisiana St Ste 1400, Houston, TX 77002-2847
Tel.: (832) 426-6001
Web Site: http://www.scotiabanc.com
Emp.: 10
International Trade Financing Services
N.A.I.C.S.: 522299
Hardeep Thind (Dir-Ops)

The Bank of Nova Scotia Trust Company of New York (2)
1 Liberty Plz 23rd Fl, New York, NY 10006 **(100%)**
Tel.: (212) 225-5470
Web Site: http://www.scotiabank.com
Investment & Corporate Banking Services
N.A.I.C.S.: 523991

Scotia International Limited (1)
Rawson Square, PO Box N-7518, Nassau, Bahamas
Tel.: (242) 3561400
Commercial Banking Services
N.A.I.C.S.: 522110

Scotia Life Insurance Company (1)
Ste 400 100 Yonge St, Toronto, M5H 1H1, ON, Canada **(100%)**
Tel.: (416) 866-7075
Web Site: http://www.scotiabank.com
Sales Range: $75-99.9 Million
Emp.: 70
Fire Insurance Services
N.A.I.C.S.: 524128

Subsidiary (Domestic):

Scotia General Insurance Company (2)
Ste 400 100 Yonge St, Toronto, M5H 1H1, ON, Canada
Tel.: (416) 866-7075
Sales Range: $75-99.9 Million
Emp.: 70
Insurance Services
N.A.I.C.S.: 524298

Scotia Mortgage Corporation (1)
Ste 200 2206 Eglinton Ave E, Scarborough, M1L 4S7, ON, Canada
Tel.: (416) 933-1973
Sales Range: $50-74.9 Million
Emp.: 47
Mortgage Services
N.A.I.C.S.: 522390

Scotia Securities, Inc. (1)
40 King St W Scotia Plz, Toronto, M5H 1H1, ON, Canada
Tel.: (416) 866-6161
Rev.: $818,640
Security Broker & Dealer
N.A.I.C.S.: 523150
Wendy G. Hannam (Exec VP-Sls & Bus Dev)

ScotiaMcLeod Direct Investing (1)
40 King St W Ste 1500, Box 402, Toronto, M5H 3Y2, ON, Canada **(100%)**
Tel.: (416) 863-7272
Sales Range: $125-149.9 Million
Emp.: 120
Securities Trading Services
N.A.I.C.S.: 523150
Shane Jones (Chief Investment Officer)

Scotiabank (Belize) Ltd. (1)
4 A Albert Street, PO Box 708, Belize, Belize
Tel.: (501) 2210135
Web Site: http://www.scotiabank.com
Sales Range: $75-99.9 Million
Emp.: 75
Banking Services
N.A.I.C.S.: 522299
Patrick Andrews (Mgr-Country)

Scotiabank (Hong Kong) Limited (1)
25/F United Ctr 95 Queensway Admiralty, Hong Kong, China (Hong Kong)
Tel.: (852) 25295511
Emp.: 200
Commercial Banking Services
N.A.I.C.S.: 522110

Subsidiary (Domestic):

Scotiatrust (Hong Kong) Limited (2)
25th Floor United Center 95 Queensway, Hong Kong, China (Hong Kong) **(100%)**
Tel.: (852) 25295511
Web Site: http://www.scotiabank.com
Sales Range: $50-74.9 Million
Emp.: 100
International Banking Services
N.A.I.C.S.: 522299

Scotiabank (Ireland) Designated Activity Company (1)
4th Floor IFSC House Custom House Quay IFSC, Dublin, Ireland
Tel.: (353) 1 790 2000
Financial Services
N.A.I.C.S.: 522320
Nicola Vavasour (CEO)

Scotiabank Azul S.A. (1)
Huerfanos 1234, Santiago, Chile **(68.19%)**
Tel.: (56) 2 679 1026
Web Site: http://www.bbva.cl
Banking Services
N.A.I.C.S.: 522110

Subsidiary (Domestic):

BBVA Seguros de Vida, S.A. (2)
Bandera 76 Piso 6 Oficina 602, Santiago, Chile
Tel.: (56) 2 640 16 60
Life Insurance Products & Services
N.A.I.C.S.: 524113

ECASA, S.A. (2)
Isidora Goyenechea 3365, Santiago, Chile
Tel.: (56) 51 543024
Financial Services
N.A.I.C.S.: 523999

Forum Servicios Financieros, S.A. (2)
Avenida Isidora Goyenechea No 3365 Level 4, Las Condes, Santiago, Chile
Tel.: (56) 2 369 3000
Sales Range: $150-199.9 Million
Emp.: 500
Automotive Financial Leasing Services
N.A.I.C.S.: 522220

Scotiabank Brasil S.A. Banco Multiplo (1)
Av Brig Faria Lima 2277 7 Andar, Sao Paulo, 01452-000, Brazil
Tel.: (55) 1122028100
Web Site: http://www.br.scotiabank.com
Corporate & Investment Banking Services
N.A.I.C.S.: 523150

Scotiabank Chile S.A. (1)
Morande 226 Casilla 90-D, Santiago, Chile **(76%)**
Tel.: (56) 26926000
Web Site: http://www.scotiabank.cl
Sales Range: $125-149.9 Million
Banking Services
N.A.I.C.S.: 522299
Daniel Kennedy (VP-Digital Banking)

Joint Venture (Domestic):

Cencosud Administradora de Tarjetas S.A. (2)
Agustinas 785 2 Piso, Santiago, Chile **(51%)**
Tel.: (56) 600 450 5000
Web Site: http://www.tarjetacencosud.cl
Retail Credit Card Administration & Sales Financing Services
N.A.I.C.S.: 522210

Scotiabank Europe plc (1)
201 Bishopsgate, London, EC2M 3NS, United Kingdom
Tel.: (44) 2076385644
Web Site: http://www.scotiabank.com
Sales Range: $100-124.9 Million
Emp.: 200
Banking Services
N.A.I.C.S.: 522299

Subsidiary (Domestic):

ScotiaMocatta Limited (2)
201 Bishopsgate 6th Floor, London, EC2M 3NS, United Kingdom **(100%)**
Tel.: (44) 2078265655
Web Site: http://www.scotiamocatta.com
Sales Range: $25-49.9 Million
Emp.: 100
Commodity Trading Services

N.A.I.C.S.: 331410

Scotiabank International Limited (1)
Broad Street, PO Box 202, Bridgetown, Barbados
Tel.: (246) 426 7000
Bank Holding Company
N.A.I.C.S.: 551111

Subsidiary (Domestic):

BNS International (Barbados) Limited (2)
Broad Street, Bridgetown, Barbados **(100%)**
Tel.: (246) 426 7000
Web Site: http://www.scotiabank.com
Sales Range: $50-74.9 Million
Emp.: 20
Investment & Corporate Banking
N.A.I.C.S.: 523150

Subsidiary (Non-US):

Corporacion Mercaban de Costa Rica, S.A. (2)
Ave Primera Calle 0-2, PO Box 5395-1000, San Jose, Costa Rica
Tel.: (506) 22104000
Web Site: http://www.scotiabankcr.com
Banking Services
N.A.I.C.S.: 522299

Subsidiary (Domestic):

Scotia Insurance (Barbados) Limited (2)
3rd Floor International Trading Centre, Warrens, Saint Michael, 22026, Barbados
Tel.: (246) 4252164
Sales Range: $75-99.9 Million
Emp.: 10
Insurance Services
N.A.I.C.S.: 524298

The Bank of Nova Scotia Trust Company (Caribbean) Limited (2)
Broad Street, PO Box 202, Bridgetown, Barbados **(100%)**
Tel.: (246) 431 3100
Web Site: http://www.scotiabank.com
International Banking
N.A.I.C.S.: 522299

Scotiabank Peru Holding S.A. (1)
Av Dionisio Derteano 102, San Isidro, Lima, Peru
Tel.: (51) 1 311 6000
Web Site: https://www.scotiabank.com.pe
Banking Services
N.A.I.C.S.: 522110

Scotiabank Peru S.A. (1)
Dionisio Derteano 102 Esquina con Miguel Seminario, PO Box 1235, Lima, Peru **(98%)**
Tel.: (51) 3116000
Web Site: https://www.scotiabank.com
Banking Services
N.A.I.C.S.: 522110

Subsidiary (Domestic):

Banco Cencosud S.A. (2)
Av Benavides No 1555 Urbanizacion, San Antonio, Lima, Peru **(51%)**
Tel.: (51) 1 626 0000
Supermarket Operator
N.A.I.C.S.: 445110
Carlos Americo Morante Ormeo (Gen Mgr)

Crediscotia Financiera S.A. (2)
Av Paseo de la Republica N 3587, San Isidro, Lima, Peru
Tel.: (51) 6119900
Web Site: https://www.crediscotia.com.pe
Rev.: $1,633,691,198
Assets: $19,599,226,504
Liabilities: $16,460,817,200
Net Worth: $3,138,409,304
Earnings: $210,377,567
Fiscal Year-end: 12/31/2023
Financial Services
N.A.I.C.S.: 523999

PROFUTURO A.F.P. (2)
Andres Reyes No 489, San Isidro, Peru
Tel.: (51) 2152800
Web Site: http://www.profuturo.com.pe

Sales Range: Less than $1 Million
Pension Fund Managing Services
N.A.I.C.S.: 525110
Miguel Uccelli Labarthe *(Chm)*

Scotiabank Republica Dominicana, S.A. (1)
Av Prolongacion 27 de Febrero, Santo Domingo Oeste, Santo Domingo, Dominican Republic
Tel.: (809) 920 3891
Financial Services
N.A.I.C.S.: 522320

Scotiabank Trinidad & Tobago Limited (1)
Scotiabank Centre 56-58 Richmond St, Port of Spain, Trinidad & Tobago **(48%)**
Tel.: (868) 6253566
Web Site: http://www.scotiabankttt.com
Sales Range: $75-99.9 Million
International Banking Services
N.A.I.C.S.: 522110
Savon Persad *(VP-Retail & Small Bus)*

Subsidiary (Domestic):

Scotiatrust & Merchant Bank Trinidad & Tobago Limited (2)
Scotia Centre 56-58 Richmond Street, Port of Spain, Trinidad & Tobago
Tel.: (868) 6253566
Web Site: http://www.scotiabankttt.com
Emp.: 4
Merchant Banking Services
N.A.I.C.S.: 522299

Scotiabank Turks & Caicos Limited (1)
PO Box 15, Providenciales, Turks & Caicos Islands
Tel.: (649) 9464750
Web Site: http://www.scotiabank.com
Sales Range: $100-124.9 Million
Emp.: 130
Banking Services
N.A.I.C.S.: 522110

Scotiabank Uruguay S.A. (1)
Misiones 1399, Montevideo, 11000, Uruguay
Tel.: (598) 29160541
Web Site: http://www.scotiabank.com.uy
Commercial Banking Services
N.A.I.C.S.: 522110

The Bank of Nova Scotia - Antigua & Barbuda (1)
PO Box 342, High Street, Saint John's, Antigua & Barbuda
Tel.: (268) 4801500
Web Site: http://ag.scotiabank.com
Sales Range: $75-99.9 Million
Emp.: 60
Banking Services
N.A.I.C.S.: 522299

The Bank of Nova Scotia - Atlantic Region (1)
1709 Hollis St 6th Fl, Halifax, B3J 1W1, NS, Canada
Tel.: (902) 420-3600
Web Site: http://www.scotiabank.com
Sales Range: $50-74.9 Million
Emp.: 100
Banking Services
N.A.I.C.S.: 522110

The Bank of Nova Scotia - British Columbia & Yukon Region (1)
650 W Georgia St 34th Fl, Vancouver, V6B 4P6, BC, Canada
Tel.: (604) 668-2094
Web Site: http://www.scotiabank.com
Banking Services
N.A.I.C.S.: 522110

The Bank of Nova Scotia - Dominican Republic (1)
Apartado 1494 John F Kennedy &, Lope de Vega Av, Santo Domingo, Dominican Republic
Tel.: (809) 5458000
Web Site: http://www.scotiabank.com
Banking Services
N.A.I.C.S.: 522299

The Bank of Nova Scotia - Guyana (1)
104 Carmichael St, PO Box 10631, Georgetown, Guyana
Tel.: (592) 2259222
Web Site: http://gy.scotiabank.com
Sales Range: $100-124.9 Million
Emp.: 186
Banking Services
N.A.I.C.S.: 522299
Adele Farier *(Sr Mgr-Credit Risk Mgmt)*

The Bank of Nova Scotia - Haiti (1)
360 Blvd JJ Dessalines, Port-au-Prince, HT6110, Haiti
Tel.: (509) 2941 3001
Web Site: http://www.scotiabank.com
Sales Range: $75-99.9 Million
Emp.: 88
Banking Services
N.A.I.C.S.: 522110

The Bank of Nova Scotia - India (1)
14th Floor Dr Gopal Das Bhavan 28 Barakhamba Road, New Delhi, 110-001, India
Tel.: (91) 1123351522
Web Site: http://www.scotiabank.com
Emp.: 28
Banking Services
N.A.I.C.S.: 522299
Ankit Sharma *(Dir & Branch Mgr-New Delhi)*

The Bank of Nova Scotia - Japan (1)
Toranomon Waiko Building 6th Floor 12-1 Toranomon 5-Chome Minato-ku, Tokyo, 105-0001, Japan
Tel.: (81) 354080900
Web Site: http://www.scotiabank.com
Sales Range: $50-74.9 Million
Emp.: 20
Banking Services
N.A.I.C.S.: 522299
Hiroshi Fujita *(Mng Dir)*

The Bank of Nova Scotia - Manitoba Region (1)
200 Portage Ave at Main, PO Box 845, Winnipeg, R3C 2R7, MB, Canada
Tel.: (204) 985-3030
Web Site: http://www.scotiabank.com
Sales Range: $50-74.9 Million
Emp.: 45
Banking Services
N.A.I.C.S.: 522110

The Bank of Nova Scotia - Ontario Region (1)
44 King Street West 22nd Floor, Toronto, M5H 1H1, ON, Canada
Tel.: (416) 866-6318
Web Site: http://www.scotiabank.com
Banking Services
N.A.I.C.S.: 522110

The Bank of Nova Scotia - Panama (1)
Ave Federico Boyd Y Esquina Calle 51, PO Box 0833, Panama, 083300174, Panama
Tel.: (507) 2087700
Web Site: http://www.scotiabank.com
Sales Range: $75-99.9 Million
Emp.: 90
Banking Services
N.A.I.C.S.: 522299

The Bank of Nova Scotia - Prairie Region (1)
700 2nd St SW Ste 4000, Calgary, T2P 2N7, AB, Canada
Tel.: (403) 221-6477
Web Site: http://www.scotiabank.com
Sales Range: $50-74.9 Million
Emp.: 10
Banking Services
N.A.I.C.S.: 522110

The Bank of Nova Scotia - Quebec & Eastern Ontario Region (1)
1002 Sherbrooke St W Ste 430, Montreal, H3A 3L6, QC, Canada
Tel.: (514) 499-5404
Web Site: http://www.scotiabank.com
Banking Services
N.A.I.C.S.: 522110

The Bank of Nova Scotia - South Korea (1)
16th Floor Dong-A Media Centre 139 Sejongno Jongno-gu, Seoul, 110-715, Korea (South)
Tel.: (82) 220202340
Web Site: http://www.scotiabank.com
Sales Range: $50-74.9 Million
Emp.: 23
Banking Services
N.A.I.C.S.: 522299

The Bank of Nova Scotia - Thailand (1)
1-2 Floor Ploenchit Tower, 898 Ploenchit Road, Bangkok, 10330, Thailand
Tel.: (66) 22630303
Web Site: http://www.scotiabank.com
Banking Services
N.A.I.C.S.: 522299

The Bank of Nova Scotia - Toronto Region (1)
40 King Street, Toronto, M5C 2W1, ON, Canada
Tel.: (416) 866-3840
Web Site: http://www.scotiabank.com
Banking Services
N.A.I.C.S.: 522110

The Bank of Nova Scotia Asia Limited (1)
10 Collyer Quay, 15-01 Ocean Building, Singapore, 049315, Singapore **(100%)**
Tel.: (65) 6535 8688
Web Site: http://www.scotiabank.com
International Banking Services
N.A.I.C.S.: 522299

The Bank of Nova Scotia Berhad (1)
Menara Boustead 69 Jalan Raja Chulan, 50200, Kuala Lumpur, Malaysia **(100%)**
Tel.: (60) 321410766
Web Site: http://www.scotiabank.my
Sales Range: $25-49.9 Million
Emp.: 120
International Banking
N.A.I.C.S.: 522299

The Bank of Nova Scotia International Limited (1)
Scotiabank Building Rawson Square, PO Box N-7518, Nassau, Bahamas
Tel.: (242) 3561518
Web Site: http://scotiabank.com
Banking Services
N.A.I.C.S.: 522299

Subsidiary (Domestic):

Scotiabank (Bahamas) Ltd. (2)
Scotiabank Building Rawson Square, PO Box N-7518, Nassau, Bahamas **(100%)**
Tel.: (242) 356 1697
Web Site: http://www.scotiabank.com
Sales Range: $50-74.9 Million
Emp.: 130
Banking Services
N.A.I.C.S.: 551112
Roger Archer *(VP)*

Scotiabank Caribbean Treasury Limited (2)
One Bay Street, PO Box N-7518, Nassau, Bahamas
Tel.: (242) 3022950
Sales Range: $50-74.9 Million
Emp.: 10
Investment Banking Services
N.A.I.C.S.: 523150

The Bank of Nova Scotia Trust Company (Bahamas) Limited (2)
Scotia House 404 East Bay Street, PO Box N3016, Nassau, Bahamas **(100%)**
Tel.: (242) 3561400
Web Site: http://www.scotiabank.com
Sales Range: $50-74.9 Million
Emp.: 80
International Banking
N.A.I.C.S.: 522299

Subsidiary (Non-US):

Scotiabank & Trust (Cayman) Limited (3)
Scotia Centre 6 Cardinal Avenue, PO Box 689 GT, Georgetown, Grand Cayman, Cayman Islands **(100%)**
Tel.: (345) 9497666
Web Site: http://www.scotiabank.com
Trust, Fiduciary & Private Banking Services
N.A.I.C.S.: 522320

The Bank of Nova Scotia Properties Inc.
Scotia Plz 44 King St W, Toronto, M5H 1H1, ON, Canada **(100%)**
Tel.: (416) 866-7872
Sales Range: $50-74.9 Million
Emp.: 100
Real Estate Manangement Services
N.A.I.C.S.: 531210

Subsidiary (Domestic):

Scotia Realty Limited (2)
Scotia Plaza 44 King Street West Woodgate Bus Park, Toronto, M5H 1H1, ON, Canada
Tel.: (416) 866-7872
Web Site: http://www.scotiabank.com
Sales Range: $125-149.9 Million
Real Estate Services
N.A.I.C.S.: 531210

Tour Scotia (1)
1002 Sherbrooke St W, Montreal, H3A 3L6, QC, Canada
Tel.: (514) 288-1002
Web Site: http://www.scotia.com
Sales Range: $50-74.9 Million
Emp.: 10
Nonresidential Building Operators
N.A.I.C.S.: 531120
Berdj Meguerian *(Gen Mgr)*

THE BANK OF OKINAWA, LTD.
10-1 3-chome Kumoji, Naha, 900 8651, Okinawa, Japan
Tel.: (81) 988672141
Web Site: http://www.okinawa-bank.co.jp
Year Founded: 1956
8397—(TKS)
Rev.: $501,307,840
Assets: $25,870,419,520
Liabilities: $24,286,655,360
Net Worth: $1,583,764,160
Earnings: $50,403,760
Emp.: 1,115
Fiscal Year-end: 03/31/21
Banking Services
N.A.I.C.S.: 522110
Yoshiaki Tamaki *(Chm)*

Subsidiaries:

Okigin General Lease Co., Ltd. (1)
2-21-1 Maejima 2nd floor Takahashi Branch Bank of Okinawa, Naha, 900-0016, Okinawa, Japan
Tel.: (81) 988673141
Web Site: http://www.okigin-lease.co.jp
Sales Range: $50-74.9 Million
Emp.: 68
Commericial Banking
N.A.I.C.S.: 522110

Okigin JCB Co., Ltd. (1)
8F Ryukyu Shimposha Izumizaki Building 1-10-3 Izumizaki, Naha, 900-8534, Okinawa, Japan
Tel.: (81) 988623201
Web Site: https://www.okigin-jcb.co.jp
Emp.: 40
Credit Card Services
N.A.I.C.S.: 522210
Kenjun Kaneshiro *(Pres)*

Okigin SPO Co., Ltd. (1)
5-5-2 Makiminato, Urasoe, 901-2131, Okinawa, Japan
Tel.: (81) 988780691
Web Site: https://www.ospo.co.jp
Emp.: 170
Data Processing Services
N.A.I.C.S.: 518210

THE BANK OF SAGA LTD.
2-7-20 Tojin, Saga, Japan
Tel.: (81) 952245111
Web Site:
https://www.sagabank.co.jp
Year Founded: 1955
8395—(TKS)
Rev.: $350,415,930
Assets: $20,894,414,910
Liabilities: $20,082,396,240
Net Worth: $812,018,670
Earnings: $297,450

THE BANK OF SAGA LTD.

The Bank of Saga Ltd.—(Continued)
Emp.: 1,160
Fiscal Year-end: 03/31/24
Banking Services
N.A.I.C.S.: 522110
Hideaki Sakai (Pres)

THE BARGAIN! SHOP HOLDINGS INC.
6877 Goreway Drive Suite 3, Mississauga, L4V 1L9, ON, Canada
Tel.: (905) 293-9700
Web Site:
 https://www.thebargainshop.com
Year Founded: 1999
Sales Range: $150-199.9 Million
Emp.: 1,000
Discount Department Store Owner & Operator
N.A.I.C.S.: 455110
Eric Claus (Chm & CEO)

THE BDRC GROUP
Kingsbourne House 229 231 High Holborn, London, WC1V 7DA, United Kingdom
Tel.: (44) 2074001000
Web Site: http://www.bva-bdrc.com
Sales Range: $25-49.9 Million
Emp.: 80
Market Research Services
N.A.I.C.S.: 541910
Crispian Tarrant (CEO)

Subsidiaries:

BDRC Asia Pte Ltd (1)
51 Goldhill Plaza 14-04/05, Singapore, 308900, Singapore
Tel.: (65) 6578 9400
Web Site: http://www.bdrc-asia.com
Market Research Services
N.A.I.C.S.: 541910
Piers Lee (Mng Dir)

BDRC China (1)
No 37 Nanmofang Lu Unit 1701-1703, Chaoyang District, Beijing, 100022, China
Tel.: (86) 10 87728052
Web Site: http://www.bdrc-china.com
Market Research Services
N.A.I.C.S.: 541910

BDRC Jones Donald Pty Ltd (1)
Level 10 117 York Street, Sydney, 2000, NSW, Australia
Tel.: (61) 2 9267 6444
Web Site: http://www.jonesdonald.com.au
Emp.: 6
Market Research Services
N.A.I.C.S.: 541910
Georgina Woodley (Gen Mgr)

Bdrc Americas Inc. (1)
1200 18th St NW Ste 700, Washington, DC 20036
Tel.: (202) 841-5855
Web Site: http://www.bdrc-americas.com
Market Research Services
N.A.I.C.S.: 541910

Continental Research Ltd. (1)
Laser House 132-140 Goswell Rd, London, EC1V 7DY, United Kingdom
Tel.: (44) 74905944
Web Site:
 http://www.continentalresearch.com
Sales Range: $10-24.9 Million
Emp.: 40
Market Research Services
N.A.I.C.S.: 541910

ESA Retail Limited (1)
10 Bricket Rd, Saint Albans, AL1 3JX, Hertfordshire, United Kingdom
Tel.: (44) 1727 847 572
Web Site: http://www.esa-retail.co.uk
Emp.: 40
Market Research Services
N.A.I.C.S.: 541910
Greg McDonald (Gen Mgr)

PT. BDRC Asia (1)
Menara DEA Tower I Kawasan Mega Kuningan, Jl Mega Kuningan Barat Kav, Jakarta, 12950, Indonesia
Tel.: (62) 21576 1253
Market Research Services
N.A.I.C.S.: 541910

Perspective Research Services (1)
12-20 Baron Street, Angel, London, N1 9LL, United Kingdom
Tel.: (44) 20 7427 2400
Web Site: http://www.perspectivemr.com
Market Research Services
N.A.I.C.S.: 541910
Ger-Jan van der Maten (Dir-Fin & Mgmt)

Viewpoint Field and Studios (1)
73 Thames Street, Middlesex, Sunbury-on-Thames, TW16 6AD, United Kingdom
Tel.: (44) 20 3176 3101
Market Research Services
N.A.I.C.S.: 541910
Bernice Baughen (Controller-Quality)

THE BECKER MILK COMPANY LIMITED
305 Milner Avenue Suite 400, Scarborough, M1B 3V4, ON, Canada
Tel.: (416) 291-4441 ON
Web Site: https://mybeckers.ca
Year Founded: 1988
BEK.B—(TSX)
Rev.: $2,422,842
Assets: $29,337,332
Liabilities: $4,194,815
Net Worth: $25,142,518
Earnings: $2,766,438
Fiscal Year-end: 04/30/21
Real Estate Management Services
N.A.I.C.S.: 531390
Brian Rattenbury (CFO)

THE BERKELEY GROUP HOLDINGS PLC
Berkeley House 19 Portsmouth Road, Cobham, KT11 1JG, Surrey, United Kingdom
Tel.: (44) 193 286 8555
Web Site:
 http://www.berkeleygroup.co.uk
Year Founded: 1976
BKG—(LSE)
Rev.: $3,187,926,560
Assets: $8,944,252,044
Liabilities: $4,686,306,352
Net Worth: $4,257,945,692
Earnings: $654,964,128
Emp.: 3,030
Fiscal Year-end: 04/30/22
Holding Company; Real Estate Development Services
N.A.I.C.S.: 551112
Karl Whiteman (Exec Dir)

Subsidiaries:

Berkeley Commercial Developments Ltd. (1)
Berkeley House, 19 Portsmouth Road, Cobham, KT111JG, Surrey, United Kingdom (100%)
Tel.: (44) 1932584555
Real Estate Development Services
N.A.I.C.S.: 531390
Rob Perrins (Mng Dir)

Berkeley First Limited (1)
Berkeley House 19 Portsmouth Road, Cobham, KT111JG, Surrey, United Kingdom (100%)
Tel.: (44) 1932584555
Sales Range: $50-74.9 Million
Emp.: 85
Activities Related to Real Estate
N.A.I.C.S.: 531390
Anthony Pidgley (Mng Dir)

Berkeley Homes (Central London) Limited (1)
380 Queenstown Road, London, SW11 8PE, United Kingdom
Tel.: (44) 2077202600
Property Development Services
N.A.I.C.S.: 531390

Berkeley Homes (East Thames) Limited (1)
5 Station Way, London, SE18 6NJ, Surrey, United Kingdom
Tel.: (44) 2083127800
Property Management Services
N.A.I.C.S.: 531311

Berkeley Homes (Eastern Counties) Limited (1)
Berkeley House Bay Tree Avenue, Leatherhead, KT22 7UE, Surrey, United Kingdom
Tel.: (44) 1732227500
Sales Range: $50-74.9 Million
Emp.: 60
Residential Property Development Services
N.A.I.C.S.: 531110
Peter Smith (Mng Dir)

Berkeley Homes (Eastern Counties) Limited (1)
Berkeley House 7 Oakhill Road, Sevenoaks, TN13 1NQ, United Kingdom
Tel.: (44) 1732 227500
Web Site: http://www.berkeleyhomes.co.uk
Emp.: 60
Residential Property Management Services
N.A.I.C.S.: 531311

Berkeley Homes (Eastern) Limited (1)
Berkeley House 19 Portsmouth Road, Woolwich, Cobham, KT11 1JG, Surrey, United Kingdom
Tel.: (44) 2077202600
Emp.: 7
Residential Property Management Services
N.A.I.C.S.: 531311
Volker Christmann (Mng Dir)

Berkeley Homes (Hampshire) Limited (1)
Berkeley House 19 Portsmouth Road, Cobham, KT11 1JG, Surrey, United Kingdom
Tel.: (44) 2392525582
Property Development Services
N.A.I.C.S.: 531390

Berkeley Homes (Kent) Limited (1)
Berkeley House, 19 Portsmouth Road, Cobham, KT11 1JG, Surrey, United Kingdom (100%)
Tel.: (44) 1932584555
Activities Related to Real Estate
N.A.I.C.S.: 531390
Anthony Pidgley (Mng Dir)

Berkeley Homes (Oxford & Chiltern) Limited (1)
Berkeley House Mill Lane, Taplow, Maidenhead, SL6 0AG, United Kingdom
Tel.: (44) 1753784400
Sales Range: $75-99.9 Million
Emp.: 8
Residential Property Development Services
N.A.I.C.S.: 531390
Rameen Firoozan (Mng Dir)

Berkeley Homes (South East London) Limited (1)
68 Alie Street, London, E1 8PX, United Kingdom (100%)
Tel.: (44) 2076017300
Sales Range: $50-74.9 Million
Emp.: 100
Activities Related to Real Estate
N.A.I.C.S.: 531390

Berkeley Homes (Southall) Limited (1)
1 Randolph Road, Southall, London, UB1 1BL, United Kingdom
Tel.: (44) 2039442713
Real Estate Services
N.A.I.C.S.: 531390

Berkeley Homes (Southern) Limited (1)
Berkeley House Bay Tree Avenue, Leatherhead, KT22 7UE, Surrey, United Kingdom
Tel.: (44) 1372370400
Emp.: 85
Residential Property Development Services
N.A.I.C.S.: 531390
Gary Hodges (Mng Dir)

Berkeley Homes (Urban Renaissance) Limited (1)
Berkeley House 19 Portsmouth Road, Cobham, KT11 1JG, Surrey, United Kingdom
Sales Range: $75-99.9 Million
Emp.: 20
Residential Property Management Services
N.A.I.C.S.: 531311
Paul Vallone (Gen Mgr)

Berkeley Homes (West London) Limited (1)
Chelsea Bridge Wharf 380 Queenstown Road, London, SW11 8PE, United Kingdom
Tel.: (44) 2036751501
Sales Range: $25-49.9 Million
Emp.: 3
New Single-Family Housing Construction
N.A.I.C.S.: 236115

Berkeley Homes (West Thames) Limited (1)
169 Brent Road Project Office, Southall, UB2 5LE, Surrey, United Kingdom
Tel.: (44) 2075872052
Real Estate Services
N.A.I.C.S.: 531390

Berkeley Homes plc (1)
Berkeley House 19 Portsmouth Road, Cobham, KT111JG, Surrey, United Kingdom (100%)
Tel.: (44) 1932584555
Web Site: http://www.berkeleygroup.co.uk
Sales Range: $75-99.9 Million
Emp.: 70
Activities Related to Real Estate
N.A.I.C.S.: 531390
Rob Perrins (Mng Dir)

Berkeley Partnership Homes Limited (1)
Berkeley House 19 Portsmouth Road, Cobham, KT11 1JG, Surrey, United Kingdom
Tel.: (44) 1732227500
Property Management Services
N.A.I.C.S.: 531311
Peter Smith (Mng Dir)

Berkeley Properties Limited (1)
68A Berkeley Road, North Earlsdon, Coventry, CV5 6NX, United Kingdom
Tel.: (44) 2476680722
Web Site: https://berkeleyproperties.co.uk
Construction & Building Services
N.A.I.C.S.: 236220
Gary Foley (Mgr)

Berkeley Strategic Land Limited (1)
Berkeley House, 19 Portsmouth Rd, Cobham, KT111JG, Surrey, United Kingdom (100%)
Tel.: (44) 193258459
Real Estate Services
N.A.I.C.S.: 531390
Matthew Biddle (Mng Dir)

Berkeley Urban Renaissance Limited (1)
Sopwith Way, London, SW84NS, United Kingdom
Tel.: (44) 2075012555
Web Site: http://www.berkeleygroup.co.uk
Sales Range: $50-74.9 Million
Emp.: 60
Real Estate Property Lessors
N.A.I.C.S.: 531190
Paul Vallone (Mng Dir)

Chelsea Bridge Wharf Car Park Limited (1)
19 Portsmouth Road, Cobham, KT11 1JG, Surrey, United Kingdom
Tel.: (44) 2039856055
Web Site: https://chelsea-bridge-wharf.uk
Construction Services
N.A.I.C.S.: 237310

Riverside West Car Park Limited (1)
Littlehampton Marina Ferry Road, Littlehampton, BN17 5DS, West Sussex, United Kingdom
Tel.: (44) 1903713553
Web Site:
 https://www.riversidewestcarpark.co.uk
Storey Car Park Services
N.A.I.C.S.: 812930

Royal Clarence Yard (Marina) Limited (1)
Berkeley House 19 Portsmouth Road, Cobham, KT11 1JG, Surrey, United Kingdom
Tel.: (44) 2392523523

AND PRIVATE COMPANIES

Web Site: https://www.rcyard.org.uk
Community Organizations Services
N.A.I.C.S.: 813410

Saad Berkeley Limited (1)
Berkeley House St George, 19 Portsmouth Road, London, SW82LE, United Kingdom
Tel.: (44) 1932584555
Emp.: 18
Real Estate
N.A.I.C.S.: 531390

St George Central London Limited (1)
Berkeley House 19 Portsmouth Road, 7 Imperial Road Fulham, Cobham, KT11 1JG, Surrey, United Kingdom (100%)
Tel.: (44) 2074714444
Web Site: http://www.stgeorgecl.com
Sales Range: $25-49.9 Million
Emp.: 40
Real Estate Property Lessors
N.A.I.C.S.: 531190

St George PLC (1)
Berkeley House 15b Portsmouth Road, Cobham, KT11 1JG, Surrey, United Kingdom (100%)
Tel.: (44) 2089174000
Sales Range: $25-49.9 Million
Emp.: 50
Real Estate Property Lessors
N.A.I.C.S.: 531190

St George South London Limited (1)
Berkeley House 19 Portsmouth Road, 17-19 Imperial Road Fulham, Cobham, KT11 1JG, Surrey, United Kingdom (100%)
Tel.: (44) 2074714444
Web Site: http://www.stgeorgesl.com
Sales Range: $25-49.9 Million
Emp.: 50
Real Estate Property Lessors
N.A.I.C.S.: 531190

St George West London Limited (1)
Berkeley House 19 Portsmouth Road, Fulham, Cobham, KT11 1JG, Surrey, United Kingdom (100%)
Tel.: (44) 2074714444
Sales Range: $50-74.9 Million
Emp.: 60
Real Estate Property Lessors
N.A.I.C.S.: 531190

St Joseph Homes Limited (1)
9 Colmore Row, Birmingham, B3 2BJ, West Midlands, United Kingdom
Tel.: (44) 1212003500
Real Estate Services
N.A.I.C.S.: 531390
Ashley Kensington *(Mng Dir)*

St. James Group Limited (1)
St James House 15b St George Wharf, London, SW8 2LE, United Kingdom (100%)
Tel.: (44) 2036751502
Web Site: http://www.stjameshomes.co.uk
Sales Range: $75-99.9 Million
Emp.: 115
Real Estate Property Lessors
N.A.I.C.S.: 531190

The Berkeley Group plc (1)
Berkeley House 19 Portsmouth Road, Cobham, KT11 1JG, Surrey, United Kingdom (100%)
Tel.: (44) 1932868555
Sales Range: $75-99.9 Million
Emp.: 120
Activities Related to Real Estate
N.A.I.C.S.: 531190

THE BEST CONNECTION GROUP LIMITED
Unit 1 Topaz Business Park Topaz Way Birmingham Road, Bromsgrove, B61 0GD, Worcs, United Kingdom
Tel.: (44) 121 504 3000 UK
Web Site:
http://www.thebestconnection.co.uk
Year Founded: 1991
Sales Range: $250-299.9 Million
Emp.: 468
Human Resource Consulting Services

N.A.I.C.S.: 541612
Andrew Sweeney *(Co-Founder & CEO)*

THE BIDVEST GROUP LIMITED
Bidvest House 18 Crescent Drive, Melrose Arch Melrose, 2196, Johannesburg, 2196, South Africa
Tel.: (27) 117728700 ZA
Web Site: https://www.bidvest.co.za
Year Founded: 1988
BDVSF—(OTCIQ)
Rev.: $6,068,479,705
Assets: $5,677,527,329
Liabilities: $3,758,849,903
Net Worth: $1,918,677,426
Earnings: $336,200,425
Emp.: 130,000
Fiscal Year-end: 06/30/23
International Services, Trading & Distribution Holding Company
N.A.I.C.S.: 551112
Lindsay Peter Ralphs *(Co-CEO)*

Subsidiaries:

Academy Brushware Products Proprietary Limited (1)
38 5th Avenue Bredell AH, Kempton Park, 1619, South Africa
Tel.: (27) 11 821 2900
Web Site:
https://www.academybrushware.co.za
Paint Brush Mfr & Distr
N.A.I.C.S.: 339994
Howard Greenstein *(CEO)*

Adcock Ingram Holdings Limited (1)
1 New Road c/o New Road 7th Street, Midrand, South Africa (37%)
Tel.: (27) 116350000
Web Site: http://www.adcock.co.za
Rev.: $593,997,894
Assets: $538,277,523
Liabilities: $180,402,781
Net Worth: $357,874,742
Earnings: $54,633,740
Emp.: 2,388
Fiscal Year-end: 06/30/2022
Pharmaceuticals Product Mfr
N.A.I.C.S.: 325412
Andrew G. Hall *(CEO)*

Subsidiary (Domestic):

Adcock Ingram Critical Care (Pty) Limited (2)
1 New Road, Aeroton, Midrand, 2013, Gauteng, South Africa
Tel.: (27) 116350000
Web Site: https://adcock.co.za
Emp.: 800
Diagnostic Equipment Distr
N.A.I.C.S.: 423450

Adcock Ingram Limited (2)
1 New Road, Midrand, 1685, Gauteng, South Africa
Tel.: (27) 116350000
Sales Range: $250-299.9 Million
Emp.: 600
Pharmaceutical Products Distr
N.A.I.C.S.: 424210
Andrew G. Hall *(CEO)*

Afcom Group Limited (1)
3 Fortune Street City Deep Industrial Park, Johannesburg, 2000, Gauteng, South Africa
Tel.: (27) 116277000
Web Site: http://www.afcom.co.za
Sales Range: $150-199.9 Million
Emp.: 350
Packaging & Fastening Products Mfr & Distr
N.A.I.C.S.: 322220

African Commerce Developing Company (Pty) Limited (1)
Unit 8 Trio Industrial Park 8 Qashana Khuzwayo Road, New Germany, 3620, Kwazulu-Natal, South Africa
Tel.: (27) 317056018
Web Site: http://www.bidvestascom.co.za
Packaging Devices Mfr
N.A.I.C.S.: 333993
Cliff Rostowsky *(Mng Dir)*

Aluminium Foil Converters Proprietary Limited (1)
184 Ohrtmann Rd, Pietermaritzburg, 3201, Kwazulu Natal, South Africa
Tel.: (27) 33 397 9758
Web Site: https://www.foilpackaging.co.za
Foil Converter Mfr
N.A.I.C.S.: 331315

Angliss China Limited (1)
47-51 Kwai Fung Crescent, Kwai Chung, New Territories, China (Hong Kong)
Tel.: (852) 24942159
Web Site: http://www.angliss.com.hk
Sales Range: $50-74.9 Million
Emp.: 100
Bakery Product Distr
N.A.I.C.S.: 424420
Johnny Kang *(Mng Dir)*

Angliss Hong Kong Food Service Limited (1)
47-51 Kwai Fung Crescent, Kwai Chung, New Territories, China (Hong Kong)
Tel.: (852) 24815111
Sales Range: $150-199.9 Million
Emp.: 300
Meat & Groceries Distr
N.A.I.C.S.: 424470

Subsidiary (Non-US):

Angliss Guangzhou Food Service Company Limited (2)
25F Jia Xing Square No 22 Baiyun Road, Guangzhou, China
Tel.: (86) 208 921 9188
Web Site: https://www.angliss.com.cn
Sales Range: $25-49.9 Million
Emp.: 170
Convenience Foods Imports & Distr
N.A.I.C.S.: 424490

Angliss Shanghai Food Service Limited (2)
5F Block B No 4 Building No 1 Hongqiao Headquarters No 100 Zixiu Road, Minhang District, Shanghai, 200235, China
Tel.: (86) 216 073 2060
Web Site: https://www.angliss.com.cn
Sales Range: $25-49.9 Million
Emp.: 50
Frozen Food Distr
N.A.I.C.S.: 424420

Angliss Macau Food Service Limited (1)
52-58 Rua dos Pescadores Edf Industrial Ocean II Fase 4 Andar C & D, Macau, China (Macau)
Tel.: (853) 28862886
Sales Range: $50-74.9 Million
Emp.: 40
Cold Food Storage & Distr
N.A.I.C.S.: 424420
Roger Chan *(Gen Mgr)*

Angliss Singapore Pte Limited (1)
232 Pandan Loop, Singapore, 128420, Singapore
Tel.: (65) 67788787
Meat & Groceries Distr
N.A.I.C.S.: 424410

Aquazania Africa Proprietary Limited (1)
22 2nd Road Linbro Park, Sandton, 2090, South Africa
Tel.: (27) 861278292
Web Site: https://www.aquazania.co.za
Bottled Water Mfr
N.A.I.C.S.: 312112

Autosure Pty. Ltd. (1)
310 HF Verwoerd Drive, Gezina, South Africa
Tel.: (27) 861331111
Web Site: https://www.autosure.co.za
Insurance Brokerage Services
N.A.I.C.S.: 524210

BFS Group Limited (1)
814 Leigh Road, Slough, SL1 4BD, United Kingdom
Tel.: (44) 3703663000
Web Site: https://www.bidfood.co.uk
Sales Range: $100-124.9 Million
Emp.: 170
Catering Supplies Distr

N.A.I.C.S.: 423220
Andy Kemp *(Grp Dir-Sls & Mktg)*

Bellco Electrical (Pty) Limited (1)
362 Victoria Road, Cape Town, 7925, Western Cape, South Africa
Tel.: (27) 214407100
Web Site: http://www.voltex.co.za
Electrical Supplies Whslr
N.A.I.C.S.: 444180
Shawn Roets *(Reg Mgr)*

Berzack Brothers (Jhb) (Pty) Limited (1)
2 Nugget Street, Johannesburg, 2094, Gauteng, South Africa
Tel.: (27) 113347634
Sales Range: $25-49.9 Million
Emp.: 30
Industrial Machinery Whslr
N.A.I.C.S.: 423830

Berzack Brothers (Pty) Limited (1)
11 Sydow Street, Cape Town, 7405, Western Cape, South Africa
Tel.: (27) 215117044
Sales Range: $25-49.9 Million
Emp.: 20
Household Appliances & Supplies Distr
N.A.I.C.S.: 423620
Johann Lourens Jr. *(Gen Mgr)*

Bid Food Ingredients (Pty) Limited (1)
31 Nguni Drive Longmeadow West, Modderfontein, Johannesburg, 2065, Gauteng, South Africa
Tel.: (27) 112019100
Web Site: http://www.bidfood.co.za
Sales Range: $75-99.9 Million
Emp.: 200
Groceries Distr
N.A.I.C.S.: 424410

Subsidiary (Domestic):

Bidfood Technologies (Pty) Limited (2)
31 Nguni Drive Long Meadow West, Edenvale, 2065, Gauteng, South Africa
Tel.: (27) 112019400
Web Site: http://www.bidfoodsolutions.co.za
Bakery Products Mfr
N.A.I.C.S.: 311821
Klaas Havenga *(CEO)*

Bid Information Exchange (Pty) Limited (1)
33 Modulus Road, Johannesburg, 3195, Gauteng, South Africa
Tel.: (27) 116619555
Web Site: http://www.oce.co.za
Sales Range: $25-49.9 Million
Emp.: 43
Printing Machinery Distr
N.A.I.C.S.: 423430
Dave Clark *(Dir-Bus Dev)*

Bid Services Division (UK) Limited (1)
The Deaf Cultural Centre Ladywood Road, Birmingham, B16 8SZ, United Kingdom
Tel.: (44) 1212466100
Web Site: https://www.bid.org.uk
Individual & Family Consulting Services
N.A.I.C.S.: 624190

BidAir Cargo (1)
Unit 9 - Boeing Street, Walmer, Port Elizabeth, 6001, Eastern Cape, South Africa
Tel.: (27) 410301080
Airfreight Sales & Cargo Handling Services
N.A.I.C.S.: 481112
Garry Marshall *(CEO)*

Bidair Services (Pty) Limited (1)
Offices Tamo-02 Terminal A Mezzanine Level OR, Tambo International Airport, Kempton Park, 1627, Gauteng, South Africa
Tel.: (27) 113839420
Web Site: http://www.bidair.co.za
Sales Range: $1-4.9 Billion
Emp.: 3,000
Aviation Support Services
N.A.I.C.S.: 488119
Bushy Mbele *(CEO)*

Bidcorp Limited (1)
3rd Fl 11th Hills St, London, W1J 5IF, United Kingdom

THE BIDVEST GROUP LIMITED

The Bidvest Group Limited—(Continued)
Tel.: (44) 2074934733
Sales Range: $25-49.9 Million
Emp.: 2
Freight Transportation Services
N.A.I.C.S.: 483111
Stephen Koseff (Chm)

Bidfreight Intermodal (Pty) Limited (1)
30 Breeder Road, Durban, 4052, Kwazulu-Natal, South Africa
Tel.: (27) 215104673
Web Site: http://www.bidintermodal.co.za
Sales Range: $25-49.9 Million
Emp.: 20
Freight Forwarding Services
N.A.I.C.S.: 488510
Ash Boodram (Mng Dir)

Bidfreight Management Services (1)
Rennies House 19 Ameshoff St, PO Box 4281, Braamfontein, 2001, South Africa
Tel.: (27) 114072111
Sales Range: $25-49.9 Million
Emp.: 25
Freight Forwarding & Transport, Cargo Services & Marine Services
N.A.I.C.S.: 483111

Bidfreight Port Operations (Pty) Limited (1)
Newark Road Richards Bay Harbour, Richards Bay, 3900, KwaZulu Natal, South Africa
Tel.: (27) 357976260
Web Site: https://www.bidports.co.za
Sales Range: $25-49.9 Million
Emp.: 89
Port Facility Operation Services
N.A.I.C.S.: 488310

Bidfreight Terminals (Pty) Limited (1)
169 Maydon Wharf Road Ground Floor Millwood House, PO Box 4536, Maydon Wharf, Durban, 4000, KwaZulu-Natal, South Africa
Tel.: (27) 312742400
Web Site: http://www.bidvest-divisions.co.za
Terminal Operation Services
N.A.I.C.S.: 488490
Mark Steyn (Dir-Fin)

Bidprocure (Pty) Limited (1)
158 Jan Smuts Avenue 1st Floor, Rosebank, Johannesburg, 2196, Gauteng, South Africa
Tel.: (27) 117317600
Sales Range: $25-49.9 Million
Emp.: 5
Business Consulting Services
N.A.I.C.S.: 541611
Derek Kinnear (Mng Dir)

Bidserv Industrial Products (Pty) Limited (1)
2 Carlisle Str, Paarden Eiland, Cape Town, 7405, South Africa
Tel.: (27) 215141400
Web Site: http://www.gfox.co.za
Sales Range: $200-249.9 Million
Emp.: 300
Industrial Supplies Distr
N.A.I.C.S.: 423450
Wayne Pollak (Mng Dir & Mgr-Johannesburg)

Bidtravel (Pty) Limited (1)
Number 1 Newton Avenue BOE Nedbank building, Killarney, 2196, Gauteng, South Africa
Tel.: (27) 115328000
Web Site: http://www.bidvest-divisions.co.za
Travel Management Services
N.A.I.C.S.: 561510
Colin Mitchley (CFO)

Bidvest (N.S.W) Limited (1)
67 Mandoon Road, Girraween, Sydney, 2145, NSW, Australia
Tel.: (61) 298402200
Web Site: http://www.bidvest.com.au
Sales Range: $550-599.9 Million
Emp.: 2,000
Groceries Distr
N.A.I.C.S.: 424410

Bidvest (UK) Limited (1)
814 Leigh Road, Slough, SL1 4BD, United Kingdom
Tel.: (44) 494555900
Web Site: http://www.bidfood.co.uk
Sales Range: $50-74.9 Million
Emp.: 2
Groceries & Food Service Equipment Retailer
N.A.I.C.S.: 423440

Subsidiary (Domestic):

PHS Group plc (2)
Block B Western Industrial Estate, Caerphilly, CF83 1XH, United Kingdom
Tel.: (44) 292 085 1000
Web Site: https://www.phs.co.uk
Office Supplies Distr
N.A.I.C.S.: 424120
Gareth Rhys Williams (CEO)

Subsidiary (Non-US):

All Water Systems Limited (3)
Unit C1 Merrywell Business Park Ballymount Road Lower, Dublin, Ireland
Tel.: (353) 800 266537
Web Site: http://www.aws.ie
Water Cooler Distr
N.A.I.C.S.: 423740
Kevin O Donovan (Acct Mgr-Field Sls)

Subsidiary (Domestic):

Epsilon Test Services Limited (3)
Epsilon House The Square Gloucester Business Park, Gloucester, GL3 4AD, United Kingdom
Tel.: (44) 8452336600
Electrical Safety Testing Services
N.A.I.C.S.: 541380

PHS All Clear Limited (3)
The Quadrant Marlborough Rd, Lancing Business Park, Lancing, BN15 8UW, United Kingdom
Tel.: (44) 1273876000
Waste Collection & Disposal Services
N.A.I.C.S.: 562119

Division (Domestic):

PHS Besafe Ltd (3)
Unit 16 Coneygree Estate, West Midlands, Tipton, DY4 8XP, United Kingdom
Tel.: (44) 1215211400
Laundry Services
N.A.I.C.S.: 812332
Lynne Vanes (Mng Dir)

Subsidiary (Domestic):

PHS Datashred Ltd (3)
Unit J Acorn Industrial Estate Crayford Road, Kent, Crayford, DA1 4AL, United Kingdom
Tel.: (44) 1322 621900
Document Processing Services
N.A.I.C.S.: 561410
Anthony Pearlgood (Mng Dir)

PHS Direct Ltd (3)
Ansley Hall Drive, Dordon, B78 1SQ, Tamworth, United Kingdom
Tel.: (44) 1827255500
Web Site: https://www.phsdirect.co.uk
Emp.: 3,000
Office Supplies Distr
N.A.I.C.S.: 424120
James Clark (Mng Dir)

PHS Investments Limited (3)
16 Mill Lane, Arlesey, SG15 6RF, Bedfordshire, United Kingdom
Tel.: (44) 2920851000
Holding Company
N.A.I.C.S.: 551112

PHS Laundryserv Ltd. (3)
Blochairn Ind Est 11 Siemens Place, Glasgow, G21 2BN, United Kingdom
Tel.: (44) 141 552 3626
Laundry Equipment Distr
N.A.I.C.S.: 423850
Lynne Vanes (Mng Dir)

PHS Treadsmart Ltd (3)
1 Dutton Rd, Coventry, CV2 2LE, United Kingdom
Tel.: (44) 2476684604
Mat Mfr
N.A.I.C.S.: 326299
Lynne Vanes (Mng Dir)

Division (Domestic):

PHS Wastekit (3)
Unit 6 Alpha Industrial Park Bevan Way, West Midlands, Smethwick, B66 1BZ, United Kingdom
Tel.: (44) 8001693534
Web Site: https://phswastekit.co.uk
Waste Treatment Services
N.A.I.C.S.: 562219

Subsidiary (Domestic):

PHS Wastemanagement Ltd. (3)
Unit 36 Moss Road Kearsley Industrial Estate, Bolton, BL4 8LD, United Kingdom
Tel.: (44) 2920 809090
Web Site: http://www.phswastemanagement.co.uk
Waste Treatment Services
N.A.I.C.S.: 562219
Clare Noble (Mng Dir)

PHS Waterlogic Ltd (3)
Dares Farm Farnham Road, Farnham, GU10 5BB, Surrey, United Kingdom
Tel.: (44) 1252 852260
Water Cooler Distr
N.A.I.C.S.: 423740
David Matthews (Mng Dir)

Teacrate Limited (3)
Phs Teacrate 151 Scrubs Lane, London, NW10 6RH, United Kingdom
Tel.: (44) 8009806996
Web Site: https://www.teacrate.co.uk
Emp.: 30
Crate Rental Services
N.A.I.C.S.: 532289
Patrick Sheehy (Dir-Sls)

Subsidiary (Non-US):

WaterCompany BV (3)
Argon 37, 4751 XC, Oud Gastel, Netherlands
Tel.: (31) 881653000
Web Site: http://www.watercompany.nl
Water Cooler Distr
N.A.I.C.S.: 423740

Subsidiary (Domestic):

Seafood Holdings Ltd (2)
Unit 14-15 Bermondsey Trading Estate Rotherhithe New Road, Camley Street, London, SE16 3LL, United Kingdom
Tel.: (44) 2073581617
Web Site: https://www.directseafoods.co.uk
Sales Range: $125-149.9 Million
Fish & Seafood Distr
N.A.I.C.S.: 424460
Brian Hall (Mng Dir)

Division (Domestic):

Daily Fish Supplies (3)
Unit 10-14 Cedar Way, Industrial Estate, London, N1C 4PD, United Kingdom
Tel.: (44) 2073833771
Fish Supplier
N.A.I.C.S.: 424460

Direct Seafoods Colchester (3)
Crown Court Severalls Business Park Clough Road, Colchester, CO4 9TZ, Essex, United Kingdom
Tel.: (44) 1206752075
Fish Supplier
N.A.I.C.S.: 424460

Direct Seafoods London (3)
Unit 14-15 Bermondsey Trading Estate Rotherhithe New Road, London, SE16 3LL, United Kingdom
Tel.: (44) 2073581617
Fish Supplier
N.A.I.C.S.: 424460
Laky Zervudachi (Dir-Sustainability & Epicurian)

Kingfisher Brixham (3)
Unit 4-5 Torbay Business Park Woodview Rd, Paignton, TQ4 7HP, Devon, United Kingdom
Tel.: (44) 1803553232
Fish Supplier
N.A.I.C.S.: 424460

Neve Fleetwood (3)
19 Copse Road, Fleetwood, FY7 6RP, Lancashire, United Kingdom
Tel.: (44) 1253774100
Sales Range: $25-49.9 Million
Emp.: 50
Fish Supplier
N.A.I.C.S.: 424460

Southbank Fresh Fish (3)
Unit 14-15 Bermondsey Trading Estate Rotherhithe New Road, Southwark, London, SE16 3LL, United Kingdom
Tel.: (44) 2076396000
Web Site: http://www.southbankfreshfish.co.uk
Emp.: 50
Fish Supplier
N.A.I.C.S.: 424460
Andrew Wilson (Owner)

Taylor's of Newcastle (3)
19a Elm Rd West Chirton, North Industrial Estate, North Shields, NE29 8SE, United Kingdom
Tel.: (44) 1912582957
Web Site: https://www.taylorfoods.co.uk
Sales Range: $25-49.9 Million
Emp.: 35
Fish Supplier
N.A.I.C.S.: 424460
Darren Leason (Owner)

Bidvest (Victoria) (Pty) Limited (1)
20 Thackray Road, Clayton, Port Melbourne, 3207, VIC, Australia
Tel.: (61) 391928666
Web Site: https://www.bidfood.com.au
Groceries Distr
N.A.I.C.S.: 424410

Bidvest (WA) (Pty) Limited (1)
71 Cocos Drive, Bibra Lake, Perth, 6163, WA, Australia
Tel.: (61) 894348800
Sales Range: $75-99.9 Million
Emp.: 200
Groceries Distr
N.A.I.C.S.: 424410
David Houston (Gen Mgr)

Bidvest Advisory Services Proprietary Limited (1)
Melrose Arch, Johannesburg, South Africa
Tel.: (27) 117728700
Web Site: https://www.bidvestalice.com
Automation Services
N.A.I.C.S.: 541512

Bidvest Afcom Proprietary Limited (1)
12 Renaissance Dr Crown City, Johannesburg, 2092, South Africa
Tel.: (27) 116277000
Web Site: https://www.bidvestafcom.co.za
Electrical Equipment Mfr & Distr
N.A.I.C.S.: 335999

Bidvest Australia Limited (1)
Level 1 31-35 Bank Street, Pyrmont, 2009, NSW, Australia
Tel.: (61) 295718666
Web Site: http://www.bidvest.com.au
Emp.: 100
Catering Supplies Distr
N.A.I.C.S.: 423220
Karenza Poynter (Gen Mgr-Adelaide)

Division (Domestic):

Bidvest Foodservice Geelong (2)
29-39 Enterprise Drive, Corio, Geelong, 3214, VIC, Australia
Tel.: (61) 352408111
Web Site: http://www.bidvest.com.au
Emp.: 50
Groceries Distr
N.A.I.C.S.: 424410

Bidvest Bank Holdings Limited (1)
1 Park Lane Wierda Valley, Sandton, 2196, South Africa
Tel.: (27) 860111177
Web Site: https://www.bidvestbank.co.za
Banking Services
N.A.I.C.S.: 523150
A. M. Mazwai (Chm)

Bidvest Bank Limited (1)
1 Park Lane, PO Box 185, Wierda Valley, Sandton, 2196, Gauteng, South Africa
Tel.: (27) 114073000

AND PRIVATE COMPANIES — THE BIDVEST GROUP LIMITED

Commercial Banking Services
N.A.I.C.S.: 522110

Bidvest Branded Products Holdings Proprietary Limited (1)
Office B03GO02 Ground Floor 20 Georgian Crescent, Charlton House Hampton Office Park, Bryanston, 2021, Gauteng, South Africa
Tel.: (27) 114635583
Office Stationery Distr
N.A.I.C.S.: 459410
Allen Kotze (CFO)

Bidvest Buffalo Tapes Proprietary Limited (1)
44 Forge Road, Spartan Kempton Park, Johannesburg, 1619, South Africa
Tel.: (27) 112812600
Web Site: https://www.buffalotapes.co.za
Emp.: 100
Dynamic Tape Mfr
N.A.I.C.S.: 325520

Bidvest Capital (Pty) Limited (1)
9th Floor 19 Ameshoff Street, Braamfontein, Johannesburg, 2001, Gauteng, South Africa
Tel.: (27) 11 570 7299
Web Site: http://www.bidvestcapital.co.za
Automobile Leasing Services
N.A.I.C.S.: 532112

Bidvest Catering Services Proprietary Limited (1)
357 Jan Smuts Ave Craighall Park, Randburg, 2196, South Africa
Tel.: (27) 101421230
Web Site: https://www.bidvestcatering.co.za
Food & Beverage Services
N.A.I.C.S.: 722310

Bidvest Commercial Products Holdings Proprietary Limited (1)
Block C First Floor - Freestone Office Park 135 Patricia Road, Sandown, Sandton, South Africa
Tel.: (27) 116277001
Electrical Product Mfr & Distr
N.A.I.C.S.: 336320
Craig Turnbull (Fin Dir)

Bidvest Czech Republic s.r.o. (1)
V Ruzovem Udoli 553, Mikovice, 278 01, Kralupy nad Vltavou, Czech Republic
Tel.: (420) 315706111
Sales Range: $650-699.9 Million
Emp.: 1,500
Frozen & Fresh Food Products Distr
N.A.I.C.S.: 424420
Jan Valecka (Dir-Sls)

Subsidiary (Non-US):

Nowaco Slovakia s.r.o. (2)
Piestanska 2321/71, 915 01, Nove Mesto nad Vahom, Slovakia
Tel.: (421) 327742811
Web Site: https://www.nowaco.sk
Frozen & Fresh Food Products Distr
N.A.I.C.S.: 424420

Bidvest Data (1)
Sibanye Park Boston Circle Airport Industria 1 Matroosfontein, Cape Town, 7490, Western Cape, South Africa
Tel.: (27) 219353300
Emp.: 500
Bulk Mail Processing & Email Services
N.A.I.C.S.: 561431

Bidvest Data (1)
Block B Stoneridge Office Park 8 Greenstone Pl Modderfontein, Edenvale, 1644, Gauteng, South Africa
Tel.: (27) 112676444
Sales Range: $25-49.9 Million
Emp.: 100
Bulk Mail Processing Services
N.A.I.C.S.: 513199
Pieter Strydo (Mng Dir)

Bidvest Facilities Management Proprietary Limited (1)
Meersig Building 269 West Avenue, Centurion, 0157, South Africa
Tel.: (27) 126418000
Web site:
https://www.bidvestfacilitiesmanage.co.za
Facility Services
N.A.I.C.S.: 561210

David Leslie (CEO)

Bidvest Foodservice International Limited (1)
60 Saturn Crescent Linbro Office Park, PO Box 1344, Johannesburg, 2000, Gauteng, South Africa
Tel.: (27) 115539600
Web Site:
http://www.bidvestfoodservice.co.za
Sales Range: $750-799.9 Million
Emp.: 2,000
Groceries Distr
N.A.I.C.S.: 424420
Brent Varcoe (Mng Dir)

Bidvest Insurance Limited (1)
2nd Floor Lincoln on the Lake 2 The High Street, Umhlanga Ridge, Durban, 4319, South Africa
Tel.: (27) 861668888
Web Site:
https://www.bidvestinsurance.co.za
Insurance Services
N.A.I.C.S.: 524210
Phillip Donnelly (Mng Dir)

Bidvest International Limited (1)
Murdoch Chambers Head Road, South Quay, Douglas, IM1 5AS, Isle of Man
Tel.: (44) 1624611225
Groceries Distr
N.A.I.C.S.: 424410

Bidvest Magnum Group Pty Ltd (1)
16 Southway Road Carlon Falco Office Park Block A-B, Kelvin, 2054, Gauteng, South Africa
Tel.: (27) 11 555 4949
Web Site: http://www.bidvestmagnum.co.za
Emp.: 40
Integrated Security Services
N.A.I.C.S.: 561612
Madie Leonard (Reg Dir)

Division (Domestic):

Bidvest Magnum Group Pty Ltd (2)
248 Cowan Ntuli Street, Middleburg, Mpumalanga, 1055, South Africa
Tel.: (27) 132430289
Web Site: http://www.provicom.co.za
Sales Range: $25-49.9 Million
Emp.: 8
Risk Managemeng Srvices
N.A.I.C.S.: 541611

Bidvest Materials Handling Proprietary Limited (1)
Unit A-2 53 Maple Street, Pomona Kempton Park, Johannesburg, 1619, South Africa
Tel.: (27) 108221877
Web Site: https://www.bidvestforklifts.co.za
Material Handling Equipment Distr
N.A.I.C.S.: 423830
Pieter Fourie (Mng Dir)

Bidvest McCarthy Brands Proprietary Limited (1)
Postnet Suite 59, Private Bag x11, Burnampark, 2015, Gauteng, South Africa
Tel.: (27) 860223344
Web Site: https://www.mccarthy.co.za
Motor Vehicle Retailing Services
N.A.I.C.S.: 441227
Steve Keys (CEO)

Bidvest Merchant Services Proprietary Limited (1)
1 Park Lane Wierda Valley, Sandton, 2196, South Africa
Tel.: (27) 860111441
Web Site: https://www.bms.co.za
Merchant Services
N.A.I.C.S.: 522320

Bidvest Namibia Commercial & Industrial Services & Products Proprietary Limited (1)
1 Ballot Street, Windhoek, Namibia
Tel.: (264) 61417450
Web Site:
https://www.bidvestnamibia.com.na
Investment Services
N.A.I.C.S.: 523150

Bidvest Namibia Limited (1)
1 Ballot Street, Windhoek, Namibia
Tel.: (264) 61417450
Web Site: http://www.bidvestnamibia.com.na

Sales Range: $200-249.9 Million
Emp.: 3,203
Investment Management Service
N.A.I.C.S.: 523940
Sebulon Inotila Kankondi (CEO)

Bidvest New Zealand Limited (1)
Tel.: (64) 9 430 4925
Web Site: https://www.bidfood.co.nz
Sales Range: $350-399.9 Million
Emp.: 600
Catering Supplies Distr
N.A.I.C.S.: 424130
Simon Hunt (Mgr)

Bidvest Noonan (ROI) Limited (1)
Hilton House Unit 3 Swords Business Park, Co Dublin, Swords, K67 X971, Ireland
Tel.: (353) 18839800
Web Site: https://www.bidvestnoonan.com
Facility Services
N.A.I.C.S.: 561210
Jim O'Hagan (Mng Dir-Northern Ireland)

Bidvest Noonan (UK) Limited (1)
Beaufort House 15 St Botolph Street Aldgate, London, EC3A 7BB, United Kingdom
Tel.: (44) 2033191750
Facility Services
N.A.I.C.S.: 561210
Cormac Sheils (COO)

Bidvest Noonan (UK) Ltd. (1)
Hilton House Unit 3, Swords Business Park, Swords, K67 X971, Dublin, Ireland
Tel.: (353) 1 883 9800
Web Site: https://www.bidvestnoonan.com
Building Support Services
N.A.I.C.S.: 561720
Peter Smyth (Mgr-Comml)

Bidvest Prestige Group (1)
22 Gerhardus Street, Strijdompark, Randburg, 2194, South Africa
Tel.: (27) 11 796 0000
Web Site: http://www.bidvestprestige.co.za
Sales Range: $25-49.9 Million
Emp.: 103
Contract Cleaning Services
N.A.I.C.S.: 561720
Jegie Padmanathan (CEO)

Bidvest Protea Coin Proprietary Limited (1)
1004 Teak Close Corner Teak Close & Witch-Hazel Ave, Centurion, South Africa
Tel.: (27) 126658000
Web Site: https://www.proteacoin.co.za
Investigation Services
N.A.I.C.S.: 561611
Costa Diavastos (CEO)

Bidvest Services (1)
Building 3 Tuscany Office Park Coombe Place, Rivonia, 2128, Gauteng, South Africa
Tel.: (27) 115198430
Web Site: https://www.bidvest.co.za
Sales Range: $25-49.9 Million
Emp.: 17
Outsourced Corporate Services
N.A.I.C.S.: 561499
Bina Gosai (CFO)

Bidvest Steiner Namibia Pty. Ltd. (1)
No 69 Lazarett Street Southern Industrial, Windhoek, Namibia
Tel.: (264) 61262160
Web Site: https://www.steiner.com.na
Cleaning Product Mfr & Distr
N.A.I.C.S.: 325611

Bidvest Tank Terminals (1)
142 Wharfside Road Island View, Durban, 4001, South Africa
Tel.: (27) 31 466 9000
Web Site: https://www.bidtanks.com
Emp.: 400
Bulk Liquid Storage Provider
N.A.I.C.S.: 493110

Bidvest Wits University Football Club (Pty) Limited (1)
Sturrock Park Raikes Road Wits University Sports Admin West Campus, PO Box 136, Braamfontein, Johannesburg, 2196, Gauteng, South Africa
Tel.: (27) 113391112
Web Site: http://www.bidvestwits.co.za
Sales Range: $50-74.9 Million
Emp.: 40
Football Club Management Services

N.A.I.C.S.: 711211
Jack Ndlovu (Mgr-Kit)

Blesston Printing and Associates (Pty) Limited (1)
280 Granville Avenue, Roodepoort, Johannesburg, 1709, Gauteng, South Africa
Tel.: (27) 114723330
Web Site: http://www.lithotech.com
Sales Range: $25-49.9 Million
Emp.: 70
Commercial Printing Services
N.A.I.C.S.: 323111
Bryan Backhouse (Mng Dir)

Bloch & Levitan (Pty) Limited (1)
Unit 10 City Deep Mini Park cnr Heidelberg and Outspan Roads, City Deep, Johannesburg, 2001, Gauteng, South Africa
Tel.: (27) 11 623 1941
Web Site: https://www.berzacks.co.za
Sales Range: $50-74.9 Million
Emp.: 128
Plumbing & Upholstery Materials Distr
N.A.I.C.S.: 423720
Johan Laurance (Mng Dir)

Buffalo Executape (Pty) Limited (1)
44 Forge Road Spartan, Kempton Park, Johannesburg, 1619, Gauteng, South Africa
Tel.: (27) 112812600
Web Site:
http://www.buffaloexecutape.co.za
Sales Range: $50-74.9 Million
Emp.: 80
Adhesive Tape Distr
N.A.I.C.S.: 424120
Lora Christie (Dir-HR)

Bulk Connections (Pty) Limited (1)
Java Road Island View, Bluff, Durban, 4036, Kwazulu-Natal, South Africa
Tel.: (27) 314669600
Web Site: https://www.bulkconnections.com
Sales Range: $50-74.9 Million
Emp.: 160
Terminal Operation Services
N.A.I.C.S.: 488490
Nonhlanhla Shange (Dir-Comml)

Burleigh Marr Distributions (Pty) Limited (1)
347 Lytton Road, Morningside, Brisbane, 4170, QLD, Australia
Tel.: (61) 738991999
Web Site: http://www.findfoodfast.com.au
Groceries Distr
N.A.I.C.S.: 424410
Silly Moody (Gen Mgr)

Bushbreaks & More Proprietary Limited (1)
2nd Floor The Travel Campus 26 Girton Road, Parktown, Johannesburg, 2193, South Africa
Tel.: (27) 861004455
Web Site: https://www.bushbreaks.co.za
Tour Operator
N.A.I.C.S.: 561520

CCW Catering Supplies (Pty) Limited (1)
21 Du Toit Viljoen Rd, Pietermaritzburg, 3201, Kwazulu Natal, South Africa
Tel.: (27) 333454505
Sales Range: $50-74.9 Million
Emp.: 65
Groceries Distr
N.A.I.C.S.: 424410
Nick Yeats (Gen Mgr)

Cannon Asset Managers Proprietary Limited (1)
5 Jellicoe Avenue, Rosebank, Johannesburg, 2196, South Africa
Tel.: (27) 11 243 4900
Web Site: https://www.cannonassets.co.za
Insurance Services
N.A.I.C.S.: 524210
J. J. van Niekerk (Chm)

Caterplus (Botswana) (Pty) Limited (1)
Plot 20594 Block 3, Gaborone, Botswana
Tel.: (267) 3924284
Web Site: http://www.caterplus.co.bw
Sales Range: $50-74.9 Million
Emp.: 53
Groceries Distr

THE BIDVEST GROUP LIMITED

The Bidvest Group Limited—(Continued)
N.A.I.C.S.: 424410
Bonolo Champane (Gen Mgr)

Caterplus Namibia (Pty) Limited (1)
4-6 Newcastle Street Northern Industria, PO Box 11496, Windhoek, Namibia
Tel.: (264) 61258313
Sales Range: $50-74.9 Million
Emp.: 80
Seafood Distr
N.A.I.C.S.: 424460

Catersales (Pty) Limited
463 Taljaard St, Hermanstad, Pretoria, 0082, Gauteng, South Africa
Tel.: (27) 123770158
Web Site: http://www.catersales.co.za
Sales Range: $50-74.9 Million
Emp.: 84
Groceries Distr
N.A.I.C.S.: 424410
Stephan Coetzee (Mgr-Sls)

Cecil Nurse (Pty) Limited (1)
1 Makro Place, Sunnyrock, Germiston, 1401, Gauteng, South Africa
Tel.: (27) 113451500
Sales Range: $125-149.9 Million
Emp.: 300
Office Furniture Mfr & Distr
N.A.I.C.S.: 337214

Chipkins Bakery Supplies (Pty) Limited (1)
279 Inanda Road Spring Field Park, Durban, 4000, KwaZulu-Natal, South Africa
Tel.: (27) 315747400
Web Site: http://www.chipbake.co.za
Sales Range: $50-74.9 Million
Emp.: 200
Bakery Products Mfr & Distr
N.A.I.C.S.: 311999
Marc Warner (Gen Mgr)

Chipkins Catering Supplies (Pty) Limited (1)
30 Paisley Road, Jacobs, Durban, 4052, Kwazulu-Natal, South Africa
Tel.: (27) 314612222
Web Site: http://www.bidvestfoodservicemt.co.za
Sales Range: $75-99.9 Million
Emp.: 300
Catering Supplies Distr
N.A.I.C.S.: 423440
Craig Rawbone (Gen Mgr)

ClickOn Communications Proprietary Limited (1)
Greenhill Village Office Park Acacia House, Cnr Nentabos & Botterklapper Streets Die Wilgers, Pretoria, 0184, South Africa
Tel.: (27) 128036783
Web Site: https://www.clickon.co.za
Residential Access Control System Services
N.A.I.C.S.: 561621

Commuter Handling Services (Pty) Limited (1)
ACSA Park One Tambo International Airport, Boksburg, 1627, Gauteng, South Africa
Tel.: (27) 11 397 6555
Web Site: http://www.bidvest.com
Aviation Support Services
N.A.I.C.S.: 488119

Concorde Travel (Pty) Limited (1)
2nd Floor 26 Girton Road, Parktown, 2193, South Africa
Tel.: (27) 116282300
Web Site: http://www.mycwt.com
Sales Range: $75-99.9 Million
Emp.: 260
Travel Management Services
N.A.I.C.S.: 561510

Contract Office Products (Pty) Limited (1)
Whartons Spencer Ofc Pk Croxley Close Heriotdale Ext 15 Germiston, PO BOX 6426, Johannesburg, 2000, Gauteng, South Africa
Tel.: (27) 113345424
Web Site: http://www.bidvest.com
Sales Range: $50-74.9 Million
Emp.: 75

Stationery Products & Computer Consumables Whslr & Distr
N.A.I.C.S.: 423430

Crown National (Pty) Limited (1)
31 Nguni Drive Longmeadow West, Modderfontein, Johannesburg, 2065, Gauteng, South Africa
Tel.: (27) 11 201 9000
Web Site: https://www.crownnational.co.za
Sales Range: $250-299.9 Million
Emp.: 600
Catering Supplies Distr
N.A.I.C.S.: 424490

Cruises International SA Proprietary Limited (1)
26 Girton Road The Travel Campus 1st Floor, Parktown, Johannesburg, 2193, South Africa
Tel.: (27) 113270327
Web Site: https://www.cruises.co.za
Cruise Reservation Services
N.A.I.C.S.: 561599

D & R Lowe Catering Supplies (Pty) Limited (1)
No 17 Eastern Service Rd Eastgate Extension 8, Sandton, Johannesburg, 2012, Gauteng, South Africa
Tel.: (27) 118043663
Web Site: http://www.drlowe.co.za
Emp.: 55
Groceries Distr
N.A.I.C.S.: 424410
Fanie Uys (Mgr-Ops)

Deli XL Belgie NV (1)
Avenue Deli XL 1, 6530, Thuin, Hainaut, Belgium
Tel.: (32) 71919725
Web Site: https://www.bidfood.be
Sales Range: $100-124.9 Million
Emp.: 351
Convenience Food Distr
N.A.I.C.S.: 445110
Thierry Legat (CEO & Mng Dir)

Ditulo Office (Pty) Limited (1)
The Office of Hyde Park Strouthos Place 2nd Road Block B 1st Floor, Johannesburg, 2093, Gauteng, South Africa
Tel.: (27) 115379860
Web Site: http://www.ditulo.co.za
Emp.: 5
Office Furniture Retailer
N.A.I.C.S.: 449110
Isla Galloway-Gaul (Gen Mgr)

Durban Coal Terminals Company Pty. Ltd. (1)
Java Road Island View, PO Box 21273, Bluff, Durban, 4036, KwaZulu Natal, South Africa
Tel.: (27) 314669600
Dry Bulk Transportation Services
N.A.I.C.S.: 484230

EMS Invirotel Energy Management Proprietary Limited (1)
1 Voyager Street, Linbro Business Park, Sandton, South Africa
Tel.: (27) 11 100 3070
Web Site: https://www.invirohub.com
Electric Power Services
N.A.I.C.S.: 221118

Eagle Lighting George Proprietary Limited (1)
Corner Knysna and Mission Roads, George, South Africa
Tel.: (27) 44 050 0177
Electrical Product Mfr & Distr
N.A.I.C.S.: 336320
Alina Gildenhuys (Mgr)

Email Connection (Pty) Limited (1)
25 Scott Street, Waverley, Johannesburg, 2090, Gauteng, South Africa
Tel.: (27) 117863116
Web Site: http://www.emc.co.za
Sales Range: $25-49.9 Million
Emp.: 25
Bulk Email Processing Services
N.A.I.C.S.: 561439

Execuflora Proprietary Limited (1)
Plot 111 Old Pretoria Rd R114 Suite 120, Private Bag X7, Nietgedacht, Northriding, 2162, Gauteng, South Africa

Tel.: (27) 110259933
Web Site: https://www.execuflora.co.za
Consumer Services
N.A.I.C.S.: 621498

Express Air Services (Namibia) (Pty) Limited (1)
Robert Mugabe Avenue 55 Eros, PO Box 98500, Windhoek, Namibia
Tel.: (264) 61252493
Sales Range: $25-49.9 Million
Emp.: 1
Freight Forwarding Services
N.A.I.C.S.: 488510
Marco Vanwyk (Office Mgr)

Farutex Sp.z.o.o. (1)
street Niciarniana 49 D, 92-320, Lodz, West Pomeranian, Poland
Tel.: (48) 426489700
Web Site: https://www.bidfood.pl
Meat & Groceries Distr
N.A.I.C.S.: 424470
Jaroslaw Rucinski (Co-Founder)

First Food Distributors (Pty) Limited (1)
Bahrain Drive and Borchards Quarry Road, Airport Industria, Cape Town, 7525, Western Cape, South Africa
Tel.: (27) 219279100
Web Site: http://www.firstfoods.co.za
Emp.: 350
Groceries Distr
N.A.I.C.S.: 424410
Jannes Kies (Mgr-Sls)

Freightbulk (Pty) Limited (1)
Rennie House, PO Box 2590, Durban, 4000, KwaZulu-Natal, South Africa
Tel.: (27) 313280404
Sales Range: $25-49.9 Million
Emp.: 50
Marine Cargo Handling Services
N.A.I.C.S.: 488320

G Fox Swaziland Proprietary Limited (1)
11th Str Matsapha Industrial Site, Matsapha, Eswatini
Tel.: (268) 25186396
Web Site: https://gfox.co.za
Electrical Product Mfr & Distr
N.A.I.C.S.: 336320

Genesis Insurance Brokers (KZN) Proprietary Limited (1)
41 Waterford Office Park Waterford Drive, Fourways, South Africa
Tel.: (27) 11 789 7845
Web Site: https://www.genesisinsurance.co.za
Insurance Services
N.A.I.C.S.: 524210

Global Payment Technologies Proprietary Limited (1)
8 Saturn Crescent Linbro Park, Frankenwald, Sandton, 2065, South Africa
Tel.: (27) 11 997 6600
Web Site: https://www.gpt.co.za
Office Equipment Distr
N.A.I.C.S.: 459410
Danie Le Roux (CEO)

Home of Living Brands Group Limited (1)
Pineslopes Shopping Centre Cnr The Straight and Witkoppen Road, Fourways, Johannesburg, South Africa
Tel.: (27) 872450029
Web Site: https://www.homeoflivingbrands.com
Household Appliance Whslr
N.A.I.C.S.: 423620

Home of Living Brands Holdings Limited (1)
Pineslopes Shopping Centre Cnr The Straight and Witkoppen Road, Fourways, Johannesburg, 2194, South Africa
Tel.: (27) 87 245 0029
Web Site: https://homeoflivingbrands.com
Sales Range: $125-149.9 Million
Emp.: 356
Home Appliance Mfr & Distr
N.A.I.C.S.: 335210
Bruce Drummond (CFO)

Horeca Trade LLC (1)

INTERNATIONAL PUBLIC

Dubai Investment Park 2 - Plot no 597-974, PO Box 73021, Dubai, 73021, United Arab Emirates
Tel.: (971) 48052000
Web Site: https://bidfoodme.com
Sales Range: $100-124.9 Million
Emp.: 160
Catering Supplies Distr
N.A.I.C.S.: 424460

Hortors Stationery (Pty) Limited (1)
Entrance 3 Pencil Park Croxley Close, Heriotdale Extension 15, Johannesburg, 2094, Gauteng, South Africa
Tel.: (27) 116204800
Web Site: http://www.hortors.co.za
Emp.: 18
Stationery Product Retailer
N.A.I.C.S.: 459410

Hotel Amenities Suppliers Proprietary Limited (1)
12 Skietlood Street, PO Box 3060, Isando, Kempton Park, 1600, Gauteng, South Africa
Tel.: (27) 119744311
Web Site: https://www.has.co.za
Hotel Services
N.A.I.C.S.: 721110

King Pie Holdings Proprietary Limited (1)
Eastside Corporate Close 807 Richards Drive, Midrand, 1685, Gauteng, South Africa
Tel.: (27) 115649701
Web Site: https://www.kirigpie.co.za
Food & Beverage Services
N.A.I.C.S.: 722310

Kolok (Namibia) (Pty) Limited (1)
40 Nickel Street Prosperita, PO Box 40797, Windhoek, Namibia
Tel.: (264) 61370500
Web Site: http://www.kolok.co.za
Sales Range: $25-49.9 Million
Emp.: 21
Computer Peripheral Equipment Distr
N.A.I.C.S.: 423430
Stanley Turter (Mgr-Warehouse)

Kolok (Pty) Limited (1)
Unit D and E Hilton Industrial Park Cnr Exton Road and Gruis Street, Private Bag X01, Hilton Postnet Suite 123, Bloemfontein, 9324, Free State, South Africa
Tel.: (27) 514331876
Web Site: https://www.koloksa.co.za
Computer Peripheral Equipment Distr
N.A.I.C.S.: 423430
Allan Thompson (Mng Dir)

Kolok Africa (Pty) Limited (1)
31 Gold Reef Road Ormonde Ext 32 2091, PO Box 4151, Johannesburg, 2000, Gauteng, South Africa
Tel.: (27) 11 248 0300
Web Site: https://www.koloksa.co.za
Sales Range: $25-49.9 Million
Emp.: 37
Computer Peripheral Equipment Distr
N.A.I.C.S.: 423430

Lithotech Afric Mail Pinetown (Pty) Limited (1)
48 Gillitts Road, Pinetown, Durban, 3610, Kwazulu-Natal, South Africa
Tel.: (27) 317927000
Bulk Mail Processing Services
N.A.I.C.S.: 492110

Lithotech Group Services (Pty) Limited (1)
Bosors Circle Epping 2, Cape Town, 7460, Western Cape, South Africa
Tel.: (27) 215074100
Web Site: https://www.lithotech.co.za
Sales Range: $125-149.9 Million
Emp.: 300
Business Forms Printing Services
N.A.I.C.S.: 323111

Lithotech Labels (Pty) Limited (1)
Cnr Shaft Street and Reduktor Avenue Stormill X3, Roodepoort, 1709, South Africa
Tel.: (27) 11 474 1828
Web Site: https://www.lithotech.co.za
Sales Range: $50-74.9 Million
Emp.: 162
Commercial Lithographic Printing Services
N.A.I.C.S.: 323111

AND PRIVATE COMPANIES — THE BIDVEST GROUP LIMITED

Wicus Maritz *(Mng Dir)*

Lithotech Manufacturing Cape (Pty) Limited (1)
Bofors Circle Epping 2, Cape Town, 8001, Western Cape, South Africa
Tel.: (27) 215074226
Sales Range: $125-149.9 Million
Emp.: 300
Business Forms Printing Services
N.A.I.C.S.: 323111
Grant McWilliams *(Mng Dir)*

Lithotech Manufacturing Pinetown (Pty) Limited (1)
Tel.: (27) 317002577
Sales Range: $50-74.9 Million
Emp.: 250
Business Forms Printing Services
N.A.I.C.S.: 323111
Bob Allan-Reynolds *(Mng Dir)*

Lithotech Print On Demand Pty. Ltd. (1)
23B Junction Road Unit 456 Dundee Park, Tygerberg Business Park, Cape Town, 7493, Western Cape, South Africa
Tel.: (27) 219511400
Web Site: http://www.lithotechafricmail.co.za
Sales Range: $25-49.9 Million
Emp.: 50
Commercial Printer Services
N.A.I.C.S.: 323111

Lithotech Sales Bloemfontein (Pty) Limited (1)
Tel.: (27) 51 447 7966
Web Site: https://www.lithotech.co.za
Sales Range: $25-49.9 Million
Emp.: 23
Commercial Printing Services
N.A.I.C.S.: 323111
W. P. Wiid *(Gen Mgr)*

Lithotech Sales Cape (Pty) Limited (1)
Tel.: (27) 215074100
Web Site: https://www.lithotech.co.za
Sales Range: $50-74.9 Million
Emp.: 200
Business Forms Printing Services
N.A.I.C.S.: 323111
Alastair Gordon-Forbes *(Mng Dir)*

Lithotech Sales East London (Pty) Limited (1)
Settlers Warehouse 3 Settlers Way, Gately, East London, 5201, Eastern Cape, South Africa
Tel.: (27) 43 731 1605
Web Site: http://www.lithotechsales.co.za
Sales Range: $25-49.9 Million
Emp.: 22
Notebooks & Paper Retailer
N.A.I.C.S.: 424120
Brian Vanderberg *(Mng Dir)*

Lithotech Sales KwaZulu-Natal (Pty) Limited (1)
Tel.: (27) 31 700 2577
Web Site: https://www.lithotech.co.za
Sales Range: $25-49.9 Million
Emp.: 30
Commercial Printing Services
N.A.I.C.S.: 323111
Tina Hinchliffe *(Branch Mgr)*

Lithotech Sales Port Elizabeth (Pty) Limited (1)
48 York Road North End, Port Elizabeth, 6001, Eastern Cape, South Africa
Tel.: (27) 41 373 3889
Web Site: https://www.lithotech.co.za
Sales Range: $25-49.9 Million
Emp.: 32
Commercial Printing Services
N.A.I.C.S.: 323111
Brian van den Berg *(Mng Dir)*

Lithotech Sales Pretoria (Pty) Limited (1)
74 Ketjen Street, Pretoria West, Pretoria, 0813, Gauteng, South Africa
Tel.: (27) 12 327 3239
Web Site: https://lithotech.co.za
Sales Range: $25-49.9 Million
Emp.: 40
Business Forms Printing Services
N.A.I.C.S.: 323111

Lithotech Solutions (Pty) Limited (1)
Bofors Circle Epping 2, Cape Town, 7405, Western Cape, South Africa
Tel.: (27) 117066751
Sales Range: $25-49.9 Million
Emp.: 10
Labeling Software Development Services
N.A.I.C.S.: 541511

Lou's Wholesalers (Pty) Limited (1)
68 Whitworth Road, Heriotdale, Johannesburg, 2000, Gauteng, South Africa
Tel.: (27) 114792600
Web Site: http://www.lous.co.za
Emp.: 150
Groceries Distr
N.A.I.C.S.: 424410
David Sayer *(Mgr-Sls)*

Luderitz Bay Shipping & Forwarding Proprietary Limited (1)
Corner of Hafen Str and Banhof Str, Luderitz, Namibia
Tel.: (264) 63207000
Web Site: https://www.lbsf.com.na
Marine Logistics Services
N.A.I.C.S.: 488390

M & M / D & R Lowe (1)
17 Eastern Service Road Tripark Block C Eastgate Ext 8, Sandton, Johannesburg, South Africa
Tel.: (27) 11 804 3663
Web Site: http://www.bidfood.co.za
Groceries Distr
N.A.I.C.S.: 424410
Bradley Singer *(Sls Mgr)*

Macardo Lodge (Pty) Limited (1)
Dennis Todd Office Park Plot 50361 Fairground, PO Box 2482, Gaborone, 2482, Botswana
Tel.: (267) 3903244
Web Site: http://www.travelwise.co.bw
Sales Range: $10-24.9 Million
Emp.: 30
Travel Management Services
N.A.I.C.S.: 561510
Fred MacDonald *(CEO & Mng Dir)*

Manica (Zambia) Limited (1)
Plot 840 Nyerere Road, Kitwe, 10101, Copperbelt, Zambia
Tel.: (260) 211273486
Freight Transportation Services
N.A.I.C.S.: 483111

Manica Africa (Pty) Limited (1)
Pencil Park Croxley Close, Heriotdale, Johannesburg, 2000, Gauteng, South Africa
Tel.: (27) 114175500
Web Site: http://www.manica-africa.com
Sales Range: $25-49.9 Million
Emp.: 65
Freight Management Services
N.A.I.C.S.: 488510

Subsidiary (Non-US):

Manica Zimbabwe Limited (2)
91 Coventry Road Workington, Harare, 990, Zimbabwe
Tel.: (263) 4 661 524
Web Site: http://www.manica-africa.com
Sales Range: $50-74.9 Million
Emp.: 100
Freight Forwarding Services
N.A.I.C.S.: 488510
Paul Mudiwa *(Dir-Fin)*

Manica Group Namibia (Pty) Limited (1)
2 Third Str, PO Box 4, Walvis Bay, Namibia
Tel.: (264) 642012911
Web Site: https://www.manica.com.na
Sales Range: $50-74.9 Million
Emp.: 760
Logistics & Warehousing Services
N.A.I.C.S.: 493110
Sean Holmes *(Dir-Financial)*

Master Currency (Pty) Limited (1)
No 33 Hammer Schlagway 6th Floor Foreshore, Cape Town, 8001, Western Cape, South Africa
Tel.: (27) 214317700
Web Site: http://www.mastercurrency.co.za
Sales Range: $50-74.9 Million
Emp.: 60
Foreign Currency Exchange Services

N.A.I.C.S.: 523160
Byron Corcoran *(CEO)*

Masterguard Fabric Protection Africa (Pty) Limited (1)
12 Skietlood Street, Isando, Kempton Park, 1600, Gauteng, South Africa
Tel.: (27) 113924411
Sales Range: $25-49.9 Million
Emp.: 5
Housekeeping Services
N.A.I.C.S.: 561720
Clive Bedell *(Gen Mgr)*

McCarthy Limited (1)
Block A Glen Gables Lynnwood Rd & Gen Louis Botha Ave, Pretoria, South Africa
Tel.: (27) 860223344
Sales Range: $50-74.9 Million
Emp.: 90
Motor Vehicle Retailers
N.A.I.C.S.: 423110

Subsidiary (Domestic):

Kunene Motor Holdings Limited (2)
Corner Or Thambo and Steenkamp Road, Witbank, 1034, Mpumalanga, South Africa
Tel.: (27) 136925010
Web Site: http://www.mccathykunene.co.za
Sales Range: $75-99.9 Million
Investment Management Service
N.A.I.C.S.: 523940
M. B. Kunene *(Chm)*

McLife Assurance Company Limited (2)
2nd Floor Lincoln On The Lake No 2 The High Street Park Side, Umhlanga Ridge, Umhlanga, 4139, KwaZulu-Natal, South Africa
Tel.: (27) 312689300
Fire Insurance Services
N.A.I.C.S.: 524113

Mocobe Properties (Pty) Limited (1)
21 Green Street, Isithebe, 4490, South Africa
Tel.: (27) 324592279
Web Site: http://www.lufil.co.za
Sales Range: $125-149.9 Million
Emp.: 300
Packing & Crating Services
N.A.I.C.S.: 488991

Monjasa Namibia Proprietary Limited (1)
2 Third Street, PO Box 4, Walvis Bay, Namibia
Tel.: (264) 64281205
Web Site: https://www.monjasa.com
Marine Logistics Services
N.A.I.C.S.: 488390
Anders Ostergaard *(CEO & Owner)*

Mubelo Electrical Proprietary Limited (1)
The Cubicle Royal Road, Phoenix, Mauritius
Tel.: (230) 698 5200
Web Site: https://www.mubelo-electrical.business.site
Electric Lighting Distr
N.A.I.C.S.: 423610

Mvelaserve Limited (1)
28 Eddington Crescent Technopark, Centurion, South Africa
Tel.: (27) 087 803 3400
Web Site: http://www.mvelaserve.co.za
Sales Range: $600-649.9 Million
Emp.: 29,069
Business Support Services
N.A.I.C.S.: 561499
Mikki Sivuyile Macmillan Xayiya *(Chm)*

Subsidiary (Domestic):

RoyalMnandi (2)
5 Eddington Crescent Technopark Highveld, PO Box 8924, Centurion, 4700, South Africa
Tel.: (27) 120017160
Web Site: http://www.royalmnandi.co.za
Emp.: 130
Catering Services
N.A.I.C.S.: 722320
Gansen Moodley *(Chief Procurement Officer)*

RoyalServe Cleaning (Proprietary) Limited (2)
22 Gerhardus St, PO Box 4268, Randburg, 2169, South Africa
Tel.: (27) 10 223 3600
Web Site: http://www.royalserve.co.za
Cleaning & Laundry Services
N.A.I.C.S.: 812320
Tseliso Pitikoe *(CEO)*

SA Water Cycle Group (Proprietary) Limited (2)
13 A Eddington Crescent Highveld Technopark, Centurion, 0157, Gauteng, South Africa
Tel.: (27) 12 665 4113
Web Site: http://www.sawater.co.za
Sales Range: $75-99.9 Million
Emp.: 13
Waste Water Treatment Services
N.A.I.C.S.: 221320

Stamford Sales (Proprietary) Limited (2)
6 Lower Jupiter Rd, PO Box 5131, Germiston, South Africa
Tel.: (27) 10 001 9500
Web Site: http://www.stamfordsales.co.za
Emp.: 80
Grocery & Frozen Food Distr & Whslr
N.A.I.C.S.: 492210
Karel Steenkamp *(CFO)*

TFMC Holdings (Proprietary) Limited (2)
The Meersig Building Cnr West & Lenchen Ave, Centurion, 0157, South Africa
Tel.: (27) 126418000
Sales Range: $50-74.9 Million
Emp.: 100
Investment Management Service
N.A.I.C.S.: 523940

Mymarket.Com (Pty) Limited (1)
2nd Floor The Travel Campus 26 Girton Road, Parktown, 2193, South Africa
Tel.: (27) 87 110 1880
Web Site: https://www.mymarket.com
Sales Range: $25-49.9 Million
Emp.: 80
Web Hosting Services
N.A.I.C.S.: 518210

NCP Yeast (Pty) Limited (1)
200 Stalwart Simelane Street, Durban, 4000, Kwazulu-Natal, South Africa
Tel.: (27) 313375242
Web Site: http://www.yeast.co.za
Yeast Mfr & Distr
N.A.I.C.S.: 311999

Namibia Bureau de Change (Pty) Limited (1)
193 Independence Avenue, Windhoek, Namibia
Tel.: (264) 61229667
Web Site: http://www.nbdc.com.na
Sales Range: $50-74.9 Million
Emp.: 16
Foreign Currency Exchange Services
N.A.I.C.S.: 523160

Namibian Sea Products Limited (1)
No 1 Fifth Street East, PO Box 4, Walvis Bay, 2715, Namibia
Tel.: (264) 26464 219 900
Web Site: http://www.unitedfishingenterprises.com
Seafood Processing Services
N.A.I.C.S.: 445250

New Frontiers Tours Proprietary Limited (1)
Ground Floor Block A One on Langford 1 Langford Road, Westville, 3629, South Africa
Tel.: (27) 312795900
Web Site: https://www.newfrontierstours.com
Travel Agency Services
N.A.I.C.S.: 561510
Craig Smith *(CEO)*

Nuclear Corporate Furniture (Pty) Limited (1)
Kasselsvlei Road, Bellville, 7530, Western Cape, South Africa
Tel.: (27) 219516850
Sales Range: $25-49.9 Million
Emp.: 80
Office Furniture Mfr

THE BIDVEST GROUP LIMITED — INTERNATIONAL PUBLIC

The Bidvest Group Limited—(Continued)
N.A.I.C.S.: 337122
Noeroon Flint *(Mgr-Fin)*

Ontime Automotive Limited (1)
Handover Centre Appletree Trading Estate Appletree Road, Chipping Warden, OX17 1LL, Northamptonshire, United Kingdom (100%)
Tel.: (44) 129 577 0040
Web Site: https://www.ontime-auto.com
Motor Vehicle Rescue & Recovery, Fleet Assistance, Distribution & Parking Support Services
N.A.I.C.S.: 561499
Justin Brinklow *(Mng Dir)*

Ozalid South Africa (Pty) Limited (1)
44 Forge Road, Spartan, Johannesburg, 1619, Gauteng, South Africa
Tel.: (27) 119758141
Paper Mfr
N.A.I.C.S.: 322120

PHS Group Limited (1)
Block B Western Industrial Estate, Caerphilly, CF83 1XH, United Kingdom
Tel.: (44) 2920809098
Web Site: https://www.phs.co.uk
Emp.: 3,000
Commercial Cleaning Services
N.A.I.C.S.: 561720

Pastry Global Food Service Limited (1)
3B Yoo Hoo Tower 38 Kwai Fung Crescent, Kwai Chung, New Territories, China (Hong Kong)
Tel.: (852) 24941907
Sales Range: $25-49.9 Million
Emp.: 20
Bakery Product Distr
N.A.I.C.S.: 424420
Christina Wong *(Exec Dir)*

Plumblink (SA) Proprietary Limited (1)
2 Ruacana Street Cnr Beatty Street, Waterfall Commercial District Woodmead, Sandton, 1685, Gauteng, South Africa
Tel.: (27) 870860129
Web Site: https://www.plumblink.co.za
Plumbing Product Distr
N.A.I.C.S.: 423720

Promo Sachets Proprietary Limited (1)
12 Skietlood Street, Isando, 1620, South Africa
Tel.: (27) 11 974 9224
Web Site: https://www.steripic.co.za
Paper Product Mfr & Distr
N.A.I.C.S.: 326111

Pureau Fresh Water Company Pty. Ltd. (1)
22 2nd Road Linbro Park, Sandton, 2090, South Africa
Tel.: (27) 861050505
Web Site: https://www.aquazania.co.za
Water Cooler Mfr & Distr
N.A.I.C.S.: 333415

Quadrel Travel Management Proprietary Limited (1)
2nd Floor Travel Campus 26 Girton Road, Parktown, Johannesburg, 2000, South Africa
Tel.: (27) 117031290
Web Site: https://www.quadreltravel.co.za
Travel & Tourism Services
N.A.I.C.S.: 561510

RFS Catering Supplies (Pty) Limited (1)
Unit F Sanlam Business Park Racecourse Road, Montague Gardens, Cape Town, 7441, Western Cape, South Africa
Tel.: (27) 215529970
Web Site: http://www.rfs.co.za
Sales Range: $50-74.9 Million
Emp.: 75
Groceries Distr
N.A.I.C.S.: 424410

Ram Fasteners (Pty) Limited (1)
Building 3 2 Old Mutual Industrial Park Fortune Road, Johannesburg, 2001, Gauteng, South Africa
Tel.: (27) 116277180
Web Site: http://www.ascom.co.za
Emp.: 10
Fasteners Retailer
N.A.I.C.S.: 423710
Vincent van der Venter *(Gen Mgr)*

Rennie Murray and Company (Pty) Limited (1)
Ground Floor Unit 28 Foregate Square FW De Klerk Boulevard, Cape Town, 8001, Western Cape, South Africa
Tel.: (27) 214214150
Web Site: https://www.renniemurray.co.za
Sales Range: $25-49.9 Million
Emp.: 4
Marine & Cargo Surveying Services
N.A.I.C.S.: 561990
Adam Baker *(Mgr-Johannesburg)*

Rennies Distribution Services (Pty) Limited (1)
45 Richard Carte Rd, Mobeni, Durban, 4092, KwaZulu-Natal, South Africa
Tel.: (27) 314521900
Web Site: http://www.rds-sa.co.za
Warehousing & Logistics Services
N.A.I.C.S.: 493110

Rennies Ships Agency (Pty) Limited (1)
Millweed House Millweed House 169-175 Maydon Road, Durban, 4001, South Africa
Tel.: (27) 313280400
Web Site: https://www.rsagency.co.za
Sales Range: $25-49.9 Million
Emp.: 50
Freight Management Services
N.A.I.C.S.: 488510
Steven Naidoo *(Mgr-Ops)*

Rennies Ships Agency Mozambique Limitada (1)
Travessa da Catembe No 21, Maputo, Mozambique
Tel.: (258) 21307540
Web Site: https://www.rsagency.co.za
Freight Transportation Services
N.A.I.C.S.: 488510

Rennies Travel (Namibia) (Pty) Limited (1)
Robert Mugabe Ave, Windhoek, Namibia
Tel.: (264) 612890760
Emp.: 25
Travel & Tour Operating Agencies
N.A.I.C.S.: 561510

Rennies Travel (Pty) Limited (1)
26 Girton Road, Parktown, Johannesburg, 2192, Gauteng, South Africa
Tel.: (27) 871101149
Web Site: https://www.renniestravelexperience.com
Emp.: 737
Corporate Travel Management Services
N.A.I.C.S.: 561599

Renttech South Africa Proprietary Limited (1)
1 Manchester Road, Wadeville, 1422, South Africa
Tel.: (27) 118240410
Web Site: https://www.renttechsa.co.za
Electrical Equipment Distr
N.A.I.C.S.: 423610

Royal Mozambique Ltda. (1)
Av kenneth kaunda Maputo, Maputo, Mozambique
Tel.: (258) 875599222
Web Site: https://www.royalmozambique.com
Supermarket Services
N.A.I.C.S.: 445110

S&N Labels Proprietary Limited (1)
44 Forge Road Spartan, Kempton Park, 1620, South Africa
Tel.: (27) 11 975 8141
Web Site: https://www.snlabels.co.za
Packaging & Labeling Mfr
N.A.I.C.S.: 333993

Safcor Panalpina (Pty) Ltd. (1)
Harbour View Oakworth Drive, Humerail, Port Elizabeth, 6001, Eastern Cape, South Africa
Tel.: (27) 415013200
Web Site: http://www.safcorpanalpina.co.za
Sales Range: $25-49.9 Million
Emp.: 80
Customs Clearing & Freight Forwarding Services
N.A.I.C.S.: 488510
Eileen Kings *(Gen Mgr-Ops)*

Sanlic International (Pty) Limited (1)
5 Faure Close, Diep River, Cape Town, 7800, Gauteng, South Africa
Tel.: (27) 212065427
Web Site: https://sanlic.org.za
Sales Range: $25-49.9 Million
Emp.: 15
Key & Lock & Security Systems Distr
N.A.I.C.S.: 424990

Seating (Pty) Limited (1)
14 Bunsen Street, Industria, Johannesburg, 2093, Gauteng, South Africa
Tel.: (27) 114741393
Sales Range: $200-249.9 Million
Emp.: 550
Office Chair Mfr
N.A.I.C.S.: 337214

Silveray Manufacturers (Pty) Limited (1)
70 Richard-Carte Road, Mobeni, Durban, 4052, Kwazulu-Natal, South Africa
Tel.: (27) 314622081
Web Site: http://www.silveray.co.za
Emp.: 300
Stationery Product Mfr
N.A.I.C.S.: 325520
Warren Straus *(Mng Dir)*

Silveray Statmark Company (Pty) Limited (1)
Tel.: (27) 116770000
Web Site: https://www.silveray.co.za
Sales Range: $75-99.9 Million
Emp.: 200
Stationery Equipment & Office Supplies Distr
N.A.I.C.S.: 424120
Carol Plummer *(Mgr-Prod)*

South African Bulk Terminals Limited (1)
156 Wharfside Road Island View, Durban, 4052, KwaZulu-Natal, South Africa
Tel.: (27) 31 327 5000
Web Site: https://sabulk.co.za
Sales Range: $25-49.9 Million
Emp.: 170
Marine Terminal Operation Services
N.A.I.C.S.: 561990

South African Container Depots (Pty) Limited (1)
Port Industrial Site Off Nereide Street, Paarden Eiland, Cape Town, 7405, Western Cape, South Africa
Tel.: (27) 218127223
Sales Range: $250-299.9 Million
Emp.: 600
Freight Import & Export Management Services
N.A.I.C.S.: 483113
Nazneen Bray *(Dir-Fin)*

South African Container Stevedores (Pty) Limited (1)
Millweed House, Durban, 4001, Kwazulu-Natal, South Africa
Tel.: (27) 312742400
Web Site: http://www.bidports.co.za
Stevedoring Services
N.A.I.C.S.: 488320
Jannie Roux *(Mng Dir)*

South African Diaries (Pty) Limited (1)
12 Stationery Centre Beach Road, Woodstock, 7925, Cape Town, Western Cape, South Africa
Tel.: (27) 214422340
Web Site: http://www.sadiaries.co.za
Sales Range: $25-49.9 Million
Emp.: 7
Diary Publishing Services
N.A.I.C.S.: 513199

Steiner Hygiene (Pty) Limited (1)
110 Loper Avenue Aeroport Spartan Ext 2, Kempton Park, 1619, Gauteng, South Africa
Tel.: (27) 119239490
Web Site: https://steiner.co.za
Sales Range: $25-49.9 Million
Emp.: 60
Contract Cleaning Services
N.A.I.C.S.: 561720
Alan Fainman *(Mng Dir)*

Steiner Hygiene Montague Gardens (Pty) Limited (1)
Unit 22 Point Business Park Merinus Street, Milnerton, Cape Town, 7441, Western Cape, South Africa
Tel.: (27) 21 552 7611
Sales Range: $25-49.9 Million
Emp.: 21
Contract Cleaning & Pest Control Services
N.A.I.C.S.: 561710

Steiner Hygiene Swaziland (Pty) Limited (1)
12th Street & 1st Avenue Unit 4 Lot 483, Matsapha, M202, Eswatini
Tel.: (268) 5184818
Sales Range: $25-49.9 Million
Emp.: 15
Housekeeping Services
N.A.I.C.S.: 561720
Andrew Mccarter *(Mgr)*

Taeuber & Corssen SWA Proprietary Limited (1)
11 Ruhr Street Northern Industrial, Windhoek, Namibia
Tel.: (264) 61 293 2000
Web Site: https://www.taeubercorssen.com
Grocery Product Whslr
N.A.I.C.S.: 424410
Gielie Van Wyk *(Gen Dir)*

Technilamp Proprietary Limited (1)
Unit 5 14 Union Street, Union Park, Alberton, South Africa
Tel.: (27) 11 621 0620
Web Site: https://www.technilamp.co.za
Ultraviolet & Infrared Lamp Mfr & Distr
N.A.I.C.S.: 335139
Charles Parsons *(Mgr)*

Top Turf Botswana (Pty) Limited (1)
Private Bag BR105, Gaborone, Botswana
Tel.: (267) 3500413
Sales Range: $25-49.9 Million
Emp.: 15
Landscaping Services
N.A.I.C.S.: 561730
Paul Kirkby *(CEO & Mng Dir)*

Top Turf Mauritius (Pty) Limited (1)
Le Coco Beach Hotel Belle Mare Coastal Road, Port Louis, Mauritius
Tel.: (230) 4155987
Landscaping Services
N.A.I.C.S.: 561730

Travel Connections (Pty) Limited (1)
The Travel Campus 26 Girton Road, Sandton, Parktown, 2193, South Africa
Tel.: (27) 871101800
Web Site: https://www.travelconnections.co.za
Sales Range: $10-24.9 Million
Emp.: 45
Travel Management Services
N.A.I.C.S.: 561510
Lindy Preston *(CEO & Mng Dir)*

UAV and Drone Solutions Pty. Ltd. (1)
2 River Road Riverview Office Park Janadel Avenue, Halfway Gardens, Midrand, South Africa
Tel.: (27) 114477337
Web Site: https://uavdronesolutions.com
Emp.: 420
Mining Infrastructure Services
N.A.I.C.S.: 541330

Vericon Outsourcing (Pty) Limited (1)
Stock Auditing Services
N.A.I.C.S.: 541614
Gustav Gericke *(Mng Dir)*

Voltex (Pty) Limited (1)
Voltex House-Block B St Andrew's Office Park 39 Wordsworth Avenue, Senderwood, Bedfordview, 2007, Gauteng, South Africa
Tel.: (27) 118792047
Emp.: 100
Electrical Material Distr
N.A.I.C.S.: 423610

Stanley Green (CEO)

Voltex Namibia (Pty) Limited (1)
69 Lazarett Street unit 2, PO Box 11508,
Southern Industrial Area, Windhoek, 11508,
Namibia
Tel.: (264) 61 228 231
Web Site: http://www.bidvestnamibia.com.na
Electrical Supplies Whslr
N.A.I.C.S.: 444180

Vulcan Catering Equipment (Pty) Ltd. (1)
2172 Albertina Sisulu Road Industria, Johannesburg, 2093, Gauteng, South Africa
Tel.: (27) 11 249 8500
Web Site: https://www.vulcan.co.za
Sales Range: $125-149.9 Million
Emp.: 350
Food Service Equipment Mfr & Distr
N.A.I.C.S.: 333310

Waltons Namibia Proprietary Limited (1)
Messum and Andimba Toiva ya Toiva Street
Southern Industrial, Windhoek, Namibia
Tel.: (264) 832838000
Web Site: https://www.waltons.com.na
Emp.: 220
Paper Product Merchant Whslr
N.A.I.C.S.: 424130
Etienne Visser (Mng Dir)

Waltons Stationery Company (Namibia) (Pty) Limited (1)
Bessemer Street, PO Box 3187, Southern
Industrial, Windhoek, Namibia
Tel.: (264) 832838000
Web Site: https://www.waltons.com.na
Sales Range: $50-74.9 Million
Emp.: 35
Office Supplies & Furniture Retailer
N.A.I.C.S.: 423210
Victor Doshoss (Mng Dir)

Walvis Bay Stevedoring Company (Pty) Limited (1)
Main Harbour Rd Port of Walvis Bay, PO
Box 4, Walvis Bay, Namibia
Tel.: (264) 64204641
Web Site: https://www.wbs.com.na
Sales Range: $25-49.9 Million
Emp.: 16
Stevedoring Services
N.A.I.C.S.: 488320
Riaan Lottering (Branch Mgr)

Woker Freight Services Proprietary Limited (1)
2 Third Street Maritime Building, PO Box 4,
Walvis Bay, Namibia
Tel.: (264) 642012027
Web Site: https://www.wfs.com.na
Logistic Services
N.A.I.C.S.: 541614

THE BIG PARTNERSHIP GROUP LIMITED

5 Pk Circus Pl, Glasgow, G3 6AH,
United Kingdom
Tel.: (44) 1413339585   UK
Web Site:
 http://www.bigpartnership.co.uk
Public Relations Agency
N.A.I.C.S.: 541820
Alex Barr (Founder)

THE BIOTECH GROWTH TRUST PLC

25 Southampton Buildings, London,
WC2A 1AL, United Kingdom
Tel.: (44) 2030084910
Web Site: https://www.biotechgt.com
BIOG—(LSE)
Assets: $447,428,961
Liabilities: $37,506,042
Net Worth: $409,922,919
Earnings: ($51,257,430)
Fiscal Year-end: 03/31/23
Investment Services
N.A.I.C.S.: 525910
Andrew Joy (Chm)

THE BLM GROUP, INC.

120 McBrine Dr, Kitchener, N2R1E7,
ON, Canada
Tel.: (519) 748-9880
Web Site: http://www.blm.com
Year Founded: 1984
Sales Range: $50-74.9 Million
Emp.: 400
Freight Services
N.A.I.C.S.: 484121
James D McConnell (Pres)

THE BLOCKCHAIN GROUP

Tour W - 102 Terrasse Boieldieu,
92800, Puteaux, France
Tel.: (33) 140075801
Web Site: https://www.theblockchain-group.com
ALTBG—(EUR)
Sales Range: $1-9.9 Million
Digital Marketing Services
N.A.I.C.S.: 541810
Xavier Latil (Chm & CEO)

THE BOMBAY BURMAH TRADING CORPORATION LIMITED

9 Wallace Street Fort, Mumbai, 400
001, Maharashtra, India
Tel.: (91) 2222197101
Web Site: https://www.bbtcl.com
501425—(BOM)
Rev.: $1,874,819,597
Assets: $1,697,537,901
Liabilities: $705,038,703
Net Worth: $992,499,199
Earnings: $174,412,752
Emp.: 3,751
Fiscal Year-end: 03/31/21
Tea Plantation Operator & Tea Distr
N.A.I.C.S.: 111998
Ness Nusli Wadia (Mng Dir)

Subsidiaries:

Electromags Autmotive Products Private Limited (1)
342/343 2nd Cross Street Nehru Nagar,
Kottivakkam, Chennai, 600 096, India
Tel.: (91) 44 2492 9277
Web Site: http://www.electromags.com
Automobile Parts Mfr
N.A.I.C.S.: 336110

Island Horti-Tech Holdings Pte. Limited (1)
Plot 13 Joan Road, Singapore, 298897,
Singapore
Tel.: (65) 62549867
Web Site: http://www.islandgroup.com.sg
Sales Range: $50-74.9 Million
Emp.: 5
Investment Management Service
N.A.I.C.S.: 523940

Subsidiary (Domestic):

Island Landscape & Nursery Pte Ltd (2)
3 Joan Road, Singapore, 298897, Singapore
Tel.: (65) 62549867
Web Site: https://www.islandgroup.com.sg
Landscaping & Nursery Services
N.A.I.C.S.: 561730

Kenafric Biscuits Limited (1)
Baba Dogo Road, PO Box 39257 00623,
Nairobi, Kenya
Tel.: (254) 730700000
Web Site: https://www.kenafricind.com
Bakery Product Mfr & Distr
N.A.I.C.S.: 311999

THE BRADNAM GROUP

136 Zillmere Road, Boondall, Brisbane, 4034, QLD, Australia
Tel.: (61) 731313777
Web Site:
 http://www.bradnams.com.au
Year Founded: 1977
Emp.: 1,000
Windows & Door Distr
N.A.I.C.S.: 423310
Jason Drewe (CEO)

THE BRAJ BINANI GROUP

Mercantile Chambers 12 J N Heredia
Marg Ballard Estate, 400 001, Mumbai, India
Tel.: (91) 22 2269 0506
Web Site:
 http://www.binaniindustries.com
Sales Range: $350-399.9 Million
Emp.: 2,000
Holding Company
N.A.I.C.S.: 551112

Subsidiaries:

Binani Industries Limited (1)
37/2 Chinar Park New Town Rajarhat Main
Road, P O Hatiara, Kolkata, 700 157, India
Tel.: (91) 8100326795
Web Site: https://www.binaniindustries.com
Rev.: $308,738,968
Assets: $1,178,089,441
Liabilities: $1,401,904,854
Net Worth: ($223,815,413)
Earnings: $3,519,890
Emp.: 31
Fiscal Year-end: 03/31/2018
Holding Company
N.A.I.C.S.: 551112
Visalakshi Sridhar (CFO, Compliance Officer, Sec & Mgr)

Subsidiary (Non-US):

3B-Fibreglass A/S (2)
Tollenesveien, 4760, Birkeland, Norway
Tel.: (47) 37 28 05 00
Fiberglass Mfr
N.A.I.C.S.: 326199

3B-Fibreglass SPRL (2)
Route de Maestricht 67, 4651, Herve, Belgium
Tel.: (32) 87 69 24 11
Web Site: http://www.3b-fibreglass.com
Fiberglass Mfr
N.A.I.C.S.: 326199
Bernard Kaesmacher (Dir-Global Process & Product)

Subsidiary (Domestic):

Asian Industry and Information Services Pvt Ltd. (2)
Peltham House 1st Floor Ballard Estate 10
J N Heredia Marg, Mumbai, 400001, Maharashtra, India
Tel.: (91) 2222660623
Magazine Publishing Services
N.A.I.C.S.: 513120
Bina Verma (Mng Dir)

BT Composites Limited (2)
C5-C9 C12-C16 Madkaim Industrial Estate,
Madkaim Mardol Post, Goa, 403 404, India
Tel.: (91) 832 2392383
Fiberglass Mfr
N.A.I.C.S.: 326199
Ajith Thayath (Mgr-Production & Maintenence)

Subsidiary (Non-US):

Bhumi Resources (Singapore) Pte Limited. (2)
29 04B Clifford Centre 24 Raffles Place,
Singapore, 048621, Singapore
Tel.: (65) 65356065
Portland Cement Mfr & Sales
N.A.I.C.S.: 327310

Binani Cement Factory LLC (2)
B-233 Jebel Ali Industrial Area 2, PO Box
37608, Dubai, United Arab Emirates
Tel.: (971) 14 8801063
Cement Mfr
N.A.I.C.S.: 327310

Subsidiary (Domestic):

Binani Energy Pvt. Ltd (2)
Mercantile Chambers 12 Ballard Estate, J N
Heredia Marg, Mumbai, 400 001, India
Tel.: (91) 2222690506
Cement Mfr
N.A.I.C.S.: 327310

Binani Metals Ltd. (2)
12 J N Heredia Marg Ballard Estate, Mumbai, 400001, Maharashtra, India
Tel.: (91) 2222617491
Cement Mfr
N.A.I.C.S.: 327310

Binani Zinc Limited (2)
Binanipuram, 683 502, Kerala, India
Tel.: (91) 484 2540276
Zinc Mfr
N.A.I.C.S.: 325180
V. N. Balagopal (Sr Mgr-Production)

Goa Glass Fibre Limited (2)
218/220 N H- 17 Colvale Village, Bardez,
Goa, 403 513, India
Tel.: (91) 2299884
Web Site: http://www.binaniglassfibre.com
Fiberglass Mfr
N.A.I.C.S.: 326199

Subsidiary (Non-US):

Krishna Holdings Pte. Ltd. (2)
29 04A Clifford Centre 24 Raffles Place,
Singapore, 048621, Singapore
Tel.: (65) 65356065
Emp.: 4
Investment Management Service
N.A.I.C.S.: 523999
Shyam Binani (Gen Mgr)

Mukundan Holdings Ltd (2)
29 04 B Clifford Centre 24 Raffles Place,
Singapore, 048621, Singapore
Tel.: (65) 65356065
Cement Mfr
N.A.I.C.S.: 327310

Murari Holdings Ltd. (2)
29 04B Clifford Centre 24 Raffles Place,
Singapore, 048621, Singapore
Tel.: (65) 65356065
Web Site: http://www.binani.com
Sales Range: $50-74.9 Million
Emp.: 5
Investment Management Service
N.A.I.C.S.: 523999

Shandong Binani Rong An Cement Co. Ltd. (2)
Fujiazhuang Village, Dongguan Town,
Rizhao, 276500, Shandong, China
Tel.: (86) 633 6567222
Cement Mfr
N.A.I.C.S.: 327310

THE BRAND AGENCY PTY. LTD.

Level 3 11 Harvest Terrace, Perth,
6005, WA, Australia
Tel.: (61) 8 9322 4433
Web Site:
 http://www.brandagency.com.au
Year Founded: 1991
Emp.: 70
Advertising Services
N.A.I.C.S.: 541810
Ken James (Chm & Mng Dir)

Subsidiaries:

TBA Communications (1)
Level 12 7 City Rd, Auckland Central, Auckland, 1140, New Zealand
Tel.: (64) 9 369 1306
Web Site: http://www.brandagency.com.au
Emp.: 8
Advertising Services
N.A.I.C.S.: 541810

The Brand Agency-Melbourne (1)
Level 8 190 Queen St, Melbourne, 3000,
VIC, Australia
Tel.: (61) 3 9602 2011
Web Site: http://www.brandagency.com.au
Advertising Services
N.A.I.C.S.: 541810

THE BRIGHTON PIER GROUP PLC

Brighton Palace Pier Madeira Drive,
Brighton, BN2 1TW, E Sussex,
United Kingdom
Tel.: (44) 1273609361

THE BRIGHTON PIER GROUP PLC

The Brighton Pier Group plc—(Continued)

Web Site:
https://www.brightonpier.co.uk
Year Founded: 2006
PIER—(AIM)
Rev.: $79,670,497
Assets: $94,721,336
Liabilities: $60,027,517
Net Worth: $34,693,819
Earnings: $8,652,750
Emp.: 681
Fiscal Year-end: 12/25/22
Bar Owner & Operator
N.A.I.C.S.: 722410
John Smith *(CFO)*

THE BRITISH LAND COMPANY PLC

York House 45 Seymour Street, London, W1H 7LX, United Kingdom
Tel.: (44) 2074864466 UK
Web Site:
https://www.britishland.com
BLND—(LSE)
Rev.: $635,412,960
Assets: $12,049,765,000
Liabilities: $3,926,526,240
Net Worth: $8,123,238,760
Earnings: ($1,399,809,320)
Emp.: 326
Fiscal Year-end: 03/31/21
Real Estate Investment Trust
N.A.I.C.S.: 525990
Nigel Webb *(Head-Dev)*

Subsidiaries:

British Land Developments Ltd. (1)
45 Seymour St York House, 45 Seymour Street, London, W1H 7LX, United Kingdom
Tel.: (44) 2074864466
Sales Range: $50-74.9 Million
Emp.: 170
Land Developer
N.A.I.C.S.: 237210

British Land Financing Ltd. (1)
York House 45 Seymour St, London, W1H 7LX, United Kingdom
Tel.: (44) 2074864466
Sales Range: $200-249.9 Million
Bank Financing Services
N.A.I.C.S.: 522299

British Land Investments Netherlands BV (1)
Leidsekada 102, 1077 ZX, Amsterdam, Netherlands (100%)
Tel.: (31) 206429848
Sales Range: $50-74.9 Million
Emp.: 5
Property Trading & Development
N.A.I.C.S.: 524126
Arend J. van der Marel *(Mng Dir)*

British Land Properties Ltd. (1)
York House, 45 Seymour Street W, London, W1H7 LX, United Kingdom
Tel.: (44) 2074864466
Web Site: http://www.britishland.com
Sales Range: $50-74.9 Million
Emp.: 200
Land Developer
N.A.I.C.S.: 237210

British Land Retail Warehouses Limited (1)
York House 45 Seymour Street, London, W1H 7JT, United Kingdom
Tel.: (44) 2074864466
Real Estate Manangement Services
N.A.I.C.S.: 531390

Broadgate Estates Ltd. (1)
York House 45 Seymour Street, London, W1H 7LX, United Kingdom
Tel.: (44) 2075054000
Web Site:
http://www.broadgateestates.co.uk
Sales Range: $50-74.9 Million
Emp.: 170
Land Developer
N.A.I.C.S.: 237210
Steve Whyman *(Mng Dir)*

Drake Circus Centre Limited (1)
1 Charles Street, Plymouth, United Kingdom
Tel.: (44) 1752223030
Web Site: https://www.drakecircus.com
Shopping Mall Operator
N.A.I.C.S.: 531120

Ludgate Investment Holdings Limited (1)
20 Old Bailey, London, United Kingdom
Tel.: (44) 2034781000
Web Site: https://ludgate.com
Investment Services
N.A.I.C.S.: 523999

Meadowhall Centre Limited (1)
Tel.: (44) 3333132000
N.A.I.C.S.: 459999

Nugent Shopping Park Limited (1)
Cray Avenue, Orpington, Kent, United Kingdom
Tel.: (44) 8081565533
Web Site: https://nugentshoppingpark.com
Shopping Mall Operator
N.A.I.C.S.: 531120

Orbital Shopping Park Swindon Limited (1)
Thamesdown Drive, Swindon, Wiltshire, United Kingdom
Tel.: (44) 80815655222
Web Site: https://orbitalshoppingpark.com
Shopping Mall Operator
N.A.I.C.S.: 531120

St. Stephens Shopping Centre Limited (1)
110 Ferensway East Riding of Yorkshire, Kingston upon Hull, HU2 8LN, United Kingdom
Tel.: (44) 1482 313 960
Web Site: http://www.ststephens-hull.com
Emp.: 60
Shopping Mall Management Services
N.A.I.C.S.: 531120
Jim Harris *(Mgr-Centre)*

Teesside Leisure Park Limited (1)
Management Suite Goodwood Square, Stockton-on-Tees, United Kingdom
Tel.: (44) 1642679447
Web Site:
https://www.teessideshopping.co.uk
Shopping Mall Operator
N.A.I.C.S.: 531120

The British Land Corporation Ltd. (1)
45 Seymour Street, London, 1H 7LX, United Kingdom
Tel.: (44) 2074864466
Sales Range: $100-124.9 Million
Emp.: 200
Property Trading & Development
N.A.I.C.S.: 523160

THE BRITISH LIBRARY

96 Euston Road, London, NW1 2DB, United Kingdom
Tel.: (44) 3303331144
Web Site: http://www.bl.uk
Rev.: $163,008,773
Assets: $1,390,231,734
Liabilities: $25,611,694
Net Worth: $1,364,620,040
Earnings: ($31,298,235)
Emp.: 1,561
Fiscal Year-end: 03/31/18
Library Services
N.A.I.C.S.: 519210
David Barclay *(Deputy Chm)*

THE BRITISH PLASTICS FEDERATION

6 Bath Pl, London, EC2A 3JE, United Kingdom
Tel.: (44) 2074575000
Web Site: http://www.bpf.co.uk
Year Founded: 1933
Sales Range: $100-124.9 Million
Emp.: 18
Trade Association for UK Plastics Industry

N.A.I.C.S.: 813910
Philip Law *(Dir Gen)*

THE BRITISH STANDARDS INSTITUTION

389 Chiswick High Road, London, W4 4AL, United Kingdom
Tel.: (44) 3450809000 UK
Web Site: http://www.bsigroup.com
Year Founded: 1901
Quality Testing Services
N.A.I.C.S.: 921190
Craig Smith *(Dir-Fin)*

Subsidiaries:

AirCert GmbH (1)
Maria-Merian-Str 8, 85521, Ottobrunn, Germany
Tel.: (49) 8944 458 2200
Web Site: https://www.aircert.org
Certification & Standard Related Services
N.A.I.C.S.: 541990
David J. Harvey *(Reg Mgr)*

BSI Assurance UK Limited (1)
Kitemark Court Davy Avenue, Knowlhill, Milton Keynes, MK5 8PP, United Kingdom
Tel.: (44) 3450809000
Web Site: http://www.bsigroup.com
Business Support Services
N.A.I.C.S.: 561499

BSI Brasil (1)
Rua Gomes de Carvalho 1069-18 andar, Vila Olimpia, Sao Paulo, 04547-004, SP, Brazil
Tel.: (55) 11 2148 9600
Web Site: http://www.bsigroup.com
Business Support Services
N.A.I.C.S.: 561499
Carlos Pitanga *(Pres)*

BSI Brasil Sistemas de Gestao Ltda (1)
Rua Gomes de Carvalho 1069-18 andar, Vila Olimpia, Sao Paulo, 04547-004, Brazil
Tel.: (55) 112 148 9600
Certification & Standard Related Services
N.A.I.C.S.: 541990

BSI Cybersecurity & Information Resilience (Ireland) Limited (1)
Corrig Court Corrig Road, Sandyford Industrial Estate, Dublin, D18 C6K1, Ireland
Tel.: (353) 1 210 1711
Certification & Standard Related Services
N.A.I.C.S.: 541990

BSI Cybersecurity and Information Resilience (UK) Limited (1)
Davy Avenue Knowlhill, Milton Keynes, MK5 8PP, United Kingdom
Tel.: (44) 345 222 1711
Web Site: http://www.bsigroup.com
Cybersecurity professional services
N.A.I.C.S.: 541511

BSI Group (Australia and New Zealand) Pty Ltd (1)
Suite 1 Level 1 54 Waterloo Road, Macquarie Park, 2113, NSW, Australia
Tel.: (61) 1300730134
Web Site: http://www.bsigroup.com
Business Support Services
N.A.I.C.S.: 561499
Marc Barnes *(Mng Dir)*

BSI Group (Thailand) Co., Ltd (1)
127/29 Panjathani Tower 24th Floor Nonsee Road, Chong Nonsi Subdistrict Yannawa District, Bangkok, 10120, Thailand
Tel.: (66) 2 294 4889 92
Web Site: http://www.bsigroup.com
Business Support Services
N.A.I.C.S.: 561499

BSI Group Canada Inc (1)
Suite 108 6205B Airport Road, Mississauga, L4V 1E3, ON, Canada
Tel.: (416) 620-9991
Web Site: http://www.bsigroup.com
Business Support Services
N.A.I.C.S.: 561499

BSI Group Deutschland GmbH (1)
Hanauer Landstrasse 115, 60314, Frankfurt am Main, Germany

Tel.: (49) 69 2222 8 9200
Web Site: http://www.bsigroup.com
Business Support Services
N.A.I.C.S.: 561499

BSI Group Eurasia Belgelendirrme Hizmetleri Limited Sirketi (1)
Degirmen Sk No 16 AR Plaza Office 61/62 A Block, Kozyatagi, Istanbul, 34742, Turkiye
Tel.: (90) 216 445 9038
Certification & Standard Related Services
N.A.I.C.S.: 541990

BSI Group Eurasia Certification Services Co. Ltd (1)
Degirmen Sk No 16 Ar Plaza Ofis 61/62 A Blok, Kozyatagi, Istanbul, Turkiye
Tel.: (90) 216 445 90 38
Web Site: http://www.bsi-turkey.com
Business Support Services
N.A.I.C.S.: 561499
Ozlem Unsal *(Mng Dir)*

BSI Group France Sarl (1)
19 Rue Alphonse de Neuville, 75017, Paris, France
Tel.: (33) 1 55 34 11 40
Web Site: http://www.bsigroup.com
Business Support Services
N.A.I.C.S.: 561499

BSI Group India Private Ltd (1)
The Mira Corporate Suites A-2 Plot 1and2 Ishwar Nagar Mathura road, New Delhi, 110065, India
Tel.: (91) 11 2692 9000
Web Site: http://www.bsigroup.co.in
Business Support Services
N.A.I.C.S.: 561499

BSI Group Italia SRL (1)
Via Gustavo Fara 35, 20124, Milan, Italy
Tel.: (39) 026679091
Web Site: http://www.bsigroup.it
Business Support Services
N.A.I.C.S.: 561499

BSI Group Japan KK (1)
Ocean Gate Minatomirai 3F 3-7-1 Minatomirai, Nishi-ku, Yokohama, 220-0012, Kanagawa, Japan
Tel.: (81) 454143021
Web Site: http://www.bsigroup.com
Business Support Services
N.A.I.C.S.: 561499

BSI Group Korea Ltd (1)
8th Floor Taehwa Building 29 Insadong 5-gil, Jongno-gu, Seoul, 03162, Korea (South)
Tel.: (82) 27774123
Web Site: http://www.bsigroup.com
Business Support Services
N.A.I.C.S.: 561499

BSI Group Mexico S dr RL de CV (1)
Torre Mayor Av Paseo de la Reforma No 505 Piso 44 B, Col Cuauhtemoc, 06500, Mexico, Mexico
Tel.: (52) 55 5241 1370
Web Site: http://www.bsigroup.com
Business Support Services
N.A.I.C.S.: 561499

BSI Group Philippines, Inc. (1)
Unit 2408 The Orient Square F Ortigas Jr Road Ortigas Business Center, Pasig, 1605, Philippines
Tel.: (63) 28 636 6430
Certification & Standard Related Services
N.A.I.C.S.: 541990

BSI Group Polska Spolka z.o.o. (1)
Al Solidarnosci 171, 00-877, Warsaw, Poland
Tel.: (48) 222090101
Web Site: http://www.bsigroup.com
Business Support Services
N.A.I.C.S.: 561499

BSI Group Singapore Pte Ltd (1)
77 Robinson Road 28-03 Robinson 77, Singapore, 068896, Singapore
Tel.: (65) 6270 0777
Web Site: http://www.bsigroup.com
Business Support Services
N.A.I.C.S.: 561499
Nuar Amanda *(Acct Mgr-Dev)*

BSI Group South Africa (Pty) Limited (1)

AND PRIVATE COMPANIES

THE BRITISH UNITED PROVIDENT ASSOCIATION LIMITED

Park Lane West 194 Bancor Avenue Glen X2, Waterkloof, Pretoria, 0181, South Africa
Tel.: (27) 12 004 0279
Certification & Standard Related Services
N.A.I.C.S.: 541990
Theuns Kotze *(Reg Mng Dir)*

BSI Group The Netherlands BV (1)
Say Building John M Keynesplein 9, 1066 EP, Amsterdam, Netherlands
Tel.: (31) 20 346 0780
Certification & Standard Related Services
N.A.I.C.S.: 541990

BSI Healthcare Saudi Arabia (1)
854 Olaya Street, Al Ghadir, Riyadh, Saudi Arabia
Tel.: (966) 1 210 7732
Business Support Services
N.A.I.C.S.: 561499

BSI Inc. (1)
12950 Worldgate Dr Ste 800, Herndon, VA 20170
Tel.: (703) 437-9000
Sales Range: $25-49.9 Million
Emp.: 90
Non-Profit Organization for Standards, Quality Services & Inspection
N.A.I.C.S.: 541990
Reg Blake *(VP-Reguatory Affairs)*

Subsidiary (Domestic):

BSI America Professional Services Inc. (2)
12950 World Gate Dr Ste 800, Herndon, VA 20170
Tel.: (703) 437-9000
Business Support Services
N.A.I.C.S.: 561499
Lauri Powell *(VP-Advisory Svcs Dev)*

BSI Services & Solutions (NYC) Inc. (2)
1115 Broadway 11th Fl Ste 1157, New York, NY 10010
Tel.: (212) 290-6323
Web Site: http://www.cescenter.com
Environmental Consulting Services
N.A.I.C.S.: 541620
Victoria Drozdov *(Pres)*

Quantum Management Group, Inc. (2)
1187 Main Ave Ste 2B, Clifton, NJ 07011
Tel.: (973) 340-9808
Scientific & Technical Consulting Services
N.A.I.C.S.: 541690

BSI Limited (1)
Charnwood Building Holywell Park Ashby Road, Loughborough, LE11 3AQ, United Kingdom
Tel.: (44) 1509 331133
Web Site: http://www.bsigroup.com
Business Support Services
N.A.I.C.S.: 561499

BSI Management Systems CIS LLC (1)
Kosmodamianskaya nab 52/3 BC Riverside Towers 9th Floor, 115035, Moscow, Russia
Tel.: (7) 4957394877
Certification & Standard Related Services
N.A.I.C.S.: 541990

BSI Management Systems Certification (Beijing) Co. Ltd. (1)
Room 2008 Donghai Center No 24 A Jianguomenwai Street, Beijing, China
Tel.: (86) 400 005 0046
Certification & Standard Related Services
N.A.I.C.S.: 541990

BSI Pacific Limited (1)
23rd Floor Cambridge House TaiKoo Place 979 King's Road Island East, Quarry Bay MTR Exit A, Hong Kong, China (Hong Kong)
Tel.: (852) 3 149 3300
Certification & Standard Related Services
N.A.I.C.S.: 541990

BSI Services (Asia Pacific) Sdn Bhd (1)
Suite 29 01 Level 29 The Gardens North Tower, 59200, Kuala Lumpur, Malaysia
Tel.: (60) 39 212 9638
Certification & Standard Related Services

N.A.I.C.S.: 541990

BSI Services Malaysia Sdn. Bhd. (1)
Suite 29 01 Level 29 The Gardens North Tower Mid Valley City, Lingkaran Syed Putra, 59200, Kuala Lumpur, Malaysia
Tel.: (60) 392129638
Web Site: http://www.bsigroup.com
Business Support Services
N.A.I.C.S.: 561499

BSI Vietnam Co., Ltd (1)
Suite 1106 11th Floor Citilight Tower 45 Vo Thi Sau Street, Dakao ward District 1, Ho Chi Minh City, Vietnam
Tel.: (84) 2838200066
Web Site: http://www.bsigroup.com
Business Support Services
N.A.I.C.S.: 561499

British Standards Institution Group Iberia SAU (1)
C/ Juan Esplandiu 15 - 3 planta, 28007, Madrid, Spain
Tel.: (34) 91 400 8620
Web Site: http://www.bsigroup.com
Business Support Services
N.A.I.C.S.: 561499

NCS International Pty. Ltd. (1)
Suite 6 22 Greenhill Road, Wayville, 5034, SA, Australia
Tel.: (61) 8 8372 7807
Web Site: http://www.ncsi.com.au
Business Support Services
N.A.I.C.S.: 561499

PT BSI Group Indonesia (1)
Talavera Office Suite 20th Floor Suite 01-06 Jl TB Simatupang, Cilandak Jakarta Selatan DKI, Jakarta, 12430, Indonesia
Tel.: (62) 2180649600
Web Site: http://www.bsigroup.com
Business Support Services
N.A.I.C.S.: 561499

THE BRITISH UNITED PROVIDENT ASSOCIATION LIMITED

1 Angel Court, London, EC2R 7HJ, United Kingdom
Tel.: (44) 2076562000 UK
Web Site: http://www.bupa.com
Year Founded: 1947
Rev.: $16,153,665,600
Assets: $21,124,629,600
Liabilities: $11,909,328,000
Net Worth: $9,215,301,600
Earnings: ($276,747,600)
Emp.: 80,517
Fiscal Year-end: 12/31/19
Holding Company; Health Care Products & Services
N.A.I.C.S.: 551112
Inaki Ereno *(CEO)*

Subsidiaries:

Anglolab S.A. (1)
Alfredo Salazar 314, San Isidro, Lima, Peru
Tel.: (51) 16148800
Web Site: https://www.anglolab.com
Laboratory Testing Services
N.A.I.C.S.: 541380

Arnica Dental Care Limited (1)
73 Leckhampton Road, Cheltenham, GL53 0BS, Gloucestershire, United Kingdom
Tel.: (44) 1242362320
Web Site: https://www.arnicadentalcare.co.uk
Dental Care Services
N.A.I.C.S.: 621210

Blueapple Dental & Implant Team Limited (1)
10 Railway Street, Belcoo, Enniskillen, BT93 5FJ, United Kingdom
Tel.: (44) 2866386111
Health Care Srvices
N.A.I.C.S.: 621999

Bupa (Asia) Limited (1)
18/F Berkshire House 25 Westlands Road, Quarry Bay, China (Hong Kong)
Tel.: (852) 2517 5175
Web Site: http://www.bupa.com.hk
Health Care Funding Services
N.A.I.C.S.: 524114

Bupa Acibadem Sigorta A.S. (1)
Basar Street No 20, Kucukbakkalkoy District Atasehir, Istanbul, Turkiye
Tel.: (90) 2165715555
Web Site: https://www.bupaacibadem.com.tr
Health Insurance Services
N.A.I.C.S.: 524114

Bupa Australia Pty Limited (1)
GPO Box 9809, Brisbane, 4001, QLD, Australia
Tel.: (61) 3 9487 6400
Web Site: http://www.bupa.com.au
Health Care Srvices
N.A.I.C.S.: 621999
Dwayne Crombie *(Mng Dir-Health Svcs)*

Bupa Care Homes (Bnh) Limited (1)
Bridge House Outwood Lane, Horsforth West Yorkshire, Leeds, LS18 4UP, United Kingdom
Tel.: (44) 113 381 6341
Women Healthcare Services
N.A.I.C.S.: 621610

Bupa Care Homes (CFG) Plc (1)
2 Arnolds Lane, Peterborough, PE7 1QD, United Kingdom
Tel.: (44) 173 320 2421
Women Healthcare Services
N.A.I.C.S.: 621610

Bupa Care Services Limited (1)
Level 19 201 Kent Street, Sydney, 2000, NSW, Australia
Tel.: (61) 1300 302 350
Web Site: http://www.bupaagedcare.com.au
Emp.: 5,000
Health Care Srvices
N.A.I.C.S.: 621999

Bupa Care Villages Australia Pty Ltd. (1)
33 Exhibition Street, Melbourne, 3000, VIC, Australia
Tel.: (61) 1800062190
Web Site: https://www.bupa.com.au
Residential Property Managing Services
N.A.I.C.S.: 531311

Bupa Dominicana, S.A. (1)
Av Winston Churchill 1099, Santo Domingo, Dominican Republic
Tel.: (809) 9552555
Health Insurance Services
N.A.I.C.S.: 524114

Bupa Guatemala, Compania de Seguros, S.A. (1)
5 Avenida 5-55 Zona 14 Europlaza World Business Center, Tower III Level 11 Office 1103, Guatemala, Guatemala
Tel.: (502) 23008000
Web Site: https://www.bupasalud.com.gt
Health Insurance Services
N.A.I.C.S.: 524114

Bupa HI Pty Ltd. (1)
33 Exhibition Street, Melbourne, 3000, VIC, Australia
Tel.: (61) 134135
Web Site: https://www.bupa.com.au
Health Care Srvices
N.A.I.C.S.: 621610

Bupa Healthcare New Zealand Limited (1)
109 Carlton Gore Road, Newmarket, Auckland, 1023, New Zealand
Tel.: (64) 95582488
Web Site: http://www.bupa.co.nz
Health Care Srvices
N.A.I.C.S.: 621999
Margaret Owens *(COO)*

Subsidiary (Domestic):

Bupa Rehabilitation Limited (2)
Level 5 5-7 Kingdon Street, Newmarket, Auckland, 1023, New Zealand
Tel.: (64) 9 985 9700
Emp.: 4,000
Brain Injury Rehabilitation Services
N.A.I.C.S.: 623990
Andria Bayer *(Mgr)*

Bupa Occupational Health Limited (1)
1 Angel Court, London, EC2R 7HJ, United Kingdom

Tel.: (44) 3456003476
Health Care Srvices
N.A.I.C.S.: 621999

Bupa Optical Pty Ltd. (1)
Level 15 33 Exhibition Street, Melbourne, 3000, VIC, Australia
Tel.: (61) 1300363992
Web Site: https://bupaoptical.bupa.com.au
Optical Goods Retailer
N.A.I.C.S.: 456130

Bupa Servicios de Salud SpA (1)
Av las Condes 8840, Santiago, Metropolitana, Chile
Tel.: (56) 227828190
Web Site: https://bupasport.cl
Medical Consulting Services
N.A.I.C.S.: 541611

Care Plus Medicina Assistencial Ltda. (1)
Alameda Mamore 687 - 12th Floor, Alphaville, Barueri, 06454-040, SP, Brazil
Tel.: (55) 1141979000
Web Site: https://www.careplus.com.br
Health Care Srvices
N.A.I.C.S.: 621999

Central MRI Centre Limited (1)
8/F Le Diamant 703-705 Nathan Road, Mongkok, Kowloon, China (Hong Kong)
Tel.: (852) 23386502
Web Site: https://www.centramri.hk
Diagnostic Imaging Services
N.A.I.C.S.: 621512

Clock Tower Dental Care Limited (1)
88 High Street, Epsom, KT19 8BJ, Surrey, United Kingdom
Tel.: (44) 1372720136
Web Site: https://www.clocktowerdental.com
Dental Care Services
N.A.I.C.S.: 621210

Dencraft (Leicester) Ltd. (1)
238 London Rd, Leicester, LE2 1RH, United Kingdom
Tel.: (44) 1162127770
Web Site: https://dencraftuk.com
Dental Product Mfr
N.A.I.C.S.: 339116

Especializada y Primaria Lhorta-Manises SA (1)
Avda Generalitat Valenciana 50, Manises, 46940, Valencia, Spain
Tel.: (34) 961845000
Web Site: http://www.hospitalmanises.es
Health Care Srvices
N.A.I.C.S.: 621999

Eurodontic Limited (1)
21 Gleadless Rd, Lowfield, Sheffield, SS2 3AA, United Kingdom
Tel.: (44) 1142766813
Web Site: https://eurodontic.co.uk
Dental Product Distr
N.A.I.C.S.: 423450

Grupo Bupa Sanitas SL (1)
Calle Ribera Del Loira 52, Madrid, 28042, Spain
Tel.: (34) 915852210
Web Site: http://www.gruposanitas.com
Health Care Srvices
N.A.I.C.S.: 621999

Luke Barnett Limited (1)
30 Clarendon Road, Watford, WD17 1JJ, Hertfordshire, United Kingdom
Tel.: (44) 1923251537
Web Site: https://www.lukebarnett.com
Dental Product Mfr
N.A.I.C.S.: 339116

Medical Services International Limited (1)
162-174 Cromwell Road, London, SW5 0TU, United Kingdom
Tel.: (44) 207 460 2000
Health Care Srvices
N.A.I.C.S.: 621999

Oasis Healthcare Limited (1)
Vantage Office Park Old Gloucester Road, Hambrook, Bristol, BS16 1GW, United Kingdom
Tel.: (44) 1179424044
Web Site: http://www.oasisdentalcare.co.uk

THE BRITISH UNITED PROVIDENT ASSOCIATION LIMITED

The British United Provident Association Limited—(Continued)

Holding Company; Dental Offices Owner & Operator
N.A.I.C.S.: 551112

Subsidiary (Domestic):

Oasis Dental Care Limited (2)
Vantage Pk Old Gloucester Rd, Hambrook, Bristol, BS16 1GW, United Kingdom
Tel.: (44) 8456029335
Web Site: http://www.oasisdentalcare.co.uk
Dental Office Operator
N.A.I.C.S.: 621210

Quality HealthCare Medical Services Limited (1)
3/F Skyline Tower 39 Wang Kwong Road, Kowloon Bay, Kowloon, China (Hong Kong) (100%)
Tel.: (852) 29753200
Web Site: http://www.qhms.com
Sales Range: $50-74.9 Million
Emp.: 400
Contract Healthcare Services & Medical Centers Network Operator
N.A.I.C.S.: 621399

Subsidiary (Domestic):

Quality HealthCare Medical Centre Limited (2)
Shop No 41 &43A 1/F Exchange Tower 33 Wang Chiu Road, Kowloon Bay, Kowloon, China (Hong Kong) (100%)
Tel.: (852) 26598399
Web Site: http://www.qhms.com
Sales Range: $25-49.9 Million
Emp.: 200
HMO Medical Centers Operator
N.A.I.C.S.: 621491

Quality HealthCare Nursing Agency Limited (2)
3/F Skyline Tower 39 Wang Kwong Road, Kowloon Bay, Kowloon, China (Hong Kong) (100%)
Tel.: (852) 29752391
Web Site: http://qhna.qhms.com
Private Nursing Services
N.A.I.C.S.: 621399

Quality HealthCare Physiotherapy Services Limited (2)
3/F Skyline Tower 39 Wang Kwong Road, Kowloon Bay, Kowloon, China (Hong Kong) (100%)
Tel.: (852) 2975 3200
Web Site: http://www.qhms.com
Physiotherapy Services
N.A.I.C.S.: 621340

Richley Dental Ceramics Limited (1)
209-215 Long Lane, Halesowen, Birmingham, B62 9JT, United Kingdom
Tel.: (44) 1214214775
Web Site: https://www.richleydental.co.uk
Dental Product Mfr
N.A.I.C.S.: 339116

Total Orthodontics Limited (1)
Bupa Dental Care Vantage Office Park Old Gloucester Road, Hambrook, Bristol, BS16 1GW, United Kingdom
Tel.: (44) 1454771594
Web Site: https://www.totalorthodontics.co.uk
Medical Consulting Services
N.A.I.C.S.: 541611

THE BROOKER GROUP PUBLIC COMPANY LIMITED

26/F The Trendy Office Building 10/190-193 Soi Sukhumvit 13, Sukhumvit Road Klong Toey Nua Wattana, Bangkok, 10110, Thailand
Tel.: (66) 21687100
Web Site: https://www.brookergroup.com
BROOK—(THA)
Rev.: $6,719,642
Assets: $85,494,138
Liabilities: $3,201,464
Net Worth: $82,292,674
Earnings: $2,011,127
Fiscal Year-end: 12/31/20
Independent Research & Consulting Services
N.A.I.C.S.: 541611
Narongchai Akrasanee (Chm)

Subsidiaries:

Binswanger Brooker (Thailand) Limited (1)
26th Fl Trendy Ofc Bldg 10 190 193, Sukhumvit Soi 13 Wattana, Bangkok, Thailand
Tel.: (66) 21687100
Web Site: http://www.binswangerbrooker.com
Sales Range: $25-49.9 Million
Emp.: 30
Real Estate Brokerage & Consulting Services
N.A.I.C.S.: 531390
Angkana Tuam-uam Sr. (Sr Mgr-Real Estate Svcs)

THE BUTCHER ENGINEERING ENTERPRISES LIMITED

2755 Lauzon Parkway, Windsor, N8T 3H5, ON, Canada
Tel.: (519) 944-9200
Web Site: http://www.butcherengineering.com
Year Founded: 1943
Rev.: $69,555,960
Emp.: 850
Packaging & Painting Services
N.A.I.C.S.: 488991
William Spencer (Pres)

THE BYKE HOSPITALITY LIMITED

Sunil Patodia Tower Plot No156-158 Near Bombay Cambridge School, Chakravarti Ashok Society J B Nagar Andheri E, Mumbai, 400 099, India
Tel.: (91) 2267079666
Web Site: https://www.thebyke.com
Year Founded: 1990
BYKE—(NSE)
Rev.: $13,842,348
Assets: $29,598,945
Liabilities: $10,474,420
Net Worth: $19,124,525
Earnings: $274,396
Emp.: 800
Fiscal Year-end: 03/31/23
Home Management Services
N.A.I.C.S.: 721110
Anil Patodia (Mng Dir)

THE CABLESHOPPE INC.

1410 Birchmount Road, Toronto, M1P 2E3, ON, Canada
Tel.: (416) 293-3634
Web Site: http://www.thecableshoppe.com
Year Founded: 1991
Rev.: $15,727,375
Emp.: 150
Telecommunication Servicesb
N.A.I.C.S.: 517810
Monty Muthulingam (Co-Chm)

THE CADILLAC FAIRVIEW CORPORATION LIMITED

20 Queen Street West 5th Floor, Toronto, M5H 3R4, ON, Canada
Tel.: (416) 598-8200
Web Site: http://www.cadillacfairview.com
Sales Range: $400-449.9 Million
Emp.: 1,700
Real Estate Managers
N.A.I.C.S.: 531210
John M. Sullivan (Pres & CEO)

Subsidiaries:

Sherway Gardens (1)
25 W Mall, Toronto, M9C 1B8, ON, Canada (100%)
Tel.: (416) 621-1070
Web Site: http://www.sherwaygardens.ca
Sales Range: $50-74.9 Million
Emp.: 100
Retail & Commercial Properties
N.A.I.C.S.: 531312
Andy Traynor (Gen Mgr)

THE CALDWELL PARTNERS INTERNATIONAL INC.

TD South Tower 79 Wellington Street West, PO Box 75, Toronto, M5K 1E7, ON, Canada
Tel.: (416) 920-7702 ON
Web Site: https://www.caldwellpartners.com
Year Founded: 1970
CWL—(TSX)
Rev.: $93,690,546
Assets: $68,162,403
Liabilities: $48,017,129
Net Worth: $20,145,275
Earnings: $3,535,123
Emp.: 131
Fiscal Year-end: 08/31/21
Executive Search & Consulting Services
N.A.I.C.S.: 541612
John Wallace (Mgr-Lorneville Plant)

Subsidiaries:

Caldwell Interim Executives Inc. (1)
165 Ave Rd, Toronto, M5R 3S4, ON, Canada
Tel.: (416) 920-7702
Human Resource Consulting Services
N.A.I.C.S.: 541612
Jhon Wallace (Pres)

Prince Arthur Advertising Inc. (1)
79 Wellington Street West TD South Tower Suite 2410, PO Box 75, Toronto, M5K 1E, ON, Canada
Tel.: (416) 920-7702
Web Site: http://www.caldwellpartners.com
Advertising Agencies & Consultants
N.A.I.C.S.: 541810

THE CALMER CO INTERNATIONAL LIMITED

96 Victoria Street, West End, 4101, QLD, Australia
Tel.: (61) 429210031
Web Site: https://www.thecalmerco.com
Year Founded: 2014
CCO—(ASX)
Rev.: $1,163,359
Assets: $2,109,846
Liabilities: $2,166,915
Net Worth: $(57,069)
Earnings: $(3,417,803)
Fiscal Year-end: 06/30/23
Health Care Srvices
N.A.I.C.S.: 621610
Pravinesh Lala (CFO)

THE CANADIAN BROADCASTING CORPORATION

181 Queen St, Ottawa, K1P, 1K9, ON, Canada
Tel.: (613) 288-6000
Web Site: http://www.cbc.ca
Year Founded: 1936
Sales Range: $500-549.9 Million
Emp.: 10,000
Television & Radio Network Operator
N.A.I.C.S.: 516120

Subsidiaries:

Radio Canada International (1)
1400 Boul Rene Levesque East, PO Box 6000, Montreal, H2L 2M2, QC, Canada
Tel.: (514) 597-7500
Web Site: http://www.rcinet.ca
Sales Range: $25-49.9 Million
Emp.: 80
Radio Networks
N.A.I.C.S.: 516210
Pia Marquard (Mng Dir)

INTERNATIONAL PUBLIC

THE CARDIFF PROPERTY PLC

56 Station Road, Egham, TW20 9LF, Surrey, United Kingdom
Tel.: (44) 1784437444 UK
Web Site: https://www.cardiff-property.com
CDFF—(LSE)
Rev.: $792,540
Assets: $35,052,912
Liabilities: $1,302,030
Net Worth: $33,750,882
Earnings: $2,728,602
Fiscal Year-end: 09/30/22
Property Investment & Management Services
N.A.I.C.S.: 531311
J. Richard Wollenberg (Chm & CEO)

Subsidiaries:

First Choice Estates plc (1)
56 Sta Rd, Egham, TW20 9LF, Surrey, United Kingdom
Tel.: (44) 1784437444
Web Site: http://www.cardiff-property.com
Emp.: 4
Real Estate Manangement Services
N.A.I.C.S.: 531311
Richard Wollenberg (Chm)

Village Residential plc (1)
56 Station Rd, Egham, TW20 9LF, Surrey, United Kingdom (100%)
Tel.: (44) 1784437444
Web Site: http://www.cardiff-property.com
Real Estate Manangement Services
N.A.I.C.S.: 531312
J.R. Wollenberg (CEO)

THE CATALYST CAPITAL GROUP INC.

181 Bay Street Suite 4700, Bay Wellington Tower Brookfield Place, Toronto, M5J 2T3, ON, Canada
Tel.: (416) 945-3000
Web Site: http://www.catcapital.com
Year Founded: 2002
Sales Range: $900-999.9 Million
Privater Equity Firm
N.A.I.C.S.: 523999
Gabriel de Alba (Partner & Mng Dir)

Subsidiaries:

Advantage Rent A Car (1)
Tower 101 Ste 1600 101 NE 3rd Ave, Fort Lauderdale, FL 33301
Tel.: (800) 777-5500
Web Site: http://www.advantage.com
Car Rental Services
N.A.I.C.S.: 532111
William N. Plamondon (Pres)

Subsidiary (Domestic):

E-Z Rent-A-Car Group Holding LLC (2)
2003 McCoy Rd Ste A, Orlando, FL 32809
Tel.: (407) 438-6922
Web Site: http://www.e-zrentacar.com
Emp.: 20
Passenger Car Rental
N.A.I.C.S.: 532111
Jeff Wedemire (Dir)

Gateway Casinos & Entertainment Limited (1)
100-4400 Dominion Street, Burnaby, V5G 4G3, BC, Canada
Tel.: (604) 412-0166
Web Site: https://www.gatewaycasinos.com
Sales Range: $350-399.9 Million
Casino & Gaming Services
N.A.I.C.S.: 721120
Tanya Gabara (Dir-PR-Western Canada)

Planet Organic Health Corp. (1)
7915 104th Street Suite 230, Edmonton, T6E 4E1, AB, Canada
Tel.: (780) 433-7278
Web Site: http://www.planetorganichealthcorp.com
Sales Range: $75-99.9 Million
Natural Foods Supermarket Operator
N.A.I.C.S.: 445110

Subsidiary (US):

Mrs. Green's Natural Markets (2)
780 White Plains Rd, Scarsdale, NY 10583
Tel.: (914) 472-0111
Web Site: http://www.mrsgreens.com
Sales Range: $25-49.9 Million
Emp.: 20
Natural Foods Supermarket Operator
N.A.I.C.S.: 445110

Subsidiary (Domestic):

Planet Organic Market Ltd. (2)
7917 - 104 Street, Edmonton, T6E 4E1, AB, Canada
Tel.: (708) 719-4667
Web Site: http://www.planetorganic.ca
Natural Foods Supermarket Operator
N.A.I.C.S.: 445110

Simply Wheelz LLC (1)
2500 450 1st Street SE, Calgary, T2P 5H1, AB, Canada
Tel.: (403) 259-6666
Web Site: http://www.advantage.com
Sales Range: $150-199.9 Million
Emp.: 600
Car Rental Services
N.A.I.C.S.: 532111
William Plamondon (Pres)

Therapure Biopharma Inc. (1)
2585 Meadowpine Blvd, Mississauga, L5N 8H9, ON, Canada
Tel.: (905) 286-6200
Web Site: http://www.therapurebio.com
Sales Range: $25-49.9 Million
Global Contract Development & Therapeutics for Biopharmaceutical Mfr
N.A.I.C.S.: 325414
Dirk Alkema (VP-Ops)

THE CEDARGLEN GROUP INC
Suite 140 550 71 Avenue SE, Calgary, T2H 0S6, AB, Canada
Tel.: (403) 255-2000
Web Site:
  http://www.cedarglenhomes.com
Year Founded: 1981
Rev.: $16,739,464
Emp.: 75
Construction Services
N.A.I.C.S.: 236115
Kimberley Holstein (Mgr-Sls-Area)

THE CENTRAL BANK OF THE BAHAMAS
Frederick Street, PO Box N 4868, Nassau, NP, Bahamas
Tel.: (242) 302 2600   BS
Web Site:
  http://www.centralbankbahama.com
Year Founded: 1974
Rev.: $60,129,009
Assets: $2,265,822,978
Liabilities: $2,039,904,967
Net Worth: $225,918,011
Earnings: $17,615,879
Emp.: 264
Fiscal Year-end: 12/31/19
Central Bank
N.A.I.C.S.: 521110
John A. Rolle (Chm & Governor)

THE CENTRE FOR GENOMIC REGULATION (CRG)
Carrer Doctor Aiguader 88 5a planta, 08003, Barcelona, Spain
Tel.: (34) 933160100
Web Site: https://www.crg.eu
Year Founded: 2000
Biotechnology Research & Development Services
N.A.I.C.S.: 541714

THE CENTURY CO., LTD.
86 Magokjungang-ro, Gangseo-gu, Seoul, Korea (South)
Tel.: (82) 233933500
Web Site:
  https://www.daehancinema.co.kr

Year Founded: 1958
002420—(KRS)
Rev.: $25,855,803
Assets: $39,609,292
Liabilities: $19,221,513
Net Worth: $20,387,779
Earnings: ($974,951)
Emp.: 45
Fiscal Year-end: 12/31/22
Theater Services
N.A.I.C.S.: 711110
Jeung-Hee Kim (Pres & CEO)

THE CG&B GROUP INC.
120 South Town Centre Blvd, Markham, L6G 1C3, ON, Canada
Tel.: (905) 479-6670
Web Site: http://www.ajjcanada.com
Year Founded: 1972
Rev.: $21,700,000
Emp.: 160
Insurance Agencies
N.A.I.C.S.: 524210
H. Larry Later (Pres & CEO)

THE CHANGE ORGANISATION LTD.
92-93 John Wilson Business Park, Whitstable, CT5 3QT, Kent, United Kingdom
Tel.: (44) 1227 779000
Web Site:
  http://www.thechange.co.uk
Year Founded: 1992
Sales Range: $25-49.9 Million
Emp.: 46
Computer Distrubution Services
N.A.I.C.S.: 423430
Peter Quinney (Dir-Ops & Sys)

THE CHARACTER GROUP PLC
2nd Floor 86-88 Coombe Road, New Malden, KT3 4QS, Surrey, United Kingdom
Tel.: (44) 2083293377
Web Site:
  https://www.thecharacter.com
CCT—(LSE)
Rev.: $190,076,727
Assets: $118,019,811
Liabilities: $57,123,354
Net Worth: $60,896,457
Earnings: $16,569,615
Emp.: 209
Fiscal Year-end: 08/31/21
Toys, Games & Gifts Mfr & Distr
N.A.I.C.S.: 339930
Kirankumar Premchand Shah (Co-Mng Dir, Fin Dir & Sec)

Subsidiaries:

Character Games Limited (1)
CityPoint 16th Floor One Ropemaker Street, London, EC2Y 9AW, Surrey, United Kingdom
Tel.: (44) 2089495898
Sales Range: $25-49.9 Million
Emp.: 12
Toys & Electronic Goods Mfr
N.A.I.C.S.: 339930

Character Gifts Limited (1)
CityPoint 16th Floor One Ropemaker Street, London, EC2Y 9AW, Surrey, United Kingdom
Tel.: (44) 2089495898
Web Site: http://www.character-online.co.uk
Sales Range: $25-49.9 Million
Emp.: 20
Toys & Collectibles Whslr
N.A.I.C.S.: 423920

Character Options Limited (1)
Lees Brook Mill Lees Road, Oldham, OL4 5JL, United Kingdom
Tel.: (44) 1616339808
Sales Range: $25-49.9 Million
Emp.: 200
Toys & Electronic Goods Mfr

N.A.I.C.S.: 339930

Chill Factor Global Pty Limited (1)
Airport Business Centre Archerfield - Unit 11 37 Mortimer Road, PO Box 150, Acacia Ridge, 4110, QLD, Australia
Tel.: (61) 732773433
Web Site: https://www.chillfactor.com.au
Refrigeration & Air Conditioning Installation Services
N.A.I.C.S.: 238220

OVG-Proxy A/S (1)
Gothersgade 14 3rd Floor, Copenhagen, 1123, Denmark
Tel.: (45) 33556120
Web Site: https://www.proxy.toys
Toy Distr
N.A.I.C.S.: 423920

Toy Options (Far East) Limited (1)
Room 1005-1007A 10 Fl, Empire Centre 68 Mody Rd E, Kowloon, 808 811, Tsim Sha Tsui, China (Hong Kong)
Tel.: (852) 21766380
Toys & Electronic Goods Mfr
N.A.I.C.S.: 339930

THE CHEMICAL SOCIETY AL-KIMIA
11 Rue des Lilas, Mahrajene, 1082, Tunis, Tunisia
Tel.: (216) 36080100
Web Site: http://www.alkimia.tn
Year Founded: 1972
Emp.: 302
Chemical Products Mfr
N.A.I.C.S.: 325998
Ali Mhiri (CEO)

Subsidiaries:

ALKIMIA-Packaging SA (1)
11 rue des lilas, 1082, Tunis, Tunisia
Tel.: (216) 71 846 052
Chemical Products Mfr
N.A.I.C.S.: 325998
Monsieur Ali Mhiri (CEO & Mng Dir)

THE CHIBA BANK, LTD.
1-2 Chiba-minato, Chuo-ku, Chiba, 260-8720, Japan
Tel.: (81) 433018459
Web Site:
  https://www.chibabank.co.jp
Year Founded: 1943
8331—(TKS)
Rev.: $2,054,004,620
Assets: $140,850,645,810
Liabilities: $133,040,910,980
Net Worth: $7,809,734,830
Earnings: $112,370
Emp.: 3,982
Fiscal Year-end: 03/31/24
Banking Services
N.A.I.C.S.: 522110
Norio Takatsu (CIO-Grp & Mng Exec Officer)

Subsidiaries:

Chiba Bank Ltd. (1)
1133 Avenue of the Americas 15th Fl, New York, NY 10036
Tel.: (212) 354-7777
Web Site: http://www.chibabank.co.jp
Sales Range: $50-74.9 Million
Emp.: 100
Banking Services
N.A.I.C.S.: 522110

Chiba Servicer Co.,Ltd. (1)
Chibagin Makuhari Building 1-10-2 Nakase, Mihama-ku, Chiba, 261-0023, Japan
Tel.: (81) 432136411
Web Site: https://www.chiba-servicer.co.jp
Nondepository Credit Intermediation Services
N.A.I.C.S.: 522299

Chibagin Accounting Service Co., Ltd. (1)
1-2 Chiba Minato Chuo-ku, Chiba, 260-8720, Japan
Tel.: (81) 432982020

Accounting, Staffing & Administration Services
N.A.I.C.S.: 541211
Hidetoshi Sakuma (Mgr)

Chibagin Asset Management Co., Ltd. (1)
2-13-7 Kotobashi, Sumida-ku, Tokyo, 130-0022, Japan
Tel.: (81) 356381450
Web Site: https://www.chibagin-am.co.jp
Sales Range: $50-74.9 Million
Emp.: 40
N.A.I.C.S.: 522210

Chibagin Capital Co., Ltd. (1)
Junichi Kuboshima 1-10-2 Nakase, Mihama-ku, Chiba, 261-0023, Japan   (25%)
Tel.: (81) 432982232
Web Site: https://www.chibagincapital.co.jp
Sales Range: $1-4.9 Billion
Emp.: 4,000
Consulting Services
N.A.I.C.S.: 523910

Chibagin Cash Business Co., Ltd. (1)
1-2 Chiba Minato Chukou, Chiba, 2608720, Tokyo, Japan   (100%)
Tel.: (81) 432451111
Web Site: http://www.chibabank.co.jp
Sales Range: $25-49.9 Million
Emp.: 197
Collection Services
N.A.I.C.S.: 561440

Chibagin Computer Service Co., Ltd. (1)
Chibagin Makuhari Building 1-10-2 Nakase, Mihama-ku, Chiba, 261-0023, Japan   (4%)
Tel.: (81) 432928881
Computer Systems Development & Commissioned Computation Tasks
N.A.I.C.S.: 541511

Chibagin DC Card Co.,Ltd. (1)
WBG Malibu East 9F 2-6-1 Nakase, Mihama-ku, Chiba, 261-0023, Japan
Tel.: (81) 432762411
Web Site: https://www.chibagindc.co.jp
Emp.: 53
Credit Card Processing Services
N.A.I.C.S.: 522320

Chibagin Guarantee Company Ltd. (1)
1-2 Chiba-minato Chuo-ku, Chiba, 260-8720, Japan   (100%)
Tel.: (81) 432451111
Web Site: http://ir.chibabank.co.jp
Sales Range: $50-74.9 Million
Emp.: 84
Housing-Loan Guarantees & Fee Collection Services
N.A.I.C.S.: 531390
Hidetoshi Sakuma (Pres)

Chibagin Heartful Co.,Ltd. (1)
4-1-10 Masago, Mihama-ku, Chiba, 261-0011, Japan
Tel.: (81) 432707341
Web Site: https://www.chibagin-heartful.co.jp
Emp.: 51
Business Management Consulting Services
N.A.I.C.S.: 541618

Chibagin JCB Card Co.,Ltd. (1)
World Business Garden Malibu East 9th floor 2-6-1 Nakase, Mihama Ward, Chiba, 261-7109, Japan
Tel.: (81) 432967288
Web Site: https://www.chibaginjcb.co.jp
Emp.: 51
Credit Card Processing Services
N.A.I.C.S.: 522320

Chibagin Lease Co., Ltd. (1)
Mihagama-Ku Nakase 1102, Mahakuhadi, Chiba, 2610023, Japan   (5%)
Tel.: (81) 432758001
Sales Range: $50-74.9 Million
Emp.: 71
Leasing & Loans
N.A.I.C.S.: 522299

Chibagin Leasing Co., Ltd. (1)
2-1-22 Hanazono, Hanamigawa-ku, Chiba,

THE CHIBA BANK, LTD.

The Chiba Bank, Ltd.—(Continued)
262-0025, Japan
Tel.: (81) 432758001
Web Site: http://www.chibabank.co.jp
Leasing Services
N.A.I.C.S.: 525990
Tetsuya Koike (Pres)

Chibagin Research Institute Co.,Ltd. (1)
2-3-12 Konakadai, Inage-ku, Chiba, 263-0043, Japan
Tel.: (81) 432451111
Computer Systems Consulting Services
N.A.I.C.S.: 541511

Chibagin Securities Co.,Ltd. (1)
2-5-1 Chuo, Chuo-ku, Chiba, 260-0013, Japan
Tel.: (81) 432221141
Web Site: http://www.chibagin-sec.co.jp
Emp.: 310
Securities Dealing Services
N.A.I.C.S.: 523150

Sobu Co., Ltd. (1)
Line 3-18-8 Nakakasai, Edogawa-ku, Tokyo, 134-0083, Japan
Tel.: (81) 338041134
Web Site: https://www.sobu-snc.com
Commercial Buildings Rental & Maintenance Services
N.A.I.C.S.: 531120

T&I Innovation Center, Co. Ltd. (1)
KABUTO ONE 11F 7-1 Nihonbashi Kabuto-cho, Chuo-ku, Tokyo, 103-0026, Japan
Tel.: (81) 356427775
Web Site: https://www.tandiic.co.jp
Financial Services
N.A.I.C.S.: 523999

The Chiba Bank Ltd. (1)
1-2 Chiba-minato, Chuo-ku, Chiba, 260-8720, Japan (100%)
Tel.: (81) 433018459
Web Site: http://www.chibabank.co.jp
Sales Range: $200-249.9 Million
Provider of Securities Services
N.A.I.C.S.: 523999
Hidetoshi Sakuma (Pres)

The Chiba Bank, Ltd. - Treasury Operation Division (1)
1 5 5 Nihombashi Muromachi, Chuo-ku, Tokyo, 103-0022, Japan
Tel.: (81) 332708459
Emp.: 50
Financial Management Consulting Services
N.A.I.C.S.: 541611
Shinichi Ikeda (Gen Mgr)

The Chiba Bank, Ltd.-Treasury Division (1)
1-5-5 Nihombashi Muromachi, Chuo-ku, Tokyo, 103-0022, Japan (100%)
Tel.: (81) 332311285
Web Site: https://www.chibabank.co.jp
Sales Range: $50-74.9 Million
Emp.: 40
Management of Rental Housing & Lot-Division Houses
N.A.I.C.S.: 522110

THE CHIBA KOGYO BANK, LTD.

1-2 Saiwaicho 2-chome, Mihama-ku, Chiba, 261-0001, Japan
Tel.: (81) 432432111
Web Site: https://www.chibakogyo-bank.co.jp
Year Founded: 1952
8337—(TKS)
Rev.: $360,800,240
Assets: $21,345,183,860
Liabilities: $20,107,263,060
Net Worth: $1,237,920,800
Earnings: $66,100
Emp.: 1,238
Fiscal Year-end: 03/31/24
Commercial Banking Services
N.A.I.C.S.: 522110
Kouichi Kyoumasu (Exec Officer)

Subsidiaries:

Chiba General Lease Co., Ltd. (1)
3rd floor Chiba Kogyo Bank Chiba Ekimae Branch Building 1-1-17 Fujimi, Chuo-ku, Chiba, 260-0015, Japan (26%)
Tel.: (81) 432279361
Web Site: https://www.chiba-general-lease.co.jp
Sales Range: $50-74.9 Million
Emp.: 40
General Insurance Services
N.A.I.C.S.: 524113

Chiba Kogin Business Service Co., Ltd. (1)
1-2 Saiwaicho 2 Chome, Mihama, Chiba, 261 0001, Japan (100%)
Tel.: (81) 432432111
Sales Range: $200-249.9 Million
Emp.: 300
Financial Services
N.A.I.C.S.: 522299

Chiba Kogin Card Service Co., Ltd. (1)
3rd floor Sodegaura Building 4-17-3 Chuo, Chuo-ku, Chiba, 260-0013, Japan (100%)
Tel.: (81) 432247811
Web Site: https://www.cuccard.co.jp
Emp.: 51,468
Credit Card Processing & Mortgage Loan Services
N.A.I.C.S.: 522320

Chiba Kogin Computer Soft Co., Ltd. (1)
Chiba Kogyo Bank Office Center 2-2-2 Saiwaicho, Mihama-ku, Chiba, 261-0001, Japan
Tel.: (81) 50 3535 2441
Web Site: http://www.chibakogin-cs.co.jp
Emp.: 86
Commercial Banking & Financial Services
N.A.I.C.S.: 522299

Chiba Kogin Finance Co., Ltd. (1)
1-17 Fujimi 1 Chome, Chuo Ku, Chiba, 600015, Japan
Tel.: (81) 432272821
Financial Services
N.A.I.C.S.: 522299

Chiba Kogin Staff Services Co., Ltd. (1)
1-2 Saiwaicho 2 Chome, Mihama Ku, Chiba, Japan
Tel.: (81) 432436161
Financial Services
N.A.I.C.S.: 522299

Chiba Kogin UC Card Co., Ltd. (1)
No 17 3rd Floor Sodegaura Building 4-chome Chiba Chuo, Chiba, 260 0013, Japan (98%)
Tel.: (81) 43 224 0821
Web Site: http://www.cuccard.co.jp
Sales Range: $50-74.9 Million
Emp.: 30
Banking & Credit Card Issuance Services
N.A.I.C.S.: 522210

Chiba Kogyo Bank-Financial Market Div (1)
3-10 Higashi-Kamba, 2-chome, Chiyoda-ku, Tokyo, Japan
Tel.: (81) 3 3561 5031
Financial Services
N.A.I.C.S.: 522299

THE CHUGOKU ELECTRIC POWER CO., INC.

4-33 Komachi, Naka-ku, Hiroshima, 730-8701, Japan
Tel.: (81) 822410211
Web Site: https://www.energia.co.jp
Year Founded: 1951
CGKEY—(OTCIQ)
Rev.: $12,150,296,340
Assets: $28,967,144,160
Liabilities: $25,701,331,050
Net Worth: $3,265,813,110
Earnings: ($1,114,060,260)
Emp.: 12,885
Fiscal Year-end: 03/31/23
Electronic Services
N.A.I.C.S.: 221122
Tomohide Karita (Chm)

Subsidiaries:

Air Water & Energia Power Yamaguchi Corporation (1)
3-1 Kanebocho, Hofu, 747-0823, Yamaguchi, Japan (100%)
Tel.: (81) 83 520 1622
Web Site: https://www.awep-yamaguchi.co.jp
Comprehensive Energy Distribution Services
N.A.I.C.S.: 221122

Chuden Engineering Consultants Co., Ltd. (1)
2-3-30 Deshio, Minami-ku, Hiroshima, 734-8510, Japan
Tel.: (81) 82 255 5501
Web Site: http://www.cecnet.co.jp
Engineeering Services
N.A.I.C.S.: 541330

Chuden Kankyo Technos Co., Ltd. (1)
4-33 Komachi, Naka-ku, Hiroshima, 730-0041, Japan
Tel.: (81) 82 242 0291
Web Site: https://www.e-ckt.jp
Electric Power Distribution Services
N.A.I.C.S.: 221121

Chuden Kogyo Co., Ltd. (1)
2-3-24 Deshio, Minami-ku, Hiroshima, 734-0001, Japan (100%)
Tel.: (81) 82 505 1500
Web Site: http://www.chuden-kogyo.co.jp
Emp.: 137
Construction & Painting Contractor
N.A.I.C.S.: 238990

Chuden Plant Co., Ltd. (1)
2-3-18 Deshio, Minami-ku, Hiroshima, 734-0001, Japan
Tel.: (81) 82 252 4311
Web Site: http://www.chuden-plant.co.jp
Sales Range: $400-449.9 Million
Emp.: 1,063
Construction Repair of Equipment
N.A.I.C.S.: 237990

Chugoku Bend Co., Ltd. (1)
4-6-23 Kusunoki-cho, Nishi-ku, Hiroshima, 733-0002, Japan
Tel.: (81) 82 509 0111
Web Site: https://www.bend.co.jp
Expansion Joint Mfr
N.A.I.C.S.: 332312

Chugoku Electric Power America, LLC (1)
1120 Avenue of the Americas Fl 4, New York, NY 10036
Tel.: (212) 626-2693
Investment Services
N.A.I.C.S.: 523999

Chugoku Record Management Inc. (1)
4-33 Komachi, Naka-ku, Hiroshima, 730-0041, Japan
Tel.: (81) 82 242 0270
Web Site: https://www.energia-crm.jp
General Management Consulting Services
N.A.I.C.S.: 541611

Denryoku Support Chugoku Co., Inc. (1)
Sumitomo Life Hiroshima Peace Boulevard Building 8F 7-22 Nakamachi, Naka-ku, Hiroshima, 730-0037, Japan
Tel.: (81) 82 541 1136
Web Site: https://www.d-sapo-c.co.jp
Electric Power Distribution Services
N.A.I.C.S.: 221121

Energia Business Service Co., Inc. (1)
Yubinbango Kokutai-ji-cho No chome 3 No 29 MRR Derutabiru, Hiroshima, 730-0042, Japan
Tel.: (81) 82 543 5060
Web Site: https://www.ebs-web.co.jp
Electric Power Distribution Services
N.A.I.C.S.: 221121

Energia Communications Inc (1)
2-11-10 Otemachi, Naka-ku, Hiroshima, 730-0051, Japan
Tel.: (81) 822478511
Web Site: http://www.enecom.co.jp
Sales Range: $200-249.9 Million
Emp.: 1,021
Information Processing
N.A.I.C.S.: 517810

Energia L&B Partners Co., Inc. (1)
4-33 Komachi, Naka-ku, Hiroshima, Japan
Tel.: (81) 82 242 7804
Web Site: https://www.energia-lbp.co.jp
Real Estate Services
N.A.I.C.S.: 531210

Energia Smile Co., Inc. (1)
4-1117 Heiseigahama, Saka-cho Aki-gun, Hiroshima, 731-4312, Japan
Tel.: (81) 82 218 0894
Web Site: https://www.energia-smile.co.jp
Vehicle Leasing Services
N.A.I.C.S.: 532112

Kaita Biomass Power Co., Ltd. (1)
2-118 Myojinmach In Hiroshima Gas Kaita Base, Kaita-cho Aki-gun, Hiroshima, 736-0056, Japan
Tel.: (81) 82 822 0770
Web Site: https://kaita-bp.co.jp
Comprehensive Energy Distribution Services
N.A.I.C.S.: 221122

Nichidenkogyo Co., Ltd. (1)
126 kotsuka, Fujisawa, 251-0013, Kanagawa, Japan
Tel.: (81) 46 622 8151
Web Site: https://www.nichiden-kogyo.co.jp
Automated Control Equipment Mfr & Distr
N.A.I.C.S.: 334519
Mitsuhiro Saiki (Plant Dir)

Tempearl Industrial Co Ltd (1)
3-1-42 Oozu, Minami-ku, Hiroshima, 732-0802, Japan
Tel.: (81) 822821341
Web Site: https://www.tempearl.co.jp
Emp.: 336
Circuit Breaker Mfr
N.A.I.C.S.: 334413
Miura Koakira (Pres)

The Chugoku Electric Manufacturing Co., Inc (1)
4-4-32 Ozu, Minami-ku, Hiroshima, 732-8564, Japan
Tel.: (81) 822863411
Web Site: https://chuki.jp
Sales Range: $75-99.9 Million
Emp.: 267
Electric Power Meter Repair Services
N.A.I.C.S.: 811114

THE CISNEROS GROUP OF COMPANIES

Edificio Venevision Quinto Piso Final Avenida La Salle, Caracas, 1050, Venezuela
Tel.: (58) 2127815066
Web Site: http://www.cisneros.com
Year Founded: 1929
Sales Range: $1-4.9 Billion
Emp.: 10,000
Holding Company; Broadcast & Pay Television, Radio & the Internet
N.A.I.C.S.: 551112
Miguel Dvorak (COO)

Subsidiaries:

Americatel Sistemas de Comunicacion C.A. (1)
C C Pza Aeropuerto 2 2-10 Zona Industrial Unare I, Puerto Ordaz, Bolivar, Venezuela
Tel.: (58) 212 700 47 00
Web Site: http://www.americatel.com.ve
Telecommunication Management Services
N.A.I.C.S.: 541618

Cuponidad Peru (1)
Miguel Dasso 117 Piso 9, San Isidro, Lima, Peru
Tel.: (51) 1 422 4649
Telecommunication Servicesb
N.A.I.C.S.: 541618

Cuponidad Venezuela CA (1)
Av Tamanaco Edif La Union Piso 6 Ofic 6-A, El Rosal, Caracas, 1060, Venezuela
Tel.: (58) 212 953 6562
Web Site: http://www.cuponidad.com.ve

Telecommunication Servicesb
N.A.I.C.S.: 541618

RedMas (1)
121 Alhambra Plz Ste 1400, Coral Gables, FL 33134
Tel.: (305) 442-3411
Web Site: http://www.redmas.com
Advertising Services
N.A.I.C.S.: 541810
Alejandro Leon Navas (Reg Dir-Ventas Pan)

THE CITY BANK LIMITED
Plot SE D 3 28 Gulshan Avenue
Gulshan1, Gulshan-2, Dhaka, 1212, Bangladesh
Tel.: (880) 258813126
Web Site: https://www.citybankplc.com
Year Founded: 1983
CITYBANK—(DHA)
Rev.: $311,436,410
Assets: $5,164,833,709
Liabilities: $4,813,072,326
Net Worth: $351,761,383
Earnings: $58,371,382
Emp.: 4,963
Fiscal Year-end: 12/31/23
Banking Services
N.A.I.C.S.: 522110
Aziz Al Kaiser (Chm)

Subsidiaries:

CBL Money Transfer Sdn. Bhd. (1)
No 2 Leboh Pasar Besar, 50050, Kuala Lumpur, Malaysia
Tel.: (60) 326933777
Web Site: https://www.cblmoneytransfer.com
Money Transfer Services
N.A.I.C.S.: 522320
Gilbert Tan (Chief Compliance Officer)

City Bank Capital Resources Limited (1)
City Centre 13th Floor Level-14 Unit ID 13D 90/1 Motijheel C/A, Dhaka, 1000, Bangladesh
Tel.: (880) 9613011011
Web Site: https://www.cbcrl.com
Commercial Banking Services
N.A.I.C.S.: 522110
Aziz Al Mahmood (Chm)

City Brokerage Limited (1)
City Centre Unit 12A and 12B 12th Floor Level-13 90/1 Motijheel C/A, Dhaka, 1000, Bangladesh
Tel.: (880) 9678111111
Web Site: https://www.citybrokerageltd.com
Brokerage Services
N.A.I.C.S.: 523150
Hossain Khaled (Chm)

THE CITY OF LONDON INVESTMENT TRUST PLC
201 Bishopsgate, London, EC2M 3AE, United Kingdom
Tel.: (44) 800832832 UK
Year Founded: 1899
TCL—(NZX)
Rev.: $151,537,845
Assets: $2,627,280,525
Liabilities: $187,923,383
Net Worth: $2,439,357,142
Earnings: $134,731,986
Fiscal Year-end: 06/30/22
Investment Management Service
N.A.I.C.S.: 525910
Philip Remnant (Chm)

THE CITY PUB GROUP PLC
2nd Floor Essel House 29 Foley Street, London, W1W 7TH, United Kingdom
Tel.: (44) 2075595106 UK
Web Site: http://www.citypubcompany.com
Year Founded: 2011

CPC—(AIM)
Rev.: $72,952,537
Assets: $171,983,085
Liabilities: $53,802,070
Net Worth: $118,181,015
Earnings: $1,200,454
Emp.: 1,053
Fiscal Year-end: 12/31/22
Entertainment Facility Operator
N.A.I.C.S.: 721310
Clive Watson (Chm)

THE CLARKE GROUP
33610 E Broadway Ave, Mission, V2V 4M4, BC, Canada
Tel.: (604) 826-9531
Web Site: http://www.clarkegroup.com
Sales Range: $10-24.9 Million
Emp.: 70
Mfr of Cedar Shingle Siding Panels, Cedar Shingle Roofing Panels & Fancy Cut Shingles
N.A.I.C.S.: 326199
Louis Clarke (Pres & COO)

Subsidiaries:

Shakertown 1992, Inc. (1)
1200 Kerron St, Winlock, WA 98596
Tel.: (360) 785-3501
Web Site: http://www.shakertown.com
Cedar Shingles Mfr
N.A.I.C.S.: 321999

THE CLASS HYOSUNG CO., LTD.
946-1 Dogok-dong, Gangnam-gu, Seoul, Korea (South)
Tel.: (82) 2 5757 500
Web Site: http://www.theclasshyosung.com
Sales Range: $25-49.9 Million
Emp.: 50
Automotive Distr
N.A.I.C.S.: 423110
Bill Ahn (Gen Mgr)

THE CLEVELAND GROUP OF COMPANIES LIMITED
Yarm Rd, PO Box 27, Darlington, Durham, DL1 4DE, United Kingdom
Tel.: (44) 325381188 UK
Web Site: http://www.clevelandbridge.com
Year Founded: 1877
Sales Range: $75-99.9 Million
Emp.: 400
Designer, Supplier, Fabrication & Erection of Bridges, Power Stations & Commercial & Industrial Structures
N.A.I.C.S.: 541330
Chris Droogan (Mng Dir)

Subsidiaries:

Cleveland Bridge International Ltd (1)
19D Yu Jia Building 1336 Huashan Rd, Shanghai, Changning District, China (100%)
Tel.: (86) 2162110500
Web Site: http://www.clevelandbridge.com
Engineering & Construction Services
N.A.I.C.S.: 541330

Cleveland Bridge Steel Company Ltd (1)
Road 106, PO Box 10017, Al Jubayl, Saudi Arabia
Tel.: (966) 3 340 8701
Web Site: http://www.clevelandbridge.sa
Emp.: 200
Construction Engineering Services
N.A.I.C.S.: 541330
Kevin Lancaster (Gen Mgr)

Cleveland Bridge UK Ltd. (1)
Cleveland House Yarm Rd, PO Box 27, Darlington, DL1 4DE, Durham, United Kingdom (100%)
Tel.: (44) 1325381188

Web Site: http://www.clevelandbridge.com
Sales Range: $100-124.9 Million
Emp.: 200
Holding Company; Bridge & Civil Engineering Construction Services
N.A.I.C.S.: 551112
Brian Rogan (Mng Dir)

Subsidiary (Domestic):

Cleveland Bridge & Engineering Co. Ltd.
Yarm Rd, PO Box 27, Darlington, DL1 4DE, United Kingdom (100%)
Tel.: (44) 1325381188
Web Site: http://www.clevelandbridge.com
Sales Range: $50-74.9 Million
Emp.: 200
Bridge & Civil Engineering Construction Services
N.A.I.C.S.: 237310
Brian Rogan (Mng Dir)

Subsidiary (Non-US):

Cleveland Bridge & Engineering Middle East (Pvt) Ltd (3)
9 Fl 7 8 Elleble Alli, PO Box 16765, Dubai, United Arab Emirates (100%)
Tel.: (971) 48835551
Web Site: http://www.clevelandbridge.co.ae
Sales Range: $25-49.9 Million
Emp.: 100
Engineering Services
N.A.I.C.S.: 541330
Michael Mack (Mng Dir)

Dorman Long UK Ltd (1)
Yarm Rd, PO Box 27, Darlington, DL1 4DE, United Kingdom (100%)
Tel.: (44) 1325390000
Web Site: http://www.dormanlongtechnology.com
Sales Range: $25-49.9 Million
Emp.: 12
Engineeering Services
N.A.I.C.S.: 541330
David Dyer (Mng Dir)

Subsidiary (Domestic):

Dorman Long Technology Ltd (2)
Whessoe Technology Centre Morton Palms, PO Box 27, Darlington, DL1 4Wb, United Kingdom (100%)
Tel.: (44) 1325390000
Web Site: http://www.dormanlongtechnology.com
Sales Range: $25-49.9 Million
Emp.: 12
Engineeering Services
N.A.I.C.S.: 541330
David Dyer (Mng Dir)

Subsidiary (Non-US):

Dorman Long Zalcon Ltd (2)
19D Yu Jia Building 1336 Huashan Rd, Shanghai, Changning District, China (100%)
Tel.: (86) 21 6211 0500
Web Site: http://www.dormanlongtechnology.com
Engineering Services
N.A.I.C.S.: 541330

THE CLIMAX ENGINEERING COMPANY LIMITED
Climaxabad GT Road, Gujranwala, Pakistan
Tel.: (92) 55 3253612
Machine Tools Mfr
N.A.I.C.S.: 333517

THE CO-OPERATIVE BANK OF KENYA LIMITED
Co-operative Bank House Haile Selassie Avenue, PO Box 48231, 00100, Nairobi, Kenya
Tel.: (254) 202776000
Web Site: https://www.co-opbank.co.ke
Year Founded: 1965
COOP—(NAI)
Rev.: $487,122,672
Assets: $4,521,088,836

Liabilities: $3,746,019,632
Net Worth: $775,069,204
Earnings: $98,397,163
Emp.: 4,016
Fiscal Year-end: 12/31/20
Investment Banking Services
N.A.I.C.S.: 523150
Macloud Malonza (Vice Chm)

Subsidiaries:

Co-op Consultancy & Bancassurance Intermediary Ltd. (1)
3rd Floor Haile Selassie Avenue, Nairobi, Kenya
Tel.: (254) 202776000
Web Site: https://insurance.co-opbank.co.ke
Insurance Advisory Services
N.A.I.C.S.: 524298

Co-optrust Investments Services Ltd. (1)
Co-operative Bank Building, PO Box 48231, 00100, Nairobi, Kenya
Tel.: (254) 203276532
Wealth Management Services
N.A.I.C.S.: 541612

THE CO-OPERATORS GROUP LIMITED
130 Macdonell Street, Guelph, N1H 6P8, ON, Canada
Tel.: (519) 824-4400
Web Site: http://www.cooperators.ca
Year Founded: 1945
Rev.: $3,922,237,620
Assets: $13,002,192,840
Liabilities: $10,207,918,980
Net Worth: $2,794,273,860
Earnings: $195,289,248
Emp.: 6,227
Fiscal Year-end: 12/31/19
Holding Company; Insurance Services
N.A.I.C.S.: 551112
Kevin Daniel (Chief Client Officer & Exec VP)

Subsidiaries:

Addenda Capital Inc. (1)
800 Rene-Levesque Blvd West Suite 2750, Montreal, H3B 1X9, QC, Canada (71.4%)
Tel.: (514) 287-7373
Web Site: https://www.addendacapital.com
Sales Range: $25-49.9 Million
Emp.: 125
Bond Portfolio Management
N.A.I.C.S.: 523999
Benoit Durocher (Exec VP)

Co-operators Financial Services Limited (1)
130 Macdonell Street, Guelph, N1H 6P8, ON, Canada
Tel.: (519) 824-4400
Web Site: http://www.cooperators.ca
Emp.: 800
Insurance Holding Company
N.A.I.C.S.: 551112

Subsidiary (Domestic):

Co-operators General Insurance Company (2)
101 Cooper Drive, Guelph, N1C 0A4, ON, Canada (100%)
Web Site: https://www.cooperators.ca
Rev.: $3,155,950,639
Assets: $7,047,176,421
Liabilities: $5,173,797,309
Net Worth: $1,873,379,111
Earnings: $400,848,877
Emp.: 4,301
Fiscal Year-end: 12/31/2021
General Insurance Services
N.A.I.C.S.: 524298
Denis Laverdiere (Vice Chm)

Co-operators Life Insurance Company (2)
1900 Albert Street, Regina, S4P 4K8, SK, Canada
Tel.: (306) 347-6200
Direct Life Insurance Carriers
N.A.I.C.S.: 524113

THE CO-OPERATORS GROUP LIMITED

The Co-operators Group Limited—(Continued)

Kathy Bardswick (Pres)

Smart Employee Benefits Inc. (2)
5500 Explorer Drive 4th Floor, Mississauga, L4C 5C7, ON, Canada
Tel.: (888) 939-8885
Web Site: http://www.seb-inc.com
Rev.: $48,329,821
Assets: $30,142,248
Liabilities: $44,223,712
Net Worth: ($14,081,464)
Earnings: ($4,462,512)
Fiscal Year-end: 11/30/2021
Investment Services
N.A.I.C.S.: 523999
John McKimm (Pres, CEO & Co-CIO)

Subsidiary (Domestic):

Adeeva Nutritionals Canada Inc. (3)
5500 Explorer Drive 4th Floor, Mississauga, L4W 5C7, ON, Canada
Web Site: https://www.adeeva.com
Pharmaceuticals Product Mfr
N.A.I.C.S.: 325412

Subsidiary (Non-US):

Inforica India Pvt. Ltd. (3)
Aditya Trade Center 3rd Floor Ameerpet, Hyderabad, 500038, India
Tel.: (91) 4066467575
Information Technology Consulting Services
N.A.I.C.S.: 541512

Subsidiary (Domestic):

Logitek Technology Ltd. (3)
5500 Explorer Drive, Mississauga, L4W 5C7, ON, Canada
Web Site: https://www.qlogitek.com
Integration Services
N.A.I.C.S.: 541512
Latiq Qureshi (Pres & CEO)

Maplesoft Group Inc. (3)
1545 Carling Ave Suite 702, Ottawa, K1Z 8P9, ON, Canada
Tel.: (613) 226-9993
Web Site: https://www.maplesoftgroup.com
Information Technology Services
N.A.I.C.S.: 541511
Scott Spencer (Sr VP)

SEB Administrative Services Inc. (3)
4th Floor 5500 Explorer Drive, Mississauga, L4W 5C7, ON, Canada
Web Site: https://www.seb-admin.com
Information Technology Services
N.A.I.C.S.: 541511
David Evans (Dir-Insurance Grp)

Subsidiary (Non-US):

SEB Administrative Services India Private Ltd. (3)
Unit 71-77 7th Floor Tower B The Corenthum Sector 62, Noida, 201309, Uttar Pradesh, India
Tel.: (91) 1204820950
Web Site: https://www.seb-inc.com
Information Technology Services
N.A.I.C.S.: 541519

Federated Agencies Limited (2)
5600 Cancross Ct, Mississauga, L5R 3E9, ON, Canada
Tel.: (905) 507-9823
Sales Range: $50-74.9 Million
Emp.: 30
Personal, Commercial & Wealth Management Products
N.A.I.C.S.: 523940

The CUMIS Group Limited (1)
151 North Service Road, PO Box 5065, Burlington, L7R 4C2, ON, Canada
Tel.: (905) 632-1221
Web Site: http://www.cumis.com
Sales Range: $200-249.9 Million
Emp.: 400
Fire, Marine & Casualty Insurance Services
N.A.I.C.S.: 524126
Alec Blundell (Pres & COO)

Subsidiary (Domestic):

CUMIS Life Insurance Company (2)
151 North Service Road, PO Box 5065, Burlington, L7R 4C2, ON, Canada
Tel.: (905) 632-1221
Web Site: http://www.cumis.com
Sales Range: $50-74.9 Million
Life Insurance Carrier
N.A.I.C.S.: 524113

The Sovereign General Insurance Company (1)
140 - 6700 Macleod Trail SE, Sovereign Centre, Calgary, T2H 0L3, AB, Canada
Tel.: (403) 298-4200
Web Site: https://www.sovereigninsurance.ca
Sales Range: $200-249.9 Million
Emp.: 80
General Insurance Carrier
N.A.I.C.S.: 524126
Matthew Campbell (VP-Fin, Ops & Claims-Toronto)

THE COCHIN MALABAR ESTATES & INDUSTRIES LIMITED

21 Strand Road, Kolkata, 700 001, West Bengal, India
Tel.: (91) 3322309601
Web Site: http://www.cochinmalabar.in
Year Founded: 1930
508571—(BOM)
Assets: $143,253
Liabilities: $553,886
Net Worth: ($410,633)
Earnings: ($78,084)
Emp.: 3
Fiscal Year-end: 03/31/23
Rubber & Tea Plantation Operator
N.A.I.C.S.: 111421

THE COLLINSON GROUP LIMITED

123 Houndsditch, London, EC3A 7BU, United Kingdom
Tel.: (44) 20 7422 1864   UK
Web Site: http://www.collinsongroup.com
Year Founded: 1991
Sales Range: $300-349.9 Million
Emp.: 2,000
Holding Company; Marketing, Insurance, Travel Enhancement & Technology Products & Services
N.A.I.C.S.: 551112
David Evans (Dir-Insurance Grp)

Subsidiaries:

Collinson Insurance Group Ltd. (1)
123 Houndsditch, London, EC3A 7BU, United Kingdom
Tel.: (44) 20 7422 4490
Web Site: http://www.collinsoninsurancegroup.com
Emp.: 400
Holding Company; Travel Insurance Products & Services
N.A.I.C.S.: 551112
David Evans (Mng Dir)

Subsidiary (Domestic):

Collinson Insurance Services Limited (2)
Sussex House Perrymount Road, Haywards Heath, RH16 1DN, W Sussex, United Kingdom
Tel.: (44) 1444442442
Sales Range: $25-49.9 Million
Emp.: 80
Holding Company; Medical, Travel & Automobile Assistance Services
N.A.I.C.S.: 551112
Tara Mead (Mgr-Market Dev)

Subsidiary (Domestic):

Astrenska Insurance Limited (3)
Sussex House Perrymount Rd, Haywards Heath, RH16 1DN, West Sussex, United Kingdom   (100%)
Tel.: (44) 1444442900
Web Site: http://www.astrenska.com
Medical, Travel & Automobile Assistance Services
N.A.I.C.S.: 541990

Subsidiary (Domestic):

Columbus Direct Limited (2)
19 Bartlett Street, Croydon, CR2 6TB, United Kingdom
Tel.: (44) 845 888 8893
Web Site: http://www.columbusdirect.com
Travel Insurance Products & Services
N.A.I.C.S.: 524128
Greg Lawson (Head-Retail)

Priority Travel Group (Holdings) Limited (1)
Cutlers Exchange, 123 Houndsditch, London, EC3A 7BU, United Kingdom
Tel.: (44) 20 8256 9035
Web Site: http://www.prioritytravelgroup.com
Emp.: 800
Holding Company; Travel Clubs & Enhancement Services
N.A.I.C.S.: 551112
Tim Gregory (Mgr-Bus Dev)

Unit (Domestic):

Lounge Club (2)
19 Bartlett Street, Croydon, CR2 6TB, Surrey, United Kingdom
Tel.: (44) 20 8827 0089
Web Site: http://www.loungeclub.com
Airport Lounge Membership Network Operator
N.A.I.C.S.: 722410
Collin Evans (CEO)

Lounge Pass (2)
19 Bartlett Street, Croydon, CR2 6TB, Surrey, United Kingdom
Tel.: (44) 20 8865 3280
Web Site: http://www.loungepass.com
Airport Lounge Membership Network Operator
N.A.I.C.S.: 722410
Jacqui Bates (Gen Mgr)

Subsidiary (Domestic):

Priority Pass Limited (2)
19 Bartlett Street, Croydon, CR2 6TB, Surrey, United Kingdom
Tel.: (44) 20 8680 1338
Web Site: http://www.prioritypass.com
Sales Range: $10-24.9 Million
Emp.: 100
Airport Lounge Membership Network Operator
N.A.I.C.S.: 722410
Jonathan French (Mgr-Mktg)

THE COLOMBO FORT LAND & BUILDING COMPANY PLC

No 8-5/2 Leyden Bastian Road York Arcade Building, 1, Colombo, Sri Lanka
Tel.: (94) 112344485
Web Site: https://www.cflbplc.com
Year Founded: 1895
CFLB.N0000—(COL)
Rev.: $252,639,249
Assets: $228,338,816
Liabilities: $189,063,176
Net Worth: $39,275,639
Earnings: $202,493
Fiscal Year-end: 03/31/24
Hardware Building Paint Material Mfr & Distr
N.A.I.C.S.: 325510
A. Rajaratnam (Chm)

THE COLONIAL MOTOR COMPANY LIMITED

Level 6 57 Courtenay Place, PO Box 6159, Wellington, 6141, New Zealand
Tel.: (64) 43849734
Web Site: https://www.colmotor.co.nz
CMO—(NZX)
Rev.: $596,426,435
Assets: $328,001,196
Liabilities: $139,052,632
Net Worth: $188,948,565
Earnings: $18,145,335
Emp.: 1,057
Fiscal Year-end: 06/30/23

INTERNATIONAL PUBLIC

Holding Company; New & Used Car, Heavy Truck & Tractor Dealerships Owner & Operator
N.A.I.C.S.: 551112
Jim P. Gibbons (Chm)

Subsidiaries:

Advance Agricentre Ltd (1)
243 Dee Street, Invercargill, 9810, New Zealand
Tel.: (64) 32111333
Web Site: http://www.advanceagricentre.co.nz
Sales Range: $50-74.9 Million
Emp.: 12
New & Used Tractor Dealers
N.A.I.C.S.: 423820

Avon City Motorcycles Ltd. (1)
Corner Main South Road Epsom Road, Sockburn, Christchurch, 8042, Canterbury, New Zealand
Tel.: (64) 33413490
Sales Range: $25-49.9 Million
Emp.: 11
Motorcycle Retailer
N.A.I.C.S.: 441227

Avon City Motors Ltd (1)
165 Main South Road, Sockburn, Christchurch, 8004, New Zealand
Tel.: (64) 33484129
Web Site: http://www.avoncityford.co.nz
Sales Range: $25-49.9 Million
Emp.: 100
New & Used Car Dealers
N.A.I.C.S.: 441110
John Luxton (Gen Mgr)

Capital City Motors Ltd (1)
97 Taranaki Street, Wellington, 6141, New Zealand
Tel.: (64) 48028750
Web Site: http://www.capitalcitymotors.co.nz
New & Used Car Dealers
N.A.I.C.S.: 441110
Matthew Carman (CEO)

Dunedin City Motors Ltd (1)
Cnr Andersons Bay & Macandrew Rd, Dunedin, 9044, New Zealand
Tel.: (64) 34664060
Web Site: http://www.dcford.co.nz
Sales Range: $25-49.9 Million
Emp.: 50
New & Used Car Dealers
N.A.I.C.S.: 441110
Steve Simpson (Mgr-Sls-Ford Used Vehicle)

Fagan Motors Ltd. (1)
75 Dixon Street, Masterton, 5810, New Zealand
Tel.: (64) 63786159
Web Site: https://www.faganford.co.nz
Sales Range: $25-49.9 Million
Emp.: 30
New Car Dealers
N.A.I.C.S.: 441110

Hutchinson Motors Ltd (1)
186 Tuam St, Christchurch, 8011, New Zealand
Tel.: (64) 33793440
Web Site: http://www.teamhutchinsonford.co.nz
Sales Range: $25-49.9 Million
Emp.: 70
New & Used Car Dealers
N.A.I.C.S.: 441110
Seth Ovens (Mgr-Retail Sls)

M.S. Motors (1998) Ltd. (1)
157 Haven Road, PO Box 106, Nelson, 7040, New Zealand
Tel.: (64) 35489189
Web Site: https://www.msford.co.nz
Sales Range: $25-49.9 Million
Emp.: 15
New Car Dealers
N.A.I.C.S.: 441110
Alan Kirby (Mng Dir)

Macaulay Motors Ltd (1)
270 Dee Street, Invercargill, 9810, New Zealand
Tel.: (64) 32111222
Web Site: http://www.macaulaymotors.co.nz
Sales Range: $25-49.9 Million
Emp.: 50
New & Used Car Dealers

AND PRIVATE COMPANIES

N.A.I.C.S.: 441110
Grant Price (CEO)

Metro Training Services Ltd. (1)
23 Parumoana Street, Porirua, 5022, Wellington, New Zealand
Tel.: (64) 6442372240
Web Site:
http://www.automotivetraining.co.nz
Sales Range: $25-49.9 Million
Emp.: 3
Automotive Repair Training Services
N.A.I.C.S.: 811198

Ruahine Motors Ltd. (1)
84 Ruataniwha Street, Poverty Bay, Waipukurau, 4200, New Zealand
Tel.: (64) 68588086
Web Site: https://www.ruahinemotors.co.nz
Sales Range: $25-49.9 Million
Emp.: 16
New & Used Car Dealers
N.A.I.C.S.: 441110
Ian Large (Mgr-Sls)

South Auckland Ford Ltd (1)
Corner Great South Road and Gladding Place, Manukau, Auckland, 2241, New Zealand
Tel.: (64) 92622739
Web Site:
http://www.southaucklandmotors.co.nz
Sales Range: $50-74.9 Million
New & Used Car Dealers
N.A.I.C.S.: 441110
Matthew Newman (Principal)

South Auckland Motors Limited (1)
231 Minukau Rd, Pukekohe, 2120, New Zealand
Tel.: (64) 92370490
Web Site:
http://www.southaucklandmotors.co.nz
Sales Range: $25-49.9 Million
Emp.: 12
New & Used Car Dealers
N.A.I.C.S.: 441110
Bruce Cullen (Mgr-Svc)

Southern Autos - Manukau Ltd. (1)
1 Bakerfield Place, Manukau, Auckland, New Zealand
Tel.: (64) 98843049
Web Site: https://www.southernautos.co.nz
Car Dealership Operator
N.A.I.C.S.: 441110

Southern Lakes Motors Ltd. (1)
142 Glenda Drive, Frankton, Queenstown, New Zealand
Tel.: (64) 34414239
Web Site:
https://www.southernlakesmotors.co.nz
Car Dealership Operator
N.A.I.C.S.: 441110

Southland Tractors Ltd (1)
853 North Road, Lorneville, Invercargill, 9876, New Zealand
Tel.: (64) 32358741
Web Site: http://www.agricentre.nz
Sales Range: $50-74.9 Million
Emp.: 10
New & Used Tractor Dealers
N.A.I.C.S.: 423820
Grant Price (Mgr)

Southpac Trucks Ltd. (1)
96-98 Wiri Station Road, PO Box 76463, Manukau, 2241, New Zealand
Tel.: (64) 92623181
Web Site: https://www.spt.co.nz
Sales Range: $50-74.9 Million
General Freight Trucking Services
N.A.I.C.S.: 484121
Maarten Durent (CEO)

Stevens Motors Ltd (1)
434 High Street, Lower Hutt, 5010, New Zealand
Tel.: (64) 45703480
Web Site: http://www.stevensmotors.co.nz
Sales Range: $25-49.9 Million
Emp.: 35
New & Used Car Dealers
N.A.I.C.S.: 441110
Paul Dikens (Bus Mgr)

The Hawkes Bay Motor Company Ltd. (1)
Cnr Heretaunga Street and Tomoana Road, St Leonards, Hastings, New Zealand
Tel.: (64) 68730065
Web Site:
https://www.hawkesbaynissan.co.nz
Car Dealership Operator
N.A.I.C.S.: 441110

Timaru Motors Ltd (1)
207 Hilton Highway, Washdyke, Timaru, 7910, New Zealand
Tel.: (64) 36874133
Web Site: http://www.timarumotors.co.nz
Sales Range: $25-49.9 Million
Emp.: 16
New & Used Car Dealers
N.A.I.C.S.: 441110

THE COMMERCIAL BANK (P.S.Q.C)
Grand Hamad Avenue, PO Box 3232, Doha, Qatar
Tel.: (974) 44490000 QA
Web Site: https://www.cbq.qa
Year Founded: 1974
CBQK—(QE)
Rev.: $2,615,592,760
Assets: $45,077,820,101
Liabilities: $38,384,874,811
Net Worth: $6,692,945,290
Earnings: $825,511,312
Emp.: 872
Fiscal Year-end: 12/31/23
Commercial Banking Services
N.A.I.C.S.: 522110
Parvez Khan (Exec Gen Mgr-Treasury & Investment)

Subsidiaries:

Alternatifbank A.S. (1)
Ayazaga Mah Cendere Cad No-109M 2D Blok, Saryer, 34485, Istanbul, Turkiye (100%)
Tel.: (90) 2123156500
Web Site: http://www.alternatifbank.com.tr
Rev.: $476,740,340
Assets: $5,032,839,713
Liabilities: $4,623,097,669
Net Worth: $409,742,044
Earnings: $32,546,163
Emp.: 952
Fiscal Year-end: 12/31/2019
Commericial Banking
N.A.I.C.S.: 522110
Omar Hussain Alfardan (Chm)

Commercial Bank Financial Services LLC (1)
2nd Floor Commercial Bank Grand Hamad St, PO Box 3232, Doha, Qatar
Tel.: (974) 4 449 5522
Web Site: https://www.cbfin.qa
Wholesale Trade Agency Services
N.A.I.C.S.: 425120

THE COMMERCIAL REAL ESTATE COMPANY K.S.C.C.
Al-Sharq Jaber Al Mubarak St Al Tijaria Head Office Building, Kuwait, 13042, Kuwait
Tel.: (965) 22902900
Web Site: https://www.altijaria.com
Year Founded: 1968
ALTIJARIA—(KUW)
Rev.: $96,287,663
Assets: $1,797,450,843
Liabilities: $779,870,113
Net Worth: $1,017,580,731
Earnings: $43,518,935
Emp.: 157
Fiscal Year-end: 12/31/22
Commercial Property Investment Services
N.A.I.C.S.: 531390
Abdulfatah M. R. Marafie (Chm)

THE COMMONWELL MUTUAL INSURANCE GROUP
336 Angeline Street South, Lindsay, K9V 0J8, ON, Canada
Tel.: (705) 324-2146
Web Site:
https://www.thecommonwell.ca
Rev.: $142,814,445
Assets: $380,321,219
Liabilities: $211,785,527
Net Worth: $168,535,692
Earnings: $6,946,083
Fiscal Year-end: 12/31/19
Insurance Services
N.A.I.C.S.: 524126
Tim Shauf (Pres & CEO)

THE COMPANY FOR COOPERATIVE INSURANCE
6507 Thumamah Road - Takhassusi, PO Box 86959, Ar Rabi District, Riyadh, 11632, Saudi Arabia
Tel.: (966) 112525800 SA
Web Site: https://www.tawuniya.com
Year Founded: 1986
8010—(SAU)
Rev.: $2,855,560,325
Assets: $5,043,326,756
Liabilities: $4,146,075,190
Net Worth: $897,251,566
Earnings: $104,253,566
Emp.: 226
Fiscal Year-end: 12/31/22
Insurance Services
N.A.I.C.S.: 524114
Soliman Saad Al-Humayyd (Co-Chm)

Subsidiaries:

Tree Digital Company (1)
8 Michael Karaoli Anemomylos Building 3rd Floor, 1095, Nicosia, Cyprus
Tel.: (357) 22396999
Web Site: https://digitaltree.com.cy
Web Development & Digital Marketing Services
N.A.I.C.S.: 518210

THE CONSULTANT & INVESTMENT GROUP P.L.C.
44 Al Kindi Street King Abdallah Gardens Intersection, PO Box 840431, Amman, 11184, Jordan
Tel.: (962) 65001000
Web Site: https://istisharihospital.com
Year Founded: 1995
CICO—(AMM)
Rev.: $20,176,580
Assets: $45,250,430
Liabilities: $17,127,355
Net Worth: $28,123,075
Earnings: ($1,527,659)
Emp.: 493
Fiscal Year-end: 12/31/20
Investment Management Service
N.A.I.C.S.: 523999
Tareq Ellauzi (Pres & CEO)

THE CONYGAR INVESTMENT COMPANY PLC
First Floor Suite 3 1 Duchess Street, London, W1W 6AN, United Kingdom
Tel.: (44) 2072588670
Web Site: https://www.conygar.com
CIC—(AIM)
Rev.: $7,993,332
Assets: $149,801,382
Liabilities: $42,163,128
Net Worth: $107,638,254
Earnings: ($56,610)
Fiscal Year-end: 09/30/22
Property Investment Services
N.A.I.C.S.: 523999
Robert Thomas Ware (CEO)

THE CORE BANKING GROUP LTD.
St Marys Court The Broadway, Buckinghamshire, Old Amersham, HP7 0UT, United Kingdom
Tel.: (44) 1494 411 202
Web Site:
http://www.corebanking.com
Banking Software Mfr
N.A.I.C.S.: 513210
Andrew Ruffell (Co-CEO)

Subsidiaries:

Verisim Limited (1)
Westpoint 4 Redheughs Rigg South Gyle, Edinburgh, EH12 9DQ, United Kingdom
Tel.: (44) 131 338 7450
Web Site: http://www.verisim.com
Emp.: 11
Software Development Services
N.A.I.C.S.: 541511

THE COVALI GROUP LLC
309 Q House Furze Road, Sandyford Industrial Estate, Dublin, 18, Ireland
Tel.: (353) 1 293 9302 UK
Web Site:
http://www.covaligroup.com
Year Founded: 2006
Sales Range: $10-24.9 Million
Emp.: 20
Business Data Intelligence Solutions
N.A.I.C.S.: 513210
Noel Shannon (Mng Dir)

THE CRANEMERE GROUP LIMITED
Floor 5 Smithson Tower St James's Street, London, SW1A 1HJ, United Kingdom
Tel.: (44) 20 7060 6530 UK
Web Site: http://www.cranemere.com
Year Founded: 2012
Sales Range: Less than $1 Million
Investment Holding Company
N.A.I.C.S.: 551112
Jeffrey Zients (CEO)

Subsidiaries:

Marmite Sp. z o.o. (1)
ul Przemyslowa 4, Zakrzewo, 62-070, Dopiewo, Poland
Tel.: (48) 618945000
Web Site: http://www.marmite.eu
Emp.: 700
Household Appliances Mfr
N.A.I.C.S.: 335220
Robert Rutkowski (CEO)

NorthStar Anesthesia P.A. (1)
6225 State Hwy 161 200, Irving, TX 75038
Tel.: (214) 687-0001
Web Site:
http://www.northstaranesthesia.com
Anesthesia Care Services
N.A.I.C.S.: 621111
Sandra Geary (Chief Compliance Officer)

THE CRESCENT TEXTILE MILLS LIMITED
Sargodha Road, Faisalabad, Pakistan
Tel.: (92) 41111105105
Web Site:
https://www.crescenttextile.com
CRTM—(KAR)
Rev.: $89,813,167
Assets: $111,867,971
Liabilities: $60,948,598
Net Worth: $50,919,373
Earnings: $1,536,513
Emp.: 3,741
Fiscal Year-end: 06/30/19
Textile Mill Mfr
N.A.I.C.S.: 313210
Khalid Bashir (Chm)

THE CROSS-HARBOUR (HOLDINGS) LIMITED
25th Floor China Resources Building 26 Harbour Road, Wanchai, China (Hong Kong)
Tel.: (852) 21611888 HK
Web Site:
https://www.crossharbour.com.hk
Year Founded: 1965
0032—(HKG)
Rev.: $89,525,400

THE CROSS-HARBOUR (HOLDINGS) LIMITED

The Cross-Harbour (Holdings) Limited—(Continued)
Assets: $999,617,340
Liabilities: $101,558,340
Net Worth: $898,059,000
Earnings: ($46,945,755)
Emp.: 500
Fiscal Year-end: 12/31/22
Transportation Management Services
N.A.I.C.S.: 551112
Shuk Mun Leung (Sec)

Subsidiaries:

NKT Driving School Limited (1)
Room C 27th Floor Ning Chun Centre 7 Shing Yip Street, Kwun Tong, China (Hong Kong)
Tel.: (852) 24664202
Web Site: https://www.nktds.com.hk
Automobile Driving Educational Services
N.A.I.C.S.: 611692

The Hong Kong School of Motoring Limited (1)
Ground Fl 138 Sha Tin Wai Rd, Siu Lek Yuen, Sha Tin, New Territories, China (Hong Kong)
Tel.: (852) 26046123
Web Site: http://www.hksm.com.hk
Sales Range: $50-74.9 Million
Automobile Driving Training Services
N.A.I.C.S.: 611692

THE CROWN PROPERTY BUREAU

173 Nakornratchasima Rd, Dusit, Bangkok, 10300, Thailand
Tel.: (66) 2787 7000
Web Site: http://www.crownproperty.or.th
Sales Range: $200-249.9 Million
Emp.: 1,000
Property & Financial Services
N.A.I.C.S.: 525990

Subsidiaries:

The Deves Insurance Public Company Limted (1)
97 99 Deves Insurance Building Ratchadamnoen-Klang Road, Pranakorn, Bangkok, 10200, Thailand (86.68%)
Tel.: (66) 26704444
Web Site: http://www.deves.co.th
Sales Range: $75-99.9 Million
Emp.: 482
Insurance Services
N.A.I.C.S.: 524298
Chirayu Isarangkul Na Ayuthaya (Chm)

THE CSL GROUP INC.

759 Square Victoria 6th Floor, Montreal, H2Y 2K3, QC, Canada
Tel.: (514) 982-3800
Web Site: http://www.cslships.com
Sales Range: $10-24.9 Million
Emp.: 1,000
Self Unloading Bulk Freight Carriers
N.A.I.C.S.: 483111
Louis Martel (Pres & CEO)

Subsidiaries:

CSL Asia Shipping Pte Ltd. (1)
Menara Kadin Indonesia 16th B Floor JL HR Rasuna Said Blok X-5, Kav 2 & 3 Kuningan, Jakarta, 12950, Indonesia
Tel.: (62) 21 5227 215
Marine Transportation Services
N.A.I.C.S.: 483111
Jakob Hansen (VP & Co-Mng Dir)

CSL Australia Ltd. (1)
486-494 Pacific Highway Suite 402, Saint Leonards, 2065, NSW, Australia
Tel.: (61) 2 9432 7500
Marine Transportation Services
N.A.I.C.S.: 483111
William Bisset (Mng Dir)

CSL Europe Limited (1)
Number One Windsor 1-2 High Street, Windsor, SL4 1LD, Berkshire, United Kingdom
Tel.: (44) 1753 251 040

Marine Transportation Services
N.A.I.C.S.: 483111
Jakob Hansen (VP & Mng Dir)

CSL International, Inc. (1)
152 Conant St, Beverly, MA 01915
Tel.: (978) 922-1300
Web Site: http://www.cslint.com
Deep Sea Freight Transportation
N.A.I.C.S.: 483111

Joint Venture (Domestic):

Marbulk Canada Inc. (2)
152 Conant St, Beverly, MA 01915 (50%)
Tel.: (978) 299-1090
Holding Company
N.A.I.C.S.: 551112

Subsidiary (Domestic):

Marbulk Shipping Inc. (3)
152 Conant St, Beverly, MA 01915
Tel.: (978) 232-4810
Provider of International Dry Bulk Shipping
N.A.I.C.S.: 483113

CSL Norway AS (1)
Sandviksbodene 68 1st Floor, 5035, Bergen, Norway
Tel.: (47) 55 33 03 80
Marine Transportation Services
N.A.I.C.S.: 483111
Helge Sandvik (Dir-Comml)

THE DACCA DYEING & MANUFACTURING COMPANY LIMITED

Sharif Mansion 4th Floor 56-57 Motijheel C/A, GPO Box No 388, Dhaka, 1000, Bangladesh
Tel.: (880) 29558131
Web Site: https://www.dacca-dyeing.com
Year Founded: 1963
DACCADYE—(CHT)
Rev.: $4,773,459
Assets: $56,286,216
Liabilities: $29,193,695
Net Worth: $27,092,522
Earnings: ($458,450)
Emp.: 57
Fiscal Year-end: 06/30/23
Dyeing Services
N.A.I.C.S.: 313310
Saifuddin Quader Chowdhury (Chm)

THE DAITO BANK LTD.

19-1 Naka-machi, Koriyama, 963-8004, Fukushima, Japan
Tel.: (81) 120601766
Web Site: https://www.daitobank.co.jp
Year Founded: 1942
8563—(TKS)
Rev.: $89,757,190
Assets: $5,796,269,340
Liabilities: $5,541,685,190
Net Worth: $254,584,150
Earnings: $198,300
Emp.: 420
Fiscal Year-end: 03/31/24
Banking Services
N.A.I.C.S.: 522110
Takao Suzuki (Chm & Pres)

THE DATABASE GROUP LTD

Colston Tower, Colston Street, Bristol, BS1 4UH, United Kingdom
Tel.: (44) 1179183500
Web Site: http://www.databasegroup.co.uk
Year Founded: 1987
Sales Range: $1-9.9 Million
Emp.: 90
Data Marketing Services
N.A.I.C.S.: 541613
Richard Lees (Chm)

THE DEPARTMENT OF DOING

91 Rose Road, Grey Lynn, Auckland, 1021, New Zealand
Tel.: (64) 94461324
Web Site: http://www.departmentofdoing.com
Year Founded: 1999
Sales Range: $10-24.9 Million
Emp.: 5
New Product Development, Package Design, Strategic Planning/Research, Technical Advertising
N.A.I.C.S.: 541810
Richard Hollingum (Owner)

THE DESCARTES SYSTEMS GROUP INC.

120 Randall Drive, Waterloo, N2V 1C6, ON, Canada
Tel.: (519) 746-8110 Ca
Web Site: https://www.descartes.com
Year Founded: 1981
DSGX—(NASDAQ)
Rev.: $572,931,000
Assets: $1,474,285,000
Liabilities: $236,251,000
Net Worth: $1,238,034,000
Earnings: $115,907,000
Emp.: 2,200
Fiscal Year-end: 01/31/24
Integrated Logistics, Supply Chain & Compliance Software Applications & Services
N.A.I.C.S.: 513210
Edward J. Ryan (CEO)

Subsidiaries:

BestTransport.com, Inc. (1)
1103 Schrock Rd Ste 100, Worthington, OH 43229
Tel.: (614) 888-2378
Web Site: http://www.besttransport.com
On-demand Transportation Management Software & Cloud Staffing Services
N.A.I.C.S.: 334610
Deborah Llaneza (VP-Professional Svcs Grp)

Core Transport Technologies NZ Limited (1)
105 Trafalgar Street 2nd Floor, Nelson, New Zealand
Tel.: (64) 35478205
Web Site: https://www.core-tt.com
Transportation & Logistics Services
N.A.I.C.S.: 541614

Datamyne, Inc. (1)
703 Waterford Way Ste 200, Miami, FL 33126-4679
Tel.: (305) 262-8600
Web Site: https://www.datamyne.com
Emp.: 200
Cloud-Based Trade Data Content Solutions
N.A.I.C.S.: 518210
Mark Segner (VP-Global Sls)

Descartes STEPcom AG (1)
Habich-Dietschy-Strasse 9A, 4310, Rheinfelden, Switzerland
Tel.: (41) 618353000
Web Site: https://www.stepcom.ch
Data Networking Services
N.A.I.C.S.: 541512

Descartes Systems (USA) LLC (1)
200 Hightower Blvd, Pittsburgh, PA 15205-1123 (100%)
Tel.: (412) 788-2466
Software Publisher & Distr
N.A.I.C.S.: 513210

Descartes Visual Compliance (USA) LLC (1)
Powers Ferry Business Park 2030 Powers Ferry Rd SE, Atlanta, GA 30339-5066
Web Site: https://www.visualcompliance.com
Trade Compliance Services
N.A.I.C.S.: 561990

OCR Services Inc. (1)
557 W Uwchlan Ave Ste 240, Exton, PA 19341-3014
Tel.: (610) 280-7971

INTERNATIONAL PUBLIC

Web Site: http://www.ocr-inc.com
Electronics Stores
N.A.I.C.S.: 449210

QuestaWeb, Inc. (1)
60 Walnut Ave Ste 300, Clark, NJ 07066
Tel.: (908) 233-2300
Web Site: http://www.questaweb.com
Sales Range: $1-9.9 Million
Emp.: 15
Data Processing, Hosting & Related Services
N.A.I.C.S.: 518210
Leon Turetsky (CEO)

Supply Vision, Inc. (1)
661 W Lake St Ste 1E, Chicago, IL 60661
Tel.: (847) 388-0065
Web Site: http://www.supply-vision.com
Logistic Software Development Services
N.A.I.C.S.: 541511
Amanda Bohl (CEO)

THE DHARAMSI MORARJI CHEMICAL CO. LTD.

Prospect Chambers 317/21 Dr Dadabhoy Naoroji Road, Mumbai, 400 001, India
Tel.: (91) 2222048881
Web Site: https://www.dmcc.com
506405—(BOM)
Rev.: $45,367,263
Assets: $52,373,658
Liabilities: $25,943,954
Net Worth: $26,429,703
Earnings: $2,912,924
Emp.: 385
Fiscal Year-end: 03/31/22
Chemical Products Mfr
N.A.I.C.S.: 325314
Bimal Lalitsingh Goculdas (CEO & Mng Dir)

THE DIVERSE INCOME TRUST PLC

Beaufort House 51 New North Road, Exeter, EX4 4EP, United Kingdom
Tel.: (44) 1392412122 UK
Web Site: http://www.mitongroup.com
Year Founded: 2011
DIVI—(LSE)
Rev.: $22,633,192
Assets: $543,785,868
Liabilities: $544,446
Net Worth: $543,241,422
Earnings: ($19,366,518)
Fiscal Year-end: 05/31/22
Investment Trust Management Services
N.A.I.C.S.: 523940
Gervais Williams (Mgr)

THE DODSAL GROUP

25th Floor UBora Towers Business Bay, PO Box 8034, Dubai, 8034, United Arab Emirates
Tel.: (971) 45038000 In
Web Site: http://www.dodsal.com
Year Founded: 1948
Sales Range: $1-4.9 Billion
Emp.: 17,500
Holding Services
N.A.I.C.S.: 551112
Rajen A. Kilachand (Chm)

Subsidiaries:

Dodsal Engineering & Construction Pte. Limited (1)
Third Floor DNI Building Sheikh Zayed Road, PO Box 8034, Dubai, United Arab Emirates
Tel.: (971) 43431515
Sales Range: $75-99.9 Million
Emp.: 220
Engineering, Procurement & Construction Services
N.A.I.C.S.: 236210
Rajen A. Kilachand (Chm & Pres)

AND PRIVATE COMPANIES — THE EDRINGTON GROUP

Subsidiary (Non-US):

AE&E I.D.E.A. India Pvt. Ltd. (2)
No 32 A & B Ambit IT Park 7th Fl Ambattur Industrial Estate, Chennai, 600058, India **(100%)**
Tel.: (91) 4466455200
Web Site: http://www.dodsal.com
Sales Range: $125-149.9 Million
Energy & Industrial Sector Construction & Engineering Services
N.A.I.C.S.: 236210

THE DORSEY GROUP INC.
330 West Street Unit 7, Brantford, N3R 7V5, ON, Canada
Tel.: (519) 759-0033
Web Site: http://www.thedorseygroup.com
Year Founded: 1957
Rev.: $10,868,119
Emp.: 45
Insurance Agencies
N.A.I.C.S.: 524128
Paula Dorsey (Pres)

THE DRIVING FORCE, INC.
11025 184 Street, Edmonton, T5S 0A6, AB, Canada
Tel.: (780) 483-9559
Web Site: http://www.drivingforce.ca
Year Founded: 1978
Rev.: $13,911,192
Emp.: 30
New & Used Car Dealers
N.A.I.C.S.: 441110
Jacob Coonan (CFO)

THE DYSON GROUP
121 McKimmies Road, Bundoora, Melbourne, 3083, VIC, Australia
Tel.: (61) 394633800
Web Site: http://www.dysongroup.com.au
Year Founded: 1952
Emp.: 790
Bus Transportation Services
N.A.I.C.S.: 485999
Vivienne Eyles (Gen Mgr-Bus Improvement & ICT)

THE E&M CO., LTD.
1 Gangnam-daero 101an-gil, Seocho-gu, Seoul, Korea (South)
Tel.: (82) 220888222
Web Site: https://theenm.com
Year Founded: 2002
089230—(KRS)
Rev.: $35,743,360
Assets: $79,874,984
Liabilities: $32,441,820
Net Worth: $47,433,164
Earnings: ($17,330,465)
Emp.: 107
Fiscal Year-end: 12/31/22
Metal Forging Product Mfr
N.A.I.C.S.: 332111
Kim Dae-kwon (CEO)

THE ECONOMICAL INSURANCE GROUP
111 Westmount Road South, PO Box 2000, Waterloo, N2J 4S4, ON, Canada
Tel.: (519) 570-8200
Web Site: http://www.economicalgroup.com
Year Founded: 1871
Rev.: $1,800,404,473
Assets: $4,185,522,569
Liabilities: $3,036,731,359
Net Worth: $1,148,791,211
Earnings: ($53,502,412)
Emp.: 2,200
Fiscal Year-end: 12/31/18
Holding Company; Property & Casualty Insurance
N.A.I.C.S.: 524126

Linda Goss (Chief Actuary & Sr VP)

Subsidiaries:

Economical Insurance (1)
5700 Yonge Street Suite 1800, Toronto, M2M 4K2, ON, Canada
Tel.: (416) 733-1777
Web Site: https://www.economical.com
Sales Range: $50-74.9 Million
Emp.: 97
Insurance For Commercial Lines
N.A.I.C.S.: 524128

Subsidiary (Domestic):

The Economical Insurance Group (2)
111 Westmount S Rd, PO Box 2000, Waterloo, N2J 4S4, ON, Canada **(100%)**
Tel.: (519) 570-8200
Web Site: http://www.economical.com
Emp.: 500
Fiscal Year-end: 12/31/2018
Life Insurance
N.A.I.C.S.: 524113
Tom Reikman (Chief Distr Officer & Sr VP)

Family Insurance Solutions Inc. (1)
1400 1177 W Hastings St, Vancouver, V6E 2K3, BC, Canada
Tel.: (604) 622-5263
Automobile Insurance Services
N.A.I.C.S.: 524126
Graham Doerr (COO)

Perth Insurance Company (1)
1600-5700 Yonge St, North York, M2M 4K2, ON, Canada
Tel.: (416) 590-0171
Emp.: 24
Automobile Insurance Services
N.A.I.C.S.: 524126
Tom Mallozzi (VP)

Petline Insurance Company (1)
301-600 Empress St, Winnipeg, R3G 0R5, MB, Canada
Tel.: (204) 942-2999
Web Site: http://www.petlineinsurance.com
Emp.: 130
Pet Health Insurance Products & Services
N.A.I.C.S.: 524128
Raegan Ahlbaum (Dir-Call Center)

The Missisquoi Insurance Company (1)
1400-5 Place Ville-Marie, Montreal, H3B 0A8, QC, Canada
Tel.: (514) 875-5790
Emp.: 100
Automobile Insurance Services
N.A.I.C.S.: 524126

THE ECONOMIST GROUP LIMITED
20 Cabot Square, London, E14 4QW, United Kingdom
Tel.: (44) 2078307000
Web Site: http://www.economistgroup.com
Year Founded: 1843
Sales Range: $450-499.9 Million
Emp.: 900
Periodical Publishers
N.A.I.C.S.: 513110
Oscar Grut (Gen Counsel, Sec & Exec VP-Corp Dev)

Subsidiaries:

CQ Roll Call (1)
77 K St NE, Washington, DC 20002
Tel.: (202) 650-6500
Web Site: http://corporate.cqrollcall.com
Sales Range: $150-199.9 Million
Emp.: 300
Books, Magazines, Daily Newspapers & E-Newsletters with Information Relating to Events on Capitol Hill, Congressional Activity & Background Information on Political Figures
N.A.I.C.S.: 513120
Jeff Steinman (Dir-Product Dev)

Subsidiary (Domestic):

Federal News Services (2)
1120 G St NW Ste 990, Washington, DC 20005
Tel.: (202) 347-1400
Web Site: http://www.fednews.com
Sales Range: $10-24.9 Million
Emp.: 20
News & Translation Agency
N.A.I.C.S.: 516210
Julieanne Rose (VP & Gen Mgr)

Capitol Advantage LLC (1)
100 SE 9th St Ste 503, Topeka, KS 66612
Tel.: (785) 235-9000
Public Relations Services
N.A.I.C.S.: 541820

Clearstate (Pte) Limited (1)
21 Biopolis Road 06-02 Nucleos, Singapore, 138567, Singapore
Tel.: (65) 6715 9200
Web Site: http://www.clearstate.com
Health Care Srvices
N.A.I.C.S.: 813212
Ivy Teh (Mng Dir)

EuroFinance (1)
Floor 5 20 Cabot Square Canary Wharf, London, E14 4QW, United Kingdom
Tel.: (44) 20 7576 8555
Web Site: http://www.eurofinance.com
Financial Services
N.A.I.C.S.: 525990
Carolyn Meier (Mng Dir)

Roll Call Inc. (1)
77 K St NE, Washington, DC 20002 **(100%)**
Tel.: (202) 650-6500
Web Site: http://www.rollcall.com
Sales Range: $10-24.9 Million
Emp.: 370
Periodical Publishers
N.A.I.C.S.: 513120
Jason Kelley (Mgr-Lead Dev-CQ Transcriptions, Capitol Advantage & Directories)

TVC Group Limited (1)
14-15 Mandela Street, London, NW1 0DU, United Kingdom
Tel.: (44) 20 7380 8000
Web Site: http://www.tvcgroup.com
Emp.: 60
Public Relations Services
N.A.I.C.S.: 541820
Greg Lappage (Exec Creative Dir)

The Economist Group (Asia/Pacific) Limited (1)
1301 Cityplaza Four 12 Taikoo Wan Road, Taikoo Shing, China (Hong Kong)
Tel.: (852) 25853888
Web Site: http://www.economistgroup.com
Emp.: 180
Newspaper Publishers
N.A.I.C.S.: 513110
Tim Pinnegar (Mng Dir)

The Economist Group (Luxembourg) Limited (1)
26 Boulevard Royal, 2449, Luxembourg, Luxembourg
Tel.: (352) 22 9999 5255
Newspaper Publishers
N.A.I.C.S.: 513110

The Economist Group (Switzerland) SA (1)
Rue De l'Athenee 32, 1206, Geneva, Switzerland
Tel.: (41) 22 566 24 70
Web Site: http://www.ecomomist.com
Emp.: 16
Newspaper Publishers
N.A.I.C.S.: 513110
Marina Haydn (Gen Mgr)

The Economist Group France S.a.r.l (1)
10 Rue du Colisee, 75008, Paris, France
Tel.: (33) 153936717
Web Site: http://www.economist.com
Emp.: 10
Newspaper Publishers
N.A.I.C.S.: 513110
Phyllis Youkbi (Mgr)

The Economist Group Singapore Pte Limited (1)
8 Cross Street Suite 23-01 PWC Building, Singapore, 048424, Singapore
Tel.: (65) 6534 5177
Newspaper Publishers
N.A.I.C.S.: 513110

The Economist Intelligence Unit, NA, Inc (1)
750 3rd Ave Ste 5, New York, NY 10017
Tel.: (212) 554-0650
Newspaper Publishers
N.A.I.C.S.: 513110

The Economist Newspaper Group, Inc (1)
750 3rd Ave The Economist Bldg, New York, NY 10017
Tel.: (212) 541-0500
Newspaper Publishers
N.A.I.C.S.: 513110

The Economist Newspaper Limited (1)
20 Cabot Square, London, E14 4QW, United Kingdom
Tel.: (44) 20 7576 8000
Web Site: http://www.economist.com
Newspaper Publishers
N.A.I.C.S.: 513110
John Prideaux (Editor-US)

THE EDINBURGH WOOLLEN MILL LTD.
Waverley Mills, Langholm, DG13 0EB, Dumfriesshire, United Kingdom
Tel.: (44) 13873 80611
Web Site: http://www.ewm.co.uk
Year Founded: 1946
Sales Range: $350-399.9 Million
Emp.: 4,955
Clothing Store Operator
N.A.I.C.S.: 458110
Philip Day (Owner)

THE EDRINGTON GROUP
100 Queen Street, Glasgow, G1 3DN, United Kingdom
Tel.: (44) 1419404000 UK
Web Site: http://www.edrington.com
Year Founded: 1887
Rev.: $997,404,416
Assets: $2,568,724,480
Liabilities: $1,515,601,408
Net Worth: $1,053,123,072
Earnings: $116,833,792
Emp.: 2,255
Fiscal Year-end: 03/31/18
Scotch & Whiskey Mfr
N.A.I.C.S.: 312140
Martin A. Cooke (Sec)

Subsidiaries:

Brugal & Co., S.A. (1)
Av J F Kennedy No 57 Edificio Brugal, Santo Domingo, Dominican Republic
Tel.: (809) 566 5651
Web Site: http://www.brugal.es
Scotch & Whisky Whslr
N.A.I.C.S.: 424820
Angel Gonell (Mgr-Mfg)

Edrington Denmark A/S (1)
Dronningens Tvaergade 9, 1302, Copenhagen, Denmark
Tel.: (45) 43 225 500
Web Site: http://www.edrington.dk
Scotch & Whisky Whslr
N.A.I.C.S.: 424820
Mickey Jensen (Key Acct Mgr)

Edrington Finland Oy (1)
Italahdenkatu 15-1, 00210, Helsinki, Finland
Tel.: (358) 20 7981 520
Scotch & Whisky Whslr
N.A.I.C.S.: 424820
Mirja Pulkkinen (Brand Mgr)

Edrington Hong Kong Ltd (1)
Wang Chiu Road Suite 1207-09A Exchange Tower 33, Kowloon Bay, Hong Kong, China (Hong Kong)
Tel.: (852) 2891 8086
Scotch & Whisky Whslr
N.A.I.C.S.: 424820
Chan William (Mng Dir)

Edrington Korea Ltd. (1)

THE EDRINGTON GROUP

The Edrington Group—(Continued)

5F 570 Samsung-ro, Gangnam-gu, Seoul, 06163, Korea (South) **(100%)**
Tel.: (82) 2 3468 4600
Web Site: http://www.edrington.com
Scotch & Whisky Whslr
N.A.I.C.S.: 424820
Dongkyu Roh *(Dir-Fin)*

Edrington Norway AS **(1)**
PO Box 4531, 0404, Oslo, Norway
Tel.: (47) 91 152 020
Scotch & Whisky Whslr
N.A.I.C.S.: 424820
Anne Sletmoe *(Brand Mgr)*

Edrington Shanghai Ltd. **(1)**
Unit 1 19/F Tower 1 Grand Gateway No 1 Hong Qiao Road, Shanghai, 200030, China
Tel.: (86) 21 64483388
Web Site: http://www.edrington.com
Scotch & Whisky Whslr
N.A.I.C.S.: 424820

Edrington Singapore Pte Ltd **(1)**
8 Marina View Asia Square Tower 1 Level 07-04, Singapore, 018960, Singapore
Tel.: (65) 6407 1230
Scotch & Whisky Whslr
N.A.I.C.S.: 424820
Milton Chee *(Gen Mgr-Sls)*

Edrington Sweden AB **(1)**
Luntmakargatan 46, Box 5314, 102 47, Stockholm, Sweden
Tel.: (46) 8440 8300
Web Site: http://www.edrington.se
Emp.: 44
Scotch & Whisky Whslr
N.A.I.C.S.: 424820
Andreas Handing *(Acct Mgr)*

Highland Park Distillery **(1)**
Holm Road, Kirkwall, KW15 1SU, Orkney, United Kingdom **(100%)**
Tel.: (44) 1856 873107
Web Site: http://www.highlandpark.co.uk
Sales Range: $25-49.9 Million
Emp.: 30
Distilled & Blended Liquors
N.A.I.C.S.: 312130

Subsidiary (Non-US):

Edrington Taiwan Ltd. **(2)**
5th Fl 310 Chung Hsiao East Rd Section 4, Taipei, 106, Taiwan **(100%)**
Tel.: (886) 287739099
Web Site: http://www.edrington.com
Sales Range: $25-49.9 Million
Sale & Distribution of Alcoholic Beverages
N.A.I.C.S.: 424820
Geoff Kirk *(Mng Dir-South East Asia)*

Plant (Domestic):

Glenrothes Distillery Co Ltd **(2)**
Burnside St, Rothes, AB38 7AA, Morayshire, United Kingdom **(100%)**
Tel.: (44) 1340872300
Web Site: http://www.glenrothes.com
Sales Range: $10-24.9 Million
Distilled & Blended Liquors
N.A.I.C.S.: 312130
Alistair Anderson *(Gen Mgr)*

Glenturret Distillery **(2)**
The Hosh, Crieff, PH7 4HA, United Kingdom
Tel.: (44) 1764656565
Web Site: http://www.theglenturret.com
Distilled & Blended Liquors
N.A.I.C.S.: 312130
Neil K Cameron *(Supvr-Production)*

The Edrington Group - Edrington Americas Central & Canada Division **(1)**
1400 16th St Ste 270, Oak Brook, IL 60523
Tel.: (773) 203-5633
Scotch & Whisky Mfr
N.A.I.C.S.: 312140

The Edrington Group - Edrington Americas Northeast Division **(1)**
150 5th Ave 11th Fl, New York, NY 10011
Tel.: (212) 352-6000
Web Site: http://www.edrington.com
Emp.: 60
Scotch & Whisky Mfr

N.A.I.C.S.: 312140
Micheal Misiorsiki *(Mgr)*

The Edrington Group - Edrington Americas South Division **(1)**
4311 Oak Lawn Ave Ste 220, Dallas, TX 75219
Tel.: (469) 453-8191
Scotch & Whisky Mfr
N.A.I.C.S.: 312140

The Edrington Group - Edrington Americas West Division **(1)**
5000 Birch Ste 440, Newport Beach, CA 92660
Tel.: (949) 892-0847
Scotch & Whisky Mfr
N.A.I.C.S.: 312140

The Macallan Distillers Limited **(1)**
Macallan Distillery Easter Elchies, Aberlour, AB38 9RX, Banffshire, United Kingdom **(100%)**
Tel.: (44) 1340 871471
Web Site: http://www.themacallan.com
Wine & Liquors Distillery & Distr
N.A.I.C.S.: 312140

Wyoming Whiskey, Inc **(1)**
100 S Nelson St, Kirby, WY 82430-4700 **(80%)**
Tel.: (307) 864-2116
Web Site: http://www.wyomingwhiskey.com
Beer, Wine & Liquor Stores
N.A.I.C.S.: 445320
David De Fazio *(Founder & COO)*

THE EHIME BANK, LTD.

1 Katsuyama-cho 2-chome, Matsuyama, 790-8580, Ehime, Japan
Tel.: (81) 899331111
Web Site: https://www.himegin.co.jp
Year Founded: 1943
8541—(TKS)
Rev.: $430,727,430
Assets: $19,089,422,210
Liabilities: $18,181,076,010
Net Worth: $908,346,200
Earnings: $112,370
Emp.: 1,248
Fiscal Year-end: 03/31/24
Banking Services
N.A.I.C.S.: 522110
Yoshinori Nishikawa *(Pres)*

Subsidiaries:

Ehime Gaiya Fund Corporation Limited **(1)**
2-1 Katsuyama-cho, Matsuyama, 790-8580, Ehime, Japan **(100%)**
Tel.: (81) 899331111
Web Site: http://www.himegin.co.jp
Investments in Agriculture, Forestry & Fisheries
N.A.I.C.S.: 523940

Ehime-JCB Co., Ltd. **(1)**
2 4 7 Katsuyama cho, Matsuyama, 790 0878, Ehime, Japan **(100%)**
Tel.: (81) 899212303
Credit Card & Credit Guarantee Services
N.A.I.C.S.: 522210
Masato Kono *(Sr Mng Dir)*

HIMEGIN Lease Co., Ltd. **(1)**
Ehime Bank Training Center 4th floor 27-1, Minamimochida-cho, Matsuyama, 790-0874, Ehime, Japan **(100%)**
Tel.: (81) 899331513
Web Site: https://www.himegin-lease.co.jp
Leasing & Investment Services
N.A.I.C.S.: 523940

Himegin Business Service Co., Ltd. **(1)**
5-6-1 Chifunemachi, Matsuyama, 790-0011, Ehime, Japan **(100%)**
Tel.: (81) 899323486
Web Site: http://www.himegin.co.jp
Automated Banking Services
N.A.I.C.S.: 522110

Himegin Soft Co., Ltd. **(1)**
27-1 Minamimochidamach, Matsuyama, 790-0878, Ehime, Japan **(100%)**
Tel.: (81) 899437767
Web Site: http://www.himegin.co.jp

Computer Software Development Services & Management of FB Terminals
N.A.I.C.S.: 541511

Himegin Staff Support Co., Ltd. **(1)**
1-13-4 Katsuyama-cho, Matsuyama, 790-0878, Ehime, Japan **(100%)**
Tel.: (81) 89 908 5010
Web Site: http://www.himegin.co.jp
Personnel, Education & Training Operations
N.A.I.C.S.: 923130

Limited Partnership for Investment Ehime Venture Fund 2013 **(1)**
2-1 Katsuyama-cho, Matsuyama, 790-8580, Ehime, Japan
Tel.: (81) 899331111
Web Site: http://www.himegin.co.jp
Venture Company Investments
N.A.I.C.S.: 523999

THE EIGHTS GROUP PTY LTD.

Level 26 1 Bligh Street, Sydney, NSW, Australia
Tel.: (61) 2 8226 8833
Web Site: http://www.the8s.com.au
Privater Equity Firm
N.A.I.C.S.: 523999
Warren Brandt *(Dir)*

Subsidiaries:

Shepparton Partners Collective Pty Ltd. **(1)**
175 Macquarie St Ste 2 Level 2, Sydney, 2000, NSW, Australia
Tel.: (61) 292792290
Web Site: http://www.spc.com.au
Food Products Mfr & Distr
N.A.I.C.S.: 311999
Hussein Rifai *(Chm)*

Subsidiary (Domestic):

SPC Ardmona Limited **(2)**
50 Camberwell Rd, Hawthorn, 3123, VIC, Australia
Tel.: (61) 398618900
Web Site: http://www.spcardmona.com.au
Packaged Fruit Distr
N.A.I.C.S.: 311411
Reg Weine *(Mng Dir)*

Subsidiary (Domestic):

Ardmona Foods Limited **(3)**
Andrew Failey Ave, Shepparton, 3630, VIC, Australia
Tel.: (61) 358333777
Web Site: http://www.spcardmona.com.au
Emp.: 700
Canned Fruit Jam & Vegetable Mfr
N.A.I.C.S.: 311411

Henry Jones Foods Pty Ltd **(3)**
PO Box 207, Shepparton, 3632, VIC, Australia
Tel.: (61) 358521111
Specialty Food Mfr & Distr
N.A.I.C.S.: 311412

Subsidiary (Non-US):

SPC Ardmona (Germany) GmbH **(3)**
Agnesstrasse 30, 22301, Hamburg, Germany
Tel.: (49) 4023841120
Web Site: http://www.spcardmona.de
Sales Range: $25-49.9 Million
Emp.: 1
Packaged Fruits & Vegetables Distr
N.A.I.C.S.: 424480

SPC Ardmona (Spain), S.L.U. **(3)**
Carretera De Caravaca Moratalla km 1, Moratalla, Murcia, 30440, Spain
Tel.: (34) 968607500
Convenience Food Retailer
N.A.I.C.S.: 445131

Subsidiary (Domestic):

SPC Ardmona Operations Limited **(3)**
50 Camberwell Road, Hawthorn East, 3123, VIC, Australia
Tel.: (61) 398618900
Processed Fruit & Vegetable Mfr
N.A.I.C.S.: 311411

INTERNATIONAL PUBLIC

Shepparton Partners Collective Pty Ltd. **(1)**
175 Macquarie St Ste 2 Level 2, Sydney, 2000, NSW, Australia
Tel.: (61) 292792290
Web Site: http://www.spc.com.au
Food Products Mfr & Distr
N.A.I.C.S.: 311999
Hussein Rifai *(Chm)*

Subsidiary (Domestic):

SPC Ardmona Limited **(2)**
50 Camberwell Rd, Hawthorn, 3123, VIC, Australia
Tel.: (61) 398618900
Web Site: http://www.spcardmona.com.au
Packaged Fruit Distr
N.A.I.C.S.: 311411
Reg Weine *(Mng Dir)*

Subsidiary (Domestic):

Ardmona Foods Limited **(3)**
Andrew Failey Ave, Shepparton, 3630, VIC, Australia
Tel.: (61) 358333777
Web Site: http://www.spcardmona.com.au
Emp.: 700
Canned Fruit Jam & Vegetable Mfr
N.A.I.C.S.: 311411

Henry Jones Foods Pty Ltd **(3)**
PO Box 207, Shepparton, 3632, VIC, Australia
Tel.: (61) 358521111
Specialty Food Mfr & Distr
N.A.I.C.S.: 311412

Subsidiary (Non-US):

SPC Ardmona (Germany) GmbH **(3)**
Agnesstrasse 30, 22301, Hamburg, Germany
Tel.: (49) 4023841120
Web Site: http://www.spcardmona.de
Sales Range: $25-49.9 Million
Emp.: 1
Packaged Fruits & Vegetables Distr
N.A.I.C.S.: 424480

SPC Ardmona (Spain), S.L.U. **(3)**
Carretera De Caravaca Moratalla km 1, Moratalla, Murcia, 30440, Spain
Tel.: (34) 968607500
Convenience Food Retailer
N.A.I.C.S.: 445131

Subsidiary (Domestic):

SPC Ardmona Operations Limited **(3)**
50 Camberwell Road, Hawthorn East, 3123, VIC, Australia
Tel.: (61) 398618900
Processed Fruit & Vegetable Mfr
N.A.I.C.S.: 311411

THE EMIRATES GROUP

PO Box 686, Dubai, United Arab Emirates
Tel.: (971) 47081111 AE
Web Site: http://www.theemiratesgroup.com
Year Founded: 1985
Rev.: $26,148,810,800
Assets: $34,686,653,460
Liabilities: $24,410,366,850
Net Worth: $10,276,286,610
Earnings: $280,438,100
Emp.: 105,286
Fiscal Year-end: 03/31/19
Airlines Holding Company
N.A.I.C.S.: 551112
Ahmed Saeed Al-Maktoum *(Chm & CEO-Emirates Airline & Grp)*

Subsidiaries:

Air Dispatch (CLC) Spolka z.o.o. **(1)**
Bokserska 66, 02-690, Warsaw, Poland
Tel.: (48) 22 445 0156
Aviation Consulting Services
N.A.I.C.S.: 488190
Marta Gorzechowska *(Acct Mgr)*

Alpha Flight US, Inc. **(1)**
301 Airport Rd Ste E, Plymouth, IN 46563

AND PRIVATE COMPANIES

THE EMIRATES GROUP

Tel.: (574) 914-4455
Web Site: https://www.alphaflt.com
Aviation Consulting Services
N.A.I.C.S.: 488190

BD4 Travel GmbH (1)
Rodelheimer Bahnweg 23, 60489, Frankfurt am Main, Germany
Tel.: (49) 69247 471 8201
Web Site: https://www.bd4travel.com
Travel Services
N.A.I.C.S.: 561510
Melanie Sickenberger *(COO & Chief Product Officer)*

Bollore Logistics LLC (1)
Plot W24 West Ring Road, Dubai Airport Free Zone, Dubai, United Arab Emirates
Tel.: (971) 4 292 3200
Logistic Services
N.A.I.C.S.: 484110
Laurent Ferry *(Gen Mgr)*

Destination Asia (Singapore) Pte Limited (1)
Suite 02-27 Vertex Tower A 33 Ubi Avenue 3, Singapore, 408868, Singapore
Tel.: (65) 6 887 5508
Travel & Tourism Services
N.A.I.C.S.: 561510
Matthew Smith *(Gen Mgr)*

Destination Asia (Thailand) Limited (1)
2034/93-96 Italthai Tower 21st Floor New Petchburi Road, Huaykwang, Bangkok, 10310, Thailand
Tel.: (66) 2 127 5888
Web Site: https://www.destination-asia.com
Travel & Tourism Services
N.A.I.C.S.: 561510
David Linde *(Gen Mgr)*

Destination Asia Destination Management Sdn Bhd (1)
Prima Tanjung Suite 98-03-13A Jalan Fettes Bandar Tanjung Tokong, 11200, Penang, Malaysia
Tel.: (60) 4 892 7378
Travel & Tourism Services
N.A.I.C.S.: 561510
Sadie Yeoh *(Gen Mgr)*

Destination Asia Japan Limited (1)
5th Floor Ichikawa building 5-13-3 Ginza, Chuo-ku, Tokyo, 104-0061, Japan
Tel.: (81) 36 278 7960
Travel & Tourism Services
N.A.I.C.S.: 561510
Peter Cools *(Gen Mgr)*

Dnata PW Airport Logistics LLC (1)
PO Box 293019, Dubai, United Arab Emirates
Tel.: (971) 4 282 6131
Web Site: https://www.palrfs.com
Logistic Services
N.A.I.C.S.: 484110

Dubai Express LLC (1)
Room 20 1st Floor Freightworks Building Street 54 Community 214v, PO Box 5514, Al Ramoul, Dubai, United Arab Emirates
Tel.: (971) 4 204 4444
Web Site: https://www.freightworks.com
Logistic Services
N.A.I.C.S.: 484110

Emirates Cuisine Solutions LLC (1)
Dubai Investment Park-1, Dubai, United Arab Emirates
Tel.: (971) 4 208 6983
Web Site: https://www.cuisinesolutionsmea.com
Food Distr
N.A.I.C.S.: 424490
Dan Wells *(Dir)*

Emirates Flight Catering Company L.L.C. (1)
PO Box 22525, Dubai, United Arab Emirates
Tel.: (971) 42823171
Web Site: http://www.ekfc.com
Flight Catering Services
N.A.I.C.S.: 722310
Saeed Mohammed *(CEO)*

Emirates Hotels (Australia) Pty Ltd. (1)
Ste 3 58 3rd Johns Young Cresent, Woolloomooloo, 2011, NSW, Australia
Tel.: (61) 292909733
Web Site: http://www.emriatesoneonlywalgen.com
Emp.: 90
Hotel Operator
N.A.I.C.S.: 721110
Michael Tayne *(Gen Mgr)*

Emirates Leisure Retail (Australia) Pty Ltd. (1)
Level 2 187 Todd Road, Port Melbourne, 3207, VIC, Australia
Tel.: (61) 3 8631 7700
Web Site: http://www.emiratesleisureretail.com
Hotel & Restaurant Operator
N.A.I.C.S.: 721110
Adam Summerville *(Mng Dir)*

Emirates Leisure Retail (Singapore) Pte. Ltd. (1)
50 Airport Boulevard Dnata Building, Singapore, 819658, Singapore
Tel.: (65) 6 511 0313
Food & Beverage Distr
N.A.I.C.S.: 445298

Emirates Leisure Retail LLC (1)
Level 5 Emirates Holidays Building Sheikh Zayed Road, PO Box 122199, Dubai, United Arab Emirates
Tel.: (971) 4 304 0400
Web Site: https://www.emiratesleisureretail.com
Food & Beverage Distr
N.A.I.C.S.: 445298

En Route International Australia Pty. Ltd. (1)
Building 1 Gateway Office Park 747 Lytton Rd, Murarrie, 4172, QLD, Australia
Tel.: (61) 73 117 3737
Restaurant Operators
N.A.I.C.S.: 722511

En Route International Limited (1)
Assurant House 6-12 Victoria Street, Windsor, SL4 1EN, Berkshire, United Kingdom
Tel.: (44) 1753465555
Web Site: http://www.en-route.com
Confectionery Distr
N.A.I.C.S.: 424450
Robert Dalboth *(Mng Dir)*

Subsidiary (Non-US):

En Route International General Trading LLC (2)
Unit 704 Burlington Tower 7th Floor Al Abraj Street, PO Box 53876, Business Bay, Dubai, United Arab Emirates
Tel.: (971) 43757154
Web Site: http://www.enroute.com
Emp.: 3
Confectionery Distr
N.A.I.C.S.: 424450

Subsidiary (US):

En Route International USA, Inc. (2)
800 Battery Ave SE Ste 100, Atlanta, GA 30339
Tel.: (678) 383-2226
Web Site: http://www.en-route.com
Emp.: 6
Confectionery Distr
N.A.I.C.S.: 424450

Harts International LLC (1)
2401 Fortune Executive Tower Cluster T Jumeirah Lakes Towers, PO Box 39074, Dubai, United Arab Emirates
Tel.: (971) 4 566 8385
Web Site: https://www.hartinternational.com
Security Services
N.A.I.C.S.: 561612
Lord Westbury *(Chm)*

Imagine Cruising (Pty) Ltd. (1)
Oxford House 17 Park Lane Grand Central Precinct, Century City, Cape Town, 7441, South Africa
Tel.: (27) 86 150 0200
Web Site: https://www.imagineholidays.co.za
Travel & Tourism Services
N.A.I.C.S.: 561510

Imagine Cruising Limited (1)
Portland House Bincknoll Lane Interface Business Park, Wootton Bassett, SN4 8SY, Wiltshire, United Kingdom
Tel.: (44) 179 385 6785
Web Site: https://www.imaginecruising.co.uk
Travel & Tourism Services
N.A.I.C.S.: 561510

Imagine Cruising Pty Ltd (1)
Level 7 301 Coronation Drive, Milton, 4064, QLD, Australia
Tel.: (61) 73 558 9874
Web Site: https://www.imagineholidays.com.au
Travel & Tourism Services
N.A.I.C.S.: 561510

Maritime & Mercantile International LLC (1)
PO Box 70, Dubai, United Arab Emirates
Tel.: (971) 4 3040400
Web Site: http://www.mmidubai.com
Wine Whslr
N.A.I.C.S.: 445320
Andrew Day *(CEO)*

Subsidiary (Domestic):

Duty Free Dubai Ports FZE (2)
Jebel Ali, PO Box 17940, Dubai, 17940, United Arab Emirates
Tel.: (971) 4 8833066
Web Site: http://www.duty-free-dubai-ports.om
Emp.: 25
Wine Whslr
N.A.I.C.S.: 445320
Vijay Katari *(Mgr-Key Acct)*

Oman United Agencies LLC (1)
Office No 33 Bldg No 17/1 Al Noor Building Way No 403 Block No 205, PO Box 985, Al Qurum, Muscat, 112, Oman
Tel.: (968) 2 464 3333
Web Site: https://www.ouaoman.com
Beverage Distr
N.A.I.C.S.: 445320

PT Destination Asia (1)
Jl By Pass Ngurah Rai No 360, Denpasar, Bali, Indonesia
Tel.: (62) 36 128 3898
Travel & Tourism Services
N.A.I.C.S.: 561510
Ketut Sedia Yasa *(Mng Dir)*

Plafond Fit Out LLC (1)
Office 3121 Building 3 Gold and Diamond Park Sheikh Zayed Road, PO Box 24689, Dubai, United Arab Emirates
Tel.: (971) 4 501 4800
Web Site: https://www.plafondme.com
Construction Services
N.A.I.C.S.: 236220
Colin Timmons *(CEO)*

Sunmaster Limited (1)
Glendale Business Park, Sandycroft, Chester, CH5 2DL, United Kingdom
Tel.: (44) 127 442 2177
Web Site: https://www.sunmaster.co.uk
Hotel Operator
N.A.I.C.S.: 721110

Travel Republic Holdings Limited (1)
Clarendon House, Kingston upon Thames, KT2 6NH, United Kingdom
Tel.: (44) 2089747200
Holding Company
N.A.I.C.S.: 551112

dnata (1)
Dubai Airline Ctr Shaik Zayed Rd, PO Box 1515, 1st Fl Dnata Agencies, Dubai, United Arab Emirates
Tel.: (971) 43166666
Web Site: http://www.dnata.com
Sales Range: $1-4.9 Billion
Emp.: 4,926
Travel Management Services such as Aircraft & Cargo Handling Provisions, Information Technology Services, Engineering Services & Sales of Tickets on Behalf of Airlines
N.A.I.C.S.: 488119
Steve Allen *(Grp CEO)*

Subsidiary (US):

121 Inflight Catering LLC (2)
45 Rason Rd, Inwood, NY 11096
Tel.: (516) 218-2721
Web Site: http://page70.com
Emp.: 350
Full-Service Restaurants
N.A.I.C.S.: 722511
Joe Savino *(Mng Partner)*

Subsidiary (Non-US):

Alpha Flight Group Limited (2)
Building 319 World Cargo Centre, Manchester Airport, Manchester, M90 5EX, United Kingdom
Tel.: (44) 20 8476 7777
Web Site: http://www.alpha-group.com
Sales Range: $1-4.9 Billion
Emp.: 5,800
Holding Company; In-Flight Catering & Retail Services
N.A.I.C.S.: 551112
Lionel Wilton *(CEO & Mng Dir-Middle East)*

Subsidiary (Domestic):

Alpha Flight UK Limited (3)
Building 319 World Cargo Centre, Manchester Airport, Manchester, M90 5EX, United Kingdom
Tel.: (44) 20 8476 7777
Web Site: http://www.alpha-group.com
In-Flight Catering & Retail Services
N.A.I.C.S.: 722320

Subsidiary (Non-US):

Alpha Flight a.s. (3)
K letisti 1018, Prague, 16100, Czech Republic
Tel.: (420) 2 3310 1800
Flight Catering Services
N.A.I.C.S.: 722320
Martin Fulier *(Project Mgr)*

Alpha Rocas SA (3)
Calea Bucurestilor Nr 224 R Henri Coanda International Airport, Otopeni, 075150, Romania
Tel.: (40) 21 204 17 85
Web Site: http://www.alpha-rocas.ro
Catering Services
N.A.I.C.S.: 722320
Dora Lucica Sabau *(Mgr-Comm & Customer Svcs)*

Subsidiary (Non-US):

Stella Travel Services (UK) Limited (2)
Glendale House Glendale Business Park Glendale Avenue Sandycroft, Deeside, CH5 2DL, United Kingdom
Tel.: (44) 1244521271
Web Site: http://www.stellatravel.co.uk
Emp.: 300
Travel Agency Support Services
N.A.I.C.S.: 561510

dnata Inc. (2)
4/F International Passenger Terminal One NAIA Avenue, Pasay, 1300, Philippines
Tel.: (63) 2 879 6113
Web Site: http://www.dnata.com.ph
Emp.: 200
Aircraft Handling Services
N.A.I.C.S.: 488190
Margaret L. Yu *(CEO)*

dnata International Pvt Ltd (2)
Windsor IT ParkTower B 1st Floor Level A-1 Sector-125, Noida, 201 301, Uttar Pradesh, India
Tel.: (91) 120 676 3500
Travel Agency
N.A.I.C.S.: 561510
JaswinderSingh Talwar *(Head-Supplier & Revenue Mgmt)*

dnata Limited (2)
Units 1 & 2 Northumberland Close, Stanwell, Spelthorne, TW19 7LN, United Kingdom
Tel.: (44) 1784 424700
Web Site: http://www.dnata.co.uk
Emp.: 800
Airport Cargo Handling Services
N.A.I.C.S.: 488119
Robin Padgett *(Sr VP-Catering-Intl)*

dnata Singapore Pte Ltd (2)
50 Airport Boulevard Singapore Changi Air-

THE EMIRATES GROUP

The Emirates Group—(Continued)
port, Singapore, 819658, Singapore
Tel.: (65) 6511 0288
Web Site: http://www.dnata.sg
Emp.: 1,800
Aircraft Management & Catering Services
N.A.I.C.S.: 722320

dnata Switzerland AG (2)
Frachtstrasse 9/OPC 4, PO Box 103, 8058,
Zurich, Switzerland
Tel.: (41) 43 815 83 11
Web Site: http://www.dnata.ch
Airport Cargo Handling Services
N.A.I.C.S.: 488119

dnata Travel (UK) Limited (2)
95 Cromwell Rd, London, SW7 4DL, United
Kingdom
Tel.: (44) 2075901444
Travel Agency
N.A.I.C.S.: 561510
Steve Barrass (Sr VP)

dnata for Airport Services Ltd. (2)
Erbil International Airport, Erbil, Iraq
Tel.: (964) 750 325 8871
Web Site: http://www.dnata.com
Airport Cargo Handling Services
N.A.I.C.S.: 488119

THE ENGINE GROUP

60 Great Portland Street, London,
W1W 7RT, United Kingdom
Tel.: (44) 203 128 8000
Web Site:
   http://www.theenginegroup.com
Year Founded: 2005
Advertising Services
N.A.I.C.S.: 541810
Steve Aldridge (Exec Dir-Creative)

Subsidiaries:

Altogether Digital (1)
60 Great Portland St, London, W1W 7RT,
United Kingdom
Tel.: (44) 020 7309 5740
Emp.: 50
Advertising Services
N.A.I.C.S.: 541810

DEEP FOCUS HONG KONG (1)
18-20 Lyndhurst Terrace, Hong Kong, China
(Hong Kong)
Tel.: (852) 3468 6973
Media Advertising Services
N.A.I.C.S.: 541810

DEEP FOCUS SHANGHAI (1)
Room 601 Building 12 207 Mengzi Road,
Shanghai, 200023, China
Tel.: (86) 21 5093 6616
Media Advertising Services
N.A.I.C.S.: 541810
Kian Fong Wong (Mng Dir)

Dave (1)
60 Great Portland St, London, W1W 7RT,
United Kingdom
Tel.: (44) 20 3128 6400
Advertising Services
N.A.I.C.S.: 541810

Deep Focus (1)
460 Park Ave S 7th Fl, New York, NY
10016
Tel.: (212) 792-6800
Web Site: http://www.deep-focus.net
Sales Range: $25-49.9 Million
Emp.: 50
Advertising Services
N.A.I.C.S.: 541810
Ian Schafer (Founder & Chm)

Edwards Groom Saunders (1)
60 Great Portland St, London, W1W 7RT,
United Kingdom
Tel.: (44) 2031286160
Web Site:
   http://www.edwardsgroomsaunders.co.uk
Advertising Services
N.A.I.C.S.: 541890
Pete Edwards (Partner)

Element (1)
5 Golden Sq, London, W1F 9BS, United
Kingdom
Tel.: (44) 20 7806 5067

Advertising Services
N.A.I.C.S.: 541810

Engine (1)
460 Park Ave S Fl 7, New York, NY 10016-
7315
Tel.: (212) 371-0088
Advertising Services
N.A.I.C.S.: 541810
John L. Bernbach (Vice Chm)

Partners Andrews Aldridge (1)
60 Great Portland St, London, W1W 7RT,
United Kingdom
Tel.: (44) 20 3128 6200
Web Site:
   http://www.partnersandrewsaldridge.com
Emp.: 45
Advertising Services
N.A.I.C.S.: 541810
Steve Aldridge (Chm & Partner-Creative)

Synergy Sponsorship (1)
60 Great Portland St, London, W1W 7RT,
United Kingdom (100%)
Tel.: (44) 203 128 6800
Web Site: http://www.synergy-
   sponsorship.com
Emp.: 35
Advertising Services
N.A.I.C.S.: 541613
Tim Crow (CEO)

WCRS (1)
60 Great Portland Street, London, W1W
7RT, United Kingdom
Tel.: (44) 20 3128 6000
Web Site: http://www.wcrs.com
Sales Range: $10-24.9 Million
Emp.: 150
Advertising Services
N.A.I.C.S.: 541810
Leon Jaume (Exec Dir-Creative)

Branch (Domestic):

Woo Communications Limited (2)
60 Great Portland St, London, W1W 7RT,
United Kingdom
Tel.: (44) 20 3128 6723
Web Site: http://www.howtowoo.com
Emp.: 15
Advertising Services
N.A.I.C.S.: 541810

THE ENTERTAINER (AMERSHAM) LTD.

Boughton Business Park Bell LaneLittle Chalfont, Amersham, HP6 6GL,
Buckinghamshire, United Kingdom
Tel.: (44) 3333205100
Web Site: http://www.thetoyshop.com
Year Founded: 1981
Toy Retailer
N.A.I.C.S.: 459120
Phil Geary (CMO)

Subsidiaries:

Early Learning Centre Limited (1)
Cherry Tree Road, Watford, WD24 6SH,
Herts, United Kingdom
Tel.: (44) 1923241000
Web Site: http://www.elc.co.uk
Sales Range: $50-74.9 Million
Emp.: 200
Pre-School Educational Toys, Games &
Books Retailer
N.A.I.C.S.: 459120
Mark Newton Jones (CEO)

THE ENVIRONMENTAL GROUP LIMITED

Level 1 Suite 110 Ferntree Place,
Mount Waverley, Melbourne, 3168,
VIC, Australia
Tel.: (61) 397636711
Web Site:
   https://www.environmental.com.au
EGL—(ASX)
Rev.: $65,606,216
Assets: $49,892,914
Liabilities: $22,553,152
Net Worth: $27,339,762
Earnings: $2,931,444
Fiscal Year-end: 06/30/24

Designing & Building Gas Cleaning
Systems
N.A.I.C.S.: 332420
Ellis Richardson (Mng Dir)

Subsidiaries:

Baltec Australia trading as Total Air
Pollution Control Pty Limited (1)
6/16 Waynote Place, Unanderra, 2526,
NSW, Australia
Tel.: (61) 242725233
Web Site: https://tapc.com.au
Air Pollution Control Equipment Mfr & Distr
N.A.I.C.S.: 334512

Baltec IES Pty Limited (1)
10 Ferntree Place, Notting Hill, Melbourne,
3168, VIC, Australia
Tel.: (61) 397636711
Web Site: https://baltecies.com.au
Gas Turbine Mfr & Distr
N.A.I.C.S.: 333611

EGL Management Services Pty
Limited (1)
Unit 1A 9 Packard Ave, Castle Hill, 2154,
New South Wales, Australia
Tel.: (61) 288583499
Web Site: http://www.environmental.com.au
Sales Range: $75-99.9 Million
Sewage Treatment Services
N.A.I.C.S.: 221320

Mine Assist Pty Limited (1)
20 Enterprise Crescent, PO Box 3107,
Singleton, New South Wales, Australia
Tel.: (61) 265723220
Web Site: http://www.mineassist.com.au
Sales Range: $25-49.9 Million
Construction Management Services
N.A.I.C.S.: 237990

RCR Energy Services Pty Ltd. (1)
Level 23 Gateway 1 Macquarie Place, Sydney, 2000, NSW, Australia
Tel.: (61) 284133000
Boiler Engineering Services
N.A.I.C.S.: 541330

Total Air Pollution Control Pty
Limited (1)
6/16 Waynote Place, Unanderra, 2526,
NSW, Australia
Tel.: (61) 24 272 5233
Web Site: https://www.tapc.com.au
Sales Range: $25-49.9 Million
Emp.: 12
Environment Control Management Services
N.A.I.C.S.: 541620

THE EQUITABLE LIFE INSURANCE COMPANY OF CANADA

1 Westmount Road North, PO Box
1603, Waterloo, N2J 4C7, ON,
Canada
Tel.: (519) 886-5110 Ca
Web Site: http://www.equitable.ca
Year Founded: 1920
Rev.: $763,082,607
Assets: $3,116,281,326
Liabilities: $2,551,127,006
Net Worth: $565,154,320
Earnings: $63,629,126
Emp.: 690
Fiscal Year-end: 12/31/18
Fire Insurance Services
N.A.I.C.S.: 524113
Ronald E. Beettam (Pres & CEO)

Subsidiaries:

262695 Holdings Limited (1)
25 Westmount Rd N Suite 101, Waterloo,
N2L 5G7, ON, Canada
Tel.: (519) 886-5210
Fire Insurance Services
N.A.I.C.S.: 524113

THE ERAWAN GROUP PUBLIC COMPANY LIMITED

Ploenchit Center 6th Floor 2
Sukhumvit Road Kwang Klongtoey,
Khet Klongtoey, Bangkok, 10110,
Thailand

INTERNATIONAL PUBLIC

Tel.: (66) 22574588
Web Site:
   https://www.theerawan.com
Year Founded: 1982
ERW—(THA)
Rev.: $205,695,077
Assets: $691,117,865
Liabilities: $505,166,619
Net Worth: $185,951,247
Earnings: $22,182,301
Emp.: 3,894
Fiscal Year-end: 12/31/23
Hotel Developer & Operator
N.A.I.C.S.: 236220
Chanin Vongkusolkit (Chm)

Subsidiaries:

Erawan Chaophraya Company
Limited (1)
ibis Bangkok Riverside, Klongsan, Bangkok,
10600, Thailand
Tel.: (66) 28059888
Public Hotel & Motel Operator
N.A.I.C.S.: 721110

Erawan Growth Management Company Limited (1)
463/79 Pattaya Sai 2 Road, Nongprue
Bang Lamung, Pattaya, 20150, Chonburi,
Thailand
Tel.: (66) 38418188
Public Hotel & Motel Operator
N.A.I.C.S.: 721110

Erawan Hotel Public Company
Limited (1)
Grand Hyatt Erawan Bangkok, Patumwan,
Bangkok, 10330, Thailand
Tel.: (66) 22541234
Emp.: 587
Public Hotel & Motel Operator
N.A.I.C.S.: 721110

Erawan Naka Company Limited (1)
494 Ploenchit Rd Lumpinee, Patumwan,
Bangkok, 10330, Thailand
Tel.: (66) 22574588
Public Hotel & Motel Operator
N.A.I.C.S.: 721110

Erawan Phuket Company
Limited (1)
Land and Building, Thalang, Phuket, 83110,
Thailand
Tel.: (66) 76371400
Public Hotel & Motel Operator
N.A.I.C.S.: 721110

Erawan Rajdamri Company
Limited (1)
Courtyard by Marriott Bangkok, Patumwan,
Bangkok, 10330, Thailand
Tel.: (66) 26901888
Public Hotel & Motel Operator
N.A.I.C.S.: 721110

Erawan Samui Company Limited (1)
208/1 Moo 4 T Marat Lamai Beach, Ko
Samui, Surat Thani, 84310, Thailand
Tel.: (66) 77429300
Public Hotel & Motel Operator
N.A.I.C.S.: 721110

THE EUROPEAN METADATA GROUP

Lutzowstrasse 102-104, 10785, Berlin, Germany
Tel.: (49) 30 25 42 22 77 10
Web Site:
   http://theeuropeanmetadata.com
Year Founded: 2016
Metadata & Editorial Services
N.A.I.C.S.: 541519

Subsidiaries:

media-press.tv AG (1)
Wollerauerstrasse 7, CH-8834, Schindellegi,
Switzerland
Tel.: (41) 44 687 71 10
Web Site: http://www.media-press.tv
TV Programme Publishing & Editorial Systems Services
N.A.I.C.S.: 541511
Krzysztof Cechnicki (Founder, Chm & Pres)

AND PRIVATE COMPANIES

Subsidiary (Non-US):

media-press.tv S.A. (2)
ul Szymanowskiego 1/15, 30-047, Krakow, Poland
Tel.: (48) 12 631 25 50
Web Site: http://www.media-press.tv
TV Programme Publishing & Editorial Systems Services
N.A.I.C.S.: 516210

Subsidiary (Non-US):

Plurimedia SA (3)
9 Place Marie-Jeanne Bassot, 92300, Levallois-Perret, France
Tel.: (33) 141349620
Web Site: http://www.plurimedia.fr
Sales Range: $25-49.9 Million
Emp.: 100
TV Metadata & Editorial Services
N.A.I.C.S.: 516210
Catherine Dutoya *(Gen Mgr)*

THE EUROPEAN SMALLER COMPANIES TRUST PLC
201 Bishopsgate, London, EC2M 3AE, United Kingdom
Tel.: (44) 2078181818
ESCT—(LSE)
Rev.: $34,256,633
Assets: $994,445,721
Liabilities: $108,582,299
Net Worth: $885,863,422
Earnings: ($237,209,977)
Fiscal Year-end: 06/30/22
Investment Management Service
N.A.I.C.S.: 525990
Christopher Casey *(Chm)*

THE EXPORT-IMPORT BANK OF KOREA
16-1 Yeouido-dong, Yeongdeungpo-gu, Seoul, 150 996, Korea (South)
Tel.: (82) 3779 6114
Web Site: http://www.koreaexim.go.kr
Sales Range: $900-999.9 Million
Emp.: 600
Provider of International Banking Services
N.A.I.C.S.: 522299
Dong Kyu Shin *(Chm & Pres)*

Subsidiaries:

KEXIM Vietnam Leasing Co (1)
9th Floor Diamond Plaza Bldg, 34 Le Duan Street Dist 1, Ho Chi Minh City, Vietnam
Tel.: (84) 8 3825 7000
Web Site: http://www.koreaexim.go.kr
Commercial Banking Services
N.A.I.C.S.: 522110
Jae-Hyung Park *(Deputy Gen Dir)*

Kexim Bank (UK) (1)
3rd fl Moorgate Hall 155 Moogate, London, EC2M 6XB, United Kingdom (100%)
Tel.: (44) 2075625500
Web Site: http://www.koreaexim.go.kr
Sales Range: $75-99.9 Million
Emp.: 8
Banking Services
N.A.I.C.S.: 522299
Ged Hally *(Gen Mgr)*

PT Koexim MANDIRI Finance (1)
Menara Mulia Twr Ste 2007, JL Jend Gatot Subroto Kav 9 11, Jakarta, 12930, Indonesia
Tel.: (62) 215257261
Web Site: http://www.kmf.co.id
Sales Range: $50-74.9 Million
Emp.: 22
Financial Services
N.A.I.C.S.: 522299
Kung Jong Lin *(Pres)*

The Export-Import Bank Of Korea (1)
1 2 2 Hidiya Taikiru Rm No 1904, Chiyoda Ku Uchisaiwaisho, Tokyo, 100 0011, Japan (100%)
Tel.: (81) 335808702
Web Site: http://www.koreaexim.co.kr

Sales Range: $75-99.9 Million
Emp.: 3
Financial Services
N.A.I.C.S.: 522299
Kim Yong Hwan *(Pres & CEO)*

The Export-Import Bank of Korea - New York (1)
460 Park Ave Fl 8, New York, NY 10022 (100%)
Tel.: (212) 355-7280
Web Site: http://www.koreaexim.go.kr
Banking & Trade Research Services
N.A.I.C.S.: 522299

The Kexim Asia Ltd. (1)
Rm 1805 18 FL Central Plz 18 Harbour Road, 1 Connaught Pl, Wanchai, China (Hong Kong) (100%)
Tel.: (852) 28100182
Sales Range: $50-74.9 Million
Emp.: 8
Deposit Banking Services
N.A.I.C.S.: 522299

THE FANTASTIC COMPANY AG
Obmoos 4, CH-6301, Zug, Switzerland
Tel.: (41) 44 3502280
Web Site: http://www.fantastic.com
Year Founded: 1996
Private Equity Investor
N.A.I.C.S.: 523999
Roger Meier-Rossi *(Vice Chm-Supervisory Bd)*

THE FAR EASTERN GROUP
Taipei Metro Bldg 207 Tun Hua S Rd Session 2, Taipei, 106, Taiwan
Tel.: (886) 227378711
Web Site: http://www.feg.com
Sales Range: $1-4.9 Billion
Emp.: 40,000
Holding Company
N.A.I.C.S.: 551112
Chia Yi Hsi *(Vice Chm)*

Subsidiaries:

Far EasTone Telecommunications Co. Ltd. (1)
468 Ruei Guang Road, Nei Hu, Taipei, Taiwan
Tel.: (886) 277235000
Web Site: http://www.fetnet.net
Rev.: $2,827,849,325
Assets: $6,168,880,912
Liabilities: $3,741,327,688
Net Worth: $2,427,553,224
Earnings: $300,375,205
Emp.: 6,428
Fiscal Year-end: 12/31/2020
Wireless Telecommunication Services
N.A.I.C.S.: 517112
Douglas Tong Hsu *(Chm)*

Far Eastern Ai Mai Co., Ltd. (1)
5F No 110 Yen Ping South Road, Taipei, Taiwan
Tel.: (886) 2 23613691
Web Site: http://www.fe-amart.com.tw
Departmental Store Operator
N.A.I.C.S.: 455110

Far Eastern Apparel (Suzhou) Co., Ltd. (1)
88 Tian Ling Rd Wuzhong, Economic Development District, Suzhou, 215128, China
Tel.: (86) 512 65621888
Web Site: http://www.feasz.com
Apparels Mfr
N.A.I.C.S.: 315990
Fendi Chu *(Mgr-Sls)*

Far Eastern Apparel (Vietnam) Ltd. (1)
46 Dai Lo Tu Do Vietnam, Singapore Industrial Park, Thuan An, Binh Duong, Vietnam
Tel.: (84) 650 3782260
Polyester & Synthetic Fiber Mfr
N.A.I.C.S.: 325220

Far Eastern Apparel Co., Ltd. (1)
36F No 207 Sec 2 Tun Hwa South Road, Taipei, Taiwan

Tel.: (886) 2 2955 1888
Web Site: http://www.fet.com.tw
Apparel Designer, Mfr & Distr
N.A.I.C.S.: 315990

Far Eastern Big City Shopping Malls Co., Ltd. (1)
20F No 207 Sec 2Tun Hwa South Road, Taipei, Taiwan
Tel.: (886) 2 77122688
Web Site: http://www.fecityonline.com
Shopping Center Operator
N.A.I.C.S.: 445110

Far Eastern City Super Ltd. (1)
7/F No 64 Sec 4 Ren - ai Rd, Taipei, Taiwan
Tel.: (886) 2 77113288
Web Site: http://www.citysuper.com.tw
Departmental Store Operator
N.A.I.C.S.: 455110

Far Eastern Department Stores Ltd. (1)
18F No 16 Xinzhan Rd, Banqiao Dist, Taipei, 220, Taiwan
Tel.: (886) 77278168
Web Site: http://www.feds.com.tw
Rev.: $1,166,294,353
Assets: $4,126,838,536
Liabilities: $2,808,241,511
Net Worth: $1,318,597,025
Earnings: $87,971,998
Emp.: 1,371
Fiscal Year-end: 12/31/2022
General Merchandise Services
N.A.I.C.S.: 423990
Douglas Tong Hsu *(Chm)*

Subsidiary (Non-US):

Chengdu Quanxing Masion Pacific Department Store Co., Ltd. (2)
No 68 RenmingZhonglu Road, Sec 2, Chengdu, 610031, China
Tel.: (86) 28 86256688
Departmental Store Operator
N.A.I.C.S.: 455110

Chongqing Metropolitan Plaza Pacific Department Store Co. Ltd. (2)
No 68 Zhourong Road, Yuzhong District, Chongqing, 400010, China
Tel.: (86) 23 63710088
Web Site: http://www.feds.com.cn
Departmental Store Operator
N.A.I.C.S.: 455110

Chougqing Far Eastern Department Store Co., Ltd. (2)
No 10 Yanghe Road, Jiangba, Chongqing, 400020, China
Tel.: (86) 23 89180088
Web Site: http://www.feds.com.cn
Departmental Store Operator
N.A.I.C.S.: 455110

Pacific Dept Stores (Dalian) Co. Ltd. (2)
No 19 Jiefang Road, Zhong Shan District, Dalian, 116001, China
Tel.: (86) 411 82306999
Web Site: http://www.feds.com.cn
Departmental Store Operator
N.A.I.C.S.: 455110

Subsidiary (Domestic):

Pacific Sogo Department Stores Ltd. (2)
No 45 Sec 4 Chung Hsiao East Road, Taipei, 11041, Taiwan
Tel.: (886) 227765555
Department Stores Operation Services
N.A.I.C.S.: 455110

Subsidiary (Non-US):

Wuxi FEDS Co., Ltd. (2)
531 Zhongshan Road, Changan District, Wuxi, 214000, Jiangsu, China
Tel.: (86) 510 81809998
Departmental Store Operator
N.A.I.C.S.: 455110

Far Eastern Dyeing & Finishing (Suzhou) Ltd. (1)
No 508 Yin Zhong South Road He Dong Industrial Park, Wu Zhong Economic Development, Suzhou, 215124, China

THE FAR EASTERN GROUP

Tel.: (86) 512 65911888
Dyeing & Fabric Product Mfr
N.A.I.C.S.: 313310

Far Eastern Electronic Toll Collection Co., Ltd. (1)
2F No 419 Ruei Guang Road, Taipei, Taiwan
Tel.: (886) 2 77106666
Web Site: http://www.fetc.net.tw
Electronic Toll Collection Services
N.A.I.C.S.: 488490
Y. C. Chang *(Pres)*

Far Eastern Fibertech Co., Ltd. (1)
No 17 Industrial 5th Road, Kuan Yin Industrial Park, Kuan-yin, 00328, Taoyuan, Taiwan
Tel.: (886) 3 272 9730
Web Site: http://www.fefc.com.tw
Polyester & Synthetic Fiber Mfr
N.A.I.C.S.: 325220

Far Eastern Industries (Shanghai) Ltd. (1)
33F Bao An Tower 800 Dongfang Road, Pudong New Area, Shanghai, 200122, China
Tel.: (86) 21 68751888
Web Site: http://www.feis.com.cn
Polyester Product Mfr
N.A.I.C.S.: 325220
Cole Yang *(Acct Mgr)*

Far Eastern Industries (Wuxi) Co., Ltd. (1)
No 20 XinZhou Load, Wuxi, 241028, Jiangsu, China
Tel.: (86) 510 85341888
Web Site: http://www.feiw.com.cn
Polyester & Synthetic Fiber Mfr
N.A.I.C.S.: 325220

Far Eastern International Bank (1)
27/F No 207 Sec 2 Dunhua S Road, Daan District, Taipei, 106, Taiwan
Tel.: (886) 223786868
Web Site: http://www.feib.com.tw
Rev.: $400,156,063
Assets: $24,082,349,190
Liabilities: $22,294,648,921
Net Worth: $1,787,700,269
Earnings: $119,592,365
Emp.: 2,574
Fiscal Year-end: 12/31/2022
Commericial Banking
N.A.I.C.S.: 522110
Ching-Ing Hou *(Chm)*

Subsidiary (Domestic):

Far Eastern Asset Management Co., Ltd. (2)
4F-1 No 267 Sec 2 Tun Hwa South Road, Taipei, 106, Taiwan
Tel.: (886) 277133688
Asset Management Services
N.A.I.C.S.: 523999

Far Eastern International Securities Co., Ltd. (2)
51F Taipei 101 No 7 Sec 5 Xin Yi Rd, Taipei, 11049, Taiwan
Tel.: (886) 8758 3399
Web Site: http://www.feis.com.tw
Financial Services
N.A.I.C.S.: 523999
Jonathan Lin *(Sr VP)*

Far Eastern International Leasing Corporation (1)
5F No 108 Section 5 Nan King East Road, Taipei, Taiwan
Tel.: (886) 2 27455038
Web Site: http://www.fei.com.tw
Financial Lending Services
N.A.I.C.S.: 522220

Far Eastern New Century Corporation (1)
36F Taipei Metro Tower 207 Tun Hua South Road Sec 2, Taipei, Taiwan
Tel.: (886) 227338000
Web Site: http://www.fenc.com
Rev.: $8,583,475,953
Assets: $21,390,287,233
Liabilities: $12,555,511,289
Net Worth: $8,834,775,944
Earnings: $433,854,198
Emp.: 30,396

THE FAR EASTERN GROUP

The Far Eastern Group—(Continued)
Fiscal Year-end: 12/31/2022
Textile Fiber Mfr & Sales
N.A.I.C.S.: 314999
Douglas Tong Hsu *(Chm)*

Subsidiary (US):

M&G Polymers USA LLC (2)
State Route 2, Apple Grove, WV 25502
Tel.: (304) 576-2041
Sales Range: $25-49.9 Million
Emp.: 100
Mfr of PET Resin
N.A.I.C.S.: 325211

Far Eastern Resource Development Ltd., Coporation (1)
34F No 207Tun Hwa South Road, Sec 2, Taipei, 106, Taiwan
Tel.: (886) 2 27338000
Web Site: http://www.tpark.com.tw
Building & Construction Services
N.A.I.C.S.: 236210

Oriental Industries (Suzhou) Co., Ltd. (1)
No 1688 Yin Zhong South Road He Dong Industrial Park, Wu Zhong Economic Development, Suzhou, 215124, China
Tel.: (86) 512 65951888
Web Site: http://www.otiz.com.cn
Polyester Product Mfr
N.A.I.C.S.: 322219

Oriental Resources Development Co., Ltd. (1)
Rm A 15F No 182 Sec 2 Dunhua S Rd, Da'an Dist, Taipei, 00106, Taiwan
Tel.: (886) 2 77188000
Web Site: http://www.ord.feg.com.tw
Recycling Services
N.A.I.C.S.: 423930

Shanghai Pacific Department Store Co., Ltd. (1)
No 932 Hengshan Road, Shanghai, 200030, China
Tel.: (86) 21 64078888
Web Site: http://www.pacific-shanghai.com.cn
Departmental Store Operator
N.A.I.C.S.: 455110

Sino-Belgian Beer (Suzhou) Co., Ltd. (1)
No 6 Hengshan Road, New District, Suzhou, 215009, Jiangsu, China
Tel.: (86) 512 68231888
Web Site: http://www.sbbz.com.cn
PET Beer Bottle Mfr
N.A.I.C.S.: 326160

Tianjing Far Eastern Department Store Co., Ltd. (1)
No 168 Tungma Road, Nankai Dist, Tianjin, 300090, China
Tel.: (86) 22 27271688
Departmental Store Operator
N.A.I.C.S.: 455110

Wuhan Far Eastern New Material Ltd. (1)
No 93 Zhushanhu Rd, Wuhan Economical-Techincal Development Zone, Wuhan, 430056, Hubei, China
Tel.: (86) 27 84291888
Polyester & Synthetic Fiber Mfr
N.A.I.C.S.: 325220

THE FEDERATION OF MALAYSIAN MANUFACTURERS

Wisma FMM No 3 Persiaran Dagang, Bandar Sri Damansara, 52200, Kuala Lumpur, Malaysia
Tel.: (60) 362867200
Web Site: http://www.fmm.org.my
Year Founded: 1968
Sales Range: $10-24.9 Million
Emp.: 100
Economic Organization Representing Manufacturing & Industrial Service Companies
N.A.I.C.S.: 813910
Mustafa Mansur *(Pres)*

Subsidiaries:

FMM Services Sdn Bhd (1)
Wisma FMM No 3 Persiaran Dagang Bandar Sri Damansara, Kuala Lumpur, 52200, Malaysia
Tel.: (60) 3 6286 7200
Web Site: http://www.fmm.org.my
Emp.: 80
Business Management Consulting Services
N.A.I.C.S.: 541611
Yeoh Oon Tean *(CEO)*

THE FEDERATION OF MIGROS COOPERATIVES

Limmatstrasse 152, CH-8031, Zurich, Switzerland
Tel.: (41) 848 84 0848 CH
Web Site: http://www.migros.ch
Year Founded: 1925
Sales Range: $15-24.9 Billion
Emp.: 82,712
Textiles, Dairy Products, Groceries, Meat, Poultry, Fish, Hardware, Agricultural Products, Laundry Products, Health/Beauty Aids, Hotel & Leisure Services & Flowers Retailer
N.A.I.C.S.: 424490
Claude Hauser *(Pres-Admin)*

Subsidiaries:

Bischofszell Foods AG (1)
Industrie Strasse 1, Bischofszell, 9220, Switzerland (100%)
Tel.: (41) 714249111
Web Site: http://www.bina.ch
Sales Range: $150-199.9 Million
Emp.: 800
Producer of Fruit, Vegetable & Meat Conserves, Fruit Juice & Iced Tea, Deep-Frozen Products, Jam & Marmalade, Tomato & Potato Products
N.A.I.C.S.: 311421

Chocolat Frey AG (1)
Bresteneggstrasse 4 Aargau, 5033, Buchs, Argovie, Switzerland (100%)
Tel.: (41) 628362626
Web Site: http://www.chocolatfrey.ch
Sales Range: $250-299.9 Million
Emp.: 850
Chcolate & Confectionery Mfr
N.A.I.C.S.: 311351
Hans Ruedi Christain *(CEO)*

Dietiker AG (1)
Hoswisenstrasse 2, Stein am Rhein, 8260, Switzerland (100%)
Tel.: (41) 527422121
Web Site: http://www.dietiker.com
Sales Range: $25-49.9 Million
Emp.: 100
Production of Chairs & Tables for Conference & Seminar Rooms, Furniture for Public Premises, Restaurants & General Purposes
N.A.I.C.S.: 337121
Nathalie Felder *(CEO)*

Estavayer Lait S.A. (1)
Case postale, CH 1470, Estavayer le Lac, Switzerland (100%)
Tel.: (41) 266649111
Web Site: http://www.elsa.ch
Emp.: 592
Producer of Dairy Products (Fresh Cheese, Desserts, Yogurt, Milk Drinks, Quark, Milk & Unpasteurized Cream), Mayonnaise, Vinegar & Salad Dressings
N.A.I.C.S.: 311514
Matthew Robins *(CEO)*

Ex Libris AG (1)
Grunaustrasse 23, 8953, Dietikon, Switzerland (100%)
Tel.: (41) 800002255
Web Site: http://www.exlibris.ch
Sales Range: $125-149.9 Million
Emp.: 355
Books, Audio & Video Media, Software, Electronics & Office Supplies Retailer
N.A.I.C.S.: 459999

Globus-Gruppe (1)
Eich Strasse 23, Zurich, 8957, Switzerland (100%)
Tel.: (41) 584552111
Web Site: http://www.globus-gruppe.ch
Sales Range: $25-49.9 Million
Emp.: 80
N.A.I.C.S.: 313310
Ronald Kistler *(Gen Mgr)*

Subsidiary (Domestic):

Globus Department Stores (2)
Schweizergasse 11, 8001, Zurich, Switzerland
Tel.: (41) 585781111
Web Site: http://www.globus.ch
Sales Range: $50-74.9 Million
Department Stores
N.A.I.C.S.: 455110

Herren Globus (2)
Kasinostr 30, 5000, Aarau, Switzerland
Tel.: (41) 585763650
N.A.I.C.S.: 313310

Hotelplan Suisse, MTCG AG (1)
Saegerei Strasse 20, Glattbrugg, 8152, Zurich, Switzerland (100%)
Tel.: (41) 432118111
Web Site: http://www.hotelplan.ch
Sales Range: $75-99.9 Million
Emp.: 500
Holiday Tour Travel Arrangement Hotel Holiday Village Operation
N.A.I.C.S.: 561510
Thomi Stirnimann *(CEO)*

Jowa AG (1)
Erlenwiesenstrasse 9, 8604, Volketswil, Zurich, Switzerland (100%)
Tel.: (41) 449479111
Web Site: http://www.jowa.ch
Sales Range: $150-199.9 Million
Emp.: 800
Producer of Bread, Confectionery, Deep-Frozen Bakeware & Noodles
N.A.I.C.S.: 311812
Heinz Lang *(Mgr-Mktg, Dev & Buying)*

Limmatdruck AG (1)
Pfadackerstrasse 10, CH 8957, Spreitenbach, Switzerland (100%)
Tel.: (41) 564175111
Web Site: http://www.limmatdruck.ch
Sales Range: $200-249.9 Million
Emp.: 602
Provider of Publishing, Communication, Printing & Packaging
N.A.I.C.S.: 513130
Andreas Young *(CEO)*

Medbase AG (1)
Schützenstrasse 3, Winterthur, Switzerland (100%)
Tel.: (41) 0522602929
Web Site: https://www.medbase.ch
Health & Human Services
N.A.I.C.S.: 621511

Mibelle AG (1)
Bolimattstrasse 1, 5033, Buchs, Switzerland (100%)
Tel.: (41) 628361111
Web Site: http://www.mibellegroup.com
Sales Range: $125-149.9 Million
Emp.: 450
Skin Care Hair Care & Oral Hygiene Soap Bath Preparation Deodorant & Toilet Water Product Mfr
N.A.I.C.S.: 325620
Marianne Meyer *(Head-Intl Sls)*

Micarna S.A. (1)
Route Del L'Industrie 25, 1784, Courtepin, Switzerland (100%)
Tel.: (41) 266849111
Web Site: http://www.micarna.ch
Sales Range: $550-599.9 Million
Emp.: 1,454
Retailer of Fresh Meat & Other Butchery Products
N.A.I.C.S.: 424470

Midor AG (1)
Bruechstrasse 70, Meilen, 8706, Switzerland (100%)
Tel.: (41) 9258111
Web Site: http://www.midor.com
Sales Range: $150-199.9 Million
Emp.: 693
Production of Biscuits, Cocktail Specialties, Ice Cream & Powdered Desserts

INTERNATIONAL PUBLIC

N.A.I.C.S.: 311520

Mifa AG (1)
Rheinstrasse 99, Frenkendorf, 4402, Switzerland (100%)
Tel.: (41) 619059111
Web Site: http://www.mibellegroup.com
Detergents & Cleansing Agents, Margarine & Edible Fats Mfr
N.A.I.C.S.: 325611
Thomas Gasser *(Dir-HR Mgmt)*

Mifroma France S.A. (1)
Rte de Pont d'Ain, 01320, Chalamont, France (100%)
Tel.: (33) 474469946
Web Site: http://www.mifroma.ch
Sales Range: $25-49.9 Million
Emp.: 70
Cheese Packaging Mfr
N.A.I.C.S.: 313310

Mifroma S.A. (1)
Rte del Plattiez 11, 1670, Ursy, Switzerland (100%)
Tel.: (41) 219091111
Web Site: http://www.mifroma.ch
Sales Range: $25-49.9 Million
Emp.: 234
Cheese Buying Warehousing Aging & Packaging Distr
N.A.I.C.S.: 493120
Gilles Oberson *(Mng Dir)*

Migro Switzerland (1)
Rue Alexandre Gavard 35, CH 1227, Geneva, Switzerland (100%)
Tel.: (41) 223075111
Web Site: http://www.migro.ch
Sales Range: $800-899.9 Million
Emp.: 3,600
N.A.I.C.S.: 313310

Migrol S.A. (1)
Badenerstrasse 569, 8048, Zurich, Switzerland (100%)
Tel.: (41) 444951111
Web Site: http://www.migrol.ch
Sales Range: $100-124.9 Million
Emp.: 320
Provider of Fuel/Heating Oil Trading, Filling Stations, Automobile Service Stations, Tank Overhauls & Installations
N.A.I.C.S.: 333921
Daniel Hofar *(Gen Mgr)*

Migros Bank (1)
Seidengasse 12, 8001, Zurich, Switzerland (100%)
Tel.: (41) 848845400
Web Site: http://www.migrosbank.ch
Sales Range: $350-399.9 Million
Emp.: 914
Banking Services
N.A.I.C.S.: 522110
Harald Nedwed *(Pres)*

Migros Betriebe Birsfelden AG (1)
Hafenstrasse 120, CH 4127, Birsfelden, Switzerland (100%)
Tel.: (41) 613157788
Web Site: http://www.mbb.ch
Sales Range: $25-49.9 Million
Emp.: 200
Provider of Roasting/Packaging of Coffee; Packaging of Peanuts; Cleaning/Blending/Packaging of Tea, Dried Fruits; Vegetables; Storage; Customs Clearance
N.A.I.C.S.: 493110
Thomas Gubler *(Gen Mgr)*

Migros Cooperative (1)
Aeschenvorstadt 24, CH 4051, Basel, Switzerland (100%)
Tel.: (41) 58 575 8750
Web Site: http://www.migros.ch
Sales Range: $750-799.9 Million
Emp.: 500
Produce, Toiletries & Cosmetics, Bakery & Fresh Seafood
N.A.I.C.S.: 424460
Andreas Munch *(Chm)*

Migros Raare Cooperative (1)
Marktgasse 28, Bern, 3011, Switzerland (100%)
Tel.: (41) 585673175
Web Site: http://www.migros.ch
Sales Range: $200-249.9 Million
Emp.: 1,000
Food Cooperative

AND PRIVATE COMPANIES

Migros Valais (1)
Rue des Finettes 45, 1920, Martigny, Switzerland
Tel.: (41) 277204400
Web Site: http://www.migrosvalais.ch
Shopping Center
N.A.I.C.S.: 459999
Alter Max *(Mng Dir)*

Migros Vaud (1)
Chemin Du Devent, CH 1024, Ecublens, Switzerland (100%)
Tel.: (41) 216946111
Web Site: http://www.migro.ch
Sales Range: $200-249.9 Million
Emp.: 800
N.A.I.C.S.: 313310

Migros Zurich (1)
Pfingstweidstrasse 101, CH 805, Zurich, Switzerland (100%)
Tel.: (41) 58561511
Web Site: http://www.migros.ch
Sales Range: $1-4.9 Billion
Emp.: 8,000
N.A.I.C.S.: 313310
Herbert Bolliger *(CEO)*

Migros-Verteilbetrieb Neuendorf AG (1)
New St 49, PO Box 18, CH 4623, Neuendorf, Switzerland (100%)
Tel.: (41) 623887111
Web Site: http://www.mvn.ch
Sales Range: $300-349.9 Million
Emp.: 1,050
Provider of Storage/Commissioning of Non-Food & Deep-Frozen Products, Bakeware & Seasonal Chocolate Articles; Logistics
N.A.I.C.S.: 493110
Hans Kuhn *(Mng Dir)*

Monte-Generoso-Bahn AG (1)
Capalogo, CH 6825, Capolago, Switzerland (100%)
Tel.: (41) 916481105
Web Site: http://www.montegeneroso.ch
Sales Range: $25-49.9 Million
Emp.: 20
Rail Services & Tourist Attractions
N.A.I.C.S.: 482112

Riseria Taverne S.A. (1)
Via Ponte Vecchio, Taverne, 6807, Switzerland (100%)
Tel.: (41) 919357300
Web Site: http://www.riseria.ch
Sales Range: $10-24.9 Million
Emp.: 27
Provider of Refining of Rice; Storage of Conserve Products
N.A.I.C.S.: 493130

Seba Aproz S.A. (1)
PO Box 1248, CH 1951, Sion, Switzerland (98%)
Tel.: (41) 273455111
Web Site: http://www.aproz.ch
Sales Range: $25-49.9 Million
Emp.: 120
Producer of Natural Mineral Water, Soft Drinks with Fruit Essence, Fruit Juices & Syrups & Aroma Additives
N.A.I.C.S.: 311411

The Federation of Migros Cooperatives (1)
Strada Cantorle, S Antonino, CH 6592, Lugano, Switzerland
Tel.: (41) 918508111
Web Site: http://www.migrosticino.ch
Sales Range: $50-74.9 Million
Emp.: 150
N.A.I.C.S.: 313310

THE FERTILISERS AND CHEMICALS TRAVANCORE LIMITED
Eloor Udyogamandal, Kochi, 683 501, Kerala, India
Tel.: (91) 4842546486
Web Site: https://www.fact.co.in
Year Founded: 1943
FACT—(NSE)
Rev.: $759,393,813
Assets: $651,556,477
Liabilities: $498,820,203
Net Worth: $152,736,275
Earnings: $73,495,030
Emp.: 1,546
Fiscal Year-end: 03/31/23
Fertilizer Mfr
N.A.I.C.S.: 212390
K. V. Balakrishnan Nair *(Sec & Exec Dir-Fin)*

THE FINANCE COMPANY PLC
No 55 Lauries Place RA De Mel Mawatha, Colombo, 4, Sri Lanka
Tel.: (94) 112580210
Web Site: http://www.thefinance.lk
Rev.: $23,129,540
Assets: $152,919,993
Liabilities: $246,872,501
Net Worth: ($93,952,509)
Earnings: ($11,642,773)
Emp.: 662
Fiscal Year-end: 03/31/18
Financial & Investment Services
N.A.I.C.S.: 523940
Kosala Wimalasiri *(CEO)*

Subsidiaries:

The Finance Company PLC - Business Leasing Division (1)
No 194 Galle Road, Dehiwala-Mount Lavinia, Western Province, Sri Lanka
Tel.: (94) 114308601
Business Leasing Services
N.A.I.C.S.: 561499

The Finance Company PLC - Corporate Finance & Treasury Division (1)
No 55 R A De Mel Mawatha, Colombo, 00400, Western Province, Sri Lanka
Tel.: (94) 112500671
Web Site: http://www.thefinance.lk
Emp.: 100
Corporate Finance & Treasury Services
N.A.I.C.S.: 541611
Aruna Lekange *(Mng Dir)*

The Finance Company PLC - Fixed Deposits Division (1)
No 97 Hyde Park Corner, Colombo, 00200, Western Province, Sri Lanka
Tel.: (94) 11 2682745
Web Site: http://www.thefinance.lk
Sales Range: $50-74.9 Million
Emp.: 50
Fixed Deposit Services
N.A.I.C.S.: 523940

The Finance Company PLC - Marketing Division (1)
No 55 Lauries Place R A De Mel Mawatha, Colombo, 00400, Western Province, Sri Lanka
Tel.: (94) 112580210
Marketing Services
N.A.I.C.S.: 541910

THE FINANCIAL CORPORATION COMPANY SAOG
PO Box 782, 131, Muscat, Oman
Tel.: (968) 24822300
Web Site: https://www.fincorp.org
FINC—(MUS)
Rev.: $1,919,221
Assets: $21,641,887
Liabilities: $2,098,252
Net Worth: $19,543,635
Earnings: $1,299,769
Emp.: 16
Fiscal Year-end: 12/31/23
Investment Banking Services
N.A.I.C.S.: 523150
Mohamed Darwish Al Khoori *(Chm)*

THE FIRST ARTIST COMPANY LTD.
First Artist House, 85 A Wembley Hill Road, Wembley, HA9 8BU, Middlesex, United Kingdom
Tel.: (44) 20 8900 1818   UK
Web Site: http://www.firstartist.com
Sales Range: $75-99.9 Million
Emp.: 275
Marketing, Sports & Entertainment Management Services
N.A.I.C.S.: 711410
Jon Smith *(CEO)*

Subsidiaries:

DeWynters Limited (1)
48 Leicester Sq, London, WC2H 7QD, United Kingdom
Tel.: (44) 20 7321 0488
Web Site: http://www.dewynters.com
Sales Range: $25-49.9 Million
Emp.: 100
N.A.I.C.S.: 541810
Anthony Pye Jeary *(Founder & Chm)*

Branch (US):

DeWynters Advertising Inc. (2)
43-01 22nd St 3rd Fl SW, Long Island City, NY 11101
Tel.: (718) 472-0424
Web Site: http://www.dewynters.com
Sales Range: $25-49.9 Million
Emp.: 4
N.A.I.C.S.: 541810

THE FIRST BANK OF TOYAMA, LTD.
5-1 Nishimachi, Toyama, 930-0062, Japan
Tel.: (81) 764241211
Web Site: https://www.first-bank.co.jp
Year Founded: 1944
7184—(TKS)
Rev.: $255,661,580
Assets: $10,449,121,050
Liabilities: $9,417,888,340
Net Worth: $1,031,232,710
Earnings: $85,930
Emp.: 629
Fiscal Year-end: 03/31/24
Banking Services
N.A.I.C.S.: 522110
Mitsuru Nomura *(Pres & CEO)*

THE FIRST CUSTODIAN FUND (INDIA) LTD.
3 Surya Mahal 3rd Floor Nagindas Master Road Fort, Mumbai, 400023, India
Tel.: (91) 2266359001
Web Site: https://www.firstcustodianfund.in
Year Founded: 1985
511122—(BOM)
Rev.: $94,496
Assets: $1,781,907
Liabilities: $287,540
Net Worth: $1,494,366
Earnings: $21,868
Fiscal Year-end: 03/31/21
Investment Management Service
N.A.I.C.S.: 525990
Manish Rajendra Banthia *(Exec Dir)*

THE FIRST INSURANCE CO., LTD.
No 54 Sec 1 Zhongxiao E Rd, Zhongzheng Dist, Taipei, Taiwan
Tel.: (886) 223913271
Web Site: https://www.firstins.com.tw
Year Founded: 1962
2852—(TAI)
Rev.: $296,288,716
Assets: $629,477,036
Liabilities: $363,685,784
Net Worth: $265,791,252
Earnings: $20,806,468
Fiscal Year-end: 12/31/23
Insurance Services
N.A.I.C.S.: 524298
C. S. Lin *(Exec VP)*

THE FLOWR CORP.
Unit A 9590 McCarthy Road, Kelowna, V4V 1S5, BC, Canada

THE FOSCHINI GROUP LIMITED

Web Site: https://www.flowr.ca
FLWR—(TSXV)
Rev.: $5,877,270
Assets: $141,591,898
Liabilities: $51,039,859
Net Worth: $90,552,039
Earnings: ($95,185,484)
Emp.: 223
Fiscal Year-end: 12/31/20
Cannabis Cultivation Services
N.A.I.C.S.: 424590
Irina Hossu *(CFO)*

THE FOOD REVOLUTION GROUP
20 Heaths Court, Mill Park, 3082, VIC, Australia
Tel.: (61) 399821451
Web Site: http://thefoodrevoluitongroup.com.au
OJC—(ASX)
Rev.: $33,018,325
Assets: $24,669,488
Liabilities: $18,382,161
Net Worth: $6,287,327
Earnings: $4,281,589
Fiscal Year-end: 06/30/24
Fruit & Vegetable Processing Services
N.A.I.C.S.: 311411
Norman Li *(Chm)*

THE FORTRESS RESORTS PLC
Tel.: (94) 4767800
Year Founded: 1967
RHTL—(COL)
Rev.: $1,447,010
Assets: $6,080,458
Liabilities: $723,961
Net Worth: $5,356,497
Earnings: ($66,051)
Emp.: 103
Fiscal Year-end: 03/31/23
Hotel & Restaurant Operator
N.A.I.C.S.: 721110
K. D. H. Perera *(Chm)*

THE FOSCHINI GROUP LIMITED
Stanley Lewis Centre 340 Voortrekker Road, Parow East, Cape Town, 7500, South Africa
Tel.: (27) 219381911   ZA
Web Site: https://www.tfglimited.co.za
Year Founded: 1924
TFG—(JSE)
Rev.: $31,500,017,020
Assets: $29,552,255,210
Liabilities: $16,494,466,040
Net Worth: $13,057,789,170
Earnings: $1,985,151,850
Emp.: 38,329
Fiscal Year-end: 03/31/22
Holding Company; Apparel, Accessories & Other Lifestyle Products Retailer; Credit Card Issuing Services
N.A.I.C.S.: 551112
Michael Lewis *(Chm)*

Subsidiaries:

Foschini Retail Group Proprietary Limited (1)
Stanley Lewis Centre 340 Voortrekker Road, Parow, 7500, Western Cape, South Africa
Tel.: (27) 219381911
Web Site: http://www.tfg.co.za
Apparel, Accessories & Other Lifestyle Products Retailer
N.A.I.C.S.: 455219

Subsidiary (Non-US):

Phase Eight (Fashion & Designs) Limited (2)
55 Kimber Road, Fulham, London, SW18 4NX, United Kingdom (85%)

THE FOSCHINI GROUP LIMITED

The Foschini Group Limited—(Continued)

Tel.: (44) 208 877 4001
Web Site: https://www.phase-eight.com
Sales Range: $25-49.9 Million
Emp.: 2,000
Women's Fashion Retailer
N.A.I.C.S.: 458110
Guy Tambling *(Dir-Information Technology-Commerce)*

Whistles Limited (2)
163 Eversholt Street, London, NW1 1BU, United Kingdom
Tel.: (44) 207 391 0923
Web Site: https://www.whistles.com
Women's & Men's Fashion Clothes Distr
N.A.I.C.S.: 458110
Justin Hampshire *(Mng Dir)*

THE FOUNTAIN STUDIOS

128 Wembley Park Dr, Wembley, HA9 8HP, Middlesex, United Kingdom
Tel.: (44) 2089005800
Web Site: http://www.ftv.co.uk
Year Founded: 1985
Sales Range: $10-24.9 Million
Emp.: 50
Television Broadcasting
N.A.I.C.S.: 516120
Tony Edwards *(Mgr-Studio)*

THE FUKUI BANK, LTD.

1-1-1 Junka, Fukui, 910-8660, Japan
Tel.: (81) 776242030
Web Site: https://www.fukuibank.co.jp
Year Founded: 1899
8362—(TKS)
Rev.: $366,346,030
Assets: $27,526,492,310
Liabilities: $26,591,131,040
Net Worth: $935,361,270
Earnings: $165,250
Emp.: 1,805
Fiscal Year-end: 03/31/24
Banking Services
N.A.I.C.S.: 522110
Masahiro Hayashi *(Chm & Pres)*

THE FUKUSHIMA BANK LTD.

Manseicho 2-5, Fukushima, 960-8625, Japan
Tel.: (81) 245252525
Web Site:
 https://www.fukushimabank.co.jp
Year Founded: 1922
8562—(TKS)
Rev.: $87,932,830
Assets: $5,479,372,720
Liabilities: $5,313,554,260
Net Worth: $165,818,460
Earnings: $33,050
Fiscal Year-end: 03/31/24
Banking Services
N.A.I.C.S.: 522110
Kunitake Konno *(Chm)*

THE FULHAM SHORE PLC

1st Floor 50-51 Berwick Street, London, W1F 8SJ, United Kingdom
Tel.: (44) 20 3026 8129 **UK**
Web Site:
 http://www.fulhamshore.com
Year Founded: 2012
FUL—(AIM)
Rev.: $54,695,750
Assets: $187,268,962
Liabilities: $139,128,284
Net Worth: $48,140,678
Earnings: ($8,561,782)
Emp.: 1,098
Fiscal Year-end: 03/28/21
Restaurants Investment Services
N.A.I.C.S.: 523999
David Page *(Chm)*

THE FURUKAWA ELECTRIC CO., LTD.

Tokiwabashi Tower 2-6-4 Otemachi, Chiyoda-ku, Tokyo, 100-8322, Japan
Tel.: (81) 362818500 **JP**
Web Site: https://www.furukawa.co.jp
Year Founded: 1884
FUWAY—(OTCIQ)
Rev.: $7,645,557,420
Assets: $6,702,781,290
Liabilities: $4,329,582,990
Net Worth: $2,373,198,300
Earnings: $128,421,870
Emp.: 51,314
Fiscal Year-end: 03/31/23
Wire & Cable Mfr
N.A.I.C.S.: 333613
Keiichiro Urakami *(VP & Gen Mgr)*

Subsidiaries:

ALPHA Industries Bhd. (1)
No 37 Jalan Kangkar Tebrau Karung Berkunci No 744, 81100, Johor Bahru, Johor, Malaysia
Tel.: (60) 73543996
Sales Range: $50-74.9 Million
Emp.: 200
Electrical Equipment
N.A.I.C.S.: 444180

Access Cable Company (1)
1-8-9 Kanda-Nishikicho, Chiyoda-ku, Tokyo, 101-0054, Japan
Tel.: (81) 335186501
Web Site: http://www.access-cable.jp
Fiber Optic Cable Mfr
N.A.I.C.S.: 335921

American Furukawa, Inc. (1)
47677 Galleon Dr, Plymouth, MI 48170
Tel.: (734) 446-2200
Web Site:
 https://www.americanfurukawa.com
Emp.: 45
Industrial Electronic Component Distr
N.A.I.C.S.: 423690

Asahi Electric Works Co., Ltd. (1)
11-16 Azamino-Minami 2-chome, Aoba-ku, Yokohama, 225-0012, Kanagawa, Japan
Tel.: (81) 45 910 2800
Web Site: http://www.aew.co.jp
Rev.: $100,368,000
Emp.: 248
Power Transmission Equipment Mfr & Distr
N.A.I.C.S.: 333613
Toshio Nakada *(Pres)*

Asia Cable Engineering Co., Pte. Ltd. (1)
623 Aljunied Rd 03 09, Aljunied Industrial Complex, Singapore, 389835, Singapore
Tel.: (65) 67413303
Web Site: http://www.sojitz-br.com
Sales Range: $700-749.9 Million
Emp.: 23
General Contractors
N.A.I.C.S.: 236220

Bangkok Telecom Co., Ltd. (1)
No 363 Soi Rama 9 13 Rama 9 Road, Huay Kwang Bang Kapi District, Bangkok, 10320, Thailand (40.74%)
Tel.: (66) 23183337
Web Site: http://www.bangkoktelecom.com
Electrical Wire & Cable Production & Sales
N.A.I.C.S.: 336320

Birla Furukawa Fibre Optics Limited (1)
Plot nos L-62 to L-64 Verna Industrial Estate, Verna Salcette, Goa, 403 722, India
Tel.: (91) 832 669 6400
Web Site: https://www.birlafurukawa.com
Optical Fiber Product Mfr
N.A.I.C.S.: 335921

C.M. Furukawa Philippines Inc. (1)
208 Veterans Center Building Western Bicutan, Tagig, Manila, Philippines
Tel.: (63) 28371485
N.A.I.C.S.: 444180

CFT Vina Copper Co., Ltd. (1)
Road No 9 Bien Hoa 1 Industrial Zone, Bien Hoa, Dong Nai, Vietnam (33%)
Tel.: (84) 613836502
Web Site: http://www.cft-vietnam.com
Sales Range: $50-74.9 Million
Emp.: 70
N.A.I.C.S.: 444180

Chongqing Changhua Automobile Harness Co., Ltd. (1)
No 8 Gang'an 2nd Road, Jiangbei District, Chongqing, China
Tel.: (86) 236 794 6790
Automotive Parts Mfr & Distr
N.A.I.C.S.: 336390

Circuit Foil Taiwan Corp. (1)
8 Tou Kung 2nd Rd Kuo Ta Industrial Park, Touliu, Taipei, 64000, Taiwan
Tel.: (886) 55571361
Sales Range: $25-49.9 Million
Emp.: 100
Metal Coatings
N.A.I.C.S.: 444180

Europtics Limited (1)
43 45 Nottinghill Gate, London, L35 1RZ, United Kingdom
Tel.: (44) 72216000
Web Site: http://www.furukawa.co.uk
N.A.I.C.S.: 444180

FE Magnet Wire (Malaysia) Sdn. Bhd. (1)
Lot 2 Persiaran Waja Bukit Raja Industrial Estate, 41720, Kelang, Selangor Darul Ehsan, Malaysia
Tel.: (60) 3 3342 7001
Web Site: http://www.femm.com.my
Emp.: 150
Magnet Wire Mfr
N.A.I.C.S.: 332618

FITEC Corp. (1)
Shinagawa Seaside West Tower 12-2 Higashi-Shinagawa 4-chome, Shinagawa-ku, Tokyo, 140-0002, Japan
Tel.: (81) 36 810 3100
Web Site: https://www.fitec.co.jp
Emp.: 302
Software Solutions Services
N.A.I.C.S.: 541511
Motohiko Taniguchi *(Pres & CEO)*

Foam Kasei Co., Ltd. (1)
4049-1 Nakatsu, Aikawa-cho, Aiko, 243-0303, Kanagawa, Japan
Tel.: (81) 46 285 6900
Web Site: https://www.foamkasei.co.jp
Plastic Foaming Material Mfr & Distr
N.A.I.C.S.: 326140

Furukawa (Thailand) Co., Ltd. (1)
191 Silom Complex Building 16th floor Units 4 C Silom Road, Kwaeng Silom Bangrak, Bangkok, 10500, Pathumwan, Thailand
Tel.: (66) 26321079
Web Site: http://www.furukawa.co.th
Emp.: 35
Electronic Telecommunication Equipment Mfr
N.A.I.C.S.: 334419

Furukawa America Inc - HIRATSUKA WORKS MAGNET WIRE PLANT (1)
5-1-9 Higashiyawata, Hiratsuka, 254-0016, Japan
Tel.: (81) 463218201
Web Site: http://www.furukawaamerica.com
Magnet Wire Mfr
N.A.I.C.S.: 332618

Furukawa America Inc - MIE WORKS, MAGNET WIRE PLANT (1)
20-16 Nobono-chyo, Kameyama, 519-0292, Mie, Japan
Tel.: (81) 5 9585 2040
Magnet Wire Mfr
N.A.I.C.S.: 332618

Furukawa Auto Parts (Huizhou) Co. Ltd. (1)
No 20 Xing San Street Jin Long Road, Xiao Jin Kou Town, Huizhou, Guangdong, China
Tel.: (86) 752 282 1111
Automotive Parts Mfr & Distr
N.A.I.C.S.: 336390

Furukawa Auto Parts(HK) Ltd. (1)
Units 1302 13/F Park Building 476 Castle Peak Road, Hong Kong, China (Hong Kong)
Tel.: (852) 3160 4562
Automotive Electric Parts Mfr & Distr
N.A.I.C.S.: 336390

Furukawa Automotive Parts (Dong Guan) Ltd. (1)
Qinghu Road West Side, Qinghu Indrstrial Park Qingxi Town, Dongguan, 523660, Guangdong, China
Tel.: (86) 7698 729 5600
Silo Mfr
N.A.I.C.S.: 335931

Furukawa Automotive Parts (Vietnam) Inc. (1)
Road No 16 Tan Thuan Export Processing Zone, Tan Thuan Dong Village District 7, Ho Chi Minh City, Vietnam
Tel.: (84) 8 770 1093
Automobile Parts Mfr
N.A.I.C.S.: 336390

Furukawa Automotive Systems Design Philippines, Inc. (1)
124 North Science Avenue SEPZ - Laguna Technopark, Binan, Laguna, Philippines
Tel.: (63) 49 502 9065
Automobile Parts Mfr
N.A.I.C.S.: 336390

Furukawa Automotive Systems Inc. (1)
1000 Amago Koura-cho, Inukami-gun, Shiga, 522-0242, Japan
Tel.: (81) 74 938 4150
Web Site: https://www.furukawaas.co.jp
Emp.: 2,181
Wire Harnesses Mfr & Distr
N.A.I.C.S.: 335931
Shigenobu Abe *(Pres)*

Furukawa Automotive Systems Lima Philippines,Inc. (1)
Block 2 Lot 3 Phase 2A JP Rizal Avenue Lima Technology Center, Lipa, 4217, Batangas, Philippines
Tel.: (63) 43 455 9600
Web Site: https://furukawalima.com
Silo Mfr
N.A.I.C.S.: 335931

Furukawa Automotive Systems Management (Shanghai) Co., Ltd. (1)
Unit C 23F Jiu Shi Fu Xing Building No 918 Huai Hai Zhong Road, Huanpu District, Shanghai, 200020, China
Tel.: (86) 216 481 1918
Automotive Parts Mfr & Distr
N.A.I.C.S.: 336390

Furukawa Automotive Systems Mexico S.A. de C.V. (1)
Carretera Federal Acambaro Jerecuaro 17 Loma Bonita, Acambaro, 38610, Guanajuato, Mexico
Tel.: (52) 417 172 1552
Automobile Parts Distr
N.A.I.C.S.: 441330

Furukawa Automotive Systems Vietnam Inc. (1)
Lot C3-C5 Giao Long Industrial Park, An Phuoc Commune, Chau Thanh, Ben Tre, Vietnam
Tel.: (84) 75 361 2792
Automobile Parts Mfr
N.A.I.C.S.: 336390

Furukawa C&B Co., Ltd. (1)
5-1-9 Higashiyawata, Hiratsuka, 254-0016, Kanagawa, Japan (100%)
Tel.: (81) 46 324 8585
Web Site: https://www.furukawa-fcb.co.jp
Emp.: 100
Communication Broadcasting Equipment Mfr & Distr
N.A.I.C.S.: 334290
Nobuya Shinoda *(Pres)*

Furukawa Circuit Foil (Hong Kong) Co., Ltd. (1)
Suite 1810 Tower 2 43 Canton Road Tsim Tsm Shatsui, Kowloon, China (Hong Kong)
Tel.: (852) 2877 1107
Emp.: 4
Electrodeposited Copper Foil Mfr
N.A.I.C.S.: 335999
Yuji Yamazaki *(Gen Mgr)*

Furukawa Circuit Foil Co., Ltd. (1)
601-2 Otorozawa Imaichi Shi, Tochigi Ken, Tochigi, 321 2336, Japan
Tel.: (81) 288223484
Web Site: http://www.fcf.co.jp
Sales Range: $125-149.9 Million
Emp.: 350
Mfr of Electro-Deposited Copper Foil

THE FURUKAWA ELECTRIC CO., LTD.

Furukawa Circuit Foil Taiwan Corporation (1)
8 Tou Kong 2Rd Tou-Liu Expansion Industrial Area, Yun-lin, Taiwan
Tel.: (886) 5 557 1361
Web Site: http://www.fcft.com.tw
Printed Circuit Board Mfr
N.A.I.C.S.: 334412

Furukawa Colombia, SAS (1)
Carrera 9A No 99-07 Torre 1 Oficina 603, Bogota, Colombia
Tel.: (57) 1 404 0817
Optic Cable Mfr & Distr
N.A.I.C.S.: 335921

Furukawa Communication & Broadcasting Co., Ltd. (1)
5-1-9 Higashiyawata, Hiratsuka, 254-0016, Kanagawa, Japan
Tel.: (81) 46 324 8585
Web Site: https://www.furukawa-fcb.co.jp
Emp.: 100
Antenna Mfr & Distr
N.A.I.C.S.: 334220
Nobuya Shinoda (Pres)

Furukawa Elecom Co., Ltd. (1)
Furukawadenko Kanda Bldg 5f, Chiyoda-Ku, Tokyo, 101-0047, Japan
Tel.: (81) 352978610
Electrical Apparatus & Equipment Whslr
N.A.I.C.S.: 423690

Furukawa Electric (Shenzhen) Co., Ltd. (1)
West Industrial Park Xinyangshe Community, Shajing Town Baoan District, Shenzhen, 518104, China
Tel.: (86) 75533848011
Web Site: http://www.furukawa.co.jp
Automobile Electric Component Mfr & Distr
N.A.I.C.S.: 336390

Furukawa Electric (Xi'an) Optical Communication Co., Ltd. (1)
No 18 Information Avenue, New Industrial Park High-tech Zone, Xi'an, China
Tel.: (86) 298 569 1220
Web Site: http://www.fxoc.com.cn
Optic Cable Mfr & Distr
N.A.I.C.S.: 335921

Furukawa Electric Advanced Engineering Co., Ltd. (1)
6 Yawatakaigandori, Ichihara, 290-8555, Chiba, Japan
Tel.: (81) 43 642 1633
Web Site: https://www.furukawa-ae.jp
Engineeering Services
N.A.I.C.S.: 541330

Furukawa Electric Autoparts Central Europe, s.r.o.(Face) (1)
Lidicka 1022, 273 51, Unhost, Czech Republic
Tel.: (420) 312818614
Web Site: http://www.furukawa.cz
Sales Range: $50-74.9 Million
Emp.: 140
Automotive Electronic Component Mfr & Distr
N.A.I.C.S.: 336390

Furukawa Electric Autoparts(Philippines)Inc. (1)
Lot3-5 Phase 4 113 East Main Avenue, Laguna Thechnopark Binan, Binan, 4024, Laguna, Philippines
Tel.: (63) 49 541 1804
Emp.: 1,400
Auto Electrical Parts Mfr
N.A.I.C.S.: 336390
Marialourden Caguicla (Gen Mgr)

Furukawa Electric Business & Life Support Inc. (1)
7F Furukawa Electric Kanda Building 16-8 Uchikanda 2-chome, Chiyoda-ku, Tokyo, 101-0047, Japan
Tel.: (81) 36 285 2980
Temporary Staffing Services
N.A.I.C.S.: 561320

Furukawa Electric Communications Southeast Asia Ltd. (1)
191 Silom Complex Building Unit C 16th Fl Silom Road, Kwaeng Silom Khet Bangrak, Bangkok, 10500, Thailand
Tel.: (66) 2 105 4057
Optical Fiber Cable Mfr
N.A.I.C.S.: 335929

Furukawa Electric Copper Foil Taiwan Co., Ltd. (1)
No 25 Kejia Rd, Yunlin County, Douliu, 64057, Taiwan
Tel.: (886) 5 551 3600
Copper Foil Mfr & Distr
N.A.I.C.S.: 331420

Furukawa Electric Ecotec Co., Ltd. (1)
6 Yawatakaigandori, Ichihara, 290-0067, Chiba, Japan
Tel.: (81) 43 641 2584
Web Site: https://www.fetec.co.jp
Optic Fiber Wire Distr
N.A.I.C.S.: 423930

Furukawa Electric Engineering Singapore Pte. Ltd. (1)
20 Harbour Drive 07-06A PSA Vista, Singapore, 117612, Singapore
Tel.: (65) 6 773 3267
Power Cable Installation Services
N.A.I.C.S.: 238210

Furukawa Electric Europe Limited (1)
Furukawa House 2 Farriers Yard, London, W6 8AH, United Kingdom
Tel.: (44) 2073135300
Web Site: https://www.furukawa.co.uk
Lumber
N.A.I.C.S.: 444180

Furukawa Electric Europe Ltd. (1)
3rd Floor Newcombe House, 43-45 Notting Hill Gate, London, W11 3FE, United Kingdom (100%)
Tel.: (44) 2072216000
Web Site: http://www.furukawa.co.uk
Sales Range: $25-49.9 Million
Emp.: 20
N.A.I.C.S.: 444180

Furukawa Electric Hong Kong Ltd. (1)
Suite 1810 18/F Tower 2 33 Canton Road China Hong Kong City, Tsim Sha Tsui, Kowloon, China (Hong Kong)
Tel.: (852) 2512 8938
Web Site: http://www.furukawaelectric.com
Electronic Components Distr
N.A.I.C.S.: 423690

Furukawa Electric Industrial Cable Co., Ltd. (1)
6-48-10 Higashi-Nippori, Arakawa-ku, Tokyo, 116-0014, Japan
Tel.: (81) 338031151
Web Site: http://www.feic.co.jp
Sales Range: $200-249.9 Million
Emp.: 380
Electric Cable Mfr & Distr
N.A.I.C.S.: 332618

Furukawa Electric Institute of Technology Co., Ltd. (1)
Kesmark street 28/A, 1158, Budapest, Hungary (100%)
Tel.: (36) 14173257
Web Site: http://www.feti.hu
Sales Range: $25-49.9 Million
Emp.: 20
N.A.I.C.S.: 444180

Furukawa Electric Latam S.A. (1)
Rua Hasdrubal Bellegard 820 Cidade Industrial Curitiba, Curitiba, 81460-120, Brazil
Tel.: (55) 413 341 4000
Optic Cable Mfr & Distr
N.A.I.C.S.: 335921

Furukawa Electric Latam SA (1)
C/Avila s/n, 28804, Alcala de Henares, Spain
Tel.: (34) 91 745 5817
Electrical & Electronic Equipment Mfr
N.A.I.C.S.: 335999

Furukawa Electric Power Systems Co., Ltd. (1)
2-11-16 Azamino-Minami, Aoba-ku, Yokohama, 225-0012, Kanagawa, Japan
Tel.: (81) 45 910 2814
Web Site: https://www.feps.co.jp
Electrical & Electronic Equipment Mfr
N.A.I.C.S.: 335999
Kazuya Ono (Pres)

Furukawa Electric Singapore Pte. Ltd. (1)
2 International Business Park 11-07/08 The Strategy, Singapore, 609930, Singapore (100%)
Tel.: (65) 6 224 4686
Web Site: https://www.furukawaelectric.com
Sales Range: $250-299.9 Million
Emp.: 20
Electrical Sales & Services
N.A.I.C.S.: 335999
Takeshi Shintoku (Pres)

Furukawa Electric Trading SZ Ltd. (1)
Room 2501A Block A United Plaza No 5022 Bin He Road, Futian District, Shenzhen, China
Tel.: (86) 755 8373 4878
Automotive Electric Parts Distr
N.A.I.C.S.: 423120

Furukawa FITEL (Thailand) Co., Ltd. (1)
Rojana Industrial Park 1/71 Moo 5 Tambol Kanharm, Amphur U-Thai Phranakorn Sri, Ayutthaya, 13210, Thailand
Tel.: (66) 35 226 581
Fiber Optic Cable Mfr
N.A.I.C.S.: 335921
Haruki Iwata (Pres)

Furukawa FITEL Optical Products (Shanghai) Co., Ltd. (1)
No 16 180 Long Jinxi Road, Songjiang, Shanghai, China
Tel.: (86) 213 352 8675
Optical Device Mfr & Distr
N.A.I.C.S.: 333310

Furukawa Fitel Optical Device Co., Ltd. (1)
6 Yawata-kaigandori, Ichihara, 290-8555, Chiba, Japan
Tel.: (81) 43 642 1600
Optical Semiconductor Mfr
N.A.I.C.S.: 333310

Furukawa Industrial Colombia, SAS (1)
Kilometro 6 via Yumbo-Aeropuerto Zona, Franca del Pacifico Lotes 1-2-3 Manzana J Bodega 2 Valle del Cauca, Palmira, Colombia
Tel.: (57) 2 280 0003
Optic Cable Mfr & Distr
N.A.I.C.S.: 335921

Furukawa Industrial Latam S.A. (1)
Ruta Nacional 2 km 37 5 Centro Industrial Ruta 2, Berazategui, Buenos Aires, Argentina
Tel.: (54) 222 949 1930
Optic Cable Mfr & Distr
N.A.I.C.S.: 335921

Furukawa Industrial Optoeletronica Ltda. (1)
AV John Dalton 301 Cj 11A e 12A Bloco A Ed 02 Techno Park, Campinas, 13069-330, Sao Paulo, Brazil
Tel.: (55) 413 341 4000
Communication Wire Mfr & Distr
N.A.I.C.S.: 335929

Furukawa Industrial Plastics Co., Ltd. (1)
195 Shimminato, Mihama-Ku, Chiba, 261-0002, Japan
Tel.: (81) 432429514
Plastic Foam Product Mfr
N.A.I.C.S.: 326199

Furukawa Industrial S.A. (1)
44th Fl Avenida Macoes Unidas 11633, 4578901, Sao Paulo, Brazil (85%)
Tel.: (55) 1155015748
Web Site: http://www.furukawa.com.br
Rev: $2,662,000
Emp.: 25
Sales of Electric Wire & Cable Production & Sales of Automotive Wire Harness
N.A.I.C.S.: 423610
Renato Cruz (Mgr-Tech & Engrg)

Furukawa Industrial S.A. Produtos Eletricos (1)
Rua Hasdrubal Bellegard 820, 81460-120, Curitiba, PR, Brazil
Tel.: (55) 4133414000
Web Site: http://www.furukawa.com.br
Electrical Wire & Cable Mfr
N.A.I.C.S.: 332618
Foad Shaikhzadeh (Pres)

Furukawa Logistics Corp. (1)
Furukawa denko Kanda Bld 6f 2-16-8 Uchikanda, Chiyoda-ku, Tokyo, 101-0047, Japan
Tel.: (81) 35 294 6721
Web Site: https://www.furukawa-logis.co.jp
Emp.: 145
Logistic Services
N.A.I.C.S.: 541614
Shingo Morita (Pres)

Furukawa Magnet Wire Co., Ltd. (1)
2-3 Marunouchi 2-chome, Marunouchi Naka-dori Building Chiyoda-ku, Tokyo, 100-0005, Japan
Tel.: (81) 332863181
Web Site: http://www.furukawa-magnetwire.co.jp
Emp.: 431
Magnet Wire Mfr & Sales
N.A.I.C.S.: 331491

Furukawa Management Shanghai, Ltd. (1)
Room 1006 Hongyi Plaza 288 Jiujiang Road, Shanghai, 200001, China
Tel.: (86) 213 366 5309
Electrical & Electronic Equipment Mfr
N.A.I.C.S.: 335999

Furukawa Mexico, S.A.DE C.V. (1)
Av Circulo de la Amistad No 2690 Parque Industrial Mexicali IV, Mexicali, Baja California, Mexico
Tel.: (52) 6865642500
Web Site: http://www.furmex.com
Sales Range: $200-249.9 Million
Emp.: 1,000
Automotive Electronic Parts Mfr
N.A.I.C.S.: 336390

Furukawa Minda Electric Private Limited (1)
325-326 Sector-3 Growth Centre, Bawal Phase-2 Dist, Rewari, 123501, Haryana, India
Tel.: (91) 128 426 4317
Electrical & Electronic Equipment Mfr
N.A.I.C.S.: 335999

Furukawa Network Solution Corporation (1)
1-9 Higashiyawata 5-chome, Hiratsuka, 254-0016, Japan
Tel.: (81) 463 24 8541
Web Site: http://www.fnsc.co.jp
Network Routers Mfr & Sales
N.A.I.C.S.: 334210

Furukawa New Leaf Co., Ltd. (1)
1-9 Higashiyawata 5 chome, Hiratsuka, 254-0016, Kanagawa, Japan
Tel.: (81) 46 324 8001
Cleaning Up In-Plant & Office Services
N.A.I.C.S.: 561720

Furukawa Nikko Power Generation Inc. (1)
273 Hosoomachi, Nikko, 321-1445, Tochigi, Japan
Tel.: (81) 28 854 1193
Web Site: https://www.furukawanh.co.jp
Electric Power Generation & Distribution Services
N.A.I.C.S.: 221118

Furukawa Precision Engineering Co., Ltd. (1)
528-5 Kiyotakishinhosoomachi, Nikko, 321-1448, Japan
Tel.: (81) 288 531025
Precision Electronic Products Mfr
N.A.I.C.S.: 332721

Furukawa Precision Thailand Co., Ltd. (1)
23rd Fl Charn Issara Tower 1 942/167 Rama 4 Rd, Sriyawongse Sub Dist, Bangkok, 10500, Thailand
Tel.: (66) 226679448

N.A.I.C.S.: 322220
Mitsuyoshi Shibata (Pres)

THE FURUKAWA ELECTRIC CO., LTD.

The Furukawa Electric Co., Ltd.—(Continued)
Sales Range: $50-74.9 Million
Emp.: 200
N.A.I.C.S.: 444180
Tatsuo Shimada *(Mng Dir)*

Furukawa Research Inc. (1)
2-4-3 Okano inside Furukawa Electric Yokohama Office, Nishi-ku, Yokohama, 220-0073, Kanagawa, Japan
Tel.: (81) 45 320 4460
Web Site: https://www.ftrcom.co.jp
Technical Information Analysis & Investigating Services
N.A.I.C.S.: 541990

Furukawa Sangyo Kaisha (H.K.) Ltd. (1)
No 2809 28/F The Metropolis Tower No 10 Metropolis Drive, Hunghom, Kowloon, China (Hong Kong)
Tel.: (852) 2 865 2128
Electronic Components Distr
N.A.I.C.S.: 423690

Furukawa Sangyo Kaisha (India) Pvt. Ltd. (1)
6/F Flat No 607 Global Foyer Golf Course Road, Sector 43, Gurgaon, 122022, Haryana, India
Tel.: (91) 124 483 1800
Optical Component Distr
N.A.I.C.S.: 423460

Furukawa Sangyo Kaisha (Malaysia) Sdn. Bhd. (1)
Suite 1106 11th Floor Menara Amcorp Amcorp Trade Centre 18, Jalan Persiaran Barat, 46050, Petaling Jaya, Selangor, Malaysia
Tel.: (60) 37 957 7000
Electronic Components Distr
N.A.I.C.S.: 423690

Furukawa Sangyo Kaisha (S.Z.) Ltd. (1)
Room B1-2-12 25F Block B Regalia Place No 4018 Jiabin Road, Luohu District, Shenzhen, 518001, Guangdong, China
Tel.: (86) 7552 590 4497
Superconducting Wire Mfr & Distr
N.A.I.C.S.: 332618

Furukawa Sangyo Kaisha Philippines, Inc. (1)
Bldg 5 and 6 Panorama Compound 5 Laguna Technopark Annex, Binan, Laguna, Philippines
Tel.: (63) 2 571 2752
Electronic Components Distr
N.A.I.C.S.: 423690

Furukawa Sangyo Kaisha, Ltd. (1)
14th 15th and 16th Floor 21-3 Shimbashi 4-chome Shimbashi Tokyu Bldg, Minato-ku, Tokyo, 105-8630, Japan (100%)
Tel.: (81) 35 405 6011
Web Site: https://www.furusan.co.jp
Emp.: 477
Sale of Electric Wire & Cable, Aluminum & Copper Products
N.A.I.C.S.: 423610
Tetsuro Yasunaga *(Pres & CEO)*

Furukawa Sangyo Korea Co., Ltd. (1)
212 Kyeongin Ilbo B/D 299 Hyowon-Ro, Paldal-Gu, Suwon, Gyeonggi, Korea (South)
Tel.: (82) 31 898 7688
Electronic Components Distr
N.A.I.C.S.: 423690

Furukawa Sangyo North America, Inc. (1)
1871 The Alameda Ste 350, San Jose, CA 95126
Tel.: (408) 496-0051
Superconducting Wire Mfr & Distr
N.A.I.C.S.: 332618

Furukawa Sangyo Shanghai Co., Ltd. (1)
RM 18 C Jiu Shi Fu Xing Mansion No 918 Huai Hai Zhong Road, Shanghai, 200020, China
Tel.: (86) 216 415 7294
Electronic Components Distr
N.A.I.C.S.: 423690

Furukawa Sangyo Vietnam Company Limited (1)
39 Nguyen Duy Hieu Street, Thao Dien Ward District 2, Ho Chi Minh City, Vietnam
Tel.: (84) 2873 049 9882
Electrical Equipment Distr
N.A.I.C.S.: 423610

Furukawa Shanghai Ltd. (1)
Room 1006 Hongyi Plaza 288 Jiujiang Road, Shanghai, 200001, China
Tel.: (86) 21 3366 5301
Web Site: http://www.furukawa-sh.cn
Sales Range: $25-49.9 Million
Emp.: 20
Fiber Optic & Electrical Component Distr
N.A.I.C.S.: 423610

Furukawa Techno Material Co., Ltd. (1)
5-1-8 Higashi-Yawata, Hiratsuka, 254-0016, Kanagawa, Japan
Tel.: (81) 46 321 7316
Web Site: https://www.furukawa-ftm.com
Sales Range: $50-74.9 Million
Emp.: 211
Electronic Communication Equipment Mfr
N.A.I.C.S.: 334290
Hiroki Suzuki *(Pres)*

Furukawa UACJ Memory Disk Co., Ltd. (1)
1351 Uwanodai, Fukaya, 366-8511, Saitama, Japan
Tel.: (81) 48 500 3387
Memory Disk Distr
N.A.I.C.S.: 423430

Furukawa Wiring Systems Mexico, S.A. de C.V. (1)
1104 Reforma Ciudad Juarez, 32040, Chihuahua, Mexico
Tel.: (52) 656 680 0500
Wire Harnesses Mfr
N.A.I.C.S.: 335999

Hirakawa Singapore Pte. Ltd. (1)
47 Pandan Road, Singapore, 609288, Singapore
Tel.: (65) 62680174
N.A.I.C.S.: 444180

Jef United Corp. (1)
1-38 Kawasaki-cho, Chuo-ku, Chiba, 260-0835, Japan
Tel.: (81) 43 663 1201
Football Club Management Operator
N.A.I.C.S.: 711211

Jiangsu OFS Hengtong Optical Technology Co., Ltd. (1)
No 688 Wangjiabei Road, Wujiang Economic and Technological Development Zone, Wujiang, 215200, Jiangsu, China
Tel.: (86) 5126 316 6117
Electrical & Electronic Equipment Mfr
N.A.I.C.S.: 335999

KANZACC Co., Ltd. (1)
5F Furukawa Osaka building west Hall 1-9 Dojimahama 2-chome, Kita-ku, Osaka, 530-0004, Japan
Tel.: (81) 663450029
Web Site: http://www.kanzacc.co.jp
Sales Range: $25-49.9 Million
Emp.: 92
Electric Wire Drawing & Mfr
N.A.I.C.S.: 332618
Hisakazu Ishibashi *(Pres)*

Kyusyu Network Cable Co., Ltd. (1)
2001 Sogawa, Kosa Town Kamimashiki District, Kumamoto, 861-3241, Japan
Tel.: (81) 96 234 1180
Web Site: https://www.knc.co.jp
Optic Fiber Cable Mfr & Distr
N.A.I.C.S.: 335921

Leoni Furukawa Wiring Systems SAS (1)
5 Avenue Newton, 78180, Montigny-le-Bretonneux, France
Tel.: (33) 130853397
Web Site: http://www.furukawa.co.jp
Automotive Electric Parts Mfr & Distr
N.A.I.C.S.: 336390

Miharu Communications Inc. (1)
1285 Iwase, Kamakura, 247-8538, Kanagawa, Japan
Tel.: (81) 46 744 9111
Broadcasting Equipment Mfr & Distr
N.A.I.C.S.: 334220

Myojodenki Co., Ltd. (1)
1-2-6 Kaji-cho, Chiyoda-ku, Tokyo, 101-0044, Japan
Tel.: (81) 33 252 5581
Web Site: https://www.myojodenki.co.jp
Emp.: 1,400
Electrical Equipment & Parts Distr
N.A.I.C.S.: 423610

NTEC Ltd. (1)
5-7-4 Yanagibashi, Yamato, 242-0022, Kanagawa, Japan
Tel.: (81) 46 268 7444
Web Site: https://www.ntec-fec.com
Heat Pipe Mfr
N.A.I.C.S.: 332996
LaVern Kenneth Lund *(CEO)*

OFS Fitel Denmark ApS (1)
Priorparken 680, 2605, Brondby, Denmark
Tel.: (45) 4 345 8888
Electrical & Electronic Equipment Mfr
N.A.I.C.S.: 335999

OFS Fitel Deutschland GmbH (1)
August-Wessels-Strasse 17, 86156, Augsburg, Germany
Tel.: (49) 8214 604 9110
Electrical & Electronic Equipment Mfr
N.A.I.C.S.: 335999

OFS Fitel LLC (1)
6305 Crescent Dr, Norcross, GA 30071
Tel.: (770) 798-2135
Web Site: http://www.ofsoptics.com
Sales Range: $50-74.9 Million
Emp.: 200
Fiber Optics Holding Company
N.A.I.C.S.: 335921
Ashish Gandhi *(CFO & Treas)*

Division (Domestic):

OFS (2)
50 Hall Rd, Sturbridge, MA 01566-1279
Tel.: (508) 347-2261
Web Site: http://www.ofsoptics.com
Sales Range: $125-149.9 Million
Multi Mode Optical Fibers Mfr
N.A.I.C.S.: 327212
Patrice Dubois *(Pres & CEO)*

OFS (2)
55 Darling Dr, Avon, CT 06001-4273
Tel.: (860) 678-0371
Web Site: http://www.specialtyphotonics.com
Mfr of Fiber Optic Cable, Connectors & Assemblies
N.A.I.C.S.: 335921

OFS Brightwave Carrollton (2)
10 Brightwave Blvd, Carrollton, GA 30117-5262
Tel.: (770) 836-8032
Web Site: http://www.ofsoptic.com
Sales Range: $75-99.9 Million
Fiber Optic Telecommunications Cable
N.A.I.C.S.: 561499

OFS Laboratories, LLC (1)
19 Schoolhouse Rd, Somerset, NJ 08873
Tel.: (732) 748-7499
Electrical & Electronic Equipment Mfr
N.A.I.C.S.: 335999

OFS RUS Fiber Optic Cable Company (1)
Street Zavodskaya 1 Industrial Park Maslovsky, Novousmansky District, 396333, Voronezh, Russia
Tel.: (7) 4732330500
Electrical & Electronic Equipment Mfr
N.A.I.C.S.: 335999

Okano Cable Co., Ltd. (1)
1-5-28 Fukaminishi, Yamato, 242-8501, Kanagawa, Japan
Tel.: (81) 46 261 3122
Web Site: https://www.okano-cable.co.jp
Optic Fiber Cable Mfr & Distr
N.A.I.C.S.: 335921
Masaru Seto *(Pres)*

Okumura Metals Co., Ltd. (1)
6 Doicho 7-chome, Amagasaki, 660-0083, Hyogo, Japan (100%)

INTERNATIONAL PUBLIC

Tel.: (81) 664117827
Web Site: http://www.fitec.co.jp
Sales Range: $75-99.9 Million
Emp.: 40
Sale of Rolled Copper & Aluminum Production
N.A.I.C.S.: 331313

P.T. Furukawa Automotive Systems Indonesia (1)
Jalan Inti Raya Block C2 No 11, Bekasi International Industrial Estate Lippo Cikarang, Bekasi, 17550, Indonesia
Tel.: (62) 218 990 8060
Automotive Parts Mfr & Distr
N.A.I.C.S.: 336390

P.T. Furukawa Electric Indonesia (1)
Sucaco Building 6th Floor Jl Kebon Sirih No 71, Jakarta, 10340, Indonesia
Tel.: (62) 213 190 6212
Web Site: https://www.furukawaelectric.com
Electrical Equipment Distr
N.A.I.C.S.: 423610
Hiroshi Suzuki *(Pres)*

P.T. Furukawa Optical Solutions Indonesia (1)
Jl Moh Toha Km 1, Tangerang, 15112, Banten, Indonesia
Tel.: (62) 215 579 6999
Optic Fiber Cable Mfr & Distr
N.A.I.C.S.: 335921

P.T. Furukawa Permintex Autoparts Indonesia (1)
Jalan Inti Raya Block C2 No 11 Bekasi International Industrial Estate, Lippo Cikarang, Bekasi, 17750, Indonesia
Tel.: (62) 21 8990 8060
Automobile Parts Distr
N.A.I.C.S.: 423120

P.T. Tembaga Mulia Semanan (1)
Jl Daan Mogot Km 16, Desa Semanan, Jakarta, 11850, Jakarta Barat, Indonesia (44%)
Tel.: (62) 216190128
Web Site: https://www.pttms.co.id
Emp.: 1,000
Production & Sales of Copper Wire Road
N.A.I.C.S.: 331420
Satoshi Tosaka *(Chm)*

PT Supreme Cable Manufacturing & Commerce (1)
Jl Kebon Sirih No 71, Jakarta, 10340, Indonesia (50%)
Tel.: (62) 213100525
Web Site: https://www.sucaco.com
Sales Range: $1-9.9 Million
Emp.: 100
N.A.I.C.S.: 444180

Permintex Furukawa Autoparts Malaysia Sdn. Bhd. (1)
Plot 73 74 Kawasan Perindustrian Bandar Baru Darulaman, Jitra, 06000, Kedah, Malaysia
Tel.: (60) 4 919 9964
Automobile Parts Mfr & Distr
N.A.I.C.S.: 336390

Riken Electric Wire Co., Ltd. (1)
Konwa Building 5F 1-12-22 Tsukiji, Chuo-ku, Tokyo, 104-0045, Japan (100%)
Tel.: (81) 33 542 3712
Web Site: https://www.rikensen.co.jp
Emp.: 210
Production & Sale of Magnet Wire & Plastic Cable
N.A.I.C.S.: 326199
Akihiro Fujiyoshi *(Pres)*

SIAM Furukawa Trading Co., Ltd. (1)
252 SPE Building Floor 11 Paholyothin Rd Paholyothin Samsennai, Phayathai, Bangkok, 10400, Thailand
Tel.: (66) 2 615 0111
Lead Acid Battery Distr
N.A.I.C.S.: 423610

STF Co., Ltd. (1)
3gongdan 3-ro, Seobuk-gu, Cheonan, Chungchongnam-Do, Korea (South)
Tel.: (82) 41 9010 500
Web Site: http://www.stf.co.kr
Electronic Component Mfr & Distr
N.A.I.C.S.: 334419

AND PRIVATE COMPANIES

Myung Soo Cho *(Pres)*

Shenyang Furukawa Cable Co., Ltd. (1)
Hujiadian Dashubo Village, Shujiatun District, Shenyang, 110115, China
Tel.: (86) 2489428599
Web Site: http://www.sf-cable.com
N.A.I.C.S.: 444180

Shianfu Optical Fiber and Cables Co., Ltd. (1)
18 Information Road, Hi-tech Industrial, Development Zone, Xi'an, Shaanxi, China
Tel.: (86) 985691220
Web Site: www.shianfu.com
Fiber Optic Cable Mfr; Owned by The Furukawa Electric Co., Ltd. & by Xi'an Xidian Optical Cable Co., Ltd.
N.A.I.C.S.: 335921

Shikoku Cable Co Ltd (1)
1576-5 Ishidanishi Sangawamachi, Sanuki, 769-2322, Kagawa, Japan
Tel.: (81) 87 943 2575
Web Site: https://www.shikokucable.co.jp
Emp.: 104
Coaxial Cable Mfr & Distr
N.A.I.C.S.: 335921
Yasuhiro Sasaki *(Pres)*

Shin Chang Connector Co., Ltd. (1)
734-2, Wonsi-dong, Ansan, Kyungki-do, Korea (South)
Tel.: (82) 3454933000
N.A.I.C.S.: 444180

Shoden Seiwa Co., Ltd. (1)
5-23-8 Nishigotanda, Shinagawa-ku, Tokyo, 141-8515, Japan
Tel.: (81) 33 493 1184
Web Site: https://www.shodenseiwa.co.jp
Emp.: 200
Information & Communications Technology Services
N.A.I.C.S.: 541519
Kamiko Michiyasu *(Pres)*

Suzhou Furukawa Power Optic Cable Co., Ltd. (1)
No 449 Fenhu Guodao Road, Lili Town Wujiang District, Suzhou, 215211, Jiangsu, China
Tel.: (86) 5126 327 2011
Web Site: https://en.sfpoc.com
Optical Device Mfr & Distr
N.A.I.C.S.: 333310

Taho Engineering Co., Ltd. (1)
No 249 Section 2 Zhongshan Road, Guanmiao District, 71802, Tainan City, Taiwan **(100%)**
Tel.: (886) 65953723
Web Site: http://www.taho.co.tw
Sales Range: Less than $1 Million
Emp.: 23
N.A.I.C.S.: 444180

Taiwan Furukawa Electric Co., Ltd. (1)
10F-4 No 23 Chang An E Road Sec 1, Taipei, 10442, Taiwan
Tel.: (886) 22 563 8148
Electronic Components Distr
N.A.I.C.S.: 423690

Taiwan SRU Co., Ltd. (1)
24 Jingjian 5th Rd, Shulin Vil Guanyin Dist, Taoyuan, 328, Taiwan
Tel.: (886) 3 476 1379
Electrical Equipment Mfr & Distr
N.A.I.C.S.: 335999

Thai Furukawa Unicomm Construction Co., Ltd. (1)
169 Soi Phayasuren, Bangkok, 10510, Thailand **(100%)**
Tel.: (66) 25180833
Web Site: http://www.tfu.co.th
Sales Range: $50-74.9 Million
Emp.: 130
N.A.I.C.S.: 444180
Hiroshi Irie *(Pres)*

Thai Furukawa Unicomm Engineering Co., Ltd. (1)
169 Soi Phayasuren 30 Phayasuren Road Bangchan, Khlongsamwa, Bangkok, 10510, Thailand
Tel.: (66) 2 540 6777

Web Site: https://www.tfu.co.th
Telecommunication Servicesb
N.A.I.C.S.: 517810
Tsuyoshi Kuwayama *(Pres)*

The Furukawa Battery Co., Ltd. (1)
2-4-1 Hoshikawa, Hodogaya-ku, Yokohama, 240-0006, Kanagawa, Japan **(52.74%)**
Tel.: (81) 453365034
Web Site: http://www.furukawadenchi.co.jp
Emp.: 2,406
Production & Sales of Batteries
N.A.I.C.S.: 335910

Tianjin Furukawa Power Component Co., Ltd. (1)
Block C1-4 Saida International Industrial City, Xiqing Economic and Technological Development Zone, Tianjin, 300385, China
Tel.: (86) 22 23975353
Electronic Parts Mfr
N.A.I.C.S.: 335999

Tianjin Jinhe Electric Engineering Co., Ltd. (1)
No 13 Haiguang Road, Zhongbei Industrial Park South Park Xiqing District, Tianjin, China
Tel.: (86) 222 739 6830
Web Site: https://www.tjjhdg.com
Automotive Parts Mfr & Distr
N.A.I.C.S.: 336390

Trocellen GmbH (1)
Mulheimer Strasse 26, 53840, Troisdorf, Germany
Tel.: (49) 2241 254 9000
Web Site: https://trocellen.com
Cross-Linked Polyolefin Foam Mfr
N.A.I.C.S.: 326150
Jozsef Takacs *(CEO & Mng Dir)*

Trocellen Iberica S.A. (1)
C/Avila s/n, 28804, Alcala de Henares, Spain
Tel.: (34) 91 885 5500
Cross-Linked Polyolefin Foam Mfr
N.A.I.C.S.: 326150
Luis Fernandez *(Mng Dir)*

Trocellen Italia Holding S.r.l. (1)
Via Della Chimica 21-23, 20867, Caponago, MB, Italy
Tel.: (39) 029 596 9555
Electrical & Electronic Equipment Mfr
N.A.I.C.S.: 335999

Trocellen Italy S.p.A. (1)
Via Dante 3, 20867, Caponago, MB, Italy
Tel.: (39) 0295 9621
Cross-Linked Polyolefin Foam Mfr
N.A.I.C.S.: 326150
Cesare Ottavi *(Mng Dir)*

Trocellen S.E.A. Sdn. Bhd. (1)
Lot 2213 Batu 9 Kebun Baru Jalan Kasawari, 42500, Teluk Panglima Garang, Selangor, Malaysia
Tel.: (60) 33 122 1213
Web Site: https://trocellen.com.my
Cross-Linked Polyolefin Foam Mfr
N.A.I.C.S.: 326150

Wuhan Furukawa Automotive Systems Co., Ltd. (1)
22 Xingfuyuan Road Xingfu Technology Industrialpark Shamao Street, Hannan District, Wuhan, China
Tel.: (86) 1354 412 8975
Wire Harnesses Mfr
N.A.I.C.S.: 335931

Xin Furukawa Metal (Wuxi) Co., Ltd. (1)
No 25 Changjiang South Road, National High-Tech Investment & Development Zone, Wuxi, 214028, Jiangsu, China **(60%)**
Tel.: (86) 510 85343445
Web Site: http://www.furukawa-metal.com.cn
Sales Range: $50-74.9 Million
Emp.: 200
Metal Products Mfr & Distr
N.A.I.C.S.: 332999

Yamakin (Japan) Co., Ltd. (1)
1-8-11 Iwamoto-cho, Chiyoda-ku, Tokyo, 101-0032, Japan
Tel.: (81) 35 687 2151
Web Site: https://www.yamakin.co.jp

Raw Material Copper Distr
N.A.I.C.S.: 423510

Yokohama Drum Manufacturing Co., Ltd. (1)
5-1-9 Higashiyawata, Hiratsuka, 254-0016, Kanagawa, Japan
Tel.: (81) 46 324 5400
Emp.: 103
Cable Drum & Machine Processing Parts Mfr & Distr
N.A.I.C.S.: 332999

Yunnan Copper Furukawa Electric Co.,Ltd. (1)
Wang-Jia-Qiao, Western Hill District, Kunming, 650102, Yunnan, China
Tel.: (86) 871 839 0059
Electric Copper Alloy Products Mfr
N.A.I.C.S.: 332999

THE FUTURA CORPORATION
2970-700 West Georgia Street, Vancouver, V7Y 1A1, BC, Canada
Tel.: (604) 608-6600
Web Site:
https://www.futuracorporation.com
Sales Range: $1-4.9 Billion
Emp.: 600
Private Asset Management & Investment Company
N.A.I.C.S.: 523999
Amardeip Singh Doman *(Founder, Pres & CEO)*

Subsidiaries:

Doman Building Materials Group Ltd. (1)
1600 - 1100 Melville Street, PO Box 39, Vancouver, V6E 4A6, BC, Canada **(100%)**
Tel.: (604) 432-1400
Web Site: https://domanbm.com
Rev.: $1,020,983,973
Assets: $684,448,257
Liabilities: $434,387,721
Net Worth: $250,060,536
Earnings: $13,176,668
Emp.: 1,152
Fiscal Year-end: 12/31/2019
Building Materials Distr
N.A.I.C.S.: 444110
Amardeip Singh Doman *(Chm & CEO)*

Subsidiary (Domestic):

Lignum Forest Products LLP (2)
999 W Hastings St Suite 1330, Vancouver, V6C 2W2, BC, Canada
Tel.: (604) 484-5000
Web Site: http://www.lignum.com
Lumber Product Distr
N.A.I.C.S.: 423310
Craig Stuart *(Pres)*

Sodisco-Howden Group, Inc. (2)
7005 Boul Taschereau Ste 301, Brossard, J4Z 1A7, QC, Canada
Tel.: (514) 286-8986
Web Site: http://www.chalifourcanada.com
Sales Range: $100-124.9 Million
Emp.: 100
Hardware & Home Renovation Products Distr
N.A.I.C.S.: 236118
Eddie Durocher *(Gen Mgr)*

THE FUTURE EDUCATION GROUP INC.
Room 501 Gaohelanfeng Building East 3rd Ring South Road, Chaoyang District, Beijing, China
Tel.: (86) 10 87663458 NV
Sales Range: $1-9.9 Million
Emp.: 128
Textbooks & Magazines Publisher; Online & Mobile Education Platforms
N.A.I.C.S.: 513130
Weifu Li *(Chm)*

THE GAEKWAR MILLS LIMITED
2/2 Plot-2 New Sion CHS Swami Vallabhdas Marg Road, No 24 Sindhi

Colony Sion, Mumbai, 400 022, India
Tel.: (91) 9820199123 In
Web Site:
http://www.gaekwarmills.com
Year Founded: 1928
Rev.: $40,798
Assets: $1,281,297
Liabilities: $8,447,941
Net Worth: ($7,166,644)
Earnings: $559,639)
Fiscal Year-end: 03/31/19
Textile Product Mfr & Distr
N.A.I.C.S.: 313110
Sheetal Gond *(Sec)*

THE GARFIELD WESTON FOUNDATION
Weston Centre 10 Grosvenor Street, London, W1K 4QY, United Kingdom
Tel.: (44) 2073996565 UK
Web Site:
http://www.garfieldweston.org
Year Founded: 1958
Grantmaking Foundations
N.A.I.C.S.: 813211
Guy Weston *(Chm)*

Subsidiaries:

Wittington Investments Limited (1)
Weston Centre 10 Grosvenor Street, London, W1K 4QY, United Kingdom **(79.2%)**
Tel.: (44) 2073996565
Web Site: http://www.wittington-investments.co.uk
Investment Holding Company
N.A.I.C.S.: 551112
Guy Weston *(Chm & CEO)*

Holding (Domestic):

Associated British Foods plc (2)
Weston Centre 10 Grosvenor Street, London, W1K 4QY, United Kingdom **(59.06%)**
Tel.: (44) 2073996500
Web Site: https://www.abf.co.uk
Rev.: $24,930,573,088
Assets: $23,786,922,494
Liabilities: $9,657,914,668
Net Worth: $14,129,007,826
Earnings: $1,348,144,408
Emp.: 133,000
Fiscal Year-end: 09/16/2023
Food Related Product Mfr
N.A.I.C.S.: 311999
George Garfield Weston *(CEO)*

Subsidiary (Domestic):

AB Agri Ltd (3)
Innovation Way, Peterborough Business Park, Peterborough,, Cambridgeshire, PE2 6FL, United Kingdom
Tel.: (44) 1733422161
Web Site: https://www.abagri.com
Animal Feed Mfr
N.A.I.C.S.: 311119
Jose Nobre *(CEO)*

Subsidiary (Domestic):

National Milk Records plc (4)
Unit 4 Fox Talbot House Greenways Business Park Bellinger Close, Chippenham, SN15 1BN, Wiltshire, United Kingdom
Tel.: (44) 3330043043
Web Site: https://www.nmr.co.uk
Rev.: $29,757,149
Assets: $17,805,140
Liabilities: $8,273,946
Net Worth: $9,531,194
Earnings: $2,769,749
Emp.: 276
Fiscal Year-end: 06/30/2021
Testing Laboratories & Services
N.A.I.C.S.: 541380
Mark C. Frankcom *(Dir-Fin)*

Subsidiary (Non-US):

AB Azucarera Iberia, S.L. (3)
Avenida de Manoteras 46, Madrid, 28050, Spain
Tel.: (34) 902101420
Web Site: http://www.azucarera.es
Sugar Mfr & Distr
N.A.I.C.S.: 311313

THE GARFIELD WESTON FOUNDATION

THE GARFIELD WESTON FOUNDATION — INTERNATIONAL PUBLIC

The Garfield Weston Foundation—(Continued)

AB Brasil Industria e Comercio de Alimentos Ltda (3)
Rua Cardeal Arcoverde 1641/12 andar, Pinheiros, Sao Paulo, 05407-002, Brazil
Tel.: (55) 1432838032
Food Products Mfr
N.A.I.C.S.: 311999

AB Enzymes GmbH (3)
Feldbergstrasse 78, 64293, Darmstadt, Germany
Tel.: (49) 61513680100
Web Site: http://www.abenzymes.com
Enzyme Mfr & Distr
N.A.I.C.S.: 325199
Karen Lewis (Mng Dir)

AB Food & Beverages (Thailand) Limited (3)
PO Box 18, Samrong Tai, Samut Prakan, 10310, Thailand
Tel.: (66) 27424330
Web Site: http://www.ovaltine.co.th
Malt Mfr
N.A.I.C.S.: 311213
Pongskorn Pongwattanasuk (Gen Mgr)

AB Food & Beverages Australia Pty Ltd. (3)
35-37 South Corporate Ave, Rowville, 3178, VIC, Australia
Tel.: (61) 397645111
Web Site: http://www.abfoodandbeverages.com.au
Sales Range: $25-49.9 Million
Emp.: 70
Food Mfg Services
N.A.I.C.S.: 311999
Will Ursell (Gen Mgr)

AB Food & Beverages Philippines, Inc. (3)
2nd Flr Valiant Bldg McKenzie Distribution Compound, 86 E Rodriguez Jr Ave Ugong Norte, Quezon City, 1110, Philippines
Tel.: (63) 26382660
Web Site: http://www.ovaltine.com.ph
Malt Mfr
N.A.I.C.S.: 311213

Subsidiary (Domestic):

AB Mauri (UK) Limited (3)
Sugar Way, Peterborough, PE2 9AY, United Kingdom
Tel.: (44) 1733 871 500
Web Site: http://www.abmauri.com
Sales Range: $1-4.9 Billion
Emp.: 70
Yeast Mfr
N.A.I.C.S.: 311999
Cathal Duffy (CEO)

Representative Office (Non-US):

AB Mauri (UK) Ltd. - Ireland Office (4)
22 Priory Hall, Stillorgan, Dublin, Ireland
Tel.: (353) 12836920
Web Site: http://www.abmauri.com
Baking Yeast Production
N.A.I.C.S.: 311423

Subsidiary (Non-US):

AB Mauri Australia Ltd. (4)
15 Grand Ave, Camellia, 2142, NSW, Australia
Tel.: (61) 296848600
Web Site: http://www.abmauri.com
Bakers' Yeast Production
N.A.I.C.S.: 311423

Plant (Domestic):

Mauri Yeast Australia Pty. Ltd. (5)
15 Grand Ave, Camellia, 2142, NSW, Australia
Tel.: (61) 296848600
Web Site: http://www.abmauri.com
Sales Range: $10-24.9 Million
Emp.: 50
Yeast Mfr
N.A.I.C.S.: 311423
Claude Alassio (Production Mgr)

Subsidiary (Non-US):

AB Mauri Brazil (4)
Rua Cardeal Arcoverde 1641 12 Andar, CEP 05407 002, Sao Paulo, Brazil
Tel.: (55) 30381800
Web Site: http://www.mauri.com.br
Yeast Mfr
N.A.I.C.S.: 311423

AB Mauri Food, S.A. (4)
Levadura 5, Villarrubia, Cordoba, 14710, Spain
Tel.: (34) 957327001
Food Ingredient Mfr
N.A.I.C.S.: 311999

AB Mauri India (Private) Limited (4)
Plot No 218 & 219 Bommasandra Jigani Link Road, Bengaluru, 560105, Karnataka, India
Tel.: (91) 8030797900
Web Site: http://www.abmauri.in
Food Ingredient Mfr
N.A.I.C.S.: 311999
Soni Sukhija Raval (Mgr-HR)

AB Mauri Italy S.p.A. (4)
Via Milano 42, Pavia, 27045, Casteggio, Italy
Tel.: (39) 03838931
Food Ingredient Distr
N.A.I.C.S.: 456191

AB Mauri Malaysia Sdn. Bhd. (4)
Lot 4185 Jalan KB 1/9 Kg, 43300, Balakong, Selangor, Malaysia
Tel.: (60) 389612209
Web Site: http://www.abmauri.com.my
Food Ingredient Mfr
N.A.I.C.S.: 311999

AB Mauri Portugal, SA (4)
Avenida Salvador Allende 99, 2770-157, Paco d'Arcos, Portugal
Tel.: (351) 214258800
Web Site: http://www.abmauri.pt
Food Ingredient Mfr
N.A.I.C.S.: 311999

Subsidiary (US):

Fleischmann's Yeast (4)
1350 Timberlake Manor Pkwy Ste 550, Chesterfield, MO 63017-6051
Tel.: (636) 349-8800
Web Site: http://www.fleischmannsyeast.com
Sales Range: $50-74.9 Million
Yeast & Other Baking Products Mfr
N.A.I.C.S.: 311942

Affiliate (Non-US):

UNIFERM GmbH & Co. (4)
Brede 4, 59368, Werne, Germany (50%)
Tel.: (49) 238978790
Web Site: http://www.uniferm.com
Sales Range: $25-49.9 Million
Emp.: 350
Yeast & Bakery Products Mfr
N.A.I.C.S.: 311999

Subsidiary (Non-US):

ABNA (Shanghai) Feed Co., Ltd (3)
20f Pacific Enterprise Center no 88, Shanghai, 200050, China
Tel.: (86) 2134533985
Animal Feed Mfr
N.A.I.C.S.: 311119

ABNA Feed (Liaoning) Co., Ltd (3)
No 145 Xincheng Road Teng'ao Economic Development Zone, Anshan, Anshan, China
Tel.: (86) 4128311558
Food Ingredient Distr
N.A.I.C.S.: 445110

Subsidiary (US):

ACH Food Companies, Inc. (3)
7171 Goodlett Farms Pkwy, Cordova, TN 38016-4909
Tel.: (901) 381-3000
Web Site: http://www.achfood.com
Sales Range: $25-49.9 Million
Emp.: 250
Miscellaneous Food Products
N.A.I.C.S.: 311225
Bill Puentes (Dir-Mktg)

Subsidiary (Non-US):

ACH Foods Mexico, S.de R.L.de C.V. (3)
Prol Paseo De La Reforma No 1015, Distrito Federal, Mexico, 01210, Mexico
Tel.: (52) 5510850100
Web Site: http://www.achfoods.mx
Food Ingredient Mfr
N.A.I.C.S.: 311999

Subsidiary (US):

Abitec Corporation (3)
501 W 1st Ave, Columbus, OH 43215
Tel.: (614) 429-6464
Web Site: http://www.abiteccorp.com
Chemical Products Mfr
N.A.I.C.S.: 325199
Jeff Walton (CEO)

Subsidiary (Non-US):

Anzchem Pty Limited (3)
52 Holker St, Silverwater, 2128, NSW, Australia
Tel.: (61) 294752200
Web Site: http://www.anzchem.com.au
Food Ingredient Mfr
N.A.I.C.S.: 311999

Bo Tian Sugar Industry Company Limited (3)
12/F Block B China International Science & Technology Convention, No 12 Yu Min Avenue Chao Yang District, Beijing, 100029, China
Tel.: (86) 1058526685
Web Site: http://www.botiansugar.com
Sugar Mfr
N.A.I.C.S.: 311313

Subsidiary (Domestic):

British Sugar plc (3)
Sugar Way, Peterborough, PE2 9AY, United Kingdom (100%)
Tel.: (44) 01733563171
Web Site: http://www.britishsugar.co.uk
Sales Range: $1-4.9 Billion
Emp.: 300
Sugar Processing & Manufacturing
N.A.I.C.S.: 311313
Paul Kenward (Mng Dir)

Subsidiary (Non-US):

Illovo Sugar (PTY) Ltd (4)
1 Nokwe Avenue Ridgeside, Umhlanga Rocks, Durban, South Africa
Tel.: (27) 315084300
Web Site: http://www.illovosugarafrica.com
Emp.: 12,600
Sugar Production
N.A.I.C.S.: 111930
Larry W. Riddle (Grp Dir-Corp & External Affairs)

Subsidiary (US):

Agriguard LLC (5)
186 N Ave E Ste 100, Cranford, NJ 07016
Tel.: (908) 272-7070
Animal Food Distr
N.A.I.C.S.: 445110

Subsidiary (Non-US):

Illovo Sugar (Malawi) Limited (5)
Illovo Sugar (Malawi) Private Bag 580, Limbe, Malawi (76%)
Tel.: (265) 1 843 988
Sales Range: $1-4.9 Billion
Emp.: 5,400
Sugar Producer
N.A.I.C.S.: 111930

Subsidiary (Domestic):

Illovo Sugar (South Africa) Limited (5)
Building 3c Gleneagles Park 10 Flanders Drive, Mount Edgecombe, South Africa
Tel.: (27) 31 508 4300
Sugar Mfr
N.A.I.C.S.: 311314
Dave Howells (Mng Dir)

Subsidiary (Non-US):

Illovo Tanzania Limited (5)
PO Box 50, Morogoro, Tanzania
Tel.: (255) 232626011
Sugar Mfr
N.A.I.C.S.: 311314

Mark Bainbridge (Gen Mgr)

Maragra Acucar SARL (5)
Caixa Postal 2789, Maputo, Mozambique (74%)
Tel.: (258) 21810024
Web Site: http://www.illovosugar.com
Emp.: 1,000
Beet Sugar Mfr
N.A.I.C.S.: 311313
Hans Veenstra (Gen Mgr)

Monitor Energy Limited (5)
35 Richardson St, West Perth, 6005, Australia
Tel.: (61) 892111555
Web Site: http://www.monitorenergy.com.au
Support Activities for Oil & Gas Operations
N.A.I.C.S.: 213112

Ubombo Sugar Limited (5)
PO Box 23, Big Bend, Mbabane, Eswatini (60%)
Tel.: (268) 3638000
Cane Sugar Refining
N.A.I.C.S.: 311314

Zambia Sugar plc (5)
PO Box 670240, Mazabuka, Zambia (90%)
Tel.: (260) 3230666
Web Site: http://www.illovo.co.za
Cane Sugar Refining
N.A.I.C.S.: 311314

Subsidiary (Non-US):

Compania Argentina de Levaduras S.A.I.C (3)
Boulevard Gobernador, Lanus Este, Rodrigues, B1824JDK, Argentina
Tel.: (54) 1143652000
Web Site: http://www.calsa.com.ar
Bakery Products Mfr
N.A.I.C.S.: 311812

George Weston Foods (NZ) Limited (3)
Building 3 Level 2 666 Great South Road, Ellerslie, Auckland, 1051, New Zealand
Tel.: (64) 99661991
Web Site: http://www.gwfbaking.co.nz
Food Ingredient Mfr
N.A.I.C.S.: 311999
Andrew Reeves (CEO)

George Weston Foods Limited (3)
Group Office Tip Top MAURI anz Jasol Building A Level 1, 11 Talavera Road, North Ryde, 2113, NSW, Australia
Tel.: (61) 2 9815 7300
Web Site: http://www.georgewestonfoods.com.au
Emp.: 550
Food Ingredient Mfr
N.A.I.C.S.: 311999
Andrew Reeves (CEO)

Guangxi Boqing Food Co., Ltd (3)
9 Gongyuan East Road, Yizhou, 546300, China
Tel.: (86) 7783146699
Sugar Mfr
N.A.I.C.S.: 311314

Guangxi Boxuan Food Co., Ltd (3)
No 41 Xianmi Road, Laibin, Wuxi, 545900, Wuxuan, China
Tel.: (86) 7725211473
Sugar Mfr
N.A.I.C.S.: 311314

Harbin Mauri Yeast Co., Ltd (3)
No 1 Tongcheng Street, Harbin, 150300, China
Tel.: (86) 45153754811
Food Products Mfr
N.A.I.C.S.: 311999

Hebei Mauri Food Co., Ltd (3)
No 1 Gongye North Avenue, Zhangjiakou, 076450, Zhangbei, China
Tel.: (86) 3135230868
Food Products Mfr
N.A.I.C.S.: 311999

Mauri Maya Sanayi A.S. (3)
Kavakpinar Mevkii Aksakal PK 101, 10200, Balikesir, Turkiye
Tel.: (90) 2667251500
Web Site: http://www.mauri.com.tr

AND PRIVATE COMPANIES — THE GLEN DIMPLEX GROUP

Bakery Products Mfr
N.A.I.C.S.: 311812

Subsidiary (US):

Primark Deutschland GmbH (3)
Kennedyplatz 2, 45127, Essen, Nordrhein-Westfalen, Germany
Tel.: (49) 20163298101
Web Site:
http://www.damenbekleidungkaufen.de
Apparel Distr
N.A.I.C.S.: 458110

Subsidiary (Domestic):

Primark Stores Limited (3)
Primark House 41 West Street, Reading, RG1 1TT, United Kingdom
Tel.: (44) 1189606370
Clothing Retailer
N.A.I.C.S.: 455110

Subsidiary (US):

SPI Pharma, Inc. (3)
503 Carr Rd, Wilmington, DE 19809-2800
Tel.: (302) 576-8554
Web Site: http://www.spipharma.com
Sales Range: $25-49.9 Million
Emp.: 80
Mfr of Raw Materials for Pharmaceutical & Food Industries
N.A.I.C.S.: 325199
Scott Thomson (CEO)

Subsidiary (Non-US):

Shanghai AB Food & Beverages Co., Ltd
8 Lancun Road Minhang Economic & Technological Development Zone, Shanghai, 200245, China
Tel.: (86) 2164303038
Web Site: http://www.abf.cn
Emp.: 200
Food Products Mfr
N.A.I.C.S.: 311999

Subsidiary (Domestic):

The Jordans & Ryvita Company Limited (3)
Weston Centre 10 Grosvenor Street, London, W1K 4QY, United Kingdom (100%)
Tel.: (44) 8082310011
Web Site: http://www.ryvita.co.uk
Crispbread & Related Products Mfr
N.A.I.C.S.: 311999
Rosalyn Sharon Schofield (Sec)

Twining & Co. Ltd. (3)
South Way, Andover, SP10 5AQ, United Kingdom (100%)
Tel.: (44) 1264334477
Web Site: http://www.twinings.com
Sales Range: $125-149.9 Million
Emp.: 500
Holding Company
N.A.I.C.S.: 551112

Subsidiary (Domestic):

R. Twining & Co. Ltd. (4)
Weston Centre 10 Grosvenor Street, London, W1K 4QY, United Kingdom (100%)
Tel.: (44) 1264313444
Web Site: http://www.twinings.co.uk
Sales Range: $75-99.9 Million
Emp.: 500
Coffee Tea Cocoa & Spice Mfr
N.A.I.C.S.: 311942
Bob Tavener (CEO)

Subsidiary (US):

Twinings North America, Inc. (5)
777 Passaic Ave Ste 230, Clifton, NJ 07012-1804
Tel.: (973) 591-0600
Web Site: http://www.twiningsusa.com
Rev.: $20,000,000

Emp.: 25
Tea, Coffee, Cocoa & Spice Whslr
N.A.I.C.S.: 311920
James Donnelly (Dir-Sls)

Subsidiary (Non-US):

Wander AG (3)
Fabrikstrasse 10, PO Box 3176, Neuenegg, Switzerland
Tel.: (41) 313772111
Web Site: http://www.wander.ch
Food Products Mfr
N.A.I.C.S.: 311999

Holding (Domestic):

Fortnum & Mason plc (2)
181 Piccadilly, London, W1A 1ER, United Kingdom
Tel.: (44) 2077348040
Web Site: http://www.fortnumandmason.com
Sales Range: $150-199.9 Million
Emp.: 500
Specialty Food & Beverage Gift Retailer
N.A.I.C.S.: 445298
Brigette Hardy (Head-Food Buying)

THE GATE WORLDWIDE LIMITED

Devon House 58 Saint Catherine's Way, London, E1W 1LB, United Kingdom
Tel.: (44) 2074234500 UK
Web Site:
http://www.thegateworldwide.com
Year Founded: 1988
Emp.: 60
Advetising Agency
N.A.I.C.S.: 541810
Phillip Hawkins (Mng Dir)

Subsidiaries:

SEA PR GmbH (1)
Bockenheimer Anlage 37, 60322, Frankfurt am Main, Germany
Tel.: (49) 691700710
Web Site: http://www.sea-pr.de
Emp.: 30
N.A.I.C.S.: 541810
Peter Kraus (Dir-Creative)

The Gate Worldwide (S) Pte Limited (1)
52 Craig Road, Singapore, 089690, Singapore (100%)
Tel.: (65) 6513 0520
Web Site: http://www.thegateworldwide.com
Emp.: 30
Graphic Design Services
N.A.I.C.S.: 541430
Sean Worrall (Mng Dir)

The Gate Worldwide Channel Islands (1)
55 Le Bordage, Saint Peter Port, GY1 1BP, Guernsey, United Kingdom
Tel.: (44) 1481 725 115
Emp.: 10
Chris Betley (Mng Dir)

The Gate Worldwide Edinburgh (1)
100 Ocean Drive, Edinburgh, EH6 6JJ, United Kingdom
Tel.: (44) 131 555 0425
Helen Hourston (Dir)

The Gate Worldwide Hong Kong (1)
13th Floor, Chinachem Hollywood Centre, 1 Hollywood Road, Central, China (Hong Kong)
Tel.: (852) 2827 2411
N.A.I.C.S.: 541810
Ellmon Fung (Mng Dir)

The Gate Worldwide New York (1)
11 E 26th St 14th Fl, New York, NY 10010
Tel.: (212) 508-3400
Web Site: http://www.thegateworldwide.com
Rev.: $85,000,000
Emp.: 50
Advetising Agency
N.A.I.C.S.: 541810
Charlie Katz (Dir-Print Production)

The Gate Worldwide Shanghai (1)
Suite 1307, BEA Finance Tower, 66 Hua Yuan Shi Qiao Road, Pu Dong District, Shanghai, 200120, China
Tel.: (86) 21 3383 0138
Wilson Feng (Mng Dir)

THE GENERAL TYRE & RUBBER COMPANY OF PAKISTAN LIMITED

H-23/2 Landhi Industrial Estate, Landhi, Karachi, Pakistan
Tel.: (92) 2135080172
Web Site: https://www.gtr.com.pk
GTYR—(KAR)
Rev.: $75,291,505
Assets: $89,570,873
Liabilities: $65,584,059
Net Worth: $23,986,815
Earnings: $882,250
Emp.: 1,130
Fiscal Year-end: 06/30/19
Tire Mfr & Sales
N.A.I.C.S.: 326211
Mussarat Ahmed (Head-Internal Audit & Sr Gen Mgr)

THE GHANA AIRPORTS COMPANY LIMITED

KA PMB 36, Accra, Ghana
Tel.: (233) 302 776171
Web Site: http://www.gacl.com.gh
Airport Operations
N.A.I.C.S.: 488119
Charles Hanson Adu (Deputy Mng Dir-Ops & Technical)

THE GLEN DIMPLEX GROUP

Old Airport Road, Cloghran, K67 VE08, Dublin, Ireland
Tel.: (353) 18523400
Web Site:
http://www.glendimplex.com
Year Founded: 1973
Electric Heating & Domestic Appliance Mfr
N.A.I.C.S.: 335210
Martin L. Naughton (Chm-Supervisory Bd)

Subsidiaries:

Burco Appliances Ltd. (1)
Talbot Road, Mexborough, S64 8AJ, S Yorkshire, United Kingdom
Tel.: (44) 1709577120
Web Site: http://www.burco.co.uk
Sales Range: $25-49.9 Million
Emp.: 100
Electric & Gas Fired Catering Boilers, Stainless Steel Kettles, Filter Coffee Equipment, Percolators, Toasters, Airpots & Flasks Mfr
N.A.I.C.S.: 333414

Chilton Electric (1)
Ardee Rd, Dunleer, County Louth, Ireland
Tel.: (353) 416862200
Web Site:
http://www.glendimplexireland.com
Sales Range: $50-74.9 Million
Emp.: 200
N.A.I.C.S.: 335210
Pat Coyne (Mng Dir)

Dimpco Ltd. (1)
Old Airport Road, Cloghran, Dublin, Ireland
Tel.: (353) 1842 4833
Web Site: http://www.dimpco.ie
Emp.: 50
Household Appliance Distr
N.A.I.C.S.: 423620

Dimplex AS (1)
Bratsbergvegen 5, NO-7493, Trondheim, Norway
Tel.: (47) 73959400
Web Site: http://www.dimplex.as
Sales Range: $25-49.9 Million
Emp.: 85
Electrical Heating Products Mfr & Distr
N.A.I.C.S.: 333414

Dimplex Cleaning Systems (1)
Clash Industrial Estate, Tralee, Co Kerry, Ireland
Tel.: (353) 66 712 1444

Dry Steam Cleaning Machines & Wet & Dry Vacuum Cleaners Mfr
N.A.I.C.S.: 335210

Dimplex Japan Ltd. (1)
2-23 East17 North46, Higashi-ku, Sapporo, 007-0846, Japan
Tel.: (81) 11 783 7989
Web Site: http://www.dimplex.jp
Household Appliance Distr
N.A.I.C.S.: 423620
Jun Nakamura (Mgr-Product Ops & Plng)

Dimplex North America Limited (1)
1367 Industrial Rd, Cambridge, N3H 4W3, ON, Canada (100%)
Tel.: (519) 650-3630
Web Site: http://www.dimplex.com
Sales Range: $100-124.9 Million
Emp.: 350
Electric Heater & Fireplace Mfr
N.A.I.C.S.: 335210
Denis Normand (Pres & CEO)

Dimplex Thermal Solutions (1)
2625 Emerald Dr, Kalamazoo, MI 49001
Tel.: (269) 349-6800
Web Site: http://www.dimplexthermal.com
Household Appliance Distr
N.A.I.C.S.: 423620
Bill Bohr (Pres)

Faber International BV (1)
Saturnus 8, NL-8448 CC, Heerenveen, Netherlands
Tel.: (31) 513656500
Web Site: http://www.faber.nl
Sales Range: $25-49.9 Million
Emp.: 30
Decorative Electric & Gas Stoves, Wood Stoves & Gas Room Heaters Researcher, Assembler & Marketer
N.A.I.C.S.: 423720
Erik Eising (CEO)

Galaxy Showers (1)
Morley Way, Peterborough, PE2 9JJ, United Kingdom
Tel.: (44) 8709000430
Web Site: http://www.applied-energy.com
Electric & Electronic Showers Mfr
N.A.I.C.S.: 332913

Glen Dimplex Americas Company (1)
2500 W 4th Plain Blvd, Vancouver, WA 98660-1354
Tel.: (360) 693-2505
Web Site:
http://www.glendimplexamericas.com
Warm Air Heating Equipment Mfr & Distr
N.A.I.C.S.: 333414
Craig Peterson (VP)

Glen Dimplex Australia Pty Ltd (1)
Unit 1 21 Lionel Road Mount Waverley, Mount Waverley, 3149, VIC, Australia
Tel.: (61) 1300 556 816
Web Site: http://www.glendimplex.com.au
Household Appliance Distr
N.A.I.C.S.: 423620

Glen Dimplex Benelux B.V. (1)
Saturnus 8, 8448 CC, Heerenveen, Netherlands
Tel.: (31) 513656500
Web Site: http://www.glendimplex.nl
Sales Range: $50-74.9 Million
Emp.: 70
Personal Care Products Whslr
N.A.I.C.S.: 423620
Van Nierop (Mng Dir)

Division (Non-US):

Glen Dimplex Benelux B.V. (2)
Gentsestraat 60, 9300, Aalst, Belgium
Tel.: (32) 53828862
Web Site: http://www.glendimplex.be
Sales Range: $25-49.9 Million
Emp.: 5
Personal Care Products Including Foot Spas, Epilators, Shavers, Hair Dryers, Curlers & Styling Brushes Distr & Sales
N.A.I.C.S.: 423620
Sandra Egbers (CEO)

Glen Dimplex Boilers (1)
Stoney Lane, Prescot, L35 2XW, Merseyside, United Kingdom
Tel.: (44) 151 424 7011

THE GLEN DIMPLEX GROUP

The Glen Dimplex Group—(Continued)
Web Site:
http://www.glendimplexboilers.com
Rev.: $52,143,300
Emp.: 120
Gas Boilers Mfr
N.A.I.C.S.: 332410

Glen Dimplex Deutschland GmbH (1)
Am Goldenenfeld 18, PO Box 1569, 95306, Kulmbach, Germany (100%)
Tel.: (49) 92217090
Web Site: http://www.glendimplex.de
Sales Range: $200-249.9 Million
Emp.: 1,000
Mfr of Electric Heaters
N.A.I.C.S.: 335210

Glen Dimplex Espana S.L. (1)
Calle Balien 20 FL 4th Gt 2nd, 080 10, Barcelona, Spain
Tel.: (34) 932386159
Web Site: http://www.glendimplex.com
Small Domestic Appliances, Portable Heaters, Electric Fireplaces & Stoves Distr
N.A.I.C.S.: 423620

Glen Dimplex Exports Ltd. (1)
Barn Road, Dunleer, Co Louth, Ireland
Tel.: (353) 419800300
Sales Range: $50-74.9 Million
Emp.: 8
Heaters, Heating Products & Appliances Exporter
N.A.I.C.S.: 423720

Glen Dimplex France (1)
ZI De l'Eglantier 20 rue des Cerisiers, 91028, Evry, Cedex, France
Tel.: (33) 169111191
Web Site: http://www.glendimplex-france.fr
Wet & Dry Ranges, Cylinders, Steamers & Other Heating Products Distr
N.A.I.C.S.: 423720

Glen Dimplex Home Appliances Ltd. (1)
Stoney Lane, Prescot, L35 2XW, Merseyside, United Kingdom
Tel.: (44) 8704449919
Web Site: www.gdha.com
Home Cooking Appliances Mfr
N.A.I.C.S.: 335220

Subsidiary (Domestic):

Lec Refrigeration (2)
Stoney Lane, Prescot, L35 2XW, Merseyside, United Kingdom
Tel.: (44) 8442484466
Web Site: http://www.gdha.com
Sales Range: $350-399.9 Million
Emp.: 1,100
Refrigerator Equipment Mfr
N.A.I.C.S.: 335220
Denzer Hewlett (CEO)

Glen Dimplex Hong Kong Limited (1)
Unit 03-05 10F Millennium City 3, 370 Kwun Tong Road, Kowloon, China (Hong Kong)
Tel.: (852) 27906600
Web Site: http://www.glendimplex.com
Sales Range: $25-49.9 Million
Emp.: 30
Heating Products & Electric Appliance Distr
N.A.I.C.S.: 423720
Jacky Choi (CEO)

Glen Dimplex Ireland (1)
Barn Road, Dunleer, A92 WV02, Co Louth, Ireland
Tel.: (353) 416872000
Web Site:
http://www.glendimplexireland.com
Sales Range: $125-149.9 Million
Emp.: 350
Heating Products Mfr
N.A.I.C.S.: 335210

Glen Dimplex Italia S.R.L. (1)
Via delle Rose 7, 24040, Lallio, BG, Italy
Tel.: (39) 035201042
Portable Heating, Wet & Dry Vacuums, Industrial Heating, Small Electrical Appliances & Electric Stoves Distr
N.A.I.C.S.: 423720

Glen Dimplex New Zealand Ltd. (1)
38 Harris Road, East Tamaki, Auckland, 2013, New Zealand
Tel.: (64) 9 274 8265
Web Site: http://www.glendimplex.co.nz
Household Appliance Distr
N.A.I.C.S.: 423620
Ross Bird (Mgr-Distr)

Glen Dimplex Nordic AS (1)
Havnegata 24, NO-7502, Stjordal, Norway
Tel.: (47) 74829100
Web Site: http://www.glendimplex.no
Sales Range: $50-74.9 Million
Emp.: 150
Electric Heating Products Mfr
N.A.I.C.S.: 333414

Subsidiary (Non-US):

Nobo Heating UK Limited (2)
Unit 15 Gravelly Industrial Park, Tyburn Road, Erdington, B24 8HZ, Birmingham, United Kingdom
Tel.: (44) 1213285671
Web Site: http://www.noboheatinguk.com
Sales Range: $25-49.9 Million
Emp.: 13
Electric Heating Products Distr
N.A.I.C.S.: 423720

Glen Dimplex Northern Ireland Limited (1)
5 Charlestown Avenue Charlestown Industrial Estate, Craigavon, BT63 5Z, Armagh, United Kingdom
Tel.: (44) 28-38-337317
Web Site: http://www.glendimplexni.co.uk
Emp.: 30
Household Appliance Distr
N.A.I.C.S.: 423620
Nmel Collins (Mng Dir)

Glen Dimplex Polska sp. zo.o. (1)
ul Strzeszynska 33, 60-479, Poznan, Poland
Tel.: (48) 618425805
Web Site: http://www.glendimplex.pl
Sales Range: $50-74.9 Million
Emp.: 15
Storage Heaters, Convector Heaters, Heat Pumps, Fan Heaters & Other Heating Products Distr; Vacuum Cleaners Distr
N.A.I.C.S.: 423720

Glen Dimplex UK (1)
Millbrook House Grange Dr, Hedge End, Southampton, SO3 02DF, United Kingdom (100%)
Tel.: (44) 8456005111
Web Site: http://www.dimplex.co.uk
Sales Range: $25-49.9 Million
Emp.: 100
Electric Space & Water Heating Products Sales
N.A.I.C.S.: 335210
Stuart MacKenzie (Gen Mgr)

Glen Electric (1)
Greenbank Industrial Estate Rampart Road, Newry, BT34 2QU, United Kingdom (100%)
Tel.: (44) 2830264621
Web Site: http://www.glenelectric.co.uk
Sales Range: $25-49.9 Million
Emp.: 100
N.A.I.C.S.: 335210
Path Purton (Mng Dir)

Koolant Koolers Inc. (1)
2625 Emerald Dr, Kalamazoo, MI 49001
Tel.: (269) 349-6800
Web Site:
http://www.dimplexkalamazoo.com
Sales Range: $25-49.9 Million
Emp.: 25
Liquid Chillers Mfr
N.A.I.C.S.: 333415
Steve Cummins (CEO)

Morphy Richards (N.I.) Ltd. (1)
Talbot Road, Mexborough, S64 8AJ, South Yorkshire, United Kingdom
Tel.: (44) 1709572570
Web Site: http://www.morphyrichards.co.uk
Home Electrical Appliance Mfr
N.A.I.C.S.: 335210
Staley Green (Mng Dir)

Morphy Richards Ltd. (1)
Adwick Park, Manvers, S63 5AB, S Yorkshire, United Kingdom (100%)
Tel.: (44) 1709582402
Web Site: http://www.morphyrichards.co.uk
Sales Range: $125-149.9 Million
Emp.: 200
Domestic Appliances Mfr & Whslr
N.A.I.C.S.: 335210
Chilit Green (CEO)

Roberts Radio Limited (1)
PO Box 130, Mexborough, S64 8YT, South Yorkshire, United Kingdom
Tel.: (44) 1709571722
Web Site: http://www.robertsradio.co.uk
Sales Range: $25-49.9 Million
Emp.: 25
Portable Radio Mfr
N.A.I.C.S.: 334220
Leslie Burrage (CEO)

Seagoe Technologies Limited (1)
Church Road Seagoe Portadown, Craigavon, BT63 5HU, Co Armagh, United Kingdom
Tel.: (44) 2838333131
Sales Range: $100-124.9 Million
Emp.: 300
Static Night Storage Heaters Mfr
N.A.I.C.S.: 333414
Neil Stewart (CEO)

Shenyang Dimplex Electronics (1)
9 Shiji Road, Shenyang Hunan Indus Zone, Shenyang, 110179, China
Tel.: (86) 2423782259
Web Site: http://www.glendimplex.com
Storage Heaters, Fireplaces & Other Heating Products Mfr
N.A.I.C.S.: 333414

Valor Ltd. (1)
Wood Lane Erdington, Birmingham, B24 9QP, United Kingdom (100%)
Tel.: (44) 844 871 1565
Web Site: http://www.valor.co.uk
Sales Range: $50-74.9 Million
Emp.: 200
Gas & Electric Fire & Heater Mfr
N.A.I.C.S.: 333414

THE GLOBAL SMALLER COMPANIES TRUST PLC

Cannon Place 78 Cannon Street, London, EC4N 6AG, United Kingdom
Tel.: (44) 2076288000 UK
GSCT—(LSE)
Rev.: $19,006,722
Assets: $1,363,206,547
Liabilities: $79,748,400
Net Worth: $1,283,458,147
Earnings: ($12,575,203)
Fiscal Year-end: 04/30/22
Investment Management Service
N.A.I.C.S.: 523940

THE GO AUTO GROUP

200 10220 - 184 St, Edmonton, T5S 0B9, AB, Canada
Tel.: (780) 777-7777
Web Site: https://www.goauto.ca
New & Used Car Dealers
N.A.I.C.S.: 441110
Phil Abram (Pres)

Subsidiaries:

Richmond Chrysler Dodge Jeep Ltd. (1)
5491 Parkwood Way, Richmond, V6V 2M9, BC, Canada
Tel.: (604) 273-7521
Web Site:
http://www.richmondchryslerjeep.com
Rev.: $28,962,500
Emp.: 75
New & Used Car Dealers
N.A.I.C.S.: 441110
Bob Macdonald (Mgr-Fixed Ops)

THE GOLDFARB CORPORATION

18 Spadina Rd Ste 100, Toronto, M2N 2S7, ON, Canada
Tel.: (416) 229-2070 ON

INTERNATIONAL PUBLIC

Year Founded: 1986
Sales Range: $1-9.9 Million
Investment Holding Company
N.A.I.C.S.: 551112
Martin Goldfarb (Chm, Pres & CEO)

THE GREAT EASTERN SHIPPING CO., LTD.

134/A Dr Annie Besant Road, Worli, Mumbai, 400 018, India
Tel.: (91) 2266613000
Web Site: https://www.greatship.com
Year Founded: 1948
GESHIP—(NSE)
Rev.: $487,082,505
Assets: $1,930,875,765
Liabilities: $879,242,910
Net Worth: $1,051,632,855
Earnings: $125,377,980
Emp.: 1,262
Fiscal Year-end: 03/31/21
Crude Oil, Petroleum Products, Gas & Dry Bulk Commodities Transportation
N.A.I.C.S.: 486110
Bharat K. Sheth (Deputy Chm & Mng Dir)

Subsidiaries:

Greatship (India) Limited (1)
One International Center Tower 3 23rd Floor Senapati Bapat Marg, Elphinstone Road West, Mumbai, 400 013, India
Tel.: (91) 2267207500
Web Site: https://greatshipglobal.com
Oil & Gas Exploration Services
N.A.I.C.S.: 213112
Ravi K. Sheth (Mng Dir)

Greatship Global Energy Services Pte. Ltd (1)
300 Beach Road 16-07 The Concourse, Singapore, 199555, Singapore
Tel.: (65) 65765600
Web Site: http://www.greatshipglobal.com
Sales Range: $25-49.9 Million
Emp.: 21
Ship Chartering Services
N.A.I.C.S.: 483111

Greatship Global Offshore Services Pte. Ltd. (1)
300 Beach Road 16-07 The Concourse, Singapore, 199555, Singapore
Tel.: (65) 65765600
Emp.: 18
Ship Chartering Services
N.A.I.C.S.: 483111

The Great Eastern Chartering L.L.C. (1)
Executive Suite Y2-112, PO Box 9271, Sharjah, United Arab Emirates
Tel.: (971) 43038740
Ship Chartering Services
N.A.I.C.S.: 483111

THE GREAT TAIPEI GAS CORPORATION

1F No 35 Ln 11 Guangfu N Rd, Songshan Dist, Taipei, 105, Taiwan
Tel.: (886) 27684999
Web Site:
https://www.taipeigas.com.tw
9908—(TAI)
Rev.: $113,437,943
Assets: $658,726,683
Liabilities: $178,242,807
Net Worth: $480,483,876
Earnings: $39,741,226
Emp.: 246
Fiscal Year-end: 12/31/23
Natural Gas Distribution Services
N.A.I.C.S.: 221210

THE GREAT WESTERN BREWING COMPANY

519 Second Ave N, Saskatoon, S7K 2C6, SK, Canada
Tel.: (306) 653-4653

Web Site: http://www.gwbc.ca
Year Founded: 1989
Sales Range: $25-49.9 Million
Emp.: 100
Brewery
N.A.I.C.S.: 312120
Michael Micovcin *(CEO)*

THE GREATER VANCOUVER CONVENTION & VISITOR BUREAU
200 Burrard St Ste 210, Vancouver, V6C3LC, BC, Canada
Tel.: (604) 682-2222
Web Site:
    http://www.tourismvancouver.com
Year Founded: 1902
Sales Range: $1-9.9 Million
Emp.: 100
Convention & Visitors Bureau
N.A.I.C.S.: 561591
David Gazley *(VP-Meeting & Convention Sls)*

THE GROB TEA COMPANY LIMITED
Haute Street 9th Floor 86A Topsia Road, Kolkata, 700 046, India
Tel.: (91) 3340031325
Web Site: https://www.grobtea.com
Year Founded: 1985
GROBTEA—(NSE)
Rev.: $15,215,978
Assets: $12,713,445
Liabilities: $2,434,462
Net Worth: $10,278,983
Earnings: $3,825,101
Emp.: 4,006
Fiscal Year-end: 03/31/21
Tea Mfr & Distr
N.A.I.C.S.: 311920
Indu Bhusan Sharaf *(Exec Dir)*

THE GROSVENOR CLEANING SERVICES LTD.
64c Heather Road Sandyford Industrial Estate, Dublin, Ireland
Tel.: (353) 12954866   IE
Web Site:
    http://www.grosvenorservices.com
Year Founded: 1959
Sales Range: $700-749.9 Million
Emp.: 5,000
Contract Janitorial & Facility Maintenance Services
N.A.I.C.S.: 561720
Bernard McCauley *(Mng Dir)*

Subsidiaries:

Grosvenor Building Services, Inc.   (1)
3398 Parkway Center Ct, Orlando, FL 32808
Tel.: (407) 292-3383
Web Site:
    http://www.grosvenorservices.com
Sales Range: $10-24.9 Million
Emp.: 500
Contract Janitorial & Facility Maintenance Services
N.A.I.C.S.: 561720

Grosvenor Cleaning Services Limited   (1)
Grosvenor House 3A Vale Industrial Estate, Spilsby, PE23 5HE, Lincolnshire, United Kingdom
Tel.: (44) 1790754580
Web Site: http://www.grosvenorservices.ie
Sales Range: $25-49.9 Million
Emp.: 12
Contract Janitorial & Facility Maintenance Services
N.A.I.C.S.: 561720

THE GROUNDS REAL ESTATE DEVELOPMENT AG
Charlottenstrasse 79-80, 10117, Berlin, Germany
Tel.: (49) 3020216866
Web Site:
    https://www.thegroundsag.com
Year Founded: 2007
AMMN—(MUN)
Rev.: $25,788,906
Assets: $159,525,146
Liabilities: $132,725,016
Net Worth: $26,800,130
Earnings: ($8,186,920)
Emp.: 14
Fiscal Year-end: 12/31/23
Real Estate Investment Services
N.A.I.C.S.: 531190

THE GUNMA BANK, LTD.
194 Motosojamachi, Maebashi, 371-8611, Gunma, Japan
Tel.: (81) 272521111
Web Site:
    https://www.gunmabank.co.jp
Year Founded: 1932
8334—(TKS)
Rev.: $1,324,353,160
Assets: $71,508,420,980
Liabilities: $67,720,263,030
Net Worth: $3,788,157,950
Earnings: $79,320
Emp.: 2,830
Fiscal Year-end: 03/31/24
Commercial Banking Services
N.A.I.C.S.: 522110
Kazuo Saito *(Chm)*

Subsidiaries:

Gungin General Maintenance Co., Ltd.   (1)
2-1-6 Ikebukuro Toshima-Ku, Tokyo, Japan
Tel.: (81) 339846121
Management Consulting Services
N.A.I.C.S.: 541618

Gungin Lease Company Limited   (1)
171-1 Motosojacho, Maebashi, 371-0846, Gunma, Japan
Tel.: (81) 272533111
Web Site: https://www.gungin-leasing.co.jp
Emp.: 96
Financial Lending Services
N.A.I.C.S.: 522220

Gungin Securities Co., Ltd.   (1)
2-2-11 Honmachi, Maebashi, Gunma, Japan
Tel.: (81) 272893833
Web Site: https://www.gunginsec.co.jp
Financial Services
N.A.I.C.S.: 522299

Gungin System Service Co., Ltd.   (1)
171-1 Motosojacho, Maebashi, 371-0846, Gunma, Japan
Tel.: (81) 272896000
Web Site: https://www.gss.co.jp
Emp.: 144
Computer Mfr & Distr
N.A.I.C.S.: 334111

Gunma Capital Co., Ltd.   (1)
194 Motosojamachi, Maebashi, 371-0846, Gunma, Japan
Tel.: (81) 272534755
Venture Capital Services
N.A.I.C.S.: 561990

Gunma Finance (Hong Kong) Limited   (1)
Room 410 16 Harcourt Road, Hong Kong, China (Hong Kong)
Tel.: (852) 25230236
Sales Range: $50-74.9 Million
Emp.: 10
Banking Services
N.A.I.C.S.: 522110
Nobuo Mashimo *(Mng Dir)*

Gunma Shinyo Hosho Co., Ltd.   (1)
3-3-1 Otemachi Gummaken Chusho Kigyokaikan 5F, Maebashi, 371-0026, Gunma, Japan
Tel.: (81) 272318816
Credit Guarantee Services
N.A.I.C.S.: 561450

The Gungin Card Co., Ltd.   (1)
194 Motosojacho, Maebashi, 371-8572, Japan
Tel.: (81) 272538111
Web Site: https://www.gungin-card.co.jp
Emp.: 60
Credit Card Processing Services
N.A.I.C.S.: 522320

The Gungin JCB Card Co., Ltd.   (1)
Miyama Building 5F, Maebashi, 371-0846, Gunma, Japan
Tel.: (81) 272536241
Web Site: http://www.gunginjcb.co.jp
Credit Card Processing Services
N.A.I.C.S.: 522320

THE GYM GROUP PLC
5th Floor OneCroydon 12-16 Addiscombe Road, Croydon, CR0 0XT, United Kingdom   UK
Web Site: https://www.tggplc.com
Year Founded: 2007
GYM—(LSE)
Rev.: $218,252,966
Assets: $751,830,346
Liabilities: $582,681,141
Net Worth: $169,149,205
Earnings: ($24,362,535)
Emp.: 2,035
Fiscal Year-end: 12/31/22
Fitness Club Operator
N.A.I.C.S.: 713940
Ann-Marie Murphy *(COO)*

THE GYM LIMITED
Woodbridge House Woodbridge Meadows, Guildford, GU1 1BA, Surrey, United Kingdom
Tel.: (44) 844 412 8137
Web Site:
    http://www.thegymgroup.com
Year Founded: 2008
Sales Range: $10-24.9 Million
Emp.: 41
Gym Operator
N.A.I.C.S.: 713940
John Treharne *(CEO)*

THE HACHIJUNI BANK LTD.
178-8 Okada, Nakagosho, Nagano, 380-8682, Japan
Tel.: (81) 262271182   JP
Web Site: https://www.82bank.co.jp
Year Founded: 1931
8359—(TKS)
Rev.: $1,402,648,610
Assets: $98,011,440,720
Liabilities: $90,619,642,970
Net Worth: $7,391,797,750
Earnings: $92,540
Emp.: 3,289
Fiscal Year-end: 03/31/24
Banking Services
N.A.I.C.S.: 522110
Shoichi Yumoto *(Chm)*

Subsidiaries:

Hachijuni Auto Lease Co., Ltd.   (1)
218-14 Okada Nakagosho, Nagano, 380-0935, Japan
Tel.: (81) 262236582
Automobile Leasing Services
N.A.I.C.S.: 532112

Hachijuni Business Service Co., Ltd.   (1)
178-8 Nakagosho, Nagano, 380-0935, Japan
Tel.: (81) 262269882
Business Services
N.A.I.C.S.: 561499

Hachijuni Capital Co., Ltd.   (1)
6F Choei Daiichi Building 1282-11 Minami-Nagano Minamiishidocho, Minaminagano, Nagano, 380-0824, Japan
Tel.: (81) 262276887
Web Site: https://www.hcc82.co.jp
Sales Range: $50-74.9 Million
Emp.: 13
Venture Capital Services
N.A.I.C.S.: 523999

Hachijuni Credit Guarantee Co., Ltd.   (1)
178-2 Okada Nakagosho, Nagano, 380-0935, Japan
Tel.: (81) 262288231
Credit Guarantee Services
N.A.I.C.S.: 522390

Hachijuni Securities Co., Ltd   (1)
2-3-3 Tsuneda, Ueda, 386-0018, Nagano, Japan   (100%)
Tel.: (81) 120104082
Web Site: https://www.82sec.co.jp
Emp.: 214
Commercial Banking & Stock Trading Services
N.A.I.C.S.: 522110
Kenichi Takegahana *(Pres)*

Hachijuni Staff Service Co., Ltd.   (1)
178-2 Okada, Nagano, 380-8568, Japan
Tel.: (81) 262273433
Web Site: https://www.82staff-service.co.jp
Emp.: 20
Staffing Services
N.A.I.C.S.: 541612

Hachijuni System Development Co., Ltd.   (1)
178-13 Okada Nakagosho, Nagano, 380-0936, Nagano Prefecture, Japan
Tel.: (81) 262173330
Web Site: https://www.82sys.co.jp
Emp.: 301
Software Development Services
N.A.I.C.S.: 541511

Yamabiko Services Co., Ltd.   (1)
178-8 Okada, Nagano, 380-0936, Japan
Tel.: (81) 262245791
Sales Range: $10-24.9 Million
Emp.: 42
Business Credit Services
N.A.I.C.S.: 561499

THE HAIGH ENGINEERING COMPANY LIMITED
Alton Road, Ross-on-Wye, HR9 5NG, Herts, United Kingdom
Tel.: (44) 1989763131
Web Site: http://www.haigh.co.uk
Year Founded: 1955
Sales Range: $10-24.9 Million
Emp.: 106
Waste Water Treatment Services
N.A.I.C.S.: 562998
David Meek *(Mgr-Svc & Spares)*

THE HANRYU TIMES CO., LTD.
55-20 3ga mullae-Dong, Yeongdeungpo-gu, Seoul, 150-834, Korea (South)
Tel.: (82) 220010072
Web Site:
    http://www.sportsseoul.com
Year Founded: 1999
039670—(KRS)
Rev.: $6,576,851
Assets: $6,358,513
Liabilities: $2,485,494
Net Worth: $3,873,020
Earnings: $187,378
Emp.: 61
Fiscal Year-end: 03/31/23
Sport & Entertainment Newspaper Publisher
N.A.I.C.S.: 513110

THE HANSHIN DIESEL WORKS, LTD.
Shinko Building 4th Floor 8 Kaigan-dori, Chuo-ku, Kobe, 650-0024, Hyogo, Japan
Tel.: (81) 783322081
Web Site: https://www.hanshin-dw.co.jp
Year Founded: 1918
6018—(TKS)

THE HANSHIN DIESEL WORKS, LTD.

The Hanshin Diesel Works, Ltd.—(Continued)
Sales Range: $75-99.9 Million
Emp.: 285
Diesel Engine Mfr & Distr
N.A.I.C.S.: 333618
Kazuhiko Kinoshita (Pres)

Subsidiaries:

The Hanshin Diesel Works, Ltd. - Akashi Factory (1)
5-8-70 Kisaki, Akashi, 673-0037, Hyogo, Japan
Tel.: (81) 789233446
Diesel Engine Mfr
N.A.I.C.S.: 333618

The Hanshin Diesel Works, Ltd. - Harima Factory (1)
6-10 Niijima Harima-cho Kako-gun, Hyogo, 675-0155, Japan
Tel.: (81) 794412817
Diesel Engine Mfr
N.A.I.C.S.: 333618

The Hanshin Diesel Works, Ltd. - Tamatsu Factory (1)
3-12 Moritomo Nishi-ku, Kobe, 651-2132, Hyogo, Japan
Tel.: (81) 789271500
Industrial Mold Mfr
N.A.I.C.S.: 333511

THE HARDMAN GROUP LIMITED

1226 Hollis Street, Halifax, B3J 1T6, NS, Canada
Tel.: (902) 429-3743
Web Site:
https://www.hardmangroup.ca
Year Founded: 1965
Sales Range: $25-49.9 Million
Emp.: 100
Real Estate & Property Management Services
N.A.I.C.S.: 531390
Mike Rose (Mgr-Property)

Subsidiaries:

Hardman Group (1)
1633 Mountain Rd, Moncton, E1G 1A5, NB, Canada
Tel.: (506) 383-4242
Web Site: http://www.hardmangroup.ca
Sales Range: $50-74.9 Million
Emp.: 3
Real Estate & Property Management Services
N.A.I.C.S.: 531390

Hardman Group (1)
One Market Square, North Market Wharf, Saint John, E2L 4Z6, NB, Canada
Tel.: (506) 658-3600
Web Site: http://www.Marketsquaresj.com
Sales Range: $50-74.9 Million
Emp.: 8
Real Estate & Property Management Services
N.A.I.C.S.: 531390
Heather Peterson (Reg Mgr)

THE HARTCOURT COMPANIES, INC.

306 Yong Teng Plaza 1065 Wuzhong Road, Shanghai, 201103, China
Tel.: (86) 21 5208 0268
Web Site: http://www.hartcourt.com
Sales Range: $1-9.9 Million
Emp.: 40
Education Training Services
N.A.I.C.S.: 611430
Rachel Zhang (CFO)

THE HARTSTONE GROUP LIMITED

65 High Street, Heathrow Business Centre, Egham, TW20 9EY, Surrey, United Kingdom
Tel.: (44) 1494 787 700
Year Founded: 1985
Sales Range: $10-24.9 Million
Emp.: 85
Holding Company; Leathergoods & Related Products
N.A.I.C.S.: 551112
Tony Cheng (Exec Dir)

Subsidiaries:

Etienne Aigner, Inc. (1)
320 5th Ave, New York, NY 10001 (100%)
Tel.: (212) 334-1079
Web Site: http://www.etienneaigner.com
Rev.: $141,700,000
Emp.: 25
Leather Handbags, Shoes & Small Leather Goods Designer, Distr & Online Retailer
N.A.I.C.S.: 424990

THE HAVEN SDN. BHD.

Jalan Haven, 31150, Ipoh, Perak, Malaysia
Tel.: (60) 5 546 66666
Web Site:
http://www.thehavenresorts.com
Sales Range: $25-49.9 Million
Emp.: 100
Real Estate Development
N.A.I.C.S.: 531390
Peter Chan (CEO)

THE HEAVITREE BREWERY PLC

Trood Lane, Matford, Exeter, EX2 8YP, United Kingdom
Tel.: (44) 1392217733
Web Site:
https://www.heavitreebrewery.co.uk
HVTA—(AIM)
Rev.: $9,884,202
Assets: $27,864,488
Liabilities: $6,921,657
Net Worth: $20,942,831
Earnings: $2,670,635
Emp.: 16
Fiscal Year-end: 10/31/22
Pub Operator
N.A.I.C.S.: 722513
Terry Wheatley (Dir-Trade)

THE HELMHOLTZ ASSOCIATION

Ahrstrasse 45, 53175, Bonn, Germany
Tel.: (49) 228308180
Web Site: https://www.helmholtz.de
Year Founded: 1995
Biotechnology Research & Development Services
N.A.I.C.S.: 541714

THE HEMPSHIRE GROUP, INC.

150-6th Avenue Suite 5100, Calgary, T2P 3Y7, AB, Canada
Tel.: (403) 803-2150
HTE.P—(TSXV)
Assets: $385,003
Liabilities: $7,823
Net Worth: $377,180
Earnings: ($56,810)
Fiscal Year-end: 12/31/20
Business Consulting Services
N.A.I.C.S.: 522299

THE HENDERSON ALTERNATIVE STRATEGIES TRUST PLC

201 Bishopsgate, London, EC2M 3AE, United Kingdom
Tel.: (44) 2078181818
Web Site:
http://www.janushenderson.com
HAST—(LSE)
Rev.: $3,001,919
Assets: $152,979,743
Liabilities: $2,312,197
Net Worth: $150,667,546
Earnings: ($24,186,424)
Fiscal Year-end: 03/31/20
Investment Management Service
N.A.I.C.S.: 525990
James De Bunsen (Mgr-Fund)

THE HERJAVEC GROUP, INC.

180 Duncan Mill Road 7th Floor, Toronto, M3B 1Z6, ON, Canada
Tel.: (416) 639-2193
Web Site:
http://www.herjavecgroup.com
Year Founded: 2003
Sales Range: $100-124.9 Million
Emp.: 225
Information Technology Security Services
N.A.I.C.S.: 541511
Jennifer Ogle (CFO)

THE HILLCORE GROUP

161 Bay Street Suite 2430, Toronto, M5J 2S1, ON, Canada
Tel.: (416) 861-8711
Web Site: https://hillcoregroup.com
Emp.: 100
Investment Services
N.A.I.C.S.: 523999
Russell Negus (Chm)

Subsidiaries:

Thompson Bros. (Constr.) LP. (1)
411 South Ave, PO Box 4300, Spruce Grove, T7X 4G2, AB, Canada
Tel.: (780) 962-1030
Web Site: https://thompsoncg.ca
Emp.: 100
Construction Services
N.A.I.C.S.: 237990
Ian McKinley (Corp Controller)

THE HINDUSTAN HOUSING COMPANY LIMITED

Bajaj Bhavan 2nd floor 226 Jamnalal Bajaj Marg, Nariman Point, Mumbai, 400 021, Maharashtra, India
Tel.: (91) 2222023626
Web Site: https://www.hhclbajaj.com
Year Founded: 1934
509650—(BOM)
Rev.: $860,512
Assets: $5,051,999
Liabilities: $387,723
Net Worth: $4,664,277
Earnings: $230,742
Emp.: 14
Fiscal Year-end: 03/31/23
Residential Building Construction Services
N.A.I.C.S.: 236116
Vijay Bohra (CFO)

THE HIROSHIMA BANK, LTD.

3-8 Kamiya-cho, Naka-ku, Hiroshima, 730-0031, Japan
Tel.: (81) 825043823
Web Site: http://www.hirogin.co.jp
Year Founded: 1878
Rev.: $1,098,452,520
Assets: $81,111,199,260
Liabilities: $76,695,436,800
Net Worth: $4,415,762,460
Earnings: $231,763,860
Emp.: 3,500
Fiscal Year-end: 03/31/19
Banking Services
N.A.I.C.S.: 522110
Koji Ikeda (Chm)

Subsidiaries:

The Bank of Hiroshima (1)
33 8 Kamiya Cho 1 Chome Naka Ku, Hiroshima, 730 0031, Japan (100%)
Tel.: (81) 825043933
Sales Range: $1-4.9 Billion
Emp.: 4,000
Banking
N.A.I.C.S.: 522110
Tsuo Ota (Mgr-Fin)

THE HOKKOKU BANK, LTD.

2-12-6 Hirooka, Kanazawa, Ishikawa, Japan
Tel.: (81) 762631111
Web Site:
https://www.hokkokubank.co.jp
Year Founded: 1945
8363—(TKS)
Rev.: $765,668,640
Assets: $53,477,285,840
Liabilities: $50,706,201,920
Net Worth: $2,771,083,920
Earnings: $65,359,360
Emp.: 2,147
Fiscal Year-end: 03/31/21
Banking Services
N.A.I.C.S.: 522110
Hideaki Hamasaki (Chm)

Subsidiaries:

The Hokkoku Capital Co. Ltd. (1)
1-16 Musashi-machi, Kanazawa, 920-0855, Ishikawa, Japan
Tel.: (81) 762631333
Banking & Financial Services
N.A.I.C.S.: 523150

The Hokkoku Credit Service Co., Ltd. (1)
Hokkoku Building 7F 2-2-15 Katamachi, Kanazawa, 920-0981, Ishikawa, Japan
Tel.: (81) 762223322
Web Site: http://www.hokkokucard.co.jp
Credit Card Processing Services
N.A.I.C.S.: 522320

The Hokkoku General Lease Co., Ltd. (1)
2-2-15 Kata-machi, Kanazawa, 920-0981, Ishikawa, Japan
Tel.: (81) 762229311
Finance Leasing Services
N.A.I.C.S.: 522220

The Hokkoku Management, Ltd. (1)
2-12-6 Hirooka, Kanazawa, 920-0855, Ishikawa, Japan
Tel.: (81) 762239711
Web Site: http://www.h-management.co.jp
Venture Capital Funding Services
N.A.I.C.S.: 525910

THE HOLY LAND INSURANCE CO.

Beer el Sabe Str, PO Box 9130, Jabal Al Hussein, Amman, 11191, Jordan
Tel.: (962) 65668598
Web Site: http://www.holylandins.com
Year Founded: 1980
Direct Insurance Carrier Services
N.A.I.C.S.: 524126
Samer B. Al Modaffar (Vice Chm)

THE HONGKONG AND SHANGHAI HOTELS LIMITED

8th Floor St Georges Building 2 Ice House Street, Central, China (Hong Kong)
Tel.: (852) 28407788
Web Site: http://www.hshgroup.com
0045—(HKG)
Rev.: $535,245,000
Assets: $7,214,077,500
Liabilities: $2,608,777,500
Net Worth: $4,605,300,000
Earnings: ($61,837,500)
Emp.: 5,885
Fiscal Year-end: 12/31/22
Hotel Rental & Leasing Services
N.A.I.C.S.: 531120
Andrew Clifford Winawer Brandler (Deputy Chm)

Subsidiaries:

HSH Management Services Limited (1)
8/F St George's Building 2 Ice House Street, Central, China (Hong Kong)
Tel.: (852) 2 840 7788

Web Site: http://www.peninsula.com
Sales Range: $50-74.9 Million
Emp.: 200
Hotel & Club Management Services
N.A.I.C.S.: 561110

Manila Peninsula Hotel, Inc. (1)
Corner of Ayala and Makati Avenues,
Makati, 1226, Metro Manila, Philippines
Tel.: (63) 28 887 2888
Web Site: https://www.peninsula.com
Sales Range: $100-124.9 Million
Emp.: 650
Home Management Services
N.A.I.C.S.: 721110
Mariano Garchitorena (Dir-PR)

Peak Tramways Company, Limited (1)
Peak Tram Lower Terminus 33 Garden Road, Central, China (Hong Kong)
Tel.: (852) 25220922
Web Site: https://www.thepeak.hk
Sales Range: $25-49.9 Million
Emp.: 70
Tramway Operation Services
N.A.I.C.S.: 487990

Subsidiary (Domestic):

The Peak Tower Limited (2)
Peak Tram Lower Terminus 33 Garden Road, Hong Kong, China (Hong Kong)
Tel.: (852) 28490668
Web Site: https://www.thepeak.hk
Sales Range: $50-74.9 Million
Emp.: 90
Shopping Mall Management Services
N.A.I.C.S.: 531120

Peninsula Chicago LLC (1)
108 E Superior St, Chicago, IL 60611-2508
Tel.: (312) 337-2888
Web Site: https://www.peninsula.com
Sales Range: $50-74.9 Million
Emp.: 400
Home Management Services
N.A.I.C.S.: 721110
Maria Zec (VP & Gen Mgr)

Peninsula Clubs and Consultancy Services Limited (1)
8 F St George's Building 2 Ice House Street, Central, China (Hong Kong)
Tel.: (852) 28407788
Web Site: http://www.hfhgroup.com
Emp.: 200
Airport Lounge & Club Management Services
N.A.I.C.S.: 713910
Martyn Fawyer (Gen Mgr)

Peninsula Merchandising Limited (1)
4/F The Peninsula Office Tower 18 Middle Road, Tsim Sha Tsui, Kowloon, China (Hong Kong)
Tel.: (852) 21936901
Web Site: http://www.peninsulahongkong.com
Branded Merchandise Whslr & Retailer
N.A.I.C.S.: 423990

Peninsula of New York, Inc. (1)
700 5th Ave 55th St, New York, NY 10019
Tel.: (212) 956-2888
Web Site: https://www.peninsula.com
Home Management Services
N.A.I.C.S.: 721110
Jonathon Crook (Gen Mgr)

Peninsula of Tokyo Limited (1)
1-8-1 Yurakucho, Chiyoda-ku, Tokyo, 100-0006, Japan
Tel.: (81) 36 270 2888
Web Site: http://www.peninsula.com
Sales Range: $100-124.9 Million
Emp.: 600
Home Management Services
N.A.I.C.S.: 721110
Noriko Murata (Mgr-Guest Rels)

Quail Lodge, Inc. (1)
8205 Valley Greens Dr, Carmel, CA 93923
Tel.: (831) 624-2888
Web Site: http://www.quaillodge.com
Golf Club & Restaurant Operation Services
N.A.I.C.S.: 713910

St. Johns Building Limited (1)
33 Garden Road, Central, China (Hong Kong)
Tel.: (852) 28497654
Office Space Rental Services
N.A.I.C.S.: 531120

Tai Pan Laundry & Dry Cleaning Services, Limited (1)
Unit 2 1/F Block B Po Yip Building 62 - 70 Texaco Road, Tsuen Wan, New Territories, China (Hong Kong)
Tel.: (852) 26122008
Emp.: 170
Laundry & Dry Cleaning Services
N.A.I.C.S.: 812320

The Peninsula Hotel Limited (1)
5/F The Peninsula Hong Kong Salisbury Road, Kowloon, China (Hong Kong)
Tel.: (852) 2 920 2888
Web Site: https://www.peninsula.com
Sales Range: $100-124.9 Million
Emp.: 800
Home Management Services
N.A.I.C.S.: 721110

The Repulse Bay Company, Limited (1)
109 Repulse Bay Road, Hong Kong, China (Hong Kong)
Tel.: (852) 2 292 2888
Web Site: https://www.therepulsebay.com
Property Rental Services
N.A.I.C.S.: 531110

THE HOUR GLASS LIMITED
302 Orchard Road Tong Building 11-01, Singapore, 238862, Singapore
Tel.: (65) 67872288
Web Site: https://www.thehourglass.com
AGS—(SES)
Rev.: $832,660,752
Assets: $782,986,184
Liabilities: $198,882,906
Net Worth: $584,103,278
Earnings: $129,180,423
Fiscal Year-end: 03/31/23
Luxury Watch Retailer
N.A.I.C.S.: 423940
Siak Yong Ng (CFO & Chief Admin Officer)

Subsidiaries:

Glajz-THG Pte Ltd (1)
391 Orchard Road 21-04 Ngee Ann City Tower B, Singapore, 238874, Singapore
Tel.: (65) 67342033
Watches & Jewelry Retailer
N.A.I.C.S.: 458310

The Hour Glass (Australia) Pty Ltd (1)
Level 6 70 Castlereagh St, Sydney, 2000, NSW, Australia
Tel.: (61) 292327775
Web Site: https://www.thehourglass.com
Watches & Jewelry Whslr
N.A.I.C.S.: 423940

The Hour Glass (Thailand) Co Ltd (1)
989 Siam Tower 19th Floor Unit A Rama 1 Road, Pathumwan, Bangkok, 10330, Thailand
Tel.: (66) 26580599
Watch & Jewelry Distr
N.A.I.C.S.: 423940
Kanitta Saisuk (Gen Mgr)

The Hour Glass Holding (Thailand) Co Ltd (1)
989 Siam Tower 19th Floor Unit A Rama 1 Road, Pathumwan, Bangkok, 10330, Thailand
Tel.: (66) 26580599
Sales Range: $50-74.9 Million
Emp.: 100
Investment Management Service
N.A.I.C.S.: 523999

The Hour Glass Japan Ltd. (1)
Royal Crystal Ginza 1F 5-4-6 Ginza, Chuo-ku, Tokyo, 104-0061, Japan
Tel.: (81) 355377888
Web Site: http://www.thehourglass.co.jp
Sales Range: $25-49.9 Million
Emp.: 10
Watches & Jewelry Retailer
N.A.I.C.S.: 458310
Atsushi Momoi (Pres)

The Hour Glass Sdn Bhd (1)
Wisma UOA II 21 Jalan Pinang Suite 10-2 10th Floor, 50450, Kuala Lumpur, Malaysia
Tel.: (60) 321613228
Web Site: https://www.thehourglass.com
Sales Range: $25-49.9 Million
Emp.: 50
Watches & Jewelry Distr
N.A.I.C.S.: 423940
S. K. Teh (Gen Mgr)

Watches of Switzerland Pte. Ltd. (1)
290 Orchard Road 01-19 to 20, Singapore, 238865, Singapore
Tel.: (65) 67329793
Watch & Jewellery Product Distr
N.A.I.C.S.: 423940

THE HOUSE OF AGRICULTURE SPIROY S.A.
Marconi 5, 122 42, Egaleo, Greece
Tel.: (30) 2103497500
Web Site: https://www.spirou.gr
Year Founded: 1987
SPIR—(ATH)
Sales Range: Less than $1 Million
Emp.: 145
Planting Seeds Production & Distribution
N.A.I.C.S.: 111191
Christos Georgiou Evangelos (VP)

Subsidiaries:

THE HOUSE OF AGRICULTURE SPIROY S.A. - SEEDLING PRODUCTION UNIT (1)
Vateri, Thebes, 32200, Greece
Tel.: (30) 22620 80603
Oilseed Production Services
N.A.I.C.S.: 111191

THE HOUSING BANK FOR TRADE & FINANCE
Prince Shaker Bin Zaid Street, PO Box 7693, Amman, 11118, Jordan
Tel.: (962) 65005555
Web Site: https://hbtf.com
Year Founded: 1973
THBK—(AMM)
Rev.: $573,246,150
Assets: $11,715,184,058
Liabilities: $10,076,453,754
Net Worth: $1,638,730,304
Earnings: $59,952,521
Emp.: 3,913
Fiscal Year-end: 12/31/20
Banking Services
N.A.I.C.S.: 522110
Ammar Al-Safadi (CEO)

Subsidiaries:

Jordan and Palestine Financial Investment Co. (1)
Farah Bldg 2nd Fl, Rukab Cir, Ramallah, 972, Palestine
Tel.: (970) 22987778
Web Site: http://www.tjps.ps
General Financial Services
N.A.I.C.S.: 522220

Specialized Lease Finance Co. (1)
Saad Bin Abi Wakkas St, Um Uthaina, Amman, 11118, Jordan
Tel.: (962) 65521230
Web Site: http://www.hbtf.com.jo
Sales Range: $50-74.9 Million
Emp.: 20
Financial Lending Services
N.A.I.C.S.: 532490
Amjad Sayeh (Gen Mgr)

THE HOUSING FINANCE CORPORATION LIMITED
3rd Floor 17 St Swithin's Lane, London, EC4N 8AL, United Kingdom
Tel.: (44) 2073379920
Web Site: http://www.thfcorp.com
Rev.: $341,176,027
Assets: $9,462,818,184
Liabilities: $9,414,469,791
Net Worth: $48,348,393
Earnings: $5,961,856
Emp.: 27
Fiscal Year-end: 03/31/19
Housing Finance Services
N.A.I.C.S.: 522310
Colin Burke (Sec & Dir-Fin)

THE HOYTS CORPORATION PTY LTD.
PO Box 110, Sydney, 2001, NSW, Australia
Tel.: (61) 2 8071 6100
Web Site: http://www.hoyts.com.au
Emp.: 3,000
Movie Theater Owner & Operator
N.A.I.C.S.: 512131
Damian Keogh (CEO)

THE HUB POWER COMPANY LIMITED
9th Floor Ocean Tower G3 Block9 Main Clifton Road, PO Box 13841, Karachi, 75600, Pakistan
Tel.: (92) 2135874677 PK
Web Site: https://www.hubpower.com
HUBC—(PSX)
Rev.: $411,061,753
Assets: $1,459,023,720
Liabilities: $890,488,145
Net Worth: $568,535,575
Earnings: $223,070,945
Emp.: 281
Fiscal Year-end: 06/30/23
Power Company
N.A.I.C.S.: 335311
Hussain Dawood (Chm)

Subsidiaries:

Laraib Energy Limited (1)
Office 12 Second Floor Executive Complex G-8 Markaz, Islamabad, 9251, Pakistan
Tel.: (92) 5122554312
Web Site: https://www.laraibenergy.com
Emp.: 35
Hydroelectric Power Generation Services
N.A.I.C.S.: 221111

THE HYAKUGO BANK, LTD.
21-27 Iwata, Tsu, 514-8666, Mie, Japan
Tel.: (81) 592272151
Web Site: https://www.hyakugo.co.jp
Year Founded: 1878
8368—(NGO)
Rev.: $738,036,780
Assets: $53,902,833,930
Liabilities: $51,091,942,980
Net Worth: $2,810,890,950
Earnings: $103,914,810
Emp.: 2,280
Fiscal Year-end: 03/31/23
Banking Services
N.A.I.C.S.: 522110
Tsuyoshi Ueda (Chm)

THE HYAKUJUSHI BANK, LTD.
5-1 Kamei-cho, Takamatsu, 760-8574, Kagawa, Japan
Tel.: (81) 878310114 JP
Web Site: https://www.114bank.co.jp
Year Founded: 1878
8386—(TKS)
Rev.: $542,985,060
Assets: $38,606,696,500
Liabilities: $36,430,777,040
Net Worth: $2,175,919,460
Earnings: $363,550
Emp.: 1,963
Fiscal Year-end: 03/31/24
Banking Services
N.A.I.C.S.: 522110
Ryuji Nishikawa (Sr Mng Exec Officer)

THE HYAKUJUSHI BANK, LTD.

The Hyakujushi Bank, Ltd.—(Continued)
Subsidiaries:

Hyakujushi DC Card, K.K. (1)
11-5 Ichida Tamachi Building, Central City 7, Takamatsu, 760 0053, Japan
Tel.: (81) 878314114
Web Site: http://www.114dc.co.jp
Emp.: 36
Nondepository Credit Intermediation
N.A.I.C.S.: 522299

Hyakujushi Ginko Kenko Hoken Kumiai K.K. (1)
5-1 Kameicho, Kagawa, Japan
Tel.: (81) 878362712
Health & Welfare Funds
N.A.I.C.S.: 525120

Hyakujushi Jinzai Center, K.K. (1)
Central 2nd Building 6F 8-1 Shioyamachi, Takamatsu, 760-0047, Japan
Tel.: (81) 878211100
Web Site: http://www.114jinzai.co.jp
Help Supply Services
N.A.I.C.S.: 561320

Hyakujushi Sogo Hosho K.K. (1)
8-1 Shioyamachi, Kagawa, 760-0047, Japan
Tel.: (81) 878229114
Sales Range: $50-74.9 Million
Emp.: 25
Nondepository Credit Intermediation
N.A.I.C.S.: 522299
Hideto Hirose *(Gen Mgr)*

THE IBN SINA PHARMACEUTICAL INDUSTRY LTD.
Tanin Center 3 Asad Gate Mirpur Road Mohammadpur, Dhaka, 1207, Bangladesh
Tel.: (880) 4102215058
Web Site:
  https://www.ibnsinapharma.com
IBNSINA—(DHA)
Rev.: $83,237,538
Assets: $45,658,496
Liabilities: $17,784,592
Net Worth: $27,873,905
Earnings: $5,525,939
Emp.: 4,000
Fiscal Year-end: 06/30/23
Health Care Srvices
N.A.I.C.S.: 621491
Shah Abdul Hannan *(Chm)*

THE IMAGINATION GROUP LIMITED
25 Store Street South Crescent, London, WC1E 7BL, United Kingdom
Tel.: (44) 207 323 3300
Web Site:
  http://www.imagination.com
Year Founded: 1978
Sales Range: $50-74.9 Million
Emp.: 300
Advertising & Creativity Services
N.A.I.C.S.: 541810
Justin Baird *(Head-Tech-APAC)*
Subsidiaries:

Imagination (Asia) Ltd. (1)
32/F Cambridge House Taikoo Place Island East, 979 King's Road, Hong Kong, China (Hong Kong)
Tel.: (852) 3513 1300
Web Site: http://www.imagination.com
Emp.: 40
Advertising Agencies
N.A.I.C.S.: 541810
Sherly Chan *(Gen Mgr)*

Imagination (Deutschland) GmbH (1)
Im Mediapark 8, 50670, Cologne, Germany
Tel.: (49) 22155405090
Web Site: http://www.imagination.com
Sales Range: $10-24.9 Million
Emp.: 9
Advertising Agencies
N.A.I.C.S.: 541810
Anton Christodoulou *(CTO-EMEA)*

Imagination (Scandinavia) AB (1)
Gotgatan 48 1st Fl, SE-118 26, Stockholm, Sweden
Tel.: (46) 8 442 1848
Emp.: 1
Advertising Agencies
N.A.I.C.S.: 541810

Imagination (USA) Inc. - Detroit (1)
1537 Monroe St Ste 100, Dearborn, MI 48124
Tel.: (313) 565-0200
Emp.: 28
Advertising Agencies
N.A.I.C.S.: 541810

Imagination (USA) Inc. - Los Angeles (1)
1720 N Vista St, Los Angeles, CA 90046
Tel.: (323) 822-6404
Advertising Agencies
N.A.I.C.S.: 541810

Imagination (USA) Inc. - New York (1)
155 Franklin St, New York, NY 10013
Tel.: (212) 813-6400
Sales Range: $25-49.9 Million
Emp.: 30
Advertising Agencies
N.A.I.C.S.: 541810

Imagination Australia Pty Limited (1)
Ste 36 Jones Bay Wharf, 26 32 Pirrama Rd, Pyrmont, 2009, NSW, Australia
Tel.: (61) 2 8572 8700
Emp.: 22
Advertising Agencies
N.A.I.C.S.: 541810
Adrian Goldthorp *(Sr Dir-Art)*

THE IMAMURA SECURITIES CO., LTD.
25 Jitsukenmachi, Kanazawa, 920-0906, Japan
Tel.: (81) 762635111
Web Site: https://www.imamura.co.jp 7175—(TKS)
Sales Range: $25-49.9 Million
Emp.: 170
Securities Brokerage
N.A.I.C.S.: 523150
Kuji Imamura *(Pres)*

THE INCE GROUP PLC
Aldgate Tower 2 Leman Street, London, E1 8QN, United Kingdom
Tel.: (44) 207 492 0000 UK
Web Site:
  http://www.theincegroup.com
INCE—(LSE)
Rev.: $1,160,851
Assets: $200,161,871
Liabilities: $142,127,487
Net Worth: $58,034,384
Earnings: $471,129
Emp.: 701
Fiscal Year-end: 03/31/21
Holding Company; Recruitment & Management Services
N.A.I.C.S.: 551112
Adrian Biles *(CEO)*
Subsidiaries:

CW Energy LLP (1)
4th Floor 40 Queen Street, London, EC4R 1DD, United Kingdom
Tel.: (44) 207 936 8300
Web Site: https://www.cwenergy.co.uk
Tax Consulting Services
N.A.I.C.S.: 541213
Phil Greatrex *(Partner)*

Hanover Financial Management Limited (1)
Michaelston Road, Llanmaes St Fagans, Cardiff, CF5 6DU, United Kingdom
Tel.: (44) 292 067 5204
Finance Management Services
N.A.I.C.S.: 541611

Hanover Pensions Limited (1)
Aldgate Tower 2 Leman Street, London, E1 8QN, United Kingdom

Tel.: (44) 207 588 8406
Web Site: https://www.hanover-pensions.co.uk
Finance Management Consulting Services
N.A.I.C.S.: 541611
Robert Young *(Partner)*

Ince & Co Middle East LLP (1)
The Maze Tower 10th Floor Sheikh Zayed Road, PO Box 123004, Dubai, United Arab Emirates
Tel.: (971) 4 307 6000
Law firm
N.A.I.C.S.: 541199
Alastair Holland *(Mng Dir)*

Ince (Gibraltar) Limited (1)
6 20 World Trade Center 6 Bayside Road, Gibraltar, GX11 1AA, Gibraltar
Tel.: (350) 2 006 8450
Law firm
N.A.I.C.S.: 541199
Peter Howitt *(Partner & Mng Dir)*

Ince Consultancy Cyprus Limited (1)
Euro House 1st Floor 82 Spyrou Kyprianou Street, 4042, Limassol, Cyprus
Tel.: (357) 2 209 0102
Professional Services
N.A.I.C.S.: 541990
George Zambartas *(Partner & Head)*

Ince Consultancy UG (1)
Grosse Elbstrasse 47, 22767, Hamburg, Germany
Tel.: (49) 4018 063 2670
Web Site: https://www.inceconsult.com
Consultancy Services
N.A.I.C.S.: 541611
Alexander Janes *(Partner & Mng Dir)*

Ince Consulting Middle East Limited (1)
Al Maqam Tower Office No 3525 ADGM Square Al Maryah Island, PO Box 35665, Abu Dhabi, United Arab Emirates
Tel.: (971) 2 418 7581
Professional Services
N.A.I.C.S.: 541990
Knut Mathiassen *(Mng Dir)*

Ince Germany Rechtsanwaltsgesellschaft mbH (1)
Grosse Elbstrasse 47, 22767, Hamburg, Germany
Tel.: (49) 4 038 0860
Law firm
N.A.I.C.S.: 541199
Jan Hungar *(Mng Dir)*

Ince Gordon Dadds LLP (1)
Aldgate Tower 2 Leman St, London, E1 8QN, United Kingdom
Tel.: (44) 20 7481 0010
Web Site: http://www.incegdlaw.com
Law firm
N.A.I.C.S.: 541110
Jonas Adolfsson *(Partner)*

Incisive Law LLC (1)
5 Shenton Way 19-01 UIC Building, Singapore, 068808, Singapore
Tel.: (65) 6 538 6660
Law firm
N.A.I.C.S.: 541199
Bill Ricquier *(Mng Dir)*

e.Legal Technology Solutions Limited (1)
East Suite Acorn House, Flackwell Heath, High Wycombe, HP10 9LS, Buckinghamshire, United Kingdom
Tel.: (44) 162 853 5570
Web Site:
  https://www.elegaltechnology.co.uk
Information Technology Services
N.A.I.C.S.: 541511

THE INCOME & GROWTH VCT PLC
5 New Street Square, London, EC4A 3TW, United Kingdom
Tel.: (44) 2079253300
Year Founded: 2000
IGV—(LSE)
Rev.: $61,751,655
Assets: $163,149,525
Liabilities: $1,842,120

INTERNATIONAL PUBLIC

Net Worth: $161,307,405
Earnings: $56,699,370
Fiscal Year-end: 09/30/21
Asset Management Services
N.A.I.C.S.: 523940
Maurice Helfgott *(Dir)*

THE INDEPENDENT ORDER OF FORESTERS
789 Don Mills Rd, Toronto, M3C 1T9, ON, Canada
Web Site: http://www.foresters.com
Year Founded: 1874
Rev.: $1,659,034,198
Assets: $14,172,565,436
Liabilities: $12,576,248,012
Net Worth: $1,596,317,423
Earnings: $70,975,245
Fiscal Year-end: 12/31/19
Fraternal Benefit Organization; Life Insurance, Financial, Retirement & Investment Products & Services
N.A.I.C.S.: 813410
Robert E. Lamoureux *(Chm)*
Subsidiaries:

Forester Holdings (Europe) Limited (1)
Foresters House Cromwell Avenue, Bromley, BR2 9BF, United Kingdom
Tel.: (44) 20 8628 3400
Web Site: http://www.foresters.co.uk
Emp.: 250
Holding Company
N.A.I.C.S.: 551112

Foresters Equity Services, Inc. (1)
6640 Lusk Blvd Ste A-202, San Diego, CA 92121 (100%)
Tel.: (858) 550-4844
Web Site: http://www.forestersequity.com
Sales Range: $50-74.9 Million
Emp.: 15
Investment Banking & Securities Dealing
N.A.I.C.S.: 523150

THE INDIA CEMENTS LIMITED
Coromandel Towers 93 Santhom High Road Karpagam Avenue R A Puram, Chennai, 600028, India
Tel.: (91) 442 852 1526
Web Site:
  http://www.indiacements.co.in
530005—(NSE)
Rev.: $621,211,459
Assets: $1,513,777,929
Liabilities: $725,861,341
Net Worth: $787,916,589
Earnings: $28,223,327
Emp.: 2,036
Fiscal Year-end: 03/31/21
Cement Manufacturing
N.A.I.C.S.: 327310
N. Srinivasan *(Vice Chm & Mng Dir)*
Subsidiaries:

Coromandel Travels Limited (1)
D No 27-23-28 Usha Estates Gopal Reddy Road, Vijayawada, 520 002, AP, India
Tel.: (91) 8662573668
Web Site: https://coromandeltravels.info
Travel Agency Services
N.A.I.C.S.: 561510

India Cements Capital Limited (1)
827 III Floor DHUN Building Anna Salai, Chennai, 600002, India
Tel.: (91) 4428572600
Web Site: https://www.iccaps.co.in
Rev.: $328,569
Assets: $8,644,313
Liabilities: $6,556,423
Net Worth: $2,087,890
Earnings: $(37,210)
Emp.: 61
Fiscal Year-end: 03/31/2021
Cement Mfr
N.A.I.C.S.: 327310
K. Suresh *(Pres, CEO & CFO)*

The India Cements Limited - Chilamkur Plant (1)

Chilamkur, Cuddapah Dist, Yerraguntla, 516310, Andhra Pradesh, India
Tel.: (91) 8563276150
Cement Mfr
N.A.I.C.S.: 327310

The India Cements Limited - Dalavoi Plant (1)
Dalavoi PO, Perambalur, 621 709, Tamil Nadu, India
Tel.: (91) 4329248201
Cement Mfr
N.A.I.C.S.: 327310

The India Cements Limited - Vishnupuram Plant (1)
Vishnupuram, Wadapally, Nalgonda, 508355, India
Tel.: (91) 8689228427
8689 228447
N.A.I.C.S.: 327310

The India Cements Limited - Yerraguntla Plant (1)
Yerraguntla, Cuddapah Dist, Yerraguntla, 516309, Andhra Pradesh, India
Tel.: (91) 8563275158
Cement Mfr
N.A.I.C.S.: 327310
M. B. K. Subramaniam *(Mgr-Mktg)*

Visaka Cement Industry Limited (1)
White House Block 3B 3rd Fl Kundanbagh, Begumpet, Hyderabad, 500016, Andhra Pradesh, India
Tel.: (91) 4023417317
Sales Range: $25-49.9 Million
Emp.: 60
Cement Mfr
N.A.I.C.S.: 327310
Rakesh Singh *(Pres-Mktg)*

THE INDIAN CARD CLOTHING COMPANY LIMITED
Katariya Capital A-19 Vidyut Nagar Society Lane No 5, Koregaon Park, Pune, 411001, India
Tel.: (91) 2026151618
Web Site: https://www.cardindia.com
509692—(BOM)
Rev.: $7,899,064
Assets: $15,619,968
Liabilities: $5,150,213
Net Worth: $10,469,755
Earnings: ($333,551)
Emp.: 221
Fiscal Year-end: 03/31/21
Card Clothing Mfr
N.A.I.C.S.: 339999
Prashant K. Trivedi *(Chm)*

THE INDIAN LINK CHAIN MANUFACTURES LIMITED
Sonawala Building 2nd Floor 59 Mumbai Samachar Marg, Mumbai, 400023, India
Tel.: (91) 2222661013
Web Site: https://www.inlinch.com
Year Founded: 1958
504746—(BOM)
Rev.: $70,581
Assets: $622,762
Liabilities: $69,944
Net Worth: $552,819
Earnings: ($52,941)
Emp.: 1
Fiscal Year-end: 03/31/21
Chain Product Mfr
N.A.I.C.S.: 332999
P. K. Nevatia *(Mng Dir)*

THE INDIAN WOOD PRODUCTS CO. LTD.
9 Brabourne Road 7th Floor, Kolkata, 700001, India
Tel.: (91) 8232023820
Web Site: https://www.iwpkatha.com
Year Founded: 1919
540954—(BOM)
Rev.: $22,024,303
Assets: $63,577,232
Liabilities: $21,279,899
Net Worth: $42,297,332
Earnings: $220,167
Emp.: 301
Fiscal Year-end: 03/31/23
Wood Products Mfr
N.A.I.C.S.: 321219
K. K. Mohta *(Chm & Mng Dir)*

THE INDUSTRIAL & PRUDENTIAL INVESTMENT COMPANY LIMITED
Paharpur House 8/1/B Diamond Harbour Road, Kolkata, 700027, West Bengal, India
Tel.: (91) 3340133000
Web Site: https://www.industrialprudential.com
501298—(BOM)
Rev.: $1,086,485
Assets: $54,924,570
Liabilities: $10,805,408
Net Worth: $44,119,161
Earnings: $414,810
Emp.: 1
Fiscal Year-end: 03/31/20
Investment Management Service
N.A.I.C.S.: 523999
Gaurav Swarup *(Chm & Mng Dir)*

THE INDUSTRIAL COMMERCIAL & AGRICULTURAL CO. LTD.
PO Box 6066, Amman, 11118, Jordan
Tel.: (962) 65533201
Web Site: https://www.ica-jo.com
Year Founded: 1961
ICAG—(AMM)
Rev.: $29,190,820
Assets: $44,447,942
Liabilities: $16,623,987
Net Worth: $27,823,954
Earnings: $1,250,654
Emp.: 194
Fiscal Year-end: 12/31/20
Chemical Products Mfr
N.A.I.C.S.: 325998
Noor Mahaini *(Gen Mgr)*

Subsidiaries:

Intaj Marketing & Distribution Co. Ltd. (1)
PO Box 6606, Amman, 11118, Jordan
Tel.: (962) 65533201
Soap & Other Detergent Mfr
N.A.I.C.S.: 325611

THE INGENIUM GROUP INC.
175 Bloor Street East North Tower 15th Floor, Toronto, M4W 3R8, ON, Canada
Tel.: (416) 675-5950
Web Site: http://www.theingeniumgroup.com
Year Founded: 1938
Sales Range: $125-149.9 Million
Architectural & Engineering Services
N.A.I.C.S.: 541310
Victor Smith *(CEO)*

Subsidiaries:

Archial NORR Limited (1)
Tennyson House 159-165 Great Portland Street, London, W1W 5PA, United Kingdom
Tel.: (44) 20 7580 0400
Architectural Engineering Services
N.A.I.C.S.: 541330
Chris Littlemore *(CEO)*

DESIGN & CONSTRUCTION GIFFELS QUEBEC INC. (1)
4333 St Catherine Street West Suite 250, Westmount, H3Z 1P9, QC, Canada
Tel.: (514) 931-1001
Construction Engineering Services
N.A.I.C.S.: 541330

Ingenium Archial Ltd. (1)
Tennyson House 159-165 Great Portland Street, London, W1W 5PA, United Kingdom
Tel.: (44) 2075800400
Web Site: http://www.archialgroup.com
Sales Range: $50-74.9 Million
Emp.: 457
Architectural Services
N.A.I.C.S.: 541310
Victor Smith *(Chm)*

NORR Architects & Engineers (Pvt.) Ltd. (1)
S-327 Greater Kailash-II, New Delhi, 110048, India
Tel.: (91) 11 4163 9294
Architectural Engineering Services
N.A.I.C.S.: 541330

NORR Asia Limited (1)
Rm 1604 16/F Kai Wong Commercial Building 222 Queen's Road, Central, China (Hong Kong)
Tel.: (852) 25422928
Architectural Engineering Services
N.A.I.C.S.: 541330

NORR Group Consultants International Limited (1)
PO Box 53150, City Tower 2 21st Floor, Dubai, United Arab Emirates
Tel.: (971) 4 354 4439
Architectural Engineering Services
N.A.I.C.S.: 541330
Thomas Wieczorek *(Sr Project Mgr)*

NORR Illinois Inc. (1)
325 N La Salle Ste 500, Chicago, IL 60654
Tel.: (312) 424-2400
Emp.: 60
Architectural Engineering Services
N.A.I.C.S.: 541330
Rachel Turner-Lauck *(Mgr-Ops)*

NORR Limited (1)
175 Bloor Street East North Tower 15th Floor, Toronto, M4W 3R8, ON, Canada
Tel.: (416) 929-0200
Web Site: https://www.norr.com
Architectural Engineering Services
N.A.I.C.S.: 541330
Michele Cohen *(Principal)*

NORR, LLC (1)
1001 G St NW Ste 800, Washington, DC 20001
Tel.: (202) 627-6870
Architectural Engineering Services
N.A.I.C.S.: 541330

WESTPRO INFRASTRUCTURE LTD. (1)
8241-129th Street Suite 710, Surrey, V3W 0A6, BC, Canada
Tel.: (604) 592-9767
Architectural Engineering Services
N.A.I.C.S.: 541330
Bryan Buis *(Sr Project Mgr)*

THE INLAND GROUP
2482 Douglas Road, Burnaby, V5C 6C9, BC, Canada
Tel.: (604) 291-6021
Web Site: http://www.inland-group.com
Emp.: 400
Holding Company
N.A.I.C.S.: 551112
Leigh N. Parker *(Chm)*

Subsidiaries:

Inland Kenworth Inc - Albuquerque Facility (1)
7711 Fortuna Rd NW, Albuquerque, NM 87121
Tel.: (505) 884-0300
Truck Repair Services
N.A.I.C.S.: 811310
Mario DeLaCruz *(Mgr-Parts)*

Inland Kenworth Inc - Burnaby Facility (1)
5550 Goring Street, Burnaby, V5B 3A4, BC, Canada
Tel.: (604) 291-6431
Truck Repair Services
N.A.I.C.S.: 811310
Bill Morrison *(Branch Mgr)*

Inland Kenworth Inc - Campbell River Facility (1)
2900 North Island Hwy, Campbell River, V9W 2H5, BC, Canada
Tel.: (250) 287-8878
Truck Repair Services
N.A.I.C.S.: 811310
Falko Heuser *(Branch Mgr)*

Inland Kenworth Inc - Carson Facility (1)
1202 E Carson St, Carson, CA 90745
Tel.: (310) 984-3430
Truck Repair Services
N.A.I.C.S.: 811310
Rob Vaughn *(Branch Mgr)*

Inland Kenworth Inc - Cranbrook Facility (1)
816 Industrial Road 1, Cranbrook, V1C 4C6, BC, Canada
Tel.: (250) 426-6205
Truck Repair Services
N.A.I.C.S.: 811310
Dale Felhauer *(Branch Mgr)*

Inland Kenworth Inc - El Cajon Facility (1)
500 N Johnson Ave, El Cajon, CA 92020
Tel.: (619) 328-1600
Truck Repair Services
N.A.I.C.S.: 811310
Kevin Nyberg *(Branch Mgr)*

Inland Kenworth Inc - Farmington Facility (1)
3924 Bloomfield Hwy, Farmington, NM 87401
Tel.: (505) 327-0200
Truck Repair Services
N.A.I.C.S.: 811310
Frank DiBenedetti *(Branch Mgr)*

Inland Kenworth Inc - Fontana Facility (1)
9730 Cherry Ave, Fontana, CA 92335
Tel.: (909) 823-9955
Truck Repair Services
N.A.I.C.S.: 811310
Joey Noriega *(Branch Mgr)*

Inland Kenworth Inc - Fort St John Facility (1)
10611 Finning Frontage Rd, Fort Saint John, V1J 4H8, BC, Canada
Tel.: (250) 785-6105
Truck Repair Services
N.A.I.C.S.: 811310
Gary Paulson *(Mgr-Parts)*

Inland Kenworth Inc - Kamloops Facility (1)
2505 West Trans-Canada Hwy, Kamloops, V1S 1Z4, BC, Canada
Tel.: (250) 374-4406
Truck Repair Services
N.A.I.C.S.: 811310
Greg Negus *(Branch Mgr)*

Inland Kenworth Inc - Kelowna Facility (1)
2485 Ross Road, West Kelowna, V1Z 1M2, BC, Canada
Tel.: (250) 769-2933
Truck Repair Services
N.A.I.C.S.: 811310
Aaron Sanders *(Mgr-Ops)*

Inland Kenworth Inc - Langley Facility (1)
26770 Gloucester Way, Langley, V4W 3V6, BC, Canada
Tel.: (604) 607-0300
Truck Repair Services
N.A.I.C.S.: 811310
Zachary Bourn *(Branch Mgr)*

Inland Kenworth Inc - Nanaimo Facility (1)
2365 Northfield Road, Nanaimo, V9S 3C3, BC, Canada
Tel.: (250) 758-5288
Truck Repair Services
N.A.I.C.S.: 811310
Steve Touhey *(Branch Mgr)*

Inland Kenworth Inc - Penticton Facility (1)
1690 Fairview Road, Penticton, V2A 6A8,

THE INLAND GROUP

The Inland Group—(Continued)
BC, Canada
Tel.: (250) 492-3939
Truck Repair Services
N.A.I.C.S.: 811310
Rick Datoff *(Branch Mgr)*

Inland Kenworth Inc - Phoenix Facility (1)
1021 N 59th Ave, Phoenix, AZ 85043
Tel.: (602) 258-7791
Truck Repair Services
N.A.I.C.S.: 811310
David Donahue *(Branch Mgr)*

Inland Kenworth Inc - Prince George Facility (1)
7337 Boundary Ave, Prince George, V2N 6C9, BC, Canada
Tel.: (250) 562-8171
Truck Repair Services
N.A.I.C.S.: 811310
Rick Bruneski *(Branch Mgr)*

Inland Kenworth Inc - Quesnel Facility (1)
3150 Highway 97 North, Quesnel, V2J 5Y9, BC, Canada
Tel.: (250) 992-7256
Truck Repair Services
N.A.I.C.S.: 811310
Ken Taylor *(Branch Mgr)*

Inland Kenworth Inc - Tucson Facility (1)
3737 N I-10 EB Frontage Rd, Tucson, AZ 85705
Tel.: (520) 888-0028
Truck Repair Services
N.A.I.C.S.: 811310
Steve Brent *(Branch Mgr)*

Inland Kenworth Inc - Vernon Facility (1)
1051 Middleton Way, Vernon, V1B 2N3, BC, Canada
Tel.: (250) 545-4424
Truck Repair Services
N.A.I.C.S.: 811310
Larry Cormier *(Branch Mgr)*

Inland Kenworth Inc - Whitehorse Facility (1)
227 Range Road, Whitehorse, Y1A 3E5, YT, Canada
Tel.: (867) 668-2127
Truck Repair Services
N.A.I.C.S.: 811310
Trevor Matthews *(Branch Mgr)*

Inland Kenworth Inc - Williams Lake Facility (1)
1560 Broadway Avenue South, Williams Lake, V2G 2X3, BC, Canada
Tel.: (250) 392-7101
Truck Repair Services
N.A.I.C.S.: 811310
Andre Bosecker *(Branch Mgr)*

Inland Kenworth Inc. (1)
1600 W Washington Blvd, Montebello, CA 90640-5422
Tel.: (323) 278-4100
Web Site: http://www.inland-group.com
Truck Dealership
N.A.I.C.S.: 423110
Mark Zucker *(VP & Gen Mgr)*

Inland PacLease (1)
2482 Douglas Road, Burnaby, V5C 6C9, BC, Canada
Tel.: (604) 291-6021
Web Site: http://www.inland-group.com
Truck Rental & Leasing
N.A.I.C.S.: 532120

Parker Pacific (1)
2482 Douglas Road, Burnaby, V5C 6C9, BC, Canada
Tel.: (604) 291-6021
Web Site: http://www.parkerpacific.com
Construction & Forestry Equipment Sales
N.A.I.C.S.: 423810

THE INNOVATION GROUP LTD.

Yarmouth House 1300 Parkway Solent Business Park, Whiteley Village, PO15 7AE, United Kingdom
Tel.: (44) 1489898300 UK
Web Site: http://www.innovation-group.com
Year Founded: 1996
Emp.: 2,498
Insurance Industry Claim Management, Outsourcing, Information & Technology Solutions Services
N.A.I.C.S.: 524292
Ashish Nanda *(Mng Dir)*

Subsidiaries:

Innovation Group (Pty) Ltd. (1)
The Innovation House 192 Bram Fischer Dr, Randburg, 2194, South Africa
Tel.: (27) 117905200
Web Site: http://www.innovation.group
IT Services
N.A.I.C.S.: 541519
Andries Van Staden *(COO)*

Innovation Group Holdings GmbH (1)
Rotebuhlstrasse 121, 70178, Stuttgart, Germany
Tel.: (49) 711664900
Web Site: http://www.innovation.group
Emp.: 3,300
Insurance Claims Management Services
N.A.I.C.S.: 524298
Bart De Groof *(Mng Dir)*

Subsidiary (Domestic):

Innovation Group Parts GmbH (2)
Finsterwalder Str 57, 01979, Lauchhammer, Germany
Tel.: (49) 3574767160
Web Site: http://www.innovation.group
Vehicle Insurance Services
N.A.I.C.S.: 524298
Matthew Whitall *(Mng Dir)*

Servicekonzept AG (2)
Am Wassermann 19, 50829, Cologne, Germany
Tel.: (49) 2217199020
Web Site: http://www.regu24.de
Property Insurance Services
N.A.I.C.S.: 524298
Matthew Whitwall *(Grp CEO)*

Motorcare Services Limited (1)
Yarmouth House 1300 Parkway Solent Business Park, Whiteley, Fareham, PO15 7AE, Hampshire, United Kingdom
Tel.: (44) 8432772353
Vehicle Insurance Services
N.A.I.C.S.: 524298

The Innovation Group (EMEA) Limited (1)
Yarmouth House 1300 Parkway Solent Business Park, Whiteley, Fareham, PO15 7AE, Hampshire, United Kingdom
Tel.: (44) 1489898300
Enterprise Management Software Development Services
N.A.I.C.S.: 541511

THE INSURANCE CORPORATION OF BRITISH COLUMBIA

151 West Esplanade, North Vancouver, V7M 3H9, BC, Canada
Tel.: (604) 661-2800
Web Site: https://www.icbc.com
Year Founded: 1973
Rev.: $4,443,810,936
Assets: $14,546,889,838
Liabilities: $14,459,867,242
Net Worth: $87,022,596
Earnings: ($845,550,527)
Fiscal Year-end: 03/31/19
Art Insurance Services
N.A.I.C.S.: 524128
Kathy Parslow *(VP-Claims Customer & Material Damage Svcs)*

THE INTERNATIONAL BANK FOR TRADE & FINANCE

Pakistan Street, PO Box 11058, Damascus, 11058, Syria
Tel.: (963) 11 23880000
Web Site: http://www.ibtf.com.sy
Year Founded: 2003
Sales Range: $10-24.9 Million
Commercial Banking Services
N.A.I.C.S.: 522110

THE INTERNATIONAL BANK OF QATAR (Q.S.C)

Po Box 27778, Doha, Qatar
Tel.: (974) 44478000 QA
Web Site: http://www.ibq.com.qa
Year Founded: 1956
Commercial Bank
N.A.I.C.S.: 522110
Khalid Al-Subeai *(CEO)*

Subsidiaries:

Barwa Bank Group (1)
Grand Hamad Street, Po Box 27778, Doha, Qatar
Tel.: (974) 44100888
Web Site: http://www.barwabank.com
Islamic Banking Services
N.A.I.C.S.: 522110
Khalid Al-Subeai *(CEO)*

Subsidiary (Domestic):

First Finance Company Q.S.C (2)
Al-Salata Al-Jadeeda C Ring Road, PO Box 7258, Doha, Qatar
Tel.: (974) 4559999
Web Site: http://www.ffcqatar.com
Sales Range: $50-74.9 Million
Consumer Financial Services
N.A.I.C.S.: 522220
Yousef Abdul Allah Al Subaie *(Mng Dir-Comml Facilities)*

THE INTERNATIONAL INVESTOR COMPANY K.S.C.C.

Arraya Tower 49th Floor Sharq, Kuwait, 13153, Kuwait
Tel.: (965) 22437070
Web Site: http://www.tii.com
Year Founded: 1992
Sales Range: $50-74.9 Million
Investment Banking & Financial Services
N.A.I.C.S.: 523150
Adnan Abdulaziz Al Bahar *(Chm & Mng Dir)*

Subsidiaries:

Courts Singapore Limited (1)
50 Tampines North Drive 2, Singapore, Singapore
Tel.: (65) 63097888
Web Site: http://www.courts.com.sg
Household Products Retailer; Owned by Baring Private Equity Asia & The International Investor Company K.S.C.
N.A.I.C.S.: 459999
Jasmine Seow *(Dir-Mdse)*

Procco Financial Services W.L.L (1)
Office 401/403 Al Moayyed Tower, Seef District, Manama, 5856, Bahrain
Tel.: (973) 17567000
Web Site: http://www.procco.net
Financial Payment Services
N.A.I.C.S.: 522320
Yzelle De Wet *(CEO & Bus Head)*

RFM Loyalty Co (1)
A 302 Falcon Gallery Building Al Mina Road, Dubai, United Arab Emirates
Tel.: (971) 43453724
Web Site: http://www.rfmloyaltyco.ae
Credit Card Processing Services
N.A.I.C.S.: 522320

The Investor For Securities Company S.S.C
King Fahd & King Abdullah Roads Jumaiah Tower 2nd Floor, PO Box 67838, Riyadh, 11517, Saudi Arabia
Tel.: (966) 12102249
Web Site: http://www.theinvestor.com.sa
Asset Management Services
N.A.I.C.S.: 531390

INTERNATIONAL PUBLIC

THE INTERTAIN GROUP LIMITED

24 Duncan Street 2nd Floor, Toronto, M5V 2B8, ON, Canada
Tel.: (416) 207-3307 ON
Web Site: http://www.intertain.com
Year Founded: 2010
Rev.: $366,932,606
Assets: $998,062,049
Liabilities: $696,095,504
Net Worth: $301,966,545
Earnings: ($53,039,626)
Emp.: 269
Fiscal Year-end: 12/31/16
Gambling Services
N.A.I.C.S.: 713290
Keith Laslop *(CFO)*

THE INVESTMENT COMPANY PLC

The Office Suite Den House, Teignmouth, Devon, TQ14 8SY, United Kingdom
Tel.: (44) 2072228989 UK
Web Site: https://www.theinvestmentplc.co.uk
Year Founded: 1868
INV—(LSE)
Rev.: $383,079
Assets: $21,297,607
Liabilities: $758,849
Net Worth: $20,538,758
Earnings: $933,093
Fiscal Year-end: 06/30/23
Investment Management Service
N.A.I.C.S.: 523999
Ian Dighe *(Chm)*

THE INVESTMENT TRUST OF INDIA LIMITED

ITI House 36 Dr R K Shirodkar Marg, Parel, Mumbai, 400 012, Maharashtra, India
Tel.: (91) 2240273600 In
Web Site: https://itiorg.com
Year Founded: 1991
THEINVEST—(NSE)
Rev.: $38,874,300
Assets: $134,008,513
Liabilities: $56,563,443
Net Worth: $77,445,069
Earnings: $1,387,651
Emp.: 14
Fiscal Year-end: 03/31/23
Banking & Investment Services
N.A.I.C.S.: 523999
Haroon Mansuri *(Compliance Officer & Sec)*

Subsidiaries:

Fortune Equity Brokers (India) Ltd. (1)
2nd Fl K K Chambers Sir P T Marg I Ft, Mumbai, 400 001, Maharashtra, India
Tel.: (91) 2222077931
Brokerage Services
N.A.I.C.S.: 523150

ITI Gold Loans Limited (1)
ITI house 36 Dr RK Shirodkar Marg, Parel, Mumbai, 400012, Maharashtra, India
Tel.: (91) 9820520200
Web Site: https://itigoldloan.com
Financial Services
N.A.I.C.S.: 523999

THE INVESTORS & EASTERN ARAB FOR INDUSTRIAL & REAL ESTATE INVESTMENTS LTD.

Fifth Circle-Um Othaina-Alkofah St -Building 44, PO Box 926175, Amman, 11190, Jordan
Tel.: (962) 65549718
Year Founded: 1995
Sales Range: $25-49.9 Million
Investment Management Service

THE INX DIGITAL COMPANY, INC
510 Burrard Street Suite 902, Vancouver, V6C 3A8, BC, Canada
Tel.: (604) 685-0201
INXDF—(OTCQB)
Assets: $352,638
Liabilities: $6,772
Net Worth: $345,866
Earnings: ($120,120)
Investment Services
N.A.I.C.S.: 523999
Shy Datika *(Co-Founder)*

Subsidiaries:

INX Limited (1)
Unit 1 02 1st Floor 6 Bayside Road, Gibraltar, GX11 1AA, Gibraltar
Tel.: (350) 20079000
Web Site: http://www.inx.co
Rev.: $2,544,000
Assets: $78,502,000
Liabilities: $301,436,000
Net Worth: ($222,934,000)
Earnings: ($215,235,000)
Emp.: 89
Fiscal Year-end: 12/31/2021
Digital Asset Brokerage Services
N.A.I.C.S.: 523160
Shy Datika *(Founder & CEO)*

THE IQ GROUP GLOBAL LTD.
Level 9, 85 Castlereagh Street, Sydney, 2000, NSW, Australia
Tel.: (61) 282359400
Web Site: http://www.iqnovate.com
IQN—(NSXA)
Rev.: $9,784,276
Assets: $37,783,042
Liabilities: $39,590,436
Net Worth: ($1,807,395)
Earnings: $5,374,804
Fiscal Year-end: 06/30/21
Biopharmaceutical Mfr & Distr
N.A.I.C.S.: 325412
George Syrmalis *(Chm & CEO)*

Subsidiaries:

iQ Capital (USA) LLC (1)
420 Lexington Ave Ste 300, New York, NY 10170
Tel.: (646) 790-5757
Web Site: https://iq-capital.com
Financial Services
N.A.I.C.S.: 523999

THE IRAQI ISLAMIC BANK
14 Ramadan Street, PO Box 6003, Al Mansour District, Baghdad, Iraq
Tel.: (964) 7721000122 IQ
Web Site: https://www.iraqiislamicb.iq
Year Founded: 1993
BIIB—(IRAQ)
Rev.: $101,466,014
Assets: $1,629,632,874
Liabilities: $1,359,698,801
Net Worth: $269,934,072
Earnings: $58,534,435
Emp.: 534
Fiscal Year-end: 12/31/23
Financial Banking Services
N.A.I.C.S.: 523999
Ahmed Waled Ahmed *(Chm)*

THE ISLAMIC INSURANCE CO. P.L.C.
Wasfi Al Tal Street Al Gardens - 94 Al Tabbaa Commercial Complex, PO Box 941000, Amman, 11194, Jordan
Tel.: (962) 65620151
Web Site: https://www.islamicinsurance.jo
Year Founded: 1996
TIIC—(AMM)
Rev.: $9,040,052
Assets: $58,607,318
Liabilities: $26,985,836
Net Worth: $31,621,482
Earnings: $2,444,223
Emp.: 102
Fiscal Year-end: 12/31/20
Insurance & Investment Management Services
N.A.I.C.S.: 524298
Musa Abdel Aziz Shehadeh *(Chm)*

THE ISRAEL ELECTRIC CORPORATION LTD.
1 Netiv Ha Or Street, PO Box 10, Haifa, 31000, Israel
Tel.: (972) 0768631555 IL
Web Site: http://www.iec.co.il
Year Founded: 1923
Rev.: $6,256,835,200
Assets: $22,798,820,800
Liabilities: $15,750,595,700
Net Worth: $7,048,225,100
Earnings: $1,079,771,000
Emp.: 11,476
Fiscal Year-end: 12/31/18
Electric Power Distr
N.A.I.C.S.: 221122
Adrian Bianu *(Sr VP-Corp Sustainability)*

Subsidiaries:

Jordan Properties Ltd. (1)
162 Madina Monawara St Office 402, PO Box 842, Amman, 11821, Jordan
Tel.: (962) 6 5533152
Web Site: http://web.jordan-properties.net
Residential & Commercial Property Development Services
N.A.I.C.S.: 236115
Khalil S. Rai *(Founder & Chm)*

National Coal Supply Corporation Ltd. (1)
20 Lincoln Street, Tel Aviv, Israel
Tel.: (972) 3 625 7000
Web Site: http://www.ncsc.co.il
Coal Distr
N.A.I.C.S.: 423520

THE ISRAEL LAND DEVELOPMENT CO., LTD.
30 Sheshet Hayamim St, Bnei Brak, 5120261, Israel
Tel.: (972) 37962222
Web Site: http://www.ildc.co.il
Year Founded: 1909
ILDC—(TAE)
Rev.: $246,514,984
Assets: $2,547,695,775
Liabilities: $1,762,563,310
Net Worth: $785,132,465
Earnings: $12,233,734
Fiscal Year-end: 12/31/23
Other Activities Related to Real Estate
N.A.I.C.S.: 531390
Ron Weissberg *(Vice Chm)*

Subsidiaries:

Hachsharat Hayishuv Hotels Ltd. (1)
Krinitzi 1, Ramat Gan, 52453, Israel **(83.36%)**
Tel.: (972) 36754444
Web Site: http://www.rimonim.com
Rev.: $54,100,241
Assets: $76,244,832
Liabilities: $38,096,284
Net Worth: $38,148,548
Earnings: ($5,486,139)
Emp.: 1,280
Fiscal Year-end: 12/31/2018
Home Management Services
N.A.I.C.S.: 721110
Assaf Shalev *(CEO)*

I.L.D. Insurance Co. Ltd. (1)
2 Ashenkar Street, Tel Aviv, 61500, Israel **(80.7%)**
Tel.: (972) 7962666
Web Site: http://www.ildinsur.co.il
Sales Range: $200-249.9 Million
Emp.: 300
Multi-Line Insurance Company
N.A.I.C.S.: 524298

ILD Hotels (1)
194 Hayarkon Street, Tel Aviv, 63405, Israel **(81.94%)**
Tel.: (972) 35200222
Sales Range: $50-74.9 Million
Emp.: 450
Deluxe & First Class Hotels in Israel
N.A.I.C.S.: 721110

Seven Stars Mall Management Company (2000) Ltd. (1)
8 Shivat Hakokhavim Blvd, Herzliya, 4670802, Israel
Tel.: (972) 9 951 9898
Web Site: https://7star.co.il
Shopping Mall Services
N.A.I.C.S.: 455219

Tel-Ad Jerusalem Studio Ltd. (1)
20 Marcus St, Jerusalem, 92233, Israel **(28%)**
Tel.: (972) 25692444
Web Site: http://www.telad2000.com
Sales Range: $50-74.9 Million
Emp.: 120
Production of Television Programs
N.A.I.C.S.: 512110

THE ITALIAN SEA GROUP S.P.A.
Viale Cristoforo Colombo 4, Marina di, 54033, Carrara, MS, Italy
Tel.: (39) 05855062
Web Site: https://www.theitalianseagroup.com
Year Founded: 1942
TISG—(ITA)
Rev.: $405,783,199
Assets: $416,590,131
Liabilities: $271,832,432
Net Worth: $144,757,700
Earnings: $40,745,115
Emp.: 658
Fiscal Year-end: 12/31/23
Construction Engineering Services
N.A.I.C.S.: 541330
Giovanni Costantino *(CEO)*

THE JAMES WALKER GROUP LTD
Lion House Oriental Road, Woking, GU22 8AP, Surrey, United Kingdom
Tel.: (44) 1483746146 UK
Web Site: http://www.jameswalker.biz
Year Founded: 1882
Sales Range: $75-99.9 Million
Emp.: 1,900
Mfr Hydraulic Packings, Jointings, Seals, Gaskets, Bellows, Protectors & Anti-Vibration Pads
N.A.I.C.S.: 339991
Peter Needham *(Chm & CEO)*

Subsidiaries:

Edilon Sedra BV (1)
Nijverheidsweg 23, Haarlem, 2031 CN, Netherlands **(100%)**
Tel.: (31) 235319519
Web Site: http://www.edilonsedra.com
Sales Range: $25-49.9 Million
Emp.: 50
Railway Infrastructure Systems
N.A.I.C.S.: 488210
Hubert C. Schwind *(Mgr-Tech)*

James Walker & Company (1)
2 Floor Gawsworth House Westmere Drive, Westmere Drive, Crewe, CW1 6XB, Cheshire, United Kingdom **(100%)**
Tel.: (44) 1270536000
Sales Range: $25-49.9 Million
Emp.: 100
Mfr of Hydraulic Packings, Jointings, Seals, Gaskets, Bellows, Protectors & Anti-Vibration Pads
N.A.I.C.S.: 339991

James Walker (Shanghai) Sealing Technology Ltd (1)
Room 1109 Cube Building 58 Chang Liu Road, Shanghai, 200135, China
Tel.: (86) 21 6876 9351
Fluid Sealing Product Distr
N.A.I.C.S.: 423840

James Walker Asia Pacific (1)
192 Pandan Loop 05-11/12 Pantech Industrial Complex, Singapore, 128381, Singapore **(100%)**
Tel.: (65) 6777 9896
Web Site: http://www.jameswalker.biz
Gasket, Jointing & Sealing Products Whslr
N.A.I.C.S.: 423840

James Walker Australia Ltd (1)
Lion Works 32 Clapham Rd, Regents Park, 2143, NSW, Australia **(100%)**
Tel.: (61) 296449755
Web Site: http://www.jameswalker.biz
Sales Range: $25-49.9 Million
Emp.: 30
Steel Mfrs
N.A.I.C.S.: 339991
Peter Miyhook *(Gen Mgr)*

James Walker Belgium (1)
Mechanicalaan 14-16, Wilrijk, 2610, Antwerp, Belgium **(100%)**
Tel.: (32) 38207900
Web Site: http://www.jameswalker.biz
Sales Range: $25-49.9 Million
Emp.: 50
Gasket, Jointing & Sealing Products Mfr & Whslr
N.A.I.C.S.: 339991
Jean Piere Gilta *(Gen Mgr)*

James Walker Benelux B.V. (1)
Rontgenstraat 7-9-11, Oud-Beijerland, 3261 LK, Netherlands
Tel.: (31) 186 633 111
Fluid Sealing Product Distr
N.A.I.C.S.: 423840

James Walker Deutschland (1)
Flughafenstrasse 54, Hamburg, 22335, Germany **(100%)**
Tel.: (49) 403860810
Web Site: http://www.jameswalker.biz
Sales Range: $25-49.9 Million
Emp.: 30
Gasket, Jointing & Sealing Products Whslr
N.A.I.C.S.: 423840
Philip Grudzinski *(Gen Mgr)*

James Walker Flemings Ltd (1)
Atlas Mill Rd, Brighouse, HD6 1ES, W Yorkshire, United Kingdom **(100%)**
Tel.: (44) 484718391
Web Site: http://www.flemings-seals.co.uk
Hydraulic Packings, Jointings, Seals & Gaskets Mfr
N.A.I.C.S.: 339991

James Walker France (1)
17 Rue Jean Elysee Dupuy, BP 36, Z I Letrochon, 69542, Lyon, Cedex, Champagne, France **(100%)**
Tel.: (33) 437497480
Sales Range: $25-49.9 Million
Emp.: 30
Gasket, Jointing & Sealing Products Whslr
N.A.I.C.S.: 423840

James Walker Iberica (1)
Calle Orixe No 16, Bilbao, 48015, Spain **(100%)**
Tel.: (34) 944470099
Web Site: http://www.jameswalker.biz
Sales Range: $25-49.9 Million
Emp.: 15
Automatic Grease Cups Whslr
N.A.I.C.S.: 424130
Peter Needham *(Chm & CEO)*

James Walker Inmarco Industries Pvt Ltd (1)
Andheri Kurla Road 104 Gayatri Complex Rimjob Mittal Industrial Estate, Andheri, Mumbai, 400 059, Maharashtra, India
Tel.: (91) 22 4080 8080
Fluid Sealing Product Distr
N.A.I.C.S.: 423840

James Walker Ireland (1)
3 Richfield Bus Pk, Ballycurreen Kinsale Rd, Cork, Ireland **(100%)**

THE JAMES WALKER GROUP LTD

The James Walker Group Ltd—(Continued)
Tel.: (353) 14542500
Sales Range: $25-49.9 Million
Emp.: 10
Packings, Mechanical Seals & Insulation Products Whslr
N.A.I.C.S.: 339991
David McCullough (Dir-Sls)

James Walker Italiana (1)
Via Ponte Veccio 2 4, 20127, Milan, Italy (100%)
Tel.: (39) 022578308
Web Site: http://www.jameswalker.it
Sales Range: $25-49.9 Million
Emp.: 100
Packings, Mechanical Seals & Insulation Products Whslr
N.A.I.C.S.: 339991

James Walker Keaflex Ltd (1)
Woolmer Way, Woolmer Trading Est, Bordon, GU35 9QE, Hampshire, United Kingdom (100%)
Tel.: (44) 1420473645
Web Site: http://www.jameswalker.biz
Sales Range: $1-9.9 Million
Emp.: 25
Seals & Mechanical Rubbers Mfr
N.A.I.C.S.: 339991

James Walker Mfg (1)
511 W 195th St, Glenwood, IL 60425-0467 (100%)
Tel.: (708) 754-4020
Web Site: http://www.jameswalkermfg.com
Sales Range: $25-49.9 Million
Emp.: 42
Mfr of Hydraulic Packings, Jointings, Seals & Gaskets
N.A.I.C.S.: 339991
Christopher May (Gen Mgr)

James Walker Moorflex Ltd (1)
John Escritt Rd, Bingley, BD16 2BS, W Yorkshire, United Kingdom (100%)
Tel.: (44) 274562211
Web Site: http://www.kea-flex-mouldings.co.uk
Gaskets Mfr
N.A.I.C.S.: 339991

James Walker New Zealand (1)
Unit B 43 Lady Ruby Dr, East Tamaki, 2013, Auckland, New Zealand (100%)
Tel.: (64) 92721599
Web Site: http://www.jameswalker.biz
Sales Range: $25-49.9 Million
Emp.: 20
Sealing Products Mfr
N.A.I.C.S.: 339991
Chris Jacob (Mng Dir)

James Walker Norge AS (1)
Ostmarkveien 27, 0687, Oslo, Norway (100%)
Tel.: (47) 22706800
Web Site: http://www.jameswalker.no
Sales Range: $25-49.9 Million
Emp.: 28
Packings, Mechanical Seals & Insulation Products Mfr
N.A.I.C.S.: 339991
Wyestig Lars (Office Mgr)

James Walker Oil & Gas Co (1)
26797 Hanna Rd Bldg 4 Oak Rdg, Conroe, TX 77385 (100%)
Tel.: (281) 875-0002
Packings, Mechanical Seals & Insulation Products Whslr
N.A.I.C.S.: 423840
Nigel Page (VP)

James Walker Rotabolt Ltd (1)
Peartree Bus Pk, Peartree Ln, Dudley, DY2 0UW, W Midlands, United Kingdom (100%)
Tel.: (44) 384214442
Web Site: http://www.rotabolt.co.uk
Fasteners & Tightening Equipment Mfr
N.A.I.C.S.: 339993

James Walker South Africa (1)
296 Magwaza Maphalala/Gale Streets, Congella, 4001, Durban, South Africa (100%)
Tel.: (27) 31 304 0770
Web Site: http://www.jameswalker.biz

Sales Range: $25-49.9 Million
Emp.: 20
Fluid Sealing Solutions
N.A.I.C.S.: 339991
Gunther Garz (Gen Mgr)

James Walker do Brasil Tecnologia em Vedacoes Industrials Ltda (1)
Av Robert Kennedy 2086 Sao Bernardo do Campo, Sao Paulo, 09860-122, Brazil
Tel.: (55) 11 4392 7360
Fluid Sealing Product Distr
N.A.I.C.S.: 423840

Tiflex Limited (1)
Tiflex House, Liskeard, PL14 4NB, Cornwall, United Kingdom (100%)
Tel.: (44) 1579320808
Web Site: http://www.tiflex.co.uk
Sales Range: $50-74.9 Million
Emp.: 150
Mfr of Cork & Rubber Bonded Materials
N.A.I.C.S.: 326299
Hugh Rogers (Mng Dir)

THE JAPAN LIVING SERVICE CO., LTD.

3F Osaka-Ekimae Dai-4 Bldg 1-11-4-300 Umeda, Kita-ku, Osaka, 530-0001, Japan
Tel.: (81) 663431841
Web Site: http://www.2110.jp
Year Founded: 1976
8854—(TKS)
Rev: $38,940,270
Assets: $70,416,570
Liabilities: $38,015,340
Net Worth: $32,401,230
Earnings: $645,300
Fiscal Year-end: 12/31/22
Real Estate Manangement Services
N.A.I.C.S.: 531390
Tomohiko Nakamura (Pres)

THE JAPAN STEEL WORKS, LTD.

Gate City Ohsaki West Tower 11-1 Osaki 1-chome, Shinagawa-ku, Tokyo, 141-0032, Japan
Tel.: (81) 357452001
Web Site: https://www.jsw.co.jp
Year Founded: 1907
JPSWF—(OTCIQ)
Rev: $1,711,629,570
Assets: $2,497,726,860
Liabilities: $1,345,966,740
Net Worth: $1,151,760,120
Earnings: $85,853,580
Emp.: 4,966
Fiscal Year-end: 03/31/23
Steel Products Mfr
N.A.I.C.S.: 331513
Takeshi Shinmoto (Exec Officer)

Subsidiaries:

Fine Crystal Co., Ltd. (1)
9-1 Chatsucho, Muroran, 051-0006, Hokkaido, Japan (100%)
Tel.: (81) 00143227401
Sales Range: $50-74.9 Million
Emp.: 170
Synthetic Crystal Mfr & Sales
N.A.I.C.S.: 326199

Subsidiary (Non-US):

Fine Crystal (H.K.) Co., Ltd. (2)
Room 903 94 Aitken Vanson Center 61 Hoi Yuen Road, Kwun Tong, Kowloon, China (Hong Kong) (100%)
Tel.: (852) 23457485
Sales Range: $25-49.9 Million
Emp.: 3
Synthetic Crystals Mfr & Sales
N.A.I.C.S.: 326199

Fine Crystal Iwaki Co., Ltd. (1)
2 6 Chubu Industrial Park, Iwaki, 972-8338, Fukushima Prefecture, Japan
Tel.: (81) 246668658
Web Site: http://www.fc-iwaki.co.jp
Molding Machine Mfr
N.A.I.C.S.: 333248

Fine Crystal Precision (S.Z.) Co., Ltd. (1)
No 14 Tongfuyu Lndustrial Estate Longtian Community, Longtian Sub District Pingshan District, Shenzhen, Guangdong, China
Tel.: (86) 75584116005
Business Support Services
N.A.I.C.S.: 561499

Hokkaido Kosan Co., Ltd. (1)
4 Chatsucho, Muroran, 051-0006, Hokkaido, Japan (100%)
Tel.: (81) 143242553
Welfare Facilities & Support Work Management Services
N.A.I.C.S.: 561990

JSW Clad Steel Plate Co., Ltd. (1)
4 Chatsucho, Muroran, 051-0006, Hokkaido, Japan
Tel.: (81) 143220752
Steel Wire Mfr & Distr
N.A.I.C.S.: 331222

JSW Electromechanical Trading (Shanghai) Co., Ltd. (1)
304 Metro Plaza 555 Loushanguan Road, Changning District, Shanghai, China
Tel.: (86) 2152067031
Industrial Machinery Mfr & Distr
N.A.I.C.S.: 333924

JSW Hiroshima Plant (1)
6-1 Funakoshi-Minami 1-chome, Aki-ku, Hiroshima, 736-8602, Japan (100%)
Tel.: (81) 82 822 3181
Web Site: http://www.jsw.co.jp
Emp.: 2,200
Molds & Machinery Parts Mfr & Processor
N.A.I.C.S.: 333511

JSW IT Korea Co., Ltd. (1)
1805 6 Samseong ro 96 gil, Gangnam-gu, Seoul, Korea (South)
Tel.: (82) 221915294
Industrial Machinery Mfr
N.A.I.C.S.: 333248

JSW IT Service Co. (1)
2 2 1 Fukuura, Kanazawa-ku, Yokohama, 236-0004, Kanagawa, Japan
Tel.: (81) 457878462
Industrial Equipment Mfr
N.A.I.C.S.: 333248

JSW Machine Center Co., Ltd. (1)
Nihonseikosho Muroran Seisakushoko-Nai 39-5 Chatsucho, Muroran, 051-0006, Hokkaido, Japan (100%)
Tel.: (81) 143232922
Sales Range: $50-74.9 Million
Emp.: 250
Steel Products Mfr & Maintenance Services
N.A.I.C.S.: 331513

JSW Machinery (Ningbo) Co., Ltd. (1)
No 1 Zhuhan Industrial Zone, Hengzhang Village Shiqi Street Yinzhou District, Ningbo, China
Tel.: (86) 57488236758
Moulding Machine Mfr & Distr
N.A.I.C.S.: 333248

JSW Machinery Trading (Shanghai) Co., Ltd. (1)
Room 301 304 Changfang International Plaza 555 Loushanguan Road, Changning District, Shanghai, China
Tel.: (86) 2152067031
Web Site: http://www.jsw-china.com
Molding Machine Mfr
N.A.I.C.S.: 333248

JSW Plastic Machinery (Shenzhen) Co., Ltd. (1)
1F YiBen Electronic & Business Industrial Park No 1063 Chaguang Road, Xili Town Nanshan District, Shenzhen, 518055, Guangdong, China
Tel.: (86) 75586020930
Molding Machine Mfr
N.A.I.C.S.: 333248

JSW Plastics Machinery (H.K.) Co., Ltd. (1)
Room 907 Corporation Park 11 On Lai Street, Sha Tin, New Territories, China (Hong Kong)
Tel.: (852) 2648 0720

INTERNATIONAL PUBLIC

Web Site: http://www.jsw.co.jp
Plastics Machinery Mfr
N.A.I.C.S.: 333998

JSW Plastics Machinery (M) SDN. BHD. (1)
D12-3A Pusat Perdagangan Dana 1, Jalan PJU 1A/46, Petaling Jaya, 47301, Selangor Darul Ehsan, Malaysia
Tel.: (60) 378426076
Web Site: http://www.jsw.com.sg
Injection Molding Machine Sales
N.A.I.C.S.: 423830

JSW Plastics Machinery (Phillippines) Inc. (1)
Unit 2205 22nd Floor Asian Star Building Asean Drive, Filinvest Corporate City, Muntinlupa, 1781, Metro Manila, Philippines
Tel.: (63) 24782533
Machine Part Mfr
N.A.I.C.S.: 333248

JSW Plastics Machinery (Shenzhen) Co., Ltd. (1)
101 Building 6 Nangang 2nd Industrial Park Songbai Road No 1026, Yangguang Xili Street Nanshan District, Shenzhen, China
Tel.: (86) 75586020930
Moulding Machine Mfr & Distr
N.A.I.C.S.: 333248

JSW Plastics Machinery (TAIWAN) Corp. (1)
1F No 21 Da Hu 1st Road, Guieshan Shiang, Taoyuan, 33373, Taiwan
Tel.: (886) 3 396 2102
Web Site: http://www.jsw.co.jp
Plastic Machine Mfr
N.A.I.C.S.: 333248

JSW Plastics Machinery Mexico S. de R.L. de C.V. (1)
Avenida Mineral de Valenciana 202 A-1 Parque Industrial Santa Fe, Silao De La Victria, 36275, Guanajuato, Mexico
Tel.: (52) 4727489412
Plastic Moulded Product Mfr & Distr
N.A.I.C.S.: 333511

JSW Plastics Machinery Vietnam Ltd. (1)
Room 103 Techno-Center Thang Long Industrial Park, Dong Anh District, Hanoi, Vietnam
Tel.: (84) 4 3951 6383
Emp.: 11
Plastic Processing Machinery Mfr
N.A.I.C.S.: 333248
Ken Kikuchi (Gen Mgr)

Japan Steel Works America, Inc. (1)
24387 Halsted Rd Unit B, Farmington Hills, MI 48335 (100%)
Tel.: (248) 536-0288
Web Site: https://www.jswamerica.com
Sales Range: $50-74.9 Million
Emp.: 4
Steel & Machinery Products Sales
N.A.I.C.S.: 423830

Japan Steel Works Europe GmbH (1)
Friedrichstrasse 19, 40217, Dusseldorf, Germany
Tel.: (49) 2113116660
Web Site: http://www.jsw.de
Military Equipment Mfr
N.A.I.C.S.: 336992

Japan Steel Works India Private Limited (1)
611 Time Tower MG Road Sector 28, Gurgaon, 122 002, Haryana, India
Tel.: (91) 124 469 4444
Web Site: http://www.jsw.co.jp
Industrial Steel Mfr
N.A.I.C.S.: 331511
Masao Oshita (Mng Exec Officer)

Japan Steel Works M&E, Inc. (1)
4 Chatsucho, Muroran, 051-8505, Hokkaido, Japan
Tel.: (81) 14 322 0143
Web Site: https://jsw-me.com
Emp.: 1,450
Industrial Equipment Mfr
N.A.I.C.S.: 333248
Takashi Iwamoto (Pres)

AND PRIVATE COMPANIES

Joyo Engineering Co., Ltd. (1)
1-5-12 Edanishi, Aoba-ku, Yokohama, 225-0014, Kanagawa, Japan **(70%)**
Tel.: (81) 459124411
Web Site: http://www.joyo-eng.co.jp
Sales Range: $50-74.9 Million
Emp.: 70
IT Devices Designer, Mfr & Sales; Engineering Research Services; Surface Treatment Technology Consulting Services; Precision Engineering Equipment Sales
N.A.I.C.S.: 334419

Jsw Afty Corporation (1)
2 35 2 Hyoe, Hachioji, 192-0918, Tokyo, Japan
Tel.: (81) 42 632 8840
Web Site: https://www.jsw-afty.co.jp
Industrial Equipment Mfr & Whslr
N.A.I.C.S.: 333248
Ishibashi Yoshinao (Pres)

Just Co., Ltd. (1)
5-7-10 Koenjiminami, Suginami-ku, Tokyo, 166-0003, Japan **(100%)**
Tel.: (81) 3 5385 8331
Web Site: http://www.just-web.co.jp
Sales Range: $125-149.9 Million
Emp.: 270
Electric & Electronic Parts Procurement Services
N.A.I.C.S.: 335999

MG Precision Co., Ltd. (1)
1-6-1 Funakoshi-Minami, Aki-ku, Hiroshima, 736-8602, Japan **(100%)**
Tel.: (81) 828221305
Sales Range: $25-49.9 Million
Emp.: 100
Injection Molded Metal Products Mfr
N.A.I.C.S.: 333511
Kengo Takeya (Pres)

Mned Co., Ltd. (1)
4 Chatsucho, Muroran, 051-8505, Hokkaido, Japan
Tel.: (81) 143220620
Business Support Services
N.A.I.C.S.: 561499

Muroran Environmental Plant Service, Ltd. (1)
14 7 Nakamachi, Muroran, 050-0087, Hokkaido, Japan
Tel.: (81) 143220005
Business Support Services
N.A.I.C.S.: 561499

Nikko Inspection Service Co., Ltd. (1)
4-1 Chatsucho, Muroran, 051-0006, Hokkaido, Japan **(100%)**
Tel.: (81) 143228386
Sales Range: $75-99.9 Million
Emp.: 160
Product Inspection Services
N.A.I.C.S.: 926150

Nikko Kosan Co., Ltd. (1)
J Tower 16F 1-1 Nikko-cho, Fuchu, Tokyo, 183-0044, Japan **(100%)**
Tel.: (81) 423308011
Sales Range: $25-49.9 Million
Emp.: 100
Clerical Support Services
N.A.I.C.S.: 561110

Nikko Kouki Co., Ltd. (1)
2 2 1 Fukuura, Kanazawa-ku, Yokohama, 236-0004, Kanagawa, Japan
Tel.: (81) 457017841
Plastic Machine Mfr
N.A.I.C.S.: 333248

Nikko Sekkei Co., Ltd. (1)
1 6 1 Funakoshiminami, Aki-ku, Hiroshima, 736-0082, Japan **(100%)**
Tel.: (81) 828221653
Web Site: http://www.nikkosekkei.co.jp
Software Development Services
N.A.I.C.S.: 541511

Nikko Techno Co., Ltd. (1)
1 6 1 Funakoshiminami, Aki-ku, Hiroshima, 736-0082, Japan
Tel.: (81) 828223232
Web Site: http://www.ntc-jsw.co.jp
Steel Products Mfr
N.A.I.C.S.: 332312

Nikko Tokki Co., Ltd. (1)
2 1 1 Nishishinjuku, Shinjuku-ku, Tokyo, 163-0429, Japan
Tel.: (81) 353268672
Ordnance Mfr
N.A.I.C.S.: 332994

Nikko Truck Co., Ltd. (1)
1 8 10 Yamato cho, Noboribetsu, Hokkaido, 059-0025, Japan
Tel.: (81) 143854255
Web Site: http://nikkoutruck.co.jp
Transportation Services
N.A.I.C.S.: 485999

Nikko Unyu Co., Ltd. (1)
4 1 Chatsucho, Muroran, 051-8505, Hokkaido, Japan
Tel.: (81) 143227923
Web Site: http://www.nikkouunyu.co.jp
Transportation Services
N.A.I.C.S.: 485999

Nikko-Ypk Shoji Co., Ltd. (1)
1 11 1 Osaki Gate City Osaki West Tower 24th Floor, Shinagawa-ku, Tokyo, 141-0032, Japan
Tel.: (81) 357452144
Web Site: http://jsw-nyc.jp
Molding Machine Whslr
N.A.I.C.S.: 423840

Nikkou Muroran Service Co., Ltd. (1)
4 Chatsucho, Muroran, 051-8505, Japan
Tel.: (81) 143242553
Web Site: http://nikkoumuroranservice.co.jp
Catering Services
N.A.I.C.S.: 722320

Ningbo To Ngyon Plastic Machinery Manufacturing Co., Ltd. (1)
No 1 Shiqi Street, Zhuhuan Industrial Zone Hengzhang Village Yinzhou District, Ningbo, China
Tel.: (86) 57483036855
Web Site: http://www.tongyongsuji.com
Plastic Machine Mfr
N.A.I.C.S.: 333248

Nippla Inc. (1)
1-6-1 Funakoshi Minami, Aki-ku, Hiroshima, 736-0082, Japan **(100%)**
Tel.: (81) 82 847 5510
Web Site: https://www.npl-jsw.co.jp
Sales Range: $25-49.9 Million
Emp.: 150
Injection Molding Machines Installation & Maintenance Services
N.A.I.C.S.: 811310
Keiji Yoshimoto (Pres & CEO)

PT. Jsw Plastics Machinery Indonesia (1)
Gajah Building Unit K JI Dr Saharjo Raya No 111, Jakarta Selatan, 12810, Indonesia
Tel.: (62) 2183702536
Molding Machine Mfr
N.A.I.C.S.: 333248

S M PLATEK Co., Ltd. (1)
687-2 Seonggok-dong, Ansan, Kyeonggi-do, Korea (South)
Tel.: (82) 314883401
Plastic Machinery Mfr & Distr
N.A.I.C.S.: 333248

SM Platex Co., Ltd. (1)
687 2 Seonggok dong, 425-836, Ansan, kyeonggi-do, Korea (South)
Tel.: (82) 31 488 3401
Web Site: https://www.smplatek.com
Twin Screw Extruder Compounding System Mfr
N.A.I.C.S.: 332721
Park Sung-Hee (CEO & Mng Dir)

Sun Tectro, Ltd. (1)
1 6 1 Funakoshiminami, Aki-ku, Hiroshima, 736-0082, Japan
Tel.: (81) 828243881
Web Site: http://www.suntec-jsw.co.jp
Industrial Equipment Mfr
N.A.I.C.S.: 333248

Tahara Machinery Ltd. (1)
2-1 Kaguro-Minami, Inzai, 270-1369, Chiba, Japan
Tel.: (81) 47 621 1991
Web Site: https://www.tahara-mc.com
Emp.: 90

Molding Machine Mfr & Whslr
N.A.I.C.S.: 333248
Tetsuya Tsuruta (Pres)

The Japan Steel Works (Singapore) Pte. Ltd. (1)
17 Gul Lane, Singapore, 629413, Singapore
Tel.: (65) 68614511
Web Site: http://www.jsw.com.sg
Injection Molding Machine Sales
N.A.I.C.S.: 423830

The Japan Steel Works (Thailand) Co., Ltd. (1)
78 6 JST Building 4th Floor Moo7 King Kaew Road, Rachatewa, Bang Phli, 10540, Samut Prakan, Thailand
Tel.: (66) 27385272
Steelworks Mfr
N.A.I.C.S.: 332312

The Japan Steel Works, Ltd. - Hiroshima Plant (1)
6-1 Funakoshi-Minami 1-chome, Aki-ku, Hiroshima, 736-8602, Japan
Tel.: (81) 82 822 3181
Web Site: http://www.jsw.co.jp
Steel Mfrs
N.A.I.C.S.: 331110

The Japan Steel Works, Ltd. - Muroran Plant (1)
4 Chatsumachi, Muroran, 051-8505, Hokkaido, Japan
Tel.: (81) 143 22 0143
Web Site: http://www.jsw.co.jp
Emp.: 800
Steel Mfrs
N.A.I.C.S.: 331110

The Japan Steel Works, Ltd. - Ordnance Division (1)
Gate City Ohsaki-West Tower 11-1 Osaki 1-chome, Shinagawa-ku, Tokyo, 141-0032, Japan
Tel.: (81) 3 5745 2086
Web Site: http://www.jsw.co.jp
Ordnance Products Mfr
N.A.I.C.S.: 332994

The Japan Steel Works, Ltd. - Yokohama Plant (1)
2-1 Fukuura 2-chome, Kanazawa-ku, Yokohama, 236-0004, Kanagawa, Japan
Tel.: (81) 45 781 1111
Web Site: http://www.jsw.co.jp
Steel Mfrs
N.A.I.C.S.: 331110

YPK Machine Trading (Shenzhen) Co., Ltd. (1)
Flat C 10/F Laifu Bldg Fuyong Road, Baoan, Shenzhen, 518103, China
Tel.: (86) 75527332114
Moulding Machine Mfr & Distr
N.A.I.C.S.: 333248

YPK Trading (Hong Kong) Co., Ltd. (1)
Unit A2 4 F Block A Po Yip Building 62 70 Texaco Road, New Territories, Tsuen Wan, China (Hong Kong)
Tel.: (852) 35210437
Molding Machine Whslr
N.A.I.C.S.: 423840

Yamato Rebuilt Co., Ltd. (1)
4882 1 Kimagase, Noda, 270-0222, Chiba, Japan
Tel.: (81) 471984556
Molding Machine Mfr
N.A.I.C.S.: 333248

THE JAPAN WOOL TEXTILE CO., LTD.
3-3-10 Kawaramachi, Chuo Ward, Osaka, 541-0048, Japan
Tel.: (81) 662056600
Web Site: https://www.nikke.co.jp
Year Founded: 1896
3201—(TKS)
Rev.: $804,693,730
Assets: $1,177,854,610
Liabilities: $368,637,460
Net Worth: $809,217,150
Earnings: $54,188,870

THE JIM PATTISON GROUP

Emp.: 944
Fiscal Year-end: 11/30/23
Textile Machinery Mfr & Whslr
N.A.I.C.S.: 333248
Kazuya Tomita (Pres & CEO)

Subsidiaries:

FUJI Corporation (1)
1-5 Giyokicho Itami, Hyogo, 664-8615, Japan **(32.95%)**
Tel.: (81) 727721101
Web Site: http://www.fujico-jp.com
Rev.: $80,090,400
Assets: $115,469,700
Liabilities: $35,062,200
Net Worth: $80,407,500
Earnings: ($5,608,140)
Emp.: 359
Fiscal Year-end: 03/31/2019
Pressed Felts, Needle Punched Felt, Needle Punched Carpets, Headwears & Other Related Goods Mfr & Sales
N.A.I.C.S.: 313230
Takayuki Nozoe (Pres)

Joint Venture (Non-US):

Dingxing Lida Hat Making Co., Ltd. (2)
No 3 Lihua Road, Dingxing, Hebei, China
Tel.: (86) 3126923013
Web Site: http://www.lihuahats.com
Sales Range: $250-299.9 Million
Hat Mfr & Whslr
N.A.I.C.S.: 315990

Subsidiary (Non-US):

Fuji Corp International Hong Kong Ltd. (2)
Rm 709 7th Floor Tower B Hung Hom Commercial Centre, 37-39 Ma Tau Wai Road, Hung Hom, Kowloon, China (Hong Kong)
Tel.: (852) 27226409
Web Site: http://www.fujico-jp.com
Piece Goods Notions & Other Dry Goods Whslr
N.A.I.C.S.: 424310
Maehara Toyoteru (Mng Dir)

Toyobo Kankyo Techno Co., Ltd. (1)
2-4-27 Kyutaromachi 5th Floor Sakaisuji Honmachi TF Building, Chuo-ku, Osaka, 541-0056, Japan
Tel.: (81) 66 266 3121
Web Site: https://www.kankyotec.toyobo.co.jp
Filtration Equipment Distr
N.A.I.C.S.: 423720

THE JEYPORE SUGAR COMPANY LIMITED
Ramakrishna Buildings No 239 Anna Salai, Chennai, 600 006, India
Tel.: (91) 44 2852 4849
Web Site: http://jeyporesugars.com
Year Founded: 1936
Rev.: $1,231,165
Assets: $102,442,524
Liabilities: $119,764,431
Net Worth: ($17,321,907)
Earnings: $76,179
Fiscal Year-end: 03/31/18
Sugar Mfr
N.A.I.C.S.: 311314
Anita Prabhu (Mng Dir)

THE JIM PATTISON GROUP
Suite 1800 - 1067 West Cordova St, Vancouver, V6C 1C7, BC, Canada
Tel.: (604) 688-6764
Web Site:
https://www.jimpattison.com
Year Founded: 1961
Sales Range: $5-14.9 Billion
Emp.: 36,000
Food Retailing & Distribution; Food Processing; Food Service, Flexible & Specialty Packaging; Electrical Signs; Automotive Retailing & Export Services
N.A.I.C.S.: 551112
David Bell (Mng Dir-Corp Fin)

THE JIM PATTISON GROUP

The Jim Pattison Group—(Continued)

Subsidiaries:

Buy-Low Foods Ltd. (1)
19580 Telegraph Trail, Surrey, V4N 4H1, BC, Canada
Tel.: (604) 888-1121
Web Site: https://buy-low.com
Sales Range: $150-199.9 Million
Emp.: 1,130
Retail Grocery Stores
N.A.I.C.S.: 445110
Sam Corea (VP-Retail)

Canadian Fishing Company (1)
301 Waterfront Road E, Vancouver, V6A 0B3, BC, Canada
Tel.: (604) 681-0211
Web Site: https://canfiscogroup.com
Sales Range: $25-49.9 Million
Emp.: 63
Fish Packaging & Product Mfr
N.A.I.C.S.: 311710

Plant (Domestic):

Canadian Fishing Company - Richmond Plant (2)
13140 Rice Mill Road, Richmond, V6W 1A1, BC, Canada
Tel.: (604) 272-2552
Web Site: http://www.canfisco.com
Emp.: 250
Seafood Canning & Distr
N.A.I.C.S.: 311710
Tom Todhunter (VP-Ops)

Everything Wine Inc. (1)
998 Marine Drive License 302893, North Vancouver, V7P 3C4, BC, Canada
Tel.: (604) 929-7277
Web Site: http://www.everythingwine.ca
Wine Mfr & Distr
N.A.I.C.S.: 312130
Trent Anderson (Pres)

Genera Solutions LP (1)
Chandler Bldg 13860 Ballantyne Corp Pl, Charlotte, NC 28277
Tel.: (980) 233-4400
Web Site: http://www.generasolutions.com
Business Process Outsourcing Services
N.A.I.C.S.: 561499
David Jones (VP-Ops)

Genpak LP. (1)
285 Industrial Parkway South, Aurora, L4G 3V8, ON, Canada
Tel.: (905) 727-0121
Food Products Mfr
N.A.I.C.S.: 311991
Rick Vanderwert (Pres)

Great Pacific Industries, Inc. (1)
19855 92A Avenue, Langley, V1M 3B6, BC, Canada
Tel.: (640) 881-3668
Web Site: http://www.saveonfoods.com
Sales Range: $1-4.9 Billion
Emp.: 12,000
Grocery Stores
N.A.I.C.S.: 424410

Jim Pattison Auto Group (1)
15393 Guildford Drive, Surrey, V3R 0H9, BC, Canada
Tel.: (604) 495-4100
Web Site: http://www.jpautogroup.com
Sales Range: $200-249.9 Million
Emp.: 700
New & Used Car Dealers
N.A.I.C.S.: 441110
Bill Harbottle (Pres)

Branch (Domestic):

Jim Pattison Auto Group (2)
623 Frances Avenue, Victoria, V8T 0C1, BC, Canada
Tel.: (604) 386-3516
Web Site: http://www.metrolexusvictoria.com
Regional Managing Office; New & Used Car Dealer
N.A.I.C.S.: 551114
Dan Hackett (Grp VP-Fin)

Jim Pattison Broadcast Group (1)
460 Pemberton Terrace, Kamloops, V2C 1T5, BC, Canada
Tel.: (250) 372-3322

Web Site: https://www.pattisonmedia.com
Sales Range: $25-49.9 Million
Emp.: 75
Radio & Television Broadcasting
N.A.I.C.S.: 516210
Rod Schween (Pres)

Unit (Domestic):

CJZN-FM (2)
Top Floor 2750 Quadra Street, Victoria, V8T 4E8, BC, Canada
Tel.: (250) 475-6611
Web Site: https://www.thezone.fm
Sales Range: $25-49.9 Million
Emp.: 60
Provider of Broadcasting Services
N.A.I.C.S.: 516210

Jim Pattison Entertainment Ltd. (1)
Ste 1800 1067 W Cordova St, Vancouver, V6C 1C7, BC, Canada
Tel.: (604) 688-6764
Sales Range: $25-49.9 Million
Emp.: 35
Amusement Park Operator
N.A.I.C.S.: 713110

Subsidiary (Non-US):

Guinness World Records Ltd. (2)
184-192 Drummond St 3rd Fl, London, NW1 3HP, United Kingdom
Tel.: (44) 2078914567
Web Site: http://www.guinnessworldrecords.com
Sales Range: $25-49.9 Million
Book Publishing
N.A.I.C.S.: 513130
Jakki Lewis (Dir-PR-EMEA & Asia Pacific)

Subsidiary (US):

Ripley Entertainment Inc. (2)
7576 Kingspointe Pkwy 188, Orlando, FL 32819
Tel.: (407) 345-8010
Web Site: http://www.ripleys.com
Sales Range: $25-49.9 Million
Amusement Park & Attractions Operator
N.A.I.C.S.: 713110
Tim O'Brien (VP-Comm)

Subsidiary (Domestic):

St. Augstine Sightseeing Trains (3)
19 San Marco Ave, Saint Augustine, FL 32084
Tel.: (904) 829-6545
Web Site: http://www.ripleys.com
Sightseeing Tour Operators
N.A.I.C.S.: 561520

Jim Pattison Lease (1)
1235 - 73rd Ave SE, Calgary, T2H 2X1, AB, Canada
Tel.: (403) 212-8900
Web Site: https://www.jimpattisonlease.com
Sales Range: $50-74.9 Million
Emp.: 100
Automobile Leasing Services
N.A.I.C.S.: 532112
Steve Akazawa (Pres)

Jim Pattison Packaging Group (1)
Ste 1800 1067 W Cordova St, Vancouver, V6C 1C7, BC, Canada
Tel.: (604) 688-6764
Web Site: http://www.jimpattison.com
Sales Range: $25-49.9 Million
Emp.: 30
Aluminum, Plastic & Foam Packaging Mfr
N.A.I.C.S.: 322220
James A. Pattison (CEO)

Subsidiary (US):

Coroplast, Inc. (2)
5001 Spring Valley Rd Ste 400 E, Dallas, TX 75244
Tel.: (972) 392-2241
Web Site: http://www.coroplast.com
Sales Range: $25-49.9 Million
Corrugated Plastic Packaging Mfr
N.A.I.C.S.: 322220
Allison Walker (Sr Dir-Fin Svcs)

Genpak LLC (2)
505 E Cotton St, Carthage, TX 75633
Tel.: (903) 693-7151

Sales Range: $50-74.9 Million
Plastic Kitchenware Products Mfr
N.A.I.C.S.: 326199

Subsidiary (Domestic):

Montebello Packaging (2)
1036 Aberdeen Street, Hawkesbury, K6A 1K5, ON, Canada
Tel.: (613) 632-7096
Web Site: http://www.montebellopkg.com
Aluminum, Laminate & Plastic Tube Packaging Mfr
N.A.I.C.S.: 331315

Meinhardt Fine Foods, Inc. (1)
3002 Granville St, Vancouver, V6H 3J8, BC, Canada
Tel.: (604) 732-4405
Web Site: http://www.meinhardtfinefoods.com
Food Products Distr
N.A.I.C.S.: 424420

Ocean Brands GP. (1)
Suite 100-3600 Lysander Lane, Richmond, V7B 1C3, BC, Canada
Tel.: (604) 242-0030
Seafood Product Mfr
N.A.I.C.S.: 311991

Overwaitea Food Group (1)
20151 Fraser Highway, Langley, V3A4E4, BC, Canada (100%)
Tel.: (604) 533-2911
Web Site: https://www.saveonfoods.com
Rev: $45,000,000
Emp.: 500
Food & Consumer Goods Retailer
N.A.I.C.S.: 445298
Darrelle Jones (Pres)

Pattison Agriculture Limited (1)
777 North Service Road West, Swift Current, S9H 5M1, Canada
Tel.: (866) 877-4321
Web Site: https://www.pattisonag.com
Farm Equipment Distr
N.A.I.C.S.: 532490
Doug Tibben (Pres)

Pattison Outdoor Advertising (1)
2700 Matheson Boulevard East Suite 500, Mississauga, L4W 4V9, ON, Canada
Tel.: (905) 282-6800
Web Site: https://www.pattisonoutdoor.com
Sales Range: $25-49.9 Million
Emp.: 400
Billboard & Outdoor Advertising
N.A.I.C.S.: 541850
Steve McGregor (Pres)

Pattison Sign Group (1)
555 Ellesmere Road, Toronto, M1R 4E8, ON, Canada
Tel.: (416) 759-1111
Web Site: http://www.pattisonsign.com
Sales Range: $200-249.9 Million
Emp.: 800
Visual Communication & Sign Mfr
N.A.I.C.S.: 339950
Nadia Palmerini (CFO & VP)

Plant (Domestic):

Pattison Sign Group (2)
555 Ellesmere Road, Toronto, M1R 4E8, ON, Canada
Tel.: (506) 735-5506
Web Site: http://www.pattisonsign.com
Sales Range: $75-99.9 Million
Emp.: 325
N.A.I.C.S.: 339950
Robert Corsetti (COO)

Plant (US):

Pattison Sign Group (NE) Inc. (2)
125 Kansas Rd Ste 100, Limestone, ME 04750
Tel.: (207) 328-4248
Sales Range: $25-49.9 Million
Emp.: 50
Sign Mfr
N.A.I.C.S.: 339950

TNG (1)
1955 Lake Park Dr Ste 400, Smyrna, GA 30080

Tel.: (770) 863-9000
Web Site: http://www.tng.com
Sales Range: $10-24.9 Million
Emp.: 10,000
Magazine & Book Distr & Surplus Reclamation Services
N.A.I.C.S.: 424920
David Parry (Pres)

Branch (Domestic):

TNG - Albuquerque (2)
5348 Pan American NE, Albuquerque, NM 87109
Tel.: (505) 764-9433
Web Site: http://www.tng.com
Sales Range: $1-9.9 Million
Magazine & Book Distr & Surplus Reclamation Services
N.A.I.C.S.: 424920

TNG - Columbia (2)
901 Idlewilde Blvd Ste 68, Columbia, SC 29201
Tel.: (803) 252-4211
Magazine & Book Distr & Surplus Reclamation Services
N.A.I.C.S.: 424920

TNG - North Fort Myers (2)
7890 Interstate Ct, North Fort Myers, FL 33917-2133
Tel.: (239) 543-5237
Web Site: http://www.tng.com
Sales Range: $10-24.9 Million
Magazine & Book Distr & Surplus Reclamation Services
N.A.I.C.S.: 424920
Kevin Coffey (Depot Mgr)

Westshore Terminals Ltd. Partnership (1)
1 Roberts Bank, Delta, V4M 4G5, BC, Canada (100%)
Tel.: (604) 946-4491
Web Site: http://www.westshore.com
Sales Range: $100-124.9 Million
Emp.: 180
Coal Shipping
N.A.I.C.S.: 212114
Glenn Dodar (VP & Gen Mgr)

THE JOHN CLARK MOTOR GROUP

Alliance Centre Greenwell Road, Aberdeen, AB12 3AX, United Kingdom
Tel.: (44) 8442 473 253
Web Site: http://www.john-clark.co.uk
Year Founded: 1986
Sales Range: $450-499.9 Million
Emp.: 900
New & Used Car Dealer
N.A.I.C.S.: 441110
John Clark (CEO)

THE JORDANIAN PHARMACEUTICAL MANUFACTURING CO., P.L.C.

PO Box 94, Naour, Amman, 11710, Jordan
Tel.: (962) 65727207
Web Site: http://www.jpm.com.jo
Year Founded: 1978
JPHM—(AMM)
Sales Range: $10-24.9 Million
Emp.: 522
Pharmaceutical Preparation Mfr
N.A.I.C.S.: 325412
Mahmoud Jarwan (CEO)

Subsidiaries:

AraGen Biotechnology Ltd. (1)
PO Box 111, Sahab, Amman, 11512, Jordan
Tel.: (962) 64025295
Web Site: http://www.aragen.com.jo
Pharmaceuticals Mfr
N.A.I.C.S.: 325412

Dellas for Natural Products Ltd. (1)
PO Box 851658, Amman, 11185, Jordan
Tel.: (962) 65828644
Web Site: http://www.delass.com.jo
Pharmaceuticals Mfr

AND PRIVATE COMPANIES

THE KANSAI ELECTRIC POWER CO., INC.

N.A.I.C.S.: 325412

THE JUPITER DRAWING ROOM (PROPRIETARY) LIMITED
River Park, 42 Holmstead Rd, Rivonia, 2128, South Africa
Tel.: (27) 11 233 8800
Web Site: http://www.jupiter.co.za
Emp.: 60
Advertising Agencies
N.A.I.C.S.: 541810
Graham Warsop *(Founder & Chm)*

Subsidiaries:

The Jupiter Drawing Room (1)
3rd Fl The Terraces Black River Park, Fir Street Observatory, Cape Town, 3000, South Africa
Tel.: (27) 21 442 7000
Web Site: http://www.jupiter.co.za
Sales Range: $10-24.9 Million
Emp.: 104
Advertising Agencies
N.A.I.C.S.: 541810

THE JUROKU BANK, LTD.
8-26 Kanda-cho, Gifu, 500-8516, Japan
Tel.: (81) 582652111
Web Site: https://www.juroku.co.jp
Year Founded: 1896
8356—(TKS)
Rev.: $1,077,829,280
Assets: $70,067,470,000
Liabilities: $66,166,342,880
Net Worth: $3,901,127,120
Earnings: $142,508,960
Fiscal Year-end: 03/31/21
Commercial Banking Services
N.A.I.C.S.: 522110

Subsidiaries:

Juroku Business Service Co., Ltd. (1)
34 Nakatakeya-cho, Gifu, 500-8047, Japan (100%)
Tel.: (81) 582662682
Clerical Work Services
N.A.I.C.S.: 561499

Juroku Capital Co., Ltd. (1)
8 26 Kandamachi, 500 8516, Gifu, Japan (100%)
Tel.: (81) 582652111
Sales Range: $200-249.9 Million
Emp.: 500
Financial Investment
N.A.I.C.S.: 523999

Juroku Computer Service Co., Ltd. (1)
7-12 Kandamachi 16th Building 4th floor, Gifu, 500-8833, Japan (100%)
Tel.: (81) 582621116
Web Site: http://www.jcs-gifu.co.jp
Sales Range: $100-124.9 Million
Emp.: 58
Computer System Development Services
N.A.I.C.S.: 541519

Juroku DC Card Co., Ltd. (1)
Juroku Bldg 1st Floor, 7-12 kandamachi, 500-8833, Gifu, Japan (100%)
Tel.: (81) 582631116
Web Site: http://www.16dc.co.jp
Sales Range: $75-99.9 Million
Emp.: 500
Business Service Centers
N.A.I.C.S.: 561439
Oriod Takashi *(Pres)*

Juroku Lease Co., Ltd. (1)
Juroku Building 1st Floor, 7-12 kandamachi, 500-8833, Gifu, Japan (100%)
Tel.: (81) 582623116
Sales Range: $150-199.9 Million
Emp.: 500
Commercial & Industrial Machinery & Equipment Rental & Leasing
N.A.I.C.S.: 532490

THE KAIN LIMITED PARTNERSHIP
55 Victoria Street N Unit J, Kitchener, N2H 5B7, ON, Canada
Tel.: (519) 576-6036
Web Site: http://www.kainlp.com
Sales Range: $1-9.9 Million
Residential Real Estate Investment & Management
N.A.I.C.S.: 523999
Harsch Khandelwal *(Mng Partner)*

THE KAMOGAWA GRAND HOTEL, LTD.
820 Hiroba, Kamogawa, 296-0044, Chiba, Japan
Tel.: (81) 470 945581
Web Site: http://www.kamogawagrandhotel.ne
Year Founded: 1947
96950—(JAS)
Sales Range: Less than $1 Million
Hotel Operator
N.A.I.C.S.: 722511
Takeshi Suzuki *(Pres & CEO)*

THE KANESHITA CONSTRUCTION CO., LTD.
471-1 Suzu, Miyazu, 629-2251, Kyoto, Japan
Tel.: (81) 772463151
Web Site: https://www.kaneshita.co.jp
Year Founded: 1951
1897—(TKS)
Rev.: $75,572,310
Assets: $157,405,090
Liabilities: $28,714,500
Net Worth: $128,690,590
Earnings: $1,914,300
Emp.: 247
Fiscal Year-end: 12/31/23
Construction Engineering Services
N.A.I.C.S.: 541330
Shoji Kaneshita *(Pres)*

THE KANOO GROUP, LLC
PO Box 245, Abu Dhabi, United Arab Emirates
Tel.: (971) 23051111 BH
Web Site: http://www.kanoogroup.com
Year Founded: 1890
Sales Range: $500-549.9 Million
Emp.: 1,200
Diversified Holding Company Chemicals; Petroleum; Shipping & Cargo Services; Travel; Real Estate; General Trading; Machinery Mfr
N.A.I.C.S.: 551112
Mishal Hamed Kanoo *(Chm)*

Subsidiaries:

Kanoo Shipping (1)
Khalid Bin Al Waleed St Bur Dubai, Dubai, United Arab Emirates (100%)
Tel.: (971) 4 393 1900
Web Site: http://www.kanooshipping.com
Regional Shipping Services
N.A.I.C.S.: 488510
Steve Blackney *(COO)*

Kanoo Travel (1)
PO Box 290, Dubai, United Arab Emirates (100%)
Tel.: (971) 4 393 8400
Web Site: http://www.kanootravel.com
Full Service Travel Agency
N.A.I.C.S.: 561510
Abdulla Abu Khamseen *(Exec Gen Mgr)*

Yusuf Bin Ahmed Kanoo (1)
Dammam Khobar Highway Opp Industrial Area 1, PO Box 37, Yusuf Bin Ahmed Kanoo Commerci, Dammam, 31411, Saudi Arabia
Tel.: (966) 38571265
Web Site: http://www.ybakanoo.com

Sales Range: $150-199.9 Million
Emp.: 300
Distr of Chemicals
N.A.I.C.S.: 424690

Yusuf Bin Ahmed Kanoo (1)
Medina Road km 9, PO Box 812, Jeddah, 21421, Saudi Arabia
Tel.: (966) 26673759
Web Site: http://www.ybakanoo.com
Distr of Chemicals
N.A.I.C.S.: 424690

Yusuf Bin Ahmed Kanoo & Co (1)
PO Box 45, Manama, Bahrain
Tel.: (973) 220220
Logistics Consulting Servies
N.A.I.C.S.: 541614

Yusuf Bin Ahmed Kanoo & Co. (1)
PO Box 45, Manama, Bahrain (100%)
Tel.: (973) 220 220
International Business Investments
N.A.I.C.S.: 522299

THE KANSAI ELECTRIC POWER CO., INC.
3-6-16 Nakanoshima, Kita-ku, Osaka, 530-8270, Japan
Tel.: (81) 664418821 JP
Web Site: https://www.kepco.co.jp
Year Founded: 1951
9503—(TKS)
Rev.: $26,832,488,580
Assets: $59,707,581,370
Liabilities: $44,284,812,090
Net Worth: $15,422,769,280
Earnings: $2,920,760,700
Emp.: 31,437
Fiscal Year-end: 03/31/24
Electric Energy Generator, Transmitter & Distr
N.A.I.C.S.: 221122
Yasuji Shimamoto *(Exec VP)*

Subsidiaries:

Clearpass Co., Ltd. (1)
Dojima Avanza 9F 1-6-20 Dojima, Kita-ku, Osaka, 530-0003, Japan (100%)
Tel.: (81) 663459251
Web Site: http://www.clearpass.co.jp
Sales Range: $50-74.9 Million
Emp.: 40
Financial Support Services
N.A.I.C.S.: 522291

Ichihara Power Co., Ltd. (1)
1 Yawatakaigandoori Mitsui Zosen Chiba Jigyosho-Nai, Ichihara, 290-0067, Chiba, Japan
Tel.: (81) 436411561
Eletric Power Generation Services
N.A.I.C.S.: 221118

K Cable Television Corporation, Inc. (1)
2-3-10 Kuzuhaasahi, Hirakata, 573-1111, Osaka, Japan
Tel.: (81) 728578601
Web Site: http://www.kcat.jp
Sales Range: $25-49.9 Million
Emp.: 80
Cable Television Broadcasting Services
N.A.I.C.S.: 516210
Junichi Tsujimura *(Pres)*

K-Opticom Corp. (1)
3-3-23 Nakanoshima Nakanoshima Dai Building, Kita-ku, Osaka, 530-6116, Japan
Tel.: (81) 675010600
Web Site: http://www.k-opti.com
Sales Range: $200-249.9 Million
Emp.: 1,000
Telecommunication Servicesb
N.A.I.C.S.: 517111
Makoto Araki *(Pres)*

KANDEN FUDOSAN CO., LTD. (1)
6-2-27 Nakanoshima Nakanoshima Center Building 15F, Kita-ku, Osaka, 530-6691, Japan
Tel.: (81) 664468821
Web Site: http://www.kanden-fudosan.co.jp
Condominium Development & Management Services
N.A.I.C.S.: 236116

KANDEN Security of Society, Inc. (1)
3-24 Taiyuji-cho Nihon Seimei Umeda No 2 Building, Kita-ku, Osaka, 530-0057, Japan
Tel.: (81) 663637051
Web Site: http://www.ksos-web.jp
Home Security Equipments Retailer
N.A.I.C.S.: 459999

KANSO Technos Co., Ltd. (1)
1-3-5 Azuchimachi, Chou-ku, Osaka, 541-0052, Japan
Tel.: (81) 662637300
Web Site: https://www.kanso.co.jp
Sales Range: $150-199.9 Million
Emp.: 532
Construction Engineering Services
N.A.I.C.S.: 541330
Masahiko Ozaki *(Sr Exec Officer)*

Kanden Amenix Corp. (1)
4-11-12 Minamisenba, Chuo-ku, Osaka, 542-0081, Japan
Tel.: (81) 66 253 0265
Web Site: https://www.k-amenix.co.jp
Emp.: 338
Hotel Services
N.A.I.C.S.: 721110

Kanden E House Corp. (1)
3rd floor Aqua Dojima NBF Tower 3F 1-4-16 Dojimahama, Kita-ku, Osaka, 530-0004, Japan
Tel.: (81) 663471854
Web Site: https://k-ehouse.com
Emp.: 151
Construction Engineering Services
N.A.I.C.S.: 541330

Kanden Energy Solution Co., Inc. (1)
Nakanoshima Festival Tower 2-3-18 Nakanoshima, Kita-ku, Osaka, 530-0005, Japan (100%)
Tel.: (81) 5071050147
Web Site: https://www.kenes.jp
Sales Range: $150-199.9 Million
Emp.: 682
Energy Consulting Services
N.A.I.C.S.: 541690
Yukio Kawasaki *(Pres & CEO)*

Kanden Engineering Corp. (1)
6-2-27 Nakanoshima, Kita-ku, Osaka, 530-6691, Japan
Tel.: (81) 664485711
Web Site: https://www.kanden-eng.co.jp
Sales Range: $500-549.9 Million
Emp.: 2,230
Heavy Construction & Engineering Services
N.A.I.C.S.: 237130

Kanden Facilities Co., Ltd. (1)
20F Matsushita IMP Bldg 3-7 Shiromi 1-Chome, Chuo-ku, Osaka, 540-6320, Japan
Tel.: (81) 66 949 2510
Web Site: https://www.kanden-fa.co.jp
Emp.: 1,239
Real Estate Services
N.A.I.C.S.: 531210
Kondo Tadashi *(Pres)*

Kanden Gas Support Co., Inc. (1)
Nakanoshima Festival Tower 2-3-18 Nakanoshima, Kita-ku, Osaka, 530-0005, Japan
Tel.: (81) 507 105 0147
Web Site: https://www.kenes.jp
Power Generation Services
N.A.I.C.S.: 221118
Yukio Kawasaki *(Pres & CEO)*

Kanden Joy Life Co., Ltd. (1)
4-14-3 Nishitenma, Kita-ku, Osaka, 530-0047, Japan
Tel.: (81) 663606369
Web Site: http://www.kjl.co.jp
Emp.: 50
Senior Citizen Homes Operation Services
N.A.I.C.S.: 623312

Kanden Plant Corp. (1)
2-9-18 Honjo Higashi, Kita-ku, Osaka, 531-8502, Osaka Prefecture, Japan
Tel.: (81) 663597539
Web Site: https://www.kanden-plant.co.jp
Emp.: 1,389
Heavy Construction & Engineering Services
N.A.I.C.S.: 237130

THE KANSAI ELECTRIC POWER CO., INC.

The Kansai Electric Power Co., Inc.—(Continued)

Kanden Power-Tech, Corp. (1)
KF Center Bldg 3-6-2 Bingo-machi, Chuo-ku, Osaka, 541-0051, Japan
Tel.: (81) 64 705 8630
Web Site: https://www.kanden-pt.co.jp
Emp.: 964
Electric Power Services
N.A.I.C.S.: 221118
Hiroshi Nakajima (Dir & Pres)

Kanden Realty & Development Co., Ltd. (1)
3-23 Nakanoshima 3-chome, Kita-ku, Osaka, 530-0005, Japan
Tel.: (81) 64 965 2111
Web Site: https://www.kanden-rd.co.jp
Emp.: 619
Leasing Services
N.A.I.C.S.: 532490
Fujino Kenichi (Pres)

Kanden System Solutions Co., Inc. (1)
26-2 Kasayacho, Nishinomiya, 663-8136, Hyogo, Japan
Tel.: (81) 798462200
Web Site: http://www.ks-sol.jp
Information Technology Consulting Services
N.A.I.C.S.: 541512

Kansai Energy Solution (Thailand) Co., Ltd. (1)
689 Bhiraj Tower at EmQuartier Unit 2313 Level 23 Sukhumvit Rd, Khlong Tan Nuea Watthana, Bangkok, 10110, Thailand
Tel.: (66) 65 512 3447
Web Site: https://kest.co.th
Electronic Services
N.A.I.C.S.: 238210

NEWJEC INC. (1)
2-3-20 Honjo-Higashi, Kita-ku, Osaka, 531-0074, Japan
Tel.: (81) 663744059
Web Site: https://www.newjec.co.jp
Sales Range: $150-199.9 Million
Emp.: 738
Construction Engineering Services
N.A.I.C.S.: 541330
Toru Shimizu (Exec Officer & VP)

NIHON NETWORK SUPPORT CO., LTD. (1)
3-6-2 Bingo-cho, Chuo-ku, Osaka, 541-0051, Japan
Tel.: (81) 675069638
Web Site: https://www.nnets.co.jp
Emp.: 412
Building Materials Distr
N.A.I.C.S.: 444180

Nuclear Engineering, Ltd. (1)
1-3-7 Tosabori, Nishi-ku, Osaka, 550-0001, Japan (56%)
Tel.: (81) 664461141
Web Site: https://www.neltd.co.jp
Sales Range: $125-149.9 Million
Emp.: 264
Nuclear Power Services
N.A.I.C.S.: 221113
Hideo Kataoka (Pres)

ORIX Electric Power Corporation (1)
2-14-5 Shiba Orix Shiba 2chome Bldg 3f, Minato-Ku, Tokyo, 105-0014, Japan
Tel.: (81) 354184810
Electric Power Distribution Services
N.A.I.C.S.: 221122

SAKAI LNG Corp. (1)
3-1-10 Chikko Shinmachi, Nishi Ward, Sakai, 592-8331, Osaka, Japan
Tel.: (81) 722803270
Web Site: https://www.sakai-lng.co.jp
Emp.: 58
Liquefied Natural Gas Distr
N.A.I.C.S.: 221210

The Kanden L&A Co., Ltd. (1)
8th and 9th floor Ujiden Building 4-8-17 Nishitenma, Kita-ku, Osaka, 530-0047, Japan
Tel.: (81) 675071350
Web Site: https://www.kla.co.jp
Sales Range: $100-124.9 Million
Emp.: 205
Car Leasing & Insurance Services
N.A.I.C.S.: 532112

THE KEEPERS HOLDINGS, INC.
No 900 Romualdez St Paco, Manila, Philippines
Tel.: (63) 285228801
Web Site: https://www.thekeepers.com.ph
Year Founded: 1963
KEEPR—(OSL)
Rev.: $250,531,596
Assets: $352,427,320
Liabilities: $110,226,014
Net Worth: $242,201,307
Earnings: $40,118,483
Emp.: 206
Fiscal Year-end: 12/31/22
Holding Company
N.A.I.C.S.: 551112

THE KEG ROYALTIES INCOME FUND
10100 Shellbridge Way, Richmond, V6X2W7, BC, Canada
Tel.: (604) 276-0242
Year Founded: 2002
KEG.UN—(TSX)
Rev.: $16,779,124
Assets: $198,965,877
Liabilities: $118,345,665
Net Worth: $80,620,212
Earnings: ($4,197,714)
Emp.: 9,700
Fiscal Year-end: 12/31/21
Investment Management Service
N.A.I.C.S.: 525990
Dean Nick (CEO)

THE KEIHIN CO., LTD.
4-20 Kaigan 3-chome, Minato-ku, Tokyo, 108-8456, Japan
Tel.: (81) 334567801
Web Site: http://www.keihin.co.jp
Year Founded: 1947
9312—(TKS)
Rev.: $307,497,200
Assets: $327,188,390
Liabilities: $140,555,040
Net Worth: $186,633,350
Earnings: $13,543,890
Emp.: 300
Fiscal Year-end: 03/31/24
Warehousing & Logistics Services
N.A.I.C.S.: 493110

Subsidiaries:

Duck Systems Co., Ltd. (1)
4-20 Kaigan 3-chome Minato-ku, Tokyo, 108-0022, Japan
Tel.: (81) 3 3456 7802
Freight Transportation Arrangement
N.A.I.C.S.: 488510

Keihin Airfreight Co., Ltd. (1)
4-20 Kaigan 3-chome, Minato-ku, Tokyo, 108-8456, Japan
Tel.: (81) 334567847
Web Site: http://www.keihinairfreight.co.jp
Emp.: 32
Freight Transportation Arrangement
N.A.I.C.S.: 488510

Keihin Container Transport Co., Ltd. (1)
2F 2-6-4 Yashio, Shinagawa-ku, Tokyo, 140-0003, Japan
Tel.: (81) 3456 7890
Web Site: http://www.kct.keihin.co.jp
Emp.: 22
Freight Transportation Services
N.A.I.C.S.: 488510

Keihin Distribution Co., Ltd. (1)
3-1 Chiwaka-cho Kanagawa-ku, Yokohama, 221-0036, Japan
Tel.: (81) 454412951
Logistic Services
N.A.I.C.S.: 488510

Keihin Harbor Transport Co., Ltd. (1)
11-47 Onohama-cho Chuo-ku, Kobe, 651-0082, Japan
Tel.: (81) 78 391 6031

Keihin Maritime Co., Ltd. (1)
15-2 Daikokufuto, Tsurumi-ku, Yokohama, 230-0054, Japan
Web Site: http://www.keihin-maritime.co.jp
Emp.: 41
Freight Transportation Arrangement
N.A.I.C.S.: 488510

Keihin Multi-Trans (Hong Kong) Limited (1)
Tel.: (852) 25453911
Freight Transportation Arrangement
N.A.I.C.S.: 488510

Keihin Multi-Trans (Shanghai) Co., Ltd. (1)
Tel.: (86) 2163578893
Freight Transportation Arrangement
N.A.I.C.S.: 488510

Keihin Multi-Trans (Singapore) Pte Ltd. (1)
Tel.: (65) 67234333
Freight Transportation Arrangement
N.A.I.C.S.: 488510

Keihin Multi-Trans (Vietnam) Company Limited (1)
2nd Floor PDD Office Building 162 Pasteur, District 1, Ho Chi Minh City, Vietnam
Tel.: (84) 2838238130
Web Site: http://www.keihin.co.jp
Freight Transportation Arrangement
N.A.I.C.S.: 488510

Keihin Multi-Trans Taiwan Co., Ltd. (1)
4FL No 69 Nanking East Road Sec 2, Taipei, Taiwan
Tel.: (886) 2 2581 0533
Freight Transportation Arrangement
N.A.I.C.S.: 488510

Keihin Transport Co., Ltd. (1)
Freight Transportation Arrangement
N.A.I.C.S.: 488510

Keihin-Everett Forwarding Co., Inc. (1)
Freight Transportation Arrangement
N.A.I.C.S.: 488510

OK Container Express Co., Ltd. (1)
790 Hazawa-cho Kanagawa-ku, Yokohama, 221-0863, Japan
Tel.: (81) 45 383 7342
Freight Transportation Arrangement
N.A.I.C.S.: 488510

THE KEIYO BANK LIMITED
11-11 Fujimi 1-chome, Chuo-ku, Chiba, Chiba, Japan
Tel.: (81) 432222121
Web Site: https://www.keiyobank.co.jp
8544—(TKS)
Rev.: $464,121,150
Assets: $43,277,302,670
Liabilities: $41,103,035,710
Net Worth: $2,174,266,960
Earnings: $82,625
Emp.: 1,863
Fiscal Year-end: 03/31/24
Commercial Banking, Bank Card & ATM Services
N.A.I.C.S.: 522110
Toshiyuki Kumagai (Pres)

THE KELLAN GROUP PLC
19-21 Great Tower Street, London, EC3R 5AR, United Kingdom
Tel.: (44) 2072686200
Web Site: https://kellangroup.com
Rev.: $29,730,557
Assets: $13,106,701
Liabilities: $10,370,685
Net Worth: $2,736,015
Earnings: $522,109
Emp.: 1,079
Fiscal Year-end: 12/31/17
Recruiting & Staffing Services
N.A.I.C.S.: 561311

Richard Ward (Chm)

Subsidiaries:

Berkeley Scott Limited (1)
4th Floor New Oxford House 16 Waterloo Street, Birmingham, B2 5UG, West Midlands, United Kingdom
Tel.: (44) 1216315890
Web Site: http://www.berkeley-scott.co.uk
Sales Range: $25-49.9 Million
Emp.: 4
Recruitment Services
N.A.I.C.S.: 561311

Quantica (1)
Quantica House, Lowfields Elland, Halifax, HX5 9DF, W Yorkshire, United Kingdom
Tel.: (44) 1422370011
Web Site: http://www.quantica-search.co.uk
Sales Range: $50-74.9 Million
Emp.: 15
Staffing & Recruitment Services
N.A.I.C.S.: 561311

Subsidiary (Domestic):

RK Group Limited (2)
Ground Fl Faulkner St, Chester, M14DY, Cheshire, United Kingdom
Tel.: (44) 1619299105
Web Site: http://www.rkfinance.co.uk
Recruitment Services
N.A.I.C.S.: 561311

THE KENNARDS HIRE GROUP
PO Box 2022, Seven Hills, 2147, NSW, Australia
Tel.: (61) 288056100
Web Site: http://www.kennards.com.au
Year Founded: 1967
Construction Equipment Distr
N.A.I.C.S.: 423810
Angus Kennard (CEO)

THE KHRUNICHEV STATE RESEARCH & PRODUCTION SPACE CENTRE
18 Novozavodskaya St, 121087, Moscow, Russia
Tel.: (7) 4997498343
Web Site: http://www.khrunichev.ru
Year Founded: 1993
Sales Range: $1-4.9 Billion
Emp.: 19,000
Space Research
N.A.I.C.S.: 927110
Andrey V. Kalinovsky (Gen Dir)

Subsidiaries:

Eurockot Launch Services GmbH (1)
Airbus-Allee 1, 28199, Bremen, Germany (49%)
Tel.: (49) 42143722509
Web Site: http://www.eurockot.com
Sales Range: $50-74.9 Million
Emp.: 9
Commercial Rocket Launch Services
N.A.I.C.S.: 927110
Elena Brandt (Mgr-Future Programs)

International Launch Services (1)
1875 Explorer St Ste 700, Reston, VA 20190
Tel.: (571) 633-7400
Web Site: http://www.ilslaunch.com
Sales Range: $25-49.9 Million
Emp.: 70
Launch Services; Owned by Lockheed Martin Corporation & by Khrunichev State Research & Production Space Center
N.A.I.C.S.: 927110
Dawn Harms (VP-Mktg & Comm)

THE KINGFISH COMPANY N.V.
Oost-Zeedijk 13, Kats, 4485 PM, Middelburg, Netherlands
Tel.: (31) 113745461 NI
Web Site: https://www.the-kingfish-company.com
Year Founded: 2015

KING—(EUR)
Rev.: $23,014,761
Assets: $174,085,825
Liabilities: $81,169,469
Net Worth: $92,916,356
Earnings: ($8,982,119)
Emp.: 137
Fiscal Year-end: 12/31/21
Seafood Product Mfr & Distr
N.A.I.C.S.: 311710
Jean Charles Valette (CFO)

THE KITA-NIPPON BANK LTD.
1-6-7 ChuoDori, Morioka, 020-8666, Iwate, Japan
Tel.: (81) 196531111
Web Site: https://www.kitagin.co.jp
Year Founded: 1942
8551—(TKS)
Rev.: $191,802,370
Assets: $10,064,888,360
Liabilities: $9,496,163,960
Net Worth: $568,724,400
Earnings: $330,500
Emp.: 759
Fiscal Year-end: 03/31/24
Banking Services
N.A.I.C.S.: 522110
Yasuji Ishizuka (Pres & CEO)

THE KIYO BANK, LTD.
1-35 Honmachi, Wakayama, 640-8656, Japan
Tel.: (81) 734239111
Web Site: https://www.kiyobank.co.jp
Year Founded: 1898
8370—(TKS)
Rev.: $560,409,020
Assets: $38,545,415,190
Liabilities: $36,971,488,260
Net Worth: $1,573,926,930
Earnings: $165,250
Emp.: 1,686
Fiscal Year-end: 03/31/24
Commercial Banking Services
N.A.I.C.S.: 522110
Hiroomi Katayama (Pres)

Subsidiaries:

Shoku En Co., Ltd. (1)
2122-3 Sano, Shingu, 647-0071, Wakayama, Japan
Tel.: (81) 735315042
Web Site: https://www.shokuen-global.com
Aqua Farming Services
N.A.I.C.S.: 112511
Masahiko Ariji (Pres & CEO)

THE KLINIQUE MEDICAL CLINIC PUBLIC COMPANY LIMITED
296-299 Chan Issara Tower Building 2 27th Floor Petchburi New Road, Bangkapi Subdistrict Huai Khwang District, Bangkok, 10310, Thailand
Tel.: (66) 23082034
Web Site: https://www.theklinique.com
KLINIQ—(THA)
Rev.: $66,703,056
Assets: $83,069,525
Liabilities: $33,361,024
Net Worth: $49,708,501
Earnings: $8,425,318
Emp.: 1,052
Fiscal Year-end: 12/31/23
Health Care Srvices
N.A.I.C.S.: 621610
Bowonrat Wanadurongwan (Chm)

THE KODENSHA CO., LTD.
5-11-10 Ginza, Chuo-ku, Tokyo, 104-0061, Japan
Tel.: (81) 335425111
Web Site: https://www.kk-kodensha.co.jp
Year Founded: 1917

1948—(TKS)
Rev.: $230,477,480
Assets: $214,322,640
Liabilities: $79,115,090
Net Worth: $135,207,550
Earnings: $5,942,390
Emp.: 1,929
Fiscal Year-end: 03/31/24
Electrical Engineering Services
N.A.I.C.S.: 541330
Hisanori Matsui (Pres)

THE KOREA ECONOMIC BROADCASTING CO., LTD
463 Cheongpa-ro, Jung-gu, Seoul, 04505, Korea (South)
Tel.: (82) 266760019
Web Site: http://www.wowtv.co.kr
Year Founded: 1999
039340—(KRS)
Rev.: $6,470,279
Assets: $149,450,429
Liabilities: $20,565,897
Net Worth: $128,884,532
Earnings: $10,590,696
Emp.: 200
Fiscal Year-end: 12/31/22
Television Broadcasting Services
N.A.I.C.S.: 516120
Park Sanggeun (Gen Mgr)

THE KOSEI SECURITIES CO., LTD.
2-1-10 Kitahama, Chuo-ku, Osaka, 541-0041, Japan
Tel.: (81) 0662090821   JP
Web Site: http://www.kosei.co.jp
Year Founded: 1961
8617—(TKS)
Sales Range: Less than $1 Million
Emp.: 44
Securities Brokerage Services
N.A.I.C.S.: 523150
Daisuke Tatsumi (Mng Dir)

THE KUSTO GROUP INC.
80 Raffles Place #32-01 UOB Plaza 1, Singapore, 048624, Singapore
Web Site: http://www.kustogroup.com
Holding Company
N.A.I.C.S.: 551112
Daniel Kunin (Mng Dir)

Subsidiaries:

Tambour Limited (1)
Haagavish 6 St Industrial Area, PO Box 8488, Kiryat Sapir, Netanya, 42504, Israel
Tel.: (972) 9 892 5561
Web Site: http://www.tambourpaints.com
Sales Range: $125-149.9 Million
Emp.: 530
Paint & Varnish Mfr & Distr
N.A.I.C.S.: 325510
Jacob Moshe (VP-Admin Mgmt & HR)

Subsidiary (Domestic):

Tzah-Serafon Ltd. (2)
Beer Tuvia Industrial Area, PO Box 1132, Kiryat Malachi, 83112, Israel
Tel.: (972) 88507755
Web Site: http://www.tzah-serafon.co.il
Sales Range: $25-49.9 Million
Emp.: 40
Printing Ink Mfr & Marketer
N.A.I.C.S.: 325910
Ronen Cohen (CEO)

Branch (Domestic):

Serafon (3)
Southern Industrial Zone, Ashkelon, 78781, Israel
Tel.: (972) 86742100
Web Site: http://www.serafon.com
Polymers & Adhesives Mfr & Marketer
N.A.I.C.S.: 325520

THE KUWAIT COMPANY FOR PROCESS PLANT CON-

STRUCTION & CONTRACTING K.S.C.
Near Shahrazad Round About Makhfar Stree 30 Shuwaikh Industrial 3, PO Box 3404, Safat, 13035, Kuwait, 13035, Kuwait
Tel.: (965) 1827000
Web Site: https://www.kcpc.com.kw
Year Founded: 1979
KCPC—(KUW)
Rev.: $84,312,266
Assets: $167,210,933
Liabilities: $64,607,235
Net Worth: $102,603,699
Earnings: $8,747,964
Emp.: 1,500
Fiscal Year-end: 12/31/22
Engineeering Services
N.A.I.C.S.: 237990
Moayed Hamad Mosaed Al-Saleh (Vice Chm & CEO)

Subsidiaries:

Mass International (Private) Limited (1)
1101-1103 Uni Plz I I Chundrigar Rd, Karachi, 74000, Pakistan
Tel.: (92) 213 242 5410
Web Site: https://www.massinternational.com
Sales Range: $25-49.9 Million
Emp.: 55
Construction Services
N.A.I.C.S.: 236210

NECON Controls Gen. Trad. & Cont. W.L.L. (1)
PO Box 842, Al Farwaniyah, 8000, Kuwait
Tel.: (965) 24340679
Web Site: http://www.neconme.com
Sales Range: $25-49.9 Million
Emp.: 13
Industrial Engineering Services
N.A.I.C.S.: 541330

Natcon (1)
2nd floor Paladin Building Damascus Road, PO Box 40086, Baabda, 961, Lebanon
Tel.: (961) 5955905
Web Site: http://www.natcon.com.lb
Sales Range: $25-49.9 Million
Emp.: 30
Engineeering Services
N.A.I.C.S.: 541330

THE KYOEI FIRE & MARINE INSURANCE CO., LTD.
18 6 Shimbashi 1 Chome, Tokyo, 105 8604, Japan
Tel.: (81) 335040131   JP
Web Site: http://www.kyoeikasai.co.jp
Year Founded: 1942
Sales Range: $1-4.9 Billion
Emp.: 2,364
Fire, Marine, Automobile & Personal Accident Insurance Carriers
N.A.I.C.S.: 524128
Hirobumi Suginaka (CEO)

Subsidiaries:

Kyoei Fire & Marine Insurance Co., (U.K.) Ltd. (1)
Level 4 City Tower, 40 Basinghall St, London, EC2V 5DE, United Kingdom (100%)
Tel.: (44) 2075885500
Sales Range: $50-74.9 Million
Emp.: 2
Fire, Marine, Automobile & Personal Casualty Insurance Carrier
N.A.I.C.S.: 524128

Kyoei Kasai Business Service Co., Ltd. (1)
1-18-6 Shimbashi 1 Chome, Minato Ku, Tokyo, 105, Japan (100%)
Tel.: (81) 335040131
Web Site: http://www.kyoerkasai.co.jp
Sales Range: $900-999.9 Million
Emp.: 2,300
N.A.I.C.S.: 524128
Katsuki Arakawa (Pres)

Kyoei Kasai Claims Research Co., Ltd. (1)
18 -6 Shimbashi 1 Chome, Minato Ku, Tokyo, 105 8604, Japan (100%)
Tel.: (81) 335040131
Web Site: http://www.kyoeikasae.co.jp
Sales Range: $1-4.9 Billion
N.A.I.C.S.: 524128

Kyoei Kasai Finance Co., Ltd. (1)
18 6 Shimbashi 1 Chome, Minato Ku, Tokyo, 105 8604, Japan (100%)
Tel.: (81) 335040131
Web Site: http://www.kyoeikasae.co.jp
Sales Range: $1-4.9 Billion
N.A.I.C.S.: 524128

Kyoei Kasai Marine Service Co., Ltd. (1)
18 6 Shimbashi 1 Chome, Minato Ku, Tokyo, 105 8604, Japan (100%)
Tel.: (81) 335040131
N.A.I.C.S.: 524128

Kyoei Kasai Training Service Co., Ltd. (1)
1-18-6 Shimbashi, Minato-ku, Tokyo, 105 8604, Japan (100%)
Tel.: (81) 335040131
Sales Range: $900-999.9 Million
Emp.: 2,300
Insurance Services
N.A.I.C.S.: 524128

Kyoei Loan Management Service Co., Ltd. (1)
18 6 Shimbashi 1 Chome, Tokyo, 105 8604, Japan (100%)
Tel.: (81) 335040131
Web Site: http://www.Kyoeika.co.jp
Sales Range: $75-99.9 Million
Emp.: 100
N.A.I.C.S.: 524128

THE KYORITSU CO., LTD.
Kyoritsu Nihonbashi Building 2-2-16 Nihonbashi, Chuo-ku, Tokyo, 103-0027, Japan
Tel.: (81) 359623100
Web Site: https://www.kyoritsu-ins.co.jp
Year Founded: 1910
7795—(TKS)
Rev.: $264,545,420
Assets: $282,954,270
Liabilities: $170,557,830
Net Worth: $112,396,440
Earnings: $5,995,270
Emp.: 259
Fiscal Year-end: 03/31/24
Insurance Services
N.A.I.C.S.: 524210
Koichi Hasegawa (Pres)

THE KYOTO HOTEL, LTD.
537-4 Ichinofunairi-cho Nijo minami-iru Kawaramachi-dori, Nakagyo-ku, Kyoto, 604-8558, Japan
Tel.: (81) 752115111
Web Site: https://www.kyotohotel.co.jp
Year Founded: 1927
9723—(TKS)
Sales Range: $25-49.9 Million
Emp.: 491
Hotel Operator
N.A.I.C.S.: 721110
Koichiro Hiraiwa (Pres)

THE LAKSHMI MILLS COMPANY LIMITED
686 Avanashi Road Pappanaickenpalayam, Coimbatore, 641 037, India
Tel.: (91) 4222245461
Web Site: https://www.lakshmimills.com
Year Founded: 1910
502958—(BOM)
Rev.: $29,308,998
Assets: $98,500,522
Liabilities: $21,643,463
Net Worth: $76,857,059

THE LAKSHMI MILLS COMPANY LIMITED

The Lakshmi Mills Company Limited—(Continued)
Earnings: ($600,923)
Emp.: 319
Fiscal Year-end: 03/31/23
Textile Mill
N.A.I.C.S.: 314999
Aditya Krishna Pathy *(Deputy Mng Dir)*

Subsidiaries:

The Lakshmi Mills Company Limited - Unit 2 **(1)**
Kuppuswamynaidupuram, Palladam Taluk, Coimbatore, 641 662, India
Tel.: (91) 4255 277468
Sales Range: $150-199.9 Million
Emp.: 900
Cotton Yarn Mfr
N.A.I.C.S.: 313110
Rudra Swamy *(VP-Tech)*

THE LAMBTON MOTORS LIMITED

101 Indian Road South, Sarnia, N7T 3W1, ON, Canada
Tel.: (519) 464-4000
Web Site:
    http://www.lambtonford.com
Year Founded: 1927
Sales Range: $25-49.9 Million
New & Used Car Dealers
N.A.I.C.S.: 441110
Mark Guy *(Mng Partner)*

THE LANKA HOSPITALS CORPORATION PLC

No 578 Elvitigala Mawatha Narahenpita, 5, Colombo, 5, Sri Lanka
Tel.: (94) 115530000
Web Site:
    https://www.lankahospitals.com
Year Founded: 2002
LHCL.N0000—(COL)
Rev.: $35,610,958
Assets: $51,043,340
Liabilities: $11,161,010
Net Worth: $39,882,330
Earnings: $10,808,083
Emp.: 2,008
Fiscal Year-end: 12/31/22
Healthcare Services
N.A.I.C.S.: 622110
Wimal Karandagoda *(Co-CEO & Dir-Medical Svcs)*

THE LAUNCH GROUP

13-14 Archer St, London, W1D 7BD, United Kingdom
Tel.: (44) 20 7758 3900
Web Site:
    http://www.launchgroup.co.uk
Sales Range: $25-49.9 Million
Emp.: 35
Digital/Interactive, Event Planning & Marketing, Experiential, Local Marketing, Media Relations, Public Relations
N.A.I.C.S.: 541820
Johnny Pitt *(Founder)*

THE LAW DEBENTURE CORPORATION P.L.C.

8th Floor 100 Bishopsgate, London, EC2N 4AG, United Kingdom
Tel.: (44)2076065451   UK
Web Site:
    https://www.lawdebenture.com
Year Founded: 1889
LWDB—(LSE)
Rev.: $168,341,328
Assets: $1,341,382,227
Liabilities: $263,082,555
Net Worth: $1,078,299,672
Earnings: $94,866,195
Emp.: 288
Fiscal Year-end: 12/31/23
Independent Fiduciary Services

N.A.I.C.S.: 523991
Christopher Smith *(Chm)*

Subsidiaries:

Delaware Corporate Services Inc. **(1)**
919 N Market St Ste 725, Wilmington, DE 19801
Tel.: (302) 482-4288
Web Site: https://www.dcsdelaware.com
Emp.: 3
Business Management Services
N.A.I.C.S.: 561499
Stefanie Hernandez *(Asst VP)*

Law Debenture Trust (Asia) Limited **(1)**
Suite 1301 Ruttonjee House Ruttonjee Centre 11 Duddell Street, Central, Hong Kong, China (Hong Kong)
Tel.: (852) 222349186
Financial Investment Services
N.A.I.C.S.: 523999

Law Debenture Trust Company of New York **(1)**
801 2nd Ave Ste 403, New York, NY 10017
Tel.: (212) 750-6474
Web Site: http://www.lawdeb.us
Emp.: 12
Business Management Services
N.A.I.C.S.: 561499

The Law Debenture Trust Corporation (Channel Islands) Limited **(1)**
IFC5 Castle Street 3rd Floor, PO Box 150, Saint Helier, JE4 5NW, Channel Islands, Jersey
Tel.: (44) 1534888050
Financial Management Services
N.A.I.C.S.: 523999

THE LAWTON TUBE CO., LTD.

Torrington Ave, Coventry, CV4 9AB, United Kingdom
Tel.: (44) 24 7646 6203   UK
Web Site:
    http://www.lawtontubes.co.uk
Year Founded: 1920
Metal Product Whslr
N.A.I.C.S.: 423510
Chris White *(Head-Air Conditioning and Refrigeration)*

THE LEAD CO., INC.

578 Yatogo, Kumagaya, 360-0203, Saitama, Japan
Tel.: (81) 485881121
Web Site: https://www.lead.co.jp
Year Founded: 1949
6982—(TKS)
Sales Range: $25-49.9 Million
Electrical Equipment Mfr & Distr
N.A.I.C.S.: 335139
Motoharu Iwasaki *(Pres & CEO)*

THE LEBANESE COMPANY FOR THE DEVELOPMENT AND RECONSTRUCTION OF BEIRUT CENTRAL DISTRICT S.A.L

Building 149 Saad Zaghloul Street, PO Box 119493, 20127305, Beirut, 20127305, Lebanon
Tel.: (961) 1980650   LB
Web Site: https://www.solidere.com
Year Founded: 1994
SOLA—(BEY)
Rev.: $69,464,110
Assets: $1,945,353,051
Liabilities: $200,882,892
Net Worth: $1,744,470,159
Earnings: ($5,165,210)
Fiscal Year-end: 12/31/22
Property Development & Real Estate Services
N.A.I.C.S.: 236220
Nasser Chammaa *(Chm & Gen Mgr)*

Subsidiaries:

Solidere International Limited **(1)**
Index Tower Office 2003 DIFC, PO Box 506640, Dubai, United Arab Emirates
Tel.: (971) 43761000
Web Site:
    http://www.solidereinternational.com
Real Estate Development Services
N.A.I.C.S.: 531390

THE LICENSING COMPANY LIMITED

1032A Southern Terrace Westfield London Shopping Centre Ariel Way, London, W12 7GB, United Kingdom
Tel.: (44) 208 222 6100
Web Site:
    http://www.licensingcompany.com
Year Founded: 1996
Sales Range: $50-74.9 Million
Emp.: 70
Retail & Brand License Services
N.A.I.C.S.: 926150
Angela Farrugia *(Founder)*

Subsidiaries:

The Licensing Company Germany GmbH **(1)**
Steinheilstrasse 17a / RGB, 80333, Munich, Germany
Tel.: (49) 895230410
Retail & Brand License Services
N.A.I.C.S.: 926150

THE LIKHACHOV PLANT PJSC

Avtozavodskaya st 23A building 2 floor 2 room 201 Business Center, Park of Legends, Moscow, 115280, Russia
Tel.: (7) 4956659676
Web Site: https://www.amo-zil.ru
ZILL—(MOEX)
Sales Range: Less than $1 Million
Automobile Mfr & Distr
N.A.I.C.S.: 336110
Yevgeny Kozhemyakin *(Deputy Gen Dir-Economy & Fin)*

THE LIMESTONE BOAT COMPANY LIMITED

65 A Hurontario Street, Collingwood, L9Y 2L7, ON, Canada
Tel.: (416) 777-5486
Web Site:
    https://limestoneboatcompany.com
BOAT—(OTCIQ)
Rev.: $5,126,771
Assets: $14,330,501
Liabilities: $13,688,810
Net Worth: $641,691
Earnings: ($10,103,616)
Fiscal Year-end: 12/31/21
Asset Management Services
N.A.I.C.S.: 523940
Scott Hanson *(CEO)*

THE LINK REAL ESTATE INVESTMENT TRUST

20/F Tower 1 The Quayside 77 Hoi Bun Road, Kwun Tong, Kowloon, China (Hong Kong)
Tel.: (852) 21751800
Web Site: https://www.linkreit.com
0823—(HKG)
Rev.: $1,559,835,000
Assets: $34,159,672,500
Liabilities: $8,715,772,500
Net Worth: $25,443,900,000
Earnings: $266,985,000
Emp.: 1,332
Fiscal Year-end: 03/31/23
Real Estate Investment Trust
N.A.I.C.S.: 525990
Christine Suk Han Chan *(Chief Investment Officer-Asia)*

INTERNATIONAL PUBLIC

Subsidiaries:

The Link Management Limited **(1)**
20/F Tower 1 The Quayside 77 Hoi Bun Road, Kwun Tong, Kowloon, China (Hong Kong)
Tel.: (852) 21751800
Web Site: https://www.linkreit.com
Sales Range: $75-99.9 Million
Emp.: 400
Management Services
N.A.I.C.S.: 541611
George Hong Choy *(CEO)*

THE LOGISTICS PARTNERSHIP LLP

Priory House, Friar Street, Droitwich, WR9 8ED, United Kingdom
Tel.: (44) 1905 827125
Web Site:
    http://www.thelogisticsnetwork.co.uk
Supply Chain & Logistics Services
N.A.I.C.S.: 541614
Ian Holford *(Mng Partner)*

Subsidiaries:

DriveLink Network Limited **(1)**
The Riverside Business Center Fort Road, Tilbury, RM18 7ND, Essex, United Kingdom **(100%)**
Tel.: (44) 1375398080
Web Site: http://www.drivelink.co.uk
Driver Supply Services
N.A.I.C.S.: 541614

MVP (Search And Selection) Limited **(1)**
Priory House Friar Street, Droitwich, WR9 8ED, Worcestershire, United Kingdom
Tel.: (44) 1905773370
Web Site: http://www.mvp-search.com
Sales Range: $25-49.9 Million
Emp.: 11
Human Resources & Executive Search Consulting Services
N.A.I.C.S.: 541612
Nick Hall-Palmer *(Mng Partner)*

More Driving Limited **(1)**
2nd Fl Homelife House, 26-32 Oxford Rd Bournemouth, Dorset, BH8 8EZ, United Kingdom **(67%)**
Tel.: (44) 1202295755
Web Site: http://www.moredriving.co.uk
Sales Range: $25-49.9 Million
Emp.: 20
Employment Placement Agencies
N.A.I.C.S.: 561311

THE LONGREACH GROUP

Suite 1902 Dina House Ruttonjee Centre, 11 Duddell Street, Hong Kong, Central, China (Hong Kong)
Tel.: (852) 31751700
Web Site:
    http://www.longreachgroup.com
Investment Management Service
N.A.I.C.S.: 523940

THE LOWE-MARTIN GROUP

400 Hunt Club Rd, Ottawa, K1V 1C1, ON, Canada
Tel.: (613) 741-0962   ON
Web Site: http://www.lmgroup.com
Year Founded: 1908
Emp.: 500
Printing Services
N.A.I.C.S.: 323111
Ward Griffin *(CEO)*

THE MABETEX GROUP

Via Cattori 7, 6902, Lugano, Switzerland
Tel.: (41) 919850101
Web Site: http://www.mabetex.com
Year Founded: 1991
Sales Range: $200-249.9 Million
Emp.: 1,500
Engineering Services
N.A.I.C.S.: 541330

Behjget Pacolli *(Founder, Pres & CEO)*

Subsidiaries:

Diamond Hotels and Resorts S.A. (1)
Via Cattori 7, CH-6902, Lugano, Switzerland
Tel.: (41) 91 965 0101
Hotel & Resort Operator
N.A.I.C.S.: 721110

Immobiliare Mabetex S.A. (1)
Via Cattori 7, 6902, Lugano, Switzerland
Tel.: (41) 919850101
Web Site: http://www.mabetex.com
Sales Range: $50-74.9 Million
Real Estate Services
N.A.I.C.S.: 531390
Behjget Pacolli *(Pres)*

Mabco Construction S.A. (1)
Via Cattori 7, Lugano, CH-6902, Switzerland
Tel.: (41) 919852060
Construction Services
N.A.I.C.S.: 236220

THE MALL OF CYPRUS (MC) PLC

Mall of Cyprus Shacolas Emporium Park 3 Verginas Street, 2025, Nicosia, Cyprus
Tel.: (357) 77776255   CY
Web Site:
    http://www.mallofcyprus.com
Year Founded: 1971
ITTL—(CYP)
Rev.: $18,002,014
Assets: $251,618,407
Liabilities: $147,128,191
Net Worth: $104,490,216
Earnings: $8,264,989
Fiscal Year-end: 12/31/19
Online Advertising Services
N.A.I.C.S.: 541850

THE MALL OF ENGOMI (ME) PLC

7-9 28th October Avenue, Engomi, 2414, Nicosia, Cyprus
Tel.: (357) 22006255   CY
Web Site:
    https://themallofengomi.com
Year Founded: 1995
WOOC—(CYP)
Rev.: $4,302,444
Assets: $50,000,794
Liabilities: $23,985,869
Net Worth: $26,014,925
Earnings: $2,958,014
Fiscal Year-end: 12/31/19
Supermarket Store Retailer
N.A.I.C.S.: 445110

THE MANCHESTER AIRPORT GROUP PLC

Manchester Airport, Manchester, M90 1QX, United Kingdom
Tel.: (44) 8712 710 711   UK
Web Site: http://www.magworld.co.uk
Sales Range: $550-599.9 Million
Emp.: 2,576
Holding Company; Airports Operator
N.A.I.C.S.: 551112
Neil Thompson *(CFO)*

Subsidiaries:

East Midlands International Airport Limited (1)
Building 34 East Midlands Airport, Castle Donington, DE74 2SA, Derby, United Kingdom
Tel.: (44) 8081697032
Web Site:
    http://www.eastmidlandsairport.com
Airport Operator
N.A.I.C.S.: 488119
Tim McDermott *(Gen Mgr)*

Manchester Airport Group Property Services Limited (1)
4M 2nd Floor Suite B, Manchester Airport, Manchester, M90 1QX, United Kingdom (100%)
Tel.: (44) 8008499747
Web Site: http://www.magproperty.co.uk
Airport Property Management Services
N.A.I.C.S.: 531312
Jonathan Haigh *(Dir-Dev Mgmt & Infrastructure)*

Manchester Airport plc (1)
Manchester Airport, Manchester, M90 1QX, United Kingdom
Tel.: (44) 871 271 0711
Web Site:
    http://www.manchesterairport.co.uk
Airport Operator
N.A.I.C.S.: 488119
Chris Formby *(Dir-Ops)*

Stansted Airport Ltd. (1)
Enterprise House Bassingbourn Road, Stansted, CM24 1QW, Essex, United Kingdom
Tel.: (44) 8443351803
Web Site: http://www.stanstedairport.com
Rev.: $423,010,000
Assets: $322,272,000
Liabilities: $229,000,053
Net Worth: $171,028,000
Earnings: $40,984,000
Emp.: 2,636
Fiscal Year-end: 12/31/2014
Airport Operator
N.A.I.C.S.: 488119
Ken O'Toole *(CEO)*

THE MANILDRA GROUP

6 Frank Street, Gladesville, 2111, NSW, Australia
Tel.: (61) 298799800
Web Site:
    http://www.manildra.com.au
Year Founded: 1952
Food Products Distr
N.A.I.C.S.: 424490
John Honan *(Mng Dir)*

THE MANITOBA HYDRO-ELECTRIC BOARD

360 Portage Avenue, Winnipeg, R3C 0G8, MB, Canada
Tel.: (204) 480-5900   MB
Web Site: http://www.hydro.mb.ca
Year Founded: 1961
Rev.: $2,378,131,200
Assets: $24,358,634,640
Liabilities: $21,851,427,240
Net Worth: $2,507,207,400
Earnings: ($202,610,520)
Emp.: 4,962
Fiscal Year-end: 03/31/22
Gas & Electricity Distr
N.A.I.C.S.: 221122
Shane Mailey *(VP-Ops)*

Subsidiaries:

Keeyask Hydropower Limited Partnership (1)
360 Portage Ave 14th floor, PO Box 815, Winnipeg, R3C 0G8, MB, Canada
Tel.: (204) 677-6831
Web Site: http://www.keeyask.com
Hydroelectric Power Generation Services
N.A.I.C.S.: 221111

Manitoba HVDC Research Centre Inc. (1)
211 Commerce Drive, Winnipeg, R3P 1A3, MB, Canada
Tel.: (204) 989-1240
Web Site: http://www.pscad.com
Emp.: 100
Electric Power Distr
N.A.I.C.S.: 221122

Manitoba Hydro International Ltd. (1)
211 Commerce Drive, Winnipeg, R3P 1A3, MB, Canada
Tel.: (204) 480-5200
Web Site: http://www.mhi.ca

Sales Range: $25-49.9 Million
Emp.: 70
Engineeering Services
N.A.I.C.S.: 541330
Shawna Pachal *(Sr Mng Dir)*

Manitoba Hydro Utility Services, Ltd. (1)
35 Sutherland Ave, Winnipeg, R2W 3C5, MB, Canada
Tel.: (204) 360-5660
Meter Reading Services
N.A.I.C.S.: 561499

THE MARKET HERALD LIMITED

Level 11 28 The Esplanade, Po Box Z5558, St Georges Tce, Perth, 6000, WA, Australia
Tel.: (61) 861693114
Web Site:
    http://themarketherald.com.au
MKT—(ASX)
Rev.: $61,075,148
Assets: $99,077,188
Liabilities: $54,411,204
Net Worth: $44,665,985
Earnings: $4,248,253
Fiscal Year-end: 06/30/24
Stock Trading Services
N.A.I.C.S.: 523150

Subsidiaries:

Subscribacar Pty. Ltd. (1)
PO Box Z5558, Perth, WA, Australia
Tel.: (61) 1300467382
Web Site: https://subscribacar.com.au
Car Subscription Services
N.A.I.C.S.: 561613

THE MARKETING DEPARTMENT

457 King St, London, N6B 1S8, ON, Canada
Tel.: (519) 439-8080
Web Site:
    http://www.marketingdepartment.ca
Year Founded: 1995
Sales Range: $10-24.9 Million
Emp.: 15
N.A.I.C.S.: 541810
Randy Timmins *(Partner & Dir-Strategy & Client Svcs)*

THE MARKETING GROUP

113 Rue Victor Hugo, 92300, Levallois-Perret, France
Tel.: (33) 141069360
Web Site:
    http://www.themarketingroup.com
Year Founded: 1991
Sales Range: $25-49.9 Million
Emp.: 800
Advertising Agencies
N.A.I.C.S.: 541810
Henri Gardette *(VP)*

THE MARKETING GROUP PLC

Henry Wood House 2 Riding House Street, Oxford Circus, London, W1W 7FA, United Kingdom
Tel.: (44) 65 8193 7625
Web Site:
    http://www.marketinggroupplc.com
Advertising Services
N.A.I.C.S.: 541810
Hannah Middleton *(Dir-Communications)*

Subsidiaries:

TDA Group, LLC (1)
3 Lagoon Dr Ste 160, Redwood City, CA 94065
Tel.: (650) 919-1200
Web Site: http://www.tdagroup.com
Sales Range: $1-9.9 Million
Emp.: 25
Publisher
N.A.I.C.S.: 513199

David Chan *(Creative Dir)*

THE MATTAMY CORPORATION

50 Hines Rd, Ottawa, K2K 2M5, ON, Canada
Tel.: (613) 831-4115
Web Site:
    http://www.mattamyhomes.com
Year Founded: 1978
New Home Builder
N.A.I.C.S.: 236115

Subsidiaries:

Royal Oaks Homes (1)
1210 Trinity Rd, Cary, NC 27513
Tel.: (919) 233-3886
Web Site: http://www.royaloakshomes.com
New Multifamily Housing Construction, except Operative Builders
N.A.I.C.S.: 236116

THE MAURITIUS COMMERCIAL BANK LTD.

9-15 Sir William Newton Street, PO Box 52, Port Louis, Mauritius
Tel.: (230) 2025000
Web Site: http://www.mcb.mu
Rev.: $463,451,257
Assets: $11,374,870,111
Liabilities: $10,102,125,721
Net Worth: $1,272,744,390
Earnings: $234,089,428
Emp.: 2,861
Fiscal Year-end: 06/30/19
Banking Services
N.A.I.C.S.: 522110
Paul Corson *(Deputy Head-Corp & Institutional Banking)*

Subsidiaries:

Fincorp Investment Limited (1)
9-15 Sir William Newton Street, Port Louis, Mauritius (57.56%)
Tel.: (230) 2025000
Rev.: $4,460,387
Assets: $264,864,148
Liabilities: $102,754,148
Net Worth: $162,110,000
Earnings: $7,759,709
Fiscal Year-end: 06/30/2023
Mortgage Services
N.A.I.C.S.: 522310

International Card Processing Services Ltd (1)
Avenue Anse Courtois Les Pailles, Port Louis, Mauritius
Tel.: (230) 2867950
Web Site: http://www.icps.mu
Commercial Banking Services
N.A.I.C.S.: 522110

MCB (Maldives) Private Ltd (1)
H Sifa Building Boduthakurufaanu Magu, Male, Maldives
Tel.: (960) 3305656
Web Site: http://www.mcbmaldives.com
Commercial Banking Services
N.A.I.C.S.: 522110
Mariyam Malveena Ismail *(Head-Fin & Admin)*

MCB Capital Partners Ltd (1)
9-15 Sir William Newton Street, Port Louis, Mauritius (100%)
Tel.: (230) 2135959
Web Site:
    http://www.mcbcapitalpartners.com
Investment Banking & Securities Dealing
N.A.I.C.S.: 523150

MCB Consulting Services Ltd (1)
3118 Washington Blvd, Arlington, VA 22210
Tel.: (703) 615-2468
Web Site: http://www.mcbcs.mu
Commercial Banking Services
N.A.I.C.S.: 522110
Jean-Michel Felix *(CEO)*

MCB Factors Ltd (1)
MCB Centre 9-15 Sir William Newton Street, Port Louis, Mauritius (100%)
Tel.: (230) 2025701

THE MAURITIUS COMMERCIAL BANK LTD.

The Mauritius Commercial Bank Ltd.—(Continued)
Web Site: http://www.mcbfactors.mu
Sales Range: $50-74.9 Million
Emp.: 20
Commercial Banking Services
N.A.I.C.S.: 522110
Rishi Dhunputh (Mng Dir)

MCB Investment Management Co. Ltd (1)
9th Floor MCB Centre Sir William Newton St, Sir William Newton Street, Port Louis, Mauritius (60%)
Tel.: (230) 2025515
Web Site: http://www.mcbim.com
Sales Range: $50-74.9 Million
Emp.: 15
Miscellaneous Financial Investment Activities
N.A.I.C.S.: 523999
Ameenah Ibrahim (Mng Dir)

MCB Properties Ltd (1)
4530 S Sheridan Rd Ste 217, Tulsa, OK 74145-1141
Tel.: (918) 270-4000
Commercial Banking Services
N.A.I.C.S.: 522110

MCB Registry & Securities Limited (1)
9th Floor Sir William Newton Street, 9-11 Sir William Newton St, Port Louis, Mauritius (100%)
Tel.: (230) 2025397
Web Site: http://www.mcbcapitalmarkets.mu
Sales Range: $50-74.9 Million
Emp.: 14
Open-End Investment Funds
N.A.I.C.S.: 525910
Marivonne Oxenhan (Mng Dir)

MCB Seychelles Ltd (1)
Manglier Street, Victoria, Mahe, Seychelles
Tel.: (248) 4284555
Web Site: http://www.mcbseychelles.com
Rev.: $20,204,248
Fiscal Year-end: 12/31/2018
Commercial Banking Services
N.A.I.C.S.: 522110
Bernard Jackson (Mng Dir)

MCB Stockbrokers Limited (1)
2nd & 9yh Floors MCB Centre Sir William Newton St, Port Louis, Mauritius (100%)
Tel.: (230) 2025427
Web Site: http://www.mcbstockbrokers.com
Sales Range: $50-74.9 Million
Emp.: 10
Securities Brokerage
N.A.I.C.S.: 523150
Shivraj Rangasami (Mng Dir & Dir)

Mauritius Commercial Bank - Madagascar (Antananarivo) S.A. (1)
Rue Solombavambohaoka Frantsay 77, BP 197, Antananarivo, Madagascar
Tel.: (261) 202227262
Web Site: http://www.mcbmadagascar.com
Commericial Banking
N.A.I.C.S.: 522110

The Mauritius Commercial Bank (Mocambique) S.A. (1)
Av Friedrich Engels No 400, Maputo, Mozambique
Tel.: (258) 21499900
Web Site: http://www.mcbmozambique.com
Sales Range: $50-74.9 Million
Emp.: 60
Commericial Banking
N.A.I.C.S.: 522110
Peter Higgins (Mng Dir)

The Mauritius Commercial Bank (Seychelles) Ltd (1)
Caravelle House Manglier Street, PO Box 122, Mahe, Seychelles
Tel.: (248) 284555
Web Site: http://www.mcbseychelles.com
Sales Range: $50-74.9 Million
Emp.: 100
Commericial Banking
N.A.I.C.S.: 522110

Union Commercial Bank S.A. (1)
Rue Solombavambohaoka Frantsay 77, BP 197, 101, Antananarivo, Madagascar (75%)
Tel.: (261) 202227262
Web Site: http://www.ucb.mg
Sales Range: $50-74.9 Million
Emp.: 70
Commericial Banking
N.A.I.C.S.: 522110
Joseph Alain Sauzier (Gen Mgr)

THE MAURITIUS DEVELOPMENT INVESTMENT TRUST COMPANY LIMITED
7th Floor Newton Tower Sir William Newton Street, Port Louis, Mauritius
Tel.: (230) 4893888
Web Site:
   https://www.website.mdit.mu
Year Founded: 1967
MDIT—(MAU)
Rev.: $1,139,167
Assets: $30,225,449
Liabilities: $2,397,481
Net Worth: $27,827,969
Earnings: ($3,338,571)
Fiscal Year-end: 06/30/23
Investment Fund Services
N.A.I.C.S.: 525910

THE MAURITIUS UNION ASSURANCE COMPANY LIMITED
4 Leoville LHomme Street, Port Louis, Mauritius
Tel.: (230) 2075500   MU
Web Site:
   http://www.mauritiusunion.com
Year Founded: 1948
Rev.: $113,044,141
Assets: $399,599,157
Liabilities: $316,972,591
Net Worth: $82,626,566
Earnings: $9,411,881
Emp.: 662
Fiscal Year-end: 12/31/18
Insurance Services
N.A.I.C.S.: 524298
Kenny Wong (Chief Underwriting Officer)

Subsidiaries:

Associated Brokers Ltd (1)
3rd Floor Travel House Sir William Newton Street, Port Louis, Mauritius
Tel.: (230) 212 30 38
Web Site: http://www.abrl.net
Emp.: 7
Securities Brokerage Services
N.A.I.C.S.: 523150
Roselyne Phanjoo (Mgr)

Feber Associates Limited (1)
2nd floor Barkly Wharf Le Caudan Waterfront, Port Louis, Mauritius
Tel.: (230) 207 25 07
Web Site: http://www.feber.mu
Pension Fund Management Services
N.A.I.C.S.: 523940
Jerome Katz (Mgr)

National Mutual Fund Ltd (1)
2nd floor Barkly Wharf Le Caudan Waterfront, Port Louis, Mauritius
Tel.: (230) 212 2520
Web Site: http://www.nmf.mu
Emp.: 5
Investment Management Service
N.A.I.C.S.: 523940
Naresh Gokulsing (Exec Dir)

THE MEDITERRANEAN AND GULF INSURANCE COMPANY P.L.C.
Bldg No 7 Abdali Boulevard Rafiq Al Hariri Ave, Abdali Area, Amman, Jordan
Tel.: (962) 65633000
Web Site: https://www.medgulf.com
Year Founded: 1980
MDGF—(AMM)
Rev.: $24,637,618
Assets: $34,638,382
Liabilities: $27,267,606
Net Worth: $7,370,776
Earnings: ($793,773)
Emp.: 76
Fiscal Year-end: 12/31/20
Insurance Related Services
N.A.I.C.S.: 524298

THE MEGILL-STEPHENSON COMPANY LTD.
35D-3965 Portage Ave, Winnipeg, R3K 2H7, MB, Canada
Tel.: (204) 831-4202
Web Site: http://www.birchwood.ca
Sales Range: $400-449.9 Million
Emp.: 800
Holding Company
N.A.I.C.S.: 551112
Mark Chipman (Pres)

Subsidiaries:

Birchwood Automotive Group Ltd. (1)
35D-3965 Portage Ave, Winnipeg, R3K 2H7, MB, Canada
Tel.: (204) 832-1676
Web Site: https://www.birchwood.ca
Emp.: 1,200
New & Used Car Dealers
N.A.I.C.S.: 441110
Stephen Chipman (Pres)

Unit (Domestic):

Birchwood Ford (2)
1300 Regent Ave W, Winnipeg, R2C 3A8, MB, Canada
Tel.: (204) 661-9555
Web Site: http://www.birchwoodford.ca
Sales Range: $25-49.9 Million
Emp.: 95
Car Dealership
N.A.I.C.S.: 441110
Tyrone Brown (Mgr-Fin Svcs)

THE MERCHANTS TRUST PLC
29 Wellington Street Link Group 10th Floor Central Square, Leeds, LS1 4DL, United Kingdom
Tel.: (44) 3716640300   UK
Web Site:
   https://www.merchantstrust.co.uk
Year Founded: 1889
MRCH—(LSE)
Rev.: $58,767,555
Assets: $1,111,753,500
Liabilities: $133,241,790
Net Worth: $978,511,710
Earnings: $48,408,855
Fiscal Year-end: 01/31/23
Investment Management Service
N.A.I.C.S.: 523940
Colin Clark (Chm)

THE MEREDITH PROPERTY GROUP PLC
4th Floor 17-19 Maddox Street, London, EC4R 1AG, United Kingdom
Tel.: (44) 2036518300
Property Management Services
N.A.I.C.S.: 523940

THE METT GROUP
20-38 Overseas Drive, Noble Park, 3174, VIC, Australia
Tel.: (61) 387962150
Web Site: http://www.mett.com.au
Year Founded: 1983
Emp.: 200
Automotive Components Mfr
N.A.I.C.S.: 336390
Vince Westphal (Mgr-Toolroom)

THE MICHINOKU BANK LIMITED
1-3-1 Katta, Aomori, 030-8622, Japan
Tel.: (81) 17 774 1111
Web Site:
   http://www.michinokubank.co.jp
Year Founded: 1921

INTERNATIONAL PUBLIC

8350—(TKS)
Rev.: $405,369,360
Assets: $22,849,581,920
Liabilities: $21,990,791,680
Net Worth: $858,790,240
Earnings: $18,798,560
Emp.: 1,355
Fiscal Year-end: 03/31/21
Banking Services
N.A.I.C.S.: 522110
Kunihiro Takada (Chm)

Subsidiaries:

Michinoku Finance (Hong Kong) Ltd. (1)
Suite 1918 Hutchison House, 10 Harcourt Road Central, Hong Kong, China (Hong Kong)
Tel.: (852) 2869 0823
Banking Services
N.A.I.C.S.: 523991

THE MIDDLE EAST NORTH AFRICA FINANCIAL NETWORK, INC.
39 Abu Sufian St, PO Box 940192, Amman, 11194, Jordan
Tel.: (962) 65690450
Web Site: http://www.menafn.com
Sales Range: $25-49.9 Million
Emp.: 100
Online & Wireless Financial Content & Financial Technology Platform Services
N.A.I.C.S.: 522320

Subsidiaries:

MENAFN.com (1)
39 Abu Sufian Street, PO Box 940192, Amman, 11194, Jordan
Tel.: (962) 65690450
Web Site: http://www.menafn.com
Sales Range: $50-74.9 Million
Emp.: 15
Online Business Information
N.A.I.C.S.: 517810
Sawsan Dababneh (Founder & CEO)

THE MIDONG CO,. LTD.
7th floor Daemyung Building 2652 Nambusunhwan-ro, Seocho-gu, Seoul, Korea (South)
Tel.: (82) 7074250614
Web Site: https://www.the-midong.com
Year Founded: 2009
161570—(KRS)
Rev.: $5,783,476
Assets: $23,703,606
Liabilities: $8,933,159
Net Worth: $14,770,447
Earnings: ($4,014,680)
Emp.: 10
Fiscal Year-end: 12/31/22
Automotive Black Boxes Mfr
N.A.I.C.S.: 336320
Hoo Seong-Yang (CEO)

THE MINAMI-NIPPON BANK LTD.
1-1 Yamashitacho, Kagoshima, 892-8611, Japan
Tel.: (81) 120422373
Web Site: https://nangin.jp
Year Founded: 1913
8554—(FKA)
Rev.: $150,010,960
Assets: $8,546,452,640
Liabilities: $8,036,945,840
Net Worth: $509,506,800
Earnings: $21,412,160
Fiscal Year-end: 03/31/22
Financial Banking Services
N.A.I.C.S.: 522110

THE MINTO GROUP INC.

200-180 Kent Street, Ottawa, K1P 0B6, ON, Canada
Tel.: (613) 230-7051
Web Site: http://www.minto.com
Year Founded: 1955
Sales Range: $250-299.9 Million
Emp.: 1,100
Real Estate Development & Management Services
N.A.I.C.S.: 531390
Roger Greenberg (Chm)

Subsidiaries:

Minto Builders Florida Inc. (1)
4400 W Sample Rd Ste 200, Coconut Creek, FL 33073
Tel.: (954) 973-4490
Web Site: http://www.mintofla.com
Sales Range: $25-49.9 Million
Emp.: 35
Single-Family Housing Construction
N.A.I.C.S.: 236115
Steve Svopa (Exec VP)

Minto Commercial Properties Inc. (1)
180 Kent Street Suite 200, Ottawa, K1P 0B6, ON, Canada
Tel.: (613) 230-7051
Web Site: http://www.minto.com
Real Estate Services
N.A.I.C.S.: 531390
Greg Rogers (Exec VP)

Minto Communities Inc. (1)
200-180 Kent Street, Ottawa, K1P 0B6, ON, Canada
Tel.: (613) 230-7051
Real Estate Services
N.A.I.C.S.: 531390

Minto Communities LLC (1)
180 Kent Street Suite 200, Ottawa, K1P 0B6, ON, Canada
Tel.: (613) 230-7051
Real Estate Services
N.A.I.C.S.: 531390
Michael J. Belmont (Pres)

THE MISSION GROUP PUBLIC LIMITED COMPANY
The Old Sawmills Filleigh, Devon, EX32 0RN, United Kingdom
Tel.: (44) 2074621415   UK
Web Site:
   https://www.themission.co.uk
Year Founded: 2006
TMG—(AIM)
Rev.: $230,604,645
Assets: $203,732,643
Liabilities: $89,904,065
Net Worth: $113,828,579
Earnings: $45,443
Emp.: 1,000
Fiscal Year-end: 12/31/22
Advertising Services
N.A.I.C.S.: 541810
Dylan Bogg (Exec Dir)

Subsidiaries:

April Six (Mobility) Ltd. (1)
1 Alfred Mews Tottenham Ct Rd, London, W1T 7AA, United Kingdom
Tel.: (44) 1895825599
Mobility Advertising & Branding Services
N.A.I.C.S.: 541810

April Six GmbH (1)
C/O Mindspace Viktualienmarkt Rosental 7, 80331, Munich, Germany
Tel.: (49) 1725189071
Mobility Advertising & Branding Services
N.A.I.C.S.: 541810

April Six Inc. (1)
900 Kearny St Ste 700, San Francisco, CA 94133
Tel.: (415) 363-6070
Marketing Consulting Services
N.A.I.C.S.: 541613
Grady Ban (Mng Dir)

April Six Proof Ltd. (1)
Tel.: (44) 1895825599
Web Site: http://www.aprilsixproof.com
Marketing Consulting Services
N.A.I.C.S.: 541613
Ellie Dobson (Mng Dir)

April Six Pte. Ltd. (1)
Tel.: (65) 88189663
Marketing Consulting Services
N.A.I.C.S.: 541613
Geri Tay (Mng Dir)

April-Six Ltd (1)
Chaplin House Widewater Place Moorhall Road, Harefield, UB9 6NS, United Kingdom
Tel.: (44) 189 582 5599
Web Site: https://www.aprilsix.com
Emp.: 70
Technology Marketing Services
N.A.I.C.S.: 541613

Big Communications Ltd. (1)
223 London Road, Leicester, LE2 1ZE, United Kingdom
Tel.: (44) 1162991144
Web Site:
   http://www.bigcommunications.co.uk
Advertising Services
N.A.I.C.S.: 541810

Bray Leino Limited (1)
Filleigh, Devon, EX32 0RX, United Kingdom
Tel.: (44) 159 876 0700
Web Site: https://www.brayleino.co.uk
Rev.: $29,444,000
Emp.: 300
Advertising Services
N.A.I.C.S.: 541810
Anna Donaghey (Head-Plng)

Bray Leino Singapore Pte. Ltd. (1)
73 Ubi Road 1 07-63 Oxley Bizhub, Singapore, 408733, Singapore
Tel.: (65) 67022763
Marketing Consulting Services
N.A.I.C.S.: 541613

Bray Leino Splash Sdn. Bhd. (1)
100 3 005 129 Offices Block J Jaya One No 72a Jalan Universiti, 46200, Petaling Jaya, Selangor Darul Ehsan, Malaysia
Tel.: (60) 379310996
Web Site:
   https://www.brayleinosplash.com.my
Emp.: 1,150
Digital Advertising & Marketing Services
N.A.I.C.S.: 541810

Chapter Agency Ltd. (1)
The Church Chapel Lane, Wythall West Midlands, Bromsgrove, B47 6JX, West Midlands, United Kingdom
Tel.: (44) 156 482 1665
Web Site: https://www.chapteragency.com
Emp.: 30
Marketing Consulting Services
N.A.I.C.S.: 541613

Destination CMS Ltd. (1)
Tel.: (44) 2071757450
Web Site: https://www.wearedestination.com
Marketing Consulting Services
N.A.I.C.S.: 541613
Matt Baker (CEO)

Gingernut Creative Ltd. (1)
55 Highfield Road, Cheshire, Lymm, WA13 0DT, United Kingdom
Tel.: (44) 1925759288
Web Site: http://www.gingernutcreative.co
Graphic & Website Design Services
N.A.I.C.S.: 541430

Influence Sports Ltd. (1)
Fourth Floor The Manufactory 1-8 Alfred Mews, London, W1T 7AA, United Kingdom
Tel.: (44) 2036974120
Web Site:
   https://www.influencesportsmedia.com
Emp.: 1,000
Digital Advertising & Marketing Services
N.A.I.C.S.: 541810

Krow Communications Limited (1)
Tel.: (44) 2075495800
Web Site: https://krowlondon.com
Brand Development & Integration, Communications, Digital/Interactive, Strategic Planning/Research, Viral/Buzz/Word of Mouth
N.A.I.C.S.: 541810

Mongoose Promotions Ltd. (1)
36 Percy St, London, W1T 2DH, United Kingdom
Tel.: (44) 2074621418
Web Site:
   http://www.mongoosepromotions.com
Advertising Material Distribution Services
N.A.I.C.S.: 541870

Mongoose Sports & Entertainment Ltd. (1)
Tel.: (44) 2086295000
Web Site:
   https://www.mongooseagency.com
Emp.: 125
Sports & Fitness Services
N.A.I.C.S.: 713940
Chris Odonoghue (CEO)

Populate Social Ltd. (1)
17 St Andrews Crescent Second Floor, Cardiff, CF10 3DB, United Kingdom
Tel.: (44) 2920253850
Web Site: https://populate.social
Social Media Marketing Services
N.A.I.C.S.: 541613

RJW & Partners Ltd. (1)
Tel.: (44) 7904222898
Web Site: https://www.rjwpartners.com
Pharmaceuticals Product Mfr
N.A.I.C.S.: 325412

RLA Group Limited (1)
Parley Green Lane, Hurn, Christchurch, BH23 6BB, United Kingdom
Tel.: (44) 1202 597 140
Web Site: http://www.rla.co.uk
Sales Range: Less than $1 Million
Emp.: 35
Advertising Services
N.A.I.C.S.: 541810
Paul Smith (Dir-Comml)

Branch (Domestic):

RLA Northern Ireland Limited (2)
90 Lisburn Road, Belfast, BT9 6AG, United Kingdom
Tel.: (44) 2890 664444
Web Site: http://www.thinkrla.co.uk
Emp.: 10
Advertising Services
N.A.I.C.S.: 541810

Solaris Healthcare Network Ltd (1)
Tel.: (44) 2083322222
Web Site: https://www.solarishealth.com
Emp.: 850
Health Care Srvices
N.A.I.C.S.: 621999

Soul (London) Ltd. (1)
LABS House 15-19 Bloomsbury Way, London, WC1A 2TH, United Kingdom
Tel.: (44) 7967820334
Web Site: https://soul.london
Advertising Services
N.A.I.C.S.: 541810

Speed Communications Agency Limited (1)
Tel.: (44) 1179733300
Web Site:
   http://www.speedcommunications.com
Sales Range: $25-49.9 Million
Emp.: 40
Public Relations
N.A.I.C.S.: 541820

Splash Interactive Company Ltd. (1)
Floor 5 SAM Building 152/11B Dien Bien Phu Str, Ward 25 Binh Thanh Dist, Ho Chi Minh City, Vietnam
Tel.: (84) 2835123004
Digital Marketing Agency Services
N.A.I.C.S.: 541613

Splash Interactive Ltd. (1)
Room 1801 Hong Kong Metropolis Building 733 Fuxing Road East, Huangpu District, Shanghai, China
Tel.: (86) 2162187770
Digital Marketing Services
N.A.I.C.S.: 541613

Splash Interactive Ltd. (1)
Room 1101 11/F Cheung Sha Wan Plaza Tower 1 833 Cheung Sha Wan Road, Lai Chi Kok, Kowloon, China (Hong Kong)
Tel.: (852) 39967916

Digital Marketing Services
N.A.I.C.S.: 541613

Splash Interactive Sdn. Bhd. (1)
100 6 047 129 Offices Block J Jaya One No 72a Jalan Universiti, 46200, Petaling Jaya, Selangor, Malaysia
Tel.: (60) 379316690
Digital Marketing Agency Services
N.A.I.C.S.: 541613

Story UK Ltd (1)
1-4 Atholl Crescent, Edinburgh, EH3 8HA, United Kingdom
Tel.: (44) 1312902650
Web Site: https://www.story.agency
Advertising Agency Services
N.A.I.C.S.: 541810

ThinkBDW Ltd (1)
4 Wyncolls Road, Severalls Industrial Estate Highwoods, Colchester, CO4 9HU, United Kingdom
Tel.: (44) 1206546965
Web Site: https://www.thinkbdw.co.uk
Advertising Agency Services
N.A.I.C.S.: 541810
Alan Day (CEO)

THE MIYAZAKI BANK, LTD.
4-3-5 Tachibanadori-Higashi, Miyazaki, 880-0805, Japan
Tel.: (81) 985273131
Web Site: http://www.miyagin.co.jp
Year Founded: 1932
8393—(TKS)
Rev.: $455,356,290
Assets: $27,172,705,280
Liabilities: $25,917,783,560
Net Worth: $1,254,921,720
Earnings: $330,500
Emp.: 860
Fiscal Year-end: 03/31/24
Banking Services
N.A.I.C.S.: 522110
Tetsuji Haraguchi (Sr Mng Dir)

Subsidiaries:

Miyagin Business Service Co., Ltd (1)
1-7-4 Higashi Tachibana-dori, Miyazaki, 880-0805, Japan
Tel.: (81) 985225493
Web Site: https://www.miyagin.co.jp
Commercial Banking Services
N.A.I.C.S.: 522110

Miyagin Card Co. Ltd. (1)
1-7-4 Higashi Tachibana-dori Daiichi Miyagin Building 7F, Miyazaki, 880-0805, Japan
Tel.: (81) 985606800
Web Site: https://www.miyagincard.co.jp
Investment & Management Consulting Services for Government & Corporate Bonds, Credit Guarantee Services & Credit Card Businesses
N.A.I.C.S.: 522210

Miyagin Computer Service Co. Ltd. (1)
1-5-14 Takachihodori, Miyazaki, 880-0812, Japan
Tel.: (81) 985324436
Web Site: https://www.miyagin-ds.jp
Sales Range: $25-49.9 Million
Emp.: 60
Computer Programming Services
N.A.I.C.S.: 541511

Miyagin Lease Co. Ltd. (1)
1-7-4 Higashi Tachibana-dori, Miyazaki, 880-0805, Japan
Tel.: (81) 985285453
Web Site: https://www.miyaginlease.co.jp
Equipment Rental & Leasing
N.A.I.C.S.: 532420

Miyagin Staff Service Co.Ltd. (1)
Daiichimiyagin Building Bekkan, Miyazaki, Japan
Tel.: (81) 985227561
Temporary Help Service
N.A.I.C.S.: 561320

Miyagin Venture Capital Co. Ltd. (1)
4-3-5 Higashi Tachibana-dori, Miyazaki,

THE MIYAZAKI BANK, LTD.

The Miyazaki Bank, Ltd.—(Continued)
880-0805, Japan
Tel.: (81) 985200822
Web Site: https://www.miyaginvc.jp
Investment Banking & Securities Dealing
N.A.I.C.S.: 523150

THE MIYAZAKI TAIYO BANK, LTD.
Tel.: (81) 985242111
Year Founded: 1941
8560—(FKA)
Rev.: $130,250,680
Assets: $6,460,301,680
Liabilities: $6,051,979,920
Net Worth: $408,321,760
Earnings: $9,775,220
Fiscal Year-end: 03/31/20
Commercial Banking Services
N.A.I.C.S.: 522110
Yoji Hayashida (Pres)

THE MONARCH PARTNERSHIP LIMITED
Monarch House 7-9 Stafford Road, Wallington, SM6 9AN, Surrey, United Kingdom
Tel.: (44) 20 8835 3535
Web Site:
  http://monarchpartnership.co.uk
Utility Contractor
N.A.I.C.S.: 926130

Subsidiaries:

Energy Intelligence Centre Ltd (1)
3 Brooklands Moons Moat Drive, North Moons Moat, Redditch, B98 9DW, United Kingdom
Tel.: (44) 1527 511 757
Web Site: http://www.eic.co.uk
Energy Management Consulting Services
N.A.I.C.S.: 541690
Neil Cressy (Head-Sls-Corp)

Branch (Domestic):

The Energy Information Centre Ltd. (2)
Linden Square, Kings Road, Bury Saint Edmunds, IP33 3DJ, Suffolk, United Kingdom
Tel.: (44) 1284 718 111
Web Site: http://www.eic.co.uk
Emp.: 30
Energy Management Consulting Services
N.A.I.C.S.: 541690
Ashley Guise (Mgr)

THE MONOGATARI CORPORATION
5-7-11 Nishi-Iwata, Toyohashi, 440-0831, Japan
Tel.: (81) 532638001
Web Site:
  https://www.monogatari.co.jp
Year Founded: 1969
3097—(TKS)
Rev.: $666,510,320
Assets: $382,716,600
Liabilities: $198,865,840
Net Worth: $183,850,760
Earnings: $35,074,580
Emp.: 1,428
Fiscal Year-end: 06/30/24
Restaurant Owner & Operator; Food Retailer
N.A.I.C.S.: 722511
Hisayuki Kato (Pres)

THE MOTOR & GENERAL FINANCE LIMITED
MGF House 4/17-B Asaf Ali Road, New Delhi, 110002, India
Tel.: (91) 1123272216
Web Site: https://www.mgfltd.com
Year Founded: 1930
501343—(BOM)
Rev.: $1,078,532
Assets: $20,844,698
Liabilities: $11,992,626
Net Worth: $8,852,071
Earnings: ($314,502)
Emp.: 18
Fiscal Year-end: 03/31/23
Retail Real Estate & Property Development Services; Car Dealership Owner & Operator
N.A.I.C.S.: 236220
Rajiv Gupta (Chm, CEO & Co-Mng Dir)

Subsidiaries:

Emaar MGF Land Limited (1)
306-308 3rd Floor Square One C-2 District Centre, Saket, New Delhi, 110017, India
Tel.: (91) 1141521155
Web Site: http://www.emaarmgf.com
Sales Range: $50-74.9 Million
Emp.: 80
Real Estate Services
N.A.I.C.S.: 531390

THE MURUGAPPA GROUP, LTD.
Dare House NSC Bose Rd Parrys Corner, George Town, Chennai, 600 001, India
Tel.: (91) 4425306789   In
Web Site:
  http://www.murugappa.com
Year Founded: 1900
Sales Range: $1-4.9 Billion
Emp.: 32,000
Holding Company
N.A.I.C.S.: 551112
M. M. Murugappan (Chm)

Subsidiaries:

Carborundum Universal Limited (1)
43 Parry House Moore Street, Chennai, 600 001, India   (42.09%)
Tel.: (91) 4430006161
Web Site: https://www.cumi.murugappa.com
Rev.: $459,264,351
Assets: $453,566,022
Liabilities: $119,180,471
Net Worth: $334,385,552
Earnings: $47,777,730
Emp.: 2,121
Fiscal Year-end: 03/31/2022
Abrasive Product Mfr
N.A.I.C.S.: 327910
K. Srinivasan (Mng Dir)

Subsidiary (US):

CUMI America Inc (2)
3940 Olympic Blvd Ste 400, Erlanger, KY 41018
Tel.: (859) 816-0234
Web Site: http://www.cumi-murugappa.com
Abrasive Product Mfr
N.A.I.C.S.: 327910

Subsidiary (Non-US):

CUMI Australia Pty Ltd (2)
29 Gipps Street, PO Box 142, Carrington, 2294, NSW, Australia
Tel.: (61) 249400035
Web Site: http://www.cumi.com.au
Sales Range: $25-49.9 Million
Emp.: 10
Industrial Ceramic Products Mfr
N.A.I.C.S.: 333994
Sushil Kumar (Mgr-Sls)

CUMI Middle East FZE (2)
Rak Free Trade Zone, PO Box 10559, Ras al Khaimah, 16190, United Arab Emirates
Tel.: (971) 72046181
Web Site: http://www.cumi.murugappa.com
Emp.: 3
Abrasive Product Mfr
N.A.I.C.S.: 327910
D. Srinavasan (Gen Mgr)

Division (Domestic):

Carborundum Universal Ltd. - Electro Minerals Division (2)
Kalamassery Development Plot PO, PO Box 1, Ernakulam, Kochi, 683 109, Kerala, India
Tel.: (91) 4843003600
Emp.: 300
Abrasive Product Mfr
N.A.I.C.S.: 327910
Jayan Ps (Sr VP)

Subsidiary (Non-US):

Foskor Zirconia (Pty) Ltd (2)
27 Selati Street, Phalaborwa, 1389, South Africa   (51%)
Tel.: (27) 15 789 2346
Web Site: http://www.foskor.co.za
Sales Range: $50-74.9 Million
Emp.: 96
Industrial Chemicals Mfr
N.A.I.C.S.: 325998
Albert Render (CEO)

Subsidiary (Domestic):

Sterling Abrasives Ltd (2)
Plot No 45/46 GIDC Estate Odhav Road, Ahmedabad, 382415, Gujarat, India
Tel.: (91) 79 22870905
Web Site: http://www.sterlingabrasives.com
Sales Range: $25-49.9 Million
Emp.: 100
Grinding Wheel Mfr
N.A.I.C.S.: 327910
Nitin Parikh (Founder)

Subsidiary (Non-US):

Thukela Refractories Isithebe (Pty) Limited (2)
1 Yellow Street, Isithebe, 4490, South Africa
Tel.: (27) 32 459 120
Sales Range: $25-49.9 Million
Emp.: 12
Mineral Materials Mfr
N.A.I.C.S.: 327999
Allan Thomson (Mgr-Comml & Admin)

Volzhsky Abrasive Works JSC (2)
Road 6 18, Volzhsky, 404130, Volgograd, Russia
Tel.: (7) 8443412312
Web Site: http://www.vabz.ru
Silicon Carbide Mfr
N.A.I.C.S.: 327910
Kostrov Sergey Vyacheslavovich (Gen Dir)

Cholamandalam Investment & Finance Company Ltd. (1)
Chola Crest C54-55 & Super B-4, Thiru-Vi-Ka Industrial Estate Guindy, Chennai, 600032, India
Tel.: (91) 4440907172
Web Site: https://www.cholamandalam.com
Rev.: $2,333,872,209
Assets: $18,830,510,079
Liabilities: $16,475,802,333
Net Worth: $2,354,707,746
Earnings: $411,021,443
Emp.: 38,235
Fiscal Year-end: 03/31/2024
Financial Services
N.A.I.C.S.: 522310
P. Sujatha (Officer-Compliance & Sec)

E.I.D. - Parry (India) Limited (1)
Dare House New No 2 Old 234 NSC Bose Road, Chennai, 600001, India (45.71%)
Tel.: (91) 4425306789
Web Site: https://www.eidparry.com
Rev.: $2,543,076,900
Assets: $1,810,482,765
Liabilities: $878,366,580
Net Worth: $932,116,185
Earnings: $136,475,430
Emp.: 2,022
Fiscal Year-end: 03/31/2021
Holding Company; Cane Sugar, Bio-Pesticides & Nutraceuticals Mfr
N.A.I.C.S.: 551112
S. K. Sathyavrdhan (Sr VP-HR)

Subsidiary (Non-US):

Alimtec S.A. (2)
Almirante Latorre 617, Santiago, CP 8370356, Chile   (100%)
Tel.: (56) 992255792
Web Site: http://www.alimtec.com
Bioactive Ingredients Mfr
N.A.I.C.S.: 325414

Holding (Domestic):

Coromandel International Limited (2)
Coromandel House 1-2-10 Sardar Patel Road, Secunderabad, 500003, Telangana, India   (63.83%)
Tel.: (91) 4066997300
Web Site: https://www.coromandel.biz
Rev.: $3,572,810,983
Assets: $1,706,708,231
Liabilities: $758,588,814
Net Worth: $948,119,417
Earnings: $241,344,044
Emp.: 3,833
Fiscal Year-end: 03/31/2023
Phosphatic Fertilizer, Specialty Agriculture Nutrients & Crop Protection Products Mfr & Distr
N.A.I.C.S.: 325312
V. Ravichandran (Vice Chm)

Subsidiary (Domestic):

Parry Sugar Industries Limited (3)
1/2 3rd Floor Venus Building Kalayanamantapa Road, Jakkasandra Koramangala Extension, Bengaluru, 560034, India
Tel.: (91) 80 49006666
Web Site: http://www.parrysugar.com
Emp.: 8
Sugar Mfr
N.A.I.C.S.: 311314
Suresh Munavalli (Assoc Mgr-Fin & Acct)

Subsidiary (Non-US):

Sabero Argentina S.A. (3)
Marcelo T De Alvear 1430, Buenos Aires, 1060, Argentina
Tel.: (54) 114 815 8721
Fertilizer Distr
N.A.I.C.S.: 424690

Sabero Europe BV (3)
Markerwaardweg 8, 1606 AS, Amsterdam, Netherlands
Tel.: (31) 228 592044
Fertilizer Distr
N.A.I.C.S.: 424690

Subsidiary (US):

Parry America Inc (2)
6565 N MacArthur Blvd Ste 225, Irving, TX 75039
Tel.: (214) 624-5115
Web Site: http://www.parryamerica.com
Biopesticides Distr
N.A.I.C.S.: 424910
K. Narasimha Rao Kothapalli (Pres & CEO)

Subsidiary (Domestic):

Parry Infrastructure Company Private Limited (2)
Dare House New No 2 Old 234, NSC Bose Road, Chennai, 600 001, India
Tel.: (91) 4425306789
Web Site: http://www.eidparry.com
Rev.: $2,429,070,044
Assets: $2,271,576,392
Liabilities: $1,612,389,440
Net Worth: $659,186,952
Earnings: $80,512,108
Fiscal Year-end: 03/31/2018
Infrastructure Development Services
N.A.I.C.S.: 561210
V. Ramesh (Mng Dir)

Parry Phytoremedies Private Limited (2)
Sr No 79/2 Near Agarwal Godown Shivane Warje-NDA Rd, Pune, 411023, Maharashtra, India   (100%)
Tel.: (91) 20 25293237
Web Site: www.parryphyto.com
Emp.: 20
Health Supplements Mfr
N.A.I.C.S.: 456191
Kuldeep Wayase (Gen Mgr)

Silkroad Sugar Private Limited (2)
Vakalapudi Kakinada, East Godavari District, Kakinada, 533005, Andhra Pradesh, India
Tel.: (91) 884 2000666
Sugar Mfr
N.A.I.C.S.: 424490

Parry Agro Industries Ltd (1)
Parry House 5th Floor 43 Moore Street, Chennai, 600 001, India
Tel.: (91) 44 25306812
Web Site: http://www.parryagro.com
Tea Mfr

Tube Investments of India Limited (1)
Dare House 234 N S C Bose Road, Chennai, 600 001, India (34.38%)
Tel.: (91) 4442177770
Web Site: https://tiindia.com
Rev.: $1,724,524,620
Assets: $1,213,254,315
Liabilities: $704,756,325
Net Worth: $508,497,990
Earnings: $135,276,960
Emp.: 3,107
Fiscal Year-end: 03/31/2022
Steel Products Mfr
N.A.I.C.S.: 331210
L. Ramkumar (Mng Dir)

N.A.I.C.S.: 311920
Gurushankar Raman (CFO)

Subsidiary (Non-US):

Sedis SAS (2)
35 rue des Bas Trevois, 10000, Troyes, Champagne-Ardenne, France
Tel.: (33) 3 25 76 29 50
Automotive Spare Parts Distr
N.A.I.C.S.: 423120

Subsidiary (Domestic):

TI Cycles of India Ltd (2)
M T H Road, PO Box 5, Ambattur, Chennai, 600 053, India
Tel.: (91) 44 42093434
Web Site: http://www.tiindia.com
Automotive Spare Parts Distr
N.A.I.C.S.: 423120
Suman Louis (Mgr-HR)

Plant (Domestic):

TI Cycles of India Ltd - Noida Plant (3)
A-32 Phase II Extn Hoisery Complex Opp Nepz Dadri Road, Gautam Bugh Nagar, Noida, 201305, Uttar Pradesh, India
Tel.: (91) 120 4332200
Automotive Spare Parts Distr
N.A.I.C.S.: 423120

Subsidiary (Domestic):

TI Metal Forming Ltd (2)
Chennai Thiruvallur High Road, Thiruninravur, Chennai, 6020204, India
Tel.: (91) 44 26390194
Automotive Spare Parts Distr
N.A.I.C.S.: 423120

Plant (Domestic):

TI Metal Forming Ltd - Ahmedabad Plant (3)
Tata Motors Vender Park Survey No 1 Northkotpura Sanand, Viroch Nagar, Ahmedabad, 382 170, India
Tel.: (91) 90072 62206
Automotive Spare Parts Distr
N.A.I.C.S.: 423120

TI Metal Forming Ltd - Baroda Plant (3)
Plot No 501-B&C Halol Industrial Estate Survey Nos 32 & 34 Dunia, Halol Panchmahals, Baroda, 389 350, India
Tel.: (91) 2676 224647
Automotive Spare Parts Distr
N.A.I.C.S.: 423120

TI Metal Forming Ltd - Bhawal Plant (3)
Plot No 245 Sector 3 Growth Centre, Rewari Haryana, Bawal, 123 501, India
Tel.: (91) 1284 260707
Automotive Spare Parts Distr
N.A.I.C.S.: 423120

TI Metal Forming Ltd - Kakkalur Plant (3)
Plot No 80 81 Sidco Industrial Estate Kakkalur, Thiruvallur, Chennai, 602 003, India
Tel.: (91) 44 27667104
Automotive Spare Parts Distr
N.A.I.C.S.: 423120

TI Metal Forming Ltd - Pune Plant (3)
Gat No 312 Sable Wadi Bahul Post Chakan Shikrapur Road, Khed Taluk, Pune, 410 501, India
Tel.: (91) 2135 202146
Automotive Spare Parts Distr
N.A.I.C.S.: 423120

Subsidiary (Domestic):

TIDC India Limited (2)
M T H Road, PO Box 11, Ambattur, Chennai, 600 053, India
Tel.: (91) 44 422355508
Web Site: http://www.tidcindia.in
Emp.: 1,000
Automotive Spare Parts Distr
N.A.I.C.S.: 423120
M. Murugappan (Chm)

Plant (Domestic):

TIDC India Limited - Haridwar Plant (3)
Khasra No 230 231, Village Gangnouli Tehsil Laksar, Haridwar, 247 663, Uttrakhand, India
Tel.: (91) 1332 259359
Automotive Spare Parts Distr
N.A.I.C.S.: 423120

TIDC India Limited - Medak Plant (3)
Plot No 1 Jinnaram Mandal, Kazipally Village, Medak, 502319, Andhra Pradesh, India
Tel.: (91) 8458 277240
Automotive Spare Parts Distr
N.A.I.C.S.: 423120

Subsidiary (Domestic):

Tube Products of India Ltd. (2)
PO Box No 4, Avadi, Chennai, 600 054, India
Tel.: (91) 44 42291999
Web Site: http://www.tubeproductsindia.com
Steel Products Mfr
N.A.I.C.S.: 331210
Kalyan Kumar Paul (Pres)

Plant (Domestic):

Tube Products of India Ltd. - Mohali Plant (3)
A-16/17 Industrial Focal Point Phase 6 - SAS Nagar, Mohali, 160 051, India
Tel.: (91) 172 267308
Web Site: http://www.tubeproductsindia.com
Steel Products Mfr
N.A.I.C.S.: 331210

Tube Products of India Ltd. - Shirwal Plant (3)
Shirwal Post Khandala Taluka, Satara, 412 801, India
Tel.: (91) 2169 244080
Web Site: http://www.tubeproductsindia.com
Steel Products Mfr
N.A.I.C.S.: 331210

THE MUSASHINO BANK, LTD.
10-8 Sakuragi-cho 1-chome, Omiyaku, Saitama, 330-0854, Japan
Tel.: (81) 486416111
Web Site: https://www.musashinobank.co.jp
Year Founded: 1952
8336—(TKS)
Rev.: $535,859,480
Assets: $35,720,539,150
Liabilities: $33,908,486,970
Net Worth: $1,812,052,180
Earnings: $363,550
Emp.: 1,943
Fiscal Year-end: 03/31/24
Commercial Banking Services
N.A.I.C.S.: 522110
Kikuo Kato (Chm)

Subsidiaries:

The Musashino Card Co., Ltd. (1)
1-10-8 Sakuragi-cho, Omiya-ku, Saitama, 330-0854, Japan
Tel.: (81) 486435081
Web Site: https://www.musashino-card.co.jp
Emp.: 34
Credit Card Services
N.A.I.C.S.: 522320

THE NAGA GROUP AG
Suhrenkamp 59, 22335, Hamburg, Germany
Tel.: (49) 4052477910   De
Web Site: https://www.thenagagroup.com
Year Founded: 2015
N4G—(DEU)
Rev.: $43,856,755
Assets: $67,203,606
Liabilities: $10,983,506
Net Worth: $56,220,099
Earnings: ($67,269,838)
Emp.: 100
Fiscal Year-end: 12/31/23
Application Software Development Services
N.A.I.C.S.: 541511
Harald Patt (Co-Mng Dir & Chief Digital Officer)

THE NAGANO BANK LTD.
2-9-38 Nagisa, Matsumoto, 390-8708, Nagano, Japan
Tel.: (81) 26 327 3311
Web Site: http://www.naganobank.co.jp
Year Founded: 1950
8521—(TKS)
Rev.: $191,518,800
Assets: $12,266,776,720
Liabilities: $11,782,060,400
Net Worth: $484,716,320
Earnings: $12,932,480
Emp.: 667
Fiscal Year-end: 03/31/22
Banking Services
N.A.I.C.S.: 522110

THE NANTO BANK, LTD.
16 Hashimotocho, Nara, 630-8677, Japan
Tel.: (81) 742271599   JP
Web Site: https://www.nantobank.co.jp
Year Founded: 1934
8367—(TKS)
Rev.: $566,714,960
Assets: $44,862,440,160
Liabilities: $42,888,489,250
Net Worth: $1,973,950,910
Earnings: $489,140
Emp.: 2,336
Fiscal Year-end: 03/31/24
Financial Investment Services
N.A.I.C.S.: 523999
Takashi Hashimoto (Pres)

Subsidiaries:

Nanto Bank Business Division (1)
16 Hashimoto-cho, Nara, 630 8677, Japan (100%)
Tel.: (81) 7 4227 1552
Web Site: http://www.nantobank.co.jp
Sales Range: $1-4.9 Billion
Emp.: 3,000
Commericial Banking
N.A.I.C.S.: 522110
Yoshiaki Morita (Gen Mgr)

Nanto Bank Securities & International Division (Nara) (1)
16 Hashimoto Cho, Nara, 630 8677, Japan (100%)
Tel.: (81) 742271560
Web Site: http://www.nantobank.com
Sales Range: $1-4.9 Billion
Emp.: 2,800
Banking Services
N.A.I.C.S.: 522110

Nanto Bank Securities & International Division (Tokyo) (1)
16 Hashimoto-Cho, Nara, 630 8677, Japan (100%)
Tel.: (81) 742271560
Web Site: http://www.nantobank.co.jp
Sales Range: $700-749.9 Million
Emp.: 2,000
Banking Services
N.A.I.C.S.: 522110

Nanto Business Service Co., Ltd. (1)
93 2 Minami Kyobate Cho 1 Chome, Nara, 630 8141, Japan (100%)
Tel.: (81) 742502120
Sales Range: $10-24.9 Million
Emp.: 50
Provider of Administrative Services
N.A.I.C.S.: 561110

Nanto Card Services Co., Ltd. (1)
Nanto Jisho Higashi-Ikoma Building 4F 1-61-7 Higashi-Ikoma, Ikoma, 630-0213, Nara, Japan
Tel.: (81) 743708881
Web Site: https://www.nantocard.jp
Emp.: 19
Credit Card Business
N.A.I.C.S.: 522210

Nanto Computer Service Co., Ltd. (1)
93 2 Minami Kyobate Cho 1 Chome, Ikoma, 630 8141, Nara, Japan (5%)
Tel.: (81) 742502125
Computer Software Development & Services
N.A.I.C.S.: 541511

Nanto Credit Guarantee Co., Ltd. (1)
2 1 Omiyacho 6 Chome, Nara, 630 8115, Japan (3%)
Tel.: (81) 742355400
Sales Range: $50-74.9 Million
Emp.: 12
Business Credit Institution
N.A.I.C.S.: 522299

Nanto DC Card Co., Ltd. (1)
4th floor Higashi-Ikoma 1-61-7 Nanto Jisho Higashi-Ikoma Building, Ikoma, 630-0213, Nara, Japan (5%)
Tel.: (81) 743716800
Web Site: https://www.nantocard.jp
Credit Card Business
N.A.I.C.S.: 522210

Nanto Lease Co., Ltd. (1)
52 1 Omori Cho, Nara, 630 8131, Japan
Tel.: (81) 742265131
Sales Range: $50-74.9 Million
Emp.: 19
Provider of Equipment Leasing Services
N.A.I.C.S.: 532210

Nanto Staff Service Co., Ltd. (1)
2-1 Omiya Cho 6 Chome, Nara, 630 8677, Japan (100%)
Tel.: (81) 742221131
Web Site: http://www.nantobank.co.jp
Sales Range: $25-49.9 Million
Emp.: 5
Temporary Staffing Solutions
N.A.I.C.S.: 561320

THE NATIONAL BANK
Al-Masyoun, PO Box 700, Ramallah, Palestine
Tel.: (970) 22946090
Web Site: http://www.tnb.ps
Year Founded: 2005
Sales Range: Less than $1 Million
Commercial Banking Services
N.A.I.C.S.: 522110
Salameh Khalil (CEO)

THE NATIONAL BANK OF KAZAKHSTAN
21 Koktem-3, 050040, Almaty, Kazakhstan
Tel.: (7) 7272704591
Web Site: http://www.nationalbank.kz
Banking Services
N.A.I.C.S.: 522110
Erbolat Askarbekovich Dossaev (Governor)

Subsidiaries:

Kazakhstan Housing Company JSC (1)
55A Mangilik El Ave, Yesil District, Z05T3E2, Astana, Kazakhstan
Tel.: (7) 7273441222
Web Site: https://www.kmc.kz
Rev.: $363,598,233

THE NATIONAL BANK OF KAZAKHSTAN

The National Bank of Kazakhstan—(Continued)

Assets: $3,258,631,194
Liabilities: $2,721,608,968
Net Worth: $537,022,226
Earnings: $91,760,650
Emp.: 195
Fiscal Year-end: 12/31/2023
Mortgage Lending Services
N.A.I.C.S.: 522310

THE NATIONAL BANK OF RAS AL-KHAIMAH PSC

RAK Operations Centre Emirates Road, PO Box 5300, Ras al Khaimah, United Arab Emirates
Tel.: (971) 42130000   AE
Web Site: http://www.rakbank.ae
Year Founded: 1976
Sales Range: $150-199.9 Million
Emp.: 723
Banking Services
N.A.I.C.S.: 522110
Peter England (CEO)

Subsidiaries:

Ras Al Khaimah National Insurance Company P.S.C.   (1)
6/F RAKBANK Building Al Jazeera Sheikh Saqr Bin Mohammad Al Qasimi, Ras al Khaimah, United Arab Emirates **(79.23%)**
Tel.: (971) 8007254
Web Site: https://www.rakinsurance.com
Rev.: $126,428,853
Assets: $164,288,979
Liabilities: $120,849,664
Net Worth: $43,439,314
Earnings: $3,958,937
Emp.: 200
Fiscal Year-end: 12/31/2023
Insurance Services
N.A.I.C.S.: 524298
Claude Zoghbi (Chief Comml Officer)

THE NATIONAL DETERGENT COMPANY SAOG

PO Box 3104, 112, Ruwi, Oman
Tel.: (968) 24493824
Web Site: https://www.ndcoman.com
Year Founded: 1981
NDTI—(MUS)
Rev.: $55,016,044
Assets: $78,855,079
Liabilities: $35,441,482
Net Worth: $43,413,598
Earnings: $1,707,886
Fiscal Year-end: 12/31/23
Soap & Detergent Mfr
N.A.I.C.S.: 325611

THE NATIONAL LIGHTING COMPANY LTD.

Unit 8 Grand Union Trading Estate Abbey Road, Park Royal, London, NW10 7UL, United Kingdom
Tel.: (44) 845 634 1515
Web Site: http://www.nationallighting.co.uk
Sales Range: $50-74.9 Million
Emp.: 110
Holding Company: Commercial Lighting
N.A.I.C.S.: 551112
Meyer Maslo (Gen Dir)

Subsidiaries:

Brilliant AG   (1)
Brilliantstr 1, 27442, Gnarrenburg, Germany   **(85%)**
Tel.: (49) 4763890
Web Site: http://www.brilliant-ag.de
Sales Range: $50-74.9 Million
Indoor & Outdoor Lighting Products Mfr
N.A.I.C.S.: 335131
Thorsten A. Spengler (CEO)

THE NATIONAL SILK & RAYON MILLS LTD.

Jaranwala Road, Faisalabad, Pakistan
Tel.: (92) 418721760
Web Site: http://www.nationalsilk.com
NSRM—(LAH)
Rev.: $6,684,128
Assets: $8,076,749
Liabilities: $2,526,187
Net Worth: $5,550,562
Earnings: $125,033
Emp.: 378
Fiscal Year-end: 06/30/19
Textile Mill
N.A.I.C.S.: 313210
Faisal Tauheed Puri (CEO)

THE NATURE HOLDINGS CO., LTD.

10 Saechang-ro 44-gil 1-4th floor, Yongsan-gu, Seoul, Korea (South)
Tel.: (82) 215882906
Web Site:
    https://www.thenatureholdings.co.kr
Year Founded: 2004
298540—(KRS)
Rev.: $381,852,829
Assets: $434,998,417
Liabilities: $189,936,561
Net Worth: $245,061,856
Earnings: $53,142,086
Emp.: 462
Fiscal Year-end: 12/31/22
Apparel Accessory Mfr
N.A.I.C.S.: 315990
Choong-Hyun Lim (CFO)

THE NEW INDIA ASSURANCE COMPANY LIMITED

87 M G Road Fort, Mumbai, 400 001, Maharashtra, India
Tel.: (91) 2222708263   In
Web Site: https://www.newindia.co.in
Year Founded: 1919
540769—(BOM)
Rev.: $274,193,529
Assets: $12,454,236,877
Liabilities: $7,193,405,160
Net Worth: $5,260,831,717
Earnings: $222,188,066
Emp.: 15,246
Fiscal Year-end: 03/31/21
Risk Managemeng Srvices
N.A.I.C.S.: 524113
Madhulika Bhaskar (Chm & Mng Dir)

Subsidiaries:

Prestige Assurance PLC   (1)
19 Ligali Ayorinde Street Victoria Island, PO Box 650, Lagos, Nigeria
Tel.: (234) 8058820333
Web Site:
    https://www.prestigeassuranceplc.com
Rev.: $9,210,888
Assets: $16,438,997
Liabilities: $6,659,801
Net Worth: $9,779,196
Earnings: $43,702
Emp.: 88
Fiscal Year-end: 12/31/2022
General Insurance Services
N.A.I.C.S.: 524113
Sarbeswar Sahoo (CEO & Mng Dir)

The New India Assurance Co. (Sierra Leone) Limited   (1)
18 Wilberforce Street, PO Box No 340, Freetown, Sierra Leone
Tel.: (232) 2 222 6453
General Insurance Services
N.A.I.C.S.: 524210

The New India Assurance Co. (Trinidad & Tobago) Limited   (1)
6 A Victoria Avenue, Post Box 884, Port of Spain, Trinidad & Tobago
Tel.: (868) 623 1868
General Insurance Services
N.A.I.C.S.: 524210
Rajeev Bhattathiripad (Mng Dir)

The New India Assurance Company (Sierra Leone) Limited   (1)

THE NEW ZEALAND FILM COMMISSION

Level 3 119 Ghuznee Street, Wellington, 6011, New Zealand
Tel.: (64) 43827680
Web Site: http://www.nzfilm.co.nz
Year Founded: 1978
Rev.: $43,292,543
Assets: $47,143,962
Liabilities: $41,705,575
Net Worth: $5,438,387
Earnings: ($3,908,575)
Emp.: 10
Fiscal Year-end: 06/30/19
Film Promoter
N.A.I.C.S.: 512199
Mladen Ivancic (COO)

THE NIGERIAN STOCK EXCHANGE

8th, 9th & 11th Floors 2/4 Customs Street, PO Box 2457, Lagos, Nigeria
Tel.: (234) 4638333
Web Site:
    http://www.nigerianexchange.com
Year Founded: 1960
Stock Exchange Services
N.A.I.C.S.: 523210
Sani Badamasi (Asst Gen Mgr & Branch Mgr-Abuja)

THE NIHON SEIMA CO., LTD.

3-3 Shimonaka, Tonami, 939-1347, Toyama, Japan
Tel.: (81) 763323111
Web Site:
    https://www.nihonseima.co.jp
Year Founded: 1947
3306—(TKS)
Rev.: $28,647,740
Assets: $30,558,030
Liabilities: $11,521,230
Net Worth: $19,036,800
Earnings: $839,470
Emp.: 1,943
Fiscal Year-end: 03/31/24
Jute Product Distr
N.A.I.C.S.: 424310
Takanobu Yamamura (Pres & CEO)

THE NISHI-NIPPON CITY BANK, LTD.

1-1 Hakata-ekimae 3-chome, Hakata-ku, Fukuoka, 812-0011, Japan
Tel.: (81) 924762481   JP
Web Site: http://www.ncbank.co.jp
Year Founded: 1944
Commercial Banking Services
N.A.I.C.S.: 522110
Seiji Isoyama (Deputy Pres)

Subsidiaries:

Kyushu Card Co., Ltd.   (1)
10-31 Hanabata-cho, Kumamoto, 860-0806, Japan
Tel.: (81) 963521171
Web Site: http://www.kyushu-card.co.jp
Sales Range: $50-74.9 Million
Emp.: 20
Credit Card Issuing Services
N.A.I.C.S.: 522210

NCB Research & Consulting Co., Ltd.   (1)
2-1 Shimokawabatamachi Hakataza Nishigin Building 13F, Hakata-ku, Fukuoka, 812-0027, Japan
Tel.: (81) 922822662
Web Site: http://www.johoza.co.jp
Sales Range: $25-49.9 Million
Emp.: 30
Economic & Financial Management Consulting Services
N.A.I.C.S.: 541611
Akira Mitsutomi (CEO)

NCB Turnaround Co., Ltd.   (1)
1-3-6 Hakataekimae, Hakata-ku, Fukuoka, 812-0011, Japan

INTERNATIONAL PUBLIC

Tel.: (81) 924762116
Debt Collection Services
N.A.I.C.S.: 561440

Nishi-Nippon City Bank Capital Markets   (1)
11-8 Kyobashi 1-chome, Chuo-ku, Tokyo, 104-0031, Japan
Tel.: (81) 335619306
Web Site: http://www.ncbank.com
Sales Range: $1-4.9 Billion
Emp.: 4,000
Financial Investment & Management Services
N.A.I.C.S.: 523999

Nishi-Nippon City Bank Hong Kong   (1)
One Pacific Place Suite 1006, 88 Queensway, Hong Kong, China (Hong Kong)
Tel.: (852) 25262259
Web Site: http://www.ncbank.co.jp
Sales Range: $50-74.9 Million
Emp.: 4
Commercial Banking Services
N.A.I.C.S.: 522110

Nishi-Nippon City Bank Securities & Intl Div   (1)
3-6 Hakata-ekimae 1-chome, Hakata-ku, Fukuoka, 812-0011, Japan
Tel.: (81) 924762501
Web Site: http://www.ncbank.co.jp
Sales Range: $100-124.9 Million
Emp.: 200
Financial Investment & Management Services
N.A.I.C.S.: 523999
Seiji Isoyama (Mng Dir)

Nishi-Nippon City Bank Shanghai   (1)
Room No 2209 Shanghai International Trade Center 2201 Yan-An Road W, Chang Nin, Shanghai, China
Tel.: (86) 2162190600
Commercial Banking Services
N.A.I.C.S.: 522110

The Bank of Nagasaki, Ltd.   (1)
3-14 Sakaemachi, Nagasaki, 850-0875, Japan
Tel.: (81) 958254151
Web Site: http://www.nagasakibank.co.jp
Commercial Banking Services
N.A.I.C.S.: 522110

The Nishi-Nippon City Bank, Ltd. - International Business Division   (1)
3-6 Hakata-ekimae 1-chome, Hakata-ku, Fukuoka, 812-0011, Japan
Tel.: (81) 924762481
Web Site: http://www.ncbank.co.jp
Sales Range: $700-749.9 Million
Emp.: 2,000
Investment Banking Services
N.A.I.C.S.: 523150
Isao Kubota (Chm)

The Nishi-Nippon City Bank, Ltd. - Treasury & Portfolio Investment Division   (1)
11-8 Kyobashi 1-chome, Chuo-ku, Tokyo, 104-0031, Japan
Tel.: (81) 335619306
Treasury & Portfolio Investment Management Services
N.A.I.C.S.: 523940

THE NISSHIN OILLIO GROUP, LTD.

1-23-1 Shinkawa, Chuo-ku, Tokyo, 104-8285, Japan
Tel.: (81) 332065005   JP
Web Site: https://www.nisshin-oillio.com
Year Founded: 1907
2602—(TKS)
Rev.: $3,394,506,010
Assets: $2,600,255,020
Liabilities: $1,327,420,200
Net Worth: $1,272,834,820
Earnings: $100,128,280
Emp.: 3,001
Fiscal Year-end: 03/31/24

AND PRIVATE COMPANIES

Edible Vegetable Oils, Processed Foods & Pharmaceutical & Chemical Products Mfr
N.A.I.C.S.: 311225
Hidetoshi Ogami (Sr Mng Officer)

Subsidiaries:

Daito Cacao Co., Ltd. (1)
2-3-23 Shimomeguro, Meguro-ku, Tokyo, 153-0064, Japan
Tel.: (81) 334927501
Web Site: https://www.daitocacao.com
Emp.: 288
Chocolate Product Mfr & Distr
N.A.I.C.S.: 311351

Subsidiary (Non-US):

T. & C. Manufacturing Co. Pte. Ltd. (2)
12 Tuas Bay Walk, Singapore, 637126, Singapore
Tel.: (65) 64967880
Web Site: https://www.tncmanufact.com.sg
Chocolate Product Mfr & Distr
N.A.I.C.S.: 311351
Shigeyuki Takeuchi (Chm)

Industrial Quimica Lasem, S.A.U. (1)
Av de la Industria 7 Pol Ind Pla del Cami, Castellgali, 08297, Barcelona, Spain
Tel.: (34) 938758840
Web Site: https://www.iql-nog.com
Cosmetic Product Distr
N.A.I.C.S.: 812199

Intercontinental Specialty Fats Sdn. Bhd. (1)
Lot 1 Lebuh Sultan Hishamuddin 2 Kawasan 20 Bandar Sultan Suleiman, PO Box 207, 42009, Port Klang, Selangor Darul Ehsan, Malaysia
Tel.: (60) 331763050
Web Site: https://isfsb.com
Emp.: 550
Food Products Distr
N.A.I.C.S.: 424490

Marketing Force Japan, Inc. (1)
8F JRE Kayabacho 2-chome Building
2-13-13 Nihonbashi Kayabacho, Chuo-ku, Tokyo, 103-0025, Japan
Tel.: (81) 336643605
Web Site: https://www.mfj-inc.co.jp
Emp.: 53
Retail Store Operator
N.A.I.C.S.: 445292

NSP Co., Ltd. (1)
Nisseki Yokohama Building 28F 1-1-8 Sakuragi-cho, Naka-ku, Yokohama, 231-0062, Kanagawa, Japan
Tel.: (81) 456501311
Web Site: https://www.nsp-ltd.co.jp
Emp.: 212
Software Development Services
N.A.I.C.S.: 541511

Nisshin Shoji Co., Ltd. (1)
1-23-17 Shinkawa Nisshin Annex Building, Chuo-ku, Tokyo, 104-0033, Japan
Tel.: (81) 36 222 3030
Web Site: https://www.nisshin-shoji.co.jp
Grocery Whslr
N.A.I.C.S.: 424410

Nisshin Shokai Co., Ltd. (1)
43-92 Hiraide Industrial Park, Utsunomiya, 321-0905, Tochigi, Japan
Tel.: (81) 286625231
Web Site: https://nisshin-sk.com
Emp.: 50
Frozen Food Product Mfr & Distr
N.A.I.C.S.: 311412

Subsidiary (US):

NI Midstar LLC (2)
370 W Anchor Dr Ste 210, North Sioux City, SD 57049-5153
Tel.: (877) 365-7447
Food Products Distr
N.A.I.C.S.: 424490

Subsidiary (Non-US):

Taiwan Nisshin Shokai Co., Ltd. (2)
4F NO 170 Dunhua N Rd, Songshan, Taipei, 105405, Taiwan
Tel.: (886) 225450909
Web Site: https://www.twnisshin.com
Food Products Distr
N.A.I.C.S.: 424490

Subsidiary (US):

US Nisshin Shokai Inc. (2)
1375 E Woodfield Rd Ste 250, Schaumburg, IL 60173
Tel.: (630) 912-2150
Web Site: http://www.usnisshinsk.com
Soybean Product Distr
N.A.I.C.S.: 424510

President Nisshin Corp. (1)
No 301-3 Zhongzheng Road, Yongkang, T'ainan, Taiwan
Tel.: (886) 62536789
Web Site: https://www.president-nisshin.com.tw
Dairy Product Mfr & Whslr
N.A.I.C.S.: 311511

Settsu Oil Mill Inc. (1)
1-5-10 Chikkoshinmachi, Nishi-ku, Sakai, 592-8331, Osaka, Japan
Tel.: (81) 72 2802650
Web Site: http://www.settsu-inc.com
Sales Range: $75-99.9 Million
Emp.: 124
Oil Product Mfr & Distr
N.A.I.C.S.: 311225
Toshikazu Ohmae (Pres)

The Golf Joy Co., Ltd. (1)
Seongseong-Dong, Seobuk-gu, Cheonan, 331-300, Chungchongnam-Do, Korea (South)
Tel.: (82) 516230507
Food Products Distr
N.A.I.C.S.: 424490

Zhangjiagang President Nisshin Food Corp. (1)
No 9 Baodao Road Free Trade Zone, Zhangjiagang, 215634, China
Tel.: (86) 51258382329
Food Products Distr
N.A.I.C.S.: 424490

THE NORINCHUKIN BANK

2-1 Otemachi 1-chome, Chiyoda-ku, Tokyo, 100-8155, Japan
Tel.: (81) 332790111   JP
Web Site: http://www.nochubank.or.jp
Year Founded: 1923
Rev.: $12,025,464,000
Assets: $1,027,419,237,680
Liabilities: $956,806,667,520
Net Worth: $70,612,570,160
Earnings: $1,793,462,000
Emp.: 3,462
Fiscal Year-end: 03/31/22
Financial Services for the Agricultural & Forestry Industries
N.A.I.C.S.: 523999
Kazuhiko Otake (Sr Mng Dir)

Subsidiaries:

Ant Capital Partners Co., Ltd. (1)
2-4-1 Marunouchi 27th Floor Marunouchi Building, Tokyo, 100-6390, Japan
Tel.: (81) 332841711
Web Site: https://www.antcapital.jp
Investment Management Service
N.A.I.C.S.: 523999

Kyodo Housing Loan Co., Ltd. (1)
5-21-11 Sendagaya, Shibuya-ku, Tokyo, 151-0051, Japan
Tel.: (81) 356569900
Web Site: http://www.kyojyu.co.jp
Emp.: 150
Mortage Loan Provider
N.A.I.C.S.: 522310

Kyodo Seminar Co., Ltd. (1)
1-12 Uchikanda 1-Chome, Chiyoda, Tokyo, 101-0047, Japan
Tel.: (81) 352831301
Web Site: http://www.kyodo-sem.co.jp
Management Development Training Services
N.A.I.C.S.: 611430

Norinchukin Australia Pty Limited (1)
Level 29 126 Phillip Street, Sydney, 2000, NSW, Australia
Tel.: (61) 289225000
Web Site: https://nochu-au.com.au
Finance Lending Services
N.A.I.C.S.: 522291

Norinchukin Bank Europe N.V. (1)
Gustav Mahlerlaan 1216 4th Floor, 1081 LA, Amsterdam, Netherlands
Tel.: (31) 202460700
Web Site: https://www.nochu-bank.eu
Commercial Banking Services
N.A.I.C.S.: 522110

Norinchukin Research Institute Co., Ltd. (1)
9th floor Agri-Square Shinjuku Bldg 5-27-11 Sendagaya, Shibuya-ku, Tokyo, 151-0051, Japan
Tel.: (81) 363627700
Web Site: http://www.nochuri.co.jp
Agricultural Research Services
N.A.I.C.S.: 541715
Shinichi Saitoh (Pres)

Norinchukin Zenkyoren Asset Management Co., Ltd. (1)
7-9 Hirakawacho 2-Chome, Chiyoda, Tokyo, 102-0093, Japan
Tel.: (81) 352108500
Asset Management & Investment Services
N.A.I.C.S.: 523940

The Norinchukin Trust & Banking Co., Ltd. (1)
1-12 Uchikanda 1-Chome, Chiyoda, Tokyo, 101-0047, Japan (100%)
Tel.: (81) 352811311
Settlement Services
N.A.I.C.S.: 523910

THE NORMANDY GROUP S.A.

RPO Headon 93113, Burlington, L7M 4A3, ON, Canada
Tel.: (905) 333-2687
Web Site: http://www.innua.com
Holding Company; PVC Resin & Plasticizer Products Buyer & Seller
N.A.I.C.S.: 551112
David Harris (Pres-INNUA)

Subsidiaries:

Innua Petrochem Limited (1)
3 Catherine Christopher Building, Box 3069, Road Town, Tortola, Virgin Islands (British)
Tel.: (284) 4950244
Web Site: http://www.innua.com
PVC Resin & Plasticizer Products Buyer & Seller
N.A.I.C.S.: 424610

Subsidiary (Non-US):

Innua Americas Ltd (2)
301 - 4145 North Service Road, Burlington, L7L 6A3, ON, Canada
Tel.: (289) 337-4123
Web Site: https://www.innua.com
Emp.: 10
Plastic Product Distr
N.A.I.C.S.: 424610
Pamela McKenna (Mgr-Intl Logistics)

Innua China Ltd (2)
Room 302-B NO 681 Lane 900 North San Xin Road, Songjiang District, Shanghai, 201620, China
Tel.: (86) 21 3772 2100
Plastic Product Distr
N.A.I.C.S.: 424610
Frank Cherng (Mng Dir)

Innua Europe Ltd (2)
Fleming court Leigh Rd, Eastleigh, SO50 9PD, Southampton, United Kingdom
Tel.: (44) 284 495 0244
Plastic Product Distr
N.A.I.C.S.: 424610
Sam Tucker (Mng Dir)

Innua Petrochem Latin America (2)
Av Presidente Masaryk 111 Piso 1 Col Chapultepec Morales, Miguel Hidalgo, Mexico, 11570, Mexico
Tel.: (52) 55 3300 6051
Plastic Product Distr
N.A.I.C.S.: 424610

Oscar Rustrian (Dir-Trade)

Branch (Non-US):

Innua Petrochem Limited (2)
301 - 4145 North Service Road, 3310 South Service Road, Burlington, L7L 6A3, ON, Canada
Tel.: (289) 337-4123
Web Site: http://www.innua.com
Sales Range: $25-49.9 Million
Emp.: 25
PVC Resin & Plasticizer Products Buyer & Seller
N.A.I.C.S.: 424610
Pamela McKenna (Mgr-Intl Logistics)

THE NORTH WEST COMPANY INC.

77 Main Street, Winnipeg, R3C 1A3, MB, Canada
Tel.: (204) 943-0881
Web Site: https://www.northwest.ca
Year Founded: 1668
NWC—(TSX)
Rev.: $1,759,188,135
Assets: $953,812,882
Liabilities: $499,930,897
Net Worth: $453,881,985
Earnings: $123,170,768
Emp.: 7,524
Fiscal Year-end: 01/31/22
Food & Consumer Product Retailer
N.A.I.C.S.: 459999
Edward S. Kennedy (Pres & CEO)

Subsidiaries:

North Star Air Ltd. (1)
1480 Walsh St, Thunder Bay, P7E 6H6, ON, Canada
Web Site: https://www.northstarair.ca
Airline Services
N.A.I.C.S.: 488190

THE OGAKI KYORITSU BANK, LTD.

3-98 Kuruwamachi, Ogaki, 503-0887, Gifu, Japan
Tel.: (81) 584742111
Web Site: http://www.okb.co.jp
8361—(TKS)
Rev.: $886,652,180
Assets: $43,965,126,050
Liabilities: $41,726,292,610
Net Worth: $2,238,833,440
Earnings: $231,350
Emp.: 2,372
Fiscal Year-end: 03/31/24
Banking Services
N.A.I.C.S.: 522110

Subsidiaries:

OKB Research Institute Co., Ltd. (1)
2-25 Kuruwamachi, Ogaki, 503-0887, Gifu, Japan
Tel.: (81) 584742611
Data Processing Services
N.A.I.C.S.: 518210

THE OITA BANK, LTD.

4-1 Funaicho 3-chome, Oita, 870-0021, Japan
Tel.: (81) 975341111
Web Site: https://www.oitabank.co.jp
Year Founded: 1983
8392—(TKS)
Rev.: $484,116,400
Assets: $30,103,149,630
Liabilities: $28,662,962,830
Net Worth: $1,440,186,800
Earnings: $330,500
Emp.: 282
Fiscal Year-end: 03/31/24
Banking Services
N.A.I.C.S.: 522110
Shoji Himeno (Chm)

THE OKINAWA ELECTRIC

THE OKINAWA ELECTRIC INTERNATIONAL PUBLIC

THE OKINAWA ELECTRIC —(CONTINUED)

POWER COMPANY, INCORPORATED
2-1 Makiminato 5-chome, Urasoe, 902-2602, Okinawa, Japan
Tel.: (81) 988772341
Web Site: https://www.okiden.co.jp 9511—(FKA)
Rev.: $1,705,925,760
Assets: $4,322,303,920
Liabilities: $2,761,045,760
Net Worth: $1,561,258,160
Earnings: $18,963,120
Emp.: 2,812
Fiscal Year-end: 03/31/22
Electric Power Distribution Services
N.A.I.C.S.: 221122
Mitsuru Omine *(Chm)*

THE OLAYAN GROUP
King Abdul Aziz Road, PO Box 1520, Al Khobar, 31952, Saudi Arabia
Tel.: (966) 38871000
Web Site:
http://www.olayangroup.com
Year Founded: 1947
Sales Range: $1-4.9 Billion
Emp.: 3,000
Commercial Real Estate Services
N.A.I.C.S.: 531210

Subsidiaries:

Arabian Business Machines Company (1)
PO Box 2006, Riyadh, 11451, Saudi Arabia
Tel.: (966) 114784909
Office Automation Products Distr
N.A.I.C.S.: 423420
Hanif Thotathil *(Sr Mgr-Technical Svcs)*

Arabian Paper Products Company (1)
PO Box 1520, Al Khobar, 31952, Saudi Arabia
Tel.: (966) 38871000
Web Site: http://www.olayangroup.com
Sales Range: $25-49.9 Million
Emp.: 75
Paper Cup Mfr
N.A.I.C.S.: 322219

Competrol Luxembourg Sarl (1)
25B Boulevard Royal, Luxembourg, 2449, Luxembourg
Tel.: (352) 262662
Financial Investment Management Services
N.A.I.C.S.: 523940

Crescent Holding GmbH (1)
Opernring 1/R/709, 1010, Vienna, Austria
Tel.: (43) 15859250
Financial Investment Management Services
N.A.I.C.S.: 523940

Drilling Equipment and Chemical Company (1)
Main Olayan Building First Floor
Dammam/Al-Khobar Highway, Al Khobar, 31952, Saudi Arabia
Tel.: (966) 38871000
Drilling Equipment Distr
N.A.I.C.S.: 423710
Sameer Al-Mubarak *(Gen Mgr)*

First Food Services L.L.C. (1)
108 Liberty Building Al-Garhoud Road, PO Box 21568, Dubai, United Arab Emirates
Tel.: (971) 42823344
Food Products Mfr
N.A.I.C.S.: 311919
Ahmad M. Jaser *(Dir-Ops)*

General Contracting Company (1)
King Abdul Aziz Road, PO Box 356, Al Khobar, 31952, Saudi Arabia
Tel.: (966) 38820888
Mechanical Component Distr
N.A.I.C.S.: 423120
Mohammed Saleh Al-Ajaji *(Gen Mgr)*

General Trading Company (1)
PO Box 593, Riyadh, 11421, Saudi Arabia
Tel.: (966) 112333111
Food Products Mfr
N.A.I.C.S.: 311919
Husam Edghaim *(Gen Mgr)*

Health Water Bottling Co. Ltd. (1)
PO Box 2948, Riyadh, 11461, Saudi Arabia
Tel.: (966) 12633300
Web Site: http://www.hwb-sa.com
Bottled Water Distr
N.A.I.C.S.: 312112
Walid Al-Jamaan *(Gen Mgr)*

Olayan Europe Limited (1)
140 Piccadilly, London, W1J 7NS, United Kingdom
Tel.: (44) 2072454000
Financial Investment Management Services
N.A.I.C.S.: 523940
Narinder Gandhi *(Mgr-IT)*

Olayan Financing Company (1)
PO Box 8772, Riyadh, 11492, Saudi Arabia
Tel.: (966) 114666555
Financial Investment Management Services
N.A.I.C.S.: 523940
Lynne Fleifel *(Portfolio Mgr)*

Olayan Food Services Company (1)
PO Box 66047, Riyadh, 11576, Saudi Arabia
Tel.: (966) 14772920
Food Products Mfr
N.A.I.C.S.: 311919
Ahmad M. Jaser *(Dir-Ops)*

Technical Trading Company Ltd. (1)
Khuraiss Road Exit 30 GCC Compound, PO Box 967, Riyadh, 11421, Saudi Arabia
Tel.: (966) 12333111
Chemical Products Distr
N.A.I.C.S.: 424690
Syed Karar Hussain *(Gen Mgr)*

Weir Arabian Metals Company (1)
PO Box 2724, Al Khobar, 31952, Saudi Arabia
Tel.: (966) 381210841104
Web Site: http://www.weiroilandgas.com
Drilling Equipment Mfr
N.A.I.C.S.: 333131
Anthony J. Dekker *(Gen Mgr)*

THE ORCHID GROUP
Park Mill Burydell Lane, Park Street, Saint Albans, AL2 2HB, United Kingdom
Tel.: (44) 1727871100
Web Site:
http://www.orchidgroup.co.uk
Year Founded: 2006
Sales Range: $550-599.9 Million
Emp.: 6,000
Pub Operator
N.A.I.C.S.: 722410
Rufus Hall *(CEO)*

Subsidiaries:

PBR Ltd. (1)
Park Mill Burydell Ln, Park St, Saint Albans, AL2 2HB, United Kingdom
Tel.: (44) 1727871100
Web Site: http://www.pbr.uk.com
Sales Range: $75-99.9 Million
Emp.: 60
Pub, Bar & Nightclub Operator
N.A.I.C.S.: 722410

THE ORTHOTIC GROUP INC.
160 Markland Street, Markham, L6C 0C6, ON, Canada
Tel.: (416) 479-8609
Web Site:
http://www.theorthoticgroup.com
Year Founded: 1985
Sales Range: $10-24.9 Million
Emp.: 160
Orthotic Devices & Customized Footwear Mfr
N.A.I.C.S.: 316210
Chris Patten *(VP-Tech)*

Subsidiaries:

TOG Orthotics International London Ltd. (1)
26 York Street, London, W1U 6PZ, United Kingdom
Tel.: (44) 207 8732269
Web Site: http://www.togorthotics.com
Orthotic Footwear Distr
N.A.I.C.S.: 424340
Michael Crowley *(Mgr)*

TOG Orthotics International Ltd (1)
1st Floor Roslevan SC Tulla Rd, Ennis, County Clare, Ireland
Tel.: (353) 65 6841140
Orthotic Footwear Distr
N.A.I.C.S.: 424340
Michael Crowley *(Mng Dir)*

THE PACIFIC SECURITIES CO., LTD.
31F Tongde Square Office Building No 926 Beijing Road, Kunming, 650224, Yunnan, China
Tel.: (86) 87168885858
Web Site: https://www.tpyzq.com
Year Founded: 2004
601099—(SHG)
Rev.: $164,584,813
Assets: $2,151,502,053
Liabilities: $853,562,067
Net Worth: $1,297,939,987
Earnings: ($64,474,909)
Fiscal Year-end: 12/31/22
Securities Brokerage Services
N.A.I.C.S.: 523150
Changwei Li *(Pres & Gen Mgr)*

THE PACK CORPORATION
2-9-3 Higashiobase, Higashinari-ku, Osaka, 537-8911, Japan
Tel.: (81) 649671221
Web Site: https://www.thepack.co.jp
Year Founded: 1952
3950—(TKS)
Rev.: $692,792,260
Assets: $700,825,230
Liabilities: $196,329,190
Net Worth: $504,496,040
Earnings: $40,072,680
Emp.: 1,183
Fiscal Year-end: 12/31/23
Packaging Products Mfr
N.A.I.C.S.: 322220
Michihisa Fujii *(Mng Dir-Corp Div)*

Subsidiaries:

Kannaru Printing Co., Ltd. (1)
3-4-23 Jusanhoncho, Yodogawa-ku, Osaka, 532-0024, Japan
Tel.: (81) 663037400
Web Site: https://www.kannaru.co.jp
Offset Printing Product Mfr
N.A.I.C.S.: 323120

Keihin Tokushu Printing Corporation (1)
16-1 Meguro-cho, Seya-ku, Yokohama, 246-0007, Kanagawa, Japan
Tel.: (81) 459211351
Web Site: http://www.keihin-t.co.jp
Paper Bag Mfr & Distr
N.A.I.C.S.: 322212

Nikko Print Corporation (1)
1-5-39 Higashikonoike-cho, Higashiosaka, 578-0973, Osaka, Japan
Tel.: (81) 729641241
Offset Printing Paper Product Mfr
N.A.I.C.S.: 323111

Nishinihon Printing Co., Ltd. (1)
3-2-1 Iaida, Hakata-ku, Fukuoka, 812-0881, Japan
Tel.: (81) 925815636
Web Site: https://www.nishiin.com
Offset Printing Product Mfr
N.A.I.C.S.: 323120

PACK TAKEYAMA CO., LTD (1)
322-1 Aza Masuda Hiruma-cho, Tsushima, 496-0004, Aichi, Japan (100%)
Tel.: (81) 567245181
Web Site: http://www.p-takeyama.co.jp
Packaging Product Mfr & Distr
N.A.I.C.S.: 322120
Toshihiro Ito *(Pres & CEO)*

The Pack (Changshu) Corporation (1)
Tel.: (86) 51252358603
Paper Bag Mfr
N.A.I.C.S.: 322220

The Pack (Shanghai) Corporation (1)
Room1401 1406 Shanghai International Group Mansion 511 Weihai Rd, Jingan District, Shanghai, 200041, China
Tel.: (86) 2152280257
Web Site: https://www.thepackshanghai.com
Packaging Sales
N.A.I.C.S.: 561910

The Pack America Corp. (1)
108 W 39th St 16th Fl, New York, NY 10018
Tel.: (212) 508-6666
Web Site: http://www.packamerica.com
Emp.: 10
Paper Bag Mfr
N.A.I.C.S.: 322220
Susumo Okada *(Pres)*

THE PAKISTAN GENERAL INSURANCE COMPANY LIMITED
Cooperative Bank House 5-Bank Square, Lahore, Pakistan
Tel.: (92) 427323569
Web Site: http://www.pgi.com.pk
Year Founded: 1947
PKGI—(PSX)
Rev.: $11,242
Assets: $1,699,149
Liabilities: $209,452
Net Worth: $1,489,697
Earnings: ($102,257)
Emp.: 17
Fiscal Year-end: 12/31/22
Insurance Services
N.A.I.C.S.: 524298
Sajid Rabbani *(Exec Dir)*

THE PALACE AMUSEMENT COMPANY (1921) LIMITED
1a South Camp Road Entrance on Blake Road, Kingston, Jamaica
Tel.: (876) 9281248
Web Site:
https://www.palaceamusement.com
Year Founded: 1921
PAL—(JAM)
Rev.: $734,051
Assets: $10,820,876
Liabilities: $6,357,644
Net Worth: $4,463,232
Earnings: ($2,658,541)
Emp.: 190
Fiscal Year-end: 06/30/21
Cinema Operator
N.A.I.C.S.: 512131
Douglas Graham *(Chm)*

THE PAN GROUP JOINT STOCK COMPANY
Vinh Loc 2 Industrial Zone Long Hiep Ward, Ben Luc District, Ho Chi Minh City, Long An, Vietnam
Tel.: (84) 2723630218 VN
Web Site:
https://www.thepangroup.vn
Year Founded: 1993
PAN—(HOSE)
Rev.: $1,409,461,098
Assets: $1,608,159,805
Liabilities: $820,321,426
Net Worth: $787,838,378
Earnings: $37,396,853
Emp.: 9,830
Fiscal Year-end: 12/31/22
Investment Holding Company
N.A.I.C.S.: 551112
Duy Hung Nguyen *(Chm)*

Subsidiaries:

Bibica Corporation (1)
443 Ly Thuong Kiet Ward 8, Tan Binh Dist,

Ho Chi Minh City, Vietnam (50.07%)
Tel.: (84) 839717920
Web Site: https://www.bibica.com.vn
Rev.: $61,292,828
Assets: $95,904,989
Liabilities: $37,716,911
Net Worth: $58,188,078
Earnings: $354,938
Fiscal Year-end: 12/31/2023
Bakery Products Mfr
N.A.I.C.S.: 311812
Chien Phu Truong *(Chm)*

Golden Beans Coffee Joint Stock
Company (1)
13 Nguyen Thiep, Ben Nghe Ward District 1, Ho Chi Minh City, Vietnam
Tel.: (84) 1900571557
Web Site: https://shincaphe.com
Coffee Powder Mfr & Distr
N.A.I.C.S.: 311920

PAN Food Joint Stock Company (1)
A1-9 Vl3 Street Vinh Loc 2 Industrial Zone, Long Hiep Ward, Ben Luc, Long An, Vietnam
Tel.: (84) 2723630218
Web Site: http://www.panfood.vn
Food Products Mfr
N.A.I.C.S.: 311999

Southern Seed Corporation (1)
282 Le Van Sy Str - 1 Ward, Tan Binh Dis, Ho Chi Minh City, Vietnam
Tel.: (84) 2838442414
Web Site: https://ssc.com.vn
Rev.: $13,048,288
Assets: $22,497,957
Liabilities: $6,463,006
Net Worth: $16,034,951
Earnings: $2,253,902
Emp.: 142
Fiscal Year-end: 12/31/2023
Seed Farming Services
N.A.I.C.S.: 111191

Vietnam National Seed
Corporation (1)
No 1-Luong Dinh Cua Phuong Mai, Dong Da, Hanoi, Vietnam
Tel.: (84) 438523294
Web Site: https://www.vinaseed.com.vn
Rev.: $83,861,652
Assets: $91,511,998
Liabilities: $31,931,236
Net Worth: $59,580,762
Earnings: $9,481,315
Fiscal Year-end: 12/31/2023
Crop Farming Services
N.A.I.C.S.: 111998
Tran Kim Lien *(Chm & CEO)*

Vietnam National Seed Group Joint
Stock Company (1)
No 1 Luong Dinh Cua Str, Phuong Mai Ward Dong Da Dist, Hanoi, Vietnam
Tel.: (84) 2438523294
Web Site: https://vinaseed.com.vn
Emp.: 722
Crop Seed Mfr
N.A.I.C.S.: 325320

Vinarice Co., Ltd. (1)
166 Binh Loi Phuong 13, Quan Binh Thanh, Ho Chi Minh City, Vietnam
Tel.: (84) 2838881882
Web Site: https://vinarice.com.vn
Nutrition Rice Mfr
N.A.I.C.S.: 311212

THE PAN ISLAMIC STEAMSHIP COMPANY LTD.
Writers Chambers Mumtaz Hassan Road, Karachi, Pakistan
Tel.: (92) 241 2110
Marine Shipping Services
N.A.I.C.S.: 488330

THE PARKMEAD GROUP PLC
4 Queen s Terrace, Aberdeen, AB10 1XL, United Kingdom
Tel.: (44) 1224622200 UK
Web Site:
 https://www.parkmeadgroup.com
PMG—(AIM)
Rev.: $16,467,786
Assets: $117,197,033
Liabilities: $39,815,139
Net Worth: $77,381,894
Earnings: ($1,105,184)
Emp.: 14
Fiscal Year-end: 06/30/22
Oil & Gas Exploration & Production
N.A.I.C.S.: 213112
Thomas P. Cross *(Chm)*

THE PEBBLE GROUP PLC
Broadway House Trafford Wharf Road, Trafford Park, Manchester, M17 1DD, United Kingdom
Tel.: (44) 1617860277 UK
Web Site:
 https://www.thepebblegroup.com
PEBB—(AIM)
Rev.: $158,077,102
Assets: $162,698,346
Liabilities: $50,069,843
Net Worth: $112,628,503
Earnings: $7,383,806
Fiscal Year-end: 12/31/23
Advertising Agencies
N.A.I.C.S.: 541810
Christopher Lee *(CEO)*

Subsidiaries:

Facilisgroup LLP (1)
1000 Clark Ave 4th Fl, Saint Louis, MO 63102
Tel.: (314) 207-5522
Web Site: http://www.facilisgroup.com
Business Support Services
N.A.I.C.S.: 561499
Ashley McCune *(Pres)*

THE PENINSULA CHITTAGONG LTD.
Bulbul Center 486/B O R Nizam Road CDA Avenue, Chittagong, 4100, Bangladesh
Tel.: (880) 233335086
Web Site:
 https://www.peninsulactg.com
Year Founded: 2002
PENINSULA—(CHT)
Rev.: $3,457,488
Assets: $38,372,057
Liabilities: $7,113,207
Net Worth: $31,258,850
Earnings: ($365,327)
Fiscal Year-end: 06/30/23
Hotel & Resort Operator
N.A.I.C.S.: 721110
Mustafa Tahseen Arshad *(Mng Dir)*

THE PENINSULA GROUP LTD.
1 Jabotinsky St, Bnei Brak, Israel
Tel.: (972) 35650100
Web Site: https://www.peninsula.co.il
PEN—(TAE)
Rev.: $45,333,225
Assets: $381,886,015
Liabilities: $244,404,045
Net Worth: $137,481,970
Earnings: $14,587,061
Fiscal Year-end: 09/30/23
Financial Services
N.A.I.C.S.: 523150
Micah Avni *(Founder & CEO)*

THE PERIA KARAMALAI TEA & PRODUCE COMPANY LIMITED
286 PANCHRATN Race Course Road, Coimbatore, 641 018, India
Tel.: (91) 4222221352
Web Site: https://www.periatea.com
Year Founded: 1913
PKTEA—(NSE)
Rev.: $6,257,694
Assets: $25,879,743
Liabilities: $4,080,787
Net Worth: $21,798,957
Earnings: ($403,261)
Emp.: 1,261
Fiscal Year-end: 03/31/23
Tea Mfr & Distr
N.A.I.C.S.: 311920
L. N. Bangur *(Chm)*

THE PERTH MINT
310 Hay Street, Perth, 6004, WA, Australia
Tel.: (61) 8 9421 7222
Web Site: http://www.perthmint.com
Rev.: $12,707,394,256
Assets: $3,345,632,440
Liabilities: $3,214,204,841
Net Worth: $131,427,599
Earnings: $9,612,314
Emp.: 397
Fiscal Year-end: 06/30/19
Coins & Other Precious Metals Distr
N.A.I.C.S.: 423940
Richard G. Hayes *(CEO)*

THE PETER KITTLE MOTOR COMPANY
46 Stuart Highway, Alice Springs, 0870, NT, Australia
Tel.: (61) 889554200
Web Site:
 http://www.peterkittle.com.au
Year Founded: 1988
Automotive Retailer
N.A.I.C.S.: 441110
Roman Wreczycki *(Mgr-ICT)*

THE PHILODRILL CORPORATION
8th Floor Quad Alpha Centrum Building 125 Pioneer Street, Mandaluyong, 1550, Philippines
Tel.: (63) 286318151
Web Site: https://www.philodrill.com
Year Founded: 1969
OV—(PHI)
Rev.: $2,138,072
Assets: $63,944,143
Liabilities: $2,057,246
Net Worth: $61,886,897
Earnings: ($5,239,128)
Emp.: 27
Fiscal Year-end: 12/31/20
Oil & Gas Exploration Services
N.A.I.C.S.: 211120
Reynaldo E. Nazarea *(Treas & VP-Admin)*

THE PHOENIX MILLS LIMITED
462 Senapati Bapat Marg, Lower Parel, Mumbai, 400013, India
Tel.: (91) 24964307
Web Site:
 https://www.thephoenixmills.com
503100—(BOM)
Rev.: $159,101,438
Assets: $1,563,614,735
Liabilities: $716,798,300
Net Worth: $846,816,434
Earnings: $6,516,974
Emp.: 82
Fiscal Year-end: 03/31/21
Real Estate Services
N.A.I.C.S.: 531312
Haresh Morajkar *(Chief HR Officer)*

Subsidiaries:

Alliance Spaces Private Limited (1)
9-17-24/1 Level-Ground Floor CBM Compound VIP Road, Sai Sree Sadan Apartment, Visakhapatnam, 530003, India
Tel.: (91) 8912760777
Web Site: https://www.alliancespaces.in
Emp.: 30
Real Estate Development & Investment Services
N.A.I.C.S.: 531390

Bellona Hospitality Services
Limited (1)
Ground Floor R R Hosiery Building Dr E Moses Road, Laxmi Woolen Mill Estate Mahalaxmi, Mumbai, 400011, Maharashtra, India
Tel.: (91) 38373727292
Web Site: https://bellonahospitality.com
Restaurant & Hotel Management Services
N.A.I.C.S.: 721110

Market City Management Private
Limited (1)
Shree Laxmi Woolen Mills Estate R R Hoisery Bldg 2nd Fl, Mahalaxmi, Mumbai, 400 011, Maharashtra, India (100%)
Tel.: (91) 2230016600
Web Site: http://www.thephoenixmills.com
Property Management Services
N.A.I.C.S.: 531312
Smitha Iyer *(Gen Mgr-HR)*

Market City Resources Private
Limited (1)
Tel.: (91) 2230016600
Web Site: http://www.phoenixmarketcity.in
Sales Range: $75-99.9 Million
Emp.: 200
Property Management Services
N.A.I.C.S.: 531311

Phoenix Digital Technologies Private
Limited (1)
MIDC Floor No 1 Wing-B Shubham Building Opp MESB Power House, Dombivali, Maharashtra, India
Tel.: (91) 9845540864
Information Technology Services
N.A.I.C.S.: 541519

Vamona Developers Private
Limited (1)
Tel.: (91) 2030489319
Web Site: http://www.phoenixmarketcity.com
Sales Range: $50-74.9 Million
Emp.: 20
Property Protection & Development Services
N.A.I.C.S.: 531311

THE PHOSPHATE COMPANY LIMITED
14 N S Road 3Rd Floor, Kolkata, 700001, India
Tel.: (91) 3340351234
Web Site: http://www.phosphate.co.in
Year Founded: 1949
26031—(KOL)
Rev.: $17,767,004
Assets: $17,017,613
Liabilities: $7,086,518
Net Worth: $9,931,095
Earnings: $563,959
Emp.: 47
Fiscal Year-end: 03/31/23
Fertilizer Mfr
N.A.I.C.S.: 325314
Suresh Kumar Bangur *(CEO)*

THE PLACE HOLDINGS LIMITED
6 Battery Road 2101, Singapore, 049909, Singapore
Tel.: (65) 67818156
Web Site:
 https://www.theplaceholdings.com
E27—(SES)
Rev.: $570,955
Assets: $183,344,032
Liabilities: $113,061,696
Net Worth: $70,282,336
Earnings: ($10,827,383)
Fiscal Year-end: 12/31/22
Printed Circuit Board Mfr
N.A.I.C.S.: 334412
Ai Li Tay *(Controller-Fin)*

Subsidiaries:

LGANG Optronics Technology Co.,
Ltd. (1)
19 Her-Jun North Road Chung-Li Industrial Park, Chung-li, 32061, Taoyuan, Taiwan
Tel.: (886) 34340771
Web Site: http://www.euconholding.com
Sales Range: $25-49.9 Million
Emp.: 110
Laser Drilling Services

THE PLACE HOLDINGS LIMITED

The Place Holdings Limited—(Continued)
N.A.I.C.S.: 541330

Shanghai Zhuo Kai Electronic Technology Co., Ltd. (1)
399 Baoqian Road Xuhang Industrial Park, Jiading District, Shanghai, China
Tel.: (86) 2139533226
Laser Drilling Services & Printed Circuit Boards Mfr
N.A.I.C.S.: 561990

Subsidiary (Domestic):

Shanghai Yaolong Electronic Technology Co., Ltd (2)
188 Yuwan Road, Jiading District, Shanghai, 201809, China
Tel.: (86) 21 3997 7791
Laser Drilling & Circuit Boards Mfr
N.A.I.C.S.: 334412

Shanghai Zeng Kang Electronic Co., Ltd. (2)
1150 Caoxin Road Xuhang Town, Jiading District, Shanghai, China
Tel.: (86) 2159949019
Mechanical & Laser Drilling Services
N.A.I.C.S.: 561990

THE PLANTING HOPE COMPANY INC.

Bentall 5 550 Burrard Street Suite 1008, Vancouver, V6C 2B5, BC, Canada
Tel.: (773) 492-2243 BC
Web Site: https://www.plantinghopeco.com
Year Founded: 2020
MYLKF—(OTCQB)
Rev.: $12,211,743
Assets: $9,840,872
Liabilities: $8,202,098
Net Worth: $1,638,774
Earnings: ($7,805,766)
Emp.: 17
Fiscal Year-end: 12/31/22
Frozen Food Product Distr
N.A.I.C.S.: 424420
Julia Stamberger *(Chm)*

THE PLATFORM GROUP AG

Schloss Elbroich Am Falder 4, 40589, Dusseldorf, Germany De
Web Site: https://corporate.the-platform-group.com
Year Founded: 2008
FSNT—(DEU)
Rev.: $477,092,614
Assets: $313,874,396
Liabilities: $225,001,822
Net Worth: $88,872,574
Earnings: $28,181,801
Emp.: 688
Fiscal Year-end: 12/31/23
Online Shopping Services
N.A.I.C.S.: 459999

Subsidiaries:

Brandfield B.V. (1)
Osloweg 105, 9723 BK, Groningen, Netherlands
Tel.: (31) 502011559
Web Site: https://www.brandfield.nl
Online Shopping Services
N.A.I.C.S.: 561320

THE PLATINUM GROUP PUBLIC COMPANY LIMITED

222/1398 The Platinum Fashion Mall Building 11th Floor Petchaburi Road, Ratchathevee, Bangkok, 10400, Thailand
Tel.: (66) 21219999
Web Site: https://theplatinumgroup.co.th
Year Founded: 2013
PLAT—(THA)
Rev.: $53,983,015
Assets: $336,810,896

Liabilities: $113,997,077
Net Worth: $222,813,819
Earnings: $5,185,210
Emp.: 670
Fiscal Year-end: 12/31/23
Property Development, Rental & Leasing
N.A.I.C.S.: 236220
Piroon Limpiviwatkul *(Exec Dir)*

THE POKEMON COMPANY

Roppongi Hills Mori Tower 8F 6-10-1, Roppongi, Minato-ku, Tokyo, 106-6108, Japan
Tel.: (81) 120 049 725
Web Site: https://corporate.pokemon.co.jp
Emp.: 100
Video Games, Card Games & Video Production; Licensing & Store Management Services
N.A.I.C.S.: 512199
Tsunekazu Ishihara *(Pres & CEO)*

Subsidiaries:

Millennium Print Group (1)
2015 Production Dr, Apex, NC 27539
Tel.: (919) 852-1117
Web Site: http://www.mprintgroup.com
Rev.: $4,891,898
Emp.: 100
Other Commercial Printing
N.A.I.C.S.: 323111
Bob Lempp *(VP-Sls & Mktg)*

THE POUL DUE JENSEN FOUNDATION

Grundfos Syd1 Birkevssnget 2, Poul Due Jensens Vej 7, DK-8850, Bjerringbro, Denmark
Tel.: (45) 87 50 12 45
Web Site: http://www.thejensenfoundation.com
Rev.: $4,125,223,380
Assets: $4,593,542,220
Liabilities: $1,366,879,380
Net Worth: $3,226,662,840
Earnings: $316,310,100
Fiscal Year-end: 12/31/19
Holding Company; Water Distr
N.A.I.C.S.: 551112
Jens Maaloe *(Chm)*

Subsidiaries:

Arnold AG (1)
Industrie Nord 12, 6105, Bern, Switzerland
Tel.: (41) 41 497 39 39
Web Site: http://www.grundfosarnold.com
Pump & Pumping Equipment Whslr
N.A.I.C.S.: 423830
Christoph Arnold *(CEO)*

BKB Aqua Engineering Pty. Ltd. (1)
1/12 O'Connor Way, Wangara, 6065, WA, Australia
Tel.: (61) 8 9408 1216
Engineeering Services
N.A.I.C.S.: 541330

BKB Building Solutions Pty. Ltd (1)
109-111 Wedgewood Rd, Hallam, 3803, VIC, Australia
Tel.: (61) 387860444
Emp.: 35
Pump Mfr & Whslr
N.A.I.C.S.: 333914
Scott Donoghue *(Gen Mgr)*

Biral AG (2)
Sudstrasse 10, 3110, Munsingen, Switzerland
Tel.: (41) 31 720 90 00
Web Site: http://www.biral.ch
Pumps Mfr
N.A.I.C.S.: 333914
Roger Weber *(CEO)*

Biral GmbH (1)
Freiherr-vom-Stein-Weg 15, 72108, Rottenburg am Neckar, Germany
Tel.: (49) 7472 16 33 0
Pump & Pumping Equipment Whslr

N.A.I.C.S.: 423830

DAB Pumpen Deutschland GmbH (1)
Tackweg 11, 47918, Tonisvorst, Germany
Tel.: (49) 2151 821 36 0
Web Site: http://www.dabpumps.de
Pump & Pumping Equipment Whslr
N.A.I.C.S.: 423830

DAB Pumps B.V. (1)
Albert Einsteinweg 4, 5151 DL, Drunen, Netherlands
Tel.: (31) 416 387280
Web Site: http://www.dabpumps.nl
Emp.: 40
Pump & Pumping Equipment Whslr
N.A.I.C.S.: 423830
Maykel Jacobs *(Gen Mgr)*

DAB Pumps Iberica S.L. (1)
Avenida De Castilla 1 - Loc 14, San Fernando De Henares, Madrid, 28830, Spain
Tel.: (34) 916569545
Pump & Pumping Equipment Whslr
N.A.I.C.S.: 423830

DAB Pumps Ltd. (1)
Units 4 & 5 Stortford Hall Industrial Park Dumow Road, Bishop's Stortford, CM23 5GZ, Hertfordshire, United Kingdom
Tel.: (44) 1279 652776
Pump & Pumping Equipment Whslr
N.A.I.C.S.: 423830

DAB Pumps S.p.A. (1)
Via Marco Polo 14, Mestrino, Padua, Italy
Tel.: (39) 049 5125000
Web Site: http://www.dabpumps.com
Emp.: 550
Pump Mfr & Whslr
N.A.I.C.S.: 333914
Giorgio Menegazzi *(Mgr-Mktg)*

Deutsche Vortex GmbH & Co. KG (1)
Kastnerstr 6, 71642, Ludwigsburg, Germany
Tel.: (49) 71 41 25 52 0
Web Site: http://www.deutsche-vortex.de
Pump Mfr & Whslr
N.A.I.C.S.: 333914
Pino Brosamle *(Gen Mgr)*

ENAQUA Inc. (1)
2410 Birch St, Vista, CA 92081
Tel.: (760) 599-2644
Web Site: http://www.enaqua.com
Emp.: 20
Water Treatment Equipment Mfr
N.A.I.C.S.: 333310
Mark Maki *(Chm)*

Grundfos Holding A/S (1)
Poul Due Jensens vej 7, 8850, Bjerringbro, Denmark
Tel.: (45) 87501400
Web Site: http://www.grundfos.com
Mechanical & Industrial Engineering Services
N.A.I.C.S.: 541330
Carsten J. Reinhardt *(Vice Chm)*

Grundfos Management A/S (1)
Poul Due Jensens Vej 7, 8850, Bjerringbro, Denmark (85%)
Tel.: (45) 87501400
Web Site: http://www.grundfos.com
Sales Range: $1-4.9 Billion
Emp.: 4,500
Pumps Mfr
N.A.I.C.S.: 333914
Poul Due Jensen *(Chief Sls Officer & Exec VP)*

Subsidiary (Non-US):

Bombas Grundfos (Portugal) S.A. (2)
Rua Calvet de Magalhaes 241, Apartado 1079, 2770-153, Paco d'Arcos, Portugal
Tel.: (351) 214407600
Web Site: http://www.grundfos.com
Sales Range: $125-149.9 Million
Emp.: 320
Pump Sales & Distr
N.A.I.C.S.: 423830
Zosa Costa *(Gen Mgr)*

Bombas Grundfos Espana S.A.U. (2)

INTERNATIONAL PUBLIC

Camino de la Fuentecilla s/n, Algete, 28110, Madrid, Spain
Tel.: (34) 918 488 800
Web Site: http://www.grundfos.es
Pump & Pumping Equipment Whslr
N.A.I.C.S.: 423830

Bombas Grundfos de Argentina S.A. (2)
Ruta Panamericana ramal Campana Km 37 500 Parque Industrial Garin, Lote 34A Esq Haendel y Mozart Garin - Pcia, 1619, Buenos Aires, Argentina
Tel.: (54) 3327414444
Web Site: http://www.ar.grundfos.com
Sales Range: $25-49.9 Million
Emp.: 50
Pump Sale & Distr
N.A.I.C.S.: 423830
Omar Bolnes *(Gen Mgr)*

Bombas Grundfos de Mexico Manufacturing S.A. de C.V. (2)
Circuito Exportacion No 272, San Luis Potosi, 78395, Mexico
Tel.: (52) 444 102 6600
Pumps Mfr
N.A.I.C.S.: 333914

Bombas Grundfos de Mexico S.A. de C.V. (2)
Blvd Tlc No 15, Apodaca, 66600, Mexico
Tel.: (52) 818 144 4000
Pump & Pumping Equipment Whslr
N.A.I.C.S.: 423830

Bombas Grundfos do Brasil Ltda (2)
Av Humberto de Alencar, Sao Bernardo do Campo, Brasilia, SP, Brazil
Tel.: (55) 1 4393 5533
Web Site: http://www.br.grundfos.com
Pump & Pumping Equipment Whslr
N.A.I.C.S.: 423830

GRUNDFOS Pumps Baltic SIA (2)
Gunara Astras iela 8b, 1082, Riga, Latvia
Tel.: (371) 67 149 640
Web Site: http://www.grundfos.lv
Emp.: 14
Pump & Pumping Equipment Whslr
N.A.I.C.S.: 423830

Grundfos (Ireland) Ltd. (2)
Unit A Merrywell Business Park, Ballymount Road Lower, Dublin, D12 PW56, Ireland
Tel.: (353) 14089800
Web Site: http://www.grundfos.com
Sales Range: $25-49.9 Million
Emp.: 25
Pump Sales & Distr
N.A.I.C.S.: 423830
Gordon Barry *(Mng Dir)*

Grundfos (Pty) Ltd. (2)
Corner Mount Joy & George Allen Roads, Wilbart Ext 2, Bedfordview, South Africa
Tel.: (27) 0115794800
Web Site: http://www.grundfos.com
Sales Range: $25-49.9 Million
Emp.: 40
Pump Sales & Distr
N.A.I.C.S.: 423830

Grundfos (Singapore) Pte. Ltd. (2)
25 Jalan Tukang, Singapore, 619264, Singapore
Tel.: (65) 68651222
Web Site: http://www.grundfos.com.sg
Sales Range: $25-49.9 Million
Emp.: 100
Pump Sales & Distr
N.A.I.C.S.: 423830

Grundfos (Thailand) Ltd. (2)
947/168 Moo 12 Bangna rad Rd KM3, Bangkok, 10260, Thailand
Tel.: (66) 27258999
Web Site: http://www.grundfos.co.th
Emp.: 95
Pump Sales & Distr
N.A.I.C.S.: 423830
Pornthip Viphatanaporn *(Gen Mgr)*

Grundfos AB (2)
Lunnagardsgatan 6, 431 90, Molndal, Sweden
Tel.: (46) 771322300
Web Site: http://www.se.grundfos.com
Rev.: $380,000,000
Emp.: 100

AND PRIVATE COMPANIES

THE POUL DUE JENSEN FOUNDATION

Pump Sales & Distr
N.A.I.C.S.: 423830
Per Frydenberg (Mng Dir)

Subsidiary (Domestic):

Grundfos BioBooster A/S (2)
Randersvej 22A, 8870, Langa, Denmark
Tel.: (45) 87501400
Pump & Pumping Equipment Whslr
N.A.I.C.S.: 423830
Thomas Rosenkilde Anderson (Grp VP-Svc)

Subsidiary (Non-US):

Grundfos Bosna i Herzegovina (2)
Trg heroja 16, 71000, Sarajevo, BIH, Bosnia & Herzegovina
Tel.: (387) 33713290
Web Site: http://www.grundfos.ba
Sales Range: $25-49.9 Million
Emp.: 4
Pump Sales & Distr
N.A.I.C.S.: 423830

Grundfos Canada Inc. (2)
2941 Brighton Road, Oakville, L6H 6C9, ON, Canada
Tel.: (905) 829-9533
Web Site: https://www.grundfos.com
Sales Range: $25-49.9 Million
Emp.: 60
Pump Sales & Distr
N.A.I.C.S.: 423830
Poul Due Jensen (Pres)

Grundfos Croatia d.o.o. (2)
Buzin Cebini 37, 10010, Zagreb, Croatia
Tel.: (385) 16595400
Web Site: http://www.grundfos.hr
Sales Range: $25-49.9 Million
Emp.: 11
Pump Sales & Distr
N.A.I.C.S.: 423830

Subsidiary (Domestic):

Grundfos DK A/S (2)
Martin Bachs Vej 3, 8850, Bjerringbro, Denmark
Tel.: (45) 87505050
Pump & Pumping Equipment Mfr
N.A.I.C.S.: 333914

Subsidiary (Non-US):

Grundfos GmbH (2)
Delta Haus Schlueterstrasse 33, D-40699, Erkrath, Germany
Tel.: (49) 211929690
Sales Range: $50-74.9 Million
Emp.: 110
Pump Sales & Distr
N.A.I.C.S.: 423830

Grundfos Gulf Distribution (2)
po 16768, PO Box 16768, Jebel Ali Free Zone, Dubai, United Arab Emirates
Tel.: (971) 48815166
Web Site: http://www.grundfos.com
Sales Range: $25-49.9 Million
Emp.: 100
Pump Sales & Distr
N.A.I.C.S.: 423830
Aliasgar Chhawniwala (Mgr-Fin)

Grundfos Handels AG (2)
14 Min Yu Rd Tunglo Hsiang, Miao-li, 36646, Taiwan
Tel.: (886) 37985015
Pump & Pumping Equipment Whslr
N.A.I.C.S.: 423830

Grundfos Hellas A.E.B.E. (2)
20th Km Athinon-Markopoulou Ave, 19002, Peania, Greece
Tel.: (30) 2106683400
Sales Range: $25-49.9 Million
Emp.: 21
Pump Sales & Distr
N.A.I.C.S.: 423830

Grundfos Hungaria Kft. (2)
Park Str 8, H-2045, Torokbalint, Hungary
Tel.: (36) 23511110
Web Site: http://www.grundfos.hu
Sales Range: $25-49.9 Million
Emp.: 75
Pump Sales & Distr
N.A.I.C.S.: 423830

Grundfos Hungary Manufacturing Ltd. (2)
Buzavirag Str 14, Tatabanya, 2800, Ipari Park, Hungary
Tel.: (36) 34520100
Web Site: http://www.gundfos.com
Sales Range: $350-399.9 Million
Emp.: 1,600
Pumps Mfr
N.A.I.C.S.: 333914
Laszlo Torok (Mng Dir)

Grundfos Istra LLC (2)
188 Leshkovo, 143581, Moscow, Russia
Tel.: (7) 4957379101
Pump & Pumping Equipment Whslr
N.A.I.C.S.: 423830

Grundfos Manufacturing Ltd. (2)
Ferryboat Lane, Castletown, Sunderland, SR5 3JL, United Kingdom
Tel.: (44) 1915495555
Web Site: http://www.grundfos.com
Sales Range: $25-49.9 Million
Emp.: 200
Pumps Mfr
N.A.I.C.S.: 333914
Lee Carlin (Mng Dir)

Grundfos Nederland B.V. (2)
Postbus 104, NL-1380 AC, Weesp, Netherlands
Tel.: (31) 294492211
Pump Sales & Distr
N.A.I.C.S.: 423830

Grundfos OOO (2)
ul Shkolnaya 39-41 building 1, 109544, Moscow, Russia
Tel.: (7) 4957373000
Web Site: http://www.grundfos.com
Pump Distr
N.A.I.C.S.: 423830

Grundfos Ofis Bulgaria (2)
105-107 Arsenalski Boulevard, BG-1421, Sofia, Bulgaria
Tel.: (359) 29633820
Web Site: http://www.grundfos.com
Pump Sales & Distr
N.A.I.C.S.: 423830

Grundfos Pompa San. ve Tic. Ltd. Sti. (2)
Gebze Organize Sanayi Bolgesi Ihsan Ded Cad 200 Sokak, 204 Gebze-Kocaeli, Istanbul, Turkiye
Tel.: (90) 2626797979
Web Site: http://www.grundfos.com.tr
Pump Mfr, Sales & Distr
N.A.I.C.S.: 333914

Grundfos Pompa Sanyi ve Ticaret Ltd. Sti. (2)
Gebze O S B Ihsan Dede Cad 200 Sok No 204, 41480, Gebze, Kocaeli, Turkiye
Tel.: (90) 262 6797900
Web Site: http://www.grundfos.tr
Pump & Pumping Equipment Whslr
N.A.I.C.S.: 423830

Grundfos Pompe Italia S.r.l. (2)
Via Gran Sasso 4, Truccazzano, 20060, Milan, Italy
Tel.: (39) 0295838112
Pump Sales & Distr
N.A.I.C.S.: 423830

Grundfos Pompe Romania S.R.L. (2)
Str Tipografilor nr 11-15 Complex S-Park Cladirea A2 Etaj 2 Sector 1, 013714, Bucharest, Romania
Tel.: (40) 21 2004100
Web Site: http://www.ro.grundfos.com
Emp.: 42
Pump & Pumping Equipment Whslr
N.A.I.C.S.: 423830
Marius Mihail Brezeanu (Mgr-Ops-SE Europe)

Grundfos Pompy Sp. z o.o. (2)
ul Klonowa 23, Baranowo k Poznania, 62-081, Przezmierowo, Poland
Tel.: (48) 616501300
Web Site: http://www.pl.grundfos.com
Sales Range: $50-74.9 Million
Emp.: 100
Pump Sales & Distr
N.A.I.C.S.: 423830

Mauricy Rataczyk (Gen Mgr)

Grundfos Pump Vietnam (2)
1073/28A Cach mang Thang Tam Ward 7, Tan Bihn, Ho Chi Minh City, Vietnam
Tel.: (84) 839 770 454
Pump & Pumping Equipment Whslr
N.A.I.C.S.: 423830

Grundfos Pumpen AG (2)
Bruggacherstrasse 10, CH-8117, Fallanden, ZH, Switzerland
Tel.: (41) 18068111
Web Site: http://www.grundfos.com
Pump Sales & Distr
N.A.I.C.S.: 423830

Grundfos Pumpen Vertrieb Ges.m.b.H. (2)
Grundfosstrasse 2, A-5082, Grodig, Austria
Tel.: (43) 62468830
Sales Range: $25-49.9 Million
Emp.: 70
Pump Sales & Distr
N.A.I.C.S.: 423830

Grundfos Pumpenfabrik GmbH (2)
Willy-Pelz-Strasse 1-5, 23812, Wahlstedt, Germany
Tel.: (49) 4554980
Web Site: http://www.grundfos.de
Sales Range: $150-199.9 Million
Emp.: 600
Pumps Mfr
N.A.I.C.S.: 333914

Grundfos Pumper A/S (2)
Alf Bjerckes vei 30, 0596, Oslo, Norway
Tel.: (47) 22904700
Web Site: http://www.no.grundfos.com
Sales Range: $25-49.9 Million
Emp.: 60
Pump Sales & Distr
N.A.I.C.S.: 423830
Per Frydenberg (Mng Dir)

Grundfos Pumps (Hong Kong) Ltd. (2)
Unit 1 Ground Floor Siu Wai Industrial Centre, 68 King Lam Street, Kowloon, China (Hong Kong)
Tel.: (852) 27861706
Pump Sales & Distr
N.A.I.C.S.: 423830

Grundfos Pumps (Philippines) Inc. (2)
5548 Osmena Highway Brgy San Isidro, Makati, 1234, Philippines
Tel.: (63) 2 465 3000
Web Site: http://www.grundfos.ph
Pump & Pumping Equipment Whslr
N.A.I.C.S.: 423830
Joy P. Cabalfin (Country Mgr)

Grundfos Pumps (Shanghai) Co. Ltd. (2)
Floor 51 Raffles City Shanghai Office Tower, 268 Xi Zang road Central, Shanghai, 200001, China
Tel.: (86) 2161225222
Pump Sales & Distr
N.A.I.C.S.: 423830

Grundfos Pumps (Taiwan) Ltd. (2)
7f 219 Min Chuan Rd, Taichung, Taiwan
Tel.: (886) 423050868
Pump & Pumping Equipment Whslr
N.A.I.C.S.: 423830

Subsidiary (US):

Grundfos Pumps Corporation (2)
17100 W 118th Ter, Olathe, KS 66061
Tel.: (913) 227-3400
Web Site: http://www.us.grundfos.com
Sales Range: $50-74.9 Million
Emp.: 115
Pump Sales & Distr
N.A.I.C.S.: 423830
Duncan Copper (Pres)

Subsidiary (Domestic):

Grundfos Pumps Manufacturing Corporation (3)
5900 E Shields Ave, Fresno, CA 93727
Tel.: (559) 292-8000
Web Site: http://www.us.grundfos.com

Sales Range: $75-99.9 Million
Emp.: 300
Pumps Mfr
N.A.I.C.S.: 333914
Tom Wing (Dir-Supply Chain-NAMREG)

Peerless Pump Company (3)
2005 Dr Martin Luther King Jr St, Indianapolis, IN 46202
Tel.: (317) 925-9661
Web Site: http://www.peerlesspump.com
Sales Range: $100-124.9 Million
Emp.: 350
Mfr of Pumps for Agricultural, Commercial Construction; General Industry; Municipal Water, Power & Utility Markets
N.A.I.C.S.: 333310
Mike Cates (VP)

Subsidiary (Non-US):

Grundfos Pumps Ghana Ltd. (2)
Plot no 302 b Adjei Tsuru St, Legon, Ghana
Tel.: (233) 302 540 172
Web Site: http://www.grundfos.com
Emp.: 7
Pump & Pumping Equipment Whslr
N.A.I.C.S.: 423830
P. Saravanan (Deputy Gen Mgr)

Grundfos Pumps India Private Ltd. (2)
118 Rajiv Gandhi Salai Thoraipakkam, Chennai, 600 097, India
Tel.: (91) 4445966800
Pump & Pumping Equipment Whslr
N.A.I.C.S.: 423830
Kalyan Panch (Mgr-HR)

Grundfos Pumps K.K. (2)
1-2-3 Shin-miyakoda, Hamamatsu, 431-2103, Shizuoka, Japan
Tel.: (81) 534284760
Web Site: http://www.grundfos.jp
Sales Range: $50-74.9 Million
Emp.: 170
Pump Sales & Distr
N.A.I.C.S.: 423830
Shirakawa Hideo (Gen Mgr)

Grundfos Pumps Korea Ltd. (2)
6th Floor Aju Building 679-5 Yeoksam-dong, Kangnam-ku, Seoul, 135-916, Korea (South)
Tel.: (82) 25317600
Web Site: http://www.grundfos.co.kr
Sales Range: $25-49.9 Million
Emp.: 90
Pump Sales & Distr
N.A.I.C.S.: 423830
Kang Ho Lee (Pres)

Grundfos Pumps Latvia Ltd. (2)
A Deglava Street 60 3rd Floor, 1035, Riga, Latvia
Tel.: (371) 7149640
Web Site: http://www.grundfos.com
Sales Range: $25-49.9 Million
Emp.: 100
Pump Sales & Distr
N.A.I.C.S.: 423830

Grundfos Pumps Ltd. (2)
Grovebury Rd, Leighton Buzzard, LU7 4TL, Bedfordshire, United Kingdom
Tel.: (44) 1525850000
Web Site: http://www.grundfos.com
Sales Range: $25-49.9 Million
Emp.: 60
Pump Sales & Distr
N.A.I.C.S.: 423830
Peter Reynolds (Mng Dir)

Grundfos Pumps NZ Ltd. (2)
17 Beatrice Tinsley Crescent North Harbour Indus Estate, Albany, 0632, Auckland, New Zealand
Tel.: (64) 94153240
Sales Range: $25-49.9 Million
Emp.: 20
Pump Sales & Distr
N.A.I.C.S.: 423830

Grundfos Pumps Pte. Ltd. (2)
24 Tuas W Rd, Singapore, 638381, Singapore
Tel.: (65) 68651222
Sales Range: $25-49.9 Million
Emp.: 120
Pumps Mfr

THE POUL DUE JENSEN FOUNDATION

The Poul Due Jensen Foundation—(Continued)
N.A.I.C.S.: 333914

Grundfos Pumps Pty. Ltd. (2)
515 South Road, Regents Park, 5010, SA, Australia
Tel.: (61) 884614611
Web Site: http://www.grundfos.com
Sales Range: $25-49.9 Million
Emp.: 100
Pump Sales & Distr
N.A.I.C.S.: 423830
Steen Jensen *(Mng Dir-Area)*

Grundfos Pumps Sdn. Bhd. (2)
7 Jalan Peguam U1/25 Hicom-glenmarie Indutrial Park, Glenmarie Industrial Park, Shah Alam, 40150, Selangor, Malaysia
Tel.: (60) 355692922
Sales Range: $25-49.9 Million
Emp.: 80
Pump Sales & Distr
N.A.I.C.S.: 423830
Chee Khuan Leong *(Gen Mgr)*

Grundfos Pumps UAB (2)
Smolensko 6, 03210, Vilnius, Lithuania
Tel.: (370) 52395430
Web Site: http://www.grundfos.lt
Sales Range: $25-49.9 Million
Emp.: 12
Pump Sales & Distr
N.A.I.C.S.: 423830
Jamie Molle *(Gen Mgr)*

Grundfos Serbia (2)
Omladinskih brigada 90a, 11070, Novi Beograd, Serbia
Tel.: (381) 11 225 8740
Web Site: http://www.grundfos.rs
Pump & Pumping Equipment Whslr
N.A.I.C.S.: 423830
Ivan Vujcic *(Mgr-Logistic)*

Grundfos Slovenija (2)
Podruznica Ljubljana Blatnica 1, 1236, Trzin, Slovenia
Tel.: (386) 15635338
Pump Sales & Distr
N.A.I.C.S.: 423830

Grundfos Srbija d.o.o. (2)
Omladinskih brigada 90a, Belgrade, 110070, Novi, Serbia
Tel.: (381) 11 225 8740
Web Site: http://www.grundfos.rs
Pump Sales & Distr
N.A.I.C.S.: 423830

Grundfos Ukraine (2)
Metropolitan Highway 103 Business Center, 0313, Kiev, Ukraine
Tel.: (380) 44 237 0400
Web Site: http://ua.grundfos.com
Pump Sales & Distr
N.A.I.C.S.: 423830
Alexandr Hamolya *(Dir-Public Works)*

Grundfos Water Treatment GmbH (2)
Reetzstrasse 85, Pfinztal, 76327, Sollingen, Germany
Tel.: (49) 7240 61 0
Pump & Pumping Equipment Whslr
N.A.I.C.S.: 423830

Grundfos o.z. (2)
Plevoznki 4D, Bratislava, Slovakia
Tel.: (421) 250201411
Web Site: http://www.grundfos.sk
Sales Range: $25-49.9 Million
Emp.: 13
Pump Sales & Distr
N.A.I.C.S.: 423830

Grundfos spol. s.r.o. (2)
Cajkovskeho 21, 77900, Olomouc, Czech Republic
Tel.: (420) 585716111
Sales Range: $25-49.9 Million
Emp.: 60
Pump Sales & Distr
N.A.I.C.S.: 423830
Peter Jelinek *(Gen Mgr)*

Mark Grundfos Ltda (2)
Av Humberto de Alencar Castelo, Branco 630, 09850-300, Sao Bernardo do Campo, SP, Brazil
Tel.: (55) 11 43935533

N.V. Grundfos Bellux S.A. (2)
Boomsesteenweg 81-83, 2630, Aartselaar, Belgium
Tel.: (32) 38707300
Pump Sales & Distr
N.A.I.C.S.: 423830
Sven Vanderbiesen *(Mgr-Fin)*

Oy Grundfos Environmental Finland Ab (2)
Kaivokselantie 3-5, FIN-00101, Vantaa, Finland
Tel.: (358) 9561420
Web Site: http://www.grundfos.com
Sales Range: $25-49.9 Million
Emp.: 140
Pumps Mfr
N.A.I.C.S.: 333914

Oy Grundfos Pumput AB (2)
Mestarintie 11, 01730, Vantaa, Finland
Tel.: (358) 207889500
Web Site: http://www.grundfos.com
Sales Range: $25-49.9 Million
Emp.: 79
Pump Sales & Distr
N.A.I.C.S.: 423830

PT Grundfos Pompa (2)
Intirub Business Park Graha Intirub 2nd & 3rd Fl Jl Cillilitan, Besar No 454, Jakarta, 13650, Halim, Indonesia
Tel.: (62) 21 4695 1900
Web Site: http://id.grundfos.com
Pump Sales & Distr
N.A.I.C.S.: 423830

Pompes Grundfos Distribution S.A.S. (2)
Parc d'Activities de Chesnes 57 rue de Malacombe, 38070, Saint-Quentin-Fallavier, France
Tel.: (33) 474821515
Web Site: http://www.fr.grundfos.com
Sales Range: $50-74.9 Million
Emp.: 200
Pump Sale & Distr
N.A.I.C.S.: 423830
Guillaume Allary *(Mng Dir)*

Pompes Grundfos S.A. (2)
Parc d Activites de Chesnes 57 Rue de Malacombe, 38070, Saint-Quentin-Fallavier, France
Tel.: (33) 474821515
Web Site: http://www.fr.grundfos.com
Sales Range: $75-99.9 Million
Emp.: 500
Pumps Mfr
N.A.I.C.S.: 333914

SIA Grundfos Pumps Baltic Eesti (2)
Priisle tee 10, 13914, Tallinn, Estonia
Tel.: (372) 6061690
Web Site: http://www.ee.grundfos.com
Sales Range: $25-49.9 Million
Emp.: 8
Pump Sale & Distr
N.A.I.C.S.: 423830
Karol Lindvere *(Branch Mgr-Sls)*

Isia S.p.A. (1)
Centro direzionale Torre Uno Via Banchina dei Molini 8, 30175, Venice, Italy
Tel.: (39) 0415381800
N.A.I.C.S.: 333310

Subsidiary (Non-US):

Isia International UAE (2)
Dubai Airport Free Zone Authority, Dubai, United Arab Emirates
Tel.: (971) 47017960
Water Treatment Equipment Mfr
N.A.I.C.S.: 333310

Sintex A/S (1)
Jyllandsvej 14, 9500, Hobro, Denmark
Tel.: (45) 9657 4300
Web Site: http://www.sintex.dk
Sintered Component Mfr
N.A.I.C.S.: 331110

Watermill Products Ltd. (1)
Gemini House Enterprise Way, Edenbridge, TN8 6HF, Kent, United Kingdom
Tel.: (44) 1732 869700

Web Site:
http://www.showerpumpselector.co.uk
Pumps Mfr
N.A.I.C.S.: 333914

Yeomans Chicago Corporation (1)
3905 Enterprise Ct, Aurora, IL 60504
Tel.: (630) 236-5500
Pump & Pumping Equipment Whslr
N.A.I.C.S.: 423830

THE PRACTICAL SOLUTION PUBLIC COMPANY LIMITED
99 Soi Cement Thai Ratchadapisek Road, Lad Yao Chatuchak, Bangkok, 10900, Thailand
Tel.: (66) 21129999 TH
Web Site:
https://www.thepractical.co.th
Year Founded: 2004
TPS—(THA)
Rev.: $39,783,112
Assets: $32,069,299
Liabilities: $15,534,253
Net Worth: $16,535,046
Earnings: $3,513,031
Emp.: 124
Fiscal Year-end: 12/31/23
Communication Equipment Mfr
N.A.I.C.S.: 334220
Bunsom Kitkasetsathaporn *(CEO)*

Subsidiaries:

X-Secure Co., Ltd. (1)
Location 99 Soi Cement Thai Ratchadapisek Road, Ladyao Subdistrict Chatuchak District, Bangkok, 10900, Thailand
Tel.: (66) 21129996
Web Site: https://www.x-secure.co.th
Computer & Cumber Security Services
N.A.I.C.S.: 541519

THE PRECEPT GROUP INC.
375 Hagey Blvd Ste 302, Waterloo, N2L 6R5, ON, Canada
Tel.: (519) 747-5210
Web Site:
http://www.alignedinsurance.net
Year Founded: 1998
Rev.: $25,300,980
Emp.: 25
Insurance Agencies
N.A.I.C.S.: 524298
Jim Mcgregor *(CEO)*

THE PREMIER BANK LIMITED
Iqbal Centre 4th Floor 42 Kemal Ataturk Avenue Banani, Dhaka, 1213, Bangladesh
Tel.: (880) 29820844 BD
Web Site:
http://www.premierbankltd.com
Year Founded: 1999
Rev.: $227,490,655
Assets: $3,038,338,299
Liabilities: $2,821,377,607
Net Worth: $216,960,692
Earnings: $38,627,079
Emp.: 1,947
Fiscal Year-end: 12/31/19
Banking Services
N.A.I.C.S.: 522110
H. B. M. Iqbal *(Chm)*

THE PREMIER SUGAR MILLS & DISTILLERY CO., LTD.
Kings Arcade 20-A Markaz F-7, Islamabad, Pakistan
Tel.: (92) 5126508057
Web Site:
https://www.premiersugarmills.com
Year Founded: 1944
PMRS—(PSX)
Rev.: $113,020,196
Assets: $132,998,553
Liabilities: $69,762,858
Net Worth: $63,235,695

INTERNATIONAL PUBLIC

Earnings: $5,774,971
Emp.: 1,229
Fiscal Year-end: 09/30/23
Sugar Products Mfr.
N.A.I.C.S.: 311314
Naveed Jafar *(Acct Mgr)*

THE PRESS TRUST OF INDIA LIMITED
PTI Building 4 Parliament Street, New Delhi, 110 001, India
Tel.: (91) 1123716621
Web Site: http://www.ptinews.com
Sales Range: $300-349.9 Million
Emp.: 1,300
Newspaper Publishers
N.A.I.C.S.: 513110
M. Shakeel Ahmed *(Gen Mgr-Admin)*

THE PROPERTY FRANCHISE GROUP PLC
2 St Stephens Court St Stephens Road, Bournemouth, BH2 6LA, Dorset, United Kingdom
Tel.: (44) 1202292829 UK
Web Site:
http://www.thepropertygroup.co.uk
Year Founded: 2013
TPFG—(AIM)
Rev.: $34,281,747
Assets: $72,972,734
Liabilities: $26,036,354
Net Worth: $46,936,380
Earnings: $9,145,418
Emp.: 3,500
Fiscal Year-end: 12/31/22
Real Estate Investment Services
N.A.I.C.S.: 531210

Subsidiaries:

Belvoir Group PLC (1)
The Old Courthouse 60A London Road, Grantham, NG31 6HR, Lincolnshire, United Kingdom
Tel.: (44) 1476584900
Web Site: http://www.belvoirgroup.com
Rev.: $41,871,012
Assets: $62,219,147
Liabilities: $14,860,621
Net Worth: $47,358,527
Earnings: $9,198,013
Emp.: 51
Fiscal Year-end: 12/31/2022
Real Estate Services
N.A.I.C.S.: 531390
Paul George *(Dir)*

Subsidiary (Domestic):

Belvoir Property Management (UK) Limited (2)
The Old Court House 60A London Road, Grantham, NG31 6HR, United Kingdom
Tel.: (44) 8453312741
Web Site: http://www.belvoir.co.uk
Emp.: 40
Real Estate Manangement Services
N.A.I.C.S.: 531390

Newton Fallowell Limited (2)
68 High Street, Grantham, NG31 6NR, Lincolnshire, United Kingdom
Tel.: (44) 1476848622
Web Site: https://www.newtonfallowell.co.uk
Real Estate Services
N.A.I.C.S.: 531210
Gavin Baker *(Branch Mgr)*

White Kite (Derby) Limited (2)
15 Friar Gate, Derby, DE1 1BU, United Kingdom
Tel.: (44) 1332265662
Real Estate Services
N.A.I.C.S.: 531110

White Kite (Leicester) Limited (2)
79 Queens Road, Leicester, LE2 1TT, United Kingdom
Tel.: (44) 1162709394
Real Estate Services
N.A.I.C.S.: 531110

EweMove Sales & Lettings Ltd. (1)
Cavendish House Littlewood Drive, Cleck-

AND PRIVATE COMPANIES

heaton, BD19 4TE, West Yorkshire, United Kingdom
Tel.: (44) 3333441199
Web Site: https://www.ewemove.com
Real Estate Development Services
N.A.I.C.S.: 531390
Sarah Makin *(Mktg Mgr)*

Hunters Property Plc (1)
Ground Floor Apollo House Eboracum Way Heworth Green, York, YO31 7RE, North Yorkshire, United Kingdom
Tel.: (44) 1904621026
Web Site: http://www.hunters.com
Sales Range: $10-24.9 Million
Emp.: 5
Real Estate Manangement Services
N.A.I.C.S.: 531210
Kevin Hollinrake *(Co-Founder & Chm)*

Subsidiary (Domestic):

Hunters Franchising Limited (2)
Hunters Franchising Apollo House Eboracum Way, York, YO31 7RE, United Kingdom
Tel.: (44) 1202292829
Web Site: https://huntersfranchise.co.uk
Real Estate Marketing Services
N.A.I.C.S.: 531390

Hunters Partners Limited (2)
Space One Beadon Road, London, W6 0EA, United Kingdom
Tel.: (44) 2082378200
Web Site: http://www.hunters.co.uk
Building Consulting Services
N.A.I.C.S.: 541690
Neil McCabe *(Co-Mng Dir)*

The Mortgage Genie Limited (1)
The Grainger Suite Dobson House Regent Centre, Newcastle upon Tyne, NE3 3PF, United Kingdom
Tel.: (44) 3333443372
Web Site: https://themortgagegenie.co.uk
Financial Loan Services
N.A.I.C.S.: 541611

THE PROTEIN PARTNERS LTD.
Dean Court 85 Adlington Road, Wilmslow, SK9 2BT, Cheshire, United Kingdom
Tel.: (44) 1625 586177 UK
Food & Dietary Supplement Products
N.A.I.C.S.: 445298
Timothy Daniel Lowth *(Dir)*

Subsidiaries:

CNP Professional Limited (1)
Unit 11 Hyde Point Dunkirk Lane, Hyde, SK14 4NL, Cheshire, United Kingdom
Tel.: (44) 1613680942
Web Site: http://www.cnpprofessional.co.uk
Food & Health Supplement Stores
N.A.I.C.S.: 456191
James Ernster *(Pres)*

THE PRS REIT PLC
Floor 3 1 St Ann Street, Manchester, M2 7LR, United Kingdom
Tel.: (44) 3339999926 UK
Web Site: https://www.theprsreit.com
Year Founded: 2017
PRSR—(LSE)
Rev.: $73,598,332
Assets: $1,472,058,895
Liabilities: $547,608,695
Net Worth: $924,450,201
Earnings: $118,396,107
Fiscal Year-end: 06/30/24
Other Activities Related to Real Estate
N.A.I.C.S.: 531390
Stephen Smith *(Chm)*

THE PUBLIC AFFAIRS INC.
Suzusen Building 4-25-6 Shimbashi, Minato-ku, Tokyo, 105-0004, Japan
Tel.: (81) 3 3433 7061 JP
Web Site: http://www.tpa.co.jp

Year Founded: 1985
Rev.: $20,000,000
Emp.: 20
Advertising, Media Planning, Planning & Consultation, Print, Production (Ad, Film, Broadcast), Public Relations, Publicity/Promotions, Radio, T.V., Web (Banner Ads, Pop-ups, etc.)
N.A.I.C.S.: 541820
Megumi Kasuga *(Pres & Exec Dir)*

THE QUARTO GROUP, INC.
The Old Brewery 6 Blundell Street, London, N7 9BH, United Kingdom
Tel.: (44) 2077006700
Web Site: http://www.quarto.com
Year Founded: 1976
QRT—(LSE)
Rev.: $126,883,000
Assets: $152,938,000
Liabilities: $109,225,000
Net Worth: $43,713,000
Earnings: $4,569,000
Emp.: 302
Fiscal Year-end: 12/31/20
Publishing Company
N.A.I.C.S.: 513130
Ken Fund *(COO)*

Subsidiaries:

Image Factory Ltd (1)
Image Centre Bumpers Farm, Chippenham, SN14 6LH, Wiltshire, United Kingdom (100%)
Tel.: (44) 1249456654
Web Site: http://www.imagefactoryuk.com
Sales Range: $25-49.9 Million
Printing Company
N.A.I.C.S.: 323111

Jacqui Small LLP (1)
7 Greenland Street, London, NW1 0ND, United Kingdom
Tel.: (44) 20 7284 7161
Web Site: http://www.quarto.com
Books Publishing Services
N.A.I.C.S.: 513130
Jacqui Small *(Publr)*

Packaged Goods Ltd (1)
Sheridan House 112-116A Western Road, Hove, BN3 1DD, East Sussex, United Kingdom
Tel.: (44) 1273 716 009
Emp.: 26
Books Publishing Services
N.A.I.C.S.: 513130
Nigel Browning *(Publr)*

ProVision Pte Ltd (1)
No 2 Jurong East St 21 03-175/176 IMM Building, Singapore, 609601, Singapore
Tel.: (65) 6334 7720
Books Publishing Services
N.A.I.C.S.: 513130

Quarto Publishing Plc (1)
The Old Brewery, 6 Blundell St, London, N7 9BH, QC, United Kingdom (100%)
Tel.: (44) 2077006700
Web Site: http://www.quarto.com
Rev.: $816,795
Emp.: 13
Publishing Company
N.A.I.C.S.: 513130

Subsidiary (Domestic):

Aurum Press Limited (2)
7 Greenland Street, London, NW1 0ND, United Kingdom
Tel.: (44) 20 7284 7160
Web Site: http://www.aurumpress.co.uk
Sales Range: $25-49.9 Million
Emp.: 25
Non Fiction Books Publishing Services
N.A.I.C.S.: 513130
Kerry Enzor *(Publr)*

Subsidiary (US):

Becker & Mayer LLC (2)
11120 NE 33rd Pl Ste 101, Bellevue, WA 98004-1444
Tel.: (425) 827-7120
Web Site: http://www.beckermayer.com

Emp.: 40
Book Publishers
N.A.I.C.S.: 513130
Mike Oprins *(Publr & VP)*

Subsidiary (Domestic):

Design Eye Publishing Ltd (2)
230 City Road, London, EC1V 2TT, United Kingdom
Tel.: (44) 20 7812 8601
Childrens Book Publishing & Printing Services
N.A.I.C.S.: 513130

Subsidiary (Non-US):

Global Book Publishing Pty Limited (2)
181 Botany Road, Waterloo, Sydney, 2017, NSW, Australia
Tel.: (61) 2 9310 5692
Web Site: http://www.globalbookpublishing.com.au
Sales Range: $25-49.9 Million
Emp.: 1
Books Publishing Services
N.A.I.C.S.: 513130

Subsidiary (US):

Harvard Common Press (2)
535 Albany St, Boston, MA 02118
Tel.: (617) 423-5803
Web Site: http://www.harvardcommonpress.com
Rev.: $3,260,000
Emp.: 10
Publisher of High-Quality Cookbooks & Parenting Books
N.A.I.C.S.: 513130
Dan Rosenberg *(Dir-Editorial)*

MBI Publishing Company LLC (2)
400 1st Ave N Ste 300, Minneapolis, MN 55401-1721
Tel.: (715) 294-3345
Rev.: $15,700,000
Emp.: 110
Book Publisher; Books, Calendars, DVDs, Diecasts & Other Car-Related Products Distr
N.A.I.C.S.: 513130

Subsidiary (Domestic):

Marshall Editions Ltd. (2)
The Old Brewery 6 Blundell Street, London, N7 9BH, United Kingdom (100%)
Tel.: (44) 20 7700 6764
Web Site: http://www.marshalleditions.com
Sales Range: $25-49.9 Million
Emp.: 70
Non-Fiction & Reference Book Publisher
N.A.I.C.S.: 513130

QED Publishing Ltd (2)
6 Blundell Street, London, N79BH, United Kingdom
Tel.: (44) 20 7812 8600
Web Site: http://www.qed-publishing.co.uk
Children Book Publishing Services
N.A.I.C.S.: 513130

Quantum Publishing Ltd (2)
The Old Brewery, 6 Blundell St, London, N7 9BH, United Kingdom (100%)
Tel.: (44) 2077006700
Web Site: http://www.quarto.com
Sales Range: $25-49.9 Million
Emp.: 10
Publishing Company
N.A.I.C.S.: 513130

Quarto Children's Books Ltd (2)
230 City Rd, London, EC1V2TT, United Kingdom (100%)
Tel.: (44) 2077006700
Web Site: http://www.quarto.com
Sales Range: $25-49.9 Million
Publishing Company
N.A.I.C.S.: 513130

Quintessence Editions Ltd (2)
6 Blundell Street, London, N7 9BH, United Kingdom
Tel.: (44) 2077006700
Web Site: http://www.quarto.com
Books Publishing Services
N.A.I.C.S.: 513130

THE RAJA GROUP

Quintet Publishing Ltd (2)
The Blundell St, London, N7 9BH, United Kingdom (100%)
Tel.: (44) 2077006700
Web Site: http://www.quarto.com
Sales Range: $25-49.9 Million
Emp.: 10
Publishing Company
N.A.I.C.S.: 513130

Subsidiary (US):

Rockport Publishers Inc (2)
100 Cummings Center St 406 L, Beverly, MA 01915 (100%)
Tel.: (978) 282-9590
Web Site: http://www.rockpub.com
Sales Range: $25-49.9 Million
Emp.: 35
Publishing Company
N.A.I.C.S.: 513130

Subsidiary (Non-US):

Apple Press Ltd (3)
7 Greenland Street, London, NW1 0ND, United Kingdom (100%)
Tel.: (44) 2072847168
Web Site: http://www.apple-press.com
Sales Range: $25-49.9 Million
Emp.: 25
Publishing Company
N.A.I.C.S.: 513130

Subsidiary (Domestic):

Fair Winds Press Inc (3)
100 Cummings Ctr Ste 406 L, Beverly, MA 01915 (100%)
Tel.: (978) 282-9590
Web Site: http://www.quartousa.com
Sales Range: $25-49.9 Million
Publishing Company
N.A.I.C.S.: 513130

Subsidiary (Non-US):

RotoVision SA (3)
Sheridan House 112-116 A Western Rd, Hove, BN3 1DD, E Sussex, United Kingdom (100%)
Tel.: (44) 1273727268
Web Site: http://www.rotovision.com
Sales Range: $25-49.9 Million
Publishing Company
N.A.I.C.S.: 513130

Subsidiary (US):

Walter Foster Publishing Inc (2)
3 Wrigley Ste A, Irvine, CA 92618 (100%)
Tel.: (949) 380-7510
Web Site: http://www.walterfoster.com
Sales Range: $25-49.9 Million
Emp.: 14
Publishing Company
N.A.I.C.S.: 513130

Western Screen & Sign Ltd (1)
The Old Brewery 6 Blundell St, London, N7 9BH, United Kingdom (100%)
Tel.: (44) 2077006700
Web Site: http://www.quarto.com
Sales Range: $25-49.9 Million
Emp.: 52
Publishing Company
N.A.I.C.S.: 513130

THE RAFT MARKETING LIMITED
The Blackbox Beech Ln, Wilmslow, SK9 5ER, Cheshire, United Kingdom
Tel.: (44) 1625547900
Web Site: http://www.theraft.co.uk
Sales Range: $10-24.9 Million
Emp.: 15
Advetising Agency
N.A.I.C.S.: 541810
Billy Evans *(Dir-Design)*

THE RAJA GROUP
ZI Paris Nord II rue de L'Etang Roissy, Ile-de-France, 95977, Paris, Cedex, France
Tel.: (33) 148 17 33 30
Web Site: http://www.raja-group.com
Year Founded: 1954

THE RAJA GROUP

The RAJA Group—(Continued)
Sales Range: $700-749.9 Million
Emp.: 1,900
Packaging Equipment & Supplies Distr
N.A.I.C.S.: 561910
Daniele Kapel-Marcovici (Pres & CEO)

Subsidiaries:

Bernard France SAS (1)
Zi de Tourcoing Nord 98 Rue de Reckem, 59960, Neuville-en-Ferrain, France
Tel.: (33) 320115555
Web Site: http://www.bernard.fr
Personal Care Product Distr
N.A.I.C.S.: 424210

MondOffice s.r.l. (1)
Via per Gattinara 17, Castelletto Cervo, 13851, Biella, Italy
Tel.: (39) 0161880880
Web Site: http://www.mondoffice.com
Sales Range: $50-74.9 Million
Emp.: 140
Office Furniture Distr
N.A.I.C.S.: 337214

RAJA SA
ZI Paris Nord II, Roissy CDG, 95977, Paris, Cedex, France
Tel.: (33) 148 17 33 30
Packaging Equipment & Supplies Distr
N.A.I.C.S.: 561910

Staples Productos de Oficina, SL (1)
Poligono Industrial Izaga Plataforma D Pabellon 1A, Apdo 3, 48960, Galdacano, Spain
Tel.: (34) 902 13 23 33
Web Site: http://www.staples.es
Office Products Distr
N.A.I.C.S.: 459410

THE RAMCO CEMENTS LIMITED

Auras Corporate Centre, 98-A Dr Radhakrishnan Salai Mylapore, Chennai, 600 004, India
Tel.: (91) 4428478666
Web Site:
  https://www.ramcocements.in
Year Founded: 1957
500260—(BOM)
Rev.: $981,978,299
Assets: $1,749,863,917
Liabilities: $926,404,892
Net Worth: $823,459,025
Earnings: $37,737,546
Emp.: 3,507
Fiscal Year-end: 03/31/23
Cement & Concrete Product Mfr
N.A.I.C.S.: 327310
K. Selvanayagam (Officer-Compliance & Sec)

THE RANK GROUP PLC

TOR Saint-Cloud Way, Maidenhead, SL6 8BN, United Kingdom
Tel.: (44) 1628504000 UK
Web Site: https://www.rank.com
Year Founded: 1937
RNK—(LSE)
Rev.: $928,589,483
Assets: $925,808,896
Liabilities: $497,345,803
Net Worth: $428,463,093
Earnings: $1,516,684
Emp.: 7,640
Fiscal Year-end: 06/30/24
Holding Company; Gaming & Leisure Operator & Franchiser
N.A.I.C.S.: 551112
Sarah Powell (Dir-IR & Corp Comm)

Subsidiaries:

Grosvenor Casinos Limited (1)
79 - 81 Queensway, London, W2 4QH, United Kingdom
Tel.: (44) 207 221 8788

Web Site:
  https://www.grosvenorcasinos.com
Casinos Services
N.A.I.C.S.: 721120

Netboost Media Limited (1)
5 Hachilazon St 8th Floor, Ramat Gan, 52522, Israel
Tel.: (972) 3 751 0033
Web Site: https://www.netboostmedia.com
Emp.: 60
Marketing Consulting Services
N.A.I.C.S.: 541613

Rank Group Gaming Division Limited (1)
Statesman House Stafferton Way, Maidenhead, SI6 1AY, United Kingdom (100%)
Tel.: (44) 1628504000
Web Site: http://www.rank.com
Sales Range: $10-24.9 Million
Emp.: 100
Casino Operator
N.A.I.C.S.: 721120
Leon Thomas (COO-Digital Bingo Brands)

Subsidiary (Domestic):

Mecca Bingo Limited (2)
TOR Saint-Cloud Way, Maidenhead, SL6 8BN, United Kingdom (100%)
Tel.: (44) 120 030 9561
Web Site: https://www.meccabingo.com
Operates Bingo & Social Clubs
N.A.I.C.S.: 713290

Rank Interactive (Gibraltar) Limited (1)
4C Leisure Island Business Centre, Ocean Village, GX11 1AA, Gibraltar, Gibraltar
Tel.: (350) 20068085
Gambling Game Services
N.A.I.C.S.: 713290

SRG Services Limited (1)
Ground Floor and 5th Floor Standard Chartered Tower Lot 19, Ebene, Mauritius
Tel.: (230) 402 1999
Gaming Entertainment Services
N.A.I.C.S.: 713210

Stride Gaming plc (1)
Unit 450 Highgate Studios 53-79 Highgate Road, London, NW5 1TL, United Kingdom
Tel.: (44) 20 72846080
Web Site: http://www.stridegaming.com
Rev.: $120,028,508
Assets: $107,885,079
Liabilities: $32,604,183
Net Worth: $75,280,896
Earnings: ($6,782,026)
Fiscal Year-end: 08/31/2018
Online Bingo & Other Gaming Services
N.A.I.C.S.: 713290
Stuart Eitan Boyd (CEO)

Stride Together Limited (1)
Unit 901 Highgate Studios 53-79 Highgate Road, London, NW5 1TL, United Kingdom
Tel.: (44) 207 284 6075
Web Site: https://www.stridetogether.com
Software Publisher
N.A.I.C.S.: 513210

Think Beyond Media Limited (1)
Hurstwood House Unit 1 Haig Road, Knutsford, WA16 8DX, Cheshire, United Kingdom
Tel.: (44) 156 563 2206
Web Site: https://www.think-beyond.co.uk
Marketing & Business Consulting Services
N.A.I.C.S.: 541613

THE REAL BROKERAGE INC.

25 York Street Suite 612, Toronto, M5J 2V5, ON, Canada
Tel.: (646) 469-7107
REAX—(NASDAQ)
Rev.: $689,158,000
Assets: $64,548,000
Liabilities: $27,464,000
Net Worth: $37,084,000
Earnings: ($27,216,000)
Emp.: 159
Fiscal Year-end: 12/31/23
Asset Management Services
N.A.I.C.S.: 523940

Ravi Jani (VP-IR, Fin Plng, and Analysis)

THE REJECT SHOP LIMITED

245 Racecourse Road, Kensington, 3031, VIC, Australia
Tel.: (61) 1800958316 AU
Web Site:
  https://www.rejectshop.com.au
Year Founded: 1981
TRS—(ASX)
Rev.: $571,075,719
Assets: $327,680,955
Liabilities: $214,110,576
Net Worth: $113,570,379
Earnings: $3,147,035
Emp.: 4,000
Fiscal Year-end: 06/30/24
Variety Merchandise Retailers
N.A.I.C.S.: 445110
Clinton Cahn (CEO & CFO)

Subsidiaries:

TRS Trading Group Pty. Ltd. (1)
245 Racecourse Rd, Kensington, 3031, VIC, Australia
Tel.: (61) 393715555
Web Site: http://www.rejectshop.com.au
Sales Range: $100-124.9 Million
Emp.: 290
Household Goods Whslr
N.A.I.C.S.: 449210

THE REMET COMPANY LTD.

9A Cody Business Centre Cody Road, London, E16 4TL, United Kingdom
Tel.: (44) 207 476 0121
Web Site:
  http://www.remetcompany.com
Year Founded: 1948
Sales Range: $250-299.9 Million
Emp.: 80
Metal Product Whslr
N.A.I.C.S.: 423510
Lorraine Hatfull (Office Mgr)

THE RENEWABLES INFRASTRUCTURE GROUP LIMITED

East Wing Trafalgar Court Les Banques, Saint Peter Port, GY1 3PP, Guernsey
Tel.: (44) 1481749700 GY
Web Site: https://www.trig-ltd.com
Year Founded: 2013
TRIG—(LSE)
Rev.: $154,758,899
Assets: $4,010,350,921
Liabilities: $3,408,230
Net Worth: $4,006,942,691
Earnings: $7,321,383
Fiscal Year-end: 12/31/23
Investment Management Service
N.A.I.C.S.: 523940
Helen Mahy (Chm)

THE RESERVE BANK OF AUSTRALIA

65 Martin Place, Sydney, 2000, NSW, Australia
Tel.: (61) 295518111
Web Site: http://www.rba.gov.au
Year Founded: 1911
Sales Range: $800-899.9 Million
Emp.: 1,378
Central Bank
N.A.I.C.S.: 521110
Tony Richards (Head-Payments Policy Dept)

Subsidiaries:

Note Printing Australia Limited (1)
1-9 Potter Street, Craigieburn, 3064, VIC, Australia
Tel.: (61) 3 9303 0444
Web Site: http://www.noteprinting.com
Banknote Printing Services

N.A.I.C.S.: 323111
Lindsay Boulton (Deputy Governor)

THE RESOURCE GROUP, INC.

15th Fl 675 W Hastings St, Vancouver, V6B 1N2, BC, Canada
Tel.: (604) 669-6463
Web Site:
  http://www.theresourcegroup.ca
Sales Range: $10-24.9 Million
Emp.: 10
Holding Company
N.A.I.C.S.: 551112
Frank Callaghan (Pres)

Subsidiaries:

Golden Cariboo Resources Ltd. (1)
804-750 West Pender St, Vancouver, V6C 2T7, BC, Canada
Tel.: (604) 682-2928
Web Site: https://www.goldencariboo.com
Mineral Exploration Services
N.A.I.C.S.: 212390
Thomas Kennedy (CEO)

THE RETHINK GROUP LIMITED

The Crane Building 22 Lavington Street, London, SE1 0NZ, United Kingdom
Tel.: (44) 2073674444 UK
Web Site:
  http://www.rethinkgroupplc.com
Year Founded: 2005
Sales Range: $150-199.9 Million
Recruiting & Other Business Services
N.A.I.C.S.: 561320
Iain Philip Blair (Member-Exec Bd & Exec Dir)

Subsidiaries:

Aiimi Ltd (1)
52-54 Southwark St, London, SE1 1UN, United Kingdom
Tel.: (44) 2073674444
Web Site: http://www.aiimi.com
Sales Range: $25-49.9 Million
Emp.: 30
Content Management & Consulting Services
N.A.I.C.S.: 541612
Steve Salvin (CEO)

KeyPower Consultants Imprimis Ltd (1)
Clarence House 22 Clarence Rd, Southend-on-Sea, SS1 1AN, United Kingdom
Tel.: (44) 1702 431666
Recruitment Agency Services
N.A.I.C.S.: 561311

ReBuild Recruitment Services Ltd (1)
5th Fl Newminster House 27-29 Baldwin St, Bristol, BS1 1LT, United Kingdom
Tel.: (44) 1173178888
Web Site: http://www.rethink-recruitment.co.uk
Sales Range: $75-99.9 Million
Recruitment Agency Services
N.A.I.C.S.: 561311

ReThink MEA FZCO (1)
Dubai Silicon Oasis Authority, PO Box 341144, Dubai, United Arab Emirates
Tel.: (971) 43724109
Web Site: http://www.rethink-recruitment.com
Sales Range: $25-49.9 Million
Emp.: 150
Human Resource Consulting Services
N.A.I.C.S.: 541612
Gavin Smith (Gen Mgr)

ReThink Recruitment Solutions Ltd (1)
19 Spring Gardens, Manchester, M2 1FB, United Kingdom
Tel.: (44) 1612147450
Web Site: http://www.rethink-recruitment.com
Sales Range: $10-24.9 Million
Emp.: 40
Recruitment Agency Services

N.A.I.C.S.: 561311
Andy Lord (COO)

THE REWARDS FACTORY LIMITED
Level 1 14 St Kilda Road, Saint Kilda, 3182, VIC, Australia
Tel.: (61) 395728500
Web Site:
http://www.rewardsfactory.com.au
Year Founded: 2001
Sales Range: $10-24.9 Million
Emp.: 30
Rewards Program & Incentive Marketing Implementation & Consulting Services
N.A.I.C.S.: 561499
David Vinson (Chm)

THE RIGHT CROWD TRUSTEES LIMITED
Finsgate 5-7 Cranwood St, London, EC1V 9EE, United Kingdom
Tel.: (44) 2072513762
Year Founded: 2005
Investment Services
N.A.I.C.S.: 523999

THE ROOF TRUSS COMPANY (NORTHERN) LIMITED
2 Rainhill Close, Stephenson Industrial Estate, Washington, NE37 3HU, United Kingdom
Tel.: (44) 1914179040
Web Site: http://www.roof-truss.co.uk
Year Founded: 1991
Roof Truss Mfr
N.A.I.C.S.: 321215

THE ROYAL CERAMIC INDUSTRY PUBLIC COMPANY LIMITED
DCC Building 37/7 Suthisarn-Vinijchai Road, Samsen-Nok Sub-district Huaykwang District, Bangkok, 10310, Thailand
Tel.: (66) 2276 9275
Web Site: http://www.rci.co.th
Year Founded: 1969
Rev.: $38,459,106
Assets: $33,847,900
Liabilities: $8,399,504
Net Worth: $25,448,396
Earnings: $5,488,081
Emp.: 367
Fiscal Year-end: 12/31/19
Ceramic Tile Product Mfr
N.A.I.C.S.: 212323
Viboon Wadcharasurang (Co-Chm)

Subsidiaries:

The Royal Ceramic Industry Public Company Limited - Nongkhae Mill (1)
No 54/7 Village No 3 Suwannasorn Road, Khokyae Sub-district, Nongkhae, 18230, Saraburi, Thailand
Tel.: (66) 3630524957
Ceramic Tile Product Mfr
N.A.I.C.S.: 327110

THE ROYAL COUNTRY CLUB AND RECREATION HOLDINGS, INC.
Room E 4F No 106 Zhouzi Street, Neihu District, Taipei, 114, Taiwan
Tel.: (886) 226582502   NV
Year Founded: 2015
Country Club Operator
N.A.I.C.S.: 713910
Fun-Ming Lo (Chm & Pres)

THE ROYAL HOTEL LIMITED
5-3-68 Nakanoshima, Kita-ku, Osaka, 530-0005, Japan
Tel.: (81) 664481121

Web Site: http://www.rihga.com
Year Founded: 1932
9713—(TKS)
Rev.: $136,615,480
Assets: $208,664,480
Liabilities: $77,277,510
Net Worth: $131,386,970
Earnings: $5,955,610
Fiscal Year-end: 03/31/24
Hotel Operator
N.A.I.C.S.: 721110
Fumiichi Ueda (Pres & CEO)

THE ROYAL LONDON MUTUAL INSURANCE SOCIETY LIMITED
55 Gracechurch Street, London, EC3V 0RL, United Kingdom
Tel.: (44) 3450502020   UK
Web Site:
http://www.royallondon.com
Year Founded: 1861
Sales Range: $200-249.9 Million
Emp.: 1,000
Insurance Products & Services
N.A.I.C.S.: 524298
Kevin Parry (Chm)

Subsidiaries:

Bright Grey (1)
2 Queen Street, Edinburgh, EH2 1BG, United Kingdom
Tel.: (44) 8456094500
Web Site: http://www.brightgrey.com
Insurance Products
N.A.I.C.S.: 524113
Roger Edwards (Dir-Propositions)

Co-operative Insurance Society Limited (1)
Miller Street, Manchester, M60 0AL, United Kingdom
Tel.: (44) 8453000374
Web Site: http://www.co-operativeinsurance.co.uk
Sales Range: $50-74.9 Million
Life, Health & Motor Insurance
N.A.I.C.S.: 524114

Royal Liver Assurance Limited (1)
Royal Liver Building Pier Head, Liverpool, L3 1HT, United Kingdom
Tel.: (44) 1512361451
Sales Range: $450-499.9 Million
Emp.: 438
Fire Insurance Services
N.A.I.C.S.: 524113

Royal London 360 (1)
London House Isle of Man Business Park, Cooil Road, Douglas, IM2 2SP, Isle of Man
Tel.: (44) 1624681681
Web Site: http://www.royallondon360.com
Sales Range: $100-124.9 Million
Emp.: 200
Offshore Investment, Savings & Tax Planning Products
N.A.I.C.S.: 523999
David Kneeshaw (Mng Dir)

Royal London Savings Limited (1)
Royal London Insurance 2nd Floor Spencer House 71 Royal Avenue, Belfast, BT1 1TL, United Kingdom
Tel.: (44) 3450502020
Banking Services
N.A.I.C.S.: 522180
Rob Regan (Dir-Ops)

Royal London Unit Trust Managers Limited (1)
55 Gracechurch Street, London, EC3V 0UF, United Kingdom
Tel.: (44) 8450502020
Web Site:
http://www.royallondongroup.co.uk
Financial Services
N.A.I.C.S.: 523999

THE ROYAL OPERA HOUSE COVENT GARDEN LTD
Covent Garden, London, WC2E 9DD, United Kingdom
Tel.: (44) 2072401200

Web Site: http://www.roh.org.uk
Sales Range: $200-249.9 Million
Emp.: 950
Opera Production
N.A.I.C.S.: 711110
Hywel David (Mgr-Corp Rels)

Subsidiaries:

ROH Developments Limited (1)
Royal Opera House Covent Garden, London, WC2E 9DD, United Kingdom
Tel.: (44) 2073044000
Real Estate Manangement Services
N.A.I.C.S.: 531390

THE RUBY MILLS LIMITED
Ruby House J K Sawant Marg Dadar West, Mumbai, 400 028, India
Tel.: (91) 2224387800
Web Site: https://www.rubymills.com
503169—(BOM)
Rev.: $18,224,456
Assets: $143,090,520
Liabilities: $74,933,013
Net Worth: $68,157,508
Earnings: $3,528,225
Emp.: 190
Fiscal Year-end: 03/31/21
Textile Mill
N.A.I.C.S.: 314999
Hiren Manharlal Shah (Chm)

THE RUSCA HOTEL
B-dul Dacia nr 10, 331086, Hunedoara, Romania
Tel.: (40) 254 717 575
Web Site: http://www.hotelrusca.ro
Sales Range: Less than $1 Million
Hotel Services
N.A.I.C.S.: 721110

THE SAGE GROUP PLC
North Park, Newcastle upon Tyne, NE13 9AA, United Kingdom
Tel.: (44) 1912943000   UK
Web Site: http://www.sage.com
Year Founded: 1981
SGE—(OTCIQ)
Rev.: $2,780,384,880
Assets: $5,010,803,520
Liabilities: $3,219,594,030
Net Worth: $1,791,209,490
Earnings: $268,617,770
Fiscal Year-end: 09/30/23
Supplier of Accounting & Business Management Software & Services
N.A.I.C.S.: 513210
Donald H. Brydon (Chm)

Subsidiaries:

Corecon Technologies, Inc. (1)
5912 Bolsa Ave Ste 109, Huntington Beach, CA 92649
Tel.: (714) 895-7222
Web Site: http://www.corecon.com
Software Publisher
N.A.I.C.S.: 513210
Norman J. Wendl (Founder & Pres)

Handisoft Software (Pty) Ltd (1)
374 Scarborough Beach Rd, Innaloo, Perth, 6018, WA, Australia
Tel.: (61) 892450600
Web Site: http://www.handisoft.com.au
Emp.: 80
Computer Software Consulting Services
N.A.I.C.S.: 541512
Alan Osrin (Mng Dir)

Micropay (Pty) Ltd (1)
Level 11 Zenith Tower B 821 Pacific Hwy, Chatswood, 2067, NSW, Australia
Tel.: (61) 298844000
Web Site: http://www.sagemicropay.com.au
Payroll Software Development Services
N.A.I.C.S.: 541511

Sage (UK) Limited (1)
C23 5 & 6 Cobalt Park Way Cobalt Business Park, Newcastle upon Tyne, NE28 9EJ, Tyne & Wear, United Kingdom

Tel.: (44) 1912943000
Sales Range: $350-399.9 Million
Emp.: 250
Business Software Consulting Services
N.A.I.C.S.: 541512

Sage Baeurer GmbH (1)
Josefstrasse 10, 78166, Donaueschingen, Germany
Tel.: (49) 771896520
Business Software Consulting Services
N.A.I.C.S.: 541512

Sage Intacct, Inc. (1)
300 Park Ave Ste 1400, San Jose, CA 95110
Tel.: (408) 878-0900
Web Site: https://www.sageintacct.com
Computer System Design Services
N.A.I.C.S.: 541512
Marc Linden (Exec VP & Gen Mgr)

Sage Logic Control, S.L (1)
Ctra de Prats 122, 08208, Sabadell, Barcelona, Spain
Tel.: (34) 93 728 54 00
Web Site: http://www.sagelogiccontrol.com
Business Management Software Development Services
N.A.I.C.S.: 541511

Sage Pay Europe Limited (1)
C23-5 6 Cobalt Park Way Cobalt Park, Newcastle upon Tyne, NE28 9EJ, United Kingdom
Tel.: (44) 8451114455
Web Site: http://www.sagepay.com
Sales Range: $1-9.9 Million
Emp.: 23
Secure Online Payment Services
N.A.I.C.S.: 522320

Sage Portugal Software S.A. (1)
Olympus II Building D Afonso Henriques 1462 - 2nd, 4450-013, Matosinhos, Portugal
Tel.: (351) 221202400
Web Site: http://www.sage.pt
Sales Range: $25-49.9 Million
Emp.: 160
Business Management Software Development Services
N.A.I.C.S.: 541511
Maria Kosta (CEO)

Sage SAS (1)
Sage 10 place de Belgique, CS 40015, La Garenne-Colombes, 92257, Paris, Cedex, France
Tel.: (33) 810303030
Web Site: https://www.sage.com
Software Development Services
N.A.I.C.S.: 541511

Sage SP, S.L. (1)
Moraleja Building One Avenida Europa 19 - planta 1, 28108, Madrid, Spain
Tel.: (34) 913349292
Web Site: https://www.sage.com
Business Software Consulting Services
N.A.I.C.S.: 541512

Sage Schweiz AG (1)
Place 10 D4, 6039, Root Langenbold, Switzerland
Tel.: (41) 58 944 19 19
Web Site: http://www.sageschweiz.ch
Emp.: 100
Business Software Consulting Services
N.A.I.C.S.: 541511
Jean-Jacques Suter (CEO)

Sage Simultan AG (1)
Via Vedeggio 4, Casella Postale 447, Manno, 6928, Switzerland
Tel.: (41) 916111313
Software Development Services
N.A.I.C.S.: 541511

Sage Software (Shanghai) Co. Ltd (1)
Room 201 Building 1 No 1412 Tongpu Road, Putuo District, Shanghai, 200333, China
Tel.: (86) 4008880540
Web Site: https://www.sagesoft.cn
Business Management Software Development Services
N.A.I.C.S.: 541511

Sage Software Asia Pte Ltd (1)
Asia Square Tower 2 12 Marina View 25-

THE SAGE GROUP PLC

The Sage Group plc—(Continued)

02, Singapore, 018961, Singapore
Tel.: (65) 63366118
Web Site: https://www.sage.com
Business Management Software Development Services
N.A.I.C.S.: 541511

Sage Software GmbH (1)
Franklinstrasse 61-63, 60486, Frankfurt am Main, Germany
Tel.: (49) 69500070
Web Site: http://www.sage.de
Business Software Consulting Services
N.A.I.C.S.: 541512

Sage Software India (P) Ltd (1)
301 3rd Floor B wing Everest Nivara Infotech Park MIDC Main Road, Indira Nagar Turbhe Maharashtra, Navi Mumbai, 400705, India
Tel.: (91) 2267687872
Web Site: https://www.sagesoftware.co.in
Sales Range: $25-49.9 Million
Emp.: 25
Business Management Software Development Services
N.A.I.C.S.: 541511

Sage Software, Inc. (1)
1715 N Brown Rd Bldg B, Lawrenceville, GA 30043 (100%)
Tel.: (949) 753-1222
Web Site: http://www.sagenorthamerica.com
Sales Range: $1-4.9 Billion
Emp.: 400
Supplier of Business Management Software & Services
N.A.I.C.S.: 513210

Subsidiary (Domestic):

Sage (2)
6700 Koll Center Pkwy Ste 125, Pleasanton, CA 94566-7032
Tel.: (925) 461-2625
Web Site: http://www.sagenorthamerica.com
Sales Range: $200-249.9 Million
Software Developer
N.A.I.C.S.: 334610
Pieter Bensch (Exec VP-Africa & Middle East)

Sage Software (2)
8800 N Gainey Ctr Dr Ste 200, Scottsdale, AZ 85258-2163
Tel.: (480) 368-3700
Sales Range: $50-74.9 Million
Emp.: 230
Software Solutions
N.A.I.C.S.: 513210

Subsidiary (Non-US):

Sage Software Canada Ltd (2)
111 5th Avenue SW Suite 3100-C, Calgary, T2P 5L3, AB, Canada
Tel.: (905) 814-0503
Web Site: https://www.sage.com
Sales Range: $1-4.9 Billion
Business Software Development Services
N.A.I.C.S.: 541511

Subsidiary (Domestic):

Sage Software, Inc. (2)
2325 Dulles Corner Blvd Ste 700, Herndon, VA 20171-4647
Web Site: http://www.bestsoftware.com
Sales Range: $75-99.9 Million
Software Solutions
N.A.I.C.S.: 541511

Timberline Software Corporation (2)
15195 NW Greenbrier Pkwy, Beaverton, OR 97006-5701
Tel.: (503) 690-6755
Web Site: http://www.timberline.com
Sales Range: $100-124.9 Million
Emp.: 315
Vertical Software Developer, Publisher & Marketer for the Construction, Architectural/Engineering & Real Estate Industries
N.A.I.C.S.: 513210

Sage Sp. z o.o. (1)
Al Jerozolimskie 132, 02-305, Warsaw, Poland
Tel.: (48) 224555600

Web Site: https://symfonia.pl
Business Software Development Services
N.A.I.C.S.: 541511
Peotr Cesiski (CEO)

Softline (Pty) Ltd (1)
102 Western Services Road Ext 6, Gallo Manor, 2191, South Africa
Tel.: (27) 11 304 1000
Web Site: http://www.softline.co.za
Emp.: 1,000
Business Management Software Development Services
N.A.I.C.S.: 541511

THE SAILOR PEN CO., LTD.

6-15-27 Shinmachi, Ome-city, Tokyo, 198-0024, Japan
Tel.: (81) 28318711
Web Site: https://www.sailor.co.jp
Year Founded: 1932
7992—(TKS)
Rev.: $32,316,220
Assets: $39,377,860
Liabilities: $22,390,220
Net Worth: $16,987,640
Earnings: ($10,698,810)
Emp.: 70
Fiscal Year-end: 12/31/23
Stationery Product Mfr
N.A.I.C.S.: 339940

Subsidiaries:

Sailor Pen Europe (1)
Mill Studio 102 Crane Mead, Ware, SG12 9PY, Hertfordshire, United Kingdom
Tel.: (44) 1920444354
Web Site: http://www.sailorpen.com
Printing Ink Mfr
N.A.I.C.S.: 325910

The Sailor Pen Co., Ltd. - Robotics Division (1)
6-15-27 Shinmachi, Ome, 198-0024, Tokyo, Japan
Tel.: (81) 428 31 8711
Web Site: http://www.sailor.co.jp
Industrial Machinery Mfr
N.A.I.C.S.: 333248

THE SALVATION ARMY INTERNATIONAL TRUST

101 Queen Victoria Street, London, EC4V 4EH, United Kingdom
Tel.: (44) 2073320101
Web Site:
  https://www.salvationarmy.org
Year Founded: 1865
Social Organization Services
N.A.I.C.S.: 813920

THE SAN-IN GODO BANK, LTD.

10 Uomachi, Matsue, 690-0062, Shimane, Japan
Tel.: (81) 852551000
Web Site: https://www.gogin.co.jp
Year Founded: 1941
8381—(TKS)
Rev.: $794,363,360
Assets: $48,653,328,040
Liabilities: $46,504,489,750
Net Worth: $2,148,838,290
Earnings: $138,810
Fiscal Year-end: 03/31/24
Commercial Banking Services
N.A.I.C.S.: 522110
Fumio Ishimaru (Chm)

Subsidiaries:

San-In Economics & Management Institute Co., Ltd. (1)
18 Shirakatahonmachi, Matsue, 690 0061, Japan
Tel.: (81) 852278248
Web Site: http://www.skeiken.co.jp
Emp.: 23
Research & Development in the Social Sciences & Humanities
N.A.I.C.S.: 541720
Yukio Sato (Pres)

The Gogin Agency Co., Ltd. (1)
10 Uomachi, Matsue, 690 0062, Japan
Tel.: (81) 852551000
Web Site: http://www.gogin.co.jp
Emp.: 100
Commercial Banking
N.A.I.C.S.: 522110

The Gogin Business Services Co., Ltd. (1)
Matsue Plaza Building 2F 1-7 Nadamachi, Shimane, Matsue, 690-0062, Japan (100%)
Tel.: (81) 852273334
Web Site: http://www.gogin.co.jp
Collection, Delivery, Sorting & Security of Cash/Checks, & Maintenance & Management of ATMs
N.A.I.C.S.: 561499

The Gogin Capital Co., Ltd. (1)
71 Shirakata Honmachi, Matsue, 690-0061, Shimane, Japan
Tel.: (81) 852287170
Web Site: https://www.g-cp.jp
Miscellaneous Financial Investment Activities
N.A.I.C.S.: 523999

The Gogin Staff Services Co., Ltd. (1)
71 Shirakatahonmachi, Matsue, 690-0061, Japan
Tel.: (81) 852554404
Temporary Help Service
N.A.I.C.S.: 561320

The San-In Servicing Co., Ltd. (1)
71 Shirakatahonmachi, Matsue, Japan
Tel.: (81) 852242001
Web Site: http://www.servicer.or.jp
Emp.: 25
Collection Agencies
N.A.I.C.S.: 561440
Hirose Masatoshi (Gen Mgr)

THE SANDESH LIMITED

Sandesh Bhavan Lad Society Road, B/H Vastrapur Gam PO Bodakdev, Ahmedabad, 380054, Gujarat, India
Tel.: (91) 7940004175
Web Site: https://www.sandesh.com
Year Founded: 1923
526725—(BOM)
Rev.: $45,971,896
Assets: $133,959,355
Liabilities: $7,466,123
Net Worth: $126,493,232
Earnings: $12,159,151
Emp.: 454
Fiscal Year-end: 03/31/23
Newspaper Publishers
N.A.I.C.S.: 513110
Falgunbhai Chimanbhai Patel (Chm & Mng Dir)

THE SAUDI BRITISH BANK

PO Box 9084, Riyadh, 11413, Saudi Arabia
Tel.: (966) 114062800
Web Site: https://www.sab.com
Year Founded: 1978
1060—(SAU)
Rev.: $4,556,310,092
Assets: $95,091,757,366
Liabilities: $78,587,407,812
Net Worth: $16,504,349,553
Earnings: $1,867,050,527
Emp.: 4,471
Fiscal Year-end: 12/31/23
Commercial Banking Services
N.A.I.C.S.: 522110
David Dew (Mng Dir)

Subsidiaries:

Alawwal Bank (1)
Al-Dhabab Street, PO Box 1467, Riyadh, 11431, Saudi Arabia
Tel.: (966) 114010288
Web Site: http://www.alawwalbank.com
Sales Range: $1-4.9 Billion
Emp.: 2,478
Banking Services

INTERNATIONAL PUBLIC

N.A.I.C.S.: 522110
Maha Al-Sudairi (Chief Compliance Officer)

Subsidiary (Domestic):

Saudi Hollandi Capital Company (2)
Al Rasheed Bldg, PO Box 1467, Al Maather St, Riyadh, 11431, Saudi Arabia
Tel.: (966) 12767808
Web Site: http://www.shc.com.sa
Financial Advisory Services
N.A.I.C.S.: 523940

HSBC Saudi Arabia Limited (1)
7267 Olaya-AlMurooj, Riyadh, 12283-2255, Saudi Arabia
Tel.: (966) 920005920
Web Site: http://www.hsbcsaudi.com
Financial & Brokerage Services
N.A.I.C.S.: 523999
Mansour Abdulaziz Al Bosaily (Chm)

SABB Takaful Company (1)
6788 Salah Ad Din Al Ayyubi Adh Dhubbat Unit No 3, Riyadh, 12627-4827, Saudi Arabia (65%)
Tel.: (966) 11 299 1666
Web Site: http://www.sabbtakaful.com
Rev.: $34,761,471
Assets: $250,763,792
Liabilities: $173,642,513
Net Worth: $77,121,279
Earnings: ($8,335,723)
Emp.: 66
Fiscal Year-end: 12/31/2020
Insurance Services
N.A.I.C.S.: 524298
Mohammad Al Shayea (Chm)

THE SCOTT TRUST LIMITED

Kings Place, 90 York Way, London, N1 9GU, United Kingdom
Tel.: (44) 2033532000
Web Site: http://www.gmgplc.co.uk
Holding Company
N.A.I.C.S.: 551112
Liz Forgan (Chm)

Subsidiaries:

Guardian Media Group.plc (1)
Kings Place 90 York Way, PO Box 68164, London, N1 9GU, United Kingdom
Tel.: (44) 2033532000
Web Site: http://www.gmgplc.co.uk
Newspapers, Websites, Radio Stations, Magazines & Business to Business Media Services
N.A.I.C.S.: 513110
Neil A. Berkett (Chm)

Subsidiary (Non-US):

GNM Australia Pty Limited (2)
35-37 Resevoir St, Surry Hills, 2010, NSW, Australia
Tel.: (61) 2 8036 7650
Newspaper Publishers
N.A.I.C.S.: 513110

Subsidiary (Domestic):

Greater Manchester Newspapers (2)
Mitchell Henry House Hollinwood Avenue, Oldham, OL9 8EF, Chadderton, United Kingdom
Tel.: (44) 1618327200
Web Site:
  http://www.manchestereveningnews.co.uk
Sales Range: $100-124.9 Million
Emp.: 500
Newspaper Publishers
N.A.I.C.S.: 513110
Rob Irvine (Editor)

The Guardian (2)
Kings Place 90 York Way, London, N1 9GU, United Kingdom
Tel.: (44) 2033532000
Web Site: http://www.guardian.co.uk
Rev.: $70,000,000
Emp.: 1,000
Newspaper Publishing
N.A.I.C.S.: 513110
Katherine Viner (Editor-in-Chief)

The Observer (2)
King's Place, 90 York Way, London, N1 9GU, United Kingdom
Tel.: (44) 2033532000

Web Site: http://www.observer.co.uk
Newspaper Publishers
N.A.I.C.S.: 513110

Joint Venture (Domestic):

Top Right Group Limited (2)
Greater London House, Hampstead Road, London, NW1 7EJ, United Kingdom
Tel.: (44) 207 728 5000
Web Site: http://www.topright-group.com
Sales Range: $1-4.9 Billion
Emp.: 600
Holding Company; Magazine Publisher & Trade Exhibition Organizer
N.A.I.C.S.: 551112
Tracey Gray (Dir-People)

Subsidiary (Non-US):

AME Info FZ LLC (3)
Dubai Media City Phase II Building 4 Office 204-205, PO Box 502100, Dubai, United Arab Emirates
Tel.: (971) 43902700
Business & Financial Information Services
N.A.I.C.S.: 516210
Phil Blizzard (Head-Brdcst)

Bounty Services Pty Ltd. (3)
54-58 Park St, Sydney, 2000, NSW, Australia
Tel.: (61) 292828000
Web Site: http://www.bountybags.com.au
Emp.: 2
Magazine Publisher
N.A.I.C.S.: 513120
Jo Runciman (Publr)

Subsidiary (Domestic):

EMAP Limited (3)
Telephone House 69-77 Paul Street, London, EC2A 4NQ, United Kingdom
Tel.: (44) 20 3033 2600
Web Site: http://www.emap.com
Sales Range: $25-49.9 Million
Emp.: 350
Magazine Publisher
N.A.I.C.S.: 513120
Natasha Christie-Miller (CEO)

Subsidiary (Non-US):

EMAP Communications BV (4)
Zonnebaan 27, 3606 CH, Maarssen, Netherlands
Tel.: (31) 302411088
Web Site: http://www.emap.nl
Sales Range: $25-49.9 Million
Magazine Publisher
N.A.I.C.S.: 513120

Subsidiary (US):

EMAP Communications USA (4)
420 Lexington Ave Ste 244, New York, NY 10170-0299
Tel.: (212) 599-5209
Provider of Business Services
N.A.I.C.S.: 513199

Subsidiary (Domestic):

EMAP Construction Networks Ltd. (4)
Greater London House Hampstead Road, London, NW1 7EJ, United Kingdom
Tel.: (44) 2077285000
Sales Range: $50-74.9 Million
Magazine Publisher
N.A.I.C.S.: 513120

Subsidiary (Domestic):

Construction Research Communications Ltd. (5)
151 Rosebery Ave, London, EC1R 4GB, United Kingdom
Tel.: (44) 2075056600
Sales Range: $25-49.9 Million
Publishers for the UK Building Research Establishment
N.A.I.C.S.: 513120

EMAP Construct Ltd. (5)
151 Roseberry Ave, London, EC1R 4QX, United Kingdom
Tel.: (44) 2074056600
Sales Range: $25-49.9 Million
Magazine & Directory Publisher
N.A.I.C.S.: 513120

EMAP Maclaren (5)
19th And 20th Floor Leon House, Croydon, CR0 9XT, Surrey, United Kingdom
Tel.: (44) 2082775000
Sales Range: $25-49.9 Million
Emp.: 150
Magazine & Directory Publisher
N.A.I.C.S.: 513120

Subsidiary (Domestic):

EMAP Public Sector Management Ltd. (4)
Greater London House Hampstead Road, London, NW1 7EJ, United Kingdom
Tel.: (44) 2078740200
Magazine & Directory Publisher & Online Information Service
N.A.I.C.S.: 513120

Subsidiary (Non-US):

Media Corporation Publishing (M) (3)
137 Jalan SS 25 2 311 Pont 01 11th Fl, Jaya Mewah, Petaling Jaya, 46500, Malaysia
Tel.: (60) 379579698
Sales Range: $25-49.9 Million
Emp.: 30
Magazine Publisher
N.A.I.C.S.: 513120

Subsidiary (Domestic):

Workthing.com (2)
12 18 Paul St, London, EC2A 4JH, United Kingdom
Tel.: (44) 8445605248
Web Site: http://www.workthing.com
Sales Range: $25-49.9 Million
Emp.: 80
N.A.I.C.S.: 513110

THE SCOTTISH AMERICAN INVESTMENT COMPANY PLC
Calton Square 1 Greenside Row, Edinburgh, EH1 3AN, United Kingdom
Tel.: (44) 1312752000
Investment Management Service
N.A.I.C.S.: 523999
Peter Moon (Chm)

THE SCOTTISH ORIENTAL SMALLER COMPANIES TRUST PLC
28 Walker Street, Edinburgh, EH3 7HR, United Kingdom
Tel.: (44) 1313780500
Web Site: https://www.scottishoriental.com
SST—(LSE)
Rev.: $37,601,704
Assets: $486,537,240
Liabilities: $46,219,796
Net Worth: $440,317,444
Earnings: $25,332,720
Fiscal Year-end: 08/31/23
Other Financial Vehicles
N.A.I.C.S.: 525990
James Ferguson (Chm)

THE SECURITIES HOUSE K.S.C.C.
18th Floor Al-Dhow Tower Khaled Ibn Al-Waleed Street, Sharq, Kuwait, 13130, Kuwait
Tel.: (965) 22245252
Web Site: https://www.sh.com.kw
Year Founded: 1982
SECH—(KUW)
Rev.: $17,612,516
Assets: $162,849,033
Liabilities: $35,947,684
Net Worth: $126,901,349
Earnings: $7,165,647
Emp.: 45
Fiscal Year-end: 12/31/22
Investment Banking & Securities Brokerage Services
N.A.I.C.S.: 523150
Ibrahim Yousef Al-Ghanim (Chm & Deputy CEO)

Subsidiaries:

Gatehouse Bank plc (1)
Fl 24 125 Old Broad St, London, EC2N 1AR, United Kingdom
Tel.: (44) 2070706000
Web Site: http://www.gatehousebank.com
Sales Range: $50-74.9 Million
Emp.: 40
Investment Banking Services
N.A.I.C.S.: 523150
James Bagshawe (CFO)

Global Securities House for Economic & Financial Consultancy K.S.C. (1)
Sharq - Khaled Bin Waleed St, Dhow Tower 15th Fl, Kuwait, Kuwait
Tel.: (965) 22332000
Web Site: http://www.gc.com.kw
Real Estate Investment & Advisory Services
N.A.I.C.S.: 525990
Abdullah Al Essa (Exec VP)

Kuwait Boxes Carton Manufacturing Company K.S.C.C. (1)
Block 4 Plots 184 186 188 190 192 Amghara Industrial Area, PO Box 892, Kuwait, 00008, Kuwait
Tel.: (965) 24573696
Web Site: http://www.kuwaitboxes.com
Coragulated Box Mfr & Distr
N.A.I.C.S.: 322211
Nael Beidas (Mgr-Sls & Mktg)

New Technology Bottling Company K.S.C.C. (1)
Kuwait Free Trade Zone Building 12, 64992 Shuwaikh B, 70460, Kuwait, Kuwait
Tel.: (965) 22275050
Web Site: http://www.abraajwater.com
Water Mfr & Distr
N.A.I.C.S.: 312112
Nixon Fernandes (Mgr-Warehouse)

THE SENTIENT GROUP LIMITED
Landmark Square 1st Floor 64 Earth Close, PO Box 10795, West Bay Beach South, Georgetown, KY1-1007, Grand Cayman, Cayman Islands
Tel.: (345) 946 0933 Ky
Web Site: http://www.thesentientgroup.com
Privater Equity Firm
N.A.I.C.S.: 523999
Greg Link (Gen Mgr)

Subsidiaries:

Iron Road Limited (1)
Level 3 63 Pirie Street, Adelaide, 5000, SA, Australia (57.87%)
Tel.: (61) 882144400
Web Site: https://www.ironroadlimited.com.au
Rev.: $545,795
Assets: $89,985,938
Liabilities: $1,550,483
Net Worth: $88,435,455
Earnings: ($993,999)
Emp.: 30
Fiscal Year-end: 06/30/2024
Iron Ore Mining & Exploration Services
N.A.I.C.S.: 212210
Peter Cassidy (Chm)

Sentient Asset Management Australia Pty. Limited (1)
Level 44 Grosvenor Place 225 George Street, Sydney, 2000, NSW, Australia (100%)
Tel.: (61) 282432900
Web Site: http://www.thesentientgroup.com
Sales Range: $50-74.9 Million
Emp.: 20
Private Equity Investment Management Services
N.A.I.C.S.: 523940
Andrew N. Pullar (CEO)

THE SHANGHAI COMMERCIAL & SAVINGS BANK, LTD.
3F-12F No 149 Sec 2 Minsheng E Rd, Zhongshan Dist, Taipei, 10483, Taiwan
Tel.: (886) 225817111
Web Site: https://www.scsb.com.tw
Year Founded: 1915
5876—(TAI)
Rev.: $2,528,591,158
Assets: $75,768,243,754
Liabilities: $68,151,810,149
Net Worth: $7,616,433,605
Earnings: $544,824,970
Emp.: 2,921
Fiscal Year-end: 12/31/23
Commercial Banking Services
N.A.I.C.S.: 522110

Subsidiaries:

China Travel Service (Taiwan) Limited (1)
No 54 Linsen North Road, Zhongshan Dist, Taipei, 104, Taiwan
Tel.: (886) 25625858
Web Site: https://www.chinatravel.com.tw
Travel Agency Services
N.A.I.C.S.: 561510

THE SHIBUSAWA WAREHOUSE CO., LTD.
2-37-28 Eidai, Koto-ku, Tokyo, Japan
Tel.: (81) 356467083
Web Site: https://www.shibusawa.co.jp
Year Founded: 1897
9304—(TKS)
Rev.: $485,286,370
Assets: $745,422,920
Liabilities: $331,458,450
Net Worth: $413,964,470
Earnings: $24,642,080
Emp.: 330
Fiscal Year-end: 03/31/24
Transportation Services
N.A.I.C.S.: 484110
Takeshi Osumi (Pres & CEO)

Subsidiaries:

Shibusawa (Hong Kong) Ltd. (1)
Tel.: (852) 24189311
Logistics Consulting Services
N.A.I.C.S.: 541614

Shibusawa Logistics (Shanghai) Ltd. (1)
Tel.: (86) 2165955789
Logistics Consulting Services
N.A.I.C.S.: 541614
Linqi Wang (Mgr)

Shibusawa Logistics Vietnam Co., Ltd. (1)
Room No E04 40 Ba Huyen Thanh Quan Street, Ward 6 District 3, Ho Chi Minh City, Vietnam (90%)
Tel.: (84) 8 3933 0922
Logistics Consulting Services
N.A.I.C.S.: 541614

THE SHIGA BANK, LTD.
1-38 Hamacho, Otsu, 520-8686, Shiga, Japan
Tel.: (81) 775212000
Web Site: https://www.shigagin.com
Year Founded: 1933
8366—(TKS)
Rev.: $810,584,300
Assets: $52,685,342,110
Liabilities: $49,440,579,040
Net Worth: $3,244,763,070
Earnings: $264,400
Emp.: 1,915
Fiscal Year-end: 03/31/24
Commercial Banking Services
N.A.I.C.S.: 522110
Shojiro Takahashi (Pres)

THE SHIGA BANK, LTD.

The Shiga Bank, Ltd.—(Continued)

Subsidiaries:

Shiga Kashiwabara Agency Company Limited (1)
851-5 Kashiwabara, Maibara, Shiga, Japan
Tel.: (81) 749571456
Business Service Centers
N.A.I.C.S.: 561439

Shiga Kutsuki Agency Company Limited, The (1)
608-2 Kutsukiichiba, Takashima, 520-1401, Japan
Tel.: (81) 740383131
Web Site: http://www.shigagin.com.jp
Sales Range: $300-349.9 Million
Emp.: 2,000
Business Service Centers
N.A.I.C.S.: 561439
Yamashi Ta (Gen Mgr)

Shigagin Business Service Company Limited, The (1)
1-38 Hamamachi, Otsu, 520-0041, Shiga, Japan
Tel.: (81) 775212490
Web Site: http://www.shigagin.com
Sales Range: $25-49.9 Million
Emp.: 80
Business Service Centers
N.A.I.C.S.: 561439

Shigagin Computer Service K.K. (1)
1-38 Hamamachi, Otsu, Japan
Tel.: (81) 775212490
Data Processing Services
N.A.I.C.S.: 518210

Shigagin Jcb, K.K. (1)
Hamaotsu Shiga Building 3F 1-10 Hamacho, Yubinbango Hamacho, Otsu, 520-0041, Shiga, Japan
Tel.: (81) 775215771
Web Site: https://www.shigaginjcb.jp
Sales Range: $50-74.9 Million
Emp.: 16
Activities Related to Credit Intermediation
N.A.I.C.S.: 522390

Shigagin Lease & Capital Co., Ltd (1)
4-28 Hamacho Hamacho Building 4th and 5th floors, Otsu, 520-0041, Shiga, Japan
Tel.: (81) 775226391
Web Site: https://www.shigagin.com
Business Service Centers
N.A.I.C.S.: 561439

The Shiga DC Card Co., Ltd. (1)
1-10 Hamamachi Hama Otsu Shiga Building 2nd Floor, Otsu, 520-0041, Shiga, Japan
Tel.: (81) 77 526 1302
Web Site: https://www.shigadc.co.jp
Credit Card Processing Services
N.A.I.C.S.: 522320

The Shigagin Economic & Cultural Center Co., Ltd. (1)
1-38 Hamamachi, Otsu, 520-0041, Shiga, Japan
Tel.: (81) 77 526 0005
Web Site: https://www.keibun.co.jp
Business Support Services
N.A.I.C.S.: 561499

The Shigagin Real Estate Company Limited (1)
1-38 Hamamachi, Otsu, 520-8686, Japan
Tel.: (81) 775212490
Emp.: 150
Real Estate Agents & Brokers
N.A.I.C.S.: 531210
Mishi Muora (Gen Mgr)

THE SHIKOKU BANK LTD.

1-1-1 Minami Harimaya-cho, Kochi, 780-8605, Japan
Tel.: (81) 888232111   JP
Web Site: https://www.shikokubank.co.jp
Year Founded: 1878
8387—(TKS)
Rev.: $346,932,460
Assets: $21,876,535,320
Liabilities: $20,764,541,630
Net Worth: $1,111,993,690
Earnings: $148,725
Fiscal Year-end: 03/31/24
Banking Services
N.A.I.C.S.: 522110
Fumiaki Yamamoto (Chm & Pres)

THE SHOKO CHUKIN BANK, LTD.

2-10-17 Yaesu, Chuo-ku, Tokyo, 104-0028, Japan
Tel.: (81) 332726111   JP
Web Site: http://www.shokochukin.co.jp
Year Founded: 1936
Rev.: $1,446,037,120
Assets: $123,784,984,400
Liabilities: $114,216,894,880
Net Worth: $9,568,089,520
Earnings: $179,292,960
Emp.: 3,685
Fiscal Year-end: 03/31/22
Retail, Commercial & Investment Banking
N.A.I.C.S.: 522110
Koushirou Umeda (Deputy Pres & Exec Officer)

Subsidiaries:

SHOKO SERVICE, LTD. (1)
3-3-2 Kyobashi, Chuo-ku, Tokyo, Japan
Tel.: (81) 3 3246 9392
Employee Health & Benefit Services
N.A.I.C.S.: 525120

SHOKOCHUKIN COMPUTER SYSTEMS CO., LTD. (1)
2-10-1 Misumicho, Higashimurayama, 189-0023, Tokyo, Japan
Tel.: (81) 42 392 8811
Web Site: http://www.shochu-comp.co.jp
Emp.: 214
Software Development Services
N.A.I.C.S.: 541511

THE SIAM CEMENT PUBLIC COMPANY LIMITED

1 Siam Cement Road, Bangsue, Bangkok, 10800, Thailand
Tel.: (66) 25864444   TH
Web Site: https://www.scg.com
Year Founded: 1913
SCC—(OTCIQ)
Rev.: $13,740,505,459
Assets: $24,574,457,553
Liabilities: $12,430,327,531
Net Worth: $12,144,130,022
Earnings: $663,036,603
Emp.: 55,578
Fiscal Year-end: 12/31/23
Chemical Products Mfr
N.A.I.C.S.: 551112
Aree Chavalitcheewingul (Pres-Cementhai Holding Co Ltd)

Subsidiaries:

Buu Long Industry & Investment Joint Stock Company (1)
Binh Thach Hamlet, Bien Hoa, Dong Nai, Vietnam
Tel.: (84) 61 3965475
Cement Mfr & Whslr
N.A.I.C.S.: 327310

Cementhai Holding Co., Ltd. (1)
1 Siam Cement Rd Bangsue, Bangkok, 10800, Thailand (100%)
Tel.: (66) 25862104
Web Site: http://www.siamcement.com
Sales Range: $50-74.9 Million
Emp.: 100
Holding Company
N.A.I.C.S.: 551112
Chaovalit Ekabut (Pres)

Joint Venture (Domestic):

SIAM KUBOTA Corporation Co., Ltd. (2)
101/19-24 Village No 20 Navanakorn Industrial Estate, Khlong Nueng Subdistrict Khlong Luang District, Pathumthani, 12120, Thailand (100%)
Tel.: (66) 20798199
Web Site: https://www.siamkubota.co.th
Agricultural Diesel Engines, Tractors & Reapers Mfr
N.A.I.C.S.: 333111

Subsidiary (Domestic):

SIAM KUBOTA Metal Technology Co., Ltd. (3)
359 Moo 3 Khao Hin Son, Phanom Sarakham, Chachoengsao, 24120, Thailand
Tel.: (66) 33051777
Web Site: https://www.skmt.co.th
Metal Products Mfr
N.A.I.C.S.: 332999

Affiliate (Domestic):

Siam Furukawa Co., Ltd. (2)
33 Moo 4 Nongplakladi Rd Tumbol Bualoy, Aumphor Nongkae, Bangkok, 18140, Saraburi, Thailand (29%)
Tel.: (66) 36373573
Sales Range: $125-149.9 Million
Emp.: 1,000
Automotive & Motorcycle Batteries
N.A.I.C.S.: 336390
Sirichai Saengthongphithak (Mng Dir)

Siam Lemmerz Co., Ltd. (2)
252 SPE Tower 11th Fl, Bangkok, 10400, Thailand (30%)
Tel.: (66) 26150187
Web Site: http://www.hayef-lemmbrf.com
Sales Range: $100-124.9 Million
Emp.: 450
Aluminum Alloy Wheels Mfr & Whslr
N.A.I.C.S.: 336390
Somchai Namsiriyothin (Mgr-Mktg)

Joint Venture (Domestic):

Siam Toyota Manufacturing Co., Ltd. (2)
700 109 111 113 Group 1 Amata Nakorn Industrial Estate, Chon Buri, 20160, Thailand
Tel.: (66) 38743313
Web Site: http://www.siamtoyota.co.th
Production & Sales of Engines; Owned by Toyota Motor Corporation & Cementhai Holding Co., Ltd.
N.A.I.C.S.: 336110

Subsidiary (Domestic):

Thai CRT Co., Ltd. (2)
Laem Chabang Industrial Estate 87 9 Moo 2 Sukhumvit Rd, Tung Sukhla, Ban Si Racha, 20230, Chon Buri, Thailand (90%)
Tel.: (66) 38490220
Television Tubes Mfr
N.A.I.C.S.: 335999

Affiliate (Domestic):

Thai Engineering Products Co., Ltd. (2)
1 Siam Cement Road, Bangsue, Bangkok, 10800, Thailand (44%)
Tel.: (66) 25293518
Web Site: http://www.tep.co.th
Mfr of Spare Parts of Casting & Aluminum for Automotives, Pickups, Trucks, Motorcycles, Agricultural Engines, Construction Materials & Computer Parts
N.A.I.C.S.: 336340

The Nawaloha Industry Co., Ltd. (2)
19 M00 3 Suwannason Road, Bualoy, Saraburi, 18230, Nonkhae, Thailand (30%)
Tel.: (66) 3633653140
Web Site: http://www.attg.co.th
Mfr of Brake Drums, Flywheels & Crankcases
N.A.I.C.S.: 336340

The Siam Construction Steel Co., Ltd. (2)
I-23 Map Taphut Industrial Estate, Muang, Rayong, 21150, Thailand
Tel.: (66) 38683968
Sales Range: $25-49.9 Million
Emp.: 100
Mfr of Round Bars & Deformed Bars
N.A.I.C.S.: 333992

The Siam Nawaloha Foundry Co., Ltd. (2)
1 Siam Cement Rd, Bangsue, Bangkok, 10800, Thailand (25%)
Tel.: (66) 25863333
Web Site: http://www.siamcement.com
Automotive Assembly, Agricultural Engine Assembly, Compressor Parts & Cement Parts
N.A.I.C.S.: 336350

Conimex Co., Ltd. (1)
40 Moo 12 Soi Shamit Sukhumvit 77 Rd Srisajorakae-Noi, Bangsaothong, Samut Prakan, 10540, Thailand
Tel.: (66) 27380305
Web Site: http://www.conimexthai.com
Emp.: 700
Plastic Container & Bottle Mfr
N.A.I.C.S.: 326160

D-In Pack Company Limited (1)
58/2 Moo 6 Prapatone-Banpaew Rd Taladjinda, Sam Phran, Nakhon Pathom, Thailand
Tel.: (66) 349814014
Corrugated Box Mfr
N.A.I.C.S.: 322211

Eco Plant Services Co., Ltd. (1)
No 1 Village No 9 Patpong Road, Ban Khrua Subdistrict Ban Mo District, Bangkok, 18270, Saraburi Province, Thailand
Tel.: (66) 36289103
Web Site: http://www.ecoplantservices.co.th
Environmental Consulting Services
N.A.I.C.S.: 541620

Grand Nawaplastic Myanmar Co., Ltd. (1)
No 12 Corner of Chindwin Street and Min Ayar Street, Shwe Than Lwin Industrial Zone Hlaing Tharyar, Yangon, Myanmar
Tel.: (95) 9450045310
Plastic Pipe Fitting Mfr
N.A.I.C.S.: 326122

Interpress Printers Sendirian Berhad (1)
Lot 34 and 36 Jalan Modal 23/2 Section 23 Kawasan MIEL, 40100, Shah Alam, Selangor, Malaysia
Tel.: (60) 35 542 1716
Web Site: https://www.interpressprinters.com
Food Packaging Services
N.A.I.C.S.: 561910

Long Son Petrochemicals Co., Ltd. (1)
R 490A 4th Floor 8 Hoang Dieu St, Vung Tau, Vietnam
Tel.: (84) 643514000
Petrochemical Products Mfr
N.A.I.C.S.: 325110

Map Ta Phut Olefins Co., Ltd. (1)
88/3 Rayong Highway 3191 Ril Map Ta Phut, Muang, Rayong, 21150, Thailand
Tel.: (66) 38937000
Plastic Materials Mfr
N.A.I.C.S.: 325211

Mariwasa Siam Holdings, Inc. (1)
Barrio San Antonio, Santo Tomas, Batangas, 4234, Philippines
Tel.: (63) 437782936
Web Site: http://www.mariwasa.com
Sales Range: $50-74.9 Million
Emp.: 643
Ceramic Tile Mfr
N.A.I.C.S.: 327120

Subsidiary (Domestic):

Mariwasa Siam Ceramics, Inc. (2)
Brgy San Antonio, Santo Tomas, Batangas, 4234, Batangas, Philippines
Tel.: (63) 2 717 6901
Web Site: https://www.mariwasa.com
Ceramic Tile Mfr
N.A.I.C.S.: 327120

Mawlamyine Cement Limited (1)
Kha Yone Gu-Chaung Hna Kwa Road, Kwan Ngan Village Kyaik Maraw Township, Yangon, Myanmar
Tel.: (95) 979 609 3056
Web Site: https://mawlamyinecementlimited.com

AND PRIVATE COMPANIES — THE SIAM CEMENT PUBLIC COMPANY LIMITED

Cement Mfr
N.A.I.C.S.: 327310
Nyan Lin Htat *(Mgr-Quality Assurance & Cement Distr Section)*

Nawa Intertech Co., Ltd. (1)
130/3 Moo 3 Nonglalok, Baan Khai, Rayong, 21120, Thailand
Tel.: (66) 388921909
Web Site: http://www.nawaintertech.com
Molding Product Mfr
N.A.I.C.S.: 333511

Nawaplastic (Cambodia) Co., Ltd. (1)
Prey Speu Village Sangkat Chom Chao Khan Posenchey, Phnom Penh, Cambodia
Tel.: (855) 23882072
Plastic Pipe Fitting Mfr
N.A.I.C.S.: 326122
Bandhit Lertpalanan *(Mng Dir)*

New Asia Industries Co., Ltd. (1)
Street 2, Binh Chieu Industrial Park Binh Chieu Ward Thu Duc Dist, Ho Chi Minh City, Vietnam
Tel.: (84) 837294160
Web Site: http://www.newasia-vn.com
Corrugated Box Mfr
N.A.I.C.S.: 322211

Nexter Digital Co., Ltd. (1)
Gateway Bangsue Floor 7 No 162/1-2 168/10 Pracharat 2 Road, Bangsue, Bangkok, 10800, Thailand
Tel.: (66) 20791112
Web Site: http://www.nexterdigital.com
Building Materials Distr
N.A.I.C.S.: 444180

Orient Containers Co., Ltd. (1)
12/5 12/8 Moo 8 Soi Liabklongchonpratansuansom Phraram 2 Rd Bankoh, Amphur Muang, Samut Sakhon, 74000, Thailand
Tel.: (66) 34 883 4224
Web Site: https://www.orientcontainers.com
Corrugated Box & Paper Mfr
N.A.I.C.S.: 322211

PT Indocorr Packaging Cikarang (1)
Jl Industri Selatan 2 Blok LL3 Tahap II, Kawasan Industrial Cikarang, Bekasi, Indonesia
Tel.: (62) 218936868
Corrugated Box Mfr
N.A.I.C.S.: 322211

PT Indoris Printingdo (1)
Jl RayaSerang KM 18 5 KM Desa Sukanagara, Cikupa, Tangerang, Indonesia
Tel.: (62) 215960772
Corrugated Box Mfr
N.A.I.C.S.: 322211

PT Nusantara Polymer Solutions (1)
Wisma Barito Pacific Lantai M Mezanin Jl Let Jend S Parman Kav 62-63, Kel Slipi Kec Palmerah, Jakarta Barat, Indonesia
Tel.: (62) 215307950
Petrochemical Products Mfr
N.A.I.C.S.: 325110

PT Primacorr Mandiri (1)
Jl Raya Serang KM 13 8 Desa Sukadamai Kecamatan Cikupa Kabupaten, Tristate Industrial Estate, Tangerang, Banten, Indonesia
Tel.: (62) 215962345
Corrugated Box Mfr
N.A.I.C.S.: 322211

PT SCG Trading Indonesia (1)
Bangkok Bank Building 6th Floor Jl M H Thamrin No 3, Jakarta, 10110, Indonesia
Tel.: (62) 213509488
International Trading Services
N.A.I.C.S.: 523160

Panel World Co., Ltd. (1)
83/1 moo11 Sethakij 1 Rd, Klongmadue Krathumban, Samut Sakhon, 74110, Thailand
Tel.: (66) 3447306770
Web Site: http://www.panelworld.co.th
Cement Bonded Particleboard Mfr
N.A.I.C.S.: 327310

Precision Print Co., Ltd. (1)
30/139 Moo 1, Sinsakhon Industrial Estate Khok Kham Muang, Samut Sakhon, 74000, Thailand
Tel.: (66) 3 411 9721
Web Site: https://www.precision-print.co.th
Packaging Design Services
N.A.I.C.S.: 541430

Prime - Ngoi Viet Joint Stock Company (1)
Binh Xuyen IZ, Huong Canh Town Binh Xuyen District, Vinh Yen, Vinh Phuc, Vietnam
Tel.: (84) 2113593468
Ceramic & Roofing Tile Mfr
N.A.I.C.S.: 327120

Prime - Truong Xuan Joint Stock Company (1)
Minh Quyet Hamlet, Khai Quang Ward, Vinh Yen, Vinh Phuc, Vietnam
Tel.: (84) 1800555595
Ceramic & Roofing Tile Mfr
N.A.I.C.S.: 327120

Prime Phong Dien Joint Stock Company (1)
CN01-B Phong Dien Industrial Zone, Phong Dien District, Yen Phong, Thua Thien Hue, Vietnam
Tel.: (84) 543625964
Web Site: http://www.fritvietnam.com
Ceramic Tile Mfr
N.A.I.C.S.: 327120

Q Mix Supply Co., Ltd. (1)
Major Tower Ramkhamheng-Rama 9 Office Building 51 Floor 8 Rama 9 Road, Huamark Bang Kapi, Bangkok, 10240, Thailand
Tel.: (66) 2 022 7888
Web Site: https://www.qmix.co.th
Readymix Concrete Mfr
N.A.I.C.S.: 327320

SCG Accounting Services Co., Ltd. (1)
1 Siam Cement Road, Bangsue, Bangkok, 10800, Thailand
Tel.: (66) 2 586 2398
Web Site: http://www.scgaccounting.co.th
Sales Range: $350-399.9 Million
Emp.: 700
Financial & Accounting Services
N.A.I.C.S.: 523999
Kan Trakulhoon *(Pres & CEO)*

SCG Building Products Co., Ltd. (1)
1 Siam Cement Road, Bangsue, Bangkok, 10800, Thailand **(100%)**
Tel.: (66) 25863333
Web Site: http://www.siamcement.com
Holding Company; Concrete, Ceramic & Gypsum Building Materials Mfr
N.A.I.C.S.: 551112

Joint Venture (Domestic):

Siam Sanitary Ware Co., Ltd. (2)
33 11 Viphavadeerangsit Rd, Bangkok, 10210, Thailand **(35.7%)**
Tel.: (66) 29735040
Web Site: http://www.siamcement.com
Mfr of Sanitary Ware
N.A.I.C.S.: 332999

Subsidiary (Domestic):

Thai Ceramic Co., Ltd. (2)
1 Siam Cement Road Bangsue, Bangkok, 10800, Thailand **(100%)**
Tel.: (66) 25864090
Web Site: http://www.cotto.co.th
Sales Range: $1-4.9 Billion
Emp.: 150
Ceramic Wall & Floor Tiles Mfr
N.A.I.C.S.: 327120

The CPAC Concrete Products Co., Ltd. (2)
181/10 Sanambinnam Road Amphur, Thasai Muang, Nonthaburi, 11000, Thailand **(100%)**
Tel.: (66) 25268860
Sales Range: $150-199.9 Million
Emp.: 487
Mfr of Precast Concrete Slabs, Concrete Blocks, Paving Blocks, Post Tension Slabs & Structures, Concrete Pipes & Concrete Walls
N.A.I.C.S.: 327331

The CPAC Ready Mixed Concrete Co., Ltd. (2)
1516 Pracharaj Sai 1 Rd, Bangkok, 10800, Thailand **(100%)**
Tel.: (66) 25555000
Web Site: http://www.mc.cementhai.co.th
Sales Range: $150-199.9 Million
Emp.: 1,000
Concrete Pump Service
N.A.I.C.S.: 238110

The CPAC Roof Tile Co., Ltd. (2)
1 Siam Cement Road, Bangsue, Bangkok, 10800, Thailand **(75%)**
Tel.: (66) 25864026
Web Site: http://www.cpacrooftile.com
Sales Range: $125-149.9 Million
Concrete Roofing Tiles & Accessories Mfr
N.A.I.C.S.: 327390

The Siam Ceramic Group Industries Co., Ltd. (2)
40 Moo 2 Rimklongrapeepat Road Tambon Nongpling, Nongkae District, Saraburi, 18140, Thailand
Tel.: (66) 36376400
Web Site: http://www.siamceramic.co.th
Ceramic Tile Mfr & Distr
N.A.I.C.S.: 423320

The Siam Fiberglass Co., Ltd. (2)
39 Moo 9 Siam Cement Industrial Land, Nongkhae, 18140, Saraburi, Thailand **(100%)**
Tel.: (66) 36373444
Web Site: http://www.siamfiberglass.com
Sales Range: $25-49.9 Million
Emp.: 100
Glass Mfr
N.A.I.C.S.: 327212

The Siam Fibre-Cement Co., Ltd. (2)
1 Siam Cement Rd, Bangsue, Bangkok, 10800, Thailand **(100%)**
Tel.: (66) 258639505
Web Site: http://www.siamfibrecement.com
Sales Range: $100-124.9 Million
Emp.: 300
Roman Tiles, Corrugated Sheets, Flat Sheets, Venetian Louver Sheets & Other Fibre-Cement Products
N.A.I.C.S.: 327120

Affiliate (Domestic):

The Siam Gypsum Industry Co., Ltd. (2)
9 Pakin Building 5th Floor Next to Fortune Tower Ratchadapisek Road, Dindang, Bangkok, 10400, Thailand **(29%)**
Tel.: (66) 25550055
Web Site: http://www.usgboral.com
Sales Range: $50-74.9 Million
Emp.: 200
Mfr of Gypsum Boards, Moisture Resistant Boards, Fire Resistant Boards, Fiol-backed Boards, PVC-laminated Boards, Jointing Plaster G-200, Bonding Plaster, Moulding Plaster
N.A.I.C.S.: 327420

Joint Venture (Domestic):

The Siam Sanitary Fittings Co., Ltd. (2)
36/11 Vibhavadi-Rangsit Rd Sanambin Don Muang, Bangkok, 10210, Thailand **(44.8%)**
Tel.: (66) 29735040
Web Site: http://www.cotto.com
Sales Range: $25-49.9 Million
Emp.: 200
Faucets, Bath & Shower Fittings, Flush Valves & Tank Trim Mfr
N.A.I.C.S.: 332913

SCG Chemicals Co., Ltd. (1)
1 Siam Cement Road, Bangkok, 10800, Thailand **(100%)**
Tel.: (66) 25864184
Web Site: http://www.chemicalsscg.co.th
Sales Range: $1-4.9 Billion
Emp.: 3,000
Holding Company; Plastic Resins & Petrochemical Mfr
N.A.I.C.S.: 551112
Cholanat Yanaranop *(Pres-Chemical Bus)*

Subsidiary (Domestic):

Flowlab & Service Co., Ltd. (2)
271 Sukhumvit Road, Muang, Rayong, 21150, Thailand
Tel.: (66) 38911321
Cement Calibration Services
N.A.I.C.S.: 541380

Joint Venture (Domestic):

Grand Siam Composites Co., Ltd. (2)
1 Siam Cement Road, Bangsue, Bangkok, 10800, Thailand
Tel.: (66) 25862500
Sales Range: $125-149.9 Million
Polypropylene Compounds Mfr & Sales; Owned 48% by Mitsui Chemicals, Inc. & 46% by SCG Chemicals Co., Ltd.
N.A.I.C.S.: 325998
Kazunori Asami *(Mng Dir)*

Subsidiary (Domestic):

Map Ta Phut Tank Terminal Co., Ltd. (2)
1 Siam Cement Road, Bangsue, Bangkok, 10800, Thailand
Tel.: (66) 2 586 5560
Web Site: https://www.mtt-terminal.com
Petrochemical Terminal Operating Services
N.A.I.C.S.: 493190

Joint Venture (Non-US):

PT Chandra Asri Pacific Tbk (2)
Wisma Barito Pacific Tower A 7th Floor Jl Let Jend S Parman Kav 62-63, Jakarta, 11410, Indonesia **(30.57%)**
Tel.: (62) 215307950
Web Site: https://www.chandra-asri.com
Rev.: $2,159,932,000
Assets: $5,614,452,000
Liabilities: $2,620,552,000
Net Worth: $2,993,900,000
Earnings: ($31,547,000)
Emp.: 1,943
Fiscal Year-end: 12/31/2023
Petrochemical Mfr & Distr
N.A.I.C.S.: 325110
Erwin Ciputra *(CEO)*

Subsidiary (Non-US):

PT TPC Indo Plastic & Chemicals (2)
Maspion Industrial Estate Desa Sidomukti Manyar, Gresik, 61151, Indonesia
Tel.: (62) 313952945
Plastic Resin & Chemical Products Mfr
N.A.I.C.S.: 325998

Subsidiary (Domestic):

Rayong Engineering & Plant Service Co., Ltd. (2)
271 Sukhumvit Rd Map Ta Phut, Muang Rayong, Rayong, 21150, Thailand
Tel.: (66) 3868 5040 8
Plant Engineering Services
N.A.I.C.S.: 541330

Rayong Olefins Co., Ltd. (2)
271 Map Ta Put Industrial Estate Sukhumvit Road, Muang, Rayong, 21150, Thailand
Tel.: (66) 38 685040
Plastic Materials Mfr & Whslr
N.A.I.C.S.: 325211

SCG Performance Chemicals Co., Ltd. (2)
1 Siam Cement Road, Bangsue, Bangkok, 10800, Thailand
Tel.: (66) 2586 4115
Chemical Products Mfr
N.A.I.C.S.: 325998

SCG Plastics Co., Ltd. (2)
1 Siam Cement Road, Bangsue, Bangkok, 10800, Thailand
Tel.: (66) 2586 6161
Web Site: http://www.scgchemicals.co.th
Plastics Product Mfr
N.A.I.C.S.: 326199

Affiliate (Domestic):

Siam Synthetic Latex Co., Ltd. (2)
75 White Group Bldg Soi Rubia Sukhumvit 42 Rd, Phra Khanong, Bangkok, 10110, Thailand **(50%)**
Tel.: (66) 23811038
Web Site: http://www.siamcement.com

THE SIAM CEMENT PUBLIC COMPANY LIMITED

The Siam Cement Public Company Limited—(Continued)
Sales Range: $50-74.9 Million
Emp.: 150
Latex Mfr
N.A.I.C.S.: 325212

Joint Venture (Domestic):

Thai PET Resin Co., Ltd.
138 Boonmitr Building 8th Floor Silom Road, Suriyawongse Bangrak, Bangkok, 10500, Thailand
Tel.: (66) 26345894
Polyethylene Terepthalate Resin Mfr & Sales; Owned 40% by Mitsui Chemicals, Inc., 40% by Toray Industries, Inc. & 20% by SCG Chemicals Co., Ltd.
N.A.I.C.S.: 325211

Subsidiary (Domestic):

Thai Polyethylene (1993) Co., Ltd. (2)
1 Siam Cement Road, Bangsue, Bangkok, 10800, Thailand
Tel.: (66) 2 586 4767
Polypropylene Resin Mfr
N.A.I.C.S.: 325211

Thai Polyethylene Co., Ltd.
10 I 1 Rd Map Ta Phut Industrial Estate, Rayong, 21150, Thailand (100%)
Tel.: (66) 38683393
Web Site: http://www.cementhai.co.th
Sales Range: $100-124.9 Million
Emp.: 400
Mfr of Plastic Resins
N.A.I.C.S.: 325211

Thai Polypropylene (1994) Co., Ltd.
1 Siam Cement Rd, Bang Sue, Bangkok, 10800, Thailand
Tel.: (66) 2586 1119
Polyolefin Mfr
N.A.I.C.S.: 325220

SCG Decor Public Company Limited (1)
1 Siam Cement Road, Bang Sue Subdistrict Bang Sue District, Bangkok, 10800, Thailand
Tel.: (66) 25863333
Web Site: https://www.scgdecor.com
Rev: $826,490,236
Assets: $1,215,870,013
Liabilities: $593,733,113
Net Worth: $622,136,900
Earnings: $13,846,277
Emp.: 10,667
Fiscal Year-end: 12/31/2023
Holding Company
N.A.I.C.S.: 551112
Numpol Malichai (CEO & Mng Dir)

Subsidiary (Non-US):

CPAC Monier Vietnam Co., Ltd. (2)
No 9 Street No 10 Vietnam - Singapore Industrial Park, Thuan An, Binh Duong, Vietnam
Tel.: (84) 650 767581
Web Site: http://www.cpacroof.com.vn
Sales Range: $25-49.9 Million
Emp.: 3
Roofing Tile Mfr
N.A.I.C.S.: 327120

Subsidiary (Domestic):

Cementhai Home Services Co., Ltd. (2)
1 Siam Cement Rd, Bangsue, Bangkok, 10800, Thailand
Tel.: (66) 25866146
Construction Materials Mfr
N.A.I.C.S.: 327120

Subsidiary (Non-US):

PT Keramika Indonesia Assosiasi (2)
Graha Mobisel 3rd floor Jl Buncit Raya No 139, Jakarta Selatan, 12740, Indonesia
Tel.: (62) 217971190
Web Site: https://www.kiaceramics.com
Rev: $36,536,588
Assets: $62,886,969
Liabilities: $9,646,913
Net Worth: $53,240,055
Earnings: ($2,202,842)
Emp.: 172
Fiscal Year-end: 12/31/2023
Ceramic Wall & Roof Tile Mfr
N.A.I.C.S.: 327110
Anusorn Potchanabanpot (Chm)

Subsidiary (Domestic):

Q-Con Eastern Co., Ltd. (2)
7/143 Moo 4 Mapyangphon Sub Dist Tumbol Mapyangphon, Amphoe Pluak Daeng, Rayong, Thailand
Tel.: (66) 38650515
Building Materials Distr
N.A.I.C.S.: 423320

SCG Ceramics Public Company Limited (2)
1 Siam Cement Road, Bangsue, Bangkok, 10800, Thailand (100%)
Tel.: (66) 25863333
Web Site: http://www.scgceramics.com
Ceramic Tile Mfr
N.A.I.C.S.: 327120
Numpol Malichai (Mng Dir)

Sosuco Ceramic Co., Ltd. (2)
444 Olympia Thai Tower Ratchadapisek Khwang Sam Saen Nok Khet, Huai Khwang, Bangkok, 10310, Thailand
Tel.: (66) 29389898
Sales Range: $25-49.9 Million
Emp.: 15
Ceramic Tile Whslr
N.A.I.C.S.: 444180
Thosapol Isarangkul (Mgr-Export)

Sosuco and Group (2008) Co., Ltd. (2)
4444 Olympia Thai Tower Ratchadapisek Road Samsennok, Huay Khwang, Bangkok, 10310, Thailand
Tel.: (66) 2938 9898
Web Site: http://www.sosuco.com
Sales Range: $50-74.9 Million
Emp.: 12
Ceramic Materials Mfr
N.A.I.C.S.: 327120
Thosapol Isarangkul (Mgr-Export)

Thai Ceramic Roof Tile Co., Ltd. (2)
1 Building Puncement Thai Rd, Bang Sue, Bangkok, 10800, Thailand
Tel.: (66) 25865999
Ceramic Roof Tiles Mfr
N.A.I.C.S.: 327120

The Fibre-Cement Products (Lampang) Co., Ltd. (2)
366 Moo 2 Chomphu, Muang, Lampang, 52100, Thailand
Tel.: (66) 2836 3965
Cement Sheet Mfr
N.A.I.C.S.: 324122

SCG Distribution Co., Ltd. (1)
1 Siam Cement Road, Bangsue, Bangkok, 10800, Thailand (100%)
Tel.: (66) 25863333
Web Site: http://www.siamcement.com
Sales Range: $650-699.9 Million
Emp.: 2,000
Holding Company; International Trading & Logistics Services
N.A.I.C.S.: 551112
Kajohndet Sangsuban (Pres)

Subsidiary (Non-US):

PT. Kokoh Inti Arebama Tbk (2)
Graha Mobisel Lt 3 Jl Buncit Raya No 139 Kalibata, Jakarta Selatan, Indonesia
Tel.: (62) 217993973
Web Site: https://www.pt-kokoh.com
Rev: $207,534,923
Assets: $65,748,377
Liabilities: $68,941,637
Net Worth: ($3,193,260)
Earnings: ($4,878,376)
Emp.: 170
Fiscal Year-end: 12/31/2023
Construction Materials Distr
N.A.I.C.S.: 423320

Subsidiary (Domestic):

SCG Experience Co., Ltd. (2)
1444 Pradit Manutham Road Along Ekamai-Raminthra Expressway, Khlong Chan Sub-district Bang Kapi District, Bangkok, 10240, Thailand
Tel.: (66) 21019922
Web Site: http://www.scgbuildingmaterials.com
Emp.: 80
Building Materials Mfr
N.A.I.C.S.: 327120

SCG Logistics Management Co., Ltd. (2)
1 Siam Cement Rd, Bangsue, Bangkok, 10800, Thailand
Tel.: (66) 2 586 6777
Web Site: https://csl.scglogistics.co.th
Logistics Consulting Servies
N.A.I.C.S.: 541614

Subsidiary (Non-US):

SCG Singapore Trading Pte. Ltd. (2)
7500A Beach Road 11-304/305 The Plaza, Singapore, 199591, Singapore
Tel.: (65) 6295 3455
Web Site: http://www.scttrading.com
Sales Range: $50-74.9 Million
Emp.: 5
Commodity Trading Services
N.A.I.C.S.: 523160

SCG Trading (Jordan) L.L.C. (2)
Office No 11 3rd Floor Zahran Plaza 7th Circle, PO Box 3818, Amman, 11821, Jordan
Tel.: (962) 6 550 3254
Web Site: http://www.scttrading.com
Sales Range: $25-49.9 Million
Emp.: 2
Construction Materials Mfr
N.A.I.C.S.: 333120

SCG Trading (M) Sdn. Bhd. (2)
Suite E410 Wisma Consplant 1 No 2 Jalan SS 16/4, 47500, Subang Jaya, Selangor Darul Ehsan, Malaysia
Tel.: (60) 3 563 20168
Construction Materials Distr
N.A.I.C.S.: 423390

Subsidiary (Domestic):

SCG Trading Co., Ltd. (2)
1 Siam Cement Road, Bangsue, Bangkok, 10800, Thailand
Tel.: (66) 2 586 1888
Web Site: http://www.scttrading.com
Construction Materials Distr
N.A.I.C.S.: 423390

Subsidiary (Non-US):

SCG Trading Guangzhou Co., Ltd. (2)
Room 1808 Yi An Plaza 33 Jian She Liu Road, Yuexiu District, Guangzhou, 510060, China
Tel.: (86) 20 83652559
Sales Range: $25-49.9 Million
Emp.: 2
Construction Materials Distr
N.A.I.C.S.: 423390
Sattha Pongprapansiri (Mng Dir)

SCG Trading Philippines Inc. (2)
Unit 903 9th Flr Lot 3 Blk 7 3rd Avenue Cor 31st St Fort Bonifacio, Global City, Taguig, 1634, Manila, Philippines
Tel.: (63) 2 501 8634
Sales Range: $25-49.9 Million
Emp.: 10
Construction Materials Distr
N.A.I.C.S.: 423390
Supanai Chandavase (Pres)

Subsidiary (US):

SCG Trading USA Inc. (2)
200 Barr Harbor Dr, Conshohocken, PA 19428-2977
Tel.: (610) 941-2959
Sales Range: $25-49.9 Million
Emp.: 3
Residential Building Construction Services
N.A.I.C.S.: 236116
Thanee Loketkravee (Gen Mgr)

Subsidiary (Non-US):

SCGT Malaysia Sdn. Bhd. (2)

INTERNATIONAL PUBLIC

Suite E410 Wisma Consplant 1 No 2 Jalan SS 16/4, Subang Jaya, 47500, Selangor, Malaysia
Tel.: (60) 3 563 20168
Web Site: http://www.sctrading.com
Sales Range: $25-49.9 Million
Emp.: 7
Construction Materials Whslr
N.A.I.C.S.: 423390
Charoon Treepictkul (Mng Dir)

Subsidiary (Domestic):

SCT Co., Ltd. (2)
1 Siam Cement Road, Bangsue, Bangkok, 10800, Thailand (100%)
Web Site: http://www.scstarch.com
Sales Range: $25-49.9 Million
Emp.: 200
Import & Export of Cement, Construction Materials, Mill Supplies, Foodstuffs, Minerals, Steel Products, Paper & Plastic Products, Metal & Chemical Products, Foundry Products & Industrial Components
N.A.I.C.S.: 444180

SCG International China (Guangzhou) Co., Ltd. (1)
Room 1808 Yian Plaza 33 Jian Sheliu Road, Yuexiu District, Guangzhou, 510060, China
Tel.: (86) 2083652559
International Trading Services
N.A.I.C.S.: 523160

SCG International Corporation Co., Ltd. (1)
1 Siam Cement Road, Bangsue, Bangkok, 10800, Thailand
Tel.: (66) 2 586 2222
Web Site: https://scginternational.com
Construction Related Material Mfr & Distr
N.A.I.C.S.: 327999

SCG Packaging Company Limited (1)
1 Siam Cement Road, Bangsue, Bangkok, 10800, Thailand (96%)
Tel.: (66) 25863333
Web Site: http://paper.scg.co.th
Sales Range: $1-4.9 Billion
Emp.: 280
Holding Company; Pulp, Paper & Corrugated Box Mfr
N.A.I.C.S.: 551112

Subsidiary (Domestic):

Siam Cellulose Co., Ltd. (2)
1 Siam Cement Road, Bangsue, Bangkok, 10800, Thailand (98%)
Tel.: (66) 5863333
Sales Range: $25-49.9 Million
Emp.: 70
Mfr of Bleached Bamboo & Eucalyptus Pulp
N.A.I.C.S.: 322120

Siam Kraft Industry Co., Ltd. (2)
1 Siam Cement Road, Bangsue, Bangkok, 10800, Thailand (100%)
Tel.: (66) 2586 4626
Web Site: http://paper.scg.co.th
Sales Range: $200-249.9 Million
Mfr of Kraft Liner Board, Corrugating Medium, Core Paper & Multi-wall Sacks for Cement, Animal-feed & Chemical Industries
N.A.I.C.S.: 322130

Joint Venture (Domestic):

Siam Toppan Packaging Co., Ltd. (2)
543 Bangpoo Industrial Estate Soi 9 Moo 4, Amphur Muang District, Samut Prakan, 10280, Thailand
Tel.: (66) 27093110
Web Site: http://www.siamtoppan.co.th
Sales Range: $100-124.9 Million
Paper Carton & Multi-Color Process Corrugated Board Mfr; Owned by Toppan Printing Co., Ltd & Siam Pulp & Paper Public Company Limited
N.A.I.C.S.: 322212

Thai Containers Group Co., Ltd. (2)
1 Siam Cement Road, Bangsue, Bangkok, 10800, Thailand (70%)
Tel.: (66) 25865555
Web Site: https://www.thaicontainersgroup.com

AND PRIVATE COMPANIES

Sales Range: $100-124.9 Million
Emp.: 500
Corrugated Box Mfr
N.A.I.C.S.: 322211
Poramate Larnroongroj (Mng Dir)

Subsidiary (Domestic):

Thai Containers Industry Co., Ltd. (2)
620 Moo 4 Bangpoo Industrial Estate, Pattana 1 Rd Praeksa Muang, Samut Prakan, 10280, Thailand **(69%)**
Tel.: (66) 27093040
Web Site: http://www.scp.co.th
Sales Range: $50-74.9 Million
Emp.: 250
Mfr of Corrugated Boxes
N.A.I.C.S.: 322211

Thai Containers Ratchaburi (1989) Co., Ltd. (2)
1 Siam Cement Road, Bangsue, Bangkok, 10800, Thailand **(69%)**
Tel.: (66) 25864289
Sales Range: $50-74.9 Million
Emp.: 180
Mfr of Corrugated Boxes
N.A.I.C.S.: 322211

Thai Kraft Paper Industry Co., Ltd. (2)
1 Siam Cement Rd, Bangkok, 10800, Thailand **(98%)**
Tel.: (66) 25863333
Web Site: http://www.scg.co.th
Sales Range: $200-249.9 Million
Mfr of Kraft Liner Board, Corrugating Medium, Extensible Sack Kraft, Core Paper & Multi-wall Sacks for Cement, Animal-feed & Chemical Industries
N.A.I.C.S.: 322130

Thai Paper Co., Ltd. (2)
1 Siam Cement Rd, Bangsue, Bangkok, 10800, Thailand **(100%)**
Tel.: (66) 25861000
Web Site: http://www.thaipaper.co.th
Sales Range: $100-124.9 Million
Emp.: 280
Mfr of Printing & Writing Paper, Coated Paper, Computer Printout Paper & Plain Paper for Copiers
N.A.I.C.S.: 322220

Thai Union Paper Public Company Limited (2)
131 Moo 2 Poochaosamingprai Road, Samut Prakan, 10130, Phra Pradaeng, Thailand **(100%)**
Tel.: (66) 27542100
Web Site: http://www.siamcement.com
Sales Range: $200-249.9 Million
Emp.: 700
Printing & Writing Paper Mfr
N.A.I.C.S.: 322120

SCG Packaging Public Company Limited (1)
1 Siam Cement Rd, Bangsue, Bangkok, 10800, Thailand
Tel.: (66) 2 586 3333
Packaging Services & Solutions
N.A.I.C.S.: 561910

Subsidiary (US):

Jordan Trading Inc. (2)
31 Albany Ave, Kingston, NY 12401-2902 **(90.1%)**
Tel.: (845) 338-5379
Sales Range: $10-24.9 Million
Emp.: 20
Broker Services
N.A.I.C.S.: 541990
Elizabeth Jordan (Pres)

Subsidiary (Non-US):

PT Fajar Surya Wisesa Tbk (2)
Jln Abdul Muis 30, Jakarta Pusat, 10160, Indonesia **(99.7%)**
Tel.: (62) 213441316
Web Site: https://www.fajarpaper.com
Rev.: $501,544,153
Assets: $814,681,651
Liabilities: $531,330,118
Net Worth: $283,351,533
Earnings: ($40,643,673)
Emp.: 3,217

Fiscal Year-end: 12/31/2023
Packing Paper Mfr
N.A.I.C.S.: 322120
Peerapol Mongkolsilp (Chm)

SCG Trading Australia Pty. Ltd. (1)
Suite 404 Level 4 1 Chandos St, Saint Leonards, 2065, NSW, Australia
Tel.: (61) 294391441
International Trading Services
N.A.I.C.S.: 523160

SCG Trading Hong Kong Limited (1)
Room 2201 Tower Two Times Square 1 Matheson St, Causeway Bay, China (Hong Kong)
Tel.: (852) 28386456
International Trading Services
N.A.I.C.S.: 523160

SCG Trading Lao Co., Ltd. (1)
Alounmai Tower 4th Floor No 407 23 Singha Road, PO Box 8156, Nongbone Village Saysettha District, Vientiane, Lao People's Democratic Republic
Tel.: (856) 21454596
International Trading Services
N.A.I.C.S.: 523160

SCG Trading Middle East DMCC (1)
Unit no 1105 Gold Crest Executive Cluster C Jumeirah Lakes Towers, PO Box 123391, Dubai, United Arab Emirates
Tel.: (971) 45520293
International Trading Services
N.A.I.C.S.: 523160

SCG Vietnam Co., Ltd. (1)
An Phu Plaza 10th floor 117-119 Ly Chinh Thang Street, Ward 7 District 3, Ho Chi Minh City, Vietnam
Tel.: (84) 83526901113
Web Site: http://www.scg.com
Chemical Products Mfr
N.A.I.C.S.: 325998

SCG-Sekisui Sales Co., Ltd. (1)
1-Siam Cement Rd, Bangsue, Bangkok, 10800, Thailand
Tel.: (66) 25864088
Modular Housing Construction Services
N.A.I.C.S.: 236220
Masaya Fujiwara (Pres)

Plant (Non-US):

PT Fajar Surya Wisesa Tbk - Factory - Pabrik (2)
Jl Kampung Gardu Sawah RT001/1-1, Desa Kalijaya, Bekasi, 17520, West Java, Indonesia
Tel.: (62) 21 890 0330
Web Site: https://www.fajarpaper.com
Sales Range: $450-499.9 Million
Paper Products Mfr
N.A.I.C.S.: 322120

SCI Eco Services Co., Ltd. (1)
1 Siam Cement Road, Bang Su, Bangkok, 10800, Thailand
Tel.: (66) 2 586 5798
Web Site: https://www.scieco.co.th
Industrial Waste Disposal & Management Services
N.A.I.C.S.: 562219

SENFI UK Limited (1)
100 Bridge Street, London, EC4V 6JA, United Kingdom
Tel.: (44) 9598633788
Research & Development Services
N.A.I.C.S.: 541715

Siam Cement Industry Co., Ltd. (1)
1 Poon Cement Thai Road, Bangsue, Bangkok, 10800, Thailand **(100%)**
Tel.: (66) 258630601
Web Site: http://www.scp.co.th
Holding Company; Cement & Concrete Mfr
N.A.I.C.S.: 551112

Subsidiary (Non-US):

PT SCG Pipe and Precast Indonesia (2)
Gd Graha Mobisel Lt 3 Jl Buncit Raya No 139, Jakarta, 12790, Indonesia
Tel.: (62) 217993068
Sales Range: $25-49.9 Million
Emp.: 70
Precast Concrete Pipe Mfr

N.A.I.C.S.: 327332
Baptis Widhiadi (Mgr-Mktg)

Subsidiary (Domestic):

Quality Construction Products Public Co .Ltd (2)
Bang Pa-in Industrial Estate No 144 Village No 16 Udomsariyat Road, Bang Krasan Subdistrict Bang Pa-in District, Phra Nakhon Si Ayutthaya, 13160, Thailand
Tel.: (66) 35258999
Web Site: https://www.qcon.co.th
Construction Materials Mfr
N.A.I.C.S.: 423320
Nithi Phatthachoke (Chm)

The Concrete Products and Aggregate Co., Ltd. (2)
1516 Pracharat 1 Rd, Bangkok, 10800, Thailand **(100%)**
Tel.: (66) 25555000
Web Site: http://www.cpac.co.th
Sales Range: $550-599.9 Million
Emp.: 2,000
Holding Company; Ready-Mixed Concrete Mfr
N.A.I.C.S.: 551112

Siam Sanitary Ware Industry Co., Ltd. (1)
36/11 Vibhavadi-Rangsit Rd, Sanambin Don Muang, Bangkok, 10210, Thailand
Tel.: (66) 29735040
Sanitary Ware Mfr
N.A.I.C.S.: 322291

TC Flexible Packaging Co., Ltd. (1)
1 Siam Cement Road, Bangsue, Bangkok, 10800, Thailand
Tel.: (66) 344406005
Web Site: http://www.tcflexpack.com
Flexographic Printing Services
N.A.I.C.S.: 323111

Texplore Co., Ltd. (1)
1 Siam Cement Road, Bangsue, Bangkok, 10800, Thailand
Tel.: (66) 25862576
Web Site: http://www.texplore.co.th
Refactory Coating & Maintenance Services
N.A.I.C.S.: 212323

Thai Cane Paper Public Company Limited (1)
26th Floor Sinn Sathorn Tower 77/107-108 Krung Thonburi Rd, Klongtonsai Klongsarn, Bangkok, 10600, Thailand
Tel.: (66) 2 440 0707
Web Site: https://www.thaicane.com
Sales Range: $150-199.9 Million
Kraft Paper Mfr
N.A.I.C.S.: 322120
Roongrote Rangsiyopash (Chm)

Thai Containers Khonkaen Co., Ltd. (1)
87 Moo 10 Banhad, Banhad, Khon Kaen, 40110, Thailand
Tel.: (66) 432183478
Corrugated Box Mfr
N.A.I.C.S.: 322211

Thai Containers Rayong Co., Ltd. (1)
7/257 Moo 6 Mabyangporn, Pluakdaeng, Rayong, 21140, Thailand
Tel.: (66) 38650750
Corrugated Box Mfr
N.A.I.C.S.: 322211

Thai Plastic & Chemicals Public Company Limited (1)
1 Siam Cement Road Bangsue, Bangkok, 10800, Thailand
Tel.: (66) 28277272
Web Site: http://www.thaiplastic.co.th
Rev.: $1,061,517,993
Assets: $854,122,976
Liabilities: $172,609,472
Net Worth: $681,513,504
Earnings: $166,469,059
Emp.: 2,221
Fiscal Year-end: 12/31/2017
Polyvinyl Chloride Polymer Mfr & Distr
N.A.I.C.S.: 325180
Cholanat Yanaranop (Chm)

Subsidiary (Domestic):

Nawaplastic Industries (Saraburi) Co., Ltd (2)

THE SIGNCRAFT GROUP

No 1 Siam Cement Road, Bang Sue, Bangkok, 10800, Thailand
Tel.: (66) 2 555 0888
Web Site: https://nawaplastic.com
Sales Range: $25-49.9 Million
Plastics Material & Resin Mfr
N.A.I.C.S.: 325211

TPC Paste Resin Co.,Ltd. (2)
183 Rajakarn Bldg, South Sathorn Rd Yannawa, Bangkok, Thailand
Tel.: (66) 26766200
Web Site: http://www.thaiplastic.co.th
Plastics Material & Resin Mfr
N.A.I.C.S.: 325211

Subsidiary (Non-US):

TPC Vina Plastic & Chemical Corporation Limited (2)
R 901 Harbour View Tower 35 Nguyen Hue Street, District 1, Ho Chi Minh City, Vietnam
Tel.: (84) 283 823 4730
Web Site: https://www.tpcvina.com.vn
Chemical Product & Preparation Mfr
N.A.I.C.S.: 325998

The Siam Cement (Kaeng Khoi) Co., Ltd. (1)
1 Siam Cement Road, Bang Su, Bangkok, 10800, Thailand
Tel.: (66) 2 5863325
Cement Mfr
N.A.I.C.S.: 327310

The Siam Cement (Lampang) Co., Ltd. (1)
279 Moo 5 Lampang-Chaehom Road, Bansa Chaehom District, Lampang, 52120, Thailand
Tel.: (66) 5423 7500
Cement Mfr & Whslr
N.A.I.C.S.: 327310

The Siam Cement (Thung Song) Co., Ltd. (1)
52 Moo 6 Thungsong-Hauiyot Road Tee Wang, Thung Song, Nakhon Si Thammarat, 80110, Thailand
Tel.: (66) 7553 8222
Cement Mfr & Distr
N.A.I.C.S.: 327310

The Siam Refractory Industry Co., Ltd. (1)
1 Siam Cement Rd, Bangsue, Bangkok, 10800, Thailand
Tel.: (66) 2 586 3246 52
Web Site: http://www.siamrefractory.com
Emp.: 400
Iron & Steel Products Mfr
N.A.I.C.S.: 331110

The Siam White Cement Co., Ltd. (1)
1Siam Cement Road, Bangsue, Bangkok, 10800, Thailand
Tel.: (66) 2 586 2229 30
Web Site: http://www.siamwhitecement.com
White Cement Mfr
N.A.I.C.S.: 327310

Unify Smart Tech Joint Stock Company (1)
234 Nguyen Van Linh Thac Gian, Thanh Khe Dist, Da Nang, Vietnam
Tel.: (84) 905559562
Web Site: http://www.unicjsc.com
Information Technology Services
N.A.I.C.S.: 541511

United Pulp & Paper Co., Inc. (1)
9th Floor Fort Legend Towers 3rd Avenue Corner 31st Street, Bonifacio Global City, Taguig, Metro Manila, Philippines
Tel.: (63) 29081724
Packing Paper Mfr
N.A.I.C.S.: 322299

Vina Kraft Paper Co., Ltd. (1)
9th Floor An Phu Plaza 117-119 Ly Chinh Thang St, Ward 7 District 3, Ho Chi Minh City, Vietnam
Tel.: (84) 83526902527
Packing Paper Mfr
N.A.I.C.S.: 322299

THE SIGNCRAFT GROUP

THE SIGNCRAFT GROUP

The Signcraft Group—(Continued)

580-598 Kororoit Creek Road, Altona, 3025, VIC, Australia
Tel.: (61) 3 9360 6222   **AU**
Web Site:
http://www.signcraft.com.au
Sales Range: $50-74.9 Million
Emp.: 50
Sign Mfr
N.A.I.C.S.: 339950
Guy Blackman *(Mgr-Ops)*

Subsidiaries:

Signcorp   (1)
79 Crockford Street, Northgate, 4013, QLD, Australia
Tel.: (61) 7 3267 8977
Web Site: http://www.signcorp.com.au
Emp.: 30
Digital Sign Board Mfr
N.A.I.C.S.: 339950
Bruce Fitzgerald *(Gen Mgr)*

Signcraft Hong Kong   (1)
10/F Block C Seaview Estate 8 Watson Road, North Point, Hong Kong, China (Hong Kong)
Tel.: (852) 3182 7800
Digital Sign Board Distr
N.A.I.C.S.: 423610

Signcraft Varisigns Pty. Ltd.   (1)
55 McDonald St East, Osborne Park, 6017, WA, Australia
Tel.: (61) 8 9443 4455
Web Site: http://www.varisigns.com.au
Digital Sign Board Mfr
N.A.I.C.S.: 339950
Dan Johnson *(Mgr-Sls)*

THE SINCERE CO. LTD.
24 F Jardine House 1 Connaught Place, Central, China (Hong Kong)
Tel.: (852) 28301016   **HK**
Web Site:
https://www.sincere.com.hk
Year Founded: 1900
0244—(HKG)
Rev.: $22,890,339
Assets: $73,763,791
Liabilities: $70,100,114
Net Worth: $3,663,677
Earnings: ($18,791,999)
Emp.: 222
Fiscal Year-end: 02/28/21
Department Stores
N.A.I.C.S.: 455110
Philip King Huen Ma *(Chm & CEO)*

THE SKIPTON BUILDING SOCIETY
The Bailey, Skipton, BD23 1DN, N Yorkshire, United Kingdom
Tel.: (44) 1756705000
Web Site: http://www.skipton.co.uk
SKIP—(LSE)
Rev.: $888,356,196
Assets: $38,373,783,448
Liabilities: $36,057,920,444
Net Worth: $2,315,863,004
Earnings: $131,698,840
Emp.: 9,458
Fiscal Year-end: 12/31/20
Real Estate Mortgage & Financial Advisory Services Organization
N.A.I.C.S.: 813910
David J. Cutter *(CEO)*

Subsidiaries:

Skipton Group Holdings Limited   (1)
The Bailey, Skipton, BD23 1DN, N Yorkshire, United Kingdom   **(100%)**
Tel.: (44) 1756 705 030
Holding Company
N.A.I.C.S.: 551112

Subsidiary (Domestic):

Amber Homeloans Limited   (2)
The Bailey, Skipton, BD23 1DN, North Yorkshire, United Kingdom   **(100%)**
Tel.: (44) 3456020750
Web Site: http://www.amber.co.uk
Sales Range: $50-74.9 Million
Mortgage & Nonmortgage Loan Brokers
N.A.I.C.S.: 522310

Bailey Computer Services Limited   (2)
The Bailey, BD231DN, Skipton, North Yorkshire, United Kingdom   **(100%)**
Tel.: (44) 1756705015
Web Site:
http://www.baileycomputerservices.co.uk
Sales Range: $25-49.9 Million
Emp.: 3
Custom Computer Programming Services
N.A.I.C.S.: 541511

Connells Limited   (2)
Cumbria House 16-20 Hockliffe Street, Leighton Buzzard, LU7 1GN, Bedfordshire, United Kingdom
Tel.: (44) 152 521 8500
Web Site: https://www.connellsgroup.co.uk
Holding Company; Real Estate Agency & Property Services
N.A.I.C.S.: 551112
David Livesey *(CEO)*

Subsidiary (Domestic):

Connell Financial Services Limited   (3)
Cumbria Ho 16 -20 Hockliffe Street, Leighton Buzzard, LU78HE, Bedfordshire, United Kingdom   **(100%)**
Tel.: (44) 1525215609
Investment Advice
N.A.I.C.S.: 523940

Connells Residential Limited   (3)
30 King Street, Maidstone, ME14 1BS, United Kingdom
Tel.: (44) 1622751034
Web Site: http://www.connells.co.uk
Sales Range: $50-74.9 Million
Real Estate Agents & Brokers
N.A.I.C.S.: 531210

Connells Survey & Valuation Limited   (3)
Cumbria House 16-20 Hockliffe Street, Leighton Buzzard, LU7 1GN, United Kingdom
Tel.: (44) 1525218500
Web Site: http://www.connells.co.uk
Real Estate Agents & Brokers
N.A.I.C.S.: 531210

Countrywide plc   (3)
Countrywide House 6 Caldecotte Lake Business Park, Caldecotte Lake Drive Caldecotte, Milton Keynes, MK7 8JT, United Kingdom
Tel.: (44) 1908465250
Web Site: https://www.countrywide.co.uk
Rev.: $653,343,573
Assets: $543,816,904
Liabilities: $415,853,273
Net Worth: $127,963,631
Earnings: ($54,659,618)
Emp.: 7,509
Fiscal Year-end: 12/31/2019
Holding Company; Real Estate Agency & Property Related Finance & Professional Services
N.A.I.C.S.: 551112
Gareth R. Williams *(Sec)*

Subsidiary (Domestic):

Bullock & Lees (Christchurch) Limited   (4)
581 Christchurch Road, Bournemouth, BH1 4BU, Dorset, United Kingdom
Tel.: (44) 120 230 2345
Web Site: https://www.bullockandlees.com
Real Estate Services
N.A.I.C.S.: 531390

Capital Private Finance Limited   (4)
6st Floor Standon House 21 Mansell Street, London, E1 8AA, United Kingdom
Tel.: (44) 208 988 6700
Web Site:
https://www.capitalprivatefinance.co.uk
Financial Services
N.A.I.C.S.: 522320

Countrywide Estate Agents (FS) Ltd.   (4)
20 High Street, Maldon, CM9 5PJ, United Kingdom
Tel.: (44) 1621854068
Direct Life Insurance Carriers
N.A.I.C.S.: 524113

Countrywide Franchising Limited   (4)
Brook House Apex Court, KT146SQ, West Byfleet, United Kingdom
Tel.: (44) 1932350314
Sales Range: $25-49.9 Million
Emp.: 15
Real Estate Agents & Brokers
N.A.I.C.S.: 531210

Countrywide Mortgage Services Limited   (4)
PO Box 186, Droitwich, WR9 1AB, United Kingdom
Tel.: (44) 8454680242
Web Site:
http://www.countrywidemortgages.com
Mortgage Broker Services
N.A.I.C.S.: 522310

Countrywide Principal Services Limited   (4)
Countrywide House 88-103 Caldecotte Lake Dr, Milton Keynes, MK7 8JT, United Kingdom
Tel.: (44) 01525383084
Web Site: http://www.cagroup.co.uk
Public Finance Activities
N.A.I.C.S.: 921130

Countrywide Property Auctions Limited   (4)
2 Cotton Street, Liverpool, L3 7DY, United Kingdom
Tel.: (44) 151 207 6315
Web Site:
https://www.countrywideauctions.co.uk
Real Estate Services
N.A.I.C.S.: 531390

Countrywide Property Lawyers Ltd   (4)
3rd Floor Lee House 90 Great Bridgewater Street, Manchester, M1 5RR, United Kingdom
Tel.: (44) 161 200 8200
Web Site: https://www.countrywide.co.uk
Law firm
N.A.I.C.S.: 541199

Countrywide Property Management Limited   (4)
Central House, Clifftown Road, Southend-on-Sea, SS11 AB, Essex, United Kingdom
Tel.: (44) 1702330073
Web Site:
http://www.click4management.co.uk
Sales Range: $75-99.9 Million
Emp.: 200
Direct Life Insurance Carriers
N.A.I.C.S.: 524113

Harrisons Estate Agents Limited   (4)
7 Whitefield Rd, New Milton, BH25 6DE, Hampshire, United Kingdom
Tel.: (44) 142 561 0016
Web Site:
https://www.harrisonestateagents.com
Real Estate Services
N.A.I.C.S.: 531390

Harvey Donaldson & Gibson Limited   (4)
3-7 Standard Buildings 94 Hope Street, Glasgow, G2 6PH, United Kingdom
Tel.: (44) 141 204 0808
Web Site: https://www.hdg.co.uk
Surveying & Mapping Services
N.A.I.C.S.: 541370

Home From Home Limited   (4)
75 Wilton Road, London, SW1V 1DE, United Kingdom
Tel.: (44) 207 233 8111
Web Site: https://www.homefromhome.co.uk
Real Estate Services
N.A.I.C.S.: 531390
Chris Willis *(Co-Founder)*

Ikon Consultancy Limited   (4)
7th Floor United Kingdom House 180 Oxford Street, Oxford, W1D 1NN, United Kingdom
Tel.: (44) 2076640400
Web Site: http://www.ikonconsultancy.com

INTERNATIONAL PUBLIC

Real Estate Services
N.A.I.C.S.: 531390
Nick Cook *(Mng Dir)*

Interlet Property Management Limited   (4)
6 Town Farm North Curry, Taunton, TA3 6NP, Somerset, United Kingdom
Tel.: (44) 182 349 1112
Web Site: https://www.interletproperty.com
Property Management Services
N.A.I.C.S.: 531311

John Curtis Lettings & Management Limited   (4)
38 High Street, Harpenden, AL5 2SX, United Kingdom
Tel.: (44) 1582742998
Web Site: http://www.johncurtis.co.uk
Real Estate Services
N.A.I.C.S.: 531390

John Frances Limited   (4)
18 Lammas Street, Carmarthen, SA31 3AJ, United Kingdom
Tel.: (44) 126 722 1554
Web Site: https://www.johnfrancis.co.uk
Property Management Services
N.A.I.C.S.: 531311

Lambert Smith Hampton Group Ltd.   (4)
55 Wells Street, London, W1T 3PT, United Kingdom
Tel.: (44) 207 198 2000
Web Site: https://www.lsh.co.uk
Sales Range: $100-124.9 Million
Emp.: 861
Commercial Real Estate Consulting Services
N.A.I.C.S.: 531210
John Hill *(Dir-Glasgow)*

Subsidiary (Non-US):

Lambert Smith Hampton Ltd.   (5)
4-10 May Street, Dublin, 2, Ireland
Tel.: (353) 90327954
Web Site: http://www.lsh.ie
Sales Range: $125-149.9 Million
Emp.: 15
Commercial Real Estate Consulting Services
N.A.I.C.S.: 531210

Subsidiary (Domestic):

Letters of Distinction Limited   (4)
169 Holgate Road, York, YO24 4DF, United Kingdom
Tel.: (44) 1904529539
Web Site:
http://www.lettersofdistinction.co.uk
Real Estate Services
N.A.I.C.S.: 531390

Lighthouse Property Services Ltd.   (4)
39a Carholme Road, Lincoln, LN1 1RN, Lincolnshire, United Kingdom
Tel.: (44) 152 262 0229
Web Site: https://www.lighthouse-property.co.uk
Property Management Services
N.A.I.C.S.: 531311
Lindsey Nesbit *(Mgr)*

Merchant Lettings Limited   (4)
2nd floor 26 Springfield Court, Glasgow, G1 3DQ, United Kingdom
Tel.: (44) 1412212998
Web Site: http://www.merchantlettings.com
Real Estate Services
N.A.I.C.S.: 531390
Ken Harkness *(Dir-Fin)*

Mortgage Bureau Limited   (4)
Davids Court Union Street, Wolverhampton, WV1 3JE, West Midlands, United Kingdom
Tel.: (44) 344 225 4321
Web Site: https://www.mortgagebureau.net
Mortgage Broker Services
N.A.I.C.S.: 522310
Helen Pierson *(Head-Bus Dev)*

Mortgage Intelligence Holdings Limited   (4)
Roddis House 12 Old Christchurch Road, Bournemouth, BH1 1LG, Dorset, United Kingdom

AND PRIVATE COMPANIES

Tel.: (44) 3451307446
Web Site: http://www.experiencemi.co.uk
Financial Services
N.A.I.C.S.: 522320
Sally Laker *(Mng Dir)*

New Space Margate Ltd. (4)
266 Kingsland Road, Hackney, London, E8 4DG, United Kingdom
Tel.: (44) 207 275 2040
Web Site:
https://www.newspacelettings.com
Real Estate Services
N.A.I.C.S.: 531390

Preston Bennett Limited (4)
37-41 Church Road, Stanmore, HA7 4AA, Middlesex, United Kingdom
Tel.: (44) 2089540044
Web Site: http://www.prestonbennett.co.uk
Real Estate Services
N.A.I.C.S.: 531390
James Townsend *(Mgr-Sls)*

Richard Dolton Limited (4)
Richard Dalton Holditch Road, Newcastle-under-Lyme, ST5 9JA, United Kingdom
Tel.: (44) 178 256 3233
Web Site: http://www.richard-dalton.com
Auto Repair Services
N.A.I.C.S.: 811111
Suzanne Dalton *(Acct Mgr)*

Spencers Estate Agents Limited (4)
469 Ecclesall Road, Sheffield, S11 8PP, United Kingdom
Tel.: (44) 114 268 3682
Web Site:
https://www.spencersestateagents.co.uk
Real Estate Services
N.A.I.C.S.: 531390
Nicola Spencer *(Mng Dir)*

The Flat Managers Limited (4)
13 Queens Road, Bournemouth, BH2 6BA, United Kingdom
Tel.: (44) 120 275 7386
Web Site: https://www.flatmanltd.co.uk
Property Management Services
N.A.I.C.S.: 531311
Daryna Walker *(Gen Dir)*

Vanet Property Asset Management Limited (4)
Unit 2 37b Millharbour, Canary Wharf, London, E14 9TX, United Kingdom
Tel.: (44) 203 733 0726
Web Site: https://www.vanet.uk.com
Real Estate Services
N.A.I.C.S.: 531390
Agata Laker *(Head-Property Mgmt)*

Subsidiary (Non-US):

Jade Software Corporation Limited (2)
5 Sir Gil Simpson Drive, Christchurch, 8053, New Zealand
Tel.: (64) 3 365 2500
Web Site: https://www.jadeworld.com
Software Development Services
N.A.I.C.S.: 541511
Charlotte Walshe *(CEO)*

Subsidiary (Non-US):

Jade Software Corporation UK Limited (3)
35 Parliament Street, York, YO1 8RU, North Yorkshire, United Kingdom
Tel.: (44) 1904635034
Financial & Mortgage Services
N.A.I.C.S.: 522390

Subsidiary (Domestic):

North Yorkshire Mortgages Limited (2)
Gateway House Gargrave Road, Skipton, BD23 2HL, North Yorkshire, United Kingdom
Tel.: (44) 3451304145
Web Site:
http://www.northyorkshiremortgages.co.uk
Mortgage Brokerage Services
N.A.I.C.S.: 522310

Subsidiary (Non-US):

Northwest Investments NZ Limited (2)
2/585 Wairakei Road Burnside, 8053, Christchurch, New Zealand **(100%)**
Tel.: (64) 3 962 3223
Web Site: https://www.nwi.co.nz
Sales Range: $25-49.9 Million
Emp.: 8
Online Information Services
N.A.I.C.S.: 519290

Subsidiary (Domestic):

Parnell Fisher Child & Co Limited (2)
8 Waltham Court Milley Lane, Hare Hatch, Reading, RG10 9AA, United Kingdom
Tel.: (44) 118 940 5600
Web Site: http://www.pearson-jones.co.uk
Sales Range: $50-74.9 Million
Emp.: 14
Financial Management Services
N.A.I.C.S.: 523999
Steve Murray *(Chrm)*

Subsidiary (Non-US):

Pink Homeloans Ltd. (2)
Number One Lichfield South, WS14 0QP, Lichfield, Staffordshire, United Kingdom - England
Tel.: (44) 8444724000
Web Site: http://www.pink.uk.net
Sales Range: $50-74.9 Million
Emp.: 50
Mortgage & Nonmortgage Loan Brokers
N.A.I.C.S.: 522310

Subsidiary (Domestic):

RED ARC Assured Limited (2)
4 Hilliards Court, Chester Business Park, Chester, CH4 9QP, United Kingdom
Tel.: (44) 1244625180
Web Site: http://www.redarc.co.uk
Sales Range: $50-74.9 Million
Direct Health & Medical Insurance Carriers
N.A.I.C.S.: 524114
Christine Husbands *(Mng Dir)*

Sequence (UK) Limited (2)
Cumbria House, 16-20 Hockliffe Street, Leighton Buzzard, LU7 1GN, Bedfordshire, United Kingdom
Tel.: (44) 1525218500
Real Estate Agents & Brokers
N.A.I.C.S.: 531210

Sharman Quinney Holdings Limited (2)
70 Albert Place, Peterborough, PE1 1DD, United Kingdom
Tel.: (44) 173 355 5185
Web Site:
https://www.sharmanquinney.co.uk
Sales Range: $50-74.9 Million
Emp.: 6
Real Estate Agents & Brokers
N.A.I.C.S.: 531210

Skipton Business Finance Limited (2)
The Bailey, Skipton, BD23 1DN, North Yorkshire, United Kingdom
Tel.: (44) 845 602 9354
Web Site:
http://www.skiptonbusinessfinance.co.uk
Sales Range: $50-74.9 Million
Emp.: 35
Financial Management Services
N.A.I.C.S.: 523999

Skipton Financial Services Limited (2)
The Bailey, PO Box 101, Skipton, BD23 1XT, North Yorkshire, United Kingdom **(100%)**
Tel.: (44) 800137832
Web Site: http://www.skiptonfs.co.uk
Emp.: 100
Miscellaneous Financial Investment Activities
N.A.I.C.S.: 523999

Subsidiary (Non-US):

Skipton Guernsey Limited (2)
Tudor House The Bordage, PO Box 509, GY1 6DS, Saint Peter Port, Guernsey **(100%)**
Tel.: (44) 1481727374

Web Site:
http://www.skiptoninternational.com
Commericial Banking
N.A.I.C.S.: 522110

Subsidiary (Domestic):

Skipton Premises Limited (2)
The Bailey, Skipton, BD231DN, North Yorkshire, United Kingdom **(100%)**
Tel.: (44) 1756705000
Web Site: http://www.skipton.co.uk
Sales Range: $25-49.9 Million
Emp.: 4
Land Subdivision
N.A.I.C.S.: 237210
David Cutter *(CEO)*

Skipton International Limited (1)
Tudor House The Bordage, Saint Peter Port, Guernsey
Tel.: (44) 1481727374
Web Site:
https://www.skiptoninternational.com
Mortgage Services
N.A.I.C.S.: 522310

Vibrant Energy Matters Limited (1)
2 Foxes Lane Oakdale Business Park, Gwent, Blackwood, NP12 4AB, United Kingdom
Tel.: (44) 1495234300
Web Site:
https://www.vibrantenergymatters.co.uk
Property Management Services
N.A.I.C.S.: 531311

THE SOCIAL CHAIN AG
Alte Jakobstrasse 8586, 10119, Berlin, Germany
Tel.: (49) 30208484010 De
Web Site:
https://www.thesocialchain.ag
Year Founded: 2019
PU11—(DEU)
Rev.: $393,245,722
Assets: $449,147,168
Liabilities: $377,890,272
Net Worth: $71,256,896
Earnings: ($136,679,213)
Emp.: 1,124
Fiscal Year-end: 12/31/22
Digital Marketing Services
N.A.I.C.S.: 541810
Andreas Schneider *(CFO)*

Subsidiaries:

BEEM Asia Limited (1)
Unit 1603 8 Jordan Road, Kowloon, China (Hong Kong)
Tel.: (852) 27392131
Web Site: https://exvhk.shoplineapp.com
Tea Machine Mfr & Distr
N.A.I.C.S.: 311920

Brand Chain GmbH (1)
Kurhausstr 48, 23795, Bad Segeberg, Germany
Tel.: (49) 38851314336
Coffee Preparation Product Mfr & Distr
N.A.I.C.S.: 311920

DEF Media GmbH (1)
Potsdamer Strasse 81/83, 10785, Berlin, Germany
Tel.: (49) 3023321110
Web Site: https://www.def-media.com
Program Organizer Services
N.A.I.C.S.: 612990

DS Holding-GmbH (1)
Stormarnring 14, Stapelfeld, 22145, Germany
Tel.: (49) 40675730
Web Site: https://www.ds-group.de
Holding Company
N.A.I.C.S.: 551112

DS Impact GmbH (1)
Stormarnring 14, 22145, Stapelfeld, Germany
Tel.: (49) 40675730
Web Site: https://www.dsinvest.de
Financial Investment Services
N.A.I.C.S.: 523999

DS Marketing GmbH (1)
Pingsdorfer Strasse 87, bei Koln, D-50321, Bruhl, Germany
Tel.: (49) 223215080
Web Site: https://www.dsmarketing.de
Program Organizer Services
N.A.I.C.S.: 812990

DS Produkte GmbH (1)
Stormarnring 14, D-22145, Stapelfeld, Germany
Tel.: (49) 40675730
Web Site: https://www.ds-group.de
Channel Network Services
N.A.I.C.S.: 516210

Drtv.agency GmbH (1)
Konigstr 42, 70173, Stuttgart, Germany
Tel.: (49) 1622840826
Web Site: https://gladtobe.com
Podcast & Social Media Services
N.A.I.C.S.: 518210

LANDMANN Germany GmbH (1)
Stormarnring 14, 22145, Stapelfeld, Germany
Tel.: (49) 4067573190
Web Site: https://www.landmann.de
Grill Product Mfr & Distr
N.A.I.C.S.: 332323

Landmann Hungaria Kft. (1)
Almaskert ut 4, Pest county, 2220, Vecses, Hungary
Tel.: (36) 29555079
Barbecue Equipment Mfr & Distr
N.A.I.C.S.: 311421

Landmann Limited (1)
Unit B2 Tower Close, Huntingdon, PE29 7DH, Cambridgeshire, United Kingdom
Tel.: (44) 480421720
Web Site: https://landmann.co.uk
Barbecue Equipment Mfr & Distr
N.A.I.C.S.: 335220

Landmann Polska Sp. z o.o. (1)
ul Kuziennicza 13b, 59-400, Jaworzno, Poland
Tel.: (48) 768702461
Web Site: https://www.landmann.pl
Barbecue Equipment Mfr & Distr
N.A.I.C.S.: 311421

RAVENSBERGER Matratzen GmbH (1)
Berliner Strasse 1, 33189, Schlangen, Germany
Tel.: (49) 5731495880
Web Site: https://www.ravensberger-matratzen.de
Mattress Mfr & Distr
N.A.I.C.S.: 326299

Urbanara Home & Living GmbH (1)
Waltgeristrasse 95, D-32049, Herford, Germany
Tel.: (49) 5221270111
Web Site:
https://www.sweetdreamsbetten.de
Mattress Mfr & Distr
N.A.I.C.S.: 337910

THE SOUTH AFRICAN RESERVE BANK
370 Helen Joseph Street, Pretoria, 2, South Africa
Tel.: (27) 123133911
Web Site: http://www.resbank.co.za
Rev.: $1,094,457,070
Assets: $60,426,643,970
Liabilities: $59,038,236,320
Net Worth: $1,388,407,650
Earnings: $433,310,570
Emp.: 2,125
Fiscal Year-end: 03/31/19
Banking Services
N.A.I.C.S.: 521110
A. Daniel Mminele *(Deputy Governor)*

Subsidiaries:

South African Mint Company (Pty) Limited (1)
Old Johannesburg Road Gateway, Centurion, 0001, South Africa
Tel.: (27) 12 677 2777
Web Site: http://www.samint.co.za
Emp.: 500

THE SOUTH AFRICAN RESERVE BANK

The South African Reserve Bank—(Continued)

Coin Mfr
N.A.I.C.S.: 339910
Tumi Tsehlo (Mng Dir)

THE SOUTH INDIA PAPER MILLS LIMITED
1205/1206 Prestige Meridian 2nd M G Road, Bengaluru, 560 001, Karnataka, India
Tel.: (91) 8041123605
Web Site: https://www.sipaper.com
Year Founded: 1959
516108—(BOM)
Rev.: $34,657,970
Assets: $58,720,964
Liabilities: $30,750,003
Net Worth: $27,970,961
Earnings: ($1,998,909)
Emp.: 347
Fiscal Year-end: 03/31/23
Paper Mfr & Whslr
N.A.I.C.S.: 322120
Manish M. Patel (Chm & Mng Dir)

THE SOUTH INDIAN BANK LIMITED
T B Road Mission Quarters, Thrissur, 680 001, Kerala, India
Tel.: (91) 4872420020
Web Site: https://www.southindianbank.com
Year Founded: 1929
532218—(BOM)
Rev.: $1,159,010,908
Assets: $12,851,362,169
Liabilities: $12,058,400,472
Net Worth: $792,961,697
Earnings: $8,450,797
Emp.: 8,314
Fiscal Year-end: 03/31/21
Commercial Banking Services
N.A.I.C.S.: 522110
T. J. Raphael (CIO & Sr Gen Mgr)

Subsidiaries:

SIB Operations & Services Ltd. (1)
Ix/839 A1-A9 SIB Building 4th Floor Rajagiri Valley, Ernakulam, Kakkanad, 682039, India
Tel.: (91) 4842990151
Web Site: https://www.sibosl.com
Front End & Back End Development Services
N.A.I.C.S.: 541714

THE SOUTHERN GAS LIMITED
Meera Classic Phase II Gogol, Borda Margao, Goa, 403 602, India
Tel.: (91) 8322724863
Web Site: https://www.southerngasindia.com
Year Founded: 1963
509910—(BOM)
Rev.: $4,395,732
Assets: $3,731,035
Liabilities: $1,215,886
Net Worth: $2,515,149
Earnings: $97,152
Emp.: 112
Fiscal Year-end: 03/31/23
Medical Gas Mfr
N.A.I.C.S.: 325120
Gautam V. Pai Kakode (Mng Dir)

THE SOUTHERN RUBBER INDUSTRY JOINT STOCK COMPANY
180 Nguyen Thi Minh Khai ward 6 District 03, Ho Chi Minh City, Vietnam
Tel.: (84) 838362369
Web Site: https://www.factlink.com.vn
Year Founded: 1976
CSM—(HOSE)
Rev.: $215,678,168

Assets: $160,033,201
Liabilities: $105,476,161
Net Worth: $54,557,040
Earnings: $2,487,450
Fiscal Year-end: 12/31/23
Rubber Products Mfr
N.A.I.C.S.: 326299

THE SPECIALIST WORKS LTD.
94 White Line Street 190th Floor, London, E1 6NF, United Kingdom
Tel.: (44) 20 7539 6100
Web Site: http://www.thespecialistworks.com
Year Founded: 2002
Sales Range: $25-49.9 Million
Emp.: 30
Media & Advertising Consulting Services
N.A.I.C.S.: 541810
Katie Lobina (Mng Partner)

THE ST. LAWRENCE SEAWAY MANAGEMENT CORPORATION
202 Pitt Street, Cornwall, K6J 3P7, ON, Canada
Tel.: (613) 932-5170
Web Site: http://www.seaway.ca
Year Founded: 1998
Rev.: $52,635,665
Emp.: 75
Waterway Transportation
N.A.I.C.S.: 483211
Terence F. Bowles (Pres & CEO)

THE STANLEY GIBBONS GROUP PLC
399 Strand, London, WC2R 0LX, United Kingdom
Tel.: (44) 2075574436   UK
Web Site: http://www.stanleygibbons.com
SGI—(AIM)
Rev.: $17,894,750
Assets: $50,860,191
Liabilities: $45,809,473
Net Worth: $5,050,718
Earnings: ($3,217,796)
Emp.: 93
Fiscal Year-end: 03/31/20
Holding Company; Stamps & Other Rare Antiquities Dealer, Appraisal Services & Book Publisher
N.A.I.C.S.: 551112
Graham Elliott Shircore (CEO)

Subsidiaries:

Mallett PLC (1)
16-17 Pall Mall St James's, London, SW1Y 5LU, United Kingdom
Tel.: (44) 1635553553
Web Site: http://mallett.co.uk
Sales Range: $10-24.9 Million
Emp.: 33
Antique Retailer
N.A.I.C.S.: 449110
Michael A. Smyth-Osbourne (Sec & Dir-Fin)

Subsidiary (Domestic):

H.J. Hatfield & Sons Limited (2)
26/28 Sidney Road, London, SW9 0TS, United Kingdom
Tel.: (44) 2076228169
Web Site: http://www.hatfieldsrestoration.com
Emp.: 10
Antique Furniture Restoration Services
N.A.I.C.S.: 811420

Mallett & Son (Antiques) Limited (2)
Ely House 37 Dover St, London, W1S 4NJ, United Kingdom
Tel.: (44) 2074997411
Web Site: http://www.Mallett.com
Sales Range: $25-49.9 Million
Emp.: 20
Antique Furniture Mfr
N.A.I.C.S.: 337126

Richard Cave (Mng Dir)

Subsidiary (US):

Mallett Inc. (2)
929 Madison Ave, New York, NY 10021
Tel.: (212) 249-8783
Web Site: http://www.mallettantiques.com
Antique Retailer
N.A.I.C.S.: 449110

Stanley Gibbons (Guernsey) Limited (1)
18-20 Le Bordage, Saint Peter Port, GY1 1DE, Guernsey
Tel.: (44) 1481 708 270
Sales Range: $10-24.9 Million
Emp.: 30
Philatelic Distr
N.A.I.C.S.: 561990
Alex Hanrahan (Head-Mktg)

Stanley Gibbons Limited (1)
399 Strand, London, WC2R 0LX, United Kingdom
Tel.: (44) 1425472363
Web Site: http://www.stanleygibbons.com
Sales Range: $25-49.9 Million
Emp.: 70
Philatelic Distr
N.A.I.C.S.: 561990

THE STAR ENTERTAINMENT GROUP LIMITED
Level 3 159 William Street, Brisbane, 4000, QLD, Australia
Tel.: (61) 732280000
Web Site: https://www.starentertainment.com
SGR—(ASX)
Rev.: $1,120,325,850
Assets: $1,267,227,559
Liabilities: $710,803,950
Net Worth: $556,423,609
Earnings: ($1,124,866,448)
Emp.: 4,027
Fiscal Year-end: 06/30/24
Casino Operator
N.A.I.C.S.: 721120
Matt Bekier (CEO & Mng Dir)

Subsidiaries:

Breakwater Island Limited (1)
Sir Leslie Thiess Drive, Townsville, 4810, QLD, Australia
Tel.: (61) 747222333
Web Site: https://www.the-ville.com.au
Casino Operator
N.A.I.C.S.: 721120
Michael Jones (CEO)

Star City Holdings Limited (1)
80 Pyrmont St, PO Box Q192, Pyrmont, 2009, NSW, Australia   (100%)
Tel.: (61) 297779000
Web Site: http://www.star.com.au
Sales Range: $1-4.9 Billion
Emp.: 4,200
Holding Company; Casino Owner & Operator
N.A.I.C.S.: 551112
Brad Schmitt (Gen Mgr-Media)

The Star Gold Coast (1)
Broadbeach Island, PO Box 1515, Broadbeach, Gold Coast, 4218, QLD, Australia
Tel.: (61) 755928100
Web Site: https://www.star.com.au
Casino Hotel Operator
N.A.I.C.S.: 721120
Geoff Hojj (Mng Dir)

The Star Pty Limited (1)
80 Pyrmont Street, Pyrmont, 2009, NSW, Australia   (100%)
Tel.: (61) 297779000
Web Site: https://www.star.com.au
Hotel & Casino Operation Services
N.A.I.C.S.: 721120
Diane Glasson (Dir-Comm & PR)

THE STEEL PUBLIC COMPANY LIMITED
1401 Ekachai Road, Bangbon-Tai Bangbon, Bangkok, 10150, Thailand

INTERNATIONAL PUBLIC

Tel.: (66) 28948889
Web Site: https://www.thesteel.co.th
Year Founded: 1991
THE—(THA)
Rev.: $200,275,628
Assets: $128,151,888
Liabilities: $69,320,217
Net Worth: $58,831,671
Earnings: ($2,975,798)
Emp.: 418
Fiscal Year-end: 12/31/23
Structural Steel Mfr
N.A.I.C.S.: 238120
Prasertsuk Nudthaisong (Mgr-Pur & Production & Plng)

Subsidiaries:

T.Y.K Industry Co., Ltd. (1)
275/4 Soi Thawi Watthana Sathupradit Road 15/Narathiwat 22, Sathupradit Road Chong Nonsi Subdistrict Yannawa District, Bangkok, 10120, Thailand
Tel.: (66) 2 211 7988
Web Site: https://www.thaiyongkiat.com
Steel Pole Mfr
N.A.I.C.S.: 331210

THE STOCK EXCHANGE OF MAURITIUS
4th Floor One Cathedral Square Building 16 Jules Koenig Street, Port Louis, Mauritius
Tel.: (230) 2129541
Web Site: http://www.mauritiusexchange.com
Rev.: $4,528,374
Assets: $20,031,950
Liabilities: $1,945,865
Net Worth: $18,086,085
Earnings: $2,678,124
Emp.: 12
Fiscal Year-end: 06/30/19
Stock Exchange Services
N.A.I.C.S.: 523210
Sunil Benimadhu (CEO)

THE STOCK EXCHANGE OF THAILAND
93 Ratchadapisek Road, Din Daeng, Bangkok, 10400, Thailand
Tel.: (66) 2009 9999   TH
Web Site: http://www.set.or.th
Year Founded: 1975
Rev.: $242,325,641
Assets: $1,496,506,892
Liabilities: $617,845,909
Net Worth: $878,660,984
Earnings: ($86,442,707)
Emp.: 741
Fiscal Year-end: 12/31/19
Securities & Commodities Exchange Operator
N.A.I.C.S.: 523210
Paveena Sriphothong (Exec VP & Head-Market Supervision Div)

Subsidiaries:

Bond Electronic Exchange (1)
The Stock Exchange of Thailand Building 5th Floor, 62 Ratchadapisek Rd Klongtoey, Bangkok, 10110, Thailand
Tel.: (66) 22292222
Web Site: http://www.set.or.th
Supports Development of Thailand's Secondary Bond Market
N.A.I.C.S.: 523210

Thai NVDR Company Limited (1)
62 Ratchadapisek Road The Stock Exchange of Thailand Bldg 4F, Klongtoey, Bangkok, 10110, Thailand
Tel.: (66) 2 229 2800
Web Site: http://www.set.or.th
Sales Range: $50-74.9 Million
Emp.: 5
Issuing & Selling Non-Voting Depository Receipts (NVDRs) to Investors
N.A.I.C.S.: 523940
Praphaphan Tharapiwattananon (Head-Depository Dept)

AND PRIVATE COMPANIES   **THE SUMITOMO WAREHOUSE CO. LTD.**

Thai Trust Fund Management Co., Ltd (1)
4/f The Stock Exchange of Thailand Building 62 Ratchadapisek Road, Klongtoey, Bangkok, 10110, Thailand
Tel.: (66) 2 229 2800
Investment Management Service
N.A.I.C.S.: 523940

Thailand Clearing House Co., Ltd. (1)
62 The Stock Exchange of Thailand Building 4th Floor, Ratchadapisek Road Klongtoey, Bangkok, 10110, Thailand
Tel.: (66) 2229 2916
Security Brokerage Services
N.A.I.C.S.: 523150
Chanisa Chutipat *(Mng Dir)*

Thailand Futures Exchange PCL (1)
Stock Exchange of Thailand Building, 62 Ratchadaphisek Rd Klongtoey, Bangkok, 10110, Thailand
Tel.: (66) 22292222
Web Site: http://www.tfex.co.th
Sales Range: $1-9.9 Million
Emp.: 16
Derivatives Exchange
N.A.I.C.S.: 523210
Kesara Manchusree *(Mng Dir)*

Thailand Securities Depository Company Limited (1)
Mail Room Floor 1 Stock Exchange of Thailand Building, No 93 Rachadaphisek Road Din DaengSub-district Din Daeng District, Bangkok, 10400, Thailand **(100%)**
Tel.: (66) 20099380
Web Site: https://www.set.or.th
Back-Office Systems Development & Promotion for After-Trade Services in Thailand
N.A.I.C.S.: 523910

THE STORE CORPORATION BERHAD
Lot 328 Jalan 51A/223 Seksyen 51A, 46100, Petaling Jaya, Malaysia
Tel.: (60) 379603233   MY
Web Site: http://www.tstore.com.my
Sales Range: Less than $1 Million
Supermarkets & Departmental Store Operators
N.A.I.C.S.: 445110
Pik Hua Hwong *(Sec)*

Subsidiaries:

Gold Shopping Centre Holdings Sdn. Bhd. (1)
Jalan Tuanku Munawir, Seremban, 70000, Negeri Sembilan, Malaysia
Tel.: (60) 67633705
Shopping Mall Management Services
N.A.I.C.S.: 531120
Habsah Nanad *(Gen Mgr)*

Milimewa Superstore Sdn. Bhd. (1)
3rd Floor Jalan Bundusan Beverly Hills Plaza, Penampang, 88000, Sabah, Malaysia
Tel.: (60) 88714157
Web Site: http://www.milimewastore.com.my
Sales Range: $25-49.9 Million
Emp.: 48
Supermarkets Operation Services
N.A.I.C.S.: 445110
Fong Nyuk Fong *(Branch Mgr)*

Pacific Hypermarket Properties Sdn. Bhd. (1)
B Megamall Pinang 2828 Jln Baru, 13700, Perai, Penang, Malaysia
Tel.: (60) 43998998
Web Site: http://www.tstore.com.my
Emp.: 200
Supermarkets Operation Services
N.A.I.C.S.: 445110

TS Universal Trading Sdn. Bhd. (1)
Lot 328 Jalan 223, 46100, Petaling Jaya, Selangor, Malaysia
Tel.: (60) 379603233
Web Site: http://www.tstore.com.my
Emp.: 400
Snacks & Mineral Water Distr
N.A.I.C.S.: 424490

The Store (Malaysia) Sdn. Bhd. (1)
Lot 328 Jalan 223, Petaling Jaya, 46100, Selangor, Malaysia
Tel.: (60) 379603233
Web Site: http://www.tstore.com.my
Sales Range: $100-124.9 Million
Emp.: 300
Supermarkets Operation Services
N.A.I.C.S.: 445110

The Store Holdings Sdn. Bhd. (1)
Lot 1-15 Ground 1 & 2 Block H Komplek Lien Hoe, Jalan Sutera Johor Bahru, Johor Bahru, 80150, Johor, Malaysia
Tel.: (60) 73318649
Web Site: http://www.holdingliststore.com.my
Emp.: 30
Supermarkets Management & Operation Services
N.A.I.C.S.: 445110

The Store Taiping Wisma Dato' Toh Eng Hoe (1)
Lot 1512-1522 Jalan Panggung Wayang, Taiping, 34000, Perak Darul Ridzuan, Malaysia
Tel.: (60) 5 806 0396
Web Site: http://www.tstore.com.my
Emp.: 100
Supermarkets Operation Services
N.A.I.C.S.: 445110

THE STRATECH GROUP LIMITED
31 International Business Park 02-02 Creative Resource, Singapore, 609921, Singapore
Tel.: (65) 63232188   SG
Web Site: http://www.thestratechgroup.com
Year Founded: 1989
Information Technology Services
N.A.I.C.S.: 541512
David Khien Meow Chew *(Founder & Chm)*

Subsidiaries:

Stratech Aerospace, Inc. (1)
245 Park Ave 39th Fl, New York, NY 10167
Tel.: (212) 372-8890
Surveillance System Services
N.A.I.C.S.: 238210
Grant C. Bishop *(COO)*

THE STRONACH GROUP INC.
455 Magna Drive, Aurora, L4G 7A9, ON, Canada
Tel.: (905) 726-7600
Web Site: http://www.stronachgroup.com
Holding Company; Racetrack & Casino Operator; Horse Breeding, Training & Aftercare Services
N.A.I.C.S.: 551112
Belinda Stronach *(Chm, Pres & CEO)*

Subsidiaries:

Adena Springs company (1)
701 Cane Ridge Rd, Paris, KY 40361
Tel.: (859) 987-1798
Web Site: http://www.adenastallions.com
Horse Racing Services
N.A.I.C.S.: 711219
Vicki Stacy *(Office Mgr)*

AmTote International, Inc. (1)
11200 Pepper Rd, Hunt Valley, MD 21031
Tel.: (410) 771-8700
Web Site: http://www.amtote.com
Sales Range: $50-74.9 Million
Emp.: 85
Betting Technology
N.A.I.C.S.: 713290
Steve Keech *(Pres)*

Subsidiary (Non-US):

AmTote Australasia Pty Ltd (2)
Unit 3 28 Leighton Plc, Hornsby, 2077, NSW, Australia
Tel.: (61) 294495744
Software & Hardware Distr
N.A.I.C.S.: 423430
Michael Laybutt *(Gen Mgr)*

Gulfstream Park Racing Association, Inc. (1)
901 S Federal Hwy, Hallandale, FL 33009-7124
Tel.: (954) 454-7000
Web Site: http://www.gulfstreampark.com
Sales Range: $100-124.9 Million
Emp.: 350
Horse Racetrack & Casino Operator
N.A.I.C.S.: 711212

Maryland Jockey Club, Inc. (1)
5201 Park Heights Ave, Baltimore, MD 21215
Tel.: (410) 542-9400
Web Site: http://www.marylandracing.com
Sales Range: $100-124.9 Million
Holding Company; Horse Racetrack Operator
N.A.I.C.S.: 551112
Sal Sinatra *(VP & Gen Mgr)*

Subsidiary (Domestic):

Laurel Racing Association, Inc. (2)
Route 198 & Racetrack Rd, Laurel, MD 20724
Tel.: (301) 725-0400
Web Site: http://www.laurelpark.com
Sales Range: $50-74.9 Million
Emp.: 600
Horse Racetrack Operator
N.A.I.C.S.: 711212

Pimlico Racing Association, Inc. (2)
5201 Park Heights Ave, Baltimore, MD 21215-5117
Tel.: (410) 542-9400
Web Site: http://www.pimlico.com
Sales Range: $50-74.9 Million
Emp.: 500
Horse Racetrack Operator
N.A.I.C.S.: 711212
Sal Sinatra *(Pres & COO)*

Prince George's Racing Ventures, LLC (1)
6336 Rosecroft Dr, Fort Washington, MD 20744
Tel.: (301) 567-4500
Web Site: http://www.rosecroft.com
Racetrack Operator
N.A.I.C.S.: 711212
Lisa Watts *(Dir-Ops)*

The Santa Anita Companies, Inc. (1)
285 W Huntington Dr, Arcadia, CA 91007 **(100%)**
Tel.: (626) 574-7223
Web Site: http://www.santaanita.com
Real Estate Investment Trust; Horse Racetrack Owner
N.A.I.C.S.: 525990
Frank Stronach *(Chm)*

Subsidiary (Domestic):

Los Angeles Turf Club, Incorporated (2)
285 W Huntington Dr, Arcadia, CA 91007
Tel.: (626) 574-7223
Web Site: http://www.santaanita.com
Sales Range: $75-99.9 Million
Emp.: 300
Horse Racetrack Operator
N.A.I.C.S.: 711212
Joe Morris *(VP)*

XpressBet, Inc. (1)
200 Racetrack Rd Bldg 26, Washington, PA 15301
Tel.: (724) 229-6918
Web Site: http://www.xpressbet.com
Sales Range: $25-49.9 Million
Horse Racetrack Operator
N.A.I.C.S.: 711212
Ronald W. Luniewski *(Pres)*

THE SUMITOMO WAREHOUSE CO. LTD.
Sumitomo Nakanoshima Building 2-18 Nakanoshima 3-chome, Kita-ku, Osaka, 530-0005, Japan
Tel.: (81) 664441181
Web Site: https://www.sumitomo-soko.co.jp
Year Founded: 1899

9303—(TKS)
Rev.: $1,220,609,210
Assets: $2,888,041,200
Liabilities: $1,137,686,760
Net Worth: $1,750,354,440
Earnings: $82,558,900
Emp.: 4,463
Fiscal Year-end: 03/31/24
Warehouses Operation
N.A.I.C.S.: 236220
Tohru Matsunaga *(Exec Officer & Gen Mgr-Kobe Branch)*

Subsidiaries:

Atsugisenso Co., Ltd. (1)
6-22 Hase, Atsugi, 243-0036, Kanagawa, Japan
Tel.: (81) 462506651
Sea Freight Transportation Services
N.A.I.C.S.: 483111

Beijing Enshu Packing Service Limited Company (1)
13-10 Chinese Businessman Building, Chaoyang District, Beijing, China
Tel.: (86) 1087303640
Packaging Services
N.A.I.C.S.: 561910

Enshu (China) Corporation Ltd. (1)
5-1 Umeyama, Fukuroi, 437-1105, Shizuoka, Japan
Tel.: (81) 538300001
Sales Range: $25-49.9 Million
Emp.: 10
Business Management Services
N.A.I.C.S.: 561110

Enshu Truck Co., Ltd. (1)
22-1 Kihara, Fukuroi, 437-0046, Shizuoka, Japan
Tel.: (81) 538421111
Web Site: https://www.enshu-truck.co.jp
Emp.: 1,303
Cargo & Trucking Services
N.A.I.C.S.: 484110

Subsidiary (Domestic):

Toyu Distribution Co., Ltd. (2)
670-1 Shiratori-cho, Higashi-ku, Hamamatsu, 435-0002, Shizuoka, Japan **(100%)**
Tel.: (81) 534215516
Web Site: http://www.toyu-distribution.co.jp
Emp.: 110
Warehousing & Freight Forwarding Services
N.A.I.C.S.: 483111
Shigeo Toyota *(Pres)*

Enshu Truck Kansai Co., Ltd. (1)
2-22 Nishihitotsuya, Settsu, 566-0044, Osaka, Japan
Tel.: (81) 648620005
General Freight Trucking Services
N.A.I.C.S.: 484110

Hakata Izumi Co., Ltd. (1)
2-20-14 Sumiyoshi in front of Sumiyoshibashi, Tamoto Hakurenkai Hospital Hakata-ku, Fukuoka, 812-0018, Japan
Tel.: (81) 922910231
Web Site: https://www.hakata-izumi.co.jp
Restaurant Services
N.A.I.C.S.: 722511

Hattori Gumi Co., Ltd. (1)
2-6-15 Kaigan-dori 2-chome, Minato-ku, Osaka, 552-0022, Japan
Tel.: (81) 665733096
Warehousing & Logistics Services
N.A.I.C.S.: 493110

ISTAR Corporation (1)
Keihanshin Yodoyabashi Building 4-4-7 Imabashi, Chuo-ku, Osaka, 541-0042, Japan
Tel.: (81) 647060061
Web Site: https://www.i-star.co.jp
Emp.: 368
Software Development & Computer Systems Management Services
N.A.I.C.S.: 541511

J-WeSco Ltd. (1)
11-1 Shiba-Koen 2-chome, Minato-ku, Tokyo, 105-0011, Japan
Tel.: (81) 364302653

THE SUMITOMO WAREHOUSE CO. LTD.   INTERNATIONAL PUBLIC

The Sumitomo Warehouse Co. Ltd.—(Continued)
Sea Freight Transportation Services
N.A.I.C.S.: 483111

Nickel & Lyons, Ltd. (1)
6-6 Hatobacho , Chuo Ward, Kobe, 650-0042, Hyogo, Japan
Tel.: (81) 783417781
Web Site: http://www.nickel.co.jp
Sales Range: $25-49.9 Million
Emp.: 100
Marine Shipping Services
N.A.I.C.S.: 488510

PT. Sumiso Logistics Indonesia (1)
Blue Bird Building 5th Floor Jl Halim Perdana Kusuma No 1, Kelurahan Kebon Pala Kecaman Makasar, Jakarta Timur, 13650, Indonesia
Tel.: (62) 2180882324
Freight Forwarding Services
N.A.I.C.S.: 488510

Qingdao JTB-Enshu Trading Co., Ltd. (1)
45 Moscow Rd, Qingdao Free Trade Zone, Qingdao, Shandong, China
Tel.: (86) 53286959101
General Freight Services
N.A.I.C.S.: 484110

Rabigh Petrochemical Logistics LLC (1)
PO Box 659, Rabigh, 21911, Saudi Arabia
Tel.: (966) 122905076
Web Site: https://www.rpl-sa.com
Sea Freight Transportation Services
N.A.I.C.S.: 483111

Rojana Distribution Center Co., Ltd. (1)
1/35 Moo 5 Rojana Road Tambol Karnham, Amphur U-Thai, Ayutthaya, 13210, Thailand
Web Site: http://www.rdc.co.th
Sales Range: $75-99.9 Million
Emp.: 150
Warehousing & Freight Forwarding Services
N.A.I.C.S.: 488510

Senso Sagyo Co., Ltd. (1)
11-50 Nanko-higashi 4-chome, Suminoe-ku, Osaka, 559-0031, Japan
Tel.: (81) 647031850
Sea Freight Transportation Services
N.A.I.C.S.: 483111

Senwa Maritime Agency, Ltd. (1)
3-1 Shibakoen 1-Chome, Minato-ku, Tokyo, 105-0011, Japan
Tel.: (81) 357337200
Web Site: www.senwa.co.jp
Sales Range: $25-49.9 Million
Emp.: 20
Overseas Shipping Services
N.A.I.C.S.: 488510
Keiichi Sano *(Pres)*

Senyo Koun Co., Ltd. (1)
1-2-31 Kaigan-dori, Chuo-ku, Kobe, 650-0024, Hyogo, Japan
Tel.: (81) 783310137
Web Site: https://www.senyokoun.co.jp
Emp.: 104
Cargo Handling Services
N.A.I.C.S.: 488320

Shanghai Enshu Distribution Co., Ltd. (1)
No 5117 Longwu Rd, Minhang-qu, Shanghai, 200241, China
Tel.: (86) 2154870788
Warehousing & Trucking Services
N.A.I.C.S.: 484110

Shanghai Jinjiang-Sumiso International Logistics Co., Ltd. (1)
No 4 Lane 251 Shendong Road, Pudong, Shanghai, 201208, China
Tel.: (86) 2156487593
Sea Freight Transportation Services
N.A.I.C.S.: 483111

Shanghai Sumiso International Logistics Co., Ltd. (1)
Tel.: (86) 2163345280
Sales Range: $25-49.9 Million
Emp.: 50
Freight Forwarding Services

Shinko Sagyo Co., Ltd. (1)
7-14 Minatojima, Chuo-ku, Kobe, 650-0045, Japan
Tel.: (81) 783025123
Sea Freight Transportation Services
N.A.I.C.S.: 483111

Sumiso (Laem Chabang) Co., Ltd. (1)
1/28 Moo 3 Takhiantia, Bang Lamung, 20150, Chonburi, Thailand
Tel.: (66) 33047351
Warehousing & Logistics Services
N.A.I.C.S.: 493110

Sumiso (Malaysia) Sdn. Bhd. (1)
Tel.: (60) 331666030
Web Site: www.sumitomo-soko.co.jp
Sales Range: $25-49.9 Million
Emp.: 20
Warehousing & Freight Forwarding Services
N.A.I.C.S.: 488510

Sumiso (Taiwan) Co., Ltd. (1)
8F-3 No 129 Sec 2 Zhongshan N Rd, Taipei, Taiwan
Tel.: (886) 225113133
Sales Range: $25-49.9 Million
Emp.: 40
Warehousing & Freight Forwarding Services
N.A.I.C.S.: 488510

Sumiso (Thailand) Co., Ltd. (1)
1/35 Moo 5 Rojana Road Tambol Karnharm, Rojana Industrial Park Amphur Uthai, Ayutthaya, 13210, Thailand
Tel.: (66) 35330141
Sales Range: $25-49.9 Million
Emp.: 150
Warehousing Services
N.A.I.C.S.: 493110

Sumiso International Logistics (Guangzhou) Co., Ltd. (1)
Rm 2103 Dongshan Plaza No 69 Xianlie Zhong Rd, Yuexiu District, Guangzhou, 510095, Guangdong, China
Tel.: (86) 2087320441
Web Site: http://www.sumitomo-soko.co.jp
Sales Range: $25-49.9 Million
Emp.: 8
Warehousing & Customs Agency
N.A.I.C.S.: 493110

Sumiso Real Estate Services Co., Ltd. (1)
1-4-19 Minamihorie Namba Sumiso Building, Nishi-ku, Osaka, 550-0015, Japan
Tel.: (81) 665383668
Web Site: https://www.sumiso.co.jp
Emp.: 56
Real Estate Services
N.A.I.C.S.: 531390

Sumitomo Warehouse (Europe) GmbH (1)
Berliner Allee 6, 40212, Dusseldorf, Germany
Tel.: (49) 211450856
Web Site: http://www.sumitomo-wh.eu
Sales Range: $25-49.9 Million
Emp.: 3
Warehousing Services
N.A.I.C.S.: 493110
Shuji Takano *(Mng Dir)*

Sumitomo Warehouse (China) Ltd. (1)
No 600 Wangqiao Road, Jinqiao Export Processing Zone South District Pudong, Shanghai, 201201, China
Tel.: (86) 2158381628
Warehousing Services
N.A.I.C.S.: 493110

Sumitomo Warehouse (Europe) GmbH (1)
Photographylaan 37-39, Wilrijk, 2610, Antwerp, Belgium
Tel.: (32) 38251515
Web Site: https://www.sumitomo-wh.eu
Sea Freight Transportation Services
N.A.I.C.S.: 483111

Sumitomo Warehouse (Europe) GmbH (1)
2nd Floor 123 Minories, London, EC3N 1NT, United Kingdom

Tel.: (44) 2039375870
Sea Freight Transportation Services
N.A.I.C.S.: 483111

Sumitomo Warehouse (Hong Kong) Ltd. (1)
Room 13012 13/F ATL Logistics Centre B Berth 3, Kwai Chung Container Terminal, Kwai Chung, NT, China (Hong Kong)
Tel.: (852) 24199168
Web Site: http://www.sumitomo-soko.co.jp
Freight Transportation Services
N.A.I.C.S.: 488510

Sumitomo Warehouse (Shanghai) Ltd. (1)
No 151 Rivingnan Road Outer Gaoqiao Free Trade Zone, Pudong New Area, Shanghai, 200131, China
Tel.: (86) 2158662032
Warehousing & Trucking Services
N.A.I.C.S.: 484110

Sumitomo Warehouse (Shenzhen) Ltd. (1)
Room 320 Shenzhen Kerry Yantian Port Logistics Centre South Area, Yantian Integrated Free Trade Zone Yantian District, Shenzhen, 518081, China
Tel.: (86) 75525281334
Warehousing Services
N.A.I.C.S.: 493110

Sumitomo Warehouse (Singapore) Pte. Ltd. (1)
No 8 Tuas Ave 5, Singapore, 639334, Singapore
Tel.: (65) 68615844
Warehousing & Freight Forwarding Services
N.A.I.C.S.: 488510

Sumitomo Warehouse (U.S.A.) Inc. (1)
19301 Pacific Gateway Dr, Torrance, CA 90502-1017
Tel.: (310) 769-0205
Web Site: https://www.sumitomo-wh.com
Sales Range: $10-24.9 Million
Emp.: 50
Warehousing Services
N.A.I.C.S.: 493110
Thom Nina *(Mgr-Warehouse)*

Division (Domestic):

Sumitomo Warehouse (U.S.A.) Inc.- Freight Forwarding Division (2)
19301 Pacific Gateway Dr, Torrance, CA 90502
Tel.: (310) 769-0205
Web Site: http://www.sumitomo-wh.com
Freight Forwarding Services
N.A.I.C.S.: 488510
Shunsuke Kato *(Pres)*

Sumitomo Warehouse (U.S.A.) Inc.- Parts Center Division (2)
19301 Pacific Gateway Dr, Torrance, CA 90502
Tel.: (310) 769-0105
Air Conditioning Parts Distr
N.A.I.C.S.: 423730

Sumitomo Warehouse (Vietnam) Co., Ltd. (1)
2F Empire Tower 26-28 Ham Nghi Street, District 1, Ho Chi Minh City, Vietnam
Tel.: (84) 2839140741
Freight Forwarding Services
N.A.I.C.S.: 488510

Sumitomo Warehouse Kyushu Co., Ltd. (1)
5-80 Okihamacho, Hakata-ku, Fukuoka, 812-0031, Japan
Tel.: (81) 922812031
Web Site: https://www.sumitomosoko-kyushu.co.jp
Cargo Storage & Merchandising Processing Services
N.A.I.C.S.: 488490

Summit Shipping Agencies Ltd. (1)
1-2-4 Hamamatsucho, Minato-ku, Tokyo, 105-0013, Japan
Tel.: (81) 364021960
Web Site: http://www.summitship.co.jp
Sales Range: $25-49.9 Million
Emp.: 20
Overseas Shipping Agents

N.A.I.C.S.: 488510
Yasutoshi Nakamura *(Pres)*

The Izumi Express Co., Ltd. (1)
1-1 Fusocho, Amagasaki, 660-0891, Hyogo, Japan
Tel.: (81) 648683500
Web Site: https://www.izumiexpress.co.jp
Cargo & Trucking Services
N.A.I.C.S.: 484110

The Osaka Packing & Transportation Co., Ltd. (1)
Bund 3-chome No 2 No 2, Minato-ku, Osaka, 552-0022, Japan
Tel.: (81) 665711581
Web Site: http://www.osakakompo.jp
Emp.: 70
Cargo Storage & Merchandise Processing Services
N.A.I.C.S.: 488320
Masahisa Ishii *(Pres)*

The Taisei Kaiun Kaisha, Ltd. (1)
2-6-15 Kaigan-dori Sumitomo Warehouse South Bank Sales Office, Minato-ku, Osaka, 552-0022, Japan
Tel.: (81) 665710668
Web Site: http://www.taiseikaiun.co.jp
Sales Range: Less than $1 Million
Emp.: 60
Cargo Shipping & Merchandise Processing Services
N.A.I.C.S.: 488510
Tadashi Takeuchi *(Pres)*

Union Services (Singapore) Pte. Ltd. (1)
150 Beach Road 13-05/07 Gateway West, Singapore, 189720, Singapore
Tel.: (65) 63911023
Web Site: http://www.unionservices.com.sg
Emp.: 200
Warehousing & Cargo Handling & Trucking & Freight Forwarding Services
N.A.I.C.S.: 488510
Tsunoda Tatsuya *(Gen Mgr)*

Division (Domestic):

Union Services (Singapore) Pte Ltd - Forwarding Division (2)
150 Beach Rd No 13-05 07 Gateway W, Singapore, Singapore
Tel.: (65) 63911037
Web Site: http://www.unionservices.com.sg
Sales Range: $25-49.9 Million
Emp.: 30
Freight Forwarding Services
N.A.I.C.S.: 488510
Philip Yap *(Mgr)*

Union Services (Singapore) Pte Ltd - Traffic Division (2)
150 Beach Rd No 13-05 07 Gateway W, Singapore, 189720, Singapore
Tel.: (65) 63911037
Web Site: http://www.unionservices.com.sg
Traffic Distribution Management Services
N.A.I.C.S.: 541614
Chieng Chian Sing *(Gen Mgr)*

Union Services (Singapore) Pte Ltd - Transport Division (2)
150 Beach Rd 13-05 07 Gateway W, Singapore, Singapore
Tel.: (65) 63911029
Web Site: http://www.unionservices.com.sg
Sales Range: $25-49.9 Million
Emp.: 50
Freight Transportation Services
N.A.I.C.S.: 488510

Vantec Sumiso Logistics (Wuhan) Co., Ltd. (1)
Tel.: (86) 2784791650
Web Site: http://www.vantec-gl.com
Logistic Services
N.A.I.C.S.: 541614

Wakasu Co., Ltd. (1)
2-3-7 Wakasu, Koto-ku, Tokyo, 136-0083, Japan
Tel.: (81) 335223041
Web Site: https://www.wakasu.co.jp
Emp.: 65
Outsourcing Services
N.A.I.C.S.: 541611

Westwood Shipping Lines Japan, Inc. (1)

3-1 Shibakoen 1-Chome, Minato-ku, Tokyo, 105-0011, Japan
Tel.: (81) 357337212
Sea Freight Transportation Services
N.A.I.C.S.: 483111

umiso (Laem Chabang) Co., Ltd. (1)
1/28 Moo 3 Takhiantia, Bang Lamung, 20150, Chonburi, Thailand
Tel.: (66) 33047351
Warehousing Services
N.A.I.C.S.: 493110

THE SUNPORK GROUP
1/29 Smallwood Place, Murarrie, 4172, QLD, Australia
Tel.: (61) 739081400
Web Site:
http://www.sunporkfreshfoods.com
Meat Product Distr
N.A.I.C.S.: 424470
Robert van Barneveld *(CEO & Mng Dir)*

THE SUPREME INDUSTRIES LIMITED
1161 Solitaire Corporate Park, Andheri Ghatkopar Link Road Chakala Andheri East, Mumbai, 400093, India
Tel.: (91) 2240430000
Web Site: https://www.supreme.co.in
Year Founded: 1942
509930—(BOM)
Rev.: $1,063,713,105
Assets: $681,936,255
Liabilities: $157,181,115
Net Worth: $524,755,140
Earnings: $132,193,425
Emp.: 5,228
Fiscal Year-end: 03/31/22
Plastics Product Mfr
N.A.I.C.S.: 326199
Vivek Kumar Taparia *(Exec Dir)*

Subsidiaries:

The Supreme Industries Overseas FZE (1)
Tel.: (971) 65574484
Plastics Product Mfr
N.A.I.C.S.: 326199

THE SWATCH GROUP LTD.
Seevorstadt 6, 2501, Biel/Bienne, Switzerland
Tel.: (41) 323436811   CH
Web Site:
https://www.swatchgroup.com
Year Founded: 1984
SWGAF—(OTCIQ)
Rev.: $8,745,011,086
Assets: $15,774,944,568
Liabilities: $2,185,144,124
Net Worth: $13,589,800,443
Earnings: $986,696,231
Emp.: 33,602
Fiscal Year-end: 12/31/23
Jewelry Product Mfr
N.A.I.C.S.: 339910
Ernst Tanner *(Vice Chm)*

Subsidiaries:

ASICentrum spol. s.r.o (1)
Novodvorska 994/138, 142 21, Prague, Czech Republic
Tel.: (420) 22 677 2111
Web Site: https://www.asicentrum.cz
Integrated Circuit & Design Mfr
N.A.I.C.S.: 334413

Assemti SA (1)
Via Campagna 23, 6595, Riazzino, Switzerland
Tel.: (41) 918503700
Watch Mfr
N.A.I.C.S.: 334519

Asulab S.A. (1)
Rue Des Sors 3, 2074, Marin, Epagnier, Switzerland (100%)
Tel.: (41) 327555666
Web Site: http://www.asulab.ch

Sales Range: $25-49.9 Million
Emp.: 100
Provider of Research & Development Services
N.A.I.C.S.: 541715

Blancpain Les Boutiques SA (1)
Le Rocher 12, 1348, Le Brassus, Switzerland
Tel.: (41) 217963636
Web Site: http://www.blancpain.com
Watch & Jewel Distr
N.A.I.C.S.: 423940
Marc Hayek *(Dir-Publ)*

Blancpain S.A. (1)
Le Rocher 12, 1348, Le Brassus, Switzerland (100%)
Tel.: (41) 21 796 3636
Web Site: https://www.blancpain.com
Emp.: 850
Watch Mfr
N.A.I.C.S.: 334519
Marc A. Hayek *(Pres & CEO)*

Breguet Les Boutiques SA (1)
Rue du Rhone 40, Geneva, 1204, Switzerland
Tel.: (41) 22 317 49 20
Web Site: http://www.breguet.ch
Watch Mfr
N.A.I.C.S.: 334519

CHH Microtechnique SA (1)
Rue de la Gare 12, 1348, Le Brassus, Switzerland
Tel.: (41) 21 845 1700
Web Site: https://www.chh-microtechnique.ch
Watch Mfr
N.A.I.C.S.: 334519

CK Watch & Jewelry Co., Ltd. (1)
Rue du Viaduc 30, Biel/Bienne, 2501, Switzerland
Tel.: (41) 32 343 65 11
Watch Mfr & Distr
N.A.I.C.S.: 334519

Certina S.A. (1)
Rue des Pres 149, 2503, Bienne, Switzerland (100%)
Tel.: (41) 32 933 3550
Web Site: https://www.certina.com
Sales Range: $25-49.9 Million
Emp.: 80
Watch Mfr
N.A.I.C.S.: 334519

Cite du Temps SA (1)
Nicolas G Hayek Strasse 2, 2502, Biel, Switzerland
Tel.: (41) 323438900
Web Site: https://www.citedutemps.com
Sales Range: $50-74.9 Million
Exhibition & Restaurant Promoting Services
N.A.I.C.S.: 711310

Comadur S.A. (1)
Col-des-Roches 33, 2400, Le Locle, Switzerland (100%)
Tel.: (41) 329308311
Web Site: https://www.comadur.ch
Sales Range: $100-124.9 Million
Emp.: 500
Mfr of Watch Components, Measurement & Automatic Control Devices, Industrial Cutting Equipment & Chromatographic Analysis Equipment
N.A.I.C.S.: 334519

Compagnie des Montres Longines, Francillon SA (1)
Rue Des Noyettes 8, 2610, Saint Imier, Switzerland
Tel.: (41) 329425425
Web Site: http://www.longines.com
Sales Range: $100-124.9 Million
Watch Mfr
N.A.I.C.S.: 334519

Deutsche Zifferblatt Manufaktur GmbH (1)
Maystrasse 6, 75172, Pforzheim, Germany
Tel.: (49) 7231586990
Sales Range: $25-49.9 Million
Emp.: 50
Watch Mfr
N.A.I.C.S.: 334519

Diantus Watch SA (1)
Via Angelo Mapoli Zona Industriale 2, Mendrisio, 6850, Switzerland (100%)
Tel.: (41) 916400500
Web Site: http://www.diantus.com
Sales Range: $200-249.9 Million
Emp.: 600
Mfr of Watches
N.A.I.C.S.: 334519

Distico SA (1)
Via San Gottardo 13, Taverne, 6807, Switzerland
Tel.: (41) 919357400
Watch Distr
N.A.I.C.S.: 423940

Dress Your Body SA (1)
Cormondreche, 2036, Corcelles, Switzerland
Tel.: (41) 327322711
Prestige Jewelry Design Services
N.A.I.C.S.: 541490

EM Microelectronic-Marin S.A. (1)
Sors 3, 2074, Marin, Neuchatel, Switzerland (100%)
Tel.: (41) 327555111
Web Site:
https://www.emmicroelectronic.com
Sales Range: $150-199.9 Million
Microelectronics
N.A.I.C.S.: 423690

ETA S.A. (1)
Schild-Rust-Strasse 17, 2540, Grenchen, Switzerland (100%)
Tel.: (41) 32 655 7111
Web Site: https://www.eta.ch
Sales Range: $650-699.9 Million
Emp.: 2,500
Provider of Real Estate Services
N.A.I.C.S.: 531210

ETA S.A. Manufacture Horlogere (1)
Schild Ruststrasse 17, 2540, Grenchen, Switzerland (100%)
Tel.: (41) 326557111
Web Site: https://www.eta.ch
Sales Range: $1-4.9 Billion
Watch Movements Mfr
N.A.I.C.S.: 334519

Subsidiary (Non-US):

ETA (Thailand) Co. Ltd. (2)
439 Bangplee Industrial Est II Moo 17 Bang Sao Thong, Samut Prakan, 10540, Samut, Thailand (100%)
Tel.: (66) 23153161
Web Site: http://www.eta.ch
Sales Range: $350-399.9 Million
Emp.: 2,500
Mfr of Watch Movements & Components
N.A.I.C.S.: 334519

Endura S.A. (1)
Ch du Long-Champ 119, 2504, Bienne, Switzerland (100%)
Tel.: (41) 323434004
Web Site: http://www.endura.ch
Sales Range: $25-49.9 Million
Emp.: 7
Watch Mfr
N.A.I.C.S.: 334519

Evaco SA (1)
Bachstrasse 10, PO Box 96, 4313, Mohlin, Switzerland
Tel.: (41) 618515800
Web Site: https://www.evaco.ch
Watch Distr
N.A.I.C.S.: 423940

Fabrique de Fournitures de Bonnetage FFB SAS (1)
Les Terres Rouges, Villers-le-Lac, 25130, France
Tel.: (33) 3 81 68 09 50
Watch Distr
N.A.I.C.S.: 423940

Francois Golay SA (1)
Route Des Ordons 4, Le Brassus, 1348, Switzerland
Tel.: (41) 21 845 17 00
Web Site: http://www.francoisgolay.ch
Sales Range: $50-74.9 Million
Emp.: 125
Watch Wheels Mfr
N.A.I.C.S.: 334519

Fresard Composants S.A. (1)
4 Rue Pierre Fresard, Charquemont, 25140, France (100%)
Tel.: (33) 381682700
Web Site: http://www.charquemont.cylex-france.fr
Sales Range: $25-49.9 Million
Emp.: 80
Mfr of Watch Components
N.A.I.C.S.: 334519

Glashutter Uhrenbetrieb GmbH (1)
Altenberger Strasse 1, Sachsen, 01768, Glashutte, Germany
Tel.: (49) 3 505 3460
Web Site: https://www.glashuette-original.com
Sales Range: $150-199.9 Million
Emp.: 500
Watch Distr
N.A.I.C.S.: 423940

Hamilton International AG (1)
Langgasse 85, 2504, Biel/Bienne, Switzerland
Tel.: (41) 323214900
Web Site: http://www.swatchgroup.com
Watch Mfr & Distr
N.A.I.C.S.: 334519

Harry Winston (Hong Kong) Limited (1)
The Peninsula Shop No E8 G/F 22 Salisbury Road Tsim Sha Tsui, Kowloon, China (Hong Kong)
Tel.: (852) 23012131
Diamond Jewelry Design Mfr
N.A.I.C.S.: 339910
Nikki Lee *(Mgr-Mktg & PR)*

Hour Passion SAS (1)
76 rue de Reuilly, 81231, Paris, Cedex 12, France
Tel.: (33) 144682727
Web Site: http://www.hourpassion.fr
Watch & Jewellery Distr
N.A.I.C.S.: 458310

Lascor S.p.A. (1)
Via Piave 98, I-21018, Sesto Calende, Italy
Tel.: (39) 0331914160
Web Site: http://www.lascor.com
Sales Range: $100-124.9 Million
Emp.: 334
Mfr of Watches & Bracelets
N.A.I.C.S.: 334519

Leon Hatot SA (1)
Av Beauregard 3, PO Box 190, 2035, Corcelles, NE, Switzerland
Tel.: (41) 327322607
Web Site: http://www.leonhatot.com
Watch Mfr & Distr
N.A.I.C.S.: 458310

MOM le Prelet SA (1)
Rue Des Prelets 24, 2206, Les Geneveys-sur-Coffrane, Switzerland
Tel.: (41) 32 858 16 16
Web Site: http://www.swatchgroup.com
Watch Dials Mfr
N.A.I.C.S.: 334519

Manufacture Favre et Perret SA (1)
Le Cret-Du-Locle 12, CP 500, 2322, La Chaux-de-Fonds, Switzerland
Tel.: (41) 32 911 95 11
Web Site: http://www.swatchgroup.com
Prestige Watch Mfr
N.A.I.C.S.: 334519

Manufacture Ruedin SA (1)
Rue De La Combe 10, Bassecourt, 2854, Switzerland (100%)
Tel.: (41) 324273131
Web Site: http://www.manufactureruedin.ch
Sales Range: $100-124.9 Million
Emp.: 300
Mfr of Watch Cases
N.A.I.C.S.: 334519
Eddy Ulmann *(Mgr-Admin)*

Meco S.A. (1)
Schutzengasse 30, 2540, Grenchen, Switzerland (100%)
Tel.: (41) 326552222
Web Site: http://www.meco.ch
Mfr of Watch Crowns
N.A.I.C.S.: 334519

Micro Crystal AG (1)

THE SWATCH GROUP LTD.

The Swatch Group Ltd.—(Continued)
Muehlestrasse 14, CH-2540, Grenchen, Switzerland
Tel.: (41) 326558282
Web Site: https://www.microcrystal.com
Emp.: 550
Watch Crystal Mfr
N.A.I.C.S.: 334519

Mido, SA (1)
Chemin des Tourelles 17, 2400, Le Locle, Switzerland **(100%)**
Tel.: (41) 32 933 3511
Web Site: https://www.midowatches.com
Sales Range: $100-124.9 Million
Emp.: 260
Mfr of Watches
N.A.I.C.S.: 334519
Frank Linder *(Pres)*

Montres Breguet S.A. (1)
Place De La Tour 23, 1344, L'Abbaye, Switzerland **(100%)**
Tel.: (41) 21 841 9090
Web Site: https://www.breguet.com
Sales Range: $200-249.9 Million
Emp.: 1,000
Mfr of Watches
N.A.I.C.S.: 458310

Montres Jaquet Droz SA (1)
Allee du Tourbillon 2, 2300, La Chaux-de-Fonds, Switzerland
Tel.: (41) 329242888
Web Site: https://www.jaquet-droz.com
Watch Mfr
N.A.I.C.S.: 334519

Nivarox-FAR S.A. (1)
Avenue du College 10, 2400, Le Locle, Switzerland
Tel.: (41) 32 933 4334
Web Site: https://www.nivarox.com
Sales Range: $400-449.9 Million
Emp.: 1,400
Mfr of Watch Components & Thin Wires
N.A.I.C.S.: 334519

O Grupo Swatch (Macau) Limitada (1)
Unit A-D 10/f fortuna business centre no 810, Av Panoramica do Lago Nam Van, Macau, China (Macau)
Tel.: (853) 85909700
Watch & Jewelry Distr
N.A.I.C.S.: 423940

Omega S.A. (1)
Rue Stampfli 96, Biel/Bienne, 2500, Switzerland **(100%)**
Tel.: (41) 323439211
Web Site: http://www.omega.ch
Sales Range: $100-124.9 Million
Emp.: 800
Mfr of Watches
N.A.I.C.S.: 334519

Pierre Balmain Montres AG (1)
Rue Des Noyettes 8, 2610, Saint Imier, Switzerland **(100%)**
Tel.: (41) 32 942 5740
Web Site: https://www.balmainwatches.com
Sales Range: $25-49.9 Million
Emp.: 25
Mfr of Watches
N.A.I.C.S.: 334519

Prestadora de Servicios Relojeros SA de CV (1)
Av Vasco de Quiroga 300 PB Santa Fe Alvaro Obregon, Mexico, Mexico
Tel.: (52) 5591773600
Watch & Clock Parts Mfr
N.A.I.C.S.: 334519

Rado Uhren AG (1)
Bielstrasse 45, 2543, Lengnau, Switzerland **(100%)**
Tel.: (41) 32 655 6111
Web Site: https://www.rado.com
Sales Range: $50-74.9 Million
Emp.: 300
Watch Mfr
N.A.I.C.S.: 334519

Renata S.A. (1)
Kreuzenstrasse 30, 4452, Itingen, Switzerland **(100%)**
Tel.: (41) 61 975 7575
Web Site: https://www.renata.com

Sales Range: $50-74.9 Million
Emp.: 250
Button Cells Battery Mfr
N.A.I.C.S.: 335910
Steven Pfrommer *(Member-Exec Bd)*

Rivoli Group L.L.C. (1)
1 Sheikh Zayed Road The H Dubai Office Tower Level 21, PO Box 121, Dubai, United Arab Emirates
Tel.: (971) 4 376 5000
Web Site: https://www.rivoligroup.com
Emp.: 1,600
Watch & Jewelry Distr
N.A.I.C.S.: 458310

SAS Centre Europeen de Service Horloger (1)
10 Rue Des Villas, 25000, Besancon, France
Tel.: (33) 381403710
Consumer Electronics Repair & Maintenance Services
N.A.I.C.S.: 811210

SEFEA S.A. (1)
15 Rue De Valeury, PO Box 251, F 74106, Annemasse, France **(100%)**
Tel.: (33) 450876161
Web Site: http://www.sefea.com
Sales Range: $25-49.9 Million
Emp.: 60
Provider of Watch Components & Electronic Assembly
N.A.I.C.S.: 334519

SGB Servicos e Comercio de Pecas Ltda (1)
Rua Ramos Batista 152 1 Andar Conjunto 11 Vila Olimpia, Sao Paulo, 04552-020, Brazil
Tel.: (55) 11 3746 2800
Web Site: http://www.swatchgroup.com
Watch Mfr
N.A.I.C.S.: 334519

SMH Immobilien S.A. (1)
Laenesereweg 119, 2504, Biel/Bienne, Switzerland **(100%)**
Tel.: (41) 323434205
Web Site: http://www.swatchimmo.ch
Sales Range: $75-99.9 Million
Emp.: 130
Real Estate & Project Management
N.A.I.C.S.: 531390

SMH Swiss Watch Trading (Shanghai) Co. Ltd (1)
4F 5F 8F No 30 Tianyaoqiao Rd, Shanghai, 200030, China
Tel.: (86) 2124125000
Sales Range: $150-199.9 Million
Emp.: 30
Watch & Jewelry Distr
N.A.I.C.S.: 423940

ST Software s.r.o. (1)
Machova 50, 460 07, Liberec, Czech Republic
Tel.: (420) 486109110
Sports Activity Services
N.A.I.C.S.: 713940

Shanghai SMH Watch Service Center Co. Ltd (1)
4F Metro City No 30 Tianyaoqiao Road, Shanghai, 200030, China
Tel.: (86) 1065839135
Web Site: http://www.smh.sh.cn
Sales Range: $75-99.9 Million
Emp.: 30
Watch Repair & Maintenance Services
N.A.I.C.S.: 811210
Susan Chen *(Gen Mgr)*

Simon et Membrez SA (1)
Habillage Horloger Haut-de-Gamme Rte de la Communance 86, 2800, Delemont, Switzerland
Tel.: (41) 32 424 5500
Web Site: https://www.simon-membrez.ch
Watch Mfr
N.A.I.C.S.: 334519
Stephane Chevrolet *(Mgr-IT)*

Swatch Group (India) Private Ltd (1)
4th Floor Rectangle - 1 Plot No D - 4, Saket District Centre, New Delhi, 110017, India
Tel.: (91) 114 609 2900
Web Site: http://www.swatchgroup.com

Sales Range: $25-49.9 Million
Emp.: 7
Watch Mfr
N.A.I.C.S.: 334519

Swatch Group Belgium S.A. (1)
Bergensesteenweg 1424 Chaussee de Mons, 1070, Brussels, Belgium **(100%)**
Tel.: (32) 2 558 3760
Web Site: https://www.swatch.com
Sales Range: $25-49.9 Million
Emp.: 100
Distr of Watches
N.A.I.C.S.: 423940

Swatch Group Espana S.A. (1)
C/ Yuca 2 - Miniparc I - Edificio C, Alcobendas, 28109, Madrid, Spain **(100%)**
Tel.: (34) 91 334 6300
Web Site: http://www.swatch.es
Sales Range: $50-74.9 Million
Emp.: 70
Distr of Watches
N.A.I.C.S.: 423940

Swatch Group do Brazil (1)
Rua Eng Antonio Jovino, 220, 6 Andar Cj 62, Sao Paulo, CEP 05727-220, SP, Brazil **(100%)**
Tel.: (55) 137462899
Watch Distr
N.A.I.C.S.: 423940

Swatch Retail AG (1)
Jakob-Stampflistrasse 94, Biel/Bienne, 2502, Switzerland
Tel.: (41) 323439580
Watch Retailer
N.A.I.C.S.: 458310

Swatch S.A. (1)
Seevorstadt 6, PO Box 2501, 2501, Biel/Bienne, Switzerland **(100%)**
Tel.: (41) 323436811
Web Site: http://www.swatch.com
Sales Range: $50-74.9 Million
Emp.: 180
Mfr of Watches
N.A.I.C.S.: 334519

Swiss Prestige Uhren Handel GmbH (1)
Rudols Diesel 7, 64760, Eschborn, Germany **(100%)**
Tel.: (49) 61736060
Web Site: http://www.swatchgroup.com
Sales Range: $25-49.9 Million
Emp.: 70
Distribution After Sales Service
N.A.I.C.S.: 334519

Swiss Timing (1)
Rue de l'Envers 1, PO Box 138, 2606, Corgemont, Switzerland
Tel.: (41) 32 488 3611
Web Site: https://www.swisstiming.com
Sales Range: $50-74.9 Million
Emp.: 140
Mfr of Sports Timing Equipment & Score-Board Information Systems
N.A.I.C.S.: 339950

Swiss Timing Ltd. (1)
Rue de l'Envers 1, PO Box 138, 2606, Corgemont, Switzerland **(100%)**
Tel.: (41) 32 488 3611
Web Site: https://www.swisstiming.com
Sales Range: $25-49.9 Million
Emp.: 150
Mfr of Sports Timing Instruments
N.A.I.C.S.: 334519

Subsidiary (Non-US):

ST Innovation GmbH (2)
Wiesenring 11, Leipzig, 4159, Germany
Tel.: (49) 341 46 21 500
Web Site: http://www.st-innovation.com
Internet Software Support Services
N.A.I.C.S.: 541511

ST Sportservice GmbH (2)
Wiesenring 11, 04159, Leipzig, Germany
Tel.: (49) 341 462 1100
Web Site: http://www.st-sportservice.com
Sports Events Information Technology Consulting Services
N.A.I.C.S.: 541512

Tech Airport Holding SAS (1)
76 Rue de Reuilly, PO Box 81231, 75583,

Paris, France
Tel.: (33) 144682727
Investment Management Service
N.A.I.C.S.: 523999

Tech Airport Orly SAS (1)
Zone Reservee Sud - Zone Publique Ouest, 91550, Orly, France
Tel.: (33) 1 74 22 03 94
Watch Distr
N.A.I.C.S.: 423940

The Swatch Group (Australia) Pty Ltd (1)
Level 2 1601 Malvern Road, Glen Iris, Glen Iris, 3146, VIC, Australia
Tel.: (61) 38 844 3300
Web Site: https://www.swatchgroup.com
Jewelry & Precious Stone Distr
N.A.I.C.S.: 423940

The Swatch Group (Belgium) SA (1)
Chaussee de Mons 1424, 1070, Brussels, Belgium
Tel.: (32) 25583700
Watch Component Mfr & Distr
N.A.I.C.S.: 334519

The Swatch Group (Canada) Ltd. (1)
555 Richmond Street West / Suite 1105, Toronto, M5V 3B1, ON, Canada **(100%)**
Tel.: (416) 703-1667
Web Site: https://www.swatchgroup.com
Sales Range: $25-49.9 Million
Emp.: 50
Wholesale Distr of Watches
N.A.I.C.S.: 423940

The Swatch Group (China) Ltd (1)
5/F Metro Tower No 30 Tian Yao Qiao Road, Shanghai, 200030, China
Tel.: (86) 2124125000
Watch Mfr & Distr
N.A.I.C.S.: 334519

The Swatch Group (Deutschland) GmbH (1)
Frankfurter Strasse 20, 65760, Eschborn, Germany **(100%)**
Tel.: (49) 619 688 7770
Web Site: http://www.swatchgroup.com
Sales Range: $75-99.9 Million
Emp.: 150
Distr of Watches
N.A.I.C.S.: 423940

The Swatch Group (Deutschland) Les Boutiques GmbH (1)
Frankfurter Strasse 20, 65760, Eschborn, Germany
Tel.: (49) 619 688 7770
Web Site: http://www.swatchgroup.com
Watch Online Retail Store Operating Services
N.A.I.C.S.: 423940

The Swatch Group (Espana) SA (1)
Edificio C Miniparc I Calle Yuca 2 Urbanizacion El Soto de la Moraleja, Alcobendas, 28109, Madrid, Spain
Tel.: (34) 913346300
Watch & Watch Component Mfr & Distr
N.A.I.C.S.: 334519

The Swatch Group (France) Les Boutiques, SAS (1)
112 Avenue Kleber, 75116, Paris, France
Tel.: (33) 153812283
Sales Range: $25-49.9 Million
Emp.: 100
Watch Retailer
N.A.I.C.S.: 458310

The Swatch Group (France) S.A. (1)
112-114 avenue Kleber, 75116, Paris, Cedex, France **(100%)**
Tel.: (33) 15 381 2200
Web Site: http://www.swatchgroup.fr
Sales Range: $150-199.9 Million
Emp.: 300
Distr of Watches
N.A.I.C.S.: 423940

The Swatch Group (Greece) SA (1)
Sygrou 3 Mantzagriotaki Street Kallithea, 17672, Athens, Greece
Tel.: (30) 2109565656
Watch Mfr & Distr
N.A.I.C.S.: 334519

AND PRIVATE COMPANIES

John Ferros *(Mng Dir)*

The Swatch Group (Hong Kong) Ltd. (1)
9/F Kerry Centre 683 Kings Road, 169 Electric Road, Quarry Bay, China (Hong Kong) **(100%)**
Tel.: (852) 2 510 5100
Web Site: http://www.swatch.com
Sales Range: $75-99.9 Million
Emp.: 200
Distr of Watches
N.A.I.C.S.: 423940

The Swatch Group (Italia) S.p.A. (1)
Via Washington 70, 20146, Milan, MI, Italy **(100%)**
Tel.: (39) 02575971
Web Site: https://www.swatch.com
Sales Range: $75-99.9 Million
Emp.: 150
Distr of Watches
N.A.I.C.S.: 423940

The Swatch Group (Japan) KK (1)
Nicolas G Hayek Center 7-9-18 Ginza, Chuo-ku, Tokyo, 104-8188, Japan
Tel.: (81) 36 254 7200
Web Site: https://www.swatchgroup.jp
Watch Mfr & Distr
N.A.I.C.S.: 334519

The Swatch Group (Korea) Ltd. (1)
1F 2F 10F 11F National Pension Service Building 36 Chungjeong-ro, Seodaemun-gu, Seoul, 120-709, Korea (South) **(100%)**
Tel.: (82) 23 149 9500
Web Site: http://www.swatchgroup.co.kr
Sales Range: $50-74.9 Million
Emp.: 200
Distr of Watches
N.A.I.C.S.: 423940

The Swatch Group (Malaysia) Sdn. Bhd. (1)
Level 22 Wisma Goldhill No 67 Jalan Raja Chulan, 50200, Kuala Lumpur, Malaysia **(51%)**
Tel.: (60) 32 050 8888
Web Site: http://www.swatch.com
Sales Range: $50-74.9 Million
Emp.: 90
Distr of Watches
N.A.I.C.S.: 423940

The Swatch Group (Netherlands) BV (1)
Kennedyplein 8, 5611 ZS, Eindhoven, Netherlands
Tel.: (31) 40 219 9999
Web Site: http://www.swatchgroup.com
Watch & Clock Parts Mfr
N.A.I.C.S.: 334519

The Swatch Group (Nordic) AB (1)
Sankt Eriksgatan 47, PO Box 12033, 112 34, Stockholm, Sweden **(100%)**
Tel.: (46) 86811800
Web Site: http://www.swatchgroup.se
Sales Range: $50-74.9 Million
Emp.: 50
Distr of Watches
N.A.I.C.S.: 423940

The Swatch Group (Oesterreich) GmbH (1)
Ares Tower Donau-City-Strasse 11, 1220, Vienna, Austria
Tel.: (43) 1981850
Watch & Watch Component Mfr & Distr
N.A.I.C.S.: 334519

The Swatch Group (Osterreich) GmbH (1)
ARES Tower Donau-City-Strasse 11/18 Stock, 1220, Vienna, Austria **(100%)**
Tel.: (43) 1 981 8545
Web Site: https://www.swatch.com
Sales Range: $50-74.9 Million
Emp.: 100
Sales of Watches
N.A.I.C.S.: 423940

The Swatch Group (Polska) Sp. z.o.o. (1)
ul Marynarska 15, 02-674, Warsaw, Poland
Tel.: (48) 222568100
Sales Range: $25-49.9 Million
Emp.: 7
Watch Retailer

N.A.I.C.S.: 458310

The Swatch Group (RUS) OOO (1)
2nd Syromyatnichesky per 1 8th floor, 105120, Moscow, Russia
Tel.: (7) 4955809845
Web Site: https://www.swatchgroup.com
Watch Mfr
N.A.I.C.S.: 334519

The Swatch Group (South Africa) (Proprietary) Ltd (1)
33 Angus Crescent Longmeadow Business Park East, ZA 1610, Edenvale, South Africa
Tel.: (27) 11 911 1200
Web Site: http://www.swatchgroup.com
Watch & Clock Distr
N.A.I.C.S.: 423940

The Swatch Group (Taiwan) Ltd (1)
6F No 126 Sec 4 Nanjing E Rd, Songshan, Taipei, 10595, Taiwan
Tel.: (886) 2 25462288
Watch Distr
N.A.I.C.S.: 423940

The Swatch Group (U.S.) Inc. (1)
1200 Harbor Blvd, Weehawken, NJ 07086 **(100%)**
Tel.: (201) 271-1400
Web Site: http://www.swatchgroup.com
Sales Range: $75-99.9 Million
Emp.: 150
Holding Company
N.A.I.C.S.: 423940
Elizabeth Petty *(Coord-Mktg)*

Subsidiary (Domestic):

EM Microelectronic - US Inc. (2)
5475 Mark Dabling Blvd Ste 200, Colorado Springs, CO 80918
Tel.: (719) 593-2883
Web Site: https://www.emmicroelectronic.com
Semiconductor Devices Mfr
N.A.I.C.S.: 334413

Harry Winston, Inc. (2)
701 5th Ave, New York, NY 10022
Tel.: (212) 399-1000
Web Site: https://www.harrywinston.com
Sales Range: $10-24.9 Million
Jewelry & Watch Mfr & Retailer
N.A.I.C.S.: 339910

Subsidiary (Non-US):

Harry Winston Japan K.K. (3)
1-8-14 Ginza, Chuo-ku, Tokyo, 104-0061, Japan
Tel.: (81) 335356441
Web Site: http://www.harrywinston.co.jp
Jewelry & Watch Mfr & Retailer
N.A.I.C.S.: 458310

Subsidiary (Domestic):

Omega Watch Company (2)
1200 Harbor Blvd, Weehawken, NJ 07086
Tel.: (201) 271-1400
Web Site: http://www.swatchgroup.com
Sales Range: $25-49.9 Million
Emp.: 30
Distr of Watches
N.A.I.C.S.: 423940

Swatch Watch U.S.A. (2)
1200 Harbor Blvd, Weehawken, NJ 07086
Tel.: (201) 271-1400
Web Site: http://www.swatch.com
Sales Range: $25-49.9 Million
Emp.: 100
Distr of Cosmetic Watches
N.A.I.C.S.: 458310
John Kelly *(CFO)*

The Swatch Group (UK) Les Boutiques (1)
Charter Court Third Avenue, Southampton, SO15 0JA, United Kingdom
Tel.: (44) 8452 743500
Watch Mfr
N.A.I.C.S.: 334519

The Swatch Group (UK) Ltd (1)
Building 1000 2nd Floor East Wing The Royals Business Park, Dockside Road, London, E16 2QU, United Kingdom
Tel.: (44) 8452743500
Emp.: 75

Precious Watch Distr
N.A.I.C.S.: 423940
Andrea Nunziata *(CEO)*

The Swatch Group Assembly SA (1)
Via Campagna Adorna 30, 6852, Genesterio, Switzerland
Tel.: (41) 91 640 30 10
Web Site: http://www.swatchgroup.com
Watch Parts Mfr
N.A.I.C.S.: 334519

The Swatch Group Customer Service (Europe) GmbH (1)
Emil-Lange-Str 3, Glashutte, 1768, Germany
Tel.: (49) 3505346400
Sales Range: $25-49.9 Million
Emp.: 35
Watch Repair & Maintenance Services
N.A.I.C.S.: 811210
Hardy Koeppe *(Gen Mgr)*

The Swatch Group Finance (Luxembourg) S.A. (1)
10 Rue Hondsbreck, 5835, Altzingen, Luxembourg **(80%)**
Tel.: (352) 226511
Web Site: http://www.swatch.com
Sales Range: $50-74.9 Million
Emp.: 5
Finance
N.A.I.C.S.: 522299

The Swatch Group Immeubles SA (1)
Faubourg de l'Hopital 3, 2001, Neuchatel, Switzerland
Tel.: (41) 327225711
Web Site: https://www.swatchimmo.ch
Real Estate Manangement Services
N.A.I.C.S.: 531390

The Swatch Group Les Boutiques SA (1)
Langgasse 85, 2504, Biel/Bienne, Switzerland
Tel.: (41) 323439611
Web Site: http://www.tourbillon.com
Sales Range: $25-49.9 Million
Emp.: 7
Watch Mfr & Distr
N.A.I.C.S.: 334519

The Swatch Group Ltd. (1)
Seevorstadt 6, PO Box 2501, 2501, Biel/Bienne, Switzerland **(100%)**
Tel.: (41) 323436811
Web Site: https://www.swatchgroup.com
Sales Range: $75-99.9 Million
Emp.: 150
Sales of Watches & Jewelry
N.A.I.C.S.: 423940

The Swatch Group Management Services SA (1)
Seevorstadt 6, 2501, Biel/Bienne, Switzerland
Tel.: (41) 323436811
Web Site: http://www.swatchgroup.com
Business Management Consulting Services
N.A.I.C.S.: 541611

The Swatch Group Mexico S.A de C.V (1)
Edifico Parque Chapultepec Av Parque Chapultepec 56 Piso, Col El Parque, 53398, Naucalpan, MX-Edo, Mexico
Tel.: (52) 559 177 3600
Web Site: https://www.swatchgroup.com
Watch Distr
N.A.I.C.S.: 423940

The Swatch Group Panama SA (1)
PH Pacific Village Business Plaza Floor Nr 6, Punta Pacifica, Panama, Panama
Tel.: (507) 304 99 00
Web Site: http://www.swatchgroup.com
Sales Range: $25-49.9 Million
Emp.: 12
Watch Distr
N.A.I.C.S.: 423940

The Swatch Group Re (Luxembourg) SA (1)
10 rue Hondsbreck, Altzingen, 5835, Luxembourg
Tel.: (352) 226 511
Watch Parts Mfr
N.A.I.C.S.: 334519

THE TAIKO BANK, LTD.

Beataang Abbet *(Gen Mgr)*

The Swatch Group Recherche et Developpement SA (1)
Rue des Sors 3, 2074, Marin, Switzerland
Tel.: (41) 32 755 56 66
Web Site: http://www.asulab.ch
Emp.: 100
Micro Technical System Research & Development Services
N.A.I.C.S.: 541715

The Swatch Group S.E.A. (S) Pte. Ltd. (1)
No 2 Boon Leat Terrace 06-01/02 Harbourside Building 2, Singapore, 119844, Singapore **(51%)**
Tel.: (65) 6 275 6388
Web Site: http://www.swatchgroup.com.sg
Sales Range: $50-74.9 Million
Emp.: 100
Distr of Watches
N.A.I.C.S.: 423940

The Swatch Group Services Ltd. (1)
Langfeldweg 119, 2504, Biel/Bienne, Switzerland
Tel.: (41) 323433911
Web Site: http://www.swatchgroup.com
Corporate Logistics, Distribution, IT, Customer & Real Estate Development Services
N.A.I.C.S.: 541614
Carmela Borloz *(Mgr-HR)*

The Swatch Group Trading (Thailand) Ltd (1)
4th Floor M Thai Tower All Seasons Place 87 Wireless Road, Pathumwan District, Bangkok, 10330, Thailand
Tel.: (66) 2 610 0200
Web Site: http://www.swatchgroup.com
Emp.: 300
Watch Distr
N.A.I.C.S.: 423940

The Swatch Group Turkey Saat Ticaret Limited Sirketi (1)
Buyukdere Caddesi No 195 K 6 Levent, Besiktas, 34360, Istanbul, Turkiye
Tel.: (90) 2123172200
Watch & Watch Component Mfr & Distr
N.A.I.C.S.: 334519

Tiffany Watch Co. Ltd (1)
Stampflistrasse 43, 2500, Biel/Bienne, Switzerland
Tel.: (41) 32 346 13 02
Web Site: http://www.tiffanywatches.com
Watch Mfr & Distr
N.A.I.C.S.: 334519

Time Flagship AG (1)
Bahnhofstrasse 48, 8001, Zurich, Switzerland
Tel.: (41) 442169000
Watch & Jewel Distr
N.A.I.C.S.: 423940

Tissot SA (1)
Chemin des Tourelles 17, PO Box 459, 2400, Le Locle, Switzerland **(100%)**
Tel.: (41) 32 933 3111
Web Site: https://www.tissotwatches.com
Sales Range: $50-74.9 Million
Emp.: 250
Mfr of Watches
N.A.I.C.S.: 334519
Francois Thiebaud *(Pres)*

Union Uhrenfabrik GmbH (1)
Fruhlingsweg 5, Saxony, 01768, Glashutte, Germany
Tel.: (49) 35053 461 6300
Web Site: https://www.union-glashuette.com
Sales Range: $25-49.9 Million
Emp.: 1,700
Watch Mfr & Distr
N.A.I.C.S.: 334519
Adrian Bosshard *(Dir)*

Universo SA (1)
Rue Louis-Joseph Chevrolet 43, 2300, La Chaux-de-Fonds, Switzerland
Tel.: (41) 32 911 9191
Web Site: https://www.universo.ch
Watch Mfr
N.A.I.C.S.: 334519

THE TAIKO BANK, LTD.

THE TAIKO BANK, LTD.

The Taiko Bank, Ltd.—(Continued)
5-6 Otedori 1-chome, Nagaoke, Niigata, 940-8651, Japan
Tel.: (81) 258364111
Web Site: http://www.taikobank.jp
8537—(TKS)
Rev.: $145,208,480
Assets: $10,742,122,520
Liabilities: $10,225,451,870
Net Worth: $516,670,650
Earnings: $165,250
Emp.: 1,244
Fiscal Year-end: 03/31/24
Banking Services
N.A.I.C.S.: 522110
Tetsuhiko Koide *(Chm)*

THE TAKIGAMI STEEL CONSTRUCTION CO., LTD.
1-1 Shinmeicho, Handa, 475-0826, Aichi, Japan
Tel.: (81) 569892101
Web Site: https://www.takigami.co.jp
Year Founded: 1937
5918—(TKS)
Rev.: $154,198,080
Assets: $386,810,590
Liabilities: $92,136,790
Net Worth: $294,673,800
Earnings: $6,517,460
Fiscal Year-end: 03/31/24
Steel Product Mfr & Distr
N.A.I.C.S.: 332312

THE THAI SETAKIJ INSURANCE PUBLIC COMPANY LIMITED
No 87 M Thai Tower Building All Seasons Place 15th Floor, Room No 1 & 4-6 Wireless Road Lumpini Pathumwan, Bangkok, 10330, Thailand
Tel.: (66) 28538888
Web Site: https://www.tsi.co.th
Year Founded: 1942
TSI—(THA)
Rev.: $16,115,135
Assets: $50,708,495
Liabilities: $45,688,060
Net Worth: $5,020,435
Earnings: ($4,655,535)
Fiscal Year-end: 12/31/23
General Insurance Services
N.A.I.C.S.: 524210
Tanaphol Bunwarut *(Chm & CEO)*

THE THAL INDUSTRIES CORPORATION LIMITED
23- Pir Khurshid Colony Gulgasht, Multan, Pakistan
Tel.: (92) 616524621
Web Site: https://www.thalindustries.com
Year Founded: 1953
TICL—(PSX)
Rev.: $110,831,051
Assets: $57,636,914
Liabilities: $24,687,589
Net Worth: $32,949,325
Earnings: $7,072,934
Emp.: 638
Fiscal Year-end: 09/30/23
Sugar Mfr
N.A.I.C.S.: 311314
Muhammad Shamim Khan *(CEO)*

Subsidiaries:

The Thal Industries Corporation Limited - Layyah Sugar Mill (1)
Layyah Sugar Mills, Layyah, Punjab, Pakistan
Tel.: (92) 606411981
Sugar Mfr
N.A.I.C.S.: 311314

The Thal Industries Corporation Limited - Safina Sugar Mill (1)
3KM Faisalabad-Sargoda Road, Chiniot District, Lalian, Pakistan
Tel.: (92) 4776299990
Sugar Mfr
N.A.I.C.S.: 311314

THE TINLEY BEVERAGE COMPANY INC.
77 King Street West Suite 2905, Toronto, M5K 1H1, ON, Canada
Tel.: (416) 402-3365 Ca
Web Site: http://drinktinley.com
Year Founded: 2005
TNYBF—(OTCQX)
Rev.: $237,944
Assets: $8,945,124
Liabilities: $2,210,917
Net Worth: $6,734,207
Earnings: ($6,015,710)
Fiscal Year-end: 12/31/20
Investment Services
N.A.I.C.S.: 523999
Jeffrey Maser *(Founder)*

THE TOA REINSURANCE COMPANY, LTD.
6-5 Kanda-Surugadai 3-chome, Chiyoda-ku, Tokyo, 101-8703, Japan
Tel.: (81) 332533171
Web Site: http://www.toare.co.jp
Year Founded: 1940
Sales Range: $125-149.9 Million
Emp.: 328
Property & Casualty Reinsurance; Accident & Health Insurance Provider
N.A.I.C.S.: 524126
Tomoatsu Noguchi *(Pres & CEO)*

Subsidiaries:

The Toa Reinsurance Company of America (1)
177 Madison Ave, Morristown, NJ 07962-1930 (100%)
Tel.: (973) 898-9480
Web Site: http://www.toare.com
Property & Casualty Reinsurance
N.A.I.C.S.: 524126
James A. Pilla *(Chief Underwriting Officer & Exec VP)*

THE TOCHIGI BANK, LTD.
2-1-18 Nishi, Utsunomiya, 320-8680, Tochigi, Japan
Tel.: (81) 286331241
Web Site: https://www.tochigibank.co.jp
Year Founded: 1942
8550—(TKS)
Rev.: $299,274,360
Assets: $21,909,122,620
Liabilities: $20,905,982,410
Net Worth: $1,003,140,210
Earnings: $19,830
Emp.: 799
Fiscal Year-end: 03/31/24
Banking Services
N.A.I.C.S.: 522110
Junnosuke Kuromoto *(Chm & Pres)*

THE TODD CORPORATION LIMITED
Level 15 The Todd Building 95 Customhouse Quay, Wellington, 6011, New Zealand
Tel.: (64) 4 471 6555 NZ
Web Site: http://www.toddcorporation.com
Year Founded: 1884
Emp.: 800
Investment Holding Company
N.A.I.C.S.: 551112
Paul Moore *(Exec VP-Todd Energy Intl)*

Subsidiaries:

Todd Energy International Limited (1)
Level 15 The Todd Building 95 Customhouse Quay, Wellington, 6011, New Zealand
Tel.: (64) 4 471 6555
Web Site: http://www.toddcorporation.com
Holding Company; Oil & Gas Exploration & Extraction; Methanol Mfr
N.A.I.C.S.: 551112
Paul Moore *(CEO)*

Subsidiary (US):

South Louisiana Methanol LP (2)
12912 Hill Country Blvd Ste F-225, Austin, TX 78738
Tel.: (512) 394-7352
Web Site: http://www.southlouisianamethanol.com
Methanol Mfr
N.A.I.C.S.: 325194
Paul Moore *(CEO & Mng Dir)*

Todd Energy Limited (1)
Level 15 The Todd Building 95 Customhouse Quay, Wellington, 6011, New Zealand
Tel.: (64) 4 471 6555
Web Site: http://www.toddenergy.co.nz
Oil & Gas Exploration & Extraction
N.A.I.C.S.: 211120
David Salisbury *(Gen Mgr-Comml & Plng)*

Todd Property Group Limited (1)
Level 28 PWC Building 188 Quay Street, Auckland, 1010, New Zealand
Tel.: (64) 9 377 7677
Web Site: http://www.toddproperty.co.nz
Commercial & Residential Property Developer Services
N.A.I.C.S.: 237210
Evan Davies *(Mng Dir)*

THE TOHO BANK, LTD.
3-25 Omachi, Fukushima, 960-8633, Fukushima, Japan
Tel.: (81) 245233131
Web Site: https://www.tohobank.co.jp
Year Founded: 1941
8346—(TKS)
Rev.: $389,884,240
Assets: $44,674,141,090
Liabilities: $43,311,297,900
Net Worth: $1,362,843,190
Earnings: $23,135
Fiscal Year-end: 03/31/24
Banking Services
N.A.I.C.S.: 522110
Minoru Sato *(Pres)*

Subsidiaries:

The Toho Card Co., Ltd. (1)
4-4 Omachi Toho Square Building 4th Fl, Fukushima, 960-8041, Fukushima Prefecture, Japan (5%)
Tel.: (81) 245211002
Web Site: https://www.tohocard.co.jp
Credit Card Services
N.A.I.C.S.: 522210

The Toho Computer Service Co., Ltd. (1)
3-3 Sakurada Hirano Izaka-machi, Fukushima, 960-0231, Japan (7.69%)
Tel.: (81) 245412140
Data Processing Services
N.A.I.C.S.: 518210

The Toho Credit Service Co., Ltd. (1)
4-4 Omachi, Fukushima, 960-8041, Fukushima Prefecture, Japan
Tel.: (81) 245241700
Emp.: 17
Activities Related to Credit Intermediation
N.A.I.C.S.: 522390

The Toho Lease Co., Ltd. (1)
5-10 Banseicho, Fukushima, 960-8033, Japan (50%)
Tel.: (81) 245211441
Plant Equipment Finance Leasing Services
N.A.I.C.S.: 523999

Toho Securities Co., Ltd. (1)
3-25 Omachi 3rd Floor Toho Bank Main Store, Fukushima, Japan
Tel.: (81) 24 523 3284
Web Site: https://toho-sec.co.jp

INTERNATIONAL PUBLIC

Security System Services
N.A.I.C.S.: 561621

THE TOHOKU BANK LTD.
3-1 Uchimaru, Morioka, 020-8606, Iwate, Japan
Tel.: (81) 196516161
Web Site: https://www.tohoku-bank.co.jp
Year Founded: 1950
8349—(TKS)
Rev.: $97,345,470
Assets: $6,693,920,560
Liabilities: $6,433,235,380
Net Worth: $260,685,180
Earnings: $165,250
Emp.: 1,311
Fiscal Year-end: 03/31/24
Commercial Banking Services
N.A.I.C.S.: 522110
Naoto Murakami *(Chm & Pres)*

THE TOPAZ GROUP, INC.
20/11 Soi Anamai-Ngamcharoen 31 Rama 2 Road, Ta-Kham Bangkatien, Bangkok, 10150, Thailand
Tel.: (66) 24179348 NV
Web Site: http://www.creativegem.com
Sales Range: $10-24.9 Million
Emp.: 2,200
Holding Company
N.A.I.C.S.: 339910
Peter J. Brongers *(CFO)*

Subsidiaries:

Creative Gems & Jewelry PCL (1)
20/11 Soi Anamai-Ngamcharoen 31 Rama 2 Road, Ta-Kham Bangkhuntien, Bangkok, Thailand
Tel.: (66) 24179348
Web Site: http://www.creativegem.com
Jewelry Mfr
N.A.I.C.S.: 339910

THE TORIGOE CO., LTD.
5-1 Hie-machi, Hakata-ku, Fukuoka, 812-0014, Japan
Tel.: (81) 924777110
Web Site: https://www.the-torigoe.co.jp
Year Founded: 1935
2009—(TKS)
Rev.: $174,969,510
Assets: $298,221,810
Liabilities: $57,718,500
Net Worth: $240,503,310
Earnings: $6,675,270
Fiscal Year-end: 12/31/22
Flour Product Mfr
N.A.I.C.S.: 311211
Toru Torikoshi *(Chm & Pres)*

THE TORONTO-DOMINION BANK
c/o General Counsel s Office Toronto-Dominion Centre, PO Box 1, Toronto, M5K 1A2, ON, Canada
Tel.: (416) 308-6963 ON
Web Site: http://www.td.com
Year Founded: 1855
TD—(NYSE)
International Banking Services
N.A.I.C.S.: 522110
Bharat B. Masrani *(Grp Pres & CEO)*

Subsidiaries:

Epoch Investment Partners, Inc. (1)
399 Park Ave 31st Fl, New York, NY 10022
Tel.: (212) 303-7200
Web Site: http://www.eipny.com
Sales Range: $25-49.9 Million
Emp.: 60
Investment Advisor
N.A.I.C.S.: 523940
William W. Priest *(Chm, Co-Chief Investment Officer & Portfolio Mgr)*

Green Line Investor Service (1)

AND PRIVATE COMPANIES — THE TORONTO-DOMINION BANK

77 Bloor Street West, Toronto, M5S 1M2, ON, Canada
Tel.: (416) 977-8077
Web Site: http://www.tdwaterhouse.ca
Sales Range: $50-74.9 Million
Emp.: 73
Securities Brokerage
N.A.I.C.S.: 523150

Meloche Monnex Inc. (1)
50 Place Cremazie 12th Floor, Montreal, H2P 1B6, QC, Canada
Tel.: (514) 382-6060
Web Site: http://www.melochemonnex.com
Sales Range: $1-4.9 Billion
Emp.: 3,000
Direct-Response Property & Casualty Insurance
N.A.I.C.S.: 524128

NatWest Stockbrokers Limited (1)
Broker Line, PO Box 549, Leeds, LS1 4WN, United Kingdom (100%)
Tel.: (44) 8706004080
Retail Brokers & Investment
N.A.I.C.S.: 531210
Jeff Williams (Sr Dir-Retail & Premium Banking)

TD Ameritrade Inc. (1)
100 Broadway, New York, NY 10005
Tel.: (212) 294-2910
Web Site: http://www.tdameritrade.com
Online Brokerages Services; Banking Services
N.A.I.C.S.: 523150

Subsidiary (Domestic):

TD Waterhouse Bank (2)
1 Harborside Financial Plz 4A 8th Fl, Jersey City, NJ 07310
Sales Range: $25-49.9 Million
Emp.: 47
National Commercial Banks
N.A.I.C.S.: 522110

TD Waterhouse Investor Services, Inc.
PO Box 2630, Jersey City, NJ 07303-2630
Web Site: http://www.tdwaterhouse.com
Security Brokers
N.A.I.C.S.: 523150

TD Auto Finance Services Inc. (1)
2425 Matheson Blvd E 3rd Fl, Mississauga, L4W 5N7, ON, Canada
Tel.: (416) 331-7576
Web Site: http://www.tdautofinanceservicesinc.ca
Motor Vehicle Financing Services
N.A.I.C.S.: 522220

TD Bank US Holding Company (1)
2 Portland Sq, Portland, ME 04112 (100%)
Tel.: (207) 761-8500
Web Site: http://www.tdbank.com
Sales Range: $5-14.9 Billion
Emp.: 20,953
Bank Holding Company; Executive Regional Managing Office
N.A.I.C.S.: 551111

Co-Headquarters (Domestic):

TD Bank US Holding Company - Cherry Hill (2)
Commerce Atrium 1701 Rte 70 E, Cherry Hill, NJ 08034-5400
Tel.: (856) 751-9000
Sales Range: $1-4.9 Billion
Emp.: 12,700
Bank Holding Company; Executive Regional Managing Office
N.A.I.C.S.: 551111
Josephine Battaglia Gallo (Asst VP)

Subsidiary (Domestic):

TD Bank, N.A. (3)
2035 Limestone Rd, Wilmington, DE 19808
Tel.: (302) 351-4560
Web Site: http://www.tdbank.com
Commercial Bank
N.A.I.C.S.: 522110
Ernie Diaz (Exec VP & Head-Consumer Distr)

Subsidiary (Domestic):

TD Auto Finance LLC (4)
27777 Inkster Rd, Farmington Hills, MI 48334-5326
Tel.: (248) 427-6800
Web Site: http://www.tdautofinance.com
Automobile Financing Services
N.A.I.C.S.: 522220

TD Canada Trust (1)
161 Bay Street, Toronto, M5J 2T2, ON, Canada (100%)
Tel.: (416) 361-5400
Web Site: http://www.tdcanadatrust.com
Sales Range: $50-74.9 Million
Emp.: 20
Full Banking Services; Estate & Trust Services
N.A.I.C.S.: 523991

TD Financing Service Inc. (1)
Station A, PO Box 4086, Toronto, M5W 5K3, ON, Canada
Tel.: (416) 463-4422
Web Site: http://www.tdfinancingservices.com
Sales Range: $100-124.9 Million
Emp.: 250
Financial Lending Services
N.A.I.C.S.: 525990

TD General Insurance Company (1)
2161 Yonge St Floor 4, Toronto, M4S 3A6, ON, Canada
Tel.: (416) 484-1112
Home & Automobile Insurance Services
N.A.I.C.S.: 524126
Ken Lalonde (VP)

TD Global Finance (1)
Level 2 Plaza 2 Custom House Plaza International, Financial Services Center, Dublin, Ireland
Tel.: (353) 1 670 2611
Web Site: http://www.tdsecurities.com
Sales Range: $50-74.9 Million
Emp.: 19
Financial Management Services
N.A.I.C.S.: 523999

TD Home and Auto Insurance Company (1)
304 The E Mall 6th Fl, Toronto, M9B 6B7, ON, Canada
Tel.: (866) 454-8910
Web Site: http://www.mytdiservice.com
Home & Automobile Insurance Services
N.A.I.C.S.: 524126

TD Ireland Unlimited Company (1)
One Molesworth Street, Dublin, D02 RF29, Ireland
Tel.: (353) 1 267 6000
Financial Services
N.A.I.C.S.: 521110

TD Securities Inc. (1)
TD Bank Tower 66 Wellington Street West, PO Box 1, Toronto, M5K 1A2, ON, Canada
Tel.: (416) 307-9360
Web Site: http://www.tdsecurities.com
Sales Range: $50-74.9 Million
Emp.: 100
Securities Brokerage Services
N.A.I.C.S.: 523150
Malcolm Lang (CFO & COO)

Subsidiary (US):

Cowen, Inc. (2)
599 Lexington Ave, New York, NY 10022
Tel.: (646) 562-1010
Web Site: http://www.cowen.com
Rev.: $2,112,799,000
Assets: $8,748,814,000
Liabilities: $7,573,210,000
Net Worth: $1,175,604,000
Earnings: $288,819,000
Emp.: 1,534
Fiscal Year-end: 12/31/2021
Investment Banking Services
N.A.I.C.S.: 523999
Stephen A. Lasota (Mng Dir & CFO)

Subsidiary (Domestic):

ATM Execution LLC (3)
599 Lexington Ave, New York, NY 10022
Tel.: (646) 562-1701
Investment Advisory Services
N.A.I.C.S.: 523940

Subsidiary (Non-US):

Cowen Asia Ltd (3)
22nd Floor LKF29 29 Wyndham Street, Central, China (Hong Kong)
Tel.: (852) 37085631
Investment Banking Services
N.A.I.C.S.: 523150

Subsidiary (Domestic):

Cowen Execution Holdco LLC (3)
1633 Broadway 48th Fl, New York, NY 10019
Tel.: (646) 690-3292
Emp.: 750
Holding Company; Investment Trading, Transaction Execution & Securities Brokerage Services
N.A.I.C.S.: 551112

Subsidiary (Domestic):

Cowen Execution Services LLC (4)
1633 Broadway 48th Fl, New York, NY 10019
Tel.: (646) 690-3292
Web Site: http://www.cowen.com
Investment Trade Execution Services
N.A.I.C.S.: 522320

Westminster Research Associates LLC (4)
1633 Broadway 48th Fl, New York, NY 10019
Tel.: (646) 690-3292
Web Site: http://www.cowen.com
Investment Research Services
N.A.I.C.S.: 523940
Christopher Tiscornia (CEO)

Subsidiary (Non-US):

Cowen Execution Services Limited (3)
16-18 New Bridge St, London, EC4V 6AG, United Kingdom
Tel.: (44) 2070700138
Security Contract Brokerage Services
N.A.I.C.S.: 523150
Noah Garland (Head-Intl Trading)

Cowen Germany AG (3)
Universitatsstrasse 14, 04109, Leipzig, Germany
Tel.: (49) 341983790
Financial Advisory Services
N.A.I.C.S.: 523940

Subsidiary (Domestic):

Cowen Prime Services LLC (3)
1010 Franklin Ave Ste 303, Garden City, NY 11530-2900
Tel.: (516) 746-5757
Web Site: http://www.conceptcapital.com
Investment Banking & Securities Dealing
N.A.I.C.S.: 523150

Cowen Prime Services Trading LLC (3)
1 Ferry Bldg Ste 255, San Francisco, CA 94111
Tel.: (415) 677-1500
Web Site: http://www.conifersecurities.com
Sales Range: $10-24.9 Million
Emp.: 120
Security Brokers & Dealers
N.A.I.C.S.: 523150
William Vastardis (Chm)

Cowen Structured Credit Group LLC (3)
599 Lexington Ave, New York, NY 10022
Tel.: (212) 845-7900
Emp.: 24
Investment Management Service
N.A.I.C.S.: 523940

Cowen Structured Holdings Inc. (3)
599 Lexington Ave Fl 19, New York, NY 10022
Tel.: (212) 845-7900
Investment Banking Services
N.A.I.C.S.: 523150
Steven Lasota (CFO)

Subsidiary (Non-US):

Cowen and Company (Asia) Limited (3)
22nd Floor LKF29 29 Wyndham Street, Central, China (Hong Kong)
Tel.: (852) 37085631
Investment Banking Services
N.A.I.C.S.: 523940

Subsidiary (Domestic):

Cowen and Company, LLC (3)
599 Lexington Ave, New York, NY 10022-7773
Tel.: (212) 845-7990
Web Site: http://www.cowen.com
Investment Banking Services
N.A.I.C.S.: 523150
Parker Anders Weil (Vice Chm-Investment Banking)

Subsidiary (Non-US):

Hollenfels Re SA (3)
97 Rue Jean-Pierre Michels, 4243, Esch-sur-Alzette, Luxembourg
Tel.: (352) 261735
Reinsurance Carrier Services
N.A.I.C.S.: 524130

Subsidiary (Domestic):

Margate Capital Partners Fund LP (3)
145 W 57th St 15th Fl, New York, NY 10019
Tel.: (212) 609-0891
Mutual Fund Agency Services
N.A.I.C.S.: 523150

Subsidiary (Non-US):

Quarton International AG (3)
Theatinerstrasse 7, 80333, Munich, Germany
Tel.: (49) 8920003930
Web Site: http://www.quartoninternational.com
Financial Investment Services
N.A.I.C.S.: 523999
Rolf Holtmann (Partner)

Quarton International AG (3)
Winkelwiese 2, 8001, Zurich, Switzerland
Tel.: (41) 442654080
Financial Investment Services
N.A.I.C.S.: 523999
Tobias Seige (Partner)

Subsidiary (Domestic):

Ramius LLC (3)
599 Lexington Ave, New York, NY 10022
Tel.: (212) 845-7900
Web Site: http://www.ramius.com
Sales Range: $75-99.9 Million
Emp.: 300
Alternative Investment Management Services
N.A.I.C.S.: 523940

Ramius Trading Strategies LLC (3)
599 Lexington Ave, New York, NY 10022
Tel.: (212) 823-0270
Web Site: http://www.cowen.com
Investment Banking Services
N.A.I.C.S.: 523150

TriArtisan Capital Advisors LLC (3)
830 3rd Ave Fl 4, New York, NY 10022
Tel.: (212) 609-0620
Web Site: http://www.triartisan.com
Holding Company
N.A.I.C.S.: 551112
Gerald Cromack (Co-Founder & Mng Dir)

Subsidiary (Domestic):

EnergySolutions of Utah, Inc. (4)
423 W 300 South Ste 200, Salt Lake City, UT 84101
Tel.: (801) 649-2000
Web Site: http://www.energysolutions.com
Rev.: $1,804,398,000
Assets: $2,420,543,000
Liabilities: $2,152,328,000
Net Worth: $268,215,000
Earnings: ($54,665,000)
Emp.: 4,950
Fiscal Year-end: 12/31/2013
Holding Company; Nuclear Material Recycling, Processing & Disposal Services
N.A.I.C.S.: 551112
Mark A. Walker (VP-Mktg & Media Rels)

Subsidiary (Domestic):

Cabrera Services, Inc. (5)

THE TORONTO-DOMINION BANK

The Toronto-Dominion Bank—(Continued)

50 Founders Plz Ste 207, East Hartford, CT 06108
Tel.: (860) 569-0095
Web Site: https://www.cabreraservices.com
Rev.: $18,900,000
Emp.: 71
Scientific & Technical Consulting Services
N.A.I.C.S.: 541690
Lorenzo Cabrera *(CEO)*

EnergySolutions, LLC (5)
299 S Main St Ste 1700, Salt Lake City, UT 84111
Tel.: (801) 649-2000
Web Site: http://www.energysolutions.com
Sales Range: $25-49.9 Million
Emp.: 100
Nuclear Material Recycling & Disposal Services
N.A.I.C.S.: 562211
Mark Walker *(VP-Mktg & Media Rels)*

Subsidiary (Domestic):

Chem-Nuclear Systems, LLC (6)
Center Point 2 100 Center Park Cir Ste 100, Columbia, SC 29210-8200 **(100%)**
Tel.: (803) 256-0450
Web Site: http://www.chemnuclear.com
Sales Range: $50-74.9 Million
Operates Low Level Radioactive Waste Disposal Facilities
N.A.I.C.S.: 562211
Steve Creimer *(Pres)*

Branch (Domestic):

EnergySolutions - Danbury (6)
100 Mill Plain Rd 2nd Fl Ste 106, Danbury, CT 06811-5188
Tel.: (203) 797-8301
Web Site: http://www.energysolutions.com
Waste Management
N.A.I.C.S.: 562112
Robert McPeak *(Gen Mgr)*

Subsidiary (Domestic):

EnergySolutions Federal EPC, Inc. (6)
2345 Stevens Dr Ste 240, Richland, WA 99354-1878
Tel.: (509) 375-9800
Hazardous Materials Transportation Services
N.A.I.C.S.: 484121

EnergySolutions Services, Inc. (6)
299 S Main St Ste 1700, Salt Lake City, UT 84111
Tel.: (801) 649-2000
Web Site: http://www.energysolutions.com
Sales Range: $25-49.9 Million
Nuclear Material Recycling & Disposal Services
N.A.I.C.S.: 562211

EnergySolutions, Spent Fuel Division, Inc. (6)
2105 S Bascom Ave Ste 230, Campbell, CA 95008 **(100%)**
Tel.: (408) 558-3500
Web Site: http://www.energysolutions.com
Sales Range: $25-49.9 Million
Emp.: 25
Waste Management
N.A.I.C.S.: 562112

Manufacturing Sciences Corporation (6)
804 S Illinois Ave, Oak Ridge, TN 37830 **(100%)**
Tel.: (865) 481-0455
Web Site: http://www.mfgsci.com
Sales Range: $25-49.9 Million
Metal Processing & Manufacturing from Specialty Metals & Depleted Uranium
N.A.I.C.S.: 332999
Richard B. Krutzik *(Sls Mgr)*

Subsidiary (Domestic):

Williams Industrial Services Group Inc. (5)
100 Cresesnt Ctr Pkwy Ste 1240, Tucker, GA 30084
Tel.: (770) 879-4400
Web Site: http://www.wisgrp.com
Rev.: $238,119,000
Assets: $108,498,000
Liabilities: $84,100,000
Net Worth: $24,398,000
Earnings: ($13,678,000)
Emp.: 506
Fiscal Year-end: 12/31/2022
Holding Company; Power Equipment Designer & Mfr
N.A.I.C.S.: 551112
Tracy D. Pagliara *(Pres & CEO)*

Subsidiary (Non-US):

Braden Manufacturing SA de CV (6)
Km 11 2 Libramiento Noroeste, San Pedro, 66000, Garza Garcia, 66000, Mexico
Tel.: (52) 81100161
Power Generating Equipment Mfr
N.A.I.C.S.: 221118

Subsidiary (Domestic):

Hetsco, Inc. (6)
1725 N Graham Rd, Franklin, IN 46131
Tel.: (317) 535-4315
Web Site: http://www.hetsco.com
Industrial Equipment Repair Services
N.A.I.C.S.: 811490
Sam Willard *(Pres & COO)*

Koontz-Wagner Custom Controls Holdings, LLC (6)
3801 Voorde Dr, South Bend, IN 46628
Tel.: (574) 387-5802
Web Site: http://www.koontz-wagner.com
Emp.: 200
Holding Company
N.A.I.C.S.: 551112

Williams Industrial Services Group, L.L.C. (6)
100 Crescent Centre Pkwy Ste 1240, Tucker, GA 30084
Tel.: (770) 879-4400
Web Site: http://www.wisgrp.com
Fiscal Year-end: 12/31/2019
Industrial Building Construction Services
N.A.I.C.S.: 236210

Williams Plant Services, LLC (6)
2076 W Park Pl Blvd, Stone Mountain, GA 30087
Tel.: (770) 879-4000
Industrial Maintenance Services
N.A.I.C.S.: 237990
Bob Badger *(VP-Nuclear Ops)*

Williams Specialty Services, LLC (6)
100 Crescent Ctr Pkwy Ste 1240, Tucker, GA 30084
Tel.: (770) 879-4800
Industrial Building Construction Services
N.A.I.C.S.: 236210

Holding (Domestic):

Hooters of America, LLC (4)
1815 The Exchange SE, Atlanta, GA 30339-2027
Tel.: (770) 951-2040
Web Site: http://www.hooters.com
Restaurants & Sports Bars Owner, Operator & Franchisor
N.A.I.C.S.: 722511
Stephen Sweetman *(Sr Dir-Domestic Dev)*

Subsidiary (Non-US):

TD Securities (Singapore) Limited (2)
1 Temasek Ave, 15 02 Millennia Tower, Singapore, 039192, Singapore
Tel.: (65) 64346280
Web Site: http://www.tdsecurities.com
Sales Range: $50-74.9 Million
Emp.: 90
International Banking Services
N.A.I.C.S.: 522299

Subsidiary (US):

TD Securities (USA) LLC (2)
31 W 52nd St Fl 18, New York, NY 10019-6118 **(100%)**
Tel.: (212) 827-7000
Web Site: http://www.tdsecurities.com
Sales Range: $50-74.9 Million
Emp.: 40
International Banking
N.A.I.C.S.: 522299

Branch (Domestic):

TD Securities (USA) LLC - Chicago (3)
230 S LaSalle St Fl 6, Chicago, IL 60604
Tel.: (312) 244-2222
Web Site: http://www.tdsecurities.com
Sales Range: $25-49.9 Million
Emp.: 3
International Banking Services
N.A.I.C.S.: 513210

TD Securities (USA) LLC - Houston (3)
909 Fannin St, Houston, TX 77010
Tel.: (713) 653-8200
Web Site: http://www.tdsecurities.com
Sales Range: $50-74.9 Million
Emp.: 14
International Banking Services
N.A.I.C.S.: 523150

Subsidiary (Non-US):

TD Securities (United Kingdom) Ltd. (2)
60 Threadneedle Street, London, EC2R 8HP, United Kingdom **(100%)**
Tel.: (44) 2079200272
Web Site: http://www.tdbank.ca
Sales Range: $75-99.9 Million
International Banking Services
N.A.I.C.S.: 522299

TD Securities Australia Ltd. (2)
24th Fl 9 Castlereagh St, Sydney, 2000, NSW, Australia **(100%)**
Tel.: (61) 296198888
Web Site: http://www.tdsecurities.com
Sales Range: $25-49.9 Million
Emp.: 35
International Banking Services
N.A.I.C.S.: 522299

TD Securities Japan Inc. (2)
Kamiya Cho M T Bldg 16F 3 20 Toranomon 4 Chome, Tokyo, 105 0001, Japan **(100%)**
Tel.: (81) 334319040
Web Site: http://www.tdsecurities.com
Sales Range: $50-74.9 Million
Emp.: 20
International Banking
N.A.I.C.S.: 522299

TD Waterhouse Canada Inc. (1)
120 Adelaide St W Ste 916, Toronto, M5H 1T1, ON, Canada **(100%)**
Tel.: (416) 308-1600
Web Site: http://www.tdwaterhouse.ca
Discount Brokerage Firm
N.A.I.C.S.: 523150

TD Waterhouse Private Investment Counsel Inc. (1)
66 Wellington Street West TD Tower 15th Floor, Toronto, M5K 1A2, ON, Canada
Tel.: (416) 308-1933
Portfolio Management Services
N.A.I.C.S.: 523940

TDAM USA Inc. (1)
31 W 52nd St, New York, NY 10019
Tel.: (212) 827-7061
Asset Management Services
N.A.I.C.S.: 523940

Toronto Dominion (New York) LLC (1)
31 W 52nd St, New York, NY 10019
Tel.: (212) 827-7000
Commercial Banking Services
N.A.I.C.S.: 522110

Toronto Dominion (South East Asia) Limited (1)
1 Temasek Avenue No 15-02 Millenia Tower, Singapore, 039192, Singapore
Tel.: (65) 6434 6280
Commercial Banking Services
N.A.I.C.S.: 522110

Toronto Dominion Holdings (U.K.) Limited (1)
60 Threadneedle Street, London, EC2R 8AP, United Kingdom
Tel.: (44) 2079200272
Sales Range: $100-124.9 Million
Emp.: 20
Financial Management Services

INTERNATIONAL PUBLIC

N.A.I.C.S.: 523999
Malcolm Lang *(Gen Mgr)*

Toronto Dominion International Inc. (1)
4th Fl Cgi Tower Warrens, Saint Michael, Barbados
Tel.: (246) 421 8760
Commercial Banking Services
N.A.I.C.S.: 522110

THE TOTTORI BANK LTD.

171 Eirakuonsen-cho, Tottori, 680-8686, Japan
Tel.: (81) 857370264
Web Site: http://www.tottoribank.co.jp
Year Founded: 1921
8383—(TKS)
Rev.: $96,810,060
Assets: $7,572,568,030
Liabilities: $7,241,916,000
Net Worth: $330,652,030
Earnings: $165,250
Emp.: 552
Fiscal Year-end: 03/31/24
Banking Services
N.A.I.C.S.: 522110

THE TOWA BANK, LTD.

2-12-6 Hon-machi, Maebashi, 371 8560, Gunma, Japan
Tel.: (81) 272341111
Web Site: https://www.towabank.co.jp
Year Founded: 1917
8558—(TKS)
Rev.: $225,652,180
Assets: $15,901,372,940
Liabilities: $15,117,393,890
Net Worth: $783,979,050
Earnings: $231,350
Emp.: 1,417
Fiscal Year-end: 03/31/24
Banking Services
N.A.I.C.S.: 522110
Kunimitsu Yoshinaga *(Exec VP)*

Subsidiaries:

The Towa Card Co., Ltd. (1)
2-14-8 Honmachi, Maebashi, 371-0023, Gunma, Japan
Tel.: (81) 272212200
Web Site: https://www.towacard.co.jp
Credit Intermediation
N.A.I.C.S.: 522390
Akira Sekihara *(Pres)*

The Towagin Lease Co., Ltd. (1)
2-14-8 Honmachi New Information Building, Maebashi, 371-0023, Gunma, Japan
Tel.: (81) 272247481
Web Site: https://www.twbl.co.jp
Machinery & Equipment Rental & Leasing
N.A.I.C.S.: 532420

THE TRAFALGAR GROUP

The Emporium Building, Ste 657 48 Carlaville Rd, Hamilton, HM12, Bermuda
Tel.: (441) 2922332
Web Site: http://www.trafalgar-group.com
Year Founded: 1994
Sales Range: $10-24.9 Million
Emp.: 100
Financial Management & Investment Services
N.A.I.C.S.: 523999
David Sheppard *(Partner)*

Subsidiaries:

Trafalgar Securities Limited (1)
Faulkner House, 108 Pitts Bay, Pembroke, HM 08, Bermuda
Tel.: (441) 292 2332
Investment Banking & Securities Dealing
N.A.I.C.S.: 523150

THE TRANG SEAFOOD PRODUCTS PUBLIC COMPANY LIMITED

29 Moo 6 Kantang Rd Khuan Pring,
Muang, Trang, 92000, Thailand
Tel.: (66) 75582134
Web Site: http://www.trstrang.com
Year Founded: 1989
Sales Range: $25-49.9 Million
Frozen Seafood Mfr
N.A.I.C.S.: 311710
Bunchoo Saisakphong *(CEO)*

THE TRAVEL NETWORK CORP.
1920 Avenue Road, Toronto, M5M 4A1, ON, Canada
Tel.: (416) 789-3271
Web Site: http://www.thetravelnetwork.com
Year Founded: 1985
Rev.: $13,563,412
Emp.: 40
Travel & Tour Agency Services
N.A.I.C.S.: 561510
Ruby Silvertown *(Owner & Pres)*

THE TRENDLINES GROUP LTD.
The Trendlines Building Misgav Business Park, 17 T'chelet Street, Misgav, 2017400, Israel
Tel.: (972) 722607000
Web Site: https://www.trendlines.com
TRNGF—(OTCQB)
Rev.: $8,147,000
Assets: $116,844,000
Liabilities: $20,509,000
Net Worth: $96,335,000
Earnings: ($3,951,000)
Emp.: 48
Fiscal Year-end: 12/31/20
Technology Investment
N.A.I.C.S.: 523999
Todd Dollinger *(Co-Chm & Co-CEO)*

THE TRUST BANK LIMITED
Shadhinata Tower Bir Srestha Shaheed Jahangir Gate, Dhaka Cantonment, Dhaka, 1206, Bangladesh
Tel.: (880) 2448700609
Web Site: https://www.tblbd.com
TRUSTBANK—(DHA)
Rev.: $207,165,602
Assets: $4,134,910,143
Liabilities: $3,930,645,080
Net Worth: $204,265,063
Earnings: $20,864,570
Emp.: 1,951
Fiscal Year-end: 12/31/20
Banking Services
N.A.I.C.S.: 522110
Mohammad Mehdi Hassan *(Head-Recovery & Monitoring Div)*

THE UAP GROUP LIMITED
Cambridge House, Le Truchot, St Peter Port, Guernsey, GY1 3HH, United Kingdom
Tel.: (44) 2078719548
Web Site: https://theuapgroup.com
Year Founded: 2020
Financial Services
N.A.I.C.S.: 523999

THE UGAR SUGAR WORKS LIMITED
Mahaveer Nagar, Sangli, 416416, Maharashtra, India
Tel.: (91) 2332623717
Web Site: https://web.ugarsugar.com
UGARSUGAR—(NSE)
Rev.: $153,402,795
Assets: $121,952,840
Liabilities: $110,946,859
Net Worth: $11,005,981
Earnings: $2,327,407
Emp.: 1,309
Fiscal Year-end: 03/31/21
Sugar Mfr
N.A.I.C.S.: 311313
Prafulla V. Shirgaokar *(Chm)*
Subsidiaries:

Galaxy Machinery Pvt. Ltd. (1)
Plot Plot no 29 A Survey No 336/1 Udyambag, Belgaum, 590008, India
Tel.: (91) 8312405771
CNC Turning Machine Mfr
N.A.I.C.S.: 332721

SB Reshellers Pvt. Limited (1)
392 E-ward Shahupuri, Kolhapur, 416001, Maharashtra, India
Tel.: (91) 2312658297
Web Site: https://www.sbreshellers.com
Mill Equipment Mfr
N.A.I.C.S.: 333519
Sachin Shirgaokar *(Mng Dir)*

Tara Tiles Pvt. Ltd. (1)
392 E Shahupuri, Kolhapur, 416001, Maharashtra, India
Tel.: (91) 2312657498
Web Site: http://www.taratiles.co.in
Tile & Paving Block Mfr
N.A.I.C.S.: 327120

Ugar Quality Packaging Pvt. Ltd. (1)
G-1/1 MIDC, Mirjole, Ratnagiri, 415 639, Maharashtra, India
Tel.: (91) 2352229501
Packaging Material Mfr & Distr
N.A.I.C.S.: 326112

iResearch Services Pvt. Ltd. (1)
Cerebrum IT Park B3 Level 4 - 2, kalyani nagar, Pune, 411 014, India
Tel.: (91) 2067253800
Business Research Services
N.A.I.C.S.: 541910

THE UNION ADVERTISING AGENCY
Union House 18 Inverleith Terrace, Edinburgh, EH3 5NS, United Kingdom
Tel.: (44) 131 625 6000 UK
Web Site: http://www.union.co.uk
Year Founded: 1996
Sales Range: $10-24.9 Million
Emp.: 70
Full Service
N.A.I.C.S.: 541810
Ian McAteer *(Owner)*
Subsidiaries:

The Union Advertising Agency (1)
Union House 66 St Ln, Leeds, LS8 2DQ, United Kingdom
Tel.: (44) 113 266 6050
Web Site: http://www.union.co.uk
Sales Range: Less than $1 Million
Emp.: 10
N.A.I.C.S.: 541810
Clive Goldstein *(Mng Dir)*

Union Digital (1)
Union House 18 Inverleith Ter, Edinburgh, EH3 5NS, United Kingdom
Tel.: (44) 131 625 6000
Web Site: http://www.union.co.uk
Sales Range: Less than $1 Million
Emp.: 8
N.A.I.C.S.: 541810
Ian McAteer *(Chm & Mng Dir)*

Union Direct (1)
Union House 18 Inverleith Ter, Edinburgh, EH3 5NS, United Kingdom
Tel.: (44) 131 467 6851
Web Site: http://www.union.co.uk
Direct Marketing
N.A.I.C.S.: 541860
Gus Chalmers *(Mng Dir)*

THE UNION MOSAIC INDUSTRY PUBLIC COMPANY LIMITED
29th Floor Chamnan Phenjati Business Center Building 65 Rama 9 Road, Huai Khwang, Bangkok, 10310, Thailand
Tel.: (66) 2487007
Web Site: https://www.umi-tiles.com
Year Founded: 1973
UMI—(THA)
Rev.: $79,581,584
Assets: $87,142,924
Liabilities: $43,043,174
Net Worth: $44,099,750
Earnings: ($968,926)
Emp.: 655
Fiscal Year-end: 12/31/23
Granites & Ceramic Tiles Mfr
N.A.I.C.S.: 327120
Serani Phenchat *(Chm & Mng Dir-Acting)*

THE UNITE GROUP PLC
South Quay House Temple Back, Bristol, BS1 6FL, United Kingdom
Tel.: (44) 1173027000
Web Site: http://www.unite-group.co.uk
UTG—(LSE)
Rev.: $292,724,432
Assets: $7,103,455,268
Liabilities: $2,677,288,068
Net Worth: $4,426,167,200
Earnings: ($165,913,384)
Emp.: 1,900
Fiscal Year-end: 12/31/20
Managed Student Accomodations
N.A.I.C.S.: 531390
Joe Lister *(CFO)*
Subsidiaries:

LDC (Holdings) Plc (1)
Core 40 St Thomas St, The Core, Bristol, BS1 6JX, United Kingdom (100%)
Tel.: (44) 1173027000
Web Site: http://www.unite-group.co.uk
Sales Range: $25-49.9 Million
Emp.: 200
Business Support Services
N.A.I.C.S.: 561499
Mark Allan *(Mng Dir)*

Unite Finance Ltd. (1)
South Quay House Temple Back, The Core, Bristol, BS1 6FL, United Kingdom (100%)
Tel.: (44) 1173027000
Web Site: http://www.unite-group.co.uk
Sales Range: $25-49.9 Million
Emp.: 150
Hotels & Motels
N.A.I.C.S.: 721110
Mark Allan *(CEO)*

Unite Finance One (Property) Ltd. (1)
South Quay House Temple Back, Bristol, BS1 6FL, Avon, United Kingdom
Tel.: (44) 1173027000
Web Site: http://www.unite-students.com
Sales Range: $50-74.9 Million
Emp.: 200
Modular Building Mfr
N.A.I.C.S.: 339999
Mark Allan *(Gen Mgr)*

Unite Holdings Plc (1)
South Quay House Temple Back, The Core, Bristol, BS1 6FL, United Kingdom (100%)
Tel.: (44) 1173027000
Sales Range: $75-99.9 Million
Emp.: 250
Real Estate Agency
N.A.I.C.S.: 531210
Richard Smith *(CEO)*

Unite London Ltd. (1)
5th Floor Swan House 17-19 Stratford Place, London, W1C 1BQ, United Kingdom (100%)
Tel.: (44) 1173027000
Web Site: http://www.unite-students.com
Emp.: 500
Student Housing
N.A.I.C.S.: 925110
Mark Allan *(CEO)*

Unite Modular Solutions Ltd. (1)
South Quay House Temple Back, Bristol, BS1 6FL, Gloscester, United Kingdom
Tel.: (44) 1453794200
Sales Range: $50-74.9 Million
Emp.: 130
Modular Building Mfr & Construction Services
N.A.I.C.S.: 236117

THE UNITED LABORATORIES INTERNATIONAL HOLDINGS LTD.
6 Fuk Wang Street Yuen Long Industrial Estate, Yuen Long, Hong Kong, New Territories, China (Hong Kong)
Tel.: (852) 26871033
Web Site: http://www.tul.com.hk
3933—(HKG)
Rev.: $1,591,330,385
Assets: $2,664,739,350
Liabilities: $1,175,175,238
Net Worth: $1,489,564,112
Earnings: $221,975,629
Emp.: 14,000
Fiscal Year-end: 12/31/22
Anti Bacterial Products Mfr
N.A.I.C.S.: 325412
Su Yan Zhu *(VP)*
Subsidiaries:

Guangdong Kaiping Kingly Capsule Co., Ltd. (1)
Dongjiao Xingchang, Kaiping, Guangdong, China
Tel.: (86) 7502387014
Pharmaceutical Products Distr
N.A.I.C.S.: 424210

Kaiping Kingly Capsules Co., Ltd (1)
Dongjiao Xingchang, Kaiping, 529300, Guangdong, China
Tel.: (86) 7502387014
Pharmaceuticals Product Mfr
N.A.I.C.S.: 325412

The United Animal Healthcare (Inner Mongolia) Co., Ltd. (1)
1 Fuyuan South Section, Linhe Chemical Industry High-tech Zone, Bayannur, Inner Mongolia, China
Tel.: (86) 4787862888
Pharmaceutical Products Distr
N.A.I.C.S.: 424210

The United Laboratories Co., Ltd. (1)
6 Fuk Wang Street, Yuen Long Industrial Estate, Yuen Long, New Territories, China (Hong Kong)
Tel.: (852) 26871033
Pharmaceuticals Product Mfr
N.A.I.C.S.: 325412

United Laboratories (Chengdu) Co., Ltd. (1)
8 South Section Mudan Avenue, Pengzhou, 611930, Sichuan, China
Tel.: (86) 2883736888
Pharmaceuticals Product Mfr
N.A.I.C.S.: 325411

United Laboratories (Inner Mongolia) Co., Ltd. (1)
1 Fuyuan South Section, Linhe Chemical Industry High-tech Zone, Bayannur, Inner Mongolia, China
Tel.: (86) 4787862600
Pharmaceutical Mfr & Distr
N.A.I.C.S.: 325412

Zhuhai United Laboratories (Zhongshan) Co., Ltd. (1)
12 Jialian Road Tanzhou Township, Zhongshan, 528467, Guangdong, China
Tel.: (86) 76087133102
Pharmaceuticals Product Mfr
N.A.I.C.S.: 325412

Zhuhai United Laboratories Co., Ltd. (1)
No 2428 Anji Road, Sanzao Town Jinwan District, Zhuhai, Guangdong, China
Tel.: (86) 7567766777
Pharmaceutical Products Distr
N.A.I.C.S.: 424210

Zhuhai United Laboratories Holding Ltd (1)

THE UNITED LABORATORIES INTERNATIONAL HOLDINGS LTD.

The United Laboratories International Holdings Ltd.—(Continued)
No 2428 Anji Road, Sanzao Town, Zhuhai, 519041, Guangdong Province, China
Tel.: (86) 7567766777
Pharmaceuticals Product Mfr
N.A.I.C.S.: 325412

Zhuhai United Laboratories Trading Company Limited (1)
Third Floor Main Office The United Laboratories, Sanzao Science And Technology Garden National Hi-Tech Zone, Zhuhai, Guangdong, China
Tel.: (86) 7567766777
Pharmaceutical Products Distr
N.A.I.C.S.: 424210

THE UNITED NILGIRI TEA ESTATES CO. LTD.
No 3 Savithri Shanmugam Road Race Course, Coimbatore, 641018, India
Tel.: (91) 4222220566
Web Site: https://unitednilgiritea.com
Year Founded: 1922
UNITEDTEA—(NSE)
Rev.: $10,147,246
Assets: $24,179,214
Liabilities: $1,582,008
Net Worth: $22,597,206
Earnings: $1,671,593
Emp.: 1,063
Fiscal Year-end: 03/31/21
Tea Mfr & Whslr
N.A.I.C.S.: 311920
S. Raghuraman (CFO)

THE URAL BANK FOR RECONSTRUCTION & DEVELOPMENT JSC
Velka Business Center 5th Floor 502 Office, 7 Bolshoi Strochenovskiy pereulok, Moscow, 115054, Russia
Tel.: (7) 495 230 01 84
Web Site: http://www.ubrr.ru
Sales Range: $400-449.9 Million
Emp.: 6,750
Banking Services
N.A.I.C.S.: 522110
Anton Solovyev (Pres & CEO)

THE VALENS COMPANY INC.
230 Carion Road, Kelowna, V4V 2K5, BC, Canada
Tel.: (778) 755-0052
Web Site: https://thevalenscompany.com
VLNS—(NASDAQ)
Rev.: $70,525,671
Assets: $269,639,400
Liabilities: $66,686,241
Net Worth: $202,953,159
Earnings: ($38,358,318)
Emp.: 445
Fiscal Year-end: 11/30/21
Holding Company; Cannabis Oils Extraction & Testing Services
N.A.I.C.S.: 551112
A. Tyler Robson (CEO)

Subsidiaries:

Citizen Stash Cannabis Corp. (1)
12556 Stave Lake Road, Mission, V2V 0A6, BC, Canada
Tel.: (604) 837-8688
Web Site: http://citizenstash.com
Rev.: $5,708,542
Assets: $9,468,960
Liabilities: $1,393,309
Net Worth: $8,075,652
Earnings: ($4,555,611)
Fiscal Year-end: 11/30/2020
Investment Services
N.A.I.C.S.: 523999
Winnie Wong (Sec)

Subsidiary (Domestic):

Experion Biotechnologies Inc. (2)
12556 Stave Lake Road, Mission, V2V 0A6, BC, Canada
Tel.: (604) 826-7237
Bio Technology Services
N.A.I.C.S.: 541714

THE VAN CARGOES & FOREIGN TRADE LOGISTICS JOINT STOCK COMPANY
No 02 Bich Cau, Quoc Tu Giam Ward Dong Da, Hanoi, Vietnam
Tel.: (84) 437321090
Web Site: https://www.vntlogistics.com
Year Founded: 1996
VNT—(HNX)
Rev.: $101,773,832
Assets: $31,681,124
Liabilities: $23,750,987
Net Worth: $7,930,137
Earnings: $440,662
Fiscal Year-end: 12/31/21
Logistic Services
N.A.I.C.S.: 541614
Tang Anh Quoc (Deputy CEO & Member-Mgmt Bd)

Subsidiaries:

Hanotrans Limited Co., (1)
No 2 Bich Cau Dong Da, Quoc Tu Giam Ward, Hanoi, Vietnam
Tel.: (84) 2437322784
Web Site: https://hanotrans.com.vn
Emp.: 200
Airfreight Forwarding & Logistic Services
N.A.I.C.S.: 541614

MPC Port Join Stock Company (1)
Dinh Vu Peninsula In Dinh Vu - Cat Hai Economic Zone, Dong Hai 2 Ward Hai An District, Haiphong, Vietnam
Tel.: (84) 2253260036
Web Site: https://www.mpcport.com
Sea Freight Agency Services
N.A.I.C.S.: 541614

THE VEGETABLE OIL INDUSTRIES COMPANY
Eastern Industrial Area, PO Box 95, Nablus, Palestine
Tel.: (970) 92324011
Web Site: https://www.voic.ps
Year Founded: 1953
VOIC—(PAL)
Rev.: $9,325,516
Assets: $108,506,652
Liabilities: $21,099,029
Net Worth: $87,407,623
Earnings: $10,954,257
Emp.: 75
Fiscal Year-end: 12/31/23
Vegetable Oil Mfr
N.A.I.C.S.: 311224

THE VEGETEXCO PORT JOINT - STOCK COMPANY
No 1 Nguyen Van Quy Street Phu Thuan ward, district 7, Ho Chi Minh City, Vietnam
Tel.: (84) 87731120
Web Site: http://www.vegeport.com
Year Founded: 1991
VGP—(HNX)
Rev.: $84,240,808
Assets: $176,001,354
Liabilities: $168,181,095
Net Worth: $7,820,259
Earnings: $266,526
Fiscal Year-end: 12/31/21
Port Support Services
N.A.I.C.S.: 488310
Hung Pham (Chm-Mgmt Bd)

THE VERY GOOD FOOD COMPANY, INC.
1701 Douglas St 6, Victoria, V8W 2G7, BC, Canada
Web Site: http://www.verygoodbutchers.com
VERY—(OTCIQ)
Rev.: $3,627,306
Assets: $27,522,642
Liabilities: $5,898,590
Net Worth: $21,624,052
Earnings: ($10,841,462)
Emp.: 87
Fiscal Year-end: 12/31/20
Food Product Mfr & Distr
N.A.I.C.S.: 311412
James Davison (Co-Founder & Chief R&D Officer)

THE VIETNAM NATIONAL GENERAL EXPORT IMPORT JOINT STOCK COMPANY NO.1
46 Ngo Quyen, Hang Bai Ward Hoan Kiem District, Hanoi, Vietnam
Tel.: (84) 248264009
Web Site: https://ge1.com.vn
Year Founded: 1982
Rev.: $3,149,400
Assets: $30,672,768
Liabilities: $35,274,192
Net Worth: ($4,601,424)
Earnings: ($881,211)
Fiscal Year-end: 12/31/18
Car Renting, Forwarding & Distribution Services
N.A.I.C.S.: 532111

THE WADIA GROUP
C1- Wadia International Centre, Pandurang Budhkar Marg, 400025, Mumbai, India
Tel.: (91) 2267420000
Web Site: http://www.wadiagroup.com
Year Founded: 1736
Holding Company; Investment Services
N.A.I.C.S.: 551112
Ness Wadia (Owner)

Subsidiaries:

Bombay Dyeing & Manufacturing Company Ltd. (1)
C-1 Wadia International Center Pandurang Budhkar Marg Worli, Mumbai, 400 025, India
Tel.: (91) 2266620000
Web Site: https://www.bombaydyeing.com
Rev.: $287,499,030
Assets: $577,497,375
Liabilities: $680,855,175
Net Worth: ($103,357,800)
Earnings: ($62,833,680)
Emp.: 472
Fiscal Year-end: 03/31/2022
Textile Mfr
N.A.I.C.S.: 314999
Nusli Neville Wadia (Chm)

Plant (Domestic):

Bombay Dyeing & Manufacturing Company Ltd. - PSF Plant (2)
A-1 Patalganga Industrial Area, Dist Raigad, Khalapur, Maharashtra, India
Tel.: (91) 2192 251096
Web Site: http://www.bombayrealty.in
Textile Products Mfr
N.A.I.C.S.: 313310

Unit (Domestic):

Bombay Dyeing & Manufacturing Company Ltd. - Textile Processing Unit (2)
B-28 MIDC Industrial Area, Ranjangaon Tal. Shirur, Pune, 412 220, India
Tel.: (91) 21 38232700
Textile Products Mfr
N.A.I.C.S.: 313210

Division (Domestic):

Bombay Realty (2)
Island City Center ICC Bombay Dyeing GD Ambekar Marg, Dadar E, Mumbai, 400 014, India
Tel.: (91) 22 61912345
Web Site: http://www.bombayrealty.in
Real Estate Management Services
N.A.I.C.S.: 531110
Bharat Dhuppar (CEO)

Britannia Industries Ltd. (1)
5/1/A Hungerford Street, Kolkata, 700 017, West Bengal, India (51%)
Tel.: (91) 3322872439
Web Site: https://www.britannia.co.in
Rev.: $1,980,266,171
Assets: $1,121,362,029
Liabilities: $693,989,569
Net Worth: $427,372,460
Earnings: $277,719,561
Emp.: 4,570
Fiscal Year-end: 03/31/2023
Biscuit, Bread & Dairy Product Mfr
N.A.I.C.S.: 311821
Nusli Neville Wadia (Chm)

Naperol Investments Limited (1)
Neville House J N Heredia Marg Ballard Estate, Pandurang Budhkar Marg Worli, Mumbai, 400025, India (70.5%)
Tel.: (91) 2266620000
Web Site: https://www.naperol.com
Rev.: $226,953
Assets: $66,997,794
Liabilities: $175,853
Net Worth: $66,821,941
Earnings: $44,991,391
Emp.: 3
Fiscal Year-end: 03/31/2023
Chemicals Mfr
N.A.I.C.S.: 325180
Y. G. Parkar (VP-Technical & Projects)

Wadia Techno-Engineering Services Limited (1)
Raheja Points I Wing A Pt Jawaharlal Nehru Road Vakola, Santacruz E, Mumbai, 400 055, India
Tel.: (91) 22 6702 1380
Web Site: http://www.wadiaengg.com
Real Estate Development Services
N.A.I.C.S.: 531120
Himanshu Mohapatra (CFO)

THE WALKER AGENCY
Wooton Grange, Wooten Mount, Bournemouth, BH1 1PJ, Dorset, United Kingdom
Tel.: (44) 1202 414200 UK
Web Site: http://www.thewalkeragency.co.uk
Year Founded: 1994
Sales Range: $10-24.9 Million
Emp.: 23
N.A.I.C.S.: 541810
Martin Walker (Mng Dir)

THE WAREHOUSE GROUP LIMITED
26 The Warehouse Way Northcote, Auckland, 0627, New Zealand
Tel.: (64) 94897000
Web Site: https://www.warehousegroup.co.nz
WHS—(NZX)
Rev.: $2,032,961,722
Assets: $1,057,974,880
Liabilities: $816,934,211
Net Worth: $241,040,670
Earnings: $17,904,904
Emp.: 5,739
Fiscal Year-end: 07/30/23
Discount Store Operator
N.A.I.C.S.: 455110
Nick Grayston (CEO)

Subsidiaries:

ChocolateWorks NZ Limited (1)
1 Innovation Way Northgate Park, Horotiu, Hamilton, 3288, New Zealand
Tel.: (64) 78558733
Web Site: https://chocolateworks.co.nz
Chocolate Mfr & Distr
N.A.I.C.S.: 311351
Jeff Andersen (Gen Mgr)

AND PRIVATE COMPANIES

Lincoln West Limited (1)
61 London Road, Kings Hill, Maidstone, ME16 8TX, Kent, United Kingdom
Tel.: (44) 1732446338
Web Site: https://www.lincolnwest.co.uk
Event Arrangement Services
N.A.I.C.S.: 561920

Noel Leeming Group Limited (1)
26 The Warehouse Way, Northcote, Auckland, 0627, New Zealand
Tel.: (64) 9 213 0202
Web Site: https://help.noelleeming.co.nz
Electronic Appliance Distr
N.A.I.C.S.: 423620

The Book Depot Limited (1)
67 Front Street North, Thorold, L2V 1X3, ON, Canada
Tel.: (905) 680-7230
Web Site: https://www.bookdepot.com
Emp.: 500
Book Whslr
N.A.I.C.S.: 424920
Wilf Wikkerink *(CEO)*

The Warehouse Limited (1)
Don McKinnon Drive, Albany, Auckland, 1311, New Zealand
Tel.: (64) 94152225
Retail Stores Operation Services
N.A.I.C.S.: 449129

THE WATER SUPPLY & SEWERAGE CONSTRUCTION & INVESTMENT JOINT-STOCK COMPANY

10 Pho Quang Ward 2, Tan Binh District, Ho Chi Minh City, Vietnam
Tel.: (84) 838475166
Web Site:
  https://www.waseco.com.vn
Year Founded: 1975
VSI—(HOSE)
Rev.: $19,158,041
Assets: $21,258,046
Liabilities: $13,251,815
Net Worth: $8,006,231
Earnings: $1,056,904
Emp.: 131
Fiscal Year-end: 12/31/23
Water Supply & Sewerage Services
N.A.I.C.S.: 237110

THE WATERBASE LIMITED

Thapar House 37 Montieth Road, Chennai, 600 008, India
Tel.: (91) 4430127000
Web Site:
  https://www.waterbaseindia.com
Year Founded: 1993
WATERBASE—(NSE)
Rev.: $36,775,097
Assets: $34,370,266
Liabilities: $12,464,013
Net Worth: $21,906,253
Earnings: ($416,881)
Emp.: 290
Fiscal Year-end: 03/31/23
Shrimp Feed Mfr
N.A.I.C.S.: 311119
Ramakanth V. Akula *(CEO)*

THE WAWANESA MUTUAL INSURANCE COMPANY

900-191 Broadway, Winnipeg, R3C 3P1, MB, Canada
Tel.: (204) 985-3923 Ca
Web Site: http://www.wawanesa.com
Year Founded: 1896
Sales Range: $1-4.9 Billion
Life, Property & Casualty Insurance Services
N.A.I.C.S.: 524126
S. Jeff Goy *(CEO)*

Subsidiaries:

The Wawanesa Life Insurance Company (1)
400 - 200 Main Street, Winnipeg, R3C 1A8, MB, Canada (100%)
Tel.: (204) 985-3940
Web Site: https://www.wawanesalife.com
Sales Range: $50-74.9 Million
Emp.: 400
Life Insurance Carrier
N.A.I.C.S.: 524113

Wawanesa General Insurance Company (1)
9050 Friars Rd, San Diego, CA 92108 (100%)
Tel.: (619) 285-6000
Web Site: http://www.wawanesaus.com
Sales Range: $200-249.9 Million
Emp.: 500
Insurance Carrier
N.A.I.C.S.: 524113
Cam Loeppky *(VP-Ops)*

Western Financial Group Inc. (1)
1010 24th Street SE, High River, T1V 2A7, AB, Canada
Tel.: (403) 652-2663
Web Site:
  https://www.westernfinancialgroup.ca
Bank Holding Company; Banking, Insurance & Financial Investment Products & Services
N.A.I.C.S.: 551111
Kenny Nicholls *(Pres & CEO)*

Subsidiary (Domestic):

The Western Investment Company of Canada Ltd. (2)
1010 24 Street SE, High River, T1V 2A7, AB, Canada
Tel.: (403) 703-9882
Web Site: https://www.winv.ca
Rev.: $1,365,193
Assets: $15,000,065
Liabilities: $5,349,589
Net Worth: $9,650,476
Earnings: $152,509
Emp.: 2
Fiscal Year-end: 12/31/2023
Holding Company; Insurance Agencies & Brokerages Operator
N.A.I.C.S.: 551112
Stacey Cross *(CFO)*

Subsidiary (Domestic):

GlassMasters Autoglass Ltd (3)
6221 Centre Street S, Calgary, T2H 0C7, AB, Canada
Tel.: (403) 692-0340
Web Site:
  http://www.glassmastersautoglass.com
Other Building Material Dealers
N.A.I.C.S.: 444180

THE WEIR GROUP PLC

1 West Regent Street, Glasgow, G2 1RW, United Kingdom
Tel.: (44) 1416377111 UK
Web Site: http://www.global.weir
Year Founded: 1871
WEIR—(OTCIQ)
Rev.: $2,667,512,484
Assets: $4,827,101,916
Liabilities: $3,038,034,272
Net Worth: $1,789,067,644
Earnings: ($202,843,368)
Emp.: 13,070
Fiscal Year-end: 12/31/20
Holding Company; Pumping Equipment, Valves, Desalination, Material Handling, Metallic Insulation & Downhole Oil Tools Mfr
N.A.I.C.S.: 551112
Jon Stanton *(CEO)*

Subsidiaries:

Carriere Industrial Supply Limited (1)
190 Magill Street Walden Industrial Park, Lively, P3Y 1K7, ON, Canada
Tel.: (705) 692-4784
Web Site: http://carriereindustrial.com
Rev.: $22,271,797
Emp.: 100
Construction Services & Mining Machinery Provider
N.A.I.C.S.: 423810

Jean-Marc Valade *(Gen Mgr)*

Durex Products Inc. (1)
112 W 1st Ave, Luck, WI 54853
Tel.: (715) 472-2111
Web Site: https://durexproducts.com
Sales Range: $25-49.9 Million
Emp.: 74
Mining Machinery
N.A.I.C.S.: 333131

ESCO (Shanghai) Trading Co., Ltd. (1)
Suite 25GH Lekai Tower 660 Shang Cheng Road, Pudong, Shanghai, 200120, China
Tel.: (86) 2158354560
Mining & Construction Equipment Mfr
N.A.I.C.S.: 333120

ESCO Corporation (1)
2141 NW 25th Ave, Portland, OR 97210
Tel.: (503) 228-2141
Web Site: http://www.escocorp.com
Engineered Metal Parts & Components Mfr
N.A.I.C.S.: 332999

Subsidiary (Domestic):

Advanced Cutting Systems Corp. (2)
891 Centennial Dr, Windber, PA 15963
Tel.: (814) 467-0822
Web Site: http://www.escocorp.com
Sales Range: $10-24.9 Million
Emp.: 48
Mining Machinery & Equipment Mfr
N.A.I.C.S.: 333131

Division (Domestic):

ESCO Engineered Products (2)
2141 NW 25th Ave, Portland, OR 97210 (100%)
Tel.: (503) 228-2141
Web Site: http://www.escocorp.com
Sales Range: $100-124.9 Million
Emp.: 1,000
Mining, Construction & Industrial Engineered Metal Components Mfr
N.A.I.C.S.: 332999

Subsidiary (Domestic):

ESCO Bucyrus Inc. (3)
260 E Beal Ave, Bucyrus, OH 44820 (100%)
Tel.: (419) 562-6015
Sales Range: $25-49.9 Million
Emp.: 24
Mfr of Cutting Edges & Related Wearing Parts for Dozers, Scrapers, Front-End Loaders & Graders
N.A.I.C.S.: 333120

ESCO Elecmetal Fundicion Limitada (1)
Calle Miraflores Numero 222 Piso Veinticuatro, 3463, Santiago, Chile
Tel.: (56) 23614020
Mining & Construction Equipment Mfr
N.A.I.C.S.: 333120
Gonzalo Camus *(Mgr-Fin)*

ESCO Hydra (UK) Limited (1)
Ings Rd, Doncaster, DN5 9SN, South Yorkshire, United Kingdom
Tel.: (44) 1302782259
Mining & Construction Equipment Mfr
N.A.I.C.S.: 333120

ESCO Mocambique S.A. (1)
Stand No 81 EN7, Moatize, Tete, Mozambique
Tel.: (258) 843113885
Mining & Construction Equipment Mfr
N.A.I.C.S.: 333120
Rui Pereira *(Branch Mgr)*

Hopkinsons Limited (1)
Britannia House Huddersfield Road, Elland, HX5 9JR, West Yorkshire, United Kingdom
Tel.: (44) 1484820820
Oil & Gas Chemical Product Distr
N.A.I.C.S.: 237120
J. Ward *(Dir-Fin)*

Mathena, Inc. (1)
3901 US Hwy 81 Service Rd, El Reno, OK 73036
Tel.: (405) 422-3600
Web Site: http://www.mathena-inc.com

THE WEIR GROUP PLC

Sales Range: $100-124.9 Million
Emp.: 70
Mud-Gas Pressure Control Equipment Mfr & Rental Services
N.A.I.C.S.: 333132
John Mathena *(Pres & CEO)*

Mesa Manufacturing Inc (1)
6510 N Golder Ave, Odessa, TX 79764
Tel.: (432) 367-8606
Web Site: http://mesamfg.com
Sales Range: $25-49.9 Million
Emp.: 100
High Pressure Fitting & Adapter Mfr
N.A.I.C.S.: 332912

Specialised Petroleum Manufacturing Ltd (1)
Badentoy Crescent Badentoy Industrial Estate, Aberdeen, AB12 4YD, United Kingdom
Tel.: (44) 1224 783666
Web Site: http://www.weiroilandgas.com
Sales Range: $25-49.9 Million
Emp.: 50
Petroleum Product Mfr
N.A.I.C.S.: 324199
Damien O'Reilly *(Mgr-Svc Centre)*

Vulco Peru SA (1)
Av Separadora Industrial N 2201 Urb Vulcano Ate, Lima, Peru
Tel.: (51) 16187575
Pumping Equipment Mfr
N.A.I.C.S.: 333914

Vulco SA (1)
San Jose No 0815, San Bernardo, Santiago, Chile
Tel.: (56) 27542100
Compressor & Pump Distr
N.A.I.C.S.: 423730

Warman International (India) Private Ltd. (1)
Plot No 471/D-1 3rd Main IV Phase, Peenya Industrial Area, Bengaluru, 560 058, India
Tel.: (91) 9886420269
Web Site: http://www.weirminerals.com
Sales Range: $1-4.9 Billion
Emp.: 9,000
Mfr of Pumps & Pumping Equipment
N.A.I.C.S.: 333914

Weir Canada Inc. (1)
2360 Millrace Court, Mississauga, L5N 1W2, ON, Canada (100%)
Tel.: (905) 812-0881
Web Site:
  http://www.weirpowerindustrial.com
Sales Range: $100-124.9 Million
Emp.: 110
Pumps & Control Systems Distr
N.A.I.C.S.: 333996

Weir Engineering Products (Shanghai) Co., Ltd. (1)
17F Longlife Mansion 1566 West Yan An Road, Shanghai, 200052, China
Tel.: (86) 18516253073
Mining & Construction Equipment Mfr
N.A.I.C.S.: 333120
Cindy Zong *(Mgr-Mktg & Comml)*

Weir Engineering Services (1)
10th Floor 1 West Regent Street, Cathcart, Glasgow, G2 1RW, United Kingdom (100%)
Tel.: (44) 416377141
Web Site: http://www.weirservices.com
Sales Range: $150-199.9 Million
Emp.: 900
Maintainence & Engineering Services to the Energy, Water, Oil & Gas & General Engineering Industries
N.A.I.C.S.: 541330

Subsidiary (Non-US):

WESCO Abu Dhabi (2)
Plot No 4 Sector MN 4 St No 6 Corniche Rd, PO Box 4752, Musaffah Industrial Area Near Third Round About, Abu Dhabi, 11111, United Arab Emirates (49%)
Tel.: (971) 2 555 4108
Web Site: https://www.wescouae.com
Sales Range: $75-99.9 Million
Emp.: 300
Pumping Equipment Mfr
N.A.I.C.S.: 333914

THE WEIR GROUP PLC

The Weir Group PLC—(Continued)

WESCO Dubai (2)
Jebel Ali Free Zn, PO Box 11419, Dubai, 11419, United Arab Emirates
Tel.: (971) 48838581
Web Site: http://www.weirservices.com
Sales Range: $25-49.9 Million
Emp.: 180
Pumping Equipment Mfr
N.A.I.C.S.: 333914

Branch (Domestic):

Weir Coatings Division (2)
Unit 19 Heysham Bus Pk, Middleton Rd, Heysham, LA3 3PP, United Kingdom
Tel.: (44) 524855625
Web Site: http://www.weircoatings.co.uk
Sales Range: $25-49.9 Million
Emp.: 12
Supplier of Protective Linings & Coatings
N.A.I.C.S.: 541330

Weir Engineering Services (2)
Badentoy Industrial Park, Portlethen, Aberdeen, AB12 4YD, Scotland, United Kingdom
Tel.: (44) 1224783666
Web Site: http://www.weirservices.com
Sales Range: $25-49.9 Million
Emp.: 60
Maintenance & Engineering Services to the Energy, Water, Oil & Gas & General Engineering Industries
N.A.I.C.S.: 541330
Ian McKey *(Gen Mgr)*

Weir Engineering Services (2)
20 Waterloo Street 4th Floor, Glasgow, G2 6DB, Scotland, United Kingdom (100%)
Tel.: (44) 1413082800
Web Site: http://www.weirpowerindustrial.com
Sales Range: $25-49.9 Million
Emp.: 150
Provider of Maintainence & Engrng Svcs to the Energy, Water, Oil & Gas & General Engineering Industries
N.A.I.C.S.: 541330

Weir Engineering Services (2)
Unit A 12 Severn Rd, Treforest Indus Est, Cardiff, CF37 5SL, United Kingdom (100%)
Tel.: (44) 443844114
Web Site: http://www.weirservices.com
Sales Range: $25-49.9 Million
Emp.: 20
Provider of Maintainence & Engrng Svcs to the Energy, Water, Oil & Gas & General Engineering Industries
N.A.I.C.S.: 541330

Weir Engineering Services (2)
Cross Green Approach, Cross Green Industrial Estate, Leeds, LS9 0SP, United Kingdom
Tel.: (44) 1132488944
Provider of Engineering Services to the Water Industry
N.A.I.C.S.: 541330

Subsidiary (Non-US):

Weir Engineering Services (India) Ltd (2)
B-212 Ansal Chambers, 1 Bhikaji Carna Place, New Delhi, 110066, India
Tel.: (91) 11 26162543
Maintenance & Engineering Services to the Energy, Water, Oil & Gas & General Engineering Industries
N.A.I.C.S.: 541330

Branch (Domestic):

Weir Turbomachinery (2)
Humber Rd, PO Box 4, Barton-upon-Humber, DN18 5BN, N Lincolnshire, United Kingdom (100%)
Tel.: (44) 652632702
Web Site: http://www.weirservices.com
Sales Range: $10-24.9 Million
Emp.: 45
Turbomachinery Engineering Svcs
N.A.I.C.S.: 541330

Weir Gabbioneta SrL (1)
Viale Casiraghi 68, 20099, Sesto San Giovanni, Milan, Italy
Tel.: (39) 02 24100 1
Sales Range: $100-124.9 Million
Emp.: 30
Heavy Duty Pump Machinery Mfr
N.A.I.C.S.: 333914
Andrea Forzi *(Mng Dir)*

Weir Materials and Foundries Ltd. (1)
Park Works Newton Heath, Manchester, M40 2BA, England, United Kingdom
Tel.: (44) 619544322
Sales Range: $25-49.9 Million
Emp.: 50
Mfr of Pre-Cast & Wrought Pumping Equipment
N.A.I.C.S.: 333914

Weir Minerals Australia Ltd (1)
1 Marden Street, Artarmon, 2064, NSW, Australia
Tel.: (61) 29 934 5100
Web Site: http://www.weirminerals.com
Sales Range: $300-349.9 Million
Emp.: 700
Pumping Equipment Mfr & Distr
N.A.I.C.S.: 423830
Craig Walker *(Mng Dir)*

Division (Domestic):

Weir Minerals Australia Ltd. (2)
15 Gindurra Rd, Somersby, 2250, NSW, Australia (100%)
Tel.: (61) 243492850
Sales Range: $25-49.9 Million
Emp.: 200
Engineering Services
N.A.I.C.S.: 541330

Weir Minerals Chile (1)
Av San Jose 0815, San Bernardo, Santiago, Chile
Tel.: (56) 22 754 2200
Web Site: http://www.weirminerals.com
Sales Range: $50-74.9 Million
Emp.: 1,000
Mfr of Pumps & Pumping Equipment
N.A.I.C.S.: 333914

Weir Minerals Europe Limited (1)
Halifax Road, Todmorden, OL14 5RT, Lancs, United Kingdom (100%)
Tel.: (44) 1706298476
Sales Range: $100-124.9 Million
Emp.: 400
Mfr of Pumping Equipment & Mill Lining Systems for the Mineral Processing & Mining Industries
N.A.I.C.S.: 333914
Tony Locke *(Mng Dir)*

Weir Minerals France SAS (1)
Parc Technoland Batiment H 6-8 Allee du Piemont, 69800, Saint Priest, France
Tel.: (33) 472817272
Sales Range: $50-74.9 Million
Emp.: 80
Pumping Machinery Distr
N.A.I.C.S.: 423830

Weir Minerals India Private Limited. (1)
NCC Urban Windsor 1st Floor, New Airport Road Opposite Jakkur Aerodrome, Bengaluru, 560 064, Karnataka, India
Tel.: (91) 8046177666
Emp.: 25
Industrial Pumping Machinery Mfr
N.A.I.C.S.: 333914
Surendra Menon *(Dir)*

Weir Minerals Ltd Australia (1)
1 Marden Street, Artarmon, 2064, NSW, Australia (100%)
Tel.: (61) 29 934 5100
Web Site: http://www.weirminerals.com
Sales Range: $100-124.9 Million
Emp.: 500
Pumps & Pumping Equipment
N.A.I.C.S.: 333914
Rob Brown *(Mng Dir)*

Weir Minerals Mongolia LLC (1)
Labor Street 52 Building No 37 Trade Union Street 20th Khoroo, Western Industrial Zone 1 Bayangol District, Ulaanbaatar, 16100, Mongolia
Tel.: (976) 99194917
Engineering Services

Weir Minerals Netherlands BV (1)
Tel.: (31) 773895200,
Web Site: https://www.weirminerals.com
Sales Range: $100-124.9 Million
Emp.: 350
Industrial Pumping Machinery Mfr
N.A.I.C.S.: 333914

Weir Minerals RFW LLC (OOO) (1)
Bolshaya Polyanka Building 2 house 2, Moscow, 199178, Russia
Tel.: (7) 8124493048
Engineering Services
N.A.I.C.S.: 541330

Weir Minerals Sweden AB (1)
Polervagen 4, 774 41, Avesta, Sweden
Tel.: (46) 97064400
Web Site: https://www.weirminerals.se
Mineral Processing Product Mfr
N.A.I.C.S.: 333131

Weir Netherlands BV (1)
Egtenrayseweg 9, PO Box 249, 5928 PH, Venlo, Netherlands
Tel.: (31) 77 389 5200
Web Site: http://www.weirminerals.com
Sales Range: $100-124.9 Million
Emp.: 360
Mfr of Pumps
N.A.I.C.S.: 333914
Marjo Cox *(Mgr-PR)*

Weir Power & Industrial France SAS (1)
ZI Du Bois Rigault Rue Jean Baptiste Grison, 62880, Vendin-le-Vieil, France
Tel.: (33) 321 79 54 50
Sales Range: $50-74.9 Million
Emp.: 160
Industrial Valve Mfr
N.A.I.C.S.: 332911
Kevin Spencer *(Mng Dir-Scotland)*

Weir Slurry Group, Inc. (1)
2701 S Stoughton Rd, Madison, WI 53716-3315
Tel.: (608) 226-5659
Sales Range: $50-74.9 Million
Emp.: 180
Heavy Duty Slurry Handling Equipment Mfr; Regional Managing Office
N.A.I.C.S.: 333914

Subsidiary (Domestic):

Weir Floway, Inc. (2)
2494 South Railroad Ave, Fresno, CA 93707
Tel.: (559) 442-4000
Web Site: http://www.floway.com
Mfr of Vertical Turbine Pumps
N.A.I.C.S.: 333914

Weir Hazleton Inc. (2)
225 N Cedar St, Hazleton, PA 18201-5551
Tel.: (570) 455-7711
Web Site: http://www.hazletonpumps.com
Sales Range: $25-49.9 Million
Emp.: 80
Mfr of Slurry Pumps
N.A.I.C.S.: 333914

Unit (Domestic):

Weir Specialty Pumps (2)
440 W 800 S, Salt Lake City, UT 84101
Tel.: (801) 359-8731
Web Site: http://www.weirsp.com
Rev: $157,100,000
Emp.: 100
Pumps & Pumping Equipment Mfr
N.A.I.C.S.: 333914

Weir Solutions FZE (1)
Office 312 3rd Floor Building 1W Al Quds Street, Dubai Airport Free Zone, Dubai, United Arab Emirates
Tel.: (971) 4 2996808
Web Site: http://www.weirminerals.com
Sales Range: $25-49.9 Million
Emp.: 22
Pumping Equipment Mfr
N.A.I.C.S.: 333914
Wayne Davidow *(Mng Dir)*

Weir Specialty Pumps (1)
440 W 800 S, Salt Lake City, UT 84110-0209
Tel.: (801) 359-8731
Web Site: http://www.weirpowerindustrial.com
Sales Range: $25-49.9 Million
Emp.: 100
Pumping Equipment Mfr & Distr
N.A.I.C.S.: 333914

Weir Valves & Controls UK Ltd. (1)
Britannia House, Huddersfield Rd, Elland, HX5 9JR, W Yorkshire, United Kingdom (100%)
Tel.: (44) 422282000
Sales Range: $50-74.9 Million
Emp.: 120
Pump & Valve Mfr
N.A.I.C.S.: 333914

Subsidiary (Non-US):

Weir Valves & Controls SEBIM SAS (2)
ZI La Palunette, 13165, Chateauneuf-les-Martigues, Cedex, France (100%)
Tel.: (33) 442070095
Web Site: http://www.weirgroup.com
Sales Range: $25-49.9 Million
Mfr of Valves for Power, Atomic Energy, Process Industries & Marine Applications
N.A.I.C.S.: 332911
Stephane Lamotte *(Dir-Sls)*

Weir Valves & Controls USA Inc. (1)
29 Old Right Rd, Ipswich, MA 01938-4544 (100%)
Tel.: (978) 744-5690
Web Site: http://www.weirgroup.com
Sales Range: $25-49.9 Million
Emp.: 110
Mfr of Valves for Power, Atomic Energy, Process Industries & Marine
N.A.I.C.S.: 332911
Linda Gagnon *(Mgr-IT)*

Subsidiary (Domestic):

Novatech, LLC (2)
8388 CF Hawn Frwy, Dallas, TX 75217
Tel.: (214) 398-1491
Web Site: http://www.novatechmfg.com
Sales Range: $50-74.9 Million
Emp.: 65
Fluid Power Valve & Seat Mfr
N.A.I.C.S.: 332912

Weir Vulco Peru (1)
Avda Argentina, Lima, Peru (100%)
Tel.: (51) 13152000
Web Site: http://www.weirvulcoperu.com
Sales Range: $25-49.9 Million
Emp.: 95
Mfr of Pumps & Pumping Equipment.
N.A.I.C.S.: 333914

Weir-EnviroTech (Pty.) Ltd. (1)
31 Isando Road, PO Box 70, Isando, Johannesburg, 1600, Gauteng, South Africa (100%)
Tel.: (27) 11 929 2600
Web Site: http://www.weirminerals.com
Sales Range: $150-199.9 Million
Emp.: 360
Pumping Equipment Whslr
N.A.I.C.S.: 423440
Grant Ramsden *(Dir-Ops)*

Wuxi Weir Minerals Equipments Co., Ltd. (1)
Lot 265 Wuxi-Singapore Industrial Park, Wuxi, 214028, Jiangsu, China
Tel.: (86) 51268786988
Mining & Construction Equipment Mfr
N.A.I.C.S.: 333120

THE WELLCOME TRUST LTD

Gibbs Building 215 Euston Road, London, NW1 2BE, United Kingdom
Tel.: (44) 20 7611 8888
Web Site: http://wellcome.org
Research & Development in the Social Sciences & Humanities
N.A.I.C.S.: 541720

Subsidiaries:

Urban&Civic plc (1)
50 New Bond Street, London, W1S 1BJ, United Kingdom
Tel.: (44) 20 7509 5555

AND PRIVATE COMPANIES

Web Site: http://www.urbanandcivic.com
Rev.: $133,932,722
Assets: $756,166,255
Liabilities: $227,548,172
Net Worth: $528,618,083
Earnings: $16,564,196
Emp.: 87
Fiscal Year-end: 09/30/2019
Property Investment & Development Services
N.A.I.C.S.: 531390
Nigel Wakefield *(Dir-Strategic Land Dev)*

Subsidiary (Domestic):

Catesby Estates plc (2)
Catesby House 5B Tournament Court Edgehill Drive, Warwick, CV34 6LG, United Kingdom
Tel.: (44) 1926836910
Web Site: http://www.catesbyestates.co.uk
Land Promoting Services
N.A.I.C.S.: 541370

Priors Hall Park Management Company (2)
1 The Courtyard Barnwell Gardens Priors Hall Park, Corby, NN17 5GS, United Kingdom
Tel.: (44) 1536428758
Web Site: http://www.priorshallparkmanagement.co.uk
Real Estate Services
N.A.I.C.S.: 531210

THE WESTAIM CORPORATION
70 York Street Suite 1700, Toronto, M5J 1S9, ON, Canada
Tel.: (416) 969-3333 AB
Web Site: https://www.westaim.com
Year Founded: 1996
WED—(OTCIQ)
Rev.: $24,855,000
Assets: $377,353,000
Liabilities: $56,831,000
Net Worth: $320,522,000
Earnings: ($34,400,000)
Emp.: 7
Fiscal Year-end: 12/31/20
Investment Services
N.A.I.C.S.: 525910
Ian W. Delaney *(Exec Chm)*

Subsidiaries:

Nucryst Pharmaceuticals Corp. (1)
101 College Rd E, Princeton, NJ 08540 (100%)
Tel.: (609) 228-8210
Sales Range: $10-24.9 Million
Emp.: 106
Medical Product Developer & Marketer
N.A.I.C.S.: 423490

THE WESTERN INDIA PLYWOODS LIMITED
Baliapatam, Kannur, 670 010, Kerala, India
Tel.: (91) 4972778151 In
Web Site: https://www.wipltd.in
Year Founded: 1942
WIPL—(NSE)
Rev.: $13,016,558
Assets: $8,375,901
Liabilities: $3,442,336
Net Worth: $4,933,565
Earnings: $418,440
Emp.: 253
Fiscal Year-end: 03/31/23
Wood Product Mfr & Distr
N.A.I.C.S.: 321211
T. Balakrishnan *(Chm)*

THE WHY HOW DO COMPANY, INC
Daisan Yamada Bldg 22 Aizumi-cho, Shinjuku-ku, Tokyo, 160-0005, Japan
Tel.: (81) 344055460
Web Site: https://www.twhdc.co.jp
Year Founded: 2004
3823—(TKS)
Rev.: $4,646,340
Assets: $9,541,480
Liabilities: $4,714,760
Net Worth: $4,826,720
Earnings: ($5,977,420)
Emp.: 643
Fiscal Year-end: 08/31/24
Consultation Services for Software Planning & Design
N.A.I.C.S.: 541512
Hiroshi Shinohara *(Pres)*

Subsidiaries:

AMS, Inc. (1)
ORIX Meguro Building 6F 1-24-12 Meguro, Meguro-ku, Tokyo, 153-0063, Japan (20%)
Tel.: (81) 364217691
Web Site: http://www.amsinc.co.jp
Sales Range: $25-49.9 Million
Emp.: 182
Mobile Product Development Services
N.A.I.C.S.: 541613
Shinichi Murai *(Pres)*

Acrodea Korea, Inc. (1)
18F Korea Sanhak Foundation Building 1337-31, Seocho-dong Seocho-gu, Seoul, Korea (South)
Tel.: (82) 56176016
Web Site: http://www.acrodea.co.kr
Mobile Communications Services
N.A.I.C.S.: 517810

THE WILLBES CO LTD
Mannam-ro 76 Sinbu-dong 494-3, Dongnam-gu, Cheonan, Chungcheongnam-do, Korea (South)
Tel.: (82) 415295700
Web Site: https://www.willbes.com
Year Founded: 1973
008600—(KRS)
Rev.: $195,476,146
Assets: $207,392,752
Liabilities: $132,015,252
Net Worth: $75,377,500
Earnings: ($7,158,062)
Emp.: 193
Fiscal Year-end: 12/31/22
Textile Mfr
N.A.I.C.S.: 313210
Byung-Hyun Jun *(Chm)*

Subsidiaries:

The Willbes (Cambodia) & Co., Ltd. (1)
Damnaktra Yeoung Vlg, Phnom Penh, 12405, Cambodia
Tel.: (855) 12464338
Children Clothes Mfr
N.A.I.C.S.: 315250

THE WILLIAM PEARS GROUP OF COMPANIES LIMITED
Clive House 2 Old Brewery Mews, Hampstead High Street, London, NW3 1PZ, United Kingdom
Tel.: (44) 2074333333
Web Site: http://www.williampears.co.uk
Commercial Property Development & Investment Services
N.A.I.C.S.: 531190
Mark Pears *(CEO)*

Subsidiaries:

Talisman Global Asset Management Limited (1)
33 Cavendish Sq, London, W1G 0PW, United Kingdom
Tel.: (44) 2074330661
Web Site: http://www.talismanglobal.co.uk
Sales Range: $200-249.9 Million
Emp.: 300
Financial Services
N.A.I.C.S.: 523999
Julian Sinclair *(Chief Investment Officer)*

Telereal Services Limited (1)
140 London Wall, London, EC2Y 5DN, United Kingdom
Tel.: (44) 2077965500
Web Site: http://www.telerealtrillium.com
Sales Range: $300-349.9 Million
Assets: $4,000,000,000
Emp.: 350
Investment Services
N.A.I.C.S.: 523999

Subsidiary (Domestic):

Trillium Holdings Limited (2)
140 London Wall, London, EC2Y 5DN, United Kingdom
Tel.: (44) 2077965500
Web Site: http://www.telerealtrillium.com
Property & Community Infrastructure Investments, Management & Services
N.A.I.C.S.: 531312
Ian D. Ellis *(Chm)*

THE WONDERFILM MEDIA CORP.
Suite 410 - 409 Granville Street, Vancouver, V6C 1T2, BC, Canada
Tel.: (604) 638-4890
Web Site: http://www.wonderfilm.com
AMNNF—(OTCQB)
Rev.: $5,171,244
Assets: $1,704,235
Liabilities: $2,138,932
Net Worth: ($434,697)
Earnings: ($9,751,264)
Fiscal Year-end: 06/30/19
Entertainment Services
N.A.I.C.S.: 711130
Dan Grodnik *(Partner)*

THE WOODBRIDGE COMPANY LIMITED
65 Queen St W Ste 2400, Toronto, M5H 2M8, ON, Canada
Tel.: (416) 364-8700
Sales Range: $25-49.9 Million
Emp.: 70
Holding Company
N.A.I.C.S.: 551112
David Thomson *(Co-Chm)*

Subsidiaries:

The Globe & Mail Inc. (1)
351 King Street East Suite 1600, Toronto, M5A 0N1, ON, Canada (85%)
Tel.: (416) 585-5000
Web Site: https://www.theglobeandmail.com
Emp.: 300
National Daily Newspaper Publisher
N.A.I.C.S.: 513110
Phillip Crawley *(CEO & Publr)*

THE WORLD FINANCIAL HOLDING GROUP CO., LIMITED
16th Floor North Tower 528 Pudong South Road, Shanghai, 200120, China
Tel.: (86) 2138932525 FL
Web Site: https://www.worldfh.com
Year Founded: 2005
WFHG—(OTCIQ)
Sales Range: Less than $1 Million
Financial Investment Services
N.A.I.C.S.: 523999
Brian K. Kistler *(Sec)*

THE YAMAGATA BANK, LTD.
1-2 Nanokamachi 3-chome, Yamagata, 990-8642, Japan JP
Web Site: http://www.yamagatabank.co.jp
Year Founded: 1896
8344—(TKS)
Rev.: $364,191,170
Assets: $20,797,479,260
Liabilities: $19,846,928,210
Net Worth: $950,551,050
Earnings: $115,675
Emp.: 1,287
Fiscal Year-end: 03/31/24
Banking Services
N.A.I.C.S.: 522110
Kichishige Hasegawa *(Pres)*

THE YAMANASHI CHUO BANK, LTD.
20-8 Marunouchi 1-chome, Kofu, 400-8601, Yamanashi, Japan
Tel.: (81) 552332111 JP
Web Site: https://www.yamanashibank.co.jp
Year Founded: 1941
8360—(TKS)
Rev.: $373,630,250
Assets: $28,860,449,800
Liabilities: $27,417,480,190
Net Worth: $1,442,969,610
Earnings: $204,910
Emp.: 1,658
Fiscal Year-end: 03/31/24
Banking Services
N.A.I.C.S.: 522110
Nakaba Shindo *(Chm)*

Subsidiaries:

Yamanashi Chugin DC Card Co., Ltd. (1)
2-9-4 Takeda, Kofu, 400-0016, Yamanashi, Japan
Tel.: (81) 552551520
Web Site: https://www.yamanashidc.co.jp
Emp.: 20
Credit Card Services
N.A.I.C.S.: 522210

THE YAMUNA SYNDICATE LIMITED
Radaur Road, Yamunanagar, 135 001, India
Tel.: (91) 1732255475
Web Site: https://www.yamunasyndicate.com
Year Founded: 1954
540980—(BOM)
Rev.: $8,968,652
Assets: $10,159,786
Liabilities: $970,690
Net Worth: $9,189,096
Earnings: $1,868,398
Emp.: 37
Fiscal Year-end: 03/31/20
Agricultural Machinery Distr
N.A.I.C.S.: 423820
Mukesh Kumar Kamboj *(CFO)*

THE YASH BIRLA GROUP
Dalamal House 1st Floor JB Marg Nariman Point, Mumbai, 400 021, India
Tel.: (91) 2266168400
Web Site: http://www.yashbirlagroup.com
Holding Company
N.A.I.C.S.: 551112
Yash Birla *(Chm)*

Subsidiaries:

Birla AccuCast Limited (1)
206 Dalamal House Nariman Point, Mumbai, 400 021, India
Tel.: (91) 22 22281173
Web Site: http://www.birlaaccucast.com
Machine Tools Mfr
N.A.I.C.S.: 333517

Birla Art Lifestyle Pvt. Ltd. (1)
Gallery BMB Queens Mansion Ground Floor G T Marg, Next to Cathedral (Middle) School, Mumbai, India
Tel.: (91) 22 22000061
Art Gallery Services
N.A.I.C.S.: 712110

Birla Cotsyn (India) Limited (1)
Dalamal House 1st Floor JB Marg, Mumbai, 400 021, India
Tel.: (91) 2266168400
Web Site: http://www.birlacotsyn.com
Sales Range: $10-24.9 Million
Emp.: 1,300
Cotton Ginning, Pressing & Oil Expelling Services

THE YASH BIRLA GROUP

The Yash Birla Group—(Continued)
N.A.I.C.S.: 115111

Birla Edutech Ltd. (1)
Melstar House G-4 M I D C Cross Road A,
Andheri E, Mumbai, 400 093, India
Tel.: (91) 22 41026565
Web Site: http://www.birlaedutech.com
Educational Support Services
N.A.I.C.S.: 611110

Birla Electricals Ltd. (1)
302 Atlanta Estate Goregaon Mulund Link
Road Goregaon E, Mumbai, 400063, India
Tel.: (91) 2 40990111
Home Appliance Product Mfr
N.A.I.C.S.: 335220

Birla Financial Services India Pvt. Ltd. (1)
335 Connection Point Mezzanine Floor Airport Exit Road, Bengaluru, 560 017, India
Tel.: (91) 80 2522 5737
Web Site: http://www.birlafin.com
Financial Consulting Services
N.A.I.C.S.: 523940

Birla Pacific Medspa Ltd (1)
Dalamal House 1st Floor JB Marg, Nariman Point, Mumbai, 400 021, Maharashtra, India
Tel.: (91) 22 66168400
Web Site: http://www.birlapacificmedspa.com
Emp.: 40
Cosmetic Dermatology, Cosmetic & Plastic Surgery, General & Specialist Dentistry & Maxillo Facial Prosthesis
N.A.I.C.S.: 622310

Birla Power Solutions Limited (1)
901 Bhikaji Cama Bhawan, 11 Bhikaji Cama Place, New Delhi, 110066, India
Tel.: (91) 42594100
Web Site: http://www.birlapower.com
Sales Range: $125-149.9 Million
Emp.: 550
Power Generator Mfr
N.A.I.C.S.: 335312

Birla Precision Technologies Limited (1)
23 Birla Mansion No 2-1st Floor D D Sathe Marg, Prarthana Samaj, Mumbai, 400 004, India **(88.5%)**
Tel.: (91) 2266168466
Web Site: https://www.birlaprecision.com
Rev.: $31,610,359
Assets: $28,139,092
Liabilities: $12,374,450
Net Worth: $15,764,642
Earnings: $1,687,333
Emp.: 300
Fiscal Year-end: 03/31/2023
Metal Working & Cutting Tool Mfr
N.A.I.C.S.: 333517
Vedant Birla *(Chm & Mng Dir)*

Subsidiary (Domestic):

Indian Tool Manufacturers Ltd. (2)
B-15/4 MIDC Waluj, Aurangabad, 431 133, Maharashtra, India
Tel.: (91) 240 2554300
Web Site: http://www.indiantool.com
Machine Tools Mfr
N.A.I.C.S.: 333517
D. C. Padalkar *(Asst VP-Mfg)*

Unit (Domestic):

Indian Tool Manufacturers Ltd. - Nashik Unit (3)
62/63 MIDC Industrial Area Satpur, 422 007, Nashik, India
Tel.: (91) 253 2350320
Machine Tools Mfr
N.A.I.C.S.: 333517

Birla Viking Travels Ltd. (1)
G - 3/4/5 Atlanta Tower Sahar Cargo Road, Near Ciggratte Factory Andheri E, Mumbai, 400 099, India
Tel.: (91) 22 4241 8000
Travel Management Services
N.A.I.C.S.: 561510

Melstar Information Technologies Ltd (1)
159 5th Floor Industry House Reclamation Churchgate, Mumbai, 400020, India
Tel.: (91) 28310505
Web Site: http://www.melstar.com
Rev.: $1,569,960
Assets: $1,686,790
Liabilities: $2,175,992
Net Worth: ($489,202)
Earnings: ($651,056)
Emp.: 81
Fiscal Year-end: 03/31/2020
IT Services
N.A.I.C.S.: 541512

THE YOC GROUP

Karl-Liebknecht-Str 1, 10178, Berlin, Germany
Tel.: (49) 30726162161
Web Site: http://www.yoc.com
Rev.: $23,600,000
N.A.I.C.S.: 541810
Gerd Schmitz-Morkramer *(Chm)*

THE YOKOHAMA RUBBER CO., LTD.

36-11 Shimbashi 5-chome, Minato-ku, Tokyo, 105-8685, Japan
Tel.: (81) 354004531 JP
Web Site: http://www.yrc.co.jp
Year Founded: 1917
5101—(TKS)
Rev.: $6,986,010,970
Assets: $11,347,247,220
Liabilities: $6,038,290,670
Net Worth: $5,308,956,550
Earnings: $476,689,060
Emp.: 33,617
Fiscal Year-end: 12/31/23
Holding Company; Rubber Products Mfr & Whslr
N.A.I.C.S.: 326211
Osamu Mikami *(Sr Mng Officer-Plng & MB & Head-Industrial Products & Hamatite)*

Subsidiaries:

ATC Tires AP Private Ltd. (1)
Unit No 1001 10th Floor Tower A Embassy 247, Lal Bahadur Shastri Marg Vikhroli West, Mumbai, India
Tel.: (91) 223 957 9600
Tiles Mfr
N.A.I.C.S.: 326211

ATC Tires Pvt. Ltd. (1)
Tel.: (91) 2239579600
Web Site: http://www.atgtire.com
Tiles Mfr
N.A.I.C.S.: 551112

Alliance Tire Company Ltd. (1)
PO Box 48, Hadera, 38100, Israel
Tel.: (972) 4 624 0520
Web Site: http://www.atgtire.com
Tire Mfr & Whslr
N.A.I.C.S.: 326211
Ozcan Demirbas *(CEO)*

Alliance Tire Europe B.V. (1)
De Entree 59, Zuidoost, 1101 BH, Amsterdam, Netherlands
Tel.: (31) 97010211125
Web Site: https://alliancetirebv.com
Tire Distr
N.A.I.C.S.: 423130

Hamagomu Aicom Inc. (1)
1-1-25 Shinurashima-cho Techno Wave 100 Building 7F, Kanagawa-ku, Yokohama, 221-0031, Japan
Tel.: (81) 45 451 6611
Web Site: https://www.aicom.co.jp
Emp.: 389
Software Development Services
N.A.I.C.S.: 513210

Mitsubishi Corporation Services (1)
Granada Business Park A4 5th Floor Airport Road Near Exit 9, PO Box 3254, Riyadh, Saudi Arabia **(100%)**
Tel.: (966) 11 511 7500
Web Site: http://www.mitsubishi.com
Emp.: 50
Tire Distr
N.A.I.C.S.: 441340

N.V. Yokohama Belgium S.A. (1)
Bosstraat 54, PO Box 8, 3560, Lummen, Belgium
Tel.: (32) 13 61 99 00
Web Site: http://www2.yokohama-online.com
Emp.: 7
Automotive Tires Distr
N.A.I.C.S.: 423130

PRGR Co., Ltd. (1)
5-36-11 Shinbashi Hama Rubber Building 3rd floor, Minato-ku, Tokyo, 105-0004, Japan
Tel.: (81) 33 436 3341
Web Site: https://www.prgr-golf.com
Rubber Products Mfr
N.A.I.C.S.: 326299

PT Yokohama Industrial Products Manufacturing Indonesia (1)
Jl Mas Surya Negara VIII No 6, Kawasan IndustriTerpaduKabil, Batam, 29467, Indonesia
Tel.: (62) 7788070100
Emp.: 142
Tiles Mfr
N.A.I.C.S.: 326211
Henny Sandra *(Mgr-Acct)*

Shandong Yokohama Rubber Industrial Products Co., Ltd. (1)
Xinzhai Local Town, Linqu County, Weifang, 262610, Shandong, China
Tel.: (86) 5363440237
Emp.: 232
Conveying Rubber Belt Mfr & Distr
N.A.I.C.S.: 326220
Zhang Yun *(Gen Mgr)*

Team Yokohama Motorsport France (1)
2 Rue Philippe Lebon, PO Box 375, Genas, 69746, Cedex, France **(100%)**
Tel.: (33) 478900111
Web Site: http://www.yokohama.fr
Emp.: 40
Sales of Tires
N.A.I.C.S.: 423130

The Yokohama Rubber Co., Ltd. - Hamatite Plant (1)
1-7-7 Shinomiya, Hiratsuka, 254-8601, Kanagawa, Japan
Tel.: (81) 46 331 3003
Web Site: http://www.yrc.co.jp
Adhesive Mfr
N.A.I.C.S.: 325520

The Yokohama Rubber Co., Ltd. - Hiratsuka-East Plant (1)
4-6-40 Higashi-Yawata, Hiratsuka, Kanagawa, Japan
Tel.: (81) 463 23 0336
Hose Coupling Mfr
N.A.I.C.S.: 332912

The Yokohama Rubber Co., Ltd. - Ibaraki Plant (1)
1 Hatori-Nishi, Omitama, 319-0128, Ibaraki, Japan
Tel.: (81) 299 46 1111
Emp.: 300
Sealing Material Mfr
N.A.I.C.S.: 339991

The Yokohama Rubber Co., Ltd. - Mie Plant (1)
1038 Takabuku Misono-cho, Ise, 516-8530, Mie, Japan
Tel.: (81) 59 628 3151
Web Site: http://www.y-yokohama.com
Automotive Tire Mfr
N.A.I.C.S.: 326211

The Yokohama Rubber Co., Ltd. - Mishima Plant (1)
8-1 Minami Futsuka-machi, Mishima, Shizuoka, Japan
Tel.: (81) 55 975 0800
Automotive Tire Mfr
N.A.I.C.S.: 326211

The Yokohama Rubber Co., Ltd. - Nagano Plant (1)
548 Yoshida Takamori-cho, Shimoina-gun, Nagano, Japan
Tel.: (81) 265 35 3211
Oil Pressure Hose Joints Mfr
N.A.I.C.S.: 326220

INTERNATIONAL PUBLIC

The Yokohama Rubber Co., Ltd. - Onomichi Plant (1)
20 Higashi-Onomichi, Onomichi, Hiroshima, Japan
Tel.: (81) 848 46 4580
Automotive Tire Mfr
N.A.I.C.S.: 326211

The Yokohama Rubber Co., Ltd. - Panama (1)
Royal Ctr Torre A Seccion B Segundo Piso Oficina 220, Panama, 1050021, Panama
Tel.: (507) 2694545
Emp.: 2
N.A.I.C.S.: 326211

The Yokohama Rubber Co., Ltd. - Shinshiro Plant (1)
1 Furuyashiki, Noda-Aza, Shinshiro, 441-1343, Aichi, Japan
Tel.: (81) 53 622 2251
Web Site: http://www.yrc.co.jp
Automotive Tire Mfr
N.A.I.C.S.: 326211

The Yokohama Rubber Co., Ltd. - Shinshiro-Minami Plant (1)
10-24 Oiri, Hitokuwada-Aza, Shinshiro, 441-1338, Aichi, Japan
Tel.: (81) 53 626 2100
Web Site: http://www.yrc.co.jp
Emp.: 1,000
Automotive Tire Mfr
N.A.I.C.S.: 326211

Trelleborg Wheel Systems AB (1)
Johan Kocksgatan 10, PO Box 153, 231 22, Trelleborg, Sweden
Tel.: (46) 41067000
Sales Range: $450-499.9 Million
Emp.: 2,064
Mfr of Tires & Rims For Forestry & Agricultural Machines, Solid Tires for Goods Handling Equipment, Moulded Products & Rubber Compounds
N.A.I.C.S.: 326211

Subsidiary (Non-US):

Trelleborg BV (2)
Foxham 57, PO Box 33, 9600 AA, Hoogezand, Netherlands **(100%)**
Tel.: (31) 598315911
Sales Range: $25-49.9 Million
Emp.: 50
N.A.I.C.S.: 326211

Trelleborg Lanka (Pvt) Ltd. (2)
Levin Drive Sapugaskanda, Makola, Kelaniya, Sri Lanka **(100%)**
Tel.: (94) 112400338
Web Site: http://www.trelleborg.com
Sales Range: $200-249.9 Million
Emp.: 900
Automotive Wheel & Tire Mfr
N.A.I.C.S.: 326211

Trelleborg Malaysia Sdn. Bhd. (2)
No B-3-7 Endah Promenade No 5 Jln 3/149E Tmn Sri Endah, Bandar Baru Sri Petaling, 57000, Kuala Lumpur, Malaysia **(100%)**
Tel.: (60) 3 9054 9266
Sales Range: $25-49.9 Million
Emp.: 5
N.A.I.C.S.: 326211

Trelleborg South Africa (Pty) Ltd. (2)
Cnr Nederveen Highway and Phillips Road, PO Box 12459, Johannesburg, Elspark, 1401, Guateng, South Africa **(100%)**
Tel.: (27) 118653110
Web Site: http://www.trelleborg.com
Sales Range: $25-49.9 Million
Emp.: 37
N.A.I.C.S.: 326211

Trelleborg Wheel Systems (2)
De Meeus Square 18 - 6, 1050, Brussels, Belgium **(100%)**
Tel.: (32) 25135477
Web Site: http://www.trelleborg.com
Sales Range: $25-49.9 Million
Emp.: 10
N.A.I.C.S.: 326211

Trelleborg Wheel Systems (2)
Helmholtz Strasse 1, 64711, Erbach, Germany **(100%)**
Tel.: (49) 6062 8095 800

AND PRIVATE COMPANIES — THE YOKOHAMA RUBBER CO., LTD.

Web Site: http://www.trelleborg.com
Sales Range: $25-49.9 Million
Emp.: 20
Agricultural Tire Sales
N.A.I.C.S.: 326211

Subsidiary (US):

Trelleborg Wheel Systems Americas, Inc. (2)
3421 Ridgewood Rd Ste 100, Fairlawn, OH 44333
Tel.: (330) 877-4800
Web Site: http://www.trelleborg.com
Sales Range: $50-74.9 Million
Emp.: 171
Industrial Wheels & Industrial, Agricultural & Forestry Tires
N.A.I.C.S.: 326291

Subsidiary (Domestic):

Maine Industrial Tire LLC (3)
107 Audubon Rd, Wakefield, MA 01880
Tel.: (781) 914-3410
Web Site: http://www.mainindustrialtires.com
Sales Range: $50-74.9 Million
Emp.: 850
Industrial Tire Mfr & Distr
N.A.I.C.S.: 326211

Subsidiary (Non-US):

Trelleborg Wheel Systems Argentina S.A (2)
Tucuman 255 - 4th Floor - Office C, C1049AAE, Buenos Aires, Argentina
Tel.: (54) 1140000070
Web Site: https://www.trelleborg.com
Sales Range: $50-74.9 Million
Emp.: 5
Tire & Wheel Distr
N.A.I.C.S.: 423130

Trelleborg Wheel Systems Australia Pty Ltd (2)
25 Darby Way, Dandenong South, Melbourne, 3175, VIC, Australia
Tel.: (61) 3 9797 4700
Web Site: http://www.trelleborg.com
Sales Range: $25-49.9 Million
Automotive Tire Mfr
N.A.I.C.S.: 326211

Subsidiary (Non-US):

TRS Tyre & Wheel Limited (3)
1 Imlay Place, Wanganui, New Zealand (100%)
Tel.: (64) 63446385
Web Site: https://www.trstyreandwheel.co.nz
Tractor Tires & Wheels Distr
N.A.I.C.S.: 423120
Mark Prentice (Sls Mgr-Natl)

Subsidiary (Non-US):

Trelleborg Wheel Systems Belgium N.V. (2)
Brugse Steenweg 7, 9940, Evergem, Belgium (100%)
Tel.: (32) 92572399
Web Site: https://www.trelleborg.com
Emp.: 50
N.A.I.C.S.: 326211

Trelleborg Wheel Systems France SAS (2)
14 Rue du Fonds Pernant, BP 10555, Cedex, 60205, Compiegne, France
Tel.: (33) 344301980
Web Site: https://www.trelleborg.com
Sales Range: $25-49.9 Million
Emp.: 14
Automotive Tire Mfr
N.A.I.C.S.: 326211

Trelleborg Wheel Systems GmbH - Industrial Tires and Wheels (2)
Kleberstrasse 2, PO Box 10 05 52, DE 408 01, Mettmann, Germany (100%)
Tel.: (49) 003292572208
Sales Range: $25-49.9 Million
Emp.: 11
N.A.I.C.S.: 326211

Trelleborg Wheel Systems Lanka Ltd. (2)
No 45 B E P Z, Walgama, Malwana, Sri Lanka (100%)

Tel.: (94) 11 481 9158
Web Site: http://www.trelleborg.com
Sales Range: $100-124.9 Million
Emp.: 438
Industrial Tire Mfr
N.A.I.C.S.: 326211

Trelleborg Wheel Systems Liepaja SIA (2)
Kapsedes Street 2, Liepaja, 3402, Latvia
Tel.: (371) 634 834 18
Web Site: http://www.trelleborg.com
Sales Range: $25-49.9 Million
Emp.: 50
Automotive Tire Mfr
N.A.I.C.S.: 326211

Trelleborg Wheel Systems Middle East Ltd (2)
Jebel Ali Free Zone, PO Box 6115, Dubai, United Arab Emirates
Tel.: (971) 42249525
Web Site: http://www.trelleborg.com
Sales Range: $25-49.9 Million
Automotive Tire Mfr
N.A.I.C.S.: 326211

Trelleborg Wheel Systems S.p.A. (2)
Via Naz Tiburtina 143, Villa Adriana, 10, Rome, Italy
Tel.: (39) 07743841
Sales Range: $100-124.9 Million
Emp.: 460
Mfr of Agricultural Radial Tires
N.A.I.C.S.: 326211

Trelleborg Wheel Systems SEA Pte Ltd (2)
4 Jalan Pesawat, Singapore, 619362, Singapore
Tel.: (65) 62650955
Web Site: http://www.trelleborg.com
Sales Range: $50-74.9 Million
Emp.: 8
Tire & Wheel Distr
N.A.I.C.S.: 423130

Subsidiary (Domestic):

Trelleborg Wheel Systems Savsjo AB (2)
Hjartlandavagen 17, 576 33, Savsjo, Sweden
Tel.: (46) 382 676 80
Web Site: http://www.trelleborg.com
Sales Range: $25-49.9 Million
Emp.: 40
Tire & Wheel Distr
N.A.I.C.S.: 423130

Subsidiary (Non-US):

Trelleborg Wheel Systems UK Limited (2)
1 Redwing Court Willow Farm Business Park, Castle Donington, DE74 2UH, Leicestershire, United Kingdom
Tel.: (44) 1530565656
Web Site: https://www.trelleborg.com
Sales Range: $25-49.9 Million
Emp.: 15
Tire & Wheel Distr
N.A.I.C.S.: 423130

Subsidiary (Domestic):

Trelleborg Wheels AB (2)
Hjartlandavagen 17, 57633, Savsjo, Sweden (100%)
Tel.: (46) 38267680
Sales Range: $25-49.9 Million
Emp.: 40
N.A.I.C.S.: 326211

Subsidiary (Non-US):

Trelleborg do Brasil Ltda. (2)
Avenida Charles Good Year 65 - sala 02 - Cururuquara, Santana de Parnaiba, 06524-115, Sao Paulo, Brazil (100%)
Tel.: (55) 1128029258
Web Site: https://www.trelleborg.com
Sales Range: $25-49.9 Million
Emp.: 15
Wheel Mfr
N.A.I.C.S.: 326211

White Baumaschinenreifen GmbH (1)
Konrad Adenauer Ring 22, Neumuhl,

47167, Duisburg, Germany
Tel.: (49) 2039353804
Web Site: https://reifen-white.de
Tire Mfr & Distr
N.A.I.C.S.: 326211

Yokohama (Suisse) S.A. (1)
La Maladaire 16, Pres Payerne, 1562, Corcelles, Switzerland (100%)
Tel.: (41) 266624000
Web Site: http://de.yokohama.ch
Emp.: 10
Sales of Tires
N.A.I.C.S.: 441340

Yokohama Asia Co., Ltd. (1)
11th Bangkok Business Building 54 Sukhumvit 21 Road Asoke, Khet Wattana, Bangkok, 10110, Thailand
Tel.: (66) 2 664 0450
Automotive Tires Distr
N.A.I.C.S.: 423130

Yokohama Austria GmbH (1)
IZ NO Sud Strasse 15 Obj 77 Stiege 2 Top 3, 2355, Wiener Neudorf, Austria (71%)
Tel.: (43) 2236677400
Web Site: http://www.yokohama.at
Emp.: 10
Sales of Tires
N.A.I.C.S.: 441340

Yokohama CEE Spolka z.o.o. (1)
Ul A Struga 66, 0-5579, Lodz, Poland
Tel.: (48) 422930531
Tire & Wheel Mfr
N.A.I.C.S.: 326211

Yokohama Corporation of North America (1)
1 MacArthur Pl Ste 900, Santa Ana, CA 92707 (100%)
Tel.: (714) 870-3800
Web Site: https://www.yokohamatire.com
Emp.: 316
Holding Company; Regional Managing Office
N.A.I.C.S.: 551112
Hideto Katsuragawa (CEO)

Subsidiary (Domestic):

Yokohama Corporation of America (2)
1 MacArthur Pl Ste 800, Santa Ana, CA 92707
Tel.: (714) 870-3800
Holding Company
N.A.I.C.S.: 551112

Subsidiary (Domestic):

Yokohama Aerospace America, Inc. (3)
22223 68th Ave S, Kent, WA 98032-1010
Tel.: (253) 395-1112
Web Site: http://www.yokohama-aero.com
Emp.: 25
Aircraft Component Mfr & Distr
N.A.I.C.S.: 336413
Kelly Stolle (Gen Mgr)

Yokohama Industries Americas Inc. (3)
Versailles Plant 105 Industry Dr, Versailles, KY 40383-1527
Tel.: (864) 850-2342
Web Site: https://www.yokohamaia.com
Emp.: 1,203
Tiles Mfr
N.A.I.C.S.: 326211
Cory Brusman (COO)

Subsidiary (Domestic):

SAS Rubber Company (4)
474 Newell St, Painesville, OH 44077-1254
Tel.: (440) 352-3321
Tiles Mfr
N.A.I.C.S.: 326211

YH America, Inc (4)
105 Kuhlman Blvd, Versailles, KY 40383
Tel.: (859) 873-2188
Web Site: http://www.yhamerica.com
Automotive Parts Mfr & Distr
N.A.I.C.S.: 336330

Subsidiary (Domestic):

Yokohama Off-Highway Tires America, Inc. (3)

201 Edgewater Dr Ste 285, Wakefield, MA 01880
Tel.: (339) 900-8080
Web Site: http://www.yokohama-oht.com
Tire Whslr
N.A.I.C.S.: 423130
Dhaval Nanavati (Pres)

Yokohama Tire Corporation (3)
1 McArthur Pl Ste 800, Santa Ana, CA 92707
Tel.: (714) 870-3800
Web Site: http://www.yokohamatire.com
Emp.: 150
Tire Mfr & Distr
N.A.I.C.S.: 441340
Thomas Masuguchi (CFO & Exec VP)

Joint Venture (Domestic):

GTY Tire Co. (4)
Po Box 1029, Mount Vernon, IL 62864
Tel.: (618) 246-2263
Sales Range: $100-124.9 Million
Tiles Mfr
N.A.I.C.S.: 326211

Subsidiary (Domestic):

Yokohama Tire Manufacturing Mississippi, LLC (4)
1 Yokohama Blvd, West Point, MS 39773
Emp.: 860
Tiles Mfr
N.A.I.C.S.: 326211

Yokohama Tire Manufacturing Virginia, LLC (4)
1500 Indiana St, Salem, VA 24153-7058
Tel.: (540) 389-5426
Emp.: 642
Tiles Mfr
N.A.I.C.S.: 326211

Subsidiary (Non-US):

Yokohama Tire (Canada), Inc. (2)
Unit 218 20353 64th Ave, Langley, V2Y 1N5, BC, Canada (100%)
Tel.: (604) 546-9656
Web Site: https://tire.yokohama.ca
Emp.: 75
Tire Design, Technology & Mfr
N.A.I.C.S.: 326211

Yokohama Danmark A/S (1)
Hammerholmen 12, 2650, Hvidovre, Denmark (100%)
Tel.: (45) 36454549
Web Site: http://www.yokohama.dk
Emp.: 14
Importer of Tires
N.A.I.C.S.: 441340

Yokohama Europe GmbH (1)
Monschauerstr 12, Monschauer 12, 40549, Dusseldorf, Germany (100%)
Tel.: (49) 21152940
Web Site: http://www.yokohama-online.com
Emp.: 35
Sales of Tires
N.A.I.C.S.: 441340
Keishi Hashimoto (Pres)

Subsidiary (Domestic):

Yokohama Industrial Products Europe GmbH (2)
Monschauerstrasse 12, 40549, Dusseldorf, Germany
Tel.: (49) 2115 374 0570
Web Site: http://www.yrc.co.jp
Industrial Supplies Distr
N.A.I.C.S.: 423840

Yokohama Reifen GmbH (2)
Monschauer Str 12, 40549, Dusseldorf, Germany (100%)
Tel.: (49) 21152940
Web Site: http://www.yokohama.de
Emp.: 20
Sales of Tires
N.A.I.C.S.: 441340

Yokohama HPT Ltd. (1)
Dawson Road Mount Farm, Milton Keynes, Bletchley, MK1 1QY, United Kingdom (100%)
Tel.: (44) 1908625625
Web Site: http://www.yokohama.co.uk
Emp.: 55

THE YOKOHAMA RUBBER CO., LTD.

The Yokohama Rubber Co., Ltd.—(Continued)
Sales & Distribution of Tires
N.A.I.C.S.: 441340

Yokohama Hamatite (Hangzhou) Co., Ltd (1)
No 12 Avenue No 18 Hangzhou Economic Technological Development Zone, Xiasha, Hangzhou, China
Tel.: (86) 5718 672 5870
Web Site: http://www.yrc.co.jp
Car Sealant Mfr & Distr
N.A.I.C.S.: 339991

Yokohama Hoses & Coupling (Hangzhou) Co., Ltd. (1)
No 12 Avenue No 18 Hangzhou Economic Technological Development Zone, Xiasha, Hangzhou, China
Tel.: (86) 5718 685 2591
Web Site: http://www.yrc.co.jp
Hydraulic Hose Mfr & Distr
N.A.I.C.S.: 332912

Yokohama Iberia, S.A. (1)
Calle Isla Graciosa 1 2 Planta Puerta 6, San Sebastian de los Reyes, 28703, Madrid, Spain
Tel.: (34) 916591560
Web Site: https://www.yokohama.eu
Tiles Mfr
N.A.I.C.S.: 326211

Yokohama India Pvt. Ltd. (1)
401-406 4th Floor Mohan Dev Building 13 Tolstoy Marg, New Delhi, 110 001, India
Tel.: (91) 11 66032066
Web Site: http://www.yokohama-india.com
Emp.: 25
Automotive Tires Distr
N.A.I.C.S.: 423130

Yokohama Industrial Products Asia-Pacific Pte. Ltd. (1)
160 Robinson Road SBF Center 15-01, Singapore, 068914, Singapore
Tel.: (65) 69709188
Emp.: 6
Tire Distr
N.A.I.C.S.: 423130
Darren Seah (Sls Mgr)

Yokohama Industrial Products Italy S.r.l. (1)
Localita Tamarete, 66026, Ortona, CH, Italy
Tel.: (39) 08590338201
Web Site: http://www.it-yokohama.com
Tiles Mfr
N.A.I.C.S.: 326211
Marco Aquino (Mgr-HR)

Yokohama Industrial Products Sales - Shanghai Co., Ltd. (1)
10F Gubei Soho 188 Ruby Road, Shanghai, 201103, China
Tel.: (86) 212368811
Web Site: http://www.yokohamamb.cn
Conveyor Belt Distr
N.A.I.C.S.: 423830

Yokohama Industrial Products-Hangzhou Co., Ltd. (1)
No 89 Sanfeng Road Qianjin Street, Xiaoshan District, Hangzhou, China
Tel.: (86) 57156975288
Emp.: 141
Tire Distr
N.A.I.C.S.: 423130

Yokohama Industries Americas Ohio Inc. (1)
474 Newell St, Painesville, OH 44077
Tel.: (440) 352-3321
Web Site: https://yokohamaiaohio.com
Industrial Rubber Hose Mfr & Distr
N.A.I.C.S.: 326220

Yokohama Italia S.p.A. (1)
Localita Taglie 44 Carpenedolo, Brescia, 25013, Italy
Tel.: (39) 03099871
Web Site: http://www.yokahama.it
Sales of Tires
N.A.I.C.S.: 441340

Yokohama Mold Co., Ltd. (1)
2227-1 Kamitamari, Omitama, 311-3436, Ibaraki, Japan
Tel.: (81) 299261417

Emp.: 120
Automotive Tire Mfr
N.A.I.C.S.: 326211
Shinichi Sakurai (Mgr)

Yokohama Rubber (China) Co., Ltd (1)
10F Gubei International Fortune Center 1452 Hongqiao Road, Shanghai, 201103, China
Tel.: (86) 21 3209 1717
Web Site: http://www.yrc.co.jp
Emp.: 160
Automotive Tire Mfr & Distr
N.A.I.C.S.: 326211

Yokohama Rubber (Thailand) Co., Ltd. (1)
Eastern Seaboard Industrial Estate Rayong 64 Moo 4 TambolPluakdaeng, AmphurPluakdaeng, Rayong, 21140, Thailand
Tel.: (66) 38954625
Emp.: 73
Tire Distr
N.A.I.C.S.: 423130

Yokohama Rubber Latin America Industria e Comercio Ltda. (1)
Rua Cubatao n86 Conjunto 1510 15 Andar, Paraiso, 04013-000, Sao Paulo, Brazil
Tel.: (55) 1132843484
Web Site: http://www.yrc.co.jp
Automotive Tires Distr
N.A.I.C.S.: 423130

Yokohama Russia L.L.C. (1)
st Panfilova possession 19 building 4 floor 2 room 1, Khimki, Moscow, 141407, Russia
Tel.: (7) 4957394844
Web Site: https://www.yokohama.ru
Emp.: 65
Automotive Tires Distr
N.A.I.C.S.: 423130
Takayuki Hamaya (Pres)

Yokohama Scandinavia AB (1) (56%)
Tel.: (46) 84457888
Web Site: http://www.yokohama.se
Sales Range: $10-24.9 Million
Emp.: 16
Sales of Tires
N.A.I.C.S.: 441340

Yokohama TWS (Malaysia) Sdn. Bhd. (1)
No 22 Jalan 30B / 146 Taman Desa Tasik Sungai Besi, MY-57000, Kuala Lumpur, Malaysia
Tel.: (60) 390596388
Tire & Wheel Mfr
N.A.I.C.S.: 326211

Yokohama TWS (Xingtai) Co. Ltd. (1)
999 Jianshe St, Xingtai, 54000, Hebei, China
Tel.: (86) 3192679578
Tire & Wheel Mfr
N.A.I.C.S.: 326211

Yokohama TWS Australia Pty. Ltd. (1)
25 Darby Way, Dandenong South, 3175, VIC, Australia
Tel.: (61) 397974700
Tire & Wheel Mfr
N.A.I.C.S.: 326211

Yokohama TWS Austria GmbH (1)
Am Teich 1 A, 4300, Sankt Valentin, Austria
Tel.: (43) 60628095800
Tire Mfr & Distr
N.A.I.C.S.: 326211

Yokohama TWS Belgium N.V. (1)
Brugse Steenweg 7, B 9940, Evergem, Belgium
Tel.: (32) 92572220
Tire & Wheel Mfr
N.A.I.C.S.: 326211

Yokohama TWS Brazil Ltda. (1)
Avenida Charles Good Year 65 - Sala 02 Cururuquara, Sao Paulo, Santana de Parnaiba, 06524-115, Brazil
Tel.: (55) 1128029258
Tire & Wheel Mfr
N.A.I.C.S.: 326211

Yokohama TWS Czech Republic a.s.
Svehlova 1900/3 Zabehlice, 106 00, Prague, Czech Republic
Tel.: (420) 283842600
Tire & Wheel Mfr
N.A.I.C.S.: 326211

Yokohama TWS Germany GmbH (1)
Helmholtzstrasse 1, D-64711, Erbach, Germany
Tel.: (49) 60628095800
Tire & Wheel Mfr
N.A.I.C.S.: 326211

Yokohama TWS Latvia LSEZ SIA (1)
Kapsedes Street 2, Liepaja, LV-3402, Latvia
Tel.: (371) 63483418
Tire & Wheel Mfr
N.A.I.C.S.: 326211

Yokohama TWS Mexico S.A. de C.V. (1)
Pedregal 3427 Col Moctezuma, 64240, Monterrey, Nuevo Leon, Mexico
Tel.: (52) 18183012021
Tire & Wheel Mfr
N.A.I.C.S.: 326211

Yokohama TWS North America, Inc. (1)
570 Trelleborg Dr, Spartanburg, SC 29301
Tire & Wheel Mfr
N.A.I.C.S.: 326211

Yokohama TWS Poland Sp. z o.o. (1)
Ul Andrzeja Struga 66, 90-557, Lodz, Poland
Tel.: (48) 422930537
Tire & Wheel Mfr
N.A.I.C.S.: 326211

Yokohama TWS RUS OOO (1)
Roschchynskiy Proezd 8 2-nd, Moscow, RU-115419, Russia
Tel.: (7) 4952325579
Tire & Wheel Mfr
N.A.I.C.S.: 326211

Yokohama TWS S.p.A. (1)
Via Giovanni Gentile 3, 20157, Milan, Italy
Tel.: (39) 02660391
Tire & Wheel Mfr
N.A.I.C.S.: 326211

Yokohama TWS Serbia d.o.o. (1)
Industrijska bb, 22400, Ruma, Serbia
Tel.: (381) 22400065
Tire Mfr & Distr
N.A.I.C.S.: 326211

Yokohama TWS Singapore Pte. Ltd. (1)
4 Jalan Pesawat, Singapore, 619362, Singapore
Tel.: (65) 62622112
Tire & Wheel Mfr
N.A.I.C.S.: 326211

Yokohama TWS Slovenia, d.o.o. (1)
Skofjeloska Cesta 6, 4000, Kranj, Slovenia
Tel.: (386) 42065883
Tire Mfr & Distr
N.A.I.C.S.: 326211

Yokohama TWS Sweden AB (1)
Johan Kocksgatan 10, SE-231 81, Trelleborg, Sweden
Tel.: (46) 41051224
Tire & Wheel Mfr
N.A.I.C.S.: 326211

Yokohama TWS Switzerland GmbH (1)
Bertiswilstrasse 52, CH 6023, Rothenburg, Switzerland
Tel.: (41) 412108200
Tire & Wheel Mfr
N.A.I.C.S.: 326211

Yokohama Tire Japan Co., Ltd. (1)
Shinagawa Intercity Tower C 13th floor 15-3 Konan 2-chome, Minato-Ku, Tokyo, 108-6213, Japan
Tel.: (81) 354004609
Emp.: 2,762
Automotive Tires Distr
N.A.I.C.S.: 423130

INTERNATIONAL PUBLIC

Yokohama Tire Korea Co., Ltd. (1)
320 Gangnam-daero, Gangnam-gu, Seoul, Korea (South)
Tel.: (82) 25881533
Web Site: https://www.yokohamakorea.com
Emp.: 7
Automotive Tire Mfr
N.A.I.C.S.: 326211

Yokohama Tire Manufacturing (Thailand) Co., Ltd. (1)
7/216 Moo 6 Amata City Industrial Estate, Tambol Map Yang Porn, Pluak Daeng, 21140, Rayong, Thailand
Tel.: (66) 38627170
Emp.: 1,858
Tiles Mfr
Tetsuya Kuze (CEO)

Yokohama Tire Philippines, Inc. (1)
Industrial Estate 5 Clark Freeport Zone, Mabalacat City, Pampanga, 2023, Philippines (100%)
Tel.: (63) 455993603
Web Site: https://www.ytpi.com
Emp.: 3,108
Tire Mfr & Distr
N.A.I.C.S.: 326211

Yokohama Tire Sales (Shanghai) Co., Ltd. (1)
10th Floor Gubei Soho 1st Floor No 188 Ruby Road, Changning District, Shanghai, 200336, Changning, China
Tel.: (86) 2162368811
Web Site: https://www.yokohamatire.cn
Emp.: 180
Automotive Tire Distr & Sales Center
N.A.I.C.S.: 423130

Yokohama Tire Sales (Thailand) Co., Ltd. (1)
12th Floor Zones A B Thanapoom Tower 1550 New Petchburi Road Makasan, Ratchathewi, Bangkok, 10400, Thailand
Tel.: (66) 26526996
Web Site: https://www.yokohamathailand.com
Automotive Tires Distr
N.A.I.C.S.: 423130

Yokohama Tire Sales Philippines, Inc. (1)
3/F Kentek Building 828 A Arnaiz Avenue, San Lorenzo, Makati, 1229, Philippines
Tel.: (63) 288175031
Web Site: https://www.yokohamatire.ph
Emp.: 24
Automotive Tires Distr
N.A.I.C.S.: 423130

Yokohama Tire Taiwan Co., Ltd. (1) (100%)
Tel.: (886) 223568528
Web Site: https://www.yokohamatire.com.tw
Emp.: 15
Sales of Tires & Related Products
N.A.I.C.S.: 441340

Yokohama Tyre Australia Pty., Ltd. (1)
123-129 Silverwater Road, Silverwater, 2128, NSW, Australia
Web Site: http://www.yokohama.com.au
Emp.: 30
Sales of Tires
N.A.I.C.S.: 441340

Yokohama Tyre Vietnam Inc. (1)
No 17 Street 10 Vietnam Singapore Industrial Park, Binh Hoa Ward, Thuan An, Binh Duong, Vietnam
Tel.: (84) 6503767909
Tire Mfr & Marketer
N.A.I.C.S.: 326211

Yokohamagomu Finance Co, Ltd. (1)
5-36-11 Shinbashi, Minato-ku, Tokyo, 105-0004, Japan
Tel.: (81) 33 431 5986
Web Site: https://www.yokohama-yfc.jp
Automobile Parts Distr
N.A.I.C.S.: 441330

THE YOMIURI SHIMBUN

1-7-1 Otemachi, Chiyoda-ku, Tokyo, 100-8055, Japan

Tel.: (81) 332421111 JP
Web Site: http://www.yomiuri.co.jp
Year Founded: 1874
Sales Range: $5-14.9 Billion
Media Holding Company; Newspaper Publisher
N.A.I.C.S.: 551112
Tsuneo Watanabe *(Editor-in-Chief)*

Subsidiaries:

Chuokoron-Shinsha, Inc. (1)
2-8-7 Kyobashi, Chuo-ku, Tokyo, 104-8320, Japan
Tel.: (81) 3 3563 1261
Web Site: http://www.chuko.co.jp
Emp.: 137
Book & Magazine Publisher
N.A.I.C.S.: 513130

THE YONDER DIGITAL GROUP LIMITED
Melford Court The Havens Ransomes Europark, Ipswich, IP3 9SJ, United Kingdom
Tel.: (44) 203 319 3747 UK
Web Site: http://www.wearewoven.com
Year Founded: 2011
Voice, Data & Contact Center Services
N.A.I.C.S.: 561421
Chris Robinson *(CEO)*

Subsidiaries:

CallScripter Limited (1)
75 Basepoint The Havens, Ipswich, IP3 9SJ, Suffolk, United Kingdom
Tel.: (44) 8445448882
Web Site: http://www.callscripter.com
Call Centre Software Services
N.A.I.C.S.: 541511
Andy Hemingway *(Dir-Dev)*

IPPlus (UK) Limited (1)
Melford Court The Havens Ransomes Europark, Ipswich, IP3 9SJ, Suffolk, United Kingdom
Tel.: (44) 1473398677
Web Site: http://www.ansaback.co.uk
Emp.: 250
Call Center Solutions
N.A.I.C.S.: 561422
Christian Pawsey *(Mng Dir)*

THE YONKYU CO., LTD.
2-318-235 Tsukiji-cho, Uwajima, 798-8691, Ehime, Japan
Tel.: (81) 895240001
Web Site: https://www.yonkyu.co.jp
Year Founded: 1975
9955—(TKS)
Rev.: $340,852,160
Assets: $414,817,040
Liabilities: $108,580,560
Net Worth: $306,236,480
Earnings: $19,340,640
Fiscal Year-end: 03/31/22
Seafood Distr
N.A.I.C.S.: 424460
Kouzo Kasaoka *(Pres)*

THE ZENITAKA CORPORATION
2-2-4 Nishihonmachi, Nishi-ku, Osaka, 550-0005, Japan
Tel.: (81) 665316431 JP
Web Site: https://www.zenitaka.co.jp
Year Founded: 1887
1811—(TKS)
Rev.: $799,657,970
Assets: $1,345,868,710
Liabilities: $731,608,020
Net Worth: $614,260,690
Earnings: $18,091,570
Emp.: 915
Fiscal Year-end: 03/31/24
Construction & Real Estate Services
N.A.I.C.S.: 541330
Hisayoshi Zenitaka *(Pres)*

THE ZOOLOGICAL SOCIETY OF LONDON
Outer Circle Regents Park, London, NW1 4RY, United Kingdom
Tel.: (44) 344 225 1826
Web Site: http://www.zsl.org
Year Founded: 1826
Rev.: $89,699,410
Assets: $98,497,525
Liabilities: $13,629,275
Net Worth: $84,868,251
Earnings: ($4,714,409)
Emp.: 977
Fiscal Year-end: 04/30/19
Zoo Operator
N.A.I.C.S.: 712130
Geoff Boxshall *(Sec)*

Subsidiaries:

Institute of Zoology (1)
Regent's Park, London, NW1 4RY, United Kingdom
Tel.: (44) 2074496610
Web Site: http://www.zoo.cam.ac.uk
Emp.: 60
Zoological Education Services
N.A.I.C.S.: 923110

Whipsnade Wild Animal Park Limited (1)
Whipsnade, Dunstable, LU6 2LF, Bedfordshire, United Kingdom
Tel.: (44) 1582 872 171
Zoo Operator
N.A.I.C.S.: 712130

Wipsnade Wild Animal Park (1)
Whipsnade Zoo, Dunstable, LU6 2LF, Befordshire, United Kingdom
Tel.: (44) 1582872171
Web Site: http://www.zsl.org
Emp.: 130
Zoo Operations
N.A.I.C.S.: 712130
Ralph Armond *(Gen Dir)*

ZSL London Zoo (1)
Regents Park, London, NW1 4RY, United Kingdom
Tel.: (44) 3442251826
Web Site: http://www.zsl.org
Zoos & Botanical Gardens
N.A.I.C.S.: 712130

ZSL Whipsnade Zoo (1)
Dunstable, Bedford, LU6 2LF, United Kingdom (100%)
Tel.: (44) 3442251826
Web Site: http://www.zsl.org
Zoos & Botanical Gardens
N.A.I.C.S.: 712130

THE ZUELLIG GROUP INC.
Suite 2003 20th Floor Shui On Centre No 6-8 Harbour Road, Wanchai, China (Hong Kong)
Tel.: (852) 25238555
Web Site: http://www.zuellig.com
Sales Range: $5-14.9 Billion
Emp.: 10,000
Holding Company
N.A.I.C.S.: 551112
Cecilia Chu *(Treas)*

Subsidiaries:

BI Nutraceuticals Asia Pacific (1)
No 2 Mechanical Workshop Export Processing Zone, High & New Tech Industrial Development Zone, Suzhou, 215151, China
Tel.: (86) 139 0149 5887
Pharmaceutical Mfr & Distr
N.A.I.C.S.: 325412
George Pontiakos *(Pres & CEO)*

C B Norwood Distributors Limited (1)
888 Tremaine Avenue, PO Box 1265, Palmerston North, 4440, New Zealand
Tel.: (64) 6 356 4920
Web Site: http://www.norwood.co.nz
Farm Machinery & Equipment Distr
N.A.I.C.S.: 423820

FPG Insurance (Thailand) Company Limited (1)
52 Thaniya Plaza Building 16th Floor Silom Road, Bangkok, 10500, Thailand
Tel.: (66) 2231 2640
Web Site: http://www.fpgins.co.th
Personal insurance services
N.A.I.C.S.: 524114

FPG Insurance Co., Inc. (1)
Zuellig Building 6F Makati Avenue corner, Paseo de Roxas, 1225, Makati, Philippines
Tel.: (63) 28591200
Web Site: http://www.fpgins.com.ph
General Insurance Services
N.A.I.C.S.: 524298

PT. Asuransi FPG Indonesia (1)
Chase Plaza Tower 4th Floor Jl Jend Sudirman Kav 21, Jakarta, 12920, Indonesia
Tel.: (62) 21 5200177
Web Site: http://www.fpgins.co.id
Personal insurance services
N.A.I.C.S.: 524114
Kuswantara Kohar *(Pres)*

Powerlift Material Handling Ltd. (1)
11A Blackburn Rd, East Tamaki, Auckland, 2013, New Zealand
Tel.: (64) 9 525 1020
Web Site: http://www.powerlift.co.nz
Material Handling Machinery Rental Services
N.A.I.C.S.: 532490

ZI-Techasia Solutions Ltd. (1)
11/F - 12/F Ploenchit Center 2 Sukhumvit Road, Kwaeng Klongtoey Khet Klongtoey, Bangkok, 10110, Thailand
Tel.: (66) 2 656 8710
Web Site: http://www.zuelligindustrial.com
Industrial Machinery & Equipment Distr
N.A.I.C.S.: 423830

Subsidiary (Non-US):

PT ZI-TECHASIA (2)
Wisma Budi 2/F Suite 202 Jl H R Rasuna Said Kav C-6, Jakarta, 12940, Indonesia
Tel.: (62) 21 5296 1448
Web Site: http://www.zi-tec.com
Industrial Machinery & Equipment Distr
N.A.I.C.S.: 423830

ZI-ARGUS AUSTRALIA PTY LTD (2)
Centerwest Industrial Estate Unit 5 108-120 Silverwater Road, Silverwater, 2128, NSW, Australia
Tel.: (61) 2 8090 3630
Web Site: http://www.zi-argus.com
Industrial Machinery & Equipment Distr
N.A.I.C.S.: 423830

Zuellig Group NA, Inc. (1)
2550 E El Presidio St, Long Beach, CA 90810-1113
Tel.: (310) 637-9566
Web Site: http://www.botanicals.com
Sales Range: $10-24.9 Million
Emp.: 70
Holding Company
N.A.I.C.S.: 424210

Subsidiary (Domestic):

AF-Zeta, Inc. (2)
163 Madison Ave Fl 4, Morristown, NJ 07960
Tel.: (973) 267-2205
Web Site: http://afzeta.en.chemnet.com
Distr of Bulk Fine Chemicals, Excipients & Generic Active Ingredients
N.A.I.C.S.: 424210

Zuellig Pharma Asia Pacific Ltd. (1)
1303 Shui On Centre 6-8 Harbour Road, Wanchai, China (Hong Kong)
Tel.: (852) 2845 2677
Web Site: http://www.zuelligpharma.com
Pharmaceutical Products Distr
N.A.I.C.S.: 424210

Subsidiary (Non-US):

P.T. Anugerah Pharmindo Lestari (2)
Cowell Tower Lt 12 Jl Senen Raya No 135, Jakarta, 10410, Indonesia
Tel.: (62) 21 345 6008
Pharmaceutical Products Distr

N.A.I.C.S.: 424210

Zuellig Pharma Bangladesh Ltd. (2)
110 Tejgaon Industrial Area, Dhaka, 1208, Bangladesh
Tel.: (880) 2 887 0391
Pharmaceutical Products Distr
N.A.I.C.S.: 424210

Zuellig Pharma Corporation (2)
Km 14 West Service Road South Superhighway cor. Edison Avenue, Sun Valley, 1700, Paranaque, Metro Manila, Philippines
Tel.: (63) 2 908 2222
Pharmaceutical Products Distr
N.A.I.C.S.: 424210

Zuellig Pharma Korea Ltd. (2)
3/F LS Yongsan Tower 92 Hangangdaero, Yongsan-gu, Seoul, 140-702, Korea (South)
Tel.: (82) 2 2006 0600
Pharmaceutical Products Distr
N.A.I.C.S.: 424210

Zuellig Pharma Ltd. (2)
8-9/F Ploenchit Center 2 Sukhumvit Road, Kwaeng Klongtoey Khet Klongtoey, Bangkok, 10110, Thailand
Tel.: (66) 2 656 9800
Pharmaceutical Products Distr
N.A.I.C.S.: 424210

Zuellig Pharma Ltd. (2)
No 266 Lum Street, Rong Chak Village Sangkat Phnom Penh Thmey Khan Sen Sok, Phnom Penh, Cambodia
Tel.: (855) 23 231 501
Pharmaceutical Products Distr
N.A.I.C.S.: 424210

Zuellig Pharma Pte. Ltd. (2)
15 Changi North Way 01-01, Singapore, 498770, Singapore
Tel.: (65) 6546 8188
Pharmaceutical Products Distr
N.A.I.C.S.: 424210

Zuellig Pharma Sdn. Bhd. (2)
15 Persiaran Pasak Bumi Seksyen U8 Perindustrian Bukit Jelutong, 40150, Shah Alam, Selangor Darul Ehsan, Malaysia
Tel.: (60) 3 5566 2288
Web Site: http://www.zuelligpharma.com
Pharmaceutical Products Distr
N.A.I.C.S.: 424210

Zuellig Pharma Vietnam Ltd. (2)
Sai Dong B Industrial Park, Long Bien, Hanoi, Vietnam
Tel.: (84) 8 3910 2650
Pharmaceutical Products Distr
N.A.I.C.S.: 424210

Zuellig Pharma, Inc. (2)
10/F 126 Nanking East Road Sec 4, Taipei, Taiwan
Tel.: (886) 2 2570 0064
Pharmaceutical Products Distr
N.A.I.C.S.: 424210

Zuellig Pharma Ltd. (1)
Ste 608 6Fl Taikoo Place Devon House 979 King's Rd, Quarry Bay, China (Hong Kong)
Tel.: (852) 28563632
Web Site: http://www.zuelligpharma.com.hk
Emp.: 7,000
Pharmaceuticals Mfr
N.A.I.C.S.: 325412
Ada Pang *(Mgr-Fin)*

THE7STARS
46 Charlotte St, London, W1T2GS, United Kingdom
Tel.: (44) 2074367275
Web Site: http://www.the7stars.co.uk
Year Founded: 2005
Sales Range: $10-24.9 Million
Emp.: 28
N.A.I.C.S.: 541810
Jenny Biggam *(Owner)*

THE9 LIMITED
17 Floor No 130 Wu Song Road, Hong Kou District, Shanghai, 200080, China
Tel.: (86) 2151729999 Ky
Web Site: https://www.the9.com

THE9 LIMITED

The9 Limited—(Continued)
NCTY—(NASDAQ)
Rev.: $24,790,800
Assets: $50,360,687
Liabilities: $25,253,095
Net Worth: $25,107,592
Earnings: $1,741,302
Emp.: 50
Fiscal Year-end: 12/31/23
Online Game Operator & Developer
N.A.I.C.S.: 513210
Jun Zhu *(Founder, Chm & CEO)*

Subsidiaries:

Red 5 Studios, Inc. (1)
24022 Calle De La Plata Ste 200, Laguna Hills, CA 92653
Tel.: (949) 754-0919
Web Site: http://www.red5studios.com
Online Game Developer & Publisher
N.A.I.C.S.: 513210
Mark Kern *(CEO & Chief Creative Officer)*

THEBE INVESTMENT CORPORATION
18 Fricker Road 2nd Floor Illovo Boulevard Illovo, Sandton, 2196, Johannesburg, South Africa
Tel.: (27) 114477800
Web Site: http://www.thebe.co.za
Year Founded: 1993
Sales Range: $450-499.9 Million
Emp.: 1,115
Commercial Banking & Financial Services
N.A.I.C.S.: 522110
Sizwe Mncwango *(CEO)*

Subsidiaries:

Reatile Timrite (Pty) Ltd (1)
Block D Palms Office Court Kudu Street Allens Nek, Roodepoort, South Africa
Tel.: (27) 11 475 1600
Web Site: http://www.timrite.co.za
Lumber Whslr
N.A.I.C.S.: 423990
Theunis Bester *(Mng Dir)*

Thebe Community Financial Services (Pty) Ltd. (1)
Thebe House 166 Jan Smuts Avenue, Rosebank, Johannesburg, 2196, South Africa
Tel.: (27) 114477800
Sales Range: $25-49.9 Million
Emp.: 35
Financial Products & Services
N.A.I.C.S.: 921130

Subsidiary (Domestic):

Creditworx (S&V) (2)
White Lodge 49 Dorado Road, Ormonde, Johannesburg, South Africa (100%)
Tel.: (27) 0112482200
Web Site: http://www.worx.co.za
Sales Range: $25-49.9 Million
Emp.: 65
Holding Company for Debt Collection Services
N.A.I.C.S.: 551112

Thebe Employee Benefits (Pty) Ltd. (2)
PO Box 4709, Johannesburg, 2000, South Africa (100%)
Tel.: (27) 0115448300
Web Site: http://www.thebe.co.za
Sales Range: $25-49.9 Million
Financial Services & Products Broker & Administrator
N.A.I.C.S.: 524210

Thebe Stockbroking (Pty) Ltd. (1)
The Crescent 2nd Floor Georgian Crescent East, PO Box 67753, Bryanston, 2021, Johannesburg, South Africa
Tel.: (27) 113751000
Web Site: http://www.thebesec.co.za
Stock Brokerage Services
N.A.I.C.S.: 523150

Thebe ya Bophelo Healthcare Administrators (Pty) Ltd (1)
Ground Floor & 2 Floor Old Trafford 4 Building Isle of Houghton, PO Box 4709, Cnr Boundry & Carse O'Gowrie Rds, Johannesburg, 2000, South Africa
Tel.: (27) 11 544 8000
Web Site: http://www.tybhealth.co.za
Health Care Srvices
N.A.I.C.S.: 621498
Wesley Nplovu *(Gen Mgr-Bus Dev)*

THEEGARTEN-PACTEC GMBH & CO. KG
Breitscheidstrasse 46, Dresden, 1237, Germany
Tel.: (49) 35125730
Web Site: http://www.theegarten-pactec.de
Rev.: $62,956,924
Emp.: 420
Packaging Machinery Mfr
N.A.I.C.S.: 333993
Markus Rustler *(Mng Dir)*

THEJO ENGINEERING LIMITED
41 Cathedral Road 3rd Floor V D Swami Building, Chennai, 600 086, India
Tel.: (91) 4442221900
Web Site: http://www.thejo-engg.com
Rev.: $33,066,878
Fiscal Year-end: 03/31/19
Industrial Machinery & Equipment Mfr
N.A.I.C.S.: 333248
V. A. George *(Mng Dir)*

Subsidiaries:

Thejo Australia Pty Ltd. (1)
Kalmia Road 5, Perth, 6163, WA, Australia
Tel.: (61) 894344811
Industrial Equipment Distr
N.A.I.C.S.: 423830
Shine Varghese *(Mng Dir)*

Thejo Hatcon Industrial Services Company (1)
PO Box 30756, Al Khobar, 31952, Saudi Arabia
Tel.: (966) 38082490
Web Site: http://www.thejohatcon.com
Conveyor Belt Distr
N.A.I.C.S.: 423910

THELLOY DEVELOPMENT GROUP
2/F Centre 600 82 King Lam Street Lai Chi Kok, Kowloon, China (Hong Kong)
Tel.: (852) 2 529 9333   Ky
Web Site: http://www.thelloy.com
Year Founded: 1982
1546—(HKG)
Rev.: $26,356,031
Assets: $35,127,058
Liabilities: $15,942,702
Net Worth: $19,184,356
Earnings: $549,971
Emp.: 69
Fiscal Year-end: 03/31/23
Building Construction Services
N.A.I.C.S.: 236220
Eddie Kin Wing Lam *(Chm & CEO)*

THELMA THERAPEUTICS CO., LTD.
218 Medi-Partner Building Bongeunsa-ro, Gangnam-gu, Seoul, Korea (South)
Tel.: (82) 25545767
Web Site: http://www.medi-plant.co.kr
Year Founded: 1981
015540—(KRS)
Rev.: $106
Assets: $8,340,393
Liabilities: $11,799,781
Net Worth: ($3,459,388)
Earnings: ($3,013,550)
Emp.: 2
Fiscal Year-end: 12/31/22

Merchandise Coupon Distr
N.A.I.C.S.: 561990

THEM ADVERTISING (SA) PTY LTD
1/26 The Parade West, Kent Town, 5067, SA, Australia
Tel.: (61) 883632717
Web Site: http://www.them.com.au
Year Founded: 1983
Sales Range: $25-49.9 Million
N.A.I.C.S.: 541810
Mark Wightman *(Mng Dir)*

THEMAC RESOURCES GROUP LIMITED
1500 - 409 Granville Street, Vancouver, V6C 1T2, BC, Canada
Tel.: (604) 868-5394
Web Site: https://www.themacresources.com
MAC—(TSXV)
Assets: $65,408,767
Liabilities: $130,368,716
Net Worth: ($64,959,949)
Earnings: ($9,818,943)
Fiscal Year-end: 06/30/24
Mineral Exploration Services
N.A.I.C.S.: 213114
Kevin Maloney *(Chm)*

THEME INTERNATIONAL HOLDINGS LIMITED
Unit 3401-03 34/F China Merchants Tower Shun Tak Centre, 168-200 Connaugh Road Central Sheung Wan, Hong Kong, China (Hong Kong)
Tel.: (852) 26155088   BM
Web Site: http://www.990.com.hk
0990—(HKG)
Rev.: $4,984,093,320
Assets: $1,736,127,083
Liabilities: $982,735,575
Net Worth: $753,391,508
Earnings: $200,069,685
Emp.: 360
Fiscal Year-end: 12/31/22
Garment Sales
N.A.I.C.S.: 424350
Lei Wu *(CFO)*

Subsidiaries:

BPI Financial Group Limited (1)
Units 3401-03 34/F China Merchants Tower Shun Tak Centre, No 168-200 Connaught Road Central, Sheung Wan, China (Hong Kong)
Tel.: (852) 37558228
Web Site: https://www.bpifinancial.com
Boutique Financial Services
N.A.I.C.S.: 541611
Kenny Mah *(CEO)*

Bright Point International Financial (UK) Ltd. (1)
83 Victoria Street, London, SW1H 0HW, United Kingdom
Tel.: (44) 2039176843
Market Leading Brokerage Services
N.A.I.C.S.: 541613

Bright Point International Futures (SG) Pte. Ltd. (1)
3 Anson Road Springleaf Tower 19-01, Singapore, 079909, Singapore
Tel.: (65) 64990618
Boutique Financial Services
N.A.I.C.S.: 541611
Brian Goh *(Head-Risk)*

THEMIS G.R.E.N. LTD
Yad-haruzim 3, Jerusalem, 93420, Israel
Tel.: (972) 98915499
TMIS—(TAE)
Rev.: $397,755
Assets: $17,269,400
Liabilities: $1,289,789
Net Worth: $15,979,611

INTERNATIONAL PUBLIC

Earnings: ($2,853,153)
Fiscal Year-end: 12/31/22
Residential & Commercial Property Development Services
N.A.I.C.S.: 531210
Nir Yehezkeli *(CEO)*

THEMIS MEDICARE LTD
11/12 Udyog Nagar SV Road, Goregaon W, Mumbai, 400 104, India
Tel.: (91) 2267607080
Web Site: https://www.themismedicare.com
530199—(BOM)
Rev.: $31,980,844
Assets: $50,660,624
Liabilities: $20,834,527
Net Worth: $29,826,096
Earnings: $4,873,446
Emp.: 976
Fiscal Year-end: 03/31/21
Pharmaceuticals Mfr
N.A.I.C.S.: 325412
Hoshang N. Sinor *(Chm)*

THEO FENNELL LTD.
169 Fulham Road, London, SW3 6PF, United Kingdom
Tel.: (44) 2075915000
Web Site: http://www.theofennell.com
Year Founded: 1975
Jewelry Designer, Mfr & Retailer
N.A.I.C.S.: 339910
Neal Sussman *(Mng Dir)*

THERACLION SA
244 avenue Pierre Brossolette, 92240, Malakoff, France
Tel.: (33) 155489070
Web Site: https://www.theraclion.com
Year Founded: 2004
ALTHE—(EUR)
Sales Range: $1-9.9 Million
Earnings: ($7,455,481)
Echotherapy Medical Equipment Mfr
N.A.I.C.S.: 334510
Jean-Yves Burel *(Pres)*

THERADIAG SA
14 rue Ambroise Croizat, CS 90136, Marne La Vallee, 77435, Croissy-Beaubourg, Cedex 2, France
Tel.: (33) 1 64 62 10 12
Web Site: http://www.theradiag.com
Year Founded: 1986
ALTER—(EUR)
Sales Range: $10-24.9 Million
In-Vitro Diagnostic Equipment Mfr
N.A.I.C.S.: 339112
Michel Finance *(CEO)*

THERAGEN ETEX CO., LTD.
Daegwan Bldg 190 Gangnam-daero, Seocho-gu, Seoul, 16229, Gyeonggi-do, Korea (South)
Tel.: (82) 234637111
Web Site: https://www.theragenetex.com
Year Founded: 1990
066700—(KRS)
Rev.: $148,321,918
Assets: $189,106,318
Liabilities: $68,174,086
Net Worth: $120,932,232
Earnings: $8,399,340
Emp.: 180
Fiscal Year-end: 12/31/22
Industrial Equipment Mfr & Distr
N.A.I.C.S.: 333248
Jin-Up Ko *(CEO)*

Subsidiaries:

Theragen Bio Co., Ltd. (1)
4th Fl Korea Bio Park Bldg C 700 Daewangpangyo-ro, Bundang-gu, Seongnam, 13488, Gyeonggi-do, Korea (South)
Tel.: (82) 15222382

Web Site: http://www.theragenbio.com
Healtcare Services
N.A.I.C.S.: 621999
Samuel Taesoon Hwang (Pres & CEO)

THERALASE TECHNOLOGIES INC.
41 Hollinger Road, Toronto, M4B 3G4, ON, Canada
Tel.: (416) 699-5273
Web Site: https://theralase.com
Year Founded: 1995
TTX—(DEU)
Rev: $790,653
Assets: $2,420,629
Liabilities: $1,013,049
Net Worth: $1,407,581
Earnings: ($3,376,582)
Fiscal Year-end: 12/31/23
Electromedical & Electrotherapeutic Apparatus Mfr
N.A.I.C.S.: 334510
Arkady Mandel (Chief Scientific Officer)

THERAMEX HQ UK LIMITED
Sloane Square House 1 Holbein Place, London, SW1W 8NS, United Kingdom
Tel.: (44) 3330096795
Web Site: https://www.theramex.com
Year Founded: 2017
Women's Health Products Mfr
N.A.I.C.S.: 325412
Robert Stewart (CEO)

THERANEXUS S.A.
Pepiniere Laennec 60 Avenue Rockefeller, 69008, Lyon, France
Tel.: (33) 146549896
Web Site: https://www.theranexus.com
Year Founded: 2013
ALTHX—(EUR)
Sales Range: Less than $1 Million
Pharmaceutical Product Mfr & Distr
N.A.I.C.S.: 325412
Franck Mouthon (Chm & CEO)

THERATECHNOLOGIES, INC.
2015 Peel Street 11th Floor, Montreal, H3A 1T8, QC, Canada
Tel.: (514) 336-7800   QC
Web Site: https://www.theratech.com
Year Founded: 1993
THTX—(NASDAQ)
Rev.: $81,764,000
Assets: $77,769,000
Liabilities: $98,639,000
Net Worth: ($20,870,000)
Earnings: ($23,957,000)
Emp.: 58
Fiscal Year-end: 11/30/23
Biopharmaceutical Mfr
N.A.I.C.S.: 325412
Marie-Noel Colussi (VP-Fin)

THERAVET SA
Avenue Jean Mermoz 32/1, 6041, Gosselies, Belgium   BE
Web Site: https://www.thera.vet
Year Founded: 2017
ALVET—(EUR)
Biotechnology Research & Development Services
N.A.I.C.S.: 541714

THERMA BRIGHT, INC.
345 Danforth Avenue, Toronto, M4K 1N7, ON, Canada
Web Site: https://www.thermabright.com
THRM—(TSXV)
Rev: $19,058
Assets: $2,332,052
Liabilities: $1,363,900
Net Worth: $968,152
Earnings: ($1,792,028)
Emp.: 7
Fiscal Year-end: 07/31/24
Medical Device Research & Development Services
N.A.I.C.S.: 621511
Victor Hugo (CFO)

THERMADOR GROUPE
60 rue de Luzais Parc d Activites de Chesnes, 38 070, Saint-Quentin-Fallavier, Cedex, France
Tel.: (33) 474956328
Web Site: https://www.thermador-groupe.fr
Year Founded: 1968
THEP—(EUR)
Rev.: $641,295,949
Assets: $576,230,268
Liabilities: $180,194,282
Net Worth: $396,035,986
Earnings: $64,354,785
Emp.: 798
Fiscal Year-end: 12/31/23
Pumps & Heating Equipment Distr
N.A.I.C.S.: 423720
Guy Vincent (Co-Founder)

Subsidiaries:

Axelair S.A.   (1)
Chesnes Business Park 65 Luzais Street, CS 41010, 38070, Saint-Quentin-Fallavier, Cedex, France
Tel.: (33) 474821935
Web Site: https://www.axelair-ventilation.fr
Ventilation Product Distr
N.A.I.C.S.: 423730

Dipra SA   (1)
107 Rue Du Ruisseau, Saint-Quentin-Fallavier, 38070, Isere, France
Tel.: (33) 474955665
Web Site: http://www.dipra.fr
Sales Range: $25-49.9 Million
Emp.: 32
Plumbing Equipment Distr
N.A.I.C.S.: 423720
Emmanuelle Desecures (Pres)

Distrilabo S.A.S.   (1)
3 avenue de l'Energie, CS 10086, 67802, Bischheim, Cedex, France
Tel.: (33) 388832058
Web Site: https://www.distrilabo.com
Measurement & Calibration Instrument Mfr
N.A.I.C.S.: 334513

Edouard Rousseau S.A.S.   (1)
9 avenue De Lattre de Tassigny, Saint-Maur-Des-Fosses, 94100, Paris, France
Tel.: (33) 155975959
Web Site: http://www.edouard-rousseau.fr
Faucet & Hydrotherapy Product Mfr
N.A.I.C.S.: 332913

Fginox S.A.S.   (1)
3 route de Lyon, 69530, Brignais, France
Tel.: (33) 437201700
Web Site: https://www.fginox.com
Industrial Valve & Flanges Mfr
N.A.I.C.S.: 332919

Jetly s.a.   (1)
28 Rue de Provence Z A C de Chesnes La Noiree, 38070, Saint-Quentin-Fallavier, CEDEX, France
Tel.: (33) 474941824
Web Site: https://www.jetly.com
Plumbing Equipment Distr
N.A.I.C.S.: 423720
Jean-Francois Bonnefond (Dir-Publ)

Opaline S.A.S.   (1)
60 rue de luzais, 38070, Saint-Quentin-Fallavier, France
Tel.: (33) 474955948
Web Site: https://www.opaline.fr
Graphic Design Development Services
N.A.I.C.S.: 541430
Arlette Berliocchi (CEO)

PB Tub Sarl   (1)
PA de Chesnes 60 Rue du Luzais, 38287, Saint-Quentin-Fallavier, France   (100%)
Tel.: (33) 474956549
Web Site: http://www.pbtub.fr

Sales Range: $25-49.9 Million
Emp.: 31
Plastics Plumbing Fixture Mfr
N.A.I.C.S.: 326191

Sectoriel SA   (1)
45 Rue Du Ruisseau, Saint-Quentin-Fallavier, 38070, Isere, France
Tel.: (33) 474949070
Web Site: http://www.sectoriel.sa
Sales Range: $25-49.9 Million
Emp.: 25
Industrial Equipment Whsr
N.A.I.C.S.: 423830

Sferaco Sarl   (1)
90 rue du Ruisseau, CS 30910, Paro d Activites de Chesnes, 38297, Saint-Quentin-Fallavier, France   (100%)
Tel.: (33) 474941590
Web Site: https://www.sferaco.fr
Sales Range: $25-49.9 Million
Emp.: 45
Plumbing Fixture Fitting & Trim Mfr
N.A.I.C.S.: 332913

Syveco S.A.   (1)
107 Rue du Ruisseau, 38070, Saint-Quentin-Fallavier, France
Tel.: (33) 474948650
Web Site: https://www.syveco.com
Industrial Valve Distr
N.A.I.C.S.: 423840

Thermador International Sarl   (1)
Parc D Activites De Chesne, Rue Du Ruissau, 38070, Saint-Quentin-Fallavier, France   (100%)
Tel.: (33) 474948650
Web Site: http://www.thermador-international.fr
Sales Range: $25-49.9 Million
Emp.: 21
Industrial Machinery & Equipment Whslr
N.A.I.C.S.: 423830

Thermador SA   (1)
Parc d'Activites de Chesnes 80 rue du Ruisseau, BP 720, Saint-Quentin-Fallavier, 38297, Isere, France
Tel.: (33) 474956328
Web Site: http://www.thermador-groupe.fr
Emp.: 5
Industrial Controls Whslr
N.A.I.C.S.: 423840

THERMAL ENERGY INTERNATIONAL INC.
850-36 Antares Drive, Ottawa, K2E 7W5, ON, Canada
Tel.: (613) 723-6776
Web Site: https://www.thermalenergy.com
Year Founded: 1991
EUW—(DEU)
Rev.: $19,118,219
Assets: $12,403,701
Liabilities: $9,875,505
Net Worth: $2,528,196
Earnings: $725,547
Fiscal Year-end: 05/31/24
Air Pollution Control, Renewable Energy & Waste Heat Recovery & Other Energy Conservation Products Developer
N.A.I.C.S.: 541330
John B. Kelly (Chm)

Subsidiaries:

Boilerroom Equipment, Inc.   (1)
11 Rich Hill Rd, Cheswick, PA 15024
Web Site: http://heatsponge.com
Plumbing, Heating & Air-Conditioning Contractors
N.A.I.C.S.: 238220

Thermal Energy International (Guangzhou) Ltd   (1)
Room 607 Wan Chai Bldg No 48, Jianshe Liu Rd, Guangzhou, China
Tel.: (86) 2083190357
Web Site: http://www.thermalenergy.com.cn
Sales Range: $25-49.9 Million
Emp.: 31
Energy Conservation Services
N.A.I.C.S.: 924120

Thermal Energy International Inc. - Bristol   (1)
1 John Street, Bristol, BS1 2HR, United Kingdom
Tel.: (44) 117 917 7010
Web Site: http://www.thermalenergy.com
Sales Range: $25-49.9 Million
Emp.: 20
Energy Conservation Services
N.A.I.C.S.: 924120

THERMAL SYSTEMS KWC LTD.
261185 Wagon Wheel Way, Rocky View, T4A 0E2, AB, Canada
Tel.: (403) 250-5507
Web Site: https://www.thermalsystems.ca
Year Founded: 1985
Insulation Contractor
N.A.I.C.S.: 238310

Subsidiaries:

Skyline Building Systems Inc.   (1)
4500-8A Street NE, Calgary, T2E 4J7, AB, Canada
Tel.: (800) 268-1078
Insulation Material Mfr
N.A.I.C.S.: 238310

THERMAX LIMITED
Thermax House 14 Mumbai-Pune Road Wakdewadi, Pune, 411 003, India
Tel.: (91) 2066051200
Web Site: https://www.thermaxglobal.com
Year Founded: 1966
THERMAX—(NSE)
Rev.: $989,148,133
Assets: $1,059,721,839
Liabilities: $595,694,503
Net Worth: $464,027,336
Earnings: $54,037,528
Emp.: 3,497
Fiscal Year-end: 03/31/23
Engineering Services
N.A.I.C.S.: 541330
M. S. Unnikrishnan (CEO & Mng Dir)

Subsidiaries:

Boilerworks A/S   (1)
Nordager 19, 6000, Kolding, Denmark
Tel.: (45) 73644850
Web Site: https://boilerworks.dk
Heat Exchanger Mfr & Distr
N.A.I.C.S.: 332410

Danstoker A/S   (1)
Industrivej Nord 13, 7400, Herning, Denmark
Tel.: (45) 99287100
Web Site: https://danstoker.com
Boiler Product Mfr & Distr
N.A.I.C.S.: 332410

Danstoker Poland Sp. z o.o.   (1)
ul Kolejowa 20, 27-400, Ostroweic Swietokrzyski, Poland
Tel.: (48) 41 246 0041
Web Site: https://danstoker.com
Boiler Distr
N.A.I.C.S.: 423720

PT Thermax International   (1)
Menara Palma 9 02B and 03 9th Floor Jl HR Rasuna Said Blok, X2 Kav 6 Kuningan, Jakarta, 12950, Indonesia
Tel.: (62) 8111 052 8866
Industrial Equipment Installation Services
N.A.I.C.S.: 238290

Rifox-Hans Richter GmbH   (1)
Bertha-von-Suttner-Str 9, 28207, Bremen, Germany
Tel.: (49) 421499750
Web Site: https://www.rifox.com
Industrial Machinery Mfr
N.A.I.C.S.: 333248

Thermax (Thailand) Limited   (1)
43 Thai CC Tower Room No 245 24th Floor South Sathorn Road, Yannawa Sathorn, Bangkok, 10120, Thailand

THERMAX LIMITED

Thermax Limited—(Continued)
Tel.: (66) 22100781
Industrial Equipment Installation Services
N.A.I.C.S.: 238290

Thermax Denmark ApS (1)
Industrivej Nord 13, 7400, Herning, Denmark
Tel.: (45) 99287100
Power Generation Services
N.A.I.C.S.: 221118

Thermax Energy & Environment Lanka (Private) Limited (1)
37th Floor West Tower World Trade Center, 01, Colombo, Sri Lanka
Tel.: (94) 117494290
Industrial Equipment Installation Services
N.A.I.C.S.: 238290

Thermax Energy & Environment Philippines Corporation (1)
Unit 4033 40/F PB Com Tower 6795 Rufino Street Corner Ayala Avenue, Salcedo Village, Makati, 1226, Philippines
Tel.: (63) 287899144
Industrial Equipment Installation Services
N.A.I.C.S.: 238290

Thermax Engineering Singapore Pte. Ltd. (1)
80 Robinson Road 25-00, Singapore, 068898, Singapore
Tel.: (65) 86860955
Power Generation Services
N.A.I.C.S.: 221118

Thermax Europe Limited (1)
Tel.: (44) 1908378914
Web Site: https://www.thermax-europe.com
Industrial Equipment Installation Services
N.A.I.C.S.: 238290

Thermax Inc. (1)
16200 Park Row Ste 190, Houston, TX 77084
Tel.: (248) 207-9959
Web Site: http://www.thermax-usa.com
Sales Range: $1-9.9 Million
Emp.: 14
Plastics Materials & Basic Forms & Shapes Merchant Whslr
N.A.I.C.S.: 424610

Thermax Nigeria Limited (1)
Tel.: (234) 8080622435
Industrial Equipment Installation Services
N.A.I.C.S.: 238290

Thermax Sdn. Bhd. (1)
23A-2 Level 23 A Oval Damansara 685 Jalan Damansara, Taman Tun Dr Ismail, 60000, Kuala Lumpur, Malaysia
Tel.: (60) 143386586
Industrial Equipment Installation Services
N.A.I.C.S.: 238290

Thermax do Brasil - Energia e Equipamentos Ltda. (1)
Tel.: (55) 21965048481
Industrial Equipment Installation Services
N.A.I.C.S.: 238290
Felipe Magazoni (Mgr)

THERMISSION AG
Alpenstrasse 9, Engelberg, 6390, Switzerland
Tel.: (41) 415110390
Web Site: http://www.thermission.com
Industrial Automation Services
N.A.I.C.S.: 541330
Ralf Kruger (CFO)

THERMO KING WESTERN INC.
15825 118 Avenue, Edmonton, T5V 1B7, AB, Canada
Tel.: (780) 447-1578
Web Site: https://www.thermokingwestern.com
Year Founded: 1964
Rev.: $14,739,135
Emp.: 67
Refrigeration Equipment Supplier
N.A.I.C.S.: 423740
Greg Gardner (VP & Gen Mgr)

THERMOKON SENSORTECHNIK GMBH
Aarstr 6, 35756, Mittenaar, Germany
Tel.: (49) 277265010
Web Site: http://www.thermokon.de
Year Founded: 1987
Rev.: $28,320,777
Emp.: 130
Wireless Sensor System Mfr
N.A.I.C.S.: 334419
Harald Zygan (Mng Dir)

THERMOPLAST NEXTRUSIONS LIMITED
3035, boul. Le Corbusier Laval, Laval, H7L 4C3, QC, Canada
Tel.: (800) 361-9261
Web Site: https://www.thermoplast.com
Year Founded: 2021
Wholesale Building Materials
N.A.I.C.S.: 444180

THERMOS RIVE NORD INC.
917 Boul Industriel, Terrebonne, J6Y 1V7, QC, Canada
Tel.: (450) 621-1333
Web Site: http://thermosrn.ca
Flat Glass Mfr
N.A.I.C.S.: 327211

THERMOTEX NAGEL GMBH
Schutterstrasse 14, 77746, Schutterwald, Germany
Tel.: (49) 78196160
Web Site: http://www.thermo-tex.de
Year Founded: 1988
Sales Range: $10-24.9 Million
Thermal Transfer Printing Systems Mfr
N.A.I.C.S.: 333248
Dietmar Nagel (Co-CEO)

THERON RESOURCE GROUP
23 Yihe Road, Luozhuang District, Linyi, 276000, Shandong, China
Tel.: (86) 5395631111
Year Founded: 2006
THRO—(OTCIQ)
Assets: $5,985
Liabilities: $274,635
Net Worth: ($268,650)
Earnings: ($56,812)
Emp.: 1
Fiscal Year-end: 12/31/19
Investment Services
N.A.I.C.S.: 523999
Zhaoyu Gu (Chm, CEO, CFO & Sec)

THESPAC S.P.A.
Via del Bravo n 14, 20121, Milan, Italy
Tel.: (39) 027788751
Web Site: https://www.thespacspa.it
Investment Management Service
N.A.I.C.S.: 523940

THESSALONIKI PORT AUTHORITY S.A.
Pier No 1 Port of Thessaloniki, 54625, Thessaloniki, Greece
Tel.: (30) 2310593118
Web Site: https://www.thpa.gr
OLTH—(ATH)
Rev.: $88,759,983
Assets: $270,658,321
Liabilities: $79,220,807
Net Worth: $191,437,513
Earnings: $20,066,911
Emp.: 499
Fiscal Year-end: 12/31/22
Freight Transportation Services
N.A.I.C.S.: 483111
Sotirios Theofanis (Chm & Mng Dir)

Subsidiaries:

ThPA Sofia EAD (1)
20 Aksakov Str, 1000, Sofia, Bulgaria
Tel.: (359) 29964206
Thessaloniki Port Operator
N.A.I.C.S.: 339930

THESSALONIKI WATER SUPPLY & SEWERAGE CO. S.A.
Egnatia 127, GR-54635, Thessaloniki, GR-54635, Greece
Tel.: (30) 2310966600
Web Site: https://www.eyath.gr
EYAPS—(ATH)
Rev.: $90,430
Assets: $280,634
Liabilities: $48,186
Net Worth: $232,448
Earnings: $13,922
Emp.: 323
Fiscal Year-end: 12/31/21
Water Supply, Waste Water Treatment & Installation Services
N.A.I.C.S.: 221320
Grigorios Penelis (Vice Chm)

THETA GOLD MINES LIMITED
Level 35 Intl Tower One 100 Barangaroo Ave, International Tower One, Sydney, 2000, NSW, Australia
Tel.: (61) 280467584
Web Site: https://www.thetagoldmines.com
Year Founded: 2011
TGMGF—(OTCIQ)
Rev.: $3,030,000
Assets: $23,803,000
Liabilities: $25,923,000
Net Worth: ($2,120,000)
Earnings: ($6,391,000)
Fiscal Year-end: 06/30/24
Gold Ore & Silver Ore Mining
N.A.I.C.S.: 212220
Johan Fourie (Mgr)

THETA INDUSTRIES LTD.
8 Truman Road, Barrie, L4N 8Y8, ON, Canada
Tel.: (705) 726-2620
Web Site: http://www.thetatts.com
Rev.: $14,846,198
Emp.: 115
Metal Stamping Mfr
N.A.I.C.S.: 332119
Glenn Gauder (Founder & Pres)

THEVENIN SA
Z I La Saussaye 193 Rue des Bruyeres, 45590, Saint-Cyr-en-Val, Loiret, France
Tel.: (33) 238417400
Web Site: http://www.thevenin.fr
Rev.: $44,100,000
Emp.: 325
N.A.I.C.S.: 238310
Daniel Thevenin (Pres)

THEWORKS.CO.UK PLC
Boldmere House Faraday Avenue Hams Hall Distribution Park, Coleshill, Birmingham, B46 1AL, United Kingdom
Tel.: (44) 1213136050
Web Site: https://www.theworks.co.uk
Year Founded: 1981
WRKS—(AIM)
Rev.: $356,716,183
Assets: $149,987,674
Liabilities: $137,250,966
Net Worth: $12,736,708
Earnings: $8,053,538
Fiscal Year-end: 05/05/24
Online Store Operator
N.A.I.C.S.: 455110
Gavin Peck (CEO & CFO)

INTERNATIONAL PUBLIC

THEY INTEGRATED INC.
226 Front Street, Belleville, K8N 2Z2, ON, Canada
Tel.: (613) 966-4915
Web Site: http://www.workwiththey.com
Year Founded: 1997
Emp.: 10
Branding, Design, Advertising & Web Development
N.A.I.C.S.: 541810
Shawn Patriquin (Pres & Founder)

THG HOLDINGS PLC
Voyager House Chicago Avenue, Manchester, M90 3DQ, United Kingdom
Tel.: (44) 168131716
Web Site: http://www.thg.com
Year Founded: 2008
Digital Commerce Group; Online Retail Organizations
N.A.I.C.S.: 561499
Matthew Moulding (Chm & Grp CEO)

Subsidiaries:

N.V. Perricone LLC (1)
639 Research Pkwy, Meriden, CT 06450
Tel.: (203) 935-0300
Web Site: http://www.perriconemd.com
Clinical Skin Care Products Marketer
N.A.I.C.S.: 424210
Nicholas V. Perricone (Founder)

UK2 Group Ltd. (1)
5th Floor Voyager House Chicago Avenue, Manchester Airport, Manchester, M90 3DQ, United Kingdom
Tel.: (44) 207 052 1717
Web Site: http://www.uk2group.com
Web Hosting Services
N.A.I.C.S.: 518210

THHEAVY ENGINEERING BERHAD
Level 26 Menara Bank Islam No 22 Jalan Perak, 50450, Kuala Lumpur, Malaysia
Tel.: (60) 327879000
Web Site: http://www.thhe.com.my
THHEAVY—(KLS)
Rev.: $4,102,504
Assets: $43,545,788
Liabilities: $162,923,556
Net Worth: ($119,377,767)
Earnings: ($73,026,072)
Fiscal Year-end: 12/31/22
Offshore Pedestal Cranes Mfr
N.A.I.C.S.: 333120
Siew Chuan Chua (Co-Sec)

Subsidiaries:

THHE Fabricators Sdn. Bhd. (1)
No 2 Jalan Sungai Chandong 13 Pulau Indah Industrial Park, 42920, Pulau Indah, Selangor Darul Ehsan, Malaysia (70%)
Tel.: (60) 33 325 6000
Web Site: https://www.thhe.com.my
Mechanical Engineering & Support Services
N.A.I.C.S.: 541330

THI INVESTMENTS GMBH
Eberhardstrabe 65, 70173, Stuttgart, Germany
Tel.: (49) 711 49050 580
Web Site: http://www.thi-investments.com
Holding Company
N.A.I.C.S.: 551112
Christoph Becker (Mng Dir)

Subsidiaries:

Learnship Networks GmbH (1)
Stolberger Str 374, 50933, Cologne, Germany
Tel.: (49) 22113062820
Web Site: http://www.learnship.com
Foreign Language Learning & Digital Media
N.A.I.C.S.: 611630

Sushel Bijganath *(Founder & CEO)*
Subsidiary (US):

GlobalEnglish Corporation (2)
1875 S Grant St Ste 700, San Mateo, CA 94402
Tel.: (415) 906-7991
Web Site: http://www.globalenglish.com
Software & Online English Learning & Support Services
N.A.I.C.S.: 513210
Tom Kahl *(Pres)*

THIBAULT BERGERON S A
le Parc, 56190, Muzillac, Morbihan, France
Tel.: (33) 297262926
Web Site: http://www.thibault-bergeron.com
Year Founded: 1890
Sales Range: $10-24.9 Million
Emp.: 245
Paperboard Boxes Mfr
N.A.I.C.S.: 322212

THIEME INTERNATIONAL
PO Box 301120, Stuttgart, 70451, Germany
Tel.: (49) 71189310
Web Site: http://www.thieme.com
Scientific & Medical Publisher
N.A.I.C.S.: 513199
Albrecht Hauff *(Pres)*

Subsidiaries:

Thieme Medical Publishers, Inc. (1)
333 7th Ave, New York, NY 10001
Tel.: (212) 760-0888
Web Site: http://www.thieme.com
Emp.: 60
Books Publishing Services
N.A.I.C.S.: 513130
Anne Vinnicombe *(VP-Production & Electronic Publ)*

Thieme Medical and Scientific Publishers Private Limited (1)
A-12 Second Floor Sector-2, Noida, 201 301, Uttar Pradesh, India
Tel.: (91) 120 427 4461
Online Book Publishing Services
N.A.I.C.S.: 513130
Rupnarayan Das *(Project Mgr)*

THIEN LONG GROUP CORPORATION
Sofic Tower 10 Mai Chi Tho Street Thu Thiem Ward, Thu Duc City, Ho Chi Minh City, Vietnam
Tel.: (84) 2837505555
Web Site: https://thienlonggroup.com
Year Founded: 1981
TLG—(HOSE)
Rev.: $352,085,800
Assets: $286,903,600
Liabilities: $91,116,400
Net Worth: $195,787,200
Earnings: $40,137,100
Emp.: 2,246
Fiscal Year-end: 12/31/22
Stationery Products Mfr & Whslr
N.A.I.C.S.: 322230
Gia Tho Co *(Chm)*

Subsidiaries:

Icco Marketing (M) Sdn. Bhd. (1)
13 Jalan Linggis 15/24 Taman Perindustrian Linggis Seksyen 15, 40200, Shah Alam, Selangor, Malaysia
Tel.: (60) 355452591
Web Site:
https://www.iccomarketing.com.my
Stationery Product Mfr & Distr
N.A.I.C.S.: 322230

THIEN NAM TRADING IMPORT EXPORT CORPORATION
111 - 121 Ngo Gia Tu, Ward 2 District 10, Ho Chi Minh City, Vietnam
Tel.: (84) 2838348980

TNA—(HOSE)
Rev.: $193,243,903
Assets: $95,827,863
Liabilities: $71,862,770
Net Worth: $23,965,092
Earnings: $139,462
Emp.: 85
Fiscal Year-end: 12/31/23
Grocery Product Distr
N.A.I.C.S.: 424490
Nguyen Van Nghia *(Gen Dir)*

Subsidiaries:

Thien Nam Confectionery Co., Ltd. (1)
7 Floor 111 - 121 Ngo Gia Tu St, Ward 2 Dist 10, Ho Chi Minh City, Vietnam
Tel.: (84) 2836100225
Food Mfr
N.A.I.C.S.: 311999

Thien Nam Education Investment Corporation (1)
28 Tran Quy Cap St, Ward 11 Binh Thanh Dist, Ho Chi Minh City, Vietnam
Tel.: (84) 981872223
Kindergarten Services
N.A.I.C.S.: 624410

THIEN QUANG GROUP JOINT STOCK COMPANY
Trung Trac Commune, Van Lam District, Hanoi, Hung Yen, Vietnam
Tel.: (84) 2213997185
Web Site: https://www.inoxthienquang.com.vn
Year Founded: 2001
ITQ—(HNX)
Rev.: $27,438,341
Assets: $20,225,223
Liabilities: $9,409,173
Net Worth: $10,816,050
Earnings: $502,964
Fiscal Year-end: 12/31/21
Steel Products Mfr
N.A.I.C.S.: 331110
Khuat Trung Thang *(Deputy Gen Dir)*

THIENSURAT PUBLIC COMPANY LIMITED
43-9 Moo 7 Soi Chuchart Anusorn 4, Bangplad Sub-district Pakkret District, Nonthaburi, 11120, Thailand
Tel.: (66) 28198888
Web Site: http://www.thiensurat.co.th
SBNEXT—(THA)
Rev.: $49,333,028
Assets: $92,609,569
Liabilities: $58,716,553
Net Worth: $33,893,016
Earnings: ($2,524,668)
Emp.: 2,018
Fiscal Year-end: 12/31/23
Water Purifiers Mfr & Distr
N.A.I.C.S.: 333310
Sahas Treetipbut *(Chm)*

Subsidiaries:

Fedders Thai Company Limited (1)
59/1 Soi Raminrta 58, Ram Inthra Sub-district Khan Na Yao District, Bangkok, Thailand
Tel.: (66) 29368990
Air Conditioner Retailer
N.A.I.C.S.: 449210

Safe Trade International Company Limited (1)
43/12 Moo 7 Soi Chuchat Arnusorn 4, Bang Talad Sub-district Pakkred District, Nonthaburi, 11120, Thailand
Tel.: (66) 296266512
Water Purifier Distr
N.A.I.C.S.: 423730

THINE ELECTRONICS, INC.
MD-Kanda Building 9-1 Kandamitoshiro-cho, Chiyoda-Ku, Tokyo, 101-0053, Japan

Tel.: (81) 352176660
Web Site: https://www.thine.co.jp
Year Founded: 1992
6769—(TKS)
Rev.: $35,577,620
Assets: $72,672,500
Liabilities: $5,742,900
Net Worth: $66,929,600
Earnings: ($489,210)
Emp.: 133
Fiscal Year-end: 12/31/23
Semiconductor Product Mfr
N.A.I.C.S.: 334413
Tetsuya Iizuka *(Founder & Chm)*

Subsidiaries:

THine Electronics Shenzhen Co., Ltd. (1)
1409 Rm Changhong Technology Building South 12 Rd Hi-Tech Park, Nanshan, Shenzhen, Guangdong, China
Tel.: (86) 75586332112
Electrical Equipment Distr
N.A.I.C.S.: 423610

THine Electronics Taiwan, Inc. (1)
Rm 2 3F No 129 Sec 2 Zhongshan N Rd, Zhongshan Dist, Taipei, 10448, Taiwan
Tel.: (886) 225642277
Web Site: https://www.thine.co.jp
Emp.: 6
Electrical Equipment Distr
N.A.I.C.S.: 423610
Jack Yang *(Mgr-Sls)*

THING ON ENTERPRISE LIMITED
17th Floor Bank of East Asia Harbour View Centre 56 Gloucester Road, Wanchai, China (Hong Kong)
Tel.: (852) 22900200
Web Site: https://www.thingon.com
Year Founded: 1950
2292—(HKG)
Rev.: $4,783,418
Assets: $167,007,150
Liabilities: $2,395,725
Net Worth: $164,611,425
Earnings: ($4,968,165)
Emp.: 18
Fiscal Year-end: 12/31/22
Investment Management Service
N.A.I.C.S.: 523940
Richard Chung Tak Wong *(Founder)*

THINK FITNESS CO., LTD.
3-3-6 Minamisuna Koto-Ku, Tokyo, 136-0076, Japan
Tel.: (81) 336459805
Web Site: http://www.thinkgroup.co.jp
Year Founded: 1986
Fitness Club Management
N.A.I.C.S.: 713940
Eiji Tezuka *(Pres & CEO)*

THINK2ACT PARTNERS BVBA
Baarbeek 1, 2070, Zwijndrecht, Antwerpen, Belgium
Tel.: (32) 3 641 16 35
Web Site: http://think2act.be
Privater Equity Firm
N.A.I.C.S.: 523940
Filip Lesaffer *(Co-founder & Mng Partner)*

THINKER AGRICULTURAL MACHINERY CO., LTD.
No 1699 Xingguang Street, Hefu Town, Huzhou, 313017, Zhejiang, China
Tel.: (86) 5723966768
Web Site: http://www.xg1688.com
Year Founded: 2004
603789—(SHG)
Rev.: $34,245,132
Assets: $151,030,035
Liabilities: $78,940,363
Net Worth: $72,089,672

Earnings: ($22,293,330)
Emp.: 400
Fiscal Year-end: 12/31/22
Agricultural Machinery Mfr
N.A.I.C.S.: 333111
Shen Qiang Zhang *(Chm & Gen Mgr)*

THINKIFIC LABS INC.
400-369 Terminal Ave, Vancouver, V6A 4C4, BC, Canada BC
Web Site:
https://investors.thinkific.com
Year Founded: 2012
THNCF—(OTCIQ)
Rev.: $51,476,010
Assets: $102,970,408
Liabilities: $15,121,973
Net Worth: $87,848,435
Earnings: ($36,421,637)
Fiscal Year-end: 12/31/22
Software Development Services
N.A.I.C.S.: 541511
Corinne Hua *(CFO)*

THINKING ELECTRONIC INDUSTRIAL CO., LTD.
8F No 93 Dashun 1st Rd, Zuoying Dist, Kaohsiung, Taiwan
Tel.: (886) 75577660
Web Site:
https://www.thinking.com.tw
Year Founded: 1979
2428—(TAI)
Rev.: $231,437,775
Assets: $446,379,165
Liabilities: $137,415,084
Net Worth: $308,964,081
Earnings: $42,877,758
Emp.: 2,731
Fiscal Year-end: 12/31/23
Thermistors Mfr
N.A.I.C.S.: 334416

Subsidiaries:

Thinking (Changzhou) Electronic Co., Ltd. (1)
No 6 Longmen Rd Wujin High & New-Tech Industrial Development Zone, Changzhou, 213161, Jiangsu, China
Tel.: (86) 51986578999
Circuit Protection Component Distr
N.A.I.C.S.: 423690

Thinking Electronic Industrial Co., Ltd. - Changzhou Factory (1)
No 82 Renmin Mld Rd Wujin High & New-Tech Industrial Development Zone, Changzhou, 213161, Jiangsu, China
Tel.: (86) 51986578999
Web Site: http://www.thinking.com.tw
Electronic Components Mfr
N.A.I.C.S.: 334416

Thinking Electronic Industrial Co., Ltd. - Kaohsiung Factory (1)
No 51 Kaifa Road NEPZ, Kaohsiung, 81170, Taiwan
Tel.: (886) 7 9616668
Electronic Components Mfr
N.A.I.C.S.: 334416

Yenyo Technology Co., Ltd. (1)
No 189 Lung Chiuan Road Tsuen Jiau-Shi Shiang, Yi-Lan County, Lungtan, 26246, Taiwan
Tel.: (886) 39287626
Web Site: https://www.yenyo.com.tw
Discrete Component Mfr
N.A.I.C.S.: 334413

THINKINGBOX MEDIA & DESIGN, INC.
200-319 W Hastings Street, Vancouver, V6B 1H6, BC, Canada
Tel.: (604) 568-0601
Web Site:
http://www.thinkingbox.com
Marketing & Advertising Services
N.A.I.C.S.: 541810

THINKINGBOX MEDIA & DESIGN, INC.

Thinkingbox Media & Design, Inc.—(Continued)

Subsidiaries:

Welikesmall Inc. (1)
252 S Edison St, Salt Lake City, UT 84111-2307
Tel.: (801) 467-2207
Web Site: http://www.welikesmall.com
Advertising Services
N.A.I.C.S.: 541810
Nick Franchi (Dir-Art)

THINKINGDOM MEDIA GROUP LTD.
Building No 5 No 3 Huayuan Hutong, Dongcheng District, Beijing, 100009, China
Tel.: (86) 1068423599
Web Site: https://www.readinglife.com
Year Founded: 2009
603096—(SHG)
Rev.: $141,204,464
Assets: $335,289,360
Liabilities: $36,609,530
Net Worth: $298,679,831
Earnings: $20,016,887
Fiscal Year-end: 12/31/21
Books Publishing Services
N.A.I.C.S.: 513130
Mingjun Chen (Chm & Gen Mgr)

THINKINK PICTUREZ LIMITED
Bunglow No 8-71 Mhada S V P Nagar 4 Bunglow Mhada, Andheri West, Mumbai, 400053, Maharashtra, India
Tel.: (91) 7718810090 In
Web Site: https://www.thinkinkpicturez.com
Year Founded: 2008
539310—(BOM)
Rev.: $300,746
Assets: $9,040,194
Liabilities: $4,896,284
Net Worth: $4,143,910
Earnings: ($25,719)
Emp.: 10
Fiscal Year-end: 03/31/21
Creative Arts & Entertainment
N.A.I.C.S.: 459920
Raj Saluja (CEO)

THINKON SEMICONDUCTOR JINZHOU CORP.
No 46 Zhongxin Road, Taihe, Jinzhou, 121000, Liaoning, China
Tel.: (86) 4167119889
Web Site: https://www.thinkon-cn.com
Year Founded: 2013
688233—(SHG)
Rev.: $75,708,805
Assets: $247,056,067
Liabilities: $20,498,203
Net Worth: $226,557,864
Earnings: $22,203,081
Fiscal Year-end: 12/31/22
Semiconductor Product Mfr & Distr
N.A.I.C.S.: 334413

THINKSMART LIMITED
Suite 5 531 Hay Street, Subiaco, 6008, WA, Australia
Tel.: (61) 893808333 AU
Web Site: http://www.thinksmartworld.com
Year Founded: 1996
TSL—(AIM)
Rev.: $4,719,435
Assets: $51,985,741
Liabilities: $1,758,247
Net Worth: $50,227,494
Earnings: ($127,734,298)
Fiscal Year-end: 06/30/22
Financial Services
N.A.I.C.S.: 523999
Ned R. Montarello (Founder & Chm)

THINKWARE SYSTEMS CORPORATION
9FL Samhwan hipex 240 Pangyoyeok-ro, Bundang-gu, Seongnam, Gyeonggi-do, Korea (South)
Tel.: (82) 25899000
Web Site: https://www.thinkware.com
Year Founded: 1997
084730—(KRS)
Sales Range: $150-199.9 Million
Communication Equipment Mfr
N.A.I.C.S.: 334290

THINKWAY TRADING CORPORATION
8885 Woodbine Ave, Markham, L3R 5G1, ON, Canada
Tel.: (905) 470-8883
Web Site: http://www.thinkwaytoys.com
Year Founded: 1990
Sales Range: $25-49.9 Million
Emp.: 14
Toys & Hobby Supplies
N.A.I.C.S.: 459120
Albert Chan (CEO)

Subsidiaries:

Thinkway Toys (1)
8885 Woodbine Ave, Markham, L3R 5G1, ON, Canada
Tel.: (905) 470-8883
Web Site: http://www.thinkwaytoys.com
Sales Range: $50-74.9 Million
Toys Mfr & Distr
N.A.I.C.S.: 459120
Albert Chan (CEO)

THINTECH MATERIALS TECHNOLOGY CO., LTD.
No 1 Luke 8th Rd, Lujhu District, Kaohsiung, 82151, Taiwan
Tel.: (886) 76955125
Web Site: https://www.e-ttmc.com.tw
Year Founded: 2000
3663—(TPE)
Rev.: $71,211,791
Assets: $56,295,475
Liabilities: $16,853,793
Net Worth: $39,441,682
Earnings: $3,954,223
Fiscal Year-end: 12/31/19
Electronic Component Mfr & Distr
N.A.I.C.S.: 334419
Song-Jan Tsai (Chm)

THIOGENESIS THERAPEUTICS, CORP.
4 King Street West Suite 401, Toronto, M5H 1B6, ON, Canada
Tel.: (647) 846-7766
Web Site: https://www.thiogenesis.com
TTIPF—(OTCIQ)
Rev.: $129,250
Assets: $5,469,334
Liabilities: $1,293,419
Net Worth: $4,175,915
Earnings: ($3,817,454)
Fiscal Year-end: 12/31/23
Asset Management Services
N.A.I.C.S.: 523940
Neil Johnson (CEO)

THIRA UTECH CO., LTD.
27F CK Building 7 Hakdongro 5gil, Gangnam-Gu, Seoul, 6044, Korea (South)
Tel.: (82) 234616531
Web Site: https://www.thirautech.com
Year Founded: 2006
322180—(KRS)
Rev.: $27,568,053
Assets: $27,458,283
Liabilities: $13,775,178
Net Worth: $13,683,106
Earnings: ($3,442,435)

Emp.: 272
Fiscal Year-end: 12/31/22
Semiconductor Machinery Mfr
N.A.I.C.S.: 333242
Jeong Ha Kim (Co-CEO)

THIRANI PROJECTS LIMITED
Subol Dutt Building 13 Brabourne Road Mezzanine Floor, Kolkata, 700 001, India
Tel.: (91) 3322315686
Web Site: https://www.thiraniprojects.com
538464—(KOL)
Rev.: $121,401
Assets: $2,704,421
Liabilities: $12,615
Net Worth: $2,691,806
Earnings: ($23,764)
Fiscal Year-end: 03/31/21
Financial Support Services
N.A.I.C.S.: 523999
Subrata Panja (CFO & Exec Dir)

THIRD POINT INVESTORS LTD.
Trafalgar Court Les Banques, Po Box 255, Saint Peter Port, GY1 3QL, Guernsey
Tel.: (44) 1481745000 GY
Web Site: https://www.thirdpointlimited.com
Year Founded: 1995
TPOU—(LSE)
Rev.: $38,342,786
Assets: $828,717,700
Liabilities: $151,874,821
Net Worth: $676,842,879
Earnings: $11,457,681
Fiscal Year-end: 12/31/22
Investment Management Service
N.A.I.C.S.: 523940
Daniel S. Loeb (Mgr-Investment)

THIRDEYE SYSTEMS LTD.
12 Beni Gaon St, Netanya, Israel
Tel.: (972) 547403352
Web Site: https://www.thirdeye-systems.com
Year Founded: 2010
THES—(TAE)
Rev.: $4,018,220
Assets: $4,653,218
Liabilities: $4,860,094
Net Worth: ($206,876)
Earnings: ($135,839)
Fiscal Year-end: 06/30/23
Software Development Services
N.A.I.C.S.: 541511
Yoel Motola (Co-Founder & CTO)

THIRDWAVE FINANCIAL INTERMEDIARIES LIMITED
601 Ambuja Neotia Ecocentre EM-4 EM Block, Sector V, Kolkata, 700091, India
Tel.: (91) 3346039630
Web Site: https://www.twfil.com
Year Founded: 1989
531652—(BOM)
Rev.: $154,411
Assets: $190,291
Liabilities: $692
Net Worth: $189,599
Earnings: ($10,637)
Fiscal Year-end: 03/31/21
Technical Consulting Services
N.A.I.C.S.: 541990
Vinay Kumar Agarwal (Chm & Mng Dir)

THIRIX
Quartier De La Pierre Plan 173 Route De Nimes, 30100, Ales, Gard, France
Tel.: (33) 466243675
Rev.: $18,900,000

Emp.: 49
N.A.I.C.S.: 445110
Jean Berthier (Dir-Fin)

THIRU AROORAN SUGARS LIMITED
Eldorado Fifth Floor 112 Nungambakkam High Road, Chennai, 600034, Tamil Nadu, India
Tel.: (91) 44 28276001 In
Web Site: http://www.tasugars.in
Year Founded: 1954
507450—(BOM)
Sales Range: $50-74.9 Million
Emp.: 417
Sugar Mfr
N.A.I.C.S.: 311314
Tyagarajan R. V. (Chm & Mng Dir)

THIRUMALAI CHEMICALS LTD
Thirumalai House Plot No 101-102 Road No 29 Sion East, Mumbai, 400022, India
Tel.: (91) 2224017841
Web Site: https://www.thirumalaichemicals.com
Year Founded: 1972
500412—(BOM)
Rev.: $259,263,833
Assets: $282,985,433
Liabilities: $140,077,933
Net Worth: $142,907,500
Earnings: $10,770,338
Emp.: 526
Fiscal Year-end: 03/31/23
Chemicals Mfr
N.A.I.C.S.: 325194
R. Parthasarathy (Chm & Mng Dir)

Subsidiaries:

Ranson Pte Ltd (1)
10 Jalan Besar Unit 12-12 Sim Lim Tower, Unit 11-06 Tong Eng Bldg, 069533, Singapore, Singapore
Tel.: (65) 62233115
Sales Range: $25-49.9 Million
Emp.: 3
Food Chemicals Mfr
N.A.I.C.S.: 311999

TCL Research (1)
25-A Sipcot Industrial Complex, Ranipet, Vellore, 632 403, Tamil Nadu, India
Tel.: (91) 4172244441
Web Site: http://www.tclresearch.com
Sales Range: $25-49.9 Million
Emp.: 45
Chemicals Mfr
N.A.I.C.S.: 325199
V. Thannikodi (Mgr)

Ultramarine & Pigments Ltd. (1)
Thirumalai House Road No 29 Near Sion Hill, Fort Sion E, Mumbai, 400 022, India
Tel.: (91) 2243686200
Web Site: https://ultramarinepigments.net
Rev.: $68,110,725
Assets: $105,648,223
Liabilities: $17,449,254
Net Worth: $88,198,969
Earnings: $8,296,805
Emp.: 462
Fiscal Year-end: 03/31/2023
Pigment & Surfactant Mfr
N.A.I.C.S.: 325130
S. Ramanan (CFO)

THITIKORN PUBLIC COMPANY LIMITED
S P Arcade Building No 69 Ramkhamhaeng Rd, Huamark Bangkapi, Bangkok, 10240, Thailand
Tel.: (66) 23107000
Web Site: https://m.tk.co.th
Year Founded: 1972
TK—(THA)
Rev.: $48,281,475
Assets: $186,966,277
Liabilities: $23,816,356
Net Worth: $163,149,921
Earnings: $2,783,571

Emp.: 1,226
Fiscal Year-end: 12/31/23
Motorcycle Hire-Purchase Services
N.A.I.C.S.: 441227
Prathama Phornprapha *(Mng Dir)*

Subsidiaries:

Sabaidee Leasing Co., Ltd. (1)
Beungkhayong Unit 5 House no 077
Thadeua Road, Sisattanak, Vientiane, Lao
People's Democratic Republic
Tel.: (856) 21316422
Web Site: https://www.sabaideeleasing.com
Automobile & Motorcycle Hire-Purchase Services
N.A.I.C.S.: 532120

Suosdey Finance PLC (1)
No 119-121 Russian Federation Boulevard
Sangkat Teuk Thla Khan, Sen Sok, Phnom Penh, Cambodia
Tel.: (855) 23884455
Web Site: https://www.suosdeyfinance.com
Automobile & Motorcycle Hire-Purchase Services
N.A.I.C.S.: 532120

THIZ TECHNOLOGY GROUP LIMITED
Unit 810 8/F Tower B Hunghom Commercial Centre 37 Ma Tau Wai Road, To Kwa Wan, Kowloon, China (Hong Kong)
Tel.: (852) 2735 2725 Ky
Web Site: http://www.thizgroup.com
Year Founded: 2000
Sales Range: $1-9.9 Million
Emp.: 43
Software Publisher
N.A.I.C.S.: 513210
Hoi Wong Wong *(Chm & CEO)*

THK CO., LTD.
2-12-10 Shibaura, Minato-ku, Tokyo, 108-8506, Japan
Tel.: (81) 357303911
Web Site: https://www.thk.com
Year Founded: 1971
6481—(TKS)
Rev.: $2,495,247,510
Assets: $3,944,528,590
Liabilities: $1,371,581,770
Net Worth: $2,572,946,820
Earnings: $130,441,820
Emp.: 13,360
Fiscal Year-end: 12/31/23
Industrial Equipment Mfr
N.A.I.C.S.: 811310
Akihiro Teramachi *(Pres & CEO)*

Subsidiaries:

ARATRON A/S (1)
Bjornerudveien 17, 1266, Oslo, Norway
Tel.: (47) 23191660
Web Site: https://www.aratron.no
Sales Range: $25-49.9 Million
Emp.: 15
Vaccum Pump Mfr
N.A.I.C.S.: 333914

Acorn Industrial Services Ltd. (1)
Unit A Denby Way Hellaby Industrial Estate, Hellaby Industrial Estate, Rotherham, S66 8HR, South Yorkshire, United Kingdom
Tel.: (44) 170 978 9999
Web Site: https://www.acorn-ind.co.uk
Power Transistor Distr
N.A.I.C.S.: 423690
Martin Povey *(Fin Dir)*

Advance Motion Control Systems Pvt Ltd (1)
Plot No R-424 MIDC TTC Industrial Area, Rabale, Navi Mumbai, 400701, India
Tel.: (91) 2227642588
Industrial Parts Mfr
N.A.I.C.S.: 336390

BIA DANILO s.r.l. (1)
Viale Europa 79/A, 43122, Parma, Italy
Tel.: (39) 052 127 2636
Web Site: https://www.biadanilo.it
Industrial Parts Mfr
N.A.I.C.S.: 336390

Bachofen-AG (1)
Ackerstrasse 42, 8610, Uster, Switzerland
Tel.: (41) 449441111
Web Site: http://www.bachofen.ch
Sales Range: $25-49.9 Million
Emp.: 120
Industrial Engineering & Consulting Services
N.A.I.C.S.: 541618
Markus Helm *(Member-Exec Bd)*

Bia Automation S.R.L. (1)
Viale Europa 79/A, 43122, Parma, Italy
Tel.: (39) 0521272636
Web Site: https://www.biadanilo.it
Industrial Machinery Component Distr
N.A.I.C.S.: 423830

Blassinger GmbH (1)
Fronleichnamsweg 15, 8940, Liezen, Austria
Tel.: (43) 3612234100
Industrial Parts Mfr
N.A.I.C.S.: 336390

Bondy A/S (1)
Hassellunden 14, DK 2765, Smorum, Denmark
Tel.: (45) 70151414
Web Site: https://bondy.dk
Electric Motor Mfr & Distr
N.A.I.C.S.: 335312

Brammer Czech a.s. (1)
Lukavecka 1735, 193 00, Prague, Czech Republic
Tel.: (420) 277003332
Industrial Parts Mfr
N.A.I.C.S.: 336390

Brammer Iberia SA (1)
P I Erletxe Plat D-152 Pab 1, 48960, Galdakao, Biscay, Spain
Tel.: (34) 944579400
Industrial Parts Mfr
N.A.I.C.S.: 336390

Brammer Magyarorszag KFT. (1)
Topark u 9, 2045, Torokbalint, Hungary
Tel.: (36) 23920777
Web Site: http://www.brammer.hu
Industrial Parts Mfr
N.A.I.C.S.: 336390

Brammer Slovakia s.r.o. (1)
Cesta do Rudiny 1098, 024 01, Kysucke Nove Mesto, Slovakia
Tel.: (421) 414216296
Industrial Parts Mfr
N.A.I.C.S.: 336390

Casa Rossier Ltda. (1)
Enrique Concha y Toro-Local 12, Santiago, Chile
Tel.: (56) 22 412 6000
Web Site: https://www.rossier.cl
Industrial Parts Distr
N.A.I.C.S.: 423840

DC Auto-Motion (Pty) Ltd (1)
11 Sunrock Close 131 Sunnyrock Ext 2, Germiston, 1401, Gauteng, South Africa
Tel.: (27) 11 453 1740
Web Site: https://www.dcauto-motion.co.za
Industrial Parts Distr
N.A.I.C.S.: 423840

DPS Vietnam Trading & Distribution Parts Co., Ltd. (1)
No 15 Street No 7A An Phu - An Khanh Residential, An Phu Ward Dist 2, Ho Chi Minh City, Vietnam
Tel.: (84) 86 296 0711
Web Site: https://www.dpsvietnam.com
Industrial Parts Mfr
N.A.I.C.S.: 336390

Daito Seiki Co., Ltd. (1)
2-26 Higashihatsushima, Amagasaki, 660-0832, Hyogo, Japan
Tel.: (81) 664891209
Web Site: http://www.daito-seiki.com
Sales Range: $50-74.9 Million
Emp.: 170
Drilling Machines Mfr
N.A.I.C.S.: 333517

Dalian THK CO., LTD. (1)
No 2 Minggu Road, Dalian Economic And Technological Development Zone, Dalian, 116650, Liaoning, China
Tel.: (86) 41184790999
Web Site: http://www.thk.com
Sales Range: $200-249.9 Million
Emp.: 1,000
Bearing Mfr
N.A.I.C.S.: 332991
Takashi Okubo *(Pres)*

Daneel Mechatronics, S.L.U. (1)
Poligon Industrial Can Vinyalets c/ Can Vinyalets n0 9 nau 6, Santa Perpetua de Mogoda, 08130, Barcelona, Spain
Tel.: (34) 934457777
Web Site: https://www.daneel-mechatronics.com
Industrial Machinery Mfr
N.A.I.C.S.: 333248

Durga Bearings (Mumbai) Co. Pvt. Ltd. (1)
32 Corporate Avenue A Wing 3rd Floor, Near Paper Box Off Mahakali Caves Road Mahal Industrial Estate Andheri, Mumbai, 400 093, Maharastra, India
Tel.: (91) 2226819000
Industrial Parts Mfr
N.A.I.C.S.: 336390

Durga Bearings Co. Pvt. Ltd. (1)
39 New Avadi Road Kilpauk, Chennai, 600 010, Tamil nadu, India
Tel.: (91) 4426440414
Industrial Parts Mfr
N.A.I.C.S.: 336390

EIBC (P) Ltd (1)
NTN Building Block 196/228P2 Opp Uttam Dairy, Village Navapura Changodhar, Ahmedabad, 382213, Gujarat, India
Tel.: (91) 851 118 6504
Web Site: https://www.eibc.in
Industrial Parts Mfr
N.A.I.C.S.: 336390

Elite Machinery Pte Ltd. (1)
29 Tessensohn Road, Singapore, 217654, Singapore
Tel.: (65) 62987600
Web Site: http://www.elitemachinery.com
Sales Range: $25-49.9 Million
Emp.: 170
Bearings & Linear Motion Guides Mfr
N.A.I.C.S.: 332991
S. Goh K *(Mgr)*

Elshin International Pte Ltd (1)
No 1 Kaki Bukit Avenue 3 KB-1, 416087, Singapore
Tel.: (65) 62867707
Web Site: http://www.elshin.com
Sales Range: $25-49.9 Million
Emp.: 25
Linear Motion Guides & Screws Mfr & Industrial Automation Services
N.A.I.C.S.: 332722

Hennlich & Zebisch GmbH (1)
Schnelldorf 51, Suben, 4975, Wiesing, Austria
Tel.: (43) 77123163533
Industrial Parts Mfr
N.A.I.C.S.: 336390

Hennlich Industrietechnik spol. Sro (1)
Mileticova 16, 821 08, Bratislava, Slovakia
Tel.: (421) 250202504
Industrial Parts Mfr
N.A.I.C.S.: 336390

Hennlich Industrietechnik spolecnost S.r.o (1)
Ceskolipska 9, 412 01, Litomerice, Czech Republic
Tel.: (420) 416711111
Web Site: http://www.hennlich.cz
Emp.: 170
Hydraulic Equipment Mfr
N.A.I.C.S.: 333248
Martin Jonas *(Mgr-PR)*

Hennlich Inudstrijska Tehnika d.o.o. (1)
Ulica Mirka Vadnova 13, 4000, Kranj, Slovenia
Tel.: (386) 4 532 0610
Web Site: https://www.hennlich.si
Industrial Parts Distr

Hennlich OOD (1)
147A Brezovsko Shosse Street, 4003, Plovdiv, Bulgaria
Tel.: (359) 3 251 1326
Web Site: https://www.hennlich.bg
Industrial Parts Distr
N.A.I.C.S.: 423840

Hennlich Sp. z o.o. (1)
Ul Thomasa Wilsona 24A, Knurow, 44-190, Katowice, Poland
Tel.: (48) 32 420 6700
Web Site: https://www.hennlich.pl
Industrial Parts Distr
N.A.I.C.S.: 423840

Hennlich industrijska tehnika d.o.o. (1)
Stupnickoobreska 17, Stupnicki Obrez Gornji Stupnik, 10255, Zagreb, Croatia
Tel.: (385) 1 387 4334
Web Site: https://www.hennlich.hr
Industrial Parts Distr
N.A.I.C.S.: 423840

INB Enterprise Company limited (1)
479/17-19 Trok Salakhin Rama IV Rd Rongmuang, Pratoomwan, Bangkok, 10330, Thailand
Tel.: (66) 261 391 6671
Web Site: https://www.inb.co.th
Industrial Parts Distr
N.A.I.C.S.: 423840

Incor S.R.L. (1)
Av Oscar R Benavides 1473-1481, Lima, Peru
Tel.: (51) 202 6000
Web Site: https://www.incor.com.pe
Industrial Parts Distr
N.A.I.C.S.: 336390

Indunorm Bewegungstechnik GmbH (1)
Obere Kaiserswerther Strasse 17, 47249, Duisburg, Germany
Tel.: (49) 2 037 6910
Web Site: https://www.indunorm.eu
Emp.: 140
Industrial Parts Mfr
N.A.I.C.S.: 336390

Josef Blassinger GmbH + Co. KG (1)
Zeppelinstrasse 18, 73760, Ostfildern, Germany
Tel.: (49) 71 116 7080
Web Site: https://www.blaessinger.com
Industrial Parts Distr
N.A.I.C.S.: 423840

KKC Bearing Service Co., Ltd. (1)
51/57 Moo 7 Bangna-Trad Km 8 Rd, Bang Kaeo Subdistrict Bang Phli District, Bang Phli, 10540, Samut Prakan, Thailand
Tel.: (66) 27528462
Web Site: http://www.kkcbearing.com
Sales Range: $25-49.9 Million
Emp.: 32
Bearing Distr
N.A.I.C.S.: 423840

Kugelfink GmbH (1)
Millennium Park 24, 6890, Lustenau, Austria
Tel.: (43) 55 772 0555
Web Site: https://www.kugelfink.at
Chemical Products Mfr
N.A.I.C.S.: 325998

L Trading Co., Ltd. (1)
283-3 Gokyu-cho, Hamamatsu, 430-0831, Shizuoka, Japan
Tel.: (81) 534258264
Industrial Parts Mfr
N.A.I.C.S.: 336390

LM Systems B.V. (1)
Kruisboog 2, 3905 TG, Veenendaal, Netherlands
Tel.: (31) 8554615
Web Site: http://www.lmsystems.nl
Sales Range: $25-49.9 Million
Emp.: 20
Bearing Mfr
N.A.I.C.S.: 332991
Richard Eshuis *(Gen Mgr)*

LM Systems B.V. (1)

THK CO., LTD.

THK CO., LTD.—(Continued)
Leuvensesteenweg 613, 1930, Zaventem, Belgium
Tel.: (32) 22524745
Industrial Parts Mfr
N.A.I.C.S.: 336390

Lineartec Srl (1)
Ombu 3737, Ciudadela, Buenos Aires, Argentina
Tel.: (54) 114 469 4800
Web Site: https://www.lineartec.com.ar
Industrial Parts Mfr
N.A.I.C.S.: 336390

Lugo Hermanos S.A. (1)
Calle 13 No 62-94, Bogota, Colombia
Tel.: (57) 1 420 2511
Web Site: https://www.lugohermanos.com
Industrial Parts Mfr
N.A.I.C.S.: 336390

Medital Comotech Ltd. (1)
36 Shaham Street, PO Box 7772, 49170, Petah Tiqwa, Israel
Tel.: (972) 39233323
Web Site: http://www.medital.co.il
Sales Range: $25-49.9 Million
Emp.: 19
Electronic Components Mfr & Distr
N.A.I.C.S.: 334419

Medital Novelty Ltd. (1)
36 Shacham St, PO Box 7772, Petach Tikva, 4951729, Israel
Tel.: (972) 3 923 3323
Web Site: http://www.medital.com
Industrial Parts Mfr
N.A.I.C.S.: 336390
Joseph Issler *(Pres & Mng Dir)*

Midland Engineering Services Ltd. (1)
Units 20 & 21 Lower Bathville, Armadale Ind Est Armadale, Edinburgh, EH48 2ND, West Lothian, United Kingdom
Tel.: (44) 150 173 9081
Web Site: http://www.mes4thk.co.uk
Power Transistor Distr
N.A.I.C.S.: 423690

Nano Control Co., Ltd. (1)
2F FINE Bldg 6-17-17 Minami-oi, Shinagawa-ku, Tokyo, 140-0013, Japan
Tel.: (81) 364042820
Web Site: http://www.nanocontrol.co.jp
Sales Range: $25-49.9 Million
Emp.: 11
Piezoelectric Actuators Mfr
N.A.I.C.S.: 334419
Katsuhiko Iida *(Pres & CEO)*

Nippon Slide CO., LTD. (1)
9-20-20 Iriya, Adachi-ku, Tokyo, 121-0836, Japan
Tel.: (81) 338572631
Web Site: http://www.n-slide.co.jp
Sales Range: $25-49.9 Million
Emp.: 60
Metal Suspension Devices Mfr
N.A.I.C.S.: 332999
Masaki Kimura *(Pres)*

OEM Motor AB/OEM Automatic AB (1)
Box 1011, 573 28, Tranas, Sweden
Tel.: (46) 75 242 4400
Web Site: https://www.oemmotor.se
Emp.: 35
Industrial Parts Mfr
N.A.I.C.S.: 336390

Osco International Co., Ltd. (1)
Lot3 Lai Xa Industrial Complex Kim Chung, Hoai Duc, Hanoi, Vietnam
Tel.: (84) 243 557 6450
Web Site: https://www.osco.vn
Emp.: 250
Industrial Parts Mfr
N.A.I.C.S.: 336390

PT Surya Sarana Dinamika (1)
Perkantoran Mega Sunter B-40 Jl Danau Sunter Selatan, Jakarta, 14350, Indonesia
Tel.: (62) 216 583 5077
Web Site: https://www.suryasarana.com
Industrial Parts Mfr
N.A.I.C.S.: 336390

PT. Flexindomas (1)
JL Prof Dr Latumenten No 17B, Jakarta, 11330, Indonesia
Tel.: (62) 21 631 3151
Web Site: https://www.id.fasflexible.com
Industrial Parts Mfr
N.A.I.C.S.: 336390

PT. SLS Bearindo (1)
Komplek Marina Mangga Dua Blok G / 3A-5 Jl Gunung Sahari No 2, Jakarta Utara, 14420, Indonesia
Tel.: (62) 216456711
Industrial Parts Mfr
N.A.I.C.S.: 336390

Qaiser Brothers (Pvt) Ltd (1)
Ist Floor Apwa Complex Opp I B A Garden Road, Karachi, Pakistan
Tel.: (92) 21322 416 4450
Web Site: https://www.qaiserbrothers.com
Bearing Product Distr
N.A.I.C.S.: 423840

REIFF Technische Produkte GmbH (1)
Tubinger Str 2-6, 72762, Reutlingen, Germany
Tel.: (49) 7 121 3230
Web Site: https://www.reiff-tp.de
Emp.: 450
Industrial Parts Mfr
N.A.I.C.S.: 336390

Rodacenter Ltda. (1)
Americo Vespucio Avenue 1391 Local 11, Quilicura, Santiago, Chile
Tel.: (56) 22 627 2727
Web Site: https://www.rodacenter.cl
Industrial Parts Mfr
N.A.I.C.S.: 336390

Rollmann Trading Company (1)
33 Manasaveena 2nd Main Road NR Colony, Bengaluru, 560019, Karnataka, India
Tel.: (91) 8026609631
Industrial Parts Mfr
N.A.I.C.S.: 336390

Rolman World Fzco (1)
PO Box 25054, Jebel Ali Free Zone, Dubai, United Arab Emirates
Tel.: (971) 4 887 3700
Web Site: https://www.rolman.com
Power Transistor Distr
N.A.I.C.S.: 423690

Rubix Czech a.s. (1)
Na Rovince 1066, Hrabova, 720 00, Ostrava, Czech Republic
Tel.: (420) 724563033
Web Site: https://rubix-group.cz
Industrial Consumable Distr
N.A.I.C.S.: 423840

Rubix Slovakia s.r.o. (1)
Banovska cesta 13, 010 01, Zilina, Slovakia
Tel.: (421) 414216296
Web Site: https://www.rubix-group.sk
Emp.: 120
Industrial Machinery Repair & Maintenance Services
N.A.I.C.S.: 811310

S.A. Vermeire-Belting N.V. (1)
Rue de la Filature 41, Ensival, 4800, Verviers, Liege, Belgium
Tel.: (32) 87322360
Web Site: www.vermeire.com
Conveyor Belts Mfr
N.A.I.C.S.: 326220

S.C. Hennlich S.R.L. (1)
Str Timotei Cipariu nr 5-7, 310213, Arad, Romania
Tel.: (40) 25 721 1119
Web Site: https://www.hennlich.ro
Industrial Parts Distr
N.A.I.C.S.: 423840

S.Factory CO., LTD. (1)
7th Floor YSD Building 3-14-11 Kamiuma, Setagaya-ku, Tokyo, 141-0031, Japan
Tel.: (81) 364590057
Web Site: http://www.thk.com
Industrial Products Mfr
N.A.I.C.S.: 811310

SKS Mekaniikka Oy (1)
Martinkylantie 50, 01721, Vantaa, Finland
Tel.: (358) 2076461

Industrial Parts Mfr
N.A.I.C.S.: 336390

SKS Sweden AB (1)
Koppargatan 8, 234 35, Lomma, Sweden
Tel.: (46) 4 041 8230
Web Site: https://www.skssweden.se
Emp.: 10
Industrial Parts Mfr & Distr
N.A.I.C.S.: 336390

SKS Tehnika OU (1)
Liimi 1, 10621, Tallinn, Estonia
Tel.: (372) 6023310
Machine Building Component & Drive Distr
N.A.I.C.S.: 423840

SLS Bearings (Malaysia) Sdn Bhd (1)
22 Jalan 51/205 Highway Centre, 46050, Petaling Jaya, Selangor, Malaysia
Tel.: (60) 377833555
Industrial Parts Mfr
N.A.I.C.S.: 336390

Sanko Seisakusho Co., Ltd. (1)
3-620 Hatanaka, Ome, 198-0061, Tokyo, Japan
Tel.: (81) 428225218
Industrial Parts Mfr
N.A.I.C.S.: 336390

TALK SYSTEM CORPORATION (1)
2-12-10 Shibaura THK Building 2nd floor, Minato-ku, Tokyo, 108-0023, Japan
Tel.: (81) 357303930
Web Site: http://www.talksystem.co.jp
Sales Range: $75-99.9 Million
Emp.: 155
Machinery Parts & Equipments Whslr
N.A.I.C.S.: 423830
Shigeru Wako *(Pres & CEO)*

THK (China) Co., Ltd. (1)
No 5-B Xuefu South Street, Dalian Economic & Technical Development Zone, Dalian, 116600, Liaoning, China
Tel.: (86) 41187337111
Web Site: http://www.thk.com
Emp.: 100
Industrial Equipment Mfr
N.A.I.C.S.: 332991
Akihiro Teramachi *(Pres & CEO)*

THK (Shanghai) Co., Ltd. (1)
1003-A Kirin Plaza 666 Gubei Road, Shanghai, 200336, China
Tel.: (86) 2162755280
Web Site: http://www.thk.com
Sales Range: $50-74.9 Million
Emp.: 200
Screw Mfr
N.A.I.C.S.: 332722
Akihiro Teramachi *(Pres)*

THK America Inc. (1)
200 E Commerce Dr, Schaumburg, IL 60173
Tel.: (847) 310-1111
Web Site: https://www.thk.com
Sales Range: $50-74.9 Million
Emp.: 250
Linear Motion Guides & Screws Mfr
N.A.I.C.S.: 333998
Masaki Sugita *(Pres & CEO)*

Subsidiary (Non-US):

THK Manufacturing of America Inc. (2)
Tel.: (740) 928-1415
Web Site: https://www.thk.com
Sales Range: $100-124.9 Million
Emp.: 300
Linear Motion Guides Mfr
N.A.I.C.S.: 333998
Tom Madden *(Acct Mgr)*

THK BRASIL INDUSTRIA E COMERCIO LTDA. (1)
Av Jaguare 818 - Galpao 20 Jaguare, Sao Paulo, 05346-000, Brazil
Tel.: (55) 1137670100
Web Site: http://www.thk.com
Sales Range: $50-74.9 Million
Emp.: 18
Bearing Distr
N.A.I.C.S.: 423840
Milton Jimenez *(Gen Mgr)*

THK Brasil LTDA. (1)

INTERNATIONAL PUBLIC

Av Corifeu de Azevedo Marques 4077, Butanta, Sao Paulo, 05346000, Brazil
Tel.: (55) 1137670100
Web Site: http://www.thk.com.br
Sales Range: $25-49.9 Million
Emp.: 16
Screw Mfr
N.A.I.C.S.: 332722
Cicero Alencar *(Gen Mgr)*

THK Co., Ltd. - Gifu Plant (1)
615 Sekigahara-cho, Fuwa-gun, Gifu, 503-1512, Japan
Tel.: (81) 584435177
Web Site: http://www.thk.com
Sales Range: $50-74.9 Million
Emp.: 200
Automobile Parts Mfr
N.A.I.C.S.: 336390

THK Co., Ltd. - Kofu Plant (1)
754 Nakadate, Chuo, 409-3801, Yamanashi, Japan
Tel.: (81) 552734321
Web Site: http://www.thk.com
Sales Range: $100-124.9 Million
Emp.: 450
Linear Motion Guides Mfr
N.A.I.C.S.: 333998
Akihiro Teramachi *(Pres)*

THK Co., Ltd. - Mie Plant (1)
1088 Hirabayashi, Nyudera-cho, Matsusaka, 515-0832, Mie, Japan
Tel.: (81) 598582811
Web Site: http://www.thk.com
Sales Range: $50-74.9 Million
Emp.: 250
Mechanical Components & Linear Motion (LM) Guide Mechanism Mfr
N.A.I.C.S.: 335999

THK Co., Ltd. - Yamagata Plant (1)
5600 Oaza Higashine-ko, Higashine, 999-3701, Yamagata, Japan
Tel.: (81) 237423611
Web Site: http://www.thk.com
Linear Motion Guides Mfr
N.A.I.C.S.: 333998

THK Europe B.V. (1)
High Tech Campus 5, 5656 AE, Eindhoven, Netherlands
Tel.: (31) 402909500
Sales Range: $25-49.9 Million
Emp.: 6
Industrial Equipment Mfr
N.A.I.C.S.: 332991
Toshihiro Teramachi *(CEO)*

THK France S. A. S. (1)
Les carres du Parc 10 rue des Rosieristes Immeuble A, 69410, Champagne-au-Mont-d'Or, Rhone, France
Tel.: (33) 437491400
Web Site: http://www.thk.com.fr
Sales Range: $25-49.9 Million
Emp.: 15
Linear Motion Guides Mfr
N.A.I.C.S.: 332991

THK GmbH (1)
Kaiserswerther Str 115, 40880, Ratingen, Germany
Tel.: (49) 21027425555
Web Site: http://www.thk.com
Sales Range: $25-49.9 Million
Emp.: 214
Roller Bearings & Industrial Equipments Mfr
N.A.I.C.S.: 332991
Tetsuya Hayashida *(Pres)*

THK GmbH (1)
Dmitrovskoye Shosse Street 60 6th Floor Office 610, 127474, Moscow, Russia
Tel.: (7) 4956498047
Electric Equipment Mfr
N.A.I.C.S.: 334419

THK INTECHS CO., LTD. (1)
2-12-10 Shibaura, Minato-ku, Tokyo, 108-0023, Japan
Tel.: (81) 357303811
Web Site: https://www.thkintechs.co.jp
Machine Tools Mfr
N.A.I.C.S.: 333517

THK India Pvt. Ltd. (1)
2nd Floor 4/4 1st Main Road Rajajinagar, Industrial Town West of Chord Road Service Road, Bengaluru, 560044, India

AND PRIVATE COMPANIES

Tel.: (91) 8023409934
Industrial Parts Mfr
N.A.I.C.S.: 336390

THK LM SYSTEM Pte. Ltd. (1)
38 Kaki Bukit Place LM Techno Building,
Singapore, 416216, Singapore
Tel.: (65) 68845500
Web Site: http://www.thk.com
Screws & Bearings Mfr
N.A.I.C.S.: 332991
Yoshiyuki Yamashita *(Pres & CEO)*

THK Manufacturing of China (Changzhou) Co., Ltd. (1)
No 152 Chunjiang Zhong Road, Xinbei District, Changzhou, 213125, jiangsu, China
Tel.: (86) 51968889000
Industrial Parts Mfr
N.A.I.C.S.: 336390

THK Manufacturing of China (Liaoning) Co., Ltd. (1)
No 5 Xuefu South Street, Dalian Economic & Technical Development Zone, Dalian, 116600, Liaoning, China
Tel.: (86) 41187337333
Web Site: http://www.thk.com
Linear Motion Guides Mfr
N.A.I.C.S.: 333998

THK Manufacturing of China (Wuxi) Co., Ltd. (1)
No 19 Changjiang South Road, Wuxi, Jiangsu, China
Tel.: (86) 51085344333
Web Site: http://www.thk.com.cn
Sales Range: $200-249.9 Million
Emp.: 530
Linear Motion Guides Mfr
N.A.I.C.S.: 333998

THK Manufacturing of Europe S.A.S. (1)
Parc d' Activites la Passerelle, 68190, Ensisheim, France
Tel.: (33) 389834400
Web Site: http://www.thk.es
Sales Range: $100-124.9 Million
Emp.: 439
Linear Motion Guides Mfr
N.A.I.C.S.: 333998
Tetsuya Hayashida *(Pres & CEO)*

THK Manufacturing of Ireland Ltd. (1)
Tallaght Business Park, Whitestown Industrial Estate Tallaght, Dublin, Ireland
Tel.: (353) 14628101
Industrial Parts Mfr
N.A.I.C.S.: 336390

THK Manufacturing of Vietnam Co., Ltd. (1)
Lot5 TS9 Tien Son IZ, Tien Du, Bac Ninh, Vietnam
Tel.: (84) 2223974970
Industrial Parts Mfr
N.A.I.C.S.: 336390

THK Niigata Co., Ltd. (1)
5836 Nakayama Yasuda, Agano, 959-2221, Niigata, Japan
Tel.: (81) 250683482
Web Site: http://www.thk-niigata.co.jp
Sales Range: $25-49.9 Million
Emp.: 275
Semiconductor Manufacturing Equipment & Machine Tools Mfr
N.A.I.C.S.: 333242
Akihiro Teramachi *(Chm)*

THK Rhythm (Thailand) Co., Ltd. (1)
Bangna Tower Tower A 1701 2/3 M 14 Bangna-Trad Highway Km 6 5 Bangkaew, Bangplee, Samut Prakan, 10540, Thailand
Tel.: (66) 27513001
Industrial Parts Mfr
N.A.I.C.S.: 336390

THK Rhythm Automotive Czech A.S. (1)
Strojirenska 160, Dacice, 380 17, Jindrichuv Hradec, Czech Republic
Tel.: (420) 38 445 6272
Web Site: https://www.thkdacice.cz
Industrial Parts Mfr
N.A.I.C.S.: 336390

THK Rhythm Changzhou Co., Ltd. (1)
150 Chunjiang Road, Xinbei District, Changzhou, 213125, China
Tel.: (86) 51969180600
Industrial Parts Mfr
N.A.I.C.S.: 336390

THK Rhythm Co., Ltd. (1)
283-3 Gokyu-cho, Minami-ku, Hamamatsu, 430-0831, Shizuoka, Japan **(100%)**
Tel.: (81) 534622111
Web Site: http://www.rhythm-mp.co.jp
Emp.: 2,000
Automobile Parts Mfr
N.A.I.C.S.: 336390
Akihiro Teramachi *(Chm)*

Subsidiary (Non-US):

Rhythm Guangzhou Corporation (2)
Sanchi N Rd E Dongfeng Rd Auto City, Huadu Dist, Guangzhou, 510800, Guangdong, China
Tel.: (86) 2086733322
Web Site: http://www.rhythm-mp.co.jp
Automobile Parts Mfr
N.A.I.C.S.: 336330
Mizutani Shinichi *(Pres)*

Subsidiary (US):

Rhythm North America Corporation (2)
549 Vista Dr, Sparta, TN 38583
Tel.: (931) 738-2250
Web Site: https://www.rhythm-na.com
Sales Range: $50-74.9 Million
Emp.: 200
Automobile Parts Distr
N.A.I.C.S.: 423120
Junzo Nakatsugawa *(Dir-Ops)*

Subsidiary (Domestic):

THK Rhythm Khushu Co., Ltd. (2)
321-1 Sankomoriyama Nakatu-shi, Oita, 871-0101, Japan
Tel.: (81) 979268111
Automobile Parts Mfr
N.A.I.C.S.: 336330

Subsidiary (US):

Thk Rhythm Automotive Michigan Corporation (2)
902 Lyons Rd, Portland, MI 48875
Tel.: (517) 647-4121
Web Site: http://www.thk-rhythm-auto.com
Industrial Parts Mfr & Distr
N.A.I.C.S.: 336390
Akihiro Teramachi *(Mng Dir)*

THK Rhythm Guangzhou Co., Ltd. (1)
No 11 Gaoxin Road Auto City Xiuquan Avenue, Huadu District, Guangzhou, 510800, China
Tel.: (86) 2086733322
Industrial Parts Mfr
N.A.I.C.S.: 336390

THK Rhythm Malaysia Sdn. Bhd. (1)
1447 Lorong Perusahaan Maju 8, Kawasan Perindustrian Prai, 13600, Perai, Penang, Malaysia
Tel.: (60) 45090082
Industrial Parts Mfr
N.A.I.C.S.: 336390

THK TAIWAN CO., LTD. (1)
7F No192-1 Sec 4 Chengde Rd, Shilin Dist, Taipei, 11167, Taiwan
Tel.: (886) 228883818
Web Site: http://www.thk.com
Sales Range: $25-49.9 Million
Emp.: 35
Screws & Linear Motion Guides Mfr
N.A.I.C.S.: 332722
Akihiro Teramachi *(Pres)*

Tech Con Czech Republic s.r.o. (1)
Ve Zlibku 1800 Big Box Facility Building B6, 193 00, Prague, Czech Republic
Tel.: (420) 27 700 4705
Web Site: https://www.tech-con.cz
Industrial Parts Distr
N.A.I.C.S.: 423840

Tech Con Hungaria Kft (1)
Veso u 9-11, 1133, Budapest, Hungary
Tel.: (36) 614124161
Web Site: http://www.tech-con.hu

Sales Range: $25-49.9 Million
Emp.: 30
Industrial Equipment Mfr
N.A.I.C.S.: 333248

Tech Con Industry SRL (1)
Calea Crangasi no 60 Sector 6, Bucharest, Romania
Tel.: (40) 21 221 9642
Web Site: http://www.tech-con.ro
Industrial Parts Distr
N.A.I.C.S.: 423840

Tech-Con Poland Sp. z.o.o. (1)
Ul Legnicka 21, 41-811, Zabrze, Poland
Tel.: (48) 79 872 1254
Web Site: https://www.tech-congroup.pl
Industrial Parts Distr
N.A.I.C.S.: 423840

Thk Rhythm Automotive Canada Limited (1)
3600B Laird Road Unit 10, Mississauga, L5L 6A7, ON, Canada
Tel.: (905) 820-7800
Industrial Parts Mfr
N.A.I.C.S.: 336390

Thk Rhythm Automotive GmbH (1)
Fichtenstrasse 37, 40233, Dusseldorf, Germany
Tel.: (49) 21 190 9550
Web Site: https://www.thk-rhythm-auto.eu
Emp.: 1,500
Industrial Parts Mfr
N.A.I.C.S.: 336390
Hauke Baumann *(Dir-Portfolio)*

Thk Rhythm Mexicana, S.A. De C.V. (1)
Circuito San Roque sur 503 Parque Santa Fe Ampliacion Silao, 36275, Guanajuato, Mexico
Tel.: (52) 4727489090
Industrial Parts Mfr
N.A.I.C.S.: 336390

United Bearing Industrial Corp. (1)
1018-1020 Benavidez Street, Binondo, Manila, 1003, Metro Manila, Philippines
Tel.: (63) 2 244 7021
Web Site: https://www.unitedbearing.com
Bearing Product Distr
N.A.I.C.S.: 423840

THN CORPORATION
43 Seongseo-ro 71-gil, Dalseo-Gu, Daegu, Korea (South)
Tel.: (82) 535833001
Web Site: https://www.th-net.co.kr
Year Founded: 1986
019180—(KRS)
Rev.: $360,234,429
Assets: $284,828,485
Liabilities: $214,698,306
Net Worth: $70,130,179
Earnings: ($3,648,958)
Emp.: 495
Fiscal Year-end: 12/31/22
Wire Harnesses Mfr
N.A.I.C.S.: 336320
Hwang Seong *(Mng Dir)*

Subsidiaries:

THN PARAGUAY. SA (1)
Crisostomo Centurion, Canadita, 2100, Itaugua, Paraguay
Tel.: (595) 213285522
Web Site: https://www.thn.com.py
Wire Product Mfr
N.A.I.C.S.: 332618

THOMAS BETEILIGUNGEN GMBH
Im Industriepark 13, 55469, Simmern, Germany
Tel.: (49) 6761901100   De
Web Site: https://www.thomas-gruppe.de
Year Founded: 1930
Construction & Building Materials Distr
N.A.I.C.S.: 423390

THOMAS FLEURS SA

THOMAS CARROLL GROUP PLC
Pendragon House Crescent Road, Caerphilly, CF83 1XX, United Kingdom
Tel.: (44) 29 2085 3788   UK
Web Site:
  http://www.thomascarroll.co.uk
Year Founded: 1972
Holding Company; Insurance Brokerage, Financial Advisory & Risk Consultancy Services
N.A.I.C.S.: 551112
John Moore *(Chm)*

Subsidiaries:

Thomas, Carroll (Brokers) Limited (1)
Pendragon House Crescent Road, Caerphilly, CF83 1XX, United Kingdom
Tel.: (44) 29 2085 3788
Web Site: http://www.thomascarroll.co.uk
Insurance Brokerage Services
N.A.I.C.S.: 524210
Rhys Thomas *(Mng Dir)*

Thomas, Carroll Independent Financial Advisers Limited (1)
Pendragon House Crescent Road, Caerphilly, CF83 1XX, United Kingdom
Tel.: (44) 29 2085 3788
Web Site: http://www.thomascarroll.co.uk
Financial Advisory Services
N.A.I.C.S.: 523940
Mark Eedy *(Mng Dir)*

THOMAS CAVANAGH CONSTRUCTION LIMITED
9094 Cavanagh Road, Ashton, K0A 1B0, ON, Canada
Tel.: (613) 257-2918
Web Site:
  https://www.thomascavanagh.ca
Year Founded: 1953
Rev.: $37,751,000
Emp.: 90
Construction Services
N.A.I.C.S.: 237310
Tom Cavanagh *(Owner)*

THOMAS COOK NORTHERN EUROPE AB
Ralambsvagen 17, Stockholm, 10520, Sweden
Tel.: (46) 8 55 51 32 00
Web Site: http://www.ving.se
Holding Company
N.A.I.C.S.: 551112
Fredrik Wessel *(Head-HR)*

Subsidiaries:

Sunclass Airlines A/S (1)
Hangar 276, 2791, Dragor, Denmark
Tel.: (45) 32 47 72 00
Web Site: http://dk.thomascookairlines.dk
Scheduled Passenger Air Transportation Services
N.A.I.C.S.: 481111

THOMAS DESIGN BUILDERS LTD.
C-2395 McGillivray Blvd, Winnipeg, R3Y 1G6, MB, Canada
Tel.: (204) 989-5400
Web Site:
  http://www.thomasdesignbuilders.ca
Year Founded: 1980
Rev.: $19,801,687
Emp.: 21
Building Construction Services
N.A.I.C.S.: 236220
Jeff Miller *(Mgr-Ops)*

THOMAS FLEURS SA
ZAC du Plan Avenue de Counoise, 84320, Entraigues-sur-la-Sorgue, France
Tel.: (33) 490832249   FR

THOMAS FLEURS SA

Thomas Fleurs SA—(Continued)
Web Site: http://www.thomasfleurs.fr
Flower Whslr
N.A.I.C.S.: 424930
Thomas van Pul *(Chm & Pres)*

Subsidiaries:

Gouverneur BV (1)
Middel Broekweg 29, 2675 KB, Honselersdyk, Netherlands
Tel.: (31) 174 63 64 30
Web Site: http://www.gouverneurexport.nl
Flower Whslr
N.A.I.C.S.: 424930
Thom Van Pul *(Mgr)*

Macfleurs S.a.r.l. (1)
ZAC du Plan 15 Avenue de Counoise, Entraigues-sur-la-Sorgue, 84320, France
Tel.: (33) 490333958
Web Site: http://www.macfleurs.com
Sales Range: $25-49.9 Million
Emp.: 12
Internet Flower Whslr
N.A.I.C.S.: 424930

THOMAS FOODS INTERNATIONAL
Lagoon Road, Murray Bridge, 5253, SA, Australia
Tel.: (61) 8 8532 1955
Web Site:
   http://www.thomasfoods.com
Sales Range: $150-199.9 Million
Emp.: 900
Meat Product Distr
N.A.I.C.S.: 424470
Chris Thomas *(Chm & Mng Dir)*

THOMAS SANDERSON
Waterberry Dr, Waterlooville, P07 7UW, Hants, United Kingdom
Tel.: (44) 2392232600
Web Site: http://www.thomas-sanderson.co.uk
Sales Range: $50-74.9 Million
Emp.: 200
Windows, Blinds & Shutters Mfr
N.A.I.C.S.: 321911
Nigel Campkin *(Mng Dir)*

THOMAS WYATT NIGERIA PLC.
10 Abebe Village Road, PMB 1006, Iganmu Ebute Meta, Lagos, 1006, Nigeria
Tel.: (234) 9122591094
Web Site: https://thomaswyattng.com
Year Founded: 1948
THOMASWY—(NIGE)
Rev.: $186,595
Assets: $2,195,780
Liabilities: $1,074,048
Net Worth: $1,121,732
Earnings: $92,324
Emp.: 28
Fiscal Year-end: 03/31/23
Stationery Product Mfr
N.A.I.C.S.: 322230
Ike Emeagwali *(Chm)*

THOMMEN MEDICAL AG
Neckarsulmstrasse 28, 2540, Grenchen, Switzerland
Tel.: (41) 619659020
Web Site:
   http://www.thommenmedical.com
Year Founded: 2001
Sales Range: $25-49.9 Million
Emp.: 70
Mfr of Dental Implants
N.A.I.C.S.: 339113
Livio Marzo *(CEO)*

Subsidiaries:

Thommen Medical Austria GmbH (1)
Simmeringer Hauptstrasse 26, 1110, Vienna, Austria

Tel.: (43) 1 93026 3014
Medical Equipment Distr
N.A.I.C.S.: 423450

Thommen Medical Benelux B.V. (1)
Dierenriem 1, 3738 TP, Maartensdijk, Netherlands
Tel.: (31) 30 68 68 468
Medical Equipment Distr
N.A.I.C.S.: 423450

Thommen Medical Deutschland GmbH (1)
Am Rathaus 2, 79576, Weil am Rhein, Germany
Tel.: (49) 7621 4 22 58 30
Medical Equipment Distr
N.A.I.C.S.: 423450

Thommen Medical France sarl (1)
10 avenue Gabriel Pierne, 77680, Roissy-en-Brie, France
Tel.: (33) 1 83 64 06 35
Web Site: http://www.implant-thommen.fr
Emp.: 5
Medical Equipment Distr
N.A.I.C.S.: 423450
Shubere Wintzinaieth *(CEO)*

Thommen Medical USA L.L.C. (1)
1375 Euclid Ave / Ste 450, Cleveland, OH 44115
Tel.: (866) 319-9800
Medical Equipment Distr
N.A.I.C.S.: 423450
Raymond Lang *(VP-Fin & Ops)*

THOMMEN-FURLER AG
Industriestrasse 10, Ruti b Buren, CH-3295, Bern, Switzerland
Tel.: (41) 32 352 08 00 CH
Web Site: http://www.thommen-furler.ch
Year Founded: 1990
Sales Range: $150-199.9 Million
Emp.: 330
Chemicals, Sepcialty & Lubricants Distr; Hazardous Waste Disposal & Recycling Services
N.A.I.C.S.: 325998
Franz Christ *(CEO)*

Subsidiaries:

K+S Entsorgung (Schweiz) AG (1)
Rue Saint Henri 2, 2800, Delemont, Switzerland
Tel.: (41) 32 423 1662
Web Site: http://www.ks-entsorgung.ch
Waste Management Services
N.A.I.C.S.: 562998

THOMPSON FORD SALES
15 Station Road, Thompson, R8N 0N6, MB, Canada
Tel.: (204) 778-6386
Web Site:
   https://www.thompsonfordsales.com
Year Founded: 1993
New & Used Car Dealers
N.A.I.C.S.: 441110
David Green *(Mgr-Fixed Ops)*

THOMPSON'S MOVING & STORAGE
51 Thornhill Dr, Dartmouth, B3B 1R9, NS, Canada
Tel.: (902) 469-5100
Web Site:
   http://www.thompsonsmoving.ca
Year Founded: 1934
Rev.: $14,693,697
Emp.: 200
Household Goods Moving & Storage Services
N.A.I.C.S.: 484210
Jack Flemming *(Pres & CEO)*

THOMPSON, AHERN & CO. LTD.
6299 Airport Road Suite 506, Mississauga, L4V 1N3, ON, Canada

Tel.: (905) 677-3471
Web Site: http://www.taco.ca
Year Founded: 1912
Rev.: $17,388,990
Emp.: 50
Trade & Logistics Ditr
N.A.I.C.S.: 488510
Rod Kyle *(Pres & Gen Mgr)*

Subsidiaries:

Tahoco Logistics, Inc. (1)
400 Riverwalk Pkwy Ste 200, Tonawanda, NY 14150
Tel.: (716) 874-6288
Freight Forwarding & Logistics Consulting Services
N.A.I.C.S.: 488510
Kim Host *(VP & Gen Mgr)*

THOMSON MEDICAL GROUP LIMITED
101 Thomson Road 20-04/05 United Square, Singapore, 307591, Singapore
Tel.: (65) 63310188 SG
Web Site:
   https://www.thomsonmedical.com
Year Founded: 1979
A50—(SES)
Rev.: $263,630,233
Assets: $1,072,828,455
Liabilities: $646,416,451
Net Worth: $426,412,004
Earnings: $30,423,120
Emp.: 695
Fiscal Year-end: 06/30/23
Holding Company
N.A.I.C.S.: 551112
Shuen Mega *(CEO-Thomson Medical Pte Ltd)*

Subsidiaries:

Rowsley Sports Pte. Ltd. (1)
Great World City 13-10 1 Kim Seng Promenade, Singapore, 237994, Singapore
Tel.: (65) 6235 5056
Web Site: http://www.rowsley.com
Investment Management Service
N.A.I.C.S.: 523999

TMC Life Sciences Berhad (1)
10th Floor Menara Hap Seng No 1 & 3 Jalan P Ramlee, 50250, Kuala Lumpur, Malaysia
Tel.: (60) 323824288
Web Site: http://www.tmclife.com
Rev.: $60,334,065
Assets: $280,380,375
Liabilities: $75,601,845
Net Worth: $204,778,530
Earnings: $10,243,778
Emp.: 1,108
Fiscal Year-end: 06/30/2022
Fertility Research Services
N.A.I.C.S.: 325413
Jimmy Wong *(Co-CFO)*

Subsidiary (Domestic):

TMC Biotech Sdn. Bhd. (2)
No 11 Jalan Teknologi, PJU 5 Kota Damansara, 47810, Petaling Jaya, Malaysia
Tel.: (60) 377293199
Sales Range: $10-24.9 Million
Emp.: 35
Healthcare Development Services
N.A.I.C.S.: 621610

Tropicana Medical Centre (M) Sdn. Bhd. (2)
No 11 Jalan Teknologi Taman Sains Selangor 1 PJU 5, Kota Damansara, 47810, Petaling Jaya, Selangor Darul Ehsan, Malaysia
Tel.: (60) 362871111
Web Site:
   https://www.thomsonhospitals.com
Sales Range: $50-74.9 Million
Emp.: 800
Healtcare Services
N.A.I.C.S.: 621610

Tropicana Medical Centre (Penang) Sdn. Bhd. (2)
12A Jln Masjid Negeri, Air Itam, 11600,

INTERNATIONAL PUBLIC

Penang, Malaysia
Tel.: (60) 48299188
Web Site:
   http://www.tropicanamedicalcentre.com
Healthcare Services
N.A.I.C.S.: 621610

Thomson Hospitals Sdn. Bhd. (1)
11 Jalan Teknologi Taman Sains Selangor 1 PJU 5 Kota Damansara, 47810, Petaling Jaya, Selangor, Malaysia
Tel.: (60) 362871111
Web Site: https://thomsonhospitals.com
Health Care Srvices
N.A.I.C.S.: 524114

Thomson Medical Pte. Ltd. (1)
339 Thomson Road, Singapore, 307677, Singapore
Tel.: (65) 62502222
Web Site: https://www.thomsonmedical.com
Health Care Srvices
N.A.I.C.S.: 621491
Lee Suen Ming *(CEO)*

Thomson Paediatric Centre Pte Ltd (1)
339 Thomson Road 03-06 Thomson Medical Centre, Singapore, 307677, Singapore
Tel.: (65) 62583353
Web Site:
   https://www.thomsonpaediatriccentre.com
Medical Devices
N.A.I.C.S.: 621610

Thomson Women Cancer Centre Pte. Ltd. (1)
101 Irrawaddy Road 17-05/06 Royal Square Medical Centre, Singapore, 329565, Singapore
Tel.: (65) 918218
Web Site:
   https://www.thomsonwomencancer.com.sg
Health Care Srvices
N.A.I.C.S.: 524114

Vantage Bay JB Sdn. Bhd. (1)
Lot 6376 and 9236 Jalan Ibrahim Sultan, 80300, Johor Bahru, Johor, Malaysia
Tel.: (60) 72218899
Healtcare Services
N.A.I.C.S.: 621610

THOMSON RESOURCES LTD
Level 1 80 Chandos Street, Saint Leonards, 2065, NSW, Australia
Tel.: (61) 299066225
Web Site:
   https://www.thomsonresources.com
TMZRF—(OTCIQ)
Rev.: $76,010
Assets: $16,154,456
Liabilities: $8,024,776
Net Worth: $8,129,680
Earnings: ($515,195)
Fiscal Year-end: 06/30/24
Metal Mining Services
N.A.I.C.S.: 212290
Eoin Rothery *(CEO & Mng Dir)*

THOMSON REUTERS CORPORATION
19 Duncan Street, Toronto, M5H 3H1, ON, Canada
Tel.: (647) 480-7000 ON
Web Site:
   https://www.thomsonreuters.com
Year Founded: 2008
TRI—(NYSE)
Rev.: $6,794,000,000
Assets: $18,684,000,000
Liabilities: $7,620,000,000
Net Worth: $11,064,000,000
Earnings: $2,695,000,000
Emp.: 25,600
Fiscal Year-end: 12/31/23
Holding Company; Financial, Legal, Tax, Accounting, Scientific & Healthcare News & Information Publisher
N.A.I.C.S.: 551112
David Thomson *(Chm)*

Subsidiaries:

Capital Confirmation, Inc (1)

AND PRIVATE COMPANIES

THOMSON REUTERS CORPORATION

214 Centerview Dr Ste 265, Brentwood, TN 37207
Tel.: (615) 844-6222
Web Site: http://www.confirmation.com
Secure Electronic Audit Confirmation Services
N.A.I.C.S.: 561621
Brian Fox *(Pres & Founder)*

Pagero Group AB (1)
Vastra Hamngatan 1, 41117, Gothenburg, Sweden
Tel.: (46) 313735890
Web Site: https://www.pagero.com
Rev: $55,091,659
Assets: $145,494,738
Liabilities: $92,378,248
Net Worth: $53,116,490
Earnings: ($25,320,460)
Emp.: 781
Fiscal Year-end: 12/31/2022
Software Development Services
N.A.I.C.S.: 541511
Jan-Olof Ohlsson *(CFO)*

Subsidiary (Non-US):

Pagero (Pty.) Ltd. (2)
Suite 18 Southdowns Ridge Office Park
John Vorster Drive, Centurion, Pretoria, 0062, South Africa
Tel.: (27) 825840907
Software Development Services
N.A.I.C.S.: 541511

Pagero France S.A.S. (2)
23 rue Danielle Casanova, 75001, Paris, France
Tel.: (33) 186478788
Software Development Services
N.A.I.C.S.: 541511

Pagero GmbH (2)
Elisabeth-Selbert Strasse 5c, D-40764, Langenfeld, Germany
Tel.: (49) 20867980000
Information Technology Services
N.A.I.C.S.: 541519

Pagero Gulf FZ-LLC (2)
No 204 Loft Office 1, PO Box 25906, Dubai Media City, Dubai, United Arab Emirates
Tel.: (971) 588179371
Software Development Services
N.A.I.C.S.: 541511

Pagero Iberica S.L. (2)
Calle de Fuencarral 121 piso 4, 28010, Madrid, Spain
Tel.: (34) 911670315
Software Development Services
N.A.I.C.S.: 541511

Subsidiary (US):

Pagero Inc. (2)
50 N Michigan Ave Ste 1950, Chicago, IL 60601
Tel.: (726) 200-4657
Information Technology Services
N.A.I.C.S.: 541519

Subsidiary (Non-US):

Pagero Italy S.R.L. (2)
Via Maurizio Gonzaga 7, 20123, Milan, Italy
Tel.: (39) 0238583586
Software Development Services
N.A.I.C.S.: 541511

Pagero Norway AS (2)
Askekroken 11, 0277, Oslo, Norway
Tel.: (47) 21497139
Software Development Services
N.A.I.C.S.: 541511

Pagero Oy (2)
Hevosenkenka 3, 02600, Espoo, Finland
Tel.: (358) 102195579
Software Development Services
N.A.I.C.S.: 541511

Pagero Poland Sp. z o.o. (2)
Belwederska 9A, 00-761, Warsaw, Poland
Tel.: (48) 532536512
Software Development Services
N.A.I.C.S.: 541511

Pagero S.R.L. (2)
Waterloo Office Park-Batiment N Dreve Richelle 161, 1410, Waterloo, Belgium
Tel.: (32) 26229888

Software Development Services
N.A.I.C.S.: 541511

Pagero UK Ltd. (2)
61 Queen Street, London, EC4R 1EB, United Kingdom
Tel.: (44) 1274015892
Software Development Services
N.A.I.C.S.: 541511

TaxWorks, Inc. (1)
1265 W Sportsplex Dr, Kaysville, UT 84037
Tel.: (801) 529-9025
Web Site: http://www.tax.thomsonreuters.com
Tax Preparation Software Solutions
N.A.I.C.S.: 513210

Thomson Reuters - Corporate Headquarters (1)
3 Times Sq, New York, NY 10036
Tel.: (646) 223-4000
Web Site: http://www.thomsonreuters.com
Corporate Office; Financial, Legal, Tax, Accounting, Scientific & Healthcare News & Information Publisher
N.A.I.C.S.: 551114
James C. Smith *(Pres & CEO)*

Unit (Domestic):

Thomson Reuters Legal (2)
610 Opperman Dr, Eagan, MN 55123
Tel.: (651) 687-7000
Web Site: http://legalsolutions.thomsonreuters.com
Sales Range: $1-4.9 Billion
Emp.: 8,500
Electronic Components Mfr
N.A.I.C.S.: 334419
Rick King *(COO)*

Subsidiary (Domestic):

BAR/BRI of Massachusetts (3)
31 St James Ave Ste 820, Boston, MA 02116
Tel.: (617) 695-9955
Web Site: http://www.barbri.com
Sales Range: $25-49.9 Million
Emp.: 10
Bar Review Services
N.A.I.C.S.: 519290

BAR/BRI of Washington (3)
4020 E Madison St Ste 321, Seattle, WA 98112-3150
Tel.: (206) 329-5250
Web Site: http://www.barbri.com
Sales Range: $10-24.9 Million
Emp.: 4
Bar Review Course
N.A.I.C.S.: 541618
Richard Conviser *(Founder & Chm)*

Clarivate Analytics (CompuMark) Inc. (3)
22 Thomson Place, Boston, MA 02210
Tel.: (800) 692-8833
Web Site: http://www.compumark.com
Trademark Search & Brand Protection Services; Intellectual Property Research
N.A.I.C.S.: 517810
Shawna Williams *(Sr Acct Mgr)*

Subsidiary (Non-US):

Complinet Group Limited (3)
Third Floor Vintners Place, 68 Upper Thames Street, London, EC4V 3BJ, United Kingdom
Tel.: (44) 8700426400
Web Site: http://www.complinet.com
Sales Range: $25-49.9 Million
Holding Company; Risk-Based Compliance Information & Technology Solutions
N.A.I.C.S.: 551112
Paul Johns *(CMO)*

Unit (Non-US):

Complinet Group Ltd. - Dubai (4)
Dubai Multi Commodities Centre Union House 5th Floor, PO Box 43659, Port Saeed Road, Dubai, United Arab Emirates
Tel.: (971) 42115146
Web Site: http://www.complinet.com
Risk-Based Compliance Information & Technology Solutions
N.A.I.C.S.: 519290
Leas Bachatene *(Mng Dir)*

Subsidiary (US):

Complinet Inc. (4)
1250 Broadway 19th Fl, New York, NY 10001
Tel.: (212) 758-7000
Web Site: http://www.complinet.com
Sales Range: $1-9.9 Million
Risk-Based Compliance Information & Technology Solutions
N.A.I.C.S.: 519290
Alex S. Viall *(CEO)*

Subsidiary (Domestic):

Complinet UK Limited (4)
Third Floor Vintners Place, 68 Upper Thames Street, London, EC4V 3BJ, United Kingdom
Tel.: (44) 8700426400
Web Site: http://www.complinet.com
Risk-Based Compliance Information & Technology Solutions
N.A.I.C.S.: 519290

Subsidiary (Domestic):

FindLaw (3)
800 W California Ave 2nd Fl, Sunnyvale, CA 94086-4834
Tel.: (408) 524-4799
Web Site: http://www.findlaw.com
Legal Research Web Site
N.A.I.C.S.: 922130
Stephanie Rahlfs *(Mgr-Digital Strategy & Social Media)*

Gilbert Law Summaries (3)
1 North Dearborn Fl 6, Chicago, IL 60602
Tel.: (312) 894-1688
Web Site: http://www.gilbertlaw.com
Sales Range: $25-49.9 Million
Emp.: 55
Book Publishing
N.A.I.C.S.: 513130

Round Table Group, Inc. (3)
980 N Michigan Ave Fl 14, Chicago, IL 60611
Tel.: (312) 635-7877
Web Site: http://www.roundtablegroup.com
Sales Range: $1-9.9 Million
Emp.: 15
Expert Witness & Consultant Location Services
N.A.I.C.S.: 561499
Robert Hull *(Co-Founder & Pres)*

Seregenti Law (3)
155 108 Ave NE Ste 650, Bellevue, WA 98004
Tel.: (425) 732-5555
Web Site: http://www.serengetilaw.com
Billing Software Developer
N.A.I.C.S.: 513210
Rob Thomas *(VP-Market Dev Grp)*

Silicon Valley Expert Witness Group, Inc. (3)
2570 W El Camino Real Ste 550, Mountain View, CA 94040
Tel.: (650) 917-0700
Web Site: http://www.bgexpertwitness.com
Sales Range: $100-124.9 Million
Emp.: 4
Technology Consulting & Litigation Support Services
N.A.I.C.S.: 561499
Richard McCloskey *(Pres)*

Thomson Elite (3)
5100 W Goldleaf Cir Ste 100, Los Angeles, CA 90056-1271
Tel.: (323) 642-5200
Web Site: http://www.elite.com
Financial & Practice Management Software & Services
N.A.I.C.S.: 519290
Steve Todd *(VP-Legal)*

Subsidiary (Domestic):

Elite Information Systems, Inc. (4)
5100 W Goldleaf Cir, Los Angeles, CA 90056-1271
Tel.: (323) 642-5200
Web Site: http://www.elite.com
Information Technology Company
N.A.I.C.S.: 541512

Elite Information Systems, Inc. (4)
530 5th Ave, New York, NY 10036
Tel.: (212) 922-1920
Web Site: http://www.elite.com
Sales Range: $75-99.9 Million
Emp.: 100
Software Publisher
N.A.I.C.S.: 334610

Holding (Non-US):

Thomson Elite (4)
Oldgate 33 Oldgate High Street, EC3N 1DL, London, United Kingdom - England
Tel.: (44) 2073697379
Web Site: http://www.elite.com
N.A.I.C.S.: 334610

Subsidiary (Domestic):

West Publishing Corporation (3)
610 Opperman Dr, Eagan, MN 55123
Tel.: (651) 687-7000
Web Site: http://www.west.thomson.com
Printing & Publishing-Legal, Educational & Electronic
N.A.I.C.S.: 513199
Kenneth M. Ross *(CTO & Sr VP)*

Subsidiary (Domestic):

Andrews Publications (4)
175 Strafford Ave Bldg 4 Ste 140, Wayne, PA 19087
Tel.: http://www.andrewsonline.com
Sales Range: $50-74.9 Million
Emp.: 45
Legal Books & Periodicals Publisher
N.A.I.C.S.: 541611

Branch (Domestic):

Thomson West (4)
50 Broad St Aqueduct Bldg, Rochester, NY 14694-0001
Tel.: (585) 546-5530
Web Site: http://www.thomson.com
Writing, Printing, Publishing & Binding of Legal Materials & Reference Works
N.A.I.C.S.: 513130

Division (Domestic):

Thomson Reuters Markets (2)
3 Times Sq, New York, NY 10006
Tel.: (646) 223-4000
Web Site: http://www.thomsonreuters.com
Sales Range: $1-4.9 Billion
Emp.: 9,300
Information & Technology Solutions to the Worldwide Financial Community
N.A.I.C.S.: 513130
Chris Ahearn *(Pres-Reuters Media)*

Subsidiary (Domestic):

FX Alliance Inc. (3)
909 3rd Ave 10th Fl, New York, NY 10022-4755
Tel.: (646) 268-9900
Web Site: http://www.fxall.com
Emp.: 205
Holding Company; Online Foreign Commodities Exchange Platform & Services
N.A.I.C.S.: 551112
Philip Zev Weisberg *(CEO)*

Subsidiary (Domestic):

FX Alliance, LLC (4)
909 3rd Ave 10th Fl, New York, NY 10022
Tel.: (646) 268-9900
Online Foreign Commodities Exchange Platform & Services
N.A.I.C.S.: 523160

Subsidiary (Domestic):

Lipper Inc. (3)
707 17th St Ste 22 Fl 22, Denver, CO 80202
Tel.: (303) 534-3472
Web Site: http://www.lipperweb.com
Mutual Fund Information & Analytical Services
N.A.I.C.S.: 519290

Subsidiary (Domestic):

HedgeWorld (4)
3 Times Sq 18th Fl, New York, NY 10036
Tel.: (646) 223-4431
Web Site: http://www.hedgeworld.com

THOMSON REUTERS CORPORATION

Thomson Reuters Corporation—(Continued)

Hedge Fund News, Research & Analysis Services
N.A.I.C.S.: 519290
Chris Clair *(Mng Editor)*

Subsidiary (Non-US):

Reuters Limited (3)
Re Bldg S Colonnate, E14 5EP, London, United Kingdom - England
Tel.: (44) 72501122
News & Information Organization
N.A.I.C.S.: 519290
Yvonne Diaz *(Global Head-External Comm, Fin & Risk)*

Subsidiary (Non-US):

Reuters Australia Pty. Ltd. (4)
60 Margaret Street Level 10, Sydney, 2000, NSW, Australia
Tel.: (61) 293731500
Sales Range: $75-99.9 Million
News Gathering & Wire Service Operations
N.A.I.C.S.: 516210

Reuters Hong Kong Limited (4)
10th Fl Cityplaza 3, 14 Taikoo Wan Rd, Hong Kong, China (Hong Kong)
Tel.: (852) 29126688
News Gathering & Wire Service Operations
N.A.I.C.S.: 516210

Reuters Italia SpA (4)
Viale Fulvio Testi 280, 20126, Milan, Italy
Tel.: (39) 02661291
News Gathering & Wire Service Operations
N.A.I.C.S.: 516210

Reuters Japan Ltd (4)
Shuwa Kamiyacho Bldg 3rd Fl, 4 3 13 Toranomon Minato Ku, Tokyo, 105 0001, Japan
Tel.: (81) 334324141
Web Site: http://jp.reuters.com
News Gathering & Wire Service Operations
N.A.I.C.S.: 516210

Reuters SA (4)
153 Route De Thonon, Collonge Bellerive, Geneva, 1245, Switzerland
Tel.: (41) 583062828
News Gathering & Wire Service Operations
N.A.I.C.S.: 516210

Reuters Services SARL (4)
6 8 Blvd Haussmann, 75457, Paris, France
Tel.: (33) 149495000
Sales Range: $75-99.9 Million
Emp.: 100
News Gathering & Wire Service Operations
N.A.I.C.S.: 516210

Reuters Singapore Pte Limited (4)
18 Science Park Drive, Singapore, 118 229, Singapore
Tel.: (65) 67755088
Web Site: http://www.thomsonreuters.com
Emp.: 820
News Gathering & Wire Service Operations
N.A.I.C.S.: 516210
Edward Haddad *(Mng Dir)*

Thomson Reuters (Markets) Deuschland GmbH (4)
Friedrich Ebert Anlage 49, 60327, Frankfurt am Main, Germany
Tel.: (49) 6975651000
Web Site: http://www.thomsonreuters.de
Sales Range: $100-124.9 Million
News Gathering & Wire Service Operations
N.A.I.C.S.: 516210

Subsidiary (Domestic):

Reuters Research (3)
3 Times Sq, New York, NY 10036-6564
Tel.: (646) 223-4000
Sales Range: $75-99.9 Million
Emp.: 560
Investment Research Company
N.A.I.C.S.: 517810
Jeff Saville *(Mgr-Mktg)*

Subsidiary (Domestic):

Reuters America Inc
717 Office Pkwy, Creve Coeur, MO 63141-7104
Tel.: (314) 468-1000
Financial News & Information Services
N.A.I.C.S.: 513199
Joyce Adeluwoye-Adams *(Editor-Newsroom Diversity)*

Subsidiary (Domestic):

StarMine Corporation (3)
425 Market St 4th fl, San Francisco, CA 94105
Tel.: (888) 578-2741
Sales Range: $10-24.9 Million
Emp.: 80
Investment Research & Analysis Services
N.A.I.C.S.: 519290

Subsidiary (Non-US):

Thomson Corporation Financial (3)
Westgate Office Building Neuhofstrasses 1 Baar, Zug, 6340, Switzerland
Tel.: (41) 41 709 04 44
Web Site: http://www.thomsonreuters.com
Sales Range: $25-49.9 Million
Emp.: 11
Mfr of Business & Financial Software & Online Services
N.A.I.C.S.: 334610

Thomson Financial (3)
Monmouth House London 58-64 City Road, London, EC1Y 2AL, United Kingdom
Tel.: (44) 2072503000
Web Site: http://www.thomsonreuters.com
Sales Range: $50-74.9 Million
Emp.: 500
Provides Online Investment Information & Research Services; Econometric & Portfolio Accounting Services
N.A.I.C.S.: 541219
James Kenigsberg *(Executives)*

Thomson Financial (3)
Antonio Vivaldistraat 50, 1083 HP, Amsterdam, Netherlands
Tel.: (31) 0104246666
Web Site: http://www.thomson.com
Sales Range: Less than $1 Million
Emp.: 15
Provider of Computer Readable Databases
N.A.I.C.S.: 334610

Thomson Financial Ltd. (3)
33 Aldgate High St, London, EC3N 1DL, United Kingdom
Tel.: (44) 2073697000
Web Site: http://thomsonreuters.com
Financial Services
N.A.I.C.S.: 522320

Thomson Financial S.A. (3)
61 Rue Lafayette, 75009, Paris, France
Tel.: (33) 153323900
Web Site: http://www.thompson.com
Provider of Financial Services
N.A.I.C.S.: 523999

Thomson Financial S.r.l. (3)
Corso Europa 2, 20122, Milan, Ronbardia, Italy
Tel.: (39) 028639111
Sales Range: $25-49.9 Million
Emp.: 20
Mfr of Business & Financial Software & Online Services
N.A.I.C.S.: 334610

Thomson Financial SA (3)
40 Monterey Avenue, Luxembourg, 2163, Luxembourg
Tel.: (352) 226660
Web Site: http://www.thomson.com
Sales Range: $25-49.9 Million
Emp.: 4
Mfr of Business & Financial Software & Online Services
N.A.I.C.S.: 334610

Subsidiary (Domestic):

Thomson Financial Vestek (3)
425 Market St Fl 6, San Francisco, CA 94105
Tel.: (415) 344-6000
Web Site: http://www.vestek.com
Sales Range: $100-124.9 Million
Emp.: 300
N.A.I.C.S.: 513110
Mark Pahlavan *(VP-Architecture)*

Thomson Global Markets Inc. (3)
22 Thomson Pl 30 T3, Boston, MA 02210-1212
Tel.: (617) 345-2000
Web Site: http://www.ifrmarkets.com
Sales Range: $10-24.9 Million
Emp.: 30
Financial Services
N.A.I.C.S.: 541512

Thomson Reuters (3)
22 Thomson Pl, Boston, MA 02210-1212
Tel.: (617) 856-2000
Web Site: http://www.thomsonreuters.com
Information Services
N.A.I.C.S.: 519290
Carr Bettis *(Executives)*

Subsidiary (Non-US):

Thomson Reuters Australia (3)
60 Margaret St Level 10, Sydney, 2000, NSW, Australia
Tel.: (61) 2 9373 1500
Web Site: http://www.thomsonreuters.com
Sales Range: $25-49.9 Million
Emp.: 500
Financial Services
N.A.I.C.S.: 523999
Darren Fittler *(Mng Dir)*

Thomson Reuters Hong Kong Limited (3)
Cityplaza 3, Hong Kong, China (Hong Kong)
Tel.: (852) 28436363
Sales Range: $25-49.9 Million
Emp.: 110
Intelligence Information Services
N.A.I.C.S.: 541690

Thomson Reuters Japan (3)
Palaceside Bldg 5th Fl, 1-1-1 Hitotsubashi Chiyoda Ku, Tokyo, 100 0003, Japan
Tel.: (81) 352186600
Web Site: http://www.thomsonreuters.co.jp
Business & Financial Software Publisher & Online Data Services
N.A.I.C.S.: 334610

Unit (Domestic):

Thomson Reuters Tax & Accounting (2)
195 Broadway, New York, NY 10007
Tel.: (212) 367-6300
Web Site: http://www.thomsonreuters.com
Sales Range: $700-749.9 Million
Tax & Accounting Technology & Information Services
N.A.I.C.S.: 541219
Brian Peccarelli *(Pres)*

Subsidiary (Domestic):

Paisley Consulting Inc. (3)
400 Cokato St E, Cokato, MN 55321
Tel.: (320) 286-5870
Sales Range: $25-49.9 Million
Emp.: 230
Consulting & Software Management Services
N.A.I.C.S.: 541611

Practitioners Publishing Co. (3)
PO Box 966, Fort Worth, TX 76101-0966
Tel.: (817) 332-3709
Web Site: http://thomsonreuters.com
Sales Range: $100-124.9 Million
Emp.: 350
Tax Information & Accounting Materials Publisher
N.A.I.C.S.: 541219

Unit (Domestic):

Thomson Reuters/ONESOURCE (3)
2395 Midway Rd, Carrollton, TX 75006-2575
Tel.: (972) 250-7000
Web Site: http://onesource.thomsonreuters.com
Computerized Tax Processing Service
N.A.I.C.S.: 541511
Joseph Harpaz *(Mng Dir-Corp Tax Products)*

THONBURI HEALTHCARE GROUP PCL

34/1 Itsaraphap Rd Ban Chang Lor, Bangkok Noi, Bangkok, 10700, Thailand
Tel.: (66) 24872000
Web Site: https://www.thg.co.th
THG—(THA)
Rev.: $255,201,089
Assets: $687,460,144
Liabilities: $372,880,937
Net Worth: $314,579,207
Earnings: $11,447,247
Emp.: 4,880
Fiscal Year-end: 12/31/23
Health Care Srvices
N.A.I.C.S.: 621610

Subsidiaries:

DS All Co., Ltd (1)
615 Jit-Uthai Bldg 11th Floor Ramkhamhaeng Rd, Bangkapi, Bangkok, 10240, Thailand
Tel.: (66) 23751516
Web Site: https://ds-all.co.th
Dental Care Product Distr
N.A.I.C.S.: 423450

DS All Co., Ltd. (1)
615 Chit Uthai Building 11th Floor Ramkhamhaeng Road, Huamark Subdistrict Bang Kapi District, Bangkok, 10240, Thailand
Tel.: (66) 23751516
Web Site: https://ds-all.co.th
Health Care Srvices
N.A.I.C.S.: 621491

Lanta Vejkij Co., Ltd. (1)
399 Moo 3 Tambol Saladan Amphur Koh Lanta, Krabi, 81150, Thailand
Tel.: (66) 815697890
Medical Business Services
N.A.I.C.S.: 524114

Modular Software Expertise Co., Ltd. (1)
667/15 Ataboon Building 3rd Floor Charan Sanit Wong Road, Arunamarin Bangkoknoi, Bangkok, 10700, Thailand
Tel.: (66) 2 882 5173
Web Site: https://www.mse-th.com
Information Technology Services
N.A.I.C.S.: 541511

Rajthanee Realty Co., Ltd. (1)
61/160 Soi Thaweemit 5 Pharam 9 Rd, Huaykwang, Bangkok, 10310, Thailand
Tel.: (66) 26430921
Property Development Services
N.A.I.C.S.: 531390

Thonburi Bamrungmuang Hospital Co., Ltd. (1)
611 Bamrungmuang Rd, Klong Mahanak Pomprapsattruphai, Bangkok, 10100, Thailand
Tel.: (66) 2 220 7999
Web Site: https://www.thonburibamrungmuang.com
Hospitality Services
N.A.I.C.S.: 621610
Chalermkul Apibunyopas *(Chm)*

Thonburi Realty Development Co., Ltd. (1)
61/160 Soi Thaweemit 5 Pharam 9 Rd, Huaykwang, Bangkok, 10310, Thailand
Tel.: (66) 264309215
Property Development Services
N.A.I.C.S.: 531390

Thung Song 888 Co., Ltd. (1)
88/8 Moo 1 Tambol Chamai, Amphur Thung Song, Nakhon Si Thammarat, 80110, Thailand
Tel.: (66) 935791188
Electricity Mfr & Distr
N.A.I.C.S.: 334515

THONBURI MEDICAL CENTRE PUBLIC COMPANY LIMITED

337 Taksin Road Sumlhae, Thon Buri, Bangkok, Thailand
Tel.: (66) 2438 0040
Year Founded: 1977
Rev.: $31,906,284
Assets: $20,727,468
Liabilities: $4,832,121
Net Worth: $15,895,347

Earnings: $825,021
Fiscal Year-end: 12/31/19
Health Care Srvices
N.A.I.C.S.: 621491
Chairat Panthuraamphorn *(Chm)*

THONG GUAN INDUSTRIES BERHAD
Lot 52 Jalan PKNK 1/6 Kawasan Perusahaan Sungai Petani, 08000, Sungai Petani, Kedah, Malaysia
Tel.: (60) 44417888
Web Site:
    https://www.thongguan.com
TGUAN—(KLS)
Rev.: $293,444,021
Assets: $276,064,762
Liabilities: $96,101,799
Net Worth: $179,962,963
Earnings: $21,515,556
Emp.: 2,378
Fiscal Year-end: 12/31/22
Plastics Product Mfr
N.A.I.C.S.: 316210
Poon Chuan Ang *(Mng Dir)*

Subsidiaries:

Everprosper Food Industries Sdn. Bhd. (1)
Plot No 33 Jalan PKNK Utama Kawasan Perusahaan Sungai Petani, 08000, Sungai Petani, Kedah, Malaysia
Tel.: (60) 44446909
Web Site:
    https://www.organicnoodle.com.my
Dry Noodle Mfr
N.A.I.C.S.: 311824

Jaya Uni'ang (Sabah) Sdn. Bhd. (1)
11 2 km Jalan Tuaran, Inanam, 89350, Kota Kinabalu, Sabah, Malaysia
Tel.: (60) 88421882
Plastics Product Mfr
N.A.I.C.S.: 325211
Alan Ang *(Mng Dir)*

Newton Research & Development Centre Sdn. Bhd. (1)
Plot 96 Jalan PKNK 1/6 Kawasan Perusahaan Sungai Petani, 08000, Sungai Petani, Kedah, Malaysia
Tel.: (60) 44424222
Web Site: https://www.newton-centre.my
Plastic Packaging Services
N.A.I.C.S.: 561910
Ang Poon Khim *(Exec Dir)*

Syarikat Thong Guan Trading Sdn. Bhd. (1)
57 Main Road, Sungai Lalang, 08100, Bedong, Kedah, Malaysia
Tel.: (60) 44422020
Web Site: https://www.888teacoffee.com.my
Sales Range: $50-74.9 Million
Emp.: 80
Tea Whslr
N.A.I.C.S.: 424490

TG Power Wrap Sdn. Bhd. (1)
Batu 33 Jalan Sungai Petani Ke Alor Setar, Sungai Lalang, 08100, Bedong, Kedah, Malaysia
Tel.: (60) 44411069
Polyvinyl Chloride Cling Food Wrap Mfr
N.A.I.C.S.: 326113

TGP Marketing Sdn. Bhd. (1)
Lot 52 Jalan PKNK 1/6 Kawasan Perusahaan Sungai, 08000, Sungai Petani, Malaysia
Tel.: (60) 44417888
Sales Range: $25-49.9 Million
Emp.: 15
Plastic Packaging Product Distr
N.A.I.C.S.: 423840
David Ang *(Gen Mgr)*

TGP Plaspack (Suzhou) Co., Ltd. (1)
No 99 Jiulong South Road Economic Developing Zone, Songling Town, Wujiang, 215200, Jiangsu, China
Tel.: (86) 51263459888
Plastic Film & Garbage Bag Mfr
N.A.I.C.S.: 326199

TGSH Plastic Industries Sdn. Bhd. (1)
Lot 3232 Jalan Paya Mengkuang Padang Lembu, 08330, Gurun, Kedah, Malaysia
Tel.: (60) 44688379
Plastic Packaging Products Mfr
N.A.I.C.S.: 326130

Thong Guan Industries Berhad - Flexible Packaging Division (1)
Plot 48 Jalan PKNK 1/6 Kawasan Perusahaan Sungai Petani, 08000, Sungai Petani, Kedah, Malaysia
Tel.: (60) 4 442 7888
Web Site: https://www.thongguan.com
Sales Range: $50-74.9 Million
Emp.: 150
Plastic Packaging Products Mfr
N.A.I.C.S.: 326199

Thong Guan Plastic & Paper Industries Sdn. Bhd. (1)
Lot 52 Jalan PKNK 1/6 Kawasan Perusahaan Sungai Petani, 08000, Sungai Petani, Kedah, Malaysia
Tel.: (60) 44417888
Web Site: https://www.thongguan.com
Sales Range: $250-299.9 Million
Emp.: 600
Plastic & Paper Products Mfr
N.A.I.C.S.: 322120

Thong Guan Plastic Industries (Suzhou) Co., Ltd. (1)
No 99 Jiulong South Road Economic Developing Zone, Songling Town, Wujiang, 215200, Jiangsu, China
Tel.: (86) 51263459888
Emp.: 500
Plastic Films & Bags Mfr
N.A.I.C.S.: 326111

Uni'ang Plastic Industries (Sabah) Sdn. Bhd. (1)
11 2km Jalan Tuaran, Inanam, 89350, Kota Kinabalu, Sabah, Malaysia
Tel.: (60) 8 842 3881
Web Site: https://www.uniang.com
Emp.: 100
Plastic Products Mfr & Whslr
N.A.I.C.S.: 325211

THONG NHAT JOINT STOCK COMPANY
Bau Xeo Industrial zone, Trang Bom District, Dong Nai, Vietnam
Tel.: (84) 613924377
BAX—(HNX)
Rev.: $7,452,300
Assets: $72,483,100
Liabilities: $51,417,500
Net Worth: $21,065,600
Earnings: $2,876,600
Fiscal Year-end: 12/31/23
Real Estate Services
N.A.I.C.S.: 531390
Tran Trung Tuan *(Chm)*

THOR ENERGY PLC
Tel.: (61) 873241935
Web Site:
    https://www.thormining.com
THR—(AIM)
Rev.: $24,014
Assets: $17,061,386
Liabilities: $304,600
Net Worth: $16,756,786
Earnings: ($3,126,889)
Fiscal Year-end: 06/30/24
Metal Exploration & Development Services
N.A.I.C.S.: 213114
Michael Robert Billing *(Chm)*

Subsidiaries:

Hale Energy Limited (1)
58 Galway Avenue, Adelaide, 5033, SA, Australia
Tel.: (61) 8 7324 1935
Web Site: http://www.thormining.com
Uranium Mining Services
N.A.I.C.S.: 212290

THOR EXPLORATIONS LIMITED
550 Burrard St Suite 2900, Vancouver, V6C 0A3, BC, Canada
Tel.: (778) 658-6391
Web Site: https://www.thorexpl.com
Year Founded: 1968
THX—(AIM)
Rev.: $141,245,328
Assets: $259,114,169
Liabilities: $146,919,399
Net Worth: $112,194,770
Earnings: $10,869,446
Fiscal Year-end: 12/31/23
Mineral Exploration Services
N.A.I.C.S.: 212290
Segun Lawson *(Pres & CEO)*

Subsidiaries:

Enorm Mining Limited (1)

Ngnira Gold SARL (1)

THOR GROUP LIMITED
Bramling House Bramling, Canterbury, CT3 1NB, Kent, United Kingdom
Tel.: (44) 1227 721699
Web Site: http://www.thor.com
Year Founded: 1983
Sales Range: $350-399.9 Million
Emp.: 1,024
Basic Chemicals Mfr
N.A.I.C.S.: 325199
Mitch Cook *(Mgr-Global Acct)*

Subsidiaries:

Thor Brasil Ltda (1)
Alameda Caiapos 861, Tambore, 06460-110, Sao Paulo, Brazil
Tel.: (55) 1141334150
Chemical Products Distr
N.A.I.C.S.: 424690

Thor Especialidades, S.A. (1)
Poligono Industrial El Pla Avda de la Industria 1, Castellgali, 8297, Barcelona, Spain
Tel.: (34) 938332800
Chemical Products Distr
N.A.I.C.S.: 424690

Thor GmbH (1)
Landwehrstrasse 1, 67346, Speyer, Germany
Tel.: (49) 62326360
Web Site: http://www.thor.com
Chemical Products Distr
N.A.I.C.S.: 424690

Thor Japan Limited (1)
19-17 Kasuga-cho, Izumiotsu, 595-0061, Osaka, Japan
Tel.: (81) 725227907
Chemical Products Distr
N.A.I.C.S.: 424690

Thor Nordic (1)
Molndalsvagen 24, 412 63, Gothenburg, Sweden
Tel.: (46) 31404146
Chemical Products Distr
N.A.I.C.S.: 424690

Thor Personal Care SAS (1)
147 rue Irene Joliot-Curie, BP 90875, Compiegne, 60208, Lacroix-Saint-Ouen, Cedex, France
Tel.: (33) 344374000
Chemical Products Distr
N.A.I.C.S.: 424690
Bertrand L'Homme *(Mng Dir)*

Thor Quimicos de Mexico, SA de CV (1)
Carretera Mexico - Queretero KM 182, Pedro Escobedo, 76700, Queretero, Mexico
Tel.: (52) 4482752200
Chemical Products Distr
N.A.I.C.S.: 424690

Thor SARL (1)
325 rue des Balmes - ZIP, Salaise-sur-Sanne, 38150, France
Tel.: (33) 474112000
Chemical Products Distr
N.A.I.C.S.: 424690

Thor Specialties (UK) Limited (1)
Wincham Avenue, Wincham, Northwich, CW9 6GB, Cheshire, United Kingdom
Tel.: (44) 1606818800
Chemical Product Mfr & Distr
N.A.I.C.S.: 325199

Thor Specialties Pty Limited (1)
67 Newton Road, Wetherill Park, 2164, NSW, Australia
Tel.: (61) 297251177
Chemical Products Distr
N.A.I.C.S.: 424690

Thor Specialties Pty Limited (1)
15 Kalmia Street, Ellerslie, Auckland, New Zealand
Tel.: (64) 95795037
Chemical Products Distr
N.A.I.C.S.: 424690

Thor Specialties Sdn Bhd (1)
Jalan Bursa 23/4, 40300, Shah Alam, Selangor Darul Ehsan, Malaysia
Tel.: (60) 355425788
Chemical Products Distr
N.A.I.C.S.: 424690
Weng Wai Kam *(Bus Mgr)*

Thor Specialties srl (1)
Via del Pontaccio 2, Casale Litta, 21020, Varese, Italy
Tel.: (39) 03321815311
Chemical Products Distr
N.A.I.C.S.: 424690
Silvio Bianchi *(Bus Mgr-Flame Retardant)*

Thor Specialties srl (1)
Turkiye Istanbul Subesi 19 Mayis Mahallesi Sumer sokak Zitas Bloklari, C1 Blok D 12 Kozyatagi, Istanbul, Turkiye
Tel.: (90) 2166586285
Chemical Products Distr
N.A.I.C.S.: 424690

Thor Specialties, Inc (1)
50 Waterview Dr, Shelton, CT 06484
Tel.: (203) 516-6980
Chemical Products Distr
N.A.I.C.S.: 424690
James Whittaker *(Area Mgr-Sls)*

Thor Specialty Chemical (Shanghai) Co Ltd (1)
Hongwell Building Room 1905 A Building No 1600 West Zhongshan Road, Xuhui District, Shanghai, 200235, China
Tel.: (86) 2164969989
Chemical Products Distr
N.A.I.C.S.: 424690
Roger Ling *(Mgr-Technical)*

THOR MEDICAL ASA
Karenslyst alle 9C NO 0278, 0884, Oslo, Norway
Tel.: (47) 97414000
Web Site: https://www.thormedical.no
Year Founded: 2009
NANO—(OSL)
Rev.: $187,871
Assets: $36,711,841
Liabilities: $15,863,072
Net Worth: $20,848,769
Earnings: ($48,668,482)
Emp.: 36
Fiscal Year-end: 12/31/20
Pharmaceuticals Mfr
N.A.I.C.S.: 325412
Jan H. Egberts *(Chm)*

Subsidiaries:

Nordic Nanovector GmbH (1)
Grafenauweg 8, 6300, Zug, Switzerland
Tel.: (41) 417232730
Pharmaceuticals Mfr
N.A.I.C.S.: 325412

THOR MOTORS
201 Gill Street, Orillia, L3V 6K7, ON, Canada
Tel.: (705) 326-6447
Web Site: http://www.thormotors.com
Year Founded: 1961
Rev.: $18,532,799

THOR MOTORS

Thor Motors—(Continued)
Emp.: 40
New & Used Car Dealers
N.A.I.C.S.: 441110
Mike Rumball *(Mgr-New Car Sls)*

THORESEN THAI AGENCIES PUBLIC COMPANY LIMITED
26/26-27 Orakarn Building 8th Floor Soi Chidlom Ploenchit Road, Kwaeng Lumpinee Khet Pathumwan, Bangkok, 10330, Thailand
Tel.: (66) 22500569
Web Site: https://www.thoresen.com
Year Founded: 1983
TTA—(THA)
Rev.: $699,892,777
Assets: $1,254,466,468
Liabilities: $428,629,199
Net Worth: $825,837,270
Earnings: $38,836,092
Fiscal Year-end: 12/31/23
Marine Shipping Services
N.A.I.C.S.: 483111
Prasert Bunsumpun *(Chm)*

Subsidiaries:

Asia Infiastructure Management (Thailand) Co., Ltd. (1)
807/26 Moo 8, Pumarin Village Tambon Khukot Amphoe Lamlukka, Pathumthani, Thailand
Tel.: (66) 25318141
Web Site: http://www.asia-infra.com
Water Utility Services
N.A.I.C.S.: 221310

Chidlom Marine Services & Supplies Ltd. (1)
206/20 Moo 9 Surasak, Aumphor, Si Racha, 20110, Chon Buri, Thailand
Tel.: (66) 384833002
Web Site: https://www.chidlommarine.com
Sales Range: $25-49.9 Million
Emp.: 15
Shipping & Logistics Services
N.A.I.C.S.: 483111

Fearnleys (Thailand) Ltd. (1)
26 55 15th Fl Orakarn Bldg Soi Chidlom Ploenchit Rd, Lumpinee Pathumwan, Bangkok, 10330, Thailand
Tel.: (66) 22536160
Web Site: http://www.fearnleys.com
Sales Range: $25-49.9 Million
Emp.: 30
Freight & Shipping Services
N.A.I.C.S.: 483111

Fearnleys Shipbroking Private Limited (1)
Office No 313 Third Floor Commercial 1 Tower Kirol Road, A Wing Kohinoor City Off LBS Marg Kurla West, Mumbai, 400 070, Maharastra, India
Tel.: (91) 226 123 7900
Web Site: http://www.fearnleys.com
Sales Range: $25-49.9 Million
Emp.: 7
Shipping Services
N.A.I.C.S.: 483111

GAC Thoresen Logistics Ltd. (1)
Amata Nakorn Industrial Estate Phase 9 700/888 Moo 1, Pan Thong, Chon Buri, 20160, Thailand
Tel.: (66) 632020693
Web Site: https://www.gac.com
Logistic Services
N.A.I.C.S.: 483111

Gulf Agency Company (Thailand) Ltd. (1)
26/30-31 9th Floor Orakarn Building Soi Chidlom Ploenchit Road, Lumpinee Pathumwan, Bangkok, 10330, Thailand
Tel.: (66) 26507400
Logistics & Shipping Services
N.A.I.C.S.: 488510
Alwyn Mendonca *(Mng Dir)*

Herakles Shipping Co., Ltd. (1)
26 32 10th Fl Orakar Bldg Ploenchit, Rd Lumpini Pathumwan, Bangkok, 10330, Thailand
Tel.: (66) 22500569
Sales Range: $125-149.9 Million
Emp.: 300
Shipping Services
N.A.I.C.S.: 483111

Heron Shipping Co.,Ltd (1)
26 32 Orakarn Bldg 10th Fl Ploenchit Rd, Lumpini Pathumwan, Bangkok, 10330, Thailand
Tel.: (66) 22500569
Shipping Services
N.A.I.C.S.: 488510

ISS Thoresen Agencies Ltd. (1)
26 27 Orakarn Bldg 8th Floor Chidlom Rd Kwaeng Lumpinee, Khet Pathumwan, Bangkok, 10330, Thailand
Tel.: (66) 22500569
Web Site: http://www.thoresen.com
Sales Range: $25-49.9 Million
Emp.: 60
Shipping Services
N.A.I.C.S.: 488510

Mermaid Maritime Public Company Limited (1)
26/28-29 Orakarn Building 9th Floor Soi Chidlom Ploenchit Road, Lumpinee Pathumwan, Bangkok, 10330, Thailand **(57.14%)**
Tel.: (66) 22553115
Web Site: https://www.mermaid-group.com
Rev.: $277,593,000
Assets: $356,579,000
Liabilities: $185,976,000
Net Worth: $170,603,000
Earnings: $9,664,000
Emp.: 500
Fiscal Year-end: 12/31/2023
Holding Company; Offshore Drilling & Marine Engineering Services
N.A.I.C.S.: 551112
Chalermchai Mahagitsiri *(Vice Chm)*

Subsidiary (Domestic):

Mermaid Drilling Ltd. (2)
26/28-29 Orakarn Building 9th Floor Soi Chidlom Ploenchit Road, Lumpinee Pathumwan, Bangkok, 10330, Thailand **(95%)**
Tel.: (66) 22553115
Web Site: http://www.mermaid-maritime.com
Offshore Drilling Services
N.A.I.C.S.: 213111

Mermaid Subsea Services (Thailand) Ltd. (2)
789/55 Moo 1 Pinthong Industrial Estate, Nongkham, Si Racha, 20230, Chon Buri, Thailand **(100%)**
Tel.: (66) 38318300
Web Site: http://www.mermaid-maritime.com
Sales Range: $25-49.9 Million
Emp.: 30
Marine Engineering Services
N.A.I.C.S.: 541330

Subsidiary (Non-US):

Seascape Surveys Pte. Ltd. (3)
8 Loyang Drive, Loyang Industrial Estate, Singapore, 508939, Singapore **(100%)**
Tel.: (65) 65010770
Web Site: http://www.seascapesurveys.com
Sales Range: $25-49.9 Million
Marine Engineering Services
N.A.I.C.S.: 541330

Subsidiary (Domestic):

Mermaid Training & Technical Services Ltd. (2)
789/55 Moo 1 Pinthong Industrial Estate, Nongkham, Si Racha, 20230, Chon Buri, Thailand **(100%)**
Tel.: (66) 38318300
Sales Range: $10-24.9 Million
Emp.: 4
Underwater Training & Technical Services
N.A.I.C.S.: 611519

Mermaid Subsea Services (UK) Limited (1)
Pavilion 11 Kingshill ParkVenture Drive, Westhill, Aberdeen, AB32 6FL, United Kingdom
Tel.: (44) 1224002480
Web Site: https://www.mermaidsubsea.co.uk
Construction Engineering Services
N.A.I.C.S.: 541330

Mermaid Subsea Services Saudi Arabia Co., Ltd. (1)
Office 602 06 Floor -Al-Mousa Building Blue Tower King Faisal Road, Al-Yarmouk, Al Khobar, 34423 - 6391, Saudi Arabia
Tel.: (966) 138824304
Offshore Oil& Gas Mfr
N.A.I.C.S.: 336611

PM Thoresen Asia Holdings Public Company Limited (1)
26-27 Orakarn Bldg 8th Floor Soi Chidlom Road, Kwaeng Lumpinee Khet Pathumwan, Bangkok, 10330, Thailand
Tel.: (66) 22500569
Web Site: https://www.pmthoresenasia.com
Rev.: $110,311,318
Assets: $73,015,722
Liabilities: $24,611,622
Net Worth: $48,404,101
Earnings: $1,697,112
Emp.: 7
Fiscal Year-end: 12/31/2023
Investment Holding Company
N.A.I.C.S.: 551112
Chalermchai Mahagitsiri *(Chm)*

Praneat Co., Ltd. (1)
No 140 One Pacific Tower 10th FloorRoom 1005-06 Sukhumvit Road, Klong Toey, Bangkok, 10110, Thailand
Tel.: (66) 979697989
Web Site: https://www.praneat.com
Design Technology Services
N.A.I.C.S.: 541512

Thor Captain Shipping Co., Ltd. (1)
26 32 Orakarn Bldg 10 Fl Soi Chitlom Ploenchit Rd, Lumpini Pathum Wan, Bangkok, 10330, Thailand
Tel.: (66) 22548437
Web Site: http://www.thoresenshipping.com
Sales Range: $125-149.9 Million
Emp.: 80
Water Transportation Services
N.A.I.C.S.: 483111

Thor Champion Shipping Co., Ltd. (1)
26 32 Orakarn Bldg 10th Fl Soi Chidlom Ploenchit Rd, Lumpini Pathum Wan, Bangkok, 10330, Thailand
Tel.: (66) 22548437
Sales Range: $125-149.9 Million
Emp.: 300
Water Transportation Services
N.A.I.C.S.: 483111

Thor Commander Shipping Co., Ltd. (1)
26 32 Orakarn Building 10th Fl Soi Chidlom Ploenchit Rd, Lumphini Pathum Wan, Bangkok, 10330, Thailand
Tel.: (66) 22548437
Water Transportation Services
N.A.I.C.S.: 483111

Thor Harmony Shipping Co., Ltd (1)
26 32 Orakan Bldg 10 Fl Soi Chitlom Ploenchit Rd, Bangkok, Thailand
Tel.: (66) 22500569
Water Transportation Services
N.A.I.C.S.: 483111

Thor Jasmine Shipping Co., Ltd. (1)
26 32 Orakarn Bldg 10th Fl Soi Chidlom Ploenchit Rd, Lumphini Pathum Wan, Bangkok, 10330, Thailand
Tel.: (66) 2 2548437
Water Transportation Services
N.A.I.C.S.: 483111

Thor Mariner Shipping Co., Ltd. (1)
26 32 Orakan Bldg 10 Fl Soi Chitlom Ploenchit Rd, Lumpini Pathum Wan, Bangkok, 10330, Thailand
Tel.: (66) 22548437
Water Transportation Services
N.A.I.C.S.: 483111

Thor Master Shipping Co., Ltd. (1)
26 32 Orakarn Bldg Fl 10 Chitlom Rd, Lumphini Pathum Wan, Bangkok, 10330, Thailand

Tel.: (66) 22548437
Water Transportation Services
N.A.I.C.S.: 483111

Thor Merchant Shipping Co., Ltd. (1)
26 32 Orakarn Bldg Fl 10 Soi Chitlom Ploenchit Rd, Lumpini Pathum Wan, Bangkok, 10330, Thailand
Tel.: (66) 22548437
Water Transportation Services
N.A.I.C.S.: 483111

Thor Navigator Shipping Co., Ltd. (1)
26 32 10th Fl Orakan Bldg Soi Chidlom Ploenchit Rd, Lumphini Pathum Wan, Bangkok, 10330, Thailand
Tel.: (66) 22548437
Web Site: http://www.thoresenshipping.com
Emp.: 76
Water Transportation Services
N.A.I.C.S.: 483111

Thor Nectar Shipping Co., Ltd. (1)
26 32 10th Fl Orakan Bldg Soi Chidlom Ploenchit Rd, Lumphini Pathum Wan, Bangkok, 10330, Thailand
Tel.: (66) 22548437
Water Transportation Services
N.A.I.C.S.: 483111

Thor Nereus Shipping Co., Ltd. (1)
26 32 Orakarn Bldg 10th Fl Ploenchit, Lumphini Pathum Wan, Bangkok, 10330, Thailand
Tel.: (66) 22548437
Web Site: http://www.thoresenshipping.com
Emp.: 80
Water Transportation Services
N.A.I.C.S.: 483111
Thinakorn Kesornsiri *(Mgr-Mktg)*

Thor Pilot Shipping Co., Ltd. (1)
26 32 Orakarn Bldg 10 Fl Soi Chitlom Ploenchit Rd, Lumpini Pathum Wan, Bangkok, 10330, Thailand
Tel.: (66) 22548437
Sales Range: $50-74.9 Million
Emp.: 200
Water Transportation Services
N.A.I.C.S.: 483111

Thor Sailor Shipping Co., Ltd. (1)
26 32 Orakarn Bldg 10th Fl Soi Chidlom Ploenchit Rd, Lumpini Pathum Wan, Bangkok, 10330, Thailand
Tel.: (66) 22548437
Sales Range: $125-149.9 Million
Emp.: 400
Water Transportation Services
N.A.I.C.S.: 483111

Thor Sea Shipping Co., Ltd. (1)
26 32 Orakan Bldg 10 Fl Soi Chitlom Ploenchit Rd, Lumpini Pathum Wan, Bangkok, 10330, Thailand
Tel.: (66) 22548437
Web Site: http://www.thoresen.com
Sales Range: $25-49.9 Million
Emp.: 100
Water Transportation Services
N.A.I.C.S.: 483111

Thor Skipper Shipping Co., Ltd. (1)
26 32 10th Orakan Bldg Soi Chidlom Ploenchit Rd, Lumpini Pathum Wan, Bangkok, 10330, Thailand
Tel.: (66) 22548437
Water Transportation Services
N.A.I.C.S.: 483111

Thor Sky Shipping Co., Ltd. (1)
26 32 Orakan Bldg 10 Fl Soi Chitlom Ploenchit Rd, Lumphini Pathum Wan, Bangkok, 10330, Thailand
Tel.: (66) 22548437
Water Transportation Services
N.A.I.C.S.: 483111

Thor Spirit Shipping Co., Ltd. (1)
26 32 Orakan Bldg 10 Fl Soi Chitlom Ploenchit Rd, Lumphini Pathum Wan, Bangkok, 10330, Thailand
Tel.: (66) 2 2548437
Web Site: http://www.thoresen.com
Water Transportation Services
N.A.I.C.S.: 488320

Thor Star Shipping Co., Ltd. (1)
26 32 10th Fl Orakan Bldg Soi Chidlom Plo-

enchit Rd, Lumphini Pathum Wan, Bangkok, 10330, Thailand
Tel.: (66) 22548437
Sales Range: $125-149.9 Million
Emp.: 400
Water Transportation Services
N.A.I.C.S.: 483111

Thor Sun Shipping Co., Ltd. (1)
26 32 Orakan Bldg 10 Fl Soi Chitlom Ploenchit Rd, Lumphini Pathum Wan, Bangkok, 10330, Thailand
Tel.: (66) 22548437
Water Transportation Services
N.A.I.C.S.: 483111

Thor Transporter Shipping Co., Ltd. (1)
26 32 Orakarn Bldg 10th Fl Soi Chidlom Ploenchit Rd, Lumphini Pathum Wan, Bangkok, 10330, Thailand
Tel.: (66) 22548437
Sales Range: $125-149.9 Million
Emp.: 500
Water Transportation Services
N.A.I.C.S.: 483111

Thoresen & Co., (Bangkok) Limited (1)
10th floor Orakarn Building 26/32-34 Soi Chidlom Ploenchit Road, Lumpinee Pathumwan, Bangkok, 10330, Thailand
Tel.: (66) 22500569
Ship Management Services
N.A.I.C.S.: 541611

Thoresen Shipping FZE (1)
Buhaira Corniche Rd, Sharjah, 27500, United Arab Emirates
Tel.: (971) 65742244
Web Site: http://www.thoresen.com
Sales Range: $25-49.9 Million
Emp.: 10
Shipping Services
N.A.I.C.S.: 483111

Thoresen Shipping Germany GmbH (1)
Stavendamm 4a, 28195, Bremen, Germany
Tel.: (49) 4213365222
Sales Range: $25-49.9 Million
Emp.: 2
Shipping & Freight Forwarding Services
N.A.I.C.S.: 483111

Thoresen Shipping Singapore Pte. Ltd. (1)
127A Telok Ayer Street, Singapore, 068596, Singapore
Tel.: (65) 65787000
Shipping Transportation Services
N.A.I.C.S.: 488330
Huang Yun *(Gen Mgr)*

Subsidiary (Non-US):

Thoresen & Company (Bangkok) Limited (2)
10th Floor Orakarn Building 26/32-34 Soi Chidlom Ploenchit Road, Lumpinee Pathumwan, Bangkok, 10330, Thailand
Tel.: (66) 22500569
Shipping Transportation Services
N.A.I.C.S.: 488330
Gulrisar Nunthakiz *(Sr Mgr-HR)*

Unique Mining Services Public Company Limited (1)
26/23 Orakarn Building 7th Floor Soi Chidlom Ploenchit Road, Lumpinee Pathumwan, Bangkok, 10330, Thailand
Tel.: (66) 26557501
Web Site: https://ums.listedcompany.com
Rev: $10,998,075
Assets: $33,526,686
Liabilities: $25,751,404
Net Worth: $7,775,281
Earnings: $(1,048,867)
Fiscal Year-end: 12/31/2023
Coal Mining Services
N.A.I.C.S.: 213113
Chalermchai Mahagitsiri *(Chm & CEO)*

THORNEY OPPORTUNITIES LIMITED
Level 45 55 Collins Street, Melbourne, 3000, VIC, Australia
Tel.: (61) 399217116 AU
Web Site: http://www.thorneyopportunities.com
TOP—(ASX)
Rev.: $38,400,629
Assets: $124,078,482
Liabilities: $17,746,528
Net Worth: $106,331,955
Earnings: $23,389,927
Fiscal Year-end: 06/30/24
Investment Management Service
N.A.I.C.S.: 523999
Craig Smith *(CFO & Sec)*

THORNEY TECHNOLOGIES LTD
Level 45 55 Collins Street, Melbourne, 3000, VIC, Australia
Tel.: (61) 399217116 AU
Web Site: http://www.thorneytechnologies.com
TEK—(ASX)
Rev.: $737,917
Assets: $69,767,708
Liabilities: $840,367
Net Worth: $68,927,341
Earnings: $(14,502,592)
Fiscal Year-end: 06/30/24
Investment Company
N.A.I.C.S.: 523999
Craig Smith *(Sec)*

Subsidiaries:

Australian Renewable Fuels Adelaide Pty Ltd (1)
166 Elder Rd, Largs Bay, Adelaide, 5016, SA, Australia
Tel.: (61) 882428600
Sales Range: $25-49.9 Million
Emp.: 5
Biodiesel Mfr
N.A.I.C.S.: 324199

THORNICO A/S
Amaliegade 16, 1256, Copenhagen, Denmark
Tel.: (45) 33 12 60 50
Web Site: http://www.thornico.com
Sales Range: $450-499.9 Million
Emp.: 1,493
Holding Company
N.A.I.C.S.: 551112
Christian Stadil *(Co-Owner)*

Subsidiaries:

ALLUNITE (1)
Tobaksvejen 23B, Copenhagen, 2860, Denmark
Tel.: (45) 70272705
Web Site: http://www.allunite.com
Advertising Services
N.A.I.C.S.: 541810

Brodrene Hartmann A/S (1)
Ornegardsvej 18, 2820, Gentofte, Denmark (70%)
Tel.: (45) 45970000
Web Site: http://www.hartmann-packaging.com
Rev.: $452,952,080
Assets: $462,889,294
Liabilities: $265,383,039
Net Worth: $197,506,255
Earnings: $12,281,208
Emp.: 2,761
Fiscal Year-end: 12/31/2021
Mfr of Moulded-Fibre Packaging
N.A.I.C.S.: 488991
Steen Parsholt *(Vice Chm)*

Subsidiary (Non-US):

Aropac S.r.l (2)
Via Ugo foscolo 11/1, Carmignano Di Brenta, 35010, Padua, Italy (100%)
Tel.: (39) 049 595 8340
Web Site: https://www.aropac.it
Sales Range: $25-49.9 Million
Emp.: 3
N.A.I.C.S.: 488991

HARTMANN Polska Sp. Z.o.o. (2)
Ul Zeromskiego 17, 95-200, Pabianice, Poland (100%)
Tel.: (48) 422252260
Web Site: http://www.hartmann.info
Sales Range: $25-49.9 Million
Emp.: 9
Packing & Crating Services
N.A.I.C.S.: 488991

Hartmann Bilokalnik Ambalaza d.o.o. (2)
Dravska BB, Koprivnica, 48000, Croatia (100%)
Tel.: (385) 48658800
Web Site: http://www.hartmann-packaging.hr
Sales Range: $50-74.9 Million
Emp.: 200
N.A.I.C.S.: 488991

Hartmann CZ s.r.o. (2)
Gabinova 867, CZ 152 00, Prague, 5, Czech Republic
Tel.: (420) 251813090
Sales Range: $25-49.9 Million
Emp.: 1
N.A.I.C.S.: 488991

Hartmann Canada Inc. (2)
58 Frank Street, PO Box 1328, Brantford, N3T 5T6, ON, Canada
Fiber Egg Packaging Container Mfr
N.A.I.C.S.: 322299

Hartmann France S.a.r.l. (2)
195 Avenue Charles de Gaulle, 92 522, Neuilly-sur-Seine, France (100%)
Tel.: (33) 17 037 5490
Web Site: http://www.hartmann-france.fr
Sales Range: $25-49.9 Million
Emp.: 7
Packing & Crating Services
N.A.I.C.S.: 488991

Hartmann India Ltd. (2)
Ramgarh Rd, Mubarakpur Sanauli, Dera Bassi, 140 507, Punjab, India
Tel.: (91) 9875944150
Web Site: https://hartmann-india.com
Paper Products Mfr
N.A.I.C.S.: 322299

Hartmann Italiana S.r.l. (2)
Via G Modena 46, 38065, Mori, TN, Italy
Tel.: (39) 0340 480 9022
Fiber Egg Packaging Container Mfr
N.A.I.C.S.: 322299

Hartmann Papirna Ambalaza d.o.o. (2)
Dravska 13, 48000, Koprivnica, Croatia
Tel.: (385) 48658800
Sales Range: $50-74.9 Million
Emp.: 200
Packaging Paper Products Mfr
N.A.I.C.S.: 322220
Melita Baci *(Gen Mgr)*

Hartmann Verpackung AG (2)
Kapellplatz 1, Adligenswil, 6004, Lucerne, Switzerland (100%)
Tel.: (41) 43 819 0991
Web Site: http://www.hartmann-suisse.ch
N.A.I.C.S.: 488991

Hartmann Verpackung GmbH (2)
Mergenthalerallee 77, 65760, Eschborn, Germany (100%)
Tel.: (49) 6 196 9320
Web Site: http://www.hartmann-packaging.de
Sales Range: $25-49.9 Million
Emp.: 35
N.A.I.C.S.: 488991

Hartmann d.o.o. (2)
Alekse Santica 48/2, 21000, Novi Sad, Serbia
Tel.: (381) 21 674 0768
Emp.: 2,800
Egg Packaging Services
N.A.I.C.S.: 561910

Hartmann-Babolna Packaging Kft. (2)
Hartmann 1, HU 2941, Acs, Hungary (100%)
Tel.: (36) 34595100
Web Site: http://wwwhartmann-packaging.com

Sales Range: $125-149.9 Million
Emp.: 500
N.A.I.C.S.: 488991

Hartmann-Hungary Kft. (2)
Hartmann U 1, 2941, Acs, Hungary
Tel.: (36) 3 459 5100
Web Site: http://www.hartmann.dk
Packaging Products Mfr
N.A.I.C.S.: 322220

Hartmann-Mai Ltd. (2)
10 Haorzim St, PO Box 13456, Industrial Zone, IL 42138, Netanya, Israel (100%)
Tel.: (972) 98621845
Sales Range: $25-49.9 Million
Emp.: 50
N.A.I.C.S.: 488991

Hartmann-Schwedt GmbH (2)
Kuhheide 32, Schwedt an der Oder, 16303, Germany (100%)
Tel.: (49) 333226550
Web Site: http://www.hartmann.dk
Sales Range: $25-49.9 Million
Emp.: 91
N.A.I.C.S.: 488991

Moldeados Argentinos SA (2)
Ingeniero Silvio Tosello 1030, 8300, Neuquen, Argentina
Tel.: (54) 299 441 3380
Fiber Egg Packaging Container Mfr
N.A.I.C.S.: 322299

Nihon Hartmann K.K. (2)
August House 3F 3 23 5 Uehara Shibuya Ku, Tokyo, 151 0064, Japan (100%)
Tel.: (81) 334653011
Sales Range: $25-49.9 Million
Emp.: 3
N.A.I.C.S.: 488991

FOODCRAFT Inc. (1)
4225 SW Kirklawn, Topeka, KS 66609
Tel.: (785) 267-9400
Web Site: http://www.foodcraft.net
Industrial Equipment Distr
N.A.I.C.S.: 423620
Michael Curtis *(Pres)*

LACTOSAN-SANOVO INGREDIENTS GROUP (1)
Ligovskiy Prospect House 246 liter B, 196084, Saint Petersburg, Russia
Tel.: (7) 812 324 4165
Food Products Distr
N.A.I.C.S.: 424490
Valery Valiev *(Dir-Country)*

Subsidiary (Non-US):

Lactosan A/S (2)
Nordbakken 2, 5750, Ringe, Denmark
Tel.: (45) 6362 0520
Web Site: http://www.lactosan.com
Food Products Mfr
N.A.I.C.S.: 311919

Subsidiary (Non-US):

Lactosan (UK) Ltd. (3)
5 Swinborne Drive Springwood Ind Estate, Braintree, CM7 2YP, Essex, United Kingdom
Tel.: (44) 1376342226
Web Site: http://www.lactosan.co.uk
Food Products Distr
N.A.I.C.S.: 424490

Lactosan China Ltd. (3)
No 386 Jinxian Road, Jinjiaba Town Development Zone, Wujiang, 215215, Jiangsu, China
Tel.: (86) 51263206111
Food Products Distr
N.A.I.C.S.: 424490

Lactosan Japan Ltd. (3)
3-2-1 Koenji-Kita, Suginami-ku, Tokyo, 166-0002, Japan
Tel.: (81) 353273500
Food Products Distr
N.A.I.C.S.: 424490

Lactosan Ltd. (3)
Bolshaya Tulskaya Street 10 Office 538, 115191, Moscow, Russia
Tel.: (7) 4952322408
Web Site: http://www.lactosan.ru
Food Products Distr

THORNICO A/S

Thornico A/S—(Continued)
N.A.I.C.S.: 424490

Lactosan Uruguay S.A. (3)
Zabala 1542 / Of 203, 11000, Montevideo, Uruguay
Tel.: (598) 29150739
Web Site: http://www.lactosan.com.uy
Food Products Distr
N.A.I.C.S.: 424490

Subsidiary (Non-US):

SANOVO Foods A/S (2)
Havnegade 36, 5000, Odense, Denmark
Tel.: (45) 66 11 17 32
Food Product Mfr & Distr
N.A.I.C.S.: 311919
Anders Wurcel (Dir-Comml)

Subsidiary (Non-US):

OVODAN FOODS (China) Ltd. (3)
No 88 Guangxin Rd Zhongyi International Building, Shanghai, China
Tel.: (86) 2166309112
Food Products Distr
N.A.I.C.S.: 424490

SANOVO Eiprodukte GmbH & Co. KG (3)
Frankenbosteler Kamp 4, 27404, Zeven, Germany
Tel.: (49) 42817560
Food Products Distr
N.A.I.C.S.: 424490

SANOVO International Asia Pacific Co. Ltd. (3)
19/125 Sukhumvit Suite Building Zone A13 Soi Sukhumvit, 13 Sukhumvit Road Klongteuy Nue Wattana, Bangkok, 10110, Thailand
Tel.: (66) 22922735
Food Products Distr
N.A.I.C.S.: 424490

SANOVO International Ltd. (3)
4th Floor no 138 Chung Hsing Road Sec 3, Hsing-Tien, Taipei, Taiwan
Tel.: (886) 229150558
Food Products Distr
N.A.I.C.S.: 424490

SANOVO GREENPACK BRAZIL (1)
Av Tres de Marco 510, 18087-180, Sorocaba, Brazil
Tel.: (55) 1532383200
Web Site: http://www.sanovo.com.br
Fiber Packaging Services
N.A.I.C.S.: 561910

SANOVO TECHNOLOGY A/S (1)
Thulevej 25-27, 5210, Odense, Denmark
Tel.: (45) 66162832
Web Site: http://www.sanovogroup.com
Household Equipment Mfr
N.A.I.C.S.: 335220
Jens Gundorph Moller (Project Mgr)

SANOVO VAX Inc. (1)
5 Emery Ave, Randolph, NJ 07869
Tel.: (973) 335-0560
Industrial Equipment Distr
N.A.I.C.S.: 423620

STANICO A/S (1)
Havnegade 36, 5000, Odense, Denmark
Tel.: (45) 24273070
Real Estate Manangement Services
N.A.I.C.S.: 531210

THORCO SHIPPING A/S (1)
Tuborg Parkvej 10, 2900, Hellerup, Denmark
Tel.: (45) 63203000
Web Site: http://www.thorcoshipping.com
Ship Management Services
N.A.I.C.S.: 532411
Thomas Mikkelsen (CEO)

Tattoodo ApS (1)
Amagertorv 1 3rd floor, 1160, Copenhagen, Denmark
Tel.: (45) 40820300
Web Site: http://www.tattoodo.com
Beauty Care Services
N.A.I.C.S.: 812112
Alexander Pinsker (CTO)

West-Star Management b.V. (1)
Westblaak 108, 3012, Rotterdam, Holland, Netherlands
Tel.: (31) 104045730
Web Site: http://www.thornicobuilding.nl
Financial Management Services
N.A.I.C.S.: 551112
Ronald Bouwens (CEO)

hummel International Sport & Leisure A/S (1)
Balticagade 20, 8000, Arhus, Denmark
Tel.: (45) 87 34 48 00
Web Site: http://www.hummel.net
Apparel Distr
N.A.I.C.S.: 424350

Subsidiary (Non-US):

HUMMEL A. LLC (2)
22 Shahamiryanneri Str, 375061, Yerevan, Armenia
Tel.: (374) 77777888
Apparel Distr
N.A.I.C.S.: 424350

hummel UK Ltd (2)
Maple House High Street Potters Bar, Hertford, EN6 5BS, United Kingdom
Tel.: (44) 1707245255
Apparel Distr
N.A.I.C.S.: 424350

THOUGHTFUL BRANDS, INC.

1199 West Hastings Street 8th Floor Suite 800, Vancouver, V6E 3T5, BC, Canada
Tel.: (604) 423-4733
Assets: $2,821,221
Liabilities: $695,672
Net Worth: $2,125,549
Earnings: ($8,353,350)
Fiscal Year-end: 12/31/19
Healthcare Product Distr
N.A.I.C.S.: 424210
Ryan Hoggan (CEO)

THQ NORDIC AB

Alvgatan 1, Karlstad, 65225, Sweden
Tel.: (46) 554854763
Web Site: http://www.thqnordic.com
Rev.: $703,313,842
Assets: $922,540,794
Liabilities: $310,300,018
Net Worth: $612,240,776
Earnings: $42,525,056
Emp.: 1,026
Fiscal Year-end: 03/31/19
Software Development Services
N.A.I.C.S.: 541511
Klemens Kreuzer (CEO)

THRACE PLASTICS HOLDING AND COMMERCIAL S.A.

20 Marinou Antypa str, Alimos, 17455, Athens, Greece
Tel.: (30) 2109875000
Web Site: https://www.thracegroup.com
Year Founded: 1977
PLAT—(ATH)
Rev.: $370,731,001
Assets: $436,092,744
Liabilities: $138,696,866
Net Worth: $297,395,878
Earnings: $19,671,533
Emp.: 1,684
Fiscal Year-end: 12/31/23
Plastic Packaging & Synthetic Materials Mfr
N.A.I.C.S.: 326199
Constantinos S. Chalioris (Chm & Exec Mgr)

Subsidiaries:

Don & Low Ltd (1)
Newfordpark House Glamis Road, Forfar, DD8 1FR, Angus, United Kingdom
Tel.: (44) 1307452200
Web Site: https://www.donlow.co.uk
Sales Range: $125-149.9 Million
Emp.: 450
Woven & Non Woven Polypropylene Mfr
N.A.I.C.S.: 325211

Synthetic Packaging Ltd (1)
Ballycumber Rd, Clara, County Offaly, Ireland
Tel.: (353) 579331282
Web Site: http://www.syntheticpackaging.com
Sales Range: $50-74.9 Million
Emp.: 14
Packaging Products & Technical Fabrics Distr
N.A.I.C.S.: 423840
Aidan Devery (Mng Dir)

Thrace Ipoma A.D. (1)
7 Nedelcho Bonchev Str, Gara Iskar, 1528, Sofia, Bulgaria
Tel.: (359) 29732333
Web Site: http://www.ipoma.com
Sales Range: $75-99.9 Million
Emp.: 200
Injection Molded Plastic Products Mfr & Distr
N.A.I.C.S.: 326199

Thrace Linq Inc. (1)
2550 W 5th N St, Summerville, SC 29483
Tel.: (843) 873-5800
Web Site: https://www.thracegroup.com
Emp.: 50
Geosynthetics Mfr & Whslr
N.A.I.C.S.: 313310
Donald O'Callaghan (Mgr-Customer Svc)

Thrace Nonwovens & Geosynthetics SA (1)
20 Marinou Antypa str, 17455, Alimos, Athens, Greece
Tel.: (30) 2109875038
Sales Range: $25-49.9 Million
Emp.: 50
Woven & Non Woven Geotextiles Mfr
N.A.I.C.S.: 313220
Christos Karageorgiou (Mgr)

Thrace Plastics Pack S.A. (1)
20 Marinou Antypa str, PO Box 1272, 17455, Alimos, Athens, Greece
Tel.: (30) 2651057320
Sales Range: $50-74.9 Million
Emp.: 190
Plastic Packaging Products Mfr
N.A.I.C.S.: 326199

Thrace Plastics Packaging DOO (1)
Cara Dusana BB, 22330, Nova Pazova, Serbia
Tel.: (381) 22321555
Plastic Packaging Products Mfr
N.A.I.C.S.: 326199

Thrace Polybulk A.S. (1)
Stromtangveien 15, PO Box 74, 3991, Brevik, Norway
Tel.: (47) 35572930
Web Site: http://www.polybulk.com
Sales Range: $25-49.9 Million
Emp.: 14
Plastics Bag Mfr
N.A.I.C.S.: 322220
Kirsti Arvesen (Mgr-Key Acct)

Thrace XPS S.A. (1)
5th km ONR, Thebes, 32200, Thivai, Chalkida, Greece
Tel.: (30) 2262056701
Web Site: http://www.thracegroup.com
Rigid Plastics Mfr
N.A.I.C.S.: 326199

THREE F CO., LTD.

6F 17 Nihon-odori, Naka-ku, Yokohama, 231-8507, Kanagawa, Japan
Tel.: (81) 456512111
Web Site: https://www.three-f.co.jp
Year Founded: 1981
7544—(TKS)
Rev.: $98,246,130
Assets: $35,357,830
Liabilities: $5,835,070
Net Worth: $29,522,760
Earnings: $1,538,530
Emp.: 33,617
Fiscal Year-end: 02/29/24
Convenience Store Operator
N.A.I.C.S.: 445131

THREE HILLS CAPITAL PARTNERS LLP

25 Maddox Street, London, W1S 2QN, United Kingdom
Tel.: (44) 20 3056 9540   UK
Web Site: http://www.thcp.eu
Privater Equity Firm
N.A.I.C.S.: 523999
Mauro Moretti (Founder & Mng Partner)

THREE SIXTY FIVE PCL

349 SJ Infinite I Business Com 23rd Floor, Vibhavadi-Rangsit Chomphon Chatuchak, Bangkok, Thailand
Tel.: (66) 27126171
TSF-F—(THA)
Rev.: $149,130
Assets: $4,399,334
Liabilities: $26,217,796
Net Worth: ($21,818,462)
Earnings: ($1,721,716)
Fiscal Year-end: 12/31/20
Telecommunication Servicesb
N.A.I.C.S.: 517112
Aran Apichari (Chm)

THREE SIXTY SOLAR LTD.

40855 Water Street Office 8312, Vancouver, V6B 1A1, BC, Canada
Web Site: https://threesixtysolar.com
VSOLF—(OTCIQ)
Rev.: $80,577
Assets: $5,902,521
Liabilities: $298,450
Net Worth: $5,604,071
Earnings: ($1,150,336)
Fiscal Year-end: 12/31/19
Solar Equipment Supply
N.A.I.C.S.: 221114

THREE SQUIRRELS, INC.

No 8 Jiusheng Road, Wuhu High-tech Industrial Development Zone Yijiang District, Wuhu, 241002, Anhui, China
Tel.: (86) 5538788323
Web Site: http://www.3songshu.com
Year Founded: 2012
300783—(SSE)
Rev.: $1,023,959,355
Assets: $636,826,854
Liabilities: $307,813,255
Net Worth: $329,013,599
Earnings: $18,119,659
Fiscal Year-end: 12/31/22
Food Product Mfr & Distr
N.A.I.C.S.: 311421

THREE'S COMPANY MEDIA GROUP CO., LTD.

Room 302B Block C City Gate Tangyan South Road, High-tech Zone, Xi'an, 710000, Shaanxi, China
Tel.: (86) 1057648016
Web Site: http://www.topsrx.com
Year Founded: 2003
605168—(SHG)
Rev.: $793,679,782
Assets: $745,171,245
Liabilities: $380,504,105
Net Worth: $364,667,140
Earnings: $103,386,081
Fiscal Year-end: 12/31/22
Digital Marketing Services
N.A.I.C.S.: 541870
Jundong Qian (Chm & Gen Mgr)

THREE-A RESOURCES BERHAD

AL 308 Lot 590 & Lot 4196 Jalan Industri U 19 Kampung Baru, Sungai

Buloh, 40160, Shah Alam, Selangor Darul Ehsan, Malaysia
Tel.: (60) 361562655
Web Site: https://www.three-a.com.my
3A—(KLS)
Rev.: $139,407,831
Assets: $107,735,026
Liabilities: $18,823,492
Net Worth: $88,911,534
Earnings: $7,427,302
Emp.: 572
Fiscal Year-end: 12/31/22
Food & Beverage Ingredients Mfr
N.A.I.C.S.: 311942
Bee Lian Ng *(Co-Sec)*

Subsidiaries:

San Soon Seng Food Industries Sdn. Bhd. (1)
AL 308 Lot 590 & Lot 4196 Jalan Industri U19, Kampung Baru Sungai Buloh, 40160, Shah Alam, Selangor, Malaysia
Tel.: (60) 36 156 2655
Web Site: https://www.sssfi.com
Sales Range: $100-124.9 Million
Emp.: 350
Food & Beverage Ingredients Mfr
N.A.I.C.S.: 311930

THREED CAPITAL INC.

130 Spadina Avenue Suite 401, Toronto, M5V 2L4, ON, Canada
Tel.: (416) 941-8900   BC
Web Site: https://www.threedcapital.com
Year Founded: 1987
B5K3—(DEU)
Rev.: $209,783
Assets: $30,104,275
Liabilities: $494,165
Net Worth: $29,610,110
Earnings: ($9,170,249)
Emp.: 4
Fiscal Year-end: 06/30/23
Investment Services
N.A.I.C.S.: 523999

THREESIXTY INVESTMENTS LIMITED

406 Duffield Road, Derby, DE22 1ES, Derbs, United Kingdom
Tel.: (44) 777 555 2202   UK
Web Site: http://www.threesixty.co.uk
Investment Services
N.A.I.C.S.: 523999
Peter Raybould *(Owner)*

Subsidiaries:

Technocover Limited (1)
Henfaes Lane, Welshpool, Powys, SY21 7BE, United Kingdom
Tel.: (44) 1938555511
Web Site: http://www.technocover.co.uk
Steel Products Mfr
N.A.I.C.S.: 332510
Terry Batten *(Mgr-Mktg)*

THREESIXTYFIVE PUBLIC COMPANY LIMITED

1555 Soi Lat Phrao 94, Phlapphla Subdistrict Wang Thonglang District, Bangkok, 10310, Thailand
Tel.: (66) 29575532
Web Site: http://tsf.co.th
Year Founded: 1989
TSF—(THA)
Rev.: $149,130
Assets: $4,399,334
Liabilities: $26,217,796
Net Worth: ($21,818,462)
Earnings: ($1,721,716)
Fiscal Year-end: 12/31/20
Communication Service
N.A.I.C.S.: 517810
Nittaya Phoemsuwa *(Mng Dir-Sls & Mktg)*

Subsidiaries:

TSF Management Company Limited (1)
1555 Soi Lat Phrao 94, Phlabphla Wangthonglang, Bangkok, 10310, Thailand
Tel.: (66) 295755323
Advertising Media Services
N.A.I.C.S.: 541810

THRIVE PRECISION HEALTH INC.

1703-1704 A Building No 1 Hongji Apartment, Jin Wei Road, He Bei District, Tianjin, China
Tel.: (86) 2258299778   DE
CNER—(OTCIQ)
Sales Range: $10-24.9 Million
Emp.: 130
Energy Utitlity Holding Company; Natural Gas Distribution, Network Development, Pipeline Construction, Operation & Maintenance Services
N.A.I.C.S.: 551112
Jiaji Shang *(Chm)*

Subsidiaries:

Willsky Development Ltd. (1)
1703-1704 A Building No 1 Hongji Apartment, Jin Wei Road, He Bei District, Tianjin, China   (100%)
Tel.: (86) 22 5829 9778
Energy Utitlity Holding Company
N.A.I.C.S.: 551112

THRIVE TRIBE TECHNOLOGIES LIMITED

Level 57 MLC Centre 19-29 Martin Place, Sydney, 2000, NSW, Australia
Tel.: (61) 292367229
Web Site: http://www.reffind.com
1TT—(ASX)
Rev.: $10,903
Assets: $2,199,380
Liabilities: $668,445
Net Worth: $1,530,935
Earnings: ($2,293,481)
Fiscal Year-end: 06/30/24
Mobile Application Software
N.A.I.C.S.: 513210
Rumi Guzder *(Chm)*

THRIVEN GLOBAL BERHAD

PS1-08 Lumi Tropicana No 2 Persiaran Tropicana PJU 3, Taman Tun Dr Ismail, 47410, Petaling Jaya, Malaysia
Tel.: (60) 376881266
Web Site: https://www.thriven.com.my
THRIVEN—(KLS)
Rev.: $17,150,265
Assets: $70,818,201
Liabilities: $36,827,513
Net Worth: $33,990,688
Earnings: ($1,594,497)
Emp.: 92
Fiscal Year-end: 12/31/22
Property Development Services
N.A.I.C.S.: 531312
Ghazie Yeoh Abdullah *(Mng Dir-Grp)*

THROGMORTON FINANCIAL SERVICES LTD.

Bridgewater Suite The Towers Towers Business Park Wilmslow Road, Didsbury, Manchester, M20 2SL, United Kingdom
Tel.: (44) 1619454411   UK
Web Site: http://www.throgmortonfs.co.uk
Year Founded: 2002
Sales Range: $700-749.9 Million
Emp.: 4
Financial Advice & Services
N.A.I.C.S.: 523940

Subsidiaries:

Throgmorton Private Capital Limited (1)
31-33 High Street, Deal, CT14 6EL, Kent, United Kingdom   (100%)
Tel.: (44) 1304371753
Web Site: http://www.throgmortonltd.co.uk
Sales Range: $50-74.9 Million
Financial Consultant
N.A.I.C.S.: 523999

THROUGHTEK CO., LTD.

9F No 364 Nangang Rd, Nangang Dist, Taipei, 11579, Taiwan
Tel.: (886) 226535111
Web Site: https://www.throughtek.com
Year Founded: 2008
6565—(TPE)
Rev.: $5,109,977
Assets: $7,272,213
Liabilities: $4,422,774
Net Worth: $2,849,439
Earnings: ($995,879)
Fiscal Year-end: 12/31/23
Security System Services
N.A.I.C.S.: 561621
Patrick Kuo *(Chm & Pres)*

THRUVISION GROUP PLC

121 Olympic Avenue Milton Park, Abingdon, OX14 4SA, Oxfordshire, United Kingdom
Tel.: (44) 1235425400   UK
Web Site: https://www.thruvision.com
THRU—(AIM)
Rev.: $10,961,632
Assets: $16,730,912
Liabilities: $5,244,800
Net Worth: $11,486,112
Earnings: ($2,176,592)
Fiscal Year-end: 03/31/22
Other Scientific & Technical Consulting Services
N.A.I.C.S.: 541690
Tom Black *(Chm)*

Subsidiaries:

Thruvision Inc. (1)
21140 Ashburn Crossing Dr Ste 140, Ashburn, VA 20147
Tel.: (540) 878-4844
Security System Services
N.A.I.C.S.: 561621

THT HEAT TRANSFER TECHNOLOGY, INC.

THT Industrial Park No 5 Nanhuan Road, Tiexi District, Siping, 136000, Jilin, China
Tel.: (86) 434 3265241   NV
Web Site: http://www.tht.cn
Year Founded: 2006
Sales Range: $50-74.9 Million
Emp.: 616
Heat Exchange Machinery Mfr
N.A.I.C.S.: 332410

Subsidiaries:

Beijing Juyuan Hanyang Heat Exchange Equipment Co., Ltd. (1)
Room 1217 Hanwei Mansion No 7, Guanghua Road Chaoyang, Beijing, 100004, China
Tel.: (86) 1084264459
Heating Equipment Mfr
N.A.I.C.S.: 333414

THU DUC HOUSING DEVELOPMENT CORP.

3-5 Pasteur street, Nguyen Thai Binh Ward District 1, Ho Chi Minh City, Vietnam
Tel.: (84) 2839143111
Year Founded: 1990
TDH—(HNX)
Real Estate Manangement Services
N.A.I.C.S.: 531390
Khac Son Nguyen *(Deputy Gen Dir)*

THU DUC TRADING IMPORT & EXPORT JOINT STOCK COMPANY

231 Vo Van Ngan P Linh Chieu, Thu Duc, Ho Chi Minh City, Vietnam
Tel.: (84) 838966819
Web Site: https://www.timexcothuduc.com.vn
Year Founded: 1995
TMC—(HNX)
Rev.: $56,713,882
Assets: $12,795,012
Liabilities: $4,936,142
Net Worth: $7,858,870
Earnings: $308,885
Fiscal Year-end: 12/31/20
Gasoline Station Operator
N.A.I.C.S.: 424710
Vo Khanh Hung *(Chm-Mgmt Bd)*

THUAN AN WOOD PROCESSING JOINT STOCK COMPANY

Binh Duong Boulevard - Binh Giao Quarter Thuan Giao Ward, Thuan An, Binh Duong, Vietnam
Tel.: (84) 2743718025
GTA—(HOSE)
Rev.: $10,267,617
Assets: $13,927,990
Liabilities: $7,222,236
Net Worth: $6,705,753
Earnings: $424,442
Fiscal Year-end: 12/31/23
Sawmilling Services
N.A.I.C.S.: 321113
Le Thi Xuyen *(CEO & Gen Dir)*

THUAN HUNG CONSTRUCTION CORPORATION

89 Hoang Quoc Viet Street, Phu Thuan Ward District 7, Ho Chi Minh City, Vietnam
Tel.: (84) 2837760875
Construction Design Services
N.A.I.C.S.: 541310

THUASNE SA

120 rue Marius Aufan, 92300, Levallois-Perret, France
Tel.: (33) 1 41 05 92 92   FR
Web Site: http://fr.thuasne.com
Year Founded: 1847
Emp.: 1,800
Wearable Medical Device Mfr & Distr
N.A.I.C.S.: 339112
Benoit Bourg *(Dir-HR-Grp)*

Subsidiaries:

Quinn Medical, Inc. (1)
1000 Calle Cordillera, San Clemente, CA 92673-6235
Tel.: (949) 784-0310
Web Site: http://www.quinnmedical.com
Emp.: 20
Orthopedic Products Mfr & Supplier
N.A.I.C.S.: 339112
Todd Thornton *(Co-Founder)*

THUDUC HOUSING DEVELOPMENT CORPORATION

13-15-17 Truong Dinh Street, Ward 6 District 3, Ho Chi Minh City, Vietnam
Tel.: (84) 839333090
Web Site: http://www.thuduchouse.vn
Year Founded: 1990
Sales Range: $25-49.9 Million
Real Estate Manangement Services
N.A.I.C.S.: 531390
Chi Hieu Le *(Chm & Gen Dir)*

Subsidiaries:

Thuduc Agriculture Wholesale Market Co., Ltd (1)
141 Quoc lo 1A Khu Pho 5 P Tam Binh,

THUDUC HOUSING DEVELOPMENT CORPORATION

Thuduc Housing Development Corporation—(Continued)
Thu Duc District, Ho Chi Minh City, Vietnam
Tel.: (84) 8 37290880
Web Site: http://www.thuducagromarket.com
Fruit & Vegetable Market Operator
N.A.I.C.S.: 445230

THUGA AKTIENGESELL-SCHAFT
Nymphenburger Strasse 39, 80335, Munich, Germany
Tel.: (49) 89381970
Web Site: http://www.thuega.de
Sales Range: $1-4.9 Billion
Emp.: 509
Natural Gas Distr
N.A.I.C.S.: 221210
Michael Riechel *(CEO & Member-Mgmt Bd)*

THULE GROUP AB
Fosievagen 13, SE-214 31, Malmo, Sweden
Tel.: (46) 406359000   SE
Web Site:
    https://www.thulegroup.com
Year Founded: 1942
THULE—(OMX)
Rev.: $906,545,968
Assets: $1,088,609,624
Liabilities: $408,700,148
Net Worth: $679,909,476
Earnings: $109,099,214
Emp.: 2,219
Fiscal Year-end: 12/31/23
Holding Company; Travel Trailer & Roofrack Mfr
N.A.I.C.S.: 551112
Kajsa von Geijer *(Sr VP-HR & Sustainability)*

Subsidiaries:

Thule GmbH   (1)
Dreichlinger Strasse 10, 92318, Neumarkt, Germany
Tel.: (49) 91819010
Sales Range: $25-49.9 Million
Roofrack Systems Mfr
N.A.I.C.S.: 336390
Michael Mitschke *(Product Mgr)*

Thule NV   (1)
Kortrijkstraat 343, 8930, Menen, Belgium
Tel.: (32) 56528899
Sales Range: $25-49.9 Million
Emp.: 140
Roofrack Systems Mfr
N.A.I.C.S.: 336390
Filip Vanverlinden *(CEO)*

Thule Towing Systems AB   (1)
Fosievagen 13, 214 31, Malmo, Sweden   (100%)
Tel.: (46) 406359000
Web Site: https://www.thule.com
Travel Trailer & Roofrack Mfr
N.A.I.C.S.: 336214

Thule, Inc.   (1)
42 Silvermine Rd, Seymour, CT 06483-3907
Tel.: (203) 881-9600
Web Site: http://www.thule.com
Sales Range: $50-74.9 Million
Roofrack Systems Mfr
N.A.I.C.S.: 336390
Fred Clark *(Pres)*

Subsidiary (Non-US):

Thule Canada Inc.   (2)
700 Bernard, Granby, J2G 9H7, QC, Canada
Tel.: (450) 777-3773
Web Site: http://www.sportrack.com
Automotive Exterior Accessories
N.A.I.C.S.: 336390

THUMBAGE CO., LTD.
6th floor, B-dong Dodam Building 246 Hwangsaeul-ro, Bundang-gu, Seongnam, Gyeonggi-do, Korea (South)
Tel.: (82) 3180601388
Web Site: https://thumbage.co.kr
Year Founded: 2014
208640—(KRS)
Rev.: $9,602,359
Assets: $36,769,683
Liabilities: $10,366,975
Net Worth: $26,402,708
Earnings: ($16,452,259)
Emp.: 64
Fiscal Year-end: 12/31/22
Financial Investment Management Services
N.A.I.C.S.: 523940

THUNDER AIRLINES LIMITED
310 Hector Dougall Way Thunder Bay Airport, Thunder Bay, P7E 6M6, ON, Canada
Tel.: (807) 475-4211
Web Site: http://www.thunderair.com
Year Founded: 1994
Oil Transportation Services
N.A.I.C.S.: 481219

THUNDER BAY TRUCK CENTRE INC.
1145 Commerce Street, Thunder Bay, P7E 6E8, ON, Canada
Tel.: (807) 577-5793
Web Site: http://www.tbtc.ca
Year Founded: 1977
Rev.: $19,552,953
Emp.: 66
Truck Repair & Services
N.A.I.C.S.: 811111
Dave Mack *(Gen Mgr)*

THUNDER GOLD CORP.
684 Squier Street, Thunder Bay, P7B 4A8, ON, Canada
Tel.: (647) 202-7686   BC
Web Site:
    https://thundergoldcorp.com
Year Founded: 1981
TNMLF—(OTCIQ)
Rev.: $5,240
Assets: $5,782,978
Liabilities: $143,730
Net Worth: $5,639,248
Earnings: ($834,622)
Fiscal Year-end: 04/30/22
Mineral Mining & Exploration
N.A.I.C.S.: 213114
Elliot Strashin *(Chm)*

Subsidiaries:

1191557 Ontario Corp.   (1)

THUNDER SOFTWARE TECHNOLOGY CO., LTD.
Chuangda Building Building 3 No 9 Qinghua East Road, Haidian District, Beijing, 100083, China
Tel.: (86) 1062662686
Web Site:
    https://www.thundersoft.com
Year Founded: 2008
300496—(CHIN)
Rev.: $738,368,687
Assets: $1,614,026,573
Liabilities: $239,997,836
Net Worth: $1,374,028,737
Earnings: $65,662,326
Fiscal Year-end: 12/31/23
Software Development Services
N.A.I.C.S.: 541511

THUNDER TIGER CORP.
No 7 6th Road Industry Park, Situn Dist, Taichung, 40755, Taiwan
Tel.: (886) 423591616
Web Site:
    https://www.thundertiger.com
Year Founded: 1979
8033—(TAI)
Rev.: $32,216,062
Assets: $71,235,159
Liabilities: $27,527,583
Net Worth: $43,707,575
Earnings: ($766,866)
Emp.: 857
Fiscal Year-end: 12/31/23
Model Airplane & Car Kits Mfr & Distr
N.A.I.C.S.: 339930
Chen Kwan-Ju *(Chm)*

Subsidiaries:

Associated Electronic Inc.   (1)
21062 Bake Pkwy, Lake Forest, CA 92630
Tel.: (949) 544-7500
Web Site:
    http://www.associatedelectrics.com
Radio Controlled Cars & Trucks Mfr
N.A.I.C.S.: 339930
Rick Hohwart *(Mgr-Reedy Electric Dept)*

Thunder Tiger Europe GmbH   (1)
Rudolf Diesel Strasse 1, 86453, Dasing, Germany
Tel.: (49) 8205959030
Web Site: http://www.thundertiger-tv.de
Electronic Equipment Distr
N.A.I.C.S.: 423690

THUNDERBIRD RESORTS INC.
Apartado, 0823-00514, Panama, Panama
Tel.: (507) 2231234   VG
Web Site:
    http://thunderbirdresorts.com
Year Founded: 1997
AGIL—(EUR)
Rev.: $15,485,000
Assets: $22,261,000
Liabilities: $18,000,000
Net Worth: $4,261,000
Earnings: $1,341,000
Emp.: 448
Fiscal Year-end: 12/31/23
Resort, Hotel & Casino Owner & Operator
N.A.I.C.S.: 721120
Albert W. Atallah *(Gen Counsel & Sec)*

Subsidiaries:

Thunderbird Hoteles Las Americas, S.A.   (1)
Alcanfores 475, 18, Lima, 18, Peru
Tel.: (51) 16163141
Web Site:
    https://www.thunderbirdhotels.com
Hotel Operator
N.A.I.C.S.: 721110

THUNDERFUL GROUP AB
Kvarnbergsgatan 2, 411 05, Gothenburg, Sweden
Tel.: (46) 739372436
Web Site:
    https://www.thunderfulgroup.com
Year Founded: 2019
THUNDR—(NASDAQ)
Rev.: $295,210,440
Assets: $336,786,660
Liabilities: $154,774,800
Net Worth: $182,011,860
Earnings: $11,126,160
Emp.: 478
Fiscal Year-end: 12/31/22
Holding Company
N.A.I.C.S.: 551112
Agostino Simonetta *(Chief Investment Officer)*

Subsidiaries:

Amo Toys A/S   (1)
Sletvej 38, 8310, Tranbjerg, Denmark
Tel.: (45) 72170187
Web Site: https://amo-toys.com
Toys & Gaming Accessories Distr
N.A.I.C.S.: 423920

INTERNATIONAL PUBLIC

Bergsala AB   (1)
Marios gata 23, 434 37, Kungsbacka, Sweden
Tel.: (46) 30050900
Nintendo Switch Mfr & Distr
N.A.I.C.S.: 339930

Bergsala AS   (1)
Elveveien 130 stubberod, 3271, Larvik, Norway
Tel.: (47) 33183324
Nintendo Switch Mfr & Distr
N.A.I.C.S.: 339930

Headup GmbH   (1)
AG Dueren HRB 5453 Nordstr 102, 52353, Duren, Germany
Tel.: (49) 24214868700
Web Site: https://www.headupgames.com
Video Game Publisher
N.A.I.C.S.: 532282

THUNDERHEAD LTD.
5th Floor Ingeni Building 17 Broadwick Street, Soho, London, W1F 0DJ, United Kingdom
Tel.: (44) 3451309340   UK
Web Site:
    http://www.thunderhead.com
Year Founded: 2001
Sales Range: $25-49.9 Million
Emp.: 94
Customer Management Software Development Services
N.A.I.C.S.: 513210
Glen Manchester *(Founder & CEO)*

Subsidiaries:

Thunderhead Pty Ltd   (1)
Level 18 175 pitt street, Sydney, 2000, NSW, Australia
Tel.: (61) 292994560
Web Site: http://www.thunderhead.com
Software Development Services
N.A.I.C.S.: 541511
Jeremy Swartz *(VP-Australia & New Zealand)*

THUNDERSTRUCK RESOURCES LTD.
1500-409 Granville Street, Vancouver, V6C 1T2, BC, Canada
Tel.: (778) 840-7180   BC
Web Site:
    https://www.thunderstruck.ca
Year Founded: 2011
AWE—(OTCIQ)
Assets: $1,416,517
Liabilities: $437,408
Net Worth: $979,109
Earnings: ($314,316)
Fiscal Year-end: 12/31/19
Investment Services
N.A.I.C.S.: 523999
Bryce Bradley *(Pres & CEO)*

THURGAUER KANTONALBANK
Bankplatz 1, 8570, Weinfelden, Switzerland
Tel.: (41) 848111444
Web Site: https://www.tkb.ch
Year Founded: 1871
TKBP—(SWX)
Sales Range: Less than $1 Million
Banking Services
N.A.I.C.S.: 522110
Thomas Koller *(Chm-Mgmt Bd & CEO)*

THURINGER ENERGIE AG
Schwerborner Strasse 30, 99087, Erfurt, Germany
Tel.: (49) 3616520   De
Web Site:
    http://www.thueringerenergie.de
Sales Range: $1-4.9 Billion
Emp.: 1,400
Energy Services
N.A.I.C.S.: 541690

AND PRIVATE COMPANIES

Olaf Werner *(Mng Dir-PR & Editor)*
Subsidiaries:

E.ON Thuringer Energie Dritte
Vermogensverwaltungs-GmbH (1)
Schwerborner Strasse 30, Erfurt, 99087,
Germany
Tel.: (49) 361 652 0
Management Consulting Services
N.A.I.C.S.: 541618

Energie- und Medienversorgung
Schwarza GmbH (EMS) (1)
Breitscheidstrasse 160, Rudolstadt, 07407,
Germany
Tel.: (49) 3672 48900
Web Site: http://www.ems-schwarza.de
Sales Range: $50-74.9 Million
Emp.: 38
Electric Power Distribution Services
N.A.I.C.S.: 221122

Thuringer Netkom GmbH (1)
Schwanseestrasse 13, 99423, Weimar,
Germany
Tel.: (49) 3643213333
Web Site: http://www.netkom.de
Emp.: 6
Telecommunication Servicesb
N.A.I.C.S.: 517810
Karsten Kluge *(Mgr)*

THYE MING INDUSTRIAL CO., LTD.
No 6 Chu Kuang 3 St Tafa Industrial
Area, Kaohsiung, Taiwan
Tel.: (886) 77872278
Web Site: https://www.tmicl.com.tw
9927—(TAI)
Rev.: $301,369,262
Assets: $249,859,469
Liabilities: $41,652,570
Net Worth: $208,206,899
Earnings: $32,595,604
Fiscal Year-end: 12/31/23
Lead Oxide Mfr
N.A.I.C.S.: 325180
Mao Shen Li *(Gen Mgr)*

Subsidiaries:

Thye Ming (Vietnam) Industrial Co.,
Ltd. (1)
C-8A-Cn C-3A-Cn Na5 Street My Phuoc 2
Industrial Park, Ben Cat, Binh Duong, Vietnam
Tel.: (84) 2743568568
Lead Acid Battery Recycle Mfr
N.A.I.C.S.: 332420

THYSSEN'SCHE HANDELSGE-SELLSCHAFT M.B.H.
Dohne 54, 45468, Mulheim an der
Ruhr, Germany
Tel.: (49) 208 9 92 18 0
Web Site:
http://www.thyssenhandel.de
Investment Firm
N.A.I.C.S.: 551112
Juergen Heite *(Mng Dir)*

Subsidiaries:

Anomatic Corporation (1)
8880 Innovation Campus Ct, New Albany,
OH 43031-3031
Tel.: (740) 522-2203
Web Site: http://www.anomatic.com
Anodized Aluminum Packaging Mfr
N.A.I.C.S.: 331318
Eric Leray *(Dir-Sls)*

Thomas GmbH (1)
Industriestrasse 6, 63505, Langenselbold,
Germany
Tel.: (49) 61848070
Web Site: https://www.thomas-holding.com
Emp.: 140
Metal Stamping
N.A.I.C.S.: 332119
Thomas Rister *(Mng Dir)*

Subsidiary (US):

Solla Eyelet Products Inc. (2)
50 Seemar Rd, Watertown, CT 06795
Tel.: (860) 274-3750
Metal Stamping
N.A.I.C.S.: 332119
Luigi Solla *(Pres)*

Subsidiary (Non-US):

Thomas (Suzhou) Metals Co.
Ltd. (2)
SIP Loufeng Exemplary IZ East Side of
Yangqing Road, Suzhou, China
Tel.: (86) 512 6745 1996
Web Site: http://www.thomas-holding.com
Mounting Cups & Aluminum Components
Mfr
N.A.I.C.S.: 331318
Yao Ying *(Asst Gen Mgr)*

Subsidiary (US):

Thomas Erie, Inc. (2)
163 Noble Rd, Girard, PA 16417
Tel.: (814) 774-5661
Web Site: http://www.thomas-holding.com
Fabricated Structural Metal Mfr
N.A.I.C.S.: 332312
David Molnar *(Supvr-Quality)*

Subsidiary (Non-US):

Thomas de Sudamerica S.A. (2)
Parque Industrial Llave Intendente Neyer
924, Beccar, San Isidro, B1643GAT, Argentina
Tel.: (54) 11 4743 8283
Web Site: http://www.thomas-holding.com
Mounting Cups & Ferrules Mfr
N.A.I.C.S.: 332119
Fernando Valle *(Pres)*

THYSSENKRUPP AG
ThyssenKrupp Allee 1, PO Box
45063, 45143, Essen, Germany
Tel.: (49) 2018440 De
Web Site:
https://www.thyssenkrupp.com
Year Founded: 1999
TKA—(MUN)
Rev.: $41,434,864,320
Assets: $36,748,936,170
Liabilities: $23,681,323,110
Net Worth: $13,067,613,060
Earnings: ($2,287,218,640)
Emp.: 99,981
Fiscal Year-end: 09/30/23
Engineeering Services
N.A.I.C.S.: 551112
Bernhard Pellens *(Chm-Supervisory Bd)*

Subsidiaries:

ASEL Ascensores S.L. (1)
Calle de la Haya 4 Bajo 3, 28044, Madrid,
Spain
Tel.: (34) 917 58 63 54
Web Site: http://www.asel-ascensores.com
Elevator Maintenance Services
N.A.I.C.S.: 811310
Montserrat Hernandez Rodriguez *(Mng Dir)*

ATLAS ELEKTRONIK GmbH (1)
Sebaldsbruecker Heerstr 235, 28309,
Bremen, Germany (51%)
Tel.: (49) 42145702
Web Site: https://www.atlas-elektronik.com
Sales Range: $450-499.9 Million
Emp.: 2,000
Maritime Combat System Developer & Mfr
N.A.I.C.S.: 334511

Subsidiary (Non-US):

ATLAS ELEKTRONIK Finland
Oy (2)
Lars Sonckin kaari 16, 02600, Espoo, Finland
Tel.: (358) 207790181
Web Site: https://www.finland.atlas-elektronik.com
Emp.: 12
Combat & Mission Management Systems
for Ships
N.A.I.C.S.: 541512
Jaakko Savisaari *(CEO)*

ATLAS ELEKTRONIK UK Ltd. (2)
Dorset Innovation Park, Winfrith Newburgh,
Dorchester, DT2 8ZB, Dorset, United Kingdom
Tel.: (44) 1305212400
Web Site: https://www.uk.atlas-elektronik.com
Sales Range: $25-49.9 Million
Emp.: 200
Maritime Defense Electronic System Designer & Mfr
N.A.I.C.S.: 334511

ATLAS MARIDAN Aps (2)
Rungsted Havn 1D, Rungsted Kyst, 2960,
Horsholm, Denmark
Tel.: (45) 45674050
Web Site: https://www.maridan.atlas-elektronik.com
Sales Range: $25-49.9 Million
Emp.: 5
Autonomous Underwater Vehicle Designer
& Mfr
N.A.I.C.S.: 334511
Allan Bertelsen *(Mng Dir)*

ATLAS NAVAL SYSTEMS MALAYSIA
SDN BHD (2)
18 Lumut Waterfront Villa, Jalan Titi Panjang, 32200, Perak, Malaysia
Tel.: (60) 56804330
Web Site: http://www.atlashydro.atlas-elektronik.com
Maritime Combat System Developer & Mfr
N.A.I.C.S.: 334511

Subsidiary (US):

ATLAS North America, LLC (2)
120 Newsome Dr Ste H, Yorktown, VA
23692-1309
Tel.: (757) 463-0670
Web Site: https://www.na.atlas-elektronik.com
Emp.: 30
Defense Products & Vehicles Distr
N.A.I.C.S.: 334511

Subsidiary (Domestic):

Hagenuk Marinekommunikation
GmbH (2)
Hamburger Chaussee 25, 24220, Flintbeck,
Germany
Tel.: (49) 43477140
Web Site: https://www.hmk.atlas-elektronik.com
Emp.: 130
Marine Integrated Communication System
Mfr
N.A.I.C.S.: 334220

Subsidiary (Non-US):

SONARTECH ATLAS Pty. Ltd. (2)
Unit G01 Ground Floor 16 Giffnock Avenue,
Macquarie Park, 2113, NSW, Australia
Tel.: (61) 284847400
Web Site: https://www.sonartech.atlas-elektronik.com
Sales Range: $25-49.9 Million
Emp.: 40
Sonar System Designer & Mfr
N.A.I.C.S.: 334511

Aguas Azuis Construcao Naval SPE
Ltda. (1)
Eugenio Pezzini 355 - room 5, Itajai, 88311-045, SC, Brazil
Tel.: (55) 4734046700
Web Site: https://aguasazuis.com.br
Ship Design Services
N.A.I.C.S.: 541330

Ascenseurs Drieux-Combaluzier
S.A.S. (1)
153 rue Noisy Le Sec, Les lilacs, 93260,
Paris, France
Tel.: (33) 149937788
Web Site: https://www.drieux-combaluzier.com
Business Supply & Equipment Distr
N.A.I.C.S.: 423830
Pascal Bulteile *(Dir Gen)*

Aspasiel S.r.l. (1)
Strada di Pentima 3, 05100, Terni, Italy
Tel.: (39) 07 44 203 1
Web Site: http://www.aspasiel.it
Sales Range: $25-49.9 Million
Emp.: 63
Software Publisher

THYSSENKRUPP AG

N.A.I.C.S.: 513210
Mathias Rist *(Chm & Mng Dir)*

Atlas Elektronik India Private
Limited (1)
Unit No 1107 11th Floor Ashoka Estate 24
Barakhamba Road, New Delhi, 110 001,
India
Tel.: (91) 1147689850
Electronic Parts & Equipment Whslr
N.A.I.C.S.: 423690
Focke Schwarzer *(Mng Dir)*

B.L.S. Aufzugservice GmbH (1)
Zum Irrgarten 3, 28844, Weyhe, Germany
Tel.: (49) 421809218000
Web Site: http://www.bls-gmbh.com
Elevator Services
N.A.I.C.S.: 238290

B.V.'Nedeximpo' Nederlandse Export-
en Importmaatschappij (1)
Prof J H Bavincklaan 2, 1183 AT, Amstelveen, Netherlands
Tel.: (31) 205732333
Web Site: http://www.nedeximpo.nl
Sales Range: $25-49.9 Million
Emp.: 14
Steel Product Distr
N.A.I.C.S.: 423510

BIS Blohm + Voss Inspection Service
GmbH (1)
Hermann Blohm Strasse 5, 20457, Hamburg, Germany
Tel.: (49) 40 756077 0
Web Site: http://www.bis-hh.de
Laboratory Testing Services
N.A.I.C.S.: 541380

BMB Steering Innovation GmbH (1)
Barbarastrasse 30, 39218, Schonebeck,
Germany
Tel.: (49) 3928442401
Power Transmission Equipment Mfr
N.A.I.C.S.: 333613

Becker & Co. GmbH (1)
Am Schlosspark 81, PO Box 12 41, 56564,
Neuwied, Germany
Tel.: (49) 2631813100
Web Site: https://www.becker-und-co.de
Iron & Steel Mfr
N.A.I.C.S.: 331110

Berco (Shanghai) Undercarriage
Technology Co., Ltd. (1)
No 129 Wanda Road, Wanxiang Town Pudong, Shanghai, 201313, China
Tel.: (86) 2160316872
Web Site: http://www.berco.com
Emp.: 80
Industrial Machinery Equipment Mfr
N.A.I.C.S.: 333248

Berco (Shanghai) Undercarriage
Trading Co., Ltd. (1)
Room 101 Building 4 Road Yangshan Free
Trade Port, Nanhui, 201306, Shanghai,
China
Tel.: (86) 21 68280368
Web Site: http://www.thyssenkrupp.com
Industrial Machinery Equipment Mfr
N.A.I.C.S.: 333248

Berco (UK) Ltd. (1)
Meadowfield Avenue Green Lane Industrial
Estate, Spennymoor, DL16 6YJ, County
Durham, United Kingdom
Tel.: (44) 1388 824888
Web Site: http://www.berco.co.uk
Sales Range: $25-49.9 Million
Emp.: 30
Industrial Machinery Mfr
N.A.I.C.S.: 333248
Michael Harrigan *(Mgr-Comml)*

Berco Undercarriages (India) Private
Ltd. (1)
Sector 1 Lane 10 Ghase II Cherlapally,
Hayathnagar Ghatkesar Mandal, Hyderabad, 500 051, Andhra Pradesh, India
Tel.: (91) 20 2742 5761
Industrial Machinery Equipment Mfr
N.A.I.C.S.: 333248

BercoSul Ltda. (1)
Av Alfried Krupp 1050, Campo Limpo, Paulista, 13231-900, Sao Paulo, Brazil
Tel.: (55) 1140399000

THYSSENKRUPP AG / INTERNATIONAL PUBLIC

ThyssenKrupp AG—(Continued)

Web Site: http://www.bercosul.com.br
Industrial Machinery Parts Mfr
N.A.I.C.S.: 333998

Blohm + Voss (Korea) Ltd. (1)
Room 1830 Ocean Tower 760-3 U-dong,
Haeundae-gu, 612-020, Pusan, Korea
(South)
Tel.: (82) 517405701
Industrial Machinery Mfr
N.A.I.C.S.: 333248

Blohm + Voss El Djazair S.a.r.l. (1)
El Mouhamadia Algeria Business Center
Tower, Algiers, 1600, Algeria
Tel.: (213) 21985081
Sales Range: $25-49.9 Million
Emp.: 1
Ship Building & Repairing Services
N.A.I.C.S.: 336611
Feriel Mekerba *(Office Mgr)*

Blohm + Voss Industries (Singapore) Pte. Ltd. (1)
33 Benoi Rd Pioneer Lot S, 627784, Singapore, Singapore
Tel.: (65) 66863373
Web Site: http://www.bv-industries.com
Sales Range: $25-49.9 Million
Emp.: 14
Industrial Machinery & Equipment Mfr
N.A.I.C.S.: 333248
C. J. Ng *(Mng Dir)*

Blohm + Voss Marine Systems GmbH (1)
Hermann-Blohm-Strasse 3, 20457, Hamburg, Germany
Tel.: (49) 4031191311
Marine Transportation Services
N.A.I.C.S.: 488390

Blohm + Voss Naval GmbH (1)
Hermann-Blohm-Str 3, 20457, Hamburg, Germany
Tel.: (49) 40 3119 0
Web Site: http://www.blohmvoss-naval.com
Emp.: 2,000
Ship Building & Repairing Services
N.A.I.C.S.: 336611
Van Beers *(Gen Mgr)*

Blohm + Voss Oil Tools, LLC (1)
11355 FM 830 Rd, Willis, TX 77318
Tel.: (936) 856-4995
Web Site: http://www.blohmvoss-oiltools.com
Sales Range: $25-49.9 Million
Emp.: 50
Industrial Machinery Whslr
N.A.I.C.S.: 423830

Blohm + Voss Shipyards & Services GmbH (1)
Hermann-Blohm-Str 3, 20457, Hamburg, Germany
Tel.: (49) 40 3119 0
Web Site: http://www.blohmvoss.com
Emp.: 2,000
Ship Building & Repairing Services
N.A.I.C.S.: 336611
Fred van Beers *(Mng Dir)*

Bobby&Carl GmbH (1)
Kaistrasse 4, 40221, Dusseldorf, Germany
Tel.: (49) 2112730470
Web Site: http://www.bobbyandcarl.com
Marketing & Advertising Services
N.A.I.C.S.: 541810

Budcan Holdings Inc. (1)
1011 Homer Watson Boulevard, Kitchener, N2G 4G8, ON, Canada
Tel.: (519) 895-1000
Investment Management Service
N.A.I.C.S.: 523940

CIAMPI S.r.l. (1)
Via Vespasiano 34, 00192, Rome, Italy
Tel.: (39) 0639723170
Web Site: https://www.ciampi.it
Piano Retailer
N.A.I.C.S.: 459140

CarValoo GmbH (1)
ThyssenKrupp Allee 1, 45143, Essen, Germany
Tel.: (49) 2018440
Web Site: https://www.carvaloo.com
Electric Vehicle Repair & Maintenance Services
N.A.I.C.S.: 811111

Carolina Building Materials, Inc. (1)
Carr Ste 860 Km 0 1, Carolina, PR 00984
Tel.: (787) 769-0176
Web Site: http://www.cbmpr.net
Emp.: 30
Building Construction Material Whslr
N.A.I.C.S.: 423390

Cimex-Nor S.A. (1)
Avenida de la Libertad 7, 20004, San Sebastian, Spain
Tel.: (34) 943423626
Sales Range: $50-74.9 Million
Emp.: 2
Industrial Machinery & Equipment Whslr
N.A.I.C.S.: 423830
Antonio Maraver Cortezo *(Pres)*

Compagnie des Ascenseurs et Elevateurs S.A.M. (1)
Rue Honore Labande 15, 98000, Monaco, Monaco
Tel.: (377) 99995010
Web Site: http://www.thyssenkrupp.com
Elevator Installation Services
N.A.I.C.S.: 238290

DE-VerwaltungsGmbH (1)
Kaiser-Wilhelm-Str 100, 47166, Duisburg, Germany
Tel.: (49) 23198395
Investment Management Service
N.A.I.C.S.: 523940

DWR - Deutsche Gesellschaft fur Weissblechrecycling mbH (1)
Graf-Adolf-Str 20, 40212, Dusseldorf, Germany
Tel.: (49) 2113106290
Web Site: https://www.rdwr.de
Waste Material Whslr
N.A.I.C.S.: 423930

Defontaine Iberica S.A. (1)
15 Poligono de la Granja, Viana, 31230, Navarra, Spain
Tel.: (34) 948 64 61 33
Web Site: http://www.defontaine.com
Emp.: 40
Motor Vehicle Parts Mfr
N.A.I.C.S.: 336390

Defontaine Tunisie S.A. (1)
55 Rue Fouchana - Z I M'Ghira 1, 2082, Fouchana, Tunisia
Tel.: (216) 79408727
Rolling Bearing Product Mfr
N.A.I.C.S.: 332991

Dr. Mertens Edelstahlhandel GmbH (1)
Lilistrasse 85, 63067, Offenbach, Germany
Tel.: (49) 698200020
Web Site: https://www.mertens-edelstahl.de
Iron & Steel Forging Mfr
N.A.I.C.S.: 332111

ELEX CemCat AG (1)
Eschenstrasse 6, 8603, Schwerzenbach, Switzerland
Tel.: (41) 448257878
Web Site: http://www.elex.ch
Sales Range: $25-49,9 Million
Emp.: 5
Electrical Engineering Services
N.A.I.C.S.: 541330
Daniel Schneider *(Member-Exec Bd & Head-Bus Unit)*

EURISOL S.A. (1)
2 Pl du Docteur J M Ryckewaert, Steenvoorde, France
Tel.: (33) 328438484
Building Equipment Installation Services
N.A.I.C.S.: 238290

Eisen- und Huttenwerke AG (1)
Koblenzer Str 141, 56626, Andernach, Germany
Tel.: (49) 2632309525
Web Site: https://www.ehw.ag
Iron & Steel Products Mfr
N.A.I.C.S.: 331110

Eisenmetall Handelsgesellschaft mbH (1)
An der Landwehr 2, PO Box 100553, 45883, Gelsenkirchen, Germany
Tel.: (49) 209 801 209
Web Site: http://www.eisenmetall-handelsgesellschaft.de
Sales Range: $25-49.9 Million
Emp.: 7
Rolled Steel Products Mfr & Distr
N.A.I.C.S.: 331221
Josef Lenz *(Mng Dir)*

Erich Weit GmbH (1)
Colditzstrasse 38-42, 12099, Berlin, Germany
Tel.: (49) 30702171
Web Site: https://www.erichweit.de
Sales Range: $25-49.9 Million
Emp.: 18
Construction Materials Whslr
N.A.I.C.S.: 423320

Ertsoverslagbedrijf Europoort C.V. (1)
Markweg 131, 3198 NB, Europoort, Netherlands
Tel.: (31) 181257899
Web Site: https://www.eecv.nl
Sales Range: $125-149.9 Million
Emp.: 280
Marine Cargo Handling Services
N.A.I.C.S.: 488320

GKI-OFU Industrieofenbau GmbH (1)
Friedrich-Uhde-Str 15, 44141, Dortmund, Germany (100%)
Tel.: (49) 2315470
Industrial Machinery Mfr
N.A.I.C.S.: 333248

GLH GmbH (1)
Heinrich-Hertz-Strasse 4-6, 22941, Bargteheide, Germany
Tel.: (49) 45322807530
Web Site: https://www.glh-europe.de
Housing Bearing Mfr
N.A.I.C.S.: 332991

GWH Aufzuge GmbH (1)
Rudolf-Diesel-Str 9, Himmelstadt, 97267, Germany
Tel.: (49) 93 64 81 33 0
Web Site: http://www.gwh-aufzuege.de
Sales Range: $25-49.9 Million
Emp.: 80
Elevator Mfr
N.A.I.C.S.: 333921

Greek Naval Shipyards Holding S.A. (1)
Skaramangas Shipyards, Chaidari, Athens, 12400, Greece
Tel.: (30) 21055783
Investment Management Service
N.A.I.C.S.: 523940

Grupo ThyssenKrupp S.L. (1)
Paseo de la Castellana Torre de Cristal 259 - C -Planta 23, 28046, Madrid, Spain
Tel.: (34) 916618642
Web Site: http://www.grupothyssenkrupp.com
Rev: $2,114,224,000
Emp.: 5,500
Elevator Mfr
N.A.I.C.S.: 333921

HF Vermogensverwaltungsgesellschaft im Ruhrtal GmbH (1)
Oeger Str 85, Hagen, 58119, Germany
Tel.: (49) 23337914172
Investment Management Service
N.A.I.C.S.: 523940

Haisch Aufzuge GmbH (1)
Brunnenstr 57, Gingen an der Fils, 73333, Germany
Tel.: (49) 716296250
Web Site: http://www.haisch-aufzuege.de
Elevator Mfr
N.A.I.C.S.: 333921

Hoesch Bausysteme Gesellschaft m.b.H. (1)
Tenscherstrasse 3, 1230, Vienna, Austria
Tel.: (43) 1 615 46 40
Web Site: http://www.hoesch-bau.com
Roofing Materials Mfr
N.A.I.C.S.: 324122

Hovelmann & Co. Eisengrosshandlung GmbH (1)
An Der Landwehr 2, Gelsenkirchen, 45883, Germany
Tel.: (49) 209 801 04
Web Site: http://www.hoevelmann-stahlhandel.de
Sales Range: $25-49.9 Million
Emp.: 7
Coal & Mineral Ore Distr
N.A.I.C.S.: 423520

Indu-Light AG (1)
Industriestrasse 23, 6215, Beromunster, Lucerne, Switzerland
Tel.: (41) 41 932 4100
Web Site: https://indu-light.ch
Lighting Equipment Installation Services
N.A.I.C.S.: 238210
Peter Denzler *(Mng Dir)*

Isocab France S.A.S. (1)
3 Rue Charles Fourier CS 30142, 59760, Grande-Synthe, Cedex, France
Tel.: (33) 328292440
Web Site: http://www.isocab.com
Mineral Wool Panel Mfr
N.A.I.C.S.: 327993

Isocab N.V. (1)
Treurnietstraat 10, Harelbeke, 8531, Bavikhove, Belgium
Tel.: (32) 56 73 43 11
Web Site: http://www.isocab.be
Mineral Wool Panel Mfr
N.A.I.C.S.: 327993

Jacob Bek GmbH (1)
Hohnerstrasse 5-11, 89079, Ulm, Germany
Tel.: (49) 7314050
Web Site: https://www.jacob-bek.de
Rolled Steel Products Mfr
N.A.I.C.S.: 331221

Krupp Canada Inc. (1)
4838 Richard Road S W Suite 400, Calgary, T3E 6L1, AB, Canada
Tel.: (403) 245-2866
Web Site: http://www.krupp.ca
Industrial Machinery & Equipment Whslr
N.A.I.C.S.: 423830

Krupp Informatik Gesellschaft mit beschrankter Haftung (1)
August-Thyssen-Strasse 1, 40211, Dusseldorf, Germany
Tel.: (49) 27434689
Computer Data Processing Services
N.A.I.C.S.: 518210

LAMINCER S.A. (1)
Aritz Bidea 81 Atela Auzotegia, 48100, Munguia, Spain
Tel.: (34) 46477700
Web Site: http://www.lamincer.com
Sales Range: $25-49.9 Million
Emp.: 76
Rolled Steel Products Mfr
N.A.I.C.S.: 331221

Lift & Engineering Services Ltd. (1)
16 Portersfield Road, Cradley Heath, B64 7BN, West Midlands, United Kingdom
Tel.: (44) 138 463 3115
Web Site: https://www.lift-engineering.co.uk
Hoist & Stair Lift Mfr
N.A.I.C.S.: 333923
Yasmin Ali *(Reg Mgr-Ops)*

LiftEquip GmbH (1)
Bernhauser Strasse 45, 73765, Neuhausen, Germany
Tel.: (49) 715 812 2929
Web Site: https://www.liftequip.de
Elevator Mfr
N.A.I.C.S.: 333921
Markus Bruckmeyer *(Head-Sls)*

Liftservice und Montage GmbH (1)
Unterturkheimer Str 35, 66117, Saarbrucken, Germany
Tel.: (49) 681 92 64 90
Web Site: http://www.liftservice-saar.de
Lift & Elevator Mfr
N.A.I.C.S.: 333921

MGTI SNEV S.A.S. (1)
Parc ICADE 7 Place de la Loire, 94150, Rungis, France
Tel.: (33) 146580265
Web Site: https://www.mgti.fr
Sales Range: $25-49.9 Million
Emp.: 25
Electrical Parts & Component Distr

AND PRIVATE COMPANIES — THYSSENKRUPP AG

N.A.I.C.S.: 423610

MONTAN GmbH Assekuranz-Makler (1)
Graf-Adolf-Strasse 49, PO Box 103854, 40210, Dusseldorf, Germany
Tel.: (49) 211 30 27 10 70
Web Site: http://www.montan-gmbh.de
Insurance Management Services
N.A.I.C.S.: 524298

Marohn thyssenkrupp Elevator Co. Ltd. (1)
Rm 805 Bldg 1 898 xiuwen Rd, Minhang District, Shanghai, 201199, China
Tel.: (86) 2133030905
Web Site: https://www.marohn-tke.com
Elevator & Moving Stairway Mfr
N.A.I.C.S.: 333921
Yaning Lu *(CEO)*

Max Cochius GmbH (1)
Rhinstrasse 50, 12681, Berlin, Germany
Tel.: (49) 3 068 2900
Web Site: https://www.cochius.de
Sales Range: $25-49.9 Million
Emp.: 27
Metal Products Mfr
N.A.I.C.S.: 332999
Michael Dreyer *(Mng Dir)*

Mulder Liftservice B.V. (1)
Handelstraat 5, 6361 KC, Nuth, 6361 KC, Netherlands
Tel.: (31) 455241242
Web Site: http://www.mulderliftservice.nl
Lift & Escalator Mfr
N.A.I.C.S.: 333921

Neomat AG (1)
Industriestrasse 23, PO Box 167, 6215, Beromunster, Switzerland
Tel.: (41) 9324141
Web Site: https://neomat.ch
Sales Range: $25-49.9 Million
Emp.: 40
Plastic Materials Mfr
N.A.I.C.S.: 325211

Nordseewerke Emden Shipyard (1)
Zum Zungenkai, 26725, Emden, Germany
Tel.: (49) 4921 85 99
Web Site: http://www.emden-dockyard.com
Ship Building & Repairing Services
N.A.I.C.S.: 336611
Christian Eckel *(Mng Dir)*

Notz Plastics AG (1)
Bielstrasse 75, PO Box 99, 2555, Brugg, Switzerland
Tel.: (41) 323667400
Web Site: https://www.notz-plastics.ch
Sales Range: $25-49.9 Million
Emp.: 30
Plastic Materials Mfr
N.A.I.C.S.: 325211

Nuova TKEI S.P.A. (1)
Via Alessandro Volta 16, 20093, Cologno Monzese, Italy
Tel.: (39) 0289696300
Web Site: https://www.tkelevator.com
Sales Range: $100-124.9 Million
Emp.: 350
Elevator Mfr
N.A.I.C.S.: 333921

OOO Polysius (1)
World Trade Centre Entrance 3 Office 1009 Krasnopresnenskaja Nab 12, Moscow, 123610, Russia
Tel.: (7) 495 258 20 10
Web Site: http://www.polysius.com
Engineeering Services
N.A.I.C.S.: 541330

OOO ThyssenKrupp Bautechnik technischer Service (1)
Pr Bolschewikow 54 Korp 5 Lit B Office 28-29-30, 193315, Saint Petersburg, Russia
Tel.: (7) 8123376510
Web Site: http://app.casagrandegroup.com
Sales Range: $50-74.9 Million
Emp.: 8
Mining Machinery Rental & Leasing Services
N.A.I.C.S.: 532412

OOO ThyssenKrupp Materials (1)
Paveletskaya Embankment 8 Building 6, 115114, Moscow, Russia
Tel.: (7) 495 921 2250
Web Site: http://www.thyssenkruppmaterials.ru
Sales Range: $25-49.9 Million
Emp.: 50
Steel Product Distr
N.A.I.C.S.: 423510
Vladimir Viktorovich *(Dir Gen)*

OOO ThyssenKrupp System Engineering (1)
Ul Gagarina 4 Office 410, 248000, Kaluga, Russia
Tel.: (7) 4842744645
Web Site: http://www.thyssenkrupp.com
Sales Range: $25-49.9 Million
Emp.: 68
Engineeering Services
N.A.I.C.S.: 541330

OOO Uhde (1)
48 Lenin Prospect Nizhny Novgorod Region, 606023, Dzerzhinsk, Russia
Tel.: (7) 8313 350 330
Web Site: http://en.uhde-russia.com
Sales Range: $100-124.9 Million
Emp.: 400
Industrial Plant Construction Services
N.A.I.C.S.: 237990
Albert Zimmermann *(Deputy Mng Dir)*

OOO thyssenkrupp Industrial Solutions (RUS) (1)
Lenin Prospect 48, 606023, Dzerzhinsk, Russia
Tel.: (7) 8313350330
Web Site: https://www.tkisrus.com
Emp.: 400
Cement Mfr
N.A.I.C.S.: 327310
Mikhail Kozlov *(Chm & Mng Dir)*

OOO thyssenkrupp Infrastructure (1)
Bolschevikov str 54 B korp 4 Lit A, 193315, Saint Petersburg, Russia
Tel.: (7) 8123376510
Web Site: http://www.thyssenkrupp-infrastructure.ru
Marine Equipment Distr
N.A.I.C.S.: 423860
Dietmar Jurges *(CEO)*

Otto Wolff U.S. Sales GmbH (1)
Graf-Adolf-Str 20, 40212, Dusseldorf, Germany
Tel.: (49) 2113106290
Web Site: https://www.rdwr.de
Real Estate Manangement Services
N.A.I.C.S.: 531390

Outokumpu Stainless USA, LLC (1)
1 Steel Dr, Calvert, AL 36513-1300
Tel.: (251) 829-3600
Web Site: http://www.thyssenkrupp-stainless-usa.com
Emp.: 950
Stainless Steel Service Center Operator
N.A.I.C.S.: 423510
Ulrich Albrecht-Frueh *(Pres & CEO)*

PALMETAL Armazenagem e Servicos S.A. (1)
Parque Industrial Autoeuropa, 2950-557, Palmela, Portugal
Tel.: (351) 212134500
Web Site: https://www.palmetal.pt
Steel Coil Distr
N.A.I.C.S.: 423510

PALMETAL Controlo e Armazenagem S.A. (1)
Parque industrial AutoEuropa, 2950-557, Palmela, Portugal
Tel.: (351) 212134500
Web Site: https://www.palmetal.pt
Sales Range: $10-24.9 Million
Emp.: 41
General Warehousing & Storage Services
N.A.I.C.S.: 493110

PSL Walzlager GmbH (1)
Tremoniastrasse 5-11, 44137, Dortmund, Germany
Tel.: (49) 23199772700
Web Site: http://www.pslofamerica.com
Industrial Machinery Equipment Mfr
N.A.I.C.S.: 333248

PSL a.s. (1)
Robotnicka Ul, 017 01, Povazska Bystrica, Slovakia
Tel.: (421) 424371460
Web Site: http://www.pslas.com
Sales Range: $200-249.9 Million
Emp.: 700
Industrial Machinery Equipment Mfr
N.A.I.C.S.: 333248
Achim Stuhlmann *(CFO & Member-Exec Bd)*

PT. ThyssenKrupp Elevator Indonesia (1)
2nd Floor Trihamas Building Jl TB Simatupang Kav 11 Tanjung Barat, Jakarta, 12530, Indonesia
Tel.: (62) 2129516466
Web Site: https://www.tkelevator.com
Sales Range: $25-49.9 Million
Emp.: 10
Elevator Mfr
N.A.I.C.S.: 333921

PT. ThyssenKrupp Polysius Indonesia (1)
Tempo Scan Tower 20th Fl Jl HR Rasuna Said Kav 3-4, Selatan, Jakarta, 12950, Indonesia
Tel.: (62) 21 2939 2800
Web Site: http://www.polysius.com
Emp.: 30
Industrial Machinery Distr
N.A.I.C.S.: 423830
Amir Sinai *(Gen Mgr)*

PT. thyssenkrupp Industrial Solutions Indonesia (1)
Tempo Scan Tower 20th Floor Jl HR Rasuna Said KAV 3-4, Jakarta Selatan, Indonesia
Tel.: (62) 2129392800
Construction Machinery & Equipment Mfr
N.A.I.C.S.: 333120
Daniel Schoenert *(Dir-Ops)*

Polysius (Shanghai) Co., Ltd. (1)
1505 Panchuan Road, Baoshan District, Shanghai, 200949, China
Tel.: (86) 2161817588
Industrial Machinery Distr
N.A.I.C.S.: 423830

Polysius Engineering Sdn. Bhd. (1)
Unit 2 01 2nd Floor Bangunan Electroscon Lot 8 Jalan Astaka U8/84, Seksyen U8 Bukit Jelutong, 40150, Shah Alam, Selangor Darul Ehsan, Malaysia
Tel.: (60) 3 7845 1886
Web Site: http://www.polysius.com
Engineeering Services
N.A.I.C.S.: 541330

Polysius Ingenieria y Servicios del Peru S.A. (1)
Av Mariscal Benavides 207 Urb Selva Alegre, Cercado, Arequipa, Peru
Tel.: (51) 54200116
Sales Range: $50-74.9 Million
Emp.: 10
Industrial Machinery Equipment Whslr
N.A.I.C.S.: 423830

Polysius Ltd. (1)
The Brackens London Road, Ascot, SL5 8BE, Berks, United Kingdom
Tel.: (44) 1344884161
Web Site: http://www.polysius.com
Sales Range: $25-49.9 Million
Emp.: 3
Engineeering Services
N.A.I.C.S.: 541330
Sue Cope *(Mgr-Facility)*

Polysius S.A. (1)
PL Manuel Gomez Moreno S/n Edificio Bronce, 28020, Madrid, Spain
Tel.: (34) 91 555 8040
Web Site: http://www.arupothyssenkrupp.com
Emp.: 50
Industrial Machinery Equipment Whslr
N.A.I.C.S.: 423830
Zlatan Azinovic *(Mgr)*

Polysius Vietnam Ltd. (1)
7th Floor Sun Red River Building 23 Phan Chu Trinh, Hoan Kiem Dist, Hanoi, Vietnam
Tel.: (84) 4 3938 7000
Web Site: http://www.thyssenkrupp-industrial-solutions.com
Sales Range: $25-49.9 Million
Emp.: 100
Industrial Machinery Equipment Whslr
N.A.I.C.S.: 423830

Polysius de Argentina S.A. (1)
25 De Mayo 596-Piso 14, 1002, Buenos Aires, Argentina
Tel.: (54) 11 43116046
Web Site: http://www.polysius.com
Construction Machinery Mfr
N.A.I.C.S.: 333120

Polysius de Mexico S.A. de C.V. (1)
Sierra Gamon No 120 D-802 Col Lomas de Chapultepec, 11000, Mexico, Mexico
Tel.: (52) 5552840100
Sales Range: $50-74.9 Million
Emp.: 100
Industrial Machinery Equipment Whslr
N.A.I.C.S.: 423830
Daniel Greune *(Mgr)*

Polysius del Peru S.A. (1)
Km 1 Carretera Matarani - Mollendo Ceticos, Matarani, Peru
Tel.: (51) 54557130
Engineeering Services
N.A.I.C.S.: 541330

Polysius do Brasil Ltda. (1)
Av Brigadeiro Faria Lima 1572 - 14 Andar Jardim Paulistano, 01451-917, Sao Paulo, Brazil
Tel.: (55) 11 38114500
Web Site: http://www.polysius.com
Sales Range: $50-74.9 Million
Emp.: 85
Industrial Machinery Equipment Whslr
N.A.I.C.S.: 423830

Proxi-Line S.a.r.l. (1)
Rue de Champfleur ZI Saint-Barthelemy, 49001, Angers, Cedex, France
Tel.: (33) 160375400
Web Site: https://www.proxi-line.com
Elevator Remote Monitoring Services
N.A.I.C.S.: 561621

RIP Comercio Ltda. (1)
Rua Moises Valezin 301 - SL 03, 13347-520, Indaiatuba, Brazil
Tel.: (55) 19 3885 7609
Web Site: http://www.ripbr.com.br
Fire Proofing & Corrosion Protection Services
N.A.I.C.S.: 922160
Jose Silvestre *(Mgr)*

RIP Servicos Industriais Ltda. (1)
Rod Eng Ermenio de Oliveira Penteado KM 57 9, Indaiatuba, 13337-300, Brazil
Tel.: (55) 1938857600
Web Site: https://www.ripbr.com.br
Industrial Machinery Installation Services
N.A.I.C.S.: 238290

Reiseburo Dr. Tigges GmbH (1)
Huyssenallee 9, 45128, Essen, Germany
Tel.: (49) 2018104050
Web Site: https://tiggesreisebuero.de
Travel Arrangement Services
N.A.I.C.S.: 561510

Rohm Italia S.r.l. (1)
Via Xx Settembre 38, 20024, Garbagnate Milanese, Milan, Italy
Tel.: (39) 02 9907051
Web Site: http://www.roehmitalia.it
Plastic Material Distr
N.A.I.C.S.: 424610

SDV Escalators Ltd. (1)
Snaygill Industrial Estate Keighley Road, Skipton, BD23 2QR, North Yorkshire, United Kingdom
Tel.: (44) 1756701649
Web Site: https://www.sdv-ltd.co.uk
Elevator & Moving Stairway Mfr
N.A.I.C.S.: 333921
Martin Monaghan *(Officer-Health Safety)*

SVG Steinwerder Verwaltungsgesellschaft mbH (1)
Hermann-Blohm-Str 3, 20457, Hamburg, Germany
Tel.: (49) 4031191323
Real Estate Prorperty Leasing Services
N.A.I.C.S.: 531190

Siegfried Schlussler Feuerungsbau GmbH (1)

THYSSENKRUPP AG

ThyssenKrupp AG—(Continued)

Sellhorner Weg 30, 29646, Bispingen, Germany
Tel.: (49) 519498970
Web Site: https://www.schluessler.com
Sales Range: $25-49.9 Million
Emp.: 100
Steel Products Mfr
N.A.I.C.S.: 331513

SkyLift B.V. (1)
Albert Plesmanstraat 24, 3772 MN, Barneveld, Netherlands
Tel.: (31) 88 505 1500
Web Site: https://www.skylift.nl
Emp.: 250
Elevator Installation & Maintenance Services
N.A.I.C.S.: 238290
Dimitri van Hensbergen (Gen Mgr-Mktg & Sls)

Steba AG (1)
Talstrasse 33, Pfaffikon, 8808, Switzerland
Tel.: (41) 55 4 16 00 66
Web Site: http://www.stebakunststoffe.ch
Construction Materials Distr
N.A.I.C.S.: 423390

Steelbuy Limited (1)
Third Floor Friars Gate 1011 Stratford Rd, Shirley, Solihull, B90 4BN, United Kingdom
Tel.: (44) 1217137290
Web Site: https://www.steel-buy.com
Software Development Services
N.A.I.C.S.: 541511

Sun Rich Enterprises Ltd. (1)
10 F-1 No 18 Sec 1 Chang-An East Road, Taipei, Taiwan
Tel.: (886) 2 2561 8310
Web Site: http://www.sre.com.tw
Sales Range: $50-74.9 Million
Emp.: 150
Elevator & Escalator Mfr & Distr
N.A.I.C.S.: 333921
Nancy Lee (CFO)

TOB ThyssenKrupp Elevator Ukraine (1)
Moskovskiy Avenue 9 Building 4A Office 4-501, 04073, Kiev, Ukraine
Tel.: (380) 44586 4923
Web Site: http://www.thyssenkrupp-elevator.com.ua
Sales Range: $25-49.9 Million
Emp.: 30
Elevator Mfr
N.A.I.C.S.: 333921

TOV Polysius Ukraine (1)
Ul Vikentija Hvojky 21 Office 624, 04655, Kiev, Ukraine
Tel.: (380) 442308734
Web Site: http://www.thyssenkrupp.com
Sales Range: $25-49.9 Million
Emp.: 2
Engineeering Services
N.A.I.C.S.: 541330

TWB Industries, S.A. de C.V. (1)
Blvd Santa Maria S/N, Ramos Arizpe, 25900, Coahuila, Mexico
Tel.: (52) 8444389650
Steel Products Mfr
N.A.I.C.S.: 331110

Tepper Aufzuge GmbH (1)
Hafen Grenzweg 11-19, PO Box 7829, 48155, Munster, Germany
Tel.: (49) 25160580
Web Site: https://www.tepper-aufzuege.de
Sales Range: $100-124.9 Million
Emp.: 300
Elevator Mfr
N.A.I.C.S.: 333921

Terninox S.p.A. (1)
Via Milano 12, Ceriano Laghetto, 20020, Monza, MI, Italy
Tel.: (39) 029 698 2402
Web Site: https://www.terninox.it
Stainless Steel Tube Mfr
N.A.I.C.S.: 331210
Emanuele Consonni (Sls Dir)

Thyssen Elevators Co., Ltd. (1)
No 279 Qiangye Road Sheshan Subarea Songjiang Industrial Area, 201602, Shanghai, China

Tel.: (86) 21 5779 6336
Web Site: http://www.thyssenkrupp.com
Elevator Mfr
N.A.I.C.S.: 333921

Thyssen Stahl GmbH (1)
Thyssenkrupp Allee 1, Essen, 45143, Germany
Tel.: (49) 2035200
Steel Products Mfr
N.A.I.C.S.: 331513
Edwin Eichler (Chm)

Thyssen Trading S.A. (1)
Rua Roberto Koch 277-Ipiranga, 04221-260, Sao Paulo, Brazil
Tel.: (55) 1161655660
Iron & Steel Mfr
N.A.I.C.S.: 331110

ThyssenKrupp (China) Ltd. (1)
22nd Floor China Life Building No 16 Chaoyangmenwai Street, Chaoyang, Beijing, 100020, China
Tel.: (86) 1085075666
Web Site: https://www.thyssenkrupp.com.cn
Sales Range: $25-49.9 Million
Emp.: 40
Elevator & Steel Product Mfr
N.A.I.C.S.: 333921

ThyssenKrupp AG-Singapore (1)
3 International Business Park 06-01 Nordic European Centre, Singapore, 609 927, Singapore
Tel.: (65) 6890 6000
Web Site: http://www.thyssenkrupp.com
Sales Range: $25-49.9 Million
Emp.: 200
Industrial Machinery Equipment Whslr
N.A.I.C.S.: 423830

ThyssenKrupp Access China Ltd. (1)
Room 105 Kaike International Building Area A No1801 Hongmei, Shanghai, 200233, China
Tel.: (86) 21 6485 5666
Web Site: http://www.tkaccess.com.cn
Sales Range: $25-49.9 Million
Emp.: 40
Elevator Mfr
N.A.I.C.S.: 333921
Ting Hu (Mgr-Mktg)

ThyssenKrupp Access Ltd. (1)
Unit E3 Eagle Court De Havilland Avenue Preston Farm Business Park, Stockton-on-Tees, TS18 3TB, United Kingdom
Tel.: (44) 1642853650
Web Site: https://www.tkelevator.com
Sales Range: $25-49.9 Million
Emp.: 72
Stairlift & Elevator Mfr
N.A.I.C.S.: 333921

ThyssenKrupp Aceros y Servicios S.A. (1)
Avda Las Americas 1021 - Cerrillos, Santiago, Chile
Tel.: (56) 22420 5500
Web Site: http://www.thyssenkrupp.cl
Steel Products Mfr
N.A.I.C.S.: 331513

ThyssenKrupp Aerospace (Shanghai) Co. Ltd. (1)
3200 Gong He Xin Road, Zhabei District, Shanghai, 200072, China
Tel.: (86) 21 5665 5959
Web Site: http://www.thyssenkruppaerospace.com
Sales Range: $25-49.9 Million
Emp.: 30
Aircraft Part Mfr
N.A.I.C.S.: 336413

ThyssenKrupp Aerospace (Xi'an) Co. Ltd. (1)
3 Bonded Warehouse Xian Export Processing Zone No 1 Fengcheng 12 Road, Xi'an, 710018, China
Tel.: (86) 29 8665 8857
Web Site: http://www.thyssenkruppaerospace.com
Sales Range: $25-49.9 Million
Emp.: 10
Aircraft Part Mfr
N.A.I.C.S.: 336413

ThyssenKrupp Aerospace Australia Pty. Ltd. (1)

Unit 2 7-10 Denoci Close, Wetherill Park, 2164, NSW, Australia
Tel.: (61) 297577777
Web Site: http://www.thyssenkruppaerospace.com
Emp.: 30
Air Freight Transportation Services
N.A.I.C.S.: 481112

ThyssenKrupp Aerospace Finland Oy (1)
Jalostamontie 1, 42300, Jamsankoski, Finland
Tel.: (358) 201274420
Sales Range: $25-49.9 Million
Emp.: 24
Aluminium Products Mfr
N.A.I.C.S.: 331313

ThyssenKrupp Aerospace Germany GmbH (1)
thyssenkrupp Allee 1, 45143, Essen, Germany
Tel.: (49) 2018440
Web Site: https://www.thyssenkrupp-aerospace.com
Aluminium Product Distr
N.A.I.C.S.: 423510

ThyssenKrupp Aerospace Nederland B.V. (1)
Celsiusweg 32-58, 5928 PR, Venlo, Netherlands
Tel.: (31) 773249999
Web Site: http://www.thyssenkruppaerospace.com
Aluminium Products Mfr
N.A.I.C.S.: 331313

ThyssenKrupp Aerospace UK Ltd. (1)
Redfern Road Tyseley, Birmingham, B11 2BH, United Kingdom
Tel.: (44) 1213355100
Web Site: http://www.thyssenkruppaerospace.com
Sales Range: $25-49.9 Million
Emp.: 100
Aluminium Products Mfr
N.A.I.C.S.: 331318

ThyssenKrupp Airport Services S.L. (1)
Poligono Industrial Vega de Baina s/n, Mieres, 33682, Asturias, Spain
Tel.: (34) 985 457 707
Web Site: http://www.thyssenkrupp.com
Emp.: 250
Airport Handling Services
N.A.I.C.S.: 237310

ThyssenKrupp Asansor Sanayi ve Tic. A.S. (1)
Defne Sokak Buyukhanli Plaza No 3 Kat 3-4, Atasehir, 34750, Istanbul, Turkiye
Tel.: (90) 216 571 3700
Web Site: http://www.thyssenkrupp-asansor.com
Elevator Mfr
N.A.I.C.S.: 333921
Tunay Isdas (Gen Mgr)

ThyssenKrupp Ascenseurs Luxembourg S.a.r.l. (1)
5 Laiteschbaach, 5324, Contern, Luxembourg
Tel.: (352) 40 08 96
Web Site: http://www.thyssenkrupp-elevator.com
Lift & Escalator Mfr
N.A.I.C.S.: 333921

ThyssenKrupp Ascenseurs S.A.S. (1)
Rue De Champfleur Zi, Saint-Barthelemy, 49001, Angers, Cedex, France
Tel.: (33) 800240020
Web Site: https://www.tkelevator.com
Elevator Mfr
N.A.I.C.S.: 333921

ThyssenKrupp Aufzuge AG (1)
Glattalstrasse 207, 8153, Rumlang, Switzerland
Tel.: (41) 432111865
Web Site: https://www.tkelevator.com
Sales Range: $25-49.9 Million
Emp.: 50
Elevator & Escalator Distr

INTERNATIONAL PUBLIC

N.A.I.C.S.: 423830

ThyssenKrupp Aufzuge Gesellschaft m.b.H. (1)
Zetschegasse 11, 1230, Vienna, Austria
Tel.: (43) 18651182
Web Site: http://www.thyssenkrupp-aufzuege.at
Elevator Mfr
N.A.I.C.S.: 333921

ThyssenKrupp Aufzuge Ltd. (1)
The Lookout 4 Bull Close Road, Lenton, Nottingham, NG7 2UL, United Kingdom
Tel.: (44) 1159868213
Elevator Mfr
N.A.I.C.S.: 333921

ThyssenKrupp Aufzuge Norge A/S (1)
Brobekkveien 38, Oslo, 0598, Norway
Tel.: (47) 23173700
Sales Range: $25-49.9 Million
Emp.: 8
Lift & Escalator Mfr
N.A.I.C.S.: 333921

ThyssenKrupp Aufzugswerke GmbH (1)
Bernhauser Strasse 45, PO Box 230370, 73765, Neuhausen, Germany
Tel.: (49) 711652220
Web Site: http://www.thyssenkrupp-aufzuege.de
Sales Range: $400-449.9 Million
Emp.: 1,500
Elevator Mfr
N.A.I.C.S.: 333921

ThyssenKrupp Aufzugswerke Konstruktions GmbH (1)
Harter Str 1a, 8101, Gratkorn, Austria
Tel.: (43) 3124239000
Elevator Mfr
N.A.I.C.S.: 333921

ThyssenKrupp Austria GmbH (1)
Tenschertstr 3, 1230, Vienna, Austria
Tel.: (43) 16150600
Steel Product Distr
N.A.I.C.S.: 423510

ThyssenKrupp Automotive Sales & Technical Center, Inc. (1)
3331W Big Beaver Rd Ste 300, Troy, MI 48084
Tel.: (248) 530-2900
Web Site: http://www.thyssenkrupp.com
Sales Range: $25-49.9 Million
Emp.: 14
Automobile Parts Distr
N.A.I.C.S.: 423140

ThyssenKrupp Automotive Systems Industrial do Brasil Ltda. (1)
Avenida Piraporinha 777 C Bairro Planalto, Sao Bernardo do Campo, 09891-001, Sao Paulo, Brazil
Tel.: (55) 11 2172 6000
Motor Vehicle Parts Mfr
N.A.I.C.S.: 336390

ThyssenKrupp Automotive Systems de Mexico S.A. de C.V. (1)
Parque Industrial Finsa No 200 Nave 11, Cuautlancingo, 72710, Puebla, Mexico
Tel.: (52) 2226221010
Motor Vehicle Parts Mfr
N.A.I.C.S.: 336390

ThyssenKrupp Bauservice GmbH (1)
Ottostrasse 30, 41836, Huckelhoven, Germany
Tel.: (49) 2433 45 30
Web Site: http://www.thyssenkruppbauservice.com
Construction Machinery Mfr
N.A.I.C.S.: 333120

ThyssenKrupp Bilstein of America Inc. (1)
8685 Bilstein Blvd, Hamilton, OH 45015
Tel.: (513) 881-7600
Web Site: http://www.bilsteinus.com
Sales Range: $125-149.9 Million
Emp.: 675
Motor Vehicle Parts Mfr & Distr
N.A.I.C.S.: 336390

AND PRIVATE COMPANIES — THYSSENKRUPP AG

ThyssenKrupp Bouwsystemen B. V. (1)
Newtonstraat 35, 3902 HP, Veenendaal, Utrecht, Netherlands
Tel.: (31) 8544644
Sales Range: $50-74.9 Million
Emp.: 10
Construction Materials Whslr
N.A.I.C.S.: 423390
Ronnie Schiltmans (Mgr)

ThyssenKrupp Byggesystem A/S (1)
Mercurvej 12 A, PO Box 19, 9530, Stovring, Denmark
Tel.: (45) 7021 7788
Web Site: http://www.thyssenkrupp-byg.dk
Sales Range: $50-74.9 Million
Emp.: 7
Construction Materials Distr
N.A.I.C.S.: 423390
Per Roddik (Mng Dir)

ThyssenKrupp Cadillac Plastic S.A.S. (1)
13 Rue Rene Cassin Z A C La Villette Aux Aulnes, 77290, Mitry-Mory, France
Tel.: (33) 1 64 67 44 24
Web Site: http://www.tk-cadillacplastic.fr
Sales Range: $50-74.9 Million
Emp.: 120
Plastic Materials Mfr
N.A.I.C.S.: 325211
Marc Schlett (Pres)

ThyssenKrupp Canada, Inc. (1)
4838 Richard Road Suite 400, Calgary, T3E 6L1, AB, Canada
Tel.: (403) 209-4444
Web Site: http://www.thyssenkrupp.com
Rev.: $1,123,181,500
Emp.: 2,300
Elevator Installation Services
N.A.I.C.S.: 238290

ThyssenKrupp Christon N.V. (1)
Brandstraat 11 Industriepark E17/3, Lokeren, 9160, Belgium
Tel.: (32) 9 349 3635
Web Site: http://www.tkchriston.be
Emp.: 65
Steel Product Distr
N.A.I.C.S.: 423510
Wim Claessens (Gen Mgr)

ThyssenKrupp Comercial Colombia S.A. (1)
Calle 33 Nr 6b-24 Piso 8, Bogota, Colombia
Tel.: (57) 13384055
Sales Range: $25-49.9 Million
Emp.: 40
Motor Vehicle Parts Mfr
N.A.I.C.S.: 336390
Juan Manuel Alvarado Baquero (Gen Mgr)

ThyssenKrupp DeliCate GmbH (1)
thyssenkrupp Allee 1, 45143, Essen, Germany
Tel.: (49) 201844553661
Web Site: https://www.thyssenkrupp-delicate.com
Catering Management Services
N.A.I.C.S.: 722320

ThyssenKrupp Elevator (CENE) Infrastruktur GmbH (1)
Fasanenweg 11, Leinfelden-Echterdingen, 70771, Germany
Tel.: (49) 7158122399
Web Site: http://www.thyssenkrupp.com
Elevator Mfr
N.A.I.C.S.: 333921

ThyssenKrupp Elevator Bergen (1)
Jordalsveien 17, Asane, 5105, Bergen, Norway
Tel.: (47) 21979701
Web Site: https://www.tkelevator.com
Emp.: 45
Elevator Installation Services
N.A.I.C.S.: 238290

ThyssenKrupp Encasa AS (1)
Brobekkveien 38, 0598, Oslo, Norway
Tel.: (47) 21979700
Web Site: http://www.tk-encasa.no
Platform Lift & Stairlift Distr
N.A.I.C.S.: 423830
Wenche Hadland Bergersen (Office Mgr)

ThyssenKrupp Encasa N.V. (1)
Kaleweg 20, Mariakerke, 9030, Gent, Belgium
Tel.: (32) 9 216 65 65
Web Site: http://www.tk-traplift.be
Sales Range: $25-49.9 Million
Emp.: 50
Platform Lift & Chairlift Distr
N.A.I.C.S.: 423830

ThyssenKrupp Encasa S.L. (1)
C/Haya 4, 28044, Madrid, Spain
Tel.: (34) 91 492 22 92
Web Site: http://www.salvaescaleras.com
Platform Lift & Chairlift Distr
N.A.I.C.S.: 423830

ThyssenKrupp Engine Components (China) Co., Ltd. (1)
Room 502 Hi-tech Innovation Service Center 391 East Tianyuan Road, Jiangning, Nanjing, 211100, China
Tel.: (86) 2566666028
Web Site: http://www.thyssenkrupp-forginggroup.com
Sales Range: $100-124.9 Million
Emp.: 300
Engine Component Mfr
N.A.I.C.S.: 333618

ThyssenKrupp Engineering (Proprietary) Ltd. (1)
71 Nanyuki Road, Sunninghill, Johannesburg, 2157, South Africa
Tel.: (27) 11 236 1000
Web Site: http://www.thyssenkrupp-engineering.co.za
Sales Range: $50-74.9 Million
Emp.: 200
Mining & Extraction Equipment Mfr
N.A.I.C.S.: 333131

ThyssenKrupp Fahrtreppen GmbH (1)
Kolumbusstrasse 8, 22113, Hamburg, Germany
Tel.: (49) 40731170
Web Site: http://www.thyssenkrupp-escalator.com
Escalator Mfr
N.A.I.C.S.: 333921

ThyssenKrupp Fawer Liaoyang Spring Co., Ltd. (1)
168 Shuangsheng Road, 111000, Liaoyang, 111000, China
Tel.: (86) 4192190298
Web Site: http://www.thyssenkrupp.com
Emp.: 600
Coil Spring Mfr
N.A.I.C.S.: 332613

ThyssenKrupp Federn GmbH (1)
Oeger Strasse 85, PO Box 5241, 58119, Hagen, Germany
Tel.: (49) 233450495533
Web Site: http://www.thyssenkrupp.com
Sales Range: $50-74.9 Million
Emp.: 250
Motor Vehicle Suspension Mfr
N.A.I.C.S.: 336330

ThyssenKrupp Ferostav, spol. s r.o. (1)
Turbinova 1, Bratislava, 831 04, Slovakia
Tel.: (421) 2 44 37 37 37
Web Site: http://www.ferostav.sk
Steel Products Mfr
N.A.I.C.S.: 331513
Krcova Anna (Bus Mgr)

ThyssenKrupp Finance Nederland B.V. (1)
Van Utrechtweg 99, 2921 LN, Krimpen aan de Ijssel, Netherlands
Tel.: (31) 180530811
Financial Management Services
N.A.I.C.S.: 523999

ThyssenKrupp Finance USA, Inc. (1)
3155 W Big Beaver Rd, Troy, MI 48084-3002
Tel.: (248) 643-3500
Financial Management Services
N.A.I.C.S.: 523999

ThyssenKrupp Galmed, S.A. (1)
Carretera Acceso IV Planta km 3 9, 46520, Sagunto, Spain
Tel.: (34) 961129600
Web Site: http://www.thyssenkrupp-galmed.com
Automotive Steel Parts Distr
N.A.I.C.S.: 423140

ThyssenKrupp Gerlach GmbH (1)
Neue Industriestrasse, 66424, Homburg, Germany
Tel.: (49) 6841 107 0
Web Site: http://www.thyssenkruppgerlach.com
Crankshaft & Engine Component Mfr
N.A.I.C.S.: 336310

ThyssenKrupp GfT Gleistechnik GmbH (1)
Thyssenkrupp Allee 1, 45143, Essen, Germany
Tel.: (49) 2018440
Web Site: https://www.tkgftgleistechnik.de
Railroad Construction & Maintenance Services
N.A.I.C.S.: 237990

ThyssenKrupp GfT Polska Sp. z o.o. (1)
Al Slowackiego 66, 30-004, Krakow, Poland
Tel.: (48) 12 62 04 130
Web Site: http://www.thyssenkruppgft.pl
Railroad Construction & Maintenance Services
N.A.I.C.S.: 237990

ThyssenKrupp GfT Tiefbautechnik GmbH (1)
Alte Liederbacher Strasse 6, 36304, Alsfeld, Germany
Tel.: (49) 66317810
Web Site: http://www.thyssenkrupp-tiefbautechnik.com
Sales Range: $50-74.9 Million
Emp.: 80
Construction Machinery Distr
N.A.I.C.S.: 423810
Johannes Kocher (Member-Exec Bd)

ThyssenKrupp Grundbesitz-Vermietungs GmbH & Co. KG (1)
Altendorfer Str 120, 45143, Essen, Germany
Tel.: (49) 201 188 0
Real Estate Manangement Services
N.A.I.C.S.: 531390

ThyssenKrupp HiServ s.r.o. (1)
Hroncova 13/3, 040 01, Kosice, Slovakia
Tel.: (421) 55 632 41 01
Iron & Steel Mfr
N.A.I.C.S.: 331110

ThyssenKrupp Industrial Services NA, Inc. (1)
22355 W 11 Mile Rd, Southfield, MI 48033
Tel.: (248) 233-5750
Sales Range: $25-49.9 Million
Emp.:
Supply Chain Management Services
N.A.I.C.S.: 541614

ThyssenKrupp Industrial Solutions (South Africa) Pty Ltd. (1)
71 Nanyuki Road, Sunninghill, Johannesburg, 2191, South Africa
Tel.: (27) 11 236 1000
Web Site: http://www.thyssenkrupp-industrial-solutions.co.za
Emp.: 400
Engineering & Technological Services
N.A.I.C.S.: 541330

ThyssenKrupp Industrial Solutions (USA), Inc. (1)
1370 Washington Pike, Bridgeville, PA 15017
Tel.: (412) 257-8277
Web Site: http://www.thyssenkrupp-industrial-solutions.com
Engineering Services
N.A.I.C.S.: 541330

ThyssenKrupp Industries India Pvt. Ltd. (1)
Pimpri Chowk Near Ksp Pumps, Pimpri, 411018, Pune, India
Tel.: (91) 20 27425461
Web Site: http://www.thyssenkrupp-industries-india.com
Sales Range: $400-449.9 Million
Emp.: 150
Industrial Machinery Mfr
N.A.I.C.S.: 333248
Vivek Bhatia (Mng Dir & CEO)

ThyssenKrupp Ingenieria Chile Ltda. (1)
Nueva de Lyon 72 Oficina 1502 Providencia, Santiago, Chile
Tel.: (56) 2 244 2299
Web Site: http://www.tkic.cl
Emp.: 100
Mining Machinery & Equipment Distr
N.A.I.C.S.: 423810

ThyssenKrupp Italia Holding S.r.l. (1)
V Cristoforo Colombo, Rome, 00125, Italy
Tel.: (39) 063243220
Investment Management Service
N.A.I.C.S.: 523999

ThyssenKrupp KH Mineral S.A.S. (1)
1 rue Rene Francois Jolly, Sarreguemines establishment Parc Industriel Sud - ZI Neuwald, 57200, Sarreguemines, France
Tel.: (33) 387987372
Web Site: http://www.khmineral.com
Emp.: 100
Industrial Machinery Installation Services
N.A.I.C.S.: 238290

ThyssenKrupp Lift Kft (1)
Korvasut sor 110, 1158, Budapest, Hungary
Tel.: (36) 1 239 5915
Web Site: http://thyssenkrupp-lift.hu
Emp.: 50
Elevator Installation Services
N.A.I.C.S.: 238290

ThyssenKrupp Liften Ascenseurs n.v.-s.a. (1)
Avenue de la Metrologielaan 10, 1130, Brussels, Belgium
Tel.: (32) 78158282
Web Site: http://www.thyssenkruppliften.be
Sales Range: $25-49.9 Million
Emp.: 65
Elevator Installation Services
N.A.I.C.S.: 238290

ThyssenKrupp Liften B.V. (1)
Fascinatio Boulevard 806-808, 2909 VA, Capelle aan den IJssel, Netherlands
Tel.: (31) 884479200
Web Site: http://www.thyssenkruppliften.nl
Emp.: 300
Elevator Installation Services
N.A.I.C.S.: 238290

ThyssenKrupp Logistics, Inc. (1)
8001 ThyssenKrupp Pkwy, Northwood, OH 43619
Tel.: (419) 662-1800
Web Site: http://www.tkmna.com
Logistics Consulting Servies
N.A.I.C.S.: 541614

ThyssenKrupp Management Consulting GmbH (1)
Thyssenkrupp Allee 1, 45143, Essen, Germany
Tel.: (49) 201844534915
Web Site: http://www.thyssenkrupp-management-consulting.com
Business Management Consulting Services
N.A.I.C.S.: 541611
Alexander Bose (Principal)

ThyssenKrupp Mannex Pty. Ltd. (1)
Level 1 267 Pacific Highway, PO Box 21 03, North Sydney, 2060, NSW, Australia
Tel.: (61) 2 99 55 09 78
Web Site: http://www.thyssen-mannesmann-handel.de
Sales Range: $25-49.9 Million
Emp.: 20
Steel Pipe & Tube Distr
N.A.I.C.S.: 331210
Joachim Koch (Mng Dir)

ThyssenKrupp Mannex Sverige AB (1)
Ekonomivagen 3, Askim, 436 33, Gothenburg, Sweden
Tel.: (46) 31 8 00 120
Web Site: http://www.tk-mannex.se
Sales Range: $25-49.9 Million
Emp.: 5
Steel Products Mfr
N.A.I.C.S.: 331110

THYSSENKRUPP AG

ThyssenKrupp AG—(Continued)

ThyssenKrupp Mannex UK Ltd. (1)
Unit 1 Woking 8 Forsyth Rd, Woking, GU21 5SB, United Kingdom
Tel.: (44) 1483 72 65 21
Web Site: http://www.thyssenkrupp.com
Sales Range: $25-49.9 Million
Emp.: 16
Carbon Steel & Steel Tubular Product Distr
N.A.I.C.S.: 423510
Irene Darcy *(Mgr)*

ThyssenKrupp Materials (Thailand) Co., Ltd. (1)
94 Moo 6 Suksawad78 Rd, Phrapradaeng Bangjak, 10130, Samut Prakan, Thailand
Tel.: (66) 2 840 4599
Web Site: http://www.thyssenkruppmaterials.co.th
Steel Products Mfr
N.A.I.C.S.: 331110

ThyssenKrupp Materials Austria GmbH (1)
Freudenauer Hafenstrasse 26, Postfach 55, 1024, Vienna, Austria
Tel.: (43) 1727310
Web Site: https://www.thyssenkrupp-materials.at
Steel Product Distr
N.A.I.C.S.: 423510

ThyssenKrupp Materials France S.A.S. (1)
Central warehouse Commercial agency Zone d'Activite Pariwest - 6, avenue Gutenberg CS 40509, 78317, Maurepas, France
Tel.: (33) 130696700
Sales Range: $150-199.9 Million
Emp.: 500
Steel & Non Ferrous Products Distr
N.A.I.C.S.: 423510
Serge Marie Weber *(Pres)*

ThyssenKrupp Materials Holding (Thailand) Ltd. (1)
94 Moo 6 Suksawad 78 Road, Phra Pradaeng, 10130, Samut Prakan, Thailand
Tel.: (66) 2 840 4599
Web Site: http://www.thyssenkruppmaterials.co.th
Iron & Steel Mfr
N.A.I.C.S.: 331110

ThyssenKrupp Materials Iberica S.A.U. (1)
Central Warehouse Carregado Apartado 32 Quinta do Peixoto, 2584-908, Carregado, Portugal
Tel.: (351) 263850100
Web Site: https://www.thyssenkrupp-materials.es
Steel Products Whslr
N.A.I.C.S.: 331513

Division (Domestic):

ThyssenKrupp Portugal - Acos e Servicos, Lda. - Non-Ferrous-Metals Division (2)
445 Hue Rua 1 Da Zona Industrial De 265, 4524-907, Rio Meao, Portugal
Tel.: (351) 263 731 300
Web Site: http://www.thyssenkrupp-portugal.com
Nonferrous Metal Products Mfr
N.A.I.C.S.: 331491

Subsidiary (Domestic):

ThyssenKrupp Tratamentos Termicos (2)
Apartado 230 Pero Neto, 2431-903, Marinha Grande, Portugal
Tel.: (351) 244 573 460
Web Site: http://www.thyssenkrupp-portugal.com
Metal Heat Treating Services
N.A.I.C.S.: 332811
Gaeme Casal *(Mng Dir)*

ThyssenKrupp Materials Korea Company Ltd. (1)
1602 Ace High End Tower 3 145 Gasan Digital 1-ro, Geumcheon-gu, Seoul, Korea (South)
Tel.: (82) 232836625
Web Site: https://www.thyssenkrupp-materials.co.kr
Sales Range: $25-49.9 Million
Emp.: 48
Aluminum Coil & Sheet Mfr
N.A.I.C.S.: 331315

ThyssenKrupp Materials Nederland B.V. (1)
Taylorweg 7, 5466 AE, Veghel, Netherlands
Tel.: (31) 413348900
Web Site: https://www.thyssenkrupp-materials.nl
Emp.: 150
Steel & Nonferrous Products Distr
N.A.I.C.S.: 423510

ThyssenKrupp Materials Poland SA (1)
Grudziadzka 159, 87-100, Torun, Poland
Tel.: (48) 56 611 9494
Web Site: https://www.thyssenkrupp-materials.pl
Steel & Nonferrous Metal Mfr
N.A.I.C.S.: 331513
Ryszard Bojarski *(Chm-Mgmt Bd)*

ThyssenKrupp Materials Romania S.R.L. (1)
256 Basarabia Blv, 030352, Bucharest, Romania
Tel.: (40) 213801006
Web Site: http://www.thyssenkrupp-materials.ro
Emp.: 75
Steel Products Mfr
N.A.I.C.S.: 331110

ThyssenKrupp Materials Schweiz AG (1)
Industriestrasse 20, 9501, Bronschhofen, Switzerland
Tel.: (41) 71 913 64 00
Web Site: http://www.thyssenkrupp-materials.ch
Steel & Nonferrous Metal Distr
N.A.I.C.S.: 423510

ThyssenKrupp Materials Sverige AB (1)
Dagjamningsgatan 2, Gothenburg, 41509, Sweden
Tel.: (46) 31 337 79 00
Web Site: http://www.thyssenkrupp.se
Sales Range: $25-49.9 Million
Emp.: 50
Nonferrous Metal Product Distr
N.A.I.C.S.: 423510

ThyssenKrupp Materials Switzerland AG (1)
Industriestrasse 20, PO Box 40, 9501, Bronschhofen, Switzerland
Tel.: (41) 719136400
Web Site: https://www.thyssenkrupp-materials.ch
Steel & Nonferrous Metal Distr
N.A.I.C.S.: 423510

ThyssenKrupp Materials Vietnam LLC (1)
Lot L5 Pho Noi B Textile and Garment Industrial Park, Di Su commune, Hung Yen, Vietnam
Tel.: (84) 2213766700
Web Site: http://www.tkmvietnam.com.vn
Steel & Nonferrous Metal Mfr
N.A.I.C.S.: 331110

ThyssenKrupp Materials d.o.o. (1)
Save Kovacevica bb, 22320, Indija, Serbia
Tel.: (381) 22520500
Web Site: https://www.thyssenkrupp-materials.rs
Sales Range: $50-74.9 Million
Emp.: 49
Steel Product Distr
N.A.I.C.S.: 423510

ThyssenKrupp Materials, LLC (1)
6811 S 204th St Ste 400, Kent, WA 98032
Tel.: (253) 239-5756
Web Site: http://www.thyssenkruppaerospace.com
Aircraft Mfr
N.A.I.C.S.: 336411

ThyssenKrupp MetalServ GmbH (1)
ThyssenKrupp Allee 1, PO Box 103817, 45143, Essen, Germany
Tel.: (49) 201 844 537280
Web Site: http://www.thyssenkrupp-metalserv.com
Steel & Nonferrous Metal Mfr
N.A.I.C.S.: 331110
Achim Boner *(Head-Product Mgmt-Tubes & Pipes)*

ThyssenKrupp Metallurgical Products Co., Ltd. Tianjin (1)
14A The International Development Building No 2 Dongting Road TEDA, Tianjin, 300457, China
Tel.: (86) 22 25288900
Web Site: http://www.thyssenkrupp.com
Metallurgical Product Mfr
N.A.I.C.S.: 331110

ThyssenKrupp Metalurgica Santa Luzia Ltda. (1)
Av Dr Angelo Teixeira da Costa N 2164 D l Carreira Comprida, Santa Luzia, 33045-170, Minas Gerais, Brazil
Tel.: (55) 3136495005
Crankshaft & Engine Component Mfr
N.A.I.C.S.: 336310

ThyssenKrupp Metalurgica Servicios S.A. de C.V. (1)
Camino A Santa Agueda No 1, 72620, San Miguel Xoxlta, Puebla, Mexico
Tel.: (52) 2222237000
Sales Range: $100-124.9 Million
Emp.: 450
Motor Vehicle Parts Mfr
N.A.I.C.S.: 336390

ThyssenKrupp Mexinox CreateIT, S.A. de C.V. (1)
Av Industrias No 4100 Zona Industrial 1a Seccion, 78395, San Luis Potosi, Mexico
Tel.: (52) 444 8 265 113
Web Site: http://www.thyssenkrupp.com
Sales Range: $150-199.9 Million
Emp.: 980
Software Development Services
N.A.I.C.S.: 541511

ThyssenKrupp MillServices & Systems GmbH (1)
Emschertalstrasse 12, 46149, Oberhausen, Germany
Tel.: (49) 20 865 6050
Web Site: https://www.thyssenkrupp-mss.com
Engineering Services
N.A.I.C.S.: 541330
Jorg Schurmann *(CEO & Mng Dir-Plant Svcs & Tech)*

ThyssenKrupp Nederland B.V. (1)
Taylorweg 7, Veghel, 5466 AE, Netherlands
Tel.: (31) 413 34 83 26
Web Site: http://www.thyssenkrupp.nl
Emp.: 3
Financial Support Services
N.A.I.C.S.: 523999

ThyssenKrupp Nederland Holding B.V. (1)
Taylorweg 7, 5466 AE, Veghel, Netherlands
Tel.: (31) 413348900
Sales Range: $100-124.9 Million
Emp.: 120
Investment Management Service
N.A.I.C.S.: 523999

ThyssenKrupp Nederland Intermediate B.V. (1)
Taylorweg 7, 5466 AE, Veghel, Netherlands
Tel.: (31) 413348900
Web Site: http://www.thyssenkrupp.com
Emp.: 160
Elevator Installation Services
N.A.I.C.S.: 238290

ThyssenKrupp Norte S.A. (1)
Pol Ind La Pereda s/n, Asturias, 33682, Mieres, Spain
Tel.: (34) 985446804
Web Site: http://www.thyssenkrupp.com
Sales Range: $100-124.9 Million
Emp.: 300
Escalator & Moving Stairway Mfr
N.A.I.C.S.: 333921

ThyssenKrupp OnlineMetals, LLC (1)
1138 W Ewing, Seattle, WA 98119

INTERNATIONAL PUBLIC

Tel.: (206) 285-8603
Web Site: http://www.onlinemetals.com
Metal & Plastic Product Distr
N.A.I.C.S.: 423510

ThyssenKrupp Otto Wolff N.V./S.A (1)
Park Ragheno Dellingstraat 57, Mechelen, 2800, Belgium
Tel.: (32) 15 453225
Web Site: http://www.thyssenkrupp-ottowolff.be
Sales Range: $25-49.9 Million
Emp.: 40
Plastic Product Whslr
N.A.I.C.S.: 424610

ThyssenKrupp Participations B.V. (1)
Taylorweg 7, 5466 AE, Veghel, Netherlands
Tel.: (31) 413348326
Steel Products Mfr
N.A.I.C.S.: 331110

ThyssenKrupp Plastic Iberica SL (1)
Poligono Industrial L'Estacio Frente estacion Renfe s/n, 46560, Massalfassar, Valencia, Spain
Tel.: (34) 900929908
Web Site: http://www.thyssenkrupp-plastics.es
Plastic Material Mfr & Distr
N.A.I.C.S.: 325211

ThyssenKrupp Plastics Austria GmbH (1)
Kornspitzstrasse 5a, 4481, Asten, Austria
Tel.: (43) 7229730210
Web Site: http://www.thyssenkrupp-plastics.at
Emp.: 50
Plastic Product Mfr & Distr
N.A.I.C.S.: 326199
Frank Schneider *(Gen Mgr)*

ThyssenKrupp Polysius AG (1)
Graf-Galen-Strasse 17, 59269, Beckum, Germany
Tel.: (49) 2525 99 0
Web Site: http://www.polysius.com
Sales Range: $25-49.9 Million
Emp.: 100
Engineeering Services
N.A.I.C.S.: 541330
Niclas Muller *(Chm-Supervisory Bd)*

Subsidiary (Non-US):

Polysius S.A.S. (2)
Departmental Road 113 intersection chemin de la Pourranque, CS 30036, 13170, Les Pennes-Mirabeau, France
Tel.: (33) 970823055
Web Site: https://www.polysius.fr
Sales Range: $50-74.9 Million
Cement Plant Construction Services
N.A.I.C.S.: 236210

ThyssenKrupp Presta Chemnitz GmbH (1)
Heinrich-Lorenz-Strasse 57, 09120, Chemnitz, Germany
Tel.: (49) 371278680
Web Site: https://karriere.thyssenkrupp.com
Sales Range: $50-74.9 Million
Emp.: 160
Automotive Engine Parts Mfr
N.A.I.C.S.: 336310

ThyssenKrupp Presta Dalian Co. Ltd. (1)
No 22 Taihe Street Dalian Development Area, 116600, Dalian, China
Tel.: (86) 411 3922 5888
Web Site: http://www.thyssenkrupp-presta-camshafts.com
Motor Vehicle Parts Mfr
N.A.I.C.S.: 336390

ThyssenKrupp Presta Esslingen GmbH (1)
Alleenstrasse 28-30, Esslingen, 73730, Germany
Tel.: (49) 71167310111
Web Site: http://www.thyssenkrupp-presta.com
Motor Vehicle Steering Mfr & Distr
N.A.I.C.S.: 336330
Sabine Scamoni *(Head-HR)*

AND PRIVATE COMPANIES — THYSSENKRUPP AG

ThyssenKrupp Presta France S.A.S. (1)
Z I Ste Agathe 8 Rue Lavoisier, BP 70001, 57192, Florange, Cedex, France
Tel.: (33) 382 82 53 53
Web Site: http://karriere.thyssenkrupp-presta.com
Motor Vehicle Steering Mfr & Distr
N.A.I.C.S.: 336330
Fernand Kiren *(Head-HR)*

ThyssenKrupp Presta Ilsenburg GmbH (1)
Trift 1, 38871, Ilsenburg, Germany
Tel.: (49) 394528006
Motor Vehicle Parts Mfr
N.A.I.C.S.: 336390

ThyssenKrupp Presta Shanghai Co. Ltd. (1)
268 Miaoqiao Road, Shanghai, 201206, China
Tel.: (86) 2161592343
Motor Vehicle Steering Mfr
N.A.I.C.S.: 336330

ThyssenKrupp Presta TecCenter AG (1)
Wirtschaftspark 37, 9492, Eschen, Liechtenstein
Tel.: (423) 399 7000
Web Site: http://www.thyssenkrupp-presta-camshafts.com
Sales Range: $50-74.9 Million
Emp.: 230
Motor Vehicle Parts Mfr
N.A.I.C.S.: 336390
Frank Altag *(CEO)*

ThyssenKrupp Presta Terre Haute, LLC (1)
1597 E Industrial Dr, Terre Haute, IN 47802
Tel.: (812) 299-5002
Motor Vehicle Parts Mfr
N.A.I.C.S.: 336330

ThyssenKrupp Rasselstein GmbH (1)
Koblenzer Strasse 141, 56626, Andernach, Germany
Tel.: (49) 263230970
Web Site: http://www.thyssenkrupp-rasselstein.com
Sales Range: $400-449.9 Million
Emp.: 2,500
Tin Plate Mfr
N.A.I.C.S.: 331110

ThyssenKrupp Robins Inc. (1)
6400 S Fiddler S Green Cir Ste 700, Greenwood Village, CO 80111-4985
Tel.: (303) 770-0808
Web Site: http://www.thyssenkrupprobins.com
Conveying Equipment Mfr
N.A.I.C.S.: 333922
Ramsis Shehata *(Pres)*

ThyssenKrupp Rulletrapper A/S (1)
Brobekkveien 38, PO Box 6877, Rodelokka, 0504, Oslo, Norway
Tel.: (47) 21979700
Web Site: http://www.rulletrapper.no
Emp.: 27
Escalator Mfr
N.A.I.C.S.: 333921
Torbjorn Endrerud *(CEO)*

ThyssenKrupp SILCO-INOX Szervizkozpont Kft (1)
Gepallomas Ut 5, Batonyterenye, 3078, Hungary
Tel.: (36) 3255 00 10
Steel Product Distr
N.A.I.C.S.: 423510

ThyssenKrupp Sagenstahlcenter GmbH (1)
Auf dem Knapp 36, Remscheid, 42855, Germany
Tel.: (49) 21 91 3 61 0
Web Site: http://www.tks-saegenstahlcenter.de
Emp.: 15
Steel Product Distr
N.A.I.C.S.: 423510
Guido Kochheim *(Mng Dir)*

ThyssenKrupp Sasa Servicios, S.A.de C.V. (1)
Eje 124 No 125, Mexico, 70395, San Luis Potosi, Mexico
Tel.: (52) 444 870 70 08
Web Site: http://www.thyssenkrupp.com
Coil Spring & Stabilizer Bar Mfr
N.A.I.C.S.: 332613

ThyssenKrupp Schulte GmbH (1)
Johanniskirchstr 63, 45329, Essen, Germany
Tel.: (49) 20183680
Web Site: http://www.thyssenkrupp-schulte.de
Steel Product Distr
N.A.I.C.S.: 423510
Ilse Henne *(CEO-Western Europe & Asia Pacific Reg)*

ThyssenKrupp Securitization Corp. (1)
22355 W 11 Mile Rd, Southfield, MI 48033-4735
Tel.: (248) 233-5600
Web Site: http://www.thyssenkrupp.com
Investment Management Service
N.A.I.C.S.: 523940

ThyssenKrupp Services AG (1)
Thyssen Krupp Trade Ctr, 40235, Dusseldorf, Germany (100%)
Tel.: (49) 2119670
Web Site: http://www.thyssenkruppservices.de
Sales Range: $5-14.9 Billion
Emp.: 40,163
Industrial Services
N.A.I.C.S.: 236210

Subsidiary (Non-US):

Cadillac Plastic France S.A.S. (2)
13 Rue Rene Cassin Z AC La Villette aux Aulnes, Mitry-Mory, 77290, Paris, France (60%)
Tel.: (33) 164674400
Web Site: https://www.thyssenkrupp-plastics.fr
Sales Range: $50-74.9 Million
Emp.: 120
Distr of Plastic in Rod, Sheet & Tube Form
N.A.I.C.S.: 424610
Mark Szanurck *(Dir-Fin)*

Subsidiary (Domestic):

ThyssenKrupp Mannex GmbH (2)
Rellinghauser Str 3, Hans Guenther Sohl Strasse 1, 45128, Essen, Germany (100%)
Tel.: (49) 201844563901
Web Site: http://www.tk-mannex.com
Sales Range: $350-399.9 Million
Emp.: 1,848
Stainless Steel Pipe & Piping Components Plastic Tubing & Fittings, Stainless Steel Sheet
N.A.I.C.S.: 331210

Subsidiary (Non-US):

ThyssenKrupp Materials (Shanghai) Co., Ltd. (2)
328 Xinteng Road Songjiang Industrial District, Shanghai, 201612, China
Tel.: (86) 21 57686710
Web Site: http://www.thyssenkrupp-materials-shanghai.com
Sales Range: $25-49.9 Million
Emp.: 40
Metal & Steel Materials Processing Services
N.A.I.C.S.: 331492
Bernd Walosek *(Gen Mgr)*

ThyssenKrupp Materials (UK) Ltd. (2)
Cox's Lane Cradley Heath, Wolverhampton, B64 5QU, West Midlands, United Kingdom
Tel.: (44) 1384563900
Web Site: http://www.thyssenkrupp-materials.co.uk
Emp.: 45
Steel Products Mfr
N.A.I.C.S.: 331510

ThyssenKrupp Materials Iberica S.A. (2)
Pol Ind Martorelles C/ Sant Marti S/N 55-63, 08107, Martorell, Barcelona, Spain
Tel.: (34) 935717400

Web Site: https://www.thyssenkrupp-materials.es
Steel Product Distr
N.A.I.C.S.: 423510

Division (US):

ThyssenKrupp Materials NA (2)
22355 W 11 Mile Rd, Southfield, MI 48033-4735 (100%)
Tel.: (248) 233-5600
Web Site: http://www.tkmna.thyssenkrupp.com
Sales Range: $50-74.9 Million
Emp.: 100
Steel Mfrs
N.A.I.C.S.: 423510
Norbert Goertz *(CFO & Exec VP)*

Subsidiary (Domestic):

Ain Plastics, Inc. (3)
60 Fullerton Ave, Yonkers, NY 10704
Tel.: (203) 265-1567
Web Site: http://www.ainplastics.com
Emp.: 20
Wholesale Distributor of Plastics
N.A.I.C.S.: 423510

Copper & Brass Sales, Inc. (3)
22355 W 11 Mile Rd, Southfield, MI 48033
Tel.: (248) 233-5700
Web Site: http://www.copperandbrass.com
Wholesale Non Ferrous Metals Manufacture Tubular Parts Assemblies
N.A.I.C.S.: 423510
Mark Yonick *(CFO)*

Ken-Mac Metals, Inc. (3)
17901 Englewood Dr, Cleveland, OH 44130-3454
Tel.: (440) 234-7500
Web Site: http://www.kenmacmetals.com
Aluminum & Stainless Metals Service Center
N.A.I.C.S.: 423510
Tim Yost *(Pres-Coil Processing Grp)*

ThyssenKrupp Airport Systems Inc. (3)
3201 N Sylvania Ave Ste 117, Fort Worth, TX 76111-3117
Tel.: (817) 210-5000
Web Site: http://www.thyssenkrupp-elevator.com
Bridge & Gate Machinery Hydraulic Mfr
N.A.I.C.S.: 333998

Subsidiary (Non-US):

ThyssenKrupp Industrial Services Canada, Inc. (3)
2480 Seminole St, Windsor, N8Y 1X3, ON, Canada
Tel.: (519) 977-8420
Web Site: http://www.tkisna.com
Industrial Management Services
N.A.I.C.S.: 541611

ThyssenKrupp Materials CA Ltd. (3)
2821 Langstaff Road, Concord, L4K 5C6, ON, Canada
Tel.: (905) 669-0247
Web Site: http://www.thyssenkrupp.com
Steel Products Mfr & Distr
N.A.I.C.S.: 331110

Subsidiary (Domestic):

ThyssenKrupp Precision Forge Inc. (3)
500 Oak Tree Dr, Selma, NC 27576-3544
Tel.: (919) 965-5555
Sales Range: $50-74.9 Million
Machine Tools Metal Forming Type Mfr
N.A.I.C.S.: 333517

Subsidiary (Non-US):

ThyssenKrupp Palmers Ltd. (2)
Access House Aviation Park Flint Road, Coventry Business Park, Chester, CH4 0GZ, United Kingdom (100%)
Tel.: (44) 1244747777
Web Site: https://palmersgroup.co.uk
Sales Range: $25-49.9 Million
Emp.: 25
Mfr & Supplier of Scaffolding, Access Equipment & Related Products & Services for the Construction Industry
N.A.I.C.S.: 423810

ThyssenKrupp Servicios S.A. de C.V. (1)
Sierra Gamon No 120, Mexico, 11000, Mexico
Tel.: (52) 5552840150
Metal Service Center Operator
N.A.I.C.S.: 423510

ThyssenKrupp Stahl Immobilien GmbH (1)
Thyssenkrupp Allee 1, Essen, 45143, Nordrhein-Westfalen, Germany
Tel.: (49) 2011882178
Web Site: http://www.thyssenkrupp.com
Emp.: 30
Steel Building Construction Services
N.A.I.C.S.: 238120

ThyssenKrupp Stahlkontor GmbH (1)
Konigsberger Strasse 80, 40231, Dusseldorf, Germany
Tel.: (49) 2117359293
Web Site: http://www.thyssenkrupp-stahlkontor.de
Rolled Steel Products Mfr & Distr
N.A.I.C.S.: 331513

ThyssenKrupp Stahlunion Polska Sp. z o.o. (1)
Ul Piastowska 7, Katowice, 40005, Poland
Tel.: (48) 32 2 01 08 54
Web Site: http://www.thyssenkrupp.com
Steel Product Distr
N.A.I.C.S.: 423510

ThyssenKrupp Stainless AG (1)
thyssenkrupp Allee 1, 45143, Essen, Germany (100%)
Tel.: (49) 2018440
Web Site: http://www.thyssenkrupp-stainless.com
Emp.: 12,000
Steel Mfrs
N.A.I.C.S.: 331513

Subsidiary (Non-US):

Acciai Speciali Terni S.p.A. (2)
V Le B Brin 218, 05100, Terni, Italy
Tel.: (39) 0744 4901
Web Site: https://www.acciaiterni.it
Emp.: 2,300
Flat Rolled Stainless Steel Products Mfr
N.A.I.C.S.: 331513
Massimiliano Burelli *(CEO)*

Subsidiary (Non-US):

Deutsche Titan GmbH (3)
Westendstr 15, 45143, Essen, Germany (100%)
Tel.: (49) 2011882245
Sales Range: $10-24.9 Million
Emp.: 200
Steel Mfrs
N.A.I.C.S.: 331513

Greening Donald Co. Ltd. (3)
16 Commerce Rd, Orangeville, L9W 2X7, ON, Canada (100%)
Tel.: (519) 941-1920
Web Site: http://www.greendon.com
Sales Range: $50-74.9 Million
Emp.: 250
Air Bag Components Mfr
N.A.I.C.S.: 336390

Martinrea Fabco (3)
3210 Langstaff Road, Vaughan, L4K 5B2, ON, Canada (100%)
Tel.: (416) 749-0314
Sales Range: $50-74.9 Million
Emp.: 150
Fabricated Steel Products & Hydroforming
N.A.I.C.S.: 331513

Silco Inox Kft (3)
Gepallomas Ut 5, 3078, Batonyterenye, Hungary (100%)
Tel.: (36) 32550010
Web Site: https://www.silcoinox.hu
Steel Products Mfr
N.A.I.C.S.: 331110

Thyssen Krupp Stainless DVP S.A. (3)
Pol Ind De La Zona Francac 62 N 3, 8040, Barcelona, Spain (100%)
Tel.: (34) 932983100

THYSSENKRUPP AG — INTERNATIONAL PUBLIC

ThyssenKrupp AG—(Continued)
Web Site: http://www.thyssenkrupp-stainless.com
Sales Range: $25-49.9 Million
Emp.: 100
Steel Mfrs
N.A.I.C.S.: 331513

Subsidiary (Non-US):

ThyssenKrupp Titanium S.p.A. (3)
Viale B Brin 218, 05100, Terni, Italy (100%)
Tel.: (39) 074454541
Mfr of Semi-Finished Products of Titanium & Titanium Alloys
N.A.I.C.S.: 331513

Subsidiary (Non-US):

Thyssenkrup Steel B.V. (3)
Boompjes 40, 3011 XB, Rotterdam, Netherlands (100%)
Tel.: (31) 0104130666
Web Site: http://www.thyssenkrupp.nl
Sales Range: $25-49.9 Million
Emp.: 4
Steel Mfrs
N.A.I.C.S.: 331513

Subsidiary (Domestic):

Tubificio di Terni S.r.l. (3)
Strada di Sabbione 91/A, 05100, Terni, Italy (100%)
Tel.: (39) 07448081
Web Site: http://www.tubiterni.it
Sales Range: $150-199.9 Million
Emp.: 140
Steel Pole Mfr
N.A.I.C.S.: 331513

Subsidiary (US):

ThyssenKrupp AST USA Inc. (2)
222 Bloomingdale Rd, White Plains, NY 10605
Tel.: (914) 428-6010
Sales Range: $25-49.9 Million
Emp.: 20
Steel Mfrs
N.A.I.C.S.: 423510

Subsidiary (Non-US):

ThyssenKrupp Mexinox S.A. de C.V. (2)
Avenida Industrias 4700 Privada Industrial Futura, Warehouse 6 Zona Industrial, 78395, San Luis Potosi, Mexico (100%)
Tel.: (52) 4448265100
Web Site: http://www.mexinox.com.mx
Sales Range: $150-199.9 Million
Emp.: 1,000
Mfr Stainless Steel Cold Rolled Flat Products
N.A.I.C.S.: 331513

Subsidiary (Domestic):

Mexinox Trading S.A. de C.V. (3)
Av Industrias No 4100, Zona Industrial 1a Seccion, 78395, San Luis Potosi, Mexico
Tel.: (52) 4448265100
Web Site: http://www.mexinox.com.mx
Stainless Steel Cold Rolled Flat Products Mfr & Whslr
N.A.I.C.S.: 331221

Subsidiary (Domestic):

ThyssenKrupp Nirosta GmbH (2)
Oberschlesienstrasse 16, Krefeld, 47807, Germany (100%)
Tel.: (49) 21518301
Web Site: http://www.thyssenkrupp-nirosta.de
Sales Range: $1-4.9 Billion
Emp.: 4,100
Steel Mfrs
N.A.I.C.S.: 331513

Plant (Domestic):

Krupp Nirosta GmbH-Werk Dillenburg (3)
Kasseler Strasse, 35683, Dillenburg, Germany (100%)
Tel.: (49) 2771390327

Web Site: http://www.thyssengroupp-nirosta.de
Sales Range: $150-199.9 Million
Emp.: 700
Steel Mfrs
N.A.I.C.S.: 331513

ThyssenKrupp Werk Dahlerbruck (3)
Volmestrasse 69, 58579, Schalksmuhle, Germany (100%)
Tel.: (49) 2355810
Web Site: http://www.nirofta-precisionstirip.com
Sales Range: $75-99.9 Million
Emp.: 250
Steel Mfrs
N.A.I.C.S.: 331513
Mathias Baerwolf (Gen Mgr)

ThyssenKrupp Werk Krefeld (3)
Oberschlesienstrasse 16, 47807, Krefeld, Germany (100%)
Tel.: (49) 21518301
Web Site: http://www.nirosta.de
Sales Range: $25-49.9 Million
Emp.: 100
Steel Mfrs
N.A.I.C.S.: 331513

ThyssenKrupp Stal Danmark A/S (1)
Agenavej 29-33, 2670, Greve, Denmark
Tel.: (45) 43950700
Web Site: http://www.thyssenkrupp.com
Rolled Steel Product Distr
N.A.I.C.S.: 423510

ThyssenKrupp Stal Serwis Polska Sp. z o.o. (1)
Ul Torunska 7, 41-300, Dabrowa Gornicza, Poland
Tel.: (48) 32 6395 900
Web Site: http://www.thyssenkrupp-stal-serwis-polska.pl
Stainless Steel Service Center Operator
N.A.I.C.S.: 423510

ThyssenKrupp Steel Distribution, LLC (1)
1 Thyssen Park, Detroit, MI 48210
Tel.: (440) 545-9063
Web Site: http://www.thyssenkrupp.com
Rolled Steel Product Distr
N.A.I.C.S.: 423510

ThyssenKrupp Steel Europe AG (1)
Kaiser-Wilhelm-Strasse 100, 47166, Duisburg, Germany (100%)
Tel.: (49) 203520
Web Site: https://www.thyssenkrupp-steel.com
Emp.: 26,000
Specialty Steels & Related Materials Mfr
N.A.I.C.S.: 331513
Arnd Kofler (Member-Exec Bd)

Subsidiary (Non-US):

Fortinox S.A. (2)
Centro Industrial Garin Rivadavia s/n, Garin, B1619ADQ, Buenos Aires, Argentina (80%)
Tel.: (54) 3327448000
Web Site: https://www.ontecfortinox.com.ar
Sales Range: $25-49.9 Million
Emp.: 54
Steel Mfrs
N.A.I.C.S.: 331513

Subsidiary (Domestic):

Hoesch Hohenlimburg GmbH (2)
Oeger Str 120, 58119, Hagen, Germany (100%)
Tel.: (49) 2334910
Web Site: http://www.hoesch-hohenlimburg.de
Sales Range: $150-199.9 Million
Emp.: 900
Steel Mfrs
N.A.I.C.S.: 331513

Subsidiary (Non-US):

Lagermex S.A. de C.V. (2)
Km 117 Autopista Mexico-Puebla Av San Lorenzo Almecatla s/n, Parque Industrial Bralemex Cuautlancingo, 72710, Puebla, Mexico (90%)
Tel.: (52) 2222298900
Web Site: http://www.lagermex.com.mx

Sales Range: $25-49.9 Million
Emp.: 120
N.A.I.C.S.: 331513

Joint Venture (US):

TWB Company, LLC (2)
1600 Nadeau Rd, Monroe, MI 48162
Tel.: (734) 289-6400
Web Site: http://www.twbcompany.com
Sales Range: $75-99.9 Million
Emp.: 400
Custom Welded Blanks Mfr; Owned 55% by ThyssenKrupp AG & 45% by Worthington Industries, Inc.
N.A.I.C.S.: 336370

Subsidiary (Domestic):

ThyssenKrupp Bausysteme GmbH (2)
Hammerstrasse 11, PO Box 10 12 15, D-57223, Kreuztal, Germany (100%)
Tel.: (49) 2732 599 1599
Web Site: http://www.thyssenkrupp-bausysteme.com
Rev: $281,303,230
Roof & Wall Products from Coated Galvanized Steel Strips
N.A.I.C.S.: 331513

Subsidiary (Non-US):

Hoesch Bausysteme GmbH (3)
Tenschertstrasse 3, A 1230, Vienna, Austria (100%)
Tel.: (43) 016154640
Web Site: http://www.hoesch.at
Sales Range: $25-49.9 Million
Emp.: 57
Building Materials from Steel & Aluminium.
N.A.I.C.S.: 331513

Hoesch Design GmbH (3)
Kastellaan 114 Bus 1, 1081, Brussels, Belgium (100%)
Tel.: (32) 25223838
Web Site: http://www.hoesch-design.com
Sales Range: $1-9.9 Million
Emp.: 100
Bath Mfr
N.A.I.C.S.: 331513

ThyssenKrupp Epitoelemek Kft (3)
Timar Utca 20, H 1034, Budapest, Hungary (100%)
Tel.: (36) 14370014
Web Site: http://www.tk-hoesch.com
Sales Range: $25-49.9 Million
Emp.: 100
Steel Sales
N.A.I.C.S.: 331513

Subsidiary (Domestic):

ThyssenKrupp Electrical Steel GmbH (2)
Kurt-Schumacher-Strasse 95, 45881, Gelsenkirchen, Germany (100%)
Tel.: (49) 2094070
Web Site: https://www.thyssenkrupp-steel.com
Engineeering Services
N.A.I.C.S.: 541330

Subsidiary (Non-US):

ThyssenKrupp Materials Sweden (2)
Dagjamningsgatan 2, PO Box 47057, 415 09, Gothenburg, Sweden (100%)
Tel.: (46) 313377900
Web Site: http://www.thyssenkrupp.se
Sales Range: $25-49.9 Million
Emp.: 32
Steel Mfrs
N.A.I.C.S.: 331513

ThyssenKrupp Presta AG (2)
Essanestrasse 10, 9492, Eschen, Liechtenstein
Tel.: (423) 3772244
Sales Range: $350-399.9 Million
Emp.: 2,500
Steel Mfrs
N.A.I.C.S.: 331513

Subsidiary (Non-US):

ThyssenKrupp Mavilor S.A. (3)
24 Ave De La Liberation, 42152, L'Horme,

Rhone-Alpes, France (100%)
Tel.: (33) 477315601
Web Site: http://www.thyssenkrupp-technologies.com
Sales Range: $10-24.9 Million
Emp.: 450
Automotive Drop Forgings
N.A.I.C.S.: 332111

ThyssenKrupp Sofedit S.A.S. (3)
1 Rue Thomas Edison, PO Box 78056, Quartier Des Chenes, Saint-Quentin-en-Yvelines, France (100%)
Tel.: (33) 139412000
Web Site: http://www.thyssenkrupp.com
Sales Range: $350-399.9 Million
Steering System Components; Precision Cold Forgings
N.A.I.C.S.: 336110

Subsidiary (Non-US):

ThyssenKrupp Sisteme pentru Constructii S.R.L. (2)
50 Petre Av Cretu Street, Bucharest, 12052, Romania
Tel.: (40) 21 319 24 16
Web Site: http://www.thyssenkrupp.com
Emp.: 1,000
Construction Machinery Mfr
N.A.I.C.S.: 333120

ThyssenKrupp Steel (Asia Pacific) Pte Ltd (2)
3 International Business Park 06-01 Nordic European Centre, Singapore, 609927, Singapore
Tel.: (65) 6890 6690
Web Site: http://www.thyssenkruppasia.com
Emp.: 50
Stainless Steel Service Center Operator
N.A.I.C.S.: 423510
Andy Goh (Gen Mgr)

Subsidiary (US):

ThyssenKrupp Steel North America, Inc. (2)
22355 W Eleven Mile Rd, Southfield, MI 48033
Tel.: (248) 233-5994
Web Site: http://www.tksna.com
Emp.: 40
Steel Product Distr
N.A.I.C.S.: 423510

Subsidiary (Non-US):

ThyssenKrupp stavebni systemy s.r.o. (2)
Mestsky Park 274, 537 01, Chrudim, Czech Republic
Tel.: (420) 469 623 134
Web Site: http://www.tk-hoesch.cz
Steel Building Construction Services
N.A.I.C.S.: 238120

Subsidiary (Domestic):

WISCO Lasertechnik GmbH (2)
Metzgerstrasse 36, 88212, Ravensburg, Germany
Tel.: (49) 751295100
Web Site: https://baosteel-lasertechnik.de
Laser System Mfr
N.A.I.C.S.: 334510
Marius Spoettl (Mng Dir)

ThyssenKrupp Steel Zweite Beteiligungsgesellschaft mbH (1)
Kaiser-Wilhelm-Str 100, Duisburg, Germany
Tel.: (49) 201844563028
Iron & Steel Mfr
N.A.I.C.S.: 331110

ThyssenKrupp Steel and Stainless USA, LLC (1)
1 AM/NS Way, Calvert, AL 36513
Tel.: (251) 289-3600
Stainless Steel Mfr & Distr
N.A.I.C.S.: 331110

ThyssenKrupp Steelcom Pty. Ltd. (1)
Suite 3 17-23 Myrtle Street, North Sydney, 2060, NSW, Australia
Tel.: (61) 294091777
Web Site: http://www.tk-steelcom.com.au
Mining Equipment Distr
N.A.I.C.S.: 423810

AND PRIVATE COMPANIES — THYSSENKRUPP AG

ThyssenKrupp Stokvis Plastics B.V. (1)
Borchwerf 10, PO Box 1575, Roosendaal, 4700 BN, Netherlands
Tel.: (31) 165585634
Web Site: http://www.thyssenkrupp-plastics.nl
Sales Range: $25-49.9 Million
Emp.: 40
Plastic Products Mfr & Distr
N.A.I.C.S.: 326199
Peter Swinkels *(Gen Mgr)*

ThyssenKrupp System Engineering (Shanghai) Co., Ltd. (1)
No 695 Jianye Road, Pudong, Shanghai, 201201, China
Tel.: (86) 2120522600
Sales Range: $50-74.9 Million
Emp.: 116
Automobile Assembly Parts Mfr
N.A.I.C.S.: 336110

ThyssenKrupp System Engineering Ltd. (1)
Unit 5 The Felbridge Centre, East Grinstead, RH19 1XP, West Sussex, United Kingdom
Tel.: (44) 134 233 0000
Web Site: http://www.thyssenkrupp-systemengineering.com
Emp.: 31
Automobile Parts Mfr
N.A.I.C.S.: 336390
Uta Anders *(CFO & Member-Exec Bd)*

ThyssenKrupp System Engineering S.A. (1)
C/Comunicacions 17 Poligon Ind Agripina, Castellbisbal, 08755, Barcelona, Spain
Tel.: (34) 935860800
Web Site: http://www.thyssenkrupp.com
Emp.: 44
System Engineering Services
N.A.I.C.S.: 541330

ThyssenKrupp System Engineering S.A.S. (1)
4 Rue de la Gare, B P 67, 68190, Ensisheim, France
Tel.: (33) 389833240
Web Site: http://www.thyssenkrupp-systemengineering.com
Sales Range: $50-74.9 Million
Emp.: 131
Automobile Assembly Parts Mfr
N.A.I.C.S.: 336390

ThyssenKrupp System Engineering S.r.l. (1)
Corso Unione Sovietica 455, 10135, Turin, Italy
Tel.: (39) 0113486270
Web Site: http://www.thyssenkrupp.com
Emp.: 15
Automobile Assembly Parts Mfr
N.A.I.C.S.: 336390

ThyssenKrupp System Engineering, S.A. de C.V. (1)
Av Del Marques 36A Parque Industrial Bernado Quintana El Marques, 76246, Queretaro, Mexico
Tel.: (52) 442 192 4000
Web Site: http://www.thyssenkrupp-system-engineering.com
Emp.: 63
Automobile Assembly Parts Mfr
N.A.I.C.S.: 336390
Michael Von Keitz *(Mgr)*

ThyssenKrupp Systembau Austria Gesellschaft m.b.H. (1)
Puchsbaumgasse 19, 1100, Vienna, Austria
Tel.: (43) 1 606 87 60
Web Site: http://www.thyssenkrupp-systembau.at
Sales Range: $25-49.9 Million
Emp.: 11
Commercial Building Wall System Mfr
N.A.I.C.S.: 332322
Christian Geppner *(Mng Dir)*

ThyssenKrupp Tailored Blanks Celik Sanayi VE Ticaret Ltd. (1)
Nilufer Org Sanayi Bolgesi No 1 Lacivert Cad, 16040, Bursa, Turkiye
Tel.: (90) 2242421233
Web Site: http://www.tailored-blanks.com
Sales Range: $25-49.9 Million
Emp.: 20
Steel Blank Mfr
N.A.I.C.S.: 332999
Selim Unal *(Acct Mgr-Fin)*

ThyssenKrupp Tailored Blanks S.A. de C.V. (1)
Cuautlancingo Av San Lorenzo Almecatla, Cuautlancingo, 72700, Puebla, Mexico
Tel.: (52) 222 229 8976
Web Site: http://www.thyssenkrupp.com
Steel Blank Mfr
N.A.I.C.S.: 331221

ThyssenKrupp Technologies AG (1)
Am Thyssenhaus 1, 45128, Essen, Nordheim, Germany (100%)
Tel.: (49) 2011060
Sales Range: $15-24.9 Billion
Emp.: 54,762
Industrial Plants, Components & Machinery Mfr
N.A.I.C.S.: 236210

Subsidiary (Non-US):

Berco S.p.A. (2)
Via 1 Maggio 237, 44034, Copparo, Italy
Tel.: (39) 0532864300
Web Site: https://www.thyssenkrupp-berco.com
Sales Range: $700-749.9 Million
Emp.: 3,000
Tracked Vehicle Components & Equipment Mfr
N.A.I.C.S.: 331513

Subsidiary (Non-US):

Berco Bulgaria EOOD (3)
58 Stara Planina STR, 5641, Apriltsi, Bulgaria
Tel.: (359) 69582130
Web Site: http://www.berco.com
Emp.: 49
Industrial Machinery Equipment Mfr
N.A.I.C.S.: 333248
Plamen Peevski *(Mng Dir)*

Berco Deutschland GmbH (3)
Hagener Str 256, 58256, Ennepetal, Germany
Tel.: (49) 023336060
Undercarriages & Undercarriage Components Mfr
N.A.I.C.S.: 331513

Subsidiary (US):

Berco of America Inc. (3)
W 229 N 1420 Westwood Dr, Waukesha, WI 53186-1175
Tel.: (262) 524-2222
Web Site: http://www.bercoamerica.com
Sales Range: $50-74.9 Million
Emp.: 75
Distr of Heavy Equipement
N.A.I.C.S.: 423810

Division (Domestic):

Berco of America, Inc. (4)
117 23rd St SE, Puyallup, WA 98372
Tel.: (253) 845-0707
Web Site: http://www.bercoamerica.com
Sales Range: $25-49.9 Million
Emp.: 9
Undercarriage Parts Mfr
N.A.I.C.S.: 331513
Amy Reichert *(Pres)*

Subsidiary (Domestic):

DOC Dortmunder Oberflachencentrum GmbH (2)
Eberhardstrasse 12, 44145, Dortmund, Germany (100%)
Tel.: (49) 2318440
Web Site: http://www.thyssenkrupp-steel.com
Sales Range: $25-49.9 Million
Emp.: 120
Steel Mfrs
N.A.I.C.S.: 331513

Rothe Erde GmbH (2)
Tremoniastrasse 5-11, 44137, Dortmund, Germany (100%)
Tel.: (49) 2311860
Web Site: http://www.rotheerde.com
Sales Range: $50-74.9 Million
Emp.: 200
Slewing Bearings, Rolled Steel & Metal Rings, Turntables & Structural Elements Mfr
N.A.I.C.S.: 331221
Winfried Schulte *(Chm-Exec Bd & CEO)*

Subsidiary (Non-US):

Defontaine S.A. (3)
Rue Saint-Eloi, La Bruffiere, 85530, La Roche-sur-Yon, France (100%)
Tel.: (33) 251459494
Web Site: https://www.defontaine.com
Sales Range: $25-49.9 Million
Emp.: 50
Steel Mfrs
N.A.I.C.S.: 331513

Subsidiary (US):

Defontaine of America Inc. (4)
16720 W Victor Rd, New Berlin, WI 53151-4131
Tel.: (262) 797-5730
Web Site: http://www.definox-usa.com
Sales Range: $25-49.9 Million
Emp.: 5
High Quality Stainless Steel Valves Mfr
N.A.I.C.S.: 423830
Steven Smith *(Mgr-Site)*

Subsidiary (Non-US):

Defontaine UK Ltd. (3)
Malmesbury Bus Pk, Tetbury Hill, Malmesbury, SN16 9JX, United Kingdom (100%)
Tel.: (44) 666824800
Web Site: http://www.defontaine.com
Sales Range: $25-49.9 Million
Emp.: 3
Steel Mfrs
N.A.I.C.S.: 331513

Nippon Roballo Co. Ltd. (3)
Fukide Bldg 7th Floor Toranomon 4-1-13, J-Minato-Ku, Tokyo, 105-0001, Japan (50%)
Tel.: (81) 334344341
Web Site: https://www.roballo.co.jp
Sales Range: $25-49.9 Million
Emp.: 30
Slewing Bearings Mfr
N.A.I.C.S.: 332991

Subsidiary (US):

PSL of America Inc. (3)
1400 S Chillicothe Rd, Aurora, OH 44202
Tel.: (330) 405-1888
Web Site: http://www.pslofamerica.com
Sales Range: $50-74.9 Million
Emp.: 5
Distr of Heavy Duty Machinery Bearing
N.A.I.C.S.: 423840
Jim D. Lemmon *(Pres)*

Subsidiary (Non-US):

Roballo Engineering Co. Ltd. (3)
2 Mill Hill North West Industrial Estate, Peterlee, SR8 2HR, Durham, United Kingdom (100%)
Tel.: (44) 915185600
Web Site: http://www.roballo.co.uk
Sales Range: $25-49.9 Million
Emp.: 100
Large Diameter Antifriction Slewing Rings Mfr
N.A.I.C.S.: 331513
Ray Carr *(Mgr-Sls & Procurement)*

Roballo France S.a.r.l. (3)
30 Blvd Bellerive, 92566, Rueil-Malmaison, Cedex, France (100%)
Tel.: (33) 41390090
Sales Range: $10-24.9 Million
Emp.: 5
Steel Mfrs
N.A.I.C.S.: 331513

Robrasa Rolamentos Especiais Rothe Erde Ltda. (3)
Rua Lidia Blank No 48, PO Box 281, 09913-010, Diadema, Brazil (100%)
Tel.: (55) 1140558400
Web Site: http://www.robrasa.com.br
Sales Range: $25-49.9 Million
Emp.: 100
N.A.I.C.S.: 331513

Subsidiary (US):

Rotek Incorporated (3)
1400 S Chillicothe Rd, Aurora, OH 44202-9282
Tel.: (330) 562-4000
Web Site: http://www.rotek-inc.com
Sales Range: $125-149.9 Million
Emp.: 150
Bearings & Rings Mfr
N.A.I.C.S.: 332991
Mark Girman *(Pres)*

Rotek Incorporated (3)
8085 Production Dr, Florence, KY 41042-3028 (100%)
Tel.: (859) 342-8430
Web Site: http://www.rotek-inc.com
Sales Range: $50-74.9 Million
Emp.: 150
Steel Mfrs
N.A.I.C.S.: 331513
Mark Girman *(Pres & CEO)*

Subsidiary (Non-US):

Rothe Erde Iberica S.A. - Roteisa (3)
Castellon Highway km 7Poligono Industrial La Cartuja E, 50720, La Cartuja Baja, Zaragoza, Spain (100%)
Tel.: (34) 976500480
Web Site: https://www.thyssenkrupp-rotheerde.com
Sales Range: $25-49.9 Million
Emp.: 45
Slewing Bearings, Rolled Steel & Metal Rings, Turntables & Structural Elements Mfr
N.A.I.C.S.: 331221
Fernando Alonso Velo *(CEO)*

Rothe Erde India (3)
Gat No 429 Gonde Nashik Maharashtra Igatpuri, Jaipur, 422 403, Wadivarhe, India (100%)
Tel.: (91) 25 53 30 2231
Web Site: http://www.rotheerdeindia.com
Steel Mfrs
N.A.I.C.S.: 331513
Sarvesh S. Verma *(Mng Dir & CFO)*

Rothe Erde India Private Ltd. (3)
Gat No 429, Wadivarhe Gonde Igatpuri, Nasik, 422 403, Maharashtra, India
Tel.: (91) 2553302231
Web Site: http://www.rotheerdeindia.com
Sales Range: $50-74.9 Million
Emp.: 180
Roller Bearing Mfr
N.A.I.C.S.: 332991

Rothe Erde Metallurgica Rossi S.p.A. (3)
Viale Kennedy 56, I - 25010, Visano, Brescia, Italy
Tel.: (39) 03095201
Web Site: http://www.rotheerde.it
Slewing Bearings, Rolled Steel & Metal Rings, Turntables & Structural Elements Mfr
N.A.I.C.S.: 331221

Subsidiary (Domestic):

Thyssen Polymer GmbH (2)
BayerwaldStrasse 18, 94327, Bogen, Germany (100%)
Tel.: (49) 94228210
Web Site: http://www.inoutic.de
Sales Range: $150-199.9 Million
Emp.: 500
Steel Door Mfr
N.A.I.C.S.: 331513
Hertoel Hans *(Pres)*

ThyssenKrupp Automotive AG (2)
ThyssenKrupp Allee 1, 45143, Essen, Germany (100%)
Tel.: (49) 2018440
Sales Range: $25-49.9 Million
Emp.: 100
Steel Mfrs
N.A.I.C.S.: 331513

Subsidiary (Domestic):

Thyssen Krupp Gerlach GmbH (3)
Neue Industriestrasse, PO Box 1252, 66424, Homburg, Germany (100%)
Tel.: (49) 6841107530

THYSSENKRUPP AG

ThyssenKrupp AG—(Continued)

Web Site:
http://www.thyssenkruppgerlach.com
Steel Mfrs
N.A.I.C.S.: 331513

Subsidiary (US):

ThyssenKrupp Crankshaft Company (4)
1000 Lynch Spur, Danville, IL 61834-5811 **(100%)**
Tel.: (217) 431-0060
Web Site:
http://www.thyssenkruppgerlach.com
Sales Range: $75-99.9 Million
Emp.: 300
Ferrous & Nonferrous Forgings
N.A.I.C.S.: 332111
Les Chewning (Sr Engr-Maintenance)

Subsidiary (Non-US):

ThyssenKrupp Automotive France S A R L (3)
Europole De Sarreguemines, 57913, Hambach, Cedex, France **(100%)**
Tel.: (33) 387282140
Web Site: http://www.thyssenkrupp-automotive.com
Emp.: 80
Steel Mfrs
N.A.I.C.S.: 331513
Christophe Flauder (Gen Mgr)

Subsidiary (Domestic):

ThyssenKrupp Automotive Systems GmbH (3)
Munchener Strasse 104 A, 45145, Essen, Germany **(100%)**
Tel.: (49) 20 150 7990
Web Site: http://www.thyssenkrupp-components-technology.com
Development, Production & Assembly of Chassis Modules & Systems for Automotive Industry
N.A.I.C.S.: 336390
Thomas Muller (CEO & CFO)

Subsidiary (Non-US):

Hoesch IMPORMOL-Industria Portuguesa de Molas S.A. (4)
Vale do Cardal, 2051, Azambuja, Codex, Portugal **(100%)**
Tel.: (351) 63 40 00 5 25
Automotive Springs: Leaf Springs, Tapered Leaf Springs
N.A.I.C.S.: 336110

Holding (US):

Krupp Hoesch Suspensions Inc. (4)
3155 W Big Beaver St, Troy, MI 48084 **(100%)**
Tel.: (248) 643-3500
Web Site: http://khaoa.com
Chassis & Suspension Springs for the Automotive Industry
N.A.I.C.S.: 336110

Joint Venture (Non-US):

Krupp Modulos Automotivos do Brasil Ltda (4)
Av Leste Km 4 Sn Campo Largo Da Roseira, 03090 900, Sao Jose dos Pinhais, Brazil **(51%)**
Tel.: (55) 4121064796
Web Site: http://www.tka-as.thyssenkrupp.com
Sales Range: $10-24.9 Million
Emp.: 296
Motor Vehicles Mfr
N.A.I.C.S.: 336110

Subsidiary (Non-US):

Liaoyang K.S. Automotive Spring Company Limited (4)
168 Shuangshang Rd, Liaoyang, 11100, China **(100%)**
Tel.: (86) 192910910
Web Site: http://www.thyssenkrupp-automotive.com
Sales Range: $75-99.9 Million
Emp.: 500
Steel Mfrs

Mure S.A. (4)
Pertxeta 22, 48810, Alonsotegui, Spain **(100%)**
Tel.: (34) 944980311
Hot-Formed & Heat-Treated Springs
N.A.I.C.S.: 336110

Thyssen Krupp Sasa S.A. de C.V. (4)
Eje 124 Numero 125, MEX 78090, San Luis Potosi, Mexico **(100%)**
Tel.: (52) 4448707000
Steel Mfrs
N.A.I.C.S.: 331513

ThyssenKrupp UK PLC (4)
Third Floor 1 Friars Gate 1011 Stratford Road, Solihull, Shirley, B90 4BN, West Midlands, United Kingdom **(100%)**
Tel.: (44) 1217137280
Web Site: https://www.thyssenkrupp-uk.com
Sales Range: $25-49.9 Million
Emp.: 64
Chassis & Suspension Springs for the Automotive Industry; Stabilizers & Antiroll Bars
N.A.I.C.S.: 336110

Subsidiary (Domestic):

ThyssenKrupp Bilstein GmbH (3)
August-Bilstein-Strasse 4, 58256, Ennepetal, Germany **(100%)**
Tel.: (49) 23337910
Web Site: https://bilstein.com
Steel Mfrs
N.A.I.C.S.: 331513

Subsidiary (US):

Krupp Bilstein of America Inc. (4)
8685 Bilstein Blvd, Hamilton, OH 45015-2205 **(100%)**
Tel.: (513) 881-7600
Web Site: http://bilsteinrocks.com
Sales Range: $25-49.9 Million
Emp.: 750
Shock Absorbers for Automotive Industry Mfr
N.A.I.C.S.: 336330
Peter Klaus Kirner (Member-Exec Bd)

Thyssen Krupp Bilstein of America Inc. (4)
14102 Stowe Dr, Poway, CA 92064-7147 **(100%)**
Tel.: (858) 386-5900
Web Site: http://www.bilstein.com
Sales Range: $25-49.9 Million
Emp.: 50
Gas-Pressure Shock Absorbers; Window Fittings; Car Jacks
N.A.I.C.S.: 336390

Subsidiary (Non-US):

ThyssenKrupp Bilstein Brasil Molas e Componentes de Suspensao Ltda. (4)
Av Abrahao Goncalves Braga 4, 04186-902, Sao Paulo, Brazil **(100%)**
Tel.: (55) 1123322400
Web Site: http://www.thyssenkrupp-brazil.com
Sales Range: $75-99.9 Million
Emp.: 300
Chassis & Suspension Springs for the Automotive Industry
N.A.I.C.S.: 336390

ThyssenKrupp Bilstein Compa S.A. (4)
Henri Coanda Str 8, 550234, Sibiu, Romania
Tel.: (40) 269207207
Web Site: http://www.bilstein.ro
Sales Range: $125-149.9 Million
Emp.: 400
Steel Mfrs
N.A.I.C.S.: 331513
Rado Betea (Gen Mgr)

Subsidiary (US):

ThyssenKrupp Budd Co. (3)
3155 W Big Beaver Rd, Troy, MI 48084 **(100%)**
Tel.: (248) 643-3500
Automotive Stampings
N.A.I.C.S.: 336370
Paul Flancbaum (Commun Mgr)

Subsidiary (Non-US):

ThyssenKrupp Metalurgica Campo Limpo Ltda. (3)
Av Alfried Krupp 1050, Campo Limpo Paulista, Sao Paulo, 13231 900, Brazil **(100%)**
Tel.: (55) 1140390099
Web Site:
http://www.thyssenkruppgermetalurgica.com
Emp.: 4,000
Motor Vehicles & Passenger Car Bodies Mfr
N.A.I.C.S.: 332111

Subsidiary (Non-US):

ThyssenKrupp Metalurgica de Mexico S.A. de C.V. (4)
Camino a Santa Agueda No 1 San Miguel Xoxtla, Puebla, Mexico **(100%)**
Tel.: (52) 2222237001
Web Site: http://www.thyssenkrupp.com
Sales Range: $75-99.9 Million
Emp.: 450
Steel Mfrs
N.A.I.C.S.: 331513

Subsidiary (Domestic):

ThyssenKrupp System Engineering GmbH (3)
Richard-Taylor-Strasse 89, 28777, Bremen, Germany **(100%)**
Tel.: (49) 42168880
Web Site: https://www.thyssenkrupp-automation-engineering.com
Sales Range: $100-124.9 Million
Jigs & Fixtures; Car Body Construction Facilities; Tooling; Prototypes
N.A.I.C.S.: 336110
Ingo Steinkruger (Chm-Exec Bd)

Division (Domestic):

ThyssenKrupp System Engineering GmbH (4)
Richard Taylor Strasse 89, 28777, Bremen, Germany **(100%)**
Tel.: (49) 421 68880
Web Site: http://www.thyssenkrupp-systemengineering.com
Emp.: 788
Steel Mfrs
N.A.I.C.S.: 331513
Ingo Steinkruger (Chm-Exec Bd)

Subsidiary (US):

ThyssenKrupp System Engineering Inc. (5)
901 Doris Rd, Auburn Hills, MI 48326-2716 **(100%)**
Tel.: (248) 340-8000
Web Site: http://www.thyssenkrupp-system-engineering.com
Sales Range: $50-74.9 Million
Emp.: 156
Machine Tools, Metal Cutting Type & Assembly Line
N.A.I.C.S.: 333517

Subsidiary (Domestic):

ThyssenKrupp Foerdertechnik GmbH (2)
Altendorfer Str 120, Essen, 45143, Germany
Tel.: (49) 20182804
Web Site: http://www.thyssenkrupp-foerdertechnik.com
Sales Range: $25-49.9 Million
Emp.: 150
Mining Equipment Mfr
N.A.I.C.S.: 333131

Subsidiary (Non-US):

ThyssenKrupp BulkTec (China) Ltd. (3)
Unit 6A 22/f China Life Tower No 16 Chaoyangmenwai Avenue, Chaoyang District, 100020, Beijing, 100020, China
Tel.: (86) 1085252999
Web Site: http://www.thyssenkrupp.com
Mineral Mining Services
N.A.I.C.S.: 212390

thyssenkrupp Industrial Solutions (Australia) Pty Ltd (3)

INTERNATIONAL PUBLIC

Level 11 140 St Georges Terrace, Perth, 6000, WA, Australia
Tel.: (61) 892000000
Web Site: http://www.thyssenkrupp-australia.com
Mining & Materials Handling Technology Services & Processing Equipment Mfr
N.A.I.C.S.: 333131

Subsidiary (Domestic):

ThyssenKrupp Industrial Solutions (2)
Graf Galen Strasse 17, 59269, Beckum, Germany
Tel.: (49) 2525 990
Web Site: http://www.thyssenkrupp-industrial-solutions.com
Sales Range: $350-399.9 Million
Emp.: 1,600
Industrial Machinery Mfr for Cement & Raw Materials Industry
N.A.I.C.S.: 333248
Marcel Fasswald (CEO & Member-Exec Bd)

Subsidiary (Non-US):

Maerz Ofenbau AG (4)
Richard-Wagner-Strasse 28, 8002, Zurich, Switzerland
Tel.: (41) 442872727
Web Site: https://www.maerz.com
Sales Range: $25-49.9 Million
Emp.: 100
Kiln Mfr
N.A.I.C.S.: 333994
Stephan Lechner (Mng Dir)

Subsidiary (US):

Polysius Corp. (3)
180 Interstate N Pkwy, Atlanta, GA 30339-2194 **(100%)**
Tel.: (770) 955-3660
Web Site: http://www.polysiususa.com
Sales Range: $25-49.9 Million
Emp.: 84
Provider of Engineering Services
N.A.I.C.S.: 541330

Subsidiary (Domestic):

A-C Equipment Services Corp. (4)
6737 W Washington St Ste 1400, Milwaukee, WI 53214
Tel.: (414) 475-2554
Web Site: http://www.a-cequipment.com
Emp.: 60
Rotary Kiln & Digester Installation Services
N.A.I.C.S.: 238990
R. William Hankes (Gen Mgr)

Subsidiary (Domestic):

Umatac Industrial Processes Inc. (4)
Suite 110 6835 Railway St SE, Calgary, T2H 2V6, AB, Canada
Tel.: (403) 910-1000
Web Site: http://www.umatac.ca
Sales Range: $10-24.9 Million
Emp.: 15
Oil & Hydrocarbon Waste Recycling Services
N.A.I.C.S.: 562920

Subsidiary (Domestic):

ThyssenKrupp Marine Systems AG (2)
Hermann-Blohm-Str 3, 20457, Hamburg, Germany **(100%)**
Tel.: (49) 4317000
Web Site: http://www.thyssenkrupp-marinesystems.com
Emp.: 9,300
Marine Systems Products & Services
N.A.I.C.S.: 111998
Rolf Wirtz (CEO & Member-Exec Bd)

Subsidiary (Non-US):

Kockums AB (3)
Stora Varvsgatan 11, Malmo, 20555, Sweden **(100%)**
Tel.: (46) 40348000
Web Site: http://www.kockums.se
Sales Range: $150-199.9 Million
Emp.: 800
Submarine Systems & Air-Independent Stirling Engines Mfr

AND PRIVATE COMPANIES — THYSSENKRUPP AG

N.A.I.C.S.: 336611

Branch (Domestic):

SAAB Kockums AB (4)
Styrmansgatan 1, 371 30, Karlskrona, Sweden (100%)
Tel.: (46) 734188797
Web Site: http://www.saab.com
Sales Range: $300-349.9 Million
Submarine Systems & Air-Independent Stirling Engines Mfr
N.A.I.C.S.: 336611

Subsidiary (Non-US):

ThyssenKrupp Marin Sistem Gemi Sanayi ve Ticaret A.S. (3)
Acisu Sok Taslik Apt No 15, 34354, Besiktas, Turkiye
Tel.: (90) 2122589983
Web Site: http://www.thyssenkrupp.com
Emp.: 4
Cargo Handling Services
N.A.I.C.S.: 488320

ThyssenKrupp Marine Systems Australia Pty Ltd (3)
32 Essingtong St, Canberra, 2911, ACT, Australia
Tel.: (61) 2 62410616
Marine Transportation Services
N.A.I.C.S.: 488390

ThyssenKrupp Marine Systems Canada Ltd. (3)
6 Gurdwara Road Suite 201, Ottawa, K2E 8A3, ON, Canada
Tel.: (613) 686-6647
Web Site: http://www.tkms.ca
Sales Range: $25-49.9 Million
Emp.: 2
Marine Engineering Services
N.A.I.C.S.: 541330

Joint Venture (Domestic):

thyssenkrupp Marine Systems GmbH (3)
Werftstrasse 112-114, 24143, Kiel, Germany
Tel.: (49) 4317000
Web Site: https://www.thyssenkrupp-marinesystems.com
Commercial Shipbuilding
N.A.I.C.S.: 336611

Subsidiary (Domestic):

MV Werften Wismar GmbH (4)
Wendorfer Weg 5, 23966, Wismar, Germany
Tel.: (49) 3841770
Web Site: http://www.mv-werften.com
Emp.: 2,948
Ship Building Services
N.A.I.C.S.: 336611

Subsidiary (Domestic):

ThyssenKrupp Real Estate GmbH (2)
thyssenkrupp Allee 1, 45143, Essen, Germany (100%)
Tel.: (49) 2018440
Web Site: https://www.thyssenkrupp.com
Sales Range: $75-99.9 Million
Emp.: 200
Real Estate Services
N.A.I.C.S.: 531390

ThyssenKrupp Umformtechnik GmbH (2)
Gotenstrasse 91, 33647, Bielefeld, Germany (100%)
Tel.: (49) 52144720
Web Site: http://www.gmf-umformtechnik.com
Sales Range: $350-399.9 Million
Emp.: 1,300
Steel Mfrs
N.A.I.C.S.: 331513

Uhde GmbH (2)
Friedrich Uhde Strasse 15, PO Box 101849, Dortmund, 44141, Germany (100%)
Tel.: (49) 2315470
Web Site: http://uhde.biz
Sales Range: $150-199.9 Million
Emp.: 1,000
Steel Mfrs
N.A.I.C.S.: 331513

Subsidiary (Non-US):

Uhde Inventa-Fischer AG (3)
Via Innovativa 31, 7013, Domat/Ems, Switzerland (100%)
Tel.: (41) 816326311
Web Site: http://www.uhde-inventa-fischer.com
Sales Range: $25-49.9 Million
Emp.: 70
Polyester, Polyamide Filaments & Fibers Mfr
N.A.I.C.S.: 325998

Uhde Inventa-Fischer Chemical Fiber Equipment (Shanghai) Ltd. (3)
Unit C1 E3 30/F Junyao Plaza No 789, Zhaojiabang Road, Shanghai, 200032, China
Tel.: (86) 2161286999
Web Site: http://www.uhde-inventa-fischer.com
Sales Range: $25-49.9 Million
Emp.: 30
Polyester, Polyamide Filaments & Fibers Mfr
N.A.I.C.S.: 325998

Subsidiary (Domestic):

Uhde Inventa-Fischer GmbH (3)
Holzhauser Str 157-159, 13509, Berlin, Germany (100%)
Tel.: (49) 30435675
Web Site: http://www.uhde-inventa-fisher.com
Sales Range: $25-49.9 Million
Emp.: 85
Polyester, Polyamide Filaments & Fibers Mfr
N.A.I.C.S.: 325998

ThyssenKrupp Tiefbautechnik GmbH (1)
Alte Liederbacher Strasse 6, Alsfeld, 36304, Germany
Tel.: (49) 66317810
Web Site: http://www.thyssenkrupp-tiefbautechnik.com
Emp.: 30
Construction Machinery Mfr
N.A.I.C.S.: 333120

ThyssenKrupp Transrapid GmbH (1)
Moosacherstrasse 58, PO Box 401867, 80809, Munich, 80809, Germany
Tel.: (49) 89 35469100
Web Site: http://www.transrapid.de
Sales Range: $25-49.9 Million
Emp.: 2
Rail Transportation Services
N.A.I.C.S.: 488210
Werner Schulte (Mng Dir)

ThyssenKrupp USA, Inc. (1)
3155 W Big Beaver Rd Ste 125, Troy, MI 48084-3007
Tel.: (248) 643-3929
Automobile Parts Mfr
N.A.I.C.S.: 336390
Kurt Moilanen (Mgr-Cash)

ThyssenKrupp Uhde GmbH (1)
Friedrich-Uhde-Strasse 15, 44141, Dortmund, Germany
Tel.: (49) 2315470
Web Site: https://www.thyssenkrupp-uhde.com
Sales Range: $200-249.9 Million
Emp.: 1,000
Plant Construction & Engineering Services
N.A.I.C.S.: 237990

Subsidiary (Domestic):

ThyssenKrupp Uhde Engineering Services GmbH (2)
Vosskuhle 38, 44141, Dortmund, Germany
Tel.: (49) 2315470
Web Site: http://www.tkues.com
Sales Range: $25-49.9 Million
Emp.: 170
Engineering Services
N.A.I.C.S.: 541330

ThyssenKrupp Veerhaven B.V. (1)
Nicolaas Pieckstraat 14, 3232 BP, Brielle, Netherlands
Tel.: (31) 18 141 9882
Web Site: https://www.thyssenkruppveerhaven.com
Sales Range: $50-74.9 Million
Emp.: 170
Push Tow Ship Operator
N.A.I.C.S.: 336611
Jos Davidse (Sr Mgr-Ops)

ThyssenKrupp Vytahy s.r.o. (1)
Nove Zahrady I/13 A, 821 05, Bratislava, Slovakia
Tel.: (421) 4020 88 88
Web Site: http://www.thyssenkrupp-vytahy.sk
Sales Range: $25-49.9 Million
Emp.: 35
Elevator Mfr
N.A.I.C.S.: 333921
Jaroslav Jenco (Mgr)

ThyssenKrupp Vytahy s.r.o. (1)
Bucharova 2641/14, 158 00, Prague, Czech Republic
Tel.: (420) 234714916
Web Site: https://www.tkelevator.com
Elevator Mfr
N.A.I.C.S.: 333921

ThyssenKrupp Xervon Co. Ltd. (1)
No 588 East Yan An Road 25th Floor, Shanghai, 200001, China
Tel.: (86) 21 6472 4736
Web Site: http://www.thyssenkrupp-materials-international.com
Sales Range: $25-49.9 Million
Emp.: 200
Engineeering Services
N.A.I.C.S.: 541330

ThyssenKrupp Xervon Corp. Sdn. Bhd. (1)
Level 12 Menara Perak 24 Jln Perak, Kuala Lumpur, 50450, Malaysia
Tel.: (60) 3 22645555
Web Site: http://www.xervon.com
Engineeering Services
N.A.I.C.S.: 541330

ThyssenKrupp Xervon Malaysia Sdn. Bhd. (1)
Level 12 Menara Perak 24 Jln Perak, 50450, Kuala Lumpur, Malaysia
Tel.: (60) 22645555
Oil & Gas Pipeline Construction Services
N.A.I.C.S.: 237120

ThyssenKrupp Xervon Norway AS (1)
Verkseier Furulundsvei 9B, Postfach 289, 0668, Oslo, Norway
Tel.: (47) 33314100
Web Site: https://www.xervon.no
Architectural Services
N.A.I.C.S.: 238390

ThyssenKrupp Xervon Saudi Arabia L.L.C. (1)
villa no. 3923 Noman Bin Haratha Road, PO Box 75328, Al Khobar, 31952, Saudi Arabia
Tel.: (966) 38657014
Emp.: 200
Construction Machinery Mfr
N.A.I.C.S.: 333120
Mayeen Ul Ahsan (Gen Mgr)

ThyssenKrupp Xervon Sweden AB (1)
Symmetrivagen 27, PO Box 2035, 19637, Kungsangen, Sweden
Tel.: (46) 104821000
Web Site: https://www.xervon.se
Emp.: 200
Construction Machinery Mfr
N.A.I.C.S.: 333120

ThyssenKrupp Xervon U.A.E. - L.L.C. (1)
Area No 1/10 South 15 Villa 1 & 2, PO Box 47616, Bain Al Jessrain, Abu Dhabi, United Arab Emirates
Tel.: (971) 25587159
Industrial Construction Services
N.A.I.C.S.: 237990

ThyssenKrupp dvigala d.o.o. (1)
Planjava 4, 1236, Trzin, Slovenia
Tel.: (386) 1 5305850
Web Site: http://www.thyssenkrupp.si
Sales Range: $25-49.9 Million
Emp.: 60
Elevator Mfr
N.A.I.C.S.: 333921

Thyssenkrupp Automation Engineering GmbH (1)
Richard-Taylor-Strasse 89, 28777, Bremen, Germany
Tel.: (49) 42168880
Web Site: https://www.thyssenkrupp-automation-engineering.com
Automation Engineering Services
N.A.I.C.S.: 541330

Thyssenkrupp Dynamic Components Changzhou Ltd. (1)
No788 West Huanghe Road, Xinbei District, Changzhou, 213136, Jiangsu Province, China
Tel.: (86) 51980118666
Emp.: 316
Automobile Parts Mfr
N.A.I.C.S.: 332119

Thyssenkrupp Dynamic Components Chemnitz GmbH (1)
Heinrich-Lorenz-Strasse 57, 09120, Chemnitz, Germany
Tel.: (49) 371278680
Emp.: 277
Dynamic Component Mfr & Distr
N.A.I.C.S.: 335312

Thyssenkrupp Dynamic Components Danville LLC (1)
75 Walz Crk Dr, Danville, IL 61834
Tel.: (217) 444-5500
Web Site: https://karriere.thyssenkrupp.com
Emp.: 385
Motor Vehicle Parts Mfr
N.A.I.C.S.: 336390
Joe Chowning (Engr-Quality)

Thyssenkrupp Dynamic Components Danville, LLC (1)
70 Walz Crk Dr, Danville, IL 61834
Tel.: (217) 444-5500
Dynamic Component Mfr & Distr
N.A.I.C.S.: 335312

Thyssenkrupp Dynamic Components TecCenter AG (1)
Wirtschaftspark 37, Furstentum, 9492, Eschen, Liechtenstein
Tel.: (423) 33997000
Emp.: 240
Dynamic Component Mfr & Distr
N.A.I.C.S.: 335312

Thyssenkrupp Industrial Solutions (CZ) S.r.o. (1)
Pekarska 7, 602 00, Brno, Czech Republic
Tel.: (420) 543423911
Construction Machinery & Equipment Mfr
N.A.I.C.S.: 333120
Jiri Richter (Head-Layout & Piping)

Thyssenkrupp Industrial Solutions (Chile) Limitada (1)
Isidora Goyenechea 2800 Piso 19 Edificio Titanium, Providencia, Las Condes, Santiago, Chile
Tel.: (56) 229989800
Construction Machinery & Equipment Mfr
N.A.I.C.S.: 333120
Gabriel Poblete Valdivia (Acct Mgr-Zona Centro)

Thyssenkrupp Industrial Solutions (France) S.A.S. (1)
Route Departementale 113 Intersection Chemin De La Pourranque CS 30036, 13170, Les Pennes-Mirabeau, France
Tel.: (33) 970823055
Web Site: https://www.polysius.fr
Cement Industry Equipment Mfr & Distr
N.A.I.C.S.: 333120

Thyssenkrupp Industrial Solutions (India) Pvt. Ltd. (1)
Uhde House Lal Bahadur Shastri Marg, Vikhroli West, Mumbai, 400 083, Maharastra, India
Tel.: (91) 224 047 8000
Web Site: https://www.thyssenkrupp-industrial-solutions.com

THYSSENKRUPP AG

ThyssenKrupp AG—(Continued)
Emp.: 1,200
Engineering & Construction Services
N.A.I.C.S.: 541330
N. R. Chitre (CFO & Exec Dir)

Thyssenkrupp Industrial Solutions (Thailand) Ltd. (1)
450 Century Industrial Park Sukhumvit Road, Huaypong Muang, Rayong, 21150, Thailand
Tel.: (66) 26128200
Engineering & Construction Services
N.A.I.C.S.: 541330

Thyssenkrupp Industrial Solutions Argentina S.A. (1)
25 de Mayo 596-Piso 14, 1002, Buenos Aires, Argentina
Tel.: (54) 11431160467
Chemical Products Mfr
N.A.I.C.S.: 325998

Thyssenkrupp Industrial Solutions Egypt Company S.A.E. (1)
6A Mostafa Refeat Street UEE Building, Sheraton Heliopolis Area, 11799, Cairo, Egypt
Tel.: (20) 222662885
Emp.: 225
Engineering & Construction Services
N.A.I.C.S.: 541330

Thyssenkrupp Material Processing Europe GmbH (1)
Heidbergsweg 102, 47809, Krefeld, Germany
Tel.: (49) 2151 6168 0
Web Site: http://www.thyssenkrupp-materials-processing-europe.com
Steel Products Service Center Operator
N.A.I.C.S.: 423510
Wilhelm Budeus (Member-Mgmt Bd)

Subsidiary (Domestic):

Herzog Coilex GmbH (2)
Am Mittelkai 50, PO Box 610161, 70329, Stuttgart, Germany
Tel.: (49) 711 3207 0
Web Site: http://www.herzog-coilex.de
Sales Range: $50-74.9 Million
Emp.: 100
Steel & Nonferrous Products Mfr
N.A.I.C.S.: 331513

Thyssenkrupp Materials Processing Europe Gmbh (1)
Heidbergsweg 102, 47809, Krefeld, Germany
Tel.: (49) 2151 6168 0
Web Site: http://www.thyssenkrupp-materials-processing-europe.com
Steel & Nonferrous Metal Mfr
N.A.I.C.S.: 331315
Marcus Wohl (Chm-Mgmt Bd)

Division (Non-US):

ThyssenKrupp Ferroglobus Kereskedelmi Zrt (2)
Fazis u 6, 1158, Budapest, Hungary
Tel.: (36) 14148700
Web Site: https://www.thyssenkrupp-materials.hu
Steel & Nonferrous Metal Mfr
N.A.I.C.S.: 331110

Subsidiary (Domestic):

thyssenkrupp Materials Processing Hungary Kft. (3)
Gerda u 3, 9011, Gyor, Hungary (100%)
Tel.: (36) 96544400
Web Site: http://thyssenkruppmaterialshungary.hu
Emp.: 50
Steel Products Mfr
N.A.I.C.S.: 331221

Thyssenkrupp Materials Services GmbH (1)
Thyssenkrupp Allee 1, 45143, Essen, Germany
Tel.: (49) 201 8440
Web Site: https://www.thyssenkrupp-materials-services.com
Steel & Nonferrous Metal Mfr & Distr
N.A.I.C.S.: 331110

Markus Bistram (Chief HR Officer)

Thyssenkrupp Materials Trading CA, Ltd. (1)
2821 Langstaff Road, Concord, L4K 56C, ON, Canada
Tel.: (905) 532-1403
Metal Product Mfr & Distr
N.A.I.C.S.: 331110

Thyssenkrupp Plastics France S.A.S. (1)
13 rue Rene Cassin, ZAC La Villette Aux Aulnes, 77290, Mitry-Mory, France
Tel.: (33) 164674400
Web Site: https://www.thyssenkrupp-plastics.fr
Plastics Product Mfr
N.A.I.C.S.: 326199

Thyssenkrupp Polysius GmbH (1)
Graf-Galen-Str 17, 59269, Beckum, Germany
Tel.: (49) 2525990
Web Site: https://www.thyssenkrupp-polysius.com
Cement & Lime Mfr
N.A.I.C.S.: 327310

Thyssenkrupp Polysius Peru S.A.C. (1)
Las Begonias No 475 DPTO 602 - Bloque A, San Isidro, Lima, Peru
Tel.: (51) 975549958
Information Technology Consulting Services
N.A.I.C.S.: 541512

Thyssenkrupp Presta North America, LLC (1)
1597 E Industrial Dr, Terre Haute, IN 47802
Tel.: (812) 299-5000
Web Site: http://www.thyssenkrupp.com
Motor Vehicle Parts Mfr
N.A.I.C.S.: 336330

Thyssenkrupp Rothe Erde Spain S.A. (1)
Carretera Castellon km 7 Poligono Industrial La Cartuja, 50720, Zaragoza, Spain
Tel.: (34) 976500480
Rolling Bearing Mfr & Distr
N.A.I.C.S.: 332991

Thyssenkrupp Uhde USA, LLC (1)
16285 Park Ten Pl Ste 420, Houston, TX 77084
Tel.: (281) 600-5770
Chemical Plant Planning & Construction Services
N.A.I.C.S.: 541330

Thyssenkrupp nucera AG & Co. KGaA (1)
Vosskuhle 38 Harpen, 44141, Dortmund, Germany
Tel.: (49) 231229727100
Web Site: https://thyssenkrupp-nucera.com
Emp.: 500
Clean Energy Distr
N.A.I.C.S.: 424690

Thyssenkrupp rothe erde (Xuzhou) Ring Mill Co., Ltd. (1)
Luoshan Road 6, Xuzhou Economic and Technological Development Zone, Jiangsu, 221004, China
Tel.: (86) 51687980163
Plastics Product Mfr
N.A.I.C.S.: 326199

Thyssenkrupp rothe erde Germany GmbH (1)
Tremoniastrasse 5-11 D, 44137, Dortmund, Germany
Tel.: (49) 2311860
Web Site: https://www.thyssenkrupp-rotheerde.com
Slewing Bearings Mfr
N.A.I.C.S.: 332991

Thyssenkrupp rothe erde Slovakia a.s. (1)
Robotnicka ul, 01701, Povazska Bystrica, Slovakia
Tel.: (421) 424371460
Rolling Bearing Mfr & Distr
N.A.I.C.S.: 332991

Trapo Kung AG (1)
Baselstrasse 49, Zwingen, 4222, Basel, Switzerland
Tel.: (41) 613196666
Web Site: https://www.trapo.ch
Emp.: 80
Lift & Escalator Mfr
N.A.I.C.S.: 333921

UAB ThyssenKrupp Baltija (1)
Minijos g 180, 93269, Klaipeda, Lithuania
Tel.: (370) 46 35 54 01
Web Site: http://www.thyssenkrupp-baltija.lt
Sales Range: $50-74.9 Million
Emp.: 5
Construction Machinery & Equipment Rental Services
N.A.I.C.S.: 532412
Ramunas Stanius (Gen Mgr)

Uhde Arabia Ltd. (1)
9th Floor Al-Subeaei Tower Cross Pepsi Cola Street, PO Box 823, Prince Faisal bin Fahad bin Abdulaziz Street, Al Khobar, 31952, Saudi Arabia
Tel.: (966) 138872414
Web Site: http://www.uhde.eu
Industrial Plant Construction Services
N.A.I.C.S.: 236210

Uhde Asia Pacific Pty. Ltd. (1)
Level 4 99 King Street, Melbourne, 3000, VIC, Australia
Tel.: (61) 392075753
Sales Range: $200-249.9 Million
Emp.: 300
Oil & Gas Exploration Services
N.A.I.C.S.: 213112
Johann Rinnhofer (CEO)

Subsidiary (Non-US):

Uhde Engineering de Mexico, S.A. de C.V. (2)
Av Sierra Gamon 120 Piso 7 Col Lomas de Chapultepec, 11000, Mexico, Mexico
Tel.: (52) 55 5284 02 00
Web Site: http://www.thyssenkrupp-uhdemexico.com
Sales Range: $100-124.9 Million
Industrial Plant Construction Services
N.A.I.C.S.: 237990
Francisco Guerrero Ramirez (Dir-Bus Dev & Strategic Market)

Uhde Edeleanu S.E. Asia Pte. Ltd. (1)
25 International Business Park, Singapore, 609916, Singapore
Tel.: (65) 65629300
Motor Vehicle Parts Mfr
N.A.I.C.S.: 336390

Uhde Edeleanu s.r.o. (1)
Pekarska 7, Brno, 602 00, Czech Republic
Tel.: (420) 543 423 911
Web Site: http://www.thyssenkrupp.com
Emp.: 10
Engineeering Services
N.A.I.C.S.: 541330

Uhde Engineering Consulting (Shanghai) Co., Ltd. (1)
4/F Building No 10 Pujiang Intelligence Valley No 1188 Lianhang Road, Pudong District, Shanghai, 201112, China
Tel.: (86) 21 6128 6999
Web Site: http://www.thyssenkrupp-uhde-asia-pacific.com
Emp.: 40
Chemical Equipment Distr
N.A.I.C.S.: 423830

Uhde Engineering Egypt Company (S.A.E.) (1)
6A Mostafa Refeat Street UEE Building, Sheraton Heliopolis Area, 11799, Cairo, Egypt
Tel.: (20) 2 2266 288 5
Web Site: http://www.uhde-engineering-egypt.com
Sales Range: $100-124.9 Million
Emp.: 170
Oil & Gas Exploration Services
N.A.I.C.S.: 213112

Uhde High Pressure Technologies GmbH (1)
Buschmuehlenstr 20, 58093, Hagen, Germany
Tel.: (49) 23319670

INTERNATIONAL PUBLIC

Web Site: http://www.uhde-hpt.com
Emp.: 350
Industrial Machinery Equipment Mfr
N.A.I.C.S.: 333248

Uhde Mexico S.A. de C.V. (1)
Sierra Gamon 120 Piso 7 Lomas De Chapultepec Miguel Hidalgo, 11000, Mexico, Mexico
Tel.: (52) 55 5284 0200
Sales Range: $25-49.9 Million
Emp.: 250
Engineeering Services
N.A.I.C.S.: 541330
Thomas Tuerk (Mng Dir)

Uhde Services Slovakia s.r.o. (1)
Lazaretska 8, 811 08, Bratislava, Slovakia
Tel.: (421) 2 57 20 04 44
Web Site: http://www.thyssenkrupp.com
Engineeering Services
N.A.I.C.S.: 541330

Uhde Shedden (Australia) Pty. Ltd. (1)
Level 2 355 Spencer Street, Melbourne, 3003, VIC, Australia
Tel.: (61) 3 9207 5777
Web Site: http://www.uhdeshedden.com
Sales Range: $200-249.9 Million
Emp.: 300
Oil & Gas Exploration Services
N.A.I.C.S.: 213112
Brian Campbell (Mgr-Bus Dev)

Uhde do Brasil Ltda. (1)
Alameda Oscar Niemeyer 119-1 andar Vila da Serra 34, Nova Lima, 34006-056, Brazil
Tel.: (55) 2133116201
Sales Range: $25-49.9 Million
Emp.: 1
Engineeering Services
N.A.I.C.S.: 541330

VDM-Unterstutzungskasse GmbH (1)
Plettenberger Str 2, 59791, Werdohl, Germany
Tel.: (49) 392 55 2725
Web Site: http://www.thyssenkrupp.com
Steel Products Mfr
N.A.I.C.S.: 331110

Vermogensverwaltungsgesellschaft TKAS mbH (1)
Marktplatz 3, Grunwald, 82031, Germany
Tel.: (49) 208656050
Steel Products Mfr
N.A.I.C.S.: 331110

Vermogensverwaltungsgesellschaft TKW mbH (1)
Obere Stahlindustrie, Bochum, 44793, Germany
Tel.: (49) 23491140
Sales Range: $50-74.9 Million
Emp.: 75
Investment Management Service
N.A.I.C.S.: 523940

Xuzhou Rothe Erde Ring Mill Co., Ltd. (1)
No 6 Luoshan Road Xuzhou Economic Development Zone, Xuzhou, 221004, Jiangsu, China
Tel.: (86) 516 8798 0101
Web Site: http://www.xrem.cn
Rolled Steel Ring Mfr
N.A.I.C.S.: 331121
Jufu Wu (Mng Dir)

thyssenkrupp AT.Pro tec GmbH (1)
Rellinghauser Strasse 3, 45128, Essen, Germany
Tel.: (49) 201844563989
Steel Shaft Furnace Product Distr
N.A.I.C.S.: 423720
Gerd Konig (Mng Partner)

thyssenkrupp Academy GmbH (1)
Thyssenkrupp Allee 1, 45143, Essen, Germany
Tel.: (49) 20184 453 8251
Web Site: https://www.thyssenkrupp-academy.com
Commercial Services
N.A.I.C.S.: 561499
David Maus (Program Dir)

thyssenkrupp Access Japan Co., Ltd. (1)

AND PRIVATE COMPANIES

THYSSENKRUPP AG

1F Akasaka Garden City 4-15-1 Akasaka, Minato-ku, Tokyo, 107-0052, Japan
Tel.: (81) 355753071
Web Site: https://www.kaidan-noboru.com
Elevator & Moving Stairway Mfr
N.A.I.C.S.: 333921

thyssenkrupp Aerospace (Suzhou) Co., Ltd. (1)
Building 2A EPZ A No 200 Suhong Middle Road, Industrial Park, Suzhou, 215021, Jiangsu, China
Tel.: (86) 13511026901
Steel Shaft Furnace Product Distr
N.A.I.C.S.: 423720
Hai Luo (Ops Mgr)

thyssenkrupp Aerospace Morocco SARL (1)
Lot 121 Parc CFCIM Ouled Salah, BP 27182, Bouskoura, Casablanca, Morocco
Tel.: (212) 669977291
Steel Shaft Furnace Product Distr
N.A.I.C.S.: 423720
Saad Amaaou (Mng Dir)

thyssenkrupp Aerospace Tunisia S.A.R.L. (1)
Rue Tozeur ZI M'Ghira 3, 2082, Fouchana, Tunisia
Tel.: (216) 130494236
Steel Shaft Furnace Product Distr
N.A.I.C.S.: 423720

thyssenkrupp Airport Solutions, S.A. (1)
Pol Industrial Vega de Baina s/n, Mieres, 33682, Asturias, Spain
Tel.: (34) 985446820
Elevator & Moving Stairway Mfr
N.A.I.C.S.: 333921
Ignacio Medina (Chm & Mng Dir)

thyssenkrupp Aufzuge GmbH, Neuhausen a. d. (1)
Bernhauser Strasse 45, 73765, Neuhausen, Germany
Tel.: (49) 711652220
Elevator & Moving Stairway Mfr
N.A.I.C.S.: 333921
Martin Slabon (Sls Mgr-Modernization)

thyssenkrupp Automata Industria de Pecas Ltda. (1)
Avenida Eurico Ambrogi Santos 1715, Pirancangaba, Taubate, 12042-010, Sao Paulo, Brazil
Tel.: (55) 1236272300
Steel Shaft Furnace Product Distr
N.A.I.C.S.: 423720

thyssenkrupp Carbon Components GmbH (1)
Frankenring 1, 01723, Kesselsdorf, Germany
Tel.: (49) 3513 203 9504
Web Site: http://www.thyssenkrupp-carbon-components.com
Carbon Wheel Mfr
N.A.I.C.S.: 335991
Jens Werner (CEO)

thyssenkrupp Components Technology Hungary Kft. (1)
Daroczi ut 1-3, 1113, Budapest, Hungary
Tel.: (36) 15059100
Web Site: http://www.thyssenkrupp.hu
Motor Vehicle Steering Component Mfr
N.A.I.C.S.: 336330
Marc de Bastos Eckstein (Mng Dir)

thyssenkrupp Dizala d.o.o. (1)
Fallerovo Setaliste 22, 10000, Zagreb, Croatia
Tel.: (385) 13535100
Web Site: http://www.thyssenkrupp-dizala.hr
Elevator & Moving Stairway Mfr
N.A.I.C.S.: 333921
Kresimir Prtenjak (Mng Dir)

thyssenkrupp Edelstahl-Service-Center GmbH (1)
Heinrich-August-Schulte-Strasse 14, 44147, Dortmund, Germany
Tel.: (49) 23182890
Steel Flat Product Distr
N.A.I.C.S.: 423510

thyssenkrupp Electrical Steel India Private Ltd. (1)
Post Gonde Village Wadivarhe Taluka Igatpuri, District Nashik, Nashik, 422 403, Maharashtra, India
Tel.: (91) 2553225182
Web Site: https://tksindia.com
Steel Products Mfr
N.A.I.C.S.: 332312

thyssenkrupp Electrical Steel Verwaltungsgesellschaft mbH (1)
Kurt-Schumacher-Strasse 95, 45881, Gelsenkirchen, Germany
Tel.: (49) 2094070
Steel Products Mfr
N.A.I.C.S.: 332312

thyssenkrupp Elevadores, S.R.L. (1)
Tte 1st Sindulfo Casco 5119 near, Laguna Grande, 1218, Asuncion, Paraguay
Tel.: (595) 214125000
Web Site: https://www.tkelevator.com
Elevator & Moving Stairway Mfr
N.A.I.C.S.: 333921

thyssenkrupp Elevator (Taiwan) Co., Ltd. (1)
36F No 16 Xinzhan Rd, Banqiao Dist, New Taipei City, 220336, Taiwan
Tel.: (886) 225618310
Elevator Installation & Maintenance Services
N.A.I.C.S.: 238290

thyssenkrupp Elevator (Thailand) Co., Ltd. (1)
65/52 Chamnan Phenjati Business Center 4th Floor Rama 9 Road, Huaykwang, Huaykwang District, Bangkok, 10310, Thailand
Tel.: (66) 22321500
Elevator Installation & Maintenance Services
N.A.I.C.S.: 238290
Worraphan Khemasingki (Mng Dir)

thyssenkrupp Elevator - Egypt S.A.E. (1)
12 Kamal El Din Hussein Street, Sheraton Heliopolis Area, Cairo, Egypt
Tel.: (20) 2226969567
Elevator & Moving Stairway Mfr
N.A.I.C.S.: 333921
Ahmed Alaa (Mng Dir)

thyssenkrupp Elevator Australia Pty. Ltd. (1)
Shed 73 The Woolstores 2/4E Huntley Street, Alexandria, 2015, NSW, Australia
Tel.: (61) 283039000
Web Site: https://www.tkelevator.com
Elevator & Moving Stairway Mfr
N.A.I.C.S.: 333921
Kevin McCreadi (Mgr-Field Engrg)

thyssenkrupp Elevator Israel LP (1)
Served Moshe 1, Rishon le Zion, Israel
Tel.: (972) 39434100
Web Site: https://www.tkelevator.com
Elevator & Moving Stairway Mfr
N.A.I.C.S.: 333921

thyssenkrupp Elevator Kuwait Trading Co. WLL. (1)
Kuwait RE Tower 5th Floor Sharq Al Shuhada Street, PO Box 115, Safat, Kuwait, Kuwait
Tel.: (965) 22278910
Elevator & Moving Stairway Mfr
N.A.I.C.S.: 333921
Hany Elkhayat (Ops Mgr)

thyssenkrupp Elevator Myanmar Limited (1)
No 33/49 Strand Condo Unit 05 7th Floor Mahabandoola Garden Street, Kyauktada Township, Yangon, Myanmar
Tel.: (95) 18252364
Elevator & Moving Stairway Mfr
N.A.I.C.S.: 333921
Win Nai (Mgr-Business Line)

thyssenkrupp Elevator New Zealand Ltd. (1)
Compass House 162 Grafton Road, Auckland, 1010, New Zealand
Tel.: (64) 99130411
Elevator & Moving Stairway Mfr
N.A.I.C.S.: 333921
David Gardner (Mgr)

thyssenkrupp Elevator UAE LLC (1)
Sheikh Zayed Road No 1 The H Dubai 11th Floor, PO Box 27278, Dubai, United Arab Emirates
Tel.: (971) 42308000
Elevator & Moving Stairway Mfr
N.A.I.C.S.: 333921
Sankalp Indwar (Sr Engr-Svc & Sls)

thyssenkrupp Elevator/Jordan Ltd. Co. (1)
1st Floor Building 58 Al-Ra'fah, PO Box 910002, Commercial Complex Abdulla Ghosheh Street, Amman, Jordan
Tel.: (962) 65828999
Elevator & Moving Stairway Mfr
N.A.I.C.S.: 333921
Khaled Assaf (Supvr-QHSE)

thyssenkrupp Escalator Co. (China) Ltd. (1)
No 2 Xunye Rd Sheshan Subarea, Songjiang Industrial Area, Shanghai, 201602, China
Tel.: (86) 2157076888
Web Site: http://www.thyssenkrupp-elevator.com.cn
Elevator & Moving Stairway Mfr
N.A.I.C.S.: 333921
Frank Chen (Chief HR Officer)

thyssenkrupp Federn und Stabilisatoren GmbH (1)
Oeger Str 85, 58119, Hagen, Germany
Tel.: (49) 233450490
Spring & Stabilizer Mfr
N.A.I.C.S.: 332613
Dieter Lechner (Dir-Global Tech & Innovation)

thyssenkrupp Fertilizer Technology GmbH (1)
Vosskuhle 38, 44141, Dortmund, Germany
Tel.: (49) 2315472937
Web Site: https://www.thyssenkrupp-industrial-solutions.com
Hydro Fertilizer Product Mfr
N.A.I.C.S.: 325314
Matthias Potthoff (Mng Dir)

thyssenkrupp Hohenlimburg Kompetenzwerkstatt GmbH (1)
Oeger Strasse 47, 58642, Iserlohn, Germany
Tel.: (49) 23749247230
Web Site: https://www.kompetenzwerkstatt-hohenlimburg.com
Steel Products Mfr
N.A.I.C.S.: 332312

thyssenkrupp Home Solutions S.r.l. (1)
Via Stanislao Cannizzaro 2, 56121, Pisa, Italy
Tel.: (39) 050955503
Web Site: http://www.thyssenkrupp-homesolutions.it
Elevator Installation & Maintenance Services
N.A.I.C.S.: 238290
Alessandro Profeti (Project Mgr)

thyssenkrupp India Private Limited (1)
5th Floor Uhde House LBS Marg, Vikhroli, Mumbai, 400083, Maharashtra, India
Tel.: (91) 2240478000
Web Site: http://www.thyssenkrupp-india.com
Engineeering Services
N.A.I.C.S.: 541330

thyssenkrupp Industrial Solutions (Asia Pacific) Pte. Ltd. (1)
3 International Business Park 06-31 Nordic European Centre, Singapore, 609927, Singapore
Tel.: (65) 68901640
Construction Machinery & Equipment Mfr
N.A.I.C.S.: 333120
Rahulraj Chavan (Head-Bus Unit-Mining)

thyssenkrupp Industrial Solutions (Canada) Inc. (1)
4838 Richard Road SW Suite 400, Calgary, T3E 6L1, AB, Canada
Tel.: (403) 245-2866
Construction Machinery & Equipment Mfr
N.A.I.C.S.: 333120

thyssenkrupp Industrial Solutions (China) Co., Ltd. (1)
No 988 Shengchang Road Building 2 7th Floor, Minhang District, Shanghai, 201106, China
Tel.: (86) 2161817588
Construction Machinery & Equipment Mfr
N.A.I.C.S.: 333120
Thorsten Heidack (CEO)

thyssenkrupp Industrial Solutions (Malaysia) Sdn. Bhd. (1)
Level 18 The Pinnacle Persiaran Lagoon, Bandar Sunway, 46150, Petaling Jaya, Selangor, Malaysia
Tel.: (60) 356229819
Construction Machinery & Equipment Mfr
N.A.I.C.S.: 333120

thyssenkrupp Industrial Solutions (Mexico) S.A. de C.V. (1)
Sierra Gamon 120 Piso 7, Col Lomas de Chapultepec Ciudad de, 11000, Mexico, Mexico
Tel.: (52) 5552840200
Emp.: 500
Cement Mfr
N.A.I.C.S.: 327310

thyssenkrupp Industrial Solutions (USA), Inc. (1)
6737 W Washington St Ste 1400, Milwaukee, WI 53214
Tel.: (414) 475-2554
Web Site: http://www.a-cequipment.com
Construction Equipment Mfr & Distr
N.A.I.C.S.: 333131
R. William Hankes (Gen Mgr)

thyssenkrupp Industrial Solutions (Vietnam) Ltd. (1)
Floor 7 Sun Red River Building 23 Phan Chu Trinh Street, Phan Chu Trinh Ward Hoan Kiem District, Hanoi, Vietnam
Tel.: (84) 2439387000
Construction Machinery & Equipment Mfr
N.A.I.C.S.: 333120
Lukas Schoeneck (CEO)

thyssenkrupp Industrial Solutions BRN Sdn. Bhd. (1)
10 First Floor Bangunan Hasbullah 3 Jalan Gadong, BE 3919, Bandar Seri Begawan, Brunei Darussalam
Tel.: (673) 2429119
Construction Machinery & Equipment Mfr
N.A.I.C.S.: 333120
Joerg H. Schiemann (CEO)

thyssenkrupp Infrastructure Brasil Ltda. (1)
Av Rio Branco 124 sl 1602, Rio de Janeiro, 20040-001, RJ, Brazil
Tel.: (55) 2132825245
Marine Equipment Distr
N.A.I.C.S.: 423860
Aline Magalhaes (Coord-Admin)

thyssenkrupp Infrastructure GmbH (1)
Hollestrasse 7a, 45127, Essen, Germany
Tel.: (49) 201844562313
Web Site: https://materials-infra.tkpharos.com
Marine Equipment Distr
N.A.I.C.S.: 423860
Dietmar Jurges (CEO)

thyssenkrupp Japan K.K. (1)
Akasaka Garden City 17th floor 4-15-1 Akasaka, Akasaka Minato-ku, Tokyo, 107-0052, Japan
Tel.: (81) 8023620622
Web Site: http://www.thyssenkrupp-japan.com
Engineeering Services
N.A.I.C.S.: 541330

thyssenkrupp Materials Australia Pty. Ltd. (1)
Unit 2 7-10 Denoci Close, Wetherill Park, 2164, NSW, Australia
Tel.: (61) 29 757 7777
Web Site: https://www.thyssenkrupp-materials.com.au
Engineering & Fabrication Product Distribution Services
N.A.I.C.S.: 541330
Brad Foster (CEO)

THYSSENKRUPP AG

ThyssenKrupp AG—(Continued)

thyssenkrupp Materials Belgium N.V. (1)
Brandstraat 11, Industriepark E17/3, 9160, Lokeren, Belgium
Tel.: (32) 93493635
Web Site: http://www.thyssenkrupp-materials.be
Steel Flat Product Distr
N.A.I.C.S.: 423510
Valerie Meyfroot *(Mgr-Pur, Stainless Steel & Toolsteel)*

thyssenkrupp Materials Bulgaria (1)
Vrajdebna Skladovo-Proizvodstvena Zona, Sofia, 1839, Bulgaria
Tel.: (359) 29427850
Web Site: http://www.thyssenkrupp-materials.bg
Steel Product Retailer & Whslr
N.A.I.C.S.: 423510
Georgi Nikolov *(CEO)*

thyssenkrupp Materials Hungary Zrt. (1)
Korvasut sor 110, 1158, Budapest, Hungary
Tel.: (36) 14148700
Web Site: http://www.thyssenkrupp-materials.hu
Emp.: 300
Steel Flat Product Distr
N.A.I.C.S.: 423510
Viktor Biro *(Mgr)*

thyssenkrupp Materials IoT GmbH (1)
Thyssenkrupp Allee 1, 45143, Essen, Germany
Tel.: (49) 208 989 9240
Web Site: https://www.thyssenkrupp-materials-iot.com
Industrial Machinery Mfr & Distr
N.A.I.C.S.: 333248
Jorg Plenert *(Chm & CTO)*

thyssenkrupp Materials Processing Europe Sp. z o.o. (1)
ul Torunska 7, 41-300, Dabrowa Gornicza, Poland
Tel.: (48) 326395900
Web Site: http://www.thyssenkrupp-materials-processing-europe.pl
Industrial Machinery Mfr
N.A.I.C.S.: 333248
Damian Trocha *(Mng Dir)*

thyssenkrupp Materials Processing Europe, S.L. (1)
Centro de Servicios El Puig Ctra al Mar s/n, El Puig, 6540, Valencia, Spain
Tel.: (34) 961472062
Web Site: http://www.thyssenkrupp-materials-processing-europe.es
Steel Product Distr
N.A.I.C.S.: 423510
Jose Almonacid *(Head-Controlling)*

thyssenkrupp Materials Slovakia spol. s r.o. (1)
Besenovska cesta 17/4757, 940 02, Nove Zamky, Slovakia
Tel.: (421) 902971701
Web Site: http://www.thyssenkrupp-materials.sk
Metal & Plastic Material Mfr
N.A.I.C.S.: 333511
Helena Uhrinova *(Mktg Mgr)*

thyssenkrupp Materials Trading Asia Pte. Ltd. (1)
No 3 International Business Park 06 - 21/23 Nordic European Centre, Singapore, 609927, Singapore
Tel.: (65) 66657665
Rolled Steel Product Distr
N.A.I.C.S.: 423510
Markus Staatsmann *(CFO)*

thyssenkrupp Materials Trading GmbH (1)
Rellinghauser Str 3, 45128, Essen, Germany
Tel.: (49) 2018440
Web Site: http://www.thyssenkrupp-materials-trading.com
Rolled Steel Product Distr
N.A.I.C.S.: 423510
Wolfgang Schnittker *(CEO)*

thyssenkrupp Materials Turkey Metal Sanayi ve Ticaret A.S. (1)
GOSB 1000 Sokak No 1030, Cayirova, 41480, Kocaeli, Turkiye
Tel.: (90) 262 677 1570
Web Site: http://www.thyssenkrupp-materials-turkey.com
Steel Product Distr
N.A.I.C.S.: 423510
Utku Cagatay Aksoy *(CFO)*

thyssenkrupp Plastics Belgium N.V./S.A. (1)
Park Ragheno' - Dellingstraat 57, 2800, Mechelen, Belgium
Tel.: (32) 15453222
Web Site: https://www.thyssenkrupp-plastics.be
Plastic Whslr
N.A.I.C.S.: 424610

thyssenkrupp Plastics GmbH (1)
Thyssenkrupp Allee 1, 45143, Essen, Germany
Tel.: (49) 2018440
Web Site: https://www.thyssenkrupp-plastics.de
Plastic Whslr
N.A.I.C.S.: 424610

thyssenkrupp Saudi Arabia Contracting Company Limited (1)
18th Floor Tamkeen Tower Olaya Street, PO Box 396376, Riyadh, 11375, Saudi Arabia
Tel.: (966) 118261730
Construction Machinery & Equipment Mfr
N.A.I.C.S.: 333120
Volker Hellberg *(CEO)*

thyssenkrupp Saudi Arabia Limited (1)
Salah Eddin Al-Ayubi Street Al Bawani Tower 6th Floor, PO Box 9812, Riyadh, 11423, Saudi Arabia
Tel.: (966) 114868900
Elevator & Moving Stairway Mfr
N.A.I.C.S.: 333921
Mohammad Abduljaleel *(Head-Svc & Modernization KSA & Branch Mgr-Western Reg)*

thyssenkrupp Steel Chile SpA (1)
Avda Las Americas 1021, Cerrillos, Chile
Tel.: (56) 224205500
Steel Products Mfr
N.A.I.C.S.: 332312

thyssenkrupp Steel Colombia S.A.S. (1)
Calle 116 15B-26 of 407, Bogota, Colombia
Tel.: (57) 16236446
Steel Products Mfr
N.A.I.C.S.: 332312

thyssenkrupp Steel Japan GK (1)
Akasaka Garden City Bldg 17th Floor 4-15-1 Akasaka, Minato-Ku, Tokyo, 107-0052, Japan
Tel.: (81) 355720681
Steel Products Mfr
N.A.I.C.S.: 332312

thyssenkrupp Steel Switzerland AG (1)
Industriestrasse 13, 9552, Bronschhofen, Switzerland
Tel.: (41) 719138300
Steel Products Mfr
N.A.I.C.S.: 332312
Urs Steiger *(Mng Dir)*

thyssenkrupp System Engineering India Private Limited (1)
Gate No 169 Chakan Industrial Area, Village- Sawardari Taluka- Khed, Pune, 410501, Maharashtra, India
Tel.: (91) 2135632100
Automobile Parts Mfr
N.A.I.C.S.: 336390
Sagar Pannase *(Engr-Design & Process)*

thyssenkrupp Technologies (Cambodia) Co., Ltd. (1)
Level 1 No 56 St 337 SangKat Boeung Kak 2, Khan Toul Kork, Phnom Penh, Cambodia
Tel.: (855) 89222663
Elevator & Moving Stairway Mfr
N.A.I.C.S.: 333921

thyssenkrupp Uhde Chlorine Electrolysis (USA) Inc. (1)
16285 Park Ten Pl Ste 150, Houston, TX 77084
Tel.: (713) 337-8700
Automobile Parts Mfr
N.A.I.C.S.: 336390

thyssenkrupp Uhde Chlorine Engineers (Italia) S.R.L. (1)
Via L Bistolfi 35, 20134, Milan, Italy
Tel.: (39) 0221291
Chlorine Product Mfr
N.A.I.C.S.: 325612
Gerhard Henssen *(Mng Dir)*

thyssenkrupp Uhde Chlorine Engineers (Japan) Ltd. (1)
7F Sakura Nihombashi Bldg 13-12 Nihombashi Kayabacho 1-chome, Chuo-ku, Tokyo, 103-0025, Okayama, Japan
Tel.: (81) 356148211
Chlorine Product Mfr
N.A.I.C.S.: 325612
Shinji Katayama *(Chm)*

thyssenkrupp Uhde Chlorine Engineers (Shanghai) Co., Ltd. (1)
No 9th Jianheng Road, Jiangning District, Shanghai, 211100, China
Tel.: (86) 2566666028
Chlorine Product Mfr
N.A.I.C.S.: 325612

thyssenkrupp Uhde Chlorine Engineers GmbH (1)
Vosskuhle 38 Harpen-Haus, 44141, Dortmund, Germany
Tel.: (49) 231229727100
Web Site: https://thyssenkrupp-nucera.com
Chlorine Product Mfr
N.A.I.C.S.: 325612
Denis Krude *(CEO)*

thyssenkrupp Valvetrain GmbH (1)
Am Industriepark 1, 38871, Ilsenburg, Germany
Tel.: (49) 394524680
Staffing & Recruiting Services
N.A.I.C.S.: 561312

thyssenkrupp rothe erde Italy S.p.A. (1)
Viale Kennedy 56, 25010, Visano, Brescia, Italy
Tel.: (39) 03428660010
Rolling Bearing Product Mfr
N.A.I.C.S.: 332991
Fabrizio Cherubini *(CEO-Sls, Mfg & Engrg)*

thyssenkrupp rothe erde Japan Ltd. (1)
Akasaka Garden City Bldg 17th Floor 4-15-1 Akasaka, Minato-Ku, Tokyo, 107-0052, Japan
Tel.: (81) 355720681
Rolling Bearing Product Mfr
N.A.I.C.S.: 332991
Michinori Yoshida *(CEO)*

thyssenkrupp rothe erde UK Ltd. (1)
Mill Hill Northwest Industrial Estate, Peterlee, SR8 2HR, Durham, United Kingdom
Tel.: (44) 1915185600
Rolling Bearing Product Mfr
N.A.I.C.S.: 332991
Edward Flood *(CEO)*

thyssenkrupp rothe erde USA Inc. (1)
1400 S Chillicothe Rd, Aurora, OH 44202
Tel.: (330) 562-4000
Web Site: http://www.rotek-inc.com
Rolling Bearing Product Mfr
N.A.I.C.S.: 332991
Frank Kuepper *(Chief Sls Officer & VP-Sls & Engrg)*

TI CLOUD INC.
28-29/F No1 Building 2nd Compound Ronghua South Road, Beijing Economic & Technological Development Zone, Beijing, China Ky
Web Site: https://www.ti-net.com.cn
Year Founded: 2006
2167—(HKG)
Rev.: $58,716,813
Assets: $87,197,480
Liabilities: $14,936,749
Net Worth: $72,260,730
Earnings: ($1,129,771)
Emp.: 477
Fiscal Year-end: 12/31/22
Software Development Services
N.A.I.C.S.: 541511
Qiang Wu *(Chm)*

TI FLUID SYSTEMS PLC
4650 Kingsgate Cascade Way, Oxford Business Park South, Oxford, OX4 2SU, Oxfordshire, United Kingdom
Tel.: (44) 1865871820 UK
Web Site: https://www.tifluidsystems.com
Year Founded: 1922
TIFS—(LSE)
Rev.: $4,125,599,596
Assets: $3,516,788,690
Liabilities: $2,662,585,206
Net Worth: $854,203,484
Earnings: ($352,183,792)
Emp.: 25,600
Fiscal Year-end: 12/31/22
Automobile Parts Mfr
N.A.I.C.S.: 333996
Ronald Hundzinski *(CFO)*

Subsidiaries:

Cascade Engineering Europe Kft. (1)
Kisgyar u 23, 2314, Halasztelek, Hungary
Tel.: (36) 24521300
Web Site: https://cee.hu
Industrial Machinery Mfr
N.A.I.C.S.: 333248

TIA MARUCA ARGENTINA SA
Av Flandes 1272, Lujan, Buenos Aires, Argentina
Tel.: (54) 800 666 6278 Ar
Web Site: http://www.tiamaruca.com
Year Founded: 1998
Cookie Mfr
N.A.I.C.S.: 311821
Alejandro Ripani *(Founder & Pres)*

Subsidiaries:

Dilexis S.A. (1)
Sarmiento 3628, Albardon, San Martin, 5419, San Juan, Argentina
Tel.: (54) 2644912660
Emp.: 400
Snack Food Mfr
N.A.I.C.S.: 311919

TIAAN CONSUMER LIMITED
405 Patel Ashwamegh Complex Jetalpur Road Near Dairy Den Circle, Sayajigunj, Vadodara, 390005, Gujarat, India
Tel.: (91) 8070827082
Web Site: http://www.tiaanstore.com
540108—(BOM)
Assets: $1,140,507
Liabilities: $179,594
Net Worth: $960,914
Earnings: ($285,474)
Fiscal Year-end: 03/31/23
Ayurvedic Product Mfr
N.A.I.C.S.: 325411
Sudharshan R. *(Mng Dir)*

TIALIS ESSENTIAL IT PLC
County Gates House 300 Poole Road, Westbourne, Poole, BH12 1AZ, Dorset, United Kingdom
Tel.: (44) 3448741000 UK
Web Site: http://www.idegroup.com
TIA—(AIM)
Rev.: $19,627,200
Assets: $21,642,057
Liabilities: $33,359,180
Net Worth: ($11,717,124)
Earnings: ($2,682,855)
Emp.: 165
Fiscal Year-end: 12/31/21

AND PRIVATE COMPANIES

Investment Services
N.A.I.C.S.: 523999

Subsidiaries:

iDE Group Limited (1)
Interchange 81 - 85 Station Road, Croydon, CR0 2RD, United Kingdom
Tel.: (44) 3448741000
Web Site: http://www.idegroup.com
Information Technology Services
N.A.I.C.S.: 541513

TIAN AN AUSTRALIA LIMITED
Level 6 99 Macquarie Street, Sydney, 2000, NSW, Australia
Tel.: (61) 282439700
Web Site: https://www.tianan.com.au
TIA—(ASX)
Rev.: $265,649
Assets: $160,563,994
Liabilities: $114,721,068
Net Worth: $45,842,926
Earnings: $3,646,891
Emp.: 15
Fiscal Year-end: 12/31/23
Residential Land Development & Sales
N.A.I.C.S.: 237210
Hai-Young Lu (COO)

Subsidiaries:

Port Bouvard Marina Pty Ltd (1)
45 Rees Pl, Wannanup, Mandurah, 6210, WA, Australia
Tel.: (61) 895346444
Web Site: https://www.portbouvardmarina.com.au
Marine Services
N.A.I.C.S.: 488320

TIAN AN CHINA INVESTMENTS COMPANY LIMITED
22/F Allied Kajima Building 138 Gloucester Road, Wanchai, China (Hong Kong)
Tel.: (852) 25333233   HK
Web Site: https://www.tiananchina.com
Year Founded: 1986
TIACF—(OTCIQ)
Rev.: $650,123,966
Assets: $6,293,946,988
Liabilities: $2,778,894,910
Net Worth: $3,515,052,079
Earnings: $198,267,793
Emp.: 1,182
Fiscal Year-end: 12/31/22
Investment Services
N.A.I.C.S.: 523999
Edwin King Yau Lo (Exec Dir)

Subsidiaries:

Asiasec Properties Limited (1)
9th Floor Allied Kajima Building 138 Gloucester Road, Wanchai, China (Hong Kong) (74.98%)
Tel.: (852) 28280288
Web Site: https://www.asiasec.com.hk
Sales Range: $1-9.9 Million
Emp.: 39
Investment Holding Company; Real Estate Development Services
N.A.I.C.S.: 551112
Cynthia Si Ying Chen (Sec)

Dalian Tian An Tower Co., Ltd. (1)
No 88 Zhongshan Rd, Zhongshan District, Dalian, China
Tel.: (86) 212 308 9090
Property Development Services
N.A.I.C.S.: 531390

Tian An (Shanghai) Investments Co., Ltd. (1)
30/F Shanghai Tian An Centre Building 338 Nanjing Road West, Huangpu District, Shanghai, China
Tel.: (86) 216 372 6666
Property Investment Services
N.A.I.C.S.: 531390

TIAN CHANG GROUP HOLDINGS LTD.
Unit 6 13/F Block B Hoi Luen Industrial Centre 55 Hoi Yuen Road, Kwun Tong, China (Hong Kong)
Tel.: (852) 28571778
Web Site: http://www.hktcgroup.com
Year Founded: 2000
2182—(HKG)
Rev.: $145,852,478
Assets: $153,588,158
Liabilities: $53,918,093
Net Worth: $99,670,065
Earnings: $13,507,988
Emp.: 1,081
Fiscal Year-end: 12/31/22
Tobacco Product Mfr
N.A.I.C.S.: 312230
Chan Yin Yan (VP-Mktg)

TIAN GE INTERACTIVE HOLDINGS LTD.
Room 322 East Tower Building 1 No 17-1 Chuxin Road, Gong Shu District, Hangzhou, China
Tel.: (86) 57188108686
Web Site: http://www.tiange.com
1980—(HKG)
Rev.: $32,255,301
Assets: $540,354,817
Liabilities: $70,965,953
Net Worth: $469,388,864
Earnings: $20,011,218
Emp.: 336
Fiscal Year-end: 12/31/21
Social Video Platform Operations
N.A.I.C.S.: 551112
Zhengjun Fu (CEO & Chm)

TIAN JIN BOHAI CHEMICAL CO., LTD.
No 189 Bohai 13th Road Lingang Economic Zone Binhai New Area, Hexi District, Tianjin, 300452, China
Tel.: (86) 2266627563
Web Site: https://www.bhcc.cn
Year Founded: 1938
600800—(SHG)
Rev.: $849,157,255
Assets: $677,452,281
Liabilities: $268,901,100
Net Worth: $408,551,181
Earnings: ($5,368,587)
Fiscal Year-end: 12/31/22
Magnetic Card Mfr
N.A.I.C.S.: 522210
Gao Yongfeng (Deputy Gen Mgr)

TIAN LUN GAS HOLDINGS LIMITED
4th FloorTianlun Group Building No 6 Huanghe Dong Rd, Zheng Dong Xin District, Zhengzhou, 450003, Henan, China
Tel.: (86) 37168081771
Web Site: http://www.tianlungas.com
1600—(HKG)
Rev.: $1,059,017,404
Assets: $2,240,606,254
Liabilities: $1,423,103,386
Net Worth: $817,502,868
Earnings: $65,885,789
Emp.: 3,355
Fiscal Year-end: 12/31/22
Gas Pipeline Transportation
N.A.I.C.S.: 486210
Yingcen Zhang (Founder & Chm)

TIAN POH RESOURCES LIMITED
C/- PKF Level 4 35-37 Havelock Street, West Perth, 6005, WA, Australia
Tel.: (61) 894268999   AU
Web Site: http://www.tianpoh.com
Rev.: $5,590
Assets: $3,765,298
Liabilities: $2,328,372
Net Worth: $1,436,926
Earnings: ($1,013,314)
Fiscal Year-end: 12/31/19
Mineral Exploration Services
N.A.I.C.S.: 213115
Poh Kay Ping (CEO)

TIAN RUIXIANG HOLDINGS LTD.
21A Jingyuan Art Center 3 Guangqu Road, Chaoyang District, Beijing, 100124, China
Tel.: (86) 1087529554   Ky
Web Site: http://www.tianrx.com
Year Founded: 2010
TIRX—(NASDAQ)
Rev.: $1,244,247
Assets: $35,479,774
Liabilities: $3,062,868
Net Worth: $32,416,906
Earnings: ($2,453,982)
Emp.: 8
Fiscal Year-end: 10/31/22
Insurance Brokerage Services
N.A.I.C.S.: 524210
Zhe Wang (Chm & CEO)

TIAN SHAN DEVELOPMENT (HOLDING) LIMITED
No 109 Tianshan Avenue Shijiazhuang Hi-Tech Industry Development Zone, Shijiazhuang, 050061, Hebei, China
Tel.: (86) 1085295302   Ky
Web Site: http://www.tian-shan.com
Year Founded: 2005
2118—(HKG)
Rev.: $826,457,026
Assets: $4,244,655,625
Liabilities: $3,905,540,152
Net Worth: $339,115,474
Earnings: ($14,218,348)
Emp.: 1,531
Fiscal Year-end: 12/31/20
Property Development Services
N.A.I.C.S.: 531312
Zhenshan Wu (Co-Founder & Chm)

Subsidiaries:

Tian Shan Real Estate Development Company Limited (1)
No 109 Tianshan Avenue Shijiazhuang Hi-Tech Industry Development Zone, Shijiazhuang, 10005, Hebei, China
Tel.: (86) 1085295302
Real Estate Services
N.A.I.C.S.: 531390

TIAN TECK LAND LTD.
9F iSQUARE 63 Nathan Road, Tsim Sha Tsui, Kowloon, China (Hong Kong)
Tel.: (852) 28100993   HK
Web Site: https://ttll.etnet.com.hk
0266—(HKG)
Rev.: $40,028,685
Assets: $1,314,588,408
Liabilities: $63,671,880
Net Worth: $1,250,916,528
Earnings: ($143,723,704)
Emp.: 39
Fiscal Year-end: 03/31/22
Holding Company
N.A.I.C.S.: 551112
Hooi Hong Cheong (Chm & CEO)

TIAN YUAN GROUP HOLDINGS LIMITED
168 Renmin South Road, Maoming, China
Tel.: (86) 37981001   Ky
Web Site: http://www.tianyuangroup.com
6119—(HKG)
Rev.: $44,633,300
Assets: $66,114,641
Liabilities: $16,947,263
Net Worth: $49,167,378
Earnings: $3,378,586
Emp.: 236
Fiscal Year-end: 12/31/22
Bulk Cargo Transportation Services
N.A.I.C.S.: 484230
Jinming Yang (Founder, Chm & CEO)

Subsidiaries:

Maoming Tianyuan Terminal Operation Company Limited (1)
Port Fort, Shuidong, Maoming, 525027, China
Tel.: (86) 6682088661
Shipping Logistic & Agent Services
N.A.I.C.S.: 488510

Maoming Zhengyuan Trade Development Company Limited (1)
East 31 Area, Maogang, Maoming, 525027, China
Tel.: (86) 6683967798
Shipping Logistic & Agent Services
N.A.I.C.S.: 488510

TIAN ZHENG INTERNATIONAL PRECISION MACHINERY CO., LTD.
No 295-2 Fengren Road, Renwu District, Kaohsiung, 814, Taiwan
Tel.: (886) 73713213
Web Site: https://tz-int-ltd.com
Year Founded: 1988
6654—(TPE)
Rev.: $17,489,604
Assets: $74,157,646
Liabilities: $42,161,899
Net Worth: $31,995,748
Earnings: $895,695
Fiscal Year-end: 12/31/22
Automobile Equipment Mfr
N.A.I.C.S.: 336110
Wan Wencai (Chm)

TIANAN INSURANCE CO., LTD.
1 Pudong Ave, Shanghai, 200135, China
Tel.: (86) 2161017878
Web Site: http://www.tianan-insurance.com
Sales Range: $300-349.9 Million
Emp.: 1,000
Accident & Health Insurance
N.A.I.C.S.: 524114
Zhengke Zhao (Gen Mgr)

TIANBAO HOLDINGS LIMITED
13Floor International Development Building No 333 Yu Feng Road, Jinshui District, Zhengzhou, 454000, China
Tel.: (86) 371 86021713
Web Site: http://www.tianbaoholdings.com
Emp.: 56
Affordable Construction Services
N.A.I.C.S.: 236210
Haitao Lian (CEO)

TIANDA GROUP LIMITED
Level 24 CITIC Tower No 1 Tim Mei Avenue, Central, China (Hong Kong)
Tel.: (852) 2295 0303
Web Site: http://www.tianda.com
Holding Company
N.A.I.C.S.: 551112
Alan Fang (Chm & Mng Dir)

Subsidiaries:

Tianda Pharmaceuticals Limited (1)
Level 24 CITIC Tower No 1 Tim Mei Avenue, Central, China (Hong Kong)
Tel.: (852) 2 545 3313

TIANDA GROUP LIMITED

Tianda Group Limited—(Continued)
Web Site: http://www.tiandapharma.com
Rev.: $65,774,002
Assets: $150,152,243
Liabilities: $48,377,319
Net Worth: $101,774,924
Earnings: ($2,795,612)
Emp.: 675
Fiscal Year-end: 03/31/2022
Pharmaceutical, Biotech & Healthcare Products Mfr & Sales
N.A.I.C.S.: 325412
Alan Wen Quan Fang *(Chm & Mng Dir)*

Subsidiary (Non-US):

Tianda Pharmaceuticals (Australia) Pty Ltd. (2)
Level 17 Gateway 1 Macquarie Place, Sydney, 2000, NSW, Australia
Tel.: (61) 2 9251 9001
Pharmaceuticals Mfr
N.A.I.C.S.: 325412

Tianda Pharmaceuticals (China) Ltd. (2)
Level 28 Block C Tian An International Building, 3012 Renmin Road South, Shenzhen, 518001, China
Tel.: (86) 755 8228 3533
Pharmaceuticals Mfr
N.A.I.C.S.: 325412

TIANDE CHEMICAL HOLDINGS LIMITED

Room 2204A 22nd Floor Bank of America Tower 12 Harcourt Road, Central, China (Hong Kong)
Tel.: (852) 28666982
Web Site: http://www.tdchem.com
0609—(HKG)
Rev.: $494,293,363
Assets: $415,615,871
Liabilities: $64,031,526
Net Worth: $351,584,345
Earnings: $134,501,375
Emp.: 1,558
Fiscal Year-end: 12/31/22
Development of Chemical Products
N.A.I.C.S.: 541715
Zijiang Wang *(Exec Dir)*

Subsidiaries:

Weifang Parasia Chem Co., Ltd. (1)
No 88 Taixiang Street Economic Development Zone, Weifang, 261041, Shandong, China
Tel.: (86) 5362103219
Web Site: http://www.tdchem.com
Emp.: 500
Fine Chemical Product Mfr & Distr
N.A.I.C.S.: 325199
Wenqiang Yang *(Gen Mgr)*

TIANDI SCIENCE & TECHNOLOGY CO., LTD.

Coal Building No 5 Qingniangou Road Heping Street, Chaoyang District, Beijing, 100013, China
Tel.: (86) 1087986209
Web Site: https://www.tdtec.com
Year Founded: 2000
600582—(SHG)
Rev.: $3,849,228,218
Assets: $6,096,175,217
Liabilities: $2,580,026,399
Net Worth: $3,516,148,818
Earnings: $274,102,597
Emp.: 21,221
Fiscal Year-end: 12/31/22
Mining Equipment Mfr
N.A.I.C.S.: 333131
Hu Shanting *(Chm)*

TIANFENG SECURITIES CO., LTD.

Building No 2 Tianfeng Building No 217 Zhongbei Road, Wuchang District, Wuhan, 430000, Hubei, China
Tel.: (86) 2787618889
Web Site: https://www.tfzq.com
Year Founded: 2000
601162—(SHG)
Rev.: $241,626,813
Assets: $13,788,446,738
Liabilities: $10,440,066,457
Net Worth: $3,348,380,281
Earnings: ($211,859,332)
Emp.: 3,000
Fiscal Year-end: 12/31/22
Investment Banking Services
N.A.I.C.S.: 523150
Pang Jiemin *(Chm)*

TIANGONG INTERNATIONAL COMPANY LIMITED

Houxiang Town, Danyang, 212312, Jiangsu, China
Tel.: (86) 51186312333
Web Site: https://www.tggj.cn
Year Founded: 1992
34T1—(DEU)
Rev.: $701,540,624
Assets: $1,850,236,902
Liabilities: $861,461,287
Net Worth: $988,775,615
Earnings: $72,567,291
Emp.: 3,203
Fiscal Year-end: 12/31/22
Steel Cutting Tool Mfr & Distr
N.A.I.C.S.: 333515

Subsidiaries:

China Tiangong (Hong Kong) Company Limited (1)
Rm 1303 13/F Jubilee Ctr, Wanchai, China (Hong Kong)
Tel.: (852) 31022386
Investment Holding Services
N.A.I.C.S.: 523940

Five Star Special Steel Europe S.R.L (1)
Via Della Zonta 2, 34122, Trieste, Italy
Tel.: (39) 030 5243724
Web Site: http://www.fssseurope.com
Steel Product Distr
N.A.I.C.S.: 423510

TGT Special Steel Company Limited (1)
1DA A-102HO Shihwa Industrial Complex 1235-2 Jungwang-Dong, Siheung, Gyeonggi, Korea (South)
Tel.: (82) 313192074
Steel Product Distr
N.A.I.C.S.: 423510

TIANGUANG FIRE-FIGHTING INCORPORATED COMPANY

Chenggong Technology Industrial Zone, Nanan, Quanzhou, 362300, Fujian, China
Tel.: (86) 595 863 11129
Web Site: http://www.tianguang.com
Year Founded: 1986
Rev.: $307,208,125
Assets: $1,299,191,911
Liabilities: $630,496,428
Net Worth: $668,695,484
Earnings: ($64,587,661)
Emp.: 460
Fiscal Year-end: 12/31/18
Fire Fighting Products Mfr
N.A.I.C.S.: 922160
Yu Houshu *(Chm)*

TIANHE CHEMICALS GROUP LTD.

100 West Jiefang Road, Tiahe District, Jinzhou, 121016, Liaoning, China
Tel.: (86) 416 5160601
Web Site: http://www.tianhechem.com
Year Founded: 1992
Chemicals Mfr
N.A.I.C.S.: 325998
Qi Wei *(CEO)*

TIANJIN 712 COMMUNICATION & BROADCASTING CO., LTD.

41 North Street, West district, Teda, 300462, China
Tel.: (86) 2265388342
Web Site: https://www.712.cn
Year Founded: 1936
603712—(SHG)
Rev.: $528,718,517
Assets: $1,315,723,049
Liabilities: $761,830,597
Net Worth: $553,892,453
Earnings: $105,454,443
Fiscal Year-end: 12/31/21
Communication Equipment Mfr
N.A.I.C.S.: 334220

TIANJIN BENEFO TEJING ELECTRIC CO., LTD.

No 12 Minhe Road Xiqing Economic Development Zone, Tianjin, 300385, China
Tel.: (86) 2283963876
Web Site: https://www.benefo.tj.cn
Year Founded: 1999
600468—(SHG)
Rev.: $313,515,180
Assets: $531,524,228
Liabilities: $230,384,480
Net Worth: $301,139,748
Earnings: $16,987,937
Emp.: 2,000
Fiscal Year-end: 12/31/22
Electrical Equipment Mfr & Distr
N.A.I.C.S.: 335999

Subsidiaries:

Dyton (Chongqing) Switchgear Co., Ltd. (1)
Dyton Park No 198 Tongxi Road, CaiJiagang Town Beibei Area, Chongqing, 400707, China
Tel.: (86) 238 608 9886
Web Site: https://www.dyton.com.cn
Electrical Equipment & Component Mfr
N.A.I.C.S.: 335999
Bill Xiao *(Mgr-Sls-Intl)*

Innova Superconductor Technology Co.,Ltd. (1)
Unit 103 Longsheng Industrial Park 7 Rongchang Dongjie, Beijing Economic Technological Development Area, Beijing, 100176, China
Tel.: (86) 106 787 1801
Web Site: https://www.innost.com
Silo Mfr
N.A.I.C.S.: 335929
Rui Bao *(Branch Mgr)*

Tianjin Pumps & Machinery Group Co., Ltd. (1)
No 4 Guantao South Road, Beichen District, Tianjin, China
Tel.: (86) 2226390373
Web Site: http://www.en.ctppumps.com
Pumping Equipment Mfr
N.A.I.C.S.: 333914

TIANJIN BINHAI ENERGY & DEVELOPMENT CO., LTD.

No 27 11th Street, Tianjin Development Zone, Tianjin, 100070, China
Tel.: (86) 1063722821
Web Site: http://www.binhaienergy.com
Year Founded: 1992
000695—(SSE)
Rev.: $58,281,893
Assets: $115,782,517
Liabilities: $69,497,621
Net Worth: $46,284,896
Earnings: ($14,382,422)
Fiscal Year-end: 12/31/22
Electric Power Distribution Services
N.A.I.C.S.: 221122
Zhigang Shen *(Deputy Gen Mgr)*

TIANJIN BINHAI TEDA LOGIS-

INTERNATIONAL PUBLIC

TICS (GROUP) CORPORATION LIMITED

No 39 Bohai Road TEDA, Tianjin, 300457, China
Tel.: (86) 2259858181
Web Site: https://www.tbtl.cn
Year Founded: 2006
8348—(HKG)
Rev.: $463,480,477
Assets: $313,850,160
Liabilities: $173,552,933
Net Worth: $140,297,227
Earnings: $8,358,574
Emp.: 1,123
Fiscal Year-end: 12/31/22
Logistics & Supply Chain Services
N.A.I.C.S.: 541614
Weihong Yang *(Chm, Chm, Compliance Officer, Compliance Officer, Sec-Party General Branch, Gen Mgr & Gen Mgr)*

Subsidiaries:

Dalian Alps Teda Logistics Co., Ltd. (1)
IC-42 Dalian Free Trade Zone, Dalian, 116600, Liaoning, China
Tel.: (86) 41187328570
Freight Forwarding Services
N.A.I.C.S.: 541614

Tianjin Alps TEDA Logistics Co., Ltd. (1)
No 21 Bohai Road TEDA, Tianjin, 300457, China
Tel.: (86) 2259883500
Freight Forwarding Services
N.A.I.C.S.: 541614

TIANJIN CAPITAL ENVIRONMENTAL PROTECTION GROUP CO., LTD.

Chuangye Environmental Protection Building No 76 Weijin South Road, Nankai District, Tianjin, 300381, China
Tel.: (86) 2223930000
Web Site: https://www.tjcep.com
600874—(SHG)
Rev.: $634,912,247
Assets: $3,224,942,230
Liabilities: $1,890,820,292
Net Worth: $1,334,121,937
Earnings: $105,476,062
Emp.: 1,739
Fiscal Year-end: 12/31/22
Sewage Treatment Services
N.A.I.C.S.: 221320
Tang Fusheng *(Chm)*

TIANJIN CHASE SUN PHARMACEUTICAL CO., LTD.

B01 Entrepreneurship Headquarters Base Wuqing Development Zone, New Technology Industrial Park, Tianjin, 301700, China
Tel.: (86) 2259623217
Web Site: https://www.chasesun.cn
Year Founded: 1996
300026—(CHIN)
Rev.: $860,432,170
Assets: $1,666,964,187
Liabilities: $417,939,825
Net Worth: $1,249,024,362
Earnings: $71,359,033
Emp.: 6,000
Fiscal Year-end: 12/31/23
Pharmaceuticals Product Mfr
N.A.I.C.S.: 325412

Subsidiaries:

Beijing Tcmages Pharmaceutical Co., Ltd. (1)
No 5 Niuhui Street Niulanshan Industrial Development Zone, Shunyi District, Beijing, 101301, China
Tel.: (86) 1069418585
Web Site: http://www.tcmages.com

AND PRIVATE COMPANIES

Pharmaceuticals Product Mfr
N.A.I.C.S.: 325412

TIANJIN DEVELOPMENT HOLDINGS LIMITED
Suites 7-13 36th Floor China Merchants Tower Shun Tak Centre, 168-200 Connaught Road, Central, China (Hong Kong)
Tel.: (852) 21628888   HK
Web Site: https://www.tianjindev.com
0882—(HKG)
Rev.: $472,403,948
Assets: $2,711,443,943
Liabilities: $616,710,743
Net Worth: $2,094,733,200
Earnings: $64,279,635
Emp.: 2,490
Fiscal Year-end: 12/31/22
Holding Company
N.A.I.C.S.: 551112
Bonnia Su Yee Lee *(Sec)*

Subsidiaries:

Tianjin Yiyao Printing Co., Ltd.   (1)
No 83 Xianyang Road, Nankai District, Tianjin, China
Tel.: (86) 2227698171
Web Site: http://en.tjyy.cn
Printing Paper Product Mfr
N.A.I.C.S.: 323111
Telea Fan *(Mgr-HR)*

TIANJIN FUTONG XINMAO SCIENCE & TECHNOLOGY CO., LTD.
No 10 Rongyuan Road, Huayuan Industrial Zone Binhai Hi-tech Zone, Tianjin, China
Tel.: (86) 2283710998
Web Site: https://www.000836.net
000836—(SSE)
Rev.: $186,813,530
Assets: $393,325,307
Liabilities: $204,930,578
Net Worth: $188,394,729
Earnings: $1,775,807
Fiscal Year-end: 12/31/22
Optic Cable Mfr
N.A.I.C.S.: 335921

Subsidiaries:

Quickgem Optoelectronic Material Science & Technology Co., Ltd.   (1)
No 85 Huaxiang Road Economic & Technical Development Zone, Langfang, China
Tel.: (86) 3166075011
Web Site: https://www.quickgem.com
Quartz Material Mfr & Distr
N.A.I.C.S.: 334419

TIANJIN GOOD HAND RAILWAY HOLDING CO., LTD.
Xinxing Road, Heping District, Tianjin, 300308, China
Tel.: (86) 22 23686400
Web Site:
    http://www.guotiekonggu.com
000594—(SSE)
Sales Range: $1-9.9 Million
Holding Company
N.A.I.C.S.: 551112
Weidong Zhang *(CFO)*

TIANJIN GUIFAXIANG 18TH STREET MAHUA FOOD CO., LTD.
No 32 Dongting Road Hexi District, Tianjin, 300221, China
002820—(SSE)
Rev.: $33,181,546
Assets: $145,015,243
Liabilities: $11,244,285
Net Worth: $133,770,958
Earnings: ($9,914,023)
Fiscal Year-end: 12/31/22
Food Mfr & Distr

N.A.I.C.S.: 311423
Huang Jingya *(Sec)*

TIANJIN HI-TECH DEVELOPMENT CO., LTD.
11F Block G Haitai Green Industrial Base No 6 Haitai Fazhan 6th Road, Huayuan Industrial Zone New Technology Industrial Park, Tianjin, 300384, China
Tel.: (86) 2285689891
Web Site: http://www.hitech-develop.com
Year Founded: 1992
600082—(SHG)
Rev.: $69,272,377
Assets: $392,564,395
Liabilities: $145,792,511
Net Worth: $246,771,884
Earnings: $1,427,194
Fiscal Year-end: 12/31/22
Industrial Building Construction & Rental Services
N.A.I.C.S.: 236210
Liu Chao *(Chm)*

TIANJIN HUMAN RESOURCE & EDUCATION CONSULTING CO., LTD.
Block B1 17F Tianjin Emperor Place, No 85 Nanjing Road, Heping District, Tianjin, 300040, China
Tel.: (86) 22 2311 2225   CN
Web Site: http://www.athuman-china.com
Year Founded: 2005
Sales Range: Less than $1 Million
Foreign Language & Computer Studies Training Services
N.A.I.C.S.: 611519
Jin Hong Wu *(Co-Owner)*

TIANJIN JIEQIANG EQUIPMENT CO., LTD.
No 3 Binhu Road, Beichen, Tianjin, 300400, China
Tel.: (86) 2286878696
Web Site: http://www.tjjqzb.com
Year Founded: 2005
300875—(SSE)
Rev.: $33,679,980
Assets: $235,875,861
Liabilities: $40,297,636
Net Worth: $195,578,225
Earnings: ($2,446,554)
Fiscal Year-end: 12/31/22
Hydraulic Parts Mfr & Distr
N.A.I.C.S.: 333611
Feng Pan *(Chm & Gen Mgr)*

TIANJIN JINBIN DEVELOPMENT CO., LTD.
No 5 Villa B2 No 2 Mingyuan Road Tianjin Development Zone, Tianjin, 300381, China
Tel.: (86) 2266225289
Web Site: https://www.jbdc.com.cn
Year Founded: 1998
000897—(SSE)
Rev.: $199,387,502
Assets: $1,157,182,921
Liabilities: $843,826,267
Net Worth: $313,356,654
Earnings: $36,950,205
Fiscal Year-end: 12/31/22
Real Estate Support Services
N.A.I.C.S.: 531390
Zhizhong Hua *(Chm)*

TIANJIN JINGWEI HUIKAI OPTOELECTRONIC CO., LTD.
No 12 Wanggang Road Jinnan Economic Development Zone, Hong Kong, Tianjin, 300353, China
Tel.: (86) 2228572578
Web Site: https://www.jwdc.cn

Year Founded: 1999
300120—(SSE)
Rev.: $379,061,748
Assets: $623,238,408
Liabilities: $252,708,768
Net Worth: $370,529,640
Earnings: $5,162,508
Emp.: 90
Fiscal Year-end: 12/31/22
Wire, Cable, Non-Ferrous Materials, Insulating Materials & Silicon Mfr & Sales
N.A.I.C.S.: 332618
Shulin Dong *(Chm & Gen Mgr)*

TIANJIN JINRAN PUBLIC UTILITIES COMPANY LIMITED
Weishan Road Chang Qing Science Industry and Trade Park, Jinnan District, Tianjin, China
Tel.: (86) 2287569853   CN
Web Site:
    http://www.jinrangongyong.com
Year Founded: 1998
1265—(HKG)
Rev.: $249,962,352
Assets: $351,464,108
Liabilities: $128,862,894
Net Worth: $222,601,214
Earnings: $9,607,865
Emp.: 695
Fiscal Year-end: 12/31/22
Gas Pipeline Infrastructure Operator & Piped Gas Sales
N.A.I.C.S.: 237120
Wang Cong *(Chm)*

TIANJIN JINRONG TIANYU PRECISION MACHINERY, INC.
No 3 Chuangxin 4th Road Haitai, Binhai High-tech Industrial Development Zone, Tianjin, 300384, China
Tel.: (86) 2283750361
Web Site: https://www.tjjinrong.com
Year Founded: 2004
300988—(SSE)
Rev.: $200,568,153
Assets: $198,364,323
Liabilities: $66,693,566
Net Worth: $131,670,756
Earnings: $11,700,964
Fiscal Year-end: 12/31/22
Industrial Mold Mfr
N.A.I.C.S.: 333511

Subsidiaries:

Dongguan Jinrong Auto Parts Co., Ltd.   (1)
Jiaoli Beifang Village, Dongguan, Guangdong, China
Tel.: (86) 76988893582
Automotive Parts Mfr & Distr
N.A.I.C.S.: 336390

Tianjin Jinrong Tiansheng Metal Surface Treatment Co., Ltd.   (1)
Building 406, Bingang High-tech Casting Industrial Park, Tianjin, China
Tel.: (86) 15022104182
Metal Coating Product Mfr
N.A.I.C.S.: 332812

Tianjin Jinrongtian New Technology Co., Ltd.   (1)
Jingbin Industrial Park, Wuqing District, Tianjin, China
Tel.: (86) 222 223 2209
Automotive Parts Mfr & Distr
N.A.I.C.S.: 336390

Wuhan Jinrong Electromechanical Co., Ltd.   (1)
Fengting 2nd Road Junshan Street, Wuhan Economic & Technological Development Zone, Wuhan, China
Tel.: (86) 2759257279
Automotive Parts Mfr & Distr
N.A.I.C.S.: 336390

Zhejiang Jiaxing Jinrong Auto Parts Co., Ltd.   (1)

No 2355 Avenue, Jiashan County, Jiaxing, Zhejiang, China
Tel.: (86) 57389116717
Automotive Parts Mfr & Distr
N.A.I.C.S.: 336390

TIANJIN JIURI NEW MATERIALS CO., LTD.
3rd 5th and 6th Floor Gate 2 Building C Zhihuishan No 1 Gonghua Road, Huayuan New Technology Industrial Park, Tianjin, 300384, China
Tel.: (86) 2258330715
Web Site: https://www.jiurichem.com
Year Founded: 1998
688199—(SHG)
Rev.: $198,098,587
Assets: $576,452,874
Liabilities: $179,603,780
Net Worth: $396,849,094
Earnings: $6,085,961
Fiscal Year-end: 12/31/22
Chemical Product Mfr & Distr
N.A.I.C.S.: 325520

TIANJIN KEYVIA ELECTRIC CO., LTD.
No 15 Haitai Development 2nd Road, Huayuan Industrial Zone, Tianjin, 300392, China
Tel.: (86) 2260128018
Web Site: https://www.keyvia.cn
Year Founded: 2000
300407—(SSE)
Rev.: $268,689,096
Assets: $407,506,788
Liabilities: $187,497,180
Net Worth: $220,009,608
Earnings: $12,488,580
Emp.: 500
Fiscal Year-end: 12/31/22
Rail Power Supply, Urban Rail Transportation Automation Equipment & Systems
N.A.I.C.S.: 336999

TIANJIN LISHENG PHARMACEUTICAL CO., LTD.
No 16 Saida North 1st Road, Xiqing, Tianjin, 300385, China
Tel.: (86) 2227364241
Web Site:
    https://www.lishengpharma.com
Year Founded: 1951
002393—(SSE)
Rev.: $160,981,152
Assets: $742,861,946
Liabilities: $132,209,176
Net Worth: $610,652,769
Earnings: $13,142,367
Fiscal Year-end: 12/31/22
Pharmaceuticals Mfr
N.A.I.C.S.: 325412
Tieshuan Qi *(Chm)*

TIANJIN LVYIN LANDSCAPE CONSTRUCTION CO., LTD.
15F Main Building Nankai Science & Technology Building, No 20 Kaihua Road Huayuan Industrial Zone Binhai High-tech Zone, Tianjin, 300384, China
Tel.: (86) 2258357570
Web Site: http://www.tjloving.com
Year Founded: 1998
002887—(SSE)
Rev.: $82,368,229
Assets: $682,334,762
Liabilities: $343,171,254
Net Worth: $339,163,508
Earnings: $21,589,434
Fiscal Year-end: 12/31/22
Landscape Management Services
N.A.I.C.S.: 541620
Qi Yong *(Chm & Pres)*

Tianjin LVYIN Landscape Construction Co., Ltd.—(Continued)

TIANJIN MOTIMO MEMBRANE TECHNOLOGY CO., LTD.
No 60 11th Street Tianjin Development Zone, Hexi District, Tianjin, 300457, China
Tel.: (86) 2266230126
Web Site: http://www.motimo.com
Year Founded: 2003
300334—(SSE)
Rev.: $34,371,324
Assets: $215,480,304
Liabilities: $123,201,000
Net Worth: $92,279,304
Earnings: ($25,926,264)
Emp.: 180
Fiscal Year-end: 12/31/22
Ultrafiltration & Micro Membrane Product Mfr
N.A.I.C.S.: 325220

TIANJIN MOTOR DIES CO., LTD.
No 77 Hangtian Road Airport Economic Zone Space, Tianjin, 300308, China
Tel.: (86) 2224890729
Web Site: https://www.tqm.com.cn
Year Founded: 1965
002510—(SSE)
Rev.: $358,324,443
Assets: $807,030,895
Liabilities: $521,560,953
Net Worth: $285,469,943
Earnings: $11,257,904
Fiscal Year-end: 12/31/22
Automobile Body Panel Dies, Gages, Fixtures & Equipment Mfr & Metal Stamping
N.A.I.C.S.: 336211

Subsidiaries:

TQM Europe GmbH (1)
August-Lapple-Strasse 1, 74076, Heilbronn, Germany
Tel.: (49) 71316495100
Web Site: http://www.tqm-eu.de
Precision Tool Mfr
N.A.I.C.S.: 332721
Helmut Reiber (Mng Dir)

TIANJIN PENGLING GROUP CO., LTD.
No 1703 Gewan Road, Zhongtang Industrial Area Binhai New Area, Tianjin, 300270, China
Tel.: (86) 2263269287
Web Site: https://www.pengling.cn
Year Founded: 1988
300375—(CHIN)
Rev.: $238,365,504
Assets: $382,320,432
Liabilities: $110,796,660
Net Worth: $271,523,772
Earnings: $10,629,684
Emp.: 1,100
Fiscal Year-end: 12/31/22
Rubber Hose Mfr
N.A.I.C.S.: 326220

Subsidiaries:

Jiangsu Pengling Rubber Hose Co., LTD. (1)
No 37 Chuangxin Avenue Xuzhuang Street, Gaogang District, Taizhou, Jiangsu, China
Tel.: (86) 52380759006
Hose Product Mfr
N.A.I.C.S.: 336330

TIANJIN PHARMACEUTICAL DA REN TANG GROUP CORPORATION LIMITED
No 17 Baidi Road, Nankai District, Tianjin, 300193, China
Tel.: (86) 2227020892
Web Site: http://www.zhongxinp.com
Year Founded: 1981
600329—(SHG)
Rev.: $1,058,304,203
Assets: $1,389,167,327
Liabilities: $391,183,433
Net Worth: $997,983,894
Earnings: $117,839,939
Fiscal Year-end: 12/31/21
Holding Company
N.A.I.C.S.: 551112
Zhang Mingrui (Chm)

TIANJIN PORT DEVELOPMENT HOLDINGS LIMITED
Suite 3904-3907 39/F Tower Two Times Square 1 Matheson Street, Causeway Bay, China (Hong Kong)
Tel.: (852) 28478888
Web Site: http://www.tianjinportdev.com
3382—(HKG)
Rev.: $1,659,709,065
Assets: $5,381,890,388
Liabilities: $1,601,058,810
Net Worth: $3,780,831,578
Earnings: $149,800,898
Emp.: 6,141
Fiscal Year-end: 12/31/22
Container Handling Operation
N.A.I.C.S.: 336611
Susan Suqin Ma (Deputy Gen Mgr)

Subsidiaries:

Tianjin Port Alliance International Container Terminal Co., Ltd. (1)
1068 Linhai Road, Tanggu district, Tianjin, 300461, China
Tel.: (86) 2225705777
Logistics & Container Services
N.A.I.C.S.: 541614

TIANJIN PORT HOLDINGS CO., LTD.
No 99 Jingang Road, Tanggu District, Tianjin, 300461, China
Tel.: (86) 2225706615
Web Site: https://www.tianjin-port.com
Year Founded: 1992
600717—(SHG)
Rev.: $2,216,686,711
Assets: $5,268,194,795
Liabilities: $1,765,483,261
Net Worth: $3,502,711,534
Earnings: $149,047,284
Fiscal Year-end: 12/31/21
Holding Company
N.A.I.C.S.: 551112
Guo Xiaowei (Sec)

TIANJIN PRINTRONICS CIRCUIT CORPORATION
No 53 Hanghai Road Airport Economic Zone, Tianjin, 300308, China
Tel.: (86) 2224893466
Web Site: http://www.en.toppcb.com
Year Founded: 2005
002134—(SSE)
Rev.: $81,533,748
Assets: $106,726,141
Liabilities: $44,642,805
Net Worth: $62,083,336
Earnings: $2,254,670
Emp.: 832
Fiscal Year-end: 12/31/22
Printed Circuit Board Mfr
N.A.I.C.S.: 334412
Qin Kejing (Chm)

TIANJIN REALTY DEVELOPMENT(GROUP) CO., LTD.
No 80 Changde Road, Heping District, Tianjin, 300050, China
Tel.: (86) 2223317185
Web Site: http://www.tffzgroup.cn
600322—(SHG)
Rev.: $471,776,025
Assets: $2,324,488,177
Liabilities: $2,219,652,354
Net Worth: $104,835,824
Earnings: ($41,566,262)
Fiscal Year-end: 12/31/22
Property Management Services
N.A.I.C.S.: 523940
Yang Bin (Pres-Interim)

TIANJIN RINGPU BIO-TECHNOLOGY CO., LTD.
No 1 Dongjiu Road Tianjin Free Trade Area, Airport Economic Area, Tianjin, 300308, China
Tel.: (86) 2288958055
Web Site: https://www.ringpubiotech.com
Year Founded: 1998
300119—(CHIN)
Rev.: $292,628,700
Assets: $857,320,308
Liabilities: $225,365,868
Net Worth: $631,954,440
Earnings: $48,676,680
Emp.: 2,700
Fiscal Year-end: 12/31/22
Biotechnology Products & Pharmaceuticals Mfr
N.A.I.C.S.: 325414
Xu Lei (Gen Mgr)

Subsidiaries:

Ringpu (Baoding) Biological Pharmaceutical Co.,LTD. (1)
No 793 Tengfei Road Scientific & Technological Industry Area, Baoding, 071000, Hebei, China
Tel.: (86) 3125922510
Veterinary Biological Products Mfr
N.A.I.C.S.: 325412

Shanxi Ruixiang Biological Pharmaceutical Co., Ltd. (1)
No 15 Dachang South Road Tanghuai Park, Taiyuan Comprehensive Reform Demonstration Zone, Taiyuan, 030032, China
Tel.: (86) 3515675157
Web Site: https://www.furuiwo.cn
Veterinary Product Mfr & Distr
N.A.I.C.S.: 325411

TIANJIN RUIXIN TECHNOLOGY CO., LTD.
No 5 Haitai North Road, Huayuan Industrial Zone Tianjin New Technology Industrial Park, Tianjin, 300834, China
Tel.: (86) 2258188590
Web Site: https://www.ruixin-eht.com
Year Founded: 2004
300828—(SSE)
Rev.: $107,506,372
Assets: $137,532,021
Liabilities: $20,296,589
Net Worth: $117,235,432
Earnings: $13,651,359
Emp.: 500
Fiscal Year-end: 12/31/22
Aluminium Products Mfr
N.A.I.C.S.: 331313
Zhanchang Guo (Chm & Gen Mgr)

TIANJIN SAIXIANG TECHNOLOGY CO., LTD.
No 9 Hitech Developing 4th RD Huanwai, Huayuan Industry Zone, Tianjin, 300384, China
Tel.: (86) 2223788188
Web Site: https://www.chinarpm.com
Year Founded: 1989
002337—(CHIN)
Rev.: $67,556,128
Assets: $255,754,325
Liabilities: $78,996,930
Net Worth: $176,757,394
Earnings: $7,234,236
Emp.: 1,000
Fiscal Year-end: 12/31/22
Radial Tire Production Equipment & Testing Instruments Mfr
N.A.I.C.S.: 333248
Zhang Xiaochen (Chm & Gen Mgr)

TIANJIN TEDA BIOMEDICAL ENGINEERING COMPANY LIMITED
Floor 9 Building A2 Tianda Science Park No 80 Fourth Street, Tianjin Development Zone, Tianjin, China
Tel.: (86) 2259816900
Web Site: https://www.bioteda.com
Year Founded: 2000
8189—(HKG)
Rev.: $63,134,504
Assets: $47,342,352
Liabilities: $35,588,997
Net Worth: $11,753,355
Earnings: ($3,741,073)
Emp.: 265
Fiscal Year-end: 12/31/22
Biomedical Engineering Services
N.A.I.C.S.: 541714
Zhihui Hao (Vice Chm)

TIANJIN TEDA CO., LTD.
No 16 Third Avenue Tianjin Development Zone, Tianjin, 300457, China
Tel.: (86) 2265175652
Web Site: http://www.tedastock.com
Year Founded: 1992
000652—(SSE)
Rev.: $2,843,296,504
Assets: $5,623,475,387
Liabilities: $4,700,014,493
Net Worth: $923,460,895
Earnings: $25,015,756
Fiscal Year-end: 12/31/22
Chemical Product Whslr
N.A.I.C.S.: 424690
Zhang Wang (Chm)

TIANJIN TIANBAO ENERGY CO., LTD.
No 35 Haibin Road No 8, Tianjin Port Free Trade Zone, Tianjin, 300461, China
Tel.: (86) 2225761863
Web Site: https://www.tjtbny.com
Year Founded: 1992
1671—(HKG)
Rev.: $100,188,598
Assets: $149,442,883
Liabilities: $84,092,720
Net Worth: $65,350,163
Earnings: $2,430,324
Emp.: 73
Fiscal Year-end: 12/31/22
Electric Power Distribution Equipment Mfr & Distr
N.A.I.C.S.: 335311
Shanzhong Zhou (Chm & Exec Dir)

TIANJIN TIANBAO INFRASTRUCTURE CO.,LTD.
No 35 West Fifth Road, Airport Economic Zone, Tianjin, 300308, China
Tel.: (86) 2284866659
Web Site: https://www.tbjijian.com
Year Founded: 1998
000965—(SSE)
Rev.: $346,071,735
Assets: $1,799,677,709
Liabilities: $1,033,344,674
Net Worth: $766,333,035
Earnings: $3,271,755
Fiscal Year-end: 12/31/22
Property Management Services
N.A.I.C.S.: 531390
Hou Haixing (Chm & Gen Mgr)

TIANJIN TIANYAO PHARMACEUTICAL CO., LTD.

No 19 Xinye 9th Street, West Area Development Zone, Tianjin, 300457, China
Tel.: (86) 2260740048
Web Site: http://www.tjpcty.com
Year Founded: 1999
600488—(SHG)
Rev.: $517,925,758
Assets: $933,758,266
Liabilities: $406,719,467
Net Worth: $527,038,799
Earnings: $4,971,030
Fiscal Year-end: 12/31/22
Pharmaceuticals Product Mfr
N.A.I.C.S.: 325412
Jian Chen *(Chm & Gen Mgr)*

Subsidiaries:

Tianjin Tianfa Pharmaceuticals Imp & Exp Corp. (1)
Jinyao Building No 109 Bawei Road, Hedong District, Tianjin, 300171, China
Tel.: (86) 222 416 0918
Web Site: https://www.kingyork.biz
Pharmaceuticals Product Mfr
N.A.I.C.S.: 325412

TIANJIN YIYI HYGIENE PRODUCTS CO., LTD.

Zhangjiawo Town Industrial Zone, Xiqing District, Tianjin, 300380, China
Tel.: (86) 2287988888
Web Site: https://www.tjyiyi.com
Year Founded: 2005
001206—(SSE)
Rev.: $212,893,883
Assets: $283,438,102
Liabilities: $29,322,891
Net Worth: $254,115,211
Earnings: $21,136,532
Fiscal Year-end: 12/31/22
Personal Care Product Distr
N.A.I.C.S.: 456199
Fuzhong Gao *(Chm & Gen Mgr)*

TIANJIN YOU FA STEEL PIPE GROUP STOCK CO., LTD.

Baiyiyuan Industrial Zone, Daqiuzhuang Town Jinghai, Tianjin, 301606, China
Tel.: (86) 2228891850
Web Site: http://www.yfgg.com
Year Founded: 2011
601686—(SHG)
Rev.: $9,457,393,196
Assets: $2,355,964,931
Liabilities: $1,319,547,645
Net Worth: $1,036,417,286
Earnings: $41,703,461
Fiscal Year-end: 12/31/22
Steel Pipe Mfr & Distr
N.A.I.C.S.: 331210
Maojin Li *(Chm)*

TIANJIN ZHUOLANG INFORMATION TECHNOLOGY CO., LTD.

No 1 Xiangtan Road, Hongqiao District, Tianjin, 300133, China
Tel.: (86) 2258301588
Web Site: http://www.tjsjgf.com.cn
Year Founded: 2001
600225—(SHG)
Rev.: $124,714,472
Assets: $1,030,208,554
Liabilities: $727,742,904
Net Worth: $302,465,650
Earnings: $119,261,728
Fiscal Year-end: 12/31/21
Real Estate Manangement Services
N.A.I.C.S.: 531390
Wang Zhigang *(Chm)*

TIANLI HOLDINGS GROUP LTD.

Unit 907909 9th Floor Three Pacific Place, 1 Queen s Road East, Hong Kong, China (Hong Kong)
Tel.: (852) 29720100
0117—(HKG)
Rev.: $50,737,331
Assets: $255,064,259
Liabilities: $130,074,142
Net Worth: $124,990,117
Earnings: ($9,086,548)
Emp.: 1,084
Fiscal Year-end: 12/31/22
Holding Company
N.A.I.C.S.: 551112

TIANLI INTERNATIONAL HOLDINGS LIMITED

Tower T25 Qingying Industrial Zone, Chengdu, Sichuan, China
Tel.: (86) 2887016688 Ky
Web Site: http://www.tianlieducation.com
1773—(HKG)
Rev.: $124,165,829
Assets: $1,141,607,984
Liabilities: $877,808,318
Net Worth: $263,799,666
Earnings: $13,500,864
Emp.: 3,018
Fiscal Year-end: 12/31/22
Educational Support Services
N.A.I.C.S.: 611710
Shi Luo *(Founder, Chm & CEO)*

TIANMA BEARING GROUP CO., LTD.

No 8 Yunhe Road, Leidian Town Deqing County, Huzhou, 313219, China
Tel.: (86) 5728487432
Web Site: https://www.zjtmb.com
002122—(SSE)
Rev.: $98,653,927
Assets: $494,197,512
Liabilities: $170,986,954
Net Worth: $323,210,558
Earnings: $11,948,686
Emp.: 6,000
Fiscal Year-end: 12/31/22
Bearing Products Mfr
N.A.I.C.S.: 332991
Maodong Xu *(Chm)*

TIANMEI BEVERAGE GROUP CORPORATION LIMITED

Level 27 Baker McKenzie 50 Brdige Street, Sydney, 2000, NSW, Australia
Tel.: (61) 280513083 AU
Web Site: http://www.tianmei.com.au
Beverage Product Distr
N.A.I.C.S.: 424490
Han Xu *(Exec Dir)*

TIANNENG BATTERY GROUP COMPANY LIMITED

No 18 Baoqiao Road, Huaxi Industrial Functional Zone Changxing County, Huzhou, 313100, Zhejiang, China
Tel.: (86) 5726029388
Web Site: https://www.cn-tn.com
Year Founded: 2003
688819—(SHG)
Rev.: $5,880,285,394
Assets: $4,545,810,365
Liabilities: $2,569,905,679
Net Worth: $1,975,904,686
Earnings: $267,909,272
Fiscal Year-end: 12/31/22
Electrical Battery Mfr & Distr
N.A.I.C.S.: 335910
Zhang Tianren *(Founder & Chm)*

TIANNENG POWER INTERNATIONAL LIMITED

Room 3202 32 Floor Central Plaza 18 Harbour Road, Wanchai, China (Hong Kong)
Tel.: (852) 28771398
Web Site: http://www.tianneng.com.hk
0819—(HKG)
Rev.: $10,473,649,196
Assets: $5,635,083,589
Liabilities: $3,224,952,760
Net Worth: $2,410,130,830
Earnings: $291,986,791
Emp.: 26,971
Fiscal Year-end: 12/31/22
Battery Production
N.A.I.C.S.: 335999
Borong Shi *(VP)*

Subsidiaries:

Zhejiang Tianneng Battery Co., Ltd. (1)
Zhicheng Industry Zone, Changxing, 313117, Zhejiang, China
Tel.: (86) 572 6709836
Web Site: http://www.tianneng.com.hk
Sales Range: $25-49.9 Million
Emp.: 20
Supplier of Motive Batteries for Electric Vehicles
N.A.I.C.S.: 335910

TIANRUI GROUP CO., LTD.

63 Guangcheng Road, Ruzhou, 467500, Henan, China
Tel.: (86) 375 603 7666 CN
Web Site: http://www.tianruigroup.cn
Year Founded: 1983
Sales Range: $1-4.9 Billion
Holding Company
N.A.I.C.S.: 551112
Liufa Li *(Owner & Chm)*

Subsidiaries:

Sanmenxia Tianyuan Aluminum Company Limited (1)
No 10 South Dongfeng Road, Sanmenxia, 472000, HEN, China
Tel.: (86) 398 2916763
Web Site: http://www.styal.com.cn
Aluminum Product Mfr & Distr
N.A.I.C.S.: 331313
Yuzhong Yang *(Deputy Gen Mgr)*

Tianrui Group Cement Co., Ltd. (1)
Guangcheng East Road, Ruzhou, 467500, Henan, China (57.1%)
Tel.: (86) 375 603 0133
Web Site: http://www.trcement.com
Cement Mfr
N.A.I.C.S.: 327310
Heping Li *(Chm)*

Tianrui Group Foundry Co., Ltd. (1)
63 Guangcheng Road, Ruzhou, 467500, Henan, China
Tel.: (86) 375 603 0123
Metal Casting Mfr
N.A.I.C.S.: 331523

TIANRUN INDUSTRY TECHNOLOGY CO., LTD.

No 2-13 Tianrun Road, Wendeng District, Weihai, 264400, Shandong, China
Tel.: (86) 6318982126
Web Site: https://www.tianrun.com
Year Founded: 1954
002283—(SSE)
Rev.: $440,340,493
Assets: $1,120,746,089
Liabilities: $327,779,806
Net Worth: $792,966,283
Earnings: $28,583,559
Emp.: 3,600
Fiscal Year-end: 12/31/22
Crankshafts, Machine Tools & Machine Accessories Mfr
N.A.I.C.S.: 333517
Xing Yunbo *(Chm)*

TIANSHAN ALUMINUM GROUP CO., LTD.

Dayangcheng Industrial Zone Daxi Town, Wenling City, Taizhou, 832014, Zhejiang, China
Tel.: (86) 2158773690
Web Site: http://www.shimge.com
Year Founded: 1989
002532—(SSE)
Rev.: $4,634,381,929
Assets: $7,962,893,729
Liabilities: $4,756,149,403
Net Worth: $3,206,744,326
Earnings: $372,126,732
Emp.: 1,000
Fiscal Year-end: 12/31/22
Pumps & Controlling Equipment Mfr
N.A.I.C.S.: 333914
Zeng Chaolin *(Chm & Gen Mgr)*

TIANSHAN MATERIAL CO.,LTD.

Tianhe Mansion No 1256 Hebei East Road, Urumqi, 830013, Xinjiang, China
Tel.: (86) 9916686781 CN
Web Site: http://www.sinoma-tianshan.cn
000877—(SSE)
Rev.: $18,614,305,106
Assets: $40,552,650,932
Liabilities: $26,891,483,688
Net Worth: $13,661,167,244
Earnings: $637,730,566
Emp.: 800
Fiscal Year-end: 12/31/22
Cement Mfr
N.A.I.C.S.: 327310
Xinjun Zhao *(Chm)*

TIANSHENG PHARMACEUTICAL GROUP CO., LTD.

No 16 Food City West Road Baoshenghu Street, Yubei District, Chongqing, 408300, China
Tel.: (86) 2374695513
Web Site: https://www.tszy.com.cn
Year Founded: 2001
002872—(SSE)
Rev.: $85,221,705
Assets: $416,963,781
Liabilities: $109,825,766
Net Worth: $307,138,015
Earnings: ($12,715,101)
Fiscal Year-end: 12/31/22
Pharmaceutical Product Mfr & Distr
N.A.I.C.S.: 325412
Liu Shuang *(Chm & Gen Mgr)*

TIANSHUI HUATIAN TECHNOLOGY CO., LTD.

No 14 Shuangqiao Road, Qinzhou District, Tianshui, 741001, Gansu, China
Tel.: (86) 9388631816 CN
Web Site: http://www.tshtkj.com
Year Founded: 2003
002185—(SSE)
Rev.: $1,671,596,854
Assets: $4,348,389,025
Liabilities: $1,652,931,320
Net Worth: $2,695,457,705
Earnings: $105,853,934
Emp.: 7,088
Fiscal Year-end: 12/31/22
Integrated Circuit Testing & Packaging Services
N.A.I.C.S.: 334418
Tiecheng Zhang *(Deputy Gen Mgr)*

Subsidiaries:

FlipChip International, LLC (1)
3701 E University Dr, Phoenix, AZ 85034
Tel.: (602) 431-6020
Web Site: http://www.flipchip.com
Wafer Level Package Bumping & Integrated Circuit Assembly Services
N.A.I.C.S.: 334413

Unisem (M) Berhad (1)

TIANSHUI HUATIAN TECHNOLOGY CO., LTD.

Tianshui Huatian Technology Co., Ltd.—(Continued)
9th Floor UBN Tower No 10 Jalan P Ramlee, Letter Box 95, 50250, Kuala Lumpur, Malaysia **(58.94%)**
Tel.: (60) 320723760
Web Site: https://www.unisemgroup.com
Rev.: $377,108,571
Assets: $638,901,376
Liabilities: $127,492,698
Net Worth: $511,408,677
Earnings: $81,557,884
Emp.: 3,256
Fiscal Year-end: 12/31/2022
Semiconductor Devices Mfr
N.A.I.C.S.: 334413
John Sin Tet Chia *(Chm & Mng Dir)*

Subsidiary (US):

Unisem (Sunnyvale) Inc. **(2)**
2241 Calle de Luna, Santa Clara, CA 95054
Tel.: (408) 734-3222
Semiconductor Product Whslr
N.A.I.C.S.: 423690

Subsidiary (Non-US):

Unisem Chengdu Co., Ltd. **(2)**
No 8-2 Kexin Road West Park of Chengdu High-tech Zone, Chengdu, 611731, China
Tel.: (86) 2887958228
Semiconductor Product Whslr
N.A.I.C.S.: 423690
Quek Suan Hong *(COO)*

TIANSHUI ZHONGXING BIO-TECHNOLOGY CO., LTD.
National Agricultural Science and Technology Park, Maiji District, Tianshui, 741030, Gansu, China
Tel.: (86) 9382851611
Web Site: http://www.tszxjy.cn
Year Founded: 2005
002772—(SSE)
Rev.: $276,626,526
Assets: $922,307,439
Liabilities: $447,099,560
Net Worth: $475,207,879
Earnings: $22,232,607
Fiscal Year-end: 12/31/22
Mushroom Farming Services
N.A.I.C.S.: 111411
Liang Liu *(CFO & Gen Mgr)*

TIANYANG NEW MATERIALS (SHANGHAI) TECHNOLOGY CO., LTD.
No 505 Huiping Rd, Jiading District, Shanghai, 201802, China
Tel.: (86) 2169890408
Web Site: https://www.hotmelt.com.cn
Year Founded: 1993
603330—(SHG)
Rev.: $200,210,372
Assets: $322,616,217
Liabilities: $178,767,908
Net Worth: $143,848,308
Earnings: ($7,945,053)
Fiscal Year-end: 12/31/22
Adhesive Mfr & Distr
N.A.I.C.S.: 325520
Li Zhelong *(Chm & Gen Mgr)*

Subsidiaries:

Kunshan Tianyang Hot Melt Adhesives Co., Ltd. **(1)**
No 366 East Wenpu Rd, Quiandeng Town, Kunshan, China
Tel.: (86) 51281639689
Adhesive Mfr
N.A.I.C.S.: 325520

Shanghai Huiping Culture Development Co., Ltd. **(1)**
No 505 Huiping Rd, Jiading District, Shanghai, China
Tel.: (86) 2169122663
Adhesive Mfr
N.A.I.C.S.: 325520

Yantai Seayu New Materials Co., Ltd. **(1)**
No 12-2 Middle Wolong Rd, Zhifu District, Yantai, Shandong, China
Tel.: (86) 4006535200
Adhesive Mfr
N.A.I.C.S.: 325520

TIANYIN PHARMACEUTICAL CO.
11th Floor South Tower Jinjiang Times Garden, 107 Jin Li Road West, Chengdu, 610072, China
Tel.: (86) 2885516696   DE
Web Site: http://www.tianyinpharma.com
Year Founded: 2002
Sales Range: $25-49.9 Million
Emp.: 1,000
Pharmaceuticals Mfr
N.A.I.C.S.: 325412
Guoqing Jiang *(Chm, Pres & CEO)*

TIANYU BIO-TECHNOLOGY CO., LTD.
2F Building C4 Wangu Science Park Lane 1688 Guoquan North Road, Yangpu District, Shanghai, 200433, China
Tel.: (86) 2165236319
Web Site: http://www.tysthj.com
Year Founded: 2000
603717—(SHG)
Rev.: $97,760,237
Assets: $510,010,044
Liabilities: $263,098,340
Net Worth: $246,911,704
Earnings: ($32,900,315)
Fiscal Year-end: 12/31/21
Ecological Garden Engineering & Landscaping Services
N.A.I.C.S.: 561730
Weiguo Luo *(Chm & Gen Mgr)*

TIANYUN INTERNATIONAL HOLDINGS LIMITED
Room 605 6/F Beautiful Group Tower 74-77 Connaught Road Central, Central, China (Hong Kong)
Tel.: (852) 28736836   VG
Web Site: http://www.tianyuninternational.com
6836—(HKG)
Rev.: $95,574,071
Assets: $192,698,719
Liabilities: $34,111,163
Net Worth: $158,587,556
Earnings: $13,563,202
Emp.: 494
Fiscal Year-end: 12/31/22
Package Fruit Product Mfr & Distr
N.A.I.C.S.: 311991
Ziyuan Yang *(Chm & CEO)*

Subsidiaries:

Shandong Tiantong Food Co., Ltd. **(1)**
Phoenix Street Middle, Hedong District, Linyi, Shandong, China
Tel.: (86) 539 808 3916
Web Site: https://www.tiantongfruit.com
Canned Fruit Product Mfr & Distr
N.A.I.C.S.: 311421
Ziyuan Yang *(Co-Founder)*

TIB CHAMICALS AG
Mulheimer Strasse 16-22, 68219, Mannheim, Germany
Tel.: (49) 621 8901 0   De
Web Site: http://www.tib.chemicals.com
Emp.: 483
Chemicals Mfr
N.A.I.C.S.: 325998
Henner Spelsberg *(Chm-Mgmt Bd)*

Subsidiaries:

Konigswarter & Ebell Chemische Fabrik GmbH **(1)**
Im Ennepeteal 19-21, 58135, Hagen, Germany **(100%)**
Tel.: (49) 2331481712
Web Site: http://www.ke-nickel.com
Chemicals Mfr
N.A.I.C.S.: 325998

TIBERIUS HOLDING AG
Langenstr 52-54, Bremen, 28195, Germany
Tel.: (49) 4215961490
Web Site: http://www.tiberius-holding.de
Sales Range: $1-9.9 Million
Emp.: 12
Financial Consulting Services
N.A.I.C.S.: 523999
Reiner Ehlerding *(Mng Dir)*

TIBET AIM PHARM INC
15A/15F Unit 4 Building C Yingdu Building No 48 Zhichun Road, Haidian District, Beijing, 100086, China
Tel.: (86) 8916862369
Web Site: https://www.emyy.cn
Year Founded: 2003
002826—(SSE)
Rev.: $120,285,496
Assets: $142,955,926
Liabilities: $37,656,459
Net Worth: $105,299,466
Earnings: $6,196,610
Fiscal Year-end: 12/31/22
Medicine Mfr & Distr
N.A.I.C.S.: 325412
Xu Ke *(Chm)*

TIBET CHEEZHENG TIBETAN MEDICINE CO. LTD.
2 Tibet Nyingchi Deji Road, Bayi District, Nyingchi, 860000, China
Tel.: (86) 8945826041
Web Site: https://www.cheezheng.com.cn
Year Founded: 1995
002287—(SSE)
Rev.: $287,088,418
Assets: $826,484,860
Liabilities: $350,858,238
Net Worth: $475,626,622
Earnings: $66,326,111
Emp.: 2,974
Fiscal Year-end: 12/31/22
Pharmaceutical Researcher, Developer & Distr
N.A.I.C.S.: 325411

TIBET DEVELOPMENT CO LTD.
No 28-5 Area A Gesanglinka Jinzhu West Road, Tibet Autonomous Region, Lhasa, 850001, China
Tel.: (86) 2885238616
000752—(SSE)
Rev.: $38,882,460
Assets: $119,857,851
Liabilities: $78,897,626
Net Worth: $40,960,226
Earnings: ($9,261,626)
Fiscal Year-end: 12/31/22
Beer Product Distr
N.A.I.C.S.: 424810

TIBET DUO RUI PHARMACEUTICAL CO., LTD.
3rd Floor Building 1 Biomedical Park Area A, Economic Development Zone, Qamdo, 854000, China
Tel.: (86) 8954892099
Web Site: https://www.duoruiyy.com
Year Founded: 2016
301075—(SSE)
Rev.: $56,307,420

INTERNATIONAL PUBLIC

Assets: $126,201,348
Liabilities: $20,422,584
Net Worth: $105,778,764
Earnings: $2,878,200
Fiscal Year-end: 12/31/22
Pharmaceutical Product Mfr & Distr
N.A.I.C.S.: 325412
Yong Deng *(Chm & Gen Mgr)*

TIBET GAOZHENG EXPLOSIVE CO., LTD.
No 18 Linqionggang Road Zone A, Economic and Technological Development Zone, Lhasa, 850000, China
Tel.: (86) 8916807952
Web Site: https://www.xzmbgf.com
Year Founded: 2014
002827—(SSE)
Rev.: $159,249,669
Assets: $297,332,830
Liabilities: $157,389,425
Net Worth: $139,943,405
Earnings: $7,495,914
Fiscal Year-end: 12/31/22
Explosive Mfr & Distr
N.A.I.C.S.: 325920
Le Yongjian *(Chm)*

TIBET HUAYU MINING CO., LTD.
Huayu Building GeSang Rd, National Economic and Technological Development Zone, Lhasa, China
Tel.: (86) 8916329000
Web Site: https://www.huayumining.com
Year Founded: 2002
601020—(SHG)
Rev.: $364,477,397
Assets: $752,994,976
Liabilities: $266,121,174
Net Worth: $486,873,802
Earnings: $11,089,340
Fiscal Year-end: 12/31/20
Non-Ferrous Metal Mfr & Distr
N.A.I.C.S.: 331410
Jianhua Xu *(Board of Directors & Exec VP)*

TIBET MINERAL DEVELOPMENT CO., LTD.
No 8 Jinzhu 2nd Road Liangdao Street, Chengguan District Tibet Autonomous Region, Lhasa, 850000, China
Tel.: (86) 8916873132
Year Founded: 1997
000762—(SSE)
Rev.: $310,170,866
Assets: $1,054,958,089
Liabilities: $484,664,619
Net Worth: $570,293,470
Earnings: $111,665,132
Fiscal Year-end: 12/31/22
Metal Mining Services
N.A.I.C.S.: 212230
Tai Zeng *(Chm)*

TIBET RHODIOLA PHARMACEUTICAL HOLDING COMPANY
No 427 Sanse Road, Jinjiang District, Chengdu, 850000, China
Tel.: (86) 2886678739
Web Site: https://www.xzyy.cn
Year Founded: 1999
600211—(SHG)
Rev.: $358,667,118
Assets: $575,557,487
Liabilities: $150,037,267
Net Worth: $425,520,220
Earnings: $51,921,043
Fiscal Year-end: 12/31/22
Holding Company
N.A.I.C.S.: 551112

TIBET SUMMIT RESOURCES CO., LTD.
7F No 305 Liuying Road, Jing An District, Shanghai, 200072, China
Tel.: (86) 2166284908
Web Site: http://www.xizangzhufeng.com
600338—(SHG)
Rev.: $276,953,166
Assets: $754,922,109
Liabilities: $265,302,704
Net Worth: $489,619,405
Earnings: $57,130,206
Emp.: 3,148
Fiscal Year-end: 12/31/22
Nonferrous Metal Product Mfr & Distr
N.A.I.C.S.: 331511
Jianrong Huang (Chm)

TIBET TIANLU CO., LTD.
No 14 Duodi Road, Lhasa, 850000, China
Tel.: (86) 8916902701
Web Site: https://www.xztianlu.com
600326—(SHG)
Rev.: $539,881,313
Assets: $1,924,237,247
Liabilities: $1,090,346,470
Net Worth: $833,890,777
Earnings: ($72,825,031)
Fiscal Year-end: 12/31/22
Road Construction Services
N.A.I.C.S.: 237310
Duoji Luobu (Chm)

TIBET TOURISM CO., LTD.
Building 11 International Headquarters City, Liuwu New District, Lhasa, 850000, Tibet, China
Tel.: (86) 8916339150
Web Site: https://www.600749.com
Year Founded: 1996
600749—(SHG)
Rev.: $16,945,859
Assets: $191,424,224
Liabilities: $51,389,405
Net Worth: $140,034,820
Earnings: ($4,125,036)
Fiscal Year-end: 12/31/22
Tourism Services
N.A.I.C.S.: 561520
Hu Feng (Pres)

TIBET URBAN DEVELOPMENT & INVESTMENT CO., LTD.
Room No 311 3rd Floor Jintai Group Office Building, A1-10 Boda Road Economic Development Zone, Lhasa, 850030, Tibet, China
Tel.: (86) 8916833922
Web Site: https://www.600773sh.com
Year Founded: 1996
600773—(SHG)
Rev.: $344,889,609
Assets: $1,957,811,759
Liabilities: $1,439,305,209
Net Worth: $518,506,551
Earnings: $16,461,423
Fiscal Year-end: 12/31/22
Real Estate Development Services
N.A.I.C.S.: 531390
Chen Weidong (Chm)

TIBET WATER RESOURCES LTD.
Unit 1611-1612 16th Floor One Island South 2 Heung Yip Road, Wong Chuk Hang, Hong Kong, China (Hong Kong)
Tel.: (852) 28913997
Web Site: http://www.twr1115.net
1115—(HKG)
Rev.: $43,797,359
Assets: $581,274,673
Liabilities: $179,806,489
Net Worth: $401,468,184

Earnings: ($14,386,226)
Emp.: 347
Fiscal Year-end: 12/31/22
Bottled Water Mfr
N.A.I.C.S.: 312112
Dong Wang (CEO)

TIBET WEIXINKANG MEDICINE CO., LTD.
3/F Building 4 Industrial Center No 5 South Road Zone B, Lhasa Economic and Technological Development Zone Tibet, Lhasa, 850000, China
Tel.: (86) 8916601760
Web Site: https://www.wxkpharma.com
Year Founded: 2006
603676—(SHG)
Rev.: $196,355,437
Assets: $233,726,435
Liabilities: $62,356,231
Net Worth: $171,370,204
Earnings: $24,845,001
Fiscal Year-end: 12/31/22
Pharmaceutical Product Mfr & Distr
N.A.I.C.S.: 325412
Zhang Yong (Chm & Gen Mgr)

TICK TRADING SOFTWARE AKTIENGESELLSCHAFT
Berliner Allee 59, 40212, Dusseldorf, Germany
Tel.: (49) 2117817670
Web Site: https://www.tick-ts.com
TBX0—(STU)
Rev.: $8,830,997
Assets: $4,437,576
Liabilities: $971,410
Net Worth: $3,466,166
Earnings: $982,448
Emp.: 30
Fiscal Year-end: 09/30/23
Software Development Services
N.A.I.C.S.: 541511
Gerd Goetz (Member-Mgmt Bd)

TICKER COMMUNICATIONS, INC
302-791 Goldstream Ave, Victoria, V9B 2X5, BC, Canada
Tel.: (250) 391-9773
Web Site: http://www.tickercom.com
Emp.: 15
Sign Mfr
N.A.I.C.S.: 339950
Aaron Gladish (Dir-Sports)

TIDE CO., LTD.
Room 2010 20th floor 128 Gasan digital 1-ro Gasan-dong STXV Tower, Geumcheon-gu, Seoul, Korea (South)
Tel.: (82) 266730930
Web Site: https://www.tidekorea.com
Year Founded: 2010
346010—(KRS)
Financial Banking Services
N.A.I.C.S.: 521110
Kevin Cho (CEO)

TIDE WATER OIL CO. (INDIA) LTD.
Yule House 8 Dr Rajendra Prasad Sarani, Kolkata, 700 001, India
Tel.: (91) 3371257700
Web Site: https://www.veedolindia.com
Year Founded: 1928
590005—(BOM)
Rev.: $224,062,107
Assets: $131,663,569
Liabilities: $40,110,305
Net Worth: $91,553,264
Earnings: $13,726,995
Emp.: 510
Fiscal Year-end: 03/31/23
Lubricant Mfr

N.A.I.C.S.: 324191
R. N. Ghosal (Mng Dir)
Subsidiaries:

Tide Water Oil Co. (India) Ltd. - Faridabad Plant (1)
Plot No 119 Sector 59 HSIDC, Ballabgarh, Faridabad, 121004, Haryana, India
Tel.: (91) 1294105228
Web Site: http://www.tidewaterindia.co.in
Sales Range: $25-49.9 Million
Emp.: 25
Lubricant Oil Mfr
N.A.I.C.S.: 324191
P. K. Jetly (Mgr)

Tide Water Oil Co. (India) Ltd. - Turbhe Plant (1)
Plot-C441 Turbhe TTC Indl Area MIDC Kalyan Dombivli Shil Road, Dist Thane, 400705, Mumbai, Maharashtra, India
Tel.: (91) 22 27618125
Web Site: http://www.tidewaterindia.co.in
Sales Range: $25-49.9 Million
Emp.: 55
Lubricant Oil Mfr
N.A.I.C.S.: 324191
J. Ramesh (VP)

TIDEHOLD DEVELOPMENT CO., LTD.
2-3FL 75 Yan-Ping S Road, Taipei, Taiwan
Tel.: (886) 223118531
Web Site: http://www.tidehold.com
9902—(TAI)
Rev.: $9,545,505
Assets: $44,754,732
Liabilities: $3,830,766
Net Worth: $40,923,966
Earnings: $1,028,680
Emp.: 17
Fiscal Year-end: 12/31/23
Automobile Whslr
N.A.I.C.S.: 423110

TIDEWATER MIDDLE EAST CO. PLC
Vozara St - No 84, Tehran, Iran
Tel.: (98) 2188553321
Web Site: https://www.tidewater.ir
Year Founded: 1968
TAYD—(THE)
Sales Range: Less than $1 Million
Underwater Pipeline Construction Services
N.A.I.C.S.: 237990

TIDEWATER MIDSTREAM AND INFRASTRUCTURE LTD.
900 222 3rd Avenue SW, Calgary, T2P 0B4, AB, Canada
Tel.: (587) 475-0210 AB
Web Site: https://www.tidewatermidstream.com
Year Founded: 2015
TWM—(TSXV)
Rev.: $1,667,531,496
Assets: $1,210,910,432
Liabilities: $953,792,072
Net Worth: $257,118,360
Earnings: ($301,443,904)
Emp.: 392
Fiscal Year-end: 12/31/23
Natural Gas Transportation
N.A.I.C.S.: 486210
Joel A. MacLeod (Chm & CEO)

TIDEWATER RENEWABLES LTD.
Suite 900 222-3rd Avenue SW, Calgary, T2P 0B4, AB, Canada
Tel.: (587) 475-0210 AB
Web Site: https://www.tidewater-renewables.com
Year Founded: 2021
LCFS—(TSX)
Rev.: $56,769,854
Assets: $741,017,466

Liabilities: $330,624,216
Net Worth: $410,393,250
Earnings: $19,352,732
Fiscal Year-end: 12/31/22
Renewable Energy Services
N.A.I.C.S.: 221210
Bryan Morin (Chief Legal Officer)

TIE KINETIX NV
De Corridor 5d 3rd Floor, 3621 ZA, Breukelen, 3621 ZA, Netherlands
Tel.: (31) 883698000
Web Site: https://www.tiekinetix.com
Year Founded: 1987
TIE—(EUR)
Rev.: $17,141,697
Assets: $12,987,016
Liabilities: $9,077,585
Net Worth: $3,909,431
Earnings: ($1,472,616)
Emp.: 115
Fiscal Year-end: 09/30/19
Computer Systems Design & Custom Computer Programming Services
N.A.I.C.S.: 541512
Jan Sundelin (CEO & Member-Exec Bd)
Subsidiaries:

TIE Commerce Inc. (1)
3 Highwood Dr Ste 101 E, Tewksbury, MA 01876
Tel.: (781) 272-4252
Sales Range: $25-49.9 Million
Emp.: 35
Business Development Software Solutions & Services
N.A.I.C.S.: 513210
Melissa Cromwell (Mgr-Fin)

TIE International BV (1)
De Corridor 5d 3rd Floor, 3621 ZA, Breukelen, Netherlands
Tel.: (31) 883698000
Web Site: https://tiekinetix.com
Sales Range: $25-49.9 Million
Emp.: 90
Business Development Software Solutions & Services
N.A.I.C.S.: 513210

TIE Kinetix S.A.S. (1)
Parc de Bellegarde Bat B 1 Chemin de Borie, 34170, Castelnau-le-Lez, France
Tel.: (33) 411950100
Electronic Data Interchange Services
N.A.I.C.S.: 518210

TIE Nederland BV (1)
City House II Antareslaan 22-24, 2132 JE, Hoofddorp, Netherlands
Tel.: (31) 206589000
Web Site: http://www.tiecommerce.com
Sales Range: $25-49.9 Million
Emp.: 35
Business Development Software Solutions
N.A.I.C.S.: 513210

TIEMCO LTD.
Kikukawa 3-1-11 Sumida-ku, Tokyo, 130-8555, Japan
Tel.: (81) 356000122
Web Site: http://www.tiemco.co.jp
Year Founded: 1969
7501—(TKS)
Rev.: $22,493,830
Assets: $38,020,720
Liabilities: $7,152,020
Net Worth: $30,868,700
Earnings: $713,880
Emp.: 68
Fiscal Year-end: 03/31/24
Fishing Tackle & Outdoor Product Mfr & Distr
N.A.I.C.S.: 339999
Yoshitada Nakayama (Mng Dir)

TIEN GIANG INVESTMENT & CONSTRUCTION COMPANY
No 46 - 48 Nguyen Cong Binh, Trung

Tien Giang Investment & Construction Company—(Continued)

An Commune, My Tho, Tien Giang, Vietnam
Tel.: (84) 733872878
Web Site: https://www.ticco.com.vn
Year Founded: 1983
THG—(HOSE)
Rev.: $68,794,936
Assets: $76,311,876
Liabilities: $47,946,747
Net Worth: $28,365,129
Earnings: $4,896,002
Fiscal Year-end: 12/31/23
Building Construction Services
N.A.I.C.S.: 236220
Vu Huy Giap *(Chm, Gen Dir & Deputy Gen Dir)*

TIEN LEN STEEL CORPORATION JOINT-STOCK COMPANY

G4A Quarter 4, Tan Hiep Ward, Bien Hoa, Dong Nai, Vietnam
Tel.: (84) 2513823187
Web Site: https://www.tienlengroup.com.vn
TLH—(HOSE)
Rev.: $253,737,923
Assets: $170,066,149
Liabilities: $93,396,687
Net Worth: $76,669,463
Earnings: $169,082
Emp.: 224
Fiscal Year-end: 12/31/23
Steel Products Mfr
N.A.I.C.S.: 331110
Nguyen Manh Ha *(Chm)*

TIEN LIANG BIOTECH CO., LTD.

No 147 Section 1 Datong Road 9F, Xizhi District, New Taipei City, Taiwan
Tel.: (886) 226483099
Web Site: https://tlb.com.tw
Year Founded: 1979
4127—(TPE)
Rev.: $16,525,123
Assets: $21,149,642
Liabilities: $6,294,094
Net Worth: $14,855,548
Earnings: $1,859,769
Fiscal Year-end: 12/31/22
Biotechnology Research & Development Services
N.A.I.C.S.: 541714
Epoch Chapter *(Pres)*

TIEN PHONG PLASTIC JOINT-STOCK COMPANY

No 222 Mac Dang Doanh Street Hung Dao Ward, Duong Kinh District, Haiphong, Vietnam
Tel.: (84) 2253813979
Web Site: https://nhuatienphong.vn
Year Founded: 1960
NTP—(HNX)
Rev.: $568,511,200
Assets: $506,383,700
Liabilities: $223,302,000
Net Worth: $283,081,700
Earnings: $47,954,000
Emp.: 2,000
Fiscal Year-end: 12/31/22
Plastic Pipe Fitting Products Mfr
N.A.I.C.S.: 326122

Subsidiaries:

CENTRAL TIEN PHONG PLASTIC COMPANY LIMITED (1)
Nam Cam Industrial Zone, Nghi Loc, Nghe An, Vietnam
Tel.: (84) 38 3791268
Plastic Pipe Fitting Mfr
N.A.I.C.S.: 326122

TIEN PHONG PLASTIC SOUTH JOINT STOCK COMPANY (1)
Dong An 2 IZ Hoa Phu ward, Thu Dau Mot, Binh Duong, Vietnam
Tel.: (84) 650 3589 544
Plastic Pipe Fitting Mfr
N.A.I.C.S.: 326122

TIEN PHONG SECURITIES CORPORATION

75-77 Nguyen Thai Binh Street, District 1, Ho Chi Minh City, Vietnam
Tel.: (84) 2873013839
Web Site: http://www.tpbs.com.vn
ORS—(HNX)
Rev.: $6,933,765
Assets: $12,968,414
Liabilities: $2,422,301
Net Worth: $10,546,113
Earnings: $1,870,737
Emp.: 80
Fiscal Year-end: 12/31/19
Investment Banking & Securities Brokerage Services
N.A.I.C.S.: 523150

TIEN SON CEMENT JOINT STOCK COMPANY

Hong Quang Commune, Ung Hoa District, Hanoi, Vietnam
Tel.: (84) 433775132
Web Site: http://www.ximangtiensonhatay.vn
Emp.: 500
Cement & Other Construction Materials Mfr
N.A.I.C.S.: 327310
Nham The Nguyen *(Chm & Gen Dir)*

TIEN THANH SERVICE & TRADING JOINT STOCK COMPANY

Viet Hung urban area Duc Giang, Long Bien, Hanoi, Vietnam
Tel.: (84) 963893958
TTH—(HNX)
Rev.: $35,339,918
Assets: $27,070,913
Liabilities: $9,512,297
Net Worth: $17,558,616
Earnings: $795,531
Emp.: 18
Fiscal Year-end: 12/31/23
Food Catering Services
N.A.I.C.S.: 722320
Nam Thanh Phan *(Gen Dir & Member-Mgmt Bd)*

TIEN TRUNG JOINT STOCK COMPANY

Tra Ly Industry Complex, Tay Luong Ward, Tien Hai District, Thai Binh, Vietnam
Tel.: (84) 363823162
Stones, Sand, Gravel & Clay Mfr & Distr
N.A.I.C.S.: 327120
Quyet Anh Hoang *(Chm-Mgmt Bd)*

TIEN WAH PRESS HOLDINGS BERHAD

12th Floor Menara Symphony No 5 Jalan Prof Khoo Kay Kim Seksyen 13, 46200, Petaling Jaya, Selangor Darul Ehsan, Malaysia
Tel.: (60) 379563866
Web Site: https://www.tienwah.com
Year Founded: 1995
TIENWAH—(KLS)
Rev.: $84,202,291
Assets: $142,924,425
Liabilities: $61,175,577
Net Worth: $81,748,848
Earnings: ($3,877,262)
Fiscal Year-end: 12/31/19
Rotogravure Printing Services
N.A.I.C.S.: 323111
Wen Hwa Yen *(Chm)*

Subsidiaries:

Alliance Print Technologies Co., Ltd. (1)
38 Huu Nghi Street Vietnam Singapore Industrial Park, Thuan An, Binh Duong, Vietnam
Tel.: (84) 2743767194
Web Site: http://www.tienwah.com
Sales Range: $50-74.9 Million
Emp.: 120
Printing Services
N.A.I.C.S.: 323111

Anzpac Services (Australia) Pty Limited (1)
32 Britton Street, Smithfield, 2164, NSW, Australia
Tel.: (61) 287871305
Web Site: http://www.anzpac.com.au
Sales Range: $50-74.9 Million
Emp.: 164
Commercial Lithographic Printing Services
N.A.I.C.S.: 323111

Max Ease International Limited (1)
Room 2804b 28F Wu Chung House 213 Queens Road East, Wanchai, China (Hong Kong)
Tel.: (852) 24672173
Printed Folding Cartons Mfr & Whslr
N.A.I.C.S.: 322299
Stephen Yen *(Mng Dir)*

Tien Wah Press (Malaya) Sdn. Bhd. (1)
9 & 11 Jalan Semangat, 46200, Petaling Jaya, Selangor, Malaysia
Tel.: (60) 379563866
Emp.: 300
Rotogravure & Photolithography Printing Services
N.A.I.C.S.: 323111

TIENS BIOTECH GROUP (USA), INC.

No 17 Xinyuan Road Wuqing New Tech Industrial Pk, Tianjin, 301700, China
Tel.: (86) 2282137914 DE
Web Site: http://www.tiens-bio.com
Year Founded: 1998
Sales Range: $25-49.9 Million
Emp.: 1,380
Nutritional & Dietary Supplements Researcher, Developer, Marketer & Mfr
N.A.I.C.S.: 325414
Jinyuan Li *(Chm, Pres, CEO & Acting CFO)*

Subsidiaries:

Tianjin Tianshi Biological Development Co., Ltd. (1)
6 Yuanquan Road Wuquing Development Area, New Tech Industrial Park, Tianjin, 301700, China (80%)
Tel.: (86) 2282124400
Web Site: http://www.tiens.com
Biological Product Researcher, Developer, Marketer & Mfr
N.A.I.C.S.: 325414
Jinyuan Li *(Pres)*

TIER ONE CAPITAL LIMITED PARTNERSHIP

161 Bay Street Suite 2460, Toronto, M5J 2S1, ON, Canada
Tel.: (416) 203-7331 ON
Web Site: https://www.tier1capital.ca
Year Founded: 2014
TLP—(CNSX)
Assets: $17,614,748
Liabilities: $225,731
Net Worth: $17,389,017
Earnings: ($2,429,696)
Fiscal Year-end: 12/31/22
Investment Services
N.A.I.C.S.: 523999

TIER ONE SILVER INC.

Suite 250-1300 997 Seymour St, Vancouver, V6B 3M1, BC, Canada
Tel.: (778) 729-0609 BC
Web Site: https://www.tieronesilver.com
Year Founded: 2020
TSLVF—(OTCQB)
Assets: $3,903,010
Liabilities: $801,608
Net Worth: $3,101,402
Earnings: $5,773,582
Emp.: 1
Fiscal Year-end: 12/31/22
Gold Exploration Services
N.A.I.C.S.: 212220
Christian Rios *(Sr VP)*

TIER1 FINANCIALS SOLUTIONS, INC.

Suite 2800 200 Yonge Street, Toronto, M4P1E4, ON, Canada
Tel.: (647) 251-3819
Web Site: http://tier1fin.com
Year Founded: 2008
Software Publisher
N.A.I.C.S.: 513210
Jiro Okochi *(CEO)*

TIERCEL TECHNOLOGY CORP.

259 Third Concession Road, PO Box 490, Princeton, N0J 1V0, ON, Canada
Tel.: (519) 458-4882
Web Site: http://www.tierceltechnology.com
Sales Range: $10-24.9 Million
Emp.: 100
Technology Services to Manufacturing Companies
N.A.I.C.S.: 541690
Bruce Seeley *(Pres)*

Subsidiaries:

John G. Wilson Machine Limited (1)
259 Third Concession Road, PO Box 490, Princeton, N0J 1V0, ON, Canada
Tel.: (519) 458-4882
Web Site: http://www.jgwmachine.com
Metal Fabricator & Contract Mfr
N.A.I.C.S.: 332999
Bruce Seeley *(Pres)*

Second Wind Air Purifier Company (1)
255 Great Arrow Ave Ste 20C, Buffalo, NY 14207
Tel.: (716) 875-5050
Web Site: http://www.secondwindairpurifier.com
Air Purification Equipment Mfr
N.A.I.C.S.: 333413
Tom Wilson *(Pres)*

TIERNAHRUNG DEUERER GMBH

Rinklinger Strasse 13-17, 75015, Bretten, Germany
Tel.: (49) 725293690
Web Site: http://www.edel-cat.de
Emp.: 800
Pet Food Mfr
N.A.I.C.S.: 311111
Hans-Jurgen Deuerer *(Mng Dir)*

TIETOEVRY OYJ

Keilalahdentie 2-4, PO Box 2, FI-02101, Espoo, Finland
Tel.: (358) 2072010 FI
Web Site: https://www.tietoevry.com
Year Founded: 1968
TIETOS—(OMX)
Rev.: $3,147,588,034
Assets: $3,883,872,393
Liabilities: $2,104,095,375
Net Worth: $1,779,777,018
Earnings: $190,087,206
Emp.: 24,159

AND PRIVATE COMPANIES — TIETOEVRY OYJ

Fiscal Year-end: 12/31/23
IT Services
N.A.I.C.S.: 518210
Kimmo Alkio *(Pres & CEO)*

Subsidiaries:

Bekk Consulting AS (1)
Akershusstranda 21 Skur 39 Vippetangen, 0150, Oslo, Norway
Tel.: (47) 23357700
Web Site: https://www.bekk.no
Consulting Services
N.A.I.C.S.: 541618

EVRY ASA (1)
Snaroyveien 30A, PB 4, 1360, Fornebu, Norway **(100%)**
Tel.: (47) 23145000
Web Site: http://www.evry.com
Rev.: $1,479,198,720
Assets: $1,328,483,584
Liabilities: $986,648,000
Net Worth: $341,835,584
Earnings: $73,284,032
Emp.: 8,807
Fiscal Year-end: 12/31/2018
Information Technology Consulting Services
N.A.I.C.S.: 541690
Wiljar I. Nesse *(Exec VP-Fin Svcs)*

Subsidiary (Non-US):

EVRY India Private Limited (2)
4th & 5th Floors E Block Global Village RVCE Post Mysore Road, Mylasandra, Bengaluru, 560059, Karnataka, India **(100%)**
Tel.: (91) 8067387000
Web Site: http://www.evry.in
Emp.: 1,979
Information Technology Consulting Services
N.A.I.C.S.: 541512
Prakash Grama *(CEO-USA)*

Subsidiary (US):

Span Systems Corporation Inc. (3)
1425 Greenway Dr Ste 490, Irving, TX 75038 **(100%)**
Tel.: (972) 514-1113
Web Site: http://www.spansystems.com
Information Technology Consulting Services
N.A.I.C.S.: 541512
Mysore S. Srinath *(Gen Mgr)*

EVRY Card Services AS (1)
Stigerplataveien 23, 8626, Mo i Rana, Norway
Tel.: (47) 23145000
Information Technology Services
N.A.I.C.S.: 541511

EVRY Card Services Oy (1)
Koivuhaantie 2-4 B, 01510, Vantaa, Finland
Tel.: (358) 102184300
Information Technology Services
N.A.I.C.S.: 541511

EVRY Financing AB (1)
Ekensbergsvagen 113, 171 41, Solna, Sweden
Tel.: (46) 2 314 5000
Web Site: https://www.evry.in
Emp.: 8
Information Technology Services
N.A.I.C.S.: 541511
Stefan Jonsson *(CEO)*

EVRY Finland Oy (1)
Mattilanniemi 6 - 8, 40100, Jyvaskyla, Finland
Tel.: (358) 40 450 3800
Information Technology Services
N.A.I.C.S.: 541511

Emric d.o.o. (1)
Bulevar Mihajla Pupina 6 22nd Floor, 11000, Belgrade, Serbia
Tel.: (381) 11 220 0024
Information Technology Services
N.A.I.C.S.: 541511

Eye-share AS (1)
Maskinveien 15, 4033, Stavanger, Norway
Tel.: (47) 48019750
Web Site: https://eye-share.no
Information Technology Services
N.A.I.C.S.: 541511

Infopulse Europe GmbH (1)
WINX-Tower Neue Mainzer Strasse 6-10, 60311, Frankfurt am Main, Germany
Tel.: (49) 695050604719
Information Technology Services
N.A.I.C.S.: 541511

Infopulse USA LLC (1)
547 N Mt Juliet Rd, Mount Juliet, TN 37122
Information Technology Services
N.A.I.C.S.: 541511

Infopulse Ukraine LLC (1)
Podil Heritage Business Center 28/12 Verkhnii Val st, 04071, Kiev, Ukraine
Tel.: (380) 445852500
Web Site: https://www.infopulse.com
Information Technology Services
N.A.I.C.S.: 541511
Artur Siebert *(VP-Sales-Marketing)*

MentorMate, Inc. (1)
1350 Lagoon Ave Ste 800, Minneapolis, MN 55408
Tel.: (612) 823-4000
Web Site: https://www.mentormate.com
Sales Range: $1-9.9 Million
Software Devolepment
N.A.I.C.S.: 513210
Bjorn Stansvik *(Founder & CEO)*

Tieto (Beijing) Technology Co., Ltd. (1)
No 36 North 3rd Ring East Road 3/F Tower A Global Trade Centre, Beijing, 100010, China
Tel.: (86) 1050831901
Information Technology Services
N.A.I.C.S.: 541511

Tieto Austria GmbH (1)
Handelskai 94-96 Millennium Tower 33rd Floor, 1200, Vienna, Austria
Tel.: (43) 1331740
Web Site: http://www.tieto.at
Sales Range: $25-49.9 Million
Emp.: 100
Information Technology Consulting Services
N.A.I.C.S.: 541611

Tieto Belgium N.V. (1)
Jaargetijdenlaan 100 Internal, 1050, Brussels, Belgium
Tel.: (32) 26393964
Web Site: http://www.tieto.com
Emp.: 1
Information Technology Consulting Services
N.A.I.C.S.: 541690

Tieto China Co., Ltd (1)
No36 North 3rd Ring East Road 3/F Tower A Global Trade Centre, Cheng District, Beijing, CN-100010, China
Tel.: (86) 1084265300
Information Technology Consulting Services
N.A.I.C.S.: 541512

Tieto Czech Support Services S.r.o. (1)
28 Rijna 3346/91 Tieto Towers, 70200, Ostrava, Czech Republic
Tel.: (420) 59 715 9900
Information Technology Services
N.A.I.C.S.: 541511

Tieto Czech s.r.o. (1)
28 Rijna 3346/91 Tieto Towers, 702 00, Ostrava, Czech Republic
Tel.: (420) 597159900
Web Site: http://www.tieto.com
Information Technology Consulting Services
N.A.I.C.S.: 541611

Tieto Denmark A/S (1)
Frederiksborggade 43, 1360, Copenhagen, Denmark
Tel.: (45) 45588888
Web Site: http://www.tieto.dk
Sales Range: $25-49.9 Million
Emp.: 16
Information Technology Consulting Services
N.A.I.C.S.: 541611

Tieto Estonia AS (1)
AHTammsaare tee 47 VII floor, 11316, Tallinn, Estonia
Tel.: (372) 6646207
Web Site: http://www.tieto.ee
Sales Range: $25-49.9 Million
Emp.: 150
Information Technology Consulting Services
N.A.I.C.S.: 541512

Subsidiary (Domestic):

Tieto Estonia Services OU (2)
Tammsaare Tee 47, 11316, Tallinn, Estonia
Tel.: (372) 6646208
Web Site: http://www.tieto.com
Sales Range: $25-49.9 Million
Emp.: 200
Information Technology Consulting Services
N.A.I.C.S.: 541512

Tieto Esy Oy (1)
Keilalahdentie 2-4, PO Box 2, 02101, Espoo, Finland
Tel.: (358) 207 2010
Information Technology Services
N.A.I.C.S.: 541511

Tieto Finland Oy (1)
Terastehtaantie 1, 55100, Imatra, Finland
Tel.: (358) 20 72 010
Web Site: http://www.tieto.com
Sales Range: $1-4.9 Billion
Emp.: 6,000
Information Technology Consulting Services
N.A.I.C.S.: 541690

Tieto Finland Support Services Oy (1)
Hatanpaan valtatie 30, PO Box 449, 33101, Tampere, Finland
Tel.: (358) 207 2010
Information Technology Services
N.A.I.C.S.: 541511

Tieto Germany GmbH (1)
Im Gewerbepark C 15, 93059, Regensburg, Germany
Tel.: (49) 941297820
Information Technology Services
N.A.I.C.S.: 541511

Tieto Healthcare & Welfare Oy (1)
Joukahaisenkatu 1, 20520, Turku, Finland
Tel.: (358) 20 72 010
Web Site: http://www.tieto.fi
Information Technology Consulting Services
N.A.I.C.S.: 541690

Tieto India Pvt. Ltd. (1)
EON Free Zone MIDC Kharadi Knowledge Park Wing 1 Cluster D, Pune, 411014, Maharashtra, India
Tel.: (91) 206 730 3000
Information Technology Services
N.A.I.C.S.: 541511

Tieto Italy S.p.A. (1)
Via Di Torre Spaccata 172, Rome, 00169, Italy
Tel.: (39) 062325160
Web Site: http://www.tieto.com
Information Technology Consulting Services
N.A.I.C.S.: 541512

Tieto Latvia SIA (1)
G Zemgala gatve 76 Jauna Teika Biroja eka Valters, Riga, 1039, Latvia
Tel.: (371) 67510000
Web Site: http://www.tieto.com
Sales Range: $150-199.9 Million
Emp.: 650
Information Technology Consulting Services
N.A.I.C.S.: 541690

Subsidiary (Domestic):

TietoEnator SIA (2)
41 Lacplesa Street, Riga, 1011, Latvia
Tel.: (371) 67286660
Sales Range: $150-199.9 Million
Emp.: 600
Information Technology Consulting Services
N.A.I.C.S.: 541512
Elmars Gengers *(Gen Mgr)*

Tieto Lietuva, UAB (1)
Lvovo g 105A, 08104, Vilnius, Lithuania
Tel.: (370) 52191000
Web Site: http://www.tieto.lt
Information Technology Consulting Services
N.A.I.C.S.: 541512
Tomas Vitkus *(Country Mgr)*

Tieto Norway AS (1)
Karenslyst Alles 53, PO Box 684, Skoyen, Oslo, 279, Norway
Tel.: (47) 21706000
Web Site: http://www.tieto.no
Sales Range: $75-99.9 Million
Emp.: 500
Information Technology Consulting Services
N.A.I.C.S.: 541690
Christine Schoen *(Mng Dir)*

Subsidiary (Domestic):

Software Innovation AS (2)
Rolfsbuktveien 4C, 1364, Fornebu, Norway
Tel.: (47) 23 89 90 00
Web Site: http://www.software-innovation.com
Information & Data Management Services
N.A.I.C.S.: 513210
Cathrine Bore *(VP-Customer Svc)*

Tieto Rus OOO (1)
1st Tverskaya-Yamskaya str 21 Four Winds Plaza, 125047, Moscow, Russia
Tel.: (7) 495 6637080
Web Site: http://www.tieto.ru
Sales Range: $25-49.9 Million
Emp.: 35
Information Technology Consulting Services
N.A.I.C.S.: 541512

Tieto Sdn Bhd (1)
Technology Park Malaysia Enterprise 4 L3-I-3 Lebuhraya Puchong Sg, Besi Bukit Jalil, 57000, Kuala Lumpur, Malaysia
Tel.: (60) 389946194
Sales Range: $25-49.9 Million
Emp.: 40
Information Technology Consulting Services
N.A.I.C.S.: 541511
Dick Vaneldik *(Country Mgr)*

Tieto Software Technologies Pvt. Ltd (1)
8th Floor D Building Weikfield IT Citi Info Park Nagar Road, 411 014, Pune, India
Tel.: (91) 2066042233
Web Site: http://www.tieto.in
Emp.: 300
Information Technology Consulting Services
N.A.I.C.S.: 541512

Tieto Support Services Sp. z o.o. (1)
ul Wadowicka 7, PL-30363, Krakow, Poland
Tel.: (48) 609207774
Information Technology Services
N.A.I.C.S.: 541511

Tieto Sweden AB (1)
Fjarde Bassangvagen 15, PO Box 1038, 651 15, Stockholm, Sweden
Tel.: (46) 104810000
Web Site: http://www.tieto.com
Sales Range: $125-149.9 Million
Emp.: 480
N.A.I.C.S.: 334418

Subsidiary (Domestic):

Avega Group AB (2)
Grev Turegatan 11A, 11446, Stockholm, Sweden **(96.7%)**
Tel.: (46) 84076500
Web Site: https://www.avegagroup.se
Sales Range: $25-49.9 Million
Emp.: 250
IT & Business Development Consulting Services
N.A.I.C.S.: 541519
Charlotte Thomsson *(CFO)*

Branch (Domestic):

Tieto Sweden AB (2)
Isafjordsgatan 39B, 164 40, Kista, Sweden
Tel.: (46) 104810000
Web Site: http://www.tieto.com
Sales Range: $100-124.9 Million
Emp.: 400
Data Processing Services
N.A.I.C.S.: 518210

Subsidiary (Domestic):

TietoEnator AB (2)
Fjarde Bassangvagen 15, Stockholm, 115 41, Sweden
Tel.: (46) 10 481 00 00
Web Site: http://www.tieto.se
Emp.: 1,538
Information Technology Consulting Services
N.A.I.C.S.: 541512
Jennifer Rebel *(Mgr-Site)*

Tieto Sweden Support Services AB (1)
Tullhusgatan 1A, PO Box 1038, 65226, Karlstad, Sweden

TIETOEVRY OYJ

TietoEVRY Oyj—(Continued)
Tel.: (46) 10 481 0000
Information Technology Services
N.A.I.C.S.: 541511

Tieto Telecom R&D Services India Pvt. Ltd (1)
5th Floor Innovator Building Itpb White Field Road, Bengaluru, 560 066, India
Tel.: (91) 8066708000
Web Site: http://www.tieto.in
Information Technology Consulting Services
N.A.I.C.S.: 541512

Tieto Ukraine Support Services LLC (1)
72 Heroiv UPA Str BC Technopark 4th and 5th Floor, 79018, Lviv, Ukraine
Tel.: (380) 676356544
Information Technology Services
N.A.I.C.S.: 541511

TietoEnator Consulting B.V. (1)
Basicweg 24, 3821 BR, Amersfoort, Netherlands
Tel.: (31) 620028355
Information Technology Consulting Services
N.A.I.C.S.: 541512

Tietokarhu Oy (1)
Mattilanniemi 6, PO Box 163, 40100, Jyvaskyla, Finland
Tel.: (358) 20 549 6500
Information Technology Services
N.A.I.C.S.: 541511

TIETTO MINERALS LTD.
Level 3 88 William Street, Perth, 6000, WA, Australia
Tel.: (61) 894864036
Web Site: http://www.tietto.com
TIE—(ASX)
Rev.: $174,149,627
Assets: $276,589,080
Liabilities: $87,591,208
Net Worth: $188,997,873
Earnings: $5,025,813
Fiscal Year-end: 12/31/23
Metal Exploration Services
N.A.I.C.S.: 213114
Caigen Wang (Mng Dir)

TIFANY INDUSTRIES SAS
Parc d'activite 1 rue de l'Empire, Phalempin, 59133, Seclin, France
Tel.: (33) 3 2005 6767   FR
Web Site: http://www.tifany.com
Sales Range: $10-24.9 Million
Emp.: 93
Laminated Paper Plates, Plastic Cups & Cutlery Mfr & Distr
N.A.I.C.S.: 322130
Benjamin Debris (Co-Owner & Chm)

TIFICO FIBER INDONESIA TBK
Jalan MH Thamrin Kel Panunggangan Kec Pinang, Tangerang, 15143, Banten, Indonesia
Tel.: (62) 2153120188
Web Site: https://www.tifico.co.id
Year Founded: 1975
TFCO—(INDO)
Rev.: $196,072,753
Assets: $335,379,399
Liabilities: $25,009,599
Net Worth: $310,369,800
Earnings: $3,297,472
Emp.: 859
Fiscal Year-end: 12/31/23
Timber Product Mfr
N.A.I.C.S.: 325220
Anton Wiratama (Chm)

TIGAR A.D. PIROT
Nikole Pasica 213, 18300, Pirot, Serbia
Tel.: (381) 10304000
Web Site: https://www.tigar.com
Year Founded: 1935
Rev.: $25,756,923
Assets: $60,077,872
Liabilities: $54,387,579
Net Worth: $5,690,293
Earnings: $3,434,118
Emp.: 1,459
Fiscal Year-end: 12/31/16
Rubber Products Mfr
N.A.I.C.S.: 326211
Vladimir Ilicic (Mng Dir)

Subsidiaries:

Tigar Incon doo (1)
Nikole Pasica Street 197, 18300, Pirot, Serbia
Tel.: (381) 10306182
Engineering Services
N.A.I.C.S.: 541330

TIGAZ TISZANTULI GAZSZOLGALTATO RESZVENYTARSASAG
Rakoczi 184, Hodmezovasarhely, 4201, Hungary
Tel.: (36) 52558100
Web Site: http://www.tigaz.com
Sales Range: $1-4.9 Billion
Emp.: 1,578
Natural Gas Distr
N.A.I.C.S.: 221210
Fabrizio Dassogno (Chm)

TIGBUR-TEMPORARY PROFESSIONAL PERSONNEL LTD.
14 Abba Hillel St, Beit oz, Ramat Gan, 52506, Israel
Tel.: (972) 772370000
Web Site: https://tigbur.co.il
Year Founded: 1978
TIGBUR—(TAE)
Rev.: $330,736,284
Assets: $115,665,974
Liabilities: $68,238,153
Net Worth: $47,427,821
Earnings: $5,464,567
Emp.: 300
Fiscal Year-end: 12/31/23
Temporary Help Service
N.A.I.C.S.: 561320

TIGER BRANDS LTD.
3010 William Nicol Drive, Bryanston, 2021, South Africa
Tel.: (27) 118404000   ZA
Web Site: https://www.tigerbrands.com
Year Founded: 1921
TBS—(NAM)
Rev.: $21,190,986,320
Assets: $15,883,940,800
Liabilities: $4,655,941,920
Net Worth: $11,227,998,880
Earnings: $739,576,880
Emp.: 11,188
Fiscal Year-end: 09/30/20
General Food & Seafood, Consumer Healthcare, Pharmaceutical & Hospital Products Distr
N.A.I.C.S.: 311230
Noel Doyle (CEO)

Subsidiaries:

Daybrook Fisheries Inc. (1)
365 Canal Pl Ste 2300, New Orleans, LA 70130
Tel.: (504) 561-6163
Web Site: https://www.daybrook.com
Emp.: 360
Supplier of Fats & Oils
N.A.I.C.S.: 311710
Scott Herbert (VP)

Langeberg & Ashton Foods Proprietary Limited (1)
Corner of Jones and Kohler Streets, Paarl, 7646, Western Cape, South Africa
Tel.: (27) 21 870 5000
Web Site: https://www.landaf.co.za
Fruit Whslr
N.A.I.C.S.: 424480

Pescanova S.A. (1)
Rua Jose Fernandez Lopez s/n, Chapela Redondela, 36320, Pontevedra, Spain
Tel.: (34) 946793394
Web Site: https://www.pescanova.com
Sales Range: $800-899.9 Million
Fresh & Frozen Seafood Processing
N.A.I.C.S.: 311710
Leopoldo Fernandez Zugazabeitia (Sec)

TIGER LOGISTICS (INDIA) LIMITED
TIGER HOUSE D 174 Ground Floor Okhla Industrial Area, Phase I, New Delhi, 110020, India
Tel.: (91) 1147351111
Web Site: https://www.tigerlogistics.in
536264—(BOM)
Rev.: $52,771,956
Assets: $14,328,865
Liabilities: $2,623,512
Net Worth: $11,705,353
Earnings: $2,783,071
Emp.: 172
Fiscal Year-end: 03/31/23
International Freight Forwarding, Custom Clearance, Transportation, Custom Consulting & Project Transportation Services
N.A.I.C.S.: 488510
Harpreet Singh Malhotra (Chm & Mng Dir)

TIGER REEF, INC.
Wellsburg Street #7, Cole Bay, Saint Martin
Tel.: (721) 9492641475   CO
Web Site: http://www.tigerreefinc.com
Year Founded: 2013
TGRR—(OTCIQ)
Investment Services
N.A.I.C.S.: 523999
Miro Zecevic (Chm)

TIGER RESOURCES LIMITED
Level 4 1 Havelock Street, West Perth, 6005, WA, Australia
Tel.: (61) 8 6188 2000   AU
Web Site: http://www.tigerresources.com.au
Year Founded: 1997
TGS—(ASX)
Copper Mining & Production Services
N.A.I.C.S.: 212230
David J Frances (Chm)

TIGER ROYALTIES AND INVESTMENTS PLC
1st Floor 7-8 Kendrick Mews, South Kensington, London, SW7 3HG, United Kingdom
Tel.: (44) 2075814477
Web Site: https://www.tiger-rf.com
TIR—(AIM)
Assets: $560,151
Liabilities: $445,574
Net Worth: $114,576
Earnings: ($509,228)
Fiscal Year-end: 12/31/23
Financial Services
N.A.I.C.S.: 523160
Colin Bird (Chm)

TIGER TASMAN MINERALS LIMITED
Ground Floor 16 Ord Street, West Perth, 6005, WA, Australia
Tel.: (61) 894820500
T1G—(ASX)
Mineral Exploration Services
N.A.I.C.S.: 212390

TIGER WHEELS LIMITED
Corner K101 & Old Pretoria Rd, Midrand, 1685, South Africa
Tel.: (27) 112564000
Web Site: http://www.tiauto.co.za

INTERNATIONAL PUBLIC

Sales Range: $450-499.9 Million
Emp.: 2,968
Wheel & Tire Mfr & Whslr
N.A.I.C.S.: 336390
Edward Ivor Keizan (Chm)

TIGERELEC CO.,LTD.
33 Yeongjeon-ro 187beon-gil, Nam-gu, 402-060, Incheon, 402-060, Korea (South)
Tel.: (82) 325794100
Web Site: https://www.tigerelec.com
Year Founded: 1991
219130—(KRS)
Rev.: $44,541,416
Assets: $55,737,668
Liabilities: $13,210,904
Net Worth: $42,526,764
Earnings: $2,753,701
Emp.: 247
Fiscal Year-end: 12/31/22
Electronic Components Mfr
N.A.I.C.S.: 334419
Moo-Young Kim (Co-CEO)

TIGERS POLYMER CORPORATION
4-1 1-chome Shinsenri Higashi-machi, Toyonaka, Osaka, 560-0082, Japan
Tel.: (81) 668341551
Web Site: https://www.tiger-poly.com
Year Founded: 1938
4231—(TKS)
Rev.: $316,367,820
Assets: $378,706,730
Liabilities: $99,183,050
Net Worth: $279,523,680
Earnings: $19,955,590
Emp.: 1,988
Fiscal Year-end: 03/31/24
Domestic Appliance Hoses, Rubber Sheeting, Plastic Gears & Industrial Hoses Mfr
N.A.I.C.S.: 326220
Kentaro Watanabe (Pres)

Subsidiaries:

Guangzhou Tigers Polymer Co., Ltd. (1)
No 55 Hefeng Road Yonghe Economic Zone, Guangzhou, 510730, Guangdong, China
Tel.: (86) 2082986998
Plastics Product Mfr
N.A.I.C.S.: 326220

Hangzhou Tigers Polymer Co., Ltd. (1)
No 18 Road Hangzhou Economic Technological Development Zone, Hangzhou, 310018, Zhejiang, China
Tel.: (86) 57186910720
Sales Range: $50-74.9 Million
Emp.: 160
Injection Molded Plastic Products Mfr
N.A.I.C.S.: 326121

Mukogawa Kasei Corporation (1)
1-45 Motohama-cho, Amagasaki, 660-0085, Hyogo, Japan
Tel.: (81) 664192556
Web Site: http://www.tiger-poly.com
Rubber Products Mfr
N.A.I.C.S.: 326299

Osaka Tigers Kouhan Co., Ltd. (1)
1-45 Motohama-cho, Amagasaki, 660-0085, Hyogo, Japan
Tel.: (81) 664111690
Rubber Products Mfr
N.A.I.C.S.: 326299

Rubber Flex Corporation (1)
1-2-16 Kurakakiuchi, Ibaraki, 567-0878, Osaka, Japan
Tel.: (81) 726265476
Sales Range: $25-49.9 Million
Emp.: 5
Rubber Products Mfr
N.A.I.C.S.: 326299

AND PRIVATE COMPANIES

Takatsuki Kasei Corporation (1)
1-1-3 Higashikammaki, Takatsuki, 569-0002, Osaka, Japan
Tel.: (81) 726693410
Sales Range: $25-49.9 Million
Emp.: 50
Injection Molded Plastic Products Mfr
N.A.I.C.S.: 326199
Seiji Shiga (Pres)

Tigerflex Corporation (1)
801 Estes Ave, Elk Grove Village, IL 60007-4903 (100%)
Tel.: (847) 640-8366
Emp.: 80
Plastic Hose Mfr
N.A.I.C.S.: 326220

Tigerpoly (Thailand) Ltd. (1)
99 Moo5 Rojana Industrial Park, U-Thai, Ayutthaya, 13210, Thailand
Tel.: (66) 35741565
Sales Range: $50-74.9 Million
Emp.: 250
Mfr of Hoses for Domestic Appliances
N.A.I.C.S.: 326220

Tigerpoly Industria de Mexico S.A. de C.V. (1)
Circuito San Roque Sur 459 Parque Industrial Santa Fe Ampliacion, 36275, Silao, Guanajuato, Mexico
Tel.: (52) 472 103 9200
Web Site: https://www.tiger-poly.com
Automobile Parts Mfr
N.A.I.C.S.: 336390
Koji Sawada (Pres)

Tigerpoly Manufacturing, Inc. (1)
6231 Enterprise Pkwy, Grove City, OH 43123-9271 (100%)
Tel.: (614) 871-0045
Web Site: http://www.tigerpoly.com
Sales Range: $150-199.9 Million
Emp.: 320
Mfr of Blow-Molded Plastics
N.A.I.C.S.: 326199

Tigers Polymer (M) Sdn Bhd (1)
No 4 Jalan Kawasan 25 Kawasan Perindustrian Sri Gading II, 83300, Batu Pahat, Johor D T, Malaysia (100%)
Tel.: (60) 74556551
Sales Range: $1-9.9 Million
Emp.: 100
Mfr of Hoses for Domestic Appliances
N.A.I.C.S.: 326220

Yamada Gomu Kougyou Co., Ltd. (1)
No 7 3 17 Asakusa Bridge, Taito-ku, Tokyo, 111-0053, Japan
Tel.: (81) 338632147
Web Site: http://www.yamada.gomu.gr.jp
Rubber Products Mfr
N.A.I.C.S.: 326299

TIGERS REALM COAL LIMITED
Suite 1 80 Wellington Street, Collingwood, 3066, VIC, Australia
Tel.: (61) 386441300
Web Site: https://www.tigersrealmcoal.com
TIG—(ASX)
Rev.: $95,446,495
Assets: $146,276,139
Liabilities: $26,607,179
Net Worth: $119,668,960
Earnings: $31,320,074
Emp.: 375
Fiscal Year-end: 12/31/23
Coal Mining
N.A.I.C.S.: 212115
David Forsyth (Sec)

TIGERTEL COMMUNICATIONS INC.
2800 Saymark Ave, Mississauga, L4W 5A6, ON, Canada
Tel.: (905) 629-7190
Web Site: http://www.tigertel.com
Sales Range: $10-24.9 Million
Emp.: 600

Call Center & Customer Relationship Management Services
N.A.I.C.S.: 541613
Douglas D. Swift (Pres & CEO)

TIGI LTD.
3 Hamechonai St, Hod Hasharon, Israel
Tel.: (972) 97748800
Web Site: http://www.tigisolar.com
Year Founded: 1979
TIGI—(TAE)
Rev.: $831,029
Assets: $5,441,679
Liabilities: $5,585,652
Net Worth: ($143,973)
Earnings: ($3,366,954)
Fiscal Year-end: 06/30/23
Solar Electric Power Generation Services
N.A.I.C.S.: 221114
Shimon Klier (Founder)

TIGNE MALL P.L.C.
The Point Shopping Mall Management Suite, Tigne Point, Sliema, SLM 3190, Malta
Tel.: (356) 22470300 Mt
Web Site: http://www.thepointmalta.com
TML—(MAL)
Rev.: $8,816,316
Assets: $98,812,235
Liabilities: $35,117,180
Net Worth: $63,695,055
Earnings: $4,063,400
Emp.: 6
Fiscal Year-end: 12/31/22
Shopping Mall Leasing Services
N.A.I.C.S.: 531120
Joseph Zammit Tabona (Chm)

TIGRE S.A
Rua Xavantes 54 Atiradores, Joinville, SC 89203-900, Brazil
Tel.: (55) 800 7074700
Web Site: http://www.tigre.com.br
Emp.: 7,000
Plastic Materials Mfr
N.A.I.C.S.: 326199

Subsidiaries:

Tigre USA, Inc. (1)
2315 Beloit Ave, Janesville, WI 53546
Tel.: (608) 754-4554
Plastic Pipe & Fitting Mfr
N.A.I.C.S.: 326122

Subsidiary (Domestic):

Dura Plastic Products, Inc. (2)
533 E 3rd St, Beaumont, CA 92223
Tel.: (951) 845-3161
Web Site: http://www.duraplastics.com
Sales Range: $1-9.9 Million
Emp.: 100
Plastics Pipe & Pipe Fitting Mfr
N.A.I.C.S.: 326122
Ron Pace (VP-Sls & Mktg)

TIH LIMITED
137 Telok Ayer Street 03-07, Singapore, 068602, Singapore
Tel.: (65) 62241211 SG
Web Site: https://www.tih.com.sg
Year Founded: 1994
T55—(SES)
Rev.: $3,862,758
Assets: $109,706,885
Liabilities: $17,911,838
Net Worth: $91,795,047
Earnings: ($3,330,304)
Emp.: 19
Fiscal Year-end: 12/31/23
Investment Holding Company
N.A.I.C.S.: 551112
Kin Chan (Chm)

TIHAMA ADVERTISING & PUB-
LIC RELATIONS COMPANY
King Fahad Road - Al oula building 4th floor, PO Box 4681, Al Muhamadiah, Riyadh, 11412, Saudi Arabia
Tel.: (966) 112079767
Web Site: https://www.tihama.com
Year Founded: 1974
4070—(SAU)
Rev.: $11,074,352
Assets: $56,128,317
Liabilities: $53,930,277
Net Worth: $2,198,040
Earnings: ($10,044,570)
Emp.: 150
Fiscal Year-end: 03/31/22
Advertising Agency Services
N.A.I.C.S.: 541810
Ayman Mohamed Abdulrahman Soliman (CFO)

TIJARA & REAL ESTATE INVESTMENT COMPANY K.S.C.C.
Khalid Ibn Al Waleed St February 25 Tower 33rd floor, PO Box 5655, Safat, 13057, Kuwait, 13057, Kuwait
Tel.: (965) 1888809
Web Site: https://www.tijara.com.kw
Year Founded: 1983
TIJARA—(KUW)
Rev.: $12,870,184
Assets: $244,129,231
Liabilities: $109,715,941
Net Worth: $134,413,289
Earnings: $6,931,554
Emp.: 34
Fiscal Year-end: 12/31/22
Real Estate & Investment Management Services
N.A.I.C.S.: 531390
Tareq Fareed Al Othman (Vice Chm & Mng Dir)

TIJARIA POLYPIPES LTD
A130 H Road No 9D V K I Area, Jaipur, 302013, Rajasthan, India
Tel.: (91) 9314669000
Web Site: https://www.tijaria-pipes.com
TIJARIA—(NSE)
Rev.: $3,362,514
Assets: $13,222,537
Liabilities: $12,272,224
Net Worth: $950,313
Earnings: ($764,045)
Emp.: 80
Fiscal Year-end: 03/31/21
Plastic Pipes & Fittings Mfr
N.A.I.C.S.: 326122
Alok Jain Tijaria (Mng Dir)

TIKCRO TECHNOLOGIES LTD.
38 Hanasi Weizmann, Hadera, 3842247, Israel
Tel.: (972) 89969800 Il
Web Site: http://www.tikcro.com
TIKRF—(OTCBB)
Rev.: $94,000
Assets: $4,422,000
Liabilities: $200,000
Net Worth: $4,222,000
Earnings: ($929,000)
Emp.: 1
Fiscal Year-end: 12/31/19
Holding Company; Biotechnology Researcher & Developer
N.A.I.C.S.: 551112
Izhak Tamir (Chm)

TIKEHAU CAPITAL ADVISORS SAS
32 Rue De Monceau, 75008, Paris, France
Tel.: (33) 1 40 06 26 26 FR
Web Site: http://www.tikehaucapital.com

Year Founded: 2004
Holding Company
N.A.I.C.S.: 551112
Guillaume Benhamou (Dir-Investments)

Subsidiaries:

ACE Management (1)
10 Avenue de Messine, 75008, Paris, France
Tel.: (33) 1 5856 2562
Web Site: http://www.acemanagement.fr
Privater Equity Firm
N.A.I.C.S.: 523999
Thierry Letailleur (Mng Partner)

Tikehau Capital SCA (1)
32 Rue De Monceau, 75008, Paris, France (51.04%)
Tel.: (33) 140062626
Web Site: https://www.tikehaucapital.com
Rev.: $355,798,653
Assets: $5,414,042,390
Liabilities: $1,892,923,060
Net Worth: $3,521,119,329
Earnings: $194,917,761
Emp.: 758
Fiscal Year-end: 12/31/2023
Holding Company; Investment Services
N.A.I.C.S.: 551112
Mathieu Chabran (Co-Founder)

Subsidiary (Non-US):

IREIT Global Group Pte Ltd (2)
1 Wallich Street 15-03 Guoco Tower, Singapore, 078881, Singapore (84.52%)
Tel.: (65) 67180590
Web Site: https://www.ireitglobal.com
Rev.: $71,726,460
Assets: $1,095,127,498
Liabilities: $492,831,438
Net Worth: $602,296,059
Earnings: ($116,266,696)
Emp.: 10
Fiscal Year-end: 12/31/2023
Real Estate Investment Trust
N.A.I.C.S.: 525990
John Kok Min Lim (Chm)

Subsidiary (Domestic):

Tikehau Ace Capital (2)
32 rue de Monceau, 75008, Paris, France
Tel.: (33) 1 40 06 26 2
Web Site: https://tikehau-ace.capital
Emp.: 100
Private Equity
N.A.I.C.S.: 523999
Guillaume Benhamou (CEO & Mng Dir)

Subsidiary (US):

Tikehau Capital North America LLC (2)
412 W 15th St 18th Fl, New York, NY 10011
Tel.: (212) 922-3734
Asset Management Services
N.A.I.C.S.: 523940

Subsidiary (Non-US):

Tikehau Investment Management Asia Pte. Ltd. (2)
1 Wallich Street 15-03 Guoco Tower, Singapore, 078881, Singapore
Tel.: (65) 67182111
Asset Management Services
N.A.I.C.S.: 523940

Tikehau Investment Management Japan K.K. (2)
Marunouchi Nakadori Bldg 6F 2-2-3, Marunouchi Chiyoda-ku, Tokyo, 100-0005, Japan
Tel.: (81) 358432770
Asset Management Services
N.A.I.C.S.: 523940

TIKFORCE LIMITED
Suite A7 435 Roberts Road, Subiaco, 6008, WA, Australia
Tel.: (61) 1800732543
Identity & Credential Verification Services
N.A.I.C.S.: 561499
Kevin Baum (Mng Dir)

TIKUN OLAM CANNBIT PHARMACEUTICALS LTD.

TikForce Limited—(Continued)

TIKUN OLAM CANNBIT PHARMACEUTICALS LTD.
Hashla 9, Tel Aviv, Israel
Tel.: (972) 35445860
Web Site: https://www.cannbit.com
Year Founded: 2006
TKUN—(TAE)
Rev.: $12,219,367
Assets: $21,155,684
Liabilities: $12,026,523
Net Worth: $9,129,161
Earnings: ($25,974,858)
Fiscal Year-end: 12/31/23
Pharmaceutical Preparation Manufacturing
N.A.I.C.S.: 325412

TIL ENVIRO LTD.
Unit 08 Level 61 CITIC Plaza, No 233 Tianhe North Road Tianhe District, Guangdong, China
Tel.: (86) 2087521681   Ky
Web Site: http://www.tilenviro.com
Year Founded: 2011
1790—(HKG)
Rev.: $27,202,253
Assets: $294,706,433
Liabilities: $126,147,480
Net Worth: $168,558,953
Earnings: $8,686,193
Emp.: 127
Fiscal Year-end: 12/31/22
Waste Water Treatment Services
N.A.I.C.S.: 221320
Kok Sun Wong (CEO)

TIL LIMITED
1Taratolla Road Garden Reach, Kolkata, 700 024, West Bengal, India
Tel.: (91) 3324693732
Web Site: https://www.tilindia.in
TIL—(NSE)
Rev.: $43,749,615
Assets: $100,818,900
Liabilities: $69,437,550
Net Worth: $31,381,350
Earnings: ($9,347,520)
Emp.: 287
Fiscal Year-end: 03/31/21
Construction Machinery Mfr
N.A.I.C.S.: 333120
Sumit Mazumder (Chm & Mng Dir)

Subsidiaries:

Myanmar Tractors Limited.   (1)
16 Mya Mar Lar Lane Tharketa Industrial Zone, Yangon, Myanmar
Tel.: (95) 1 547304
Web Site: http://www.mspcat.com
Sales Range: $100-124.9 Million
Emp.: 400
Mining Equipment Mfr
N.A.I.C.S.: 333131
Heinz Ludi (CEO)

TIL Overseas Pte. Limited.   (1)
Tel.: (65) 65367475
Construction & Mining Equipment Leasing Services
N.A.I.C.S.: 532412

Tractors India Pvt. Ltd.   (1)
1 Taratolla Road Garden Reach, Kolkata, 700 024, West Bengal, India
Tel.: (91) 33 2469 3732
Web Site: http://www.tiplindia.in
Emp.: 300
Construction & Mining Equipment Leasing Services
N.A.I.C.S.: 532412
Aloke Banerjee (Dir-Fin)

Subsidiary (Domestic):

SITECH India North & East   (2)
705 7th Floor Godrej Waterside Tower II Block DP Sector V, Salt Lake City, Kolkata, 700091, West Bengal, India
Tel.: (91) 120 665 9600
Web Site: https://www.sitechindia-ne.com

Sales Range: $250-299.9 Million
Emp.: 100
Construction & Mining Equipment Leasing Services
N.A.I.C.S.: 532412
Sumit Mazumder (Mng Dir)

TILAK VENTURES LIMITED
E-109 Crystal Plaza New Link Road, Opp Infinity Mall Andheri W, Mumbai, 400 053, India
Tel.: (91) 2261522222
Web Site: https://tilakfinance.wordpress.com
Year Founded: 1980
503663—(BOM)
Rev.: $1,140,555
Assets: $9,251,652
Liabilities: $371,117
Net Worth: $8,880,535
Earnings: $282,009
Emp.: 8
Fiscal Year-end: 03/31/23
Securities Investment Services
N.A.I.C.S.: 523150
Girraj Kishor Agrawal (Mng Dir)

Subsidiaries:

Yosto Venture (India) Private Limited   (1)
306 Mahavir Industrial Estate Ramchandra Lane Ext, Kanchpada Malad West, Mumbai, 400064, Maharashtra, India
Tel.: (91) 9322006555
Web Site: https://yosto.in
Office Equipment Whslr
N.A.I.C.S.: 423420

TILAKNAGAR INDUSTRIES LTD
3rd Floor Industrial Assurance Building Churchgate, Mumbai, 400 020, Maharashtra, India
Tel.: (91) 2222831718
Web Site: https://www.tilind.com
507205—(BOM)
Rev.: $211,876,014
Assets: $151,208,596
Liabilities: $153,640,788
Net Worth: ($2,432,192)
Earnings: $37,761,864
Emp.: 270
Fiscal Year-end: 03/31/20
Alcoholic Beverages Mfr
N.A.I.C.S.: 424820
Amit Dahanukar (Chm & Mng Dir)

TILL CAPITAL CORPORATION
666 Burrard St 1700, Vancouver, V6C 2X8, BC, Canada
Tel.: (208) 635-5415   BM
Web Site: https://www.tillcap.com
Year Founded: 2012
TIL—(TSXV)
Rev.: $250,000
Assets: $16,443,200
Liabilities: $108,489
Net Worth: $16,334,711
Earnings: ($4,109,175)
Fiscal Year-end: 12/31/23
Investment Holding Company
N.A.I.C.S.: 551112
William A. Lupien (Chief Investment Officer)

Subsidiaries:

Silver Predator Corp.   (1)
Suite 700-250 Howe Street, Vancouver, V6C 357, BC, Canada   (55%)
Tel.: (604) 806-7000
Web Site: http://www.silverpredator.com
Sales Range: Less than $1 Million
Silver Ore Exploration & Mining Development Services
N.A.I.C.S.: 213114
Nathan A. Tewalt (Chm)

Subsidiary (US):

Springer Mining Company   (2)
9000 N Hwy 400 Imlay, Lovelock, NV 89418   (100%)
Tel.: (775) 538-7384
Mineral Mining Services
N.A.I.C.S.: 212390

TILLING TIMBER PTY. LIMITED
31-45 Orchard Street, PO Box 189, Kilsyth, 3137, VIC, Australia
Tel.: (61) 3 9725 0222   AU
Web Site: http://www.tilling.com.au
Year Founded: 1963
Sales Range: $10-24.9 Million
Emp.: 212
Lumber & Wood Construction Materials Whslr
N.A.I.C.S.: 423310
Norm Tilling (Chm, CEO & Mng Dir)

TILON INC.
22 Magokjungang 14-ro, Gangseo-gu, Seoul, Korea (South)
Tel.: (82) 226279000
Web Site: https://en.tilon.co.kr
Year Founded: 2001
Cloud Computing Solution Services
N.A.I.C.S.: 541512

TILRAY BRANDS, INC.
1100 Maughan Rd, Nanaimo, V9X 1J2, BC, Canada   DE
Web Site: http://www.tilray.com
Year Founded: 2013
TLRY—(NASDAQ)
Rev.: $788,942,000
Assets: $4,221,665,000
Liabilities: $778,487,000
Net Worth: $3,443,178,000
Earnings: ($222,404,000)
Emp.: 2,650
Fiscal Year-end: 05/31/24
Cannabis Research, Cultivation, Processing & Distribution
N.A.I.C.S.: 325412
Irwin David Simon (Chm, Pres & CEO)

Subsidiaries:

Aphria Inc.   (1)
98 Talbot St W, Leamington, N8H 1M8, ON, Canada
Web Site: http://www.aphria.com
Rev.: $439,209,498
Assets: $1,911,905,460
Liabilities: $505,132,628
Net Worth: $1,406,772,832
Earnings: ($64,765,322)
Emp.: 1,200
Fiscal Year-end: 05/31/2020
Medical Marijuana Mfr
N.A.I.C.S.: 325411
Carl Merton (CFO)

Fresh Hemp Foods Ltd.   (1)
69 Eagle Drive, Winnipeg, R2R 1V4, MB, Canada
Tel.: (204) 953-0233
Web Site: http://manitobaharvest.com
Carbon Neutral Food Mfr
N.A.I.C.S.: 311999
Bill Chiasson (CEO)

Hexo Corp.   (1)
120 chemin de la rive, Gatineau, J8M 1V2, QC, Canada
Tel.: (416) 750-4949
Web Site: http://www.hexocorp.com
Rev.: $96,822,013
Assets: $1,026,197,251
Liabilities: $453,360,987
Net Worth: $572,836,264
Earnings: ($89,776,017)
Emp.: 1,277
Fiscal Year-end: 07/31/2021
Holding Company
N.A.I.C.S.: 551111
Sebastien St-Louis (Co-Founder)

INTERNATIONAL PUBLIC

Subsidiary (Domestic):

48North Cannabis Corp.   (2)
257 Adelaide St W Suite 500, Toronto, M5H 1X9, ON, Canada
Tel.: (416) 639-5891
Web Site: http://www.48nrth.com
Rev.: $8,191,823
Assets: $45,196,109
Liabilities: $5,565,978
Net Worth: $39,630,131
Earnings: ($31,505,355)
Emp.: 145
Fiscal Year-end: 06/30/2020
Cannabis-infused Products Distr
N.A.I.C.S.: 115112
Kevin Helfand (COO)

HEXO Operations Inc.   (2)
3000 Solandt Rd, Kanata, K2K 2X2, ON, Canada
Pharmaceuticals Product Mfr
N.A.I.C.S.: 325412

Newstrike Brands Ltd   (2)
390 Bay Street Suite 612, Toronto, M5H 2Y2, ON, Canada
Tel.: (877) 541-9151
Web Site: http://newstrike.ca
Assets: $19,820,295
Liabilities: $9,801,227
Net Worth: $10,019,068
Earnings: ($11,223,808)
Fiscal Year-end: 03/31/2018
Pharmaceuticals Product Mfr
N.A.I.C.S.: 325412
Jason Redman (CFO)

Revolver Brewing, LLC   (1)
5650 Matlock Rd, Granbury, TX 76049-5347
Tel.: (817) 736-8034
Web Site: https://www.revolverbrewing.com
Beer Brewer & Whslr
N.A.I.C.S.: 312120
Rhett Keisler (Owner)

Terrapin Beer Company, LLC   (1)
265 Newton Bridge Rd, Athens, GA 30607
Tel.: (706) 549-3377
Web Site: https://www.terrapinbeer.com
Craft Beer Breweries
N.A.I.C.S.: 312120
John Cochran (Co-Founder)

TILTING CAPITAL CORP.
555 Burrard Street Suite 900, Vancouver, V7X 1MB, BC, Canada
Tel.: (403) 560-4951
Investment Company
N.A.I.C.S.: 523999
Scott P. Hayduk (CEO & CFO)

TIM S.P.A.
Corso D Italia 41, 00198, Rome, Italy
Tel.: (39) 0636881   IT
Web Site: https://www.gruppotim.it
Year Founded: 1994
TI—(NYSE)
Rev.: $21,173,193,020
Assets: $78,506,665,440
Liabilities: $53,168,713,080
Net Worth: $25,337,952,360
Earnings: $1,025,791,760
Emp.: 55,198
Fiscal Year-end: 12/31/19
Telecommunication Servicesb
N.A.I.C.S.: 517121
Lorenzo Forina (Chief Revenue Officer)

Subsidiaries:

TI Sparkle Argentina S.A.   (1)
Avenida Del Libertador 602 Piso 12, 1101, Buenos Aires, Argentina
Tel.: (54) 114 850 0600
Telecommunication Servicesb
N.A.I.C.S.: 517810

TI Sparkle Austria GmbH   (1)
Stadiongasse 6-8/23, 1010, Vienna, Austria
Tel.: (43) 6991 958 6610
Telecommunication Servicesb
N.A.I.C.S.: 517810

AND PRIVATE COMPANIES

TIM S.P.A.

TI Sparkle Brasil Participacoes Ltda. (1)
Avenida Das Americas 3500 Sala 606 Edificio Londres Barra Da Tijuca, Rio de Janeiro, 22640-102, Brazil
Tel.: (55) 212 429 2500
Telecommunication Servicesb
N.A.I.C.S.: 517810

TI Sparkle France S.A.S. (1)
15 Rue De Faubourg Montmartre, 75009, Paris, France
Tel.: (33) 17 856 9955
Telecommunication Servicesb
N.A.I.C.S.: 517810

TI Sparkle Germany GmbH (1)
Wilhelm Leuschner Strasse 23, 60329, Frankfurt am Main, Germany
Tel.: (49) 693 103 6160
Telecommunication Servicesb
N.A.I.C.S.: 517810

TI Sparkle Greece S.A. (1)
Zaimi 1 and Psatha, Melissia, 15127, Athens, Greece
Tel.: (30) 210 810 2633
Telecommunication Servicesb
N.A.I.C.S.: 517810

TI Sparkle Romania S.r.l. (1)
Bd Mircea Voda N 24 Et2 Sector 3, Bucharest, Romania
Tel.: (40) 21 310 7546
Telecommunication Servicesb
N.A.I.C.S.: 517810

TI Sparkle Russia LLC (1)
1 St Tverskaya-yamskaya Str Bld 23/1, 125047, Moscow, Russia
Tel.: (7) 495 783 8736
Telecommunication Servicesb
N.A.I.C.S.: 517810

TI Sparkle Singapore Pte. Ltd. (1)
6 Temasek Boulevard 23-01 Suntec City Tower 4, Singapore, 038986, Singapore
Tel.: (65) 6 235 7067
Telecommunication Servicesb
N.A.I.C.S.: 517810

TI Sparkle Turkey Telekomunikasyon Anonim Sirketi (1)
Eski Buyukdere Cad No 14 Park Plaza kat 1 6/A, Maslak, 34398, Istanbul, Turkiye
Tel.: (90) 212 258 3878
Telecommunication Servicesb
N.A.I.C.S.: 517810

TI Sparkle UK Ltd. (1)
5 Harbour Exchange Square, Docklands, London, E14 9GE, United Kingdom
Tel.: (44) 799 003 5092
Telecommunication Servicesb
N.A.I.C.S.: 517810

TIM S.p.A. - Rome Corporate Office (1)
Corso d'Italia 41, 00198, Rome, Italy
Tel.: (39) 0636881
Web Site: http://www.telecomitalia.it
Telecommunications Services; Corporate Managing Office
N.A.I.C.S.: 517121
Franco Rosario Brescia *(Head-Pub Affairs & Regulatory Affairs)*

Subsidiary (Domestic):

FLAGSHIP STORE BOLOGNA 1 S.r.l. (2)
Via Francesco Rizzoli 7/B, 40125, Bologna, Italy
Tel.: (39) 051271871
Telecommunication Equipment Distr
N.A.I.C.S.: 423690

FLAGSHIP STORE CATANIA 1 S.r.l. (2)
Corso Italia 112, 95129, Catania, Italy
Tel.: (39) 095536009
Telecommunication Equipment Distr
N.A.I.C.S.: 423690

FLAGSHIP STORE MILANO 2 S.r.l. (2)
47 Via Della Moscova, 20121, Milan, Italy
Tel.: (39) 0262694039
Telecommunication Equipment Distr
N.A.I.C.S.: 423690

FLAGSHIP STORE MODENA 1 S.r.l. (2)
Via Luigi Farini 34, 41121, Modena, Italy
Tel.: (39) 059221817
Telecommunication Equipment Distr
N.A.I.C.S.: 423690

FLAGSHIPSTORE ROMA 1 S.r.l. (2)
Via Cola Di Rienzo 189, 192, Rome, Italy
Tel.: (39) 063240336
Telecommunication Equipment Distr
N.A.I.C.S.: 423690

FLAGSHIPSTORE ROMA 2 S.r.l. (2)
Via Del Corso 87, 186, Rome, Italy
Tel.: (39) 0669921460
Telecommunication Equipment Distr
N.A.I.C.S.: 423690

FLAGSHIPSTORE TARANTO 1 S.r.l. (2)
Via T D Aquino 91, 74123, Taranto, Italy
Tel.: (39) 0994593641
Sales Range: $25-49.9 Million
Emp.: 5
Telecommunication Equipment Distr
N.A.I.C.S.: 423690
Cosimo Amapi *(Gen Mgr)*

FLAGSHIPSTORE TORINO 1 S.r.l. (2)
20 Via Lagrange Giuseppe Luigi, 10123, Turin, Italy
Tel.: (39) 0115 625 247
Telecommunication Equipment Distr
N.A.I.C.S.: 423690

I.T. TELECOM S.r.l. (2)
SS 148 Pontina Km 29 100, 00040, Pomezia, Rome, Italy
Tel.: (39) 06 91197426
Sales Range: $10-24.9 Million
Emp.: 40
Information Technology Consulting Services
N.A.I.C.S.: 541512

INWIT SpA (2)
Largo Donegani n 2, 20121, Milan, Italy
Tel.: (39) 028020911
Web Site: https://www.inwit.it
Rev.: $909,458,891
Assets: $9,875,019,220
Liabilities: $5,112,895,125
Net Worth: $4,762,124,095
Earnings: $312,758,576
Emp.: 256
Fiscal Year-end: 12/31/2022
Telecommunication Tower Structure Mfr
N.A.I.C.S.: 237130
Giovanni Ferigo *(CEO)*

MATRIX S.p.A. (2)
Piazza Luigi Einaudi 8, 20124, Milan, Italy
Tel.: (39) 02 290471
Telecommunication Servicesb
N.A.I.C.S.: 517810

Subsidiary (Non-US):

MEDITERRANEAN NAUTILUS GREECE S.A. (2)
1 Zaimi Street Esatha, Melissia, 15127, Athens, Greece
Tel.: (30) 210 8102633
Web Site: http://www.mednautilus.gr
Sales Range: $25-49.9 Million
Emp.: 2
Telecommunication Servicesb
N.A.I.C.S.: 517810
Paolo Ficini *(Gen Mgr)*

MEDITERRANEAN NAUTILUS ISRAEL Ltd (2)
12 Abba Hillel Silver Street, Ramat Gan, 52506, Israel
Tel.: (972) 3 7533600
Emp.: 15
Network Integration Services
N.A.I.C.S.: 541512

MEDITERRANEAN NAUTILUS TELEKOMUNIKASYON HIZMETLERI TICARET ANONIM SIRKETI (2)
Cobancesme Mah Kimiz Sok No 30, Yenibosna, 34196, Istanbul, Turkiye
Tel.: (90) 2124547316
Web Site: http://www.mednautilus.com
Sales Range: $25-49.9 Million
Emp.: 20
Telecommunication Servicesb

N.A.I.C.S.: 517810
Joint Venture (Non-US):

Nortel Inversora S.A. (2)
Alicia Moreau de Justo 50 Piso 13, C1107AAB, Buenos Aires, Argentina
Tel.: (54) 1149683631
Web Site: http://www.nortelsa.com.ar
Rev.: $3,349,688,040
Assets: $3,013,726,680
Liabilities: $1,762,163,820
Net Worth: $1,251,562,860
Earnings: $250,463,340
Emp.: 1
Fiscal Year-end: 12/31/2016
Holding Company; Owned by Telecom Italia S.p.A. & by Gregorio, Numo y Noel Werthein S.A.
N.A.I.C.S.: 551112

Subsidiary (Domestic):

Olivetti S.p.A. (2)
Via Jervis 77, 10015, Ivrea, Italy
Tel.: (39) 0125 7751
Web Site: http://www.olivetti.it
Emp.: 1,000
Computer & Office Products & Services
N.A.I.C.S.: 541512
Federico Maurizio d'Andrea *(Pres)*

Subsidiary (Domestic):

ADVALSO S.p.A. (3)
Via Guglielmo Jervis 77, Ivrea, 10015, Italy
Tel.: (39) 08639941
Telecommunication Servicesb
N.A.I.C.S.: 517810

Subsidiary (Non-US):

OLIVETTI DEUTSCHLAND GmbH (3)
Further Str 212, 90429, Nuremberg, Germany
Tel.: (49) 911 93120
Web Site: http://www.olivetti.com
Office Equipment Distr
N.A.I.C.S.: 423420

Subsidiary (Domestic):

OLIVETTI GESTIONI IVREA S.r.l. (3)
Via Guglielmo Jervis 77, Ivrea, 10015, Torino, Italy
Tel.: (39) 01257751
Real Estate Development Services
N.A.I.C.S.: 531390

OLIVETTI I-JET S.p.A. (3)
Localita Le Vieux 41, Arnad, 11020, Italy
Tel.: (39) 0125 96 60 29
Ink Jet Component Mfr & Distr
N.A.I.C.S.: 325910

Subsidiary (Non-US):

OLIVETTI ENGINEERING S.A. (4)
Avenue Des Sports 28, Case Postale 1022, 1401, Yverdon-les-Bains, Switzerland
Tel.: (41) 24 423 41 41
Web Site: http://www.olivetti-engineering.com
Sales Range: $10-24.9 Million
Emp.: 28
Information Technology Consulting Services
N.A.I.C.S.: 541512

Subsidiary (Non-US):

Olivetti Argentina S.A. (3)
Manuela Pedraza 2665, C1429CCN, Buenos Aires, Argentina
Tel.: (54) 1147012318
Web Site: http://www.olivetti.com.ar
Rev.: $16,194,640
Emp.: 112
Sales of Office Machines
N.A.I.C.S.: 423420

Olivetti Lexikon Espana S.A. (3)
Avenida Diagonal 188 Planta 5a Olivetti Espana S A, 08018, Barcelona, Spain
Tel.: (34) 934861900
Rev.: $126,632,640
Emp.: 35
Mfr of Personal Computers, Typewriters & Printers
N.A.I.C.S.: 334111

Olivetti Tecnost Africa (Pty.) Ltd. (3)
6 Milcliff Rd, Paulshof, Sandton, 2056, Gauteng, South Africa
Tel.: (27) 2363000
Web Site: http://www.olivetti.com
Sales Range: $25-49.9 Million
Emp.: 23
Sales of Office Equipment
N.A.I.C.S.: 423420

Olivetti Tecnost Belux (3)
Minerva Office Minervastraat 14 Bis, 1930, Zaventem, Belgium
Tel.: (32) 027090210
Web Site: http://www.olivetti.com
Sales Range: $25-49.9 Million
Emp.: 14
Sales of Office Products
N.A.I.C.S.: 424120

Olivetti Tecnost Deutschland GmbH (3)
Further Strasse 212, 90429, Nuremberg, Germany
Tel.: (49) 91193120
Web Site: http://www.olivetti.de
Sales Range: $25-49.9 Million
Emp.: 25
Sales of Office Machines
N.A.I.C.S.: 423420

Olivetti UK Limited (3)
500 Avebury Blvd, Milton Keynes, MK9 2BE, United Kingdom
Tel.: (44) 1908547980
Web Site: http://www.olivetti.co.uk
Rev.: $2,840,801
Emp.: 14
Sales of Office Machines
N.A.I.C.S.: 423420

Olivetti de Chile S.A. (3)
Avenida La Dehesa 1201 Office 632, Santiago, Chile
Tel.: (56) 2 656 9648
Web Site: http://www.olivetti.cl
Sales Range: $10-24.9 Million
Emp.: 150
Office Machinery Mfr
N.A.I.C.S.: 423420

Olivetti do Brasil S.A. (3)
Avenida Da Paulista 453, 01311 907, Sao Paulo, Brazil
Tel.: (55) 1150852500
Web Site: http://www.olivetti.com.br
Sales Range: $350-399.9 Million
Mfr & Sales of Typewriters, Calculators & Printers
N.A.I.C.S.: 333310

Subsidiary (Domestic):

PATH.NET S.p.A. (2)
Viale Parco de' Medici 61, 00148, Rome, Italy
Tel.: (39) 06 5030425
Telecommunication Servicesb
N.A.I.C.S.: 517810

Affiliate (Domestic):

Sirti S.p.A. (2)
Via Stamira dAncona 9, 20127, Milan, Italy
Tel.: (39) 0295881
Web Site: http://www.sirti.com
Sales Range: $350-399.9 Million
Emp.: 1,200
Engineers of Telecommunications Networks
N.A.I.C.S.: 517111

Subsidiary (Non-US):

TELECOM ITALIA CAPITAL S.A. (2)
12 Rue Eugene Ruppert, Luxembourg, 2453, Luxembourg
Tel.: (352) 45 60 60 440
Web Site: http://www.ticap.lu
Emp.: 4
Financial Management Services
N.A.I.C.S.: 523999

TELECOM ITALIA FINANCE S.A. (2)
12 Rue Eugene Ruppert, Luxembourg, 2453, Luxembourg
Tel.: (352) 45 6060 1
Web Site: http://www.tifinance.lu
Sales Range: $50-74.9 Million
Emp.: 15
Financial Management Services

TIM S.P.A.

TIM S.p.A.—(Continued)
N.A.I.C.S.: 523999

Subsidiary (Domestic):

TELECOM ITALIA MEDIA BROAD-CASTING S.r.l. (2)
Via Pineta Sacchetti 229, 00168, Rome, Italy
Tel.: (39) 06 35584 1
Television Broadcasting Services
N.A.I.C.S.: 516120

TELECONTACT CENTER S.p.A. (2)
Via Della Stadera 66, Naples, 80143, Italy
Tel.: (39) 081 21 79111
Telemarketing Services
N.A.I.C.S.: 561422

TELSY ELETTRONICA E TELECO-MUNICAZIONI S.p.A. (2)
C so Svizzera 185, 10149, Turin, Italy
Tel.: (39) 011 771 43 43
Web Site: http://www.telsy.com
Communication System Software Development Services
N.A.I.C.S.: 541511

Subsidiary (Non-US):

TIM Brasil Servicios e Participacoes S.A. (2)
Avenida das Americas 3434 Bloco 1 6o andar, Barra da Tijuca, 22640-102, Rio de Janeiro, RJ, Brazil (100%)
Tel.: (55) 2140093742
Web Site: http://www.tim.com.br
Sales Range: $1-4.9 Billion
Emp.: 9,531
Holding Company; Telecommunications Products & Services
N.A.I.C.S.: 551112

Holding (Domestic):

TIM Participacoes S.A. (3)
Joao Cabral de Melo Neto Avenue 850-North Tower-12th Floor, 22775-057, Rio de Janeiro, RJ, Brazil (69.67%)
Tel.: (55) 2141094167
Web Site: http://www.tim.com.br
Rev.: $4,302,245,691
Assets: $9,989,586,604
Liabilities: $4,435,917,103
Net Worth: $5,553,669,500
Earnings: $896,766,203
Emp.: 9,700
Fiscal Year-end: 12/31/2019
Holding Company; Mobile Telecommunications Network Services
N.A.I.C.S.: 551112
Jaques Horn *(Officer-Legal)*

Subsidiary (Domestic):

TIM Celular S.A. (4)
Avenida Giovanni Gronchi 7, 7143, Sao Paulo, SP, Brazil (100%)
Tel.: (55) 11 2847 6144
Web Site: http://www.timcelular.com.br
Mobile Telecommunications Services
N.A.I.C.S.: 517112

Subsidiary (Domestic):

Telecom Italia Lab (2)
Via G Reiss Romoli 274, 10148, Turin, Italy
Tel.: (39) 0112285111
Sales Range: $350-399.9 Million
Emp.: 1,100
Researcher for Telecommunications & Information Technology
N.A.I.C.S.: 517111

Telecom Italia Sparkle S.p.A. (2)
Via Cristoforo Colombo 142, Rome, 00147, Italy
Tel.: (39) 06 52741
Web Site: http://www.ti-sparkle.it
Sales Range: $1-4.9 Billion
Emp.: 10,000
Telecommunication Servicesb
N.A.I.C.S.: 517810
Alessandro Talotta *(CEO)*

Subsidiary (Non-US):

LAN MED NAUTILUS Ltd (3)
3 Harbourmaster Place IFSC, Dublin, Ireland
Tel.: (353) 1 439 2700
Web Site: http://www.mednautilus.com
Telecommunication Network Services
N.A.I.C.S.: 517810

Subsidiary (Non-US):

LATIN AMERICAN NAUTILUS PERU S.A. (4)
Av De La Floresta 497 Urb Chacarilla Del Estanque, Lima, Peru
Tel.: (51) 13727373
Sales Range: $10-24.9 Million
Emp.: 2
Submarine Cable System Repair & Maintenance Services
N.A.I.C.S.: 811210
Alfonso Belosheros *(Gen Mgr)*

Subsidiary (US):

LATIN AMERICAN NAUTILUS USA Inc. (4)
200 S Biscayne Blvd Ste 4400, Miami, FL 33131
Tel.: (786) 425-2460
Emp.: 30
Telecommunication Servicesb
N.A.I.C.S.: 517810
Laurie Bowen *(CEO)*

Subsidiary (Non-US):

TI BELGIUM S.P.R.L.-B.V.B.A (3)
Drukpersstraat 4, Brussels, 1000, Belgium
Tel.: (32) 22271111
Web Site: http://www.telecomitalia.it
Telecommunication Servicesb
N.A.I.C.S.: 517810
Doriana Baldassari *(Mgr)*

TIS France S.A.S. (3)
15 Rue Du Fg Montmartre, 75009, Paris, France
Tel.: (33) 1 46 46 13 14
Telecommunication Equipment Repair & Maintenance Services
N.A.I.C.S.: 811310

Telecom Italia Spain SL (3)
Avenida De Bruselas 13-1C Edif America, Madrid, 28109, Spain
Tel.: (34) 916574655
Web Site: http://www.tisparkle.com
Sales Range: $25-49.9 Million
Emp.: 4
Telecommunication Servicesb
N.A.I.C.S.: 517810

Subsidiary (US):

Telecom Italia Sparkle of North America, Inc. (3)
745 5th Ave 27th Fl, New York, NY 10151
Tel.: (212) 310-9000
Telecommunication Servicesb
N.A.I.C.S.: 517810
Salvatore Brancato *(Dir-Carrier Rels)*

Subsidiary (Non-US):

Telecom Italia Sparkle Singapore Pte. Ltd. (2)
6 Temasek Boulevard 23-01 Suntec Tower 4, Singapore, 38986, Singapore
Tel.: (65) 62357067
Telecommunication Servicesb
N.A.I.C.S.: 517810

Subsidiary (Domestic):

Telecom Italia Wireline (2)
Via Di Val Cannuta 182, 166, Rome, Italy
Tel.: (39) 0000636881
Providers of Domestic & International WirelineTelecommunications Services
N.A.I.C.S.: 517111

Telenergia S.r.l. (1)
107A E De Filippis Street, Cava De' Tirreni, 84013, Salerno, Italy
Tel.: (39) 0347 333 6162
Telecommunication Servicesb
N.A.I.C.S.: 517810

Telsy S.p.A. (1)
Corso Svizzera 185, 10149, Turin, Italy
Tel.: (39) 011 771 4343
Web Site: https://www.telsy.com
Telecommunication Servicesb
N.A.I.C.S.: 517810

Stefano Grassi *(Chm)*

TIM W.E. SGPS, S.A.
Avenida Infante Santo 2H 3, 1350-178, Lisbon, Portugal
Tel.: (351) 212487800 PT
Web Site: http://www.timwe.com
Year Founded: 2002
Sales Range: $300-349.9 Million
Emp.: 330
Mobile Marketing, Entertainment & Money Services
N.A.I.C.S.: 513210
Diogo Ahrens Teixeira Salvi *(CEO)*

TIM-BR MARTS LTD.
Suite 705 1601 Airport Road NE, Calgary, T2E 6Z8, AB, Canada
Tel.: (403) 717-1990
Web Site: http://www.timbermart.ca
Year Founded: 1967
Rev.: $145,648,433
Emp.: 250
Building Material Supplier
N.A.I.C.S.: 423330
Timothy H. Urquhart *(Pres & CEO)*

TIMAS A.D.
Izvorski put bb, Zajecar, Serbia
Tel.: (381) 19 426 074
Year Founded: 2000
Sales Range: $1-9.9 Million
Emp.: 39
Passenger Transportation Services
N.A.I.C.S.: 485999

TIMBER PRO LOGGING LTD.
Grande Prairie, PO Box 3005, Clairmont, T8X 0T8, AB, Canada
Tel.: (780) 567-3612
Web Site: https://www.tproltd.com
Year Founded: 2006
Logging Services
N.A.I.C.S.: 113310

TIMBERCREEK ASSET MANAGEMENT INC.
1000 Yonge Street Suite 500, Toronto, M4W 2K2, ON, Canada
Tel.: (416) 306-9967 ON
Web Site: http://www.timbercreek.com
Year Founded: 1999
Emp.: 600
Real Estate Investment & Asset Management Services
N.A.I.C.S.: 531390
Ugo Bizzarri *(CIO, Sr Mng Dir & Global Head-Direct & Debt Investment)*

Subsidiaries:

Timbercreek Financial Corp. (1)
25 Price Street, Toronto, M4W 1Z1, ON, Canada
Tel.: (416) 923-9967
Web Site: https://www.timbercreekfinancial.com
Rev.: $96,047,556
Assets: $1,338,842,493
Liabilities: $802,941,579
Net Worth: $535,900,914
Earnings: $25,034,525
Fiscal Year-end: 12/31/2020
Closed-End Investment Fund
N.A.I.C.S.: 525990
R. Blair Tamblyn *(Chm)*

TIMBERWELL BERHAD
2nd Floor Wisma BSN Sabah Jalan Kemajuan Karamunsing, 88867, Kota Kinabalu, Sabah, Malaysia
Tel.: (60) 88222190
Web Site: https://timwell.com.my
Year Founded: 1996
TIMWELL—(KLS)
Rev.: $4,112,973
Assets: $16,702,220

INTERNATIONAL PUBLIC

Liabilities: $2,722,682
Net Worth: $13,979,539
Earnings: ($515,455)
Emp.: 53
Fiscal Year-end: 12/31/23
Timber Related Products Mfr
N.A.I.C.S.: 321215
Chiong Ung Pau *(CEO)*

TIME DOTCOM BERHAD
No 14 Jalan Majistret U1/26 HICOM Glenmarie Industrial Park, 40150, Shah Alam, Selangor, Malaysia
Tel.: (60) 350326000
Web Site: https://www.time.com.my
TIMECOM—(KLS)
Rev.: $302,734,328
Assets: $965,394,293
Liabilities: $210,447,023
Net Worth: $754,947,270
Earnings: $80,908,740
Emp.: 653
Fiscal Year-end: 12/31/20
Holding Company; Communications Solutions & Services
N.A.I.C.S.: 551112
Afzal Abdul Rahim *(CEO)*

Subsidiaries:

AIMS Data Centre Pte. Ltd. (1)
c/o 9 Raffles Place 26-01 Republic Plaza, Singapore, 048619, Singapore
Tel.: (65) 64381330
Telecommunication Servicesb
N.A.I.C.S.: 517810

AIMS Data Centre Sdn. Bhd. (1)
Changkat Raja Chulan Bukit Ceylon, 50200, Kuala Lumpur, Malaysia
Tel.: (60) 350212188
Web Site: https://www.aims.com.my
Network & System Integration Services
N.A.I.C.S.: 541519

Global Transit (Hong Kong) Limited (1)
Room 1301 13/F Blissful Building Des Voeux Road 243-247, Central, China (Hong Kong)
Tel.: (852) 28742828
Telecommunication Servicesb
N.A.I.C.S.: 517810

Global Transit 2 Limited (1)
Lot A020 Level 1 Podium Level Financial Park Jalan Merdeka, 87000, Labuan, Sabah, Malaysia
Tel.: (60) 87427745
Telecommunication Servicesb
N.A.I.C.S.: 517810

TIME dotNet Bhd. (1)
No 14 Jalan Majistret U1/26 HICOM, Glenmarie Industrial Park, 40150, Shah Alam, Selangor, Malaysia
Tel.: (60) 35 032 6000
Web Site: https://www.time.com.my
Domestic & International Data Communication Services
N.A.I.C.S.: 517112

TT dotCom Sdn. Bhd (1)
No 14 Jalan Majistret U1/26 HICOM Glenmarie Industrial Park, Glenmarie Industrial Park, 40150, Shah Alam, Selangor, Malaysia
Tel.: (60) 350393000
Web Site: https://www.time.com.my
Sales Range: $100-124.9 Million
Emp.: 500
Domestic & International Data Communication Services
N.A.I.C.S.: 517112

TIME FINANCE PLC
St James House The Square Lower Bristol Road, Bath, BA2 3BH, United Kingdom
Tel.: (44) 1225474230
Web Site: https://www.timefinance.com
TIME—(AIM)
Rev.: $41,946,561
Assets: $264,756,899

AND PRIVATE COMPANIES

Liabilities: $181,267,716
Net Worth: $83,489,183
Earnings: $5,604,656
Fiscal Year-end: 05/31/24
Consumer Lending
N.A.I.C.S.: 522291
R. Ian Smith (CEO)

Subsidiaries:

Car Finance 2U Limited (1)
Unit 10 Woodside Business Park, Birkenhead, Wirral, CH41 1EL, United Kingdom
Tel.: (44) 1517056778
Web Site: http://www.carfinance2u.co.uk
Automobile Finance Services
N.A.I.C.S.: 522220
Diane Faulkner (Mgr-Relationship)

TIME INTERCONNECT TECHNOLOGY LIMITED
Unit 601 6/F Photonics Centre 2 Science Park East Avenue, Hong Kong Science Park, Sha Tin, China (Hong Kong)
Tel.: (852) 24254611   Ky
Web Site: http://www.time-interconnect.com
Year Founded: 1992
1729—(HKG)
Rev.: $735,016,973
Assets: $778,637,910
Liabilities: $632,768,985
Net Worth: $145,868,925
Earnings: $27,525,465
Emp.: 3,949
Fiscal Year-end: 03/31/23
Telecommunication Product Mfr & Distr
N.A.I.C.S.: 335929
Simon Tin Yin Cua (Exec Dir)

Subsidiaries:

Linkz International Limited (1)
Units 213-221 2/F Building 5E 5 Science Park East Avenue, Hong Kong Science Park New Territories, Hong Kong, China (Hong Kong)
Tel.: (852) 24254611
Web Site: https://www.linkzcables.com
Largest Digital Cable Mfr
N.A.I.C.S.: 335921

TIME Interconnect Technology (Huizhou) Limited (1)
38 Xia Tangzai Road, Chenjiang Zhongkai Hi-tech Industrial Development Zone, Huizhou, 516229, Guangdong, China
Tel.: (86) 7528459888
Electric Equipment Mfr
N.A.I.C.S.: 335999

TIME INTERNATIONAL
Centennial Tower 28th Floor, Jalan Gatot Subroto kav 24-25, Jakarta, 12930, Indonesia
Tel.: (62) 2129272708
Web Site: http://www.timeinternational.co.id
Year Founded: 1965
Brand Builder & Retailer Organization
N.A.I.C.S.: 423940
Irwan Dany Mussry (Pres & CEO)

TIME OUT GROUP PLC
1st Floor 172 Drury Lane, London, WC2B 5QR, United Kingdom
Tel.: (44) 2078133000   UK
Web Site: https://www.timeout.com
Year Founded: 1968
TMO—(AIM)
Rev.: $91,031,226
Assets: $150,720,150
Liabilities: $111,851,202
Net Worth: $38,868,948
Earnings: $(24,414,792)
Emp.: 365
Fiscal Year-end: 06/30/22
Media Monitoring Services
N.A.I.C.S.: 541840
Julio Bruno (CEO)

Subsidiaries:

Time Out Chicago LLC (1)
916 W Fulton Market, Chicago, IL 60607
Tel.: (312) 637-3888
Advertising Services
N.A.I.C.S.: 541890

Time Out Market Porto, Lda (1)
Mercado da Ribeira Avenida 24 de Julho, 1200-479, Lisbon, Portugal
Tel.: (351) 213951274
Advertising Services
N.A.I.C.S.: 541890

TIME PRODUCTS LTD.
27 Berkeley Square, London, W1J 6EL, United Kingdom
Tel.: (44) 20 7343 7200
Web Site: http://www.timeproducts.co.uk
Year Founded: 1966
Sales Range: $75-99.9 Million
Emp.: 183
Watch Distribution Services
N.A.I.C.S.: 423940
Marcus Margulies (Chm)

Subsidiaries:

Accurist Watches Ltd (1)
Asher House Blackburn Road, West Hampstead, London, NW6 1AW, United Kingdom
Tel.: (44) 2074473945
Web Site: http://www.accurist.co.uk
Watch Distr
N.A.I.C.S.: 458310

SEKONDA (1)
Chartwell Dr, Wigston, LE18 2EZ, United Kingdom
Tel.: (44) 1162573535
Web Site: http://www.sekonda.co.uk
Watch Distr
N.A.I.C.S.: 458310

TIME PUBLISHING AND MEDIA CO., LTD.
Publishing Media Square No 1118 Feicui Road, Shushan District, Hefei, 230071, Anhui, China
Tel.: (86) 55165321668
Web Site: http://www.press-mart.com
Year Founded: 1999
600551—(SHG)
Rev.: $1,209,367,731
Assets: $1,137,352,903
Liabilities: $361,641,480
Net Worth: $775,711,423
Earnings: $55,045,289
Fiscal Year-end: 12/31/21
Publishing Services
N.A.I.C.S.: 513120
Dong Lei (Chm)

TIME TECHNOLOGY CO., LTD.
813 & 912 Mecca-dong 50 Wanam-ro SK Techno Park, Seongsan-gu, Changwon, 51573, Gyeongsangnam-do, Korea (South)
Tel.: (82) 552816540
Web Site: https://www.timett.co.kr
Year Founded: 2004
318660—(KRS)
Information Technology Services
N.A.I.C.S.: 541512
Ju Yanghyo (CEO)

TIME TECHNOPLAST LIMITED
2nd Floor 55 Corporate Avenue Saki Vihar Road Andheri E, Mumbai, 400 072, India
Tel.: (91) 2271119999
Web Site: https://www.timetechnoplast.com
532856—(BOM)
Rev.: $514,739,800
Assets: $459,121,647
Liabilities: $180,070,320
Net Worth: $279,051,328
Earnings: $26,828,919
Emp.: 2,502
Fiscal Year-end: 03/31/23
Polymer Product Mfr
N.A.I.C.S.: 326199
Anil Jain (Mng Dir)

Subsidiaries:

Elan Incorporated FZE (1)
SAIF Zone, PO Box 9410, Sharjah, United Arab Emirates
Tel.: (971) 65576111
Web Site: https://www.uaeelan.com
Sales Range: $25-49.9 Million
Emp.: 10
Industrial Packaging Product Mfr
N.A.I.C.S.: 326199

Gulf Powerbeat WLL (1)
Building 1369 Road 5138 South Alba, South Alba, Askar, 951, Bahrain
Tel.: (973) 1 783 0831
Web Site: https://www.gulfpowerbeat.com
Sales Range: $25-49.9 Million
Emp.: 10
Plastics Product Mfr
N.A.I.C.S.: 326199

NED Energy Ltd. (1)
Sy No 823 & 827 Medchal -Sameerpet Road, Medchal, Hyderabad, 501401, Telangana, India
Tel.: (91) 9866778671
Web Site: https://www.nedenergy.in
Battery Mfr
N.A.I.C.S.: 335910

Novo Tech SP Z.o.o. (1)
Aleja Milenijna 15, 66-470, Kostrzyn, Poland
Tel.: (48) 95 752 8130
Web Site: http://www.novo-tech.eu
Sales Range: $25-49.9 Million
Emp.: 4
Polymer Product Mfr & Distr
N.A.I.C.S.: 326199

TPL PLASTECH LIMITED (1)
203 Centre Point J B Nagar Andheri Kurla Road, Near J B Nagar Chakala Metro Station Andheri East, Mumbai, 400059, India
Tel.: (91) 2240624200
Web Site: https://www.tplplastech.in
Rev.: $23,279,191
Assets: $25,932,515
Liabilities: $13,385,563
Net Worth: $12,546,952
Earnings: $1,092,705
Emp.: 171
Fiscal Year-end: 03/31/2021
Plastic Drum Mfr
N.A.I.C.S.: 326199
Sanjaya Shrikrishna Kulkarni (Chm)

Yung Hsin Contain Industry Co. Ltd. (1)
No 22 Wen Hua road, Hsinchu Industrial park Ho Kou hsiang, Hsin-chu, 30352, Taiwan
Tel.: (886) 3 5978 918
Web Site: http://www.yunghsincontain.com
Emp.: 100
Industrial Packaging Product Mfr
N.A.I.C.S.: 326199

TIME WATCH INVESTMENTS LTD
27th Floor Ceo Tower, 77 Wing Hong Street, Kowloon, China (Hong Kong)
Tel.: (852) 2411 3567
Web Site: http://www.timewatch.com.hk
Year Founded: 1988
2033—(HKG)
Rev.: $247,379,384
Assets: $396,973,225
Liabilities: $57,266,475
Net Worth: $339,706,750
Earnings: $34,634,612
Emp.: 4,500
Fiscal Year-end: 06/30/21
Watch Mfr & Retailer
N.A.I.C.S.: 339910

TIMELESS RESOURCES HOLDINGS LIMITED

Michael Koon ming Tung (Founder, Chm & CEO)

Subsidiaries:

Balco Switzerland SAGL (1)
Via Penate 16, 6850, Mendrisio, Switzerland
Tel.: (41) 91 646 7152
Web Site: https://www.balcowatch.ch
Watch Whslr
N.A.I.C.S.: 423940

Tian Wang Electronics (Shenzhen) Company Limited (1)
4-5F Building 4 Jincheng Science and Technology Industrial Park, Industrial East Road Longhua Street Longhua District, Shenzhen, 518109, China
Tel.: (86) 75581719888
Web Site: https://www.tianwangwatch.cn
Watch Whslr
N.A.I.C.S.: 423940

TIMELESS CAPITAL CORP.
520-3rd Avenue Southwest Suite 1900, Calgary, T2P 0R3, AB, Canada
Tel.: (604) 340-5101
Year Founded: 2018
TLC.P—(TSXV)
Assets: $16,841
Liabilities: $68,743
Net Worth: $(51,902)
Earnings: $(236,943)
Fiscal Year-end: 12/31/23
Business Consulting Services
N.A.I.C.S.: 541611
Fahim Gadallah (CEO)

TIMELESS INVESTMENTS BV
Rubensstraat 66, 1077 MZ, Amsterdam, Netherlands
Tel.: (31) 207234321
Web Site: http://www.timeless.nl
Year Founded: 2000
Holding Company
N.A.I.C.S.: 551112
Hans Van Veggel (Partner)

Subsidiaries:

StoneBridge Investments BV (1)
Rubensstraat 66, 1077 MZ, Amsterdam, Netherlands
Tel.: (31) 207234321
Web Site: http://www.stonebridgeinvestments.com
Emp.: 6
Real Estate Investment Services
N.A.I.C.S.: 523999
Kees F. Bruggen (Mng Dir & Dir-Statutory)

Subsidiary (US):

StoneBridge Investments (2)
1054 31st St NW Ste 320, Washington, DC 20007
Tel.: (202) 337-1023
Real Estate Investment Services
N.A.I.C.S.: 523999

TIMELESS RESOURCES HOLDINGS LIMITED
Room 2208 118 Connaught Road West, Hong Kong, China (Hong Kong)
Tel.: (852) 35860280   HK
Web Site: https://www.timeless.com.hk
Year Founded: 1996
8028—(HKG)
Rev.: $10,343,809
Assets: $23,383,816
Liabilities: $4,248,859
Net Worth: $19,134,957
Earnings: $4,724,795
Emp.: 22
Fiscal Year-end: 03/31/22
Software Development Services
N.A.I.C.S.: 541511
Felipe Tan (Chm)

TIMES CHINA HOLDINGS LIMITED

Timeless Resources Holdings Limited—(Continued)

TIMES CHINA HOLDINGS LIMITED
Times Property Center 410-412
Dongfeng Road, Guangzhou,
510030, Guangdong, China
Tel.: (86) 2083486668   CN
Web Site: https://www.timesgroup.cn
Year Founded: 1999
1233—(HKG)
Rev.: $3,429,088,182
Assets: $21,049,799,378
Liabilities: $18,254,933,096
Net Worth: $2,794,866,282
Earnings: ($1,350,583,697)
Emp.: 2,656
Fiscal Year-end: 12/31/22
Holding Company
N.A.I.C.S.: 551112
Jianhui Guan *(Exec Dir)*

TIMES GREEN ENERGY INDIA LIMITED
602 6th Floor Times Green House
Dhruvathara Apts Somajiguda,
Hyderabad, 500082, Telangana, India
Tel.: (91) 7702632033
Web Site:
   https://www.timesgreenenergy.com
543310—(BOM)
Rev.: $2,465,661
Assets: $4,586,837
Liabilities: $535,817
Net Worth: $4,051,021
Earnings: $18,528
Fiscal Year-end: 03/31/23
Natural Gas Exploration Service
N.A.I.C.S.: 211130
Dinne Lakshmi Jumaal *(Mng Dir)*

TIMES NEIGHBORHOOD HOLDINGS LIMITED
R4706-4707 Building 47 Two Exchange Square 8 Connaught Place,
Central, Hong Kong, China (Hong Kong)
Tel.: (852) 4001119928   Ky
Web Site: http://www.shidaiwuye.com
Year Founded: 1998
9928—(HKG)
Rev.: $365,888,297
Assets: $411,215,173
Liabilities: $173,940,858
Net Worth: $237,274,315
Earnings: ($28,023,138)
Emp.: 9,128
Fiscal Year-end: 12/31/22
Holding Company
N.A.I.C.S.: 551112
Xihong Bai *(Chm)*

TIMES UNIVERSAL GROUP HOLDINGS LIMITED
Unit 3002 30/F Workington Tower 78
Bonham Strand East, Sheung Wan,
Hong Kong, China (Hong Kong)
Tel.: (852) 29073080
Web Site:
   https://www.timesuniversal.com
2310—(HKG)
Rev.: $12,247,013
Assets: $17,507,153
Liabilities: $19,402,568
Net Worth: ($1,895,415)
Earnings: ($3,614,370)
Emp.: 262
Fiscal Year-end: 12/31/22
Electronic Components Mfr
N.A.I.C.S.: 334416
So Mui Yeung *(Co-Chm)*

Subsidiaries:

Shenzhen Kwang Sung Electronics Co., Ltd. (1)
Ste 208-209 2 F Bio-Informatics Ctr No 2
Science Park, Hong Kong Science Park,
Sha Tin, New Territories, China (Hong Kong)
Tel.: (852) 29467600
Web Site: http://www.kse.cpm.hk
Sales Range: $25-49.9 Million
Emp.: 30
IFT & Coil Products Mfr
N.A.I.C.S.: 334416

TIMESCAN LOGISTICS (INDIA) LIMITED
Rajah Annamalai Buildings Annexe
3rd Floor, 18/3 Rukmani Lakshmipathy Road Marshalls Road Egmore,
Chennai, 600008, India
Tel.: (91) 9840442322
Web Site: https://www.timescan.in
Year Founded: 2006
TIMESCAN—(NSE)
Rev.: $23,010,146
Assets: $5,460,819
Liabilities: $3,670,239
Net Worth: $1,790,580
Earnings: $397,242
Emp.: 49
Fiscal Year-end: 03/31/22
Freight Air Transportation Services
N.A.I.C.S.: 481112

TIMEX GROUP B.V.
Herengracht 466, 1017 CA, Amsterdam, Netherlands
Tel.: (31) 23 556 3660
Holding Company; Watches Mfr
N.A.I.C.S.: 551112
Anette Olsen *(Chm)*

Subsidiaries:

Timex Group Luxury Watches BV (1)
Herengracht 466, 1017, Amsterdam, Netherlands
Tel.: (31) 23 556 3660
Jewelry & Watches Mfr
N.A.I.C.S.: 423940

Subsidiary (Non-US):

Timex Group India Ltd. (2)
Unit no - 303 3rd Floor Tower-B World Trade Tower C-1 Sector-16, Noida, 201301, Uttar Pradesh, India (74.93%)
Tel.: (91) 1204741300
Web Site: https://www.timexindia.com
Rev.: $19,398,015
Assets: $14,428,050
Liabilities: $12,714,975
Net Worth: $1,713,075
Earnings: ($1,093,365)
Emp.: 348
Fiscal Year-end: 03/31/2021
Watches & Jewel Mfr & Distr
N.A.I.C.S.: 334519
Sharmila Sahai *(Mng Dir)*

Timex Group USA, Inc. (1)
555 Christian Rd, Middlebury, CT 06762
Tel.: (203) 346-5000
Web Site: http://www.timex.com
Sales Range: $600-649.9 Million
Emp.: 7,500
Watches & Clocks Mfr
N.A.I.C.S.: 334519
Bob Lapointe *(Dir-Global Facilities Mgmt)*

TIMMINS GARAGE INC.
1395 Riverside Drive, Timmins, P4R 1A6, ON, Canada
Tel.: (705) 268-4122
Web Site:
   http://www.timminsgarage.com
Rev.: $23,240,233
Emp.: 55
New & Used Car Dealers
N.A.I.C.S.: 441110
Marc Cloutier *(Mgr-Svc)*

TIMOK A.D.
Save Dragojevica 23, Negotin, Serbia
Tel.: (381) 19 542 629
Year Founded: 2000
Sales Range: Less than $1 Million
Emp.: 9
Concrete Products Mfr
N.A.I.C.S.: 327390

TIMPSON GROUP PLC
Timpson House Claverton Road,
Wythenshawe, Manchester, M23 9TT,
United Kingdom
Tel.: (44) 1619466200   UK
Web Site: http://www.timpson-group.co.uk
Year Founded: 1989
Holding Company; Shoe Repair,
Locksmith, Engraving, Photo & Dry-cleaning Service Shops Operator
N.A.I.C.S.: 551112
John Timpson *(Chm)*

Subsidiaries:

Jeeves of Belgravia Limited (1)
8-10 Pont Street, Belgravia, London, SW1X 9EL, United Kingdom
Tel.: (44) 20 8809 3232
Web Site:
   http://www.jeevesofbelgravia.co.uk
Dry Cleaning Services
N.A.I.C.S.: 812320
Paul Ogle *(Mng Dir)*

Johnson Cleaners UK Ltd. (1)
Pittman Way, Fulwood, Preston, PR2 9ZD, Lancs, United Kingdom (100%)
Tel.: (44) 1772 662 590
Web Site: http://www.johnsoncleaners.com
Dry Cleaning Services
N.A.I.C.S.: 812320
Paul Ogle *(Mng Dir)*

Snappy Snaps Franchises Limited (1)
86 Aldgate High Street, Aldgate, London, EC3N 1LH, United Kingdom
Tel.: (44) 20 7702 4477
Web Site: http://www.snappysnaps.co.uk
Photo Printing Services
N.A.I.C.S.: 323111
James Timpson *(CEO)*

Timpson Ltd. (1)
Timpson House Claverton Road, Wythenshawe, Manchester, M23 9TT, United Kingdom
Tel.: (44) 1619466200
Web Site: http://www.timpson.co.uk
Shoe Care & Repair, Sign Making & Engraving Services
N.A.I.C.S.: 811430
James Timpson *(CEO)*

Subsidiary (Domestic):

Timpson Locksmiths Ltd. (2)
Timpson House Claverton Road, Wythenshawe, Manchester, M23 9TT, United Kingdom
Tel.: (44) 1619466200
Web Site:
   http://www.timpsonlocksmiths.co.uk
Locksmith Services
N.A.I.C.S.: 561622
Perry Watkins *(Dir-Ops)*

TIMPURI NOI S.A.
Sos Giurgiului 5B, Ilfov, Jilava, 077120, Romania
Tel.: (40) 21 318 83 00
Web Site: http://www.timpurinoi.ro
Sales Range: $1-9.9 Million
Engine & Turbine Mfr
N.A.I.C.S.: 333618

TIN NGHIA CORP.
96 Ha Duy Giap Street NR 1, Quyet Thang ward, Bien Hoa, Dong Nai, Vietnam
Tel.: (84) 61 3822 486
Web Site:
   http://www.tinnghiacorp.com
Year Founded: 1989
Sales Range: $400-449.9 Million
Holding Company
N.A.I.C.S.: 551112
Van Duc Quach *(Chm & CEO)*

INTERNATIONAL PUBLIC

Subsidiaries:

Dong Thuan Tourism Joint-Stock Company (1)
Ninh Chu Beach Yen Ninh Street, Van Hai Ward, Phan Rang-Thap Cham, Ninh Thuan, Vietnam
Tel.: (84) 68 3874 047
Web Site: http://www.bautrucresort.com
Resort Operator
N.A.I.C.S.: 721110

Nhon Trach Investment Joint Stock Company (1)
The 7th Street Dong SaiGon Urban Area, Long Tan Commune, Nhon Trach, Dong Nai, Vietnam
Tel.: (84) 613 561 462
Web Site: http://www.dongsaigon.vn
Real Estate Development Services
N.A.I.C.S.: 531390

Tin Nghia - A Chau Joint-Stock Company (1)
A2/377A Bui Huu Nghia Street, Ward Tan Van, Bien Hoa, Dong Nai, Vietnam
Tel.: (84) 618 851 689
Web Site: http://www.centria.com.vn
Real Estate Development Services
N.A.I.C.S.: 531390

Tin Nghia Corp. - Tin Nghia Granite Factory (1)
Section 8, Long Binh Ward, Bien Hoa, Dong Nai, Vietnam
Tel.: (84) 61 3982 195
Building Materials Whslr
N.A.I.C.S.: 423390

Tin Nghia Laos Joint Stock Company (1)
Luong Ward, Pakse, Champasak, Lao People's Democratic Republic
Tel.: (856) 31254138
Bricks Mfr
N.A.I.C.S.: 327331

Tin Nghia Logistics Joint-Stock Company (1)
Km01 900 Highway 51, Long Binh Tan ward, Bien Hoa, Dong Nai, Vietnam
Tel.: (84) 61 3831576
Web Site: http://www.icdbienhoa.com
N.A.I.C.S.: 541614
Van Nghi *(Mgr-Logistics)*

Tin Nghia Petrol Joint Stock Company (1)
95 A CMT 8 Street, Bien Hoa, Dong Nai, Vietnam
Tel.: (84) 61 3827 758
Web Site: http://www.tinexpetrol.com.vn
Petroleum Product Distr
N.A.I.C.S.: 424720

Tin Nghia Project Management Company Limited (1)
C15-C16 Tan Bien 2 Dieu Xien Street, Tan Bien Ward, Bien Hoa, Dong Nai, Vietnam
Tel.: (84) 61 3983029
Engineeering Services
N.A.I.C.S.: 541330

TIN ONE MINING JSC
Al-Farabi Ave 75v/7 3rd floor, 50051, Almaty, Kazakhstan
Tel.: (7) 7016479957
Web Site: https://www.tinone.kz
Year Founded: 1998
SRBT—(KAZ)
Assets: $30,281,710
Liabilities: $12,154,251
Net Worth: $18,127,459
Earnings: ($634,866)
Fiscal Year-end: 12/31/20
Metal Exploration Services
N.A.I.C.S.: 213114
Lawrence Rossouw *(Pres)*

TINC COMM. VA
Karel Oomsstraat 37, 2018, Antwerp, Belgium
Tel.: (32) 32902173
Web Site: https://www.tincinvest.com
Year Founded: 2007

TINC—(EUR)
Rev.: $42,974,025
Assets: $501,445,493
Liabilities: $1,095,379
Net Worth: $500,350,114
Earnings: $26,951,772
Emp.: 800
Fiscal Year-end: 06/30/22
Portfolio & Investment Services
N.A.I.C.S.: 523940
Manu Vandenbulcke *(CEO & Member-Exec Bd)*

Subsidiaries:

GlasDraad BV (1)
Prinses Margrietplantsoen 87, 2595 BR, Hague, Netherlands
Tel.: (31) 850479225
Web Site: http://www.glasdraad.nl
Fiber Optic Cable Installation Services
N.A.I.C.S.: 238210

T&D Invest NV (1)
Waregemstraat 527, 8540, Deerlijk, Belgium
Tel.: (32) 56190302
Web Site: https://www.tdinvest.be
Real Estate Development Services
N.A.I.C.S.: 531210

TINCI HOLDINGS LIMITED
FL 18 Wuyangxincheng Plaza No 115 Siyouxin Road, Guangzhou, China
Tel.: (86) 20 87382888   HK
Year Founded: 2001
Sales Range: $10-24.9 Million
Emp.: 61
Environmental Engineering Services
N.A.I.C.S.: 541330
Jinfu Xu *(Founder & CEO)*

TINE AGRO LTD.
39 Sardar Patel Nagar Nr Hotel Nest, Navrangpura, Ahmedabad, 380009, Gujarat, India
Tel.: (91) 7600916324
Web Site: https://www.tineagrolimited.in
Year Founded: 1994
531205—(BOM)
Rev.: $8,703,424
Assets: $8,263,431
Liabilities: $362,752
Net Worth: $7,900,679
Earnings: $1,393,402
Fiscal Year-end: 03/31/24
Textile Products Mfr
N.A.I.C.S.: 313110
Karan Bairawa *(Chm & Mng Dir)*

TINE SA
Lakkegata 23, 0187, Oslo, Norway
Tel.: (47) 75663080   NO
Web Site: http://www.tine.no
Year Founded: 1881
Sales Range: $1-4.9 Billion
Emp.: 5,400
Dairy Products Distr
N.A.I.C.S.: 424490
Trond Reierstad *(Chm)*

Subsidiaries:

Bunes Fryselager AS (1)
Stromtangvegen 38, 3950, Brevik, Porsgrunn, Norway
Tel.: (47) 90 19 89 89
Dairy Products Distr
N.A.I.C.S.: 424430

Diplom-Is AS (1)
Brennaveien 10, 1481, Hagan, Norway
Tel.: (47) 51371604
Web Site: http://www.diplom-is.no
Frozen Food Mfr & Distr
N.A.I.C.S.: 311520
Bjorn Moldskred *(Mng Dir)*

Subsidiary (Domestic):

Isdalen AS (2)
Hovfaret 17, 0275, Oslo, Norway
Tel.: (47) 22 73 08 77
Web Site: http://www.isdalen.no
Ice Cream & Frozen Yogurt Mfr
N.A.I.C.S.: 311520
Erik Bjorn Hansen *(Mng Dir)*

Kulinaris AS (2)
Trollasveien 8, 1414, Trollasen, Norway
Tel.: (47) 66 80 02 05
Web Site: http://www.kulinaris.no
Ice Cream Mfr
N.A.I.C.S.: 311520
Roar Langli *(CEO)*

Laguna Produkter AS (2)
Bentsrudveien 8, 3083, Holmestrand, Norway
Tel.: (47) 33 07 85 01
Web Site: http://www.lagunaprodukter.no
Beverages Mfr
N.A.I.C.S.: 312111
Christian Faureng *(Mng Dir)*

Fjordland AS (1)
Brynsengveien 10, 0667, Oslo, Norway
Tel.: (47) 22 97 49 00
Web Site: http://www.fjordland.no
Convenience Food Distr
N.A.I.C.S.: 445131

Subsidiary (Domestic):

Matvarehuset AS (2)
Hallheimslien 12 Olsvik, 5184, Bergen, Norway
Tel.: (47) 400 06 499
Web Site: http://www.matvarehuset.no
Food Preparation & Transportation
N.A.I.C.S.: 311991
Ken Are Ostlid *(CEO)*

Safari Nringsmidler AS (2)
Kjokkelvikveien 75, 5178, Loddefjord, Norway
Tel.: (47) 55 50 75 00
Web Site: http://www.safaricatering.no
Food Preparation And Catering Services
N.A.I.C.S.: 311991
Heine Eliassen *(Mng Dir)*

Ilchester Cheese Company (1)
Ilchester, Somerset, United Kingdom
Tel.: (44) 1935 842800
Cheese Mfr
N.A.I.C.S.: 311513

Norseland Ltd. (1)
Somerton Road, Ilchester, Somerset, BA22 8JL, United Kingdom
Tel.: (44) 1935 842800
Web Site: http://www.norseland.co.uk
Cheese Mfr & Distr
N.A.I.C.S.: 311513

Norseland, Inc. (1)
3 Parklands Dr Ste 102, Darien, CT 06902-3555
Tel.: (203) 324-5620
Web Site: http://www.norseland.com
Sales Range: $75-99.9 Million
Emp.: 35
Dairy Products Distr
N.A.I.C.S.: 424430
John Solomon *(Pres)*

Subsidiary (Domestic):

Alpine Dairy, LLC (2)
238 Tucker Rd, Ethel, WA 98542
Tel.: (330) 359-6291
Cheese Mfr
N.A.I.C.S.: 311513
Brian Barbey *(Gen Mgr)*

Lotito Foods LLC (2)
240 Carter Dr, Edison, NJ 08817
Tel.: (732) 248-0222
Cheese & Other Dairy Mfr
N.A.I.C.S.: 311513
Chris Lotito *(Pres)*

Sunniva Drikker AS (1)
Bedriftsveien 7, 0950, Oslo, Norway
Tel.: (47) 75663080
Web Site: http://www.sunniva.no
Beverage Distr
N.A.I.C.S.: 424490

TINE Meieriet Vest BA (1)
Minde Alle 10, PO Box 6030, 5892, Bergen, Norway
Tel.: (47) 3080

Web Site: http://www.tinevest.no
Rev.: $125,000,000
Emp.: 400
Mfr of Dairy Products
N.A.I.C.S.: 311512

Wernersson Ost AB (1)
Industrivagen 5, 523 90, Ulricehamn, Sweden
Tel.: (46) 321 261 50
Web Site: http://www.wernerssonost.se
Emp.: 200
Cheese Mfr & Distr
N.A.I.C.S.: 311513
Magnus Ekstrand *(Mng Dir)*

Subsidiary (Non-US):

Wernersson Ost Danmark AS (2)
Stengardsvej 5, 4340, Tollose, Denmark
Tel.: (45) 5918 5090
Web Site: http://www.we-to.dk
Cheese Distr
N.A.I.C.S.: 424430

TINEXTA S.P.A.
Piazza Sallustio 9, 00187, Rome, Italy
Tel.: (39) 0642012631
Web Site: https://www.tinexta.com
TNXT—(ITA)
Rev.: $330,499,732
Assets: $641,073,727
Liabilities: $427,506,127
Net Worth: $213,567,599
Earnings: $46,567,491
Emp.: 1,403
Fiscal Year-end: 12/31/20
Investment Services
N.A.I.C.S.: 523999
Enrico Salza *(Chm)*

Subsidiaries:

Ascertia Ltd. (1)
33 Queen Street, London, EC4R 1AP, United Kingdom
Tel.: (44) 2036331177
Web Site: https://www.ascertia.com
Software Development Services
N.A.I.C.S.: 518210

Ascertia Software Trading LLC (1)
Office No 1816 Burlington Tower Business Bay, PO Box No 418687, Dubai, United Arab Emirates
Tel.: (971) 45704760
Information Technology Services
N.A.I.C.S.: 541511

Camerfirma Colombia S.A.S. (1)
Parque Central Bavaria Manzana 2 Piso 2 Carrera 13 N 28 - 38, Bogota, Colombia
Tel.: (57) 3054645979
Web Site: https://camerfirma.com.co
Digital Trust Services
N.A.I.C.S.: 541519

CertEurope S.A.S. (1)
41 Rue de lEchiquier, 75010, Paris, France
Tel.: (33) 149702930
Web Site: https://www.certeurope.fr
Computer & Network Security Services
N.A.I.C.S.: 541519

Co.Mark TES S.L (1)
Torre Diagonal One Placa De Ernest Lluch I Martin 5 Planta, 08019, Barcelona, Spain
Tel.: (34) 930130263
Web Site: https://www.comark.es
Business Information Services
N.A.I.C.S.: 541611

Europroject OOD (1)
26 William Gladstone str ap 7, 1000, Sofia, Bulgaria
Tel.: (359) 29431176
Web Site: https://europroject.bg
Management Consultancy Services
N.A.I.C.S.: 541618

Euroquality S.A.S. (1)
39 Rue Saint-Lazare, 75009, Paris, France
Tel.: (33) 144699980
Web Site: https://www.euroquality.fr
Funding Program & Research Services
N.A.I.C.S.: 541715

PrivacyLab S.R.L. (1)
Via del Fante 45, 42124, Reggio Emilia, Italy
Tel.: (39) 0522215092
Web Site: https://www.privacylab.it
Data Processing Services
N.A.I.C.S.: 518210

Queryo Advance S.R.L. (1)
Via Riccione 7, 09045, Quartu Sant'Elena, Italy
Tel.: (39) 0709791458
Web Site: https://www.queryo.com
Web Marketing Services
N.A.I.C.S.: 541910

Re Valuta S.p.A. (1)
Via dei Valtorta 48, 20127, Milan, Italy
Tel.: (39) 0223330800
Web Site: https://www.revaluta.it
Real Estate Investment Services
N.A.I.C.S.: 531390

Sferabit S.R.L. (1)
Via Monte Rosa 81, 10154, Turin, Italy
Tel.: (39) 03292525455
Web Site: https://www.sferabit.com
Software Development Services
N.A.I.C.S.: 541511

Studio Fieschi & Soci S.R.L. (1)
C so Vittorio Emanuele II 18, 10123, Turin, Italy
Tel.: (39) 0116599677
Web Site: https://studiofieschi.it
Business Consulting Services
N.A.I.C.S.: 541618

Tinexta Cyber S.p.A. (1)
Vetra Building Via Fernanda Wittgens 2, Milan, 20123, Italy
Tel.: (39) 0266661440
Web Site: https://tinexta.com
Security System Services
N.A.I.C.S.: 561621

Subsidiary (Domestic):

Swascan S.R.L. (2)
Via Fabio Filzi 2B, Cernusco Sul Naviglio, Milan, 20063, Italy (100%)
Tel.: (39) 0278620700
Web Site: https://www.swascan.com
Security System Services
N.A.I.C.S.: 561621

Trix S.R.L. (1)
Via F lli Vicentini 18, 24126, Bergamo, Italy
Tel.: (39) 035313646
Web Site: https://www.trixsrl.com
Emp.: 15
Auto Spare Parts Distr
N.A.I.C.S.: 423120

Visura S.p.A. (1)
Lungotevere dei Mellini 44, 00193, Romano Canavese, Italy
Tel.: (39) 066841781
Web Site: https://www.visura.it
Environmental Consulting Services
N.A.I.C.S.: 541620

Warrant Hub S.p.A. (1)
Corso Mazzini 11, 42015, Correggio, Italy
Tel.: (39) 0522733711
Web Site: https://www.warranthub.it
Business Management Consulting Services
N.A.I.C.S.: 541611

Yoroi S.R.L. (1)
Via Paisiello 42, 00198, Romano Canavese, Italy
Tel.: (39) 0510301005
Security System Services
N.A.I.C.S.: 561612

TING SIN CO., LTD.
407 14th Floor No 386 Zhengyi Road, Xitun Dist, Taichung, 407, Taiwan
Tel.: (886) 422521638
Web Site: https://www.tingsin.com.tw
2358—(TAI)
Rev.: $68,710,012
Assets: $129,020,889
Liabilities: $63,921,312
Net Worth: $65,099,577
Earnings: ($114,958)
Emp.: 240
Fiscal Year-end: 12/31/22

TING SIN CO., LTD.

Ting Sin Co., Ltd.—(Continued)
Aluminum Alloy Mfr
N.A.I.C.S.: 331314
Fu-Tao Wu *(Chm)*

Subsidiaries:

ACE Accessories Co., Ltd. (1)
3F No 190 Gongye 9th Rd, Dali Dist, Taichung, 412037, Taiwan
Tel.: (886) 424921638
Web Site: https://en.aceaccessories.com.tw
Leather Belt Mfr & Distr
N.A.I.C.S.: 326220

TINGYI (CAYMAN ISLANDS) HOLDING CORP.
Suite 5607 56th Floor Central Plaza
18 Harbour Road, Wanchai, China
(Hong Kong)
Tel.: (852) 25111911   Ky
Web Site: http://www.tingyi.com
0322—(OTCIQ)
Rev.: $10,899,066,792
Assets: $8,092,781,624
Liabilities: $5,764,542,396
Net Worth: $2,328,239,228
Earnings: $425,874,225
Emp.: 64,302
Fiscal Year-end: 12/31/22
Holding Company
N.A.I.C.S.: 551112
Junichiro Ida *(Vice Chm)*

Subsidiaries:

Beijing Ting Tong Logistics Co., Ltd. (1)
No 888 West Daxian Road Wan Zi District Hei Zhuanghu Village, Chaoyang District, Beijing, 100024, China
Tel.: (86) 1085308468
Web Site: http://www.tingtong.com.cn
Logistics Management Services
N.A.I.C.S.: 541614

Chongqing Fumanduo Food Co., Ltd. (1)
No F32 Di Pingchang Industrial Zone, Beibu New Area, Chongqing, 401122, Sichuan, China
Tel.: (86) 2367390075
Instant Noodles Mfr & Whslr
N.A.I.C.S.: 311824

Chongqing Tingjin Food Co., Ltd. (1)
No 29 Danlong Road Economic Technology Development Zone, Nan'an District, Chongqing, 400060, Sichuan, China
Tel.: (86) 2362796734
Beverages Mfr & Distr
N.A.I.C.S.: 312111

Chongqing Tingyi Food Co., Ltd. (1)
No 29 Danlong Road, Nanan District, Chongqing, 400060, Sichuan, China
Tel.: (86) 2362826999
Instant Noodles Mfr & Sales
N.A.I.C.S.: 311824

Guangzhou Tingjin Beverage Co., Ltd. (1)
No 16 Hongyuan Rd E of Economic Technology Development Zone, Guangzhou, Guangdong, China
Tel.: (86) 2082089838
Beverages Mfr & Distr
N.A.I.C.S.: 424810

Guangzhou Tingyi Food Co., Ltd. (1)
No 12 & 14 Hongming Road East Area, Guangzhou, Guangdong, China
Tel.: (86) 2082268331
Instant Noodles Mfr & Sales
N.A.I.C.S.: 311824

Jiangmen Tingyi Food Co., Ltd. (1)
Banqiao Road, Beiyang Village Daze Town Xinhui District, Jiangmen, Guangdong, China
Tel.: (86) 7506638828
Web Site: http://www.junying-food.com
Dried Food Mfr
N.A.I.C.S.: 311423

Master Kong (Taiwan) Foods Co., Ltd. (1)
11 Chang Lin Rd, Toulie, Taipei, 640, Taiwan
Tel.: (886) 55325003
Web Site: http://www.masterkong.com.tw
Sales Range: $25-49.9 Million
Emp.: 140
Food Products
N.A.I.C.S.: 311423

Nanjing Tingjin Food Co., Ltd. (1)
No 649 Jiangjun Road Jiangning Economic and Technological, Development Zone, Nanjing, 211100, Jiangsu, China
Tel.: (86) 2552733265
Beverages Mfr & Distr
N.A.I.C.S.: 424820

Tianjin Kameda Food Co., Ltd. (1)
No 5 Xintai Street Development Zone, Tianjin, China
Tel.: (86) 2266200458
Rice Crackers Mfr & Sales
N.A.I.C.S.: 311821

Tianjin Tingyi International Food Co., Ltd. (1)
No 218 Muning Road Economic Development Zone, Tianjin, 300457, China
Tel.: (86) 2225325954
Web Site: http://www.masterkong.com.cn
Convenience Food & Beverages Mfr
N.A.I.C.S.: 311412

Tianjin Tingyu Consulting Co., Ltd. (1)
No 15 No 3 Avenue Tianjin Economic Development Area, Tianjin, 300457, China
Tel.: (86) 2265298888
Management Consulting Services
N.A.I.C.S.: 541618

Wuhan Tingyi Food Co., Ltd. (1)
No 63 Zhushanhu Avenue Economic Technology Development Zone, Wuhan, 430056, Hubei, China
Tel.: (86) 2784892668
Instant Noodles Mfr & Whslr
N.A.I.C.S.: 311824

TINKA RESOURCES LIMITED
1305 1090 West Georgia Street, Vancouver, V6E 3V7, BC, Canada
Tel.: (604) 685-9316   BC
Web Site:
https://www.tinkaresources.com
Year Founded: 1987
TK—(OTCIQ)
Rev.: $78,021
Assets: $52,496,857
Liabilities: $466,392
Net Worth: $52,030,465
Earnings: ($1,607,307)
Fiscal Year-end: 09/30/21
Zinc & Silver Ore Exploration
N.A.I.C.S.: 213114
Nick DeMare *(CFO)*

Subsidiaries:

Tinka Resources S.A.C. (1)
Av Benavides 1579 Of 306, Miraflores, Lima, 18, Peru (100%)
Tel.: (51) 14476017
Zinc & Silver Ore Exploration
N.A.I.C.S.: 213114
John Nebocat *(VP-Exploration)*

TINKERINE STUDIOS LTD.
113A 8275 92nd St, Delta, V4G 0A4, BC, Canada
Tel.: (604) 288-8778   BC
Web Site: https://www.tinkerines.com
Year Founded: 2006
TTD—(OTCIQ)
Sales Range: $800-899.9 Million
Three Dimensional Printers & Software Mfr
N.A.I.C.S.: 333248
Eugene Suyu *(Co-founder & CEO)*

TINKOFF BANK JSC
5 Golovinskoye shosse, Moscow, Russia
Tel.: (7) 4956481000
Web Site: http://tinkoff-group.com
Sales Range: Less than $1 Million
Commercial Banking Services
N.A.I.C.S.: 522110
Oliver Charles Hughes *(CEO)*

TINNA RUBBER & INFRASTRUCTURE LIMITED
Tinna House No 6 Sultanpur Mandi Road, Mehrauli, New Delhi, 110030, India
Tel.: (91) 1149518530
Web Site: https://www.tinna.in
Year Founded: 1984
530475—(BOM)
Rev.: $36,157,029
Assets: $23,132,006
Liabilities: $11,623,788
Net Worth: $11,508,219
Earnings: $2,613,668
Emp.: 651
Fiscal Year-end: 03/31/23
Bituminous Product Mfr
N.A.I.C.S.: 326220
Bhupinder Kumar Sekhri *(Chm & Mng Dir)*

TINONE RESOURCES INC.
Suite 600 1111 West Hastings Street, Vancouver, V6E 2J3, BC, Canada
Tel.: (604) 364-2215   BC
Web Site: https://www.tinone.ca
Year Founded: 2019
TORCF—(OTCQB)
Assets: $4,170,288
Liabilities: $409,407
Net Worth: $3,760,881
Earnings: $2,202,905
Fiscal Year-end: 06/30/22
Mineral Mining Services
N.A.I.C.S.: 213115
Ben Meka *(VP)*

TINSELTOWN INVESTMENTS B.V.
Maliebaan 6, 3581 CM, Utrecht, Netherlands
Tel.: (31) 302332269
Web Site: http://www.tinseltown-investments.com
Privater Equity Firm
N.A.I.C.S.: 523999
Erik Mouthaan *(Co-Founder)*

TINTAS ROBBIALAC S.A.
Apartado 1404 EC, Bobadela, 2696 901, Loures, Portugal
Tel.: (351) 219947700
Web Site: http://www.robbialac.pt
Sales Range: $75-99.9 Million
Emp.: 400
Paints Mfr
N.A.I.C.S.: 325510

TINTINA MINES LIMITED
82 Richmond Street East, Toronto, M5C 1P1, ON, Canada
Tel.: (416) 848-0106
Year Founded: 1961
TNNTF—(OTCIQ)
Rev.: $192,669
Assets: $7,231,486
Liabilities: $9,898,224
Net Worth: ($2,666,738)
Earnings: ($235,431)
Fiscal Year-end: 12/31/23
Mineral Exploration Services
N.A.I.C.S.: 212290
Eugenio Ferrari *(CEO)*

TINTOMETER GMBH
Schleefstrasse 8-12, 44287, Dortmund, Germany
Tel.: (49) 231945100
Web Site: http://www.lovibond.com

INTERNATIONAL PUBLIC

Year Founded: 1885
Rev.: $19,816,563
Emp.: 370
Water Test Equipment Mfr
N.A.I.C.S.: 333613
Cay-Peter Voss *(Co-CEO)*

Subsidiaries:

The Tintometer Limited (1)
Lovibond House Solar Way Solstice Park, Amesbury, SP4 7SZ, United Kingdom
Tel.: (44) 1980 664800
Web Site: http://www.lovibond.com
Emp.: 50
Water Testing Equipment Mfr
N.A.I.C.S.: 333613
Paul Banning *(Dir-Fin)*

Tintometer AG (1)
Hauptstrasse 2, 5212, Hausen, Switzerland
Tel.: (41) 56 4422829
Water Testing Equipment Mfr
N.A.I.C.S.: 333613

Tintometer China (1)
Room 1001 China Life Tower 16 Chaoyangmenwai Avenue, Beijing, 100020, China
Tel.: (86) 10 85251111
Water Testing Equipment Mfr
N.A.I.C.S.: 333613

Tintometer Inc. (1)
6456 Parkland Dr, Sarasota, FL 34243
Tel.: (941) 756-6410
Web Site: http://lovibond.us
Emp.: 250
Water Testing Equipment Mfr
N.A.I.C.S.: 334519
Brad Martell *(Pres)*

Tintometer South East Asia (1)
Unit B-3-12 BBT One Boulevard Lebuh Nilam 2, Klang, 41200, Selangor D.E, Malaysia
Tel.: (60) 3 3325 2285
Water Testing Equipment Mfr
N.A.I.C.S.: 333613

TINTRA PLC
2nd Floor Berkeley Square House, Berkeley Square, London, W1J 6BD, United Kingdom
Tel.: (44) 2037950421
Web Site: https://www.tintra.com
TNT—(AIM)
Rev.: $140,323
Assets: $15,070,485
Liabilities: $14,491,806
Net Worth: $578,679
Earnings: ($1,973,220)
Emp.: 12
Fiscal Year-end: 01/31/23
Lottery & Gaming Services; Payment Processing Services
N.A.I.C.S.: 713290
E. T. Razzall *(Chm)*

Subsidiaries:

Soccerdome Limited (1)
The Soccerdome 132 Birkenhead Road, Seacombe, Wirral, CH44 7BZ, United Kingdom
Tel.: (44) 1516373213
Sports Facility Services
N.A.I.C.S.: 611620

TINYBEANS
L5 126 Phillip Street, Sydney, 2000, NSW, Australia
Tel.: (61) 280721400   AU
Web Site: https://www.tinybeans.com
Year Founded: 2012
TNYYF—(OTCQB)
Rev.: $5,413,302
Assets: $5,632,888
Liabilities: $2,148,504
Net Worth: $3,484,384
Earnings: ($4,499,476)
Fiscal Year-end: 06/30/24
Online Information Services
N.A.I.C.S.: 513120

Jessica Jones (Head-Talent & Happiness)

Subsidiaries:

Tinybeans USA Ltd (1)
228 Park Ave S, New York, NY 10003-1502
Tel.: (347) 326-0632
Web Site: https://tinybeans.com
Online Journal Publishing Services
N.A.I.C.S.: 513120

TIO TECH A
Unter den Linden 21, 10117, Berlin, Germany
Tel.: (49) 3020924040 Ky
Year Founded: 2021
TIOA—(NASDAQ)
Rev.: $18,532,328
Assets: $348,982,359
Liabilities: $360,082,803
Net Worth: ($11,100,444)
Earnings: $15,771,043
Emp.: 2
Fiscal Year-end: 12/31/22
Investment Management Service
N.A.I.C.S.: 523999
Dominik Richter (Chm)

TIONG NAM LOGISTICS HOLDINGS BERHAD
Lot 30462 Jalan Kempas Baru, 81200, Johor Bahru, Johor, Malaysia
Tel.: (60) 72321299
Web Site: https://www.tiongnam.com
TNLOGIS—(KLS)
Rev.: $170,731,688
Assets: $520,867,958
Liabilities: $323,036,258
Net Worth: $197,831,700
Earnings: $1,557,023
Emp.: 3,000
Fiscal Year-end: 03/31/22
Logistic Services
N.A.I.C.S.: 484230
Kwee Lian Yong (Exec Dir)

Subsidiaries:

G-Force Logistics Solutions Sdn. Bhd. (1)
Lot 204 Jalan Bukit Belimbing 26/38 Section 26, Off Persipan Tengku Ampuan Lion Industrial Park, 40400, Shah Alam, Selangor, Malaysia
Tel.: (60) 351914733
Transportation Services
N.A.I.C.S.: 484110

LT Growth Sdn. Bhd. (1)
38 9 Jalan Bukit Belimbing 26/28 Kampung Baru Hicom, 40400, Shah Alam, Selangor, Malaysia
Tel.: (60) 351915555
Food Grocery Product Distr
N.A.I.C.S.: 445110

Tiong Nam Heavy Transport & Lifting Sdn. Bhd. (1)
Lot 2-10B Jalan SU 6A Persiaran Tengku Ampuan Section 26, Lion Industrial Park, 40400, Shah Alam, Selangor, Malaysia
Tel.: (60) 351915555
Web Site: https://www.tnheavylift.com
Emp.: 30
Container Trucking Services
N.A.I.C.S.: 484110

Tiong Nam Logistics Solutions (LAO) Co., Ltd. (1)
Lot 304 and 305 Savan-Seno Special Economic Zone C KM 9 Route 9, Nongdeun Village Kaysone Phomvihane, Savannakhet, Lao People's Democratic Republic
Tel.: (856) 305303117
Logistic Services
N.A.I.C.S.: 484110

Tiong Nam Logistics Solutions Sdn. Bhd. (1)
Lot 30462 Jalan Kempas Baru, 81200, Johor Bahru, Johor, Malaysia
Tel.: (60) 72321299
Web Site: http://www.tiongnam.com

Sales Range: $75-99.9 Million
Emp.: 400
Logistics Consulting Servies
N.A.I.C.S.: 541614

Subsidiary (Domestic):

TNTT Packages Express Sdn. Bhd. (2)
Lot 2-10B Jln SU6A Persiaran Tengku Ampuan Section 26, Lion Industrial Park, 40400, Shah Alam, Selangor, Malaysia
Tel.: (60) 351913837
Web Site: https://www.tnpexpress.com
Sales Range: $25-49.9 Million
Emp.: 60
Courier Service
N.A.I.C.S.: 492110

Tiong Nam Properties Sdn. Bhd. (1)
Lot 30462 Jalan Bukit Kempas Baru, 81200, Johor Bahru, Johor, Malaysia
Tel.: (60) 72341180
Web Site: https://www.tiongnamproperties.com
Property Development Services
N.A.I.C.S.: 531390

TIONG SENG HOLDINGS LIMITED
21 Fan Yoong Road, Singapore, 629796, Singapore
Tel.: (65) 63560822
Web Site: https://www.tiongseng.com.sg
Year Founded: 1959
BFI—(SES)
Rev.: $359,803,075
Assets: $389,342,573
Liabilities: $332,422,177
Net Worth: $56,920,397
Earnings: ($10,299,932)
Emp.: 1,394
Fiscal Year-end: 12/31/23
Residential & Commercial Property Construction & Development Services
N.A.I.C.S.: 236117
Lian Guan Pek (CEO)

Subsidiaries:

Steeltech Industries Pte. Ltd. (1)
16 Tuas Link 2, Singapore, 638562, Singapore
Tel.: (65) 6 862 7504
Web Site: https://www.steeltech.com.sg
Fabricated Metal Mfr
N.A.I.C.S.: 332312

Suzhou Changhe Investment & Development Co., Ltd. (1)
No 37 Sutong Road Suzhou Industrial Park, Suzhou, 215021, China
Tel.: (86) 65206601
Web Site: http://www.cytzjt.com
Automobile Mfr
N.A.I.C.S.: 336110

TIONG WOON CORPORATION HOLDING LTD.
15 Pandan Crescent, Singapore, 128470, Singapore
Tel.: (65) 62617888
Web Site: https://www.tiongwoon.com
BQM—(SES)
Rev.: $100,640,978
Assets: $364,218,599
Liabilities: $146,887,736
Net Worth: $217,330,863
Earnings: $11,600,593
Emp.: 1,110
Fiscal Year-end: 06/30/23
Marine Transportation Services
N.A.I.C.S.: 488320
Kah Hong Ang (Chm & Mng Dir)

Subsidiaries:

J Oasis Airbag Technology Pte. Ltd (1)
39 Woodlands Close 08-10 Mega Woodlands, Singapore, 737856, Singapore
Tel.: (65) 66659016

Sales Range: $25-49.9 Million
Emp.: 20
Ship Repairing Services
N.A.I.C.S.: 336611
Jeffery Toethiansero (Mng Dir)

P.T. TWC Indonesia (1)
Komplek Ruko Grand Niaga Mas Blok B No 80 Batam Center-Kepulauan, Riau Islands, Indonesia
Tel.: (62) 7784804502
Transportation & Logistic Services
N.A.I.C.S.: 488510

TWC Arabia Ltd. (1)
Jubail Industrial City, PO Box 37407, Off Street 274 Near Municipality of West Branch, Al Jubayl, 31961, Saudi Arabia
Tel.: (966):133633263
Web Site: https://www.tiongwoon.com
Sales Range: $100-124.9 Million
Emp.: 120
Oil Field Drilling Services
N.A.I.C.S.: 213111

Thai Contracting & Enterprises Co., Ltd. (1)
196 Moo 1, Banchang, Rayong, 21130, Thailand
Tel.: (66) 38941920
Transportation & Logistic Services
N.A.I.C.S.: 488510

Tiong Woon China Consortium Pte. Ltd. (1)
No 15 Pandan Crescent, Singapore, 128470, Singapore (100%)
Tel.: (65) 62617888
Marine Engineering Services
N.A.I.C.S.: 541330

Subsidiary (Non-US):

Tiong Woon (Huizhou) Industrial Services Co., Ltd (2)
Yifa Industrial Area Dushi Village Pingtan Town, Huiyang District, Huizhou, 516259, Guangdong, China
Tel.: (86) 7523307755
Crane Rental Services
N.A.I.C.S.: 238990

Tiong Woon Crane & Transport (M) Sdn Bhd (1)
Lot 1265 1266 Jalan Seelong, Senai Kulaijaya, 81400, Johor Bahru, Malaysia
Tel.: (60) 1127613680
Web Site: https://www.tiongwoon.com
Sales Range: $25-49.9 Million
Emp.: 30
Construction Equipment Leasing Services
N.A.I.C.S.: 532412

Tiong Woon Crane & Transport Lanka (Pvt) Ltd. (1)
888 Negombo Road, Keragapokuna, Wattala, Sri Lanka
Tel.: (94) 1143838057
Transportation & Logistic Services
N.A.I.C.S.: 488510

Tiong Woon Crane Pte Ltd (1)
No 15 Pandan Crescent, Singapore, 128470, Singapore
Tel.: (65) 62617888
Emp.: 100
Crane Rental Services
N.A.I.C.S.: 532412

Tiong Woon Crane and Transport (Pte) Ltd (1)
No 15 Pandan Crescent, Singapore, 128470, Singapore
Tel.: (65) 62617888
Web Site: http://www.tiongwoon.com
Emp.: 150
Cranes & Transportation Equipments Hiring Services
N.A.I.C.S.: 532412

Tiong Woon Enterprise Pte Ltd (1)
No 15 Pandan Crescent, Singapore, 128470, Singapore
Tel.: (65) 62617888
Emp.: 150
Construction Equipment Distr
N.A.I.C.S.: 423810

Tiong Woon International Pte Ltd (1)
No 15 Pandan Crescent, Singapore,

128470, Singapore
Tel.: (65) 62617888
Web Site: https://www.tiongwoon.com
Emp.: 150
Oil Field Drilling Services
N.A.I.C.S.: 213111

Tiong Woon Marine Pte Ltd (1)
No 15 Pandan Crescent, Singapore, 128470, Singapore
Tel.: (65) 62617888
Emp.: 100
Marine Transportation Services
N.A.I.C.S.: 483112
Kah Hong Ang (Mgr)

Subsidiary (Domestic):

TW (Sabah) Pte Ltd (2)
No 15 Pandan Crescent, Singapore, 128470, Singapore
Tel.: (65) 62617888
Web Site: https://www.tiongwoon.com
Sales Range: $200-249.9 Million
Emp.: 800
Marine Transportation & Logistics Services
N.A.I.C.S.: 483112

Tiong Woon Offshore Pte Ltd (2)
No 15 Pandan Crescent, Singapore, 128470, Singapore
Tel.: (65) 62617888
Sales Range: $150-199.9 Million
Emp.: 1,000
Offshore Marine Engineering Services
N.A.I.C.S.: 541330
Kah Hong Ang (Chm)

Tiong Woon Myanmar Company Limited (1)
No 141/145 4th Floor Left Bo Aung Kyaw Street, Kyauktada Township, Yangon, Myanmar
Tel.: (95) 9421133765
Transportation & Logistic Services
N.A.I.C.S.: 488510

Tiong Woon Philippines, Inc. (1)
Diezmo Road Barangay Pulo, Cabuyao, Laguna, Philippines
Tel.: (63) 495504686
Transportation & Logistic Services
N.A.I.C.S.: 488510

Tiong Woon Project & Contracting Pte Ltd (1)
No 15 Pandan Crescent, Singapore, 128470, Singapore
Tel.: (65) 62617888
Emp.: 150
Marine Engineering Services
N.A.I.C.S.: 541330
Ang Kah Hong (Chm)

Subsidiary (Non-US):

Tiong Woon Project & Contracting India Private Limited (2)
2nd Floor No 194 Block O Ganapathy Colony Near RTO Office, Anna Nagar East, Chennai, 600102, India
Tel.: (91) 4443331116
Web Site: https://www.tiongwoon.com
Marine Equipments Installation Services
N.A.I.C.S.: 541330

Tiong Woon Thai Co., Ltd. (1)
196 Moo 1 Banchang, Rayong, 21130, Thailand
Tel.: (66) 38941920
Web Site: https://www.tiongwoon.com
Construction Equipment Rental Services
N.A.I.C.S.: 532412
Ben Kat (Country Mgr)

Tiong Woon Tower Crane Pte. Ltd. (1)
12 Benoi Place, Singapore, 629932, Singapore
Tel.: (65) 68614944
Web Site: http://www.tiongwoon.com
Crane Hiring Services
N.A.I.C.S.: 532412

Tiong Woon Vietnam Company Limited (1)
Section 1 Mid Floor Trung Yen Plaza Building Lot O17 Trung Yen Urban, Trung Hoa Ward Cau Giay, Hanoi, Vietnam
Tel.: (84) 437866060

TIONG WOON CORPORATION HOLDING LTD.

Tiong Woon Corporation Holding Ltd.—(Continued)
Web Site: http://www.tiongwoon.com
Construction Engineering Services
N.A.I.C.S.: 541330

Tower Cranes Services Pte. Ltd. (1)
12 Benoi Place, Singapore, 629932, Singapore
Tel.: (65) 68614944
Transportation & Logistic Services
N.A.I.C.S.: 488510

TIPCO FOODS PUBLIC COMPANY LIMITED
118/1 Tipco Tower 28th-28th Floor
Rama 6 Road, Phaya Thai District,
Bangkok, 10400, Thailand
Tel.: (66) 22736200
Web Site: https://www.tipco.net
TIPCO—(THA)
Rev.: $77,230,884
Assets: $185,953,557
Liabilities: $64,350,781
Net Worth: $121,602,775
Earnings: $7,173,791
Emp.: 662
Fiscal Year-end: 12/31/23
Beverage Producer
N.A.I.C.S.: 312111
Laksana Supsakorn *(Chm)*

Subsidiaries:

Tipco Asphalt Public Company Limited (1)
Tipco Tower 1 118/1 Rama 6 Road
Phayathai, Phayathai District, Bangkok,
10400, Thailand
Tel.: (66) 22736000
Web Site: https://www.tipcoasphalt.com
Sales Range: $125-149.9 Million
Emp.: 500
Asphalt Shingle & Coating Materials Mfr
N.A.I.C.S.: 324122
Chainoi Puankosoom *(Chm)*

Tipco Biotech Co., Ltd. (1)
118/1 Rama 6 Road, Phayathai Phayathai,
Bangkok, 10400, Thailand
Tel.: (66) 22736200
Web Site: http://www.tipcobiotech.com
Agriculture & Biotechnology Services
N.A.I.C.S.: 541714

Tipco F&B Co., Ltd. (1)
118/1 Tipco Tower Floor 27-29 Rama 6
Road, Phaya Thai Subdistrict Phaya Thai
District, Bangkok, 10400, Thailand (49.99%)
Tel.: (66) 22736200
Sales Range: $100-124.9 Million
Emp.: 400
Fruit Juices & Syrups Mfr
N.A.I.C.S.: 311411

Tipco Food Co., Ltd. (1)
118/1 Tipco Tower 28th Floor Rama 6
Road, Samsen Nai Phaya Thai, Bangkok,
10400, Thailand
Tel.: (66) 22736200
Sales Range: $25-49.9 Million
Emp.: 200
Fruit Juices Mfr
N.A.I.C.S.: 311411
Viwat Lim Sakdakul *(Gen Mgr)*

TIPIAK S.A.
D2A Nantes Atlantique Saint-Aignan
de Grand-Lie, 44860, Pont-Saint-Martin, France
Tel.: (33) 240321125
Web Site: https://www.tipiak.fr
Year Founded: 1830
TIPI—(EUR)
Sales Range: $200-249.9 Million
Frozen Food Product Mfr
N.A.I.C.S.: 311813
Hubert Groues *(Chm & Mng Dir)*

Subsidiaries:

Tipiak Inc (1)
37 N Ave Ste 203, Norwalk, CT 06851
Tel.: (203) 961-9117
Web Site: http://groupe.tipiak.fr
Sales Range: $25-49.9 Million
Emp.: 2
Frozen Food Product Mfr
N.A.I.C.S.: 311412

Tipiak International (1)
D2A Nantes Atlantique Saint Aignan de
Grand Lieu, BP 5, 44860, Pont-Saint-Martin, France
Tel.: (33) 240 32 11 25
Sales Range: $75-99.9 Million
Emp.: 15
Food Products Distr
N.A.I.C.S.: 424420
Hubert Groues *(Mgr)*

TIPIK S.A.
Avenue de Tervueren 270, 1150,
Brussels, Belgium
Tel.: (32) 2 235 56 70   BE
Web Site: http://www.tipik.eu
Year Founded: 1988
Sales Range: $25-49.9 Million
Emp.: 100
Advertising & Public Relations Services
N.A.I.C.S.: 541810
Benoit Goossens *(Dir-Art)*

TIPMEFAST, INC.
HaShnura St 1, Zichron Yaakov,
30950, Israel
Tel.: (972) 37370057   NV
Year Founded: 2017
TMEF—(OTCIQ)
Liabilities: $17,720
Net Worth: ($17,720)
Earnings: ($15,000)
Fiscal Year-end: 12/31/22
Software Development Services
N.A.I.C.S.: 541511
Raid Chalil *(Founder, Pres, CEO, CFO, Treas & Sec)*

TIPOPLASTIKA A.D.
Radovana Grkovica bb, 32300, Gornji
Milanovac, Serbia
Tel.: (381) 32770905
Web Site: https://www.tipoplastika.rs
Year Founded: 1959
Sales Range: $10-24.9 Million
Emp.: 176
Packaging Materials Mfr
N.A.I.C.S.: 326112
Milica Todorovic *(Sec)*

TIPPERARY CO-OPERATIVE CREAMERY LTD.
Station Road, Tipperary, Ireland
Tel.: (353) 6233111
Web Site: http://www.tipperary-coop.ie
Sales Range: $25-49.9 Million
Emp.: 250
Dairy Products Including Butter,
Cheese & Milk Powder; Operation of
Supermarkets
N.A.I.C.S.: 311514
Michael Dunlea *(Controller-Fin)*

Subsidiaries:

Azbar Ltd (1)
Knockanrawley, Tipperary, Ireland
Tel.: (353) 62 80476
Sales Range: $25-49.9 Million
Emp.: 8
Dairy Products Mfr
N.A.I.C.S.: 311119

Tippagral S.A. (1)
1 Rue Professeur Louis Neel, BP 20,
Longvic, 21601, France
Tel.: (33) 3 80 31 66 19
Web Site: http://www.tippagral.net
Sales Range: $25-49.9 Million
Emp.: 20
Dairy Products Mfr
N.A.I.C.S.: 311119
Oisin Morrin *(Mgr)*

TIPS INDUSTRIES LIMITED
601 Durga Chambers Linking Road
Khar West, Mumbai, 400052, MH,
India
Tel.: (91) 2266431188
Web Site: https://www.tips.in
Year Founded: 1977
TIPSINDLTD—(BOM)
Rev.: $23,036,700
Assets: $23,103,603
Liabilities: $6,775,937
Net Worth: $16,327,666
Earnings: $9,174,702
Emp.: 49
Fiscal Year-end: 03/31/23
Music Publishers
N.A.I.C.S.: 512230
Kumar S. Taurani *(Chm & Mng Dir)*

TIPTEH D.O.O.
Ratarska 35, Zagreb, 10000, Croatia
Tel.: (385) 13141556   HR
Motion Control Systems Mfr
N.A.I.C.S.: 335314

TIPTEL AG
Halskestr 1, 40880, Ratingen, Germany
Tel.: (49) 21024280
Web Site: http://www.tiptel.com
Year Founded: 1973
Sales Range: $25-49.9 Million
Emp.: 272
Producer of Comfort Telephone
(ISDN) & Telecommunications System Safety Engineering Services
N.A.I.C.S.: 517112
Erhard Schaefer *(Exec Dir)*

TIPTON AND COSELEY BUILDING SOCIETY
70 Owen Street, Tipton, DY4 8HG,
West Midlands, United Kingdom
Tel.: (44) 121 5572551
Web Site: http://www.thetipton.co.uk
Year Founded: 1901
Rev.: $13,361,269
Assets: $521,838,422
Liabilities: $468,241,200
Net Worth: $53,597,222
Earnings: $1,451,941
Emp.: 55
Fiscal Year-end: 12/31/19
Mortgage Lending & Other Financial Services
N.A.I.C.S.: 522310
Richard Newton *(CEO)*

TIRATHAI PUBLIC COMPANY LIMITED
516/1 Moo 4 Bangpoo Industrial Estate Sukhumvit Road T Praksa A
Muang, Samut Prakan, 10280, Thailand
Tel.: (66) 27697699
Web Site: https://www.tirathai.co.th
Year Founded: 1987
TRT—(THA)
Rev.: $61,615,199
Assets: $95,328,713
Liabilities: $61,884,933
Net Worth: $33,443,780
Earnings: $3,782,695
Fiscal Year-end: 12/31/23
Transformer Mfr
N.A.I.C.S.: 334416
Sumpan Vongphan *(Mng Dir)*

Subsidiaries:

L.D.S. Metal Works Company Limited (1)
55/4 Moo 2 Soi Watrathburana (Watbangpla) Theparak Road Km 17 Bangpla, Bang
Plee, Samut Prakan, 10540, Thailand
Tel.: (66) 27524364
Web Site: http://www.ldsmetalwork.com
Fabricated Structural Metal Mfr

N.A.I.C.S.: 332312
Pisit Leeahtam *(Chm)*

Thai Fin Co., Ltd. (1)
653 Moo 2 Bangpu Industrial Est Soi 1 B
Phatthana 1, Tumbol Bang Pu Mai, Samut
Prakan, 10280, Thailand
Tel.: (66) 23233094
Transformer Accessory Mfr
N.A.I.C.S.: 334416

TIREMASTER LIMITED
145 Orenda Road, Brampton, L4W
1W3, ON, Canada
Tel.: (905) 453-4300
Web Site: http://www.tiremaster.ca
Year Founded: 1991
Sales Range: $10-24.9 Million
Emp.: 50
Tire Mfr & Distr
N.A.I.C.S.: 423130
Ron Cherry *(Pres)*

TIRTH PLASTICS LIMITED
Nr Vakil Bridge Bopal Ambli Road,
Village vejalpur, Ahmedabad, 380051,
Gujarat, India
Tel.: (91) 9408647410
Web Site: https://www.tirthlimited.in
Year Founded: 1986
526675—(BOM)
Rev.: $22,378
Assets: $400,015
Liabilities: $75,533
Net Worth: $324,482
Earnings: ($2,029)
Emp.: 1
Fiscal Year-end: 03/31/22
Plastics Product Mfr
N.A.I.C.S.: 326199
Varis Mahendrabhai Doshi *(Mng Dir)*

TIRUPATI FINCORP LTD.
2nd Floor Plot No 36 Pushpa Park
Daftary Road, Malad, Mumbai,
400097, India
Tel.: (91) 2271148504
Web Site: https://tirupatifincorp.in
Financial Investment Management Services
N.A.I.C.S.: 523940
Sudhir Bhikhalal Parekh *(Chm & Mng Dir)*

TIRUPATI FINLEASE LTD.
B/10 Madhavpura Market Nr Police
Commissioner Market Shahiabug
Road, Ahmedabad, 380 004, Gujarat,
India
Tel.: (91) 7940097020
Web Site: https://www.tirupatifinlease.co.in
Year Founded: 1993
539488—(BOM)
Rev.: $1,178,952
Assets: $826,308
Liabilities: $402,959
Net Worth: $423,350
Earnings: $15,919
Emp.: 5
Fiscal Year-end: 03/31/23
Financial Investment Services
N.A.I.C.S.: 523999
Pushpadevi Bajranglal Agarwal *(Exec Dir)*

TIRUPATI FOAM LTD.
Tirupati House 4th Floor Nr Topaz
Restaurent University Road, Polytechnic Char Rasta Ambawadi,
Ahmedabad, 380 015, Gujarat, India
Tel.: (91) 7926304652
Web Site: https://www.tirupatifoam.com
Year Founded: 1986
540904—(BOM)
Rev.: $10,055,856
Assets: $12,964,000

AND PRIVATE COMPANIES — TIS INC.

Liabilities: $9,446,154
Net Worth: $3,517,846
Earnings: $148,547
Emp.: 38
Fiscal Year-end: 03/31/21
Polyurethane Foam Mfr
N.A.I.C.S.: 326140
Satishkumar Amrutlal Mehta *(Exec Dir)*

TIRUPATI FORGE LTD.
Survey No 92/1 Plot No 1-5 Hadamtala Industrial Area, National Highway 27 Hadamtala Tal Kotdasangani, Rajkot, 360 311, Gujarat, India
Tel.: (91) 2827270512
Web Site: https://tirupatiforge.com
Year Founded: 2012
TIRUPATIFL—(NSE)
Rev.: $11,250,968
Assets: $6,148,888
Liabilities: $1,804,017
Net Worth: $4,344,871
Earnings: $1,130,460
Emp.: 73
Fiscal Year-end: 03/31/23
Automobile Equipment Mfr
N.A.I.C.S.: 336110
Atul L. Natu *(CFO)*

TIRUPATI GRAPHITE PLC
Eastcastle Street, London, W1W 8DH, United Kingdom
Tel.: (44) 2039849894   UK
Web Site: https://www.tirupatigraphite.co.uk
Year Founded: 2017
TGR—(LSE)
Rev.: $3,588,814
Assets: $26,494,459
Liabilities: $5,572,438
Net Worth: $20,922,020
Earnings: ($2,940,191)
Emp.: 290
Fiscal Year-end: 03/31/23
Mining Services
N.A.I.C.S.: 212290
Ameya Gogate *(CFO)*

TIRUPATI INDUSTRIES (INDIA) LIMITED
14 Sagar Samruddhi Plot Nos 1-2-3 Takai Post Sajgaon, Taluka Khalapur Raigad, Mumbai, 410203, Maharashtra, India
Tel.: (91) 8104529381   In
Web Site: https://www.tirupatiind.com
Year Founded: 1973
531547—(BOM)
Sales Range: $1-9.9 Million
Edible Oil & Specialty Chemical Mfr
N.A.I.C.S.: 311225
Milee J. Shah *(Sec)*

TIRUPATI INKS LIMITED
101 DDA Market Hargovind Enclave Vikas Marg Extension, New Delhi, 110092, India
Tel.: (91) 1122379709
Web Site: http://www.tirupatiinks.com
Year Founded: 1999
Sales Range: $10-24.9 Million
Printing Ink Mfr
N.A.I.C.S.: 325910
Sanjiv Agrawal *(Chm & Mng Dir)*

TIRUPATI SARJAN LTD.
A/11 12 13 Satymav Complex Opp Gujarat High Court S G Highway, Ahmedabad, 380060, Gujarat, India
Tel.: (91) 7927662013
Web Site: https://www.tirupatisarjan.com
Year Founded: 1995
531814—(BOM)
Rev.: $9,190,258
Assets: $24,072,280
Liabilities: $13,821,676
Net Worth: $10,250,604
Earnings: $155,201
Fiscal Year-end: 03/31/21
Real Estate Development Services
N.A.I.C.S.: 531390
Jitendrakumar Ishvarlal Patel *(Chm & Mng Dir)*

Subsidiaries:
Tirupati Development (U) Ltd (1)
Tirupati House Plot 705 Mawanda Road Kamwokya, PO Box 2412, Kampala, 256, Uganda
Tel.: (256) 414663031
Web Site: http://www.tirupati-uganda.com
Sales Range: $75-99.9 Million
Emp.: 200
Real Estate Development Services
N.A.I.C.S.: 531390
Sam Atina *(Head-Mktg)*

TIRUPATI STARCH & CHEMICALS LIMITED
Shreeram Chember 1st Floor 12 Agrawal Nagar, Indore, 452 001, Madhya Pradesh, India
Tel.: (91) 7312405001
Web Site: https://www.TIRUPATIstarch.com
Year Founded: 1985
524582—(BOM)
Rev.: $27,307,385
Assets: $18,182,919
Liabilities: $14,390,963
Net Worth: $3,791,956
Earnings: $140,008
Emp.: 263
Fiscal Year-end: 03/31/21
Starch Mfr
N.A.I.C.S.: 311221
Ramdas Goyal *(Chm)*

TIRUPATI TYRES LTD.
B1/A Utkarsh Co-op Housing Society M A Road, Andheri West, Mumbai, 400058, India
Tel.: (91) 2226204220
Web Site: http://www.tirupatityresltd.com
Year Founded: 1988
539040—(BOM)
Assets: $160,487
Liabilities: $18,393
Net Worth: $142,094
Earnings: ($94,901)
Fiscal Year-end: 03/31/21
Tiles Mfr
N.A.I.C.S.: 326199

TIS INC.
Sumitomo Fudosan Shinjuku Grand Tower 17-1 Nishishinjuku 8-chome, Shinjuku-ku, Tokyo, 160-0023, Japan
Tel.: (81) 353377070
Web Site: https://www.tis.com
Year Founded: 2008
3626—(TKS)
Rev.: $3,628,916,440
Assets: $3,473,264,160
Liabilities: $1,326,831,910
Net Worth: $2,146,432,250
Earnings: $323,050,530
Emp.: 21,972
Fiscal Year-end: 03/31/24
Information & Communication Services
N.A.I.C.S.: 519290
Toru Kuwano *(Chm & Chm)*

Subsidiaries:
AGREX DNP Vietnam Co., Ltd. (1)
10th Floor Detech Tower 8 Ton That Thuyet Street, My Dinh II Ward Nam Tu Liem District, Hanoi, Vietnam
Tel.: (84) 243 837 1000
Web Site: https://www.agrexvn.com
Business Process Outsourcing Services
N.A.I.C.S.: 541611
Fukuda Atsushi *(Gen Dir)*

AGREX Fine Techno Co., Ltd. (1)
Shigeru Makoto No 10 Bldg 10th Fl, 2 5 10 Shinjuku, Shinjuku Shinjuku 2-chome, Tokyo, 160 0022, Japan
Tel.: (81) 333500431
Sales Range: $25-49.9 Million
Emp.: 140
Software Development Services
N.A.I.C.S.: 541511

AJS Inc. (1)
Sumitomo Fudosan Shinjuku Grand Tower 8-17-1, Nishi Shinjuku, Tokyo, 160-0023, Japan
Tel.: (81) 367425500
Web Site: http://www.ajs.co.jp
Emp.: 356
System Development & Operation Services
N.A.I.C.S.: 541512
Kazunori Kawasaki *(Pres)*

ALMEC Co.,Ltd. (1)
5-5-3 Shinjuku, Shinjuku-ku, Tokyo, 160-0022, Japan
Tel.: (81) 333533200
Web Site: https://www.almec.co.jp
Medical Devices
N.A.I.C.S.: 423450
Katsuhide Nagayama *(Mng Dir)*

Agrex, Inc. (1)
Tokyo Opera City Building 3-20-2 Nishi-shinjuku, Shinjuku-ku, Tokyo, 163-1438, Japan (100%)
Tel.: (81) 353711500
Web Site: http://www.agrex.co.jp
Sales Range: $300-349.9 Million
Emp.: 2,300
Data Processing, Entry & Collecting, Printing, Mailing & Other Office Services
N.A.I.C.S.: 518210
Toshimasa Nakai *(Mng Corp Officer)*

CST Co., Ltd. (1)
Emubiru Jay 6 No 9 Fl 3, 2-chome Taito-ku, Tokyo, Japan
Tel.: (81) 338620201
Web Site: http://www.cstweb.co.jp
Rev.: $274,536,000
Emp.: 380
Software Development & System Management Services
N.A.I.C.S.: 541511

Chuo System Corporation (1)
Sumitomo Fudosan Shinjuku Grand Tower 15F 8-17-1, Nishi-Shinjuku Shinjuku-ku, Tokyo, 160-0023, Japan
Tel.: (81) 353313636
Web Site: https://www.chuosystem.co.jp
Sales Range: $75-99.9 Million
Emp.: 467
Business Application Development Services
N.A.I.C.S.: 541511

Cloud Scope Technologies, Inc. (1)
2-9-3 Aoyama Bldg 1F, Aoyama Minato-ku, Tokyo, 107-0062, Japan
Tel.: (81) 334038321
Web Site: http://www.cloud-scope.com
Sales Range: $25-49.9 Million
Emp.: 18
Business Development & Marketing Services
N.A.I.C.S.: 541611
Toshimitsu Takaoka *(Pres)*

Hokkoku Intec Service Inc. (1)
2-1 Kurazuki, IT Comprehensive Human Resource Development Center Building 5F, Kanazawa, 920-8203, Ishikawa, Japan
Tel.: (81) 762663000
Web Site: http://www.hokkoku-intec.co.jp
Sales Range: Less than $1 Million
Emp.: 95
Software Development Services
N.A.I.C.S.: 541511
Wakabayashi Hiroshi *(Pres)*

I AM Consulting Co., Ltd. (1)
219 Pracha-u-thit, Huaykwang, Bangkok, 10310, Thailand
Tel.: (66) 2 690 3663
Web Site: https://www.iamconsulting.co.th
Business Consulting Services
N.A.I.C.S.: 541611
Thanawat Taro Lertwattanarak *(Co-Founder)*

INTEC IT Capital, Inc. (1)
1-3-3 shinsuna Koto-ku, Tokyo, 136 0075, Japan
Tel.: (81) 356655070
Web Site: http://www.inteccap.co.jp
Sales Range: $50-74.9 Million
Emp.: 4
Asset Management Services
N.A.I.C.S.: 531390
Hideki Kondo *(Pres & CEO)*

INTEC Solution Power Inc. (1)
Aioi Nissay Dowa Insurance Shinjuku Building 3-25-3 Yoyogi, Shibuya-ku, Tokyo, 151-0053, Japan
Tel.: (81) 333724440
Web Site: https://www.intec-sp.co.jp
Emp.: 1,239
Software Development & System Operation Services
N.A.I.C.S.: 541511

KOUSHI INTEC Inc. (1)
5-23 In Shimoshinmachi, Toyama, 930-0804, Toyama Prefecture, Japan
Tel.: (81) 764324632
Web Site: https://www.koushi-intec.co.jp
Sales Range: $75-99.9 Million
Emp.: 547
Software Development & System Operation Services
N.A.I.C.S.: 541511

LANSA Japan Ltd. (1)
2-3-21 Kouraku, Bunkyo-ku, Tokyo, 112-0004, Japan
Tel.: (81) 356159912
Web Site: https://lansa.com
Software Development Services
N.A.I.C.S.: 541511

MITEC Inc. (1)
18-21 Nabeta, Toyama, 930 0831, Toyama, Japan
Tel.: (81) 764510101
Web Site: http://www.mitec-toyama.com
Sales Range: $25-49.9 Million
Emp.: 50
Electronic Components Mfr
N.A.I.C.S.: 423690

Medical Toukei Co., Ltd. (1)
2-8-4 Core 1F Nihonbashi Bldg, Cho Chuo-ku, Tokyo, 103 0012, Japan
Tel.: (81) 336398720
Web Site: http://www.md-stat.co.jp
Sales Range: $25-49.9 Million
Emp.: 18
Medical Products Manufacturing Support Services
N.A.I.C.S.: 423450
Kota Hideyo *(CEO)*

MicroMates Corp. (1)
1-6-21 Nishi-Shimbashi NBF Toranomon Building 6F, Minato-ku, Tokyo, 105-0003, Japan
Tel.: (81) 35 512 5252
Web Site: https://www.micromates.co.jp
Software Development Services
N.A.I.C.S.: 541511

NEOAXIS Co., Ltd. (1)
Sumitomo Fudosan Shinjuku Grand Tower 25th Floor 8-17-1 Nishishinjuku, Shinjuku-ku, Tokyo, 160-0023, Japan (100%)
Tel.: (81) 35330 5300
Web Site: http://www.neoaxis.co.jp
Sales Range: $25-49.9 Million
Emp.: 188
System Operation & Management Services
N.A.I.C.S.: 541512
Masayuki Takahashi *(Pres & CEO)*

Oartech, Inc. (1)
Ogawamachikita Building 4F 1-8-3 Kanda-ogawamachi, Chiyoda-ku, Tokyo, 101 0052, Japan
Tel.: (81) 352893160
Web Site: http://www.oartech.co.jp
Rev.: $18,200,720
Emp.: 62
Investment Banking Services & Foreign Securities
N.A.I.C.S.: 523999

PT AINO Indonesia (1)
Jl Acasia Sekip UGM Blok L No 1, Yogya-

TIS INC.

TIS Inc.—(Continued)
karta, 55281, Indonesia
Tel.: (62) 27 451 8682
Web Site: https://www.ainosi.co.id
Information Technology Services
N.A.I.C.S.: 541511
Hastono Bayu Trisnanto *(Pres)*

PromptNow Co., Ltd. (1)
333 Lao Peng Nguan Tower I 16th Floor,
Soi Choei Phuang Vibhavadi-Rangsit Road
Chompol Chatuchak, Bangkok, 10900,
Thailand
Tel.: (66) 83 842 8534
Web Site: https://www.promptnow.com
Software Development Services
N.A.I.C.S.: 541511

QUALICA (Thailand) Co., Ltd. (1)
UBC II Building 20th Floor 591 Sukhumvit
Road, North Klongton Wattana, Bangkok,
10110, Thailand
Tel.: (66) 2 666 4851
Web Site: https://www.qualica-th.co.th
Emp.: 8
Software Development Services
N.A.I.C.S.: 541511
Kazuya Takeuchi *(Mng Dir)*

QUALICA Asia Pacific Pte. Ltd. (1)
2 Venture Drive 18-28 Vision Exchange,
Singapore, 608526, Singapore
Tel.: (65) 6 499 9160
Web Site: https://www.qualica.com.sg
Software Development Services
N.A.I.C.S.: 541511
Kaoru Nakamura *(Mng Dir)*

QUALICA(Shanghai) Inc. (1)
Room 2707-2709 New Hongqiao Center
Building No 83 Loushanguan Road, Changning, Shanghai, 200336, China
Tel.: (86) 2162411205
Web Site: https://www.qualica-sh.com
Emp.: 45
IT Solution Provider
N.A.I.C.S.: 541511

SORUN CORPORATION (1)
3 11 24 Mita, Minato ku, Tokyo, 1088368,
Tokyo, Japan
Tel.: (81) 354275555
Web Site: http://www.sorun.co.jp
Rev.: $624,342,654
Assets: $312,638,485
Liabilities: $126,267,658
Net Worth: $186,370,828
Earnings: $19,166,995
Emp.: 2,729
Software Development Services
N.A.I.C.S.: 513210

Sky Intec Inc. (1)
5-5 Ushijimashinmachi Tower 111, Toyama,
930-0804, Japan
Tel.: (81) 76 444 8711
Web Site: http://www.skyintec.co.jp
Sales Range: $25-49.9 Million
Emp.: 207
Advertising Services
N.A.I.C.S.: 541810
Sano Hiroshi *(Pres & CEO)*

SorunPure Inc.
8-17-1 Nishi-Shinjuku, Shinjuku-ku, Tokyo,
160-0023, Japan
Tel.: (81) 35 337 4549
Web Site: https://www.tis.co.jp
Shiitake Mushroom Services
N.A.I.C.S.: 111411

TIS Hokkaido Inc. (1)
1-3 Minami 1 Johigashi Park East Sapporo
6F, Chuo-ku, Sapporo, 060-0051, Japan
Tel.: (81) 11 251 5514
Web Site: https://www.tis-h.co.jp
Software Development Services
N.A.I.C.S.: 541511

TIS Solution Link Inc. (1)
18th Floor Shinjuku Square Tower 6-22-1,
Nishi- Shinjuku Shinjuku-ku, Tokyo, 163-
1118, Japan
Tel.: (81) 35 322 6220
Web Site: https://www.tsolweb.co.jp
Software Development Services
N.A.I.C.S.: 541511

TIS System Service Inc. (1)
1-1-5 Dojima Zymax Umeda Shindo Building 4F, Kita-ku, Osaka, 530-0003, Japan
Tel.: (81) 647970500
Web Site: http://www.tss-j.co.jp
Sales Range: $150-199.9 Million
Emp.: 940
Software Development & System Operation Services
N.A.I.C.S.: 541511
Itaru Bun Matsuoka *(Chm)*

TIS Tohoku Inc. (1)
1-226 Shintera 9th Floor of Odakyu Sendai
East Exit Building, Wakabayashi-ku, Sendai, 984-0051, Miyagi, Japan
Tel.: (81) 22 791 2770
Web Site: https://www.tis-t.co.jp
Computer & Software Product Distr
N.A.I.C.S.: 449210

TIS Total Service Co,. Ltd. (1)
Shinjuku Square Tower 17F 6-22-1, Nishi-
Shinjuku Shinjuku-ku, Tokyo, 163-1117,
Japan
Tel.: (81) 359097718
Web Site: https://www.tts21.co.jp
Sales Range: $25-49.9 Million
Emp.: 148
Security Systems Whslr
N.A.I.C.S.: 561621

TIS West Japan Inc. (1)
Urbannet Hakata Building 3F 2-5-1 Hakataekihigashi, Hakata-ku, Fukuoka, 812-
0013, Japan
Tel.: (81) 92 452 8400
Web Site: https://www.tis-w.co.jp
Computer & Software Product Distr
N.A.I.C.S.: 423430

TISI(Shanghai) Co., Ltd. (1)
Room 1901 Building T1 Raffles City Changning No 1133 Changning Road, Changning, Shanghai, China
Tel.: (86) 2133728011
Web Site: https://www.tisi.com.cn
System Integration & Outsourcing Services
N.A.I.C.S.: 541512

TKSOFT Singapore PTE. Ltd. (1)
2 Venture Drive 18-28 Vision Exchange,
Singapore, 608526, Singapore
Tel.: (65) 64999160
Web Site: https://www.qualica.com.sg
Sales Range: $25-49.9 Million
Emp.: 1
Software Development Services
N.A.I.C.S.: 541511

TinhVan Technologies JSC. (1)
8th Floor Sport Hotel, Hacinco Student Village Thanh Xuan District, Hanoi, Vietnam
Tel.: (84) 43 558 9970
Web Site: https://www.tinhvan.vn
Software Development Services
N.A.I.C.S.: 541511
Hoang To *(CEO & Chm)*

Tis Inc (1)
Shin-Daibiru Building 2-1 Dojimahama
1-chome, Kita-ku, Osaka, 530-0004, Japan
Tel.: (81) 647963060
Web Site: http://www.tis.co.jp
Sales Range: $700-749.9 Million
Emp.: 2,827
Software Development & Outsourcing Services
N.A.I.C.S.: 541511

Subsidiary (Domestic):

QUALICA Inc. (2)
23F Sumitomofudosan Shinjuku Grand
Tower 8-17-1, Nishishinjuku Shinjuku-ku,
Tokyo, 160-0023, Japan
Tel.: (81) 359370700
Web Site: https://www.qualica.co.jp
Sales Range: $150-199.9 Million
Emp.: 970
Software Development & System Operation Services
N.A.I.C.S.: 541511

UFIT Co., Ltd. (1)
Shibansu No 2 No 3 S Hall Zip Shibaura
1-Chome, Minato-ku, Tokyo, 105 8007, Japan
Tel.: (81) 357651200
Web Site: http://www.ufit.co.jp
Sales Range: $350-399.9 Million
Emp.: 1,342
Software Development & Solution Services

N.A.I.C.S.: 541512

UPSHE Co., Ltd. (1)
Core Build 1F 2-8-4 Horidome-cho, Nihonbashi Chuo-ku, Tokyo, 103 0012, Japan
Tel.: (81) 356528661
Pharmaceutical Sales & Marketing Services
N.A.I.C.S.: 456110

WITHINTEC INC. (1)
6-22 city, Toyama Intec Bldg No 6, Toyama,
930 0803, Toyama, Japan
Tel.: (81) 764448057
Sales Range: $50-74.9 Million
Emp.: 180
Data Entry & Facility Management Services
N.A.I.C.S.: 518210

aidec Corporation (1)
Bldg 1-10-6 Taito, Taito-ku, Tokyo, 110
0016, Japan
Tel.: (81) 338365401
Web Site: http://www.aidec.co.jp
System Integration Services
N.A.I.C.S.: 541512

TISA A.D.
Glavni trg 11, Senta, Serbia
Tel.: (381) 24 812 368
Web Site: http://www.tisasenta.com
Year Founded: 1991
Sales Range: Less than $1 Million
Emp.: 16
Home Management Services
N.A.I.C.S.: 721110

TISCALI S.P.A.
Giacomo Robustelli loc Sa Illetta,
09123, Cagliari, Italy
Tel.: (39) 07046011 IT
Web Site: http://www.tiscali.it
Year Founded: 1998
TIS—(EUR)
Sales Range: Less than $1 Million
Holding Company; Internet Services
N.A.I.C.S.: 551112
Alberto Trondoli *(Chm)*

Subsidiaries:

Tiscali International Network B.V. (1)
Ebweg 1e, Barendrecht, 2991 LS, South
Holland, Netherlands
Tel.: (31) 180532953
Internet Service Provider
N.A.I.C.S.: 517810

World Online International Nv (1)
Ebweg 1e, 2991 LS, Barendrecht, South
Holland, Netherlands
Tel.: (31) 180532953
Internet Service Provider
N.A.I.C.S.: 517810

TISCO FINANCIAL GROUP PUBLIC COMPANY LIMITED
Tower 48/2 North Sathorn Road, Bangrak, Bangkok, 10500, Thailand
Tel.: (66) 26336000
Web Site: https://www.tisco.co.th
Year Founded: 1969
TSCFY—(OTCIQ)
Rev.: $526,536,614
Assets: $8,486,813,672
Liabilities: $7,247,673,455
Net Worth: $1,239,140,217
Earnings: $213,148,147
Emp.: 4,839
Fiscal Year-end: 12/31/23
Banking Services
N.A.I.C.S.: 522110
Suthas Ruangmanamongkol *(Chm-Exec Bd & CEO)*

Subsidiaries:

Hi-Way Co., Ltd. (1)
2046/16 New Petchaburi Road, Bangkapi
Huay-Kwang, Bangkok, 10320, Thailand
Tel.: (66) 2319 1717
Motorcycle Leasing Services
N.A.I.C.S.: 532284

INTERNATIONAL PUBLIC

TISCO Asset Management Company Limited (1)
48/16-17 TISCO Tower 9th Floor North
Sathorn Road Silom, Bangrak, Bangkok,
10500, Thailand (100%)
Tel.: (66) 26336000
Web Site: https://www.tiscoasset.com
Sales Range: $100-124.9 Million
Emp.: 150
Asset Management Services
N.A.I.C.S.: 523999
Theeranat Rujimethapass *(Pres)*

TISCO Bank Public Company Limited (1)
1st Fl TISCO Tower 48/2 North Sathorn
Road, Bangrak, Bangkok, 10500, Thailand
Tel.: (66) 26336000
Web Site: https://www.tisco.co.th
Banking Services
N.A.I.C.S.: 522110

TISCO Information Technology Company Limited (1)
6th Fl TISCO Tower 48/12 North Sathorn
Road Silom, Bangrak, Bangkok, 10500,
Thailand
Tel.: (66) 26334299
Banking Services
N.A.I.C.S.: 522110

TISCO Insurance Solution Company Limited (1)
48/50-48/51 TISCO Tower Building 22nd
Floor North Sathorn Road, Silom Subdistrict
Bang Rak District, Bangkok, 10500, Thailand
Tel.: (66) 26336060
Web Site: https://www.tiscoinsure.com
Banking Services
N.A.I.C.S.: 522110

TISCO Learning Center Company Limited (1)
12th Fl Zone A TISCO Tower 48/20 North
Sathorn Road Silom, Bangrak, Bangkok,
10500, Thailand
Tel.: (66) 26337154
Banking Services
N.A.I.C.S.: 522110

TISCO Securities Company Limited (1)
48/8 TISCO Tower 4th Floor North Sathorn
Road, Silom Subdistrict Bang Rak District,
Bangkok, 10500, Thailand (100%)
Tel.: (66) 26336000
Web Site: https://www.tiscosec.com
Sales Range: $50-74.9 Million
Emp.: 100
Securities Dealer
N.A.I.C.S.: 523150

TISDALE CLEAN ENERGY CORP.
2200-885 W Georgia St, Vancouver,
V6C 3E8, BC, Canada
Tel.: (604) 970-4330 BC
Web Site:
  https://www.tisdalecleanenergy.com
Year Founded: 1972
C9OO—(DEU)
Rev.: $24,341
Assets: $1,691,818
Liabilities: $204,871
Net Worth: $1,486,948
Earnings: ($814,065)
Fiscal Year-end: 12/31/23
Mineral Exploration Services
N.A.I.C.S.: 213114
Alex Klenman *(CEO)*

TISO BLACKSTAR GROUP SE
North West House 119 Marylebone
Road, Marylebone, London, NW1
5PU, United Kingdom
Tel.: (44) 203 965 6799 Mt
Web Site:
  http://www.tisoblackstar.com
TBG—(JSE)
Sales Range: $150-199.9 Million
Privater Equity Firm
N.A.I.C.S.: 523999

AND PRIVATE COMPANIES

Andrew David Bonamour *(Founder & CEO)*

Subsidiaries:

Adreach Group (Pty) Limited (1)
33 A Bath Avenue, Rosebank, Johannesburg, 2196, Gauteng, South Africa
Tel.: (27) 113277110
Web Site: http://www.streetpoleads.co.za
Sales Range: $25-49.9 Million
Emp.: 70
Outdoor Advertising Solutions
N.A.I.C.S.: 541850

Ferro Industrial Products (Pty) Limited (1)
1 Atomic St, Brakpan, 1540, Gauteng, South Africa
Tel.: (27) 117464000
Web Site: http://www.ferrosa.co.za
Sales Range: $125-149.9 Million
Emp.: 400
Powder Coating Mfr
N.A.I.C.S.: 325510
Trevor I'Ons *(Dir-Engrg & Ops)*

Global Roofing Solutions (Pty) Ltd. (1)
154 Monteer Road, Isando, 1600, Gauteng, South Africa
Tel.: (27) 115704600
Web Site: http://www.global-roofing-solutions.co.za
Sales Range: $100-124.9 Million
Emp.: 325
Holding Company; Metal Roof Covering, Wall Cladding & Floor Decking Products Mfr
N.A.I.C.S.: 551112

Unit (Domestic):

Brownbuilt Metal Sections (2)
cnr of Tile & Paul Smit Roads, Boksburg, 1508, South Africa
Tel.: (27) 118982903
Web Site: http://www.global-roofing-solutions.co.za
Metal Roof Covering, Wall Cladding & Floor Decking Products Mfr
N.A.I.C.S.: 332323
Johan van der Westhuizen *(Gen Mgr)*

Stainless Steel & Aluminum Corporation (1)
Cnr Linton Jones & Brammer Streets, Industria East, Germiston, 1600, South Africa
Tel.: (27) 118716900
Web Site: http://www.stalcor.co.za
Emp.: 200
Hot & Cold Rolled, Flat Rolled & Fabricated Structural Steel & Aluminum Products Mfr & Distr
N.A.I.C.S.: 331221
Chris Ransome *(Chm)*

Times Media Group Limited (1)
4 Biermann Avenue Rosebank, Johann Gauteng ZAF, Johannesburg, 2196, Gauteng, South Africa
Tel.: (27) 112803000
Web Site: http://www.timesmedia.co.za
Sales Range: $750-799.9 Million
Emp.: 5,000
Media Holding Company
N.A.I.C.S.: 551112
Andrew David Bonamour *(CEO)*

Subsidiary (Domestic):

Times Media (Pty) Limited (2)
4 Biermann Avenue Rosebank, Johann Gauteng ZAF, Johannesburg, 2196, Gauteng, South Africa
Tel.: (27) 11 280 3000
Web Site: http://www.timesmedia.co.za
Business Management Services
N.A.I.C.S.: 561110
Andrew David Bonamour *(CEO)*

Division (Domestic):

Times Media (Pty) Limited - Books Division (3)
4 Biermann Avenue Rosebank, Johannesburg Gauteng ZAF, Johannesburg, 2196, Gauteng, South Africa
Tel.: (27) 11 280 3000

Sales Range: $25-49.9 Million
Emp.: 30
General & Academic Books Retailer
N.A.I.C.S.: 459210

Times Media (Pty) Limited - Media Division (3)
4 Biermann Avenue Rosebank, Johannesburg Gauteng ZAF, Johannesburg, 2196, Gauteng, South Africa
Tel.: (27) 11 280 3000
Web Site: http://www.timesmedia.co.za
Sales Range: $200-249.9 Million
Emp.: 1,000
Newspaper & Magazine Publisher
N.A.I.C.S.: 513110
Shaun Smith *(Mgr-Circulation & Mktg)*

Tiso Blackstar Group Proprietary Limited (1)
1st Floor 4 Biermann Avenue, Rosebank, 2196, South Africa
Tel.: (27) 11 214 8500
Web Site: http://www.tisoblackstar.com
Privater Equity Firm
N.A.I.C.S.: 523999
Nkululeko Leonard Sowazi *(Chm)*

TISSUE REGENIX GROUP PLC
Unit 1 and 2 Astley Way Swillington, Leeds, LS26 8XT, United Kingdom
Tel.: (44) 3304303052
Web Site: http://www.tissueregenix.com
TRX—(AIM)
Rev.: $24,476,000
Assets: $46,039,000
Liabilities: $15,638,000
Net Worth: $30,401,000
Earnings: ($2,596,000)
Emp.: 85
Fiscal Year-end: 12/31/22
Tissue Cell Technology
N.A.I.C.S.: 325413
Mike Izon *(Dir-R&D)*

TISSUE REPAIR LTD.
Level 10 255 Pitt Street, Sydney, 2000, NSW, Australia
Tel.: (61) 419557663   AU
Web Site: https://www.tissuerepair.com.au
Year Founded: 2012
TRP—(ASX)
Rev.: $1,023,012
Assets: $14,591,522
Liabilities: $324,279
Net Worth: $14,267,243
Earnings: ($2,721,793)
Fiscal Year-end: 06/30/23
Biotechnology Research & Development Services
N.A.I.C.S.: 541714
Darryl Reed *(COO)*

TITAANIUM TEN ENTERPRISE LIMITED
Shop No 901/914 Rajhans Complex 9 thFloor Ring Road, Surat, 395002, Gujarat, India
Tel.: (91) 2612320240
Web Site: https://www.titaaniumten.co.in
Year Founded: 1991
539985—(BOM)
Rev.: $27,888,796
Assets: $7,773,071
Liabilities: $5,855,440
Net Worth: $1,917,631
Earnings: $192,123
Emp.: 28
Fiscal Year-end: 03/31/23
Textile Product Mfr & Distr
N.A.I.C.S.: 313240
Ilaben Rohitkumar Kapadia *(Chm)*

TITAGARH RAIL SYSTEMS LIMITED.
Titagarh Towers 756 Anandapur E M Bypass, Kolkata, 700 107, West Bengal, India
Tel.: (91) 3340190800
Web Site: https://www.titagarh.in
532966—(BOM)
Rev.: $210,960,573
Assets: $337,659,804
Liabilities: $222,924,183
Net Worth: $114,735,621
Earnings: ($2,564,357)
Emp.: 453
Fiscal Year-end: 03/31/21
Railway Wagon Mfr
N.A.I.C.S.: 333924
Jagdish Prasad Chowdhary *(Chm)*

Subsidiaries:

Titagarh Firema S.p.A. (1)
Via Prov le Appia 8/10 Loc Ponteselice, 81100, Caserta, CE, Italy
Tel.: (39) 0823379111
Passenger Rolling Stock Mfr
N.A.I.C.S.: 336510

TITAN BIOTECH LIMITED
903-909 9th Floor Bigjos Tower Netaji Subhash Place, Delhi, 110034, India
Tel.: (91) 1127355742
Web Site: https://titanbiotechltd.com
Year Founded: 1992
524717—(BOM)
Rev.: $17,498,040
Assets: $16,127,930
Liabilities: $2,949,979
Net Worth: $13,177,951
Earnings: $2,978,730
Emp.: 396
Fiscal Year-end: 03/31/23
Biological Product Mfr
N.A.I.C.S.: 325414
Charanjit Singh *(Officer-Compliance & Sec)*

TITAN CEMENT COMPANY S.A.
22A Halkidos Str, 111 43, Athens, Greece
Tel.: (30) 2102591111   GR
Web Site: http://www.titan.gr
Year Founded: 1902
TITCF—(OTCIQ)
Rev.: $2,811,539,905
Assets: $3,545,027,045
Liabilities: $1,797,457,777
Net Worth: $1,747,569,268
Earnings: $300,966,994
Emp.: 5,621
Fiscal Year-end: 12/31/23
Cement Mfr
N.A.I.C.S.: 327310
Nellos Canellopoulos *(Chm)*

Subsidiaries:

Adocim Cimento Beton Sanayi ve Ticaret A.S. (1)
No1 Kat 13 Dereboyu Cad Meydan Sok Beybi Giz Plaza, Maslak, Istanbul, Turkiye
Tel.: (90) 2122866982
Web Site: http://www.adocim.com
Cement Mfr
N.A.I.C.S.: 327310
Murat Erserim *(Reg Mgr-Black Sea)*

Aeas Netherlands B.V. (1)
Schiphol Boulevard 231 Toren B5E, Luchthaven Schiphol, 1118 BH, Schiphol, North Holland, Netherlands
Tel.: (31) 204054747
Emp.: 15
Investment Management Service
N.A.I.C.S.: 523999

CemAI Inc. (1)
5700 Lake Wright Dr Ste 300, Norfolk, VA 23502
Tel.: (904) 509-5800
Web Site: https://www.cemai.com
Artificial Intelligence Monitoring Service
N.A.I.C.S.: 518210

Cementara Kosjeric AD (1)
Zivojina Misica 50, 31260, Kosjeric, Serbia
Tel.: (381) 31590333
Web Site: http://www.titan.rs
Sales Range: $125-149.9 Million
Emp.: 300
Cement Mfr
N.A.I.C.S.: 327310
Miroslav Gligorijevic *(Gen Mgr)*

Cementi Crotone S.R.L. (1)
Via Delle Industrie 54, 30175, Venice, 30175, Italy
Tel.: (39) 0415317874
Cement Import & Distr
N.A.I.C.S.: 423320
Nikolaos Vlasspoulos *(Pres & Owner)*

Essex Cement Co LLC (1)
182 Calcutta St, Newark, NJ 07114-3332
Tel.: (973) 522-4200
Web Site: http://www.titanamerica.com
Sales Range: $50-74.9 Million
Emp.: 9
Cement Whslr
N.A.I.C.S.: 423320

INTERMIX, A.E. (1)
22A Chalkidos, 11143, Athens, Greece
Tel.: (30) 2102591111
Web Site: http://www.intermix.gr
Dry Mortar Mfr
N.A.I.C.S.: 327120

Interbeton Construction Materials S.A. (1)
22a Halkidos Street, 111 43, Athens, Greece
Tel.: (30) 210 259 3661
Web Site: http://www.interbeton.gr
Ready Mix Concrete Mfr & Distr
N.A.I.C.S.: 327320

Ionia S.A. (1)
Andrea Metaxa 9, Kifisia, 14564, Athens, Greece
Tel.: (30) 2106299999
Web Site: http://www.ionia.gr
Porcelain Tableware Products Mfr
N.A.I.C.S.: 327110

Mechanicsville Concrete, Inc. (1)
3501 Warboro Rd, Midlothian, VA 23112
Tel.: (804) 744-1472
Web Site: http://www.powmix.com
Rev.: $17,756,371
Emp.: 80
Ready Mixed Concrete
N.A.I.C.S.: 327320

ST Equipment & Technology LLC (1)
101 Hampton Ave, Needham, MA 02494
Tel.: (781) 972-2300
Web Site: http://www.steqtech.com
Specialized Processing Equipment Mfr
N.A.I.C.S.: 423830
Michael J. Allen *(Pres)*

ST Equipment & Technology LLC (1)
101 Hampton Ave, Needham, MA 02494
Tel.: (781) 972-2300
Web Site: http://www.steqtech.com
Specialized Processing Equipment Mfr
N.A.I.C.S.: 423830
Michael J. Allen *(Pres)*

Separation Technologies Canada Ltd (1)
1558 Main St, Belledune, E8G 2M3, NB, Canada
Tel.: (506) 522-1829
Readymix Concrete Mfr
N.A.I.C.S.: 327320

Separation Technologies U.K. Ltd. (1)
No 12 Shed King George Dock, Kingston upon Hull, HU9 5PR, East Yorkshire, United Kingdom
Tel.: (44) 14 82 784012
Waste Materials Processing Services
N.A.I.C.S.: 562920

Sharrcem SH.P.K. (1)
No 280 Adem Jashari Hani Elezit, 71510, Pristina, Kosovo
Tel.: (383) 38777011
Web Site: http://www.sharrcem.com
Cement Mfr

TITAN CEMENT COMPANY S.A.

Titan Cement Company S.A.—(Continued)

Titan America LLC (1)
5700 Lake Wright Dr Ste 300, Norfolk, VA 23502-5601 **(100%)**
Tel.: (757) 858-6500
Web Site: http://www.titanamerica.com
Sales Range: $900-999.9 Million
Emp.: 2,300
Cement & Ready Mix
N.A.I.C.S.: 327310
Lawrence H. Wilt (CFO & VP)

Subsidiary (Domestic):

Central Concrete Supermix Inc. (2)
4300 SW 74th Ave, Miami, FL 33155
Tel.: (305) 262-3250
Web Site: http://www.supermix.com
Sales Range: $50-74.9 Million
Emp.: 225
Ready Mix Concrete Mfr & Dsitr
N.A.I.C.S.: 327320
Bernardo Dias (Pres)

Pennsuco Cement Co. LLC (2)
11000 NW 121st Way, Medley, FL 33178
Tel.: (305) 364-2230
Sales Range: $100-124.9 Million
Emp.: 300
Cement Mfr
N.A.I.C.S.: 327310

Division (Domestic):

S&W Ready Mix Concrete Co. (2)
217 Lisbon St, Clinton, NC 28328
Tel.: (910) 592-1733
Sales Range: $50-74.9 Million
Emp.: 250
Provider of Ready-Mixed Concrete Services
N.A.I.C.S.: 327320

Subsidiary (Domestic):

Separation Technologies LLC (2)
188 Summerfield Ct Ste 101, Roanoke, VA 24019
Tel.: (540) 512-7663
Web Site: http://proash.com
Cement Mfr & Distr
N.A.I.C.S.: 325520

Division (Domestic):

Tarmac America (2)
455 Fairway Dr, Deerfield Beach, FL 33441-1809
Tel.: (954) 481-2800
Web Site: http://www.titanamerica.com
Sales Range: $25-49.9 Million
Emp.: 90
Mfr of Cement; Quarrying of Aggregate Stone
N.A.I.C.S.: 327331

Titan Cement UK Ltd. (1)
No 12 Shed King George Dock, Hull, HU9 5PR, East Yorkshire, United Kingdom
Tel.: (44) 1482784012
Web Site: http://www.titanuk.co.uk
Sales Range: $50-74.9 Million
Emp.: 9
Cement Import & Distr
N.A.I.C.S.: 423320

Usje Cementarnica AD (1)
Bul Boris Trajkovski no 94, 1000, Skopje, North Macedonia
Tel.: (389) 2 2782 500
Web Site: http://www.usje.mk
Sales Range: $125-149.9 Million
Emp.: 300
Cement Mfr
N.A.I.C.S.: 327310
Boris Hrisafov (CEO)

Zlatna Panega Cement AD (1)
Shipka 2 St, Zlatna Panega Yablanitsa, 1528, Lovech, Bulgaria
Tel.: (359) 29760070
Web Site: http://www.zlatnapanegacement.bg
Cement Mfr
N.A.I.C.S.: 327310
Bisser Dossev (Dir-Fin)

Subsidiary (Domestic):

Zlatna Panega Beton EOOD (2)
ul Poruchik Nedelcho Bonchev 6, 1528, Sofia, Bulgaria
Tel.: (359) 29760081
Sales Range: $100-124.9 Million
Emp.: 300
Cement Mfr
N.A.I.C.S.: 327310

TITAN CEMENT INTERNATIONAL SA
Rue de la Loi 23 7th floor, PO Box 4, 1040, Brussels, Belgium
Tel.: (32) 27268058
Web Site: https://www.titan-cement.com
Year Founded: 1902
TITC—(EUR)
Rev.: $1,973,822,212
Assets: $3,290,372,668
Liabilities: $1,734,581,940
Net Worth: $1,555,790,728
Earnings: $1,906,228
Emp.: 5,363
Fiscal Year-end: 12/31/20
Cement & Building Material Mfr
N.A.I.C.S.: 327120
Michael Colakides (Mng Dir & CFO-Grp)

TITAN COMPANY LIMITED
3 Sipcot Industrial Complex, Hosur, 635126, Tamil Nadu, India
Tel.: (91) 4344664199
Web Site: https://www.titancompany.in
Year Founded: 1984
500114—(BOM)
Rev.: $4,901,744,500
Assets: $3,239,973,623
Liabilities: $1,812,721,060
Net Worth: $1,427,252,563
Earnings: $392,542,414
Emp.: 7,857
Fiscal Year-end: 03/31/23
Watch, Jewelry & Eyewear Mfr
N.A.I.C.S.: 339910
N. N. Tata (Vice Chm)

TITAN ECHIPAMENTE NUCLEARE S.A.
250 Basarabia Boulevard, Postal Office 49, 3rd District, 030352, Bucharest, Romania
Tel.: (40) 212556480
Web Site: http://www.titan-ten.ro
Year Founded: 1982
Nuclear Equipment Mfr
N.A.I.C.S.: 339999

TITAN INTECH LIMITED
5th Floor 54-1-7/21 Panchajanya Plot No 48 Vijayalakshmi Colony Road 2, Gunadala, Vijayawada, 520007, India
Tel.: (91) 8790814671
Web Site: https://www.titanintech.com
Rev.: $3,077,445
Assets: $171,943
Liabilities: $513,859
Net Worth: $(341,916)
Earnings: $842
Fiscal Year-end: 03/31/18
Electronic Component Mfr & Whslr
N.A.I.C.S.: 334419
Zameer Ahammed Kottala (CFO & Compliance Officer)

TITAN INTERNATIONAL LTD.
Hang Wai Industrial Center Block C 6th Floor Room 601 Kin Tai Street, Tuen Mun, China (Hong Kong)
Tel.: (852) 25494888
Web Site: http://www.titanhk.com
Year Founded: 1974
Emp.: 30
Hardware & Industrial Equipment Distr
N.A.I.C.S.: 423830
John W. H. Chan (Mng Dir-Hong Kong)

TITAN INVO TECHNOLOGY LIMITED
18/F Block C SP Tower Tsinghua University Science Park, Haidian District, Beijing, China
Tel.: (86) 31757707
Web Site: http://www.tus-i.com
Year Founded: 1997
0872—(HKG)
Rev.: $111,889,110
Assets: $256,502,343
Liabilities: $222,508,568
Net Worth: $33,993,775
Earnings: ($35,373,584)
Emp.: 368
Fiscal Year-end: 12/31/20
Automotive Safety Airbag Systems Researcher, Developer, Mfr & Sales
N.A.I.C.S.: 336390
Xiao Shen (Pres)

Subsidiaries:

Troitec Automotive Electronics Co., Ltd. (1)
Unit 2 Building 38 No 2 Jing Yuan North Street Beijing Economic, Technological Development Area, Beijing, 100176, China
Tel.: (86) 1080361892
Automobile Parts Distr
N.A.I.C.S.: 441330

TITAN KOGYO, LTD.
1978-25 Oaza Kogushi, Ube, 755-8567, Yamaguchi, Japan
Tel.: (81) 836314155
Web Site: https://www.titankogyo.co.jp
Year Founded: 1936
4098—(TKS)
Rev.: $52,569,330
Assets: $98,370,020
Liabilities: $62,048,070
Net Worth: $36,321,950
Earnings: ($11,104,800)
Fiscal Year-end: 03/31/24
Chemical Products Mfr
N.A.I.C.S.: 325180
Hajime Watanabe (Pres)

Subsidiaries:

Titan Kogyo, Ltd. - Ube Nishi Plant (1)
1804-8 Oaza Tsumazakigaisaku, Ube, Yamaguchi, Japan
Tel.: (81) 836 39 7558
Chemical Products Mfr
N.A.I.C.S.: 325180

TITAN LOGIX CORP.
4130-93 Street NW, Edmonton, T6E 5P5, AB, Canada
Tel.: (780) 462-4085
Web Site: https://www.titanlogix.com
Year Founded: 1979
TPCFF—(OTCIQ)
Rev.: $3,386,168
Assets: $13,689,338
Liabilities: $626,574
Net Worth: $13,062,764
Earnings: $880,739
Emp.: 30
Fiscal Year-end: 08/31/22
Oil Field Instruments Mfr
N.A.I.C.S.: 333132
Angela Schultz (CFO)

Subsidiaries:

Titan Logix Corp. - Overland Park Branch (1)
10100 W 87 St Ste 350, Overland Park, KS 66212
Tel.: (913) 541-8200
Fluid Meter Distr
N.A.I.C.S.: 423830

INTERNATIONAL PUBLIC

TITAN MEDICAL INC.
76 Berkeley Street, Toronto, M5A 2W7, ON, Canada
Tel.: (416) 548-7522 ON
Web Site: https://www.titanmedicalinc.com
Year Founded: 2007
TMDI—(NASDAQ)
Rev.: $308,000
Assets: $8,762,000
Liabilities: $3,977,000
Net Worth: $4,785,000
Earnings: ($6,953,000)
Emp.: 4
Fiscal Year-end: 12/31/23
Medical Device Mfr
N.A.I.C.S.: 339112
Curtis R. Jensen (VP-Quality & Regulatory Affairs)

TITAN MINERALS LIMITED
Suite 1 295 Rokeby Road, Subiaco, 6008, WA, Australia
Tel.: (61) 865552950
Web Site: https://www.titanminerals.com.au
TTM—(ASX)
Rev.: $3,850,000
Assets: $52,104,000
Liabilities: $6,007,000
Net Worth: $46,097,000
Earnings: ($1,589,000)
Emp.: 300
Fiscal Year-end: 12/31/23
Gold Mining Services
N.A.I.C.S.: 212220
Matthew Carr (Exec Dir)

Subsidiaries:

Core Gold Inc. (1)
Suite 1201-1166 Alberni Street, Vancouver, V6E 3Z3, BC, Canada
Tel.: (604) 345-4822
Web Site: http://www.coregoldinc.com
Rev.: $27,270,000
Assets: $23,764,000
Liabilities: $23,879,000
Net Worth: $(115,000)
Earnings: ($6,250,000)
Emp.: 255
Fiscal Year-end: 12/31/2018
Metal Mining Services
N.A.I.C.S.: 212290

TITAN MINING CORP.
Suite 555 - 999 Canada Place, Vancouver, V6C 3E1, BC, Canada
Tel.: (604) 687-1717
Web Site: https://titanminingcorp.com
TI—(TSX)
Rev.: $32,638,000
Assets: $78,896,000
Liabilities: $61,255,000
Net Worth: $17,641,000
Earnings: ($13,668,000)
Fiscal Year-end: 12/31/20
Mineral Exploration Services
N.A.I.C.S.: 213114
Donald R. Taylor (Pres)

Subsidiaries:

Balmat Holdings Corp. (1)

Empire State Mines, LLC (1)
408 Sylvia Lake Rd, Gouverneur, NY 13642
Tel.: (315) 535-3200
Gold Mining Services
N.A.I.C.S.: 212220

Titan Mining (US) Corporation (1)

TITAN PETROCHEMICALS GROUP LIMITED
4902 Sun Hung Kai Centre 30 Harbour Road, Wanchai, China (Hong Kong)
Tel.: (852) 2116 1388 BM
Web Site: http://www.petrotitan.com
1192—(HKG)

Sales Range: $25-49.9 Million
Emp.: 134
Holding Company
N.A.I.C.S.: 551112
Shing Chi Wong (Sec)

TITAN SECURITIES LIMITED
A23 IIIrd Floor Lusa Tower Azadpur Commercial Complex, Delhi, 110033, India
Tel.: (91) 1127674181
Web Site:
https://titansecuritieslimited.com
Year Founded: 1993
530045—(BOM)
Rev.: $415,275
Assets: $9,652,143
Liabilities: $220,826
Net Worth: $9,431,317
Earnings: $1,644,602
Emp.: 2
Fiscal Year-end: 03/31/23
Financial Lending Services
N.A.I.C.S.: 522299
Manju Singla (Mng Dir)

TITAN TOOL & DIE LIMITED
2801 Howard Ave, Windsor, N8X 3Y1, ON, Canada
Tel.: (519) 966-1234
Web Site: http://www.titantool.ca
Year Founded: 1956
Rev.: $45,294,703
Emp.: 145
Metal Stamping Services
N.A.I.C.S.: 332119
Joseph Szecsei (Founder, Pres & CEO)

TITAN WIND ENERGY (SUZHOU) CO., LTD.
No 28 Ningbo East Road Taicang Economic Development Zone, Suzhou, 200051, Jiangsu, China
Tel.: (86) 51282757666   CN
Web Site:
http://www.titanwind.com.cn
Year Founded: 2005
002531—(SSE)
Rev.: $946,025,098
Assets: $2,791,521,996
Liabilities: $1,624,257,091
Net Worth: $1,167,264,905
Earnings: $88,191,432
Emp.: 480
Fiscal Year-end: 12/31/22
Wind Turbine Towers & Related Equipment Mfr & Distr
N.A.I.C.S.: 331210
Yan Junxu (Chm & Gen Mgr)

Subsidiaries:

Titan Wind Energy (Europe) A/S   (1)
Engdraget 20, 6800, Varde, Denmark   **(100%)**
Tel.: (45) 7070 7150
Web Site: http://www.titan-wind.com
Sales Range: $50-74.9 Million
Emp.: 120
Wind Turbine Towers Mfr & Distr
N.A.I.C.S.: 331210

TITANIUM GROUP LIMITED
Suite 2101 21/F Chinachem Century Tower 178 Gloucester Road, Wanchai, China (Hong Kong)
Tel.: (852) 36793110
Web Site: http://www.ttnuf.com
Sales Range: $1-9.9 Million
Emp.: 192
Electric Wire Product Mfr
N.A.I.C.S.: 335929
Huamin Lai (Chm)

TITANIUM TRANSPORTATION GROUP INC.
32 Simpson Road, Bolton, L7E 1G9, ON, Canada
Tel.: (905) 266-3010   Ca
Web Site: https://www.ttgi.com
TTR—(TSXV)
Rev.: $331,259,817
Assets: $268,818,944
Liabilities: $189,871,904
Net Worth: $78,947,041
Earnings: $7,724,122
Emp.: 1,300
Fiscal Year-end: 12/31/23
Trucking & Logistics
N.A.I.C.S.: 484121
Theodor Daniel (Co-Founder & CEO)

Subsidiaries:

Crane Transport, Inc.   (1)
4125 W White Rd, Oakwood, GA 30566
Tel.: (770) 532-0057
Rev.: $2,200,000
Emp.: 30
General Freight Trucking, Long-Distance, Truckload
N.A.I.C.S.: 484121
Allison Crane (Sec & Treas)

Titanium American Trucking, Inc.   (1)

TITAS GAS TRANSMISSION & DISTRIBUTION COMPANY LIMITED
105 Kazi Nazrul Islam Avenue Kawranbazar Commercial Area, Dhaka, 1215, Bangladesh
Tel.: (880) 29103960
Web Site: https://www.titasgas.org.bd
Year Founded: 1964
TITASGAS—(CHT)
Rev.: $2,072,483,121
Assets: $2,094,072,444
Liabilities: $1,261,387,069
Net Worth: $832,685,375
Earnings: $40,133,142
Emp.: 1,956
Fiscal Year-end: 06/30/21
Natural Gas Transmission Services
N.A.I.C.S.: 221210
A. S. M. Ziaul Hoque (Fin Dir)

TITIJAYA LAND BERHAD
N-16-01 Penthouse Level 16 First Subang Jalan SS15 4G, 47500, Subang Jaya, Selangor, Malaysia
Tel.: (60) 380229999
Web Site: https://titijaya.com.my
TITIJYA—(KLS)
Rev.: $76,746,126
Assets: $485,642,230
Liabilities: $212,142,597
Net Worth: $273,499,632
Earnings: $1,254,675
Emp.: 77
Fiscal Year-end: 06/30/23
Property Development
N.A.I.C.S.: 237210
Soon Peng Lim (Mng Dir-Grp)

Subsidiaries:

NPO Development Sdn. Bhd.   (1)
N-16-01 Penthouse Level 16 First Subang Jalan SS15/4G, 47500, Subang Jaya, Selangor, Malaysia
Tel.: (60) 380229999
Innovative Property Development Services
N.A.I.C.S.: 531390

Riveria City Sdn. Bhd.   (1)
Level 18 Menara Sentral Vista Jalan Sultan Abdul Samad, Brickfields, 50470, Kuala Lumpur, Malaysia
Tel.: (60) 1300229898
Web Site: https://www.riveriacity.my
Property Development Services
N.A.I.C.S.: 531390

TITOMIC LIMITED
Tel.: (61) 395588822   AU
Web Site: https://www.titomic.com
Year Founded: 2014

TTT—(ASX)
Rev.: $5,139,842
Assets: $5,392,152
Liabilities: $4,704,090
Net Worth: $688,062
Earnings: ($7,940,874)
Fiscal Year-end: 06/30/24
Industrial Product Mfr & Distr
N.A.I.C.S.: 332999
Jeffrey Lang (Founder, CTO & Exec Dir)

TITON HOLDINGS PLC
894 The Crescent Colchester Business Park, Colchester, CO4 9YQ, Essex, United Kingdom
Tel.: (44) 8009704190   UK
Web Site: https://www.titon.com
Year Founded: 1981
TON—(LSE)
Rev.: $31,786,941
Assets: $29,823,678
Liabilities: $6,990,900
Net Worth: $22,832,777
Earnings: $1,361,793
Emp.: 202
Fiscal Year-end: 09/30/21
Window Vents & Fittings
N.A.I.C.S.: 332321
John N. Anderson (Deputy Chm)

Subsidiaries:

Titon Hardware Limited   (1)
Falconer Road, Haverhill, CB9 7XU, Suffolk, United Kingdom
Tel.: (44) 120 671 3800
Web Site: https://www.titon.com
Sales Range: $50-74.9 Million
Emp.: 90
Window Vents & Fittings Mfr
N.A.I.C.S.: 326199

Titon Inc   (1)
51129 Brandychase W, Granger, IN 46530-9004
Tel.: (574) 271-9699
Web Site: https://www.titon.com
Electronic Equipment Whslr
N.A.I.C.S.: 423690

TITTOT COMPANY LIMITED
22F No 80 Sec 1 ChengGong Rd, Yonghe District, New Taipei City, Taiwan
Tel.: (886) 277055168
Web Site: https://www.tittot.com
Year Founded: 1994
9949—(TPE)
Rev.: $6,329,081
Assets: $14,757,590
Liabilities: $2,109,308
Net Worth: $12,648,282
Earnings: ($1,102,054)
Fiscal Year-end: 12/31/22
Crystal Glass Product Mfr
N.A.I.C.S.: 327215
Yung-Shan Wang (Chm & Pres)

TIUMBIO CO., LTD.
6F Pangyo IT Center 30 Changup-ro 40 beon-gil, Sujeong-gu, Seongnam, 13469, Gyeonggi-do, Korea (South)
Tel.: (82) 316001500
Web Site: https://www.tiumbio.com
Year Founded: 2016
321550—(KRS)
Rev.: $965,034
Assets: $78,523,215
Liabilities: $2,617,165
Net Worth: $75,906,050
Earnings: ($11,149,317)
Emp.: 46
Fiscal Year-end: 12/31/20
Research & Experimental Development Services
N.A.I.C.S.: 541715
Huntaek Kim (CEO)

TIV TAAM HOLDINGS 1 LTD.
1 Zvi Hanachal Street Industrial Park, Emek Hefer, Haifa, 38830, Israel
Tel.: (972) 46179048
TTAM—(TAE)
Rev.: $433,590,098
Assets: $321,405,564
Liabilities: $250,180,847
Net Worth: $71,224,717
Earnings: $16,565,533
Fiscal Year-end: 12/31/22
Supermarket Store Retailer
N.A.I.C.S.: 445110
Shalom Haggai (Board of Directors & CEO)

TIV TEXTILE GROUP 1969 LTD.
11 ort Israel st, Bat Yam, 59594, Israel
Tel.: (972) 3 5553222
Web Site: http://www.tivtex.com
Year Founded: 1948
Sales Range: $50-74.9 Million
Textile Products Mfr
N.A.I.C.S.: 313110
Joseph Gutreich (Chm)

TIVOLI A/S
Vesterbrogade 3, 1620, Copenhagen, Denmark
Tel.: (45) 33151001
Web Site: https://www.tivoli.dk
Year Founded: 1843
TIV—(CSE)
Rev.: $163,519,555
Assets: $242,161,161
Liabilities: $99,144,854
Net Worth: $143,016,307
Earnings: $9,419,629
Emp.: 1,014
Fiscal Year-end: 12/31/22
Amusement Park Operator
N.A.I.C.S.: 713110
Dorthe Dinesen (Dir-HR)

Subsidiaries:

TivoliCasino.com Limited   (1)
Quantum House 75 Abate Rigord Street, Ta' Xbiex, XBX 1120, Malta
Tel.: (356) 21316590
Web Site: http://www.tivolicasino.com
Entertainment Services
N.A.I.C.S.: 713210

TIVOLI CONSTRUCTION LIMITED
4th Floor Raheja Chambers Linking Road & Main Avenue, Mumbai, 400 054, India
Tel.: (91) 2267694400
Web Site:
https://www.tivoliconstruction.in
Year Founded: 1985
511096—(BOM)
Rev.: $13,759
Assets: $314,201
Liabilities: $999
Net Worth: $313,202
Earnings: ($3,446)
Emp.: 1
Fiscal Year-end: 03/31/23
Construction Engineering Services
N.A.I.C.S.: 541330
A. Unnikrishnan (Compliance Officer)

TIVOLY S.A.
266 Route Portes de Tarentaise, 73790, Tours, France
Tel.: (33) 4 79 59 58 85
Web Site: http://www.tivoly.fr
Year Founded: 1917
TVLY—(EUR)
Sales Range: $75-99.9 Million
Cutting Tool Mfr
N.A.I.C.S.: 333517
Marc Tivoly (Deputy CEO)

TIVOLY S.A.

Tivoly S.A.—(Continued)

Subsidiaries:

Elite Tooling Limited (1)
Unit 5 Central Business Park Masbrough Street, Rotherham, S60 1EW, South Yorkshire, United Kingdom
Tel.: (44) 1709740640
Cutting Tool Mfr
N.A.I.C.S.: 333515

FFDM-Tivoly SA (1)
78-80 Avenue de la Prospective, 18020, Bourges, Cedex, France
Tel.: (33) 248232727
Web Site: http://www.ffdm-pneumat.fr
Cutting Tool Mfr
N.A.I.C.S.: 333515
David Risset *(Sls Mgr-Bu Pneumat)*

Nueva Herramienta de Corte SA (1)
B Urkizuaran, 48230, Elorrio, Bizkaia, Spain
Tel.: (34) 946231680
Cutting Tool Mfr
N.A.I.C.S.: 333515

Tivoly Df S.A. de C.V. (1)
Refugio 13 Col Nativitas, Delegacion Benito Juarez, 03050, Mexico, Mexico
Tel.: (52) 5555322778
Cutting Tool Mfr
N.A.I.C.S.: 333515

Tivoly Inc. (1)
434 Baxter Ave Derby Line, Derby Line, VT 05830
Tel.: (802) 873-3106
Sales Range: $50-74.9 Million
Emp.: 160
Cutting Tool Mfr
N.A.I.C.S.: 333515
Marc Tivoly *(CEO)*

TIYO A.S.
Pricna 2071, 508 01, Horice, Czech Republic
Tel.: (420) 493546800
Web Site: http://www.swell.cz
Emp.: 100
Industrial Machinery & Equipment Distr
N.A.I.C.S.: 423830

TIZ A.D.
Cara Dusana 212, Zemun, Serbia
Tel.: (381) 11 2619 428
Web Site: http://www.tiz-ad.com
Year Founded: 1975
Sales Range: Less than $1 Million
Emp.: 2
Textile Products Mfr
N.A.I.C.S.: 313220

TIZIANA LIFE SCIENCES PLC
14/15 Conduit Street, London, W1S 2XJ, United Kingdom
Tel.: (44) 2074952379
Web Site:
https://www.tizianalifesciences.com
TLSA—(NASDAQ)
Assets: $26,477,000
Liabilities: $6,906,000
Net Worth: $19,571,000
Earnings: ($15,397,000)
Emp.: 9
Fiscal Year-end: 12/31/22
Pharmaceuticals Mfr
N.A.I.C.S.: 325412
Gabriele Marco Antonio Cerrone *(Founder, Chm & Acting CFO)*

TJ MEDIA CO., LTD.
84 Sangam IT Tower 434 World Cup buk-ro, Mapo-gu, Seoul, 03922, Korea (South)
Tel.: (82) 236634700
Web Site:
http://www.taijinmedia.co.kr
Year Founded: 1981
032540—(KRS)
Rev.: $65,894,120
Assets: $103,377,935
Liabilities: $37,954,259
Net Worth: $65,423,676
Earnings: $3,449,350
Emp.: 186
Fiscal Year-end: 12/31/22
Audio & Video Equipment Mfr
N.A.I.C.S.: 334310
Jung Sin *(Head)*

Subsidiaries:

TJ media Phil. Co., Ltd. (1)
Unit E-1601 East Tower Phil Stock Exchange Center Exchange Road, Ortigas Center, Pasig, 1605, Philippines
Tel.: (63) 2 470 9022
Audio Equipment Distr
N.A.I.C.S.: 423990

TJ media Thailand Co., Ltd. (1)
896/41-42 SV-City Office Tower 1 24 floor Rama 3 Rd, Bang-Pongpang Yannawa, Bangkok, Thailand
Tel.: (66) 2 682 7215
Audio Equipment Distr
N.A.I.C.S.: 423990

TJK MACHINERY (TIANJIN) CO., LTD.
Wuwei Road, Lulugang Logistics Industrial Park, Tianjin, 300408, China
Tel.: (86) 2226993766
Web Site: https://www.tjkmachinery-group.com
Year Founded: 2002
300823—(SSE)
Rev.: $61,394,997
Assets: $170,237,724
Liabilities: $33,474,182
Net Worth: $136,763,542
Earnings: $4,976,001
Emp.: 600
Fiscal Year-end: 12/31/22
Construction Equipment Mfr & Distr
N.A.I.C.S.: 333120
Zhendong Chen *(Chm)*

TK CHEMICAL CORPORATION
Magok Jungang 8-ro 78 SM R&D Center 11F, Gangseo-gu, Seoul, 702-713, Korea (South)
Tel.: (82) 220016000
Web Site: https://www.tkchemi.co.kr
Year Founded: 1965
104480—(KRS)
Rev.: $577,817,527
Assets: $1,097,918,139
Liabilities: $370,855,932
Net Worth: $727,062,206
Earnings: $211,102,449
Emp.: 648
Fiscal Year-end: 12/31/22
Chemicals, Yarns & Resins Mfr
N.A.I.C.S.: 325998
Dong-Soo Lee *(CEO)*

Subsidiaries:

TK Chemical Corporation - Synthetic Resin Plant (1)
300 Gongdan-dong, Gumi, Gyeongsangbuk-do, Korea (South)
Tel.: (82) 54 463 0380
Sales Range: $25-49.9 Million
Emp.: 65
Synthetic Resin Mfr
N.A.I.C.S.: 325211

TK CORPORATION
117-12 Noksansaneop-daero, Gangseo-gu, Busan, 46752, Korea (South)
Tel.: (82) 519706600
Web Site: https://www.tkbend.co.kr
Year Founded: 1965
023160—(KRS)
Rev.: $191,552,631
Assets: $455,594,277
Liabilities: $53,507,768
Net Worth: $402,086,509
Earnings: $27,436,220
Emp.: 336
Fiscal Year-end: 12/31/22
Pipe Fitting Mfr
N.A.I.C.S.: 332919
Sung Duk Yoon *(Pres & CEO)*

Subsidiaries:

TK Corporation - Hwajeon Plant (1)
51 Hwajeonsandan 5-ro, Gangseo-gu, Busan, 618-280, Korea (South)
Tel.: (82) 51 971 1681
Pipe Fitting Services
N.A.I.C.S.: 238220

TK GROUP (HOLDINGS) LIMITED
Workship No 19 9th Floor Block B Hi Tech Industrial Centre, 491-501 Castle Peak Road, Tsuen Wan, NT, China (Hong Kong)
Tel.: (852) 24113628
Web Site: http://www.tkmold.com
Year Founded: 1983
2283—(HKG)
Rev.: $290,613,428
Assets: $343,934,183
Liabilities: $139,220,820
Net Worth: $204,713,363
Earnings: $28,930,898
Emp.: 3,313
Fiscal Year-end: 12/31/22
Holding Company; Plastic Products & Molds Mfr
N.A.I.C.S.: 551112
Pui Leung Li *(Co-Founder & Chm)*

Subsidiaries:

TK Mold (Shenzhen) Limited (1)
South Gate TK Technology Park HuiYe Road 11 GuangMing Hi-Tech Park, Guangming New District, Shenzhen, 518107, Guangdong, China
Tel.: (86) 75523690000
Mold Mfr
N.A.I.C.S.: 333511

TK Plastic Products (Suzhou) Limited (1)
No 666 of JianLin Rd, Hi-Tech Development District, Suzhou, 215151, Jiangsu, China
Tel.: (86) 51267369500
Plastics Product Mfr
N.A.I.C.S.: 326199

TK-HOLD PLC
Goritsa St No 6, 1618, Sofia, Bulgaria
Tel.: (359) 8551170
Web Site: https://www.tkhold.com
TCH—(BUL)
Sales Range: Less than $1 Million
Holding Company
N.A.I.C.S.: 551112

TKC CO LTD
280 Sihwa-ro, Danwon-gu, Ansan, 405 300, Gyeonggi-do, Korea (South)
Tel.: (82) 314322121
Web Site: https://tkc21.com
Year Founded: 1996
Electrical Component Mfr
N.A.I.C.S.: 334418
Sang-Bong Kim *(CEO)*

TKC CORPORATION
1758 Tsurutamachi, Utsunomiya, 320-8644, Tochigi, Japan
Tel.: (81) 286482111
Web Site: https://www.tkc.jp
Year Founded: 1966
9746—(TKS)
Rev.: $509,877,350
Assets: $824,964,040
Liabilities: $149,230,320
Net Worth: $675,733,720
Earnings: $76,756,340
Emp.: 2,409
Fiscal Year-end: 09/30/23
Software Development Services
N.A.I.C.S.: 541512

INTERNATIONAL PUBLIC

Kazuyuki Sumi *(Chm)*

Subsidiaries:

SkyCom Corporation (1)
10th floor Akihabara Building 19 Kanda Matsunaga-cho, Chiyoda-ku, Tokyo, 101-0023, Japan
Tel.: (81) 352890788
Telecommunication Services
N.A.I.C.S.: 517810

TKC Financial Gurantee Co., Ltd. (1)
1-21 Agebacho Iidabashi Masumoto Building 5th Floor, Shinjuku-ku, Tokyo, 162-0824, Japan
Tel.: (81) 35 227 5055
Web Site: https://www.tkk-tkc.co.jp
Financial Services
N.A.I.C.S.: 523210

TKC Shuppan Corporation (1)
2-17 Central Building 2nd floor, Kagurazaka Shinjuku-ku, Tokyo, 162-0825, Japan
Tel.: (81) 33 268 0561
Web Site: https://www.tkcshuppan.co.jp
Book Publication Services
N.A.I.C.S.: 513130

TKC METALS CORPORATION
Unit 201/2nd Floor W Tower Condominium 39th St, Bonifacio Global City, 1231, Taguig, 1231, Metro Manila, Philippines
Tel.: (63) 28640734
Web Site: https://www.tkcmetals.ph
Year Founded: 1996
T—(PHI)
Rev.: $24,027,181
Assets: $88,660,885
Liabilities: $94,889,319
Net Worth: ($6,228,434)
Earnings: ($8,491,350)
Emp.: 9
Fiscal Year-end: 12/31/21
Steel Products Mfr & Distr
N.A.I.C.S.: 331110
Wilfrido O. Gamboa *(CIO & Head-Corp Svcs)*

TKD SCIENCE AND TECHNOLOGY CO., LTD.
1311 Jiaotong Avenue, Suizhou, China
Tel.: (86) 7223309660
Web Site: https://www.sztkd.com
Year Founded: 2005
603738—(SHG)
Rev.: $128,657,225
Assets: $289,647,039
Liabilities: $34,234,673
Net Worth: $255,412,367
Earnings: $26,463,743
Fiscal Year-end: 12/31/22
Crystal Component Mfr & Distr
N.A.I.C.S.: 334419
Xindong Yu *(Chm & Pres)*

Subsidiaries:

Shenzhen Tkd Industrial Co., Ltd. (1)
5 Floor Jianda West Building Keyuan Road No 10, Science and Technology Park Nanshan District, Shenzhen, China
Tel.: (86) 75527328578
Crystal Frequency Component Mfr
N.A.I.C.S.: 334419

Suizhou Taihua Electronic Technology Co., Ltd. (1)
Taihua Industrial Park Economic Development Zone, Suizhou, China
Tel.: (86) 7227509668
Crystal Frequency Component Mfr
N.A.I.C.S.: 334419

TKG HUCHEMS CO.,LTD
173 Toegye-ro Chungmuro3-ga Kukdong Bldg 19 F, Jung-gu, Seoul, 100-705, Korea (South)
Tel.: (82) 222620600

AND PRIVATE COMPANIES — TKH GROUP N.V.

Web Site: https://tkg.huchems.com
Year Founded: 2002
069260—(KRS)
Rev.: $947,887,647
Assets: $722,017,655
Liabilities: $154,291,291
Net Worth: $567,726,364
Earnings: $62,747,835
Emp.: 269
Fiscal Year-end: 12/31/22
Chemical Products Mfr
N.A.I.C.S.: 325998
Jin Yong Shin *(Pres & CEO)*

Subsidiaries:

Huchems Fine Chemical Corporation
- Yeosu Plant (1)
963 Sangam-ro, 555-260, Yeosu,
Jeollanam-do, Korea (South)
Tel.: (82) 616804500
Fine Chemical Product Mfr
N.A.I.C.S.: 325311

TKH GROUP N.V.

Spinnerstraat 15, PO Box 5, 7480
AA, Haaksbergen, Netherlands
Tel.: (31) 535732900 Nl
Web Site: https://www.tkhgroup.com
Year Founded: 1930
TWSA—(DEU)
Rev.: $2,039,443,647
Assets: $2,348,801,193
Liabilities: $1,426,278,839
Net Worth: $922,522,354
Earnings: $182,980,461
Emp.: 6,899
Fiscal Year-end: 12/31/23
Holding Company; Telecommunication, Electrotechnical Engineering & Industrial Electronic Components & Systems Designer, Mfr & Distr
N.A.I.C.S.: 551112
J. M. Alexander van der Lof *(Chm-Exec Bd & CEO)*

Subsidiaries:

ASP AG (1)
Luttringhauser Str 9, 42897, Remscheid, Germany
Tel.: (49) 21914 374 9883
Web Site: http://www.grundig-cctv.com
Electronic Product Mfr & Distr
N.A.I.C.S.: 334419

Aasset Security International SAS (1)
153 rue Michel Carre, 95100, Argenteuil, France
Tel.: (33) 130 76 30 30
Web Site: http://www.aasset-security.fr
Security System Mfr & Distr
N.A.I.C.S.: 334290

Subsidiary (Non-US):

AASSET SECURITY Italia SpA. (2)
Via Palu 38 H/i, San Vendemiano, 31020, Italy
Tel.: (39) 0 438 179 2811
Web Site: http://www.aasset-security.it
Emp.: 10
Security System Mfr & Distr
N.A.I.C.S.: 334290
Flavio Venz *(Mng Dir)*

AASSET SECURITY Ltd. (2)
Unit 9 Beaufort Court-Roebuck Way, Knowlhill, Milton Keynes, MK5 8HL, United Kingdom
Tel.: (44) 845 230 8330
Security System Mfr & Distr
N.A.I.C.S.: 334290
Joanne Livings *(Office Mgr)*

Aasset Germany GmbH (2)
Max-planck-Str 15 a-c, 40699, Erkrath, 40699, Germany
Tel.: (49) 211 2470160
Web Site: http://www.aasset.de
Security System Mfr & Distr
N.A.I.C.S.: 334290
Torsten Anstadt *(Office Mgr)*

Alphatronics B.V. (1)
Boekdrukker 5-7, 3861 SE, Nijkerk, Netherlands
Tel.: (31) 33 245 99 44
Web Site: http://www.alphatronics.nl
Security System Mfr & Distr
N.A.I.C.S.: 334290

B.V. Twentsche Kabelfabriek (1)
Spinnerstraat 15, 7481 KJ, Haaksbergen, Netherlands
Tel.: (31) 53 573 2255
Web Site: https://www.tkf.nl
Cable Mfr
N.A.I.C.S.: 335921

BB Lightconcepts B.V (1)
Fabriekstraat 16-04, 7005 AR, Doetinchem, 7005 AR, Netherlands
Tel.: (31) 314392348
Web Site: http://www.bb-lightconcepts.eu
Emp.: 7
Lighting Fixture Mfr & Distr
N.A.I.C.S.: 335131
Jan Baartmans *(Mgr)*

C&C Partners Sp. z o.o (1)
17 Stycznia Street 119 121, 64-100, Leszno, Poland
Tel.: (48) 65 525 5500
Web Site: https://www.ccpartners.pl
Security System Services
N.A.I.C.S.: 561621
Artur Hejdysz *(CEO)*

C&C Partners Telecom Sp. z o.o (1)
ul 17 Stycznia 119 121, 64-100, Leszno, Poland
Tel.: (48) 655255500
Web Site: http://www.ccpartners.pl
Electronic Product Mfr & Distr
N.A.I.C.S.: 334419

CAE Data SAS (1)
3 Rue Jeanne Garnerin, 91320, Wissous, France
Tel.: (33) 1 69 79 14 14
Web Site: http://www.cae-groupe.fr
Emp.: 100
Communication Equipment Mfr & Distr
N.A.I.C.S.: 335929

Capable B.V. (1)
Weidehek 109, 4824 AT, Breda, Netherlands
Tel.: (31) 76 541 64 56
Web Site: http://www.capable.nl
Emp.: 30
Electronic Cable Mfr
N.A.I.C.S.: 334419

Capassy B.V (1)
Guldenweg 109, 4879 NL, Etten-Leur, Netherlands
Tel.: (31) 76 564 48 80
Web Site: http://www.capassy.com
Electronic Product Mfr & Distr
N.A.I.C.S.: 334419

Chromasens GmbH (1)
Max-Stromeyer-Strasse 116, 78467, Konstanz, Germany
Tel.: (49) 75318760
Web Site: https://www.chromasens.de
Semiconductor Product Distr
N.A.I.C.S.: 423690
Martin Hund *(CEO)*

Commend Benelux B.V. (1)
De Lind 3, 4841 KC, Prinsenbeek, Netherlands
Tel.: (31) 76 20 00 100
Web Site: http://www.commend.nl
Software Development Services
N.A.I.C.S.: 541511

Subsidiary (Non-US):

Commend AG (2)
Mulistrasse 4, 8320, Fehraltorf, Switzerland
Tel.: (41) 44 955 02 22
Web Site: http://www.commend.ch
Software Development Services
N.A.I.C.S.: 541511

Commend Australia Integrated Security and Communication Systems Pty Ltd (2)
9/38 Corporate Blvd, Bayswater, 3153, VIC, Australia
Tel.: (61) 3 9729 3700
Web Site: http://www.commend.com.au
Software Development Services
N.A.I.C.S.: 541511
Peter Zanon *(Mng Dir)*

Commend Business Hub Nordic (2)
Solkraftsvagen 35, 13570, Stockholm, Sweden
Tel.: (46) 8 993060
Web Site: http://www.commend.se
Software Development Services
N.A.I.C.S.: 541511

Commend France S.A.S (2)
155 Dr Bauer Street, 93400, Saint-Ouen, France
Tel.: (33) 1 49 18 16 40
Web Site: http://www.commend.fr
Emp.: 30
Software Development Services
N.A.I.C.S.: 541511

Commend Iberica S.L. (2)
C/ Mallorca n 1 Planta 2 Oficina 11, 08014, Barcelona, Spain
Tel.: (34) 937006546
Web Site: http://www.commend.es
Software Development Services
N.A.I.C.S.: 541511

Subsidiary (US):

Commend Inc. (2)
63 Ramapo Valley Rd Ste 201, Mahwah, NJ 07430
Tel.: (201) 529-2425
Web Site: http://www.commendusa.com
Emp.: 20
Software Development Services
N.A.I.C.S.: 541511
Thomas J. Reilly *(Pres)*

Subsidiary (Non-US):

Commend Italia s.r.l. (2)
Via L da Vinci 3, 24060, Carobbio degli Angeli, BG, Italy
Tel.: (39) 035 95 39 63
Web Site: http://www.commend.it
Emp.: 4
Software Development Services
N.A.I.C.S.: 541511

Commend Osterreich GmbH (2)
Barichgasse 40-42, 1030, Vienna, Austria
Tel.: (43) 1 715 30 79
Web Site: http://www.commend.at
Emp.: 150
Software Development Services
N.A.I.C.S.: 541511
Christian Schmid *(Mng Dir)*

Subsidiary (Non-US):

Commend Adria d.o.o. (3)
Josipa Vogrinca 18, 10000, Zagreb, Croatia
Tel.: (385) 1 369 11 23
Web Site: http://www.commend.hr
Software Development Services
N.A.I.C.S.: 541511
Drago Labazan *(Mng Dir)*

Commend Slovakia s.r.o. (3)
Stare grunty 12, 841 04, Bratislava, Slovakia
Tel.: (421) 2 5810 1040
Web Site: http://www.commend.sk
Software Development Services
N.A.I.C.S.: 541511
Martin Buncak *(Mng Dir)*

Subsidiary (Non-US):

Commend UK ltd (2)
Commend House Unit 2 M11 Business Link Parsonage Lane, Stansted, CM24 8GF, Essex, United Kingdom
Tel.: (44) 1279872020
Web Site: https://www.commend.co.uk
Software Development Services
N.A.I.C.S.: 541511

Commend Scandinavia AB (1)
Soderbymalmsvagen 8, 136 45, Handen, Sweden
Tel.: (46) 10 220 3054
Security System Services
N.A.I.C.S.: 561621

Commend South East Asia Pte. Ltd. (1)
25 Tai Seng Avenue Office 05-01, Singapore, 534104, Singapore
Tel.: (65) 6 272 2371
Telecommunication Products Mfr
N.A.I.C.S.: 334290
Arya Varma *(Mng Dir)*

Cross Hardware B.V. (1)
Koolhovenstraat 1E, 3772 MT, Barneveld, Netherlands
Tel.: (31) 342407060
Web Site: http://www.cross.nl
Communication & Electrical Equipment Mfr
N.A.I.C.S.: 334210

Cruxin B.V. (1)
Bunsenstraat 125, 3316 GC, Dordrecht, Netherlands
Tel.: (31) 10 285 5285
Web Site: https://www.cruxin.nl
Information Technology Services
N.A.I.C.S.: 541511

Dewetron Test & Measurement Equipment (Beijing) Co. Ltd. (1)
Room 1510A Huateng Building Jinsong, Chaoyang District, Beijing, 100021, China
Tel.: (86) 1381 805 9086
Web Site: https://www.dewetron-cn.com
Emp.: 120
Measuring Instrument Mfr & Distr
N.A.I.C.S.: 334513

Dewetron Test & Measurement Equipment (Shanghai) Co. Ltd. (1)
Room 1403 CITS Building No 1277 Beijing Rd W, Jing'an District, Shanghai, 200040, China
Tel.: (86) 216 289 0027
Measuring Instrument Mfr & Distr
N.A.I.C.S.: 334513

EEB Kabeltechnik GmbH (1)
Holunderweg 2, Brandenburg, 03149, Forst, Brandenburg, Germany
Tel.: (49) 35626924180
Web Site: http://www.eeb-kabeltechnik.de
Cable Mfr
N.A.I.C.S.: 335929

EFB Elektronik Austria GmbH (1)
Belgradpl 5, 1100, Vienna, Austria
Tel.: (43) 1 6001785
Emp.: 2
Electronic Product Distr
N.A.I.C.S.: 423690
Mathias Fischer *(Gen Mgr)*

EFB Elektronik GmbH (1)
Striegauer Strasse 1, 33719, Bielefeld, Germany
Tel.: (49) 521404180
Web Site: https://www.efb-elektronik.de
Emp.: 330
Cable Product Mfr & Distr
N.A.I.C.S.: 335929

Subsidiary (Non-US):

EFB Elektronik Ltd (2)
Sultan Sokak Mavi Plaza No 22 D 11/22A, 34381, Istanbul, Turkiye
Tel.: (90) 212 222 92 50
Web Site: http://www.efb-elektronik.com.tr
Cable Product Distr
N.A.I.C.S.: 423610

EFB Nordics A/S (1)
Naverland 22, 2600, Glostrup, Denmark
Tel.: (45) 4 466 2911
Cable Mfr
N.A.I.C.S.: 335921
Kim Haugaard Sorensen *(Mng Dir)*

EKB Zuid B.V. (1)
Lage Akkerweg 17, 5711 DD, Someren, Netherlands
Tel.: (31) 493 496 665
Industrial Automation Services
N.A.I.C.S.: 238210

Eldra B.V. (1)
Spinnerstraat 15, 7481 KJ, Haaksbergen, Netherlands
Tel.: (31) 47 556 6767
Web Site: https://www.eldra.nl
Information Technology Services
N.A.I.C.S.: 541511

Electro-Draad B.V. (1)
Branskamp 7, PO Box 3720, 6014 CB, Ittervoort, Netherlands

TKH GROUP N.V.

TKH Group N.V.—(Continued)

Tel.: (31) 47556 67 67
Electrical Equipment Mfr & Distr
N.A.I.C.S.: 335999

Eminent Europe B.V (1)
Middelweg 27, PO Box 276, 6160 AG, Geleen, Netherlands
Tel.: (31) 208080932
Web Site: http://www.eminent-online.com
Electronic Product Mfr & Distr
N.A.I.C.S.: 334419

Ernst & Engbring GmbH (1)
Industriestrasse 9, 45739, Oer-Erkenschwick, Germany
Tel.: (49) 236869010
Web Site: https://www.ee-cables.com
Emp.: 450
Cable Mfr
N.A.I.C.S.: 335929
Alexander van der Lof *(Mng Dir)*

Flexposure B.V. (1)
Industrieweg 22, 4153 BW, Beesd, Netherlands
Tel.: (31) 885008700
Web Site: http://www.flexposure.nl
Communication Software Development Services
N.A.I.C.S.: 541511

Funea Broadband Services B.V (1)
Gouden Rijderstraat 1, 4903 RD, Oosterhout, Netherlands
Tel.: (31) 162 47 58 00
Web Site: http://www.funea.com
Electrical Products Distr
N.A.I.C.S.: 423610

ID Cables SAS (1)
3 Avenue Jeanne Garnerin, 91320, Wissous, France
Tel.: (33) 16 979 1404
Web Site: https://www.id-cables.fr
Cable Mfr
N.A.I.C.S.: 335921

IV-Tec GmbH (1)
Grubstr 8, Vorstetten, 79279, Freiburg, Germany
Tel.: (49) 88 06 92 34 0
Web Site: http://www.iv-tec.com
Video & Image Processing Services
N.A.I.C.S.: 518210

Inec N.V. (1)
Herenthoutseweg 236, 2200, Herentals, Belgium
Tel.: (32) 14 220 334
Web Site: http://www.intronics.be
Emp.: 10
Communication Equipment Distr
N.A.I.C.S.: 423690
Marijke van Diependaele *(Mgr-HR)*

Internacional Negocio Electronica y Componentes Espana SAU (1)
Calle Eslovenia 15 Nave 72 Poligono Industrial Guadalhorce, 29004, Malaga, Spain
Tel.: (34) 952 24 55 57
Web Site: http://www.intronics.es
Communication Equipment Distr
N.A.I.C.S.: 423690

Intronics B.V. (1)
Koolhovenstraat 1E, 3772 MT, Barneveld, Netherlands
Tel.: (31) 34 240 7040
Web Site: https://www.intronics.nl
Software Development Services
N.A.I.C.S.: 541511

Isolectra B.V. (1)
Wilhelminakade 957, 3072 AP, Rotterdam, Netherlands
Tel.: (31) 102855444
Web Site: http://www.isolectra.nl
Communication & Electrical Equipment Distr
N.A.I.C.S.: 423690

Isolectra Communications Technology Sdn Bhd (1)
Suite 2 02 2nd Floor Lot 10 Mercu Picorp Jalan Astaka U8/84 Bukit, Jelutong, 40150, Shah Alam, Selangor, Malaysia
Tel.: (60) 7846 9988
Web Site: http://www.isolectra.com.my
Project Management Services
N.A.I.C.S.: 561110

Isolectra Far East Pte Ltd (1)
29 Tai SENG Avenue 05-06 Natural Cool lifestyle Building, Singapore, 534119, Singapore
Tel.: (65) 6272 2371
Web Site: http://www.isolectra.com.sg
Project Management Services
N.A.I.C.S.: 561110

Ithaca (1)
170 Route de lOasis, 20110, Casablanca, Morocco
Tel.: (212) 22 98 66 66
Electrical Equipment Mfr & Distr
N.A.I.C.S.: 335999

Jacques Technologies Pty. Ltd. (1)
28-30 Bank St, West End, 4101, QLD, Australia
Tel.: (61) 73 846 8400
Web Site: https://www.jacques.com.au
Communication Equipment Mfr
N.A.I.C.S.: 334290
Erik Jansson *(Mng Dir)*

Jobarco B.V. (1)
Verbreepark 15, 2731 BR, Benthuizen, Netherlands
Tel.: (31) 79 331 93 13
Web Site: http://www.jobarco.com
Electrical Cable Distr
N.A.I.C.S.: 423610
Maria Ditmar *(Deputy Dir)*

KC Industrie Srl (1)
via Dante Alighieri 33, 29010, Villanova sull'Arda, PC, Italy
Tel.: (39) 0523 837 899
Web Site: http://www.kcindustrie.it
Electrical Cables Mfr
N.A.I.C.S.: 333248

KLS Netherlands B.V (1)
Buitenvaart 1401, 7905 SJ, Hoogeveen, Netherlands
Tel.: (31) 368 200 101
Web Site: http://www.klsnetherlands.nl
Logistics Consulting & Software Development Services
N.A.I.C.S.: 541614

Keyprocessor B.V. (1)
Paasheuvelweg 20, 1105 BJ, Amsterdam, Netherlands
Tel.: (31) 20 462 07 00
Web Site: http://www.keyprocessor.com
Emp.: 60
Security Management Services
N.A.I.C.S.: 561621

LMI (Shanghai) Trading Co. Ltd. (1)
B-510 Venture International Business Park 2679 Hechuan Road, Minhang District, Shanghai, 201103, China
Tel.: (86) 215 441 0711
Sensor Accessory Mfr & Distr
N.A.I.C.S.: 334413

LMI Technologies Co. Ltd. (1)
Ginza East Square 6F 3-12-7, Kyobashi Chuo-ku, Tokyo, 104-0031, Japan
Tel.: (81) 36 264 4651
Sensor Accessory Mfr & Distr
N.A.I.C.S.: 334413

LMI Technologies Inc. (1)
9200 Glenlyon Parkway, Burnaby, V5J 5J8, BC, Canada
Tel.: (604) 636-1011
Web Site: http://www.lmi3d.com
Emp.: 128
Scanning Sensor Mfr
N.A.I.C.S.: 334513
Mark Radford *(CEO)*

Subsidiary (Non-US):

LMI Technologies B.V. (2)
Wiebachstraat 25B, 6466 NG, Kerkrade, Netherlands
Tel.: (31) 45 850 7000
Web Site: http://www.lmi3d.com
Emp.: 6
Scanning Sensor Mfr
N.A.I.C.S.: 334513
Mark Radford *(CEO)*

Mextal B.V. (1)
De Tienden 48, 5674 TB, Nuenen, Netherlands
Tel.: (31) 40 290 75 10

Web Site: http://www.mextal.com
Emp.: 30
Security Software Development Services & Monitoring Device Mfr
N.A.I.C.S.: 541511

Mikrotron GmbH (1)
Landshuter Str 20-22, 85716, Unterschleissheim, Germany
Tel.: (49) 897 263 4200
Web Site: https://www.mikrotron.de
Emp.: 35
Electronic Circuits Mfr
N.A.I.C.S.: 334419
Walter Denk *(Mng Dir)*

Multi Media Connect (Aust) Pty ltd (1)
U3/ 5 Bounty Cl, Tuggerah, 2259, NSW, Australia
Tel.: (61) 2 4351 5092
Telecommunication Servicesb
N.A.I.C.S.: 517111

NET Japan Co. Ltd. (1)
Nissei Building 1F 1-12-17 Okano, Nishi-ku, Yokohama, 220-0073, Kanagawa, Japan
Tel.: (81) 452906660
Web Site: http://www.net-japan.com
Camera Distr
N.A.I.C.S.: 423410

Pantaflex B.V. (1)
Verbreepark 15, 2731 BR, Benthuizen, Netherlands
Tel.: (31) 793310007
Web Site: http://www.pantaflex.nl
Electronic Components Distr
N.A.I.C.S.: 423690

Park Assist LLC (1)
125 Commerce Ct Ste 11, Cheshire, CT 06410
Tel.: (203) 220-6544
Web Site: https://www.parkassist.com
Information Technology Services
N.A.I.C.S.: 541511

Park Assist Pty. Ltd. (1)
T58 Level 5 East Village 4 Defries Avenue, Zetland, 2017, NSW, Australia
Tel.: (61) 28 315 7900
Information Technology Services
N.A.I.C.S.: 541511

S-Com A/S (1)
Naverland 22, 2600, Glostrup, Denmark
Tel.: (45) 44 66 29 11
Web Site: http://www.s-comdirect.dk
Electronic Components Distr
N.A.I.C.S.: 423690
Kim Sorensen *(Gen Mgr)*

SVS-Vistek GmbH (1)
Ferdinand-Porsche-Str 3, 82205, Gilching, Germany
Tel.: (49) 8105398760
Web Site: https://www.svs-vistek.com
Camera Mfr
N.A.I.C.S.: 333310
Walter Denk *(Mng Dir)*

SVS-Vistek Inc. (1)
4400 State Hwy 121 Ste 313, Lewisville, TX 75056
Camera Mfr & Distr
N.A.I.C.S.: 333310

SVS-Vistek K.K. (1)
Unit 801 8F 1-4-3 Sengencho, Nishi-ku, Yokohama, 220-0072, Kanagawa, Japan
Tel.: (81) 807 033 1689
Camera Mfr & Distr
N.A.I.C.S.: 333310

Schneider Intercom GmbH (1)
Heinrich-Hertz-Strasse 40, 40699, Erkrath, Germany
Tel.: (49) 211882850
Web Site: https://www.schneider-intercom.de
Emp.: 55
Security Management Services
N.A.I.C.S.: 561621
Detlef Witte *(Mng Dir)*

Schrade Kabel- und Elektrotechnik GmbH (1)
Carl-Benz-Strasse 1, 89604, Allmendingen, Germany
Tel.: (49) 7391 7074 0

Web Site: http://www.schrade-kabel.de
Cable Mfr
N.A.I.C.S.: 335929

Schreinermacher Kabelconfektionen GmbH (1)
Gutenbergstrasse 8, 41564, Kaarst, Germany
Tel.: (49) 2131 20137 0
Web Site: http://www.schreinermacher.de
Cable Mfr
N.A.I.C.S.: 335929

TKD Kabel GmbH (1)
An der Kleinbahn 16, 41334, Nettetal, Germany
Tel.: (49) 2157 8979 0
Web Site: http://www.tkd-kabel.de
Emp.: 100
Cable Mfr & Distr
N.A.I.C.S.: 335929

Subsidiary (Non-US):

HPM Cables Sarl (2)
14 rue du Bon Repos, 41600, Chaon, France
Tel.: (33) 254 95 88 00
Web Site: http://www.tkd-kabel.de
Cable Mfr & Distr
N.A.I.C.S.: 335929

Subsidiary (US):

Kaweflex Wire and Cable Inc. (2)
PO Box 62027, Cincinnati, OH 45262-0027
Tel.: (513) 232-9300
Electrical Cable Distr
N.A.I.C.S.: 423610

Subsidiary (Non-US):

TKD Cable (Suzhou) Co., Ltd (2)
No 12 Chuangye Road, Jinfeng, Zhangjiagang, Jiangsu, China
Tel.: (86) 512 56971382
Web Site: http://www.tkd-kabel.de
Cable Distr
N.A.I.C.S.: 423510

TKD Italia S.r.l. (2)
Via Matteotti 37, 40064, Ozzano dell'Emilia, BO, Italy
Tel.: (39) 051 790636
Web Site: http://www.tkditalia.it
Cable Distr
N.A.I.C.S.: 423510

TKD Kabel Mexico S. de R.L. de C.V. (2)
Av Piramide de la Luna No 286 Col Las Trojes C P, Corregidora, 76900, El Pueblito, Mexico
Tel.: (52) 14424847117
Web Site: http://www.tkdkabel.mx
Cable Distr
N.A.I.C.S.: 423510

TKD Polska Sp. z o.o. (2)
ul Szyszkowa 35/37, 02-285, Warsaw, Poland
Tel.: (48) 22 878 31 35
Cable Distr
N.A.I.C.S.: 423510

TKF GmbH (1)
Potsdamer Strasse 14b, 14513, Teltow, Germany
Tel.: (49) 332833660310
Web Site: http://www.tkf.eu
Emp.: 11
Cable Mfr & Distr
N.A.I.C.S.: 335929
Andreas Baitz *(Gen Mgr)*

TKF Nordics (1)
Annebergsvagen 3, Box 191, 645 41, Strangnas, Sweden
Tel.: (46) 152333400
Web Site: http://www.vmc.se
Electrical Equipment Distr
N.A.I.C.S.: 423610

TKH Airport Solutions A/S (1)
Kobenhavnsvej 1, 4800, Nykobing, Denmark
Tel.: (45) 5 486 0200
Aerospace Services
N.A.I.C.S.: 488190

TKH Airport Solutions B.V. (1)

Elektrostraat 17, 7483 PG, Haaksbergen, Netherlands
Tel.: (31) 53 574 1456
Web Site: https://www.tkh-airportsolutions.com
Aeronautical Engineering Services
N.A.I.C.S.: 541330
Erik Velderman (CEO)

TKH Building Solutions Shanghai Co. Ltd. (1)
1104-1105 11th floor No 509 Wuning Road, Putuo District, Shanghai, 200063, China
Tel.: (86) 21 3133 57 63
Web Site: http://www.tkhchina.com
Electronic Product Mfr & Distr
N.A.I.C.S.: 334419

TKH Security & Airport Solutions Pte. Ltd. (1)
05-51 25 Tai Seng Avenue Cityneon Building, Singapore, 534104, Singapore
Tel.: (65) 6 272 2371
Web Site: https://www.tkhsaa.com.sg
Telecommunication Product Distr
N.A.I.C.S.: 423690

TKH Security B.V. (1)
Platinastraat 65, 2718 SZ, Zoetermeer, Netherlands
Tel.: (31) 20 462 0700
Web Site: https://www.tkhsecurity.com
Emp.: 300
Security System Services
N.A.I.C.S.: 561621

TKH Security UK Ltd. (1)
Unit 2 M11 Business Link Stanstead, Maida Vale, London, CM24 8GF, Essex, United Kingdom
Tel.: (44) 8455280004
Security System Services
N.A.I.C.S.: 561621

TKH Technologie Deutschland AG (1)
Willy-Brandt-Platz 3, 81829, Munich, Germany
Tel.: (49) 8943571550
Sales Range: $125-149.9 Million
Emp.: 548
Holding Company; Optical Sensor & Digital Imaging Technologies Mfr
N.A.I.C.S.: 551112
Berth Hausmann (Member-Mgmt Bd)

Subsidiary (Domestic):

Allied Vision Technologies GmbH (2)
Taschenweg 2a, 07646, Stadtroda, Germany (100%)
Tel.: (49) 364286770
Web Site: https://www.alliedvisiontec.com
Sales Range: $25-49.9 Million
Emp.: 80
Specialty Industrial & Life Science Image Processing Equipment Designer, Mfr & Whslr
N.A.I.C.S.: 333310

Subsidiary (Non-US):

Allied Vision Technologies (Canada) Inc.
4621 Canada Way 300, Burnaby, V5G 4X8, BC, Canada (100%)
Tel.: (604) 875-8855
Web Site: http://www.alliedvision.com
Specialty Industrial & Life Science Image Processing Equipment Designer, Mfr & Whslr
N.A.I.C.S.: 333310

Allied Vision Technologies (Shanghai) Co., Ltd. (3)
2-2109 Hongwell Int Plaza 1602 Zhong-ShanXi Road, Shanghai, 200235, China
Tel.: (86) 21 64861133
Web Site: http://www.alliedvision.com
Camera Component Mfr & Distr
N.A.I.C.S.: 333310

Allied Vision Technologies Pte. Ltd. (3)
82 Playfair Rd 07-02 D Lithium, Singapore, 368001, Singapore
Tel.: (65) 6634 9027
Web Site: http://www.alliedvision.com
Camera Component Mfr & Distr
N.A.I.C.S.: 333310

Subsidiary (US):

Allied Vision Technologies, Inc. (3)
102 Pickering Way Ste 502, Exton, PA 19341 (100%)
Tel.: (978) 225-2030
Web Site: http://www.alliedvision.com
Emp.: 20
Specialty Industrial & Life Science Image Processing Equipment Whslr
N.A.I.C.S.: 423410

Subsidiary (Non-US):

DEWETRON Elektronische Messgerate Gesellschaft m.b.H. (2)
Parkring 4, 8074, Grambach, Austria (100%)
Tel.: (43) 31630700
Web Site: http://www.dewetron.com
Sales Range: $25-49.9 Million
Emp.: 75
Computer-Based Test & Measuring Equipment, Components & Software Developer, Mfr & Distr
N.A.I.C.S.: 334118
Oskar Dohrau (Mng Dir)

Subsidiary (Non-US):

DEWESoft d.o.o. (3)
Gabrsko 11a, 1420, Trbovlje, Slovenia
Tel.: (386) 3 56 25 300
Web Site: http://www.dewesoft.com
Software Development Services & Electronic Equipment Mfr
N.A.I.C.S.: 541511

Subsidiary (Non-US):

DEWESoft China Ltd. (4)
Room 2312 Block C Wanda Plaza, Tongzhou, Beijing, 101100, China
Tel.: (86) 1056862785
Web Site: http://www.dewesoft.cn
Electronic Equipment Mfr & Distr
N.A.I.C.S.: 334419

DS NET CO., LTD. (4)
D-902 SK Technopark Bldg 1345 Sohadong, Gwangmyeong, 423-050, Gyeonggi-do, Korea (South)
Tel.: (82) 2 866 9030
Web Site: http://www.dsnet.kr
Software Development Services & Hardware Mfr & Distr
N.A.I.C.S.: 541511

Dewesoft Co., Ltd. (4)
26/56 TPI Tower 20th Floor Nanglingee Rd Thungmahamek, Sathorn, 10120, Bangkok, Thailand
Tel.: (66) 2678 6779
Electronic Equipment Mfr & Distr
N.A.I.C.S.: 334419

Subsidiary (US):

Dewesoft LLC (4)
8720 Heller Rd, Whitehouse, OH 43571
Tel.: (855) 339-3669
Electronic Equipment Mfr & Distr
N.A.I.C.S.: 334419

Subsidiary (Non-US):

DEWETRON Benelux B.V. (3)
Postbus 8808, 4820 BC, Breda, Netherlands
Tel.: (31) 76 544 25 44
Web Site: http://www.dewetron.nl
Software Development Services & Electrical Equipment Mfr & Distr
N.A.I.C.S.: 541511

DEWETRON Finland Oy (3)
Paatsamakatu 4, 53810, Lappeenranta, Finland
Tel.: (358) 5 5411425
Web Site: http://www.dewetron.fi
Emp.: 3
Software Development Services & Electrical Equipment Mfr & Distr
N.A.I.C.S.: 541511

DEWETRON GmbH (3)
Rudolf-Diesel-Str 32, 73760, Ostfildern, Germany
Tel.: (49) 711 673100 60
Software Development Services & Electrical Equipment Mfr & Distr

DEWETRON Korea Ltd. (3)
1451-1 Guanyang-Dong, Dongan-ku, Anyang, Gyeonggi-do, Korea (South)
Tel.: (82) 31 425 4024
Web Site: http://www.dewetron.co.kr
Software Development Services & Electrical Equipment Mfr & Distr
N.A.I.C.S.: 541511

DEWETRON Schweiz AG (3)
Moosacherstrasse 15, 8804, Au, Switzerland
Tel.: (41) 44 727 7530
Web Site: http://www.dewetron.ch
Software Development Services & Electronic Product Mfr & Distr
N.A.I.C.S.: 541511

DEWETRON U.K. Ltd. (3)
1 Appley Court Appley Wood Corner, Haynes, Bedford, MK45 3QQ, Bedfordshire, United Kingdom
Tel.: (44) 1234381261
Web Site: http://dewesoft.com
Software Development Services & Electronic Product Mfr & Distr
N.A.I.C.S.: 541511
Andy Hathway (Mgr-Bus Dev)

Subsidiary (US):

DEWETRON, Inc. (3)
10 High St Ste K, Wakefield, RI 02879-3144
Tel.: (401) 284-3750
Web Site: http://www.dewamerica.com
Computer-Based Test & Measuring Equipment, Components & Software Distr
N.A.I.C.S.: 423430

Subsidiary (Non-US):

DEWETRON-PRAHA spol. s r.o. (3)
Tehovska 25/1237, 100 00, Prague, Czech Republic
Tel.: (420) 274 822925
Web Site: http://www.dewetron.com
Software Development Services & Electronic Product Mfr & Distr
N.A.I.C.S.: 541511

Dew Japan Co., Ltd. (3)
330-0064 Koike Building 4F 6-1-2 Kishi-cho, Urawa-ku, Saitama, 330-0064, Japan
Tel.: (81) 488140800
Web Site: https://www.dewejapan.com
Software Development Services & Electrical Equipment Mfr & Distr
N.A.I.C.S.: 541511

Dewe Solutions Pte Ltd (3)
50 Bukit Batok Street 23 04-06 Midview Building, Singapore, 659578, Singapore
Tel.: (65) 63167320
Web Site: https://www.dewesolutions.sg
Software Development Services & Hardware Mfr & Distr
N.A.I.C.S.: 541511
Kelvin Kek (Mgr)

Techno Specials N.V. (1)
Krimperslaan 1, 9140, Temse, Belgium
Tel.: (32) 9 325 82 12
Web Site: http://www.technospecials.be
Electronic Product Mfr & Distr
N.A.I.C.S.: 334419
Frank Bobbaerts (Mng Dir)

Texim Europe B.V. (1)
Elektrostraat 17, 7483 PG, Haaksbergen, Netherlands
Tel.: (31) 535733333
Web Site: http://www.texim-europe.com
Electronic Component Mfr & Distr
N.A.I.C.S.: 334419

Subsidiary (Non-US):

Texim Europe BVBA (2)
Zuiderlaan 14, Box 10, 1731, Zellik, Belgium
Tel.: (32) 2 462 01 00
Web Site: http://www.texim-europe.com
Emp.: 3
Electronic Components Distr
N.A.I.C.S.: 423690

Texim Europe GmbH (2)
Bahnhofstrasse 92, 25451, Quickborn, Germany
Tel.: (49) 4106627070
Electronic Components Distr
N.A.I.C.S.: 423690

Twentsche (Nanjing) Fibre Optics Co. Ltd. (1)
No 2 Xinke 4 Road New High Technology Industry Development Zone, Pukou, Nanjing, 210061, Jiangsu, China
Tel.: (86) 2558844888660
Web Site: http://www.tfo.com.cn
Emp.: 100
Cable Mfr
N.A.I.C.S.: 335929

USE-System Engineering Holding B.V. (1)
Elektrostraat 17, 7483 PG, Haaksbergen, Netherlands
Tel.: (31) 535741456
Web Site: http://www.usetechnology.nl
Emp.: 20
Information Technology Consulting Services
N.A.I.C.S.: 541512

VDG Security B.V. (1)
Platinastraat 65, 2718 SZ, Zoetermeer, Netherlands
Tel.: (31) 79 363 81 11
Web Site: http://www.vdgsecurity.com
Security Software Development Services
N.A.I.C.S.: 541511

VMC Denmark A/S (1)
Industriparken 16, 2750, Ballerup, Denmark
Tel.: (45) 44342342
Electrical Equipment Mfr & Distr
N.A.I.C.S.: 335999

VMI Holland B.V. (1)
Gelriaweg 16, 8161 RK, Epe, Netherlands
Tel.: (31) 578 679 111
Web Site: http://www.vmi-group.com
Industrial Machinery Mfr & Distr
N.A.I.C.S.: 333511
Harm Voortman (Pres & CEO)

Subsidiary (Non-US):

VMI (Yantai) Machinery Co. Ltd. (2)
No 886 Yongfu Yuan Road Fushan High, New Techn Industrial Park, Yantai, 265500, Shandong, China
Tel.: (86) 535 630 01 39
Industrial Machinery Mfr & Distr
N.A.I.C.S.: 333511
Xu Kangyuan (Pres)

VMI Ltd. (2)
Internal 41 No 50 Beijing Zhong Road ETDZ, Yantai, 264000, Shandong, China (100%)
Tel.: (86) 535 630 16 11
Web Site: http://www.vmi.com.cn
Industrial Machinery Mfr
N.A.I.C.S.: 333511

VMI South America Ltda. (2)
Condominio Industrial Sergio Gregori Rodovia Presidente, KM 316 sentido, 27580-000, Itatiaia, Brazil
Tel.: (55) 24 21089425
Industrial Machinery Mfr & Distr
N.A.I.C.S.: 333511

VMI-AZ Extrusion GmbH (2)
Bahnhofstrasse 6, 93486, Runding, Germany
Tel.: (49) 9971 761390
Industrial Machinery Mfr & Distr
N.A.I.C.S.: 333511
G. Roncken (Gen Mgr)

bv Elspec (1)
Verbreepark 15, 2731 BR, Benthuizen, Netherlands
Tel.: (31) 297330300
Web Site: http://www.elspec.nl
Telecommunication Equipment Distr
N.A.I.C.S.: 238210

TKL & FAMILY PTE. LTD.
50 East Coast Road #B1-18 Roxy Square, Singapore, 428769, Singapore
Tel.: (65) 64409878   SG
Year Founded: 2021

TKL & FAMILY PTE. LTD.

TKL & Family Pte. Ltd.—(Continued)
Investment Holding Company
N.A.I.C.S.: 551112
Teo Hong Lim *(Dir)*

Subsidiaries:

Roxy-Pacific Holdings Pte. Ltd. (1)
50 East Coast Road B1-18 Roxy Square,
Singapore, 428769, Singapore
Tel.: (65) 64409878
Web Site: http://www.roxypacific.com.sg
Rev.: $149,809,452
Assets: $1,220,224,792
Liabilities: $859,749,266
Net Worth: $360,475,526
Earnings: ($24,617,307)
Emp.: 243
Fiscal Year-end: 12/31/2020
Holding Company; Property Investment & Development Services
N.A.I.C.S.: 551112
Seng Geok Koh *(Deputy CEO & Sec)*

Subsidiary (Domestic):

RP Properties Pte. Ltd. (2)
50 East Coast Road 03-11 Roxy Square, Singapore, 428769, Singapore
Tel.: (65) 64409878
Sales Range: $25-49.9 Million
Emp.: 30
Property Management Services
N.A.I.C.S.: 531311

Roxy Homes Pte Ltd (2)
50 East Coast Road 03-11 Roxy Square Shopping Center, Singapore, 428769, Singapore
Tel.: (65) 64409878
Web Site: http://www.roxypacific.com.sg
Residential Property Development Services
N.A.I.C.S.: 236117

Roxy Land Pte. Ltd. (2)
Roxy Sq 03-11 50 E Coast Rd, Singapore, 428769, Singapore
Tel.: (65) 64409878
Sales Range: $50-74.9 Million
Emp.: 25
Real Estate Property Development Services
N.A.I.C.S.: 531210

Roxy-Pacific Developments Pte Ltd (2)
50 East Coast Road B1-18 Roxy Square, Singapore, 428769, Singapore
Tel.: (65) 64409878
Web Site: http://www.roxypacific.com.sg
Sales Range: $25-49.9 Million
Emp.: 30
Property Development Services
N.A.I.C.S.: 531210

TKP CORPORATION
2F TKP Ichigaya Building 8 Ichigaya-Hachiman-cho, Shinjuku-ku, Tokyo, 162-0844, Japan
Tel.: (81) 352277321
Web Site: https://www.tkp.jp
Year Founded: 2005
3479—(TKS)
Rev.: $259,104,050
Assets: $564,874,480
Liabilities: $279,608,330
Net Worth: $285,266,150
Earnings: $49,452,750
Emp.: 2,388
Fiscal Year-end: 02/29/24
Meeting Room Rental Services
N.A.I.C.S.: 531120
Takateru Kawano *(Pres & CEO)*

Subsidiaries:

Konbinisuteshon Co., Ltd (1)
Kanda Abe Building 7F 3-2 Kandamitoshiro-cho, Chiyoda-ku, Tokyo, 101-0053, Japan
Tel.: (81) 352175577
Web Site: http://convenistation.jp
Room Rental Management Services
N.A.I.C.S.: 531120

TKP International Limited (1)
23/F Euro Trade Centre 21-23 Des Voeux Road Central, Central, China (Hong Kong)
Tel.: (852) 25280108

Rental Management Services
N.A.I.C.S.: 531120

TKP Medicalink Co., Ltd. (1)
14 Ichigaya Hachiman-cho Ichigaya Central Building 7F, Shinjuku-ku, Tokyo, 162-0844, Japan
Tel.: (81) 352064001
Web Site: https://www.tkp-medicalink.co.jp
Medical Office Management Services
N.A.I.C.S.: 561110

TKP New York, Inc. (1)
109 W 39th St, New York, NY 10018
Tel.: (212) 444-7342
Web Site: http://tkpny.com
Room Rental Management Services
N.A.I.C.S.: 531120

TKP Telemarketing Corporation (1)
Sancho Building 2F 3-12-13 Sancho, Matsuyama, 790-0914, Ehime, Japan
Tel.: (81) 899556990
Web Site: http://tkpcom.jp
Business Management Services
N.A.I.C.S.: 561110

Tokiwaken Foods Co., Ltd. (1)
Minamirokugo 2-chome 33 No 9 No, Ota-ku, Tokyo, 144-0045, Yubinbango, Japan
Tel.: (81) 337304700
Web Site: http://tokiwaken-foods.jp
Food Mfr
N.A.I.C.S.: 311991

TKPH PTY LTD.
113 Clayton Street, Bellevue, Perth, 6056, WA, Australia
Tel.: (61) 0892508949 AU
Web Site: https://otrtyres.com
Emp.: 100
Wheel Servicing & Fleet Maintenance Services
N.A.I.C.S.: 811198
Darryl Bentley *(Mng Dir)*

Subsidiaries:

Titan Australia Pty. Ltd., (1)
6 Wonderland Drive, Eastern Creek, 2766, NSW, Australia
Tel.: (61) 2 9757 3407
Web Site: http://titanaust.com.au
Wheels & Undercarriage Components Mfr
N.A.I.C.S.: 326211

Titan Wheels Australia Pty. Ltd. - MUSWELLBROOK Wheel and Undercarriage Refurbish Facility (1)
26 Strathmore Road, PO Box 666, Muswellbrook, 2333, NSW, Australia
Tel.: (61) 265413207
Web Site: http://www.titanaustralia.com.au
Sales Range: $10-24.9 Million
Emp.: 5
Wheel & Undercarriage Refurbishing Services
N.A.I.C.S.: 811114

TL NATURAL GAS HOLDINGS LTD.
Jingzhou Primary Station Dong Fang Road, Economic Development Zone, Jingzhou, Hubei, China
Tel.: (86) 7168838666 Ky
Web Site: http://www.tl-cng.com
Year Founded: 2007
8536—(HKG)
Rev.: $9,489,776
Assets: $13,382,507
Liabilities: $1,858,334
Net Worth: $11,524,172
Earnings: ($511,618)
Emp.: 64
Fiscal Year-end: 12/31/22
Natural Gas Distr
N.A.I.C.S.: 221210
Yong Cheng Liu *(Chm, CEO & Compliance Officer)*

TLA WORLDWIDE PLC
2-6 Boundary Row, London, SE1 8HP, United Kingdom
Tel.: (44) 203 714 4154 UK

Web Site: http://tlaworldwide.com
Year Founded: 2011
Holding Company; Media Representation & Sports Marketing Services
N.A.I.C.S.: 551112
Scott Davidson *(CEO)*

TLB CO., LTD.
16Bl 17Lt 305 Sinwon-Ro, Danwon-Gu, Ansan, Gyeonggi-do, Korea (South)
Tel.: (82) 3180402071
Web Site: https://www.tlbpcb.com
Year Founded: 2011
356860—(KRS)
Rev.: $169,927,440
Assets: $126,495,686
Liabilities: $40,349,378
Net Worth: $86,146,308
Earnings: $23,430,664
Emp.: 432
Fiscal Year-end: 12/31/22
Printed Circuit Board Mfr
N.A.I.C.S.: 334412
Baek Seong Hyeon *(Pres & CEO)*

TLOU ENERGY LIMITED
210 Alice Street, Brisbane, 4000, QLD, Australia
Tel.: (61) 30409084
Web Site: https://www.tlouenergy.com
Year Founded: 2009
TOU—(ASX)
Rev.: $8,907
Assets: $51,771,340
Liabilities: $9,976,481
Net Worth: $41,794,859
Earnings: ($2,838,947)
Fiscal Year-end: 06/30/24
Crude Petroleum Extraction Services
N.A.I.C.S.: 211120
Colm Cloonan *(Fin Dir & Fin Dir)*

TM INSURANCE HF.
Sidumula 24, 108, Reykjavik, Iceland
Tel.: (354) 515 2000
Web Site: http://www.tm.is
Year Founded: 1956
Insurance Services
N.A.I.C.S.: 524126
Sigurdur Vidarsson *(CEO)*

TM TECHNOLOGY, INC.
No 6 Technology Road 5 Hsinchu Science Park, Hsinchu, Taiwan
Tel.: (886) 35787720
Web Site: https://www.tmtech.com.tw
Year Founded: 1994
5468—(TPE)
Rev.: $4,996,873
Assets: $17,075,227
Liabilities: $6,649,095
Net Worth: $10,426,133
Earnings: ($99,647)
Fiscal Year-end: 12/31/22
Electronic Material Mfr & Distr
N.A.I.C.S.: 334419
Bingnan Hu *(Chm)*

TMA GROUP OF COMPANIES LIMITED
4-6 Straits Avenue, Locked Bag 60, Granville, 2142, NSW, Australia
Tel.: (61) 298929999
Web Site: http://www.tmagroup.com.au
Sales Range: $50-74.9 Million
Emp.: 300
Thermal Coatings, Film & Paper Mfr; Commercial Printing
N.A.I.C.S.: 322220
Corriene Karam *(COO)*

TMBTHANACHART BANK PUBLIC COMPANY LIMITED

INTERNATIONAL PUBLIC

3000 Phahonyothin Rd., Khwang Chomphon, Khet Chatuchak, Bangkok, 10900, Thailand
Tel.: (66) 22991111
Web Site: https://www.ttbbank.com
Year Founded: 1957
TTB—(THA)
Rev.: $2,176,217,721
Assets: $50,172,805,269
Liabilities: $43,865,648,736
Net Worth: $6,307,156,533
Earnings: $507,719,605
Emp.: 15,320
Fiscal Year-end: 12/31/23
Commercial Banking Services
N.A.I.C.S.: 522110
Vikran Paovarojkit *(Chief Risk Officer)*

Subsidiaries:

Thanachart Bank Public Co. Ltd. (1)
16th-17th Floor MBK Tower 444 Phayathai Rd, Wangmai, Pathumwan, 10330, Bangkok, Thailand
Tel.: (66) 22178000
Web Site: http://www.thanachartbank.co.th
Banking Services
N.A.I.C.S.: 522110
Somjate Moosirilert *(Pres & CEO)*

Subsidiary (Domestic):

Ratchthani Leasing Public Company Limited (2)
77/35 - 36 11th Floor Sinsathorn Tower Building Krungthonburi Road, Klong Ton Sai Sub-district Klongsan District, Bangkok, 10600, Thailand
Tel.: (66) 24319000
Web Site: http://www.ratchthani.com
Rev.: $134,206,734
Assets: $1,613,137,487
Liabilities: $1,242,839,315
Net Worth: $370,298,172
Earnings: $37,568,073
Emp.: 494
Fiscal Year-end: 12/31/2023
Car Lending Services
N.A.I.C.S.: 532112
Virat Chinprapinporn *(Chm)*

TMC CONTENT GROUP AG
Poststrasse 24, Box 1546, CH-6300, Zug, Switzerland
Tel.: (41) 417662530 CH
Web Site: https://www.contentgroup.ch
Year Founded: 1999
ERO—(DEU)
Rev.: $6,962,306
Assets: $11,962,306
Liabilities: $964,523
Net Worth: $10,997,783
Earnings: ($2,549,889)
Emp.: 18
Fiscal Year-end: 12/30/23
Adult Entertainment Content Marketing & Distribution Services
N.A.I.C.S.: 512120
John Engelsma *(Chm)*

TMC THE METALS COMPANY INC.
595 Howe Street, Vancouver, V6C 2T5, BC, Canada
Tel.: (574) 252-9333 BC
Web Site: https://metals.co
TMC—(NASDAQ)
Rev.: $1,111,000
Assets: $94,777,000
Liabilities: $53,272,000
Net Worth: $41,505,000
Earnings: $170,964,000
Emp.: 39
Fiscal Year-end: 12/31/22
Mineral Exploration; Polymetallic Nodules Processing & Refining
N.A.I.C.S.: 331410
Stephen T. Jurvetson *(Vice Chm)*

TMF OPERATING SAS

AND PRIVATE COMPANIES — TNR GOLD CORP.

37 Rue Paul Sain, PO Box 50119, 84918, Avignon, Cedex 9, France
Tel.: (33) 428380440   FR
Web Site: http://www.tmf-operating.com
Sales Range: $50-74.9 Million
Emp.: 200
Multimodal Freight Transportation & Logistics Services
N.A.I.C.S.: 488510
Andy Brassart *(Mgr-Comml)*

TMK ENERGY LTD.
1202 Hay Street, West Perth, 6005, WA, Australia
Tel.: (61) 863191900   AU
Web Site: https://www.tmkenergy.com.au
TMK—(ASX)
Rev.: $85,164
Assets: $12,465,647
Liabilities: $336,350
Net Worth: $12,129,297
Earnings: ($1,765,960)
Fiscal Year-end: 12/31/23
Oil & Gas Exploration Services
N.A.I.C.S.: 211120
Brett Lawrence *(Mng Dir, Mng Dir & Exec Dir)*

TMM REAL ESTATE DEVELOPMENT PUBLIC LTD.
Volodymyrska st 49a, 01001, Kiev, Ukraine
Tel.: (380) 445930711
Web Site: https://www.tmm.ua
Year Founded: 2006
TR61—(DEU)
Rev.: $3,115,000
Assets: $16,948,000
Liabilities: $17,001,000
Net Worth: ($53,000)
Earnings: ($2,579,000)
Emp.: 282
Fiscal Year-end: 12/31/22
Real Estate Development Services
N.A.I.C.S.: 531190
Larysa Chyvurina *(CFO)*

TMP GROUP S.P.A.
Via Arcivescovo Calabiana 6, 20139, Milan, Italy
Tel.: (39) 0287199855
Web Site: https://www.tmpgroup.it
Year Founded: 2012
TMP—(EUR)
Emp.: 25
Advertising Media Services
N.A.I.C.S.: 541840
Margherita Leder *(CFO)*

TMT (INDIA) LTD.
A-28 2nd Floor Journalist Colony Road No 70 Jubilee Hills, Hyderabad, 500001, India
Tel.: (91) 4023556089
Web Site: https://www.tmtindia.in
Year Founded: 1994
522171—(BOM)
Rev.: $1,234
Assets: $90,771
Liabilities: $762,631
Net Worth: ($671,860)
Earnings: ($203,100)
Emp.: 4
Fiscal Year-end: 03/31/23
Engineeering Services
N.A.I.C.S.: 541330
Tumbalam Gooty Veera Prasad *(Mng Dir)*

TMT FINANCE SA
Via Bagutti 14, 6900, Lugano, Switzerland
Tel.: (41) 91 972 13 15
Holding Company; Financial Investments
N.A.I.C.S.: 551112

Angelo Mastrolia *(Pres)*

Subsidiaries:

Newlat SpA   (1)
Via J F Kennedy 16, 42124, Reggio Emilia, Italy
Tel.: (39) 0522 7901
Web Site: http://www.newlat.it
Sales Range: $350-399.9 Million
Emp.: 1,000
Dairy, Pasta & Bread Substitutes Mfr
N.A.I.C.S.: 112120

Plant (Domestic):

Newlat - Sansepolcro   (2)
Newlat Zona Industriale Altotevere 1, 52037, Sansepolcro, Italy
Tel.: (39) 0575 7471
Web Site: http://www.newlat.eu
Sales Range: $125-149.9 Million
Emp.: 400
Pasta & Bread Substitute Mfr
N.A.I.C.S.: 311824

TMT INVESTMENTS PLC
13 Castle Street, Saint Helier, JE1 1ES, Jersey
Tel.: (44) 3707074040   JE
Web Site: https://www.tmtinvestments.com
Year Founded: 2010
TMT—(AIM)
Rev.: $7,394,443
Assets: $209,829,519
Liabilities: $1,717,816
Net Worth: $208,111,703
Earnings: $6,377,773
Emp.: 7
Fiscal Year-end: 12/31/23
Investment Management Service
N.A.I.C.S.: 523999
Alexander Selegenev *(Exec Dir)*

TMT MOTORS CORPORATION
Floor 9 10 CONINCO Building no 4 Ton That Tung Trung Tu Wark, Dong Da District, Hanoi, Vietnam
Tel.: (84) 2438628205
Web Site: https://www.tmtmotors.vn
Year Founded: 1976
TMT—(HOSE)
Rev.: $108,539,711
Assets: $89,393,782
Liabilities: $71,370,719
Net Worth: $18,023,064
Earnings: $117,585
Emp.: 480
Fiscal Year-end: 12/31/23
Trucks Mfr
N.A.I.C.S.: 336120

TMT STEEL PUBLIC COMPANY LIMITED
179 Bangkok City Tower 22nd Floor South Sathorn Road Thungmahamek, Sathorn, Bangkok, 10120, Thailand
Tel.: (66) 26854000
Web Site: https://www.tmtsteel.co.th
Year Founded: 1992
TMT—(THA)
Rev.: $583,597,818
Assets: $261,007,651
Liabilities: $163,916,486
Net Worth: $97,091,165
Earnings: $9,713,334
Emp.: 1,410
Fiscal Year-end: 12/31/23
Steel Products Mfr
N.A.I.C.S.: 331210
Paisal Tarasansombat *(CEO)*

TMW LIMITED
Avoncroft House Unit 7 Shottery Brook Ofc Park Timothys Bridge Rd, Stratford-upon-Avon, CV379NQ, Warwickshire, United Kingdom
Tel.: (44) 1789404180
Rev.: $15,000,000

Emp.: 8
N.A.I.C.S.: 541810
Chris Phillips *(Mng Dir)*

TMX GROUP LIMITED
300 - 100 Adelaide St West, Toronto, M5H 1S3, ON, Canada
Tel.: (416) 947-4700   ON
Web Site: https://www.tmx.com
9TX—(DEU)
Rev.: $901,688,792
Assets: $48,582,457,488
Liabilities: $45,319,055,384
Net Worth: $3,263,402,104
Earnings: $293,137,584
Emp.: 1,803
Fiscal Year-end: 12/31/23
Holding Company; Securities Exchange Operator & Financial Transaction Processing Services
N.A.I.C.S.: 551112
Charles Winograd *(Chm)*

Subsidiaries:

TMX Group Inc.   (1)
130 King Street West, PO Box 38, The Exchange Tower, Toronto, M5X 1A9, ON, Canada   (100%)
Tel.: (416) 343-2777
Web Site: http://www.tmx.com
Sales Range: $300-349.9 Million
Holding Company; Stock Exchanges
N.A.I.C.S.: 551112
Paul Malcolmson *(Dir-IR)*

Subsidiary (Domestic):

Montreal Exchange Inc.   (2)
1800- 1190 Ave des Canadienes-de-Montreal, PO Box 37, Montreal, H3B 0G7, QC, Canada
Tel.: (514) 871-2424
Web Site: http://www.m-x.ca
Derivative Markets Exchange Operator & Clearinghouse Services
N.A.I.C.S.: 523210
Luc Fortin *(Pres & CEO)*

Subsidiary (Domestic):

Canadian Derivatives Clearing Corporation   (3)
1800- 1190 Ave des Canadienes-de-Montreal, PO Box 37, Montreal, H3B 0G7, QC, Canada   (100%)
Tel.: (514) 871-3545
Web Site: http://www.cdcc.ca
Financial Clearinghouse Services
N.A.I.C.S.: 522320
Joseph Ernst *(Chief Compliance Officer)*

Subsidiary (Domestic):

Shorcan Brokers Limited   (2)
20 Adelaide Street East Suite 1000, Toronto, M5C 2T6, ON, Canada
Tel.: (416) 360-2500
Web Site: http://www.shorcan.com
Fixed Income Brokerage & Dealing Services
N.A.I.C.S.: 523160

TSX Inc.   (2)
130 King Street West, The Exchange Tower, Toronto, M5X 1J2, ON, Canada   (100%)
Tel.: (416) 947-4700
Web Site: http://www.tmx.com
Sales Range: $200-249.9 Million
Emp.: 510
Securities & Equities Exchange
N.A.I.C.S.: 523210

The Canadian Depository for Securities Limited   (1)
100 Adelaide Street West, Toronto, M5H 1S3, ON, Canada
Tel.: (416) 365-8400
Web Site: https://www.cds.ca
Sales Range: $75-99.9 Million
Emp.: 400
Security & Commodity Services
N.A.I.C.S.: 523210
David Wood *(Chm)*

Tradesignal GmbH   (1)

Trayport Limited   (1)
7th Floor 9 Appold Street, London, EC2A 2AP, United Kingdom
Tel.: (44) 2079605500
Web Site: http://www.trayport.com
Securities Trading Software Developer
N.A.I.C.S.: 513210
Richard Everett *(COO)*

Subsidiary (Non-US):

Trayport Pte Ltd   (2)
One Raffles Place Office Tower 1 #31-02, Singapore, 048616, Singapore
Tel.: (65) 6411 4700
Web Site: http://www.trayport.com
Securities Trading Software Services
N.A.I.C.S.: 513210

TNC INDUSTRIAL CO., LTD.
19F 1 No 1071 Zhong Zheng Rd, Taoyuan, Taiwan
Tel.: (886) 3 356 6289
Web Site: http://www.tnc.com.tw
1724—(TAI)
Rev.: $62,117,278
Assets: $111,699,404
Liabilities: $42,461,474
Net Worth: $69,237,930
Earnings: $906,217
Fiscal Year-end: 12/31/21
Nitrocellulose Mfr
N.A.I.C.S.: 325211

Subsidiaries:

TNC Industrial Co., Ltd. - Coating Raw Materials Division   (1)
29-25 Kang-Kou Village Lu-Chu Shiang, Taoyuan, 33844, Taiwan
Tel.: (886) 33241126
Coating Chemical Mfr
N.A.I.C.S.: 325510
Crystal Hsiao *(Mgr)*

TNG INVESTMENT & TRADING JSC
434/1 Bac Kan, Thai Nguyen, Vietnam
Tel.: (84) 2803858508
Web Site: http://www.tng.vn
Year Founded: 1979
TNG—(HNX)
Rev.: $292,322,446
Assets: $215,493,057
Liabilities: $139,071,136
Net Worth: $76,421,921
Earnings: $9,041,010
Emp.: 18,154
Fiscal Year-end: 12/31/23
Financial Investment Services
N.A.I.C.S.: 523999

TNG LIMITED
Suite 20 22 Railway Road, Subiaco, 6008, WA, Australia
Tel.: (61) 893270900   AU
Web Site: http://www.tngltd.com.au
TVN—(ASX)
Rev.: $8,681
Assets: $18,462,206
Liabilities: $9,226,095
Net Worth: $9,236,111
Earnings: ($45,296)
Fiscal Year-end: 06/30/24
Mining & Exploration Services
N.A.I.C.S.: 213114
Paul E. Burton *(CEO & Mng Dir)*

Subsidiaries:

Enigma Mining Limited   (1)
Level 1 282 Rokeby Rd, Subiaco, 6008, Western Australia, Australia
Tel.: (61) 894814101
Sales Range: $50-74.9 Million
Emp.: 4
Nickel Ore Mining Services
N.A.I.C.S.: 212230

TNR GOLD CORP.

TNR GOLD CORP.

TNR Gold Corp.—(Continued)

1120 - 789 West Pender Street, Vancouver, V6C 1H2, BC, Canada
Tel.: (604) 229-8129 BC
Web Site: https://www.tnrgoldcorp.com
TNR—(TSXV)
Rev.: $362
Assets: $484,934
Liabilities: $26,657
Net Worth: $458,276
Earnings: $5,959,337
Fiscal Year-end: 12/31/23
Gold & Other Metal Mining Services
N.A.I.C.S.: 212220
Kirill Klip *(Chm, Pres & CEO)*

Subsidiaries:

International Lithium Corp. (1)
1120-789 West Pender Street, Vancouver, V4A 2H9, BC, Canada
Tel.: (604) 449-6520
Web Site: https://www.internationallithium.ca
Assets: $7,042,101
Liabilities: $7,749,927
Net Worth: ($707,826)
Earnings: ($1,334,721)
Fiscal Year-end: 12/31/2020
Lithium Mining Services
N.A.I.C.S.: 212290
John Wisbey *(Chm & CEO)*

TNS ENERGO KUBAN PJSC

Gimnazicheskaya Street 51/1, Krasnodar, 350000, Russia
Tel.: (7) 8612990720
KBSB—(MOEX)
Sales Range: Less than $1 Million
Electrical Energy Distr
N.A.I.C.S.: 423610
Ivan Kostanov *(Mng Dir & Deputy Gen Dir)*

TNS ENERGO MARI EL PJSC

Iyvana Kyrlya Street 21, Yoshkar-Ola, 424019, Russia
Tel.: (7) 8362465180
Web Site: http://www.corp.tns-e.ru
MISB—(MOEX)
Sales Range: Less than $1 Million
Electric Power Distribution Services
N.A.I.C.S.: 221122
Maxim Ye Belousov *(Mng Dir)*

TNS ENERGO NIZHNIY NOVG

Nastasinsky per. 4 bldg. 1, Moscow, 127006, Russia
Tel.: (7) 4952872484
Web Site: http://www.nsk.elektra.ru
NNSB—(MOEX)
Sales Range: Less than $1 Million
Electric Power Distribution Services
N.A.I.C.S.: 221122
Oleg Borisovich Shavin *(Mng Dir)*

TNS ENERGO ROSTOV-ON-DON PJSC

Zhuravlev Street 47, Rostov-na-Donu, 344022, Russia
Tel.: (7) 8632035957
Web Site: http://www.rostov.tns-e.ru
RTSB—(MOEX)
Sales Range: Less than $1 Million
Fishing Equipment Distr
N.A.I.C.S.: 423830
Roman Lutikov *(Mng Dir)*

TNS ENERGO VORONEZH PJSC

Merkulova 7A, Voronezh, 394029, Russia
Tel.: (7) 4732618708
VRSB—(MOEX)
Sales Range: Less than $1 Million
Electric Power Distribution Services
N.A.I.C.S.: 221122
Evgeny Severgin *(Gen Dir-PJSC TNS Energo Grp)*

TNS ENERGO YAROSLAVL AO

Prospekt Lenina 21b, Yaroslavl, 150003, Russia
Tel.: (7) 4852781909
Web Site: http://www.yar.tns-e.ru
YRSB—(MOEX)
Sales Range: Less than $1 Million
Electric Power Distribution Services
N.A.I.C.S.: 221122
Alexey Ermakov *(Mng Dir)*

TNT GROUP JOINT STOCK COMPANY

No 115 Group 5 Lang Ha, Dong Da, Hanoi, Vietnam
Tel.: (84) 02462510894
Web Site: http://www.tainguyen.vn
TNT—(HOSE)
Rev.: $26,265,371
Assets: $66,111,374
Liabilities: $38,159,316
Net Worth: $27,952,058
Earnings: $769,616
Emp.: 8
Fiscal Year-end: 12/31/23
Investment Advisory Services
N.A.I.C.S.: 523940
Nguyen Gia Long *(Chm & Gen Dir)*

TO PROSPERITY TECHNOLOGY INC.

Suite 08 Floor 24 Unit 1 Building 1 No 88 Shujin Road, High-New Tech District, Chengdu, 610041, Sichuan, China
Tel.: (86) 2887099772 Ky
Year Founded: 2019
Rev.: $820,833
Assets: $545,591
Liabilities: $418,887
Net Worth: $126,704
Earnings: ($603,142)
Emp.: 40
Fiscal Year-end: 09/30/18
Holding Company
N.A.I.C.S.: 551112
Zhengbo Ju *(CEO)*

TO-LE-DO FOODSERVICE

2430 McGillivray Blvd, Winnipeg, R3Y 1G6, MB, Canada
Tel.: (204) 487-3340 Ca
Web Site: http://www.toledofoodservice.ca
Year Founded: 1988
Meat & Meat Products Distr
N.A.I.C.S.: 424470
Mitch Rooney *(Mgr-Pur & Distribution)*

TOA CORPORATION

7-2-1 Minatojima-Nakamachi, Chuo-ku, Kobe, 650-0046, Japan
Tel.: (81) 783035620 JP
Web Site: https://toa-global.com
Year Founded: 1934
6809—(TKS)
Rev.: $322,660,540
Assets: $427,891,740
Liabilities: $102,421,950
Net Worth: $325,469,790
Earnings: $13,200,170
Emp.: 3,025
Fiscal Year-end: 03/31/24
Professional & Commercial Sound Products Mfr & Developer
N.A.I.C.S.: 334310
Kazuhiro Takeuchi *(Pres & CEO)*

Subsidiaries:

TOA Corporation (1)
7-2-1 Minatojima-Nakamachi, Chuo-ku, Kobe, 650-0046, Hyogo, Japan **(100%)**
Tel.: (81) 783035620
Web Site: http://www.toa.jp
Sales Range: $300-349.9 Million
Professional & Commercial Sound Products Mfr & Distr
N.A.I.C.S.: 532490
Kenji Itani *(Chm)*

Subsidiary (Domestic):

ACOUS Corporation (2)
113 Fuma, Maibara, 521-0224, Shiga, Japan
Tel.: (81) 749550711
Web Site: https://www.acous.co.jp
Communication Equipment Mfr
N.A.I.C.S.: 334419

Subsidiary (Non-US):

Dynatron Industrial Co., Ltd (2)
NO 89 Din Pin Rd, Ruifang Industrial Park Ruifang Dist, New Taipei City, Taiwan
Tel.: (886) 224979801
Web Site: https://www.dynatron.com.tw
Sales Range: $25-49.9 Million
Emp.: 250
Electronic Components Mfr
N.A.I.C.S.: 334419

Subsidiary (Domestic):

Hino Seiki Co., Ltd. (2)
2140 Nishioji, Hino-cho, Gamo, 529-1628, Shiga, Japan
Tel.: (81) 748521075
Web Site: https://www.hinoseiki.com
Sales Range: $25-49.9 Million
Emp.: 105
N.A.I.C.S.: 237310

Subsidiary (Non-US):

P.T. TOA-Galva Industries (2)
Jalan Raya Jakarta Bogor Km 34-35, Desa Sukamaju Baru TAPOS, Depok, Indonesia **(100%)**
Tel.: (62) 218740809
Sales Range: $150-199.9 Million
Emp.: 600
Mfr of Sound Products
N.A.I.C.S.: 512240

PT. TOA-GALVA Prima Karya (2)
Galva Building Lantai 4 Jl Hayam Wuruk No 27, Kel Kebon Kelapa Kec Gambir, Jakarta Pusat, 10120, Indonesia
Tel.: (62) 213456650
Web Site: https://toa.co.id
Emp.: 300
Electronic Component Mfr & Distr
N.A.I.C.S.: 334419

Subsidiary (Domestic):

TAKEX Co., Ltd. (2)
1-3-5 Esakacho, Takeo-Shi, Suita, 564-0063, Osaka Prefecture, Japan **(100%)**
Tel.: (81) 668212577
Web Site: https://takex-co.com
Sales Range: $50-74.9 Million
Emp.: 120
N.A.I.C.S.: 237310

Subsidiary (Non-US):

TOA (China) Limited (2)
Room 708 Building 2 No 1535 Hong Mei Road, Xu Hui District, Shanghai, 200042, China
Tel.: (86) 2162722584
Web Site: https://www.toachina.com.cn
Sales Range: $25-49.9 Million
Emp.: 3
Communication Equipment Distr
N.A.I.C.S.: 423690

TOA (Hong Kong) Ltd. (2)
Flat 710 7/F Fortress Tower 250 King's Road, North Point, China (Hong Kong) **(100%)**
Tel.: (852) 27820311
Web Site: https://www.toa.com.hk
Sales Range: $25-49.9 Million
Emp.: 15
Mfr of Sound Products
N.A.I.C.S.: 512240

Division (Domestic):

TOA Active Noise Control Division (2)

INTERNATIONAL PUBLIC

1-10 Takamatsu-cho, Takarazuka, 665-0043, Japan **(100%)**
Tel.: (81) 797719011
Web Site: http://www.toa.jp
Sales Range: $25-49.9 Million
Emp.: 15
Mfr, Developer & Distr of Professional & Commercial Sound Products
N.A.I.C.S.: 532490

Subsidiary (Non-US):

TOA Canada Corporation (2)
3670 Odyssey Drive Unit 1, Mississauga, L5M 0Y9, ON, Canada **(100%)**
Tel.: (905) 564-3570
Web Site: https://www.toacanada.com
Sales Range: $25-49.9 Million
Emp.: 15
Mfr of Sound Products
N.A.I.C.S.: 512240
Don Angus *(Reg Mgr-Sales)*

Subsidiary (US):

TOA Communication Systems, Inc. (2)
341 New Albany Rd Ste105, Moorestown, NJ 08057
Tel.: (856) 235-0637
Web Site: http://www.toa.jp
Communication Equipment Mfr
N.A.I.C.S.: 334290

Subsidiary (Non-US):

TOA Corporation (UK) Limited (2)
HQ3 Unit 2 Hook Rise South, Surbiton, KT6 7LD, Surrey, United Kingdom **(100%)**
Tel.: (44) 8707740987
Web Site: http://www.toa-corp.co.uk
Sales Range: $25-49.9 Million
Emp.: 13
Mfr of Sound Products
N.A.I.C.S.: 512240
Kosuke Tanaka *(Mng Dir)*

TOA ELECTRONICS (M) SDN. BHD. (2)
3rd Floor Wisma Kemajuan No 2 Jalan 19/1B, 46300, Petaling Jaya, Selangor Darul Ehsan, Malaysia
Tel.: (60) 379601128
Web Site: https://www.toamys.com.my
Sales Range: $25-49.9 Million
Emp.: 13
Communication Equipment Distr
N.A.I.C.S.: 423690
Hirokazu Ichino *(Mng Dir)*

TOA ELECTRONICS PTE LTD (2)
491B River Valley Road 19-03/04 Valley Point Office Tower, Singapore, 248373, Singapore
Tel.: (65) 68359119
Web Site: https://www.toa.com.sg
Sales Range: $25-49.9 Million
Emp.: 24
Communication Equipment Distr
N.A.I.C.S.: 423690
Nishino Takashi *(Mng Dir)*

TOA ELECTRONICS SOUTHERN AFRICA (PROPRIETARY) LIMITED (2)
70 Mangold Street Newton Park, Port Elizabeth, 6045, Eastern Cape, South Africa
Tel.: (27) 413641170
Web Site: https://www.toasa.co.za
Sales Range: $25-49.9 Million
Emp.: 29
Electronic Component & Equipment Distr
N.A.I.C.S.: 423690

TOA Electronics (Thailand) Co., Ltd. (2)
15th Floor Serm-Mit Tower 159/24 Sukhumvit 21 Road, North Klongtoey Wattana, Bangkok, 10110, Thailand
Tel.: (66) 26652600
Web Site: https://www.toathailand.com
Sales Range: $25-49.9 Million
Emp.: 35
Communication Equipment Distr
N.A.I.C.S.: 423690
Ninomiya Yosuke *(Mng Dir)*

TOA Electronics Europe G.m.b.H (2)
ZA Central Parc 2 allee du Daim, 93421, Villepinte, Cedex, France

Tel.: (33) 141511550
Web Site: www.toa.fr
Sales Range: $25-49.9 Million
Emp.: 16
Sound System Mfr
N.A.I.C.S.: 334419

TOA Electronics Europe G.m.b.H. Sp. z.o.o. (2)
Ul Migdalowa 4, 02-796, Warsaw, Poland
Tel.: (48) 226451198
Web Site: https://www.toa.pl
Emp.: 9
Communication Equipment Distr
N.A.I.C.S.: 423690

TOA Electronics Europe GmbH (2)
SuderstraSSe 282, 20537, Hamburg, Germany **(100%)**
Tel.: (49) 402517190
Web Site: https://www.toa.eu
Sales Range: $25-49.9 Million
Emp.: 22
Mfr of Sound Products
N.A.I.C.S.: 512240

TOA Electronics Taiwan Corporation (2)
4F No 18 Chang An E Rd Section 1, Taipei, Taiwan **(100%)**
Tel.: (886) 225433601
Web Site: http://www.toataiwan.com.tw
Sales Range: $25-49.9 Million
Emp.: 15
Mfr of Sound Products
N.A.I.C.S.: 512240

Subsidiary (US):

TOA Electronics, Inc. (2)
1 Harmon Plz Ste 602, Secaucus, NJ 07094 **(100%)**
Tel.: (650) 452-1200
Web Site: http://www.toaelectronics.com
Sales Range: $25-49.9 Million
Emp.: 11
Mfr of Sound Products
N.A.I.C.S.: 423690

Subsidiary (Domestic):

TOA Engineering Corporation (2)
5-5-2 Kiba CN-1 Building 3F, Koto-ku, Tokyo, 135-0042, Japan **(100%)**
Tel.: (81) 356461293
Web Site: https://www.toae.co.jp
Emp.: 132
Construction & Civil Engineering
N.A.I.C.S.: 237310

Division (Domestic):

TOA International Division (2)
7-2-1 Minatojima-Nakamachi, Chuo-ku, Kobe, 650-0046, Japan **(100%)**
Tel.: (81) 783035660
Web Site: http://www.toa.jp
Sales Range: $50-74.9 Million
Emp.: 100
Mfr, Developer & Distributor of Professional & Commercial Sound Products
N.A.I.C.S.: 532490

Subsidiary (Domestic):

TOA Tokyo Office (2)
CN-1 Bldg 4F 5-5-2 Kiba, Koto-ku, Tokyo, 135-0042, Japan **(100%)**
Tel.: (81) 356215761
Web Site: http://www.toa.jp
Sales Range: $50-74.9 Million
Emp.: 100
Mfr, Developer & Distributor of Professional & Commercial Sound Products
N.A.I.C.S.: 532490

Subsidiary (Non-US):

TOA VIETNAM CO., LTD. (2)
Lot D1 - Thang Long Industrial Park, Vong La Commune Dong Anh District, Hanoi, Vietnam
Tel.: (84) 2438811707
Web Site: https://www.toa.com.vn
Sales Range: $25-49.9 Million
Emp.: 191
Conferencing System Equipment Mfr
N.A.I.C.S.: 334419
Koji Kawaguchi (Gen Dir)

Subsidiary (Domestic):

XEBEC Corporation (2)
7-2-1 Minatojima Nakamachi, Chuo-Ku, Kobe, 650-0046, Hyogo-ken, Japan **(100%)**
Tel.: (81) 783035600
Web Site: https://www.xebec.co.jp
Emp.: 16
Software Publisher
N.A.I.C.S.: 513210

TOA GROUP HOLDING CO., LTD.
31/2 Moo 3 Bangna-Trad Road, Bangsaothong, Bang Sao Thong, 10570, Samutprakan, Thailand
Tel.: (66) 2335 5555 TH
Holding Company
N.A.I.C.S.: 551112
Nattavuth Tangkaravakoon (Principal)

Subsidiaries:

TOA Paint (Thailand) Public Company Limited (1)
31/2 Moo 3 Bangna-Trad Road, Bangsaothong, Bang Sao Thong, 10570, Samutprakan, Thailand **(30%)**
Tel.: (66) 23355555
Web Site: http://www.toagroup.com
Rev.: $542,982,605
Assets: $549,323,174
Liabilities: $169,294,763
Net Worth: $380,028,410
Earnings: $67,463,334
Fiscal Year-end: 12/31/2020
Paint & Coating Mfr & Whslr
N.A.I.C.S.: 325510
Jatuphat Tangkaravakoon (CEO & Mng Dir-Acting)

Subsidiary (Domestic):

British Paints Co., Ltd. (2)
31/2 Moo 3 Debaratana Road, Bangsaothong, Bang Sao Thong, 10570, Samutprakan, Thailand
Tel.: (66) 2 335 5777
Paint & Coating Distr
N.A.I.C.S.: 424950

Subsidiary (Non-US):

TOA Paint (Laos) Ltd. (2)
Unit 6 Ban Nahai, Hatsaifong District, Vientiane, Lao People's Democratic Republic
Tel.: (856) 21 812 082
Paint & Coating Distr
N.A.I.C.S.: 424950
Prakorn Makjumroen (Acting Mng Dir)

TOA Paint (Vietnam) Co., Ltd. (2)
Floor 8 Room 85 E-town 3 Building 364 Cong Hoa Street, Ward 13 Tan Binh District, Ho Chi Minh City, Vietnam
Tel.: (84) 8 3813 1999
Web Site: http://www.toagroup.com.vn
Paint & Coating Mfr & Whslr
N.A.I.C.S.: 325510

TOA Venture Holding Company Limited (1)
31/1 Moo 3 Debaratana Road, Bangsaothong, Bang Sao Thong, 10570, Samutprakan, Thailand **(100%)**
Tel.: (66) 2 335 5555
Holding Company; Industrial Paint, Auto Parts & Chemicals Mfr; Car Dealer; Real Estate Development
N.A.I.C.S.: 551112
Nattavuth Tangkaravakoon (Pres)

Subsidiary (Domestic):

Sherwood Corp (Thailand) Public Co., Ltd. (2)
1065 Srinakarin Road, Suanluang, Bangkok, 10250, Thailand
Tel.: (66) 23202288
Web Site: http://www.sherwood.co.th
Rev.: $55,386,595
Assets: $43,175,980
Liabilities: $19,786,781
Net Worth: $23,389,199
Earnings: $5,760,136
Fiscal Year-end: 12/31/2019
Industrial Chemical Product Mfr & Distr

N.A.I.C.S.: 325199
Thongchai Charoenkulmetee (CEO)

Sherwood Corporation (Thailand) Public Company Limited (2)
1065 Srinakarin Road Suanluang Suanluang, Bangkok, 10250, Thailand **(69.41%)**
Tel.: (66) 23202288
Web Site: https://www.sherwood.co.th
Rev.: $50,017,522
Assets: $33,438,377
Liabilities: $14,104,433
Net Worth: $19,333,944
Earnings: $1,785,708
Emp.: 386
Fiscal Year-end: 12/31/2023
Chemicals Mfr
N.A.I.C.S.: 325998
Chanin Yensudchai (Chm)

TOA Performance Coating Corporation Co., Ltd. (2)
31/1 Moo 3 Debaratana Road KM 23, Bangsaothong, Bang Sao Thong, 10570, Samutprakan, Thailand **(95.09%)**
Tel.: (66) 2335 5555
Web Site: http://www.toapc.com
Industrial Paints & Coatings Mfr & Whslr
N.A.I.C.S.: 325510
Terdsak Surakitbovorn (Mng Dir)

TOA HOLDINGS, INC.
C/O Toa Shoko 1-1-36 Nishiawaji, Higashiyadogawa-ku, Osaka, 533-0031, Japan
Tel.: (81) 6 6325 5035 DE
Year Founded: 2012
Sales Range: Less than $1 Million
Emp.: 1
Wholesale Trade Agents & Other Business Services
N.A.I.C.S.: 425120
Shunji Fukumoto (Sec)

TOA ROAD CORPORATION
7-3-7 Roppongi, Minato-ku, Tokyo, 106-0032, Japan
Tel.: (81) 334051811
Web Site: https://www.toadoro.co.jp
Year Founded: 1930
1882—(TKS)
Rev.: $780,376,600
Assets: $614,035,950
Liabilities: $243,380,200
Net Worth: $370,655,750
Earnings: $25,071,730
Fiscal Year-end: 03/31/24
Construction Engineering Services
N.A.I.C.S.: 541330
Kyouichi Morishita (Pres)

Subsidiaries:

Fujikensetsu Corporation (1)
NMF Shiba Park Building 3-5-5 Shiba, Minato-ku, Tokyo, 105-0014, Japan
Tel.: (81) 354765561
Web Site: http://www.fujikensetsu.com
Emp.: 265
Engineeering Services
N.A.I.C.S.: 541330
Tadao Yonekawa (Pres & CEO)

Toa-Tone Boring Co., Ltd. (1)
3rd Floor Toa Road Corp Bldg 3-7 Roppongi 7-chome, Minato-ku, Tokyo, 106-0032, Japan
Tel.: (81) 357753321
Web Site: https://www.toa-tone.jp
Emp.: 120
Mining Machinery & Equipment Mfr & Distr
N.A.I.C.S.: 333131
Haruhiko Ito (Pres)

Umetsugumi Corporation (1)
9-75 Midoricho, Nagai, 993-0081, Yamagata, Japan
Tel.: (81) 238842032
Web Site: https://www.umetu.co.jp
Emp.: 75
Engineeering Services
N.A.I.C.S.: 541330

TOABO CORPORATION
18th Floor Crystal Tower 2-27 Shiromi 1-chome, Chuo-ku, Osaka, 540-6018, Japan
Tel.: (81) 671781151
Web Site: https://www.toabo.co.jp
Year Founded: 2003
3204—(TKS)
Rev.: $135,007,780
Assets: $244,285,950
Liabilities: $155,377,350
Net Worth: $88,908,600
Earnings: $4,062,570
Emp.: 117
Fiscal Year-end: 12/31/23
Textile Product Mfr & Distr
N.A.I.C.S.: 313220
Wataru Nagai (Pres)

TOADMAN INTERACTIVE AB
Ringvägen 100, 118 60, Stockholm, Sweden
Web Site: http://toadmaninteractive.com
Year Founded: 2013
Computer Games Developer
N.A.I.C.S.: 513210

Subsidiaries:

Petrol Advertising, Inc. (1)
443 N Varney St, Burbank, CA 91502-1733
Tel.: (323) 644-3720
Web Site: http://www.petrolad.com
Services Related to Advertising
N.A.I.C.S.: 541890
Al Herrera (Sr Acct Exec)

TOAGOSEI CO. LTD.
1-14-1 Nishi-Shimbashi, Minato-ku, Tokyo, 105-8419, Japan
Tel.: (81) 335977215
Web Site: https://www.toagosei.co.jp
Year Founded: 1944
4045—(TKS)
Rev.: $1,129,940,390
Assets: $1,930,500,650
Liabilities: $423,748,030
Net Worth: $1,506,752,620
Earnings: $86,349,110
Emp.: 2,554
Fiscal Year-end: 12/31/23
Organic & Inorganic Chemicals Mfr
N.A.I.C.S.: 325110
Nobuhiro Ishikawa (VP & Gen Mgr-Corp Strategy Div)

Subsidiaries:

Aron Ever Grip Ltd. (1)
1 14 1 Nishi Shimbashi, Minato ku, Tokyo, 105 8419, Japan
Tel.: (81) 3 3539 4481
Web Site: http://www.toagosei.co.jp
Adhesives Mfr & Distr
N.A.I.C.S.: 325520

Aron Packaging Co., Ltd. (1)
2-1-3 Fushiki Takaoka, Toyama, 933-0195, Japan
Tel.: (81) 766447427
Web Site: http://www.toagosei.co.jp
Sales Range: $25-49.9 Million
Emp.: 100
Adhesives Filling & Packaging Services
N.A.I.C.S.: 325520

Aronkasei Co., Ltd. (1)
8F Sumitomo Fudosan Hibiya BLDG 8-6 2-Chome, 8-6 2-Chome Nishishimbashi Minato-ku, Tokyo, 105-0003, Japan
Web Site: http://www.aronkasei.co.jp
Plastics Product Mfr
N.A.I.C.S.: 326122

Subsidiary (Domestic):

Mikuni Plastics Co. Ltd. (2)
14 17 Juhachijo 3 Chome, Yodogawa Ku, Osaka, 532 0001, Japan
Tel.: (81) 663954011
Web Site: http://www.mikumipla.co.jp
Sales Range: $25-49.9 Million
Emp.: 5
Mfr & Distribution of Plastic Products
N.A.I.C.S.: 326199

TOAGOSEI CO. LTD.

Toagosei Co. Ltd.—(Continued)

Elmer's & Toagosei Co. (1)
6655 Peachtree Dunwoody Rd, Atlanta, GA 30228
Adhesive Mfr
N.A.I.C.S.: 325520

MT AquaPolymer, Inc (1)
2-6-2 Kajicho Ueno Bldg 3rd Floor, Chiyoda-ku, Tokyo, 101-0044, Japan (90%)
Tel.: (81) 362064507
Web Site: http://www.mtaqua.co.jp
Organic Flocculant Mfr
N.A.I.C.S.: 325199
Koji Kimura (Pres)

MT AquaPolymer, Inc. (1)
Ueno Bldg 3rd Floor 2-6-2 Kajicho, Chiyoda-ku, Tokyo, 101-0044, Japan
Tel.: (81) 362064505
Web Site: https://www.mtaqua.co.jp
Water Treatment Chemicals Mfr & Distr
N.A.I.C.S.: 325998
Satoshi Shikama (Pres)

Plant (Domestic):

MT AquaPolymer, Inc. - Mobara Plant (2)
1900 Togo, Mobara, 297-0017, Chiba, Japan
Tel.: (81) 475251277
Web Site: http://www.mtaqua.co.jp
Water Treatment Chemical Mfr
N.A.I.C.S.: 325998

MT AquaPolymer, Inc. - Sakaide Plant (2)
2-4-1 Showamachi, Sakaide, 762-0004, Kagawa, Japan
Tel.: (81) 877463161
Web Site: http://www.mtaqua.co.jp
Water Treatment Chemical Mfr
N.A.I.C.S.: 325998

MT Ethylene Carbonate Co., Ltd. (1)
1-14-1 Nishi-Shimbashi, Minato-ku, Tokyo, 105-8419, Japan
Tel.: (81) 335977359
Ethylene Carbonate Mfr
N.A.I.C.S.: 325998

Nihon Junyaku Co., Ltd. (1)
1-14-1 Nishi-Shinbashi, Minato-ku, Tokyo, 105 8419, Japan
Tel.: (81) 355118211
Web Site: http://www.nihon-junyaku.co.jp
Sales Range: $75-99.9 Million
Emp.: 131
Chemical Products Mfr & Distr
N.A.I.C.S.: 424690

Oita Chemical Co., Ltd. (1)
2 Oaza-Nakanosu, Oita, 870-0111, Japan
Tel.: (81) 975223265
Chemical Products Mfr
N.A.I.C.S.: 325998

TG Corporation (1)
1-14-1 Nishi-Shimbashi, Minato-ku, Tokyo, 105-8419, Japan
Tel.: (81) 335014847
Web Site: http://www.tg-corp.co.jp
Sales Range: $25-49.9 Million
Emp.: 20
Chemical Products Distr
N.A.I.C.S.: 424690
Hideo Kato (Pres)

Taiwan Toagosei Co., Ltd. (1)
Room 602 No 88 Sec 2 Zhongxiao East Road, Zhongzheng District, Taipei, Taiwan
Tel.: (886) 223965658
Web Site: https://toagosei.com.tw
Sales Range: $50-74.9 Million
Emp.: 4
Chemical Products Distr
N.A.I.C.S.: 424690
Kouji Sumita (Gen Mgr)

Toa Business Associe Co., Ltd. (1)
1-14-1 Nishi Shimbashi, Minato ku, Tokyo, 105-8419, Japan
Tel.: (81) 335012538
Real Estate Management & Brokerage Services
N.A.I.C.S.: 531390

Toa Kenso Co., Ltd. (1)
1-42 Funamicho, Minato-ku, Nagoya, 455-0027, Japan
Tel.: (81) 526125916
Construction Materials Distr
N.A.I.C.S.: 444180

Toa Kogyo Co., Ltd. (1)
1-42 Funami cho, Minato ku, Nagoya, 455-0027, Japan
Tel.: (81) 526125700
Web Site: http://www.toagosei.co.jp
Metal Product Mfr & Distr
N.A.I.C.S.: 332999

Toa Logistics Co., Ltd. (1)
17-23 Showacho, Minato-ku, Nagoya, 455-0026, Japan
Tel.: (81) 526117661
Chemical Products Mfr
N.A.I.C.S.: 325998

Toa Techno-Gas Co., Ltd. (1)
6th floor Taiki Seimei Nagoya Building 1-4-6 Nishiki, Naka-ku, Nagoya, 460-0003, Japan
Tel.: (81) 522098840
Sales Range: $25-49.9 Million
Industrial Gases Mfr & Distr
N.A.I.C.S.: 325120

Toa-Jet Chemical Co., Ltd. (1)
No 15 Rong-Kong South Road, Guan-Inn Industrial Distnct, Taoyuan, 328-49, Taiwan
Tel.: (886) 34832953
Chemical Product Mfr & Whslr
N.A.I.C.S.: 325998

Toagosei (Shanghai) Management Co., Ltd. (1)
Rm 1608 16F Metro Plaza No 555 Loushanguan Road, Shanghai, 200051, China
Tel.: (86) 2162293191
Chemical Product Mfr & Distr
N.A.I.C.S.: 325998

Toagosei (Thailand) Co., Ltd. (1)
890/4 Moo 3 Khaokansong, Si Racha, 20110, Chonburi, Thailand
Tel.: (66) 83126031
Chemical Product Mfr & Whslr
N.A.I.C.S.: 325998

Toagosei (Zhangjiagang) New Technology Co., Ltd. (1)
No 509 East Changjiang Road, Yangtze River International Chemical Industrial Park, Zhangjiagang, 215633, Jiangsu, China
Tel.: (86) 51258727220
Web Site: http://www.toagosei-zjg.com
Chemical Product Mfr & Distr
N.A.I.C.S.: 325998

Toagosei (Zhuhai) Limited (1)
3/F No2 Factory Bldg No 2372 Meihua West Road, Xiangzhou Ind Park Of Science Technology Qianshan, Zhuhai, 519070, Guangdong, China
Tel.: (86) 7568508810
Web Site: https://www.toagosei-zh.com
Adhesive Mfr
N.A.I.C.S.: 325520

Toagosei America, Inc. (1)
1450 W Main St, West Jefferson, OH 43162
Tel.: (614) 718-3855
Web Site: http://aronalpha.net
Sales Range: $50-74.9 Million
Emp.: 60
Chemical Products Mfr
N.A.I.C.S.: 424690

Toagosei Co. Ltd. - Hirono Plant (1)
1-16 Iwasawa Oaza-Kamikitasako, Hirono Town, Futaba, 979-0401, Fukushima, Japan
Tel.: (81) 240280111
Chemical Products Mfr
N.A.I.C.S.: 325998

Toagosei Co. Ltd. - Kawasaki Plant (1)
7-4 Ukishimacho, Kawasaki-ku, Kawasaki, 210-0862, Kanagawa, Japan
Tel.: (81) 442772211
Chemical Products Mfr
N.A.I.C.S.: 325998

Toagosei Co. Ltd. - Nagoya Plant (1)
17-23 Showacho, Minato-ku, Nagoya, 455-0026, Aichi, Japan
Tel.: (81) 526119804
Chemical Products Mfr
N.A.I.C.S.: 325998

Toagosei Co. Ltd. - Sakaide Plant (1)
2-4-1 Showacho, Sakaide, 762-0004, Kagawa, Japan
Tel.: (81) 877463161
Chemical Products Mfr
N.A.I.C.S.: 325998

Toagosei Co. Ltd. - Takaoka Plant (1)
2-1-3 Fushiki, Takaoka, 933-0195, Toyama, Japan
Tel.: (81) 766447401
Chemical Products Mfr
N.A.I.C.S.: 325998

Toagosei Co. Ltd. - Tokushima Plant (1)
575-1 Nakashima, Kawauchicho, Tokushima, 771-0188, Japan
Tel.: (81) 886652111
Chemical Products Mfr
N.A.I.C.S.: 325998

Toagosei Co. Ltd. - Yokohama Plant (1)
1-7 Suehirocho, Tsurumi-ku, Yokohama, 230-0045, Kanagawa, Japan
Tel.: (81) 455037300
Chemical Products Mfr
N.A.I.C.S.: 325998

Toagosei Hong Kong Limited (1)
Room 607-9 6th Floor 1 Hung To Road, Kwun Tong, Kowloon, China (Hong Kong)
Tel.: (852) 27631086
Web Site: https://www.toagosei.com.hk
Sales Range: $25-49.9 Million
Emp.: 5
Adhesive Mfr
N.A.I.C.S.: 325520

Toagosei Korea Co., Ltd. (1)
Cambridge BL 19F 110 Teheran-ro, Gangnam-gu, Seoul, 06232, Korea (South)
Tel.: (82) 25672252
Web Site: https://www.toagosei.co.kr
Emp.: 1,339
Chemical Products Mfr
N.A.I.C.S.: 325998

Toagosei Singapore Pte Ltd. (1)
460 Alexandra Road 22-04 mTower, Singapore, 119963, Singapore
Tel.: (65) 62730800
Emp.: 20
Chemical Products Mfr & Distr
N.A.I.C.S.: 424690

Tsurumi Soda Co., Ltd. (1)
1 7 Suehiro cho, Tsurumi ku, Yokohama, 230 0045, Japan
Tel.: (81) 455037300
Web Site: http://www.tsurumi.co.jp
Sales Range: $75-99.9 Million
Emp.: 200
Chemical Products Mfr
N.A.I.C.S.: 424690

TOAMI CORPORATION

1020 Nakanoshinmachi, Shijonawate, 575-0054, Osaka, Japan
Tel.: (81) 728761121
Web Site: https://www.toami.co.jp
Year Founded: 1940
5973—(TKS)
Rev.: $116,521,080
Assets: $128,967,710
Liabilities: $56,317,200
Net Worth: $72,650,510
Earnings: $1,632,670
Emp.: 207
Fiscal Year-end: 03/31/24
Construction Material Mfr & Distr
N.A.I.C.S.: 332618
Yoshihito Kitagawa (Pres)

Subsidiaries:

SMC Toami LLC (1)
124 Ung Van Khiem Street, Ward 25 Binh Thanh, Ho Chi Minh City, Vietnam
Tel.: (84) 2835125555
Web Site: https://www.toami.co.jp
Emp.: 42
Construction Materials Whslr

INTERNATIONAL PUBLIC

N.A.I.C.S.: 423390

Sumikurakouzai Co., Ltd. (1)
2-1-18 Higashino, Kokura Kita-ku, Kitakyushu, 803-0802, Japan
Tel.: (81) 935612483
Web Site: https://www.sk-kouzai.co.jp
Emp.: 40
Construction Machinery Mfr
N.A.I.C.S.: 333120

TOAN MY CORPORATION-JSC

KP Hoa Lan 1, Thuan Giao, Thuan An, Binh Duong, Vietnam
Tel.: (84) 2743747263 VN
Web Site: http://www.toanmy.com
Solar Water Heater Mfr
N.A.I.C.S.: 333414

TOBA PULP LESTARI TBK

Uniplaza East Tower Lantai 3 Jl Letjen Haryono Mt No A-1, Medan, 20231, North Sumatra, Indonesia
Tel.: (62) 614532088
Web Site: https://www.tobapulp.com
INRU—(INDO)
Rev.: $95,656,000
Assets: $480,875,000
Liabilities: $370,743,000
Net Worth: $110,132,000
Earnings: ($25,755,000)
Emp.: 1,232
Fiscal Year-end: 12/31/23
Wood Products Mfr
N.A.I.C.S.: 321999
Vinod Kesavan (Chm)

TOBA, INC.

8-6 Suido 2-chome Bunkyo-ku, Tokyo, 112-0005, Japan
Tel.: (81) 339443221
Web Site: http://www.toba.co.jp
Year Founded: 1906
7472—(TKS)
Rev.: $188,047,890
Assets: $212,339,640
Liabilities: $76,894,130
Net Worth: $135,445,510
Earnings: $7,099,140
Emp.: 262
Fiscal Year-end: 03/31/24
Machinery Tool Mfr & Distr
N.A.I.C.S.: 333515
Shigeyoshi Toba (Pres)

Subsidiaries:

Toba (Shanghai) Trading Co., Ltd. (1)
Rm 921 Yongsheng Building No 2025 Zhongshan Road West, Shanghai, 200235, China
Tel.: (86) 2164812233
Industrial Machinery Distr
N.A.I.C.S.: 423830
Naoyuki Miura (Chm)

Toba (Thailand) Co., Ltd. (1)
No1 MD Tower 8th floor Soi Bangna-trad 25, Bang Na, Bangkok, 10260, Thailand
Tel.: (66) 21864980
Industrial Machinery Distr
N.A.I.C.S.: 423830

TOBAR LTD.

Yare House 62-64 Thorpe Road, Norwich, NR1 1RY, Norfolk, United Kingdom
Tel.: (44) 4618591522
Web Site: http://www.tobar.co.uk
Year Founded: 1973
Sales Range: $10-24.9 Million
Emp.: 100
Electronic Shopping & Mail-Order Services
N.A.I.C.S.: 459420
David Morcecai (CEO)

Subsidiaries:

Letterbox Mail Order Limited (1)
The Old Aerodrome, Beccles, NR34 7SP,

Suffolk, United Kingdom
Tel.: (44) 8445734000
Web Site: http://www.letterbox.co.uk
Electronic Shopping & Mail-Order Services
N.A.I.C.S.: 425120

TOBESOFT CO., LTD.
2-5F Intops Building 617 Bongeunsa-Ro, Gangnam-gu, Seoul, 06083, Korea (South)
Tel.: (82) 221407700
Web Site: https://www.tobesoft.com
Year Founded: 2000
079970—(KRS)
Rev.: $33,145,269
Assets: $80,575,558
Liabilities: $46,088,995
Net Worth: $34,486,564
Earnings: ($12,011,705)
Emp.: 280
Fiscal Year-end: 12/31/22
Software Products Development & Marketing Services
N.A.I.C.S.: 541511
Kyong Lee *(CEO)*

Subsidiaries:

Nexaweb Europe (1)
Herengacht 478, 1017 CB, Amsterdam, Netherlands
Tel.: (31) 202621820
Application Software Development Services
N.A.I.C.S.: 541511

Nexaweb Japan, Inc. (1)
10F Akihabara OS Building 5-3-1 Sotokanda, Chiyoda-ku, Tokyo, 101-0021, Japan
Tel.: (81) 358126358
Web Site: https://www.nexaweb.co.jp
Software Development Services
N.A.I.C.S.: 541511
David U. Moon *(CEO)*

TOBII AB
Karlsrovagen 2D, S 182 53, Danderyd, Sweden
Tel.: (46) 86636990
Web Site: https://www.tobii.com
Year Founded: 2001
TOBII—(OMX)
Rev.: $75,247,683
Assets: $114,062,781
Liabilities: $58,073,740
Net Worth: $55,989,041
Earnings: ($19,655,727)
Emp.: 550
Fiscal Year-end: 12/31/23
Eye Tracking & Eye Control Computer Technology
N.A.I.C.S.: 541519
Henrik Eskilsson *(Founder & CEO)*

Subsidiaries:

Phasya S.A. (1)
Rue du Bois Saint-Jean 29, 4102, Seraing, Belgium
Tel.: (32) 42463537
Web Site: https://www.phasya.com
Psychological Care Services
N.A.I.C.S.: 621330

Tobii Dynavox LLC (1)
2100 Wharton St Ste 400, Pittsburgh, PA 15203
Tel.: (412) 381-4883
Web Site: http://us.tobiidynavox.com
Sales Range: $25-49.9 Million
Emp.: 300
Mfr of Hearing Machines for Disabled
N.A.I.C.S.: 339112

Subsidiary (Domestic):

Mayer-Johnson LLC (2)
2100 Wharton St Ste 400, Pittsburgh, PA 15203
Tel.: (412) 381-4883
Web Site: http://www.mayer-johnson.com
Sales Range: $50-74.9 Million
Emp.: 150
Special Education Software Developer
N.A.I.C.S.: 513210
Fredrik Ruben *(Pres)*

Tobii Technology Inc. (1)
12007 Sunrise Valley Dr Ste 400, Reston, VA 20191
Tel.: (703) 738-1300
Information Technology Services
N.A.I.C.S.: 541511

Tobii Technology Japan Ltd. (1)
3F SG Square 7-7-7 Nishigotanda, Shinagawa-ku, Tokyo, 141-0031, Japan
Tel.: (81) 364203990
Information Technology Services
N.A.I.C.S.: 541511

TOBILA SYSTEMS, INC.
2-5-12 Nishiki Pacific Square Nagoya Nishiki 7F, Naka-Ku, Nagoya, 460-0003, Aichi, Japan
Tel.: (81) 5036122677
Web Site: https://www.tobila.com
Year Founded: 2006
4441—(TKS)
Sales Range: Less than $1 Million
Software Development Services
N.A.I.C.S.: 541511
Atsushi Akita *(Pres & CEO)*

TOBINSNET OIL & GAS LTD.
101 - 6th Avenue SW Suite 1200, Calgary, T2P 3P4, AB, Canada
Tel.: (403) 264-4737
Web Site: https://www.tobinsnet.com
Oil & Gas Dist
N.A.I.C.S.: 333132
Ejovwoke Ann Agbokutaye *(Supvr)*

Subsidiaries:

Dejour Energy (Alberta) Ltd. (1)
505-2nd Street SW Suite 802, Calgary, T2P 1N8, AB, Canada
Tel.: (403) 266-3825
Emp.: 4
Oil & Gas Exlporation Services
N.A.I.C.S.: 211120
Robert Hodgkinson *(CEO)*

TOBISHIMA CORPORATION
1-8-15 Konan, Minato-ku, Tokyo, 108-0075, Japan
Tel.: (81) 364558390   JP
Web Site: https://www.tobishima.co.jp
Year Founded: 1883
1805—(TKS)
Rev.: $872,843,890
Assets: $997,244,090
Liabilities: $674,656,260
Net Worth: $322,587,830
Earnings: $22,507,050
Emp.: 1,425
Fiscal Year-end: 03/31/24
Construction, Engineering & Real Estate Services
N.A.I.C.S.: 236620
Masahiro Norikyo *(Pres & CEO)*

Subsidiaries:

E&CS Co., Ltd. (1)
1-8-15 Konan, Minato-ku, Tokyo, 108-0075, Japan
Tel.: (81) 364558433
Web Site: https://www.kk-ecs.co.jp
Emp.: 23
Construction Engineering Services
N.A.I.C.S.: 541330

NXTField, Inc. (1)
4th Floor Next Site Shibuya Building 2-12-4, Shibuya-ku, Tokyo, 150-0002, Japan
Tel.: (81) 364341502
Web Site: https://nxtfield.co.jp
Information & Communications Technology Services
N.A.I.C.S.: 541430

Tobishima (Brunei) Sdn Bhd (1)
Unit 6 2nd floor Block J, Abdul Razak Complex Gadong, BE 2719, Bandar Seri Begawan, Negara, Brunei Darussalam
Tel.: (673) 2425946
Sales Range: $25-49.9 Million
Emp.: 30
Civil Engineering Services

N.A.I.C.S.: 237990

TOBLER S.A.S.
4 avenue de la Vieille, 95380, Louvres, France
Tel.: (33) 134473314   FR
Web Site: http://www.altifort-tobler.com
Year Founded: 1945
Emp.: 65
Mandrels & Chucks Mfr
N.A.I.C.S.: 333515
Olivier Coreau *(Mng Dir & Dir Gen)*

TOBU RAILWAY CO., LTD.
1-1-2 Oshiage, Sumida-ku, Tokyo, 131-8522, Japan
Tel.: (81) 338412871
Web Site: https://www.tobu.co.jp
Year Founded: 1897
9001—(TKS)
Rev.: $4,898,302,640
Assets: $16,357,796,400
Liabilities: $11,912,556,480
Net Worth: $4,445,239,920
Earnings: $130,225,040
Emp.: 3,531
Fiscal Year-end: 03/31/22
Railway & Bus Services; Station Kiosks, Amusement Parks & Department Stores
N.A.I.C.S.: 485112
Yutaka Tsuzuki *(Pres & CEO)*

Subsidiaries:

ASAHI Motor Corporation (1)
5F 2nd Tobukan 1-33-12 Mukojima, Sumida-ku, Tokyo, 131-0033, Japan
Tel.: (81) 489785021
Web Site: https://www.asahibus.jp
Emp.: 584
Cargo Transportation Services
N.A.I.C.S.: 561613

Asahi Motor Co., Ltd (1)
1119 Fukuroyama, Koshigaya, 343-0032, Saitama Prefecture, Japan
Tel.: (81) 489785021
Web Site: https://www.asahibus.jp
Emp.: 584
Food Transportation Services
N.A.I.C.S.: 488490

Jomo Electric Railway Co., Ltd. (1)
4-1-1 Jotomachi, Maebashi, 371-0016, Gunma, Japan
Tel.: (81) 27 231 3597
Web Site: https://www.jomorailway.com
Rail Transportation Services
N.A.I.C.S.: 488210

Nishi-Ikebukuro Heat Supply Co., Ltd (1)
1-10-10 Nishi Ikebukuro, Toshima-ku, Tokyo, 171-0021, Japan
Tel.: (81) 339853451
Heat Distribution Services
N.A.I.C.S.: 221330

TOBU Bus Co., Ltd. (1)
2-18-12 Oshiage, Sumida-ku, Tokyo, 131-8508, Japan
Tel.: (81) 33 621 0102
Web Site: https://www.tobu-bus.com
Movable & Real Estate Leasing Services
N.A.I.C.S.: 531190

TOBU Utsunomiya Department Store Co., Ltd (1)
5-4 Miyazonocho, Utsunomiya, 320-8560, Tochigi, Japan
Tel.: (81) 286362211
Web Site: https://www.tobu-u-dept.jp
Emp.: 344
General Merchandise Retailer
N.A.I.C.S.: 459999

Tobu Construction Co., Ltd. (1)
138 Okuwacho, Nikko, 321-2492, Tochigi, Japan
Tel.: (81) 288218321
Web Site: https://www.tobukensetsu.co.jp
Emp.: 363
Construction & Civil Engineering Services

N.A.I.C.S.: 532412

Tobu Delivery Co., Ltd. (1)
Logi Square Urawa Misono 2500 Daimon, Midori-ku, Saitama, 336-0963, Japan
Tel.: (81) 486330950
Web Site: http://www.tobu-tdc.co.jp
Emp.: 199
Freight & Cargo Delivery Services
N.A.I.C.S.: 488510

Tobu Department Store Co., Ltd. (1)
1-1-25 Nishi-ikebukuro, Toshima-ku, Tokyo, 171-8512, Japan
Tel.: (81) 339812211
Web Site: https://www.tobu-dept.co.jp
Emp.: 631
Retail Services
N.A.I.C.S.: 455110

Tobu Hotel Management Co., Ltd. (1)
5F Tobu Hotel Levant Tokyo 1-2 2 Kinshi, Sumida-ku, Tokyo, 130-0013, Japan
Tel.: (81) 336260301
Web Site: https://www.tobuhotel.com
Sales Range: $125-149.9 Million
Emp.: 658
Home Management Services
N.A.I.C.S.: 713210

Tobu Kaihatsu Co., Ltd. (1)
658-1 Maruyama Oaza, Oita, Oita Prefecture, Japan
Tel.: (81) 975223111
Web Site: https://www.tobukaihatsu.jp
Emp.: 52
Engineeering Services
N.A.I.C.S.: 541330

Tobu Keibi Support Co., Ltd. (1)
1-4-10 Nishiikebukuro, Toshima-ku, Tokyo, 171-0021, Japan
Tel.: (81) 339898356
Web Site: https://www.tobukeibi.com
Emp.: 64
Building Maintenance & Cleaning Services
N.A.I.C.S.: 561790

Tobu Kogyo Co., Ltd (1)
2-18-12 Oshiage, Sumida-ku, Tokyo, 131-0045, Japan
Tel.: (81) 336255271
Web Site: https://www.tobu-kogyo.com
Home Management Services
N.A.I.C.S.: 721110

Tobu Store Co., Ltd. (1)
3-1-1 Kamiitabashi, Itabashi-ku, Tokyo, 174-0076, Japan   (100%)
Tel.: (81) 359225111
Web Site: https://www.tobustore.co.jp
Emp.: 842
Supermarket & Management Services
N.A.I.C.S.: 459999
Hiroyuki Wada *(Exec Officer)*

Tobu Top Tours Co., Ltd. (1)
1-1-2 Oshiage, Sumida-ku, Tokyo, Japan
Tel.: (81) 353483895
Web Site: http://www.tobutoptours.com
Emp.: 2,280
Travel Services
N.A.I.C.S.: 561510
Nobuaki Sakamaki *(Pres)*

Tobu Transportation Co., Ltd (1)
4-13-25 Kawabata Miyashiro-cho, Minamisaitama-gun, Saitama, 345-0804, Japan
Tel.: (81) 480311311
Web Site: https://www.tobuunyu.co.jp
Freight Transportation Services
N.A.I.C.S.: 488999

Tobu World Square (1)
209-1 Ohara Kinugawa Onsen, Nikko, 321-2593, Tochigi, Japan
Tel.: (81) 288771055
Web Site: https://www.tobuws.co.jp
Emp.: 64
Amusement & Entertainment Services
N.A.I.C.S.: 713110

Tobu Yachida Construction Co., Ltd. (1)
3-44-4 Mukojima, Sumida Ward, Tokyo, 131-8524, Japan
Tel.: (81) 336251011
Web Site: https://www.tobu-yachida.co.jp
Emp.: 182

TOBU RAILWAY CO., LTD.

Tobu Railway Co., Ltd.—(Continued)
Construction Services
N.A.I.C.S.: 236220
Ryokichi Yauchida (Pres)

Tobu Zoological Garden (1)
110 Suga Miyashiro-cho, Minamisaitama-gun, Saitama, 345-0831, Japan
Tel.: (81) 480931200
Web Site: https://www.tobuzoo.com
Emp.: 130
Theme Park Services
N.A.I.C.S.: 713110

Tobu ryokuchi Co., Ltd. (1)
1-26-5 Mukojima, Sumida-ku, Tokyo, 131-0033, Japan
Tel.: (81) 336225621
Web Site: https://www.toburyokuchi.co.jp
Real Estate Agency Services
N.A.I.C.S.: 531210

TOC CO., LTD.
7-22-17 Nishi-Gotanda, Shinagawa-ku, Tokyo, 141-0031, Japan
Tel.: (81) 334942111
Web Site: http://www.toc.co.jp
Year Founded: 1926
T3O—(DEU)
Rev.: $90,656,150
Assets: $783,589,060
Liabilities: $103,975,300
Net Worth: $679,613,760
Earnings: $33,863,030
Emp.: 103
Fiscal Year-end: 03/31/24
Real Estate Manangement Services
N.A.I.C.S.: 531390
Takuo Otani (Pres)

TOCALO CO., LTD.
6-4-4 Minatojimaminami-Machi, Chuo-Ku, Kobe, 650-0047, Japan
Tel.: (81) 783033433
Web Site: https://www.tocalo.co.jp
Year Founded: 1951
3433—(TKS)
Rev.: $308,918,350
Assets: $515,183,400
Liabilities: $119,085,760
Net Worth: $396,097,640
Earnings: $41,814,860
Emp.: 1,389
Fiscal Year-end: 03/31/24
Thermal Spray Equipment Mfr
N.A.I.C.S.: 333517
Noriyuki Mifune (Pres)

Subsidiaries:

Tocalo & Han Tai (Kunshan) Co., Ltd. (1)
No 58 Dongyue Road, Shipai Bacheng City, Kunshan, Jiangsu, China
Tel.: (86) 51236827900
Web Site: https://www.tocalo-hantai-ks.com
Electronic Parts & Other Various Equipment Mfr
N.A.I.C.S.: 334510

Tocalo & Han Tai Co., Ltd. (1)
No 9 Hefeng 2nd Street, Yonghe Town Huangpu District, Guangzhou, 511356, China
Tel.: (86) 2082986789
Web Site: https://www.tocalo-hantai.com.cn
Emp.: 70
Coating Mfr
N.A.I.C.S.: 325510

Tocalo Co., Ltd. - AKASHI No.2 PLANT (1)
22-7 Minamifutami, Futami-Cho, Akashi, 674-0093, Hyogo, Japan
Tel.: (81) 789427871
Thermal Spray Coating Mfr
N.A.I.C.S.: 325510

Tocalo Co., Ltd. - AKASHI No.4 PLANT (1)
11-1 Minamifutami, Futami-Cho, Akashi, 674-0093, Hyogo, Japan
Tel.: (81) 789491256
Thermal Spray Coating Mfr
N.A.I.C.S.: 325510

Tocalo Co., Ltd. - AKASHI PLANT (1)
14-1 Minamifutami, Futami-Cho, Akashi, 674-0093, Hyogo, Japan
Tel.: (81) 789426501
Thermal Spray Coating Mfr
N.A.I.C.S.: 325510

Tocalo Co., Ltd. - KITA-KYUSYU PLANT (1)
1-48 Torigoe-Cho Kanda-Machi, Miyako-Gun, Fukuoka, 800-0304, Japan
Tel.: (81) 934361221
Thermal Spray Coating Mfr
N.A.I.C.S.: 325510
Kazuya Kobayashi (Dir)

Tocalo Co., Ltd. - MIZUSHIMA PLANT (1)
2030-28 Kojimaunotsu, Kurashiki, 711-0935, Okayama, Japan
Tel.: (81) 864703433
Thermal Spray Coating Mfr
N.A.I.C.S.: 325510

Tocalo Co., Ltd. - NAGOYA PLANT (1)
33-3 Nibanwarishimo Nawamachi, Midori-Ku, Tokai, 476-0002, Aichi, Japan
Tel.: (81) 526033520
Thermal Spray Coating Mfr
N.A.I.C.S.: 325510

Tocalo Co., Ltd. - TOKYO PLANT (1)
1-1-1 Gyoda, Funabashi, 273-0044, Chiba, Japan
Tel.: (81) 474395511
Thermal Spray Coating Mfr
N.A.I.C.S.: 325510

TOCVAN VENTURES CORP.
820 - 1130 West Pender St, Vancouver, V6E 4A4, BC, Canada
Tel.: (403) 829-9877
Web Site: https://www.tocvan.com
TCVNF—(OTCQB)
Assets: $2,219,030
Liabilities: $64,450
Net Worth: $2,154,579
Earnings: ($1,126,539)
Fiscal Year-end: 08/31/21
Mineral Exploration Services
N.A.I.C.S.: 213115
Derek Wood (Founder)

Subsidiaries:

Burgencio S.A. de C.V. (1)

TOD'S S.P.A.
Via Filippo Della Valle 1, Sant Elpidio a Mare, 63811, Ascoli Piceno, Italy
Tel.: (39) 07348661 IT
Web Site: https://www.todsgroup.com
Year Founded: 1900
TOD—(ITA)
Rev.: $794,724,094
Assets: $2,536,615,291
Liabilities: $1,299,561,440
Net Worth: $1,237,053,850
Earnings: ($89,894,886)
Emp.: 4,588
Fiscal Year-end: 12/31/20
Footwear, Clothing, Leather Goods & Related Accessories Mfr, Designer & Marketer
N.A.I.C.S.: 315990
Diego Della Valle (CEO)

Subsidiaries:

Del.Com S.r.l. (1)
Contrada Lecco 3, Rende, 87036, Cosenza, Italy
Tel.: (39) 0984403818
Leather Goods Mfr & Distr
N.A.I.C.S.: 316990

Deva Inc. (1)
2651 Dow Ave, Tustin, CA 92780
Tel.: (714) 368-1717
Web Site: https://www.devainc.com
Electronic Related Product Distr
N.A.I.C.S.: 423690

TOD'S Austria GmbH (1)
Graben 17, 1010, Vienna, Austria
Tel.: (43) 153220060
Jean Apparel Mfr
N.A.I.C.S.: 315250

TODS France Sas (1)
Rue du Faubourg st, 75008, Paris, France
Tel.: (33) 153431616
Web Site: http://www.tods.com
Leather Goods Distr
N.A.I.C.S.: 424990

Tod's Deutschland GmbH (1)
Domagk strasse 1 B, 80807, Munich, Germany (100%)
Tel.: (49) 892080770
Web Site: http://www.tods.com
Sales Range: $25-49.9 Million
Emp.: 15
Shoes, Clothing & Accessories Retailer
N.A.I.C.S.: 458210

Tod's International BV (1)
De Bijenkorf 3rd Floor Woman Shoes Dam 1 1012, 1101 BA, Amsterdam, Netherlands (100%)
Tel.: (31) 631642266
Web Site: http://www.tods.com
Holding Company; Administrative Services
N.A.I.C.S.: 551112

Subsidiary (Non-US):

Gen.Del. SA (2)
Boutique Tods Bahnhofstrasse 32, 8001, Zurich, Switzerland
Tel.: (41) 434228422
Web Site: http://www.tods.com
Sales Range: $25-49.9 Million
Emp.: 10
Leather Goods Retailer
N.A.I.C.S.: 458320

TOD'S Espana SL (2)
Calle Jose Ortega Y Gasset 17, 28006, Madrid, Spain
Tel.: (34) 915776343
Web Site: http://www.tods.com
Sales Range: $25-49.9 Million
Emp.: 7
Leather Goods Whslr
N.A.I.C.S.: 424990

TOD'S Japan KK (2)
5-1-5 Jingumae, Shibuya-Ku, Tokyo, 150-0001, Japan
Tel.: (81) 364192350
Web Site: http://www.tods.com
Leather Goods Distr
N.A.I.C.S.: 424990

Tod's Belgique S.p.r.l. (2)
46 Blvd de Waterloo, 1000, Brussels, Belgium (100%)
Tel.: (32) 25133005
Web Site: http://www.tods.com
Sales Range: $25-49.9 Million
Emp.: 8
Shoes, Clothing & Accessories Retailer
N.A.I.C.S.: 458210

Tod's Hong Kong Limited (2)
Room 3501 35/f Lee Garden One 33 Hysan Avenue, Causeway Bay, China (Hong Kong)
Tel.: (852) 28109080
Web Site: http://www.tods.com
Shoe Retailer
N.A.I.C.S.: 458210

Tod's Massachussets Inc. (1)
100 Huntington Ave Space D015B, Boston, MA 02116
Tel.: (617) 236-5091
Jean Apparel Mfr
N.A.I.C.S.: 315250

TODA CORPORATION
2-8-5 Hatchobori, Chuo-ku, Tokyo, 104-0032, Japan
Tel.: (81) 335352094 JP
Web Site: https://www.toda.co.jp
Year Founded: 1881
1860—(TKS)
Rev.: $3,453,288,740

INTERNATIONAL PUBLIC

Assets: $5,764,316,600
Liabilities: $3,414,302,960
Net Worth: $2,350,013,640
Earnings: $106,427,610
Emp.: 1,988
Fiscal Year-end: 03/31/24
Construction of Industrial, Commercial & Residential Buildings; Civil Engineering; Real Estate
N.A.I.C.S.: 236210
Masanori Imai (Chm)

Subsidiaries:

Chiyoda Kenkou Co., Ltd. (1)
6th Floor Yasaka Hatchobori Building 2-19-6 Hatchobori, Chuo-ku, Tokyo, 104-0032, Japan
Tel.: (81) 351172771
Web Site: http://www.chiyodakenkou.co.jp
Construction Material Distr & Engineering Services
N.A.I.C.S.: 423390

Chiyoda Staff Service Co., Ltd (1)
2-9-2 Higashinihombashi Kosei Building 3 F, Chuo-ku, Tokyo, 103-0004, Japan
Tel.: (81) 338652207
Web Site: http://www.chiyoda-staff.com
Human Resource Consulting Services
N.A.I.C.S.: 561311

Chiyoda Tochi Tatemono Co., Ltd., (1)
3-1-11 Higashiyama Sun Sara Higashiyama 3 F, Meguro-ku, Tokyo, 153-0043, Japan
Tel.: (81) 357047451
Real Estate Manangement Services
N.A.I.C.S.: 531390

Construtora Toda do Brasil S.A. (1)
Rua Manuel da Nobrega 1280-3 Andar, Jardim Paulista, Sao Paulo, 04001-902, Brazil
Tel.: (55) 1138865844
Web Site: http://www.toda.com.br
Sales Range: $100-124.9 Million
Emp.: 400
Civil Engineering & Construction; Real Estate Development
N.A.I.C.S.: 237990

P.T. Toda Group Indonesia (1)
Sampoerna Strategic Square South Tower 28Floor, Jl Jend Sudirman Kav 45-46, Jakarta, 12930, Indonesia
Tel.: (62) 212527897
Real Estate Lending Services
N.A.I.C.S.: 531110

Sato Kogyo Co., Ltd. (1)
4-12-19 Nihonbashi Honcho, Chuo-Ku, Tokyo, 103-8639, Japan
Tel.: (81) 336610502
Web Site: https://www.satokogyo.co.jp
Emp.: 1,557
General Contractors
N.A.I.C.S.: 236220

Subsidiary (Non-US):

Kedah Sato Sdn. Bhd. (2)
No 131 Ground Floor Taman Tunku Hosna Jalan Tanjung Bendahara, Aras, Alor Setar, 05300, Kedah Darul Aman, Malaysia
Tel.: (60) 47318322
Web Site: https://ecq.bdb.com.my
Sales Range: $25-49.9 Million
Emp.: 23
General Contractors-Non-Residential Buildings, other than Industrial Buildings & Warehouses
N.A.I.C.S.: 236220
Mohd Sobri Hussein (Gen Mgr)

Sato Amoy Construction (Malaysia) (2)
405 Level 4 Uptown 2,2 Jalan SS21/37, Petaling Jaya, 47400, Malaysia
Tel.: (60) 377288000
Web Site: http://www.satoamoy.com
Sales Range: $25-49.9 Million
Emp.: 30
General Contractors
N.A.I.C.S.: 236220

Sato Kogyo (Cambodia) Co., Ltd. (2)
PPSEZ Trapaingkol Village National Road

No 4, Sangkat Kantouk Khan Kambol,
Phnom Penh, 5384418, Cambodia
Tel.: (855) 23729343
Web Site: https://www.satokogyo.com.kh
Construction Engineering Services
N.A.I.C.S.: 541330

Sato Kogyo (M) Sdn. Bhd. (2)
405 Level 4 Uptown 2 No 2 Jalan SS 21/37
Damansara Uptown, 47400, Petaling Jaya,
Selangor Darul Ehsan, Malaysia
Tel.: (60) 377288000
Web Site: https://www.satokogyo.com.my
Sales Range: $1-9.9 Million
Emp.: 150
General Contractor Services
N.A.I.C.S.: 236220

Sato Kogyo (Singapore) Pte.Ltd. (2)
149 Rochor Road 04-14/15 Fu Lu Shou
Complex, Singapore, 188425, Singapore
Tel.: (65) 63367333
Web Site: https://www.satokogyo.com.sg
Emp.: 300
Construction Engineering Services
N.A.I.C.S.: 541330
Hajime Matsui (Gen Mgr-Fin & Admin Div)

Sato Kogyo (Xi'an) Co., Ltd. (2)
38 Gao Xin 6 Road Block A 01-106 Ascendas Building, Xi'an, 710054, China
Tel.: (86) 29 8833 9187
Web Site: http://www.satokogyo.com.cn
Construction Engineering Services
N.A.I.C.S.: 541330
Ito Makoto (Gen Mgr)

Sato Kogyo Bangkok Co., Ltd. (2)
25 Bangkok Insurance/YWCA Building 20th
Floor South Sathorn Road, Khwang Tungmahamek Khet Sathorn, Bangkok, 10120,
Thailand
Tel.: (66) 26774146
Web Site: https://www.satobkk.co.th
Sales Range: $75-99.9 Million
General Contractor & Engineering Services
N.A.I.C.S.: 236220
Kazuo Ogihara (Gen Mgr)

Showa Construction Co., Ltd. (1)
743-2 Kokubuncho, Kurume, 839-0863, Fukuoka, Japan
Tel.: (81) 942213311
Web Site: https://www.showacr.co.jp
Construction & Civil Engineering Services
N.A.I.C.S.: 532412

Sipco Industries Co., Ltd (1)
107-7717 Beedie Way, Delta, V4G 0A5,
BC, Canada
Tel.: (604) 940-9922
Web Site: http://www.sipcobio.com
Medical Detergents Mfr & Distr
N.A.I.C.S.: 325998
Sheila Oakes (Pres & CEO)

Thai Toda Corporation Ltd. (1)
199 Column Tower 20th Fl Ratchadapisek
Rd, Klongtoey, Bangkok, 10110, Thailand
Tel.: (66) 22616544
Web Site: https://www.thaitoda.co.th
Emp.: 145
Civil Engineering & Construction; Real Estate Development
N.A.I.C.S.: 237990
Kazuyoshi Nitahara (Mng Dir)

Toda America, Inc. (1)
4750 W Dickman Rd, Battle Creek, MI
49037
Tel.: (269) 962-0353
Web Site: http://www.todaamerica.com
Sales Range: $25-49.9 Million
Emp.: 3
Civil Engineering & Construction; Real Estate Development
N.A.I.C.S.: 236220

Toda Bldg. Partners Co., Ltd. (1)
5F TFT Building West Building 3-4-10 Ariake, Koto-ku, Tokyo, 135-8072, Japan
Tel.: (81) 335278211
Web Site: https://bp.toda.co.jp
Construction & Building Management Services
N.A.I.C.S.: 532412

Toda Construction (Shanghai) Co., Ltd. (1)
6A 9 Joy Tower 9 Zhenning Road, Changning District, Shanghai, 200050, China
Tel.: (86) 2162520777
Web Site: http://www.toda.co.jp
Sales Range: $25-49.9 Million
Emp.: 30
Civil Engineering & Construction; Real Estate Development
N.A.I.C.S.: 237990
Satoru Kikuchi (Pres)

Toda Finance Co., Ltd (1)
1-8-13 Kyobashi 1 Chome, Chuo-ku, Tokyo,
104-0031, Japan
Tel.: (81) 335353793
Real Estate Manangement Services
N.A.I.C.S.: 531390

Toda Reform Co., Ltd. (1)
1-8-14 Kyobashi Todakensetsu kabu kyobashidaiichibekkan, Chuo-ku, Tokyo, 104-0031, Japan
Tel.: (81) 335628571
Web Site: http://www.toda-reform.jp
Sales Range: $25-49.9 Million
Emp.: 42
Real Estate Manangement Services
N.A.I.C.S.: 531390

Toda Road Co., Ltd (1)
2-13-6 Kakigara- cho Nihonbashi, Chuo-ku,
Tokyo, 103-0014, Japan (100%)
Tel.: (81) 336698051
Web Site: https://www.toda-road.co.jp
Emp.: 108
Road Construction Services
N.A.I.C.S.: 488490

Toda Staff Service Co., Ltd. (1)
4F MG Kodenmacho Building 7-10 Nihonbashi Kodenmacho, Chuo-ku, Tokyo, 103-0001, Japan
Tel.: (81) 362648991
Web Site: https://www.toda-staff.co.jp
Human Resource Consulting Services
N.A.I.C.S.: 541612

Toda Vietnam Co., Ltd. (1)
33ter-33bis Mac Dinh Chi Street 10th Floor
Star Building, Da Kao Ward District 1, Ho
Chi Minh City, Vietnam
Tel.: (84) 2862914127
Sales Range: $25-49.9 Million
Emp.: 20
Civil Engineering, Construction & Real Estate Developments
N.A.I.C.S.: 237990
Katsuharo Tsuchayi (Pres)

Towa Kanko Kaihatsu Co., Ltd (1)
5-9 Tanakamachi Toda Building 7 F, Naka-Ku, Hiroshima, 730-0026, Japan
Tel.: (81) 825457630
Emp.: 50
Real Estate Manangement Services
N.A.I.C.S.: 531390
Ehiaroyuki Ito (Pres)

Yachiyo Urban Co., Ltd. (1)
1-8-13 Kyobashi, Chuo-ku, Tokyo, 104-0031, Japan
Tel.: (81) 335679119
Real Estate Manangement Services
N.A.I.C.S.: 531390

TODA INTERNATIONAL HOLDINGS INC.
No 18-2-401 Gangjing Garden Dandong Street, Zhongshan District, Dalian, 116001, Liaoning, China
Tel.: (86) 411 8278 9758 Ky
Year Founded: 2006
Sales Range: $25-49.9 Million
Emp.: 84
Holding Company
N.A.I.C.S.: 551112
Chuan-Tao Zheng (Chm, Pres & CEO)

TODAK PJSC
5/7 Kurenivska str, Kiev, 04073, Ukraine
Tel.: (380) 44 230 87 83
Web Site: http://www.todak.com.ua
Industrial Machinery Mfr
N.A.I.C.S.: 811310

TODD RIVER RESOURCES LIMITED
Unit 4 24 Parkland Road, Osborne Park, 6017, WA, Australia
Tel.: (61) 861660255
Web Site: http://www.trrltd.com.au
TRT—(ASX)
Rev.: $76,342
Assets: $11,210,122
Liabilities: $1,038,393
Net Worth: $10,171,729
Earnings: ($3,289,937)
Fiscal Year-end: 06/30/24
Mineral Exploration Services
N.A.I.C.S.: 213113
Simon Robertson (Sec)

TODO SEISAKUSHO LTD.
Ste 24 Hase-Bldg., 391, Osaka-cho, Karasuma Gojyo, Shimogyo-Ku, Kyoto, 600-8177, Japan
Tel.: (81) 753710701
Web Site: http://www.todo-ltd.co.jp
Sales Range: $10-24.9 Million
Emp.: 100
Semiconductor Technology
N.A.I.C.S.: 334413
Toshiyuki Todo (Pres)

TODOROFF AD-SOFIA
Bul Todor Aleksandrov 137 et 6 ofis A16, Sofia, 1309, Bulgaria
Tel.: (359) 2 850 4666
Web Site: http://www.todoroff-wines.com
Wineries Mfr
N.A.I.C.S.: 312130
Ivan Dimitrov Todorov (Chm & CEO)

TODOS MEDICAL LTD.
121 Derech Menachem Begin 30th Floor, Tel Aviv, 6701203, Israel
Tel.: (972) 732077259
Web Site: https://www.todosmedical.com
Year Founded: 2010
TOMDF—(OTCIQ)
Rev.: $7,695,000
Assets: $15,267,000
Liabilities: $50,778,000
Net Worth: ($35,511,000)
Earnings: ($24,994,000)
Fiscal Year-end: 12/31/22
Biotechnology Research & Development Services
N.A.I.C.S.: 541714
Philippe J. Goix (Chief Comml Officer)

TOEBOX KOREA, LTD.
609 Building A 178 Digital-ro, Geumcheon-gu, Seoul, Korea (South)
Tel.: (82) 261013639
Web Site: https://www.toebox.co.kr
Year Founded: 2015
215480—(KRS)
Rev.: $39,295,611
Assets: $31,892,102
Liabilities: $6,898,190
Net Worth: $24,993,913
Earnings: $3,186,462
Emp.: 33
Fiscal Year-end: 12/31/22
Financial Investment Management Services
N.A.I.C.S.: 523940
Sun-Gen Lee (CEO)

TOEI ANIMATION CO., LTD.
5F Nakano Central Park East 4-10-1 Nakano, Nakano-ku, Tokyo, 164-0001, Japan
Tel.: (81) 353180678
Web Site: https://corp.toei-anim.co.jp
Year Founded: 1948
4816—(TKS)
Rev.: $586,002,940
Assets: $1,075,704,790
Liabilities: $205,081,860
Net Worth: $870,622,930
Earnings: $124,234,950
Emp.: 911
Fiscal Year-end: 03/31/24
Animation Picture Producer
N.A.I.C.S.: 512110
Katsuhiro Takagi (Pres)

Subsidiaries:

TAVAC CO., LTD. (1)
Sato Bldg 1-5-2 Kita-Shinjuku, Shinjuku-Ku, Tokyo, 169-0074, Japan
Tel.: (81) 359473015
Web Site: https://www.toei-anim.co.jp
Motion Picture Production Services
N.A.I.C.S.: 512191

TOEI ANIMATION EUROPE S.A.S (1)
5 rue Greffulhe, 75008, Paris, France
Tel.: (33) 145482882
Web Site: https://www.toei-animation.com
Motion Picture Production Services
N.A.I.C.S.: 512191

TOEI ANIMATION INCORPORATED (1)
11150 W Olympic Blvd Ste 1150, Los Angeles, CA 90064
Tel.: (310) 996-2240
Web Site: http://www.toei-anim.com
Emp.: 5
Motion Picture Production Services
N.A.I.C.S.: 512191
Osamu Honma (Mgr-Production)

TOEI ANIMATION MUSIC PUBLISHING CO., LTD. (1)
5F Nakano Central Park East 4-10-1 Nakano, Nakano-ku, Tokyo, 164-0001, Japan
Tel.: (81) 353180695
Web Site: https://corp.toei-anim.co.jp
Music Publishing Services
N.A.I.C.S.: 512230

TOEI ANIMATION PHILS., INC. (1)
9th floor Cyber One Building Eastwoodcity Cyberpark E Rodriguez Jr, Avenue Bagumbayan, Quezon City, Philippines
Tel.: (63) 26871720
Emp.: 160
Motion Picture Production Services
N.A.I.C.S.: 512191

TOEI CO., LTD.
2-17 3-chome Ginza, Chuo-ku, Tokyo, 104-8108, Japan
Tel.: (81) 335354641 JP
Web Site: https://www.toei.co.jp
Year Founded: 1949
9605—(TKS)
Rev.: $1,132,590,450
Assets: $2,719,393,660
Liabilities: $629,113,360
Net Worth: $2,090,280,300
Earnings: $92,348,310
Emp.: 382
Fiscal Year-end: 03/31/24
Motion Pictures, Television Programs & Animation; Theatres, Hotels & Theme Parks Owner & Operator; Cable Television Channel Operator
N.A.I.C.S.: 512110
Noriyuki Tada (Chm)

Subsidiaries:

Amazonlaterna Co., Ltd. (1)
3-50-11 Sendagaya Myojo Building 4F, Shibuya-ku, Tokyo, 151-8507, Japan
Tel.: (81) 357705600
Web Site: https://www.amalate.co.jp
Emp.: 70
Film Production Services
N.A.I.C.S.: 512110

Sanei Electric Inc. (1)
2-51-13 Ikebukuro, Toshima-ku, Tokyo, 171-0014, Japan
Tel.: (81) 339860646
Web Site: https://www.sanei-elec.co.jp

TOEI CO., LTD.

Toei Co., Ltd.—(Continued)
Laser Printer Mfr
N.A.I.C.S.: 334118

Tes-Service Co., Ltd.
3rd Floor Fukuoka Toei Hotel 1-1-23 Takasago, Chuo-ku, Fukuoka, 810-0011, Japan
Tel.: (81) 925321086
Web Site: https://www.tes-service.co.jp
Emp.: 59
Machinery & Equipment Maintenance Services
N.A.I.C.S.: 811310

Toei Advertising, Ltd. (1)
Kyobashi Daiichi Seimei building 7F 2-4-12 Kyobashi, Chuo-ku, Tokyo, 104-0031, Japan
Tel.: (81) 332712821
Web Site: http://www.toeiad.co.jp
Advertising Services
N.A.I.C.S.: 541810
Takaaki Murayama (Mng Dir)

Toei Commercial Film Co., Ltd. (1)
11th Floor Tsukiji Hamarikyu Building 5-3-3 Tsukiji, Chuo-ku, Tokyo, 104-0045, Japan
Tel.: (81) 335421811
Web Site: https://toei-cm.co.jp
Film & Television Production Services
N.A.I.C.S.: 512110

Toei Digital Labo Tech Co., Ltd. (1)
2-34-5 Higashi - Oizumi, Nerima-ku, Tokyo, 178-8666, Japan
Tel.: (81) 338675009
Web Site: https://www.toeilab.co.jp
Film Production Services
N.A.I.C.S.: 512110

Toei Foods Co., Ltd. (1)
3-2-17 Toei Kaikan 3rd floor Ginza, Chuo-ku, Tokyo, 104-8108, Japan
Tel.: (81) 335630881
Web Site: https://www.toeifoods.com
Food Products Mfr
N.A.I.C.S.: 311999

Toei Hotel Chain Co., Ltd. (1)
1-1-23 Takasago, Chuo-ku, Fukuoka, 810-0011, Japan
Tel.: (81) 925242121
Web Site: https://www.toei-hotels.jp
Hotel Operator
N.A.I.C.S.: 721110

Toei Kenko Co., Ltd. (1)
111 Tomizawacho 11-1 Nihonbashi Tomizawacho, Chuo-ku, Tokyo, 103-0006, Japan
Tel.: (81) 356142311
Web Site: https://www.toei-kenko.com
Emp.: 53
Construction Services
N.A.I.C.S.: 236220

Toei Kyoto Studio Co., Ltd. (1)
10 Uzumasa Higashihachiokacho, Ukyo-ku, Kyoto, 616-8586, Japan
Tel.: (81) 570064349
Web Site: https://www.toei-eigamura.com
Film Production Services
N.A.I.C.S.: 512110
Yamaguchi Kihiro (Pres)

Toei Labo Tech Co., Ltd. (1)
8-9-1 Kokuryo- cho, Chofu, 182-0022, Tokyo, Japan
Tel.: (81) 334303331
Web Site: https://www.toeilab.co.jp
Emp.: 160
Film Production Services
N.A.I.C.S.: 512110

Toei Music Publishing Co., Ltd. (1)
Deux Mille Un GINZA BLDG 3F 5-15 1 - CHOME GINZA, Chuo-ku, Tokyo, 104-0061, Japan
Tel.: (81) 335642131
Web Site: https://www.toeimusic.co.jp
Film Production Services
N.A.I.C.S.: 512110

Toei Video Company, Ltd. (1)
10th Floor Konwa Building 1-12-22 Tsukiji, Chuo-ku, Tokyo, 104-0045, Japan
Tel.: (81) 335454511
Web Site: https://www.toei-video.co.jp
Emp.: 63
Film Production Services

N.A.I.C.S.: 512110

TOEI REEFER LINE LTD.
8F Shiba Koen Bldg 3-5-5 Shiba, Minato-Ku, Tokyo, 105-0014, Japan
Tel.: (81) 354762085
Web Site: http://www.toeireefer.co.jp
Year Founded: 1959
Sales Range: $50-74.9 Million
Emp.: 154
Marine Transportation Services
N.A.I.C.S.: 488390
Hirofumi Kawai (Pres)

TOELL CO., LTD.
1-5-21 Takada-Nishi, Kohoku-ku, Yokohama, 223-8510, Kanagawa, Japan
Tel.: (81) 455927777
Web Site: https://www.toell.co.jp
Year Founded: 1963
3361—(TKS)
Rev.: $179,144,220
Assets: $184,987,460
Liabilities: $43,540,070
Net Worth: $141,447,390
Earnings: $14,396,580
Emp.: 455
Fiscal Year-end: 04/30/24
Gas Distr & Mfr
N.A.I.C.S.: 221210
Michi Nakata (Chm & CEO)

TOENEC CORPORATION
20-31 Sakae 1-chome, Naka-ku, Nagoya, 460-0008, Aichi, Japan
Tel.: (81) 522211111
Web Site: https://www.toenec.co.jp
Year Founded: 1944
1946—(TKS)
Rev.: $1,671,424,430
Assets: $2,015,593,910
Liabilities: $1,148,758,510
Net Worth: $866,835,400
Earnings: $61,770,450
Emp.: 4,868
Fiscal Year-end: 03/31/24
Electric Equipment Mfr
N.A.I.C.S.: 335999
Isao Takagi (Exec Officer & Exec VP)

Subsidiaries:

FILLTECH CORPORATION (1)
1-32 Chitose 3-chome, Minato-ku, Nagoya, 455-0011, Aichi, Japan
Tel.: (81) 526529938
Electric Equipment Mfr
N.A.I.C.S.: 334515
Mitsuo Hashimoto (Pres)

TOENEC (THAILAND) CO., LTD. (1)
Room 1402 Bangkok Tower 2170 New Petchburi Road, Bangkapi Huaykwang, Bangkok, 10310, Thailand
Tel.: (66) 23080320
Electric Equipment Mfr
N.A.I.C.S.: 334515
Hiroyuki Kawata (Mng Dir)

TOENEC CONSTRUCTION (SHANGHAI) CO., LTD. (1)
Room No 604 Changfa Building No 128 Weihai Road, Huang Pu District, Shanghai, 200003, China
Tel.: (86) 2163581878
Electric Equipment Mfr
N.A.I.C.S.: 334515
Toshiyuki Maeshima (Pres)

TOENEC PHILIPPINES INC. (1)
4F Valderrama Building 107 Esteban Street, Legaspi Village, Makati, 1229, Philippines
Tel.: (63) 276216800
Web Site: https://www.toenec.co.jp
Electric Equipment Mfr
N.A.I.C.S.: 334515

Toenec Corporation (1)
2F No 62 Quyun Rd, Banqiao Dist, New Taipei City, 220, Taiwan
Tel.: (886) 229620720

Construction Engineering Services
N.A.I.C.S.: 237990

Toenec Corporation (1)
128 Lion Star Building room 104 St Russian Federation Blvd 110, Sangkat Toek Laak 1 Khan Toul Kork, Phnom Penh, Cambodia
Tel.: (855) 15861282
Construction Engineering Services
N.A.I.C.S.: 237990

Toenec Corporation (1)
Room 909 La Pyatt Wun Plaza No 37 Alanpya Pagoda Road, Dagon Township, Yangon, Myanmar
Tel.: (95) 1393189
Construction Engineering Services
N.A.I.C.S.: 237990

Toenec Service Corporation (1)
22-20 Nishiki 3-chome, Naka-ku, Nagoya, 460-0003, Aichi, Japan
Tel.: (81) 529576950
Electric Equipment Mfr
N.A.I.C.S.: 334515
Michio Tomita (Pres)

TOFANE GLOBAL SAS
112 avenue Kleber, 75116, Paris, France
Tel.: (33) 186957816 FR
Web Site: http://www.tofaneglobal.com
Year Founded: 2017
Telecommunication & Digital Services
N.A.I.C.S.: 517810
Alexander Pebereau (CEO)

Subsidiaries:

Altice France SA
10 rue Albert Einstein, 77420, Champs-sur-Marne, France
Tel.: (33) 1 7001 7001
Rev.: $13,075,839,760
Assets: $35,671,072,940
Liabilities: $32,267,952,680
Net Worth: $3,403,120,260
Earnings: $(856,469,900)
Emp.: 16,671
Fiscal Year-end: 12/31/2017
Fiber-Optic Telecommunication Services
N.A.I.C.S.: 335921

Subsidiary (Domestic):

Societe Francaise du Radiotelephone S.A. (2)
1 Square Bela Bartok, 75015, Paris, France (77.75%)
Tel.: (33) 185060000
Web Site: http://www.sfr.fr
Sales Range: $1-4.9 Billion
Wireless Telecommunication Services
N.A.I.C.S.: 517112
Jean-Pascal Van Overbeke (Exec Dir-Consumer)

Subsidiary (Domestic):

5 sur 5 S.A. (3)
Immeuble Antares 2 Rue Blaise Pascal Jardin d entreprises, BP 30099, 28002, Chartres, Cedex, France
Tel.: (33) 2 37 88 58 88
Web Site: http://www.5sur5.fr
Telecommunication Services
N.A.I.C.S.: 517810

La Poste Telecom (3)
855 Avenue Roger Salengro, Chaville, 92370, France
Tel.: (33) 147054709
Web Site: http://www.lapostemobile.fr
Telecommunication Services
N.A.I.C.S.: 517810

iBasis, Inc. (1)
Building 3 10 Maguire Rd, Lexington, MA 02421
Tel.: (781) 505-7500
Web Site: https://www.ibasis.com
Internet-Based Telecommunications Services
N.A.I.C.S.: 517121
Feddo Hazewindus (CEO)

Subsidiary (Non-US):

iBasis Europe Ltd. (2)

INTERNATIONAL PUBLIC

2 Honey Lane 3rd Floor, London, EC2V 8BT, United Kingdom
Tel.: (44) 2076009692
Web Site: http://www.ibasis.net
Sales Range: $25-49.9 Million
Emp.: 20
Internet-Based Telecommunications Services
N.A.I.C.S.: 517121

TOGAMI ELECTRIC MFG. CO., LTD.
1-1 Ohtakara-Kitamachi, Saga, 840-0802, Japan
Tel.: (81) 952244111
Web Site: https://www.togami-elec.co.jp
Year Founded: 1925
6643—(TKS)
Rev.: $176,691,910
Assets: $207,540,780
Liabilities: $68,063,170
Net Worth: $139,477,610
Earnings: $13,814,900
Emp.: 455
Fiscal Year-end: 03/31/24
Electric Equipment Mfr
N.A.I.C.S.: 335999
Shinichi Togami (Pres & CEO)

Subsidiaries:

Sankyo Manufacturing Co., Ltd. (1)
5-9-15 Ohtakara, Saga, 840-0811, Saga Prefecture, Japan
Tel.: (81) 952231739
Web Site: http://www.togami-sankyo.co.jp
Spring Product Mfr
N.A.I.C.S.: 332613

Togami Control Co., Ltd. (1)
3144-1 Shimoizumi Kuboizumi-cho, Second Factory 2028-1 Shimoizumi, Saga, 849-0903, Japan
Tel.: (81) 952373022
Web Site: https://www.togami-control.co.jp
Emp.: 169
Electric Equipment Mfr
N.A.I.C.S.: 335999

Togami Denso Co., Ltd. (1)
5-7-25 Ozai, Saga, 840-0811, Saga Prefecture, Japan
Tel.: (81) 952254151
Web Site: https://www.togami-denso.co.jp
Emp.: 130
Electric Equipment Mfr
N.A.I.C.S.: 335999

Togami Electrical Soft Co., Ltd. (1)
1-1 Ozaikita-cho, Saga, 840-0802, Japan
Tel.: (81) 952234262
Web Site: https://www.togami-soft.co.jp
Emp.: 19
Computer Software Mfr & Distr
N.A.I.C.S.: 334118

Togami Kasei Co., Ltd. (1)
2778-1 Shimoiwazumi, Kuboizumi-cho, Saga, 849-0903, Japan
Tel.: (81) 952982821
Web Site: https://www.togami-kasei.jp
Mold Product Mfr
N.A.I.C.S.: 333511

Togami Metalix Co., Ltd. (1)
3200-1 Shimoizumi, Kuboizumi-cho, Saga, 849-0903, Saga Prefecture, Japan
Tel.: (81) 952982131
Web Site: https://www.togami-metalix.jp
Emp.: 177
Electrical Equipment Mfr & Retailer
N.A.I.C.S.: 335999

Tokyo Togami Electric Sales Co., Ltd. (1)
Togami Building 4-1-13 Aobadai, Meguro-ku, Tokyo, 153-0042, Japan
Tel.: (81) 334653111
Web Site: https://www.tokyo-togami.jp
Measuring Equipment Distr
N.A.I.C.S.: 423830

TOGETHER PHARMA LTD.
HaTidhar Street 17, Ra'anana, 43665, Israel

Tel.: (972) 97733045
Web Site: http://www.together-pharma.com
TGTR—(TAE)
Rev.: $25,143,251
Assets: $38,277,386
Liabilities: $38,982,179
Net Worth: ($704,793)
Earnings: ($700,097)
Fiscal Year-end: 12/31/23
Medicinal & Botanical Manufacturing
N.A.I.C.S.: 325411

TOGGLE3D.AI INC.
Royal Bank Plaza, PO Box 64039, Toronto, M5J 2T6, ON, Canada
Tel.: (631) 655-6733 ON
Web Site: https://www.toggle3d.com
Year Founded: 2023
TGGLF—(OTCQB)
Emp.: 10
Software Development Services
N.A.I.C.S.: 541511

TOGO TELECOM
Place de la Reconciliation quartier Atchante, PO Box 333, Lome, Togo
Tel.: (228) 22 21 44 01
Web Site: http://www.togotelecom.tg
Sales Range: $150-199.9 Million
Emp.: 900
Telecommunication Servicesb
N.A.I.C.S.: 517111
Petchetibadi Bikassam *(CEO)*

TOHAN CORPORATION
6-24 Higashigokencho Shinjuku-ku, Tokyo, 162-8710, Japan
Tel.: (81) 0332696111 JP
Web Site: https://www.tohan.jp
Year Founded: 1949
Books Publishing Services
N.A.I.C.S.: 513130

Subsidiaries:

Japan Publications Trading Co., Ltd (1)
Sarugaku-cho SS Building 3F 1-5-15 Kanda Sarugaku-cho, Chiyoda-ku, Tokyo, 101-0064, Japan (64.84%)
Tel.: (81) 332923751
Web Site: https://www.jptco.co.jp
Rev.: $56,541,940
Assets: $48,424,860
Liabilities: $32,144,430
Net Worth: $16,280,430
Earnings: $2,075,540
Emp.: 119
Fiscal Year-end: 03/31/2024
Book Periodical & Newspaper Whslr
N.A.I.C.S.: 424920
Toyohiko Ayamori *(Pres)*

Subsidiary (Non-US):

Culture Japon S.A.S. (2)
101 bis quai Branly, 75015, Paris, France
Tel.: (33) 1 4579 0200
Web Site: http://www.boutiqueculturejapon.fr
Emp.: 3
Language Learning Materials, Books, Magazines & Art Craft Sales
N.A.I.C.S.: 459210
Anil Prabhakaran *(Gen Mgr)*

Subsidiary (US):

Hakubundo, Inc. (2)
98-029 Hekaha St, Aiea, HI 96701
Tel.: (808) 379-2545
Web Site: https://hakubundo.com
Book & Stationery Product Whslr
N.A.I.C.S.: 424120

JPT AMERICA, INC. (2)
243 E Redondo Beach Blvd, Gardena, CA 90248-2130
Tel.: (310) 719-9999
Web Site: https://www.jptamerica.com
Book & Stationery Product Distr
N.A.I.C.S.: 424120

Subsidiary (Non-US):

JPT Europe Ltd. (2)
Office 1 289 Kennington Lane, London, SE11 5QY, United Kingdom
Tel.: (44) 20 7839 4839
Web Site: http://shop.jpbooks.co.uk
Emp.: 6
Books, Magazines & Art Craft Sales
N.A.I.C.S.: 459210

Subsidiary (Domestic):

Japan Publications, Inc. (2)
5-2-2 Hongo, Bunkyo-ku, Tokyo, 113-0033, Japan
Tel.: (81) 3 5805 3303
Web Site: http://www.nichibou.co.jp
Emp.: 17
Publishing Services
N.A.I.C.S.: 513199

TOHBU NETWORK CO., LTD.
7F Tobu Yokohama Building 2-9 Sakaemachi, Kanagawa-ku, Yokohama, 221-0052, Kanagawa, Japan
Tel.: (81) 454611651
Web Site: https://www.tohbu.co.jp
Year Founded: 1943
90360—(TKS)
Sales Range: Less than $1 Million
Lorry Transportation Services
N.A.I.C.S.: 484110
Yoshitaka Wakayama *(Pres & CEO)*

TOHO CHEMICAL INDUSTRY CO., LTD.
Nichirei Akashi-cho Bldg 6-4 Akashi-cho, Chuo-ku, Tokyo, 104-0044, Japan
Tel.: (81) 355503733
Web Site: https://www.toho-chem.co.jp
Year Founded: 1938
4409—(TKS)
Rev.: $334,439,560
Assets: $462,276,960
Liabilities: $335,629,360
Net Worth: $126,647,600
Earnings: $3,609,060
Emp.: 677
Fiscal Year-end: 03/31/24
Specialty Chemicals Mfr
N.A.I.C.S.: 325199
Tatsuo Nakasaki *(Pres & CEO)*

Subsidiaries:

Kindai Chemical Industry Co., Ltd. (1)
4-5-32 Daidou Higashi, Yodogawa-ku, Osaka, 533-0011, Osaka Prefecture, Japan
Tel.: (81) 663281541
Web Site: https://toho-chem.co.jp
Chemical Product Mfr & Distr
N.A.I.C.S.: 325199

Toho Chemical (Thailand) Co., Ltd. (1)
Bangpoo Industrial Estate No 371 Moo 4 Tambol Praeksa, Amphur-Muang, Samut Prakan, 10280, Thailand
Tel.: (66) 27093723
Chemical Products Distr
N.A.I.C.S.: 424690

Toho Huaiji Chemical Co., Ltd. (1)
Longwen Huai Cheng, Huaiji County, Huaicheng, 526400, Guangdong, China
Tel.: (86) 7585571650
Chemical Product Mfr & Distr
N.A.I.C.S.: 325199

TOHO CO., LTD.
Mukouyocho Nishi 5-9, Higashinada Ward, Kobe, 658-0033, Japan
Tel.: (81) 788452400 JP
Web Site: https://www.to-ho.co.jp
Year Founded: 1947
8142—(TKS)
Rev.: $1,736,553,700
Assets: $626,025,730
Liabilities: $430,596,970
Net Worth: $195,428,760
Earnings: $25,559,450
Emp.: 377
Fiscal Year-end: 01/31/24
Holding Company; Food & Other Consumer Products Distr & Retailer
N.A.I.C.S.: 551112
Yoshishige Shimatani *(Pres)*

Subsidiaries:

TOHO Powerlarks Co., Ltd. (1)
2-8-13 Asahigaoka, Tokyo, 191-0065, Hino, Japan (100%)
Tel.: (81) 42 581 9111
Web Site: http://www.t-powerlarks.com
Sales Range: $1-4.9 Billion
Emp.: 186
Liquor Store & Processed Foods Operations
N.A.I.C.S.: 445320
Kasai Takeo *(Pres)*

TOHO CO., LTD.
1-2-2 Yuraku-cho, Chiyoda-Ku, Tokyo, Japan
Tel.: (81) 335911214 JP
Web Site: https://www.toho.co.jp
Year Founded: 1932
9602—(TKS)
Rev.: $2,008,930,230
Assets: $4,366,206,340
Liabilities: $929,293,390
Net Worth: $3,436,912,950
Earnings: $321,056,470
Emp.: 3,088
Fiscal Year-end: 02/29/24
Holding Company; Motion Picture & Television Program Production & Distribution; Real Estate Investment & Leasing Services
N.A.I.C.S.: 551112
Yoshishige Shimatani *(Chm & Pres)*

Subsidiaries:

TOHO REAL ESTATE CO., LTD. (1)
1-5-2 Yuraku-cho, Chiyoda-ku, Tokyo, 100-0006, Japan (100%)
Tel.: (81) 3 3504 3333
Web Site: http://www.toho-re.co.jp
Emp.: 62
Commercial Real Estate Investment, Management & Leasing Services
N.A.I.C.S.: 531390
Naoyoshi Hachiuma *(Chm)*

TOHO GAS CO., LTD.
19-18 Sakurada-cho, Atsuta-ku, Nagoya, 456-8511, Japan
Tel.: (81) 528729341
Web Site: https://www.tohogas.co.jp
9533—(TKS)
Rev.: $4,184,030,850
Assets: $4,855,203,640
Liabilities: $1,835,411,920
Net Worth: $3,019,791,720
Earnings: $180,479,440
Emp.: 6,080
Fiscal Year-end: 03/31/24
Gas Distr
N.A.I.C.S.: 221210
Koichi Yasui *(Chm)*

Subsidiaries:

Mizushima Gas Co., Ltd. (1)
3-30 Mizushima Fukusakicho, Kurashiki, 712-8611, Okayama, Japan
Tel.: (81) 864448141
Web Site: http://www.mizushima-gas.co.jp
Sales Range: $50-74.9 Million
Emp.: 72
Gas Production Services
N.A.I.C.S.: 211120

Toho Gas Customer Service Co., Ltd. (1)
8 Takayokosuka-cho-cho-shinden, Tokai, 477-0037, Japan
Tel.: (81) 562330901
Web Site: https://www.thgcs.co.jp
Sales Range: $10-24.9 Million
Emp.: 600
Gas Meter Reading Services
N.A.I.C.S.: 561990

Toho Gas Engineering Co., Ltd. (1)
19-18 Sakurada-cho, Atsuta-ku, Nagoya, 456-8511, Japan
Tel.: (81) 528729431
Sales Range: $50-74.9 Million
Emp.: 2,764
Gas Production & Engineering Services
N.A.I.C.S.: 325120

Toho Gas Information System Co., Ltd. (1)
19-18 Sakurada-cho, Atsuta-ku, Nagoya, 456-8511, Japan
Tel.: (81) 528810487
Data Processing & Engineering System Services
N.A.I.C.S.: 541618

Toho Gas Living Co., Ltd. (1)
19-18 Sakurada-cho, Atsuta-ku, Nagoya, 456-0004, Aichi, Japan
Tel.: (81) 52 882 6289
Web Site: https://www.tohogas-living.jp
Exterior Material & Household Goods Whslr
N.A.I.C.S.: 423390

Toho Gas Safety Life Co., Ltd. (1)
3-7-7 Fukue, Showa-ku, Nagoya, Japan
Tel.: (81) 52 882 5388
Web Site: https://www.tgsl.co.jp
Gas Safety Security Inspection Services
N.A.I.C.S.: 541990

Toho Gas Techno Co., Ltd. (1)
19-18 Sakurada-cho, Atsuta-ku, Nagoya, 456-0004, Japan
Tel.: (81) 528723757
Web Site: http://www.thg-group.tohogas.co.jp
Emp.: 248
Gas Field Piping & Plumbing Services
N.A.I.C.S.: 237120
Hiroyuki Hasegawa *(Pres)*

Toho LNG Shipping Co., Ltd. (1)
19-18 Sakurada-cho, Atsuta-ku, Nagoya, 456-0004, Aichi, Japan
Tel.: (81) 52 872 9592
Liquefied Natural Gas Carrier Rental Services
N.A.I.C.S.: 532490

Toho Liquefied Gas Co., Ltd. (1)
19-18 Sakurada-cho, Atsuta-ku, Nagoya, 456-0004, Aichi, Japan
Tel.: (81) 528729378
Web Site: http://www.tohoekika.jp
Emp.: 624
Liquefied Gas Mfr
N.A.I.C.S.: 211130
Ohji Hiroshi *(Sr Mng Dir)*

Subsidiary (Domestic):

Customer Service Co., East Solution (2)
Sakurada-cho Atsuta-ku, 456 0004, Nagoya, Japan
Tel.: (81) 528715888
Customer Care Services
N.A.I.C.S.: 541613

TOEKI Eco Life Corporation (2)
Sakurada-cho Atsuta-ku, 456 0004, Nagoya, Japan
Tel.: (81) 566235955
Gas Equipment Repairing Services
N.A.I.C.S.: 811412

Toho Real Estate Co., Ltd. (1)
19-18 Sakurada-cho, Atsuta-ku, Nagoya, 456-0004, Aichi, Japan
Tel.: (81) 528810487
Web Site: https://www.toho-fudosan.jp
Emp.: 160
Commercial Property Management & Leasing Services
N.A.I.C.S.: 531120

Toho Service Co., Ltd. (1)
19-18 Sakurada-cho Atsuta-ku, 456-8511, Aichi, Japan
Tel.: (81) 528729341
Web Site: http://www.tohogas.co.jp
Emp.: 3,000

TOHO GAS CO., LTD.

Toho Gas Co., Ltd.—(Continued)
Car Sales, Lease & Maintenance; Equipment Leases; Insurance Services & Tour Operations
N.A.I.C.S.: 524210

Yamasa Sohgyou Co., Ltd. (1)
20-18 Sakurada-cho, Atsuta-ku, Nagoya, 456-0004, Japan
Tel.: (81) 52 871 3331
Home Delivery Water Mfr & Distr
N.A.I.C.S.: 312112

TOHO HOLDINGS CO., LTD.
2-2-1 Yaesu Chuo, Tokyo, 155-8655, Japan
Tel.: (81) 368382800   JP
Web Site: https://www.tohohd.co.jp
Year Founded: 1948
8129—(TKS)
Rev.: $9,761,066,320
Assets: $5,112,352,470
Liabilities: $3,463,573,900
Net Worth: $1,648,778,570
Earnings: $136,542,770
Emp.: 7,572
Fiscal Year-end: 03/31/24
Holding Company; Pharmaceutical Whslr, Drug Store Operator & Clinical Research & Development Services
N.A.I.C.S.: 551112
Norio Hamada (Chm & CEO)

Subsidiaries:

ALF Inc. (1)
3-6-11 Daisawa, Setagaya-ku, Tokyo, 155-0032, Japan
Tel.: (81) 5031931935
Web Site: https://datalogic.alf-net.co.jp
Sales Range: $25-49.9 Million
Emp.: 75
Handheld Terminal Devices Mfr & Whslr
N.A.I.C.S.: 334118
Yasuyoshi Iwamoto (CEO)

Kokando & Kyoso Mirai Asia Pte. Ltd. (1)
20 Maxwell Rd 03-01B Maxwell House, Singapore, 069113, Singapore
Tel.: (65) 6 222 2508
Pharmaceutical Product Whslr
N.A.I.C.S.: 424210

Koyo Co., Ltd. (1)
1-5-1 Fukuura, Kanazawa-ku, Yokohama, 236-0004, Kanagawa, Japan
Tel.: (81) 45 701 2210
Business Management Services
N.A.I.C.S.: 541611
Katsumasa Takagi (Chm)

Nextit Research Institute, Inc. (1)
85-1 Edomachi Bay Wing Kobe Building 5F, Chuo-ku, Kobe, 650-0033, Hyogo, Japan
Tel.: (81) 783932151
Web Site: https://www.nextit.co.jp
Emp.: 74
Medical Software Development Services
N.A.I.C.S.: 541511

Orphan Trust Japan Co., Ltd. (1)
GranTokyo South Tower 12F 1-9-2 Marunouchi, Chiyoda-ku, Tokyo, 100-6613, Japan
Tel.: (81) 36 838 2829
Web Site: https://www.tohohd.co.jp
Emp.: 10
Pharmaceutical Products Distr
N.A.I.C.S.: 424210
Shigeki Nakata (Pres)

PharmaCluster Co., Ltd. (1)
GranTokyo South Tower 12F 1-9-2 Marunouchi, Chiyoda-ku, Tokyo, 100-6612, Japan
Tel.: (81) 716602123
Pharmaceutical Whslr & Distr
N.A.I.C.S.: 456110

Subsidiary (Domestic):

Chuoh Medical Co., Ltd. (2)
1459-2 Kurikuma Nishi Ayakamachi, Chuo-ku, Marugame, 761-2405, Kagawa, Japan
Tel.: (81) 878137212
Web Site: https://c-medical.net
Emp.: 65
Pharmaceutical Product Retailer
N.A.I.C.S.: 456110

J.Mirai Medical Co., Ltd. (2)
8F Wakita Kyobashi Building 1 2-5-1 Higashinodamachi, Miyakojima-ku, Osaka, 534-0024, Japan
Tel.: (81) 663609215
Web Site: https://www.jmirai.com
Emp.: 143
Pharmaceutical Product Retailer
N.A.I.C.S.: 456110

Pharma Daiwa Co., Ltd. (2)
1-56 Ryutsudanchi, Minami-ku, Kumamoto, 862-0967, Japan
Tel.: (81) 963341060
Web Site: http://www.pharma-daiwa.co.jp
Emp.: 206
Pharmaceutical Products Mfr & Distr
N.A.I.C.S.: 456110

Pharma Square Co. Ltd. (2)
4-4-2 Nihombashihoncho Higashiyama Building 2F, Chuo-ku, Tokyo, 103-0023, Japan
Tel.: (81) 332423420
Web Site: http://www.phms.co.jp
Pharmaceutical Product Retailer
N.A.I.C.S.: 456110

Sunmedical Co., Ltd. (1)
571-2 Furutaka-cho, Moriyama, 524-0044, Shiga, Japan
Tel.: (81) 775829978
Web Site: https://www.sunmedical.co.jp
Emp.: 128
Dental Material Mfr & Distr
N.A.I.C.S.: 339114
Takayuki Inagaki (Pres & CEO)

Toho Pharmaceutical Co., Ltd. (1)
5-2-1 Daisawa, Setagaya-ku, Tokyo, 155-8655, Japan
Tel.: (81) 334197811
Web Site: https://www.tohoyk.co.jp
Sales Range: $50-74.9 Million
Pharmaceutical Preparation, Research & Development Services
N.A.I.C.S.: 325412
Hiromi Edahiro (Pres)

Subsidiary (Domestic):

Kyushu Toho Co., Ltd. (2)
3-4-46 Hakozakifuto, Higashi-ku, Fukuoka, 812-8585, Japan
Tel.: (81) 926413141
Web Site: http://www.kyushu-toho.co.jp
Emp.: 831
Pharmaceutical Products Distr
N.A.I.C.S.: 424210

Toho System Service Co., Ltd. (2)
1-30-17 Daita, Setagaya-ku, Tokyo, 155-0033, Japan
Tel.: (81) 289765353
Medical Software Development Services
N.A.I.C.S.: 541511

Yamaguchi Toho K.K. (2)
2-2-27 Manabe, Tsuchiura, 300-0051, Ibaraki, Japan
Tel.: (81) 298220821
Pharmaceutical Products Distr
N.A.I.C.S.: 424210

Zenkaido Yakkyoku Co., Ltd. (2)
3-5-13 Heijima Y Building 1kai, Nishi-ku, Niigata, 950-2004, Japan
Tel.: (81) 25 231 6030
Pharmaceutical Product Retailer
N.A.I.C.S.: 456110

Tokyo Clinical CRO Co., Ltd. (1)
20 Samoncho Yotsuya Medical Building 5F, Shinjuku-ku, Tokyo, 160-0017, Japan
Tel.: (81) 353661720
Web Site: http://www.tokyorinsho-cro.co.jp
Clinical Laboratory Testing Services
N.A.I.C.S.: 621512

Tokyo Research Center of Clinical Pharmacology Co., Ltd. (1)
Yotsuya Medical Building 20 Samoncho, Shinjuku-ku, Tokyo, 160-0017, Japan
Tel.: (81) 353663417
Web Site: https://www.trcp.co.jp
Clinical Research & Development Services
N.A.I.C.S.: 541715

TOHO KOKI CO., LTD.
2500 Koizumi, Yamatokoriyama, Nara, 639-1042, Japan
Tel.: (81) 743 52 4172
Web Site: http://www.hittools.co.jp
Year Founded: 1938
Hand Tool Mfr
N.A.I.C.S.: 332216
Kihachiro Kawakami (Pres)

TOHO LAMAC CO., LTD.
3-42-6 Yushima Bunkyo-ku, Tokyo, 113-8513, Japan
Tel.: (81) 3 3832 0131
Web Site: http://www.toho-lamac.co.jp
Year Founded: 1958
7422—(JAS)
Sales Range: $200-249.9 Million
Emp.: 112
Cycle & Shoes Import & Export
N.A.I.C.S.: 424990
Hiroka Machida (Auditor)

TOHO SYSTEM SCIENCE CO., LTD.
5F Nippon Life Koishikawa Building 1-12-14 Koishikawa, Bunkyo-ku, Tokyo, 112-0002, Japan
Tel.: (81) 338686060
Web Site: https://www.tss.co.jp
Year Founded: 1971
4333—(TKS)
Sales Range: $75-99.9 Million
Software Development Services
N.A.I.C.S.: 541511
Seiji Shinohara (CEO & Chm)

TOHO TITANIUM CO., LTD.
JR Yokohama Tower 22nd Floor 1-1-1 Minamisaiwai, Nishi-ku, Yokohama, 220-0005, Kanagawa, Japan
Tel.: (81) 453945522
Web Site: https://www.toho-titanium.co.jp
Year Founded: 1953
5727—(TKS)
Rev.: $518,250,440
Assets: $832,873,220
Liabilities: $459,097,550
Net Worth: $373,775,670
Earnings: $32,726,110
Emp.: 1,195
Fiscal Year-end: 03/31/24
Titanium Metal Producer
N.A.I.C.S.: 331491
Takeshi Shirai (Exec Officer & Gen Mgr-Titanium Engrg Dept)

Subsidiaries:

Toho Titanium Co., Ltd. - Hitachi Plant (1)
3453 Miyata-cho, Hitachi, 317-0055, Ibaraki, Japan
Tel.: (81) 294237267
Titanium Metal Mfr
N.A.I.C.S.: 331491

Toho Titanium Co., Ltd. - Kurobe Plant (1)
8 Tenjinshin, Kurobe, Toyama, 938-0042, Japan
Tel.: (81) 765549381
Titanium Metal Mfr
N.A.I.C.S.: 331491

Toho Titanium Co., Ltd. - Wakamatsu Plant (1)
1-62-1 Hibiki-machi, Wakamatsu-ku, Kitakyushu, 808-0021, Fukuoka, Japan
Tel.: (81) 937717553
Titanium Metal Mfr
N.A.I.C.S.: 331491

Toho Titanium Co., Ltd. - Yahata Plant (1)
2-3 Nishikukioka Maeda, Yahatahigashi-ku, Kitakyushu, 805-0058, Fukuoka, Japan
Tel.: (81) 936631483
Titanium Metal Mfr
N.A.I.C.S.: 331491

INTERNATIONAL PUBLIC

N.A.I.C.S.: 331491

Toho Titanium Europe Co., Ltd. (1)
2nd Floor Bury House 31 Bury Street, London, United Kingdom
Tel.: (44) 2076210888
Emp.: 2
Titanium Metal Distr
N.A.I.C.S.: 423840
Nobutoshi Nomoto (Dir)

TOHO ZINC CO., LTD.
Tekko Building 1-8-2 Marunouchi, Chiyoda-ku, Tokyo, 100-8207, Japan
Tel.: (81) 362121711
Web Site: https://www.toho-zinc.co.jp
Year Founded: 1937
5707—(TKS)
Rev.: $864,607,830
Assets: $716,761,960
Liabilities: $698,881,910
Net Worth: $17,880,050
Earnings: ($307,047,720)
Emp.: 963
Fiscal Year-end: 03/31/24
Lead, Zinc & Silver Mining, Smelting & Refining & Exploration; Electronic Components Mfr
N.A.I.C.S.: 212230
Kimiyasu Marusaki (Pres)

Subsidiaries:

CBH Resources Limited (1)
(100%)
Tel.: (61) 29 925 8100
Web Site: https://www.cbhresources.com.au
Sales Range: $100-124.9 Million
Emp.: 5
Zinc, Lead & Silver Mining & Exploration
N.A.I.C.S.: 212220
Visko Sulicich (COO)

Subsidiary (Domestic):

Carrington Facilities Pty Ltd (2)
2 Dyke Berth, PO Box 55, Carrington, 2294, NSW, Australia
(100%)
Tel.: (61) 249621666
Web Site: http://www.cbhresources.com.au
Ship Loading Services
N.A.I.C.S.: 488320

TDE Co Ltd (1)
2-53-5 Kyoda, Sakata, 998-0102, Yamagata, Japan
(100%)
Tel.: (81) 234314511
Web Site: https://www.tde-kk.co.jp
Building Equipment & Machinery Installation Contractors
N.A.I.C.S.: 238990

Toho Career Co., Ltd (1)
10 Aza Yoshihama Onahama, Fukushima, Iwaki, 971-8101, Japan
(100%)
Tel.: (81) 246544537
Web Site: https://www.toho-carrier.com
Environmental Consulting Services
N.A.I.C.S.: 541620

Toho Development Engineering Co., Ltd. (1)
Kyobashi Nisshoku Building 1-8-7 Kyobashi, Chuo-ku, Tokyo, 104-0031, Japan
Tel.: (81) 335627191
Web Site: https://www.tdekk.co.jp
Emp.: 52
Civil Engineering Services
N.A.I.C.S.: 541330

Toho Trade Co Ltd (1)
2-3-6 Shinmeicho, Takahama, 444-1305, Japan
(100%)
Tel.: (81) 566520451
Sales Range: $25-49.9 Million
Emp.: 5
Industrial Building Construction
N.A.I.C.S.: 236210
Masayuki Tsuchiya (Mng Dir)

TOHOKU CHEMICAL CO., LTD.
1-3-1 Kanda, Hirosaki, 036-8061, Aomori, Japan
Tel.: (81) 172338131
Web Site: https://www.t-kagaku.co.jp
Year Founded: 1953

7446—(TKS)
Rev.: $223,798,800
Assets: $119,983,440
Liabilities: $67,734,720
Net Worth: $52,248,720
Earnings: $1,649,520
Fiscal Year-end: 09/30/24
Industrial Chemical Whslr
N.A.I.C.S.: 424690
Yukihiro Kudo (Pres & CEO)

Subsidiaries:

NICHIEI-TOKAI Co., Ltd. (1)
2-35-25 Shakujiidai, Nerima-ku, Tokyo, 177-0045, Japan
Tel.: (81) 369132070
Web Site: https://www.kk-nichieitokai.jp
Industrial Chemical Distr
N.A.I.C.S.: 424690

Tohoku Systems Co., Ltd. (1)
1-2-14 Kanda, Hirosaki, 036-8061, Aomori, Japan
Tel.: (81) 172329821
Computer Distr
N.A.I.C.S.: 423430

TOHOKU ELECTRIC POWER CO., INC.

1-7-1 Honcho, Aoba-ku, Sendai, 980-8550, Miyagi, Japan
Tel.: (81) 222252111 JP
Web Site: https://www.tohoku-epco.co.jp
Year Founded: 1951
9506—(TKS)
Rev.: $18,625,743,930
Assets: $35,619,459,030
Liabilities: $29,597,233,450
Net Worth: $6,022,225,580
Earnings: $1,494,534,220
Emp.: 4,763
Fiscal Year-end: 03/31/24
Electric Power Distr
N.A.I.C.S.: 221122
Makoto Kaiwa (Chm)

Subsidiaries:

Higashi Nihon Kougyou Co., Inc. (1)
3-7-1 Ichibancho, Aoba-ku, Sendai, 980-8534, Miyagi, Japan
Tel.: (81) 22 225 1191
Web Site: https://www.hnk-i.co.jp
Emp.: 176
Real Estate Management, Building Construction Contractors & Damage & Life Insurance Services
N.A.I.C.S.: 531390
Shinsuke Matsuzawa (Chm)

Joban Joint Power Co., Ltd (1)
1-1-1 Kanda Sudacho, Chiyoda-ku, Tokyo, 101-0041, Japan
Tel.: (81) 33 256 5411
Web Site: https://www.joban-power.co.jp
Emp.: 244
Wholesale Thermal Power Generation Electricity Services
N.A.I.C.S.: 221122
Toshiaki Koizumi (Mng Dir)

Kitanihon Electric Cable Co., Ltd. (1)
6-2 Mukaiharamae Kagitori, Hakutori- ku Taishiro-ku, Sendai, 982-8511, Miyagi, Japan
Tel.: (81) 22 307 1736
Web Site: https://www.kitaniti-td.co.jp
Emp.: 380
Electric Wires & Cable Mfr & Distr
N.A.I.C.S.: 335921

Nihonkai LNG Co., Ltd (1)
1-1612-32 Higashiko Seiro-cho, Kita-Gamahara-gun, Niigata, 957-0195, Japan
Tel.: (81) 25 256 2131
Web Site: https://www.nihonkai-lng.co.jp
Sales Range: $125-149.9 Million
Emp.: 153
Natural Gas Distr
N.A.I.C.S.: 221210

Sakata Kyodo Power Co., Ltd. (1)
1-19 Miyaumi Minamihara, Sakata, 998-8622, Yamagata, Japan
Tel.: (81) 23 434 2321
Web Site: https://www.sakata-power.co.jp
Emp.: 107
Electric Power Generation
N.A.I.C.S.: 221113

Soma Kyodo Power Co., Ltd. (1)
65-16 Tsukanomachi Nakamura Shinko Bldg 3 F Soma, Fukushima, 976-0042, Japan
Tel.: (81) 244361200
Web Site: http://www.somakyoda.co.jp
Sales Range: $125-149.9 Million
Emp.: 150
Elctric Power Generation Services
N.A.I.C.S.: 221118

Tohoku Electric Power Engineering & Construction Co., Inc. (1)
Omachi 2-15-29, Aoba-ku, Sendai, 980-0804, Miyagi, Japan
Tel.: (81) 22 261 5431
Web Site: https://www.tohatu.co.jp
Emp.: 1,817
Civil Engineering Services
N.A.I.C.S.: 237990
Toshiro Sasagawa (Pres)

Tohoku Information Systems Co., Inc. (1)
2-9-10 Central, Aoba-ku, Sendai, 980-0021, Miyagi, Japan
Tel.: (81) 22 799 5555
Web Site: https://www.toinx.co.jp
Sales Range: $150-199.9 Million
Emp.: 720
Information Systems Network Services
N.A.I.C.S.: 541512
Eiji Hayasaka (Pres)

Tohoku Intelligent Telecommunication Co., Inc. (1)
Denryoku Building 2F 3-7-1 Ichibancho, Aoba ku, Sendai, 980-0811, Miyagi, Japan
Tel.: (81) 22 799 4201
Web Site: https://www.tohknet.co.jp
Sales Range: $100-124.9 Million
Emp.: 376
Telecommunication Services Provider
N.A.I.C.S.: 517810

Tohoku Ryokka Kankyohozen Co., Ltd. (1)
2-5-1 Honcho Oak Sendai Building, Aoba-ku, Sendai, 980-0014, Miyagi, Japan
Tel.: (81) 222630607
Web Site: http://www.tohoku-aep.co.jp
Emp.: 448
Civil Engineering Services
N.A.I.C.S.: 541330

Tsuken Electric Ind Co., Ltd. (1)
3-9 Akedori, Izumi-ku, Sendai, 981-3206, Miyagi, Japan
Tel.: (81) 22 377 2800
Web Site: https://www.2ken.co.jp
Emp.: 436
Electronic Equipment Supplier
N.A.I.C.S.: 423690

TOHOKU STEEL CO., LTD.

23 Nishigaoka Muratacho, Muratamachi Shibata-gun, Miyagi, 989-1393, Japan
Tel.: (81) 224821010
Web Site: https://www.tohokusteel.com
Year Founded: 1937
5484—(TKS)
Rev.: $141,037,570
Assets: $229,981,730
Liabilities: $47,750,640
Net Worth: $182,231,090
Earnings: $6,438,140
Emp.: 244
Fiscal Year-end: 03/31/24
Steel Products Mfr
N.A.I.C.S.: 331110
Shinji Naruse (Pres)

Subsidiaries:

TOHOKU Manufacturing (Thailand)Co., Ltd. (1)
789/166 Moo1, Nong Kham Amphur Sriracha, Tambol, 20230, Chonburi, Thailand
Tel.: (66) 38348548
Web Site: https://www.tohoku-tmt.co.th
Automobile Parts Mfr
N.A.I.C.S.: 333514
Hitoshi Ogata (Pres)

Tohoku Steel Co., Ltd. - Tsuchiura Plant (1)
20-26 Harayama Hongo, Tsuchiura, 300-4102, Ibaraki, Japan
Tel.: (81) 298306018
Web Site: https://www.tohokusteel.com
Steel Products Mfr
N.A.I.C.S.: 332999

TOHOKU TATSUMI KK

51-6 Oki Fushiogami, Aza, Fukushima, 960-8154, Japan
Tel.: (81) 24 545 5131 JP
Web Site: http://www.t-tatsumi.com
Year Founded: 1980
Sales Range: $400-449.9 Million
Emp.: 100
Digital Home Appliance & Automotive Assembly Control Equipment Mfr; Press Die Mold Connector Mfr & Distr
N.A.I.C.S.: 335999
Tsutomu Yoshioka (CEO)

Subsidiaries:

Hangzhou JALCO Electronics Co., Ltd. (1)
No 8 Yang Building Industrial Park Baijia Yuan Road, Liuxia Town Xihu District, Hangzhou, Zhejiang, China
Tel.: (86) 571 8522 4647
Electronic Parts & Equipment Mfr
N.A.I.C.S.: 334419

JALCO Electronics Hong Kong Ltd. (1)
Room 712 7/F Sterling Centre 11 Cheung Yue Street, Cheung Sha Wan, Kowloon, China (Hong Kong)
Tel.: (852) 2759 3778
Sales Range: $50-74.9 Million
Emp.: 5
Electronic Components Distr
N.A.I.C.S.: 423690
Fujinoki Etsuo (Mgr)

TOHOKUSHINSHA FILM CORPORATION

4-8-10 Akasaka, Minato-ku, Tokyo, 107-8460, Japan
Tel.: (81) 354140211 JP
Web Site: https://www.tfc.co.jp
Year Founded: 1961
2329—(TKS)
Rev.: $349,133,590
Assets: $646,927,310
Liabilities: $102,137,720
Net Worth: $544,789,590
Earnings: $26,578,810
Emp.: 1,561
Fiscal Year-end: 03/31/24
Motion Picture Production, Post-Production & Distribution; Television Broadcasting
N.A.I.C.S.: 512110
Kiyotaka Ninomiya (Pres & CEO)

Subsidiaries:

CENTE SERVICE CORP. (1)
8981 Sunset Blvd, Los Angeles, CA 90069
Tel.: (310) 858-8981
Sales Range: $1-9.9 Million
Emp.: 10
Marketing Consulting Services
N.A.I.C.S.: 541613
Toshi Katsumi (Office Mgr)

IGO & SHOGI CHANNEL INC. (1)
7-2 Gobancho Nihon Kiin Kaikan B1F, Chiyoda-ku, Tokyo, 102-0076, Japan
Tel.: (81) 335111981
Emp.: 50
Television Broadcasting Services
N.A.I.C.S.: 516120

Kimura Brewery Inc.. (1)
2-1-11 Tamachi, Yuzawa, 012-0844, Akita, Japan
Tel.: (81) 183733155
Sake Mfr
N.A.I.C.S.: 312140

National Trading Inc. (1)
Izak Higashi Azabu Building 3-3-1 Higashi-azabu, Minatoku, Tokyo, 106-0047, Japan
Tel.: (81) 355709761
Web Site: https://www.vgi.jp
Retail Store Operator
N.A.I.C.S.: 459420

Nibankohboh Productions Corp. (1)
Nittochi Ginza Building 7-14-13 Ginza, Chuo-ku, Tokyo, 104-0061, Japan
Tel.: (81) 335448870
Television Commercials Production Services
N.A.I.C.S.: 512110

Omnibus Japan Inc. (1)
7-9-11 Akasaka, Minato-ku, Tokyo, 107-0052, Japan
Tel.: (81) 362290601
Emp.: 371
Television Commercial Post Production Services
N.A.I.C.S.: 512191
Banjiro Uemura (Founder)

Soda! Communications Inc. (1)
REVZO Toranomon 5F/6F 1-8-1 Nishi-Shinbashi, Minato-ku, Tokyo, 105-0003, Japan
Tel.: (81) 362067560
Emp.: 50
Boutique Mfr
N.A.I.C.S.: 339910

Star Channel, Inc. (1)
4-8-10 Akasaka, Minato-ku, Tokyo, 107-0052, Japan (100%)
Tel.: (81) 354140436
Sales Range: $50-74.9 Million
Cable Television Broadcasting Services
N.A.I.C.S.: 516120

Tohokushinsha Creates Inc. (1)
Akasaka-zaka Higashi Building 4-8-14 Akasaka, Minato-ku, Tokyo, 107-0052, Japan
Tel.: (81) 3 5414 0335
Web Site: http://www.tfc.co.jp
Film Production Services
N.A.I.C.S.: 512110
Uemura Tsuuemura (CEO)

White Box Co., Ltd. (1)
4-8-10 Akasaka, Minato-ku, Tokyo, 107-0052, Japan
Tel.: (81) 354140282
Web Site: http://www.whiteboxandco.com
Public Event Organizer
N.A.I.C.S.: 561920

TOHTO SUISAN CO., LTD.

6-6-2 Toyosu, Koto-ku, Tokyo, 135-8134, Japan
Tel.: (81) 366331003
Web Site: https://www.tohsui.co.jp
Year Founded: 1948
8038—(TKS)
Rev.: $692,741,220
Assets: $266,032,670
Liabilities: $88,038,590
Net Worth: $177,994,080
Earnings: $16,445,680
Emp.: 4,763
Fiscal Year-end: 03/31/24
Fish Whslr
N.A.I.C.S.: 424460
Koh Ehara (Pres)

Subsidiaries:

Aero Trading Company Limited (1)
Suite 200-8592 Fraser Street, Vancouver, V5X 3Y3, BC, Canada
Tel.: (604) 327-6331
Web Site: http://www.aerotrading.ca
Fish Whslr
N.A.I.C.S.: 424460

Chiba Gyorui K.K. (1)
Chiba Regional Wholesale Market 2-2-1 Takahama, Mihama-ku, Chiba, 261-0003, Japan
Tel.: (81) 432483271
Web Site: https://chibagyorui.co.jp
Fish Whslr
N.A.I.C.S.: 424460

TOHTO SUISAN CO., LTD.

TOHTO SUISAN Co., Ltd.—(Continued)

Kawagoe Suisanshijo K.K. (1)
650 Oubukuro, Kawagoe, 350-1168, Saitama-ken, Japan
Tel.: (81) 492 40 2102
Fish Whslr
N.A.I.C.S.: 424460

Kushiro Tohsui Reito K.K. (1)
3-1-3 Kaiun, Kushiro, 085-0023, Hokkaido, Japan
Tel.: (81) 154 25 0191
Cold Storage Services
N.A.I.C.S.: 493120

Saitamaken Uoichiba K.K. (1)
2-226-1 Yoshino-cho, Kita-ku, Saitama, 331-9675, Japan
Tel.: (81) 486663101
Web Site: https://www.saitamauoiti.co.jp
Emp.: 89
Fish Whslr
N.A.I.C.S.: 424460

Tohsui Foods K.K. (1)
3-3-4 Hama-cho, Funabashi, 273-0012, Chiba-ken, Japan
Tel.: (81) 47 435 2223
Cold Storage Services
N.A.I.C.S.: 493120

Toyomi Tohto Suisan Reizo K.K. (1)
13-5 Toyomi-cho, Chuoh-ku, Tokyo, 104-0055, Japan
Tel.: (81) 335321581
Cold Storage Services
N.A.I.C.S.: 493120

TOIN CORPORATION
1-4-2 Kameido, Koto Ward, Tokyo, 136-0071, Japan
Tel.: (81) 356279111
Web Site: https://www.toin.co.jp
Year Founded: 1955
7923—(TKS)
Rev.: $89,281,270
Assets: $127,810,960
Liabilities: $61,644,860
Net Worth: $66,166,100
Earnings: $3,219,070
Emp.: 465
Fiscal Year-end: 03/31/24
Plastic & Paper Product Mfr
N.A.I.C.S.: 326199
Kimiaki Haru (Pres, CEO & COO)

Subsidiaries:

TOIN CORPORATION - Kashiwa Factory (1)
16-1 Shintoyofuta, Kashiwa-shi, Chiba, 277-0804, Japan
Tel.: (81) 471312111
Packaging & Labelling Services
N.A.I.C.S.: 561910

TOIN CORPORATION - Noda Factory (1)
231-5 Nakazato, Noda, 270-0237, Chiba, Japan
Tel.: (81) 471208805
Web Site: http://www.toin.co.jp
Packaging & Labelling Services
N.A.I.C.S.: 561910

TOITURES COUTURE ET ASSOCIES INC.
6565 Maricourt Boulevard, Saint-Hubert, J3Y 1S8, QC, Canada
Tel.: (450) 678-2562
Web Site: http://www.toiturecouture.com
Emp.: 175
Roofing Services
N.A.I.C.S.: 238160
Laurent Couture (Chm)

TOKAI CARBON CO., LTD.
Aoyama Building 1-2-3 Kita Aoyama, Minato-ku, Tokyo, 107-8636, Japan
Tel.: (81) 337465100   JP
Web Site: https://www.tokaicarbon.co.jp
Year Founded: 1918
TKCBY—(OTCQB)
Rev.: $1,950,926,560
Assets: $4,449,983,120
Liabilities: $2,273,773,920
Net Worth: $2,176,209,200
Earnings: $9,863,920
Emp.: 4,242
Fiscal Year-end: 12/31/20
Carbon & Graphite Mfr
N.A.I.C.S.: 325180
Toshiaki Fukuda (Mng Exec Officer)

Subsidiaries:

Cancarb Limited (1)
1702 Brier Park Cres NW, Medicine Hat, T1C 1T9, AB, Canada (100%)
Tel.: (403) 527-1121
Web Site: https://www.cancarb.com
Sales Range: $25-49.9 Million
Emp.: 80
Carbon Black Mfr
N.A.I.C.S.: 335991
Peter Donnelly (VP-Mktg)

Daiya Tsusho Co., Ltd. (1)
2nd floor Daiwa Shibuya Shinsen Building 9-1 Shinsencho, Shibuya-ku, Tokyo, 150-0045, Japan
Tel.: (81) 339411171
Web Site: https://www.capita-inc.jp
Petroleum Product Whslr
N.A.I.C.S.: 424720

Mitomo Brake Co., Ltd. (1)
218-1 Aoyama, Ogawamachi Hiki-Gun, Saitama, 355-0324, Japan
Tel.: (81) 493720974
Chemicals Mfr
N.A.I.C.S.: 325998

Oriental Sangyo Co., Ltd. (1)
180 Kamijo-Araimachi, Kofu, 400-0052, Yamanashi, Japan
Tel.: (81) 552413221
Web Site: http://www.oriental-ind.co.jp
Rev.: $15,252,000
Emp.: 74
Carbon Mfr
N.A.I.C.S.: 325180

Shanghai Tokai Konetsu Co., Ltd. (1)
No 878 Boxuenan Road, Malu Jiading, Shanghai, China
Tel.: (86) 2159100169
Chemicals Mfr
N.A.I.C.S.: 325998

Svensk Specialgrafit AB (1)
Kardanvaegen 40, 461 38, Trollhattan, Sweden
Tel.: (46) 52081185
Web Site: http://www.specialgrafit.se
Sales Range: $25-49.9 Million
Emp.: 10
Graphite Mfr
N.A.I.C.S.: 335991

Thai Tokai Carbon Product Company Ltd. (1)
54 9th Floor Harinthorn Tower North Sathorn Road, Silom Bang Rak, Bangkok, 10500, Thailand (100%)
Tel.: (66) 2 266 3232
Web Site: https://www.tcp.co.th
Carbon Black Mfr
N.A.I.C.S.: 325180
Shunji Yamamoto (Mng Dir)

Tokai COBEX Polska sp. z o.o. (1)
Piastowska 29, 47-400, Raciborz, Poland
Tel.: (48) 324595212
Graphite Product Mfr & Distr
N.A.I.C.S.: 335991

Tokai COBEX Savoie S.A.S. (1)
30 Rue Louis Jouvet, 69200, Venissieux, France
Tel.: (33) 479223010
Graphite Product Mfr & Distr
N.A.I.C.S.: 335991

Tokai Carbon (Dalian) Co., Ltd. (1)
Room 1804 Tian An international Tower No 88 Zhongshan Road, Zhongshan District, Dalian, Liaoning, China
Tel.: (86) 41182311183
Chemicals Mfr
N.A.I.C.S.: 325998

Tokai Carbon (Shanghai) Co., Ltd. (1)
Rm No 513 Guoli Bldg, Beijing Xi-lu, 1465, Shanghai, China
Tel.: (86) 2162181010
Sales Range: $25-49.9 Million
Emp.: 7
Carbon Mfr
N.A.I.C.S.: 335991

Tokai Carbon (Suzhou) Co., Ltd. (1)
A2 Building 59 Qiye Road, Industrial Park, Suzhou, China
Tel.: (86) 51262800695
Chemicals Mfr
N.A.I.C.S.: 325998

Tokai Carbon CB Ltd. (1)
301 Commerce St Ste 500, Fort Worth, TX 76102
Tel.: (817) 567-2929
Web Site: https://www.tokaicarboncb.com
Tiles Mfr
N.A.I.C.S.: 326211
William R. Jones (Pres)

Tokai Carbon Co., Ltd. - Chita Plant (1)
5gouchi -1 Taketoyocho, Chita, 470-2341, Aichi, Japan
Tel.: (81) 569721011
Chemicals Mfr
N.A.I.C.S.: 325998

Tokai Carbon Co., Ltd. - Hofu Plant (1)
569 Hamakata, Hofu, 747-0833, Yamaguchi, Japan
Tel.: (81) 835233204
Chemicals Mfr
N.A.I.C.S.: 325998

Tokai Carbon Co., Ltd. - Kyushu-Wakamatsu Plant (1)
2-26 Fujinoki 3-chome, Wakamatsu-ku, Kitakyushu, 808-0074, Fukuoka, Japan
Tel.: (81) 937910731
Chemicals Mfr
N.A.I.C.S.: 325998

Tokai Carbon Co., Ltd. - Shonan Plant (1)
370 Enzo, Chigasaki, 253-0084, Kanagawa, Japan
Tel.: (81) 467820104
Chemicals Mfr
N.A.I.C.S.: 325998

Tokai Carbon Co., Ltd. - Tanoura Plant (1)
959-1 Kodanoura Ashikita-cho, Ashikita-gun, Kumamoto, 869-5393, Japan
Tel.: (81) 966870006
Chemicals Mfr
N.A.I.C.S.: 325998

Tokai Carbon Deutschland GmbH (1)
Industriepark 25, Mendt, 53567, Buchholz, Germany
Tel.: (49) 268397830
Sales Range: $25-49.9 Million
Emp.: 35
Carbon & Graphite Materials Mfr
N.A.I.C.S.: 335991
John Diviney (Gen Mgr)

Tokai Carbon Europe GmbH (1)
Aluminiumstrasse 4, 41515, Grevenbroich, Germany
Tel.: (49) 21814952261
Carbon Mfr
N.A.I.C.S.: 335991

Tokai Carbon Europe Ltd. (1)
Roway Lane, Oldbury, B69 3EJ, West Midlands, United Kingdom
Tel.: (44) 121 552 5577
Web Site: https://en.tokaicarbon.eu
Sales Range: $25-49.9 Million
Emp.: 31
Carbon & Graphite Products Mfr
N.A.I.C.S.: 335991

Tokai Carbon GE LLC (1)
6210 Ardrey Kell Rd Ste 270, Charlotte, NC 28277
Tel.: (980) 260-1130
Web Site: https://www.tokaicarbonusa.com
Chemicals Mfr
N.A.I.C.S.: 325998
Scott L. Carlton (Pres)

Tokai Carbon Italia S.R.L. (1)
Via Cagliari 40, 20060, Trezzano Rosa, Italy
Tel.: (39) 029 096 9190
Web Site: https://www.tokaicarbon.co.jp
Carbon Mfr
N.A.I.C.S.: 335991

Tokai Carbon Korea Co., Ltd. (1)
71 Gaejeongsaneopdanji-ro, Miyang-myeon, Anseong, Gyeonggi-do, Korea (South) (58.57%)
Tel.: (82) 316770277
Web Site: https://www.tck.co.kr
Rev.: $245,104,695
Assets: $368,576,526
Liabilities: $48,834,441
Net Worth: $319,742,086
Earnings: $72,141,296
Emp.: 469
Fiscal Year-end: 12/31/2022
Carbon Products Mfr
N.A.I.C.S.: 335991
Yeong-Soon Park (CEO)

Tokai Carbon U.S.A., Inc. (1)
4495 NE 59th Ave, Hillsboro, OR 97124
Tel.: (503) 640-2039
Web Site: https://www.tokaicarbon.com
Emp.: 25
Carbon And Graphite Products
N.A.I.C.S.: 335991

Tokai Carbon US Holdings Inc (1)
6210 Ardrey Kell Rd Ste 270, Charlotte, NC 28277
Tel.: (980) 260-1130
Web Site: http://www.tokaielectrodes.com
Sales Range: $25-49.9 Million
Emp.: 1
Electric Furnace Mfr & Distr
N.A.I.C.S.: 333994
Michael Slabe (CFO)

Tokai Carbon US Holdings Inc. (1)
6210 Ardrey Kell Rd Ste 270, Charlotte, NC 28277
Tel.: (980) 260-1130
Chemicals Mfr
N.A.I.C.S.: 325998

Tokai Erftcarbon GmbH (1)
Aluminiumstrasse 4, 41515, Grevenbroich, Germany
Tel.: (49) 2181 495 2100
Web Site: https://tokai-erftcarbon.com
Sales Range: $50-74.9 Million
Emp.: 200
Produces Large-Format Graphite Electrodes for Electric Steel Industries
N.A.I.C.S.: 335991

Tokai Fine Carbon Co., Ltd. (1)
370 Enzo, Chigasaki, 253-0084, Kanagawa, Japan
Tel.: (81) 467858000
Web Site: https://tokaifinecarbon.co.jp
Carbon & Graphite Mfr
N.A.I.C.S.: 335991

Tokai Konetsu (Suzhou) Co., Ltd. (1)
No 569 Fangqiao Road Xiangcheng Economic Development Area, A2 Aviation Industrial Park Cao Lake Industrial Park, Suzhou, Jiangsu, China
Tel.: (86) 51286860650
Chemicals Mfr
N.A.I.C.S.: 325998

Tokai Konetsu Engineering Co., Ltd (1)
705 Chokoji-cho, Omihachiman, 523-0013, Shiga, Japan
Tel.: (81) 748372014
Sales Range: $50-74.9 Million
Emp.: 250
Electric Furnaces Mfr
N.A.I.C.S.: 333994

Tokai Konetsu Engineering Co., Ltd. (1)
705 Chokoji-cho Oumihachiman, Shiga, 523-0013, Japan
Tel.: (81) 748372014
Chemicals Mfr

N.A.I.C.S.: 325998

Tokai Konetsu Kogyo Co., Ltd. (1)
1-2-3 Kita-Aoyama 3F Aoyama Bldg,
Minato-Ku, Tokyo, 107-0061, Japan
Tel.: (81) 35 772 8211
Web Site: https://www.tokaikonetsu.co.jp
Sales Range: $50-74.9 Million
Emp.: 250
Industrial Furnace & Heating Equipment Mfr
N.A.I.C.S.: 333994
Akihiko Sato (Pres)

Tokai Noshiro Seiko Co., Ltd. (1)
1-2 Ogida, Ogida, Noshiro, 016-0122, Akita,
Japan
Tel.: (81) 18 558 3125
Web Site: https://www.tokai-noshiroseiko.co.jp
Emp.: 72
Friction Materials Mfr
N.A.I.C.S.: 336350

Tokai Unyu Co., Ltd. (1)
1-10 Shigeyoshi-cho, Chome Chuo-ku, Ishinomaki, 986-0844, Miyagi, Japan
Tel.: (81) 225968921
Graphite Product Mfr
N.A.I.C.S.: 335991

TOKAI CORP.
9-16 Wakamiyacho, Gifu, 500-8828,
Japan
Tel.: (81) 582635111   JP
Web Site: https://www.tokai-corp.com
Year Founded: 1955
9729—(TKS)
Rev.: $913,647,420
Assets: $759,660,860
Liabilities: $185,985,570
Net Worth: $573,675,290
Earnings: $38,404,100
Emp.: 180
Fiscal Year-end: 03/31/24
Hospital Equipment & Linen Sales,
Rental & Leasing Services
N.A.I.C.S.: 423450
Koji Onoki (Pres)

Subsidiaries:

QUERY Co. Ltd. (1)
1-32-7 Higashiikebukuro Taiki Seimei Ikebukuro Building 9F, Toshima-ku, Tokyo, 170-0013, Japan
Tel.: (81) 359264363
Software Development & Contract Services
N.A.I.C.S.: 541511

TOKAI HOLDINGS CORPORATION
2-6-8 Tokiwa-cho, Aoi-ku, Shizuoka,
420-0034, Shizuoka, Japan
Tel.: (81) 542750007
Web Site:
https://www.tokaiholdings.co.jp
Year Founded: 2011
3167—(TKS)
Rev.: $1,530,300,930
Assets: $1,357,039,610
Liabilities: $753,546,610
Net Worth: $603,493,000
Earnings: $56,059,410
Emp.: 4,732
Fiscal Year-end: 03/31/24
Holding Company
N.A.I.C.S.: 551112
Katsuhiko Tokita (Pres & CEO)

Subsidiaries:

AM's Brain Inc. (1)
2nd Floor Kitanagase MK Building 1201-1
Kitanagase, Kita-ku, Okayama, 700-0963,
Okayama Prefecture, Japan
Tel.: (81) 862500067
Software Development Services
N.A.I.C.S.: 541511

Atsugi Isehara Cable Network Corporation (1)
3050 Okada Atsugi Axto Main Tower 4F,
Atsugi, 243-0021, Kanagawa, Japan
Tel.: (81) 462202018
Television Broadcasting Services
N.A.I.C.S.: 516120

CYZE Inc. (1)
7F Dogenzaka TR Building 1-18-1 Dogenzaka, Shibuya-ku, Tokyo, 150-0043, Japan
Tel.: (81) 354593817
System Development Services
N.A.I.C.S.: 541511

Cable Television Tsuyama Co., Ltd. (1)
1308-9 Odanaka, Tsuyama, 708-0006,
Okayama Prefecture, Japan
Tel.: (81) 868244000
Web Site: https://www.tvt-catv.jp
Television Broadcasting Services
N.A.I.C.S.: 516120

Chuo Denki Construction Co., Ltd. (1)
4-11-6 Kaminagoya, Nishi-ku, Nagoya, 451-0025, Aichi, Japan
Tel.: (81) 525315321
Web Site: https://chuo-denki.co.jp
Emp.: 26
Construction Electrical Equipment Mfr
N.A.I.C.S.: 336320

CloudMaster Co., Ltd. (1)
102 No 2 Chengdu Road, 108 Wanhua District, Taipei, Taiwan
Tel.: (886) 223118191
System Development Services
N.A.I.C.S.: 541511

East Communications Company Limited (1)
1-20 Asumigaoka, Midori-ku, Chiba, 267-0066, Japan
Tel.: (81) 120336368
Web Site: http://www.eastcom.ne.jp
Television Broadcasting Services
N.A.I.C.S.: 516120

Energy Line Corporation (1)
2-20-25 Furusho, Aoi-ku, Shizuoka, 420-0812, Japan
Tel.: (81) 542734927
Emp.: 229
Liquefied Petroleum Gas Distr
N.A.I.C.S.: 457210

Ichihara Cable Television Corporation (1)
2-23-18 Goi Chuohigashi, Ichihara, 290-0054, Japan
Tel.: (81) 120241991
Web Site: https://www.icntv.ne.jp
Cable Television Broadcasting Services
N.A.I.C.S.: 561492

Ichihara Community Network Television Corporation (1)
2-23-18 Goichuohigashi, Goi Chuohigashi,
Ichihara, 290-0054, Chiba, Japan
Tel.: (81) 120241991
Television Broadcasting Services
N.A.I.C.S.: 516120

Inoue Technica Co., Ltd. (1)
3-20 Nakaharacho, Numazu, 410-0818,
Japan
Tel.: (81) 559350550
Web Site: https://www.inoue-t.jp
Emp.: 110
Building Maintenance Business Services
N.A.I.C.S.: 541350

Isesaki Gas Co., Ltd. (1)
108 Hinodecho, Isesaki, 372-0022, Gunma
Prefecture, Japan
Tel.: (81) 270254520
Liquefied Petroleum Gas Distr
N.A.I.C.S.: 221210

J-support Co., Ltd. (1)
4-3-30 Tenjin, Chuo-ku, Fukuoka, 810-0001,
Japan
Tel.: (81) 927381410
Web Site: https://www.jsup.co.jp
Emp.: 28
Logistics Consulting Servies
N.A.I.C.S.: 541614

JOYNET Co., Ltd. (1)
3551-1 Mannohara Shinden, Fujinomiya,
418-0001, Shizuoka Prefecture, Japan
Tel.: (81) 544271178
Liquefied Petroleum Gas Distr
N.A.I.C.S.: 221210

Kurashiki Cable Television Inc. (1)
2661-1 Nakajima, Kurashiki, 710-0803,
Okayama, Japan
Tel.: (81) 120021337
Emp.: 111
Television Broadcasting Services
N.A.I.C.S.: 516120

LCV Corporation (1)
821 Shiga, Suwa, 392-8609, Nagano, Japan
Tel.: (81) 120123833
Television Broadcasting Services
N.A.I.C.S.: 516120

Nikaho Gas Corporation (1)
4 Funabashi Hirasawa, Nikaho, 018-0402,
Akita, Japan
Tel.: (81) 184747870
Liquefied Petroleum Gas Distr
N.A.I.C.S.: 457210

Nissan Tri Star Construction, Inc. (1)
Hagiwarachoatotsu 439-1, Gero, 509-2504,
Gifu Prefecture, Japan
Tel.: (81) 576522114
Cable Network Services
N.A.I.C.S.: 516120

Okinawa Cable Network Inc. (1)
1-2-20 Kumoji, Naha, 900-0015, Japan
Tel.: (81) 120984141
Web Site: https://nirai.ne.jp
Emp.: 75
Cable Television Broadcasting Services
N.A.I.C.S.: 561492

Osuga Gas Service, Ltd. (1)
903-2 Yokosuka, Kakegawa, 437-1301, Shizuoka Prefecture, Japan
Tel.: (81) 537482001
Liquefied Petroleum Gas Distr
N.A.I.C.S.: 221210

SENDAI CATV Co., Ltd. (1)
Honcho 1-15-5, Aoba-ku, Sendai, 980-0014,
Miyagi Prefecture, Japan
Tel.: (81) 222252211
Liquefied Petroleum Gas Distr
N.A.I.C.S.: 221210

T&T Energy Co., Ltd. (1)
2-33-10 Meisei, Nishi-ku, Nagoya, 451-0064, Aichi, Japan
Tel.: (81) 525242560
Liquefied Petroleum Gas Distr
N.A.I.C.S.: 457210

TOKAI (Shanghai) Trade & Commerce Co., Ltd. (1)
Room 302-1 No 1 Lane 777 WanRong
Road, JinAn District, Shanghai, 200072,
China
Tel.: (86) 2163510076
Bottled Water Mfr
N.A.I.C.S.: 312112

TOKAI Bay Network Co., Ltd. (1)
Toyocho SH Building 4F 4-10-4 Toyo, Koto-ku, Tokyo, 135-0016, Japan
Tel.: (81) 336402001
Television Broadcasting Services
N.A.I.C.S.: 516120

TOKAI Cable Network Corporation (1)
8-28 Kotobukicho, Numazu, 410-0053, Shizuoka, Japan
Tel.: (81) 559224701
Web Site: https://www.thn.ne.jp
Emp.: 275
Cable Network Services
N.A.I.C.S.: 516120

TOKAI City Service Corporation (1)
Koya-machi 17-1, Aoi-ku, Shizuoka, 420-0852, Shizuoka Prefecture, Japan
Tel.: (81) 542735003
Wedding & Banquet Hall Services
N.A.I.C.S.: 561990

TOKAI Communications Corporation (1)
8 TOKAI Building 2-6 Tokiwacho, Aoi Ward,
Shizuoka, 420-0034, Shizuoka Prefecture,
Japan
Tel.: (81) 542543781
Web Site: https://www.tokai-com.co.jp
Emp.: 1,313
Information Communications Technology
Services
N.A.I.C.S.: 517810

TOKAI Corporation (1)
TOKAI Building 2-6-8 Tokiwa-cho, Aoi-ku,
Shizuoka, 420-0034, Japan
Tel.: (81) 542548181
Emp.: 1,501
Energy & Telecommunications Products &
Services
N.A.I.C.S.: 424720
Katsuhiko Tokita (Chm)

TOKAI Gas Corporation (1)
74-3 Shiotsu, Yaizu, 425-0085, Shizuoka,
Japan
Tel.: (81) 546287151
LP Gas Distr
N.A.I.C.S.: 457210

TOKAI Home Gas Corporation (1)
Hama Rikyu Intercity 1-9-1 Kaigan, Minato-ku, Tokyo, 105-0022, Japan
Tel.: (81) 35 404 7513
Web Site: https://www.tokai-homegas.co.jp
Liquefied Petroleum Gas Distr
N.A.I.C.S.: 457210

TOKAI Human Resources Evol Corporation (1)
2-6-8 Tokiwa-cho, Aoi-ku, Shizuoka, 420-0034, Japan
Tel.: (81) 542734941
Dispatching Services
N.A.I.C.S.: 561320

TOKAI Kids Touch Corporation (1)
2-6-8 Tokiwacho, Aoi Ward, Shizuoka, 420-0034, Japan
Tel.: (81) 549080033
Web Site: https://www.tokai-kidstouch.co.jp
Day-Care Centre Operator
N.A.I.C.S.: 624410

TOKAI Life Plus Corporation (1)
TOKAI Building Tokiwa-cho 2-6-8, Aoi-ku,
Shizuoka, 420-0034, Shizuoka Prefecture,
Japan
Tel.: (81) 542734916
Web Site: https://www.tokai-lifeplus.co.jp
Adult Day Care & Nursing Care Services
N.A.I.C.S.: 623990

TOKAI Management Service Corporation (1)
TOKAI Building Tokiwa-cho 2-6-8, Aoi-ku,
Shizuoka, 420-0034, Shizuoka Prefecture,
Japan
Tel.: (81) 542735566
Accounting & Payroll Services
N.A.I.C.S.: 541214

TOKAI Myanmar Company Limited (1)
130 Shwegonedine Road Rm 419 4th Floor
Yuzana Hotel, Bahan Tsp, Yangon, Myanmar
Tel.: (95) 9254066141
Emp.: 3,888
LP Gas Piping System Services
N.A.I.C.S.: 237120

Tender Co., Ltd. (1)
Hagiwarachoatotsu 439-1, Gero, 509-2504,
Gifu Prefecture, Japan
Tel.: (81) 576523462
Nursing Care Welfare Services
N.A.I.C.S.: 623110

Toco Channel Shizuoka Corporation (1)
1st floor Suzuyo Information Center Building
2-1-5 Nakanogo, Shimizu-ku, Shizuoka,
424-0888, Japan
Tel.: (81) 543479811
Television Broadcasting Services
N.A.I.C.S.: 516120

Tokai Nondestructive Inspection Co., Ltd. (1)
813-1 Hagiwara, Gero, 509-2517, Gifu,
Japan
Tel.: (81) 576524091
Non-Destructive Inspection Services
N.A.I.C.S.: 541380

Tokaizosen-unyu Corporation (1)
3899-4 Ogawa, Yaizu, 425-0033, Shizuoka,
Japan

TOKAI HOLDINGS CORPORATION

TOKAI Holdings Corporation—(Continued)
Tel.: (81) 546243131
Ship Maintenance & Repair Services
N.A.I.C.S.: 336611

Tokai Corporation (1)
2-6-8 Tokiwa-Cho, Aoi-ku, Shizuoka, 420-0034, Japan
Tel.: (81) 120987242
Web Site: https://www.tokai.jp
Emp.: 1,501
Energy Information Communication Services
N.A.I.C.S.: 541350

Tokyo Bay Network Co., Ltd. (1)
4F Toyocho Sh Building 4-10-4 Toyo, Koto-ku, Tokyo, 135-0016, Japan
Tel.: (81) 120443404
Web Site: https://www.baynet.ne.jp
Telecommunication Broadcasting Services
N.A.I.C.S.: 561492

Wae Co., Ltd.
11-29 Minamimachi, Suruga-ku, Shizuoka, 422-8067, Shizuoka Prefecture, Japan
Tel.: (81) 542822277
Electronic Products Mfr
N.A.I.C.S.: 335132

TOKAI KISEN CO., LTD.
1-16-1 Kaigan, Minato-ku, Tokyo, 105-6891, Japan
Tel.: (81) 354729999
Web Site:
https://www.tokaikisen.co.jp
Year Founded: 1889
9173—(TKS)
Rev.: $93,417,840
Assets: $159,383,200
Liabilities: $117,722,360
Net Worth: $41,660,840
Earnings: ($4,112,200)
Emp.: 365
Fiscal Year-end: 12/31/23
Marine Transportation Services
N.A.I.C.S.: 488510
Junichi Yamazaki (Pres)

TOKAI LEASE CO., LTD.
2-6 Tenjinbashi, Kita-ku, Osaka, 530-0041, Japan
Tel.: (81) 663520001
Web Site: https://www.tokai-lease.co.jp
Year Founded: 1968
9761—(TKS)
Rev.: $113,526,750
Assets: $228,368,890
Liabilities: $121,081,980
Net Worth: $107,286,910
Earnings: $4,461,750
Emp.: 465
Fiscal Year-end: 03/31/24
Building Lease Services
N.A.I.C.S.: 531110
Hiroaki Tsukamoto (Pres)

TOKAI RIKA CO., LTD.
3-260 Toyota Oguchi-cho, Niwa-gun, Oguchi, 480-0195, Aichi, Japan
Tel.: (81) 587955211
Web Site: https://www.tokai-rika.co.jp
Year Founded: 1948
6995—(TKS)
Rev.: $4,119,972,418
Assets: $3,433,880,770
Liabilities: $1,190,815,656
Net Worth: $2,243,065,114
Earnings: $180,614,419
Emp.: 20,247
Fiscal Year-end: 03/31/24
Human Interface Systems & Controls, Security Systems, Safety Systems, Exterior, Electrical Appliances & Devices, Housing Equipment & Agricultural Device Mfr
N.A.I.C.S.: 336340
Koki Sato (Exec VP)

Subsidiaries:

Ena Tokai Rika Co., Ltd. (1)
22 Shintakeori Takenami cho, Ena, 509-7126, Gifu, Japan
Tel.: (81) 573283000
Sales Range: $150-199.9 Million
Emp.: 480
Automotive Resin Parts Mfr & Distr
N.A.I.C.S.: 423120

Foshan Tokairika Automotive Parts Co., Ltd. (1)
No 10 Wusha Section of Shunpan Road, Daliang Town Shunde, Foshan, Guangdong, China
Tel.: (86) 75722803921
Web Site: http://www.tokai-rika.co.jp
Sales Range: $200-249.9 Million
Emp.: 1,000
Automotive Parts Mfr & Distr
N.A.I.C.S.: 336390

NSK Co., Ltd. (1)
2188 45 Aza Minamiyama, Mitake cho Kani-gun, Gifu, 505 0116, Japan
Tel.: (81) 574681070
Sales Range: $50-74.9 Million
Emp.: 170
Automotive Switches Mfr & Distr
N.A.I.C.S.: 336320

PT. TOKAI RIKA INDONESIA (1)
Sales Range: $25-49.9 Million
Emp.: 20
Automotive Parts Mfr & Distr
N.A.I.C.S.: 336390

Quality Safety Systems Company (1)
255 Patillo Rd RR 1, Old Castle, N8N 2L9, ON, Canada
Tel.: (519) 973-7400
Sales Range: $250-299.9 Million
Emp.: 950
Automotive Seat Belts Mfr & Distr
N.A.I.C.S.: 423120

Rica Auto Parts Co Ltd (1)
No 1076 Sec 3 Fuguo Rd, Luzhu Dist, Taoyuan, 338, Taiwan
Tel.: (886) 33221381
Web Site: http://www.rica-auto-parts.com
Sales Range: $75-99.9 Million
Emp.: 115
Automotive Switches & Key locks Mfr & Distr
N.A.I.C.S.: 423120
Ushiroda Kazunori (Chm)

Rikaseiki Co., Ltd. (1)
3-260 Toyota, Oguchi-cho, Niwa, 480-0134, Aichi, Japan
Tel.: (81) 587228716
Web Site: http://www.rikaseiki.co.jp
Sales Range: $75-99.9 Million
Emp.: 92
Automotive Parts Mfr & Distr
N.A.I.C.S.: 423120

Sandenzaisha Co., Ltd. (1)
331-7 Hamaike Nishisaiwai-cho, Nishimiyuki-cho, Toyohashi, 441-8113, Aichi, Japan
Tel.: (81) 532385631
Web Site: https://www.sandenzai.co.jp
Sales Range: $50-74.9 Million
Emp.: 125
Automotive Part Whslr
N.A.I.C.S.: 423120

TAC Manufacturing, Inc. (1)
4111 County Farm Rd, Jackson, MI 49201
Tel.: (517) 789-7000
Web Site: http://www.tacmfg.com
Sales Range: $250-299.9 Million
Emp.: 700
Automotive Parts Mfr & Distr
N.A.I.C.S.: 423120

TRAM, Inc. (1)
47200 Port St, Plymouth, MI 48170
Tel.: (734) 254-8500
Web Site: https://www.tokai-rika.co.jp
Sales Range: $25-49.9 Million
Emp.: 190
Electronic Component Research Services
N.A.I.C.S.: 541715

TRB Limited (1)
1 TRB Drive, St Asaph Business Park, Saint Asaph, LL17 0JB, Denbighshire, United Kingdom
Tel.: (44) 1745584000
Web Site: https://trb-ltd.com
Sales Range: $75-99.9 Million
Emp.: 110
Automobile Component Distr
N.A.I.C.S.: 423120
Naohisa Goto (Mng Dir)

TRBR Industria e Comercio Ltda. (1)
Avenida Marginal 1515 Bairro Polo Industrial, Santa Barbara d'Oeste, 13458-840, SP, Brazil
Tel.: (55) 1930262300
Sales Range: $50-74.9 Million
Emp.: 235
Automotive Switches Mfr & Distr
N.A.I.C.S.: 423120

TRCZ s.r.o. (1)
Prumyslova 1165, 410 02, Lovosice, Czech Republic
Tel.: (420) 41 642 1111
Web Site: https://www.trcz.cz
Automotive Parts Mfr & Distr
N.A.I.C.S.: 336390

TRMI, Inc. (1)
100 Hill Brady Rd, Battle Creek, MI 49037
Tel.: (269) 966-0100
Web Site: https://tramgroup.com
Sales Range: $150-199.9 Million
Emp.: 535
Automotive Switches Mfr
N.A.I.C.S.: 423120
Vickey Bobberteen (Mgr-HR)

TRP, Inc. (1)
Toyota Sta Rosa Laguna Industrial Complex Barangay Pulong, Sta Cruz, Santa Rosa, 4026, Laguna, Philippines
Tel.: (63) 495413015
Sales Range: $200-249.9 Million
Emp.: 1,595
Automotive Switches Mfr & Distr
N.A.I.C.S.: 335931

TRQSS, Inc (1)
255 Patillo Rd RR 1, Tecumseh, N8N 2L9, ON, Canada
Tel.: (519) 973-7400
Sales Range: $200-249.9 Million
Emp.: 830
Automotive Seat Belt Mfr & Distr
N.A.I.C.S.: 336360

Thai Seat Belt Co Ltd (1)
700/56 M 6, T Nongmaidaeng A Muang, Chon Buri, 20000, Thailand
Tel.: (66) 38214705
Sales Range: $100-124.9 Million
Emp.: 465
Automotive Seat Belts Mfr & Distr
N.A.I.C.S.: 336360

Tianjin Tokairika Automotive Parts Co., Ltd (1)
200 Huang Hai lu, Tianjin Economic-Technological Development Area, Tianjin, China
Tel.: (86) 22 25320790
Web Site: http://www.tokai-rika.co.jp
Sales Range: $200-249.9 Million
Emp.: 625
Automotive Switches Mfr & Distr
N.A.I.C.S.: 335931

Tokai Rika Asia Co., Ltd. (1)
700/104 M 6 T Nongmaidaeng, A Muang, Chon Buri, 20000, Thailand
Tel.: (66) 3 846 5670
Web Site: http://www.tokai-rika.co.jp
Sales Range: $50-74.9 Million
Emp.: 25
Investment Management Service
N.A.I.C.S.: 523999

Tokai Rika Belgium NV (1)
Ikaroslaan 37, 1930, Zaventem, Belgium
Tel.: (32) 27110300
Sales Range: $50-74.9 Million
Emp.: 20
Automotive Part Whslr
N.A.I.C.S.: 423120

Tokai Rika Co., Ltd. - Hagi Plant (1)

INTERNATIONAL PUBLIC

1-3 Nakayama Hagi-cho, Toyokawa, 441-0201, Aichi, Japan
Tel.: (81) 53 388 7051
Web Site: https://www.tokai-rika.co.jp
Sales Range: $50-74.9 Million
Emp.: 125
Automobile Parts Mfr
N.A.I.C.S.: 336390

Tokai Rika Co., Ltd. - Otowa Plant (1)
1 Hirayama Akasaka-Cho, Toyokawa, 441-0295, Aichi, Japan
Tel.: (81) 53 388 4111
Web Site: https://www.tokai-rika.co.jp
Sales Range: $400-449.9 Million
Emp.: 1,675
Automobile Parts Mfr
N.A.I.C.S.: 336390

Tokai Rika Co., Ltd. - Toyota Plant (1)
2-47-1 Konosu-cho, Toyota, 471-0836, Aichi, Japan
Tel.: (81) 565 28 1141
Sales Range: $200-249.9 Million
Emp.: 840
Automobile Parts Mfr
N.A.I.C.S.: 336390

Tokai Rika Create Corporation (1)
2-3-10 Aoi, Higashi-ku, Nagoya, 461-0004, Aichi, Japan
Tel.: (81) 529342111
Web Site: https://www.torica.co.jp
Emp.: 319
Automotive Components, Resin, Nonferrous Metal Materials & Industrial Machineries Equipments Mfr
N.A.I.C.S.: 423620
Masaki Matsuyama (Pres)

Tokai Rika Eletec Co., Ltd. (1)
5-3-16 Odabuchi-ch, Toyokawa, 442-0844, Aichi, Japan
Tel.: (81) 53 388 6195
Emp.: 250
Automotive Parts Mfr & Distr
N.A.I.C.S.: 336320

Tokai Rika Eletech Co., Ltd. (1)
5-3-16 Odabuchi-cho, Toyokawa, 442-0844, Aichi, Japan
Tel.: (81) 533 88 6195
Web Site: http://www.tokai-rika.co.jp
Emp.: 250
Automotive Key Cylinder & Electronic Parts Mfr & Distr
N.A.I.C.S.: 333995

Tokai Rika Mexico, S.A. de C.V. (1)
Blvd Interpuerto Monterrey No 103 Parque Industrial Interpuerto, 65500, Salinas Victoria, Nuevo Leon, Mexico
Tel.: (52) 812 314 3300
Emp.: 810
Automotive Parts Mfr & Distr
N.A.I.C.S.: 336390

Tokai Rika Minda India Private Limited (1)
Plot No 365 Kiadb Industrial Area Sompura 1st Stage Dobbaspet, Nelamangala Taluk, Bengaluru, 562111, India
Tel.: (91) 80 2801 4700
Sales Range: $25-49.9 Million
Emp.: 6
Automotive Seat Belt Mfr & Distr
N.A.I.C.S.: 336360
Yoshihiro Kondo (Mng Dir)

Tokai Rika Next Co., Ltd. (1)
22 Shintakeori Takenami-cho, Ena, Gifu, 509-7126, Japan
Tel.: (81) 57 328 3000
Emp.: 750
Automotive Parts Mfr & Distr
N.A.I.C.S.: 336320

Tokai Rika Service Co., Ltd. (1)
48 Izumi Nishibiwajima-cho, Kiyosu, 452-0015, Aichi, Japan
Tel.: (81) 52 501 8111
Web Site: https://www.tokai-rika.co.jp
Sales Range: $125-149.9 Million
Emp.: 295
Overland Transportation Services
N.A.I.C.S.: 488999

Tokai Rika Thailand Co Ltd (1)

7/114 Mu 4 Map Yang Phon, Pluak Daeng, Rayong, 21140, Thailand
Tel.: (66) 38015030
Sales Range: $550-599.9 Million
Emp.: 1,405
Automotive Switches & Key Locks Mfr & Distr
N.A.I.C.S.: 423120

Trin, Inc. (1)
803 HL Thompson Jr Dr, Ashley, IN 46705
Tel.: (260) 587-9282
Sales Range: $75-99.9 Million
Emp.: 150
Automotive Switches Mfr
N.A.I.C.S.: 423120
Jessica Curran *(Mgr-Assembly Section)*

Wuxi Risho Technology Co., Ltd. (1)
38 Changjiang Road, Wuxi National Hi-Tech Industrial Development Zone, Jiangsu, China
Tel.: (86) 510 8521 1511
Web Site: http://www.tokai-rika.co.jp
Sales Range: $200-249.9 Million
Emp.: 815
Automotive Seat Belt Mfr & Distr
N.A.I.C.S.: 336360

TOKAI SENKO K.K.
Dai Nagoya Building 8F 28-12 Meieki 3-chome, Nakamura-ku, Nagoya, 450-6432, Japan
Tel.: (81) 528568141
Web Site: https://www.tokai-senko.co.jp
Year Founded: 1941
3577—(TKS)
Rev.: $87,351,150
Assets: $96,195,330
Liabilities: $43,255,840
Net Worth: $52,939,490
Earnings: $852,690
Emp.: 180
Fiscal Year-end: 03/31/24
Textile Product Mfr & Whslr
N.A.I.C.S.: 333248
Yoshiaki Yashiro *(Chm)*

Subsidiaries:

P.T. Dessin junn Indonesia (1)
Jl Jababeka Raya B 4-10 Cikarang Industrial Estate, Bekasi, 17530, West Java, Indonesia
Tel.: (62) 2189835836
Industrial Machinery Distr
N.A.I.C.S.: 423830

Tex Tracing Co., Ltd (1)
14/2 Mu 9 Puchaosamingpri Rd Samrongklag, Phra Pradaeng, 10130, Samutprakarn, Thailand
Tel.: (66) 27543521
Industrial Machinery Distr
N.A.I.C.S.: 423830

Tokai Dyeing Co., (THAILAND) Ltd. (1)
69 Mu 1 Puchaosamingpri Rd Samrongklag, Phra Pradaeng, 10130, Samutprakarn, Thailand
Tel.: (66) 23943013
Dyeing Product Mfr
N.A.I.C.S.: 313310

Tokai Trading Co., Ltd. (1)
Tokai Bldg 1-18-2 Honcho, Yokosuka, Kanagawa, Japan
Tel.: (81) 468213411
Web Site: https://www.tkijp.com
Industrial Machinery Distr
N.A.I.C.S.: 423830

Tokaitex Phils. Inc. (1)
Unit 3B 3rd Floor Corinthian Plaza 121 Paseo De Roxas Legaspi Village, Makati, 1229, Philippines
Tel.: (63) 25502419
Fabric Distr
N.A.I.C.S.: 424210

TOKAI SOFTWARE CO., LTD.
2-15-1 Shindo, Nishi-Ku, Nagoya, 451-0043, Japan
Tel.: (81) 525633572
Web Site: http://www.tokai-soft.co.jp
4430—(TKS)
Sales Range: $50-74.9 Million
Software Development Services
N.A.I.C.S.: 541511
Hidekazu Ito *(Pres)*

TOKAI TOKYO FINANCIAL HOLDINGS, INC.
2-5-1 Nihonbashi, Chuo-ku, Tokyo, 103-6130, Japan
Tel.: (81) 335178100   JP
Web Site: https://www.tokaitokyo-fh.jp
Year Founded: 1929
8616—(NGO)
Rev.: $589,368,847
Assets: $9,252,458,592
Liabilities: $7,977,698,460
Net Worth: $1,274,760,132
Earnings: $78,037,639
Emp.: 2,655
Fiscal Year-end: 03/31/24
Holding Company
N.A.I.C.S.: 551112
Mikio Fujii *(Deputy Pres & Head-Investment Banking Company)*

Subsidiaries:

Ace Securities Co., Ltd. (1)
2-6-11 Honmachi, Chuo-ku, Osaka, 541-0053, Japan   **(94.86%)**
Tel.: (81) 662672111
Web Site: http://www.ace-sec.co.jp
Emp.: 343
Securities Brokerage
N.A.I.C.S.: 523150
Yoshinori Deguchi *(Pres & Dir)*

Subsidiary (Domestic):

Ace Consulting Co., Ltd. (2)
3-2-12 Nihonbashi Kayabacho, Chuo-ku, Tokyo, Japan
Tel.: (81) 3 5695 5078
Management Consulting Services
N.A.I.C.S.: 541611
Nobuhiro Tokuhara *(Pres)*

CHEER Securities Inc. (1)
1-17-21 Shinkawa, Chuo-ku, Tokyo, 104-0033, Japan
Tel.: (81) 363873355
Web Site: https://www.cheer-sec.co.jp
Financial Management Services
N.A.I.C.S.: 551112

Eternal Co., Ltd. (1)
2nd Floor Prem Minami-Aoyama Building 4-20-19 Minami-Aoyama, Minato-ku, Tokyo, 107-0062, Japan
Tel.: (81) 782414201
Web Site: https://www.e-fca.jp
Emp.: 207
Financial Planning Services
N.A.I.C.S.: 522320

Mebius Co., Ltd. (1)
Tobu Tateno Building 5F 2-10-27 Kitasai, Nishi-ku, Yokohama, 220-0004, Japan
Tel.: (81) 452900135
Web Site: https://www.mebius.co.jp
Emp.: 103
Software Development Services
N.A.I.C.S.: 541511

Nishi-Nippon City Tokai Tokyo Securities Co., Ltd. (1)
1-10-20 Tenjin 3rd floor of Tenjin Business Center, Chuo-ku, Fukuoka, 810-0001, Japan
Tel.: (81) 92 707 3000
Web Site: https://www.nctt.co.jp
Emp.: 197
Financial Management Services
N.A.I.C.S.: 523999

Tokai Tokyo Academy Co., Ltd. (1)
Educational Support Services
N.A.I.C.S.: 611710

Tokai Tokyo Business Service Co., Ltd. (1)
1-17-21 Shinkawa, Chuo, 104-0033, Japan
Tel.: (81) 3 3553 6364
Business Support Services

N.A.I.C.S.: 561439

Tokai Tokyo Global Investments Pte. Ltd. (1)
60 Anson Road 13-03 Mapletree Anson, Singapore, 079914, Singapore
Tel.: (65) 6 634 2177
Fund Investment & Research Services
N.A.I.C.S.: 523940

Tokai Tokyo Investment Co., Ltd. (1)
9th Floor Kayabacho First Building 1-17-21 Shinkawa, Chuo-ku, Tokyo, 104-0033, Japan
Tel.: (81) 33 553 7174
Fund Operation Management Services
N.A.I.C.S.: 523940

Tokai Tokyo Investment Management Pte. Ltd. (1)
250 North Bridge Road 06-00 Raffles City Tower, Singapore, 179101, Singapore
Tel.: (65) 6 230 8133
Fund Management Services
N.A.I.C.S.: 523940

Tokai Tokyo Investment Management Singapore Pte. Ltd. (1)
Tel.: (65) 64364250
Portfolio Management Services
N.A.I.C.S.: 523940

Tokai Tokyo Research Center Co., Ltd. (1)
1-19-30 Aoi 5th Floor Mazak Art Plaza Office Building, Higashi-ku, Tokyo, 461-0004, Aichi, Japan
Tel.: (81) 52 979 8591
Market Research Services
N.A.I.C.S.: 541613

Tokai Tokyo Research Institute Co., Ltd. (1)
1-19-30 Aoi Mazak Art Plaza Office Building 5F, Higashi-ku, Nagoya, 461-0004, Aichi, Japan
Tel.: (81) 52 979 8591
Web Site: https://www.ttrc.co.jp
Investment Advisory Services
N.A.I.C.S.: 523940

Tokai Tokyo Securities (Asia) LTD. (1)
15/F 33 Des Voeux Road, Central, China (Hong Kong)
Tel.: (852) 28100822
Security Brokerage Services
N.A.I.C.S.: 523150
Sam Omata *(Mng Dir)*

Tokai Tokyo Securities (USA), Inc. (1)
3 Columbus Cir Ste 1715, New York, NY 10019
Tel.: (646) 979-2200
Marketing Consulting Services
N.A.I.C.S.: 541613
Miki Ohtsubo *(Pres)*

Tokai Tokyo Securities Co., Ltd (1)
7-1, Meieki 4-chome, Nakamura-ku, Nagoya-shi, Aichi, Japan
Tel.: (81) 0525271111
Web Site: https://www.tokaitokyo.co.jp
Financial Instruments Business
N.A.I.C.S.: 334513

Tokai Tokyo Securities Europe Limited (1)
4th Floor Salisbury House, London Wall, London, EC2M 5QQ, United Kingdom
Tel.: (44) 2070704600
Emp.: 10
Security Brokerage Services
N.A.I.C.S.: 523150

Tokai Tokyo Services Co., Ltd. (1)
3rd floor Urbannet Nunoike Building 1-13-8 Aoi, Higashi-ku, Nagoya, 460-0004, Aichi, Japan
Tel.: (81) 525086661
Real Estate Lending Services
N.A.I.C.S.: 531110

Tokai Tokyo Wealth Consulting Co., Ltd. (1)
3rd floor Sakuradori Toyota Building 4-5-28 Meieki, Nakamura-ku, Nagoya, 450-0002, Aichi, Japan
Tel.: (81) 525271160

Inheritance Property Services
N.A.I.C.S.: 523991

TOKAIDO REIT, INC.
2-2-1 Otemachi, Chiyoda-ku, Tokyo, 100-0004, Japan
Tel.: (81) 335017822
Web Site: https://www.tokaido-reit.co.jp
2989—(TKS)
Real Estate Investment Services
N.A.I.C.S.: 531190

TOKATSU HOLDINGS CO., LTD.
3-21-1 Kogane Kiyoshigaoka, Matsudo, 270-0013, Chiba, Japan
Tel.: (81) 473461190
Web Site: https://www.tkhd.co.jp
Year Founded: 1969
2754—(TKS)
Rev.: $56,442,790
Assets: $52,761,020
Liabilities: $17,675,140
Net Worth: $35,085,880
Earnings: $2,313,500
Fiscal Year-end: 03/31/24
Automobile Whslr
N.A.I.C.S.: 441110
Toshiyuki Ishizuka *(Pres)*

TOKEN CORPORATION
Token Headquarters Marunouchi Building 1-33 2-chome Marunouchi, Naka-ku, Nagoya, 460-0002, Japan
Tel.: (81) 522328027   JP
Web Site: https://www.token.co.jp
Year Founded: 1974
1766—(NGO)
Rev.: $2,093,485,299
Assets: $1,311,192,600
Liabilities: $549,448,299
Net Worth: $761,744,301
Earnings: $34,615,130
Emp.: 6,370
Fiscal Year-end: 04/30/23
Apartment Building Management & Leasing Services
N.A.I.C.S.: 531110
Minoru Souda *(Pres & Chm)*

Subsidiaries:

Nasluck Co., Ltd. (1)
Alpen Power 8 Floor, 2940 Narunouchi Nakaku, Nagoya, Japan
Tel.: (81) 522328030
Web Site: https://www.nasluck.co.jp
Kitchen Fixtures & Accessories Mfr & Whslr
N.A.I.C.S.: 337110

Token Building Management Co., Ltd. (1)
2-1-33 Marunouchi Tokenhonshamarunochi Building, Naka-ku, Nagoya, 460-0002, Aichi, Japan   **(100%)**
Tel.: (81) 522328020
Residential Property Management Services
N.A.I.C.S.: 531311

Token Lease Fund Co., Ltd. (1)
2-133 Marunouchi Token Headquarters Marunouchi Building 9F, Naka-ku, Nagoya, 460-0002, Aichi, Japan
Tel.: (81) 522328080
Web Site: http://www.leasefund.co.jp
Financial Lending Services
N.A.I.C.S.: 522220

Token Resort Japan Co., Ltd. (1)
2-1-33 Marunouchi, Naka-ku, Nagoya, 460-0002, Aichi, Japan
Tel.: (81) 574659111
Web Site: http://www.token-resort-j.com
Hotels & Resorts Operation Services
N.A.I.C.S.: 721110

Token TADO Country Co., Ltd. (1)
2692 Tadochokono, Kuwana, 511-0122, Mie, Japan
Tel.: (81) 594485811

TOKEN CORPORATION

Token Corporation—(Continued)
Sales Range: $50-74.9 Million
Emp.: 100
Golf & Country Clubs Operation Services
N.A.I.C.S.: 713910
Minoru Soda (Pres)

Token Tado Country K.K. (1)
2692 Furuno Tadocho, Kuwana, 511-0122, Mie, Japan
Tel.: (81) 594485811
Web Site: http://www.token-tado.co.jp
Sales Range: $50-74.9 Million
Emp.: 100
Golf Courses & Country Clubs
N.A.I.C.S.: 713910

Totsu Agency Co., Ltd (1)
3-35-34 Sakae Sakae Tower Hills 3F, Naka-ku, Nagoya, 460-0008, Aichi, Japan
Tel.: (81) 522328050
Web Site: http://www.totsu-ag.com
Event Planning & Advertising Services
N.A.I.C.S.: 541810
Minoru Souda (Pres & CEO)

Totsu Travel Co., Ltd. (1)
Sakae Tower Hills 1st floor 3-35-34 Sakae, Naka-ku, Nagoya, 460-0008, Aichi, Japan
Tel.: (81) 522438500
Web Site: http://www.totsu-tr.co.jp
Travel & Tour Operating Agencies
N.A.I.C.S.: 561520

TOKENS.COM CORP.
Suite 3200 Bay Adelaide Centre-North Tower 40 Temperance St, Toronto, M5H 0B4, ON, Canada
Tel.: (647) 578-7490 BC
Web Site: https://www.tokens.com
Year Founded: 1998
SMURF—(OTCQB)
Investment Management Service
N.A.I.C.S.: 523999
Eric Abrahams (COO)

TOKENS.COM CORP.
3200-40 Temperance St Bay Adelaide Center - North Tower, Toronto, M5H 0B4, ON, Canada
Tel.: (647) 578-7490
Web Site: https://www.realbotix.ai
Year Founded: 2020
XBOTF—(OTCIQ)
Rev.: $17,985
Assets: $2,418,345
Liabilities: $62,579
Net Worth: $2,355,766
Earnings: ($30,369)
Emp.: 3
Fiscal Year-end: 12/31/19
Technology Investment Company
N.A.I.C.S.: 513210
Eric Abrahams (COO)

TOKENTUS INVESTMENT AG
Taunusanlage 8 c/o WeWork, 60329, Frankfurt am Main, Germany
Tel.: (49) 1772421383
Web Site: https://www.tokentus.com
Year Founded: 2019
14D—(DEU)
Assets: $10,166,643
Liabilities: $231,813
Net Worth: $9,934,830
Earnings: ($2,583,056)
Emp.: 4
Fiscal Year-end: 12/31/23
Investment Management Service
N.A.I.C.S.: 523999
Oliver Michel (Founder)

TOKIO MARINE HOLDINGS, INC.
2-6-4 Otemachi, Chiyoda-ku, Tokyo, 100-0004, Japan
Tel.: (81) 367044547 JP
Web Site: https://www.tokiomarinehd.com
Year Founded: 1879
TKOMY—(OTCIQ)
Rev.: $47,670,462,000
Assets: $196,442,355,060
Liabilities: $170,623,765,830
Net Worth: $25,818,589,230
Earnings: $2,699,124,990
Emp.: 971
Fiscal Year-end: 03/31/23
Holding Company; Casualty & Property Insurance
N.A.I.C.S.: 551112
Tsuyoshi Nagano (Chm)

Subsidiaries:

Asahi Mutual Life Insurance Company (1)
2-6-1 Asahi Seimei Otemachi Building, Chiyoda-ku, Tokyo, 100-8103, Japan (100%)
Tel.: (81) 362253111
Web Site: http://www.asahi-life.co.jp
Sales Range: $350-399.9 Million
Emp.: 700
Provider of Life Insurance
N.A.I.C.S.: 524113
Hiroki Kimura (Pres)

Baoviet Tokio Marine Insurance Joint Venture Company (1)
Room 601 6th Floor Sun Red River Building 23 Phan Chu Trinh, Hoan Kiem District, Hanoi, Vietnam
Tel.: (84) 439330704
Web Site: http://www.baoviettokiomarine.com
Sales Range: $1-9.9 Million
Emp.: 50
Non-Life Insurance Products & Services
N.A.I.C.S.: 524128
Hidaki Mishima (Gen Mgr)

Delphi Financial Group, Inc. (1)
1105 N Market St Ste 1230, Wilmington, DE 19899
Tel.: (302) 478-5142
Web Site: https://www.delphifin.com
Sales Range: $900-999.9 Million
Emp.: 1,964
Holding Company; Integrated Employee Benefit Services
N.A.I.C.S.: 551112
Robert Rosenkranz (Chm)

Subsidiary (Domestic):

Delphi Capital Management, Inc. (2)
590 Madison Ave Ste 430, New York, NY 10022 (100%)
Tel.: (212) 838-7000
Sales Range: $25-49.9 Million
Emp.: 40
Medical Insurance Provider
N.A.I.C.S.: 524113

Matrix Absence Management, Inc. (2)
3979 Freedom Cir Ste 650, Santa Clara, CA 95054 (100%)
Tel.: (408) 360-8370
Web Site: https://www.matrixcos.com
Sales Range: $50-74.9 Million
Emp.: 90
Financial Services
N.A.I.C.S.: 524292
Kenneth F. Cope (Pres)

Reliance Standard Life Insurance Company (2)
1700 Market St Ste 1200, Philadelphia, PA 19103 (100%)
Tel.: (610) 994-7800
Web Site: https://www.reliancestandard.com
Sales Range: $150-199.9 Million
Emp.: 300
Life Insurance Dental Insurance & General Insurance
N.A.I.C.S.: 524113
Robert M. Smith Jr. (Chief Investment Officer)

Subsidiary (Domestic):

First Reliance Standard Life Insurance Company (3)
590 Madison Ave 29th Fl, New York, NY 10022
Tel.: (212) 303-8400

Web Site: http://www.rsli.com
Emp.: 17
Business Insurance Services
N.A.I.C.S.: 524128
Lawrence E. Daurelle (CEO)

Subsidiary (Domestic):

Safety National Casualty Corporation (2)
1832 Schuetz Rd, Saint Louis, MO 63146 (100%)
Tel.: (314) 995-5300
Web Site: https://www.safetynational.com
Sales Range: $50-74.9 Million
Emp.: 285
Property & Casualty Insurance Specializing in the Issuance of Excess Workers Compensation Policies for Self Insured Employers
N.A.I.C.S.: 524126
Duane A. Hercules (CEO)

Subsidiary (Domestic):

Midlands Management Corporation (3)
3817 NW Expy Ste 1000, Oklahoma City, OK 73112
Tel.: (405) 840-0074
Web Site: http://www.midlandsmgt.com
Insurance Management Services
N.A.I.C.S.: 524298
Charles C. Caldwell (Founder & CEO)

E. design Insurance Co., Ltd. (1)
3-20-2 Nishi-Shinjuku, Shinjuku-ku, Tokyo, 163-1413, Japan
Tel.: (81) 12 009 8035
Web Site: https://www.edsp.co.jp
General Insurance Services
N.A.I.C.S.: 524210
Teraji Ine (Mng Dir)

First Insurance Company of Hawaii, Ltd. (1)
1100 Ward Ave, Honolulu, HI 96814-1600
Tel.: (808) 527-7777
Web Site: https://www.ficoh.com
Sales Range: $200-249.9 Million
Emp.: 310
Casualty, Marine, Automobile & Fire Insurance Services
N.A.I.C.S.: 524126
Lance Kawano (Pres-First Risk Mgmt Svcs & VP)

Kiln Hong Kong (1)
3804 The Lee Gardens 33 Hysan Avenue, Causeway Bay, China (Hong Kong)
Tel.: (852) 2500 3300
Web Site: http://www.tokiomarinekiln.com
Emp.: 11
General Insurance Services
N.A.I.C.S.: 524210
Adelina Leong (Reg Dir-Ops)

Kiln Regional UnderWriting Limited (1)
Suite 1011 10th Floor Peter House Oxford Street, Manchester, M1 5AN, United Kingdom
Tel.: (44) 161 932 1041
Web Site: http://www.kilngroup.com
Sales Range: $50-74.9 Million
Emp.: 5
Fire Insurance Services
N.A.I.C.S.: 524126
Michael Brook (Reg Mgr-Cargo)

La Rural S.A. de Seguros (1)
Avenida Mcal Lopez 1082, Esq Mayor Bullo, Asuncion, Paraguay
Tel.: (595) 21491917
Non-Life Insurance
N.A.I.C.S.: 524126

Millea Asia Pte Ltd. (1)
6 Shenton Way Unit 25 09 DBS Bldg Tower Two, Singapore, 068809, Singapore (100%)
Tel.: (65) 63722988
Web Site: http://www.milleaasia.com
Sales Range: $1-9.9 Million
Emp.: 35
Management & Consulting Services
N.A.I.C.S.: 541611

Subsidiary (Non-US):

P.T. Asuransi Tokio Marine Indonesia (2)

INTERNATIONAL PUBLIC

Sentral Senayan I Lantai 3 & 4 Jl Asia Afrika No 8, Jakarta, 10270, Indonesia (80%)
Tel.: (62) 215725772
Web Site: http://www.tokiomarine.co.id
Insurance Services
N.A.I.C.S.: 524128

The Tokio Marine & Fire Insurance Company (Hong Kong) Limited (2)
27A United Centre 95 Queensway, Hong Kong, China (Hong Kong) (100%)
Tel.: (852) 2 529 4401
Web Site: https://www.tokiomarine.com.hk
N.A.I.C.S.: 524128
Daisuke Fujii (Mng Dir)

Tokio Marine Insurance (Malaysia) Bhd. (2)
29th Floor Menara Dion 27 Jalan Sultan Ismail, 50250, Kuala Lumpur, 50250, Malaysia (100%)
Tel.: (60) 320269808
Web Site: http://www.tokiomarine.com.my
Provider of Insurance & Related Services
N.A.I.C.S.: 524128
Jayakumar Somasundram (COO)

Tokio Marine Malayan Insurance Co., Inc. (2)
6th & 7th Floors Y Tower II Alfaro Cor Gallardo Streets, Saloodo Village, Makati, Metro Manila, Philippines
N.A.I.C.S.: 524128

Nisshin Fire & Marine Insurance Co., Ltd. (1)
2-3 Kanda Surugadai, Chiyoda-Ku, Tokyo, 101-8329, Japan
Tel.: (81) 33 292 8000
Web Site: https://www.nisshinfire.co.jp
Sales Range: $700-749.9 Million
Emp.: 2,180
General Insurance Services
N.A.I.C.S.: 524210
Masato Murashima (Pres)

Subsidiary (Domestic):

Nisshin Fire Insurance Service Company, Limited (2)
2-3 Kanda Surugadai, Chiyoda-ku, Tokyo, 101-8329, Japan
Tel.: (81) 35 282 5663
Web Site: https://www.nisshinfire-is.co.jp
Emp.: 120
Insurance Agency Services
N.A.I.C.S.: 524210

Nisshin Information System Development Company, Limited (2)
2-7-5 Kamikizaki, Urawa-Ku, Saitama, 330-9311, Japan
Tel.: (81) 48 834 1382
Web Site: http://www.nisshin-info.co.jp
Emp.: 182
Insurance Software Development Services
N.A.I.C.S.: 541512

Nisshin Kasai Sogo Service Company, Limited (2)
2-3 Kandasurugadai Nisshinkasai Honsha Bldg, Chiyoda-Ku, Tokyo, 101-0062, Japan
Tel.: (81) 335182030
Business Process Outsourcing Services
N.A.I.C.S.: 561499

Universal Risk Solution Company, Limited (2)
2-3 Kandasurugadai, Chiyoda-Ku, Tokyo, 101-0062, Japan
Tel.: (81) 352825633
General Insurance Services
N.A.I.C.S.: 524210

Philadelphia Consolidated Holding Corporation (1)
1 Bala Plz Ste 100, Bala Cynwyd, PA 19004-0950
Tel.: (610) 617-7900
Web Site: https://www.phly.com
Sales Range: $1-4.9 Billion
Emp.: 1,324
Property & Casualty Insurance Services
N.A.I.C.S.: 524126
James J. Maguire Jr. (Chm)

Subsidiary (Domestic):

Liberty American Insurance Group, Inc. (2)

1 Bala Plz Ste W100, Bala Cynwyd, PA
19004-1401
Tel.: (727) 546-8911
Web Site: http://www.libertyamerican.com
Homeowner & Flood Insurance Carrier
N.A.I.C.S.: 524210

**Philadelphia Insurance
Companies** (2)
1 Bala Plz Ste 100, Bala Cynwyd, PA
19004
Tel.: (610) 617-7900
Web Site: http://www.phly.com
Insurance Agency & Broker
N.A.I.C.S.: 524210
James J. Maguire Jr. *(Chm)*

Subsidiary (Domestic):

**The Allen J. Flood Companies,
Inc.** (3)
2 Madison Ave, Larchmont, NY 10538
Tel.: (914) 834-9326
Web Site: http://www.ajfusa.com
Sales Range: $1-9.9 Million
Emp.: 40
Insurance Agencies & Brokerages
N.A.I.C.S.: 524210
Michael Flood *(Pres)*

**Philadelphia Indemnity Insurance
Company** (1)
1 Bala Plz Ste 100, Bala Cynwyd, PA
19004
Web Site: https://www.phly.com
Property Insurance Services
N.A.I.C.S.: 524126

Sino Life Insurance Co., Ltd. (1)
22/F Tower B East Pacific International
Center 7888 Shennan Road, Futian, Shenzhen, China
Tel.: (86) 4008200035
Web Site: http://www.sino-life.com
Life Insurance
N.A.I.C.S.: 524113

**TM Casualty Insurance
Company** (1)
230 Park Ave, New York, NY 10169
Tel.: (212) 297-6600
Web Site: http://www.tokiomarine.us
Sales Range: $100-124.9 Million
Emp.: 200
Casualty Insurance
N.A.I.C.S.: 524126

TM Claims Service, Inc. (1)
499 Washington Blvd Ste 1500, Jersey City,
NJ 07310 (100%)
Tel.: (212) 297-6700
Web Site: http://www.tmclaims.com
Sales Range: $200-249.9 Million
Emp.: 300
Product Liability Claims Handling
N.A.I.C.S.: 524291

TM Claims Service, Inc. (1)
800 E Colorado Blvd, Pasadena, CA 91101-2103
Tel.: (626) 568-7600
Provider of Insurance Services
N.A.I.C.S.: 524291
Timothy J. Doonan *(VP)*

**TM Specialty Insurance
Company** (1)
230 Park Ave, New York, NY 10169
Tel.: (212) 297-6600
Web Site: http://www.tokiomarine.us
Sales Range: $125-149.9 Million
Emp.: 200
N.A.I.C.S.: 524128

The Arab-Eastern Insurance Company Limited E.C. (1)
2nd Floor AFS Tower Building, 155 Road
2004, Manama, 320, Bahrain (33%)
Tel.: (973) 17296869
Web Site: http://www.tokiomarine-nichido.co.jp
Property & Casualty Insurance
N.A.I.C.S.: 524126

**The Sri Muang Insurance Company,
Limited** (1)
195 Empire Tower 40 Fl S Sathorn Rd
Sathorn District, Bangkok, 10120, Thailand
Tel.: (66) 26868888
Web Site: http://www.srimuang.co.th

Sales Range: $100-124.9 Million
Emp.: 220
Property & Casualty Insurance
N.A.I.C.S.: 524126
Sonjai Kamthonkittikul *(CFO)*

**The Tokio Marine & Fire Insurance
Company (Singapore) Pte.
Limited** (1)
20 McCallum St 09-01 Tokyo Marine Ctr,
Singapore, 069406, Singapore (100%)
Tel.: (65) 62216111
Web Site: http://www.tokiomarine.com.sg
Sales Range: $100-124.9 Million
Emp.: 200
Property & Casualty Insurance
N.A.I.C.S.: 524126
Minoru Yuki *(Mng Dir)*

**The Tokio Marine & Fire Insurance
Company (UK) Limited** (1)
150 Leadenhall St, London, EC3V 4TE,
United Kingdom (100%)
Tel.: (44) 2072838844
Web Site: http://www.tokyomarine.co.uk
Sales Range: $100-124.9 Million
Emp.: 120
Property & Casualty Insurance
N.A.I.C.S.: 524126

**The Tokio Marine & Fire Insurance
Company, Ltd.** (1)
c/o Kuwait Insurance Company S.A.K., PO
Box 769, Safat, 13008, Kuwait, Kuwait
Tel.: (965) 2420135
N.A.I.C.S.: 524128

**The Tokio Marine & Fire Insurance
Company, Ltd.** (1)
c/o Hussein Aoueini & Co Ltd Apartment
202-204 Shaker Building, PO Box 25, Ibrahim Shaker St, Jeddah, 21411, Saudi Arabia
Tel.: (966) 26433334
Web Site: http://www.tokiomarine.com
Sales Range: $50-74.9 Million
Emp.: 50
N.A.I.C.S.: 524128

**The Tokio Marine & Fire Insurance
Company, Ltd.** (1)
3rd Fl Deira City, PO Box 152, Ctr Office
Bldg Deira, Dubai, United Arab Emirates
Tel.: (971) 42951693
Sales Range: $50-74.9 Million
Emp.: 30
N.A.I.C.S.: 524128

**The Tokio Marine & Fire Insurance
Company, Ltd.** (1)
c/o IAG New Zealand Insurance Ltd. Level
10, PO Box 1609, NZI House 151 Queen
St, Auckland, 1, New Zealand
Tel.: (64) 9 3909 7090
N.A.I.C.S.: 524128

**The Tokio Marine Europe Insurance
Limited** (1)
Havenlaan 86c, Brussels, 1000,
Belgium (100%)
Tel.: (32) 22182728
Web Site: http://www.tokiomarine.com
Sales Range: $50-74.9 Million
Emp.: 10
Property & Casualty Insurance
N.A.I.C.S.: 524126
Makano Kazumi *(Mgr)*

**The Tokio Marine Europe Insurance
Limited** (1)
C/o Citius Insurance AS Skoyen Atrium
Drammensveien 147 B, PO Box 170,
Skoyen, Oslo, 10213, Norway (100%)
Tel.: (47) 22128000
Sales Range: $50-74.9 Million
Emp.: 2
Property & Casualty Insurance
N.A.I.C.S.: 524126

**The Tokio Marine Europe Insurance
Limited** (1)
Benrather starsse 18-20, 40213, Dusseldorf, Germany (100%)
Tel.: (49) 211172370
Sales Range: $75-99.9 Million
Emp.: 20
N.A.I.C.S.: 524128

**The Tokio Marine Europe Insurance
Limited** (1)

Prof WH Keesmolaan 1, Amstelveen, 1183
DJ, Netherlands (100%)
Tel.: (31) 206766757
Sales Range: $75-99.9 Million
Emp.: 7
N.A.I.C.S.: 524128

**The Tokio Marine Europe Insurance
Limited, Spain Branch** (1)
Torre Diagonal Mar Josep Pla 2 10th Floor,
08019, Barcelona, Spain (100%)
Tel.: (34) 935307300
Web Site: https://www.tmhcc.com
Sales Range: $50-74.9 Million
Emp.: 22
Property & Casualty Insurance
N.A.I.C.S.: 524126
Fernendo Rodrigues *(Mng Dir)*

**The Tokio Marine Europe Insurance
Ltd.** (1)
Burmester Duncker and Joly Trostbrucke 1,
Hamburg, 20457, Germany (100%)
Tel.: (49) 40376030
Sales Range: $50-74.9 Million
Emp.: 65
Property & Casualty Insurance
N.A.I.C.S.: 524126
Johann Paschin *(Mng Dir)*

**The Tokio Marine Europe Insurance
Ltd.** (1)
Peiazzale Lodi 3, I 20137, Milan,
Italy (100%)
Tel.: (39) 0026554791
Sales Range: $50-74.9 Million
Emp.: 3
Property & Casualty Insurance
N.A.I.C.S.: 524126
Satoshi Ohkuma *(Gen Mgr)*

Tokio Marine & Nichido Anshin Consulting Co., Ltd. (1)
8th floor of Nihonbashi Dia Building 1-19-1
Nihonbashi, Chuo-ku, Tokyo, 103-0027,
Japan
Tel.: (81) 33 243 7034
Web Site: https://www.web-tac.co.jp
Emp.: 200
Property & Casualty Insurance Services
N.A.I.C.S.: 524126

Tokio Marine & Nichido Career Service Co., Ltd. (1)
6th floor Shinjuku Eastside Square 6-27-30,
Shinjuku-ku, Tokyo, 160-0022, Japan
Tel.: (81) 36 233 2300
Web Site: https://www.tokiomarine-tcs.jp
Sales Range: $75-99.9 Million
Emp.: 500
Human Resource Consulting Services
N.A.I.C.S.: 541612

**Tokio Marine & Nichido Facilities,
Inc.** (1)
1310 Omiya-cho Muza Kawasaki Central
Tower 22nd floor, Saiwai-Ku, Kawasaki,
212-8554, Kanagawa, Japan
Tel.: (81) 44 543 2300
Web Site: https://www.tkn-f.co.jp
Emp.: 1,572
Real Estate Manangement Services
N.A.I.C.S.: 531390

Tokio Marine & Nichido Fire Insurance Co. (1)
195 Empire Twr 40th Fl Rm 4001-4003
4007-4009 4012 S Sathorn R, Bangkok,
10120, Thailand
Tel.: (66) 26868888
Web Site: http://www.tokiomarine-nichido.co
Sales Range: $450-499.9 Million
Emp.: 600
N.A.I.C.S.: 524128

Tokio Marine & Nichido Fire Insurance Co., Ltd. (1)
2-6-4 Otemachi, Chiyoda-ku, Tokyo, 100-8050, Japan
Tel.: (81) 12 006 5095
Web Site: https://www.tokiomarine-nichido.co.jp
Emp.: 17,176
Insurance Services
N.A.I.C.S.: 524298
Koichi Takano *(Sr Mng Dir)*

Joint Venture (Non-US):

Alinma Tokio Marine Co. (2)

King Fahad Road Alanoud Tower 2 Floor
21, Riyadh, Saudi Arabia
Tel.: (966) 11 212 9307
Web Site: http://www.atmc.com.sa
Rev.: $84,234,685
Assets: $174,692,001
Liabilities: $120,962,514
Net Worth: $53,729,487
Earnings: ($1,550,665)
Emp.: 178
Fiscal Year-end: 12/31/2020
Insurance & Reinsurance Services
N.A.I.C.S.: 524113
Abdulmohsen Abdulaziz Al Fares *(Chm)*

Subsidiary (US):

HCC Insurance Holdings, Inc. (2)
13403 NW Fwy, Houston, TX
77040 (100%)
Tel.: (713) 462-1000
Web Site: https://www.tmhcc.com
Holding Company; Insurance Products &
Services
N.A.I.C.S.: 551112
Michael J. Schell *(Exec VP)*

Subsidiary (Domestic):

Avemco Insurance Company (3)
8490 Progress Dr Ste 200, Frederick, MD
21701
Tel.: (301) 694-5700
Web Site: https://www.avemco.com
Emp.: 2,500
Aviation Insurance & Financial Services
N.A.I.C.S.: 524114
Mike Adams *(Sr VP-Underwriting)*

Continental Underwriters Ltd. (3)
2235 N Hwy 190, Covington, LA 70433
Tel.: (985) 898-5300
Web Site: https://www.cultd.com
Marine Insurance Brokerage Services
N.A.I.C.S.: 524210
Joe Morency *(Specialist-Excess Liability)*

**HCC Casualty Insurance Services,
Inc.** (3)
2300 Clayton Rd Ste 1100, Concord, CA
94520-2157
Tel.: (925) 685-1600
Emp.: 12
Casualty Insurance Services
N.A.I.C.S.: 524126

HCC Credit Group, Inc. (3)
600 Lexington Ave 22nd Fl, New York, NY
10022
Tel.: (212) 326-9393
Web Site: http://www.tmhcc.com
Insurance Coverage Consulting Services
N.A.I.C.S.: 524298
Mark P. Reynolds *(Pres-Credit Grp)*

**HCC Global Financial Products
LLC** (3)
8 Forest Park Dr, Farmington, CT 06032-1449
Tel.: (860) 674-1900
Insurance Underwriting Services
N.A.I.C.S.: 524126

**HCC Indemnity Guaranty Agency,
Inc.** (3)
600 Lexington Ave 22nd Fl, New York, NY
10022
Tel.: (212) 751-8383
Web Site: http://www.tmhcc.com
Insurance Underwriting Services
N.A.I.C.S.: 524127

Subsidiary (Non-US):

HCC International Insurance Company PLC (3)
1 Aldgate, London, EC3N 1RE, United
Kingdom
Tel.: (44) 20 7702 4700
Web Site: http://www.tmhcc.com
Property & Casualty Insurance Services
N.A.I.C.S.: 524126

Subsidiary (Domestic):

HCC Life Insurance Company (3)
225 Townpark Dr NW Ste 350, Kennesaw,
GA 30144-5885
Tel.: (770) 973-9851
Web Site: http://www.tmhcc.com

TOKIO MARINE HOLDINGS, INC.   INTERNATIONAL PUBLIC

Tokio Marine Holdings, Inc.—(Continued)
Emp.: 175
Insurance Services
N.A.I.C.S.: 524210
Jay Ritchie (CEO)

HCC Medical Insurance Services, LLC (3)
251 N Illinois St Ste 600, Indianapolis, IN 46204
Tel.: (317) 262-2132
Web Site: http://www.hccmis.com
Medical Insurance Brokerage Services
N.A.I.C.S.: 524298
Andrew Bard (Sr VP & Gen Mgr)

HCC Public Risk Claim Service, Inc. (3)
1700 Opdyke Ct, Auburn Hills, MI 48326
Tel.: (248) 371-3100
Web Site: http://www.tmhcc.com
Insurance Claims Processing Services
N.A.I.C.S.: 524292

HCC Risk Management Corporation (3)
13403 NW Fwy, Houston, TX 77040
Tel.: (713) 462-1000
Insurance Claims Processing Services
N.A.I.C.S.: 524292

HCC Specialty Underwriters, Inc. (3)
401 Edgewater Pl Ste 400, Wakefield, MA 01880
Tel.: (781) 994-6000
Web Site: http://www.tmhcc.com
Emp.: 500
Insurance Underwriting Services
N.A.I.C.S.: 524127
Matthew C. Overlan (CEO)

Subsidiary (Non-US):

HCC Underwriting Agency Ltd. (3)
1 Aldgate, London, EC3N 1RE, United Kingdom
Tel.: (44) 20 7702 4700
Web Site: http://www.tmhcc.com
Insurance Underwriting Services
N.A.I.C.S.: 524127

Subsidiary (Domestic):

Houston Casualty Company (3)
13403 Northwest Fwy, Houston, TX 77040
Tel.: (713) 462-1000
Web Site: http://www.tmhcc.com
Property & Casualty Insurance Services
N.A.I.C.S.: 524126

InsPro Corporation (3)
401 Edgewater Pl Ste 400, Wakefield, MA 01880
Tel.: (781) 994-6000
Web Site: http://www.tmhcc.com
Insurance Services
N.A.I.C.S.: 524298

LDG Reinsurance Corporation (3)
401 Edgewater Pl Ste 400, Wakefield, MA 01880
Tel.: (781) 245-2220
Insurance Brokerage Services
N.A.I.C.S.: 524210

NAS Insurance Services LLC (3)
16501 Ventura Blvd Ste 200, Encino, CA 91436 (100%)
Tel.: (818) 382-2030
Web Site: http://www.nasinsurance.com
Sales Range: $1-9.9 Million
Emp.: 180
Insurance Agencies & Brokerages
N.A.I.C.S.: 524210
Richard Robin (CEO)

On Call International, LLC (3)
11 Manor Pkwy, Salem, NH 03079
Tel.: (603) 328-1926
Web Site: https://www.oncallinternational.com
Medical & Emergency Assistance Services
N.A.I.C.S.: 621493
Jennifer Brunelle (VP)

Privilege Underwriters, Inc. (3)
44 S Broadway Ste 301, White Plains, NY 10601
Web Site: https://www.pureinsurance.com
Insurance Agencies & Brokerages
N.A.I.C.S.: 524210
Michelle Dieter (Mgr-Agency Ops)

Producers Ag Insurance Group, Inc. (3)
5601 Interstate 40 W, Amarillo, TX 79106
Tel.: (806) 372-6785
Web Site: https://www.proag.com
Group Insurance Services
N.A.I.C.S.: 524298
Russ Klein (CFO)

Subsidiary (Domestic):

Producers Agriculture Insurance Company (4)
5601 Interstate 40 W Ste 204, Amarillo, TX 79106
Tel.: (806) 372-6785
Web Site: https://www.proag.com
Emp.: 500
Insurance Services
N.A.I.C.S.: 524210

Subsidiary (Domestic):

Professional Indemnity Agency, Inc. (3)
401 Edgewater Pl Ste 400, Wakefield, MA 01880
Tel.: (781) 994-6000
Web Site: http://www.tmhcc.com
Insurance Underwriting Services
N.A.I.C.S.: 524127

U.S. Specialty Insurance Company (3)
13403 NW Fwy, Houston, TX 77040
Tel.: (713) 744-3700
Web Site: http://www.tmhcc.com
Emp.: 200
Property & Casualty Insurance Services
N.A.I.C.S.: 524126

United States Surety Company (3)
20 W Aylesbury Rd, Timonium, MD 21093
Tel.: (410) 453-9522
Web Site: http://www.tmhcc.com
Emp.: 20
Surety Insurance Brokerage Services
N.A.I.C.S.: 524292

Subsidiary (Non-US):

Kiln Group Limited (3)
106 Fenchurch St, London, EC3M 5NR, United Kingdom
Tel.: (44) 2078869000
Web Site: http://www.kilngroup.com
Sales Range: $900-999.9 Million
Emp.: 166
Holding Company; Specialty Insurance & Reinsurance Products & Services
N.A.I.C.S.: 551112
Reeken Patel (CFO)

Subsidiary (Non-US):

Kiln Europe SA (3)
Avenue du Luxembourg 35, 4020, Liege, Belgium
Tel.: (32) 4 340 10 50
Web Site: http://www.kilngroup.com
Sales Range: $50-74.9 Million
Emp.: 10
Marine Insurance Services
N.A.I.C.S.: 524126
Pierre Cobus (Reg Mgr-Underwriting)

Kiln Singapore PTE Limited (3)
8 Marina View #14-01 Asia Square Tower 1, Singapore, 018960, Singapore
Tel.: (65) 6632 7168
Web Site: http://www.kilngroup.com
Health Insurance Services
N.A.I.C.S.: 524114
Mike McFarlane (Mgr-Claims)

Kiln South Africa (Proprietary) Limited (3)
Ground Fl Blk 1 Tuscany Office Pk, 6 Coombe St, Johannesburg, 2128, Rivonia, South Africa (100%)
Tel.: (27) 116129300
Web Site: http://www.kilngroup.com
Sales Range: $50-74.9 Million
Emp.: 33
Insurance Agencies & Brokerages
N.A.I.C.S.: 524210
Alan Morgan (Mng Dir)

Subsidiary (Domestic):

Kiln Underwriting Limited (3)
Furness House 106 Fenchurch Street, London, EC3M 5NR, United Kingdom
Tel.: (44) 20 7886 9000
Sales Range: $75-99.9 Million
Emp.: 20
Property & Casualty Insurance Services
N.A.I.C.S.: 524126

R.J. Kiln & Co. Limited (3)
Furness House 106 Fenchurch Street, London, EC3M 3BY, United Kingdom
Tel.: (44) 2078869000
Web Site: http://www.tokiomarine.com
Sales Range: $150-199.9 Million
Insurance Services
N.A.I.C.S.: 524210

Tokio Marine Kiln Insurance Services Limited (3)
Furness House 106 Fenchurch Street, London, EC3M 5NR, United Kingdom
Tel.: (44) 20 7886 9000
Web Site: http://www.tokiomarinekiln.com
Emp.: 700
General Insurance Services
N.A.I.C.S.: 524210
Anna McNamara (Grp COO)

Subsidiary (Non-US):

P.T. Asuransi Tokio Marine Indonesia (2)
Sentral Senayan I Lantai 3 & 4 Jl Asia Afrika No 8, Jakarta, 10270, Indonesia
Web Site: http://www.tokiomarine.co.id
N.A.I.C.S.: 524128

Subsidiary (Domestic):

PT Asuransi Parolamas (3)
Pondok Indah Office Tower 2 Lantai 16 Suite 1601, Jalan Sultan Iskandar Muda Kav V-TA Pondok Pinang, Jakarta Selatan, 12310, Indonesia (80%)
Tel.: (62) 5363226110
Web Site: http://www.parolamas.co.id
Insurance Company
N.A.I.C.S.: 524298

Subsidiary (Non-US):

TM Claims Service Asia Pte. Ltd. (2)
20 McCallum Street 14-01 Tokio Marine Centre, Singapore, 69046, Singapore
Tel.: (65) 6592 6090
Sales Range: $50-74.9 Million
Emp.: 11
Claims Management Services
N.A.I.C.S.: 524292

The Tokio Marine & Nichido Fire Insurance Company (China) Limited (2)
38F Hang Seng Bank Tower 1000 Lujiazui Ring Road, Pilot Free Trade Zone, Shanghai, 200120, China
Tel.: (86) 216 841 4455
Web Site: https://www.tokiomarine.com.cn
Emp.: 25
Property & Casualty Insurance Services
N.A.I.C.S.: 524126
Kenichi Komiya (Pres)

Subsidiary (Domestic):

The Tokio Marine Claims Service Co., Ltd. (2)
1-2-1 Marunouchi Tokyokaijonichido Bldg Shinkan 4F, Chiyoda-Ku, Tokyo, 100-0005, Japan
Tel.: (81) 332400211
Emp.: 48
Marine Insurance Services
N.A.I.C.S.: 524126
Yoshihiro Tahara (Pres)

Tokio Marine & Nichido ANSHIN 110 Co., Ltd. (2)
2-28-8 Honkomagome, Bunkyo-ku, Tokyo, 113-0021, Japan
Tel.: (81) 35 977 7800
Web Site: https://www.anshin110ban.co.jp
Emp.: 982
General Insurance Services
N.A.I.C.S.: 524210

Tokio Marine & Nichido Adjusting Services Co., Ltd. (2)
1-5-1 Omorikita JRE Omori Station East Exit Building 6F, Ota-Ku, Tokyo, 143-0016, Japan
Tel.: (81) 33 765 6021
Web Site: https://www.tas-ajnet.co.jp
Emp.: 1,496
Marine Insurance Services
N.A.I.C.S.: 524126

Tokio Marine & Nichido Agent Support Co., Ltd. (2)
1-2-1 Marunouchi, Chiyoda-ku, Tokyo, 100-8050, Japan
Tel.: (81) 3 6269 9211
Web Site: http://www.tokio-hspack-tmnds.com
Risk Managemeng Srvices
N.A.I.C.S.: 541618

Tokio Marine & Nichido Communications Co., Ltd. (2)
19-4 Yokoyama-cho, Hachioji, 192-0081, Tokyo, Japan
Tel.: (81) 42 644 5612
Web Site: http://www.tcc21.com
Emp.: 809
Employee Training & Information Technology Consulting Services
N.A.I.C.S.: 541512
Kenichi Iwakoshi (Pres)

Tokio Marine & Nichido Finance Co., Ltd. (2)
1-5-1 Omori North JRE Omori Station East Exit, Ota-ku, Tokyo, 143-0016, Japan
Tel.: (81) 33 298 8181
Web Site: https://www.tmarinecard.co.jp
Credit Card Operating Services
N.A.I.C.S.: 522299

Tokio Marine & Nichido Human Resources Academy Co., Ltd. (2)
2-2-1 Otemachi New Otemachi Building 9th Floor, Chiyoda-ku, Tokyo, 100-0004, Japan
Tel.: (81) 36 630 3750
Web Site: https://www.tmn-hra.co.jp
Emp.: 73
Human Resource Consulting Services
N.A.I.C.S.: 541612
Hiroyuki Watabiki (Pres & CEO)

Subsidiary (Non-US):

Tokio Marine Asia Pte. Ltd. (2)
20 McCallum Street 13-01 Tokio Marine Centre, Singapore, 069046, Singapore
Tel.: (65) 6 372 2988
Web Site: https://www.tokiomarine.com
General Insurance Services
N.A.I.C.S.: 524210
Ian Brimecome (Mng Dir)

Subsidiary (Non-US):

IFFCO-Tokio General Insurance Co., Ltd. (3)
IFFCO Tower Plot No 3 Sector 29, Gurgaon, 122001, Haryana, India (26%)
Tel.: (91) 124 428 5499
Web Site: https://www.iffcotokio.co.in
Emp.: 4,238
Insurance Services
N.A.I.C.S.: 524210
K. Srinivasa Gowda (Chm)

Subsidiary (Domestic):

Tokio Marine Insurance Singapore Ltd. (3)
20 McCallum Street 07-01 Tokio Marine Centre, Singapore, 069046, Singapore
Tel.: (65) 6 592 6100
Web Site: https://www.tokiomarine.com
General Insurance Services
N.A.I.C.S.: 524210

Subsidiary (Non-US):

Tokio Marine Life Insurance (Thailand) Public Company Limited (3)
Empire Tower 26th Floor 1 South Sathorn Road Yannawa, Sathorn, Bangkok, 10120, Thailand
Tel.: (66) 2 670 1400
Web Site: http://www.tokiomarinelife.co.th
General Insurance Services
N.A.I.C.S.: 524210

TOKIO MARINE HOLDINGS, INC.

Subsidiary (Domestic):

Tokio Marine Life Insurance Singapore Ltd. (3)
20 McCallum Street 07-01 Tokio Marine Centre, Singapore, 69046, Singapore
Tel.: (65) 6 592 6100
Web Site: https://www.tokiomarine.com
Emp.: 180
Fire Insurance Services
N.A.I.C.S.: 524113
Cheng Han Tan (Chm)

Tokio Marine Retakaful Pte. Ltd. (3)
180 Cecil Street 14-03 Bangkok Bank Building, Singapore, 069546, Singapore
Tel.: (65) 6324 7530
Sales Range: $50-74.9 Million
Emp.: 6
Life Reinsurance Services
N.A.I.C.S.: 524113
Kamsani Tati (CEO)

Subsidiary (Domestic):

Tokio Marine Asset Management Co., Ltd. (2)
19F Tekko Building 8-2 Marunouchi 1-chome, Chiyoda-ku, Tokyo, 100-0005, Japan
Tel.: (81) 33 212 8421
Web Site: https://www.tokiomarineam.com
Emp.: 397
Investment Advisory & Asset Management Services
N.A.I.C.S.: 523940
Nobuki Goto (Mng Dir)

Subsidiary (Non-US):

Tokio Marine Asset Management (London) Limited (3)
20 Fenchurch Street, London, EC3M 3BY, United Kingdom (100%)
Tel.: (44) 207 280 8580
Web Site: http://www.tokiomarineam.com
Sales Range: $700-749.9 Million
Emp.: 120
Insurance Services
N.A.I.C.S.: 524128
Watts Itoh (Head-Bus Dev)

Subsidiary (US):

Tokio Marine Asset Management (USA) Ltd. (3)
60 E 42nd St Ste 2300, New York, NY 10165 (100%)
Tel.: (212) 476-8291
Web Site: http://www.tokiomarineam.com
Investment Advisory Services
N.A.I.C.S.: 524128
Takeo Mitsuhashi (CEO & CIO)

Subsidiary (Non-US):

Tokio Marine Asset Management International Pte. Ltd. (3)
20 Mccallum Street 18-02 Tokio Marine Centre, Singapore, 069046, Singapore (100%)
Tel.: (65) 65926279
Web Site: http://www.tmai.com.sg
Investment & Asset Management Services
N.A.I.C.S.: 523940
Tenji Kudama (CEO)

Subsidiary (Non-US):

Tokio Marine Brasil Seguradora S.A. (2)
Rua 13 de Maio 1529, Sao Paulo, 01327-001, Brazil
Tel.: (55) 1132657500
Web Site: http://www.tokiomarine.com.br
General Insurance Services
N.A.I.C.S.: 524210

Tokio Marine Europe Limited (2)
60 Gracechurch Street 6th Floor, London, EC3V OHR, United Kingdom
Tel.: (44) 20 7283 8844
Insurance Management Services
N.A.I.C.S.: 524298

Subsidiary (Domestic):

Tokio Marine Financial Solutions Ltd. (2)
Tokyo Club Building 2-6 Kasumigaseki 3-chome, Chiyoda-ku, Tokyo, 100-0013, Japan
Tel.: (81) 3 4540 4000
Web Site: http://www.tokiomarine-fs.co.jp
Sales Range: $25-49.9 Million
Emp.: 48
Financial Management Services
N.A.I.C.S.: 523999
Kyoichi Katsuda (CEO)

Subsidiary (US):

Tokio Marine Management, Inc. (2)
230 Park Ave Fl 3, New York, NY 10169 (100%)
Tel.: (212) 297-6600
Sales Range: $150-199.9 Million
Emp.: 300
Property & Casualty Insurance
N.A.I.C.S.: 524210
Koki Umeda (CEO)

Subsidiary (Non-US):

Tokio Millennium Re Ltd. (2)
Tokio Millennium House, 3 Waterloo Lane, Pembroke, HM 08, Bermuda
Tel.: (441) 2966700
Web Site: http://www.tokiomillennium.com
Sales Range: $50-74.9 Million
Emp.: 85
Reinsurance Services
N.A.I.C.S.: 524130
Stephen O'Flynn (Head-Underwriting)

Subsidiary (US):

Trance Pacific Insurance Company (2)
1221 ave of americas suite 1500, New York, NY 10020
Tel.: (212) 297-6600
Web Site: http://www.tokiomarine-nichido.co.jp
General Insurance Services
N.A.I.C.S.: 524210

Tokio Marine & Nichido Fire Insurance Co., Ltd. - France (1)
36 rue de Chateaudun, 75009, Paris, Cedex 09, France
Tel.: (33) 15 329 3000
Web Site: http://www.tokiomarine.fr
Sales Range: $50-74.9 Million
Emp.: 50
Property & Casualty Insurance
N.A.I.C.S.: 524126

Tokio Marine & Nichido Fire Insurance Company, Ltd. (1)
8F-13F No 130 Sec 3 Nanjing E Rd, Taipei, 104, Zhongshan, Taiwan
Tel.: (886) 2 8772 7777
Web Site: http://www.tokiomarine-nichido.co.jp
Sales Range: $250-299.9 Million
Emp.: 400
Insurance & Risk Management Services
N.A.I.C.S.: 524128

Tokio Marine & Nichido Life Insurance Co., Ltd. (1)
Tokiwabashi Tower Customer Center 2-6-4 Otemachi, Chiyoda-ku, Tokyo, 100-0004, Japan (100%)
Tel.: (81) 12 001 6234
Web Site: https://www.tmn-anshin.co.jp
Emp.: 2,524
Fire Insurance Services
N.A.I.C.S.: 524113

Tokio Marine & Nichido Medical Service Co., Ltd. (1)
1-1-1 Minami Aoyama Shin-Aoyama Building East Building, Minato-ku, Tokyo, 107-0062, Japan
Tel.: (81) 36 704 4000
Web Site: https://www.tokio-mednet.co.jp
Health Care Srvices
N.A.I.C.S.: 621999

Tokio Marine & Nichido Risk Consulting Co., Ltd. (1)
Otemachi First Square West Tower 23F 1-5-1, Chiyoda-ku Otemachi, Tokyo, 100-0004, Japan
Tel.: (81) 352886580
Web Site: http://www.tokiorisk.co.jp
Sales Range: $25-49.9 Million
Emp.: 250
Management Consulting Services
N.A.I.C.S.: 541618
Taizo Shimakura (Pres & CEO)

Tokio Marine Business Support Co., Ltd. (1)
1-2-1 Marunouchi, Chiyoda-ku, Tokyo, 100-0005, Japan
Tel.: (81) 3 3212 6102
Business Support Services
N.A.I.C.S.: 561499

Tokio Marine Compania de Seguros, S.A. de C.V. (1)
Paseo De La Reforma No 505 Piso 34 Col Cuauhtemoc Del Cuauhtemoc, Aluvaro Odregon, Mexico, 06500, Mexico (100%)
Tel.: (52) 5552782100
Sales Range: $75-99.9 Million
Emp.: 70
N.A.I.C.S.: 524128
Jorge Farrel Zermeno (Pres)

Tokio Marine Compania de Seguros, S.A. de C.V. (1)
Blvd Rodolfo Sanchez Taboada 10488 Suite 914 Zona Urbana Rio, 22010, Tijuana, Mexico (100%)
Tel.: (52) 6646158023
Sales Range: $75-99.9 Million
Emp.: 2
N.A.I.C.S.: 524128

Tokio Marine Compania de Seguros, S.A. de C.V. (1)
Sierra Morena 512 Desp 103 Fraccionamiento Bosques del Prado, 1a Secc 20127, 20127, Aguascalientes, Mexico
Tel.: (52) 4499125352
N.A.I.C.S.: 524128

Tokio Marine Europe (1)
66 Rue De La Chaussee D Antin, F 75441, Paris, Cedex, France (100%)
Tel.: (33) 0153293000
Sales Range: $10-24.9 Million
Emp.: 44
N.A.I.C.S.: 524128

Tokio Marine Europe Insurance Ltd. (1)
c/o Willis Kendriki S A, 8 Achilleous Street, 176 74, Athens, Kallithea, Greece (100%)
Tel.: (30) 2199999200
Sales Range: $50-74.9 Million
Emp.: 4
Non-Life Insurance
N.A.I.C.S.: 524126

Tokio Marine Insurance (Malaysia) Bhd. (1)
29th Floor Menara Dion 27 Jalan Sultan Ismail, 50250, Kuala Lumpur, Malaysia (100%)
Tel.: (60) 327838383
Web Site: http://www.tokiomarine.com
Sales Range: $1-9.9 Million
Emp.: 20
N.A.I.C.S.: 524128
Chew Boon Kheng (Mgr-Mktg)

Tokio Marine Insurance (Malaysia) Bhd. (1)
46-48 Jalan Merdeka, Taman Melaka Raya, 75000, Melaka, Malaysia (100%)
Tel.: (60) 62823663
Web Site: http://www.tokiomarine.com.my
Sales Range: $75-99.9 Million
Emp.: 25
N.A.I.C.S.: 524128
Lim Teng Huan (Gen Mgr)

Tokio Marine Investment Services, Limited (1)
Suite 1112 11 Fl 2 Pacific Pl 88 Queensway, Hong Kong, China (Hong Kong) (100%)
Tel.: (852) 25270822
Web Site: http://www.tokiomarine-nichido.co.jp
Sales Range: $50-74.9 Million
Emp.: 4
Investment Advisory Services
N.A.I.C.S.: 523940

Tokio Marine Kiln Group Limited (1)
20 Fenchurch Street, London, EC3M 3BY, United Kingdom
Tel.: (44) 207 886 9000
Web Site: https://www.tmkiln.com
Property Insurance Services
N.A.I.C.S.: 524126
Brad Irick (CEO)

Tokio Marine Life Insurance Malaysia Bhd. (1)
Ground Floor Menara Tokio Marine Life 189 Jalan Tun Razak, 50400, Kuala Lumpur, Malaysia
Tel.: (60) 32 059 6188
Web Site: https://www.tokiomarine.com
Sales Range: $200-249.9 Million
Emp.: 30
General Insurance Services
N.A.I.C.S.: 524210
Yahya Awang (Chm)

Tokio Marine Management (Australasia) Pty. Ltd. (1)
Level 3 1 Chifley Square, Sydney, 2000, NSW, Australia (100%)
Tel.: (61) 29 225 7500
Web Site: https://www.tokiomarine.com.au
Sales Range: $50-74.9 Million
Emp.: 60
Underwriting Agent of Property & Casualty Insurance
N.A.I.C.S.: 524298
Shigekazu Ueno (CEO)

Branch (Domestic):

Tokio Marine Management (Australasia) Pty. Ltd. (2)
Level 13 North Tower 459 Collins Street, Melbourne, 3000, VIC, Australia
Tel.: (61) 39 621 1911
Web Site: https://www.tokiomarine.com.au
Sales Range: $50-74.9 Million
Emp.: 3
Provider of Insurance & Related Services
N.A.I.C.S.: 524128
Shigekazu Ueno (CEO)

Tokio Marine Middle East Limited (1)
Level 15 Unit OT Office Tower 15-33 Central Park Towers, PO Box 506616, International Financial Center, Dubai, United Arab Emirates
Tel.: (971) 4 425 5678
Web Site: http://www.tmmena.com
General Insurance Services
N.A.I.C.S.: 524210
Hisato Hamada (Chm)

Tokio Marine Millea SAST Insurance Co., Ltd. (1)
2-2-1-1 Minatomirai Yokohama Landmark Tower 35F, Nishi-ku, Yokohama, 220-8135, Kanagawa, Japan
Tel.: (81) 36 629 8810
Web Site: https://www.tmssi.co.jp
Insurance Services
N.A.I.C.S.: 524210

Tokio Marine Nichido Better Life Service Co., Ltd. (1)
Hatsudai TN Building 1F 1-34-14 Hatsudai, Shibuya-ku, Tokyo, 151 0061, Japan
Tel.: (81) 333704951
Sales Range: $25-49.9 Million
Emp.: 150
Residential Care Services
N.A.I.C.S.: 623990

Tokio Marine Nichido Samuel Co., Ltd (1)
2-14-4 Shin-Yokohama, Kohoku-ku, Yokohama, 222-0033, Kanagawa, Japan
Tel.: (81) 454762080
Web Site: www.hyldemoer.com
Nursing Care Facility Services
N.A.I.C.S.: 623110

Tokio Marine Property Investment Management, Inc. (1)
San Marino Shiodome 7F 2-4-1 Higashishimbashi, Minato Ward, Tokyo, 105-0021, Japan
Tel.: (81) 3 5733 3001
Web Site: http://www.tokiomarine-pim.com
Sales Range: $25-49.9 Million
Emp.: 3
Real Estate Investment Services
N.A.I.C.S.: 531390
Minoru Kato (Mng Dir-Fund Mgmt 1)

Tokio Marine Property Limited (1)

TOKIO MARINE HOLDINGS, INC.

Tokio Marine Holdings, Inc.—(Continued)
150 Leadenhall St, London, EC3V 4TE, United Kingdom **(100%)**
Tel.: (44) 2073983109
Real Estate Investment
N.A.I.C.S.: 525990

Tokio Marine Safety Insurance (Thailand) Public Company Limited **(1)**
Orakarn Building 1st 2n 4th and 6th Floors, No 26/5-8 26/10-11 26/16-19 Chidlom Road Lumpini Pathumwan, Bangkok, 10330, Thailand
Tel.: (66) 2 257 8080
Motor Insurance Services
N.A.I.C.S.: 524126

Tokio Marine South-East Servicing Company Limited **(1)**
195 Empire Tower 40 Floor Unit 4001 4003 South Sathorn Road, Yannawa Sathorn Dis, Bangkok, 10120, Thailand
Tel.: (66) 26868888
Web Site: http://www.srimuang.co.th
Sales Range: $50-74.9 Million
Emp.: 40
Insurance Services
N.A.I.C.S.: 524128

Tokyo Marine Brasil Seguradora SA **(1)**
Rua Treze De Maio 1529, 01327 001, Sao Paulo, SP, Brazil
Tel.: (55) 132657500
Web Site: http://www.tokiomarine.com.br
Sales Range: $200-249.9 Million
Emp.: 400
Provider of Property Casualty Insurance
N.A.I.C.S.: 524126

Branch (Domestic):

Tokio Marine Brasil **(2)**
Assembleia St 23, CEP 20011 901, Rio de Janeiro, Brazil **(100%)**
Tel.: (55) 122213892
Web Site: http://www.tokiomarine.com.br
Sales Range: $75-99.9 Million
Emp.: 10
N.A.I.C.S.: 524128

Tokio Marine Brasil **(2)**
Av Cristovao Colombo 400 2 Andar, 30140-150, Belo Horizonte, Brazil
Tel.: (55) 3132622233
Web Site: http://www.americalatinaseguros.com.br
Sales Range: $75-99.9 Million
Emp.: 10
N.A.I.C.S.: 524128

Trans Pacific Insurance Company **(1)**
230 Park Ave, New York, NY 10169-0005 **(100%)**
Tel.: (212) 865-1700
Web Site: http://www.tokiomarine.us
Sales Range: $100-124.9 Million
Emp.: 200
Property & Casualty Insurance
N.A.I.C.S.: 524210

Vietnam International Assurance Company **(1)**
6th Fl Sun Red River 23 Phan Chu Trinh St, Hanoi, Vietnam **(100%)**
Tel.: (84) 49330704
Web Site: http://www.via.com.vn
Sales Range: $75-99.9 Million
Emp.: 10
N.A.I.C.S.: 524128

TOKIO MARINE NEWA INSURANCE CO. LTD.
8 13F No 130 Section 3 Nanjing East Road, Zhongshan District, Taipei, 104505, Taiwan
Tel.: (886) 28 772 7777
Web Site: https://www.tmnewa.com.tw
Year Founded: 1991
Sales Range: $350-399.9 Million
Emp.: 909
Property & Casualty Insurance Services
N.A.I.C.S.: 524126

TOKMANNI GROUP CORPORATION
Isolammintie 1, 04600, Mantsala, Finland
Tel.: (358) 300472220
Web Site: https://ir.tokmanni.fi
Year Founded: 1989
TOKMAN—(HEL)
Rev.: $1,260,540,686
Assets: $856,705,159
Liabilities: $590,183,466
Net Worth: $266,521,692
Earnings: $63,342,327
Emp.: 4,241
Fiscal Year-end: 12/31/22
Consumer Product Retailer
N.A.I.C.S.: 423620
Seppo Saastamoinen *(Chm)*

Subsidiaries:

Tokmanni Oy **(1)**
Isolammintie 1, 04600, Mantsala, Finland
Tel.: (358) 300472220
Web Site: https://ir.tokmanni.fi
General Discount Distr
N.A.I.C.S.: 455219
Maarit Mikkonen *(Head-IR & Comm)*

TOKUDEN CO., LTD.
Tel.: (81) 755812111
Web Site: https://www.tokuden.co.jp
Year Founded: 1933
3437—(TKS)
Rev.: $63,370,070
Assets: $76,510,750
Liabilities: $28,528,760
Net Worth: $47,981,990
Earnings: $2,505,190
Fiscal Year-end: 03/31/24
Welding Equipment Mfr
N.A.I.C.S.: 333992
Katsuhiko Kanbayashi *(Pres)*

Subsidiaries:

Tokuden Topal Co., Ltd. **(1)**
11th Floor Zone A Thaniya Plaza Building 52 Silom Rd, Bangrak, Bangkok, 10500, Thailand
Tel.: (66) 22312486
Web Site: http://www.tokuden-topal.com
Die Casting Part Mfr
N.A.I.C.S.: 331524

TOKURA CONSTRUCTION CO., LTD.
13-5 Nishiki 3-chome, Nakaku, Nagoya, 460-8615, Aichi, Japan
Tel.: (81) 529613271
Web Site: https://tokura.co.jp
Year Founded: 1947
18920—(NGO)
Rev.: $648,221,200
Assets: $430,779,360
Liabilities: $265,648,240
Net Worth: $165,131,120
Earnings: $16,252,720
Fiscal Year-end: 03/31/22
Construction Services
N.A.I.C.S.: 236220
Katsumi Tokura *(Pres)*

Subsidiaries:

Kawamura Quantity Surveyors Co., Ltd. **(1)**
1-12-15 Suido, Bunkyo-ku, Tokyo, 112-0005, Japan
Tel.: (81) 332641800
Construction Estimation & Construction Cost-Management Services
N.A.I.C.S.: 541990

TC Pacific Construction, LLC **(1)**
E-W Business Ctr Bldg D Ste 201 718 N Marine Corps Dr, Tamuning, GU 96913
Tel.: (671) 922-0109
Civil Engineering & Building Construction Services
N.A.I.C.S.: 541330

TOKUSHU TOKAI PAPER CO., LTD.
Tekko Building 11F 1-8-2 Marunouchi, Chuo-ku, Tokyo, 100-0005, Japan
Tel.: (81) 352191810 JP
Web Site: https://www.tt-paper.co.jp
Year Founded: 2007
3708—(TKS)
Rev.: $571,877,370
Assets: $878,984,580
Liabilities: $324,227,110
Net Worth: $554,757,470
Earnings: $30,339,900
Fiscal Year-end: 03/31/24
Holding Company; Paper Products Mfr & Distr
N.A.I.C.S.: 551112
Yuji Matsuda *(Pres)*

Subsidiaries:

Meiji Seishi Co., Ltd. **(1)**
Atshhara 167-1, Fuji, Shizuoka, Japan
Tel.: (81) 545 71 1122
Web Site: http://www.tt-ecology.co.jp
Paper Products Mfr
N.A.I.C.S.: 322299

REX Co., Ltd. **(1)**
1-1-2 Yokoi, Shimada, 411-0024, Shizuoka, Japan
Tel.: (81) 547393112
Container Mfr
N.A.I.C.S.: 322219

Shizuoka Logistics Co., Ltd. **(1)**
Tel.: (81) 559881357
Logistics Support Services
N.A.I.C.S.: 488510

Techno Support Co., Ltd. **(1)**
4379 Mukoujima-cho, Shimada, Shizuoka, Japan
Tel.: (81) 547 35 6505
Business Support Services
N.A.I.C.S.: 561499

Tokai Forest Co., Ltd. **(1)**
1-753-1 Kanayahigashi, Shimada, 428-0013, Shizuoka, Japan
Tel.: (81) 547461551
Emp.: 20
Forest Management Services
N.A.I.C.S.: 115310

Tokai Paper Converting Co., Ltd. **(1)**
Yokoi 1-1-1, Shimada, Shizuoka, Japan
Tel.: (81) 547 37 6111
Paper Products Mfr
N.A.I.C.S.: 322299
Masami Kuruebsahi *(Gen Mgr)*

Tokushu Matel Co., Ltd. **(1)**
Hara 1063, Numazu, Shizuoka, Japan
Tel.: (81) 55 966 1357
Paper Mfr
N.A.I.C.S.: 322299

Tokushu Paper Trading Co., Ltd. **(1)**
6th floor 2-4-1 Yaesu, Chuo-ku, Tokyo, 104-0028, Japan
Tel.: (81) 332738516
Web Site: https://www.tokushu-papertrade.jp
Emp.: 19
Business Support Services
N.A.I.C.S.: 561499
Naoki Konagaya *(Gen Mgr)*

Tokushu Tokai Materialz Co., Ltd. **(1)**
4379 Mukojima-cho, Shimada, 427-0045, Shizuoka, Japan
Tel.: (81) 54736151
Web Site: https://www.tt-materialz.co.jp
Waste Paper Recycling Services
N.A.I.C.S.: 562219
Satoru Ida *(Pres & CEO)*

Tokushu Tokai Paper Co., Ltd. - Gifu Plant **(1)**
814 Kamikawate, Gifu, 500-8245, Japan
Tel.: (81) 582469111
Paper Products Mfr
N.A.I.C.S.: 322299

Tokushu Tokai Paper Co., Ltd. - Mishima Mill **(1)**
501 Honjyuku Nagaizumi-Cho, Sunto-gun,

INTERNATIONAL PUBLIC

Shizuoka, 411-8750, Japan
Tel.: (81) 559881115
Paper Products Mfr
N.A.I.C.S.: 322299

TOKUSUI CORPORATION
2-2-21 Minato, Chuo-ku, Fukuoka, 810-0075, Japan
Tel.: (81) 92 721 0931 JP
Web Site: http://www.tokusui.co.jp
Year Founded: 1924
Holding Company; Fish Processing & Whslr
N.A.I.C.S.: 551112
Chihiro Tokushima *(Chm)*

Subsidiaries:

Orca Bay Seafoods, Inc. **(1)**
900 Powell Ave SW, Renton, WA 98057-2907
Tel.: (425) 204-9100
Web Site: http://www.orcabayseafoods.com
Sales Range: $50-74.9 Million
Emp.: 200
Seafood Processor & Distr
N.A.I.C.S.: 311710
Roger Fickenscher *(Dir-Product Dev)*

Tohoku Tokusui, Ltd. **(1)**
6-7-5 Kachidoki, Chuo-ku, Tokyo, 104-0054, Japan
Tel.: (81) 3 3533 5121
Frozen Food Product Distr
N.A.I.C.S.: 424460

Plant (Domestic):

Tohoku Tokusui, Ltd. - Shiogama factory **(2)**
3-3-17 Shinhama-tyou, Shiogama, 985-0001, Miyagi, Japan
Tel.: (81) 22 366 6829
Frozen Food Product Mfr
N.A.I.C.S.: 311710

TOKUYAMA CORPORATION
1-7-5 Front Place Akihabara Sotokanda, Chiyoda-ku, Tokyo, 101-8618, Japan
Tel.: (81) 352072500 JP
Web Site: https://www.tokuyama.co.jp
Year Founded: 1918
TKYMY—(OTCIQ)
Rev.: $2,522,334,300
Assets: $3,429,712,140
Liabilities: $1,697,425,800
Net Worth: $1,732,286,340
Earnings: $67,139,880
Emp.: 5,909
Fiscal Year-end: 03/31/23
Holding Company; Chemicals, Cement, Synthetic Resins & Construction Materials Mfr & Sales
N.A.I.C.S.: 551112
Hideki Adachi *(Sr Mng Exec Officer & Gen Mgr-Tokuyama Factory)*

Subsidiaries:

A&T Corporation **(1)**
10F Yokohama Plaza Bldg 2-6 Kinko-cho, Kanagawa-ku, Yokohama, 221-0056, Kanagawa, Japan
Tel.: (81) 45 440 5813
Web Site: https://www.aandt.co.jp
Emp.: 477
Chemicals, Analyzers, Computers & Lab-Logistics Development, Mfr, Sales & Services
N.A.I.C.S.: 424210

Astom Corporation **(1)**
2-6-2 Nishi-Shimbashi, Minato-ku, Tokyo, 105-0003, Japan
Tel.: (81) 33 597 5019
Web Site: https://www.astom-corp.jp
Electrode Apparatus Mfr & Distr
N.A.I.C.S.: 333992
Hiroyuki Yanagi *(Pres)*

Chugoku Ready Mixed Concrete Co., Ltd. **(1)**
2-2 Dejima 3-chome, Minami-ku, Hiroshima,

Eurodia Industrie S.A. (1)
Zac St Martin Impasse St Martin, 84120,
Pertuis, France **(100%)**
Tel.: (33) 49 008 7500
Web Site: https://www.eurodia.com
Sales Range: $25-49.9 Million
Emp.: 35
Sale of Ion Exchange Membranes & Electrodialyzers
N.A.I.C.S.: 238160

Excel Shanon Corporation (1)
2-7-8 Nihonbashibakurocho Ichigo Nihonbashi East Building 4th Floor, Chuo-ku, Tokyo, 103-0002, Japan **(51%)**
Tel.: (81) 36 458 2941
Web Site: https://www.excelshanon.co.jp
Construction Machinery Mfr & Distr
N.A.I.C.S.: 333120

FL Tokuyama Corporation (1)
2-7-8 Nihonbashibakurocho Ichigo Nihonbashi East Building 4th Floor, Chuo-ku, Tokyo, 103-0002, Japan
Tel.: (81) 33 527 2556
Web Site: https://www.fltokuyama.com
Building Material Plaster Sheet Mfr & Distr
N.A.I.C.S.: 327420

Hiroshima Tokuyama Ready Mixed Concrete Co., Ltd. (1)
5-3 Taibi 1-chome, Saka-cho Aki-gun, Hiroshima, 731-4325, Japan
Tel.: (81) 828855611
Cement Mfr & Distr
N.A.I.C.S.: 327310

Kagawa Tokuyama Co., Ltd. (1)
1-45 Kozaihonmachi, Takamatsu, 761-8012, Kagawa, Japan
Tel.: (81) 878820612
Cement Mfr & Distr
N.A.I.C.S.: 327310

Kansai Tokuyama Trading Co., Ltd. (1)
2-2-7 Nakanoshima Nakanoshima Central Tower 19F, Kita-ku, Osaka, 530-0005, Japan
Tel.: (81) 66 201 7290
Web Site: https://www.kansai-tokuyama.jp
Cement Distr
N.A.I.C.S.: 423320

Kawasaki Tokuyama Ready Mixed Concrete Co., Ltd. (1)
13-7 Ogicho, Kawasaki-ku, Kawasaki, 210-0867, Kanagawa, Japan **(100%)**
Tel.: (81) 443227730
Readymix Concrete Mfr
N.A.I.C.S.: 327320

Kyushu Tokuyama Ready Mixed Concrete Co., Ltd. (1)
82-2 Higashihama 2-chome, Higashi-ku, Fukuoka, 812-0055, Japan **(100%)**
Tel.: (81) 926518667
Ready-Mix Concrete Mfr & Retailer
N.A.I.C.S.: 327320

Oita Mining Co., Ltd. (1)
2426-1 Kamiaoe, Tsukumi, 879-2461, Oita, Japan
Tel.: (81) 972823171
Limestone Mining Services
N.A.I.C.S.: 212312

Sanyo Tokuyama Ready Mixed Concrete Co., Ltd. (1)
636 Toba, Kurashiki, 710-0012, Okayama, Japan **(50%)**
Tel.: (81) 86 464 0500
Web Site: https://www.sanyo-tokuyama.co.jp
Readymix Concrete Mfr
N.A.I.C.S.: 327320

Seibu Tokuyama Ready Mixed Concrete Co., Ltd. (1)
1-1 Mikage-cho, Shunan, Yamaguchi, 745 8648, Japan **(100%)**
Tel.: (81) 834342000
Sales Range: $25-49.9 Million
Emp.: 100
Production & Sale of Ready Mixed Concrete
N.A.I.C.S.: 327320

Shanghai Tokuyama Plastics Co., Ltd. (1)
138 Xintao Road, Qingpu Industrial Zone, Shanghai, 201707, China
Tel.: (86) 215 970 5669
Web Site: https://www.tokuyama.com.cn
Plastics Product Mfr
N.A.I.C.S.: 326199

Shanon Co., Ltd. (1)
Mita 43 MT Building 4F 3-13-16 Mita, Minato-ku, Tokyo, 108-0073, Japan **(100%)**
Tel.: (81) 36 743 1551
Web Site: https://www.shanon.co.jp
Emp.: 245
Mfr, Processing & Sales of Building Materials, Including Plastic Sashes & Doors
N.A.I.C.S.: 326199

Branch (Domestic):

Shanon Co., Ltd. - Hokkaido Branch (2)
Toyokawa Bldg 2 Fl Kita 1 31 Nango Dori 19 Chome Shiraishi Ku, Sapporo, Hokkaido, 003 0023, Japan **(100%)**
Tel.: (81) 118638511
Sales of Plastic Windows
N.A.I.C.S.: 423220

Shanon Tohoku Trading Co., Ltd (1)
Hokushin Building 4 Floor 6 10 Uesugi 1 Chome Aoba Ku, Sendai, Miyagi, 980 0011, Japan **(100%)**
Tel.: (81) 222159871
Web Site: http://www.shanon.co.jp
Sales Range: $50-74.9 Million
Emp.: 10
Sales of Plastic Windows
N.A.I.C.S.: 423220

Shin Dai-ichi Vinyl Corporation (1)
1-7-5 Sotokanda, Chiyoda-ku, Tokyo, 101-0021, Japan **(85.5%)**
Tel.: (81) 35 207 2561
Web Site: https://www.zest-pvc.co.jp
Vinyl Chloride Resin Mfr & Distr
N.A.I.C.S.: 325211

Shirokawa co., Ltd. (1)
1-13-11 Bakurocho Nihonbashi, Chuo-ku, Tokyo, 103-0002, Japan
Tel.: (81) 336631701
Web Site: https://www.k-shirakawa.com
Emp.: 192
Ready-Mix Concrete Mfr & Distr
N.A.I.C.S.: 327320

Shunan Bulk Terminal Co., Ltd. (1)
8 Harumi-cho, Shunan, 745-0024, Yamaguchi, Japan
Tel.: (81) 83 434 2031
Web Site: https://www.shunanbulk.jp
Port Services
N.A.I.C.S.: 488310

Shunan Swimming Club Co., Ltd. (1)
1-1-26 Eguchi, Shunan, 745-0862, Yamaguchi, Japan
Tel.: (81) 83 431 8819
Web Site: https://www.shunansc.jp
Fitness & Recreational Services
N.A.I.C.S.: 713940

Shunan System Sangyo Co., Ltd. (1)
1-1-1 Eguchi, Shunan, 745-0862, Yamaguchi, Japan
Tel.: (81) 83 434 2380
Web Site: https://www.shunan.co.jp
Emp.: 441
Engineeering Services
N.A.I.C.S.: 541330

Sun Arrow Kasei Co., Ltd. (1)
1-2 Harumi-cho, Shunan, 745-0024, Yamaguchi, Japan
Tel.: (81) 83 434 2672
Web Site: https://www.sun-arrow.co.jp
Emp.: 28
Vinyl Chloride Resin Mfr & Distr
N.A.I.C.S.: 325211

Taiwan Tokuyama Corporation (1)
No 21 Shin Chen Road Hu Kou Country, Hsinchu Industrial Park, Hukou, Taiwan **(100%)**
Tel.: (886) 35979108
Sales Range: $25-49.9 Million
Emp.: 20
Production & Sales of Solvent for Semiconductor Base Materials
N.A.I.C.S.: 334413

Tohoku Shanon Co., Ltd. (1)
46-1 Dai 1 Chiwari Kitayuguchi, Hanamaki, 025 03, Iwate, Japan **(72%)**
Tel.: (81) 19 827 4300
Web Site: https://www.tohoku-shanon.jp
Sales Range: $125-149.9 Million
Emp.: 300
Production of Plastic Sashes
N.A.I.C.S.: 326199

Tokushin Co., Ltd. (1)
11F Hiroshima Nissei Midori Building 8-18 Teppocho, Naka-ku, Hiroshima, 730-0017, Japan
Tel.: (81) 82 221 9477
Web Site: https://www.tokushin-tg.co.jp
Cement Distr
N.A.I.C.S.: 423320

Tokushou Co., Ltd. (1)
2-8-38 Tenjin 7th floor Kyowa Building, Chuo-ku, Fukuoka, 810-0001, Japan
Tel.: (81) 92 732 6706
Web Site: https://www.tokushou.jp
Cement Mfr & Distr
N.A.I.C.S.: 327310

Tokuyama (Shanghai) Co., Ltd. (1)
1003 Shanghai International Group Mansion 511 WeiHai Road, Shanghai, 200041, China
Tel.: (86) 2162181177
Cement Mfr & Distr
N.A.I.C.S.: 327310

Tokuyama America Inc. (1)
3655 Torrance Blvd 3rd Fl, Torrance, CA 90503 **(100%)**
Tel.: (424) 247-1142
Web Site: http://www.tokuyama-a.com
Sales Range: $1-9.9 Million
Emp.: 3
Marketing of Tokuyama Products, Specialty Chemicals Ceramics
N.A.I.C.S.: 424690
Tsuyoshi Habe (Pres)

Tokuyama Asia Pacific Pte. Ltd. (1)
61 Robinson Road 14-02 Robinson Centre, Singapore, 068893, Singapore **(100%)**
Tel.: (65) 65335258
Web Site: http://www.tokuyama-asia.com
Sales Range: $50-74.9 Million
Emp.: 10
Sales of Plastic & Chemical Products
N.A.I.C.S.: 424690
Toshihiro Katayama (Mng Dir)

Tokuyama Chemicals (Zhejiang) Co., Ltd. (1)
No 555 Yashan West Road, Economic Development Zone Zhapu Port, Jiaxing, 314201, Zhejiang, China
Tel.: (86) 5738 552 7887
Web Site: https://www.tokuyama.net.cn
Emp.: 200
Chemical Products Mfr
N.A.I.C.S.: 325998
Tetsuya Nakano (Co-Pres)

Tokuyama Chiyoda Gypsum Co., Ltd. (1)
928 Takamatsu, Kawagoe-cho Mie-gun, Mie, 510-8121, Japan
Tel.: (81) 59 361 3073
Web Site: https://www.tc-g.co.jp
Waste Disposal Services
N.A.I.C.S.: 562998

Tokuyama Dental Corporation (1)
1-38-9 Taito 7F Itopia Kiyosubashidori Building, Taito-ku, Tokyo, 110-0016, Japan
Tel.: (81) 33 835 2260
Web Site: https://www.tokuyama-dental.co.jp
Emp.: 200
Dental Material & Equipment Mfr & Distr
N.A.I.C.S.: 339114
Hideki Kazama (Pres)

Tokuyama Electronic Chemicals Pte. Ltd. (1)
21 Gul Road, Singapore, 629355, Singapore **(100%)**
Tel.: (65) 68621081
Web Site: http://www.tokuyama-asia.com
Sales Range: $25-49.9 Million
Emp.: 30
Production of Solvent for Semiconductor Base Materials
N.A.I.C.S.: 325998

Tokuyama Europe GmbH (1)
Am Gierath 20a, 40885, Ratingen, Germany **(100%)**
Tel.: (49) 2102 565 0660
Web Site: https://www.tokuyama-europe.com
Sales Range: $50-74.9 Million
Emp.: 4
Marketer of Specialty Chemicals, Ceramics & Dental Materials
N.A.I.C.S.: 424690
Kanji Yoshinari (Mng Dir)

Tokuyama Information Service Corporation (1)
1-7 Shinjuku dori, Shunan, 745-0056, Yamaguchi, Japan
Tel.: (81) 83 433 3330
Web Site: https://www.tokuyama-js.co.jp
Emp.: 60
IT Infrastructure Design & Construction Services
N.A.I.C.S.: 541330

Tokuyama Kairiku Unso K.K. (1)
2-18 Chikkocho, Shunan, 745-0025, Yamaguchi, Japan
Tel.: (81) 83 431 3614
Web Site: https://www.t-kairiku.co.jp
Coastal Transportation Services
N.A.I.C.S.: 483113

Tokuyama Korea Co., Ltd. (1)
604 Korea Air City Terminal Bldg 22 Teheran-ro 87-gil, Gangnam-Gu, Seoul, 06164, Korea (South)
Tel.: (82) 2 517 3851
Web Site: https://www.tokuyama.co.jp
Chemical Products Mfr
N.A.I.C.S.: 325998

Tokuyama Metel Corporation (1)
1-1 Minamiwatarida-cho Keihin Building 8th floor, Kawasaki-ku, Kawasaki, 210-0855, Kanagawa, Japan
Tel.: (81) 44 328 7747
Web Site: https://www.t-metel.co.jp
Cleaning Solvent Mfr & Distr
N.A.I.C.S.: 325612

Tokuyama Mtech Corporation (1)
4-8-16 Nihonbashihoncho KDX Shin Nihonbashi Ekimae Building 3F, Chuo-ku, Tokyo, 103-0023, Japan **(100%)**
Tel.: (81) 36 265 1075
Web Site: https://www.tokuyama.co.jp
Sales Range: $25-49.9 Million
Emp.: 30
Sale of Construction Materials
N.A.I.C.S.: 444180

Tokuyama Nouvelle Caledonie S.A. (1)
Pointe Kuari Baie de Numbo, BP 310, 98845, Noumea, New Caledonia **(74.1%)**
Tel.: (687) 243295
Sales Range: $10-24.9 Million
Emp.: 34
Cement Mfr & Whslr
N.A.I.C.S.: 327310
Hideyoshi Koya (Pres)

Tokuyama Polypropylene Co., Ltd. (1)
1-1 Harumicho, Shunan, 745-8648, Yamaguchi, Japan
Tel.: (81) 83 434 2707
Web Site: https://www.tokuyamapp.co.jp
Emp.: 63
Polypropylene Mfr
N.A.I.C.S.: 327910

Tokuyama Siam Silica Co., Ltd. (1)
38th Floor Ocean Tower II Bldg 75/106 Sukhumvit 19, North Klongtoey Wattana, Bangkok, 10110, Thailand **(99.18%)**
Tel.: (66) 26652903
Sales Range: $25-49.9 Million
Emp.: 15
Production & Sale of Precipitated Silica

TOKUYAMA CORPORATION

Tokuyama Corporation—(Continued)
N.A.I.C.S.: 325998

Tokuyama Singapore Pte. Ltd. (1)
21 Gul Road, Singapore, 629355, Singapore
Tel.: (65) 68621081
Electronic Products Mfr
N.A.I.C.S.: 334419

Tokuyama Soda Trading Co., Ltd. (1)
Ichigo Nihonbashi East Building 7-8 Nihonbashibakurocho 2-chome, Chuo-ku, Tokyo, 103-0002, Japan
Tel.: (81) 335272553
Soda Ash & Calcium Chloride Mfr
N.A.I.C.S.: 325180

Tokuyama Trading (Shanghai) Co., Ltd. (1)
1003 Shanghai International Group Mansion 511 WeiHai Road, Shanghai, 200041, China
Tel.: (86) 216 218 1177
Web Site: http://www.tokuyama.co.jp
Sales Range: $25-49.9 Million
Emp.: 20
Chemicals Mfr
N.A.I.C.S.: 325998

Tokuyama Tsusho Trading Co., Ltd. (1)
4-8-16 Nihonbashihoncho KDX Shin Nihonbashi Ekimae Building 4F, Chuo-ku, Tokyo, 103-0023, Japan
Tel.: (81) 33 241 4131
Web Site: https://www.tokuyamatsusho.jp
Emp.: 60
Cement Distr
N.A.I.C.S.: 423320

Tokuyama-Dowa Power Materials Co., Ltd. (1)
29-17 Misasa-cho, Shunan, 746-0004, Yamaguchi, Japan
Tel.: (83) 464 7211
Web Site: https://www.td-power.biz
Aluminum Plate Mfr & Distr
N.A.I.C.S.: 331315

Tokyo Tokuyama Concrete Co., Ltd. (1)
1-1-8 Wakasu, Koto-ku, Tokyo, 136-0083, Japan
Tel.: (81) 36 457 0225
Web Site: https://www.tokyotokuyama.co.jp
Construction Machinery Mfr
N.A.I.C.S.: 333120

Tomitec Co., Ltd. (1)
3055-1 Ogo Tabuse-cho, Kumage, Yamaguchi, 742-1513, Japan
Tel.: (81) 82 055 5678
Web Site: https://www.ymg-tomitec.com
Chemicals Mfr
N.A.I.C.S.: 325998

Towa Giken Co., Ltd. (1)
7 6 Takejima 5 Chome, Nishiyodogawa ku, Osaka, 555 0011, Japan **(100%)**
Tel.: (81) 664755200
Rev.: $10,000,000
Emp.: 7
Producer & Sales of Dental & Medical Materials
N.A.I.C.S.: 339114

Toyomi Co., Ltd. (1)
4-9 Toyomi 5-chome, Oita, 870-0018, Japan
Tel.: (81) 975346081
Ready-Mix Concrete Mfr & Distr
N.A.I.C.S.: 327320

TOKYO AIRCRAFT INSTRUMENT CO., LTD.
2-6 Oyamagaoka 2-chome, Machida, 194-0296, Tokyo, Japan
Tel.: (81) 427986643
Web Site: http://www.tkk-air.co.jp
Year Founded: 1937
Sales Range: $100-124.9 Million
Emp.: 400
Aircraft Instrument Mfr
N.A.I.C.S.: 336413
Shinji Wakasugi (Pres)

Subsidiaries:

Toko Co., Ltd. (1)
9-11 Kamitsuruma 1-chome, Minami-ku, Sagamihara, 252-0302, Kanagawa, Japan
Tel.: (81) 427420243
Aircraft Instrument Mfr
N.A.I.C.S.: 336413

Toko Engineering co., Ltd. (1)
2-6,Oyamagaoka 2-chome, Machida-shi, Tokyo, 194-0215, Japan
Tel.: (81) 42 798 6639
Aircraft Instrument Mfr
N.A.I.C.S.: 336413

United Instruments, Inc. (1)
3625 Comotara Ave, Wichita, KS 67226
Tel.: (316) 636-9203
Web Site: http://www.unitedinst.com
Aircraft Instrument Mfr
N.A.I.C.S.: 336413

TOKYO AUTOMATIC MACHINERY WORKS, LTD.
Tojiki Building 3-10-7, Chiyoda-ku, Tokyo, 101-0032, Japan
Tel.: (81) 338667171
Web Site: https://www.tam-tokyo.co.jp
Year Founded: 1944
6360—(TKS)
Sales Range: $50-74.9 Million
Emp.: 250
Packaging Machinery Mfr & Whslr
N.A.I.C.S.: 333993
Haruo Yamamoto (Chm, Pres & CEO)

Subsidiaries:

Tokyo Automatic Machinery Works, Ltd. - Kashiwa Factory (1)
7-3-1 Nishihara, Kashiwa, 277-0085, Chiba, Japan
Tel.: (81) 4 7152 2121
Packaging Machinery Mfr
N.A.I.C.S.: 333993

TOKYO BASE CO.,LTD.
1-14-6 Dougenzaka, Shibuya-ku, Tokyo, Japan
Tel.: (81) 364550644
Web Site: http://www.studious.co.jp
3415—(TKS)
Rev.: $141,700,740
Assets: $84,285,920
Liabilities: $45,056,950
Net Worth: $39,228,970
Earnings: $2,375,150
Fiscal Year-end: 01/31/24
Apparel Store Operator
N.A.I.C.S.: 315990
Masato Tani (CEO)

TOKYO BOARD INDUSTRIES CO., LTD.
2-11-1 Shinkiba Koto-ku, Tokyo, 136-0082, Japan
Tel.: (81) 335224138
Web Site: https://www.t-b-i.co.jp
7815—(TKS)
Rev.: $47,162,350
Assets: $78,130,200
Liabilities: $64,467,330
Net Worth: $13,662,870
Earnings: ($6,325,770)
Emp.: 266
Fiscal Year-end: 03/31/24
Particleboard Mfr
N.A.I.C.S.: 322130
Hiroyuki Inoue (Pres)

TOKYO CEMENT COMPANY (LANKA) PLC
Tel.: (94) 112558100
Web Site: https://www.tokyocement.com
TKYO—(COL)
Rev.: $228,560,134
Assets: $208,191,899
Liabilities: $90,901,246
Net Worth: $117,290,653
Earnings: $28,786,392
Emp.: 1,431
Fiscal Year-end: 03/31/21
Cement & Mixed Concrete Mfr
N.A.I.C.S.: 327320
W. Christopher Fernando (Exec Dir)

Subsidiaries:

Tokyo Supermix (Private) Limited (1)
No 12D Haig Road, 04, Colombo, Sri Lanka
Tel.: (94) 112004455
Cement Mfr
N.A.I.C.S.: 327310

TOKYO CENTURY CORPORATION
FUJISOFT Bldg 3 Kanda-neribeicho, Chiyoda-ku, Tokyo, 101-0022, Japan
Tel.: (81) 352097055   JP
Web Site: https://www.tokyocentury.co.jp
Year Founded: 1969
8439—(TKS)
Rev.: $8,897,806,930
Assets: $42,706,747,300
Liabilities: $36,022,873,940
Net Worth: $6,683,873,360
Earnings: $476,818,960
Emp.: 7,876
Fiscal Year-end: 03/31/24
Diversified Leasing Services
N.A.I.C.S.: 523999
Shunichi Asada (Chm)

Subsidiaries:

Amada Lease Co., Ltd. (1)
200 Ishida, Isehara, 259-1196, Kanagawa, Japan **(60%)**
Tel.: (81) 463963663
Web Site: https://www.amadalease.co.jp
Lease of Metalworking Machines, Machine Tools & Related Products
N.A.I.C.S.: 532490

Aviation Capital Group LLC (1)
840 Newport Center Dr Ste 300, Newport Beach, CA 92660 **(100%)**
Tel.: (949) 219-4600
Sales Range: $25-49.9 Million
Emp.: 90
Commercial Jet Aircraft Leasing
N.A.I.C.S.: 532411
Tom Baker (Pres & CEO)

BPI Century Tokyo Lease & Finance Corporation (1)
21F NEX Tower 6786 Ayala Avenue, Brgy Bel-Air Metro Manila, Makati, 1229, Philippines **(51%)**
Tel.: (63) 285395000
Automobile Leasing Services
N.A.I.C.S.: 532112

CSI Leasing, Inc. (1)
9990 Old Olive Street Rd, Saint Louis, MO 63141
Tel.: (314) 997-7010
Web Site: http://www.csileasing.com
Emp.: 1,300
Information Technology & Healthcare Equipment Leasing & Distr
N.A.I.C.S.: 532420
Paul Keefe (CFO & Exec VP)

Subsidiary (Domestic):

CSI Latina Financial, Inc. (2)
220 Alhambra Cir Ste 350, Coral Gables, FL 33134
Tel.: (305) 860-1616
Holding Company; Equipment Leasing Services
N.A.I.C.S.: 551112
Arnaldo Rodriguez (Pres)

Subsidiary (Non-US):

CSI Latina Arrendamento Mercantil S/A (3)
Alameda Rio Negro No 585 Bloco A - Suite 71, Alphaville, Barueri, 06454-000, SP, Brazil

INTERNATIONAL PUBLIC

Tel.: (55) 1135142800
Web Site: http://br.en.csileasing.com
Emp.: 50
Information Technology & Healthcare Equipment Leasing & Distr
N.A.I.C.S.: 532420
Arnaldo Rodriguez (Pres)

CSI Leasing Mexico, S. de R.L. de C.V. (3)
Av Insurgentes Sur 1602 Piso 10 Oficina 1002 Col Credito Constructor, Del Benito Juarez, 03940, Mexico, Mexico
Tel.: (52) 5591404200
Web Site: https://www.csimexico.com
Emp.: 90
Information Technology & Healthcare Equipment Leasing & Distr
N.A.I.C.S.: 532420

CSI Leasing de Centroamerica SRL (3)
Plaza Roble Edificio Las Terrazas A primer piso, Escazu, San Jose, Costa Rica
Tel.: (506) 25064900
Web Site: https://www.csileasing.com
Information Technology & Communications Equipment Leasing Services
N.A.I.C.S.: 532420

Subsidiary (Non-US):

CSI Leasing Guatemala, S.A. (4)
12 Calle 1-25 Zona 10 Edificio Geminis10 Torre Norte 14 Nivel oficina, 1412, Guatemala, Guatemala
Tel.: (502) 22281400
Web Site: http://www.csicentroamerica.com
Information Technology & Communications Equipment Leasing Services
N.A.I.C.S.: 532420

Subsidiary (Non-US):

CSI Renting Chile, S.A. (3)
Calle El Golf 40 Piso 20, Las Condes, Santiago, Chile
Tel.: (56) 2089441
Equipment Leasing Services
N.A.I.C.S.: 532420

CSI Renting Colombia S.A. (3)
Calle 109 No 18C 17 Ofc 401, Bogota, Colombia
Tel.: (57) 14894400
Information Technology & Healthcare Equipment Leasing & Distr
N.A.I.C.S.: 532420

CSI Renting Peru S.A.C. (3)
Av Emilio Cavenecia N 151 Ofc 408 409, Miraflores, 15073, Lima, Peru
Tel.: (51) 12089430
Information Technology & Healthcare Equipment Leasing & Distr
N.A.I.C.S.: 532420

Subsidiary (Non-US):

CSI Leasing (Shenzhen) Limited (3)
Office 102 44/F Tower A NEO Building 6011 Shennan Avenue, Futian District, Shenzhen, 518034, China
Tel.: (86) 75588326966
Web Site: http://cn.csileasingasia.com
Information Technology & Healthcare Equipment Leasing & Distr
N.A.I.C.S.: 532420
Monika Tureckova (COO-Asaia Pacific)

CSI Leasing (Singapore) Pte. Ltd. (2)
No 6 Raffles Quay 14-03, Singapore, 048580, Singapore
Tel.: (65) 62360279
Web Site: http://www.csileasingasia.com
Information Technology & Healthcare Equipment Leasing & Distr
N.A.I.C.S.: 532420
Ong Cheng Chiin (Mng Dir-Asia Pacific)

CSI Leasing Canada Ltd. (2)
2400 Winston Park Drive Unit 4, Oakville, L6H 0G7, ON, Canada
Tel.: (905) 829-9600
Web Site: https://www.csileasing.ca
Information Technology & Healthcare Equipment Leasing & Distr
N.A.I.C.S.: 532420

CSI Leasing Czech s.r.o. (2)

AND PRIVATE COMPANIES

Krizikova 237/36a, 186 00, Prague, Czech Republic
Tel.: (420) 227030503
Web Site: https://cz.en.csileasing.com
Information Technology & Healthcare Equipment Leasing & Distr
N.A.I.C.S.: 532420

CSI Leasing Malaysia Sdn. Bhd. (2)
C1-2-1 Solaris Dutamas Jalan Dutamas 1, 50480, Kuala Lumpur, Malaysia
Tel.: (60) 327792020
Information Technology & Healthcare Equipment Leasing & Distr
N.A.I.C.S.: 532420

CSI Leasing Polska Sp.z o.o. (2)
Ul Przyokopowa 33 Pietro 8, 01-042, Warsaw, Poland
Tel.: (48) 224040913
Web Site: https://pl.en.csileasing.com
Information Technology & Healthcare Equipment Leasing & Distr
N.A.I.C.S.: 532420
Patryk Krajewski (Sls Dir)

CSI Leasing Slovakia, s.r.o. (2)
Digital Park II Einsteinova 23, 851 01, Bratislava, Slovakia
Tel.: (421) 258103815
Web Site: https://sk.en.csileasing.com
Information Technology & Healthcare Equipment Leasing & Distr
N.A.I.C.S.: 532420
Martin Kardos (Mng Dir-Central & Eastern Europe)

CSI Leasing UK Ltd. (2)
1-2 Chambers Way Newton Chambers Road, Chapeltown, Sheffield, S35 2PH, South Yorkshire, United Kingdom
Tel.: (44) 2045244936
Web Site: https://csileasing.co.uk
Information Technology & Healthcare Equipment Leasing & Distr
N.A.I.C.S.: 532420
James Gunson (Mng Dir)

CSI LifeCycle Leasing GmbH (2)
Martin-Behaim-Strasse 22, 63263, Neu-Isenburg, Germany
Tel.: (49) 610288220
Web Site: https://www.csilifecycle.de
Information Technology & Healthcare Equipment Leasing & Distr
N.A.I.C.S.: 532420
Arnaldo Rodriguez (Pres)

CSI LifeCycle Services Italia S.r.l. (2)
Via Pier Capponi 13, 20145, Milan, Italy
Tel.: (39) 0284940906
Web Site: https://www.csilifecycle.it
Information Technology & Healthcare Equipment Leasing & Distr
N.A.I.C.S.: 532420
Federico Marchese (Country Mgr)

CSI Lifecycle Europe, s.r.o. (2)
Digital Park II Einsteyn 23, 851 01, Bratislava, Slovakia
Tel.: (421) 903426898
Web Site: http://www.csilifecycle.eu
Equipment Leasing Services
N.A.I.C.S.: 532420
Martin Kardos (Mng Dir-Central & Eastern Europe)

CSI Renting de Tecnologia SAU (2)
Avda Diagonal 514 3-4, 08006, Barcelona, Spain
Tel.: (34) 932402300
Web Site: https://es.en.csileasing.com
Information Technology & Healthcare Equipment Leasing & Distr
N.A.I.C.S.: 532420
Javier Heredia (Sr Mng Dir-Europe)

Subsidiary (Domestic):

Executive Personal Computers Inc. (2)
3941 Harry S Truman, Saint Charles, MO 63301 (100%)
Tel.: (636) 443-1999
Web Site: http://www.epcusa.com
Emp.: 500
Computer Reconditioning, Refurbishing & Storage
N.A.I.C.S.: 423430

FFG Lease Co., Ltd. (1)
3-11-1 Hakataeki Higashi, Hakata-ku, Fukuoka, 812-0013, Japan
Tel.: (81) 924520590
Web Site: https://www.fflease.co.jp
Emp.: 74
Machinery & Equipment Leasing Services
N.A.I.C.S.: 532490

Fujitsu Leasing Co., Ltd. (1)
3-Kanda Neribemachi, Chiyoda-ku, Tokyo, 101-0022, Japan
Tel.: (81) 358436301
Web Site: https://www.flcs.co.jp
Sales Range: $25-49.9 Million
Emp.: 170
Computer Leasing Services
N.A.I.C.S.: 541519

IHI Finance Support Corporation (1)
FUJISOFT Bldg 3 Kanda-neribeicho, Chiyoda-ku, Tokyo, 101-0022, Japan
Tel.: (81) 332528501
Web Site: http://www.ctl.co.jp
Sales Range: $50-74.9 Million
Emp.: 20
Finance & Leasing Services
N.A.I.C.S.: 522220

ITEC Leasing Co., Ltd. (1)
1-4-1 Jinnan, Shibuya-ku, Tokyo, 150-0041, Japan
Tel.: (81) 354564760
Web Site: https://iteclease.com
Emp.: 8
Broadcasting Equipment Leasing Services
N.A.I.C.S.: 532490

Nippon Car Solutions Co., Ltd. (1)
Akihabara UDX 9th floor 4-14-1 Sotokanda, Chiyoda-ku, Tokyo, 101-0021, Japan (59.5%)
Tel.: (81) 352072000
Web Site: https://www.ncsol.co.jp
Emp.: 1,126
Automobile Leasing Services
N.A.I.C.S.: 532112

Nippon Rent-A-Car Service, Inc. (1)
14F FUJISOFT Bldg 3 Kanda-neribeicho, Chiyoda-ku, Tokyo, 101-0022, Japan (89%)
Tel.: (81) 368596111
Web Site: https://www.nrgroup-global.com
Sales Range: $5-14.9 Billion
Emp.: 5,336
Car Rental Services
N.A.I.C.S.: 532111
Yoshimitsu Arahata (Pres)

Orico Auto Leasing Co., Ltd. (1)
Nittochi Okachimachi Building 2-27-5, Taito-ku, Tokyo, 110-0016, Japan
Tel.: (81) 368655515
Web Site: https://www.oal-net.co.jp
Automobile Leasing Services
N.A.I.C.S.: 532112

P.T. Tokyo Century Indonesia (1)
World Trade Center 2 Lantai 9 Jalan Jenderal Sudirman Kavling 29-31, Jakarta, 12920, Indonesia
Tel.: (62) 2130404080
Finance & Leasing Services
N.A.I.C.S.: 522220

Q'sai Co., Ltd. (1)
1-7-16 Kusagae, Chuo-ku, Fukuoka, 810-8606, Japan
Tel.: (81) 927240831
Web Site: http://corporate.kyusai.co.jp
Sales Range: $50-74.9 Million
Emp.: 498
Health Food Products Mfr & Distr
N.A.I.C.S.: 311999
Satoshi Kambe (Pres)

S.D.L. Co., Ltd. (1)
Shinbashi Kikuei Building 5-13-1 Shinbashi, Minato-ku, Tokyo, 105-0004, Japan
Tel.: (81) 332892028
Automobile Leasing Services
N.A.I.C.S.: 532112

Shinko Real Estate Co., Ltd. (1)
2-2-4 Wakinohamakaigan-dori, Chuo-ku, Kobe, 651-0073, Hyogo, Japan (70%)
Tel.: (81) 782612121
Web Site: https://www.kobelco2103.jp
Emp.: 285

Real Estate Brokerage & Leasing Services
N.A.I.C.S.: 531210
Masahiro Hanaoka (Pres)

TC Agency Corporation (1)
Akihabara UDX 4-14-1 Sotokanda, Chiyoda-ku, Tokyo, 101-0021, Japan
Tel.: (81) 352976015
Web Site: http://www.ctl.co.jp
Casualty Insurance & Financial Support Services
N.A.I.C.S.: 522291

TC Business Experts Corporation (1)
Akihabara UDX 4-14-1 Sotokanda, Chiyoda-ku, Tokyo, 101-0021, Japan
Tel.: (81) 352976080
Web Site: http://www.ctl.co.jp
Business Inspection Services
N.A.I.C.S.: 813910

TC Business Service Corporation (1)
Nittochi Okachimachi Bldg 2-27-5 Taito, Taito-ku, Tokyo, 110-0016, Japan (100%)
Tel.: (81) 358188076
Web Site: http://www.tokyocentury.co.jp
Business Processing Service
N.A.I.C.S.: 541990
Yasuo Mori (Pres)

TRY, Inc. (1)
2-10-10 Hironodai, Zama, 252-0012, Kanagawa, Japan
Tel.: (81) 462598124
Web Site: http://www.ctl.co.jp
Data Deletion & Computer Recycling Services
N.A.I.C.S.: 518210

Tokyo Century (USA) Inc. (1)
2500 Westchester Ave Ste 310, Purchase, NY 10466 (100%)
Tel.: (914) 697-9030
Web Site: https://tokyocentury.com
Leasing Services
N.A.I.C.S.: 522220
Chris A. Enbom (CEO)

Tokyo Century Capital (Malaysia) Sdn. Bhd. (1)
Suite 20 01 20 01A Level 20 Menara Citibank No 165 Jalan Ampang, 50450, Kuala Lumpur, Malaysia
Tel.: (60) 321629633
Web Site: https://www.tokyocentury.co.jp
General Leasing Services
N.A.I.C.S.: 561990

Tokyo Century Leasing (Singapore) Pte. Ltd. (1)
8 Cross Street No 09-04/05 Manulife Tower, Singapore, 048424, Singapore
Tel.: (65) 65323436
Web Site: https://tcls.com.sg
Leasing Services
N.A.I.C.S.: 522220
Foo Siang Seng (Officer-ASEAN Reg)

Tokyo Century Leasing China Corporation (1)
Unit 06 12F Tower I No 523 Loushanguan Road, Changning District, Shanghai, 200051, China (80%)
Tel.: (86) 2162889388
Web Site: https://www.tokyocentury.co.jp
Leasing Services
N.A.I.C.S.: 522220

Tokyo Leasing (Hong Kong) Ltd. (1)
Room 301 3rd Floor Sun Hung Kai Centre 30 Harbour Road, 30 Harbour Road, Wan Chai, Hong Kong, China (Hong Kong) (100%)
Tel.: (852) 25214373
Sales Range: $75-99.9 Million
Emp.: 50
Leasing Services
N.A.I.C.S.: 532210

Tokyo Leasing (UK) Plc (1)
5 Argosy Court Scimitar Way, Whitley Business Park, Coventry, CV3 4GA, Mddx, United Kingdom (100%)
Tel.: (44) 2084291963
Leasing Services
N.A.I.C.S.: 522220

TOKYO CHUO AUCTION

TOKYO COSMOS ELECTRIC CO., LTD.

HOLDINGS LTD.
Room 2601 26/F Wing On Centre No 111 Connaught Road Central, Hong Kong, China (Hong Kong)
Tel.: (852) 28059016   HK
Web Site: https://www.chuo-auction.com
Year Founded: 2010
1939—(HKG)
Rev.: $9,277,155
Assets: $59,415,128
Liabilities: $25,871,408
Net Worth: $33,543,720
Earnings: ($1,055,955)
Emp.: 42
Fiscal Year-end: 03/31/23
Online Advertising Services
N.A.I.C.S.: 541810
Shokei Ando (Chm & Exec Dir)

Subsidiaries:

Tokyo Chuo Auction Co., Ltd. (1)
3-7-5 Kyobashi, Chuo-ku, Tokyo, 104-0031, Japan
Tel.: (81) 335643321
Web Site: http://www.chuo-auction.co.jp
Advertising Services
N.A.I.C.S.: 541810

Tokyo Chuo Taiwan Auction Company Limited (1)
Room 1303 13F No 88 Sec 2 Zhongxiao E Rd, Zhongzheng, Taipei, 100, Taiwan
Tel.: (886) 223932081
Painting & Calligraphies Distr
N.A.I.C.S.: 424950

TOKYO COMMODITY EXCHANGE, INC.
10-7 Nihonbashi Horidomecho 1-chome, Chuo-ku, Tokyo, 103-0012, Japan
Tel.: (81) 3 3661 9191
Web Site: http://www.tocom.or.jp
Emp.: 83
Commodity Stock Exchange
N.A.I.C.S.: 523210
Takamichi Hamada (Pres & CEO)

TOKYO CONE PAPER MFG. CO., LTD.
87 Niigatafukuro, Kasukabe, 344-0056, Japan
Tel.: (81) 48 761 7166
Web Site: http://www.toptone.co.jp
Year Founded: 1964
Speakers & Amplifier Components Mfr & Sales
N.A.I.C.S.: 334310
Masato Oshida (Pres)

Subsidiaries:

Toptone Acoustics (Malaysia) Sdn. Bhd. (1)
Lot 5613 Sungai Ketapang, 08300, Gurun, Malaysia
Tel.: (60) 4 4687489
Web Site: http://www.toptone.co.jp
Speakers & Parts Mfr
N.A.I.C.S.: 334310

TOKYO COSMOS ELECTRIC CO., LTD.
2-12-1 Sobudai, Zama, 252-8550, Kanagawa, Japan
Tel.: (81) 462532111
Web Site: https://www.tocos-j.co.jp
Year Founded: 1957
6772—(TKS)
Rev.: $68,968,740
Assets: $82,063,150
Liabilities: $35,773,320
Net Worth: $46,289,830
Earnings: $6,358,820
Emp.: 696
Fiscal Year-end: 03/31/24
Electrical Component Mfr
N.A.I.C.S.: 334416

TOKYO COSMOS ELECTRIC CO., LTD.

Tokyo Cosmos Electric Co., Ltd.—(Continued)

Hideo Nakajima *(Mng Dir)*

Subsidiaries:

TOCOS America, Inc. (1)
1177 E Tower Rd, Schaumburg, IL 60173
Tel.: (847) 884-6664
Electronic Components Distr
N.A.I.C.S.: 423690

Taiwan Tocos Electric Co., Ltd (1)
8F-2 No 59 Tianxiang Rd, Zhongshan, Taipei, 10452, Taiwan
Tel.: (886) 225867862
Web Site: http://www.tocos.com.tw
Electronic Components Distr
N.A.I.C.S.: 423690

TOKYO ELECTRIC POWER COMPANY HOLDINGS, INCORPORATED

1-1-3 Uchisaiwai-cho, Chiyoda-ku, Tokyo, 100-8560, Japan
Tel.: (81) 363731111 JP
Web Site: https://www.tepco.co.jp
Year Founded: 1951
9501—(TKS)
Rev.: $45,730,551,290
Assets: $96,476,122,800
Liabilities: $73,089,797,380
Net Worth: $23,386,325,420
Earnings: $1,770,488,500
Emp.: 37,891
Fiscal Year-end: 03/31/24
Electricity Generation, Transmission & Distribution Services
N.A.I.C.S.: 221122
Seiichi Fubasami *(Exec VP)*

Subsidiaries:

Familynet Japan Corporation (1)
29th floor Atago Green Hills MORI Tower 2-5-1 Atago, Minato-ku, Tokyo, 105-6229, Japan
Tel.: (81) 367592200
Web Site: https://www.fnj.co.jp
Internet Connection Services
N.A.I.C.S.: 517111

Houseplus Corporation, Inc. (1)
1-11-1 Kaigan New Pier Takeshiba North Tower 18th Floor, Minato-ku, Tokyo, 105-0022, Japan
Tel.: (81) 345317200
Insurance Services
N.A.I.C.S.: 524210

Japan Facility Solutions, Inc. (1)
17th floor Shin-Osaki Kogyo Building 1-6-4 Osaki, Shinagawa-ku, Tokyo, 141-0032, Japan (45%)
Tel.: (81) 363712500
Web Site: http://www.j-facility.com
Sales Range: $25-49.9 Million
Emp.: 200
Facilities Environmental Management Consulting Services
N.A.I.C.S.: 541620

Japan Natural Energy Company Limited (1)
(58%)
Web Site: http://www.natural-e.co.jp
Natural Energy Power Generation Services
N.A.I.C.S.: 221118
Keiki Kato *(Pres)*

Japan Nuclear Fuel Limited (1)
4-108 Aza Okitsuke Oaza Obuchi, Rokkasho Kamikita-gun, Aomori, 039 3212, Japan (20.6%)
Tel.: (81) 175712000
Web Site: https://www.jnfl.co.jp
Emp.: 3,142
Nuclear Fuel
N.A.I.C.S.: 221113

Japan e-Market Co., Ltd. (1)
2-21-6 Mita, Tokyo, 108-0073, Minato-ku, Japan
Tel.: (81) 3 3299 3275
Web Site: http://www.j-emarket.com
Sales Range: $25-49.9 Million
Emp.: 28
Electricity Commodities & Services

N.A.I.C.S.: 423610

Nuclear Fuel Transport Co., Ltd. (1)
1-1-3 Shiba-daimon, Minato-ku, Tokyo, 105-0012, Japan
Tel.: (81) 334383241
Web Site: https://www.nft.co.jp
Emp.: 136
Nuclear Fuel Transportation
N.A.I.C.S.: 483111
Atsuhiro Yoshizawa *(Pres)*

Recyclable-Fuel Storage Company (1)
596-1 Mizukawame, Mutsu, 035-0022, Aomori, Japan
Tel.: (81) 175252990
Fuel Power Generation Services
N.A.I.C.S.: 221112

TEPCO Fuel & Power, Inc. (1)
1 - 1 - 3 Uchisaiwai - cho, Chiyoda-ku, Tokyo, 100-8560, Japan
Tel.: (81) 363731111
Fuel Power Generation Services
N.A.I.C.S.: 221112

TEPCO HomeTech, Inc. (1)
12th floor Olinas Tower 4-1-3 Taihei, Sumida-ku, Tokyo, 130-0012, Japan
Tel.: (81) 368472004
Building Equipment Distr
N.A.I.C.S.: 444180
Tatsuyuki Iwasaki *(Chm)*

TEPCO Humming Work Co., Ltd. (1)
460 Momogusa Hino City, Tokyo, Japan
Tel.: (81) 428487300
Emp.: 217
Electrical Material Distr
N.A.I.C.S.: 423610

TEPCO Life Service, Inc. (1)
2-9 Higashi-Shimbashi Circles Shiodome 7th Floor, Minato-ku, Tokyo, Japan
Tel.: (81) 368092705
Web Site: https://www.tepco-ls.co.jp
Business Development Services
N.A.I.C.S.: 541611

TEPCO Logistics Co. Ltd. (1)
16th floor Shinagawa Seaside Canal Tower 4-12-6 Higashishinagawa, Shinagawa-ku, Tokyo, 140-0002, Japan
Tel.: (81) 363617900
Emp.: 531
Warehousing Services
N.A.I.C.S.: 493110

TEPCO Optical Network Engineering Inc. (1)
8F Koishikawa Daikoku Building 1-3-25 Koishikawa, Bunkyo-ku, Tokyo, 112-0002, Japan
Tel.: (81) 363670100
Emp.: 271
Communication Equipment Maintenance Services
N.A.I.C.S.: 811210
Hidetsu Kuroda *(Mng Dir)*

TEPCO Renewable Power, Inc. (1)
1-3 Uchisaiwai-cho 1 chome, Chiyuda-ku, Tokyo, 100-8560, Japan
Tel.: (81) 363731111
Web Site: https://www.tepco.co.jp
Electric Power Production & Distribution Services
N.A.I.C.S.: 221111
Masashi Nagasawa *(Pres)*

TEPCO Ventures, Inc. (1)
1-1-3 Uchisaiwaicho, Chiyoda-ku, Tokyo, 100-8560, Japan
Tel.: (81) 368598295
Web Site: https://www.tepcoventures.co.jp
Emp.: 38
Electric Power Distribution Services
N.A.I.C.S.: 221122
Masashi Takase *(Pres)*

Tepco FinTech, Inc. (1)
2-9 Higashi-Shimbashi Circles Shiodome 7th Floor, Minato-ku, Tokyo, Japan
Tel.: (81) 368092745
Web Site: https://www.tepco-ft.co.jp
Financial Development Services
N.A.I.C.S.: 541611

Tepco Solution Advance Co., Ltd. (1)

8th floor Icon Place Shibakoen 3-2-18 Shiba, Minato-ku, Tokyo, 105-0014, Japan
Tel.: (81) 342122092
Emp.: 2,279
Electric Work Contracting Services
N.A.I.C.S.: 238210
Akira Tanehashi *(Pres)*

Tepco Town Planning Co., Ltd. (1)
New Pier Takeshiba North Tower 1-11-1 Kaigan, Minato-ku, Tokyo, 105-0022, Japan
Tel.: (81) 363718111
Emp.: 2,308
Electric Power Distribution Services
N.A.I.C.S.: 221122
Yusuke Suzuki *(Pres)*

The Tokyo Electric Generation Company, Incorporated (1)
1604 Azanakagoshi Iwaki, Itoigawa, 941-0078, Niigata, Japan
Tel.: (81) 25552 0537
Eletric Power Generation Services
N.A.I.C.S.: 221121
Koichi Kimura *(Chm)*

Toden KoKoku Co.,Ltd. (1)
22-2 Shinsencho, Shibuya-Ku, Tokyo, 150-0045, Japan
Tel.: (81) 363718111
Contract Advertising Services
N.A.I.C.S.: 541890

Toden Kogyo Co., Ltd. (1)
1-3-13 Takanawa, Minato-Ku, Tokyo, 108-0074, Japan
Tel.: (81) 363724800
Web Site: http://www.todenkogyo.co.jp
Sales Range: $300-349.9 Million
Emp.: 1,327
Power Generation Facility Repair & Maintenance Services
N.A.I.C.S.: 561210

Toden Real Estate Co., Inc. (1)
1-6-1 Kyobashi Mitsuisumitomokaijo Tepuko Building, Chuo-ku, Tokyo, 104-0031, Japan
Tel.: (81) 363721010
Real Estate Manangement Services
N.A.I.C.S.: 531390

Tokyo Electric Power Company International B.V. (1)
Herikerbergweg, Amsterdam, 1101 CM, Netherlands
Tel.: (31) 205755600
Eletric Power Generation Services
N.A.I.C.S.: 221118

Tokyo Electric Power Services Company, Limited (1)
9F KDX Toyosu Grandsquare 7-12 Shinonome 1-chome, Koto-ku, Tokyo, 135-0062, Japan
Tel.: (81) 363725111
Emp.: 890
Consultancy Services
N.A.I.C.S.: 541690
Noriaki Taketani *(Chm)*

Tokyo Power Technology Ltd. (1)
5-5-13 Toyosu, Koto-ku, Tokyo, 135-0061, Japan
Tel.: (81) 363727000
Emp.: 2,396
Fire Insurance Services
N.A.I.C.S.: 524113
Kazuyuki Shiokawa *(Pres)*

Tokyo Records Management Co., Inc. (1)
2nd floor BR Gotanda 2-30-4 Nishigotanda, Shinagawa-ku, Tokyo, 141-0031, Japan
Tel.: (81) 363720200
Emp.: 233
Electronic Document Management Services
N.A.I.C.S.: 561410

e-Mobility Power Co., Inc. (1)
7th floor NSS-II Building 2-13-34 Konan, Minato- ku, Tokyo, 108-0075, Japan
Tel.: (81) 362751745
Electric Vehicle Charging Services
N.A.I.C.S.: 457120
Naoko Yotsuyanagi *(Pres)*

TOKYO ELECTRON LIMITED

Akasaka Biz Tower 3-1 Akasaka

INTERNATIONAL PUBLIC

5-chome, Minato-ku, Tokyo, 107-6325, Japan
Tel.: (81) 355617000
Web Site: https://www.tel.com
Year Founded: 1963
TOELF—(OTCIQ)
Rev.: $15,838,709,250
Assets: $16,574,128,980
Liabilities: $5,105,541,900
Net Worth: $11,468,587,080
Earnings: $3,381,257,280
Emp.: 17,522
Fiscal Year-end: 03/31/23
Semiconductor Production Equipment Mfr
N.A.I.C.S.: 334413
Kenji Washino *(Sr VP & Gen Mgr-Backend Process Bus Div)*

Subsidiaries:

TEL Magnetic Solutions Ltd. (1)
Unit J, Furry Park Industrial Estate Santry, Dublin, Ireland
Tel.: (353) 1 854 7900
Magnetic Annealing Mfr
N.A.I.C.S.: 332420
James Traynor *(Chm)*

TEL Solar AG (1)
Hauptsrrasse 1a, Trubbach, 9477, Switzerland (100%)
Tel.: (41) 81 784 8000
Web Site: http://www.solar.tel.com
Sales Range: $350-399.9 Million
Emp.: 400
Holding Company; Thin Film Silicon Solar Module Developer, Mfr & Distr
N.A.I.C.S.: 551112
Hannes Reinhardt *(Head-Ops)*

Subsidiary (Non-US):

TEL Solar (Shanghai) Ltd. (2)
Room 1001 New Town Center No 83 Lou Shan Guan Road, Shanghai, 200336, China
Tel.: (86) 21 5048 5958
Sales Range: $25-49.9 Million
Emp.: 29
Thin Film Silicon Solar Module Device Distr
N.A.I.C.S.: 423690

Subsidiary (Domestic):

TEL Solar Switzerland AG (2)
Hauptstrasse 1a, 9477, Trubbach, Switzerland (100%)
Tel.: (41) 817848000
Web Site: http://www.solar.tel.com
Sales Range: $100-124.9 Million
Emp.: 414
Thin Film Silicon Solar Modules Mfr & Distr
N.A.I.C.S.: 333242
Hannes Reinhardt *(Head-Ops)*

Subsidiary (Non-US):

TEL Solar Taiwan Ltd. (2)
416-1 Sec 3 Chunghsin Rd, Chutung, Hsinchu, 310, Taiwan (100%)
Tel.: (886) 3 500 1688
Sales Range: $25-49.9 Million
Emp.: 2
Thin Film Silicon Solar Module Device Distr
N.A.I.C.S.: 423690
Eric Chan *(Gen Mgr)*

Subsidiary (Domestic):

TEL Solar-Lab SA (2)
Rue du Puits-Godet 12, CH-2000, Neuchatel, Switzerland (100%)
Tel.: (41) 32 732 55 80
Sales Range: $25-49.9 Million
Emp.: 24
Thin Film Silicon Solar Module Developer
N.A.I.C.S.: 541715

Tokyo Electron (Malaysia) Sdn. Bhd. (1)
No 11-1 and 11-2 Jalan Perda Jaya, Kawasan Perniagaan Perda Jaya, 14000, Bukit Mertajam, Pulau Pinang, Malaysia
Tel.: (60) 4 530 7511
Semiconductor Distr
N.A.I.C.S.: 423690
Hideki Ito *(Pres & Mng Dir)*

Tokyo Electron Agency Limited (1)
30 7 Sumiyoshi Cho 2 Chome, Tokyo, 183 8705, Fuchu, Japan **(100%)**
Tel.: (81) 423338300
Web Site: http://www.tel.com
Sales Range: $25-49.9 Million
Emp.: 15
N.A.I.C.S.: 334220

Tokyo Electron America, Inc. (1)
2400 Grove Blvd, Austin, TX 78741-6500 **(100%)**
Tel.: (512) 424-1000
Sales Range: $150-199.9 Million
Emp.: 300
N.A.I.C.S.: 334220
Larry Smith *(Pres)*

Subsidiary (Domestic):

TEL Manufacturing and Engineering of America, Inc. (2)
3455 Lyman Blvd, Chaska, MN 55318-3052
Tel.: (952) 448-5440
Sales Range: $125-149.9 Million
Special Industry Machinery Mfr
N.A.I.C.S.: 333248
Kenji Washino *(Chm)*

TEL Technology Center, America, LLC (2)
255 Fuller Rd Ste 244, Albany, NY 12203
Tel.: (518) 292-4200
Web Site: http://www.tel.com
Sales Range: $25-49.9 Million
Emp.: 130
Semiconductor Research & Development Services
N.A.I.C.S.: 541715
Gishi Chung *(Chm)*

Branch (Domestic):

Tokyo Electron America (2)
2545 W Frye Rd Ste 1, Chandler, AZ 85224
Tel.: (480) 539-2000
Web Site: http://www.tel.com
Sales Range: $25-49.9 Million
Emp.: 75
N.A.I.C.S.: 334220
Larry Smith *(Pres)*

Tokyo Electron BP Limited (1)
30-7 Sumiyoshi-cho 2-chome, Fuchu, 183-8705, Tokyo, Japan
Tel.: (81) 423338100
Web Site: http://www.tel.com
Sales Range: $75-99.9 Million
Emp.: 322
Delivery, Facility Management & Support Services
N.A.I.C.S.: 541614
Jinzaburo Sakamoto *(Pres)*

Tokyo Electron Device Asia Pacific Limited (2)
Suite 1010-11 10/F Ocean Centre Harbour City 5 Canton Road, Tsim Sha Tsui, Kowloon, China (Hong Kong)
Tel.: (852) 2169 0707
Sales Range: $50-74.9 Million
Emp.: 25
Holding Company; Regional Managing Office
N.A.I.C.S.: 551112
Atsushi Tokushige *(Mng Dir)*

Subsidiary (Non-US):

SABIC (Shanghai) Trading Co. Ltd. (2)
2550 Xiupu Road, Pudong New Area, Shanghai, 201319, China
Tel.: (86) 2120378188
Emp.: 10
Plastic Resins Distr
N.A.I.C.S.: 424610
Khalid Abdulaziz *(Gen Mgr)*

Tokyo Electron (Kunshan) Limited (2)
No 8 Dongguang Road, Kunshan Economic & Technical Development Zone, Kunshan, 215300, Jiangsu, China
Tel.: (86) 512 5500 8000
Web Site: http://www.tel.com
Electric Equipment Mfr
N.A.I.C.S.: 336320

Tokyo Electron (Shanghai) Limited (2)
No 555 Gaosi Road Zhangjiang Hi-Tech Park, Shanghai, 201203, China
Tel.: (86) 2138954800
Web Site: http://www.tokyoelectron.com
Sales Range: $25-49.9 Million
Emp.: 200
Semiconductor Mfr
N.A.I.C.S.: 334413

Subsidiary (Domestic):

Tokyo Electron (Shanghai) Logistic Center Limited (3)
Level 1 No 126 Hedan Road Waigaoqiao FTZ, Pudong, Shanghai, 201206, China
Tel.: (86) 2158681626
Web Site: http://www.tel.com
Semiconductor Parts Distr
N.A.I.C.S.: 334413
Jay Chen *(Pres)*

Subsidiary (Non-US):

Tokyo Electron Device Singapore Pte. Ltd. (2)
175A Bencoolen Street 05-01/02 Burlington Square, Singapore, 189650, Singapore
Tel.: (65) 6542 1776
Sales Range: $25-49.9 Million
Emp.: 5
Electronic Components Distr
N.A.I.C.S.: 423690
Atsushi Tokushige *(Pres)*

Tokyo Electron Korea Limited (2)
56 Samsung 1-ro 1-gil, Hwaseong, 18449, Gyeonggi, Korea (South) **(100%)**
Tel.: (82) 312605000
Web Site: http://www.telkorea.co.kr
Sales Range: $1-9.9 Million
Emp.: 350
N.A.I.C.S.: 334220

Subsidiary (Domestic):

Tokyo Electron Korea Solution Limited (3)
325-230 Dongchun-Dong, Suji-Gu, Yongin, 449-120, Kyonggi-do, Korea (South)
Tel.: (82) 312605000
Semiconductor Modification, Relocation & Re-Engineering Services
N.A.I.C.S.: 541519

Subsidiary (Non-US):

Tokyo Electron Taiwan Limited (2)
No 7 Dusing Rd Hsinchu Science Park, Hsin-chu, 30078, Taiwan
Tel.: (886) 36662266
Web Site: http://www.tel.com
Sales Range: $25-49.9 Million
Emp.: 140
Provider of Electronic Components
N.A.I.C.S.: 334419

Tokyo Electron Device Limited (1)
Yokohama East Square 1-4 Kinko-cho, Kanagawa-ku, Yokohama, 221-0056, Kanagawa, Japan **(50%)**
Tel.: (81) 454434000
Web Site: https://www.teldevice.co.jp
Emp.: 1,279
N.A.I.C.S.: 334220
Atsushi Tokushige *(Pres)*

Tokyo Electron EE Limited (1)
2 41 Machiya 1 Chome, Shiroyama Machi, Tsukui, 220-0101, Kanagawa, Japan **(100%)**
Tel.: (81) 427831331
Web Site: http://www.tel.co.jp
Sales Range: $75-99.9 Million
Emp.: 200
N.A.I.C.S.: 334220

Tokyo Electron Europe Limited (1)
Pioneer Crawley Business Quarter Fleming Way, Crawley, RH10 9QL, West Sussex, United Kingdom **(100%)**
Tel.: (44) 1293655800
Web Site: http://www.tel.com
Sales Range: $50-74.9 Million
Emp.: 70
N.A.I.C.S.: 334220

Branch (Non-US):

Tokyo Electron Europe Limited-France (2)
Les Jardins d'Entreprise Batiment Alicante 1 Chemin De La Dhuy, 38240, Meylan, France **(100%)**
Tel.: (33) 476041244
Web Site: http://www.telcustomer.com
Sales Range: $25-49.9 Million
Emp.: 43
N.A.I.C.S.: 334220

Tokyo Electron Europe Limited-Germany (2)
Moritzburger Weg 67 Haus D, 01109, Dresden, Germany
Tel.: (49) 35185034100
Web Site: http://www.tel.com
Sales Range: $25-49.9 Million
Emp.: 65
Semiconductor Mfr
N.A.I.C.S.: 334413

Tokyo Electron Europe Limited-Ireland (2)
Unit 1 Block K Maynooth Bus Campus, Maynooth, RH10 9QL, Co Kildare, Ireland **(100%)**
Tel.: (353) 16014970
Web Site: http://www.tel.co.jp
Sales Range: $25-49.9 Million
N.A.I.C.S.: 334220

Tokyo Electron Europe Limited-Italy (2)
Via Monza 7, 20871, Vimercate, MB, Italy
Tel.: (39) 0039656081
Sales Range: $25-49.9 Million
Emp.: 22
N.A.I.C.S.: 334220

Tokyo Electron Europe Limited-Netherlands (2)
Kerkenbos 10 15 Unit C, 6546 BB, Nijmegen, Netherlands **(100%)**
Tel.: (31) 243726630
Web Site: http://www.tal-europe.com
Sales Range: $25-49.9 Million
Emp.: 11
N.A.I.C.S.: 334220

Tokyo Electron FE Limited (1)
30-7 Sumiyoshi-cho 2-chome, Fuchu, 183-8705, Tokyo, Japan **(100%)**
Tel.: (81) 423338411
Web Site: http://www.tel.co.jp
Sales Range: $250-299.9 Million
Emp.: 1,000
N.A.I.C.S.: 334220

Tokyo Electron Israel Limited (1)
Leshem 1 Industrial Area, PO Box 8625, Kiryat Gat, 82000, Israel **(89%)**
Tel.: (972) 86810860
Sales Range: $50-74.9 Million
Emp.: 80
N.A.I.C.S.: 334220
Eyal Shekel *(Gen Mgr)*

Tokyo Electron Miyagi Limited (1)
1 Techno-Hills, Taiwa-cho Kurokawa-gun, Miyagi, 981-3629, Japan
Tel.: (81) 22 346 3000
Web Site: http://www.tel.com
Plasma Etch System Mfr
N.A.I.C.S.: 334413

Tokyo Electron Singapore Pte. Ltd. (1)
1 Paya Lebar Link 14-05 PLQ 2 Paya Lebar Quarter, Singapore, 408533, Singapore
Tel.: (65) 6 439 7000
Semiconductor Distr
N.A.I.C.S.: 423690
Hideki Ito *(Pres & Mng Dir)*

Tokyo Electron Technology Development Institute, Inc. (1)
2-1 Osawa 3-chome, Izumi-ku, Sendai, 981-3137, Miyagi, Japan
Tel.: (81) 22 772 8130
Emp.: 12
Electronic Components Mfr
N.A.I.C.S.: 334419
Satoshi Kawakami *(Pres)*

Tokyo Electron Technology Solutions Ltd. (1)
2381-1 Kitagejo Fujii-cho, Nirasaki, 407-8511, Yamanashi, Japan
Tel.: (81) 55 122 8611
Semiconductor Mfr
N.A.I.C.S.: 334413

Sadao Sasaki *(Pres)*

TOKYO ENERGY & SYSTEMS INC.
1-3-1 Nihonbashi Kayabacho, Chuo-ku, Tokyo, 103-0025, Japan
Tel.: (81) 363711947
Web Site: https://www.qtes.co.jp
Year Founded: 1947
1945—(TKS)
Rev.: $584,766,870
Assets: $710,383,310
Liabilities: $257,281,030
Net Worth: $453,102,280
Earnings: $19,565,600
Emp.: 1,308
Fiscal Year-end: 03/31/24
Industrial Construction Services
N.A.I.C.S.: 237990
Tsutomu Kumagai *(Pres)*

TOKYO FINANCE LIMITED
601-A Dynasty Business Park Andheri Kurla Road Near J B Nagar, Andheri East, Mumbai, 400059, Maharashtra, India
Tel.: (91) 2261453300
Web Site: https://www.tokyofinance.in
Year Founded: 1994
531644—(BOM)
Rev.: $84,120
Assets: $1,335,627
Liabilities: $107,416
Net Worth: $1,228,212
Earnings: $14,819
Emp.: 9
Fiscal Year-end: 03/31/23
Consumer Financial Services
N.A.I.C.S.: 522291
Velji L. Shah *(Chm & Mng Dir)*

TOKYO FINANCIAL EXCHANGE INC.
Tekko Building 8th Floor 1-8-2 Marunouchi, Chiyoda-ku, Tokyo, 100-0005, Japan
Tel.: (81) 345782400
Web Site: http://www.tfx.co.jp
Year Founded: 1989
Sales Range: $50-74.9 Million
Emp.: 113
Futures Exchange Services
N.A.I.C.S.: 523210
Shozo Ohta *(Pres & CEO)*

TOKYO GAS CO., LTD.
1-5-20 Kaigan, Minato-ku, Tokyo, 105-8527, Japan
Tel.: (81) 570033800 JP
Web Site: https://www.tokyo-gas.co.jp
Year Founded: 1885
9531—(NGO)
Rev.: $17,086,613,280
Assets: $26,507,208,640
Liabilities: $15,101,545,360
Net Worth: $11,405,663,280
Earnings: $479,208,400
Emp.: 16,858
Fiscal Year-end: 03/31/21
Gas Producer, Distr, Refiner & Sales; Gas Appliances Developer & Sales; Natural Gas Whslr ; Cold Water & Heat Supply Distr
N.A.I.C.S.: 221210
Michiaki Hirose *(Chm)*

Subsidiaries:

Capty Co., Ltd. (1)
Tel.: (81) 368973320
Web Site: http://www.capty.co.jp
Emp.: 1,255
Gas Pipe Construction Services
N.A.I.C.S.: 237120

TG Natural Resources LLC (1)

TOKYO GAS CO., LTD.

Tokyo Gas Co., Ltd.—(Continued)

717 Texas Ave Ste 2000, Houston, TX 77002
Tel.: (346) 308-2250
Web Site: http://www.tgnr.com
Natural Gas Mfr & Distr
N.A.I.C.S.: 333912

Tokyo Gas America Ltd. (1)
5051 Westheimer Rd Ste 1900, Houston, TX 77056
Tel.: (713) 465-1811
Web Site: https://www.tgamerica.com
Natural Gas Distr
N.A.I.C.S.: 221210

Tokyo Gas Australia Pty Ltd (1)
Level 11 Brookfield Place Tower 2 123 St Georges Terrace, Perth, 6000, WA, Australia
Tel.: (61) 894255100
Web Site: https://www.tokyo-gas.com.au
Natural Gas Distr
N.A.I.C.S.: 221210
Hideto Kurokawa (Gen Mgr)

Tokyo Gas Chemicals Co., Ltd. (1)
2-4-1 Shibakoen, Minato-ku, Tokyo, 105-0011, Japan
Tel.: (81) 364021061
Web Site: https://www.tgc.jp
Natural Gas Distr
N.A.I.C.S.: 221210
Toshiyasu Ishii (Pres)

Tokyo Gas Co., Ltd. - US Office (1)
5051 Westheimer Rd Ste 1900, Houston, TX 77056
Tel.: (713) 465-1811
Web Site: http://www.tgny.com
Sales Range: $75-99.9 Million
Emp.: 5
Production & Distribution of Natural Gas
N.A.I.C.S.: 221210

TOKYO ICHIBAN FOODS CO., LTD.
Shinjuku Yawaragi Bldg 4F 5-6-1, Shinjuku-ku, Tokyo, 160-0022, Japan
Tel.: (81) 353632132
Web Site: https://www.tokyo-ichiban-foods.co.jp
Year Founded: 1996
3067—(TKS)
Rev.: $51,452,130
Assets: $32,486,380
Liabilities: $21,255,820
Net Worth: $11,230,560
Earnings: $772,810
Fiscal Year-end: 09/30/23
Restaurant Operators
N.A.I.C.S.: 722511
Daichi Sakamoto (Pres & CEO)

TOKYO INFRASTRUCTURE ENERGY INVESTMENT CORP.
8F Kojimachi Place 2-3 Kojimachi, Chiyoda-Ku, Tokyo, 100-0004, Japan
Tel.: (81) 365512838
Web Site: https://tokyo-infra.com
Year Founded: 2017
9285—(TKS)
Sales Range: Less than $1 Million
Investment Services
N.A.I.C.S.: 523999
Toshihiko Nagamori (Exec Dir)

TOKYO KAIKAN CO., LTD.
3-2-1 Marunouchi, Chiyoda-Ku, Tokyo, 100-0005, Japan
Tel.: (81) 332152111
Web Site: https://www.kaikan.co.jp
Year Founded: 1920
9701—(TKS)
Sales Range: $75-99.9 Million
Restaurant Operators
N.A.I.C.S.: 722511
Yukihiro Fujiwara (Pres)

TOKYO KEIKI INC.
2-16-46 Minami-Kamata, Ohta-ku, Tokyo, 144-8551, Japan
Tel.: (81) 337322111
Web Site: http://www.tokyo-keiki.co.jp
Year Founded: 1896
7721—(TKS)
Rev.: $311,767,260
Assets: $442,724,580
Liabilities: $195,715,490
Net Worth: $247,009,090
Earnings: $15,050,970
Emp.: 1,700
Fiscal Year-end: 03/31/24
Marine Instruments, Hydraulic Equipment, Aerospace & Defense Equipment, Instruments & Systems Mfr & Sales
N.A.I.C.S.: 334519
Hidemitsu Yamada (Sr Exec Dir)

Subsidiaries:

MOCOS JAPAN CO., LTD. (1)
A-Place Bashamichi 5F 4-43 Honcho, Naka-Ku, Yokohama, 231-0005, Kanagawa, Japan
Tel.: (81) 456718301
Web Site: https://www.tokyokeiki.jp
Sales Range: $25-49.9 Million
Emp.: 9
Telecommunication Servicesb
N.A.I.C.S.: 517810

TOKYO KEIKI AVIATION INC. (1)
2-1-1 Misugidai, Hanno, 357-0041, Saitama, Japan
Tel.: (81) 429710550
Emp.: 110
Aircraft Equipment Repair Services
N.A.I.C.S.: 811114

TOKYO KEIKI CUSTOMER SERVICE INC. (1)
2-16-46 Minami-Kamata, Ota-Ku, Tokyo, 144-8551, Japan
Tel.: (81) 357106441
Marine Equipment Distr
N.A.I.C.S.: 423860
Hisao Kitajima (Pres)

TOKYO KEIKI INC. - Hanno Plant (1)
2-1-1 Misugidai, Hanno, 357-0041, Saitama, Japan
Tel.: (81) 429710550
Web Site: http://www.tokyo-keiki.co.jp
Marine Equipment Mfr
N.A.I.C.S.: 333618

TOKYO KEIKI INC. - Nasu Plant (1)
3-1 Takakukou Nasu-Machi, Nasu-Gun, Tochigi, 325-0001, Japan
Tel.: (81) 287633711
Marine Equipment Mfr
N.A.I.C.S.: 336999

TOKYO KEIKI INC. - Sano Plant (1)
1-1 Sakae-Cho, Sano, 327-0816, Tochigi, Japan
Tel.: (81) 283233311
Web Site: http://www.tokyo-keiki.co.jp
Emp.: 1,000
Marine Equipment Mfr
N.A.I.C.S.: 336999

TOKYO KEIKI INC. - Tanuma Plant (1)
168 Tada-Cho, Sano, 327-0311, Tochigi, Japan
Tel.: (81) 283627330
Marine Equipment Mfr
N.A.I.C.S.: 336999

TOKYO KEIKI INC. - Yaita Plant (1)
333-4 Azuma-Cho, Yaita, 329-2136, Tochigi, Japan
Tel.: (81) 287432121
Marine Equipment Mfr
N.A.I.C.S.: 336999

TOKYO KEIKI INFORMATION SYSTEMS INC. (1)
2-16-46 Minami Kamata, Ota-Ku, Tokyo, 144-8551, Japan
Tel.: (81) 337310511
Web Site: http://www.tokyo-keiki.co.jp
Emp.: 50

Information Development & Communication Technology
N.A.I.C.S.: 541512

TOKYO KEIKI POWER SYSTEMS INC. (1)
168 Tadacho, Sano, 327-0311, Tochigi, Japan
Tel.: (81) 283627330
Sales Range: $25-49.9 Million
Emp.: 70
Hydraulic Equipment Mfr & Distr
N.A.I.C.S.: 333995
Shigeki Shirayama (Pres)

TOKYO KEIKI RAIL TECHNO INC. (1)
2-16-46 Minami-Kamata, Ohta-ku, Tokyo, 144-8551, Japan
Tel.: (81) 337327061
Sales Range: $25-49.9 Million
Emp.: 65
Railway Equipment Maintenance Services
N.A.I.C.S.: 811114

TOKYO KEIKI TECHNOPORT INC. (1)
2-16-46 Minami-Kamata, Ohta-Ku, Tokyo, 144-8551, Japan
Tel.: (81) 337353731
Web Site: https://www.tokyokeiki.jp
Transportation Equipment Mfr
N.A.I.C.S.: 336999

Technoport Inc. (1)
2-16-46 Minami-Kamata, Ota-ku, Tokyo, 144-8551, Japan
Tel.: (81) 337353731
Emp.: 40
Electronic Equipment Import & Sales; Real Estate & Hotel Businesses Management & Sales
N.A.I.C.S.: 423690

Tokimec Aviation Inc. (1)
2-1-1 Misugidai, Hanno, 357-0041, Saitama, Japan **(100%)**
Tel.: (81) 429710550
Aeronautical Equipment Repair & Sales
N.A.I.C.S.: 811210

Tokimec Construction Systems Inc (1)
2 16 46 Minami Kamata Ohta ku, Tokyo, 144 8551, Japan **(100%)**
Tel.: (81) 337312631
Web Site: http://www.tokyo-keiki.co.jp
Sales Range: $100-124.9 Million
Emp.: 400
Machines for Road & Building Construction Production & Sales
N.A.I.C.S.: 333120

Tokimec Information Systems Inc. (1)
2-16-46 Minami Kamata, Ota-ku, Tokyo, 144-8551, Japan **(100%)**
Tel.: (81) 337310511
Web Site: https://www.tokyokeiki.jp
Emp.: 50
Navigational Information Systems Mfr
N.A.I.C.S.: 334511

Tokimec Korea Power Control Co. Ltd. (1)
70 Seonyu-ro, Yeongdeungpo-gu, Seoul, 07294, Korea (South)
Tel.: (82) 226706632
Web Site: https://eng.tokimec.co.kr
Sales Range: $50-74.9 Million
Emp.: 63
Hydraulic Equipment Production & Sales & Engineering of Hydraulic/Pneumatic Systems
N.A.I.C.S.: 333120

Tokimec Rail Techno Inc. (1)
2-16-46 Minami Kamata Ohta ku, Tokyo, 144 8551, Japan **(100%)**
Tel.: (81) 337327061
Web Site: http://www.tokyo-keiki.co.jp
Sales Range: $25-49.9 Million
Emp.: 46
Rail Track Maintenance Equipment Mfr
N.A.I.C.S.: 811210

Tokyo Keiki Power Systems Inc. (1)
168 TadaCho, Sano, 327-0311, Tochigi, Japan

INTERNATIONAL PUBLIC

Tel.: (81) 283627330
Web Site: https://www.tokyokeiki.jp
Emp.: 60
Hydraulic Equipment Mfr
N.A.I.C.S.: 332912
Shigeki Shirayama (Pres)

Tokyo Keiki Precision Technology Co., Ltd. (1)
Lot A15-6 Central Road Da Nang Hi-tech Park, Hoa Lien Commune Hoa Vang Dist, Da Nang, Vietnam
Tel.: (84) 2363733833
Hydraulic Equipment Mfr
N.A.I.C.S.: 336612

Tokyo Keiki U.S.A., Inc. (1)
3452 E Foothill Blvd Ste 420, Pasadena, CA 91107
Tel.: (626) 403-1500
Sales Range: $50-74.9 Million
Emp.: 10
Electronic Components & Optical Electronic Products Import & Export
N.A.I.C.S.: 423690

TOKYO KEISO CO., LTD.
Shiba Toho Bldg 1-7-24 Shibakoen, Minato-ku, Tokyo, 105-8558, Japan
Tel.: (81) 3 3431 1625
Web Site: http://www.tokyokeiso.co.jp
Emp.: 650
Flow Control Instrument Mfr
N.A.I.C.S.: 334514
Ryoichi Sugi (CEO)

Subsidiaries:

CHONGQING ENDURANCE & TOKYO KEISO INSTRUMENT CO., LTD. (1)
No 6 Yangliu Road Huangshan Branch, New Northern District, Chongqing, 401121, China
Tel.: (86) 2367300733
Measuring Instrument Distr
N.A.I.C.S.: 423830

PT. TOKYO KEISO INDONESIA (1)
Wisma Slipi 3rd Floor JL Let Lend S parman Kav 12, Jakarta, 12210, Indonesia
Tel.: (62) 215307248
Measuring Instrument Distr
N.A.I.C.S.: 423830

TOKYO KEISO (BEIJING) CO., LTD. (1)
Room H1 Floor 3 East Area HuikeBuilding No158, West Fourth Ring North Road Haidian, Beijing, 100097, China
Tel.: (86) 1088591468
Web Site: http://www.tokyokeiso.bj.cn
Measuring Instrument Distr
N.A.I.C.S.: 423830

TOKYO KEISO (MALAYSIA) SDN.BHD. (1)
No 5-1 Block E2 Jalan Pju 1/42A Dataran Prima, Petaling Jaya, Selangor, Malaysia
Tel.: (60) 378048335
Measuring Instrument Distr
N.A.I.C.S.: 423830

TOKYO KEISO (SHANGHAI) CO., LTD. (1)
703F Building 11 No 518 Xinzhuan Rd, Songjiang, Shanghai, 201612, China
Tel.: (86) 2157633151
Measuring Instrument Distr
N.A.I.C.S.: 423830

TOKYO KEISO (XIA MEN) CO., LTD. (1)
Room1305 Building A Hai Fu Center No 597 Sishui Road, Huli, Xiamen, China
Tel.: (86) 5925323699806
Measuring Instrument Distr
N.A.I.C.S.: 423830

TOKYO KEISO CORPORATION OF AMERICA (1)
4900 Hopyard Rd Ste 290, Pleasanton, CA 94588
Tel.: (925) 251-0852
Measuring Instrument Distr
N.A.I.C.S.: 423830

TOKYO KEISO EUROPE B.V. (1)

Liendense Singel 39, 4033 KH, Buren, Netherlands
Tel.: (31) 344601157
Web Site: http://www.tokyokeiso-europe.nl
Measuring Instrument Distr
N.A.I.C.S.: 423830

TOKYO KEISO KOREA CO., LTD. (1)
Rm 1314 E & C Dream Tower 46 Yangpyoung-dong 3 Ga, Youngdeungpo, Seoul, Korea (South)
Tel.: (82) 226280460
Measuring Instrument Distr
N.A.I.C.S.: 423830

TOKYO KEISO SALES (THAILAND) CO., LTD. (1)
58 Soi Ramkhamhaeng 18 Meankhian 3 Ramkhamhaeng Rd Huamark, Bangkapi, Bangkok, 10240, Thailand
Tel.: (66) 23693585
Measuring Instrument Distr
N.A.I.C.S.: 423830

TOKYO KEISO TAIWAN CO., LTD. (1)
Room 6 9F No 8 Zihciang S Rd, Zhubei, Hsin-chu, 30264, Taiwan
Tel.: (886) 36599979
Web Site: http://www.tokyokeiso.com.tw
Measuring Instrument Distr
N.A.I.C.S.: 423830

TOKYO KIHO CO., LTD.
Aurum Bldg 1-26-2 Higashi-Ueno, Taito-Ku, Tokyo, 110-0015, Japan
Tel.: (81) 3 38346262
Web Site: http://www.tokyokiho.com
Year Founded: 1960
7597—(JAS)
Sales Range: $25-49.9 Million
Emp.: 102
Jewel Mfr & Distr
N.A.I.C.S.: 339910

TOKYO KIKAI SEISAKUSHO LTD.
Mita Nitto Daibiru Bldg 6F 3-11-36 Mita, Minato-ku, Tokyo, 108-8375, Japan
Tel.: (81) 334518141
Web Site: https://www.tks-net.co.jp
6335—(TKS)
Rev.: $61,572,150
Assets: $100,472,000
Liabilities: $40,248,290
Net Worth: $60,223,710
Earnings: ($548,630)
Fiscal Year-end: 03/31/24
Press Control Systems Mfr
N.A.I.C.S.: 323111

Subsidiaries:

Iga Machinery Co., Ltd. (1)
98 Sanagu-cho, Iga, 518-0001, Mie, Japan
Tel.: (81) 595233151
Sales Range: $25-49.9 Million
Emp.: 58
Printing Equipment Mfr
N.A.I.C.S.: 325910

KKS, Ltd. (1)
4-11-54 Takeshima, Nishiyodogawa-ku, Osaka, 555-0011, Japan
Tel.: (81) 664717771
Web Site: https://www.kks-j.co.jp
Sales Range: $10-24.9 Million
Emp.: 115
Printing Machinery Mfr
N.A.I.C.S.: 333248
Kiyoshi Tsunami (Mng Dir)

TKS (U.S.A.), Inc. (1)
101 E Park Blvd Ste 614, Plano, TX 75074
Tel.: (972) 871-8857
Web Site: http://www.tksusa.com
Sales Range: $25-49.9 Million
Emp.: 10
Printing Equipment Mfr
N.A.I.C.S.: 333248
Mike Shafer (Dir-Sls & Mktg)

TOKYO KIKAI SEISAKUSHO LTD. - Tamagawa Factory (1)
1135 Shinmaruko-higashi 3-chome, Nakahara-ku, Kawasaki, 211-0004, Kanagawa, Japan
Tel.: (81) 444350511
Printing Equipment Mfr
N.A.I.C.S.: 333248

Tohki Electronics Co., Ltd. (1)
1-8-2 Haneda-kuko Ota-ku, Tokyo, 144-0041, Japan
Tel.: (81) 3 5708 7730
Web Site: http://www.tkel.co.jp
Rev.: $18,597,272
Emp.: 53
Software Development Services
N.A.I.C.S.: 541511
Yoshimaro Shiba (Pres)

Toki Fudosan Co., Ltd (1)
Mita Nitto Daibiru Bldg 6F 3-11-36 Mita, Minato-ku, Tokyo, 108-0073, Japan
Tel.: (81) 3 3454 1650
Web Site: http://www.tks-net.co.jp
Printing Machinery Mfr
N.A.I.C.S.: 333248

Toki Service Co., Ltd. (1)
Mitsuba Seiki Bldg 15-21 Shimomaruko 1-chome, Ota-Ku, Tokyo, 146-0092, Japan
Tel.: (81) 337564921
Web Site: http://www.tks-net.co.jp
Printing Machinery Mfr
N.A.I.C.S.: 333248

TOKYO KIRABOSHI FINANCIAL GROUP, INC.
10-43 Minamiaoyama3-chome, Minato-ku, Tokyo, 107-0062, Japan
Tel.: (81) 353414301 **JP**
Web Site: https://www.tokyo-kiraboshifg.co.jp
Year Founded: 2014
7173—(TKS)
Rev.: $914,367,910
Assets: $47,549,054,830
Liabilities: $45,135,552,140
Net Worth: $2,413,502,690
Earnings: $528,800
Fiscal Year-end: 03/31/24
Bank Holding Company
N.A.I.C.S.: 551111
Satoru Nobeta (Sr Mng Dir)

Subsidiaries:

The Tokyo Tomin Bank, Limited (1)
2-3-11 Roppongi 2-chome, Minato-ku, Tokyo, 106-8525, Japan
Tel.: (81) 335828663
Web Site: http://www.tominbank.co.jp
Sales Range: $400-449.9 Million
Emp.: 1,535
Commercial & Investment Banking
N.A.I.C.S.: 522110
Satoru Nobeta (Mng Dir)

Subsidiary (Domestic):

Tomin Card Co., Ltd. (2)
2-61-3 Higashiikebukuro, Toshima-ku, Tokyo, 170-0013, Japan **(73%)**
Tel.: (81) 359271233
Web Site: https://www.kiraboshijcb.co.jp
Credit Card Services
N.A.I.C.S.: 522210

Tomin Computer System Co., Ltd. (2)
Tomin Roppongi Building 8F 2-4-1 Roppongi, Minato-ku, Tokyo, 106-0032, Japan
Tel.: (81) 3 3585 0923
Web Site: http://www.tcsweb.co.jp
Data Processing & Information Technology Management Services
N.A.I.C.S.: 518210
Hideo Kato (Pres)

Tomin Credit Guarantee Co., Ltd. (2)
3-3 Kanda Ogawa 6-chome, Chiyoda-ku, Tokyo, 101-0052, Japan **(100%)**
Tel.: (81) 3 3292 7511
Web Site: http://www.tomin-tcg.co.jp
Loan Credit Services
N.A.I.C.S.: 522180

Tomin Management Research Institute Co., Ltd. (2)
Consulting Unit Kiraboshi Bank 3-10-43 Minami-Aoyama, Minato-ku, Tokyo, 107-0062, Japan **(80.7%)**
Tel.: (81) 364475886
Web Site: https://www.kiraboshi-consul.co.jp
Financial Management Consulting Services
N.A.I.C.S.: 541618

The Yachiyo Bank, Limited (1)
5-9-2 Shinjuku, Shinjuku-ku, Tokyo, 160-8431, Japan
Tel.: (81) 3 3352 2295
Web Site: http://www.yachiyobank.co.jp
Sales Range: $450-499.9 Million
Emp.: 1,623
Commercial & Investment Banking
N.A.I.C.S.: 522110
Kazuyuki Takahashi (Chm)

TOKYO KISEN CO., LTD.
2 Yamashita-cho Japan Industrial Trade Center Building, Naka-ku, Yokohama, 231-0023, Kanagawa, Japan
Tel.: (81) 456717711
Web Site: https://www.tokyokisen.co.jp
Year Founded: 1947
9193—(TKS)
Rev.: $82,724,150
Assets: $192,469,980
Liabilities: $43,077,370
Net Worth: $149,392,610
Earnings: $3,780,920
Emp.: 232
Fiscal Year-end: 03/31/24
Tugboat Services
N.A.I.C.S.: 488330
Masaya Saito (Chm)

Subsidiaries:

Miyagi Marine Service Co., Ltd. (1)
1-Chome 8-35 Teizan-Dori, Shiogama, 985-0011, Miyagi-Ken, Japan
Tel.: (81) 223642301
Web Site: http://www.miyagimarine.co.jp
Shipping Agency Services
N.A.I.C.S.: 488510
Yoshinori Sato (Pres)

Pacific Marine Services Co., Ltd. (1)
37C Nguyen Thien Thuat St, Thang Nhat Ward, Vung Tau, Vietnam
Tel.: (84) 2543563606
Web Site: http://pmarine.com.vn
Marine Cargo Services
N.A.I.C.S.: 488390
Trieu Minh Triet (Mgr-Design & Fabrication Dept)

South China Towing Co., Ltd. (1)
Unit 3203-06 Singga Commercial Centre 148 Connaught Road West, Hong Kong, China (Hong Kong)
Tel.: (852) 25485205
Web Site: https://www.southchinatowing.com.hk
Coastal Towage Services
N.A.I.C.S.: 488410
Jacka Ho (Gen Mgr)

TOKYO KOKI CO., LTD.
1-9 Kandasakumacho, Chiyoda-ku, Tokyo, 101-0025, Japan
Tel.: (81) 427801650
Web Site: https://www.tksnet.co.jp
Year Founded: 1923
7719—(TKS)
Rev.: $23,857,850
Assets: $25,977,760
Liabilities: $15,200,960
Net Worth: $10,776,800
Earnings: $645,190
Emp.: 50
Fiscal Year-end: 02/29/24
Testing Machine Mfr & Distr
N.A.I.C.S.: 334519
Hiroshi Takenaka (Pres)

TOKYO LIVING SERVICE CO., LTD.
5 F Step Roppongi Building 6-8-10 Roppongi, Minato-ku, Tokyo, 106-0032, Japan
Tel.: (81) 363715676
Web Site: http://www.ryokou-tls.com
Sales Range: $150-199.9 Million
Real Estate Manangement Services
N.A.I.C.S.: 531390

TOKYO METRO CO., LTD.
19-6 Higashi-Ueno 3-Chome, Tokyo, 110-8614, Japan
Tel.: (81) 338377041
Web Site: http://www.tokyometro.jp
Sales Range: $1-4.9 Billion
Emp.: 8,379
Rapid Transit & Subway Services
N.A.I.C.S.: 485999
Akiyoshi Yamamura (Sr Mng Dir)

Subsidiaries:

Metro Ad Agency Co., Ltd. (1)
NBF Toronanomon Building 4th Floor 6-21 Nishishinbashi, Minato-ku, Tokyo, 105-0003, Japan **(100%)**
Tel.: (81) 3 5501 7831
Web Site: http://www.metro-ad.co.jp
Sales Range: $25-49.9 Million
Emp.: 368
Advertising Services
N.A.I.C.S.: 541810
Kenichi Higo (Pres)

Metro Commerce Co., Ltd. (1)
9th Sumitomo Real Estate Ueno Building No 9 Higashi Ueno 6 chome, Taito-ku, Tokyo, 110-0015, Japan **(100%)**
Tel.: (81) 3 5246 8125
Web Site: http://www.metocan.co.jp
Emp.: 524
Food Shops, Rapid Transit & Subway Services
N.A.I.C.S.: 485999
Shigeru Ishii (Dir)

Metro Food Service Co., Ltd. (1)
5-6-6 Higashi Ueno, Taito-ku, Tokyo, 110-0115, Japan **(100%)**
Tel.: (81) 3 5806 9655
Web Site: http://www.metrofood.co.jp
Emp.: 195
Food & Beverage Retailer
N.A.I.C.S.: 722513
Atae Akira Muramatsu (Pres)

TOKYO OHKA KOGYO CO., LTD.
150 Nakamaruko, Nakahara-ku, Kawasaki, 211-0012, Kanagawa, Japan
Tel.: (81) 444453000
Web Site: https://www.tok.co.jp
Year Founded: 1940
4186—(TKS)
Rev.: $1,150,494,300
Assets: $1,785,715,760
Liabilities: $399,762,560
Net Worth: $1,385,953,200
Earnings: $90,128,080
Emp.: 1,877
Fiscal Year-end: 12/31/23
Photoresists & High Purity Chemicals Mfr & Sales
N.A.I.C.S.: 325998
Kunio Mizuki (Exec Officer & Mgr-Gen Affairs Dept)

Subsidiaries:

CHANG CHUN TOK (CHANGSHU) CO., LTD. (1)
Changchun Road Riverside Industrial Park Changshu, Economic Development Zone, Changshu, 215537, Jiangsu, China
Tel.: (86) 51252648000
Chemical Products Mfr
N.A.I.C.S.: 325998

ElgaEurope s.r.l (1)
via della Merlata 8, Nerviano, 20014, Milan, Italy
Tel.: (39) 0331586947
Web Site: https://www.elgaeurope.it
Dry Film Resists & Chemicals

TOKYO OHKA KOGYO CO., LTD.

Tokyo Ohka Kogyo Co., Ltd.—(Continued)
N.A.I.C.S.: 325998

Kumagaya Ohka Co., Ltd. (1)
823 8 Saitama Ken, Kumagayashi Migeahara, Kumagaya, 360 0844, Saitama, Japan
Tel.: (81) 485331171
Chemicals Mfr
N.A.I.C.S.: 325998

Ohka Eruope Ltd. (1)
Nettlehill Rd Houstoun Industrial Estate, Livingston, EH54 5DL, United Kingdom
Tel.: (44) 1506438755
Photoresists & High Purity Chemicals Mfr & Sales
N.A.I.C.S.: 325998

Ohka Service Co., Ltd. (1)
150 Nakamaruko, Nakahara-ku, Kawasaki, 211-0012, Kanagawa, Japan
Tel.: (81) 444353117
Sales Range: $50-74.9 Million
Emp.: 2
Insurance Services
N.A.I.C.S.: 524298

TOK Engineering Co., Ltd. (1)
3-9 Daikokuya Building 2-9-8 Akebonocho, Tachikawa, 190-0012, Tokyo, Japan
Tel.: (81) 425483530
Web Site: http://www.tok-eng.co.jp
Sales Range: $25-49.9 Million
Emp.: 96
Automatic Chemical Supplying Machines Mfr & Sales
N.A.I.C.S.: 325998

TOK KOREA CO., LTD. (1)
1106 Diplomatic Center Building 1376-1 Seocho Dong, Seocho-Gu, Seoul, 137-072, Korea (South)
Tel.: (82) 25885035
Web Site: http://www.tok.co.jp
Semiconductor Equipment Distr
N.A.I.C.S.: 423690

TOK Taiwan Co., Ltd. (1)
4F No 95 Beida Rd, Hsin-chu, 30044, Taiwan
Tel.: (886) 35345953
Web Site: https://toktaiwan.com
Sales Range: $25-49.9 Million
Emp.: 40
Photolithography Materials Mfr & Supplier; Owned by ChangChung Group & Tokyo Ohka Kogyo Co., Ltd.
N.A.I.C.S.: 425120

TOK Techno Service Co., Ltd. (1)
7-8-16 Kanagawa Prefecture dais gun samukawa, Ichinomiya, 253 0111, Japan
Tel.: (81) 467749202
Web Site: http://www.tok-technoservice.co.jp
Emp.: 20
Processing Equipment Maintenance & Services
N.A.I.C.S.: 811310
Motokawa Tsukasa (Pres)

Tok Advanced Materials Co., Ltd. (1)
45 Cheomdan Daero 60Beon-Gi, Yeonsu-Gu, Incheon, Korea (South)
Tel.: (82) 328502000
Semiconductor Material Mfr & Distr
N.A.I.C.S.: 334413

Tok China Co., Ltd. (1)
703B GIFCII 1438 Hongqiao Road, Chang-Ning, Shanghai, China
Tel.: (86) 2158408800
Semiconductor Material Distr
N.A.I.C.S.: 423690

Tokyo Ohka Kogyo America, inc. (1)
4600 NE Brookwood Pkwy, Hillsboro, OR 97124
Tel.: (503) 693-7711
Web Site: https://www.tokamerica.com
Sales Range: $50-74.9 Million
Emp.: 100
Photoresists & High Purity Chemicals Mfr & Sales
N.A.I.C.S.: 325180
Shoji Otaka (Pres)

Tokyo Ohka Kogyo Co., Ltd. - Aso Plant
4454-1 Miyaji, Ichinomiya-machi, Aso, 869-2612, Kumamoto, Japan
Tel.: (81) 967224411
Web Site: http://www.tok.co.jp
Semiconductor Photoresists Mfr
N.A.I.C.S.: 334413

Tokyo Ohka Kogyo Co., Ltd. - Electronic Material Marketing Division (1)
150 Nakamaruko, Nakahara-ku, Kawasaki, 211-0012, Kanagawa, Japan
Tel.: (81) 444353000
Web Site: https://www.tok.co.jp
Emp.: 1,950
Semiconductor Equipment Mfr
N.A.I.C.S.: 334413

Tokyo Ohka Kogyo Co., Ltd. - Gotemba Plant (1)
1-1 Komakado, Gotemba, 412-0038, Shizuoka, Japan
Tel.: (81) 550873003
Web Site: http://www.tok.co.jp
Semiconductor Photoresists Mfr
N.A.I.C.S.: 334413

Tokyo Ohka Kogyo Co., Ltd. - Koriyama Plant (1)
1-23 Machiikedai, Koriyama, 963-0215, Fukushima, Japan
Tel.: (81) 249596911
Web Site: http://www.tok.co.jp
Chemical Products Mfr
N.A.I.C.S.: 325998

Tokyo Ohka Kogyo Co., Ltd. - Kumagaya Plant (1)
823-8 Kamibayashi Miizugahara, Kumagaya, 360-0844, Saitama, Japan
Tel.: (81) 485331171
Web Site: http://www.tok.co.jp
Industrial Chemicals Mfr
N.A.I.C.S.: 325998

Tokyo Ohka Kogyo Co., Ltd. - Utsunomiya Plant (1)
21-5 Kiyohara Kogyo Danchi, Utsunomiya, 321-3231, Tochigi, Japan
Tel.: (81) 286673711
Web Site: http://www.tok.co.jp
Semiconductor Photoresists Mfr
N.A.I.C.S.: 334413

Yamanashi Ohka Co., Ltd. (1)
10234 Shimoyama Minobu-cho, Minami Koma-gun, Yamanashi, 409 2522, Japan
Tel.: (81) 556623151
Web Site: http://www.tok.co.jp
Emp.: 80
Mfr of Photopolymer Plates for Flexographic Printing
N.A.I.C.S.: 326130
Hiroshi Fujiwara (Pres)

TOKYO PLAST INTERNATIONAL LIMITED

A/401 Gala Quest Paranjape B Scheme Road No 1, Vile Parle East, Mumbai, 400057, Maharashtra, India
Tel.: (91) 2261453300
Web Site: https://www.tokyoplast.com
Year Founded: 1992
500418—(BOM)
Rev.: $8,586,866
Assets: $11,832,208
Liabilities: $3,990,974
Net Worth: $7,841,233
Earnings: $16,494
Emp.: 359
Fiscal Year-end: 03/31/21
Plastics Product Mfr
N.A.I.C.S.: 326199
Velji L. Shah (Chm & Mng Dir)

TOKYO PRINTING INK MANUFACTURING CO., LTD.

1-12-4 Oji, Kita-ku, Tokyo, 114-0002, Japan
Tel.: (81) 359027629 JP
Web Site: https://www.tokyoink.co.jp
Year Founded: 1923
4635—(TKS)
Rev.: $400,761,680
Assets: $457,951,120
Liabilities: $209,271,920
Net Worth: $248,679,200
Earnings: $7,018,000
Emp.: 880
Fiscal Year-end: 03/31/22
Printing Inks, Color & Additive Concentrates & Compounds Mfr
N.A.I.C.S.: 325910
Satoshi Horikawa (Pres)

Subsidiaries:

Tokyo Ink (Thailand) Co., Ltd. (1)
2525 Two FYI Center 5th Floor Rama 4 Road, Klongtoei, Bangkok, Thailand
Tel.: (66) 22586893
Web Site: https://www.tokyoinkthailand.com
Chemical Products Mfr
N.A.I.C.S.: 325998

Tokyo Printing Ink Corporation U.S.A (1)
2695 Temple Ave, Signal Hill, CA 90755 (100%)
Tel.: (562) 424-2226
Web Site: www.tokyoink.co.jp
Sales Range: $50-74.9 Million
Distr of Printing Ink
N.A.I.C.S.: 423840

TOKYO RAKUTENCHI CO., LTD.

4-27-14 Kotobashi, Sumida-ku, Tokyo, 130-8535, Japan
Tel.: (81) 33 631 3123
Web Site: http://www.rakutenchi.co.jp
Year Founded: 1937
8842—(TKS)
Rev.: $79,559,920
Assets: $410,674,000
Liabilities: $111,358,720
Net Worth: $299,315,280
Earnings: $3,804,240
Fiscal Year-end: 01/31/22
Real Estate Lending Services
N.A.I.C.S.: 531120

TOKYO ROPE MANUFACTURING CO., LTD.

2-37-28 Eidai Shibusawa City Place Eidai, Koto-ku, Tokyo, 135-8306, Japan
Tel.: (81) 363667777
Web Site:
https://www.tokyorope.co.jp
Year Founded: 1887
5981—(TKS)
Rev.: $424,566,910
Assets: $567,428,840
Liabilities: $338,934,360
Net Worth: $228,494,480
Earnings: $13,484,400
Fiscal Year-end: 03/31/24
Wire Product Mfr & Distr
N.A.I.C.S.: 332618
Hideyuki Harada (Pres & CEO)

Subsidiaries:

Jiangsu Tokyo Rope Co., Ltd. (1)
Cheng-Chang Industrial Park, Huangtu Town, Jiangyin, Jiangsu, China
Tel.: (86) 51086058001
Wire Rope Mfr & Distr
N.A.I.C.S.: 332618

Nippon Tokushu Goukin MFG Co., Ltd. (1)
11-3 Hakusan, Toyooka-cho, Gamagori, 443-0011, Aichi, Japan
Tel.: (81) 533691100
Emp.: 125
Industrial Mold Mfr
N.A.I.C.S.: 333511

TOKYO ROPE DO BRASIL LTDA. (1)
Av Ibirapuera 2907 - Conjunto 1710, Sao Paulo, 04029-200, SP, Brazil
Tel.: (55) 2125866034
Wire Product Distr
N.A.I.C.S.: 423510

Toko Steel Cord Co., Ltd (1)
7-1 Kitakogyoudanchi, Kitakami, 024-0002, Iwate, Japan
Tel.: (81) 197662101
Emp.: 400
Steel Pole Mfr
N.A.I.C.S.: 331222
Nakahara Ryo (Pres)

Tokyo Rope (Changzhou) Co., Ltd. (1)
No 328 West Hehai Road Xinbei District, Changzhou, Jiangsu, China
Tel.: (86) 51985966289
Steel Cord Mfr & Distr
N.A.I.C.S.: 331222

Tokyo Rope (Hong Kong) Co., Ltd. (1)
Suite 610 6/F Tower 1 The Gateway Harbour City 25 Canton Road, Tsim Sha Tsui, Kowloon, China (Hong Kong)
Tel.: (852) 25910008
Elevator Ropes Distr
N.A.I.C.S.: 423510

Tokyo Rope (Shanghai) Trading Co., Ltd. (1)
RM 2008 No 83 Lon Shan Guan Road New Hong Qiao Center Building, Shanghai, 200336, China
Tel.: (86) 2162368788
Steel Wire Product Distr
N.A.I.C.S.: 423510

Tokyo Rope Engineering LLC (1)
Leninskaya Sloboda street 26 building 28 business center Slobodskoy, 115280, Moscow, Russia
Tel.: (7) 4956450403
Web Site: http://www.tokyorope.ru
Construction Materials Distr
N.A.I.C.S.: 423390

Tokyo Rope Manufacturing Co., Ltd. - Sakai Plant (1)
2-6-1 Chikkoshinmachi Nishi-ku, Sakai, Osaka, Japan
Tel.: (81) 722453493
Wire Product Mfr
N.A.I.C.S.: 314994

Tokyo Rope Manufacturing Co., Ltd. - Tsuchiura Plant (1)
5707 Shishikura, Kasumigaura, Ibaraki, Japan
Tel.: (81) 298312222
Wire Product Mfr
N.A.I.C.S.: 314994

Tokyo Rope USA, Inc. (1)
8301 Ronda Dr, Canton, MI 48187
Tel.: (734) 335-6037
Fiber Composite Cable Distr
N.A.I.C.S.: 423510

Tokyo Rope Vietnam Co., Ltd. (1)
30 VSIP II Street 3 Vietnam Singapore Industrial Park II, Hoa Phu Ward, Thu Dau Mot, Binh Duong, Vietnam
Tel.: (84) 2743861901
Wire Rope Mfr & Distr
N.A.I.C.S.: 332618

Tokyo Seiko Rope Mfg. Co., Ltd. (1)
1-1 Nakamura, Toyooka-cho, Gamagori, 443-0011, Aichi, Japan
Tel.: (81) 533683151
Emp.: 100
Wire Product Mfr & Distr
N.A.I.C.S.: 332618
Yoshinori Matsumoto (Pres)

TOKYO SANGYO CO., LTD.

8th Floor Shin Otemachi Building 2-1 Otemachi 2-chome, Chiyoda-ku, Tokyo, 100-0004, Japan
Tel.: (81) 352037690
Web Site: https://www.tscom.co.jp
Year Founded: 1942
8070—(TKS)
Rev.: $429,841,690
Assets: $534,054,950
Liabilities: $402,667,980
Net Worth: $131,386,970
Earnings: ($9,525,010)
Emp.: 381
Fiscal Year-end: 03/31/24

AND PRIVATE COMPANIES

TOKYO SEIMITSU CO., LTD.

Industrial Machinery & Equipment Whslr
N.A.I.C.S.: 423830
Toshio Satomi (Pres)

Subsidiaries:

CO2 Reducation Co., Ltd. (1)
Shin Otemachi Building 2-1 Otemachi 2-chome, Chiyoda-ku, Tokyo, 100-0004, Japan
Tel.: (81) 352030642
Industrial Machinery Distr
N.A.I.C.S.: 423830

Innovation of Social Environment Co., Ltd. (1)
Wakuya Building 10-14 Nakamachi, Koriyama, 963-8004, Fukushima, Japan
Tel.: (81) 249831118
Web Site: https://www.isec2016.co.jp
Emp.: 6
Industrial Machinery Distr
N.A.I.C.S.: 423830

PT. Tokyo Sangyo Indonesia (1)
Indonesia Stock Exchange Tower 1 17Th FL Suite 1707A, Ji Jend Sudirman Kav 52-53, Jakarta Selatan, 12190, Indonesia
Tel.: (62) 215151267
Industrial Machinery Distr
N.A.I.C.S.: 423830

Shandong Tokyo-Union Technology Development Co., Ltd. (1)
Room 0221 Block A Huoqiao Road, Innovation And Entrepreneurship Base No 213-2 Gao District, Weihai, Shandong, China
Tel.: (86) 631569600
Web Site: https://ja.tokyounion.cn
Project Management Services
N.A.I.C.S.: 541611

TOKYO SANGYO Japan Co., Ltd. (1)
14F-5 No 85 Sec 1 Zhongxiao E Rd, Taipei, Taiwan
Tel.: (886) 223966131
Industrial Machinery Distr
N.A.I.C.S.: 423830

TR Energy Co., Ltd. (1)
Shin Otemachi Building 2-1 Otemachi 2-chome, Chiyoda-ku, Tokyo, 100-0004, Japan
Tel.: (81) 356560362
Industrial Machinery Distr
N.A.I.C.S.: 423830

TSC (Shanghai) Co., Ltd. (1)
No85 Loushanguan Road Room 405 Block D Oriental International Building, Changning District, Shanghai, 200336, China
Tel.: (86) 2162351333
Web Site: https://www.tscom.com.cn
Industrial Machinery Distr
N.A.I.C.S.: 423830

Tokyo Sangyo (Thailand) Co., Ltd. (1)
323 United Center Building Unit 2901 29 Floor Silom Road Bangrak, Bangrak, 10500, Thailand
Tel.: (66) 26311981
Industrial Machinery Distr
N.A.I.C.S.: 423830

Tokyo Sangyo Asia Trading Co., Ltd. (1)
323 United Center Building Unit 2901 29 Floor Silom Road, Bangrak, Bangkok, Thailand
Tel.: (66) 26311981
Industrial Machinery Distr
N.A.I.C.S.: 423830

Tokyo Sangyo Europe GmbH (1)
An der Welle 4, 60322, Frankfurt, Germany
Tel.: (49) 6975938556
Web Site: https://tsce.eu
Industrial Machinery Distr
N.A.I.C.S.: 423830
Hiroaki Nishioka (Mng Dir)

Tokyo Sangyo Fudosan Co., Ltd. (1)
Shin Otemachi Building 2-1 Otemachi 2-chome, Chiyoda-ku, Tokyo, 100-0004, Japan
Tel.: (81) 352037868
Industrial Machinery Distr
N.A.I.C.S.: 423830

Tokyo Sangyo Machinery, S. A. de C. V. (1)
Edificio Montecarlo Av Las Americas 608-203 Fracc La Fuente, 20239, Aguascalientes, Mexico
Tel.: (52) 4499155091
Industrial Machinery Distr
N.A.I.C.S.: 423830

Tokyo Sangyo Malaysia Sdn. Bhd. (1)
Level 33 Ilham Tower No 8 Jalan Binjai, 50450, Kuala Lumpur, Malaysia
Tel.: (60) 321696336
Industrial Machinery Distr
N.A.I.C.S.: 423830

Tokyo Sangyo Singapore (Pte.) Ltd. (1)
3 Temasek Avenue Level 21 Centennial Tower, Singapore, 039190, Singapore
Tel.: (65) 68297117
Web Site: https://tssin.sg
Emp.: 3
Industrial Machinery Distr
N.A.I.C.S.: 423830

Tokyo Sangyo Vietnam Co., Ltd. (1)
6th Floor The Imperial Suites 01-N1 Alley 40 Van Bao Street, Lieu Giai Ba Dinh District, Hanoi, Vietnam
Tel.: (84) 2471099805
Industrial Machinery Distr
N.A.I.C.S.: 423830

TOKYO SECURITIES TRANSFER AGENT CO., LTD.

Togin Bldg 1-4-2 Marunouchi, Chiyoda-ku, Tokyo, 100-0005, Japan
Tel.: (81) 3 3212 4611
Web Site: http://www.tosyodai.co.jp
Year Founded: 1962
Financial Services
N.A.I.C.S.: 523999

TOKYO SEIMITSU CO., LTD.

2968-2 Ishikawa-machi, Hachioji, 192-8515, Tokyo, Japan
Tel.: (81) 426421701 JP
Web Site: https://www.accretech.jp
Year Founded: 1949
7729—(TKS)
Rev.: $890,234,800
Assets: $1,490,713,640
Liabilities: $443,511,170
Net Worth: $1,047,202,470
Earnings: $128,088,580
Emp.: 2,658
Fiscal Year-end: 03/31/24
Semiconductor & Precision Measuring Systems Mfr
N.A.I.C.S.: 332216
Hitoshi Yoshida (Chm, Pres & CEO)

Subsidiaries:

Accretech (China) Co., Ltd. (1)
Room2101C No 1077 ZuChongZhi Road Zhang Jiang Hi-Tech Park, Pudong New Area, Shanghai, 201203, China
Tel.: (86) 213 887 0801
Measuring Instrument Mfr & Distr
N.A.I.C.S.: 334515

Accretech (Europe) GmbH (1)
Landsbergerstr 396, 81241, Munich, Germany
Tel.: (49) 895467880
Web Site: http://www.accretech.eu
Sales Range: $25-49.9 Million
Emp.: 70
Semiconductor Devices Mfr
N.A.I.C.S.: 334413
Wolfgang Bonatz (CEO)

Accretech (Malaysia) Sdn. Bhd. (1)
No 15 Jalan PJS 8/17 Dataran Mentari, Bandar Sunway, 46150, Petaling Jaya, Selangor, Malaysia
Tel.: (60) 377173088
Web Site: http://www.accretech.jp
Sales Range: $25-49.9 Million
Emp.: 21
Semiconductor Devices Mfr
N.A.I.C.S.: 334413
K. H. Tee (Mng Dir)

Accretech (Singapore) Pte. Ltd. (1)
140 Paya Lebar Road 06-07 AZ Paya Lebar, Singapore, 409015, Singapore
Tel.: (65) 6 341 6052
Measuring Instrument Mfr & Distr
N.A.I.C.S.: 334515

Accretech (Thailand) Co., Ltd. (1)
2/3 Moo 14 Bangna Tower A 16th Fl Bangna-Trad Road KM 6 5, Bangkaew, Bang Phli, 10540, Samut Prakan, Thailand
Tel.: (66) 2 751 9573
Measuring Instrument Mfr & Distr
N.A.I.C.S.: 334515

Accretech Adamas (Thailand) Co., Ltd. (1)
56/27 Moo 20, Tambol Klongnueng, Khlong Luang, 12120, Pathumthani, Thailand
Tel.: (66) 2 119 5489
Measuring Instrument Mfr & Distr
N.A.I.C.S.: 334515

Accretech America Inc. (1)
2280 Campbell Creek Blvd Ste 300, Richardson, TX 75082
Tel.: (214) 459-1688
Measuring Instrument Mfr & Distr
N.A.I.C.S.: 334515

Accretech Create Corp. (1)
2968-2 Ishikawa-machi, Hachioji, 192-0032, Tokyo, Japan
Tel.: (81) 426422691
Web Site: http://www.accretech.jp
Sales Range: $200-249.9 Million
Emp.: 737
Semiconductor Devices Mfr
N.A.I.C.S.: 334413

Accretech Finance Co., Ltd. (1)
2968-2 Ishikawa-machi Hachioji-shi, Tokyo, 192-8515, Japan
Tel.: (81) 426421701
Web Site: http://www.accretech.jp
Investment Management Service
N.A.I.C.S.: 541618
Hitoshi Yoshida (CEO)

Accretech Korea Co., Ltd. (1)
205 IMS Bldg 31-8 Dongtan-daero, Hwaseong, 18463, Gyeonggi, Korea (South)
Tel.: (82) 317864000
Web Site: http://www.accretechkorea.jp
Sales Range: $25-49.9 Million
Emp.: 44
Semiconductor Devices Mfr
N.A.I.C.S.: 334413
Hane Yutaka (Pres)

Accretech Powertro System Co., Ltd. (1)
50 Matsukawadaisaku Furudono-machi, Ishikawa-gun, Fukushima, 963-8304, Japan
Tel.: (81) 24 753 4111
Measuring Instrument Mfr & Distr
N.A.I.C.S.: 334515

Accretech SBS Inc. (1)
2451 NW 28th Ave, Portland, OR 97210
Tel.: (503) 595-4270
Web Site: https://www.accretechsbs.com
Precision Grinding Machine Mfr
N.A.I.C.S.: 333517

Accretech Taiwan Co., Ltd. (1)
No 55 Fenggong Rd Neighborhood 5, Fengshan Vil Hukou Township, Hsinchu, 303035, Taiwan
Tel.: (886) 3 553 1300
Measuring Instrument Mfr & Distr
N.A.I.C.S.: 334515

Accretech Vietnam Co., Ltd. (1)
Lot 06 1F Riverside Garden Bldg at No 349 Vu Tong Phan street, Khuong Dinh ward Thanh Xuan district, Hanoi, Vietnam
Tel.: (84) 243 941 3309
Measuring Instrument Mfr & Distr
N.A.I.C.S.: 334515

Accretech-SBS UK Ltd. (1)
Unit 2 Leofric Court Progress Way, Binley Industrial Estate, Coventry, CV3 2NT, United Kingdom
Tel.: (44) 247 665 1774
Measuring Instrument Mfr & Distr

Accretech-Tosei Hungary kft. (1)
Liget Utca 1 Ground Floor, 2040, Budaors, Hungary
Measuring Instrument Mfr & Distr
N.A.I.C.S.: 334515

Accretech-Tosei do Brasil Ltda. (1)
Av Presidente Vargas 2 921 - Sala 314 Condominio Sky Towers Office, Vila Homero, Indaiatuba, 13338-705, Sao Paulo, Brazil
Measuring Instrument Mfr & Distr
N.A.I.C.S.: 334515

PT Accretech Indonesia (1)
Jl Kenari Timur Blok G-1A No 23 Delta Silicon 5, Lippo Cikarang Cicau Chkarang Pusat, Bekasi, 17530, Jawa Barat, Indonesia
Tel.: (62) 212 961 2374
Measuring Instrument Mfr & Distr
N.A.I.C.S.: 334515

PT Tosei Indonesia (1)
Jl Kenari Timur Blok G1A No 23 Delta Silicon 5, Lippo Cikarang, Bekasi, 17530, Indonesia
Tel.: (62) 212 961 7698
Web Site: https://www.toseiindonesia.co.id
Emp.: 15
Measuring Instrument Mfr & Distr
N.A.I.C.S.: 334515
Nobuhide Takagi (Pres)

Tokyo Seimitsu Co., Ltd. - Hachioji Plant (1)
2968-2 Ishikawa-machi, Hachioji, 192-0032, Tokyo, Japan
Tel.: (81) 426420381
Web Site: http://www.accretech.jp
Sales Range: $200-249.9 Million
Emp.: 737
Semiconductor Devices Mfr
N.A.I.C.S.: 541810

Tokyo Seimitsu Co., Ltd. - Tsuchiura Plant (1)
4 Higashi-Nakanuki-machi, Tsuchiura, 300-0006, Ibaraki, Japan
Tel.: (81) 298311234
Web Site: http://www.accretech.jp
Sales Range: $200-249.9 Million
Emp.: 737
Semiconductor Devices Mfr
N.A.I.C.S.: 541850

Tosei (Thailand) Co., Ltd. (1)
700/633 Moo 7 Tambol Donhuaroh Phase 6C, Amatanakorn Industrial Estate, Amphur Muang, 20000, Chonburi, Thailand
Tel.: (66) 38193282
Web Site: http://www.tosei.co.th
Sales Range: $25-49.9 Million
Emp.: 11
Semiconductor Devices Mfr
N.A.I.C.S.: 334413
Hiroyuki Kobayashi (Pres)

Tosei America, Inc. (1)
8790 Governer Hill Dr Ste 207, Cincinnati, OH 45249
Tel.: (513) 373-4844
Sales Range: $25-49.9 Million
Emp.: 7
Measuring Equipment Mfr
N.A.I.C.S.: 334515

Subsidiary (Domestic):

Schmitt Measurement Systems, Inc. (2)
2765 NW Nicolai, Portland, OR 97210 (100%)
Tel.: (503) 227-7908
Web Site: http://www.schmitt-ind.com
Sales Range: $100-124.9 Million
Emp.: 40
Precision Manufacturing Systems
N.A.I.C.S.: 332721

Tosei Box Corp. (1)
Urban Center Tachikawa 2F 1-22-17, Akebono-cho, Tachikawa, 190-0012, Tokyo, Japan
Tel.: (81) 425957023
Web Site: https://www.toseibox.com
Sales Range: $100-124.9 Million
Emp.: 500
Semiconductor Devices Mfr

TOKYO SEIMITSU CO., LTD.

Tokyo Seimitsu Co., Ltd.—(Continued)
N.A.I.C.S.: 334413

Tosei Canada Measuring Inc. (1)
2355 Derry Rd East Unit 48, Mississauga, L5S 1V6, ON, Canada
Tel.: (647) 995-8828
Precision Grinding Machine Mfr
N.A.I.C.S.: 333517

Tosei Engineering Corp. (1)
4-6 Higashi-Nakanuki-machi, Tsuchiura, 300-0006, Ibaraki, Japan
Tel.: (81) 298301888
Web Site: http://www.toseieng.co.jp
Emp.: 584
Semiconductor Devices Mfr
N.A.I.C.S.: 334413
Katsuhiro Tago (Pres)

Tosei Engineering Pvt. Ltd. (1)
Plot No 150 Sector-3 HSIIDC IMT Manesar, Golf Course Rd, Gurgaon, 122 050, Haryana, India
Tel.: (91) 1244241673
Web Site: https://www.toseieng.co.jp
Sales Range: $25-49.9 Million
Emp.: 23
Semiconductor Devices Mfr
N.A.I.C.S.: 541820

Tosei Korea Co., Ltd. (1)
168 Gasan digital 1-ro 371-2B Gasan Dong B 511 Woolim Lion Valley, Geumcheon-gu, Seoul, Korea (South)
Tel.: (82) 707 500 2136
Web Site: https://www.toseikorea.co.kr
Measuring Instrument Mfr & Distr
N.A.I.C.S.: 334515
Goto Katsushi (CEO)

Tosei Mexico, S.A. de C.V. (1)
Plateros 125 Col Valle del Campestre, 37150, Leon, Guanajuato, Mexico
Tel.: (52) 477 330 7793
Precision Grinding Machine Mfr
N.A.I.C.S.: 333517

Tosei Philippines Corp. (1)
Unit 407 Humana Wellness Center Sta Rosa-Tagaytay Road Brgy, Don Jose, Santa Rosa Laguna, 4026, Philippines
Tel.: (63) 49 536 1180
Measuring Instrument Mfr & Distr
N.A.I.C.S.: 334515

Tosei Systems Co., Ltd. (1)
2968-2 Ishikawa-machi, Hachioji, 192-0032, Tokyo, Japan
Tel.: (81) 426319757
Web Site: http://www.toseisys.co.jp
Sales Range: Less than $1 Million
Emp.: 102
Software Development Services
N.A.I.C.S.: 513210
Koichi Kawamura (Pres)

Tosei Taiwan Co., Ltd. (1)
4 of 11th Floor No 295 Section 2 Guangfu Road, East District, Hsinchu, 30017, Taiwan
Tel.: (886) 3 573 5161
Web Site: https://www.toseitaiwan.com.tw
Measuring Instrument Mfr & Distr
N.A.I.C.S.: 334515

TOKYO SOIR CO., LTD.

Shin Aoyama Bldg West Wing 1-1-1 Minami Aoyama, Minato-ku, Tokyo, 107-8604, Japan
Tel.: (81) 334751251
Web Site: http://www.soir.co.jp
Year Founded: 1949
8040—(TKS)
Sales Range: $150-199.9 Million
Emp.: 299
Apparel Product Mfr & Distr
N.A.I.C.S.: 315250
Tomio Hagiwara (Chm)

TOKYO STEEL MANUFACTURING CO., LTD.

15th floor Kasumigaseki Kantokyu Building 3-7-1 Kasumigaseki, Chiyoda-ku, Tokyo, 100-0013, Japan
Tel.: (81) 335017721

Web Site: https://www.tokyosteel.co.jp
Year Founded: 1934
5423—(TKS)
Sales Range: $1-4.9 Billion
Emp.: 1,070
Steel Products Mfr & Sales
N.A.I.C.S.: 331221
Toshikazu Nishimoto (Pres)

TOKYO TATEMONO CO. LTD.

1-9-9 Yaesu, Chuo-ku, Tokyo, 103-8285, Japan
Tel.: (81) 332740111
Web Site: https://www.tatemono.com
Year Founded: 1896
TYTMF—(OTCIQ)
Rev.: $2,665,457,140
Assets: $13,508,640,810
Liabilities: $9,906,672,660
Net Worth: $3,601,968,150
Earnings: $319,645,560
Emp.: 807
Fiscal Year-end: 12/31/23
Commercial Building Leasing & Real Estate Business
N.A.I.C.S.: 531110
Hitoshi Nomura (Pres & CEO)

Subsidiaries:

E-State Online Co., Ltd. (1)
7F Tokyo Tatemono Jinbocho Building 2-4 Kandajinbocho, Chiyoda-ku, Tokyo, 101-0051, Japan
Tel.: (81) 332889700
Web Site: http://www.e-state.ne.jp
Internet Service Provider
N.A.I.C.S.: 517810

EXPERT OFFICE Co., Ltd. (1)
2F Nakano Central Park South 4-10-2 Nakano, Nakano-ku, Tokyo, 164-0001, Japan
Tel.: (81) 120587560
Web Site: https://www.expertoffice.jp
Emp.: 44
Rental Office Management Services
N.A.I.C.S.: 561110

Japan Rental Guaranty Co., Ltd. (1)
Tokyo Tatemono TG Building 1-2-16 Yaesu, Chuo-ku, Tokyo, 103-0028, Japan
Tel.: (81) 368377670
House Rental & Leasing Services
N.A.I.C.S.: 531110

Nihon Parking Corporation (1)
4F Tokyo Tatemono Jinbocho Building 2-4 Kandajinbocho, Chiyoda-ku, Tokyo, 101-0051, Japan
Tel.: (81) 332220015
Parking Lot Services
N.A.I.C.S.: 812930

Parking Support Center Corporation (1)
4F Kyugetsu Kanda Building 2-4-7 Kandajinbocho, Chiyoda-ku, Tokyo, 101-0051, Japan
Tel.: (81) 332346515
Parking Lot Services
N.A.I.C.S.: 812930

Prime Place Co., Ltd. (1)
1-8-12 Yaesu, Chuo-ku, Tokyo, Japan
Tel.: (81) 332422266
Web Site: http://www.prime-place.jp
Sales Range: $50-74.9 Million
Emp.: 64
Property Management Services
N.A.I.C.S.: 531311

Seishin Service Co., Ltd. (1)
2F Tokyo Tatemono Dai-3 Muromachi Building 4-8-14 Nihonbashi Honcho, Chuo-ku, Tokyo, 103-0023, Japan
Tel.: (81) 362627790
Facility Management Services
N.A.I.C.S.: 561210

Shinjuku Center Building Management Co., Ltd. (1)
4F Shinjuku Center Building 1-25-1 Nishishinjuku, Shinjyuku-ku, Tokyo, 163-0604, Japan
Tel.: (81) 333451281

Building Management Services
N.A.I.C.S.: 561790

Tokyo Building Service Co., Ltd. (1)
5F Olinas Tower 4-1-3 Taihei, Sumida-ku, Tokyo, 130-0012, Japan
Tel.: (81) 356108700
Building Cleaning Services
N.A.I.C.S.: 561720

Tokyo Fudosan Kanri Co., Ltd. (1)
5th Floor Olinas Tower 4-1-3 Taihei, Sumida-ku, Tokyo, 130-0012, Japan
Tel.: (81) 356372550
Web Site: https://www.etfk.jp
Emp.: 908
Real Estate Management Services
N.A.I.C.S.: 531210

Tokyo Realty Investment Management, Inc. (1)
3F 1-4-16 Yaesu, Chuo-ku, Tokyo, 103-0028, Japan (100%)
Tel.: (81) 335161591
Asset Management Services
N.A.I.C.S.: 523940

Tokyo Tatemono (Shanghai) Real Estate Consulting Co., Ltd. (1)
Room 606 Shanghai Kerry Centre 1515 Nanjing Road West, Jingan District, Shanghai, 200040, China
Tel.: (86) 2162881000
Real Estate Consulting Service
N.A.I.C.S.: 531390

Tokyo Tatemono (U.S.A.) Inc. (1)
222 N Sepulveda Blvd Ste 2000, El Segundo, CA 90245
Tel.: (310) 607-0355
Sales Range: $50-74.9 Million
Emp.: 5
Real Estate Management Services
N.A.I.C.S.: 531390

Tokyo Tatemono Amenity Support Co., Ltd. (1)
5F-6F TG Building 1-2-16 Yaesu, Chuo-ku, Tokyo, 103-0028, Japan
Tel.: (81) 367776700
Condominium Residential Management Services
N.A.I.C.S.: 531311

Tokyo Tatemono Asia Pte. Ltd. (1)
20 Collyer Quay 19-01, Singapore, 049319, Singapore
Tel.: (65) 62245826
Real Estate Development Services
N.A.I.C.S.: 531390

Tokyo Tatemono Fund Management Co., Ltd. (1)
Chome 9 9 Yaesu, Chuo-ko, Tokyo, 103-0028, Japan (100%)
Tel.: (81) 332723944
Web Site: http://www.ttfm.co.jp
Real Estate & Brokerage Services
N.A.I.C.S.: 531210
Masami Kamo (Pres)

Tokyo Tatemono Investment Advisors Co., Ltd. (1)
7F Nihonbashi First Building 1-2-19 Nihonbashi, Chuo-ku, Tokyo, 103-0027, Japan
Tel.: (81) 335483351
Real Estate Investment Services
N.A.I.C.S.: 531390

Tokyo Tatemono Kids Co., Ltd. (1)
5F 1-9-9 Yaesu, Chuo-ku, Tokyo, 103-0028, Japan (90%)
Tel.: (81) 332740952
Nursery School Operator
N.A.I.C.S.: 624410

Tokyo Tatemono Real Estate Sales Co., Ltd. (1)
Tokyo Tatemono Yaesu Sakura-dori Building 1-5-20 Yaesu, Chuo-ku, Tokyo, 103-0028, Japan (100%)
Tel.: (81) 36 837 7700
Web Site: https://www.ttfuhan.co.jp
Sales Range: $350-399.9 Million
Brokerage Services
N.A.I.C.S.: 523150

Tokyo Tatemono Resort Co., Ltd. (1)
6F 1-9-9 Yaesu, Chuo-ku, Tokyo, 103-0028, Japan

Tel.: (81) 332740865
Web Site: http://www.regina-resorts.com
Sales Range: $25-49.9 Million
Emp.: 10
Resort Management Services
N.A.I.C.S.: 561110

Subsidiary (Domestic):

Kawaguchiko Country Club Co., Ltd. (2)
6236 Funatsu Fuji Kawaguchiko, Minamitsuru, Yamanashi, 401 0301, Japan
Tel.: (81) 555 73 1211
Web Site: http://www.kawaguchiko-cc.co.jp
Golf Club
N.A.I.C.S.: 713910

Tokyo Tatemono Senior Life Support Co., Ltd. (1)
6F 1-9-9 Yaesu, Chuo-ku, Tokyo, 103-0028, Japan
Tel.: (81) 332740451
Nursing Care Services
N.A.I.C.S.: 623110

Tokyo Tatemono Staffing Co., Ltd. (1)
6F 1-9-9 Yaesu, Chuo-ku, Tokyo, 103-0028, Japan
Tel.: (81) 332742734
Human Resource Dispatch Services
N.A.I.C.S.: 541612

TOKYO TEKKO CO., LTD.

12th Floor Stage Building 272 Fujimi, Chiyoda-ku, Tokyo, 102-0071, Japan
Tel.: (81) 352769700
Web Site: https://www.tokyotekko.co.jp
Year Founded: 1939
5445—(TKS)
Rev.: $526,268,370
Assets: $514,938,830
Liabilities: $163,551,230
Net Worth: $351,387,600
Earnings: $52,133,070
Emp.: 815
Fiscal Year-end: 03/31/24
Steel Product Mfr & Distr
N.A.I.C.S.: 331110
Takao Shibata (Mng Dir)

Subsidiaries:

Ttk Korea Co., Ltd. (1)
1708 West Wing Hanshin Intervalley 24 Bldg 322 Teheran-ro, Gangnam-gu, Seoul, 06211, Korea (South)
Tel.: (82) 221830692
Software Development Services
N.A.I.C.S.: 541511

TOKYO THEATRES COMPANY INCORPORATED

1-1-8 Gyoen Theatre Building Shinjuku, Shinjuku-ku, Tokyo, 160-0022, Japan
Tel.: (81) 333551082
Web Site: https://www.theatres.co.jp
Year Founded: 1946
9633—(TKS)
Rev.: $112,945,070
Assets: $162,368,040
Liabilities: $78,189,690
Net Worth: $84,178,350
Earnings: $1,540,130
Emp.: 449
Fiscal Year-end: 03/31/24
Catering & Film Distribution Services
N.A.I.C.S.: 722511
Takeshi Matsuoka (Mng Exec Officer & Gen Mgr-Mgmt)

TOKYO TSUSHIN GROUP CO., LTD.

1-1-9 Ebisu-Minami, Shibuya-Ku, Tokyo, 150-0022, Japan
Tel.: (81) 364524523
Web Site: http://www.tokyo-tsushin.com
Year Founded: 2015

AND PRIVATE COMPANIES

7359—(TKS)
Rev.: $44,092,710
Assets: $35,414,550
Liabilities: $23,042,500
Net Worth: $12,372,050
Earnings: ($1,446,360)
Fiscal Year-end: 12/31/23
Advertising Agency Services
N.A.I.C.S.: 541810
Yuki Furuya *(Founder, Pres & CEO)*

TOKYOTOKEIBA CO., LTD.
6-8 Omorikita 1-chome, Ota-ku, Tokyo, 143-0016, Japan
Tel.: (81) 357679055
Web Site: https://www.tokyotokeiba.co.jp
Year Founded: 1949
9672—(TKS)
Rev.: $266,186,960
Assets: $820,965,280
Liabilities: $205,645,450
Net Worth: $615,319,830
Earnings: $59,924,680
Emp.: 62
Fiscal Year-end: 12/31/23
Race Track Services
N.A.I.C.S.: 711212
Tarao Mitsuchika *(Pres & CEO)*

Subsidiaries:

Tokyo Property Service Co., Ltd. (1)
Inside Oi Racecourse 2-1-2 Katsushima, Shinagawa-ku, Tokyo, 140-0012, Japan
Tel.: (81) 33 764 5652
Web Site: https://www.tokyops.co.jp
Commercial Property Management Services
N.A.I.C.S.: 531312

Tokyo Summerland Co., Ltd. (1)
600 Kamiyotsugi Shiraiwa, Akiruno, 197-0832, Japan
Tel.: (81) 42 558 6511
Web Site: https://www.summerland.co.jp
Amusement Park Operator
N.A.I.C.S.: 713110

TOKYU AGENCY INC.
4-8-18 Akasaka, Minato-ku, Tokyo, 107-8417, Japan
Tel.: (81) 3 3404 5321   JP
Web Site: http://www.tokyu-agc.co.jp
Year Founded: 1961
Sales Range: $1-4.9 Billion
Emp.: 869
Advetising Agency
N.A.I.C.S.: 541810
Tsuneyasu Kuwahara *(Chm)*

TOKYU CONSTRUCTION CO., LTD.
1-16-14 Shibuya, Shibuya-ku, Tokyo, 150-8340, Japan
Tel.: (81) 354665020
Web Site: https://www.tokyu-cnst.co.jp
Year Founded: 2003
1720—(TKS)
Rev.: $1,888,351,410
Assets: $1,748,510,250
Liabilities: $1,082,294,960
Net Worth: $666,215,290
Earnings: $48,028,260
Emp.: 2,471
Fiscal Year-end: 03/31/24
Construction Engineering Services
N.A.I.C.S.: 236210
Junichi Omuro *(Exec Officer & Gen Mgr-Real Estate Div)*

Subsidiaries:

Ch. Karnachang-Tokyu Construction Co., Ltd. (1)
7-8th Floor Viriyathavorn Building 587 Sutthisarn Road, Dindaeng, Bangkok, 10400, Thailand
Tel.: (66) 2 277 5004
Web Site: https://www.chtokyu.co.th
Construction Contractor Services

N.A.I.C.S.: 236220
Khajonwit Sae Chea *(Mng Dir)*

Golden Tokyu Construction Co., Ltd (1)
Room No - 04-01 04-02 Crystal Tower No - 37 Kyun Taw Street Quarter, Kamayut Township, Yangon, Myanmar
Tel.: (95) 19339281
Construction Engineering Services
N.A.I.C.S.: 541330

Indochine Engineering Limited (1)
Unit 12-01 Pearl Plaza 561A Dien Bien Phu Street, Binh Thanh District, Ho Chi Minh City, Vietnam
Tel.: (84) 283 512 4100
Web Site: https://www.indoeng.com
Engineering Consultancy Services
N.A.I.C.S.: 541330
Carl Gay *(Gen Dir)*

PT. Tokyu Construction Indonesia (1)
2nd Floor Wisma Haka Building Jalan K H Wahid Hasyim No 71, Jakarta, 10350, Indonesia
Tel.: (62) 213147613
Construction Engineering Services
N.A.I.C.S.: 541330

Plantaardig Farm Co., Ltd. (1)
1306-1 Tsuchiura, Miho-mura, Inashiki, 300-0404, Ibaraki, Japan
Tel.: (81) 29 875 7833
Web Site: https://www.vege-innovation.jp
Farm Management Services
N.A.I.C.S.: 115116

Richfield Miho Co., Ltd (1)
102 Kobayashi-corpo 574-1 Shida, Miho Inashiki District, Ibaraki, 300-0414, Japan
Tel.: (81) 354666247
Construction Engineering Services
N.A.I.C.S.: 541330

Token Industry Co., Ltd. (1)
1-24-8 Shibuya Tokyu Shibuya 1-chome Building 3rd Floor, Shibuya-ku, Tokyo, 150-0002, Japan
Tel.: (81) 35 466 9511
Web Site: https://www.token-sangyo.co.jp
Wastewater Treatment Maintenance Services
N.A.I.C.S.: 562998

Tokyu Renewal Co., Ltd. (1)
5F Shibuya Subway Building 1-16-14 Shibuya, Shibuya-ku, Tokyo, 150-0002, Japan
Tel.: (81) 363698600
Web Site: https://www.tokyu-renewal.co.jp
Construction Engineering Services
N.A.I.C.S.: 541330

TOKYU CORPORATION
5-6 Nanpeidai-cho, Shibuya-ku, Tokyo, 150-8511, Japan
Tel.: (81) 334770109
Web Site: https://www.tokyu.co.jp
Year Founded: 1922
TOKUY—(OTCIQ)
Rev.: $6,677,370,810
Assets: $18,742,466,040
Liabilities: $13,154,368,800
Net Worth: $5,588,097,240
Earnings: $186,384,150
Emp.: 24,655
Fiscal Year-end: 03/31/23
Railway Management, Commercial & Residential Construction Services & Retail Store Operator
N.A.I.C.S.: 236220
Kazuo Takahashi *(Pres)*

Subsidiaries:

Izukyu Corp. (1)
1151 Yawata, Ito, 413-0292, Shizuoka, Japan   **(100%)**
Tel.: (81) 55 753 1111
Web Site: https://www.izukyu.co.jp
Sales Range: $100-124.9 Million
Emp.: 300
Railroad Rolling Stock Manufacturing
N.A.I.C.S.: 336510

Jotetsu Corporation (1)

1-1-8 Higashi Sapporo, Shiroishi-ku, Sapporo, 003-0001, Japan
Tel.: (81) 11 811 6141
Web Site: https://www.jotetsu.co.jp
Sales Range: $200-249.9 Million
Emp.: 303
Real Estate
N.A.I.C.S.: 531210

Sendai International Airport Co., Ltd. (1)
Aza-Minamihara, Shimomasuda, Natori, 989-2401, Miyagi, Japan
Tel.: (81) 22 383 4301
Web Site: https://www.sendai-airport.co.jp
Airport Facility Management Services
N.A.I.C.S.: 488119
Akito Toba *(CEO)*

Tokyu Bus Corporation (1)
3-8-1 Higashiyama, Meguro-ku, Tokyo, 153-8518, Japan
Tel.: (81) 36 412 0190
Web Site: https://www.tokyubus.co.jp
Cargo Transportation Services
N.A.I.C.S.: 488490

Tokyu Card, Inc. (1)
4-10-1 Yoga Setagaya Business Square Tower, Setagaya-ku, Tokyo, 158-8534, Japan
Tel.: (81) 33 700 2109
Web Site: https://www.topcard.co.jp
Credit Card Handling Services
N.A.I.C.S.: 522320

Tokyu Corporation - Building Management Division (1)
31 2 Sakuragaoka Cho, Shibuya Ku, Tokyo, 150 8511, Japan   **(100%)**
Tel.: (81) 334776367
Web Site: http://www.tokyu.co.jp
Sales Range: $100-124.9 Million
Emp.: 500
General Contractors
N.A.I.C.S.: 236220

Tokyu Corporation - Resort Development Division (1)
31 2 Sakuragaoka Cho, Shibuya Ku, Tokyo, 150 8511, Japan   **(100%)**
Tel.: (81) 334776367
Web Site: http://www.tokyu.co.jp
Sales Range: $100-124.9 Million
Emp.: 500
General Contractors
N.A.I.C.S.: 236220

Tokyu Corporation - Transport Division (1)
31 2 Sakuragaoka Cho, Shibuya Ku, Tokyo, 150 8511, Japan   **(100%)**
Tel.: (81) 334776367
Web Site: http://www.tokyu.co.jp
Sales Range: $100-124.9 Million
Emp.: 500
General Contractors
N.A.I.C.S.: 236220

Tokyu Department Store Co., Ltd. (1)
2-24-1 Dogenzaka, Shibuya-ku, Tokyo, 150-8019, Japan   **(100%)**
Tel.: (81) 33 477 3111
Web Site: https://www.tokyu-dept.co.jp
Sales Range: $10-24.9 Million
Emp.: 1,994
Departmental Store Operator
N.A.I.C.S.: 455110

Subsidiary (Domestic):

Nagano Tokyu Department Store Co. (2)
1-1-1 Minami Chitose, Nagano, 380-8539, Japan   **(100%)**
Tel.: (81) 26 226 8181
Web Site: https://www.nagano-tokyu.co.jp
Emp.: 231
Department Stores
N.A.I.C.S.: 455110
Masayuki Nakajina *(Pres)*

Tokyu Geox Co., Ltd. (1)
1-16-14 Shibuya Shibuya Subway Building 3rd Floor, Shibuya-ku, Tokyo, 150-0002, Japan
Tel.: (81) 33 406 7111
Web Site: https://www.tokyu-geox.co.jp
Building Equipment Distr

TOKYU FUDOSAN HOLDINGS CORPORATION

N.A.I.C.S.: 444180

Tokyu Hospital (1)
3-27-2 Kitasenzoku, Ota-ku, Tokyo, 145-0062, Japan   **(100%)**
Tel.: (81) 33 718 3331
Web Site: https://www.tokyu-hospital.jp
Hospital Operator
N.A.I.C.S.: 622110

Tokyu Hotels Co., Ltd. (1)
Goto Ikueikai Bldg 3F 1-10-7 Dogenzaka, Shibuya-ku, Tokyo, 150-0043, Japan
Tel.: (81) 33 477 6019
Web Site: https://www.tokyuhotelsjapan.com
Sales Range: $25-49.9 Million
Emp.: 225
Hotel Management Trust
N.A.I.C.S.: 721110
Akihito Kobayashi *(Pres)*

Tokyu Kidsbasecamp Co., Ltd. (1)
2-14-9 Tamagawa Twin City H 3F, Setagaya-ku, Tokyo, 158-0094, Japan
Tel.: (81) 35 797 3566
Web Site: https://www.kidsbasecamp.com
Preschooler Childcare Services
N.A.I.C.S.: 624410

Tokyu Malls Development Corporation (1)
1-10-7 Dogenzaka 4th Floor Goshima Ikueikai Building, Shibuya-ku, Tokyo, 150-0043, Japan
Tel.: (81) 33 477 5150
Web Site: https://www.tokyu-tmd.co.jp
Property Development Services
N.A.I.C.S.: 531390

Tokyu Recreation Co., Ltd. (1)
No 5 Fuji Shoji Building 24-4 Sakuragaoka-cho, Shibuya-ku, Tokyo, 150-0031, Japan   **(50.16%)**
Tel.: (81) 33 462 8888
Web Site: https://www.tokyu-rec.co.jp
Sales Range: $75-99.9 Million
Emp.: 393
Recreational Services
N.A.I.C.S.: 713990
Kanno Shinzo *(Pres)*

Tokyu Security Co., Ltd. (1)
4-1-1 Taishido Carrot Tower 21F, Setagaya-ku, Tokyo, 154-0004, Japan
Tel.: (81) 36 866 7101
Web Site: https://www.tokyu-security.co.jp
Patrol Security Services
N.A.I.C.S.: 561612

Tokyu Stay Co., Ltd. (1)
4F Shibuya Place Dogenzaka 1-10-5, Shibuya-ku, Tokyo, 150-0043, Japan
Tel.: (81) 33 476 1008
Web Site: https://www.tokyustay.co.jp
Hotel & Resort Operator
N.A.I.C.S.: 721110
Shogo Takatani *(Pres)*

Tokyu Store Chain Co., Ltd. (1)
1-21-12 Kamimeguro, Meguro-Ku, Tokyo, 153-8577, Japan   **(100%)**
Tel.: (81) 33 711 0109
Web Site: https://www.tokyu-store.co.jp
Emp.: 6,222
Retail Store Operator
N.A.I.C.S.: 445298
Ogawa Nobuyuki *(Chm)*

Tokyu Technosystem Co., Ltd. (1)
11-21 Imaikamicho, Nakahara-ku, Kawasaki, 211-0067, Kanagawa, Japan
Tel.: (81) 44 733 4351
Web Site: https://www.tokyu-techno.co.jp
Transportation Services
N.A.I.C.S.: 485210

Tokyu World Transport (U.S.A.) Inc. (1)
991 Francisco St, Torrance, CA 90502-1217
Tel.: (310) 727-1500
Sales Range: $50-74.9 Million
Emp.: 120
Provider of Freight Transportation Arrangement Services
N.A.I.C.S.: 488510

TOKYU FUDOSAN HOLDINGS CORPORATION
Shibuya Solasta 1-21-1 Dogenzaka,

TOKYU FUDOSAN HOLDINGS CORPORATION

Tokyu Fudosan Holdings Corporation—(Continued)
Shibuya-ku, Tokyo, 150-0043, Japan
Tel.: (81) 364551122   JP
Web Site: https://www.tokyu-fudosan-hd.co.jp
Year Founded: 2013
TTUUF—(OTCIQ)
Rev.: $7,211,844,120
Assets: $19,634,743,860
Liabilities: $14,610,710,520
Net Worth: $5,024,033,340
Earnings: $345,787,590
Emp.: 21,614
Fiscal Year-end: 03/31/23
Holding Company; Real Estate Investment, Management & Brokerage Services
N.A.I.C.S.: 551112
Hitoshi Uemura *(Operating Officer)*

Subsidiaries:

Hunter Mountain shiobara Co., Ltd. (1)
Yumoto-Shiobara, Nasushiobara, 329-2922, Tochigi, Japan
Tel.: (81) 28 732 4580
Web Site: https://www.hunter.co.jp
Resort Services
N.A.I.C.S.: 721110

Infield Co., Ltd. (1)
4-2-5 Kanda Surugadai Ochanomizu NK Building, Tri-edge Ochanomizu 11th Floor Chiyoda-ku, Tokyo, 101-0062, Japan
Tel.: (81) 35 289 0211
Web Site: https://www.infield95.com
Conference Hall Rental Services
N.A.I.C.S.: 531120

Ishikatsu Exterior Inc. (1)
2-2-1 Tamagawa, Setagaya-ku, Tokyo, 158-0094, Japan
Tel.: (81) 33 709 5591
Web Site: https://www.ishikatsu.co.jp
Civil Engineering Services
N.A.I.C.S.: 541330

Livable Asset Management Inc. (1)
1-9-5 Dogenzaka, Shibuya Square A Shibuya-ku, Tokyo, 150-0043, Japan
Tel.: (81) 33 463 3792
Web Site: https://www.livable-am.co.jp
Real Estate Rental Services
N.A.I.C.S.: 531110

Marimo Community Co. Ltd. (1)
1-3-2 Kamiyacho Ginsen Hiroshima Building 11th Floor, Naka-ku, Hiroshima, 730-0031, Japan
Tel.: (81) 82 258 5500
Web Site: https://www.marimo-mc.co.jp
Building Contracting Services
N.A.I.C.S.: 236220

Miki Yokawa Country Club Co., Ltd. (1)
487-68 Makiyokawa Kuchiyokawa-cho, Miki, 673-075, Hyogo, Japan
Tel.: (81) 79 488 0236
Web Site: https://www.tokyu-golf-resort.com
Resort Services
N.A.I.C.S.: 721110

Niseko Tokyu Resort Co., Ltd. (1)
204 Aza Yamada Kutchan-cho, Abuta-gun, Hokkaido, 44-0081, Japan
Tel.: (81) 13 622 0109
Web Site: https://www.grand-hirafu.jp
Property Management Services
N.A.I.C.S.: 531312

Ohtakijo Golf Club Corporation (1)
1090 Uebara Otaki-cho, Isumi-gun, Chiba, 298-0223, Japan
Tel.: (81) 47 082 3311
Golf Club Services
N.A.I.C.S.: 713910

PT. Tokyu Land Indonesia (1)
Noble House 33rd Floor Jl Dr Ide Anak Gde Agung Kav E 4 2 No 2, Lingkar Mega Kuningan, Jakarta, 12950, Indonesia
Tel.: (62) 212 918 3109
Web Site: https://www.tokyuland-id.com
Real Estate Services
N.A.I.C.S.: 531390

Hidetatsu Ikeda *(Pres)*

Pacific Islands Development Corp. (1)
PO Box 308, Koror, PW 96940
Tel.: (680) 488-2600
Web Site: https://www.palauppr.com
Resort Services
N.A.I.C.S.: 721110

Sigma Japan Co. Ltd. (1)
9-2-28 Kegoya, Kure, 737-0012, Hiroshima, Japan
Tel.: (81) 82 328 0121
Web Site: https://www.sigma-k.co.jp
Emp.: 180
Transport Equipment Mfr & Distr
N.A.I.C.S.: 336320
Toshitaka Shitanaka *(Pres & CEO)*

TC Forum Corp. (1)
4F Shinjuku Ki Kaede Building 7-2-4 Nishi-Shinjuku, Shinjuku-ku, Tokyo, 160-0023, Japan
Tel.: (81) 35 338 0109
Web Site: https://www.tc-forum.co.jp
Conference Hall Rental Services
N.A.I.C.S.: 531120

TLC REIT Management Inc. (1)
Shibuya Solasta 18th Floor 21-1 Dougen-Zaka 1-Chome, Shibuya-ku, Tokyo, 150-0043, Japan
Tel.: (81) 36 455 3442
Web Site: https://www.tokyu-trm.co.jp
Investment Management Service
N.A.I.C.S.: 523940
Hiroyuki Tohmata *(Chm)*

Tokyu Building Maintenance Co., Ltd. (1)
19th Floor of Carrot Tower 4-1-1 Taishido, Setagaya-ku, Tokyo, 154-0004, Japan
Tel.: (81) 35 430 1919
Web Site: https://www.tokyu-bm.co.jp
Building Maintenance Services
N.A.I.C.S.: 561790

Tokyu Corporate Housing Management Inc. (1)
Shinjuku Monolith 22F 2-3-1 Nishi-Shinjuku, Shinjuku-ku, Tokyo, 163-0922, Japan
Tel.: (81) 33 344 3109
Web Site: https://www.tokyu-corporate-housing-management.co.jp
Real Estate Agency Services
N.A.I.C.S.: 531210
Hitoshi Takagi *(Pres)*

Tokyu E-Life Design Inc. (1)
1-10-8 Dogenzaka Shibuya Dogenzaka Tokyu Building, Shibuya-ku, Tokyo, 150-0043, Japan
Tel.: (81) 36 455 1236
Web Site: https://www.e-life-design.co.jp
Nursing Care Services
N.A.I.C.S.: 623110

Tokyu Hands Singapore Pte. Ltd. (1)
181 Orchard Road B1-07 Orchard Central, Singapore, 238896, Singapore
Tel.: (65) 6 834 3755
Web Site: https://www.tokyu-hands.com.sg
General Merchandise Product Distr
N.A.I.C.S.: 455219

Tokyu Land Capital Management Inc. (1)
Shibuya Solasta Building 21-1 1-Chome, Dogenzaka Shibuya-ku, Tokyo, Japan
Tel.: (81) 36 455 2637
Web Site: https://www.tokyu-tlcm.co.jp
Emp.: 63
Real Estate Asset Management Services
N.A.I.C.S.: 531390
Tsuyoshi Tsuneyoshi *(Pres & CEO)*

Tokyu Land Corporation (1)
SHIBUYA SOLASTA 1-21-1 Dogenzaka, Shibuya-ku, Tokyo, 150-0043, Japan
Tel.: (81) 36 455 1121
Web Site: https://www.tokyu-land.co.jp
Emp.: 1,145
Real Estate Investment, Development, Management & Brokerage Services
N.A.I.C.S.: 531390
Hitoshi Uemura *(Vice Chm & Sr Exec Officer)*

Tokyu Land US Corporation (1)
12100 Wilshire Blvd Ste 1650, Los Angeles, CA 90025
Tel.: (424) 372-3400
Web Site: https://www.tlusc.com
Real Estate Services
N.A.I.C.S.: 531390

Tokyu Livable Staff Corporation (1)
24-4 Sakuragaoka-cho Tobu Fuji Building 2nd Floor, Shibuya-ku, Tokyo, 150-0031, Japan
Tel.: (81) 36 416 3056
Web Site: https://www.livable-staff.co.jp
Employment Agency Services
N.A.I.C.S.: 561311

Tokyu Livable Texas Investment Advisors, LLC (1)
5851 Legacy Cir Ste 600, Plano, TX 75024
Tel.: (469) 626-5142
Real Estate Rental Services
N.A.I.C.S.: 531110

Tokyu Livable, Inc. (1)
1-9-5 Dogenzaka, Shibuya-ku, Tokyo, 150-0043, Japan
Tel.: (81) 12 094 1303
Web Site: https://www.livable.co.jp
Emp.: 3,581
Real Estate Investment, Management & Brokerage Services
N.A.I.C.S.: 531390
Kenji Sakaki *(Pres)*

Tokyu PM Vietnam Co., Ltd. (1)
Floor 3 Tower B Moonlight Residences No 102 Dang Van Bi Street, Binh Tho Ward Thu Duc District, Ho Chi Minh City, Vietnam
Tel.: (84) 283 636 2078
Web Site: https://www.tokyupm.vn
Building Maintenance Services
N.A.I.C.S.: 561790

Tokyu Resort Corporation (1)
1-10-8 Dogenzaka Shibuya Dogenzaka Tokyu Building, Shibuya-ku, Tokyo, 150-0043, Japan
Tel.: (81) 12 008 9109
Web Site: https://www.tokyu-resort.co.jp
Emp.: 165
Real Estate Brokerage Services
N.A.I.C.S.: 531210
Hideaki Ito *(Pres & CEO)*

Tokyu Sports Oasis Inc. (1)
01-10-2008 Shibuya Dogenzaka Tokyu Building, Shibuya-ku, Tokyo, 150-0043, Japan
Tel.: (81) 36 427 0028
Web Site: https://www.sportsoasis.co.jp
Fitness Center Services
N.A.I.C.S.: 713940

TOKYU REIT, INC.
1-12-1 Dogenzaka, Shibuya-ku, Tokyo, 150-0043, Japan
Tel.: (81) 354285828
Web Site: https://www.tokyu-reit.co.jp
Year Founded: 2003
89570—(TKS)
Sales Range: Less than $1 Million
Real Estate Related Services
N.A.I.C.S.: 531390
Kazuyoshi Kashiwazaki *(Exec Dir)*

TOLERANZIA AB
Arvid Wallgrens backe 20 8th floor, 413 26, Gothenburg, Sweden
Tel.: (46) 763199898
Web Site: https://www.toleranzia.com
Pharmaceuticals Product Mfr
N.A.I.C.S.: 325412
Ola Ronn *(Chm)*

TOLI CORPORATION
5-125 Higashi-Arioka, Itami, 664-8610, Hyogo, Japan
Tel.: (81) 354032078
Web Site: https://www.toli.co.jp
7971—(TKS)
Rev.: $677,326,700
Assets: $600,511,890
Liabilities: $298,038,290
Net Worth: $302,473,600
Earnings: $24,384,290

Emp.: 1,883
Fiscal Year-end: 03/31/24
Building Product Mfr
N.A.I.C.S.: 327120
Motohiro Nagashima *(Pres)*

Subsidiaries:

Kirony Co., Ltd. (1)
Tori Tokyo Building 2F 2-10-4 Higashi-Shinbashi, Minato-ku, Tokyo, 105-0021, Japan
Tel.: (81) 368950112
Web Site: https://www.kirony.co.jp
Interior Decoration Products Sales
N.A.I.C.S.: 449110
Hiroyasu Furuno *(Pres & CEO)*

TOLKO INDUSTRIES LTD.
3000 - 28th Street, Vernon, V1T 9W9, BC, Canada
Tel.: (250) 545-4411   Ca
Web Site: http://www.tolko.com
Year Founded: 1956
Emp.: 3,000
Wood Product Mfr & Distr
N.A.I.C.S.: 321113
J. Allan Thorlakson *(Chm)*

Subsidiaries:

Meadow Lake OSB Limited Partnership (1)
12 km South of Hwy 55 on the Matchee/Neeb Road, PO Box 280, Meadow Lake, S9X 1Y2, SK, Canada   (100%)
Tel.: (306) 236-6565
Web Site: http://www.tolko.com
Emp.: 155
Oriented Strand Board Mfr & Distr
N.A.I.C.S.: 321219
Greg Jhonson *(Plant Mgr)*

Tolko Industries Ltd. - Armstrong Lumber-Plywood/Veneer Mill (1)
844 Otter Lake X-Road, Armstrong, V0E 1B6, BC, Canada
Tel.: (250) 546-3171
Web Site: http://www.tolko.com
Emp.: 400
Sawmill Operator, Lumber Distr, Plywood & Veneer Mfr & Distr
N.A.I.C.S.: 321113
David Smith *(Gen Mgr)*

Tolko Industries Ltd. - Athabasca Mill (1)
6 km East Mitsue Industrial Park, PO Box 1400, Slave Lake, T0G 2A0, AB, Canada
Tel.: (780) 805-3800
Web Site: http://www.tolko.com
Emp.: 188
Engineered Wood Products Mfr & Distr
N.A.I.C.S.: 321219
Mark Cunningham *(Plant Mgr)*

Tolko Industries Ltd. - Eagle Rock Reforestation Centre Division (1)
844 Otter Lake Cross Road, Armstrong, V0E 1B6, BC, Canada
Tel.: (250) 546-3171
Web Site: https://
Reforestation Services
N.A.I.C.S.: 115310

Tolko Industries Ltd. - Heffley Creek Mill (1)
6275 Old Highway 5, Kamloops, V2H 1T8, BC, Canada
Tel.: (250) 578-7212
Web Site: http://www.tolko.com
Emp.: 250
Plywood & Veneer Mfr
N.A.I.C.S.: 321211
Kristen Gammel *(Mgr-Reg HR)*

Tolko Industries Ltd. - High Level Lumber Mill (1)
11401-92 Street, High Level, T0H 1Z0, AB, Canada
Tel.: (780) 926-3781
Web Site: http://www.tolko.com
Emp.: 325
Sawmill Operator
N.A.I.C.S.: 321113
Dean Lamberton *(Mgr-Maintenance)*

Tolko Industries Ltd. - Kraft Paper Mill (1)

Highway 10 North, PO Box 1590, The Pas, R9A 1L4, MB, Canada
Tel.: (204) 623-7411
Web Site:
http://www.canadiankraftpaper.com
Kraft Paper Mfr
N.A.I.C.S.: 322120

Tolko Industries Ltd. - Lake Country Division
400 Beaver Lake Road, Kelowna, V4V 1S5, BC, Canada
Tel.: (250) 766-1207
Timber Product Mfr
N.A.I.C.S.: 321912

Tolko Industries Ltd. - Lakeview Lumber Division
180 Hodgson Road, Williams Lake, V2G 3P6, BC, Canada
Tel.: (250) 392-3371
Wood Products Mfr
N.A.I.C.S.: 321911

Tolko Industries Ltd. - Lavington Planer Mill (1)
6200 Jeffers Drive, Coldstream, Lavington, V1B 3G4, BC, Canada
Tel.: (250) 545-4992
Web Site: http://www.tolko.com
Emp.: 215
Lumber Planing Mill Operator
N.A.I.C.S.: 321912

Tolko Industries Ltd. - White Valley Division (1)
4280 Highway 6, Lumby, V0E 2G7, BC, Canada
Tel.: (250) 547-2111
Veneer Mfr
N.A.I.C.S.: 321211

TOLO TOYS LTD.
5th Floor Tower 2 South Seas Centre, 75 Mody Road, Kowloon, China (Hong Kong)
Tel.: (852) 2369 0261
Web Site: http://www.tolotoys.com
Year Founded: 1985
Children's Toy Mfr
N.A.I.C.S.: 339930
Stephen D. Reardon *(Mng Dir)*

Subsidiaries:

Tolo Toys Learning Ltd. (1)
101 Ridley Wood, Bryn Lane, Wrexham, LL13 9UT, Wales, United Kingdom
Tel.: (44) 1978 667777
Sales Range: $50-74.9 Million
Emp.: 7
Distr of Learning Products to Educational Establishments
N.A.I.C.S.: 423920

TOLY BREAD CO., LTD.
No 1066 Jichang Road, Sujiatun District, Shenyang, 110000, Liaoning, China
Tel.: (86) 2422817166
Web Site: http://www.tolybread.cn
Year Founded: 1997
603866—(SHG)
Rev.: $938,751,367
Assets: $929,734,753
Liabilities: $224,061,636
Net Worth: $705,673,117
Earnings: $89,864,073
Fiscal Year-end: 12/31/22
Bakery Product Mfr & Distr
N.A.I.C.S.: 311812
Xueliang Wu *(Chm & Exec Gen Mgr)*

TOLYPERS COMPANY
No 27-Africa St-Western Shahid Atefi Ave, Tehran, 19177 96941, Iran
Tel.: (98) 2122019940
Year Founded: 1973
Emp.: 356
Toilet Preparation Mfr
N.A.I.C.S.: 325620
Bijan Esmaili *(Chm)*

TOM TAILOR HOLDING SE
Garstedter Weg 14, 22453, Hamburg, Germany
Tel.: (49) 4018047237
Web Site: https://www.tom-tailor.eu
Year Founded: 1962
Clothing Retailer
N.A.I.C.S.: 458110
Thomas Dressendorfer *(Co-CFO & Member-Mgmt Bd)*

Subsidiaries:

Tom Tailor (Schweiz) AG (1)
Ruessenstrasse 12, 6340, Baar, Zug, Switzerland
Tel.: (41) 417667050
Branded Apparels Retailer
N.A.I.C.S.: 458110
Peter Kuhn *(Acct Mgr)*

Tom Tailor France S.A.R.L. (1)
23 Rue Louis le Grand, 75002, Paris, France
Tel.: (33) 147036280
Web Site: http://www.tomtailor.com
Emp.: 100
Branded Apparels Retailer
N.A.I.C.S.: 458110

Tom Tailor Gesellschaft m.b.H. (1)
Bahnhofstrasse 53, Worgl, 6300, Tyrol, Austria
Tel.: (43) 533277953
Web Site: http://www.tomtailor.com
Sales Range: $25-49.9 Million
Emp.: 19
Branded Apparels Retailer
N.A.I.C.S.: 458110
Christian Schroeder *(Mng Dir)*

Tom Tailor GmbH (1)
Garstedter Weg 14, 22453, Hamburg, Germany
Tel.: (49) 40589560
Web Site: http://www.tom-tailor.com
Sales Range: $100-124.9 Million
Emp.: 450
Apparel Retail Stores Operation Services
N.A.I.C.S.: 458110

Tom Tailor International Holding B.V. (1)
De Kreek 1, 4906 BB, Oosterhout, Noord-Brabant, Netherlands
Tel.: (31) 162472575
Web Site: http://www.tomtailor.com
Sales Range: $25-49.9 Million
Emp.: 20
Management Services
N.A.I.C.S.: 551112

Tom Tailor Retail GmbH (1)
Garstedter Weg 14, 22453, Hamburg, Germany
Tel.: (49) 1805824567
Web Site: http://www.tom-tailor.de
Online Apparel Retailer
N.A.I.C.S.: 458110

TOM'S CO., LTD.
6-13-10 Todoroki, Setagaya-Ku, Tokyo, 158-0082, Japan
Tel.: (81) 337046191
Web Site:
http://www.tomsracing.co.jp
Automotive Parts Mfr & Distr
N.A.I.C.S.: 336390

TOMA A.S.
class Tomas Bata 332, 76502, Otrokovice, Czech Republic
Tel.: (420) 577662001
Web Site: https://www.tomaas.cz
Year Founded: 1935
TOMA—(PRA)
Sales Range: Less than $1 Million
Energy Distribution Services
N.A.I.C.S.: 221122
Miroslav Sevcik *(Chm & Chm-Mgmt Bd)*

TOMAGOLD CORPORATION
410 St-Nicolas Suite 236, Montreal, H2Y-2P5, QC, Canada
Tel.: (514) 583-3490
Web Site:
https://www.tomagoldcorp.com
OTM—(DEU)
Assets: $513,928
Liabilities: $464,509
Net Worth: $49,420
Earnings: ($2,284,212)
Emp.: 2
Fiscal Year-end: 08/31/23
Gold Ore Mining Services
N.A.I.C.S.: 212220
David Grondin *(Pres & CEO)*

TOMAL AB
Bol 110, 311 65, Vessigebro, Sweden
Tel.: (46) 346713100
Web Site: http://www.tomal.se
Sales Range: $10-24.9 Million
Emp.: 75
Metering Equipment
N.A.I.C.S.: 333310
Magnus Dahl *(Mgr-IT)*

TOMASZ GENERAL CONTRACTING LTD.
5480 Bourget Dr, Mississauga, L5R 3C8, ON, Canada
Tel.: (416) 518-8038
Web Site: http://www.tgchomes.com
Sales Range: $1-9.9 Million
Emp.: 2
General Contracting & Construction
N.A.I.C.S.: 236115

Subsidiaries:

TGC Homes (1)
5480 Bourget Dr, Mississauga, L5R 3C8, ON, Canada
Tel.: (416) 518-8038
Web Site: http://www.tgchomes.com
Specializes in Assisting Home Owners With the Design, Architecture, Technical Support & Execution of Building Homes
N.A.I.C.S.: 541310

TOMATO BANK LTD.
2-3-4 Bancho, Kita-Ku, Okayama, 700-0811, Japan
Tel.: (81) 862211010
Web Site:
https://www.tomatobank.co.jp
Year Founded: 1931
8542—(TKS)
Rev.: $159,069,650
Assets: $8,873,931,610
Liabilities: $8,498,298,530
Net Worth: $375,633,080
Earnings: $165,250
Emp.: 1,482
Fiscal Year-end: 03/31/24
Commercial Banking Services
N.A.I.C.S.: 522110
Shougo Takagi *(Pres)*

Subsidiaries:

TOMATO CARD, LTD (1)
1-9-1 Nakayamashita, Kita Ward, Okayama, Okayama Prefecture, Japan
Tel.: (81) 862318131
Web Site: https://www.tomatocard.co.jp
Emp.: 6
Credit Card Issuing Services
N.A.I.C.S.: 522210

TOMATO SYSTEM CO., LTD.
5F 6F & 8F 5 Nonhyeon-ro 128-gil, Gangnam-Gu, Seoul, 06104, Korea (South)
Tel.: (82) 234452194
Web Site: https://tomatosystem.co.kr
Year Founded: 2000
393210—(KRS)
Software Development Services
N.A.I.C.S.: 541511
Sang-Don Lee *(CEO)*

TOMBADOR IRON LIMITED
Level 1 3 Ord Street, West Perth, 6005, WA, Australia
Tel.: (61) 863821805
Web Site:
https://www.tombadoriron.com
Year Founded: 2004
TI1—(ASX)
Rev.: $21,739,584
Assets: $37,005,116
Liabilities: $13,611,098
Net Worth: $23,394,018
Earnings: $2,332,589
Fiscal Year-end: 06/30/22
Iron Ore Mining Services
N.A.I.C.S.: 212210
Stephen Quantrill *(Exec Dir)*

TOMBAO ANTIQUES & ART GROUP
No 77 Xianlie Middle Road Rm 818 Suite A Huifeng Building, Guangzhou, China
Tel.: (86) 2087321478
TAAI—(OTCIQ)
Sales Range: Less than $1 Million
Art Product Distr
N.A.I.C.S.: 459999

TOMBOLA GOLD LTD.
Level 14 309 Kent Street, Sydney, 2000, NSW, Australia
Tel.: (61) 292480104
Web Site:
http://www.ausmexgroup.com.au
TBA—(ASX)
Rev.: $122,734
Assets: $4,227,384
Liabilities: $976,800
Net Worth: $3,250,584
Earnings: ($2,427,537)
Fiscal Year-end: 06/30/21
Metal Mining
N.A.I.C.S.: 212290
Joseph Yosse Goldberg *(Chm)*

TOMCO ENERGY PLC
111 Park Street, London, W1K 7JL, United Kingdom
Tel.: (44) 2038233635
Web Site:
https://www.tomcoenergy.com
TOM—(AIM)
Rev.: $79,254
Assets: $8,140,518
Liabilities: $2,015,316
Net Worth: $6,125,202
Earnings: ($781,218)
Fiscal Year-end: 09/30/22
Oil & Gas Exploration Services
N.A.I.C.S.: 211120
Malcolm Groat *(Chm)*

TOMEI CONSOLIDATED BERHAD
8-1 Jalan 2/131A Project Jaya Industrial Estate, Batu 6 Jalan Kelang Lama, 58200, Kuala Lumpur, Malaysia
Tel.: (60) 377848136
Web Site: https://www.tomei.com.my
Year Founded: 1968
TOMEI—(KLS)
Rev.: $206,209,947
Assets: $138,939,894
Liabilities: $61,612,063
Net Worth: $77,327,831
Earnings: $14,276,614
Emp.: 800
Fiscal Year-end: 12/31/22
Jewelry Mfr
N.A.I.C.S.: 212390
Kok Jong Teoh *(Sec)*

TOMEN DEVICES CORPORATION

TOMEN DEVICES CORPORATION

Tomen Devices Corporation—(Continued)
8-12 Harumi 1-chome, Chuo-ku, Tokyo, 104-6230, Japan
Tel.: (81) 335369150
Web Site: https://www.tomendevices.co.jp
Year Founded: 1992
2737—(TKS)
Rev.: $2,450,168,360
Assets: $860,707,930
Liabilities: $559,900,050
Net Worth: $300,807,880
Earnings: $13,854,560
Emp.: 187
Fiscal Year-end: 03/31/24
Electronic Parts Whslr
N.A.I.C.S.: 423690
Ichiro Tsumaki *(Pres)*

Subsidiaries:

ATMD (Hong Kong) Limited (1)
Rm 1906 19/F Tower 2 Enterpriase Square 9 Sheung Yuet Road, Kowloon Bay, Kowloon, China (Hong Kong) (100%)
Tel.: (852) 31060488
Web Site: http://www.atmd.com.hk
Electronic Products Mfr
N.A.I.C.S.: 334419

ATMD Electronics (Shanghai) Limited (1)
Room 1602-03 Oriental Center Building NO 699 West Nanjing Road, Jing'an District, Shanghai, 200041, China
Tel.: (86) 2158207816
Electronic Products Mfr
N.A.I.C.S.: 334419

ATMD Electronics (Shenzhen) Limited (1)
Rm07-08 11F Tower C China Resources Land Building 9668 Shennan Avenue, Nanshan, Shenzhen, 518057, China
Tel.: (86) 23612882
Electronic Products Mfr
N.A.I.C.S.: 334419

ATMD Electronics (Singapore) Limited (1)
600 North Bridge Road 16-04 Parkview Square, Singapore, 188778, Singapore
Tel.: (65) 63231505
Electronic Parts Mfr
N.A.I.C.S.: 334419

NEXTY Electronics Corporation (1)
2-3-13 Konan Shinagawa Front Building, Minato-ku, Tokyo, 108-8510, Japan
Tel.: (81) 354629611
Web Site: https://www.nexty-ele.com
Electronic Products Mfr
N.A.I.C.S.: 334419
Kiyotaka Nakao *(Mng Dir)*

TOMER ENERGY ROYALTIES 2012 LTD.
Greenworks Complex B, Yakum, 6097200, Israel
Tel.: (972) 733242742
Web Site: https://www.tomerenergy.co.il
Year Founded: 2012
TOEN—(TAE)
Rev.: $22,786,000
Assets: $161,922,000
Liabilities: $62,948,000
Net Worth: $98,974,000
Earnings: $4,638,000
Fiscal Year-end: 09/30/23
Natural Gas Exploration Service
N.A.I.C.S.: 211130
Miryam Sophie Guez *(CEO)*

TOMI S.A.I.E.D.W.
Meandroupoleos 11-13 Ambelokipi, 115 24, Athens, Greece
Tel.: (30) 2106980680   GR
Web Site: http://www.tomh-ae.gr
Year Founded: 1987
Sales Range: $25-49.9 Million
Emp.: 35

Infrastructures Design & Construction Services
N.A.I.C.S.: 236220
Christos Ntalas *(Pres)*

TOMITA CO., LTD.
8-3-10 Ginza, Chuo-Ku, Tokyo, 104-0061, Japan
Tel.: (81) 337651181
Web Site: https://www.tomitaj.co.jp
Year Founded: 1943
8147—(TKS)
Rev.: $140,878,930
Assets: $122,013,990
Liabilities: $43,341,770
Net Worth: $78,672,220
Earnings: $3,708,210
Emp.: 89
Fiscal Year-end: 03/31/24
Industrial Machinery & Tools Distr
N.A.I.C.S.: 423830
Kaoru Tomita *(Pres & CEO)*

Subsidiaries:

PT. Tomita Indonesia (1)
Ruko River Town Ba-3 No 18 Grand Wisata Desa Lambangsari, Kec Tambun Selatan, Bekasi, 17510, Jawa Barat, Indonesia
Tel.: (62) 2182621062
Industrial Machinery Distr
N.A.I.C.S.: 423830

Tomita Asia Co., Ltd. (1)
1035 22 1st 6th Fl Soi Pridi Phanomyong 41 Sukhumvit 71 Rd, Khlong Tan Nuea Watthana, Bangkok, 10110, Thailand
Tel.: (66) 2392506670
Web Site: https://www.tomitaasia.com
Industrial Machinery Mfr & Distr
N.A.I.C.S.: 333248

Tomita Canada Inc. (1)
178 Pennsylvania Ave Unit 8, Concord, L4K 3Z4, ON, Canada
Tel.: (905) 760-9863
Web Site: http://www.tomitacanada.com
Industrial Machinery Distr
N.A.I.C.S.: 423830

Tomita China Co., Ltd. (1)
Room 1501 Guangdong traffic Building south block No 27-1 Baiyun Road, Yuexiu District, Guangzhou, 510100, China
Tel.: (86) 2037621705
Industrial Machinery Distr
N.A.I.C.S.: 423830
Nitin Khandelwal *(Deputy Mgr)*

Tomita Mexico, S.DE R.L.DE C.V. (1)
Blvd Jose Maria Morelos No 807 Local 29 col Los Murales, 37219, Leon, Guanajuato, Mexico
Tel.: (52) 4777118549
Industrial Machinery Distr
N.A.I.C.S.: 423830

Tomita UK Ltd. (1)
Unit 3 Mead Park Thorpe Mead, Banbury, OX16 4RY, Oxfordshire, United Kingdom
Tel.: (44) 1295277317
Web Site: https://www.tomita.co.uk
Cutting Tool Mfr & Distr
N.A.I.C.S.: 333515

Vietnam Tomita Co., Ltd. (1)
13Floor Hoa Binh Building 106 Hoang Quoc Viet St, Nghia Tan Ward Cau Glay District, Hanoi, Vietnam
Tel.: (84) 2439590252
Industrial Machinery Distr
N.A.I.C.S.: 423830
Thanh Nguyen *(Engr-Sls)*

TOMITA ELECTRIC CO., LTD.
123 Saiwai-cho, Tottori, 680-0823, Japan
Tel.: (81) 857228441

Web Site: https://www.tomita-electric.com
Year Founded: 1960
6898—(TKS)
Rev.: $10,578,280
Assets: $33,301,730
Liabilities: $6,501,530
Net Worth: $26,800,200
Earnings: ($233,970)
Emp.: 45
Fiscal Year-end: 01/31/24
Electronic Components Mfr
N.A.I.C.S.: 334419
Tetsuro Kamitani *(Pres)*

Subsidiaries:

TOMITA FERRITE LTD. (1)
Rm 814 Hong Leong Industrial Complex 4 Wang Kwong Road, Kowloon Bay, China (Hong Kong)
Tel.: (852) 34254300
Web Site: http://www.tomita-electric.com
Electrical Equipment Distr
N.A.I.C.S.: 423610

Zhuhai Tomita Electronics Ltd. (1)
No 41 Qinshi Road Sanzao Town, Jinwan District, Zhuhai, China
Tel.: (86) 7567766009
Electronic Equipment Mfr & Distr
N.A.I.C.S.: 335999

TOMIZONE LIMITED
Level 32 101 Miller Street, Sydney, 2060, NSW, Australia
Tel.: (61) 2 9025 3995   AU
Web Site: http://www.tomizone.com
Rev.: $4,036,742
Assets: $3,292,829
Liabilities: $8,363,956
Net Worth: ($5,071,127)
Earnings: ($4,860,215)
Fiscal Year-end: 06/30/18
Wireless Internet Services
N.A.I.C.S.: 517112
Phillip Joe *(Founder)*

Subsidiaries:

Bluesky Online Services Limited (1)
110 Wairau Rd Wairau Valley, Auckland, 0627, New Zealand
Tel.: (64) 5082583759
Web Site: http://blueskyonlineservices.co.nz
Online Computer Product Distr
N.A.I.C.S.: 541512
Gary Myburgh *(Mng Dir)*

TOMLIN INDUSTRIES INC
145 Northfield Drive West, Waterloo, N2L 5J3, ON, Canada
Tel.: (519) 884-5290
Web Site: http://www.camltomlin.com
Sales Range: $25-49.9 Million
Emp.: 10
Acrylic Bath Tub Mfr
N.A.I.C.S.: 326191
Jean-Louis Cloutier *(Pres)*

TOMO HOLDINGS LIMITED
3018 Bedok North Street 5 02-08 Eastlink, Singapore, 486132, Singapore
Tel.: (65) 64455777   Ky
Web Site: https://www.thetomogroup.com
Year Founded: 1995
6928—(HKG)
Rev.: $6,870,603
Assets: $11,086,717
Liabilities: $1,052,178
Net Worth: $10,034,539
Earnings: ($8,014,990)
Emp.: 46
Fiscal Year-end: 12/31/23
Electronic Accessory Distr
N.A.I.C.S.: 423690
Yew Khuen Siew *(Co-Founder, Chm & CEO)*

Subsidiaries:

TOMO-CSE Autotrim Pte. Ltd. (1)
3018 Bedok North Street 5 02-08 Eastlink, Singapore, 486132, Singapore
Tel.: (65) 64455777
Web Site: https://www.tomocse.com.sg
Electronic Equipment Whslr
N.A.I.C.S.: 423690
David Siew *(CEO)*

TOMOE ENGINEERING CO., LTD.
Osaki Bright Core 5-15 Kitashinagawa 5-chome, Shinagawa-ku, Tokyo, 141-0001, Japan
Tel.: (81) 334425120
Web Site: https://www.tomo-e.co.jp
Year Founded: 1941
6309—(TKS)
Rev.: $351,862,520
Assets: $347,459,630
Liabilities: $86,320,750
Net Worth: $261,138,880
Earnings: $19,376,970
Emp.: 767
Fiscal Year-end: 10/31/23
Machinery & Equipment Mfr
N.A.I.C.S.: 238290
Yoshito Honma *(Mng Dir)*

Subsidiaries:

Interstella Plastics (Shenzhen) Co., Ltd. (1)
No 4 Longshan 7th Road Luotian Community Songgang Road, Bao'an District, Shenzhen, 518055, Guangdong, China
Tel.: (86) 75586000643
Web Site: https://interstella.com.cn
Sales Range: $50-74.9 Million
Emp.: 130
Plastic Materials Mfr
N.A.I.C.S.: 325211

TOMOE Advanced Materials s.r.o. (1)
Karolinska 661/4, 186 00, Prague, Czech Republic
Tel.: (420) 227031209
Machinery Equipment Mfr
N.A.I.C.S.: 333924

TOMOE Engineering (Hong Kong) Co., Ltd. (1)
Unit 211 2/F Two Harbourfront 22 Tak Fung Street, Hunghom, Kowloon, China (Hong Kong)
Tel.: (852) 28901120
Centrifugal Machinery Products Mfr
N.A.I.C.S.: 333120

TOMOE Engineering Co., Ltd. - Sagami Factory (1)
193 Kamisoyagi, Yamato, 242-0029, Kanagawa, Japan
Tel.: (81) 462620511
Web Site: http://www.tomo-e.co.jp
Sales Range: $150-199.9 Million
Emp.: 500
Industrial Machinery Mfr
N.A.I.C.S.: 423830

TOMOE Engineering Co., Ltd. - Shonan Factory (1)
357-12 Higashitoyoda, Hiratsuka, 254-0082, Kanagawa, Japan
Tel.: (81) 463557711
Sales Range: $50-74.9 Million
Emp.: 60
Industrial Machinery Mfr
N.A.I.C.S.: 423830
Shouzo Nagai *(Pres)*

TOMOE Machinery Co., Ltd. (1)
9-31-36 Fukayanaka, Ayase, 252-1107, Kanagawa, Japan
Tel.: (81) 467787933
Web Site: https://www.tomoe-masy.co.jp
Sales Range: $25-49.9 Million
Emp.: 51
Centrifuge Frames & Casings Mfr
N.A.I.C.S.: 332313
Ryoji Tanaka *(Mng Dir)*

TOMOE Machinery Service Co., Ltd. (1)

357-12 Higashi - Toyoda, Hiratsuka, 254-0082, Kanagawa, Japan
Tel.: (81) 463557711
Web Site: https://www.tomo-e-service.co.jp
Sales Range: $25-49.9 Million
Emp.: 60
Centrifuges Maintenance & Repair Services
N.A.I.C.S.: 811310

TOMOE SHOKAI CO., LTD.
Kamata Bldg 1-2-5 Kamata-honcho, Ohta-ku, Tokyo, 144-8505, Japan
Tel.: (81) 3 3734 1111   JP
Web Site: http://www.tomoeshokai.co.jp
Year Founded: 1950
Emp.: 852
Industrial Gas Mfr
N.A.I.C.S.: 325120
Sadao Fukao (Pres)

Subsidiaries:

Vietnam Japan Gas Joint Stock Company   (1)
No 33 Road 3A Bien Hoa Industrial Zone 2, Bien Hoa, Dong Nai, Vietnam
Tel.: (84) 2513836706
Web Site: http://www.vijagas.vn
Sales Range: $25-49.9 Million
Emp.: 70
Industrial Gas Mfr
N.A.I.C.S.: 325120
Haruhiro Yasuga (Gen Dir)

TOMOEGAWA CO., LTD.
7th Floor Kyobashi Trust Tower 2-1-3 Kyobashi, Chuo-ku, Tokyo, Japan
Tel.: (81) 335163401
Web Site: https://www.tomoegawa.co.jp
Year Founded: 1917
3878—(TKS)
Rev.: $222,704,120
Assets: $302,162,930
Liabilities: $173,955,370
Net Worth: $128,207,560
Earnings: $3,926,340
Emp.: 1,305
Fiscal Year-end: 03/31/24
Paper Products & Office Supplies Mfr
N.A.I.C.S.: 322130
Hiroshi Kawashima (VP-Production Div)

Subsidiaries:

Nihon Rika Seishi Co., Ltd.   (1)
3-1-1 Nakanogo, Shimizu-ku, Shizuoka, 424-0888, Japan
Tel.: (81) 543453411
Web Site: http://www.nihonrika.co.jp
Adhesive Tapes Mfr & Whslr
N.A.I.C.S.: 325520

Nippon Card Co., Ltd.   (1)
2-2-40 Katamachi Osaka Daihatsu Building, Miyakojima-ku, Osaka, 534-0025, Japan
Tel.: (81) 648005710
Web Site: https://www.nippon-card.co.jp
Credit Card Processing Services
N.A.I.C.S.: 522320

Sanwa Co., Ltd.   (1)
2-1-3 Kyobashi Kyobashi Trust Tower, Chuo-ku, Tokyo, 104-0031, Japan
Tel.: (81) 335172070
Web Site: http://www.sanwa-shiko.co.jp
Sales Range: $50-74.9 Million
Emp.: 115
Packaging Paper Products Mfr
N.A.I.C.S.: 322299

Plant (Domestic):

Sanwa Co., Ltd. - Kashima Factory   (2)
3075-8 Shimasu, Itako, 311-2434, Ibaraki, Japan
Tel.: (81) 299646921
Packaging Materials Mfr
N.A.I.C.S.: 322220

Sanwa Co., Ltd. - Okayama Factory   (2)
846-1 Saidaijihama, Higashi-ku, Okayama, 704-8126, Okayama Prefecture, Japan
Tel.: (81) 869434123
Paper & Packaging Materials Mfr
N.A.I.C.S.: 322130

Shin Tomoegawa Kakoh Co., Ltd.   (1)
3-1 Mochimune Tomoe-cho, Suruga-ku, Shizuoka, 422-8067, Japan
Tel.: (81) 542594153
Sales Range: $75-99.9 Million
Emp.: 200
Paper & Packaging Products Distr
N.A.I.C.S.: 423840

TFC Co., Ltd.
34-23-2 Azono, Tsuruga, 914-8501, Fukui, Japan   (14.5%)
Tel.: (81) 770211711
Web Site: http://www.tomoegawa.co.jp
Optical Film Mfr
N.A.I.C.S.: 326112

Technica Tomoegawa Co., Ltd.   (1)
Itako Industrial Park 3075-8 Shimasu, Itako, 311-2434, Ibaraki, Japan
Tel.: (81) 299646926
Electronic Products Finishing Services
N.A.I.C.S.: 334514

Tomoegawa (U.S.A.) Inc.   (1)
742 Glenn Ave, Wheeling, IL 60090-6079   (100%)
Tel.: (847) 541-3001
Web Site: https://www.tomoegawa.com
Sales Range: $25-49.9 Million
Emp.: 98
Printing Toner Mfr
N.A.I.C.S.: 325910
Kimihiko Nakamura (Pres & COO)

Tomoegawa Europe B.V.   (1)
Prof J H Bavincklaan 2, 1183 AT, Amstelveen, Netherlands
Tel.: (31) 206621011
Web Site: https://www.tomoegawa.nl
Emp.: 5
Electronic & Stationery Products Distr
N.A.I.C.S.: 423690
Shigeru Ishigaki (Chm & CEO)

Tomoegawa Hong Kong Co., Ltd.   (1)
Unit 1213 12/F Tower II Cheung Sha Wan Plaza 833 Cheung Sha Wan Road, Lai Chi Kok, Kowloon, China (Hong Kong)
Tel.: (852) 35496722
Web Site: http://www.tomoegawa.co.jp
Sales Range: $50-74.9 Million
Emp.: 9
Paper Products & Adhesives Whslr
N.A.I.C.S.: 424130

Tomoegawa Imaging Technology Huizhou Co., Ltd.   (1)
No 1 Songbai Road Huinan Hi-Tech Industrial Park Huiao Highway, Huizhou, 516025, Guangdong, China
Tel.: (86) 7522598801
Sales Range: $25-49.9 Million
Emp.: 100
Toner Mfr & Whslr
N.A.I.C.S.: 339999

Tomoegawa Korea Co., Ltd.   (1)
Illumistate 417-1904 180, Beoman-ro, Bucheon, 08862, Gyeonggi, Korea (South)
Tel.: (82) 1090834180
Electronic Parts Whslr
N.A.I.C.S.: 423690

Tomoegawa Logistics Service Co., Ltd.   (1)
3-1 Mochimune Tomoe-cho, Suruga-ku, Shizuoka, 422-8067, Japan
Tel.: (81) 542594155
Freight Trucking & Warehousing Services
N.A.I.C.S.: 484110
Yukinori Sakumoto (Dir)

Tomoegawa Paper Co., Ltd.   (1)
3-1 Mochimune tomoe-cho, Suruga-ku, Shizuoka, 421-0126, Japan
Tel.: (81) 542564111
Web Site: http://paper.tomoegawa.co.jp
Sales Range: $25-49.9 Million
Emp.: 72
Paper Products Mfr
N.A.I.C.S.: 322120

TOMOIKE ELECTRONICS (SHANGHAI) CO., LIMITED
3-4F Yong Fu Building 85 Tai Gu Road Wai Gao Qiao FTZ, Pudong New Area, Shanghai, 200131, China
Tel.: (86) 2158682105
Year Founded: 2003
Sales Range: $25-49.9 Million
Emp.: 93
Flat Panel Display Component Mfr & Distr
N.A.I.C.S.: 334419

TOMOKU CO., LTD.
Marunouchi Mitsui Building 2-2-2 Marunouchi, Chiyoda-ku, Tokyo, 100-0005, Japan
Tel.: (81) 332136811   JP
Web Site: https://www.tomoku.co.jp
Year Founded: 1948
3946—(SAP)
Rev.: $1,406,124,876
Assets: $1,290,901,883
Liabilities: $757,654,443
Net Worth: $533,247,440
Earnings: $34,694,417
Emp.: 3,717
Fiscal Year-end: 03/31/23
Holding Company; Packaging Products Mfr & Distr
N.A.I.C.S.: 551112
Mitsuo Nakahashi (Pres & COO)

Subsidiaries:

Atsuta Shiki Co., Ltd.   (1)
680 Iwasaki, Komaki, 485-0011, Aichi, Japan
Tel.: (81) 568 72 3738
Corrugated Paper Product Mfr
N.A.I.C.S.: 322211

B-Staff Co., Ltd.   (1)
180 Shimono-go-shinden, Iwanuma, 989-2421, Miyagi, Japan
Tel.: (81) 223242321
Transportation Services
N.A.I.C.S.: 484110

Chubu Tohun Co., Ltd.   (1)
588 Shimizu Jyu Hachi Jyo, Mizuho-shi, Gifu, 501-0314, Japan
Tel.: (81) 583287533
Warehouse & Factory Operation Services
N.A.I.C.S.: 811310

Cosmos Kogyo Co., Ltd.   (1)
2756-1 Kanazawa, Chino, 391-0012, Japan
Tel.: (81) 266727145
Container Boards Mfr & Distr
N.A.I.C.S.: 321920

Daiichi Container Co., Ltd.   (1)
1001 Nakagawa, Shimada, 427-0103, Shizuoka, Japan   (70%)
Tel.: (81) 54 738 1235
Web Site: https://www.tomoku.co.jp
Cardboard Mfr & Distr
N.A.I.C.S.: 322212
Yoshio Okamoto (Pres)

Enshu Kami Kogyo Co., Ltd.   (1)
2600 Kuramatsu-cho, Minami-ku, Hamamatsu, 430-0846, Shizuoka, Japan
Tel.: (81) 534152600
Textile Products Mfr
N.A.I.C.S.: 314999

Gavle Tomoku Hus AB   (1)
PO Box 1343, 801 38, Gavle, Sweden
Tel.: (46) 26 667110
Prefabricated Wood Building Mfr
N.A.I.C.S.: 321992

Hoju Unyu Co., Ltd.   (1)
160-20 Nougawa, Wakayama, 640-8481, Japan
Tel.: (81) 734644020
Container Boards Mfr & Distr
N.A.I.C.S.: 321920

Hokuyo Co., Ltd.   (1)
2-15-11 Uchikanda Showa Kanda Building 4th floor, Chiyoda-ku, Tokyo, 101-0047, Japan
Tel.: (81) 35 298 5631
Web Site: https://www.hokuyo2006.co.jp
Industrial Supplies Whslr
N.A.I.C.S.: 423840

Hokuyo Koeki Co., Ltd.   (1)
7th Floor Musashi-Kosugi Building 1-403 Kosugi-cho, Nakahara-ku, Kawasaki, 211-0063, Kanagawa, Japan
Tel.: (81) 447114480
Textile Products Mfr
N.A.I.C.S.: 314999

Kadoma Shiki Co., Ltd.   (1)
117 Kuwazai, Kadoma, 571-0035, Osaka, Japan
Tel.: (81) 72 881 2791
Corrugated Paper Product Mfr
N.A.I.C.S.: 322211

Kanesawa Shiki Kogyo Co., Ltd.   (1)
2364-1 Honyonezaki, Naka, 311-0101, Ibaraki, Japan
Tel.: (81) 29 295 4801
Corrugated Paper Product Mfr
N.A.I.C.S.: 322211

Kansai Hoju Unyu Co., Ltd.   (1)
1132 Hanyuno, Habikino, Osaka, 583-0866, Japan
Tel.: (81) 729374011
Container Boards Mfr & Distr
N.A.I.C.S.: 321920

Kanto Tohun Co., Ltd.   (1)
12-9 Kougouki, Kazo, 347-0111, Japan
Tel.: (81) 480538131
Passenger Vehicle Transportation Services
N.A.I.C.S.: 488999

Kyoshinsha Co., Ltd.   (1)
6-48-18 Higashi-mukojima, Sumida, Tokyo, 131-0032, Japan
Tel.: (81) 3 3213 6811
Corrugated Paper Product Mfr
N.A.I.C.S.: 322211

Nansai Shiki Co., Ltd.   (1)
1285-2 Kanamuro-higashi, Iwatsuki-ku, Saitama, 339-0001, Japan
Tel.: (81) 48 794 1616
Corrugated Paper Product Mfr
N.A.I.C.S.: 322211

Nichiei Shikou Co., Ltd.   (1)
1265 Okubo-cho, Nishi-ku, Hamamatsu, 432-8006, Shizuoka, Japan
Tel.: (81) 534854433
Textile Products Mfr
N.A.I.C.S.: 314999

Ota Danboru Co., Ltd.   (1)
280-11 Nitta-ichinokuracho, Ota, 373-0306, Gunma, Japan
Tel.: (81) 276 57 7166
Corrugated Paper Product Mfr
N.A.I.C.S.: 322211

Prime Truss Co., Ltd.   (1)
2nd floor of MA Building 2-15-12 Kiba, Koto-ku, Tokyo, 135-0042, Japan
Tel.: (81) 33 643 3310
Web Site: https://www.primetruss.com
Construction Services
N.A.I.C.S.: 236220

Sapporo Tohun Co., Ltd.   (1)
2-755-5 Shinko-chuo, Ishikari, 016-3242, Japan
Tel.: (81) 133645313
Vehicle Inspection Services
N.A.I.C.S.: 811198

Sekiya Co., Ltd.   (1)
735-1 Jyoka-2-chome, Gosen, 959-1758, Niigata, Japan
Tel.: (81) 250586184
Textile Products Mfr
N.A.I.C.S.: 314999

Sendai Shiki Kogyo Co., Ltd.   (1)
180 Shinden Shimono-go, Iwanuma, 989-2421, Miyagi, Japan   (100%)
Tel.: (81) 22 322 4041
Web Site: http://www.tomoku.co.jp
Corrugated Paper Product Mfr
N.A.I.C.S.: 322211

Sendai Tohun Co., Ltd.   (1)
80 Shimono-Go-Shinden, Iwanuma, 989-2421, Japan
Tel.: (81) 223242321
Container Boards Mfr & Distr

TOMOKU CO., LTD.

Tomoku Co., Ltd.—(Continued)
N.A.I.C.S.: 321920

Shimizu Danboru Co., Ltd. (1)
180 Nagasakishinden, Shimizu, Shizuoka, 424-0064, Japan
Tel.: (81) 543 45 1155
Corrugated Paper Product Mfr
N.A.I.C.S.: 322211

Southland Box Company (1)
4201 Fruitland Ave, Vernon, CA 90058 **(100%)**
Tel.: (323) 583-2231
Web Site: https://www.southlandbox.com
Sales Range: $50-74.9 Million
Emp.: 130
Corrugated Paper Mfr
N.A.I.C.S.: 322211
Hideya Takagi (Pres)

Sweden House Co., Ltd. (1)
Carrot Tower 23F 4-1-1 Taishido, Setagaya-ku, Tokyo, 131 0004, Japan **(87.5%)**
Tel.: (81) 35 430 7620
Web Site: https://www.swedenhouse.co.jp
Emp.: 150
Sale & Construction of Swedish Style Houses
N.A.I.C.S.: 321999
Sumio Mitani (Mng Dir & Exec Officer)

Sweden House Reform Co., Ltd. (1)
7th Floor Musashi-Kosugi Building 1-403 Kosugi-cho, Nakahara-ku, Kawasaki, 211-0063, Kanagawa, Japan
Tel.: (81) 447114158
Construction Services
N.A.I.C.S.: 236220

Tamazen Co., Ltd. (1)
14KT Building 3F 1-17-2 Marunouchi, Naka-ku, Nagoya, 460-0002, Aichi, Japan
Tel.: (81) 522111030
Web Site: https://www.tamazen.co.jp
Emp.: 82
Detached House Construction Distr
N.A.I.C.S.: 236115

Tohun Co., Ltd. (1)
GM Omiya Building 8F 1-49-8 Dotemachi, Omiya Ward, Saitama, 330-8541, Japan
Tel.: (81) 486473381
Web Site: https://tohun.co.jp
Emp.: 686
Passenger Vehicle Transportation Services
N.A.I.C.S.: 488999

Tohun Logitem Co., Ltd. (1)
8th Floor GM Omiya Building Dote-cho 1-49-8, Omiya-ku, Saitama, 330-8541, Japan
Tel.: (81) 487294661
Transportation Services
N.A.I.C.S.: 484110

Tohun Ryutsu Service Co., Ltd. (1)
2-755-5 Shinko-chuo, Ishikari, 016-3242, Hokkaido, Japan
Tel.: (81) 133 64 5312
Automotive Inspection Services
N.A.I.C.S.: 488490

Tohun Service Co., Ltd. (1)
GM Omiya Building 8F 1-49-8 Dotecho, Omiya-ku, Saitama, 330-8541, Japan **(61.5%)**
Tel.: (81) 48 647 3381
Web Site: https://www.tohun.co.jp
Emp.: 650
Logistics Consulting Servies
N.A.I.C.S.: 541614

Tohun Traffic Co., Ltd. (1)
12-9 Kouguki, Kazo, 347-0111, Saitama, Japan
Tel.: (81) 480538131
Transportation Services
N.A.I.C.S.: 484110

Tokachi Package Co., Ltd. (1)
145-1 Shihoro-nishi-nisen, Kato, Shihoro, 080-1253, Hokkaido, Japan
Tel.: (81) 1564 5 2016
Corrugated Paper Product Mfr
N.A.I.C.S.: 322211

Tomoku Co., Ltd. - Aomori Works (1)
513 Hazirosawada, Aomori, 038-0058, Japan
Tel.: (81) 17 788 1191
Corrugated Paper Product Mfr
N.A.I.C.S.: 322211

Tomoku Co., Ltd. - Atsugi Works (1)
3008 Kamiechi, Atsugi, 243-0801, Kanagawa, Japan
Tel.: (81) 46 284 2525
Corrugated Paper Product Mfr
N.A.I.C.S.: 322211

Tomoku Co., Ltd. - Chiba Folding Carton Works (1)
Chonan Industrial Complex 1-15 Miharadai Chonan-machi, Chosei-gun, Chiba, 297-0143, Japan
Tel.: (81) 47 546 1170
Web Site: http://www.tomoku.co.jp
Corrugated Paper Product Mfr
N.A.I.C.S.: 322211

Tomoku Co., Ltd. - Hamamatsu Works (1)
2402 Nippashi-cho, Hamamatsu, 432-8058, Shizuoka, Japan
Tel.: (81) 53 441 6131
Corrugated Paper Product Mfr
N.A.I.C.S.: 322211

Tomoku Co., Ltd. - Iwatsuki Works (1)
839-1 Kanamuro, Iwatsuki, Saitama, 339-8566, Japan
Tel.: (81) 48 794 3111
Corrugated Paper Product Mfr
N.A.I.C.S.: 322211
Shoichi Yamashita (Gen Mgr)

Tomoku Co., Ltd. - Kyushu Works (1)
360 Nagano Kiyama-cho, Miyaki-gun, Saga, 841-0202, Japan
Tel.: (81) 94 292 5111
Web Site: http://www.tomoku.co.jp
Corrugated Paper Product Mfr
N.A.I.C.S.: 322211

Tomoku Co., Ltd. - Niigata Works (1)
3-182-4 Higashiko Seiro-machi, Kitakanbara, Niigata, 957-0101, Japan
Tel.: (81) 25 256 2100
Corrugated Paper Product Mfr
N.A.I.C.S.: 322211

Tomoku Co., Ltd. - Osaka Works (1)
4-11 Fukadacho, Kadoma, 571-0042, Osaka, Japan
Tel.: (81) 6 6909 2131
Corrugated Paper Product Mfr
N.A.I.C.S.: 322211
Hidetoshi Murai (Gen Mgr)

Tomoku Co., Ltd. - Sapporo Works (1)
4-157-2 Zenibako, Otaru, 061-3271, Hokkaido, Japan
Tel.: (81) 133 72 5151
Corrugated Paper Product Mfr
N.A.I.C.S.: 322211

Tomoku Co., Ltd. - Sendai Works (1)
155 Shinden Shimono-go, Iwanuma, 989-2421, Miyagi, Japan
Tel.: (81) 223 22 1021
Corrugated Paper Product Mfr
N.A.I.C.S.: 322211

Tomoku Co., Ltd. - Tatebayashi Works (1)
906-1 Nobe-machi, Tatebayashi, 374-0047, Gunma, Japan
Tel.: (81) 276 74 9111
Corrugated Paper Product Mfr
N.A.I.C.S.: 322211
Takashi Arai (Gen Mgr)

Tomoku Co., Ltd. - Tomoprest Works (1)
238-1 Oowa Meiwa-machi, Oura, 370-0718, Gunma, Japan
Tel.: (81) 276 70 3071
Corrugated Paper Product Mfr
N.A.I.C.S.: 322211

Tomoku Co., Ltd. - Yamagata Works (1)
3-1410 Tachiyagawa, Yamagata, 990-2251, Japan
Tel.: (81) 23 686 2251
Corrugated Paper Product Mfr
N.A.I.C.S.: 322211

Tomoku Hus AB (1)
Timmervagen 50, 793 40, Insjon, Sweden
Tel.: (46) 24744000
Web Site: https://www.tomokuhus.se
Emp.: 18
Mfr of Wooden Components for Housing
N.A.I.C.S.: 321999
Olle Deras (Mgr-Fin)

Tomoku Vietnam Co., Ltd. (1)
Lot B_5BI_CN Road DE4&NE5A, My Phuoc IP 3, Ben Cat, Binh Duong, Vietnam
Tel.: (84) 2742220435
Textile Products Mfr
N.A.I.C.S.: 314999
Genzo Yoshitomi (Gen Mgr-Admin Dept)

Toshin Package Co., Ltd. (1)
516-1 Kitaokuwa, Kazo, 349-1147, Saitama, Japan
Tel.: (81) 48 031 7260
Web Site: https://www.toshinpackage.co.jp
Emp.: 98
Corrugated Paper Product Mfr
N.A.I.C.S.: 322211

TOMONY HOLDINGS, INC.

7 1 Kamei cho, Takamatsu, 760 0050, Kagawa, Japan
Tel.: (81) 878120102
Web Site: https://www.tomony-hd.co.jp
Year Founded: 2010
8600—(TKS)
Rev.: $580,470,370
Assets: $31,797,087,720
Liabilities: $29,963,037,460
Net Worth: $1,834,050,260
Earnings: $36,355
Fiscal Year-end: 03/31/24
Bank Holding Company
N.A.I.C.S.: 551111
Shinichi Kakiuchi (Chm)

Subsidiaries:

TOMONY Card, Inc. (1)
1-37 Showa-cho, Tokushima, 770-0942, Tokushima Prefecture, Japan
Tel.: (81) 886242244
Emp.: 28
Commercial Banking Services
N.A.I.C.S.: 522110

The Kagawa Bank, Ltd. (1)
6-1 Kamei-cho, Kagawa, 760-8576, Japan
Tel.: (81) 878613121
Web Site: http://www.kagawabank.co.jp
Sales Range: $400-449.9 Million
Emp.: 1,200
Banking Services
N.A.I.C.S.: 522110
Seiji Toyama (Chm)

The Tokushima Bank, Ltd. (1)
1 16 Tomidahama, Tokushima, 770 8648, Japan
Tel.: (81) 886233111
Emp.: 1,000
Banking Services
N.A.I.C.S.: 522110
Hirofumi Hunto (Gen Mgr)

Tokugin Capital Co., Ltd. (1)
1-11 Honmachi Nishi Terashima, Tokushima, 770-0942, Japan
Tel.: (81) 886794321
Investment Banking Services
N.A.I.C.S.: 523150

TOMRA SYSTEMS ASA

Tel.: (47) 66799100 NO
Web Site: https://www.tomra.com
Year Founded: 1972
TMRAF—(OTCIQ)
Solid Waste Recycling
N.A.I.C.S.: 423930
Espen Gundersen (Deputy CEO & CFO)

INTERNATIONAL PUBLIC

Subsidiaries:

Bottlecycler Australia Pty. Ltd. (1)
7A Rocklea Dr, Port Melbourne, 3207, VIC, Australia
Tel.: (61) 1300306039
Web Site: https://bottlecycler.com
Glass Recycling Mfr
N.A.I.C.S.: 333248

OY Tomra AB (1) **(100%)**
Tel.: (358) 98254820
Web Site: http://www.tomra.fi
Sales Range: $25-49.9 Million
Emp.: 26
Industrial Machinery & Equipment Whslr
N.A.I.C.S.: 423830

Odenberg B.V. (1)
Zeemanlaan 15, NL-3401 MV, IJsselstein, Netherlands
Tel.: (31) 30 6006155
Fruit & Vegetable Processing Equipment Mfr
N.A.I.C.S.: 333111

Subsidiary (Non-US):

Tomra Sorting Ltd. Ireland (2)
4034 Kingswood Avenue Citywest Business Campus, Citywest, Dublin, 24, Ireland
Tel.: (353) 14136200
Sensor-Based Food Sorting Machinery Mfr
N.A.I.C.S.: 333241

QVision AS (1)
Ryensvingen 11B, 0680, Oslo, Norway **(100%)**
Tel.: (47) 23302300
Sales Range: $25-49.9 Million
Emp.: 3
Industrial Machinery Mfr
N.A.I.C.S.: 333248

TOMRA Collection Solutions Taiwan Co., Ltd. (1)
3F No 118 Sec 2 Zhongshan Rd, Guiren District Southern Taiwan, Tainan City, 711, Taiwan
Tel.: (886) 62305221
Can & Bottle Recycling Services
N.A.I.C.S.: 423930

Tomra Brasil Solucoes EM segregacao Ltda. (1)
Rua Fernandes Moreira 883 Chac Sto Antonio, Sao Paulo, 04716-002, Brazil
Tel.: (55) 1134763500
Can & Bottle Recycling Services
N.A.I.C.S.: 423930

Tomra Butikksystemer AS (1)
PO Box 362, 1372, Asker, Norway **(100%)**
Tel.: (47) 66799100
Web Site: http://www.tomra.com
Sales Range: $50-74.9 Million
Emp.: 230
Industrial Machinery Mfr
N.A.I.C.S.: 333248

Tomra Canada Inc (1)
20500 Av Clark-Graham, Baie-d Urfe, Montreal, H9X 4B6, QC, Canada
Tel.: (514) 457-4177
Web Site: https://tomracollectioncanada.com
Sales Range: $25-49.9 Million
Emp.: 80
Industrial Machinery & Equipment Whslr
N.A.I.C.S.: 423830

Tomra Collection Portugal, Unipessoal Ltda. (1)
Rua Mira Parque 1, 2655-482, Ericeira, Portugal
Tel.: (351) 261131010
Web Site: https://collection-pt.tomra.com
Automatic Machine Mfr & Distr
N.A.I.C.S.: 333517

Tomra Collection Romania S.R.L. (1)
Strada Barbu Vacarescu Nr 164A Etaj 3 Sector 2, Bucharest, Romania
Tel.: (40) 4915122659374
Web Site: https://collection-ro.tomra.com
Automatic Beverage Packaging System Services
N.A.I.C.S.: 812310

AND PRIVATE COMPANIES — TOMRA SYSTEMS ASA

Tomra Collection Slovakia s.r.o. (1)
Prologist Park Senec DC 8 Highway 5019/26, 903 01, Senec, Slovakia
Tel.: (421) 232343920
Web Site: https://collection-sk.tomra.com
Can & Bottle Recycling Services
N.A.I.C.S.: 423930

Tomra Collection Turkey Makine Teknoloji Sanayi ve Ticaret Anonim Sirketi (1)
Atalar Mah Canakkale Cad Can Blok 61/A, Kartal, 34862, Istanbul, Turkiye
Tel.: (90) 2167661227
Automatic Machine Mfr & Distr
N.A.I.C.S.: 333517

Tomra Environmental Protection Technology (Xiamen) Co.Ltd. (1)
6 E/F No 8 Xinfeng Road Torch High-Tech Industrial Development Zone, Xiamen, 361006, China
Tel.: (86) 592 5720780
Web Site: http://www.tomra.com
Emp.: 2
Industrial Machinery Mfr
N.A.I.C.S.: 333248

Tomra Europe AS (1)
Drengsrudhagen 2, 1385, Asker, Norway (100%)
Tel.: (47) 66799100
Holding Company
N.A.I.C.S.: 551112

Subsidiary (Non-US):

Tomra AG (2)
Holzliwisenstrasse 12, 8604, Volketswil, Switzerland
Tel.: (41) 449475500
Web Site: http://www.tomra.com
Office Equipment Whslr
N.A.I.C.S.: 423420

Tomra Leergutsysteme GmbH (2)
Campus 21 Businesspark Wien Sud Liebermannstrasse F03 402, 2345, Brunn am Gebirge, Lower Austria, Austria
Tel.: (43) 16655400
Sales Range: $25-49.9 Million
Emp.: 20
Automatic Vending Machine Mfr
N.A.I.C.S.: 333310

Tomra System AS (2)
Brogrenen 3, 2635, Ishoj, Denmark
Tel.: (45) 4 356 5050
Web Site: https://www.tomra.com
Sales Range: $25-49.9 Million
Emp.: 35
Vending Machine Operators
N.A.I.C.S.: 445132

Tomra Systems AB (2)
Djupdalsvagen 32, PO Box 66, 192 51, Sollentuna, Sweden (100%)
Tel.: (46) 86258000
Web Site: http://www.tomra.se
Sales Range: $25-49.9 Million
Emp.: 20
Industrial Machinery & Equipment Whslr
N.A.I.C.S.: 423830

Tomra Systems B.V. (2)
Laan van Malkenschoten 80, 7333 NP, Apeldoorn, Netherlands
Tel.: (31) 555998844
Web Site: https://www.tomra.nl
Sales Range: $25-49.9 Million
Emp.: 100
Industrial Machinery & Equipment Whslr
N.A.I.C.S.: 423830

Tomra Systems GmbH (2)
Felix-Wankel-Strasse 9, 40764, Langenfeld, Germany (100%)
Tel.: (49) 217349900
Web Site: https://www.tomra.com
Sales Range: $25-49.9 Million
Emp.: 80
Automatic Vending Machine Mfr
N.A.I.C.S.: 333310
Thomas Lostegard *(Mng Dir)*

Tomra Systems Ltd (2)
Unit 13 Apex Business Centre, Boscombe Road, Dunstable, LU5 4SB, United Kingdom (100%)
Tel.: (44) 8004346156
Web Site: http://www.tomra.com
Sales Range: $25-49.9 Million
Emp.: 11
Industrial Machinery & Equipment Whslr
N.A.I.C.S.: 423830

Tomra Systems N.V. (2)
Hagelberg 31, B-2250, Olen, Belgium (100%)
Tel.: (32) 33092145
Web Site: https://www.tomra.be
Sales Range: $25-49.9 Million
Emp.: 12
Industrial Machinery & Equipment Whslr
N.A.I.C.S.: 423830

Tomra Systems SAS (2)
Centre Initia Parc de la Porte Nord Rue Christophe Colomb, 62700, Bruay-la-Buissiere, France
Tel.: (33) 638924465
Web Site: http://www.tomra.com
Industrial Machinery Mfr
N.A.I.C.S.: 333248

Tomra s.r.o. (2)
Mochovska 1671, Celakovice, 250 88, Prague, Czech Republic
Tel.: (420) 32 699 1089
Web Site: http://www.tomra.orwak.cz
Sales Range: $25-49.9 Million
Emp.: 10
Electronic Parts & Equipment Whslr
N.A.I.C.S.: 423690

Tomra Food (Valencia) S.L. (1)
Carrer Arquitecte Gaudi Num 45, Roses, 17480, Girona, Spain
Tel.: (34) 972154373
Automatic Machine Mfr & Distr
N.A.I.C.S.: 333517

Tomra Production AS (1)
PO Box 278, 1372, Asker, Norway (100%)
Tel.: (47) 66799100
Web Site: http://www.tomra.com
Sales Range: $50-74.9 Million
Emp.: 250
Industrial Machinery Mfr
N.A.I.C.S.: 333248

Tomra Recycling Technology (Xiamen) Co. Ltd. (1)
No 8 Xinfeng 2nd Road, Torch Hi-tech Industrial Zone, Xiamen, 361006, Fujian, China
Tel.: (86) 5925720780
Can & Bottle Recycling Services
N.A.I.C.S.: 423930

Tomra Sorting AS (1)
Drengsrudhagen 2, PO Box 278, 1385, Asker, Norway
Tel.: (47) 66752440
Web Site: http://www.tomrasorting.com
Automatic Sorting Sensor Mfr
N.A.I.C.S.: 334511

Subsidiary (Non-US):

Tomra Sorting (Pty) Ltd. (2)
Unit 7, West Square Office Park 407 West Avenue, Ferndale, 2194, South Africa
Tel.: (27) 879413840
Mining Machinery & Equipment Mfr
N.A.I.C.S.: 333131

Tomra Sorting , S.L. (2)
C Arquitecte Gaudi 45, Roses, 17480, Girona, Spain
Tel.: (34) 972154373
Web Site: https://www.tomra.com
Automated Recycling Sorting Systems Mfr
N.A.I.C.S.: 333248

Tomra Sorting Co,. Ltd. (2)
7th Fl 454 Chungang-ro, Deokyang-gu, Goyang, 10486, Kyeonggi-do, Korea (South)
Tel.: (82) 319387171
Web Site: http://www.tomra.com
Automatic Sensor Sorting Machine Mfr
N.A.I.C.S.: 334511

Tomra Sorting GmbH (2)
Feldstrasse 128, 22880, Wedel, Germany
Tel.: (49) 410318880
Web Site: https://www.tomra.com
Sorting Machine Sensor Mfr
N.A.I.C.S.: 333248

Tomra Sorting GmbH (2)
Feldstrasse 128, Wedel, 22880, Schleswig-Holstein, Germany
Tel.: (49) 410318880
Sales Range: $25-49.9 Million
Emp.: 13
Automatic Sorting Machine Sensor Mfr
N.A.I.C.S.: 334511
Andreas Gohr *(Project Mgr & Mgr-Sls-Americas)*

Tomra Sorting Inc. (2)
Unit 8 - 19122 27th Ave, Surrey, V3S 5T1, BC, Canada
Tel.: (778) 242-9480
Web Site: http://www.tomra.com
Emp.: 5
Automatic Sorting Machine Sensor Mfr
N.A.I.C.S.: 334413

Tomra Sorting JLT (2)
Unit No 3702-21 floor No 37 Mayfair Executive Offices JLT, Jumeirah Business Center 2 Jumeirah Lake Towers, Dubai, United Arab Emirates
Tel.: (971) 4 374 5744
Web Site: http://www.titech.com
Automatic Sorting Machine Mfr
N.A.I.C.S.: 333248

Tomra Sorting K.K. (2)
3-2-5 Magamoto, Minato-ku, Saitama, 336-0033, Japan
Tel.: (81) 487113135
Web Site: https://www.tomra.com
Recyclable Material Whslr
N.A.I.C.S.: 423930

Tomra Sorting Ltd. (2)
Tomra House Centurion Way Meridian, Leicester, LE19 1WH, United Kingdom
Tel.: (44) 116 218 1430
Web Site: https://www.tomra.com
Sales Range: $25-49.9 Million
Automatic Sorting Sensor Machine Mfr
N.A.I.C.S.: 334511

Tomra Sorting S.r.l. (2)
Strada Martinella 74 A/B, Alberi, 43124, Parma, Italy
Tel.: (39) 0521681082
Web Site: https://www.tomra.com
Food Product Machinery Mfr
N.A.I.C.S.: 333241

Subsidiary (Domestic):

Tomra Sorting Solutions AS (2)
Drengsrudhagen 2, Asker, 1372, Norway
Tel.: (47) 66 79 91 00
Web Site: http://www.tomra.com
Food Shorting Machinery Mfr
N.A.I.C.S.: 333241

Subsidiary (Non-US):

Tomra Sorting Solutions SRL (2)
Veas Minerva - 40 Avenue des Gardians, 34160, Castries, France
Tel.: (33) 467 56 39 66
Web Site: http://www.tomrasorting.com
Sales Range: $25-49.9 Million
Emp.: 1
Industrial Machinery Mfr
N.A.I.C.S.: 333248

Tomra Sorting sp. z o.o. (2)
Ul Ligocka 103, 40-568, Katowice, Poland
Tel.: (48) 323526093
Web Site: https://www.tomra.com
Sensor Sorting System Mfr
N.A.I.C.S.: 333248

Tomra Sorting India Private Limited (1)
Jain Heights Solus Floor 10 Office 10E No2 1st cross J C Road, Bengaluru, 560 027, Karnataka, India
Tel.: (91) 8022224223901
Can & Bottle Recycling Services
N.A.I.C.S.: 423930

Tomra Sorting N.V. (1)
Research Park Haasrode 1622 Romeinse Straat 20, 3001, Leuven, Belgium
Tel.: (32) 16396396
Food Mfr & Distr
N.A.I.C.S.: 311412

Tomra of North America, Inc. (1)
1 Corporate Dr Ste 710, Shelton, CT 06484 (100%)
Tel.: (203) 447-8800
Web Site: http://www.tomranorthamerica.com
Holding Company; Regional Managing Office; Waste Collection, Recycling Services & Recycling Reverse Vending Machine Mfr
N.A.I.C.S.: 551112

Subsidiary (Domestic):

BICS LLC (2)
57 Maple Ave, Thomaston, CT 06787
Tel.: (860) 283-1561
Web Site: http://www.bics.net
Computer Networking Services
N.A.I.C.S.: 541519

Camco Recycling Inc. (2)
100 Fair St, Dillonvale, OH 43917-0656
Tel.: (740) 769-2366
Web Site: http://www.tomra.com
Recyclable Material Whslr
N.A.I.C.S.: 423930

Orwak LLC (2)
480 Lordship Blvd Ste 1, Stratford, CT 06615-7149
Tel.: (203) 447-8787
Web Site: http://www.orwak.us
Sales Range: $25-49.9 Million
Emp.: 5
Industrial Machinery & Equipment Whslr
N.A.I.C.S.: 423830
J. Mark Lanning *(Pres)*

Returnable Services LLC (2)
150 Mt Vernon Ave, Augusta, ME 04330
Tel.: (207) 623-2944
Web Site: http://www.returnableservices.com
Sales Range: $25-49.9 Million
Emp.: 50
Packaging Box & Bag Mfr
N.A.I.C.S.: 322220

Synergistics LLC (2)
4820 Holtz Dr, Wixom, MI 48393
Tel.: (248) 529-2400
Web Site: http://www.synergisticsllc.com
Logistics Management Services
N.A.I.C.S.: 541614

Subsidiary (Non-US):

Tomra Metro, LLC (2)
Tel.: (315) 656-7238
Web Site: http://www.tomranorthamerica.com
Recyclable Waste Collection & Material Recovery Services
N.A.I.C.S.: 562920

Subsidiary (Domestic):

Tomra NY Recycling LLC (2)
5923 Loomis Rd, Farmington, NY 14425
Tel.: (585) 742-3790
Web Site: http://www.tomra.com
Recyclable Material Whslr
N.A.I.C.S.: 423930

Subsidiary (Domestic):

Tomra Mass LLC (3)
260 Kenneth Welch Dr, Lakeville, MA 02347-1348 (100%)
Tel.: (508) 946-8184
Recyclable Material Whslr
N.A.I.C.S.: 423930

Subsidiary (Domestic):

Tomra/CBSI, LLC (2)
2525 SE Stubb St, Milwaukie, OR 97222 (100%)
Tel.: (503) 236-8906
Recycling Reverse Vending Machine Mfr
N.A.I.C.S.: 333310

UBCR LLC (2)
4820 Holtz Dr, Wixom, MI 48393
Tel.: (248) 529-2600
Web Site: https://www.ubcrllc.com
Sales Range: $25-49.9 Million
Metal Container Mfr
N.A.I.C.S.: 332439
Nickolas Kronsbein *(Gen Mgr)*

WESTERN NY BICS LLP (2)
4284 Walden Ave, Lancaster, NY 14086

TOMRA SYSTEMS ASA

Tomra Systems ASA—(Continued)
Tel.: (716) 685-7400
Garbage Collection Services
N.A.I.C.S.: 562111

TOMSK RASPREDELIT KOMP AP
Pr Kirova 36T, Omsk, 634041, Russia
Tel.: (7) 3822277777
Web Site: http://www.trk.tom.ru
TORSP—(RUS)
Sales Range: Less than $1 Million
Electric Power Distribution Services
N.A.I.C.S.: 221122

TOMSKPROMSTROYBANK PJSC
Frunze Street 90, 634061, Tomsk, Russia
Tel.: (7) 3822265931
Web Site:
http://www.tpsbank.tomsk.ru
Financial Lending Services
N.A.I.C.S.: 522220
Nadezhda Yu Kaydash *(Chm-Mgmt Bd)*

TOMSON GROUP LIMITED
Rooms 1507-12 15th Floor Wing On Centre 111 Connaught Road, Hong Kong, China (Hong Kong)
Tel.: (852) 28481668
Web Site: http://www.tomson.com.hk
0258—(HKG)
Rev.: $58,656,248
Assets: $2,396,402,535
Liabilities: $776,313,330
Net Worth: $1,620,089,205
Earnings: $2,391,263
Emp.: 400
Fiscal Year-end: 12/31/22
Property Development & Investing Services
N.A.I.C.S.: 531312
Yuen Lee *(Sec)*

Subsidiaries:

Shanghai Tomson Huangpu Real Estate Development Co., Ltd. (1)
No 188 Zhangyang Rd, Shanghai, 200122, China
Tel.: (86) 2158766858
Sales Range: $50-74.9 Million
Emp.: 80
Real Estate Property Development Services
N.A.I.C.S.: 531210

Tomson (China) Limited (1)
Rooms 1507-12 15th Floor Wing On Centre 111 Connaught Road, Central, China (Hong Kong)
Tel.: (852) 28481668
Web Site: https://www.tomson.com.hk
Sales Range: $50-74.9 Million
Emp.: 20
Investment Holding Services
N.A.I.C.S.: 523999

Tomson Golf (Shanghai) Limited (1)
No 1 Longdong Avenue, Pudong, Shanghai, 201203, China
Tel.: (86) 2158338888
Web Site: http://www.tomson-golf.com
Sales Range: $150-199.9 Million
Emp.: 300
18 Hole Golf Course & Club Operation Services
N.A.I.C.S.: 713910

TOMTOM N.V.
De Ruijterkade 154, 1011 AC, Amsterdam, Netherlands
Tel.: (31) 207575000
Web Site: https://www.tomtom.com
Year Founded: 1991
TOM2—(EUR)
Rev.: $578,829,052
Assets: $871,468,811
Liabilities: $656,051,155
Net Worth: $215,417,656
Earnings: ($110,873,084)
Emp.: 3,010
Fiscal Year-end: 12/31/22
Personal Navigation Products Mfr
N.A.I.C.S.: 334511
Harold Goddijn *(CEO & Member-Mgmt Bd)*

Subsidiaries:

Fratino B.V (1)
De Ruyterkade 154, 1011 AC, Amsterdam, Netherlands
Tel.: (31) 20 757 5000
Automobile Parts Mfr
N.A.I.C.S.: 336390

Tele Atlas BV (1)
Reitscheweg 7F, NL 5232 BX, 's-Hertogenbosch, Netherlands
Tel.: (31) 736402121
Sales Range: $350-399.9 Million
Emp.: 1,628
Holding Company; Digital Geographic Database Developer
N.A.I.C.S.: 551112

Subsidiary (Domestic):

Bene-Fin B.V. (2)
Reitscheweg 7F, NL 5232 BX, 's-Hertogenbosch, Netherlands
Tel.: (31) 73 640 2121
Sales Range: $25-49.9 Million
Emp.: 52
Mapping Software Publisher
N.A.I.C.S.: 513210

Affiliate (Non-US):

PT Tele Atlas Navindo (2)
Menara Sudirman 12th Floor, Jl Jend Sudirman Kav 60, 12190, Jakarta, Indonesia
Tel.: (62) 215213986
Sales Range: $25-49.9 Million
Emp.: 17
Management Consulting Services
N.A.I.C.S.: 541618

Subsidiary (Domestic):

Tele Atlas Datas (2)
Reitscheweg 7F, NL 5232 BX, 's-Hertogenbosch, Netherlands
Tel.: (31) 736402121
Sales Range: $25-49.9 Million
Emp.: 52
Mapping Software Publisher
N.A.I.C.S.: 513210

Subsidiary (Non-US):

Tele Atlas Germany (2)
Am Neuen Horizont 1, 31177, Harsum, Germany
Tel.: (49) 51274080
Digital Map Data
N.A.I.C.S.: 541360

Tele Atlas Polska Sp. Z.o.o. (2)
2 Ludna Str, 00-406, Warsaw, Poland
Tel.: (48) 22 594 36 36
Web Site: http://www.tomtom.com
Sales Range: $25-49.9 Million
Emp.: 24
Digital Map Data
N.A.I.C.S.: 541360

Tele Atlas Russia (2)
Kazakova ulitsa 6 st 1, 105064, Moscow, Russia
Tel.: (7) 4955850916
Sales Range: $10-24.9 Million
Emp.: 26
Digital Mapping Products
N.A.I.C.S.: 541370

Subsidiary (Domestic):

Tele Atlas Survey B.V. (2)
Reitscheweg 7F, NL 5232 BX, 's-Hertogenbosch, Netherlands
Tel.: (31) 736402121
Sales Range: $25-49.9 Million
Emp.: 52
Mapping Software Publisher
N.A.I.C.S.: 513210

Subsidiary (Non-US):

Tele Atlas Taiwan Co. Ltd (2)
3rd Floor 11 No 79 Sec 1Hsin Tai Wu Rd Hsichih, Taipei, Taiwan
Tel.: (886) 286432680
Web Site: http://www.teleatlas.com
Sales Range: $25-49.9 Million
Emp.: 20
Data Processing Hosting & Related Services
N.A.I.C.S.: 518210

Tele Atlas UK (2)
Chiswick Place, 272 Gunnersbury Avenue, London, W4 5QB, United Kingdom
Tel.: (44) 2089963800
Sales Range: $10-24.9 Million
Emp.: 50
Digital Map Data
N.A.I.C.S.: 541360

Tele Atlas Malaysia SDN. BHD (1)
Uoa Ii, Kuala Lumpur, Malaysia
Tel.: (60) 3 2166 4219
Sales Range: $25-49.9 Million
Emp.: 20
Automotive Accessories Mfr
N.A.I.C.S.: 336390

TomTom Asia Ltd. (1)
32nd Fl No 66 Sec 1 Jhongsiao W Rd, 10018, Taipei, Taiwan **(100%)**
Tel.: (886) 223315889
Sales Range: $25-49.9 Million
Emp.: 90
Search Detection Navigation Guidance Aeronautical & Nautical System & Instrument Mfr
N.A.I.C.S.: 334511

TomTom Development Germany GmbH (1)
Inselstrase 22, Leipzig, 4103, Germany
Tel.: (49) 341244950
Web Site: http://www.tomtom.com
Automobile Parts Mfr
N.A.I.C.S.: 336390

TomTom Inc (1)
150 Baker Ave Ext, Concord, MA 01742 **(100%)**
Tel.: (978) 287-9555
Web Site: http://www.tomtom.com
Sales Range: $25-49.9 Million
Emp.: 60
Search Detection Navigation Guidance Aeronautical & Nautical System & Instrument Mfr
N.A.I.C.S.: 334511

TomTom Inc. (1)
11 Lafayette St, Lebanon, NH 03766-1445
Tel.: (603) 643-0330
Digital Mapping Products
N.A.I.C.S.: 541360
Charles Cautley *(Mng Dir)*

TomTom International BV. (1)
De Ruijterkade 154, 1011 AC, Amsterdam, Netherlands **(100%)**
Tel.: (31) 208500800
Web Site: https://www.tomtom.com
Sales Range: $50-74.9 Million
Emp.: 150
Search Detection Navigation Guidance Aeronautical & Nautical System & Instrument Mfr
N.A.I.C.S.: 334511

TomTom Places B.V (1)
Oosterdoksstraat 114, Amsterdam, 1011 DK, Netherlands
Tel.: (31) 882456222
Web Site: http://www.places.tomtom.com
Automobile Parts Mfr
N.A.I.C.S.: 336390

TomTom Places Development B.V (1)
Oosterdoksstraat 114, Amsterdam, 1011 DK, Netherlands
Tel.: (31) 882456222
Sales Range: $25-49.9 Million
Emp.: 32
Navigation Device Mfr
N.A.I.C.S.: 334511

TomTom Polska Sp. Z.o.o (1)
Marynarska 15, Poland, 02-674, Poland
Tel.: (48) 225943616
Sales Range: $50-74.9 Million
Emp.: 200
Automobile Parts Mfr
N.A.I.C.S.: 336390

TomTom Sales BV (1)
Oosterdokstraat 114, 1011 DK, Amsterdam, Netherlands **(100%)**
Tel.: (31) 208500800
Search Detection Navigation Guidance Aeronautical & Nautical System & Instrument Mfr
N.A.I.C.S.: 334511

TomTom Software Ltd. (1)
20th Fl Euston Tower 286 Euston Rd, NW1 2AE, London, United Kingdom - England **(100%)**
Tel.: (44) 2073875444
Web Site: https://www.tomtom.com
Software Publisher
N.A.I.C.S.: 511210

TomTom Treasury I B.V (1)
Oosterdoksstraat 114, Amsterdam, 1011 DK, Netherlands
Tel.: (31) 207575000
Automobile Parts Mfr
N.A.I.C.S.: 336390
Harold Goddijn *(Mng Dir)*

TomTom Work GmbH (1)
Maximilianallee 4, 04129, Leipzig, Germany **(100%)**
Tel.: (49) 341244950
Web Site: http://www.tomtomwork.com
Sales Range: $25-49.9 Million
Emp.: 50
Custom Computer Programming Services
N.A.I.C.S.: 541511

ilocal International BV (1)
Wijersstraat 1, 3811 MZ, Amersfoort, Netherlands
Tel.: (31) 384600146
Sales Range: $25-49.9 Million
Emp.: 50
Online Information Services
N.A.I.C.S.: 519290

TOMY COMPANY, LTD.
7-9-10 Tateishi, Katsushika-ku, Tokyo, 124-8511, Japan
Tel.: (81) 356541548 JP
Web Site:
https://www.takaratomy.co.jp
Year Founded: 1924
7867—(TKS)
Rev.: $1,377,034,860
Assets: $1,098,925,720
Liabilities: $437,932,330
Net Worth: $660,993,390
Earnings: $64,830,880
Emp.: 2,476
Fiscal Year-end: 03/31/24
Toy Mfr & Sales
N.A.I.C.S.: 459120
Kantaro Tomiyama *(Chm & CEO)*

Subsidiaries:

Boon, Inc. (1)
5005 S Ash Ave Ste A-18, Tempe, AZ 85282-6882
Tel.: (480) 456-0224
Web Site: http://www.booninc.com
Sales Range: $10-24.9 Million
Emp.: 9
Toy Mfr
N.A.I.C.S.: 339930

T-ARTS Korea Company, Ltd. (1)
10th floor Sangjeong Building 163 Seongan-ro, Gangdong-gu, Seoul, 134-864, Korea (South)
Tel.: (82) 24875803
Web Site: https://www.tarts-korea.co.kr
Toy Product Mfr
N.A.I.C.S.: 339930

T-FIELDTEC Company, Ltd. (1)
3-19-3 Tateishi, Katsushika-ku, Tokyo, Japan
Tel.: (81) 336966018
Web Site: https://www.t-fieldtec.co.jp
Toy Product Mfr
N.A.I.C.S.: 339930

AND PRIVATE COMPANIES

Tomy (Hong Kong) Ltd. (1)
Room 901-7 Tower 1 Enterprise Square 9 Sheung Yuet Road, Kowloon Bay, Kowloon, China (Hong Kong)
Tel.: (852) 27517239
Children Toys Distr
N.A.I.C.S.: 423920

Tomy (Shenzhen) Ltd. (1)
10F Wenjindu Customs Declaration Building, 1028 Dongmen South Road, Shenzhen, 518001, Guangdong, China
Tel.: (86) 75582287149
Children Toys Mfr
N.A.I.C.S.: 339930

Tomy (Thailand) Ltd. (1)
60/59 Moo 19 Tambol Klongnuang, Amphur, Khlong Luang, 12120, Pathumthani, Thailand
Tel.: (66) 25290680
Web Site: https://www.tomy-thailand.com
Sales Range: $400-449.9 Million
Emp.: 1,500
Toy Mfr
N.A.I.C.S.: 339930

Tomy France SARL (1)
Parc d'affaires internationales, 74160, Archamps, Haute-Savoie, France
Tel.: (33) 450820620
Web Site: http://www.tomy.fr
Sales Range: $25-49.9 Million
Emp.: 20
Children Toys & Games Distr
N.A.I.C.S.: 423920
Lionel Delisle (Gen Mgr)

Tomy International, Inc. (1)
2015 Spring Rd Ste 700, Oak Brook, IL 60523
Tel.: (630) 573-7200
Web Site: http://us.tomy.com
Sales Range: $400-449.9 Million
Emp.: 780
Design & Marketing of Toys & Infant Products
N.A.I.C.S.: 339930
Peter J. Henseler (Chm)

Subsidiary (Domestic):

The First Years Inc. (2)
45 Shawmut Rd Ste 3, Canton, MA 02021-1400
Tel.: (781) 828-2824
Web Site: http://www.thefirstyears.com
Sales Range: $75-99.9 Million
Emp.: 182
Infant & Toddler Products
N.A.I.C.S.: 423920

Subsidiary (Non-US):

Tomy International-Australia (2)
942 - 956 Taylors Rd, Dandenong, 3175, VIC, Australia (100%)
Tel.: (61) 397995500
Web Site: http://www.rc2corp.com
Sales Range: $150-199.9 Million
Emp.: 40
Mfr, Designer & Sales of Juvenile & Infant Products
N.A.I.C.S.: 423920

Tomy International-China (2)
RC2 Industrial Zone, Dongguan, China (100%)
Tel.: (86) 21735333
Web Site: http://www.rc2corp.com
Sales Range: $25-49.9 Million
Emp.: 50
Mfr, Designer & Sales of Juvenile & Infant Products
N.A.I.C.S.: 423920

Tomy International-Germany (2)
Oskar-Jager-Strasse 173 K4, 50825, Cologne, Germany (100%)
Tel.: (49) 2218014760
Web Site: https://de.tomy.com
Sales Range: $10-24.9 Million
Emp.: 7
Mfr, Designer & Sales of Juvenile & Infant Products
N.A.I.C.S.: 423920

Tomy International-Hong Kong (2)
Room 901-7 Tower 1 Enterprise Square 9 Sheung Yuet Road, Kowloon Bay, 81000, China (Hong Kong) (100%)
Tel.: (852) 27517239
Web Site: http://us.tomy.com
Sales Range: $150-199.9 Million
Mfr, Designer & Sales of Juvenile & Infant Products
N.A.I.C.S.: 423920

Tomy International-United Kingdom (2)
Hembury House Pynes Hill, Rydon Lane, Exeter, EX2 5AZ, United Kingdom (100%)
Tel.: (44) 1392281900
Sales Range: $150-199.9 Million
Mfr, Designer & Sales of Juvenile & Infant Products
N.A.I.C.S.: 423920

Tomy UK Ltd. (1)
Velocity 1 Brooklands Drive Brooklands, Weybridge, KT13 0SL, Surrey, United Kingdom
Tel.: (44) 1932338630
Web Site: http://www.tomy.co.uk
Toys & Hobby Goods Distr
N.A.I.C.S.: 423920

TOMYPAK HOLDINGS BERHAD
11 Jalan Tahana Kawasan Perindustrian Tampoi, District of Kulai, 81400, Johor Bahru, Johor Darul Takzim, Malaysia
Tel.: (60) 75352222
Web Site: https://www.tomypak.com.my
Year Founded: 1979
TOMYPAK—(KLS)
Rev.: $12,244,021
Assets: $45,986,032
Liabilities: $10,200,423
Net Worth: $35,785,608
Earnings: $17,955,979
Emp.: 137
Fiscal Year-end: 06/30/23
Investment Holding Company
N.A.I.C.S.: 551112
Hun Swee Lim (Mng Dir)

Subsidiaries:

Tomypak Flexible Packaging (S) Pte. Ltd.
PTD 109476 Jalan Cyber 4, Senai, 81400, Johor, Malaysia
Tel.: (60) 75352222
Food Package Material Mfr
N.A.I.C.S.: 326112
Tan Sri Arshad Ayub (Chm)

Tomypak Flexible Packaging Sdn Bhd (1)
PTD 109476 Jalan Cyber 4 Kawasan Perindustrian Senai Fasa 3, 81400, Senai, Johor Darul Takzim, Malaysia (100%)
Tel.: (60) 7 535 2222
Web Site: https://www.tomypak.com.my
Food Packaging Materials Mfr & Whslr
N.A.I.C.S.: 326199
Eddie Hun Swee Lim (Mng Dir)

TONAMI HOLDINGS CO., LTD.
3-2-12 Showa-cho, Chuo-ku, Takaoka, 933-8788, Toyama, Japan
Tel.: (81) 336645402
Web Site: https://www.tonamiholdings.co.jp
Year Founded: 1943
9070—(TKS)
Rev.: $939,095,920
Assets: $1,118,702,840
Liabilities: $504,627,230
Net Worth: $614,075,610
Earnings: $26,843,210
Fiscal Year-end: 03/31/24
Truck Transportation, Parcel Deliveries, Air Freight, Moving, Warehousing, Van Operations & Direct Marketing Services
N.A.I.C.S.: 541614
Katsusuke Watanuki (Pres)

Subsidiaries:

Fukui Tonami Transportation Co., Ltd. (1)
13-3 Haori-cho, Tsuruga, 914-0039, Fukui, Japan
Tel.: (81) 770222448
Web Site: https://www.f-tonami.co.jp
Emp.: 173
Vehicles Transportation Services
N.A.I.C.S.: 532411

Tonami System Solutions Co., Ltd. (1)
20-2 Chudoji Mibukawa-cho, Shimogyo-ku, Kyoto, 600-8806, Japan
Tel.: (81) 758422101
Web Site: https://www.tonami-syssol.co.jp
Emp.: 141
Courier Delivery Services
N.A.I.C.S.: 624210

TONDA CONSTRUCTION LIMITED
1085 Wilton Grove Rd, London, N6N 1C9, ON, Canada
Tel.: (519) 686-5200
Web Site: https://www.tonda.on.ca
Year Founded: 1979
Rev.: $22,434,000
Emp.: 30
General Contractors
N.A.I.C.S.: 238190
Tom Weller (Pres)

TONDO SMART LTD.
Ha Yotzrim 5 StOrYehuda, Tel Aviv, 6022411, Israel
Tel.: (972) 502833266
Web Site: https://www.tondo-iot.com
TNDO—(TAE)
Rev.: $5,459,303
Assets: $7,057,914
Liabilities: $7,956,727
Net Worth: ($898,812)
Earnings: ($2,094,789)
Fiscal Year-end: 06/30/23
Information Technology Services
N.A.I.C.S.: 541519
Yair Gamliel (Chm)

TONE COMPANY LTD
1-57 Minatomachi 2-Chome, Naniwa-ku, Osaka, 556-0017, Japan
Tel.: (81) 667225967
Web Site: https://www.tonetool.co.jp
Year Founded: 1938
5967—(TKS)
Rev.: $50,090,580
Assets: $98,310,530
Liabilities: $27,781,830
Net Worth: $70,528,700
Earnings: $6,226,620
Emp.: 45
Fiscal Year-end: 05/31/24
Work Tools Mfr & Distr
N.A.I.C.S.: 332618
Shozo Matsumura (Chm)

Subsidiaries:

Tone Company Ltd - Kawachinagano Factory (1)
Number 6 Kotobukicho Number 25, Kawachinagano, 586-0026, Osaka, Japan
Tel.: (81) 721568721
Hand Tool Mfr
N.A.I.C.S.: 332216

TONELI NUTRITION TITU SA
Sos Bucuresti Ploiesti Nr 42-44 Cladirea Nr 1 Et 3 Birouri 1 2 14, Sect 1, Bucharest, Romania
Tel.: (40) 21 3610531
Sales Range: $10-24.9 Million
Emp.: 48
Animal Feed Mfr
N.A.I.C.S.: 311119

TONG HSING ELECTRONIC INDUSTRIES, LTD.

TONG HERR RESOURCES BERHAD
No 2515 Tingkat Perusahaan 4A, Perai Free Trade Zone, 13600, Perai, Penang, Malaysia
Tel.: (60) 43903970 MY
Web Site: https://www.tong.com.my
TONGHER—(KLS)
Rev.: $209,224,339
Assets: $148,343,069
Liabilities: $17,740,106
Net Worth: $130,602,963
Earnings: $18,498,836
Fiscal Year-end: 12/31/22
Holding Company; Stainless Steel Bolts, Screws, Nuts & Other Fastener Products Mfr & Whslr; Aluminum Extruded Products Mfr
N.A.I.C.S.: 551112
Angelina Gaik Suan Cheah (Co-Sec)

Subsidiaries:

Tong Heer Aluminium Industries Sdn. Bhd. (1)
Plot 17-A Jalan Perusahaan, Prai Industrial Estate, 13600, Perai, Penang, Malaysia
Tel.: (60) 45079079
Web Site: https://www.tong-al.com.my
Stainless Steel Mfr
N.A.I.C.S.: 331210

Tong Heer Fasteners Co. Sdn. Bhd. (1)
No 2515 Tingkat Perusahaan 4A, Perai Free Trade Zone, 13600, Perai, Penang, Malaysia (100%)
Tel.: (60) 43903970
Web Site: https://www.tong.com.my
Bolts, Screws, Nuts & Other Fastener Products Mfr & Whslr
N.A.I.C.S.: 332722
Yi Ting Tsai (Mng Dir)

Tong Heer Fasteners Thailand Co., Ltd. (1)
Amata Nakorn Industrial Estate 700/553 Moo 7 T Don Hua Roh, Amphur Muang, 20000, Chonburi, Thailand (100%)
Tel.: (66) 38454537
Stainless Steel Bolts, Screws, Nuts & Other Fastener Products Mfr & Whslr
N.A.I.C.S.: 332722

TONG HSING ELECTRONIC INDUSTRIES, LTD.
No 55 Lane 365 Yingtao Rd, Yinko Dist, Taipei, 23942, Taiwan
Tel.: (886) 226790122
Web Site: https://www.theil.com
Year Founded: 1974
6271—(TAI)
Rev.: $385,132,625
Assets: $1,100,834,845
Liabilities: $301,545,984
Net Worth: $799,288,861
Earnings: $37,624,283
Emp.: 2,308
Fiscal Year-end: 12/31/23
Semiconductor Mfr
N.A.I.C.S.: 334413
Shao-Ping Lu (Pres)

Subsidiaries:

Tong Hsing Electronic Industries, Ltd. - ChungLi Plant (1)
8F No 27 Ji-Lin Rd Chung-Li Industrial Park Tao-Yuan, Hsien, Taiwan
Tel.: (886) 34335998
Electronic Parts Distr
N.A.I.C.S.: 423930

Tong Hsing Electronic Industries, Ltd. - Longtan Plant (1)
21 Longyuan 5th Rd Longtan Dist, Taoyuan, 325, Taiwan
Tel.: (886) 34893700
Electronic Parts Distr
N.A.I.C.S.: 423930

Tong Hsing Electronics Phils Inc. (1)
103 Prosperity Avenue Carmelray international Business Park Brgy, Canlubang,

Tong Hsing Electronic Industries, Ltd.—(Continued)
Calamba, Laguna, Philippines
Tel.: (63) 495494250
Web Site: https://www.tonghsing.ph
Electronic Products Mfr
N.A.I.C.S.: 334419

TONG HUA HOLDING PUBLIC COMPANY LIMITED
877-881 New Road Talatnoi, Samphanthawong, Bangkok, 10100, Thailand
Tel.: (66) 22369171 TH
Web Site:
   http://www.thaizhonghua.com
Year Founded: 1960
TH—(THA)
Rev.: $13,042,096
Assets: $49,974,317
Liabilities: $2,721,275
Net Worth: $47,253,042
Earnings: $2,819,069
Fiscal Year-end: 12/31/23
Newspaper Publishing Services
N.A.I.C.S.: 513110
Somnuk Kyavatanakij *(Chm)*

TONG HWA SYNTHETIC FIBER COMPANY LIMITED
9F No 56 Sec 1, Xinsheng S Road, Taipei, 100, Taiwan
Tel.: (886) 223967768
Web Site:
   http://www.tonghwa.com.tw
1418—(TAI)
Rev.: $860,427
Assets: $146,443,273
Liabilities: $104,860,783
Net Worth: $41,582,490
Earnings: $1,307,237
Fiscal Year-end: 12/31/23
Acrylic Fiber Mfr
N.A.I.C.S.: 313110

TONG KEE (HOLDING) LTD.
Room 2502 25/F 148 Electric Road North Point, Hong Kong, China (Hong Kong)
Tel.: (852) 24076298
Web Site: http://www.tongkee.com.hk
Year Founded: 1994
8305—(HKG)
Rev.: $19,895,810
Assets: $30,378,917
Liabilities: $17,941,505
Net Worth: $12,437,412
Earnings: ($5,499,191)
Emp.: 131
Fiscal Year-end: 12/31/21
Commercial Building Construction Services
N.A.I.C.S.: 236220
Chung Sum Heung *(Founder, Chm & Compliance Officer)*

TONG MING ENTERPRISE CO., LTD.
No 88 East ChangSheng Road, Economic Development Zone, Jiaxing, 314003, Zhejiang, China
Tel.: (86) 57382203125
Web Site: https://www.the.com.cn
Year Founded: 1996
5538—(TAI)
Rev.: $1,405,140,695
Assets: $1,356,740,124
Liabilities: $716,764,948
Net Worth: $639,975,176
Earnings: $75,811,985
Emp.: 800
Fiscal Year-end: 12/31/20
Stainless Steel Fasteners, Bolts, Nuts, Rivets, Washers & Wires
N.A.I.C.S.: 339993

TONG PETROTECH CORP.
Floor 13 Building A Rensheng First Center No 51 Tangyan Road, Xi'an High-Tech Zone, Xi'an, 710065, Shaanxi, China
Tel.: (86) 2987607460
Web Site:
   https://www.tongoiltools.com
Year Founded: 1995
300164—(CHIN)
Rev.: $144,976,553
Assets: $257,610,805
Liabilities: $68,697,531
Net Worth: $188,913,274
Earnings: $7,081,896
Fiscal Year-end: 12/31/23
Oil & Gas Extraction Support Services
N.A.I.C.S.: 213112
Ren Yanzhong *(Chm)*

TONG REN TANG TECHNOLOGIES CO., LTD.
No 20 Nansanhuan Zhonglu Road, Fengtai District, Beijing, 100079, China
Tel.: (86) 4006000988 CN
Web Site:
   https://www.tongrentangkj.com
Year Founded: 1669
1666—(HKG)
Rev.: $841,254,476
Assets: $1,752,861,427
Liabilities: $486,883,332
Net Worth: $1,265,978,095
Earnings: $140,627,448
Emp.: 4,089
Fiscal Year-end: 12/31/22
Medicinal Product Mfr
N.A.I.C.S.: 325411
Di Shu Bing *(Chm)*

Subsidiaries:

Beijing Tong Ren Tang Czech Republic SE (1)
Myslikova 171/31, 110 00, Prague, Czech Republic
Tel.: (420) 720979830
Web Site: http://www.trtprague.cz
Pharmaceutical Products Distr
N.A.I.C.S.: 424210

TONG TEIK PTE LTD
1 Temasek ave ste 16-01 Millenia Tower, 7 Temasek Boulevard, Singapore, 39192, Singapore
Tel.: (65) 63322282
Web Site: http://www.rcma-commodities.com
Rev.: $56,600,000
Emp.: 40
Natural Rubber Trading, Shipping, Handling & Packaging Services
N.A.I.C.S.: 326299
Oei Hong Bie *(Chm & Mng Dir)*

Subsidiaries:

RCMA Americas Inc. (1)
115 College Pl, Norfolk, VA 23510-9998
Tel.: (757) 627-4000
Web Site: http://www.rcma-rubber.com
Emp.: 15
Non-Durable Goods Whslr
N.A.I.C.S.: 424990
Christopher Foord-Kelcey *(Sr VP)*

Tong Teik (Nantong) Trading Ltd (1)
Room 2503 Nantong International Trade Center 88 Chongchuan Road, Nantong, Jiangsu, China
Tel.: (86) 0550 18151
Rubber Product Distr
N.A.I.C.S.: 424990

Tong Teik (Thailand) Limited (1)
5 Siamcitycenter 1 Road, Tambol Hatyai, Hat Yai, 90110, Songkhla, Thailand
Tel.: (66) 74 233067
Rubber Product Distr
N.A.I.C.S.: 424990

Wurfbain B.V. - Zaandam (1)
Saentower 14th Floor Ankersmidplein 2, NL-1506 CK, Zaandam, Netherlands
Tel.: (31) 756810810
Web Site: http://www.rcma-commodities.com
Sales Range: $25-49.9 Million
Emp.: 25
Coal, Commodities & Coffee Trading
N.A.I.C.S.: 523160
Albert F. van Feggelen *(Mng Dir)*

TONG YANG INDUSTRY CO., LTD.
No 98 Section 2 Anhe Road, T'ainan, 709401, Taiwan
Tel.: (886) 63560511
Web Site: https://www.tyg.com.tw
Year Founded: 1952
1319—(TAI)
Rev.: $780,234,968
Assets: $1,146,086,552
Liabilities: $298,704,492
Net Worth: $847,382,060
Earnings: $99,652,699
Emp.: 2,693
Fiscal Year-end: 12/31/23
Automotive & Motorcycle Parts Mfr
N.A.I.C.S.: 336390

Subsidiaries:

Kai Ming Industrial Co., Ltd (1)
91 Cheng-An Road, T'ainan, Taiwan
Tel.: (886) 635592212
Sales Range: $25-49.9 Million
Emp.: 70
Motor Vehicle Parts Mfr
N.A.I.C.S.: 336390

Taiwan Kai Yih Industrial Company Ltd. (1)
98 section 2 An- ho Rd, 70969, Taipei, Taiwan
Tel.: (886) 63555757
Motor Vehicle Parts Mfr
N.A.I.C.S.: 336390

TONG-TAI MACHINE TOOL CO., LTD.
No 3 Luke 3rd Rd, Luzhou Dist, Kaohsiung, 82151, Taiwan
Tel.: (886) 79761588
Web Site: https://www.tongtai.com.tw
Year Founded: 1969
4526—(TAI)
Rev.: $249,207,290
Assets: $413,760,768
Liabilities: $247,014,478
Net Worth: $166,746,290
Earnings: $3,972,890
Emp.: 650
Fiscal Year-end: 12/31/23
Photoelectric Mfr
N.A.I.C.S.: 334413
Yu-Pin Chen *(VP)*

Subsidiaries:

Anger Machining GmbH (1)
Zaunermuhlstrasse 3/5, 4050, Traun, Austria
Tel.: (43) 7229710410
Web Site: https://www.anger-machining.com
Emp.: 90
Automotive Component Mfr & Distr
N.A.I.C.S.: 336390

Anger Machining Inc. (1)
4630 Freedom Dr, Ann Arbor, MI 48108
Tel.: (734) 973-5530
Machine Tool Mfr & Distr
N.A.I.C.S.: 333517

Asia Pacific Elite Corp. (1)
No 7 Jingke N Rd, Nantun Dist, Taichung, 40852, Taiwan
Tel.: (886) 423589313
Web Site: https://www.apeccnc.com
Machine Tool Mfr & Distr
N.A.I.C.S.: 333517

Eastai Technology (M) Sdn. Bhd. (1)
No 22 Jalan U5 24 Seksyen U5 Mahsing

Intergrated Industrial Pk, 40150, Shah Alam, Selangor, Malaysia
Tel.: (60) 378456815
Sales Range: $50-74.9 Million
Emp.: 3
Industrial Machinery Distr
N.A.I.C.S.: 423830

HPC Producktions GmbH (1)
Seebacher Strasse 40, 9871, Seeboden, Austria
Tel.: (43) 47 624 9310
Web Site: https://www.hellmerich.com
Emp.: 100
Precision Parts Mfr & Distr
N.A.I.C.S.: 332721
Gunther Kranabether *(CEO)*

HPC Produktions GmbH (1)
Seebacher Strasse 40, 9871, Seeboden, Austria
Tel.: (43) 476249310
Web Site: https://www.hellmerich.com
Emp.: 100
Machine Tools Mfr
N.A.I.C.S.: 333511

Honor Seiki Co., Ltd. (1)
No 6 Sec 2 Chung-shan Rd, Hu-nei District, Kaohsiung, Taiwan
Tel.: (886) 79759888
Web Site: https://www.honorseiki.com
Emp.: 200
Machine Tool Mfr & Distr
N.A.I.C.S.: 333517
Charles Chen *(Pres)*

Process Conception Ingenierie S.A (1)
Rue Copernic, 42030, Saint Etienne, France
Tel.: (33) 4 77 42 61 61
Web Site: http://www.pci.fr
Emp.: 130
Machine Tools Mfr
N.A.I.C.S.: 333517
Patrice Gambier *(Mgr-Site)*

Quick-Tech Machinery Co., Ltd. (1)
Rm 208 Research Building 3 No 31 Gongye 2nd Rd, Annan Dist, Tainan City, 709, Taiwan
Tel.: (886) 6 384 1166
Web Site: https://www.quicktech.com.tw
Lathe Machinery Mfr & Distr
N.A.I.C.S.: 333517

SKTD Co., Ltd. (1)
Matsudo Bld 6F 1307-1 Matsudo, Matsudo, 271-0092, Chiba, Japan
Tel.: (81) 473826040
Web Site: https://www.sktd.co.jp
Machine Tools Mfr
N.A.I.C.S.: 333517

TTGroup France SA (1)
Campus Industriel Rue de Copernic, 42100, Saint-Etienne, Cedex, France
Tel.: (33) 149170745
Web Site: https://www.ttgroupfrance.fr
Machine Tool Mfr & Distr
N.A.I.C.S.: 333517

Tong-tai Seiki USA INC. (1)
157 Route 303 Unit No 1 Valley Cottage, New York, NY 10989
Tel.: (845) 267-5500
Web Site: http://www.tongtaiusa.com
Sales Range: $25-49.9 Million
Emp.: 15
Machine Tool Distr
N.A.I.C.S.: 423830

Tongtai Europe B.V. (1)
Burgemeester Krollaan 23, 5126 PT, Gilze, Netherlands
Tel.: (31) 161454639
Web Site: https://www.tongtai.eu
Machine Tool Distr
N.A.I.C.S.: 423830

Tongtai Machine & Tool Japan Co., Ltd. (1)
Matsudo Bldg 6F 1307-1, Matsudo, 271-0092, Chiba, Japan
Tel.: (81) 477120835
Electric Automation Equipment Distr
N.A.I.C.S.: 423610

Tongtai Seiki Vietnam Co., Ltd. (1)
2/62 Nguyen Chi Thanh, Lang Thuong

Dong Da, Hanoi, Vietnam
Machine Tool Mfr & Distr
N.A.I.C.S.: 333517

Topper Europe B.V. (1)
Vloeiveld 16, 5126 RG, Gilze, Netherlands
Tel.: (31) 161454639
Web Site: http://www.tongtai.eu
Sales Range: $50-74.9 Million
Emp.: 4
Machine Tool Distr
N.A.I.C.S.: 423830

TONGA COMMUNICATIONS CORPORATION
Private Bag 4, Nuku'alofa, Tonga
Tel.: (676) 20000
Web Site: http://www.tcc.to
Year Founded: 2001
Sales Range: $75-99.9 Million
Emp.: 300
Telecommunications Carrier
N.A.I.C.S.: 517111
Tai'atu Ataata (Mgr-Sls & Mktg)

TONGAAT HULETT LIMITED
Amanzimnyama Hill Road, PO Box 3, Tongaat, 4400, KwaZulu-Natal, South Africa
Tel.: (27) 324394000 ZA
Web Site: https://www.tongaat.com
Year Founded: 1892
TON—(JSE)
Rev.: $1,017,855,140
Assets: $905,821,480
Liabilities: $909,505,900
Net Worth: ($3,684,420)
Earnings: $185,585,600
Fiscal Year-end: 03/31/21
Holding Company; Sugar, Starch & Property
N.A.I.C.S.: 551112
Rob David Aitken (CFO)

Subsidiaries:

Hippo Valley Estates Limited (1)
PO Box 1, PO Box 1, Chiredzi, Zimbabwe
Tel.: (263) 2312313141
Rev.: $384,806,648
Assets: $405,164,510
Liabilities: $193,571,614
Net Worth: $211,592,896
Earnings: $47,587,060
Fiscal Year-end: 03/31/2023
Sugarcane Farming Services
N.A.I.C.S.: 111930

Tambankulu Estates Limited (1)
Private Bag, Mhlume, Eswatini
Tel.: (268) 3 737 111
Web Site: http://www.tongaat.co.za
Sugar Mfr
N.A.I.C.S.: 311314

Tongaat Hulett Acucar Limitada (1)
Caixa Postal 583, Maputo, 258, Mozambique
Tel.: (258) 21303106
Web Site: http://www.huletts.co.za
Sugar Mfr
N.A.I.C.S.: 311314
Rosario Cumbi (Gen Mgr)

Tongaat Hulett Acucareira de Mocambique, SARL (1)
Caixa Postal 1121, Beira, Mozambique
Tel.: (258) 23960014
Web Site: http://www.huletts.co.za
Sugar Mfr
N.A.I.C.S.: 311314

Tongaat Hulett Developments (Pty) Ltd
305 Umhlanga Rocks Drive, PO Box 22319, La Lucia, Durban, 4022, South Africa
Tel.: (27) 315601900
Web Site: http://www.thdev.co.za
Sales Range: $25-49.9 Million
Emp.: 84
City Developing Services
N.A.I.C.S.: 236220
Michael Deighton (Mng Dir)

Tongaat Hulett Estates (Pty) Limited (1)
305 Umhlanga Rocks Dr, Umhlanga Rocks, Umhlanga, 4319, Kwazulu-Natal, South Africa
Tel.: (27) 315601900
Sales Range: $50-74.9 Million
Emp.: 60
Residential Property Development Services
N.A.I.C.S.: 531210
Mike Deighton (Mng Dir)

Tongaat Hulett Starch (Pty) Limited (1)
2 Dick Kemp Street 2019 Isando Meadowdale, 1600, Germiston, Gauteng, South Africa
Tel.: (27) 114585000
Web Site: http://www.tongaathulettstarch.co.za
Sales Range: $25-49.9 Million
Emp.: 120
Starch & Glucose Mfr
N.A.I.C.S.: 311221
Gary Summer (Mgr-Mktg)

Tongaat Hulett Sugar Limited (1)
Amanzimnyama Hill Road, Tongaat, 4400, KwaZulu-Natal, South Africa
Tel.: (27) 324394300
Web Site: http://www.huletts.co.za
Sales Range: $25-49.9 Million
Emp.: 40
Sugarcane Mills
N.A.I.C.S.: 311314

Tongaat Hulett Sugar South Africa Limited (1)
444 South Coast Road, Rossburgh, Durban, 4094, South Africa
Tel.: (27) 314600289
Agricultural Services
N.A.I.C.S.: 115116

Triangle Sugar Corporation Limited (1)
Private Bag 801, Triangle, Masvingo, Zimbabwe
Tel.: (263) 336221
Web Site: http://www.huletts.co.za
Sugar Mfr
N.A.I.C.S.: 311314

Voermol Feeds Proprietary Limited (1)
Main Avenue Off Gopalall Hurbans Road, Maidstone Village Maidstone, Tongaat, 4399, South Africa
Tel.: (27) 324395599
Web Site: https://voermol.co.za
Animal Food Mfr & Distr
N.A.I.C.S.: 311119

TONGCHENG TRAVEL HOLDINGS LIMITED
Tongcheng Mansion No 188 Yuxin Road, Suzhou Industrial Park, Jiangsu, China
Tel.: (86) 51280717992 Ky
Web Site: http://www.tcelir.com
Year Founded: 1999
0780—(HKG)
Rev.: $924,487,106
Assets: $3,514,871,880
Liabilities: $1,269,839,938
Net Worth: $2,245,031,942
Earnings: ($22,965,228)
Emp.: 6,134
Fiscal Year-end: 12/31/22
Holding Company
N.A.I.C.S.: 551112
Heping Ma (CEO)

TONGDA GROUP HOLDINGS LIMITED
Room 1201-1202 12/F Shui On Centre 6-8 Harbour Road, Wanchai, China (Hong Kong)
Tel.: (852) 28722628 Ky
Web Site: https://www.tongda.com
Year Founded: 1988
0698—(HKG)
Rev.: $963,798,638
Assets: $1,814,182,838
Liabilities: $841,251,248
Net Worth: $972,931,590
Earnings: $19,341,878
Emp.: 18,000
Fiscal Year-end: 12/31/22
Holding Company; Consumer Electronics Components Mfr & Whslr
N.A.I.C.S.: 551112
Wang Ming Che (Exec Dir)

Subsidiaries:

Tong Da General Holdings (H.K.) Limited (1)
Room 1201-1202 12/F Shui On Centre 6-8 Harbour Road, Wanchai, China (Hong Kong)
Tel.: (852) 28722628
Web Site: https://www.tongda.com
Emp.: 3
Holding Company; Raw Materials Sourcing Services
N.A.I.C.S.: 551112

Tongda Electrics Company Limited (1)
Tongda Industrial Park Shihu Road, Shishi, Fujian, China
Tel.: (86) 59588686188
Electrical Appliance Products Mfr & Whslr
N.A.I.C.S.: 334419

TONGDA HONG TAI HOLDINGS LIMITED
Shui On Centre 6-8 Harbour Road, Wanchai, China (Hong Kong)
Tel.: (852) 31881681 Ky
Web Site: http://www.tongdahongtai.com
Year Founded: 2010
2363—(HKG)
Rev.: $19,194,488
Assets: $18,663,323
Liabilities: $44,599,245
Net Worth: ($25,935,923)
Earnings: ($29,506,433)
Emp.: 312
Fiscal Year-end: 12/31/22
Holding Company; Electronic Notebook & Tablet Casings Mfr & Whslr
N.A.I.C.S.: 551112
Ming Li Wong (Gen Mgr-Grp)

TONGDAO LIEPIN GROUP
8th Floor Building C Rongxin Technology Centre No 34 Chuangda Road, Chaoyang District, Beijing, 100044, China
Tel.: (86) 1085532000 Ky
Web Site: http://www.liepin.com
6100—(HKG)
Rev.: $370,364,108
Assets: $691,359,084
Liabilities: $221,557,939
Net Worth: $469,801,145
Earnings: $12,578,015
Emp.: 5,165
Fiscal Year-end: 12/31/22
Online Advertising Services
N.A.I.C.S.: 541810
Kebin Dai (Chm & CEO)

TONGDING INTERCONNECTION INFORMATION CO., LTD.
No 8 Xiaoping Rd Badu Economic Development Zone, Zhenze Town Wujiang District, Suzhou, 215233, Jiangsu, China
Tel.: (86) 51263873510
Web Site: https://www.tdgd.com.cn
Year Founded: 1999
002491—(SSE)
Rev.: $465,549,763
Assets: $840,136,345
Liabilities: $524,659,398
Net Worth: $315,476,947
Earnings: $17,613,615
Emp.: 1,500
Fiscal Year-end: 12/31/22
Fiber Optic Cable Mfr
N.A.I.C.S.: 335921
Xiaoping Shen (Chm)

TONGFU MICROELECTRONICS CO., LTD.
No 288 Chongchuan Road, Nantong, 226004, Jiangsu, China
Tel.: (86) 51385058919
Web Site: https://www.tfme.com
Year Founded: 1997
002156—(SSE)
Rev.: $3,008,572,155
Assets: $5,002,371,733
Liabilities: $2,957,873,153
Net Worth: $2,044,498,580
Earnings: $70,481,474
Emp.: 18,000
Fiscal Year-end: 12/31/22
Integrated Circuit Packaging Services
N.A.I.C.S.: 334412
Shi Lei (Chm & Pres)

TONGGUAN GOLD GROUP LTD.
Room 1306 13-F Bank of America Tower 12 Harcourt Road, Admiralty, Hong Kong, China (Hong Kong)
Tel.: (852) 22950822
Web Site: http://www.tongguangold.com
0340—(HKG)
Rev.: $158,720,160
Assets: $465,395,018
Liabilities: $206,142,128
Net Worth: $259,252,890
Earnings: $7,268,265
Emp.: 206
Fiscal Year-end: 12/31/22
Molybdenum Mining Services
N.A.I.C.S.: 212290
Kwok Kuen Yeung (CFO)

Subsidiaries:

Wuyi Star Tea Industrial Co., Ltd. (1)
Room 701 7/F Fortune Centre 44-48 Yun Ping Road, Causeway Bay, China (Hong Kong)
Tel.: (852) 3 153 4428
Web Site: https://www.wuyistar.hk
Sales Range: $25-49.9 Million
Emp.: 10
Tea Mfr
N.A.I.C.S.: 311920

TONGHUA DONGBAO PHARMACEUTICAL CO., LTD.
Dongbao New Village, Tonghua, 134123, Jilin, China
Tel.: (86) 4355088025
Web Site: https://www.thdb.com
Year Founded: 1985
600867—(SHG)
Rev.: $390,094,815
Assets: $947,744,043
Liabilities: $28,183,910
Net Worth: $919,560,133
Earnings: $222,097,595
Emp.: 388
Fiscal Year-end: 12/31/22
Pharmaceutical Mfr & Whslr
N.A.I.C.S.: 325412
Chunsheng Leng (Chm, Vice Chm & Gen Mgr)

TONGHUA GOLDEN-HORSE PHARMACEUTICAL INDUSTRY CO.
No 999 Golden-horse Road, Erdaojiang District, Tonghua, 134001, Jilin, China
Tel.: (86) 4353910701
Web Site: https://www.thjm.cn
Year Founded: 1990
000766—(SSE)
Rev.: $206,493,132
Assets: $657,790,146

TONGHUA GOLDEN-HORSE PHARMACEUTICAL INDUSTRY CO. INTERNATIONAL PUBLIC

Tonghua Golden-horse Pharmaceutical Industry Co.—(Continued)
Liabilities: $325,252,578
Net Worth: $332,537,568
Earnings: $4,233,243
Fiscal Year-end: 12/31/22
Pharmaceuticals Product Mfr
N.A.I.C.S.: 325412
Zhang Yufu *(Chm & Gen Mgr)*

TONGHUA GRAPE WINE CO., LTD.
Tonghua Winery No 28 Qianxing Road, Dongchang District, Tonghua, 134002, Jilin, China
Tel.: (86) 4353948012
Web Site: https://www.tonhwa.com
Year Founded: 1937
600365—(SHG)
Rev.: $115,276,389
Assets: $132,771,310
Liabilities: $86,171,483
Net Worth: $46,599,827
Earnings: ($7,286,100)
Fiscal Year-end: 12/31/22
Liquor Product Mfr & Distr
N.A.I.C.S.: 312130
Weimin He *(Pres & Sec-Party)*

TONGJITANG CHINESE MEDICINES COMPANY
5/F Block B Baiying Medical Device Park Nanhai Ave S, Nanshan District, Shenzhen, 518067, Guangdong, China
Tel.: (86) 75526891550 Ky
Web Site: http://www.tongjitang.com
Year Founded: 1995
Sales Range: $50-74.9 Million
Emp.: 2,440
Pharmaceuticals Mfr
N.A.I.C.S.: 325412
Xiaochun Wang *(Chm & CEO)*

Subsidiaries:

Unisource Enterprises Limited (1)
Baiying Medical Device Park Nanhai Avenue South, Nanshan District, Shenzhen, 518067, China
Tel.: (86) 75526670969
Holding Company
N.A.I.C.S.: 551112

Subsidiary (Domestic):

Guizhou Tongjitang Pharmaceutical Co., Ltd. (2)
Fuzhong International Plaza, Xinhua Road, Guiyang, 550002, China
Tel.: (86) 851 5516218
Development, Mfg, Marketing & Sales of Pharmaceutical Products
N.A.I.C.S.: 325412

Guizhou Tongjitang Pharmaceutical Distribution Co., Ltd. (2)
69 Mid Hauxi Ave, Guiyang, China
Tel.: (86) 851 3816378
Pharmaceutical Products Distribution Services
N.A.I.C.S.: 541614

TONGKAH HARBOUR PUBLIC COMPANY LIMITED
7th Floor Muang Thai-Phatra Complex Tower 1 252/11 Ratchadapisek Road, Huay Khwang, Bangkok, 10310, Thailand
Tel.: (66) 2695491228
Web Site: http://www.tongkahharbour.com
Year Founded: 1906
THL—(THA)
Rev.: $13,194,559
Assets: $51,003,406
Liabilities: $7,600,727
Net Worth: $43,402,679
Earnings: $2,802,867
Emp.: 90

Fiscal Year-end: 12/31/20
Gold & Tin Mining Services; Rock Crushing Services
N.A.I.C.S.: 212220
Wijit Jiemwijitkul *(Chm & CEO)*

Subsidiaries:

Cholsin Company Limited (1)
7 th Floor Muang Thai-Phatra Office Building 1, 252/11 Ratchadapisek Rd Huai-Khwang, Bangkok, 10310, Thailand
Tel.: (66) 2695491228
Pyrolusite Distr
N.A.I.C.S.: 423520

Pure Nergy Co., Ltd. (1)
7th Floor Muang Thai-Phatra 1 Office Building 252/11 Ratchadapisek Rd, Bangkok, Thailand
Tel.: (66) 2695491228
Renewable Energy Services
N.A.I.C.S.: 221118

SEA MINERALS LIMITED (SML) (1)
7 Fl Muang Thai-Phatra Ofc Tower 1, 252 11 Ratchadapisek Rd, Bangkok, 10320, Thailand
Tel.: (66) 2695491228
Offshore Tin Mining Services
N.A.I.C.S.: 212290

SKY CLIFF LIMITED(SCL) (1)
14 Ratchadapisek Rd, Huay Kwang, Bangkok, 10320, Thailand
Tel.: (66) 2247 2728
Residential Building Rental Services
N.A.I.C.S.: 531110

Sea Mineral Limited (1)
7th Floor Muang Thai-Phatra 1 Office Building 252/11 Ratchadapisek Rd, Huai-Khwang, Bangkok, 10310, Thailand
Tel.: (66) 2695491228
Mineral Mining Services
N.A.I.C.S.: 213114

TONGKUN GROUP CO., LTD.
No 518 Phoenix Lake Avenue Wutong Street, Tongxiang, 314500, Zhejiang, China
Tel.: (86) 57388187878
Web Site: http://www.zjtkgf.com
Year Founded: 1999
601233—(SHG)
Rev.: $8,703,866,256
Assets: $12,655,659,861
Liabilities: $7,740,760,206
Net Worth: $4,914,899,655
Earnings: $18,281,400
Fiscal Year-end: 12/31/22
Polyester Filament Mfr
N.A.I.C.S.: 313110
Chen Lei *(Chm & Pres)*

Subsidiaries:

Tongkun Group Zhejiang Hengtong Chemical Fibre Co., Ltd. (1)
No 1 Desheng Road Zhouquan Industrial Zone, Tongxiang, 314513, Zhejiang, China
Tel.: (86) 57389392889
Emp.: 1,600
Polyester Filament Mfr
N.A.I.C.S.: 313110

TONGLING JIEYA BIOLOGIC TECHNOLOGY CO., LTD.
No 528 Dizhi Avenue Shizishan Economic Development Zone, Tongling, 244031, Anhui, China
Tel.: (86) 5626868001
Web Site: https://www.babywipes.com.cn
Year Founded: 1999
301108—(CHIN)
Rev.: $87,688,324
Assets: $302,644,055
Liabilities: $40,819,746
Net Worth: $261,824,309
Earnings: $16,224,859
Fiscal Year-end: 12/31/23
Sanitary Product Mfr & Distr
N.A.I.C.S.: 322291

Yingchuan Cai *(Chm & Gen Mgr)*

TONGLING JINGDA SPECIAL MAGNET WIRE CO., LTD.
No 988 Northern Section Huangshan Avenue, Tongling Economic and Technological Development Zone, Tongling, 244061, Anhui, China
Tel.: (86) 5622836952
Web Site: https://www.jingda.cn
Year Founded: 1990
600577—(SHG)
Rev.: $2,462,953,578
Assets: $1,524,143,874
Liabilities: $770,362,866
Net Worth: $753,781,008
Earnings: $53,503,084
Emp.: 2,925
Fiscal Year-end: 12/31/22
Magnet Wire Mfr & Distr
N.A.I.C.S.: 331420
Xiao Li *(Chm)*

Subsidiaries:

Changzhou Hengfeng Special Conductor Co., Ltd. (1)
No 26 Fenghuang Road, Tianning District, Changzhou, 213018, China
Tel.: (86) 5622839654
Web Site: https://www.czhftc.com
Copper Wires Mfr
N.A.I.C.S.: 331420

Tongling Jingxun Special Enamelled Wire Co., Ltd. (1)
No 5151 Taishan Road Tong Ling Economical and Technological New Zone, Anhui, 244000, China
Tel.: (86) 5622839654
Web Site: https://tljx.jingda.cn
Aluminum Wire Product Mfr
N.A.I.C.S.: 331318

TONGLING NONFERROUS METALS GROUP HOLDINGS CO., LTD
West Changjiang Road, Tongling, 244001, Anhui, China
Tel.: (86) 5625861313
Web Site: http://www.tnmg.com.cn
Year Founded: 1952
Sales Range: $5-14.9 Billion
Copper Mining & Smelting Services
N.A.I.C.S.: 212230

Subsidiaries:

Corriente Resources, Inc. (1)
Unit S209-5811 Cooney Road, Richmond, V6X 3M1, BC, Canada
Tel.: (604) 282-7212
Web Site: https://www.corriente.com
Sales Range: $200-249.9 Million
Emp.: 252
Copper & Gold Mining Services
N.A.I.C.S.: 212230
Shouhua Jin *(Chm & Mng VP)*

Tongling Nonferrous Metals Group Co., Ltd. (1)
Changjiang West Road, Tongling, 244001, Anhui, China
Tel.: (86) 5625860159
Web Site: http://www.tlys.cn
Rev.: $19,031,602,736
Assets: $10,833,673,668
Liabilities: $5,365,014,940
Net Worth: $5,468,658,728
Earnings: $373,722,890
Fiscal Year-end: 12/31/2023
Non Ferrous Metal Mfr
N.A.I.C.S.: 331410
Huadong Gong *(Chm)*

TONGQINGLOU DINING CO., LTD.
Building 9 No 10 Wangang Road, Baohe, Hefei, 230031, Anhui, China
Tel.: (86) 55163642210
Web Site: https://www.tongqinglou.cn
Year Founded: 2005

605108—(SHG)
Rev.: $234,532,781
Assets: $407,392,123
Liabilities: $128,546,898
Net Worth: $278,845,225
Earnings: $13,141,229
Fiscal Year-end: 12/31/22
Hotel & Restaurant Operator
N.A.I.C.S.: 721110
Jishui Shen *(Chm & Gen Mgr)*

TONGWEI CO., LTD.
No 588 Middle Section of Tianfu Avenue High-tech Zone, Gaoxin District, Chengdu, Sichuan, China
Tel.: (86) 2885188888
Web Site: https://en.tongwei.com.cn
600438—(SHG)
Rev.: $19,996,121,527
Assets: $20,392,228,621
Liabilities: $10,108,597,796
Net Worth: $10,283,630,826
Earnings: $3,611,993,187
Fiscal Year-end: 12/31/22
Feedstuff Mfr
N.A.I.C.S.: 311119
Liu Shuqi *(CEO)*

Subsidiaries:

Inner Mongolia Tongwei Silicon Co., Ltd. (1)
No 1 Ronghua Street Metal Deep Processing Park, Kundulun District Inner Mongolia, Baotou, China
Tel.: (86) 4728599031
Crystalline Silicon & Solar Cell Mfr
N.A.I.C.S.: 334413

Sichuan TW Food Co., Ltd. (1)
No 2 Chuangye Road High-tech Zone, Chengdu, China
Tel.: (86) 4008666720
Crystalline Silicon & Solar Cell Mfr
N.A.I.C.S.: 334413

TW Agricultural Development Co., Ltd. (1)
No 588 Middle Section of Tianfu Avenue High-tech Zone, Chengdu, China
Tel.: (86) 2885188888
Crystalline Silicon & Solar Cell Mfr
N.A.I.C.S.: 334413

TW Solar (Chengdu) Co., Ltd. (1)
No 888 Linjiaci Road, Huangjia Subdistrict Shuangliu District, Chengdu, China
Tel.: (86) 2860666006
Crystalline Silicon & Solar Cell Mfr
N.A.I.C.S.: 334413

TW Solar (Hefei) Co., Ltd. (1)
No 888 Changning Avenue, High-tech Zone, Hefei, Anhui, China
Tel.: (86) 55162896556
Crystalline Silicon & Solar Cell Mfr
N.A.I.C.S.: 334413

TW Solar (Jintang) Co., Ltd. (1)
No 1 East section of Jinle Road, huaikou Town Jintang County, Chengdu, China
Tel.: (86) 2860666999
Crystalline Silicon & Solar Cell Mfr
N.A.I.C.S.: 334413

TW Solar (Meishan) Co., Ltd. (1)
No 999 Kangding Avenue, Xiuwen Town Dongpo District, Meishan, China
Tel.: (86) 2860666777
Crystalline Silicon & Solar Cell Mfr
N.A.I.C.S.: 334413

Tonghe New Energy (Jintang) Co., Ltd. (1)
No 888 East Jinle Road Jintang Avenue, Jintang County, Chengdu, China
Tel.: (86) 2860666888
Crystalline Silicon & Solar Cell Mfr
N.A.I.C.S.: 334413

Tongwei New Energy Co., Ltd. (1)
No 888 Linjiaci Road, Huangjia Subdistrict Shuangliu District, Chengdu, China
Tel.: (86) 4000835858
Crystalline Silicon & Solar Cell Mfr
N.A.I.C.S.: 334413

TONGXIN INTERNATIONAL LTD.
Hunan Tongxin Jiangbei Town, Changsha, 410135, Hunan, China
Tel.: (86) 73186264578 VG
Year Founded: 2008
TXIC—(OTCIQ)
Sales Range: Less than $1 Million
Motor Vehicle Body Mfr & Distr
N.A.I.C.S.: 336211
Duanxiang Zhang *(Chm, CEO & Chief Admin Officer)*

TONGXING ENVIRONMENTAL PROTECTION TECHNOLOGY CO., LTD.
Building B10 Binhu Financial Port, Baohe, Hefei, 230091, Anhui, China
Tel.: (86) 55164276188
Web Site: https://www.ahtxhb.com
Year Founded: 2006
003027—(SSE)
Rev.: $131,732,841
Assets: $378,971,990
Liabilities: $127,365,152
Net Worth: $251,606,839
Earnings: $16,831,391
Fiscal Year-end: 12/31/22
Waste Management Services
N.A.I.C.S.: 562998
Guangming Zheng *(Chm)*

TONGYANG GROUP
13th Floor TONGYANG Securities Building 76 Eulgiro, Jung-gu, Seoul, 100-845, Korea (South)
Tel.: (82) 2 3770 5874
Web Site: http://www.tongyang.co.kr
Holding Company
N.A.I.C.S.: 551112
Jae-Hyun Hyun *(Chm & CEO)*

Subsidiaries:

Geumjin Biotech (1)
Gangneung Science Industry Park Room 215 Saimdang-ro 641-22, Gangneung, 210-341, Gangwon-do, Korea (South)
Tel.: (82) 33 641 7393
Biotechnology Research & Development Services
N.A.I.C.S.: 541714

TONGYANG A&D Co., Ltd. (1)
Alpha Bldg Jonno 34, Jonno-gu, Seoul, 110-110, Korea (South)
Tel.: (82) 2 3770 2969
Web Site: http://www.tycement.com
Cement Mfr
N.A.I.C.S.: 327310

TONGYANG Cement E&C (1)
Tongyanggil 20, Samcheok, 245-150, Gangwon-do, Korea (South)
Tel.: (82) 33 571 7000
Cement Mfr
N.A.I.C.S.: 327310

TONGYANG Inc. (1)
3-4F Samsung Life Yeouido Bldg 24 Gukjegeumyungro 2-gil, Yeongdeungpo-gu, Seoul, Korea (South)
Tel.: (82) 261507000
Web Site: http://www.tongyanginc.co.kr
Rev.: $588,811,739
Assets: $754,383,035
Liabilities: $153,413,994
Net Worth: $600,969,040
Earnings: ($3,375,186)
Emp.: 533
Fiscal Year-end: 12/31/2022
Holding Company; Engineering & Construction, Cement Production & Financial Services
N.A.I.C.S.: 551112

Subsidiary (Domestic):

TONGYANG Engineering & Construction Group (2)
Alpha Bldg Jonno 34, Jonno-gu, Seoul, 110-110, Korea (South)
Tel.: (82) 2 3770 3148
Web Site: http://www.tycon.co.kr

Construction Engineering Services
N.A.I.C.S.: 541330
Chul-Won Park *(CEO)*

TONGYANG Investment Co., Ltd. (1)
19th floor Hi-Living Bldg Teheran-ro 420, Gangnam-gu, Seoul, 135-280, Korea (South)
Tel.: (82) 2 561 0056
Web Site: http://www.tyinvest.co.kr
Venture Capital Investment Firm
N.A.I.C.S.: 523999

TONGYANG Leisure Co., Ltd. (1)
TONGYANG Bldg Unjoo-ro 729, Gangnam-gu, Seoul, 135-995, Korea (South)
Tel.: (82) 2 318 8600
Web Site: http://www.tyleisure.co.kr
Sales Range: $25-49.9 Million
Emp.: 30
Golf Course & Country Club Management Services
N.A.I.C.S.: 713910

TONGYANG Life Science Corp. (1)
TONGYANG Bldg 70-11 Nonhyeon-dong, Gangnam-gu, Seoul, 135-010, Korea (South)
Tel.: (82) 2 6906 1054
Web Site: http://www.tongyangls.com
Health Care Products Developer & Distr
N.A.I.C.S.: 541715

TONGYANG Networks Inc. (1)
Cosmo Tower 326 Wangsimni-ro, Seongdong-gu, Seoul, 04709, Korea (South)
Tel.: (82) 24057700
Web Site: http://www.tynetworks.com
Rev.: $20,830,223
Assets: $90,801,088
Liabilities: $86,576,288
Net Worth: $4,224,801
Earnings: ($28,695,837)
Emp.: 6
Fiscal Year-end: 12/31/2021
IT Services
N.A.I.C.S.: 541519
Choi Jangrim *(CEO)*

Subsidiary (Domestic):

TONGYANG Online Co., Ltd. (2)
21F Nurikum Square IT Business Tower Worldcup-ro 396, Mapo-gu, Seoul, 121-795, Korea (South) **(85.15%)**
Tel.: (82) 70 7090 0900
Web Site: http://www.tyonline.co.kr
Information Technology Consulting Services
N.A.I.C.S.: 541512

Yuanta Securities Korea Co., Ltd. (1)
100-845 Yuanta Securities Korea Building 76 Uljiro, Jung-gu, Seoul, 100-845, Korea (South)
Tel.: (82) 237702000
Web Site: http://www.yuantakorea.com
Sales Range: $400-449.9 Million
Emp.: 1,717
Asset Management & Investment Banking Services
N.A.I.C.S.: 523150
Jae-Hyun Hyun *(Chm)*

TONGYANG PILE INC.
16-127 Asanoncheon-ro Yeomchi-eup, Asan, Chungcheongnam-do, Korea (South)
Tel.: (82) 237703157
Web Site: http://www.tongyangphc.com
Year Founded: 2013
228340—(KRS)
Rev.: $55,672,403
Assets: $99,259,495
Liabilities: $4,984,223
Net Worth: $94,275,273
Earnings: $3,763,324
Emp.: 37
Fiscal Year-end: 12/31/22
Concrete Product Mfr & Distr
N.A.I.C.S.: 327390
Kim See-Nyun *(Pres & CEO)*

TONGYU COMMUNICATION INC.
No 1 Dongzhendong 2nd RD Torch Hi-Tech Industrial Development Zone, Zhongshan, 528437, Guandong, China
Tel.: (86) 76085318111 CN
Web Site: https://www.tycc.cn
Year Founded: 1996
002792—(SSE)
Rev.: $197,511,940
Assets: $501,574,662
Liabilities: $114,212,213
Net Worth: $387,362,449
Earnings: $11,446,896
Fiscal Year-end: 12/31/22
Telecommunication Component Mfr & Distr
N.A.I.C.S.: 335929
Wu Zhonglin *(Chm & Fin Dir)*

Subsidiaries:

Shenzhen OPWAY Communication Co., Ltd. (1)
Block 5 No 1002 Songbai Road Xili Street, Nanshan District, Shenzhen, 518055, Guangdong, China **(100%)**
Tel.: (86) 75526713789
Web Site: https://www.opwaytech.com
Emp.: 300
Fiber Optic Cable Mfr
N.A.I.C.S.: 335921

Tongyu Technology India Private Limited (1)
Level 12 Tower C Building 8 DLF Cyber City Complex DLF City Phase II, Gurgaon, 122 002, Haryana, India
Tel.: (91) 1244696969
Telecommunication Products Mfr
N.A.I.C.S.: 334419
Tim Hau *(Mng Dir)*

Tongyu Technology Oy (1)
Yrttipellontie 1, 90230, Oulu, Finland
Tel.: (358) 504702316
Web Site: http://www.tongyutechnology.com
Telecommunication Products Mfr
N.A.I.C.S.: 334419
Robert Lindell *(Mng Dir)*

TONGYU HEAVY INDUSTRY CO., LTD
National High-Tech Industrial Development Zone, Dezhou, Yucheng, 251200, Shandong, China
Tel.: (86) 5347520668
Web Site: https://www.tongyuheavy.com
Year Founded: 2002
300185—(CHIN)
Rev.: $830,169,756
Assets: $2,214,706,104
Liabilities: $1,239,800,796
Net Worth: $974,905,308
Earnings: $34,538,400
Emp.: 1,425
Fiscal Year-end: 12/31/22
Large Forging Products Mfr & Sales
N.A.I.C.S.: 335999
Si Yong *(Gen Mgr)*

Subsidiaries:

Qingdao Bortome Import & Export Co., Ltd (1)
Room 703 Bldg A No 63 Haier Road, Qingdao, China
Tel.: (86) 53255579725
Web Site: https://www.bortome.com
Iron Casting Mfr
N.A.I.C.S.: 331511

TONIES SE
Oststrasse 119, 40210, Dusseldorf, Germany
Tel.: (49) 15157846012 LU
Web Site: https://www.ir.tonies.com
Year Founded: 2013
TNIE—(DEU)
Rev.: $389,542,413
Assets: $531,351,176
Liabilities: $180,261,170
Net Worth: $351,090,006
Earnings: ($12,745,521)
Emp.: 453
Fiscal Year-end: 12/31/23
Audio & Video Equipment Mfr
N.A.I.C.S.: 334310
Jan Middelhoff *(CFO)*

Subsidiaries:

Tonies France S.A.S. (1)
23 rue d Anjou, 75008, Paris, France
Tel.: (33) 175859726
Audio System Mfr & Distr
N.A.I.C.S.: 334310

TONKENS AGRAR AG
Welsleber Strasse 1, Sulzetal, 39171, Magdeburg, Germany
Tel.: (49) 39205417410
Web Site: https://www.tonkens-agrar.de
Year Founded: 2010
GTK—(DEU)
Rev.: $21,525,632
Assets: $40,112,064
Liabilities: $27,692,608
Net Worth: $12,419,456
Earnings: $1,485,632
Emp.: 95
Fiscal Year-end: 06/30/23
Agricultural Product Mfr & Distr
N.A.I.C.S.: 333111
Gerrit Tonkens *(Member-Mgmt Bd)*

TONKING NEW ENERGY GROUP HOLDINGS LIMITED
Room 1302 13th Floor Chevalier House 45-51 Chatham Road South, Tsim Sha Tsui, Kowloon, China (Hong Kong)
Tel.: (852) 25055566
Web Site: http://www.tonkinggroup.com.hk
Year Founded: 2004
8326—(HKG)
Rev.: $87,843,038
Assets: $65,800,583
Liabilities: $33,172,058
Net Worth: $32,628,525
Earnings: $3,703,875
Emp.: 128
Fiscal Year-end: 03/31/23
Investment Services
N.A.I.C.S.: 523999
Jian Nong Wu *(Chm & CEO)*

Subsidiaries:

JC Group (HK) Limited (1)
Unit B 6/F Dragon Industrial Building No 93 King Lam Street, Cheung Sha Wan, Kowloon, China (Hong Kong)
Tel.: (852) 3 618 6749
Web Site: https://www.jcgroup.hk
Restaurant Operators
N.A.I.C.S.: 722511

PHO Hoi An Limited (1)
Shop 303 3/F iSquare 63 Nathan Road Tsim Sha Tsui, Kowloon, China (Hong Kong)
Tel.: (852) 23270077
Restaurant Operators
N.A.I.C.S.: 722511

TONLIN DEPARTMENT STORE CO., LTD.
10F-6 No 197 Section 4 Zhongxiao East Road, Taipei, 10690, Taiwan
Tel.: (886) 227522222
Web Site: https://www.tonlin.com.tw
Year Founded: 1971
2910—(TAI)
Rev.: $22,370,875
Assets: $182,918,663
Liabilities: $98,218,120
Net Worth: $84,700,543
Earnings: $6,700,971
Fiscal Year-end: 12/31/23

TONLIN DEPARTMENT STORE CO., LTD.

Tonlin Department Store Co., Ltd.—(Continued)
Departmental Store Operator
N.A.I.C.S.: 455110
Wenlong Chen (Deputy Gen Mgr)

TONNA ELECTRONIQUE S.A.
36 Avenue Hoche, FR-51100, Reims, France
Tel.: (33) 326055050
Web Site: http://www.tonna.com
Year Founded: 1949
Rev.: $12,858,275
Earnings: ($125,160)
Fiscal Year-end: 12/31/16
Telecommunication Servicesb
N.A.I.C.S.: 517810

TONNELERIE RADOUX
10 Avenue Faidherbe, Jonzac, 17500, Angouleme, France
Tel.: (33) 546481028
Rev.: $26,600,000
Emp.: 90
Wood Containers
N.A.I.C.S.: 321920
Nicolas Mahler Besse (Dir)

TONNELLERIE FRANCOIS FRERES
Departmental road 17, 21190, Le Puy, France
Tel.: (33) 380212333   FR
Web Site:
 https://www.francoisfreres.com
Year Founded: 1910
TFF—(EUR)
Sales Range: $25-49.9 Million
Oak Barrels Mfr & Distr
N.A.I.C.S.: 332439
Thierry Simonel (Dir-Fin & Admin)

Subsidiaries:

A.P. John & Sons Pty Ltd   (1)
24 - 26 Basedow Road, Tanunda, 5352, SA, Australia
Tel.: (61) 8 8563 2178
Web Site: http://www.apjohn.com.au
Sales Range: $25-49.9 Million
Emp.: 20
Barrel Mfr
N.A.I.C.S.: 321920
Jarrod Schmidt (Mgr-Sls)

BOUYOUD DISTRIBUTION   (1)
Zone Industrielle Cana Est Rue Francois Labrousse, 19100, Brive-la-Gaillarde, France
Tel.: (33) 5 55 87 63 39
Sales Range: $25-49.9 Million
Emp.: 49
Wine Barrel Distr
N.A.I.C.S.: 423840
Laurent Lacroix (Gen Mgr)

Barrels Unlimited, Inc.   (1)
13455 S Bryan Flats Rd, Jackson, WY 83001
Tel.: (307) 733-1993
Web Site: http://www.barrelsunlimited.com
Rev.: $7,100,000
Emp.: 50
Barrel Manufacturing for Wine & Spirits Industry
N.A.I.C.S.: 423840
Mary Gabrielson (Treas)

Classic Oak Products (AUS) Pty Ltd   (1)
Suite 39 14 Narabang Way, Belrose, 2085, NSW, Australia
Tel.: (61) 2 9986 2277
Web Site:
 http://www.classicoakproducts.com
Barrel Distr
N.A.I.C.S.: 423840

Classic Oak Products (NZ) Ltd   (1)
L13 45 Johnston Street, Wellington, 6011, New Zealand
Tel.: (64) 4 472 6050
Oak Products Distr
N.A.I.C.S.: 424990

DEMPTOS ESPANA   (1)
Pol Ind Casablanca 12, 1300, Laguardia, Alava, Spain
Tel.: (34) 945 62 52 20
Sales Range: $25-49.9 Million
Emp.: 18
Wine Barrel Mfr

DEMPTOS NAPA Cooperage, Inc   (1)
1050 Soscol Ferry Rd, Napa, CA 94558
Tel.: (707) 257-2628
Web Site: http://www.demptos.fr
Wood Container Mfr
N.A.I.C.S.: 321920

DEMPTOS SA (PTY) LTD   (1)
13 Planken St, Stellenbosch, 7600, South Africa
Tel.: (27) 21 883 9434
Web Site: http://www.demptos.fr
Sales Range: $75-99.9 Million
Emp.: 102
Wine Barrel Distr
N.A.I.C.S.: 423840
Patrick Ghiot (Mgr-Market)

FRANCOIS FRERES MANAGEMENT   (1)
Village Bas, 21190, Saint-Romain, France
Tel.: (33) 3 80 21 23 33
Web Site: http://www.francoisfreres.com
Sales Range: $25-49.9 Million
Emp.: 50
Wine Barrel Mfr
N.A.I.C.S.: 321920
Jerome Francois (Mgr)

ISLA Cooperage Co. Ltd.   (1)
Isla Road, Keith, AB55 5DQ, Banffshire, United Kingdom
Tel.: (44) 1542 882337
Sales Range: $25-49.9 Million
Emp.: 2
Wooden Cask Repair & Maintenance Services
N.A.I.C.S.: 811490

LAGREZE   (1)
18 Avenue De Luzanne, 3380, Saint-Caprais-de-Bordeaux, France
Tel.: (33) 5 57 97 12 50
Wine Barrel Mfr
N.A.I.C.S.: 321920

Speyside Cooperage   (1)
Dufftown Road, Craigellachie, AB38 9RS, Banffshire, United Kingdom
Tel.: (44) 1340 871108
Web Site:
 http://www.speysidecooperage.co.uk
Emp.: 60
Wooden Cask Mfr
N.A.I.C.S.: 321920

TONNELLERIE DEMPTOS SA   (1)
18 Avenue le Luzanne, 33880, Saint-Caprais-de-Bordeaux, France
Tel.: (33) 5 57 97 12 50
Web Site: http://www.demptos.fr
Sales Range: $25-49.9 Million
Emp.: 7
Wine Barrel Mfr
N.A.I.C.S.: 321920
Jerome Francois (CEO)

TONNELLERIE PROVENCALE   (1)
Zone Industrielle Cana Est Rue Francois Labrousse, 19100, Brive-la-Gaillarde, France
Tel.: (33) 4 94 66 80 14
Wine Barrel Mfr
N.A.I.C.S.: 321920

TONOLLI CANADA LTD.
1333 Tonolli Rd, Mississauga, L4Y 4C2, ON, Canada
Tel.: (905) 279-9555
Web Site: http://www.tonolli.ca
Year Founded: 1958
Sales Range: $25-49.9 Million
Emp.: 80
Lead Acid Battery Recycler
N.A.I.C.S.: 335910
Ross Atkinson (Pres)

TONS LIGHTOLOGY, INC.
4F 236 Bo ai St, Shulin Dist, New Taipei City, 23845, Taiwan
Tel.: (886) 286857855
Web Site: https://www.tonslight.com
Year Founded: 1992
4972—(TPE)
Rev.: $28,571,460
Assets: $41,222,181
Liabilities: $5,758,434
Net Worth: $35,463,746
Earnings: $1,638,183
Emp.: 529
Fiscal Year-end: 12/31/22
Lighting Equipment Mfr
N.A.I.C.S.: 335139
Hung Chia-Cheng (Exec VP)

TONTEK DESIGN TECHNOLOGY CO., LTD.
6F No 166 Jian 1st Rd, Zhonghe Dist, New Taipei City, 235, Taiwan
Tel.: (886) 282265916
Web Site: https://www.tontek.com.tw
Year Founded: 1986
5487—(TPE)
Rev.: $7,371,291
Assets: $19,624,082
Liabilities: $2,096,708
Net Worth: $17,527,374
Earnings: ($56,843)
Emp.: 54
Fiscal Year-end: 12/31/22
Electronic Products Mfr
N.A.I.C.S.: 334419
Y. J. Lin (Chm)

Subsidiaries:

Tontek Technology (Shenzhen) Co., Ltd.   (1)
Unit 1907 tower A world Trade Plaza No 9 Fuhong Road, Futian District, Shenzhen, China
Tel.: (86) 75583662916
Electronic Components Mfr
N.A.I.C.S.: 334419

TONY FUN, INC.
555 Taishan Street, Tai'an, Shandong, China
Tel.: (86) 5388077188
Year Founded: 2017
Rev.: $2,019,848
Assets: $18,026,647
Liabilities: $23,255,016
Net Worth: ($5,228,369)
Earnings: ($2,676,500)
Fiscal Year-end: 12/31/19
Holding Company
N.A.I.C.S.: 551112
Zhiqiang Han (Chm, CEO & CFO-Interim)

TONYMOLY CO., LTD.
2557 Nambusunhwan-ro, Seocho-gu, Seoul, Korea (South)
Tel.: (82) 803562222
Web Site: https://corp.tonymoly.com
Year Founded: 2006
214420—(KRS)
Rev.: $97,213,427
Assets: $152,680,595
Liabilities: $77,987,812
Net Worth: $74,692,783
Earnings: ($1,824,392)
Emp.: 137
Fiscal Year-end: 12/31/22
Cosmetics, Skin Care, Hair Care & Body Care Mfr
N.A.I.C.S.: 325620
Haedong Bae (Pres & CEO)

TONZE NEW ENERGY TECHNOLOGY CO., LTD.
No 12-12 Block Chaoshan Road, Jinyuan Industrial City, Shantou, 5150021, China
Tel.: (86) 75488118888

INTERNATIONAL PUBLIC

Web Site: https://www.tonze.com
002759—(SSE)
Rev.: $459,756,648
Assets: $873,019,836
Liabilities: $291,370,716
Net Worth: $581,649,120
Earnings: $73,892,520
Emp.: 230
Fiscal Year-end: 12/31/22
Small Household Appliances, Electronic Products & Medical Devices Mfr & Distr
N.A.I.C.S.: 335210

Subsidiaries:

Shantou Tonze Electric Appliance Industry Co., Ltd.   (1)
West side of C03 Unit, Nanshanwan Industrial Park, Shantou, China
Tel.: (86) 75486702288
Lithium Battery Mfr
N.A.I.C.S.: 335910

TOOLGEN, INC.
8F 172 Magokjungang-ro, Gangseo-gu, Seoul, 151-724, Korea (South)
Tel.: (82) 236601300
Web Site: https://www.toolgen.com
Year Founded: 1999
199800—(KRS)
Biotechnology Products Researcher, Developer & Mfr
N.A.I.C.S.: 541714
Jin-Su Kim (Pres)

TOOLS INDUSTRIBEHOV GJOVIK AS
Kasper Andresensvei 7, Gjovik, 2815, Norway
Tel.: (47) 61146600
Web Site: http://www.tools.no
Year Founded: 1988
Sales Range: $1-9.9 Million
Emp.: 12
Tool Reselling Services
N.A.I.C.S.: 423830
Terje Terjesamsdengen (Chm & Mng Dir)

TOOLUX SANDING S.A.
Ganlin Town, Shaoxing, Zhe Jiang, China
Tel.: (86) 83272505
Web Site: https://www.toolux.com
Year Founded: 1992
ALTLX—(EUR)
Sales Range: $10-24.9 Million
Emp.: 181
Hand Tool Mfr
N.A.I.C.S.: 332216
Ji Nan Xu (Chm)

TOOPLE PLC
Phoenix House Elland Road, PO Box 501, Churwell, Leeds, LS27 7TB, Hertfordshire, United Kingdom
Tel.: (44) 8000499499   UK
Web Site: https://www.toople.com
Year Founded: 2016
TOOP—(LSE)
Rev.: $4,090,723
Assets: $2,840,688
Liabilities: $3,760,996
Net Worth: ($920,307)
Earnings: ($1,653,719)
Emp.: 20
Fiscal Year-end: 09/30/21
Broadband Internet Service Provider
N.A.I.C.S.: 517112
Andrew James Holingworth (CEO)

TOOSLA SA
24 Rue des Compagnons, 51350, Cormontreuil, France
Tel.: (33) 153673632
Web Site: https://apps.apple.com
Year Founded: 2016

AND PRIVATE COMPANIES

ALTOO—(EUR)
Vehicle Rental Services
N.A.I.C.S.: 532120
Eric Poncin (Chm)

TOP 10 CANADIAN FINANCIAL TRUST
121 King Street West Suite 2600, PO Box 113, Toronto, M5H 3T9, ON, Canada
Tel.: (416) 681-3966
Web Site:
   http://www.strathbridge.com
Year Founded: 2000
TCT.UN—(TSX)
Rev.: $1,921,242
Assets: $9,232,350
Liabilities: $1,733,484
Net Worth: $7,498,867
Earnings: $1,623,532
Fiscal Year-end: 12/31/19
Financial Investment Services
N.A.I.C.S.: 523999
John P. Mulvihill (Chm & CEO)

TOP 10 SPLIT TRUST
121 King Street West Suite 2600, PO Box 113, Toronto, M5H 3T9, ON, Canada
Tel.: (416) 681-3966
Web Site: https://mulvihill.com
TXT.UN—(TSX)
Rev.: $2,781,726
Assets: $13,881,640
Liabilities: $10,930,038
Net Worth: $2,951,602
Earnings: $1,761,231
Fiscal Year-end: 12/31/19
Financial Investment Services
N.A.I.C.S.: 523999
John P. Mulvihill (Chm & CEO)

TOP BRIGHT HOLDING CO., LTD.
955 Zhongzheng Rd 5th Floor, Zhonghe, New Taipei City, Taiwan
Tel.: (886) 222265102
8499—(TAI)
Rev.: $60,454,264
Assets: $367,274,946
Liabilities: $23,098,367
Net Worth: $344,176,579
Earnings: $18,673,076
Fiscal Year-end: 12/31/23
Electronic Component Mfr & Distr
N.A.I.C.S.: 334419
Ching-Hsuan Fu (Chm & Pres)

TOP BUILDERS CAPITAL BERHAD
No 35 37 And 39 Jalan PJU 1A/41B Pusat Dagangan NZX, 47301, Petaling Jaya, Selangor, Malaysia
Tel.: (60) 378850626 MY
Web Site: http://www.ikhmasjaya.com
Year Founded: 1992
Rev.: $48,523,164
Assets: $80,466,803
Liabilities: $73,742,633
Net Worth: $6,724,170
Earnings: ($38,798,396)
Fiscal Year-end: 12/31/19
Bridge Construction Services
N.A.I.C.S.: 237310
Cheng Siong Ang (Mng Dir)

TOP CREATION INVESTMENTS LIMITED
Queensway House Hilgrove Street, Saint Helier, JE1 1ES, Jersey
Tel.: (44) 20 86762514
Web Site: http://www.topcltd.com
Real Estate Investment Services
N.A.I.C.S.: 531390
Yu Sun Wong (Dir-Fin)

TOP CULTURE CO., LTD.
4-9-1 Kobari, Nishi-ku, Niigata, 950-2022, Japan
Tel.: (81) 252320008
Web Site:
   https://www.topculture.co.jp
Year Founded: 1986
7640—(TKS)
Rev.: $134,376,770
Assets: $122,203,240
Liabilities: $104,407,340
Net Worth: $17,795,900
Earnings: ($9,755,840)
Fiscal Year-end: 10/31/23
Merchandise Store Operator
N.A.I.C.S.: 455219
Hideo Shimizu (Founder & Pres)

TOP EDUCATION GROUP LTD.
Suite 1 Biomedical Building 1 Central Avenue, Eveleigh, Sydney, 2015, NSW, Australia
Tel.: (61) 292094888 AU
Web Site: https://www.top.edu.au
Year Founded: 2001
1752—(HKG)
Rev.: $19,391,693
Assets: $51,669,337
Liabilities: $18,203,793
Net Worth: $33,465,545
Earnings: $1,275,374
Emp.: 58
Fiscal Year-end: 06/30/24
Educational Support Services
N.A.I.C.S.: 611710
Zhu Minshen (CEO & Chm)

TOP END ENERGY LIMITED
Level 2 10 Outram Street, West Perth, 6005, WA, Australia
Tel.: (61) 862459836
Web Site:
   https://www.topendenergy.com.au
Year Founded: 2021
TEE—(ASX)
Oil & Gas Exploration Services
N.A.I.C.S.: 213112
Oliver Oxenbridge (Mng Dir)

TOP ENERGY COMPANY LTD.
No 272 Changzhi Road, Xiaodian District, Taiyuan, 030006, Shanxi, China
Tel.: (86) 3517021857
Web Site: http://www.600780.com.cn
Year Founded: 1992
600780—(SHG)
Rev.: $1,561,030,534
Assets: $1,408,433,313
Liabilities: $483,605,104
Net Worth: $924,828,208
Earnings: $119,922,112
Fiscal Year-end: 12/31/22
Thermal Electric Power Generation & Distribution Services
N.A.I.C.S.: 221116
Li Xin (Chm)

TOP ENGINEERING CO., LTD.
130 Gongsumul-gil Wollong-myeon, Paju, Gyeonggi-do, Korea (South)
Tel.: (82) 319563300
Web Site: http://www.topengnet.com
Year Founded: 1993
065130—(KRS)
Rev.: $718,253,193
Assets: $393,175,754
Liabilities: $164,089,950
Net Worth: $229,085,804
Earnings: ($32,957,704)
Emp.: 338
Fiscal Year-end: 12/31/22
Dispaly & Semiconductor Equipment Mfr
N.A.I.C.S.: 334413
Seo Sik (VP)

TOP FINANCIAL GROUP LIMITED
Unit 1101 118 Connaught Road West, Hong Kong, China (Hong Kong)
Tel.: (852) 31070731 Ky
Web Site: https://zyfgl.com
Year Founded: 2019
TOP—(NASDAQ)
Rev.: $8,037,105
Assets: $57,642,843
Liabilities: $17,111,938
Net Worth: $40,530,905
Earnings: $1,051,539
Emp.: 11
Fiscal Year-end: 03/31/24
Holding Company
N.A.I.C.S.: 551112
Ka Fai Yuen (CEO)

TOP FORM INTERNATIONAL LTD
7/F Port 33 33 Tseuk Luk Street San Po Kong, Kowloon, China (Hong Kong)
Tel.: (852) 23930171
Web Site:
   http://www.topformbras.com
0333—(HKG)
Rev.: $184,252,057
Assets: $120,787,577
Liabilities: $54,940,321
Net Worth: $65,847,257
Earnings: $921,562
Emp.: 7,681
Fiscal Year-end: 06/30/21
Apparel Distr & Mfr
N.A.I.C.S.: 315120
Eddie Chung chong Wong (Founder & Chm)

Subsidiaries:

Top Form International Ltd - China Nanhoi factory (1)
Block A Jian She Xi Road Yan Bu, Dali Town Nanhai, Foshan, 528247, Guangdong, China
Tel.: (86) 75785773050
Web Site: http://www.topform.com
Sales Range: $25-49.9 Million
Emp.: 200
Brassieres Mfr
N.A.I.C.S.: 315250

Top Form International Ltd - China Shenzhen Factory (1)
2-4/F Block 424 3 Bagua Ling Road, Futian District, Shenzhen, 518029, Guangdong, China
Tel.: (86) 755 82262786
Brassieres Mfr
N.A.I.C.S.: 315210

TOP FRONTIER INVESTMENT HOLDINGS, INC.
5th Floor ENZO Building 399 Sen Gil J Puyat Avenue, Makati, Philippines
Tel.: (63) 86323481 PH
Web Site:
   https://www.topfrontier.com.ph
Year Founded: 2008
TFHI—(PHI)
Rev.: $26,805,964,307
Assets: $45,259,390,402
Liabilities: $32,300,421,701
Net Worth: $12,958,968,702
Earnings: $424,618,779
Emp.: 50,496
Fiscal Year-end: 12/31/22
Holding Company
N.A.I.C.S.: 551112
Inigo U. Zobel (Chm)

Subsidiaries:

San Miguel Corporation (1)
40 San Miguel Avenue, PO Box 271, Manila Central Post Office, Mandaluyong, 1550, Metro Manila, Philippines (66.13%)
Tel.: (63) 286323000

TOP FRONTIER INVESTMENT HOLDINGS, INC.

Web Site: https://www.sanmiguel.com.ph
Rev.: $15,096,577,600
Assets: $39,773,905,600
Liabilities: $26,148,075,200
Net Worth: $13,625,830,400
Earnings: $455,083,200
Emp.: 45,522
Fiscal Year-end: 12/31/2020
Alcoholic & Non-Alcoholic Beverages, Food & Packaging Products Mfr & Whslr
N.A.I.C.S.: 312120
Ferdinand K. Constantino (CFO & Treas)

Subsidiary (Domestic):

Eagle Cement Corporation (2)
155 EDSA Brgy Wack Wack 2F SMITS Corporate Center, Mandaluyong, Philippines (100%)
Tel.: (63) 253013453
Web Site: http://www.eaglecement.com.ph
Rev.: $289,247,699
Assets: $1,032,910,365
Liabilities: $227,647,213
Net Worth: $805,263,151
Earnings: $70,540,965
Emp.: 516
Fiscal Year-end: 12/31/2020
Construction Material Mfr & Distr
N.A.I.C.S.: 327310
Ramon S. Ang (Chm)

Ginebra San Miguel, Inc. (2)
3rd 5th & 6th Floors San Miguel Properties Centre St Francis Street, Ortigas Center, Mandaluyong, 1550, Metro Manila, Philippines (79.62%)
Tel.: (63) 288415100
Web Site:
   https://www.ginebrasanmiguel.com
Rev.: $954,406,077
Assets: $494,080,329
Liabilities: $166,678,426
Net Worth: $327,401,904
Earnings: $125,369,084
Emp.: 1,200
Fiscal Year-end: 12/31/2023
Gin & Other Alcoholic Beverages Distiller & Whslr
N.A.I.C.S.: 312140
Ramon S. Ang (Pres)

Subsidiary (Domestic):

Distileria Bago, Inc. (3)
Km 13 5 Taloc, Bago City, Bago, Philippines (100%)
Tel.: (63) 26899100
Web Site: http://www.ginebrasanmiguel.com
Alcohol Distillery
N.A.I.C.S.: 312140

Subsidiary (Non-US):

Petron Malaysia Refining & Marketing Bhd. (2)
Level 12A Menara I&P 1 No 46 Jalan Dungun Damansara Heights, 50490, Kuala Lumpur, Malaysia
Tel.: (60) 320828400
Web Site: https://www.petron.com.my
Sales Range: $150-199.9 Million
Petroleum Products, Lubricating Oil & Grease, Ammonia & Sulphur
N.A.I.C.S.: 211120

Subsidiary (Domestic):

San Miguel Brewery Inc. (2)
40 San Miguel Avenue, Mandaluyong, 1550, Metro Manila, Philippines (100%)
Tel.: (63) 26323000
Web Site:
   https://www.sanmiguelbrewery.com.ph
Beer Brewer & Whslr
N.A.I.C.S.: 312120

Subsidiary (Non-US):

San Miguel Brewery Hong Kong Ltd. (3)
9/F Citimark Building 28 Yuen Shun Circuit, Siu Lek Yuen, Sha Tin, New Territories, China (Hong Kong) (65.78%)
Tel.: (852) 24910411
Web Site: https://info.sanmiguel.com.hk
Rev.: $86,848,283
Assets: $91,716,360
Liabilities: $16,527,188
Net Worth: $75,189,173

TOP FRONTIER INVESTMENT HOLDINGS, INC.

Top Frontier Investment Holdings, Inc.—(Continued)
Earnings: $4,224,713
Emp.: 460
Fiscal Year-end: 12/31/2022
Beer Brewer & Distr
N.A.I.C.S.: 312120
Ramon S. Ang *(Chm)*

Subsidiary (Non-US):

Guangzhou San Miguel Brewery Co., Ltd. (4)
63 Xizeng Road, Xicun, Guangzhou, 510160, China (70%)
Tel.: (86) 2086509983
Web Site: http://info.sanmiguel.com.hk
Beer Brewer & Whslr
N.A.I.C.S.: 312120

San Miguel (Guangdong) Brewery Co., Ltd. (4)
Renmin Road, Longjiang, 528310, Shunde, China (100%)
Tel.: (86) 75723888222
Web Site: http://www.sanmiguel.com.ph
Beer Brewer & Whslr
N.A.I.C.S.: 312120

Subsidiary (Domestic):

San Miguel Food and Beverage, Inc. (2)
40 San Miguel Avenue, Mandaluyong, 1550, Philippines (85.4%)
Tel.: (63) 26323417
Web Site: https://www.smfb.com.ph
Rev.: $6,857,849,533
Assets: $6,423,670,608
Liabilities: $3,370,226,564
Net Worth: $3,053,444,044
Earnings: $688,002,160
Emp.: 9,780
Fiscal Year-end: 12/31/2023
Beef & Poultry Meat Processing & Marketing; Flour Milling; Animal Feed Mfr
N.A.I.C.S.: 311612
Ramon S. Ang *(Vice Chm, Pres & CEO)*

Subsidiary (Domestic):

Magnolia, Inc. (3)
21st Floor The JMT Corporate Condominium ADB Avenue cor J Vargas St, Ortigas Center, Pasig, 1605, Philippines
Tel.: (63) 2 632 2000
Web Site: http://www.magnolia.com.ph
Sales Range: $100-124.9 Million
Emp.: 322
Milk, Butter, Cheese, Margarine, Edible Fats & Oils Mfr & Whslr
N.A.I.C.S.: 424490

San Miguel Foods, Inc. (3)
No 100 E Rodriguez Jr Avenue C5 Road, Barangay Ugong, Pasig, 1604, Philippines (63.89%)
Tel.: (63) 27025000
Web Site: http://www.sanmiguel.com.ph
Emp.: 100
Poultry Processor & Animal Feed Mfr
N.A.I.C.S.: 311615

The Purefoods-Hormel Company, Inc. (3)
17 Fl JMT Corporate Condominium, ADB Ave Ortigas Ctr, Pasig, Philippines (60%)
Tel.: (63) 29141111
Sales Range: $50-74.9 Million
Emp.: 105
Processed Meats & Canned Meat Products Mfr & Marketer
N.A.I.C.S.: 311612

Subsidiary (Domestic):

San Miguel Properties, Inc. (2)
3/F San Miguel Head Office Complex, 40 San Miguel Ave Ortigas Center, Mandaluyong, 1550, Philippines (98.45%)
Tel.: (63) 28632300
Web Site: https://www.sanmiguelproperties.com.ph
Sales Range: $10-24.9 Million
Emp.: 22
Real Estate Development, Sales & Leasing Services
N.A.I.C.S.: 531390
Ramon S. Ang *(Chm & Pres)*

San Miguel Yamamura Asia Corporation (2)
Km 27 Aguenaldo Hwy, Cavite, Philippines (60%)
Tel.: (63) 26322650
Web Site: http://www.sanmiguel.com.ph
Glass Container Mfr
N.A.I.C.S.: 327213

San Miguel Yamamura Packaging Corporation (2)
9th Fl San Miguel Properties Centre 7 St Francis St Ortigas Center, Mandaluyong, 1550, Metro Manila, Philippines (65%)
Tel.: (63) 27024200
Web Site: http://www.smypc.com.ph
Sales Range: $100-124.9 Million
Emp.: 163
Total Packaging Solutions; Glass, Plastics, Metal, Flexibles, PET, Molds & Paper
N.A.I.C.S.: 327213

TOP GLOBAL LIMITED

302 Orchard Road 18-02 Tong Building, Singapore, 238862, Singapore
Tel.: (65) 67464333
Web Site: http://www.topglobal.com.sg
Rev.: $43,277,388
Assets: $439,569,393
Liabilities: $146,501,885
Net Worth: $293,067,508
Earnings: $3,965,840
Fiscal Year-end: 12/31/19
Holding Company; Commercial Real Estate Investment, Property Development & Management Services
N.A.I.C.S.: 551112
Rose Ling *(Dir-Admin, Sls & Collaboration)*

Subsidiaries:

Raintree Cove Pte. Ltd. (1)
1 Scotts Road 20-03 Shaw Centre, Singapore, 228208, Singapore
Tel.: (65) 67464333
Facility Management Services
N.A.I.C.S.: 561210

Top Global Real Estate Investment Pte. Ltd. (1)
302 Orchard Road Tong Building Unit 18-02, Singapore, 238862, Singapore
Tel.: (65) 67464333
Web Site: http://www.topglobal.com.sg
Emp.: 22
Real Estate Investment Trust
N.A.I.C.S.: 525990
Rose Ling *(Dir-HR)*

TOP GLOVE CORPORATION BHD.

Level 21 Top Glove Tower, 16 Persiaran Setia Dagang Setia Alam Seksyen U13, 40170, Shah Alam, Selangor DE, Malaysia
Tel.: (60) 333623098 MY
Web Site: https://www.topglove.com
Year Founded: 2001
TOPGLOV—(KLS)
Rev.: $4,049,457,143
Assets: $2,421,149,940
Liabilities: $634,160,340
Net Worth: $1,786,989,600
Earnings: $1,936,438,020
Emp.: 22,000
Fiscal Year-end: 08/31/21
Rubber Glove Mfr
N.A.I.C.S.: 315990
Kim Meow Lee *(Mng Dir)*

Subsidiaries:

Great Glove (Xinghua) Co. Ltd. (1)
No 4 Shazhuang Road, Economic Development District Xinghua, Taizhou, 225700, Jiang Su, China
Tel.: (86) 52383268976
Glove Mfr & Distr
N.A.I.C.S.: 339113

Kevenoll Do Brasil Produtos Medicos Hospitalares Ltda (1)
Rod Antonio Heil 1001-KM0 Sala 203 Itaipava, Itajai, 88316-001, Santa Catarina, Brazil
Tel.: (55) 4733496168
Web Site: https://www.kevenoll.com.br
Medical Product Distr
N.A.I.C.S.: 423450
Lim Wee Chai *(Chm)*

TG Ecommerce Sdn. Bhd. (1)
5090 Jalan Teratai Meru, 41050, Klang, Selangor, Malaysia
Tel.: (60) 129116897
Web Site: https://www.tgebuy.com
Ecommerce Services
N.A.I.C.S.: 423690

TG Medical (U.S.A.) Inc. (1)
155 N Aspan Ave, Azusa, CA 91702
Tel.: (626) 969-8808
Sales Range: $25-49.9 Million
Emp.: 21
Rubber Gloves Whslr
N.A.I.C.S.: 315990

TG Medical Sdn. Bhd. (1)
Lot 5091 Jalan Teratai Batu 5 Off Jalan Meru, 41050, Kelang, Selangor, Malaysia
Tel.: (60) 333927880
Rubber Gloves Mfr & Whslr
N.A.I.C.S.: 315990
Wee Chai Lim *(Chm)*

Plant (Domestic):

TG Medical Sdn. Bhd. - Factory 14 (2)
Lot 5104 Jalan Teratai Batu 5 Off Jalan Meru, 41050, Kelang, Selangor, Malaysia
Tel.: (60) 333923626
Sales Range: $150-199.9 Million
Emp.: 400
Rubber Glove Mfr
N.A.I.C.S.: 315990
Kim Meow Lee *(Mng Dir)*

Top Glove Europe GmbH (1)
Bliersheimer Str 80 A, 47229, Duisburg, Germany
Tel.: (49) 2065764210
Web Site: https://www.topglove.de
Glove Mfr & Distr
N.A.I.C.S.: 339113

Top Glove Sdn. Bhd. (1)
Lot 4969 Jalan Teratai Batu 6 Off Jalan Meru, 41050, Kelang, Selangor, Malaysia
Tel.: (60) 333921992
Rubber Gloves Mfr & Whslr
N.A.I.C.S.: 315990
Kim Meow Lee *(Mng Dir)*

Subsidiary (Non-US):

B Tech Industry Co. Ltd. (2)
268 Moo 5 Tambon Kampangphet, Amphur Rattaphum, 90180, Songkhla, Thailand
Tel.: (66) 74302888
Latex Concentrates Mfr & Distr
N.A.I.C.S.: 325212

Subsidiary (Domestic):

Flexitech Sdn Bhd (2)
Lot 124 and 126 Jalan 8 Kompleks Perabot Olak Lempit 13KM, Jalan Banting Dengkil, 42700, Banting, Selangor Darul Ehsan, Malaysia
Tel.: (60) 331491998
Web Site: http://www.medi-flex.com.sg
Sales Range: $50-74.9 Million
Disposal Gloves Mfr
N.A.I.C.S.: 339113
Noraziah Mahmud *(Sr Gen Mgr-Mktg)*

Subsidiary (Non-US):

Great Glove (Thailand) Co. Ltd. (2)
180/3 Moo 7 Srisoontorn Road Tambon Srisoontorn, Amphur Thalang, Phuket, 83110, Thailand
Tel.: (66) 76620190
Web Site: https://www.topglove.com.my
Sales Range: $75-99.9 Million
Emp.: 350
Rubber Glove Mfr
N.A.I.C.S.: 315990

INTERNATIONAL PUBLIC

Top Glove Medical (Thailand) Co. Ltd. (2)
188 Moo 5 Kanchanawanich Road, Tamboi Samnakhan Amphur Sadao, Songkhla, 90320, Thailand
Tel.: (66) 74410000
Sales Range: $150-199.9 Million
Emp.: 700
Rubber Glove Mfr
N.A.I.C.S.: 339113

Plant (Domestic):

Top Glove Sdn. Bhd. - Factory 11 (2)
Lot 4967 Jalan Teratai Batu 6 Off Jalan Meru, 41050, Klang, Selangor Darul Ehsan, Malaysia
Tel.: (60) 33 392 1899
Web Site: http://www.topglove.com.my
Emp.: 8,000
Rubber Glove Mfr
N.A.I.C.S.: 315990

Top Glove Sdn. Bhd. - Factory 13 (2)
Lot 4947 Jalan Teratai Batu 6 Off Jalan Meru, 41050, Kelang, Selangor, Malaysia
Tel.: (60) 333931288
Sales Range: $1-4.9 Billion
Emp.: 5,000
Rubber Glove Mfr
N.A.I.C.S.: 326299
Kim Lee Meow *(Mng Dir)*

Top Glove Sdn. Bhd. - Factory 19 (2)
Lot 4987 Jalan Bunga Raya Batu 6 Off Jalan Meru, 41050, Klang, Selangor Darul Ehsan, Malaysia
Tel.: (60) 33 392 5900
Web Site: http://www.topglove.com.my
Sales Range: $200-249.9 Million
Emp.: 628
Rubber Glove Mfr
N.A.I.C.S.: 326299

Top Glove Sdn. Bhd. - Factory 4 (2)
Lot 5987 Jalan Teratai Batu 5 Off Jalan Meru, 41050, Kelang, Selangor Darul Ehsan, Malaysia
Tel.: (60) 33 392 8588
Web Site: http://www.topglove.com.my
Rubber Glove Mfr
N.A.I.C.S.: 315990

Top Glove Sdn. Bhd. - Factory 5 (2)
Lot 18 27 38 57 Medan Tasek, Kawasan Perindustrian Tasek, 31400, Ipoh, Perak Darul Ridzuan, Malaysia
Tel.: (60) 554792715
Sales Range: $200-249.9 Million
Emp.: 500
Rubber Glove Mfr
N.A.I.C.S.: 326299

Subsidiary (Non-US):

Top Glove Technology (Thailand) Co. Ltd. (2)
188 Moo 5 Tambol Pangla, Amphur Sadao, Songkhla, 90170, Thailand
Tel.: (66) 7441888
Web Site: https://www.topglove.com.my
Latex Concentrates Mfr & Distr
N.A.I.C.S.: 325212

TOP HIGH IMAGE CORP.

No 20 Juguang 2nd Street, Daliao Dist, Kaohsiung, 83100, Taiwan
Tel.: (886) 77877690
Web Site: https://www.ctptop.com.tw
Year Founded: 1998
3284—(TPE)
Rev.: $24,941,313
Assets: $50,923,366
Liabilities: $19,919,426
Net Worth: $31,003,940
Earnings: $1,111,903
Fiscal Year-end: 12/31/22
Printing Services
N.A.I.C.S.: 323120
Chi-Sun Wang *(CEO)*

TOP KINGWIN LTD.

Room 1304 Building No 25 Tian'an Headquarters Center, No 555 North Panyu Avenue Donghuan Street Panyu District, Guangzhou, 511400, Guangdong, China
Tel.: (86) 4006613113 Ky
Year Founded: 2018
TCJH—(NASDAQ)
Rev.: $6,294,667
Assets: $5,878,748
Liabilities: $3,081,794
Net Worth: $2,796,954
Earnings: $2,308,626
Emp.: 40
Fiscal Year-end: 12/31/21
Investment Management Service
N.A.I.C.S.: 523999
Ruilin Xu *(Chm & CEO)*

TOP KINISIS TRAVEL PUBLIC LTD
2 Leonidou & Acropoleos Ave, PO Box 27031, 2007, Strovolos, Cyprus
Tel.: (357) 22713755
Web Site: https://www.topkinisis.com
Year Founded: 1987
TOP—(CYP)
Sales Range: Less than $1 Million
Emp.: 70
Tour Operating Services
N.A.I.C.S.: 561520

Subsidiaries:

Kinisis Travel & Tours Inc. (1)
29 - 13 23rd Ave Fl 2, Astoria, NY 11105
Tel.: (718) 267-6880
Travel & Tour Operator
N.A.I.C.S.: 561510

Top Kinisis Hellas (1)
Filellinon 22 3rd Floor, Syntagma, 10557, Athens, Greece
Tel.: (30) 210 3232501
Web Site: http://www.taxidiamprosta.com
Sales Range: $25-49.9 Million
Emp.: 3
Travel & Tour Operator
N.A.I.C.S.: 561510
George Antonarosh *(Gen Mgr)*

TOP MATERIAL CO., LTD.
554-30 Deokpyeong ro Hobeopmyeon, Icheon, Gyeonggi-do, Korea (South)
Tel.: (82) 316329876
Web Site: https://www.topmaterial.co.kr
Year Founded: 2012
360070—(KRS)
Engineeering Services
N.A.I.C.S.: 541330

TOP RAMDOR SYSTEMS & COMPUTERS 1990 CO LTD.
Raoul Wallenberg 24, PO Box 58184, Tel Aviv, Israel
Tel.: (972) 37667711
Web Site: https://top-group.co.il
Year Founded: 1990
TOPS—(TAE)
Rev.: $65,402,955
Assets: $79,586,129
Liabilities: $59,263,157
Net Worth: $20,322,972
Earnings: $3,472,855
Emp.: 187
Fiscal Year-end: 12/31/23
Custom Computer Programming Services
N.A.I.C.S.: 541511
Gilad Har-Oz *(Co-CEO)*

TOP RESOURCE ENERGY CO., LTD.
22A Building B Vantone Center No 6 Chaoyangmenwai Street, Chaoyang District, Beijing, 100082, China
Tel.: (86) 1062215518

Web Site: https://www.thny.cc
Year Founded: 2007
300332—(CHIN)
Rev.: $539,394,196
Assets: $1,304,818,070
Liabilities: $718,927,438
Net Worth: $585,890,632
Earnings: $51,315,526
Fiscal Year-end: 12/31/22
Natural Gas Supply & Related Equipment Installation; Power Plants Investment, Construction & Operations
N.A.I.C.S.: 237990
Chen Zuotao *(Chm & Gen Mgr)*

TOP SCORE FASHION CO., LTD.
No 31 Yinsha Street Dongyong Town, Nansha District, Guangzhou, 511475, Guangdong, China
Tel.: (86) 2039301538
Web Site: https://www.topscore.com.cn
Year Founded: 2004
603608—(SHG)
Rev.: $178,700,488
Assets: $300,991,078
Liabilities: $111,497,635
Net Worth: $189,493,443
Earnings: ($25,107,451)
Fiscal Year-end: 12/31/22
Footwear Mfr & Distr
N.A.I.C.S.: 316210
Yang Lu *(Sec)*

TOP SHELF INTERNATIONAL HOLDINGS LTD.
16-18 National Boulevard, Campbellfield, 3061, VIC, Australia
Tel.: (61) 383179990 AU
Web Site: https://www.topshelfgroup.com.au
Year Founded: 2013
TSI—(ASX)
Rev.: $17,961,140
Assets: $51,800,222
Liabilities: $37,016,366
Net Worth: $14,783,856
Earnings: ($31,486,601)
Fiscal Year-end: 06/30/23
Holding Company
N.A.I.C.S.: 551112

TOP SHIPS, INC.
1 Vasilisis Sofias and Megalou Alexandrou Str, 15124, Maroussi, Greece
Tel.: (30) 2108128000 MH
Web Site: http://www.topships.org
TOPS—(NASDAQ)
Rev.: $82,949,000
Assets: $459,189,000
Liabilities: $319,725,000
Net Worth: $139,464,000
Earnings: ($22,370,000)
Emp.: 178
Fiscal Year-end: 12/31/23
Liquid & Petroleum Transportation & Dry Bulk Freight Shipping
N.A.I.C.S.: 483111
Evangelos J. Pistiolis *(Founder, Pres & CEO)*

TOP SPRING INTERNATIONAL HOLDINGS LIMITED
Rooms 04-08 26th Floor Shui On Centre 6-8 Harbour Road, Wanchai, China (Hong Kong)
Tel.: (852) 31062350
Web Site: http://www.topspring.com
3688—(HKG)
Rev.: $467,563,283
Assets: $2,783,661,600
Liabilities: $1,600,205,835
Net Worth: $1,183,455,765
Earnings: ($23,414,228)
Emp.: 883

Fiscal Year-end: 12/31/22
Residential Real Estate Property Developer
N.A.I.C.S.: 237210
Chun Hong Wong *(Founder, Chm & CEO)*

TOP STANDARD CORPORATION
Flat 2202 22/F West Exchange Tower 322 Des Voeux Road, Central, Sheung Wan, China (Hong Kong)
Tel.: (852) 21329610 Ky
Web Site: https://www.topstandard.com.hk
Year Founded: 2008
8510—(HKG)
Rev.: $1,609,670
Assets: $1,304,246
Liabilities: $3,338,647
Net Worth: ($2,034,402)
Earnings: ($1,137,475)
Emp.: 31
Fiscal Year-end: 12/31/22
Restaurant Operators
N.A.I.C.S.: 722511

Subsidiaries:

MOW Limited (1)
Unit 3C 3/F Yue Xiu Industrial Building 87 Hung To Road, Kwun Tong, Kowloon, China (Hong Kong)
Tel.: (852) 56400900
Web Site: https://mow.com.hk
Red Wine Mfr & Distr
N.A.I.C.S.: 312130

TOP TASTE HOLDING BV
Korenhalmdijk 17, 4431 NE, 's-Gravenpolder, Netherlands
Tel.: (31) 113 315 050
Web Site: http://www.toponions.com
Holding Company
N.A.I.C.S.: 551112
Adrie Murre *(Mng Dir)*

Subsidiaries:

Lion Foods B.V. (1)
Nijverheidsweg 5, PO Box 57, 4695 ZH, Saint Maartensdijk, Netherlands (100%)
Tel.: (31) 166663644
Web Site: http://www.lionfoods.nl
Sales Range: $25-49.9 Million
Emp.: 100
Crispy Fried Onions Mfr
N.A.I.C.S.: 311999
Rien van Meel *(Mng Dir)*

Triumfus Onion Products Onions b.v. (1)
Baarlandsezandweg 5, 4431 NJ, 's-Gravenpolder, Netherlands
Tel.: (31) 113 315 050
Web Site: http://www.toponions.com
Emp.: 100
Onion Growing & Processing
N.A.I.C.S.: 111219
Adrie Murre *(Mng Dir)*

TOP UNION ELECTRONICS CORP.
No 480 Nioupu E Rd, Siangshan Dist, Hsinchu, Taiwan
Tel.: (886) 35386139
Web Site: https://www.topunion.com.tw
Year Founded: 1990
6266—(TPE)
Rev.: $103,013,757
Assets: $99,673,670
Liabilities: $32,261,576
Net Worth: $67,412,094
Earnings: $10,300,034
Emp.: 511
Fiscal Year-end: 12/31/22
Electronic Products Mfr
N.A.I.C.S.: 334419
Shih-Ho Tsui *(Chm & Pres)*

TOP VISION EYE SPECIALIST CENTRE
Unit 11-2 & 11-3 No 2 Block 2 Jalan Setia Prima S U13/S Seksyen U13, Setia Alam, 40170, Shah Alam, Selangor, Malaysia
Tel.: (60) 333439911
Web Site: http://www.tvesc.com
Year Founded: 2010
Healthcare Services
N.A.I.C.S.: 621999
Kenny Liew *(Founder & CEO)*

TOP WEALTH GROUP HOLDING LIMITED
Units 714 & 715 Hong Kong Plaza Connaught Road West, Hong Kong, China (Hong Kong)
Tel.: (852) 36158567 Ky
Year Founded: 2023
TWG—(NASDAQ)
Rev.: $16,943,287
Assets: $7,348,982
Liabilities: $2,396,346
Net Worth: $4,952,636
Earnings: $2,438,095
Emp.: 12
Fiscal Year-end: 12/31/23
Holding Company
N.A.I.C.S.: 551112

TOPASIA COMPUTER LIMITED
Unit 2001-2 Lipo chun Chambers Voeux Road, Central, China (Hong Kong)
Tel.: (852) 28 896289
Web Site: http://www.topasia.com
Year Founded: 1992
Sales Range: $25-49.9 Million
Emp.: 10
Computer Network System Integration Services
N.A.I.C.S.: 541512

TOPBI INTERNATIONAL HOLDINGS LIMITED
2F No 97 Xinhu 1st Road, Neihu District, Taipei, 11494, Taiwan
Tel.: (886) 227938077
Web Site: https://www.topbi.com.tw
Year Founded: 2012
2929—(TAI)
Rev.: $78,036,427
Assets: $133,061,966
Liabilities: $41,453,905
Net Worth: $91,608,061
Earnings: ($2,230,550)
Fiscal Year-end: 12/31/23
Children's Clothing & Accessories Mfr
N.A.I.C.S.: 315250
Xun-Cai Zhou *(Chm)*

TOPCHOICE MEDICAL CORPORATION
Building 5 Hesheng International Trade Center No 21 Lingxi North Road, Hangzhou, 310013, Zhejiang, China
Tel.: (86) 57188923999
Web Site: https://www.tcmedical.com.cn
Year Founded: 1995
600763—(SHG)
Rev.: $381,693,195
Assets: $723,685,187
Liabilities: $215,685,807
Net Worth: $507,999,380
Earnings: $76,976,968
Fiscal Year-end: 12/31/22
Dental Care Services
N.A.I.C.S.: 622110
Jianming Lu *(Co-Chm)*

TOPCO OILSITE PRODUCTS LTD.

TOPCO OILSITE PRODUCTS LTD.

Topco Oilsite Products Ltd.—(Continued)
Bay 7 3401 - 19th Street NE, Calgary, T2E 6S8, AB, Canada
Tel.: (403) 219-0255
Web Site:
https://www.topcooilsite.com
Year Founded: 1959
Sales Range: $25-49.9 Million
Emp.: 80
Oilfield Product Mfr & Distr
N.A.I.C.S.: 213111
Tom Lemmon *(Coord-Safety)*

Subsidiaries:

Topco Oilsite Products (USA) Inc. (1)
8200 W Reno, Oklahoma City, OK 73127
Tel.: (405) 491-8521
Oilfield Product Distr
N.A.I.C.S.: 423120
Larry McDonald *(Mgr-Ops)*

TOPCO SCIENTIFIC CO., LTD.

No 483 Sec 2 Tiding Blvd, Neihu, Taipei, 11493, Taiwan
Tel.: (886) 287978020
Web Site: https://www.topco-global.com
Year Founded: 1990
5434—(TAI)
Rev.: $1,611,349,395
Assets: $1,034,551,091
Liabilities: $532,758,670
Net Worth: $501,792,420
Earnings: $93,296,507
Emp.: 1,842
Fiscal Year-end: 12/31/23
Electronic Product Whslr
N.A.I.C.S.: 423690

Subsidiaries:

Anyong Biotechnology Co., Ltd. (1)
No 483 Sec 2 Tiding Blvd Neihu Dist, Taipei, 11493, Taiwan
Tel.: (886) 287978020
Semiconductor & Electronic Component Distr
N.A.I.C.S.: 333242

Anyong Freshmart, Inc. (1)
No 483 Sec 2 Tiding Blvd, Neihu District, Taipei, 11493, Taiwan
Tel.: (886) 800538835
Web Site: https://
Semiconductor & Electronic Component Distr
N.A.I.C.S.: 333242

Chien Yueh Technology Engineering Co., Ltd. (1)
8F No 483 Sec 2 Tiding Blvd Neihu, Taipei, 11493, Taiwan
Tel.: (886) 287978020
Water Purification Services
N.A.I.C.S.: 423720

Jia Yi Energy Co., Ltd. (1)
3F-10 No 12 Fuxing 4th Rd Qianzhen District, Kaohsiung, 80661, Taiwan
Tel.: (886) 75377626
Web Site: http://www.jiayi-global.com
Machinery & Electronic Mfr
N.A.I.C.S.: 333517

Jing Yueh Energy Co., Ltd. (1)
4F No 483 Section 2 Tiding Avenue, Neihu District, Taipei, Taiwan
Tel.: (886) 287978020
Renewable Energy Development Services
N.A.I.C.S.: 541690

Kanbo Biomedical Co., Ltd. (1)
5th Floor No 483 Section 2 Dingding Avenue, Neihu District, 11493, Taipei, Taiwan
Tel.: (886) 287978020
Web Site: http://www.kanbo-bio.com
Food Products Distr
N.A.I.C.S.: 424220

Kuan Yueh Technology Engineering Co., Ltd. (1)
No 483 Sec 2 Tiding Blvd Neihu District, Taipei, 11493, Taiwan
Tel.: (886) 287978020
Fishery Product Distr
N.A.I.C.S.: 311710

Ping Yue Technologies Sdn. Bhd. (1)
1-21-03A Suntech Penang Cybercity Lintang Mayang Pasir 3, 11950, Bayan Baru, Penang, Malaysia
Tel.: (60) 42877454
Semiconductor Equipment Distr
N.A.I.C.S.: 423690

Shin-Etsu Handotai Taiwan Co., Ltd. (1)
No 12 Gongye E 9th Rd East Dist, Hsinchu, 30075, Taiwan
Tel.: (886) 35771188
Semiconductor & Electronic Component Distr
N.A.I.C.S.: 333242

Shin-Etsu Opto Electronic Co., Ltd. (1)
1F No 30 Gongye E 4th Rd East Dist, Hsinchu, 30077, Taiwan
Tel.: (886) 35784566
Semiconductor & Electronic Component Distr
N.A.I.C.S.: 333242

Shunkawa Co., Ltd. (1)
Googolplex Millennium 5F 4-4-20 Shiba, Minato-ku, Tokyo, 108-0014, Japan
Tel.: (81) 366658323
Web Site: https://www.shunkawa.com
Electronic Components Distr
N.A.I.C.S.: 423610

Taiwan E&M System Inc. (1)
1F No 16 Prosperity 2nd Road, Science Based Industrial Park, Hsinchu, 30078, Taiwan
Tel.: (886) 35641224
Web Site: https://www.tteam.com.tw
Electronic Material Distr
N.A.I.C.S.: 423690

Topchem Materials Corp. (1)
No 483 Sec 2 Tiding Blvd, Neihu District, Taipei, 11493, Taiwan
Tel.: (886) 287978020
Semiconductor & Electronic Component Distr
N.A.I.C.S.: 333242

Topco Quartz Products Co., Ltd. (1)
No 8 Wenhua Rd Hukou Township, Hsinchu, 30352, Taiwan
Tel.: (886) 35985668
Semiconductor & Electronic Component Distr
N.A.I.C.S.: 333242

Topco Scientific USA Corp. (1)
10429 S 51st St Ste 105, Phoenix, AZ 85044
Tel.: (480) 597-3161
Semiconductor Material Whslr
N.A.I.C.S.: 423690

Topscience (s) Pte. Ltd. (1)
140 Paya Lebar Rd 08-03/04 AZ, Paya Lebar, 409015, Singapore
Tel.: (65) 67866800
Emp.: 18
Semiconductor Distr
N.A.I.C.S.: 423690

Unitech New Energy Engineering Co., Ltd. (1)
Room 7 17F No 77 Section 1 Xintai 5th Road, Xizhi District, New Taipei City, Taiwan
Tel.: (886) 226981277
Environment Related Engineering Services
N.A.I.C.S.: 541330

Xprots Sports Co., Ltd. (1)
2F No 483 Section 2 Tiding Avenue, Neihu District, New Taipei City, Taiwan
Tel.: (886) 287978020
Sports Training Services
N.A.I.C.S.: 611620

TOPCON CORPORATION

75-1 Hasunuma-cho, Itabashi-ku, Tokyo, 174 8580, Japan
Tel.: (81) 335582532   **JP**
Web Site: https://www.topcon.co.jp
Year Founded: 1932
TOPCF—(OTCIQ)
Rev.: $1,546,031,250
Assets: $1,490,571,300
Liabilities: $794,794,500
Net Worth: $695,776,800
Earnings: $84,649,020
Emp.: 5,543
Fiscal Year-end: 03/31/23
Optical Instruments & Lenses Mfr & Sales
N.A.I.C.S.: 333310
Makoto Iwasaki *(Sr Mng Exec Officer & Gen Mgr-Gen Admin & Legal Div)*

Subsidiaries:

Asia General Holding Co.,Ltd. (1)
No 501/503 Pyay Road Corner of Pyi Yeik Thar Street, Kamaryut Township, Yangon, Myanmar
Tel.: (95) 12304273
Web Site: https://wp.agholding.com
Emp.: 800
Switch Gear Mfr & Distr
N.A.I.C.S.: 335313

ClearEdge3D, Inc. (1)
7960 Donegan Dr Ste 223, Manassas, VA 20109
Tel.: (886)
Web Site: http://www.clearedge3d.com
Software Publisher
N.A.I.C.S.: 513210
Tim Lowery *(VP-Sls & Bus Dev)*

Ivolve Pty. Ltd. (1)
Level 6 52 Merivale Street South, Brisbane, 4101, QLD, Australia
Tel.: (61) 73 253 6700
Web Site: https://www.ivolve.com
Computer Software Development Services
N.A.I.C.S.: 513210
David Eagles *(CTO)*

Mehra Eyetech Pvt. Ltd. (1)
801 B Wing Lotus Corporate Park, Graham Firth Steel Compound Goregaon East, Mumbai, 400063, Maharashtra, India
Tel.: (91) 2261285455
Optical Equipment Mfr
N.A.I.C.S.: 333310

Shanghai Topcon-Sokkia Technology & Trading Co., Ltd. (1)
Section E 5F Building 1 No 389 Gangao Road, Shanghai Pilot Free Trade Zone, Shanghai, 200131, China
Tel.: (86) 2163541844
Optical Equipment Mfr
N.A.I.C.S.: 333310

Sokkia Korea Co., Ltd. (1)
2nd Floor 541 Dosan-daero Cheongdamdong Seshin Building, Gangnam-gu, Seoul, Korea (South)
Tel.: (82) 2 514 0491
Web Site: https://www.sokkia.co.kr
Computer Software Development Services
N.A.I.C.S.: 513210

Thunderbuild BV (1)
Beukenlaan 119, 5616 VC, Eindhoven, Netherlands
Tel.: (31) 882411000
Optical Equipment Mfr
N.A.I.C.S.: 333310

Tierra S.p.a. (1)
C so Ferrucci 112, 10138, Rivalta di Torino, Italy
Tel.: (39) 011 382 5304
Web Site: https://www.tierratelematics.com
Emp.: 110
Engineeering Services
N.A.I.C.S.: 541330

Topcon (Beijing) Medical Technology Co., Ltd. (1)
Room 2808 Tower C JinChangAn Building No 82, Middle Section of East 4th Ring Road Chaoyang District, Beijing, 100124, China
Tel.: (86) 1087945176
Optical Equipment Mfr
N.A.I.C.S.: 333310

Topcon (Beijing) Opto-Electronics Corporation (1)
Building B No 9 Kangding Street, Beijing Economic-Technological Development Area, Beijing, 100176, China
Tel.: (86) 10 6780 2799
Web Site: http://www.topcon.com.sg
Optical Equipment Mfr
N.A.I.C.S.: 333310 (75%)

Topcon (Great Britain) Medical Ltd. (1)
Kennetside Bone Lane, Newbury, RG14 5PX, United Kingdom
Tel.: (44) 1635551120
Digital Transformation Technology Services
N.A.I.C.S.: 541512

Topcon Agriculture Canada, Inc. (1)
3702 Kinnear Place, Saskatoon, S7P 0A6, SK, Canada
Tel.: (306) 664-6700
Web Site: https://www.norac.ca
Agricultural Machinery Mfr
N.A.I.C.S.: 333111

Topcon Agriculture S.p.a. (1)
Via Nizza 262 int 25, Turin, 10126, Italy
Tel.: (39) 0110243906
Optical Equipment Mfr
N.A.I.C.S.: 333310

Topcon America Corporation (1)
111 Bauer Dr, Oakland, NJ 07436
Tel.: (201) 599-5100
Web Site:
https://www.topconpositioning.com
Precision Positioning Equipment Mfr
N.A.I.C.S.: 332216
Paula Louzeiro *(Dir-HR Ops)*

Subsidiary (Domestic):

Topcon Medical Systems, Inc. (2)
111 Bauer Dr, Oakland, NJ 07436
Tel.: (201) 599-5100
Web Site: https://topconhealthcare.com
Ophthalmic Diagnostic Equipment Mfr
N.A.I.C.S.: 339115
Corey Nielson *(VP-Sales)*

Subsidiary (Domestic):

Topcon Medical Laser Systems, Inc. (3)
606 Enterprise Ct, Livermore, CA 94550
Tel.: (925) 245-3394
Web Site: http://www.tmlsinc.com
Medical Laser Device Mfr & Distr
N.A.I.C.S.: 334510

Subsidiary (Domestic):

Topcon Positioning Systems, Inc (2)
7400 National Dr, Livermore, CA 94550
Tel.: (925) 245-8300
Web Site:
https://www.topconpositioning.com
Precision Positioning Equipment Mfr
N.A.I.C.S.: 332216
Scott Langbein *(Dir)*

Topcon Australia Pty. Ltd. (1)
Unit 18 4 Avenue of Americas, Newington, 2127, NSW, Australia
Tel.: (61) 2 8748 8777
Web Site: http://www.topcon.com.au
Optical Instrument Mfr
N.A.I.C.S.: 333310

Topcon Canada, Inc. (1)
110 Provencher Avenue, Boisbriand, J7G 1N1, QC, Canada
Tel.: (450) 430-7771
Web Site: https://topconhealthcare.ca
Sales Range: $25-49.9 Million
Emp.: 15
Ophthalmic Equipment & Supplies Distr
N.A.I.C.S.: 423460
Jean-Philippe Simard *(Mgr-Territory-Quebec)*

Topcon Deutschland Medical GmbH (1)
Hanns-Martin-Schleyer Strasse 41, 47877, Willich, Germany
Tel.: (49) 21548850
Digital Transformation Technology Services
N.A.I.C.S.: 541512

Topcon Deutschland Positioning G.m.b.H. (1)
Alter Teichweg 55b, 22049, Hamburg, Germany
Tel.: (49) 4022633160

AND PRIVATE COMPANIES • TOPCON CORPORATION

Electrical & Electronic Mfr
N.A.I.C.S.: 335999

Topcon Electronics GmbH & Co. KG (1)
Industriestrasse 7, 65366, Geisenheim, Germany
Tel.: (49) 67 224 0260
Web Site: https://www.topcon-electronics.de
Electrical & Electronic Mfr
N.A.I.C.S.: 335999
Albert Zahalka *(CEO)*

Topcon Essilor Japan, Co., Ltd. (1)
75-1 Hasunuma-cho, Itabashi-ku, Tokyo, 174-8580, Japan
Tel.: (81) 33 558 2514
Web Site: https://www.topcon-essilor.co.jp
Computer Software Development Services
N.A.I.C.S.: 513210

Topcon Europe B.V. (1)
Essebaan 11, 2908 LJ, Capelle aan den IJssel, Netherlands
Tel.: (31) 10 4585077
Medical Equipment Distr
N.A.I.C.S.: 423450

Subsidiary (Non-US):

Topcon (Great Britain) Ltd. (2)
Kennetside Bone Lane, Newbury, RG14 5PX, Berkshire, United Kingdom
Tel.: (44) 163 5551120
Web Site: http://www.topcon-medical.co.uk
Sales Range: $25-49.9 Million
Emp.: 44
Medical Equipment Distr
N.A.I.C.S.: 423450

Topcon Deutschland GmbH (2)
Giesserallee 31-33, 47877, Willich, Germany
Tel.: (49) 21 548850
Web Site: http://www.topcon-medical.de
Emp.: 5
Surveying & Medical Equipment Mfr
N.A.I.C.S.: 334519

Topcon Espana S.A. (2)
Frederic Mompou 4, 8960, Sant Just Desvern, Barcelona, Spain
Tel.: (34) 93 4734057
Emp.: 48
Medical Equipment Mfr
N.A.I.C.S.: 334510
Frank Esderts *(Gen Mgr)*

Subsidiary (Domestic):

Topcon Europe Medical B.V. (2)
Essebaan 11, 2908 LJ, Capelle aan den IJssel, Netherlands
Tel.: (31) 10 4585077
Web Site: http://www.topcon-medical.eu
Medical Equipment Mfr
N.A.I.C.S.: 339112

Subsidiary (Non-US):

Topcon S.A.R.L. (2)
Bat A1 3 Route de la Revolte, 93206, Saint Denis, France
Tel.: (33) 14 9212323
Sales Range: $25-49.9 Million
Emp.: 3
Medical Equipment Mfr
N.A.I.C.S.: 334510
Damien Nogier *(Gen Mgr)*

Topcon Scandinavia AB (2)
Neongatan 2, 431 51, Molndal, Sweden
Tel.: (46) 31 7109200
Medical Equipment Mfr
N.A.I.C.S.: 334510

Topcon France Medical S.A.S. (1)
1 rue des Vergers Parc Swen Batiment 2, 69760, Limonest, France
Tel.: (33) 43 758 1940
Web Site: https://www.topconhealthcare.eu
Optical Equipment Mfr
N.A.I.C.S.: 333310

Topcon G.S. Corporation (1)
75-1 Hasunuma-cho, Itabashi-ku, Tokyo, 174-8580, Japan
Tel.: (81) 335582598
Optical Equipment Mfr
N.A.I.C.S.: 333310

Topcon HK (BD) Ltd. (1)
Plot no 12 and 13 Sector 6 CEPZ, South Halishahar, Chittagong, Bangladesh
Tel.: (880) 31742005
Optical Equipment Mfr
N.A.I.C.S.: 333310

Topcon Healthcare Solutions Asia Pacific Pte. Ltd. (1)
1 Jalan Kilang Timor 09-01, Pacific Tech Centre, Singapore, 159303, Singapore
Tel.: (65) 68720606
Optical Equipment Mfr
N.A.I.C.S.: 333310

Topcon Healthcare Solutions Australia Pty Ltd. (1)
14 Park Way, Varsity Lakes, 5095, SA, Australia
Tel.: (61) 457414673
Web Site: https://topconhealthcare.com.au
Medical Equipment Mfr
N.A.I.C.S.: 339112

Topcon Healthcare Solutions Emea Oy (1)
Saaristonkatu 9, 90100, Oulu, Finland
Tel.: (358) 20 734 8190
Web Site: https://www.topconhealthcare.eu
Optical Equipment Mfr
N.A.I.C.S.: 333310
Akifumi Baba *(Pres)*

Topcon Healthcare Solutions, Inc. (1)
111 Bauer Dr, Oakland, NJ 07436
Tel.: (201) 599-5100
Web Site: https://www.topconhealthcare.com
Health Care Srvices
N.A.I.C.S.: 621610
Akifumi Baba *(Pres)*

Topcon Infomobility S.r.l. (1)
Polo Tecnologico Topcon - Via per Vallalta - SP 7 snc, Concordia Sulla Secchia, 41033, Modena, Italy
Tel.: (39) 05 354 0818
Web Site: https://www.topconinfomobility.com
Engineeering Services
N.A.I.C.S.: 541330

Topcon Instruments (Malaysia) Sdn. Bhd. (1)
No 6 Jalan Pensyarah U1/28 HICOM Glenmarie Inds Park, 40150, Shah Alam, Selangor, Malaysia
Tel.: (60) 350223688
Web Site: http://www.topcon.com.my
Global Positioning System & Medical Equipment Mfr
N.A.I.C.S.: 334519

Topcon Instruments (Thailand) Co., Ltd. (1)
77/162 Sinnsathorn Tower 37th floor Krungdhonburi Road, Klongtonsai Klongsarn, Bangkok, 10600, Thailand (49%)
Tel.: (66) 2 440 1152
Web Site: http://www.topcon.co.th
Sales Range: $50-74.9 Million
Emp.: 25
Surveying & Medical Instruments Distr
N.A.I.C.S.: 423490

Topcon Korea Corporation (1)
4th floor 30 Bangbaejungang-ro Bangbaedong Jiho Building, Seocho-gu, Seoul, 137-876, Korea (South)
Tel.: (82) 2 2055 0321
Web Site: http://www.topcon.co.kr
Ophthalmic Instrument Mfr
N.A.I.C.S.: 339112
Lee In Goo *(CEO)*

Topcon Medical Japan Co., Ltd. (1)
75-1 Hasunuma-cho, Itabashi-ku, Tokyo, 174-8580, Japan
Tel.: (81) 359151800
Optical Equipment Mfr
N.A.I.C.S.: 333310

Topcon Mirage Technologies, S.L. (1)
Edificio Europa Planta 12 Local I Avenida de Aragon 30, 46021, Valencia, Spain
Tel.: (34) 963294950
Web Site: https://www.topconmirage.com
Software Solutions Services

N.A.I.C.S.: 541511

Topcon Optical (Dongguan) Technology Ltd. (1)
Room 101 201 301 501 2 Fumin Street, Zhongshandong Shilong Town, Dongguan, Guangdong, China
Tel.: (86) 76939018899
Optical Equipment Mfr
N.A.I.C.S.: 333310

Topcon Optical (H.K.) Ltd. (1)
2/F Meeco Industrial Bldg No 53-55 Au Pui Wan Street Fo Tan Road, Sha Tin, China (Hong Kong)
Tel.: (852) 26049688
Optical Equipment Mfr
N.A.I.C.S.: 333310

Topcon Optonexus Co., Ltd. (1)
35 Hinokuchi Kubo Tokiwa-machi, Tamura, 963-4605, Fukushima, Japan
Tel.: (81) 247772010
Optical Equipment Mfr
N.A.I.C.S.: 333310
Katsuhiko Muramatsu *(Pres)*

Topcon Polska Sp. zo. o. (1)
ul Warszawska 23, Siewierz, 42-470, Zawiercie, Poland
Tel.: (48) 32 670 5045
Web Site: https://www.topconhealthcare.eu
Electrical & Electronic Mfr
N.A.I.C.S.: 335999

Topcon Positioning (Great Britain) Ltd. (1)
Sandy Hill Business Park Sandy Way, Amington, Tamworth, B77 4DU, Staffordshire, United Kingdom
Tel.: (44) 8454504300
Electrical & Electronic Mfr
N.A.I.C.S.: 335999

Topcon Positioning Asia (Malaysia) Sdn. Bhd. (1)
No 6 Jalan Pensyarah U1/28 HicomGlenmarie Inds Park, 40150, Shah Alam, Selangor, Malaysia
Tel.: (60) 350223688
Web Site: https://www.topcon.com.my
Geo-Positioning Services
N.A.I.C.S.: 541360

Topcon Positioning Asia Co., Ltd. (1)
75-1 Hasunuma-cho, Itabashi-ku, Tokyo, 174-8580, Japan
Tel.: (81) 335582517
Optical Equipment Mfr
N.A.I.C.S.: 333310

Topcon Positioning Belgium BV BA (1)
Doornveld Business Park Asse 3 Nr 11-B1, 1731, Zellik, Belgium
Tel.: (32) 24668230
Optical Equipment Mfr
N.A.I.C.S.: 333310

Topcon Positioning Canarias, S.L. (1)
Panama 3 Edificio Luna 20 Oficina 18, 38009, Santa Cruz de Tenerife, Spain
Tel.: (34) 922228905
Optical Equipment Mfr
N.A.I.C.S.: 333310

Topcon Positioning France S.A.S. (1)
576 Rue des Grands Crus, 71000, Macon, France
Tel.: (33) 385519800
Industrial Machinery Mfr
N.A.I.C.S.: 333248

Topcon Positioning Italy s.r.l. (1)
via Caduti del Lavoro 40, Ancona, Italy
Tel.: (39) 071213251
Electrical & Electronic Mfr
N.A.I.C.S.: 335999

Topcon Positioning Middle East and Africa FZE (1)
LIU J-11 Dubai Airport Free Zone, PO Box 371028, Dubai, United Arab Emirates
Tel.: (971) 42990203
Global Positioning System Mfr
N.A.I.C.S.: 334220
Yoshiaki Kataoka *(Mng Dir)*

Topcon Positioning Portugal, Lda. (1)
Parque Industrial da Figueira da Foz - Rua das Tilias Lote 66A, 3090-380, Figueira da Foz, Portugal
Tel.: (351) 233900020
Web Site: http://www.topconpositioningportugal.com
Electrical & Electronic Mfr
N.A.I.C.S.: 335999

Topcon Positioning Spain, S.L.U. (1)
Avenida de la Industria 35, 28760, Tres Cantos, Madrid, Spain
Tel.: (34) 914841900
Optical Equipment Mfr
N.A.I.C.S.: 333310

Topcon Positioning Systems (Australia) Pty Ltd. (1)
7/52 Merivale St South, Brisbane, 4101, QLD, Australia
Tel.: (61) 734560999
Optical Equipment Mfr
N.A.I.C.S.: 333310

Topcon Precision Ag Europe S.L. (1)
Avenida de la Industria 35, 28760, Tres Cantos, Madrid, Spain
Tel.: (34) 918049231
Optical Equipment Mfr
N.A.I.C.S.: 333310

Topcon Precision Agriculture Pty Ltd. (1)
14 Park way, Mawson Lakes, Adelaide, 5095, SA, Australia
Tel.: (61) 882033300
Optical Equipment Mfr
N.A.I.C.S.: 333310

Topcon Singapore Holdings Pte. Ltd. (1)
100G Pasir Panjang Road 05-05 Interlocal Centre, Singapore, 118523, Singapore
Tel.: (65) 6278 0222
Web Site: http://www.topcon.com.sg
Sales Range: $50-74.9 Million
Emp.: 1
Investment Management Service
N.A.I.C.S.: 523940

Subsidiary (Domestic):

Topcon Singapore Medical Pte Ltd (2)
Pacific Tech Centre, Singapore, 159303, Singapore
Tel.: (65) 68720606
Medical Equipment Distr
N.A.I.C.S.: 423450
Leo Hiroshi Nagatake *(Mng Dir)*

Topcon Singapore Positioning Pte. Ltd. (2)
1 Jalan Kilang Timor 09-01 Pacific Tech Centre, Singapore, 159303, Singapore
Tel.: (65) 6778 3456
Web Site: http://www.topconpositioining.com
Ophthalmic Instrument Mfr
N.A.I.C.S.: 339112

Subsidiary (Domestic):

Topcon Singapore Positioning Sales Pte Ltd (3)
1 Jalan Kilang Timor 09-01 Pacific tech centre, Singapore, 159303, Singapore
Tel.: (65) 67783456
Web Site: http://www.topcon.com.sg
Surveying Equipment Distr
N.A.I.C.S.: 423490

Topcon Sokkia India Pvt. Ltd. (1)
Unit No 101-106A 1st Floor ABW Tower M G Road Sector 25 IFFCO Chowk, Gurgaon, 122001, Haryana, India
Tel.: (91) 1244847676
Web Site: http://www.topconsokkia.ind.in
Sales Range: $25-49.9 Million
Emp.: 5
Precision Surveying Instrument Mfr
N.A.I.C.S.: 334519

Topcon Sokkia Positioning Japan Co., Ltd. (1)
75-1 Hasunuma-cho, Itabashi-ku, Tokyo, 174-8580, Japan
Tel.: (81) 35 994 0671
Web Site: https://www.topconsokkia.co.jp

TOPCON CORPORATION

Topcon Corporation—(Continued)
Emp.: 136
Industrial Machinery Mfr
N.A.I.C.S.: 333248

Topcon Technohouse Corporation (1)
75-1 Hasunuma-cho, Itabashi-ku, Tokyo, 174-8580, Japan
Tel.: (81) 33 558 2642
Web Site: https://www.topcon-techno.co.jp
Optical Equipment Mfr
N.A.I.C.S.: 333310

Topcon Technology Finland Oy (1)
Vaisalantie 6, 02130, Espoo, Finland
Tel.: (358) 923132100
Optical Equipment Mfr
N.A.I.C.S.: 333310

Topcon Technology Ltd. (1)
Cirencester Road, Minchinhampton, Stroud, GL6 9BH, Gloucestershire, United Kingdom
Tel.: (44) 145 373 3300
Web Site: https://www.rdstec.com
Industrial Machinery Mfr
N.A.I.C.S.: 333248
Gareth Thomas (Gen Mgr)

Topcon Yamagata Co., Ltd. (1)
547 Ishida Oaza Urushiyama, Yamagata, 990-2196, Japan
Tel.: (81) 23 686 3987
Web Site: https://www.topcon-yamagata.co.jp
Optical Equipment Mfr
N.A.I.C.S.: 333310

TOPDANMARK A/S
Borupvang 4, DK-2750, Ballerup, Denmark
Tel.: (45) 44683311 DK
Web Site: https://www.topdanmark.com
Year Founded: 1899
TOP—(CSE)
Rev.: $1,407,880,077
Assets: $3,331,452,301
Liabilities: $2,391,225,709
Net Worth: $940,226,592
Earnings: $296,479,576
Emp.: 2,378
Fiscal Year-end: 12/31/22
Insurance Services
N.A.I.C.S.: 524126
Peter Hermann (CEO & Member-Exec Bd)

Subsidiaries:

Risk & Insurance Services S.A. (1)
1A Rue du Nord, 2229, Luxembourg, Luxembourg
Tel.: (352) 2224741
General Insurance Services
N.A.I.C.S.: 524210

Topdanmark Ejendom A/S (1)
Borupvang 4, 2750, Ballerup, Denmark
Tel.: (45) 4 477 7233
Web Site: https://www.topdanmarkejendom.dk
Insurance Services
N.A.I.C.S.: 524210
Thomas Junker Guldborg (Portfolio Mgr)

TOPGREEN TECHNOLOGY CO., LTD.
No 19 Ln 412 Sec 1 Jieshou Rd, Sanxia Dist, New Taipei City, 23743, Taiwan
Tel.: (886) 226685678
Web Site: http://www.topgreentech.com
Year Founded: 2000
1585—(TPE)
Rev.: $5,936,522
Assets: $33,086,576
Liabilities: $23,148,717
Net Worth: $9,937,860
Earnings: ($3,734,573)
Fiscal Year-end: 12/31/19
Hand Tool Mfr
N.A.I.C.S.: 332216

Chao-Feng Tsai (Vice Chm)

TOPHATMONOCLE CORP.
151 Bloor Street West Suite 200, Toronto, M5S 1S4, ON, Canada
Tel.: (888) 588-5341
Web Site: http://www.tophat.com
Educational Computer Software Development Services
N.A.I.C.S.: 513210
Joe Rohrlich (CEO)

Subsidiaries:

Morton Publishing Company, LLC (1)
925 W Kenyon Ave Ste 12, Englewood, CO 80110
Tel.: (303) 761-4805
Web Site: http://www.morton-pub.com
Book Publishers
N.A.I.C.S.: 513130
Doug Morton (Chm)

bluedoor, LLC (1)
10949 Bren Rd E, Minneapolis, MN 55343
Web Site: http://www.bluedoorpublishing.com
Publishing Services
N.A.I.C.S.: 513130
Jon Earl (CEO)

TOPHEDGE AKTIENGESELLSCHAFT
Inside the bag 3, 76227, Karlsruhe, Germany
Tel.: (49) 160 962 810 67 De
Web Site: http://www.tophedge.de
Hedge Fund Investment & Management Services
N.A.I.C.S.: 525910
Paul Bosmediano (Member-Mgmt Bd)

TOPKEY CORPORATION
No 18 20th Road Industrial Park, Taichung, 40850, Taiwan
Tel.: (886) 423591229
Web Site: https://www.topkey.com.tw
Year Founded: 1980
4536—(TAI)
Rev.: $303,036,288
Assets: $448,913,878
Liabilities: $172,756,820
Net Worth: $276,157,058
Earnings: $48,511,558
Emp.: 3,563
Fiscal Year-end: 12/31/23
Plastics Product Mfr
N.A.I.C.S.: 326199
Jerry Lin (Officer-Technical)

Subsidiaries:

Keentech Composite Tech. Co., Ltd. - Houxi Plant (1)
No 399 Houxi Avenue Houxi Town Jimei, Xiamen, China
Tel.: (86) 5926366001
Helmets Mfr
N.A.I.C.S.: 339920

TOPLOFIKATSIA ROUSSE EAD
Tez Iztok str, Ruse, 7009, Bulgaria
Tel.: (359) 82 883313
Web Site: http://www.toplo-ruse.com
Eletric Power Generation Services
N.A.I.C.S.: 221118
Petr Pashnin (Exec Dir)

TOPLUS GLOBAL CO., LTD.
13th Floor No 216 Section 3 Zhonghua Road, Xinzhuang District, New Taipei City, 235, Taiwan
Tel.: (886) 222266277
Web Site: https://www.toplusglobal.com
3522—(TPE)
Rev.: $20,459,275
Assets: $52,595,785

Liabilities: $44,357,534
Net Worth: $8,238,252
Earnings: ($3,272,582)
Fiscal Year-end: 12/31/22
Restaurant Operators
N.A.I.C.S.: 722511
Hsiang-Hung Hsu (CEO)

TOPOINT TECHNOLOGY CO., LTD.
No 203 Sec 3 Jiayuan Rd, Shulin Dist, Taipei, 238, Taiwan
Tel.: (886) 226805868
Web Site: https://www.topoint.tw
8021—(TAI)
Rev.: $91,413,483
Assets: $220,285,384
Liabilities: $59,836,716
Net Worth: $160,448,668
Earnings: ($1,260,571)
Emp.: 98
Fiscal Year-end: 12/31/23
Circuit Board Mfr
N.A.I.C.S.: 334412
Chang-Long Yan (Dir-Admin Center)

Subsidiaries:

Cosmos Vacuum Technology Corporation (1)
No 550 Jujin Road, Zhangpu Town, Kunshan, 215321, Jiangsu Province, China
Tel.: (86) 51257455188
Web Site: https://www.cosmostech.com.tw
Emp.: 122
Coated Router Bits Mfr
N.A.I.C.S.: 333515

Shanghai Topoint Precision Technology Co., Ltd. (1)
No 505 Fengden Road, Malu Industrial Park Jiading District, Shanghai, 201801, China
Tel.: (86) 2159157365
Precision Equipment Mfr
N.A.I.C.S.: 332721

TOPOLA A.D. BACKA TOPOLA
Marsala Tita 3, Backa Topola, 24300, Serbia
Tel.: (381) 24 712 360
Web Site: http://www.imtopola.rs
Year Founded: 1960
Meat Product Producer
N.A.I.C.S.: 445240
Vukoje Muhadinovic (Gen Mgr)

TOPOLA LIVAR A.D.
Pilota Zorana Tomica 23, Topola, Serbia
Tel.: (381) 34 812 151
Year Founded: 1991
Sales Range: $1-9.9 Million
Emp.: 208
Iron Casting Mfr
N.A.I.C.S.: 331511

TOPOLA UNIVERZAL A.D.
Glavna 55/a, Backa Topola, Serbia
Tel.: (381) 24 711 137
Web Site: http://www.topolaunivrzal.com
Year Founded: 1946
Sales Range: Less than $1 Million
Real Estate Property Management Services
N.A.I.C.S.: 531311

TOPPAN HOLDINGS INC.
1-3-3 Suido, Bunkyo-ku, Tokyo, 112-8531, Japan
Tel.: (81) 338355111
Web Site: https://www.toppan.com
Year Founded: 1900
TOPPY—(OTCIQ)
Rev.: $14,199,930,800
Assets: $22,878,709,040
Liabilities: $8,812,081,520
Net Worth: $14,066,627,520
Earnings: $793,730,960

INTERNATIONAL PUBLIC

Emp.: 52,401
Fiscal Year-end: 03/31/21
Commercial, Packaging, Publications & Securities & Cards Printing Services; Electronics-Related & Industrial Materials Mfr
N.A.I.C.S.: 323111
Tetsuro Ueki (Sr Mng Exec Officer-Electronics Div & Ortus Subdiv)

Subsidiaries:

Asutoro Publishing Co., Ltd. (1)
48-23 Sakaecho Toshobunko Bldg, Kita-Ku, Tokyo, 114-0005, Japan
Tel.: (81) 339111461
Web Site: http://www.asutoro.co.jp
Books Publishing Services
N.A.I.C.S.: 513130

Beijing Nippo Printing Co., Ltd. (1)
No 6 Yongchang Road N Beijing Technical Economic Development Zone, Beijing, 100176, China
Tel.: (86) 10 67881680
Commercial Printing Services
N.A.I.C.S.: 323111

Beijing Toppan Digital Products Co., Ltd. (1)
Room 1506 Suite B Fenglan International Centre No 32 Xizhime, Beijing, 100082, China
Tel.: (86) 1062264572
Web Site: http://www.bjtoppan.com
Computer Software Development Services
N.A.I.C.S.: 541511

Decotec Printing, S.A. (1)
Pol Ind Can Busca Sud s/n, 08490, Tordera, Spain
Tel.: (34) 93 764 3708
Web Site: https://www.decotec.com
Decor Paper Mfr
N.A.I.C.S.: 322299

Digi-Book Japan Inc. (1)
Aoyama Building 3F 1-2-3 Kitaaoyama, Minato-ku, Tokyo, 107-0061, Japan
Tel.: (81) 345006740
Web Site: http://www.dbook.co.jp
Online Comic Books Publishing Services
N.A.I.C.S.: 513130

Froebel-Kan Co., Ltd. (1)
6-14-9 Honkomagome, Bunkyo-Ku, Tokyo, 113-8611, Japan
Tel.: (81) 35 395 6600
Web Site: https://www.froebel-kan.co.jp
Sales Range: $125-149.9 Million
Emp.: 407
Books & Magazines Publishing Services
N.A.I.C.S.: 323111
Akihiko Iida (Pres)

Gakko Tosho Co., Ltd. (1)
3-10-36 Higashijujo, Kita-Ku, Tokyo, 114-0001, Japan
Tel.: (81) 3 5843 9430
Web Site: http://www.gakuto.co.jp
Sales Range: $25-49.9 Million
Emp.: 61
Educational Books Publishing Services
N.A.I.C.S.: 513130
Norio Nakajima (CEO)

I.N.T. Co., Ltd. (1)
3-7 Kawama-cho, Minato-Ku, Nagoya, 455-0076, Aichi, Japan
Tel.: (81) 52 665 2920
Web Site: https://www.intgroup.co.jp
Commercial Printing Services
N.A.I.C.S.: 323111

Interprint GmbH (1)
Westring 22, 59759, Arnsberg, Germany
Tel.: (49) 2 932 9500
Web Site: https://www.interprint.com
Printing & Packaging Services
N.A.I.C.S.: 561910
R. Bierfreund (CEO)

Kagawa Prefecture Information Services Co., Ltd. (1)
2-1 Sunport Symbol Tower Building 4th and 5th floors, Takamatsu, 760-0019, Kagawa, Japan
Tel.: (81) 87 822 0111
Web Site: https://www.e-topia-kagawa.jp

Sales Range: $25-49.9 Million
Emp.: 25
Commercial Printing Services
N.A.I.C.S.: 323111
Michihiro Baba (Gen Mgr)

Kita-Osaka Shigyo Co., Ltd. (1)
3-22-61 Ebie, Fukushima-Ku, Osaka, 553-0001, Japan
Tel.: (81) 664543541
Paper Products Mfr
N.A.I.C.S.: 322120

Livretech Co., Ltd. (1)
1-28-1 Horifune, Kita-ku, Tokyo, 114-0004, Japan
Tel.: (81) 33 927 6411
Web Site: https://www.livretech.co.jp
Emp.: 447
Commercial Printing Services
N.A.I.C.S.: 323111

Mapion Co., Ltd. (1)
3-19-26 Shibaura Toppan Shibaura Bldg 4f, Minato-Ku, Tokyo, 108-0023, Japan
Tel.: (81) 337693503
Web Site: http://www.mapion.co.jp
Advertising Agency Services
N.A.I.C.S.: 541810

NEC Toppan Circuit Solutions Philippines, Inc. (1)
1 Ring Road Light Industry and Science Park II Brgy La Mesa, Calamba, 4027, Laguna, Philippines
Tel.: (63) 495456111
Web Site: http://www.tncsi.com
Printed Circuit Board Mfr
N.A.I.C.S.: 334412

NEC Toppan Circuit Solutions USA Inc. (1)
631 River Oaks Pkwy, San Jose, CA 95134-1907
Tel.: (408) 232-0944
Printed Circuit Board Mfr
N.A.I.C.S.: 334412

Okinawa Business Forms Co., Ltd. (1)
4-9-3 Nishizakicho, Itoman, 901-0306, Okinawa, Japan
Tel.: (81) 989924116
Commercial Printing Services
N.A.I.C.S.: 323111

Ortus Technology Co., Ltd. (1)
2-8-7 Asahigaoka, Hino, 191-0065, Tokyo, Japan
Tel.: (81) 42 514 0640
Web Site: http://www.ortustech.co.jp
Sales Range: $50-74.9 Million
Emp.: 100
Medium Sized Display Mfr & Distr
N.A.I.C.S.: 334118
Jin Endo (Pres)

Subsidiary (Non-US):

Giantplus Technology Co., Ltd. (2)
No 15 Gongye Rd, Lu-Chu Li, Toufen, Miauli, Taiwan
Tel.: (886) 37611611
Web Site: http://www.giantplus.com
Rev.: $295,696,872
Assets: $382,304,345
Liabilities: $123,360,210
Net Worth: $258,944,135
Earnings: $7,722,816
Emp.: 2,098
Fiscal Year-end: 12/31/2023
TFT-LCD Display Mfr
N.A.I.C.S.: 334419

Plant (Domestic):

Giantplus Technology Co., Ltd. - Bade Plant (3)
No 1127 Heping Road, Bade District, Taoyuan, 334, Taiwan
Tel.: (886) 3 3679978
Web Site: http://www.giantplus.com
TFT-LCD Display Panels Mfr
N.A.I.C.S.: 334419

Giantplus Technology Co., Ltd. - Hsinchu Plant (3)
No 2-1 Wenhua Rd, Hukou Township, Hsinchu, 303, Taiwan
Tel.: (886) 3 3679978

Web Site: http://www.giantplus.com
TFT-LCD Display Mfr

Subsidiary (Non-US):

Kunshan Giantplus Optoelectronics Technology Co., Ltd. (3)
88 Huang Qing Rd Kunshan Hi Tech Park, Kunshan, 215316, Jiangsu, China
Tel.: (86) 51257780988
Touch Panels & Modules Display Mfr
N.A.I.C.S.: 334419

Shenzhen Giantplus Optoelectronics Display Co., Ltd. (3)
Bldg A District A Min Zhu 99 Industrial City Sha Jing Indus Park, Bao An District, Shenzhen, 518104, Guangdong, China
Tel.: (86) 75529720088
TFT-LCD Display Mfr
N.A.I.C.S.: 334419

P.T. Toppan Printing Indonesia (1)
Jl Teuku Umar Km 44 Ds Telaga Asih Cikarang Barat, Bekasi, 17530, Jawa Barat, Indonesia
Tel.: (62) 21 8831153
Web Site: http://www.toppan.co.id
Packaging & Printing Services
N.A.I.C.S.: 323111

P.T. Toppan Sampoerna Indonesia (1)
Jl Raya Cibitung Desa Telaga Asih, Kecamatan Cibitung, Bekasi, 17520, Jawa Barat, Indonesia
Tel.: (62) 218831153
Mfr of Flexible Packaging Materials, Paper Carton Packaging Materials, Calenders & Other Commercial Printing
N.A.I.C.S.: 322212

Pouchfill Packaging, LLC. (1)
811 Fentress Ct, Daytona Beach, FL 32117
Tel.: (386) 274-1600
Web Site: https://www.toppan.com
Printing & Packaging Services
N.A.I.C.S.: 561910

Sansei Printing Ltd. (1)
6-6-5 Higashikanamachi Mitsuiseimei Kanamachi Bldg, Katsushika-Ku, Tokyo, 125-0041, Japan
Tel.: (81) 336276881
Commercial Printing Services
N.A.I.C.S.: 323111

Shanghai Toppan Advertisement Co., Ltd. (1)
15/F Yasheng Mansion No 188 Jiangning Rd, Jing An Dist, Shanghai, 200041, China
Tel.: (86) 2132520808
Sales Range: $25-49.9 Million
Emp.: 100
Advertising Agency Services
N.A.I.C.S.: 541810

Shanghai Toppan Co., Ltd. (1)
No 2300 Shengang Road, Dong Bu New District Songjiang Industrial Zone, Shanghai, 201612, China
Tel.: (86) 2167600860
Packaging Materials Mfr
N.A.I.C.S.: 326112

Shanghai Toppan International Trading Co., Ltd. (1)
9f Global Harbor Tower B 1188 North Kaixuan Rd, Putuo District, Shanghai, 200063, China (100%)
Tel.: (86) 2162231000
Web Site: http://www.toppan.com
Sales Range: $25-49.9 Million
Emp.: 75
Distr of Commercial Printing
N.A.I.C.S.: 323111

Shanghai Toppan Printing Co., Ltd. (1)
No 2300 Shengang Road, Songjiang Industrial Zone Dong Bu New District, Shanghai, 201612, China
Tel.: (86) 216 760 0860
Web Site: http://www.pac.toppan.com.cn
Sales Range: $50-74.9 Million
Emp.: 250
Packaging Materials Printing Services
N.A.I.C.S.: 323111

Shenzhen Ruixing Printing Company Ltd. (1)
Block1 Huihua Industrial Park Tenth Industrial Zone, Longhua Town Bao An District, Shenzhen, 518109, China
Tel.: (86) 755 28064993
Web Site: http://www.rxpapers.com
Printing Machinery Mfr
N.A.I.C.S.: 333248

Siam Toppan Packaging Co., Ltd. (1)
543 Bangpoo Industrial Estate Soi 9 Moo 4, Amphur Muang District, Samut Prakan, 10280, Thailand
Tel.: (66) 27093110
Web Site: http://www.siamtoppan.co.th
Sales Range: $100-124.9 Million
Emp.: 200
Paper Carton & Multi-Color Process Corrugated Board Mfr; Owned by Toppan Printing Co., Ltd & Siam Pulp & Paper Public Company Limited
N.A.I.C.S.: 322212

Sobi Calendars Co., Ltd. (1)
1-3-3 Suido Toppan Koishikawa Bldg 4f, Bunkyo-Ku, Tokyo, 112-0005, Japan
Tel.: (81) 358402060
Calendar Mfr & Whslr
N.A.I.C.S.: 322299

T&T Enertechno Co., Ltd. (1)
1-5-1 Taito, Taito-ku, Tokyo, 110-0016, Japan
Tel.: (81) 33 835 5200
Web Site: https://www.tt-enertechno.co.jp
Storage Battery Mfr
N.A.I.C.S.: 335910
Kazuhiko Nagahara (Pres)

T.M.G. Prepress Toppan Co., Ltd. (1)
1-16-2 Azusawa, Itabashi-Ku, Tokyo, 174-0051, Japan
Tel.: (81) 3 3968 5800
Prepress Printing Services
N.A.I.C.S.: 323120

TOPPAN Edge Inc. (1)
1-7-3 Higashi Shimbashi, Minato-ku, Tokyo, 105-8311, Japan
Tel.: (81) 362536000
Web Site: https://www.edge.toppan.com
Emp.: 2,625
Communication Media Services
N.A.I.C.S.: 541840

Tama Kako Co., Ltd. (1)
1207-2 Yoshida Oizumimachi, Oura, 370-0523, Gunma, Japan
Tel.: (81) 276636611
Commercial Printing Services
N.A.I.C.S.: 323111

Tamapoly Co., Ltd. (1)
Diagate Ikebukuro 10F 1-16-15 Minamiikebukuro, Toshima-Ku, Tokyo, 171-0022, Japan
Tel.: (81) 33 981 1431
Web Site: https://www.tamapoly.co.jp
Sales Range: $200-249.9 Million
Emp.: 415
Polyethylene Film Mfr & Distr
N.A.I.C.S.: 326113
Yasuo Matsuki (Pres)

Techno Toppan Forms Co., Ltd. (1)
1-7-3 Higashishimbashi Toppan Forms Bldg 15f, Minato-Ku, Tokyo, 105-0021, Japan
Tel.: (81) 362535900
Web Site: http://www.ttf.co.jp
Computer Peripheral Equipment Maintenance Services
N.A.I.C.S.: 811210

Tipografia Manson, Limitada (1)
Ed Indl Cheong Long, Macau, China (Macau)
Tel.: (853) 2830 4278
Commercial Printing Services
N.A.I.C.S.: 323111

Tokyo Shoseki Co., Ltd (1)
2-17-1 Horifune, Kita-ku, Tokyo, 114-8524, Japan
Tel.: (81) 35 390 7200
Web Site: https://www.tokyo-shoseki.co.jp
Emp.: 500
Textbook Publishing Services
N.A.I.C.S.: 513130

Toppan (Shanghai) Management Co., Ltd. (1)
15th Floor Yasheng Building No 188 Jiang Ning Road, Jing an District, Shanghai, 200041, China
Tel.: (86) 21 3252 0707
Sales Range: $50-74.9 Million
Emp.: 200
Commercial Printing Services
N.A.I.C.S.: 323111

Toppan Best-Set Premedia (Guangzhou) Ltd. (1)
3 Da Song Gang Jiang Nan Main Avenue C, Guangzhou, 55140, China
Tel.: (86) 20 8441 5873
Emp.: 200
Journals & Books Publishing Services
N.A.I.C.S.: 513120
Johnson Yueng (Mng Dir)

Toppan Best-Set Premedia Ltd. (1)
20/F Manulife Tower 169 Electric Road, North Point, China (Hong Kong)
Tel.: (852) 2897 6033
Web Site: http://www.toppanbestset.com
Emp.: 50
Journals & Books Publishing Services
N.A.I.C.S.: 513130
Johnson Yeung (Mng Dir)

Toppan Character Production Co., Ltd. (1)
1-5-1 Taito Taito-ku, Taito-Ku, Tokyo, 110-8560, Japan
Tel.: (81) 338356542
Web Site: http://www.chara-pro.com
Sales Range: $25-49.9 Million
Emp.: 10
Character Development & Merchandising Services
N.A.I.C.S.: 541490
Yasuhiro Iba (Pres)

Toppan Chunghwa Electronics Corporation (1)
1127-3 Hoping Road, Bade Dist, Taoyuan, 33444, Taiwan (100%)
Tel.: (886) 3 364 3300
Web Site: https://www.tce.com.tw
Photomasks Mfr
N.A.I.C.S.: 325992

Toppan Co., Ltd. (1)
1-5-1 Taito Toppan Insatsu-Nai, Taito-Ku, Tokyo, 110-0016, Japan (100%)
Tel.: (81) 338356520
Web Site: http://www.toppan.co.jp
Commercial Printing Services
N.A.I.C.S.: 323111

Subsidiary (Domestic):

Tosho Printing Company Limited (2)
3-10-36 Higashi-Jujo, Kita-ku, Tokyo, 114-0001, Japan
Tel.: (81) 3 58439700
Web Site: http://www.tosho.co.jp
Rev.: $476,713,920
Assets: $955,425,840
Liabilities: $281,052,000
Net Worth: $674,373,840
Earnings: $7,770,000
Emp.: 1,547
Fiscal Year-end: 03/31/2018
Commercial Printing Services
N.A.I.C.S.: 323111
Kazuaki Kawada (Pres)

Subsidiary (Domestic):

Kirihara Shoten KK (3)
3-10-36 Higashijujo, 4-15-3 Nishi-Shinjuku, Tokyo, 114-0001, Japan (51%)
Tel.: (81) 35 302 7020
Web Site: https://www.kirihara.co.jp
Sales Range: Less than $1 Million
Emp.: 150
Book Publishers
N.A.I.C.S.: 513130
Satoshi Saito (Pres)

Toppan Communication Products Co., Ltd. (1)
1-5-1 Taito, Taito-ku, Tokyo, Japan
Tel.: (81) 48 482 4602
Web Site: https://www.toppan-c.co.jp
Semiconductor & Related Device Mfr
N.A.I.C.S.: 334413

TOPPAN HOLDINGS INC.   INTERNATIONAL PUBLIC

TOPPAN Holdings Inc.—(Continued)

Toppan Cosmo Europe GmbH (1)
Elisabeth Strasse 40, D 402 17, Dusseldorf, Germany (100%)
Tel.: (49) 211356648
Web Site: http://www.toppan.co.uk
Sales Range: $25-49.9 Million
Emp.: 5
Interior Decor & Industrial Materials Sales & Marketing
N.A.I.C.S.: 541410

Toppan Cosmo, Inc. (1)
1 Kanda Izumicho Kanda Izumicho Building, Chiyoda-ku, Tokyo, 101-0024, Japan
Tel.: (81) 33 835 6280
Web Site: https://www.toppan-cosmo.jp
Sales Range: $125-149.9 Million
Emp.: 300
Decorative Sheet Mfr
N.A.I.C.S.: 326112
Yoshio Sakamura (Chm)

Toppan Editorial Communications Co., Ltd. (1)
6th floor Kanda Izumicho Building 1 Kanda Izumicho, Chiyoda-ku, Tokyo, 101-0024, Japan
Tel.: (81) 33 835 6153
Web Site: https://www.toppan-tec.co.jp
Planning & Editing Services
N.A.I.C.S.: 541511

Toppan Electronics (Taiwan) Co., Ltd. (1)
10th Floor No 109 Sec 3 Min Sheng East Road, Taipei, Taiwan
Tel.: (886) 227190065
Web Site: http://www.toppanelectronics.co.tw
Seller of Electronic Precision Components
N.A.I.C.S.: 449210

Toppan Electronics Co., Ltd. (1)
3 Floor -1 165 19 East Road 416, Section 3, Taipei, 10580, Taiwan (100%)
Tel.: (886) 227191641
Web Site: http://www.toppan.com.tw
Distr of Commercial Printing
N.A.I.C.S.: 323111

Toppan Electronics Fuji Co., Ltd. (1)
32-1 Otsuka, Numazu, 410-0306, Shizuoka, Japan
Tel.: (81) 559672231
Electronic Components Mfr
N.A.I.C.S.: 334419

Toppan Electronics, Inc. (1)
14107 Stowe Dr, Poway, CA 92064-7145 (100%)
Tel.: (858) 693-1908
Sales Range: $100-124.9 Million
Emp.: 350
Mfr & Sales of Printed Wiring Boards
N.A.I.C.S.: 334412

Toppan Europe GmbH (1)
Toulouser Allee 19a, 40211, Dusseldorf, Germany
Tel.: (49) 211 732 7600
Web Site: https://www.toppan-europe.com
Printing & Packaging Services
N.A.I.C.S.: 561910
Kiyoshi Okayasu (CEO)

Toppan Europe GmbH (1)
15 Basinghall Street, London, EC2V 5BR, United Kingdom
Tel.: (44) 2072130501
Printing & Packaging Services
N.A.I.C.S.: 561910

Toppan Excel (Thailand) Co., Ltd. (1)
37-57 Saint Louis Square Building 3rd Floor Soi Chan 18/7, Tung Wat Don Sathorn, Bangkok, 10120, Thailand
Tel.: (66) 2 212 7898
Sales Range: $25-49.9 Million
Emp.: 4
Novelty Books Publishing Services
N.A.I.C.S.: 513120
Foong Kee Loon (Gen Mgr)

Toppan Excel Printing (Guangzhou) Co., Ltd. (1)
No 88 Qishan Road Shiji Town, Panyu District, Guangzhou, 511450, Guangdong, China

Tel.: (86) 2084852823
Commercial Printing Services
N.A.I.C.S.: 323111

Toppan Forms (Sanyo) Co., Ltd. (1)
1-8-38 Takayadai, Higashi-hiroshima, 739-2117, Hiroshima, Japan
Tel.: (81) 824347300
Commercial Printing Services
N.A.I.C.S.: 323111

Toppan Forms Co., Ltd. (1)
1-7-3 Higashi Shimbashi, Minato-ku, Tokyo, 105-8311, Japan (60.7%)
Tel.: (81) 362536000
Web Site: http://www.toppan-f.co.jp
Rev: $2,112,476,080
Assets: $2,174,340,960
Liabilities: $499,788,080
Net Worth: $1,674,552,880
Earnings: $41,943,440
Emp.: 9,545
Fiscal Year-end: 03/31/2021
Holding Company; Printing Services, Data Card Mfr, Information Technology Products Whslr & Support Services
N.A.I.C.S.: 551112
Koichi Sakata (Pres)

Subsidiary (Non-US):

T.F. Company, Ltd. (2)
Unit 1075A KITEC 1 Trademark Drive, Kowloon, China (Hong Kong) (100%)
Tel.: (852) 2519 0118
Web Site: http://www.toppanforms.net
Holding Company
N.A.I.C.S.: 551112

Subsidiary (Domestic):

Toppan Forms (Hong Kong) Ltd. (3)
Unit 1075A KITEC 1 Trademark Drive, Kowloon, China (Hong Kong) (100%)
Tel.: (852) 25118870
Business Form & Other Commercial Printing Services, Printing Machinery Whslr & Data Management Services
N.A.I.C.S.: 323111

Toppan Forms Card Technologies Ltd. (3)
Unit 1051 10/F Kitec 1 Trademark Drive, Kowloon Bay, China (Hong Kong)
Tel.: (852) 25196388
Web Site: https://www.toppanforms.com
Sales Range: $25-49.9 Million
Emp.: 100
Plastic Data Card Mfr & Printing Services
N.A.I.C.S.: 323111

Toppan Forms Computer Systems Ltd. (3)
Unit 1075A KITEC 1 Trademark Drive, Kowloon, China (Hong Kong)
Tel.: (852) 25132134
Emp.: 500
Information Technology Products Whslr & Support Services
N.A.I.C.S.: 541519

Subsidiary (Non-US):

Toppan Forms (S) Pte. Ltd. (2)
41 Joo Koon Circle, Singapore, 629065, Singapore
Tel.: (65) 6 862 3811
Web Site: https://www.tfs.com.sg
Data Printing & Business Form Printing Services
N.A.I.C.S.: 323111

Joint Venture (Non-US):

CFM Toppan Forms (Malaysia) Sdn. Bhd. (3)
Lot 2 Block B Jalan Usahawan 5 Off Jalan Genting Kelang, PKNS Setapak Industrial Area, 53300, Kuala Lumpur, Malaysia
Tel.: (60) 340237628
Web Site: http://www.cfmtf.com.my
Outsource Data Printing & Direct Mailer Services; Owned by Computer Forms (Malaysia) Berhad, by Toppan Forms (Singapore) Pte. Ltd. & by Cardsys Sdn. Bhd.
N.A.I.C.S.: 323111

Subsidiary (Domestic):

Toppan Forms Operation Co., Ltd. (2)

Toppan Forms Building 1-7-3 Higashi-Shimbashi, Minato-ku, Tokyo, 105-8312, Japan (100%)
Tel.: (81) 36 253 5800
Web Site: https://www.tfo.co.jp
Emp.: 2,298
Information Technology Management & Support Services
N.A.I.C.S.: 541519

Toppan Forms Kansai Co., Ltd. (1)
3-1-3 Esakacho, Suita, 564-0063, Osaka, Japan
Tel.: (81) 663372334
Business Forms Printing Services
N.A.I.C.S.: 323111

Toppan Forms Nishinihon Co., Ltd. (1)
1-35-12 Matsushima, Higashi-Ku, Fukuoka, 812-0062, Japan
Tel.: (81) 926234221
Commercial Printing Services
N.A.I.C.S.: 323111

Toppan Forms Tokai Co., Ltd (1)
Fukuroi Factory 2228 Toyosawa, Higashi-Ku, Fukuroi, 435-0029, Shizuoka, Japan
Tel.: (81) 53 844 3310
Web Site: https://tokai.toppan-f.co.jp
Emp.: 590
Business Forms Printing Services
N.A.I.C.S.: 323111

Toppan Graphic Communications Co., Ltd. (1)
1-11-1 Shimura, Itabashi-Ku, Tokyo, 174-8558, Japan
Tel.: (81) 33 968 5046
Web Site: https://www.toppan-tgc.co.jp
Commercial Printing Services
N.A.I.C.S.: 323111

Toppan Gravity Limited (1)
20th Floor Lee and Man Commercial Center, 169 Electric Road North Point, Hong Kong, China (Hong Kong)
Tel.: (852) 29125200
Financial Services
N.A.I.C.S.: 523999

Toppan Hall Co., Ltd. (1)
1-3-3 Suido, Bunkyo-ku, Tokyo, 112-0005, Japan
Tel.: (81) 35 840 2200
Web Site: https://www.toppanhall.com
Musical Concert Hall Management & Operation Services
N.A.I.C.S.: 713990

Toppan Harima Products Co., Ltd. (1)
3-13-1 Koto Kamigooricho, Akou-Gun, Hyogo, 678-1205, Japan
Tel.: (81) 791598180
Plastic Container Mfr
N.A.I.C.S.: 326199

Toppan Hokkaido Insatsukako Co., Ltd. (1)
1-1-30 4jo Nijuyonken, Nishi-Ku, Sapporo, Hokkaido, Japan
Tel.: (81) 116146231
Book Binding Services
N.A.I.C.S.: 323120

Toppan Human Information Services Co., Ltd. (1)
1-5-1 Taito, Taito-Ku, Tokyo, 110-0016, Japan
Tel.: (81) 338355199
Human Resource Consulting Services
N.A.I.C.S.: 541612

Toppan Infomedia Co., Ltd. (1)
3-19-26 Shibaura, Minato-ku, Tokyo, 108-0023, Japan
Tel.: (81) 36 367 5550
Web Site: https://www.toppan-im.co.jp
Semiconductor & Related Device Mfr
N.A.I.C.S.: 334413
Yuji Sato (Chm)

Toppan Insurance Service Co., Ltd. (1)
1-5-1 Taito, Taito-Ku, Tokyo, 110-0016, Japan
Tel.: (81) 338356741
Insurance Management Services
N.A.I.C.S.: 524298

Toppan Interamerica, Inc. (1)
1131 Highway 155 S, McDonough, GA 30253
Tel.: (770) 957-5060
Web Site: https://toppaninteramerica.com
Sales Range: $75-99.9 Million
Emp.: 145
Mfr & Sales of Interior Decor Materials
N.A.I.C.S.: 323111

Toppan Leefung Advertising (Shanghai) Co., Ltd. (1)
Room 2013 Beijing Fortune Bldg, 5 Dong San Huan Bei Lu Chao Yang District, Beijing, 100004, China
Tel.: (86) 1065528766
Decor Paper Mfr
N.A.I.C.S.: 322299

Toppan Leefung Packaging & Printing (Beijing) Co., Ltd. (1)
Block 3 No 3 Kechuang East 2nd Street, Tong Zhou District, Beijing, 101111, China
Tel.: (86) 105 901 1288
Web Site: http://www.toppanleefung.com
Commercial Printing & Packaging Services
N.A.I.C.S.: 323111

Toppan Leefung Printing Ltd. (1)
20/F Concoy Tower 169 Electric Road, North Point, China (Hong Kong)
Tel.: (852) 28106801
Emp.: 100
Book Printing Services
N.A.I.C.S.: 323111
Steven Lo (Mng Dir)

Toppan Leefung Pte. Ltd. (1)
1 Kim Seng Promenade 18-01 Great World City East Lobby, 18-01 Great World City East Tower, Singapore, 237994, Singapore
Tel.: (65) 6 826 9600
Web Site: https://www.toppanleefung.com
Books Publishing Services
N.A.I.C.S.: 513120
Chee Tong Yeo (Pres & CEO)

Subsidiary (Non-US):

Toppan Leefung (Hong Kong) Ltd. (2)
20/F Lee & Man Commercial Center 169 Electric Road, North Point, China (Hong Kong)
Tel.: (852) 2 912 5200
Web Site: http://www.toppanleefung.com
Color Magazine Printing Services
N.A.I.C.S.: 323111

Subsidiary (Domestic):

Toppan Yau Yue Paper Products Ltd. (3)
20/F Lee and Man Commercial Center 169 Electric Road, North Point, China (Hong Kong)
Tel.: (852) 2 912 5200
Web Site: https://www.toppanleefung.com
Corrugated Paper Board Mfr & Distr
N.A.I.C.S.: 424130
Xiao Gang Luo (Mng Dir)

Subsidiary (Domestic):

Toppan Security Printing Pte. Ltd. (2)
97 Ubi Avenue 4, Singapore, 408754, Singapore
Tel.: (65) 6 741 2500
Web Site: http://www.toppanleefung.com
Commercial Printing Services
N.A.I.C.S.: 323111

Subsidiary (Non-US):

Toppan Vite Ltd. (2)
8th Floor Gloucester Tower 15 Queen's Road, Central, China (Hong Kong)
Tel.: (852) 2877 8773
Web Site: http://www.toppanvite.com
Emp.: 150
Financial Printing Services
N.A.I.C.S.: 323111
Christabel Lee (Mng Dir)

Subsidiary (Domestic):

Toppan Vite Pte. Ltd. (2)
3 Church Street 10-03 Samsung Hub, Singapore, 049483, Singapore

Tel.: (65) 6578 6522
Web Site: http://www.toppanvite.com
Financial Printing Services
N.A.I.C.S.: 323111
Maggie Ma *(Gen Mgr)*

Toppan Logistics Co., Ltd. (1)
1-16-5 Azusawa, Itabashi-ku, Tokyo, 174-8510, Japan
Tel.: (81) 35 915 6311
Web Site: https://www.toppan-b.co.jp
Emp.: 483
Logistics Consulting Servies
N.A.I.C.S.: 541614

Toppan M&I Ltd. (1)
1-5-22 Shimoochiai Arimino Bldg 5f, Shinjuku-Ku, Tokyo, 161-0033, Japan
Tel.: (81) 3 5330 8080
Web Site: http://www.toppanmi.jp
Software Development Services
N.A.I.C.S.: 541511

Toppan Management Systems (S) Pte. Ltd. (1)
97 Ubi Avenue 4, Singapore, 408754, Singapore
Tel.: (65) 6 336 6936
Web Site: https://www.tms.com.sg
Sales Range: $25-49.9 Million
Emp.: 20
Information Technology Consulting Services
N.A.I.C.S.: 541512
Gentaro Matsunaga *(Mng Dir)*

Toppan Media Printec Kansai Co., Ltd. (1)
3-22-61 Ebie, Fukushima-ku, Osaka, Japan
Tel.: (81) 66 454 3666
Web Site: https://www.toppan-tmk.co.jp
Emp.: 100
Multicolor Offset Printing Services
N.A.I.C.S.: 323111

Toppan Media Printec Tokyo Co., Ltd (1)
3-1-8 Asahigaoka, Hino, 191-0065, Tokyo, Japan
Tel.: (81) 42 582 3261
Web Site: https://www.toppan-mpt.co.jp
Newspaper Printing Services
N.A.I.C.S.: 323111

Toppan Media Printing Hokkaido Co., Ltd. (1)
8-2-3 Kogyodanchi Omagari, Kitahiroshima, 061-1274, Hokkaido, Japan
Tel.: (81) 113703151
Newspaper Printing Services
N.A.I.C.S.: 323111

Toppan Mind Wellness Co., Ltd. (1)
1-5-1 Taito, Taito-Ku, Tokyo, 110-8560, Japan
Tel.: (81) 33 835 6865
Web Site: https://www.mindupnavi.com
Business Management Consulting Services
N.A.I.C.S.: 541618

Toppan Packs Co., Ltd. (1)
Toppaninsatsuk K Gummakojonai, Oura, 370-0523, Gunma, Japan
Tel.: (81) 276621115
Commercial Printing Services
N.A.I.C.S.: 323111

Toppan Photomasks France S.A.S. (1)
224 Boulevard John Kennedy, 91105, Corbeil-Essonnes, France
Tel.: (33) 16 493 7520
Web Site: http://www.electronics.toppan.co.jp
Photomasks Mfr
N.A.I.C.S.: 325992

Toppan Photomasks Germany GmbH (1)
Rahnitzer Allee 9, 01109, Dresden, Germany
Tel.: (49) 3 518 1090
Web Site: http://www.amtc-erestem.com
Sales Range: $25-49.9 Million
Emp.: 20
Photomasks Mfr
N.A.I.C.S.: 325992
Isamu Ishida *(Gen Mgr)*

Toppan Photomasks GmbH (1)
Rahnitzer Allee 9, 01109, Dresden, Germany
Tel.: (49) 351 81090
Web Site: http://www.photomasks.com
Photomasks Mfr
N.A.I.C.S.: 325992

Toppan Photomasks, Inc. (1)
131 Old Settlers Blvd, Round Rock, TX 78664-2211
Tel.: (512) 310-6500
Web Site: https://www.photomasks.com
Sales Range: $350-399.9 Million
Emp.: 1,540
Semiconductor Equipment & Materials Mfr
N.A.I.C.S.: 333242
Franklin Kalk *(CTO & Exec VP)*

Branch (Domestic):

Toppan Photomasks, Inc. - Colorado Springs (2)
400 Texas Ave, Round Rock, TX 78664
Tel.: (512) 310-6000
Web Site: https://www.photomask.com
Sales Range: $25-49.9 Million
Emp.: 1
Photographic Services
N.A.I.C.S.: 812921
Kurlin Peter *(CEO)*

Toppan Photomasks, Inc. - Santa Clara (2)
2920 Coronado Dr, Santa Clara, CA 95054
Tel.: (408) 492-1900
Web Site: http://www.photomask.com
Sales Range: $25-49.9 Million
Emp.: 240
Die Cut Cards Folders & Mats
N.A.I.C.S.: 334413
Don Needham *(Dir-Sls)*

Toppan Plastic Co., Ltd. (1)
1-8 Omanocho, Koshigaya, 343-0844, Saitama, Japan
Tel.: (81) 489881321
Plastics Product Mfr
N.A.I.C.S.: 326199

Toppan Printing Co. (America), Inc. (1)
2175 Greenhill Dr, Round Rock, TX 78664 (100%)
Tel.: (512) 310-6212
Web Site: https://www.toppan.com
Sales Range: $25-49.9 Million
Emp.: 25
Book & Magazine Printing Sales, Commercial Printing Sales, Sales Promotion, Copyright & Joint Publication Negotiation
N.A.I.C.S.: 323111

Toppan Printing Co. (UK) Ltd. (1)
Old Change House 2nd Floor 128 Queen Victoria St, London, EC4V 4BJ, United Kingdom (100%)
Tel.: (44) 20 7213 0500
Web Site: http://www.toppan.co.uk
Sales Range: $25-49.9 Million
Emp.: 20
Interior Decor Materials, Electronic Precision Components Sales, Book Printing & Marketing
N.A.I.C.S.: 323120

Toppan Printing Co. (HK) Ltd. (1)
Unit 417 InnoCentre 72 Tat Chee Avenue, Kowloon Tong, Kowloon, NT, China (Hong Kong) (100%)
Tel.: (852) 2 561 0101
Web Site: https://www.toppan.com.hk
Sales Range: $125-149.9 Million
Emp.: 350
Book, Magazine & Commercial Printing
N.A.I.C.S.: 323111

Toppan Printing Co., (Shanghai) Ltd. (1)
No 2300 Shengang Road, Dong Bu New District, Shanghai, 201612, China (100%)
Tel.: (86) 216 760 0860
Web Site: https://www.toppansh.com.cn
Sales Range: $1-9.9 Million
Emp.: 300
Mfr of Bank Cards, Credit Cards & Prepaid Cards
N.A.I.C.S.: 522210
Tsuginura Kauyoshi *(Mng Dir)*

Toppan Printing Co., (Shenzhen) Ltd. (1)
No 27 Industrial Zone Chuang Ye Rd Baoan, Shenzhen, 518133, China (100%)
Tel.: (86) 75527963311
Web Site: http://www.poptan.com.jp
Sales Range: $450-499.9 Million
Emp.: 20
Book, Magazine & Commercial Printing & Paper Carton Packaging
N.A.I.C.S.: 323111

Toppan Printing Co., Ltd. (1)
Room 4015 Chang Fu Gong Office Bldg 26, Jia Guo Men Wai Da Jie Chao Yang-Qu, Beijing, 100022, China
Tel.: (86) 1065138039
Decor Paper Mfr
N.A.I.C.S.: 322299

Toppan Printing Co., Ltd. (1)
97 Ubi Avenue 4, Singapore, 408754, Singapore
Tel.: (65) 65895454
Packaging Materials Mfr
N.A.I.C.S.: 326112

Toppan Printing Co., Ltd. (1)
Crosscoop Delhi NCR 3rd Floor Building No 9-A, DLF Cyber City Phase III, Gurgaon, 122002, Haryana, India
Tel.: (91) 1244545030
Packaging Materials Mfr
N.A.I.C.S.: 326112

Toppan Printing Co., Ltd. - Chubu Division (1)
19 Nominami-cho, Nishi-ku, Nagoya, 452-0847, Aichi, Japan
Tel.: (81) 52 503 5111
Commercial Printing Services
N.A.I.C.S.: 323111

Toppan Printing Co., Ltd. - Electronics Division (1)
Yomiuri Kyoto Building 630 Shichikannoncho Rokkakusagaru Karasuma, Nakagyo-ku, Kyoto, 604-8162, Japan
Tel.: (81) 75 257 7231
Electronic Components Mfr
N.A.I.C.S.: 334419

Toppan Printing Co., Ltd. - Higashinihon Division (1)
3-30 Akedori, Izumi-ku, Sendai, 981-3296, Miyagi, Japan
Tel.: (81) 22 377 5111
Web Site: http://www.toppan.co.jp
Commercial Printing Services
N.A.I.C.S.: 323111

Toppan Printing Co., Ltd. - Hokkaido Division (1)
1-1-30 Nijuyonken 4-jo, Nishi-ku, Sapporo, 063-8555, Hokkaido, Japan
Tel.: (81) 11 614 6111
Commercial Printing Services
N.A.I.C.S.: 323111

Toppan Printing Co., Ltd. - Information and Communication Division (1)
1-3-3 Suido, Bunkyo-ku, Tokyo, 112-8531, Japan
Tel.: (81) 3 5840 3111
Emp.: 3,000
Commercial Printing Services
N.A.I.C.S.: 323111

Toppan Printing Co., Ltd. - International Division (1)
1 Kanda Izumi-cho, Chiyoda-ku, Tokyo, 101-0024, Japan
Tel.: (81) 3 3835 5743
Commercial Printing Services
N.A.I.C.S.: 323111

Toppan Printing Co., Ltd. - Kansai Division (1)
3-22-61 Ebie, Fukushima-ku, Osaka, 553-8580, Japan
Tel.: (81) 6 6454 3011
Paper Products Mfr
N.A.I.C.S.: 322299

Toppan Printing Co., Ltd. - Living Environment Division (1)
1-5-1 Taito, Taito-ku, Tokyo, 110-8560, Japan
Tel.: (81) 338356826
Web Site: http://www.toppan.co.jp
Commercial Printing Services
N.A.I.C.S.: 323111

Toppan Printing Co., Ltd. - Nishinihon Division (1)
1-17-28 Yakuin, Chuo, Fukuoka, 810-0022, Japan
Tel.: (81) 92 722 2000
Web Site: http://www.toppan.co.jp
Commercial Printing Services
N.A.I.C.S.: 323111

Toppan Printing Co., Ltd. International Business Law Center (1)
275 Battery St Ste 2600, San Francisco, CA 94111 (100%)
Tel.: (415) 393-9839
Sales Range: $25-49.9 Million
Emp.: 1
Mfr of Electronics & Printing
N.A.I.C.S.: 541110
Yutaka Konosu *(Pres)*

Toppan Printing Greece S.A. (1)
212 Kifisias Avenue, Neo Psychico, 154 51, Athens, Greece
Tel.: (30) 210 67 55 477
Printing Machine Sales & Maintenance Services
N.A.I.C.S.: 423830

Toppan Prosprint Co., Ltd. (1)
3-5-6 Etchujima, Koto-Ku, Tokyo, 135-0044, Japan
Tel.: (81) 35 646 6222
Web Site: https://www.toppan-pp.co.jp
Sales Range: $125-149.9 Million.
Emp.: 255
Printing Materials Mfr & Distr
N.A.I.C.S.: 325910

Toppan Security Service Co., Ltd. (1)
1-5-1 Taito, Taito-Ku, Tokyo, 110-0016, Japan (100%)
Tel.: (81) 338355100
Security Consulting Services
N.A.I.C.S.: 541690

Toppan Seihon Co., Ltd. (1)
Azusawa 2-11-22, Tokyo, Japan
Tel.: (81) 3 3960 1151
Book Printing Services
N.A.I.C.S.: 323117

Toppan Semiconductor Singapore Pte. Ltd. (1)
c/o Toppan Leefung Pte Ltd 1 Kim Seng Promenade 18-01 Great World City, East Tower, Singapore, 237994, Singapore
Tel.: (65) 6826 9644
Semiconductor Devices Mfr
N.A.I.C.S.: 334413

Toppan Smic Electronics (Shanghai) Co., Ltd. (1)
SO3-5F 965 Guoshoujing Road, Pudong New Area District, Shanghai, 201203, China
Tel.: (86) 215 080 5800
Web Site: http://www.toppan.co.jp
Microlense Component Mfr
N.A.I.C.S.: 334419

Toppan System Solutions Co., Ltd. (1)
3-10-36 Higashijujo, Kita-Ku, Tokyo, 114-0001, Japan
Tel.: (81) 3 5959 5030
Web Site: http://www.toppan-ss.co.jp
Business Support Services
N.A.I.C.S.: 561499

Toppan TDK Label Co., Ltd. (1)
1-5-1 Taito, Taito-ku, Tokyo, 110-0016, Japan
Tel.: (81) 3 3833 7520
Web Site: http://www.toppan-tl.co.jp
Magnetic & Other Recording Media Applied Devices Mfr
N.A.I.C.S.: 334610
Yuji Shimizu *(Pres)*

Plant (Domestic):

Toppan TDK Label Co., Ltd. - Fukushima Plant (2)
30-2 Aza Miyata Okajima, Fukushima, 960-8201, Japan
Tel.: (81) 24 536 6111
Labels & Stickers Printing Services
N.A.I.C.S.: 323111

Toppan TDK Label Co., Ltd. - Sagamihara Plant (2)

TOPPAN HOLDINGS INC.

TOPPAN Holdings Inc.—(Continued)
2-29-20 Onodai, Sagamihara, 229-0011, Kanagawa, Japan
Tel.: (81) 42 759 2221
Printing Machinery Mfr
N.A.I.C.S.: 333248

Toppan TDK Label Co., Ltd. - Takino Plant (2)
1816-173 Kotaka, Kato, 679-0221, Hyogo, Japan
Tel.: (81) 795 48 1171
Printing Machinery Mfr
N.A.I.C.S.: 333248

Toppan TOMOEGAWA Optical Films Co., Ltd. (1)
1-5-1 Taito, Taito-Ku, Tokyo, 110-0016, Japan
Tel.: (81) 338356200
Antiglare & Functional Film Mfr & Distr
N.A.I.C.S.: 326112

Toppan Technical Design Center Co., Ltd. (1)
1-5-1 Taito, Taito-ku, Tokyo, 110-0016, Japan
Tel.: (81) 338356188
Web Site: http://www.toptdc.com
Semiconductor Devices Mfr
N.A.I.C.S.: 334413
Kaname Arai *(Pres & CEO)*

Toppan Techno Co., Ltd. (1)
1-18-4 Shimura, Itabashi-Ku, Tokyo, 174-0056, Japan
Tel.: (81) 33 965 6841
Web Site: https://www.toppan-techno.co.jp
Emp.: 450
Building Maintenance Services
N.A.I.C.S.: 561730

Toppan Travel Service Corp. (1)
2-6-2 Hamamatsucho Hamamatsucho 262 Building Reception 8th floor, Minato-ku, Tokyo, 105-0013, Japan
Tel.: (81) 34 570 0600
Web Site: https://www.toppantravel.com
Sales Range: $25-49.9 Million
Emp.: 131
Tours & Travel Management Services
N.A.I.C.S.: 561520

Toppan USA, Inc. (1)
603 Rehoboth Rd, Griffin, GA 30224
Tel.: (770) 467-5900
Web Site: https://www.toppan-usa.com
Barrier Film Mfr
N.A.I.C.S.: 326112
Masa Tatewaki *(Pres)*

Tosho Estate Co., Ltd. (1)
4-3-10 Meieki, Nakamura-Ku, Nagoya, 450-0002, Aichi, Japan
Tel.: (81) 525412057
Commercial Printer Services
N.A.I.C.S.: 323111

Total Media Development Institute Co., Ltd. (1)
Bungei Spring Autumn New Building 3-23 Kioicho, Chiyoda-Ku, Tokyo, 102-0094, Japan
Tel.: (81) 33 221 5558
Web Site: https://www.totalmedia.co.jp
Visual Media Development Services
N.A.I.C.S.: 561499

TOPPESFIELD LTD

Toppesfield House Hill View Business Park Old Ipswich Rd, Claydon, Ipswich, IP6 0AJ, Suffolk, United Kingdom
Tel.: (44) 1473 829129
Web Site: http://www.toppesfield.com
Sales Range: $25-49.9 Million
Emp.: 200
Fiscal Year-end: 12/31/14
Highway & Street Tarmacing
N.A.I.C.S.: 237310
Sean Gorman *(Dir-Sls & Strategy)*

TOPPS TILES PLC

Thorpe Way Grove Park, Enderby, LE19 1SU, Leicester, United Kingdom
Tel.: (44) 1162828000
Web Site: https://www.toppsgroup.com
Year Founded: 1963
TPT—(LSE)
Rev.: $334,454,489
Assets: $222,026,735
Liabilities: $188,432,846
Net Worth: $33,593,889
Earnings: $4,989,179
Emp.: 1,744
Fiscal Year-end: 09/30/23
Floor & Window Covering Sales
N.A.I.C.S.: 449121
Stephen Hopson *(CFO)*

Subsidiaries:

Multi-Tile Ltd (1)
Earl Road Cheadle Humle, Unit Q Oak Green Business Park, Cheadle, United Kingdom (100%)
Tel.: (44) 1625446700
Sales Range: $25-49.9 Million
Emp.: 70
Ceramic Wall & Floor Tile Mfr
N.A.I.C.S.: 327120

Strata Tiles Limited (1)
Barnsdale Way Grove Park, Enderby, LE19 1SN, Leicester, United Kingdom
Tel.: (44) 116 282 8000
Web Site: https://www.stratatiles.co.uk
Ceramic Floor Tile Distr
N.A.I.C.S.: 423220
Dan Little *(Mng Dir-Commercial)*

Tiles4less Limited (1)
3rd Floor 207 Regent Street, London, W1B 3HH, United Kingdom
Tel.: (44) 204 571 0589
Web Site: https://www.tiles4less.co.uk
Ceramic Floor Tile Distr
N.A.I.C.S.: 423220

Topps Tiles (UK) Ltd (1)
Thorpe Way Grove Park, Leicester, LE19 1SU, United Kingdom (100%)
Tel.: (44) 1162828000
Sales Range: $250-299.9 Million
Emp.: 1,500
Construction Material Merchant Whsl
N.A.I.C.S.: 423390

TOPRAY SOLAR CO., LTD.

Tel.: (86) 75586612689
Web Site: https://www.topraysolar.com
Year Founded: 2002
002218—(SSE)
Rev.: $185,732,184
Assets: $1,002,681,468
Liabilities: $408,050,010
Net Worth: $594,631,459
Earnings: $13,512,054
Fiscal Year-end: 12/31/22
Solar Cell Module Mfr
N.A.I.C.S.: 334419
Hongxia Fu *(Deputy Gen Mgr)*

Subsidiaries:

Kashi Ruicheng New Energy Technology Co., Ltd. (1)
Room 901 Unit 2 No 56 Hengchang Phase III, Kashi, China
Tel.: (86) 9982313695
Photovoltaic Equipment Mfr & Distr
N.A.I.C.S.: 335999

Leshan Topray Solar Cell Co., Ltd. (1)
No 9 Jianye Road High-tech Industrial Development Zone, Leshan, Sichuan, China
Tel.: (86) 8333525666
Web Site: http://www.topraycell.com
Solar Product Mfr
N.A.I.C.S.: 334413

Qinghai Topray Solar Co., Ltd. (1)
Economic and Technological Development Zone, Dongchuan Industrial Park Road South of the Silica, Xining, Qinghai, China
Tel.: (86) 9716251814
Solar Product Mfr
N.A.I.C.S.: 334413

Qinghai Tuori New Energy Technology Co., Ltd. (1)
Economic & Technological Development Zone, Dongchuan Industrial Park Road South of the Silica, Xining, Qinghai, China
Tel.: (86) 9716251814
Electronic Component Mfr & Distr
N.A.I.C.S.: 334419

Shaanxi Topray Solar Co., Ltd. (1)
East Extension Sun City, Chengcheng County Daigo Village, Weinan, Shaanxi, China
Tel.: (86) 9136900800
Solar Product Mfr
N.A.I.C.S.: 334413

Shaanxi Tuori New Energy Technology Co., Ltd. (1)
East Extension West Yu The Direction Of Export 3 8 km, Chengcheng County Taiyuan Daigo Village, Weinan, China
Tel.: (86) 9136900800
Photovoltaic Equipment Mfr & Distr
N.A.I.C.S.: 335999

Topray Solar (United States) Co., Ltd. (1)
Figueroa St Rm 288 350s, Los Angeles, CA 90012-2543
Tel.: (213) 628-9888
Solar Product Whslr
N.A.I.C.S.: 423690

Topray Solar GmbH (1)
Hanauer Landstrasse 291B, 60314, Frankfurt am Main, Germany
Tel.: (49) 69710475301
Solar Product Whslr
N.A.I.C.S.: 423690

TOPRE CORPORATION

Asahi Bldg 12-2 Nihonbashi 3-chome, Chuo-ku, Tokyo, 103-0027, Japan
Tel.: (81) 332710711
Web Site: https://www.topre.co.jp
Year Founded: 1935
5975—(TKS)
Rev.: $2,346,034,420
Assets: $2,416,120,250
Liabilities: $983,561,390
Net Worth: $1,432,558,860
Earnings: $113,024,390
Emp.: 5,621
Fiscal Year-end: 03/31/24
Automobile Parts Mfr
N.A.I.C.S.: 336390
Yutaka Yamamoto *(Pres)*

Subsidiaries:

PT. topre Refrigerator Indonesia (1)
Jl Raya Serang Km 24 Desa, Balaraja, Tangerang, 15610, Banten, Indonesia
Tel.: (62) 215951624
Web Site: https://topre.co.id
Refrigeration & Insulated Container Mfr
N.A.I.C.S.: 332439
Toshiaki Taneda *(Pres)*

TOPRE (THAILAND) CO., LTD. (1)
Asia Industrial Estate 111 Moo 3, Klongsuan Sub-district Bangbo district, Bangkok, 10560, Samutprakarn, Thailand
Tel.: (66) 21365370
Automobile Component Distr
N.A.I.C.S.: 441330
Rissara Winitchaiyanan *(Asst Mgr-Gen Affairs)*

Toho Transportation Co., Ltd. (1)
2-11 Minami Hashimoto 3-chome, chuo-ku, Sagamihara, 252-0253, Kanagawa, Japan
Tel.: (81) 427721367
Vehicles Transportation Services
N.A.I.C.S.: 488490

Tokyo Kinzoku Co. Ltd. (1)
3767 Kaminokawa Kaminokawa-machi, Kawachi, 329-0611, Tochigi, Japan
Tel.: (81) 285562089
Automotive Components Mfr
N.A.I.C.S.: 336390

Tokyo Metal Pack Co., Ltd. (1)
3-2-25 Minamihashimoto, Chuo-ku, Sagamihara, 252-0253, Kanagawa, Japan
Tel.: (81) 427728167
Web Site: https://metalpack.co.jp
Emp.: 38

INTERNATIONAL PUBLIC

Automotive Components Mfr

Tokyo Multifastener Co. Ltd. (1)
12-2 Nihonbashi 3-chome, Chuo-ku, Tokyo, 103-0027, Japan
Tel.: (81) 427728169
Pierce Nut Mfr
N.A.I.C.S.: 332722

Topre (FOSHAN) Autoparts Corporation (1)
No 19 Beiyuan Middle Road, Shishan Science and Technology Industrial Park Nanhai District, Foshan, 528225, Guangdong, China
Tel.: (86) 75781208935
Emp.: 290
Automotive Component Mfr & Distr
N.A.I.C.S.: 336390

Topre (Wuhan) Autoparts Corporation (1)
No 10 Huayuanwan 2nd Road Zhashan Street, Caidian District, Wuhan, 430100, China
Tel.: (86) 2784750711
Automotive Part Mfr & Distr
N.A.I.C.S.: 336350

Topre (Xiangyang) Autoparts Corporation (1)
No 82 Dongfeng Motor Avenue, High-tech Industrial Development Zone, Xiangyang, 441004, Hubei, China
Tel.: (86) 7103330711
Emp.: 197
Automotive Component Mfr & Distr
N.A.I.C.S.: 336390
Bing Zeng *(Coord-IT)*

Topre America Corporation (1)
1580 County Rd 222, Cullman, AL 35057
Tel.: (256) 735-2600
Automotive Component Mfr & Distr
N.A.I.C.S.: 336390
Hideo Shimizu *(Gen Mgr)*

Topre Autoparts Mexico, S.A. de C.V. (1)
Yaquis Numero 9 Colonia Nuevo Parque Industrial, 76806, San Juan del Rio, Queretaro, Mexico
Tel.: (52) 4272682200
Automotive Component Mfr & Distr
N.A.I.C.S.: 336390
Enrique Dominguez *(Project Mgr)*

Topre Gifu Corporation (1)
372-7 Shimo Kawabe Kawabe-cho, Kamogun, Gifu, 509-0306, Japan
Tel.: (81) 574532180
Air Conditioning Equipment Mfr
N.A.I.C.S.: 333415

Topre India Pvt. Ltd. (1)
Plot No 56 to 61, Mandal Industrial Estate Japanese Industrial Park Vithalapur, Gujarat, 382130, India
Tel.: (91) 2715661011
Automotive Press Parts Mfr
N.A.I.C.S.: 336390

Topre Kyushu Corporation (1)
150 Akinari, Tanushimaru-cho, Kurume, 839-1203, Fukuoka, Japan
Tel.: (81) 943747150
Web Site: https://toprekyushu.jp
Emp.: 560
Automotive Components Mfr
N.A.I.C.S.: 336390

Topre Saitama Corporation (1)
874-1 Tamagawa Tokigawa-machi, Hiki-gun, Saitama, 355-0342, Japan
Tel.: (81) 493661211
Automotive Components Mfr
N.A.I.C.S.: 336390

Topre Tokai Corporation (1)
200 Sekoizumi, Toin-cho, Inabe, 511-0252, Mie, Japan
Tel.: (81) 594861010
Web Site: https://www.topretokai.jp
Emp.: 276
Automotive Press Parts Mfr
N.A.I.C.S.: 336390

Toprec Corporation (1)
1-13-12 Nihonbashi Kayabacho Sakura Nihonbashi Building 8F, Chuo-ku, Tokyo, 103-

AND PRIVATE COMPANIES

0025, Japan (100%)
Tel.: (81) 368927811
Web Site: https://www.toprec.co.jp
Emp.: 179
Cold Storage Equipment Mfr
N.A.I.C.S.: 423740

TOPSOE A/S
Haldor Topsoes Alle 1, DK-2800, Lyngby, Denmark
Tel.: (45) 45272000 DK
Web Site: http://www.topsoe.com
Year Founded: 1940
Rev.: $889,116,210
Assets: $1,038,276,660
Liabilities: $750,299,550
Net Worth: $287,977,110
Earnings: $93,993,570
Emp.: 2,238
Fiscal Year-end: 12/31/19
Heterogeneous Catalysts, Equipment & Consumables Design & Mfr
N.A.I.C.S.: 325998
Vagn B. Villadsen *(VP-Fin)*

Subsidiaries:

Haldor Topsoe A/S (1)
1-2 Bolshoy Gnezdnikovskiy Pereulok 6 floor, 125009, Moscow, Russia
Tel.: (7) 4959563274
Web Site: http://www.topsoe.com
Sales Range: $25-49.9 Million
Emp.: 45
Catalytic Process Technologies
N.A.I.C.S.: 334519

Haldor Topsoe America Latina S.A. (1)
Dardo Rocha 2070 Martinez, B1640FSZ, Buenos Aires, Argentina
Tel.: (54) 1147170172
Chemical Products Distr
N.A.I.C.S.: 424690
Frederik Soeby *(Gen Mgr)*

Haldor Topsoe Canada Limited (1)
RPO Meadowlark, PO Box 92560, Edmonton, T5R 5Y3, AB, Canada
Tel.: (780) 720-9143
Chemical Products Distr
N.A.I.C.S.: 424690

Haldor Topsoe India Private Limited (1)
Vatika Mindscapes Tower A 3rd Floor 12/3 Mathura Road NH-2, Faridabad, 121003, Haryana, India
Tel.: (91) 129 661 7000
Web Site: http://www.topsoe.com
Catalytic Process Technologies
N.A.I.C.S.: 334519
Rasmus Breivik *(Mng Dir)*

Haldor Topsoe International A/S (1)
2301 West Tower Prosper Center 5 Guanghua Road, Chaoyang Distict, Beijing, 100020, China
Tel.: (86) 1065158886
Web Site: http://www.topsoe.dk
Emp.: 99
Catalytic Process Technologies
N.A.I.C.S.: 334519
Kim Hedejaard *(Mng Dir)*

Haldor Topsoe International A/S (1)
Fukoku Seimei Building 17F, 2-2-2 Uchisaiwaicho, Chiyoda-Ku, 100-0011, Tokyo, Japan
Tel.: (81) 355118115
Web Site: http://www.topsoe.jp
Sales Range: $25-49.9 Million
Emp.: 2
Catalytic Process Technologies
N.A.I.C.S.: 334519

Haldor Topsoe International A/S (1)
Almoayyed Tower 2504 Off No 3401 34th Floor Rd No 2832, PO Box 20274, Manama, Bahrain
Tel.: (973) 17550485
Technical Consulting Services
N.A.I.C.S.: 541690

Haldor Topsoe SA (Pty) Ltd. (1)
200 on Main Cnr of Main Street & Bowwood Road, Claremont, 7708, Cape Town, South Africa

Tel.: (27) 218358350
Chemical Products Mfr
N.A.I.C.S.: 325199
Helge Rosenberg *(Mng Dir)*

Haldor Topsoe Sdn. Bhd. (1)
A-38-1 Tower A Menara UOA Bangsar 5 Jala Bangsar Utama 1, Bangsar, 59000, Kuala Lumpur, Malaysia
Tel.: (60) 322010166
Web Site: http://www.topsoe.com
Emp.: 17
Chemical Products Distr
N.A.I.C.S.: 424690

Haldor Topsoe, Inc. (1)
17629 El Camino Real, Houston, TX 77058
Tel.: (281) 228-5000
Web Site: http://www.haldortopsoe.com
Catalytic Process Technologies
N.A.I.C.S.: 334519
Dorna Rohrman *(Dir-HR)*

Haldor Topsoe, Inc. (1)
770 The City Dr Ste 8400, Orange, CA 92668
Tel.: (714) 621-3800
Web Site: http://www.topsoe.com
Sales Range: $25-49.9 Million
Emp.: 10
Catalytic Process Technologies
N.A.I.C.S.: 334519

Topsoe Fuel Cell A/S (1)
Nymollevej 55, DK-2800, Lyngby, Denmark
Tel.: (45) 45272000
Web Site: http://www.topsoefuelcell.com
Sales Range: $200-249.9 Million
Emp.: 900
Fuel Cell Solutions
N.A.I.C.S.: 335910
Lars Martiny *(CEO)*

ZAO Haldor Topsoe (1)
42 Respublikanskaya, 150040, Yaroslavl, Russia
Tel.: (7) 852730173
Chemical Products Mfr
N.A.I.C.S.: 325199

TOPSPORTS INTERNATIONAL HOLDINGS LIMITED
30-34 Kwai Wing Road 6th floor M1 The Edge, Kwai Chung, China (Hong Kong) Ky
Web Site: https://www.topsports.com.cn
Year Founded: 1999
6110—(HKG)
Rev.: $3,748,504,652
Assets: $2,328,962,672
Liabilities: $967,420,802
Net Worth: $1,361,541,870
Earnings: $254,292,202
Emp.: 9,844
Fiscal Year-end: 02/28/23
Holding Company
N.A.I.C.S.: 551112
Kam Kwan Leung *(Sec)*

TOPSUN CO., LTD.
B-101 GIDC Electronic ZoneSector 25, Gandhinagar, 382028, Gujarat, India
Tel.: (91) 7573006633
Web Site: https://www.topsunenergy.com
Renewable Energy Consulting Services
N.A.I.C.S.: 221114
Chintan Patel *(Mng Dir)*

TOPTEC CO., LTD.
28 5gongdan 4-ro Sandong-eup, Gumi, Gyeongsangbuk-do, Korea (South)
Tel.: (82) 544721100
Web Site: https://www.toptec.co.kr
Year Founded: 1992
108230—(KRS)
Rev.: $264,598,609
Assets: $366,757,773
Liabilities: $113,924,873

Net Worth: $252,832,900
Earnings: $4,578,054
Emp.: 439
Fiscal Year-end: 12/31/22
Automated Machinery Mfr
N.A.I.C.S.: 334512
Jeong Ji-yong *(CEO)*

TOPTICA PHOTONICS AG
Lochhamer Schlag 19, Munich, 82166, Germany
Tel.: (49) 89858370
Web Site: http://www.toptica.com
Year Founded: 1998
Rev.: $18,312,675
Emp.: 100
Laser System Mfr
N.A.I.C.S.: 334413
Wilhelm Kaenders *(CTO)*

Subsidiaries:

Toptica Photonics Inc (1)
1286 Blossom Dr, Victor, NY 14564
Tel.: (585) 657-6663
Laser Diode Mfr
N.A.I.C.S.: 334413

TOPVIEW OPTRONICS CORP.
No 10 Dacheng Rd, Taoyuan, 33068, Taiwan
Tel.: (886) 33628528
Web Site: https://www.topviewcorp.com
Year Founded: 1994
6556—(TPE)
Rev.: $70,427,196
Assets: $77,376,356
Liabilities: $35,597,349
Net Worth: $41,779,008
Earnings: $9,093,018
Emp.: 215
Fiscal Year-end: 12/31/22
Security System Services
N.A.I.C.S.: 561621
Hung-Ming Lee *(Chm & Pres)*

TOPY INDUSTRIES, LTD.
Art Village Osaki Central Tower 1-2-2 Osaki, Shinagawa-ku, Tokyo, 141-8634, Japan
Tel.: (81) 334930777 JP
Web Site: https://www.topy.co.jp
Year Founded: 1921
7231—(NGO)
Rev.: $2,206,751,942
Assets: $1,970,868,295
Liabilities: $1,039,332,382
Net Worth: $931,535,914
Earnings: $30,895,267
Emp.: 5,621
Fiscal Year-end: 03/31/24
Steel & Aluminum Wheels Mfr
N.A.I.C.S.: 332111
Takanori Kawano *(Supervisory Board of Directors & Operating Officer)*

Subsidiaries:

ATC Holdings Co., Ltd. (1)
3311-1 Higashi-Yokoji, Kikugawa, Shizuoka, Japan
Tel.: (81) 537363111
Steel Material Mfr
N.A.I.C.S.: 332999

Akemi Electric Power, Ltd. (1)
1 Akemi-cho, Toyohashi, 441-8510, Aichi, Japan
Tel.: (81) 532 25 6284
Emp.: 42
Eletric Power Generation Services
N.A.I.C.S.: 221111

Akemi Gas, Ltd. (1)
1 Akemi-cho, Toyohashi, 441-8510, Aichi, Japan
Tel.: (81) 532251035
Web Site: http://www.topy.co.jp
High Pressure Gas Production Equipment Mfr & Sales
N.A.I.C.S.: 333132

TOPY INDUSTRIES, LTD.

Akemi Recycling Center, Ltd. (1)
1 Akemi-cho, Toyohashi, 441-8510, Aichi, Japan
Tel.: (81) 532251211
Web Site: https://www.akemi-rc.co.jp
Raw Steel Processing & Industrial Waste Treatment Services
N.A.I.C.S.: 331110

Asahi Tec Aluminium (Thailand) Company Limited (1)
Amata Nacorn Industrial Estate 700/145 Moo 5, Klongtamharu, Amphur Muang, 20000, Chon Buri, Thailand
Tel.: (66) 38214218
Automotive Wheel Mfr & Whslr
N.A.I.C.S.: 336390

Asahi Tec Corp., Ltd. (1)
1569-1 Kamisaigo, Kyobashi, Kakegawa, 436-0342, Shizuoka, Japan (100%)
Tel.: (81) 53 725 7007
Web Site: https://www.asahitec.co.jp
Emp.: 1,127
Malleable Iron Casting & Aluminum Alloy Products Mfr
N.A.I.C.S.: 336390
Kenichi Ando *(Co-CEO)*

Autopia, Ltd. (1)
2003-6 Uchikoshi-machi, Hachioji, 192-0911, Tokyo, Japan
Tel.: (81) 42 632 5018
Web Site: https://www.autopia-ab.com
Emp.: 129
Automotive Parts Retailer
N.A.I.C.S.: 441330

Fujian Topy Autoparts Co., Ltd. (1)
Qingkou Investment Zone, Minhou, Fuzhou, Fujian, China
Tel.: (86) 59122768398
Automotive Wheel Mfr & Whslr
N.A.I.C.S.: 336390

Guangzhou Asahi Dongling Research & Development Co., Ltd. (1)
No 498 Xianning Road, Xiancun Town Zengcheng District, Guangzhou, 511335, China
Tel.: (86) 2032982813
Construction Machinery Mfr
N.A.I.C.S.: 333120

Guangzhou Dicastal Asahi Aluminium Co., Ltd. (1)
DongLing Industrial Park, Yonghe Zengcheng, Guangzhou, China
Tel.: (86) 2082983008
Aluminium Wheel Mfr & Distr
N.A.I.C.S.: 331314

Hokko Shouji, Inc. (1)
316-1 Kaneko Shinden, Sanjo, 955-0814, Niigata, Japan
Tel.: (81) 25 634 5865
Web Site: https://www.hokkou-eco.co.jp
Industrial Metal Waste Recycling Services
N.A.I.C.S.: 562920

Hokuetsu Kogyo, Ltd. (1)
221-31 Seiryo-machi, Nagaoka, 940-2045, Niigata, Japan
Tel.: (81) 258 21 4511
Wire Mesh & Reinforced Bar Processing Services & Industrial Fasteners Mfr
N.A.I.C.S.: 238210

Hokuetsu Turnbuckle Co., Ltd. (1)
8-4-1 Imaichi, Mitsuke, 954-0111, Niigata, Japan
Tel.: (81) 258667415
Web Site: http://www.topy.co.jp
Turnbuckle & Rockbolt Mfr
N.A.I.C.S.: 332722

Kotecs Co., Ltd. (1)
4th Floor Sanko Building 1-1 Kagurazaka, Shinjuku-ku, Tokyo, 162-0825, Japan
Tel.: (81) 35 227 3511
Web Site: https://www.kotecs.co.jp
Automotive Wheel Whslr
N.A.I.C.S.: 423120

Kotecs Kogyo Co., Ltd. (1)
Sanko Building 1-1 Kagurazaka, Shinjuku-ku, Tokyo, 162-0825, Japan
Tel.: (81) 352273782
Machinery Maintenance Management Services

TOPY INDUSTRIES, LTD.

Topy Industries, Ltd.—(Continued)
N.A.I.C.S.: 811310

Kyushu Wheel Kogyo, Ltd. (1)
45 Nagahama-cho Kanda-cho, Miyako-gun, Fukuoka, 800-0311, Japan (100%)
Tel.: (81) 93 434 4731
Web Site: https://www.kyushuwheel.co.jp
Sales Range: $100-124.9 Million
Emp.: 330
Automotive Wheel Mfr
N.A.I.C.S.: 336390

Metal Transport Ltd. (1)
2-14-11 Hokuyou, Nagaoka, 940-0871, Niigata, Japan
Tel.: (81) 258244554
General Freight Trucking Services
N.A.I.C.S.: 484110

N. E. Tojitsu, Ltd. (1)
2-3-8 Tekkodori, Urayasu, 279-0025, Chiba, Japan
Tel.: (81) 473905131
Web Site: http://www.topy.co.jp
Raw Steel Mfr & Distr
N.A.I.C.S.: 331110

Ring Techs Co., Ltd. (1)
2670 Tsurushinden Tsurajima-cho, Kurashiki, 712-8006, Okayama, Japan
Tel.: (81) 86 444 8111
Web Site: https://www.ring-techs.co.jp
Automotive Wheel Mfr & Whslr
N.A.I.C.S.: 336390

Ring-Techs Guangzhou Company Limited (1)
8 Xian Tang Road Yong He Section, Economic and Technological Development District, Guangzhou, China
Tel.: (86) 2032223377
Automotive Wheel Mfr & Whslr
N.A.I.C.S.: 336390

Sanwa Buhin Co., Ltd. (1)
3479 Yumida, Bando, 306-0607, Ibaraki, Japan (100%)
Tel.: (81) 297357121
Web Site: http://www.sanwa-buhin.com
Construction Machinery Components Mfr & Sales
N.A.I.C.S.: 333120
Kaneko Masayoshi *(Pres)*

Sanwa Kogyo Co., Ltd. (1)
3-7-43 Terajima, Itoigawa, 941-0066, Niigata, Japan
Tel.: (81) 255529014
Steel Material Mfr
N.A.I.C.S.: 332999

Seibu Wheels Co., Ltd. (1)
2670 Tsurushinden Tsurajima-cho, Kurashiki, 712-8006, Okayama, Japan
Tel.: (81) 864482866
Steel Material Mfr
N.A.I.C.S.: 332999

TEC-SAN Co., Ltd. (1)
847-10 Nae-ri Guji-Myeon, Dalseong-gun, Daegu, 711-890, Korea (South)
Tel.: (82) 161 2 12 30
Automotive Steel Wheels Mfr
N.A.I.C.S.: 331110

Tanagura Development Co., Ltd. (1)
286 Kawaharada Nikogi Tanagura-cho, Higashishirakawa-gun, Fukushima, 963-6122, Japan
Tel.: (81) 24 733 3193
Web Site: https://www.tanagura-cc.co.jp
Emp.: 40
Golf & Country Clubs Operation Services
N.A.I.C.S.: 713910
Shinichi Hirokawa *(Pres)*

Tojitsu, Ltd. (1)
1 Akemicho, Toyohashi, 441-8510, Aichi, Japan
Tel.: (81) 53 225 9355
Web Site: https://www.tojitu.co.jp
Emp.: 76
Scrap Iron Processing & Treatment Services
N.A.I.C.S.: 331110

Topy Agency, Ltd. (1)
Art Village Osaki Central Tower 6th floor
1-2-2 Osaki, Shinagawa-ku, Tokyo, 141-0032, Japan
Tel.: (81) 354360211
Web Site: https://www.topy-agency.co.jp
Emp.: 26
Insurance, Travel & Financial Support Services
N.A.I.C.S.: 522291

Topy America, Inc. (1)
980 Chenault Rd, Frankfort, KY 40601
Tel.: (502) 695-6163
Web Site: https://www.topyamerica.com
Automotive Steel Wheels Mfr
N.A.I.C.S.: 331110
Sue Shields *(Asst Mgr-Pur)*

Topy Enterprises (Dalian Free Trade Zone) Co., Ltd. (1)
Senmao Bldg 17F 147 Zhongshan Rd, Xigana, Dalian, 116011, Liaoning, China
Tel.: (86) 4118 368 6909
Web Site: http://www.topy.co.jp
International & Commission Trading Services
N.A.I.C.S.: 523160

Topy Enterprises, Ltd. (1)
1-2-2 Osaki Art Village Osaki Central Tower 6F, Yonban-cho, Shinagawa-ku, Tokyo, 141-8667, Japan
Tel.: (81) 33 495 6500
Web Site: https://www.topy-ep.co.jp
Sales Range: $125-149.9 Million
Emp.: 470
Automotive Components & Steel Materials Mfr & Whslr
N.A.I.C.S.: 336330

Topy Fastener (Thailand) Ltd. (1)
Amata City Chonburi 700/337 Moo 6 Bangna-Trad Rd Km 57, Tambol Donhualor Amphur Muang, Chon Buri, 20000, Thailand
Tel.: (66) 3 821 4401
Web Site: http://www.topy-fas.co.jp
Industrial Fasteners Mfr & Distr
N.A.I.C.S.: 339993

Topy Fasteners (Thailand) Ltd. (1)
700/337 Moo 6 Bangna-Trad Rd Km 57, Tambol Donhualor, Amphur Muang, 20000, Chon Buri, Thailand
Tel.: (66) 382144013
Web Site: https://www.topy.co.th
Construction Machinery Mfr
N.A.I.C.S.: 333120

Topy Fasteners Mexico S.A. DE C.V. (1)
Av Asia 603 Desarrollo Parque Industrial Llogistik II, Municipio Villa de Reyes, 79526, San Luis Potosi, Mexico
Tel.: (52) 4444781050
Steel Material Mfr
N.A.I.C.S.: 332999

Topy Fasteners Vietnam Co., Ltd. (1)
Plot No F-1 Thang Long Industrial Park II, Lieu Xa Commune Yen My District, Yen My, Hung Yen, Vietnam
Tel.: (84) 2213974884
Web Site: https://www.fact-link.com.vn
Emp.: 190
Construction Machinery Mfr
N.A.I.C.S.: 333120

Topy Fasteners, Ltd. (1)
5652-36 Sasaga, Matsumoto, 399-0033, Nagano, Japan
Tel.: (81) 26 325 6219
Web Site: https://www.topy-fas.co.jp
Emp.: 396
Construction Machinery Mfr
N.A.I.C.S.: 333120
Tani Toshiyuki *(Pres)*

Topy Fasteners, Ltd. - Kanra Factory (1)
550-3 Zenkeiji Kanra-machi Oaza, Kanra-gun, Gunma, 370-2206, Japan
Tel.: (81) 274 74 5571
Industrial Fastener Mfr
N.A.I.C.S.: 339993

Topy Industries Ltd. - Akemi Plant (1)
5-29 Akemi-cho, Toyohashi, 441-8074, Aichi, Japan
Tel.: (81) 53 223 3191
Web Site: https://www.topy.co.jp
Sales Range: $50-74.9 Million
Emp.: 60
Tire Sets Mfr
N.A.I.C.S.: 326211

Topy Industries Ltd. - Ayase Factory (1)
2-3-1 Ogami, Ayase, 252-1104, Kanagawa, Japan
Tel.: (81) 467781111
Automotive Wheel Mfr
N.A.I.C.S.: 331110

Topy Industries Ltd. - Hamura Plant (1)
3-5-10 Nagaoka Mizuho-cho, Nishitama-gun, Tokyo, 190-1232, Japan
Tel.: (81) 425795871
Tire Sets Mfr
N.A.I.C.S.: 326211

Topy Industries Ltd. - Kanagawa Factory (1)
830 Yabata, Chigasaki, 253-8650, Kanagawa, Japan
Tel.: (81) 46 782 1171
Web Site: https://www.topy.co.jp
Sales Range: $50-74.9 Million
Emp.: 250
Construction Machinery Components Mfr & Sales
N.A.I.C.S.: 333120

Topy Industries Ltd. - Kurate Plant (1)
765-1 Iwakawauchi Muroki Kuratemachi, Kurate-gun, Fukuoka, 807-1307, Japan
Tel.: (81) 94 942 8051
Web Site: http://www.topy.co.jp
Tire Sets Mfr
N.A.I.C.S.: 326211

Topy Industries Ltd. - Sagami Plant (1)
2-13-7 Hashimotodai, Midori-ku, Sagamihara, 252-0132, Kanagawa, Japan
Tel.: (81) 427002450
Web Site: http://www.topy.co.jp
Tire Sets Mfr
N.A.I.C.S.: 326211

Topy Industries Ltd. - Toyohashi Factory (1)
1 Akemi-cho, Toyohashi, 441-8510, Aichi, Japan
Tel.: (81) 53 225 1111
Web Site: https://www.topy.co.jp
Sales Range: $250-299.9 Million
Emp.: 800
Steel Products, Construction Machinery Components & Synthetic Mica Mfr
N.A.I.C.S.: 327999

Topy Industries Ltd. - Toyokawa Factory (1)
3-30 Honohara, Toyokawa, 442-8506, Aichi, Japan
Tel.: (81) 53 386 5121
Web Site: https://www.topy.co.jp
Motor Vehicle Parts Mfr
N.A.I.C.S.: 336390

Topy MW Manufacturing Mexico S.A. DE C.V. (1)
Av Mina de Guadalupe 798 Parque Industrial Santa Fe Ampliacion Silao, 36275, Guanajuato, Mexico
Tel.: (52) 4721350300
Automotive Wheel Mfr & Whslr
N.A.I.C.S.: 336390

Topy Marine Transport, Ltd. (1)
3-15 Jinnofutocho, Toyohashi, 441-8075, Aichi, Japan
Tel.: (81) 53 232 3261
Web Site: https://www.topy-kaiun.co.jp
Emp.: 279
Marine & Overland Transport & Warehousing Services
N.A.I.C.S.: 488390
Okazaki Yhirno *(Pres)*

Topy Precision Mfg., Inc. (1)
1375 Lunt Ave, Elk Grove Village, IL 60007
Tel.: (847) 439-6560
Web Site: http://www.topyprecision.com
Sales Range: $25-49.9 Million
Emp.: 50
Steel Fasteners Mfr & Distr
N.A.I.C.S.: 339993

Topy Undercarriage (China) Co., Ltd. (1)
No 91 Kewen Road, Qingdao Hi-tech Industrial Development Zone, Qingdao, 266111, China
Tel.: (86) 53266726888
Construction Machinery Mfr
N.A.I.C.S.: 333120

Topy-Rec, Ltd. (1)
6-7-15 Minamisuna, Koto-ku, Tokyo, 136-0076, Japan
Tel.: (81) 35 634 5401
Web Site: https://www.topyrec.co.jp
Sports Club Facilities Management Services
N.A.I.C.S.: 713940

TORAY CONSTRUCTION CO., LTD.

19th Fl Nakanoshima Mitsui Bldg Nakanoshima 3-chome, Kita-ku, Osaka, 530-8222, Japan
Tel.: (81) 664475152 JP
Web Site: http://www.toray-tcc.co.jp
Year Founded: 1982
Emp.: 346
Construction Engineering Services
N.A.I.C.S.: 541330
Tomiyama Motogyo *(Pres & CEO)*

TORAY INDUSTRIES, INC.

Nihonbashi Mitsui Tower 1-1
Nihonbashi-Muromachi 2-Chome,
Chuo-ku, Tokyo, 103-8666, Japan
Tel.: (81) 332455111 JP
Web Site: https://www.toray.com
Year Founded: 1926
3402—(TKS)
Rev.: $16,290,979,560
Assets: $22,913,683,980
Liabilities: $10,709,231,160
Net Worth: $12,204,452,820
Earnings: $144,739,170
Emp.: 48,140
Fiscal Year-end: 03/31/24
Real Estate Manangement Services
N.A.I.C.S.: 531390
Koichi Abe *(Exec VP)*

Subsidiaries:

Alcantara S.p.A. (1)
Via Mecenate 86, 20138, Milan, Italy
Tel.: (39) 02580301
Web Site: https://www.alcantara.com
Sales Range: $25-49.9 Million
Emp.: 100
Synthetic Organic Fibers
N.A.I.C.S.: 325220

Alva Confecvoes, S.A. (1)
Rua do Mercado no21 S Carlos, 2725-393, Mem Martins, Portugal
Tel.: (351) 219216692
Automobile Parts Mfr
N.A.I.C.S.: 336390

Alva Sweden AB (1)
Goteborgsvagen 89, 431 30, Molndal, Sweden
Tel.: (46) 317272200
Automobile Parts Distr
N.A.I.C.S.: 423120

Alva Tunisia S.A. (1)
ZI Charguia 2 Rue des Entrepreneurs Impasse 9104, 2035, Ariana, Tunisia
Tel.: (216) 71940800
Automobile Parts Mfr
N.A.I.C.S.: 336390

Chiba Shokusan Inc. (1)
2-1 Chigusa-Kaigan, Ichihara, 299-0196, Chiba, Japan
Tel.: (81) 436230750
Web Site: http://www.toray.com
Ancillary & Eco-Recycling Services & Construction Materials Marketing
N.A.I.C.S.: 423930

Composite Materials (Italy) S.R.L. (1)
Via Quasimodo 33, 20025, Legnano, Milano, Italy

Daehan Precision Co., Ltd. (1)
21-4 Sameun-Ri Jicksan-Eup, Cheonan, 331-816, Chungnam, Korea (South) **(100%)**
Tel.: (82) 415838162
Web Site: https://www.spinneret-dpc.com
Emp.: 50
Mfr & Marketing of Precision Equipment & Parts in Synthetic Fiber Production
N.A.I.C.S.: 325220

Delta-Preg S.P.A. (1)
Localita Bonifica del Tronto, Sant'Egidio alla Vibrata, 64016, Teramo, TE, Italy
Tel.: (39) 0861815106
Web Site: http://www.delta-preg.com
Fiber Material Mfr
N.A.I.C.S.: 313110

Delta-Tech S.P.A. (1)
Localita Rifoglieto 60/a, Altopascio, 55011, Lucca, LU, Italy
Tel.: (39) 0583269080
Web Site: http://www.delta-tech.it
Fiber Material Mfr
N.A.I.C.S.: 313110

Dow Corning Toray Silicon Co., Ltd. (1)
AIG Bldg 1 1 3 4th Fl Dow Corning Toray Marunouchi Chiyoda Ku, Tokyo, 1000005, Japan **(50%)**
Tel.: (81) 332871011
Web Site: http://www.dowcorning.co.jp
Silicon & Organosilicon Polymer Products & Compounds Mfr & Whslr
N.A.I.C.S.: 325211

Du Pont-Toray Co., Ltd. (1)
1-1-1 Nihonbashi Honcho METLIFE Nihonbashi Honcho Building, Chuo-ku, Tokyo, 103-0023, Japan **(50%)**
Tel.: (81) 332455081
Web Site: http://www.td-net.co.jp
Producer of Synthetic Fiber & Film
N.A.I.C.S.: 325220
Shinichiro Hata (Pres & CEO)

Eitopia Co., Ltd. (1)
5th Fl 1-17 Nihonbashi Ningyocho 3-chome, Chuo-ku, Tokyo, 103-0013, Japan
Tel.: (81) 356957165
Web Site: http://www.pro.fiber.com
Sales Range: $25-49.9 Million
Emp.: 1
Electronic Commerce Website Development Services
N.A.I.C.S.: 518210
Kazuaki Takabayashi (Pres)

Euro Advanced Carbon Fiber Composites GmbH (1)
Fritz-Muller-Strasse 11-27, 73730, Esslingen am Neckar, Germany
Tel.: (49) 7111856780
Web Site: https://www.eacc.de
Automobile Parts Mfr
N.A.I.C.S.: 336390

Greenerity GmbH (1)
Industriegebiet Sud E11, 63755, Alzenau, Germany
Tel.: (49) 61884468100
Web Site: https://www.greenerity.com
Emp.: 40
Semiconductor Product Mfr
N.A.I.C.S.: 334413

Ichimura Sangyo Co., Ltd. (1)
Nakanoshima Daibiru Bldg 18th floor 3-3-23 Nakanoshima, Kita-ku, Osaka, 530-6118, Japan
Tel.: (81) 67 223 8300
Web Site: https://www.ichimura.co.jp
Emp.: 126
Textile Products Mfr
N.A.I.C.S.: 314999
Atsushi Fujiwara (VP & Gen Mgr-Textiles Div)

Subsidiary (Non-US):

Ichimura (Shanghai) Trading Co.,Ltd (2)
Room 2707 Yanan Road West 2201, 200336, Shanghai, China
Tel.: (86) 2162097575
Textile Products Mfr
N.A.I.C.S.: 314999

Japan Apparel System Science Inc. (1)
4-87 Iwato-cho 2nd floor Iwato-cho Building, Shinjuku-ku, Tokyo, 162-0832, Japan
Tel.: (81) 352275540
Web Site: https://www.jassnet.co.jp
Textile Pattern Making Equipment Whslr
N.A.I.C.S.: 423830

KTP Industries, Inc. (1)
1018 Ungmyung Dong, Kimch'on, Gyungsanbuk Do, Korea (South) **(30%)**
Tel.: (82) 5474208306
Web Site: http://www.toray.com
Sales Range: $25-49.9 Million
Emp.: 85
Synthetic Organic Fibers Except Cellulosic
N.A.I.C.S.: 325220

Kamakura Techno-Science Inc. (1)
6-11 1-1 Tehiro, Kamakura, 248-0036, Kanagawa, Japan
Tel.: (81) 46 732 9775
Web Site: https://www.kamakura-ts.co.jp
Emp.: 70
Bio Research Reagent Mfr & Distr
N.A.I.C.S.: 325180
Nicholas Parts (Gen Mgr)

LIBI Plastic Compounding (Shenzhen) Co., Ltd. (1)
Ist Bldg Shatou Jiaotan, Baoan Industrial District, Shenzhen, 518104, Guangdong, China **(90%)**
Tel.: (86) 75527235000
Synthetic Organic Fibers Except Cellulosic Mfr
N.A.I.C.S.: 325220

Marusa Co., Ltd. (1)
Nohi Nissei Building 11F/12F 2-8 Hashimotocho, Gifu, 500-8856, Japan
Tel.: (81) 582548710
Web Site: https://www.marusa-site.co.jp
Emp.: 55
Textile Yarn Distr
N.A.I.C.S.: 424990

Ogaki Fuso Spinning Co., Ltd. (1)
1688 Miwa-cho, Ogaki, 503-0857, Gifu, Japan
Tel.: (81) 584825252
Web Site: https://www.ogakifuso.co.jp
Emp.: 101
Spun Yarn Mfr & Whslr
N.A.I.C.S.: 313110

P.T. Acryl Textile Mills (1)
Summitmas II 3rd Floor Jl Jend Sudirman Kav 61-62, Jakarta, 12190, Indonesia **(100%)**
Tel.: (62) 212526841
Web Site: http://www.toray.co.id
Sales Range: $125-149.9 Million
Emp.: 211
Production of Acrylic Yarns & Acrylic Yarn Wools
N.A.I.C.S.: 325220
Tsuyoshi Sumida (Pres)

P.T. Century Textile Industry (1)
Jl Raya Bogor Km 27, Ciracas, Jakarta, 13740, Indonesia **(27%)**
Tel.: (62) 218710724
Web Site: http://www.toray.co.id
Sales Range: $10-24.9 Million
Emp.: 638
Synthetic Organic Fibers Except Cellulosic
N.A.I.C.S.: 325220

P.T. Easterntex (1)
Summitmas II 3rd Floor Jl Jend Sudirman Kav 61-62, Jakarta, 12190, Indonesia **(69.84%)**
Tel.: (62) 21 520 1282
Web Site: https://www.toray.co.id
Sales Range: $25-49.9 Million
Emp.: 12
Spinning & Weaving of Blended Polyester & Cotton Fabrics
N.A.I.C.S.: 313210
Echio Kidachi (Pres)

P.T. Indonesia Synthetic Textile Mills (1)
Summitmas II 3rd Fl Jalan Jenderal Sudirman Kav 61-62, Jakarta, 12190, Indonesia **(100%)**
Tel.: (62) 21 551 5388
Web Site: http://www.toray.com
Sales Range: $200-249.9 Million
Emp.: 400
Spinning & Weaving of Polyester, Rayon Textiles
N.A.I.C.S.: 325220
Hisai Sasaki (Pres)

P.T. Indonesia Toray Synthetics (1)
JL Moh Toha Km 1 Tangerang West Java, Jakarta, 12190, Indonesia **(100%)**
Tel.: (62) 215524467
Web Site: https://www.toray.co.id
Sales Range: $25-49.9 Million
Emp.: 50
Mfr of Synthetic Fibers & Textiles
N.A.I.C.S.: 325220

P.T. OST Fibre Industries (1)
3rd floor Summitmas Tower II 61-62 Jl Jenderal Sudirman, PO Box 53, Jakarta, 12190, Indonesia
Tel.: (62) 212526841
Web Site: https://www.toray.co.id
Sales Range: $25-49.9 Million
Emp.: 50
Sewing Thread Mfr
N.A.I.C.S.: 325220

P.T. Petnesia Resindo (1)
Jl Moch Toha Km 1 Pabuaran Tumpeng, Tangerang, 15112, Banten, Indonesia
Tel.: (62) 215533083
N.A.I.C.S.: 325220

P.T. Ti Matsuoka Winner Industry (1)
Summitmas II 3rd Floor Jl Jend Sudirman Kav 61-62, Jakarta, 12190, Indonesia
Tel.: (62) 215201756
Garment Product Mfr
N.A.I.C.S.: 314999

P.T. Toray Industries Indonesia (1)
Summitmas II 3rd Floor Jl Jend Sudirman Kav 61-62, Jakarta, 12190, Indonesia
Tel.: (62) 212526841
Polyester Film Mfr
N.A.I.C.S.: 326113

P.T. Toray International Indonesia (1)
Summitmas II 3rd Fl Jl Jend Sudirman Kav 61-62, Jakarta, 12190, Indonesia
Tel.: (62) 215201756
Sales Range: $25-49.9 Million
Emp.: 18
Chemical Product Whslr
N.A.I.C.S.: 424690

P.T. Toray Polytech Jakarta (1)
Jl Moch Toha Km1 Kel Pabuaran Tumpeng Kec, Karawaci Kota, Tangerang, Banten, Indonesia
Tel.: (62) 2129519000
Web Site: https://www.toray.co.id
Polyester Film Mfr
N.A.I.C.S.: 326113

PMC Performance Materials (Guangzhou) Ltd. (1)
Bldg 11 48 Hongmian Ave, Xinhua Town Huadu District, Guangzhou, 510800, China
Tel.: (86) 2036872887
Thermoplastic Material Mfr
N.A.I.C.S.: 325211

Penfabric Sdn. Berhad (1)
Plot 117-119 200-202 Prai Free Industrial Zone 1, 13600, Prai, Penang, Malaysia **(100%)**
Tel.: (60) 43854188
Web Site: http://www.penfabric.com.my
Sales Range: $150-199.9 Million
Emp.: 600
Dyeing of Blended Polyester & Cotton Fabrics
N.A.I.C.S.: 313210
M. Okamoto (Dir-Fin)

Penfibre Sdn. Berhad (1)
Lot 109-114 128-130 Prai Free Industrial Zone 1, 13600, Prai, Penang, Malaysia **(100%)**
Tel.: (60) 43907788
Web Site: http://www.penfibre.com
Sales Range: $50-74.9 Million
Emp.: 200
Synthetic Organic Fibers Except Cellulosic
N.A.I.C.S.: 325220

Pentex Sdn. Berhad (1)
Plot 1-2 Prai Free Industrial Zone, 13600, Prai, Penang, Malaysia **(100%)**
Tel.: (60) 43907003
Sales Range: $200-249.9 Million
Emp.: 900
Synthetic Organic Fibers Except Cellulosic
N.A.I.C.S.: 325220
Y. K. Cheng (Gen Mgr)

STEMCO, Ltd. (1)
79-44 Gwahaksaneop4-ro Oksan-Myeon, Heungdeok-Gu, Cheongju, 28122, Chungcheongbuk-do, Korea (South)
Tel.: (82) 432407004
Web Site: http://www.toray.com
Film & Tape Mfr
N.A.I.C.S.: 322230

Societe des Fibres de Carbone S.A. (1)
Route de Lagor, 64150, Abidos, France **(70%)**
Tel.: (33) 559607100
Web Site: http://www.soficar-carbon.com
Sales Range: $50-74.9 Million
Emp.: 250
Mfr & Sales of Carbon Fibres
N.A.I.C.S.: 335991
Michael Bresson (Pres)

Soda Aromatic Co., Ltd. (1)
221 Nihonbashi Horidomecho, Chuo-ku, Tokyo, 103-8366, Japan **(66%)**
Tel.: (81) 356457347
Web Site: http://www.soda.co.jp
Emp.: 400
Industrial Chemical Mfr & Distr
N.A.I.C.S.: 325998
Tsukazaki Jyunichiro (Gen Mgr)

Suido Kiko Kaisha, Ltd. (1)
5-48-16 Sakuragaoka, Setagaya-ku, Tokyo, 156-0054, Japan
Tel.: (81) 334262131
Web Site: https://www.suiki.co.jp
Rev.: $143,000,740
Assets: $159,552,180
Liabilities: $93,511,670
Net Worth: $66,040,510
Earnings: $2,425,870
Fiscal Year-end: 03/31/2024
Water Treatment Machinery Mfr
N.A.I.C.S.: 333310
Masanobu Kadokawa (Pres & CEO)

Sunrich Mode Inc. (1)
5F Segi Building 1-7-1 Iwamoto-cho, Chiyoda-ku, Tokyo, 101-0032, Japan
Tel.: (81) 358213345
Web Site: https://www.sunrichmode.co.jp
Apparel Mfr & Whslr
N.A.I.C.S.: 315120

TAL Knits Ltd. (1)
8th Fl 49 Austin Rd Tal Bldg, Kowloon, China (Hong Kong) **(100%)**
Tel.: (852) 21967278
Web Site: http://www.toray.co.jp
Sales Range: $1-9.9 Million
Emp.: 100
Synthetic Organic Fibers Except Cellulosic
N.A.I.C.S.: 325220

TM Textiles & Garments Limited (1)
Kashor Hobirbari Union PS-Bhaluka, Mymensingh, 2240, Bangladesh
Tel.: (880) 28415520
Fiber Material Mfr
N.A.I.C.S.: 313110

Thai PET Resin Co., Ltd. (1)
138 Boonmitr Building 8th Floor Silom Road, Suriyawongse Bangrak, Bangkok, 10500, Thailand
Tel.: (66) 26345894
Polyethylene Terepthalate Resin Mfr & Sales; Owned 40% by Mitsui Chemicals, Inc., 40% by Toray Industries, Inc. & 20% by SCG Chemicals Co., Ltd.
N.A.I.C.S.: 325211

Thai Toray Synthetic Co., Ltd. (1)
4th 6th Floor Bubhajit Building 20 North Sathorn Road Silom, Bangrak, Bangkok, 10500, Thailand **(65%)**
Tel.: (66) 22666596
Sales Range: $50-74.9 Million
Emp.: 200

TORAY INDUSTRIES, INC.

Toray Industries, Inc.—(Continued)

Mfr & Marketing of Polyester Filament Yarns
N.A.I.C.S.: 325220

Tong Shing, Inc. (1)
6th Floor Shinkong Life Insurance Building 123, Nanking East Road Section 2, Taipei, 104, Taiwan (70%)
Tel.: (886) 225060700
Sales Range: $25-49.9 Million
Emp.: 30
Trading of Raw Materials for Fibers, Woven Fabrics & Plastics
N.A.I.C.S.: 313310

Toray ACE Co., Ltd. (1)
12-2 Nihonbashi Daidenmacho, Chuo-ku, Tokyo, 103-0011, Japan
Tel.: (81) 356233631
Web Site: https://www.toray-ace.com
Ceramic Products Mfr & Distr
N.A.I.C.S.: 327910

Toray Advanced Composites Ads LLC (1)
2450 Cordelia Rd, Fairfield, CA 94534
Tel.: (707) 359-3400
Thermoplastic Material Mfr
N.A.I.C.S.: 325211

Toray Advanced Composites B.V. (1)
G van der Muelenweg 2, 7443 RE, Nijverdal, Netherlands
Tel.: (31) 548633933
Web Site: http://www.toraytac.com
Composite & Ceramic Aerospace & Armor Products Mfr
N.A.I.C.S.: 336992
Nick Stiffin (Dir-Sales)

Subsidiary (US):

Ten Cate Advanced Armor USA Inc. (2)
23 Sisal St, Newark, OH 43055
Tel.: (740) 345-5574
Web Site: http://www.tencateadvancedarmor.com
Protective Flat Plate Mfr
N.A.I.C.S.: 332215

Toray Advanced Composites USA Inc. (2)
18255 Sutter Blvd, Morgan Hill, CA 95037
Tel.: (408) 465-8500
Web Site: http://www.toraytac.com
Advanced Composite Materials Mfr
N.A.I.C.S.: 325998

Subsidiary (Domestic):

Toray Advanced Composites (3)
2450 Cordelia Rd, Fairfield, CA 94534
Tel.: (707) 747-2750
Web Site: http://www.toraytac.com
Aerospace Composites Mfr
N.A.I.C.S.: 336413

Toray Performance Materials Corporation (3)
1150 Calle Suerte, Camarillo, CA 93012
Tel.: (805) 482-1722
Web Site: http://www.toraytac.com
Thermoplastic Molded Parts, Components & Other Materials Mfr
N.A.I.C.S.: 325211

Toray Advanced Composites Netherlands B.V. (1)
G van der Muelenweg 2, 7443 RE, Nijverdal, Netherlands
Tel.: (31) 548633933
Thermoplastic Material Mfr
N.A.I.C.S.: 325211

Toray Advanced Composites UK Ltd. (1)
Amber Drive, Langley Mill, Nottingham, NG16 4BE, United Kingdom
Tel.: (44) 1773530899
Thermoplastic Material Mfr
N.A.I.C.S.: 325211

Toray Advanced Composites Usa Inc. (1)
18255 Sutter Blvd, Morgan Hill, CA 95037
Tel.: (408) 465-8500
Web Site: https://www.toraytac.com
Thermoplastic Material Mfr
N.A.I.C.S.: 325211

Toray Advanced Computer Solution, Inc. (1)
4th Fl Isomura Bldg 1-1-3 Toranomon, Minato-ku, Tokyo, 105-0001, Japan
Tel.: (81) 363277000
Web Site: https://www.toray-acs.co.jp
Emp.: 60
Apparel Software Development Services
N.A.I.C.S.: 541511

Toray Advanced Film Co., Ltd. (1)
Nihonbashi Muromachi Bldg 3F 3-3-16 Nihonbashi Hongoku-cho, Chuo-ku, Tokyo, 103-0021, Japan
Tel.: (81) 35 200 5611
Web Site: https://www.toray-taf.co.jp
Emp.: 669
Plastics Films Mfr
Susumu Yamaguchi (Chm)

Subsidiary (Non-US):

Toray Advanced Film Kaohsiung Co., Ltd. (2)
Kaohsiung Science Park NO 99 Minzhu Rd, Gangshan Dist, Kaohsiung, 82059, Taiwan
Tel.: (886) 76955668
Polyolefin Film Mfr & Distr
N.A.I.C.S.: 325992

Subsidiary (Domestic):

Toyo Shinko Co., Ltd (2)
33-1 Nagafushi, Mishima, 411-0824, Shizuoka, Japan
Tel.: (81) 55 977 0680
Web Site: http://www.toray-taf.co.jp
Plastics Films Mfr
N.A.I.C.S.: 322220

Plant (Domestic):

Toyo Shinko Co., Ltd - Nagaoka Factory (3)
1396 Kitaema, Izunokuni, 410-2223, Shizuoka, Japan
Tel.: (81) 559484655
Plastics Films Mfr
N.A.I.C.S.: 322220

Toray Advanced Materials Korea Inc. (1)
7 Magokdong-ro 10-gil, Gangseo-gu, Seoul, 07790, Korea (South)
Tel.: (82) 232791000
Web Site: https://www.torayamk.com
Emp.: 2,400
Polyester Film Mfr
N.A.I.C.S.: 326113

Subsidiary (Domestic):

Toray Chemical Korea Inc. (2)
34F/36F FKI Tower 24 Yeoui-daero, Yeongdeungpo-gu, Seoul, 07230, Korea (South)
Tel.: (82) 2 3279 7000
Web Site: http://www.toray-tck.com
Chemicals & Textiles Mfr & Distr
N.A.I.C.S.: 313310
Youngkwan Lee (Chm & CEO)

Subsidiary (Non-US):

PT. TCK Textiles Indonesia (3)
Korea Ctr Rm 604 6th Fl Jl Gatot Subroto Kav 58, Jakarta Selatan, Jakarta, 12950, Indonesia
Tel.: (62) 215223364
Sales Range: $150-199.9 Million
Emp.: 600
Textile Products Mfr
N.A.I.C.S.: 314999
Kim Dukyong (Pres)

TCK Shanghai Co., Ltd. (3)
Rm 2307 International Trade Center, 2200 Yanan Rd W, Shanghai, 200339, China
Tel.: (86) 21 6219 0119
Sales Range: $25-49.9 Million
Emp.: 20
Textile Products Whslr
N.A.I.C.S.: 313310

Plant (Domestic):

Toray Chemical Korea - Gumi I Plant (3)

102 Gumidero, Gumi, 39349, Gyeongsangbuk-do, Korea (South)
Tel.: (82) 544694114
Textile Products Mfr
N.A.I.C.S.: 313310

Toray Chemical Korea - Yugu Plant (3)
122 Yugumagoksa-ro Yugu-eup, Gongju, 314895, Chungcheongnam-do, Korea (South)
Tel.: (82) 41 840 6100
Synthetic Textile Products Mfr
N.A.I.C.S.: 313310

Toray Advanced Materials Research Laboratories (China) Co., Ltd. (1)
369 Ziyue Road, Zizhu Hi-Tech Industrial Development Zone Minhang District, Shanghai, 200241, China
Tel.: (86) 2134292928
Water Treatment Product Distr
N.A.I.C.S.: 221310

Toray Advanced Textile Mexico, S.A. De C.V. (1)
Carr El Salto a la Capilla Km 3 S/N, Parque Industrial, 45680, El Salto, Jalisco, Mexico
Tel.: (52) 3332843333
Fiber Material Mfr & Distr
N.A.I.C.S.: 313110

Toray Asia Pte. Ltd. (1)
111 Somerset Road 14-01 Devonshire Wing Singapore Power Bldg, Singapore 238164, Singapore
Tel.: (65) 62260525
Marketing Consulting Services
N.A.I.C.S.: 541613

Toray Basf Pbt Resin Sdn. Berhad (1)
Jalan Gebeng 2/1, Kawasan Perindustrian Gebeng, 26080, Kuantan, Pahang, Malaysia
Tel.: (60) 95857200
Polyester Film Mfr
N.A.I.C.S.: 326113

Toray Battery Separator Film Korea Limited (1)
50 Cheomdangieop 7-ro Sandong-myeon, Gumi, Gyeongsangbuk-do, Korea (South)
Tel.: (82) 54 440 7022
Web Site: https://www.toray-bsf.com
Battery Product Mfr
N.A.I.C.S.: 335910

Toray Bluestar Membrane Co., Ltd. (1)
No 28 Yu An Road Zone B, Airport Industrial Zone Shunyi District, Beijing, 101318, China
Tel.: (86) 1080485216
Web Site: https://www.tbmc-bj.com
Chemical Product Mfr & Distr
N.A.I.C.S.: 325998

Toray Bsf Coating Korea Limited (1)
81 2 sandan-ro Ochang-eup, Cheongwongu, Cheongju, 28117, Chungcheongbuk-do, Korea (South)
Tel.: (82) 439065000
Battery Product Mfr
N.A.I.C.S.: 335910

Toray Carbon Fibers Europe S.A. (1)
Route Departementale 817, 64170, Lacq, France
Tel.: (33) 559607100
Web Site: https://www.toray-cfe.com
Fiber Material Mfr
N.A.I.C.S.: 313110

Toray Coatex Co., Ltd. (1)
15 Ochiaicho Kisshoin, Minami-ku, Kyoto, 601-8324, Japan
Tel.: (81) 756915191
Web Site: https://www.tcx.co.jp
Sales Range: $25-49.9 Million
Emp.: 195
Nonwoven Fabric Mfr
N.A.I.C.S.: 313230

Toray Composite Materials America, Inc. (1)
19002 50th Ave E, Tacoma, WA 98446
Tel.: (248) 273-3486
Web Site: https://www.toraycma.com

INTERNATIONAL PUBLIC

Fiber Material Mfr
N.A.I.C.S.: 313110

Toray Coms Chiba Co., Ltd. (1)
2-1 Chikusa Kaigan, Ichihara, 299-0196, Chiba, Japan
Tel.: (81) 436230750
Web Site: https://www.coms.toray
Emp.: 55
Eco Recycling Services
N.A.I.C.S.: 512240

Toray Corporate Business Research, Inc. (1)
1-8-1 Mihama, Urayasu, 279-8555, Chiba, Japan
Tel.: (81) 47 350 6149
Web Site: http://www.tbr.co.jp
Sales Range: $25-49.9 Million
Emp.: 25
Strategic Planning Consulting Services
N.A.I.C.S.: 541611
Shinichi Sanbongi (Pres)

Toray Diplomode, Inc. (1)
4-16-13 Nishiazabu Nishiazabu Roppongi Dori Building, Minato-ku, Tokyo, 106-0031, Japan (100%)
Tel.: (81) 334067191
Web Site: http://www.toray-tdm.co.jp
Sales Range: $50-74.9 Million
Emp.: 160
Apparel & Accessories Mfr & Whslr
N.A.I.C.S.: 315990
Toru Chiba (Pres)

Toray Do Brasil Ltda. (1)
Avenida Paulista 1048-Conj 71 Bela Vista, Sao Paulo, 01310-100, SP, Brazil
Tel.: (55) 1131710502
Web Site: https://toray.com.br
Fiber Material Mfr
N.A.I.C.S.: 313110

Toray ECSAINE Plaza, Inc. (1)
3rd Fl Higashi-Nihonbashi EX Bldg 4-18 Higashi-Nihonbashi 3-chome, Chuo-ku, Tokyo, 103-0004, Japan
Tel.: (81) 3 5695 3501
Web Site: http://www.toray-ecsaine-plaza.com
Miscellaneous Accessories Mfr & Whslr
N.A.I.C.S.: 315990

Toray Engineering (Korea) Co., Ltd. (1)
512 10 Yatap-ro 81 Beon-gil, Bundang-gu, Seongnam, Gyeonggi, Korea (South)
Tel.: (82) 316220060
Web Site: https://www.tekor.co.kr
Emp.: 56
Electric Equipment Mfr
N.A.I.C.S.: 334419

Toray Engineering Co., Ltd. (1)
6th Floor Yaesu Ryumeikan Bldg 3-22 Yaesu 1-chome, Chuo-ku, Tokyo, 103-0028, Japan (99.99%)
Tel.: (81) 332411541
Web Site: https://www.toray-eng.com
Sales Range: $400-449.9 Million
Emp.: 2,005
Design, Manufacture & Market Industrial Plants, Machinery & Tools
N.A.I.C.S.: 333517

Toray Engineering West Co., Ltd. (1)
4th Floor Kansai Technical Center 1-1 Sonoyama 1-Chome, Otsu, 520-0842, Shiga, Japan
Tel.: (81) 775340956
Electronic Equipment Mfr & Distr
N.A.I.C.S.: 334419

Toray Enterprise Corp. (1)
8th floor Nihonbashi Honmachi YS Building 2-2-2 Nihonbashi Honmachi, Chuo-ku, Tokyo, 103-0023, Japan
Tel.: (81) 332700678
Web Site: https://www.toray-enter.co.jp
Sales Range: $75-99.9 Million
Emp.: 158
Real Estate Manangement Services
N.A.I.C.S.: 531390

Toray Europe Ltd. (1)
Thomas House 84 Eccleston Square, London, SW1V 1PX, United Kingdom (85%)
Tel.: (44) 2076637700
Web Site: https://www.toray.eu

AND PRIVATE COMPANIES — TORAY INDUSTRIES, INC.

Sales Range: $25-49.9 Million
Emp.: 37
Trading of Fiber & Fabric & Plastics Products
N.A.I.C.S.: 313310

Toray Fibers & Textiles Research Laboratories (China) Co., Ltd. (1)
58 Xin Kai Road South Nantong Economic Technological Development Zone, Nantong Economic and Technological Development Zone, Nantong, 226009, Jiangsu, China
Tel.: (86) 51383593300
Fiber Material Mfr
N.A.I.C.S.: 313110

Toray Fibers (Nantong) Co., Ltd. (1)
58 Xin Kai Road South, Nantong Economic and Technological Development Zone, Nantong, 226009, Jiangsu, China
Tel.: (86) 51389053000
Fiber Material Mfr
N.A.I.C.S.: 313110

Toray Fibers (Nantong) Co., Ltd. (TFNL) (1)
58 Xin Kai Road South Nantong Economic Technological Development Zone, Nantong, 226009, Jiangsu, China (100%)
Tel.: (86) 51389053000
Web Site: http://www.toray.com
Sales Range: $125-149.9 Million
Emp.: 400
Manufacture & Marketing of Synthetic Fibers & Chips
N.A.I.C.S.: 325220

Toray Film Products (Hong Kong) Ltd. (1)
19th Floor Sun Life Tower Gateway, Harbour City, Kowloon, China (Hong Kong)
Tel.: (852) 21967251
Vapor Deposition Film Distr
N.A.I.C.S.: 423410

Toray Film Products (Zhongshan) Ltd. (1)
20 Torch Road Zhongshan Torch Development Zone, Zhongshan, 528437, Guangdong, China
Tel.: (86) 76085338288
Polyester Film Mfr
N.A.I.C.S.: 326113

Toray Film Products (Zhougshan) Ltd. (1)
Torch Road Zhongshan Torch Development Zone Zhongshan Port, Zhongshan, 528437, Guangdong, China
Tel.: (86) 76085338288
Vapor Deposition Film Mfr
N.A.I.C.S.: 326113

Toray Films Europe S.A.S. (1)
Place d'Armenie, 01700, Saint-Maurice-de-Beynost, France
Tel.: (33) 47 288 1600
Web Site: https://www.torayfilms.eu
Emp.: 414
Polyester & Polypropylene Film Product Mfr
N.A.I.C.S.: 326113

Toray Fine Chemicals Co., Ltd. (1)
2-3-1 Kanda-Sudacho, Chiyoda-ku, Tokyo, 101-0041, Chiba, Japan
Tel.: (81) 368591111
Web Site: http://www.torayfinechemicals.com
Rev.: $223,220,880
Emp.: 366
Polysulfide Polymer Mfr
N.A.I.C.S.: 325180

Toray Fine Chemicals Co., Ltd. - Chiba Plant (1)
2-3 Chigusakaigan, Ichihara, 299-0196, Chiba, Japan
Tel.: (81) 436223716
Polysulfide Polymer Mfr
N.A.I.C.S.: 325211

Toray Fine Chemicals Co., Ltd. - Matsuyama Plant (1)
360 Okaga 3-chome, Matsuyama, 791-8057, Ehime, Japan
Tel.: (81) 899511191
Cellulose Sponge Mfr
N.A.I.C.S.: 325220

Toray Fine Chemicals Co., Ltd. - Moriyama Plant (1)

1-1 Katsube 6-chome, Moriyama, 524-0041, Shiga, Japan
Tel.: (81) 775832570
Web Site: http://www.torayfinechemicals.com
Computer Peripheral Equipment Mfr
N.A.I.C.S.: 334118

Toray Fine Chemicals Co., Ltd. - Tokai Plant (1)
31 Shinpo-machi, Tokai, 476-8567, Aichi, Japan
Tel.: (81) 526016616
Polysulfide Polymer Mfr
N.A.I.C.S.: 325211

Toray Hybrid Cord, Inc. (1)
3 Shinmeiji Kamiyata-cho, Nishio, 444-0394, Aichi, Japan
Tel.: (81) 563594000
Tire Cord Fabric Mfr
N.A.I.C.S.: 314994

Toray Industries (America), Inc. (1)
461 5th Ave, New York, NY 10017 (100%)
Tel.: (212) 697-8150
Web Site: http://www.toray.com
Sales Range: $25-49.9 Million
Emp.: 50
U.S. Branch Office
N.A.I.C.S.: 551112

Subsidiary (Domestic):

Toray Capital (America), Inc. (2)
461 5th Ave Fl 9, New York, NY 10017
Tel.: (212) 697-8150
Web Site: http://www.torayusa.com
Emp.: 30
Synthetic Organic Fibers Except Cellulosic
N.A.I.C.S.: 561110

Toray Carbon Fibers America, Inc. (2)
700 Parker Sq Ste 275, Flower Mound, TX 75028
Tel.: (972) 899-2930
Web Site: http://www.toraycfa.com
Sales Range: $25-49.9 Million
Emp.: 12
Carbon Fiber Products Mfr
N.A.I.C.S.: 335991
Jeff Cross (Dir-Bus Dev)

Toray Composites (America), Inc. (2)
19002 50th Ave E, Tacoma, WA 98446-3752 (91.61%)
Tel.: (253) 846-1777
Web Site: http://www.toraycompam.com
Carbon Fiber Prepreg Mfr & Marketer
N.A.I.C.S.: 335991
Toshiyuki Kondo (Pres & CEO)

Toray Fluorofibers (America), Inc. (2)
2032 Hwy 20, Decatur, AL 35601
Tel.: (256) 260-5900
Web Site: http://www.torayfluorofibers.com
Fluoropolymer Fiber & Packing Yarn Mfr
N.A.I.C.S.: 313210

Toray Marketing and Sales (America), Inc. (2)
461 5th Ave 9th Fl, New York, NY 10016
Tel.: (212) 697-8150
Web Site: http://www.torayusa.com
Sales Range: $25-49.9 Million
Emp.: 40
Synthetic Organic Fibers Except Cellulosic
N.A.I.C.S.: 423690

Toray Membrane USA, Inc. (2)
13435 Danielson St, Poway, CA 92064
Tel.: (858) 218-2360
Emp.: 100
Water Treatment Membrane Mfr & Distr
N.A.I.C.S.: 333310
Karen Zhao (Mgr-Engrg)

Toray Plastics (America), Inc. (2)
50 Belver Ave, North Kingstown, RI 02852-7520 (80.85%)
Tel.: (401) 294-4511
Web Site: http://www.toraytpa.com
Mfr & Marketing of Polypropylene & Polyester Films
N.A.I.C.S.: 326113
Christopher Roy (Pres & COO)

Toray Resin Company (2)
Troy Officentre Bldg D 2800 Livernois Rd Ste 115, Troy, MI 48083
Tel.: (248) 269-8800
Web Site: http://www.torayusa.com
Sales Range: $25-49.9 Million
Emp.: 15
Resin Product Mfr
N.A.I.C.S.: 325211

Plant (Domestic):

Toray Resin Co. - Indiana Factory (3)
821-W Marusolem Rd, Shelbyville, IN 46176
Tel.: (317) 398-7833
Web Site: http://www.toray.com
Resin Product Mfr
N.A.I.C.S.: 325211

Subsidiary (Domestic):

Zoltek Companies, Inc. (2)
3101 McKelvey Rd, Bridgeton, MO 63044
Tel.: (314) 291-5110
Web Site: http://www.zoltek.com
Sales Range: $100-124.9 Million
Assets: $352,865,000
Liabilities: $45,649,000
Net Worth: $307,216,000
Earnings: $5,236,000
Emp.: 70
Mfr & Marketer of Carbon Fibers for Use in Aircraft Brakes & Other Composite Materials
N.A.I.C.S.: 335991
Andrew W. Whipple (CFO)

Subsidiary (Non-US):

Zoltek Zrt. (3)
Varga Jozsef Ter 1, 2537, Nyergesujfalu, Hungary
Tel.: (36) 33536021
Sales Range: $1-4.9 Billion
Emp.: 850
Carbon Fiber Mfr
N.A.I.C.S.: 444180

Toray Industries (China) Co., Ltd. (1)
8th Floor Park Place 1601 West Nanjing Road, Jing An District, Shanghai, 200040, China
Tel.: (86) 2132518558
Web Site: https://www.toray.cn
Business Support Services
N.A.I.C.S.: 561499

Toray Industries (H.K.) Ltd. (1)
9th Floor North Tower World Finance Centre Harbour City, Kowloon, 999077, China (Hong Kong) (100%)
Tel.: (852) 2 196 7000
Web Site: http://www.toray.co.jp
Sales Range: $25-49.9 Million
Emp.: 75
Trading of Fibers, Textiles & Garments
N.A.I.C.S.: 313310
Masataka Hamazaki (Mng Dir & Gen Mgr)

Toray Industries (India) Private Limited (1)
1800 EMC Road Sricity, Chitoor, Satyavedu, 517646, Andhra Pradesh, India
Tel.: (91) 8576669669
Web Site: https://www.toray.in
Fiber Material Mfr
N.A.I.C.S.: 313110

Toray Industries (Singapore) Pte. Ltd. (1)
111 Somerset Road 14-22, Singapore, 238164, Singapore (70%)
Tel.: (65) 65333288
Sales Range: $25-49.9 Million
Emp.: 41
Trading of Fibers & Textiles
N.A.I.C.S.: 313310

Toray Industries (South China) Co., Ltd. (1)
9th Floor North Tower World Finance Centre, Harbour City, Kowloon, China (Hong Kong)
Tel.: (852) 21967000
Business Support Services
N.A.I.C.S.: 561499

Toray Industries (Thailand) Co., Ltd. (1)

6th Floor Bubhajit Bldg 20 North Sathorn Road, Silom Bangrak, Bangkok, 10500, Thailand
Tel.: (66) 22666595
Fiber Material Mfr
N.A.I.C.S.: 313110

Toray Industries (Thailand) Co., Ltd. (TTH) (1)
6th Fl Bubhajit Bldg 20 North Sathorn Rd, Bangrak, Bangkok, 10500, Thailand (100%)
Tel.: (66) 22666595
Web Site: http://www.toray.com
Sales Range: $25-49.9 Million
Emp.: 30
Spinning, Weaving & Dyeing of Blended Polyester & Rayon Fabrics; Manufacture of Knitted Fabrics
N.A.I.C.S.: 313240

Toray Industries Europe GmbH (1)
Hugenottenallee 175, 63263, Neu-Isenburg, Germany
Tel.: (49) 610279991000
Polyester Film Distr
N.A.I.C.S.: 512120

Toray Industries Hungary Kft. (1)
Toray utca 1, 2536, Nyergesujfalu, Hungary
Tel.: (36) 14751451
Plastics Product Mfr
N.A.I.C.S.: 326199

Toray Industries Korea Inc. (1)
8Fl Korea Toray R D center 7 Magokdong-ro 10-gil, Gangseo-gu, Seoul, 07790, Korea (South)
Tel.: (82) 232791488
Fiber Material Mfr
N.A.I.C.S.: 313110

Toray Industries, Inc. - Aichi Plant (1)
1-1 Horikoshi 1-chome, Nishi-ku, Nagoya, 451-8666, Japan
Tel.: (81) 525213111
Timber Product Mfr
N.A.I.C.S.: 325220

Toray Industries, Inc. - Chiba Plant (1)
2-1 Chigusa-Kaigan, Ichihara, 299-0196, Chiba, Japan
Tel.: (81) 436215211
Resin Mfr
N.A.I.C.S.: 325211

Toray Industries, Inc. - Ehime Plant (1)
1515 Oaza Tsutsui Masaki-cho, Iyo-gun, Matsuyama, 791-3193, Ehime, Japan
Tel.: (81) 899842121
Industrial Chemicals Mfr
N.A.I.C.S.: 325998

Toray Industries, Inc. - Gifu Plant (1)
900-1 Oaza-Yasutsugu Godo-cho, Anpachigun, Gifu, 503-2395, Japan
Tel.: (81) 584272085
Plastics Films Mfr
N.A.I.C.S.: 322220

Toray Industries, Inc. - Ishikawa Plant (1)
Ri-1 Kitaichi-machi, Nomi, 923-1294, Ishikawa, Japan
Tel.: (81) 761514111
Carbonizing Textile Fiber Mfr
N.A.I.C.S.: 313310

Toray Industries, Inc. - Nagoya Plant (1)
9-1 Oe-cho, Minato-ku, Nagoya, 455-8502, Japan
Tel.: (81) 526135111
Automobile Parts Mfr
N.A.I.C.S.: 336390

Toray Industries, Inc. - Okazaki Plant (1)
1 Aza-Deguchi, Yahagi-cho, Okazaki, 444-8522, Aichi, Japan
Tel.: (81) 564342111
Web Site: http://www.toray.com
Emp.: 600
Textile Products Mfr
N.A.I.C.S.: 314999

Toray Industries, Inc. - Seta Plant (1)

TORAY INDUSTRIES, INC.

Toray Industries, Inc.—(Continued)
1-1 Oe 1-chome, Otsu, 520-2141, Shiga, Japan
Tel.: (81) 775443500
Industrial Chemicals Mfr
N.A.I.C.S.: 325998

Toray Industries, Inc. - Shiga Plant (1)
1-1 Sonoyama 1-chome, Otsu, 520-8558, Shiga, Japan
Tel.: (81) 775338020
Timber Product Mfr
N.A.I.C.S.: 325220

Toray Industries, Inc. - Tokai Plant (1)
31 Shinpo-cho, Tokai, 476-8567, Aichi, Japan
Tel.: (81) 526891500
Chemical Products Mfr
N.A.I.C.S.: 325998

Toray International (China) Co., Ltd. (1)
8th Floor Park Place 1601 West Nanjing Road, Jing An District, Shanghai, 200040, China
Tel.: (86) 2132518558
Logistic Services
N.A.I.C.S.: 488510

Toray International (Korea) , Inc. (1)
17th Floor FKI Tower 24 Yeoui-daero, Yeongdeungpo-gu, Seoul, 07320, Korea (South)
Tel.: (82) 232788600
Logistic Services
N.A.I.C.S.: 488510

Toray International De Mexico, S.A. De C.V. (1)
Carr El Salto a la Capilla Km 3 S/N, Parque Industrial, 45680, El Salto, Jalisco, Mexico
Tel.: (52) 3332843333
Logistic Services
N.A.I.C.S.: 488510

Toray International Europe GmbH (1)
Hugenottenallee 175, 63263, Neu-Isenburg, Germany
Tel.: (49) 61 027 9990
Web Site: http://www.toray.us
Sales Range: $25-49.9 Million
Emp.: 40
Chemical & Plastic Products Distr
N.A.I.C.S.: 424690
Ryuji Hirai *(Mng Dir)*

Toray International Guangzhou Trading Co., Ltd. (1)
Room 1002 10/F Tower1 Taikoo Hui Office 385 Tianhe Road, Tianhe District, Guangzhou, 510620, China
Tel.: (86) 2087521672
Logistic Services
N.A.I.C.S.: 488510

Toray International India Private Limited (1)
Tower 3 East Wing 6th Floor Equinox Business Park, Lal Bahadur Shastri Marg Kurla, Mumbai, 400070, India
Tel.: (91) 1244128450
Fiber Material Mfr
N.A.I.C.S.: 313110

Toray International Italy S.r.l. (1)
Via Mecenate 86, 20138, Milan, Italy
Tel.: (39) 02 580 3911
Web Site: http://www.toray.com
Medical Equipment Whslr
N.A.I.C.S.: 423460
Ryuji Hirai *(Mng Dir)*

Toray International Singapore Pte. Ltd. (1)
111 Somerset Road 14-01, Singapore, 238164, Singapore
Tel.: (65) 65333288
Web Site: http://www.toray.com
Emp.: 30
Apparel Distr
N.A.I.C.S.: 424350

Toray International Taipei Inc. (1)
6th Fl Shinkong Life Insurance Bldg No 123 Nanking E Road Sec 2, Taipei, Taiwan
Tel.: (886) 227165000
Textile Products Distr
N.A.I.C.S.: 424350

Toray International Trading (Thailand) Co., Ltd. (1)
9th Fl Bubhajit Building 20 North Sathorn Road, Silom Bangrak, Bangkok, 10500, Thailand
Tel.: (66) 26338486
Logistic Services
N.A.I.C.S.: 488510

Toray International U.K. Ltd. (1)
Thomas House 84 Eccleston Square, London, SW1V 1PX, United Kingdom
Tel.: (44) 2076637700
Web Site: http://www.toray-intl.co.uk
Chemical & Plastic Products Distr
N.A.I.C.S.: 424690

Toray International Vietnam Co., Ltd. (1)
Rm 1905 Saigon Trade Center 37 Ton Duc Thang, District 1, Ho Chi Minh City, Vietnam
Tel.: (84) 2839103878
Logistic Services
N.A.I.C.S.: 488510

Toray International, Inc. (1)
2-1-1 Nihombashi Muromachi Nihonbashi Mitsui Tower, Chuo-ku, Tokyo, 103-8666, Japan
Tel.: (81) 332455111
Web Site: http://www.ultrasuede.us
Sales Range: $200-249.9 Million
Emp.: 444
Textile Products Mfr
N.A.I.C.S.: 314999
Taisuke Minakuchi *(Mng Dir)*

Subsidiary (US):

Toray International America Inc. (2)
461 Fifth Ave 9th Fl, New York, NY 10017
Tel.: (212) 697-8150
Web Site: http://www.toray.us
Emp.: 50
Textile Products Distr
N.A.I.C.S.: 424310
Takako Kawana *(Asst Mgr)*

Toray Italia S.r.l. (1)
Via Mecenate 86, 20138, Milan, Italy (100%)
Tel.: (39) 025803911
Sales Range: $25-49.9 Million
Emp.: 9
Trading of Fibers & Textiles
N.A.I.C.S.: 313310

Toray KP Films Inc. (1)
510 Furuouchi, Noguchi-cho, Kakogawa, 675-8558, Hyogo, Japan
Tel.: (81) 794220151
Emp.: 154
Synthetic Resin Film Mfr
N.A.I.C.S.: 322220

Toray Kusumgar Advanced Textile Private Limited (1)
Plot No 5001/A GIDC, Sarigam, Gujarat, 396 155, India
Tel.: (91) 7069069333
Web Site: https://www.toray.in
Fiber Material Mfr
N.A.I.C.S.: 313110

Toray Malaysia Systems Solution Sdn. Bhd. (1)
108-B-2-21 22 23 & 23A Setia SPICE Canopy Jalan Tun Dr Awang, 11900, Bayan Lepas, Penang, Malaysia
Tel.: (60) 4 638 1688
Web Site: https://www.tms.toray
Information Technology Services
N.A.I.C.S.: 541511
Peter Chan *(Mng Dir)*

Toray Marketing e Vendas (Brasil) Ltda. (1)
Avenida Paulista 1048 -Conj 71 Bela Vista, Sao Paulo, 01310-100, Brazil
Tel.: (55) 1131710502
Web Site: https://www.toray.com.br
Sales Range: $25-49.9 Million
Emp.: 7
Marketing Research Service
N.A.I.C.S.: 541910

Tsubasa Shimonishi *(Gen Mgr)*

Toray Medical (Qingdao) Co., Ltd. (1)
No 63 Kongquehe 4 Road, Garment Industrial Zone Jimo, Qingdao, 266200, Shandong, China
Tel.: (86) 53281721030
Web Site: https://www.toray-medical.com
Dialysis Equipment Mfr
N.A.I.C.S.: 334510

Toray Medical Co., Ltd. (1)
Toray Bldg 5F 8-1 Mihama 1-chome, Urayasu, 279-8555, Chiba, Japan
Tel.: (81) 477007511
Web Site: http://www.toray-medical.com
Rev.: $356,000,000
Emp.: 500
Dialysis Equipment Mfr & Distr
N.A.I.C.S.: 334510

Toray Membrane (Beijing) Co.,Ltd. (1)
Beijing Fortune Bldg No 918 5 Dong San Huan Bei-lu, Chao Yang District, Beijing, 100004, China
Tel.: (86) 1065908365
Waste Treatment Services
N.A.I.C.S.: 221310

Toray Membrane (Foshan) Co., Ltd. (1)
1 Tengfei Rd Jiujiang Ave, Jiujiang Town Nanhai District, Foshan, 528203, Guangdong, China
Tel.: (86) 75786511501
Water Treatment Product Distr
N.A.I.C.S.: 221310

Toray Membrane Europe AG (1)
Grabenackerstrasse 8b, 4142, Munchenstein, Switzerland
Tel.: (41) 614158710
Semiconductor Product Distr
N.A.I.C.S.: 423690

Toray Membrane Middle East LLC (1)
3515 3rd Industrial City 8682, PO Box 20279, Dammam, 34857, Saudi Arabia
Tel.: (966) 135680091
Water Treatment Product Distr
N.A.I.C.S.: 221310

Toray Membrane Spain S.L. (1)
Paseo de la Castellana 141 5th floor, 28046, Madrid, Spain
Tel.: (34) 915726504
Water Treatment Product Distr
N.A.I.C.S.: 221310

Toray Monofilament Co., Ltd. (1)
Showacho, Okazaki, 444-8512, Aichi, Japan
Tel.: (81) 564 31 6211
Web Site: http://www.toray-mono.com
Sales Range: $50-74.9 Million
Emp.: 199
Synthetic Monofilament Mfr & Distr
N.A.I.C.S.: 339999
Masaharu Mizuno *(Pres)*

Toray Opelontex Co., Ltd. (1)
20th Fl Nakanoshima Mitsui Bldg 3-3 Nakanoshima 3-chome, Kita-ku, Osaka, 530-8222, Japan
Tel.: (81) 664486570
Fiber Material Mfr
N.A.I.C.S.: 313110

Toray PEF Products Inc. (1)
1916 Shimoda, Konan, 520-3201, Shiga, Japan (100%)
Tel.: (81) 748 75 0761
Web Site: http://www.toray-pef.co.jp
Polyolefin Foam Mfr
N.A.I.C.S.: 325220

Toray Plastics (Chengdu) Co., Ltd. (1)
No 320 Ping Tang Xi Lu Pu Xing Jie Xin Jin Qu, Gongye Yuanqu, Chengdu, 611400, Sichuan, China
Tel.: (86) 2885574088
Thermoplastic Material Mfr
N.A.I.C.S.: 325211

Toray Plastics (China) Co., Ltd. (1)
9th Floor North Tower World Finance Centre, Harbour City, Kowloon, China (Hong Kong)

INTERNATIONAL PUBLIC

Tel.: (852) 21967200
Plastic Component Whslr
N.A.I.C.S.: 424610

Toray Plastics (Malaysia) Sdn. Bhd. (1)
2628 MK 1 SPT Lorong Perusahaan 4 Prai Free Industrial Zone, 13600, Prai, Penang, Malaysia (100%)
Tel.: (60) 4 398 8088
Web Site: https://www.torayplastics.com.my
Sales Range: $125-149.9 Million
Emp.: 305
Synthetic Organic Fibers Except Cellulosic
N.A.I.C.S.: 325220
Takehiko Cakayama *(Mng Dir)*

Toray Plastics (Shenzhen) Ltd. (1)
No 450 Nanhuan Road West, Shajing Baoan, Shenzhen, 518104, Guangdong, China
Tel.: (86) 75527235000
Thermoplastic Material Mfr
N.A.I.C.S.: 325211

Toray Plastics (SuZhou) Co., Ltd. (1)
318 Dongxin Rd Xujiang Industrial Park, Xukou Town Wuzhong District, Suzhou, 215164, China
Tel.: (86) 5126 651 7008
Web Site: http://www.toray.com
Emp.: 155
Compounded Resin Mfr
N.A.I.C.S.: 325211
Inoue Atfuto *(Gen Mgr)*

Toray Plastics Europe S.A. (1)
Place d'Armenie, 01700, Saint-Maurice-de-Beynost, France
Tel.: (33) 472881600
Web Site: https://www.torayfilms.eu
Sales Range: $200-249.9 Million
Emp.: 400
Mfr of Plastic Products
N.A.I.C.S.: 326199

Toray Plastics Precision (Hong Kong) Ltd. (1)
9th Floor North Tower World Finance Centre, Harbour City, Kowloon, China (Hong Kong)
Tel.: (852) 21967334
Thermoplastic Material Mfr
N.A.I.C.S.: 325211

Toray Plastics Precision (Zhongshan) Ltd. (1)
No 14 Torch Road Zhongshan Torch Development Zone Zhongshan Port, Zhongshan, 528437, Guangdong, China
Tel.: (86) 76085594368
Thermoplastic Material Mfr
N.A.I.C.S.: 325211

Toray Plastics Precision Co., Ltd. (1)
Nihonbashi Nichigin-Dori Building 3Fl 4-6-7 Nihonbashi-Hongokucho, Chuo-ku, Tokyo, 103-0021, Japan
Tel.: (81) 33 241 3972
Web Site: https://www.toplaseiko.com
Emp.: 327
Injection Molding Product Mfr
N.A.I.C.S.: 326199
Kuniharu Nojiri *(Pres)*

Toray Polytech (Foshan) Co. Ltd. (1)
No 6 Jiujiang Avenue, Jiujiang Town Nanhai District, Foshan, Guangdong, China
Tel.: (86) 75786512547
Fiber Material Mfr
N.A.I.C.S.: 313110

Toray Polytech (Nantong) Co., Ltd. (1)
56 Xin Kai Road South, Nantong Economic & Technological Development Zone, Nantong, 226010, Jiangsu, China
Tel.: (86) 51389198300
Fiber Material Mfr
N.A.I.C.S.: 313110

Toray Precision Co., Ltd. (1)
1-1-40 Oe, Otsu, 520-2141, Shiga, Japan
Tel.: (81) 77 545 8804
Web Site: https://www.tpc.toray
Sales Range: $50-74.9 Million
Emp.: 150
Precision Equipment Mfr & Distr
N.A.I.C.S.: 332216

AND PRIVATE COMPANIES / TOREX SEMICONDUCTOR LTD.

Tamio Watanabe *(Mgr-Sls)*

Toray Research Center, Inc. (1)
1-1-1 Nihonbashi-Honcho, Chuo-ku, Tokyo, 103-0023, Japan **(100%)**
Tel.: (81) 332455633
Web Site: https://www.toray-research.co.jp
Sales Range: $75-99.9 Million
Emp.: 403
Analysis of Industrial Materials & Biological Investigation & Research of Technologies
N.A.I.C.S.: 561611

Toray Resin Mexico, S.A. De C.V. (1)
Carr El Salto a La Capilla Km 3 S/N, Parque Industrial, 45680, El Salto, Jalisco, Mexico
Tel.: (52) 3332843348
Thermoplastic Material Mfr
N.A.I.C.S.: 325211

Toray Resins Europe GmbH (1)
Frankfurter Strasse 227, 63263, Neu-Isenburg, Germany
Tel.: (49) 610279992700
Polyester Film Distr
N.A.I.C.S.: 512120
Masahiro Minami *(Pres)*

Toray Sakai Weaving & Dyeing (Nantong) Co., Ltd. (1)
301 Rui Xin Road Nantong Economic and Technological Development Zone, Nantong, 226009, Jiangsu, China
Tel.: (86) 51383595501
Fiber Material Mfr
N.A.I.C.S.: 313110

Toray Sakai Weaving & Dyeing (Nantong) Co., Ltd. (TSD) (1)
301 Rui Xin Road Nantong Economic Technological Development Zone, Nantong, 226009, Jiangsu, China **(80%)**
Tel.: (86) 51383595501
Sales Range: $50-74.9 Million
Emp.: 1,000
Weaving & Dyeing of Synthetic Organic Fibers
N.A.I.C.S.: 325130

Toray Sanko Precision (Hong Kong) Ltd. (1)
7th Fl TAL Bldg 49 Austin Rd, Kowloon, China (Hong Kong)
Tel.: (852) 21967194
Web Site: http://www.toray.com
Sales Range: $25-49.9 Million
Emp.: 5
Synthetic Organic Fibers Except Cellulosic
N.A.I.C.S.: 325220

Toray Sanko Precision (Zhongshan) Ltd. (1)
Torch Road Zhongshan Torch Development Zone, Zhongshan Port, Zhongshan, 528437, Guangdong, China **(70%)**
Tel.: (86) 7605594368
Sales Range: $200-249.9 Million
Emp.: 800
Molded Plastics; Manufacture & Marketing of Assembled Plastic Components
N.A.I.C.S.: 326199

Toray Systems Center, Inc. (1)
3F Nihonbashi Honmachi Tokyu Building 2-4-1 Nihonbashi Honmachi, Chuo-ku, Tokyo, 103-0023, Chiba, Japan
Tel.: (81) 368956960
Web Site: https://www.toray-system.co.jp
Sales Range: $5-14.9 Billion
Emp.: 422
Software Development Services
N.A.I.C.S.: 541511

Toray Textiles (Thailand) Public Company Limited (1)
5th Floor Bubhajit Building 20 North Sathorn Road Silom, Bangrak, Bangkok, 10500, Thailand
Tel.: (66) 22666600
Web Site: http://www.toray.co.th
Rev.: $262,781,293
Assets: $243,267,353
Liabilities: $47,055,409
Net Worth: $196,211,944
Earnings: $7,480,142
Emp.: 1,949
Fiscal Year-end: 03/31/2024
Filament Fabrics, Blended Polyester & Rayon Textile Mfr
N.A.I.C.S.: 314999
Masahiro Kimura *(Chm)*

Subsidiary (Domestic):

Luckytex (Thailand) Public Company Limited (2)
5th Fl Bubhajit Bldg 20 N Sathorn Rd, Bangrak, Bangkok, 10500, Thailand **(100%)**
Tel.: (66) 22666600
Web Site: http://www.toray.com.th
Sales Range: $450-499.9 Million
Emp.: 2,000
Synthetic Organic Fibers Except Cellulosic
N.A.I.C.S.: 325220
Warun Laoitthi *(Gen Mgr)*

Thai Toray Textile Mills Public Company Limited (2)
5th Fl Bubhajit Building 20 North Sathorn Road Silom, Bangrak, Bangkok, 10500, Thailand
Tel.: (66) 22666593
Web Site: http://www.toray.co.th
Rev.: $36,814,860
Assets: $52,126,745
Liabilities: $6,397,921
Net Worth: $45,728,824
Earnings: $626,241
Fiscal Year-end: 03/31/2018
Textile Products Mfr
N.A.I.C.S.: 314999

Toray Textiles Central Europe s.r.o. (1)
Prumyslova 4235/4, 796 01, Prostejov, Czech Republic **(100%)**
Tel.: (420) 582303111
Web Site: https://www.toray.cz
Sales Range: $125-149.9 Million
Emp.: 400
Synthetic Organic Fibers Except Cellulosic
N.A.I.C.S.: 325220

Toray Textiles Europe Ltd. (1)
Crown Farm Way, Forest Town, Mansfield, NG19 0FT, Nottinghamshire, United Kingdom **(100%)**
Tel.: (44) 1623415000
Web Site: https://www.ttel.co.uk
Sales Range: $125-149.9 Million
Emp.: 370
Weaving & Dyeing of Textured Polyester Fabrics
N.A.I.C.S.: 325220

Toray Textiles Inc. (1)
1-1 Kamimiyake Heiwacho, Inazawa, 490-1303, Aichi, Japan
Tel.: (81) 567462111
Web Site: https://www.toray-textiles.co.jp
Emp.: 116
Synthetic Textured Yarn Mfr & Whslr
N.A.I.C.S.: 313110

Toray Trading (Shanghai) Co., Ltd. (1)
8th Floor Park Place 1601 West Nanjing Road, Jing An District, Shanghai, 200040, China **(100%)**
Tel.: (86) 2132518558
Web Site: http://www.toray.cn
Sales Range: $50-74.9 Million
Emp.: 120
Synthetic Organic Fibers Except Cellulosic
N.A.I.C.S.: 325220

Toray Travel Co., Ltd. (1)
3-4 Nihonbashi-Honcho 2-chome, Chuo-ku, Tokyo, 103-0023, Japan
Tel.: (81) 3 3245 5010
Web Site: http://www.toray-travel.co.jp
Sales Range: $10-24.9 Million
Emp.: 30
Travel Agency Services
N.A.I.C.S.: 561510
Hideki Koike *(Mgr-Sls)*

Toray Wbd Membrane Technology (JS) Co., Ltd. (1)
No 9 Huanbao Street, Environmental Protection District, Yancheng, Jiangsu, China
Tel.: (86) 51589815111
Pharmaceutical Product Mfr & Distr
N.A.I.C.S.: 325412

Towa Orimono Co., Ltd. (1)
1-65 Nishiitamochi-cho 8-chome, Tondabayashi, 584-0048, Osaka, Japan
Tel.: (81) 721341234
Carpet Mfr & Distr
N.A.I.C.S.: 314110

Toyo Business Support Inc. (1)
2-1-1 Nihonbashi Muromachi, Chuo-ku, Tokyo, 103-8666, Japan
Tel.: (81) 332455371
Web Site: https://www.tybs.co.jp
Emp.: 56
Business Support Services
N.A.I.C.S.: 561499

Toyo Jitsugyo Co., Ltd. (1)
1-5 Sakaemachi, Otsu, 520-0855, Shiga, Japan
Tel.: (81) 775373553
Web Site: https://www.toyo-jitsugyo.co.jp
Sales Range: $150-199.9 Million
Emp.: 718
Paper Products Recycling Services
N.A.I.C.S.: 562920

Toyo Shokusan Inc. (1)
1515 Oaza Tsutsui Masaki-cho, Iyo, 791-3191, Ehime, Japan
Tel.: (81) 899840079
Web Site: http://www.toray.com
Timber Product Mfr
N.A.I.C.S.: 322219

Tsuchiura Shokusan Inc. (1)
1 Kitakandatsu-machi 2-chome, Tsuchiura, 300-0015, Ibaraki, Japan
Tel.: (81) 298326955
Web Site: http://www.toray.com
Contract Provision of Ancillary Services, Mfr, Processing & Marketing of Various Products
N.A.I.C.S.: 561499

Vietnam Tnt Fibers Co., Ltd. (1)
DT 743 St, An Phu Ward Thuan An Dist, Binh Dong, Binh Duong, Vietnam
Tel.: (84) 2743740358
Fiber Material Mfr
N.A.I.C.S.: 313110

Yihua Toray Polyester Film Co., Ltd. (1)
East side of YouGang Rd, XuPu, Yizheng, 211900, Jiangsu, China
Tel.: (86) 51483234812
Web Site: https://www.jsytp.com
Polyester Film Mfr
N.A.I.C.S.: 326113

Zoltek Corporation (1)
3101 McKelvey Rd, Bridgeton, MO 63044
Tel.: (314) 291-5110
Web Site: http://www.zoltek.com
Building Materials Distr
N.A.I.C.S.: 444180

Zoltek De Mexico S.A. De C.V. (1)
Km 3 Carretera a El Salto, 45680, El Salto, Jalisco, Mexico
Tel.: (52) 3332843333
Web Site: https://zoltek.com
Fiber Material Mfr
N.A.I.C.S.: 313110

TORBRAM ELECTRIC SUPPLY CORPORATION
10 Perdue Ct Unit 6, Caledon, L7C 3M6, ON, Canada
Tel.: (905) 495-0535
Web Site: http://www.torbramelectric.com
Year Founded: 1951
Rev.: $26,083,485
Emp.: 120
Electrical Products Distr
N.A.I.C.S.: 238210
Andrew Dawes *(Gen Mgr)*

TOREAD HOLDINGS GROUP CO., LTD.
No 28 Hongfu Technology Park, Beiqijia County Changping District, Beijing, 102209, China
Tel.: (86) 1081788188
Web Site: http://www.toread.com.cn
Year Founded: 2008
300005—(CHIN)
Rev.: $195,881,630
Assets: $371,311,559
Liabilities: $74,786,265
Net Worth: $296,525,294
Earnings: $10,112,734
Fiscal Year-end: 12/31/23
Outdoor Product Mfr
N.A.I.C.S.: 315210
Li Ming *(Chm)*

TOREX GOLD RESOURCES INC.
130 King St West Suite 740, Toronto, M5X 2A2, ON, Canada
Tel.: (647) 260-1500 BC
Web Site: https://www.torexgold.com
Year Founded: 1980
TORXF—(OTCIQ)
Rev.: $882,600,000
Assets: $1,835,800,000
Liabilities: $340,700,000
Net Worth: $1,495,100,000
Earnings: $204,400,000
Emp.: 1,212
Fiscal Year-end: 12/31/23
Gold & Other Precious Metal Mining Services
N.A.I.C.S.: 212220
Fred Stanford *(Chm)*

TOREX SEMICONDUCTOR LTD.
3F Daiho Annex 1-24-1 Shinkawa, Chuo-ku, Tokyo, 104-0033, Japan
Tel.: (81) 362222851
Web Site: https://www.torexsemi.com
Year Founded: 1995
6616—(TKS)
Rev.: $170,214,110
Assets: $242,163,960
Liabilities: $106,315,240
Net Worth: $135,848,720
Earnings: ($28,403,170)
Emp.: 1,042
Fiscal Year-end: 03/31/24
Semiconductor Devices Mfr
N.A.I.C.S.: 334413
Koji Shibamiya *(Chm & Pres)*

Subsidiaries:

Phenitec Semiconductor Corp (1)
6833 Kinoko-cho, Ibara, 715-8602, Okayama, Japan
Tel.: (81) 866624121
Emp.: 721
Semiconductor Chips Mfr
N.A.I.C.S.: 333242

Affiliate (Domestic):

Phenitec Semiconductor - Kagoshima Factory (2)
1770-1 Kitakata, Yusui-cho, Aira, 899-6202, Kagoshima, Japan
Tel.: (81) 995743611
Web Site: http://www.phenitec.co.jp
Semiconductor Components Mfr
N.A.I.C.S.: 334413

Phenitec Semiconductor Corp - 1st Factory (2)
6833 Kinoko-cho Ibara, Okayama, 715-8602, Japan
Tel.: (81) 866624400
Semiconductor Chips Mfr
N.A.I.C.S.: 333242

TOREX (HONG KONG) LIMITED (1)
Units 505 Energy Plaza 92 Granville Road TST East, Kowloon, China (Hong Kong)
Tel.: (852) 23127489
Semiconductor Device Distr
N.A.I.C.S.: 423690
Jack Hayashi *(Gen Mgr)*

TOREX SEMICONDUCTOR (S) PTE LTD (1)
60 Kaki Bukit Place Eunos Techpark 05-17, Singapore, 415979, Singapore

TOREX SEMICONDUCTOR LTD.

Torex Semiconductor Ltd.—(Continued)
Tel.: (65) 67451352
Emp.: 5
Semiconductor Device Distr
N.A.I.C.S.: 423690
Kenichi Rikukawa (Mng Dir)

TOREX SEMICONDUCTOR DEVICE (Shanghai) CO., LTD. (1)
RM1705 E BLDG of Baoneng Center No 3008 North Baoan Road, Luohu District, Shenzhen, China
Tel.: (86) 75583266338
Semiconductor Device Distr
N.A.I.C.S.: 423690

TOREX SEMICONDUCTOR TAIWAN LTD. (1)
11F-1 No 21 Sec 6 Zhong Xiao E Rd, Taipei, 11575, Taiwan
Tel.: (886) 227892089
Semiconductor Device Distr
N.A.I.C.S.: 423690

TOREX VIETNAM SEMICONDUCTOR CO., LTD. (1)
20 VSIP II Street 6 Vietnam-Singapore Industrial Park II, Binh Duong Industry-Service-Urban Complex Hoa Phu Ward, Thu Dau Mot, Binh Duong, Vietnam
Tel.: (84) 6503628115
Semiconductor Device Distr
N.A.I.C.S.: 423690

Torex Semiconductor Ltd. - Sales Division (1)
6F Daiho Annex 1-24-1 Shinkawa, Chuo-ku, Tokyo, 104-0033, Japan
Tel.: (81) 362222860
Semiconductor Device Distr
N.A.I.C.S.: 423690

TORGAN MANAGEMENT INC
4950 Yonge Street Suite 1010, Toronto, M2N 6K1, ON, Canada
Tel.: (416) 221-9348
Web Site: http://www.torgan.com
Year Founded: 1980
Rev.: $50,000,000
Emp.: 30
Real Estate Services
N.A.I.C.S.: 531390
Eli Swirsky (Pres)

TORGOTERM PLC
1 Ovoshtarska Street, 2500, Kyustendil, Bulgaria
Tel.: (359) 78 528195
Web Site: http://www.torgoterm-bg.com
Year Founded: 1965
Kitchen Equipment Mfr
N.A.I.C.S.: 332215

TORIASE PUBLIC COMPANY LTD.
15 Ayion Omologiton, Nicosia, Cyprus
Tel.: (357) 22452600
TORIA—(CYP)
Rev.: $4,995
Assets: $26,504
Liabilities: $11,308
Net Worth: $15,195
Earnings: ($4,794)
Fiscal Year-end: 12/31/19
Business Management Services
N.A.I.C.S.: 561110

TORIDOLL HOLDINGS CORPORATION
Shibuya Solasta 19th floor 1-21-1 Dogenzaka, Shibuya-ku, Tokyo, 150-0043, Japan
Tel.: (81) 342218900
Web Site: https://www.toridoll.com
Year Founded: 1990
3397—(TKS)
Rev.: $1,533,202,720
Assets: $2,122,272,700
Liabilities: $1,526,480,350
Net Worth: $595,792,350
Earnings: $37,511,750
Emp.: 5,795
Fiscal Year-end: 03/31/24
Holding Company; Restaurant Management Services
N.A.I.C.S.: 551112
Kimihiro Tanaka (COO)

Subsidiaries:

Dream Dining Corp. (1)
1585 Kapiolani Blvd, Honolulu, HI 96814
Tel.: (808) 947-9596
Sales Range: $1-9.9 Million
Emp.: 100
Eating Place
N.A.I.C.S.: 722511
Tepsuya Emura (Principal)

Marugame Seimen Inc. (1)
11F Nihon-Seimei Sannomiya-eki-mae Bldg 7-1-1 Onoedori, Chuo, Kobe, 651-0088, Japan
Tel.: (81) 782003430
Emp.: 823
Restaurant Services
N.A.I.C.S.: 722511
Hiroshi Yamaguchi (Pres & CEO)

Wok To Walk Franchise B.V. (1)
WOK TO WALK Leidsestraat 85, 1017NX, Amsterdam, Netherlands
Tel.: (31) 206250721
Web Site: https://www.woktowalk.com
Fast Food Franchise Restaurant Operator
N.A.I.C.S.: 722513

TORII PHARMACEUTICAL CO., LTD.
Torii Nihonbashi Bldg 4-1 Nihonbashi-Honch 3-chome, Chuo-ku, Tokyo, 103-8439, Japan
Tel.: (81) 332316811
Web Site: https://www.torii.co.jp
Year Founded: 1921
4551—(TKS)
Rev.: $403,656,000
Assets: $1,219,931,680
Liabilities: $105,850,800
Net Worth: $1,114,080,880
Earnings: $33,831,600
Emp.: 568
Fiscal Year-end: 12/31/20
Pharmaceutical Product Mfr & Whslr
N.A.I.C.S.: 325412
Masaki Sunami (Sr Exec Officer)

TORIKIZOKU CO., LTD.
1-2-12 Tateba, Naniwa-ku, Osaka, Japan
Tel.: (81) 665625333
Web Site: http://www.torikizoku.co.jp
3193—(TKS)
Rev.: $260,705,080
Assets: $128,467,880
Liabilities: $74,403,640
Net Worth: $54,064,240
Earnings: $13,229,940
Emp.: 420
Fiscal Year-end: 07/31/24
Drinking Establishment
N.A.I.C.S.: 722410
Tadashi Okura (Pres)

TORISHIMA PUMP MFG. CO., LTD.
1-1-8 Miyatacho, Takatsuki City, Osaka, 569-8660, Japan
Tel.: (81) 726950551
Web Site: https://www.torishima.co.jp
6363—(TKS)
Rev.: $536,090,830
Assets: $671,311,600
Liabilities: $323,414,080
Net Worth: $347,897,520
Earnings: $41,147,250
Emp.: 48,140
Fiscal Year-end: 03/31/24
Pumping & Wind Power Generation Equipment Mfr
N.A.I.C.S.: 333914

Kotaro Harada (Pres & CEO)

Subsidiaries:

Kyushu Torishima Co.,Ltd (1)
9857-13 Kawako Wakagi-cho, Takeo Industrial Park, Takeo, 843-0151, Saga, Japan
Tel.: (81) 954263081
Web Site: https://www.torishima.co.jp
Emp.: 90
Industrial Pump Mfr
N.A.I.C.S.: 333914

TORISHIMA EUROPE LTD (1)
327 5th Floor - Door 3, 28043, Madrid, Spain
Tel.: (34) 910027541
Web Site: https://www.torishima.es
Sales Range: $25-49.9 Million
Emp.: 3
Industrial Pump Mfr
N.A.I.C.S.: 333914

TORISHIMA MALAYSIA SDN.BHD (1)
Lot 19 1st Floor Bangunan Ipmuda Jalan 13/2, 46200, Petaling Jaya, Selangor, Malaysia
Tel.: (60) 3 7960 5771
Web Site: http://www.torishima.co.jp
Sales Range: $25-49.9 Million
Emp.: 7
Industrial Pumps Mfr & Distr
N.A.I.C.S.: 333914

TORISHIMA SERVICE SOLUTIONS EUROPE LTD. (1)
Unit 3 - M8 Interlink Estate Kirkshaws Road, Coatbridge, ML5 4RP, Scotland, United Kingdom
Tel.: (44) 1236 442390
Web Site: http://www.torishima.eu
Sales Range: $25-49.9 Million
Emp.: 23
Industrial Engineering Services
N.A.I.C.S.: 541330
Gerry Clocherty (Mng Dir)

TORISHIMA SERVICE SOLUTIONS FZCO (1)
Plot of Land TP010501 National Industries Park, PO Box 37603, Jebel Ali, Dubai, United Arab Emirates
Tel.: (971) 48807344
Hydraulic Pump Distr
N.A.I.C.S.: 423830

Torishima (Hong Kong) Limited (1)
Unit 2203A 22/F One Harbour Square 181 Hoi Bun Road, Kwun Tong, Kowloon, China (Hong Kong)
Tel.: (852) 27951838
Web Site: http://www.torishima.co.jp
Sales Range: $25-49.9 Million
Emp.: 20
Water Sewer & Pipeline Construction
N.A.I.C.S.: 237120

TORLYS INC.
1900 Derry Road East, Mississauga, L5S1Y6, ON, Canada
Tel.: (905) 612-8772
Web Site: http://www.torlys.com
Year Founded: 1988
Rev.: $11,040,923
Emp.: 70
Flooring Contract Services
N.A.I.C.S.: 238330

TORM A/S
Tuborg Havnevej 18, DK-2900, Hellerup, Denmark
Tel.: (45) 39179200
Web Site: http://www.torm.com
Year Founded: 1889
TRMD-A—(CSE)
Rev.: $1,443,351,000
Assets: $2,614,176,000
Liabilities: $1,110,502,000
Net Worth: $1,503,674,000
Earnings: $562,574,000
Emp.: 442
Fiscal Year-end: 12/31/22
International Shipping & Related Services

INTERNATIONAL PUBLIC

N.A.I.C.S.: 483111
Jacob Meldgaard (CEO)

Subsidiaries:

TORM Shipping India Pte Ltd (1)
2nd Floor Leela Business Park Andheri-Kurla Road, Andheri E, Mumbai, 400059, Maharashtra, India
Tel.: (91) 2266407200
Web Site: https://www.torm.com
Sales Range: $25-49.9 Million
Emp.: 90
Shipping Agents
N.A.I.C.S.: 488320
Valerian Pinto (Deputy Gen Mgr)

TORM Singapore Pte. Ltd (1)
6 Battery Road Ste 27-02, Singapore, 049909, Singapore
Tel.: (65) 65343431
Sales Range: $25-49.9 Million
Emp.: 20
Bulk Cargo Handling Services
N.A.I.C.S.: 488320
Frank Yap (Gen Mgr)

TORM USA LLC (1)
1 Station Pl, Stamford, CT 06902
Tel.: (203) 602-6700
Web Site: http://www.torm.com
Sales Range: $25-49.9 Million
Emp.: 10
Shipping Agents
N.A.I.C.S.: 488320

TORM PLC
Office 105 20 St Dunstan's Hill, London, EC3R 8HL, United Kingdom
Tel.: (44) 2037952794   UK
Web Site: https://www.torm.com
Year Founded: 1889
TRMD—(NASDAQ)
Rev.: $1,443,351,000
Assets: $2,614,176,000
Liabilities: $1,110,502,000
Net Worth: $1,503,674,000
Earnings: $562,574,000
Emp.: 355
Fiscal Year-end: 12/31/22
Petroleum Product Distr
N.A.I.C.S.: 424720
David N. Weinstein (Deputy Chm)

TORNADO AIR PLC
145-147 St John Street, London, EC1V 4PW, United Kingdom
Tel.: (44) 207 1930 107
Web Site: http://www.tornado-air.com
Air Compressor Mfr
N.A.I.C.S.: 333912
Kyung Jai Youh (CEO)

TORNADO GLOBAL HYDROVACS LTD.
Suite 1800 300 5th Avenue S W, Calgary, T2P 3C4, AB, Canada
Tel.: (403) 742-6121
Web Site: https://www.tornadotrucks.com
Year Founded: 1984
TGH—(TSX)
Rev.: $46,240,392
Assets: $18,235,669
Liabilities: $6,764,722
Net Worth: $11,470,948
Earnings: ($1,250,402)
Fiscal Year-end: 12/31/19
Hydrovac Truck Mfr
N.A.I.C.S.: 336120
George Tai (Sec)

TORNOS HOLDINGS S.A
Rue Industrielle 111, 2740, Moutier, Switzerland
Tel.: (41) 32 494 4444
Web Site: http://www.tornos.ch
TOHN—(SWX)
Rev.: $194,205,015
Assets: $164,110,758
Liabilities: $52,258,961

Net Worth: $111,851,797
Earnings: $23,021,983
Emp.: 640
Fiscal Year-end: 12/31/21
Lathe Machine Mfr
N.A.I.C.S.: 333517
Francois Frote *(Chm)*

Subsidiaries:

Tornos (Taichung) Machine Works Ltd. (1)
12-3 Zhuangqian Road, Shengang district, Taichung, 42951, Taiwan
Tel.: (886) 42 563 1125
Machine Tools Mfr
N.A.I.C.S.: 333517

Tornos (Xi'an) Machine Works Co., Ltd. (1)
No190 Xibudadao Xian High-tech Zone, Xi'an, 710119, China
Tel.: (86) 298 844 5670
Machine Tools Mfr
N.A.I.C.S.: 333517

Tornos Technologies (Thailand) Co. Ltd. (1)
18/3 Soi Udomsuk 31, Bangjak Phrakanong, Bangkok, 10260, Thailand
Tel.: (66) 21 062 6012
Machine Tools Mfr
N.A.I.C.S.: 333517

Tornos Technologies Asia Limited (1)
Rm 1803-06 corporation park 11 on Lai street Shek Mun, Tai Wai, Sha Tin, New Territories, China (Hong Kong)
Tel.: (852) 26912633
Web Site: http://www.tornos.com
Sales Range: $25-49.9 Million
Emp.: 10
Precision Machine Tools Mfr
N.A.I.C.S.: 332216
Kevin Lee *(Mgr-Logistics)*

Tornos Technologies Deutschland GmbH (1)
Karlsruher Strasse 38, 75179, Pforzheim, Baden-Wurttemberg, Germany
Tel.: (49) 723191070
Web Site: http://www.tornos.com
Sales Range: $25-49.9 Million
Emp.: 50
Machine Tools Mfr
N.A.I.C.S.: 333517

Tornos Technologies France SAS (1)
275 rue du Rhone St-Pierre en Faucigny, 74807, Saint-Pierre-en-Faucigny, France
Tel.: (33) 450038333
Web Site: http://www.tornos.ch
Sales Range: $25-49.9 Million
Emp.: 25
Machine Tool Distr
N.A.I.C.S.: 423830
Patrice Armeni *(Mng Dir)*

Tornos Technologies Italia Srl (1)
Via Achille Grandi 1-B e 1-C, 20017, Rho, Italy
Tel.: (39) 025 768 1501
Machine Tools Mfr
N.A.I.C.S.: 333517

TORO CORP.
223 Christodoulou Chatzipavlou St, Hawaii Royal Gardens, 3036, Limassol, Cyprus
Tel.: (357) 25357768   MH
Web Site: https://www.torocorp.com
Year Founded: 2022
TORO—(NASDAQ)
Rev.: $78,468,574
Assets: $308,104,130
Liabilities: $131,362,931
Net Worth: $176,741,199
Earnings: $140,636,993
Fiscal Year-end: 12/31/23
Transportation Services
N.A.I.C.S.: 488510

TORO ENERGY LTD
60 Havelock Street, West Perth, 6005, WA, Australia
Tel.: (61) 892142100   AU
Web Site: http://www.toroenergy.com.au
TOE—(ASX)
Rev.: $327,541
Assets: $21,134,025
Liabilities: $836,780
Net Worth: $20,297,245
Earnings: ($5,391,388)
Fiscal Year-end: 06/30/24
Uranium Development & Exploration Services
N.A.I.C.S.: 212290
Greg Shirtliff *(Mgr-Geology)*

TOROMONT INDUSTRIES LTD.
3131 Highway 7 West, PO Box 5511, Concord, L4K 1B7, ON, Canada
Tel.: (416) 667-5511   Ca
Web Site: https://www.toromont.com
Year Founded: 1961
TMTNF—(OTCIQ)
Rev.: $3,414,568,220
Assets: $3,377,297,038
Liabilities: $1,394,891,778
Net Worth: $1,982,405,260
Earnings: $390,859,866
Emp.: 7,000
Fiscal Year-end: 12/31/23
Holding Company
N.A.I.C.S.: 551112
Scott J. Medhurst *(Pres & CEO)*

Subsidiaries:

Battlefield - The CAT Rental Store (1)
880 South Service Road, PO Box 9340, Stoney Creek, L8E 5M7, ON, Canada
Tel.: (905) 643-9410
Web Site: http://www.battlefieldequipment.ca
Equipment Rentals; Distributor of Caterpillar Compact Construction Equipment
N.A.I.C.S.: 532412

CIMCO Refrigeration (1)
65 Villiers St, Toronto, M5A 3S1, ON, Canada   **(100%)**
Tel.: (416) 465-7581
Web Site: http://www.cimcorefrigeration.com
Sales Range: $200-249.9 Million
Engineering & Design of Industrial Refrigeration Systems; Manufacturing of Components, Installation & After-Sales Service
N.A.I.C.S.: 333415

Toromont CAT (1)
3131 Highway 7 W - Bldg B, PO Box 5511, Concord, L4K 5E1, ON, Canada
Tel.: (416) 667-5511
Web Site: http://www.toromontcat.com
Sales Range: $350-399.9 Million
Emp.: 1,800
Heavy Equipment Dealer; Rebuilds Caterpillar & OEM Engines, Transmissions, Hydraulic Pumps, Cylinders & Components
N.A.I.C.S.: 811210

Toromont CAT - Quebec (1)
5001 Trans Canada Highway, Pointe-Claire, H9R 1B8, QC, Canada
Tel.: (514) 630-3100
Web Site: https://www.toromontcat.com
Heavy Equipment Rental & Sales
N.A.I.C.S.: 423820

Toromont Energy (1)
268 Orenda Road, Brampton, L6T 1E9, ON, Canada   **(100%)**
Tel.: (905) 488-2500
Web Site: https://www.toromontenergy.com
Sales Range: $25-49.9 Million
N.A.I.C.S.: 333415

Toromont Material Handling (1)
4000 Trans-Canada Highway, Pointe-Claire, H9R 1B2, QC, Canada
Tel.: (514) 426-6700
Web Site: http://succursale.toromontcatqc.com
Heavy Equipment Rental & Sales
N.A.I.C.S.: 423830

TORONTO AIRWAYS LTD.
2833 16th Avenue, PO Box 100, Markham, L3R 0P8, ON, Canada
Tel.: (905) 477-8100
Web Site: http://www.torontoairways.com
Year Founded: 1965
Rev.: $41,472,741
Emp.: 108
Pilot & Aviation Related Services
N.A.I.C.S.: 488119
Derek Sifton *(Pres)*

TORONTO HONDA
2300 Danforth Ave, Toronto, M4C 1K6, ON, Canada
Tel.: (416) 423-2300
Web Site: http://www.torontohonda.com
Year Founded: 1955
New & Used Car Dealers
N.A.I.C.S.: 441110
Jenny Lam *(Mgr-Fin Svcs)*

TORONTO HYDRO CORPORATION
14 Carlton Street, Toronto, M5B 1K5, ON, Canada
Tel.: (416) 542-3100   ON
Web Site: http://www.torontohydro.com
Year Founded: 1999
Rev.: $2,545,384,919
Assets: $3,836,511,574
Liabilities: $2,454,276,748
Net Worth: $1,382,234,826
Earnings: $170,195,634
Emp.: 1,400
Fiscal Year-end: 12/31/18
Electric & Telecommunications Services
N.A.I.C.S.: 335311
Brian Chu *(Vice Chm)*

Subsidiaries:

Toronto Hydro Energy Services Inc. (1)
14 Carlton Street, Toronto, M5B 1K5, ON, Canada
Tel.: (416) 542-8000
Web Site: http://www.torontohydroenergy.com
Energy Services
N.A.I.C.S.: 221122

Toronto Hydro Street Lighting Inc. (1)
500 Commissioners Street, Toronto, M4M 3N7, ON, Canada
Tel.: (416) 542-8000
Municipal Lighting Services
N.A.I.C.S.: 335132

Toronto Hydro-Electric System Limited (1)
14 Carlton Street, Toronto, M5B 1K5, ON, Canada
Tel.: (416) 542-8000
Power Transmission & Distribution Services
N.A.I.C.S.: 221122
Anthony Haines *(Pres & CEO)*

TORONTO SYMPHONY ORCHESTRA
212 King St W, Toronto, M5H 1K5, ON, Canada
Tel.: (416) 598-3375
Web Site: http://www.tso.ca
Sales Range: $50-74.9 Million
Emp.: 150
Symphony Orchestra
N.A.I.C.S.: 711190
Roberta Smith *(VP)*

TORPOL S.A.
St Michaels Street 43, 61-119, Poznan, Poland
Tel.: (48) 618782700   PL
Web Site: https://www.torpol.pl

Year Founded: 1991
TOR—(WAR)
Rev.: $277,490,853
Assets: $288,360,009
Liabilities: $159,002,286
Net Worth: $129,357,723
Earnings: $25,919,461
Emp.: 800
Fiscal Year-end: 12/31/23
Transport Infrastructure Engineering & Construction Services
N.A.I.C.S.: 237990
Krzysztof Miler *(Chief Production Officer, Member-Mgmt Bd & VP)*

TORQ INC.
2-7-4 Minami-Horie, Nishi-ku, Osaka, 550-0015, Japan
Tel.: (81) 665353690
Web Site: https://www.torq.co.jp
Year Founded: 1941
8077—(TKS)
Rev.: $154,257,130
Assets: $231,765,010
Liabilities: $144,246,050
Net Worth: $87,518,960
Earnings: $5,991,050
Emp.: 236
Fiscal Year-end: 10/31/23
Screw Product Mfr & Distr
N.A.I.C.S.: 332722
Toshiyuki Higaki *(Pres & Dir-Rep)*

Subsidiaries:

Kobax Co., Ltd. (1)
2-7-4 Minamihorie, Nishi-ku, Osaka, 550-0015, Japan
Tel.: (81) 665358590
Building Material Retailer
N.A.I.C.S.: 444180

Nakajimakoki Coporation (1)
3-11-7 Minamisenjyu, Arakawaku, Tokyo, 116-0003, Japan
Tel.: (81) 356151804
Rivet Product Retailer
N.A.I.C.S.: 423710

Nakasho Machine Co., Ltd. (1)
2-7-4 Minamihorie, Nishi-ku, Osaka, 550-0015, Japan
Tel.: (81) 665353670
Peripheral Equipment Retailer
N.A.I.C.S.: 423430
Takashi Shigaki *(Pres)*

Owa Hagane Industry Co., Ltd. (1)
5-11-5 Namiyoke, Minato-ku, Osaka, 552-0001, Japan
Tel.: (81) 665810721
Stainless Steel Product Retailer
N.A.I.C.S.: 423510

TORQ RESOURCES INC.
1400-1199 West Hastings Street, Vancouver, V6E 3T5, BC, Canada
Tel.: (778) 729-0500
Web Site: https://www.torqresources.com
TORQ—(OTCIQ)
Rev.: $66,262
Assets: $7,114,718
Liabilities: $158,738
Net Worth: $6,955,980
Earnings: ($1,633,272)
Fiscal Year-end: 12/31/20
Mineral Exploration Services
N.A.I.C.S.: 213114
Shawn Kristen Wallace *(Chm & CEO)*

TORQUEST PARTNERS INC.
161 Bay St Suite 4240, Toronto, M5J 2S1, ON, Canada
Tel.: (416) 956-7022
Web Site: http://www.torquest.com
Year Founded: 2002
Privater Equity Firm
N.A.I.C.S.:
Brent S. Belzberg *(Co-Founder & Sr Mng Partner)*

TORQUEST PARTNERS INC.

TorQuest Partners Inc.—(Continued)

Subsidiaries:

A&W Food Services of Canada Inc. (1)
171 W Esplanade Ste 300, North Vancouver, V7M 3K9, BC, Canada
Tel.: (604) 988-2141
Web Site: http://www.aw.ca
Sales Range: $400-449.9 Million
Emp.: 100
Restaurant Operators
N.A.I.C.S.: 722511
Paul F. B. Hollands (Chm)

Subsidiary (Domestic):

A&W Revenue Royalties Income Fund (2)
300 171 West Esplanade, North Vancouver, V7M 3K9, BC, Canada
Tel.: (604) 988-2141
Web Site: https://www.awincomefund.ca
Rev.: $36,830,525
Assets: $295,212,133
Liabilities: $62,407,952
Net Worth: $232,804,181
Earnings: $23,508,296
Fiscal Year-end: 12/31/2021
Trademark Owner & Licenser
N.A.I.C.S.: 533110
Donald T. Leslie (CFO)

A&W Trade Marks Limited Partnership (2)
171 West Esplanade Ste 300, North Vancouver, V7M 3K9, BC, Canada
Tel.: (604) 988-2141
Web Site: http://www.aw.ca
Food Restaurant Business Service
N.A.I.C.S.: 722513

Can Art Aluminum Extrusion L.P. (1)
85 Parkshore Drive, Brampton, L6T 5M1, ON, Canada
Tel.: (905) 791-1464
Web Site: http://www.canart.ca
Aluminum Extrusions & Fabrication Services
N.A.I.C.S.: 331318
Tyler Menary (Sls Mgr)

Cando Rail Services Ltd. (1)
Unit 400 740 Rosser Avenue, Brandon, R7A 0K9, MB, Canada
Tel.: (204) 725-2627
Web Site: https://www.candorail.com
Emp.: 400
Heavy Construction Services
N.A.I.C.S.: 336510
Brian Cornick (CEO)

Subsidiary (Domestic):

Central Manitoba Railway Inc. (2)
2675 Day Street, PO Box 27, Sunnyside, R5R 0H7, MB, Canada
Tel.: (204) 235-1175
Web Site: http://www.cemrr.com
Railroad Construction Services
N.A.I.C.S.: 237990

Envirosystems Inc. (1)
11 Brown Ave, Dartmouth, B3B 1Z7, NS, Canada
Tel.: (902) 481-8008
Web Site: http://www.envirosystemsglobal.com
Industrial & Environmental Services
N.A.I.C.S.: 444180
Mike Ryan (Pres & CEO)

Subsidiary (US):

Rocky Mountain Industrial Services, LLC (2)
8571 Rosemary St Ste B, Commerce City, CO 80022
Tel.: (303) 789-9307
Web Site: http://www.rmisusa.com
Chemical Cleaning & Engineering Services
N.A.I.C.S.: 459999
Charles Wigglesworth (Owner)

Indiana Limestone Company, Inc. (1)
301 Main St, Oolitic, IN 47451
Tel.: (812) 275-3341
Web Site: http://www.indianalimestonecompany.com
Limestone Supplier
N.A.I.C.S.: 212312
Duffe Elkins (VP)

Madden Manufacturing Co., Inc. (1)
469 Dogwood Rd, Lake Ozark, MO 65049
Tel.: (573) 365-7040
Web Site: http://www.maddenmetals.com
Rev.: $1,240,000
Emp.: 10
Other Building Finishing Contractors
N.A.I.C.S.: 238390
Cory Hofeldt (VP-Ops)

Polycor Inc. (1)
76 rue Saint-Paul Suite 100, Quebec, G1K 3V9, QC, Canada
Tel.: (418) 692-4695
Web Site: http://www.polycor.com
Natural Stone Products Mfr & Distr
N.A.I.C.S.: 212311
Patrick Perus (Pres & CEO)

Subsidiary (US):

Elliott Stone Co., Inc. (2)
3326 Mitchell Road, Bedford, IN 47421
Tel.: (812) 275-5556
Cut Stone & Stone Product Mfr
N.A.I.C.S.: 327991
Ralph Morgan (Treas)

Subsidiary (Non-US):

Rocamat S.A. (2)
58 Quai de la Marine, L'Ile Saint-Denis, 93450, Paris, France
Tel.: (33) 149332600
Web Site: http://www.rocamat.com
Sales Range: $100-124.9 Million
Stone Mining, Cutting & Sales
N.A.I.C.S.: 327991
Philippe Karmin (Chm & CEO)

Subsidiary (US):

Swenson Granite Company LLC (2)
369 N State St, Concord, NH 03301-3233
Tel.: (603) 225-4322
Web Site: http://www.swensongranite.com
Granite Quarring Cut Stone & Stone Product Services
N.A.I.C.S.: 212311
Bill Bonneau (Mgr-Rowley)

Subsidiary (Domestic):

Rock of Ages Corporation (3)
560 Graniteville Rd, Graniteville, VT 05654
Tel.: (802) 476-3121
Web Site: http://www.rockofages.com
Quarrying; Granite Memorial Products Mfr
N.A.I.C.S.: 327991
Paul H. Hutchins (VP-Admin)

Subsidiary (Domestic):

Carolina Quarries, Inc. (4)
805 Harris Granite Rd, Salisbury, NC 28146-7810
Tel.: (704) 636-6780
Dimensional Stone Quarrying; Stone Products Mfr
N.A.I.C.S.: 212311

Pennsylvania Granite Corp. (4)
410 Trythall Rd, Elverson, PA 19520
Tel.: (610) 286-0094
Dimensional Stone Quarrying; Stone & Granite Memorial Products Mfr
N.A.I.C.S.: 212311

Subsidiary (Non-US):

Rock of Ages Canada, Inc. (4)
4 Rue Rock Of Ages, Stanstead, J0B 3E2, QC, Canada
Tel.: (819) 876-2745
Web Site: https://rockofages.com
Dimensional Stone Quarrying Stone & Granite Memorial Product Mfr
N.A.I.C.S.: 212311
Donald Labonte (Pres)

S.i. Systems ULC (1)
Suite 309 401 9th Avenue SW, Calgary, T2P 3C5, AB, Canada
Tel.: (403) 263-1200
Web Site: https://www.sisystems.com
Staffing & Recruiting Services

N.A.I.C.S.: 561311
Derek Bullen (CEO)

Subsidiary (Domestic):

Annex Consulting Group Inc. (2)
Suite 950 555 Burrard Street Two Bentall Centre, Vancouver, V7X 1M9, BC, Canada
Tel.: (604) 638-8878
Web Site: http://www.annexgroup.com
Business Consulting Services
N.A.I.C.S.: 541611
Stacey Cerniuk (CEO)

Eagle Professional Resources Inc. (2)
170 Laurier Avenue W Suite 902, Ottawa, K1P 5V5, ON, Canada
Tel.: (613) 234-1810
Web Site: http://www.eagleonline.com
Employment & Consulting Agencies
N.A.I.C.S.: 561311
Kevin Dee (Chm)

SCM Insurance Services, Inc. (1)
8560 Roper Road NW Suite 200, Edmonton, T6E 6V4, AB, Canada
Tel.: (780) 484-0364
Web Site: https://scminsuranceservices.com
Insurance Services
N.A.I.C.S.: 524210
Mike Ackroyd (CIO)

Subsidiary (US):

Arm Claims Incorporated (2)
3500 Market Place Ave, Bryant, AR 72022
Tel.: (501) 228-0900
Insurance Related Activities
N.A.I.C.S.: 524298

Nixon & Company (2)
13205 Manchester Blvd Ste 100, Saint Louis, MO 63131
Tel.: (314) 821-4888
Web Site: http://www.nixonandco.com
Sales Range: $1-9.9 Million
Emp.: 46
Claims Adjusting & Management Services
N.A.I.C.S.: 524291
Ken Pini (Principal)

TORQX CAPITAL PARTNERS B.V.

Brediusweg 43, Bussum, 1401 AC, Netherlands
Tel.: (31) 35 3037110
Web Site:
    http://www.torqxcapital.com
Year Founded: 2017
Venture Capital & Private Equity
N.A.I.C.S.: 523940
Harmen Geerts (Mng Partner)

Subsidiaries:

Diamond Tools Group B.V. (1)
De Vest 1-C, 5555 XL, Valkenswaard, Netherlands
Tel.: (31) 40 208 2363
Web Site: http://www.contour-diamonds.com
Emp.: 460
Diamond Cutting Tools & Diamond Wire Dies Mfr
N.A.I.C.S.: 333515

Subsidiary (US):

Esteves USA (2)
1921 Patterson St, Decatur, IN 46733
Tel.: (260) 728-9272
Web Site: http://www.estevesgroup.com
Sales Range: $10-24.9 Million
Emp.: 95
Wire Drawing & Straightening Dies
N.A.I.C.S.: 333514
Gary Kantz (Dir-Sls)

TORR METALS INC.

Suite 780 1111 West Hastings Street, Vancouver, V6E 2J3, BC, Canada
Tel.: (780) 437-6624
Web Site: https://torrmetals.com
TMET—(TSXV)
Rev.: $54,274
Assets: $6,416,868
Liabilities: $39,959

Net Worth: $6,376,909
Earnings: ($19,077)
Fiscal Year-end: 04/30/24
Business Consulting Services
N.A.I.C.S.: 522299
Sean Mager (CEO)

Subsidiaries:

1306043 B.C. Ltd. (1)

TORREAL, S.A.

Fortuny 1, 28010, Madrid, Spain
Tel.: (34) 91 575 66 22   ES
Web Site: http://www.torreal.com
Year Founded: 1990
Privater Equity Firm
N.A.I.C.S.: 523999
Juan Abello Gallo (Chm)

Subsidiaries:

Aernnova Aerospace Corporation S.A. (1)
Leonardo da Vinci 13, Parque Tecnologico de Alava, 01510, Minano, Spain
Tel.: (34) 945 185 600
Web Site: http://www.aernnova.com
Rev.: $789,786,995
Fiscal Year-end: 12/31/2018
Aerostructures & Aircraft Components Designer, Mfr & Distr
N.A.I.C.S.: 336413
Juan Ignacio Gandasegui (Chm & CEO)

TORRENT CAPITAL LTD.

1969 Upper Water Street Suite 2001 Purdy's Wharf Tower II, Halifax, B3J 3R7, NS, Canada
Tel.: (902) 536-1976
Web Site: https://torrentcapital.ca
0MLA—(DEU)
Rev.: $22,260
Assets: $12,120,863
Liabilities: $287,279
Net Worth: $11,833,584
Earnings: ($4,435,613)
Fiscal Year-end: 12/31/23
Investment Services
N.A.I.C.S.: 523999
Wade Dawe (Pres & CEO)

TORRENT GOLD INC.

710-1030 W Georgia Street, Vancouver, V6E 2Y3, BC, Canada
Tel.: (208) 926-6379
Web Site: https://torrentgoldinc.com
TGLD—(DEU)
Assets: $1,807,690
Liabilities: $25,983
Net Worth: $1,781,708
Earnings: ($904,723)
Fiscal Year-end: 01/31/22
Mineral Exploration Services
N.A.I.C.S.: 213115
Alexander Kunz (Pres & CEO)

TORRENT PHARMACEUTICALS LIMITED

Torrent House Off Ashram Road, Ahmedabad, 380 009, Gujarat, India
Tel.: (91) 7926599000   In
Web Site:
    https://www.torrentpharma.com
Year Founded: 1959
500420—(BOM)
Rev.: $1,188,177,900
Assets: $1,788,128,160
Liabilities: $975,550,485
Net Worth: $812,577,675
Earnings: $106,085,070
Emp.: 13,682
Fiscal Year-end: 03/31/22
Pharmaceuticals Product Mfr
N.A.I.C.S.: 325412
Chaitanya Dutt (Dir-R&D)

AND PRIVATE COMPANIES

Subsidiaries:

Heuman Pharman GmbH & Co., Ltd. (1)
Sudwestpark 50, 90449, Nuremberg, Germany
Tel.: (49) 9 114 3020
Web Site: https://www.heumann.de
Pharmaceutical Product Mfr & Distr
N.A.I.C.S.: 325412
Ludwig Heumann (Founder)

Heunet Pharma GmbH (1)
Sudwestpark 50, 90449, Nuremberg, Germany
Tel.: (49) 9114302980
Web Site: https://www.heunet.de
Pharmaceutical Product Mfr & Distr
N.A.I.C.S.: 325412
Nirav Jhaveri (Mng Dir)

Laboratories Torrent, S.A. de C.V. (1)
Av Insurgentes Sur No 2453 Piso 8, Col Tizapan, 01090, Mexico, Mexico
Tel.: (52) 5552020856
Web Site: https://www.torrentpharma.com.mx
Pharmaceuticals Mfr
N.A.I.C.S.: 325412

Laboratorios Torrent Malaysia Sdn. Bhd. (1)
Suite E-08-08 Plaza Mont Kiara No 2 Jalan Kiara, Mont Kiara, 50480, Kuala Lumpur, Malaysia
Tel.: (60) 362011415
Pharmaceutical Product Mfr & Distr
N.A.I.C.S.: 325412

Laboratorios Torrent, S.A. de CV (1)
Av Insurgentes Sur No 2453 Floor 8, Col Tizapan, 01090, Mexico, Mexico
Tel.: (52) 555 202 0856
Web Site: https://www.torrentpharma.com.mx
Pharmaceutical Product Mfr & Distr
N.A.I.C.S.: 325412

Torrent Do Brasil Ltda. (1)
Avenida Dr Chucri Zaidan 1240 Morumbi Building Golden Tower-Tower A, 24th Floor Santo Amaro, Sao Paulo, CEP 04711-130, SP, Brazil
Tel.: (55) 1155012585
Web Site: https://www.torrent.com.br
Pharmaceutical Product Mfr & Distr
N.A.I.C.S.: 325412

Torrent Pharma (UK) Ltd. (1)
Third Floor Nexus Building 4 Gatwick Road, Crawley, RH10 9BG, United Kingdom
Tel.: (44) 1293574180
Pharmaceuticals Product Mfr
N.A.I.C.S.: 325412

Torrent Pharma Inc. (1)
Tel.: (908) 280-3333
Web Site: http://www.torrentpharma.com
Pharmaceutical Preparation Mfr
N.A.I.C.S.: 325412

Torrent Pharma Philippines Inc. (1)
Units 3 and 4 34th Floor Zuellig Building Makati Avenue Corner, Paseo de Roxas, Makati, Philippines
Tel.: (63) 28952097
Pharmaceutical Product Mfr & Distr
N.A.I.C.S.: 325412

TORRENT POWER LIMITED
Samanvay 600 Tapovan Ambawadi, Ahmedabad, 380015, Gujarat, India
Tel.: (91) 7926628000
Web Site: https://www.torrentpower.com
Year Founded: 1996
TORNTPOWER—(NSE)
Rev.: $1,680,925,155
Assets: $3,213,035,280
Liabilities: $1,817,923,380
Net Worth: $1,395,111,900
Earnings: $176,886,255
Emp.: 7,803
Fiscal Year-end: 03/31/21
Power Generation Services
N.A.I.C.S.: 221111

Sanjay Dalal (CFO)

Subsidiaries:

Dadra and Nagar Haveli and Daman and Diu Power Distribution Corporation Limited (1)
Vidhyut Bhavan 66 KV Road Near Secreteriat Amli, Silvassa, 396230, Dadra & Nagar Haveli, India
Tel.: (91) 2602406500
Web Site: https://www.dnhddpcl.in
Power Distribution Services
N.A.I.C.S.: 221122

Latur Renewable Private Limited (1)
Samanvay 600 Tapovan, Ambavadi, Ahmedabad, 380 015, Gujarat, India
Tel.: (91) 7926628000
Web Site: https://www.laturrenewable.com
Electric Power Distribution Services
N.A.I.C.S.: 221122
Pradip Mehta (Chm)

Surya Vidyut Limited (1)
6 Church Lane Ground Floor, Kolkata, 700001, India
Tel.: (91) 3322109658
Web Site: http://www.suryavidyut.in
Wind Energy Generation Services
N.A.I.C.S.: 221115

Visual Percept Solar Projects Private Limited (1)
Off National Highway No 48 Kamrej, Surat, Gujarat, 394155, India
Tel.: (91) 2621261165
Web Site: https://vpspenergy.com
Solar Power Generation Services
N.A.I.C.S.: 221114

TORSLANDA PROPERTY INVESTMENT AB
c/o AB Sagax Engelbrektsplan 1, 114 34, Stockholm, Sweden
Tel.: (46) 08 545 83 540
Web Site: http://www.torslandaproperties.com
TORSAB—(OMX)
Rev.: $27,785,408
Assets: $399,287,056
Liabilities: $227,581,536
Net Worth: $171,705,520
Earnings: $20,143,200
Fiscal Year-end: 12/31/20
Real Estate Investment
N.A.I.C.S.: 531390

TORSTAR CORPORATION
8 Spadina Avenue, Toronto, M5V 0S8, ON, Canada
Tel.: (416) 869-4010 ON
Web Site: https://www.torstar.com
Year Founded: 1967
TS.B—(TSX)
Rev.: $366,530,829
Assets: $276,335,051
Liabilities: $134,382,266
Net Worth: $141,952,785
Earnings: ($39,731,261)
Emp.: 2,380
Fiscal Year-end: 12/31/19
Holding Company; Newspaper & Book Publishing
N.A.I.C.S.: 551112
Marie E. Beyette (Gen Counsel, Sec & Sr VP)

Subsidiaries:

Metroland Media Group Ltd. (1)
10 Tempo Ave, Toronto, M2H 2N8, ON, Canada
Tel.: (905) 279-0440
Web Site: https://www.metroland.com
Newspaper Publishers
N.A.I.C.S.: 513110
Ian Oliver (Pres-Community Brands)

Group (Domestic):

Hamilton Community News (2)
333 Arvin Avenue, Stoney Creek, L8E 2M6, ON, Canada

Tel.: (905) 523-5800
Web Site: http://www.hamiltonnews.com
Sales Range: $25-49.9 Million
Emp.: 36
Newspaper Publishers
N.A.I.C.S.: 513110

Subsidiary (Domestic):

Dundas Star News Inc. (3)
333 Arvin Ave, Stoney Creek, L8E 2M6, ON, Canada (100%)
Tel.: (905) 523-5800
Web Site: http://www.dundasstarnews.com
Sales Range: $25-49.9 Million
Emp.: 30
Newspaper Publishers
N.A.I.C.S.: 513110

Unit (Domestic):

Peterborough Examiner (2)
171A Rink Street Suite 125, Peterborough, K9J 2J6, ON, Canada
Tel.: (705) 745-4641
Web Site: https://www.peterboroughexaminer.com
Daily Newspaper
N.A.I.C.S.: 513110

The St. Catharines Standard (2)
55 King Street, Saint Catharines, L2R 3H5, ON, Canada
Tel.: (905) 684-7251
Web Site: http://www.stcatharinesstandard.ca
Daily Newspaper
N.A.I.C.S.: 513110

The Hamilton Spectator (1)
211 Pritchard Road Unit 4, PO Box 300, Hamilton, L8J 0G5, ON, Canada
Tel.: (905) 575-4004
Web Site: http://www.thespec.com
Sales Range: $100-124.9 Million
Emp.: 500
Newspaper Publishing
N.A.I.C.S.: 513110
Nancy Kimmins (Controller-Bus Office)

The Record (1)
160 King St E, Kitchener, N2G 4E5, ON, Canada
Tel.: (519) 895-5687
Web Site: http://www.therecord.com
Sales Range: $50-74.9 Million
Emp.: 200
Daily Newspaper
N.A.I.C.S.: 513110
Joanne Good (Acct Exec)

Toronto Star Newspapers Ltd. (1)
8 Spadina Avenue 10th Floor, Toronto, M5V 0S8, ON, Canada (100%)
Tel.: (416) 367-2000
Web Site: http://www.thestar.com
Sales Range: $400-449.9 Million
Emp.: 800
Newspaper Publishing
N.A.I.C.S.: 513110

TORTEL COMMUNICATIONS INC.
151 N Rivermede Rd, Concord, L4K 0C4, ON, Canada
Tel.: (905) 660-9661
Web Site: http://www.tortel.ca
Emp.: 45
Telephone & Office Equipment Retailer
N.A.I.C.S.: 423420
Dominic Ogbonna (CTO)

Subsidiaries:

Tortel USA LLC (1)
221 Commerce Dr, Amherst, NY 14228
Tel.: (716) 691-5536
Sales Range: $50-74.9 Million
Emp.: 5
Telephone & Office Equipment Retailer
N.A.I.C.S.: 423420
Lakhi Singh (Mgr)

Subsidiary (Domestic):

Citel Technologies, Inc. (2)
221 Commerce Dr, Amherst, NY 14228
Tel.: (206) 957-6270

Web Site: http://www.citel.com
Sales Range: $25-49.9 Million
Emp.: 5
Voice-over-IP Telecommunications Services
N.A.I.C.S.: 517810

TORTILLA MEXICAN GRILL PLC
1st Floor Evelyn House 142 New Cavendish Street, London, W1W 6YF, United Kingdom UK
Web Site: https://www.tortilla.co.uk
Year Founded: 2007
MEX—(AIM)
Rev.: $78,338,390
Assets: $71,084,006
Liabilities: $66,208,457
Net Worth: $4,875,549
Earnings: ($866,527)
Emp.: 1,000
Fiscal Year-end: 01/01/23
Full-Service Restaurants
N.A.I.C.S.: 722511

TORUNLAR GAYRIMENKUL YATIRIM ORTAKLIGI AS
Ruzgarlibahce Mahallesi Ozalp Cikmazi No 4, Beykoz, 34805, Istanbul, Turkiye
Tel.: (90) 2164250328
Web Site: https://www.torunlarreic.com
Year Founded: 1996
TRGYO—(IST)
Rev.: $82,220,383
Assets: $1,213,286,220
Liabilities: $169,428,580
Net Worth: $1,043,857,639
Earnings: $569,452,209
Fiscal Year-end: 12/31/22
Real Estate Development Services
N.A.I.C.S.: 531390
Aziz Torun (Chm & CEO)

Subsidiaries:

Yuksel Insaat A.S. (1)
Sogutozu Cad No 14 / A-B Bestepeler, 06560, Ankara, Turkiye
Tel.: (90) 3122842545
Web Site: https://www.yuksel.net
Construction Services
N.A.I.C.S.: 236220
Emin Sazak (Chm)

TOSCANA (WA) PTY LTD.
65 Kurnall Road, Welshpool, Perth, 6106, Australia
Tel.: (61) 8 9458 6044
Private Investment Firm
N.A.I.C.S.: 523999

Subsidiaries:

Frankland River Olive Company Limited (1)
1-29 McDowell Street, Welshpool, 6106, WA, Australia
Tel.: (61) 894586044
Olive Oil Processor & Exporter
N.A.I.C.S.: 111191

TOSE CO., LTD.
Higashinotoindori Shijo Sagaru, Shimogyo-ku, Kyoto, 600-8091, Japan
Tel.: (81) 753422525
Web Site: https://www.tose.co.jp
Year Founded: 1979
4728—(TKS)
Rev.: $28,705,300
Assets: $44,951,940
Liabilities: $7,140,560
Net Worth: $37,811,380
Earnings: $1,617,200
Fiscal Year-end: 08/31/24
Software Development Services
N.A.I.C.S.: 541511
Shigeru Saito (Chm & CEO)

TOSE CO., LTD.

Tose Co., Ltd.—(Continued)

Subsidiaries:

PHONEX COMMUNICATIONS INC. (1)
A-PLACE Shibuya Kinno 7F 3-3-1 Shibuya, Shibuya-ku, Tokyo, 150-0002, Japan
Tel.: (81) 354660970
Web Site: https://www.phonex.co.jp
Software Development Services
N.A.I.C.S.: 541511

Tose Philippines, Inc. (1)
Unit 1501 EcoTower 32nd st cor 9th ave32nd St cor 9th Ave, Bonifacio Global City Metro Manila, Taguig, 1634, Philippines
Tel.: (63) 285561103
Web Site: https://www.tose.com.ph
Software Development Services
N.A.I.C.S.: 541511

Tose Software (Hangzhou) Co., Ltd. (1)
Room 2101 YuanMao Tower No 1 Wen'er xi road, Hangzhou, 310012, China
Tel.: (86) 5718 827 1880
Web Site: https://www.tose.com.cn
Software Development Services
N.A.I.C.S.: 541511

TOSE-E MELLI GROUP INVESTMENT COMPANY
No 1 Didar St Haghani Blvd, Tehran, Iran
Tel.: (98) 85598
Web Site: http://www.bmiic.ir
Investment Services
N.A.I.C.S.: 523999
Behrooz Sangani (Mgr-IT)

TOSEE MELLI INVESTMENT COMPANY
No 89 Shahid Khodami St above Vanak Square, Valiasr St after Tehran Bridge, Tehran, 1958698856, Iran
Tel.: (98) 2185549000
Web Site: http://www.tmico.ir
Year Founded: 2003
TMEL1—(THE)
Sales Range: Less than $1 Million
Investment Management Service
N.A.I.C.S.: 523150
Hossamuddin Saeedi (Deputy CEO)

TOSEI REIT INVESTMENT CORPORATION
4-5-4 Shibaura, Minato-ku, Tokyo, Japan
Tel.: (81) 354252704
Web Site: https://www.tosei-reit.co.jp
Year Founded: 2014
34510—(TKS)
Sales Range: Less than $1 Million
Real Estate Related Services
N.A.I.C.S.: 531390
Takayoshi Kitajima (Exec Dir)

TOSHIN GROUP CO., LTD.
1-3-7 Shinjuku, Shinjuku-Ku, Tokyo, 160-0022, Japan
Tel.: (81) 3 33564611
Web Site: http://www.toshingroup.co.jp
Year Founded: 1977
27610—(JAS)
Rev.: $393,279,040
Assets: $420,237,840
Liabilities: $59,928,880
Net Worth: $360,308,960
Earnings: $14,142,480
Fiscal Year-end: 05/31/21
Electrical Material & Lighting Equipment Distr
N.A.I.C.S.: 423610
Mitsuaki Kato (Pres & CEO)

TOSHIN HOLDINGS CO., LTD.
3421 Toshin Sakae Building, Naka-ku, Nagoya, 460-0008, Aichi, Japan

Tel.: (81) 522621122
Web Site: https://www.toshin-group.com
Year Founded: 1988
9444—(TKS)
Rev.: $115,086,710
Assets: $165,342,540
Liabilities: $140,693,850
Net Worth: $24,648,690
Earnings: $2,848,910
Emp.: 25
Fiscal Year-end: 04/30/24
Mobile Communication Equipment Distr
N.A.I.C.S.: 423610

TOSHKENT REPUBLIC STOCK EXCHANGE
10 Bukhara Street, Tashkent, 700187, Uzbekistan
Tel.: (998) 12360740
Web Site: http://www.uzse.uz
Year Founded: 1994
Stock Exchange Services
N.A.I.C.S.: 523210

TOSHO CO., LTD.
1-16-5 Mikawaanjocho, Anjo, 446-0056, Aichi-ken, Japan
Tel.: (81) 566793111 JP
Web Site: https://www.to-sho.net
Year Founded: 1979
8920—(TKS)
Rev.: $204,427,470
Assets: $490,587,590
Liabilities: $224,085,610
Net Worth: $266,501,980
Earnings: ($14,733,690)
Emp.: 413
Fiscal Year-end: 03/31/24
Fitness Club Center
N.A.I.C.S.: 713940
Yumiko Sakurai (Auditor)

Subsidiaries:

Tosho Asset Management Co., Ltd. (1)
Tosho Building 2F 1-16-5 Mikawaanjocho, Anjo, Aichi, Japan
Tel.: (81) 566713123
Asset Management Services
N.A.I.C.S.: 523940

TOSNET CORPORATION
1-10-1 Miyagino, Miyagino-ku, Sendai, 983-0045, Miyagi, Japan
Tel.: (81) 222995761
Web Site: https://www.tosnet.co.jp
Year Founded: 1977
4754—(TKS)
Rev.: $80,450,640
Assets: $77,882,400
Liabilities: $22,710,480
Net Worth: $55,171,920
Earnings: $6,201,360
Fiscal Year-end: 09/30/24
Security Services
N.A.I.C.S.: 561612
Yasuhiro Sato (Chm)

Subsidiaries:

EIKO Co., Ltd. (1)
6-5-15 Minamiterakatahigashidori, Moriguchi, Osaka, 570-0043, Japan
Tel.: (81) 671634575
Web Site: https://eik-o.co.jp
Emp.: 12
Security Services
N.A.I.C.S.: 561612

Mailing Japan Co., Ltd. (1)
3-3-19 Oroshimachi, Wakabayashi-ku, Sendai, 984-0015, Miyagi, Japan
Tel.: (81) 222313677
Emp.: 30
Packaging Services
N.A.I.C.S.: 488991

TOSO CO., LTD.

1-4-9 Shinkawa, Chuo-ku, Tokyo, 104-0033, Japan
Tel.: (81) 366934550
Web Site: https://www.toso.com
Year Founded: 1949
5956—(TKS)
Rev.: $142,809,050
Assets: $143,152,770
Liabilities: $47,876,230
Net Worth: $95,276,540
Earnings: $1,943,340
Emp.: 928
Fiscal Year-end: 03/31/24
Interior Decoration Product Mfr & Whslr
N.A.I.C.S.: 337920
Keiji Maekawa (Pres)

Subsidiaries:

TOSO Ryutsu Service Co., Ltd. (1)
551 Kokinu Tsukubamirai, Ibaraki, 300-2494, Japan
Tel.: (81) 297520781
Curtain Product Mfr
N.A.I.C.S.: 337920

TOSO Window Treatment (Shanghai) Co., Ltd. (1)
Floor 1 Building 3 No 1288 Zhongchun Road, Minhang Shanghai Golden Weixin Minhang Science and Technology Park, Shanghai, 201109, China
Tel.: (86) 2164795156
Emp.: 30
Window Blind Product Mfr
N.A.I.C.S.: 337920

TOSOH CORPORATION
3-8-2 Shiba, Minato-ku, Tokyo, 105-8623, Japan
Tel.: (81) 354275118 JP
Web Site: http://www.tosoh.com
Year Founded: 1935
4042—(TKS)
Rev.: $6,647,280,400
Assets: $8,526,562,890
Liabilities: $2,850,119,630
Net Worth: $5,676,443,260
Earnings: $378,911,640
Emp.: 14,394
Fiscal Year-end: 03/31/24
Mfr of Basic & Fine Chemicals, Petrochemicals & Specialty Products
N.A.I.C.S.: 325199
Toshinori Yamamoto (Pres & Exec Officer)

Subsidiaries:

Ace Pack Co., Ltd. (1)
3-62-36 Hibarigaoka, Zama, 252-0003, Kanagawa, Japan
Tel.: (81) 462552211
Web Site: https://acepack.co.jp
Emp.: 35
Polyethylene Film Mfr
N.A.I.C.S.: 326113

Asia Industry Co., Ltd. (1)
6-32-1 Machiya, Arakawa-ku, Tokyo, 116-0001, Japan
Tel.: (81) 3 895 4041
Web Site: https://www.asia-kogyo.co.jp
Emp.: 164
Synthetic Resin Mfr & Distr
N.A.I.C.S.: 325211
Takanori Nakamoto (Pres)

Delamine B.V. (1)
Stationsplein 121 Argonaut, 3818 LE, Amersfoort, Netherlands
Tel.: (31) 334224600
Web Site: https://www.delamine.com
Ethylene Amines Mfr
N.A.I.C.S.: 325199

Hokuetsu Kasei Co., Ltd. (1)
7-3-19 Imamachi, Mitsuke, 954-0111, Niigata, Japan
Tel.: (81) 258663292
Web Site: https://hokuetsukasei.com
Emp.: 127
Synthetic Resin Mfr
N.A.I.C.S.: 325211

INTERNATIONAL PUBLIC

Hyuga Unyu Co., Ltd. (1)
1-16 Funaba-cho, Hyuga, 883-0065, Miyazaki, Japan
Tel.: (81) 98 252 2148
Web Site: https://www.hyugaunyu.co.jp
Warehousing Services
N.A.I.C.S.: 493110

Izumi Sangyo Co., Ltd. (1)
10 Kisshoin Miyanonishicho, Minami-ku, Kyoto, 601-8306, Japan
Tel.: (81) 753126551
Web Site: https://www.izumi-ib.co.jp
Industrial Machinery Mfr
N.A.I.C.S.: 333248

Kansai Shipping Co., Ltd. (1)
3-11-46 Karumojimacho, Nagata-ku, Kobe, 653-0033, Hyogo, Japan
Tel.: (81) 78 652 8488
Web Site: https://www.ceres.dti.ne.jp
Warehousing Services
N.A.I.C.S.: 493110

Kasumi Kyodo Jigyo Co., Ltd. (1)
1-1 Kasumi, Yokkaichi, 510-0011, Mie, Japan
Tel.: (81) 593641161
Web Site: https://www.kkj.co.jp
Emp.: 42
Waste Water Treatment Services
N.A.I.C.S.: 221310
Kaduhisa Watanabe (Mgr)

Mabuhay Vinyl Corporation (1)
22F The Salcedo Towers 169 H V Dela Costa Street, Salcedo Village, Makati, 1227, Philippines (87.97%)
Tel.: (63) 288178971
Web Site: https://www.mvc.com.ph
Rev.: $55,498,280
Assets: $78,248,119
Liabilities: $10,896,034
Net Worth: $67,352,085
Earnings: $7,386,085
Emp.: 160
Fiscal Year-end: 12/31/2023
Caustic Soda & Hydrochloric Acid Mfr
N.A.I.C.S.: 325998
Edwin L. L. Umali (Co-Pres & Co-COO)

Nippon Polyurethane (Ruian) Co., Ltd. (1)
No 2727 Kaifaqu Dadao Economic Development Zone, Ruian, 325200, Zhejiang, China
Tel.: (86) 577 6500 1111
Web Site: http://www.npu.co.jp
Plastic Material & Resin Mfr
N.A.I.C.S.: 325211

Nippon Polyurethane Industry Co., Ltd. (1)
15F Mita NN Bldg 1-23 Shiba 4-chome, Minato-Ku, Tokyo, 108-0014, Japan
Tel.: (81) 3 5439 8600
Web Site: http://www.npu.co.jp
Rev.: $1,143,434,620
Emp.: 617
Plastic Materials & Resin Mfr
N.A.I.C.S.: 325211
O. Hamada (Pres & CEO)

P.T. Satomo Indovyl Polymer (1)
UIC Building 4th Floor JL Jend Gatot Subroto Kav 6-7, Jakarta, 12930, Indonesia
Tel.: (62) 215264618
PVC Resins Mfr & Whslr
N.A.I.C.S.: 325211

P.T. Standard Toyo Polymer (1)
Plaza Bank Index 7th Floor Jl M H Thamrin No 57, Jakarta, 10350, Indonesia (50%)
Tel.: (62) 213903132
Web Site: https://www.statomer.com
Sales Range: $25-49.9 Million
Emp.: 135
PVC Resin Mfr
N.A.I.C.S.: 325211
Toshiharu Nakagima (Pres)

Philippine Resins Industries, Inc. (1)
Mezzanine Floor BDO Towers Paseo 8741 Paseo de Roxas Bel-Air, Makati, 1209, Philippines (100%)
Tel.: (63) 2 810 4956
Web Site: https://www.prii.com.ph
Sales Range: $25-49.9 Million
Emp.: 15
PVC Resin Mfr

Plas-Tech Corporation (1)
1-1 Kasumi-no-sato, Ami-cho, Inashiki, 300-0315, Ibaraki, Japan
Tel.: (81) 298892222
Web Site: https://www.plas-tech.co.jp
Emp.: 218
Plastic Materials Mfr & Distr
N.A.I.C.S.: 326199

Rensol Co., Ltd. (1)
7-3-19 Imamachi, Mitsuke, 954111, Niigata, Japan
Tel.: (81) 258663292
Plastic Film & Sheet Mfr
N.A.I.C.S.: 322220
Yutake Takeuchi *(Mgr)*

Rinkagaku Kogyo Co., Ltd. (1)
34 Shinbori, Imizu, 934-8534, Toyama, Japan
Tel.: (81) 766862511
Web Site: https://www.rinka.co.jp
Emp.: 88
Specialty Chemicals Mfr
N.A.I.C.S.: 325998
Hajime Otsuka *(Pres)*

Sankyo Kasei Industry Corporation (1)
8-13 Shimbashicho, Fuji, 417-0004, Shizuoka, Japan
Tel.: (81) 545525731
Chemical Products & Plastic Materials Mfr
N.A.I.C.S.: 424690

TOSOH America, Inc. (1)
3600 Gantz Rd, Grove City, OH 43123-1895 **(100%)**
Tel.: (614) 539-8622
Web Site: http://www.tosohamerica.com
Sales Range: $150-199.9 Million
Emp.: 290
Holding Company
N.A.I.C.S.: 424690

Subsidiary (Domestic):

Tosoh USA, Inc. (2)
3600 Gantz Rd, Grove City, OH 43123-1895 **(100%)**
Tel.: (614) 277-4348
Web Site: http://www.tosohusa.com
Sales Range: $25-49.9 Million
Emp.: 12
Importer of Chemicals & Ceramics
N.A.I.C.S.: 424690

Subsidiary (Domestic):

TOSOH SET, Inc. (3)
3530 Bassett St, Santa Clara, CA 95054-2704
Tel.: (925) 560-6000
Web Site: http://www.tosohset.com
Sales Range: $25-49.9 Million
Mfr, Sales & Maintenance of Shielding for Use in Sputtering & Chemical/CVD Vapor Depositional Devices
N.A.I.C.S.: 332710

Tosoh Quartz, Inc. (3)
14380 NW Science Park Dr, Portland, OR 97229-5419 **(100%)**
Tel.: (503) 605-5600
Web Site: http://www.tosohquartz.com
Sales Range: $50-74.9 Million
Mfr & Sale of Glass Products & Related Components; Designs & Produces Equipment for Silica Wafer Processing Furnaces
N.A.I.C.S.: 327212

Tosoh SMD, Inc. (3)
3600 Gantz Rd, Grove City, OH 43123-1895 **(100%)**
Tel.: (614) 875-7912
Web Site: http://www.tosohsmd.com
Sales Range: $100-124.9 Million
Supplier of High Parity Film Deposition Materials
N.A.I.C.S.: 333413

Taihei (Shanghai) Co., Ltd. (1)
Room 2617 Shanghai International Trade Centre 2201 Yan An Road West, Shanghai, 200336, China
Tel.: (86) 216 278 1170
Chemical Product Mfr & Distr
N.A.I.C.S.: 325998

Taihei Chemicals Limited (1)
4-5-19 Ryoke, Kawaguchi, 332-0004, Saitama, Japan
Tel.: (81) 482221122
Web Site: https://www.taihei-chemicals.com
Sales Range: $50-74.9 Million
Emp.: 168
Chemical Products Mfr
N.A.I.C.S.: 325998
Masahide Iizuka *(Mng Dir & Sr Gen Mgr-Admin)*

Plant (Domestic):

Taihei Chemicals Limited - Kawaguchi Factory (2)
4-5-19 Ryoke, Kawaguchi, 332-0004, Japan
Tel.: (81) 482243141
Emp.: 150
Chemical Products Mfr
N.A.I.C.S.: 325998
Eisuke Kanazawa *(Dir-Auditing)*

Taihei Chemicals Limited - Souka Factory (2)
1-2-15 Aoyagi, Soka, 340-0002, Saitama, Japan
Tel.: (81) 489353141
Specialty Chemicals Mfr
N.A.I.C.S.: 325998

Taiyo Vinyl Corporation (1)
No 2 Shiba Sanchome 8F Shiba Park Shiba Park Fuji 8F, Minato-Ku, Tokyo, 105-0014, Japan
Tel.: (81) 354275441
Web Site: http://www.taiyo-vinyl.co.jp
Polyvinyl Chloride Mfr
N.A.I.C.S.: 325211
Shinhachiro Emori *(Pres)*

Plant (Domestic):

Taiyo Vinyl Corporation - Yokkaichi Plant (2)
1-8 Kasumi, Yokkaichi, 510-8540, Mie, Japan
Tel.: (81) 593646627
Sales Range: $50-74.9 Million
Emp.: 15
Polyvinyl Chloride Mfr
N.A.I.C.S.: 325211

Toho Acetylene Co., Ltd. (1)
2-3-32 Sakae, Tagajo, 985-0833, Miyagi, Japan
Tel.: (81) 223666110
Web Site: https://www.toho-ace.co.jp
Rev: $234,146,030
Assets: $222,492,600
Liabilities: $93,743,020
Net Worth: $128,749,580
Earnings: $9,353,150
Emp.: 764
Fiscal Year-end: 03/31/2024
Gas Mfr & Distr
N.A.I.C.S.: 325120

Toho Unyu Co., Ltd. (1)
145-1 Shimookata, Iwata, Shizuoka, Japan
Tel.: (81) 53 836 1018
Web Site: https://www.toho-unyu.co.jp
Freight Transportation Services
N.A.I.C.S.: 488510

Tohoku Denki Tekko Co., Ltd. (1)
Ohama No 4 No 57 1-chome, Sakata, 998-0064, Yamagata, Japan
Tel.: (81) 234 33 9111
Web Site: http://www.dtekko.co.jp
Sales Range: $25-49.9 Million
Emp.: 170
Electrical & Instrumentation Equipment Mfr
N.A.I.C.S.: 335999
Yamane Shuji *(Pres & CEO)*

Tohoku Tosoh Chemical Co., Ltd (1)
1-4-16 Ohama, Sakata, 998-0064, Yamagata, Japan **(100%)**
Tel.: (81) 234336111
Web Site: https://www.t-tosoh-chem.jp
Emp.: 152
Chemical Products Mfr
N.A.I.C.S.: 325180

Tokuyama Sekisui Co., Ltd. (1)
4560 Kaisei-cho, Shunan, 746-0006, Yamaguchi, Japan
Tel.: (81) 834630188
Web Site: https://tokuyamasekisui.co.jp

Emp.: 130
Plastic Materials & Chemical Products Mfr
N.A.I.C.S.: 325211

Tosoh (Guangzhou) Chemical Industries, Inc. (1)
No 2 Huzhen Road, Huangge Town Nansha District, Guangzhou, 511455, China
Tel.: (86) 2039911301
Web Site: https://www.tosoh-guangzhou.com
Plastic Material & Resin Mfr
N.A.I.C.S.: 325211

Tosoh (Shanghai) Co., Ltd. (1)
Room 2618A International Trade Center No 2201 Yan-An West Road, Changning, Shanghai, 200336, China
Tel.: (86) 2162702810
Web Site: http://www.tosoh.com
Sales Range: $25-49.9 Million
Emp.: 50
Plastic Material & Chemical Product Mfr
N.A.I.C.S.: 325211

Tosoh Analysis and Research Center Co., Ltd. (1)
Chugoku, Yamaguchi, 746-0006, Japan
Tel.: (81) 834639603
Web Site: https://www.tosoh-arc.co.jp
Emp.: 130
Chemical Products Research & Development Services
N.A.I.C.S.: 541715

Tosoh Asia Pte. Ltd. (1)
9 Battery Road 11-01 MYP Centre, Singapore, 049910, Singapore **(100%)**
Tel.: (65) 62265106
Web Site: https://www.tosohasia.com
Sales Range: $50-74.9 Million
Emp.: 19
Chemicals Mfr
N.A.I.C.S.: 325998

Tosoh Bioscience GmbH (1)
Im Leuschnerpark 4, 64347, Griesheim, Germany
Tel.: (49) 61557043700
Web Site: http://www.tosohbioscience.com
Sales Range: $25-49.9 Million
Emp.: 25
Biological Product Mfr
N.A.I.C.S.: 325414
Michael Marquardt *(Sr Mgr-Sls-EMEA)*

Subsidiary (US):

Tosoh Bioscience LLC (2)
3604 Horizon Dr Ste 100, King of Prussia, PA 19406 **(100%)**
Tel.: (484) 805-1219
Web Site: http://www.separations.tosohscience.com
Sales Range: $25-49.9 Million
Markets Process-Scale & Laboratory-Scale Liquid Chromatography Products
N.A.I.C.S.: 541613

Subsidiary (Domestic):

Tosoh Bioscience, Inc. (3)
6000 Shoreline Ct Ste 101, South San Francisco, CA 94080-1948 **(100%)**
Tel.: (650) 615-4970
Web Site: http://www.diagnostics.tosohscience.com
Sales Range: $50-74.9 Million
Emp.: 19
Sale & Marketing of Diagnostic Systems & Reagents
N.A.I.C.S.: 423450

Subsidiary (Non-US):

Tosoh Bioscience Ltd. (2)
100 Longwater Avenue Green Park, Reading, RG2 6GP, Berkshire, United Kingdom **(100%)**
Tel.: (44) 1527592901
Web Site: http://www.tosohbioscience.com
Sales Range: $50-74.9 Million
Emp.: 12
Chemicals Mfr
N.A.I.C.S.: 325998

Tosoh Bioscience N.V. (2)
Transportstraat 4, 3980, Tessenderlo, Belgium **(100%)**
Tel.: (32) 13668830

Web Site: https://www.diagnostics.tosohscience.com
Sales Range: $25-49.9 Million
Emp.: 50
Markets Clinical Diagnostic Systems & Related Products
N.A.I.C.S.: 423450
Masanobu Kasai *(Gen Mgr)*

Tosoh Bioscience S.A. (2)
Industriestrasse 12, 6210, Sursée, Switzerland
Tel.: (41) 800554188
Web Site: http://www.tosoh.com
Emp.: 1
Chemicals Mfr
N.A.I.C.S.: 325998

Tosoh Bioscience SRL (2)
Via Chivasso 15a, Cascine Vica, 10098, Rivoli, TO, Italy
Tel.: (39) 0119519453
Web Site: http://www.tosohbioscience.com
Surgical & Medical Instrument Mfr
N.A.I.C.S.: 339112

Tosoh Bioscience Shanghai Co., Ltd. (2)
Room 1001 Kaike International Building Area A No 1801 Hongmei Road, Xuhui District, Shanghai, 200233, China
Tel.: (86) 2134610856
Web Site: https://www.diagnostics.tosohscience.com
Sales Range: $25-49.9 Million
Emp.: 20
Surgical & Medical Instrument Mfr
N.A.I.C.S.: 339112

Tosoh Bioscience, A.G. (2)
Fanghofli 14, Littau, 6014, Lucerne, Switzerland
Tel.: (41) 2504480
Emp.: 1
Biological Product Mfr
N.A.I.C.S.: 325414

Subsidiary (Domestic):

Tosoh Biosep GmbH (2)
Im Leuschnerpark 4, 464347, Griesheim, Germany **(100%)**
Tel.: (49) 61557043700
Web Site: https://www.separations.tosohscience.com
Sales Range: $25-49.9 Million
Emp.: 16
Mfr of Process-Scales & Laboratory-Scales
N.A.I.C.S.: 332216

Tosoh Bioscience Wisconsin, Inc. (1)
601 Science Dr, Madison, WI 53711
Tel.: (608) 441-8009
Web Site: https://www.sembabio.com
Chromatographic Instruments Mfr
N.A.I.C.S.: 334516

Tosoh Ceramics Co., Ltd. (1)
2 Iwasekoshi-machi, Toyama, 931-8371, Japan
Tel.: (81) 764374551
Web Site: https://www.tosoh-ceramics.co.jp
Emp.: 80
Ceramic Tile Mfr
N.A.I.C.S.: 327120

Tosoh Corporation (1)
4560 Kaisei Cho, Shunan, Yamaguchi, 746 8501, Japan **(100%)**
Tel.: (81) 834639800
Sales Range: $300-349.9 Million
Emp.: 1,000
N.A.I.C.S.: 325998
Komura Minoru *(Mgr)*

Tosoh Corporation (1)
Sendai Green Place 2F 1-11-1, Aoba Ku Honmachi, Sendai, 980-0014, Miyagi, Japan **(100%)**
Tel.: (81) 222662341
Web Site: http://www.tosoh.com
Regional Sales
N.A.I.C.S.: 325998

Tosoh Corporation (1)
1-8 Kasumi, Yokkaichi, 510-8540, Mie, Japan **(100%)**
Tel.: (81) 593641111
Web Site: http://www.tosoh.com

TOSOH CORPORATION

Tosoh Corporation—(Continued)
Sales Range: $300-349.9 Million
Emp.: 900
Chemical Production
N.A.I.C.S.: 325998

Tosoh Corporation - Fukuoka Regional Office (1)
Kogin Building 1-13-2 Tenjin, Chuo-ku, Fukuoka, 810-0001, Japan
Tel.: (81) 927810481
Web Site: http://www.tosoh.com
Chemical Products Mfr
N.A.I.C.S.: 325998

Tosoh Corporation - Osaka Regional Office (1)
4-4-9 Kouraibashi, Chuo-ku, Osaka, 541-0043, Japan
Tel.: (81) 662091901
Web Site: http://www.tosoh.com
Chemical Mfr & Distr
N.A.I.C.S.: 325998

Tosoh Europe B.V. (1)
Rembrandt Tower Amstelplein 1, 1096 HA, Amsterdam, Netherlands (100%)
Tel.: (31) 205650010
Web Site: https://www.tosoheurope.com
Sales Range: $25-49.9 Million
Emp.: 17
Marketing & Business Development
N.A.I.C.S.: 541720
Kazutoyo Kawahara (Mng Dir)

Tosoh Europe N.V. (1)
Transportstraat 4, 3980, Tessenderlo, Belgium (100%)
Tel.: (32) 13668830
Web Site:
https://www.diagnostics.tosohscience.com
Sales Range: $50-74.9 Million
Emp.: 50
Mfr of Reagents
N.A.I.C.S.: 424210
Kasai Masanobu (Mng Dir)

Tosoh F-TECH, Inc. (1)
Shiba-koen First Building 3-8-2 Shiba, Minato-ku, Tokyo, 105-0014, Japan
Tel.: (81) 3 5427 5490
Web Site: http://www.f-techinc.co.jp
Sales Range: $25-49.9 Million
Emp.: 100
Specialty Chemicals Mfr
N.A.I.C.S.: 325998

Plant (Domestic):

Tosoh F-TECH, Inc. - Nanyo Plant (2)
4988 Kaisei-cho, Shunan, 746-0022, Yamaguchi, Japan
Tel.: (81) 834 62 1301
Web Site: http://www.f-techinc.co.jp
Emp.: 100
Specialty Chemicals Mfr
N.A.I.C.S.: 325998
Abe Yoshiko (Gen Mgr)

Tosoh Finechem Corporation (1)
4988 Kaiseicho, Shunan, Yamaguchi, Japan
Tel.: (81) 834623718
Web Site: https://tosoh-finechem.co.jp
Sales Range: $50-74.9 Million
Emp.: 150
Specialty Chemicals Mfr
N.A.I.C.S.: 325998

Tosoh Hellas A.I.C. (1)
Sindos, 57022, Thessaloniki, Greece (65%)
Tel.: (30) 2310717800
Web Site: http://www.tosoh-hellas.gr
Sales Range: $25-49.9 Million
Emp.: 100
Electrolytic Manganese Dioxide Mfr
N.A.I.C.S.: 325998
Efi Pavlidou (Environment & Customer Svc)

Tosoh Hyuga Corporation (1)
1 Funabacho, Hyuga, 883-0065, Miyazaki, Japan
Tel.: (81) 982525351
Web Site: https://tosoh-hyuga.co.jp
Emp.: 89
Chemical Products Mfr
N.A.I.C.S.: 325998

Tosoh India Pvt. Ltd. (1)
E 302 Lotus Corporate Park, Graham Fifth Compound Western Express Highway Goregaon East, Mumbai, 400 063, India
Tel.: (91) 226 148 5200
Web Site: https://www.tosohindia.com
Chemical Product Mfr & Distr
N.A.I.C.S.: 325998

Tosoh Information Systems Corporation (1)
Shiba Park ND Building 2-5-10 Shiba, Minato-Ku, Tokyo, 105-0014, Japan (100%)
Tel.: (81) 354465541
Web Site: http://www.tosis.co.jp
Information Technology Consulting Services
N.A.I.C.S.: 541512
Shigeki Hattori (Pres)

Tosoh Kasumi Engi Inc. (1)
1-1-1 Kasumi, Yokkaichi, 510-0011, Mie, Japan
Tel.: (81) 59 364 8373
Web Site: https://www.kec.tosoh.gr.jp
Instrumentation Equipment Distr
N.A.I.C.S.: 423490

Tosoh Logistics Corporation (1)
1-23-15 Nomura, Shunan, 746-0022, Yamaguchi, Japan
Tel.: (81) 834630077
Logistics Consulting Servies
N.A.I.C.S.: 541614

Subsidiary (Non-US):

Tosoh Logistics Warehouse Co., Ltd. (2)
South of Xiao Hu Road Xiaohu Island, Huangge Town Nansha District, Guangzhou, 511455, Guangdong, China
Tel.: (86) 2039911339
General Warehousing & Storage Services
N.A.I.C.S.: 493110
Suetake Kazuhiro (Gen Mgr)

Tosoh Organic Chemical Co., Ltd. (1)
4988 Kaisei-cho, Shunan, 746-0006, Yamaguchi, Japan
Tel.: (81) 834 62 1455
Web Site: http://www.tosoh-organic.co.jp
Sales Range: $25-49.9 Million
Emp.: 90
Specialty Chemicals Mfr
N.A.I.C.S.: 325998
Masanobu Okamura (Mgr-Sls)

Tosoh Polyvin Corporation (1)
Special Economic Zone LIMA Technology Center, Lipa City, Batangas, 4217, Philippines
Tel.: (63) 439813002
Sales Range: $75-99.9 Million
Mfr & Sales of PVC Compounds; JV with Plas-Tech Corporation
N.A.I.C.S.: 325998

Tosoh Quartz Co., Ltd. (1)
No 92 Da-Soong 7th Road Tainan-Science-Based Industrial Park, Hsin-She Shing, Tainan City, Taiwan (100%)
Tel.: (886) 65050860
Web Site: http://www.tqt.com.tw
Sales Range: $50-74.9 Million
Emp.: 846
Chemicals Mfr
N.A.I.C.S.: 325998

Tosoh Quartz Co., Ltd. (1)
92 Da-Soong 7th Road Tainan Science Park, Xinshi, T'ainan, Taiwan
Tel.: (886) 65050860
Emp.: 880
Semiconductor Quartz Mfr & Distr
N.A.I.C.S.: 334419

Tosoh Quartz, Ltd. (1)
Unit 2 Greencroft Industrial Park, Stanley, DH9 7YB, Co Durham, United Kingdom (99.99%)
Tel.: (44) 1207524400
Web Site: http://www.tosohquartz.com
Sales Range: $25-49.9 Million
Emp.: 25
Mfr of Quartzwave
N.A.I.C.S.: 425120

Tosoh SGM Corporation (1)
4555 Kaisei-cho, Shunan, 746-0006, Yamaguchi, Japan
Tel.: (81) 834622830
Web Site: https://tosoh-sgm.jp
Glass Products Mfr
N.A.I.C.S.: 327215

Tosoh SMD Korea, Ltd. (1)
163 Sandan-ro 121 Beon-gil, Pyeongtaek, 17744, Gyeonggi-do, Korea (South) (49%)
Tel.: (82) 316690200
Web Site: http://www.tosohsmd.com
Sales Range: $25-49.9 Million
Emp.: 24
Supplier of High Parity Film Deposition Materials
N.A.I.C.S.: 333310

Tosoh SMD Taiwan, Ltd. (1)
4F-1 No 29 Pu-Ding Road, Hsin-chu, 300, Taiwan (100%)
Tel.: (886) 35775768
Web Site: http://www.tosohsmd.com
Sales Range: $25-49.9 Million
Emp.: 12
Sales of Chemical Products
N.A.I.C.S.: 424690

Tosoh Silica Corporation (1)
4560 Kaisei-cho, Shunan, 746-0006, Yamaguchi, Japan
Tel.: (81) 834623590
Web Site: https://www.n-silica.co.jp
Emp.: 100
Rubber & Plastic Silica Filler Mfr
N.A.I.C.S.: 326299

Tosoh Speciality Materials Corporation (1)
2-1-6 Zao Matsugaoka, Yamagata, 990-2338, Japan
Tel.: (81) 236890150
Electronic Components Mfr
N.A.I.C.S.: 334419

Tosoh Specialty Chemicals USA, Inc. (1)
1720 Windward Concourse Ste 125, Alpharetta, GA 30005
Tel.: (770) 442-9501
Web Site: http://www.tosohscu.com
Chemical Product Mfr & Distr
N.A.I.C.S.: 325998

Tosoh Techno-System, Inc. (1)
2-5-10 Shiba, Minato-ku, Tokyo, 105-0014, Japan
Tel.: (81) 35 446 1110
Web Site: https://www.tosoh-technosystem.co.jp
Diagnostic Equipment Installation Services
N.A.I.C.S.: 811210

Toyo Polymer Co., Ltd. (1)
5-5-17 Miyahara, Yodogawa-ku, Osaka, 532-0003, Niigata, Japan
Tel.: (81) 663978015
Web Site: https://toyopolymer.co.jp
Plastic Film & Sheet Mfr
N.A.I.C.S.: 326113

Yamaguchi Koun Corporation (1)
3-2 Rinkai-cho, Shunan, 746-0019, Yamaguchi, Japan
Tel.: (81) 83 463 3313
Warehousing Services
N.A.I.C.S.: 493110

TOSRIFA INDUSTRIES LTD.
No 4/2 A Plot 49 & 57 135 Gopalpur Munnu Nagar, Tongi, Gazipur, 1213, Bangladesh
Tel.: (880) 2224410051
Web Site: http://www.til.com.bd
Year Founded: 2002
TOSRIFA—(CHT)
Rev.: $34,882,994
Assets: $51,093,356
Liabilities: $28,510,233
Net Worth: $22,583,123
Earnings: $496,214
Emp.: 3,738
Fiscal Year-end: 06/30/21
Knit Garment Product Mfr
N.A.I.C.S.: 315990
Rafiq Hassan (Chm)

INTERNATIONAL PUBLIC

TOT BIOPHARM INTERNATIONAL COMPANY LIMITED
No 120 changyang Street, Suzhou Industrial Park, Suzhou, Jiangsu, China
Tel.: (86) 51262965186   HK
Web Site:
https://www.totbiopharm.com
Year Founded: 2009
1875—(HKG)
Rev.: $62,081,791
Assets: $177,189,152
Liabilities: $76,741,517
Net Worth: $100,447,636
Earnings: ($7,026,458)
Emp.: 431
Fiscal Year-end: 12/31/22
Pharmaceutical Product Mfr & Distr
N.A.I.C.S.: 325412
Ming Liu (Chief Medical Officer & Deputy Gen Mgr)

TOT PUBLIC COMPANY LIMITED
89/2 Moo 3 Chaeng Watthana Road, Thungsong-Hong Laksi, Bangkok, 10210, Thailand
Tel.: (66) 22400701
Web Site: http://www.tot.co.th
Year Founded: 1954
Sales Range: $1-4.9 Billion
Emp.: 48
Telecommunication Servicesb
N.A.I.C.S.: 517112
Montchai Noosong (Pres)

TOTAL ENERGY SERVICES INC.
Suite 1000 734 - 7th Ave SW, Calgary, T2P 3P8, AB, Canada
Tel.: (403) 216-3939   BC
Web Site: https://www.totalenergy.ca
Year Founded: 1997
TOT—(TSX)
Rev.: $286,118,910
Assets: $664,608,660
Liabilities: $264,873,750
Net Worth: $399,734,910
Earnings: ($23,824,337)
Emp.: 1,976
Fiscal Year-end: 12/31/20
Oil & Natural Gas Drilling & Production Services
N.A.I.C.S.: 213112
Bruce Pachkowski (Chm)

Subsidiaries:

Bidell Equipment LP (1)
6900-112 Avenue SE, Calgary, T2C 4Z1, AB, Canada
Tel.: (403) 235-5877
Web Site: https://bidell.com
Sales Range: $50-74.9 Million
Emp.: 150
Gas Compressors Suppliers
N.A.I.C.S.: 333912
Sean Ulmer (Pres)

Bidell Gas Compression Inc. (1)
1400 Main St, Weirton, WV 26062
Tel.: (610) 764-1232
Natural Gas Compressor Mfr & Distr
N.A.I.C.S.: 333912

Chinook Drilling (1)
2550 300 5th Ave SW, Calgary, T2P 3C4, AB, Canada
Tel.: (403) 269-2612
Web Site: http://www.chinookdrilling.ca
Sales Range: $50-74.9 Million
Emp.: 15
Drilling Services
N.A.I.C.S.: 213111

Opsco Process Corp. (1)
285175 Kleysen Way, Rocky View, T1X 0K1, AB, Canada
Tel.: (403) 723-3400
Web Site: https://opsco.ca
Pressure Vessel Mfr & Distr

AND PRIVATE COMPANIES

N.A.I.C.S.: 334513

Savanna Drilling LLC (1)
1500 Windway St, Odessa, TX 79761
Tel.: (432) 614-1055
Drilling Rig Services
N.A.I.C.S.: 213111

Savanna Energy Services Corp. (1)
Suite 800 311-6th Avenue SW, Calgary, T2P 3H2, AB, Canada
Tel.: (403) 503-9990
Web Site: http://www.savannaenergy.com
Sales Range: $200-249.9 Million
Oil Field Services
N.A.I.C.S.: 213112

Subsidiary (Domestic):

Savanna Well Servicing Inc. (2)
311 6th Avenue Southwest Suite 800, Calgary, T2P 3H2, AB, Canada
Tel.: (403) 503-9990
Web Site: http://www.savannaenergy.com
Oil Well Support Services
N.A.I.C.S.: 213112

Subsidiary (US):

Savanna Well Servicing Corp. (3)
3056 Hwy 22 N, Dickinson, ND 58601
Tel.: (701) 483-5488
Oil Well Support Services
N.A.I.C.S.: 213112

Savanna Energy Services Pty. Ltd. (1)
339 Anzac Avenue, Toowoomba, 4350, QLD, Australia
Tel.: (61) 74 633 6700
Drilling Rig Services
N.A.I.C.S.: 213111

TES Services Inc. (1)
600 Railhead Rd Ste 200, Fort Worth, TX 76106
Tel.: (817) 625-6100
Web Site: https://www.tesservice.com
Semiconductor Component Mfr & Distr
N.A.I.C.S.: 334413

Total Oilfield Rentals (1)
800 311 - 6th Avenue SW, Calgary, T2P 3H2, AB, Canada
Tel.: (403) 698-8448
Web Site: http://www.totaloilfield.ca
Oil Drilling Equipment Rental Services
N.A.I.C.S.: 213111

Total Oilfield Rentals Inc. (1)
6850 W Yellowstone Hwy, Casper, WY 82604
Drilling Oil Gas Services
N.A.I.C.S.: 213111

TOTAL HELIUM LTD.
Suite 3123 595 Burrard Street, PO Box 49139, Vancouver, V7X 1J1, BC, Canada
Tel.: (604) 609-6110   BC
Web Site: https://www.totalhelium.com
Year Founded: 2006
TTLHF—(OTCIQ)
Rev.: $10,411
Assets: $11,296,684
Liabilities: $2,162,117
Net Worth: $9,134,567
Earnings: ($2,848,535)
Fiscal Year-end: 03/31/22
Industrial Gas Mfr
N.A.I.C.S.: 325120
Robert B. Price (CEO)

TOTAL HOSPITALITY LTD.
1004 Tower B 10th Floor Millenium Plaza Sushant Lok Sector 27, Near Huda City Center Metro Station, Gurgaon, 122002, India
Tel.: (91) 124 6541514
Web Site:
 http://www.totalhospitality.in
Assets: $565,991
Liabilities: $107,888
Net Worth: $458,103
Earnings: ($57,009)

Fiscal Year-end: 03/31/17
Home Management Services
N.A.I.C.S.: 721110
Divya Seengal (Mng Dir)

Subsidiaries:

SKD Restaurants Pvt. Ltd. (1)
S C O 5-6-7 Sector - 15 Part - II, Gurgaon, 122001, Haryana, India
Tel.: (91) 124 4276040
Web Site: http://www.skdrestaurants.com
Hotel Operator
N.A.I.C.S.: 721110
Sanjay Nagar (Mgr-Restaurant)

TOTAL MEDIA GROUP LTD.
125 Kensington High Street, London, W8 5SF, United Kingdom
Tel.: (44) 2079373793   UK
Web Site:
 http://www.totalmedia.co.uk
Year Founded: 1982
Sales Range: $50-74.9 Million
Media Buying Services, New Product Development, Planning & Consultation
N.A.I.C.S.: 541830
Mike Sell (Chm)

Subsidiaries:

Total Media Direct (1)
125 Kensington High St, London, W8 5SF, United Kingdom
Tel.: (44) 20 7361 0909
Web Site: http://www.totalmedia.co.uk
Emp.: 63
N.A.I.C.S.: 541870
Lucas Brown (Mng Dir)

Total Media North (1)
Unit 5 The Courtyard Nunhold Farm Business Centre, Dark Lane, Warwick, CV35 8XB, Hatton, United Kingdom
Tel.: (44) 1564 741 700
Web Site: http://www.totalmedia.co.uk
Emp.: 5
N.A.I.C.S.: 541810
Barry Took (Mng Dir)

Total Production Line (TPL) (1)
125 Kensington High St, London, W8 5SF, United Kingdom
Tel.: (44) 20 7361 0900
Web Site: http://www.totalmedia.co.uk
Sales Range: $10-24.9 Million
Emp.: 2
N.A.I.C.S.: 541810
David Proud (Mng Dir)

TOTAL SOFT BANK LTD.
66-39 Bansong-ro 513beon-gil, Haeundae-gu, Busan, 48002, Korea (South)
Tel.: (82) 7047331000
Web Site: https://www.tsb.co.kr
Year Founded: 1988
045340—(KRS)
Rev.: $10,644,139
Assets: $22,025,860
Liabilities: $7,592,896
Net Worth: $14,432,964
Earnings: $2,026,578
Emp.: 109
Fiscal Year-end: 12/31/22
Software Mfr & Distr
N.A.I.C.S.: 541511
J. S. Choi (Chm & CEO)

TOTAL SYSTEMS PLC
394 City Rd, London, EC1V 2QA, United Kingdom
Tel.: (44) 2072944888
Web Site:
 http://www.totalsystems.co.uk
Sales Range: $1-9.9 Million
Emp.: 56
Software for Insurance & Financial Companies
N.A.I.C.S.: 513210
Terrence P. Bourne (Chm & Mng Dir)

TOTAL TELCOM INC.
540 - 1632 Dickson Ave, Kelowna, V1Y 7T2, BC, Canada
Tel.: (250) 860-3762   AB
Web Site:
 https://www.totaltelcom.com
Year Founded: 1999
TTLTF—(OTCIQ)
Rev.: $1,440,864
Assets: $4,042,335
Liabilities: $466,454
Net Worth: $3,575,881
Earnings: $213,124
Fiscal Year-end: 06/30/24
Designs, Constructs & Operates Fiber Optic Cable Networks
N.A.I.C.S.: 517112
Lawrence R. Cunningham (Sec)

Subsidiaries:

ROM Communications, Inc. (1)
540 - 1632 Dickson Ave, Kelowna, V1Y 7T2, BC, Canada
Tel.: (250) 860-3762
Web Site: https://www.romcomm.com
Internet Technology Focused on Wireless Monitoring, Tracking, Remote Control, Data Retrieval & Asset Management Solutions
N.A.I.C.S.: 517810

TOTAL TRANSPORT SYSTEMS LIMITED
7th Floor T Square Opposite Chandivali Petrol Pump Saki-Vihar Road, Sakinaka Andheri East, Mumbai, 400072, Maharashtra, India
Tel.: (91) 2266441500
Web Site: https://www.ttspl.in
Year Founded: 1994
TOTAL—(NSE)
Rev.: $70,823,548
Assets: $14,974,246
Liabilities: $5,666,483
Net Worth: $9,307,763
Earnings: $628,272
Emp.: 352
Fiscal Year-end: 03/31/23
Freight Transportation Services
N.A.I.C.S.: 488510
Makrand Prabhakar Pradhan (Mng Dir)

TOTALBANKEN A/S
Bredgade 95, 5560, Arup, Denmark
Tel.: (45) 6 345 7000
Web Site: http://www.totalbanken.dk
TOTA—(OMX)
Rev.: $28,210,463
Assets: $637,449,168
Liabilities: $556,454,271
Net Worth: $80,994,897
Earnings: $6,548,327
Emp.: 88
Fiscal Year-end: 12/31/20
Banking Services
N.A.I.C.S.: 522110

TOTALENERGIES MARKETING MAROC S.A.
146 Boulevard Zerktouni, 20000, Casablanca, Morocco
Tel.: (212) 801000023
Web Site: https://www.totalenergies.ma
Year Founded: 1927
TMA—(CAS)
Sales Range: Less than $1 Million
Oil & Gas Distribution Services
N.A.I.C.S.: 221210
Olivier Chalvon-Demersay (Chm)

TOTALENERGIES SE
Tour Coupole - 2 place Jean Millier, 92078, Paris, La Defense, France
Tel.: (33) 147444546   FR
Web Site: https://totalenergies.com
Year Founded: 1924

TOTALENERGIES SE

TTE—(NYSE)
Rev.: $237,128,000,000
Assets: $283,654,000,000
Liabilities: $164,201,000,000
Net Worth: $119,453,000,000
Earnings: $21,510,000,000
Emp.: 102,579
Fiscal Year-end: 12/31/23
Oil & Gas Distribution Services
N.A.I.C.S.: 221210
Laurent Wolffsheim (Sr VP-People, Strategy, and Growth)

Subsidiaries:

AS24 (1)
1 boulevard du Zenith, BP 90272, 44800, Saint-Herblain, France
Tel.: (33) 240922424
Web Site: https://www.as24.com
Petroleum & Lubricant Distr
N.A.I.C.S.: 424720
Daude Lagrave (VP-Compensation & Benefits)

AS24 Belgie N.V. (1)
Boulevard Anspach 1-Bte 2, 1000, Brussels, Belgium
Tel.: (32) 22742780
Oil & Gas Exploration Services
N.A.I.C.S.: 213112
Scheirman Jean (Mng Dir)

AS24 Espanola S.A. (1)
c/ Valencia 307 4e planta, 08009, Barcelona, Spain
Tel.: (34) 934593686
Oil & Gas Exploration Services
N.A.I.C.S.: 213112
Jose Luis Ramos Rodriguez (Dir Gen)

AS24 Fuel Cards Limited (1)
11-19 Station Road, Watford, WD17 1AP, United Kingdom
Tel.: (44) 1923801060
Oil & Gas Exploration Services
N.A.I.C.S.: 213112
Orlando Roach (Mgr-Cards Sls)

AS24 Polska SP Z O.O. (1)
Al Janan Pawla II 80 / 12 A, 00-175, Warsaw, Poland
Tel.: (48) 223318080
Oil & Gas Exploration Services
N.A.I.C.S.: 213112
Vincent Gales (Officer-Digital Mktg)

Air Total International SA (1)
24 Cours Michelet, 92069, Paris, France
Tel.: (33) 141354000
Web Site: http://www.total.com
Aviation Fuel & Lubricant Distr
N.A.I.C.S.: 424720

BioQuercy S.A.S. (1)
ZI Le Perie, 46500, Gramat, France
Tel.: (33) 553779744
Web Site: https://www.bioquercy.fr
Biogas Mfr & Distr
N.A.I.C.S.: 325120

BlueCharge Pte. Ltd. (1)
16 Science Park Drive 04-01 DNV GL Technology Centre, Singapore, 118227, Singapore
Tel.: (65) 97383985
Web Site: https://www.bluecharge.sg
Electric Vehicle Charging Services
N.A.I.C.S.: 238210

Bostik Holding S.A. (1)
2 Place Jean Millier, 92 400, Courbevoie, France
Tel.: (33) 147445649
Investment Management Service
N.A.I.C.S.: 523999

Core Solar, LLC (1)
1221 S MoPac Expy Ste 225, Austin, TX 78746
Tel.: (512) 684-1995
Web Site: https://www.coresolarllc.com
Solar Product Development & Installation Services
N.A.I.C.S.: 221114

Egedis SAS (1)
21 rue Frederic Mistral, 38400, Saint-Martin-d'Heres, France
Tel.: (33) 476445281

TOTALENERGIES SE

TotalEnergies SE—(Continued)
Web Site: http://www.egedis.com
Oil & Gas Exploration Services
N.A.I.C.S.: 213112

Fioulmarket.fr SAS (1)
8 rue Eugene et Armand Peugeot Immeuble Ampere - Bat B, CS 60104, 92566, Rueil-Malmaison, Cedex, France
Tel.: (33) 972722021
Web Site: http://www.fioulmarket.fr
Oil & Gas Exploration Services
N.A.I.C.S.: 213112
Christophe Doussoux *(CEO)*

Gasket (Suzhou) Valve Components Company, Limited (1)
No 6 Building No 88 East Jin Ling Road, Jinling Industrial Park Weiting Town of Suzhou Industrial Park, Suzhou, China
Tel.: (86) 51287770862
Web Site: https://www.gasketsuzhou.cn
Industrial Valve Component Mfr
N.A.I.C.S.: 332911
Simone Ventura *(Gen Mgr)*

Greenflex Actirent Group, S.L. (1)
C/Aragon 208, 08011, Barcelona, Spain
Tel.: (34) 932181183
Web Site: http://www.greenflex.com
Renewable Energy Services
N.A.I.C.S.: 221118

Greenflex S.A.S. (1)
7-11 boulevard Haussmann, 75009, Paris, France
Tel.: (33) 140221460
Renewable Energy Services
N.A.I.C.S.: 221118
Sandra Thevenaz *(Dir-Publication)*

HBA Hutchinson Brasil Automotive Ltda. (1)
Estrada do Barreiro S/N, Caixa Postal 141, Distrito Industrial 1 Extrema, Gerais, 37640, Brazil
Tel.: (55) 3534359214
Rubber & Plastic Belting Product Mfr
N.A.I.C.S.: 326220

Hetty SAS (1)
2 bis rue Louis Armand, 75015, Paris, France
Tel.: (33) 518070190
Web Site: http://www.hetty.fr
Investment Services
N.A.I.C.S.: 523999

Hutchinson (Wuhan) Automotive Rubber Products Company Limited (1)
Economic and Technological Development Zone Zhuan Yang Avenue n 5, Wuhan, 430056, China
Tel.: (86) 2759805888
Automobile Parts Mfr
N.A.I.C.S.: 336390
David Liu *(Fin Mgr)*

Hutchinson Corporation (1)
460 Fuller Ave NE, Grand Rapids, MI 49503-1912
Tel.: (616) 459-4541
Rubber Products Mfr
N.A.I.C.S.: 326299

Hutchinson GmbH (1)
Hansastrasse 66, 68169, Mannheim, Germany
Tel.: (49) 62139710
Rubber & Plastic Belting Product Mfr
N.A.I.C.S.: 326220
Michael Klein *(Mng Dir)*

Hutchinson Industrial Rubber Products (Suzhou) Company, Limited (1)
No 6 Linbu Street, Weiting Town Suzhou Industrial Park, Jiangsu, 215121, China
Tel.: (86) 51285188298
Rubber & Plastic Belting Product Mfr
N.A.I.C.S.: 326220
Ning Song *(Gen Mgr)*

Hutchinson Japan Company Limited (1)
NSS-II Building 4th floor, Minato-ku, Tokyo, 108-0075, Japan
Tel.: (81) 367118080
Rubber & Plastic Belting Product Mfr
N.A.I.C.S.: 326220

Hutchinson Korea Limited (1)
180-6 Bangi-2dong, Songpa-gu, 138-830, Seoul, 057-86, Korea (South)
Tel.: (82) 24252600
Rubber & Plastic Belting Product Mfr
N.A.I.C.S.: 326220

Hutchinson Poland SP ZO.O. (1)
Ul Kurczaki 130, 93-331, Lodz, Poland
Tel.: (48) 426893098
Rubber & Plastic Belting Product Mfr
N.A.I.C.S.: 326220
Michal Blonski *(Production Mgr)*

Hutchinson Porto Lda. (1)
R D Afonso Henriques n 153, Gandra, 4585-237, Parede, Portugal
Tel.: (351) 224119500
Rubber & Plastic Belting Product Mfr
N.A.I.C.S.: 326220
Jorge Pocas *(Project Mgr)*

Hutchinson S.A. (1)
2 Rue Balzac, 75008, Paris, France
Tel.: (33) 40748300
Web Site: http://www.hutchinson.com
Rev.: $3,870,108,200
Emp.: 27,474
Rubber Products Processing & Mfr
N.A.I.C.S.: 326299

Subsidiary (Non-US):

Atotech Deutschland GmbH (2)
Erasmusstrasse 20, 10553, Berlin, Germany (100%)
Tel.: (49) 30349850
Sales Range: $600-649.9 Million
Emp.: 360
Mfr of Production Systems & Equipment for Electroplating, Semiconductor & Printed Circuit Board Manufacturing
N.A.I.C.S.: 332813
Geoffrey Wild *(Co-CEO)*

Subsidiary (Non-US):

Atotech (Malaysia) Sdn Bhd (3)
Tingkat 4B-2 Wisma Fiamma No 20 Jalan 7A/62A Bandar Manjalara, 52200, Kuala Lumpur, Malaysia
Tel.: (60) 362725966
Web Site: http://www.atotech.com
Sales Range: $25-49.9 Million
Emp.: 40
Specialty Chemicals Distr
N.A.I.C.S.: 424690

Atotech (Thailand) Co., Ltd. (3)
11th Floor 1 TP&T Tower Soi 19 Vibhavadee Rungsit Road, Chatuchak, Bangkok, 10900, Thailand
Tel.: (66) 293 618 71
Web Site: http://www.atotech.com
Metal Plating Chemical Equipment Mfr
N.A.I.C.S.: 332812

Atotech Argentina S.A. (3)
Parana 4574, 1605, Buenos Aires, Argentina
Tel.: (54) 1147567167
Emp.: 7
Chemical Distr
N.A.I.C.S.: 424690
Vicente Pastalle Mas *(Bus Dir)*

Atotech Asia Pacific Ltd. (3)
Unit 906-909 9/F Mira Place Tower A 132 Nathan Road, Tsim Sha Tsui, Kowloon, China (Hong Kong)
Tel.: (852) 27220108
Emp.: 7
Chemical Distr
N.A.I.C.S.: 424690

Atotech CZ, a.s. (3)
Belgicka 5119, 466 05, Jablonec nad Nisou, Czech Republic
Web Site: http://www.atotech.com
Sales Range: $25-49.9 Million
Emp.: 6
Chemical Preparations Mfr
N.A.I.C.S.: 325998

Plant (Domestic):

Atotech Deutschland GmbH (3)
Industriestrasse 69, Feucht, 90537, Germany (100%)
Tel.: (49) 91287250
Web Site: http://www.atotech.com

Sales Range: $50-74.9 Million
Emp.: 180
Mfr of Production Systems & Equipment for Electroplating, Semiconductor & Printed Circuit Board Manufacturing
N.A.I.C.S.: 332813

Subsidiary (Non-US):

Atotech Deutschland GmbH (3)
Zweigniederlassung Basel WRO-1059 P Mattenstrasse, 4002, Basel, Switzerland
Tel.: (41) 61 468 31 60
Chemical Processing Equipment Mfr
N.A.I.C.S.: 333248
Norbert Galster *(Gen Mgr)*

Atotech Espana S.A. (3)
Sucursal em Portugal Av Europa n 473 C, 9A Oia, 3800-228, Aveiro, Portugal
Tel.: (351) 234729800
Electroplating Chemical Distr
N.A.I.C.S.: 424690
Miguel Majuelos *(Gen Mgr)*

Atotech France SA (3)
ZA Du Vert Galant 29 Avenue De l'Eguillette, 95310, Saint Ouen L'Aumone, France
Tel.: (33) 134302060
Emp.: 4
Industrial Lubricants Mfr
N.A.I.C.S.: 333914
Jeremy Hooper *(Pres & Dir Gén)*

Atotech Istanbul Kimya Sanayi Tic. Ltd. Sti. (3)
Barbaros St Nesime Hanim No 4, Tuzla, 34956, Istanbul, Turkiye
Tel.: (90) 2165932390
Chemical Product Whslr
N.A.I.C.S.: 424690
Kansav Atila *(Gen Mgr)*

Atotech Italia S.r.l. (3)
Via Lecco 6, 20045, Lainate, Milan, Italy
Tel.: (39) 02933021
Electroplating Chemical Distr
N.A.I.C.S.: 424690

Atotech Japan K.K. (3)
German Industry Park 1-18-2 Hakusan, Midori-ku, Yokohama, 226-0006, Kanagawa, Japan
Tel.: (81) 459376116
Web Site: http://www.atotech.com
Industrial Chemicals & Equipment Mfr
N.A.I.C.S.: 325998

Atotech Korea Ltd. (3)
37 Jangangongdan 1-gil, Jangan-Myeon, Hwaseong, 18579, Gyeonggi, Korea (South)
Tel.: (82) 313593000
Printed Circuit Board Mfr
N.A.I.C.S.: 334412

Atotech Nederland B.V. (3)
Strijkviertel 35-2, 3454 PJ, De Meern, Netherlands
Tel.: (31) 302409010
Graphite Lubricant Distr
N.A.I.C.S.: 424720

Atotech Osterreich GmbH (3)
Linzer Strasse 63, 3002, Purkersdorf, Austria
Tel.: (43) 2231682400
Web Site: https://www.atotech.com
Sales Range: $25-49.9 Million
Emp.: 18
Electroplating Chemical Distr
N.A.I.C.S.: 424690

Atotech Osterreich GmbH (3)
Niederlassung Ungarn Magyarorszagi Fioktelepe Francia ut 43, 1143, Budapest, Hungary
Tel.: (36) 1 273 14 84
Chemical Distr
N.A.I.C.S.: 424690
Irene Batzower *(Mng Dir)*

Atotech Poland Sp.z o.o. (3)
Ul Marcelinska 92/94, 60-324, Poznan, Poland
Tel.: (48) 616622735
Emp.: 20
Organic Chemical Mfr & Whslr
N.A.I.C.S.: 424690

INTERNATIONAL PUBLIC

Atotech S.E.A (Phils) Pte Ltd (3)
CTP Alpha Building 401-402 Investment Dr Madrigal Bus Park, Muntinlupa, 1780, Philippines
Tel.: (63) 2817 8040
Web Site: http://www.atotech.com
Sales Range: $25-49.9 Million
Emp.: 7
Chemical Processing Equipment Mfr
N.A.I.C.S.: 333310

Atotech S.E.A Pte Ltd (3)
8 Buroh Street Unit 03-01 Surface Engineering Hub, Singapore, 627563, Singapore
Tel.: (65) 68622618
Web Site: https://www.atotech.com
Printed Circuit Board Mfr
N.A.I.C.S.: 334412

Atotech Skandinavien AB (3)
Slottsgatan 33, Box 5, 601 02, Norrkoping, Sweden
Tel.: (46) 11361100
Chemical Products Distr
N.A.I.C.S.: 424690

Atotech Slovenija, proizvodnja kemicnih izdelkov, d.d. (3)
Podnart 43, 4244, Podnart, Slovenia
Tel.: (386) 45376000
Printed Circuit Board Mfr & Distr
N.A.I.C.S.: 334412

Atotech Spain SA (3)
Sociedad Unipersonal Apartado 156 - 48950 Erandio Ribera de Axpe 39, 48950, Erandio, Bizkaia, Spain
Tel.: (34) 944803055
Chemical Products Distr
N.A.I.C.S.: 424690

Atotech Srl Italia Lainate (3)
Sucursala Bucuresti Str Italiana Nr 24 Et 4, 20976, Bucharest, Romania
Tel.: (40) 371064033
Web Site: http://www.atotech.com
Sales Range: $50-74.9 Million
Emp.: 5
Chemical Products Distr
N.A.I.C.S.: 424690

Atotech Taiwan Ltd. (3)
4F No 285 Sec 3 Nanjing E Rd, Taipei, 10550, Taiwan
Tel.: (886) 227176868
Printed Circuit Board Mfr
N.A.I.C.S.: 334412

Plant (Domestic):

Atotech Taiwan Ltd. - Guanyin Plant (4)
11 Jingjian 2nd Rd Guanyin Industrial Park, Guanyin, 32853, Taoyuan, Taiwan
Tel.: (886) 34389788
Electric Equipment Mfr
N.A.I.C.S.: 334419

Subsidiary (Non-US):

Atotech UK Ltd. (3)
William Street, West Bromwich, B70 0BG, West Midlands, United Kingdom
Tel.: (44) 1216067777
Sales Range: $25-49.9 Million
Emp.: 25
Printed Circuit Board Mfr
N.A.I.C.S.: 334412
Russell Gregory *(Mng Dir)*

Subsidiary (US):

Atotech USA Inc. (3)
1750 Overview Dr, Rock Hill, SC 29730
Tel.: (803) 817-3500
Web Site: https://www.atotech.com
Sales Range: $50-74.9 Million
Emp.: 135
Mfr of Production Systems & Equipment for Electroplating, Semiconductor & Printed Circuit Board Manufacturing
N.A.I.C.S.: 332813
John Kochilla *(VP)*

Subsidiary (Non-US):

Atotech Canada Ltd. (4)
1180 Corporate Dr, Burlington, L7L 5R6, ON, Canada (100%)
Tel.: (905) 332-0111
Web Site: http://www.atotechcanada.com

AND PRIVATE COMPANIES

Sales Range: $25-49.9 Million
Emp.: 55
Mfr of Production Systems & Equipment for Electroplating, Semiconductor & Printed Circuit Board Manufacturing
N.A.I.C.S.: 332813
Sue Guida *(Sls Dir)*

Subsidiary (Non-US):

Atotech Vietnam Co., Ltd. (3)
5F Hai Au Building 39B Truong Son Street, Ward 4 Tan Binh District, Ho Chi Minh City, Vietnam
Tel.: (84) 862961670
Emp.: 38
Printed Circuit Board Distr
N.A.I.C.S.: 423690
Khajorn Phongnarin *(Mng Dir & Head-Bus Unit-Electronics)*

Atotech de Mexico S.A. de C.V. (3)
Carretera Estatal 100 No 4200 Lote 33/34 Interior 4-H/4-G, Parque Industrial Aeropuerto San Ildefonso Colon Queretaro, 76295, Mexico, CP, Mexico
Tel.: (52) 4422958862
Electronic Equipment Mfr & Electroplating Services
N.A.I.C.S.: 423690

Atotech do Brasil Galvanotecnica Ltda. (3)
Rua Maria Patricia da Silva 205, Taboao da Serra, 06787-480, Sao Paulo, Brazil
Tel.: (55) 1141389900
Semiconductor & Printed Circuit Board Mfr
N.A.I.C.S.: 334413

OOO Atotech-Chemeta (3)
Volokolamskoe Highway Chaussee 73 Building Office 623, 125424, Moscow, Russia
Tel.: (7) 495 780 31 50
Emp.: 10
Metal Finishing Product Whslr
N.A.I.C.S.: 423510
Grazina Kontrimaviciute *(Mng Dir)*

Subsidiary (US):

Barry Controls Incorporated (2)
82 S St, Hopkinton, MA 01748-2205
Tel.: (508) 417-7000
Sales Range: $100-124.9 Million
Emp.: 350
Designs, Manufactures & Markets Shock, Vibration, Noise & Motion Solutions for Defense, Industrial & Commercial Aerospace Markets
N.A.I.C.S.: 333515

Division (Domestic):

Barry Controls Aerospace (3)
4510 Vanowen St, Burbank, CA 91505
Tel.: (818) 843-1000
Web Site: http://www.barrycontrols.com
Sales Range: $50-74.9 Million
Emp.: 150
Vibration & Shock Isolation Components & Systems for the Aerospace Industry
N.A.I.C.S.: 326299
Shano Cristilli *(CFO)*

Subsidiary (Non-US):

Stop Choc Limited (3)
Banbury Avenue, Slough, SL1 4LR, United Kingdom
Tel.: (44) 753533223
Web Site: http://www.stopchoc.co.uk
Designs, Manufactures & Markets Shock, Vibration, Noise & Motion Solutions for Defense, Industrial & Commercial Aerospace Markets
N.A.I.C.S.: 336330

Unit (Non-US):

Barry Controls Aerospace (4)
40 Rue Raymond Grimaud, 31700, Blagnac, France
Tel.: (33) 561167080
Web Site: http://www.barrycontrols.com
Sales Range: $50-74.9 Million
Emp.: 20
Designs, Manufactures & Markets Shock, Vibration, Noise & Motion Solutions for Defense, Industrial & Commercial Aerospace Markets

N.A.I.C.S.: 336330

Subsidiary (US):

Hutchinson Antivibration Systems, Inc. (2)
460 Fuller Ave NE, Grand Rapids, MI 49503-1912
Tel.: (616) 459-4541
Web Site: http://www.hutchinson.com
Anti-Vibration Devices Mfr
N.A.I.C.S.: 326299

Plant (Domestic):

Paulstra CRC Corp. (3)
600 7th St, Cadillac, MI 49601-1345
Tel.: (231) 775-9737
Sales Range: $100-124.9 Million
Mfr of Anti-Vibration Devices
N.A.I.C.S.: 326299
Tom Kelley *(Plant Mgr)*

Subsidiary (Non-US):

Hutchinson FTS Inc. (2)
Tel.: (931) 864-7827
Web Site: http://www.hutchinsonfts.com
Emp.: 60
Automotive Rubber Parts Mfr
N.A.I.C.S.: 326220

Plant (Domestic):

Hutchinson FTS Inc. (3)
315 Tubular Dr, Livingston, TN 38570
Tel.: (931) 823-1284
Web Site: http://www.hutchinsonworldwide.com
Sales Range: $125-149.9 Million
Emp.: 430
Mfr of Automotive Rubber Parts
N.A.I.C.S.: 336390

Hutchinson FTS, Inc. (3)
1835 Technology Dr, Troy, MI 48083-4244
Tel.: (248) 589-7710
Web Site: http://www.hutchinsonrubber.com
Sales Range: $25-49.9 Million
Emp.: 100
Mfr of Industrial Rubber Products
N.A.I.C.S.: 336390

Subsidiary (US):

Hutchinson Industries, Inc. (2)
460 Southard St, Trenton, NJ 08638-4224
Tel.: (609) 587-4156
Web Site: http://www.hutchinsoninc.com
Sales Range: $125-149.9 Million
Emp.: 350
Mfr of Industrial Rubber Products
N.A.I.C.S.: 326299

Subsidiary (Non-US):

Hutchinson Brasil Automotive Ltda (3)
Rua Dr Carlos Kielander 02, Monte Alto, CEP 15910 000, Sao Paulo, Brazil
Tel.: (55) 1632413500
Web Site: http://www.hutchinsoninc.com
Mfr of Automotive Rubber Products
N.A.I.C.S.: 336340

Subsidiary (US):

Hutchinson Precision Sealing Systems, Inc. (2)
39 Wauregan Rd, Danielson, CT 06239-0300
Tel.: (860) 779-0300
Web Site: http://www.hutchinson.com
Precision Rubber Components Mfr
N.A.I.C.S.: 326299

Subsidiary (Domestic):

Hutchinson S.A - Centre de Recherche (2)
BP 31, 45120, Chalette-sur-Loing, France
Tel.: (33) 238944900
Web Site: http://www.hutchinsonrubber.com
Research & Development Operations
N.A.I.C.S.: 541715

Subsidiary (US):

Hutchinson Sealing Systems Inc. (2)
1060 Ctr Rd, Auburn Hills, MI 48326-2600
Tel.: (248) 375-3720
Web Site: http://www.hutchinsonrubber.com

Sales Range: $25-49.9 Million
Emp.: 65
Automotive Door & Window Seals, Deck Lid & Hood-to-Cowl Seals
N.A.I.C.S.: 326299
Andre Cadet *(Pres)*

Hutchinson Sealing Systems North America, Inc. (2)
171 Rte 85, Newfields, NH 03856-0169
Tel.: (603) 772-3771
Sales Range: $50-74.9 Million
Emp.: 250
Auto Glass Run Channels & Metal Fabrications
N.A.I.C.S.: 326299
Paul McDonald *(Plant Mgr)*

Subsidiary (Domestic):

Hutchinson Sealing Systems, Inc. (3)
1150 S Third St, Wytheville, VA 24382-3925
Tel.: (276) 223-7000
Web Site: http://www.hutchinsonrubber.com
Sales Range: $50-74.9 Million
Emp.: 250
Mfr of Rubber Seals
N.A.I.C.S.: 326299

Division (Domestic):

Hutchinson Sealing Systems, Inc. (3)
309 Press Rd, Church Hill, TN 37642-4602
Tel.: (423) 357-6991
Mfr of Rubber Automotive Products
N.A.I.C.S.: 326299

Subsidiary (Domestic):

Techlam S.A. (2)
1 rue de l Industrie, 68700, Cernay, France (100%)
Tel.: (33) 389756667
Sales Range: $25-49.9 Million
Emp.: 60
Mechanical Assembly Mfr
N.A.I.C.S.: 326291

Hutchinson Stop - Choc GmbH & CO. KG (1)
Benzstrasse 42, 71272, Renningen, Germany
Tel.: (49) 715992190
Web Site: https://www.stop-choc.de
Rubber & Plastic Belting Product Mfr
N.A.I.C.S.: 326220
Wiljan Stenssen *(Mng Dir)*

Lampiris S.A. (1)
Rue Saint-Laurent 54, 4000, Liege, Belgium
Tel.: (32) 43406464
Web Site: https://www.lampiris.be
Natural Gas & Electric Power Distribution Services
N.A.I.C.S.: 221210
Brieuc Feneuil *(Portfolio Mgr)*

Methanergy SA (1)
74 rue Lieutenant de Montcabrier Technoparc de Mazeran, CS 10034, 34536, Beziers, Cedex, France
Tel.: (33) 467326330
Web Site: http://www.methanergy.fr
Biomass Power Generation Services
N.A.I.C.S.: 221117

Mide Technology Corporation (1)
475 Wildwood Ave, Woburn, MA 01801
Tel.: (781) 306-0609
Web Site: https://www.mide.com
Engineering Services
N.A.I.C.S.: 541330
Marthinus Van Schoor *(CEO & CTO)*

PT Total Oil Indonesia (1)
Menara FIF 15th Fl Jl TB Simatupang Kav 15, Jakarta, 12440, Indonesia
Tel.: (62) 21 75916999
Oil & Gas Exploration Services
N.A.I.C.S.: 213112

Paulstra S.N.C. (1)
61 rue Marius Aufan, 92309, Levallois-Perret, Cedex, France
Tel.: (33) 140895331
Web Site: https://www.paulstra-industry.com
Rubber & Plastic Belting Product Mfr
N.A.I.C.S.: 326220

TOTALENERGIES SE

Petroleum Development Oman LLC (1)
Mina Alfahal, Postal Office Box 81, Muscat, 100, Oman
Tel.: (968) 24678111
Web Site: https://www.pdo.co.om
Sales Range: $1-4.9 Billion
Emp.: 8,500
Petroleum Refiner
N.A.I.C.S.: 324110
Mohammed Saif Al Rumhy *(Chm)*

Polyblend GmbH (1)
Tel.: (49) 6751857670
Web Site: http://www.polyblend.de
Plastics Product Mfr
N.A.I.C.S.: 326199
Rene Herbiet *(Mng Dir)*

Quadrica SARL (1)
17 Rue Drouot, 75009, Paris, France
Tel.: (33) 144541010
Web Site: https://www.quadriga.fr
Photography & Production Agency Services
N.A.I.C.S.: 541921

Saft (Zhuhai FTZ) Batteries Company Limited (1)
No 201 Lianfeng Road Building 8, Hengli Industrial Park Xiangzhou District, Zhuhai, Guangdong, China
Tel.: (86) 7566290288
Battery Mfr
N.A.I.C.S.: 335910
Jun Lu *(Gen Mgr)*

Saft Batterie Italia S.R.L. (1)
Via Cesare Battisti 68, 20862, Arcore, MB, Italy
Tel.: (39) 0398947361
Battery & Electrochemical Accumulator Mfr
N.A.I.C.S.: 335910
Mauro Fassina *(Gen Mgr)*

Saft Do Brasil Ltda. (1)
Alameda Araguaia 2044 - 11 andar Cj 1110/11/12 CEA I Torre II, Alphaville Industrial, Barueri, 06455-000, SP, Brazil
Tel.: (55) 1140823292
Battery Mfr
N.A.I.C.S.: 335910
Marcos Soares *(Country Mgr)*

Saft Groupe S.A. (1)
26 quai Charles Pasqua, 92300, Levallois-Perret, France (100%)
Tel.: (33) 33158631600
Web Site: http://www.saftbatteries.com
Advanced Battery Product Mfr
N.A.I.C.S.: 335910
Bertrand de La Noue *(CFO)*

Subsidiary (Non-US):

Friemann & Wolf Batterietechnik GmbH (2)
Industrie Strasse 22, 63654, Budingen, Germany
Tel.: (49) 6042954150
Web Site: http://www.friemann-wolf.de
Industrial Batteries Mfr
N.A.I.C.S.: 335910

Subsidiary (US):

Go Electric Inc. (2)
1920 Purdue Pkwy Ste 400, Anderson, IN 46016
Tel.: (765) 400-1347
Web Site: https://www.goelectricinc.com
Current-Carrying Wiring Device Mfr
N.A.I.C.S.: 335931
Janel Bland *(Sr Project Mgr)*

Subsidiary (Non-US):

SGH UG (2)
Lessingstrasse 42, 21629, Neu Wulmstorf, Germany
Tel.: (49) 4076111101
Web Site: http://www.sgh-ug.de
Bus Coaches Retailer
N.A.I.C.S.: 441227

Saft AB (2)
Jungnergatan 25, PO Box 709, 572 32, Oskarshamn, Sweden
Tel.: (46) 49168000
Advanced Battery Product Mfr
N.A.I.C.S.: 335910

7837

TOTALENERGIES SE

TotalEnergies SE—(Continued)

Subsidiary (Domestic):

Alcad A.B. (3)
Norra Strandgatan 35, PO Box 504, SE-572 25, Oskarshamn, Sweden
Tel.: (46) 49168100
Web Site: http://www.alcad.com
Industrial Machinery Equipment Whslr
N.A.I.C.S.: 423830

Subsidiary (Non-US):

Tadiran Batteries Ltd (3)
PO Box 1, Kiryat Ekron, 7695001, Israel
Tel.: (972) 89444503
Web Site: http://www.tadiranbat.com
Lithium Thionyl Chloride Batteries Mfr
N.A.I.C.S.: 335910

Subsidiary (Non-US):

Saft AS (2)
Griniveien 363, Bekkestua, 1356, Baerum, Norway
Tel.: (47) 67164160
Industrial Batteries Mfr
N.A.I.C.S.: 335910
Trond Beyer *(Mgr)*

Subsidiary (US):

Saft America Inc. (2)
711 Gil Harbin Industrial Blvd, Valdosta, GA 31601-6512
Tel.: (229) 247-2331
Advanced Battery Product Mfr
N.A.I.C.S.: 335910

Plant (Domestic):

Saft America Inc. (3)
107 Beaver Ct, Cockeysville, MD 21030
Tel.: (410) 771-3200
Web Site: http://www.saftbatteries.com
Advanced Battery Product Mfr
N.A.I.C.S.: 335910

Saft America Inc. (3)
313 Crescent St, Valdese, NC 28690
Tel.: (828) 874-4111
Web Site: http://www.saftbatteries.com
Battery Mfr
N.A.I.C.S.: 335910

Subsidiary (Domestic):

Saft Federal Systems, Inc. (3)
2001 Marcus Ave Ste 125 E, Lake Success, NY 11042
Tel.: (516) 621-4980
Web Site: https://www.tadiranbat.com
Industrial Battery Mfr
N.A.I.C.S.: 335910

Subsidiary (Non-US):

Saft Australia Pty. Ltd. (2)
167 Prospect Hwy, PO Box 883, Seven Hills, 2147, NSW, Australia
Tel.: (61) 296740701
Advanced Battery Product Mfr
N.A.I.C.S.: 335910

Subsidiary (Domestic):

Saft Batteries Pty Ltd (3)
Unit 9 167 Prospect Highway, Seven Hills, 2147, NSW, Australia
Tel.: (61) 296740701
Industrial Batteries Mfr
N.A.I.C.S.: 335132

Subsidiary (Non-US):

Saft Baterias SL (2)
C de la Calendula 93 Miniparc II Edif H Floor 1, 28109, Alcobendas, Madrid, Spain
Tel.: (34) 916593480
Batteries Mfr
N.A.I.C.S.: 335910

Saft Batterien GmbH (2)
Loeffelholzstrasse 20, 90441, Nuremberg, Germany
Tel.: (49) 91194740
Web Site: https://de.saft.com
Industrial Batteries Mfr
N.A.I.C.S.: 335910
Holger Schuh *(Mng Dir)*

Saft Batteries Pte. Ltd. (2)
03 03 Ruby Land Complex II, 54 Genting Ln, Singapore, 349562, Singapore
Tel.: (65) 65121500
Advanced Battery Product Mfr
N.A.I.C.S.: 335910

Subsidiary (Non-US):

Amco-Saft India Pvt Ltd (3)
Plot No 10/1A 1B & 1C Abbanakupe Area, Bidadi Industrial Area Bangalore, Karnataka, 562109, India
Tel.: (91) 8027287947
Web Site: http://www.amcosaft.com
Industrial Nickel Cadmium Mfr & Whslr
N.A.I.C.S.: 335910

Subsidiary (Non-US):

Saft Ferak AS (2)
Raskovice 247, 739 04, Frydek-Mistek, Czech Republic
Tel.: (420) 558426111
Industrial Batteries Mfr
N.A.I.C.S.: 335910
Peter Pavlasek *(Mng Dir)*

Saft Hong Kong Ltd. (2)
30/F Cambridge House 979 King's Road Taikoo Place, Quarry Bay, Kowloon, China (Hong Kong)
Tel.: (852) 37566399
Advanced Battery Product Mfr
N.A.I.C.S.: 335910
Zhang Xiaoming *(Deputy Gen Mgr)*

Saft Nife ME Ltd (2)
Kanika Business Center 319 A 28th Oktovriou Street 5th Floor, Limassol, CY-3600, Cyprus
Tel.: (357) 25820040
Aircraft Components Mfr
N.A.I.C.S.: 336411

Saft Sweden AB (2)
Jungnergatan 25, PO Box 709, 572 32, Oskarshamn, Kalmar, Sweden
Tel.: (46) 49168000
Industrial Batteries Mfr
N.A.I.C.S.: 335910

Tadiran Batteries GmbH (2)
Industriestr 22, 63654, Budingen, Germany
Tel.: (49) 60429540
Web Site: https://www.tadiranbatteries.de
Lithium Batteries Mfr
N.A.I.C.S.: 335910

Saft Japan KK (1)
8F Akasaka Shasta East 4-2-19 Akasaka, Minato-ku, Tokyo, 107-0052, Japan
Tel.: (81) 362066269
Web Site: https://jp.saft.com
Battery Mfr
N.A.I.C.S.: 335910
Takahiro Fujii *(Sr Mgr-Sls)*

Saft LLC (1)
Lesnaya St 7 7th Floor, 125196, Moscow, Russia
Tel.: (7) 4959661673
Web Site: http://www.saftbatteries.ru
Battery Mfr
N.A.I.C.S.: 335910
Sergey Varnavskiy *(Acct Mgr)*

Saudi Aramco Total Refining and Petrochemical Company (1)
Saeed Tower Dammam Khobar Highway, PO Box 151, Al Khobar, Saudi Arabia
Tel.: (966) 38106999
Web Site: http://www.satorp.com
Petrochemical Refining Services
N.A.I.C.S.: 324110
Sulaiman Mansour Ababtain *(Pres & CEO)*

Saudi Total Petroleum Products Co., Ltd. (1)
Zahran Business Centre Sultan St Tower A - Office 704, PO Box 4861, Jeddah, 21463, Saudi Arabia
Tel.: (966) 122256300
Web Site: https://lubricants.totalenergies.sa
Petroleum & Coal Product Mfr
N.A.I.C.S.: 324199
Tony Abraham *(Mgr-Strategic)*

Socap S.A.S. (1)
5 Rue Longues Raies, BP 511, Sens, 89105, France

Tel.: (33) 386950900
Oil & Gas Exploration Services
N.A.I.C.S.: 213112

Societe du Pipeline Sud-Europeen (1)
195 Ave Charles De Gaulle, 92521, Neuilly-sur-Seine, Cedex, France (27.8%)
Tel.: (33) 141432164
Web Site: http://www.spse.fr
Sales Range: $50-74.9 Million
Emp.: 180
Crude Oil Pipeline Transport Services
N.A.I.C.S.: 486110

Sofax Banque SA (1)
Tour Coupole 2 Place de la Coupole Cedex 45, Paris, 92078, France
Tel.: (33) 147443645
Commercial Banking Services
N.A.I.C.S.: 522110

TOTAL (Philippines) Corp. (1)
7th Floor, Bonifacio Global City, Taguig, 1634, Metro Manila, Philippines
Tel.: (63) 28490888
Web Site: http://www.totalol.com.ph
Container Terminal Operation Services
N.A.I.C.S.: 493190

TOTAL AMERICAN SERVICES, INC. (1)
100 Pavonia Ave Ste 401, Jersey City, NJ 07310
Tel.: (713) 483-5070
Oil & Gas Exploration Services
N.A.I.C.S.: 213112

TOTAL CAMBODGE (1)
108-112 Preah Sothearos Blvd, Sangkat Chaktomok, Phnom Penh, Cambodia
Tel.: (855) 23 218 630
Web Site: http://www.total.com.kh
Sales Range: $200-249.9 Million
Emp.: 350
Oil & Gas Exploration Services
N.A.I.C.S.: 213112

TOTAL CESKA REPUBLIKA S.R.O. (1)
Rohanske nabrezi 678/29, Karlin, 186 00, Prague, Czech Republic
Tel.: (420) 224890511
Web Site: https://totalenergies.cz
Emp.: 70
Refining And Marketing
N.A.I.C.S.: 541613

TOTAL CHILE SA (1)
Calle Uno, 3010, Quilicura, Santiago, Chile
Tel.: (56) 251 97 800
Web Site: http://www.total-chile.com
Emp.: 100
Lubricant & Engine Oil Distr
N.A.I.C.S.: 424720
Marin de Montbel *(Gen Dir)*

TOTAL DENMARK A/S (1)
Aldersrogade 6C 4 Sal, 2100, Copenhagen, Denmark
Tel.: (45) 45813701
Web Site: http://www.totalnordec.com
Emp.: 40
Lubricant & Engine Oil Distr
N.A.I.C.S.: 424720

TOTAL E & P Malaysia (1)
Level 21 Menara HLA 3 Jalan Kia Peng, Kuala Lumpur, 50450, Malaysia
Tel.: (60) 321616670
Oil & Gas Exploration Services
N.A.I.C.S.: 213112

TOTAL E&P Nederland B.V. (1)
Bordewijklaan 18, Hague, 2591 XR, Netherlands
Tel.: (31) 705129449
Web Site: http://www.nl.total.com
Emp.: 270
Exploration & Oil Production
N.A.I.C.S.: 213112

TOTAL ENERGIE GAZ SA (1)
La Defense 2 Place Jean Millier, Courbevoie, 92400, Hauts de Seine, France
Tel.: (33) 147444546
Web Site: http://www.tegaz.fr
Natural Gas Distribution Services
N.A.I.C.S.: 221210

TOTAL FIJI LIMITED (1)

INTERNATIONAL PUBLIC

Rona Street Walu Bay, PO Box 168, Suva, Fiji
Tel.: (679) 3313 933
Web Site: http://www.total.com.fj
Sales Range: $75-99.9 Million
Emp.: 121
Petroleum Product Distr
N.A.I.C.S.: 424720

TOTAL Finance Exploitation (1)
2 Place Jean Millier La Defense 6, 92400, Courbevoie, France
Tel.: (33) 1 47 44 45 46
Web Site: http://www.total.com
Financial Management Services
N.A.I.C.S.: 523999

TOTAL Finance USA, Inc. (1)
900 1st Ave, King of Prussia, PA 19406-1308
Tel.: (610) 205-7000
Sales Range: $350-399.9 Million
Emp.: 600
Financial Management Services
N.A.I.C.S.: 523999

TOTAL GUADELOUPE (1)
Immeuble Adonis ZAC de Houelbourg Sud, BP 2142, Jarry, 97194, Pointe-a-Pitre, Guadeloupe
Tel.: (590) 590264532
Web Site: http://www.totalguadeloupe.com
Emp.: 42
Engine Oil Distr
N.A.I.C.S.: 424720

TOTAL Gasandes S.A. (1)
2 Place Jean Millier La Defense 6, 92078, Courbevoie, France
Tel.: (33) 147444546
Web Site: http://www.total.com
Emp.: 1,000
Petroleum Product Distr
N.A.I.C.S.: 424720

TOTAL Gaz & Electricite Holdings France (1)
2 Place Jean Millier La Defense, 92400, Courbevoie, France
Tel.: (33) 1 47 44 77 96
Natural Gas Distribution Services
N.A.I.C.S.: 221210

TOTAL HUNGARIA KFT (1)
Neumann Janos u 1, 2040, Budaors, Hungary
Tel.: (36) 23507500
Web Site: https://totalenergies.hu
Sales Range: $50-74.9 Million
Emp.: 55
Oil & Gas Distribution Services
N.A.I.C.S.: 213112

TOTAL LUBRICANTS JAPAN Co, Ltd. (1)
4-2-19 Akasaka, Minato - ku, Tokyo, 107 -0052, Japan
Tel.: (81) 355625930
Emp.: 73
Petroleum Product Whslr
N.A.I.C.S.: 424720

TOTAL LUXEMBOURG S.A. (1)
310 Rte d'Esch, BP 1404, 1014, Luxembourg, Luxembourg
Tel.: (352) 4804811
Oil & Gas Exploration Services
N.A.I.C.S.: 213112

TOTAL Mineraloel und Chemie GmbH (1)
Schneemann 2, Berlin, 10117, Germany
Tel.: (49) 30202760
Web Site: http://www.total.de
Petroleum Product Whslr
N.A.I.C.S.: 424720

TOTAL Oil Asia-Pacific Pte Ltd. (1)
182 Cecil Street 27-01 Frasers Tower, Singapore, 069547, Singapore
Tel.: (65) 68792200
Emp.: 260
Engine Oil Lubricant Distr
N.A.I.C.S.: 424720

Plant (Domestic):

TOTAL Oil Asia-Pacific Pte Ltd. - Lubricants Plant (2)

AND PRIVATE COMPANIES

10 Pandan Avenue, Singapore, 609385,
Singapore
Tel.: (65) 6266 28 00
Web Site: http://www.total.sg
Sales Range: $25-49.9 Million
Emp.: 15
Petroleum Product Mfr
N.A.I.C.S.: 324199

**TOTAL PETROLEO COSTA RICA
S.A.** (1)
Lubcostarica, Tres Rios, Costa Rica
Tel.: (506) 22 79 77 77
Lubricant Product Whslr
N.A.I.C.S.: 424720

TOTAL POLSKA S.P. ZO.O. (1)
Al Jana Pawla II 80, 00-175, Warsaw, Poland
Tel.: (48) 224819400
Web Site: https://www.totalpolska.pl
Emp.: 60
Engine Oil Lubricant Distr
N.A.I.C.S.: 424720

TOTAL Profils Petroliers (1)
2 Place Jean Millier La Defense, Courbevoie, 92078, France
Tel.: (33) 1 47 44 45 46
Petroleum Product Whslr
N.A.I.C.S.: 424720

TOTAL SENEGAL SA (1)
3 Bld du Centenaire de la Commune de Dakar, BP 355, Dakar, Senegal
Tel.: (221) 33 839 54 54
Web Site: http://www.total-senegal.com
Petroleum Product Distr
N.A.I.C.S.: 424720

TOTAL SLOVENSKO S.R.O. (1)
Panenska 21, 811 03, Bratislava, Slovakia
Tel.: (421) 2 52620895
Web Site: http://www.total.sk
Lubricant Distr
N.A.I.C.S.: 424720

TOTAL SWEDEN AB (1)
Alberfgoade 6C, Box 50326, 202 13, Copenhagen, Denmark
Tel.: (45) 40383650
Web Site: http://www.totalsweden.se
Petroleum & Lubricant Distr
N.A.I.C.S.: 424720

TOTAL South Pars (1)
2 Place Jean Millier La Defense, 92400, Courbevoie, France
Tel.: (33) 147444546
Oil & Gas Exploration Services
N.A.I.C.S.: 213112

TOTAL TUNISIA (1)
Rue du Lac Huron Les Berges du Lac, 1053, Tunis, Tunisia
Tel.: (216) 71965858
Web Site: https://totalenergies.com
Engine Oil Distr
N.A.I.C.S.: 424720

TOTAL Treasury (1)
2 Place Jean Millier La Defense 6, 92400, Courbevoie, France
Tel.: (33) 1 47 44 45 46
Financial Management Services
N.A.I.C.S.: 523999

TOTAL VENEZUELA SA (1)
2 Place Jean Millier, Courbevoie, 92400, Hauts De Seine, France
Tel.: (33) 147444546
Web Site: http://www.total.com
Lubricant Distr
N.A.I.C.S.: 424720

**TOTAL Yemen LNG Company
Ltd.** (1)
Hadda Area Opposite Hadda Hotel Adhban Building, PO Box 15347, Sana'a, Yemen
Tel.: (967) 1 438 000
Web Site: http://www.yemenlng.com
Sales Range: $350-399.9 Million
Emp.: 700
Oil & Gas Exploration Services
N.A.I.C.S.: 213112

TOTSA Total Oil Trading S.A (1)
(100%)
Tel.: (41) 227101112
Web Site: http://www.totsa.com
Sales Range: $75-99.9 Million
Oil Trading & Risk Management Services
N.A.I.C.S.: 541330

Subsidiary (US):

Atlantic Trading & Marketing, Inc. (2)
5847 San Felipe Plz Ste 2100, Houston, TX 77057-3193 (100%)
Tel.: (713) 243-2200
Web Site: http://www.totsa.com
Sales Range: $25-49.9 Million
Emp.: 75
Petroleum Trading & Risk Management Services
N.A.I.C.S.: 424720

Subsidiary (Non-US):

Total Trading & Shipping (2)
Tour Coupole La Defense 6 2 place Jean Millier, 92078, Paris, Cedex, France (100%)
Tel.: (33) 147446000
Web Site: http://www.totsa.com
Petroleum Trading & Risk Management Services
N.A.I.C.S.: 424720

Total Trading Asia Pte Ltd (2)
250 N Bridge Rd 39-00 Raffles City Tower, 179101, Singapore, Singapore (100%)
Tel.: (65) 68494242
Web Site: http://www.totsa.com
Sales Range: $25-49.9 Million
Emp.: 80
Petroleum Trading & Risk Management Services
N.A.I.C.S.: 541330

Total Trading International S.A (2)
Akasaka Shasta E 4 2 19, Akasaka, Tokyo, 107 0052, Japan (100%)
Tel.: (81) 55625211
Web Site: http://www.totsa.com
Petroleum Trading & Risk Management Services
N.A.I.C.S.: 541330

Terneftegaz JSC (1)
No 11 Building 2, Territory Industrial Area Yamalo-Nenets Autonomous District, 629380, Krasnoyarsk, Russia
Tel.: (7) 4993943295
Web Site: http://www.terneftegaz.ru
Oil & Gas Operation Services
N.A.I.C.S.: 213112

Total (Suisse) S.A. (1)
Ruessenstrasse 18, 6340, Baar, Switzerland (100%)
Tel.: (41) 800011011
Web Site: https://totalenergies.ch
Petroleum Trading
N.A.I.C.S.: 425120

Total - Bitumen (1)
562 Avenue du Parc de l ile, 92029, Nanterre, France
Tel.: (33) 141354000
Web Site: http://www.total.com
Petroleum Product Distr
N.A.I.C.S.: 424720

Subsidiary (Non-US):

**TOTAL Bitumen Deutschland
GmbH** (2)
Bitumenwerk Brunsbuttel Industrial Area South, 25541, Brunsbuttel, Germany
Tel.: (49) 48528880
Petroleum Refining Services
N.A.I.C.S.: 324110

Total - CSTJF (1)
2 Place Eanmillier, La Defense, Paris, 92078, Cedex, France
Tel.: (33) 5 59 83 40 00
Oil & Gas Exploration Services
N.A.I.C.S.: 213112

Total - Marine Fuels (1)
562 Avenue du Parc de l'ile, 92029, Nanterre, France
Tel.: (33) 141354000
Web Site: http://www.marinefuels.total.com
Petroleum Product Distr
N.A.I.C.S.: 424720

**Total Additifs et Carburants Speciaux
SA** (1)
Place du Bassin, 69700, Givors, France
Tel.: (33) 472498410
Web Site: http://www.acs.total.com
Oil & Gas Exploration Services
N.A.I.C.S.: 213112
Denis Marcel *(Mgr-Publ)*

Total Austral S.A. (1)
Moreno 877-Piso 15, C1091AAQ, Buenos Aires, Argentina
Tel.: (54) 43466400
Oil & Gas Operation Services
N.A.I.C.S.: 213112
Fernando Garcia Bonini *(Mgr-Legal)*

Total Austria GmbH (1)
Otto Probst-Strasse 36/II, 1100, Vienna, Austria
Tel.: (43) 161646110
Web Site: http://www.total.co.at
Engine Oil Distr
N.A.I.C.S.: 424720

Total Aviation Ltd. (1)
562 Avenue du Parc de l ile, 92029, Nanterre, France
Tel.: (33) 1 41 35 40 00
Aviation Fuel Mfr
N.A.I.C.S.: 324110

Total Belgium SA/NV (1)
93 Rue du Commerce, B-1040, Brussels, Belgium
Tel.: (32) 22889933
Web Site: http://www.be.total.com
Sales Range: $1-4.9 Billion
Emp.: 4,741
Holding Company; Chemicals Mfr & Whslr; Oil & Natural Gas Refining & Marketing
N.A.I.C.S.: 551112

Subsidiary (Domestic):

**Total Gas & Power North Europe
S.A.** (2)
52 Rue de l'Industrie, B-1040, Brussels, Belgium (100%)
Tel.: (32) 22889111
Web Site: http://www.be.total.com
Sales Range: $200-249.9 Million
Emp.: 600
Oil Company
N.A.I.C.S.: 324191

Total Bitumen UK Ltd (1)
Chain Caul Way Preston Riversway, Preston, PR2 2TZ, United Kingdom
Tel.: (44) 1772729302
Web Site: http://www.bitumen.total.co.uk
Sales Range: $25-49.9 Million
Emp.: 7
Asphalt Paving Mixture Mfr
N.A.I.C.S.: 324121

Total Burkina S.A. (1)
1080 Avenue Kwame N Krumah 101, BP 21, Ouagadougou, Burkina Faso
Tel.: (226) 50 32 50 00
Web Site: http://www.total.bf
Sales Range: $50-74.9 Million
Emp.: 100
Lubricant & Engine Oil Distr
N.A.I.C.S.: 424720

Total Capital S.A. (1)
2 Place Jean Millier La Defense 6, Paris, 92078, France
Tel.: (33) 147445853
Financial Management Services
N.A.I.C.S.: 523999

Total Carbon Neutrality Ventures Europe SA (1)
2 Place Jean Millier-La Defense 6, 92400, Courbevoie, France
Tel.: (33) 147444546
Web Site: http://www.ventures.total
Renewable Energy Services
N.A.I.C.S.: 221118
Girish Nadkarni *(CEO)*

Total Chemical Division (1)
2 place Jean Millier La Defense 6, Paris, 92078, France
Tel.: (33) 147444546
Web Site: http://www.total.com
Sales Range: $25-49.9 Billion
Petrochemicals, Fertilizers & Specialty Chemicals Mfr

TOTALENERGIES SE

N.A.I.C.S.: 325110

Subsidiary (Domestic):

Cray Valley S.A. (2)
12 Pl Del Iris La Defense 2, 92062, Paris, Cedex, France
Tel.: (33) 0147969850
Web Site: http://www.crayvalley.com
Sales Range: $25-49.9 Million
Emp.: 100
Mfr of Resins & Coating Additives
N.A.I.C.S.: 325211

Subsidiary (Non-US):

Cray Valley Iberica SA (3)
Carretera D Olzinelles Sant Celoni, 08470, Barcelona, Spain
Tel.: (34) 938674000
Web Site: http://www.crayvalley.com
Sales Range: $50-74.9 Million
Coating Resins Mfr
N.A.I.C.S.: 325211

Cray Valley Italia Srl (3)
Viale Col Di Lana 9, Treviglio, BG 24047, Italy
Tel.: (39) 0522968611
Web Site: http://www.crayvalley.com
Mfr of Resins
N.A.I.C.S.: 325211

Cray Valley Korea (3)
13Floor Taeyoung Building 252-2 Gongdeok 2-dong, Mapo-gu, Seoul, 121-717, Korea (South)
Tel.: (82) 232713310
Web Site: http://www.ccpcomposites.com
Sales Range: $50-74.9 Million
Emp.: 100
Resin Mfr
N.A.I.C.S.: 325211
Seil Kin *(Mng Dir)*

Cray Valley Kunstharze GmbH (3)
Flurstrasse, Postfach 808, Zwickau, 8056, Germany
Tel.: (49) 3758280
Sales Range: $50-74.9 Million
Resin Mfr
N.A.I.C.S.: 325211

Cray Valley Ltd (3)
Laporte Road, Near Grimsby, Stallingborough, DN41 8DR, Lincolnshire, United Kingdom
Tel.: (44) 1469552570
Emp.: 24
Resin Mfr
N.A.I.C.S.: 325211

**Cray Valley Resins South Africa Pty.
Ltd.** (3)
4 Baltex Rd Isipingo Rail, PO Box 32211, Mobeni, 4060, South Africa
Tel.: (27) 319103574
Sales Range: $25-49.9 Million
Emp.: 92
Mfr of Resins
N.A.I.C.S.: 325211

Plant (US):

Cray Valley USA, LLC (3)
569 24 1/4 Rd, Grand Junction, CO 81505-1113 (100%)
Tel.: (970) 245-8148
Sales Range: $25-49.9 Million
Emp.: 31
Mfr of Industrial Inorganic Chemicals
N.A.I.C.S.: 325180

Cray Valley USA, LLC (3)
105 Ontario St, Stratford, CT 06615-7135 (100%)
Tel.: (203) 375-0668
Web Site: http://www.crayvalley.com
Sales Range: $25-49.9 Million
Emp.: 23
Mfr of Industrial Inorganic Chemicals
N.A.I.C.S.: 325180

**Total China Investment Company
Limited** (1)
Floor 30 Office Building 3 Huamao Center No 77 Jianguo Road, Chaoyang District, Beijing, 100025, China
Tel.: (86) 1085905666
Oil & Gas Exploration Services
N.A.I.C.S.: 213112

TOTALENERGIES SE

INTERNATIONAL PUBLIC

TotalEnergies SE—(Continued)
Justine Guo *(Country Mgr-Com & Ben)*

Total Congo SA (1)
Rue de la Corniche, BP 1037, Brazzaville, Congo, Republic of
Tel.: (242) 52021414
Oil & Gas Exploration Services
N.A.I.C.S.: 213112

Total Costa Rica (1)
Contiguo a la Casa Presidencial Centro-Langer-Zapote, 1937-1002, San Jose, Costa Rica
Tel.: (506) 2279 77 77
Lubricant & Engine Oil Distr
N.A.I.C.S.: 424720

Total Cote D'Ivoire SA (1)
Rive Gauche building 100 rue des brasseurs - Zone 3, Abidjan, Cote d'Ivoire
Oil & Gas Exploration Services
N.A.I.C.S.: 213112
Ahmed Yao *(Reg Sls Mgr)*

Total Deutschland GmbH (1)
Jean-Monnet-Str 2, Berlin, 10557, Germany **(100%)**
Tel.: (49) 30202760
Web Site: http://www.total.de
Sales Range: $10-24.9 Million
Emp.: 500
Diesel Products
N.A.I.C.S.: 324110

Subsidiary (Domestic):

Total Raffinerie Mitteldeutschland GmbH (2)
Maienweg 1, Spergau, 06237, Leipzig, Germany
Tel.: (49) 3461480
Web Site: http://www.total.de
Petroleum Refining
N.A.I.C.S.: 324110

Total Direct Energie S.A. (1)
2bis rue Louis Armand, 75015, Paris, France
Tel.: (33) 988813006
Web Site: http://www.total.direct-energie.com
Natural Gas & Electric Power Distribution Services
N.A.I.C.S.: 221210

Total Direction Generale Gaz & Electricite (1)
2 Pl Jean Millier, F 92078, Paris, Cedex, France **(100%)**
Tel.: (33) 147444546
Web Site: http://www.total.com
Gas Distribution & Power Generation Services
N.A.I.C.S.: 221122

Total E&P Bolivie S.A. (1)
Calle Las Violetas No 40 Equipetrol Norte, Santa Cruz, Bolivia
Tel.: (591) 33634500
Oil & Gas Operation Services
N.A.I.C.S.: 213112
Borja Guzman *(Mgr-Comml & Bus Dev)*

Total E&P Borneo B.V. (1)
2nd Floor RBA Plaza Jalan Sultan, BS8811, Bandar Seri Begawan, Brunei Darussalam
Tel.: (673) 2229269
Web Site: http://www.total.com.bn
Emp.: 95
Oil & Gas Operation Services
N.A.I.C.S.: 213112
Josephine Tan *(Mgr-Contracts & Procurement)*

Total E&P Bulgaria B.V. (1)
Infinity Tower fl 13 69 Bulgaria Blvd, 1404, Sofia, Bulgaria
Tel.: (359) 29047000
Oil & Gas Operation Services
N.A.I.C.S.: 213112
Stanislav Yankov *(Officer-HSE)*

Total E&P Danmark A/S (1)
Britanniavej 10, 6700, Esbjerg, Denmark
Tel.: (45) 75451366
Oil & Gas Operation Services
N.A.I.C.S.: 213112

Total E&P Mozambique Area 1, Limitada (1)
Av Julius Nyerere n 3412 JN 3412 Office Park, Maputo, Mozambique
Tel.: (258) 21500000
Web Site: https://mzlng.totalenergies.co.mz
Oil & Gas Exploration Services
N.A.I.C.S.: 213112
Paulo Jorge Roberts *(Mgr-HR)*

Total E&P Nigeria Limited (1)
Total House Plot 247 Herbert Macaulay Way, Central Business District, Abuja, Nigeria
Tel.: (234) 8039037007
Web Site: http://www.nigeria.total.com
Oil & Gas Operation Services
N.A.I.C.S.: 213112
Ibifuro Olayomi *(Mgr-Industrial Rels)*

Total E&P North Sea UK Limited (1)
18th Floor 10 Upper Bank Street, Canary Wharf, London, E14 5BF, United Kingdom
Tel.: (44) 1224 242 000
Web Site: http://www.total.uk
Oil & Gas Exploration Services
N.A.I.C.S.: 213112

Total E&P PNG Limited (1)
Level 7 Deloitte Haus MacGregor Street-CBD, PO Box 1145, National Capital District, 123, Port Moresby, Papua New Guinea
Tel.: (675) 70910000
Web Site: https://totalenergies.com.pg
Oil & Gas Exploration Services
N.A.I.C.S.: 213112
Philippe Blanchard *(Mng Dir)*

Total E&P Uganda B.V. (1)
Course View Towers Plot 21 Yusuf Lule Road, PO Box 34867, Kampala, Uganda
Tel.: (256) 204916000
Oil & Gas Operation Services
N.A.I.C.S.: 213112
Marion Adengo Muyobo *(Head-Social Affairs)*

Total Energie Developpement SAS (1)
Tour CBX-1 passerelle des Reflets, 92400, Courbevoie, France
Tel.: (33) 170375580
Web Site: https://renewables.totalenergies.com
Electronic Components Mfr
N.A.I.C.S.: 334419

Total Energie Gas GmbH (1)
Hohenstrasse 17, 70736, Fellbach, Germany
Tel.: (49) 711128590
Web Site: http://www.gas-strom.total.de
Natural Gas & Electric Power Distribution Services
N.A.I.C.S.: 221210
Franck Maurin *(Mng Dir)*

Total Energies Lubrifiants Algerie SPA (1)
20 rue Sfindja, El Biar, 16023, Algiers, Algeria
Tel.: (213) 21920333
Oil & Natural Gas Mfr
N.A.I.C.S.: 325194

Total Energies Marketing (Cambodia) Co. Ltd. (1)
Anina Building 6th floor No 240 St 271, BP 600, Phnom Penh, 120606, Cambodia
Tel.: (855) 23218630
Web Site: https://kh.totalenergies.com
Emp.: 140
Petroleum Product Distr
N.A.I.C.S.: 424720

Total Energies Marketing Espana, S.A.U. (1)
Calle Ribera del Loira 46 Building 2, Floor 3 - Puerta de las Unidas Business Park, 28042, Madrid, Spain
Tel.: (34) 917220840
Web Site: https://services.totalenergies.es
Engine Oil & Hydraulic Lubricant Distr
N.A.I.C.S.: 423120

Total Energies Marketing UK Limited (1)
10 Upper Bank Street 19th floor, Canary Wharf, London, United Kingdom
Tel.: (44) 1932334498
Web Site: https://services.totalenergies.uk

Emp.: 1,800
Industrial Lubricant Product Mfr & Distr
N.A.I.C.S.: 324191

Total Energies Marketing Uganda Ltd. (1)
Plot 4 8th street industrial area, PO Box 3079, Kampala, Uganda
Tel.: (256) 414390700
Petroleum Product Distr
N.A.I.C.S.: 424720

Total Energies Marketing Zambia Ltd. (1)
Plot Number 1708/9 Mungwi Road Industrial Area, PO Box 31724, Lusaka, Zambia
Tel.: (260) 211374400
Web Site: https://totalenergies.co.zm
Petroleum Product Distr
N.A.I.C.S.: 424720

Total Espana SA (1)
Calle Ribera Del Loira 46 2nd Fl, 28042, Madrid, Spain
Tel.: (34) 917220840
Web Site: http://www.total.es
Sales Range: $50-74.9 Million
Emp.: 100
Petroleum & Gas Products
N.A.I.C.S.: 424720

Total Especialidades Argentina S.A. (1)
Avenida Del Libertador 1295 Piso 2, Vicente Lopez, Buenos Aires, 1638, Argentina
Tel.: (54) 1148376300
Web Site: http://www.total-argentina.com.ar
Sales Range: $75-99.9 Million
Emp.: 25
Lubricant & Engine Oil Distr
N.A.I.C.S.: 424720

Total Especialidades Venezuela, C.A. (1)
Torre Corp Banca Avenida Blandin con Calle Los Chaguaramos Municipio, Chacoa Estado Miranda, Caracas, Venezuela
Tel.: (58) 212 277 60 01
Lubricant & Engine Oil Distr
N.A.I.C.S.: 424720

Total Ethiopia S.C. (1)
Mullege Building 7th Floor, PO Box 1462, Addis Ababa, Ethiopia
Tel.: (251) 114668327
Oil & Gas Exploration Services
N.A.I.C.S.: 213112
Anteneh Begashaw *(Mgr-Corp Affairs)*

Total Exploration & Production (1)
2 Place Jean Miller, La Defense, F-92078, Paris, Cedex, France
Tel.: (33) 147444546
Web Site: http://www.total.com
Oil & Gas Exploration & Production
N.A.I.C.S.: 211120

Subsidiary (Non-US):

Elf Petroleum Nigeria Ltd. (2)
35 Kofo Abayomi St, PO Box 927, Victoria Island, Lagos, Nigeria **(100%)**
Tel.: (234) 1262 3720
Web Site: http://www.total.com
Oil & Gas Production
N.A.I.C.S.: 211120

PT. Total E&P Indonesie (2)
Kuningan Plaza North Tower 4th - 9th Floor, Jl HR Rasuna Said Kav C 11- 14, Jakarta, 12940, Indonesia
Tel.: (62) 215231999
Oil & Gas Exploration Services
N.A.I.C.S.: 213112

Total Abu Al Bu Khoosh S.A. (2)
11th Floor East Tower Abu Dhabi Mall Tourist Club Area, 4058, Abu Dhabi, United Arab Emirates
Tel.: (971) 2 6986666
Oil & Gas Exploration Services
N.A.I.C.S.: 213112
Amer Al Ali *(CEO)*

Total E&P Algerie (2)
17 chemin de la Madeleine, El Biar, 16030, Algiers, Algeria **(99.8%)**
Tel.: (213) 21691512
Web Site: http://www.total.com
Petrochemicals Exploration & Production

N.A.I.C.S.: 325110

Total E&P Angola SA (2)
Avenue 4 Fevereiro North 37, Luanda, Angola
Tel.: (244) 222674000
Oil & Gas Exploration Services
N.A.I.C.S.: 213112

Total E&P Australia (2)
Level 13 28 The Esplanade, Perth, 6000, WA, Australia
Tel.: (61) 8 9442 2000
Emp.: 50
Petroleum Exploration & Production Services
N.A.I.C.S.: 211120
David Mendelson *(Mng Dir)*

Total E&P Azerbaidjan B.V. (2)
69 Nizami str Isr Plaza 15 floor, AZ1005, Baku, Azerbaijan
Tel.: (994) 124978380
Emp.: 40
Oil & Gas Exploration Services
N.A.I.C.S.: 213112
Anna Merzlyakova *(Dir-Fin)*

Total E&P Cameroon (2)
83 Bd Liberte, BP 2214-2215, Douala, Cameroon **(75.4%)**
Tel.: (237) 3421366
Web Site: http://www.total.com
Oil & Gas Production
N.A.I.C.S.: 211120

Total E&P Canada Ltd. (2)
(100%)
Tel.: (403) 571-7599
Web Site: http://www.total-ep-canada.com
Sales Range: $150-199.9 Million
Emp.: 368
Petroleum Exploration & Production
N.A.I.C.S.: 211120

Subsidiary (Domestic):

Total E&P France (2)
Route de Bayonne, BP 22 - RN 117, F-64170, Lacq, France **(100%)**
Tel.: (33) 5 5992 2222
Sales Range: $700-749.9 Million
Emp.: 900
Petrochemicals Exploration & Production
N.A.I.C.S.: 325110

Subsidiary (Non-US):

Total E&P Iran (2)
No 42 Saba St Africa Ave, Tehran, Iran
Tel.: (98) 21 26200263
Oil & Gas Exploration Services
N.A.I.C.S.: 213112

Total E&P Iraq (2)
Hay Al-Wahda Mahalat 906 Zukak 8 House No 21, PO Box 2301, Alwiyah, Baghdad, Iraq
Tel.: (964) 1 719 2908
Oil & Gas Exploration Services
N.A.I.C.S.: 213112

Total E&P Italia SpA (2)
Via Cornelia 498, 166, Rome, Italy
Tel.: (39) 06612481
Web Site: http://www.it.total.com
Emp.: 50
Oil & Gas Exploration Services
N.A.I.C.S.: 213112

Total E&P Kuwait (2)
Salmiya Andash Salem Mubarak Street Marina Plaza Bldg, PO Box 7633, Al-Salmiya, 22087, Kuwait, Kuwait
Tel.: (965) 571 7960
Petroleum Exploration & Production Services
N.A.I.C.S.: 211120

Total E&P Libye (2)
Dhat El Imad Bldg Tower 3 1st Fl, PO Box 91171, Tripoli, Libya **(99.9%)**
Tel.: (218) 213350317
Web Site: http://www.total.com
Petrochemicals Exploration & Production
N.A.I.C.S.: 325110

Total E&P Mauritanie (2)
Lot M No 0058 Tevragh Zeina, BP 5111, Nouakchott, Mauritania
Tel.: (222) 733 0011

Sales Range: $650-699.9 Million
Emp.: 2,000
Oil & Gas Exploration Services
N.A.I.C.S.: 213112

Total E&P Nederland B.V. (2)
(100%)
Tel.: (31) 705129449
Web Site: http://www.ep.total.nl
Sales Range: $150-199.9 Million
Emp.: 300
Oil & Gas Production
N.A.I.C.S.: 211120

Total E&P Norge AS (2)
Finnestadveien 44, Dusavik, Stavanger, 4001, Norway (100%)
Tel.: (47) 51503000
Web Site: https://corporate.totalenergies.no
Sales Range: $5-14.9 Billion
Emp.: 300
Oil & Gas Exploration & Production
N.A.I.C.S.: 213111

Affiliate (Domestic):

Conoco Phillips Norge (3)
Ekofiskvegen 35, PO Box 3, 4056, Tananger, Norway (28%)
Tel.: (47) 52020000
Web Site: https://www.conocophillips.no
Sales Range: $250-299.9 Million
Emp.: 1,800
Oil & Gas Terminal & Pipeline Operator
N.A.I.C.S.: 424710

Unit (Domestic):

Total E&P Norge AS - Harstad (3)
Havnegt 3B, 9404, Harstad, Norway
Tel.: (47) 51503000
Web Site: http://www.total.no
Oil & Gas Exploration & Production
N.A.I.C.S.: 213112

Total E&P Norge AS - Oslo (3)
Haakon VIIs Gt 1, 161, Oslo, Norway
Tel.: (47) 51503000
Web Site: http://www.total.no
Sales Range: $50-74.9 Million
Emp.: 5
Oil & Gas Exploration & Production
N.A.I.C.S.: 213112

Subsidiary (Non-US):

Total E&P Oman (2)
PC 114 Muttrah Way 2241 Bldg 2072, PO Box 663, Qurum, Muscat, Oman
Tel.: (968) 24 571 780
Petroleum Exploration & Production
N.A.I.C.S.: 211120

Total E&P Qatar (2)
Elf Building 25 Al Eahil Street, PO Box 9803, Doha, Qatar
Tel.: (974) 44208111
Web Site: http://www.total.com
Sales Range: $150-199.9 Million
Emp.: 271
Oil & Gas Exploration Services
N.A.I.C.S.: 213112

Total E&P Russia (2)
7 Lesnaya st, 125196, Moscow, Russia
Tel.: (7) 4952286200
Web Site: http://www.ru.total.com
Petroleum Exploration & Production Services
N.A.I.C.S.: 211120

Total E&P Syrie (2)
16 Villat Gharbia Mezzeh Dar Es Saada, Damascus, 9645, Syria
Tel.: (963) 116621400
Oil & Gas Exploration Services
N.A.I.C.S.: 213112

Total E&P Thailand (2)
123 Soi Choeiphuang Vibhavadi Rangsit Road, Bangkok, 10900, Thailand
Tel.: (66) 2 617 6464
Oil & Gas Exploration Services
N.A.I.C.S.: 213112

Total E&P UK Ltd. - London Executive Office (2)
33 Cavendish Sq, London, W1G OPW, United Kingdom
Tel.: (44) 2074164200
Web Site: http://www.uk.total.com

Sales Range: $50-74.9 Million
Emp.: 150
Executive Office
N.A.I.C.S.: 921110

Total E&P UK Limited (3)
Crawpeel Road Altens, Aberdeen, AB12 3FG, United Kingdom
Tel.: (44) 1224297000
Web Site: http://www.uk.total.com
Sales Range: $25-49.9 Million
Emp.: 600
Petroleum Exploration & Production Services
N.A.I.C.S.: 211120

Subsidiary (US):

Total E&P USA Inc. (2)
1201 Louisana St Ste 1800, Houston, TX 77002 (67%)
Tel.: (713) 647-3000
Web Site: http://www.total.com
Sales Range: $75-99.9 Million
Emp.: 250
Oil & Gas Exploration & Production
N.A.I.C.S.: 211120

Subsidiary (Non-US):

Total E&P Yemen (2)
Off Hadda Street, PO Box 15347, Sana'a, Yemen
Tel.: (967) 1414137
Petroleum Exploration & Production Services
N.A.I.C.S.: 211120

Total E&P do Brasil (2)
Republica do chile 500-24, Centro, Rio de Janeiro, 20031-170, Brazil
Tel.: (55) 2121029000
Web Site: http://www.totalbrazil.com.br
Emp.: 100
Petroleum Product Distr
N.A.I.C.S.: 424720

Total Petroleum Ghana PLC (2)
Total House 25 Liberia Road, PO Box 553, Accra, Ghana
Tel.: (233) 302611530
Web Site: https://totalenergies.com.gh
Rev.: $548,619,550
Assets: $192,796,780
Liabilities: $121,637,225
Net Worth: $71,159,556
Earnings: $17,739,353
Emp.: 216
Fiscal Year-end: 12/31/2021
Petroleum Products Marketer
N.A.I.C.S.: 424720

Total Fluides S.A. (1)
24 Cours Michelet La Defense 10, Paris, 92069, France
Tel.: (33) 1 41 35 36 56
Web Site: http://www.totalfluides.fr
Oil & Gas Exploration Services
N.A.I.C.S.: 213112

Total Fuels (Wuhan) Co., Ltd. (1)
Room A11 F/11 New World CenterA No 634 Jiefang Avenue, Wuhan, 430032, Hubei, China
Tel.: (86) 27 83760099
Web Site: http://www.total.com.cn
Industrial Fuel Distr
N.A.I.C.S.: 424720

Total Gabon (1)
Hourcq Boulevard, PO Box 525, Port-Gentil, Gabon (58%)
Tel.: (241) 556000
Web Site: http://www.total-gabon.com
Rev: $237,128,000,000
Assets: $283,654,000,000
Liabilities: $164,201,000,000
Net Worth: $119,453,000,000
Earnings: $21,510,000,000
Fiscal Year-end: 12/31/2023
Crude Petroleum Extraction
N.A.I.C.S.: 211120
Guy Maurice (Chm)

Total Gas & Power (1)
Onur Ofis Park Is Merkezi Inkilap Mahalessi Untel Sok No 10 B1 Blok, Umraniye, 34768, Istanbul, Turkiye
Tel.: (90) 216 63 37 300

Natural Gas Distribution Services
N.A.I.C.S.: 221210

Total Gas & Power North America, Inc (1)
1201 Loisiana Ste 1600, Houston, TX 77002 (100%)
Tel.: (713) 647-4000
Web Site: http://www.total.com
Sales Range: $700-749.9 Million
Emp.: 65
Natural Gas Distribution
N.A.I.C.S.: 221210
Fundi Mwamba (Pres)

Subsidiary (Domestic):

Total Gas & Power New Energies USA, Inc. (2)
Emery Sta 1 5858 Horton St Ste 253, Emeryville, CA 94608
Tel.: (510) 788-6700
Web Site: http://www.usa.total.com
Natural Gas Distribution Services
N.A.I.C.S.: 221210

Total Gas & Power Ventures USA, Inc (2)
Total Plz 1201 Louisiana Ste 1600, Houston, TX 77002
Tel.: (713) 647-4003
Oil & Gas Exploration Services
N.A.I.C.S.: 213112

Plant (Domestic):

Total Port Arthur Refinery (2)
Hwy 366 & 32nd St, Port Arthur, TX 77642
Tel.: (409) 963-6800
Web Site: http://www.usa.total.com
Sales Range: $200-249.9 Million
Petroleum Refining Services
N.A.I.C.S.: 324110
Nagel Tranter (Pres)

Total Guinea Ecuatorial SA (1)
Rotonda de Malabo II Apdo 647, Malabo, Equatorial Guinea
Tel.: (240) 350091800
Oil & Gas Exploration Services
N.A.I.C.S.: 213112

Total Guinee SA (1)
Coleah - Km 4 Route du Niger, BP 306, Conakry, Guinea
Tel.: (224) 623236262
Oil & Gas Exploration Services
N.A.I.C.S.: 213112

Total Hellas S.A. (1)
74-76 Voreiou Ipeirou, Maroussi, Greece
Tel.: (30) 2105440540
Web Site: http://www.total.gr
Emp.: 3
Petroleum & Lubricant Distr
N.A.I.C.S.: 424720

Total Holdings Europe S.A.S. (1)
2 Place Jean Millier, 92078, Courbevoie, France
Tel.: (33) 1 41 35 40 00
Web Site: http://www.total.com
Investment Management Service
N.A.I.C.S.: 523999

Total Holdings UK Limited (1)
33 Cavendish Sq, London, W1G OPW, United Kingdom (100%)
Tel.: (44) 2074164200
Web Site: http://www.uk.total.com
Sales Range: $25-49.9 Million
Emp.: 20
Holding Company
N.A.I.C.S.: 551112

Subsidiary (Domestic):

Total UK Ltd (2)
40 Clarendon Rd, Watford, WD17 1TQ, United Kingdom (100%)
Tel.: (44) 1923694000
Web Site: http://www.uk.total.com
Petroleum Refining & Marketing Operations
N.A.I.C.S.: 324110

Subsidiary (Domestic):

Total Gas and Power Limited (3)
13th Fl 10 Upper Bank St, London, E14 5BF, Canary Wharf, United Kingdom (100%)

Tel.: (44) 2077186000
Web Site: http://www.totalgp.com
Sales Range: $10-24.9 Million
Emp.: 170
Energy Distribution Services
N.A.I.C.S.: 221210

Subsidiary (Domestic):

Elf Business Energy (4)
Bridge Gate 55 57 High Street, Redhill, RH1 1RX, United Kingdom (100%)
Tel.: (44) 1737275500
Energy Sales
N.A.I.C.S.: 221210

Elf Business Energy (4)
Unit 1280 Octagen Century Way, Thorpe Park, Leeds, LS15 8ZB, United Kingdom (100%)
Tel.: (44) 32321000
Energy Sales
N.A.I.C.S.: 221210

Total Honduras, S.A. de C.V. (1)
Colonia El Carrizal Salida Al Norte, Contiguo Gasolinera Dippsa, Tegucigalpa, Honduras
Tel.: (504) 22231008
Sales Range: $50-74.9 Million
Emp.: 2
Oil & Gas Exploration Services
N.A.I.C.S.: 213112
Laurent Gouy (Mng Dir)

Total Italia S.p.A (1)
Via Arconati 1, 20135, Milan, Italy (99.7%)
Tel.: (39) 02540681
Web Site: http://www.totalitalia.it
Sales Range: $200-249.9 Million
Emp.: 300
Oil & Gas Production
N.A.I.C.S.: 211120

Total Jamaica Limited (1)
86 Hope Road, Kingston, Jamaica
Tel.: (876) 9789522
Web Site: https://totalenergies.com.jm
Oil & Gas Exploration Services
N.A.I.C.S.: 213112
Kerrith Annikie (Mgr-Maintenance)

Total Jordan PSC (1)
Reem Center 4th Floor 244 Arar Street Wadi Saqra, Amman, Jordan
Tel.: (962) 65008005
Web Site: http://www.total.jo
Oil & Gas Exploration Services
N.A.I.C.S.: 213112
Stephane Lapauw (Mng Dir)

Total Kenya Plc (1)
Regal Plaza Limuru Road, PO Box 30736, 100, Nairobi, Kenya (87.3%)
Tel.: (254) 202897000
Web Site: https://www.total.co.ke
Rev: $885,901,571
Assets: $391,183,265
Liabilities: $146,754,563
Net Worth: $244,428,703
Earnings: $29,998,441
Emp.: 396
Fiscal Year-end: 12/31/2020
Oil & Petroleum Products Mfr
N.A.I.C.S.: 486110
Irene K. Muinde (Mgr-HR & Admin)

Total Liban SAL (1)
Tel.: (961) 1212250
Oil & Gas Exploration Services
N.A.I.C.S.: 213112
Michele Khalife (Dir-Publication)

Total Lubricantes Do Brasil Ltda (1)
Rua Gomes de Carvalho 1 356 - 5 Andar, Vila Olimpia, Sao Paulo, 04547-005, Brazil
Tel.: (55) 11 3848 2600
Web Site: http://www.totalbras.com.br
Sales Range: $75-99.9 Million
Emp.: 130
Lubricant Distr
N.A.I.C.S.: 424720

Total Lubricants Algerie (1)
60s Boulevard Colonel Ahmed, El Biar, 16406, Algiers, Algeria
Tel.: (213) 21 92 03 33
Engine Oil Lubricant Distr
N.A.I.C.S.: 424720

Total Lubricants Blending UAE Co Ltd (1)

TOTALENERGIES SE INTERNATIONAL PUBLIC

TotalEnergies SE—(Continued)

Rooftop, PO Box 17575, Jebel Ali, United Arab Emirates
Tel.: (971) 48129500
Petroleum & Lubricant Distr
N.A.I.C.S.: 424720

Total Lubricants China Co., Ltd. (1)
Room 3803-06 Raffles Office Building No 268 Xizang Middle Road, Huangpu District, Shanghai, 200001, China
Tel.: (86) 2123202000
Web Site: https://lubricants.totalenergies.cn
Petroleum & Lubricant Distr
N.A.I.C.S.: 424720

Total Lubricants Hong Kong Ltd. (1)
30/F Cambridge House Taikoo Place, Quarry Bay, China (Hong Kong)
Tel.: (852) 25201511
Emp.: 4
Oil & Gas Exploration Services
N.A.I.C.S.: 213112

Total Lubricants USA (1)
5 N Stiles St, Linden, NJ 07036
Tel.: (908) 862-9300
Web Site: http://www.total-us.com
Sales Range: $25-49.9 Million
Emp.: 30
Production of Lubricating Oils & Greases
N.A.I.C.S.: 324191

Total Lubrifiants Algerie SPA (1)
20 rue Sfindja, El Biar, 16023, Algiers, Algeria
Tel.: (213) 21920333
Oil & Gas Exploration Services
N.A.I.C.S.: 213112
Redouane Karar (Dir-Lubricants)

Total Lubrifiants SA (1)
562 Avenue du Parc de l'Ile, 92029, Nanterre, Cedex, France
Oil & Gas Exploration Services
N.A.I.C.S.: 213112
Jean-Gabriel Klingsheim (Dir-Publication)

Total Malawi Limited (1)
Maselema, Private Bag 5125, Limbe, Blantyre, Malawi
Tel.: (265) 1847766
Oil & Gas Exploration Services
N.A.I.C.S.: 213112
Arnold Njikho (Mgr-Technical Sls)

Total Marketing Middle East LLC (1)
Burjuman Business Towers 11th Floor Sheikh Khalifa Bin Zayed Road, PO Box 14871, Dubai, United Arab Emirates
Tel.: (971) 4.7095000
Web Site: http://www.totalmarketingmiddleeast.com
Automotive & Industrial Lubricant Mfr
N.A.I.C.S.: 324191

Total Mauritius Ltd (1)
Chaussee Tromelin, PO Box 1202, Port Louis, Mauritius
Tel.: (230) 2075600
Web Site: https://services.totalenergies.mu
Petroleum Product Distr
N.A.I.C.S.: 424720

Total Mayotte SAS (1)
Immeuble jacaranda 1 Lotissement 3 Vallees, BP 867, Kaweni, 97600, Mamoudzou, France
Tel.: (33) 269601294
Oil & Gas Exploration Services
N.A.I.C.S.: 213112

Total Mexico S.A De C.V (1)
8 de Julio Avenue number 2462, ona Industrial neighborhood, 44940, Guadalajara, Jalisco, Mexico
Tel.: (52) 3338122300
Web Site: https://totalenergies.mx
Lubricant Distr
N.A.I.C.S.: 424720

Total Mozambique SA
Av Sociedade de Geografia n 83 5th Floor, PO 2073, Maputo, Mozambique
Tel.: (258) 21307230
Web Site: http://www.total.co.mz
Oil & Gas Exploration Services
N.A.I.C.S.: 213112
Guy-Mohamed Hoguie (Compliance Officer)

Total Nederland N V (1)
Nieuwe Havenstraat 2, 2272 AD, Voorburg, Netherlands **(100%)**
Tel.: (31) 703180480
Web Site: http://www.total.nl
Sales Range: $75-99.9 Million
Emp.: 250
Holding Company
N.A.I.C.S.: 551112
Alwin Kautz (Mgr-Shop-Food & Svcs)

Total Nigeria PLC (1)
Total House 4 Churchgate Street, Victoria Island, Lagos, Nigeria
Tel.: (234) 14631681
Web Site: http://www.total.com.ng
Oil & Gas Exploration Services
N.A.I.C.S.: 213112
Adesua Adewole (Gen Mgr-HR)

Total Oil (Thailand) Co. Ltd (1)
173/5 Asia Centre Building 12th Floor South Sathorn Road, Thungmahamek Sathorn, Bangkok, 10120, Thailand
Tel.: (66) 2163636471
Web Site: https://services.th.totalenergies.com
Automotive Lubricant Mfr & Distr
N.A.I.C.S.: 324191

Total Oil India Pvt Ltd (1)
138 Ground Floor & First Floor Raheja Paramount Residency Road, Bengaluru, 560 025, India
Tel.: (91) 80 42730000
Web Site: http://www.total.com
Sales Range: $50-74.9 Million
Emp.: 100
Oil & Gas Exploration Services
N.A.I.C.S.: 213112

Total Oil India Pvt. Ltd. (1)
3rd Floor The Leela Galleria, Andheri E, Mumbai, 400059, Maharashtra, India
Tel.: (91) 8001023339
Web Site: https://totalenergies.in
Sales Range: $150-199.9 Million
Emp.: 30
Petroleum & Lubricant Distr
N.A.I.C.S.: 424720

Total Oil Malaysia Sdn Bhd (1)
2nd Level Wisma Kemajuan 2 Jalan 19/1B, 46300, Petaling Jaya, Selangor Darul Ehsan, Malaysia
Tel.: (60) 377112000
Web Site: https://totalenergies.my
Oil & Gas Exploration Services
N.A.I.C.S.: 213112
Krishnan As (Mng Dir)

Total Oil Turkey A.S. (1)
Total Gebze Terminali Limantepe Mevkii TavSancil Gebze, Gebze, Kocaeli, Turkiye
Tel.: (90) 262 754 71 84
Web Site: http://www.total.com.tr
Petroleum Product Whslr
N.A.I.C.S.: 424720

Total Opslag En Pijpleiding Nederland NV (1)
Luxemburgweg 1, 4455 TM, Nieuwdorp, Netherlands
Tel.: (31) 635250396
Web Site: http://www.tspn.nl
Oil Fluid Pipeline Storage Services
N.A.I.C.S.: 237120

Total Outre-Mer S.A. (1)
2 Place Jean Millier La Defense, Courbevoie, 92400, France
Tel.: (33) 141354000
Web Site: http://www.total.com
Oil & Natural Gas Distribution Services
N.A.I.C.S.: 221210

Total Pacifique SA (1)
30 Route de la Baie des Dames Building Le Center, BP 717, Ducos, 98845, Noumea, New Caledonia
Tel.: (687) 279050
Web Site: http://www.total.nc
Oil & Gas Exploration Services
N.A.I.C.S.: 213112
Nicolas Favre (Mng Dir)

Total Parco Pakistan Limited (1)
10 - Tariq Block, New Garden Town, Lahore, Pakistan
Tel.: (92) 42111709709

Engine Oil Lubricant Distr
N.A.I.C.S.: 424720
Mehmet Celepoglu (CEO)

Total Parco Pakistan Ltd. (1)
10 Tariq Block, New Garden Town, Lahore, 54700, Pakistan
Tel.: (92) 42111709709
Fuel & Petroleum Products Retail
N.A.I.C.S.: 424720

Total Petrochemicals (1)
52 Rue De L Industrie, 1040, Brussels, 1040, Belgium **(100%)**
Tel.: (32) 22889111
Web Site: http://www.totalpetrochemicals.com
Sales Range: $200-249.9 Million
Emp.: 600
Fuel Distribution Services
N.A.I.C.S.: 424690

Unit (Domestic):

Fina Antwerp Olefins
Scheldelaan 10, B-2030, Antwerp, Belgium
Tel.: (32) 35452011
Petrochemical Mfr
N.A.I.C.S.: 325110

Joint Venture (Non-US):

Qatar Petrochemical Company Ltd. (2)
PO Box 756, Doha, Qatar
Tel.: (974) 40338000
Web Site: http://www.qapco.com
Sales Range: $300-349.9 Million
Mfr of Petrochemicals; Owned 80% by Qatar Petroleum & 20% by Total S.A.
N.A.I.C.S.: 325110
Abdulaziz Jassim M. Al-Muftah (Chm)

Affiliate (Domestic):

Qatar Plastic Products Company W.L.L. (3)
Nike Industrial Area, PO Box 50174, Mesaieed, 50174, Qatar
Tel.: (974) 4770815
Web Site: https://www.qppc.net
Emp.: 38
N.A.I.C.S.: 326199

Joint Venture (Non-US):

Samsung Total Petrochemicals Co., Ltd. (2)
103 Dokgot2-Ro Daesan-Eup, Seosan, 356-711, ChungNam, Korea (South) **(50%)**
Tel.: (82) 41 660 6114
Web Site: http://www.samsungchem.com
Olefin, Polyolefin & Aromatic Chemical Products Mfr & Distr
N.A.I.C.S.: 325110
Seog-Weon Son (Pres & CEO)

Subsidiary (US):

Total Petrochemicals & Refining USA, Inc. (2)
1201 Louisiana St Ste 1800, Houston, TX 77002 **(100%)**
Tel.: (713) 483-5000
Web Site: http://www.totalpetrochemicalsusa.com
Emp.: 5,000
Polypropylene, Polyethylene & Polystyrene, Styrene, Base Chemicals & Transportation Fuels Mfr
N.A.I.C.S.: 325110

Plant (Domestic):

Total Petrochemicals (3)
6325 Hwy 75 & River Rd, Carville, LA 70721
Tel.: (225) 642-5454
Web Site: http://www.totalpetrochemicalsusa.com
Sales Range: $50-74.9 Million
Emp.: 200
Mfr of Styrene & Polystyrene
N.A.I.C.S.: 325110

Total Petrochemicals & Refining USA, Inc. - Bayport (3)
12212 Port Dr, Pasadena, TX 77507-1800
Tel.: (281) 474-6000

Web Site: http://www.totalpetrochemicalsusa.com
Sales Range: $350-399.9 Million
Emp.: 116
Petrochemical Mfr
N.A.I.C.S.: 325110

Total Petrochemicals USA, Inc. - La Porte (3)
1818 Independence Pkwy S, La Porte, TX 77571
Tel.: (281) 476-3700
Web Site: http://www.totalpetrochemicalsusa.com
Sales Range: $75-99.9 Million
Emp.: 300
Mfr of Polypropylene
N.A.I.C.S.: 325110

Total Petrochemicals USA, Inc. - Port Arthur (3)
Hwy 336 & 32 nd St, Port Arthur, TX 77642 **(100%)**
Tel.: (409) 963-6800
Emp.: 600
Mfr of Transportation Fuel, Propane, Butane, Base Chemicals & Asphalt
N.A.I.C.S.: 324110
Brayn Canfield (Gen Mgr)

Subsidiary (Domestic):

Total Petrochemicals, Inc. (3)
1818 Independence Pkwy S, La Porte, TX 77551
Tel.: (281) 476-3700
Web Site: http://www.petrochemicals.com
Sales Range: $50-74.9 Million
Emp.: 149
Research & Technology Center
N.A.I.C.S.: 324110

Subsidiary (Non-US):

Total Petrochemicals (Foshan) Co., Ltd. (2)
No 61 Jinben Industry Avenue Xi-nan Subdistrict, Sanshui District, Foshan, 528132, Guangdong, China
Tel.: (86) 757 8751 7888
Web Site: http://www.cn.total.com
Petrochemical Products Mfr
N.A.I.C.S.: 325110

Total Petrochemicals (Hong Kong) Ltd. (2)
Unit 2905-07 Millennium City 6 392 Kwun Tong Road, Kwun Tong, Kowloon, China (Hong Kong)
Tel.: (852) 21101188
Web Site: http://www.cn.total.com
Emp.: 35
Petrochemical Products Mfr
N.A.I.C.S.: 325110

Unit (Domestic):

Total Petrochemicals Antwerpen (2)
Scheldelaan 10, Antwerp, B 2030, Belgium
Tel.: (32) 35452011
Web Site: http://www.be.total.com
Sales Range: $200-249.9 Million
Petrochemical Mfr
N.A.I.C.S.: 325110

Total Petrochemicals Feluy (2)
Zoning Industriel Zone C, 7181, Feluy, Hainaut, Belgium **(100%)**
Tel.: (32) 64517211
Web Site: http://www.totalpetrochemicals.com
Sales Range: $125-149.9 Million
Emp.: 500
Mfr of Petrochemicals
N.A.I.C.S.: 325110

Subsidiary (Non-US):

Total Petrochemicals Taipei (2)
8/F-5 National Enterprise Center No 188 Nanking East Road Sec 5, Taipei, Taiwan
Tel.: (886) 227476979
Web Site: http://www.total.com.cn
Petrochemical Mfr
N.A.I.C.S.: 325110

Total Petrochemicals UK Limited (2)
Globe House Bayley St, Stalybridge, SK15 1PY, Cheshire, United Kingdom
Tel.: (44) 01613384411

AND PRIVATE COMPANIES — TOTALENERGIES SE

Web Site: http://www.totalpetrochemicals.com
Sales Range: $350-399.9 Million
Emp.: 220
Specialty Chemicals & Plastics Raw Materials Mfr & Sales
N.A.I.C.S.: 325211

Subsidiary (Domestic):

Sovereign Chemicals Limited (3)
Park Road, Barrow-in-Furness, LA14 4QU, Cumbria, United Kingdom (100%)
Web Site: http://www.sovchem.co.uk
Sales Range: $25-49.9 Million
Emp.: 60
Building Chemicals & Paint Mfrs.
N.A.I.C.S.: 325510

Plant (Domestic):

Sovereign Chemicals Ltd (4)
Park Road Barrow-In-Furness, Barrow-in-Furness, LA14 4EQ, Cumbria, United Kingdom
Tel.: (44) 1416479117
Web Site: http://www.sovchem.co.uk
Sales Range: $75-99.9 Million
Emp.: 9
Building Chemicals & Sealants Mfr
N.A.I.C.S.: 325520

Sovereign Chemicals Ltd (4)
Park Rd, Barrow-in-Furness, LA14 4EQ, Cumbria, United Kingdom
Tel.: (44) 870800
Web Site: http://www.sovchem.co.uk
Building Chemicals & Paint Mfrs.
N.A.I.C.S.: 325180

Unit (Domestic):

Total Raffinaderij Antwerpen (2)
Haven 447 Scheldelaan 16, B 2030, Antwerp, Belgium (100%)
Tel.: (32) 035455011
Web Site: http://www.be.total.com
Sales Range: $200-249.9 Million
Crude Oil Refining
N.A.I.C.S.: 324110

Total Research & Technology Feluy (2)
Zone Industrielle Feluy C, Seneffe, BE 7181, Feluy, Belgium (100%)
Tel.: (32) 64514111
Web Site: http://www.totalrefiningchemicals.com
Sales Range: $100-124.9 Million
Emp.: 500
Petrochemical Research & Development
N.A.I.C.S.: 541715

Total Petroleum Hong Kong Ltd. (1)
No 9 South Runway Road Hong Kong International Airport, Lantau, Hong Kong, China (Hong Kong)
Tel.: (852) 21802559
Web Site: http://www.total.com.cn
Petroleum Product Distr
N.A.I.C.S.: 424720

Total Petroleum Puerto Rico Corp. (1)
Millennium Park Plz Ste 15 Calle 2 Ste 525, Guaynabo, PR 00968
Tel.: (787) 783-4625
Web Site: https://totalenergies.com.pr
Emp.: 65
Petroleum Product Distr
N.A.I.C.S.: 424720

Total Polynesie S.A. (1)
Tahiti, BP 64, 98713, Papeete, French Polynesia
Tel.: (689) 40485050
Web Site: http://www.total.pf
Oil & Gas Exploration Services
N.A.I.C.S.: 213112

Total Projects India Ltd (1)
6B 6th Floor Lotus Towers Community Centre New Friends Colony, New Delhi, 110 025, India
Tel.: (91) 114 103 70 00
Sales Range: $25-49.9 Million
Emp.: 15
Petroleum & Lubricant Distr
N.A.I.C.S.: 424720
Ashutosh Agrawal *(Gen Mgr-Bus Dev)*

Total R&M Trinidad & Tobago Ltd. (1)
25 Warner Street, Port of Spain, Trinidad & Tobago
Tel.: (868) 6282906
Sales Range: $50-74.9 Million
Emp.: 5
Engine Oil Lubricant Distr
N.A.I.C.S.: 424720

Total RDC SA (1)
Kinshasa - 24 Av Cadeco, Gombe, Congo, Democratic Republic of
Tel.: (243) 808518881
Web Site: http://www.total.cd
Oil & Gas Exploration Services
N.A.I.C.S.: 213112

Total Raffinage France SA (1)
Plateforme de Donges, CS 9005, 44480, Donges, France
Tel.: (33) 240905500
Web Site: http://www.donges.total.fr
Oil Refinery Services
N.A.I.C.S.: 324110

Total Reunion S.A. (1)
3 rue Jacques Prevert La Reunion, CS 11190, 97829, Le Port, France
Tel.: (33) 262552030
Web Site: http://www.total.re
Oil & Gas Exploration Services
N.A.I.C.S.: 213112

Total Romania S.A. (1)
42-44 Bucuresti Ploiesti Road Entrance A A2 Building 1st Floor, District 1, 13696, Bucharest, Romania
Tel.: (40) 213610551
Web Site: http://www.total.com.ro
Emp.: 10
Petroleum & Lubricant Distr
N.A.I.C.S.: 424720

Total Solar International SAS (1)
2 Place Jean Millier La Defense, Courbevoie, 92400, France (100%)
Tel.: (33) 1 47 44 27 90
Oil & Gas Exploration Services
N.A.I.C.S.: 213112

Total Solar Intl SAS (1)
Tour CBX-1 passerelle des Reflets, 92400, Courbevoie, France
Tel.: (33) 170375580
Web Site: http://www.solar.total.com
Solar Electric Power Generation Services
N.A.I.C.S.: 221114

Total South Africa (Pty.) Ltd. (1)
Saxonwold, PO Box 579, Johannesburg, 2196, Johannes, South Africa (100%)
Tel.: (27) 117782000
Sales Range: $200-249.9 Million
Emp.: 550
Oil Refining & Marketing
N.A.I.C.S.: 324110

Subsidiary (Non-US):

Total Botswana (2)
LOT 22010 Kgomokasitwa Road, Gaborone, Botswana
Tel.: (267) 356673
Petroleum Products Sales
N.A.I.C.S.: 424720

Total Lesotho (Pty) Ltd (2)
Motsoane Road, Maseru, 100, Lesotho
Tel.: (266) 316 187
Web Site: http://www.outremer.total.com
Petroleum Products
N.A.I.C.S.: 424720

Total Namibia (Pty) Ltd (2)
2nd Fl Southern Life Tower, Post Street Mall, Windhoek, Namibia
Tel.: (264) 61237650
Web Site: http://www.total.com
Sales & Marketing of Petroleum Products
N.A.I.C.S.: 424720

Total Swaziland (Pty) Ltd (2)
193 Manzini King Sobhuza 2nd Ave, 200, Matsapha, Eswatini
Tel.: (268) 5184238
Sales Range: $25-49.9 Million
Emp.: 8
Petroleum Products
N.A.I.C.S.: 424720

Total Special Fluids (1)
51 Esplanade du General de Gaulle, 92907, Paris, France
Tel.: (33) 141352701
Web Site: http://www.totalspecialfluids.com
Petroleum Product Mfr
N.A.I.C.S.: 324199

Plant (Domestic):

Total Special Fluids - The Oudalle Plant (2)
ZI du Havre Route du Canal de Tancarville, 76430, Oudalle, France
Tel.: (33) 2 32 79 52 52
Web Site: http://www.totalspecialfluids.com
Petroleum Product Mfr
N.A.I.C.S.: 324199

Total Specialties USA Inc. (1)
1201 Louisiana St Ste 1800, Houston, TX 77002
Tel.: (713) 969-4600
Web Site: http://www.totalspecialties.com
Oil & Gas Exploration Services
N.A.I.C.S.: 213112
Peter Egan *(VP-Special Fluids)*

Total Tanzanie Ltd. (1)
Nkruma Street, PO Box 1503, Dar es Salaam, Tanzania
Tel.: (255) 222113484
Sales Range: $50-74.9 Million
Emp.: 10
Petroleum Product Distr
N.A.I.C.S.: 424720

Total Togo SA (1)
69 Bd de la Paix, Lome, Togo
Tel.: (228) 22236800
Web Site: http://www.totaltogo.com
Oil & Gas Exploration Services
N.A.I.C.S.: 213112

Total Trading Canada Limited (1)
500-5940 Macleod Trail SW, Calgary, T2H 2G4, AB, Canada
Tel.: (587) 888-9987
Web Site: http://www.totaltradingcanada.com
Trading & Marketing Services
N.A.I.C.S.: 425120
Tae Kim *(Pres & CEO)*

Total Transport Maritime (1)
2 Place Jean Millier, 92078, Paris, France (100%)
Tel.: (33) 0147444546
Web Site: http://www.total.fr
Sales Range: $200-249.9 Million
Emp.: 1,000
Oil Shipping & Other Marine Activities
N.A.I.C.S.: 483111

Total Uganda Limited (1)
Plot 4 8th Street Industrial Area, PO Box 3079, Kampala, Uganda
Tel.: (256) 752793555
Oil & Gas Exploration Services
N.A.I.C.S.: 213112
Ted Mugisa *(Mgr-Sls & Mktg)*

Total Upstream Danmark A/S (1)
Amerika Plads 29, 2100, Copenhagen, Denmark
Tel.: (45) 33647000
Oil & Gas Operation Services
N.A.I.C.S.: 213112
Rasmus Havsteen *(Project Mgr-Wells)*

Total Upstream Nigeria Ltd. (1)
35 Kofo Abayomi Street, Lagos, Nigeria
Tel.: (234) 12623720
Oil & Gas Exploration Services
N.A.I.C.S.: 213112
Elisabeth Proust *(CEO & Mng Dir)*

Total Vietnam Limited (1)
No 1601 16th Floor Sailing Building No 111a Pasteur, Ben Nghe Ward District 1, Ho Chi Minh City, Vietnam
Tel.: (84) 862998400
Web Site: http://www.total.com.vn
Oil & Gas Exploration Services
N.A.I.C.S.: 213112
Hoang Anh *(Sls Mgr)*

Total Vostok OOO (1)
Lesnaya Street 7 Building A Floor 6 Room 26, 125196, Moscow, Russia
Tel.: (7) 4959373784

Web Site: http://www.total-lub.ru
Oil & Gas Exploration Services
N.A.I.C.S.: 213112
Alexey Klepikov *(Dir-Supply Chain Logistics)*

Total Zimbabwe Pvt. Ltd. (1)
Number 1 Auckland Road, Southerton, Harare, Zimbabwe
Tel.: (263) 8677004344
Oil & Gas Exploration Services
N.A.I.C.S.: 213112

TotalEnergies (Beijing) Corporate Management Co., Ltd. (1)
30/F Tower 3 China Central Place No 77 Jianguo Road, Chaoyang District, Beijing, China
Tel.: (86) 1085905666
Web Site: https://corporate.totalenergies.cn
Emp.: 4,000
Oil Exploration & Refining Services
N.A.I.C.S.: 211120

TotalEnergies Additives and Fuels Solutions (1)
3 Place du Bassin, 69700, Givors, France
Tel.: (33) 472492700
Web Site: https://additives-fuels.totalenergies.com
Motor Vehicles Mfr
N.A.I.C.S.: 336370

TotalEnergies Distribuidora Brasil LTDA. (1)
Av Tobias Salgado 45 Distrito Industrial, Pindamonhangaba, Sao Paulo, CEP 12412-770, Brazil
Tel.: (55) 8000335045
Petroleum Product Distr
N.A.I.C.S.: 424720

TotalEnergies EP Danmark A/S (1)
Britanniavej 10, 6700, Esbjerg, Denmark
Tel.: (45) 75451366
Oil & Gas Field Exploration Services
N.A.I.C.S.: 213112

TotalEnergies EP Nederland B.V. (1)
Prinses Catharina-Amaliastraat 5, 2496 XD, Hague, Netherlands
Tel.: (31) 705129449
Web Site: https://services.totalenergies.nl
Emp.: 165
Petroleum Product Distr
N.A.I.C.S.: 424720

TotalEnergies EP Nigeria Ltd. (1)
TotalEnergies House Plot 247 Herbert Macaulay Way, Central Business District Federal Capital Territory, Abuja, Nigeria
Tel.: (234) 8039037007
Web Site: https://corporate.totalenergies.ng
Oil & Gas Field Exploration Services
N.A.I.C.S.: 213112

TotalEnergies EP Norge AS (1)
Finnestadveien 44 Dusavik, N-4029, Stavanger, Norway
Tel.: (47) 51503000
Web Site: https://corporate.totalenergies.no
Oil & Gas Exploration Services
N.A.I.C.S.: 213112

TotalEnergies EP PNG Ltd. (1)
Level 7 Deloitte Haus MacGregor Street-CBD, PO Box 1145, National Capital District, 121, Port Moresby, Papua New Guinea
Tel.: (675) 70910000
Web Site: https://totalenergies.com.pg
Oil & Gas Field Exploration Services
N.A.I.C.S.: 213112

TotalEnergies Glass Lubricants Europe GmbH (1)
Zeithstrasse 136, Seelscheid, D-53819, Neunkirchen, Germany
Tel.: (49) 22476608
Glass Lubrication Mfr & Distr
N.A.I.C.S.: 325998

TotalEnergies Marine Fuels Pte. Ltd. (1)
182 Cecil Street 27-01 Frasers Tower, Singapore, 069547, Singapore
Tel.: (65) 68495266
Web Site: https://marinefuels.totalenergies.com
Oil & Gas Exploration Services

TOTALENERGIES SE

TotalEnergies SE—(Continued)
N.A.I.C.S.: 213112

TotalEnergies Marketing (Fiji) Pte. Ltd. (1)
16 Rona Street Walu Bay, Suva, Fiji
Tel.: (679) 9997768
Web Site: https://totalenergies.com.fj
Engine Oil & Transmission Oil Mfr
N.A.I.C.S.: 336390

TotalEnergies Marketing Ceska republika S.R.O. (1)
Rohanske nabrezi 678/29 River Garden Budova D 8 - Karlin, 186 00, Prague, Czech Republic
Tel.: (420) 224890511
Web Site: https://totalenergies.cz
Automotive Oil Distr
N.A.I.C.S.: 423120

TotalEnergies Marketing Egypt (1)
Corner st 254 & 206 Degla, Maadi, Cairo, Egypt
Tel.: (20) 25225600
Web Site: https://totalenergies.eg
Petroleum Product Distr
N.A.I.C.S.: 424720

TotalEnergies Marketing Ethiopia Share Company (1)
Mullege Building 7th Floor, PO Box 1462, Addis Ababa, Ethiopia
Tel.: (251) 114668327
Web Site: https://totalenergies.et
Petroleum Product Distr
N.A.I.C.S.: 424720

TotalEnergies Marketing Ghana PLC (1)
TotalEnergies House 25 Liberia Road, Accra, GA-077-7769, Ghana
Tel.: (233) 302611530
Web Site: https://totalenergies.com.gh
Petroleum Product Distr
N.A.I.C.S.: 424720

TotalEnergies Marketing Italia S.p.A. (1)
Via Rombon 11, 20132, Milan, Italy
Tel.: (39) 02540681
Web Site: https://services.totalenergies.it
Lubricants Product Distr
N.A.I.C.S.: 424720

TotalEnergies Marketing Jamaica Ltd. (1)
86 Hope Road 6, Kingston, Jamaica
Tel.: (876) 9789522
Web Site: https://totalenergies.com.jm
Automotive Engine Services
N.A.I.C.S.: 811111

TotalEnergies Marketing Kenya PLC (1)
Regal Plaza Limuru Road, PO Box 30736, Nairobi, Kenya
Tel.: (254) 2897000
Web Site: https://totalenergies.ke
Petroleum Product Distr
N.A.I.C.S.: 424720

TotalEnergies Marketing Luxembourg S.A. (1)
310 route d Esch, 1471, Luxembourg, Luxembourg
Tel.: (352) 80026060
Web Site: https://my.totalenergies.lu
Heating Oil Distr
N.A.I.C.S.: 424710

TotalEnergies Marketing Madagasikara S.A. (1)
Immeuble Fitaratra Ankorondrano, 101, Antananarivo, Madagascar
Tel.: (261) 202239040
Web Site: https://totalenergies.mg
Petroleum Product Distr
N.A.I.C.S.: 424720

TotalEnergies Marketing Malawi Ltd. (1)
Private Bag 5125, Limbe - Maselema, Blantyre, Malawi
Tel.: (265) 1847766
Web Site: https://totalenergies.mw
Emp.: 500
Petroleum Fuel Product Distr
N.A.I.C.S.: 424720

TotalEnergies Marketing Mauritius Ltd. (1)
Chaussee Tromelin, PO Box 1202, 11609, Port Louis, Mauritius
Tel.: (230) 2075600
Web Site: https://services.totalenergies.mu
Vehicle Maintenance Services
N.A.I.C.S.: 811198

TotalEnergies Marketing Mexico S.A. de C.V. (1)
Avenida 8 de Julio Numero 2462 Colonia Zona Industrial, 44940, Guadalajara, Jalisco, Mexico
Tel.: (52) 3338122300
Web Site: https://totalenergies.mx
Fuel & Lubricant Product Distr
N.A.I.C.S.: 424720

TotalEnergies Marketing Mocambique S.A. (1)
Av Julius Nyerere nr 3412-R/C TotalEnergies Card- 1, Postal 2073, Escritorios Caixa, Maputo, Mozambique
Tel.: (258) 823171340
Web Site: https://services.totalenergies.co.mz
Petroleum Product Distr
N.A.I.C.S.: 424720

TotalEnergies Marketing Namibia (Pty.) Ltd. (1)
No 55 Rehobother Road Ausspannplatz, Windhoek, Namibia
Tel.: (264) 61374900
Hydrocarbon Distr
N.A.I.C.S.: 486210

TotalEnergies Marketing Nigeria PLC (1)
Total House 4 Churchgate Street Victoria Island, Lagos, Nigeria
Tel.: (234) 14631681
Web Site: https://services.totalenergies.ng
Emp.: 470
Petroleum Product Distr
N.A.I.C.S.: 424720

TotalEnergies Marketing Romania S.A. (1)
Strada Stejarilor nr 2, Cristian, 507055, Brasov, Romania
Tel.: (40) 268401711
Web Site: https://totalenergies.ro
Motorcycles & Transport Vehicle Engine Oil Mfr
N.A.I.C.S.: 336390

TotalEnergies Marketing South Africa (Pty.) Ltd. (1)
Total House 3 Biermann Avenue, Rosebank, South Africa
Tel.: (27) 117782000
Web Site: https://totalenergies.co.za
Petroleum Product Mfr & Distr
N.A.I.C.S.: 324191

TotalEnergies Marketing Taiwan Ltd. (1)
9th Floor No 178 Section 3 Minquan East Road, Songshan District, Taipei, Taiwan
Tel.: (886) 227198201
Web Site: https://totalenergies.tw
Automotive Lubricant Oil Distr
N.A.I.C.S.: 424720

TotalEnergies Marketing Tanzania Ltd. (1)
Total House Msasani Peninsula Haile Sellasie Road Plot No 1720, PO Box 1503, Dar es Salaam, Tanzania
Tel.: (255) 800750242
Web Site: https://totalenergies.co.tz
Petroleum Product Distr
N.A.I.C.S.: 424720

TotalEnergies Marketing USA Inc. (1)
1201 Louisiana St Ste 1800, Houston, TX 77002
Tel.: (713) 969-4600
Web Site: https://services.us.totalenergies.com
Glass Lubricant & Coating Mfr
N.A.I.C.S.: 324191

TotalEnergies Marketing Vietnam Company Ltd. (1)
Unit 1601 Sailing Tower 111A Pasteur Street, District 1, Ho Chi Minh City, Vietnam
Tel.: (84) 906954596
Web Site: https://totalenergies.vn
Industrial Lubricant Oil Mfr & Distr
N.A.I.C.S.: 324191

TotalEnergies Marketing Zimbabwe (Private) Ltd. (1)
Number 1 Auckland Road, Southerton, Harare, Zimbabwe
Tel.: (263) 8677004344
Web Site: https://zw.totalenergies.com
Petroleum Product Distr
N.A.I.C.S.: 424720

TotalEnergies Raffinerie Mitteldeutschland GmbH (1)
Maienweg 1, 06237, Leuna, Germany
Tel.: (49) 8004848112
Natural Gas Mfr & Distr
N.A.I.C.S.: 325194

TotalEnergies SE (1)
2 Place Jean Millier, 92078, Paris, Cedex, France (73.04%)
Tel.: (33) 147444546
Web Site: http://www.totalenergies.com
Sales Range: $100-149.9 Billion
Emp.: 100,000
Electricity & Gas Supplier
N.A.I.C.S.: 221122
Xavier Caitucoli (Chm & CEO)

Subsidiary (Domestic):

Total Quadran SAS (2)
74 rue Lieutenant de Montcabrier Mazeran Technopark CS 10034, 34536, Beziers, France
Tel.: (33) 4 67 32 63 30
Web Site: http://renouvelables.totalenergies.fr
Wind, Photovoltaics, Hyraulics, Biogas & Biomass Electricity Generation
N.A.I.C.S.: 221115
Karine Pallandre (Sec)

TotalEnergies Trading Canada L.P. (1)
4700 888-3rd Street SW, Calgary, T2P 5C5, AB, Canada
Tel.: (403) 571-7599
Petrochemical Product Mfr & Distr
N.A.I.C.S.: 324110

TotalEnergies Turkey Pazarlama A.S. (1)
Saray Mh Dr Adnan Buyukdeniz Cd Akkom Ofis Park 3 Blok No 2 Kat 3, Umraniye, Istanbul, Turkiye
Tel.: (90) 2166390200
Web Site: https://tr.totalenergies.com
Engine Parts & Component Mfr
N.A.I.C.S.: 336310

TotalEnergies Upstream Danmark A/S (1)
Amerika Plads 29, 2100, Copenhagen, Denmark
Tel.: (45) 33647000
Oil & Gas Field Exploration Services
N.A.I.C.S.: 213112

TotalEnergies Warme&Kraftstoff Deutschland GmbH (1)
Am Blumenkampshof 55, 47059, Duisburg, Germany
Tel.: (49) 30202760
Web Site: https://www.heizoel.com
Heating Oil Distr
N.A.I.C.S.: 424710

Urbaine Des Petroles Sas (1)
8 Rue Eugene Armand Peugeot, 92567, Rueil-Malmaison, France
Tel.: (33) 1 47 14 65 00
Oil & Gas Exploration Services
N.A.I.C.S.: 213112

V Energy S.A. (1)
Acropolis Tower 10th Floor Av Winston Churchill, Ensanche Piantini, Santo Domingo, Dominican Republic
Tel.: (809) 8092620200
Web Site: http://www.total.com.do
Oil & Gas Exploration Services
N.A.I.C.S.: 213112
Philippe Jaurrey (CEO)

Vibrachoc S.A.U. (1)
C/ Vereda de las Yeguas s/n, Pol Industrial El Guijar, 28500, Arganda del Rey, Madrid, Spain
Tel.: (34) 918760806
Metal Products Mfr
N.A.I.C.S.: 332999
Sergio Anda Perez (Sls Mgr)

Zeeland Refinery NV (1)
Luxemburgweg 1, 4455 TM, Nieuwdorp, Netherlands
Tel.: (31) 113619000
Crude Oil Extraction Services
N.A.I.C.S.: 211120
Stefan Burggraaf (Engr-Mechanical)

TOTALLY HIP TECHNOLOGIES INC.

Suite 702 - 889 West Pender Street, Vancouver, V6C 3B2, BC, Canada
Tel.: (604) 683-3288
Web Site: http://www.totallyhip.com
Year Founded: 1995
THP—(TSXV)
Assets: $34,530
Liabilities: $350,836
Net Worth: ($316,306)
Earnings: ($93,632)
Fiscal Year-end: 09/30/23
Custom Computer Programming Services
N.A.I.C.S.: 541511
John Brydle (Pres & CEO)

TOTALLY PLC

Cardinal Square West 10 Nottingham Road, Derby, DE1 3QT, United Kingdom
Tel.: (44) 2038663330   UK
Web Site: https://www.totallyplc.com
Year Founded: 1999
TLY—(AIM)
Rev.: $134,660,439
Assets: $79,944,459
Liabilities: $37,366,827
Net Worth: $42,577,632
Earnings: ($3,956,072)
Emp.: 1,403
Fiscal Year-end: 03/31/24
Software Development Services
N.A.I.C.S.: 541511
Wendy Lawrence (CEO)

Subsidiaries:

About Health Limited (1)
Cardinal Square West 10 Nottingham Road, Derby, DE1 3QT, United Kingdom
Tel.: (44) 1254282930
Web Site: http://www.abouthealthgroup.com
Healthcare Services
N.A.I.C.S.: 621999
Richard Benson (Founder)

Premier Physical Healthcare Limited (1)
Cardinal Square West 10 Nottingham Road, Derby, DE1 3QT, United Kingdom
Tel.: (44) 2076877600
Web Site: https://www.premierphysicalhealth.co.uk
Healthcare Services
N.A.I.C.S.: 621999
Lisa Barter (Grp Dir-Fin)

Totally Health Limited (1)
999 Finchley Road, London, NW11 7HB, United Kingdom
Tel.: (44) 2084559939
Web Site: https://totalhealthltd.co.uk
Health Care Srvices
N.A.I.C.S.: 621999

Totally Healthcare Limited (1)
Cardinal Square West 10 Nottingham Road, Derby, DE1 3QT, United Kingdom
Tel.: (44) 2038663330
Web Site: http://www.totallyhealthcarelimited.com
Healtcare Services
N.A.I.C.S.: 621999

Vocare Limited (1)
Vocare House Balliol Business Park Benton

Lane, Newcastle upon Tyne, NE12 8EW, United Kingdom
Tel.: (44) 3001231182
Web Site: https://www.vocare.org.uk
Healtcare Services
N.A.I.C.S.: 621999
Wendy Lawrence *(Chm & CEO)*

TOTALPLAN INC.
350-1095 W Pender Street, Vancouver, V6E 2M6, BC, Canada
Tel.: (604) 689-7241
Web Site: https://www.totalplan-inc.com
Year Founded: 1966
Interior Design Services
N.A.I.C.S.: 541410
Maria Theresa Araujo *(Controller)*

TOTECH CORPORATION
3-11-11 Nihonbashi Honcho, Chuo-ku, Tokyo, 103-0023, Japan
Tel.: (81) 366327000
Web Site: https://www.totech.co.jp
Year Founded: 1955
9960—(TKS)
Rev.: $930,238,520
Assets: $664,166,190
Liabilities: $310,947,620
Net Worth: $353,218,570
Earnings: $46,296,440
Emp.: 1,076
Fiscal Year-end: 03/31/24
Air Conditioning Equipment Distr
N.A.I.C.S.: 423730
Tomoyuki Kusano *(Chm)*

Subsidiaries:

Nippon Builcon Corporation (1)
2-11-10 Tachikawa, Sumida-ku, Tokyo, 130-0023, Japan
Tel.: (81) 356002381
Web Site: https://www.nipponbuilcon.co.jp
Emp.: 728
Electrical Equipment Repair & Maintenance Services
N.A.I.C.S.: 811210

Tottori Builcon Corporation (1)
722 Minamikuma, Tottori, 680-0903, Japan
Tel.: (81) 857307400
Web Site: https://www.t-builcon.com
Emp.: 22
Water & Energy Distr
N.A.I.C.S.: 221310

TOTENKO CO., LTD.
1-4-1 Ikenohata, Taito-ku, Tokyo, 110-8707, Japan
Tel.: (81) 0338286272   JP
Web Site: https://www.totenko.co.jp
Year Founded: 1961
8181—(TKS)
Sales Range: $10-24.9 Million
Emp.: 527
Restaurant Operators
N.A.I.C.S.: 722511
Keiji Matsumoto *(Sls Dir-Ueno Store & Dir)*

TOTETSU KOGYO CO., LTD.
4th Floor JR Shinanomachi Building 34 Shinanomachi, Shinjuku-ku, Tokyo, 160-8589, Japan
Tel.: (81) 353697698
Web Site: https://www.totetsu.co.jp
Year Founded: 1943
1835—(TKS)
Rev.: $937,595,450
Assets: $1,111,253,370
Liabilities: $374,350,740
Net Worth: $736,902,630
Earnings: $54,836,560
Emp.: 1,853
Fiscal Year-end: 03/31/24
Civil Engineering Services
N.A.I.C.S.: 541330
Naomichi Yagishita *(Pres)*

Subsidiaries:

Kowa Kasei Co., Ltd. (1)
17-22 Shioiri-cho, Mizuho-ku, Nagoya, 467-0851, Aichi, Japan
Tel.: (81) 528217710
Web Site: https://www.kowa-kasei.co.jp
Electric Equipment Mfr
N.A.I.C.S.: 335999

Totetsu Maintenance Koji Co., Ltd. (1)
5-6-11 Higashi-Shinagawa, Shinagawa, 140-0002, Japan
Tel.: (81) 354601718
Web Site: https://www.totetsu-maintenance.com
Emp.: 26
Civil Engineering Services
N.A.I.C.S.: 541330

Totetsu Soken Co., Ltd. (1)
oak Kanda Kajicho 5F 3-4 Kanda Kajicho, Chiyoda-ku, Tokyo, 101-0045, Japan
Tel.: (81) 352950211
Web Site: https://www.totetsu-soken.com
Emp.: 52
Civil Engineering Services
N.A.I.C.S.: 541330

TOTO LTD.
1-1 Nakashima 2-chome, Kokurakita-ku, Kitakyushu, 802-8601, Fukuoka, Japan
Tel.: (81) 939512052   JP
Web Site: https://jp.toto.com
Year Founded: 1917
5332—(FKA)
Rev.: $4,642,097,240
Assets: $5,223,585,550
Liabilities: $1,848,810,390
Net Worth: $3,374,775,160
Earnings: $245,865,560
Emp.: 35,027
Fiscal Year-end: 03/31/24
Sanitary Ware & Water-Related Products Mfr
N.A.I.C.S.: 332999
Madoka Kitamura *(Chm)*

Subsidiaries:

Bulthaup GmbH & Co. (1)
Werkstrasse 6, Bodenkirchen, 84155, Aich, Germany   (35%)
Tel.: (49) 8001004190
Web Site: https://bulthaup.com
Sales Range: $100-124.9 Million
Emp.: 540
Mfr of Modular Kitchens
N.A.I.C.S.: 337110

CERA TRADING LTD. (1)
TOTO Nogizaka Building 7F/8F 1-24-3 Minami Aoyama, Minato-ku, Tokyo, 107-0062, Japan
Tel.: (81) 337966151
Web Site: https://www.cera.co.jp
Sales Range: $25-49.9 Million
Emp.: 60
Building Materials Distr
N.A.I.C.S.: 423390

ICOT HONG KONG LTD. (1)
Dragon Centre Cheung Sha Wan, Sham Shui Po District, Hong Kong, China (Hong Kong)
Tel.: (852) 2959 3461
Ceramic Tile Mfr
N.A.I.C.S.: 327120

Nakayama Kenzai LTD. (1)
369 Kamino, Kumagaya, 360-0012, Saitama, Japan
Tel.: (81) 485217607
Residential Equipment Distr
N.A.I.C.S.: 423390

P.T. Surya Toto Indonesia (1)
Jl Letjen S Parman Kav 81, Jakarta, 11420, Barat, Indonesia   (51%)
Tel.: (62) 2129298686
Web Site: http://www.toto.co.id
Sales Range: $25-49.9 Million
Emp.: 100
Mfr of Sanitary Ware & Metal Fittings
N.A.I.C.S.: 332999

Royal Toto Metal Co., Ltd. (1)
414 3 Cheongneon 2 Dong Bupyeong Gu, Incheon, Korea (South)   (25%)
Tel.: (82) 325184646
Sales Range: $100-124.9 Million
Emp.: 335
Mfr of Faucets & Bathroom Fixtures
N.A.I.C.S.: 332913
Jeong Hoon *(CEO)*

SUNAQUA TOTO LTD. (1)
1-2-1 Maigaoka, Kokuraminami-ku, Kitakyushu, 802-0823, Fukuoka, Japan
Tel.: (81) 939640141
Web Site: https://sat.jp.toto.com
Emp.: 145
Plumbing Fixture Fittings Mfr
N.A.I.C.S.: 332913

Siam Sanitary Ware Co., Ltd. (1)
33 11 Viphavadeerangsit Rd, Bangkok, 10210, Thailand   (35.7%)
Tel.: (66) 29735040
Web Site: https://www.siamcement.com
Mfr of Sanitary Ware
N.A.I.C.S.: 332999

TOTO (SHANGHAI) CO., LTD. (1)
No 717 Lianyang Rd, Songjiang Industrial Park, Shanghai, 201613, China
Tel.: (86) 2157741193
Sanitary Equipment Mfr
N.A.I.C.S.: 322291

TOTO AMERICAS HOLDINGS, INC. (1)
1155 Southern Rd, Morrow, GA 30260
Tel.: (770) 282-8686
Web Site: http://www.toto.com
Investment Management Service
N.A.I.C.S.: 523999
William Strang *(Pres)*

TOTO AQUAIR LTD. (1)
6-12-12 Honkomagome, Bunkyo, Tokyo, 113-0021, Japan
Tel.: (81) 3 3944 5551
Web Site: http://www.toto-aquair.co.jp
Emp.: 128
Building Materials Distr
N.A.I.C.S.: 423390
Atsushi Sakamoto *(Pres & CEO)*

TOTO ASIA OCEANIA PTE. LTD. (1)
10 Eunos Road 8 12-07 Singapore Post Center, Singapore, 408600, Singapore
Tel.: (65) 67446955
Web Site: https://www.asia.toto.com
Washroom Products Mfr
N.A.I.C.S.: 325620

TOTO BUSINETZ LTD. (1)
2-1-1 Nakajima, Kokura Kita Ward, Kitakyushu, 802-8601, Fukuoka, Japan
Tel.: (81) 939512619
Real Estate Management Services
N.A.I.C.S.: 531390
Koji Hatakeda *(Pres)*

TOTO Bath Create LTD. (1)
2-5-1 Daisaku, Sakura, 285-8585, Chiba, Japan
Tel.: (81) 434983211
Web Site: https://tbc.jp.toto.com
Emp.: 587
Restroom Accessories Mfr
N.A.I.C.S.: 326220
Hiroaki Hashiguchi *(CEO)*

TOTO Chubu Sales LTD. (1)
3-76 Kasatori-cho, Nishi-Ku, Nagoya, 451-0072, Aichi, Japan
Tel.: (81) 525321491
Web Site: https://tcu.jp.toto.com
Building Materials Distr
N.A.I.C.S.: 423390
Hiroshi Okubo *(Pres)*

TOTO Do Brasil Distribuicao e Comercio, Ltd. (1)
Rua Dona Inacia Uchoa 59, Vila Mariana, Sao Paulo, SP, Brazil
Tel.: (55) 1150842147
Web Site: https://www.totobrasil.com.br
Sanitary Ware Products Distr
N.A.I.C.S.: 424130

TOTO EAST CHINA CO., LTD. (1)
No 1108 Nanle Rd, Songjiang Industrial Park, Shanghai, 201613, China
Tel.: (86) 2157749688
Sanitary Ware Mfr
N.A.I.C.S.: 325620

TOTO ENPLA LTD. (1)
7-11 Saiwaimachi, Miyako, 800-0314, Fukuoka, Japan
Tel.: (81) 93 434 1331
Web Site: http://www.totoenpla.co.jp
Emp.: 30
Plastics Product Mfr
N.A.I.C.S.: 326199
Christian Reagan *(Gen Mgr)*

TOTO EXCERA LTD. (1)
2-26-5 Takanodai, Nerima, Tokyo, 177-0033, Japan
Tel.: (81) 339976211
Web Site: http://www.totoexcera.jp
Building Materials Distr
N.A.I.C.S.: 423390

TOTO EXPERT LTD. (1)
1-28-15 Shinjuku Toshinjuku Bldg 7kai, Shinjuku, Tokyo, 160-0022, Japan
Tel.: (81) 3 5269 4071
Web Site: http://www.tes-haken.co.jp
Residential Equipment Mfr
N.A.I.C.S.: 531110

TOTO Engineering LTD. (1)
3-44-1 Mukojima, Sumida, Tokyo, 131-0033, Japan
Tel.: (81) 356081010
Web Site: http://www.toto-eng.co.jp
Construction Materials Distr
N.A.I.C.S.: 423390

TOTO Europe GmbH (1)
Zollhof 2, 40221, Dusseldorf, Germany
Tel.: (49) 21127308200
Web Site: https://eu.toto.com
Emp.: 3
Sanitary Products Mfr
N.A.I.C.S.: 325620

TOTO Finance LTD. (1)
2-1-1 Nakashima, Kokurakita-Ku, Kitakyushu, 802-8601, Fukuoka, Japan
Tel.: (81) 939512103
Web Site: http://www.toto.co.jp
Financial Management Services
N.A.I.C.S.: 523999
Madoka Kitamura *(CEO)*

TOTO Fine Ceramics LTD. (1)
1-4 Azanakamaru Yamadaoka Narahamachi, Futaba, 979-0513, Fukushima, Japan
Tel.: (81) 240251010
Building Materials Mfr
N.A.I.C.S.: 332311

TOTO Germany GmbH (1)
Armelerstrasse 20-22, 46242, Bottrop, Germany
Tel.: (49) 20412460
Web Site: http://www.totoge.com
Emp.: 55
Toilet Seat Mfr
N.A.I.C.S.: 325620
Bernd Kuetemann *(Dir-Sls)*

TOTO High Living Ltd. (1)
3210-1 Honno, Mobara, 299-4114, Chiba, Japan
Tel.: (81) 475 34 3155
Web Site: http://thl.jp.toto.com
Sales Range: $250-299.9 Million
Emp.: 507
House Furniture Mfr & Distr
N.A.I.C.S.: 337126

TOTO INDIA INDUSTRIES PVT. LTD. (1)
1002 Kamla Executive Park Opposite Vazir Glass Works, Andheri Kurla Road Andheri E, Mumbai, 400 059, Maharashtra, India
Tel.: (91) 2243112111
Web Site: https://in.toto.com
Emp.: 45
Sanitary Ware Paper Products Mfr
N.A.I.C.S.: 322291
Tatsuhiko Yasaka *(Mng Dir)*

TOTO INFOM LTD. (1)
2-1-1 Nakajima, Kokura Kita-ku, Kitakyushu, 802-8601, Fukuoka, Japan
Tel.: (81) 939523366
Web Site: https://tim.jp.toto.com

TOTO LTD.

Toto Ltd.—(Continued)
Software Development Services
N.A.I.C.S.: 541511
Takayuki Usami (Pres)

TOTO KOREA LTD. (1)
Tel.: (82) 231418236
Web Site: http://kr.toto.com
Sanitary Ware Products Mfr
N.A.I.C.S.: 322291

TOTO MALAYSIA SDN. BHD. (1)
Lot No 74 Part 76 Part 80 81 84 and 85,
Senawang Industrial Park, 70400, Seremban, Negeri Sembilan, Malaysia
Tel.: (60) 66782506
Washlets Mfr
N.A.I.C.S.: 325620

TOTO MEXICO, S.A. DE C.V. (1)
Av TOTO 1100 Parque Industrial Multiparque Aeropuerto, 65583, Cienega de Flores, N L, Mexico
Tel.: (52) 81 8288 2600
Web Site: http://www.toto.co.jp
Sanitary Ware Products Mfr
N.A.I.C.S.: 332999

TOTO MTEC LTD. (1)
6-24-1 Nishi-Shinjuku, Shinjuku-ku, Tokyo, 160-0023, Japan
Tel.: (81) 353390700
Web Site: https://tmt.jp.toto.com
Emp.: 471
Construction Materials Distr
N.A.I.C.S.: 423390

TOTO Maintenance LTD. (1)
3-44-1 MukojimaTeg Bldg 2f, Sumida, Tokyo, 131-0033, Japan
Tel.: (81) 356086672
Restroom Accessories Repair & Maintenance Services
N.A.I.C.S.: 811490

TOTO VIETNAM CO., LTD. (1)
Lot F1 F2 F3 F4, Thang Long Industrial Park Dong Anh, Hanoi, Vietnam
Tel.: (84) 2438811926
Web Site: https://vn.toto.com
Sanitary Ware Product Mfr
N.A.I.C.S.: 325620

TOTO WASHLET TECHNO LTD. (1)
2-1-1 Nakajima, Kokurakita-ku, Kitakyushu, 802-8601, Fukuoka, Japan
Tel.: (81) 933308600
Web Site: https://twt.jp.toto.com
Emp.: 678
Research, Development & Production of Hot Water Cleaning Bidets
N.A.I.C.S.: 332913

Taiwan Toto Co., Ltd. (1)
1F No 99 Songren Road, Taipei, 110, Taiwan
Tel.: (886) 277356780
Web Site: https://www.twtoto.com.tw
Sales Range: $50-74.9 Million
Emp.: 200
Sanitary Ware Mfr & Sales
N.A.I.C.S.: 325620

The Siam Sanitary Fittings Co., Ltd. (1)
36/11 Vibhavadi-Rangsit Rd Sanambin Don Muang, Bangkok, 10210, Thailand **(45.8%)**
Tel.: (66) 29735040
Web Site: http://www.cotto.com
Sales Range: $25-49.9 Million
Emp.: 200
Faucets, Bath & Shower Fittings, Flush Valves & Tank Trim Mfr
N.A.I.C.S.: 332913

Toto (Beijing) Co., Ltd. (1)
No 8 Jiancai City Zhong Rd, Xisanqi East Haidian District, Beijing, 100096, China
Tel.: (86) 1082910003
Ceramic Sanitary Equipment & Plumbing Mfr
N.A.I.C.S.: 327110

Toto (China) Co. Ltd.
unit1915 north tower 0003 kerry center 1 guang hua road, chaoyang district, Beijing, 100020, China **(100%)**
Tel.: (86) 1085298600
Web Site: http://www.toto.com.cn
Emp.: 100

Sales & Management
N.A.I.C.S.: 332999

Subsidiary (Non-US):

Beijing Toto Co., Ltd. (2) **(55%)**
Web Site: http://www.bjtoto.com
Sales Range: $150-199.9 Million
Mfr of Sanitary Ware
N.A.I.C.S.: 332999

Affiliate (Non-US):

Nanjing Toto Co., Ltd. (2)
Web Site: http://www.toto.com.cn
Cast Iron & Acrylic Bathtubs Mfr
N.A.I.C.S.: 332999

Subsidiary (Domestic):

Toto (China) Co., Ltd. (2)
5F Tower 1 Jing An Kerry Center 1515 Nanjing Road West, Shanghai, 200040, China
Tel.: (86) 2162701010
Sales Range: $25-49.9 Million
Emp.: 70
Sale & Distribution of Ceramic Sanitary Equipment & Plumbing Hardware
N.A.I.C.S.: 423720

Toto (China) Co., Ltd., - Beijing (2)
Unit 1915 North Tower Kerry Centre No 1 Guang Hua Rd, Chao Yang District, Beijing, Chao Yang, China **(60%)**
Tel.: (86) 10 8529 8600
Web Site: http://www.toto.com.cn
Mfr of Sanitary Ceramics Products
N.A.I.C.S.: 332999

Toto Dalian Co., Ltd. (2)
No 17 Dongbei 2nd Street, Economic Technical Development Zone, Dalian, 116600, China **(75%)**
Tel.: (86) 41187624383
Faucet Mfr
N.A.I.C.S.: 332913

Toto (Fujian) Co., Ltd. (1)
16 Gu Nong Farm Economic Development Zone, Taikun Industrial Park Shun Xiang Road Changtai County, Zhangzhou, Fujian, China
Tel.: (86) 5967070700
Ceramic Sanitary Equipment & Plumbing Mfr
N.A.I.C.S.: 327110

Toto (Guangzhou) Co., Ltd. (1)
Plant No 2 No715 Xing Nan Road, Nan Cun Town Panyu, Guangzhou, 511422, China
Tel.: (86) 2034764020
Ceramic Sanitary Equipment & Plumbing Mfr
N.A.I.C.S.: 327110

Toto (H.K.) Ltd. (1)
RM 1101 11/F No 3 Lockhart Rd, Wanchai, China (Hong Kong)
Tel.: (852) 28613177
Web Site: https://www.hk.toto.com
Ceramic Sanitary Equipment & Plumbing Mfr
N.A.I.C.S.: 327110

Toto (Thailand) Co., Ltd. (1)
12th Floor South Wing G Tower Grand Rama 9 9 Rama IX Road, Huaykwang District, Bangkok, 10310, Thailand
Tel.: (66) 21179520
Ceramic Sanitary Equipment & Plumbing Mfr
N.A.I.C.S.: 327110

Toto Kiki (H.K.) Ltd. (1)
Rm 1101 11th Fl AON Insurance No 3 Lockhardt Rd, Wan Chai, Hong Kong, China (Hong Kong) **(100%)**
Tel.: (852) 28613177
Web Site: http://www.toto.com.hk
Sales Range: $25-49.9 Million
Emp.: 10
Plumbing Fixture Mfr
N.A.I.C.S.: 332999

Toto Logicom Ltd. (1)
2-1-1 Nakashima, Kokurakita-Ku, Kitakyushu, 802-0076, Fukuoka, Japan
Tel.: (81) 939512380
Logistics Consulting Servies

N.A.I.C.S.: 541614

Toto Materia Ltd. (1)
304-701 Oroshicho, Toki, 509-5202, Gifu, Japan
Tel.: (81) 572574815
Ceramic Tile Mfr & Distr
N.A.I.C.S.: 423320

Toto USA, Inc. (1)
1155 Southern Rd, Morrow, GA 30260-2917 **(100%)**
Tel.: (770) 282-8686
Web Site: http://www.totousa.com
Sales Range: $550-599.9 Million
Emp.: 1,500
Plumbing Supplies Mfr
N.A.I.C.S.: 423720
Lenora Campos (Sr Mgr-PR & Corp Spokesperson)

TOTTENHAM ACQUISITION I LTD.

Unit 902 Lucky Building 39-41 Wellington Street, Central, China (Hong Kong)
Tel.: (852) 39984852
TOTAU—(NASDAQ)
Rev.: $857,005
Assets: $48,777,222
Liabilities: $43,777,221
Net Worth: $5,000,001
Earnings: ($450,215)
Fiscal Year-end: 12/31/19
Asset Management Services
N.A.I.C.S.: 523940
Jason Ma (Chm & CEO)

TOTTENHAM HOTSPUR PLC

Bill Nicholson Way 748 High Road Tottenham, London, N17 0AP, United Kingdom
Tel.: (44) 2083655006
Web Site:
http://www.tottenhamhotspur.com
Sales Range: $250-299.9 Million
Emp.: 315
Soccer Team Operator
N.A.I.C.S.: 551112
Daniel P. Levy (Chm)

Subsidiaries:

Tottenham Hotspur Football and Athletic Co. Limited (1)
748 High Road, London, N17 0AP, United Kingdom **(100%)**
Tel.: (44) 2083655000
Web Site: http://www.tottenhamhotspur.com
Sales Range: $50-74.9 Million
Emp.: 100
Sports Teams & Clubs
N.A.I.C.S.: 711211
Daniel Levy (Chm)

TOTVS S.A.

Av Braz Leme 1000, 02511-000, Sao Paulo, SP, Brazil
Tel.: (55) 1120997773
Web Site: http://www.en.totvs.com
TOTS3—(BRAZ)
Rev.: $896,804,866
Assets: $1,760,666,068
Liabilities: $819,281,284
Net Worth: $941,384,784
Earnings: $146,539,037
Fiscal Year-end: 12/31/23
Software Development Services
N.A.I.C.S.: 541511

Subsidiaries:

Eurototvs Ltda. (1)
Avenida Liberdade 69 4 E, 1250-140, Lisbon, Portugal
Tel.: (351) 936299680
Sales Range: $25-49.9 Million
Emp.: 18
Software Programming Services
N.A.I.C.S.: 541511

Gesplan S.A. (1)
Av Santos Dumont 831, Joinville, Brazil

INTERNATIONAL PUBLIC

Tel.: (55) 4721017070
Web Site: https://www.gesplan.com.br
Software Operating Services
N.A.I.C.S.: 541714

Lexos Solucao em Tecnologia Ltda. (1)
Av Sao Joao 1080 Jardim Esplanada, Sao Jose dos Campos, SP, Brazil
Tel.: (55) 12988791338
Web Site: https://www.lexos.com.br
Emp.: 80
Online Product Retailer
N.A.I.C.S.: 424490

R.J. Consultores e Informatica Ltd. (1)
Av Raja Gabaglia 2664 2nd floor, Estoril, Belo Horizonte, Minas Gerais, Brazil
Tel.: (55) 3121225232
Web Site: https://www.rjconsultores.com.br
Digital Transport Services
N.A.I.C.S.: 488490

Soft Team Consultoria e informatica Ltda. (1)
Rua Dom Aguirre 576 Jardim Marajoara, Sao Paulo, 04671-245, Brazil
Tel.: (55) 11 5504 0000
Software Programming Services
N.A.I.C.S.: 541511

Supplier Sociedade De Credito Direto S.A. (1)
Av Paulista 1728 - 14 Andar, Bela Vista, Sao Paulo, 01310-200, Brazil
Tel.: (55) 1140814000
Web Site: https://www.supplier.com.br
Credit Card Processing Services
N.A.I.C.S.: 522320

TQTVD Software Ltda. (1)
Rua Da Assembleia 66 21 Andar Centro, Rio de Janeiro, 20011-000, Brazil
Tel.: (55) 2131478600
Web Site: http://www.tqtvd.com.br
Emp.: 40
Digital Television Software Development Services
N.A.I.C.S.: 541511

Tail Target Tecnologia de Informacao Ltd. (1)
Av Pedroso de Morais 1553 cj 51, Alto de Pinheiros, Sao Paulo, 05419-001, Brazil
Tel.: (55) 1130811585
Software Operating Services
N.A.I.C.S.: 541714

YMF Arquitetura Financeira de Negocios S.A. (1)
27 Calcada Canopo - Centro De Apoio II, Santana de Parnaiba, 06541-078, Sao Paulo, Brazil
Tel.: (55) 11 3528 9700
Web Site: http://www.ymfold.com
Investment Management Service
N.A.I.C.S.: 523999

TOUBANI RESOURCES LIMITED

65 Queen Street West Suite 805, PO Box 71, Toronto, M5H 2M5, ON, Canada
Tel.: (416) 644-8892
Web Site:
https://toubaniresources.com
Year Founded: 2002
TRE—(ASX)
Rev.: $13,641
Assets: $4,043,341
Liabilities: $612,629
Net Worth: $3,430,712
Earnings: ($3,568,461)
Fiscal Year-end: 12/31/22
Gold Exploration Services
N.A.I.C.S.: 212220
Ryan Ptolemy (CFO)

TOUBANI RESOURCES LIMITED

100 King Street West 1600, Toronto, M5X 1G5, ON, Canada
Web Site:
https://www.toubaniresources.com

Year Founded: 2002
TRE—(TSXV)
Rev.: $13,641
Assets: $4,043,341
Liabilities: $612,629
Net Worth: $3,430,712
Earnings: ($3,568,461)
Fiscal Year-end: 12/31/22
Exploration & Mining Services
N.A.I.C.S.: 213115
Paul Bozoki (CFO)

TOUBUJYUHAN CO., LTD.
11-46 Misakimachi, Shimonoseki, 750-0014, Yamaguchi, Japan
Tel.: (81) 832221111
Web Site: https://www.toubu.co.jp
Year Founded: 1984
3297—(TKS)
Sales Range: $25-49.9 Million
Emp.: 100
Real Estate Services
N.A.I.C.S.: 531390
Toshihiro Ogino (Pres & CEO)

TOUCH VENTURES LIMITED
Gateway Tower Level 36 1 Macquarie Place, Sydney, 2000, NSW, Australia
Tel.: (61) 393219834
Web Site: https://www.touchventures.com
Year Founded: 2016
TVL—(ASX)
Rev.: $1,780,661
Assets: $71,445,524
Liabilities: $415,987
Net Worth: $71,029,536
Earnings: ($10,056,074)
Emp.: 4
Fiscal Year-end: 12/31/23
Asset Management Services
N.A.I.C.S.: 523999
Gerard Pais (CFO)

Subsidiaries:

PlanPay Pty. Ltd. (1)
Level 8 11 York St, Sydney, 2000, NSW, Australia
Tel.: (61) 1800780880
Web Site: https://planpay.com
Tourist Plan Pay Services
N.A.I.C.S.: 561599

TOUCHSTAR PLC
7 Commerce Way, Trafford Park, Manchester, M17 1HW, United Kingdom
Tel.: (44) 1618745050   UK
Web Site: https://www.touchstarplc.com
TST—(AIM)
Rev.: $8,511,739
Assets: $10,031,558
Liabilities: $6,329,210
Net Worth: $3,702,348
Earnings: $704,368
Emp.: 53
Fiscal Year-end: 12/31/22
Mobile Computing Solutions
N.A.I.C.S.: 513210
Mark W. Hardy (CEO)

Subsidiaries:

Belgravium Limited (1)
Campus Road Listerhills Science Park, Bradford, BD7 1HR, West Yorkshire, United Kingdom
Tel.: (44) 1274741860
Web Site: http://www.warehouse-logistics-it.com
Sales Range: $25-49.9 Million
Emp.: 15
Data Capture Systems Services
N.A.I.C.S.: 518210

Touchstar Technologies Ltd. (1)
7 Commerce Way, Trafford Park, Manchester, M17 1HW, United Kingdom
Tel.: (44) 161 874 5050

Web Site: https://www.touchstar.co.uk
Sales Range: $10-24.9 Million
Emp.: 35
Mobile Computing Services
N.A.I.C.S.: 541519

TOUCHSTONE EXPLORATION INC.
Suite 4100 350-7th Avenue SW, Calgary, T2P 3N9, AB, Canada
Tel.: (403) 750-4400   AB
Web Site: https://www.touchstone.com
Year Founded: 1983
PNW1—(DEU)
Rev.: $27,176,769
Assets: $104,923,924
Liabilities: $59,790,402
Net Worth: $45,133,522
Earnings: ($15,555,472)
Emp.: 98
Fiscal Year-end: 12/31/23
Oil & Natural Gas Exploration Services
N.A.I.C.S.: 211120
Paul R. Baay (Pres & CEO)

Subsidiaries:

Touchstone Exploration (Trinidad) Ltd. (1)
30 Forest Reserve Road, Fyzabad, Trinidad & Tobago
Tel.: (868) 6777411
Oil & Gas Exploration Services
N.A.I.C.S.: 213112

TOUCHSTONE GROUP PLC
46 Worship Street, London, EC2A 2EA, United Kingdom
Tel.: (44) 2071214700
Web Site: http://www.touchstone.co.uk
Year Founded: 1982
Sales Range: $25-49.9 Million
Emp.: 150
Computer Products & Services
N.A.I.C.S.: 541512
Keith Birch (CEO)

Subsidiaries:

Touchstone (CI) Limited (1)
Commercial Street Commercial House, Saint Helier, JE2 3RU, Jersey
Tel.: (44) 1534 818900
Business Software Distribution Servcies
N.A.I.C.S.: 423430
Peter Le Broco (Mng Dir)

Touchstone CRM Limited (1)
3rd Floor 64 Clarendon Road, Watford, WD17 1DA, United Kingdom
Tel.: (44) 1923 652100
Web Site: http://www.touchstonecrm.co.uk
Software Development Services
N.A.I.C.S.: 541511
Dean Carroll (Gen Mgr)

Touchstone Ltd. (1)
1 Triton Square 3rd Fl, London, NW13DX, United Kingdom
Tel.: (44) 2071214700
Web Site: http://www.touchstone.co.uk
Sales Range: $25-49.9 Million
Emp.: 120
Computer Services
N.A.I.C.S.: 541512
Keith Birch (CEO)

TOUCHSTONE INTERNATIONAL MEDICAL SCIENCE CO., LTD.
No 278 Dongping Street, Suzhou Industrial Park, Suzhou, 215123, Jiangsu, China
Tel.: (86) 51262991900
Web Site: https://www.touchstone.hk
Year Founded: 2003
688013—(SHG)
Rev.: $32,577,447
Assets: $76,301,208

Liabilities: $4,920,290
Net Worth: $71,380,918
Earnings: $6,064,592
Fiscal Year-end: 12/31/22
Medical Product Mfr & Distr
N.A.I.C.S.: 339112
Wangyu Chen (Chm & Sec)

TOUCHWOOD ENTERTAINMENT LTD.
Thapar Farms Church/Mall Road Opp Shanti Kunj Gate No 1 Vasant Kunj, New Delhi, 110070, India
Tel.: (91) 9810108253
Web Site: https://www.touchwood.in
TOUCHWOOD—(NSE)
Rev.: $4,413,093
Assets: $4,066,291
Liabilities: $930,232
Net Worth: $3,136,059
Earnings: $292,273
Emp.: 16
Fiscal Year-end: 03/31/23
Stage Set Contract Operator
N.A.I.C.S.: 711510
Vijay Arora (Exec Dir)

Subsidiaries:

MakeMeUp Private Limited (1)
Touchwood Thapar Farms Church Road Vasant Kunj, New Delhi, 110070, India
Tel.: (91) 9015122222
Web Site: https://www.makemeupindia.com
Online Beauty Product Services
N.A.I.C.S.: 518210

TOUKEI COMPUTER CO., LTD.
150 Ichinotsubo, Nakahara-ku, Kawasaki, 211-8550, Kanagawa, Japan
Tel.: (81) 444301311
Web Site: https://www.toukei.co.jp
Year Founded: 1970
4746—(TKS)
Rev.: $138,694,580
Assets: $295,468,660
Liabilities: $53,976,170
Net Worth: $241,492,490
Earnings: $28,133,120
Emp.: 821
Fiscal Year-end: 12/31/23
Software Devalopment Sercives
N.A.I.C.S.: 541511
Hiroyasu Koda (Founder & Chm)

Subsidiaries:

Toukei (Thailand) Co., Ltd. (1)
2 Ploenchit Center G Floor Room No 24 Sukhumvit Rd Klongtoey, Bangkok, 10110, Thailand
Tel.: (66) 917264301
Web Site: http://www.toukei.co.th
Software Development Services
N.A.I.C.S.: 541511

TOULON DIFFUSION AUTO
469 R Henri Ste Claire Deville, 83100, Toulon, France
Tel.: (33) 494617171
Web Site: http://www.toulon-diffusion-auto.concessions-toyota.fr
New Car Dealers
N.A.I.C.S.: 441110
Thierry Bernaud (Mgr-Comml)

TOUMEI CO., LTD.
2-1-39 Hatsuta, Yokkaichi, 510-0001, Mie, Japan
Tel.: (81) 593302151
Web Site: https://www.toumei.co.jp
4439—(TKS)
Rev.: $148,769,960
Assets: $88,149,840
Liabilities: $40,635,260
Net Worth: $47,514,580
Earnings: $9,653,440
Emp.: 447
Fiscal Year-end: 08/31/24
Information Technology Services

N.A.I.C.S.: 541519
Fumihiko Yamamoto (Founder & Pres)

Subsidiaries:

Gifu Recomm Co., Ltd. (1)
2-1-39 Hatta, Yokkaichi, 510-0001, Japan
Tel.: (81) 593337232
Web Site: https://www.gifu-recomm.jp
Emp.: 17
LED Light Fixing Distr
N.A.I.C.S.: 423610

TOUNG LOONG TEXTILE MFG CO., LTD.
19F No 31 Sec 2 Sanmin Rd, Banqiao District, New Taipei City, 220, Taiwan
Tel.: (886) 229612112
Web Site: https://www.toungloong.com
Year Founded: 1960
4401—(TPE)
Rev.: $128,189,444
Assets: $187,067,911
Liabilities: $99,796,798
Net Worth: $87,271,113
Earnings: $5,387,237
Emp.: 666
Fiscal Year-end: 12/31/22
Textile Products Mfr
N.A.I.C.S.: 314999
Chih-Cheng Yu (Pres)

TOUPARGEL GROUPE SA
13 chemin des Pres Secs, 69380, Civrieux-d'Azergues, France
Tel.: (33) 472541000
Web Site: http://www.toupargel-groupe.fr
Year Founded: 1947
TOU—(EUR)
Sales Range: $300-349.9 Million
Frozen Food Product Distr
N.A.I.C.S.: 424420
Valerie Bedouet (Dir-Quality Assurance)

Subsidiaries:

Toupargel SAS (1)
Rue Maurice Ravel, Orne, 61200, Argentan, France
Tel.: (33) 233679040
Packaged Frozen Food Whslr
N.A.I.C.S.: 424420

TOUQUET SAVOUR S.A.S.
RD 1001, BP 60018, 80160, Essertaux, Somme, France
Tel.: (33) 322353290
Web Site: http://www.touquetsavour.com
Year Founded: 1967
Sales Range: $25-49.9 Million
Potato Farming & Whlslr
N.A.I.C.S.: 111211
Helene Maillard (Gen Mgr)

TOURIN PROPERTIES REIT
Kiril Blagoev 10, Sofia, 1271, Bulgaria
Tel.: (359) 29350366
Web Site: http://www.turinimoti.com
TPS—(BUL)
Real Estate Investment Services
N.A.I.C.S.: 531210

TOURISM ENTERPRISES COMPANY
Eastern Region, PO Box 8383, Dammam, 31482, Saudi Arabia
Tel.: (966) 138366669
Web Site: https://www.shamstourism.sa
Year Founded: 1991
4170—(SAU)
Rev.: $2,666,555

TOURISM ENTERPRISES COMPANY

Tourism Enterprises Company—(Continued)
Assets: $152,170,592
Liabilities: $5,307,547
Net Worth: $146,863,045
Earnings: ($1,928,518)
Emp.: 55
Fiscal Year-end: 12/31/22
Resort Management Services
N.A.I.C.S.: 721110
Hisham Ahmed Abulola (Vice Chm)

TOURISM FINANCE CORPORATION OF INDIA LTD.
4th Floor Tower 1 NBCC Plaza Sector V, Pushp Vihar Saket, New Delhi, 110017, India
Tel.: (91) 1129561180
Web Site: https://www.tfciltd.com
526650—(BOM)
Rev.: $27,780,445
Assets: $245,164,187
Liabilities: $123,216,474
Net Worth: $121,947,713
Earnings: $10,544,871
Emp.: 35
Fiscal Year-end: 03/31/23
Financial Services
N.A.I.C.S.: 523999
Sanjay Ahuja (Compliance Officer, Sec & VP)

TOURISM HOLDINGS LIMITED
The Beach House Level 1 83 Beach Rd, PO Box 4293, Auckland, 1010, New Zealand
Tel.: (64) 93364299
Web Site: https://thlonline.com
Year Founded: 1986
THL—(ASX)
Rev.: $397,034,091
Assets: $803,570,574
Liabilities: $438,166,866
Net Worth: $365,403,708
Earnings: $29,819,378
Emp.: 2,377
Fiscal Year-end: 06/30/23
Tour Operator
N.A.I.C.S.: 561520
Kate Meldrum (Gen Mgr-Australian Ops)

Subsidiaries:

Apollo Tourism & Leisure Ltd. (1)
698 Nudgee Road, Northgate, 4013, QLD, Australia
Tel.: (61) 401485450
Rev.: $224,762,603
Assets: $273,312,232
Liabilities: $243,873,680
Net Worth: $29,438,552
Earnings: ($13,678,790)
Fiscal Year-end: 06/30/2021
Tourism Services
N.A.I.C.S.: 561510

Subsidiary (Domestic):

Apollo Motorhome Holidays Pty. Ltd. (2)
698 Nudgee Road, Brisbane, Northgate, 4013, QLD, Australia
Tel.: (61) 732659200
Recreational Vehicle Distr
N.A.I.C.S.: 423110

Apollo Rv Service & Repair Centre Pty. Ltd. (2)
38 Fraser Rd, Northgate, 4013, Australia
Tel.: (61) 732659288
Motorhome Repair Services
N.A.I.C.S.: 561990

Subsidiary (Non-US):

Bunk Campers Ltd. (2)
Cyril Johnston Complex Ballynahinch Road, Belfast, BT8 8DJ, United Kingdom
Tel.: (44) 2890813057
Web Site: https://www.bunkcampers.com
Camper Van Rental Services
N.A.I.C.S.: 532112

CanaDream Corporation (2)
292154 Crosspointe Drive, Rocky View County, Calgary, T4A 0V2, AB, Canada
Tel.: (403) 291-1000
Web Site: http://www.canadream.com
Recreational Vehicle Rental Services
N.A.I.C.S.: 721211

Hippie Camper Ltd. (2)
13 Manu Tapu Drive Auckland Airport, Auckland, 2022, New Zealand
Tel.: (64) 800113131
Web Site: https://www.hippiecamper.co.nz
Camper Van Rental Services
N.A.I.C.S.: 532112

Subsidiary (Domestic):

Hippie Camper Pty. Ltd. (2)
733A Nudgee Road, Northgate, 4013, QLD, Australia
Tel.: (61) 800777779
Web Site: https://www.hippiecamper.com
Camper Van Rental Services
N.A.I.C.S.: 532112

Subsidiary (Non-US):

Nomad Campervans Ltd. (2)
843 Finchley Road, London, NW11 8NA, United Kingdom
Tel.: (44) 3304030034
Web Site: https://www.nomadcampervans.com
Camper Van Mfr & Distr
N.A.I.C.S.: 336214

El Monte Rents Inc. (1)
12818 Firestone Blvd, Santa Fe Springs, CA 90670
Tel.: (562) 404-9300
Web Site: https://www.elmonterv.com
Motor Home Rental Services
N.A.I.C.S.: 532120

Fullers Bay of Islands Limited (1)
Maritime Building Marsden Rd, Marsden Road, Paihia, 2020, New Zealand
Tel.: (64) 94027421
Web Site: http://www.dolphincruzers.co.nz
Emp.: 100
Tour Operator
N.A.I.C.S.: 561520
Charles Parker (Gen Mgr)

Tourism Holdings Australia Pty Limited (1)
Building 2 9 Ashley Street, Braybrook, 3019, VIC, Australia
Tel.: (61) 383988855
Web Site: https://www.britz.com
Sales Range: $50-74.9 Million
Emp.: 20
Truck Utility Trailer & RV Recreational Vehicle Rental & Leasing
N.A.I.C.S.: 532120
Rebecca Mason (Mgr-Market Dev-Maui & Britz)

Waitomo Caves Limited (1)
584 State Highway 3, PO Box 501, Waitomo Caves, Otorohanga, 3977, New Zealand
Tel.: (64) 78737397
Web Site: https://www.waitomo.com
Sales Range: $50-74.9 Million
Emp.: 300
Adventure & Sightseeing Accommodation Services
N.A.I.C.S.: 721199
Liz Lindsay (Brand Mgr)

TOURISM NEW ZEALAND
Level 22 Vodafone House 157 Lambton Quay, PO Box 95, Wellington, 6011, New Zealand
Tel.: (64) 44628000
Web Site: http://www.tourismnewzealand.com
Sales Range: $50-74.9 Million
Emp.: 125
New Zealand Tourism Information & Services
N.A.I.C.S.: 926110
Sue Parcell (CFO)

Subsidiaries:

Tourism New Zealand (1)
501 Santa Monica Blvd Ste 300, Santa Monica, CA 90401
Tel.: (310) 395-7480
Sales Range: $50-74.9 Million
Emp.: 10
Promoter of Tourism to New Zealand
N.A.I.C.S.: 921110

TOURIST TRANSPORT (FIJI) LIMITED
Nadi Airport, Nadi, Fiji
Tel.: (679) 6723311
Web Site: http://www.touristtransportfiji.com
Sales Range: $100-124.9 Million
Emp.: 75
All Other Support Activities for Transportation
N.A.I.C.S.: 488999
Ashneel Kumar (Controller)

TOURIST VILLAGE OF MOSUL DAM
Al-Salhiya Sec 222 St 22 H 8 8, Baghdad, Iraq
Tel.: (964) 15370371
Year Founded: 1990
HTVM—(IRAQ)
Sales Range: Less than $1 Million
Tour Operator
N.A.I.C.S.: 561520
Immortalized Muhyiddin Younis (Mng Dir)

TOURISTIC ENTERPRISES COMPANY
Al Jahra Street Ops Kuwait Sporting Club, PO Box 23310, Safat, Kuwait, 13094, Kuwait
Tel.: (965) 24965555 KW
Web Site: http://www.kuwaittourism.com
Year Founded: 1976
Sales Range: $100-124.9 Million
Emp.: 980
Tourism, Recreation & Entertainment Services
N.A.I.C.S.: 561520

TOURMALINE OIL CORP.
2900 250 6th Ave SW, Calgary, T2P 3H7, AB, Canada
Tel.: (403) 266-5992 AB
Web Site: http://www.tourmalineoil.com
Year Founded: 2008
TRMLF—(OTCIQ)
Rev.: $3,953,056,807
Assets: $14,846,254,709
Liabilities: $4,492,593,632
Net Worth: $10,353,661,077
Earnings: $1,282,322,523
Emp.: 288
Fiscal Year-end: 12/31/23
Intermediate Crude Oil & Natural Gas Exploration & Production Services
N.A.I.C.S.: 211120
Brian G. Robinson (CFO & VP-Fin)

Subsidiaries:

Bonavista Energy Corporation (1)
1500 525 - 8th Ave SW, Calgary, T2P 1G1, AB, Canada
Tel.: (403) 213-4300
Web Site: http://www.bonavistaenergy.com
Rev.: $377,455,362
Assets: $2,142,990,986
Liabilities: $1,005,286,679
Net Worth: $1,137,704,306
Earnings: $8,660,041
Emp.: 195
Fiscal Year-end: 12/31/2018
Oil & Gas Services
N.A.I.C.S.: 333132
Lynda J. Robinson (VP-HR & Admin)

INTERNATIONAL PUBLIC

Chinook Energy Inc. (1)
Suite 1610 222 3rd Avenue SW, Calgary, T2P 0B4, AB, Canada
Tel.: (403) 261-6883
Web Site: https://www.chinookenergyinc.com
Oil & Gas Exploration Services
N.A.I.C.S.: 211120
Tim Halpen (COO)

Crew Energy Inc. (1)
Suite 800 250 - 5th Street SW, Calgary, T2P 0R4, AB, Canada
Tel.: (403) 266-2088
Web Site: https://www.crewenergy.com
Rev.: $247,495,111
Assets: $1,264,727,834
Liabilities: $278,511,665
Net Worth: $986,216,170
Earnings: $90,383,333
Fiscal Year-end: 12/31/2023
Petroleum & Natural Gas Exploration, Drilling & Extraction
N.A.I.C.S.: 211120
John A. Brussa (Chm)

Subsidiary (Domestic):

Crew Resources Inc. (2)
Ste 800 250 5th St SW, Calgary, T2P 0R4, AB, Canada
Tel.: (403) 266-2088
Web Site: http://www.crewenergy.com
Oil & Gas Exploration Services
N.A.I.C.S.: 213112

Polar Star Canadian Oil & Gas, Inc. (1)
700 9th Avenue SW Ste 1310, Calgary, T2P 3V4, AB, Canada
Tel.: (403) 775-8061
Web Site: http://www.polarstar.ca
Sales Range: $75-99.9 Million
Emp.: 15
Oil & Gas Real Estate Investment Trust
N.A.I.C.S.: 525990

TOURNAMENT SPORTS MARKETING INC.
185 Weber St S, Waterloo, N2J 2B1, ON, Canada
Tel.: (519) 888-6500
Web Site: http://www.tournament-sports.com
Sales Range: $10-24.9 Million
Golf, Skate & Curling Products Mfr
N.A.I.C.S.: 339920
Kim Bauer (Pres)

Subsidiaries:

Nancy Lopez Golf (1)
185 Weber St S, Waterloo, N2J 2B1, ON, Canada (75%)
Tel.: (519) 888-6872
Web Site: http://www.nancylopezgolf.com
Sales Range: $25-49.9 Million
Emp.: 30
Golf Clubs & Accessories Mfr
N.A.I.C.S.: 339920
Gary Pollock (Product Mgr)

TOUS WOOLLEN COMPANY
No 75-2nd Floor-Bokharast St Tala Bldg-Argantin Sq, Tehran, Iran
Tel.: (98) 21 88532174
Year Founded: 1976
Emp.: 162
Textile Products Mfr
N.A.I.C.S.: 313210
Mohammad Ramazan Qasem (Chm)

TOUTATIS CLIENT SERVICES DO BRASIL S.A.
Rua G1909 3 andar, Sao Paulo, 01012-010, SP, Brazil
Tel.: (55) 11 2395 2500 BR
Web Site: http://www.toutatisglobal.com
Business Process Outsourcing Services
N.A.I.C.S.: 561499

TOVARNA OLJA GEA D.D.

Trg svobode 3, 2310, Slovenska Bistrica, Slovenia
Tel.: (386) 28432610
Web Site: http://www.gea.si
Emp.: 100
Oil & Seed Products Mfr
N.A.I.C.S.: 311224
Igor Hustic *(Dir-IR, Pub & Admin)*

TOVIS CO., LTD

15 Harmony-ro 226beon-gil, Yeonsu-gu, Incheon, 790-829, Korea (South)
Tel.: (82) 327125100
Web Site: https://www.tovism.com
Year Founded: 1998
051360—(KRS)
Rev.: $251,744,062
Assets: $306,418,410
Liabilities: $160,440,880
Net Worth: $145,977,530
Earnings: ($3,823,405)
Emp.: 248
Fiscal Year-end: 12/31/22
Display Unit Mfr
N.A.I.C.S.: 334419
Yong-Beom Kim *(Co-CEO)*

Subsidiaries:

Tovis CO., Ltd - Wonju Factory (1)
92 dongwha-ri munmak-eup, Wonju, Kwangwon-do, Korea (South)
Tel.: (82) 31 345 7708
Electronic Components Mfr
N.A.I.C.S.: 334419

TOW CO., LTD.

3F Hulic Kamiyacho Bldg 4-3-13 Toranomon, Minato-ku, Tokyo, 105-0001, Japan
Tel.: (81) 357771888   JP
Web Site: https://www.tow.co.jp
Year Founded: 1976
4767—(TKS)
Rev.: $108,868,660
Assets: $87,608,700
Liabilities: $29,750,260
Net Worth: $57,858,440
Earnings: $8,739,100
Emp.: 126
Fiscal Year-end: 06/30/24
Event Planning, Production & Management
N.A.I.C.S.: 711320
Osamu Kawamura *(Chm)*

TOWA CORPORATION

5 Kamichoshi-cho Kamitoba, Minami-ku, Kyoto, 601-8105, Japan
Tel.: (81) 756920250
Web Site:
 https://www.towajapan.co.jp
Year Founded: 1979
6315—(TKS)
Rev.: $333,613,310
Assets: $580,761,210
Liabilities: $194,505,860
Net Worth: $386,255,350
Earnings: $42,594,840
Emp.: 623
Fiscal Year-end: 03/31/24
Semiconductor Mfr
N.A.I.C.S.: 333242
Hirokazu Okada *(Pres & CEO)*

Subsidiaries:

Bandick Corporation (1)
596-146 Shimojo Minamiwari, Tatsuoka-cho, Nirasaki, 407-0033, Yamanashi, Japan
Tel.: (81) 551228700
Web Site: https://bandick.co.jp
Emp.: 125
Molded Plastic Product Mfr
N.A.I.C.S.: 424610

HI-TEK International Inc. (1)
9F Kumsan bldg 750 Gukhoe-Daero, Youngdeungpo-ku, Seoul, 07202, Korea (South)
Tel.: (82) 27843014
Web Site: https://www.i-hitek.com
Sales Range: $25-49.9 Million
Emp.: 53
Electric Equipment Mfr
N.A.I.C.S.: 335999
Chang-Ho Choo *(Pres & CEO)*

JIPAL (H.K.) Company Ltd. (1)
Unit 1615 16/F Golden Era Plaza 39-55 Sai Yee Street, Mongkok, Kowloon, China (Hong Kong)
Tel.: (852) 31044761
Web Site: http://www.towam.com.my
Industrial Equipment Mfr
N.A.I.C.S.: 811310

Jipal Corporation (1)
18F-8 No 295 Sec 2 Guangfu Rd, Hsinchu, 300195, Taiwan
Tel.: (886) 35725325
Web Site: https://www.jipal.com
Sales Range: $50-74.9 Million
Emp.: 100
Semiconductor Packaging Equipments & Materials Distr & Support Services
N.A.I.C.S.: 423830
Eric Tsai *(Founder & Chm)*

TOWA (Nantong) Co., Ltd. (1)
No 8 Dong He Road, Economic and Technological Development Area, Nantong, 226017, Jiangsu, China
Tel.: (86) 5136 998 6969
High Precision Mold Mfr
N.A.I.C.S.: 333511

TOWA Asia-Pacific Pte. Ltd. (1)
1A International Business Park 05-03, Singapore, 609933, Singapore
Tel.: (65) 6 567 1551
Web Site: https://www.sg-towa-ap.com
Semiconductor Mfr
N.A.I.C.S.: 334413

TOWA Europe B.V. (1)
Geograaf 14, 6921 EW, Duiven, Netherlands
Tel.: (31) 26 379 1500
Semiconductor Equipment Distr
N.A.I.C.S.: 423690

TOWA Korea Co., Ltd. (1)
Room A 302 123 Bongeunsa-ro Richehill Sinnonhyeon Officetel, Gangnam-gu Nonhyeon-dong, Seoul, Korea (South)
Tel.: (82) 2 784 0256
Web Site: https://www.towakorea.com
Molding Equipment Mfr
N.A.I.C.S.: 333248

TOWA Laserfront Corporation (1)
1120 Shimokuzawa, Chuo-ku, Sagamihara, 252-5298, Kanagawa, Japan
Tel.: (81) 42 700 3431
Web Site: https://www.laserfront.jp
Emp.: 78
Laser Processing Machine Mfr & Distr
N.A.I.C.S.: 333517
Yoshizumi Tamura *(Pres & CEO)*

TOWA Taiwan Co., Ltd. (1)
15F-2 No 295 Sec 2 Guangfu Road, East District, Hsinchu, 300, Taiwan
Tel.: (886) 35737646
Web Site: http://www.towam.com.my
Sales Range: $25-49.9 Million
Emp.: 6
Semiconductor Manufacturing Equipment Distr
N.A.I.C.S.: 334413

TOWA Thai Company Limited (1)
No 88 Nimitikul Tower 2nd Floor Soi Rama IX 57/1 Wiset Suk 2, Rama IX Road Suan Luang Sub-district Suan Luang District, Bangkok, 10250, Thailand
Tel.: (66) 2 187 2204
Semiconductor Equipment Distr
N.A.I.C.S.: 423690

TOWAM Sdn. Bhd. (1)
PMT 768 Persiaran Cassia Selatan 7, Taman Perindustrian Batu Kawan Bandar Cassia, 14110, Pulau Penang, Malaysia
Tel.: (60) 4 585 5888
Web Site: https://www.towam.com.my
Semiconductor Mfr
N.A.I.C.S.: 334413

Towa (Shanghai) Co., Ltd. (1)
Unit A 20F Global Harbor Tower B No 1188 North Kaixuan Road, Putuo District, Shanghai, 200063, China
Tel.: (86) 2168886860
Web Site: https://www.towa-sh.com
Semiconductor Manufacturing Equipment Sales & Service
N.A.I.C.S.: 333242

Towa (Suzhou) Co., Ltd. (1)
No 1 Su Hong Zhong Road, Suzhou Industrial Park Pilot Free Trade Zone, Suzhou, 215027, Jiangsu, China
Tel.: (86) 51262588010
Sales Range: $50-74.9 Million
Emp.: 110
Semiconductor Manufacturing Equipment & High Precision Molds Mfr
N.A.I.C.S.: 333242

Towa Corporation - Kyoto East Plant (1)
Ujitawara Industrial Park 1-35 Ujitawara-cho, Tsuzuki-gun, Kyoto, 610-0231, Japan
Tel.: (81) 774885071
Semiconductor Manufacturing Equipment Mfr
N.A.I.C.S.: 333242

Towa Europe GmbH (1)
Am Wammesknopf 39, 70439, Stuttgart, Germany
Tel.: (49) 71122724790
Web Site: https://www.towaeurope.com
Sales Range: $50-74.9 Million
Emp.: 3
Semiconductor Manufacturing Equipment Sales & Repair & Maintenance Services
N.A.I.C.S.: 423690

Towa Semiconductor Equipment Philippines Corporation (1)
121 East Science Avenue, Laguna Technopark, Binan, 4024, Laguna, Philippines
Tel.: (63) 495410971
Web Site: http://www.towam.com.my
Sales Range: $25-49.9 Million
Emp.: 13
Semiconductor Manufacturing Equipment Sales & Maintenance Services
N.A.I.C.S.: 333242

Towatec Co., Ltd. (1)
5 Kamitoba Kamichoncho, Minami-ku, Kyoto, 601-8105, Japan
Tel.: (81) 756920271
Web Site: https://towatec.towagrp.co.jp
Sales Range: $25-49.9 Million
Emp.: 58
Semiconductor Equipment Repair & Maintenance Services
N.A.I.C.S.: 811310

TOWA FOOD SERVICE CO., LTD.

6th floor TOWAJ'S Building 3-20-1 Shinbashi, Minato-Ku, Tokyo, 105-0004, Japan
Tel.: (81) 358347666
Web Site: https://www.towafood-net.co.jp
Year Founded: 1981
33290—(TKS)
Sales Range: Less than $1 Million
Restaurant Operators
N.A.I.C.S.: 722511
Masato Kishino *(Pres & CEO)*

TOWA HI SYSTEM CO., LTD.

3-12-33 Noda, Kita-Ku, Okayama, 700-0971, Japan
Tel.: (81) 862433003
Web Site: https://www.towa-hi-sys.co.jp
Year Founded: 1978
4172—(TKS)
Software Development Services
N.A.I.C.S.: 541511
Shigehisa Ishii *(Founder, Chm, Pres & Dir-Rep)*

TOWA PHARMACEUTICAL CO. LTD.

2-11 Shinbashi-cho, Kadoma, 571-8580, Osaka, Japan
Tel.: (81) 669009100
Web Site:
 https://www.towayakuhin.co.jp
4553—(TKS)
Rev.: $1,506,643,740
Assets: $2,846,616,330
Liabilities: $1,816,163,600
Net Worth: $1,030,452,730
Earnings: $106,903,530
Emp.: 3,519
Fiscal Year-end: 03/31/24
Pharmaceuticals Product Mfr
N.A.I.C.S.: 325412
Itsuro Yoshida *(Pres)*

Subsidiaries:

Daichi Kasei Co., Ltd. (1)
6 1004 Ohnuki, Fukusaki-cho, Kanzaki, 679-2201, Hyogo Prefecture, Japan
Tel.: (81) 790243600
Web Site: https://www.daichikasei.com
Emp.: 80
Medical Drug Mfr
N.A.I.C.S.: 325412

Greencaps Pharmaceutical Co., Ltd. (1)
2201-2 Yamamiya, Fujinomiya, 418-0111, Shizuoka, Japan
Tel.: (81) 544592360
Web Site: https://www.greencaps.co.jp
Medical Drug Mfr
N.A.I.C.S.: 325412

J-DOLPH Pharmaceutical Co., Ltd. (1)
2-5-15 Hiyoshi-cho, Moriguchi, 570-0081, Osaka, Japan
Tel.: (81) 675072530
Web Site: https://www.j-dolph.co.jp
Medical Drug Mfr & Whslr
N.A.I.C.S.: 325412

T-Square Solutions Co., Ltd. (1)
2-5-15 Hiyoshicho, Moriguchi, 570-0081, Osaka, Japan
Tel.: (81) 669916711
Web Site: https://www.t2-sol.co.jp
IT Management Services
N.A.I.C.S.: 541611

TOWELLERS LIMITED

Towellers House WSA 30/31, FB Area Block 1, Karachi, 75950, Pakistan
Tel.: (92) 2136326600
Web Site: https://www.towellers.com
TOWL—(PSX)
Rev.: $39,885,227
Assets: $35,910,019
Liabilities: $8,710,206
Net Worth: $27,199,812
Earnings: $8,592,054
Emp.: 1,736
Fiscal Year-end: 06/30/23
Towels, Bed Linens, Blankets, Apparel & Socks Mfr
N.A.I.C.S.: 313210
Mehreen Obaid Agha *(CEO)*

TOWER CAPITAL ASIA PTE. LTD.

3 Church Street #22-05, Singapore, 049483, Singapore
Tel.: (65) 6850 7728   SG
Web Site:
 http://www.towercapitalasia.com
Year Founded: 2016
Private Equity & Real Estate Investment Management
N.A.I.C.S.: 523940
Danny Koh *(Founder & CEO)*

Subsidiaries:

Poh Tiong Choon Logistics Limited (1)
48 Pandan Road, Singapore, 609289, Singapore
Tel.: (65) 62682522
Web Site: http://www.ptclogistics.com.sg
Logistics Management Services

TOWER CAPITAL ASIA PTE. LTD.

Tower Capital Asia Pte. Ltd.—(Continued)
N.A.I.C.S.: 541614
Francis Kwan Yew Lai *(Deputy Gen Mgr-Transportation Dept)*

Subsidiary (Domestic):

Bitubulk Pte Ltd (2)
21 Merbau Road Jurong Island, Singapore, 627858, Singapore
Tel.: (65) 65151311
Bitumen Distr
N.A.I.C.S.: 424690

PTC Express Pte Ltd (2)
48 Pandan Road, Singapore, 609289, Singapore
Tel.: (65) 62682522
Web Site: http://www.ptclogistics.com.sg
Freight Forwarding Services
N.A.I.C.S.: 488510

PTC Marine Private Limited (2)
48 Pandan Road, Singapore, 609289, Singapore
Tel.: (65) 62682522
Web Site: http://www.ptclogistics.com.sg
Stevedoring Services
N.A.I.C.S.: 488320

PTC-Chien Li Transportation Pte Ltd (2)
48 Pandan Road, Singapore, 608289, Singapore
Tel.: (65) 66628808
Web Site: http://www.ptclogistics.com
Warehousing & Logistics Services
N.A.I.C.S.: 493110

PTC-Xin Hua Transportation Pte Ltd (2)
48 Pandan Road, Singapore, 609289, Singapore
Tel.: (65) 62615108
Web Site: http://www.ptclogistics.com.sg
General Freight Trucking Services
N.A.I.C.S.: 484110

TOWER INVESTMENTS S.A.
Plac Malachowskiego 2, 00-066, Warsaw, Poland
Tel.: (48) 222997334
Web Site:
https://www.towerinvestments.pl
Year Founded: 2005
TOW—(WAR)
Rev.: $6,059,020
Assets: $19,496,619
Liabilities: $8,279,118
Net Worth: $11,217,502
Earnings: ($2,435,652)
Fiscal Year-end: 12/31/22
Construction Engineering Services
N.A.I.C.S.: 541330
Bartosz Kazimierczuk *(Chm & Chm-Mgmt Bd)*

TOWER LIMITED
Level 5 136 Fanshawe Street, PO Box 90347, Auckland, New Zealand
Tel.: (64) 93692000
Web Site: https://www.tower.co.nz
TWR—(ASX)
Rev.: $290,965,639
Assets: $576,863,047
Liabilities: $325,414,367
Net Worth: $251,448,680
Earnings: $13,887,485
Emp.: 775
Fiscal Year-end: 09/30/21
Risk Insurance & Wealth Management Products & Services
N.A.I.C.S.: 524298
Michelle James *(Mng Dir-Tower Direct)*

Subsidiaries:

Southern Cross Marine Limited (1)
Unit 12 Parkers Close Downton Business Park, Downton, Salisbury, SP5 3RB, Wiltshire, United Kingdom
Tel.: (44) 1725 511 601
Marine Insurance Services

N.A.I.C.S.: 524126

TOWER Health & Life Limited (1)
Level 11 Tower Centre 22 Fanshawe Street, PO Box 90347, Auckland, 1142, New Zealand
Tel.: (64) 93692000
Web Site: http://www.towerlimited.com
Emp.: 500
Medical Insurance Services
N.A.I.C.S.: 524114
Richard Harding *(CEO)*

TOWER ONE WIRELESS CORP.
600-535 Howe Street, Vancouver, V6C 2Z4, BC, Canada
Tel.: (917) 546-3016 BC
Web Site:
http://www.toweronewireless.com
Year Founded: 2006
TO—(CNSX)
Rev.: $8,360,716
Assets: $17,121,740
Liabilities: $28,698,087
Net Worth: ($11,576,348)
Earnings: ($3,594,020)
Emp.: 68
Fiscal Year-end: 12/31/21
Wireless Infrastructure Owner & Operator
N.A.I.C.S.: 334290
Alejandro Ochoa *(Pres, CEO, Interim CFO & Interim Sec)*

TOWER REAL ESTATE INVESTMENT TRUST
Level 10 Wisma Hong Leong 18 Jalan Perak, 50450, Kuala Lumpur, Malaysia
Tel.: (60) 321641818
Web Site: https://www.tower-reit.com.my
Year Founded: 2006
TWRREIT—(KLS)
Rev.: $7,168,466
Assets: $171,054,815
Liabilities: $65,008,042
Net Worth: $106,046,772
Earnings: ($3,724,868)
Emp.: 9
Fiscal Year-end: 06/30/23
Real Estate Investment Trust Services
N.A.I.C.S.: 531110
Chua Song Yong *(CEO)*

TOWER RECORDS JAPAN INC.
2-15-9 Minami Shinagawa, Shinagawa-ku, Tokyo, 140-8667, Japan
Tel.: (81) 334964171 JP
Web Site: http://www.tower.jp
Year Founded: 1981
Sales Range: $5-14.9 Billion
Music Compact Disc, DVD & Other Media Retailer
N.A.I.C.S.: 449210
Tetsumi Takaga *(Pres & CEO)*

TOWER RESOURCES LTD.
Suite 912-1112 West Pender St, Vancouver, V6E 2S1, BC, Canada
Tel.: (604) 558-2565
Web Site:
https://www.towerresources.ca
Year Founded: 1988
T7Y1—(DEU)
Rev.: $2,628
Assets: $6,628,519
Liabilities: $213,292
Net Worth: $6,415,227
Earnings: ($196,281)
Fiscal Year-end: 10/31/23
Mineral Exploration Services
N.A.I.C.S.: 212290
Gerald Shields *(Chm)*

TOWER RESOURCES PLC
140 Buckingham Palace Road, Westminster, London, SW1W 9SA, United Kingdom
Tel.: (44) 2071579625 UK
Web Site:
https://www.towerresources.co.uk
Year Founded: 2004
TRP—(AIM)
Assets: $32,539,636
Liabilities: $3,176,317
Net Worth: $29,363,319
Earnings: ($1,009,122)
Emp.: 6
Fiscal Year-end: 12/31/22
Crude Petroleum Extraction Services
N.A.I.C.S.: 211120
Jeremy Asher *(Chm & CEO)*

Subsidiaries:

Neptune Petroleum (Uganda) Limited (1)
Plot 5 Kitante Rd Nakasero, PO Box 20093, Nakawa, Kampala, Uganda
Tel.: (256) 414340963
Web Site:
http://www.neptunepetroleum.co.ug
Sales Range: $50-74.9 Million
Oil & Gas Exploration Services
N.A.I.C.S.: 213112

TOWER SEMICONDUCTOR LTD.
Ramat Gavriel Industrial Park, PO Box 619, Migdal Ha'Emeq, 2310502, Israel
Tel.: (972) 46506611 IL
Web Site:
https://www.towersemi.com
Year Founded: 1988
TSEM—(NASDAQ)
Rev.: $1,508,166,000
Assets: $2,231,241,000
Liabilities: $615,852,000
Net Worth: $1,615,389,000
Earnings: $150,012,000
Emp.: 5,887
Fiscal Year-end: 12/31/21
Semiconductor Mfr
N.A.I.C.S.: 334413
Amir Elstein *(Chm)*

Subsidiaries:

Jazz Technologies, Inc. (1)
4321 Jamboree Rd, Newport Beach, CA 92660
Tel.: (949) 435-8000
Rev.: $221,469,000
Assets: $250,598,000
Liabilities: $169,881,000
Net Worth: $80,717,000
Earnings: ($11,265,000)
Fiscal Year-end: 12/31/2014
Semiconductor Foundry Focused on Specialty Process Technologies
N.A.I.C.S.: 334413
Ronit Vardi *(CFO)*

Subsidiary (Domestic):

Jazz Semiconductor, Inc. (2)
4321 Jamboree Rd, Newport Beach, CA 92660-3007
Tel.: (949) 435-8000
Web Site: http://www.jazzsemi.com
Sales Range: $200-249.9 Million
Emp.: 780
Semiconductor Wafer Foundry
N.A.I.C.S.: 334413

Newport Fab LLC (2)
4321 Jamboree Rd, Newport Beach, CA 92660
Tel.: (949) 435-8000
Semiconductor Devices Mfr
N.A.I.C.S.: 334413

Tower Semiconductor Newport Beach, Inc. (1)
4321 Jamboree Rd, Newport Beach, CA 92660
Tel.: (949) 435-8000

INTERNATIONAL PUBLIC

Semiconductor Mfr
N.A.I.C.S.: 334413

Tower Semiconductor San Antonio, Inc. (1)
9651 Westover Hills Blvd, San Antonio, TX 78251
Tel.: (210) 522-7000
Semiconductor Mfr
N.A.I.C.S.: 334413

Tower Semiconductor USA Inc. (1)
2350 Mission College Blvd Ste 500, Santa Clara, CA 95054
Tel.: (408) 327-8900
Sales Range: $25-49.9 Million
Emp.: 19
Current-Carrying Wiring Device Mfr
N.A.I.C.S.: 335931

TOWERBANK INTERNATIONAL, INC.
Tower Financial Center Calle 50 and Elvira Mendez, Panama, Panama
Tel.: (507) 8006900
Web Site:
https://www.towerbank.com
Year Founded: 1971
TOWI—(PAN)
Sales Range: Less than $1 Million
Financial Banking Services
N.A.I.C.S.: 522110
Giuseppina Buglione Cassino *(VP-Credit)*

TOWERGATE PARTNERSHIP LIMITED
77 Laden hall, London, EC 3A 3DE, United Kingdom
Tel.: (44) 622 754 754 UK
Web Site:
http://www.towergatepartners.co.uk
Year Founded: 1914
Sales Range: $1-4.9 Billion
Emp.: 400
Insurance Carrier
N.A.I.C.S.: 524128
Tim Grant *(Controller-Fin Grp)*

Subsidiaries:

Open GI Limited (1)
Buckholt Drive, Warndon, Worcester, WR4 9SR, United Kingdom
Tel.: (44) 9 0575 4455
Web Site: http://www.opengi.co.uk
Sales Range: $125-149.9 Million
Emp.: 300
IT Insurance Solutions Services
N.A.I.C.S.: 541512
Chris Guillaume *(Mng Dir)*

Towergate Financial (West) Ltd. (1)
Pegasus Court Olympus Avenue, Tachbrook Park, Warwick, CV34 6LW, United Kingdom
Tel.: (44) 1926439499
Web Site:
http://www.towergatefinancial.co.uk
Financial Investment Services
N.A.I.C.S.: 523940
Andrew Hunt *(Mgr-Compliance)*

TOWN CENTRE SECURITIES PLC
Town Centre House The Merrion Centre, Leeds, LS2 8LY, United Kingdom
Tel.: (44) 1132221234 UK
Web Site: https://www.tcs-plc.co.uk
Year Founded: 1959
TOWN—(LSE)
Rev.: $38,207,599
Assets: $509,237,325
Liabilities: $265,792,698
Net Worth: $243,444,627
Earnings: $14,951,213
Emp.: 27
Fiscal Year-end: 06/30/22
Holding Company
N.A.I.C.S.: 551112
Edward M. Ziff *(Chm & CEO)*

AND PRIVATE COMPANIES — TOYE & CO. PLC

Subsidiaries:

TCS (Mill Hill) Limited (1)
Town Centre House Merrion center Street, Leeds, LS2 8LY, West Yorkshire, United Kingdom
Tel.: (44) 1132221234
Web Site: http://www.tcs-plc.com
Emp.: 50
Property Investment Services
N.A.I.C.S.: 523999

TCS Freehold Investments Limited (1)
Town Ctr House Merrion Cntr, Leeds, LS2 8LY, West Yorkshire, United Kingdom
Tel.: (44) 1132221234
Web Site: http://www.tcs.plc.com
Emp.: 50
Property Investment Services
N.A.I.C.S.: 523999

TCS Holdings Limited (1)
Town Ctr House, Merrion St, Leeds, LS2 8LY, West Yorkshire, United Kingdom
Tel.: (44) 1132221284
Property Investment
N.A.I.C.S.: 523999

TCS Trustees Limited (1)
Town Ctr House Merrion Ctr, Leeds, LS2 8LY, West Yorkshire, United Kingdom
Tel.: (44) 1132221260
Web Site: http://www.tcs-plc.co.uk
Property Investment Services
N.A.I.C.S.: 523999

TOWN HEALTH INTERNATIONAL MEDICAL GROUP LIMITED
2/F Town Health Technology Centre 10-12 Yuen Shun Circuit, Siu Lek Yuen, Sha Tin, China (Hong Kong)
Tel.: (852) 22102194
Web Site: https://www.townhealth.com
Year Founded: 1989
3886—(HKG)
Rev.: $191,392,390
Assets: $610,123,123
Liabilities: $65,126,645
Net Worth: $544,996,477
Earnings: $9,682,787
Emp.: 1,170
Fiscal Year-end: 12/31/21
Medical & Dental Products & Services
N.A.I.C.S.: 621111
Jinhao Chen (CEO)

Subsidiaries:

Audio Health Hearing Care(Shatin) Limited (1)
Shop 37 R Level 3 Hilton Plz, 3-9 Shatin Ctr St, Sha Tin, New Territories, China (Hong Kong)
Tel.: (852) 26963832
Web Site: http://www.hearingaids.com.hk
Sales Range: $25-49.9 Million
Emp.: 14
Hearing Aid Devices Whslr
N.A.I.C.S.: 423450

First Oriental Cyclotron Limited (1)
NE Portion of Basement of N Wing St Teresa, 327 Prince Edward Rd, Kowloon, China (Hong Kong)
Tel.: (852) 22445370
Sales Range: $25-49.9 Million
Emp.: 5
Radioactive Isotopes Mfr
N.A.I.C.S.: 325180

Hong Kong Medical Consultants Limited (1)
9th Floor Central Building 1-3 Pedder Street Central, Hong Kong, China (Hong Kong)
Tel.: (852) 22199992
Web Site: https://www.hkmedicalconsultants.com
Medical Healthcare Services
N.A.I.C.S.: 621112

Nu/Hart Hair Solutions Limited (1)
14 F Plz 2000, 2-4 Russell St, Causeway Bay, China (Hong Kong)
Tel.: (852) 22010606
Web Site: http://www.nuhart.com.hk
Sales Range: $25-49.9 Million
Emp.: 10
Hair Treatment Services
N.A.I.C.S.: 812199

Town Health Medical & Dental Services Limited (1)
2/F Town Health Technology Centre 10-12 Yuen Shun Circuit, Siu Lek Yuen New Territories, Sha Tin, China (Hong Kong)
Tel.: (852) 22102194
Web Site: https://thmd.townhealth.com
Medical Healthcare Services
N.A.I.C.S.: 621610

TOWN RAY HOLDINGS LIMITED
10th Floor Block A Chung Mei Centre 15 Hing Yip Street, Kwun Tong, Kowloon, China (Hong Kong)
Tel.: (852) 27500775 Ky
Web Site: http://www.townray.com
Year Founded: 2005
1692—(HKG)
Rev.: $105,016,395
Assets: $74,185,875
Liabilities: $29,570,310
Net Worth: $44,615,565
Earnings: $17,124,653
Emp.: 1,044
Fiscal Year-end: 12/31/22
Holding Company
N.A.I.C.S.: 551112
Wai Ming Chan (Exec Dir)

Subsidiaries:

Tunbow Group Limited (1)
10/F Block A Chung Mei Centre 15 Hing Yip Street, Kwun Tong, Kowloon, China (Hong Kong)
Tel.: (852) 2 750 0775
Web Site: https://www.tunbow.com
Small Electrical Appliance Mfr & Distr
N.A.I.C.S.: 335210

TOWNGAS SMART ENERGY COMPANY LIMITED
23/F 363 Java Road, North Point, China (Hong Kong)
Tel.: (852) 29633298
Web Site: https://www.towngasenergy.com
TGASF—(OTCIQ)
Rev.: $2,535,753,575
Assets: $6,832,811,865
Liabilities: $3,608,344,473
Net Worth: $3,224,467,392
Earnings: $231,487,980
Emp.: 24,220
Fiscal Year-end: 12/31/23
Oil & Gas Distribution Services
N.A.I.C.S.: 221210
John Hon-Ming Ho (Sec)

TOWNNEWS-SHA CO., LTD.
1-3 Eda Nishi 2-chome, Aoba-ku, Yokohama, 225-0014, Kanagawa, Japan
Tel.: (81) 459134111
Web Site: https://www.townnews.co.jp
2481—(TKS)
Sales Range: Less than $1 Million
Newspaper Publishers
N.A.I.C.S.: 513110
Tomonari Uyama (Chm & Pres)

TOX PRESSOTECHNIK GMBH & CO. KG
Riedstrasse 4, 88250, Weingarten, Germany
Tel.: (49) 75150070
Web Site: http://www.de.tox-pressotechnik.com
Year Founded: 1978
Sales Range: $75-99.9 Million
Emp.: 300
Pneumatic Tool & Equipment Mfr
N.A.I.C.S.: 332216
Eugen Rapp (Founder & Co-Owner)

Subsidiaries:

SUZHOU TOX PRESSOTECHNIK Co. Ltd. (1)
No 58 East Nanjing Road, 215400, Taicang, Jiangsu, China
Tel.: (86) 512 53582248
Web Site: http://www.tox-cn.com
Cylinder Liner Mfr
N.A.I.C.S.: 333995
Wang Hui (Supvr-Mktg Adv)

TOX PRESSOTECHNIK (Pty) Ltd (1)
433 Strauss Crescent Cnr Crocker & Strauss Road, PO Box 4821, Atlaspark, 1428, Wadeville, Gauteng, South Africa
Tel.: (27) 11 865 5831
Industrial Machinery & Equipment Distr
N.A.I.C.S.: 423830

TOX PRESSOTECHNIK DO BRASIL LTDA. (1)
Rua Bento Goncalves 74, Gloria, 216-110, Joinville, Brazil
Tel.: (55) 47 3419 9000
Web Site: http://www.tox-br.com
Industrial Machinery & Tool Distr
N.A.I.C.S.: 423830

TOX PRESSOTECHNIK India Pvt Ltd. (1)
Gat No 343 Survey No 7 - 10 Pune Paud Road, At post Ambadvet Tal Mulshi, Pune, 412108, India
Tel.: (91) 20 66538300
Web Site: http://www.tox-in.com
Industrial Machinery & Equipment Distr
N.A.I.C.S.: 423830
Vinit Sonawane (Project Mgr & Mgr-Bus Dev)

TOX PRESSOTECHNIK Ltd. (1)
210-2 Shinho-dong, Gangseo-ku, Busan, 618-290, Korea (South)
Tel.: (82) 51 8321274
Web Site: http://www.tox-kr.com
Emp.: 30
Industrial Machinery & Equipment Distr
N.A.I.C.S.: 423830
Jaeho Kim (Gen Mgr)

TOX PRESSOTECHNIK Sdn Bhd (1)
56 Jalan Industri USJ 1/1 Taman Perindustrian USJ 1, 47600, Subang Jaya, Malaysia
Tel.: (60) 3 80231448
Industrial Machinery & Equipment Distr
N.A.I.C.S.: 423830

TOX-RIX PRESSOTECHNIK Co. (1)
1261-1 Satani Sue-machi, Kasuya-gun, Fukuoka, 811-2112, Japan
Tel.: (81) 92 934 4888
Web Site: http://www.tox-jp.com
Emp.: 11
Industrial Machinery & Equipment Distr
N.A.I.C.S.: 423830
Sadayuki Koga (Gen Mgr)

Tox-Pressotechnik LLC (1)
4250 Weaver Pkwy, Warrenville, IL 60555
Tel.: (630) 393-0300
Web Site: http://www.tox-us.com
Rev.: $15,000,000
Emp.: 42
Pneumatic Tools & Equipment
N.A.I.C.S.: 423830

TOY MARINE S.P.A
Zona 2/3 Porto di, 17100, Savona, Italy
Tel.: (39) 019 800757
Web Site: http://www.toymarine.it
Ship Building & Repair Services
N.A.I.C.S.: 336611

Subsidiaries:

W Service SpA (1)
Zona 2/3 Porto di Savona, 17100, Savona, Italy
Tel.: (39) 0198485379
Web Site: http://www.w-service.com
Emp.: 30
Ship Building & Repair Services
N.A.I.C.S.: 336611

TOYA S.A.
13-15 Soltysowicka Street, 51-168, Wroclaw, Poland
Tel.: (48) 713246200
Web Site: https://www.toya.pl
Year Founded: 1990
TOA—(WAR)
Rev.: $186,076,219
Assets: $140,606,707
Liabilities: $33,911,839
Net Worth: $106,694,868
Earnings: $17,357,215
Emp.: 550
Fiscal Year-end: 12/31/23
Power-Driven Handtool Manufacturing
N.A.I.C.S.: 333991

Subsidiaries:

Toya Romania S.A. (1)
109-123 Sos Odai, Bucharest, 13602, Romania
Tel.: (40) 317108692
Sales Range: $25-49.9 Million
Emp.: 4
Hand & Power Tools Distr
N.A.I.C.S.: 423830
Grzegorz Pinkosz (Gen Mgr)

Yato Tools (Jiaxing) Co. Ltd. (1)
No 1033 Yan Hu Road, Baibu Town Haiyan County, Jiaxing, Zhejiang, China
Tel.: (86) 2120981107
Power Tool Mfr & Distr
N.A.I.C.S.: 333991

Yato Tools (Shanghai) Co. Ltd. (1)
No 1 Lane 1300 East Kangqiao Road, Shanghai, China
Tel.: (86) 2168182950
Power Tool Mfr & Distr
N.A.I.C.S.: 333991

TOYAM SPORTS LIMITED
503 Shri Krishna Complex Fun Republic Lane New Link Road, Opp Laxmi Industrial Estate Andheri West, Mumbai, 400053, Maharashtra, India
Tel.: (91) 2267425111
Web Site: https://toyamsportsltd.com
Year Founded: 1985
538607—(BOM)
Rev.: $408,273
Assets: $8,540,939
Liabilities: $840,513
Net Worth: $7,700,426
Earnings: ($1,465,404)
Emp.: 9
Fiscal Year-end: 03/31/23
Asset Securitization & Reconstruction Services
N.A.I.C.S.: 522299
Budhwani Rajabali (Chm & Mng Dir)

Subsidiaries:

Pacific Star Sports Services L.L.C. (1)

TOYAMA ELECTRIC LTD.
#38-A2 KIADB Industrial Estate Hoskote, Bengaluru, 562 114, India
Tel.: (91) 8027971457
Web Site: http://www.toyamaindia.com
Sales Range: $1-9.9 Million
Electronic Components Mfr & Distr
N.A.I.C.S.: 334419
Mustafa Kamal Basha (Chm, Mng Dir & Compliance Officer)

TOYE & CO. PLC
Russell Court Entrance C basement Coram Street, London, WC1N 1HA, United Kingdom
Tel.: (44) 2476848800 UK

TOYE & CO. PLC

Toye & Co. plc—(Continued)

Web Site: http://www.toye.com
Year Founded: 1685
Sales Range: $10-24.9 Million
Emp.: 133
Apparel & Accessories Industry
N.A.I.C.S.: 315210
Fiona A. Toye (*CEO*)

Subsidiaries:

Toye, Kenning & Spencer Limited (1)
Regalia House Newtown Rd, Bedworth,
CV12 8QR, Warwickshire, United Kingdom
Tel.: (44) 2476848890
Web Site:
 http://www.toyekenningandspencer.com
Sales Range: $25-49.9 Million
Emp.: 120
Giftware & Furnishings Sales
N.A.I.C.S.: 449129
Steve Goode (*Mgr-Masonic*)

TOYO ASANO FOUNDATION CO., LTD.

315-2 Hara, Numazu, 410-0312, Shizuoka, Japan
Tel.: (81) 559673535
Web Site:
 https://www.toyoasano.co.jp
Year Founded: 1951
5271—(TKS)
Rev.: $106,825,030
Assets: $106,477,620
Liabilities: $78,613,920
Net Worth: $27,863,700
Earnings: $4,275,270
Emp.: 3,519
Fiscal Year-end: 02/29/24
Concrete Product Mfr & Distr
N.A.I.C.S.: 327332
Yasusuke Uematsu (*Pres & CEO*)

TOYO CONSTRUCTION CO., LTD.

11th Floor Jinbocho Mitsui Building
1-105 Kandajimbocho, Chiyoda-ku, Tokyo, 101-0051, Japan
Tel.: (81) 363615450
Web Site: http://www.toyo-const.co.jp
Year Founded: 1929
1890—(TKS)
Rev.: $1,234,622,410
Assets: $1,085,097,600
Liabilities: $551,009,600
Net Worth: $534,088,000
Earnings: $46,375,760
Emp.: 1,527
Fiscal Year-end: 03/31/24
Civil Engineering Services
N.A.I.C.S.: 237990
Kyoji Takezawa (*Pres & Exec Officer*)

Subsidiaries:

CCT Constructors Corporation (1)
3rd Floor Planters Products Building 109 Esteban Street, Legaspi Village, Makati, 1229, Philippines
Tel.: (63) 28102001
Web Site: https://www.cctconst.com
Engineering Services
N.A.I.C.S.: 541830
Hiroki Nakazawa (*Chm*)

Orient Ecology Co., Ltd. (1)
11th Floor Jinbocho Mitsui Building 1-105, Kandajimbocho Chiyoda-ku, Tokyo, 101-0051, Japan
Tel.: (81) 363615550
Engineering Services
N.A.I.C.S.: 541330

Tecuos Co., Ltd. (1)
3rd Floor Yagi Bldg 2-20-4 Kandamisaki-cho, Chiyoda-ku, Tokyo, 101-0061, Japan
Tel.: (81) 352167504
Civil Engineering & Construction Services
N.A.I.C.S.: 541330

Token Shoji Co., Ltd. (1)
3-19 Kanda Nishiki-cho Hirose 2nd Building 3F, Chiyoda-ku, Tokyo, 101-0054, Japan
Tel.: (81) 352445693
Web Site: https://www.token-shoji.co.jp
Insurance Agency Services
N.A.I.C.S.: 524210

Token Techno Co., Ltd. (1)
1-25-1 Naruohama, Nishinomiya, 663-8142, Hyogo, Japan
Tel.: (81) 798465555
Engineeering Services
N.A.I.C.S.: 541330

TOYO CORPORATION

1-6 Yaesu 1-chome, Chuo-ku, Tokyo, 103-8284, Japan
Tel.: (81) 332790771 JP
Web Site: https://www.toyo.co.jp
Year Founded: 1953
8151—(TKS)
Rev.: $199,739,480
Assets: $283,273,860
Liabilities: $82,534,690
Net Worth: $200,739,170
Earnings: $10,876,060
Emp.: 591
Fiscal Year-end: 09/30/23
Test & Measurement Equipment Mfr
N.A.I.C.S.: 334513
Shuuzou Totoki (*CFO & Exec VP*)

Subsidiaries:

TOYO Corporation China (1)
Room 310 Enterprise Plaza No 228 Meiyuan Road, Jing'an District, Shanghai, 200070, China
Tel.: (86) 216 380 9633
Web Site: https://www.toyochina.com.cn
Emp.: 20
Industrial Measuring Equipment Distr
N.A.I.C.S.: 423830
Toshiya Kohno (*Mng Dir*)

Tochiku Corporation (1)
806 Nonoi Toride, 302-0032, Ibaraki, Japan
Tel.: (81) 297785311
Sales Range: $25-49.9 Million
Emp.: 7
Electromedical & Electrotherapeutic Apparatus Mfr
N.A.I.C.S.: 334510

Toyo EMC Engineering Co., Ltd. (1)
398 Shibokuchi, Takatsu -ku, Kawasaki, 213-0023, Kanagawa, Japan
Tel.: (81) 447515331
Web Site: http://www.tee.tokin.jp
Electronic Components Mfr
N.A.I.C.S.: 334416

Uila, Inc. (1)
2975 Scott Blvd Ste 110, Santa Clara, CA 95054
Tel.: (408) 400-3706
Web Site: https://www.uila.com
Information Technology Services
N.A.I.C.S.: 541511

TOYO DENKI SEIZO K.K.

5F Tokyo Tatemono Yaesu Builiding
5F 1-4-16 Yaesu, Chuou-ku, Tokyo, 103-0028, Japan
Tel.: (81) 352028121
Web Site: https://www.toyodenki.co.jp
Year Founded: 1918
6505—(TKS)
Rev.: $212,445,400
Assets: $341,419,720
Liabilities: $169,097,020
Net Worth: $172,322,700
Earnings: $6,180,350
Emp.: 1,147
Fiscal Year-end: 05/31/24
Electrical Traffic Equipment Mfr & Sales
N.A.I.C.S.: 336320
Hiroshi Shimotakahara (*Sr Exec Officer*)

Subsidiaries:

Beijing Jingche Shuangyang Traction System Co., Ltd. (1)
F-2 Bodaxing Industrial Park No 24 Kechuang 3rd Street, East District Economy Technology Development Zone Yizhuang, Beijing, 100176, China
Tel.: (86) 1067892383
Electrical Equipment Distr
N.A.I.C.S.: 423610

Chalco-Toyo Permanent Magnet Motor Co., Ltd. (1)
Jiadi Changshu International Industrial Park No 1150 Southeast Avenue, Block G Changshu Hi-Tech Industrial Development Zone, Changshu, 215500, Jiangsu, China
Tel.: (86) 51252861933
Web Site: en.chinalcotoyo.com
Electric Motor & Parts Mfr & Distr
N.A.I.C.S.: 335312

Changzhou Ruiyang Transmission Technology Co., Ltd. (1)
No 12 Fukang Road, Xuejia Xinbei District, Changzhou, 213125, Jiangsu, China
Tel.: (86) 51985967359
Web Site: https://www.cz-ruiyang.com
Gear Transmission Equipment Mfr & Distr
N.A.I.C.S.: 333612

Changzhou Taiping Zhanyun Automatic Door Co., Ltd. (1)
No 182 Xuecheng Rd Xueyan, Wujin, Changzhou, 213171, Jiangsu, China
Tel.: (86) 51986160768
Door Operating Equipments Mfr & Sales
N.A.I.C.S.: 335999

Changzhou Yangdian Zhanyun Transport Equipment Co., Ltd. (1)
Innovative Industrial Park 1 No 377 Wuyi South Road, Wujin National High-Tech Industrial Development District, Changzhou, 213166, Jiangsu, China
Tel.: (86) 51986160768
Electrical Equipment Mfr & Distr
N.A.I.C.S.: 335999

Chengdu Yonggui Toyo Rolling Stock Equipment Co., Ltd. (1)
No 369 Chuang Fei Rd, Shibantan Town Xindu District, Chengdu, 610500, Sichuan, China
Tel.: (86) 2862365686
Electrical Equipment Mfr & Distr
N.A.I.C.S.: 335999

TD Drive Manufacturing Co., Ltd. (1)
2911-6 Oaza Okaya Ryuo-cho, Gamo-gun, Moriyama, 520-2541, Shiga, Japan
Tel.: (81) 748585258
Web Site: https://www.toyodenki.co.jp
Emp.: 46
Motor Maintenance Services
N.A.I.C.S.: 811310

Taihei Electric Co., Ltd. (1)
8-4 1-chome Azusawa, Itabashi-ku, Tokyo, 174-0051, Japan
Tel.: (81) 339667411
Web Site: https://www.taihei-electric.co.jp
Sales Range: $25-49.9 Million
Emp.: 80
Bus Door Operating Equipment Mfr & Sales
N.A.I.C.S.: 335999

Tianjin Toyodenki International Trade Co., Ltd. (1)
Rm 911 Bohai Wisdom Ctr No 42 Xinkai Rd, Hedong, Tianjin, 300011, China
Tel.: (86) 22 2489 7537
Web Site: http://www.ct-toyodenki.com
Industrial Equipment Mfr & Maintenance Services
N.A.I.C.S.: 333248

Toyo Denki (Beijing) Co., Ltd. (1)
Rm 3005 3rd Floor Building No 2 No 26 Jianguomenwai Avenue, Chaoyang District, Beijing, 100022, China
Tel.: (86) 1065132132
Electrical Equipment Distr
N.A.I.C.S.: 423610

Toyo Denki USA, Inc. (1)
2507 Lovi Rd Tri-County Commerce Park Bldg 3, Freedom, PA 15042
Tel.: (724) 774-1760
Web Site: http://www.toyodenkiusa.com
Sales Range: $25-49.9 Million
Emp.: 30

INTERNATIONAL PUBLIC

Light Rail Vehicle Electrical Equipment Mfr & Sales
N.A.I.C.S.: 336320
Ichiro Sueoka (*VP-Mktg & Sls*)

Toyo Shoji K.K. (1)
3-8 Fukuura, Kanazawa-ku, Yokohama, 236-0004, Kanagawa, Japan
Tel.: (81) 457890470
Web Site: https://www.toyosyoji.co.jp
Office Equipment Distr
N.A.I.C.S.: 423420

Toyokouki Co., Ltd. (1)
2-46 Kuryotsuzumi, Hiratsuka, 254-0801, Kanagawa, Japan
Tel.: (81) 463215932
Web Site: https://www.toyokouki.co.jp
Emp.: 130
Railway Components Mfr
N.A.I.C.S.: 335999
Etsunori Yatatsu (*Pres*)

Toyosangyo K.K. (1)
1-6-1 Omorihoncho Omori Park Building 5th floor, Ota-ku, Tokyo, 143-0011, Japan
Tel.: (81) 357675781
Web Site: http://www.toyosangyou.co.jp
Sales Range: $1-9.9 Million
Emp.: 135
Electrical Equipment Services
N.A.I.C.S.: 811114
Nagahisa Seno (*Pres*)

TOYO DRILUBE CO., LTD.

1-26-4 Daizawa, Setagaya-ku, Tokyo, 155-0032, Japan
Tel.: (81) 334125711
Web Site: https://www.drilube.co.jp
Year Founded: 1962
4976—(TKS)
Rev.: $29,227,780
Assets: $74,714,640
Liabilities: $14,977,760
Net Worth: $59,736,880
Earnings: $3,837,740
Emp.: 509
Fiscal Year-end: 06/30/24
Dry Lube Products & Coatings Developer, Mfr & Marketer
N.A.I.C.S.: 324191
Mitsuhiko Iino (*Pres, Pres & CEO*)

TOYO ENGINEERING CORPORATION

2-8-1 Akanehama Narashino-shi, Chiba, 275-0024, Japan
Tel.: (81) 474511111 JP
Web Site: http://www.toyo-eng.com
Year Founded: 1961
6330—(TKS)
Rev.: $1,724,053,250
Assets: $1,890,433,560
Liabilities: $1,466,382,230
Net Worth: $424,051,330
Earnings: $64,916,810
Emp.: 7,283
Fiscal Year-end: 03/31/24
Industrial Plants Design & Construction Services
N.A.I.C.S.: 236210
Masayuki Yoshizawa (*Exec VP & Dir-Future Architect, Security Mgmt Dept & Procurement*)

Subsidiaries:

Business Engineering Corporation (1)
KDDI Otemachi Bldg 1-8-1 Otemachi, Chiyoda-ku, Tokyo, 100-0004, Japan
Tel.: (81) 335101600
Web Site: https://www.b-en-g.co.jp
Rev.: $128,848,730
Assets: $103,895,980
Liabilities: $31,516,480
Net Worth: $72,379,500
Earnings: $17,351,250
Emp.: 699
Fiscal Year-end: 03/31/2024
Technical Consulting Services
N.A.I.C.S.: 541690
Masakazu Haneda (*Pres & CEO*)

AND PRIVATE COMPANIES

Chiba Data Center Corporation (1)
6-5-3 Tendai, Inage-ku, Chiba, 263-0016, Japan
Tel.: (81) 432843611
Web Site: http://www.chiba-data.co.jp
Data Entry, Documentation & Printing Services
N.A.I.C.S.: 518210

Estaleiros do Brasil Ltda. (1)
Estrada publica S/n - Bairro Cocuruto, Sao Jose do Norte, Sao Paulo, 96225-000, RS, Brazil
Tel.: (55) 5332381695
Industrial Engineering & Construction Services
N.A.I.C.S.: 541330

PT. Inti Karya Persada Tehnik (1)
Jl MT Haryono Kav 4-5, Jakarta Selatan, 12830, Indonesia
Tel.: (62) 218292177
Web Site: https://www.ikpt.com
Plant & Facility Construction Services
N.A.I.C.S.: 236220
Yasuhiro Hime *(Pres & CEO)*

Saudi Toyo Engineering Company (1)
B-504 Mada Commercial Tower 1 Prince Turki Street, PO Box 1720, Corniche District, Al Khobar, 31952, Eastern Province, Saudi Arabia
Tel.: (966) 38970072
Web Site: http://www.toyo-eng.co.jp
Plants & Facilities Construction Engineering Services
N.A.I.C.S.: 541330

TEC Accounting & Consulting, Ltd. (1)
2-8-1 Akanehama, Narashino, 275-0024, Chiba, Japan
Tel.: (81) 474541690
Web Site: http://www.ta-c.co.jp
Accounting & Business Support Consulting Services
N.A.I.C.S.: 541219

TEC Air Service Corporation (1)
2-6-7 Ginza Meijiya Ginza Building, Chuo-ku, Tokyo, 104-0061, Japan
Tel.: (81) 335640130
Web Site: http://www.tec-air.co.jp
Sales Range: $10-24.9 Million
Emp.: 50
Travel & Insurance Services
N.A.I.C.S.: 561599

TEC Business Services Corporation (1)
8-1 Akanehama 2-chome, Narashino, 275-0024, Chiba, Japan
Tel.: (81) 474137672
Web Site: http://www.tbiz.co.jp
Business Support Services
N.A.I.C.S.: 561499

TEC Project Services Corporation (1)
2-8-1 Akanehama, Narashino, 275-0024, Chiba, Japan
Tel.: (81) 474541178
Web Site: https://tec-tps.com
Emp.: 230
Environmental Engineering & Construction Services
N.A.I.C.S.: 541330
Shigeyuki Imai *(Pres)*

TTCL Public Company Limited (1)
159/41-44 Sermmit Tower 27th-30th Floor Sukhumvit 21 Asoke Road, North Klongtoey Wattana, Bangkok, 10110, Thailand
Tel.: (66) 22608505
Web Site: http://www.ttcl.com
Rev.: $211,483,453
Assets: $454,657,828
Liabilities: $356,837,732
Net Worth: $97,820,096
Earnings: $9,744,061
Emp.: 1,012
Fiscal Year-end: 12/31/2021
Engineering Contracting Services
N.A.I.C.S.: 237990
Hironobu Iriya *(Chm, Pres & CEO)*

Toyo Engineering & Construction Sdn. Bhd. (1)
Level 25 Menara Haw Par Jalan Sultan Ismai, 50250, Kuala Lumpur, Malaysia
Tel.: (60) 327311100
Web Site: http://www.toyo-m.com.my
Emp.: 200
Construction Engineering Services
N.A.I.C.S.: 541330
Azhan Salleh *(Exec Dir)*

Toyo Engineering Canada Ltd. (1)
Suite 300 150-13th Avenue S W, Calgary, T2R 0V2, AB, Canada
Tel.: (403) 266-4400
Web Site: http://www.toyo-eng.com
Emp.: 200
Construction Engineering Services
N.A.I.C.S.: 237120

Toyo Engineering Corporation (China) (1)
7F New Bund Oriental Plaza I No 512 Haiyang West Road, Pudong New District, Shanghai, 200124, China
Tel.: (86) 2161871270
Web Site: http://www.toyo-eng.com
Construction Engineering Services
N.A.I.C.S.: 541330
Masahiko Kita *(Chm)*

Toyo Engineering Europe S.A. (1)
PO Box 1473, 1014, Luxembourg, Luxembourg
Tel.: (352) 497511
Web Site: http://www.toyo-eng.co.jp
Procurement Services
N.A.I.C.S.: 812990

Toyo Engineering Europe, S.r.l (1)
10 Via Alzata, Villa d'Adda, 24030, Bergamo, Italy
Tel.: (39) 0354390520
Procurement Services
N.A.I.C.S.: 541990

Toyo Engineering India Limited (1)
Toyo House Lal Bahadur Shastri Marg, Kanjurmarg West, Mumbai, 400 078, Maharashtra, India
Tel.: (91) 2225737000
Web Site: http://www.toyoindia.com
Engineering Consulting Services
N.A.I.C.S.: 541330
S. B. Shelke *(Exec Dir-Comml & Sls)*

Toyo Engineering India Private Limited (1)
Toyo House Lal Bahadur Shastri Marg Kanjurmarg West, Mumbai, 400 078, Maharashtra, India
Tel.: (91) 2250727000
Web Site: https://www.toyoindia.com
Engineering Consulting Services
N.A.I.C.S.: 541330

Toyo Engineering Korea Limited (1)
Toyo B/D 11 Teheran-ro 37-gil, Yeoksam-dong Gangnam-gu, Seoul, 06142, Korea (South)
Tel.: (82) 221891620
Web Site: http://www.toyo-eng.com
Sales Range: $75-99.9 Million
Emp.: 400
Construction Engineering Services
N.A.I.C.S.: 541330

Toyo Ingenieria de Venezuela, C.A. (1)
Edif Cavendes Piso 10 Av Francisco de Miranda c/1ra Av, Urb Los Palos Grandes, 1062, Caracas, Venezuela
Tel.: (58) 2122868696
Web Site: http://www.toyo-eng.co.jp
Plant Construction & Engineering Services
N.A.I.C.S.: 339999

Toyo Setal Empreendimentos Ltda. (1)
Birmann Building 12 Rua Alexandre Dumas n 1 711 1st floor, Chacara Santo Antonio, Sao Paulo, 04717-911, SP, Brazil
Tel.: (55) 1155254990
Web Site: https://www.toyosetal.com
Industrial Engineering & Construction Services
N.A.I.C.S.: 541330

Toyo Transport Engineering Co., Ltd. (1)
2-8-1 Akanehama, Narashino, 275-0024, Chiba, Japan
Tel.: (81) 474541660
Transportation Consulting Services
N.A.I.C.S.: 541614

Toyo U.S.A., Inc. (1)
15415 Katy Freeway Ste 600, Houston, TX 77094
Tel.: (281) 579-8900
Emp.: 17
Plant Construction & Engineering Services
N.A.I.C.S.: 236210
Michael McInchak *(Mgr-Admin)*

Toyo do Brasil - Consultoria E Construcoes Industriais Ltda. (1)
Praia do Botafogo 228-Sala 801C-Ala B, 22250-906, Botafogo, Rio de Janeiro, Brazil
Tel.: (55) 2136216100
Sales Range: $25-49.9 Million
Emp.: 20
Construction Engineering Services
N.A.I.C.S.: 541330
Moto Kamoshima *(Pres)*

TOYO ENGINEERING WORKS, LTD.

1634 Shimotsuruma, Yamato, 242-0001, Kanagawa, Japan
Tel.: (81) 46 272 3000
Web Site: http://www.h.toyo-ew.co.jp
Year Founded: 1952
Air Conditioning Equipment Mfr
N.A.I.C.S.: 333415
Eiki Kurokawa *(Pres)*

TOYO GOSEI CO., LTD.

1-22-16 Asakusabashi Hulic Asakusabashi Building 8F, Taito-ku, Tokyo, 111-0053, Japan
Tel.: (81) 358226170
Web Site: https://www.toyogosei.co.jp
Year Founded: 1954
49700—(TKS)
Sales Range: $250-299.9 Million
Emp.: 688
Chemical Products Mfr
N.A.I.C.S.: 325199
Masateru Kimura *(Chm)*

TOYO INK SC HOLDINGS CO., LTD.

Kyobashi Edogrand Bldg 2-1 Kyobashi 2-Chome, Chuo-ku, Tokyo, 104-8377, Japan
Tel.: (81) 332725731
Web Site: http://www.toyoink.co.jp
Year Founded: 1896
4634—(TKS)
Rev.: $2,283,844,980
Assets: $3,174,887,820
Liabilities: $1,362,308,050
Net Worth: $1,812,579,770
Earnings: $69,035,330
Emp.: 7,836
Fiscal Year-end: 12/31/23
Commercial Printing Inks Mfr
N.A.I.C.S.: 325910
Katsumi Kitagawa *(Chm & CEO-Grp)*

Subsidiaries:

Aichi Toyo Ink Co., Ltd. (1)
3701-1 Kinoko-cho, Ibara, 715-0004, Okayama, Japan
Tel.: (81) 866633100
Plastic Colorants Mfr & Whslr
N.A.I.C.S.: 325130

Chengdu Toyo Ink Co., Ltd. (1)
B-4-2 Yang'an Industrial Park, Yang'an Town Qionglai City, Chengdu, 611534, Sichuan, China
Tel.: (86) 2861788557
Printing Material Mfr
N.A.I.C.S.: 323111

Hanil Toyo Co., Ltd. (1)
7F MGL Blue Fin Tower 42 Seochojungang-ro Seocho-gu, Seoul, 137-877, Korea (South)
Tel.: (82) 2 588 7855
Web Site: http://www.haniltoyo.co.kr
Plastic Colorants & Compounds Mfr & Sales
N.A.I.C.S.: 325998

Heubach Toyo Colour Pvt. Ltd. (1)
2nd Fl Landmark Bldg Race Course Rd Paris Nagar, Diwalipura, Vadodara, 390007, Gujarat, India
Tel.: (91) 2652343310
Organic Pigment Whslr
N.A.I.C.S.: 424690

Jiangmen TOYO INK CO., LTD. (1)
32-33 Longwan Road West, Jiangmen, Guangdong, China
Tel.: (86) 7503532618
Web Site: http://www.jm-toyoink.com
Sales Range: $150-199.9 Million
Emp.: 300
Inks Mfr & Whslr
N.A.I.C.S.: 325910

Jiangsu Toyo Renxin Pigment Co., Ltd. (1)
59 Hubin Rd N Niutang, Wujin District, Changzhou, 213163, Jiangsu, China
Tel.: (86) 51988319782
Printing Material Whslr
N.A.I.C.S.: 424110

Logi Co-Net Corp. (1)
3-23-3 Edo, Kawaguchi, 334-0074, Saitama, Japan
Tel.: (81) 48 283 1731
Web Site: https://www.lcn-co.com
Emp.: 133
Freight Transportation Services
N.A.I.C.S.: 484110

Matsui Chemical Co., Ltd. (1)
130 Jibu-cho, Fushimi-ku, Kyoto, 612-8374, Japan **(100%)**
Tel.: (81) 756110231
Web Site: http://www.toyoink.co.jp
Metal Decorating & Ultraviolet Curing Inks Mfr & Whslr
N.A.I.C.S.: 325910

P.T. Toyo Ink Indonesia (1)
Greenland International Industrial Center GIIC Blok AB No 03, Desa Nagasari Kecamatan Serang Baru Nagasari, Bekasi, 17330, Jawa Barat, Indonesia
Tel.: (62) 2129568040
Web Site: https://artience-id.com
Gravure Inks & Coating Materials Mfr & Distr
N.A.I.C.S.: 325910

PT. Toyo Ink Trading Indonesia (1)
Greenland International Industrial Center GIIC Blok AB No 03, Desa Nagasari Kecamatan Serang Baru Nagasari, Bekasi, 17330, Jawa Barat, Indonesia
Tel.: (62) 2129568040
Web Site: https://artience-id.com
Printing Material Mfr
N.A.I.C.S.: 323111

Sam Young Ink & Paint Mfg. Co. Ltd. (1)
18-2 Dangjung-Dong, Gunpo, 451-831, Kyungki, Korea (South)
Tel.: (82) 55258236
Web Site: http://www.syink.co.kr
Printing Inks Mfr & Distr
N.A.I.C.S.: 325910
Chang Hyung Soon *(CEO)*

Shanghai Toyo Ink Co., Ltd. (1)
590 Lianyang Road Songjiang Industrial Zone, Shanghai, 201613, China
Tel.: (86) 21 6760 6226
Web Site: http://www.toyoink.com.cn
Sales Range: $25-49.9 Million
Emp.: 30
Pigment Whslr
N.A.I.C.S.: 424950
Tant Wei *(Mgr-Sls)*

Shanghai Toyo Ink Mfg. Co., Ltd. (1)
Tel.: (86) 2167600606
Web Site: http://www.toyoink.co.jp
Colorants Mfr & Whslr
N.A.I.C.S.: 325130

Shenzhen Toyo Ink Co., Ltd. (1)
Room 05-06 25/F 5002 Shen Nan Dong Road, Shun Hing Square DiWang Commercial Center Louhu District, Shenzhen, 518001, Guangdong, China
Tel.: (86) 75528459829

TOYO INK SC HOLDINGS CO., LTD.

INTERNATIONAL PUBLIC

Toyo Ink SC Holdings Co., Ltd.—(Continued)
Sales Range: $25-49.9 Million
Emp.: 30
Printing Inks Whslr
N.A.I.C.S.: 424120

Sichuan Toyo Ink Mfg. Co., Ltd. (1)
South Side on Xinhua 2nd Rd, Chengdu New Materials Industry Function Zone Xinjin County, Chengdu, 611436, Sichuan, China
Tel.: (86) 2867779008
Printing Material Mfr & Whslr
N.A.I.C.S.: 323111

Sumika Polymer Compounds (Thailand) Co., Ltd. (1)
130 Moo 9 Wellgrow Industrial Estate T Bangwua, Bang Pakong, 24180, Chachoengsao, Thailand
Tel.: (66) 389891747
Polypropylene Resin Mfr
N.A.I.C.S.: 325211

TOYO INK (THAILAND) CO., LTD. (1)
34/1 Moo 14 Bangchan Industrial Estate Serithai Road, Minburi, Bangkok, 10510, Thailand
Tel.: (66) 25170143
Web Site: http://www.toyoink.co.th
Printing Ink Mfr
N.A.I.C.S.: 325910

Plant (Domestic):

TOYO INK (THAILAND) CO., LTD. - Plastic Colorant Factory (2)
130 Moo 9 Wellgrow Industrial Estate Bangwua, Bangpakong, Chachoengsao, 24180, Thailand
Tel.: (66) 3 898 9099
Web Site: http://www.toyoink.co.th
Plastic Colorants Mfr
N.A.I.C.S.: 325130
Hideyasu Kambayashi *(Pres)*

TOYO INK EUROPE (Paris) S.A.S. (1)
Boulevard Dambourney, CS 90051, Oissel, 76350, Villers-Saint-Paul, France
Tel.: (33) 235644043
Web Site: http://www.toyoink-europe.com
Sales Range: $25-49.9 Million
Emp.: 10
Printing Ink Distr
N.A.I.C.S.: 423840

TOYO INK EUROPE SPECIALTY CHEMICALS S.A. (1)
Tel.: (33) 235644043
Color Pigments Mfr
N.A.I.C.S.: 325130

TOYO INK KOREA CO., LTD. (1)
4F Yuil Bldg 25 Soecho-daero, Seocho-gu, Seoul, 137-838, Korea (South)
Tel.: (82) 53 794 9592
Inks Distr
N.A.I.C.S.: 423840
Tae Sun Kwon *(Mgr)*

TOYO INK NEW ZEALAND LTD. (1)
57E Mclaughlins Road Wiri, Maanukau, Auckland, 2104, New Zealand
Tel.: (64) 92504444
Web Site: http://www.toyoink.au
Emp.: 3
Offset Inks Distr
N.A.I.C.S.: 423840

TOYO INK Tohoku CO., LTD. (1)
27 Ake-dori 3-chome, Izumi-ku, Sendai, 981-3206, Miyagi, Japan
Tel.: (81) 22 378 5131
Web Site: http://www.toyoink.co.jp
Sale & Servicing Ink Products
N.A.I.C.S.: 325910

TOYO INK VIETNAM CO., LTD. (1)
Lot 201 Amata Street, Amata Industrial Park Long Bing Ward, 0084, Bien Hoa, Dong Nai, Vietnam
Tel.: (84) 25139366468
Web Site: https://toyoink.vn
Sales Range: $25-49.9 Million
Emp.: 20
Printing Supplies Distr
N.A.I.C.S.: 423840
C. F. Tan *(Chm)*

Tianjin Toyo Ink Co., Ltd. (1)
No 12 Second Branch Xinghua Road, Xiqing Economic Development Zone, Tianjin, 300385, China
Tel.: (86) 2223971610
Web Site: https://www.tjtoyoink.com.cn
Printing Inks Mfr & Whslr
N.A.I.C.S.: 325910

Tipps Pte. Ltd. (1)
31 Tuas Ave 2, Singapore, 639462, Singapore
Tel.: (65) 68615880
Printing Material Mfr
N.A.I.C.S.: 323111

Toyo ADL Co., Ltd. (1)
2-1 Kyobashi 2-Chome, Chuo-ku, Tokyo, 104-8377, Japan (100%)
Tel.: (81) 332725731
Web Site: http://www.toyoink.co.jp
Sales Range: $25-49.9 Million
Emp.: 50
Polymers Mfr
N.A.I.C.S.: 325211

Plant (Domestic):

Toyo ADL Corp. - Chiba Plant (2)
6-13 Onodai 2-chome, Midori-ku, Chiba, 267-0056, Japan
Tel.: (81) 432050811
Adhesives & Waxes Mfr
N.A.I.C.S.: 325520

Toyo Advanced Science Taiwan Co., Ltd. (1)
6F No 318 Songjiang Rd, Zhongshan Dist, Taipei, 10469, Taiwan
Tel.: (886) 22 536 2628
Web Site: https://www.toyoinkgroup.com.tw
Printing Material Mfr & Whslr
N.A.I.C.S.: 323111

Toyo B Net Co., Ltd. (1)
2-2-1 Kyobashi 2-chome, Chuo-ku, Tokyo, 104-0031, Japan
Tel.: (81) 332723741
Web Site: http://www.toyo-b-net.co.jp
Sales Range: $150-199.9 Million
Emp.: 300
Real Estate Management & Leasing Services
N.A.I.C.S.: 531110

Toyo Fpp Co., Ltd. (1)
23-3 Edo 3-chome, Kawaguchi, 334-0074, Saitama, Japan
Tel.: (81) 482848593
Web Site: http://www.topc.co.jp
Sales Range: $125-149.9 Million
Emp.: 260
Printing Cylinders Mfr & Whslr
N.A.I.C.S.: 333248
Masayuki Kawashima *(Pres)*

Plant (Domestic):

Toyo Fpp Co., Ltd. - 1st Plant (2)
Edo 3-23-3, Kawaguchi, 334-0074, Saitama, Japan
Tel.: (81) 482848502
Gravure Printing Services
N.A.I.C.S.: 323111
Tetsuo Iga *(Pres)*

Toyo Human Asset Co., Ltd. (1)
3-13 Kyobashi 2-chome, Chuo-ku, Tokyo, 104-0031, Japan
Tel.: (81) 3 3272 6941
Web Site: http://www.toyoink.co.jp
Human Resource Management Services
N.A.I.C.S.: 541612

Toyo Ink (Middle East) FZE (1)
RAO 8ZF02, PO Box 17734, Jebel Ali Fz, Dubai, United Arab Emirates
Web Site: http://www.toyoink.co.jp
Emp.: 8
Printing Supplies Whslr
N.A.I.C.S.: 424110
Yasushi Namise *(Mng Dir)*

Toyo Ink (Philippines) Co., Inc. (1)
106-B Integrity Ave, Carmelray Industrial Park 1 Calamba, Calamba, 4028, Laguna, Philippines
Tel.: (63) 495491647
Web Site: http://www.toyoinkgroup.com

Sales Range: $25-49.9 Million
Emp.: 55
Printing Inks Mfr & Whslr
N.A.I.C.S.: 325910

Toyo Ink (Shanghai) RHQ Co., Ltd. (1)
2450 Shengang Road Songjiang Industrial District East, Shanghai, China
Tel.: (86) 21 6760 0606
Web Site: http://www.toyoink.co.jp
Printing Ink Mfr
N.A.I.C.S.: 325910

Toyo Ink Arets India Pvt. Ltd. (1)
Prakash Deep Building 308-309 7 Tolstoy Marg, New Delhi, 110 001, India
Tel.: (91) 1143522548
Printing Material Whslr
N.A.I.C.S.: 424110

Toyo Ink Arets Middle East Fze. (1)
PO Box 9364, Saif Zone, Sharjah, United Arab Emirates
Tel.: (971) 65575410
Printing Material Whslr
N.A.I.C.S.: 424110

Toyo Ink Asia Ltd. (1)
Room 513-522 5/F Leader Industrial Centre 57-59 Au Pui Wan Street, Fotan, New Territories, China (Hong Kong)
Tel.: (852) 26935663
Web Site: http://www.toyoink.co.jp
Printing Machinery & Materials Distr
N.A.I.C.S.: 423830

Toyo Ink Australia PTY. LTD. (1)
29 Garden Street, Kilsyth, 3137, VIC, Australia
Tel.: (61) 2 9728 4977
Web Site: http://www.toyoink.co.jp
Sales Range: $75-99.9 Million
Emp.: 110
Printing Trades Machinery, Equipment & Supplies Mfr
N.A.I.C.S.: 325910

Toyo Ink Brasil Ltda (1)
Rua Gustavo Henrique Meerson 350 Aglomeracao Urbana de Jundiai, Jundiai, 13213-105, Sao Paulo, Brazil
Tel.: (55) 1129235100
Web Site: https://www.toyoink.com.br
Sales Range: $50-74.9 Million
Emp.: 100
Printing Inks & Related Products Whslr
N.A.I.C.S.: 424110
Sergo Pera *(Dir-Comml)*

Toyo Ink Chemicals Taiwan Co., Ltd. (1)
No 50 Gongye 3rd Road Tainan Technology Industrial Park, Annan District, T'ainan, 70955, Taiwan
Tel.: (886) 6 384 0650
Web Site: http://schd.toyoinkgroup.com
Sales Range: $75-99.9 Million
Emp.: 120
Color Resist Inks Mfr & Distr
N.A.I.C.S.: 325910

Toyo Ink Chushikoku Co., Ltd. (1)
11th Fl Hiroshima NS Bldg 10-6 Hashimotocho, Naka-ku, Hiroshima, 730-0015, Japan
Tel.: (81) 82 511 3411
Web Site: http://www.toyoink.co.jp
Printing Ink Mfr
N.A.I.C.S.: 325910

Toyo Ink Co., Ltd. (1)
Kyobashi Edgrand 2-2-1 Kyobashi, Chuo-ku, Tokyo, 104-8378, Japan
Tel.: (81) 332723435
Web Site: http://www.toyoink.jp
Emp.: 660
Printing Inks Mfr & Sales
N.A.I.C.S.: 325910
Katsumi Yamazaki *(Pres & CEO)*

Toyo Ink Compounds Corporation. (1)
106 A Integrity Avenue Carmelray Industrial Park 1, Canlubang, Calamba, 4027, Laguna, Philippines
Tel.: (63) 495491444
Plastic Colorants Mfr & Distr
N.A.I.C.S.: 325180
Masaru Kato *(Chm)*

Toyo Ink Compounds Vietnam Co., Ltd. (1)
Lot G9 Que Vo Industrial Park Van Duong Commune, Bac Ninh, Vietnam
Tel.: (84) 2413634340
Web Site: http://www.toyoinkgroup.com
Emp.: 200
Plastic Colorants Distr
N.A.I.C.S.: 424950
Junichi Suzuki *(Gen Dir)*

Toyo Ink Engineering Co., Ltd. (1)
1-22-1 Kaga, Itabashi-ku, Tokyo, 173-8666, Japan
Tel.: (81) 33 962 2137
Web Site: https://www.toyoink-eng.co.jp
Sales Range: $200-249.9 Million
Emp.: 1,000
Chemical Factories & Plants Construction Services
N.A.I.C.S.: 236210

Toyo Ink Europe Deutschland GmbH (1)
Wolfener Str 32/34 Haus E, 12681, Berlin, Germany
Tel.: (49) 3099273940
Printing Material Whslr
N.A.I.C.S.: 424110

Toyo Ink Europe France S.A.S. (1)
ZE des Recoux, Soyaux, 16800, Angouleme, France
Tel.: (33) 545683057
Web Site: https://www.toyoink.eu
Printing Material Whslr
N.A.I.C.S.: 424110

Toyo Ink Europe Plastic Colorant S.A.S. (1)
Rue Albert Thomas, Rieux, 60870, Villers-Saint-Paul, France
Tel.: (33) 344744646
Web Site: http://www.toyoink-europe.com
Sales Range: $25-49.9 Million
Emp.: 32
Plastic Colorants Mfr
N.A.I.C.S.: 325130

Toyo Ink Europe SA (1)
Gulledelle 94, 1200, Brussels, Belgium
Tel.: (32) 27053440
Inks & Printing Materials Whslr
N.A.I.C.S.: 423840

Toyo Ink Europe UK Ltd. (1)
45 Monckton Road Industrial Estate, Wakefield, WF2 7AL, West Yorkshire, United Kingdom
Tel.: (44) 1924280905
Printing Material Whslr
N.A.I.C.S.: 424110

Toyo Ink Graphics Co., Ltd. (1)
22-1 Kaga 1-chome, Itabashi-ku, Tokyo, 173-0003, Japan
Tel.: (81) 33 962 3661
Web Site: http://www.toyoink.co.jp
Printing Machinery & Supplies Whslr
N.A.I.C.S.: 423830

Toyo Ink Graphics Nishinihon Co., Ltd. (1)
6-6 Sanra Nishi-machi, Neyagawa, 572-0818, Osaka, Japan
Tel.: (81) 72 822 2670
Web Site: http://www.toyoink.co.jp
Printing Machinery & Supplies Mfr
N.A.I.C.S.: 325910

Toyo Ink Hokkaido Co., Ltd. (1)
1-36 Nishi-machi Minami 11-chome, Nishi-ku, Sapporo, 063-0062, Hokkaido, Japan
Tel.: (81) 116624733
Printing Ink Mfr
N.A.I.C.S.: 325910

Toyo Ink India Pvt. Ltd. (1)
Plot No 17 Ecotech - III Udyog Kendra, Greater Noida Distt Gautam Budh Nagar, Noida, 201306, Uttar Pradesh, India
Tel.: (91) 120 677 7222
Web Site: https://www.toyoinkindia.com
Printing Material Mfr & Whslr
N.A.I.C.S.: 323111
Haruhiko Akutsu *(Chm & Mng Dir)*

Toyo Ink International Corp. (1)
610 5th Ave Rockefeller Ctr Ste 305, New York, NY 10020

Tel.: (212) 554-2310
Web Site: http://www.tii.toyoink.com
Rev.: $100,000,000
Emp.: 200
Printing Supplies Whslr
N.A.I.C.S.: 424110

Subsidiary (Domestic):

LioChem, Inc. (2)
2145 E Park Dr, Conyers, GA 30013
Tel.: (770) 922-0800
Sales Range: $25-49.9 Million
Emp.: 100
Printing Chemicals Mfr
N.A.I.C.S.: 325998
Ronnie Robertson *(Mgr-HR)*

Toyo Ink America, LLC (2)
1225 N Michael Dr, Wood Dale, IL 60191
Tel.: (630) 930-5100
Web Site: https://www.toyoink.com
Sales Range: $25-49.9 Million
Emp.: 75
Printing Supplies Whslr
N.A.I.C.S.: 424110
John Copeland *(Pres & COO)*

Toyo Ink Mfg. America, LLC, (2)
Glen Pointe Ctr E 7th Fl 300 Frank W Burr Blvd Ste 70, Teaneck, NJ 07666
Tel.: (201) 287-4000
Web Site: http://www.tima.toyoink.com
Printing Supplies Whslr
N.A.I.C.S.: 424110

Plant (Domestic):

Toyo Ink Mfg. America, LLC - Texas Factory (3)
2400 N Harvey Mitchell Pkwy, Bryan, TX 77807
Tel.: (979) 778-1538
Web Site: http://www.toyoink.com
Sales Range: $25-49.9 Million
Emp.: 32
Printing Ink Mfr
N.A.I.C.S.: 325910
Danny Vessells *(Mgr-Admin)*

Toyo Ink Kyushu Co., Ltd. (1)
12-1 Matsushima 4-chome, Higashi-ku, Fukuoka, 813-0062, Japan
Tel.: (81) 926217106
Web Site: http://www.toyoink.co.jp
Sales Range: $25-49.9 Million
Emp.: 46
Printing Ink Mfr
N.A.I.C.S.: 325910

Toyo Ink Mexico, S.A. De C.V. (1)
Paseo de Los Adobes 1081 Bodega 2, Fraccionamiento Guadalajara Technology Park, 45010, Zapopan, Jalisco, Mexico
Tel.: (52) 3336271145
Printing Material Mfr
N.A.I.C.S.: 323111

Toyo Ink Mfg. Co., Ltd. - Saitama Factory (1)
1 Sakae, Kawagoe, 350-0803, Saitama, Japan
Tel.: (81) 492332211
Web Site: http://www.toyoink.co.jp
Sales Range: $200-249.9 Million
Emp.: 750
Printing Ink Mfr
N.A.I.C.S.: 325910

Toyo Ink Myanmar Co,. Ltd. (1)
Printing Material Mfr & Whslr
N.A.I.C.S.: 323111

Toyo Ink North Africa S.A.R.L. (1)
Parc Industriel Sapono Lot 684, Nouaceur, 27182, Casablanca, Morocco
Tel.: (212) 646650188
Printing Material Mfr
N.A.I.C.S.: 323111

Toyo Ink Pan Pacific Pte. Ltd. (1)
31 Tuas Avenue 2, 639462, Singapore, Singapore
Tel.: (65) 67947875
Web Site: http://schd.toyoinkgroup.com
Sales Range: $50-74.9 Million
Emp.: 8
Printing Ink Mfr & Distr
N.A.I.C.S.: 325910

Toyo Ink Taiwan Co., Ltd. (1)
1F No 250 Section 3 Bei Shen Road, Shenkeng Township, Taipei, Taiwan
Tel.: (886) 226628222
Web Site: http://www.toyoink.com.tw
Printing Inks & Pigments Distr
N.A.I.C.S.: 424110

Toyo Management Service Co., Ltd. (1)
Kyobashi Edogrand Bldg 2-1 Kyobashi 2-chome, Chuo-ku, Tokyo, 104-0031, Japan
Tel.: (81) 332725727
Emp.: 71
Information Processing & Accounts Outsourcing Services
N.A.I.C.S.: 541219

Toyo Matbaa Murekkepleri Sanayi Ve Ticaret A.S. (1)
Kecilikoy OSB Mah Hasan Turek Blv 6, Merkez Koyu Merkez Bucagi Yunusemre, Manisa, Turkiye
Tel.: (90) 236 226 5000
Web Site: https://www.toyoink.com.tr
Printing Material Mfr
N.A.I.C.S.: 323111
Engin Kurt *(Sls Dir)*

Toyo SC Trading Co., Ltd. (1)
Kyobashi Edogrand Bldg 2-1 Kyobashi 2-chome, Chuo-ku, Tokyo, 104-0031, Japan
Tel.: (81) 33 272 8671
Web Site: https://www.toyo-sc-trading.com
Emp.: 26
Raw Material Product Whslr
N.A.I.C.S.: 424590
Hiroyuki Matsumoto *(Pres)*

Toyo Visual Solutions Co., Ltd. (1)
Kyobashi Edogrand Bldg 2-1 Kyobashi 2-chome, Chuo-ku, Tokyo, 104-0031, Japan
Tel.: (81) 33 272 5743
Web Site: https://www.toyo-visual.com
Emp.: 215
Raw Material Product Mfr & Whslr
N.A.I.C.S.: 325211
Toshikazu Tamura *(Pres)*

Toyo-Morton, Ltd. (1)
Kyobashi EDOGRAND Bldg 2-1 Kyobashi 2-chome, Chuo-ku, Tokyo, 104-0031, Japan (50%)
Tel.: (81) 332720717
Sales Range: $25-49.9 Million
Emp.: 30
Specialty Chemicals Mfr
N.A.I.C.S.: 325998

Plant (Domestic):

Toyo-Morton, Ltd. - Saitama Plant (2)
25-26 Miyako, Namegawamachi Hikigun, Saitama, 355-0812, Japan
Tel.: (81) 49 356 4361
Web Site: http://www.toyoink.co.jp
Adhesive Mfr
N.A.I.C.S.: 325520

Toyochem Co., Ltd. (1)
2-2-1 Kyobashi, Chuo-ku, Tokyo, 104-8379, Japan
Tel.: (81) 3 3272 5743
Web Site: http://www.toyo-chem.com
Emp.: 365
Polymers, Coatings, Colorants & Functional Materials Mfr & Sales
N.A.I.C.S.: 325510

Subsidiary (Non-US):

TOYOCHEM CORPORATION SDN. BHD. (2)
10 Jalan Pengapit 15/19 Section 15, 40000, Shah Alam, Selangor, Malaysia
Tel.: (60) 355109606
Emp.: 300
Printing Inks Mfr & Distr
N.A.I.C.S.: 325910
Lilian Low *(Mgr-Fin)*

Plant (Domestic):

Toyochem Co., Ltd. - Kawagoe Factory (2)
286 Nakafuku, Kawagoe, 350-1156, Saitama, Japan
Tel.: (81) 492421331
Polymers, Coatings-Related Products & Plastic Colorants Mfr
N.A.I.C.S.: 325211

Toyochem Co., Ltd. - Seishin Plant (2)
5-7 Takatsukadai 1-chome, Nishi-ku, Kobe, 651-2271, Hyogo, Japan
Tel.: (81) 789915952
Polymer-Related Products Mfr
N.A.I.C.S.: 325211

Subsidiary (Non-US):

Toyochem Printing Chemical Sdn. Bhd. (2)
10 Jalan Pengapit 15/19 Section 15, 40000, Shah Alam, 40000, Selangor, Malaysia
Tel.: (60) 355109606
Web Site: http://www.toyochem.com.my
Emp.: 300
Printing Ink Mfr
N.A.I.C.S.: 325910

Toyochem Specialty Chemical Sdn. Bhd. (2)
10 Jalan Pengapit 15/19 Section 15, 40000, Shah Alam, Selangor, Malaysia
Tel.: (60) 355109606
Sales Range: $125-149.9 Million
Emp.: 300
Printing Inks Mfr & Distr
N.A.I.C.S.: 325910
H. Matsumoto *(Chm)*

Plant (Domestic):

Toyochem Specialty Chemical Sdn. Bhd. - Seremban Plant (3)
Lot 17942-44 & 17950-52 Tuanku Jaafar Industrial Park, Sungai Gadut, 71450, Seremban, Negeri Sembilan, Malaysia
Tel.: (60) 6 679 1800
Web Site: http://www.toyochem.com.my
Sales Range: $25-49.9 Million
Emp.: 100
Printing Ink Mfr
N.A.I.C.S.: 325910
Liang Yat Hong *(Gen Mgr)*

Toyocolor Co., Ltd. (1)
Kyobashi Edogrand Bldg 2-1 Kyobashi 2-chome, Chuo-ku, Tokyo, 104-8381, Japan (100%)
Tel.: (81) 33 272 3443
Web Site: https://www.toyo-color.com
Emp.: 501
Pigment Dispersions Mfr & Whslr
N.A.I.C.S.: 325510
Hideki Okaichi *(Pres)*

Toyocolor Co., Ltd. (1)
Kyobashi East Bldg 2-1 Kyobashi 2, Chuo-ku, Tokyo, 104-8378, Japan (100%)
Tel.: (81) 332720000
Web Site: http://www.toyo-color.com
Emp.: 744
Colorants & Functional Materials Related Products Mfr & Sales
N.A.I.C.S.: 325910

Plant (Domestic):

Toyocolor Co., Ltd. - Moriyama Factory (2)
436-1 Miyake-cho, Moriyama, 524-0051, Shiga, Japan
Tel.: (81) 775827200
Color Resist Inks Mfr
N.A.I.C.S.: 325998

Toyocolor Co., Ltd. - Okayama Plant (2)
3701-1 Kinoko-cho, Ibara, 715-0004, Okayama, Japan
Tel.: (81) 866633100
Plastic Colorants Mfr
N.A.I.C.S.: 325998

Toyocolor Co., Ltd.- Fuji Factory (2)
400 Tenma, Fuji, 419-0205, Shizuoka, Japan
Tel.: (81) 545711221
Inks & Organic Pigments Mfr
N.A.I.C.S.: 325130

UAB Toyo Ink Europe Baltica (1)
Europos pr 85, Kauno miestas, 46333, Kaunas, Lithuania
Tel.: (370) 37295231
Printing Material Whslr
N.A.I.C.S.: 424110

Zhuhai Toyo Color Co., Ltd. (1)
2 Fushan Ave, Fushan Industrial Park Doumen District, Zhuhai, 519175, Guangdong, China
Tel.: (86) 756 687 9998
Web Site: https://www.zhtoyocolor.com
Printing Material Mfr & Whslr
N.A.I.C.S.: 323111

Zhuhai Toyo Ink Co., Ltd. (1)
229 Qiaohu Road South East of Jinganzhen, Doumen District, Zhuhai, 519125, Guangdong, China
Tel.: (86) 756 522 2869
Web Site: http://schd.toyoinkgroup.com
Pigments Mfr & Whslr
N.A.I.C.S.: 325130

TOYO KANETSU K.K.

2-11-1 Minamisuna, Koto-ku, Tokyo, 136-8666, Japan
Tel.: (81) 358573100
Web Site: https://www.toyokanetsu.co.jp
6369—(TKS)
Rev.: $355,532,070
Assets: $448,759,510
Liabilities: $199,218,790
Net Worth: $249,540,720
Earnings: $23,491,940
Emp.: 1,147
Fiscal Year-end: 03/31/24
Logistics Systems & Machinery Mfr
N.A.I.C.S.: 238290
Toru Yanagawa *(Pres)*

Subsidiaries:

Kankyo Research Institute Inc. (1)
104 Komoncho, Tokyo, 192-0054, Japan
Tel.: (81) 426552501
Web Site: https://www.kankyo-research.co.jp
Varnish & Supplies Merchant Whslr
N.A.I.C.S.: 424950

P.T. Toyo Kanetsu Indonesia (1)
Midplaza Building 1 8th Floor JL Jend, Sudirman Kav 10-11, Jakarta, 10220, Indonesia
Tel.: (62) 215707805
Web Site: https://www.pttki.com
Sales Range: $50-74.9 Million
Emp.: 250
Storage Tank Mfr
N.A.I.C.S.: 332420
Toru Kiritani *(Personnel Dir)*

TKK Plant Engineering K.K. (1)
2-11-1 Minamisuna, Koto-ku, Tokyo, 136-8666, Japan
Tel.: (81) 358573159
Web Site: https://tkkplanteng.co.jp
Storage Tank Mfr & Distr
N.A.I.C.S.: 332420

TKL Co., Ltd. (1)
19-20 Higashi-Suna 8-chome, Koto-ku, Tokyo, 136-8666, Japan
Tel.: (81) 336405164
Web Site: http://www.web-tkl.co.jp
Sales Range: $75-99.9 Million
Emp.: 10
Insurance & Travel Agencies
N.A.I.C.S.: 524210

Toyo Kanetsu K.K. - Chiba Plant (1)
2 Tsukiji Kisarazu, Chiba, 292-0835, Japan
Tel.: (81) 438367161
Web Site: http://www.toyokanetsu.co
Storage Tank Mfr
N.A.I.C.S.: 332420

Toyo Kanetsu Singapore Pte. Ltd. (1)
16 Ayer Rajah Crescent 03-04 Tempco Technominium 3rd Floor, Singapore, 139965, Singapore
Tel.: (65) 67762393
Storage Tank Mfr & Distr
N.A.I.C.S.: 332420

Toyo Kanetsu Solutions K.K. (1)
11-1 Minamisuna 2-chome, Koto-ku, Tokyo, 136-8666, Japan
Tel.: (81) 358573126
Web Site: http://www.tksl.co.jp

TOYO KANETSU K.K.

TOYO KANETSU K.K.—(Continued)
Sales Range: $75-99.9 Million
Emp.: 310
Logistics Solutions
N.A.I.C.S.: 541614
Toru Yanagawa *(Pres & CEO)*

Toyo Koken K.K. (1)
1-1 Minamisuna 2-chome, Koto-ku, Tokyo, 136-8666, Japan
Tel.: (81) 358573161
Web Site: https://www.toyokoken.co.jp
Machine Tools Mfr
N.A.I.C.S.: 333517

Toyo Service System K.K. (1)
11-1 Minamisuna 2-chome, Koto-ku, Tokyo, 136-8666, Japan
Tel.: (81) 358573200
Web Site: https://www.toyoservice.co.jp
Real Estate Manangement Services
N.A.I.C.S.: 531390

TOYO KNIFE (SHANGHAI) CO., LTD.

Room 323-324 331 No 38 Yinglun Road, Wai Gao Qiao Free Trade Zone, Shanghai, 200131, China
Tel.: (86) 21 50483386
Knife Distr
N.A.I.C.S.: 423710

TOYO KNITEX (CEPZ) LIMITED

South Avenue Tower 6th Floor House 50 Road 3 Gulshen 1, Dhaka, 1212, Bangladesh
Tel.: (880) 9847926
Web Site: https://mkdl-cepz.com.bd
Year Founded: 1991
MITHUNKNIT—(DHA)
Sales Range: Less than $1 Million
Knit Fabric Mfr
N.A.I.C.S.: 313240

TOYO LOGISTICS CO., LTD.

6-17 Meiekiminami 2-chome, Nakamura-ku, Nagoya, 450-8614, Aichi, Japan
Tel.: (81) 525810251
Web Site: https://www.toyo-logistics.co.jp
Year Founded: 1926
9306—(TKS)
Rev.: $184,253,750
Assets: $314,199,740
Liabilities: $147,647,570
Net Worth: $166,552,170
Earnings: $9,049,090
Emp.: 297
Fiscal Year-end: 03/31/24
Transportation Services
N.A.I.C.S.: 481112
Yoshitaka Shiraishi *(Chm)*

Subsidiaries:

Toyo Logistics (S) Pte Ltd (1)
10 Anson Road International Plaza 33-12, Singapore, Singapore
Tel.: (65) 62201193
Freight Forwarding Services
N.A.I.C.S.: 488510
Tomotaka Kobayashi *(Gen Mgr)*

Toyo Logistics America, Inc. (1)
20675 S Western Ave Ste 208, Torrance, CA 90501
Tel.: (310) 533-8300
Air Freight Transportation Services
N.A.I.C.S.: 481212
Yoshinori Yamagiwa *(Pres)*

Toyo Logistics Co., Ltd. (1)
Room No 1406 Shanghai Jinjiang int'l Shopping Center No 527 HuaiHai Rd, Shanghai, 200020, China
Tel.: (86) 2153067290
Logistics Consulting Servies
N.A.I.C.S.: 541614

TOYO MACHINERY & METAL CO., LTD.

523-1 Fukusato Futami-cho, Akashi, 674-0091, Hyogo, Japan
Tel.: (81) 789422345 JP
Web Site: https://www.toyo-mm.co.jp
Year Founded: 1925
6210—(TKS)
Rev.: $190,645,620
Assets: $198,709,820
Liabilities: $75,869,580
Net Worth: $122,840,240
Earnings: ($8,546,730)
Emp.: 771
Fiscal Year-end: 03/31/24
Industrial Machinery Mfr
N.A.I.C.S.: 333248
Tabata Yoshiaki *(Pres & CEO)*

Subsidiaries:

Toyo Machinery & Metal (Guangzhou) Co., Ltd. (1)
Room 612-613 Tianhe Commercial Building Linhe Rd, Guangzhou, China
Tel.: (86) 2038880271
Plastic Injection Molding Machine Mfr
N.A.I.C.S.: 333924

Toyo Machinery & Metal (Shanghai) Co., Ltd. (1)
1903 Xiandai Plaza No 369 Xianxia Road, Shanghai, China
Tel.: (86) 2161921000
Plastic Injection Molding Machine Mfr
N.A.I.C.S.: 333924

Toyo Machinery & Metal (Taiwan) Co., Ltd. (1)
E5F-2 No 88 Section 2 Chung Hsiao East Road, Taipei, Taiwan
Tel.: (886) 223930272
Machinery & Equipment Mfr
N.A.I.C.S.: 333132

Toyo Machinery (Changshu) Co., Ltd. (1)
Unit 1 No 56 Xiangjiang Road Economic Zone, Changshu, Jiangsu, China
Tel.: (86) 51252889300
Plastic Injection Molding Machine Mfr
N.A.I.C.S.: 333924

Toyo Machinery (M) Sdn. Bhd. (1)
E-G-49 Jalan Pju 1/45 Aman Suria Damansara, 47301, Petaling Jaya, Selangor, Malaysia
Tel.: (60) 378805921
Plastic Injection Molding Machine Mfr
N.A.I.C.S.: 333924

Toyo Machinery Vietnam Co., Ltd. (1)
R 301C 3F DMC Tower 535 Kim Ma Street, Ngoc Khanh Ward Ba Dinh District, Hanoi, Vietnam
Tel.: (84) 2435211082
Web Site: https://toyo-mmvn.com
Plastic Injection Molding Machine Mfr
N.A.I.C.S.: 333924

TOYO SECURITIES CO., LTD.

4-7-1 Hatchobori, Chuo-ku, Tokyo, 104-8678, Japan
Tel.: (81) 351171040
Web Site: https://www.toyo-sec.co.jp
Year Founded: 1916
8614—(TKS)
Rev.: $79,472,030
Assets: $533,757,500
Liabilities: $273,297,060
Net Worth: $260,460,440
Earnings: $8,626,050
Emp.: 646
Fiscal Year-end: 03/31/24
Investment Services
N.A.I.C.S.: 523999
Manabu Ishioka *(Sr Exec Officer)*

Subsidiaries:

Toyo Capital Co., Ltd. (1)
2-8-5 Kyobashi, Chuo-ku, Tokyo, 104-0031, Japan
Tel.: (81) 3 5524 1040
Integrated Financial Services
N.A.I.C.S.: 523999

Toyo Securities Asia Ltd. (1)
Unit 502 5 Fl Henley Bldg 5 Queens Road, Central, China (Hong Kong)
Tel.: (852) 22355567
Sales Range: $50-74.9 Million
Securities Brokerage Services
N.A.I.C.S.: 523150

TOYO SEIKAN GROUP HOLDINGS, LTD.

Osaki Forest Building 2-18-1, Higashi-Gotanda Shinagawa-ku, Tokyo, 141-8627, Japan
Tel.: (81) 345142000 JP
Web Site: https://www.tskg-hd.com
Year Founded: 1917
5901—(TKS)
Rev.: $6,283,882,430
Assets: $7,804,982,240
Liabilities: $3,193,297,610
Net Worth: $4,611,684,630
Earnings: $152,578,630
Emp.: 19,673
Fiscal Year-end: 03/31/24
Plastic Containers & Aluminum Cans Mfr
N.A.I.C.S.: 332431
Masanori Honda *(Operating Officer)*

Subsidiaries:

Bangkok Can Manufacturing Co., Ltd. (1)
1 13 Soi Rangsit-Nakornnayok 46, Prachatipat Tanyaburi, Pathumthani, 12130, Thailand
Tel.: (66) 25 330 2758
Web Site: https://www.bcm.co.th
Can Mfr
N.A.I.C.S.: 332431

Crown Seal Public Company Limited (1)
5 Soi Rangsit-Nakornnayok 46, Prachatipat Tanyaburi, Pathumthani, 12130, Thailand
Tel.: (66) 25330450
Web Site: https://www.crownseal.co.th
Rev.: $105,677,144
Assets: $140,374,275
Liabilities: $24,378,746
Net Worth: $115,995,528
Earnings: $5,178,436
Emp.: 946
Fiscal Year-end: 12/31/2023
Container Seal Mfr
N.A.I.C.S.: 332439
Dhep Vongvanich *(Chm)*

Fukuoka Packing Co., Ltd. (1)
2-1 Shono, Kazo, 347-0107, Saitama, Japan
Tel.: (81) 48 073 4871
Web Site: https://www.fukuoka-pac.com
Sealant Mfr & Distr
N.A.I.C.S.: 325520

Global Eco-Can Stock (Thailand) Co., Ltd. (1)
300/135 Moo1 Tambol Tasit Amphur, Pluak Daeng, 21140, Rayong, Thailand
Tel.: (66) 3 802 6527
Web Site: https://www.gest-ecocan.com
Resin Coated Aluminum Sheet Mfr & Distr
N.A.I.C.S.: 331315

Honshu Seikan Co., Ltd. (1)
7 Wakamiya, Yuki, 307-0017, Ibaraki, Japan
Tel.: (81) 29 633 7771
Web Site: https://www.honshu-seikan.co.jp
Can Mfr
N.A.I.C.S.: 332431

Ichinose-Trading Co., Ltd. (1)
Matsuo Building 7F 3-14-3 Honmachi, Shibuya-ku, Tokyo, 151-0071, Japan
Tel.: (81) 35 304 4510
Glassware Distr
N.A.I.C.S.: 423460

Ishikawa Ink Co., Ltd. (1)
6-1-11 Ueno, Iwatsuki-ku, Saitama, 339-0073, Japan
Tel.: (81) 48 793 2311
Web Site: https://www.ishikawaink.co.jp
Synthetic Resin Mfr & Distr
N.A.I.C.S.: 325998

Japan Bottled Water Co., Ltd. (1)
581-1 Shioshinden, Iwata, 437-1213, Shizuoka, Japan
Tel.: (81) 53 855 5975
Web Site: https://www.jbwater.co.jp
Water Related Product Mfr & Distr
N.A.I.C.S.: 312112

Kanagata (Thailand) Co., Ltd. (1)
80 89 Moo1 Bangna-Trad Km 36 Homseal, Bang Pakong, 24180, Chachoengsao, Thailand
Tel.: (66) 38 570 1446
Web Site: https://www.katmould.com
Emp.: 58
Mold Product Mfr
N.A.I.C.S.: 333511

Kohan Kogyo Co., Ltd. (1)
1394 Nishitoyoi, Kudamatsu, 744-0011, Yamaguchi, Japan
Tel.: (81) 83 341 2747
Web Site: https://www.i-koko.jp
Steel Plate Mfr
N.A.I.C.S.: 331110

Kohan Shoji Co., Ltd. (1)
2-18-1 Higashigotanda Osaki Forest Building, Shinagawa-ku, Tokyō, 141-0022, Japan
Tel.: (81) 34 531 6880
Web Site: https://www.kohanshoji.co.jp
Steel Sheet Distr
N.A.I.C.S.: 423510

Kyodo Kaiun Co., Ltd. (1)
1302 Higashitoyoi, Kudamatsu, 744-0002, Yamaguchi, Japan
Tel.: (81) 83 341 2612
Marine Transportation Services
N.A.I.C.S.: 488320

Mebius Packaging Co., Ltd. (1)
Osaki Forest Building 2-18-1 Higashi-Gotanda, Shinagawa-ku, Tokyo, 141-0022, Japan
Tel.: (81) 34 514 6800
Web Site: https://www.mebius-pkg.co.jp
Emp.: 785
Plastic Closure Mfr & Distr
N.A.I.C.S.: 326199
Hiroaki Sakazaki *(Pres)*

NCC Europe GmbH (1)
Industriestrasse 7, Foritztal, 96524, Neuhaus-Schierschnitz, Germany
Tel.: (49) 3676 480 0830
Web Site: https://www.ncceurope.de
Metal Closure Distr
N.A.I.C.S.: 423840

Next Can Innovation Co., Ltd. (1)
10 Moo 14 Pahonyothin Road, Nongkhae Industrial Estate Khokyae, Nongkhae, 18230, Saraburi, Thailand
Tel.: (66) 3 637 4225
Web Site: https://www.nextcan.co.th
Metal Can Mfr & Distr
N.A.I.C.S.: 332431

Nippon Closures Co., Ltd. (1)
Osaki Forest Building 2-18-1 Higashigotanda, Shinagawa-ku, Tokyo, 141-0022, Japan
Tel.: (81) 34 514 2158
Web Site: https://www.ncc-caps.co.jp
Emp.: 1,449
Plastic Closure Mfr & Distr
N.A.I.C.S.: 326199
Hisashi Nakajima *(Pres)*

Nippon Tokan Package Co., Ltd. (1)
2-18-1 Higashigotanda Osaki Forest Building 17th Floor, Shinagawa-ku, Tokyo, 141-0022, Japan
Tel.: (81) 34 514 2130
Paper Container Product Mfr & Distr
N.A.I.C.S.: 322220

PT. Tomatec Indonesia (1)
B2-3A Desa Lolawang, Kawasan Ngoro Industrial Park, Mojokerto, 61385, Jawa Timur, Indonesia
Tel.: (62) 321 681 5477
Frit Mfr & Distr
N.A.I.C.S.: 325510

Riguan Closure (Changshu) Co., Ltd. (1)
No 88 Yinfeng Road, New and Hi-tech Industrial Development Zone, Changshu, 215533, Jiangsu, China

AND PRIVATE COMPANIES — TOYO SEIKAN GROUP HOLDINGS, LTD.

Tel.: (86) 5125 290 5155
Metal & Plastic Closure Distr
N.A.I.C.S.: 424610

Ryukyu Seikan Kaisha, Ltd. (1)
11 of 854 Yabu, Nago, 905-0007, Okinawa, Japan
Web Site: https://www.ryucan.com
Can Mfr
N.A.I.C.S.: 332431

Shin-Sankyo-Pd. Co., Ltd. (1)
370 Enzo, Chigasaki, 253-0084, Kanagawa, Japan
Tel.: (81) 46 788 4466
Web Site: https://www.shin-sankyo-pd.co.jp
Freight Transportation Services
N.A.I.C.S.: 488510

Shosando Co., Ltd. (1)
2-18-8 Kisonishi, Machida-shi, Tokyo, 194-0037, Japan
Tel.: (81) 42 791 0611
Paper Container Product Mfr & Distr
N.A.I.C.S.: 322220

Stolle Asia Pacific Co., Ltd. (1)
Factory No 2 Tien Phong 5 Street, Mapletree Binh Duong Industrial Park Hoa Phu Ward, Thu Dau Mot, Binh Duong, Vietnam
Tel.: (84) 274 380 3300
Can Mfr & Distr
N.A.I.C.S.: 332431

Stolle EMS Precision Limited (1)
Unit B3 Sykeside Drive Altham Business Park, Accrington, BB5 5YE, Lancashire, United Kingdom
Tel.: (44) 128 241 4444
Can Mfr & Distr
N.A.I.C.S.: 332431

Stolle Europe Ltd. (1)
Kingstown Broadway, Kingstown Industrial Estate, Carlisle, CA3 0HA, United Kingdom
Tel.: (44) 122 881 8125
Can Mfr & Distr
N.A.I.C.S.: 332431

Stolle European Manufacturing Solutions Limited (1)
Unit 3B Barnfield Way Altham Business Park, Accrington, BB5 5WJ, Lancashire, United Kingdom
Tel.: (44) 128 285 8930
Can Mfr & Distr
N.A.I.C.S.: 332431

Stolle Machinery (Guangdong) Co., Ltd. (1)
No 5 Xingye 14th Road, Guanglong Industrial Zone Chencun Town Shunde District, Foshan, 528300, Guangdong, China
Tel.: (86) 7572 927 1018
Can Mfr & Distr
N.A.I.C.S.: 332431

Stolle Machinery (Shanghai) Co., Ltd. (1)
Part A 1st Floor South Building No 168 Meisheng Road, Pilot Free Trade Zone, Shanghai, 200131, China
Tel.: (86) 216 088 5168
Can Mfr & Distr
N.A.I.C.S.: 332431

Stolle Machinery Company, LLC (1)
6949 S Potomac St, Centennial, CO 80112-4036
Tel.: (303) 708-9044
Web Site: http://www.stollemachinery.com
Sales Range: $100-124.9 Million
Emp.: 350
Industrial Machinery & Parts Mfr
N.A.I.C.S.: 333248
Gus Reall (CEO)

Branch (Domestic):

Stolle Machinery Company - Canton (2)
4337 Excel St, Canton, OH 44720-6995
Tel.: (330) 493-0444
Web Site: http://www.stollemachinery.com
Sales Range: $25-49.9 Million
Emp.: 55
Dies & Handling Equipment & Press Designer Mfr
N.A.I.C.S.: 333998

Division (Domestic):

Stolle Machinery Company - Container Machinery (2)
6949 S Potomac St, Centennial, CO 80112-4036
Tel.: (303) 708-9044
Web Site: http://www.stollemachinery.com
Sales Range: $125-149.9 Million
Industrial Mfr
N.A.I.C.S.: 333248

Stolle Machinery Company - End & Metal Forming (2)
2900 Campbell Rd, Sidney, OH 45365-8865
Tel.: (937) 497-5400
Web Site: http://www.stollemachinery.com
Sales Range: $50-74.9 Million
Emp.: 150
Industrial Mfr
N.A.I.C.S.: 333248

Stolle Machinery do Brasil Industria e Comercio Equipamentos Ltda. (1)
Alameda Venus No 104 American Park Empresarial NR, Indaiatuba, Sao Paulo, 13347-659, Brazil
Tel.: (55) 193 801 8400
Can Mfr & Distr
N.A.I.C.S.: 332431

Sunnap Co., Ltd. (1)
3-8-5 Asakusabashi, Taito-ku, Tokyo, 111-0053, Japan
Tel.: (81) 33 862 8965
Web Site: https://www.sunnap.co.jp
Sanitary Paper Product Mfr & Distr
N.A.I.C.S.: 322291

TM Pack Co., Ltd. (1)
2-4-1 Minato, Miyagino-ku, Sendai, 983-8502, Miyagi, Japan
Tel.: (81) 22 388 7610
Web Site: https://www.tm-pack-co.com
Pet Bottled Beverage Mfr & Distr
N.A.I.C.S.: 326160

Taiyo Plastic Corporation of the Philippines (1)
Special Export Processing Zone Gateway Business Park, Javalera Gen Trias, Cavite, Philippines
Tel.: (63) 46 433 0037
Mold Product Mfr
N.A.I.C.S.: 333511
Kunio Owaki (Pres)

Tohoku Keisya Co., Ltd. (1)
26 Nakagabukuro Oura, Oishida-cho Kitamurayama-gun, Yamagata, 999-4131, Japan
Tel.: (81) 23 735 3626
Web Site: https://www.tohoku-keisya.co.jp
Silica Sand Mfr
N.A.I.C.S.: 327211

Tokan (Changshu) High Technology Containers Co., Ltd. (1)
No 50 Xiangjiang Rd Dongnan Economic Development, Changshu, 215500, Jiangsu, China
Tel.: (86) 5125 233 1111
Web Site: https://www.lamicon.com
Container Mfr & Distr
N.A.I.C.S.: 332439

Tokan Kogyo Co., Ltd. (1)
2-18-1 Higashigotanda Osaki Forest Building 17th Floor, Shinagawa-ku, Tokyo, 141-0022, Japan
Tel.: (81) 34 514 2100
Emp.: 1,092
Paper Container Product Mfr & Distr
N.A.I.C.S.: 322220
Toshiya Kasai (Pres)

Tokan Kosan Co., Ltd. (1)
1-2-14 Hamamatsu-cho Uden Building, Minato-ku, Tokyo, 105-0013, Japan
Tel.: (81) 35 472 5111
Web Site: https://www.tokan.co.jp
Paper Products Mfr
N.A.I.C.S.: 322299

Tokan Kyoei Kaisha, Ltd. (1)
2-18-1 Higashigotanda 2nd Floor of Osaki Forest Building, Shinagawa- ku, Tokyo, 141-0022, Japan
Tel.: (81) 34 514 2210
Web Site: https://www.tokan-kyoei.co.jp

Real Estate Rental Management Services
N.A.I.C.S.: 531311

Tokan Logitech Co., Ltd. (1)
Osaki Forest Building 2-18-1 Higashigotanda, Shinagawa-ku, Tokyo, 141-0022, Japan
Tel.: (81) 34 514 6818
Paper Container Product Mfr & Distr
N.A.I.C.S.: 322220

Tokan Takayama Co., Ltd. (1)
2466-1 Nyukawa-cho, Takayama, Gifu, Japan
Tel.: (81) 57 778 0088
Web Site: https://www.tokantakayama.com
Paper Container Product Mfr & Distr
N.A.I.C.S.: 322220

Tokan Trading Corporation (1)
2-18-1 Higashigotanda Osaki Forest Building, Shinagawa-ku, Tokyo, 141-0022, Japan
Tel.: (81) 34 514 2200
Web Site: https://www.tokan-shoji.co.jp
Packing Material Mfr & Distr
N.A.I.C.S.: 326112

Tomatec (Shanghai) Fine Materials Co., Ltd. (1)
No 418 Minfa Road of Yexie Industry Area, Songjiang, Shanghai, China
Tel.: (86) 215 788 7266
Frit Mfr & Distr
N.A.I.C.S.: 325510

Tomatec (Xiamen) Fine Material Co., Ltd. (1)
No 450-458 Sanshe Rd, Guankou Jimei District, Xiamen, China
Tel.: (86) 592 313 3111
Frit Mfr & Distr
N.A.I.C.S.: 325510

Tomatec America, Inc. (1)
7914 Tanners Gate Ln, Florence, KY 41042
Tel.: (859) 746-0407
Web Site: https://www.tomatec.com
Frit Mfr & Distr
N.A.I.C.S.: 325510

Tomatec Co., Ltd. (1)
1-27 Oyodo Kita 2 chome, Kita-ku, Osaka, 531-8526, Japan
Tel.: (81) 66 456 0001
Web Site: https://www.tomatec.co.jp
Emp.: 261
Frit Mfr & Distr
N.A.I.C.S.: 325510
Shuichi Takata (Pres)

Tosho Glass Co., Ltd. (1)
Osaki Forest Building 2-18-1 Higashigotanda, Shinagawa- ku, Tokyo, 141-0022, Japan
Tel.: (81) 34 514 2060
Glassware Distr
N.A.I.C.S.: 423460

Tosyali Toyo Celik Anonim Sirketi (1)
Sutcuyolu Cad Tosyali Plaza No 72 Atasehir, Barbaros Mah, 34746, Istanbul, Turkiye
Tel.: (90) 2164705191
Steel Sheet Mfr & Distr
N.A.I.C.S.: 332322

Toyo - Sasaki Glass Co., Ltd. (1)
2-1-3 Nihombashi Bakurocho, Chuo-ku, Tokyo, 103-8373, Japan
Tel.: (81) 33 663 1273
Web Site: https://www.toyo.sasaki.co.jp
Emp.: 470
Glassware Mfr & Distr
N.A.I.C.S.: 327215
Shuto Hirofumi (Pres & CEO)

Toyo Aerosol Industry Co., Ltd. (1)
2-18-1 Higashi-Gotanda, Shinagawa-ku, Tokyo, 141-0022, Japan
Tel.: (81) 34 514 2170
Web Site: https://www.toyoa.co.jp
Emp.: 600
Aerosol Mfr & Distr
N.A.I.C.S.: 325998
Masato Sugiyama (Pres)

Toyo Filling International Co., Ltd. (1)
500/45 Moo3 Tanbol Tasit Amphur, WHA Eastern Seaboad Industriar Estate I, Pluak Daeng, 21140, Rayong, Thailand
Tel.: (66) 33 895 0300

Personal Care Product Mfr & Distr
N.A.I.C.S.: 325620

Toyo Glass Co., Ltd. (1)
Osaki Forest Building 2-18-1 Higashi-Gotanda, Shinagawa-ku, Tokyo, 141-0022, Japan
Tel.: (81) 34 514 2068
Web Site: https://www.toyo-glass.co.jp
Emp.: 815
Glassware Mfr & Distr
N.A.I.C.S.: 327215
Shingo Noguchi (Pres)

Toyo Glass Logistics Co., Ltd. (1)
Shintoyofuta 1-1, Kashiwa, 277-0804, Chiba, Japan
Tel.: (81) 47 137 3065
Web Site: https://www.tg-l.co.jp
Freight Transportation Services
N.A.I.C.S.: 488510

Toyo Glass Machinery Co., Ltd. (1)
1-1-70 Yako, Tsurumi-ku, Yokohama, 230-0001, Japan
Tel.: (81) 45 585 1910
Web Site: https://www.tgmm.co.jp
Emp.: 115
Glassware Mfr & Distr
N.A.I.C.S.: 327215
Kazutoshi Nagasawa (Pres)

Toyo Kohan Co., Ltd. (1)
Osaki Forest Bldg 2-18-1 Higashi-Gotanda, Shinagawa-ku, Tokyo, 141-8260, Japan (95%)
Tel.: (81) 345316850
Web Site: https://www.toyokohan.co.jp
Emp.: 1,528
Steel Products Mfr & Whslr
N.A.I.C.S.: 331110
Toshiyuki Tanabe (Pres)

Subsidiary (Domestic):

Fuji Technica & Miyazu Inc. (2)
20 Matoba Shimizu-cho, Sunto-gun, Shizuoka, 411-0915, Japan (100%)
Tel.: (81) 559772301
Web Site: http://www.fuji-miyazu.co.jp
Automobile Parts Mfr
N.A.I.C.S.: 336370
Hiroshi Hasegawa (Pres)

Toyo Kohan Shanghai Co., Ltd. (1)
Xianxia Road No 137 Sheng International Building Room 2701, Shanghai, 200051, China
Tel.: (86) 216 259 1708
Web Site: https://www.toyokohan.cn
Steel Related Product Mfr & Distr
N.A.I.C.S.: 332312

Toyo Mebius Co., Ltd. (1)
8-3-6 Nishigotanda TK Gotanda Building, Shinagawa-ku, Tokyo, 141-0031, Japan
Tel.: (81) 35 436 0251
Freight Transportation Services
N.A.I.C.S.: 488510

Toyo Mebius Logistics (Thailand) Co., Ltd. (1)
14th Floor A2 Lake Rajada Office Complex 193/52 Rachadapisek Rd, Klongtoey, Bangkok, 10110, Thailand
Tel.: (66) 2 661 8655
Web Site: https://www.toyo-mebius.com
Freight Transportation Services
N.A.I.C.S.: 488510
Shoko Kanemoto (Mng Dir)

Toyo Pack (Changshu) Co., Ltd. (1)
No 88 Yinfeng Road, New and Hi-tech Industrial Development Zone, Changshu, China
Tel.: (86) 512 528 8112
Web Site: https://www.toyopackch.com
Beverage Drink Mfr
N.A.I.C.S.: 312111

Toyo Packs Co., Ltd. (1)
1292-5 Higashitoyoi, Kudamatsu, 744-0002, Yamaguchi, Japan
Tel.: (81) 83 345 2275
Packing Material Mfr & Distr
N.A.I.C.S.: 326112

Toyo Partner Co., Ltd. (1)
1302-1 Higashitoyoi, Kudamatsu, 744-0002, Yamaguchi, Japan
Tel.: (81) 83 344 2519

TOYO SEIKAN GROUP HOLDINGS, LTD.

Toyo Seikan Group Holdings, Ltd.—(Continued)
Employee Welfare Facility Services
N.A.I.C.S.: 561210

Toyo Seihan Co., Ltd. (1)
6-19-45 Yako, Tsurumi-ku, Yokohama, 230-0001, Japan
Tel.: (81) 45 586 1091
Web Site: https://www.toyo-seihan.co.jp
Printing Plate Mfr & Distr
N.A.I.C.S.: 323120

Toyo Seikan (Thailand) Co., Ltd. (1)
95 Moo3 Tambol, Rojana industrial park2
Bancharig Amphur U-Thai, Phra Nakhon Si Ayutthaya, 13210, Thailand
Tel.: (66) 3 574 6655
Web Site: https://www.toyoseikan.co.th
Plastic Product Mfr & Distr
N.A.I.C.S.: 325211

Toyo Seikan Co., Ltd. (1)
Osaki Forest Building 2-18-1 Higashi-Gotanda, Shinagawa-ku, Tokyo, 141-8640, Japan
Tel.: (81) 34 514 2300
Web Site: https://www.toyo-seikan.co.jp
Emp.: 2,621
Food Packaging Machinery Mfr & Distr
N.A.I.C.S.: 333241
Masanori Honda *(Pres)*

Toyo Seikan Group Engineering Co., Ltd. (1)
6-19-45 Yako, Tsurumi-ku, Yokohama, 230-0001, Kanagawa, Japan
Tel.: (81) 45 571 1310
Web Site: https://www.tskg-eng.com
Food Packaging Machinery Mfr & Distr
N.A.I.C.S.: 333241

Toyo-Memory Technology Sdn. Bhd. (1)
Plot 3, Kulim Hi-Tech Industrial Zone Phase II, 09090, Kulim, Kedah, Malaysia
Tel.: (60) 4 403 1642
Web Site: https://www.toyomemory.com.my
Aluminum Substrate Mfr
N.A.I.C.S.: 332999

Yangon Can Manufacturing Co., Ltd. (1)
Lot No B-15 Zone A Thilawa SEZ, Yangon, Myanmar
Tel.: (95) 1 230 9131
Beverage Can Mfr & Distr
N.A.I.C.S.: 332431

TOYO SHUTTER CO., LTD.
232 Minamisenba Minamisenba Heart Building 12F, Chuo-ku, Osaka, 542-0081, Japan
Tel.: (81) 647052110
Web Site: https://www.toyo-shutter.co.jp
Year Founded: 1955
5936—(TKS)
Rev.: $142,029,070
Assets: $134,361,470
Liabilities: $75,036,720
Net Worth: $59,324,750
Earnings: $6,338,990
Emp.: 518
Fiscal Year-end: 03/31/24
Shutter Mfr & Distr
N.A.I.C.S.: 332321
Toshio Okada *(Pres)*

TOYO SUISAN KAISHA, LTD.
13-40 Konan 2-chome, Minato-ku, Tokyo, 108-8501, Japan
Tel.: (81) 334585111   JP
Web Site: https://www.maruchan.co.jp
Year Founded: 1953
2875—(TKS)
Rev.: $3,232,375,930
Assets: $3,774,270,340
Liabilities: $637,600,600
Net Worth: $3,136,669,740
Earnings: $367,866,330
Emp.: 1,736
Fiscal Year-end: 03/31/24
Frozen Fish, Instant Noodles & Processed Foods Producer & Marketer
N.A.I.C.S.: 445250
Kazuo Mori *(Founder)*

Subsidiaries:

Choshi Toyo Kaisha, Ltd. (1)
Shiomi-cho address 6 1, Choshi, 288-0025, Chiba, Japan
Tel.: (81) 479253881
Web Site: http://choshitoyo.co.jp
Emp.: 78
Frozen Seafood Distr
N.A.I.C.S.: 424460

Fresh Diner Corporation (1)
7-9 Takasecho, Funabashi, 273-0014, Chiba, Japan
Tel.: (81) 474337511
Web Site: https://www.freshdiner.co.jp
Emp.: 1,150
Processed Meats Mfr & Whslr
N.A.I.C.S.: 311612

Fukushima Foods Co., Ltd. (1)
10-1 Nihongi Narita Koori-cho, Date-gun, Fukushima, 969-1652, Japan
Tel.: (81) 245822260
Web Site: https://www.fukushimafoods.jp
Emp.: 239
Instant Noodles & Rice Mfr
N.A.I.C.S.: 311824

Hachinohe Toyo Co., Ltd. (1)
3-6-5 Kikyono Industrial Park, Hachinohe, 039-2283, Aomori, Japan   **(100%)**
Tel.: (81) 178204860
Web Site: https://www.hachinohetoyo.jp
Emp.: 190
Convenience Foods Mfr
N.A.I.C.S.: 311821
Yasuko Shimazaki *(Mng Dir)*

Imari Toyo Co., Ltd. (1)
929-53 Kusuku Yamashiro-cho, Imari, 849-4251, Saga, Japan
Tel.: (81) 955284818
Convenience Foods Mfr
N.A.I.C.S.: 311999

Ishikari Toyo Kaisha, Ltd. (1)
5-61-1 Zenibako, Otaru, 061-3271, Hokkaido, Japan
Tel.: (81) 133762722
Processed Meats Mfr & Whslr
N.A.I.C.S.: 311612

Kofu Toyo Co., Ltd. (1)
91 Fuse, Chuo, 409-3841, Yamanashi, Japan
Tel.: (81) 552732511
Web Site: https://www.kofutoyo.co.jp
Emp.: 167
Convenience Foods Mfr
N.A.I.C.S.: 311612

Maruchan Inc. (1)
15800 Laguna Canyon Rd, Irvine, CA 92618
Tel.: (949) 789-2300
Web Site: http://www.maruchan.com
Sales Range: $100-124.9 Million
Emp.: 500
Mfr of Dehydrated Instant Noodle Soups & Won Ton Soup & Related Products
N.A.I.C.S.: 311824

Maruchan Virginia, Inc. (1)
8101 Whitepine Rd, North Chesterfield, VA 23237-2288
Tel.: (804) 275-2800
Web Site: https://www.maruchan.co.jp
Sales Range: $100-124.9 Million
Emp.: 500
Instant Noodles Mfr
N.A.I.C.S.: 311813
Kiyoshi Fukagawa *(Pres)*

Maruchan de Mexico, S.A. de C.V. (1)
688 piso 3 colonia Del Valle, Col Del Valle Del Benito Juarez, 03100, Mexico, Mexico
Tel.: (52) 5556691794
Web Site: https://www.maruchan.com.mx
Convenience Food Distr
N.A.I.C.S.: 445298
Kiyoshi Fukagawa *(Gen Dir)*

Miyagi Toyo Kaisha, Ltd. (1)
3-12-3 Sakanamachi, Ishinomaki, 986-0022, Miyagi, Japan
Tel.: (81) 22 594 3311
Web Site: https://www.miyagitoyo.co.jp
Fish Distr
N.A.I.C.S.: 445250

Pac-Maru, Inc. (1)
4209 21st Ave W Ste 222, Seattle, WA 98199
Tel.: (206) 282-0196
Web Site: http://www.pacmaru.com
Emp.: 4
Seafood Whslr
N.A.I.C.S.: 424460

Sanriku Toyo Kaisha, Ltd. (1)
106 Akaiwaminato, Kesennuma, 988-0103, Miyagi, Japan
Tel.: (81) 226226030
Sales Range: $25-49.9 Million
Emp.: 50
Convenience Foods Mfr
N.A.I.C.S.: 311612
Akira Sasaki *(Pres)*

Shimaya Co., Ltd. (1)
1-57 Miyakomachi, Shunan, Yamaguchi, Japan
Tel.: (81) 83 432 7771
Liquid Seasoning Product Mfr
N.A.I.C.S.: 311942

Shuetsu Co., Ltd. (1)
7th floor Shinagawa TS Building 2-13-40 Konan, Minato-ku Shinagawa, Tokyo, 108-0075, Japan
Tel.: (81) 334585372
Web Site: https://www.shuetsu.co.jp
Convenience Foods Mfr
N.A.I.C.S.: 311612

Suruga Toyo Kaisha, Ltd. (1)
2307 Tajiri, Yaizu, 425-0052, Shizuoka, Japan
Tel.: (81) 546234411
Web Site: https://www.surugatoyo.co.jp
Refrigerated Warehousing & Storage Services
N.A.I.C.S.: 493120

Tokyo Commercial Co., Ltd. (1)
8-15 Toyomi-cho, Chuo-ku, Tokyo, 104-0055, Japan
Tel.: (81) 335345311
Convenience Foods Mfr
N.A.I.C.S.: 311612

Toyo Reito Kaisha, Ltd. (1)
3-12-3 Sakana-machi, Ishinomaki, 986-0022, Miyagi, Japan
Tel.: (81) 225943311
Sales Range: $25-49.9 Million
Emp.: 100
Convenience Foods Mfr
N.A.I.C.S.: 311999

Yaizu Shinto Co., Ltd. (1)
2322 Tajiri, Yaizu, 425-0052, Shizuoka, Japan
Tel.: (81) 546561688
Convenience Foods Mfr
N.A.I.C.S.: 311612

TOYO TANSO CO., LTD.
1-13-1 Umeda, Kita-ku, Osaka, 530-0001, Japan
Tel.: (81) 5030974950
Web Site: https://www.toyotanso.co.jp
Year Founded: 1947
5310—(TKS)
Rev.: $349,189,590
Assets: $684,979,080
Liabilities: $85,703,920
Net Worth: $599,275,160
Earnings: $53,217,540
Emp.: 1,736
Fiscal Year-end: 12/31/23
Graphite & Carbon Products Mfr & Sales
N.A.I.C.S.: 335991
Naotaka Kondo *(Chm, Pres & CEO)*

Subsidiaries:

Chengdu Toyo Tanso Industrial Co., Ltd. (1)
Building D3 Zone D Bosch Road, Helian New Industrial Park Shou'an Town Pujiang County, Chengdu, China
Tel.: (86) 2863966628
Carbon Brush Mfr
N.A.I.C.S.: 335991

GTD Graphit Technologie GmbH (1)
Raiffeisenstrasse 1, 35428, Langgons, Germany
Tel.: (49) 64 039 5140
Web Site: https://www.gtd-graphit.de
Sales Range: $25-49.9 Million
Emp.: 45
Graphite Product & Composite Product Distr
N.A.I.C.S.: 423710
Arno Cloos *(CEO)*

Graphites Technologie et Industrie S.A. (1)
Z I Du Manet Et Du Bois De La Couldre 9 10, Rue Eugne Hnaff, Trappes, 78190, France
Tel.: (33) 30663535
Sales Range: $25-49.9 Million
Emp.: 13
Sales & Processing of Isotropic Graphite Products & Carbon Brushes
N.A.I.C.S.: 335991

Ohwada Carbon Industrial Co., Ltd. (1)
2-1-16 Hinode-cho, Toyonaka, 561-0821, Osaka, Japan
Tel.: (81) 663332301
Carbon & Graphite Product Mfr
N.A.I.C.S.: 335991

PT. Toyo Tanso Indonesia (1)
BM Rental Factory Unit B2 Kav L9 Jl Madura I Kawasan Industri MM2100, Kel Cikedokan Kec Cikarang Barat Prop Jawa Barat, Bekasi, 17845, Indonesia
Tel.: (62) 2128080180
Carbon & Graphite Product Mfr
N.A.I.C.S.: 335991
Teppei Tsuchiya *(Pres)*

Shanghai Toyo Tanso Co., Ltd. (1)
No 486 Xinfei Road, Songjiang, Shanghai, China
Tel.: (86) 2137742888
Carbon & Graphite Product Mfr
N.A.I.C.S.: 335991

Shanghai Toyo Tanso Industrial Co., Ltd. (1)
No 486 Xinfei Road, Songjiang, Shanghai, China
Tel.: (86) 2157736628
Carbon & Graphite Product Mfr
N.A.I.C.S.: 335991

Shanghai Yongxin Toyo Tanso Co., Ltd. (1)
Xianghua Town, Chongming County, Shanghai, China
Tel.: (86) 2159441531
Brush Holder Mfr
N.A.I.C.S.: 339994

Totan Kako Co., Ltd. (1)
1335-22 Saitakami Saita-cho, Mitoyo, 769-0401, Kagawa, Japan
Tel.: (81) 875672655
Web Site: https://www.totankako.com
Carbon & Graphite Product Mfr
N.A.I.C.S.: 335991

Toyo Tanso (Thailand) Co., Ltd. (1)
333/5 Moo 9 Bangplee, Bangpla, Samut Prakan, 10540, Thailand
Tel.: (66) 21366240
Carbon & Graphite Product Mfr
N.A.I.C.S.: 335991

Toyo Tanso (Zhejiang) Co., Ltd. (1)
No 88 Pu Xian Road Pinghu Economic Technological Development Zone, Ningbo, Zhejiang, China
Tel.: (86) 57385299866
Carbon & Graphite Product Mfr
N.A.I.C.S.: 335991

Toyo Tanso Europe S.p.A. (1)
Via Leonardo Da Vinci N 5, Roncello, 20877, Milan, Monza and Brianza, Italy
Tel.: (39) 039627841
Web Site: http://www.toyotansoeurope.com

Sales Range: $25-49.9 Million
Emp.: 33
Sales & Processing of Carbon Brushes & Isotropic Graphite Products
N.A.I.C.S.: 335991

Toyo Tanso France S.A. (1)
Z A du Buisson de la Couldre 9-10 Rue Eugene Henaff, 78190, Trappes, France
Tel.: (33) 13 066 3535
Web Site: https://www.toyotansofrance.com
Carbon & Graphite Product Mfr
N.A.I.C.S.: 335991

Toyo Tanso Korea Co., Ltd. (1)
211 Hanshin Intervalley 24 East Tower 322 Teheran-ro, Gangnam-Gu, Seoul, 06211, Korea (South)
Tel.: (82) 221831660
Web Site: http://www.toyotanso-korea.co.kr
Carbon & Graphite Product Mfr
N.A.I.C.S.: 335991

Toyo Tanso Mexico, S.A. de C.V. (1)
Mina de Guadalupe 950-H Parque Industrial Santa Fe IV Silao, 36275, Guanajuato, Mexico
Tel.: (52) 4727489382
Carbon & Graphite Product Mfr
N.A.I.C.S.: 335991

Toyo Tanso Singapore Pte. Ltd. (1)
20 Cross Street 02-07/08 China Square Central, Singapore, 048422, Singapore
Tel.: (65) 67186520
Carbon & Graphite Product Mfr
N.A.I.C.S.: 335991

Toyo Tanso Taiwan Co., Ltd. (1)
No 168 Lunping 5th Rd, Guanyin District, Taoyuan, 32846, Taiwan **(97.2%)**
Tel.: (886) 34985577
Carbon & Graphite Product Mfr
N.A.I.C.S.: 335991

Toyo Tanso USA Inc. (1)
2575 NW Graham Cir, Troutdale, OR 97060
Tel.: (503) 661-7700
Web Site: http://www.ttu.com
Sales Range: $50-74.9 Million
Emp.: 150
Mfr of Brush Blocks & Carbon Molded Graphite
N.A.I.C.S.: 335991

TOYO TEC CO., LTD.
1-7-18 Sakuragawa, Naniwa-ku, Osaka, 556-0022, Japan
Tel.: (81) 665632111
Web Site: https://www.toyo-tec.co.jp
Year Founded: 1972
9686—(TKS)
Rev: $206,555,890
Assets: $236,452,920
Liabilities: $95,580,600
Net Worth: $140,872,320
Earnings: $4,137,860
Emp.: 518
Fiscal Year-end: 03/31/24
Security System Services
N.A.I.C.S.: 561621
Takashi Tanaka *(Chm)*

TOYO TIRE CORPORATION
2-2-13 Fujinoki, Hyogo, Itami, 664-0847, Japan
Tel.: (81) 727899100   JP
Web Site: http://www.toyotires.co.jp
Year Founded: 1945
5105—(TKS)
Rev: $3,919,529,250
Assets: $4,576,453,200
Liabilities: $1,774,492,290
Net Worth: $2,801,960,910
Earnings: $512,415,570
Emp.: 11,656
Fiscal Year-end: 12/31/23
Tires & Rubber Chemical Products Mfr
N.A.I.C.S.: 326211
Tatsuo Mitsuhata *(Corp Officer)*

Subsidiaries:

Ayabe Toyo Rubber Co.,Ltd (1)
115 Kuri-cho, Ayabe, 623-0222, Kyoto, Japan
Tel.: (81) 773480001
Rubber Products Mfr
N.A.I.C.S.: 326299

F.T.G Co.,Ltd (1)
17-18 Edobori 1 Chome, Osaka, 550-0002, Japan
Tel.: (81) 664418804
Web Site: http://www.toyo-rubber.co.jp
Rubber Tire Mfr
N.A.I.C.S.: 326211

Fukushima Rubber Co.,Ltd (1)
28 Aza Domae Miyashiro, Fukushima, 960-0116, Japan
Tel.: (81) 245531356
Web Site: http://www.toyo-rubber.co.jp
Rubber Products Mfr
N.A.I.C.S.: 326299

GTY Tire Co. (1)
Po Box 1029, Mount Vernon, IL 62864
Tel.: (618) 246-2263
Sales Range: $100-124.9 Million
Tiles Mfr
N.A.I.C.S.: 326211

Kuwana Service Co.,Ltd (1)
2400 Oaza Nakagami Toin-cho, Inabe-gun, Mie, 511-0294, Japan
Tel.: (81) 594860117
Rubber Tire Mfr
N.A.I.C.S.: 326211

NITTO TIRE CANADA INC. (1)
7791 Nelson Rd Unit No 120, Richmond, V6W 1G3, BC, Canada
Tel.: (604) 304-1970
Web Site: http://www.toyo-rubber.co.jp
Sales Range: $25-49.9 Million
Emp.: 50
Tiles Mfr
N.A.I.C.S.: 326211

NT Mexico S. de R.L. de C.V. (1)
Insurgentes Sur 800 Piso 9 Oficina B Del Valle Benito Juarez, 03100, Mexico, Mexico
Tel.: (52) 5559989558
Tire Mfr & Distr
N.A.I.C.S.: 326211

New Pacific Industry Co., Ltd. (1)
44 Sec 1 Chung Shan Rd, Chung Chuang Vlg Hua Tan, Chang-Hua, Taiwan
Tel.: (886) 47869711
Sales Range: $50-74.9 Million
Emp.: 120
Mfr of Automotive Parts
N.A.I.C.S.: 336340

Nitto Japan Co., Ltd (1)
2-17-22 Takada, Toshima-ku, Tokyo, 171-8544, Japan
Tel.: (81) 359553210
Web Site: http://www.toyo-rubber.co.jp
Rubber Tire Mfr
N.A.I.C.S.: 326299

Nitto Tire U.S.A Inc (1)
6021 Katella Ave Ste 250, Cypress, CA 90630
Tel.: (714) 236-1863
Web Site: http://www.nittotire.com
Tiles Mfr
N.A.I.C.S.: 326211
Keiko Brockel *(Pres)*

Orient Koki Co.,Ltd (1)
3-6 Fujinoki 2 Chome, Itami, 664-0847, Hyogo, Japan
Tel.: (81) 727877651
Web Site: http://www.toyo-rubber.co.jp
Sales Range: $25-49.9 Million
Emp.: 60
Rubber Products Mfr
N.A.I.C.S.: 326299

Orient Machinery Co., Ltd. (1)
3-6 Fujinoki 2-chome, Itami, 664-0847, Hyogo, Japan
Tel.: (81) 727877651
Tire Mfr & Distr
N.A.I.C.S.: 326211

Sendai Service Co.,Ltd (1)
3-5-1 Fukiage, Iwanuma, 989-2484, Miyagi, Japan
Tel.: (81) 223244570
Web Site: http://www.toyo-rubber.co.jp
Industrial Machinery Equipments Mfr & Sales
N.A.I.C.S.: 333248

Showa Estate Co.,Ltd (1)
1-6 Tosabori 2 Chome, Nishi-ku, Osaka, 550-0001, Japan
Tel.: (81) 664433180
Real Estate Manangement Services
N.A.I.C.S.: 531390
Naoki Nishimura *(Pres)*

Silverstone Berhad (1)
Lot 5831 Kawasan Perusahaan Kamunting II, PO Box 2, Kamunting, Taiping, 34600, Perak, Malaysia
Tel.: (60) 58911077
Web Site: http://www.silverstone.com.my
Sales Range: $450-499.9 Million
Emp.: 1,005
Rubber Tire Mfr
N.A.I.C.S.: 326211

Silverstone Marketing Sdn. Bhd. (1)
Level 2 Wisma Comcorp No 37 Jalan Pelukis U1/46 Section U1, Temasya Industrial Park Glenmarie, 40150, Shah Alam, Selangor Darul Ehsan, Malaysia
Tel.: (60) 355683188
Tire Mfr & Distr
N.A.I.C.S.: 326211

Soflan Wiz CO., LTD (1)
17-18 Edobori 1 Chome, Nishi-ku, Osaka, 550-8661, Japan
Tel.: (81) 6 6441 8702
Web Site: http://www.soflan-wiz.com
Rubber Product Mfr & Sales
N.A.I.C.S.: 326299

TOYO AUTOMOTIVE PARTS (GUANGZHOU) CO., LTD. (1)
No 10 St 2 Hefeng Erzong Lu Yonghe Economic Zone GETDD, Guangzhou, China
Tel.: (86) 2082986828
Emp.: 239
Rubber Tire Mfr
N.A.I.C.S.: 326211

TOYO AUTOMOTIVE PARTS (USA) INC (1)
521 Page Dr, Franklin, KY 42134
Tel.: (270) 598-4100
Emp.: 30
Automotive Parts Retailer
N.A.I.C.S.: 424990
Shay Smith *(Dir-HR)*

TOYO RUBBER CHEMICAL & INDUSTRIAL PRODUCTS (HK) LTD (1)
Room 301 3rd Floor Sun Hung Kai Centre 30 Harbour Road, Wan Chai, Hong Kong, China (Hong Kong)
Tel.: (86) 28508990
Web Site: http://www.toyo-rubber.co.jp
Emp.: 100
Rubber Tire Mfr & Sales
N.A.I.C.S.: 326211

TOYO TIRE HOLDINGS OF AMERICAS INC. (1)
5665 Poeza Dr Ste 200, Cypress, CA 90630
Tel.: (562) 431-6502
Web Site: http://www.toyotires.com
Sales Range: $25-49.9 Million
Emp.: 140
Tiles Mfr
N.A.I.C.S.: 326211

TOYO TIRE MEXICO LLC (1)
860 Kuhn Dr Ste 106, Chula Vista, CA 91914
Tel.: (619) 691-1077
Web Site: http://www.toyotiremexico.com
Tiles Mfr
N.A.I.C.S.: 326211
Angelina Ramirez *(Office Mgr)*

TOYO TIRE NORTH AMERICA MANUFACTURING INC (1)
3660 Hwy 411 NE, White, GA 30184-2427
Tel.: (678) 721-7200
Emp.: 1,550
Tiles Mfr
N.A.I.C.S.: 326211
Takuji Yamamoto *(Chief Risk Mgmt Officer & Chief Compliance Mgmt Officer)*

TOYO TIRE NORTH AMERICA OE SALES LLC (1)
3660 Hwy 411 NE, White, GA 30184
Tel.: (678) 721-7200
Web Site: http://www.toyotires.co.jp
Sales Range: $25-49.9 Million
Emp.: 40
Rubber Tire Distr
N.A.I.C.S.: 423130
James L. Hawk *(Pres)*

TOYO TIRE RUS LLC (1)
st Butyrsky Val 68/70 building 1 office 26B, Moscow, 127055, Russia
Tel.: (7) 4959871835
Web Site: https://www.toyotire.ru
Sales Range: $25-49.9 Million
Emp.: 10
Rubber Tire Mfr
N.A.I.C.S.: 326211
Kenta Kuribayashi *(Chm & CEO)*

Toyo Automotive Parts de Mexico, S.A. de C.V. (1)
Carretera Estatal 431 Int63 Parque Tenologico Innovacion Queretaro, El Marques, 76246, Queretaro, Mexico
Tel.: (52) 4422216183
Tire Mfr & Distr
N.A.I.C.S.: 326211

Toyo Chemical / Industrial Products Sales Corporation (1)
10 Tenjin-cho, Shinjuku-Ku, Tokyo, 162-8622, Japan
Tel.: (81) 332351711
Web Site: http://www.toyo-kohan.co.jp
Sales Range: $75-99.9 Million
Emp.: 114
Rubber Products Sales
N.A.I.C.S.: 423990
Masato Kanetsuki *(Gen Mgr)*

Toyo Chemical Industrial Products Co., Ltd. (1)
Rokubuichi 1183 Inami-cho, kako-gun, Hyogo, 675-1112, Japan
Tel.: (81) 794951519
Tire Mfr & Distr
N.A.I.C.S.: 326211

Toyo Reifen GmbH (1)
Wersterftstrasse 47, D 40549, Dusseldorf, Germany **(60%)**
Tel.: (49) 2115690911
Web Site: http://www.toyo.de
Sales Range: $25-49.9 Million
Emp.: 35
Sale & Marketing of Tires
N.A.I.C.S.: 441340

Toyo Rubber Chemical Products (Thailand) Limited (1)
99/8 30 31 Moo 4 Tambol Kanham, Amphur U-Thai, Ayutthaya, 13210, Thailand
Tel.: (66) 35352347
Tire Mfr & Distr
N.A.I.C.S.: 326211

Toyo Seiki Co.,Ltd (1)
878 Nunobikihara, Makinohara, 421-0407, Shizuoka, Japan
Tel.: (81) 548272234
Web Site: http://www.toyo-rubber.co.jp
Emp.: 20
Synthetic Rubber Mfr
N.A.I.C.S.: 325212

Toyo Soflan Tec Co., LTD (1)
10 Tenjin-cho, Shinjuku-Ku, Tokyo, 162-0808, Japan
Tel.: (81) 332351744
Web Site: http://www.toyo-rubber.co.jp
Rubber Tire Mfr
N.A.I.C.S.: 326211

Toyo Tire & Benelux (1)
Kooldreef 2 6, Postbus 1083, 4700 BB, Roosendaal, Netherlands **(100%)**
Tel.: (31) 165556475
Web Site: http://www.toyotires.nl
Sales Range: $25-49.9 Million
Emp.: 14
Sales of Tires
N.A.I.C.S.: 441340
Steven Laurijssen *(Gen Mgr)*

Toyo Tire (Shangai) Co Ltd (1)
6 Floor No 39 Wu Zhong Road Xu Hui Dis-

TOYO TIRE CORPORATION

Toyo Tire Corporation—(Continued)
trict, New Concept Building, Shanghai, China
Tel.: (86) 2158820880
Web Site: http://www.toyo-tire.com.cn
Tiles Mfr
N.A.I.C.S.: 326211

Toyo Tire (U.S.A.) Corporation (1)
5665 Plz Dr Ste 300, Cypress, CA 90630 **(100%)**
Tel.: (714) 236-2080
Web Site: https://www.toyotires.com
Sales Range: $25-49.9 Million
Emp.: 50
Tires Distributer & Mfr
N.A.I.C.S.: 423130
Lori Simonelli *(Sr Dir-Tech Svcs)*

Toyo Tire Benelux B.V (1)
Kooldreef 2-6, Roosendaal, 4703, Netherlands
Tel.: (31) 165556475
Web Site: http://www.toyo-rubber.co.jp
Sales Range: $25-49.9 Million
Emp.: 16
Rubber Tire Mfr
N.A.I.C.S.: 326211

Toyo Tire Canada, Inc. (1)
1645 Cliveden Avenue, Delta, V3M 6V5, BC, Canada **(60%)**
Tel.: (604) 540-1331
Sales Range: $25-49.9 Million
Emp.: 15
Distribution of Tires
N.A.I.C.S.: 441340

Toyo Tire Deutschland GmbH (1)
Halskestr 3-5, 47877, Willich, Germany
Tel.: (49) 21548911111
Web Site: https://www.toyo.de
Tire Mfr & Distr
N.A.I.C.S.: 326211

Toyo Tire Europe Gmbh (1)
Halskestrasse 3-5, 47877, Willich, Germany
Tel.: (49) 2154 891 1111
Web Site: http://www.toyo.de
Rubber Tire Mfr
N.A.I.C.S.: 326211
David Stinissen *(Mgr-Mktg)*

Toyo Tire Holdings of Europe GmbH (1)
Halskestrasse 3-5, 47877, Willich, Germany
Tel.: (49) 21548911111
Web Site: https://www.toyotires.eu
Tire Mfr & Distr
N.A.I.C.S.: 326211

Toyo Tire Italia S.P.A (1)
via Napoli n 33, 57014, Colle Salvetti, Li, Italy
Tel.: (39) 0586962243
Web Site: https://www.toyo.it
Rubber Tire Distr
N.A.I.C.S.: 423130

Toyo Tire Japan Co.,Ltd (1)
3-1-2 Iwamoto-cho 3 Chome, Chiyoda-ku, Tokyo, 101-0032, Japan
Tel.: (81) 358255740
Web Site: http://www.toyotire.co.jp
Rubber Tire Mfr
N.A.I.C.S.: 326299

Toyo Tire Refine Corporation (1)
2-2-13 Fujinoki, Itami, 664-0847, Hyogo, Japan
Tel.: (81) 727899088
Tire Mfr & Distr
N.A.I.C.S.: 326211

Toyo Tire Zhangjiagang Co., Ltd. (1)
58 Donghai Road, Jiangsu Yangtze River International Chemical Industrial Park, Zhangjiagang, Jiangsu, China
Tel.: (86) 51235007100
Tire Mfr & Distr
N.A.I.C.S.: 326211

Toyo Tires Canada Inc. (1)
7791 Nelson Road Unit 120, Richmond, V6W 1G3, BC, Canada
Web Site: https://www.toyotires.ca
Tire Mfr & Distr
N.A.I.C.S.: 326211

Toyo Tires Logistics Co.,Ltd
17-18 Edobori 1 Chome, Nishi-Ku, Osaka, 550-8661, Japan
Tel.: (81) 664432730
Warehousing & Logistics Services
N.A.I.C.S.: 493110

Toyo Tyre (Uk) Ltd (1)
Shipton Way, Rushden, NN10 6GL, Northants, United Kingdom
Tel.: (44) 1933411144
Web Site: https://www.toyo.co.uk
Sales Range: $25-49.9 Million
Emp.: 18
Rubber Tire Mfr
N.A.I.C.S.: 326211

Toyo Tyre Australia Pty. Ltd. (1)
137-149 Airds Rd, PO Box 5084, Minto, 2566, NSW, Australia
Tel.: (61) 287960222
Web Site: https://www.toyotires.com.au
Tire Mfr & Distr
N.A.I.C.S.: 326211

Toyo Tyre Malaysia Sdn. Bhd. (1)
PT 23101 Jalan Tembaga Kuning Kawasan Perindustrian Kamunting Raya, PO Box 1, 34600, Taiping, Perak Darul Ridzuan, Malaysia
Tel.: (60) 58206600
Emp.: 1,572
Tire Mfr & Distr
N.A.I.C.S.: 326211

Toyo Tyre Sales & Marketing Malaysia Sdn. Bhd.
Level 2 Wisma Comcorp No 37 Jalan Pelukis U1/46 Section U1, Temasya Industrial Park, 40150, Shah Alam, Selangor Darul Ehsan, Malaysia
Tel.: (60) 355683188
Web Site: https://www.toyotiresasia.com
Emp.: 121
Tire Mfr & Distr
N.A.I.C.S.: 326211

Toyo Tyre and Rubber Australia Limited (1)
137-149 Airds Rd, Minto, Sydney, 2566, NSW, Australia **(74%)**
Tel.: (61) 296420177
Web Site: http://www.toyo.com.au
Sales Range: $25-49.9 Million
Emp.: 30
Automotive Parts, Rubber Materials & Tires Sales & Mfr
N.A.I.C.S.: 336340

TOYO VENTURES HOLDINGS BERHAD

PT 3477 Jalan 6/1 Kawasan Perusahaan, 43300, Seri Kembangan, Selangor, Malaysia
Tel.: (60) 389423335 MY
Web Site: https://www.toyoventures.com.my
Year Founded: 2020
TOYOVEN—(KLS)
Rev.: $17,739,661
Assets: $124,909,230
Liabilities: $94,257,510
Net Worth: $30,651,720
Earnings: $192,860
Fiscal Year-end: 09/30/23
Holding Company
N.A.I.C.S.: 551112
Song Kok Cheong *(Mng Dir)*

Subsidiaries:

EDM Machining Solutions (M) Sdn. Bhd. (1)
No 10 Jalan TPP 1/1A, Taman Industri Puchong, 47160, Puchong, Selangor Darul Ehsan, Malaysia **(100%)**
Tel.: (60) 380602503
Web Site: https://www.emssb.com.my
Sales Range: $25-49.9 Million
Emp.: 50
Graphite Electrode Mfr
N.A.I.C.S.: 335991
Chew Cheong Loong *(Mng Dir)*

EDM-Tools (M) Sdn. Bhd. (1)
No 6 8 Jalan TPP 1/1A, Taman Industri Puchong, 47160, Puchong, Selangor, Malaysia **(100%)**
Tel.: (60) 380625918
Web Site: http://www.edmtools.com.my
Sales Range: $25-49.9 Million
Emp.: 80
Machine Tool Distr
N.A.I.C.S.: 423830

Toyo Ink Group Berhad (1)
PT 3477 Jalan 6/1 Kawasan Perusahaan, 43300, Seri Kembangan, Selangor, Malaysia **(100%)**
Tel.: (60) 389423335
Web Site: http://www.toyoink.com.my
Holding Company; Printing Ink Mfr
N.A.I.C.S.: 551112
Kok Cheong Song *(Mng Dir)*

Toyo Ink Sdn. Bhd. (1)
PT 3477 Jalan 6/1 Kawasan Perusahaan, 43300, Seri Kembangan, Selangor, Malaysia **(100%)**
Tel.: (60) 389423335
Web Site: http://www.toyoink.com.my
Emp.: 80
Gravure & Flexographic Printing Inks Mfr
N.A.I.C.S.: 325910
Steven Kok Cheong Song *(Mng Dir)*

Subsidiary (Domestic):

EDM-Tools (Penang) Sdn. Bhd. (2)
No 6 Lorong Industri Sungai Lokan 3, Taman Industri Sungai Lokan, 13800, Butterworth, Pulau Pinang, Malaysia **(100%)**
Tel.: (60) 43581833
Web Site: http://www.edmtools.com.my
Sales Range: $25-49.9 Million
Emp.: 10
Machine Tools Mfr
N.A.I.C.S.: 333517
Chew Cheong Loong *(Mng Dir)*

TOYO WHARF & WAREHOUSE CO., LTD.

19th floor Harumi Triton Square W Building 1-8-8 Harumi, Chuo-ku, Tokyo, 104-0053, Japan
Tel.: (81) 355602701
Web Site: https://www.toyofuto.co.jp
Year Founded: 1940
9351—(TKS)
Rev.: $229,347,170
Assets: $320,155,350
Liabilities: $144,653,240
Net Worth: $175,502,110
Earnings: $6,477,800
Emp.: 1,953
Fiscal Year-end: 03/31/24
Warehousing Services
N.A.I.C.S.: 493110

TOYOBO CO., LTD.

2-8 Dojima Hama 2-chome, Kita-ku, Osaka, 530-8230, Japan
Tel.: (81) 663484208 JP
Web Site: https://www.toyobo-global.com
Year Founded: 1882
3101—(TKS)
Rev.: $2,738,291,650
Assets: $4,012,203,900
Liabilities: $2,491,328,830
Net Worth: $1,520,875,070
Earnings: $16,227,550
Emp.: 10,668
Fiscal Year-end: 03/31/24
Textile Mfr
N.A.I.C.S.: 313110
Ikuo Takeuchi *(Pres, CEO & Co-COO)*

Subsidiaries:

Arabian Japanese Membrane Company, LLC (1)
Rabigh PlusTech Park, PO Box 214, Rabigh, 21911, Saudi Arabia
Tel.: (966) 12 289 1532
Desalination Kit Mfr & Distr
N.A.I.C.S.: 325998

Industrias Unidas, S.A. (1)
Km 11 5 Carretera Panamericana Oriente frente Aduana San Bartolo, Ilopango, San Salvador, El Salvador

INTERNATIONAL PUBLIC

Tel.: (503) 2 250 9500
Web Site: https://www.iusa.com.sv
Textile Mfr
N.A.I.C.S.: 314999

Japan Exlan Company, Limited (1)
Toyobo Bldg 6F 2-2-8 Dojimahama, Kita-ku, Osaka, 530-0004, Japan
Tel.: (81) 66 348 3431
Web Site: https://www.exlan.co.jp
Emp.: 345
Textile Mfr
N.A.I.C.S.: 314999
Susumu Fujimoto *(Pres)*

Kureha Ltd. (1)
255 Oka, Ritto, 520-3012, Shiga, Japan
Tel.: (81) 77 552 1280
Web Site: https://www.kurehatech.co.jp
Sales Range: $25-49.9 Million
Emp.: 270
Nonwoven Fabric Mfr
N.A.I.C.S.: 313230

Subsidiary (US):

Toyobo Kureha America Co., Ltd. (2)
11630 Mosteller Rd, Cincinnati, OH 45241
Tel.: (513) 771-6788
Web Site: http://www.tkamerica.com
Sales Range: $1-9.9 Million
Emp.: 40
Nonwoven Fabric Mfr
N.A.I.C.S.: 313230

Miyukikeori Co., Ltd. (1)
Miyuki Building 390 Ichibagi-cho, Nishi-ku, Nagoya, 452-8570, Japan
Tel.: (81) 52 509 1600
Web Site: https://www.miyukikeori.co.jp
Textile Fabric Product Mfr & Distr
N.A.I.C.S.: 314999
Naoto Yoshida *(Pres)*

P.T. Indonesia Toyobo Film Solutions (1)
JI M H Thamrin Kel Panunggangan Kec, Tangerang, 15143, Banten, Indonesia
Tel.: (62) 2153122115
Films & Plastics Mfr
N.A.I.C.S.: 326112
Yuichi Hanawa *(Pres)*

PT. Shinko Toyobo Gistex Garment (1)
JI Panyawungan Km 19 Desa Cileunyi Wetan, Bandung, Indonesia
Tel.: (62) 22 779 8893
Sewing Sportswear Mfr
N.A.I.C.S.: 315250

PT. Toyobo Indonesia (1)
Kawasan Kiic Block B-3, Karawang, Jawa Barat, Indonesia
Tel.: (62) 267 845 8108
Textile Products Distr
N.A.I.C.S.: 459130

PT. Toyobo Manufacturing Indonesia (1)
Kawasan Kiic Block B-3, Karawang, Jawa Barat, Indonesia
Tel.: (62) 21 890 2544
Knitting Fabric Mfr
N.A.I.C.S.: 313240

PT. Toyobo Trias Ecosyar (1)
Desa Keboharan KM 26 Krian, Sidoarjo, 61262, Indonesia
Tel.: (62) 31 897 5825
Vapor Deposition Product Mfr
N.A.I.C.S.: 326112

Santoyoko (Hong Kong) Co., Ltd. (1)
Suite 1122 11/F Ocean Centre 5 Canton Road, Tsim Tsa Tsui, Kowloon, China (Hong Kong)
Tel.: (852) 23145939
Engineering Plastic Products Whslr
N.A.I.C.S.: 424610

Spinreact SA (1)
Ctra Sta Coloma 7, Sant Esteve de'n Bas, 17176, Girona, Catalonia, Spain
Tel.: (34) 972 69 08 00
Web Site: https://www.spinreact.com
Diagnostic Reagent Mfr
N.A.I.C.S.: 621511
Joan Beltran *(Mgr-Sales-Marketing)*

AND PRIVATE COMPANIES / TOYODA GOSEI CO., LTD.

Spinreact, S.A.U. (1)
Ctra Sta Coloma 7 17176 Sant Esteve den Bas, Girona, Spain
Tel.: (34) 972690800
Web Site: https://www.spinreact.com
Clinical Vitro Diagnostic Product Mfr & Distr
N.A.I.C.S.: 325413

TOYOBO MC U.S.A. Inc. (1)
39555 Orchard Hill Pl Ste 230, Novi, MI 48375
Tel.: (248) 449-3323
Web Site: https://www.toyobousa.com
Biotechnology Product Services
N.A.I.C.S.: 541714

Toyo Cloth Co., Ltd. (1)
Tarui 6-chome 29-1, Sennan, 590-0521, Osaka, Japan
Tel.: (81) 72 483 6101
Web Site: https://www.toyocloth.co.jp
Synthetic Leather Mfr
N.A.I.C.S.: 316990

Toyo Knit Co., Ltd. (1)
4-1-15 Nakagawara, Yokkaichi, 510-0833, Mie, Japan
Tel.: (81) 59 359 2160
Web Site: https://www.toyoknit.co.jp
Sewing Sportswear Mfr
N.A.I.C.S.: 315250

Toyobo (Shanghai) Biotech Co., Ltd. (1)
Unit AL 28th Floor China Resources Times Square 500 Zhangyang Road, Pudong New Area, Shanghai, 200122, China
Tel.: (86) 215 879 4900
Web Site: https://www.bio-toyobo.cn
Medical Equipment Mfr & Distr
N.A.I.C.S.: 339112

Toyobo (Shanghai) Co., Ltd. (1)
Room 2301-A Building B Dongyin Center 500 Ruby Road, Changning District, Shanghai, 201103, China
Tel.: (86) 216 208 3030
Web Site: https://www.sh-toyobo.com.cn
Resin & Film Product Mfr
N.A.I.C.S.: 325211

Toyobo (Taiwan) Co., Ltd. (1)
Room 702 7th Floor No 96 Section 2, Zhongshan District, Taipei, 10449, Taiwan
Tel.: (886) 22 561 0325
Web Site: https://www.toyobo.com.tw
Polymer Distr
N.A.I.C.S.: 424610

Toyobo (Thailand) Co., Ltd. (1)
No 944 Mirrtown Office Tower 11th Floor Room 1103-1106 Rama 4 Road, Wangmai Pathumwan, Bangkok, 10330, Thailand
Tel.: (66) 276 639 4248
Web Site: https://www.toyobo.co.th
Industrial Material Distr
N.A.I.C.S.: 423390

Toyobo America Inc. (1)
666 Third Ave Ste 603, New York, NY 10017 **(100%)**
Tel.: (212) 398-0550
Web Site: http://www.toyobousa.com
Sales Range: $1-9.9 Million
Emp.: 6
Marketing & Sales of Textiles Thread
N.A.I.C.S.: 541910

Toyobo Automotive Textiles (Changshu) Co., Ltd. (1)
3 Jingshun Industrial Square No9 Maqiao Road Riverside Industrial Park, Changshu Economic and Technological Development Zone, Changshu, 215513, Jiangsu, China
Tel.: (86) 5125 226 5550
Airbag Fabric Mfr & Distr
N.A.I.C.S.: 336360

Toyobo Binh Duong Co., Ltd. (1)
Lot 03 Viet Huong, Industrial Park, Thuan An, Binh Duong, Vietnam
Tel.: (84) 274 371 5421
Casual Wear Mfr
N.A.I.C.S.: 315210

Toyobo Chemicals (Thailand) Co., Ltd. (1)
700/922 Moo 3, T Nongkakha A Phanthong, Chon Buri, 20160, Thailand
Tel.: (66) 3 821 2376
Polyester Resin Mfr
N.A.I.C.S.: 325211

Toyobo Chemicals Europe GmbH (1)
Am Wehrhahn 50, 40211, Dusseldorf, Germany
Tel.: (49) 2119 762 2913
Web Site: https://www.toyobo-europe.com
Textile Product Mfr & Distr
N.A.I.C.S.: 314999

Toyobo Do Brasil Participacoes Ltda. (1)
Av Dr Chucri Zaidan 771, Vila Cordeiro, Sao Paulo, 04583-913, Brazil
Tel.: (55) 115 509 7801
Web Site: https://www.toyobo.com.br
Emp.: 250
Polymer Mfr & Distr
N.A.I.C.S.: 325211

Toyobo Engineering Co., Ltd. (1)
Fujita Toyobo Building 1-16 Dojima 2-chome, Kita-ku, Osaka, 530-0003, Japan
Tel.: (81) 66 348 3935
Web Site: https://www.toyobo-eng.co.jp
Emp.: 254
Construction Equipment Mfr
N.A.I.C.S.: 333120
Makoto Marutani *(Pres)*

Toyobo India Private Limited (1)
308 Time Tower sector 28 MG Road, Gurgaon, 122 002, Haryana, India
Tel.: (91) 12 443 9270
Polymer Distr
N.A.I.C.S.: 424610

Toyobo Industrial Material (Thailand) Ltd. (1)
159 Serm-Mit Tower 9th Floor Unit 903/1 Sukhumvit 21 Road Soi Asoke, Kwaeng Klongtoey Nua Khet Wattana Metropolis, Bangkok, Thailand
Tel.: (66) 2 661 7250
Airbag Fabric Distr
N.A.I.C.S.: 424990

Toyobo Industrial Materials America, Inc. (1)
7526 Roy Owens Blvd, Scottsboro, AL 35769
Tel.: (256) 575-2579
Airbag Fabric Distr
N.A.I.C.S.: 424990

Toyobo Information System Create Co., Ltd. (1)
12F Toyo Spinning Building 2-2-8 Dojimahama, Kita-ku, Osaka, 530-8230, Japan
Tel.: (81) 66 348 3500
Web Site: https://www.toyobo.co.jp
Software Development Services
N.A.I.C.S.: 541511

Toyobo Korea Co., Ltd. (1)
Suite 1002 10/F Trade Tower 511 Yeongdong-daero, Gangnam-gu, Seoul, Korea (South)
Tel.: (82) 2 555 6353
Web Site: https://www.toyobo.co.kr
Industrial Material Distr
N.A.I.C.S.: 423390

Toyobo Logistics Co., Ltd. (1)
2-2-8 Dojimahama, Kita-ku, Osaka, 530-0004, Japan
Tel.: (81) 66 348 3401
Web Site: https://www.tlc.toyobo.co.jp
Logistic Services
N.A.I.C.S.: 541614

Toyobo MC Mexico S.A. de C.V. (1)
Prolongacion Bernardo Quintana 300 Int 1002 Colonia Centro Sur, CP 76090, Queretaro, Qro, Mexico
Tel.: (52) 4421995091
Industrial Material Mfr & Distr
N.A.I.C.S.: 333248

Toyobo Mexico, S.A. de C.V. (1)
Prolongacion Bernardo Quintana 300 Int 1002 Colonia Centro Sur, 76090, Santiago de Queretaro, Mexico
Tel.: (52) 442 199 5091
Polymer Mfr & Distr
N.A.I.C.S.: 325211

Toyobo Photo Chemicals Co., Ltd. (1)
Toyobo Bldg 2-2-8 Dojima Hama, Kita-ku, Osaka, 530-0004, Japan
Tel.: (81) 66 348 3058
Photopolymer Mfr
N.A.I.C.S.: 325211

Toyobo Real Estate Co., Ltd. (1)
Sakaisujihonmachi TF Bldg 2-4-27 Kyutaromachi, Chuo-ku, Osaka, 541-0056, Japan
Tel.: (81) 67 669 8610
Property Insurance Services
N.A.I.C.S.: 524210

Toyobo STC Co., Ltd. (1)
2-2-8 Dojimahama, Kita-ku, Osaka, 530-0004, Japan
Tel.: (81) 64 797 6000
Web Site: https://www.stc.toyobo.co.jp
Textile Product Mfr & Distr
N.A.I.C.S.: 314999
Takayuki Tabo *(Pres & COO)*

Toyobo Saha Safety Weave Co., Ltd. (1)
49/1 Mu 3 Poochaosamingprai Rd, Samrongtai, Phra Pradaeng, 10130, Samut Prakan, Thailand
Tel.: (66) 2 183 3904
Airbag Fabric Mfr
N.A.I.C.S.: 336360

Toyobo Textile (Malaysia) Sdn. Bhd. (1)
Kuala Kangsar Industrial Estate, Kuala Kangsar, 33000, Perak, Malaysia
Tel.: (60) 5 776 1388
Web Site: https://www.toyobo.com.my
Cotton Textile Mfr
N.A.I.C.S.: 313310
Masato Hirakawa *(Mng Dir)*

Yuho Co., Ltd. (1)
2-1-16 Dojima Fujita Toyobo Building, Kita-ku, Osaka, 530-0003, Japan
Tel.: (81) 66 348 4311
Web Site: https://www.yuho.toyobo.co.jp
Nonwoven Fabric Mfr
N.A.I.C.S.: 313230

TOYODA GOSEI CO., LTD.
1 Haruhinagahata, Kiyosu, 452-8564, Aichi, Japan
Tel.: (81) 524001055   JP
Web Site: https://www.toyoda-gosei.com
Year Founded: 1949
7282---(TKS)
Rev.: $7,080,017,270
Assets: $6,169,423,670
Liabilities: $2,423,311,930
Net Worth: $3,746,111,740
Earnings: $340,110,940
Emp.: 38,951
Fiscal Year-end: 03/31/24
Automotive Parts & Accessories Mfr & Sales
N.A.I.C.S.: 336390
Tomonobu Yamada *(Exec VP)*

Subsidiaries:

Chusei Gomu Co., Ltd. (1)
400 Uchida Ano-cho, Tsu, 514-2396, Mie, Japan
Tel.: (81) 59 268 2201
Web Site: https://www.chuseigomu.co.jp
Automotive Rubber Mfr
N.A.I.C.S.: 326220

FTS Co., Ltd. (1)
2-26 Konosu-cho, Toyota, 471-8510, Aichi, Japan
Tel.: (81) 56 529 2211
Web Site: https://www.fts-com.co.jp
Fuel Tank Mfr
N.A.I.C.S.: 332420
Hiroyuki Ochiai *(Pres)*

Fong Yue Co., Ltd. (1)
No 6-1 Kuangfu Road 10 Hunan Village, Hukou, 30351, Hsinchu, Taiwan
Tel.: (886) 35983716
Web Site: http://www.toyoda-gosei.com
Rev.: $26,928,000
Emp.: 194
Automobile Parts Mfr
N.A.I.C.S.: 336360

Hoshin Gosei Co., Ltd. (1)
6487-15 Katagiri, Nakagawa Kamiina-gun, Nagano, 399-3802, Japan
Tel.: (81) 26 588 4011
Web Site: https://www.toyoda-gosei.com
Interior & Exterior Parts Mfr
N.A.I.C.S.: 336390

Ichiei Kogyo Co., Ltd. (1)
1 Inouchi Meichi, Ichinomiya, 494-0012, Aichi, Japan
Tel.: (81) 58 669 2991
Web Site: https://www.ichiei-ind.co.jp
Automobile Parts Mfr
N.A.I.C.S.: 336110

Lexedis Lighting GmbH (1)
Technologiepark 10, Jennersdorf, 8380, Burgenland, Austria
Tel.: (43) 5901065054
Web Site: https://www.lexedis.com
Rev.: $23,256,000
Emp.: 1
Optoelectronic Product Mfr
N.A.I.C.S.: 334413
Motoo Tanaka *(Co-Mng Dir)*

P.T. TG Inoac Indonesia (1)
Jl Hayam Wuruk No 8 Wisma Hayam Wuruk LT 3 Suite 325 RT 6/RW 2 Kb, Jakarta, 10120, Indonesia
Tel.: (62) 21 351 9717
Rubber Seal Parts Mfr & Distr
N.A.I.C.S.: 326299

P.T. Toyoda Gosei Safety Systems Indonesia (1)
JL Raya Jakarta-Bogor KM 47 5 RT 002/RW 03, Nanggewer-Cibinong, Bogor, 16912, West Java, Indonesia
Tel.: (62) 251650411
Web Site: https://www.toyoda-gosei.com
Rev.: $4,896,000
Emp.: 59
Automobile Parts Mfr
N.A.I.C.S.: 336330

Pecval Industria Ltda. (1)
Rua Antonio Barnabe 990, Distrito Industrial Domingos Giomi, 13347-340, Indaiatuba, SP, Brazil
Tel.: (55) 19 39 36 9999
Web Site: http://www.pecval.com.br
Automotive Components Mfr
N.A.I.C.S.: 441330

TG Logistics Co., Ltd. (1)
25-2 Nagahara Higashimiyashige Hagiwaracho, Ichinomiya, 491-0363, Aichi, Japan
Tel.: (81) 58 667 1128
Automobile Parts Distr
N.A.I.C.S.: 423120

TG Maintenance Inc. (1)
1 Nishisukabata Haruhi, Kiyosu, 452-0961, Aichi, Japan
Tel.: (81) 52 409 4040
Automotive Parts Mfr & Distr
N.A.I.C.S.: 336390

TG Minto Corporation (1)
300 Toronto St, Palmerston, N0G 2P0, ON, Canada
Tel.: (519) 343-2800
Web Site: http://www.toyoda-gosei.com
Rev.: $139,536,000
Emp.: 800
Automobile Parts Mfr
N.A.I.C.S.: 336110
Jim Whelan *(Pres)*

TG Opseed Co., Ltd. (1)
5-6-1 Sakuradai, Nishi-ku, Hamamatsu, 431-1104, Shizuoka, Japan
Tel.: (81) 53 414 5770
Web Site: https://www.tg-opseed.co.jp
Light Emitting Diode Product Mfr & Distr
N.A.I.C.S.: 335139

TG Sports Co., Ltd. (1)
1-16-4 Orizukitayama, Inazawa, 492-8094, Aichi, Japan
Tel.: (81) 58 721 0615
Automotive Parts Mfr & Distr
N.A.I.C.S.: 336390

TG Welfare Co., Ltd. (1)
100 Kasuga Nagahata, Kiyosu, 452-0961, Aichi, Japan
Tel.: (81) 52 400 4678
Web Site: https://www.tgwelfare.co.jp

TOYODA GOSEI CO., LTD.

Toyoda Gosei Co., Ltd.—(Continued)
Prescription Product Distr
N.A.I.C.S.: 424210

TG-Techno Co., Ltd. (1)
30 Nishinocho Kitajima-cho, Inazawa, 492-8540, Aichi, Japan
Tel.: (81) 58 736 7191
Web Site: https://www.tg-techno.co.jp
Software Development Services
N.A.I.C.S.: 541511

TGAP Co., Ltd. (1)
425 Inouenishi Chiakicho Kanomanba, Ichinomiya, 491-0811, Aichi, Japan
Tel.: (81) 58 676 0611
Interior & Exterior Parts Mfr
N.A.I.C.S.: 336390

TS Opto Co., Ltd. (1)
5-1 Yawatakaigandori, Ichihara, 290-0067, Chiba, Japan
Tel.: (81) 43 642 0051
Automotive Parts Mfr & Distr
N.A.I.C.S.: 336390

Tai-Yue Rubber Industrial Co., Ltd. (1)
No 360 Sec 6 Minzu Rd, Zhongli Dist, Taoyuan, 32050, Taiwan
Tel.: (886) 3 490 1148
Web Site: https://www.taiyue.com.tw
Automotive Rubber Mfr
N.A.I.C.S.: 326220

Tecno Art Research Co., Ltd. (1)
5-1 Buheicho Nagoya Sakae Building 8F, Higashi-ku, Nagoya, 461-0008, Japan
Tel.: (81) 52 962 9911
Web Site: https://www.tar.co.jp
Automotive Interior & Exterior Parts Mfr
N.A.I.C.S.: 336390

Tianjin Star Light Rubber And Plastic Co., Ltd. (1)
No 6 Tianhe Road, Zhongbei Town Xiqing District, Tianjing, 300112, China
Tel.: (86) 22273952
Web Site: http://www.toyoda-gosei-china.com
Emp.: 805
Mechanical Rubber Goods Mfr
N.A.I.C.S.: 326291
Hidenori Saba (Gen Mgr)

Toyoda Gosei (Thailand) Co., Ltd. (1)
700/489 Moo 4 Amata Nakorn Industrial Estate Bangna-Trad Highway KM 57, Tambon Bankao Amphur Pantong, Chon Buri, 20160, Thailand
Tel.: (66) 3845408994
Web Site: http://www.toyoda-gosei.com
Rev.: $315,792,000
Emp.: 1,500
Automobile Parts Mfr
N.A.I.C.S.: 336310

Toyoda Gosei Asia Co., Ltd. (1)
700/489 Moo 4 Amata Nakorn Industrial Estate Bangna-Trad Highway KM 57, Tambon Bankao Amphur Pantong, Chon Buri, 20160, Thailand
Tel.: (66) 38454589
Web Site: http://www.toyoda-gosei.co.jp
Rev.: $372,096,000
Emp.: 2,500
Automobile Parts Distr
N.A.I.C.S.: 423120

Toyoda Gosei Australia Pty. Ltd. (1)
1028 South Road, Edwardstown, 5039, SA, Australia
Tel.: (61) 883720200
Web Site: http://www.toyodagosei.com.au
Rev.: $36,686,000
Emp.: 140
Automobile Parts Mfr
N.A.I.C.S.: 336330

Toyoda Gosei Co., Ltd. - Bisai Plant (1)
40 Higashishimoshiro, Meichi, Ichinomiya, 494-8502, Aichi, Japan
Tel.: (81) 586691811
Web Site: http://www.toyoda-gosei.com
Sales Range: $250-299.9 Million
Emp.: 759
Automobile Parts Mfr
N.A.I.C.S.: 336330

Toyoda Gosei Co., Ltd. - Fukuoka Plant (1)
2223-1 Kurahisa, Miyawaka, 823-0017, Fukuoka, Japan
Tel.: (81) 949347167
Web Site: http://www.toyoda-gosei.com
Sales Range: $150-199.9 Million
Emp.: 276
Automobile Parts Mfr
N.A.I.C.S.: 336310

Toyoda Gosei Co., Ltd. - Haruhi Plant (1)
1 Haruhinagahata, Kiyosu, 452-8564, Aichi, Japan
Tel.: (81) 524005141
Sales Range: $200-249.9 Million
Emp.: 622
Automotive Functional Parts Mfr
N.A.I.C.S.: 336310

Toyoda Gosei Co., Ltd. - Heiwacho Plant (1)
710 Origuchi Shimomiyake, Heiwa, Inazawa, 490-1312, Aichi, Japan
Tel.: (81) 567462222
Web Site: http://www.toyoda-gosei.com
Sales Range: $300-349.9 Million
Emp.: 999
Automotive & Optoelectronic Products Mfr
N.A.I.C.S.: 334413

Toyoda Gosei Co., Ltd. - Inazawa Plant (1)
1 Komeyasakai, Kitajima, Inazawa, 492-8542, Aichi, Japan
Tel.: (81) 587361111
Web Site: http://www.toyoda-gosei.com
Automobile Parts Mfr
N.A.I.C.S.: 336310

Toyoda Gosei Co., Ltd. - Iwate Plant (1)
1-1 Nishine Moriyama Kanegasaki-cho, Isawa-gun, Iwate, 029-4503, Japan
Tel.: (81) 19 741 0661
Automobile Parts Mfr
N.A.I.C.S.: 336330

Toyoda Gosei Co., Ltd. - Kitakyushu Plant (1)
1-2 Kita-Horaoka Maeda, Yahatahigashi-ku, Kitakyushu, 805-0058, Fukuoka, Japan
Tel.: (81) 936631820
Web Site: http://www.toyoda-gosei.com
Automobile Parts Mfr
N.A.I.C.S.: 336310

Toyoda Gosei Co., Ltd. - Morimachi Plant (1)
1310-128 Mutsumi Mori, Shuchi, Shizuoka, 437-0213, Japan
Tel.: (81) 538852165
Sales Range: $200-249.9 Million
Emp.: 999
Automobile Parts Mfr
N.A.I.C.S.: 336310

Toyoda Gosei Co., Ltd. - Nishimizoguchi Plant (1)
1-1 Daininuma, Nishimizoguchi, Inazawa, 492-8452, Aichi, Japan
Tel.: (81) 587365761
Sales Range: $50-74.9 Million
Emp.: 234
Jigs & Machine Tools Mfr
N.A.I.C.S.: 333517

Toyoda Gosei Co., Ltd. - Saga Plant (1)
9966-9 Kawako Oaza Wakaki-cho, Takeo, 843-0151, Saga, Japan
Tel.: (81) 954262678
Web Site: http://www.toyoda-gosei.com
Sales Range: $25-49.9 Million
Emp.: 81
Optoelectronic Product Mfr
N.A.I.C.S.: 334419

Toyoda Gosei Co., Ltd. - Seto Plant (1)
141 Sousaku, Seto, 489-8452, Aichi, Japan
Tel.: (81) 561973602
Web Site: http://www.toyoda-gosei.com
Sales Range: $50-74.9 Million
Emp.: 119
Automotive Interior & Exterior Parts Mfr
N.A.I.C.S.: 336330

Toyoda Gosei Czech, s.r.o. (1)
Prumyslova 2, PO Box 21, 431 51, Klasterec nad Ohri, Czech Republic
Tel.: (420) 47 710 1111
Web Site: https://www.tgcz.cz
Emp.: 1,500
Automobile Parts Mfr
N.A.I.C.S.: 326220
Hiroshi Yasuda (Pres)

Toyoda Gosei East Japan Co., Ltd. (1)
3-3 Takashimizuosawa, Kurihara, 987-2014, Miyagi, Japan
Tel.: (81) 22 824 8680
Weather Strip Mfr
N.A.I.C.S.: 332321

Toyoda Gosei Europe N.V. (1)
Planet II Unit E3 0 Leuvensesteenweg 542, 1930, Zaventem, Flemish Brabant, Belgium
Tel.: (32) 25132453
Web Site: http://www.toyoda-gosei.com
Rev.: $4,896,000
Emp.: 23
Automobile Parts Distr
N.A.I.C.S.: 423120

Toyoda Gosei Foshan Rubber Parts Co., Ltd. (1)
No 5 Wusha Section Shunpan Road, Daliang Town Shunde, Foshan, Guangdong, China
Tel.: (86) 75722801260
Web Site: http://www.toyoda-gosei.com
Rev.: $38,844,000
Emp.: 652
Automobile Parts Mfr
N.A.I.C.S.: 336390

Toyoda Gosei Haiphong Co., Ltd. (1)
Land Plot M Nomura-Haiphong Industrial Zone Km13, An Duong District, Haiphong, Vietnam
Tel.: (84) 31743028
Web Site: http://www.toyoda-gosei.com
Rev.: $100,368,000
Emp.: 2,287
Automobile Parts Mfr
N.A.I.C.S.: 336330

Toyoda Gosei Hinode Co., Ltd. (1)
260-1 Yamadacho, Yokkaichi, 512-1111, Mie, Japan
Tel.: (81) 59 328 2911
Weather Strip Mfr
N.A.I.C.S.: 332321

Toyoda Gosei India Pvt. Ltd. (1)
Plot No SP2-30 & 31 RIICO Industrial Area, Majrakath Area Neemrana, Alwar, Rajasthan, Rajasthan, India
Tel.: (91) 494 246418
Web Site: http://www.toyoda-gosei.com
Rev.: $1,224,000
Emp.: 28
Automobile Parts Mfr
N.A.I.C.S.: 336330

Subsidiary (Domestic):

Metzeler Automotive Profiles India Pvt. Ltd. (2)
Plot No 24A Site IV Sahibabad Industrial Area, Ghaziabad, 201 010, Uttar Pradesh, India
Tel.: (91) 1204181715
Automobile Parts Mfr
N.A.I.C.S.: 336370
Enrique Noguerolef (Mng Dir)

Toyoda Gosei South India Pvt. Ltd. (2)
Building No 1 Toyota Techno Park Plot No 20, Bidadi Industrial Area Bidadi Ramanagara Dist, Bengaluru, 562109, Karnataka, India
Tel.: (91) 8027287160
Web Site: https://www.tgsin.in
Emp.: 1,095
Automobile Parts Mfr
N.A.I.C.S.: 336370

Toyoda Gosei Interior Manufacturing Co., Ltd. (1)
158 Kitayama Morowa Togo, Nagoya, 470-0151, Aichi, Japan
Tel.: (81) 56 139 1241
Interior & Exterior Parts Mfr

INTERNATIONAL PUBLIC

N.A.I.C.S.: 336390

Toyoda Gosei Kyushu Co., Ltd. (1)
2223-1 Kurahisa, Miyawaka, 823-0017, Fukuoka, Japan
Tel.: (81) 94 934 7167
Weather Strip Mfr
N.A.I.C.S.: 332321

Toyoda Gosei North America Corporation (1)
1400 Stephenson Hwy, Troy, MI 48083
Tel.: (248) 280-2100
Web Site: https://www.toyodagosei.com
Rev.: $1,252,152,000
Emp.: 220
Automotive Parts & Optoelectronics Mfr
N.A.I.C.S.: 326220

Subsidiary (Domestic):

TG Automotive Sealing Kentucky, LLC (2)
501 Frank Yost Ln, Hopkinsville, KY 42240
Tel.: (270) 475-1400
Web Site: http://www.toyoda-gosei.com
Rev.: $59,976,000
Emp.: 193
Automobile Parts Mfr
N.A.I.C.S.: 336370
Allan Abdalla (Pres)

TG Fluid Systems USA Corporation (2)
100 Brighton Interior Dr, Brighton, MI 48116
Tel.: (810) 220-6161
Web Site: http://www.toyoda-gosei.com
Rev.: $50,184,000
Emp.: 194
Automobile Parts Mfr
N.A.I.C.S.: 336390
Scott Maly (Pres)

TG Kentucky, LLC (2)
633 E Main St, Lebanon, KY 40033
Tel.: (270) 699-3300
Web Site: https://www.toyoda-gosei.com
Emp.: 1,100
Automobile Parts Mfr
N.A.I.C.S.: 336310
Takashi Fujii (Pres)

TG Missouri Corporation (2)
2200 Plattin Rd, Perryville, MO 63775
Tel.: (573) 547-1041
Web Site: http://www.tgmissouri.com
Automobile Parts Mfr
N.A.I.C.S.: 336390
Brian Robinson (Mgr-Payroll & HRIS)

TGR Technical Center, LLC (2)
47050 Port St, Plymouth, MI 48170
Tel.: (734) 451-4310
Web Site: http://www.toyoda-gosei.com
Rev.: $3,672,000
Emp.: 8
Automotive Safety Systems Evaluation Services
N.A.I.C.S.: 541380
Hal Charogoff (Branch Mgr)

Subsidiary (Non-US):

Tapex Mexicana S.A. DE C.V. (2)
Diagonal Lorenzo de la Garza 61 Ciudad Industrial, 84799, Matamoros, Tamaulipas Mexico, Mexico
Tel.: (52) 8183167660
Rev.: $19,584,000
Emp.: 172
Automobile Parts Mfr
N.A.I.C.S.: 336330

Toyoda Gosei Automotive Sealing Mexico S.A. DE C.V. (2)
Highway San Luis - Zacatecas Km 12 5 Industrial park, Pueblo Viejo Mexquitic De Carmona, 78480, San Luis Potosi, Mexico
Tel.: (52) 4441027500
Web Site: https://www.toyodagosei.com.mx
Automobile Parts Mfr
N.A.I.C.S.: 336370

Subsidiary (Domestic):

Toyoda Gosei Texas, LLC (2)
1 Lone Star Pass Bldg 31, San Antonio, TX 78264-3640
Tel.: (210) 302-4600
Rev.: $26,928,000
Emp.: 116

AND PRIVATE COMPANIES / TOYOTA BOSHOKU CORPORATION

Automobile Parts Mfr
N.A.I.C.S.: 336360

Toyoda Gosei Opto-Electronics Shanghai Co., Ltd. (1)
Room 801 Aetna Tower No 107 Zunyi Road, Shanghai, 200051, China
Tel.: (86) 2132233221
Web Site: http://www.toyoda-gosei.com
Rev: $35,607,000
Emp.: 12
Optoelectronic Products Distr
N.A.I.C.S.: 423690
Sugiura Tsugumori *(Pres)*

Toyoda Gosei Shanghai Co., Ltd. (1)
No.879 Shenfu Road, Xin Zhuang Industry Zone, Shanghai, 201108, China
Tel.: (86) 2132233203
Web Site: http://www.toyoda-gosei.com
Rev: $2,158,000
Emp.: 30
Automobile Parts Distr
N.A.I.C.S.: 423120

Toyoda Gosei South Africa Pty. Ltd. (1)
15 Beechgate Crescent Southgate Business Park Moss Kolnik Drive, Umbogintwini, 4012, Kwazulu Natal, South Africa
Tel.: (27) 319495733
Rev: $11,016,000
Emp.: 11
Automobile Parts Mfr
N.A.I.C.S.: 336330

Toyoda Gosei Tianjin Precise Plastic Co., Ltd. (1)
No 15 Zi Jing Road Tianjin Airport Industrial Park, Free Trade Zone, Tianjin, 300380, China
Tel.: (86) 2284909105
Rev: $10,790,000
Emp.: 414
Precision Plastic Products Mfr
N.A.I.C.S.: 326199

Toyoda Gosei UK Ltd. (1)
Bessemer Way Centurion Business Park, Templeborough, Rotherham, S60 1FB, South Yorkshire, United Kingdom
Tel.: (44) 1709323150
Rev: $47,736,000
Emp.: 484
Automobile Parts Mfr
N.A.I.C.S.: 336370

Toyoda Gosei Zhangjiagang Co., Ltd. (1)
113 Zhonghua Road Zhangjiagang Free Trade Zone, Zhangjiagang, 215634, Jiangsu, China
Tel.: (86) 51258389351
Rev: $104,663,000
Emp.: 702
Automobile Parts Mfr
N.A.I.C.S.: 336330
Kuwahara Yukihiro *(Gen Mgr)*

Toyoda Gosei Zhangjiagang Plastic Parts Co., Ltd. (1)
111 Zhonghua Rd Zhangjiagang Free Trade Zone, Zhangjiagang, Jiangsu, China
Tel.: (86) 51258323001
Web Site: http://www.toyoda-gosei.com
Rev: $42,081,000
Emp.: 519
Automobile Parts Mfr
N.A.I.C.S.: 336360

Waterville TG Inc. (1)
10 Depot, Waterville, J0B 3H0, QC, Canada **(100%)**
Tel.: (819) 837-2421
Web Site: https://www.watervilletg.ca
Sales Range: $400-449.9 Million
Emp.: 1,300
Sealing Systems Mfr for Automotive OEMs
N.A.I.C.S.: 339991

TOYODA IRON WORKS CO., LTD.
50 Hosoya-cho 4-chome, Toyota, 471-8507, Aichi, Japan
Tel.: (81) 565 26 1212
Web Site: http://www.tiw.co.jp
Year Founded: 1946
Automobile Parts Mfr
N.A.I.C.S.: 336211

Kazuhio Takarada *(Pres)*
Subsidiaries:

Guangzhou Toyotetsu Automobile Parts Co., Ltd. (1)
20 Huangge Middle Road Nansha Development Zone, Nansha, Guangzhou, China
Tel.: (86) 2034683218
Emp.: 848
Automobile Parts Distr
N.A.I.C.S.: 423120

PT. Nusa Toyotetsu (1)
Jl Bali Kawasan Industri MM 2100 Bl J/12-14-15, Cibitung, Bekasi, 17520, Jawa Barat, Indonesia
Tel.: (62) 218980777
Emp.: 1,420
Automobile Parts Distr
N.A.I.C.S.: 423120
Karl Jones *(Mgr-Sls-Midlands & Wales)*

PT. Nusa Toyotetsu Engineering (1)
Jl Mitra Raya II No 4, Clampel, Karawang, 41363, Jawa Barat, Indonesia
Tel.: (62) 2678637856
Emp.: 86
Automobile Parts Distr
N.A.I.C.S.: 423120

Stanzen Toyotetsu India Pvt. Ltd. (1)
No 2 Plot No 20 Ramanagar Taluk Bidadi Industrial Area, Bengaluru, Karnataka, India
Tel.: (91) 8027287158
Web Site: http://www.stanzentoyotetsu.com
Emp.: 669
Automobile Parts Distr
N.A.I.C.S.: 423120

Tianjin Toyotetsu Automobile Parts Co., Ltd. (1)
45 Gaoxin Avenue Beichen Technology Park, Beichen, Tianjin, China
Tel.: (86) 2226991001
Emp.: 970
Automobile Parts Distr
N.A.I.C.S.: 423120

Toyoda Iron Works Co., Ltd. - Hirokute Plant (1)
8 Hirokute-cho 6-chome, Toyota, Japan
Tel.: (81) 565358880
Automobile Parts Mfr
N.A.I.C.S.: 336390

Toyoda Iron Works Co., Ltd. - Nukata Plant (1)
8-4 Aza Osarada, Nakainishi-cho, Okazaki, Japan
Tel.: (81) 564843211
Automobile Parts Mfr
N.A.I.C.S.: 336390

Toyoda Iron Works Co., Ltd. - Sasahara Plant (1)
37-8 Shikida, Sasabara-cho, Toyota, Japan
Tel.: (81) 565486730
Emp.: 128
Automobile Parts Mfr
N.A.I.C.S.: 336390

Toyotetsu (Thailand) Co., Ltd. (1)
106 Moo 7, Si Maha Phot, 25140, Prachinburi, Thailand
Tel.: (66) 37270450
Emp.: 50
Automobile Parts Distr
N.A.I.C.S.: 423120

Toyotetsu America, Inc. (1)
100 Pin Oak Dr, Somerset, KY 42503
Tel.: (606) 274-9005
Web Site: http://www.ttna.com
Emp.: 685
Automobile Parts Mfr
N.A.I.C.S.: 336390
Jiro Iwase *(Pres)*

Toyotetsu Fukuoka Co., Ltd. (1)
620-45 Shimoaruki, Miyawaka, Fukuoka, Japan
Tel.: (81) 949556033
Emp.: 260
Automobile Parts Mfr
N.A.I.C.S.: 336390

Toyotetsu India, Auto Parts Pvt. Ltd. (1)
1 Oss Park Toyota Kirloskar Motors Campus Bidadi Industrial Area, Bidadi, Bengaluru, 562109, Karnataka, India
Tel.: (91) 9243602790
Emp.: 324
Automobile Parts Distr
N.A.I.C.S.: 423120

Toyotetsu Otomotiv Parcalari Sanayi Ve Ticaret A.S. (1)
Tosb Otomotiv Yan Sanayi ihtisas Organize Sanayi Bolgesi 5 Cadde No 4, Sekerpinar, 41420, Cayirova, Kocaeli, Turkiye
Tel.: (90) 2626588710
Web Site: http://www.toyotetsu.com.tr
Emp.: 777
Automobile Parts Mfr
N.A.I.C.S.: 336390

Toyotetsu Tohoku Co., Ltd. (1)
1 Aza Higashitominaga, Hasama-cho Kitakata, Tome, Miyagi, Japan
Tel.: (81) 220215201
Automobile Parts Mfr
N.A.I.C.S.: 336390

TOYOKUMO, INC.
2-27-3 Nishi-Gotanda, Shinagawa-Ku, Tokyo, 141-0031, Japan
Tel.: (81) 5038166666
Web Site: http://www.toyokumo.co.jp
Year Founded: 2010
4058—(TKS)
Application Development Services
N.A.I.C.S.: 541511
Yuji Yamamoto *(Chm & Pres)*

TOYOSHIMA & CO., LTD.
15-15 Nishiki 2 chome Nakaku, Nagoya, 460-8671, Japan
Tel.: (81) 522047711 JP
Web Site: http://www.toyoshima.co.jp
Year Founded: 1841
Rev: $1,923,202,440
Assets: $1,165,197,540
Liabilities: $456,977,340
Net Worth: $708,220,200
Earnings: $29,743,980
Emp.: 574
Fiscal Year-end: 06/30/19
Yarns, Textiles, Garments & other Raw Materials Whslr
N.A.I.C.S.: 313310
Hanshichi Toyoshima *(Pres)*
Subsidiaries:

PT. TYSM Indonesia (1)
Mid Plaza2 17th Floor Jl Jend Sudirman Kav 10-11, Jakarta, 10220, Indonesia
Tel.: (62) 215723910
Textile Raw Material Whslr
N.A.I.C.S.: 424590

Toyoshima (Asia) Co., Ltd. (1)
Rm 1111-1113A 11/F One Harbourfront 18 Tak Fung Street, Hung Hom, Kowloon, China (Hong Kong)
Tel.: (852) 23694071
Textile Raw Material Whslr
N.A.I.C.S.: 424590

Toyoshima (U.S.A.), Inc. (1)
19600 Magellan Dr, Torrance, CA 90502
Tel.: (310) 879-4400
Textile Raw Material Whslr
N.A.I.C.S.: 424590

Toyoshima Do Brasil Comercial Importadora E Exportadora Ltda. (1)
Av Das Nacoes Unidas 12399-96A, Brooklin Paulista, Sao Paulo, 04578-000, Brazil
Tel.: (55) 1126268385
Textile Raw Material Whslr
N.A.I.C.S.: 424590

Toyoshima International (Shanghai) Co., Ltd. (1)
Room 1513 Shanghai International Trade Center 2201 West Yan'an Road, Changning District, Shanghai, China
Tel.: (86) 2162098181
Web Site: http://www.toyoku.com.cn
Textile Raw Material Whslr
N.A.I.C.S.: 424590

Toyoshima International America, Inc. (1)
19600 Magellan Dr 3F, Torrance, CA 90502
Tel.: (310) 879-4450
Textile Raw Material Whslr
N.A.I.C.S.: 424590

Toyoshima Long An Garment Co., Ltd. (1)
D6 Kizuna Lot K, Tan Kim Industrial Park, Can Giuoc, Long An, Vietnam
Tel.: (84) 2723733550
Textile Raw Material Whslr
N.A.I.C.S.: 424590

Toyoshima Vietnam Co., Ltd. (1)
Lot A5-A6 Nhi Xuan Industrial Zone, Xuan Thoi Son Commune Hoc Mon District, Ho Chi Minh City, Vietnam
Tel.: (84) 2835950197
Textile Raw Material Whslr
N.A.I.C.S.: 424590

TOYOTA BOSHOKU CORPORATION
1-1 Toyoda-cho, Kariya, 448-8651, Aichi, Japan
Tel.: (81) 566236611
Web Site: https://www.toyota-boshoku.com
Year Founded: 1950
3116—(TKS)
Rev: $12,913,461,250
Assets: $7,459,325,510
Liabilities: $4,196,351,890
Net Worth: $3,262,973,620
Earnings: $382,619,850
Emp.: 46,972
Fiscal Year-end: 03/31/24
Automobile Interior Systems Mfr; Automotive Filtration & Power Train Components Mfr
N.A.I.C.S.: 336360
Shuhei Toyoda *(Chm)*
Subsidiaries:

Araco Co., Ltd. (1)
34-1 Toei, Yoshiwara-cho, Toyota, 473-0916, Aichi, Japan **(59.49%)**
Tel.: (81) 565528501
Seats & Seat Covers Mfr & Distr
N.A.I.C.S.: 336360

Boshoku Automotive (Thailand) Co., Ltd. (1)
Eastern Seaboard Industrial Estate 300/300 M 1 T Tasit, A Pluakdaeng, Rayong, 21140, Thailand
Tel.: (66) 38923600
Web Site: https://www.boshoku-automotive.co.th
Seat Interior Component Mfr & Distr
N.A.I.C.S.: 336360

Chengdu Toyota Boshoku Automotive Parts Co., Ltd. (1)
No 336 South Three Road, Chengdu Economic & Technological Development Zone Longquanyi, Chengdu, 610100, China
Tel.: (86) 2888435070
Automotive Seat Mfr & Distr
N.A.I.C.S.: 336360

Cowerk Co., Ltd. (1)
4-33 Nakayamacho, Kariya, 448-0026, Aichi, Japan
Tel.: (81) 566252228
Web Site: https://www.cowerk.jp
Automotive Seat Mfr
N.A.I.C.S.: 336360

Feng'ai (Guangzhou) Automotive Seat Parts Co., Ltd. (1)
No 1 Wuzhou Shanbei Road, Huangge Town Nansha District, Guangzhou, 511455, Guangdong, China
Tel.: (86) 203 468 2662
Web Site: https://www.toyota-boshoku.com
Automotive Mfr & Sales of Seats & Interior Components
N.A.I.C.S.: 336360

Kawashima Textile Manufacturers (Shanghai) Ltd. (1)
2F 3F Building 35 Shengchuang Enterprise

TOYOTA BOSHOKU CORPORATION

Toyota Boshoku Corporation—(Continued)
Homeland Lane 1661, Jialuo Road Jiading, Shanghai, 201808, China
Tel.: (86) 2139533366
Transportation Vehicle Interior Material Mfr & Distr
N.A.I.C.S.: 336360

Kyowa Sangyo Corp. (1)
3-1 Korugahara, Toyota, 471-0856, Aichi, Japan
Tel.: (81) 565324651
Web Site: https://www.kyowa-sangyo.co.jp
Emp.: 517
Automobile Parts Mfr
N.A.I.C.S.: 334290

Master Trim de Argentina S.R.L. (1)
Gral Lavalle 4024, Villa Martelli, Buenos Aires, B1603AUR, Argentina
Tel.: (54) 1147618927
Web Site: http://www.mta.com.ar
Automotive Interiors Mfr & Distr
N.A.I.C.S.: 336360

Naruco Corporation (1)
18 Kanayamaura Kamekubi-cho, Toyota, 470-0375, Aichi, Japan
Tel.: (81) 565450515
Auto Component Mfr & Distr
N.A.I.C.S.: 336370

Ningbo Toyota Boshoku Automotive Parts Co., Ltd. (1)
No 9 GangXi Road Free Trade Zone West Zone, Ningbo, 315800, China
Tel.: (86) 57486820678
Automobile Seat Cover Mfr & Distr
N.A.I.C.S.: 336360

P.T. Toyota Boshoku Indonesia (1)
Jl Jawa 1 Blok J-11 Kawasan Industri MM2100, Cikarang Barat, Bekasi, 17520, Indonesia
Tel.: (62) 218981274
Automotive Seat Mfr & Distr
N.A.I.C.S.: 336360

S.K. Auto Interior Co., Ltd. (1)
184 Moo 7, Gateway City Industrial Estate Huasamrong Plaengyao, Chachoengsao, 24190, Thailand
Tel.: (66) 38575251
Web Site: http://www.toyota-boshoku.com
Automobile Parts Mfr
N.A.I.C.S.: 336360

STB Textiles Industry Co., Ltd. (1)
199/3 Moo 3 Sukhumvit Road, Si Racha, 20230, Chon Buri, Thailand
Tel.: (66) 38493780
Seat Fabrics Mfr
N.A.I.C.S.: 313220

Seiwa Co., Ltd. (1)
Ueno Chuo Building 7-11-6 Ueno, Taito-ku, Tokyo, 110-0005, Japan
Tel.: (81) 358286781
Web Site: https://www.seiwa-tr.co.jp
Seat Cover Mfr & Distr
N.A.I.C.S.: 336360

Shin San Shing Co., Ltd. (1)
8 Jen Yi Road Feng Shan Village, Hukou, 30352, Hsinchu, Taiwan
Tel.: (886) 35983226
Automotive Parts Mfr & Distr
N.A.I.C.S.: 336360

TB CORPORATE SERVICE CORPORATION (1)
1-1 Maehata, Oshima-cho, Toyota, 473-0935, Aichi, Japan (70.2%)
Tel.: (81) 565528787
Web Site: https://www.tb-corporateservice.com
Emp.: 274
Stationery Products Retailer & Corporate Support Services
N.A.I.C.S.: 459410
Naoyuki Niii (Mng Dir)

TB Create Staff Corporation (1)
1-1 Maehata Oshima-cho, Toyota, 473-0935, Aichi, Japan
Tel.: (81) 565523251
Emp.: 50
General Labor Dispatch Services
N.A.I.C.S.: 561320
Hiroshi Nagao (Gen Mgr)

TB Engineering Corporation (1)
1-11-1 Kosakahonmachi, Toyota, 471-0034, Aichi, Japan
Tel.: (81) 565370371
Web Site: https://www.tb-eng.co.jp
Sales Range: $25-49.9 Million
Emp.: 261
Manpower Dispatch Services
N.A.I.C.S.: 561320

TB KAWASHIMA CO., Ltd. (1)
923 Toendo Aisho-cho, Echi-gun, Shiga, 529-1325, Japan
Tel.: (81) 749424012
Web Site: https://www.tb-kawashima.co.jp
Emp.: 1,181
Automobile Seat Cover Mfr & Distr
N.A.I.C.S.: 336360

TB Sewtech Kyushu Corporation (1)
1076-5 Nagaheta Ouchi-Cho, Karatsu, 849-3217, Saga, Japan
Tel.: (81) 955623722
Seat Cover Mfr & Distr
N.A.I.C.S.: 336360

TB Sewtech Tohoku Corporation (1)
61 Matsunagane Iwayado, Esashi-ku, Oshu, 023-1101, Iwate, Japan
Tel.: (81) 197310606
Seat Cover Mfr & Distr
N.A.I.C.S.: 336360

TB Technogreen Corporation (1)
8-54 Obayashi-cho, Toyota, 473-0902, Aichi, Japan
Tel.: (81) 565291381
Web Site: https://www.tb-technogreen.com
Emp.: 28
Construction Engineering Services
N.A.I.C.S.: 541330

TB Unifashion Corporation (1)
1-20 Shiroshita-cho, Minami-ku, Nagoya, 457-0047, Aichi, Japan
Tel.: (81) 528193555
Web Site: https://www.tb-unifashion.com
Uniform Mfr & Whslr
N.A.I.C.S.: 315210

TB de Mexico, S.A. de C.V. (1)
Boulevard Jaime Benavides No 850, Los Rodriguez, Ramos Arizpe, 25900, Coahuila, Mexico
Tel.: (52) 18448669240
Seats & Seat Covers Mfr & Distr
N.A.I.C.S.: 336360

TOYOTA BOSHOKU EUROPE N.V.
Ikaroslaan 20, 1930, Zaventem, Vlaams Brabant, Belgium
Tel.: (32) 28991000
Sales Range: $25-49.9 Million
Emp.: 109
Automotive Parts Mfr & Distr
N.A.I.C.S.: 336360
Yoshiomi Matsushima (Exec VP)

Joint Venture (Non-US):

TBMECA Poland Sp. z o.o. (2)
ul Jaworzynska 291 a, 59-220, Legnica, Poland (54.9%)
Tel.: (48) 768508120
Web Site: http://www.tbmeca.pl
Emp.: 115
Automotive Components Mfr
N.A.I.C.S.: 336390

Taketech Co., Ltd. (1)
1-1 Maehata Oshima-cho, Toyota, 473-0935, Aichi, Japan
Tel.: (81) 565524035
Web Site: http://www.toyota-boshoku.co.jp
Sales Range: $25-49.9 Million
Emp.: 30
Automotive Interior Components Mfr & Distr
N.A.I.C.S.: 336360

Tb Kawashima USA, Inc. (1)
412 Groves St, Lugoff, SC 29078
Tel.: (803) 421-0033
Transportation Interior Material Mfr & Distr
N.A.I.C.S.: 336360

Tb Logistics Corporation (1)
17-1 Kirito Ikoma-cho, Toyota, 473-0928, Aichi, Japan
Tel.: (81) 565593135
Web Site: https://www.tb-logistics.co.jp

Emp.: 704
Industrial Vehicle Seat Mfr
N.A.I.C.S.: 336360

Tbai Poland Sp. z o.o. (1)
Ul Wyzwolenia 56, 59-730, Wykroty, Dolnyslask, Poland
Tel.: (48) 756479900
Web Site: http://www.tbaipl.com
Sales Range: $50-74.9 Million
Emp.: 200
Car Seat Frames & Covers Mfr
N.A.I.C.S.: 336360

Technical Links Design Co., Ltd. (1)
1-225 Hirako Asada, Nisshin, 470-0128, Aichi, Japan
Tel.: (81) 528080041
Web Site: https://www.links-d.co.jp
Sales Range: $25-49.9 Million
Emp.: 26
Product & Visual Design Services
N.A.I.C.S.: 541430

Tianjin Intex Auto Parts Co., Ltd. (1)
No 61 11th Street Tianjin Economic & Technological Development Area, Tianjin, 300457, China
Tel.: (86) 2266231188
Automotive Seat Mfr & Distr
N.A.I.C.S.: 336360

Toyota Boshoku (China) Co. Ltd. (1)
No 169 Yiwei Road Waigaoqiao, Pudong New District, Shanghai, 200131, China
Tel.: (86) 2120596266
Web Site: https://www.toyota-boshoku-china.com
Sales Range: $50-74.9 Million
Emp.: 228
Automotive Interiors Mfr & Distr
N.A.I.C.S.: 336360

Subsidiary (Domestic):

Guangzhou Intex Auto Parts Co., Ltd. (2)
No 3 Wuzhou Shanbei Road, Huangge Town Nansha, Guangzhou, 511455, Guangdong, China
Tel.: (86) 2034683060
Automobile Parts Mfr & Sales
N.A.I.C.S.: 336360

Kunshan Toyota Boshoku Automotive Parts Co., Ltd. (2)
No 333 Qingfeng West Road, Kunshan Economic and Technological Development Zone, Jiangsu, 215301, China
Tel.: (86) 51257308309
Sales Range: $25-49.9 Million
Emp.: 176
Automobile Parts Mfr
N.A.I.C.S.: 336360

Shanghai Toyota Automotive Parts Co. Ltd. (2)
No 218 Xinling Road Waigaoqiao, Pudong New District, Shanghai, 200131, China
Tel.: (86) 2150463237
Web Site: http://www.toyota-boshoku.com
Automotive Parts Mfr & Distr
N.A.I.C.S.: 336360

TOYOTA BOSHOKU FOSHAN Co., Ltd. (2)
No 13 Beiyuanzhong Road, Shishan Nanhai Zone, Foshan, 528225, Guangdong, China
Tel.: (86) 75781203988
Web Site: http://www.toyota-boshoku.com
Automobile Parts Mfr
N.A.I.C.S.: 336360

Toyota Boshoku (Guangzhou) Automotive Parts Co., Ltd. (1)
No 1 Wuzhou Shanbei Road, Huangge Town Nansha District, Guangzhou, 511455, China
Tel.: (86) 2034682662
Automotive Seat Mfr & Distr
N.A.I.C.S.: 336360

Toyota Boshoku (Tianjin) Automotive Parts Co., Ltd. (1)
No 135 Taifeng Road, Tianjin Economic and Technological Development Area, Tianjin, 300457, China
Tel.: (86) 2266231808
Automotive Seat Mfr & Distr

INTERNATIONAL PUBLIC

N.A.I.C.S.: 336360

Toyota Boshoku America, Inc. (1)
1360 Dolwick Dr Ste 125, Erlanger, KY 41018-3159
Tel.: (859) 817-4000
Sales Range: $100-124.9 Million
Emp.: 270
Development, Design, Manufacture & Sales of Automobile Seats & Interior Components
N.A.I.C.S.: 336360
Yoshihiro Ito (Chm)

Subsidiary (Non-US):

Toyota Boshoku Canada, Inc. (2)
230 Universal Road, Woodstock, N4S 7W3, ON, Canada
Tel.: (519) 421-7556
Web Site: https://toyotaboshoku.ca
Automobile Seats & Interior Components Mfr
N.A.I.C.S.: 336360
Takahito Kobayashi (Pres)

Subsidiary (Domestic):

Toyota Boshoku Indiana, LLC (2)
1698 S 100 W, Princeton, IN 47670-9531 (100%)
Tel.: (812) 491-9100
Automotive Seats & Door Trims Mfr
N.A.I.C.S.: 336360

Toyota Boshoku Argentina S.R.L. (1)
Camino a Capilla del Senor a 500mts Ruta9 Altura Km 80, Buenos Aires, CP2804, Campana, Argentina
Tel.: (54) 3489412000
Automotive Seat Mfr & Distr
N.A.I.C.S.: 336360

Toyota Boshoku Asia Co., Ltd. (1)
801 Kanchanapisek Road, Prawet Sub-District Prawet District, Bangkok, 10250, Thailand
Tel.: (66) 23295000
Web Site: https://toyota-boshoku-asia.com
Emp.: 271
Automotive Parts Mfr & Distr
N.A.I.C.S.: 336390
Masaki Kuroyanagi (Exec VP-Sls, Pur, PE & Production)

Toyota Boshoku Australia Pty. Ltd. (1)
235-239 Boundary Rd, Laverton North, Laverton, 3026, VIC, Australia
Tel.: (61) 383691100
Emp.: 370
Automobile Parts Mfr
N.A.I.C.S.: 336360
Mark Curnow (Dir-Bus & Admin)

Toyota Boshoku Automotive India Private Limited (1)
No 41 Bhimenahalli M N Halli Post, Bidadi Ramanagaram District, Karnataka, 562 109, India
Tel.: (91) 8022632999
Web Site: http://www.tbi-india.com
Sales Range: $200-249.9 Million
Emp.: 1,000
Automotive Parts Mfr & Distr
N.A.I.C.S.: 336330

Toyota Boshoku Corporation - Fujioka Plant (1)
143-1 Shinzayashiki, Nishinakayama-cho, Toyota, 470-0431, Aichi, Japan
Tel.: (81) 565761511
Automotive Door Trims Mfr

Toyota Boshoku Corporation - Fujisusono Plant (1)
2810-4 Suyama, Susono, 410-1231, Shizuoka, Japan
Tel.: (81) 559651311
Web Site: http://www.toyota-boshoku.co.jp
Automotive Seats & Door Trims Mfr
N.A.I.C.S.: 336360

Toyota Boshoku Corporation - Gifu Plant (1)
3-3 Maruno, Yanaizu-cho, Gifu, 501-6115, Japan
Tel.: (81) 583872141
Web Site: http://www.toyota-boshoku.co.jp
Bumpers Mfr

AND PRIVATE COMPANIES

TOYOTA INDUSTRIES CORPORATION

N.A.I.C.S.: 336390

Toyota Boshoku Corporation - Inabe Plant (1)
2181-59 Fujitani Oizumi Inabe-cho, Inabe, 511-0224, Mie, Japan
Tel.: (81) 594 84 2611
Web Site: http://www.toyota-boshoku.co.jp
Automotive Interiors Mfr
N.A.I.C.S.: 336360

Toyota Boshoku Corporation - Kariya Plant (1)
1-1 Toyoda-cho, Kariya, 448-8651, Aichi, Japan
Tel.: (81) 566267711
Sales Range: $250-299.9 Million
Emp.: 920
Automotive Components Mfr
N.A.I.C.S.: 334511

Toyota Boshoku Corporation - Kisogawa Plant (1)
1-1 Shimoinaba Sotowariden, Kisogawa-cho, Ichinomiya, 493-0007, Aichi, Japan
Tel.: (81) 586872111
Sales Range: $25-49.9 Million
Emp.: 84
Automotive Components Mfr
N.A.I.C.S.: 336360

Toyota Boshoku Corporation - Oguchi Plant (1)
3-201 Kamioguchi, Niwa-gun, Oguchi, 480-0141, Aichi, Japan
Tel.: (81) 587959750
Web Site: http://www.toyota-boshoku.co.jp
Automotive Mfr of Molded Headliners, Fender Liners, Seat Fabrics & Airbag Base Fabrics
N.A.I.C.S.: 336360

Toyota Boshoku Corporation - Sanage Plant (1)
88 Kanayama, Kamekubi-cho, Toyota, 470-0395, Aichi, Japan
Tel.: (81) 565451131
Automotive Interiors Mfr
N.A.I.C.S.: 336360

Toyota Boshoku Corporation - Tahara Plant (1)
39-22 Kizuka Ura-cho, Tahara, 441-3403, Aichi, Japan
Tel.: (81) 531 24 0351
Web Site: http://www.toyota-boshoku.co.jp
Automotive Interiors Mfr
N.A.I.C.S.: 336360

Toyota Boshoku Corporation - Takaoka Plant (1)
1-1 Maehata, Oshima-cho, Toyota, 473-0935, Aichi, Japan
Tel.: (81) 565523131
Web Site: http://www.toyota-boshoku.co.jp
Sales Range: $100-124.9 Million
Emp.: 500
Automotive Seats & Door Trims Mfr
N.A.I.C.S.: 336360
Ikuo Mochizuki *(Pres & CEO)*

Toyota Boshoku Corporation - Tokyo Plant (1)
4-6-1 Shinmeidai, Hamura, 205-0023, Tokyo, Japan
Tel.: (81) 425546094
Web Site: http://www.toyota-boshoku.co.jp
Automotive Door Trims & Manifolds Mfr
N.A.I.C.S.: 336360

Toyota Boshoku Corporation - Toyohashi-Higashi Plant (1)
3-56 Akemi-cho, Toyohashi, 441-8074, Aichi, Japan
Tel.: (81) 532233261
Floor Carpets Mfr
N.A.I.C.S.: 314110

Toyota Boshoku Corporation - Toyohashi-Kita Plant (1)
4-46 Akemi-cho, Toyohashi, 441-8074, Aichi, Japan
Tel.: (81) 532232801
Web Site: http://www.toyota-boshoku.com
Automobile Seats Mfr
N.A.I.C.S.: 336360

Toyota Boshoku Corporation - Toyohashi-Minami Plant (1)
5-12 Akemi-cho, Toyohashi, 441-8074, Aichi, Japan
Tel.: (81) 532231460
Automotive Door Trims & Seat Covers Mfr

Toyota Boshoku Corporation - Tsuchihashi Plant (1)
5-1-1 Shimizu-cho, Toyota, 471-0843, Aichi, Japan
Tel.: (81) 565283135
Automotive Seats & Seat Covers Mfr
N.A.I.C.S.: 336360

Toyota Boshoku Corporation - Tsutsumi Plant (1)
18-1 Kitanagane Wakabayashinishi-machi, Toyota, 473-0917, Aichi, Japan
Tel.: (81) 565510701
Web Site: http://www.toyota-boshoku.com
Automotive Floor Carpets & Interior Components Mfr
N.A.I.C.S.: 321999

Toyota Boshoku France S.A.S. (1)
Parc d'activites de la Vallee de l'Escaut Sud, 59264, Onnaing, France
Tel.: (33) 327514220
Web Site: http://www.toyota-boshoku.com
Sales Range: $25-49.9 Million
Emp.: 40
Bumpers Mfr & Distr
N.A.I.C.S.: 336390
Kennedy Jones *(Pres)*

Toyota Boshoku Haiphong Co., Ltd. (1)
Land Plot No M-1 2 M8 9 10 Japn Haiphong Industrial Zone, An Duong, 04159, Haiphong, Vietnam
Tel.: (84) 2253743155
Automotive Components Mfr & Distr
N.A.I.C.S.: 336360
Takatoshi Sekihara *(Gen Dir)*

Toyota Boshoku Hanoi Co., Ltd. (1)
No 144 Tran Phu Street, Phuc Thang Ward, 15908, Phuc Yen, Vinh Phuc, Vietnam
Tel.: (84) 2113868300
Motor Vehicle Seat Mfr & Distr
N.A.I.C.S.: 336360

Toyota Boshoku Hirose Corporation (1)
635-26 Komugyo Nishihirose-cho, Toyota, 470-0309, Aichi, Japan
Tel.: (81) 565464691
Emp.: 926
Automotive Component Mfr & Distr
N.A.I.C.S.: 336370

Toyota Boshoku Illinois, LLC (1)
100 Trim Masters Dr, Lawrenceville, IL 62439
Tel.: (618) 943-5300
Web Site: https://www.tbillinois.com
Automotive Interior Component Mfr & Distr
N.A.I.C.S.: 336360

Toyota Boshoku Kentucky, LLC (1)
1051 Withrow Ct, Bardstown, KY 40004
Tel.: (502) 349-6000
Door Trim Component Mfr & Distr
N.A.I.C.S.: 336360

Toyota Boshoku Kyushu Corporation (1)
1600 Tsuru, Kanzaki, 842-0107, Saga, Japan
Tel.: (81) 952527111
Web Site: https://www.tb-kyushu.co.jp
Sales Range: $500-549.9 Million
Emp.: 1,409
Automotive Components Mfr & Distr
N.A.I.C.S.: 336330

Toyota Boshoku Legnica Sp. z o.o. (1)
Ul Jaworzynska 291 A, 59-220, Legnica, Poland
Tel.: (48) 768508120
Web Site: https://www.tble.pl
Emp.: 115
Motor Vehicle Parts Mfr & Distr
N.A.I.C.S.: 336211

Toyota Boshoku Manufacturing Kentucky LLC (1)
200 Francis Marion Dr, Lebanon, KY 40033-1993
Tel.: (270) 699-2872
Automotive Parts Mfr & Sales
N.A.I.C.S.: 336360

Toyota Boshoku Mississippi LLC (1)
1 TB Way, Mantachie, MS 38855
Tel.: (662) 862-1340
Door Trim Component Mfr & Distr
N.A.I.C.S.: 336360

Toyota Boshoku Philippines Corporation (1)
111 Commerce Road Phase 2 Industriar Zone, Laguna Technopark, Binan, 4024, Laguna, Philippines
Tel.: (63) 495411323
Sales Range: $50-74.9 Million
Emp.: 200
Automotive Parts Mfr & Distr
N.A.I.C.S.: 336360

Toyota Boshoku Poland Sp. Z O.O. (1)
Ul Wyzwolenia 56, Nowogrodziec, 59-730, Wykroty, Poland
Tel.: (48) 756479900
Web Site: https://toyota-boshoku.pl
Seat Component Mfr & Distr
N.A.I.C.S.: 336360

Toyota Boshoku Seiko Corporation (1)
1-1 Nitta-cho, Takahama, 444-1301, Aichi, Japan
Tel.: (81) 566535820
Web Site: https://www.tbseiko.co.jp
Emp.: 1,551
Auto Component Mfr & Distr
N.A.I.C.S.: 336370

Toyota Boshoku Shiga Corporation (1)
1-14 Sasagaoka, Minakuchi-cho, Koka, 528-0061, Shiga, Japan
Tel.: (81) 748630031
Automotive Components Mfr & Distr
N.A.I.C.S.: 336390

Toyota Boshoku Siam Metal Com., Ltd. (1)
700/617 Moo 4 Amata City Chonburi Industrial Estate, Ban Kao Subdistrict Phan Thong District, Chon Buri, 20160, Thailand
Tel.: (66) 38210011
Web Site: https://www.jobthai.com
Automotive Seat Mfr & Distr
N.A.I.C.S.: 336360

Toyota Boshoku Somain S.A.S. (1)
Zone Industrielle de la Renaissance BP 67, Nord, 59490, Somain, France
Tel.: (33) 327933700
Automotive Seats Mfr & Distr
N.A.I.C.S.: 336360

Toyota Boshoku South Africa (PTY) LTD. (1)
1 Beechgate Crescent Southgate Business Park Moss Kolnik Drive, Umbogintwini, 4120, Kwazulu-Natal, South Africa
Tel.: (27) 319494000
Web Site: http://www.toyota-boshoku.sa.com
Sales Range: $200-249.9 Million
Emp.: 700
Automotive Components Mfr & Distr
N.A.I.C.S.: 336360

Toyota Boshoku Tennessee, LLC (1)
3300 Ridgecrest Rd Extended, Jackson, TN 38305
Tel.: (731) 927-8000
Metal Parts Mfr & Distr
N.A.I.C.S.: 332999

Toyota Boshoku Tohoku Corporation (1)
15-13 Hirabayashi, Aisari-cho, Kitakami, 024-0051, Iwate, Japan
Tel.: (81) 197671111
Automotive Parts Mfr & Distr
N.A.I.C.S.: 336360

Toyota Boshoku Turkiye Otomotiv Sanayi Ve Ticaret A.S. (1)
1 Organized Industrial Zone 1st Street, 54580, Arifiye, Sakarya, Turkiye
Tel.: (90) 2642952525
Web Site: https://www.toyota-boshokutr.com
Sales Range: $10-24.9 Million
Emp.: 2,135
Automotive Parts Mfr & Distr
N.A.I.C.S.: 336360
Halim Turhan *(Pres)*

Toyota Boshoku do Brasil Ltda. (1)
Avenida Antonio Comitre no 1650 Bairro Itavuvu, Sorocaba, Sao Paulo, Brazil
Tel.: (55) 1534160700
Automotive Seat Mfr & Distr
N.A.I.C.S.: 336360

TOYOTA CAETANO PORTUGAL S.A.

Av Vasco da Gama n1410, 4430-247, Vila Nova de Gaia, Portugal
Tel.: (351) 227867000
Web Site: https://www.toyotacaetano.pt
Year Founded: 1946
SCT—(EUR)
Rev.: $592,896,324
Assets: $502,812,643
Liabilities: $315,123,036
Net Worth: $187,689,607
Earnings: $19,282,066
Emp.: 1,576
Fiscal Year-end: 12/31/23
Automotive Distr
N.A.I.C.S.: 423110
Jose Reis da Silva Ramos *(Chm, Pres & CEO)*

Subsidiaries:

Caetano Auto, S.A. (1)
Av Vasco da Gama 1008 V N GAIA, Oliveira do Douro, 4430-247, Vila Nova de Gaia, Porto, Portugal
Tel.: (351) 227867032
New Car Distr
N.A.I.C.S.: 441110

CaetanoBus - Fabricacao de Carrocarias, S.A. (1)
Av Vasco da Gama 1410, 4431-901, Vila Nova de Gaia, Portugal
Tel.: (351) 227867000
Web Site: https://www.caetanobus.pt
Bus & Chassis Mfr
N.A.I.C.S.: 336211

TOYOTA INDUSTRIES CORPORATION

2-1 Toyoda-cho, Kariya, 448-8671, Aichi, Japan
Tel.: (81) 566222511   JP
Web Site: https://www.toyota-industries.com
Year Founded: 1926
6201—(TKS)
Rev.: $25,337,485,050
Assets: $73,228,633,820
Liabilities: $32,554,930,830
Net Worth: $40,673,702,990
Earnings: $1,512,222,580
Emp.: 77,824
Fiscal Year-end: 03/31/24
Automobiles, Materials Handling Equipment, Electronic Components & Textile Machinery Mfr
N.A.I.C.S.: 333248
Tetsuro Toyoda *(Chm)*

Subsidiaries:

ALT Logistics Co., Ltd. (1)
8 Chaya Kyowa-cho, Obu, 474-0057, Aichi, Japan
Tel.: (81) 562 48 9891
Logistics Consulting Servies
N.A.I.C.S.: 541614

Advanced Logistics Solutions Co., Ltd. (1)
Toyota Shokki Takahama Factory 2-1-1, Toyoda-cho, Takahama, 444-1304, Aichi, Japan (100%)
Tel.: (81) 566876420
Web Site: http://www.al-so.co.jp
Sales Range: $25-49.9 Million
Emp.: 94

TOYOTA INDUSTRIES CORPORATION

Toyota Industries Corporation—(Continued)
Logistics Planning & Operation of Distribution Centers
N.A.I.C.S.: 541614
Takashi Okubo (Pres)

Altex Co., Ltd. (1)
521 Nagashima, Hamakita-ku, Hamamatsu, 434-0013, Shizuoka, Japan
Tel.: (81) 535866116
Aluminum Die Casting Mfr & Distr
N.A.I.C.S.: 331523

Asahi Security Co., Ltd. (1)
2-4-2 Kaigan, Minato-ku, Tokyo, 105-0022, Japan (100%)
Tel.: (81) 354418383
Web Site: http://www.assjapan.co.jp
Sales Range: $300-349.9 Million
Emp.: 6,038
Secured Transportation Services
N.A.I.C.S.: 488999
Kenichi Yamaguchi (Sr Mng Dir)

ELETT CORPORATION (1)
Marunouchi Building 29F 2-4-1 Marunouchi, Chiyoda-ku, Tokyo, 100-6329, Japan
Tel.: (81) 3 5293 2550
Sales Range: $25-49.9 Million
Emp.: 14
Industrial Motor Mfr & Distr
N.A.I.C.S.: 333248

HANDA Casting Company (1)
4-1-8 Kawasaki-cho, Handa, 475-0832, Aichi, Japan
Tel.: (81) 569254711
Sales Range: $25-49.9 Million
Emp.: 58
Foundry Parts Mfr & Dsitr
N.A.I.C.S.: 331511
Hiroshi Suzuki (Pres)

Hakuai Nursing Villa Co., Ltd. (1)
95 North Exit Noda-cho, Kariya, 448-0803, Aichi, Japan
Tel.: (81) 566251600
Web Site: https://www.hakuai.co.jp
Home Care Nursing Services
N.A.I.C.S.: 623110

Hara Corporation (1)
1080 Yawata Ikeda-cho, Ibi-gun, Gifu, 503-2426, Japan
Tel.: (81) 585 45 0570
Sales Range: $50-74.9 Million
Emp.: 113
Textile Machinery Mfr & Distr
N.A.I.C.S.: 333248
Noriaki Miyamoto (Pres)

Haratechs Corporation (1)
1080 Yawata Ikeda-cho, Ibi-gun, Gifu, 503-2426, Japan
Tel.: (81) 585450570
Web Site: http://www.haratechs.co.jp
Emp.: 110
Textile Machinery Mfr
N.A.I.C.S.: 333248

IZUMI MACHINE MFG. CO., LTD. (1)
1-3 Shimizu Kitasaki-cho, Obu, 474-8510, Aichi, Japan
Tel.: (81) 562 47 3141
Web Site: http://www.en.izumi-mfg.co.jp
Sales Range: $200-249.9 Million
Emp.: 600
Machine Tools & Automotive Parts Mfr
N.A.I.C.S.: 336390
Kiyotsugu Kurimoto (Pres)

Iwama Loom Works, Ltd. (1)
56 Higashigomae Akita Oguchi-cho, Niwa-gun, Oguchi, 480-0132, Aichi, Japan
Tel.: (81) 587956011
Sales Range: $50-74.9 Million
Emp.: 135
Compressor Parts Mfr & Distr
N.A.I.C.S.: 333912

Kirloskar Toyoda Textile Machinery Pvt. Ltd. (1)
Plot 10 13 Phase II, Jigani Industrial Area, Bengaluru, 560 105, India (95.1%)
Tel.: (91) 8110419555
Web Site: http://kttm.toyota-industries.com
Sales Range: $200-249.9 Million
Emp.: 564

Spinning Frames & Automotive Parts Mfr & Sales; Industrial Equipment Sales
N.A.I.C.S.: 336390

Kirloskar Toyota Textile Machinery Pvt. Ltd. (1)
Plot No 10-13 Phase II Jigani Industrial Area, Bengaluru, 560 105, Karanataka, India
Tel.: (91) 8110419555
Web Site: https://kttm.toyota-industries.com
Textile Machinery Parts Mfr
N.A.I.C.S.: 333924

Miduho Industry Co., Ltd. (1)
6-1-109 MinamiTsumori, Nishinari-ku, Osaka, 557-0063, Aichi, Japan (100%)
Tel.: (81) 666584001
Web Site: http://www.mizuho-ind.co.jp
Emp.: 130
Industrial Equipment Mfr & Distr
N.A.I.C.S.: 333248

Nagao Kogyo Co., Ltd. (1)
1-63 Juichiya, Minato-ku, Nagoya, 455-0831, Aichi, Japan
Tel.: (81) 52 381 0913
Web Site: http://www.nagaokogyo.co.jp
Sales Range: $50-74.9 Million
Emp.: 136
Industrial Machinery Equipment Mfr & Distr
N.A.I.C.S.: 333248

Nishina Industrial Co., Ltd. (1)
1671 Asano Toyono-machi, Nagano, 389-1196, Japan
Tel.: (81) 26 257 6111
Web Site: http://www.nishina-ind.co.jp
Sales Range: $100-124.9 Million
Emp.: 353
Industrial Hydraulic Machinery Mfr & Distr
N.A.I.C.S.: 333248

Plant (Domestic):

Nishina Industrial Co., Ltd. - Suzaka Factory (2)
601-1 Aza-Kozasahara Oaza-Yonamochi, Suzaka, 382-0041, Nagano, Japan
Tel.: (81) 26 248 1172
Web Site: http://www.nishina-ind.co.jp
Industrial Hydraulic Machinery Mfr
N.A.I.C.S.: 333248

P.T. TD Automotive Compressor Indonesia (1)
Jl Kalimantan Blok E 1-2 Kw Industri MM 2100, Cikarang Barat, Bekasi, 17520, Jawa Barat, Indonesia
Tel.: (62) 21 8980303
Web Site: http://www.toyota-industries.com
Sales Range: $125-149.9 Million
Emp.: 304
Air Conditioning Compressors Mfr & Distr
N.A.I.C.S.: 333912

SKM CORPORATION (1)
3-3-9 Kumano-cho, Kariya, 448-0831, Aichi, Japan (100%)
Tel.: (81) 566 27 5233
Web Site: http://www.skm-t.co.jp
Emp.: 840
Real Estate Manangement Services
N.A.I.C.S.: 531390

Shine's Co., Ltd (1)
2-18 Toyocho, Kariya, 448-0842, Aichi, Japan
Tel.: (81) 566243348
Sales Range: $10-24.9 Million
Emp.: 80
Restaurant Management Services
N.A.I.C.S.: 722511
Toshihiko Ishikawa (Pres)

Sugiyama Industries Co., Ltd. (1)
Oyabu 2627-1 Wanouchicho, Anpachigun, Gifu, 503-0202, Gifu Pref, Japan
Tel.: (81) 584765892
Web Site: http://sugiyama-c.co.jp
Industrial Equipment Mfr
N.A.I.C.S.: 333248

Sun River Co., Ltd. (1)
13-14 Yoshino-cho, Suita, 564-0054, Osaka, Japan
Tel.: (81) 6 6384 4314
Web Site: http://www.amenity-esaka.com
Sales Range: $50-74.9 Million
Emp.: 60
Sports Facilities Management Services

N.A.I.C.S.: 713940

Sun Staff, Inc. (1)
1-95 Wakamatsucho Meitetsu Kariya Building 3F 5F, Kariya, 448-0858, Aichi, Japan
Tel.: (81) 566240039
Web Site: http://www.sunstaff.co.jp
Sales Range: $10-24.9 Million
Emp.: 729
Human Resource Consulting Services
N.A.I.C.S.: 541612
Kyoichi Maruyama (Pres)

Sun Valley Inc. (1)
SKm Bldg 3F 4-15 Hirokoji, Kariya, 448-0844, Aichi, Japan
Tel.: (81) 566252211
Sales Range: $50-74.9 Million
Emp.: 66
Tube Amplifiers Distr
N.A.I.C.S.: 423830

TD Automotive Compressor Kunshan Co., Ltd. (1)
412 San Xiang Road Kunshan Economic & Technical Development Zone, Kunshan, Jiangsu, China (59.8%)
Tel.: (86) 51257630770
Web Site: http://www.toyota-industries.com
Sales Range: $25-49.9 Million
Emp.: 82
Car Air-Conditioning Compressors Mfr & Sales
N.A.I.C.S.: 336390
Shinji Matsuura (Pres)

TOYOTA L&F Akita Co., Ltd. (1)
2-1-18 Goshonoyumoto, Akita, 010-1415, Japan
Tel.: (81) 18 826 0800
Web Site: http://www.lf-akita.com
Emp.: 32
Industrial Equipment Distr & Leasing Services
N.A.I.C.S.: 423830

TOYOTA L&F Hyogo Co., Ltd (1)
27-9 Uozakihamamachi, Higashinada-ku, Kobe, 658-0024, Hyogo, Japan
Tel.: (81) 784118887
Sales Range: $75-99.9 Million
Emp.: 221
Industrial Equipment Sales & Leasing Services
N.A.I.C.S.: 423830

TOYOTA L&F Shizuoka Co., Ltd. (1)
9-12 Hijicho, Aoi-ku, Shizuoka, 420-0837, Japan
Tel.: (81) 54 251 0333
Web Site: https://toyota-lf-shizuoka.jp
Emp.: 301
Material Handling System Distr & Leasing Services
N.A.I.C.S.: 423830
Nobuyoshi Egashira (Pres)

TOYOTA L&F Tokyo Co., Ltd. (1)
3-7-6 Higashi-Shinagawa, Shinagawa-ku, Tokyo, 140-0002, Japan
Tel.: (81) 334725221
Web Site: http://www.toyota-lf-tokyo.co.jp
Sales Range: $200-249.9 Million
Emp.: 312
Material Handling System Distr & Leasing Services
N.A.I.C.S.: 532490

TOYOTA MATERIAL HANDLING TAIWAN LTD. (1)
2nd Floor No 158 Section 2 Zhonghua Road, Tucheng District, New Taipei City, Taiwan
Tel.: (886) 222688266
Web Site: http://www.toyota-lf.com.tw
Industrial Equipment Distr
N.A.I.C.S.: 423830

Taikoh Transportation Co., Ltd. (1)
2-38 Shinsakaemachi, Kariya, 448-0843, Aichi, Japan
Tel.: (81) 566 21 3416
Web Site: http://www.taikoh.co.jp
Sales Range: $550-599.9 Million
Emp.: 1,625
Warehousing & Distribution Consulting Services
N.A.I.C.S.: 484122
Yutaka Murodono (Pres)

Takeuchi Industrial Equipment Manufacturing Co., Ltd. (1)

INTERNATIONAL PUBLIC

1-25 Nakada Fuki Oaza, Taketoyo-cho, Chita, 470-2531, Aichi, Japan
Tel.: (81) 569727172
Web Site: http://www.takeuchitekkou.co.jp
Emp.: 60
Fork Mfr
N.A.I.C.S.: 339992

Tokaiseiki Co., Ltd. (1)
2830 Nakaizumi, Iwata, 438-0078, Shizuoka, Japan
Tel.: (81) 538322126
Web Site: http://www.toukai-seiki.co.jp
Emp.: 496
Aluminum Die Casting Products & Engine Parts Mfr
N.A.I.C.S.: 331523
Satoshi Kaseda (Pres)

Tokyu Co., Ltd. (1)
1-60 Yono Oguchi-cho, Niwa-gun, Oguchi, 480-0146, Aichi, Japan
Tel.: (81) 587 95 1211
Web Site: http://www.tokyu-jp.com
Sales Range: $125-149.9 Million
Emp.: 380
Industrial Machinery Mfr & Distr
N.A.I.C.S.: 333248
Masafumi Kunito (Pres)

Toyoda High System, Incorporated (1)
Skm Bldg 2F 4-15 Hirokoji, Kariya, 448-0844, Aichi, Japan
Tel.: (81) 566 62 8700
Web Site: http://www.ths.co.jp
Sales Range: $25-49.9 Million
Emp.: 180
Software Development Services
N.A.I.C.S.: 541511

Toyota Advance Logistics North America (1)
10585 N Meridian St, Indianapolis, IN 46290 (100%)
Tel.: (317) 324-4767
Web Site: http://www.toyota-logistics.com
End-to-End Supply Chain & Logistics Consulting Services
N.A.I.C.S.: 541614
Troy Donnelly (VP-Integration)

Subsidiary (Domestic):

Bastian Solutions, LLC (2)
10585 N Meridian St 3rd Floor, Indianapolis, IN 46290 (100%)
Tel.: (317) 575-9992
Web Site: http://www.bastiansolutions.com
Material Handling Machinery Mfr
N.A.I.C.S.: 333310
Aaron Jones (Pres)

Subsidiary (Non-US):

Bastian Solutions India Pvt. Ltd. (3)
#1329 13th Cross 2nd Stage Indiranagar, Bengaluru, 560 038, India
Tel.: (91) 7353 777262
Web Site: http://www.bastiansolutions.com
System Integration for Industrial Automation & Material Handling Solutions
N.A.I.C.S.: 541420
Manoj Daniel (Project Coord)

Toyota Industrial Equipment Vietnam Co., Ltd. (1)
A1-A2 Thang Long Industrial Park II, Yen My, Hung Yen, Vietnam
Tel.: (84) 3213974664
Lift Truck Parts & Warehouse Equipment Mfr
N.A.I.C.S.: 333248

Toyota Industries Corporation - Anjo Plant (1)
201 Nishiishitani, Nesaki-cho, Anjo, 444-1295, Aichi, Japan
Tel.: (81) 566732411
Sales Range: $50-74.9 Million
Emp.: 584
Electric Equipment Mfr
N.A.I.C.S.: 334419

Toyota Industries Corporation - Hekinan Plant (1)
3 Hama-machi, Hekinan, 447-8507, Aichi, Japan
Tel.: (81) 566483111
Web Site: http://www.toyota-industries.com

AND PRIVATE COMPANIES — TOYOTA INDUSTRIES CORPORATION

Sales Range: $400-449.9 Million
Emp.: 1,885
Automobile Engine & Industrial Equipment Mfr
N.A.I.C.S.: 333618

Toyota Industries Corporation - Higashichita Plant (1)
4-15 Nittou-cho, Handa, 475-0033, Aichi, Japan
Tel.: (81) 569265500
Sales Range: $400-449.9 Million
Emp.: 1,269
Foundry Parts & Engines Mfr
N.A.I.C.S.: 333248

Toyota Industries Corporation - Higashiura Plant (1)
1-1 Shimomeotosaka Ogawa, Higashiura-cho Chita-gun, Higashiura, 470-2102, Aichi, Japan
Tel.: (81) 562850601
Web Site: http://www.toyota-industries.com
Sales Range: $50-74.9 Million
Emp.: 209
Car Air Conditioning Compressor Mfr
N.A.I.C.S.: 336390

Toyota Industries Corporation - Kyowa Plant (1)
8 Chaya Kyowa-machi, Obu, 474-8601, Aichi, Japan
Tel.: (81) 562461115
Web Site: http://www.toyota-industries.com
Sales Range: $400-449.9 Million
Emp.: 1,614
Automotive Electronic Parts Mfr
N.A.I.C.S.: 336390

Toyota Industries Corporation - Morioka Works (1)
60-1 Sakaekita Morioka, Higashiura-cho, Chita, 470-2101, Aichi, Japan
Tel.: (81) 562822302
Sales Range: $25-49.9 Million
Emp.: 31
Automobile Parts Mfr
N.A.I.C.S.: 336390

Toyota Industries Corporation - Nagakusa Plant (1)
9-2 Yamaguchi Nagakusa-machi, Obu, 474-8686, Aichi, Japan
Tel.: (81) 562463113
Web Site: http://www.toyota-industries.com
Sales Range: $800-899.9 Million
Emp.: 2,874
Automobile Parts Mfr
N.A.I.C.S.: 336390

Toyota Industries Corporation - Obu Plant (1)
1-1 Ebata-cho, Obu, 474-8668, Aichi, Japan
Tel.: (81) 562461215
Sales Range: $200-249.9 Million
Emp.: 765
Air Condition Compressor Mfr
N.A.I.C.S.: 333912

Toyota Industries Corporation - Takahama Plant (1)
2-1-1 Toyoda-cho, Takahama, 444-1393, Aichi, Japan
Tel.: (81) 566537007
Sales Range: $400-449.9 Million
Emp.: 2,373
Industrial Equipment Mfr
N.A.I.C.S.: 333248

Toyota Industries Engine India Pvt Ltd. (1)
Plot No 9 Phase II, Jigani Industrial Area Jigani, Bengaluru, 560 105, Karnataka, India
Tel.: (91) 811 042 4000
Web Site: https://tiei.toyota-industries.com
Diesel Engine Mfr & Whslr
N.A.I.C.S.: 333618
Hiroshi Matsumoto *(Chm)*

Toyota Industries Europe AB (1)
30 Svarvargatan 8, 595 81, Mjolby, Sweden (100%)
Tel.: (46) 14286100
Web Site: http://www.toyota.com
Sales Range: $550-599.9 Million
Emp.: 2,000
Holding Company
N.A.I.C.S.: 551112

Subsidiary (Non-US):

TD Deutsche Klimakompressor GmbH (2)
Weissiger Strasse 6, 02994, Bernsdorf, Germany (65%)
Tel.: (49) 3572394300
Web Site: http://tddk.de
Sales Range: $75-99.9 Million
Emp.: 500
Car Air-Conditioning Compressor Mfr & Sales
N.A.I.C.S.: 336390

Toyota Anyagmozgatas Magyarorszag Kft.
Epitesz utca 28, 1116, Budapest, Hungary
Tel.: (36) 1 482 0900
Web Site: https://www.toyota-forklifts.hu
Emp.: 40
Industrial Equipment Distr
N.A.I.C.S.: 423830
Norbet Szabo *(Mgr-Mktg)*

Subsidiary (Domestic):

Toyota Industries Finance International AB (2)
Svarvargatan 8, 595 81, Mjolby, Sweden (100%)
Tel.: (46) 14286100
Web Site: http://www.toyota-forklifts.eu
Financial Services
N.A.I.C.S.: 561499

Toyota Industries Sweden AB (2)
Voltavagen 15, Bromma, 161 84, Sweden (100%)
Tel.: (46) 87044000
Web Site: http://www.toyota-forklifts.se
Sales Range: $500-549.9 Million
Emp.: 1,500
Holding Company
N.A.I.C.S.: 551112
Per Wass *(Pres)*

Toyota Material Handling Europe AB (2)
Svarvargatan 8, 595 35, Mjolby, Sweden (100%)
Tel.: (46) 1 428 6000
Web Site: https://www.toyota-forklifts.eu
Emp.: 1,700
Warehouse Equipment Mfr & Sales
N.A.I.C.S.: 333924
Matthias Fischer *(Pres & CEO)*

Subsidiary (Non-US):

BT France S.a.r.l (3)
Tour Ariane 5 place de la Pyramide, BP 22, La Defense, 92088, Paris, Cedex, France
Tel.: (33) 178412000
Web Site: https://www.globalservices.bt.com
Sales Range: $50-74.9 Million
Emp.: 150
Industrial Equipment Distr
N.A.I.C.S.: 423830
Protais Patrick *(Gen Dir)*

Subsidiary (Domestic):

BT Products AB (3)
Svarvargatan 8, 595 81, Mjolby, Sweden
Tel.: (46) 142 860 00
Sales Range: $50-74.9 Million
Forklift Truck Mfr
N.A.I.C.S.: 333924
Matthias Fischer *(Gen Mgr)*

Subsidiary (Non-US):

CESAB Carrelli Elevatori S.p.A. (3)
Via Persicetana Vecchia 10, 40132, Bologna, Italy (100%)
Tel.: (39) 051205411
Web Site: http://www.cesab-forklifts.com
Sales Range: $125-149.9 Million
Emp.: 393
Industrial Equipment Sales
N.A.I.C.S.: 423830
Andrea Stach *(Dir-Sls & Svcs-Europe)*

Toyota Carrelli Elevatori Italia S.r.l. (3)
Via del Tappezziere 3 ZI Roveri, 40138, Bologna, Italy (100%)
Tel.: (39) 0516027611

Sales Range: $25-49.9 Million
Emp.: 49
Industrial Equipment Sales
N.A.I.C.S.: 423830

Toyota Industrial Equipment Europe, S.A.R.L. (3)
ZAC de l'Aeropole, BP 30077, F-44152, Ancenis, France (100%)
Tel.: (33) 251145144
Web Site: http://www.toyota-tiee.com
Sales Range: $25-49.9 Million
Emp.: 300
Industrial Equipment Sales
N.A.I.C.S.: 423830
Philippe Mahe *(Pres)*

Toyota Industrial Equipment, S.A. (3)
ZAC de l'Aeropole, BP 30077, F-44152, Ancenis, France (80%)
Tel.: (33) 251145100
Web Site: http://www.toyota-tlee.com
Sales Range: $125-149.9 Million
Emp.: 488
Industrial Equipment Mfr & Sales
N.A.I.C.S.: 333248

Toyota Material Handling Austria GmbH (3)
Griesfeldstrasse 3, 2351, Wiener Neudorf, Austria (100%)
Tel.: (43) 505700
Web Site: http://toyota-forklifts.at
Sales Range: $25-49.9 Million
Emp.: 100
Industrial Equipment Sales
N.A.I.C.S.: 423830

Toyota Material Handling Belgium NV/SA (3)
Schoondonkweg 1, 2830, Willebroek, Belgium (100%)
Tel.: (32) 3 820 7600
Web Site: https://toyota-forklifts.be
Sales Range: $50-74.9 Million
Emp.: 180
Industrial Equipment Sales
N.A.I.C.S.: 423830
Van Espen *(Pres)*

Toyota Material Handling CZ s.r.o. (3)
K Vypichu 1049, 252 19, Rudna, Czech Republic
Tel.: (420) 311651111
Web Site: http://www.toyota-forklifts.cz
Sales Range: $50-74.9 Million
Emp.: 160
Forklift Truck Mfr
N.A.I.C.S.: 333924

Toyota Material Handling Danmark A/S (3)
Industrivej 3, 3550, Slangerup, Denmark (100%)
Tel.: (45) 7 022 0260
Web Site: https://toyota-forklifts.dk
Sales Range: $25-49.9 Million
Emp.: 47
Industrial Equipment Sales
N.A.I.C.S.: 423830
Claus Christensen *(Pres)*

Toyota Material Handling Deutschland GmbH (3)
Hannoversche Strasse 113, 30916, Isernhagen, Germany (100%)
Tel.: (49) 5 117 2620
Web Site: https://toyota-forklifts.de
Industrial Equipment Sales
N.A.I.C.S.: 423830
Matthias Fischer *(Pres)*

Toyota Material Handling Eesti AS (3)
Punane 73, 75301, Tallinn, Estonia (100%)
Tel.: (372) 606 6020
Web Site: http://www.toyota-forklifts.ee
Emp.: 18
Industrial Equipment Sales
N.A.I.C.S.: 423830
Hans Gehlen *(Pres)*

Toyota Material Handling Espana, S.A. (3)
Avenida Arrahona 25 Conjunto C Pol Ind Can Salvatella, 08210, Barbera del Valles, Spain (100%)

Tel.: (34) 90 242 0422
Web Site: https://www.toyota-forklifts.es
Sales Range: $50-74.9 Million
Emp.: 120
Industrial Equipment Sales
N.A.I.C.S.: 423830
Ernesto Dominguez *(Mng Dir)*

Toyota Material Handling Europe Brussels NV/SA (3)
Avenue du Bourget 42, 1130, Brussels, Belgium
Tel.: (32) 2 790 30 00
Web Site: http://www.toyota-forklifts.eu
Sales Range: $900-999.9 Million
Emp.: 40
Industrial Machinery Mfr & Distr
N.A.I.C.S.: 333248
Matthias Fischer *(Pres & CEO)*

Toyota Material Handling Europe, NV/SA (3)
Leopold Square Bourgetlaan 42, Brussels, 1130, Belgium (100%)
Tel.: (32) 27905000
Web Site: http://www.toyota-industries.eu
Sales Range: $25-49.9 Million
Emp.: 40
Business Support Services
N.A.I.C.S.: 561499
Lenaers Veronique *(Dir-HR)*

Toyota Material Handling Finland Oy (3)
Korpivaarantie 1, 01450, Vantaa, Finland (100%)
Tel.: (358) 1 057 5700
Web Site: https://toyota-forklifts.fi
Industrial Equipment Sales
N.A.I.C.S.: 423830
Pasey Nieminen *(Mng Dir)*

Toyota Material Handling Greece SA (3)
2nd Street Olympic Shooting Range, 19003, Markopoulo Mesogaias, Greece (100%)
Tel.: (30) 229 902 0200
Web Site: https://toyota-forklifts.gr
Sales Range: $25-49.9 Million
Emp.: 35
Industrial Equipment Sales
N.A.I.C.S.: 423830
Luk Smeets *(Gen Mgr)*

Toyota Material Handling Ireland (3)
Killeen Road, Dublin, D12 AW94, Ireland
Tel.: (353) 14190200
Web Site: http://www.toyota-forklifts.ie
Sales Range: $25-49.9 Million
Emp.: 75
Forklift Truck Mfr
N.A.I.C.S.: 333924

Toyota Material Handling Italia S.r.l. (3)
Via del Lavoro 93/1, 40033, Casalecchio di Reno, Bologna, Italy
Tel.: (39) 0800688776
Web Site: http://www.toyota-forklifts.it
Material Handling Equipment Distr
N.A.I.C.S.: 423830

Toyota Material Handling Latvija Ltd. (3)
11 Duntes Str, Riga, LV 1013, Latvia (100%)
Tel.: (371) 67364036
Web Site: http://www.toyota-forklifts.lv
Sales Range: $25-49.9 Million
Emp.: 100
Industrial Equipment Sales
N.A.I.C.S.: 423830
Hans Gehlen *(Pres)*

Toyota Material Handling Lietuva UAB (3)
Tignagu 10, Lt-02244, Vilnius, Lithuania (100%)
Tel.: (370) 70055095
Web Site: http://www.toyota-forklifts.lt
Industrial Equipment Sales
N.A.I.C.S.: 423830

Toyota Material Handling Nederland B.V. (3)
Stevinlaan 4, 6716 WB, Ede, Netherlands (100%)
Tel.: (31) 88 864 2000

TOYOTA INDUSTRIES CORPORATION — INTERNATIONAL PUBLIC

Toyota Industries Corporation—(Continued)
Web Site: https://toyota-forklifts.nl
Sales Range: $125-149.9 Million
Emp.: 320
Industrial Equipment Sales
N.A.I.C.S.: 423830
Pank Hertsenberg *(Pres)*

Toyota Material Handling Norway AS (3)
Haakon VIIs gt 23C, 7041, Trondheim, Norway **(100%)**
Tel.: (47) 73827300
Web Site: http://www.toyota-forklifts.no
Industrial Equipment Sales
N.A.I.C.S.: 423830
Tor Marius Dahl *(Pres)*

Toyota Material Handling Polska Sp. z o.o. (3)
ul Wiejska 4, 05-800, Pruszkow, Poland
Tel.: (48) 22 753 20 00
Web Site: http://www.toyota-forklifts.pl
Forklift Truck Mfr
N.A.I.C.S.: 333924

Toyota Material Handling Romania s.r.l. (3)
Soseaua Berceni no 104V sector 4, 041912, Bucharest, Romania
Tel.: (40) 73 058 4982
Web Site: https://www.toyota-forklifts.ro
Emp.: 18
Material Handling Equipment Mfr
N.A.I.C.S.: 333310
Daniel Preda *(Mng Dir)*

Toyota Material Handling Schweiz AG (3)
Feldstrasse 62, 8180, Bulach, Zurich, Switzerland
Tel.: (41) 844 869 682
Web Site: http://www.toyota-forklifts.ch
Emp.: 25
Construction Machinery Mfr
N.A.I.C.S.: 333120

Toyota Material Handling Slovensko s.r.o. (3)
Vajnorska 134/B, 831 04, Bratislava, Slovakia
Tel.: (421) 24 825 2520
Web Site: http://www.toyota-forklifts.sk
Industrial Equipment Whsr
N.A.I.C.S.: 423830
Lubos Imre *(Mng Dir)*

Subsidiary (Domestic):

Toyota Material Handling Sweden AB (3)
Hemvarngatan 9, 171 54, Solna, Sweden **(100%)**
Tel.: (46) 77 122 0220
Web Site: https://www.toyota-forklifts.se
Sales Range: $125-149.9 Million
Emp.: 500
Industrial Equipment Sales
N.A.I.C.S.: 423830
Per Wass *(Sr VP)*

Subsidiary (Non-US):

Toyota Material Handling UK Limited
Stirling Road Trading Estate, Slough, SL1 4SY, Berks, United Kingdom **(100%)**
Tel.: (44) 370 850 1409
Web Site: https://www.toyota-forklifts.co.uk
Sales Range: $25-49.9 Million
Emp.: 30
Industrial Equipment Sales
N.A.I.C.S.: 423830
Mike Mathias *(Mng Dir)*

Subsidiary (Non-US):

Toyota Textile Machinery Europe, AG (2)
Turbinenweg 5, 8610, Uster, Switzerland **(100%)**
Tel.: (41) 449433612
Web Site: http://www.ttm-europe.com
Sales Range: $25-49.9 Million
Emp.: 10
Textile Machinery Sales & Service
N.A.I.C.S.: 333248

Subsidiary (Domestic):

Uster Technologies AG (3)
Sonnenbergstrasse 10, 8610, Uster, Switzerland
Tel.: (41) 43 366 3636
Web Site: https://www.uster.com
Yarn Quality Measurement & Cotton Classing Instruments Development, Mfr & Sales
N.A.I.C.S.: 314999
Thomas Nasiou *(CEO)*

Subsidiary (Non-US):

Uster Technologies Ltd. (4)
Industrial Park Caesarea North Bareket 7, POB 3047, Caesarea, 3088900, Israel
Tel.: (972) 4 610 7600
Web Site: http://www.uster.com
Automatic Visual Inspection & Monitoring Systems for the Textile & Fabric Industries
N.A.I.C.S.: 334513
Ira Girel *(Coord-HR)*

Subsidiary (Domestic):

ScanMaster Systems, Ltd. (5)
5b Atir Yeda St Industrial Park, Kfar Saba, 4464305, Israel
Tel.: (972) 9 779 1990
Web Site: https://www.scanmaster-irt.com
Instrumentation, Automated Ultrasonic Inspection & Imaging Systems & Transducers Mfr
N.A.I.C.S.: 333310
Micha Kemelman *(VP-Sls)*

Subsidiary (US):

Uster Technologies Vision Systems Inc. (5)
319 Garlington Rd Ste B4, Greenville, SC 29615
Tel.: (864) 288-9777
Web Site: http://www.uster.com
Visual Inspection Instruments
N.A.I.C.S.: 334513

Subsidiary (Domestic):

Uster Technologies Ltd. (3)
Sonnenbergstrasse 10, 8610, Uster, Switzerland **(50.3%)**
Tel.: (41) 43 366 3636
Web Site: https://www.uster.com
Sales Range: $200-249.9 Million
Emp.: 498
Textile Quality Measurement & Certification Instrument Mfr
N.A.I.C.S.: 334519
Philip Mosimann *(Co-Chm)*

Subsidiary (Domestic):

Ruf Telematik AG (4)
Rutistrasse 13, 8952, Schlieren, Switzerland **(70%)**
Tel.: (41) 447338333
Web Site: http://www.ruf.ch
Sales Range: $25-49.9 Million
Emp.: 175
IT Solutions, Telematics & Multimedia Solutions
N.A.I.C.S.: 519290
Fred Engler *(CEO)*

Subsidiary (US):

Uster Technologies, Inc. (4)
319 Garlington Rd Ste B4, Greenville, SC 29615 **(100%)**
Tel.: (864) 288-9777
Web Site: http://www.uster.com
Sales Range: $25-49.9 Million
Emp.: 60
Mfr of Monitoring & Control Data Systems & Testing Instruments
N.A.I.C.S.: 334519
Galyon Mike *(Mgr-R&D)*

Unit (Domestic):

Uster Technologies, Inc. - Charlotte (5)
2748 Interstate St Ste B, Charlotte, NC 28208
Tel.: (704) 392-7421
Web Site: http://www.uster.com
Sales Range: $50-74.9 Million
Emp.: 12

Monitoring & Control Data Systems & Testing Instruments Mfr
N.A.I.C.S.: 334519
Alvin Ellison *(VP-Sls & Svcs)*

Toyota Industries IT Solutions Inc. (1)
1-72-1 Minamisakuramachi Albax Tower Kariya Ekimae Akariya, Kariya, 448-0841, Aichi, Japan
Tel.: (81) 566892291
Web Site: http://www.tiis.global
Emp.: 437
IT Infrastructure Construction Services
N.A.I.C.S.: 236220

Toyota Industries North America, Inc. (1)
25 NW Point Blvd Ste 925, Elk Grove Village, IL 60007 **(100%)**
Tel.: (847) 228-8462
Web Site: http://www.toyotaindustries.com
Sales Range: $25-49.9 Million
Emp.: 25
Holding Company
N.A.I.C.S.: 551112

Subsidiary (Domestic):

ACTIS Manufacturing, Ltd. LLC (2)
4051 Freeport Pkwy Bldg H Ste 400, Grapevine, TX 76051-2315 **(60%)**
Tel.: (972) 724-3600
Sales Range: $25-49.9 Million
Emp.: 40
Compressors Remanufacture & Sales
N.A.I.C.S.: 333912

Cascade Corporation (2)
2201 NE 201st Ave, Fairview, OR 97024-9718
Tel.: (503) 669-6300
Web Site: http://www.cascorp.com
Sales Range: $450-499.9 Million
Emp.: 1,005
Designer, Mfr & Marketer of Materials Handling Equipment & Related Technologies
N.A.I.C.S.: 333924
Richard S. Anderson *(CEO)*

Subsidiary (Domestic):

American Compaction Equipment, Inc. (3)
29380 Hunco Way, Lake Elsinore, CA 92530
Tel.: (949) 661-2921
Web Site: https://www.acewheels.com
Construction Machinery Mfr
N.A.I.C.S.: 333120
Mike Shoemaker *(Gen Mgr)*

Subsidiary (Non-US):

Booforge Steel AB (3)
PO Box 55, Karlskoga, 691 80, Sweden **(100%)**
Tel.: (46) 58682000
Web Site: http://www.scana.no
Sales Range: $50-74.9 Million
Emp.: 100
Hardware Mfr
N.A.I.C.S.: 332510

Holding (Non-US):

Cascade (Africa) Pty. Ltd. (3)
60A Steel Rd Spartan, PO Box 625, Isando, Kempton Park, 1600, South Africa **(100%)**
Tel.: (27) 119759240
Web Site: http://www.cascorp.com
Sales Range: Less than $1 Million
Emp.: 7
Sales & Marketing of Hydraulic Lift Truck Attachments
N.A.I.C.S.: 333924
Wendy Gerber *(Mng Dir)*

Subsidiary (Non-US):

Cascade (Australia) Pty. Ltd. (3)
36 Kiln Street, Darra, 4076, QLD, Australia
Tel.: (61) 733737300
Sales Range: $25-49.9 Million
Emp.: 6
Construction Machinery Mfr
N.A.I.C.S.: 333120

Holding (Non-US):

Cascade (Canada), Inc.-Mississauga (3)
5570 Timberlea Blvd, Mississauga, L4W 4M6, ON, Canada **(100%)**
Tel.: (905) 629-7777
Web Site: http://www.cascorp.com
Sales Range: $25-49.9 Million
Emp.: 60
Mfr & Sales of Hydraulic Lift Truck Attachments
N.A.I.C.S.: 333924

Cascade (Japan) Ltd. (3)
2-23 2-Chome Kukuchi Nishinomi, Amagasaki, 661-0978, Hyogo, Japan **(100%)**
Tel.: (81) 664209771
Web Site: http://www.cascadejapan.com
Sales Range: $10-24.9 Million
Emp.: 20
Sales & Marketing of Hydraulic Lift Truck Attachments
N.A.I.C.S.: 333924

Cascade (Korea) Ltd. (3)
140-35 Neungheo - daero 625 beon-gil Namdong Indus Park 121B-9L, Namdong-gu, Incheon, Gojan-dong, Korea (South) **(100%)**
Tel.: (82) 328212051
Web Site: http://www.cascorp.com
Sales Range: $1-9.9 Million
Emp.: 17
Designer, Manufacturer & Marketer of Materials Handling Equipment & Related Technologies
N.A.I.C.S.: 333924
Hoyoung Jang *(Gen Mgr)*

Cascade (U.K.) Ltd. (3)
3 Kelbrook Road, Parkhouse Industrial Estate, Manchester, M11 2DD, Openshaw, United Kingdom **(100%)**
Tel.: (44) 1614384020
Web Site: http://www.cascadeeurope.com
Sales Range: $10-24.9 Million
Emp.: 12
Hydraulic Cylinders & Rams Mfr
N.A.I.C.S.: 333995
Charlie Mitchelson *(Gen Mgr)*

Cascade Canada, Inc. (3)
RR 3 Nicholas Beaver Industrial Park Road, PO Box 1508, Guelph, N1H 6H9, ON, Canada **(100%)**
Tel.: (519) 763-3675
Web Site: http://www.cascade.com
Sales Range: $50-74.9 Million
Emp.: 150
Designer, Manufacturer & Marketer of Materials Handling Equipment & Related Technologies
N.A.I.C.S.: 333924
Vince Purzomato *(Gen Mgr)*

Cascade Europe N.V. (3)
Damsluisweg 56, PO Box 3009, 1300 EL, Almere, Netherlands **(100%)**
Tel.: (31) 365492950
Web Site: http://www.cascade.com
Sales Range: $50-74.9 Million
Emp.: 30
Hydraulic Lift Truck Attachments Mfr & Marketer
N.A.I.C.S.: 333924
Robert C. Warren Jr. *(Pres)*

Subsidiary (Non-US):

Cascade GmbH (3)
Max-Planck-Str 15b, 40699, Erkrath, Germany
Tel.: (49) 2115989550
Web Site: http://www.cascorp.com
Sales Range: $25-49.9 Million
Emp.: 2
Construction Machinery Mfr
N.A.I.C.S.: 333120

Cascade India Material Handling Private Limited (3)
Gat No 319/1 319/2 Village Kuruli, Taluka Khed, Pune, 410 501, Maharashtra, India
Tel.: (91) 7720025745
Construction Machinery Mfr
N.A.I.C.S.: 333120

Cascade Xiamen Forklift Truck Attachment Co., Ltd. (3)
No 668 Yangguang Rd, Xinyang Industrial Zone Haicang, Xiamen, 361026, Fujian, China
Tel.: (86) 5926512500

AND PRIVATE COMPANIES / TOYOTA MOTOR CORPORATION

Web Site: http://www.cascorp.com.cn
Fork Lift Trucks Mfr
N.A.I.C.S.: 333924

Subsidiary (Domestic):

Lift Technologies, Inc. (3)
7040 South Hwy 11, Westminster, SC 29693
Tel.: (864) 647-1119
Web Site: http://www.lift-tek.com
Industrial Machinery Mfr
N.A.I.C.S.: 333998

Subsidiary (Non-US):

Lift-Tek Elecar S.p.A. (3)
Via G Galilei, 29015, Castel San Giovanni, Piacenza, Italy
Tel.: (39) 052 373 6001
Web Site: https://www.lift-tekelecar.it
Emp.: 130
Industrial Machinery Mfr
N.A.I.C.S.: 333998
Marco Vignola (Mgr-Pur Dept)

Subsidiary (Domestic):

PSM, LLC (3)
21307 87th Ave SE, Woodinville, WA 98072
Tel.: (425) 486-1232
Web Site: https://www.psmcorp.com
Construction Machinery Mfr
N.A.I.C.S.: 333120

Subsidiary (Non-US):

G. N. Johnston Equipment Co., Ltd. (2)
5990 Avebury Road, Mississauga, L5R 3R2, ON, Canada
Tel.: (905) 712-6000
Web Site:
https://www.johnstonequipment.com
Emp.: 1,200
Industrial Equipment Distr
N.A.I.C.S.: 423830
Michael Marcotte (Pres & CEO)

Subsidiary (Domestic):

Hoist Material Handling, Inc. (2)
4407 Railroad Ave, East Chicago, IN 46312
Tel.: (708) 458-2200
Web Site: http://www.hoistlift.com
Heavy Duty Lift Trucks Mfr
N.A.I.C.S.: 333924
Marty Flaska (Founder)

Indiana Hydraulic Equipment Corp. (2)
2000 Commerce Pkwy, Franklin, IN 46131 (100%)
Tel.: (317) 736-2500
Sales Range: $25-49.9 Million
Emp.: 33
Hydraulic Control Valves Mfr & Sales
N.A.I.C.S.: 332911
Ryosuke Ushigome (Pres)

Subsidiary (Non-US):

Lift-Rite Inc. (2)
5975 Falbourne Street - Unit 3, Mississauga, L5R 3L8, ON, Canada
Tel.: (905) 507-2099
Web Site: https://www.liftrite.com
Sales Range: $25-49.9 Million
Emp.: 6
Hand Pallet Truck Machinery Mfr
N.A.I.C.S.: 333924

Subsidiary (Domestic):

Michigan Automotive Compressor, Inc. (2)
2400 N Dearing Rd, Parma, MI 49269 (60%)
Tel.: (517) 796-3200
Web Site: http://www.michauto.com
Car Air-Conditioning Compressors & Magnetic Clutches Mfr & Sales
N.A.I.C.S.: 336390
Masaharu Suzuki (Pres)

North Vernon Industry Corp. (2)
3750 4th St, North Vernon, IN 47265
Tel.: (812) 346-8772
Web Site: http://www.nvic-cwt.com
Forklift Counterweight Mfr & Distr
N.A.I.C.S.: 333924

Raymond-Muscatine Inc. (2)
3305 N Hwy 38, Muscatine, IA 52761-8801
Tel.: (563) 262-7700
Warehouse Equipment Mfr & Distr
N.A.I.C.S.: 332311

TD Automotive Compressor Georgia, LLC (2)
1000 Valentine Industrial Pkwy, Pendergrass, GA 30567 (65%)
Tel.: (706) 693-6000
Web Site: http://www.tacglink.com
Sales Range: $75-99.9 Million
Emp.: 303
Car Air-Conditioning Compressors Mfr & Sales
N.A.I.C.S.: 336390

The Raymond Corporation (2)
22 S Canal St, Greene, NY 13778-1202
Tel.: (607) 656-2311
Web Site: http://www.raymondcorp.com
Warehouse Equipment Mfr & Sales
N.A.I.C.S.: 333924
John F. Everts (VP-Fin)

Subsidiary (Domestic):

Associated Material Handling Industries Inc. (3)
133 N Swift Rd, Addison, IL 60101-1447
Tel.: (630) 588-8800
Web Site:
https://www.associated-solutions.com
Rev: $42,300,000
Emp.: 400
Industrial Machinery & Equipment
N.A.I.C.S.: 423830
Dale Lamaster (VP)

Subsidiary (Domestic):

Allied Handling Equipment Co (4)
3 Quest Dr Ste 206, Bloomington, IL 61705-8903
Tel.: (309) 691-7620
Web Site: http://www.associated-allied.net
Rev: $10,000,000
Emp.: 17
Materials Handling Machinery
N.A.I.C.S.: 423830

Peach State Integrated Technologies Inc. (4)
3005 Business Park Dr, Norcross, GA 30071
Tel.: (678) 327-2000
Web Site: http://www.peachstate.com
Emp.: 35
Logistics Management Services
N.A.I.C.S.: 541614
Jeff Boudreau (Global Dir-Retail & Consumer Products)

Stoffel Equipment Company, Inc. (4)
7764 N 81st St, Milwaukee, WI 53223
Web Site: http://www.stoffelequip.com
Commercial, Industrial Machinery & Equipment Repair & Maintenance
N.A.I.C.S.: 811310
Ross Martin (Acct Mgr)

Subsidiary (Non-US):

G.N. Johnston Equipment Co., Ltd. (3)
5990 Avebury Road, Mississauga, L5R 3R2, ON, Canada (100%)
Tel.: (905) 712-6000
Web Site:
http://www.johnstonequipment.com
Sales Range: $125-149.9 Million
Emp.: 1,200
Industrial Equipment Sales
N.A.I.C.S.: 423830

Subsidiary (Domestic):

Toyoda Textile Machinery, Inc. (2)
8300 Arrowridge Blvd, Charlotte, NC 28273 (100%)
Tel.: (704) 527-5400
Web Site:
https://www.toyotatextilemachinery.com
Emp.: 15
Textile Machinery Sales & Service
N.A.I.C.S.: 333248
Noriharu Teraoka (Pres)

Toyota Industrial Equipment Mfg., Inc. (2)
5555 Inwood Dr, Columbus, IN 47202 (100%)
Tel.: (812) 342-0060
Sales Range: $50-74.9 Million
Industrial Equipment & Spare Parts Mfr
N.A.I.C.S.: 333924

Toyota Industries Personnel Service of America, Inc. (2)
25 Northwest Point Blvd Ste 925, Elk Grove Village, IL 60007 (100%)
Tel.: (847) 228-3118
Personnel Placement Services
N.A.I.C.S.: 561311

Toyota Material Handling, U.S.A., Inc. (2)
1 Park Plz Ste 1000, Irvine, CA 92614 (100%)
Tel.: (949) 474-1135
Web Site: http://www.toyotaforklift.com
Industrial Equipment Sales
N.A.I.C.S.: 423830
Bret Bruin (VP-Aftermarket Ops)

Toyota Industries Well Support Corporation (1)
2-1 Toyoda-cho, Kariya, 448-8671, Aichi, Japan
Tel.: (81) 566275137
Sales Range: $100-124.9 Million
Emp.: 140
Administrative Processing Services
N.A.I.C.S.: 524292

Toyota L&F Fukui Co., Ltd. (1)
38-10 Imaichicho, Fukui, 918-8152, Japan
Tel.: (81) 776380018
Web Site: http://www.toyota-lf-fukui.co.jp
Emp.: 51
Logistic Services
N.A.I.C.S.: 541330

Toyota L&F Kinki Co., Ltd. (1)
1-1-51 Nishikujo, Konohana-ku, Osaka, 554-0012, Japan
Tel.: (81) 664625301
Web Site: http://www.toyota-lf-kinki.co.jp
Emp.: 532
Industrial Vehicle Repair Services
N.A.I.C.S.: 811198

Toyota Maquinas Texteis Brasil Ltda (1)
Avenida Ibirapuera 2907 Conj 117-120, Moema, 04029-200, Sao Paulo, Brazil (100%)
Tel.: (55) 1150539912
Web Site: http://www.toyota-industries.com
Sales Range: $25-49.9 Million
Emp.: 12
Textile Machinery Sales & Service
N.A.I.C.S.: 333248
Markus Lichtenstein (Dir)

Toyota Material Handling (Shanghai) Co., Ltd. (1)
17F Metro Plaza No 555 Loushanguan Road, Shanghai, 200051, China (100%)
Tel.: (86) 2162287722
Web Site: http://www.toyota-forklift.cn
Lift Truck Sales
N.A.I.C.S.: 423830
Takanobu Watanabe (Mgr)

Toyota Material Handling Australia Pty Limited (1)
8 Secombe Place, Moorebank, 2170, NSW, Australia (100%)
Tel.: (61) 80 042 5438
Web Site:
https://www.toyotamaterialhandling.com
Sales Range: $50-74.9 Million
Emp.: 150
Industrial Equipment Sales
N.A.I.C.S.: 423830
Takashi Unnai (Pres)

Toyota Material Handling India Pvt. Ltd. (1)
43 Milestone Delhi- Jaipur Highway NH-8, Meharuli-Grugaon, Gurgaon, 122 004, Haryana, India
Tel.: (91) 1243877100
Web Site:
https://www.toyotamaterialhandling.com
Sales Range: $25-49.9 Million
Emp.: 15
Industrial Equipment Distr
N.A.I.C.S.: 423830

Toyota Material Handling Mercosur Comercio de Equipamentos Ltda (1)
Estrada Particular Sadae Takagi 2235 - Ordinance 1, Sao Bernardo do Campo, 09852-070, SP, Brazil (100%)
Tel.: (55) 1135110400
Web Site:
https://www.toyotaempilhadeiras.com.br
Sales Range: $50-74.9 Million
Emp.: 100
Industrial Equipment Sales
N.A.I.C.S.: 423830
Hiroyuki Ogata (Pres)

Toyota Material Handling, Inc. (1)
5559 Inwood Dr, Columbus, IN 47201
Web Site: https://www.toyotaforklift.com
Forklift Mfr & Distr
N.A.I.C.S.: 333924

Toyota Textile Machinery (Shanghai) Co., Ltd. (1)
Room 1002 Want Want Plaza Jingan Qu No 211 Shimen Yi Road, Shanghai, 200041, China
Tel.: (86) 2163170992
Sales Range: $25-49.9 Million
Emp.: 41
Textile Machinery Parts Distr
N.A.I.C.S.: 423830

Unica Co., Ltd. (1)
170 Hasuike Nishitanaka, Kiyosu, 452-0933, Aichi, Japan
Tel.: (81) 524003811
Web Site: https://www.unica-co.com
Sales Range: $25-49.9 Million
Emp.: 54
House Transporter Mfr & Distr
N.A.I.C.S.: 336999

Vanderlande Industries Holding B.V. (1)
Vanderlandelaan 2, 5466 RB, Veghel, Netherlands
Tel.: (31) 41 349 4949
Web Site: https://www.vanderlande.com
Emp.: 9,000
Holding Company; Logistic Process Automation Systems Mfr
N.A.I.C.S.: 551112
Remo Brunschwiler (Chm-Mgmt Bd & CEO)

Subsidiary (Domestic):

Vanderlande Industries B.V. (2)
Vanderlandelaan 2, 5466 RB, Veghel, Netherlands
Tel.: (31) 413 49 49 49
Web Site: http://www.vanderlande.com
Sales Range: $1-4.9 Billion
Emp.: 5,500
Logistic Process Automation Systems Designer, Mfr, Whslr & Installer
N.A.I.C.S.: 334513
Remo Brunschwiler (CEO)

Subsidiary (US):

Vanderlande Industries Inc. (3)
1975 W Oak Cir, Marietta, GA 30062
Tel.: (770) 250-2800
Web Site: http://www.vanderlande.com
Logistic Process Automation Systems Sales & Installation Services
N.A.I.C.S.: 423830
Nick Porter (Pres)

Wanbishi Archives Co., Ltd. (1)
4-1-28 Toranomon, Minato-ku, Tokyo, 105-0001, Japan
Tel.: (81) 354255100
Web Site: https://www.wanbishi.co.jp
Sales Range: $150-199.9 Million
Emp.: 819
Information Management & Life & Property Insurance Services
N.A.I.C.S.: 519290
Hideaki Tabuchi (Pres)

TOYOTA MOTOR CORPORATION

1 Toyota-Cho, Toyota, 471-8571, Aichi, Japan
Tel.: (81) 565282121
JP

TOYOTA MOTOR CORPORATION

Web Site: https://www.toyota-global.com
Year Founded: 1937
TM—(NYSE)
Rev.: $280,530,801,573
Assets: $560,586,617,129
Liabilities: $341,368,333,725
Net Worth: $219,218,283,404
Earnings: $31,548,498,614
Emp.: 380,793
Fiscal Year-end: 03/31/24
Automotive Products, Industrial Vehicles, Parts, Lubricants & Appliances Mfr & Whslr
N.A.I.C.S.: 336210
Takeshi Uchiyamada *(Chm)*

Subsidiaries:

Aisin Corporation (1)
2-1 Asahi-machi, Kariya, 448-8650, Aichi, Japan
Tel.: (81) 566248441
Web Site: https://www.aisin.com
Automotive Parts Mfr & Distr
N.A.I.C.S.: 336390

Bauda A/S (1)
Carbell Gaten 6, PO Box 54, 0508, Oslo, Okern, Norway (40%)
Tel.: (47) 22700200
Web Site: https://www.bauda.no
Sales Range: $50-74.9 Million
Emp.: 5
Motor Vehicle Whslr
N.A.I.C.S.: 423110
Henrik Baumann *(Chm)*

Daihatsu Motor Co., Ltd. (1)
1-1 Daihatsu-cho, Ikeda-shi, Osaka, 563-0044, Japan
Tel.: (81) 727518811
Web Site: https://www.daihatsu.com
Compact Automobile Mfr
N.A.I.C.S.: 336110
Sunao Matsubayashi *(Chm)*

Subsidiary (Domestic):

Akashi-Kikai Industry Co., Ltd. (2)
2337 Inami Inami-cho, Kako-gun, Hyogo, 675-1111, Japan
Tel.: (81) 794957901
Web Site: https://akasi-kk.co.jp
Sales Range: $350-399.9 Million
Emp.: 1,200
Automobile Parts Mfr
N.A.I.C.S.: 336390

Aoi Machine Industry Co., Ltd. (2)
1-7 Kosunacho, Konan, 520-3212, Aichi, Japan
Tel.: (81) 748758583
Sales Range: $200-249.9 Million
Emp.: 700
Automotive Parts & Equipment Mfr
N.A.I.C.S.: 336390

BUSINESS SUPPORT CENTER CO., Ltd. (2)
4-15-1 Nihombashihoncho Takako Bldg 5f, Chuo-ku, Tokyo, 103-0023, Japan
Tel.: (81) 368251160
Business Support Services
N.A.I.C.S.: 561499
Shin Kimura *(Pres)*

Subsidiary (Non-US):

DAIHATSU DE GUATEMALA, S.A. (2)
10a Avenida 31-71 Zona 5, Guatemala, Guatemala
Tel.: (502) 2204 0451
Web Site: http://www.daihatsu.com
New Car Dealers
N.A.I.C.S.: 441110

DAIHATSU DE NICARAGUA, S.A. (2)
Kilometro Tres Y Medio Carretera Sur Apartado 1595, Managua, Nicaragua
Tel.: (505) 22666455
Web Site: http://www.autonica.com
Emp.: 35
Automobile Parts Mfr

DAIHATSU IRELAND LTD. (2)
Clonlara Avenue Baldonnell Business Park, Baldonnell, Dublin, 22, Ireland
Tel.: (353) 14698700
Sales Range: $25-49.9 Million
Emp.: 5
Car Dealer
N.A.I.C.S.: 441110
Tommy Smith *(Gen Mgr)*

Daihatsu (UK) Ltd. (2)
Ryder St, West Bromwich, B70 7EJ, United Kingdom (100%)
Tel.: (44) 1215205000
Web Site: http://www.daihatsu.co.uk
Sales Range: $75-99.9 Million
Emp.: 300
Importers of Automobiles
N.A.I.C.S.: 441110

Daihatsu Australia Pty. Ltd. (2)
Unit 6002 Bayside Plaza 380 Bay St, Brighton-Le-Sands, Sydney, 2229, Australia
Tel.: (61) 295344999
Sales Range: $50-74.9 Million
Emp.: 130
Automobiles & Automotive Parts Distr
N.A.I.C.S.: 423110

Daihatsu Belgium S.A. (2)
Hermesstraat 8C, 1930, Zaventem, Belgium
Tel.: (32) 27197010
Web Site: http://www.daihatsu.be
Sales Range: $25-49.9 Million
Emp.: 3
Automobiles & Automotive Parts Distr
N.A.I.C.S.: 441227

Joint Venture (Domestic):

Daihatsu Briggs & Stratton Co., Ltd. (2)
722 Kagami Ryuo Cho, Shiga, 520 2573, Japan
Tel.: (81) 748582151
Sales Range: $50-74.9 Million
Emp.: 92
Overhead Valve Engines Mfr
N.A.I.C.S.: 336412

Subsidiary (Domestic):

Daihatsu Credit Co., Ltd. (2)
1-1 Daihatsu-cho, Ikeda, 563-0044, Osaka, Japan
Tel.: (81) 727544061
Credit Card Services
N.A.I.C.S.: 522320

Daihatsu Diesel Mfg. Co., Ltd. (2)
1-30 Oyodo Naka 1-Chome, Kita-ku, Osaka, 531-0076, Japan (51%)
Tel.: (81) 664542331
Web Site: https://www.dhtd.co.jp
Rev.: $540,532,750
Assets: $670,439,080
Liabilities: $334,366,850
Net Worth: $336,072,230
Earnings: $34,034,890
Emp.: 833
Fiscal Year-end: 03/31/2024
Marine Diesel & Auxiliary Ship Engine Mfr
N.A.I.C.S.: 333618
Shigeki Kinoshita *(Chm)*

Subsidiary (US):

Daihatsu Diesel (America) Inc. (3)
380 N Broadway Ste 302, Jericho, NY 11753
Tel.: (516) 822-3483
Web Site: http://www.dhtd.co.jp
Sales Range: $50-74.9 Million
Emp.: 4
Diesel Engines & Parts Whslr
N.A.I.C.S.: 423830

Subsidiary (Non-US):

Daihatsu Diesel (Europe) Ltd. (3)
Floor28 One Canada Square Canary Wharf, London, E14 5AA, United Kingdom
Tel.: (44) 2045665600
Sales Range: $25-49.9 Million
Emp.: 12
Internal Combustion Engines Mfr
N.A.I.C.S.: 333998

Subsidiary (Non-US):

Daihatsu France S.A.S. (2)
PA des Bethunes 1 avenue du Fief, BP 80520, Cergy Pontoise, 95005, Saint-Ouen-l'Aumone, Cedex, France
Tel.: (33) 134306363
Web Site: https://www.daihatsu.fr
New Car Dealers
N.A.I.C.S.: 441110

Daihatsu Holland B.V. (2)
Steurweg 8, Raamsdonksveer, 4941VR, Netherlands (35%)
Tel.: (31) 347750500
Web Site: http://www.daihatsu.nl
Sales Range: $25-49.9 Million
Emp.: 3
Automobile Importer & Distr
N.A.I.C.S.: 423110

Subsidiary (Domestic):

Daihatsu Metal Co., Ltd. (2)
2-1-13 HigashiKushiro, Kawanishi, 666-0023, Hyogo, Japan
Tel.: (81) 727591215
Web Site: https://www.d-metal.co.jp
Sales Range: $200-249.9 Million
Emp.: 851
Casting & Machine Tool Parts Mfr
N.A.I.C.S.: 331523

Plant (Domestic):

Daihatsu Motor Co., Ltd. - Kyoto Plant
1 Koaza Kitahosoike Aza Shimoueno Oyamazaki-cho, Otokuni-gun, Kyoto, 618-0081, Japan
Tel.: (81) 759561141
Sales Range: $350-399.9 Million
Emp.: 1,062
Automobile Parts Mfr
N.A.I.C.S.: 336390

Subsidiary (Domestic):

Daihatsu Motor Kyushu Co., Ltd. (2)
1 Ooaza-Showashinden, Nakatsu, 879-0107, Oita, Japan
Tel.: (81) 979331230
Web Site: http://www.daihatsu-kyushu.co.jp
Sales Range: $350-399.9 Million
Emp.: 340
Automotive Truck Mfr
N.A.I.C.S.: 336390

KANBISHI Corporation (2)
6 Takumidai, Ono, 675-1322, Hyogo, Japan
Tel.: (81) 794631800
Web Site: https://www.kanbishi.co.jp
Automotive Die Casting Parts Mfr
N.A.I.C.S.: 336390

Subsidiary (Non-US):

P.T. Astra Daihatsu Motor (2)
Jl Gaya Motor III/5, PO Box 2126, Sunter II, Jakarta, 14330, Indonesia (100%)
Tel.: (62) 1500898
Web Site: https://daihatsu.co.id
Sales Range: $150-199.9 Million
Emp.: 700
Motor Vehicle Metal Stamping
N.A.I.C.S.: 336370

Paifat Hong Ltd. (2)
Rm 4038 Asian House 1 Hennessy Road, Hong Kong, China (Hong Kong)
Tel.: (852) 25283038
Sales Range: $25-49.9 Million
Emp.: 3
Automotive Distr
N.A.I.C.S.: 423110
Fukhung Lau *(Mng Dir)*

TOYOTA GABON S.A. (2)
Industrial Zone of Oloumi, BP 31, Libreville, Gabon
Tel.: (241) 11792685
Web Site: https://toyota-gabon.com
Car Dealer
N.A.I.C.S.: 441110

TOYOTA MAURITANIE S.A. (2)
Ksar-Nord Industrial Zone Opposite the old airport, Route d'Akjoujt, Nouakchott, Mauritania
Tel.: (222) 45254730

INTERNATIONAL PUBLIC

Web Site: https://www.toyota-mauritanie.com
Car Dealer
N.A.I.C.S.: 441110

Delphys Inc. (1)
Waterasutawa 9F 2-101 Kanda Awajicho, Chiyoda-Ku, Tokyo, 101-8343, Japan (100%)
Tel.: (81) 367578200
Web Site: http://www.delphys.co.jp
Advetising Agency
N.A.I.C.S.: 541810
Takako Ueno *(Mng Dir)*

Hino Motors, Ltd. (1)
3-1-1 Hinodai Hino-shi, Tokyo, 191-8660, Japan (50.21%)
Tel.: (81) 425865488
Web Site: https://www.hino-global.com
Rev.: $10,018,200,036
Assets: $9,675,418,500
Liabilities: $6,613,509,876
Net Worth: $3,061,908,624
Earnings: $166,633,584
Emp.: 33,314
Fiscal Year-end: 03/31/2024
Medium & Heavy Duty Diesel Trucks, Buses & Light Commercial Vehicles Mfr
N.A.I.C.S.: 336211
Yoshio Shimo *(Chm)*

Subsidiary (Domestic):

Aomori Hino Motor Ltd. (2)
164-82 Nogiyamaguchi, Aomori, 030-0142, Japan
Tel.: (81) 177293800
Web Site: https://www.aomori-hino.co.jp
Emp.: 155
New Car Dealers
N.A.I.C.S.: 441110
Mikio Todate *(Gen Mgr)*

CJK Co., Ltd. (2)
1115-1 Teradake, Iruma, 358-0045, Saitama, Japan
Tel.: (81) 429363185
Automotive Distr
N.A.I.C.S.: 423110

Chiba Hino Motor Ltd. (2)
177 Shin-minato, Mihama-ku, Chiba, 261-0002, Japan
Tel.: (81) 43 241 6661
Web Site: http://www.hino-global.com
Automotive Truck Mfr
N.A.I.C.S.: 336212

Fukui Hino Motors Ltd. (2)
1-501 Owada, Fukui, 910-8579, Japan
Tel.: (81) 776540855
Web Site: https://www.fukui-hino.co.jp
Emp.: 54
Automotive Distr & Services
N.A.I.C.S.: 423110
Kato Mikihiro *(Pres)*

Fukushima Hino Motor Ltd. (2)
5-1 Hachida Sasagawa, Azumi-cho, Koriyama, 963-0102, Fukushima, Japan
Tel.: (81) 249451665
Web Site: https://www.fukushima-hino.co.jp
Emp.: 225
Automotive Distr
N.A.I.C.S.: 423110

Fukushima Steel Work Co., Ltd. (2)
8-1 Tenjikuta Sasakino, Fukushima, 960-8661, Japan
Tel.: (81) 245345161
Web Site: https://www.f-seiko.co.jp
Automotive Parts Mfr
N.A.I.C.S.: 336390

Higashi Hokkaido Hino Motor Ltd. (2)
1-7-6 Nishi 19 Kita, Obihiro, 080-2459, Hokkaido, Japan
Tel.: (81) 155334441
Web Site: https://www.hh-hino.co.jp
Emp.: 231
Automotive Distr
N.A.I.C.S.: 423110

Subsidiary (US):

Hino Diesel Trucks (U.S.A.), Inc.-New York (2)
25 Corporate Dr, Orangeburg, NY 10962-2615

AND PRIVATE COMPANIES — TOYOTA MOTOR CORPORATION

Tel.: (845) 365-1400
Web Site: http://www.hino.com
Sales Range: $25-49.9 Million
Emp.: 25
Trucks Marketer & Distr
N.A.I.C.S.: 423110

Subsidiary (Domestic):

Hino Engineering Annex, Ltd. (2)
689-1 Kamikayama, Hidaka, 350-1234, Saitama, Japan
Tel.: (81) 429859120
Web Site: https://www.hinoannex.com
Emp.: 124
Industrial Machinery Mfr
N.A.I.C.S.: 333248

Hino Hutech Co., Ltd. (2)
1-9-5 Hinodai, Hino, 191-0003, Tokyo, Japan
Tel.: (81) 425894355
Web Site: https://www.hinohutech.co.jp
Emp.: 859
Automobile Parts Mfr
N.A.I.C.S.: 336390

Hino Logistics and Packing, Ltd. (2)
1-5-1 Suehirocho, Ome, 198-0025, Tokyo, Japan
Tel.: (81) 428335101
Logistics Consulting Servies
N.A.I.C.S.: 541614

Subsidiary (Non-US):

Hino Motor Sales (Canada) Ltd. (2)
6975 Creditview Road Unit 2, Mississauga, L5N 8E9, ON, Canada **(100%)**
Tel.: (905) 670-3352
Web Site: http://www.hinocanada.com
Sales Range: $25-49.9 Million
Emp.: 45
Trucks & Parts Whslr
N.A.I.C.S.: 441330

Hino Motor Sales (Thailand) Limited (2)
212 Moo 4 Vibhavadi Rangsit Road, Talad Bang Khen Subdistrict Lak Si District, Bangkok, 10210, Thailand
Tel.: (66) 29005000
Web Site: http://www.hinothailand.com
Sales Range: $125-149.9 Million
Emp.: 500
Automobile Whslr
N.A.I.C.S.: 423110

Hino Motor Sales Australia Pty. Ltd. (2)
6-10 Parraweena Rd, PO Box 225, Caringbah, 2229, NSW, Australia **(100%)**
Tel.: (61) 300014466
Web Site: https://www.hino.com.au
Sales Range: $25-49.9 Million
Emp.: 75
Automobile Whslr
N.A.I.C.S.: 423110
Sam Suda *(Pres & CEO)*

Subsidiary (US):

Hino Motor Sales USA, Inc. (2)
45501 12 Mile Rd, Novi, MI 48377
Tel.: (248) 699-9300
Web Site: http://www.hino.com
Sales Range: $25-49.9 Million
Emp.: 4
Truck & Truck Part Distr
N.A.I.C.S.: 423120

Hino Motor Sales USA, Inc. (2)
41180 Bridge St, Novi, MI 48375
Tel.: (248) 699-9300
Web Site: http://www.hino.com
Sales Range: $25-49.9 Million
Emp.: 50
Motor Vehicle Parts Whslr
N.A.I.C.S.: 423110

Subsidiary (Non-US):

Hino Motors (China) Co., Ltd. (2)
Beijing Fortune Building 1609A No 5 Dong San Huan Bei Lu, Chao Yang District, Beijing, China
Tel.: (86) 10 6590 8858
Truck & Engine Distr
N.A.I.C.S.: 423120

Hino Motors (Europe) N.V. (2)
Blarenberglaan 19, 2800, Mechelen, Belgium
Tel.: (32) 15281740
Web Site: https://www.hino.be
Sales Range: $25-49.9 Million
Emp.: 25
Import & Sales of Auxiliary Parts for Vehicles
N.A.I.C.S.: 423120

Hino Motors (Malaysia) Sdn. Bhd. (2)
Lot PT 24 Jalan 223 Seksyen 51A, 46100, Petaling Jaya, Selangor, Malaysia
Tel.: (60) 379575199
Web Site: https://www.hino.com.my
Sales Range: $25-49.9 Million
Emp.: 80
Motor Vehicle Body Mfr
N.A.I.C.S.: 336211

Hino Motors Canada, Ltd. (2)
6975 Creditview Road Unit 2, Mississauga, L5N 8E9, ON, Canada
Tel.: (905) 670-3352
Web Site: http://www.hinocanada.com
Sales Range: $25-49.9 Million
Emp.: 35
Automobile Mfr
N.A.I.C.S.: 336110

Hino Motors Manufacturing Colombia, S.A. (2)
Parque Industrial Hipodromo Km 1 5, Cota, Colombia
Tel.: (57) 18773377
Truck Mfr & Distr
N.A.I.C.S.: 336110

Subsidiary (US):

Hino Motors Manufacturing USA, Inc. (2)
4550-A Wineville Rd, Mira Loma, CA 91752
Tel.: (951) 316-7416
Motor Vehicle Body Mfr
N.A.I.C.S.: 336211
Shigehiro Matsuoka *(Pres & CEO-Hino Trucks-North America)*

Subsidiary (Non-US):

Hino Motors Philippines Corporation (2)
Industrial Park Road Canlubang Industrial Estate, Canlubang, Calamba, 4027, Philippines **(70%)**
Tel.: (63) 273685800
Web Site: https://www.hino.com.ph
Motor Vehicle Body Mfr & Distr
N.A.I.C.S.: 336211

Hino Motors Sales (Thailand) Ltd. (2)
212 Moo 4 Vibhavadi Rangsit Road, Talad Bang Khen Subdistrict Lak Si District, Bangkok, 10210, Thailand
Tel.: (66) 29005000
Web Site: http://www.hinothailand.com
Sales Range: $75-99.9 Million
Emp.: 400
Automobile Mfr
N.A.I.C.S.: 336211

Affiliate (Non-US):

Hino Motors Vietnam, Ltd. (2)
Alley 83 Ngoc Hoi Str, Hoang Liet Hoang Mai, Hanoi, Vietnam
Tel.: (84) 2438616017
Web Site: https://hino.vn
Sales Range: $25-49.9 Million
Emp.: 195
Motor Vehicle Parts Mfr
N.A.I.C.S.: 336340

Subsidiary (Non-US):

Hino Motors de Venezuela, C.A. (2)
Av Don Eugenio Mendoza Edificio Iasa Piso 7 Oficina, 701B 702 y 703 La Castellana, Caracas, 1060, Venezuela
Tel.: (58) 2122673041
Web Site: http://www.hino-global.com
Emp.: 24
Truck Repair & Manintenance Services
N.A.I.C.S.: 811198

Plant (Domestic):

Hino Motors, Ltd. - Hamura Plant (2)
3-1-1 Midorigaoka, Hamura, 205-8660, Tokyo, Japan
Tel.: (81) 425790411
Web Site: http://www.hino-global.com
Automobile Mfr
N.A.I.C.S.: 336110

Hino Motors, Ltd. - Koga Plant (2)
1 Nasaki, Koga, 306-0110, Ibaraki, Japan
Tel.: (81) 280673500
Sales Range: $25-49.9 Million
Emp.: 150
Automobile Mfr
N.A.I.C.S.: 336110

Hino Motors, Ltd. - Nitta Plant (2)
10-1 Nitta, Hayakawa-cho, Ota, 370-0344, Gunma, Japan
Tel.: (81) 276565111
Automobile Mfr
N.A.I.C.S.: 336110

Subsidiary (Domestic):

Hino U-Truck & Engineering, Ltd. (2)
689-1 Kamikayama, Hidaka, 350-1234, Saitama, Japan
Tel.: (81) 429840662
Truck Sales & Maintenance Services
N.A.I.C.S.: 423110

Subsidiary (Non-US):

Hinopak Motors Limited (2)
D-2 SITE Manghopir Road, PO Box 10714, Karachi, 75700, Pakistan **(100%)**
Tel.: (92) 2132563510
Web Site: https://www.hinopak.com
Sales Range: $100-124.9 Million
Emp.: 300
Mfr, Assembler & Marketer of Diesel Trucks & Buses
N.A.I.C.S.: 336211
Muhammad Aslam Sanjrani *(Chm)*

Affiliate (Non-US):

Ho-Tai Motor Co. Ltd. (2)
8 Fl Bangkok Bldg 121 Sung Chiang Rd Chungshan Dist, Taipei, Taiwan
Tel.: (886) 225062121
Web Site: http://www.hotaimotor.com.tw
Sales Range: $350-399.9 Million
Emp.: 500
Motor Vehicle Body Mfr
N.A.I.C.S.: 336211
Justin Su *(Pres)*

Subsidiary (Domestic):

Hokkaido Hino Motor Ltd. (2)
2-3-2-15 Higashi Naebo, Higashi, Sapporo, 007-8507, Hokkaido, Japan
Tel.: (81) 117812121
Web Site: https://hokkaido-hino.co.jp
Emp.: 386
Truck & Parts Distr
N.A.I.C.S.: 423110

Kobe Hino Motor Ltd. (2)
5-11 West Koyo-cho, Higashinada-ku, Kobe, 658-0033, Hyogo, Japan
Tel.: (81) 788577111
Web Site: https://www.kobe-hino.co.jp
Sales Range: $350-399.9 Million
Emp.: 339
Automobile Mfr
N.A.I.C.S.: 336110
Hitoshi Matsuyama *(Gen Mgr)*

Kumamoto Hino Motor Ltd. (2)
3-2-115 Minamitakae, Minami Ward, Kumamoto, 861-4106, Kumamoto Prefecture, Japan
Tel.: (81) 963573111
Web Site: https://www.kumamoto-hino.co.jp
Emp.: 158
Commercial Vehicle Mfr
N.A.I.C.S.: 336110

Kyoto Hino Motor Ltd. (2)
37-1 Sayama Futakuri, Kuse-gun, Kyoto, 613-0034, Japan
Tel.: (81) 774465200
Web Site: https://www.kyoto-hino.co.jp
Emp.: 143
Automotive Repair & Maintenance Services
N.A.I.C.S.: 811198

Meiyu Kiko Co., Ltd. (2)
466 Shimojominamiwari Tatsuokamachi, Nirasaki, 407-0033, Yamanashi, Japan
Tel.: (81) 551224045
Web Site: http://www.hino-global.com
Bus Chassis Diesel Engines Mfr
N.A.I.C.S.: 561499

Nishi Tohoku Hino Motor Ltd. (2)
3553-1 Tatetanigawa 3-chome, Yamagata, 990-2251, Yamagata Prefecture, Japan
Tel.: (81) 236863001
Web Site: https://www.nisitouhoku-hino.co.jp
Emp.: 231
Automotive Distr
N.A.I.C.S.: 423110

Nissha Butsuryu Co., Ltd. (2)
1268-1 Matsumotomachi, Hakusan, 924-0057, Ishikawa, Japan
Tel.: (81) 762740050
Automobile Mfr
N.A.I.C.S.: 336110

Osaka Hino Motor Ltd. (2)
1-4-45 Chifune, Nishiyodogawa-ku, Osaka, 555-0013, Japan
Tel.: (81) 664741851
Web Site: https://www.osaka-hino.co.jp
Emp.: 503
Automotive Sales & Repair Services
N.A.I.C.S.: 423110

Subsidiary (Non-US):

P.T. Hino Motors Manufacturing (2)
Bukit Indah City Industrial Estate Jl Damar Blok D1 No 1, Purwakarta, 41181, West Java, Indonesia
Tel.: (62) 264351911
Web Site: https://www.hino.co.id
Sales Range: $75-99.9 Million
Emp.: 2,047
Motor Vehicle Body Mfr
N.A.I.C.S.: 336211

Subsidiary (Domestic):

Riken Forge Co., Ltd. (2)
395-3 Motosouja-cho, Maebashi, 371-0846, Gunma, Japan
Tel.: (81) 27 251 1831
Web Site: http://www.riken-forge.co.jp
Rev.: $201,443,800
Emp.: 263
Forging & Forging Die Mfr
N.A.I.C.S.: 332111
Hisao Ishibashi *(Pres)*

Serio Co., Ltd. (2)
5F Kinoshita Building 2-3-5 Horidomecho, Nihonbashi Chuo-ku, Tokyo, 103-0012, Japan
Tel.: (81) 362649758
Emp.: 15
Industrial Machinery Mfr
N.A.I.C.S.: 333248

Subsidiary (Non-US):

Shanghai Hino Engine Co., Ltd. (2)
No 179 Huancheng East Road South Bridge, Fengxian District, Shanghai, China
Tel.: (86) 2167108800
Web Site: https://www.shanghaihino.com
Automotive Engine Mfr
N.A.I.C.S.: 327910

Subsidiary (Domestic):

Shimane Hino Motor Ltd. (2)
881 Izumo-go, Higashi-Izumo-cho, Matsue, 699-0108, Shimane Prefecture, Japan
Tel.: (81) 852527231
Web Site: https://www.shimane-hino.jp
Emp.: 156
Automotive Truck Mfr
N.A.I.C.S.: 336212

Shizuoka Hino Motor Ltd. (2)
2-5-1 Kuniyoshida, Suruga-ku, Shizuoka, 422-8004, Shizuoka Prefecture, Japan
Tel.: (81) 542612900
Web Site: https://www.shizuoka-hino.co.jp
Emp.: 385
Automotive Electric Motor Mfr
N.A.I.C.S.: 336320

Sohshin Co., Ltd. (2)
1115-1 Teradake, Iruma, 358-0045, Saitama Prefecture, Japan
Tel.: (81) 429363161
Web Site: https://www.sohshin-global.com

TOYOTA MOTOR CORPORATION

INTERNATIONAL PUBLIC

Toyota Motor Corporation—(Continued)
Emp.: 714
Automobile Parts Mfr
N.A.I.C.S.: 336390

Takebe Tekkosho Co., Ltd. (2)
Midorigaoka 5-18-1, Atsugi, 243-0041, Kanagawa, Japan
Tel.: (81) 462215210
Web Site: https://www.takebe.co.jp
Emp.: 500
Truck Chassis Mfr
N.A.I.C.S.: 336214
Kazuaki Takebe (Pres & CEO)

Tokyo Hino Motor Ltd. (2)
18-1 Shinbashi 5-chome, Minato-ku, Tokyo, 105-0004, Japan
Tel.: (81) 3 3578 3955
Emp.: 800
Automotive Truck Mfr
N.A.I.C.S.: 336212
Hashimoto Shuithi (Office Mgr)

Trantechs, Ltd. (2)
670 Tokumaru-cho, Hakusan, 924-8580, Ishikawa, Japan
Tel.: (81) 762742816
Web Site: https://www.trantechs.co.jp
Emp.: 1,100
Automobile Parts Mfr
N.A.I.C.S.: 336211

Wakayama Hino Motor Ltd. (2)
10-1 Naka, Wakayama, 640-8451, Wakayama Prefecture, Japan
Tel.: (81) 734514180
Web Site: https://www.wakayama-hino.co.jp
Emp.: 87
Automobile Sales & Maintenance Services
N.A.I.C.S.: 423110

Yokohama Hino Motor Ltd. (2)
730-1 Nishitomi, Fujisawa, 251-0001, Kanagawa, Japan
Tel.: (81) 466 81 0135
Web Site: http://www.hino-global.com
Automotive Truck Distr
N.A.I.C.S.: 423110

Yoshizawa Ironworks Co., Ltd. (2)
2010 Enzan Koyashiki, Koshu, 404-0053, Yamanashi, Japan
Tel.: (81) 553336010
Steel Mfrs
N.A.I.C.S.: 331513

Indus Motor Company Limited (1)
Plot No N W Z/P-1 Port Qasim Authority, Karachi, Pakistan
Tel.: (92) 2134721100
Web Site: http://www.toyota-indus.com
Rev.: $1,710,890,881
Assets: $1,328,724,848
Liabilities: $993,316,066
Net Worth: $335,408,782
Earnings: $98,129,476
Emp.: 3,139
Fiscal Year-end: 06/30/2022
Automobile Mfr; Owned by Toyota Motor Corporation, by Toyota Tsusho Corporation & by House of Habib
N.A.I.C.S.: 336110
Ali S. Habib (Founder & Chm)

JTEKT Automotive Malaysia (1)
Lot 24 Jalan Delima 1/3 Subang Hi-Tech Industrial Park Batu Tiga, 40000, Shah Alam, Malaysia (60%)
Tel.: (60) 358296800
Sales Range: $100-124.9 Million
Emp.: 300
Automotive Parts Mfr & Whslr
N.A.I.C.S.: 336340

Kuozui Motors, Ltd. (1)
11F No 121 Sung Chiang Rd, Taipei, Taiwan (56.66%)
Tel.: (886) 225062875
Web Site: http://www.kuozui.com.tw
Sales Range: $400-449.9 Million
Emp.: 2,000
Automobile Mfr & Distr; Jointly Owned by Toyota Motor Corporation & Hinto Motors, Ltd.
N.A.I.C.S.: 336340

N.V. Toyota Motor Europe Marketing & Engineering S.A. (1)
Ave Du Bourgep 60, 1140, Brussels, Belgium (100%)
Tel.: (32) 27452111
Web Site: http://www.toyota.be
Sales Range: $350-399.9 Million
Emp.: 2,000
Automobile Testing, Research, Information Gathering, Automotive Design Research & CBU Vehicle Import & Sales
N.A.I.C.S.: 541380

Nippon Soken, Inc. (1)
500-20 Minamiyama, Komenoki-cho, Nisshin, 470-0111, Aichi, Japan
Tel.: (81) 561570400
Web Site: https://www.soken-labs.com
Emp.: 441
Vehicle Safety & Pollution Prevention; Owned 75% by Denso Corporation & 25% by Toyota Motor Corporation
N.A.I.C.S.: 541715
Kato Yoshifumi (Pres & CEO)

OOO TOYOTA MOTOR (1)
Mkad 84-I Km Tpz Altufevo Vladenie 5 Str 1, Mytishchi, Russia
Tel.: (7) 4952583465
Web Site: http://www.toyota.ru
Sales Range: $150-199.9 Million
Emp.: 30
Automotive Distr
N.A.I.C.S.: 423110
Takeshi Isogaya (Pres)

P.T. Toyota Motor Manufacturing Indonesia (1)
Jl Gaya Motor Raya Sunter II, Jakarta, 14330, Utara, Indonesia
Tel.: (62) 216511210
Web Site: https://www.toyota.co.id
Sales Range: $1-4.9 Billion
Emp.: 5,915
Automobile Mfr
N.A.I.C.S.: 336110

P.T. Toyota-Astra Motor (1)
Jalan Laks Yos Sudarso, Sunter II, Jakarta, 14330, Indonesia (49%)
Tel.: (62) 216515551
Web Site: https://www.toyota.astra.co.id
Sales Range: $1-4.9 Billion
Emp.: 5,314
CKD Unit Assembly & Sales & Production of Automotive Parts & Engines
N.A.I.C.S.: 441330

Siam Toyota Manufacturing Co., Ltd. (1)
700 109 111 113 Group 1 Amata Nakorn Industrial Estate, Chon Buri, 20160, Thailand
Tel.: (66) 38743313
Web Site: http://www.siamtoyota.co.th
Production & Sales of Engines; Owned by Toyota Motor Corporation & Cementhai Holding Co., Ltd.
N.A.I.C.S.: 336110

TOYOTA ALGERIE SPA (1)
Lotissement Muchacho N 2 High site of Hydra, Hydra, Algiers, 16405, Alger, Algeria
Tel.: (213) 21983000
Web Site: https://www.toyotaalgerie.com
Automobile Parts Mfr
N.A.I.C.S.: 336390

TOYOTA CHILE S.A. (1)
Avenida Americo Vespucio Norte 098, Pudahuel, Santiago, Chile
Tel.: (56) 800004300
Web Site: https://toyota.cl
Automobile Parts Mfr
N.A.I.C.S.: 336390

TOYOTA TANZANIA LIMITED (1)
5 Nyerere Rd, PO Box 9060, Dar es Salaam, Tanzania
Tel.: (255) 800750134
Web Site: https://toyota.co.tz
Automotive Distr
N.A.I.C.S.: 423110
Jatin Pandya (Dir-Sls)

Tianjin FAW Toyota Motor Co., Ltd. (1)
No 2 Liuli Road, Yangliuqing Village, Tianjin, 300380, Xiqing, China
Tel.: (86) 2227944050
Web Site: http://en.tjfaw.com
Motor Vehicles Mfr

N.A.I.C.S.: 336390

Towa Real Estate Co., Ltd. (1)
324-6 Nishinakashinden, Nakamura-Ku, Kurashiki, 710-0833, Okayama, Japan
Tel.: (81) 864368008
Web Site: https://www.towa-realestate.com
Real Estate Mangement Services
N.A.I.C.S.: 531390

Toyoda Boshoku Corporation (1)
1-1 Toyotacho, Kariya, 448-8651, Aichi, Japan (11.02%)
Tel.: (81) 566236611
Web Site: https://www.toyota-boshoku.com
Sales Range: $350-399.9 Million
Emp.: 44,581
Cotton Thread, Cotton Cloth, Auto Parts & Household Appliances Mfr & Whslr
N.A.I.C.S.: 313110
Shuhei Toyoda (Chm)

Toyota (GB) PLC (1)
Great Burgh, Burgh Heath, Epsom, KT18 5UX, Surrey, United Kingdom
Tel.: (44) 8708505533
Web Site: http://www.toyota.co.uk
Sales Range: $150-199.9 Million
Emp.: 400
Vehicle Import & Sales
N.A.I.C.S.: 423110
Chris Hayes (Dir-People & Plng)

Toyota Argentina S.A. (1)
Ruta 12 Km 81, B2800OFA, Zarate, Buenos Aires, Argentina (99%)
Tel.: (54) 3487443000
Web Site: https://www.toyota.com.ar
Sales Range: $200-249.9 Million
Emp.: 1,000
Automobile Mfr
N.A.I.C.S.: 336110

Toyota Auto Body Co., Ltd. (1)
100 Kanayama, Ichiriyamacho, Kariya, 448-8666, Aichi, Japan
Tel.: (81) 566362121
Web Site: http://www.toyota-body.co.jp
Emp.: 18,609
Auto & Special Vehicle Bodies & Parts Mfr
N.A.I.C.S.: 336110

Subsidiary (US):

Auto Parts Manufacturing Mississippi Inc. (2)
100 Tab Way, Guntown, MS 38849-8001
Tel.: (662) 365-3082
Web Site: https://www.apmmguntown.com
Emp.: 600
Automobile Parts Mfr
N.A.I.C.S.: 336390

Subsidiary (Non-US):

P.T.Toyota Auto Body-Tokai Extrusion (2)
Kawasan Industri Mm 2100 Blok LI-3, Bekasi, 17520, Indonesia
Tel.: (62) 218980357
Rubber & Plastic Extruded Products Mfr
N.A.I.C.S.: 326291

Plant (Domestic):

Toyota Auto Body Co., Ltd. - Inabe Plant (2)
10 Ichinohara, Inabe, 511-0201, Mie, Japan
Tel.: (81) 594745250
Automotive Stamping & Plastic Products Mfr
N.A.I.C.S.: 336370

Toyota Auto Body Co., Ltd. - Kariya Plant (2)
2-1 Showa-cho, Kariya, 448-0029, Aichi, Japan
Tel.: (81) 566225311
Web Site: http://www.toyota-body.co.jp
Automotive Truck Mfr
N.A.I.C.S.: 336212

Toyota Auto Body Co., Ltd. - Yoshiwara Plant (2)
25 Kamihujiike, Yoshiwara-cho, Toyota, 473-8512, Aichi, Japan
Tel.: (81) 565512104
Automobile Mfr
N.A.I.C.S.: 336110

Toyota Canada, Inc. (1)
1 Toyota Place, Toronto, M1H 1H9, ON, Canada
Tel.: (416) 438-6320
Web Site: https://www.toyota.ca
Sales Range: $250-299.9 Million
Emp.: 575
CBU Vehicle Import & Sales; Joint Venture of Mitsui & Co., Ltd. (50%) & Toyota Motor Corporation (50%)
N.A.I.C.S.: 423120
Stephen Beatty (VP-Corp)

Toyota Central R&D Labs., Inc. (1)
41-1 Yokomichi, Nagakute, 480-1192, Aichi, Japan
Tel.: (81) 561636509
Web Site: https://www.tytlabs.co.jp
Sales Range: $350-399.9 Million
Emp.: 929
Environmental Equipment Research & Development Services
N.A.I.C.S.: 541715
Noboru Kikuchi (Pres)

Toyota Credit Canada, Inc. (1)
80 Micro Court Suite 200, Markham, L3R 9Z5, ON, Canada (100%)
Tel.: (905) 513-8200
Web Site: http://www.toyotafinancialservices.ca
Sales Range: $100-124.9 Million
Emp.: 120
Financing for Dealers & Customers
N.A.I.C.S.: 522299

Toyota Deutschland GmbH (1)
Toyota Allee 2, Marsdorf, 50858, Cologne, Germany (100%)
Tel.: (49) 2341021221
Web Site: http://www.toyota.de
Sales Range: $150-199.9 Million
Emp.: 300
Holding Company
N.A.I.C.S.: 551112

Subsidiary (Domestic):

Toyota Kreditbank GmbH (2)
Toyota Allee 5, 50858, Cologne, Germany (100%)
Tel.: (49) 223410210
Web Site: http://www.toyota-bank.de
Sales Range: $75-99.9 Million
Emp.: 200
Financial Services
N.A.I.C.S.: 522299
Elo Ljubica (Mng Dir)

Toyota Leasing GmbH (2)
Toyota Allee 5, 50858, Cologne, Germany (100%)
Tel.: (49) 223410210
Web Site: http://www.toyota-ff.de
Sales Range: $75-99.9 Million
Emp.: 200
Motor Vehicle Lessor
N.A.I.C.S.: 532112

Toyota Finance Finland Oy (1)
Korpivaarantie 1, PO Box 49, 01450, Vantaa, Finland (100%)
Tel.: (358) 985182634
Web Site: https://myfinance.toyota.fi
Sales Range: $200-249.9 Million
Emp.: 450
Financial Services
N.A.I.C.S.: 522299

Toyota Financial Services (1)
Level 3 Toyota Building The Millennium Centre 602 Great South Road, Greenlane, Auckland, 1051, New Zealand (54.5%)
Tel.: (64) 95714150
Web Site: http://www.tfs.co.nz
Sales Range: $50-74.9 Million
Emp.: 60
Financial Services
N.A.I.C.S.: 522220
Julia Wada (Grp VP)

Toyota Financial Services (UK) PLC (1)
Great Burgh, Epsom, KT18 5UZ, Surrey, United Kingdom (100%)
Tel.: (44) 8009151571
Web Site: http://www.toyota.co.uk
Sales Range: $100-124.9 Million
Emp.: 150
Financial Services
N.A.I.C.S.: 523940

AND PRIVATE COMPANIES — TOYOTA MOTOR CORPORATION

Toyota Financial Services Corporation (1)
Nagoya Lucent Tower 15F 6-1 Ushijima-cho, Nishi-ku, Nagoya, 451-6015, Japan
Tel.: (81) 525277111
Web Site: https://www.tfsc.jp
Emp.: 144
Automotive Financial Leasing Services
N.A.I.C.S.: 522220
Akihiro Fukutome (CEO-Grp)

Subsidiary (US):

Toyota Motor Credit Corporation (2)
6565 Headquarters Dr, Plano, TX 75024 (100%)
Tel.: (469) 486-9300
Web Site: https://www.toyotafinancial.com
Rev.: $11,920,000,000
Assets: $135,041,000,000
Liabilities: $116,940,000,000
Net Worth: $18,101,000,000
Earnings: $2,535,000,000
Emp.: 3,700
Fiscal Year-end: 03/31/2022
Automobile Sales Financing Services
N.A.I.C.S.: 522220
Mark S. Templin (Pres & CEO)

Toyota France S.A. (1)
20 boulevard de la Republique, 92423, Vaucresson, Cedex, France (60%)
Tel.: (33) 147016030
Web Site: https://www.toyota.fr
Sales Range: $50-74.9 Million
Emp.: 200
Automobile Mfr
N.A.I.C.S.: 336110

Toyota Fudosan Co., Ltd. (1)
16F Midland Square Meieki 4-7-1, Nakamura Ward, Nagoya, 450-6216, Japan
Tel.: (81) 525847111
Web Site: https://www.toyotafudosan.com
Real Estate Investment Services
N.A.I.C.S.: 531390

Toyota Housing Corporation (1)
1-23-22 Izumi, Higashi-ku, Nagoya, 461-0001, Aichi, Japan
Tel.: (81) 529523111
Web Site: https://www.toyotahome.co.jp
Emp.: 800
Real Estate Manangement Services
N.A.I.C.S.: 531311

Subsidiary (Domestic):

Misawa Homes Co., Ltd. (2)
2-4-1 Nishi-Shinjuku, Shinjuku-ku, Tokyo, 163-0850, Japan (100%)
Tel.: (81) 333451111
Web Site: http://www.misawa.co.jp
Rev.: $3,618,083,820
Assets: $2,556,206,520
Liabilities: $1,980,226,080
Net Worth: $575,980,440
Earnings: $48,108,600
Emp.: 8,859
Fiscal Year-end: 03/31/2019
Mfr & Sales of Prefabricated Housing Materials, Construction Works, Golf Course & Resort Facilities
N.A.I.C.S.: 321992
Yuji Goto (Mng Dir & Head-Sls & Mktg Center)

Subsidiary (US):

Impression Homes LLC (3)
2325 Dean Wy Ste 150, Southlake, TX 76092
Tel.: (817) 717-5103
Web Site: http://www.impressionhomes.net
Single-Family Housing
N.A.I.C.S.: 236115
Bruce Heikkinen (CEO)

Subsidiary (Domestic):

Media MG Co Ltd (3)
5th floor Shinjuku NS Building 2-4-1 Nishi-Shinjuku, Shinjuku-ku, Tokyo, 163-0805, Japan
Tel.: (81) 353398500
Web Site: https://www.mediamg.com
Sales Range: $25-49.9 Million
Emp.: 42
Housing Consulting Services
N.A.I.C.S.: 541618

Misawa Homes Ceramics Co., Ltd (3)
2-4-5 Takaidohigashi, Suginami-ku, Tokyo, 168-8533, Japan
Tel.: (81) 332472060
Web Site: http://www.ceramic.misawa.co.jp
Emp.: 135
Residential Building Sales & Construction Services
N.A.I.C.S.: 236115

Misawa Homes Chugoku Co., Ltd (3)
2-13-17 Noda, Okayama, 700 0971, Japan (68.42%)
Tel.: (81) 862453111
Web Site: http://www.misawa-c.co.jp
Rev.: $267,025,380
Assets: $163,596,420
Liabilities: $111,057,480
Net Worth: $52,538,940
Earnings: $489,240
Emp.: 548
Fiscal Year-end: 03/31/2019
Residential Home Builder
N.A.I.C.S.: 236115

Misawa Homes Higashikanto Co., Ltd (3)
388-13 Sonnocho, Inage-ku, Chiba, 263-0051, Japan
Tel.: (81) 433093119
Web Site: http://www.hkanto.misawa.co.jp
Residential Building Rental & Sales
N.A.I.C.S.: 236117

Misawa Homes Hokkaido Co., Ltd. (3)
2-6-8-1 Higashi Sapporo, Shiroishi-ku, Sapporo, 003-8558, Hokkaido, Japan (100%)
Tel.: (81) 118221111
Web Site: https://www.hokkaido.misawa.co.jp
Emp.: 339
Prefabricated Houses Construction & Sales
N.A.I.C.S.: 236118

Misawa Homes Institute of Research and Development Co Ltd (3)
2-4-5 Takaido Higashi, Suginami-ku, Tokyo, 168-0072, Japan
Tel.: (81) 332475644
Web Site: https://soken.misawa.co.jp
Housing Research & Development Services
N.A.I.C.S.: 541715

Misawa Homes Kinki Co., Ltd (3)
13th floor Kintetsu Dojima Building 2-2-2 Dojima, Kita-ku, Osaka, 530-0003, Japan
Tel.: (81) 663411301
Web Site: https://misawa-kinki.jp
Emp.: 340
Residential Building Sales & Rental Services
N.A.I.C.S.: 531110

Misawa Homes Shin-etsu Co., Ltd (3)
2-1-53 Sekishin, Chuo-ku, Niigata, 951-8141, Japan
Tel.: (81) 252323330
Web Site: http://www.shin-etsu.misawa.co.jp
Residential Building Development Services
N.A.I.C.S.: 236115

Misawa Homes Shizuoka Co., Ltd (3)
367 Tegoshi, Suruga-ku, Shizuoka, 421-0102, Japan
Tel.: (81) 542571111
Web Site: https://www.shizuoka.misawa.co.jp
Emp.: 243
Residential Building Sales & Rental Services
N.A.I.C.S.: 531110

Misawa Homes Tokai Co., Ltd. (3)
20 1 Higashiyama Dori 5 Chome, Chikusa Ku, Nagoya, 464 8663, Aichi, Japan (100%)
Tel.: (81) 527822131
Web Site: http://www.misawa-tokai.co.jp
Sales Range: $125-149.9 Million
Emp.: 460
Sales of Wooden Prefabricated Houses, Houses & Land; Contracted Construction of Single-Family Houses & Apartments; Extending & Remodeling Works; Real Estate Agency
N.A.I.C.S.: 321992

Misawa Homes Tokyo Co., Ltd (3)
2-4-5 Takaidohigashi, Suginami-ku, Tokyo, 168-0072, Japan (100%)
Tel.: (81) 353446811
Residential Building Rental & Sales
N.A.I.C.S.: 531110

Joint Venture (Domestic):

RESOL HOLDINGS Co., Ltd. (3)
6-24-1 Nishi-Shinjuku, Shinjuku-Ku, Tokyo, 160 0023, Japan
Tel.: (81) 333448811
Web Site: http://www.resol.jp
Rev.: $169,989,370
Assets: $284,249,830
Liabilities: $187,307,570
Net Worth: $96,942,260
Earnings: $9,326,710
Emp.: 1,796
Fiscal Year-end: 03/31/2024
Holding Company; Resort Related & Development Business
N.A.I.C.S.: 551112
Hideaki Hirata (Chm & CEO)

Subsidiary (Domestic):

Tohoku Misawa Homes Co., Ltd. (3)
TM Building 8F 1-3-1 Ichibancho, Aoba-ku, Sendai, 980-0811, Miyagi, Japan (100%)
Tel.: (81) 227060330
Web Site: https://tohoku.misawa.co.jp
Sales Range: $200-249.9 Million
Emp.: 602
Construction & Sales of System-Built Homes
N.A.I.C.S.: 236115

Toyota Ireland (1)
Long Mile Road, Dublin, 12, Ireland
Tel.: (353) 14190200
Web Site: http://www.toyota.ie
Sales Range: $50-74.9 Million
Emp.: 76
Automotive Distr
N.A.I.C.S.: 423120

Toyota Kirloskar Motor Private Ltd. (1)
Plot No 1 Bidadi Industrial Area, Ramanagar Taluk, Bengaluru, 562 101, Karnataka, India
Tel.: (91) 8066553300
Web Site: https://www.toyotabharat.com
Sales Range: $100-124.9 Million
Emp.: 40
Automobile Mfr
N.A.I.C.S.: 336110
Raju B. Ketkale (Deputy Mng Dir-Mfg)

Toyota Leasing (Thailand) Co., Ltd. (1)
990 Abdulrahim Building 18th 19th Floor Rama 4 Road Silom, Bangkok, 10500, Thailand (33%)
Tel.: (66) 26605555
Web Site: https://www.tlt.co.th
Sales Range: $300-349.9 Million
Emp.: 1,260
Passenger Car Leasing
N.A.I.C.S.: 532112

Toyota Motor (China) Investment Co., Ltd. (1)
3806-11 Jingguang Centre, Hujialou Chaoyang District, Beijing, 100020, China
Tel.: (86) 1065978728
Investment Management Service
N.A.I.C.S.: 523999

Toyota Motor (China) Ltd. (1)
Unit 2702 27 F Tower 1 Admiralty Ctr 18 Harcourt Rd, Hong Kong, China (Hong Kong) (75%)
Tel.: (852) 25280768
Web Site: http://www.tmcl.com.cn
Sales Range: $50-74.9 Million
Emp.: 60
CBU Vehicle Import & Sales
N.A.I.C.S.: 423120

Toyota Motor Asia Pacific Engineering and Manufacturing Co., Ltd. (1)
99 Moo 5 Ban-ragad, Bang-Bo, Samut Prakan, 10560, Thailand
Tel.: (66) 27905000
Web Site: https://www.tdem.toyota-asia.com

Automobile Evaluation Services
N.A.I.C.S.: 561990

Toyota Motor Asia Pacific Pte Ltd. (1)
20 Anson Road 13-01 Twenty Anson, Singapore, 079912, Singapore
Tel.: (65) 62278011
Sales Range: $150-199.9 Million
Emp.: 35
Automotive Distr
N.A.I.C.S.: 423110

Toyota Motor Asia Pte. Ltd. (1)
3 Temasek Ave 1301 20 Enson Rd, 20 enson rd 13-01 20 Enson, Singapore, 079910, Singapore (100%)
Tel.: (65) 62278011
Web Site: http://www.toyota-asia.com
Sales Range: $150-199.9 Million
Emp.: 300
Services & Trading of Automobiles & Parts
N.A.I.C.S.: 423120

Toyota Motor Corporation - Hirose Plant (1)
543 Kirigabora, Nishihirose-cho, Toyota, 470-0309, Aichi, Japan
Tel.: (81) 565455111
Web Site: http://www.toyota.co.jp
Sales Range: $400-449.9 Million
Emp.: 1,589
Electronic Control Device Mfr
N.A.I.C.S.: 334419

Toyota Motor Corporation - Honsha Plant (1)
1Toyota-cho, Toyota, 471-8571, Aichi, Japan
Tel.: (81) 565282121
Automobile Parts Mfr
N.A.I.C.S.: 336390

Toyota Motor Corporation - Tahara Plant (1)
3-1 Midorigahama, Tahara, 441-3401, Aichi, Japan
Tel.: (81) 531235111
Sales Range: $1-4.9 Billion
Emp.: 8,089
Automobile Mfr
N.A.I.C.S.: 336110

Toyota Motor Corporation Australia Ltd. (1)
155 Bertie Street, Port Melbourne, 3207, VIC, Australia (49%)
Tel.: (61) 396474444
Web Site: http://www.toyota.com.au
Sales Range: $800-899.9 Million
Emp.: 4,760
CKD (Passenger) Unit Assembly, CBU (Passenger) Vehicle Import & Sales
N.A.I.C.S.: 336110

Branch (Domestic):

Toyota Motor Corporation Australia Ltd. - Caringbah (2)
4 Murray Rose Avenue, Sydney Olympic Park, 2127, NSW, Australia
Tel.: (61) 297103333
Web Site: http://www.toyota.com.au
CBU (Commercial) Vehicle Import, Semi-Knockdown SKD (Commercial) Assembly & Sales
N.A.I.C.S.: 423120

Toyota Motor East Japan, Inc. (1)
1 Chuo-daira, Kurokawa-gun, Ohira, 981-3609, Miyagi, Japan
Tel.: (81) 227656000
Web Site: https://www.toyota-ej.co.jp
Sales Range: $1-4.9 Billion
Emp.: 7,100
Automobile Mfr
N.A.I.C.S.: 336110
Takeshi Shirane (Chm)

Plant (Domestic):

Toyota Motor East Japan, Inc. - Higashi Fuji Plant (2)
1501 Mishuku, Susono, 410-1198, Shizuoka, Japan
Tel.: (81) 559971111
Web Site: http://www.toyota-ej.co.jp
Automobile Mfr
N.A.I.C.S.: 336110

TOYOTA MOTOR CORPORATION

Toyota Motor Corporation—(Continued)

Toyota Motor East Japan, Inc. - Iwate Plant (2)
1 Nishine Moriyama Kanegasaki-cho, Isawa-gun, Iwate, 029-4503, Japan
Tel.: (81) 197411120
Automobile Mfr
N.A.I.C.S.: 336110

Toyota Motor East Japan, Inc. - Miyagi Taiwa Plant (2)
5-1-1 Matsusaka-daira Taiwa-cho, Kurokawa-gun, Miyagi, 981-3408, Japan
Tel.: (81) 223456711
Automobile Mfr
N.A.I.C.S.: 336110

Toyota Motor East Japan, Inc. - Suyama Plant (2)
2810-1 Suyama, Susono, 410-1231, Shizuoka, Japan
Tel.: (81) 559651700
Automobile Mfr
N.A.I.C.S.: 336110

Toyota Motor Finance (Netherlands) B.V. (1)
WTC Amsterdam Tower H Level 10 Zuidplein 90, 1077 XV, Amsterdam, Netherlands (100%)
Tel.: (31) 205025310
Web Site: https://toyotamotorfinance.com
Sales Range: $50-74.9 Million
Emp.: 2
Financing for Subsidiaries & Affiliates
N.A.I.C.S.: 522299

Toyota Motor Finland Oy (1)
Korpivaarantie 12, PO Box 12, Vantaa, 1450, Finland (100%)
Tel.: (358) 985181
Web Site: http://www.toyota.fi
Sales Range: $25-49.9 Million
Emp.: 80
Holding Company
N.A.I.C.S.: 551112

Toyota Motor Hokkaido Inc. (1)
145-1 Yufutsu, Tomakomai, 059-1393, Hokkaido, Japan (100%)
Tel.: (81) 144572121
Web Site: https://www.tmh.co.jp
Sales Range: $5-14.9 Billion
Emp.: 3,490
Automotive Transmission & Power Train Parts Mfr
N.A.I.C.S.: 336350
Yuji Yoshida *(Sr Mng Dir)*

Toyota Motor Hungary Kft. (1)
Szabadkikoto U 4, 1211, Budapest, Hungary (50%)
Tel.: (36) 12773844
Web Site: http://www.toyota.hu
Sales Range: $25-49.9 Million
Emp.: 60
CBU Vehicle Import & Sales
N.A.I.C.S.: 441110

Toyota Motor Industries Poland SP. z.o.o. (1)
Ul Japonska 6 Leg, 55-220, Jelcz-Laskowice, Poland
Tel.: (48) 713020000
Sales Range: $200-249.9 Million
Emp.: 664
Diesel Engine Mfr & Distr
N.A.I.C.S.: 333618

Toyota Motor Italia S.p.A. (1)
Via Kiiciro Toyoda 2, 00148, Rome, Italy (100%)
Tel.: (39) 026291000
Web Site: https://www.toyota.it
Sales Range: $150-199.9 Million
Emp.: 300
CBU Vehicle Import & Sales
N.A.I.C.S.: 423120

Toyota Motor Kyushu, Inc. (1)
1 Kamiaruki, Miyawaka, 823-0015, Fukuoka, Japan
Tel.: (81) 949325151
Web Site: https://www.toyota-kyushu.com
Rev.: $10,175,127,000
Emp.: 7,700
Automobile & Engine Mfr
N.A.I.C.S.: 336110
Nagata Osamu *(Pres)*

Plant (Domestic):

Toyota Motor Kyushu, Inc. - Kanda Plant (2)
9-2 Torigoe, Kanda, Miyako, 800-0304, Fukuoka, Japan
Tel.: (81) 934354300
Industrial Casting Machinery Mfr
N.A.I.C.S.: 333248

Toyota Motor Manufacturing (UK) Ltd (1)
Deeside Industrial Park Tenth Ave, Deeside, CH5 2TW, Flintshire, United Kingdom
Tel.: (44) 24482121
Sales Range: $200-249.9 Million
Emp.: 900
Automotive Parts Mfr & Whslr
N.A.I.C.S.: 336390

Toyota Motor Manufacturing (UK) Ltd. (1)
East Midlands, Burnaston, DE1 9TA, Derby, United Kingdom (100%)
Tel.: (44) 24482121
Web Site: https://www.toyotauk.com
Sales Range: $800-899.9 Million
Emp.: 4,000
Automobile Parts Production & Sales
N.A.I.C.S.: 336110

Toyota Motor Manufacturing Canada, Inc. (1)
1055 Fountain Street North, Cambridge, N3H 4R7, ON, Canada (100%)
Tel.: (519) 653-1111
Web Site: http://www.tmmc.ca
Sales Range: $800-899.9 Million
Emp.: 4,000
Automobiles & Parts Mfr & Whslr
N.A.I.C.S.: 336110

Toyota Motor Manufacturing France S.A.S. (1)
Scheldt Valley Business Park south BP16, 59264, Onnaing, France
Tel.: (33) 327512121
Web Site: https://tmmf.toyota-europe.com
Sales Range: $800-899.9 Million
Emp.: 400
Automobile Mfr
N.A.I.C.S.: 336110

Toyota Motor Manufacturing Poland SP. z.o.o. (1)
st Uczniowska 26, 58-306, Walbrzych, Dolnoslaskie, Poland
Tel.: (48) 748888000
Sales Range: $400-449.9 Million
Emp.: 2,105
Automotive Transmission Mfr
N.A.I.C.S.: 336350

Toyota Motor Manufacturing Turkey Inc. (1)
Toyota Caddesi No 2, Arifiye, 54580, Sakarya, Turkiye
Tel.: (90) 2642950295
Web Site: https://www.toyotatr.com
Sales Range: $800-899.9 Million
Emp.: 2,536
Automobile Mfr
N.A.I.C.S.: 336110

Toyota Motor Manufacturing de Baja California S .de R.L.de C.V. (1)
Carretera Tijuana - Tecate No 33143, Tecate Km 143 - 144, 22550, Tijuana, Baja California, Mexico
Tel.: (52) 6649692800
Web Site: http://www.toyota.com
Sales Range: $200-249.9 Million
Emp.: 683
Truck Trailer Mfr
N.A.I.C.S.: 336212

Toyota Motor North America, Inc. (1)
1114 Avenue of the Americas, New York, NY 10036 (100%)
Tel.: (212) 223-0303
Web Site: http://www.toyota.com
Sales Range: $1-4.9 Billion
Emp.: 31,543
Holding Company
N.A.I.C.S.: 551112
Peggy P. Turner *(VP-Guest Retention)*

Subsidiary (Domestic):

Calty Design Research, Inc. (2)
2810 Jamboree Rd, Newport Beach, CA 92660-3201 (60%)
Tel.: (949) 759-1701
Web Site: http://www.toyota.com
Sales Range: $10-24.9 Million
Emp.: 106
Automobile Design Research Services
N.A.I.C.S.: 541330
Kevin Hunter *(Pres)*

TABC, Inc. (2)
6375 N Paramount Blvd, Long Beach, CA 90805-3301 (100%)
Tel.: (562) 428-3604
Sales Range: $200-249.9 Million
Emp.: 350
Truck Assembly
N.A.I.C.S.: 336390

Branch (Domestic):

TABC (3)
6375 N Paramount Blvd, Long Beach, CA 90805-2720
Tel.: (562) 984-3305
Web Site: http://www.toyota.com
Sales Range: $125-149.9 Million
Emp.: 500
Coating of Metals & Formed Products
N.A.I.C.S.: 336390

Subsidiary (Domestic):

Toyota Motor Engineering & Manufacturing North America, Inc. (2)
25 Atlantic Ave, Erlanger, KY 41018-3151
Tel.: (859) 746-4000
Web Site: http://www.toyota.com
Sales Range: $1-4.9 Billion
Emp.: 22,387
Motor Vehicles & Car Bodies Mfr
N.A.I.C.S.: 336110
Shinichi Yasui *(Pres)*

Subsidiary (Domestic):

Bodine Aluminum Inc. (3)
2100 Walton Rd, Saint Louis, MO 63114-5808
Tel.: (314) 423-8200
Web Site: http://www.bodinealuminum.com
Rev.: $28,000,000
Emp.: 180
Aluminum Die-Castings
N.A.I.C.S.: 331523

Toyota Motor Manufacturing, Alabama, Inc. (3)
1 Cottonvalley Dr, Huntsville, AL 35810
Tel.: (256) 746-5000
Web Site: http://www.toyota.com
Sales Range: $200-249.9 Million
Emp.: 1,800
Automobile Mfr
N.A.I.C.S.: 336110
Hiroyuki Fukui *(Chm)*

Toyota Motor Manufacturing, Indiana, Inc. (3)
4000 Tulip Tree Dr, Princeton, IN 47670-2300
Tel.: (812) 387-2000
Web Site: http://www.tourtoyotaindiana.com
Emp.: 7,550
Automotive Vehicles Assembly & Mfr
N.A.I.C.S.: 336110
Leah Curry *(Pres)*

Toyota Motor Manufacturing, Kentucky, Inc. (3)
1001 Cherry Blossom Way, Georgetown, KY 40324-9564 (100%)
Tel.: (502) 868-2000
Web Site:
 Sales Range: $1-4.9 Billion
Emp.: 7,773
Automobile Assembly
N.A.I.C.S.: 336110
Susan Elkington *(Pres)*

Toyota Motor Manufacturing, Mississippi, Inc. (3)
1200 Magnolia Way, Blue Springs, MS 38828
Tel.: (662) 317-3015
Sales Range: $400-449.9 Million
Emp.: 2,250
Automobile Mfr
N.A.I.C.S.: 336110

Sean M. Suggs *(Pres & Gen Mgr-Quality Plng)*

Toyota Motor Manufacturing, Texas, Inc. (3)
1 Lone Star Pass, San Antonio, TX 78264
Tel.: (210) 263-4000
Sales Range: $400-449.9 Million
Emp.: 9,400
Automobile Mfr
N.A.I.C.S.: 336110
Kevin Voelkel *(Pres)*

Toyota Motor Manufacturing, West Virginia, Inc. (3)
1 Sugar Maple Ln, Buffalo, WV 25033
Tel.: (304) 937-7000
Sales Range: $400-449.9 Million
Emp.: 1,200
Automobile Engine & Transmission Mfr
N.A.I.C.S.: 333618

Subsidiary (Domestic):

Toyota Motor Insurance Services (2)
19001 South Western Ave, Torrance, CA 90501-1106
Tel.: (310) 468-4000
Web Site: http://www.toyotafinancial.com
Rev.: $22,100,000
Emp.: 5,000
Automobile Insurance
N.A.I.C.S.: 524210

Toyota Motor Sales, U.S.A., Inc. (2)
19001 S Western Ave, Torrance, CA 90501-1106 (100%)
Tel.: (310) 468-4000
Web Site: https://www.toyota.com
Passenger Cars, 4-Wheel Drive Vehicles, Trucks & Vans Distr
N.A.I.C.S.: 423110

Subsidiary (Domestic):

Airflite Inc. (3)
3250 Airflite Way, Long Beach, CA 90807-5312 (100%)
Tel.: (562) 490-6200
Web Site: http://www.airflite.toyota.com
Sales Range: $25-49.9 Million
Emp.: 100
Airport Terminal Services
N.A.I.C.S.: 481219
Craig Grucza *(Pres)*

Division (Domestic):

Lexus Division (3)
19001 S Western Ave, Torrance, CA 90501
Tel.: (310) 468-4000
Web Site: https://www.lexus.com
Cars Mfr & Sales
N.A.I.C.S.: 336110

Subsidiary (Domestic):

TRD USA Inc. (3)
335 Baker St E, Costa Mesa, CA 92626-4518
Tel.: (714) 444-1188
Web Site: http://www.trdusa.com
Sales Range: $50-74.9 Million
Emp.: 217
Testing Laboratories
N.A.I.C.S.: 541715

Subsidiary (Domestic):

Toyota Technical Center, U.S.A., Inc. (2)
1555 Woodridge Ave, Ann Arbor, MI 48105-9748
Tel.: (734) 995-2600
Web Site: http://www.toyotamotor.com
Sales Range: $25-49.9 Million
Emp.: 110
Automobile Testing Research & Information Gathering
N.A.I.C.S.: 541715

Toyota Textile Machinery Corp. in U.S.A. (2)
8300 Arrowridge Blvd, Charlotte, NC 28273-5679 (100%)
Tel.: (704) 527-5400
Web Site:
 https://www.toyotatextilemachinery.com
Sales Range: $25-49.9 Million
Emp.: 10
Textile Machinery Distr

AND PRIVATE COMPANIES — TOYOTA TSUSHO CORPORATION

N.A.I.C.S.: 423830
Oak Mirua *(Pres)*

Toyota de Puerto Rico Corp. (2)
654 Ave Luis Munoz Rivera FL 20, San
Juan, PR 00918 **(100%)**
Tel.: (787) 641-3800
Web Site: https://www.toyotapr.com
Sales Range: $75-99.9 Million
Emp.: 107
Automobile Import & Sales
N.A.I.C.S.: 423110

**Toyota Motor Poland Company, Ltd.
Sp zoo** (1)
Ul Konstruktorska 5, 02-673, Warsaw,
Poland **(50%)**
Tel.: (48) 225490500
Web Site: https://www.toyota.com.pl
Sales Range: $75-99.9 Million
Emp.: 120
CBU Vehicle Import & Sales
N.A.I.C.S.: 423120

Toyota Motor Thailand Co., Ltd. (1)
186/1 Moo 1 Old Railway Road Samrong
Tai, Samut Prakan, 10130, Phra Phradeng,
Thailand **(86.4%)**
Tel.: (66) 23861000
Web Site: https://www.toyota.co.th
Sales Range: $1-4.9 Billion
Emp.: 15,000
CBU Vehicle Import; CKD Unit Assembly &
Sales
N.A.I.C.S.: 423120
Vudhigorn Suriyachantananont *(Exec VP)*

Affiliate (Domestic):

**Toyota Auto Body Thailand Co.,
Ltd.** (2)
82/1 Moo 2 Old Railway Road, Samrong Tai
Phrapadaeng, Bangkok, 10270, Samut Pra-
karn, Thailand **(48.9%)**
Tel.: (66) 23861000
Web Site: http://www.toyota.co.th
Sales Range: $25-49.9 Million
Emp.: 250
Automobile Parts Mfr
N.A.I.C.S.: 336340

Toyota Motor Vietnam Co., Ltd. (1)
Viglacera Building 8th Floor No 1 Thang
Long Avenue, Me Tri Tu Liem, Hanoi, Vinh
Phuc, Vietnam **(70%)**
Tel.: (84) 211868100
Sales Range: $1-4.9 Billion
Emp.: 3,000
CKD Unit Assembly CBU Vehicle Import &
Sales
N.A.I.C.S.: 423120

Toyota Motorsport GmbH (1)
Toyota Allee 7, 50858, Cologne,
Germany **(100%)**
Tel.: (49) 223418230
Web Site: https://www.tgr-europe.com
Sales Range: $200-249.9 Million
Emp.: 600
Design & Development of Motor Sports
Vehicles
N.A.I.C.S.: 339920
Yoshiaki Kinoshita *(Pres)*

Toyota New Zealand Ltd. (1)
Roberts Line, PO Box 46, Palmerston
North, 4440, New Zealand **(100%)**
Tel.: (64) 800869682
Web Site: https://www.toyota.co.nz
Rev: $514,754,112
Emp.: 180
CBU Vehicle Import; CKD Unit & SKD Set
Assembly & Sales
N.A.I.C.S.: 423120

Toyota Norge A/S (1)
Svelvikvn 59 B, PO Box 665, 3039, Dram-
men, Norway
Tel.: (47) 32205000
Web Site: https://www.toyota.no
Sales Range: $50-74.9 Million
Emp.: 80
Automobile Sales
N.A.I.C.S.: 423120
Espen Olsen *(Mgr-Information)*

Toyota South Africa Limited (1)
Stand 1 Eastern Service Road, Wesco
Park, Sandton, 2012, South Africa **(27.8%)**
Tel.: (27) 118099111
Web Site: http://www.toyota.co.za
Sales Range: $250-299.9 Million
Emp.: 800
Holding Company
N.A.I.C.S.: 551112

Holding (Domestic):

**Toyota South Africa Motors (Pty.)
Ltd.** (2)
Stand 1 Eastern Service Road, Wesco
Park, Sandton, 2012, South Africa
Tel.: (27) 118099111
Web Site: http://www.toyota.co.za
Automobile Mfr; Owned 75% by Toyota Mo-
tor Corporation & 25% by Wesco Invest-
ments Limited
N.A.I.C.S.: 336110
Calvyn Hamman *(Sr VP-Sls & Mktg)*

Toyota Sweden AB (1)
Mademvagan 7, PO Box 1103, 172 22,
Sundbyberg, Sweden **(100%)**
Tel.: (46) 87067190
Web Site: https://www.toyota.se
Sales Range: $50-74.9 Million
Emp.: 75
Holding Company
N.A.I.C.S.: 551112

**Toyota Turkiye Motorlu Araclar
A.S.** (1)
Gulsuyu Mevkii Ankara Asfalti, 34846, Istan-
bul, Turkiye **(25%)**
Tel.: (90) 2164585858
Web Site: http://www.toyotasa.com.tr
Sales Range: $50-74.9 Million
Emp.: 150
Automobiles Mfr; Joint Venture of Haci
Omer Sabanci Holding A.S., Toyota Motor
Corp. & Mitsui & Co., Ltd.
N.A.I.C.S.: 336110

Toyota de Venezuela C.A. (1)
Ave Francisco De Miranda C/2da Ave, Ca-
racas, Venezuela
Tel.: (58) 2122108757
Web Site: https://www.toyota.com.ve
Emp.: 300
Automobile Parts Mfr
N.A.I.C.S.: 336390

Toyota del Peru S.A. (1)
Av Elmer Faucett 3548, Callao, Lima,
Peru **(100%)**
Tel.: (51) 15753800
Web Site: https://www.toyotaperu.com.pe
Sales Range: $25-49.9 Million
Emp.: 45
CBU Vehicle Import, CKD Unit Assembly &
Sales; Joint Venture of Toyota Motor Corpo-
ration & Mitsui & Co., Ltd.
N.A.I.C.S.: 423120

Toyota do Brasil Ltda. (1)
Rua Max Mangels Senior N 1024, Sao Ber-
nardo do Campo, 0989002, Sao Paulo,
Brazil
Tel.: (55) 1143315199
Web Site: https://www.toyota.com.br
Sales Range: $25-49.9 Million
Emp.: 55
Automobile Mfr
N.A.I.C.S.: 336110

TOYOTA TSUSHO CORPORATION

9-8 Meieki 4-chome, Nakamura-ku,
Nagoya, 450-8575, Japan
Tel.: (81) 525845000 JP
Web Site: https://www.toyota-tsusho.com
Year Founded: 1948
8015—(NGO)
Rev: $65,071,423,852
Assets: $42,134,549,058
Liabilities: $28,467,360,423
Net Worth: $13,667,188,636
Earnings: $2,079,557,317
Emp.: 66,944
Fiscal Year-end: 03/31/23
Construction Engineering Services
N.A.I.C.S.: 541330
Richard Bielle *(CEO-Africa Div)*

Subsidiaries:

Aichi Kokan Industries, Ltd. (1)
3-9 Toshincho, Obu, 474-0073, Aichi, Japan
Tel.: (81) 562 46 1295
Steel Pipes Whslr
N.A.I.C.S.: 423840

**C.I. Toyota Tsusho de Colombia
S.A.** (1)
Calle 110 No 9 - 25 Oficina 902 Edificio
Torre Empresarial Petrobras, Bogota, Co-
lombia
Tel.: (57) 16378700
Automotive Parts Mfr & Distr
N.A.I.C.S.: 336390

CFAO SAS (1)
18 Rue Troyon, 92310, Sevres, France
Tel.: (33) 14 623 5656
Web Site: https://www.cfaogroup.com
Emp.: 21,000
Automotive, Pharmaceuticals & Technology
Products Distr
N.A.I.C.S.: 425120
Alain Pecheur *(CFO)*

Subsidiary (Non-US):

Alliance Auto Nigeria Limited (2)
Plot 1090 Adeola Odeku Street, Victoria
Island, Lagos, Nigeria
Tel.: (234) 1 4627888
Web Site: https://www.allianceautosng.com
New Car Dealers
N.A.I.C.S.: 441110
Henry Monuh *(Reg Mgr)*

Asian Hall Algerie SARL (2)
114 Rte du Cap Bordj El Kiffan, 16412, Al-
giers, Algeria
Tel.: (213) 21 21 36 26
Web Site: http://www.cfaogroup.com
Sales Range: $25-49.9 Million
Emp.: 30
New Car Dealers
N.A.I.C.S.: 441110

Bavaria Motors Algerie SARL (2)
150 Rue de Tripoli, Hussein Dey, 16008,
Algiers, Algeria
Tel.: (213) 21 49 80 60
Sales Range: $25-49.9 Million
Emp.: 50
New Car Dealers
N.A.I.C.S.: 441110
Christophe de Coatpont *(Mgr)*

CFAO (Ghana) Limited (2)
CFAO Building, House No. 6, Otublohum
Road, Industrial Area, Accra, Ghana
Tel.: (233) 21244071
Automobiles, Office Equipment Sales &
Services; Car Rental Services
N.A.I.C.S.: 441110

CFAO Malawi Limited (2)
Plot BC1131 Kaoshiung Road, PO Box 467,
Top Mandala, Blantyre, Malawi
Tel.: (265) 1879011
Web Site: http://www.cfaomw.com
Automobile Dealers
N.A.I.C.S.: 441110
David Blair *(Mng Dir)*

CFAO Motors Burkina S.A. (2)
2280 Boulevard Tansoba Kiema 01, BP 23,
Ouagadougou, Kadiogo, Burkina Faso
Tel.: (226) 50498830
Automotive Distr
N.A.I.C.S.: 441110

CFAO Motors Guinee Bissau (2)
Tel.: (245) 6752090
Automobile Parts Distr
N.A.I.C.S.: 423120

**CFAO Motors Guinee
Equatoriale** (2)
Los cocos - carretera del aeropuerto, BP
127, Bata, Equatorial Guinea
Tel.: (240) 333083538
Web Site: http://www.cfao-automotive.com
Automotive Distr
N.A.I.C.S.: 441110

CFAO Motors Maroc SA (2)
Rte D El Jadida Km 13 Lissasfa, Casa-
blanca, Morocco
Tel.: (212) 522659040
Automotive Distr
N.A.I.C.S.: 441110

CFAO Motors RCA (2)
Rue des Missions, BP 837, Bangui, Central
African Republic
Tel.: (236) 21 61 32 78
Web Site: http://www.cfao-automotive.com
Automotive Distr
N.A.I.C.S.: 441110

CFAO Senegal (2)
Km 2 5 Boulevard du Centenaire de la
commune, Dakar, Senegal
Tel.: (221) 33 849 77 77
Automotive Distr
N.A.I.C.S.: 441110
Fabraeca Dacraequar *(Mgr)*

CFAO Technologies Burkina S.A. (2)
BP 4841, Ouagadougou, Burkina Faso
Tel.: (226) 50328000
Sales Range: $25-49.9 Million
Emp.: 35
Pharmaceuticals Distr
N.A.I.C.S.: 424210

CFAO Technologies Gabon S.A. (2)
ZI Oloumi, BP 2231, Libreville, Gabon
Tel.: (241) 74 73 00
Business Management Software Develop-
ment Services
N.A.I.C.S.: 541511

CFAO Technologies Mali SA (2)
Hamdallaye ACI 2000 Avenue Tombouctou
Immeuble, Trelenium, Bamako, Mali
Tel.: (223) 20 22 50 50
Web Site: http://www.cfao-te.com
Sales Range: $1-9.9 Million
Emp.: 22
Information & Communication Technology
Services
N.A.I.C.S.: 541512

CFAO Technologies Senegal (2)
103 Sotrac Mermoz, BP 878, Dakar, 4218,
Senegal
Tel.: (221) 338698900
Web Site: http://www.cfao-te.com
Sales Range: $25-49.9 Million
Emp.: 67
Information & Communication Technology
Services
N.A.I.C.S.: 541512

CFAO Zambia Ltd. (2)
Plot 9558 Sheki Sheki Road, PO Box
31238, Lusaka, Zambia
Tel.: (260) 211243112
Web Site: http://www.cfao-automotive.com
Sales Range: $50-74.9 Million
Emp.: 120
New Car Dealers
N.A.I.C.S.: 441110
Susan Mennell *(Mng Dir)*

CMM Automobiles (2)
4 Chemin Grand Canal, 97490, Sainte Clo-
tilde, Reunion
Tel.: (262) 2 62 48 25 00
Rev: $169,896,000
Emp.: 201
Automotive Distr
N.A.I.C.S.: 441110
Harsc Hsald *(Mng Dir)*

**Cameroon Motors Industries
S.A.** (2)
Zone Industrielle Bonaberi, BP 1217,
Douala, Cameroon
Tel.: (237) 233398056
Web Site: http://www.cfao-automotive.com
Motorbikes Distr
N.A.I.C.S.: 441110

Capstone International Ltd (2)
4th Floor Harbour Front Building President
John Kennedy Street, Port Louis, Mauritius
Tel.: (230) 2130005
Pharmaceuticals Distr
N.A.I.C.S.: 424210

Subsidiary (Domestic):

Continental Pharmaceutique (2)
ZAC du Grand-Launay - 8 avenue Paul De-
lorme, BP 90237, 76121, Grand Quevilly,
Cedex, France
Tel.: (33) 2 35 79 42 00
Web Site: http://www.eurapharma.com
Emp.: 121
Pharmaceutical Products Distr
N.A.I.C.S.: 424210

TOYOTA TSUSHO CORPORATION INTERNATIONAL PUBLIC

Toyota Tsusho Corporation—(Continued)

Subsidiary (Non-US):

DT Dobie Kenya (2)
Lusaka Road, PO Box 30160, Industrial Area, 00100, Nairobi, Kenya
Tel.: (254) 207604000
Web Site: http://www2.dtdobie.co.ke
New Car Dealers
N.A.I.C.S.: 441110

Distribution Automobiles & Materiels en Algerie, Spa (2)
CW No 31 Les Annassers Bir Mourad Rais, Algiers, Algeria
Tel.: (213) 21449600
Sales Range: $100-124.9 Million
Emp.: 337
Automobile Dealers
N.A.I.C.S.: 441110

Subsidiary (Domestic):

EPDIS S.A. (2)
ZAC du Grand Launay 8 Avenue Paul Delorme, 76120, Le Grand-Quevilly, France
Tel.: (33) 232184700
Web Site: http://www.eurapharma.com
Sales Range: $25-49.9 Million
Emp.: 50
Pharmaceutical Products Distr
N.A.I.C.S.: 424210
Jean-Marc Leccia (CEO)

Subsidiary (Non-US):

Epdis Kenya Limited (2)
Mombasa Road, PO Box 72030, 00200, Nairobi, Kenya
Tel.: (254) 20 693 90 00
Pharmaceutical Products Distr
N.A.I.C.S.: 424210

Subsidiary (Domestic):

Eurapharma S.A. (2)
ZAC du Grand-Launay - 8 avenue Paul Delorme, 76120, Grand Quevilly, France
Tel.: (33) 235794200
Web Site: http://www.eurapharma.com
Sales Range: $550-599.9 Million
Emp.: 1,300
Pharmaceuticals Distr
N.A.I.C.S.: 424210
Didier Lefebvre (VP-IT & Ops Div)

Subsidiary (Non-US):

Gokals Laborex Ghana (2)
7 Barnes Road - Farrar Avenue, PO Box GP 623, Adabraka, Accra, Ghana
Tel.: (233) 302230800
Web Site: https://www.gokals-laborex.com
Pharmaceutical Preparation Whslr
N.A.I.C.S.: 424210

Subsidiary (Domestic):

Holdinter S.A.R.L. (2)
18 Rue Troyon, Sevres, 92310, Hauts-de-Seine, France
Tel.: (33) 146235656
Office Administrative Services
N.A.I.C.S.: 561110

Subsidiary (Non-US):

Laborex Burkina S.A. (2)
ZAD secteur 50 Arrondissement 11 commune de Ouagadougou 01, BP 6179, Ouagadougou, 01, Kadiogo, Burkina Faso
Tel.: (226) 25372751
Web Site: https://www.laborex-burkina.com
Pharmaceutical Product Whslr
N.A.I.C.S.: 424210

Laborex Cameroun SA (2)
1394 Rue Pasteur Lottin Same, BP 483, Douala, Cameroon
Tel.: (237) 233422235
Web Site: https://www.laborex-cameroun.com
Pharmaceutical Products Distr
N.A.I.C.S.: 424210

Laborex Kenya Limited (2)
Tel.: (254) 206939000
Pharmaceutical Product Whslr
N.A.I.C.S.: 424210

Laborex Mali S.A (2)
Hamdallaye ACI 2000 - Rue 267, BP 1696, Bamako, Mali
Tel.: (223) 44202020
Web Site: https://www.laborex-mali.com
Pharmaceutical Product Whslr
N.A.I.C.S.: 424210

Laborex Senegal (2)
Corniche des HLM 1 x Rue Y Face HLM 1, BP 2066, Dakar, Senegal
Tel.: (221) 338690222
Web Site: https://www.laborex-senegal.com
Pharmaceutical Product Whslr
N.A.I.C.S.: 424210

Laborex Tanzanie (2)
Plot No 238-241 Nyerer Road, PO Box 70032, Dar es Salaam, Tanzania
Tel.: (255) 784622626
Sales Range: $25-49.9 Million
Emp.: 15
Pharmaceutical Products Distr
N.A.I.C.S.: 424210
Leonard Netto (CEO)

Laborex Uganda Limited (2)
Sure House Plot 1 Bombo Road, Kampala, 22705, Uganda
Tel.: (256) 414255371
Sales Range: $25-49.9 Million
Emp.: 33
Pharmaceutical Product Whslr
N.A.I.C.S.: 424210

Menard Automobiles (2)
21 rue Jean Chalier - PK4, BP H2, 98849, Noumea, Cedex, New Caledonia
Tel.: (687) 414471
Web Site: http://www.menard-automobiles.com
Emp.: 200
Automotive Distr
N.A.I.C.S.: 441110
Sebastien Marrec (Gen Mgr)

Nigerian Motor Industries Ltd. (2)
Plot 1 Block D Amuwo-Odofin Industrial Scheme Apapa-Oshodi Expressway, Lagos, Nigeria
Tel.: (234) 1621 1876
New Car Dealers
N.A.I.C.S.: 441110

Pens & Plastics (Ghana) Ltd. (2)
Otublohum Road, PO Box 10348, Accra, Ghana
Tel.: (233) 21 21 34 60
Ball Point Pens Mfr
N.A.I.C.S.: 339940

PharmaGabon S.A.S. (2)
Owendo Barracuda, BP 2224, Owendo, Libreville, Gabon
Tel.: (241) 17798989
Web Site: https://www.pharmagabon.com
Pharmaceutical Product Whslr
N.A.I.C.S.: 424210

Promopharma S.A.. (2)
Zone industrielle d'Akpakpa, BP 08 931, Cotonou, Littoral, Benin
Tel.: (229) 21331393
Web Site: https://www.promopharma-benin.com
Pharmaceutical Product Whslr
N.A.I.C.S.: 424210

Subsidiary (Domestic):

SECA Sarl (2)
ZI Champs a la Perdrix, 21140, Semur-en-Auxois, France
Tel.: (33) 380974380
Web Site: https://www.seca.com
Sales Range: $50-74.9 Million
Medical Weighing Equipments Distr
N.A.I.C.S.: 423450

Subsidiary (Non-US):

SPG (Guiana) (2)
11 Rue des Bois Tropiques, 97351, Matoury, French Guiana
Tel.: (594) 594351858
Web Site: http://www.spg-guyane.com
Emp.: 12
Pharmaceutical Product Whslr
N.A.I.C.S.: 424210

SPLV Cameroun (2)
Boulevard du General Leclerc, BP 4080, Douala, Cameroon
Tel.: (237) 33 42 64 10
Sales Range: $25-49.9 Million
Emp.: 25
New Car Dealers
N.A.I.C.S.: 441110

Subsidiary (Domestic):

Societe Francaise de Commerce Europeen S.A. (2)
18 Rue Troyon, Sevres, 92316, Hauts-de-Seine, France
Tel.: (33) 146235656
New Car Dealers
N.A.I.C.S.: 441110

Societe Pharmaceutique Des Caraibes (2)
8 Avenue Paul Delorme, 76120, Le Grand-Quevilly, Seine-Maritime, France (81.74%)
Tel.: (33) 2 35 79 42 00
Pharmaceutical Product Whslr
N.A.I.C.S.: 424210

Subsidiary (Non-US):

Societe Pharmaceutique Gabonaise (2)
BP 2224, Libreville, Gabon
Tel.: (241) 76 13 43
Pharmaceutical Product Whslr
N.A.I.C.S.: 424210

Somaphar S.A. (2)
Ankadimbahoaka Lot III U 49 Ter A, BP 427, 101, Antananarivo, Madagascar
Tel.: (261) 202254492
Web Site: https://www.somaphar.com
Pharmaceutical Product Whslr
N.A.I.C.S.: 424210

Sopharma Antilles (2)
ZAC de Moudong Center, 97122, La Baie Mahault, Guadeloupe
Tel.: (590) 5 90 32 06 32
Web Site: http://www.sopharma-guadeloupe.com
Pharmaceutical Product Whslr
N.A.I.C.S.: 424210

Tahiti Motor Yet Sing (2)
Immeuble Le Bihan, Pirae, 51564, French Polynesia
Tel.: (689) 424 190
New Car Dealers
N.A.I.C.S.: 441110

Tahiti Pharm (French Polynesia) S.A (2)
Quartier Tavararo PK 4-8 Cote Mer FAA, BP 510, 97813, Papeete, Tahiti, French Polynesia
Tel.: (689) 80 02 00
Pharmaceutical Products Distr
N.A.I.C.S.: 424210

CFT Vina Cooper Co., Ltd. (1)
Long Duc Industrial Park Road D3-3, Long Duc Commune Long Thanh District, Bien Hoa, Dong Nai, Vietnam
Tel.: (84) 2513833500
Web Site: https://www.cft-vietnam.com
Sales Range: $50-74.9 Million
Copper Rod & Wire Distr
N.A.I.C.S.: 423610

Central Motor Wheel Co., Ltd. (1)
1-7 Maruda Ozakicho, Anjo, 446-0004, Aichi, Japan
Tel.: (81) 566966250
Web Site: http://www.chuoseiki.co.jp
Automotive Wheels Mfr & Whslr
N.A.I.C.S.: 326211

Chubu Syokuryo Kaisha, Ltd. (1)
8 Ryukoda Iwatsuka-cho, Nakamura-ku, Nagoya, 453-0862, Japan
Tel.: (81) 52 413 1234
Web Site: http://www.chushoku.jp
Frozen Food Whslr
N.A.I.C.S.: 424420

Daihatsu Italia S.R.L. (1)
Via Bergamo 43, 24047, Treviglio, BG, Italy
Tel.: (39) 0363311411
Web Site: https://www.daihatsu.it
Automobile Parts Distr
N.A.I.C.S.: 423120

Daiichisekken Co., Ltd. (1)
7208 Ebise Itakura-cho, Oura-gun, Gunma, 374-0111, Gunma Prefecture, Japan
Tel.: (81) 276823761
Web Site: https://www.daiichisekken.co.jp
Emp.: 272
Detergents Mfr & Whslr
N.A.I.C.S.: 325611

ELAMOTORS TOYOTA TSUSHO (S.I.) LTD. (1)
Prince Philip Highway Ranadi, GPO Box 140, Honiara, Solomon Islands
Tel.: (677) 30314
Web Site: https://www.elamotorssolomon.com
Sales Range: $25-49.9 Million
Automotive Distr
N.A.I.C.S.: 423110

Elematec Corporation (1)
Sumitomo Fudosan Tokyo Mita Garden Tower 26F 3-5-19 Mita, Minato-ku, Tokyo, 108-0073, Japan
Tel.: (81) 334543526
Web Site: https://www.elematec.com
Rev.: $1,284,653,500
Assets: $774,771,320
Liabilities: $317,035,430
Net Worth: $457,735,890
Earnings: $37,868,690
Fiscal Year-end: 03/31/2024
Electrical Insulation Materials, Industrial Heaters, Crimp Contacts & Connectors, Printed Circuit Boards, Industrial Tapes, Small Batteries & Power Supplies Mfr & Distr
N.A.I.C.S.: 423610
Akira Yokode (Chm, Pres, Pres & CEO)

Subsidiary (Non-US):

ELEMATEC VIETNAM CO., LTD. (2)
Suite 505 5th Floor V-Tower Building 649 Kim Ma Street, Ba Dinh District, 132138, Hanoi, Vietnam
Tel.: (84) 2437666408
Web Site: http://www.elematec.com
Sales Range: $25-49.9 Million
Electrical & Electronic Components Distr
N.A.I.C.S.: 423610

Elematec (Shanghai) Trading Co., Ltd. (2)
Rm 1101 Shanghai Lippo Plaza 222 Huaihaizhong Road, Shanghai, 200021, China
Tel.: (86) 2153838801
Sales Range: $25-49.9 Million
Emp.: 30
Electric Component Whslr
N.A.I.C.S.: 423690
Fugiyama Sogiro (Gen Mgr)

Subsidiary (Domestic):

Elematec (Qingdao) Trading Co., Ltd. (3)
Rm 710 Yihe International Building A No 10 Hong Kong Middle Road, South City District, Qingdao, 266071, Shandong, China
Tel.: (86) 53266888228
Electric Component Whslr
N.A.I.C.S.: 423690

Subsidiary (Non-US):

Elematec (Thailand) Co., Ltd. (2)
399 Interchange 21 Building Unit 2704-6 27th Floor Sukhumvit Road, Klongtoey-Nua Wattana, Bangkok, 10110, Thailand
Tel.: (66) 22584412
Web Site: http://www.elematec.com
Sales Range: $25-49.9 Million
Electrical & Electronic Components Distr
N.A.I.C.S.: 423610

Elematec (Tianjin) International Trading Co., Ltd. (2)
Rm 3108 Golden Crown Bldg No 20 Nanjing Rd, Hexi District, Tianjin, China
Tel.: (86) 2223161070
Sales Range: $25-49.9 Million
Emp.: 10
Electronic Components Distr
N.A.I.C.S.: 423690

Elematec Czech s.r.o. (2)
SMICHOV GATE Building 1st Floor Plzenska 3217/16, Smichov, 150 00, Prague, 5, Czech Republic
Tel.: (420) 246050070

AND PRIVATE COMPANIES

TOYOTA TSUSHO CORPORATION

Sales Range: $25-49.9 Million
Emp.: 5
Consumer Electronics Distr
N.A.I.C.S.: 423620

Elematec Electronics (Dalian) Co., Ltd. (2)
No 35-3 ID Free Trade Zone, Dalian, 116600, Liaoning, China
Tel.: (86) 41187544828
Circuit Board Assembling Services
N.A.I.C.S.: 334514

Elematec Hong Kong Limited (2)
Unit 504B 505B 5/F Empire Centre No 68 Mody Road, Tsim Sha Tsui, Kowloon, China (Hong Kong)
Tel.: (852) 27965713
Electric Component Whslr
N.A.I.C.S.: 423690

Elematec International Trading (Shenzhen) Co., Ltd. (2)
Room 3609-3615 ShunHing Square Di Wang Commercial Center, 5002 Shennan Road East, Shenzhen, 518022, Guangdong, China
Tel.: (86) 75582170257
Sales Range: $25-49.9 Million
Electric Component Whslr
N.A.I.C.S.: 423690

Elematec Korea Co., Ltd. (2)
Rm 501 527 Eonju-ro, Gangnam-gu, Seoul, 06138, Korea (South)
Tel.: (82) 234541257
Web Site: https://www.elematec.com
Sales Range: $25-49.9 Million
Electrical & Electronics Component Whslr
N.A.I.C.S.: 423610

Elematec Philippines, Inc. (2)
18/F 6788 Ayala Ave Oledan Square, Makati, 1226, Philippines
Tel.: (63) 28177552
Web Site: http://www.elematec.com
Sales Range: $25-49.9 Million
Electrical & Electronic Components Distr
N.A.I.C.S.: 423610

Elematec Singapore (Pte.) Ltd. (2)
305 Alexandra Road ste 04-01/02 Vantage Automotive Centre, Singapore, Singapore
Tel.: (65) 62731844
Sales Range: $50-74.9 Million
Emp.: 9
Electrical & Electronic Components Distr
N.A.I.C.S.: 423610
So Thara (Mng Dir)

Elematec Taiwan Corporation (2)
13F No 36-10 Sec 1 Fu-Hsing South Road, Taipei, 104698, Taiwan
Tel.: (886) 227312112
Emp.: 20
Electrical & Electronic Components Distr
N.A.I.C.S.: 423610
Hiroshi Aozei (Gen Mgr)

Elematec Trading (Dalian) Co., Ltd. (2)
5/F No 35-3 ID Free Trade Zone, Dalian, 116600, Liaoning, China
Tel.: (86) 41187308830
Electrical & Electronic Components Distr
N.A.I.C.S.: 423610

Elematec Trading India Private Limited (2)
Unit No 601 6th Floor Prestige Meridian-1 No 29 M G Road, Bengaluru, 560 001, Karnataka, India (100%)
Tel.: (91) 8040935645
Web Site: http://www.elematec.com
Sales Range: $750-799.9 Million
Import, Export & Domestic Sales of Electrical Materials & Electronic Components
N.A.I.C.S.: 334419

Subsidiary (US):

Elematec USA Corporation (2)
4909 Murphy Canyon Rd, San Diego, CA 92123
Tel.: (858) 527-1700
Web Site: http://www.elematecusa.com
Sales Range: $25-49.9 Million
Electronic Components Distr
N.A.I.C.S.: 423690
Yoichi Sugao (CEO)

Subsidiary (Non-US):

KORIN TECHNOLOGY CO., LIMITED (2)
Dafapu Village Bantian Buji Longgang, Shenzhen, Guangdong, China
Tel.: (86) 755 8995 1338
Electronic Components Mfr
N.A.I.C.S.: 334419

Subsidiary (Domestic):

Ohnishi Denki Co., Ltd. (2)
138-2 Higashi Ku-jo Matsuda-cho, Minami-ku, Kyoto, 601-8036, Japan
Tel.: (81) 756935231
Web Site: http://www.elematec.jp
Sales Range: $100-124.9 Million
Emp.: 90
Electrical Insulation Materials, Industrial Heaters, Crimp Contacts & Connectors, Printed Circuit Boards, Industrial Tapes, Small Batteries & Power Supplies Mfr & Distr
N.A.I.C.S.: 423610

Subsidiary (Non-US):

Wuxi Takachiho-Sun Industry Co., Ltd. (2)
No 6 Block 8 South Station Industry Concentrated District B, Wuxi, 214028, Jiangsu, China
Tel.: (86) 51088558108
Electronic Components Mfr
N.A.I.C.S.: 334419

Ene Vision Co., Ltd (1)
5th floor Nissei Imaike Building 4-1-29 Imaike, Chikusa-ku, Nagoya, 464-0850, Aichi, Japan
Tel.: (81) 527443931
Web Site: https://www.enev.co.jp
Emp.: 50
Construction Engineering Services
N.A.I.C.S.: 541330

Eurus Energy Holdings Corporation (1)
Hulic Kamiyacho Building 7th Floor 3-13 Toranomon 4-Chome, Minato-ku, Tokyo, 105-0001, Japan (99.99%)
Tel.: (81) 35 404 5300
Web Site: https://www.eurus-energy.com
Sales Range: $10-24.9 Million
Emp.: 366
Electricity Generation Services
N.A.I.C.S.: 221118
Hideyuki Inazumi (Pres & CEO)

Fukuske Corporation (1)
Kyocera Bldg 4 F 6-27-8 Jingumae, Shibuya-ku, Tokyo, 150-0001, Japan
Tel.: (81) 3 6418 1400
Web Site: http://www.fukuske.com
Emp.: 651
Sock, Stocking & Underwear Mfr
N.A.I.C.S.: 315120
Hiroshi Tasaka (Pres)

Grand Place Corporation (1)
17 Yachimata-ha, Yachimata, 289-1107, Chiba, Japan
Tel.: (81) 434436471
Web Site: https://grand-place.co.jp
Emp.: 80
Confectionery Mfr & Whslr
N.A.I.C.S.: 311351

Green Metals Hokuriku Inc. (1)
79-1-1 Awatabecho, Echizen, 915-0242, Fukui, Japan
Tel.: (81) 778438700
Metal Scrap Recycling Services
N.A.I.C.S.: 561990

Guangzhou Fengzhong Aluminium Smelting Technology Co., Ltd. (1)
11 Wuzhoushan North Road, Huangge Town Nansha District, Guangzhou, 511400, Guangdong, China
Tel.: (86) 20 34971999
Web Site: http://www.gfast.com.cn
Sales Range: $100-124.9 Million
Emp.: 500
Aluminium Products Mfr
N.A.I.C.S.: 331314
Kotaro Watanabe (Gen Mgr)

Hot-Line International Transport Ltd. (1)
Osakatoyota Bldg 6F, Osaka, 542-0081, Japan
Tel.: (81) 662436739
Web Site: http://www.tlsnet.co.jp
Emp.: 150
Freight Forwarding Services
N.A.I.C.S.: 488510
Naoki Ishii (Gen Mgr)

Subsidiary (Non-US):

Hot-Line International Transport (China) Limited (2)
1717 West Nanjing Road 2nd Floor Wheelock Square, Shanghai, 100040, Jinganqu, China
Tel.: (86) 21 3633 8000
Freight Forwarding Services
N.A.I.C.S.: 488510

Hot-Line International Transport (H.K.) Limited (2)
Room 2601-2603 26/F Saxon Tower 7 Cheung Shun Street, Cheung Sha Wan, Kowloon, China (Hong Kong)
Tel.: (852) 23684228
Web Site: http://www.hithk.com
Emp.: 40
Warehousing & Logistics Consulting Services
N.A.I.C.S.: 493110
Peggy Shek (Gen Mgr)

Hot-Line Logistics Center (2)
2nd Floor Kerry Warehouse Tsuen Wan No 3 Shing Yiu Street, Kwai Chung, New Territories, China (Hong Kong)
Tel.: (852) 2439 0312
Web Site: http://www.hithk.com
Logistics Consulting Servies
N.A.I.C.S.: 541614
Peggy Shek (Gen Mgr)

Shanghai Toyota Tsusho Hot-Line Logistics Co., Ltd. (2)
Wuhua Road 288 Hongkou Dist Room 607 Building-1, Shanghai, 200080, China
Tel.: (86) 21 3633 8000
Emp.: 100
Logistics Consulting Servies
N.A.I.C.S.: 541614
Sadashi Takizawa (Mgr)

JV "Business Car" Co. Ltd. (1)
74 Rublevskoe Highway, Moscow, 121609, Russia
Tel.: (7) 4957213392
Web Site: http://www.business-car.ru
Sales Range: $550-599.9 Million
Emp.: 1,500
Automotive Distr
N.A.I.C.S.: 423110

Kanto Coil Center Co., Ltd. (1)
58 Minato, Urayasu, 279-0024, Chiba, Japan
Tel.: (81) 473532031
Steel Sheets Whslr
N.A.I.C.S.: 423510

Kanto Grain Terminal Co., Ltd. (1)
2-3 Higashifukashiba, Kamisu, 314-0103, Ibaraki, Japan
Tel.: (81) 299926531
Web Site: https://www.kanto-grain.co.jp
General Warehousing & Storage Services
N.A.I.C.S.: 493110

Kyushu Smelting Technology Corporation (1)
9-2 Torigoe-cho Kanda-machi, Miyako-gun, Miyako, 800-0304, Japan
Tel.: (81) 9 3435 3318
Aluminum Alloys Mfr & Whslr
N.A.I.C.S.: 331314

Natural Cotton Exchange Co., Ltd. (1)
5/6 Baan Piyasathorn 7th Fl Soi Suan-plu South Sathorn Rd, Thungmahamek Sathirn, Bangkok, 10120, Thailand
Tel.: (66) 26775255
Web Site: http://www.toyocotton.co.jp
Sales Range: $50-74.9 Million
Emp.: 5
Cotton Products Distr
N.A.I.C.S.: 424590

Oleos "MENU" Industria e Comercio Ltda. (1)
Rua Afonso Pena S/N - Bairro Industrial, Guararapes, 16700-000, SP, Brazil
Tel.: (55) 1836068200
Web Site: http://www.oleosmenu.com.br
Sales Range: $50-74.9 Million
Oilseed Products Mfr & Distr
N.A.I.C.S.: 311224

Oriental Steel Co., Ltd. (1)
2-33-7 Ariso, Imizu, 933-0251, Toyama, Japan
Tel.: (81) 766864000
Metal Sheets Whslr
N.A.I.C.S.: 423510

P.T. Toyota Tsusho Logistic Center (1)
Jl Irian V Blok KK-8 Kawasan Industri MM2100 Cikarang Barat, Bekasi, 17520, West Java, Indonesia
Tel.: (62) 2189981701
Web Site: https://ttlc.co.id
Warehousing & Logistics Services
N.A.I.C.S.: 493110

PROSTEEL Co., Ltd. (1)
1-1908 Daikonyama, Midori-ku, Nagoya, 459-8501, Aichi, Japan (61.3%)
Tel.: (81) 526291811
Web Site: https://www.prosteel.co.jp
Sales Range: $1-4.9 Billion
Emp.: 92
Steel Products Import & Distr
N.A.I.C.S.: 423510

Poland Smelting Technologies Sp. z.o.o. (1)
ul Jachimowicza 2, 58-306, Walbrzych, Poland
Tel.: (48) 748869800
Web Site: https://www.polst.com.pl
Sales Range: $50-74.9 Million
Emp.: 912
Aluminum Products Whslr
N.A.I.C.S.: 423510

S.C. Toyota Tsusho do Brasil Ltda. (1)
Avenida Paulista 37 - 5 Floor, Paraiso, 01311-902, Sao Paulo, Brazil
Tel.: (55) 1131781500
Web Site: https://www.toyotsu.com.br
Sales Range: $50-74.9 Million
Emp.: 85
Steel Products Import & Distr
N.A.I.C.S.: 423510

T-ST Corporation (1)
2-1-25 Midorigahama, Tahara, 441-3401, Aichi, Japan
Tel.: (81) 531237381
Web Site: https://www.tst-japan.co.jp
Emp.: 137
Aluminum Alloy Mfr & Whslr
N.A.I.C.S.: 331314

T. T. H. K. Co., Ltd. (1)
Russian Federation Blvd Phum Borey 100 Khnong, Sangkat Tuk Thla Khan Sen Sok, Phnom Penh, Cambodia
Tel.: (855) 17333521
Web Site: https://www.toyota.com.kh
Sales Range: $50-74.9 Million
Emp.: 120
Automotive Distr
N.A.I.C.S.: 423110
Masaaki Kawabata (Pres)

T.T.A.S. Co., Ltd. (1)
No 87 A Kaba Aye Pagoda Road, PO 11201, Bahan Township, Yangon, Myanmar
Tel.: (95) 1540740
Web Site: https://toyota-ayeandsons.com
Sales Range: $50-74.9 Million
Emp.: 86
Automotive Part Whslr
N.A.I.C.S.: 423120

TEMCO Corporation (1)
2-3-6 Kamishirane, Asahi-ku, Yokohama, 241-0002, Kanagawa, Japan
Tel.: (81) 459533434
Industrial Machinery & Equipment Mfr & Whslr
N.A.I.C.S.: 333248

TOMEN ELECTRONICS (SHENZHEN) CO., LTD (1)
Suite A03-04 12/F Anlian Plaza 4018 Jintian

TOYOTA TSUSHO CORPORATION

Toyota Tsusho Corporation—(Continued)
Road, Futian District, Shenzhen, 518026, China
Tel.: (86) 755 88286262
Electronic Component Mfr & Whslr
N.A.I.C.S.: 334419

TOMEN ELECTRONICS INDIA PRIVATE LIMITED (1)
812-15 Krishna Apra Netaji Subhash Place, Pitam Pura Distt Centre, New Delhi, 110034, India
Tel.: (91) 11 4563 9200
Emp.: 13
Electronic Component Mfr & Whslr
N.A.I.C.S.: 334419
Sunny Malhotra *(Pres)*

TOMEN ELECTRONICS MALAYSIA SDN. BHD. (1)
Room 1406 Wisma Lim Foo Yong 86 Jalan Raja Chulan, 50200, Kuala Lumpur, Malaysia
Tel.: (60) 3 2143 0173
Electronic Component Mfr & Whslr
N.A.I.C.S.: 334419

TOYOTA (CAMBODIA) CO., LTD. (1)
Russian Federation Blvd 110 Sangkat Teuk Thlar, Khan Sen Sok, Phnom Penh, 12100, Cambodia
Tel.: (855) 17222730
Web Site: https://www.toyota.com.kh
Sales Range: $50-74.9 Million
Automotive Distr
N.A.I.C.S.: 423120

TOYOTA DIGITAL CRUISE, INC. (1)
DNI Nishiki Bldg 2F 1-8-11 Nishiki, Naka-ku, Nagoya, 460-0003, Aichi, Japan
Tel.: (81) 52 202 0333
Web Site: http://www.d-cruise.co.jp
Rev.: $192,168,000
Emp.: 514
Information Technology Consulting Services
N.A.I.C.S.: 541512
Shozaburo Tomita *(Sr Mng Dir)*

Subsidiary (Non-US):

PT. TT NETWORK INTEGRATION INDONESIA (2)
Mid Plaza Building 2 14th Floor JL Jend Sudirman Kav 10-11, Jakarta Pusat, Jakarta, 10220, Indonesia
Tel.: (62) 2180511660
Web Site: https://www.ttsystems.com
Sales Range: $10-24.9 Million
Emp.: 18
Information Technology Consulting Services
N.A.I.C.S.: 541512

TT Network Integration (Thailand) Co., Ltd. (2)
49th Floor CRC Tower All Seasons Place 87/2 Wireless Road, Lumpini Pathumwan, Bangkok, 10330, Thailand
Tel.: (66) 26853077
Web Site: https://www.ttsystems.com
Sales Range: $25-49.9 Million
Emp.: 241
Information Technology Consulting Services
N.A.I.C.S.: 541512
Hirotoshi Watanabe *(Mng Dir)*

TOYOTA TSUSHO TECHNICS CENTRAL ASIA LLP (1)
Tashkent 505 yr St Momyshuly Building, Almaty, 050061, Kazakhstan
Tel.: (7) 727 315 01 01
Web Site: http://www.forklift.kz
Sales Range: $50-74.9 Million
Emp.: 57
Construction Machinery Distr
N.A.I.C.S.: 423810

TT NETWORK INTEGRATION INDIA PRIVATE LIMITED (1)
Embassy Diamante Level II 34 Vital Mallya Road, Bengaluru, 560 001, India
Tel.: (91) 8043341000
Web Site: https://www.ttsystems.com
Information Technology Consulting Services
N.A.I.C.S.: 541512

Techno Steel Processing De Mexico S.A. de C.V. (1)
Boulevard Interamerican No 316 Parque Industrial Finsa Monterrey, 66626, Apodaca, Nuevo Leon, Mexico
Tel.: (52) 8181963080
Web Site: https://tspmx.com
Steel Processing Center & Distr
N.A.I.C.S.: 423510
Yoshiyuki Tajiri *(Gen Mgr)*

Thai Chemical Terminal Co., Ltd. (1)
90 Phethung Road Bangyor, Phra Pradaeng, Samut Prakan, 10130, Thailand
Tel.: (66) 2 4610005
Logistics Consulting Servies
N.A.I.C.S.: 541614

Tianjin Fengtian Logistics Co., Ltd. (1)
No 15 11th Avenue Teda, Technological Development Zone, Tianjin, 300457, China
Tel.: (86) 22 2532 7977
Web Site: http://www.tfl-global.com
Emp.: 1,400
Logistics Consulting Servies
N.A.I.C.S.: 541614

Tianjin Toyota Tsusho Steel Co., Ltd. (1)
No 15 Huayang Street Economic Technology Development Zone, Tianjin, 300457, China
Tel.: (86) 2266230050
Steel Mfrs
N.A.I.C.S.: 331110

Tianjin Toyotsu Aluminium Smelting Technology Co., Ltd. (1)
No 185 Taifeng Road Teda, Tianjin, 300457, China
Tel.: (86) 2266231101206
Aluminum Products Mfr & Whslr
N.A.I.C.S.: 331314

Tianjin Toyotsu Automotive Equipment Manufacturing Co., Ltd. (1)
East Side of Plant D Fenghua Industrial Park No 66 9th Ave Teda, Tianjin, China
Tel.: (86) 22 25293951
Automobile Equipment Mfr
N.A.I.C.S.: 336390

Tohoku Grain Terminal Co., Ltd. (1)
24-4 Kaigan Kawaragi, Hachinohe, 039-1161, Aomori, Japan
Tel.: (81) 178202025
General Warehousing & Storage Services
N.A.I.C.S.: 493110

Tomen Electronics Corporation (1)
Shinagawa Front Building 2-3-13 Konan, Minato-ku, Tokyo, 108-8208, Japan (63%)
Tel.: (81) 354629611
Web Site: http://www.tomen-ele.co.jp
Electronic Component Mfr & Whslr
N.A.I.C.S.: 334419

Tomen Iran Ltd. (1)
Unit 5 2nd Floor No 1 4th Park Alley Movahed Danesh, PO Box 15875/3141, Aqdasiyeh, 19576-47776, Tehran, Iran
Tel.: (98) 2126117086
Web Site: http://www.toyota-tsusho.com
Steel Import & Distr
N.A.I.C.S.: 423510

Tomen Power (Singapore) Pte. Ltd. (1)
600 North Bridge Road 04-09 Parkview Square, Unit 03-01 Odeon Towers, Singapore, 188778, Singapore
Tel.: (65) 62271128
Power Generation Services
N.A.I.C.S.: 221118

Tomen Toyota Tsusho Petroleum (S) Pte. Ltd. (1)
600 North Beach Road Unit 16-08//09/10 Parkview Square, Singapore, 188778, Singapore
Tel.: (65) 62214002
Petroleum Product Mfr
N.A.I.C.S.: 324199
Haruhiko Murata *(Mng Dir)*

Tomuki Corporation (1)
Pacific Square Sengoku 6F 2-29-24 Honkomagome, Bunkyou-ku, Tokyo, 113-0021, Japan
Tel.: (81) 3 5978 8360
Web Site: http://www.tomuki.co.jp
Rev.: $64,872,000
Emp.: 95
Electric Component Whslr
N.A.I.C.S.: 423690
Kazuyuki Hashimoto *(Pres)*

Toyo Cotton (Japan) Co. (1)
8-2 Utsubo-Honmachi 1-Chome, Nishi-ku, Osaka, 550-0004, Japan
Tel.: (81) 664791422
Web Site: http://www.toyocotton.net
Cotton Products Distr
N.A.I.C.S.: 424590

Subsidiary (Non-US):

Sang Jee Trading Co. (2)
Room 402 Keunwha Bldg 120-13 Seosomoon-Dong, Chung-ku, Seoul, Korea (South)
Tel.: (82) 2 778 1186
Web Site: http://www.toyocotton.co.jp
Cotton Products Distr
N.A.I.C.S.: 424590

Subsidiary (US):

Toyo Cotton Company (2)
11611 Forest Central Dr, Dallas, TX 75243-3928
Tel.: (214) 349-1376
Web Site: http://www.toyocotton.net
Sales Range: $1-9.9 Million
Emp.: 20
Cotton Merchants
N.A.I.C.S.: 424590

Toyo Grain Terminal Co., Ltd. (1)
14-9 Kitahamamachi, Chita, 478-0046, Aichi, Japan
Tel.: (81) 562325371
General Warehousing & Storage Services
N.A.I.C.S.: 493110

Toyoda Machinery (Dalian) Co., Ltd (1)
Inside of No 46 Area Economic Technology Development Zone, Dalian, 116600, Liaoning, China
Tel.: (86) 41187334601
Machine Tools Mfr
N.A.I.C.S.: 333517

Toyota Adria, podjetje za izvoz in promet z vozili, d.o.o. (1)
Brnciceva Ulica 51, 1231, Ljubljana, Slovenia
Tel.: (386) 15305060
Web Site: http://www.toyota.se
Emp.: 35
Automotive Distr
N.A.I.C.S.: 423110
Akira Kimura *(Pres)*

Toyota Chemical Engineering Co., Ltd. (1)
4-9-8 Meieki, Nakamura-ku, Nagoya, 450-8575, Aichi, Japan (100%)
Tel.: (81) 569249925
Web Site: https://www.toyochemi.co.jp
Emp.: 115
Waste Management Services
N.A.I.C.S.: 562998

Toyota Europe Engineering & Maintenance, NV/SA (1)
Bourgetlaan 60, Brussels, 1130, Belgium
Tel.: (32) 27452111
Industrial Machinery Maintenance Services
N.A.I.C.S.: 811310

Toyota Istif Makineleri A.S. (1)
Esenkent Mah Kartopu Sok No 20, Umraniye, 34776, Istanbul, Turkiye
Tel.: (90) 4447898
Web Site: https://www.toyota-forklifts.com.tr
Construction Machinery Mfr
N.A.I.C.S.: 333120

Toyota Jamaica Ltd. (1)
427 Spanish Town Road, Kingston, 11, Jamaica
Tel.: (876) 9 237 2315
Web Site: https://www.toyotajamaica.com
Automotive Distr
N.A.I.C.S.: 423110
Howard Foster *(Gen Mgr-Sls & Mktg)*

Toyota Kenya Ltd. (1)
Uhuru Highway/Lusaka Road, PO Box 3391, Nairobi, 506, Kenya
Tel.: (254) 71 902 9000
Web Site: https://toyotakenya.com
Automotive Distr
N.A.I.C.S.: 423110
Denis Awori *(Chm)*

Toyota Lakozy Auto Private Ltd. (1)
504 Link Road Chicholi Bunder Malad West, Mumbai, 400064, India
Tel.: (91) 2261927777
Web Site: https://www.lakozytoyota.com
Sales Range: $50-74.9 Million
Emp.: 100
Automotive Distr
N.A.I.C.S.: 423110

Toyota Lanka (Private) Limited (1)
Toyota Plaza No 337 Negombo Road, Wattala, Sri Lanka
Tel.: (94) 112 939 0006
Web Site: https://www.toyota.lk
Sales Range: $150-199.9 Million
Emp.: 400
Automotive Distr
N.A.I.C.S.: 423110
Sachio Yotsukura *(Chm)*

Toyota Malawi Ltd. (1)
Queens Corner Masauko Chipembere Highway, PO Box 430, Blantyre, Malawi
Tel.: (265) 31 000 2444
Web Site: https://www.toyotamalawi.com
Automotive Distr
N.A.I.C.S.: 423110
Andrew Katimba *(Gen Mgr-Corp Affairs)*

Toyota Steel Center Co., Ltd. (1)
33-4 Shinhocho, Tokai, 476-8533, Aichi, Japan
Tel.: (81) 526035561
Web Site: https://www.toyotasc.jp
Emp.: 403
Metal Sheet Distr
N.A.I.C.S.: 423510

Toyota Techno Park India Pvt. Ltd. (1)
Plot No 20 Bidadi Industrial Area, Ramanagar Tk District, Bengaluru, 562109, Karnataka, India
Tel.: (91) 8027287157
Industrial Park Construction & Management Services
N.A.I.C.S.: 237990

Toyota Tsusho (Australasia) Pty. Ltd. (1)
231-233 Boundary Road, Laverton, 3026, VIC, Australia
Tel.: (61) 383687900
Web Site: http://www2.toyotatsusho.com.au
Sales Range: $50-74.9 Million
Emp.: 108
Basic Material Trading Services
N.A.I.C.S.: 238990

Subsidiary (Non-US):

Myanmar Toyota Tsusho Co. Ltd (2)
Sedona Business Suite 03-12 No 1 Kaba Aye Pagoda Road Yankin Township, Yangon, Myanmar
Tel.: (95) 1 651 638
Chemical Products Distr
N.A.I.C.S.: 424690

P.T. Toyota Tsusho Indonesia (2)
14th Floor New Summitmas Jl Jend Sudirman Kav 61-62, Jakarta, 12069, Indonesia
Tel.: (62) 215703203
Web Site: http://www.toyotatsusho.com
Emp.: 150
Automobile Product Distr
N.A.I.C.S.: 423120
Jun Karube *(Pres)*

Subsidiary (Domestic):

TT Logistics (Australasia) Pty Ltd (2)
231-233 Boundary Road, Laverton North, Melbourne, 3026, VIC, Australia
Tel.: (61) 3 8368 7900
Web Site: http://ttlogistics.com.au
Logistics Consulting Servies
N.A.I.C.S.: 541614

TT Steel Centre (Australasia) Pty Ltd (2)

AND PRIVATE COMPANIES — TOYOTA TSUSHO CORPORATION

231-233 Boundary Road, Laverton North, Melbourne, 3026, VIC, Australia
Tel.: (61) 3 8368 7900
Emp.: 33
Steel Products Mfr
N.A.I.C.S.: 331110

Subsidiary (Non-US):

Toyota Tsusho (Hong Kong) Co., Ltd. (2)
27th Floor United Centre No 95 Queensway, Hong Kong, China (Hong Kong)
Tel.: (852) 28042832
Automotive Part Whslr
N.A.I.C.S.: 423140

Toyota Tsusho Korea Corporation (2)
30F Mirae Asset CENTER1 West Tower 67 Suha-dong, Jung-gu, Seoul, 100-210, Korea (South)
Tel.: (82) 267446744
Web Site: http://www.toyotatsusho.co.kr
Sales Range: $25-49.9 Million
Emp.: 45
Automotive Part Whslr
N.A.I.C.S.: 423120

Toyota Tsusho (China) Co., Ltd. (1)
Room No 220 Beijing Fortune Building No 5 Dong San Huan Bei Lu, Chaoyang District, Beijing, 100004, China
Tel.: (86) 106 590 8920
Web Site: http://www.toyota-tsusho.com
Emp.: 65
Steel Products Import & Distr
N.A.I.C.S.: 423510
Takahiro Kondo (Gen Mgr)

Toyota Tsusho (Dalian) Co., Ltd. (1)
7F Senmao Building 147 Zhongshan Road, Dalian, Liaoning, China
Tel.: (86) 41183607568
Web Site: http://www.toyota-tsusho.com
Steel Products Import & Distr
N.A.I.C.S.: 423510

Toyota Tsusho (Guangzhou) Co., Ltd. (1)
Room 2201 Taikoo Hui Tower 1 No 385 Tianhe Road, Tianhe District, Guangzhou, 510620, Guangdong, China
Tel.: (86) 2086663948
Trading Services
N.A.I.C.S.: 238990

Toyota Tsusho (H.K.) Corporation Limited (1)
Room 2702 Block 1 27/F Admiralty Centre 18 Harcourt Road, Hong Kong, China (Hong Kong)
Tel.: (852) 36671000
Web Site: http://www.toyota-tsusho.com
Emp.: 80
Steel Products Import & Distr
N.A.I.C.S.: 423510

Toyota Tsusho (Malaysia) Sdn. Bhd. (1)
Room 1404 Wisma Lim Foo Yong 86 Jalan Raja Chulan, 50200, Kuala Lumpur, Malaysia (70%)
Tel.: (60) 32 336 3366
Web Site: http://www.toyotsu.com.my
Sales Range: $25-49.9 Million
Emp.: 70
Material Trading Services
N.A.I.C.S.: 238990
Lee Meng Hui (Head-Metals & Non-Ferrous Matls)

Toyota Tsusho (Shanghai) Co., Ltd. (1)
2nd Floor Wheelock Square 1717 Nanjing West Road, Jinganqu, Shanghai, China
Tel.: (86) 215 404 2222
Web Site: http://www.toyota-tsusho.com
Steel Products Import & Distr
N.A.I.C.S.: 423510

Toyota Tsusho (Singapore) Pte., Ltd. (1)
6 Shenton Way 11-08 OUE Downtown 2, Singapore, 068809, Singapore
Tel.: (65) 62223711
Web Site: https://www.toyotsu.com.sg
Sales Range: $50-74.9 Million
Emp.: 150
Worldwide Trading Services

N.A.I.C.S.: 238990
Avalon Goh (Mgr-Admin)

Toyota Tsusho (Taiwan) Co., Ltd. (1)
5F No 101 Songren Rd, Sinyi Dist, Taipei, 110, Taiwan
Tel.: (886) 28 786 2500
Web Site: https://www.toyotsu.com.tw
Emp.: 177
Metal Products Import & Distr
N.A.I.C.S.: 423510
Issei Hata (Pres)

Toyota Tsusho Africa (Pty) Ltd. (1)
15 Beechgate Crescent Southgate Business Park Moss Kolnik Drive, Umbogintwini, 4120, Kwazulu Natal, South Africa
Tel.: (27) 319495000
Web Site: http://www.ttaf.co.za
Sales Range: $150-199.9 Million
Emp.: 600
Logistic Services
N.A.I.C.S.: 541614

Division (Domestic):

Toyota Tsusho Africa (Pty) Ltd. - Green Metals Division (2)
15-17 Power Drive, Prospecton, Durban, 4110, South Africa
Tel.: (27) 31 910 7850
Emp.: 26
Logistics Consulting Servies
N.A.I.C.S.: 541614
Antom Dreyer (Gen Mgr)

Toyota Tsusho America, Inc. (1)
805 3rd Ave 17th Fl, New York, NY 10022
Tel.: (212) 355-3600
Web Site: http://www.taiamerica.com
Sales Range: $50-74.9 Million
Emp.: 100
Trading & Investment Services
N.A.I.C.S.: 425120
Kenji Yodose (Project Mgr)

Subsidiary (Domestic):

Deepwater Chemicals, Inc. (2)
196122 E County Rd 40, Woodward, OK 73801-5656
Tel.: (580) 256-0500
Web Site: https://www.deepwaterchemicals.com
Sales Range: $25-49.9 Million
Chemical Products Mfr
N.A.I.C.S.: 325180

Dewey Chemical Inc. (2)
5801 Broadway Ext Ste 305, Oklahoma City, OK 73118-7334
Tel.: (405) 848-8611
Sales Range: $25-49.9 Million
Emp.: 1
Iodine Producer & Sales
N.A.I.C.S.: 325180

Feroleto Steel Company, Inc. (2)
300 Scofield Ave, Bridgeport, CT 06605
Tel.: (203) 366-3263
Web Site: https://www.feroletosteel.com
Sales Range: $25-49.9 Million
Emp.: 65
Rolled Steel Mfr
N.A.I.C.S.: 331221
Jim Hillas (Sr VP)

Industrial Tech Services, Inc. (2)
321 Triport Rd, Georgetown, KY 40324
Tel.: (502) 863-4941
Web Site: https://www.itslex.com
Sales Range: $10-24.9 Million
Industrial Engineering Services
N.A.I.C.S.: 541330

Joint Venture (Domestic):

Silver Springs Citrus Inc. (2)
25411 Mare Ave, Howey in the Hills, FL 34737 (49%)
Tel.: (352) 324-2101
Web Site: http://www.silverspringscitrus.com
Sales Range: $100-124.9 Million
Emp.: 227
Grower, Harvester & Processor of Citrus Fruits
N.A.I.C.S.: 311411

Subsidiary (Domestic):

Tomen Grain Co. (2)
221 Margaret St, Pekin, IL 61554-3180
Tel.: (309) 347-3184
Sales Range: $10-24.9 Million
Emp.: 11
Grain Elevators
N.A.I.C.S.: 111199

Subsidiary (Non-US):

Toyota Tsusho Canada, Inc. (2)
1080 Fountain St, Cambridge, N3E 1A3, ON, Canada
Tel.: (519) 653-6600
Web Site: http://www.taiamerica.com
Sales Range: $25-49.9 Million
Emp.: 40
Automotive & MRO Products Distr
N.A.I.C.S.: 441330
Kengo Suzuki (Pres)

Subsidiary (Domestic):

Toyota Tsusho Material Handling America, Inc. (2)
12001 SE Jennifer St, Clackamas, OR 97015
Tel.: (503) 657-6900
Web Site: http://www.toyotaliftnorthwest.com
Sales Range: $25-49.9 Million
Emp.: 35
Forklifts & Material Handling Equipment Sales & Rentals
N.A.I.C.S.: 423830

Toyota Tsusho Argentina S.A. (1)
Ruta Panamericana KM 29 4 1618, El Talar, Buenos Aires, Argentina
Tel.: (54) 11 4726 4250
Web Site: http://www.toyotsu.com.ar
Industrial Supplies Distr
N.A.I.C.S.: 423840

Toyota Tsusho Auto Valenciennes S.A.R.L. (1)
Zone Industrielle 4 Ld Les Pres Sud 200 Rue Henri Durre, 59880, Saint-Saulve, Nord, France
Tel.: (33) 327329400
Automotive Distr
N.A.I.C.S.: 423110

Toyota Tsusho Automobile London Holdings Limited (1)
The Hyde Edgware Road, London, NW9 6BH, United Kingdom
Tel.: (44) 2082031888
Financial Management Services
N.A.I.C.S.: 523999

Toyota Tsusho Automobiles Paris Est S.A.S. (1)
3 Rue Des Ardennes, 75019, Paris, France
Tel.: (33) 140031600
Motor Vehicle Parts Distr
N.A.I.C.S.: 423120

Toyota Tsusho Electronics Corporation (1)
Nagoya Lucent Tower 33F 6-1 Ushijimacho, Nishi-ku, Nagoya, 451-6033, Japan
Tel.: (81) 525593333
Web Site: http://www.toyotsu-electronics.co.jp
Rev.: $266,832,000
Emp.: 284
Semiconductor Equipment Distr
N.A.I.C.S.: 423690
Atsushi Aoki (Sr Mng Dir)

Subsidiary (Domestic):

JasPar (2)
2-3-13 Konan, Minato-ku, Tokyo, 108-0075, Japan
Tel.: (81) 354957530
Web Site: https://www.jaspar.jp
Sales Range: $25-49.9 Million
Emp.: 198
Automotive Software Development Services
N.A.I.C.S.: 541511
Shunichi Toyomasu (Sr Exec Dir)

T.A.Q.S Toyotsu Automotive Quality Support Center (2)
1-3 Onawa TAQS Ozakicho, Anjo, 446-0004, Aichi, Japan
Tel.: (81) 566 96 4433
Web Site: http://www.taqs.net
Computer Software Development Services
N.A.I.C.S.: 541511

Van Partners (2)
1-8-27 Nishin Building 8th Fl, Minato-ku, Tokyo, 108-0075, Japan
Tel.: (81) 3 5495 7550
Web Site: http://www.van-partners.com
Computer Software Development Services
N.A.I.C.S.: 541511
Tomonori Nakamura (Gen Mgr)

e License Inc. (2)
Shibuya Hiroo 5-6-6 Hiroo Plaza 8 Floor, Minato-ku, Tokyo, 150-0012, Shibuya-ku, Japan
Tel.: (81) 354471080
Web Site: http://www.elicense.co.jp
Emp.: 30
Computer Software Development Services
N.A.I.C.S.: 541511
Akihiro Mino (CEO)

Toyota Tsusho Euroleasing Hungary KFT (1)
Szallas Utca 20-22, Budapest, 1107, Hungary
Tel.: (36) 12601811
Web Site: http://www.toyotatsusho.hu
Automobile Parts Distr
N.A.I.C.S.: 423120

Toyota Tsusho Europe SA (1)
Belgicastraat 13, 1930, Zaventem, Belgium
Tel.: (32) 25414700
Web Site: http://www.toyota-tsusho-europe.com
Sales Range: $25-49.9 Million
Emp.: 38
Trading Services
N.A.I.C.S.: 238990

Division (Non-US):

Toyota Tsusho Europe SA (2)
65B Immermannstrasse, 40210, Dusseldorf, Germany
Tel.: (49) 2118 825 2101
Web Site: http://www.toyota-tsusho-europe.com
Sales Range: $25-49.9 Million
Emp.: 75
Trading Services & Supply Chain Management
N.A.I.C.S.: 425120
Christoph Warnar (Mgr-QA)

Toyota Tsusho Foods Corporation (1)
2-3-13 Konan, Minato-ku, Tokyo, 108-0075, Japan
Tel.: (81) 343068541
Web Site: http://www.toyotsu-shokuryo.com
Emp.: 165
Food Products & Liquors Whslr
N.A.I.C.S.: 424420

Toyota Tsusho Forklift (Thailand) Co., Ltd. (1)
Amata City Chonburi Industrial Estate Phase 4 700/412 Moo 7 T, Don Huaroh A Muang, Chon Buri, 20000, Thailand
Tel.: (66) 38454428
Web Site: http://www.toyotaforkliftthailand.com
Forklift Truck Distr
N.A.I.C.S.: 423830

Toyota Tsusho ID Systems GmbH (1)
Immermannstrasse 65 B, 40210, Dusseldorf, Germany
Tel.: (49) 21188252450
Web Site: http://www.ttid-systems.com
Barcode Handheld Terminals & Scanners Whslr
N.A.I.C.S.: 423430

Toyota Tsusho Insurance Partners Corporation. (1)
4-60-12 Hiraikecho Nakamura-ku Nagoya, Aichi, 453-6129, Japan
Tel.: (81) 525844701
Web Site: https://www.tip-net.com
Emp.: 444
Insurance Agents
N.A.I.C.S.: 524210

Toyota Tsusho Machinery, LLC (1)
Sofiyskaya ul 66 Lit B, 192289, Saint Petersburg, Russia
Tel.: (7) 812 331 5640
Industrial Machinery Mfr

TOYOTA TSUSHO CORPORATION

Toyota Tsusho Corporation—(Continued)
N.A.I.C.S.: 333248
Yuakiharu Hashiga (Mgr)

Toyota Tsusho Mexico, S.A. de C.V. (1)
Calle Septima No 300 Suite 1020 Parque Industrial Monterrey, Apodaca, 66603, Nuevo Leon, Mexico
Tel.: (52) 81 1156 6800
Web Site: http://www.toyota-tsusho.com
Emp.: 200
Automobile Parts Distr
N.A.I.C.S.: 423120
Tetsuo Horimoto (VP)

Toyota Tsusho Re Singapore Pte. Ltd. (1)
2 Shenton Way 26-01 SGX Centre I, Singapore, 068804, Singapore
Tel.: (65) 62223711
Web Site: http://www.toyota.com.sg
Reinsurance Carrier Services
N.A.I.C.S.: 524130

Toyota Tsusho Tekhnika LLC (1)
Balaklavsky prospect 26, 141401, Moscow, Russia
Tel.: (7) 4952237726
Web Site: http://toyota-forklift.ru
Forklifts Distr
N.A.I.C.S.: 423810

Toyota Tsusho U.K. Ltd. (1)
2 Pond End Willow Farm Business Park, Castle Donington, DE74 2UB, Derbyshire, United Kingdom
Tel.: (44) 1332815210
Web Site: https://www.toyota-tsusho-europe.com
Emp.: 200
Steel Products Import & Distr
N.A.I.C.S.: 423510
Takashi Hirobe (Mng Dir)

Subsidiary (Domestic):

Green Metals UK Ltd (2)
2 Pond End Willow Farm Business Park, Castle Donington, DE74 2UB, Derbyshire, United Kingdom
Tel.: (44) 1332284888
Web Site: https://www.ttgmuk.com
Sales Range: $10-24.9 Million
Waste Management Services
N.A.I.C.S.: 562998

Toyota Tsusho Vietnam Co., Ltd. (1)
Sun Red River Building 7th Fl 23 Phan Chu Trinh Street, Hoan Kiem District, Hanoi, Vietnam
Tel.: (84) 2439331018
Automobile Parts Distr
N.A.I.C.S.: 423120

Toyota Tsusho de Venezuela, C.A. (1)
Av Francisco de Miranda con Av Arturo Uslar Pietri, Edificio Torre Meta Iica Piso 14 Urb, Chacao, Estado Miranda, Venezuela
Tel.: (58) 2122659662
Emp.: 15
Steel Products Import & Distr
N.A.I.C.S.: 423510

Toyota Uganda Limited (1)
Plot 1A & 1B First Street Industrial Area, PO Box 31732, Kampala, 31732, Uganda
Tel.: (256) 80 021 1033
Web Site: https://www.toyota.co.ug
Sales Range: $75-99.9 Million
Emp.: 160
Automotive Distr
N.A.I.C.S.: 423110
Omar Mahmood (Mng Dir)

Toyota Zimbabwe (Private) Ltd. (1)
67 Mutare Road, PO Box HG747, Msasa, Harare, Zimbabwe
Tel.: (263) 867 706 7067
Web Site: http://www.toyota.co.zw
Sales Range: $50-74.9 Million
Emp.: 110
Motor Car Dealers
N.A.I.C.S.: 441110
Ian Howden (Mng Dir)

Toyotsu Auto Service Co., Ltd. (1)
3rd Floor Chitose Building 26-13 Meieki 4-chome, Nakamura-ku, Nagoya, 450-0002, Japan
Tel.: (81) 52 618 7522
Web Site: http://www.tautos.jp
Rev.: $50,600,160
Emp.: 100
Automotive Part Whslr
N.A.I.C.S.: 423120
Masaru Tanaka (Pres)

Toyotsu Business Service Corporation (1)
Century Toyoda Bldg 4-9-8 It Meieki, Nakamura-ku, Nagoya, 450-0002, Aichi, Japan
Tel.: (81) 525845459
N.A.I.C.S.: 541219
Yoshiki Asakura (Gen Mgr)

Toyotsu Chemiplas Corporation (1)
Shinagawa Front Building 3-13 Konan 2-chome, Minato-ku, Tokyo, 108-8216, Japan
Tel.: (81) 34 306 8660
Web Site: https://toyotsu-chemiplas.com
Sales Range: $150-199.9 Million
Emp.: 479
Chemical Product Whslr
N.A.I.C.S.: 424690
Yasuhiko Mimura (Chief Div Officer-Chemicals Div)

Toyotsu Energy Corporation (1)
106 Yokoyama, Ikoma-cho, Toyota, 473-0928, Aichi, Japan
Tel.: (81) 565572563
Web Site: http://www.toyotsuene.co.jp
Petroleum Product Whslr
N.A.I.C.S.: 424720

Toyotsu Family Life Corporation (1)
4-11-27 Meieki No 2 Toyota Bldg Higashi-kan, Nakamura-Ku, Nagoya, 450-0002, Aichi, Japan
Tel.: (81) 3 4306 8554
Web Site: http://www.toyotsu-fl.co.jp
General Insurance Services
N.A.I.C.S.: 524210

Toyotsu Fashion Express Co., Ltd. (1)
Kojimachi Tsuruya Hachiman Bldg 8F 2-4 Kojimachi, Chiyoda-ku, Tokyo, 102-0083, Japan
Tel.: (81) 356577000
Web Site: https://www.toyotsufashionexpress.com
Sales Range: $50-74.9 Million
Emp.: 125
Fashion Apparels Retailer
N.A.I.C.S.: 458110

Toyotsu Hitetsu Center Corporation (1)
1 Onawa Ozakicho, Anjo, 446-0004, Aichi, Japan
Tel.: (81) 566963411
Aluminum Sheet Whslr
N.A.I.C.S.: 423510

Toyotsu Hoken Customer Center Corporation (1)
3-12 Sumiyoshicho Toyotsu Bldg Kariya, Kariya, 448-0852, Aichi, Japan
Tel.: (81) 566626991
Web Site: http://www.thcc-net.com
General Insurance Services
N.A.I.C.S.: 524210

Toyotsu Human Resources Corporation (1)
4-9-8 Meieki, Nakamura-ku, Nagoya, 450-0002, Japan
Tel.: (81) 525848050
Web Site: https://www.thr-net.jp
Emp.: 105
Human Resource Consulting Services
N.A.I.C.S.: 541612

Toyotsu Lifecare Corporation (1)
3-162 Hongo, Meito-ku, Nagoya, 465-0024, Aichi, Japan
Tel.: (81) 527775705
Web Site: https://www.toyotsu-facilities.com
Emp.: 72
Nursing Care Services
N.A.I.C.S.: 623110

Toyotsu Machinery Corporation (1)
Symphony Toyota Building 4-11-27 Meieki, Nakamura-ku, Nagoya, 450-0002, Aichi, Japan
Tel.: (81) 525582800
Web Site: https://www.toyotsu-machinery.co.jp
Emp.: 697
Industrial Equipment Repair & Maintenance Services
N.A.I.C.S.: 811310

Toyotsu Material Inc. (1)
Symphony Toyota Bldg 14F 4-11 27 Meieki, Nakamura-ku, Nagoya, 450-0002, Aichi, Japan
Tel.: (81) 525584400
Web Site: https://www.toyotsumaterial.co.jp
Sales Range: $50-74.9 Million
Emp.: 257
Metal Product Whslr
N.A.I.C.S.: 423510

Toyotsu New Pack Co., Ltd. (1)
2-1 Ishizaka Uchikoshicho, Miyoshi, 470-0213, Aichi, Japan
Tel.: (81) 56 133 3988
Web Site: https://www.toyotsu-newpack.jp
Emp.: 34
Packing Products Mfr & Whslr
N.A.I.C.S.: 339991
Yasuo Takanezawa (Gen Mgr)

Toyotsu Office Service Corporation (1)
Century Toyota Building 4-9-8 Meieki, Nakamura-ku, Nagoya, 450-0002, Aichi, Japan
Tel.: (81) 525848152
Web Site: https://www.toyotsu-os.com
Emp.: 109
Office Supplies Distr
N.A.I.C.S.: 424120

Toyotsu Petrotex Corporation (1)
Matsubara Chome No 2 No 8 Teruweru Shinmatsubara building 6th floor, Naka-ku, Nagoya, 460-0017, Aichi, Japan
Tel.: (81) 523245680
Web Site: http://www.toyotsu-sekihan.jp
Sales Range: $50-74.9 Million
Emp.: 60
Petroleum Product Whslr
N.A.I.C.S.: 424720

Toyotsu Rare Earths Corporation (1)
Shinagawa Front Bldg 3-13 Konan 2-chome, Minato-ku, Tokyo, 108-0075, Japan
Tel.: (81) 3 4306 8293
Web Site: http://www.toyotsu-rare-earths.com
Emp.: 15
Metal Mining Services
N.A.I.C.S.: 212290
Sugimoto Atsushi (Pres)

Toyotsu Recycle Corporation (1)
519-1 Kawarada, Nishihirose-cho, Toyota, 470-0309, Aichi, Japan
Tel.: (81) 565469520
Web Site: https://www.toyotsurecycle.co.jp
Emp.: 89
Steel Products Import & Distr
N.A.I.C.S.: 423510

Toyotsu Syscom Corporation (1)
4-11-27 Meieki Symphony Toyota Building, Nakamura-ku, Nagoya, 450-0002, Japan (100%)
Tel.: (81) 5031423500
Web Site: https://www.tsyscom.co.jp
Emp.: 373
Information Systems Consulting & Maintenance Services
N.A.I.C.S.: 517112
Shigeki Tani (CEO)

Toyotsu Tekkou Hambai Co., Ltd. (1)
Century Toyota Building 4-9-8 Meieki, Nakamura-ku, Nagoya, 450-0002, Aichi, Japan
Tel.: (81) 525848450
Web Site: http://www.toyotsuth.co.jp
Emp.: 301
Steel Pipes Whslr
N.A.I.C.S.: 423840

Toyotsu Tekkou Hanbai Co., Ltd. (1)
11th floor Century Toyota Building 4-9-8 Meieki, Nakamura-ku, Nagoya, 450-0002, Aichi, Japan
Tel.: (81) 525848450
Emp.: 301
Metal Sheets Whslr
N.A.I.C.S.: 423510

Toyotsu-Living Co., Ltd. (1)
2-24-2 Hatchobori Nichibei Bldg 8f, Chuo-ku, Tokyo, 104-0032, Japan
Tel.: (81) 3 3551 1300
Web Site: http://www.toyotsu-living.co.jp
Condominium Construction Management Services
N.A.I.C.S.: 236117

UMW Toyotsu Motors Sdn. Bhd. (1)
No 2 Jalan Q15/Q Section 15, 40200, Shah Alam, Selangor, Malaysia (51%)
Tel.: (60) 355136800
Web Site: https://www.toyota.com.my
Sales Range: $50-74.9 Million
Emp.: 140
Car Dealer
N.A.I.C.S.: 441110
Norio Yanai (Mng Dir)

Yamakichi Co., Ltd. (1)
28-7 Tomisuharacho, Yokkaichi, 510-8016, Mie, Japan
Tel.: (81) 593653261
Web Site: http://www.kk-yamakichi.co.jp
Commercial Foodstuffs Whslr
N.A.I.C.S.: 424420

TOYOTA TSUSHO SOUTH SEA LIMITED
Ratu Mara Road Nabua, PO Box 355, Suva, Fiji
Tel.: (679) 3384888
Web Site: http://www.asco.com.fj
TTS—(SPSE)
Rev.: $79,050,021
Assets: $68,163,856
Liabilities: $13,110,336
Net Worth: $55,053,520
Earnings: $7,640,952
Emp.: 402
Fiscal Year-end: 03/31/23
Automobile Parts Mfr
N.A.I.C.S.: 336110
Craig Joseph Sims (CEO)

TOYOU FEIJI ELECTRONICS CO., LTD.
Tongyou Technology Building Building 2 No 9 Dijin Road, Haidian District, Beijing, China
Tel.: (86) 1062491977
Web Site: https://www.toyou.com.cn
300302—(CHIN)
Rev.: $61,114,716
Assets: $266,373,900
Liabilities: $54,243,540
Net Worth: $212,130,360
Earnings: ($2,837,484)
Emp.: 200
Fiscal Year-end: 12/31/22
Data Storage, Protection & Disaster Recovery Products & Software
N.A.I.C.S.: 334112
Zexiang Zhou (Chm & Pres)

TOYS "R" US IBERIA, S.A.U.
Poligono Industrial, Ctra Antigua De Barcelona, 28802, Madrid, Spain
Tel.: (34) 918878200   ES
Web Site: http://www.tru.com
Sales Range: $50-74.9 Million
Emp.: 50
Toy Retailer
N.A.I.C.S.: 459120

TOYS R US ANZ LIMITED
Unit 3 45-47 McNaughton Road, Clayton, 3168, VIC, Australia
Tel.: (61) 800244543
Web Site:
https://www.funtastic.com.au
Year Founded: 1994
TOY—(ASX)
Rev.: $5,120,192
Assets: $12,035,924

Liabilities: $22,173,477
Net Worth: ($10,137,553)
Earnings: ($7,679,621)
Fiscal Year-end: 07/31/24
Children's Toys & Related Merchandise Distr & Marketer
N.A.I.C.S.: 423920
Howard Abbey *(CFO & Sec)*

Subsidiaries:

Fun International Ltd (1)
Rm 508a 5th Floor Empire Ctr, Tsim Sha Tsui, Kowloon, China (Hong Kong) **(100%)**
Tel.: (852) 31037300
Sales Range: $25-49.9 Million
Emp.: 30
Non-Durable Goods Whslr
N.A.I.C.S.: 424990

Funtastic International Limited (1)
1502 Chinachem Golden Plz 77 Mody Rd Tsim Sha Tsui E, Kowloon, China (Hong Kong)
Tel.: (852) 31037300
Web Site: http://www.funtastic.com.au
Sales Range: $25-49.9 Million
Emp.: 20
Toy Mfr
N.A.I.C.S.: 339930

JNH Australia Pty Ltd (1)
635 Waverley Rd, 3150, Glen Waverley, VIC, Australia **(100%)**
Tel.: (61) 395355888
Sales Range: $150-199.9 Million
Confectionery Whslr
N.A.I.C.S.: 424450

TOZA MARKOVIC D.O.O
Basaidski road 62, 23300, Kikinda, Serbia
Tel.: (381) 230422640
Web Site: https://toza.rs
Construction Machinery Mfr
N.A.I.C.S.: 333120

TOZAI CAPITAL CO. LTD.
Com-Box Building 7th Floor, 1-32-16 Ebisu-Nishi Shibuya-ku, Tokyo, 150-0021, Japan
Tel.: (81) 334621755
Web Site: http://www.tozaicapital.com
Privater Equity Firm
N.A.I.C.S.: 523150
Andrew Mankiewicz *(Pres & CEO)*

TP DC SARAJEVO D.D. SARAJEVO
Rajlovacka bb, 71000, Sarajevo, Bosnia & Herzegovina
Tel.: (387) 3 375 4081
Web Site: http://www.tpdc.ba
DCNSR—(SARE)
Rev.: $3,236,898
Assets: $30,950,063
Liabilities: $2,218,333
Net Worth: $28,731,731
Earnings: $25,359
Emp.: 29
Fiscal Year-end: 12/31/20
Logistics Consulting Servies
N.A.I.C.S.: 541614

TP DUNAV A.D.
Karadordeva 20, Vucak, Serbia
Tel.: (381) 26 636 033
Web Site: http://www.tp-dunav.com
Year Founded: 1989
Sales Range: $1-9.9 Million
Real Estate Manangement Services
N.A.I.C.S.: 531390

TP ICAP FINANCE PLC
135 Bishopsgate, London, EC2M 3TP, United Kingdom
Tel.: (44) 2072007000
TPAC—(LSE)
Rev.: $2,669,780,358
Assets: $7,400,908,861
Liabilities: $4,673,062,358
Net Worth: $2,727,846,503
Earnings: $133,804,595
Emp.: 5,200
Fiscal Year-end: 12/31/23
Financial Investment Services
N.A.I.C.S.: 523999
Philip Price *(Gen Counsel-Grp)*

Subsidiaries:

Coex Partners Limited (1)
135 Bishopsgate, London, EC2M 3TP, United Kingdom
Tel.: (44) 203 859 5120
Web Site: https://www.tpicap.com
Financial Brokerage Services
N.A.I.C.S.: 523150

Cosmorex A.G. (1)
Zuercherstrasse 66, 8800, Thalwil, Switzerland
Tel.: (41) 447239400
Web Site: http://www.cosmorex.ch
Sales Range: $50-74.9 Million
Emp.: 30
Securities Brokerage Services
N.A.I.C.S.: 523150
Patrik Epstein *(Pres)*

ICAP (Singapore) Pte Limited (1)
50 Raffles Place 41-00 Singapore Land Tower, Singapore, 048623, Singapore
Tel.: (65) 6 831 0888
Financial Services
N.A.I.C.S.: 523999

ICAP do Brasil Corretora De Titulos E Valores Mobiliarios Ltda. (1)
Le Monde-Av das Americas 3500 Block 01-London Building-Room 219, Barra da Tijuca, Rio de Janeiro, 22640-102, Brazil
Tel.: (55) 2 114 0500
Web Site: https://www.mycap.com.br
Financial Services
N.A.I.C.S.: 523999

Liquidnet Asia Limited (1)
Suite 2501 25/F One Hennessy 1 Hennessy Road Wan Chai, Hong Kong, China (Hong Kong)
Tel.: (852) 37986888
Business Consulting Services
N.A.I.C.S.: 541611

Liquidnet Australia Pty Ltd. (1)
Level 29 Suite 2 9 Castlereagh Street, Sydney, 2000, NSW, Australia
Tel.: (61) 292277000
Financial Services
N.A.I.C.S.: 522320

Liquidnet Holdings, Inc. (1)
620 8th Ave 20th Fl, New York, NY 10018-6753
Tel.: (646) 674-2000
Web Site: http://www.liquidnet.com
Sales Range: $300-349.9 Million
Emp.: 379
Holding Company; Securities Brokerage Services
N.A.I.C.S.: 551112
Seth Merrin *(Founder & CEO)*

Subsidiary (Non-US):

Liquidnet Canada Inc. (2)
1 Toronto Street Suite 808, Toronto, M5C 2V6, ON, Canada
Web Site: https://www.liquidnet.com
Sales Range: $25-49.9 Million
Emp.: 1
Securities Brokerage Services
N.A.I.C.S.: 523150

Liquidnet Europe Ltd. (2)
135 Bishopsgate 4th Floor, London, EC2M 3TP, United Kingdom
Tel.: (44) 2039330200
Web Site: http://www.liquidnet.com
Sales Range: $25-49.9 Million
Emp.: 40
Securities Brokerage Services
N.A.I.C.S.: 523150
Mark Pumfrey *(CEO)*

Subsidiary (Domestic):

Liquidnet, Inc. (2)
498 Fashion Ave Fl 15, New York, NY 10018-6753
Tel.: (646) 674-2000
Web Site: http://www.liquidnet.com
Sales Range: $50-74.9 Million
Emp.: 100
Securities Brokerage Services
N.A.I.C.S.: 523150
Seth Merrin *(Founder & CEO)*

Liquidnet Japan, Inc. (1)
Akasaka Tameike Tower 4F 2-17-7 Akasaka, Minato-ku, Tokyo, 107-0052, Japan
Tel.: (81) 355796252
Web Site: https://www.liquidnet.co.jp
Asset Management Services
N.A.I.C.S.: 531390

Louis Capital Markets France SA (1)
42 Rue Washington, 75008, Paris, France
Tel.: (33) 15 504 0455
Financial Broker Offering Services
N.A.I.C.S.: 523150
Michael Benhamou *(CEO)*

Louis Capital Markets Israel Ltd. (1)
45 Rotschild Blvd, 6578403, Tel Aviv, Israel
Tel.: (972) 54 344 3000
Financial Broker Offering Services
N.A.I.C.S.: 523150

Louis Capital Markets UK LLP (1)
135 Bishopsgate, London, EC2M 3TP, United Kingdom
Tel.: (44) 207 936 1700
Financial Broker Offering Services
N.A.I.C.S.: 523150
Patrice Cohen *(CEO)*

Marshalls (Bahrain) WLL (1)
Manama Centre 104/105 Government Road, Manama, Bahrain
Tel.: (973) 17228787
Securities Brokerage Services
N.A.I.C.S.: 523150
Sanjiv Mohapatra *(Gen Mgr)*

Marshalls Bahrain Limited (1)
Manama Ctr 104 105 Government Rd, Manama, 316, Bahrain
Tel.: (973) 17228787
Sales Range: $1-9.9 Million
Emp.: 15
Financial Brokers
N.A.I.C.S.: 522320

PT. Inti Tullett Prebon Indonesia (1)
Menara DEA Tower II 12th Floor Kawasan Jl Mega Kuningan Barat Kav E43, Mega Kuningan, Jakarta, 12950, Selatan, Indonesia
Tel.: (62) 2139504488
Web Site: http://www.intiprebon.co.id
Sales Range: $50-74.9 Million
Emp.: 33
Loan Company
N.A.I.C.S.: 522310

PVM Futures Inc. (1)
101 Hudson St 24th Fl, Jersey City, NJ 07302
Tel.: (201) 984-6800
Data Processing Services
N.A.I.C.S.: 518210

PVM Oil Associates Inc. (1)
5177 Richmond Ave Ste 590, Houston, TX 77056
Tel.: (713) 255-3434
Data Processing Services
N.A.I.C.S.: 518210

PVM Oil Associates Pte. Ltd. (1)
50 Raffles Place 41-00 Singapore Land Tower, Singapore, 048623, Singapore
Tel.: (65) 6 780 3700
Crude Oil Product Brokerage Services
N.A.I.C.S.: 425120

PVM Oil Futures Limited (1)
117 Jermyn Street, London, SW1Y 6HH, United Kingdom
Tel.: (44) 207 451 5100
Financial Brokerage Services
N.A.I.C.S.: 523150

Prebon Yamane (India) Limited (1)
Maneckji Wadia Building 4th Floor 127 Mahatma Gandhi Road, Fort, Mumbai, 400 001, India
Tel.: (91) 2222624341
Web Site: http://www.tullettprebon.com
Financial Institution

N.A.I.C.S.: 523940
Irene Pinto *(Head-HR & Admin)*

TP ICAP (Dubai) Limited (1)
Office 7 and 8 Level 1 Gate Village Building 1 DIFC, PO Box 506627, Dubai, United Arab Emirates
Tel.: (971) 4 302 3900
Financial Services
N.A.I.C.S.: 523999

TP ICAP EMEA Investments Limited (1)
135 Bishopsgate, London, EC2M 3TP, United Kingdom
Tel.: (44) 2072007000
Information Technology Services
N.A.I.C.S.: 519290

TP ICAP Management Services (Singapore) Pte. Ltd. (1)
50 Raffles Place 41-00 Singapore Land Tower, Singapore, Singapore
Tel.: (65) 6 922 1388
Financial Services
N.A.I.C.S.: 523999

Tullett Liberty (Bahrain) Co. W.L.L. (1)
Manama Centre Ent 4 Flat 11 Bldg 104 Government Avenue 383, PO Box 20526, Manama, Bahrain
Tel.: (973) 1 722 6363
Interdealer Broker Services
N.A.I.C.S.: 523150

Tullett Prebon (Australia) Pty. Limited (1)
Level 29 9 Castlereagh St, Sydney, 2000, NSW, Australia
Tel.: (61) 292761900
Web Site: http://www.tullettprebon.com
Sales Range: $50-74.9 Million
Emp.: 66
Energy Brokers
N.A.I.C.S.: 523160

Tullett Prebon (Canada) Limited (1)
1 Toronto Street Suite 803, Toronto, M5C 2V6, ON, Canada
Tel.: (416) 941-0606
Web Site: https://www.tullettprebon.com
Sales Range: $50-74.9 Million
Emp.: 40
Financial Institution
N.A.I.C.S.: 523940

Tullett Prebon (Equities) Limited (1)
155 Bishop St, London, EC2M3TQ, United Kingdom
Tel.: (44) 2072007000
Web Site: http://www.tullettprebon.com
Sales Range: $700-749.9 Million
Emp.: 2,000
Securities & Commodity Exchanges
N.A.I.C.S.: 523210

Tullett Prebon (Europe) Limited (1)
P89-91 rue du Faubourg Saint-Honore, 75008, Paris, France
Tel.: (33) 149241800
Sales Range: $50-74.9 Million
Emp.: 60
Financial Brokers
N.A.I.C.S.: 522310
Ivan Ljubic *(Gen Mgr)*

Tullett Prebon (Hong Kong) Limited (1)
Suite 1001 10Fl, Citic Tower 1 Tim Mei Avenue, Central, China (Hong Kong)
Tel.: (852) 25278027
Sales Range: $50-74.9 Million
Emp.: 65
Financial Institution
N.A.I.C.S.: 523940

Tullett Prebon (Japan) Limited (1)
Akasaka Tameike Tower 4th Floor 2-17-7, Akasaka Minato-Ku, Tokyo, 107-0052, Japan
Tel.: (81) 355498100
Security Brokerage Services
N.A.I.C.S.: 523150

Tullett Prebon (Luxembourg) S.A. (1)
2 Rue Henri Schnadt, L 2530, Luxembourg, Luxembourg
Tel.: (352) 268991

TP ICAP FINANCE PLC

TP ICAP Finance PLC—(Continued)
Web Site: http://www.tullettprebon.com
Sales Range: $50-74.9 Million
Emp.: 17
Financial Brokers
N.A.I.C.S.: 522310

Tullett Prebon (Philippines) Inc (1)
25th Floor Rufino Pacific Tower 6784 Ayala Avenue, Makati, 1226, Philippines
Tel.: (63) 28607600
Web Site: http://www.prebon.com.ph
Sales Range: $50-74.9 Million
Emp.: 43
Financial Institution
N.A.I.C.S.: 523940
Jose Ma F. Bonifacio *(Deputy Mng Dir)*

Tullett Prebon (Polska) SA (1)
ul Wspolna 47/49, 00-684, Warsaw, Poland
Tel.: (48) 228307080
Web Site: http://www.tullettprebon.com
Sales Range: $50-74.9 Million
Emp.: 12
Securities Brokerage
N.A.I.C.S.: 523150

Tullett Prebon (Singapore) Limited (1)
50 Raffles Place 39-00 Singapore Land Tower, 39 00 Singapore Land Tower, Singapore, 048623, Singapore
Tel.: (65) 69221388
Rev.: $5,000,000
Emp.: 200
Financial Institution
N.A.I.C.S.: 523940

Tullett Prebon (UK) Limited (1)
155 Bishopsgate, London, EC2 M3TQ, United Kingdom
Tel.: (44) 2072007000
Web Site: http://www.tullettprebon.com
Emp.: 2,000
Securities & Commodity Exchanges
N.A.I.C.S.: 523210

Tullett Prebon Americas Corp. (1)
101 Hudson St, Jersey City, NJ 07302-3908
Tel.: (201) 557-5995
Web Site: http://www.tullettprebon.com
Sales Range: $50-74.9 Million
Emp.: 3
Intermediary Wholesale Security & Financial Brokers
N.A.I.C.S.: 425120

Subsidiary (Domestic):

Chapdelaine Tullett Prebon, LLC (2)
1 Seaport Plz 17th Fl, New York, NY 10038
Tel.: (212) 208-9000
Web Site: http://www.chappy.com
Sales Range: $10-24.9 Million
Emp.: 60
Municipal Bond Dealer & Broker
N.A.I.C.S.: 523150

Moab Oil, Inc. (2)
47 Water St, Norwalk, CT 06854
Tel.: (203) 857-6622
Web Site: http://www.moaboil.com
Rev.: $1,300,000
Emp.: 15
Investment Banking & Securities Dealing
N.A.I.C.S.: 523150

Prebon Energy Inc (2)
101 Hudson St, Jersey City, NJ 07302-3908
Tel.: (201) 557-5000
Web Site: http://www.prebonenergy.com
Natural Gas Distribution
N.A.I.C.S.: 221210

Prebon Financial Products Inc (2)
300 Champion Ave Ste 260, Palm Beach Gardens, FL 33418
Tel.: (561) 622-0005
Web Site: http://www.tullettprebon.com
Sales Range: $25-49.9 Million
Emp.: 31
Investment Banking & Securities Dealing
N.A.I.C.S.: 523150

Tullett Prebon Americas Corp. (2)
1 Seaport Plz 17th Fl, New York, NY 10038
Tel.: (212) 208-9000
Web Site: http://www.tullettprebon.com
Sales Range: $75-99.9 Million
Security Brokers & Dealers
N.A.I.C.S.: 523150

Tullett Prebon Brasil Corretora De Valores E Cambio Ltda. (1)
Rua Sao Tom 86-21st Floor, Vila Olimpia, Sao Paulo, 04551-080, Brazil
Tel.: (55) 112 111 4800
Web Site: https://www.tullettprebon.com.br
Interdealer Broker Services
N.A.I.C.S.: 523150

Tullett Prebon ETP (Japan) Ltd. (1)
Akasaka Tameike Tower 4th Floor 2-17-7, Akasaka Minato-ku, Tokyo, 107-0052, Japan
Tel.: (81) 35 549 8100
Interdealer Broker Services
N.A.I.C.S.: 523150

Tullett Prebon Energy (Japan) Limited (1)
Akasaka Tameike Tower 4th Floor 2-17-7 Akasaka, Minato-ku, Tokyo, 107-0052, Japan
Tel.: (81) 355498100
Bond Financial Services
N.A.I.C.S.: 523150

Tullett Prebon Energy (Singapore) Pte. Ltd. (1)
50 Raffles Place 39-00 Singapore Land Tower, Singapore, 048623, Singapore
Tel.: (65) 69221388
Web Site: http://www.tullettprebon.com
Emp.: 200
Commodity Broking Services
N.A.I.C.S.: 523160

Tullett Prebon Mexico S.A. de C.V. (1)
Av De Vasco Quiroga No 1900 Piso 4 Oficina 403, Delegation Alvaro Obregon Colonia Centro de Ciudad Santa Fe, 01210, Mexico, Mexico
Tel.: (52) 551 105 9670
Interdealer Broker Services
N.A.I.C.S.: 523150

Tullett Prebon Money Brokerage (Korea) Limited (1)
6th Floor Booyoung Eulji Bldg 29 Euljiro, Jung-gu, Seoul, 04523, Korea (South)
Tel.: (82) 2 728 0100
Interdealer Broker Services
N.A.I.C.S.: 523150

Tullett Prebon SITICO (China) Limited (1)
10F DBS Tower No 1318 Lujiazui Ring Road, Shanghai, 200120, China
Tel.: (86) 2138789777
Web Site: https://www.tpsitico.com.cn
Financial Institution
N.A.I.C.S.: 523940

Tullett Prebon South Africa (Pty) Limited (1)
2nd Floor West Tower Nelson Mandela Square Maude Street, Sandton, 2146, Johannesburg, South Africa
Tel.: (27) 11 036 3700
Interdealer Broker Services
N.A.I.C.S.: 523150

Wall Street Tullett Prebon Limited (1)
33/64 Wall St Tower 13th Fl, Surawong Rd bangrak, 10500, Bangkok, Thailand
Tel.: (66) 22668889
Web Site: http://www.tullettprebon.com
Sales Range: $50-74.9 Million
Emp.: 20
Securities Brokerage
N.A.I.C.S.: 523150

Wall Street Tullett Prebon Securities Limited (1)
33/64 Wall St Twr 13th Fl, Surawong Rd bangrak, Bangkok, 10500, Thailand
Tel.: (66) 22668889
Web Site: http://www.tullettprebon.com
Sales Range: $50-74.9 Million
Emp.: 20
Securities Brokerage
N.A.I.C.S.: 523150

Yamane Tullett Prebon (Japan) Limited (1)
Akasaka Tameike Tower 4th Floor, 2 17 7 Akasaka Minato ku, Tokyo, 107 0052, Japan

Tel.: (81) 355498100
Web Site: http://www.tullettprebon.com
Financial Institution
N.A.I.C.S.: 523940

tpSEF Inc. (1)
101 Hudson St, Jersey City, NJ 07302
Tel.: (201) 557-5599
Interdealer Broker Services
N.A.I.C.S.: 523940

TP MLAVA A.D.
Karadordeva 20, 11300, Vucak, Serbia
Tel.: (381) 26636033
Web Site: https://www.admlava.com
Year Founded: 1989
MLVP—(BEL)
Sales Range: Less than $1 Million
Retail Store Operator
N.A.I.C.S.: 459999
Zoran Rajic *(Gen Dir)*

TP ZVEZDA A.D.
Zorza Klemansoa 19, Belgrade, Serbia
Tel.: (381) 11 328 53 39
Web Site: http://www.tpzvezda.rs
Year Founded: 2001
Sales Range: Less than $1 Million
Real Estate Manangement Services
N.A.I.C.S.: 531190

TPBI PUBLIC COMPANY LIMITED
42/174 Moo 5 Soi Srisatian Niwes Raiking Sampran, Nakhon Pathom, 73210, Thailand
Tel.: (66) 24290354
Web Site: https://www.tpbigroup.com
TPBI—(THA)
Rev.: $153,707,107
Assets: $132,343,256
Liabilities: $53,517,639
Net Worth: $78,825,617
Earnings: $5,947,864
Fiscal Year-end: 12/31/23
Packaging Manufacturer
N.A.I.C.S.: 326112
Banchong Chittchang *(Chm)*

TPC CO., LTD.
120-3 Seonhwa-ri Jillyang-eup, Gyeongsan, Gyeongbuk, Korea (South)
Tel.: (82) 538547500
Web Site: https://www.tc21.co.kr
Year Founded: 1998
130740—(KRS)
Rev.: $62,391,060
Assets: $90,958,563
Liabilities: $28,277,194
Net Worth: $62,681,369
Earnings: $1,699,875
Emp.: 199
Fiscal Year-end: 12/31/22
Steel Pipes & Automotive Components Mfr
N.A.I.C.S.: 331210
Jeong Hun Lee *(CEO)*

TPC CONSOLIDATED LIMITED
Suite 05 Level 29 225 George Street, Sydney, 2000, NSW, Australia
Tel.: (61) 1300731574 AU
Web Site: https://www.tpc.com.au
Year Founded: 1996
TPC—(ASX)
Rev.: $106,675,976
Assets: $43,765,248
Liabilities: $21,097,653
Net Worth: $22,667,595
Earnings: $3,600,182
Fiscal Year-end: 06/30/24
Holding Company; Mobile Telecommunications Services
N.A.I.C.S.: 551112
Jeffrey Ma *(CFO & Sec)*

INTERNATIONAL PUBLIC

Subsidiaries:

Realtime Mobile Pty. Limited (1)
Level 10 Tower B 821 Pacific Highway, Chatswood, 2071, NSW, Australia (100%)
Tel.: (61) 2 8448 0633
Mobile Telecommunications Services
N.A.I.C.S.: 517121
Charles Chiao-Heng Huang *(CEO & Mng Dir)*

TPC MECHATRONICS CORPORATION
Unit 1201 An-Gang Private tower 1cha Magok Joonang-ro 165, Gangseo-ku, Seoul, 07788, Korea (South)
Tel.: (82) 226918888
Web Site: https://www.tpcpage.com
Year Founded: 1979
048770—(KRS)
Rev.: $72,312,653
Assets: $86,748,830
Liabilities: $53,967,222
Net Worth: $32,781,608
Earnings: $20,288
Emp.: 329
Fiscal Year-end: 12/31/22
Electronic Components Mfr
N.A.I.C.S.: 334419
Jae-Yun Uhm *(Vice Chm & CEO)*

Subsidiaries:

TPC Pneumatics Inc. (1)
12411 McCann Dr, Santa Fe Springs, CA 90670
Tel.: (562) 946-8459
Pneumatic Product Distr
N.A.I.C.S.: 423830

TPC PLUS BERHAD
Lot 942 Simpang Empat Alor Gajah, 78000, Melaka, Malaysia
Tel.: (60) 65529355
Web Site: https://www.tpc.com.my
TPC—(KLS)
Rev.: $92,712,186
Assets: $48,198,716
Liabilities: $33,343,643
Net Worth: $14,855,074
Earnings: $1,548,805
Fiscal Year-end: 12/31/22
Poultry Farming Services
N.A.I.C.S.: 112340
Yew Chua Lim *(Mng Dir)*

TPC POWER HOLDING PUBLIC COMPANY LIMITED
4/2 Soi prasert-Manukitch 29 Yak 8 Prasert-Manukitch Rd Chaorakhebua, Ladprao, Bangkok, 10230, Thailand
Tel.: (66) 29432935
Web Site: https://www.tpcpower.co.th
TPCH—(THA)
Rev.: $84,462,294
Assets: $226,508,377
Liabilities: $130,500,950
Net Worth: $96,007,427
Earnings: $8,420,132
Fiscal Year-end: 12/31/23
Electric Power Generation & Distribution
N.A.I.C.S.: 221118
Thanu Kulachol *(Co/Co-Chm)*

TPCS PUBLIC COMPANY LIMITED
489 Rama 3 Rd Bang Khlo Bang Kho Laem, Bangkok, 10120, Thailand
Tel.: (66) 22940071
Web Site: https://tpcsplc.com
Year Founded: 1976
TPCS—(THA)
Rev.: $41,952,289
Assets: $86,032,727
Liabilities: $7,801,075
Net Worth: $78,231,652
Earnings: $2,454,654

Emp.: 763
Fiscal Year-end: 12/31/23
Textile Products Mfr
N.A.I.C.S.: 314999
Manu Leelanuwatana (Chm)

Subsidiaries:

Prestige Embroidery Co., Ltd. (1)
220 Moo 5 Suwanasorn Road Tambon
Nonsi, Amphoe Kabin Buri, Prachin Buri,
25110, Thailand
Tel.: (66) 37 205 062
Fabric Lace Mfr
N.A.I.C.S.: 313220

TPI - TRIUNFO PARTICIPA-COES E INVESTIMENTOS S.A.
Rua Olimpiadas no 205 Conjunto
143, Vila Olimpia, 04551-000, SP,
Brazil
Tel.: (55) 1121693999   BR
Web Site: https://www.triunfo.com
Year Founded: 1999
TPIS3—(BRAZ)
Rev.: $184,303,279
Assets: $504,736,942
Liabilities: $343,754,482
Net Worth: $160,982,459
Earnings: ($1,880,374)
Fiscal Year-end: 12/31/23
Highway & Port Development Services
N.A.I.C.S.: 237310
Joao Villar Garcia (Chm)

Subsidiaries:

Empresa Concessionaria de Rodovias do Norte S.A. Econorte (1)
Rua Seimu Oguido 242, Londrina, 86075-140, PR, Brazil
Tel.: (55) 43 377 1505
Highway Construction Services
N.A.I.C.S.: 237310
Sandro Antonio De Lima (CFO, Chief Admin Officer & Dir-IR)

TPI INDIA LIMITED
Plot No J61 Additional MIDC, Murbad
District, Thane, 420 401, India
Tel.: (91) 2240026214   In
Web Site: https://www.tpiindia.in
Year Founded: 1982
Rev.: $2,287,999
Assets: $1,092,232
Liabilities: $4,861,693
Net Worth: ($3,769,461)
Earnings: ($407,357)
Fiscal Year-end: 03/31/20
Flexible Container Product Mfr & Distr
N.A.I.C.S.: 314910
Bharat C. Parekh (Mng Dir)

TPI POLENE POWER PCL
26/56 Chan Tat Mai Road, Thungmahamek Sathorn, Bangkok, 10120,
Thailand
Tel.: (66) 22131039
Web Site:
https://www.tpipolenepower.co.th
Year Founded: 1991
TPIPP—(THA)
Rev.: $320,814,321
Assets: $1,744,721,580
Liabilities: $775,501,790
Net Worth: $969,219,790
Earnings: $106,642,966
Emp.: 1,141
Fiscal Year-end: 12/31/23
Eletric Power Generation Services
N.A.I.C.S.: 221118
Prachai Leophairatana (Chm)

TPI POLENE PUBLIC COMPANY LIMITED
26/56 Chan Tat Mai Rd, Tungmahamek Sathorn, Bangkok, 10120,
Thailand
Tel.: (66) 22855090
Web Site: https://www.tpipolene.co.th
Year Founded: 1990
TPIPL—(THA)
Rev.: $1,249,633,971
Assets: $4,770,396,378
Liabilities: $2,883,824,302
Net Worth: $1,886,572,076
Earnings: $125,675,459
Emp.: 10,037
Fiscal Year-end: 12/31/23
Cement Mfr
N.A.I.C.S.: 327310
Prachai Leophairatana (CEO)

Subsidiaries:

TPI Concrete Co., Ltd. (1)
26/56 5th Floor TPI Tower Chan Tat Mai
Rd, Thungmahamek Sathorn, Bangkok,
10120, Thailand
Tel.: (66) 678535074
Web Site: http://www.tpipolene.co.th
Sales Range: $250-299.9 Million
Emp.: 600
Concrete Mfr
N.A.I.C.S.: 327320

Thai Nitrate Co.,Ltd (1)
26/56 21st Floor TPI Tower Building Chan
Tad Mai Road, Thungmahamek Sathorn,
Bangkok, 10120, Thailand
Tel.: (66) 267854502
Web Site: https://www.thainitrate.com
Nitric Acid & Ammonium Nitrate Mfr
N.A.I.C.S.: 325311

United Grain Industry Co., Ltd. (1)
27th Floor TPI Building 26/56 New Chan
Tadmai Road, Sathorn Thung Mahamek,
Bangkok, Thailand
Tel.: (66) 26786988
Sales Range: $1-4.9 Billion
Emp.: 3,085
Agricultural Product Packaging Mfr
N.A.I.C.S.: 322220

TPK HOLDING CO., LTD.
No 13-18 Sec 6 Minquan E Rd,
Neihu District, Taipei, Taiwan
Tel.: (886) 277271199
Web Site: https://www.tpk.com
Year Founded: 2003
3673—(TAI)
Rev.: $2,284,614,551
Assets: $2,872,014,248
Liabilities: $1,663,776,810
Net Worth: $1,208,237,438
Earnings: $7,393,505
Emp.: 11,397
Fiscal Year-end: 12/31/23
Computer Terminal & Touch Screen
Technology Mfr
N.A.I.C.S.: 334118
Michael Chao-Juei Chiang (Chm)

Subsidiaries:

TPK Touch Solutions Inc. (1)
No 13-18 Sec 6 Minquan E Rd, Neihu Dist,
Taipei, 114, Taiwan
Tel.: (886) 277271199
Web Site: http://www.tpk-solutions.com
Sales Range: $25-49.9 Million
Emp.: 100
Computer Terminal & Touch Screen Technology Mfr
N.A.I.C.S.: 334118

Division (Non-US):

TPK Touch Solutions (Xiamen) Inc. (2)
199 Banxang Road Xiamen Torch High-Tech Industrial Development Zone, Xiamen,
China
Tel.: (86) 5925738999
Web Site: http://www.tpk-solutions.com
Touch Screen Technology Mfr
N.A.I.C.S.: 334118

TPL CORP LIMITED
20th Floor Sky Tower East Wing Dolmen City HC 3 Block 4 Abdul Sattar
Edhi Avenue Clifton, Karachi, Pakistan
Tel.: (92) 2134390300   PK
Web Site: https://tplcorp.com
Year Founded: 2000
Investment Holding Company
N.A.I.C.S.: 551112
Ali Jameel (CEO)

Subsidiaries:

TPL Insurance Limited (1)
Plot no 19 Block B Sindhi Muslim CHS
SMCHS 74900, Karachi, Pakistan
Tel.: (92) 42111000300
Web Site: https://tplinsurance.com
Life, Health, Property & Casualty Insurance Services
N.A.I.C.S.: 524113
Saad Nisar (CEO)

Subsidiary (Domestic):

TPL Life Insurance Limited (2)
54 C III Gulberg III, Lahore, Pakistan
Tel.: (92) 425878643
Rev.: $146,325
Assets: $2,858,935
Liabilities: $3,708,072
Net Worth: ($849,137)
Earnings: ($35,429)
Emp.: 15
Fiscal Year-end: 06/30/2019
Textile Products Mfr
N.A.I.C.S.: 313110

TPLEX CO., LTD.
75 MTV1-ro, Danwon-gu, Ansan,
Gyeonggi-do, Korea (South)
Tel.: (82) 314888800
Web Site: https://www.tplex.co.kr
Year Founded: 1982
081150—(KRS)
Rev.: $197,686,799
Assets: $182,490,563
Liabilities: $60,619,880
Net Worth: $121,870,683
Earnings: $12,002,159
Emp.: 73
Fiscal Year-end: 12/31/22
Steel Products Mfr
N.A.I.C.S.: 331210
Kim Young-Guk (CEO)

TPR CO., LTD.
10th Floor Shinmarunouchi Center
Building 1-6-2 Marunouchi, Chiyoda-ku, Tokyo, 100-0005, Japan
Tel.: (81) 352932811
Web Site: https://www.tpr.co.jp
Year Founded: 1939
6463—(TKS)
Rev.: $1,281,242,740
Assets: $1,917,620,490
Liabilities: $664,100,090
Net Worth: $1,253,520,400
Earnings: $54,168,950
Emp.: 6,959
Fiscal Year-end: 03/31/24
Automobile Related Components Mfr
N.A.I.C.S.: 332510
Keisuke Miyasaka (Mng Exec Officer & Head-Production-Multi Materials)

Subsidiaries:

ALTIA Co., Ltd. (1)
6th floor Office Tower Z Building 1-8-12
Harumi, Harumi Island Triton Square Chuo-ku, Tokyo, 104-6206, Japan
Tel.: (81) 367770111
Emp.: 300
Automobile Production Equipment Mfr
N.A.I.C.S.: 336320

Anqing ATGE Engineering Co., Ltd. (1)
No 16 Yingbin Road of Economic Technical
Development Zone, Anqing, Anhui, China
Tel.: (86) 5565305600
Automobile Related Parts Mfr
N.A.I.C.S.: 336390

Anqing Art TP Pistons Co., Ltd. (1)
No 317 Yingbin Road of Development
AREA, Anqing, Anhui, China
Tel.: (86) 5565345382
Automobile Related Parts Mfr
N.A.I.C.S.: 336390

Anqing TP Powder Metallurgy Co., Ltd. (1)
No 1777 Tianzhu Shandong Road, Yixiu
District, Anqing, 246001, Anhui, China
Tel.: (86) 5565357761
Web Site: https://www.aqatp.com
Sales Range: $125-149.9 Million
Emp.: 300
Vehicle Equipments Mfr & Whslr
N.A.I.C.S.: 336390

Anqing TPR Engineering Plastic Co., Ltd. (1)
No 1777 Tianzhushan Road, Laofeng Town
Yixiu District, Anqing, Anhui, China
Tel.: (86) 5565520761
Automobile Related Parts Mfr
N.A.I.C.S.: 336390

China United Piston Ring Co.,Ltd. (1)
No 28 Baihe Street Lang Sen Industrial
Area, Lang Fang Economic Technical Development Zone, Langfang, Hebei, China
Tel.: (86) 3165918087
Piston Rings Mfr & Supplier
N.A.I.C.S.: 336310

Edogawa Metals Co., Ltd. (1)
2147-1 Ohta, Sakura, 285-0808, Chiba,
Japan
Tel.: (81) 434866611
Web Site: http://www.ekmetals.co.jp
Sales Range: $25-49.9 Million
Emp.: 25
Rolled Iron Sheets & Iron Bars Mfr
N.A.I.C.S.: 331221

FALTEC Co., Ltd. (1)
580 Horikawacho, Saiwai-ku, Kawasaki,
212-0013, Kanagawa, Japan   (55.5%)
Tel.: (81) 445200019
Web Site: https://www.faltec.co.jp
Rev.: $541,266,460
Assets: $456,354,400
Liabilities: $330,295,090
Net Worth: $126,059,310
Earnings: ($5,221,900)
Emp.: 2,030
Fiscal Year-end: 03/31/2024
Automotive Parts & Accessories Mfr
N.A.I.C.S.: 336390
Tsuyoshi Kobayashi (Sr VP)

Subsidiary (Non-US):

FALTEC Europe Limited (2)
Unit 5 Didcot Way Boldon Business Park,
Boldon, NE35 9PD, Tyne and Wear, United
Kingdom
Tel.: (44) 191 519 0088
Web Site: http://www.falteceurope.com
Sales Range: $50-74.9 Million
Emp.: 450
Automobile Parts Mfr
N.A.I.C.S.: 336390
Chris Pennison (Mng Dir)

Federal-Mogul TP Europe GmbH & Co. KG (1)
Buergermeister-Schmidt-Strasse 17, 51399,
Burscheid, Germany
Tel.: (49) 2174692870
Web Site: http://www.tpr.co.jp
Sales Range: $25-49.9 Million
Emp.: 6
Automobile Parts Mfr
N.A.I.C.S.: 336310
Masayuki Ohira (Engr)

Federal-Mogul TP Liner Europe Otomotiv Ltd. Sti. (1)
Istanbul Industry and Trade Free Zone
Aydinli SBMAH 4 Sokak No 6, Istanbul Industry and Commerce Free Zone Tuzla,
34957, Istanbul, Turkiye
Tel.: (90) 2163941978
Automobile Related Parts Mfr
N.A.I.C.S.: 336390

Federal-Mogul TP Liners Europe Otomotiv Ltd. Sti. (1)

TPR CO., LTD.

TPR Co., Ltd.—(Continued)

Aydinli S B Mah 4 Sokak No 6, Istanbul Endustri Ve Ticaret Serbest Bolgesi Tuzla, 34957, Istanbul, Turkiye
Tel.: (90) 2163941978
Sales Range: $25-49.9 Million
Emp.: 37
Cylinder Liners Mfr
N.A.I.C.S.: 441330

Federal-Mogul TP Liners, Inc. (1)
520N 8th St, Lake City, MN 55041
Tel.: (651) 345-8083
Sales Range: $25-49.9 Million
Emp.: 100
Transmission Equipment Mfr
N.A.I.C.S.: 333612

KT Motors Co., Ltd. (1)
1-2-83 Deguchi, Hirakata, 573-0065, Osaka, Japan
Tel.: (81) 728450121
Web Site: http://www.keihan-kt.jp
Emp.: 140
Automobile Parts Mfr
N.A.I.C.S.: 336310

Kitakyushu Faltec Co., Ltd. (1)
10-1 Mukaihirocho, Wakamatsu-ku, Kitakyushu, 808-0002, Japan
Tel.: (81) 937522727
Web Site: https://www.kitakyushufaltec.com
Emp.: 35
Decorative Plating Product Mfr
N.A.I.C.S.: 332813

Nanjing TP Thermal Engineering Co., Ltd. (1)
No 6-1 Xingwen Road, Development Zone Nanjing Economic and Technological Development Zone, Nanjing, 210038, Jiangsu, China
Tel.: (86) 2585803553
Web Site: https://www.cn-ntec.com
Sales Range: $25-49.9 Million
Emp.: 60
Valve Mfr
N.A.I.C.S.: 336310

PT TPR Sales Indonesia (1)
Gedung Mid Plaza 1 Floor 19 Jl Jenderal Sudirman Kav 10-11, Jakarta, 10220, West Java, Indonesia
Tel.: (62) 215720720
Web Site: https://www.tsin.co.id
Sales Range: $25-49.9 Million
Emp.: 21
Cylinder Liners Mfr & Supplier
N.A.I.C.S.: 336310

PT. Art Piston Indonesia (1)
Suryacipta City of Industry Jl Surya Kencana Kav 1-M1FGH, Kutamekar Ciampel, Karawang, 41363, Jawa Barat, Indonesia
Tel.: (62) 2129614021
Web Site: http://www.art-piston.co.id
Piston Ring Product Mfr
N.A.I.C.S.: 336310

PT. TPR Enpla Indonesia (1)
Kawasan Industri MM2100 Jl Irian IV Blok LL No 4 Jatiwangi, Cikarang Barat, Bekasi, 17520, Jawa Barat, Indonesia
Tel.: (62) 218 998 1520
Web Site: https://www.tprenpla.co.id
Plastic Multi Profile Extrusion Mfr
N.A.I.C.S.: 326199
Kakutani Tomoyuki (Pres)

PT. TPR Indonesia (1)
Kawasan Greenland International Industrial Center GIIC Blok AE No 1, Kota Deltamas Desa Nagasari Serang Baru, Bekasi, 17330, Indonesia
Tel.: (62) 2150555670
Emp.: 190
Piston Ring Product Mfr
N.A.I.C.S.: 336310

Sunlight Rubber Products (Shang Hai) Co., Ltd. (1)
No 625 Xinge Road Xinqiaozhen, Songjiang District, Shanghai, China
Tel.: (86) 2157687272
Automobile Related Parts Mfr
N.A.I.C.S.: 336390

TEIKOKU PISTON RING CO. LTD. - Gifu Plant (1)
3-3 Himegaoka, Kani, 509-0249, Gifu-ken, Japan
Tel.: (81) 574626711
Web Site: http://www.tpr.co.jp
Sales Range: $25-49.9 Million
Emp.: 100
Mechanical Component Mfr
N.A.I.C.S.: 336330

TEIKOKU PISTON RING CO. LTD. - Nagano Plant (1)
2-1-13 Shinmei-cho, Okaya, 394-8511, Nagano-ken, Japan
Tel.: (81) 266232811
Web Site: http://www.tpr.co.jp
Sales Range: $200-249.9 Million
Emp.: 900
Mechanical Component Mfr
N.A.I.C.S.: 336330

TP ARN International Trading (Shanghai) Co.,Ltd. (1)
Rm 605 Shenggao Guoji Daxia Xian Xia Lu 137, Shanghai, China
Tel.: (86) 2162094771
Web Site: http://www.tas.sh.cn
Sales Range: $25-49.9 Million
Emp.: 14
Piston Rings Distr
N.A.I.C.S.: 423830

TPR (Tianjin) Co., Ltd. (1)
Room 1101 The Exchange Tower 2 189 Nanjing Road, Heping District, Tianjin, 300051, China
Tel.: (86) 2223371182
Automobile Related Parts Mfr
N.A.I.C.S.: 336390

TPR Altec Co., Ltd. (1)
99-1 Jingo, Tsuyama, 708-0015, Okayama, Japan
Tel.: (81) 868288001
Automobile Related Parts Mfr
N.A.I.C.S.: 336390

TPR America, Inc. (1)
10 N Martingale Rd Ste 145, Schaumburg, IL 60173
Tel.: (847) 446-5336
Sales Range: $50-74.9 Million
Emp.: 6
Industrial Equipments & Parts Whslr
N.A.I.C.S.: 423830

TPR Asian Sales (Thailand) Ltd. (1)
23/83-84 21st floor Sorachai Building Soi Sukhumvit 63 Sukhumvit Road, Klongton-Nua Wattana, Bangkok, 10110, Thailand
Tel.: (66) 27143300
Automobile Related Parts Mfr
N.A.I.C.S.: 336390

TPR Autoparts Mfg. India Pvt Ltd. (1)
Plot No SP2-37 & SP2-38 A Japanese Zone Phase-III, New industrial Complex Majrakath Neemrana, Alwar, 301705, Rajasthan, India
Tel.: (91) 1494246092
Automobile Related Parts Mfr
N.A.I.C.S.: 336390

TPR Business Co., Ltd. (1)
2-1-13 Shinmei-cho, Okaya, 394-8511, Nagano, Japan
Tel.: (81) 266232515
Automobile Related Parts Mfr
N.A.I.C.S.: 336390

TPR EK Metals Co., Ltd. (1)
2147-1 Ota, Sakura, 285-0808, Chiba, Japan
Tel.: (81) 43 486 6611
Web Site: https://www.ekmetals.co.jp
Emp.: 25
Electrode Material Mfr
N.A.I.C.S.: 333992

TPR Engineering Co., Ltd. (1)
2-1-34 Goda, Okaya, 394-0021, Nagano, Japan
Tel.: (81) 266244250
Automobile Related Parts Mfr
N.A.I.C.S.: 336390

TPR Enpla Co., Ltd. (1)
558 Akimoto, Samukawa-cho, Tonami, 939-1304, Toyama, Japan
Tel.: (81) 763336600
Web Site: https://www.tprenpla.com
Resin Product Mfr & Distr
N.A.I.C.S.: 325211

TPR Europe GmbH (1)
Berliner Allee 47, 40212, Dusseldorf, Germany
Tel.: (49) 211329773
Web Site: https://www.tpr-europe.com
Sales Range: $25-49.9 Million
Emp.: 6
Automotive Part Whslr
N.A.I.C.S.: 336310

TPR Industria de Pecas Automotivas do Brasil Ltda. (1)
Av Armando Lopes Ribeiro 410, Colonia Rodrigo e Silva Porto Feliz, Sao Paulo, 18547-360, Brazil
Tel.: (55) 1540629760
Cylinder Liner Product Mfr
N.A.I.C.S.: 336310

TPR Industry Co., Ltd. (1)
1 Chuokogyodanchi, Sagae, 990-0561, Yamagata, Japan
Tel.: (81) 23 786 4131
Web Site: https://www.tpkk.jp
Emp.: 434
Cylinder & Casting Liner Product Mfr
N.A.I.C.S.: 332999

TPR Nobukawa Co., Ltd. (1)
3-3 Kanda Kajicho, Chiyoda-ku, Tokyo, 101-0045, Japan
Tel.: (81) 332582335
Anti Vibration Pad & Extruded Rubber Product Mfr
N.A.I.C.S.: 326299

TPR Nobukawa Trading Co., Ltd. (1)
3-3 Kaji-cho, Kanda Chiyoda-ku, Tokyo, 101-0045, Japan
Tel.: (81) 332585888
Automobile Related Parts Mfr
N.A.I.C.S.: 336390

TPR Premec Co., Ltd. (1)
2-1-13 Shinmei-cho, Okaya, 394-8511, Nagano, Japan
Tel.: (81) 266239278
Automobile Related Parts Mfr
N.A.I.C.S.: 336390

TPR Sunlight Co., Ltd. (1)
2-4-2 Misato Second Tokushige Building, Misato, 341-0024, Saitama, Japan
Tel.: (81) 489514705
Industrial Rubber Product Mfr & Distr
N.A.I.C.S.: 326299

TPR Thermal Engineering Co., Ltd. (1)
1-2-17 Deguchi, Hirakata, 573-0065, Osaka, Japan
Tel.: (81) 728410881
Automobile Related Parts Mfr
N.A.I.C.S.: 336390

TPR Total Service Co., Ltd. (1)
2-16-6 Kamo-cho, Okaya, 394-0003, Nagano, Japan
Tel.: (81) 266238817
Web Site: https://www.tpr-ts.co.jp
Emp.: 85
Automobile Related Parts Mfr
N.A.I.C.S.: 336390

TPR Trading Co., Ltd. (1)
Shinjuku Centland Building 3-5-1 Nishi-Shinjuku, Shinjuku-ku, Tokyo, 160-0023, Japan
Tel.: (81) 333484581
Emp.: 50
Piston Ring & Cylinder Liner Product Mfr
N.A.I.C.S.: 336310

TPR Vietnam Co., Ltd. (1)
26VSIP II Street2, Vietnam Singapore Industrial Park II, Thu Dau Mot, Binh Duong, Vietnam
Tel.: (84) 2743635005
Emp.: 936
Automobile Related Parts Mfr
N.A.I.C.S.: 336390

Teipi Altec Co., Ltd. (1)
Jingo 99 1 Kobe Tsuyama-shi, Okayama, 708-0015, Japan
Tel.: (81) 868288001
Web Site: http://www.tpr.co.jp

INTERNATIONAL PUBLIC

Mechanical Component Mfr
N.A.I.C.S.: 336310

Teipi Business Co., Ltd. (1)
2-1-13 Shinmei-cho, Okaya, 394-8511, Nagano, Japan
Tel.: (81) 266232515
Emp.: 700
Automobile Parts Mfr
N.A.I.C.S.: 441330

Teipi Engineering Co., Ltd. (1)
2-1-34 Goda, Okaya, 394-0021, Nagano, Japan
Tel.: (81) 266244250
Sales Range: $25-49.9 Million
Emp.: 26
Automobile Parts Mfr
N.A.I.C.S.: 441330

Teipi Industries Co., Ltd. (1)
1 Central Industrial Park, Sagae, 990-0561, Yamagata, Japan
Tel.: (81) 237864131
Web Site: https://tpkk.jp
Sales Range: $150-199.9 Million
Emp.: 434
Mechanical Component Mfr
N.A.I.C.S.: 423830

Teipi Kosan Co., Ltd. (1)
Tel.: (81) 266238817
Emp.: 85
Automobile Parts Mfr
N.A.I.C.S.: 441330

Teipi Premec Co., Ltd (1)
2-1-13 Shinmei-cho, Okaya, 394-8511, Nagano, Japan
Tel.: (81) 266239278
Automobile Parts Mfr
N.A.I.C.S.: 441330

Teipi Sales Co., Ltd. (1)
3 5 1 Nishi-shinjuku Shinjuku-ku, Tokyo, 160-0023, Japan
Tel.: (81) 333484581
Web Site: http://www.tp-sales.co.jp
Sales Range: $25-49.9 Million
Emp.: 50
Mechanical Products Whslr
N.A.I.C.S.: 423830

United Piston Ring, Inc. (1)
2318 Waldo Blvd, Manitowoc, WI 54220-0910
Tel.: (920) 684-4609
Emp.: 200
Piston Rings Mfr
N.A.I.C.S.: 336310
David Ourada (Mgr)

Y&T Power Tech., Inc. (1)
110 High-Tech Sandan-ro, Samseong-myeon, Eumseong, Chungcheongbuk, Korea (South)
Tel.: (82) 438801200
Cylinder Liners Mfr
N.A.I.C.S.: 332994

TPR FIBERDUR GMBH & CO. KG

Industriepark Emil Mayrisch, PO Box 1265, Aldenhoven, 52457, Germany
Tel.: (49) 24649720 De
Web Site: http://www.fiberdur.com
Sales Range: $10-24.9 Million
Emp.: 180
Glass Reinforced Plastic Pipe & Pipe Systems Mfr
N.A.I.C.S.: 326122
Michael Stotzel (Mng Dir)

TPS EASTERN AFRICA LIMITED

4th Floor Williamson House 4th Ngong Avenue, PO Box 48690, 00100, Nairobi, Kenya
Tel.: (254) 202842000 KE
Web Site: https://www.serenahotels.com
TPSE—(NAI)
Rev.: $52,776,303
Assets: $134,576,972
Liabilities: $61,296,724
Net Worth: $73,280,248

AND PRIVATE COMPANIES

Earnings: $2,885,659
Emp.: 2,264
Fiscal Year-end: 12/31/22
Hotel Operator
N.A.I.C.S.: 721110

TPS S.P.A.
Via Lazzaretto 12, 21013, Gallarate, Italy
Tel.: (39) 0331797010
Web Site: https://www.tps-group.it
Year Founded: 1964
TPS—(ITA)
Sales Range: $25-49.9 Million
Information Technology Support Services
N.A.I.C.S.: 541512
Alessandro Rosso *(Chm & CEO)*

TPSH S.A.
3 rue du Gevaudan, SILIC 1 735 Lisses, 91017, Evry, Cedex, France
Tel.: (33) 1 69 11 91 91
Web Site: http://www.tpsh.fr
Sales Range: $1-9.9 Million
Consulting & Engineering Services
N.A.I.C.S.: 541611
Claude Leonetti *(Founder)*

TPV TECHNOLOGY CO., LTD.
No 77 Tianyou Road, Qixia District, Nanjing, 210033, Jiangsu, China
Tel.: (86) 2566852685
Web Site: https://www.tpv-tech.com
Year Founded: 1967
000727—(SSE)
Rev.: $8,688,358,697
Assets: $4,941,397,333
Liabilities: $3,734,346,775
Net Worth: $1,207,050,558
Earnings: $12,171,781
Fiscal Year-end: 12/31/22
Electronic Component Mfr & Distr
N.A.I.C.S.: 334419
Jason Hsuan *(Chm & CEO)*

Subsidiaries:

TPV Technology Limited (1)
Room 1208-16 12th Fl Sibao International Building 108 Wai Yip Street, Kwun Tong, Kowloon, China (Hong Kong) **(51%)**
Tel.: (852) 28585736
Web Site: http://www.tpv-tech.com
Computer Monitors Mfr
N.A.I.C.S.: 334118
Jason Hsuan *(Chm & CEO)*

Subsidiary (Non-US):

AOC International (Europe) GmbH (2)
Lahnstrasse 86a, D 12055Berlin, Berlin, Germany
Tel.: (49) 306840990
Web Site: https://www.aoc-europe.com
Computer Monitors Mfr
N.A.I.C.S.: 334419

AOC do Brasil Monitores Ltda. (2)
Al Raja Gabaglia 188 9th fl, CEP 04551 090, Sao Paulo, Brazil
Tel.: (55) 1121399999
Web Site: http://www.aoc.com.br
Sales Range: $25-49.9 Million
Emp.: 90
Computer Monitors Mfr
N.A.I.C.S.: 334419
Atul Jasra *(Head-Tablets & Smart Phones-India & SAARC)*

PTC Technology Company Limited (2)
6th Floor Block D Yantian Hi-Tech Park No 108, Hongshiqiao Industrial Zone Yantian Village Fenggang, Dongguan, China
Tel.: (86) 76982060291
Web Site: https://www.ptctech.cn
Emp.: 100
Computer Terminal Product Mfr
N.A.I.C.S.: 334118

TPV CIS Ltd. (2)
Russian Federation St Moskovskoe shosse 177A, Shushary, Saint Petersburg, 196626, Russia
Tel.: (7) 8126005091
Web Site: https://tpvrussia.ru
Electronics Mfr
N.A.I.C.S.: 334419

TPV Electronics (Fujian) Company Limited (2)
Yuanhong Rd, Fuqing, Fujian, China
Tel.: (86) 59185285555
Web Site: https://www.tpvtechnology.com
Electronic Components Mfr
N.A.I.C.S.: 334419

TPV Technology (Wuhan) Company Limited (2)
No 8 Zhuankou Area Economic Tech, Development Zone, Wuhan, China
Tel.: (86) 2768849600
Electronic Components Mfr
N.A.I.C.S.: 334419

Top Victory Electronics (Fujian) Company Limited (2)
Shangzheng Yuanhong Rd, 350301, Fuqing, Fujian, China
Tel.: (86) 59185285555
Web Site: http://www.tpv-tech.com
Monitors Mfr
N.A.I.C.S.: 334118

Top Victory Electronics (Taiwan) Company Limited (2)
18F 738 Chung Cheng Rd, Chung Ho, Taipei, 23553, Taiwan
Tel.: (886) 282261668
Display Systems Mfr
N.A.I.C.S.: 334118

Top Victory Investments Limited (2)
604 Tower B Millennium Plz, Sector 27, Gurgaon, 122002, Haryana, India
Tel.: (91) 1242806116
Web Site: https://www.aocmonitor.co.in
Sales Range: $25-49.9 Million
Emp.: 50
Computer Monitors Mfr
N.A.I.C.S.: 334118

TPXIMPACT HOLDINGS PLC
The Hickman 2 Whitechapel Road Second Floor, London, E1 1EW, United Kingdom
Tel.: (44) 2072262805 UK
Web Site: https://www.thepanoply.com
Year Founded: 2016
TPX—(AIM)
Rev.: $103,913,824
Assets: $142,956,016
Liabilities: $60,146,583
Net Worth: $82,809,433
Earnings: ($21,803,524)
Emp.: 800
Fiscal Year-end: 03/31/23
Information Technology Management Services
N.A.I.C.S.: 541512
Neal Narendra Gandhi *(Co-Founder & CEO)*

Subsidiaries:

Bene Agere Norden AS (1)
Bygdoy Alle 2, Postboks 573, 0105, Oslo, Norway
Tel.: (47) 91184009
Web Site: http://www.beneagere.no
Management Consulting Services
N.A.I.C.S.: 541611

Deeson Group Limited (1)
27 Castle Street, Canterbury, CT1 2PX, Kent, United Kingdom
Tel.: (44) 2071868239
Web Site: https://www.deeson.co.uk
Digital Marketing Services
N.A.I.C.S.: 541613

Questers Bulgaria EOOD (1)
17 H Ibsen Str fl 5, Sofia, Bulgaria
Tel.: (359) 24444132
Information Technology Development Services
N.A.I.C.S.: 541519

TRABZONSPOR SPORTIF YATIRIM VE FUTBOL A.S.

TQM CORP PCL
123 Ladplakao Road Jorakhaebua, Lat Phrao, Bangkok, 10230, Thailand
Tel.: (66) 21198888
Web Site:
  http://www.en.tqmcorp.co.th
TQM—(THA)
Rev.: $108,614,551
Assets: $159,370,621
Liabilities: $63,793,957
Net Worth: $95,576,664
Earnings: $25,092,966
Emp.: 4,254
Fiscal Year-end: 12/31/23
Insurance Services
N.A.I.C.S.: 524210
Unchalin Punnipa *(Chm & Pres)*

TQMP GLASS MANUFACTURING CORP.
168 Sapang Bakaw Lawang Bato, Valenzuela, 1447, Metro Manila, Philippines
Tel.: (63) 28288 8767
Web Site: http://tqmp.biz
Year Founded: 1998
Glass & Aluminum Products Mfr
N.A.I.C.S.: 327211
Paul Vincent Go *(Pres)*

Subsidiaries:

Pioneer Float Glass Mfg Inc. (1)
Asez 730 MH Del Pilar St, Brgy Pinagbuhatan, Pasig, 1600, Philippines
Tel.: (63) 26411981
Web Site: http://www.pfg.com.ph
Flat Glass Mfr
N.A.I.C.S.: 327211

TQR PUBLIC COMPANY LIMITED
46/7 Rungrojthanakul Building Building A 8th floor Ratchadapisek Road, Huaykwang, Bangkok, 10310, Thailand
Tel.: (66) 21508560 TH
Web Site: https://www.tqr.co.th
Year Founded: 2012
TQR—(THA)
Rev.: $7,295,992
Assets: $17,269,144
Liabilities: $2,684,877
Net Worth: $14,584,268
Earnings: $2,928,356
Emp.: 48
Fiscal Year-end: 12/31/23
Insurance Services
N.A.I.C.S.: 524298
Chanaphan Piriyaphan *(CEO)*

TR HOTEL JARDIN DEL MAR SA
Huguet des Far S/N, 07180, Calvia, Spain
Tel.: (34) 971690911
Web Site:
  https://www.hoteltrhjardindelmar.com
0QH9—(LSE)
Sales Range: Less than $1 Million
Hotel & Resort Operator
N.A.I.C.S.: 721110
Andres Gilabert Sanchez *(Chm & CEO)*

TR PROPERTY INVESTMENT TRUST PLC
13 Woodstock Street, London, W1C 2AG, United Kingdom
Tel.: (44) 35306375
Web Site: https://www.trproperty.com
TRY—(LSE)
Rev.: $283,244,131
Assets: $1,502,609,192
Liabilities: $94,501,389
Net Worth: $1,408,107,803
Earnings: $247,850,291

Fiscal Year-end: 03/31/24
Real Estate Investment Trust
N.A.I.C.S.: 525990
Marcus A. Phayre-mudge *(Mgr-Fund)*

TRAAS ON PRODUCT INC.
4-3 Kioicho Izumikan Kioicho Building 3F, Chiyoda-ku, Tokyo, 220-8117, Japan
Tel.: (81) 332392020
Web Site: http://www.pthree.co.jp
6696—(TKS)
Rev.: $5,672,480
Assets: $9,050,800
Liabilities: $2,023,120
Net Worth: $7,027,680
Earnings: ($3,552,560)
Fiscal Year-end: 01/31/21
Communication Product Mfr & Distr
N.A.I.C.S.: 334515
Hidehiko Fujiyoshi *(Founder & Pres)*

Subsidiaries:

TRANZAS Asia Pacific Pte. Ltd. (1)
60 Paya Lebar Road 05-22 Paya Lebar Square, Singapore, 409051, Singapore
Tel.: (65) 63856987
Web Site: http://www.cygnuswearable.com
Broadcasting Equipment Mfr & Distr
N.A.I.C.S.: 334220

TRABAJOS INDUSTRIALES Y MECANICOS, C.A.
Av Este/Oeste Calle 103 Manzana M-2, Parcela No P-2 Zona Industrial, Catillito, Valencia, 2006, Edo Carabobo, Venezuela
Tel.: (58) 241 871 4985 VE
Web Site: http://www.trime.com
Year Founded: 1976
Sales Range: $100-124.9 Million
Emp.: 1,250
Industrial & Civil Infrastructure Construction Services
N.A.I.C.S.: 236210
Enrique Pradella *(Pres)*

Subsidiaries:

Trinel C.A. (1)
Urbanizacion Industrial Mesones Manzana 20 Sector La Ponderosa, Parcela P B-8 Anzoategui, Barcelona, Venezuela
Tel.: (58) 2812765501
Web Site: http://www.trinelca.com
Other Motor Vehicle Electrical & Electronic Equipment Mfr
N.A.I.C.S.: 336320

TRABZON LIMAN ISLETMECILI AS
Iskenderpasa Mah Rihtim Sok No 13, Ortahisar, Trabzon, Turkiye
Tel.: (90) 4623776050
Web Site:
  https://www.trabzonport.com.tr
Year Founded: 2003
TLMAN—(IST)
Sales Range: Less than $1 Million
Marine Transportation & Logistic Services
N.A.I.C.S.: 488510
Nuri Albayrak *(Chm)*

TRABZONSPOR SPORTIF YATIRIM VE FUTBOL ISLETMECILIGI TAS
Mehmet Ali Yilmaz Tesisleri Havaalani Yani, Trabzon, 61010, Turkiye
Tel.: (90) 4623250967
Soccer Club Management Services
N.A.I.C.S.: 711211
Ahmet Ali Agaoglu *(Chm)*

TRABZONSPOR SPORTIF YATIRIM VE FUTBOL A.S.
Mehmet Ali Yilmaz Facilities University, Main Education Ahmet Suat

TRABZONSPOR SPORTIF YATIRIM VE FUTBOL A.S.

Trabzonspor Sportif Yatirim ve Futbol A.S.—(Continued)
Ozyazici Street No 31-35, Trabzon, Türkiye
Tel.: (90) 4623250967
Web Site: http://www.trabzonspor.org.tr
TSPOR—(IST)
Rev.: $59,931,405
Assets: $200,816,457
Liabilities: $185,603,720
Net Worth: $15,212,737
Earnings: ($25,195,779)
Fiscal Year-end: 12/31/23
Sports Club Operator
N.A.I.C.S.: 713940
Ertugrul Dogan (Chm)

TRACE GROUP
224-232 St John Street, London, EC1V 4QR, United Kingdom
Tel.: (44) 2078251000
Web Site: http://www.tracegroup.com
Year Founded: 1974
Sales Range: $125-149.9 Million
Emp.: 250
Software Developer Services
N.A.I.C.S.: 541512
Peter Stolerman (Dir-Fin)

Subsidiaries:

Trace Financial (1)
224-232 St John St, London, EC1V 4QR, United Kingdom
Tel.: (44) 2078251000
Web Site: http://www.tracefinancial.com
Sales Range: $25-49.9 Million
Emp.: 33
Advanced Messaging Solutions to Major Financial Institutions
N.A.I.C.S.: 513210
John Murphy (Mng Dir)

Trace Isys Limited (1)
224-232 St John St, London, EC1V 4QR, United Kingdom
Tel.: (44) 2076088400
Web Site: http://www.traceisys.com
Sales Range: $25-49.9 Million
Emp.: 40
Software Solutions & Services
N.A.I.C.S.: 513210
Simon Howden (CEO)

Trace Payroll Services Limited (1)
224-232 St John St, London, EC1V 4QR, United Kingdom
Tel.: (44) 20 7825 1000
Web Site: http://www.tracepayroll.com
Sales Range: $25-49.9 Million
Emp.: 40
Payroll Processes & Legislation Services
N.A.I.C.S.: 541214
Andrew Bell (Mng Dir)

Trace Solutions (1)
224-232 St John Street, London, EC1V 4QR, United Kingdom
Tel.: (44) 2078251000
Web Site: http://www.tracesolutions.co.uk
Sales Range: $25-49.9 Million
Emp.: 100
Property Management Software Services
N.A.I.C.S.: 513210
Mick Flynn (Mng Dir)

TRACE GROUP HOLD PLC
South Park Residential Group 12 Nikola Obrazopisov Str, 1408, Sofia, 1408, Bulgaria
Tel.: (359) 28066700
Web Site: https://www.tracebg.com
Year Founded: 2007
T57—(BUL)
Rev.: $121,545,635
Assets: $149,412,317
Liabilities: $76,253,725
Net Worth: $73,158,592
Earnings: ($102,638)
Emp.: 768
Fiscal Year-end: 12/31/22
Construction Services
N.A.I.C.S.: 237310
Nikolay Mihaylov (Chm-Supervisory Bd)

Subsidiaries:

AVGUSTA TRACE LTD. (1)
190 Patriarh Evtimij Blvd, Stara Zagora, 6000, Bulgaria
Tel.: (359) 42 61 37 13
Highway Construction Services
N.A.I.C.S.: 237310

Asphalt Commerce EOOD Ltd. (1)
12 Nikola Obrazopisov Str, 1408, Sofia, Bulgaria
Tel.: (359) 28066700
Commodity Trade Intermediation Services
N.A.I.C.S.: 523160

Asphalt Commerce Ltd. (1)
12 Nikola Obrazopisov Str, 1408, Sofia, Bulgaria
Tel.: (359) 28066700
Construction Services
N.A.I.C.S.: 236220

INFRASTROJ LTD. (1)
Pleven 4 G Kovachev Blvd Fl 3, Pleven, 5800, Bulgaria
Tel.: (359) 64 80 14 60
Highway Construction Services
N.A.I.C.S.: 237310

Infra Commerce EOOD Ltd. (1)
71 James Bourchier Blvd, 1404, Sofia, Bulgaria
Tel.: (359) 24053277
Commodity Trade Intermediation Services
N.A.I.C.S.: 523160

PATNA SIGNALIZATSIA I SAORAZHENIA JSC (1)
Stara Zagora Golesh USM base, Stara Zagora, 6000, Bulgaria
Tel.: (359) 42 690 995
Highway Construction Services
N.A.I.C.S.: 237310

PSF MOSTINZHENERING JSC (1)
16 D Blagoev Blvd, Yambol, 8600, Bulgaria
Tel.: (359) 46 66 32 62
Highway Construction Services
N.A.I.C.S.: 237310

PSI JSC (1)
Stara Zagora 190 P Evtimii Str, Stara Zagora, 6000, Bulgaria
Tel.: (359) 42 61 37 10
Web Site: http://www.tracebg.com
Highway Construction Services
N.A.I.C.S.: 237310

RODOPA TRACE LTD. (1)
Smolyan 6 Bulgaria Blvd Fl 2, Smolyan, 4700, Bulgaria
Tel.: (359) 301 6 59 20
Highway Construction Services
N.A.I.C.S.: 237310

TRACE - BOURGAS JSC (1)
15 Odrin Str Fl 7, Burgas, 8000, Bulgaria
Tel.: (359) 56 81 36 39
Highway Construction Services
N.A.I.C.S.: 237310

TRACE KARJALI JSC (1)
76 Bulgaria Blvd Fl 4, Kardjhali, 6600, Bulgaria
Tel.: (359) 361 61 347
Highway Construction Services
N.A.I.C.S.: 237310

TRACE PLOVDIV LTD. (1)
1 Kozloduj office No 2 3, Plovdiv, 4000, Bulgaria
Tel.: (359) 32 39 30 00
Highway Construction Services
N.A.I.C.S.: 237310

TRACE ROADS JSC (1)
15 Metlichina Polyana, Sofia, 1404, Bulgaria
Tel.: (359) 2 819 36 06
Highway Construction Services
N.A.I.C.S.: 237310

Trace BG EOOD Ltd. (1)
Gotse Delchev Quarter 15 Metlichina polyana Street fl 2, 1404, Sofia, Bulgaria
Tel.: (359) 28193600

Railway Station Construction Services
N.A.I.C.S.: 236220

Trace Bg JSC (1)
Gotse Delchev Quarter 15 Metlichina Polyana Street Fl 2, 1404, Sofia, Bulgaria
Tel.: (359) 28193600
Construction Services
N.A.I.C.S.: 236220
George Ivanov (Exec Dir)

Trace Properties Ltd. (1)
71 James Bourchier Blvd, 1407, Sofia, Bulgaria
Tel.: (359) 28066700
Construction Services
N.A.I.C.S.: 236220

Trace Serbia JSC (1)
13 a GeneralaTranijea Str, 18000, Nis, Serbia
Tel.: (381) 18517000
Construction Services
N.A.I.C.S.: 236220
Stoyko Meshkov (Exec Dir)

Trace Yambol JSC (1)
2 d-r Petar Branekov str, 8600, Yambol, Bulgaria
Tel.: (359) 46663263
Construction Services
N.A.I.C.S.: 236220
Ivan Hristov (Exec Dir)

USM JSC (1)
Golesh, Stara Zagora, 6000, Bulgaria
Tel.: (359) 42 61 33 43
Highway Construction Services
N.A.I.C.S.: 237310

Vior Velika Morava a.d. (1)
Kneza Milosa 9/5, Belgrade, Serbia
Tel.: (381) 11 3241 439
Sales Range: Less than $1 Million
Emp.: 6
Hydraulic Structure Construction Services
N.A.I.C.S.: 236210

TRACE SOFTWARE INTERNATIONAL
Parc Eco-Normandie, 76430, Saint-Romain-de-Colbosc, France
Tel.: (33) 232794424
Web Site: http://www.trace-software.com
Year Founded: 1990
Emp.: 200
Development of Software Solutions & Services to Industrial Engineering
N.A.I.C.S.: 513210

Subsidiaries:

Trace Software China (1)
Shangda International Room D408 No 3100 Hutai Road, Baoshan District, Shanghai, 200436, China (100%)
Tel.: (86) 21 6236 0850
Web Site: http://www.trace-software.com
Online Media & 3D Digital Engineering Content Mfr
N.A.I.C.S.: 513210

Trace Software Iberia (1)
Via Augusta 48-54, 08006, Barcelona, Spain (100%)
Tel.: (34) 934 531 206
Web Site: http://www.trace-software.com
3D Content Software Mfr
N.A.I.C.S.: 513210
Guillem Fiter (CMO)

Trace Software Morocco (1)
104 Bis Boulevard Abdelmoumen 4th Floor, 20042, Casablanca, Morocco (100%)
Tel.: (212) 645 51 08 27
3D Digital Content Software
N.A.I.C.S.: 513210

TraceParts GmbH (1)
Fuggerstrasse 9A, D-92224, Amberg, Germany (100%)
Tel.: (49) 9621 9173 0
Web Site: http://www.traceparts.de
Digital Engineering 3D Content Applications
N.A.I.C.S.: 513210
Christian Baumgartner (Mng Dir)

TraceParts Inc. (1)

INTERNATIONAL PUBLIC

402 Amherst St Suite 304, Nashua, NH 03063 (100%)
Tel.: (603) 577-1876
Web Site: http://www.tracepartsusa.com
Online Media Business Solutions in Digital Engineering 3D Content
N.A.I.C.S.: 541840
Bob Noftle (Pres)

TraceParts S.A. (1)
Parc Eco Normandie, 76430, Saint-Romain-de-Colbosc, France (100%)
Tel.: (33) 232 794 426
Web Site: http://www.traceparts.com
3D Digital Engineering Content
N.A.I.C.S.: 513210
Gabriel Guigue (Mng Dir)

TraceParts UK Ltd. (1)
431 Maidstone Road, Bluebell Hill, Nottingham, ME5 9RX, Kent, United Kingdom (100%)
Tel.: (44) 1622370100
Web Site: http://www.traceparts.com
3D Digital Engineering Content
N.A.I.C.S.: 513210
Thierry Bourgeay (Mktg Dir-Intl)

TraceParts srl (1)
via Aristotele 109, Reggio Emilia, 42122, Italy (100%)
Tel.: (39) 0522 39 17 27
Web Site: http://www.traceparts.com
3D Digital Engineering Content
N.A.I.C.S.: 513210
Nino Mazza (Mng Dir)

TRACE SOFTWARE PRIVATE LIMITED
2nd Floor Plot No 2 Sector 42 Golf Course Road, Gurgaon, 122001, Haryana, India
Tel.: (91) 1242578797
Web Site: http://www.tracesoftware.in
Year Founded: 2003
Sales Range: $25-49.9 Million
Emp.: 200
Bespoke Software & Applications for Desktop & Web
N.A.I.C.S.: 513210
Vaibhav Agarwal (Dir-Dev)

TRACKNET HOLDING
Steindleren 3, 3210, Fribourg, Switzerland
Tel.: (41) 317500070
Web Site: http://www.tracknet-group.ch
Holding Company; Track Equipment Maintenance
N.A.I.C.S.: 551112

Subsidiaries:

Tensol Rail Ltd. (1)
Tensol Rail SA, Giornico, 6745, Switzerland
Tel.: (41) 918736611
Web Site: http://www.tensolrail.com
Sales Range: $25-49.9 Million
Emp.: 100
Railway Material Mfr
N.A.I.C.S.: 541330

TRACKWISE DESIGNS PLC
1 Ashvale Alexandra Way, Tewkesbury, GL20 8NB, Gloucestershire, United Kingdom
Tel.: (44) 1684299930 UK
Web Site: http://www.trackwise.co.uk
Year Founded: 1989
TWD—(AIM)
Rev.: $10,876,695
Assets: $49,740,072
Liabilities: $16,542,460
Net Worth: $33,197,612
Earnings: ($2,242,953)
Emp.: 132
Fiscal Year-end: 12/31/21
Electronic Components Mfr
N.A.I.C.S.: 334413
Philip Johnston (CEO)

TRACKX HOLDINGS INC.

800 West Pender St Suite1430, Vancouver, V6C 2V6, BC, Canada
Tel.: (303) 325-7300 BC
Web Site: http://www.trackx.com
Year Founded: 2004
TKX—(TSXV)
Rev.: $2,732,613
Assets: $1,281,722
Liabilities: $2,365,598
Net Worth: ($1,083,876)
Earnings: ($593,534)
Fiscal Year-end: 09/30/21
Gold & Precious Metals Mining & Exploration Services
N.A.I.C.S.: 212220
Michael Himmelfarb *(CMO)*

TRACOE MEDICAL GMBH
Reichsforststr 32, D-60528, Frankfurt am Main, Germany
Tel.: (49) 696656680
Web Site: http://www.tracoe.com
Year Founded: 1972
Rev.: $11,173,140
Emp.: 112
Tracheostomy Tube Mfr
N.A.I.C.S.: 339112
Stephan Kohler *(Mng Dir)*

Subsidiaries:

MC Europe B.V. (1)
Flight Forum 1500, 5657 EZ, Eindhoven, Netherlands
Tel.: (31) 854872121
Web Site: https://www.mc-europe.nl
Emp.: 8
Medical Equipment Mfr & Distr
N.A.I.C.S.: 339112
Mathilde Kirk *(Mgr-Comml Bus Unit)*

TRACOMA HOLDINGS BERHAD
Lot 13 33 Tingkat 13 Kompleks Pertama Jalan Tuanku Abdul Rahman, 50100, Kuala Lumpur, Malaysia
Tel.: (60) 326931011
Sales Range: $50-74.9 Million
Emp.: 770
Automotive Parts & Components Mfr
N.A.I.C.S.: 423120
Mohamed Niza Abu Bakar *(CEO)*

Subsidiaries:

Mindus (M) Sdn. Bhd. (1)
18-02 Jalan Permas 10/7 Bandar Baru Permas Jaya, 81750, Masai, Johor, Malaysia
Tel.: (60) 73863206
Web Site: http://www.mindus.biz
Sales Range: $25-49.9 Million
Emp.: 10
Construction Engineering Services
N.A.I.C.S.: 541330
Zainal Ariffin Yahya *(Mgr)*

Profen Manufacturing Sdn. Bhd. (1)
Lot 52 Bbt 7 Jalan Jasmine 2 Kawasan Perindustrian Bukit Beruntung, Rawang, 48300, Selangor, Malaysia
Tel.: (60) 360282800
Metal Stamping Machinery Mfr
N.A.I.C.S.: 333517

Profen Sdn. Bhd. (1)
Lot 9 Kawasan MIEL Fasa II Jalan Bursa 23/4 Section 23, 40300, Shah Alam, Selangor Darul Ehsan, Malaysia
Tel.: (60) 355424800
Web Site: http://www.profen.com.my
Sales Range: $50-74.9 Million
Emp.: 240
Car Components Mfr & Distr
N.A.I.C.S.: 336390

Propoly (M) Sdn. Bhd. (1)
Lot 14 Jalan Lada Sulah 18/11 Section 16, 40000, Shah Alam, Selangor, Malaysia
Tel.: (60) 3 5511 5235
Automotive Components Mfr
N.A.I.C.S.: 336310

TRACSIS PLC
Nexus Discovery Way, Leeds, LS2 3AA, United Kingdom
Tel.: (44) 8451259162 UK
Web Site: https://www.tracsis.com
Year Founded: 2004
TRCS—(AIM)
Rev.: $101,852,436
Assets: $125,297,620
Liabilities: $41,140,834
Net Worth: $84,156,786
Earnings: $8,456,658
Fiscal Year-end: 07/31/23
Software Publisher
N.A.I.C.S.: 513210
Max Cawthra *(CFO)*

Subsidiaries:

Railcomm LLC (1)
1387 Fairport Rd Ste 900D, Fairport, NY 14450
Tel.: (585) 377-3360
Web Site: http://www.railcomm.com
Sales Range: $10-24.9 Million
Emp.: 43
Technology Solutions for Railroad & Industrial Operations
N.A.I.C.S.: 238210
Joe Denny *(Founder)*

Sky High Technology (1)
12-14 Westgate Tadcaster, Leeds, LS24 9AB, United Kingdom
Tel.: (44) 1937 833 933
Web Site: http://skyhightechnology.com
Sales Range: $1-9.9 Million
Emp.: 458
Traffic Data Capturing Services
N.A.I.C.S.: 518210
Alex Johnson *(Sec & Dir-Fin)*

Subsidiary (Domestic):

Sky High Technology Limited (2)
12-14 Westgate, Tadcaster, LS24 9AB, North Yorkshire, United Kingdom (100%)
Tel.: (44) 1937833933
Web Site: http://www.skyhightechnology.com
Traffic & Transportation Surveys
N.A.I.C.S.: 541614
Mark Mattison *(CEO)*

Sky High Technology (1)
Topfloor Unit E6 Centrepoint Business Park Oak Drive, 12, Dublin, Eire, Ireland
Tel.: (353) 142 43132
Web Site: http://www.skyhightechnology.com
Transport Survey & Data Consultancy Services
N.A.I.C.S.: 541614
Grant Wilson *(Exec Dir)*

Tracsis Passenger Counts Limited (1)
Recorder Rd, 14 Lovelstaithe, Norwich, NR1 1LW, United Kingdom
Tel.: (44) 1603625604
Railway Strategic Planning & Consulting Service Providers
N.A.I.C.S.: 541611

Tracsis Rail Consultancy Limited (1)
Ste 7 Loughborough Tech Ctr, Epinal Way, Loughborough, LE11 3GE, United Kingdom
Tel.: (44) 1509210110
Sales Range: $25-49.9 Million
Emp.: 25
Strategic Planning & Consulting Service Providers
N.A.I.C.S.: 541611

TRACTION URANIUM INC.
100 521 3rd Avenue SW, Calgary, T2P 3T3, AB, Canada
Tel.: (604) 425-2271 BC
Web Site: https://www.tractionuranium.com
Year Founded: 2020
TRCTF—(OTCQB)
Assets: $2,865,681
Liabilities: $17,070
Net Worth: $2,848,611
Earnings: ($9,405,944)
Fiscal Year-end: 09/30/22

Mineral Mining Services
N.A.I.C.S.: 213115
Lester Esteban *(CEO)*

TRACXN TECHNOLOGIES LIMITED
No L-248 2nd Floor 17th Cross Sector 6 HSR Layout, Bengaluru, 560102, Karnataka, India
Tel.: (91) 9036090116
Web Site: https://www.tracxn.com
Year Founded: 2012
TRACXN—(NSE)
Rev.: $8,894,061
Assets: $7,372,985
Liabilities: $4,555,474
Net Worth: $2,817,512
Earnings: ($661,707)
Fiscal Year-end: 03/31/22
Information Technology Services
N.A.I.C.S.: 541512
Neha Singh *(Chm & Mng Dir)*

TRADE & DEVELOPMENT BANK OF MONGOLIA LLC
Street 1 Peace Avenue 19, Sukhbaatar District, Ulaanbaatar, 14210, Mongolia
Tel.: (976) 1900 1977
Web Site: http://www.tdbm.mn
Year Founded: 1990
Rev.: $263,759,645
Assets: $2,767,840,079
Liabilities: $2,414,903,648
Net Worth: $352,936,431
Earnings: $4,803,097
Emp.: 1,500
Fiscal Year-end: 12/31/18
Retail & Corporate Banking
N.A.I.C.S.: 522110
Doljin Erdenebileg *(Chm)*

TRADE PARTNERS LIMITED
86-1 Sukhumvit Soi 23 Sukhumvit Road, Bangkok, 10110, Thailand
Tel.: (66) 22584086
Web Site: http://www.thailand-accounting.com
Year Founded: 1978
Emp.: 13
Accounting Services
N.A.I.C.S.: 541219

TRADE UNION COOPERATIVE INSURANCE & REINSURANCE COMPANY
NSH Tower 6389 King Fahed Bin Abdul Aziz Rd South Rakah, PO Box 1022, Al Khobar, 34227-2453, Saudi Arabia
Tel.: (966) 920006262
Web Site: http://www.tuci-sa.com
Year Founded: 2008
8170—(SAU)
Rev.: $276,751,490
Assets: $482,770,702
Liabilities: $332,055,206
Net Worth: $150,715,496
Earnings: $9,338,451
Emp.: 250
Fiscal Year-end: 12/31/22
Insurance Management Services
N.A.I.C.S.: 524298

TRADE WINGS LIMITED
A-2 Kaveri CHS Plot No 63 Sector 17 Vashi, Bhogilal Building 1st Floor Kalaghoda Fort, Navi Mumbai, 400705, India
Tel.: (91) 9168835801
Web Site: https://www.tradewings.in
Year Founded: 1949
509953—(BOM)
Rev.: $10,770,182
Assets: $6,683,400
Liabilities: $9,015,191

Net Worth: ($2,331,791)
Earnings: ($377,735)
Emp.: 110
Fiscal Year-end: 03/31/22
Freight Transportation Services
N.A.I.C.S.: 488510
Shailendra P. Mittal *(Chm & Mng Dir)*

TRADE WORKS CO., LTD.
Askasaka Park Building 10F 2-20 Akasaka 5-chome, Minato-ku, Tokyo, 107-6110, Japan
Tel.: (81) 362308900
Web Site: https://www.tworks.co.jp
3997—(TKS)
Rev.: $26,608,770
Assets: $21,574,870
Liabilities: $11,755,220
Net Worth: $9,819,650
Earnings: ($375,770)
Emp.: 2,030
Fiscal Year-end: 12/31/23
Securities Trading Development Services
N.A.I.C.S.: 523150
Katsuhiro Asami *(Founder, Chm & Pres)*

TRADE-MARK INDUSTRIAL INC.
1197 Union Street, Kitchener, N2H 6N6, ON, Canada
Tel.: (519) 570-1511
Web Site: http://www.trade-markind.com
Year Founded: 1998
Rev.: $22,002,300
Emp.: 300
Commercial & Industrial Building Construction Services
N.A.I.C.S.: 236220
Terry Moore *(VP-Electrical)*

TRADE-VAN INFORMATION SERVICES CO.
6F No 19-13 Sanchung Road, Nangang District, Taipei, 115, Taiwan
Tel.: (886) 226551188
Web Site: https://www.trade-van.com
6183—(TAI)
Rev.: $75,124,887
Assets: $119,637,132
Liabilities: $34,888,909
Net Worth: $84,748,223
Earnings: $15,718,793
Emp.: 673
Fiscal Year-end: 12/31/23
Internet Information Services
N.A.I.C.S.: 513199
Lu-Sheng Chang *(Chm-Acting & Pres)*

TRADEDOUBLER AB
Centralplan 15, 11120, Stockholm, Sweden
Tel.: (46) 84050800 SE
Web Site: https://www.tradedoubler.com
TRAD—(OMX)
Rev.: $153,563,367
Assets: $97,168,507
Liabilities: $68,347,336
Net Worth: $28,821,171
Earnings: $2,275,235
Emp.: 294
Fiscal Year-end: 12/31/22
Digital Marketing Solutions
N.A.I.C.S.: 541890
Matthias Stadelmeyer *(Pres & CEO)*

Subsidiaries:

TD Search (1)
24th Floor Portland House, Bressenden Place, London, SW1E 5BH, United Kingdom
Tel.: (44) 207 798 6400
Web Site: http://www.thesearchworks.com

TRADEDOUBLER AB

TradeDoubler AB—(Continued)
Search Engine Optimization
N.A.I.C.S.: 541810
Gavin Ailes *(Dir-Comml)*

TradeDoubler BV (1)
Stationsplein 45 Unit A5 209, 3013 AK, Rotterdam, Netherlands
Tel.: (31) 102863977
Marketing Services
N.A.I.C.S.: 541613

TradeDoubler Espana SL (1)
C/Martires de Alcala n 4-3 Left, 28015, Madrid, Spain
Tel.: (34) 915321247
Marketing Services
N.A.I.C.S.: 541613

TradeDoubler GmbH (1)
Mainzer Strasse 13, 80804, Munich, Germany
Tel.: (49) 89693113071
Marketing Services
N.A.I.C.S.: 541613

TradeDoubler International AB (1)
Malmskillnadsgatan 32, 111 51, Stockholm, Sweden
Tel.: (46) 84050800
Advertising & Marketing Services
N.A.I.C.S.: 541810

TradeDoubler Ltd. (1)
4th Floor 90 High Holborn, London, WC1V 6BH, United Kingdom
Tel.: (44) 2077985800
Marketing Services
N.A.I.C.S.: 541613

TradeDoubler Sp zoo (1)
Unii Ul Pulawska 2 budynek C, 02-566, Warsaw, Poland
Tel.: (48) 223076402
Marketing Services
N.A.I.C.S.: 541613

TRADEGATE AG WERTPAPIERHANDELSBANK
Kurfurstendamm 119, 10711, Berlin, Germany
Tel.: (49) 30896060
Web Site: https://www.tradegate.ag
Year Founded: 1986
T2G—(DEU)
Emp.: 160
Electronic Finance Services
N.A.I.C.S.: 522320
Holger Timm *(Chm)*

TRADEGO FINTECH LTD.
Office No 10 16th Floor Hong Kong Plaza 188 Connaught Road West, Hong Kong, China (Hong Kong)
Tel.: (852) 23375966 Ky
Web Site: http://www.tradego8.com
8017—(HKG)
Rev.: $12,492,420
Assets: $21,779,927
Liabilities: $5,857,007
Net Worth: $15,922,920
Earnings: $3,306,413
Emp.: 152
Fiscal Year-end: 03/31/23
Integrated Security Services
N.A.I.C.S.: 561621
Leon Lau *(Chm & CEO)*

TRADEHOLD LIMITED
Suite 1603 Portside Building 4 Bree Street, Cape Town, 8001, South Africa
Tel.: (27) 763341430 ZA
Web Site:
https://www.tradehold.co.za
CPP—(JSE)
Rev.: $64,075,458
Assets: $671,611,939
Liabilities: $386,973,645
Net Worth: $284,638,294
Earnings: $65,767,857
Fiscal Year-end: 02/29/24

Investment Holding Company
N.A.I.C.S.: 551112
C. H. Wiese *(Chm)*

Subsidiaries:

Collins Group
1 Richefond Circle Ridgeside Office Park, Umhlanga, 4319, South Africa
Tel.: (27) 315368005
Web Site: https://collinsresidential.co.za
Commercial Property Development & Construction Company
N.A.I.C.S.: 236220

TRADELINK ELECTRONIC COMMERCE LIMITED
11/F and 12/F Tower B Regent Centre 63 Wo Yi Hop Road, Kwai Chung, China (Hong Kong)
Tel.: (852) 25991600
Web Site:
https://www.tradelink.com.hk
0536—(HKG)
Rev.: $32,998,913
Assets: $67,901,528
Liabilities: $21,438,870
Net Worth: $46,462,658
Earnings: $6,672,458
Emp.: 255
Fiscal Year-end: 12/31/22
E-Commerce Service Provider
N.A.I.C.S.: 541511
Harry Nai Shee Lee *(Chm)*

Subsidiaries:

Digi-Sign Certification Services Limited (1)
11/F 12/F Tower B Regent Centre 63 Wo Yi Hop Road, Kwai Chung, China (Hong Kong)
Tel.: (852) 25991777
Web Site: https://www.dg-sign.com
Computer Programming Services
N.A.I.C.S.: 541511
Kam Keung *(Chm)*

Digital Trade and Transportation Network Limited (1)
11/F 12/F Tower B Regent Centre 63 Wo Yi Hop Road, Kwai Chung, New Territories, China (Hong Kong)
Tel.: (852) 25991771
Web Site: https://www.hk-dttn.com
Emp.: 100
Electronic Document Exchange Services
N.A.I.C.S.: 561410

VSHIP Limited (1)
11/F and 12/F Tower B Regent Centre 63 Wo Yi Hop Road, Kwai Chung, China (Hong Kong)
Tel.: (852) 25991600
Web Site: http://www.vship.com
Logistic Services
N.A.I.C.S.: 541614

TRADERS HOLDINGS CO., LTD.
Yebisu Garden Place Tower 28F 4-20-3 Ebisu, Shibuya-ku, Tokyo, 150-6028, Japan
Tel.: (81) 343304700
Web Site: https://www.tradershd.com
Year Founded: 1999
8704—(TKS)
Rev.: $66,780,830
Assets: $781,255,730
Liabilities: $687,915,920
Net Worth: $93,339,810
Earnings: $22,037,740
Emp.: 25
Fiscal Year-end: 03/31/24
Holding Company
N.A.I.C.S.: 551112
Takayuki Kanamaru *(Chm & Pres)*

Subsidiaries:

Nextop Co., Ltd. (1)
Level 12 70 Building Keangnam Landmark Tower, Me Tri Ward Nam Tu Liem Dist, Hanoi, Vietnam

Tel.: (84) 2485874050
Online Game Development Services
N.A.I.C.S.: 541511

Nextop Software (Dalian) Co., Ltd. (1)
Room A1702 Namai Daxia No 3 Huoqiao Road, Hi-Tech Park, Dalian, China
Tel.: (86) 41139570586
Mobile Application Development Services
N.A.I.C.S.: 541511

PT. Pialang Jepang Berjangka (1)
Sumitmas II Lantai 17 Jl Jend Sudirman Kav 61-62, Lot 8 6 - 8 7 Kawasan Mega Kuningan, Jakarta, 12190, Indonesia
Tel.: (62) 2127510027
Web Site: http://www.pjbindo.com
Financial Brokerage Services
N.A.I.C.S.: 523160

ZE Energy Inc. (1)
Taisei Building 6F 1-11-7 Nihonbashi Kayabacho, Chuo-ku, Tokyo, 103-0025, Japan
Tel.: (81) 364324331
Power Generation System Mfr & Distr
N.A.I.C.S.: 333611
Kohei Matsushita *(Pres)*

Subsidiary (Domestic):

ZE Design Inc. (2)
9F Kyoto-cloto bldg 376 Ichinofunairi-cho Nakagyo-ku, Kyoto, Japan
Tel.: (81) 752536375
Power Generation Services
N.A.I.C.S.: 221117

TRADETOOL AUTO CO., LTD.
Rm 7 4F No 213 Chaofu Rd, Xitun Dist, Taichung, 407, Taiwan
Tel.: (886) 422585821
Web Site:
https://www.tradetools.com.tw
Year Founded: 1983
3685—(TPE)
Rev.: $48,504,487
Assets: $82,997,843
Liabilities: $37,246,975
Net Worth: $45,750,868
Earnings: ($1,750,274)
Emp.: 192
Fiscal Year-end: 12/31/22
Plastics Product Mfr
N.A.I.C.S.: 326199
Ming-Hung Chang *(Gen Mgr)*

TRADEWINDS CORPORATION BERHAD
Lot 6875 Jalan Kerja Ayer Lama, 68000, Ampang, Selangor Darul Ehsan, Malaysia
Tel.: (60) 3 2727 7000
Web Site:
http://www.tradewindscorp.com
Sales Range: $150-199.9 Million
Home Management Services
N.A.I.C.S.: 721110
Arief Nasran Abdul Wahab *(COO)*

Subsidiaries:

Mutiara Hotels & Resorts Sdn. Bhd. (1)
Lobby Level Hotel Istana Kuala Lumpur, 72 Jalan Raja Chulan, 50200, Kuala Lumpur, Malaysia
Tel.: (60) 3 2782 2222
Web Site: http://www.mutiarahotels.com
Hotel & Resort Operators Services
N.A.I.C.S.: 721110
Cassendra Grace *(Asst Dir-Sls)*

Mutiara-TCB Hotel Management Sdn. Bhd. (1)
21st Floor Wisma Zelan No 1 Jalan Tasik Pemaisuri 2, Bandar Tun Razak Cheras, 56000, Kuala Lumpur, Malaysia
Tel.: (60) 3 9106 3000
Web Site: http://www.tradewindscorp.com
Home Management Services
N.A.I.C.S.: 721110

Prism Protection Services Sdn. Bhd. (1)

INTERNATIONAL PUBLIC

B-10-8 Megan Avenue 1 189 Jalan Tun Razak, 50350, Kuala Lumpur, Malaysia
Tel.: (60) 3 26988888
Web Site: http://www.prism-alarm.com.my
Sales Range: $75-99.9 Million
Emp.: 400
Integrated Security Services
N.A.I.C.S.: 561621

Prism Security Management Sdn. Bhd. (1)
B-10-8 Megan Avenue 1 189 Jalan Tun Razak, Jalan Raja Laut, Kuala Lumpur, 50400, Malaysia
Tel.: (60) 3 2698 8888
Web Site: http://www.prism-alarm.com.my
Sales Range: $10-24.9 Million
Emp.: 33
Security System Services
N.A.I.C.S.: 561621
Ab Hamid Shafie *(CEO)*

Sincere Leasing Sdn. Bhd. (1)
1st Floor 40 Jalan SS 2/63, 47300, Petaling Jaya, Selangor, Malaysia
Tel.: (60) 378747416
Web Site: http://www.tradewindscorp.com
Sales Range: $50-74.9 Million
Emp.: 5
Financial Management Services
N.A.I.C.S.: 523999
Chine Lee Loh *(Sr Mgr)*

TCB Land Sdn. Bhd. (1)
21st Floor Wisma Zelan No 1 Jalan Tasik Pemaisuri 2 Bandar Tun Razak, Cheras, 56000, Kuala Lumpur, Malaysia
Tel.: (60) 3 9106 3000
Web Site: http://www.tradewindscorp.com
Property Management Services
N.A.I.C.S.: 531312

THR Hotel (Johor) Sdn. Bhd. (1)
21st Floor Wisma Zelan No 1 Jalan Tasik Pemaisuri 2, Bandar Tun Razak Cheras, 56000, Kuala Lumpur, Malaysia
Tel.: (60) 3 9106 3000
Web Site: http://www.tradewindscorp.com
Home Management Services
N.A.I.C.S.: 721110

THR Hotel (Kuala Tahan) Sdn. Bhd. (1)
21st Floor Wisma Zelan No 1 Jalan Tasik Pemaisuri 2, Bandar Tun Razak Cheras, 56000, Kuala Lumpur, Malaysia
Tel.: (60) 3 9106 3000
Home Management Services
N.A.I.C.S.: 721110
Shaharul Farez Hassan *(CEO)*

THR Hotel (Penang) Sdn. Bhd. (1)
21st Floor Wisma Zelan No 1 Jalan Tasik Pemaisuri 2, Bandar Tun Razak Cheras, Kuala Lumpur, 56000, Malaysia
Tel.: (60) 3 9106 3000
Web Site: http://www.tradewindscorp.com
Home Management Services
N.A.I.C.S.: 721110

THR Hotel (Selangor) Berhad (1)
21st Floor Wisma Zelan No 1 Jalan Tasik Pemaisuri 2, Bandar Tun Razak Cheras, 56000, Kuala Lumpur, Malaysia
Tel.: (60) 3 9106 3000
Home Management Services
N.A.I.C.S.: 721110

Tradewinds Hotels & Resorts Sdn. Bhd. (1)
21st Floor Wisma Zelan No 1 Jalan Tasik Pemaisuri 2, Bandar Tun Razak Cheras, 56000, Kuala Lumpur, Malaysia
Tel.: (60) 3 9106 3000
Web Site: http://www.tradewindscorp.com
Home Management Services
N.A.I.C.S.: 721110

Tradewinds International Insurance Brokers Sdn. Bhd. (1)
37th Floor CAP Square Tower No 10 Jalan Munshi Abdullah, Kuala Lumpur, 50100, Malaysia
Tel.: (60) 3 23804800
Web Site: http://www.tradewinds-insbrok.com
Sales Range: $50-74.9 Million
Emp.: 60
Insurance Broking Services
N.A.I.C.S.: 524210

AND PRIVATE COMPANIES

TRAFIGURA BEHEER B.V.

Norhayati Mohamed *(CEO)*

Tradewinds Johor Sdn. Bhd. (1)
21st Floor Wisma Zelan No 1 Jalan Tasik Pemaisuri 2, 56000, Kuala Lumpur, Malaysia
Tel.: (60) 3 9106 3000
Web Site: http://www.tradewindscorp.com
Financial Management Services
N.A.I.C.S.: 523999

Tradewinds Properties Sdn. Bhd. (1)
21st Floor Wisma Zelan No 1 Jalan Tasik Pemaisuri 2, Bandar Tun Razak Cheras, 56000, Kuala Lumpur, Malaysia
Tel.: (60) 3 9106 3166
Web Site: http://www.tradewindscorp.com
Property Management Services
N.A.I.C.S.: 531311

Tradewinds Travel & Tours Sdn. Bhd. (1)
29-5 Block V Jaya One No 72 A Jalan Universiti, Petaling Jaya, 46200, Selangor, Malaysia
Tel.: (60) 379670888
Web Site: http://www.tradewindtravel.com.my
Sales Range: $10-24.9 Million
Emp.: 28
Travel Agency Services
N.A.I.C.S.: 561510
Mohamed Khairy Abdul Rahim *(Gen Mgr)*

TRADEWINDS PLANTATION BERHAD
No 7 Jalan 5/65C Off Jalan Pahang Barat, Pekeliling Business Centre, 53000, Kuala Lumpur, Malaysia
Tel.: (60) 342897888
Web Site: http://www.tpb.com.my
Sales Range: $550-599.9 Million
Palm Oil Producer
N.A.I.C.S.: 311224

TRADEX FOODS INC.
Suite 410 3960 Quadra Street, Victoria, V8X 4A3, BC, Canada
Tel.: (250) 479-1355
Web Site: https://www.tradexfoods.com
Year Founded: 1991
Rev.: $10,595,724
Emp.: 24
Fresh Frozen Seafood Supplier
N.A.I.C.S.: 424460
Robert Reierson *(Pres & CEO)*

TRADI S.A.
Prolongacion Huamanga No 1500, La Victoria, Lima, Peru
Tel.: (51) 7122222
Web Site: https://www.tradisa.com.pe
Year Founded: 1976
TRADIC1—(LIM)
Sales Range: Less than $1 Million
Solid Waste Recycling Services
N.A.I.C.S.: 562998
Enrique Miguel Ferrand Rubini *(Chm)*

TRADIA CORPORATION
1-2-22 Kaigan-dori, Chuo-ku, Kobe, 650-0024, Japan
Tel.: (81) 783917170
Web Site: https://www.tradia.co.jp
Year Founded: 1941
9365—(TKS)
Rev.: $99,196,270
Assets: $68,823,320
Liabilities: $39,739,320
Net Worth: $29,084,000
Earnings: $2,154,860
Fiscal Year-end: 03/31/24
Marine Transportation Services
N.A.I.C.S.: 483111

Subsidiaries:

Dainichi Butsuryu Co., Ltd. (1)
SuzueBaydium Bldg 8F 1-15-1 Kaigan, Minato-ku, Tokyo, 105-0022, Japan
Tel.: (81) 669044840

Personnel Dispatch Services
N.A.I.C.S.: 561499

Hirose Sangyo Kaiun Co., Ltd. (1)
1-7-23 Chikko, Minato-ku, Osaka, 552-0021, Japan
Tel.: (81) 665733841
Barge Transportation Services
N.A.I.C.S.: 483211

Mikasa Rikuun Co. Ltd. (1)
8-11-6 Minatojima, Chuo-ku, Kobe, 650-0045, Japan
Tel.: (81) 783045165
General Trucking Services
N.A.I.C.S.: 484121

Om Trax Packaging Solutions Ltd. (1)
Plot No-159 Transport Centre Punjabi Bagh, New Delhi, 110035, India
Tel.: (91) 1148316700
Web Site: http://www.omtrax.com
Material Packing Services
N.A.I.C.S.: 561910

Sea Union International Logistics (Hong Kong) Ltd. (1)
Unit 01-02 32/F Saxon Tower 7 Cheung Shun Street Lai Chi Kok, Kowloon, China (Hong Kong)
Tel.: (852) 34230610
Freight Forwarding Logistics Services
N.A.I.C.S.: 541614

Sea Union International Logistics (ShenZhen) Co., Ltd. (1)
22/F Block B Nanfang Securities Building Jian She Rd, Shenzhen, 518001, China
Tel.: (86) 75582617228
Freight Forwarding Logistics Services
N.A.I.C.S.: 541614

TRADING EMISSIONS PLC
IOMA House Hope Street, Douglas, IM1 1AP, Isle of Man
Tel.: (44) 1624681335
Web Site: http://www.tradingemissionsplc.com
Sales Range: Less than $1 Million
Investment Services; Carbon Products
N.A.I.C.S.: 523999

TRADITION FINE FOODS LTD.
663 Warden Avenue, Toronto, M1L 3Z5, ON, Canada
Tel.: (416) 444-4777
Web Site: http://www.tradition.ca
Year Founded: 1982
Sales Range: $25-49.9 Million
Emp.: 80
Bakery Products Mfr & Distr
N.A.I.C.S.: 311813
Thomas Glowczewski *(Pres)*

TRAFAIR CAPITAL AG
Rutihofstrasse 2, Niederteufen, 9052, Teufen, Switzerland
Tel.: (41) 71 333 47 00
Investment Services
N.A.I.C.S.: 523999
Michael von Borzyszkowski *(Chm)*

TRAFALGAR PROPERTY GROUP PLC
Chequers Barn Chequers Hill, Bough Beech, Edenbridge, TN8 7PD, Kent, United Kingdom
Tel.: (44) 1732700000   UK
Web Site: https://www.trafalgarproperty.group
Year Founded: 2001
TRAF—(AIM)
Rev.: $3,103,476
Assets: $3,169,967
Liabilities: $7,191,846
Net Worth: ($4,021,879)
Earnings: ($446,953)
Emp.: 3
Fiscal Year-end: 03/31/21
Offices of Other Holding Companies

N.A.I.C.S.: 551112
Christopher Charles Johnson *(CEO)*

Subsidiaries:

Trafalgar Retirement + Limited (1)
Raven House 29 Linkfield Lane, Redhill, RH1 1SS, United Kingdom
Tel.: (44) 1737452111
Web Site: https://www.beauforthomes.co.uk
Property Management Services
N.A.I.C.S.: 531311

TRAFCO GROUP B.S.C.
Mina Salman Avenue 40, PO Box 20202, Manama, Bahrain
Tel.: (973) 17729000   BH
Web Site: https://www.trafco.com
Year Founded: 1977
TRAFCO—(BAH)
Rev.: $112,922,315
Assets: $140,011,230
Liabilities: $51,751,784
Net Worth: $88,259,447
Earnings: $4,073,958
Emp.: 300
Fiscal Year-end: 12/31/22
Fast Moving Consumer Goods Import & Distr
N.A.I.C.S.: 424420
Yusuf Saleh Abdulla Alsaleh *(Vice Chm)*

Subsidiaries:

Awal Dairy Company W.L.L. (1)
Building No 791 Road No 55 Block No 463 Off Budaiya Road, PO Box 601, Al Hajar Village, Manama, Bahrain
Tel.: (973) 17598598
Web Site: https://www.awaldairy.com
Food Ingredient & Dairy Product Mfr
N.A.I.C.S.: 311999

TRAFFIC CONTROL TECHNOLOGY CO., LTD.
TCT Building No 3 Zhicheng North Street, Fengtai District, Beijing, 100070, China
Tel.: (86) 1083606005
Web Site: https://www.bj-tct.com
Year Founded: 2009
688015—(SHG)
Rev.: $346,464,827
Assets: $788,819,036
Liabilities: $429,955,105
Net Worth: $358,863,930
Earnings: $32,221,084
Fiscal Year-end: 12/31/22
Traffic Control Equipment Mfr & Distr
N.A.I.C.S.: 334290
Chunhai Gao *(Chm & Gen Mgr)*

TRAFFIC TECHNOLOGIES LTD.
Tel.: (61) 394300222
Web Site: https://www.trafficltd.com.au
Year Founded: 2004
TTI—(ASX)
Rev.: $21,272,861
Assets: $14,040,569
Liabilities: $19,106,045
Net Worth: ($5,065,476)
Earnings: ($10,199,728)
Fiscal Year-end: 06/30/24
Traffic Control Equipment Manufacturing
N.A.I.C.S.: 336999
Peter Kenneth Crafter *(CFO & Sec)*

Subsidiaries:

Aldridge Traffic Systems Pty Ltd (1)
12-14 Leeds Street, Rhodes, 2138, NSW, Australia
Tel.: (61) 29 701 9900
Web Site: http://www.aldridgetraffic.com.au
Roadway Lighting Product Mfr
N.A.I.C.S.: 335139

De Neefe Pty Ltd (1)

25 Brisbane Street, PO Box 132, Eltham, Melbourne, 3095, VIC, Australia
Tel.: (61) 39 430 0266
Web Site: https://www.deneefe.com
Building Equipment Mfr & Distr
N.A.I.C.S.: 333120

Excelsior Diecasting Pty Limited (1)
PO Box 201, Concord West, 2138, NSW, Australia
Tel.: (61) 296480094
Web Site: http://www.excelsiordiecasting.com.au
Die Casting Material Mfr
N.A.I.C.S.: 331524

L&M Traffic Services Pty Ltd (1)
Unit 1 2-4 Souffi Place, Dandenong South, 3175, VIC, Australia
Tel.: (61) 397682637
Web Site: http://www.lmts.com.au
Traffic Signal Installation Services
N.A.I.C.S.: 238210
Trevor Chambers *(Gen Mgr)*

Sunny Sign Company Pty Ltd (1)
10 Boulder Rd, Malaga, 6090, WA, Australia
Tel.: (61) 89 248 1002
Web Site: https://www.sunnysigns.com.au
Road Safety Accessory Distr
N.A.I.C.S.: 441330
Dale Chapman *(Project Mgr-Bus Dev)*

TRAFFORD HOLDINGS LTD.
2333 Government St Ste 6E, Victoria, V8T 4P4, BC, Canada
Tel.: (250) 383-6864
Web Site: http://www.trafford.com
Year Founded: 1991
Sales Range: $25-49.9 Million
Emp.: 70
Book Publishers
N.A.I.C.S.: 513130
Kingstone Reed *(CFO & VP)*

Subsidiaries:

Trafford Publishing, Inc. (1)
301 S Front St Ste 8, New Bern, NC 28560
Tel.: (252) 633-4816
Web Site: http://www.trafford.com
Book Publishers
N.A.I.C.S.: 513199

TRAFIGURA BEHEER B.V.
Evert van de Beekstraat 1 82 The Base Tower B 5th Floor, 1118 CL, Schiphol, Netherlands
Tel.: (31) 205041800   Nl
Web Site: http://www.trafigura.com
Year Founded: 1993
Sales Range: Less than $1 Million
Commodities Trader
N.A.I.C.S.: 523160
Andrew Vickerman *(Chm)*

Subsidiaries:

Galena Asset Management S.A. (1)
1 rue de Jargonnant, 1207, Geneva, Switzerland
Tel.: (41) 22 594 6900
Web Site: http://www.galena-invest.com
Alternative Investment & Asset Management Services
N.A.I.C.S.: 523940

Subsidiary (Non-US):

Galena Asset Management Limited (2)
Portman House 2 Portman St, London, W1H 6DU, United Kingdom
Tel.: (44) 207 009 1726
Web Site: http://www.galena-invest.com
Alternative Investment & Asset Management Services
N.A.I.C.S.: 523940

Greenergy International Limited (1)
198 High Holborn, London, WC1V 7BD, United Kingdom
Tel.: (44) 2074047700
Web Site: http://www.greenergy.com

TRAFIGURA BEHEER B.V.

Trafigura Beheer B.V.—(Continued)
Sales Range: $15-24.9 Billion
Emp.: 35
Independent Oil Company
N.A.I.C.S.: 213112
Andrew Owens *(CEO)*

Subsidiary (Non-US):

Greenergy Asia DMCC (2)
Unit No R30-36 Floor No 30 Serviced Offices JLT Reef Tower Plot No 01, Jumeirah Lake Towers, Dubai, United Arab Emirates
Tel.: (971) 44487149
Fuel Distr
N.A.I.C.S.: 424720

Greenergy Brasil Trading SA (2)
Rua Gomes de Carvalho 1 069 cj 82 Advance Tower - Vila Olimpia, Sao Paulo, 04547-004, Brazil
Tel.: (55) 1130350800
Fuel Distr
N.A.I.C.S.: 424720

Subsidiary (US):

Greenergy USA Inc. (2)
111 Bridgepoint Plz Ste 310, Rome, GA 30161
Tel.: (706) 232-4010
Fuel Distr
N.A.I.C.S.: 424720

Iberian Minerals Corp. plc (1)
65 Front Street East Suite 200, Toronto, M5E 1B5, ON, Canada
Tel.: (416) 815-8558
Web Site: http://www.iberianminerals.com
Mineral Exploration Services
N.A.I.C.S.: 213114

Impala USA Inc (1)
263 Tresser Blvd, Stamford, CT 06901-3236
Tel.: (203) 504-7642
General Warehousing & Storage Services
N.A.I.C.S.: 493110

Subsidiary (Domestic):

Impala Terminals Burnside LLC (2)
4258 Hwy 44, Darrow, LA 70725-2400
Tel.: (225) 289-5211
Logistics Consulting Servies
N.A.I.C.S.: 541614

Puma Energy Holdings B.V. (1)
20th Floor Ito Tower, Gustav Mahlerplein 102, 1082 MA, Amsterdam, Netherlands
Tel.: (31) 205041800
Holding Company
N.A.I.C.S.: 551112

Subsidiary (Non-US):

Puma Energy International B.V. (2)
45 rue du Stand, CH 1204, Geneva, Switzerland
Tel.: (41) 22 594 69 00
Web Site: http://www.pumaenergy.net
Sales Range: $600-649.9 Million
Emp.: 1,800
Supply, Storage & Transportation of Petroleum Products
N.A.I.C.S.: 424710

Joint Venture (Non-US):

BP Malawi Limited (3)
8 Independence Drive, PO Box 469, Blantyre, Malawi (50%)
Tel.: (265) 1 824244
Web Site: http://www.bp.com
Petroleum Products Marketing
N.A.I.C.S.: 424720

BP Tanzania Limited (3)
Bandari Road, PO BOX 9043, Kurasini, Dar es Salaam, Tanzania (50%)
Tel.: (255) 222112725
Sales Range: $100-124.9 Million
Emp.: 225
Petroleum & Petroleum Products Whslr; Gasoline Service Stations; Owned 50% by BP plc & 50% by Tanzanian Government
N.A.I.C.S.: 424720

Subsidiary (Non-US):

Puma Dominicana, S.A. (3)
Carretera San Pedro La Romana Km 3 El Penon, Santo Domingo, Dominican Republic
Tel.: (809) 893 5200
Web Site: http://www.pumaenergy.net
Petroleum Storage & Distr
N.A.I.C.S.: 424710

Puma Energy Botswana (Pty) Ltd. (3)
Plot 682 3 Botswana Road Main Mall, PO Box 183, Gaborone, Botswana
Tel.: (267) 3951077
Web Site: http://www.bp.com
Sales Range: $250-299.9 Million
Emp.: 68
Petroleum & Fuels Distr
N.A.I.C.S.: 424710
Mahube Mpugwa *(Mng Dir)*

Puma Energy Cote d'Ivoire SA (3)
Rue de Canal de Vridi, BP 15, 522 Abidjan 15, Abidjan, Cote d'Ivoire
Tel.: (225) 21 27 00 72
Web Site: http://www.pumaenergy.com
Sales Range: $50-74.9 Million
Emp.: 50
Petroleum Storage, Transport & Distr
N.A.I.C.S.: 424710

Puma Energy Guatemala S.A. (3)
5 Ave 5-55 Zona 14 Europlaza Torre II Oficina 903, 01014, Guatemala, Guatemala
Tel.: (502) 23389000
Petroleum Storage & Distr
N.A.I.C.S.: 424710

Puma Energy Namibia (Pty) Limited (3)
Mutual Tower Independence Ave 4th Fl, Windhoek, Namibia
Tel.: (264) 612808111
Web Site: http://www.puma-energy.com
Sales Range: $50-74.9 Million
Emp.: 7
Petroleum & Petroleum Products Production & Marketing; Gasoline Service Stations
N.A.I.C.S.: 424720
Angela Katjimune *(Mgr-HR)*

Puma Energy Paraguay SA (3)
tsgto Nicasio Vilaba No 650c Delfin Chamorro, Fernando de la Mora Zona Norte, Asuncion, Paraguay
Tel.: (595) 21672456
Emp.: 105
Petroleum Storage & Distr
N.A.I.C.S.: 424710
Rodrigo Zavala *(Gen Mgr)*

Subsidiary (US):

Puma Energy Puerto Rico, Inc. (3)
Carr 28 km 0 .2 Zona Portuaria, Guaynabo, PR 00965
Tel.: (787) 679-7350
Petroleum Storage & Distr
N.A.I.C.S.: 424710

Subsidiary (Non-US):

Puma Energy Services South Africa Pty Ltd (3)
32 Jellicoe Ave 8th Fl, Rosebank, Johannesburg, 2196, South Africa
Tel.: (27) 117506800
Web Site: http://www.trafigura.com
Emp.: 300
Petroleum Storage & Distr
N.A.I.C.S.: 424710
Jean-Pierre Valentini *(Gen Mgr)*

Puma Energy Zambia plc (3)
Mukuba Pension House, Dedani Kamathi Road, 10101, Lusaka, Zambia
Tel.: (260) 122868498
Sales Range: $100-124.9 Million
Emp.: 135
Oil & Gas Refining, Storage & Marketing
N.A.I.C.S.: 213112
Sidy Bane *(CEO)*

Puma International Congo S.A. (3)
Immeuble SVP Construction 50 Avenue Felix Eboue Zone Portuaire, BP 1180, Pointe Noire, Congo, Republic of
Tel.: (242) 660 84 10
Web Site: http://www.pumaenergy.net
Petroleum, Storage, Transport & Distr

Pumangol Lda (3)
Edificio Caravela 1 Andar Rua Dr Agostinho Neto, Lote 1 Bairro Praia do Bispo, Ingombota, Luanda, Angola
Tel.: (244) 934 764 587
Petroleum Distr
N.A.I.C.S.: 457120

Trafigura AG (1)
Zurichstrasse 31, Postfach 4268, Lucerne, 6002, Switzerland
Tel.: (41) 41 419 43 43
Commodity Trading Services
N.A.I.C.S.: 523160

Trafigura Calgary Ltd. (1)
1700 400 3 ave SW, Devon Tower, Calgary, T2P 4H2, AB, Canada
Tel.: (403) 294-0400
Petroleum Product Distr
N.A.I.C.S.: 424720

Trafigura Chile Limitada (1)
Avenida El Golf 40 Oficina 702 Las Condes, Santiago, 7550120, Chile
Tel.: (56) 2 7563800
Commodity Trading Services
N.A.I.C.S.: 523160

Trafigura Eurasia LLC (1)
Business Center LOTTE 19th Floor 8 Novinsky Blvd, Moscow, 121099, Russia
Tel.: (7) 495 641 1728
Petroleum Product Distr
N.A.I.C.S.: 424720
Dmitry Kuranov *(Dir-Trading)*

Trafigura India Private Limited (1)
2 North Avenue Maker Maxity Bandra Kurla Complex, Bandra, 400 051, Mumbai, India
Tel.: (91) 22 42268550
Petroleum Product Distr
N.A.I.C.S.: 424720

Trafigura Investment (China) Co., Ltd (1)
56F Tower 2 IFC Building 8 Century Avenue, Pudong, Shanghai, 200120, China
Tel.: (86) 21 61258300
Metal Product Distr
N.A.I.C.S.: 423510
Rita Zhang *(Office Mgr)*

Trafigura Mexico, S.A. de C.V. (1)
Reforma 115 Oficina 2102 Col Lomas de Chapultepec, Delegacion Miguel Hidalgo, Mexico, 11000, Mexico
Tel.: (52) 55 5201 4100
Metal Product Distr
N.A.I.C.S.: 423510

Trafigura Peru S.A.C. (1)
Av Santo Toribio 173 Edificio, Real Ocho Piso 4 Centro, Lima, Peru
Tel.: (51) 1 412 0800
Metal Product Distr
N.A.I.C.S.: 423510

Trafigura Pte. Ltd. (1)
10 Collyer Quay Ocean Financial Centre, Singapore, 99315, Singapore
Tel.: (65) 63 19 2960
Commodity Trading Services
N.A.I.C.S.: 523160
Rebecca Tham *(Mgr-HR)*

Trafigura Services South Africa (Pty) Ltd (1)
15 Alice Lane, 3rd Floor, Sandton, Johannesburg, 2196, South Africa
Tel.: (27) 11 750 6800
Emp.: 250
Commodity Trading Services
N.A.I.C.S.: 523160
Jean Pierre Valentine *(Gen Mgr)*

TRAIL APPLIANCES

6880 11th Street SE, Calgary, T2H 2T9, AB, Canada
Tel.: (403) 253-5442
Web Site:
  http://www.trailappliances.com
Year Founded: 1974
Rev.: $40,126,060
Emp.: 375
Household Appliance Retailer
N.A.I.C.S.: 449210
Paul Broderick *(Pres)*

INTERNATIONAL PUBLIC

TRAILSTONE LLP

110 Bishopsgate, London, EC2N 4AY, United Kingdom
Tel.: (44) 203 425 9720   UK
Web Site:
  http://www.trailstonegroup.com
Year Founded: 2013
Emp.: 80
Investment Holding Company
N.A.I.C.S.: 551112
Ante Pogacic *(Head-Power & Renewables-Global)*

Subsidiaries:

TRAILSTONE AUSTRALIA PTY LTD (1)
Grafton Bond Building Level 5 201 Kent Street, Sydney, 2000, NSW, Australia
Tel.: (61) 282922600
Financial Investment Services
N.A.I.C.S.: 523940
Raymond Key *(Mng Partner)*

TRAILSTONE GmbH (1)
Hardenbergstr 27, 10623, Berlin, Germany
Tel.: (49) 30340446770
Financial Investment Services
N.A.I.C.S.: 523940
Linn Solheim *(Mgr-Bus)*

TRAILSTONE MANAGEMENT CORP (1)
400 Madison Ave Ste 4B, New York, NY 10017
Tel.: (646) 774-1020
Financial Investment Services
N.A.I.C.S.: 523940
Jarek Kozlowski *(CFO)*

TRAILSTONE NETHERLANDS I COOPERATIEF u.a. (1)
Herengracht 450, 1017 CA, Amsterdam, Netherlands
Tel.: (31) 202404442
Financial Investment Services
N.A.I.C.S.: 523940

TRAINERS' HOUSE PLC

Itamerentalo Tammasaarenlaituri 3, 180, Helsinki, Finland
Tel.: (358) 306888500
Web Site:
  https://www.trainershouse.fi
Year Founded: 1990
TRH1V—(HEL)
Rev: $10,522,340
Assets: $8,374,703
Liabilities: $2,935,463
Net Worth: $5,439,240
Earnings: $625,944
Emp.: 111
Fiscal Year-end: 12/31/22
Technology Dependent Training Services
N.A.I.C.S.: 611430
Aarne Aktan *(Chm)*

TRAIS CO., LTD.

Shihwa Industrial Complex 4Ma-701 714 Seonggok-dong, Danwon-Gu, Ansan, Gyeonggi-do, Korea (South)
Tel.: (82) 31 4998960
Web Site: http://www.trais.co.kr
Rev.: $3,273,786
Assets: $34,015,224
Liabilities: $18,208,594
Net Worth: $15,806,631
Earnings: ($34,230,496)
Emp.: 15
Fiscal Year-end: 12/31/17
Electronic Component Mfr & Distr
N.A.I.C.S.: 334413
Kwang-Gu Lee *(CEO)*

TRAITAFINA AG

Niederlenzer Kirchweg 12, 5600, Lenzburg, Switzerland
Tel.: (41) 628852121
Web Site: http://www.traitafina.ch
Sales Range: $100-124.9 Million

Emp.: 300
Meat & Sausage Mfr
N.A.I.C.S.: 424470
Hermann Bader *(Chm)*

TRAJAN GROUP HOLDINGS LIMITED
7 Argent Place, Ringwood, 3134, VIC, Australia
Tel.: (61) 398374200
Web Site: https://www.trajanscimed.com
Year Founded: 2014
TRJ—(ASX)
Rev.: $103,514,289
Assets: $125,532,852
Liabilities: $56,856,971
Net Worth: $68,675,881
Earnings: ($16,913,061)
Fiscal Year-end: 06/30/24
Holding Company; Pharmaceuticals, Biotechnology & Life Sciences
N.A.I.C.S.: 551112
Stephen Tomisich *(CEO)*

Subsidiaries:

Trajan Scientific & Medical Pty Ltd. (1)
7 Argent Place, Ringwood, 3134, VIC, Australia
Tel.: (61) 3 9837 4200
Web Site: http://www.trajanscimed.com
Medical Analysis Services
N.A.I.C.S.: 621511
Stephen Tomisich *(Grp CFO)*

Subsidiary (US):

Chromatography Research Supplies, Inc. (2)
2601 Technology Dr, Louisville, KY 40299
Tel.: (502) 491-6300
Web Site: http://www.chromres.com
Analytical Laboratory Instrument Mfr
N.A.I.C.S.: 334516
Paul Carroll *(CIO)*

Leap Technologies, Inc. (2)
610 Jones Ferry Rd, Carrboro, NC 27510
Tel.: (919) 929-8814
Web Site: http://www.leaptec.com
Rev.: $2,900,000
Emp.: 30
All Other Health & Personal Care Stores
N.A.I.C.S.: 456199
Michael Sabatino *(Dir-Channel Sls)*

TRAJANO IBERIA SOCIMI SA
Zurbano 49 oficina 10, 28010, Madrid, Spain
Tel.: (34) 914129145
Web Site: https://www.trajanoiberia.es
YTRA—(MAD)
Sales Range: Less than $1 Million
Real Estate Manangement Services
N.A.I.C.S.: 531390
Jose Moya Sanabria *(Chm)*

TRAKA RESOURCES LIMITED
Suite 2 Ground Floor 43 Ventnor Avenue, West Perth, 6005, WA, Australia
Tel.: (61) 893221655
Web Site: https://www.trakaresources.com.au
TKL—(ASX)
Rev.: $30,524
Assets: $517,837
Liabilities: $92,753
Net Worth: $425,084
Earnings: ($688,761)
Fiscal Year-end: 06/30/24
Minerals Exploration
N.A.I.C.S.: 213115
Peter Ruttledge *(Sec)*

TRAKCJA PRKII S.A.
Al Jerozolimskie 100 IIp, 00-807, Warsaw, Poland
Tel.: (48) 223509431
Web Site: https://www.grupatrakcja.com
Year Founded: 2004
TRK—(WAR)
Rev.: $26,111,028
Assets: $39,207,819
Liabilities: $31,196,789
Net Worth: $8,011,030
Earnings: ($819,803)
Emp.: 2,262
Fiscal Year-end: 12/31/21
Rail Transport Infrastructure Construction Services
N.A.I.C.S.: 237990
Pawel Nogalski *(CFO & Exec VP)*

Subsidiaries:

Bahn Technik Wroclaw Sp. z o.o. (1)
Ul Opolska 199, 52-013, Wroclaw, Poland
Tel.: (48) 517302729
Web Site: http://www.btw-wroc.pl
Railway Construction Services
N.A.I.C.S.: 488210
Adam Siwek *(Pres)*

Dalba Sp. z o.o (1)
102 Produkcyjna Street First Floor Rooms 122-123, 15-688, Bialystok, Poland
Tel.: (48) 856611750
Web Site: http://www.dalba.eu
Engineeering Services
N.A.I.C.S.: 541330

PRK 7 Nieruchomosci Sp. z o.o. (1)
Ul Leszno 12 IIp, 01-192, Warsaw, Poland
Tel.: (48) 226914646
Web Site: http://www.prk7nieruchomosci.com.pl
Construction Services
N.A.I.C.S.: 236220

Przedsiebiorstwo Eksploatacji Ulic i Mostow Sp. z o.o. (1)
102 Produkcyjna Street, 15-680, Bialystok, Poland
Tel.: (48) 856530773
Web Site: http://www.peuim.com.pl
Road Construction Services
N.A.I.C.S.: 237310

Torprojekt Sp. z o.o. (1)
Ul Gniewkowska 1, 01-253, Warsaw, Poland
Tel.: (48) 222034750
Web Site: http://www.torprojekt.pl
Railway Construction Services
N.A.I.C.S.: 488210
Henryk Kozlowski *(Chm)*

TRAKIISKO PIVO AD
18 St Stambolov St, 4400, Pazardzhik, Bulgaria
Tel.: (359) 34445465
Web Site: https://trakpivo.eu
Year Founded: 1997
TRPV—(BUL)
Sales Range: Less than $1 Million
Real Estate Services
N.A.I.C.S.: 531390

TRAKM8 HOLDINGS PLC
4 Roman Park Roman Way, Coleshill, Birmingham, B46 1HG, West Midlands, United Kingdom
Tel.: (44) 3303334120
Web Site: https://www.trakm8.com
TRAK—(AIM)
Rev.: $24,589,667
Assets: $50,036,055
Liabilities: $23,050,012
Net Worth: $26,986,043
Earnings: $253,894
Emp.: 165
Fiscal Year-end: 03/31/22
Internet Based Global Positioning System Hardware & Software Designer & Developer
N.A.I.C.S.: 334511
Matt Cowley *(Founder & Dir-Big Data)*

Subsidiaries:

Trakm8 Limited (1)
Lydden House Wincombe Business Park, Shaftesbury, Dorset, SP7 9QJ, United Kingdom
Tel.: (44) 1747858444
Web Site: http://www.trakm8.com
Sales Range: $25-49.9 Million
Emp.: 50
Tracking Device Mfr & Supplier
N.A.I.C.S.: 517810
John Watkins *(CEO)*

Trakm8 s.r.o. (1)
U Pruhonu 11a/1588, 170 00, Prague, Czech Republic
Tel.: (420) 225852900
Automotive Parts & Accessories Retailer
N.A.I.C.S.: 441330

TRAKNIAGA SDN. BHD
Level 5 Block F2 31-5 Jalan PJU 1/42a Dataran Prima, 47301, Petaling Jaya, Selangor, Malaysia
Tel.: (60) 378871121
Emp.: 100
Investment Services
N.A.I.C.S.: 523999

TRAKOPOLIS IOT CORP.
Suite 810 940 6th Ave S W, Calgary, T2P 3T1, AB, Canada
Tel.: (403) 450-7854
Web Site: http://www.trakopolis.com
Year Founded: 1999
Rev.: $4,646,015
Assets: $2,741,474
Liabilities: $4,788,030
Net Worth: ($2,046,556)
Earnings: ($3,110,281)
Fiscal Year-end: 12/31/18
Asset Management Software Solutions
N.A.I.C.S.: 513210

TRANAUTO
9 Avenue Claude Vellefaux, 75010, Paris, France
Tel.: (33) 142061805
Web Site: http://www.tranauto.net
Rev.: $21,000,000
Emp.: 30
Automobile Dealership
N.A.I.C.S.: 441110
Eng Tran *(Mng Partner)*

TRANCOM CO., LTD.
1-19-30 Aoi, Higashi-ku, Nagoya, Aichi, Japan
Tel.: (81) 529392011 JP
Web Site: https://www.trancom.co.jp
Year Founded: 1959
9058—(NGO)
Rev.: $1,119,325,752
Assets: $489,573,698
Liabilities: $157,621,363
Net Worth: $331,952,335
Earnings: $30,525,264
Emp.: 6,582
Fiscal Year-end: 03/31/24
Logistics Products & Services
N.A.I.C.S.: 541614
Yutaka Tsunekawa *(Pres)*

Subsidiaries:

Mechanos Co., Ltd (1)
4-276 Nakaotai, Nishi-Ku, Nagoya, Japan
Tel.: (81) 525036215
General Automotive Repair
N.A.I.C.S.: 811111

Monoful Inc. (1)
1-5-2 Higashi-Shimbashi Shiodome City Center 34th Floor, Minato-ku, Tokyo, 105-7134, Japan
Tel.: (81) 12 050 7765
Web Site: https://www.monoful.co.jp
Logistics Consulting Servies
N.A.I.C.S.: 541614

Sergent Services Pte. Ltd. (1)
1 Ubi View 04-23 Focus One, Singapore, 408555, Singapore
Tel.: (65) 6 570 6733
Web Site: https://www.sergent.com.sg
Cleaning Service
N.A.I.C.S.: 561720
Kelvin Boo Hui Meng *(Dir-Ops)*

Smile Staff Co., Ltd. (1)
6-4-3 Imaizumi Hazime, Tochigi, Utsunomiya, 321-0954, Japan
Tel.: (81) 28 661 2500
Web Site: http://www.smilestaff.co.jp
Sales Range: $75-99.9 Million
Employment Placement Agency
N.A.I.C.S.: 561311

Trancom DS Co., Ltd. (1)
1-19-30 Aoi, Higashi-ku, Nagoya, Japan
Tel.: (81) 523253007
Freight Forwarding Services
N.A.I.C.S.: 488510

Trancom ITS Co., Ltd. (1)
1-16-38 Aoi Garden Building 4F, Higashi-ku, Nagoya, 461-0004, Aichi, Japan
Tel.: (81) 52 937 2450
Web Site: https://www.trancom-its.co.jp
Emp.: 251
Logistics Software & Support Services
N.A.I.C.S.: 541511
Takeshi Tsunekawa *(Pres, CEO & Dir)*

TRANE TECHNOLOGIES PLC
170/175 Lakeview Dr Airside Business Park, Swords, Co Dublin, Ireland
Tel.: (353) 18707400 IE
Web Site: https://www.tranetechnologies.com
Year Founded: 1885
TT—(NYSE)
Rev.: $17,677,600,000
Assets: $19,391,900,000
Liabilities: $12,374,900,000
Net Worth: $7,017,000,000
Earnings: $2,023,900,000
Emp.: 40,000
Fiscal Year-end: 12/31/23
Holding Company; Commercial Products Mfr
N.A.I.C.S.: 551112
Jason E. Bingham *(Pres-Residential HVAC & Supply)*

Subsidiaries:

CALMAC CORP. (1)
3 00 Banta Pl, Fair Lawn, NJ 07410
Tel.: (201) 797-1511
Web Site: http://www.calmac.com
Cooling Equipment Mfr
N.A.I.C.S.: 333415
Mark M. MacCracken *(Pres-LEED Fellow)*

FELLON-MCCORD & ASSOCIATES, LLC (1)
10200 Forest Green Blvd Ste 601, Louisville, KY 40223
Tel.: (502) 214-9400
Web Site: http://www.fellonmccord.com
Management Consulting Services
N.A.I.C.S.: 541618
Drew Fellon *(Pres & CEO)*

GLOBAL ENERGY MARKET SERVICES, LLC (1)
2790 Mosside Blvd, Monroeville, PA 15146
Tel.: (412) 372-2631
Web Site: http://www.fmenergychoice.com
Emp.: 5
Natural Gas Distribution Services
N.A.I.C.S.: 221210

Nuvolo Technologies Corporation (1)
16 Mica Ln., Wellesley, MA 02481
Web Site: http://www.nuvolo.com
Sales Range: $1-9.9 Million
Software Development Services
N.A.I.C.S.: 541511

Thermo King Corporation (1)
314 W 90th St, Minneapolis, MN 55420
Tel.: (952) 887-2200
Sales Range: $150-199.9 Million
Emp.: 600

TRANE TECHNOLOGIES PLC

Trane Technologies Plc—(Continued)
Mfr of Mechanical Refrigeration Systems for Trucks, Trailers & Rail Cars; Bus Air Conditioning
N.A.I.C.S.: 333415

Subsidiary (Non-US):

Ingersoll-Rand Equipment Manufacturing Czech Republic Limited (2)
Havlrska 202, Kolin, 28059, Czech Republic
Tel.: (420) 321757111
Web Site: http://www.Ingersoll-Rand.com
Sales Range: $75-99.9 Million
Emp.: 500
Mfr of Mechanical Refrigeration Systems for Trucks, Trailers & Rail Cars; Bus Air Conditioning
N.A.I.C.S.: 333415

Ingersoll-Rand Equipment Manufacturing Czech Republic S.R.O. (2)
Florianova 2460, Hostivice, 25301, Czech Republic
Tel.: (420) 257109111
Sales Range: $25-49.9 Million
Emp.: 60
Mfr of Mechanical Refrigeration Systems for Trucks, Trailers & Rail Cars; Bus Air Conditioning
N.A.I.C.S.: 333415

Reftrans, S.A. (2)
Calle San Jose 140/142, Barcelona, 8980, Spain
Tel.: (34) 936857700
Web Site: http://www.thermoking.com
Sales Range: $25-49.9 Million
Emp.: 100
Mfr of Mechanical Refrigeration Systems for Trucks, Trailers & Rail Cars; Bus Air Conditioning
N.A.I.C.S.: 333415

THERMO KING CONTAINER TEMPERATURE CONTROL (SUZHOU) CORPORATION LTD. (2)
No 2a Suchun Industrial Workshop No 428 Xinglong Street, Suzhou, 215126, Jiangsu, China
Tel.: (86) 51262836628
Refrigeration & Heating Equipment Mfr
N.A.I.C.S.: 333415

THERMO KING DO BRASIL, LTDA. (2)
Web Site: http://www.thermoking.com.br
Sales Range: $10-24.9 Million
Emp.: 30
Vehicle Air Conditioning Mfr
N.A.I.C.S.: 333415

Subsidiary (Domestic):

THERMO KING ENTERPRISES COMPANY (2)
548 Spring St, Windsor Locks, CT 06096
Tel.: (860) 627-9015
Industrial Machinery & Equipment Mfr
N.A.I.C.S.: 423830

Subsidiary (Non-US):

THERMO KING INDIA PRIVATE LIMITED (2)
Plot No 35 KIADB Industrial Area, Bidadi Ramanagaram Taluk, Bengaluru, 562 109, India
Tel.: (91) 8022166000
Sales Range: $125-149.9 Million
Emp.: 600
Transport Temperature Control System Mfr
N.A.I.C.S.: 336320

THERMO KING IRELAND LIMITED (2)
Monivea Rd Mervue, Galway, Ireland
Tel.: (353) 91751231
Sales Range: $75-99.9 Million
Emp.: 450
Air Conditioning Equipment Mfr
N.A.I.C.S.: 333415
Cormac McDonncha (Plant Mgr)

Subsidiary (Domestic):

THERMO KING EUROPEAN MANUFACTURING LIMITED (3)
Monivea Rd Mervue, Galway, Ireland

Tel.: (353) 91751231
Industrial Machinery & Equipment Mfr
N.A.I.C.S.: 423830
Cormac Mac Macdonncha (Gen Mgr)

THERMO KING SERVICES LIMITED (3)
Monivea Road, Mervue, Galway, Ireland
Tel.: (353) 91751231
Management Consulting Services
N.A.I.C.S.: 541618

Subsidiary (Non-US):

THERMO KING MARITIMES INC. (2)
125 Urquhart Ave, Moncton, E1H 2R4, NB, Canada
Tel.: (506) 858-8849
Refrigerator Equipment Mfr
N.A.I.C.S.: 333415

THERMO KING MONTREAL INC. (2)
6100 Chemin Saint-Francois, Saint Laurent, H4S 1B7, QC, Canada
Tel.: (514) 333-5133
Refrigerator Equipment Mfr
N.A.I.C.S.: 333415

THERMO KING ONTARIO INC. (2)
6243 Netherhart Rd, Mississauga, L5T 1G5, ON, Canada
Tel.: (905) 564-2800
Refrigerator Equipment Mfr
N.A.I.C.S.: 333415

Subsidiary (Domestic):

THERMO KING SVC, INC. (2)
314 W 90th St MS-40, Minneapolis, MN 55420
Tel.: (952) 886-6014
Web Site: http://www.thermoking.com
Refrigeration Equipment Repair & Maintenance Services
N.A.I.C.S.: 811310

Subsidiary (Non-US):

THERMO KING TRANSPORTKOELING B.V. (2)
Driemanssteeweg 60, 3084 CB, Rotterdam, Netherlands
Tel.: (31) 10 2100666
Web Site: http://www.thermoking.nl
Emp.: 30
Refrigerated Storage Services
N.A.I.C.S.: 493120
Andre van Asselt (Mgr-Special Acct & Bus Dev)

Thermo King Container - Denmark A/S (2)
Industrivej 2, 5550, Langeskov, Denmark
Tel.: (45) 63384200
Web Site: http://www.thermoking.com
Sales Range: $1-9.9 Million
Emp.: 12
Mfr of Mechanical Refrigeration Systems for Trucks, Trailers & Rail Cars; Bus Air Conditioning
N.A.I.C.S.: 333415

Thermo King Container Antwerp (2)
Wilmingtonstraat 3, 2030, Antwerp, Belgium
Tel.: (32) 35441170
Mechanical Refrigeration Systems Mfr; Trailers & Rail Cars; Bus Air Conditioning; Container Warehouse Facilities
N.A.I.C.S.: 333415
Peter Verheyleweghen (Mgr)

Branch (Domestic):

Thermo King Corp. (2)
1800 Centennial Ave, Hastings, NE 68901-6712
Tel.: (402) 463-6751
Web Site: http://www.thermoking.com
Sales Range: $75-99.9 Million
Emp.: 300
Mfr of Refrigeration Equipment
N.A.I.C.S.: 333415

Subsidiary (Non-US):

Thermo King Corporation (2)
Honda Denki Bldg 5F 4 5 37 Kamiosaki, Shingawa Ku, Tokyo, 141-0021, Japan
Tel.: (81) 369106600

Web Site: http://www.thermoking.com
Sales Range: $25-49.9 Million
Emp.: 100
Mfr of Mechanical Refrigeration Systems for Trucks, Trailers & Rail Cars; Bus Air Conditioning
N.A.I.C.S.: 333415

Thermo King Ingersoll Rand Svenska AB (2)
Trankarrsgatan 5 Hisings Karra, 425 37, Gothenburg, Sweden
Tel.: (46) 31 72 77 600
Web Site: http://www.thermoking.se
Cooling Equipment Maintenance Services
N.A.I.C.S.: 811310

Subsidiary (Domestic):

Thermo King de Puerto Rico (2)
Calle B Parque Zeno Gandia, Arecibo, PR 00612
Tel.: (787) 815-0546
Sales Range: $75-99.9 Million
Emp.: 500
Refrigeration & Heating Equipment
N.A.I.C.S.: 333415
Ivan Collazo (Gen Mgr)

Trane Inc. (1)
1 Centennial Ave, Piscataway, NJ 08855-6820
Tel.: (732) 652-7100
Sales Range: $5-14.9 Billion
Emp.: 29,600
Air Conditioning Equipment Whslr
N.A.I.C.S.: 423730

Subsidiary (Non-US):

Airco Ltd. (2)
302/60 Moo 5 Maliwant Road, Tombon Banpet Amphur Muang, Khon Kaen, Thailand
Tel.: (66) 43345454
Web Site: http://www.trane.com
Sales Range: $25-49.9 Million
Emp.: 10
Air Conditioning & Heating Equipment Mfr & Whslr
N.A.I.C.S.: 333415

TRANE AIR CONDITIONING SYSTEMS (CHINA) CO. LTD. (2)
No 88 Suzhou Middle Road, Taicang, 215412, China
Tel.: (86) 51253597229
Air Conditioning Equipment Whslr
N.A.I.C.S.: 423730

TRANE AIRCONDITIONING BV (2)
Nieuwegracht 22, 3736 LB, Soest, Netherlands
Tel.: (31) 356039300
Web Site: https://trane.eu
Air Conditioning Equipment Distr
N.A.I.C.S.: 423730

TRANE AIRE ACONDICIANDO S.L. (2)
Idorsoro 13 Edif San Isidro I Dpto 3, 48160, Derio, Vizcaya, Spain
Tel.: (34) 944541876
Air Conditioning Equipment Distr
N.A.I.C.S.: 423730

TRANE CANADA LP (2)
6210 Hawthorne Dr, Windsor, N8T 1J9, ON, Canada
Tel.: (519) 256-7922
Air Conditioning Equipment Distr
N.A.I.C.S.: 423730
Norn Clarke (Gen Mgr)

TRANE CANADA ULC (2)
4051 Gordon Baker Road, Scarborough, M1W 2P3, ON, Canada
Tel.: (416) 499-1616
Sales Range: $25-49.9 Million
Emp.: 150
Air Conditioning Equipment Mfr & Distr
N.A.I.C.S.: 333415

TRANE DE MEXICO, S.A. DE C.V. (2)
Felix Guzman No 21 Col El Parque, 53398, Naucalpan, Mexico
Tel.: (52) 5521222300
Air Conditioning Equipment Distr
N.A.I.C.S.: 423730

INTERNATIONAL PUBLIC

TRANE DESIGN CENTRE PRIVATE LTD. (2)
Ascendas International Technology Park, Crest Building Phase - II 5th Floor Unit 1 Taramani High Road Taramani, Chennai, 600 113, India
Tel.: (91) 4442990993
Web Site: http://www.ingersollrand.co.in
Emp.: 150
Software Development Services
N.A.I.C.S.: 541511

TRANE DISTRIBUTION PTE LTD (2)
30 Boon Lay Way 04-01, Singapore, 609957, Singapore
Tel.: (65) 64688622
Air Conditioning Equipment Distr
N.A.I.C.S.: 423730
Sin Yew Cheng (VP)

TRANE DO BRASIL INDUSTRIA E COMERCIO DE PRODUCTOS PARA CONDICIONAMENTO DE AR LTDA. (2)
Rua Pinheirinho 144 Bairro Jabaquara, Sao Paulo, 04321-170, Brazil
Tel.: (55) 1150146300
Air Conditioning System Mfr
N.A.I.C.S.: 333415

TRANE DOMINCANA, C. POR A. (2)
Aut Duarte 1, Santiago, Dominican Republic
Tel.: (809) 971 8717
Web Site: http://www.paginasamarillas.com
Air Conditioning Equipment Distr
N.A.I.C.S.: 423730

TRANE EUROPE HOLDINGS B.V. (2)
Nieuwegracht 22, Soest, 3763 LB, Netherlands
Tel.: (31) 356039300
Emp.: 50
Investment Management Service
N.A.I.C.S.: 523940
E. Oossanen (Gen Mgr)

TRANE ITALIA S.R.L (2)
Viale Europa 30/C2, Cusago, 20090, Italy
Tel.: (39) 02 903351
Web Site: http://www.trane.com
Air Conditioning Equipment Distr
N.A.I.C.S.: 423730

TRANE ROMANIA S.R.L (2)
Strada Cauzasi 22B, 030802, Bucharest, Romania
Tel.: (40) 213086420
Web Site: https://trane.eu
Emp.: 29
Air Conditioning Equipment Distr
N.A.I.C.S.: 423730

TRANE VIETNAM SERVICES COMPANY LTD. (2)
Web Site: http://www.tranevietnam.com
Sales Range: $10-24.9 Million
Emp.: 60
Air Conditioning Equipment Maintenance Services
N.A.I.C.S.: 811412

TRANE, S.A. DE C.V. (2)
Felix Guzman No 21 Col El Parque, 53398, Naucalpan, Mexico
Tel.: (52) 21222300
Sales Range: $50-74.9 Million
Emp.: 181
Air Conditioning Equipment Whslr
N.A.I.C.S.: 423730

Subsidiary (Domestic):

The Trane Company (2)
6200 Troup Hwy, Tyler, TX 75707
Tel.: (903) 581-3200
Web Site: http://www.trane.com
Sales Range: $700-749.9 Million
Emp.: 3,200
Residential & Small Commercial Air Conditioning Mfr
N.A.I.C.S.: 333415

Subsidiary (Domestic):

Pacific Coast Sales & Service, Inc. (3)

AND PRIVATE COMPANIES   TRANG CORPORATION

310 Soquel Way, Sunnyvale, CA 94085
Tel.: (408) 481-3600
Sales Range: $200-249.9 Million
Emp.: 120
Air Conditioning & Heating Equipment Mfr & Whslr
N.A.I.C.S.: 333415
Greg Clemente *(Mgr-Building Automation Sys Ops)*

TRANE CENTRAL AMERICA, INC. (3)
7650 NW 19th St Ste 270, Miami, FL 33126
Tel.: (305) 592-8646
Web Site: http://www.trane.com
Air Conditioning Equipment Distr
N.A.I.C.S.: 423730

TRANE COMFORT SOLUTIONS INC. (3)
288 Fairforest Way, Greenville, SC 29607
Tel.: (864) 672-6000
Web Site: http://www.trane.com
Emp.: 200
Air Conditioning Equipment Distr
N.A.I.C.S.: 423730

TRANE INC. OF DELAWARE (3)
66 Southgate Blvd Southgate Industrial Park, New Castle, DE 19720
Tel.: (302) 395-0200
Air Conditioning Equipment Distr
N.A.I.C.S.: 423730

TRANE PUERTO RICO INC. (3)
San Juan Industrial Park PR 1 KM25 1, San Juan, PR 00926
Tel.: (787) 798-0999
Web Site: https://www.tranepuertorico.com
Sales Range: $100-124.9 Million
Emp.: 80
Air Conditioning Equipment Distr
N.A.I.C.S.: 423730

TRANE U.S. INC. (3)
4145 Delmar Ave, Rocklin, CA 95677
Tel.: (916) 577-1100
Web Site: http://www.trane.com
Air Conditioning & Warm Air Heating Equipment Mfr
N.A.I.C.S.: 333415

TRANE VIDALIA LLC (3)
1 Centennial Ave, Piscataway, NJ 08855
Tel.: (912) 538-4003
Air Conditioning Equipment Mfr
N.A.I.C.S.: 333415

Unit (Domestic):

Trane - Nashville (3)
601 Grassmere Park Dr Ste 10, Nashville, TN 37211
Tel.: (615) 242-0311
Web Site: http://www.trane.com
Sales Range: $75-99.9 Million
Emp.: 90
Air Conditioning & Heating Equipment Mfr & Whslr
N.A.I.C.S.: 333415

Trane Equipment/Controls/Parts (3)
2525 Larson St, La Crosse, WI 54603
Web Site: http://www.trane.com
Sales Range: $50-74.9 Million
Emp.: 15
Heating, Ventilating, Air Conditioning & Building Management Equipment & Systems Mfr
N.A.I.C.S.: 333415

Subsidiary (Domestic):

Trane Leasing Services (3)
2105 Elm Hill Pike, Nashville, TN 37210
Tel.: (800) 724-6026
Web Site: http://www.traneleasing.com
Financial Management Services
N.A.I.C.S.: 523999

Subsidiary (Non-US):

Trane (Ireland) Ltd. (2)
F7 Centrepoint Business Park Oak Road, Dublin, Ireland
Tel.: (353) 14606030
Web Site: http://www.trane.com
Sales Range: $25-49.9 Million
Emp.: 16
Air Conditioning & Heating Equipment Mfr & Whslr
N.A.I.C.S.: 333415

Trane (Schweiz) AG (2)
Lerzenstrasse 8, 8953, Dietikon, Switzerland
Tel.: (41) 447453030
Web Site: http://www.trane.com
Sales Range: $10-24.9 Million
Emp.: 30
Air Conditioning & Heating Equipment Mfr & Whslr
N.A.I.C.S.: 333415

Trane (United Kingdom) Ltd. (2)
Harrow House Bessemer Road, Basingstoke, RG21 3NB, Hampshire, United Kingdom
Tel.: (44) 8457165162
Web Site: http://www.trane.com
Sales Range: $10-24.9 Million
Emp.: 50
Air Conditioning & Heating Equipment Mfr & Whslr
N.A.I.C.S.: 333415

Trane Belo Horizonte (2)
Av Raja Gabaglia 4055 Sala 311, Belo Horizonte, Brazil
Tel.: (55) 3132966746
Web Site: http://www.trane.com.br
Sales Range: $25-49.9 Million
Emp.: 6
Air Conditioning & Heating Equipment Mfr & Whslr
N.A.I.C.S.: 333415

Trane CR Spol, s.r.o. (2)
Thamova 183/11, 186 00, Prague, 6, Czech Republic
Tel.: (420) 296337219
Web Site: https://trane.eu
Sales Range: $25-49.9 Million
Emp.: 25
Air Conditioning & Heating Equipment Mfr & Whslr
N.A.I.C.S.: 333415

Trane Central Ontario (2)
4051 Gordon Baker Road, Scarborough, M1W 2P3, ON, Canada
Tel.: (416) 499-3600
Web Site: http://www.trane.com
Sales Range: $25-49.9 Million
Emp.: 175
Air Conditioning & Heating Equipment Mfr & Whslr
N.A.I.C.S.: 333415

Trane GmbH (2)
Tel.: (43) 2236378400
Web Site: http://www.trane.com
Sales Range: $25-49.9 Million
Emp.: 20
Air Conditioning & Heating Equipment Mfr & Whslr
N.A.I.C.S.: 333415

Trane Hellas SA (2)
Sales Range: $10-24.9 Million
Emp.: 30
Air Conditioning & Heating Equipment Mfr & Whslr
N.A.I.C.S.: 333415

Trane Hungary Kft. (2)
Tel.: (36) 23422572
Sales Range: $10-24.9 Million
Emp.: 40
Air Conditioning & Heating Equipment Mfr & Whslr
N.A.I.C.S.: 333415

Trane Japan, Ltd. (2)
Tel.: (81) 354356441
Sales Range: $10-24.9 Million
Emp.: 30
Air Conditioning & Heating Equipment Mfr & Whslr
N.A.I.C.S.: 333415

Trane Klima Ticaret A.S. (2)
Ataturk Mah Meric Cad No 5 Turkuaz Plaza D 43 53 Atasehir, Altunizade Uskudar, Istanbul, Turkiye
Tel.: (90) 2165565000
Web Site: http://www.trane.com
Sales Range: $10-24.9 Million
Emp.: 35
Air Conditioning & Heating Equipment Mfr & Whslr
N.A.I.C.S.: 333415

Trane Korea, Inc. (2)
8th Fl TRUTEC Building 12 Worldcupbuk-ro 56-gi Mapo-gu, GilMapo-Gu, Seoul, 121-835, Korea (South)
Tel.: (82) 221860900
Web Site: http://www.trane.com
Sales Range: $25-49.9 Million
Emp.: 70
Air Conditioning & Heating Equipment Mfr & Whslr
N.A.I.C.S.: 333415

Trane Malaysia Sales & Services Sdn. Bhd. (2)
Lot 4881 Jalan SS 13/2, 47500, Subang Jaya, Selangor Darul Ehsan, Malaysia
Tel.: (60) 356357600
Sales Range: $25-49.9 Million
Emp.: 160
Air Conditioning & Heating Equipment Mfr & Whslr
N.A.I.C.S.: 333415

Trane Phillipines (2)
Door 2 Anilson Bldg ML Quezon St Cabancalan Mandaue City, Cebu, Philippines
Tel.: (63) 323459117
Web Site: http://www.trane.com
Sales Range: $25-49.9 Million
Emp.: 15
Air Conditioning & Heating Equipment Mfr & Whslr
N.A.I.C.S.: 333415

Trane Polska sp. Z.o.o. (2)
Ul Kolejowa 5/7, 01-217, Warsaw, Poland
Tel.: (48) 224347700
Web Site: http://www.trane.com
Sales Range: $10-24.9 Million
Emp.: 50
Air Conditioning & Heating Equipment Mfr & Whslr
N.A.I.C.S.: 333415

Trane Reinetsu Service, Ltd. (2)
4 3 9 Morooka Hataka ku, Kukuok, Fukuoka, 8160094, Japan
Tel.: (81) 929150443
Air Conditioning & Heating Equipment Mfr & Whslr
N.A.I.C.S.: 333415

Trane ServicFirst C.A. (2)
Final Ave Principal Boleitas Norte, Calle Miraima Galpon Trane No, Caracas, 1070, Venezuela
Tel.: (58) 2122736900
Web Site: http://www.tranevenezuela.com
Sales Range: $25-49.9 Million
Emp.: 12
Air Conditioning & Heating Equipment Mfr & Whslr
N.A.I.C.S.: 333415

Trane Service Hong Kong (2)
12/F Manhattan Centre 8 Kwai Cheong Road Kwai Chung, Kowloon, Hong Kong, New Territories, China (Hong Kong)
Tel.: (852) 27439010
Web Site: http://www.tranehk.com
Air Conditioning & Heating Equipment Mfr & Whslr
N.A.I.C.S.: 333415

Trane Singapore (2)
27 Benoi Sector, Singapore, 629859, Singapore
Tel.: (65) 64688622
Web Site: http://www.trane.com
Sales Range: $25-49.9 Million
Emp.: 100
Air Conditioning & Heating Equipment Mfr & Whslr
N.A.I.C.S.: 333415

Trane Sweden AB (2)
Flygfaltsgatan 8, 128 30, Skarpnack, Sweden
Tel.: (46) 855613450
Sales Range: $25-49.9 Million
Emp.: 9
Air Conditioning & Heating Equipment Mfr & Whslr
N.A.I.C.S.: 333415

Trane Technologies LLC (2)
Bld 19/6 Leninskaya Sloboda Str, 129226, Moscow, Russia
Tel.: (7) 4959211671
Web Site: http://www.trane.com

Sales Range: $10-24.9 Million
Emp.: 30
Air Conditioning & Heating Equipment Mfr & Whslr
N.A.I.C.S.: 333415

Trane Thailand Ltd. (2)
30th-31st Floor Vanit Building II 1126/2 New Petchburi Road, Bangkok, Makkasan, Thailand
Tel.: (66) 27611111
Web Site: http://www.trane.com
Sales Range: $75-99.9 Million
Emp.: 350
Air Conditioning & Heating Equipment Mfr & Whslr
N.A.I.C.S.: 333415

Trane de Argentina S.A. (2)
Tel.: (54) 1147306000
Web Site: http://www.trane.com.ar
Sales Range: $25-49.9 Million
Emp.: 80
Air Conditioning & Heating Equipment Mfr & Whslr
N.A.I.C.S.: 333415

Trane de Chile SA (2)
Calle Nueva 1820 Huechuraba, Santiago, Chile
Web Site: http://www.trane.cl
Air Conditioning & Heating Equipment Mfr & Whslr
N.A.I.C.S.: 333415

Trane de Colombia, SA (2)
Av Cra 45 108-27 Parallel Building 108 Tower 3 17th Floor, Carrera 14 98-73, Bogota, Colombia
Tel.: (57) 6016517272
Sales Range: $25-49.9 Million
Emp.: 30
Air Conditioning & Heating Equipment Whslr
N.A.I.C.S.: 423730

TRANG AN SECURITIES JOINT STOCK COMPANY
Tang 9 59 Quang Trung, Hai Ba Trung, Hanoi, Vietnam
Tel.: (84) 439446218
Web Site: http://www.tas.com.vn
Sales Range: $25-49.9 Million
Emp.: 90
Investment Banking & Securities Brokerage Services
N.A.I.C.S.: 523150
Khoi Ho Le *(Chm)*

TRANG CORPORATION
Lot A 14b Hiep Phuoc Industry Park, Nha Be Dist, Ho Chi Minh City, Vietnam
Tel.: (84) 2837800933
Web Site:
   https://www.trangcorporation.vn
Year Founded: 2004
TFC—(HNX)
Rev.: $85,012,600
Assets: $71,362,900
Liabilities: $50,836,400
Net Worth: $20,526,500
Earnings: $2,911,700
Fiscal Year-end: 12/31/22
Frozen Seafood Mfr
N.A.I.C.S.: 311710

Subsidiaries:

Trangs China Corporation (1)
18B1002 ChengshiChuntian Beihubei Rd, Xixiangtang, Nanning, Guangxi, China
Tel.: (86) 7713398796
Food Products Mfr
N.A.I.C.S.: 311999

Trangs Food Pty Ltd (1)
Unit 1B/9 Mvis Street, Revesby, 2212, NSW, Australia
Tel.: (61) 279030663
Food Products Mfr
N.A.I.C.S.: 311999

Trangs Group USA Incorporated (1)
7108 Katella Ave No 404, Stanton, CA 90680

TRANG CORPORATION

Trang Corporation—(Continued)
Food Products Mfr
N.A.I.C.S.: 311999

Trangs UK Limited (1)
Suite 215 Crown House North Circular Road, London, NW10 7PN, United Kingdom
Tel.: (44) 2089653176
Food Products Mfr
N.A.I.C.S.: 311999

TRANS ASIA CORPORATION LIMITED

110 Royal Ratan 7 M G Road, Indore, 452 001, MP, India
Tel.: (91) 731 2526767
Web Site:
  http://www.transasiagroup.org
Year Founded: 1993
530783—(BOM)
Assets: $923,025
Liabilities: $102,879
Net Worth: $820,146
Earnings: ($11,244)
Fiscal Year-end: 03/31/20
Steel & Agro Product Whslr
N.A.I.C.S.: 423510
Vikram Khandelwal *(Chm & Mng Dir)*

TRANS ASIA HOTELS PLC

No 115 Sir Chittampalam A Gardiner Mawatha, 2, Colombo, 2, Sri Lanka
Tel.: (94) 112449100
Web Site:
  http://www.transasiahotel.com
Year Founded: 1981
TRAN—(COL)
Rev.: $11,880,513
Assets: $28,816,701
Liabilities: $9,036,314
Net Worth: $19,780,387
Earnings: ($324,546)
Emp.: 601
Fiscal Year-end: 03/31/23
Hotel & Restaurant Operator
N.A.I.C.S.: 721110
Krishan Niraj Jayasekara Balendra *(Chm)*

TRANS ASIAN SHIPPING SERVICES PVT. LTD.

Trans Asian Corporate Park XIV/396-C Seaport-Airport Road, Chittethukara Kakkanad, Cochin, 682 037, India
Tel.: (91) 4844096000   In
Web Site: http://www.tassgroup.com
Year Founded: 1992
Sales Range: $100-124.9 Million
Emp.: 250
Freight Transportation Services
N.A.I.C.S.: 488510
Wilson Thomas *(Gen Mgr-Cochin)*

TRANS CANADA GOLD CORP.

Tel.: (604) 681-3131   BC
Year Founded: 2006
TTG—(TSXV)
Rev.: $67,152
Assets: $1,475,175
Liabilities: $87,856
Net Worth: $1,387,319
Earnings: ($423,612)
Fiscal Year-end: 06/30/21
Oil & Gas Exploration Services
N.A.I.C.S.: 211120
Tim Coupland *(Pres, Pres, CEO & CEO)*

TRANS CONSULT INTERNATIONAL SA

92 rue de Levis, 75017, Paris, France
Tel.: (33) 142936843
Web Site:
  http://www.transconsultnational.com
Year Founded: 2001

Sales Range: $1-9.9 Million
Emp.: 5
Crises, Strategic Analysis, Restructuring & Negotiations Management Services
N.A.I.C.S.: 561499
Arnaud Christian Alain Marion *(Founder)*

TRANS FREIGHT CONTAINERS LTD.

72-73 Nariman Bhavan, Nariman Point, Mumbai, 400021, India
Tel.: (91) 2222022172
Web Site: https://www.tfcl.in
Year Founded: 1975
513063—(BOM)
Rev.: $953,036
Assets: $4,856,855
Liabilities: $420,466
Net Worth: $4,436,389
Earnings: $702,979
Emp.: 7
Fiscal Year-end: 03/31/23
Container Mfr
N.A.I.C.S.: 321920
Chandrabhan R. Singh *(CFO)*

TRANS GENIC INC.

2-3-36 Tenjin, Chuo-ku, Fukuoka, 810-0001, Japan
Tel.: (81) 922888470
Web Site: https://transgenic-group.co.jp
Year Founded: 1998
2342—(TKS)
Rev.: $86,478,630
Assets: $64,844,100
Liabilities: $25,197,320
Net Worth: $39,646,780
Earnings: $26,440
Emp.: 236
Fiscal Year-end: 03/31/24
Biotechnology Research & Development Services
N.A.I.C.S.: 541714
Kenji Fukunaga *(Pres & CEO)*

Subsidiaries:

BioSafety Research Center Inc. (1)
582-2 Shioshinden, Iwata, 437-1213, Shizuoka, Japan
Tel.: (81) 538581266
Web Site: https://www.anpyo.co.jp
Biotechnology Research & Development Services
N.A.I.C.S.: 541714

Medicinal Chemistry Pharmaceutical Co., Ltd. (1)
452-1 Toiso, Eniwa, 061-1405, Hokkaido, Japan
Tel.: (81) 123295934
Web Site: https://soyaku.co.jp
Pharmaceuticals Mfr
N.A.I.C.S.: 325412

New Drug Research Center, Inc. (1)
452-1 Toiso, Eniwa, 061-1405, Hokkaido, Japan
Tel.: (81) 123340412
Emp.: 54
Biotechnology Research & Development Services
N.A.I.C.S.: 541714

Primmune Inc. (1)
7-1-14 Minatojimaminami-cho, Chuo-ku, Kobe, 650-0047, Japan
Tel.: (81) 783060304
Web Site: https://www.primmune.com
Biotechnology Research & Development Services
N.A.I.C.S.: 541714

TRANS HEX GROUP LIMITED

Sidvale Street, Parow, 7500, Cape Town, South Africa
Tel.: (27) 219372000   ZA
Web Site: http://www.transhex.co.za
Year Founded: 1965

TSX—(JSE)
Rev.: $15,549,692
Assets: $79,196,406
Liabilities: $58,861,118
Net Worth: $20,335,287
Earnings: ($15,084,918)
Emp.: 176
Fiscal Year-end: 03/31/18
Diamond Mining, Exploration & Marketers
N.A.I.C.S.: 212390
Llewellyn Delport *(CEO)*

TRANS INDIA HOUSE IMPEX LIMITED

B1101 Titanium Square B/H Sarveshwar Tower Opp B M W Show Room Thaltej, Sector-125, Ahmedabad, 380054, Uttar Pradesh, India
Tel.: (91) 8487064057
Web Site: https://tihil.co.in
523752—(BOM)
Rev.: $24
Assets: $24,182
Liabilities: $504,671
Net Worth: ($480,489)
Earnings: ($100,293)
Emp.: 3
Fiscal Year-end: 03/31/21
Office Automation Equipment Mfr
N.A.I.C.S.: 541512

TRANS MEDITERRANEAN AIRLINES S.A.L.

Beirut International Airport, PO Box 30, Beirut, 1001, Lebanon
Tel.: (961) 1629210
Web Site: http://www.tma.com.lb
Year Founded: 1953
Sales Range: $75-99.9 Million
Emp.: 300
Oil Transportation Services
N.A.I.C.S.: 481111
Hassan Kassem *(Asst VP-Traffic)*

TRANS POLONIA S.A.

Ul Rokicka 16, 83-110, Tczew, Poland
Tel.: (48) 585339015
Web Site: https://transpolonia.com
TRN—(WAR)
Rev.: $52,215,193
Assets: $62,345,020
Liabilities: $26,606,707
Net Worth: $35,738,313
Earnings: $1,024,136
Fiscal Year-end: 12/31/23
Transportation & Logistics Services
N.A.I.C.S.: 488510
Gregorz Wanio *(Chm & Chm-Supervisory Bd)*

Subsidiaries:

OTP S.A. (1)
ul Chemikow 7, 09-411, Plock, Poland
Tel.: (48) 24 365 71 77
Web Site: http://otpsa.pl
Hazardous Material Transportation Services
N.A.I.C.S.: 488999
Miroslaw Zubek *(Chm-Mgmt Bd & Gen Dir)*

TRANS POWER UTILITY CONTRACTORS INC.

585 Applewood Cres, Concord, L4K 5V7, ON, Canada
Tel.: (905) 660-9575
Web Site: http://www.transpower.ca
Year Founded: 1990
Rev.: $13,284,960
Emp.: 70
Utility Contracting Services
N.A.I.C.S.: 238990
Vince De Gasperis *(Chief Bus Officer)*

TRANS-NATIONWIDE EXPRESS PLC.

INTERNATIONAL PUBLIC

28 Oshodi Apapa Expressway, Oshodi, Lagos, Nigeria
Tel.: (234) 8123682573   NG
Web Site: https://www.tranex-ng.com
Year Founded: 1984
TRANSEXPR—(NIGE)
Rev.: $390,275
Assets: $532,873
Liabilities: $247,453
Net Worth: $285,420
Earnings: $11,862
Emp.: 119
Fiscal Year-end: 12/31/23
Logistics Consulting Servies
N.A.I.C.S.: 541614
Sulaiman Adedokun *(Chm)*

TRANSACTION CAPITAL LIMITED

342 Jan Smuts Avenue Hyde Park, Johannesburg, 2196, South Africa
Tel.: (27) 110496700   ZA
Web Site:
  https://www.transactioncapital.co.za
TCP—(JSE)
Rev.: $1,278,448,500
Assets: $2,266,951,960
Liabilities: $1,831,544,260
Net Worth: $435,407,700
Earnings: ($72,704,100)
Emp.: 11,155
Fiscal Year-end: 09/30/23
Financial Services
N.A.I.C.S.: 522299
Christopher Stefan Seabrooke *(Chm)*

Subsidiaries:

BDB Data Bureau (PTY) Ltd (1)
115 West Street, Sandton, Johannesburg, 2196, South Africa
Tel.: (27) 115606000
Web Site: https://www.nutun.com
Payroll Processing Services
N.A.I.C.S.: 541214

Capital Debt Recovery Proprietary Limited (1)
No 42 wierda road west, Sandton, Johannesburg, 2196, Gauteng, South Africa
Tel.: (27) 11 448 6262
Financial Support Services
N.A.I.C.S.: 522390

Company Unique Finance Proprietary Limited (1)
Rennie House 18 Hoofd St, Johannesburg, 2001, South Africa
Tel.: (27) 11 719 6538
Financial Management Services
N.A.I.C.S.: 523999

Principa Decisions Proprietary Limited (1)
Mezzanine Level The Colosseum Building Cnr, Century Way and Century Blvd Century City, Cape Town, 7441, South Africa
Tel.: (27) 216806000
Web Site: https://www.principa.co.za
Software Development Services
N.A.I.C.S.: 541511

Subsidiary (Domestic):

TC Corporate Support Proprietary Limited (2)
14 Pongola Crescent, Johannesburg, 2144, South Africa
Tel.: (27) 11 531 5300
Financial Management Services
N.A.I.C.S.: 523999

RC VAS Direct Proprietary Limited (1)
112 4th Street Parkmore, Sandton, 2196, South Africa
Tel.: (27) 86 072 6837
Web Site: https://www.roadcover.co.za
Financial Services
N.A.I.C.S.: 523999

Rand Trust Financiers Proprietary Limited (1)
348 Rivonia Boulevard Edenburg Terraces Block B Ground Floor, Rivonia, South Africa

AND PRIVATE COMPANIES

Tel.: (27) 11 844 7160
Web Site: http://www.randtrust.co.za
Financial Support Services
N.A.I.C.S.: 522299

Recoveries Corporation Proprietary Limited (1)
PO Box 13159, Law Courts, Melbourne, 8010, VIC, Australia
Tel.: (61) 38 627 0600
Web Site:
  https://www.recoveriescorp.com.au
Insurance Related Activity Services
N.A.I.C.S.: 524298
Nicholas Harrak *(CEO)*

SA Taxi Finance Holdings (Pty) Ltd (1)
179 - 15th Road, Randjespark, Midrand, South Africa
Tel.: (27) 115509300
Web Site: https://www.sataxi.co.za
Vehicle Financing Services
N.A.I.C.S.: 525990

SA Taxi Protect Proprietary Limited (1)
179 15th Road, Randjespark, Midrand, South Africa
Tel.: (27) 86 182 9448
Web Site: https://sataxi.co.za
Taxi Insurance Services
N.A.I.C.S.: 485310

Transaction Capital Transactional Services Proprietary Limited (1)
Victoria Gate South Hyde Park Lane, cnr William Nicol Drive and Jan Smuts Avenue Hyde Park, Johannesburg, 2196, South Africa
Tel.: (27) 10 447 4024
Web Site:
  https://www.tctransactionalservices.co.za
Investment Management Service
N.A.I.C.S.: 541611

Zebra Cabs Proprietary Limited (1)
179 15th Street, Randjespark, Midrand, South Africa
Tel.: (27) 86 110 5105
Web Site: https://www.zebracabs.co.za
Taxi Service
N.A.I.C.S.: 485310

TRANSACTION CO., LTD.
Shibuya Shinminamiguchi Building 8F 2813 Shibuya 3chome, Shibuya-ku, Tokyo, 150-0002, Japan
Tel.: (81) 354689033
Web Site: https://www.trans-action.co.jp
Year Founded: 1987
7818—(TKS)
Rev.: $155,792,340
Assets: $138,830,400
Liabilities: $25,949,840
Net Worth: $112,880,560
Earnings: $23,405,860
Emp.: 481
Fiscal Year-end: 08/31/24
Household Goods & Healthcare Products Mfr & Sales
N.A.I.C.S.: 325611
Satoshi Ishikawa *(Pres)*

Subsidiaries:

Kraftwerk Co., Ltd. (1)
1124 Hongo Sugito-cho, Kitakatsushika-gun, Saitama, 345-0023, Japan
Tel.: (81) 480370070
Web Site: https://www.kraft-werk.jp
Printing Services
N.A.I.C.S.: 323113
Atsushi Ishikawa *(Pres)*

Shanghai Trade Works Asia Limited (1)
Rm 2607 Feidiao International Building No Jia 1065 Zhao Jia Bang Road, Xu Hui District, Shanghai, China
Tel.: (86) 2133762706
Consumer Goods Distr
N.A.I.C.S.: 423990

Trade Works Asia Limited (1)
1602A-3A Tower 6 China Hong Kong City 33 Canton Road, Tsim Sha Tsui, Kowloon, China (Hong Kong)
Tel.: (852) 27367070
Consumer Goods Distr
N.A.I.C.S.: 423990
Hajime Akashi *(Pres)*

Trade Works Co., Ltd. (1)
7th floor Shibuya New South Exit Building 3-28-13 Shibuya, Shibuya-ku, Tokyo, 150-0002, Japan
Tel.: (81) 354687271
Emp.: 173
Fabless Product Mfr & Distr
N.A.I.C.S.: 334419
Keiichi Chiba *(Pres)*

Trans Co., Ltd. (1)
9F Shibuya Shin-South Exit Building 3-28-13 Shibuya, Shibuya-ku, Tokyo, 150-0002, Japan
Tel.: (81) 354689411
Emp.: 130
Fabless Product Mfr
N.A.I.C.S.: 334419
Kazuaki Hosoda *(Pres)*

TRANSACTION MEDIA NETWORKS INC.
18th floor Taiyo Life Nihonbashi Building 2-11-2 Nihonbashi, Chuo-ku, Tokyo, 103-0027, Japan
Tel.: (81) 335173800
Web Site: https://www.tm-nets.com
Year Founded: 2008
5258—(TKS)
Rev.: $68,545,700
Assets: $168,753,300
Liabilities: $97,173,610
Net Worth: $71,579,690
Earnings: $3,866,850
Emp.: 286
Fiscal Year-end: 03/31/24
Electronic Payment Services
N.A.I.C.S.: 522320
Atsushi Ohtaka *(Pres & CEO)*

TRANSADRIA MEDUNARODNA SPEDICIJA D.D.
Riva Boduli 1, 51000, Rijeka, Croatia
Tel.: (385) 51212111
Web Site: http://www.transadria.hr
Year Founded: 1947
Sales Range: $10-24.9 Million
Emp.: 575
Freight Transportation Services
N.A.I.C.S.: 488510
Marijan Kljucaricek *(Pres)*

Subsidiaries:

Transglob mednarodna spedicija d.o.o. Ljubljana (1)
Slovenska cesta 54, Ljubljana, 1000, Slovenia
Tel.: (386) 1 2306800
Web Site: http://www.transglob.si
Freight Forwarding Services
N.A.I.C.S.: 488510
Mihael Lah *(Gen Mgr)*

TRANSAKT LTD.
Unit 8 3F Wah Yiu Industrial Centre 3032 Au Pui Wan Street, Fotan, China (Hong Kong)
Tel.: (852) 52389111 NV
Web Site:
  https://www.transaktltd.com
Year Founded: 1996
TAKD—(OTCIQ)
Assets: $3,000
Liabilities: $13,000
Net Worth: ($10,000)
Earnings: ($15,000)
Emp.: 2
Fiscal Year-end: 12/31/22
Agricultural Equipment Mfr & Distr
N.A.I.C.S.: 333111
Chi-Wah Yam *(CFO)*

TRANSALLIANCE

5 bis rue Saint Leon, 54000, Nancy, France
Tel.: (33) 3 8390 2000 FR
Web Site: http://www.transalliance.eu
Sales Range: $600-649.9 Million
Emp.: 2,750
Freight Transportation & Logistics Services
N.A.I.C.S.: 488510
Alexandre Michel *(CEO)*

Subsidiaries:

Proxidis Express (1)
13 rue de l'Aqueduc, ZA de Charpenay, 69210, Lentilly, France
Tel.: (33) 437496850
Web Site: http://www.proxidis-express.com
Sales Range: $25-49.9 Million
Emp.: 80
Express Delivery, Storage & Logistics Services
N.A.I.C.S.: 492110

TRANSALTA CORPORATION
TransAlta Place Suite 1400 1100 1 St SE, PO Box 1900, Calgary, T2G 1B1, AB, Canada
Tel.: (403) 267-7110 AB
Web Site: https://www.transalta.com
Year Founded: 1911
TAC—(NYSE)
Rev.: $2,478,392,554
Assets: $6,396,542,809
Liabilities: $5,167,319,199
Net Worth: $1,229,223,609
Earnings: $588,018,025
Emp.: 1,257
Fiscal Year-end: 12/31/23
Power Generation & Distribution Services
N.A.I.C.S.: 221112
Brent Ward *(Treas & Sr VP-Strategy & M&A)*

Subsidiaries:

TransAlta Centralia Generation LLC (1)
913 Big Hanaford Rd, Centralia, WA 98531-9100
Tel.: (360) 736-9901
Power Generation Services
N.A.I.C.S.: 221112

TransAlta Energy (Australia) Pty. Ltd. (1)
Level 36 Central Park, 152 158 Saint Georges Ter, Perth, 6000, WA, Australia
Tel.: (61) 893222101
Power Generation Services
N.A.I.C.S.: 221112

TransAlta Energy Marketing (U.S.) Inc. (1)
110 12 Ave SW, Calgary, T2R 0G7, AB, Canada
Tel.: (403) 267-7987
Electric Power Distribution Services
N.A.I.C.S.: 221122

TransAlta Energy Marketing Corp. (1)
110 12 Ave SW, Calgary, T2R 0G7, AB, Canada
Tel.: (403) 267-7987
Electric Power Generation & Distribution Services
N.A.I.C.S.: 221118

TransAlta Generation Partnership (1)
110 12 Ave SW, Calgary, T2P 2M1, AB, Canada
Tel.: (403) 267-7110
Web Site: http://www.transalta.com
Sales Range: $1-4.9 Billion
Emp.: 200
Eletric Power Generation Services
N.A.I.C.S.: 221118

TransAlta Renewables Inc. (1)
110 12th Avenue Southwest, PO Box 1900, Station M, Calgary, T2P 2M1, AB, Canada
Tel.: (403) 267-2520

TRANSASIA BIO-MEDICALS LTD.

Web Site:
  https://www.transaltarenewables.com
Rev.: $367,671,600
Assets: $2,932,767,720
Liabilities: $1,271,987,280
Net Worth: $1,660,780,440
Earnings: $108,736,920
Fiscal Year-end: 12/31/2021
Renewable Power Generation
N.A.I.C.S.: 221115
Brent Ward *(Co-CFO)*

TRANSART GRAPHICS CO., LTD.
No 6 The 12th Road Taichung Ind Park, Taichung, 407269, Taiwan
Tel.: (886) 423593687 TW
Web Site:
  https://www.transart.com.tw
Year Founded: 1973
8481—(TAI)
Rev.: $32,495,698
Assets: $58,734,685
Liabilities: $6,853,069
Net Worth: $51,881,616
Earnings: $4,084,241
Emp.: 160
Fiscal Year-end: 12/31/23
Label Printing Services
N.A.I.C.S.: 323113
Hong Zhaoyi *(Chm)*

Subsidiaries:

Transart Europe B.V. (1)
Dieselstraat 15, 8263 AE, Kampen, Netherlands
Tel.: (31) 383372300
Sporting Goods Decorating Product Distr
N.A.I.C.S.: 423920

Transart Graphics (Shenzhen) Co., Ltd. (1)
No 61 Youlian Minzhi Village Longhua Town, Shenzhen, 518109, China
Tel.: (86) 75529828811
Printing Products Mfr
N.A.I.C.S.: 323113

Transart Graphics (Taicang) Co,. Ltd. (1)
No 155 Bai Yun Du Road Lu-Du Town, Taicang, Jiangsu, China
Tel.: (86) 51253458033
Printing Product Mfr & Distr
N.A.I.C.S.: 323113

Transart Graphics (Tianjin) Co,. Ltd. (1)
No 28 Wuhai Road Jinghai Economic Development Zone, Tianjin, 301600, China
Tel.: (86) 2259591688
Printing Products Mfr
N.A.I.C.S.: 323113

Transart Graphics (Vietnam) Co,. Ltd. (1)
Lot A3 N2 Road, Dai Dang Industrial Zone Phu Tan Ward, Thu Dau Mot, Binh Duong, Vietnam
Tel.: (84) 2743800604
Sporting Goods Decorating Product Distr
N.A.I.C.S.: 423920

TRANSASIA BIO-MEDICALS LTD.
Transasia House 8 Chandivali Studio Road, Andheri East, Mumbai, 400 072, India
Tel.: (91) 22 40309000 In
Web Site:
  http://www.erbamannheim.com
Year Founded: 1979
Holding Company; Surgical Appliance & Supplies Mfr
N.A.I.C.S.: 551112

Subsidiaries:

ERBA Diagnostics Mannheim GmbH (1)
Mallaustrasse 69-73, 68219, Mannheim, Germany (100%)
Tel.: (49) 621 8799770
Web Site: http://www.erbamannheim.com

TRANSASIA BIO-MEDICALS LTD.

Transasia Bio-Medicals Ltd.—(Continued)
Surgical Supplies Mfr
N.A.I.C.S.: 339113
Suresh Vazirani *(Chm & Mng Dir)*

Subsidiary (US):

ERBA Diagnostics, Inc. (2)
14100 NW 57th Ct, Miami Lakes, FL
33014 (82.4%)
Tel.: (305) 324-2300
Web Site: http://www.erbadiagnostics.com
Sales Range: $10-24.9 Million
Emp.: 134
Diagnostic Test Kits & Materials Mfr & Distr
N.A.I.C.S.: 325412
David Barka *(Interim CEO)*

Subsidiary (Domestic):

Calbiotech, Inc. (3)
1935 Cordell Ct, El Cajon, CA 92020
Tel.: (619) 660-6162
Web Site: http://www.calbiotech.com
Immunoassay Products Developer & Mfr
N.A.I.C.S.: 325413
Noori Barka *(Founder & Pres)*

Subsidiary (Non-US):

Delta Biologicals S.r.l. (3)
Via Nicaragua 12-14, 00040, Pomezia, Italy
Tel.: (39) 0691190
Web Site: http://www.deltabiologicals.it
Sales Range: $25-49.9 Million
Emp.: 25
In-Vitro Diagnostic Products Mfr
N.A.I.C.S.: 325413
Coriano Onder Traetta *(Gen Mgr)*

Subsidiary (Domestic):

Diamedix Corporation (3)
14100 NW 57th Ct, Miami, FL 33014
Tel.: (305) 324-2300
Web Site: http://www.diamedix.com
Diagnostic Test Kit Mfr
N.A.I.C.S.: 325413
Greg Vega *(Mgr-Facility)*

Drew Scientific, Inc. (3)
14100 NW 57 Ct, Miami Lakes, FL 33014
Tel.: (214) 210-4900
Web Site: http://www.drew-scientific.com
Sales Range: $25-49.9 Million
Emp.: 70
Surgical & Medical Instrument Mfr
N.A.I.C.S.: 339112

ImmunoVision, Inc. (3)
1820 Ford Ave, Springdale, AR
72764 (100%)
Tel.: (479) 751-7005
Web Site: http://www.immunovision.com
Mfr & Marketer of Autoimmune Reagents &
Research Products
N.A.I.C.S.: 325413

JAS Diagnostics, Inc. (3)
14100 NW 57th Court, Miami Lakes, FL
33014
Tel.: (305) 418-2320
Web Site: http://www.erbadiagnostics.com
Chemistry Reagents Mfr
N.A.I.C.S.: 325413

TRANSAT A.T., INC.
Place du Parc 300-Leo Pariseau
Street Suite 600, Montreal, H2X 4C2,
QC, Canada
Tel.: (514) 987-1660 Ca
Web Site: http://www.transat.com
Year Founded: 1987
TRZBF—(OTCIQ)
Rev.: $1,018,582,537
Assets: $1,577,132,022
Liabilities: $1,525,261,382
Net Worth: $51,870,640
Earnings: ($388,609,324)
Emp.: 5,180
Fiscal Year-end: 10/31/20
Travel Industry; Retail Sales through
Travel Agencies, Organizes & Distributes Vacation Packages through Tour
Operators, Air Transportation, Hotel
Management
N.A.I.C.S.: 561520

Jean-Marc Eustache *(Pres, CEO, Founder & Chm)*

Subsidiaries:

Air Transat A T Inc (1)
5959 Cote-vertu, Saint Laurent, H4S 2E6,
QC, Canada
Tel.: (514) 906-0330
Web Site: http://www.airtransat.com
Sales Range: $125-149.9 Million
Emp.: 400
Commercial Passenger Air Transportation
N.A.I.C.S.: 481111

Trafictours de Mexico S.A. de
C.V. (1)
Lago Alberto 319 Piso 6 Oficina 610 Col
Granada, 11520, Mexico, Mexico
Tel.: (52) 4 124 0713
Web Site:
https://trafictoursdemexico.com.mx
Travel Agency Services
N.A.I.C.S.: 561510

Transat Holidays USA Inc. (1)
4050 SW 11th Ter, Fort Lauderdale, FL
33315
Tel.: (954) 929-2200
Web Site:
https://www.transatholidaysusa.com
Destination Management Services
N.A.I.C.S.: 561599

TRANSCANNA HOLDINGS, INC.
2489 Bellevue Avenue, West Vancouver, V7V 1E1, BC, Canada
Tel.: (604) 207-5548
Web Site:
https://www.transcanna.com
Year Founded: 2017
TCAN—(CNSX)
Rev.: $3,128,339
Assets: $20,061,394
Liabilities: $17,512,065
Net Worth: $2,549,328
Earnings: ($10,242,125)
Fiscal Year-end: 11/30/21
Holding Company
N.A.I.C.S.: 551112
Stephanie Wesik *(Pres)*

TRANSCARD FINANCIAL SERVICES EAD
43 Cherni Vrah Blvd, 1407, Sofia,
Bulgaria
Tel.: (359) 2 4969010
Web Site: http://www.transcard.bg
Credit Card Services
N.A.I.C.S.: 522210
Yuriy Stanchev *(Chm)*

TRANSCARGO
Zac De L Anjoly 18 Voie D Irlande,
13127, Vitrolles, Bouches Du Rhone,
France
Tel.: (33) 442108700 FR
Web Site: http://www.transcargo.fr
Rev.: $11,100,000
Emp.: 39
Freight Transportation Arrangement
Services
N.A.I.C.S.: 488510
Marc Grolleau *(Pres)*

TRANSCEND INFORMATION, INC.
No 70 Xingzhong Road, Neihu District, Taipei, 114, Taiwan
Tel.: (886) 227928000 TW
Web Site: https://tw.transcend-info.com
Year Founded: 1988
2451—(TAI)
Rev.: $343,247,706
Assets: $728,908,079
Liabilities: $98,779,257
Net Worth: $630,128,823
Earnings: $64,908,431

Emp.: 592
Fiscal Year-end: 12/31/23
Memory Module, Computer Peripheral & Other Consumer Electronic
Components Designer, Mfr & Marketer
N.A.I.C.S.: 334419
Shu Chongwan *(Chm, CEO & Gen Mgr)*

Subsidiaries:

Transcend Information (Shanghai),
Ltd. (1)
Room 801-802 T1 Building Changning International No 1388 Kaixuan Road, Changning District, Shanghai, 200052, China
Tel.: (86) 2161619388
Computer Memory Module Mfr & Whslr
N.A.I.C.S.: 334118

Transcend Information Inc. (1)
1645 N Brian St, Orange, CA 92867
Tel.: (714) 921-2000
Web Site: http://www.transcend-info.com
Sales Range: $25-49.9 Million
Emp.: 50
Memory Module, Computer Peripheral &
Other Consumer Electronic Components
Designer, Mfr & Marketer
N.A.I.C.S.: 334419

Transcend Information Trading
GmbH (1)
Flughafenstrasse 52b Airport-Center,
22335, Hamburg, Germany
Tel.: (49) 405389070
Web Site: https://www.de.transcend-info.com
Sales Range: $25-49.9 Million
Emp.: 30
Memory Module, Computer Peripheral &
Other Consumer Electronic Components
Marketer
N.A.I.C.S.: 423690

Transcend Information UK
Limited (1)
1st Floor Nexus House Boundary Way,
Nexus House, Hemel Hempstead, HP2
7SJ, Hertfordshire, United Kingdom
Tel.: (44) 1442000000
Web Site: http://www.uk.transcend-info.com
Memory Module, Computer Peripheral &
Other Consumer Electronic Components
Marketer
N.A.I.C.S.: 423430

Transcend Korea Inc. (1)
159-1 Mokdongseo-ro 12th Floor CBS
Building, Yangcheon-gu, Seoul, Korea
(South)
Tel.: (82) 27828088
Web Site: https://kr.transcend-info.com
Computer Memory Module & Peripheral
Product Whslr
N.A.I.C.S.: 423430

TRANSCEND RESIDENTIAL PROPERTY FUND LTD.
54 Peter Place Peter Place Office
Park Block G, Glasgow House
Ground Floor Bryanston, Johannesburg, 2191, South Africa
Tel.: (27) 113008600
Web Site:
http://www.transcendproperty.co.za
Year Founded: 2016
TPF—(JSE)
Rev.: $20,417,720
Assets: $120,604,618
Liabilities: $47,579,170
Net Worth: $73,025,448
Earnings: $6,105,291
Fiscal Year-end: 03/31/23
Real Estate Investment Services
N.A.I.C.S.: 531190
Solly Mboweni *(CEO)*

TRANSCENTA HOLDING LIMITED
218 Xinghu Street Biobay B6-501,
Suzhou, 215123, China
Tel.: (86) 2162370929 Ky

INTERNATIONAL PUBLIC

Web Site:
https://www.transcenta.com
Year Founded: 2010
6628—(HKG)
Rev.: $7,455,832
Assets: $234,451,014
Liabilities: $92,166,870
Net Worth: $142,284,144
Earnings: ($64,046,577)
Emp.: 215
Fiscal Year-end: 12/31/23
Holding Company
N.A.I.C.S.: 551112
Christopher Hwang *(CTO)*

Subsidiaries:

Lisheng Industrial Co., Ltd. (1)
No 669 East 2nd Road Nanbin Street,
Ruian City, Wenzhou, Zhejiang, China
Tel.: (86) 57758189489
Web Site: https://www.lishg.com
Flex Printing Machine Mfr & Distr
N.A.I.C.S.: 323120

TRANSCENTURY LIMITED
48 Apple Cross Road Off James
Gichuru Road, PO Box 42334, Lavington, 100, Nairobi, Kenya
Tel.: (254) 709916000 KE
Web Site:
https://www.transcentury.co.ke
Year Founded: 1997
Rev.: $41,538,183
Assets: $163,014,810
Liabilities: $195,333,661
Net Worth: ($32,318,851)
Earnings: ($34,255,653)
Emp.: 1,039
Fiscal Year-end: 12/31/18
Electrical Component Mfr
N.A.I.C.S.: 335999
Martin Munyiri *(CFO-Grp)*

TRANSCHEM LTD.
304 Ganatra Estate Pokhran Road
No 1 Kopat, Thane, 400 601, India
Tel.: (91) 2225477077
Web Site: https://www.transchem.net
500422—(BOM)
Rev.: $909,158
Assets: $9,120,002
Liabilities: $69,997
Net Worth: $9,050,005
Earnings: $391,509
Emp.: 17
Fiscal Year-end: 03/31/22
Chemical Products Mfr
N.A.I.C.S.: 325998
Neeraja Deepak Karandikar *(Compliance Officer & Sec)*

TRANSCOM S.A.
Tel.: (40) 213177178
Web Site: https://transcom.ro
Year Founded: 1991
TRSB—(BUC)
Rev.: $460,423
Assets: $3,155,567
Liabilities: $305,269
Net Worth: $2,850,297
Earnings: $13,578
Emp.: 14
Fiscal Year-end: 12/31/20
Automotive Repair & Maintenance
Services
N.A.I.C.S.: 811198
Mihaela Nicoleta Ungureanu *(Pres)*

TRANSCONTINENTAL GOLD CORP.
580 Hornby Street Suite 890, Vancouver, V6C 2E7, BC, Canada
Tel.: (604) 694-6539
Assets: $106,544
Liabilities: $48,914
Net Worth: $57,630
Earnings: ($162,682)

TRANSCONTINENTAL INC.
1 Place Ville Marie Suite 3240, Montreal, H3B 0G1, QC, Canada
Tel.: (514) 954-4000 QC
Web Site:
 https://www.transcontinental.com
Year Founded: 1976
53L—(DEU)
Rev.: $2,220,493,845
Assets: $2,794,155,402
Liabilities: $1,354,753,454
Net Worth: $1,439,401,948
Earnings: $64,788,945
Emp.: 8,131
Fiscal Year-end: 10/29/23
Newspapers, Magazines, Websites, Flyers & Catalogs Publishing & Printing Services
N.A.I.C.S.: 323111
Donald LeCavalier (CFO)

Subsidiaries:

Americ Disc, Inc. (1)
2525 Rue Canadien, Drummondville, J2C 7W2, QC, Canada (100%)
Tel.: (819) 474-2655
Sales Range: $200-249.9 Million
Emp.: 700
N.A.I.C.S.: 323117

Multifilm Packaging Corp. (1)
1040 North McLean Blvd, Elgin, IL 60123
Tel.: (847) 695-7600
Web Site: http://www.multifilm.com
Coated & Laminated Paper Mfr
N.A.I.C.S.: 322220
Olle Mannertorp (CEO)

Transcontinental Printing Inc. (1)
1603 boul de Montarville, Boucherville, J4B 5Y2, QC, Canada (100%)
Tel.: (514) 337-8560
Sales Range: $200-249.9 Million
Emp.: 150
N.A.I.C.S.: 323117

Subsidiary (Domestic):

Ad-Bag Distribution (2)
523 Lebeau Blvd, Saint Laurent, H4M 1S2, QC, Canada (100%)
Tel.: (514) 337-6920
Web Site: http://www.transcontinental.ca
Sales Range: $50-74.9 Million
Emp.: 120
Newspaper Publishing
N.A.I.C.S.: 513110

Interglobe Printing, Inc. (2)
150 181st Street, Beauceville, G5X 3P3, QC, Canada (100%)
Tel.: (418) 774-3367
Web Site: http://www.tc.tc
Sales Range: $100-124.9 Million
Emp.: 5,000
N.A.I.C.S.: 323117
Nathalie Gregoire (Plant Mgr)

Metrolitho (2)
4137 Blvd Portland, Sherbrooke, J1L 2Z1, QC, Canada (100%)
Tel.: (819) 563-4001
Web Site: http://www.metrolitho.com
Sales Range: $50-74.9 Million
Emp.: 150
N.A.I.C.S.: 323117

Subsidiary (US):

Trans-Continental Printing USA Inc (2)
67 Irving Pl 9th Fl, New York, NY 10003
Tel.: (212) 473-5679
Rev.: $1,200,000
Emp.: 20
Market Analysis & Research
N.A.I.C.S.: 541910

Plant (Domestic):

Transcontinental Printing Inc. - Northern California Plant (3)
47540 Kato Rd, Fremont, CA 94538
Tel.: (510) 580-7700
Web Site: http://www.tctranscontinental.com
Emp.: 200
Newspaper Publishing & Marketing Services
N.A.I.C.S.: 513110
Brenda York (Mgr-HR)

Subsidiary (Domestic):

Transcontinental Acme Direct (2)
999 90E Avenue, La Salle, H8R 3A4, QC, Canada (100%)
Tel.: (514) 328-7070
Web Site: http://www.tcprinting.tc
Sales Range: $100-124.9 Million
Emp.: 350
Books Printing
N.A.I.C.S.: 323117

Transcontinental Digital Services Inc. (2)
6688 Kitimat Rd, Mississauga, L5N 1P8, ON, Canada (100%)
Tel.: (905) 826-4664
Web Site: http://www.transcontinental-printing.com
Sales Range: $50-74.9 Million
N.A.I.C.S.: 323117

Transcontinental Direct, Inc. (2)
210 Duffield Dr, Markham, L6G 1C9, ON, Canada (100%)
Tel.: (416) 848-8500
Sales Range: $100-124.9 Million
Provider of Commercial Web, Half Web, Sheetfed & Laser Printing Services
N.A.I.C.S.: 323111

Transcontinental Interweb Inc. (2)
1603 de Montarville Blvd, Boucherville, J4B 5Y2, QC, Canada (100%)
Tel.: (450) 655-2801
Web Site: http://www.interwebinc.com
Sales Range: $100-124.9 Million
Magazine & Newspaper Printing
N.A.I.C.S.: 513110
Norman Preville (Gen Mgr)

Transcontinental LGM Graphics (2)
737 Moray Street, Winnipeg, R3J 3S9, MB, Canada (100%)
Tel.: (204) 982-1717
Web Site: http://www.transcontinental-printing.com
Sales Range: $50-74.9 Million
Emp.: 140
Printing Services
N.A.I.C.S.: 323120
Monique Therien (Controller)

Transcontinental PLM (2)
210 Duffield Dr, Markham, L6G 1C8, ON, Canada
Tel.: (416) 848-8500
Web Site: http://www.tcimprimeries.tc
Sales Range: $125-149.9 Million
Business Visual Communications & Commercial Printing
N.A.I.C.S.: 323111

Subsidiary (Domestic):

Mailer Magic (3)
195 Duffield Drive, Markham, L6G 1C9, ON, Canada
Tel.: (416) 848-8500
Web Site: http://corp.plmgroup.com
Other Commercial Printing
N.A.I.C.S.: 323111

Plant (Domestic):

Transcontinental Printing Inc. - Aurora (2)
275 Wellington Street East, Aurora, L4G 6J9, ON, Canada
Tel.: (905) 841-4400
Web Site: http://www.transcontinental.ca
Sales Range: $100-124.9 Million
Commercial Printing Services
N.A.I.C.S.: 323111

Transcontinental Printing Inc. - Brampton (2)
394-A Orenda Road East, Brampton, L6T 1G9, ON, Canada
Tel.: (905) 799-5920
Web Site: http://www.transcontinental-printing.com
Sales Range: $25-49.9 Million
Emp.: 50
N.A.I.C.S.: 323117

Transcontinental Printing Inc. - Calgary Plant (2)
5516 Fifth Street South East, Calgary, T2H 1L3, AB, Canada
Tel.: (403) 258-3788
Web Site: http://www.tctranscontinental.com
Sales Range: $100-124.9 Million
Emp.: 320
Newspaper Printing Services
N.A.I.C.S.: 323117

Transcontinental Printing Inc. - Concord Plant (2)
89 Connie Crescent, Concord, L4K 1L3, ON, Canada
Tel.: (905) 669-2386
Sales Range: $50-74.9 Million
Emp.: 12
Newspaper Publishing Services
N.A.I.C.S.: 513110
Mark Dominato (Gen Mgr)

Transcontinental Printing Inc. - Halifax Plant (2)
11 Ragged Lake Blvd, Halifax, B3S 1R3, NS, Canada
Tel.: (902) 450-5611
Web Site: http://www.tctranscontinental.com
Newspaper Publishing Services
N.A.I.C.S.: 513110

Transcontinental Printing Inc. - Lasalle Plant (2)
7743 Bourdeau St, Lasalle, Montreal, H8N 2G8, QC, Canada
Tel.: (514) 366-4580
Web Site: http://www.tctranscontinental.com
Newspaper Publishing Services
N.A.I.C.S.: 513110

Transcontinental Printing Inc. - Metropolitan Plant (2)
12300 Metropolitan Blvd East, Pointe-aux-Trembles, H1B 5Y2, QC, Canada
Tel.: (514) 640-1840
Sales Range: $25-49.9 Million
Emp.: 80
Newspaper Publishing Services
N.A.I.C.S.: 513110
Francois Cormier (Gen Mgr)

Transcontinental Printing Inc. - Prince Edward Island Plant (2)
169 Industrial Drive Borden-Carleton Industrial Park, Borden-Carleton, C0B 1X0, PE, Canada
Tel.: (902) 437-2125
Web Site: http://www.tctranscontinental.com
Sales Range: $25-49.9 Million
Emp.: 3
Commercial Printing Services
N.A.I.C.S.: 323111

Transcontinental Printing Inc. - Qualimax Plant (2)
130 Adrien-Robert Street, Gatineau, J8Y 3S2, QC, Canada
Tel.: (819) 777-6045
Sales Range: $25-49.9 Million
Emp.: 45
Newspaper Publishing Services
N.A.I.C.S.: 513110
Daniel Beaulne (Gen Mgr)

Transcontinental Printing Inc. - Saint-Hyacinthe (2)
2700 Casavant West Blvd, Saint-Hyacinthe, J2S 7S4, QC, Canada (100%)
Tel.: (450) 773-0289
Web Site: http://www.imprimeries-transcontinental.com
Sales Range: $50-74.9 Million
N.A.I.C.S.: 323117

Transcontinental Printing Inc. - Transmag (2)
10807 Mirabeau Street, Anjou, H1J 1T7, QC, Canada
Tel.: (514) 355-4134
Web Site: http://www.transcontinental-printing.com
Sales Range: $50-74.9 Million
N.A.I.C.S.: 323117
Pierre Des Longchamps (Gen Mgr)

Transcontinental Printing Inc. - Vaughan Plant (2)
100B Royal Group Crescent, Vaughan, L4H 1X9, ON, Canada
Tel.: (905) 663-0050
Web Site: http://www.tctranscontinental.com
Newspaper Publishing Services
N.A.I.C.S.: 513110

Subsidiary (Domestic):

Transcontinental RBW Graphics (2)
2049 Twentieth Street East, Owen Sound, N4K 5R2, ON, Canada (100%)
Tel.: (519) 376-8330
Web Site: http://www.transcontinental.ca
Sales Range: $200-249.9 Million
Emp.: 100
N.A.I.C.S.: 323117
Bryan Reid (Pres)

Transcontinental Ross-Ellis (2)
999 90e Avenue, La Salle, H8R 3A4, QC, Canada (100%)
Tel.: (514) 861-2411
Web Site: http://www.ross-ellis.com
Sales Range: $100-124.9 Million
Packaging Solutions
N.A.I.C.S.: 561910

Transmedia (1)
1500 boulevard Jules-Poitras, Saint Laurent, H4N 1X7, QC, Canada (100%)
Tel.: (514) 334-8420
Web Site: http://www.tctranscontinental.com
Sales Range: $50-74.9 Million
Emp.: 125
Book Publishing
N.A.I.C.S.: 323117

TRANSCOR ASTRA GROUP S.A.
Parc de l'Alliance Boulevard de France 7, 1420, Braine-l'Alleud, Belgium
Tel.: (32) 2663 1900 BE
Web Site:
 http://www.astratranscor.com
Year Founded: 2012
Holding Company
N.A.I.C.S.: 551112
Albert Frere (CEO)

Subsidiaries:

AOT Deutschland GmbH (1)
Lilienstrasse 11, 20095, Hamburg, Germany
Tel.: (49) 40209321042
Fuel Distr
N.A.I.C.S.: 424720

AOT Energy Poland Sp. z o.o. (1)
ul Krolewska 16, 00-103, Warsaw, Poland
Tel.: (48) 226603711
Fuel Distr
N.A.I.C.S.: 424720
Grzegorz Bujnowski (Head-Sls)

AOT Trading AG (1)
Grafenaweg 4, 6300, Zug, Switzerland
Tel.: (41) 417276900
Fuel Distr
N.A.I.C.S.: 424720
Alexander Paulus (Mgr-Trading)

Astra Oil Company Pte Ltd (1)
38 Beach Road 26-12 South Beach Tower, Singapore, 189767, Singapore
Tel.: (65) 63398868
Fuel Distr
N.A.I.C.S.: 424720
Luke Ng (Mgr-Trading)

Astra Transcor France SAS (1)
247 C route de Bethune, 62300, Lens, France
Tel.: (33) 323650060
Fuel Distr
N.A.I.C.S.: 424720

PT Transcor Indonesia (1)
Sentral Senayan 2 16th Flr Jl Asia Afrika No 8, gelora bung karno senayan, Jakarta, Indonesia
Tel.: (62) 2129241917
Fuel Distr
N.A.I.C.S.: 424720

Transcor Astra Luxembourg S.A. (1)

AND PRIVATE COMPANIES

Gold Mining Services
N.A.I.C.S.: 212220
Wenhong Jin (CFO)

TRANSCOR ASTRA GROUP S.A.

Transcor Astra Group S.A.—(Continued)

76-78 rue de Merl, 2146, Luxembourg, Luxembourg
Tel.: (352) 442242
Fuel Distr
N.A.I.C.S.: 424720

Transcor Corporation (Energy) (1)
4955 Steubenville Pike Ste 300, Pittsburgh, PA 15205
Tel.: (412) 787-6355
Coal Wholesale Trade Distr
N.A.I.C.S.: 425120

TRANSCORP HOLDINGS LIMITED

1 Kim Seng Promenade #17-04
Great World City, Singapore, 237994, Singapore
Tel.: (65) 62352182
T19—(SES)
Sales Range: $1-9.9 Million
Real Estate Services
N.A.I.C.S.: 531390
Choon Hwee Sim (Mgr-Bus Dev)

TRANSCORP INTERNATIONAL LIMITED

Plot No 3 HAF Pocket Sector-18A Phase-II, Kargil Apartment Near Veer Awas, New Delhi, 110 075, India
Tel.: (91) 1130418901
Web Site: https://www.transcorpint.com
Year Founded: 1993
532410—(BOM)
Rev.: $346,437,971
Assets: $16,183,406
Liabilities: $9,345,974
Net Worth: $6,837,432
Earnings: $60,584
Emp.: 297
Fiscal Year-end: 03/31/23
Money Transfer Services
N.A.I.C.S.: 522320
Amitava Ghosh (CEO)

Subsidiaries:

Ritco Travels & Tours Pvt. Ltd. (1)
Tel.: (91) 1414004888
Web Site: https://www.ritcotravels.com
Travel Agency
N.A.I.C.S.: 561510
Severine Fernandes (VP)

TRANSCOSMOS INC.

Shibuya First Tower 1-2-20 Higashi, Shibuya-ku, Tokyo, 150-0011, Japan
Tel.: (81) 5017517700   JP
Web Site: https://www.trans-cosmos.co.jp
Year Founded: 1985
9715—(TKS)
Rev.: $2,394,148,610
Assets: $1,318,338,060
Liabilities: $537,928,410
Net Worth: $780,409,650
Earnings: $66,741,170
Emp.: 69,674
Fiscal Year-end: 03/31/24
Business-To-Business Services
N.A.I.C.S.: 541439
Koichi Iwami (Co-Pres & Dir-Representative)

Subsidiaries:

9FRUITSMEDIA, Inc. (1)
725-21 Yeoksam 2-dong, Gangnam-gu, Seoul, 135-921, Korea (South)
Tel.: (82) 25664498
Web Site: http://www.9fruits.com
Internet Advertisement Services
N.A.I.C.S.: 541810

Brightcove KK (1)
PMO Tamachi 9F 5-31-17 Shiba, Minato-ku, Tokyo, 108-0014, Japan
Tel.: (81) 364537730
Sales Range: $25-49.9 Million
Emp.: 14
Internet Hosting Services
N.A.I.C.S.: 518210
Jeremy D. Allaire (Chm)

Crossco Co., Ltd. (1)
EX Roppongi Building 5F 7-18-23 Roppongi, Minato-ku, Tokyo, 106-0032, Japan
Tel.: (81) 364471920
Web Site: https://www.crossco.co.jp
Sales Range: $25-49.9 Million
Emp.: 100
Advertising Services
N.A.I.C.S.: 541810

FJ transcosmos Human Resource Professionals Limited (1)
Shin-Kawasaki Twin Tower W Building 25F 1-1-2 Kashimada, Saiwai-ku, Kawasaki, 211-8588, Kanagawa, Japan
Tel.: (81) 447542115
Web Site: https://www.trans-cosmos.co.jp
Emp.: 220
Human Resource Consulting Services
N.A.I.C.S.: 541612

Fujisan Magazine Service Co., Ltd. (1)
16-11-7th floor Nanpeidai-cho, Shibuya-Ku, Tokyo, 150-0036, Japan
Tel.: (81) 354597072
Web Site: https://www.fujisan.co.jp
Rev.: $40,916,390
Assets: $41,285,070
Liabilities: $24,637,750
Net Worth: $16,647,320
Earnings: $1,573,980
Emp.: 82
Fiscal Year-end: 12/31/2023
Magazine Publishing Agencies
N.A.I.C.S.: 513199

Heroleads (Thailand) Co., Ltd. (1)
32/32 Floor 11 Sino-Thai Tower Sukhumvit 21 Road, Klongtoey Nua Wattana, Bangkok, 10110, Thailand
Tel.: (66) 655061444
Marketing Consulting Services
N.A.I.C.S.: 541613

Infracommerce Ltd. (1)
Av Dr Cardoso de Melo 1855 - 15 andar, Sao Paulo, Brazil
Tel.: (55) 11384813
Web Site: http://www.infracommerce.com.br
Information Technology & Services
N.A.I.C.S.: 541511

Japan Public Fare Services Co., Ltd. (1)
4-9-8 Ginza chome, Chuo-ku, Tokyo, 104-0061, Japan
Tel.: (81) 335440871
Web Site: http://www.ryoukin.co.jp
Sales Range: $50-74.9 Million
Emp.: 16
Electronic Financial Processing Services
N.A.I.C.S.: 522320

Listen Japan, Inc. (1)
3-25-18 Shibuya, Shibuya-ku, Tokyo, 150-0002, Japan
Tel.: (81) 343634141
Web Site: http://www.listenjapan.jp
Sales Range: $25-49.9 Million
Emp.: 20
Music Downloads Sales
N.A.I.C.S.: 512230

Marketswitch Japan KK (1)
3-25-18 Shibuya, Shibuya-ku, Tokyo, 150-0002, Japan
Tel.: (81) 3 6418 1980
Business Consulting Services
N.A.I.C.S.: 541611

NetMile, Inc. (1)
3F Toranomon 372 Building 3-7-2 Toranomon, Minato-ku, Tokyo, 105-0001, Japan
Tel.: (81) 352113110
Web Site: https://www.netmile.co.jp
Sales Range: $25-49.9 Million
Emp.: 30
Computer Programming Services
N.A.I.C.S.: 541511

Nielsen Co., Ltd. (1)
11th floor Akasaka Tameike Tower 2-17-7 Akasaka, Minato-ku, Tokyo, 107-0052, Japan
Tel.: (81) 368376500
Web Site: https://www.netratings.co.jp
Internet Audience Surveys
N.A.I.C.S.: 541910

Ookbee Co., Ltd. (1)
Noble Pattanakan Village 1104 / 207-209 Pattanakan Road, Suan Luang Subdistrict Suan Luang District, Bangkok, 10250, Thailand
Tel.: (66) 21872222
Web Site: https://www.ookbee.com
Book Publishers
N.A.I.C.S.: 513130

PT. transcosmos Commerce (1)
Atria Sudirman Building 21st floor JI Jenderal Sudirman, No Kav 33A RT 3/RW 2 Karet Tengsin Kecamatan Tanah Abang, Jakarta Pusat, 10220, Indonesia
Tel.: (62) 81223454219
BPO Services
N.A.I.C.S.: 561990
Naoto Osada (CEO)

PT. transcosmos Indonesia (1)
RDTX Tower lt 7 JI E-IV No 6 JI Kuningan Barat Raya No 2 RT 5/RW 2, Kuningan East Kuningan Setiabudi, South Jakarta, 12940, Jakarta, Indonesia
Tel.: (62) 2129652345
BPO Services
N.A.I.C.S.: 561990

RaBlock Co., Ltd. (1)
Win Aoyama 942 2-2-15 Minami-Aoyama, Minato-ku, Tokyo, 107-0062, Japan
Tel.: (81) 334087688
Web Site: https://rablock.co.jp
Block Chain Development Services
N.A.I.C.S.: 541511
Yoshihide Nagase (CTO)

Sankei Human Learning Co., Ltd. (1)
Nishi-Shinjuku Prime Square 7-5-25, Nishi-Shinjuku Shinjuku-ku, Tokyo, 160-0023, Japan
Tel.: (81) 363880110
Web Site: https://human.sankei.co.jp
Foreign Language School Business Services
N.A.I.C.S.: 611630

Skylight Consulting Inc. (1)
Akasaka Tameike Tower 2-17-7 Akasaka, Minato-ku, Tokyo, 107-0052, Japan
Tel.: (81) 335601480
Web Site: https://www.skylight.co.jp
Sales Range: $25-49.9 Million
Emp.: 163
Business Consulting Services
N.A.I.C.S.: 541611
Toshiki Habutsu (Pres)

Social Gear Pte. Ltd. (1)
66A Tras Street, Singapore, 079005, Singapore
Tel.: (65) 62244265
Web Site: http://www.social-gear.jp
Marketing Consulting Services
N.A.I.C.S.: 541613
Shunsuke Sato (Founder & CEO)

Soft Space Sdn. Bhd. (1)
Q Sentral Level 15 Unit 15-15 2A Jalan Stesen Sentral 2, Kuala Lumpur Sentral, 50470, Kuala Lumpur, Malaysia
Tel.: (60) 374941222
Financial Technology Services
N.A.I.C.S.: 523940

TT Human Asset Service Corporation (1)
Shin-Kawasaki Twin Tower WEST TOWER 24F 1-1-2 Kashimada, Saiwai-ku, Kawasaki, 212-8604, Kanagawa, Japan
Tel.: (81) 5068654733
Web Site: https://www.trans-cosmos.co.jp
Emp.: 121
Human Resource Consulting Services
N.A.I.C.S.: 541612

TT Process Management Inc. (1)
2-8-12 Shin-Yokohama, Kohoku-ku, Yokohama, 222-0033, Japan
Tel.: (81) 454702911
BPO Services
N.A.I.C.S.: 561990

Takashimaya Transcosmos International Commerce Pte. Ltd. (1)
63 Chulia Street 15-01 OCBC Centre East, Singapore, 049514, Singapore
Tel.: (65) 62216001
Web Site: https://www.takatrans.com
Financial Technology Services
N.A.I.C.S.: 523940

Team Lab Inc. (1)
Ogawamachi Shinko Building 2-12 Kanda Ogawamachi, Chiyoda-ku, Tokyo, 101-0052, Japan
Tel.: (81) 358042356
Web Site: https://www.team-lab.com
Sales Range: $25-49.9 Million
Emp.: 200
Computer Programming Services
N.A.I.C.S.: 541511

Transcosmos (Malaysia) Sdn. Bhd. (1)
Level 20 No 211 Menara Shell Jalan Tun Sambanthan, 50470, Kuala Lumpur, Malaysia
Tel.: (60) 327336790
BPO Services
N.A.I.C.S.: 561990
Toshio Tozaki (Mng Dir)

Transcosmos (Thailand) Co., Ltd. (1)
Exchange Tower 37th Floor 388 Sukhumvit Road, Klongtoey Klongtoey, Bangkok, 10110, Thailand
Tel.: (66) 26130600
Web Site: https://www.trans-cosmos.co.th
Sales Range: $25-49.9 Million
Emp.: 170
Marketing & Call Center Services
N.A.I.C.S.: 541613

Transcosmos America Inc. (1)
879 W 190th St Ste 410, Gardena, CA 90248
Tel.: (310) 630-0072
Web Site: https://transcosmos.com
Marketing Management Services
N.A.I.C.S.: 541613

Subsidiary (Domestic):

Digital Operative, Inc. (2)
404 Camino del Rio S Ste 200, San Diego, CA 92110
Tel.: (619) 795-0630
Web Site: https://www.digitaloperative.com
Sales Range: $1-9.9 Million
Emp.: 24
Advertising & Marketing Services
N.A.I.C.S.: 541810
B. J. Cook (Co-Founder & CEO)

Transcosmos Analytics Inc. (1)
Sunshine 60 15F 3-1-1 Higashi-Ikebukuro, Toshima-ku, Tokyo, 170-6015, Japan
Tel.: (81) 343630210
Web Site: https://www.trans-cosmos.jp
Analytic Services
N.A.I.C.S.: 518210

Transcosmos Business Service Outsourcing (Dalian) Co., Ltd. (1)
501B 24th Building Software Park, No 44 Software Park East Road, Dalian, China
Tel.: (86) 411 8473 6660
Office Supplies Distr
N.A.I.C.S.: 424120

Transcosmos Business Service Outsourcing Suzhou Co., Ltd. (1)
3F No 68 Jixian Street, Suzhou Industrial Park, Suzhou, 215123, Jiangsu, China
Tel.: (86) 51269568900
Web Site: https://www.trans-cosmos-bpochina.com
Emp.: 249
BPO Services
N.A.I.C.S.: 561990

Transcosmos CRM Miyazaki Inc. (1)
1-16-1 Aoshima, Miyazaki, 889-2162, Japan
Tel.: (81) 985651500
Web Site: http://www.tci-crm.jp
Call Center Services
N.A.I.C.S.: 561422

Transcosmos Field Marketing Inc. (1)
3-22-7 Yoyogi Shinjuku Bunka Quint Building 13F, Shibuya-ku, Tokyo, 151-0053, Japan

Tel.: (81) 353547220
Web Site: https://www.tcpartners.co.jp
Sales Range: $25-49.9 Million
Emp.: 200
Call Center Services
N.A.I.C.S.: 561422

Transcosmos Information Creative (China) Co., Ltd. (1)
No 9 Kaihua Road, Huayuan Industrial Zone High-tech Zone, Tianjin, 300384, China
Tel.: (86) 2283710681
Web Site: https://www.trans-cosmos.com.cn
Professional & Management Development Training Services
N.A.I.C.S.: 611430

Transcosmos Information Creative Japan Inc. (1)
2-28-5 Nishigotanda 6F Okura Building 2, Shinagawa-ku, Tokyo, 141-0031, Japan
Tel.: (81) 368931700
Emp.: 250
Professional & Management Development Training Services
N.A.I.C.S.: 611430

Transcosmos Information Systems Limited (1)
Challenge House Sherwood Dr, Bletchley, Milton Keynes, MK3 6DP, United Kingdom
Tel.: (44) 1280824331
Web Site: https://transcosmos.co.uk
Information Technology & Services
N.A.I.C.S.: 541511

Transcosmos Korea Inc. (1)
3F Yongsan Building 44-3 Hangang- ro 2 ga, Seoul, 135-934, Korea (South)
Tel.: (82) 27908106
Web Site: https://www.trans-cosmos.co.kr
Sales Range: $800-899.9 Million
Emp.: 5,000
Direct Mail & IT Solution Services
N.A.I.C.S.: 541860
Kwon Sang Chuel *(Pres & COO)*

Transcosmos Logicall Inc. (1)
1133 Chino Roces Ave Corner Metropolitan Ave, Makati, 1203, Manila, Philippines
Tel.: (63) 2 8603663
Sales Range: $25-49.9 Million
Emp.: 120
Call Center Services
N.A.I.C.S.: 561422

Transcosmos OmniConnect, LLC (1)
879 W 190th St Ste 410, Gardena, CA 90248
Tel.: (310) 630-0072
Web Site: https://www.transcosmos.com
BPO Services
N.A.I.C.S.: 561990
Shinichi S. Nagakura *(CEO & Chm)*

Transcosmos Taiwan Inc. (1)
TEL-5 7th Floor No 188 Section 5 Nanjing East Road, Songshan District, Taipei, Taiwan
Tel.: (886) 227511560
BPO Services
N.A.I.C.S.: 561990

Transcosmos Technologies Inc. (1)
8F Yokohama West Exit KN Building 2-8-4 Kitasai, Nishi-ku, Yokohama, 220-0004, Kanagawa, Japan
Tel.: (81) 453135539
Web Site: https://www.trans-cosmos-digtec.co.jp
Sales Range: $50-74.9 Million
Emp.: 270
Website Hosting Services
N.A.I.C.S.: 518210

Vaimo AB (1)
Master Samuelsgatan 36, 111 57, Stockholm, Sweden
Tel.: (46) 84522650
Ecommerce Services
N.A.I.C.S.: 541870
David Holender *(Co-Founder & CEO)*

Web-Star Japan Co., Ltd. (1)
1-8-8 Ginza Tokyo Mikami AL Building 3F, Chuo-ku, Tokyo, 104-0061, Japan
Tel.: (81) 355245391
Web Site: https://www.webstarjapan.com
Sales Range: $25-49.9 Million
Emp.: 30
Computer Programming Services

N.A.I.C.S.: 541511
Jun Okawa *(Pres & CEO)*

transcosmos Asia Philippines, Inc. (1)
32F One Corporate Center Meralco Ave Cor Julia Vargas Ave, Ortigas Center, Pasig, 1605, Philippines
Tel.: (63) 26261400
BPO Services
N.A.I.C.S.: 561990
Mary Grace Parilla Quinones *(Ops Mgr)*

transcosmos Technologic Arts Co., Ltd. (1)
15th Floor TTC Tower 253 Hoang Van Thu Street, Ward 2 Tan Binh, Ho Chi Minh City, Vietnam
Tel.: (84) 2839201276
Web Site: https://www.trans-tech.vn
Emp.: 110
Information Technology & Services
N.A.I.C.S.: 541511
Nguyen Hong Phuc *(Mgr-HR)*

transcosmos Vietnam Co., Ltd. (1)
20th Floor VTC Online Tower 18 Tam Trinh Street, Hai Ba Trung District, Hanoi, Vietnam
Tel.: (84) 438622288
BPO Services
N.A.I.C.S.: 561990
Yohei Komura *(Gen Dir)*

TRANSCU LTD.
50 Raffles Quay 45-01/02 Singapore Land Tower, Singapore, 48623, Singapore
Tel.: (65) 65322533
Emp.: 50
Pharmaceutical & Cosmetics Distr
N.A.I.C.S.: 424210

Subsidiaries:

TTI Ellebeau, Inc. (1)
4-8-8 Higashi Shinagawa, Shinagawa-ku, Tokyo, 140-0002, Japan
Tel.: (81) 367449640
Web Site: http://www.ellebeau.com
Cosmetics Mfr
N.A.I.C.S.: 325620

TRANSEASTERN POWER TRUST
181 Bay Street Suite 1800, Toronto, M5J 2T9, ON, Canada
Tel.: (647) 987-7663 ON
Web Site: http://www.transeastern.com
Year Founded: 2014
Sales Range: Less than $1 Million
Hydroelectric Power Generation Investment Trust
N.A.I.C.S.: 525910

TRANSENSE TECHNOLOGIES PLC
1 Landscape Close Weston-On-The-Green, Bicester, OX25 3SX, Oxfordshire, United Kingdom
Tel.: (44) 1869238380
Web Site: https://www.transense.com
Year Founded: 1991
TRT—(AIM)
Rev.: $3,573,519
Assets: $5,103,669
Liabilities: $905,599
Net Worth: $4,198,070
Earnings: $1,190,720
Emp.: 16
Fiscal Year-end: 06/30/22
Automotive Sensors Mfr
N.A.I.C.S.: 336390
Melvyn Segal *(CFO)*

TRANSFAR GROUP CO., LTD.
Xiaoshan Economic & Technological Development Zone, Hangzhou, China
Tel.: (86) 571 82602688
Web Site: http://www.etransfar.com
Year Founded: 1986

Emp.: 12,000
Holding Company; Specialty Chemical Mfr
N.A.I.C.S.: 551112
Guanju Xu *(Founder, Chm & Pres)*

Subsidiaries:

Transfar Zhilian Co., Ltd. (1)
Xiaoshan Economy & Technology Development Zone, Hangzhou, 311215, Zhejiang, China
Tel.: (86) 57183783068
Web Site: https://www.transfarchem.com
Rev.: $5,194,479,565
Assets: $5,771,061,424
Liabilities: $3,187,622,913
Net Worth: $2,583,438,512
Earnings: $104,576,196
Fiscal Year-end: 12/31/2022
Chemical Products Mfr
N.A.I.C.S.: 325199
Zhou Jiahai *(Chm & Gen Mgr)*

Subsidiary (Non-US):

Tanatex Chemicals BV (2)
Einsteinstraat 1-11, PO Box 46, 6710 BA, Ede, Netherlands
Tel.: (31) 318670911
Web Site: http://www.tanatexchemicals.com
Chemical Product Mfr & Distr
N.A.I.C.S.: 325998
Marco de Koning *(CEO)*

Subsidiary (Non-US):

NEW TANATEX S.p.A. (3)
Via della Mosa 6, 20017, Milan, Italy
Tel.: (39) 02 9392341
Web Site: http://www.newtanatex.com
Chemical Products Distr
N.A.I.C.S.: 424690

TANATEX Chemicals (Thailand) Co., Ltd. (3)
Hemaraj Eastern Seaboard I E 500/107 Moo 2 Tambol Tasit, Amphur Pluakdaeng, Rayong, Thailand
Tel.: (66) 33010460
Web Site: http://www.tanatexchemicals.com
Chemical Products Distr
N.A.I.C.S.: 424690

TANATEX Chemicals Argentina SA. (3)
M Lezica 3045 Piso 1, San Isidro, B1642GJA, Buenos Aires, Argentina
Tel.: (54) 1155501601
Web Site: http://www.tanatexchemicals.com
Chemical Products Distr
N.A.I.C.S.: 424690
Giselle Pisano *(Mgr-Fin & Acctg)*

TANATEX Chemicals Hong Kong Limited (3)
Unit 2605 26/F Skyline Tower 39 Wang Kwong Road, Kowloon Bay, Kowloon, China (Hong Kong)
Tel.: (852) 27630061
Web Site: http://www.tanatexchemicals.com
Chemical Products Distr
N.A.I.C.S.: 424690
Gillen Yuen *(Mgr-Brand & Retail)*

TANATEX Chemicals Iberica, S.L.U. (3)
World Trade Center Moll de Barcelona s/n Edifici NORD 4a Planta, 08039, Barcelona, Spain
Tel.: (34) 93 481 33 22
Web Site: http://www.tanatexchemicals.com
Chemical Products Distr
N.A.I.C.S.: 424690
Charles Alex *(Mng Dir)*

TANATEX Chemicals India Private Limited (3)
ACE Business Centre 401 4th Floor Gokul Nagar LBS Road, Thane, 400 601, India
Tel.: (91) 22 4129 2020
Web Site: http://www.tanatexchemicals.com
Chemical Products Distr
N.A.I.C.S.: 424690
Pradeep Karhade *(Dir)*

TANATEX Chemicals Japan K.K. (3)
3-10 Kawaramachi 2-chome Kawaramachi Chuo Building 3F, Chuo-ku, Osaka, 541-0048, Japan

Tel.: (81) 662286213
Web Site: http://www.tanatexchemicals.com
Chemical Products Distr
N.A.I.C.S.: 424690

TANATEX Chemicals Trading (Shanghai) Co., Ltd. (3)
RM 701-704 Wuzhong Business Building No 1099 Wuzhong Road, Shanghai, 201103, China
Tel.: (86) 2161271988
Web Site: http://tanatexchemicals.com
Chemical Products Distr
N.A.I.C.S.: 424690

TRANSFIN-M OJSC
34 Mashi Poryvaevoy street, 107078, Moscow, Russia
Tel.: (7) 4994180404
Web Site: http://www.transfin-m.ru
TRFM—(MOEX)
Sales Range: Less than $1 Million
Residential Property Management Services
N.A.I.C.S.: 531311
Maksim Anishchenkov *(Gen Dir)*

TRANSFORM EXPLORATION PTY LTD.
Level 1 373 Rokeby Road, Subiaco, 6011, WA, Australia
Tel.: (61) 861453010
Web Site: http://www.transformex.com.au
Oil & Gas Exploration Services
N.A.I.C.S.: 211120
Agu J. Kantsler *(Mng Dir)*

TRANSFORMA RESOURCES CORP.
9th Floor - 570 Granville Street, Vancouver, V6C 1T1, BC, Canada
Tel.: (604) 682-3701
Web Site: http://www.cresval.com
Year Founded: 2004
TFM—(DEU)
Assets: $193,612
Liabilities: $392,848
Net Worth: ($199,237)
Earnings: $88,995
Fiscal Year-end: 12/31/22
Metal Mining Services
N.A.I.C.S.: 212290
Douglas Yee *(CFO-Interim & Sec)*

TRANSFORMATEUR FEDERAL LTEE.
5059 Boul St Jean Baptiste, Montreal, H1B 5V3, QC, Canada
Tel.: (514) 640-5059
Web Site: http://www.transfed.ca
Year Founded: 1963
Sales Range: $10-24.9 Million
Signage & Display Media Distr & Services
N.A.I.C.S.: 423690
Pierre Venne *(Mgr-Pur)*

TRANSFORMERS & RECTIFIERS INDIA LTD
Survey No 427 P-3-4 & 431 P-1-2 Sarkhej-Bavla Highway, Moraiya Village Sanand Dist, Ahmedabad, 382213, Gujarat, India
Tel.: (91) 2717661661
Web Site: https://www.infinityads.in
532928—(BOM)
Rev.: $166,537,977
Assets: $142,159,523
Liabilities: $94,096,937
Net Worth: $48,062,586
Earnings: $5,077,058
Emp.: 538
Fiscal Year-end: 03/31/23
Transformer Mfr
N.A.I.C.S.: 334416
Jitendra U. Mamtora *(Chm)*

TRANSFORMERS & RECTIFIERS INDIA LTD

Transformers & Rectifiers India Ltd—(Continued)

Subsidiaries:

Savas Engineering Company Private Limited (1)
498 Changodhar, Radhe Industrial estate Village Sanand, Ahmedabad, 382213, Gujarat, India
Tel.: (91) 8238080274
Web Site: https://www.savasengg.com
Emp.: 64
Vacuum Product Mfr
N.A.I.C.S.: 333310
Sunil Jain (CEO)

Transpares Limited (1)
Plot No-14-15 Sarkhej-Bavala Highway Village P O, Ashwamegh Industrial Estate Changodar Sanand, Ahmedabad, 382213, Gujarat, India
Tel.: (91) 8037402508
Web Site: http://www.transpares.co.in
Emp.: 130
Eminent Radiator Mfr & Retailer
N.A.I.C.S.: 333414
Hitendra M. Doshi (Mng Dir)

TRANSGAZ S.A.

Piata C I Motas Nr 1, 551130, Medias, Sibiu, Romania
Tel.: (40) 269803333
Web Site: https://www.transgaz.ro
Year Founded: 2000
TGN—(BUC)
Rev.: $725,855,934
Assets: $1,737,828,867
Liabilities: $851,065,817
Net Worth: $886,763,050
Earnings: $79,441,122
Emp.: 4,145
Fiscal Year-end: 12/31/22
Gas Transmission Services
N.A.I.C.S.: 221210
Emil Florin Cosma (Dir-Exploitation & Maintenance Div)

TRANSGENE BIOTEK LTD.

69 70 IDA Bollaram, Sangareddy District, Medak, 502 325, Telangana, India
Tel.: (91) 8458279103
Web Site: https://www.transgenebiotek.com
526139—(BOM)
Rev.: $27,633
Assets: $17,068,307
Liabilities: $15,705,223
Net Worth: $1,363,084
Earnings: ($720,412)
Fiscal Year-end: 03/31/23
Pharmaceuticals Product Mfr
N.A.I.C.S.: 325412
K. Koteswara Rao (Chm & Mng Dir)

TRANSGLOBE FOODS LIMITED

Office No G 191 Ground Floor Raghuleela Mega Mall Behind Poisar Depot, Kandivali West, Mumbai, 400067, India
Tel.: (91) 8097095677
Web Site: https://www.transglobefoods.com
Year Founded: 1986
519367—(BOM)
Rev.: $21,605
Assets: $35,322
Liabilities: $41,688
Net Worth: ($6,367)
Earnings: ($2,074)
Emp.: 5
Fiscal Year-end: 03/31/23
Food Products Mfr
N.A.I.C.S.: 311999
Prabhakar Khakhar (Chm & Mng Dir)

TRANSGLOBE LIFE INSURANCE INC.

238 Jian Guo N Rd Sec 2, Zhong-Shan District, Taipei, 10484, Taiwan
Tel.: (886) 223707270
Web Site: http://www.transglobe.com.tw
Year Founded: 2001
Sales Range: $125-149.9 Million
Emp.: 500
Life Insurance Products
N.A.I.C.S.: 524113
James H.C. Liu (Chm)

TRANSGROUP AS, LTD.

6 Building 2 Dokuchaev Pereulok, 107078, Moscow, Russia
Tel.: (7) 495 777 2755   RU
Freight Forwarding Services & Railway Services
N.A.I.C.S.: 541614
Victor Sukhorukov (Gen Dir)

Subsidiaries:

JSC RailTransAuto (1)
6 Building 2 Dokuchaev Pereulok, 107078, Moscow, Russia (49%)
Tel.: (7) 495 777 02 55
Web Site: http://www.railtransauto.ru
Motor Vehicle Rail Transportation Services
N.A.I.C.S.: 482111

TRANSILVANIA BROKER DE ASIGURARE S.A.

Str Calea Moldovei Nr 13, Jud Bistrita-Nasaud, 420096, Bistrita, Romania
Tel.: (40) 263235900
Web Site: https://www.transilvaniabroker.ro
TBK—(BUC)
Rev.: $24,222,978
Assets: $6,465,965
Liabilities: $3,913,349
Net Worth: $2,552,616
Earnings: $1,643,388
Emp.: 43
Fiscal Year-end: 12/31/23
Insurance Brokerage Services
N.A.I.C.S.: 524210
Ion Cotiac (Exec Dir)

TRANSILVANIA INVESTMENTS ALLIANCE S.A.

2 Nicolae Iorga Street, 500057, Brasov, 500057, Romania
Tel.: (40) 268415529
Web Site: https://transilvaniainvestments.ro
SIF3—(BUC)
Rev.: $65,628,480
Assets: $327,453,040
Liabilities: $32,732,819
Net Worth: $294,720,221
Earnings: $8,699,381
Emp.: 43
Fiscal Year-end: 12/31/20
Investment Services
N.A.I.C.S.: 523999

Subsidiaries:

Mecanica Codlea SA (1)
Str Rampei nr1, Brasov, 505100, Codlea, Romania
Tel.: (40) 268254200
Web Site: https://www.mecod.ro
Agricultural Machinery & Equipment Mfr
N.A.I.C.S.: 333922

Sembraz SA (1)
Str Henri Coanda Nr 12, 550234, Sibiu, Romania
Tel.: (40) 369409926
Web Site: https://www.sembraz.ro
Agricultural Machinery & Equipment Mfr
N.A.I.C.S.: 333922

Tratament Balnear Buzias S.A. (1)
12 Avram Iancu Street, Timis County, 305100, Buzias, Romania
Tel.: (40) 747111316
Web Site: https://www.buzias.ro
Hotel & Resort Management Services
N.A.I.C.S.: 721110

Turism, Hoteluri, Restaurante Marea Neagra S.A. (1)
Str Lavrion nr 29 Statiunea Saturn, Judetul Constanta, 905500, Mangalia, Romania
Tel.: (40) 241752452
Web Site: https://www.thrmareaneagra.ro
Hotel & Resort Management Services
N.A.I.C.S.: 721110

Tusnad SA (1)
Str Garii nr 599, Harghita, 537336, Baile Tusnad, Romania
Tel.: (40) 266334091
Web Site: https://www.tusnad.ro
Mineral Water Bottle Mfr & Distr
N.A.I.C.S.: 312112

Utilaj Greu S.A. (1)
Murfatlar Str Ciocirliei nr1 Jud, Constanta, Romania
Tel.: (40) 241234395
Web Site: https://www.utilaj-greu.ro
Construction Equipment Rental Services
N.A.I.C.S.: 532412

TRANSILVANIA LEASING & CREDIT IFN S.A.

Centrul de Afaceri Cristiana B-dul Eroilor Nr 3A mezanin, Brasov, Romania
Tel.: (40) 268315172
Web Site: https://www.transilvanialeasing.ro
Year Founded: 1977
TSLA—(BUC)
Sales Range: Less than $1 Million
Financial Lending Services
N.A.I.C.S.: 533110
Sorin Donca (Gen Mgr)

TRANSIMEX CORPORATION

Floor 9-10, 172 Hai Ba Trung Street Dakao Ward District 1, Ho Chi Minh City, Vietnam
Tel.: (84) 822202888
Web Site: https://transimex.com.vn
Year Founded: 1983
TMS—(HOSE)
Rev.: $98,460,502
Assets: $309,545,570
Liabilities: $113,077,149
Net Worth: $196,468,421
Earnings: $7,129,660
Emp.: 1,435
Fiscal Year-end: 12/31/23
Logistic Services
N.A.I.C.S.: 541614
Bui Tuan Ngoc (Chm-Mgmt Bd)

Subsidiaries:

Transimex Hi Tech Park Logistics Co., Ltd. (1)
Lot BT Road D2 Saigon Hi Tech Park, Tang Nhon Phu B Ward Dist 9, Ho Chi Minh City, Vietnam
Tel.: (84) 2837206666
Logistic Services
N.A.I.C.S.: 541614

Transimex Property Company Ltd. (1)
172 Hai Ba Trung, Dakao Ward Dist 1, Ho Chi Minh City, Vietnam
Tel.: (84) 2822202882
Real Estate Services
N.A.I.C.S.: 531210

TRANSINTRA GMBH

Schlachte 3-5, 28195, Bremen, Germany
Tel.: (49) 421175880
Web Site: http://www.transintra.de
Year Founded: 1977
Rev.: $17,932,200
Emp.: 20
Transport Logistic & Customer Focused Service
N.A.I.C.S.: 541614
Pascal Bretthauer (Mng Dir)

INTERNATIONAL PUBLIC

Subsidiaries:

Transintra Shipping and Forwarding Sp. z o.o. (1)
Ul Bulwar Beniowskiego 5, 70-642, Szczecin, Poland
Tel.: (48) 914624355
Logistics Consulting Servies
N.A.I.C.S.: 541614

TRANSINVESTMENT SPV

Sofia Silistra St No 8, 1527, Sofia, Bulgaria
Tel.: (359) 24960020
Web Site: https://www.transinvestment.bg
TRIV—(BUL)
Sales Range: Less than $1 Million
Investment Services
N.A.I.C.S.: 523999

TRANSIT SUPPORT SERVICES LTD.

26 Oshodi Apapa Expressway, Lagos, Nigeria
Tel.: (234) 12901693   NG
Web Site: http://www.transitsupports.com
Year Founded: 2007
Transportation Services
N.A.I.C.S.: 485999
Dave Chukwudulue (Gen Mgr)

TRANSITION EVERGREEN

6 Square de l'Opéra Louis Jouvet, 75009, Paris, France
Tel.: (33) 18916610
Web Site: https://www.transition-evergreen.com
Year Founded: 1985
EGR—(EUR)
Sound Equipment Distr
N.A.I.C.S.: 423620
Jacques Pierrelee (CEO)

Subsidiaries:

90 Degrees North, Inc. (1)
502/503/509 Emerald Court Bldg 54 Road 3 Project 6, Quezon City, Philippines
Tel.: (63) 23980356
Web Site: http://www.90northmedia.com
Telecommunication Equipment Distr
N.A.I.C.S.: 423690
John Achilles Denna (Pres & CEO)

Ace Medias Tools JSC (1)
9 rue de l'echelle, 75001, Paris, France
Tel.: (33) 144820057
Web Site: http://www.acemediastools.fr
Broadcast Software & Web Application Services
N.A.I.C.S.: 516120

Ade Corporation (1)
4 Fl No 336 Chien-Kuo S Road Sec 1, Taipei, 106, Taiwan
Tel.: (886) 227077707
Web Site: http://www.ade.com.tw
Telecommunication Equipment Distr
N.A.I.C.S.: 423690
Michael Yu (Founder & Chm)

Audio Pro Heilbronn Elektroakustik GmbH (1)
Pfaffenstrasse 25, 74078, Heilbronn, Germany
Tel.: (49) 71312636400
Web Site: http://www.audiopro.de
Broadcasting Equipment Mfr
N.A.I.C.S.: 334220

Audiopole JSC (1)
22 rue Edouard Buffard Z A C de la, Charbonniere Montevrain, 77771, Marne-la-Vallee, Cedex, France
Tel.: (33) 160543200
Web Site: http://www.audiopole.net
Audio Visual Equipment Distr
N.A.I.C.S.: 449210

Bionics Corporation Ltd. (1)
Hurstwood Grange Hurstwood Lane, Haywards Heath, RH17 7QX, West Sussex, United Kingdom

Tel.: (44) 1444473999
Web Site: http://www.bionics.co.uk
Software Technology Services
N.A.I.C.S.: 541512
Dan McQuillin (Mng Dir)

Broadcast Hungary Kft. (1)
Ujvilag u 15, 1145, Budapest, Hungary
Tel.: (36) 205850003
Broadcasting Equipment Distr
N.A.I.C.S.: 423690
Kristof Toth (Mng Dir)

Concilium Technologies (Pty) Ltd. (1)
1 Stanford Office Park 12 Bauhinia Street Highveld Technopark, Centurion, Pretoria, 0157, South Africa
Tel.: (27) 126789200
Web Site: http://www.concilium.co.za
Broadcasting Equipment Distr
N.A.I.C.S.: 423690
Alan Mendes (Sr Acct Mgr)

Crosspoint S.A.L (1)
Po Marques de Monistrol 7 - 2 Dcha, 28011, Madrid, Spain
Tel.: (34) 915474867
Web Site: http://www.crosspoint.es
Audio Visual Equipment Distr
N.A.I.C.S.: 449210

Digigram Asia Pte Ltd (1)
60 Albert Street 09-11 Og Albert Complex, Singapore, 189969, Singapore
Tel.: (65) 62912234
Sound Equipment Distr
N.A.I.C.S.: 423690

Gbs Alliance Pte Ltd. (1)
159 Sin Ming Road 04-07 Lobby 2 Amtech Building, Singapore, 575625, Singapore
Tel.: (65) 64549233
Web Site: http://www.gbsalliance.com
Audio Visual Consulting Services
N.A.I.C.S.: 512290
Y. C. Tan (Founder & Mng Dir)

High Grade Technologies & Energy Systems Nigeria Ltd. (1)
Suite C10 J-Plus Plaza No 39 Jimmy Carter Street, Asokoro, Abuja, Nigeria
Tel.: (234) 35912470
Web Site: http://www.highgradetech.com
Broadcasting Equipment Distr
N.A.I.C.S.: 423690
Ahmed Agberankhe (CEO)

Ivamod D.O.O. (1)
Kneza Mislava 5, 10410, Velika Gorica, Croatia
Tel.: (385) 16226400
Web Site: http://www.ivamod.hr
Broadcasting Equipment Distr
N.A.I.C.S.: 423690

Media Utilities B.V (1)
Kweekgrasstraat 30, 1313 BX, Almere, Netherlands
Tel.: (31) 367501430
Web Site: http://www.media-utilities.nl
Audio Visual Equipment Distr
N.A.I.C.S.: 449210

Omniwave Ltd. (1)
10 Polemiston Str, Lykovrysi-Pefki, 141 23, Athens, Greece
Tel.: (30) 2102834000
Web Site: http://www.omniwave.gr
Broadcasting & Telecommunication System Equipment Distr
N.A.I.C.S.: 423690
Nectarios Labadarios (Owner)

Pantalha, Lda. (1)
Rua Cidade de Lobito 267A, 1800-088, Lisbon, Portugal
Tel.: (351) 217543640
Web Site: http://www.pantalha.pt
Audio Visual Equipment Distr
N.A.I.C.S.: 449210
Bonifacio Ribeiro (CEO)

Profi Audio Sp. Z O O (1)
ul Zeganska 1 Budynek ABB, 04-713, Warsaw, Poland
Tel.: (48) 607205073
Broadcasting Equipment Distr
N.A.I.C.S.: 423690

Radikal Ltd. (1)
Ihlamur-Yildiz Cad Kessaf Sok No 4/12, Besiktas, 34353, Istanbul, Turkiye
Tel.: (90) 2122597971
Web Site: http://www.radikaltr.com
Audio Visual Equipment Distr
N.A.I.C.S.: 449210

Sca Sound Solutions Co. (1)
1-29-2 Nishihara, Shibuya-ku, Tokyo, 151-0066, Japan
Tel.: (81) 333723661
Web Site: http://www.ss.sc-a.jp
Broadcasting Equipment Distr
N.A.I.C.S.: 423690

Slg Broadcast Ag (1)
Poststrasse 5, 8105, Regensdorf, Switzerland
Tel.: (41) 445332260
Web Site: http://www.slgbroadcast.com
Broadcasting Equipment Distr
N.A.I.C.S.: 423690

Sonotechnique Pjl Inc. (1)
200 Gince Street, Montreal, H4N 2W6, QC, Canada
Tel.: (514) 332-6868
Web Site: http://www.sonotechnique.ca
Audio Visual Equipment Distr
N.A.I.C.S.: 449210
Patrice Delhaes (Pres)

Soundfox International Co., Ltd. (1)
Rm 524 Ion Square 188 Wiryegwangjangro, Songpa-gu, Seoul, 05849, Korea (South)
Tel.: (82) 7070193725
Web Site: http://www.soundfox.co.kr
Broadcasting Equipment Distr
N.A.I.C.S.: 423690
Peter Youngsuk Moh (CEO)

Soundware Denmark A/S (1)
Nybrovej 99, Gentofte, 2820, Copenhagen, Denmark
Tel.: (45) 45968890
Web Site: http://www.soundware.dk
Broadcasting Equipment Distr
N.A.I.C.S.: 423690
William Dion (Sls Mgr)

Soundware Norge As (1)
Brynsveien 18C, 0667, Oslo, Norway
Tel.: (47) 23400400
Web Site: http://www.no.soundware.shop
Audio Visual Equipment Distr
N.A.I.C.S.: 449210

Synthax Inc. (1)
6600 NW 16th St Ste 10, Fort Lauderdale, FL 33313
Tel.: (754) 206-4220
Audio Visual Equipment Distr
N.A.I.C.S.: 449210
Mathias Von Heydekampf (Mng Dir)

Tv Tools Oy (1)
Italahdenkatu 15-17, 00210, Helsinki, Finland
Tel.: (358) 95259700
Web Site: http://www.tvtools.fi
Emp.: 40
Medical Software Development Services
N.A.I.C.S.: 513210
Mikko Kujala (CEO)

TRANSITION METALS CORP.
9C 1351 Kelly Lake Road, Sudbury, P3E 5P5, ON, Canada
Tel.: (705) 669-1777   ON
Web Site:
   https://www.transitionmetalscorp.com
Year Founded: 2009
XTM—(TSXV)
Sales Range: Less than $1 Million
Gold Mining
N.A.I.C.S.: 212220
Scott McLean (Pres & CEO)

TRANSITION SA
49 bis avenue Franklin Roosevelt, 75008, Paris, France
Web Site:
   https://www.spactransition.com
Year Founded: 2021
TRAN—(EUR)
Investment Management Service

N.A.I.C.S.: 523999
Xavier Caitucoli (CEO)

TRANSLATEMEDIA LTD.
1-11 Carteret Street, London, SW1H 9DJ, United Kingdom
Tel.: (44) 20 8834 4840   UK
Web Site:
   http://www.translatemedia.com
Emp.: 90
Language Translation Software & Services
N.A.I.C.S.: 541930
Rupert Evans (Mng Dir)

Subsidiaries:

Ralph Mcelroy & Associates, Ltd. (1)
504 Leewarker Ste 940, Austin, TX 78701
Tel.: (512) 472-6753
Web Site:
   http://www.mcelroytranslation.com
Sales Range: $1-9.9 Million
Emp.: 45
Translation & Interpretation Services
N.A.I.C.S.: 541930
Jennifer Cardenas (Dir-Production)

TranslateMedia Asia Ltd (1)
907 Silvercord Tower 2 30 Canton Road, Tsim Sha Tsui, Kowloon, China (Hong Kong)
Tel.: (852) 37537559
Translation & Interpretation Services
N.A.I.C.S.: 541930
Rachel Wang (Dir-Bus Dev)

TranslateMedia GmbH (1)
Zeltnerstr 1-3, 90443, Nuremberg, Germany
Tel.: (49) 8922061095
Web Site: http://www.translatemedia.com
Translation & Interpretation Services
N.A.I.C.S.: 541930

TranslateMedia Translation Services LLC (1)
27 W 24th St Ste 407, New York, NY 10010
Tel.: (212) 796-5636
Translation & Interpretation Services
N.A.I.C.S.: 541930
Anne Haerling (Sr Project Mgr)

TRANSMASHHOLDING JSC
10 Efremova St, 119048, Moscow, Russia
Tel.: (7) 4956608950
Web Site: http://tmh.global
Year Founded: 2002
Sales Range: Less than $1 Million
Railway Freight Transportation Services
N.A.I.C.S.: 488999
Sergo-Shakhzada Kurbanov (VP)

TRANSMETRO CORPORATION LIMITED
Suite 53 Level 3 330 Wattle Street, Ultimo, Sydney, 2007, NSW, Australia
Tel.: (61) 282173333   AU
Web Site:
   http://www.metrohotels.com.au
Year Founded: 1976
TCO—(ASX)
Rev.: $15,327,618
Assets: $27,694,866
Liabilities: $11,697,707
Net Worth: $15,997,159
Earnings: $1,308,542
Fiscal Year-end: 06/30/24
Investment Management Service
N.A.I.C.S.: 523940
John A. C. McEvoy (Chm & Mng Dir)

TRANSMILE AIR SERVICES SDN. BHD.
Transmile Centre Cargo Complex, Sultan Abdul Aziz Shah Airport, Subang Jaya, 47200, Selangor Darul Ehsan, Malaysia
Tel.: (60) 378849898   MY
Web Site: http://www.transmile.com

Year Founded: 1993
Sales Range: $50-74.9 Million
Emp.: 300
Air Freight Transportation & Chartering Services
N.A.I.C.S.: 481112
Krishasamy Rengasamy (Gen Mgr-Flight Ops)

Subsidiaries:

Transmile Air Services Sdn. Bhd. - Engineering Division (1)
Transmile Air Engineering Complex Lot 4060 AA/4/65, Sultan Abdul Aziz Shah Airport, 47200, Subang Jaya, Selangor Darul Ehsan, Malaysia
Tel.: (60) 378465066
Aircraft Maintenance, Repair & Engineering Services
N.A.I.C.S.: 488190

TRANSMISSION ENGINEERING INDUSTRIES LIMITED
B-14 Block-A SMCHS, Karachi, 74400, Pakistan
Tel.: (92) 21111000862
Web Site: http://www.transmission-eng.com
Year Founded: 1986
Sales Range: $1-9.9 Million
Transmission Components Mfr
N.A.I.C.S.: 336350

TRANSMISSORA ALIANCA DE ENERGIA ELETRICA S.A.
Praca Quinze de Novembro n 20 10 andar sala 1003 parte Centro, Rio de Janeiro, 20010-010, Brazil
Tel.: (55) 2122126000
Web Site: http://www.taesa.com.br
Sales Range: $150-199.9 Million
Electric Power Structure Management Services
N.A.I.C.S.: 221121
Djalma Bastos de Morais (Chm)

TRANSMIT ENTERTAINMENT LIMITED
Flat B 14/F Neich Tower 128 Gloucester Road, Wan Chai, Hong Kong, China (Hong Kong)
Tel.: (852) 2 180 9018   Ky
Web Site: http://www.transmit-ent.com
Year Founded: 2012
1326—(HKG)
Rev.: $58,942,312
Assets: $210,350,902
Liabilities: $178,130,667
Net Worth: $32,220,236
Earnings: $1,060,345
Emp.: 220
Fiscal Year-end: 06/30/21
Film Production
N.A.I.C.S.: 512110
Patrick Hin kwong Lee (Exec Dir)

Subsidiaries:

Chili Advertising & Promotions Limited (1)
1806 Westlands Center Westlands Road, Quarry Bay, China (Hong Kong)
Tel.: (852) 2 369 6883
Web Site: https://www.chilipromotions.com
Advertising Agency Services
N.A.I.C.S.: 541810

Cinema City (Chai Wan) Limited (1)
G/F to 4/F Wynn Plaza 333 Chai Wan Road, Chai Wan, China (Hong Kong)
Tel.: (852) 23600910
Web Site: https://www.cinemacity.com.hk
Motion Picture & Video Production Services
N.A.I.C.S.: 512110

Cinema City (Langham Place) Limited (1)
8-11/F Langham Place Shopping Centre 8

TRANSMIT ENTERTAINMENT LIMITED

Transmit Entertainment Limited—(Continued)
Argyle Street, Mong Kok, China (Hong Kong)
Tel.: (852) 23600910
Web Site: https://www.cinemacity.com.hk
Motion Picture & Video Production Services
N.A.I.C.S.: 512110

Cinema City (TW) Limited (1)
Shop 1036 Level 1 398 Castle Peak Road, Discovery Park Tsuen Wan, Tsuen Wan, China (Hong Kong)
Tel.: (852) 23600910
Web Site: https://www.cinemacity.com.hk
Motion Picture & Video Production Services
N.A.I.C.S.: 512110

Skywork Media Limited (1)
Unit 37 7/F Sino Industrial Plaza 9 Kai Cheung Road, Kowloon Bay, Kowloon, China (Hong Kong)
Tel.: (852) 31882036
Web Site: http://www.skyworkhk.com
Motion Picture & Video Production Services
N.A.I.C.S.: 512110
Jenny Wong (Mng Dir)

TRANSNATIONAL CANNABIS LTD
Suite 810 - 789 West Pender Street, Vancouver, V6C 1H2, BC, Canada
Tel.: (604) 687-2038 BC
Web Site:
  http://www.intlcannabiscorp.com
Year Founded: 2010
WLDCF—(OTCIQ)
Rev.: $14,313
Assets: $51,131,833
Liabilities: $5,070,972
Net Worth: $46,060,860
Earnings: ($44,204,710)
Fiscal Year-end: 02/28/19
Cannabinoid Extracts Mfr
N.A.I.C.S.: 111419

TRANSNATIONAL COMPANY KAZCHROME JSC
Tel.: (7) 132973388
Web Site: https://kazchrome.com
Year Founded: 1938
KZCR—(KAZ)
Rev.: $2,882,895,065
Assets: $3,439,087,764
Liabilities: $2,982,751,315
Net Worth: $456,336,450
Earnings: $1,086,518,112
Emp.: 19,987
Fiscal Year-end: 12/31/22
Metal Mining Services
N.A.I.C.S.: 212290
Sergey Prokopyev (Gen Dir)

TRANSNATIONAL CORPORATION OF NIGERIA PLC.
Transnational House 38 Glover Road, Ikoyi, Lagos, Nigeria
Tel.: (234) 8145652652 NG
Web Site:
  http://www.transcorpnigeria.com
Year Founded: 2004
TRANSCORP—(NIGE)
Rev.: $99,720,342
Assets: $327,687,786
Liabilities: $213,124,586
Net Worth: $114,563,200
Earnings: $12,464,729
Emp.: 1,391
Fiscal Year-end: 12/31/22
Hospitality Services
N.A.I.C.S.: 621491
Tony O. Elumelu (Chm)

Subsidiaries:

Transcorp Hotels Plc. (1)
1 Aguiyi Ironsi St, Abuja, 900001, Nigeria
Tel.: (234) 94613000
Web Site: https://www.transcorphotels.com
Rev.: $23,273,240
Assets: $89,184,511
Liabilities: $42,707,768

Net Worth: $46,476,742
Earnings: $1,937,760
Emp.: 1,224
Fiscal Year-end: 12/31/2022
Hotel Operator
N.A.I.C.S.: 721110
Irene Nwankwo (Head-Internal Audit)

TRANSNATIONAL DIVERSIFIED GROUP OF COMPANIES
The Penthouse Net Quad Building 4th Avenue Corner 30th Street, E-Square Crescent Park West Bonifacio Global City, Taguig, 1634, Philippines
Tel.: (63) 28308888
Web Site: http://www.tdgworld.com
Year Founded: 1976
Sales Range: $1-4.9 Billion
Emp.: 18,000
Holding Company; Logistics, Ship Management, Air & Travel Services, Information & Communications Technology & Investments
N.A.I.C.S.: 551112
J. Roberto C. Delgado (Founder & Chm)

Subsidiaries:

Adventure International Tours, Inc. (1)
3-4/F Eurovilla 2 118 VA Rufino Street, Legaspi Village, Makati, 1229, Philippines
Tel.: (63) 2 884 9400
Web Site: http://www.travelnow.ph
Travel Tour Operator
N.A.I.C.S.: 561520

Clark Airport Support Services Corporation (1)
Bldg 7585 CASS Cargo Center DMIA Civil Aviation Complex, Clark Freeport Zone Clarkfield, Pampanga, Philippines
Tel.: (63) 45 599 6688
Cargo Handling Services
N.A.I.C.S.: 488320
Diana Navarro (Mgr-Flight Ops)

TDG Orion Shanghai (1)
Room 508 5F Fuxing Building No 109 Yandang Road, Shanghai, 200020, China
Tel.: (86) 21 5351 0773
Information Technology Consulting Services
N.A.I.C.S.: 541512

TDG Tokyo (1)
10F Park Side Sepia Building 3-13-10 Nishi-azabu, Minato-ku, Tokyo, 106-0031, Japan
Tel.: (81) 3 5775 3778
Ship Building Services
N.A.I.C.S.: 336611

Transnational Aero Corporation (1)
Rm 211 MIASCOR Cargo Center NAIA Ave. Paranaque, Philippines
Tel.: (63) 2 852 8894
Aircraft Distr
N.A.I.C.S.: 441227

Transnational Diversified Group, Inc. (1)
The Penthouse Net Quad Building 4th Ave Corner 30th St, E-Square Crescent Park West Bonifacio Global City, Taguig, 1634, Philippines
Tel.: (63) 288308888
Web Site: https://www.tdgworld.com
Management Services Transnational Diversified Group
N.A.I.C.S.: 561499

Transnational Financial Services, Inc. (1)
Ground Floor Mary Bachrach Building 25th St corner AC Delgado St, Port Area, Manila, Philippines
Tel.: (63) 2 301 9271
Financial Services
N.A.I.C.S.: 522320

Transnational Logistics Solutions Corp. (1)
2F TDG-NYK Harbor Center Bldg Railroad cor 23rd St, Port Area, Manila, Philippines
Tel.: (63) 2 528 0502

Web Site: http://www.tlsc.com.ph
Emp.: 100
Logistics Consulting Servies
N.A.I.C.S.: 541614
Maria Neria Oliver (VP)

Transnational Medical & Diagnostic Center, Inc. (1)
Casa Marinero II Bldg 551 Cabildo St, Intramuros, Manila, Philippines
Tel.: (63) 2 527 6310
Diagnostic Services
N.A.I.C.S.: 621512

Transnational Ship Management, Inc. (1)
G/F Harbor Center Building I AC Delgado corner 23rd Street, Port Area, Manila, Philippines
Tel.: (63) 2 527 9494
Web Site: http://www.transhipmanage.com
Ship Management Services
N.A.I.C.S.: 336611
Rogelio Sobremonte (Chief Engr)

Universal Holidays, Inc. (1)
Mezzanine Floor Dusit Thani Hotel Ayala Center, Makati, 1223, Philippines **(88.9%)**
Tel.: (63) 2 859 3827
Web Site: http://www.universalholidays.com
Sales Range: $25-49.9 Million
Emp.: 30
Travel Agency
N.A.I.C.S.: 561510
Susie Lou (Gen Mgr)

Vision Air and Sea Services Inc. (1)
Suite 147 Bldg 8015 Subic Bay International Airport, Subic Bay Freeport Zone, Subic, Philippines
Tel.: (63) 47 252 7571
Airport Ground Handling Services
N.A.I.C.S.: 481211

TRANSNET LTD.
Carlton Centre, 150 Commissioner Street, Johannesburg, 2001, South Africa
Tel.: (27) 113083000
Web Site: http://www.transnet.net
Year Founded: 1990
Sales Range: $5-14.9 Billion
Emp.: 54,726
Transportation & Logistics Services
N.A.I.C.S.: 488510
Tau Morwe (Acting Grp CEO)

Subsidiaries:

National Ports Authority of South Africa (1)
PO Box 32696, Braamfontein, 2017, South Africa
Tel.: (27) 0113519001
Web Site: http://www.npa.co.za
Sales Range: $1-4.9 Billion
Emp.: 3,367
Ports Authority
N.A.I.C.S.: 926120

Protekon (1)
Carlton Centre 7th Fl, 150 Commissioner St, Johannesburg, South Africa
Tel.: (27) 11 3083100
Web Site: http://www.protekon.co.za
Multidisciplinary Engineering Services
N.A.I.C.S.: 237990

South African Port Operations (1)
Transmith Port Terminal, 10124, Marine Parade, 4033, Durban, South Africa
Tel.: (27) 313088333
Web Site: http://www.transmith.com
Sales Range: $25-49.9 Million
Emp.: 100
Port Terminal Management Services
N.A.I.C.S.: 488310

Transnet Freight Rail (1)
15 Girton Road Inyanda House 2, Parktown, 2193, South Africa
Tel.: (27) 860690730
Web Site: http://www.transnetfreightrail-tfr.net
Sales Range: $1-4.9 Billion
Emp.: 38,329
Rail Freight & Long Distance Passenger Transport Services

N.A.I.C.S.: 485112
Bheka Xaba (Exec Mgr-Sls-Iron, Ore & Manganese)

Transnet Pipelines (1)
202 Anton Lembede Smith Street, 4001, Durban, South Africa
Tel.: (27) 313611456
Web Site: http://www.transnetpipelines.net
Sales Range: $200-249.9 Million
Emp.: 550
Gas Pipeline Services
N.A.I.C.S.: 486990
Lennie Moodley (Gen Mgr-Strategy & Comml)

Transwerk (1)
Transwerk Park, Lynette Street Kilner Park, Pretoria, 0186, South Africa
Tel.: (27) 123911304
Web Site: http://www.transwerk.co.za
Rail Related Products Mfr
N.A.I.C.S.: 336510
John Mathew (Mgr-Mktg)

TRANSOCEAN HOLDINGS BHD.
No 38 Jalan Chow Kit, 50350, Kuala Lumpur, Malaysia
Tel.: (60) 340477878
Web Site:
  https://www.transocean.com.my
Year Founded: 1977
TOCEAN—(KLS)
Rev.: $6,112,455
Assets: $14,940,080
Liabilities: $2,015,534
Net Worth: $12,924,546
Earnings: $372,225
Fiscal Year-end: 12/31/22
Freight Forwarding Services
N.A.I.C.S.: 481212
Sook Fun Thum (Co-Sec)

Subsidiaries:

Gerak Intensif Sdn. Bhd. (1)
2955 2956 & 2957 Jalan Perusahaan Sg Lokan 3 Kawasan, Perusahaan Sungai Lokan, 13400, Butterworth, Penang, Malaysia
Tel.: (60) 43234768
Web Site: http://www.transocean.com.my
Sales Range: $50-74.9 Million
Emp.: 200
Container Trucking Services
N.A.I.C.S.: 484110

TFS Logistics Pte. Ltd. (1)
71 Tuas View Place 02-05 Westlink Two, Singapore, 637434, Singapore
Tel.: (65) 62626090
Logistic Services
N.A.I.C.S.: 541614

Transocean (KL) Sdn. Bhd. (1)
F1 29 Klas Cargo Complex Klia, 64000, Sepang, Selangor, Malaysia
Tel.: (60) 387788700
Web Site: http://www.tfs.net.my
Emp.: 9
Freight Forwarding & Trucking Services
N.A.I.C.S.: 484110

Transocean Distribution Hub Sdn. Bhd. (1)
2955 2956 and 2957 Jalan Perusahaan Sg Lokan 3 Kawasan, Perusahaan Sg Lokan, 13400, Butterworth, Penang, Malaysia
Tel.: (60) 43322650
Web Site: https://www.transocean.com.my
Sales Range: $100-124.9 Million
Emp.: 300
Warehousing & Trucking Services
N.A.I.C.S.: 493110

Transocean Logistics Sdn. Bhd. (1)
2955 2956 and 2957 Jalan Perusahaan Sg Lokan 3, Kawasan Perusahaan Sg Lokan, 13400, Butterworth, Penang, Malaysia
Tel.: (60) 43322650
Web Site: https://www.transocean.com.my
Sales Range: $50-74.9 Million
Emp.: 90
Freight Forwarding Services
N.A.I.C.S.: 488510
Datuk Mazmi (Owner & Mng Dir)

Usmeta Manufacturing Sdn. Bhd. (1)
Batu 1 1/2Jalan Sungai Chua Peti Surat
No3, 43007, Kajang, Selangor, Malaysia
Tel.: (60) 387335803
Logistic Services
N.A.I.C.S.: 541614

TRANSOCEAN LTD.
Turmstrasse 30, 6312, Steinhausen,
Switzerland
Tel.: (41) 417490500   CH
Web Site:
  https://www.deepwater.com
Year Founded: 2008
RIG—(NYSE)
Rev.: $2,832,000,000
Assets: $20,254,000,000
Liabilities: $9,838,000,000
Net Worth: $10,416,000,000
Earnings: ($954,000,000)
Emp.: 5,430
Fiscal Year-end: 12/31/23
Holding Company; Offshore Oil Drilling Contractor Services
N.A.I.C.S.: 551112
Keelan I. Adamson (Pres & COO)

Subsidiaries:

Global Dolphin Drilling Company
Limited (1)
1001 Raheja Center, Nariman Point, Mumbai, India
Tel.: (91) 2222832242
Ship Building & Repairing Services
N.A.I.C.S.: 336611

GlobalSantaFe Drilling Company (1)
15375 Memorial Dr, Houston, TX 77079
Tel.: (281) 496-8000
Oil & Gas Well Drilling Services
N.A.I.C.S.: 213111

Intermarine Servicos Petroliferos
Ltda. (1)
Av luis carlos prestes 290, Rio de Janeiro, 22775-055, Brazil
Tel.: (55) 11 3652 5252
Water Transportation Services
N.A.I.C.S.: 488390

Ocean Rig UDW Inc. (1)
c/o Ocean Rig Cayman Management Services SEZC Limited, 3rd Floor Flagship Building Harbour Drive Grand Cayman, Georgetown, Cayman Islands
Tel.: (345) 327 9232
Web Site: http://www.ocean-rig.com
Rev.: $1,007,520,000
Assets: $2,851,965,000
Liabilities: $648,745,000
Net Worth: $2,203,220,000
Earnings: ($5,402,000)
Emp.: 1,160
Fiscal Year-end: 12/31/2017
Oil Drilling
N.A.I.C.S.: 213111
Josselin Gere (VP-Mktg & Contracts)

Affiliate (Non-US):

Ocean Rig Partners LP (2)
Tribune House 10 Skopa Street, CY-1075, Nicosia, Cyprus
Tel.: (357) 22761542
Offshore Drilling Services
N.A.I.C.S.: 213111
George Economou (Chm, Pres & CEO)

R&B Falcon (A) Pty Ltd (1)
220 St George's Tce, Perth, 6000, WA, Australia
Tel.: (61) 892135777
Oil & Gas Well Drilling Services
N.A.I.C.S.: 213111

R&B Falcon B.V. (1)
Schouwburgplein 30-34, 3012 CL, Rotterdam, Netherlands
Tel.: (31) 102245333
Oil & Gas Well Drilling Services
N.A.I.C.S.: 213111

R&B Falcon Drilling (International & Deepwater) Inc. LLC (1)
2000 W Sam Houston Pkwy S, Houston, TX 77042-3615
Tel.: (713) 278-6000
Oil & Gas Well Drilling Services
N.A.I.C.S.: 213111

R&B Falcon International Energy Services B.V. (1)
west bleek 98, 3012 CL, Rotterdam, Netherlands
Tel.: (31) 102245333
Oil & Gas Exploration Services
N.A.I.C.S.: 213112
Hueb Kanter (CEO)

Resource Rig Supply Inc. (1)
15375 Memorial Dr, Houston, TX 77079-4101
Tel.: (281) 925-7300
Construction & Mining Machinery Whslr
N.A.I.C.S.: 423320
Bert Morris (VP)

Services Petroliers Transocean (1)
Tour Egee Faubourg de l'Arche 9-11 Allee de l'Arche, Courbevoie, 92400, Paris, France
Tel.: (33) 1 46 67 21 50
Sales Range: $25-49.9 Million
Emp.: 4
Petroleum Product Distr
N.A.I.C.S.: 424720
Marc Deleglise (Pres)

Transocean Drilling Limited (1)
Crawpeel Rd, Aberdeen, AB12 3LG, United Kingdom
Tel.: (44) 1224 427700
Sales Range: $200-249.9 Million
Emp.: 500
Oil & Gas Wells Drilling Services
N.A.I.C.S.: 213111
Adrian P. Rose (Mng Dir)

Transocean Drilling Offshore
S.a.r.l. (1)
25 Route d Esch, 1470, Luxembourg, Luxembourg
Tel.: (352) 270241
Sales Range: $50-74.9 Million
Emp.: 6
Oil & Gas Wells Drilling Services
N.A.I.C.S.: 213111
Mark Jones (Dir-Asset)

Transocean Enterprise Inc. (1)
1100 E Colorado St, Glendale, CA 91205-1309
Tel.: (818) 637-8579
Household Furniture & Goods Whslr
N.A.I.C.S.: 423210

Transocean Inc. (1)
1414 Enclave Pkwy, Houston, TX 77077 (100%)
Tel.: (713) 232-7500
Holding Company; Offshore Oil & Natural Gas Drilling Contractor Services
N.A.I.C.S.: 551112

Subsidiary (Non-US):

Applied Drilling Technology Inc. (2)
Tel.: (832) 587-5300
Sales Range: $50-74.9 Million
Emp.: 70
Turnkey Oil & Gas Well Construction Services
N.A.I.C.S.: 213111

Subsidiary (Non-US):

Applied Drilling Technology
International (3)
Tel.: (44) 1224654400
Web Site: http://www.gsfdrill.com
Sales Range: $100-124.9 Million
Shaft Drilling
N.A.I.C.S.: 213111

Subsidiary (Domestic):

Challenger Minerals Inc. (2)
1311 Broadfield Blvd Ste 500, Houston, TX 77084-4966
Tel.: (281) 925-7200
Web Site:
  http://www.challengerminerals.com
Sales Range: $50-74.9 Million
Emp.: 25
Offshore Oil & Gas Prospect Screening, Facilitating & Funding Services
N.A.I.C.S.: 213112

Subsidiary (Non-US):

PT Hitek Nusantara Offshore
Drilling (2)
Jl Longikis, PO Box 249, Balikpapan, Kalimantan Timur, Indonesia
Tel.: (62) 542410478
Oil Drilling Services
N.A.I.C.S.: 213111

PT Transocean Indonesia (2)
Sentra Mulia Building Suite 1801, Jl HR Rasuna Said Kav, X-6 No 8 Kuningan, Jakarta, Indonesia
Tel.: (62) 215227250
Oil Drilling Services
N.A.I.C.S.: 213111

Transocean Brasil Ltda. (2)
Av Praia de Botafogo 186 13 Andar Ed Torre Oscar Neimeyer, Rio de Janeiro, Botafogo, 22250-145, RJ, Brazil
Tel.: (55) 2130359900
Emp.: 20
Oil Drilling Services
N.A.I.C.S.: 213111

Transocean Drilling (Nigeria) Ltd. (2)
Maersk House 121 Louis Solomon Close, Victoria Island, Lagos, Nigeria
Tel.: (234) 12719770
Oil Drilling Services
N.A.I.C.S.: 213111

Transocean Eastern Pte Ltd. (2)
391B Orchard Road Level 22 Ngee Ann City Tower B, Singapore, 238874, Singapore
Tel.: (65) 69501704
Sales Range: $50-74.9 Million
Emp.: 85
Oil Drilling Services
N.A.I.C.S.: 213111

Transocean I AS (2)
Stavanger Main Office, PO Box 8200, 4069, Stavanger, Norway
Tel.: (47) 51504300
Web Site: http://www.transocean.com
Sales Range: $50-74.9 Million
Emp.: 80
Oil Drilling Services
N.A.I.C.S.: 213111

Transocean Norway Drilling AS (2)
Maskinveien 26, 4033, Stavanger, Norway (100%)
Tel.: (47) 51504300
Sales Range: $150-199.9 Million
Emp.: 392
Offshore Drilling
N.A.I.C.S.: 213111

Transocean Offshore (North Sea)
Ltd. (2)
Hareness Circle Altens Industrial Estate, Aberdeen, AB12 3LG, United Kingdom
Tel.: (44) 1224427700
Web Site: http://www.deepwater.com
Oil Drilling Services
N.A.I.C.S.: 213111

Transocean Offshore International
Ventures Limited (2)
One Boulevard 4th Floor Office No 2 Lake Boulevard Street, Hiranandani Business Park Powai, Mumbai, 400 076, India
Tel.: (91) 2240000000
Sales Range: $50-74.9 Million
Emp.: 100
Oil Drilling Services
N.A.I.C.S.: 213111

Subsidiary (Domestic):

Transocean Offshore USA, Inc. (2)
4 E Greenway Plz, Houston, TX 77046
Tel.: (713) 232-7500
Web Site: http://www.deepwater.com
Sales Range: $25-49.9 Million
Emp.: 35
Drilling Oil & Gas Wells
N.A.I.C.S.: 213111
Terry Bonno (Sr VP-Mktg)

Subsidiary (Non-US):

Transocean Pty Ltd. (2)
PO Box 7757 Cloisters Square, Perth, 6850, WA, Australia
Tel.: (61) 892133700
Web Site: http://www.deepwater.com
Sales Range: $50-74.9 Million
Emp.: 40
Oil Drilling Services
N.A.I.C.S.: 213111

Transocean Support Services Pvt.
Ltd. (2)
One Boulevard 4th Floor Office No 2 Lake Boulevard Street, Hiranandani Business Park Powai, Mumbai, 400076, India
Tel.: (91) 2240000000
Sales Range: $75-99.9 Million
Emp.: 200
Oil Drilling Services
N.A.I.C.S.: 213111

Transocean Management Ltd. (1)
Chemin de Blandonnet 10, 1214, Vernier, Switzerland
Tel.: (41) 229309000
Web Site: http://www.deepwater.com
Offshore Drilling Services
N.A.I.C.S.: 213111

Transocean Offshore Canada Services Ltd. (1)
66 Kenmount Rd Suite 302, Saint John's, A1B 3V7, NL, Canada
Tel.: (709) 724-6600
Oil & Gas Well Drilling Services
N.A.I.C.S.: 213111

Transocean Offshore Deepwater Drilling Inc. (1)
4 Greenway Plz, Houston, TX 77046-0400
Tel.: (713) 232-7500
Web Site: http://www.deepwater.com
Oil Well Drilling Services
N.A.I.C.S.: 213111

Transocean Onshore Support Services Limited (1)
Langlands House Huntly Street, Aberdeen, AB10 1SH, United Kingdom
Tel.: (44) 1224654400
Oil Well Drilling Services
N.A.I.C.S.: 213111

Triton Asset Leasing GmbH (1)
Turmstrasse 30, 6300, Zug, Switzerland
Tel.: (41) 417288100
Oil & Gas Well Drilling Services
N.A.I.C.S.: 213111

TRANSPACIFIC BROADBAND GROUP INTERNATIONAL, INC.
1751 Chico Street Clark Special Economic Zone, Clarkfield, Pampanga, Philippines
Tel.: (63) 284040239   PH
Web Site: https://www.tbgi.net.ph
Year Founded: 1995
TBGI—(PHI)
Rev.: $620,293
Assets: $11,906,791
Liabilities: $1,227,638
Net Worth: $10,679,153
Earnings: $38,601
Emp.: 11
Fiscal Year-end: 12/31/23
Internet & Specialty Broadband Telecommunications Services
N.A.I.C.S.: 517810
Arsenio T. Ng (Chm, Pres & CEO)

TRANSPACO LTD.
331 6th Street, Wynberg, Johannesburg, 2090, South Africa
Tel.: (27) 118870430
Web Site:
  https://www.transpaco.co.za
Year Founded: 1951
TPC—(JSE)
Rev.: $136,834,673
Assets: $77,245,271
Liabilities: $30,476,980
Net Worth: $46,768,291
Earnings: $9,328,626
Emp.: 1,559
Fiscal Year-end: 06/30/23
Holding Company
N.A.I.C.S.: 551112

TRANSPACO LTD.

Transpaco Ltd.—(Continued)
Phillip N. Abelheim *(CEO)*

Subsidiaries:

Britepak Trading (Pty) Ltd (1)
36 Derrick Rd, Spartan, Kempton Park, 1619, Gauteng, South Africa
Tel.: (27) 115708700
Web Site: https://www.britepak.co.za
Sales Range: $50-74.9 Million
Emp.: 110
Packaging Materials Printing Services
N.A.I.C.S.: 323111
John Latter *(Mng Dir)*

East Rand Plastics (Pty) Ltd. (1)
87 Uranium Road, Vulcania, Brakpan, 1541, South Africa
Tel.: (27) 118179000
Web Site: http://www.transpaco.com
Plastic Packaging Products Mfr
N.A.I.C.S.: 322220
Ryan Gravett *(Mgr-Natl Key Accts)*

Future Packaging & Machinery (Pty) Ltd. (1)
32 Raft St Laser Park, Roodepoort, South Africa
Tel.: (27) 117943310
Web Site: https://www.futurepack.co.za
Industrial Packaging Distr
N.A.I.C.S.: 488991

Future Packaging & Machinery Cape (Pty) Ltd. (1)
15 3rd St Montague Gardens, Cape Town, 7442, South Africa
Tel.: (27) 215511313
Web Site: http://www.futurepack.co.za
Corrugated Board Distr
N.A.I.C.S.: 424130

TRANSPACO RECYCLING (PTY) LTD (1)
180 Barbara Road, Germiston, 1429, Gauteng, South Africa
Tel.: (27) 118226470
Plastic Waste Recycling Services
N.A.I.C.S.: 562998
Willi Henning *(Gen Mgr)*

Transpaco Administrative And Financial Services (Pty) Ltd (1)
331 6th Street, Wynberg, Johannesburg, 2018, Gauteng, South Africa
Tel.: (27) 118870430
Emp.: 200
Financial Support Services
N.A.I.C.S.: 523999
Louis Weinberg *(Dir-Fin)*

Transpaco Cores & Tubes (Pty) Ltd. (1)
20 Goodenough Ave Epping 2, Cape Town, 7475, South Africa
Tel.: (27) 215352610
Paper & Plastic Packaging Mfr & Distr
N.A.I.C.S.: 322220

Transpaco Flexibles Mpumalanga (Pty) Ltd (1)
196/1 Manganese Road Ekandustria, Bronkhorstspruit, 1020, Western Cape, South Africa
Tel.: (27) 139333764
Sales Range: $50-74.9 Million
Emp.: 250
Plastic Packaging Materials Mfr
N.A.I.C.S.: 326112

Transpaco Flexibles Pty Limited (1)
Glucose Way, Bellville South, Cape Town, 7530, South Africa
Tel.: (27) 219511241
Web Site: https://www.transpaco.co.za
Emp.: 200
Packaging Bags Mfr
N.A.I.C.S.: 326199

Transpaco Packaging (Pty) Ltd (1)
9 Booysens Station Road, Stafford, Johannesburg, 2197, Gauteng, South Africa
Tel.: (27) 118911300
Sales Range: $50-74.9 Million
Emp.: 60
Packaging Plastic Bags Mfr & Distr
N.A.I.C.S.: 326112
Steve Harmse *(Mng Dir)*

Transpaco Polymer Recyclers (Pty) Ltd (1)
180 Barbara Road, Germiston, 1429, Gauteng, South Africa
Tel.: (27) 118226470
Sales Range: $25-49.9 Million
Emp.: 125
Plastic Waste Recycling Services
N.A.I.C.S.: 562998
Jako Breytenbach *(Mng Dir)*

Transpaco Specialised Films (Pty) Ltd (1)
199/1 Manganese Road Ekandustria, Bronkhorstspruit, Pretoria, 1020, Gauteng, South Africa
Tel.: (27) 139333554
Plastics Films Mfr
N.A.I.C.S.: 326113

TRANSPACT ENTERPRISES LIMITED

204 Timmy Arcade Makwana Road, Marol Andheri East, Mumbai, 400059, India
Tel.: (91) 2240231431
Web Site: https://www.transpact.in
Year Founded: 2013
542765—(BOM)
Rev.: $45,861
Assets: $125,268
Liabilities: $61,327
Net Worth: $63,941
Earnings: ($7,901)
Emp.: 8
Fiscal Year-end: 03/31/23
Software Development Services
N.A.I.C.S.: 541511
Aslam Khan *(Co-Founder & CEO)*

TRANSPED A.D.

Veselina Maslese 11, 78000, Banja Luka, Bosnia & Herzegovina
Tel.: (387) 51212495
TRAN-R-A—(BANJ)
Rev.: $192,614
Assets: $2,167,432
Liabilities: $1,718,519
Net Worth: $448,913
Earnings: $2,563
Emp.: 12
Fiscal Year-end: 12/31/12
Travel Agency Services
N.A.I.C.S.: 561510
Zdravko Tolj *(Chm)*

TRANSPEK INDUSTRY LIMITED

4 th Floor Lilleria 1038 Gotri- Sevasi Road, Vadodara, 390 021, Gujarat, India
Tel.: (91) 2656700300
Web Site: https://www.transpek.com
Year Founded: 1965
506687—(BOM)
Rev.: $101,277,393
Assets: $106,332,846
Liabilities: $35,997,039
Net Worth: $70,335,807
Earnings: $10,008,645
Emp.: 566
Fiscal Year-end: 03/31/23
Cement Mfr & Distr
N.A.I.C.S.: 327310
Bimal Vasantlal Mehta *(Mng Dir)*

Subsidiaries:

Sam Fine O Chem Ltd. (1)
Shyam Villa Sapta Sindhu Compound Rokadia Lane, Borivali, Mumbai, 400 092, India
Tel.: (91) 222 890 0066
Web Site: https://www.samfinechem.com
Emp.: 150
Pharmaceuticals Product Mfr
N.A.I.C.S.: 325412
Deepak Mehta *(Mng Dir)*

Transpek Creative Chemistry Private Limited (1)
4th Floor Lilleria 1038 Gotri Sevasi Road, Vadodara, 390021, Gujarat, India
Tel.: (91) 2656700300
Acrylic Sheet Mfr
N.A.I.C.S.: 326113

Transpek Industry (Europe) Ltd. (1)
2nd Floor 1 Risborough Street, Shooters Hill Woolwich, London, SE1 0HF, United Kingdom
Tel.: (44) 207 9287771
Inorganic Chemical Mfr & Whslr
N.A.I.C.S.: 325180

TRANSPORT & INVESTMENT BARTER COMPANY

Al-jeezah-Main Road Amman-Aqaba, PO Box 930506, Amman, 11193, Jordan
Tel.: (962) 64460600
Web Site: http://www.naqel.com
Year Founded: 1979
NAQL—(AMM)
Rev.: $5,247,395
Assets: $15,208,491
Liabilities: $1,985,310
Net Worth: $13,223,181
Earnings: ($112,736)
Emp.: 170
Fiscal Year-end: 12/31/20
Transportation Services
N.A.I.C.S.: 488999

TRANSPORT CORPORATION OF INDIA LTD.

TCI House 69 Institutional Area Sector-32, Gurgaon, 122001, Haryana, India
Tel.: (91) 1242381603
Web Site: https://www.tcil.com
532349—(BOM)
Rev.: $457,147,054
Assets: $251,893,292
Liabilities: $47,854,205
Net Worth: $204,039,086
Earnings: $38,437,624
Emp.: 3,687
Fiscal Year-end: 03/31/23
Logistics Solutions Distr
N.A.I.C.S.: 541614
D. P. Agarwal *(Mng Dir & Chm)*

Subsidiaries:

TCI Bangladesh Ltd. (1)
UTC Building 19th Floor, Kawranbazar, Dhaka, 1215, Bangladesh
Tel.: (880) 1779540900
Web Site: https://www.tcibangladesh.com
Logistic Services
N.A.I.C.S.: 541614

TCI Cold Chain Solutions Ltd. (1)
TCI House 69 Institutional Area Sector 32, Gurgaon, 122 001, India
Tel.: (91) 124238160307
Web Site: https://www.tciscs.com
Logistic Services
N.A.I.C.S.: 541614

TCI Developers Limited (1)
TCI House 69 Institutional Area Sector-32, Gurgaon, 122 001, Haryana, India
Tel.: (91) 1242381603
Web Site: http://www.tcidevelopers.com
Rev.: $1,450,900
Assets: $15,150,717
Liabilities: $3,305,972
Net Worth: $11,844,745
Earnings: $272,146
Emp.: 27
Fiscal Year-end: 03/31/2021
Real Estate Development Services
N.A.I.C.S.: 531390
D. P. Agarwal *(Chm)*

TCI Freight (1)
TCI House 69, Institutional Area Sector-32, Gurgaon, 122 001, Haryana, India
Tel.: (91) 1242381603
Web Site: http://www.tcifreight.in
Sales Range: $50-74.9 Million
Emp.: 250
Freight Services

INTERNATIONAL PUBLIC

N.A.I.C.S.: 484110
I. S. Sigar *(CEO)*

TCI Global (HKG) Ltd. (1)
19A On Hing Building No 1 On Hing Terrace, Central, China (Hong Kong)
Tel.: (852) 23101112
Web Site: http://www.tciglobal.com
Logistic Services
N.A.I.C.S.: 541614

TCI Global (Sanghai) Co., Ltd. (1)
Rm 2607 No-1701 Bei jing Xi Lu, Jing An Dist, Shanghai, 200040, China
Tel.: (86) 2161370870
Sales Range: $25-49.9 Million
Emp.: 50
Logistic Services
N.A.I.C.S.: 541614

TCI Global (Thailand) Co., Ltd. (1)
138 billet bldg, Suriyawong Bangrak, Bangkok, 10500, Thailand
Tel.: (66) 263435502
Web Site: http://www.tciglobal.com
Sales Range: $25-49.9 Million
Emp.: 2
Logistic Services
N.A.I.C.S.: 541614

TCI Global Logistik Gmbh (1)
Ecos Ofc Ctr Ventura Bldg 23 11th Fl, Mergenthalerallee 10 -12, 65760, Eschborn, Germany
Tel.: (49) 6196400193
Web Site: http://www.tciglobal.com
Sales Range: $25-49.9 Million
Emp.: 3
Logistic Services
N.A.I.C.S.: 541614
Chanda Agarwal *(Gen Mgr)*

TCI Global Pte Ltd. (1)
10 Anson Rd 35-04, International Plz, Singapore, 79903, Singapore
Tel.: (65) 62728300
Web Site: http://www.tciglobal.com
Sales Range: $25-49.9 Million
Emp.: 6
Logistic Services
N.A.I.C.S.: 541614

TCI Nepal Pvt. Ltd. (1)
B-327 Shankardeep Building 4th Floor New Road, Khichapokhari, Kathmandu, Nepal
Tel.: (977) 14249786
Web Site: https://tcinepal.com
Logistic Services
N.A.I.C.S.: 541614

TCI Seaways (1)
TCI House 69, Institutional Area Sector-32, Gurgaon, 122 001, Haryana, India
Tel.: (91) 1242381603
Web Site: http://www.tciseaways.com
Sales Range: $25-49.9 Million
Emp.: 5
Shipping Services
N.A.I.C.S.: 488510
K. Singh *(Co-Pres-Tech)*

TCI Supply Chain Solutions (1)
TCI House 69, Institutional Area Sector-32, Gurgaon, 122 001, Haryana, India
Tel.: (91) 1242381603
Web Site: http://www.tciscs.com
Sales Range: $150-199.9 Million
Emp.: 400
Logistic Services
N.A.I.C.S.: 481112
Jasjit Singh Sethi *(Pres & CEO)*

TCI XPS (1)
69 Institutional Area Sector 32, Sector-32, Gurgaon, 122001, Haryana, India
Tel.: (91) 1242381603
Web Site: http://www.tcixps.com
Sales Range: $125-149.9 Million
Emp.: 300
Air Courier Services
N.A.I.C.S.: 481112
Phool Chand Sharma *(CEO)*

TCI-CONCOR Multimodal Solutions Pvt. Ltd. (1)
69 Institutional Area Sector-32, Gurgaon, 122001, Haryana, India
Tel.: (91) 124238160307
Web Site: https://www.tciconcor.com
Logistic Services

AND PRIVATE COMPANIES

Transport Co of India (Mauritius) Ltd. (1)
14 Lancaster Ct Lavoquer St, Port Louis, Mauritius
Tel.: (230) 2134510
Web Site: http://www.tciglobal.com
Sales Range: $25-49.9 Million
Emp.: 10
Logistic Services
N.A.I.C.S.: 541614
Jhumka Zabeen (Mgr)

TRANSPORT HERVE LEMIEUX
6500 Chemin St Francois, Saint Laurent, H4S 1B7, QC, Canada
Tel.: (514) 337-2203
Web Site:
http://www.transportlemieux.com
Year Founded: 1947
Rev.: $30,381,409
Emp.: 350
Transportation Services
N.A.I.C.S.: 488999
Richard Lemieux (Pres)

TRANSPORT INTERNATIONAL HOLDINGS LIMITED
15/F No 9 Po Lun Street Lai Chi Kok, Kowloon, China (Hong Kong)
Tel.: (852) 27868888
Web Site: http://www.tih.hk
Year Founded: 1997
0062—(HKG)
Rev.: $842,414,303
Assets: $2,696,711,190
Liabilities: $991,026,263
Net Worth: $1,705,684,928
Earnings: $18,314,100
Emp.: 12,028
Fiscal Year-end: 12/31/22
Transportation Services
N.A.I.C.S.: 488999

Subsidiaries:

Hoi Tai Tours Limited (1)
Room 9A1/F 9 Po Lun Street Lai Chi Kok, Kowloon, China (Hong Kong)
Tel.: (852) 23091116
Bus Transportation Services
N.A.I.C.S.: 485113

Sun Bus Limited (1)
Room 15A 15/F 9 Po Lun Street, Lai Chi Kok, Kowloon, China (Hong Kong)
Tel.: (852) 2 372 0638
Web Site: https://www.sunbus.com.hk
Bus Transportation Services
N.A.I.C.S.: 485113

The Kowloon Motor Bus Company (1933) Limited (1)
9 Po Lun Street, Lai Chi Kok, Kowloon, China (Hong Kong)
Tel.: (852) 2 745 4466
Web Site: https://www.kmb.hk
Bus Transportation Services
N.A.I.C.S.: 485113

TRANSPORT JACQUES AUGER INC.
860 rue Archimede, Levis, G6V 7M5, QC, Canada
Tel.: (418) 835-9266
Web Site: http://www.tja.ca
Year Founded: 1986
Rev.: $34,343,255
Emp.: 300
Transportation Services
N.A.I.C.S.: 488999

TRANSPORT VOZDOVAC A.D.
Vozdovacki kruzni put 6, Belgrade, Serbia
Tel.: (381) 11 2473 837
Web Site: http://www.transport-ad.com
Year Founded: 1960
TRVZ—(BEL)
Sales Range: Less than $1 Million

Emp.: 72
Marine Cargo Handling Services
N.A.I.C.S.: 488320
Sreten Cirovic (CEO)

TRANSPORTADORA DE GAS DEL PERU S.A.
Victor A Belaunde 147 Centro Empresarial Real Torre Real 3 Oficina 501, San Isidro, 27, Lima, Peru
Tel.: (51) 1 617 7777   Pe
Web Site: http://www.tgp.com.pe
Year Founded: 2000
Emp.: 14,000
Natural Gas Transportation & Distribution Services
N.A.I.C.S.: 486210
Ricardo Ferreiro (CEO)

TRANSPORTATION & TRADING SERVICES JOINT STOCK COMPANY
R 427-430 Thanh Dat 1 Bulding No 3 Le Thanh Tong St, May To Ward Ngo Quyen Dist, Haiphong, Vietnam
Tel.: (84) 2253821037
Web Site: http://www.transco.com.vn
TJC—(HNX)
Rev.: $16,744,600
Assets: $17,408,200
Liabilities: $2,158,800
Net Worth: $15,249,400
Earnings: $4,936,200
Fiscal Year-end: 12/31/22
Cargo Transportation & Maritime Services
N.A.I.C.S.: 488320

TRANSPORTES MARITIMOS INSULARES, S.A.
Edificio Goncalves Zarco Doca de Alcantara lado Norte, 1399-015, Lisbon, Portugal
Tel.: (351) 211128000
Web Site: http://www.transinsular.pt
Maritime Transportation Services
N.A.I.C.S.: 541330
Matthieu Roger (CEO)

TRANSPORTS BAUDOUIN
Route De Niort, 79230, Prahecq, Deux Sevres, France
Tel.: (33) 549264111
Web Site: http://www.transports-baudouin.fr
Year Founded: 1957
Rev.: $13,100,000
Emp.: 99
Freight Trucking Services
N.A.I.C.S.: 484121
Denis Baudouin (Pres)

TRANSPORTS DESERT SA
Zone Artisanale de Piquet, CS 36015, 35370, Etrelles, France
Tel.: (33) 299963210   FR
Web Site: https://www.groupe-desert.com
Truck Transportation Services
N.A.I.C.S.: 484110

Subsidiaries:

Tratel S.a.s (1)
Les Technodes, 78931, Guerville, Cedex, France
Tel.: (33) 134777800
Web Site: http://www.tratel.fr
Cement Transportation Services
N.A.I.C.S.: 484110

Subsidiary (Domestic):

Tratel Airvault (2)
28 Rue De L Aumonerie, 79600, Airvault, France
Tel.: (33) 549647125
Logistic Services
N.A.I.C.S.: 541614

Tratel Moult (2)
ZI De La Gare, 14370, Moult, France
Tel.: (33) 2 31 38 38 38
Logistics Consulting Servies
N.A.I.C.S.: 541614

Tratel Pessac (2)
162 Avenue de Haut Leveque, 33600, Pessac, France
Tel.: (33) 5 57 26 27 81
Logistics Consulting Servies
N.A.I.C.S.: 541614

TRANSPORTS GOUBET
Chemin de pra Paris, Noyarey, Sassenage, 38360, France
Tel.: (33) 476539344   FR
Year Founded: 1994
Sales Range: $10-24.9 Million
Emp.: 68
Freight Truck Transportation Services
N.A.I.C.S.: 484121
Oliver Zoynoz (Pres)

TRANSPORTS GUIDEZ
Zone Artoipole 34 Allee De Grande Bretagne, 62118, Monchy-le-Preux, France
Tel.: (33) 321506565
Web Site: http://www.tps-guidez.fr
Year Founded: 1985
Emp.: 420
Perishable Goods Transportaion Services
N.A.I.C.S.: 484121
Christophe Pavy (Dir-Transportation)

TRANSPORTS JOLLIVET CHRISTIAN
Parc D'' Activites 1 Rue De La Grand Maison, 49800, Trelaze, Maine Et Loire, France
Tel.: (33) 241185185
Rev.: $25,000,000
Emp.: 200
Trucking Except Local
N.A.I.C.S.: 484121
Christian Jollivet (Personnel Dir)

TRANSPORTS KLINZING FRERES ET CIE
2 Rue Des Faisans, 68270, Mulhouse, France
Tel.: (33) 389529911
Web Site: http://www.klinzing.fr
Sales Range: $25-49.9 Million
Emp.: 194
Trucking Service
N.A.I.C.S.: 484121
Cathy Klinzing (Dir-Personnel)

TRANSPORTURI AUTO GIULESTI SA
Sos Giulesti 177 s6, Bucharest, Romania
Tel.: (40) 212205469
TRGI—(BUC)
Rev.: $375,930
Assets: $4,226,326
Liabilities: $18,830
Net Worth: $4,207,497
Earnings: $177,876
Emp.: 10
Fiscal Year-end: 12/31/23
Food Transportation Services
N.A.I.C.S.: 484121
Ioana-Valeria Avram (Pres & Gen Mgr)

TRANSPRO FREIGHT SYSTEMS LTD.
8600 Escarpment Way, Milton, L9T 0M1, ON, Canada
Tel.: (905) 693-0699
Web Site:
https://www.transprofreight.com

TRANSTEMA GROUP AB

Year Founded: 1990
Rev.: $14,067,500
Emp.: 30
Transportation Services
N.A.I.C.S.: 488999
Frank Prosia (Pres)

TRANSPROM A.D.
Neznanih Junaka 69, 76300, Bijeljina, Bosnia & Herzegovina
Tel.: (387) 65689216   BA
Emp.: 1
Real Estate Manangement Services
N.A.I.C.S.: 531390

TRANSRAIL LIGHTING LIMITED
Fortune 2000 A wing 5th floor Bandra Kurla Complex, Mumbai, 400051, India
Tel.: (91) 22 6197 9600   In
Web Site: http://www.transrail.in
Year Founded: 2008
Construction Engineering Services
N.A.I.C.S.: 541330
D. C. Bagde (Mng Dir)

TRANSSTROY-AM AD
29 Klokotnitsa St, 1202, Sofia, Bulgaria
Tel.: (359) 28310039
Web Site: https://transstroyam.com
Year Founded: 1903
TRNB—(BUL)
Sales Range: Less than $1 Million
Electricity & Communication Related Construction Services
N.A.I.C.S.: 237130

TRANSSTROY-BURGAS AD
ul Uspenska 8, 8000, Burgas, 8000, Bulgaria
Tel.: (359) 56857070
Web Site: https://www.transstroy.com
Year Founded: 1934
TSBS—(BUL)
Sales Range: Less than $1 Million
Building Construction Services
N.A.I.C.S.: 236210

TRANSTECH OPTELECOM SCIENCE HOLDINGS LTD.
No 3 Dai Kwai Street Tai Po industrial Estate, Tai Po, China (Hong Kong)
Tel.: (852) 26657799
Web Site:
http://www.transtechoptel.com
Year Founded: 2016
9963—(HKG)
Rev.: $29,676,008
Assets: $77,804,963
Liabilities: $12,408,045
Net Worth: $65,396,918
Earnings: ($9,029,550)
Emp.: 177
Fiscal Year-end: 12/31/22
Fiber Optic Electrical Equipment Mfr
N.A.I.C.S.: 335921

TRANSTELE - CANAL FRANCE INTERNATIONAL
131 Avenue De Wagram, 75017, Paris, France
Tel.: (33) 140623232
Web Site: http://www.cfi.fr
Sales Range: $25-49.9 Million
Emp.: 44
Motion Picture & Video Production
N.A.I.C.S.: 512110
Pascale Deruelle (Mgr-Personnel)

TRANSTEMA GROUP AB
EA Rosengrens gata 31, 431 31, Vastra Frolunda, Sweden
Tel.: (46) 31 746 83 00   SE

TRANSTEMA GROUP AB

Transtema Group AB—(Continued)

Web Site:
http://www.transtemagroup.se
Year Founded: 1997
Emp.: 130
Holding Company; Information Technology Infrastructure Services
N.A.I.C.S.: 551112
Magnus Johansson (CEO)

Subsidiaries:

Fiberdata AB (1)
Kvarnkronen 7, 805 92, Gavle, Sweden
Tel.: (46) 83659500
Web Site: http://www.fiberdata.se
Information Technology Network Integration & Installation Services
N.A.I.C.S.: 541519
Mats Erik Devert (CEO)

Transtema AB (1)
Flojelbergsgatan 12, 421 31, Molndal, Sweden
Tel.: (46) 31 746 8300
Web Site: http://www.transtema.com
Information Technology Infrastructure Services
N.A.I.C.S.: 541519
Magnus Johansson (CEO)

TRANSTOUCH TECHNOLOGY, INC.

333 No 50 Hwa-ya 3 Rd Kwei-san shian, Taoyuan, Taiwan
Tel.: (886) 33978800
Web Site:
https://www.transtouch.com.tw
Year Founded: 2000
3623—(TPE)
Rev.: $11,171,810
Assets: $16,656,724
Liabilities: $4,701,748
Net Worth: $11,954,976
Earnings: ($862,239)
Fiscal Year-end: 12/31/22
Hardware Product Mfr
N.A.I.C.S.: 332510
Chien-Hua Yu (Pres)

TRANSTURIST D.D.

Bosne srebrene 60, 75 000, Tuzla, Bosnia & Herzegovina
Tel.: (387) 35320303
Web Site: http://www.transturist.ba
TRTURK2—(SARE)
Rev.: $3,222,030
Assets: $6,378,521
Liabilities: $2,884,778
Net Worth: $3,493,742
Earnings: ($136,176)
Emp.: 108
Fiscal Year-end: 12/31/21
Passenger Transportation Services
N.A.I.C.S.: 485999

TRANSTURK HOLDING A.S.

Atakoy 7-8-9-10 Kisim Mah E-5 Yan Yol Cad, No 8/2 D 37 Bakirkoy, Istanbul, Turkiye
Tel.: (90) 212 275 50 26
Web Site: http://www.transturk.com.tr
Year Founded: 1940
Holding Company
N.A.I.C.S.: 551112

TRANSUNIVERS VOYAGE

8 Cite Nollez, 75018, Paris, France
Tel.: (33) 1 42 23 77 77
Web Site: http://www.transunivers.fr
Rev.: $14,700,000
Emp.: 25
Tour Operator
N.A.I.C.S.: 561510
Emmanuelle Ulrich (Dir & Fin)

TRANSURBAN LIMITED

Tower Five Collins Square 727 Collins Street, Docklands, Melbourne, 3008, VIC, Australia
Tel.: (61) 386568900
Web Site: http://www.transurban.com
Year Founded: 1996
TRAUF—(OTCIQ)
Rev.: $2,220,773,293
Assets: $25,405,881,202
Liabilities: $15,476,951,164
Net Worth: $9,928,930,038
Earnings: $10,432,288
Emp.: 1,925
Fiscal Year-end: 06/30/22
Property Management Services
N.A.I.C.S.: 531311
Andrew Head (CEO-WestConnex)

Subsidiaries:

Transurban Infrastructure Management Limited (1)
Level 3 505 Collins St, Melbourne, 3000, Victoria, Australia
Tel.: (61) 386568900
Web Site: http://www.transurban.com.au
Sales Range: $100-124.9 Million
Emp.: 500
Toll Road Operation Services
N.A.I.C.S.: 237310

TRANSVOY LOGISTICS INDIA LIMITED

B-504 Mondeal Heights B/S Novotel Hotel Sarkhej-Gandhinagar Hwy, Ahmedabad, 380015, Gujarat, India
Tel.: (91) 9687604073 In
Web Site: https://www.transvoy.com
Year Founded: 2015
543754—(BOM)
Logistic Services
N.A.I.C.S.: 541614
Ravindrakumar Kumarchandra Joshi (Chm)

TRANSWARRANTY FINANCE LIMITED

403 Regent Chambers Nariman Point, Mumbai, 400 021, India
Tel.: (91) 2240010900
Web Site:
https://www.transwarranty.com
Year Founded: 1994
TFL—(NSE)
Rev.: $1,442,467
Assets: $12,732,582
Liabilities: $8,720,364
Net Worth: $4,012,217
Earnings: ($1,113,842)
Emp.: 24
Fiscal Year-end: 03/31/23
Financial Management Services
N.A.I.C.S.: 523999
Kumar Nair (Chm, CEO & Mng Dir)

TRANSWIND INFRASTRUCTURES LIMITED

74 Newyork Tower-A Opp Jain Derasar S G Highway Thaltej, Ahmedabad, 380054, India
Tel.: (91) 7926854899
Web Site: https://www.transwind.in
Year Founded: 1997
TRANSWIND—(NSE)
Rev.: $2,923,877
Assets: $2,442,180
Liabilities: $606,606
Net Worth: $1,835,573
Earnings: $60,152
Emp.: 18
Fiscal Year-end: 03/31/23
Civil Construction Services
N.A.I.C.S.: 236220
Khyati Shah (Sec & Compliance Officer)

TRANTER HOLDINGS (PTY) LIMITED

Ground Floor Turnberry Building Roos Street, Fourways Golf Park, Bryanston, 2191, Gauteng, South Africa
Tel.: (27) 861 8726837 ZA
Web Site:
http://www.tranterholdings.com
Sales Range: $10-24.9 Million
Holding Company; Investments, Energy & Mining Services
N.A.I.C.S.: 551112
Joshua Ngoma (Co-Founder & CEO)

Subsidiaries:

Tranter Energy & Mining Services (1)
144 Main Reef Rd (Corner Wilson & Main Reef Rd) Manufacta, Roodepoort, 1724, Gauteng, South Africa
Tel.: (27) 11 761 2200
Mining & Energy Equipment Mfr
N.A.I.C.S.: 333131

Subsidiary (Domestic):

Tranter Rock Drills (2)
144 Main Reef Road, Manufacta, Roodepoort, 1725, Gauteng, South Africa
Tel.: (27) 117612200
Web Site:
http://www.energyandminingservices.com
Exploratory Drilling Equipment Mfr
N.A.I.C.S.: 333132

TRANWAY TECHNOLOGIES LIMITED

No 1914 5th Cross 18th A Main J P Nagar 2Nd Phase, Bengaluru, 560078, Karnataka, India
Tel.: (91) 8046730800
Web Site: http://www.tranwayinc.com
Year Founded: 2014
542923—(BOM)
Computer Programming Services
N.A.I.C.S.: 541511
Kalavathy Bylappa (Chm & Mng Dir)

TRAP OIL LTD.

4 Park Pl, St James Mayfair, London, SW1A 1LP, United Kingdom
Tel.: (44) 2031705586 UK
Web Site: http://www.trapoil.com
Year Founded: 2007
Oil & Gas Exploration Services
N.A.I.C.S.: 211120
John Church (Sec)

TRAPHACO JOINT STOCK COMPANY

75 Yen Ninh Street Quan Thanh Ward, Ba Dinh District, Hanoi, Vietnam
Tel.: (84) 18006612
Web Site: https://traphaco.com.vn
Year Founded: 1972
TRA—(HOSE)
Rev.: $94,859,430
Assets: $87,504,707
Liabilities: $26,155,649
Net Worth: $61,349,057
Earnings: $11,753,079
Emp.: 1,021
Fiscal Year-end: 12/31/23
Pharmaceutical Products Mfr & Whslr
N.A.I.C.S.: 325412
Thi Thuan Vu (Chm)

Subsidiaries:

Dak Lak Pharmaceuticals and Medical Equipments joint stock company (1)
9A Hung Vuong, Buon Ma Thuot, Daklak, Vietnam
Tel.: (84) 5003852462
Medical Equipment Mfr & Distr
N.A.I.C.S.: 339112

TRAPROCK MINING LIMITED

Level 16 344 Queen Street, Brisbane, 4000, QLD, Australia

INTERNATIONAL PUBLIC

Tel.: (61) 732216022
Web Site: http://www.traprock.com.au
Year Founded: 2016
Mineral Exploration Services
N.A.I.C.S.: 213113
Anthony Fawdon (Chm)

TRAPY PRO

Zae Saltgourde Avenue De L Industrie, Marsac Sur L Isle, 24430, Bordeaux, France
Tel.: (33) 553079090
Web Site: http://www.trapy.com
Sales Range: $25-49.9 Million
Emp.: 72
Electrical Apparatus & Equipment
N.A.I.C.S.: 423610
Jean-Jacques Trapy (Pres)

TRAQER CORP.

No 436 North Dongjiao Road Room 516, Liwan, Guangzhou, 510145, Guangdong, China
Tel.: (86) 2066685362
TAQR—(OTCIQ)
Software Development Services
N.A.I.C.S.: 541511
Linfeng Li (Chm, Pres, CEO, CFO, Treas & Sec)

TRAUMHAUS AG

Borsigstrasse 20a, 65205, Wiesbaden, Germany
Tel.: (49) 6122586530
Web Site: https://www.traumhaus-familie.de
Year Founded: 1993
TRU—(DEU)
Metal Building Component Mfr
N.A.I.C.S.: 332311
Ottfried Sinner (Chm)

TRAVEL EXPERT (ASIA) ENTERPRISES LIMITED

9/F LiFung Tower 868 Cheung Sha Wan Road, Kowloon, China (Hong Kong)
Tel.: (852) 21116900 Ky
Web Site: http://www.tegroup.com.hk
1235—(HKG)
Rev.: $5,134,425
Assets: $13,433,528
Liabilities: $5,835,165
Net Worth: $7,598,363
Earnings: ($281,138)
Emp.: 114
Fiscal Year-end: 03/31/23
Travel Agency
N.A.I.C.S.: 561510
Daniel Wai Ming Ko (Chm)

Subsidiaries:

Travel Expert Business Services Limited (1)
Units A-C 9/F D2 Place Two 15 Cheung Shun Street Lai Chi Kok, Kowloon, China (Hong Kong)
Tel.: (852) 25291999
Web Site: http://www.tebsl.com
Travel Agency Services
N.A.I.C.S.: 561510

Travel Expert Online Limited (1)
8/F Guangdong Finance Building No 88 Connaught Road, Hong Kong, China (Hong Kong)
Tel.: (852) 21116900
Web Site: https://www.texpert.com
Travel Agency Services
N.A.I.C.S.: 561510

TRAVEL INVESTMENT & SEAFOOD DEVELOPMENT CORP.

National Road 80 Vam Cong IP, Lap Vo, Binh Thanh, Dong Thap, Vietnam
Tel.: (84) 2773680657
Year Founded: 2008
DAT—(HNX)

TRAVEL TECHNOLOGY INTERACTIVE SA
11 rue du Colisee, 75008, Paris, France
Tel.: (33) 171181515
Web Site: https://www.ttinteractive.com
Year Founded: 2001
ALTTI—(EUR)
Sales Range: $1-9.9 Million
Emp.: 52
Air Transportation Software Products
N.A.I.C.S.: 513210
Eric Kourry *(Chm-Supervisory Bd)*

TRAVELERS FINANCIAL GROUP LIMITED
800 9900 King George Blvd, Surrey, V3T 0K7, BC, Canada
Tel.: (604) 293-0202
Web Site: http://www.travelersfinancial.com
Year Founded: 1986
Sales Range: $75-99.9 Million
Emp.: 150
Commercial Financial & Leasing Services
N.A.I.C.S.: 525990
Dennis Holmes *(Chm)*

Subsidiaries:

Crelogix Acceptance Corporation (1)
4445 Lougheed Hwy Ste 900, Burnaby, V5C 0E4, BC, Canada
Tel.: (604) 293-1131
Web Site: http://www.crelogix.com
Credit Services
N.A.I.C.S.: 522390
Karl E. Sigerist *(Pres & CEO)*

Travelers Financial (Alberta) Corporation (1)
Ste 210 2880 Glenmore Trl SE, Calgary, T2C 2E7, AB, Canada
Tel.: (403) 296-0180
Web Site: http://www.travelersfinancial.com
Sales Range: $25-49.9 Million
Emp.: 12
Financial Services
N.A.I.C.S.: 561499

Travelers Financial Corporation (1)
Ste 500 4180 Lougheed Hwy, Burnaby, V5C 6A7, BC, Canada
Tel.: (604) 293-0202
Web Site: http://www.travelersfinancial.com
Sales Range: $10-24.9 Million
Emp.: 40
Financial Services
N.A.I.C.S.: 561499
Roberto Cortese *(COO)*

TRAVELERS TRANSPORTATION SERVICES
195 Heart Lake Road South, Brampton, L6W 3N6, ON, Canada
Tel.: (905) 457-8789
Web Site: http://www.travelers.ca
Year Founded: 1985
Sales Range: $50-74.9 Million
Emp.: 365
Freight Transportation Services
N.A.I.C.S.: 488510

TRAVELEX HOLDINGS LIMITED
4th Floor Kings Place 90 York Way, London, N1 9AG, United Kingdom
Tel.: (44) 207 812 5500 UK
Web Site: http://www.travelex-corporate.com
Year Founded: 1976
Sales Range: $900-999.9 Million
Emp.: 7,196

Holding Company; Currency Exchange Services
N.A.I.C.S.: 551112
James Birch *(Gen Counsel)*

Subsidiaries:

Banque Travelex S.A. (1)
17 Route de la Reine, 92100, Boulogne-Billancourt, France
Tel.: (33) 1 76 77 45 20
Web Site: http://www.travelex.fr
Currency Exchange Services
N.A.I.C.S.: 523160

GWK Travelex N.V. (1)
De Entree 47-49, 1101 BH, Amsterdam, Netherlands
Tel.: (31) 205690690
Web Site: http://www.gwktravelex.nl
Money Exchange & Transfer Services
N.A.I.C.S.: 523999

Travelex Bahrain WLL (1)
Jawad House 171 Sh Issa Avenue, PO Box 24344, Manama, Bahrain
Tel.: (973) 173 39283
Web Site: http://www.travelex.bh
Currency Exchange Services
N.A.I.C.S.: 523160

Travelex Currency Exchange (China) Co., Ltd. (1)
1168 Century Avenue Pudong Financial Center East Room 1702 Block B, Shanghai, China
Tel.: (86) 4008216825
Web Site: http://www.travelex.com.cn
Currency Exchange Services
N.A.I.C.S.: 523160

Travelex Currency Services Inc. (1)
122 E 42nd St Ste 2800, New York, NY 10168
Tel.: (516) 300-1622
Web Site: http://www.travelex.com
Foreign Currency Exchange Services
N.A.I.C.S.: 522320
Pamela Henning *(VP-Retail Partnerships & Bus Dev-North America)*

Travelex Deutschland GmbH (1)
Flughafen Frankfurt Gebaude 234 HBK 5 Hugo-Eckener-Ring, 60549, Frankfurt am Main, Germany
Tel.: (49) 69 90721276
Web Site: http://www.travelex.de
Currency Exchange Services
N.A.I.C.S.: 523210

Travelex Emirates LLC (1)
Sheikh Ahmed bin Hamid Al Hamid Building Sheikh Zayed I Street, Abu Dhabi, United Arab Emirates
Tel.: (971) 25759660
Web Site: http://www.travelexae.com
Currency Exchange Services
N.A.I.C.S.: 523160
Dylan D'Souza *(Mgr-Retail Sls)*

Travelex India Pvt Limited (1)
A Wing 2nd Floor Paradigm Tower Mindspace Link Road Malad West, Mumbai, 400 064, India
Tel.: (91) 22 66757500
Web Site: http://www.travelex.co.in
Currency Exchange Services
N.A.I.C.S.: 523160

Travelex Italia Ltd (1)
via Gian Lorenzo Bernini 11, Fiumicino, 00054, Rome, Italy
Tel.: (39) 06658721
Web Site: http://www.travelex.it
Currency Exchange Services
N.A.I.C.S.: 522320

Travelex Japan KK (1)
6F Orix Akasaka 2-Chome Building 2-9-11 Akasaka, Minato-ku, Tokyo, 107-0052, Japan
Tel.: (81) 3 3568 1061
Web Site: http://www.travelex.co.jp
Currency Exchange Services
N.A.I.C.S.: 523160
Kozo Watanabe *(CEO)*

Travelex Limited (1)
Level 28 20 Bond Street, Sydney, 2000, NSW, Australia
Tel.: (61) 2 9696 9000
Web Site: http://www.travelex.com.au
Currency Exchange Services
N.A.I.C.S.: 523160

Travelex Malaysia Sdn Bhd (1)
Johor Bahru City Square 28-06 Jalan Wong Ah Fook, Bandar Johor Bahru, 80000, Johor Bahru, Malaysia
Tel.: (60) 7 2220 0701
Currency Exchange Services
N.A.I.C.S.: 523160

Travelex Money Exchange Limited (1)
Room 2301 23rd Floor Des Voeux Road Central, Hongkong Dragon Center 188, Hong Kong, China (Hong Kong)
Tel.: (852) 2854 4938
Web Site: http://www.travelex.hk
Currency Exchange Services
N.A.I.C.S.: 523160

Travelex Qatar Q.S.C. (1)
Souq Al Badi, PO Box 30808, Doha, Qatar
Tel.: (974) 44432043
Web Site: http://www.travelex.qa
Currency Exchange Services
N.A.I.C.S.: 523160
Shankar Soman *(Gen Mgr)*

Travelex SA/NV (1)
Steendam 108, 9000, Gent, Belgium
Tel.: (32) 09 269 1720
Web Site: http://www.travelex.be
Currency Exchange Services
N.A.I.C.S.: 523160

TRAVELITE HOLDINGS LTD.
53 Ubi Avenue 3 Travelite Building, Singapore, 408863, Singapore
Tel.: (65) 67858000
Web Site: https://www.etravelite.com
Year Founded: 1968
BCZ—(SES)
Rev.: $34,377,177
Assets: $50,393,479
Liabilities: $32,540,941
Net Worth: $17,852,538
Earnings: $2,540,200
Emp.: 224
Fiscal Year-end: 03/31/23
Luggage Bags Mfr
N.A.I.C.S.: 316990
Woon Hong Wee *(Co-Sec)*

Subsidiaries:

Demarco Pte. Ltd. (1)
Block 9005 Tampines St 93 04-254, Singapore, 528839, Singapore
Tel.: (65) 67858000
Web Site: http://www.etravelite.com
Sales Range: $50-74.9 Million
Emp.: 70
Luggage & Travel Accessories Distr
N.A.I.C.S.: 423990
Simon Guan Hong Yeo *(Gen Mgr)*

Fashion Way Sdn. Bhd. (1)
No 8 Jalan TPP 6/12 Taman Perindustrian Puchong, Puchong, 47160, Selangor Darul Ehsan, Malaysia
Tel.: (60) 380606000
Sales Range: $25-49.9 Million
Emp.: 50
Women's Shoes Whslr
N.A.I.C.S.: 424340
Raymond Pong *(Mng Dir)*

YG Marketing Pte. Ltd. (1)
YGM Building 205A Kallang Bahru, Singapore, 339342, Singapore
Tel.: (65) 62953811
Men Apparel Whslr
N.A.I.C.S.: 424350

TRAVELODGE LAKESHORE
718 Lakeshore Drive, North Bay, P1A 2G4, ON, Canada
Tel.: (705) 472-7171
Web Site: http://www.travelodgenorthbay.com
Sales Range: $10-24.9 Million
Emp.: 21
Hotel Operations
N.A.I.C.S.: 721110
Amith Talreja *(Mgr)*

TRAVELPERK SL
Avinguda Catedral 6-8 1a Planta, 08002, Barcelona, Spain
Tel.: (34) 931227581
Web Site: http://www.travelperk.com
Travel Management Services
N.A.I.C.S.: 561599
Avi Meir *(Co-Founder & CEO)*

Subsidiaries:

Click Travel Ltd. (1)
Alpha Tower Suffolk Street Queensway, Birmingham, B1 1TT, United Kingdom
Tel.: (44) 844 745 2121
Web Site: http://www.clicktravel.com
Sales Range: $75-99.9 Million
Emp.: 76
Travel Management Services
N.A.I.C.S.: 561520
James McClean *(Dir-Fin)*

TRAVELSKY TECHNOLOGY LIMITED
TravelSky High-Tech Industrial Park Houshayu Town, Shunyi District, Beijing, 101318, China
Tel.: (86) 1057650696
Web Site: https://www.travelskyir.com
0696—(OTCIQ)
Rev.: $721,381,504
Assets: $3,494,191,937
Liabilities: $760,868,429
Net Worth: $2,733,323,509
Earnings: $86,743,858
Emp.: 6,570
Fiscal Year-end: 12/31/22
Aviation Information Technology Solutions
N.A.I.C.S.: 541512
Yinhong Xiao *(CEO & Gen Mgr)*

Subsidiaries:

China TravelSky International Limited (1)
TravelSky High-Tech Industrial Park, Houshayu Town Shunyi District, Beijing, 101318, China
Tel.: (86) 1057650696
Web Site: https://www.travelskyir.com
Emp.: 6,620
Application Development Services
N.A.I.C.S.: 541511

InfoSky Technology Co., Ltd. (1)
2nd Floor Building B No 11 Dong Xing Li Xing Fu San Cun, Chao Yang District, Beijing, 100027, China (100%)
Tel.: (86) 1065669939
Web Site: http://www.infosky.com.cn
Logistic Services
N.A.I.C.S.: 481112

TravelSky Technology (Japan) Limited (1)
Holland Hills Mori Tower 16th Fl 5-11-2 Toranomon, Minato-Ku, Tokyo, 105-0001, Japan
Tel.: (81) 354252122
Web Site: http://www.travelsky.co.jp
Sales Range: $25-49.9 Million
Emp.: 4
Aviation Information Technology Services
N.A.I.C.S.: 541512

TRAVELSTART ONLINE TRAVEL OPERATIONS PTY. LTD
Longkloof Studios Block B Darters Road Gardens, Cape Town, South Africa
Tel.: (27) 214684300
Web Site: http://www.travelstart.co.za
Online Travel Agency
N.A.I.C.S.: 561599
Stephan Ekbergh *(CEO)*

TRAVELSTART ONLINE TRAVEL OPERATIONS PTY. LTD

Travelstart Online Travel Operations Pty. Ltd—(Continued)

Subsidiaries:

Club Travel SA (Pty) Ltd. (1)
Unit 1100 11th Floor Picbel Parkade 58 Strand Street, Cape Town, 8000, South Africa
Tel.: (27) 860555777
Web Site: http://www.clubtravel.co.za
Emp.: 3
Travel Tour Operator
N.A.I.C.S.: 561520
Wally Gaynor (Mng Dir)

TRAVERSE ENERGY LTD.
Suite 780 839 - Fifth Avenue SW, Calgary, T2P 3C8, AB, Canada
Tel.: (403) 264-9223
Web Site: http://www.traverseenergy.com
Rev.: $4,689,071
Assets: $21,031,648
Liabilities: $8,847,116
Net Worth: $12,184,532
Earnings: ($12,977,306)
Emp.: 10
Fiscal Year-end: 12/31/18
Oil & Gas Exploration Service
N.A.I.C.S.: 213112
Sharon A. Supple (CFO)

TRAVERTINE COMPANY PLC
Ghore Damia-Hay Fanoush, PO Box 941499, Amman, 11194, Jordan
Tel.: (962) 53539300
Web Site: https://www.travco.com.jo
Year Founded: 1999
TRAV—(AMM)
Rev.: $409,149
Assets: $4,165,307
Liabilities: $2,275,899
Net Worth: $1,889,408
Earnings: ($933,831)
Emp.: 38
Fiscal Year-end: 12/31/20
Limestone Mining Services
N.A.I.C.S.: 212311

TRAVIS PERKINS PLC
Tel.: (44) 1604752424   UK
Web Site:
https://www.travisperkinsplc.co.uk
Year Founded: 1988
TPRKY—(OTCIQ)
Rev.: $6,016,236,600
Assets: $4,982,293,800
Liabilities: $2,450,193,900
Net Worth: $2,532,099,900
Earnings: $231,504,900
Fiscal Year-end: 12/31/22
Other Building Material Dealers
N.A.I.C.S.: 444180
Frank M. Elkins (COO)

Subsidiaries:

BSS Group Ltd (1)
1st Fl Ct 7 Bartan Close Grow Park, Leicester, LE1 3QQ, United Kingdom
Tel.: (44) 1162623232
Web Site: http://www.bssgroup.com
Sales Range: $1-4.9 Billion
Emp.: 4,966
Heating, Plumbing, Process, Pipeline & Mechanical Services Equipment Marketing & Distribution
N.A.I.C.S.: 423720

Subsidiary (Domestic):

PTS Plumbing Trade Supplies (2)
Buccaneer Way, Magna Park, Lutterworth, LE17 4YZ, Leicestershire, United Kingdom (100%)
Tel.: (44) 455551210
Web Site: http://www.ptsplumbing.com
Sales Range: $25-49.9 Million
Emp.: 100
Heating, Plumbing, Process & Mechanical Service Equipment Supplier
N.A.I.C.S.: 423720

Pegler & Louden (2)
Martin Close, Blenheim Industrial Estate, Bulwell, Nottingham, NG6 8UW, United Kingdom (100%)
Tel.: (44) 59739580
Web Site: http://www.peglerandlouden.com
Valve & Flow Control Product Supplier
N.A.I.C.S.: 423720

Benchmarx Kitchens and Joinery Limited (1)
Lodge Way House Lodge Way Harlestone Road, Northampton, NN5 7UG, Northamptonshire, United Kingdom
Tel.: (44) 1604585208
Web Site:
http://www.benchmarxjoinery.co.uk
Kitchen & Joinery Products Retailer
N.A.I.C.S.: 424990
Robert Dicks (Mgr-Sls)

CCF Ltd. (1)
123 Gillette way, Reading, RG2 OBS, Berks, United Kingdom
Tel.: (44) 1189491092
Web Site: http://www.ccfltd.co.uk
Sales Range: $25-49.9 Million
Emp.: 55
Building Supply Retailer
N.A.I.C.S.: 444180

City Plumbing Supplies (1)
Lodge Way House Lodge Way Harlestone Rd, Northampton, NN5 7UG, United Kingdom
Tel.: (44) 3306780267
Web Site: http://www.cityplumbing.co.uk
Sales Range: $200-249.9 Million
Emp.: 1,000
Plumbing Supply Retailer
N.A.I.C.S.: 444180
Stephen Kemp (Mgr-Audit, Security & Loss Prevention)

Keyline Builders Merchant (1)
Keyline Civils Specialist Ltd 130 Salkeld Street, Glasgow, G5 8HD, United Kingdom
Tel.: (44) 414203333
Web Site: http://www.keyline.co.uk
Sales Range: $25-49.9 Million
Emp.: 20
Building Supply Retailer
N.A.I.C.S.: 444180

National Shower Spares Limited (1)
Units 16-17 Bamel Way Gloucester Business Park, Brockworth, Gloucester, GL3 4BH, Gloucestershire, United Kingdom
Tel.: (44) 1452619836
Web Site: http://www.showerspares.com
Plumbing & Heating Equipment Whslr
N.A.I.C.S.: 423720

Primaflow Limited (1)
Stargate Business Park, Nechells, Birmingham, B7 5SE, United Kingdom
Tel.: (44) 121 322 4800
Web Site: http://www.primaflow.co.uk
Emp.: 130
Plumbing, Heating & Ventilation Supplies Distr
N.A.I.C.S.: 423720

Solfex Limited (1)
Units 3-4, Charnley Fold Industrial Estate Bamber Bridge, Preston, PR5 6PS, United Kingdom
Tel.: (44) 1772312847
Web Site: http://www.solfex.co.uk
Energy Equipment Distr
N.A.I.C.S.: 423690

TP Plumbing & Heating (1)
Lodge Way House Lodge Way Harlestone Rd, Northampton, NN5 7UG, United Kingdom
Tel.: (44) 1604752424
Web Site: http://www.tpph.co.uk
Sales Range: $200-249.9 Million
Emp.: 1,000
Plumbing Supply Retailer
N.A.I.C.S.: 444180

The Underfloor Heating Store Limited (1)
Lodge Way House Lodge Way Harlestone Road, Northampton, NN5 7UG, United Kingdom
Tel.: (44) 1268567016

Web Site:
http://www.theunderfloorheatingstore.com
Plumbing & Heating Equipment Whslr
N.A.I.C.S.: 423720
Dominic Lodge (Mgr-Sls)

Tile Giant Limited (1)
Anchor Road, Longton, Stoke-on-Trent, ST3 1NF, Staffordshire, United Kingdom
Tel.: (44) 1782597777
Web Site: http://www.tilegiant.co.uk
Sales Range: $25-49.9 Million
Emp.: 20
Ceramic Tiles Retailer
N.A.I.C.S.: 423320

Travis Perkins (Properties) Limited (1)
Navigation Road, Chelmsford, CM2 6HX, Essex, United Kingdom
Tel.: (44) 1245490000
Sales Range: $25-49.9 Million
Emp.: 30
Commercial Property Management Services
N.A.I.C.S.: 531312
Mark Junnar (Gen Mgr)

Travis Perkins Trading Company (1)
Lodge Way House Lodge Way Harlestone Rd, Northampton, NN5 7UG, United Kingdom
Tel.: (44) 3335778811
Web Site: http://www.travisperkins.co.uk
Sales Range: $150-199.9 Million
Emp.: 700
Retail Support Services
N.A.I.C.S.: 561499

Wickes Building Supplies Limited (1)
Rhosili Road Brackmills Industrial Estate, Northampton, NN5 5AF, Northamptonshire, United Kingdom
Tel.: (44) 1604753221
Web Site: http://www.wickes.co.uk
Hardware Retailer
N.A.I.C.S.: 444140

TRAVUNIJA A.D.
Kralja Petra I Oslobodioca 40, 89000, Trebinje, Bosnia & Herzegovina
Tel.: (387) 59 274 080
Sales Range: Less than $1 Million
Emp.: 10
Real Estate Prorperty Leasing Services
N.A.I.C.S.: 531190

TRAX TECHNOLOGY SOLUTIONS PTE LTD
65 Chulia Street #19-01 OCBC Centre, Singapore, 049513, Singapore
Tel.: (65) 62249145
Web Site: http://traxretail.com
Year Founded: 2010
Computer Vision Solutions
N.A.I.C.S.: 513210
Joel Bar-El (CEO)

Subsidiaries:

Bet Information Systems, Inc. (1)
2059 Camden Ave Ste 223, San Jose, CA 95124
Tel.: (408) 850-1227
Web Site: http://www.survey.com
Market Research Solutions
N.A.I.C.S.: 541910
Ron Magliocco (Chief Customer Officer)

Shopkick, Inc. (1)
2317 Broadway St, Redwood City, CA 94063
Tel.: (650) 326-1667
Web Site: http://www.shopkick.com
Emp.: 51
Mobile Software Development Services
N.A.I.C.S.: 513210
Adam Sand (CEO)

TRAXALL INTERNATIONAL LTD.
Silverdale Business Park Fleet House Maries Way Newcastle,, Staffordshire, ST5 6PA, United Kingdom
Tel.: (44) 8445677988

INTERNATIONAL PUBLIC

Web Site:
https://www.traxallinternational.com
Year Founded: 2015
Business Consulting & Services
N.A.I.C.S.: 541618
Ross Jackson (CEO)

TRAYAL KORPORACIJA A.D.
Parunovacka 18 V, 37000, Krusevac, Serbia
Tel.: (381) 37422328   RS
Web Site: https://www.trayal.rs
Year Founded: 1889
TRAY—(BEL)
Rev.: $82,126,704,919
Assets: $114,821,089,377
Liabilities: $58,456,134,258
Net Worth: $56,364,955,119
Earnings: $5,396,596,052
Emp.: 1,230
Fiscal Year-end: 12/31/23
Tiles Mfr
N.A.I.C.S.: 326211
Milos Nenezic (Dir)

TRC CONSTRUCTION PUBLIC COMPANY LIMITED
No 8 Soi Sukhapiban 5 soi 32 Tha Raeng, Bang Khen District, Bangkok, 10220, Thailand
Tel.: (66) 20227777   TH
Web Site: https://www.trc-con.com
Year Founded: 2001
TRC—(THA)
Rev.: $64,043,626
Assets: $114,633,259
Liabilities: $121,601,606
Net Worth: ($6,968,347)
Earnings: ($15,772,884)
Emp.: 229
Fiscal Year-end: 12/31/23
Construction Services
N.A.I.C.S.: 236210
Paichit Rattananon (Chm)

Subsidiaries:

Sahakarn Wisavakorn Co., Ltd. (1)
8 Soi Sukhaphiban 5 Soi 32 Tha Raeng, Bang Khen District, Bangkok, 10220, Thailand
Tel.: (66) 2 022 7777
Construction Engineering Services
N.A.I.C.S.: 541330

TRC Engineering LLC (1)
Office No 41 Fourth Floor Ghoubra Plaza Building No 19, Plot No 105, Muscat, Oman
Tel.: (968) 24614048
Civil Engineering Services
N.A.I.C.S.: 541330

TRC Middle East LLC (1)
180 Al-Athaibah, Muscat, Oman
Tel.: (968) 24613335
Construction Engineering Services
N.A.I.C.S.: 541330

TRC SYNERGY BERHAD
TRC Business Centre Jalan Andaman Utama, 68000, Ampang, Selangor Darul Ehsan, Malaysia
Tel.: (60) 341038000
Web Site: https://www.trc.com.my
TRC—(KLS)
Rev.: $188,625,443
Assets: $287,864,033
Liabilities: $175,240,890
Net Worth: $112,623,143
Earnings: $4,490,393
Emp.: 765
Fiscal Year-end: 12/31/21
Construction Services
N.A.I.C.S.: 236220
Abdul Aziz Mohamed (Sec)

Subsidiaries:

TRC Land Sdn. Bhd. (1)
Ground Floor Block 1 Impian Senibong Apartments, Persiaran Senibong Taman

Bayu Senibong, 81750, Johor Bahru, Johor Darul Takzim, Malaysia
Tel.: (60) 73864496
Web Site: https://www.trcland.com.my
Emp.: 6
Residential Property Development Services
N.A.I.C.S.: 531110
Fuziah Ibrahim (Office Mgr)

Subsidiary (Domestic):

TRC Development Sdn. Bhd. (2)
TRC Business Centre Jalan Andaman Utama, Ampang, 68000, Selangor, Malaysia
Tel.: (60) 341080105
Web Site: https://www.trc.com.my
Sales Range: $150-199.9 Million
Emp.: 500
Residential & Commercial Property Development Services
N.A.I.C.S.: 531311
Rafidah Mansor (Sr Mgr)

Trans Resources Corporation Sdn. Bhd. (1)
TRC Business Centre Jalan Andaman Utama, 68000, Ampang, Selangor, Malaysia
Tel.: (60) 341038000
Web Site: https://www.trc.my
Construction Services
N.A.I.C.S.: 236220
Abdul Aziz Mohamad (CEO & Exec Dir)

TRE HOLDINGS CORPORATION
Tel.: (81) 363272620
Web Site: https://tre-hd.co.jp
92470—(TKS)
Holding Company
N.A.I.C.S.: 551112
Matsuoka Nato (Chm & CEO)

TREA CAPITAL PARTNERS, SOCIEDAD DE VALORES S.A.
Avda Diagonal 640 3 E, 08017, Barcelona, Spain
Tel.: (34) 93 467 5510   ES
Web Site: http://www.treaam.com
Year Founded: 2006
Emp.: 47
Investment Management Service
N.A.I.C.S.: 523940
Carlos Tusquets (Founder & Chm)

Subsidiaries:

TREA Asset Management S.G.I.I.C., S.A. (1)
Avenida Diagonal 640 3 E, 08017, Barcelona, Spain
Tel.: (34) 93 467 5510
Web Site: http://www.treacapital.com
Investment Management Service
N.A.I.C.S.: 523940
Carlos Tusquets (Founder & Chm)

TREASURE FACTORY CO., LTD.
2F Daito Bldg 3 Kandaneribeicho, Chiyoda-ku, Tokyo, 101-0022, Japan
Tel.: (81) 338808822
Web Site: https://www.treasurefactory.co.jp
Year Founded: 1995
3093—(TKS)
Rev.: $244,278,860
Assets: $125,691,520
Liabilities: $65,242,180
Net Worth: $60,449,340
Earnings: $15,888,690
Fiscal Year-end: 02/29/24
Recycle Store Operator
N.A.I.C.S.: 459510
Eigo Nosaka (Pres & CEO)

TREASURY CORPORATION OF VICTORIA
Level 12 1 Collins Street, Melbourne, 3000, VIC, Australia
Tel.: (61) 396514800
Web Site: http://www.tcv.vic.gov.au
Rev.: $58,868,356
Assets: $36,986,223,237
Liabilities: $36,826,393,738
Net Worth: $159,829,499
Earnings: $35,172,323
Emp.: 43
Fiscal Year-end: 06/30/19
Financial Management Services
N.A.I.C.S.: 523999
William Whitford (Mng Dir)

TREASURY WINE ESTATES LIMITED
Level 8 161 Collins Street, Melbourne, 3000, VIC, Australia
Tel.: (61) 385333000   AU
Web Site: https://www.tweglobal.com
TSRYF—(OTCIQ)
Rev.: $2,056,377,341
Assets: $4,814,891,198
Liabilities: $2,063,349,670
Net Worth: $2,751,541,528
Earnings: $191,547,500
Emp.: 2,600
Fiscal Year-end: 06/30/21
Wineries
N.A.I.C.S.: 312130
Timothy Ford (CEO & Mng Dir)

Subsidiaries:

Daou Vineyards (1)
2777 Hidden Mtn Rd, Paso Robles, CA 93446-8712
Tel.: (805) 226-5460
Web Site: http://www.daouvineyards.com
Grape Vineyards
N.A.I.C.S.: 111332
Brandon Carlisle (Mgr-Lab)

Leo Buring Pty. Ltd (1)
L 8 5 Rider Bvd, Rhodes, 2138, NSW, Australia
Tel.: (61) 292171200
Alcoholic Beverages Mfr & Whslr
N.A.I.C.S.: 312140

Lindemans Wines Pty. Ltd. (1)
58 Queensbridge Street, Southbank, 3006, VIC, Australia
Tel.: (61) 130 065 1650
Web Site: https://www.lindemans.com
Wine Mfr
N.A.I.C.S.: 312130

Treasury Wine Estates (1)
555 Gateway Dr, Napa, CA 94558-7516   (72%)
Tel.: (707) 259-4500
Web Site: https://www.tweglobal.com
Sales Range: $200-249.9 Million
Emp.: 600
California Wines Producer & Marketer
N.A.I.C.S.: 312130
Kinyi Choo (Mng Dir-Southeast Asia, Middle East, Africa, Hong Kong & Taiwan)

Subsidiary (Domestic):

Chateau St. Jean Winery (2)
8555 Sonoma Hwy, Kenwood, CA 95452-0293   (100%)
Tel.: (707) 257-5784
Sales Range: $25-49.9 Million
Emp.: 70
Produces & Markets California Wines
N.A.I.C.S.: 312130

Etude Wines, Inc (2)
1250 Cuttings Wharf Rd, Napa, CA 94559-9738
Tel.: (707) 257-5782
Web Site: https://www.etudewines.com
Alcoholic Beverage Distr
N.A.I.C.S.: 424820

St. Clement Vineyards (2)
555 Gateway Dr, Napa, CA 94558 (100%)
Tel.: (707) 257-5783
Web Site: http://www.stclement.com
Winery
N.A.I.C.S.: 312130

Treasury Chateau & Estates (2)
240 Gateway Rd W, Napa, CA 94558   (100%)
Tel.: (800) 373-5896
Web Site: http://tcewines.com
Wine Mfr
N.A.I.C.S.: 312130

Unit (Domestic):

Beaulieu Vineyard (3)
1960 St Helena Hwy, Rutherford, CA 94573
Tel.: (707) 257-5749
Vineyard & Winery
N.A.I.C.S.: 312130

Sterling Vineyards (3)
1111 Dunaweal Ln, Calistoga, CA 94515
Tel.: (707) 942-3300
Vineyard & Winery
N.A.I.C.S.: 312130

Treasury Wine Estates (China) Holding Co. Pty. Ltd. (1)
161 Collins Street, Melbourne, 3000, VIC, Australia
Tel.: (61) 38 533 3000
Beverages Mfr
N.A.I.C.S.: 312111
Kerrin Petty (Chief Supply Officer)

Treasury Wine Estates (NZ) Limited (1)
Level 3 Fosters House 16 College Cell Freemans Bay, PO Box 8264, Simon St, Auckland, New Zealand
Tel.: (64) 9145920
Sales Range: $25-49.9 Million
Emp.: 25
Brewery
N.A.I.C.S.: 312120

Subsidiary (Domestic):

Bulmer Harvest Limited (2)
91 Custom House St, Gisborne, 4010, New Zealand
Tel.: (64) 68688300
Web Site: http://www.harvestcider.co.nz
Sales Range: $25-49.9 Million
Emp.: 12
Alcoholic Beverages Mfr & Distr
N.A.I.C.S.: 312140
Hamish Jackson (Gen Mgr)

Treasury Wine Estates Canada, Inc (1)
3335 Boul Pitfield Suite 100, Saint Laurent, H4S 1H3, QC, Canada
Tel.: (514) 289-2057
Web Site: http://www.treasurywineestate.com
Sales Range: $25-49.9 Million
Emp.: 14
Alcoholic Beverages Mfr & Distr
N.A.I.C.S.: 312140

Treasury Wine Estates EMEA Ltd. (1)
Regal House London Road, Twickenham, TW1 3QS, Middlesex, United Kingdom
Tel.: (44) 2088438400
Wine Marketing & Distr
N.A.I.C.S.: 424820

Treasury Wine Estates Pte. Ltd. (1)
50 Scotts Road 02 -01A, Singapore, 228242, Singapore
Tel.: (65) 65089144
Sales Range: $25-49.9 Million
Emp.: 15
Wine Distr
N.A.I.C.S.: 424820

Winemaker Choice Pty Ltd. (1)
Unit E 75-77 St Hilliers Road, Auburn, 2144, NSW, Australia
Tel.: (61) 296468333
Web Site: http://www.winemakerschoice.com.au
Alcoholic Beverages Mfr & Whslr
N.A.I.C.S.: 312130

Wolf Blass Wines Pty. Ltd (1)
97 Sturt Highway, Nurioopta, 5355, SA, Australia
Tel.: (61) 88 568 7311
Web Site: https://www.wolfblass.com
Wine Mfr
N.A.I.C.S.: 312130

Wynns Coonawarra Estate Pty. Ltd (1)
77 Memorial Dr, Coonawarra, 5263, SA, Australia
Tel.: (61) 887362225
Sales Range: $25-49.9 Million
Emp.: 200
Alcoholic Beverages Mfr & Whslr
N.A.I.C.S.: 312130

TREATT PLC
2 Gresham Street, London, EC2V 7QP, Suffolk, United Kingdom
Tel.: (44) 2075975970
Web Site: https://www.treatt.com
Year Founded: 1886
TET—(LSE)
Rev.: $168,799,897
Assets: $202,866,449
Liabilities: $58,542,171
Net Worth: $144,324,278
Earnings: $20,566,743
Emp.: 423
Fiscal Year-end: 09/30/21
Essential Oils, Natural Specialties, Aroma Chemicals & Flavours Producer & Distr
N.A.I.C.S.: 325998
Richard Andrew Hope (CFO)

Subsidiaries:

R C Treatt & Co Ltd (1)
Skyliner Way, Bury Saint Edmunds, IP32 7FR, Suffolk, United Kingdom   (100%)
Tel.: (44) 128 470 2500
Web Site: https://www.treatt.com
Sales Range: $50-74.9 Million
Emp.: 130
Mfr & Distributor of Essential Oils, Natural Specialties, Aroma Chemicals & Flavours
N.A.I.C.S.: 325998

Treatt USA Inc (1)
4900 Lakeland Commerce Pkwy, Lakeland, FL 33805   (100%)
Tel.: (863) 668-9500
Sales Range: $50-74.9 Million
Emp.: 52
Mfr & Distributor of Essential Oils, Natural Specialties, Aroma Chemicals & Flavours
N.A.I.C.S.: 424490

TREDJE AP-FONDEN
Vasagatan 16, Box 1176, SE-11191, Stockholm, Sweden
Tel.: (46) 8 555 17 100
Web Site: http://www.ap3.se
Rev.: $6,404,586,370
Assets: $43,257,562,950
Liabilities: $1,065,055,460
Net Worth: $42,192,507,490
Earnings: $6,381,866,330
Emp.: 58
Fiscal Year-end: 12/31/19
Investment & Funding Services
N.A.I.C.S.: 523999
Christina Lindenius (Chm)

Subsidiaries:

Polhem Infra AB (1)
Norrlandsgatan 12, Stockholm, Sweden
Tel.: (46) 738 00 67 25
Web Site: http://www.polheminfra.se
Privater Equity Firm
N.A.I.C.S.: 523999
Mikael Lundin (CEO & VP)

Subsidiary (Domestic):

Telia Carrier AB (2)
Stjarntorget 1, 169 94, Solna, Sweden
Tel.: (46) 850455000
Web Site: http://www.teliasoneraic.com
Sales Range: $25-49.9 Million
Mobile Network Services
N.A.I.C.S.: 517112
Staffan Gojeryd (CEO)

TREE HOUSE EDUCATION & ACCESSORIES LIMITED
702/C Morya House Off Link Road Near Infinity Mall, Andheri West, Mumbai, 400 052, India
Tel.: (91) 7777051421

TREE HOUSE EDUCATION & ACCESSORIES LIMITED

Tree House Education & Accessories Limited—(Continued)
Web Site:
https://www.treehouseplaygroup.net
TREEHOUSE—(NSE)
Rev.: $1,321,942
Assets: $26,426,256
Liabilities: $1,008,935
Net Worth: $25,417,320
Earnings: ($5,354,869)
Emp.: 16
Fiscal Year-end: 03/31/23
Educational Support Services
N.A.I.C.S.: 611710
Jugal Shah *(Exec Dir)*

TREE ISLAND STEEL LTD.
3933 Boundary Road, Richmond, V6V 1T8, BC, Canada
Tel.: (604) 524-3744   Ca
Web Site: https://www.treeisland.com
Year Founded: 1964
TSL—(TSX)
Rev.: $168,889,558
Assets: $114,642,352
Liabilities: $74,692,094
Net Worth: $39,950,257
Earnings: $4,013,879
Emp.: 420
Fiscal Year-end: 12/31/20
Fabricated Wire Product Mfr
N.A.I.C.S.: 332618
Nancy Davies *(CFO & VP-Fin)*

Subsidiaries:

Tree Island Steel Ltd. - Rancho Cucamonga Plant (1)
12459 Arrow Rte, Rancho Cucamonga, CA 91739
Tel.: (800) 255-6974
Chemical Products Mfr
N.A.I.C.S.: 325998

TREELINE WELL SERVICES INC.
750 333 11th Avenue SW, Calgary, T2R 1L9, AB, Canada
Tel.: (403) 266-2868
Web Site: http://www.treelinewell.com
Year Founded: 1997
Rev.: $19,027,216
Emp.: 70
Rigs Supplier
N.A.I.C.S.: 213112
Dan Bryson *(Pres)*

TREET CORPORATION LIMITED
72B Peco Road Kot Lakhpat Industrial Area, Lahore, 54770, Pakistan
Tel.: (92) 42111187338
Web Site: https://treetcorp.com
TREET—(KAR)
Rev.: $85,959,391
Assets: $188,281,707
Liabilities: $112,994,604
Net Worth: $75,287,103
Earnings: ($15,259,266)
Emp.: 2,208
Fiscal Year-end: 06/30/19
Shaving Products Mfr
N.A.I.C.S.: 325620
Muhammad Shafique Anjum *(Exec Dir)*

Subsidiaries:

Global Econo Trade (Pvt) Limited (1)
72-B Kot Lakhpat Industrial Area, Lahore, 54660, Pakistan
Tel.: (92) 35830881
Web Site: http://www.treetonline.com
Emp.: 1,200
Shaving Products Sales
N.A.I.C.S.: 424210
Syed Shahid Ali *(CEO)*

Plant (Domestic):

First Treet Manufacturing Modaraba (2)
72-B Industrial Area Kot Lakhpat, Rohi Nala, Lahore, Pakistan
Tel.: (92) 35830881
Web Site: https://ftmm.com.pk
Packaging Products Mfr
N.A.I.C.S.: 322211

Subsidiary (Domestic):

TCL Labor-Hire Company (Private) Limited (2)
72-B Kot Lakhpat Industrial Area, Lahore, Pakistan
Tel.: (92) 42 3583 0881
Workforce Supply Services
N.A.I.C.S.: 561499

Treet Services (Private) Limited (2)
72-B Kot Lakhpat Industrial Area, Lahore, Pakistan (100%)
Tel.: (92) 42 3583 0881
Export Services
N.A.I.C.S.: 561499

Renacon Pharma Limited (1)
72-B Peco Road Kot Lakhpat, Lahore, Pakistan
Tel.: (92) 42111187338
Web Site: https://www.renaconpharma.com
Pioneer Equipment Mfr
N.A.I.C.S.: 326130

Treet Battery Limited (1)
Plot Number 1-Phase 2 M-3 Industrial City, FIEDMC Sahianwala Interchange, Faisalabad, 37700, Pakistan
Tel.: (92) 4232590691
Web Site: https://treetbattery.com
Automobile Equipment Mfr
N.A.I.C.S.: 336310
Syed Shahid Shahid Ali *(Chm)*

TREIBACHER INDUSTRIE AG
Auer-von-Welsbach-Strasse 1, Althofen, 9330, Austria
Tel.: (43) 4262 505 0
Web Site: http://www.treibacher.com
Year Founded: 1898
Sales Range: $700-749.9 Million
Emp.: 670
Ceramic Materials, Chemicals & Steel & Foundry Products Mfr
N.A.I.C.S.: 325998
Jon Dodge *(Mng Dir-Advanced Ceramic Materials)*

Subsidiaries:

Austria Email AG (1)
Austriastrasse 6, AT-8720, Knittelfeld, Austria (88.5%)
Tel.: (43) 35127000
Web Site: http://www.austria-email.at
Emp.: 350
Water Heater Mfr
N.A.I.C.S.: 333414
Walter Persch *(Member-Mgmt Bd)*

Leuchtstoffwerk Breitungen GmbH (1)
Lange Soemme 17, 98597, Breitungen, Germany
Tel.: (49) 36848 840
Web Site: http://www.webinfo.leuchtstoffwerk.com
Industrial Chemicals Mfr
N.A.I.C.S.: 325998
Hans-Jurgen Limburg *(Mng Dir-Technical)*

Treibacher Industrie Inc. (1)
515 Consumers Road Suite 212, Toronto, M2J 4Z2, ON, Canada
Tel.: (416) 535-2600
Web Site: http://www.treibacher.com
Emp.: 6
Chemicals & Metal Materials Whslr
N.A.I.C.S.: 424690
Ulfried Pirker *(Pres)*

TREJHARA SOLUTIONS LTD.
Unit no 601 Sigma IT Park Plot no R-203 R-204, T T C Industrial Estate, Mumbai, 400701, Maharashtra, India
Tel.: (91) 2266172700
Web Site: https://www.trejhara.com
Year Founded: 2017
542233—(BOM)
Rev.: $8,316,564
Assets: $41,532,234
Liabilities: $17,758,420
Net Worth: $23,773,815
Earnings: ($35,864,600)
Emp.: 262
Fiscal Year-end: 03/31/23
Software Development Services
N.A.I.C.S.: 541511
Nilesh Kharche *(Sec)*

Subsidiaries:

Trejhara Pte. Limited (1)
438B Alexandra Road Alexandra Techno Park 05-11, Singapore, 119968, Singapore
Tel.: (65) 65364852
Freight Forwarding Services
N.A.I.C.S.: 488510

TREK 2000 INTERNATIONAL LTD
30 Loyang Way 07-13/14/15 Loyang Industrial Estate, Singapore, 508769, Singapore
Tel.: (65) 65466088
Web Site:
http://www.trek2000.com.sg
Sales Range: $100-124.9 Million
Mobile Media Solution Services
N.A.I.C.S.: 334220
Kuok Keong Tan *(CFO)*

Subsidiaries:

Racer Technology Pte Ltd (1)
28 Changi South Street 1 Changi South Industrial Estates, Singapore, 486772, Singapore
Tel.: (65) 65468318
Web Site: http://www.racer.com.sg
Precision Plastic Component Mfr
N.A.I.C.S.: 326121
Willy Koh *(Mng Dir)*

S-Com System (S) Pte Ltd (1)
30 Loyang Way 07-13/14/15 Loyang Industrial Estate, Singapore, 508769, Singapore
Tel.: (65) 6546 3933
Web Site: http://www.trek2000.com.sg
Sales Range: $25-49.9 Million
Emp.: 30
Computer Peripheral Equipment Mfr
N.A.I.C.S.: 334112
Teng Pin Poo *(Gen Mgr)*

Tracer Technology Pte Ltd (1)
28 Changi South Street 1, Singapore, 486772, Singapore
Tel.: (65) 65468318
Sales Range: $25-49.9 Million
Emp.: 20
Injection Molded Plastic Products Mfr
N.A.I.C.S.: 326121

Trek Systems (M) Sdn Bhd (1)
Block B 303-5-8 Krystal Point Jalan Sultan Azlan Shah, 11900, Sungai Nibong, Penang, Malaysia
Tel.: (60) 4 643 8811
Sales Range: $50-74.9 Million
Emp.: 5
Storage Devices Whslr
N.A.I.C.S.: 423430
Eddie Chan *(Mgr)*

Trek Technology (HK) Co. Ltd. (1)
Unit 02 8/F Block B New Trade Plaza No 6 On Ping Street, Sha Tin, New Territories, China (Hong Kong)
Tel.: (852) 27731696
Web Site: http://www.thumbdrive.com
Emp.: 2
Computer Peripheral Equipment Distr
N.A.I.C.S.: 423430
Heou Lin *(Office Mgr)*

Trek Technology (Singapore) Pte Ltd (1)
30 Loyang Way 07-13/14/15 Loyang Industrial Estate, Singapore, 508769, Singapore
Tel.: (65) 6546 3933

INTERNATIONAL PUBLIC

Web Site: http://www.trek2000.com
Sales Range: $25-49.9 Million
Emp.: 30
Computer Peripheral Equipment Mfr
N.A.I.C.S.: 334112
Teng Pin Poo *(Mgr)*

TREK METALS LTD.
5/2 Centro Avenue, PO Box 8209, Subiaco, 6008, WA, Australia
Tel.: (61) 863837844   BM
Web Site: https://trekmetals.com.au
TKM—(ASX)
Rev.: $104,779
Assets: $12,110,428
Liabilities: $707,340
Net Worth: $11,403,088
Earnings: ($1,111,749)
Fiscal Year-end: 03/31/24
Copper & Gold
N.A.I.C.S.: 212220
Derek Marshall *(CEO)*

TRELLEBORG AB
Johan Kocksgatan 10, PO Box 153, 231 22, Trelleborg, Sweden
Tel.: (46) 41067000   SE
Web Site: https://www.trelleborg.com
Year Founded: 1905
TREL.B—(OMX)
Rev.: $3,147,454,800
Assets: $5,462,375,400
Liabilities: $1,631,836,800
Net Worth: $3,830,538,600
Earnings: $319,555,800
Emp.: 15,646
Fiscal Year-end: 12/31/23
Industrial Holding Company; Engineering Services, Automotive Noise Damping Products, Industrial Seals & Wheel Systems
N.A.I.C.S.: 551112
Hans Biorck *(Chm)*

Subsidiaries:

Bloch S.A. (1)
12 Rue Joannes Carret, Lyon, 69009, France
Tel.: (33) 4 78 83 28 48
Web Site: http://www.bloch-sa.fr
Emp.: 17
Industrial Hose Mfr
N.A.I.C.S.: 326220

Dormviltre AB (1)
Johan Kocksgatan 10, Trelleborg, 231 45, Sweden
Tel.: (46) 41067000
Engineering Consulting Services
N.A.I.C.S.: 541330

Interfit Ltd (1)
Web Site: http://www.interfit-uk.com
Emp.: 30
Forklift Tire & Wheel Sales, Installation & Repair Services
N.A.I.C.S.: 423130

Interfit Sas (1)
Zone Industrielle B 35-15 rue de Luyot, Seclin, 59113, France
Tel.: (33) 3 20 16 63 40
Web Site: http://www.interfit-fr.com
Industrial Tire Mfr
N.A.I.C.S.: 326211

MHT Takentreprenoren i Malmo AB (1)
Aspogatan 5, 211 24, Malmo, Sweden
Tel.: (46) 40181205
Roofing Contractor Services
N.A.I.C.S.: 238160

Mehren Rubber AS (1)
Kalosjegata 15, PO Box 143, 3015, Krokstadelva, Norway
Tel.: (47) 33785500
Web Site: http://www.mehren.no
Sales Range: $25-49.9 Million
Emp.: 30
Fabricated Rubber Products
N.A.I.C.S.: 326299

Mitas d.o.o. Ruma (1)

AND PRIVATE COMPANIES   TRELLEBORG AB

Industrijska bb, 22400, Ruma, Serbia
Tel.: (381) 122400065
Coaxial Mechanical Face Seal Mfr
N.A.I.C.S.: 339991

OOO Mitas (1)
Proyektiruemyj Proezd 4062 b 6 corp 16 Off 25 26, 115432, Moscow, Russia
Tel.: (7) 4952696202
Tire Mfr & Distr
N.A.I.C.S.: 326211

PT. Trelleborg Indonesia (1)
Wisma Korindo 4th Floor Jl M T Haryono Kav 62, Jakarta, 12780, Indonesia
Tel.: (62) 21 797 6211
Web Site: http://www.trelleborg.com
Automotive Tire Mfr
N.A.I.C.S.: 326211

Polypac SpA (1)
Via G March 11, PO Box 546, 57121, Livorno, Italy
Tel.: (39) 0586226111
Web Site: http://www.polypac.com
Sales Range: $50-74.9 Million
Emp.: 200
Provider of Industrial Seals
N.A.I.C.S.: 333310

QEW Engineered Rubber B.V. (1)
Foxham 57, 9601 LE, Hoogezand, Netherlands
Tel.: (31) 598 31 59 11
Web Site: http://www.qewrubber.com
Sales Range: $25-49.9 Million
Emp.: 50
Engineered Rubber Product Mfr
N.A.I.C.S.: 326299

QEW Engineered Rubber BV (1)
Foxham 57, 9601 LE, Hoogezand, Netherlands
Tel.: (31) 598 315911
Web Site: http://www.qewrubber.com
Rubber Products Mfr
N.A.I.C.S.: 326291

Subsidiary (Domestic):

Trelleborg Pipe Seals Lelystad BV (2)
Pascallaan 80, PO Box 62, NL-8200, Lelystad, Netherlands
Tel.: (31) 320267979
Web Site: https://www.trelleborg.com
Sales Range: $25-49.9 Million
Emp.: 30
Sealing Device Distr
N.A.I.C.S.: 423840

Reynolds S.A.S. (1)
Immeuble Lumiere 17 Rue Des Deux Gares, 92565, Rueil-Malmaison, Cedex, France (100%)
Tel.: (33) 147145555
Web Site: http://www.reynolds-european.fr
Sales Range: $25-49.9 Million
Emp.: 66
Distr of Semi-Manufactured Products Such as Tubes & Sheets & Wire in Copper, Brass & Aluminum; Joint Venture of Trelleborg AB & Nordic Capital
N.A.I.C.S.: 332439

Subsidiary (Non-US):

Reyton Metals Ltd. (2)
1 Malvern View Business Park, Stella Way, Bishops Cleeve, Cheltenham, GL52 4RP, Glos, United Kingdom
Tel.: (44) 1242631000
N.A.I.C.S.: 326211

Reyton Wire Ltd (2)
Unit 1 Miners Rd Llay Industrial Estate Llay, Wrexham, LL12 0PJ, United Kingdom (100%)
Tel.: (44) 1978855668
Web Site: http://www.reytonwire.co.uk
N.A.I.C.S.: 326211

Signum Technology Ltd. (1)
Commerce Business Centre, West Wilts Trading Estate, Westbury, BA13 4LS, Wiltshire, United Kingdom
Tel.: (44) 1373827100
Web Site: http://www.signumtl.com
Environmental Protection Services
N.A.I.C.S.: 541620
Chris Braithwaite (Chm)

Subsidiary (Domestic):

Gall Thomson Environmental Limited (2)
Suffling, Great Yarmouth, NR30 3QP, Norfolk, United Kingdom
Tel.: (44) 1493857936
Web Site: http://www.gall-thomson.co.uk
Pumping & Filtration Equipment Installation Services
N.A.I.C.S.: 238220

Trelleborg Antivibration Solutions Germany GmbH (1)
Berliner Strasse 17, 16727, Velten, Germany
Tel.: (49) 33043650
Web Site: https://www.schwab-vc.com
Vibration Control Components & Systems Mfr
N.A.I.C.S.: 334519

Trelleborg Applied Technology (1)
Halfpenny Lane, Knaresborough, HG5 0PP, North Yorkshire, United Kingdom
Tel.: (44) 1423 862677
Sales Range: $25-49.9 Million
Emp.: 50
Mfr of Engineered Polymer Solutions That Seal, Damp & Protect Critical Applications in Demanding Environments
N.A.I.C.S.: 326150

Trelleborg Automotive Group AB (1)
Johan Kocksgatan 10, PO Box 153, Johankokaf gatan 10, 231 22, Trelleborg, Sweden (100%)
Tel.: (46) 41067000
Sales Range: $25-49.9 Million
Emp.: 70
Mfr of Products for the Vehicle Industry Including Molded Products, Profiles & Hoses, Materials & Methods for Noise Dampening & Products Which Solve Structural Noise & Vibration Problems
N.A.I.C.S.: 326220

Subsidiary (Non-US):

Dowty Automotive (2)
Thornton Trading Estate, Milford Haven, SA73 2RS, Dyfed, United Kingdom
Tel.: (44) 1646691600
Provider of Industrial Seals
N.A.I.C.S.: 333310

Elastomeros de Cantabria S.A. (2)
Fastino Cavatads 79, PO Box 816, Penacastillo, ES 39011, Santander, Spain (100%)
Tel.: (34) 942336033
Sales Range: $25-49.9 Million
N.A.I.C.S.: 326211

Trellebog Ceiling Solutions (2)
Calle Colinas 11850 Seccion Colinas, Parque Indus El Florido, Tijuana, 22597, BC, Mexico
Tel.: (52) 6646450353
Web Site: http://www.polymersealing.com
Sales Range: $75-99.9 Million
Provider of Industrial Seals
N.A.I.C.S.: 339991

Subsidiary (US):

Trelleborg Automotive (2)
200 Veterans Blvd Ste 3, South Haven, MI 49090-8663 (100%)
Tel.: (269) 639-9891
Sales Range: $25-49.9 Million
Mfr of Molded Products
N.A.I.C.S.: 326291

Plant (Domestic):

Trelleborg YSH (3)
PO Box 329, Morganfield, KY 42437-0329 (100%)
Tel.: (270) 389-1954
Web Site: http://www.trelleborg.com
Sales Range: $50-74.9 Million
Mfr of Custom Molded Rubber Products
N.A.I.C.S.: 326291

Trelleborg YSH (3)
180 Dawson St, Sandusky, MI 48471-1034 (100%)
Tel.: (810) 648-2100

Sales Range: $125-149.9 Million
Mfr of Custom Molded Rubber Products
N.A.I.C.S.: 326291

Trelleborg YSH (3)
102 Industrial Ave, Carmi, IL 62821
Tel.: (618) 382-2318
Sales Range: $25-49.9 Million
Emp.: 62
Mfr of Antivibration & Acoustic Systems
N.A.I.C.S.: 326291

Subsidiary (Non-US):

Trelleborg Automotive AVS Europe (2)
Poligono Industrial Villanoluejar, Calle Lopez Bravo No 35, 09001, Burgos, Spain (100%)
Tel.: (34) 947473026
Sales Range: $50-74.9 Million
N.A.I.C.S.: 326211

Subsidiary (Domestic):

Trelleborg Automotive China Holding AB (2)
Kontinehtgatan 2, 231 42, Trelleborg, Sweden
Tel.: (46) 41067000
Investment Management Service
N.A.I.C.S.: 523940

Subsidiary (Non-US):

Trelleborg Automotive Czech Republic S.r.o (2)
Industry Park Bezdecin 105, 293 01, Mlada Boleslav, Czech Republic
Tel.: (420) 326709939
Automobile Parts Mfr
N.A.I.C.S.: 339999

Subsidiary (Domestic):

Trelleborg Automotive Forsheda AB (2)
Storgatan 26-28, 330 12, Forsheda, Sweden
Tel.: (46) 370 890 00
Sales Range: $25-49.9 Million
Automobile Parts Mfr
N.A.I.C.S.: 336390

Subsidiary (Non-US):

Trelleborg Automotive Mexico SA de CV (2)
Calle 2 y Calle 4 Sur Parque Industrial Toluca 2000, Toluca, 52060, Mexico
Tel.: (52) 722 2620200
Sales Range: $75-99.9 Million
Automobile Parts Mfr
N.A.I.C.S.: 336390

Trelleborg Automotive Spain SA (2)
Camino Can Bros 4, Martorell, 08760, Spain
Tel.: (34) 937 76 62 00
Sales Range: $25-49.9 Million
Automobile Parts Mfr
N.A.I.C.S.: 336390

Trelleborg Automotive do Brasil Industria e Comercio de autopecas Ltd (2)
Av Rotary 1 350, Guarulhos, 07042-000, Sao Paulo, Brazil
Tel.: (55) 1121475722
Polymer Coated Fabrics Mfr
N.A.I.C.S.: 313320

Subsidiary (US):

Trelleborg Fillite Inc. (2)
1325 Satellite Blvd Nw Ste 104, Suwanee, GA 30024-4697
Tel.: (770) 729-8030
Web Site: http://www.fillite.com
Sales Range: $25-49.9 Million
Mfr of Automotive Switch Insulators
N.A.I.C.S.: 517121

Subsidiary (Non-US):

Trelleborg Fillite Ltd. (2)
Goddard Rd Astmoor Industrial Estate, Runcom, WA7 1QF, Cheshire, United Kingdom (100%)
Tel.: (44) 928566661
Web Site: http://www.fillite.com

Sales Range: $25-49.9 Million
N.A.I.C.S.: 326211

Subsidiary (Domestic):

Trelleborg Industri AB (2)
Johan KocksGatan 10, 231 45, Trelleborg, Sweden (100%)
Tel.: (46) 41051000
Sales Range: $100-124.9 Million
N.A.I.C.S.: 326211
Peter Nilsson (Pres & CEO)

Trelleborg Rubore AB (2)
Franska Vagen 18B, 393 54, Kalmar, Sweden (100%)
Tel.: (46) 480499400
Web Site: http://www.rubore.com
Sales Range: $50-74.9 Million
Mfr & Distr of Tires, Hoses & Other Rubber & Plastic Industrial Products
N.A.I.C.S.: 326211

Subsidiary (US):

Trelleborg Rubore Inc. (3)
1325 Satellite Blvd Nw Ste 104, Suwanee, GA 30024-4697
Tel.: (770) 729-8030
Web Site: http://www.rubore.com
Sales Range: $25-49.9 Million
Emp.: 14
Mfr of Automotive Switch Insulators
N.A.I.C.S.: 423120

Branch (Non-US):

Trelleborg Rubore-Australia (3)
141 Osborne Street, South Yarra, Melbourne, 3141, VIC, Australia (100%)
Tel.: (61) 392793956
Web Site: http://www.rubore.com
Sales Range: $125-149.9 Million
N.A.I.C.S.: 326211

Subsidiary (Domestic):

Trelleborg Sigma AB (2)
Stalgatan 2, 703 63, Orebro, Sweden (100%)
Tel.: (46) 19164700
Sales Range: $25-49.9 Million
N.A.I.C.S.: 326211

Subsidiary (Non-US):

Trelleborg YSH S.A. de C.V. (2)
Viena 22 Col Juarez C P, Calle 3 No 108, 6600, Mexico, Mexico
Tel.: (52) 5557195005
Sales Range: $100-124.9 Million
N.A.I.C.S.: 326211

Trelleborg Bohemia a.s (1)
Akademika Bedrny 531/8a, Vekose, 500 03, Hradec Kralove, Czech Republic
Tel.: (420) 495753111
Web Site: https://www.trelleborgbohemia.com
Seal & Rubber Product Mfr
N.A.I.C.S.: 326299
Jan Stritesky (Mgr-Supply Chain)

Trelleborg Boots France SAS (1)
ZI de Nantes-Carquefou 24 Rue de Grande Bretagne, BP 90436, 44474, Carquefou, Cedex, France
Tel.: (33) 384811253
Sales Range: $25-49.9 Million
Automobile Parts Mfr
N.A.I.C.S.: 336390

Trelleborg China Holding AB (1)
Johan Kocksgatan 10, 231 45, Trelleborg, Sweden
Tel.: (46) 41067000
Emp.: 200
Polymer Coated Fabrics Mfr
N.A.I.C.S.: 313320

Trelleborg Coated System France SAS (1)
3 Rue de l Industrie, BP 30160, 68702, Cernay, Cedex, France
Tel.: (33) 3 89 38 43 43
Web Site: http://www.trelleborg.com
Printing Blanket Mfr
N.A.I.C.S.: 322299

Trelleborg Coated Systems (Shanghai) Co., Ltd. (1)

TRELLEBORG AB

Trelleborg AB—(Continued)
No 1345 Haixu Road, Pudong New Area,
CN-200137, Shanghai, China
Tel.: (86) 21 5131 3188
Web Site: http://www.trelleborg.com
Printing Blanket Mfr. & Distr
N.A.I.C.S.: 322120

Trelleborg Corporation (1)
400 Aylworth Ave, South Haven, MI 49090
Tel.: (269) 637-2116
Copper Ore Mining Services
N.A.I.C.S.: 212230

Subsidiary (Domestic):

ADC Acquisition Company, Inc. (2)
2 Commerce Park Dr, Niskayuna, NY 12309
Tel.: (518) 377-6471
Web Site:
http://www.automateddynamics.com
Plastics Material & Resin Mfr
N.A.I.C.S.: 325211
Dave Hauber (Mgr-Engrg)

Group (Domestic):

Engineered Fabrics Group (2)
715 Railroad Ave, Rutherfordton, NC 28139-2207
Tel.: (828) 286-9126
Sales Range: $50-74.9 Million
Emp.: 220
Plastic & Synthetic Rubber Coating of Fabrics
N.A.I.C.S.: 325220

Subsidiary (Domestic):

Maritime International, Inc. (2)
1186 Petroleum Way, Broussard, LA 70518
Tel.: (337) 321-4240
Web Site:
http://www.maritimeinternational.com
Sales Range: $10-24.9 Million
Emp.: 50
Marine System Products & Services
N.A.I.C.S.: 541330

Trelleborg Coated Systems US Inc. (2)
715 Railroad Ave, Rutherfordton, NC 28139
Tel.: (828) 286-9126
Polymer Coated Fabrics Mfr
N.A.I.C.S.: 313320

Trelleborg Industrial AVS USA, Inc (2)
200 Veterans Blvd Ste 3, South Haven, MI 49090
Tel.: (269) 639-9891
Web Site: http://www.trelleborg.com
Vibration Isolator Mfr
N.A.I.C.S.: 336330

Trelleborg Offshore Boston, Inc. (2)
24 Teed Dr, Randolph, MA 02368
Tel.: (774) 719-1400
Web Site: http://www.trelleborg.com
Syntactic Foams Mfr
N.A.I.C.S.: 326150

Trelleborg Offshore US Inc (2)
Millennium Tower 10375 Richmond Ave Ste 1725, Houston, TX 77042
Tel.: (832) 456-8300
Sales Range: $150-199.9 Million
Offshore Oil & Gas Drilling Services
N.A.I.C.S.: 213111

Trelleborg Pipe Seals Milford, Inc. (2)
250 Elm St, Milford, NH 03055
Tel.: (603) 673-8680
Pipe Sealing Device Distr
N.A.I.C.S.: 423840

Trelleborg Croatia d.o.o. (1)
Slavonska Avenija 24/6, HR-10000, Zagreb, Croatia
Tel.: (385) 12456387
Coaxial Mechanical Face Seal Mfr
N.A.I.C.S.: 339991

Trelleborg Engineered Systems Group AB (1)
Johan Kocksgatan 10, 23122, Trelleborg, Sweden **(100%)**
Tel.: (46) 41051000

Sales Range: $1-4.9 Billion
Emp.: 3,204
Mfr of Industrial & Special Hoses, Protective Products & Diving Suits, Laminated Polymer Products & Industrial Rubber Products for Offshore, Infrastructure, Paper & Pulp Industries
N.A.I.C.S.: 326220

Subsidiary (US):

Polymer Sealing Solutions (2)
445 Enterprise Ct, Bloomfield, MI 48302-0307
Tel.: (248) 888-8100
Sales Range: $25-49.9 Million
Emp.: 22
Mfr & Distribution of Speciality Polymers
N.A.I.C.S.: 541330

Subsidiary (Non-US):

Trelleborg Building Systems UK Ltd. (2)
Maybrook Rd Castle Vale Industrial Estate, Minworth, Sutton Coldfield, B76 1AX, W Midlands, United Kingdom **(100%)**
Tel.: (44) 213523800
Sales Range: $25-49.9 Million
Emp.: 80
N.A.I.C.S.: 326211

Trelleborg ETM GmbH (2)
Alte Neckarelz Strasse 24, 74821, Mosbach, Germany **(100%)**
Tel.: (49) 626192350
Sales Range: $25-49.9 Million
Emp.: 100
N.A.I.C.S.: 326211

Trelleborg Ede BV (2)
Knutteiweg 8, NL-6718 ZD, Ede, Netherlands
Tel.: (31) 318617112
Sales Range: $25-49.9 Million
Emp.: 150
Engineering Systems Services
N.A.I.C.S.: 541330

Trelleborg Engineered Systems Australia Pty Ltd (2)
25 Glassford Road, Kewdale, 6105, WA, Australia
Tel.: (61) 8 9256 6000
Web Site: http://www.trelleborg.com.au
Sales Range: $25-49.9 Million
Emp.: 40
Industrial Supplies Mfr
N.A.I.C.S.: 332999

Subsidiary (Domestic):

Trelleborg Engineered Systems China Holding AB (2)
Box 153, 231 22, Trelleborg, Sweden
Tel.: (46) 8835500
Polymer Coated Fabrics Mfr
N.A.I.C.S.: 313320

Subsidiary (Non-US):

Trelleborg Engineered Systems Italy S.p.A. (2)
SP 140, 26855, Lodi Vecchio, Italy
Tel.: (39) 0371406233
Sales Range: $1-9.9 Million
Emp.: 250
Mfr of Offset Printing Blankets & Industrial Coated Fabrics
N.A.I.C.S.: 313320

Trelleborg Engineered Systems Ltd (2)
Community Community North Nanwan Jihongtan, Chengyang, Qingdao, 266111, China
Tel.: (86) 532 8965 0700
Web Site: http://www.trelleborg.cn
Industrial Rubber Hose Mfr
N.A.I.C.S.: 326220

Subsidiary (Domestic):

Trelleborg Horda AB- Materials Division (2)
Jonkopengsv, PO Box 1004, SE 001 29, Varnamo, Sweden **(100%)**
Tel.: (46) 37048100

Sales Range: $100-124.9 Million
Emp.: 500
N.A.I.C.S.: 326211

Subsidiary (Non-US):

Trelleborg ITM (2)
Alte Neckarelz St 24, 74821, Mosbach, Germany **(100%)**
Tel.: (49) 6261923520
Sales Range: $25-49.9 Million
Emp.: 20
N.A.I.C.S.: 326211

Trelleborg Ibercaucho Alava S.A. (2)
C San Vicente 23, 1140, Izarra, Alava, Spain **(100%)**
Tel.: (34) 945437090
Sales Range: $200-249.9 Million
Emp.: 600
N.A.I.C.S.: 326211

Trelleborg Industri Benelux (2)
Brugse Steenweg 7, 9940, Evergem, Belgium **(100%)**
Tel.: (32) 92572399
Sales Range: $25-49.9 Million
Emp.: 50
Rubber Membranes
N.A.I.C.S.: 326299

Trelleborg Industri Iberica S.A. (2)
C/ Jose Echegaray 8 Edificio 3, Planta 2 Oficinas 4 y 5, 28015, Madrid, Spain **(100%)**
Tel.: (34) 917105730
Sales Range: $25-49.9 Million
Emp.: 7
N.A.I.C.S.: 326211

Subsidiary (Domestic):

Trelleborg Industrial AB (2)
Johan Kocksgatan 10, 23 181, Trelleborg, Sweden **(100%)**
Tel.: (46) 41051866
Sales Range: $25-49.9 Million
Emp.: 6
N.A.I.C.S.: 326211

Subsidiary (Non-US):

Trelleborg Industrie S.A. (2)
ZI La Combaude Rue de Chantemerle CS 10725, Clermont-Ferrand, FR-63050, Cedex 2, France **(100%)**
Tel.: (33) 4 73 25 81 00
Sales Range: $100-124.9 Million
Emp.: 650
N.A.I.C.S.: 326211

Trelleborg Izarra, S.A.U. (2)
C/San Vicente 23, 1440, Izarra, Alava, Spain
Tel.: (34) 945 43 70 90
Web Site: http://www.trelleborg.com
Rubber Sheeting, Matting & Flooring Mfr
N.A.I.C.S.: 326299

Subsidiary (US):

Trelleborg Marine Systems USA (2)
3470 Martinsburg Pike, Clear Brook, VA 22624
Tel.: (540) 667-5191
Web Site: http://www.trelleborg.com
Rev: $15,000,000
Emp.: 50
Berthing & Mooring Engineering Solutions for Port, Inshore & Marine Industries
N.A.I.C.S.: 541330

Division (Domestic):

Virginia Harbour Services (3)
3470 Martinsburg Pike, Clear Brook, VA 22624
Tel.: (540) 667-5191
Web Site: http://www.trelleborg.com
Designer & Fabricator of Air-Supported Rubber Structures, Concrete & Steel Pilings
N.A.I.C.S.: 488320

Subsidiary (Non-US):

Trelleborg Offshore Norway AS (2)
Kalosjegata 15, PO Box A, NO 3051, Mjondalen, Norway **(100%)**
Tel.: (47) 32232000
Sales Range: $25-49.9 Million
Emp.: 200
Mfr & Sales of Engineered Products

INTERNATIONAL PUBLIC

N.A.I.C.S.: 541330
Thor Hegg Eriksen (Mng Dir)

Subsidiary (Domestic):

Trelleborg Sealing Profiles Sweden AB (2)
Kavsjovagen 38, SE 331-29, Varnamo, Sweden **(100%)**
Tel.: (46) 41051000
Sales Range: $75-99.9 Million
Emp.: 300
Sealant Mfr
N.A.I.C.S.: 339991

Subsidiary (US):

Carolina Seal, Inc. (3)
1424 Cross Beam Dr, Charlotte, NC 28217
Tel.: (704) 523-4450
Web Site: http://www.carolinaseal.com
Sales Range: $1-9.9 Million
Emp.: 12
Industrial Supplies Merchant Whslr
N.A.I.C.S.: 423840

Trelleborg Ersmark AB (1)
Fabriksv 1-3, SE-934 41, Ersmark, Sweden
Tel.: (46) 910714200
Web Site: https://www.skeegaseals.se
Sales Range: $50-74.9 Million
Emp.: 250
Engineered Rubber Product Mfr
N.A.I.C.S.: 326299

Trelleborg Fittings SAS (1)
22 Rue de la Gare, 69009, Lyon, France
Tel.: (33) 4 72 20 89 50
Web Site: http://www.trelleborg.com
Industrial Rubber Hose Mfr
N.A.I.C.S.: 326220

Trelleborg Forsheda AB (1)
Storgatan 28, Forsheda, Sweden
Tel.: (46) 370510700
Web Site: https://www.trelleborg.com
Pipe Seal Distr
N.A.I.C.S.: 423840

Trelleborg Holding Danmark A/S (1)
Fabriksvej 17, Helsingor, 3000, Denmark
Tel.: (45) 49270333
Emp.: 350
Investment Management Service
N.A.I.C.S.: 523940

Trelleborg Holdings Italy S.r.l (1)
Via Giovanni March 11, Livorno, 57121, Italy
Tel.: (39) 0586226111
Sales Range: $50-74.9 Million
Emp.: 30
Investment Management Service
N.A.I.C.S.: 523999

Trelleborg India Pvt Ltd. (1)
22/9 Beratena Agrahara Hosur Main Road, Bengaluru, 560100, Karnataka, India
Tel.: (91) 8066729200
Web Site: https://www.trelleborg.com
Engineering Consulting Services
N.A.I.C.S.: 541330

Trelleborg Industri O.O.O (1)
Projected proezd 4062 6 building 16 office 25, 109548, Moscow, Russia
Tel.: (7) 4952696200
Web Site: http://www.trelleborg.ru
Emp.: 10
Roller Bearing Mfr
N.A.I.C.S.: 332991

Trelleborg Industrial AVS (1)
1 Hoods Close, Leicester, LE4 2BN, United Kingdom **(100%)**
Tel.: (44) 116 2670 455
Sales Range: $50-74.9 Million
Emp.: 220
Mfr of Vibration Control Products for Automotive, Rail & Marine Usage; Manufacturer of Automotive Water & Fuel Hoses
N.A.I.C.S.: 336340

Trelleborg Industrial AVS AB (1)
PO Box 153, Trelleborg, 231 22, Sweden
Tel.: (46) 41 05 10 00
Emp.: 100
Engineered Rubber Product Mfr
N.A.I.C.S.: 326299

Trelleborg Industrial Products Estonia OU (1)

TRELLEBORG AB

Pikk Tn 62E, PO Box 127, 93815, Kuressaare, Estonia
Tel.: (372) 45 30 400
Sales Range: $50-74.9 Million
Emp.: 200
Engineered Rubber Product Mfr

Trelleborg Industrial Products Finland Oy (1)
Kikkerlantie 72, FI-383 00, Sastamala, Finland
Tel.: (358) 35126000
Web Site: https://www2.trelleborg.com
Fiber Optic Cable Mfr
N.A.I.C.S.: 335921

Trelleborg Industrial Products Germany GmbH (1)
Kleberstr 2, 408 22, Mettmann, Germany (100%)
Tel.: (49) 2104 217 0
Sales Range: $25-49.9 Million
Emp.: 13
Industrial Hoses & Assemblies Distr
N.A.I.C.S.: 423830

Trelleborg Industrial Products India Pvt Ltd (1)
19/1 Kalena Agrahara Bannerghata Main Road, Bengaluru, 560 076, India
Tel.: (91) 80 25189700
Industrial Rubber Hose Mfr
N.A.I.C.S.: 326220

Trelleborg Industrial Products Norway AS (1)
PO Box 58, Leirdal, 1008, Oslo, Norway
Tel.: (47) 22 90 49 00
Industrial Rubber Hose Mfr
N.A.I.C.S.: 326220

Trelleborg Industrial Products Sancheville SAS (1)
7 Place du Marche, 28800, Sancheville, France
Tel.: (33) 2 37 44 62 15
Industrial Rubber Hose Mfr
N.A.I.C.S.: 326220

Trelleborg Industrial Products Sweden AB (1)
Ronevagen 1, 620 12, Hemse, Sweden
Tel.: (46) 498 48 49 00
Web Site: http://www.trelleborg.com
Sales Range: $50-74.9 Million
Industrial Rubber Hose Mfr
N.A.I.C.S.: 326220

Trelleborg Industrial Products UK Ltd (1)
1 Hoods Close, Leicester, LE4 2BN, United Kingdom
Tel.: (44) 1162670455
Polymer Coated Fabrics Mfr
N.A.I.C.S.: 313320

Trelleborg Industrial Tyres UK Ltd (1)
Riverside Court Beaufort Park Way, Chepstow, NP16 5UH, United Kingdom
Tel.: (44) 1291 637660
Web Site: http://www.trelleborg.com
Forklift Tire & Wheel Sales, Installation & Repair Services
N.A.I.C.S.: 423130

Trelleborg Industries Polska Sp. z o.o. (1)
Ul Andrzeja Struga 66, 90-557, Lodz, Poland
Tel.: (48) 42 293 05 37
Web Site: http://www.trelleborg.com
Sales Range: $25-49.9 Million
Emp.: 15
Industrial Rubber Hose Mfr
N.A.I.C.S.: 326220

Trelleborg Izarra S.A.U. (1)
C/San Vicente 25, 01440, Izarra, Alava, Spain
Tel.: (34) 945 43 70 90
Web Site: http://www.trelleborg.com
Sales Range: $50-74.9 Million
Engineered Rubber Product Mfr
N.A.I.C.S.: 326299

Trelleborg Japan K.K. (1)
Kdx Shin-yokohama 381 Bldg 7f 3-8-11 Shin-yokohama, Kohoku-ku, Yokohama, 222-0033, Kanagawa-Ken, Japan
Tel.: (81) 45 478 0731
Web Site: http://www.tbvc.com
Automotive Vibration Isolator Mfr
N.A.I.C.S.: 336330

Trelleborg Kunhwa Co Ltd (1)
1209-4 Sinsang-ri Jillyang-eup, 712-838, Gyeongsan, Gyeongsangbuk-do, Korea (South)
Tel.: (82) 53 850 9902
Web Site: http://www.kunhwa-trelleborg.com
Sales Range: $125-149.9 Million
Emp.: 350
Automotive Component Mfr & Distr
N.A.I.C.S.: 336390

Trelleborg Marine Systems Asia Pte Ltd (1)
4 Jalan Pesawat, Singapore, 619362, Singapore
Tel.: (65) 62688005
Sales Range: $25-49.9 Million
Marine Engineering Services
N.A.I.C.S.: 541330

Trelleborg Marine Systems Australia Pty Ltd (1)
Suite 504 Level 5 5 Hunter Street, Sydney, 2000, NSW, Australia
Tel.: (61) 292850200
Sales Range: $25-49.9 Million
Marine Engineering Services
N.A.I.C.S.: 541330

Trelleborg Marine Systems FZE (1)
JAFZA View Building 19 Office 408/409 Jebel Ali, PO Box 261758, Dubai, United Arab Emirates
Tel.: (971) 48086000
Marine Engineering Services
N.A.I.C.S.: 541330

Trelleborg Marine Systems India Pvt Ltd (1)
801 Parswanath Esquare Corporate Road Nr Prahaladnagar, Garden Satellite, Ahmedabad, 380054, Gujarat, India
Tel.: (91) 79 4001 3333
Web Site: http://www.trelleborg.com
Sales Range: $25-49.9 Million
Marine Engineering Services
N.A.I.C.S.: 541330

Trelleborg Marine Systems Melbourne Pty Ltd (1)
Level 3 Building 1 195 Wellington Road, Clayton, 3168, VIC, Australia
Tel.: (61) 3 9575 9999
Web Site: http://www.trelleborg.com
Sales Range: $25-49.9 Million
Marine Engineering Services
N.A.I.C.S.: 541330

Trelleborg Materials & Mixing Forsheda AB (1)
Storgatan 28, PO Box 1004, Forsheda, 331 29, Varnamo, Sweden
Tel.: (46) 370 481 00
Web Site: http://www.trelleborg.com
Emp.: 20
Fiber Optic Cable Mfr
N.A.I.C.S.: 335921
Joakim Hansson *(Gen Mgr)*

Trelleborg Modyn SAS (1)
Zone Industrielle De Nantes, Carquefou, 44470, France
Tel.: (33) 2 40 68 63 91
Automotive Rubber Parts Mfr
N.A.I.C.S.: 326299

Trelleborg Offshore & Construction AB (1)
Johan Kocksgatan 10, 231 81, Trelleborg, Sweden
Tel.: (46) 41051000
Coaxial Mechanical Face Seal Mfr
N.A.I.C.S.: 339991
Jean-Pierre Schumacher *(Mgr-Project-EMSA)*

Trelleborg PPL (1)
Trinity Park Randall Way, Retford, DN22 7AX, Nottinghamshire, United Kingdom
Tel.: (44) 1777 712 500
Sales Range: $25-49.9 Million
Polyurethane Material Mfr
N.A.I.C.S.: 326150

Trelleborg Pipe Seals Duisburg GmbH (1)
Dr-Alfred-Herrhausen-Allee 36, 47228, Duisburg, Germany
Tel.: (49) 2065 999 0
Sales Range: $25-49.9 Million
Sewer Pipeline Repair & Maintenance Services
N.A.I.C.S.: 237110

Trelleborg Pipe Seals Rochefort SAS (1)
Zl des Soers, 17300, Rochefort, France
Tel.: (33) 5 46 87 85 85
Web Site: http://www.trelleborg.com
Pipe Sealing Device Mfr
N.A.I.C.S.: 339991

Trelleborg Pipe Seals Santander S.A. (1)
B San Martin 79, PO Box 816, 39011, Santander, Penacastillo, Spain
Tel.: (34) 942 336 033
Web Site: http://www.trelleborg.com
Sales Range: $25-49.9 Million
Emp.: 40
Pipe Sealing Device Mfr
N.A.I.C.S.: 325520

Trelleborg Pipe Seals Spydeberg AS (1)
Handverkveien 4, 1820, Spydeberg, Norway
Tel.: (47) 69 83 68 68
Sales Range: $25-49.9 Million
Pipe Sealing Device Mfr
N.A.I.C.S.: 325520

Trelleborg Praha s.r.o. (1)
Touzimska 720, 199 00, Prague, Czech Republic
Tel.: (420) 2 838 426 00
Web Site: http://www.trelleborg.com
Pipe Sealing Device Mfr
N.A.I.C.S.: 339991

Trelleborg Reims SAS (1)
17 Rue Du Moulin Florent, Witry-les-Reims, 51420, France
Tel.: (33) 326844800
Polymer Coated Fabrics Mfr
N.A.I.C.S.: 313320

Trelleborg Ridderkerk BV (1)
Verlengde Kerkweg 15, Ridderkerk, 2985 AZ, Netherlands
Tel.: (31) 180 495 595
Sales Range: $50-74.9 Million
Emp.: 125
Engineered Rubber Product Mfr
N.A.I.C.S.: 326299

Trelleborg Sealing Solutions A/S (1)
Pilestraede 58, 1112, Copenhagen, Denmark
Tel.: (45) 48228080
Web Site: https://www.tss.trelleborg.com
Sales Range: $700-749.9 Million
Emp.: 5,806
Automotive, Industrial & Aerospace Seal Developer & Mfr
N.A.I.C.S.: 339991

Subsidiary (Non-US):

Trelleborg Sealing Profiles Germany GmbH (2)
Auweg 27, 63920, Grossheubach, Germany
Tel.: (49) 937166910
Web Site: https://www.trelleborg.com
Sales Range: $25-49.9 Million
Pipe Sealing Device Mfr
N.A.I.C.S.: 339991

Trelleborg Sealing Profiles Hungary Ltd (2)
Kalaszi 3, Szentendre, 2000, Hungary
Tel.: (36) 26 801 850
Sales Range: $25-49.9 Million
Emp.: 6
Pipe Sealing Device Mfr
N.A.I.C.S.: 339991

Subsidiary (US):

Trelleborg Sealing Profiles North America Inc. (2)
285 Lena Dr, Aurora, OH 44202
Tel.: (330) 995-9725
Emp.: 100
Automotive, Industrial & Aerospace Sealing Component Mfr
N.A.I.C.S.: 339991

Subsidiary (Domestic):

Trelleborg Sealing Profiles U.S., Inc (3)
285 Lena Dr, Aurora, OH 44202
Tel.: (330) 995-9725
Gasket & Sealing Device Mfr
N.A.I.C.S.: 339991
Andrew Boer *(Mgr-Bus Dev-North America)*

Subsidiary (Domestic):

Anderson Seal, Inc. (4)
16555 W Lincoln Ave, New Berlin, WI 53151
Tel.: (262) 821-0344
Web Site: http://www.andersonseal.com
Sales Range: $1-9.9 Million
Emp.: 50
Sealing Products Distributor
N.A.I.C.S.: 339991

Trelleborg Sealing Solutions Detroit, Inc (4)
15701 Centennial Dr, Northville, MI 48168
Tel.: (734) 354-1250
Web Site: http://www.trelleborg.com
Sales Range: $25-49.9 Million
Emp.: 14
Automotive Shim Mfr
N.A.I.C.S.: 336390

Trelleborg Sealing Solutions El Segundo, Inc. (4)
2051 E Maple Ave, El Segundo, CA 90245
Tel.: (310) 322-8030
Precision Seals & Bearings Mfr
N.A.I.C.S.: 339991

Subsidiary (Non-US):

Trelleborg Sealing Solutions Canada Inc. (3)
43 Voyager Court North, Etobicoke, M9W 4Y2, ON, Canada
Tel.: (416) 213-9444
Web Site: http://www.tss.trelleborg.com
Sales Range: $25-49.9 Million
Emp.: 12
Hydraulic Seal & Gasket Mfr
N.A.I.C.S.: 339991

Subsidiary (Non-US):

Trelleborg Sealing Solutions (China) Co., Ltd. (2)
5118 YuanJiang Road Xinzhuang Industrial Park, Shanghai, 201108, China
Tel.: (86) 2161451830
Sales Range: $50-74.9 Million
Emp.: 250
Pipe Seal Distr
N.A.I.C.S.: 423840

Trelleborg Sealing Solutions Austria GmbH (2)
Handelskai 94-96 Millennium Tower 26 OG, 1200, Vienna, Austria
Tel.: (43) 1 406 4733
Web Site: http://www.tss.trelleborg.com
Sales Range: $25-49.9 Million
Emp.: 18
Automotive, Industrial & Aerospace Sealing Component Mfr
N.A.I.C.S.: 339991
Martin Unterberger *(Mgr-Sales-Engineering)*

Trelleborg Sealing Solutions Belgium SA (2)
Boulevard du Centenaire 4 Bte 4, B-1325, Dion Valmont, Belgium
Tel.: (32) 10225750
Web Site: https://www.tss.trelleborg.com
Sales Range: $25-49.9 Million
Emp.: 16
Automotive, Industrial & Aerospace Seal Mfr
N.A.I.C.S.: 339991

Trelleborg Sealing Solutions Bulgaria EOOD (2)
80 Christophor Columb Blvd Floor 7, 1592, Sofia, Bulgaria
Tel.: (359) 29699599
Web Site: https://www.tss.trelleborg.com

TRELLEBORG AB   INTERNATIONAL PUBLIC

Trelleborg AB—(Continued)
Sales Range: $25-49.9 Million
Emp.: 20
Automotive, Industrial & Aerospace Seal Mfr
N.A.I.C.S.: 339991

Trelleborg Sealing Solutions Czech s.r.o. (2)
Evropska 423/178, 160 00, Prague, 6, Vokovice, Czech Republic
Tel.: (420) 220400288
Web Site: https://www.tss.trelleborg.com
Sales Range: $25-49.9 Million
Emp.: 25
Automotive, Industrial & Aerospace Seal Mfr
N.A.I.C.S.: 339991

Subsidiary (Domestic):

Trelleborg Sealing Solutions Denmark A/S (2)
Pilestraed 58, 1112, Copenhagen, Denmark
Tel.: (45) 48228080
Web Site: http://www.tss.trelleborg.com
Sales Range: $25-49.9 Million
Emp.: 12
Automotive, Industrial & Aerospace Seal Mfr
N.A.I.C.S.: 339991

Subsidiary (Non-US):

Trelleborg Sealing Solutions Espana SAU (2)
Parque Empresarial Alvia C/ Jose Echegaray 8 Building 3 Floor 2, Offices 4 y 5 Las Rozas, 28230, Madrid, Spain
Tel.: (34) 917105730
Web Site: http://www.tss.trelleborg.com
Sales Range: $25-49.9 Million
Emp.: 14
Automotive, Industrial & Aerospace Seal Mfr
N.A.I.C.S.: 339991

Trelleborg Sealing Solutions Finland Oy (2)
Ayritie 12B, 01510, Vantaa, Finland
Tel.: (358) 207121350
Web Site: https://www.tss.trelleborg.com
Hydraulic Seal & Gasket Mfr
N.A.I.C.S.: 339991

Trelleborg Sealing Solutions France SAS (2)
38 Rue Jean Mermoz, BP 106, 78602, Maisons-Laffitte, Cedex, France   **(100%)**
Tel.: (33) 130865600
Web Site: https://www.tss.trelleborg.com
Sales Range: $25-49.9 Million
Emp.: 73
Automotive, Industrial & Aerospace Seal Mfr
N.A.I.C.S.: 339991

Trelleborg Sealing Solutions Germany GmbH (2)
Schockenriedstr 1, 70565, Stuttgart, Germany
Tel.: (49) 7 117 8640
Web Site: http://www.tss.trelleborg.com
Sales Range: $400-449.9 Million
Emp.: 500
Automotive, Industrial & Aerospace Seal Mfr
N.A.I.C.S.: 339991
Carsten Stehle *(Chm & Mng Dir)*

Subsidiary (Domestic):

Saint-Gobain Performance Plastics MG Silikon GmbH (3)
Robert-Bosch-Str 17, 88131, Lindau, Germany
Tel.: (49) 838270560
Web Site: http://www.process.saint-gobain.eu
Plastics Product Mfr
N.A.I.C.S.: 326199

Subsidiary (Non-US):

Trelleborg Sealing Solutions Hong Kong Ltd. (2)
31/F Aitken Vanson Centre 61 Hoi Yuen Road, Kwun Tong, Kowloon, China (Hong Kong)
Tel.: (852) 23669165
Web Site: https://www.tss.trelleborg.com
Automotive, Industrial & Aerospace Seal Mfr
N.A.I.C.S.: 339991

Trelleborg Sealing Solutions Italy SpA (2)
Via G March 11, PO Box 466, Livorno, 57121, Italy
Tel.: (39) 0586226111
Web Site: http://www.tss.trelleborg.com
Sales Range: $50-74.9 Million
Emp.: 130
Automotive, Industrial & Aerospace Seal Mfr
N.A.I.C.S.: 339991

Trelleborg Sealing Solutions Japan KK (2)
Eastnet Building 2F 7-1-1 Toyo, Koto-ku, Tokyo, 135-0016, Japan
Tel.: (81) 356338008
Web Site: https://www.tss.trelleborg.com
Sales Range: $25-49.9 Million
Emp.: 84
Automotive, Industrial & Aerospace Seal Mfr
N.A.I.C.S.: 339991

Trelleborg Sealing Solutions Korea Ltd (2)
1502 Hyundai 41 tower 917-9-Mok-1dong, Yangchun-gu, Seoul, 158-723, Korea (South)
Tel.: (82) 27613476
Web Site: https://www.tss.trelleborg.com
Sales Range: $25-49.9 Million
Hydraulic Seal & Gasket Mfr
N.A.I.C.S.: 339991

Trelleborg Sealing Solutions Mexico S.A de C.V (2)
Viena 22 Col Juarez, 06600, Cuauhtemoc, Mexico
Tel.: (52) 55 57 19 50 05
Web Site: http://www.tss.trelleborg.com
Hydraulic Seal & Gasket Mfr
N.A.I.C.S.: 339991

Trelleborg Sealing Solutions Netherlands BV (2)
Zeemanstraat 33, 2991 XR, Barendrecht, Netherlands
Tel.: (31) 102922111
Web Site: http://www.tss.trelleborg.com
Sales Range: $25-49.9 Million
Emp.: 25
Automotive, Industrial & Aerospace Seal Mfr
N.A.I.C.S.: 339991

Trelleborg Sealing Solutions Norway AS (2)
Brobekkveien 40, PO Box 188, Okern, Oslo, 510, Norway
Tel.: (47) 22646080
Web Site: http://www.tss.trelleborg.com
Sales Range: $25-49.9 Million
Emp.: 15
Automotive, Industrial & Aerospace Seal Mfr
N.A.I.C.S.: 339991

Trelleborg Sealing Solutions Polska Sp.z.o.o (2)
ul Twarda 18, 00-105, Warsaw, Poland
Tel.: (48) 228633011
Web Site: https://www.tss.trelleborg.com
Sales Range: $25-49.9 Million
Emp.: 10
Hydraulic Seal & Gasket Mfr
N.A.I.C.S.: 339991

Trelleborg Sealing Solutions Silcotech Switzerland AG (2)
Kaltenbacherstrasse 46, CH-8260, Stein am Rhein, Switzerland
Tel.: (41) 52 742 0100
Sales Range: $25-49.9 Million
Emp.: 130
Molded Silicon Product Mfr
N.A.I.C.S.: 339991

Trelleborg Sealing Solutions Singapore Pte Ltd (2)
56 Kallang Pudding Road 08-05 HH, Kallang, Singapore, 349328, Singapore
Tel.: (65) 6577 1778
Web Site: http://www.tss.trelleborg.com
Sales Range: $25-49.9 Million
Emp.: 11
Hydraulic Seal & Gasket Mfr
N.A.I.C.S.: 339991

Trelleborg Sealing Solutions Switzerland SA (2)
Route Sous Riette 29, Crissier, CH-1023, Lausanne, Switzerland

Tel.: (41) 216314111
Web Site: https://www.tss.trelleborg.com
Sales Range: $25-49.9 Million
Emp.: 20
Automotive, Industrial & Aerospace Seal Mfr
N.A.I.C.S.: 339991

Trelleborg Sealing Solutions Taiwan Ltd (2)
No 19 Wen-Shan 11th Street, Nantun District, Taichung, 40869, Taiwan
Tel.: (886) 4 2382 8886
Web Site: http://www.tss.trelleborg.com
Hydraulic Seal & Gasket Mfr
N.A.I.C.S.: 339991

Trelleborg Sealing Solutions UK Ltd. (2)
1 Cranbrook Way, Solihull Business Park, Solihull, B90 4GT, West Midlands, United Kingdom
Tel.: (44) 1217441221
Web Site: https://www.tss.trelleborg.com
Sales Range: $50-74.9 Million
Emp.: 115
Automotive, Industrial & Aerospace Seal Mfr
N.A.I.C.S.: 339991

Trelleborg Sealing Solutions o.o.o. (2)
17 Vereyskaya Ul Str 134 B Vereyskaya Plaza-2 Office 601 A, Moscow, 121357, Russia
Tel.: (7) 495 982 3921
Web Site: http://www.trelleborg.com
Sales Range: $25-49.9 Million
Emp.: 7
Hydraulic Seal & Gasket Mfr
N.A.I.C.S.: 339991

Trelleborg Sealing Solutions Hungary Kft (1)
Gyar Utca 2 Bitep Industrial Park 100/2-Building, 2040, Budaors, Hungary
Tel.: (36) 23502121
Coaxial Mechanical Face Seal Mfr
N.A.I.C.S.: 339991

Trelleborg Sealing Solutions Italia S.p.A. (1)
Via G March 11, PO Box 466, 57121, Livorno, Italy
Tel.: (39) 0586226111
Engineering Consulting Services
N.A.I.C.S.: 541330

Trelleborg Sealing Solutions Kalmar AB (1)
Franska Vagen 18B, 393 54, Kalmar, Sweden
Tel.: (46) 480499400
Web Site: https://www.rubore.com
Automotive Parts Mfr & Distr
N.A.I.C.S.: 336390

Trelleborg Sealing Solutions Sweden AB (1)
Huskvarnavagen 62, Box 5046, 550 05, Jonkoping, Sweden
Tel.: (46) 36 34 15 00
Web Site: http://www.tss.trelleborg.com
Emp.: 6,900
Hydraulic Seal & Gasket Mfr
N.A.I.C.S.: 339991

Subsidiary (US):

Trelleborg Sealing Solutions Delano, LLC (2)
740 7th St S Ste 2, Delano, MN 55328
Tel.: (763) 972-9206
Synthetic Rubber Mfr
N.A.I.C.S.: 325212
Kevin Carver *(Dir-Business Optimization)*

Tri-Tec Seal LLC (2)
2111 W Thompson Rd, Fenton, MI 48430
Tel.: (810) 655-3900
Web Site: http://www.tritecseal.com
Rev.: $2,333,333
Emp.: 24
Gasket, Packing & Sealing Device Mfr
N.A.I.C.S.: 339991
Greg Watson *(VP-Engrg)*

Trelleborg Singapore Pte Ltd (1)
4 Jalan Pesawat SG, Singapore, 619362, Singapore
Tel.: (65) 62650955

Sales Range: $50-74.9 Million
Emp.: 100
Rubber Hose & Hydraulic Seal Mfr
N.A.I.C.S.: 326220

Trelleborg Slovenija d.o.o (1)
Skofjeloska C 6, 4000, Kranj, Slovenia
Tel.: (386) 42066080
Web Site: https://www.savatech.eu
Industrial Rubber Product Mfr
N.A.I.C.S.: 326299
Alen Adilic *(Mgr-Design)*

Trelleborg Trading Wuxi Co., Ltd. (1)
8 Zhong Tong Road, New District Wuxi, CN - PRC 214143, Wuxi, Jiang Su, China
Tel.: (86) 510 8530 8808
Web Site: http://www.trelleborg.com
Emp.: 2
Industrial Rubber Hose Distr
N.A.I.C.S.: 423840

Trelleborg Treasury (1)
Jakobsbergsgatan 22, PO Box 7365, SE-103 90, Stockholm, Sweden   **(100%)**
Tel.: (46) 84403500
Sales Range: $25-49.9 Million
Emp.: 20
N.A.I.C.S.: 326211

Trelleborg Tyres Lanka (Private) Ltd (1)
Levin Drive Sapugaskanda Makola, Colombo, Western Province, Sri Lanka
Tel.: (94) 11 4829400
Automotive Tire Mfr
N.A.I.C.S.: 326211

Trelleborg Wheel Systems Moto d.o.o. (1)
Skofjeloska cesta 6, Kranj, Slovenia
Tel.: (386) 42065883
Web Site: https://www.mitas-moto.com
Motor Vehicle Tire Mfr
N.A.I.C.S.: 326211

Trelleborg Wheel Systems Netherlands B.V. (1)
Zadelmakerstraat 4, 2984 CC, Ridderkerk, Netherlands
Tel.: (31) 180414350
Engineering Consulting Services
N.A.I.C.S.: 541330

Trelleborg Wheel Systems Nordic AB (1)
Henry Dunkers Gata 1, 231 81, Trelleborg, Sweden
Tel.: (46) 41051000
Engineering Consulting Services
N.A.I.C.S.: 541330

Trelleborg do Brasil Solucoes em Vedacao Ltda (1)
Russian Federation St Moskovskoe shosse 177A, Sao Jose dos Campos, 12237-823, SP, Brazil
Tel.: (55) 1239327600
Web Site: https://www.trelleborgab.com
Emp.: 43
Automotive Rubber Product Mfr
N.A.I.C.S.: 326299

Wuxi Trelleborg Vibration Isolators Co., Ltd. (1)
36 Ximei Road State Hi-Tech Develop Zone, Wuxi, 214112, Jiangsu, China
Tel.: (86) 51088666222
Automotive Vibration Isolator Mfr
N.A.I.C.S.: 336330

TRELLEBORG OFFSHORE UK LTD

Stanley Way, Skelmersdale, WN8 8EA, Lancashire, United Kingdom
Tel.: (44) 1695 712000
Web Site: http://www.trelleborg.com
Emp.: 400
Offshore Oil & Gas Drilling Services
N.A.I.C.S.: 213111
Alan Burgess *(Co-Owner)*

TRELLIDOR HOLDINGS LIMITED

20 Aberdare Drive, Phoenix Industrial Park, Durban, South Africa
Tel.: (27) 315080800

Web Site:
https://www.holdings.trellidor.co.za
Year Founded: 1976
TRL—(JSE)
Rev.: $26,526,489
Assets: $22,734,954
Liabilities: $13,586,903
Net Worth: $9,148,052
Earnings: $183,530
Fiscal Year-end: 06/30/23
Security Door Mfr
N.A.I.C.S.: 332321
Terence Mark Dennison *(CEO)*

Subsidiaries:

Trellidor Ghana Limited (1)
Century Plaza Spintex Road Behind Herbal Life, Accra, Ghana
Tel.: (233) 561242424
Web Site: https://franchises.trellidor.co.za
Security Grille Mfr
N.A.I.C.S.: 327215

Trellidor Innovations Proprietary Limited (1)
Unit 9 Moon River 6 River Close, Barbeque Downs Kyalami, Johannesburg, South Africa
Tel.: (27) 117941743
Web Site: https://www.taylorblinds.co.za
Emp.: 180
Shutters Mfr
N.A.I.C.S.: 327215

Trellidor Proprietary Limited (1)
20 Aberdare Drive, Phoenix Industrial Park, Durban, South Africa
Tel.: (27) 861873554367
Web Site: https://www.trellidor.co.za
Security Gate Mfr & Distr
N.A.I.C.S.: 327215
Terry Dennison *(CEO)*

Trellidor UK Limited (1)
41 Walkers Road Moons Moat North, Manorside Industrial Estate, Redditch, United Kingdom
Tel.: (44) 1212850900
Web Site: https://www.trellidor.co.uk
Security Barrier Installation Services
N.A.I.C.S.: 561621

TRELLUS HEALTH PLC

Avon House 19 Stanwell Road, Penarth, Cardiff, CF64 2EZ, United Kingdom
Tel.: (44) 18008664165 UK
Web Site:
https://www.trellushealth.com
Year Founded: 2020
TRLS—(AIM)
Rev.: $18,000
Assets: $25,914,000
Liabilities: $822,000
Net Worth: $25,092,000
Earnings: ($8,810,000)
Emp.: 31
Fiscal Year-end: 12/31/22
Health Care Srvices
N.A.I.C.S.: 621610
Marla Dubinsky *(Co-Founder & CEO)*

Subsidiaries:

Trellus Health Inc. (1)
44 S Broadway Ste 100, White Plains, NY 10601
Healthcare Medical Treatment Services
N.A.I.C.S.: 622110

TREMATON CAPITAL INVESTMENTS LTD.

3rd Floor North Wharf 42 Hans Strijdom Avenue, Cape Town, 8001, South Africa
Tel.: (27) 214215550 ZA
Web Site: https://www.trematon.co.za
TMT—(JSE)
Rev.: $29,270,036
Assets: $133,811,683
Liabilities: $80,664,646
Net Worth: $53,147,037
Earnings: $6,424,803
Emp.: 544
Fiscal Year-end: 08/31/23
Financial Investment Services
N.A.I.C.S.: 523999
Arnold J. Shapiro *(CEO)*

Subsidiaries:

Aria Property Group (Pty) Limited (1)
Level 2 / 56 Boundary Street, South Brisbane, Brisbane, 4101, QLD, Australia
Tel.: (61) 732260111
Web Site: https://www.ariaproperty.com.au
Residential Services
N.A.I.C.S.: 721110
Tim Forrester *(Founder & Mng Dir)*

Club Mykonos Langebaan (Pty) Limited (1)
Mykonos Access Road, Langebaan, 7357, Western Cape, South Africa
Tel.: (27) 227077000
Web Site: https://www.clubmykonos.co.za
Resort Services
N.A.I.C.S.: 721110
Jacques Blom *(Fin Mgr)*

TREMCAR INC.

790 Avenue Montrichard, Saint-Jean-sur-Richelieu, J2X 5G4, QC, Canada
Tel.: (450) 347-7822
Web Site: http://www.tremcar.com
Year Founded: 1962
Sales Range: $100-124.9 Million
Tank Trailer Mfr
N.A.I.C.S.: 336212
Allan Paaren *(VP-Sls-Trailers-Ontario)*

Subsidiaries:

Tremcar Industries Inc. (1)
20 Alness Street, Toronto, M3J 3H4, ON, Canada
Tel.: (416) 661-9330
Tank Trailer Mfr
N.A.I.C.S.: 336212
Joe DeSimone *(VP-Sls-Tanks)*

Tremcar London inc. (1)
2060 Oxford Street E, London, N5V 2Z8, ON, Canada
Tel.: (519) 452-7732
Tank Trailer Mfr
N.A.I.C.S.: 336212
Denny Radlein *(Project Mgr)*

Tremcar St-Cesaire inc. (1)
1025 rue Neveu, Saint-Cesaire, J0L 1T0, QC, Canada
Tel.: (450) 469-4840
Tank Trailer Mfr
N.A.I.C.S.: 336212

Tremcar USA inc. (1)
436 - 12th St NE, Strasburg, OH 44680
Tel.: (330) 878-7708
Tank Trailer Mfr
N.A.I.C.S.: 336212
Andy Mulvey *(VP-Sls-Intl)*

Tremcar West inc. (1)
1750 Aurum Road, Edmonton, T6S 0A4, AB, Canada
Tel.: (780) 371-1579
Tank Trailer Mfr
N.A.I.C.S.: 336212
Ross Longson *(Mgr-Svc)*

TREMISIS ENERGY ACQUISITION CORPORATION II

545-7 Dogok-Dong, SoftForum B/D 7th Floor, Gangnam-Gu, Seoul, Korea (South)
Tel.: (82) 2 575 0466 DE
Year Founded: 2007
Sales Range: $1-9.9 Million
Investment Services
N.A.I.C.S.: 523999
Sang-Chul Kim *(Chm)*

TREMULA NAV SA

Str Industriala 7, Constanta, Romania
Tel.: (40) 341 449868
Forestry Services
N.A.I.C.S.: 115310

TRENCH METALS CORP.

2200-885 West Georgia St, Vancouver, V6C 3E8, BC, Canada
Tel.: (604) 339-0339 AB
Web Site: https://trenchmetals.com
Year Founded: 2012
NVTQF—(OTCIQ)
Assets: $645,174
Liabilities: $56,233
Net Worth: $588,940
Earnings: ($230,772)
Fiscal Year-end: 10/31/22
Investment Services
N.A.I.C.S.: 523999
Simon Cheng *(CEO)*

TRENCHANT CAPITAL CORP.

1021 West Hastings Street 9th Floor, Vancouver, V6E 0C3, BC, Canada
Tel.: (604) 307-4274 BC
Web Site:
http://www.trenchantcapital.net
Year Founded: 2009
Investment Services
N.A.I.C.S.: 523999
Eric Boehnke *(CEO)*

TRENCOR LIMITED

Suite 304 Sea Point Medical Centre, 11 Kloof Road Sea Point 8005, Cape Town, 8005, South Africa
Tel.: (27) 214217310
Web Site: https://www.trencor.net
TRE—(JSE)
Rev.: $5,718,300
Assets: $77,278,740
Liabilities: $490,140
Net Worth: $76,788,600
Earnings: $6,753,040
Emp.: 184
Fiscal Year-end: 12/31/23
Marine Cargo Services
N.A.I.C.S.: 423840
David Morris Nurek *(Chm)*

TREND ELECTRONICS LTD.

Gut No 350 Beed Road, Village Bhalgaon, Aurangabad, 431201, Maharashtra, India
Tel.: (91) 7385335100
Web Site:
https://www.trendelectronics.in
Year Founded: 1989
Electrical Home Appliance Mfr
N.A.I.C.S.: 335999
Milind M. Deshpande *(CFO)*

TREND EXPLORATION, LTD.

2F-2 No 669 Sec 5 Zhongxiao E Rd C, Xinyi Dist, Taipei, 11061, Taiwan
Tel.: (886) 287850039 NV
Year Founded: 1999
TRDX—(OTCIQ)
Rev.: $18,000
Assets: $20,000
Liabilities: $188,000
Net Worth: ($168,000)
Earnings: ($28,000)
Fiscal Year-end: 12/31/23
Holding Company
N.A.I.C.S.: 551112
Hsin Jung Lee *(Sec)*

TREND GAYRIMENKUL YATIRIM ORTAKLIGI A.S.

Egitim Mah Poyraz Sk Er Togay Is Merkezi No 3/21, Kadikoy, 34400, Istanbul, Turkiye
Tel.: (90) 2122103344
Web Site:
https://www.trendgyo.com.tr
Year Founded: 2006
TDGYO—(IST)
Sales Range: Less than $1 Million
Asset Management Services
N.A.I.C.S.: 531390
Hamid Abdullah Hussein Alahmar *(Chm)*

TREND MICRO INC.

JR Shinjuku Miraina Tower4-1-6 Shinjuku, Shinjuku-ku, Tokyo, 160-0022, Japan
Tel.: (81) 353343600 JP
Web Site:
https://success.trendmicro.com
Year Founded: 1988
TMICY—(OTCIQ)
Rev.: $1,478,658,738
Assets: $3,110,664,024
Liabilities: $1,599,735,712
Net Worth: $1,510,928,312
Earnings: $197,178,725
Emp.: 7,500
Fiscal Year-end: 12/31/22
Anti-Virus Software Producer
N.A.I.C.S.: 334610
Steve Ming-Jang Chang *(Chm)*

Subsidiaries:

Trend Micro (EMEA) Limited (1)
Median House Cork Business Technology Park Model Farm Road, Cork, Co Cork, Ireland
Tel.: (353) 21 730 7300
Web Site: http://www.trendmicor.com
Sales Range: $25-49.9 Million
Emp.: 200
Security Software Development Services
N.A.I.C.S.: 541511

Trend Micro (UK) Ltd. (1)
Podium Level East 2 Kingdom Street Paddington Central, London, W2 6BD, United Kingdom
Tel.: (44) 2035493300
Web Site: http://www.trendmicro.co.uk
Sales Range: $25-49.9 Million
Emp.: 50
Mfr of Anti-Virus Software
N.A.I.C.S.: 334610

Trend Micro Australia Pty. Ltd. (1)
Level 3 2-4 Lyon Park Road, North Ryde, 2113, NSW, Australia
Tel.: (61) 2 9870 4888
Web Site: http://www.trendmicro.com.au
Sales Range: $25-49.9 Million
Emp.: 60
Security Software Development Services
N.A.I.C.S.: 541511
Peter Hewett *(Dir-Channel-Australia & New Zealand)*

Trend Micro Deutschland GmbH (1)
Parkring 29, 85748, Garching, Germany (100%)
Tel.: (49) 89839329700
Web Site: http://www.trendmicro.com
Sales Range: $25-49.9 Million
Emp.: 100
Mfr of Anti-Virus Software
N.A.I.C.S.: 334610

Trend Micro France S.A. (1)
85 rue Albert Premier, 92500, Rueil-Malmaison, France (100%)
Tel.: (33) 17 668 6500
Web Site: http://www.trendmicro.fr
Sales Range: $1-9.9 Million
Emp.: 30
Mfr of Anti-Virus Software
N.A.I.C.S.: 334610

Trend Micro Incorporated (1)
225 E John Carpenter Fwy Ste 1500, Irving, TX 75062
Tel.: (817) 569-8900
Web Site: http://us.trendmicro.com
Sales Range: $100-124.9 Million
Emp.: 300
Anti-Virus Software Mfr
N.A.I.C.S.: 541511

Trend Micro Latin America (1)
Viamonte 1646 Piso 8 Oficina 62, 1055, Buenos Aires, Argentina
Tel.: (54) 48161663

TREND MICRO INC.

Trend Micro Inc.—(Continued)
Web Site: http://www.trendmicro-la.com
Mfr of Anti-Virus Software
N.A.I.C.S.: 334610

Trend Micro Latinoamerica BU (1)
Insurgentes Sur 688 - piso 6 Col Del Valle,
03100, Mexico, Mexico
Tel.: (52) 55 3067 6000
Web Site: http://la.trendmicro.com
Distr of Anti-Virus Software
N.A.I.C.S.: 334610

Trend Micro Middle East (1)
Unit 3301 Swiss Tower Cluster Y Jumeirah
Lakes Towers, PO Box 488075, Dubai Internet City, Dubai, United Arab Emirates
Tel.: (971) 44573080
Web Site: http://www.trendmicro.com
Antivirus & Security Software Solutions
N.A.I.C.S.: 513210

Trend Micro do Brasil, Ltda. (1)
Rua Joaquim Floriano 1120 2o andar, Itaim
Bibi, 04534 004, Sao Paulo, Brazil
Tel.: (55) 11 2149 5655
Web Site: http://br.trendmicro.com
Anti-Virus Software Distr
N.A.I.C.S.: 334610

Trend Micro, Inc. (1)
8F No 198 Tun-Hwa S Road Sec 2, Sector
2, Taipei, 106, Taiwan
Tel.: (886) 22 378 9666
Web Site: http://www.trendmicro.com
Sales Range: $100-124.9 Million
Emp.: 500
Mfr of Anti-Virus Software
N.A.I.C.S.: 334610

TREND NETWORKS LIMITED
Stokenchurch House Oxford Road,
Stokenchurch, High Wycombe, HP14
3SX, Buckinghamshire, United Kingdom
Tel.: (44) 1925 428 380 UK
Web Site: http://www.trend-networks.com
Sales Range: Less than $1 Million
Data Cable & Network Testers Mfr
N.A.I.C.S.: 335999
Paul Walsh (CEO)

Subsidiaries:

Terahertz Technologies Inc. (1)
169 Clear Rd, Oriskany, NY 13424-4301
Tel.: (315) 736-3642
Web Site: http://www.teratec.us
Sales Range: Less than $1 Million
Instrument Mfr
N.A.I.C.S.: 334515
Michael Mazzatti (Founder & VP-Fiber Res & Dev)

TRENDEVICE S.P.A.
Via Copernico 38, 20125, Milan, Italy
Tel.: (39) 0235959520
Web Site:
  https://www.trendevice.com
Year Founded: 2013
TD—(EUR)
Electronic Device Retailer
N.A.I.C.S.: 425120
Antonio Capaldo (Chm)

TRENDMAKER, INC. LIMITED
Lot 56935 Jalan 9/8 Seksyen 9,
43650, Bandar Baru Bangi, Selangor,
Malaysia
Tel.: (60) 389231880 NV
Year Founded: 2013
TMIN—(OTCIQ)
Assets: $185,013
Liabilities: $225,140
Net Worth: ($40,127)
Earnings: ($39,990)
Fiscal Year-end: 12/31/22
Investment Management Service
N.A.I.C.S.: 523999
Chin Yee Tan (CEO)

TRENDZON HOLDINGS

GROUP LIMITED
38 Senoko Road, Singapore, 758110,
Singapore Ky
Web Site:
  https://www.trendzon1865.com
Year Founded: 1996
1865—(HKG)
Rev.: $44,537,236
Assets: $89,183,401
Liabilities: $47,576,880
Net Worth: $41,606,521
Earnings: ($1,540,571)
Emp.: 340
Fiscal Year-end: 03/31/23
Holding Company
N.A.I.C.S.: 551112
Fung Chun Tse (Sec)

TRENT LIMITED
Trent House G Block Plot No C 60
Beside Citibank Bandra Kurla Complex, Bandra East, Mumbai, 51, India
Tel.: (91) 7506401234
Web Site: https://www.westside.com
500251—(BOM)
Rev.: $381,457,440
Assets: $781,289,145
Liabilities: $459,487,665
Net Worth: $321,801,480
Earnings: ($24,724,245)
Emp.: 7,112
Fiscal Year-end: 03/31/21
Retail Stores
N.A.I.C.S.: 459999
Noel N. Tata (Chm)

Subsidiaries:

Booker India Private Limited (1)
Tel.: (91) 2268830900
Web Site: https://www.bookerindia.net
Food Product Whslr
N.A.I.C.S.: 424420

Common Wealth Developers Limited (1)
CD Fountainhead-Murida Opp CD Countryside, Fatorda Salcete, Goa, 403602, India
Tel.: (91) 8322742082
Web Site: https://www.cdhomes.com
Real Estate Development Services
N.A.I.C.S.: 531390

TRENTION AB
Ankdammsgatan 35, 171 67, Solna,
Sweden
Tel.: (46) 84664500 SE
Web Site: http://www.trention.se
TRENT—(OMX)
Rev.: $6,365,898
Assets: $33,377,025
Liabilities: $258,280
Net Worth: $33,118,745
Earnings: ($828,424)
Emp.: 2
Fiscal Year-end: 12/31/19
Power Generation & Engine Efficiency Technology Development Services
N.A.I.C.S.: 335311
Mats Gabrielsson (Chm)

Subsidiaries:

Opcon Bioenergy AB (1)
Varmdovagen 120, PO Box 79, Nacka,
13160, Sweden
Tel.: (46) 850410580
Web Site: http://www.faxlund.se
Power Generating Equipment Mfr
N.A.I.C.S.: 335312

Opcon Technology Suzhou Co., Ltd (1)
No 3 Binhe Road, 215011, Suzhou, Jiangsu, China
Tel.: (86) 51268073990
Sales Range: $50-74.9 Million
Emp.: 140
Small Engine Ignition Systems Mfr
N.A.I.C.S.: 336320
Ingemar Pettersson (CEO & Gen Mgr)

TRENTON COLD STORAGE, INC.
21 Albert St, Trenton, K8V 5R1, ON,
Canada
Tel.: (613) 394-3317
Web Site: http://www.trencold.com
Sales Range: $25-49.9 Million
Emp.: 250
Provider of Warehouse Storage Space
N.A.I.C.S.: 493120

Subsidiaries:

Trenton Cold Storage, Inc. - Edmonton Facility (1)
12425 66th Street NW, Edmonton, T5B 1K5, AB, Canada
Tel.: (780) 378-3317
Cold Storage & Logistics Services
N.A.I.C.S.: 493120

Trenton Cold Storage, Inc. - Toronto Facility (1)
3691-3695 Weston Rd, North York, M9L 1W4, ON, Canada
Tel.: (613) 394-3317
Cold Storage & Logistics Services
N.A.I.C.S.: 493120

TRES-OR RESOURCES LTD.
1934 - 131 Street White Rock, Vancouver, V4A 7R7, BC, Canada
Tel.: (604) 688-8700
Web Site: https://www.tres-or.com
TRSFF—(OTCIQ)
Rev.: $3,824
Assets: $2,171,821
Liabilities: $479,032
Net Worth: $1,692,789
Earnings: ($176,465)
Fiscal Year-end: 02/29/24
Metal Mining Exploration Service
N.A.I.C.S.: 213114
Laura Duffett Lee (Pres & CEO)

Subsidiaries:

Vaaldiam do Brasil Mineracao Ltda. (1)
Rua Brasilia 251 Bairro Canaan, Sete Lagoas, Minas Gerais, Brazil
Tel.: (55) 3137720938
Gold Mining & Exploration Services
N.A.I.C.S.: 213114

TRESCON LIMTED
203-204 Second Floor Orbit Plaza
New Prabhadevi Road, Prabhadevi,
Mumbai, 400025, Maharashtra, India
Tel.: (91) 2249153599
Web Site: https://www.trescon.com
532159—(BOM)
Rev.: $594,976
Assets: $13,040,034
Liabilities: $179,498
Net Worth: $12,860,536
Earnings: $337,594
Emp.: 3
Fiscal Year-end: 03/31/23
Real Estate Services
N.A.I.C.S.: 531210
Vilas Kharche (Chm)

TRESMAN STEEL INDUSTRIES LTD.
286 Statesman Drive, Mississauga,
L5S 1X7, ON, Canada
Tel.: (905) 795-8757 ON
Web Site:
  https://www.tresmansteel.com
Year Founded: 1976
Emp.: 60
Structured Steel Distr
N.A.I.C.S.: 238120
Andras Kenedi (Partner)

TRESTON OY
Sorakatu 1, 20730, Turku, Finland
Tel.: (358) 10446911

INTERNATIONAL PUBLIC

Web Site: https://www.treston.fi
Emp.: 100
Industrial Furniture & Office Equipment Whslr
N.A.I.C.S.: 423210
Esa Siljander (CEO)

Subsidiaries:

Treston Holding, Inc. (1)
156 Bluffs Ct, Canton, GA 30114
Tel.: (770) 721-7980
Holding Company
N.A.I.C.S.: 551112

Subsidiary (Domestic):

Treston IAC LLC (2)
3831 S. Bullard Ave, Goodyear, AZ 85338
Tel.: (714) 990-8997
Industrial Furniture & Office Equipment Whslr
N.A.I.C.S.: 337127
Donald Murphy (Gen Mgr)

Subsidiary (Domestic):

IAC Industries, Inc. (3)
3831 S Bullard Ave, Goodyear, AZ 85338
Tel.: (714) 990-8997
Web Site: https://www.iacindustries.com
Industrial Work Benches, Anti-Static Materials & Laminar Flow Work Stations Mfr
N.A.I.C.S.: 337127
Donald Murphy (CEO)

TREVALI MINING CORPORATION
1900 - 999 West Hastings Street,
Vancouver, V6C 2W2, BC, Canada
Tel.: (778) 655-5885 BC
Web Site: https://www.trevali.com
Year Founded: 1993
TREVQ—(OTCEM)
Rev.: $386,110,000
Assets: $744,570,000
Liabilities: $296,121,000
Net Worth: $448,449,000
Earnings: ($35,411,000)
Emp.: 1,138
Fiscal Year-end: 12/31/19
Gold, Silver & Other Metal Mining Exploration & Services
N.A.I.C.S.: 212220
Ricus Grimbeek (Pres & CEO)

TREVI FINANZIARIA INDUSTRIALE SPA.
Via Larga 201, 47522, Cesena, FC,
Italy
Tel.: (39) 0547319311 IT
Web Site: https://www.trevigroup.com
TFIN—(ITA)
Rev.: $656,693,896
Assets: $787,410,310
Liabilities: $625,246,716
Net Worth: $162,163,594
Earnings: $28,626,780
Emp.: 3,189
Fiscal Year-end: 12/31/23
Soil Engineering Services
N.A.I.C.S.: 237990
Cesare Trevisani (VP)

Subsidiaries:

Arabian Soil Contractors Ltd. (1)
77006 16th Street cross Prince Nasser St, Al Khobar, 31952, Saudi Arabia
Tel.: (966) 138678288
Web Site: https://www.treviasc.com
Soil Contracting Services
N.A.I.C.S.: 541330

Idt FZCO (1)
Jebel Ali Freezone Jazfa 19 Office no 1502, Dubai, United Arab Emirates
Tel.: (971) 48810560
Construction Engineering Services
N.A.I.C.S.: 541330

PSM S.p.A. (1)
Via del lavoro 7, Casella D, 31011, Asolo, Italy

AND PRIVATE COMPANIES — TRF LTD

Tel.: (39) 0423541211
Construction Mfr & Distr
N.A.I.C.S.: 333120

Soilmec Algeria Sarl (1)
17 rue Djurdura, El Mohammadia, Algeria
Tel.: (213) 21826042
Soil Engineering Services
N.A.I.C.S.: 541330

Soilmec Australia Pty. Ltd. (1)
19 Precision Place, Mulgrave, 2756, NSW, Australia
Tel.: (61) 245879588
Web Site: https://www.soilmec.com.au
Soil Engineering Services
N.A.I.C.S.: 541330

Soilmec Colombia S.A.S. (1)
Calle 93B no 18-12 Ofic 308, Bogota, Colombia
Tel.: (57) 16360990
General Construction Services
N.A.I.C.S.: 541990

Soilmec Deutschland GmbH (1)
Raiffeisenstrasse 43, 57462, Olpe, Germany
Tel.: (49) 2761941280
Soil Engineering Services
N.A.I.C.S.: 541330

Soilmec F. Equipment Pvt. Ltd. (1)
G7 Kothari Compound Opp Tikuji-Ni-Wadi Manpada, Mumbai, Thane, 400607, India
Tel.: (91) 2225899258
Web Site: http://www.soilmecindia.co
Piling Machine Tool Mfr & Distr
N.A.I.C.S.: 333517

Soilmec France S.A.S. (1)
Boite Postale 820, Le Buisson Saint Aubin sur, 27600, Gaillon, France
Tel.: (33) 232533126
Construction Equipment Mfr & Distr
N.A.I.C.S.: 333120

Soilmec H.K. Ltd. (1)
1059-1061 Tung Chau West Street Unit A 7th Floor, Sun Kwong Industrial Building, Kowloon, China (Hong Kong)
Tel.: (852) 21560963
Construction Equipment Mfr & Distr
N.A.I.C.S.: 333120

Soilmec Japan Co., Ltd. (1)
7F Suitengumae Tokyu Building 1-29-6 Kakigara-cho, Nihonbashi Chuo-ku, Tokyo, 103-0014, Japan
Tel.: (81) 356431271
Web Site: https://www.soilmec-j.com
Industrial Machinery Mfr & Distr
N.A.I.C.S.: 333248

Soilmec North America Inc. (1)
18320 Imperial Valley Dr, Houston, TX 77060
Tel.: (281) 885-0777
Web Site:
  https://soilmecna.squarespace.com
Underground Construction Services
N.A.I.C.S.: 541990

Soilmec S.p.A. (1)
Via Dismano 5819, 47522, Cesena, Forli Cesena, Italy
Tel.: (39) 0547319111
Web Site: https://www.soilmec.com
Emp.: 1,300
Machinery Product Mfr & Distr
N.A.I.C.S.: 333120

Soilmec Singapore Pte. Ltd. (1)
101B Pioneer Road, Tuas West, 639607, Singapore
Tel.: (65) 68630280
Web Site: https://www.soilmec.com.sg
Ground Engineering Services
N.A.I.C.S.: 541330

Soilmec U.K. Ltd. (1)
New Lodge, Polebrook Oundle, Peterborough, PE8 5LL, United Kingdom
Tel.: (44) 1832274602
Web Site: https://www.soilmec.co.uk
Building Construction Services
N.A.I.C.S.: 541990

Soilmec do Brasil S.A. (1)
Rodovia Bunjiro Nakao 52 800 CEP, Cotia, 06726-300, SP, Brazil

Tel.: (55) 11982300058
Soil Engineering Services
N.A.I.C.S.: 541330

Swissboring & Co. LLC (1)
PO Box 2694, P C 112, Ruwi, Oman
Tel.: (968) 26884195
Engineeering Services
N.A.I.C.S.: 541330

Swissboring Overseas Piling Corp. Ltd. (1)
Building No -P/77 Unit No M-01 Al Nahyan, Abu Dhabi, United Arab Emirates
Tel.: (971) 26324155
Engineeering Services
N.A.I.C.S.: 541330

Swissboring Qatar WLL (1)
PO Box 3020, Doha, Qatar
Tel.: (974) 44553102
Soil Engineering Services
N.A.I.C.S.: 541330

Trevi Algerie E.U.R.L. (1)
9 rue de Jardins, Algiers, 16035, Hydra, Algeria
Tel.: (213) 23477288
Geotechnical Reconnaissance Services
N.A.I.C.S.: 541330

Trevi Australia Pty. Ltd. (1)
Level 19 644 Chapel Street, South Yarra, 3141, VIC, Australia
Tel.: (61) 491149397
Soil Engineering Services
N.A.I.C.S.: 541330

Trevi Chile S.p.A. (1)
Hendaya 60 Torre Napoleon Piso 10, Las Condes, Santiago, Chile
Tel.: (56) 11964390435
Construction Engineering Services
N.A.I.C.S.: 541330

Trevi Cimentaciones C.A. (1)
Torre Forum entre Las Mercedes Carabobo y la Calle Guaicaipuro, Piso 3 Oficina 3-B El Rosal, Caracas, 1060, Venezuela
Tel.: (58) 2129523593
Soil Engineering Services
N.A.I.C.S.: 541330

Trevi Cimentacones y Consolidaciones S.A. (1)
Via Panamericana-Caceres Distrito Arraijan 1003-Prov, 1060, Panama, Panama Oeste, Panama
Tel.: (507) 66751100
Construction Engineering Services
N.A.I.C.S.: 541330

Trevi Construction Co., Ltd. (1)
7/F Sun Kwong Industrial Building 1059 Tung Chau West St, Cheung Sha Wan, Kowloon, China (Hong Kong)
Tel.: (852) 21166966
General Construction Services
N.A.I.C.S.: 541990

Trevi Fondations Speciales S.A.S. (1)
23 Allee des Impressionnistes-Immeuble Le Sisley Parc d Activite, Paris Nord II, 93420, Villepinte, France
Tel.: (33) 185101530
Web Site: https://www.trevifrance.eu
Geotechnical & Foundation Engineering Services
N.A.I.C.S.: 541330

Trevi Foundations Kuwait Co. WLL (1)
PO Box 1032, Dasman, 15461, Kuwait
Tel.: (965) 22468591
Web Site: https://www.trevikuwait.com
Emp.: 400
Engineeering Services
N.A.I.C.S.: 541330

Trevi Foundations Nigeria Ltd. (1)
Plot 4 Block B Gbagada Industrial scheme Gbagada Expressway Gbagada, Lagos, Nigeria
Tel.: (234) 8150892906
Web Site: https://www.trevinigeria.com
Building Construction Services
N.A.I.C.S.: 541990

Trevi Foundations Philippines Inc. (1)

Unit 2301 23rd Floor 88 Corporate Center, 141 Valero corner Sedeno Streets Salcedo Village, Makati, 1227, Philippines
Tel.: (63) 28673181
Web Site: https://www.trevi.com.ph
Drilling & Grouting Services
N.A.I.C.S.: 532412

Trevi Galante S.A. (1)
Av El Dorado No 96J-66 Oficina 209, Bogota, Colombia
Tel.: (57) 16814395
General Construction Services
N.A.I.C.S.: 541990

Trevi Geotechnik GmbH (1)
Gauermanngasse 2, 1010, Wien, Austria
Tel.: (43) 457319311
Building Construction Services
N.A.I.C.S.: 541990

Trevi Icos Corporation (1)
38 3rd Ave Unit 300, Charlestown, MA 02129-4503
Tel.: (617) 241-4800
Web Site: http://www.treviicos.com
Sales Range: $50-74.9 Million
Emp.: 120
Bridge Construction
N.A.I.C.S.: 237310

Trevi Insaat Ve Muhendislik AS (1)
Omer Avni Mah Inonu Cd Gumussu Palas 18/10, Beyoglu, 34427, Istanbul, Turkiye
Tel.: (90) 21224306
Web Site: https://www.trevi-tr.com
Geotechnical & Foundation Engineering Services
N.A.I.C.S.: 541330

Trevi S.p.A. (1)
Via Dismano 5819, 47522, Cesena, Italy
Tel.: (39) 0547319311
Web Site: https://www.trevispa.com
Civil Engineering Services
N.A.I.C.S.: 541330

Trevi Spezialtiefbau GmbH (1)
Linprunstrasse 49, 80335, Munich, Germany
Tel.: (49) 457319311
Soil Engineering Services
N.A.I.C.S.: 541330

Treviicos Soletanche JV (1)
38 3rd Ave, Charlestown, MA 02129
Tel.: (617) 241-4800
General Construction Services
N.A.I.C.S.: 541990

TREVISA INVESTIMENTOS SA
Av Padre Cacique 320 6 andar, Porto Alegre, 90810240, RS, Brazil
Tel.: (55) 5121031188
Web Site: https://www.trevisa.com.br
Year Founded: 1930
LUXM4—(BRAZ)
Rev.: $24,413,578
Assets: $30,483,008
Liabilities: $8,948,714
Net Worth: $21,534,294
Earnings: $3,305,089
Fiscal Year-end: 12/31/23
Sea Transportation Services
N.A.I.C.S.: 483111
Jorge Lindemann *(Dir-IR)*

TREVISAN COMETAL SPA
Via Antonio Meucci 4, 37135, Verona, Italy
Tel.: (39) 0458203711
Web Site: http://www.trevisan.com
Sales Range: $125-149.9 Million
Emp.: 855
Aluminium Coating Mfr
N.A.I.C.S.: 332812
Luca Negri *(Chm)*

Subsidiaries:

Autel S.r.l. (1)
Via Bagnoli 9, 41049, Sassuolo, Italy (60.2%)
Tel.: (39) 0536802104
Web Site: http://www.aeautel.it

Sales Range: $25-49.9 Million
Emp.: 100
Machine Tools Mfr
N.A.I.C.S.: 333517

Cometal Engineering S.p.A. (1)
Via Brognolo 5, Rodengo Saiano, 25050, Brescia, Italy (100%)
Tel.: (39) 0306817200
Machine Tools Mfr
N.A.I.C.S.: 333517

Effecta Koine S.r.l. (1)
C da San Benedetto-zona Industriale, Favara, 92026, Catania, Italy (71%)
Tel.: (39) 0922613069
Machine Tools Mfr
N.A.I.C.S.: 333517

R.G.Automation S.p.A. (1)
Via Monti Berici 4, San Giovanni Lupatoto, Verona, Italy (100%)
Tel.: (39) 0458751168
Relay & Industrial Control Mfr
N.A.I.C.S.: 335314

Trevisan Cometal North America Inc (1)
1818 N Interstate 35e Ste 118, Carrollton, TX 75006-3768 (100%)
Tel.: (972) 242-9799
Industrial Machinery Mfr
N.A.I.C.S.: 333248

Trevisan Nanhai Co. Ltd (1)
Muyuan shishan Nanhai, 528225, Foshan, Guangdong, China (99.99%)
Tel.: (86) 75786696995
Sales Range: $50-74.9 Million
Emp.: 11
Clay & Ceramic & Refractory Minerals Mining
N.A.I.C.S.: 212323

TREVOR BAYLIS BRANDS PLC
Building 3/001 Building Research Establishment, Bucknalls Lane, Watford, WD25 9XX, United Kingdom
Tel.: (44) 1784737050   UK
Web Site:
  http://www.trevorbaylisbrands.com
Year Founded: 2003
Management Consulting Services
N.A.I.C.S.: 541618
David Bunting *(CEO)*

TREYO LEISURE AND ENTERTAINMENT LTD
Level 2 371 Spencer Street, Melbourne, 3000, Australia
Tel.: (61) 438949009
Web Site: http://www.treyo.com.au
Sales Range: $50-74.9 Million
Emp.: 770
Automatic Mahjong Tables Mfr
N.A.I.C.S.: 713990
Allan Mao *(Chm)*

TRF LTD
11 Station Road Burmamines, Jamshedpur, 831007, India
Tel.: (91) 6572345727
Web Site: https://www.trf.co.in
505854—(BOM)
Rev.: $26,775,458
Assets: $77,833,296
Liabilities: $102,312,469
Net Worth: ($24,479,173)
Earnings: ($25,257,100)
Emp.: 1,254
Fiscal Year-end: 03/31/20
Engineeering Services
N.A.I.C.S.: 541330
Anil Kumar Singh *(VP-Ops)*

Subsidiaries:

Qingdao YTE Special Products Co. Ltd. (1)
No 18 Huishui Rd, Qingdao, 266101, Licang, China
Tel.: (86) 53280923091

TRF Ltd—(Continued)

Sales Range: $25-49.9 Million
Emp.: 30
Axles Mfr
N.A.I.C.S.: 336999

YORK Transport Equipment (Malaysia) Sdn Bhd (1)
Ste 8 03A 8th Fl N Block The Ampwalk 218 Jalan Ampang, 50450, Kuala Lumpur, Malaysia
Tel.: (60) 68610577
Axles Mfr
N.A.I.C.S.: 336999

TRG PAKISTAN LIMITED
24th floor Sky Tower West Wing Dolmen, HC-3 Block 4 Marine Drive Clifton, Karachi, 75600, Pakistan
Tel.: (92) 21111874874
Web Site: https://trg.com.pk
TRG—(KAR)
Rev.: $1,527,413
Assets: $150,455,672
Liabilities: $25,491,516
Net Worth: $124,964,156
Earnings: $490,503
Emp.: 1
Fiscal Year-end: 06/30/20
Business Process Outsourcing Services
N.A.I.C.S.: 561439

TRGOAUTO A.D.
Trg Srpskih Junaka 3, 78000, Banja Luka, Bosnia & Herzegovina
Tel.: (387) 51 215 465
Sales Range: Less than $1 Million
Emp.: 1
Motor Vehicle Parts Whslr
N.A.I.C.S.: 423120

TRGOCENTAR A.D.
Kralja Petra Prvog 9, Leskovac, Serbia
Tel.: (381) 16246903
Web Site: http://www.trgocentar.co.rs
Year Founded: 1995
TRGC—(BEL)
Sales Range: Less than $1 Million
Emp.: 46
Hardware Product Whslr
N.A.I.C.S.: 423710
Slobodan Arsic (Exec Dir & Dir)

TRGOPROMET A.D.
Aerodromska 4b, Kraljevo, 36 000, Serbia
Tel.: (381) 36 384 135
Web Site: http://www.trgopromet-ad.com
Year Founded: 2000
Sales Range: $1-9.9 Million
Emp.: 2
Food Product Retailer
N.A.I.C.S.: 445298

TRGOVINA 22 A.D.
19 Oktobar br 2, 34000, Kragujevac, Serbia
Tel.: (381) 34 33 60 48
Web Site: http://www.trgovina22.rs
Year Founded: 1949
Sales Range: Less than $1 Million
Emp.: 16
Apparel Product Mfr
N.A.I.C.S.: 315250
Dragan Spasojevic (Exec Dir)

TRGOVINA BORAC D.D. TRAVNIK
ul Tornicka bb, 72270, Travnik, Bosnia & Herzegovina
Tel.: (387) 3 051 1118
Web Site: http://www.borac-trgovina.com

TBOTRK1—(SARE)
Rev.: $472,283
Assets: $9,233,864
Liabilities: $413,036
Net Worth: $8,820,828
Earnings: ($387,745)
Emp.: 3
Fiscal Year-end: 12/31/20
Trading Services
N.A.I.C.S.: 238990

TRI CHEMICAL LABORATORIES INC.
8154-217 Uenohara Uenohara-shi, Yamanashi, 409-0112, Japan
Tel.: (81) 554636600
Web Site: https://www.trichemical.com
Year Founded: 1978
4369—(TKS)
Rev.: $79,734,140
Assets: $225,915,760
Liabilities: $30,444,460
Net Worth: $195,471,300
Earnings: $17,512,300
Emp.: 214
Fiscal Year-end: 01/31/24
Chemicals Mfr
N.A.I.C.S.: 325998
Jumpei Takenaka (Chm)

TRI VIET ASSET MANAGEMENT CORPORATION JOINT STOCK COMPANY
142 Doi Can, Ba Dinh District, Hanoi, Vietnam
Tel.: (84) 437224999
Web Site: http://tcorp.vn
TVC—(HNX)
Rev.: $2,688,053
Assets: $81,471,929
Liabilities: $8,514,433
Net Worth: $72,957,496
Earnings: $11,480,050
Emp.: 18
Fiscal Year-end: 12/31/23
Management Consulting Services
N.A.I.C.S.: 541611
Thanh Tung Pham (Chm)

TRI VIET SECURITIES JSC
2 nd Floor 142 Doi Can, Ba Dinh district, Hanoi, Vietnam
Tel.: (84) 2462735059
Web Site: https://www.tvsc.vn
TVB—(HNX)
Financial Investment Services
N.A.I.C.S.: 523999
Pham Thanh Tung (Chm)

TRI-MODE SYSTEM (M) BHD
No 1 Lot 48 Jalan Sungai Chandong 24/KS11, Taman Perindustrian Pulau Indah Fasa 3, 42920, Port Klang, Selangor, Malaysia
Tel.: (60) 330938118
Web Site: https://www.trimode-malaysia.com.my
Year Founded: 1992
199—(KLS)
Rev.: $26,375,486
Assets: $31,970,545
Liabilities: $12,663,093
Net Worth: $19,307,451
Earnings: $2,216,704
Emp.: 243
Fiscal Year-end: 12/31/22
Logistic Services
N.A.I.C.S.: 541614
Hew Han Seng (Mng Dir)

TRI-RIVER VENTURES INC.
Suite 2050 736 6th Avenue SW, Vancouver, BC, Canada
Tel.: (604) 306-5867

Web Site: http://www.tririver-venture.com
Year Founded: 1992
Rev.: $12,828
Assets: $764,011
Liabilities: $7,418
Net Worth: $756,593
Earnings: ($56,945)
Fiscal Year-end: 12/31/18
Mineral Mining Exploration Service
N.A.I.C.S.: 213114

TRI-STAR MUTUAL FUND LIMITED
A/33 Central Commercial Area Block 7/8 Main Shahrah-e-Faisal, Karachi, 75350, Pakistan
Tel.: (92) 2571598
TSMF—(PSX)
Assets: $224,952
Liabilities: $75,576
Net Worth: $149,376
Earnings: ($60,884)
Fiscal Year-end: 06/30/23
Financial Services
N.A.I.C.S.: 523999

TRI-STAR POWER LIMITED
A/33 Central Commercial Area Block 7/8, Main Shahrah-e-Faisal KCHSU, Karachi, 75350, Pakistan
Tel.: (92) 212571598
Web Site: https://tristar.com.pk
Year Founded: 1993
TSPL—(PSX)
Rev.: $21,872
Assets: $733,462
Liabilities: $39,526
Net Worth: $693,935
Earnings: $21,934
Fiscal Year-end: 06/30/23
Power Generation & Distribution Services
N.A.I.C.S.: 221114
Shamima Begum (Chm)

TRI-STAR RESOURCES PLC
16 Great Queen Street, London, WC2B 5DG, United Kingdom
Tel.: (44) 1233619550
Web Site: http://www.tri-starresources.com
Rev.: $54,568
Assets: $23,226,873
Liabilities: $1,695,411
Net Worth: $21,531,462
Earnings: ($2,571,035)
Emp.: 10
Fiscal Year-end: 12/31/18
Metal Mining Services
N.A.I.C.S.: 212290
David Facey (CEO & CFO)

TRI-TECH HOLDING INC.
#1205 Tower B Haidian Cultural and Arts Jia 28 Zhongguancun St, Haidian District, Beijing, 100086, China
Tel.: (86) 13601134582
Web Site: http://www.tri-tech.cn
Year Founded: 2002
Sales Range: Less than $1 Million
Sewage Treatment & Odor Control Systems Mfr
N.A.I.C.S.: 333310
Warren Zhao (Chm & CEO)

Subsidiaries:

Tri-Tech Infrastructures, LLC. - J&Y Water Division (1)
123 Center Park Dr Ste 224, Knoxville, TN 37922
Tel.: (865) 392-5926
Water Treatment System Mfr
N.A.I.C.S.: 333248

TRI-WALL K.K.

1-11-32 Nagata-cho Chiyoda-ku, Tokyo, 100-0014, Japan
Tel.: (81) 335195100
Web Site: http://www.tri-wall.com
Year Founded: 1974
Sales Range: $10-24.9 Million
Emp.: 70
Heavy-Duty Packaging Materials Mfr
N.A.I.C.S.: 322299
Yuji Suzuki (Chm & CEO)

TRIACTA BV
Torenlaan 19, 3742 CR, Baarn, Netherlands
Tel.: (31) 35 538 5444
Web Site: http://www.triacta.nl
Private Equity Services
N.A.I.C.S.: 523999
Gerben Willems (Mng Partner)

Subsidiaries:

Rademakers Gieterij B.V. (1)
Langestraat 12, 7891 GA, Klazienaveen, Netherlands
Tel.: (31) 591 547 000
Web Site: http://www.rademakersgieterij.com
Components for Sewage & Water Transport Systems Mfr
N.A.I.C.S.: 237110

TBS Soest B.V. (1)
Koningsweg 30, 3762 EC, Soest, Utracht, Netherlands
Tel.: (31) 356095611
Web Site: http://www.tbs.nl
Water & Road Construction Products Mfr
N.A.I.C.S.: 221320

TRIAD GROUP PLC
Huxley House Weyside Park Catteshall Lane, Godalming, GU7 1XE, Surrey, United Kingdom
Tel.: (44) 1908278450
Web Site: https://www.triad.co.uk
Year Founded: 1988
TRD—(LSE)
Rev.: $231,016,058
Assets: $12,055,196
Liabilities: $3,884,437
Net Worth: $8,170,759
Earnings: $1,587,175
Emp.: 104
Fiscal Year-end: 03/31/22
IT Consulting & Integrated Systems Design
N.A.I.C.S.: 541512
John Rigg (Chm)

Subsidiaries:

Generic Software Consultants Limited (1)
St Andrew House, Caldecotte Business Park, Milton Keynes, MK7 8LE, Buckinghamshire, United Kingdom
Tel.: (44) 1908278450
Web Site: http://www.generic-software.com
Sales Range: $25-49.9 Million
IT Consulting Services
N.A.I.C.S.: 541611
Adrian Leer (Mgr-Sls)

TRIALTO WINE GROUP LTD.
300-1260 Hamilton Street, Vancouver, V6B 2S8, BC, Canada
Tel.: (778) 331-8999
Web Site: https://www.trialto.com
Rev.: $13,294,786
Emp.: 35
Wine Distr
N.A.I.C.S.: 424820

TRIAN INVESTORS 1 LIMITED
PO Box 286 Fl 2 Trafalgar Court Les Banques, Saint Peter Port, GY1 4LY, Guernsey
Tel.: (44) 1481742074
Web Site: http://www.trianinvestors1.com

TI1—(LSE)
Rev.: $106,855,279
Assets: $540,730,998
Liabilities: $80,105
Net Worth: $540,650,893
Earnings: $105,999,916
Fiscal Year-end: 12/31/20
Investment Management Service
N.A.I.C.S.: 525990
Chris Sherwell (Chm)

TRIANGLE ENERGY (GLOBAL) LIMITED
Suite 2 Ground Floor 100 Havelock Street, West Perth, 6005, WA, Australia
Tel.: (61) 892197111 AU
Web Site:
https://www.triangleenergy.com.au
TEG—(ASX)
Rev.: $833,232
Assets: $12,349,523
Liabilities: $14,187,739
Net Worth: ($1,838,216)
Earnings: ($1,473,906)
Fiscal Year-end: 06/30/24
Natural Resources Exploration
N.A.I.C.S.: 213112
Conrad Todd (Mng Dir)

TRIANGLE TIRE CO. LTD
No 56 Qingdao Middle Road, Weihai, 264200, Shandong, China
Tel.: (86) 6315305527
Web Site: http://www.triangle.com.cn
Year Founded: 2001
601163—(SHG)
Rev.: $1,294,505,382
Assets: $2,484,141,763
Liabilities: $841,965,701
Net Worth: $1,642,176,062
Earnings: $103,564,923
Fiscal Year-end: 12/31/22
Tire Mfr & Distr
N.A.I.C.S.: 326211
Ding Mu (Chm)

TRIBAL GROUP PLC
City Lab 4-6 Dalton Square, Lancaster, LA1 1PP, United Kingdom
Tel.: (44) 3300164000 UK
Web Site:
https://www.tribalgroup.com
TRB—(LSE)
Rev.: $99,051,105
Assets: $115,441,501
Liabilities: $63,552,158
Net Worth: $51,889,343
Earnings: $8,632,384
Emp.: 893
Fiscal Year-end: 12/31/20
Holding Company; Education, Government & Training Market Consulting Services
N.A.I.C.S.: 551112
Richard Last (Chm)

Subsidiaries:

Class Measures Inc. (1)
100 Tower Office Park Dr Ste A, Woburn, MA 01801
Tel.: (781) 939-5699
Educational Support Services
N.A.I.C.S.: 611710

International Graduate Insight Group Limited (1)
Kings Orchard One Queen Street, Bristol, BS2 0HQ, United Kingdom
Tel.: (44) 115 666 3380
Web Site: https://www.i-graduate.org
Educational Support Services
N.A.I.C.S.: 611710

Tribal Consulting Limited (1)
Parkway House, Palatine Road, M224DB, Manchester, United Kingdom (100%)
Tel.: (44) 1619021100

Sales Range: $25-49.9 Million
Emp.: 40
Management Consulting Services
N.A.I.C.S.: 541618

Tribal Education Limited (1)
Tribal Education Limited, London, W1T 3EY, United Kingdom (100%)
Tel.: (44) 2073237100
Web Site: http://www.tribalgroup.com
Sales Range: $10-24.9 Million
Emp.: 30
Educational Support Services
N.A.I.C.S.: 611710

Tribal Group Pty Limited (1)
West 7-8 Federal Mills Park 3-35 Mackey Street, North Geelong, 3215, VIC, Australia
Tel.: (61) 38 580 0100
Educational Support Services
N.A.I.C.S.: 611710

Tribal Resourcing Limited (1)
155 Great Charles Street, Birmingham, B338HW, United Kingdom (99%)
Tel.: (44) 1212337777
Web Site: http://www.tribalresourcing.com
Sales Range: $25-49.9 Million
Emp.: 40
Advertising Agencies
N.A.I.C.S.: 541810

Tribal Systems Canada Limited (1)
Suite 400-601 West Broadway, Vancouver, V5Z 4C2, BC, Canada
Tel.: (604) 900-0120
Educational Support Services
N.A.I.C.S.: 611710

TRIBECA GLOBAL NATURAL RESOURCES LIMITED
Level 23 1 O'Connell Street, Sydney, 2000, NSW, Australia
Tel.: (61) 296402600 AU
Web Site: https://www.tribecaip.com
Year Founded: 1997
TGF—(ASX)
Rev.: $1,550,174
Assets: $160,010,767
Liabilities: $50,346,646
Net Worth: $109,664,121
Earnings: ($6,403,138)
Fiscal Year-end: 06/30/24
Investment Management Service
N.A.I.C.S.: 525910
David Aylward (CEO, Mng Dir & Portfolio Mgr)

TRIBECA RESOURCES CORPORATION
1305 - 1090 West Georgia Street, Vancouver, V6E 3V7, BC, Canada
Tel.: (604) 685-9316
Web Site:
https://tribecaresources.com
TRRCF—(OTCQB)
Rev.: $89,460
Assets: $2,791,710
Liabilities: $182,106
Net Worth: $2,609,604
Earnings: ($1,786,534)
Fiscal Year-end: 12/31/23
Metal Exploration Services
N.A.I.C.S.: 213114
Nick DeMare (CFO)

TRIBHOVANDAS BHIMJI ZAVERI LIMITED
241/43 Zaveri Bazar, Mumbai, 400 002, India
Tel.: (91) 2240465000
Web Site:
https://www.tbztheoriginal.com
TBZ—(NSE)
Rev.: $184,864,284
Assets: $165,781,298
Liabilities: $94,407,700
Net Worth: $71,373,598
Earnings: $5,905,973
Emp.: 904
Fiscal Year-end: 03/31/21

Jewelry Mfr & Retailer
N.A.I.C.S.: 339910
Niraj Rohitkumar Oza (Officer-Compliance, Sec & Head-Legal)

TRIBOO SPA
Viale Sarca 336 Edificio 16, 20126, Milan, Italy
Tel.: (39) 0264741401
Web Site: https://www.triboo.com
Year Founded: 2001
TB—(ITA)
Sales Range: Less than $1 Million
E-Commerce & Internet Marketing & Advertising
N.A.I.C.S.: 541613
Riccardo Maria Monti (Chm)

TRIBORON INTERNATIONAL AB
Hadar Grudes gata 6, 164 74, Kista, Sweden
Tel.: (46) 86431000
Web Site: https://www.triboron.com
Year Founded: 2013
TRIBO.B—(OMX)
Rev.: $39,066
Assets: $2,822,490
Liabilities: $504,190
Net Worth: $2,318,299
Earnings: ($1,635,872)
Emp.: 4
Fiscal Year-end: 12/31/20
Petroleum Product Distr
N.A.I.C.S.: 424720
Par Krossling (CEO & COO)

TRIBUILD CONTRACTING (CALGARY) LTD.
3 Skyline Crescent NE, Calgary, T2K 5X2, AB, Canada
Tel.: (403) 295-6100
Web Site: https://www.tribuild.com
Year Founded: 1982
Rev.: $11,362,976
Emp.: 36
General Building Contractors
N.A.I.C.S.: 236220
Matt McCaig (Pres)

TRIBUNE RESOURCES LTD.
Unit G1 49 Melville Parade, South Perth, 6151, WA, Australia
Tel.: (61) 894742113
Web Site: https://www.tribune.com.au
TBR—(ASX)
Rev.: $72,076,649
Assets: $209,156,750
Liabilities: $17,896,695
Net Worth: $191,260,055
Earnings: $5,263,964
Fiscal Year-end: 06/30/24
Mineral Exploration Services
N.A.I.C.S.: 213115
Otakar Demis (Co-Sec)

TRIBURY CONSTRUCTION (1995) INC.
1549 Fairburn Avenue, Sudbury, P3A 1N6, ON, Canada
Tel.: (705) 560-8743
Web Site: http://www.tribury.com
Rev.: $20,678,568
Emp.: 35
Construction Services
N.A.I.C.S.: 236220
Bob Cecchetto (Pres)

TRIBUTE RESOURCES INC.
2807 Woodhull Road, London, N6J 1Y4, ON, Canada
Tel.: (519) 657-7624
Web Site:
http://www.tributeresources.com
Year Founded: 1997
Assets: $1,553,991

Liabilities: $608,842
Net Worth: $945,149
Earnings: ($852,057)
Fiscal Year-end: 12/31/17
Gas Exploration Services
N.A.I.C.S.: 213112
Jane Lowrie (Pres & CEO)

TRICAN WELL SERVICE, LTD.
2900 645 - 7th Avenue SW, Calgary, T2P 4G8, AB, Canada
Tel.: (403) 266-0202
Web Site:
https://www.tricanwellservice.com
Year Founded: 1996
TCW—(TSX)
Rev.: $440,016,072
Assets: $452,031,893
Liabilities: $69,184,061
Net Worth: $382,847,832
Earnings: $13,470,862
Emp.: 1,032
Fiscal Year-end: 12/31/21
Specialized Products, Equipment & Services Used in Drilling, Completion, Stimulation & Reworking of Gas & Oil Wells
N.A.I.C.S.: 213111
G. Allen Brooks (Dir-Lead)

Subsidiaries:

Trican Well Service, L.P. (1)
1104 Dallas Dr Ste 220, Denton, TX 76205
Tel.: (940) 243-1120
Sales Range: $25-49.9 Million
Emp.: 6
Pumping Equipment Mfr
N.A.I.C.S.: 333914
Robert Hoskins (Pres)

TRICKLESTAR LIMITED
80 Robinson Road 02-00, Singapore, 068898, Singapore
Tel.: (65) 62363510 SG
Web Site: http://www.tricklestar.com
Year Founded: 2008
CYW—(SES)
Rev.: $13,820,102
Assets: $8,817,840
Liabilities: $3,500,146
Net Worth: $5,317,694
Earnings: $164,303
Emp.: 18
Fiscal Year-end: 12/31/22
Energy Saving Product Mfr
N.A.I.C.S.: 334513
Bernard Christopher Emby (Chm & CEO)

TRICOM FRUIT PRODUCTS LIMITED
Gat No 336 338-341 Village Andori Taluka Khandala, Satara, 415521, Maharashtra, India
Tel.: (91) 2169266251
Web Site:
https://www.tricomfruitproducts.com
531716—(BOM)
Assets: $18,291
Liabilities: $11,757,671
Net Worth: ($11,739,380)
Earnings: ($3,693,992)
Emp.: 2
Fiscal Year-end: 03/31/21
Fruit Product Mfr
N.A.I.C.S.: 311411
Chetan Kothari (CFO)

TRICOR PACIFIC CAPITAL, INC.
The Waterfront Centre 200 Burrard Street Suite 1560, Vancouver, V6C 3L6, BC, Canada
Tel.: (604) 688-7669
Web Site:
http://www.tricorpacific.com
Privater Equity Firm

TRICOR PACIFIC CAPITAL, INC.

Tricor Pacific Capital, Inc.—(Continued)
N.A.I.C.S.: 523999
Rod Senft *(Co-Founder)*

Subsidiaries:

CPI Card Group Inc. (1)
10368 W Centennial Rd, Littleton, CO 80127
Tel.: (720) 681-6304
Web Site: https://www.cpicardgroup.com
Rev.: $475,745,000
Assets: $296,666,000
Liabilities: $378,743,000
Net Worth: ($82,077,000)
Earnings: $36,540,000
Emp.: 1,375
Fiscal Year-end: 12/31/2022
Financial Payment Card Mfr
N.A.I.C.S.: 326199
Lane R. Dubin *(Chief Dev & Digital Officer & Exec VP)*

Subsidiary (Non-US):

CPI Card Group-Colchester Limited (2)
Graphic House Telford Way Severalls Business Park, Colchester, CO4 9QF, Essex, United Kingdom
Tel.: (44) 1206845555
Web Site: http://www.cpicardgroup.com
Sales Range: $25-49.9 Million
Emp.: 100
Plastic Card Mfr
N.A.I.C.S.: 326199
Alex Smith *(Mgr-HR)*

Subsidiary (Domestic):

CPI Card Group-Liverpool Limited (3)
2 Seddon Place, Skelmersdale, WN8 8EB, Lancashire, United Kingdom
Tel.: (44) 169550622
Web Site: http://www.cpicardgroup.com
Sales Range: $25-49.9 Million
Emp.: 70
Plastic Card Mfr
N.A.I.C.S.: 326199
Nick Khan *(Mng Dir)*

Parallel49 Equity (1)
225 E Deerpath Rd Ste 200, Lake Forest, IL 60045
Tel.: (847) 295-4410
Web Site: http://www.p49equity.com
Holding Company
N.A.I.C.S.: 551112
Brad Seaman *(Mng Partner)*

Holding (Domestic):

Twin Traffic Marking Corp. (2)
626 N 47th St, Kansas City, KS 66102
Tel.: (913) 428-2575
Web Site: http://www.twintraffic.com
Highway, Street & Bridge Construction
N.A.I.C.S.: 237310
James R. Francis *(Pres)*

Strong Precision Technologies, Inc. (1)
880 Nicholas Blvd, Elk Grove Village, IL 60007
Tel.: (847) 956-0126
Web Site: http://www.comettool.net
Precision Machined Metal Parts & Tools Mfr
N.A.I.C.S.: 333517
Jim Ray *(Pres & COO)*

Subsidiary (Domestic):

Duro-Life Corporation (2)
2401 Huntington Dr N, Algonquin, IL 60102-4400
Tel.: (847) 854-1044
Web Site: http://www.duro-life.com
Sales Range: $25-49.9 Million
Emp.: 100
Industrial Machinery Mfr
N.A.I.C.S.: 332710

Tiger Calcium Services Inc. (1)
603 - 15 Avenue, Nisku, T9E 7M6, AB, Canada
Tel.: (780) 955-5004
Web Site: http://www.tigercalcium.com
Chemical Product Mfr & Distr
N.A.I.C.S.: 325180

Plant (Domestic):

Tiger Calcium Services Inc. - Slave Lake Plant (2)
4505 Township Road 724 E c, Slave Lake, T0G 2A0, AB, Canada
Tel.: (780) 849-3114
Chemical Products Mfr
N.A.I.C.S.: 325180

TRICOR PACIFIC FOUNDERS CAPITAL, INC.

1111 West Hastings St Suite 200, Vancouver, V6E 2J3, BC, Canada
Tel.: (604) 646-4363
Web Site: https://www.tricorpacific.com
Privater Equity Firm
N.A.I.C.S.: 523999
Derek Senft *(Mng Dir)*

Subsidiaries:

Ganache Gourmet, Inc. (1)
200-1111 West Hastings St., Vancouver, V6E 2J3, BC, Canada
Tel.: (604) 646-4363
Edible Gift Products
N.A.I.C.S.: 445298

Subsidiary (US):

Totally Chocolate, Inc. (2)
2025 Sweet Rd, Blaine, WA 98230
Tel.: (360) 332-3900
Web Site: http://www.totallychocolate.com
Chocolate & Confectionery Mfr
N.A.I.C.S.: 311351
Ken Strong *(Pres)*

TRICOR PLC

Finsgate 5-7 Cranwood Street, London, EC1V 9EE, United Kingdom
Tel.: (44) 207 099 7703
Web Site: http://www.tricor-plc.org.uk
Sales Range: Less than $1 Million
Emp.: 2
Environmental Trading & Investment Solutions
N.A.I.C.S.: 523999
Fook Meng Chan *(CEO)*

TRICORN GROUP PLC

Spring Lane Malvern Link, Malvern, WR14 1DA, Worcestershire, United Kingdom
Tel.: (44) 1684569956   UK
Web Site: http://www.tricorn.uk.com
Rev.: $28,886,702
Assets: $19,091,137
Liabilities: $9,813,332
Net Worth: $9,277,805
Earnings: $1,121,814
Emp.: 304
Fiscal Year-end: 03/31/19
Holding Company; Pipe & Pipe Fitting Developer & Mfr
N.A.I.C.S.: 551112
Phillip Lee *(Dir-Fin)*

Subsidiaries:

Malvern Tubular Components Limited (1)
Spring Ln, Malvern, WR14 1DA, Worcestershire, United Kingdom
Tel.: (44) 1684892600
Web Site: http://www.mtc.uk.com
Sales Range: $25-49.9 Million
Emp.: 80
Tubular Components Mfr
N.A.I.C.S.: 313220
Jo Howard *(Mgr-HR & HSE)*

Maxpower Automotive Limited (1)
Bank St Hall End, West Bromwich, B71 1HB, West Midlands, United Kingdom
Tel.: (44) 1215882605
Web Site: http://www.maxaut.co.uk
Sales Range: $50-74.9 Million
Emp.: 120
Automotive Tubular & Pipe Components Mfr
N.A.I.C.S.: 313220
Rob Fairclough *(Dir-Ops)*

Redman Fittings Limited (1)
Unit B Spring Ln, Malvern Link, Malvern, WR14 1BY, Worcestershire, United Kingdom
Tel.: (44) 1684892600
Web Site: http://www.redmanfittings.com
Sales Range: $25-49.9 Million
Emp.: 6
Pipe Fittings Mfr & Distr
N.A.I.C.S.: 326122

TRICORONA AB

Kungsgatan 32, PO Box 70426, SE 107 25, Stockholm, Sweden
Tel.: (46) 8 506 885 00
Web Site: http://www.tricorona.com
Year Founded: 1988
Sales Range: $75-99.9 Million
Emp.: 25
Environmental Investment Services in the Carbon Emissions Trading Sector
N.A.I.C.S.: 523999
Niels von Zweigbergk *(Pres & CEO)*

Subsidiaries:

Carbon Asset Services Sweden AB (1)
Kungsgatan 32, PO Box 70426, 111 35, Stockholm, Sweden
Tel.: (46) 850688500
Web Site: http://www.tricorona.com
Sales Range: $50-74.9 Million
Investment Management Service
N.A.I.C.S.: 523999

Svensk Kraftmakling AB (1)
Norrlandsgatan 22, PO Box 70426, 111 43, Stockholm, Sweden
Tel.: (46) 850626300
Web Site: http://www.skm.se
Sales Range: $50-74.9 Million
Emp.: 10
Electric Power Brokering
N.A.I.C.S.: 425120
Peter Chudi *(VP)*

Svenska Vanadin AB (1)
Observatoriegatan 23, 113 29, Stockholm, Sweden
Tel.: (46) 854542630
Mineral Ore Mining Services
N.A.I.C.S.: 212390

Tricorona Carbon Asset Management Pte. Ltd. (1)
50 Raffles Pl No 35-01, Singapore Land Tower, Singapore, 048623, Singapore
Tel.: (65) 64991288
Web Site: http://www.tricorona.com
Sales Range: $50-74.9 Million
Emp.: 9
Develops & Buys & Trades Carbon Credits
N.A.I.C.S.: 523999
Moe Moe Oo *(Mng Dir)*

Tricorona Climate Partner AB (1)
Kungsgatan 32, PO Box 70426, 107 25, Stockholm, Sweden
Tel.: (46) 850688500
Web Site: http://www.tricorona.com
Sales Range: $50-74.9 Million
Investment Management Service
N.A.I.C.S.: 523999

TRIDENT LIFELINE LIMITED

2001 2 nd floor kurshi bazar APMC sahara darwaja choriyasi, Surat, 395003, Gujarat, India
Tel.: (91) 2612490224
Web Site: https://www.tridentlifeline.com
Year Founded: 2014
543616—(BOM)
Pharmaceutical Product Mfr & Distr
N.A.I.C.S.: 325412

Subsidiaries:

TNS Pharma Private Limited (1)
Plot No 4232 Road No 42 Sachin Gidc, Surat, 394230, Gujarat, India
Tel.: (91) 9825018791
Web Site: https://tnspharma.com
Pharmaceutical Tablet & Capsule Mfr
N.A.I.C.S.: 325412

INTERNATIONAL PUBLIC

TRIDENT LIMITED

E-212 Kitchlu Nagar, Ludhiana, 141 001, Punjab, India
Tel.: (91) 161 503 9999
Web Site: http://www.tridentindia.com
Year Founded: 1990
521064—(NSE)
Rev.: $958,261,395
Assets: $885,766,245
Liabilities: $360,967,425
Net Worth: $524,798,820
Earnings: $113,806,875
Emp.: 14,998
Fiscal Year-end: 03/31/22
Textile Products Mfr
N.A.I.C.S.: 314999
Rajinder Gupta *(Founder & Co-Chm)*

TRIDENT LIMITED PARTNERSHIP

3100 888-3 Street SW, Calgary, T2P 5C5, AB, Canada
Tel.: (403) 770-0333   DE
Web Site: http://www.tridentexploration.ca
Year Founded: 2003
Sales Range: $25-49.9 Million
Emp.: 100
Holding Company; Natural Gas Exploration, Development & Extraction
N.A.I.C.S.: 551112
Alan G. Withey *(Pres & CEO)*

Subsidiaries:

Trident Exploration Corp. (1)
444 7th Ave SW Ste 1000, Calgary, T2P 0X8, AB, Canada
Tel.: (403) 770-0333
Web Site: http://www.tridentexploration.ca
Natural Gas Exploration, Development & Extraction
N.A.I.C.S.: 213112
Todd A. Dillabough *(Pres, CEO & COO)*

Subsidiary (Domestic):

Trident Exploration (WX) Corp. (2)
444 5th Avenue SW Suite 1950, Calgary, T2P 2T8, AB, Canada
Tel.: (403) 290-6800
Sales Range: $1-9.9 Million
Emp.: 10
Natural Gas Exploration, Development & Extraction
N.A.I.C.S.: 213112

TRIDENT TECHLABS LIMITED

White House 1/18-20 2nd Floor Rani Jhansi Road, New Delhi, 110055, India
Tel.: (91) 1161811100
Web Site: https://www.tridenttechlabs.com
Year Founded: 2000
TECHLABS—(NSE)
Emp.: 84
Electric Equipment Mfr
N.A.I.C.S.: 331110

TRIDENT TEXOFAB LIMITED

2004 3rd Floor North Extension Begumpura Falsadwali Ring Road, Surat, 395 003, Gujarat, India
Tel.: (91) 2612451284
Web Site: https://www.tridenttexofab.com
Year Founded: 2008
540726—(BOM)
Rev.: $7,067,894
Assets: $9,251,088
Liabilities: $7,616,265
Net Worth: $1,634,822
Earnings: $48,206
Emp.: 55
Fiscal Year-end: 03/31/21
Textile Material Mfr & Distr
N.A.I.C.S.: 313210
Hardik Jigishkumar Desai *(Chm & Mng Dir)*

TRIDENT TOOLS LIMITED
Gut No 171 Tembhode Shirgaon Road, Dhansar Village, Palghar, 401 404, India
Tel.: (91) 2228847191
Web Site:
 https://www.magicuttools.com
Year Founded: 1982
531972—(BOM)
Sales Range: $1-9.9 Million
Emp.: 58
Cutting Tool Mfr
N.A.I.C.S.: 333515
Narendra R. Gupta *(Chm)*

TRIESSE LIMITED
Sherburn Enterprise Park Sherburn in Elmet, Leeds, LS25 6NS, United Kingdom
Tel.: (44) 1977687600
Web Site: http://www.triesseltd.co.uk
Rev.: $14,919,267
Emp.: 58
Wood Based Panel Products Distr
N.A.I.C.S.: 423310
John Nield *(Gen Mgr)*

TRIFAST PLC
Trifast House Bellbrook Park, Uckfield, TN22 1QW, East Sussex, United Kingdom
Tel.: (44) 8454811800
Web Site:
 https://www.trfastenings.com
TRI—(LSE)
Rev.: $296,822,031
Assets: $346,240,324
Liabilities: $157,320,374
Net Worth: $188,919,949
Earnings: $12,188,252
Emp.: 1,280
Fiscal Year-end: 03/31/22
Fastener Mfr
N.A.I.C.S.: 339993
Mark R. Belton *(CEO)*

Subsidiaries:

Lancaster Fastener Co Ltd (1)
Stevant Way Northgate, White Lund Industrial Estate, Morecambe, LA3 3PU, United Kingdom
Tel.: (44) 1524389232
Web Site: http://www.lancasterfastener.com
Sales Range: $25-49.9 Million
Emp.: 22
Fastener Distr
N.A.I.C.S.: 423710
Elaine Hollier *(Dir-Sls)*

Power Steel & Electro-Plating Works Sdn Bhd (1)
Jalan Pengapit 15/19 Section 15, 40000, Shah Alam, Selangor, Malaysia
Tel.: (60) 35 519 1444
Industrial Machinery Mfr
N.A.I.C.S.: 333248

Precision Technology Supplies Ltd. (1)
The Birches Industrial Estate, East Grinstead, RH19 1XZ, United Kingdom
Tel.: (44) 134 241 0758
Web Site: https://www.pts-uk.com
Fastening Distr
N.A.I.C.S.: 423710

Special Fasteners Engineering Co.,Ltd. (1)
9F-3 No 366 Bo Ai 2nd Rd, Kaohsiung, 81358, Taiwan
Tel.: (886) 75576366
Web Site: http://www.sfe.com.tw
Sales Range: $25-49.9 Million
Emp.: 20
Fasteners Mfr & Distr
N.A.I.C.S.: 339993
Cosette Wang *(Deputy Mgr-Sls)*

TR Asia Investment Holdings Pte Ltd (1)
57 Senoko Road, Singapore, 758121, Singapore
Tel.: (65) 6 759 6033
Fastening Distr

TR Fastenings AB (1)
Smedjegatan 6 7tr, PO Box 4133, 131 04, Nacka, Sweden
Tel.: (46) 857844900
Web Site: http://www.trfastenings.com
Sales Range: $25-49.9 Million
Emp.: 24
Fastener Distr
N.A.I.C.S.: 423710

TR Fastenings Espana - Ingenieria Industrial, S.L. (1)
Calle de la Ciencia Numero 43, Viladecans, 08840, Barcelona, Spain
Tel.: (34) 93 647 2245
Fastening Distr
N.A.I.C.S.: 423710

TR Fastenings Ltd (1)
Trifast House Bellbrook Park, Uckfield, TN22 1QW, Sussex, United Kingdom
Tel.: (44) 8454811800
Web Site: http://www.trfastenings.com
Sales Range: $50-74.9 Million
Emp.: 150
Fastenings Mfr
N.A.I.C.S.: 339993
Dan Baldock *(Gen Mgr)*

TR Formac (Shanghai) Pte Ltd (1)
No 1222 JinHu Road, Pudong New District, Shanghai, 201206, China
Tel.: (86) 215032 5696
Web Site: http://www.trformac.com.cn
Fastening Distr
N.A.I.C.S.: 423710

TR Formac (Suzhou) Pte Ltd (1)
No 6 Lansheng Road Suzhou Industrial Park, Suzhou, 205126, Jiangsu, China
Tel.: (86) 51289570683
Web Site: http://www.trfastenings.com
Fasteners Mfr & Distr
N.A.I.C.S.: 339993

TR Formac Co. Ltd. (1)
28 3rd Floor Motorway Road, Prawet, Bangkok, 10250, Thailand
Tel.: (66) 2 130 6562
Fastening Distr
N.A.I.C.S.: 423710

TR Formac Fastenings Private Ltd. (1)
Door No 6 05th Cross Street Mangala Nagar, Porur, Chennai, 600 116, India
Tel.: (91) 444 280 3932
Fastening Mfr & Distr
N.A.I.C.S.: 339993

TR Formac Pte Ltd (1)
57 Senoko Rd, Singapore, 758121, Singapore
Tel.: (65) 67596033
Web Site: http://www2.trfastenings.com
Sales Range: $25-49.9 Million
Emp.: 100
Fasteners Mfr & Distr
N.A.I.C.S.: 339993

TR Hungary Kft (1)
Leshegy u 8, Szigetszentmiklos, 2310, Budapest, Hungary
Tel.: (36) 24516970
Sales Range: $25-49.9 Million
Emp.: 25
Fastener Distr
N.A.I.C.S.: 423710
Zoltan Csengeri *(Gen Mgr)*

TR Keba Ltd (1)
Baysal, 34755, Istanbul, Turkiye
Tel.: (90) 2164661333
Sales Range: $25-49.9 Million
Emp.: 40
Fastener Distr
N.A.I.C.S.: 423710

TR Kuhlmann GmbH (1)
Lerchenweg 99, 33415, Verl, Germany
Tel.: (49) 524 650 3200
Industrial Machinery Mfr
N.A.I.C.S.: 333248

TR Miller Holding B.V. (1)
Kelvinstraat 5, 7575 AS, Oldenzaal, Netherlands
Tel.: (31) 541511515
Web Site: http://www.trfastenings.com
Sales Range: $25-49.9 Million
Emp.: 24
Fastener Distr
N.A.I.C.S.: 423710
Ron Vlutters *(Mng Dir)*

TR Norge AS (1)
Masteveien 8, 1481, Hagan, Norway
Tel.: (47) 67067000
Web Site: http://www.trfastenings.com
Fastening Distr
N.A.I.C.S.: 423710
Jan Storsve *(Gen Mgr)*

TR Southern Fasteners Ltd (1)
Mallow Business & Technology Park, Mallow, Cork, P51 HV12, Ireland
Tel.: (353) 2222301
Web Site: http://www2.trfastenings.com
Sales Range: $25-49.9 Million
Emp.: 11
Fastenings Mfr
N.A.I.C.S.: 339993

Trifast Systems Ltd (1)
Trifast House Bellbrook Park, Uckfield, TN22 1QW, East Sussex, United Kingdom
Tel.: (44) 8454 811 800
Web Site: http://www.trfastenings.com
Sales Range: $75-99.9 Million
Emp.: 150
Various Industrial & Electronic Components Mfr & Supplier
N.A.I.C.S.: 423430
Malcolm Diamond *(Mng Dir)*

TRIFECTA GOLD LTD.
5101100 Melville Street, Vancouver, V6E 4A6, BC, Canada
Tel.: (604) 687-2522
Web Site:
 https://www.trifectagold.com
R0B—(DEU)
Rev.: $22,189
Assets: $3,137,709
Liabilities: $39,321
Net Worth: $3,098,388
Earnings: ($153,404)
Emp.: 3
Fiscal Year-end: 12/31/23
Metal Exploration Services
N.A.I.C.S.: 213114
Quinn Martin *(CFO)*

TRIGEM COMPUTER, INC.
Danwon-gu Shingil-Dong, Ansan, 425-839, Kyonggi, Korea (South)
Tel.: (82) 314893000
Web Site: http://www.trigem.com
Sales Range: $800-899.9 Million
Emp.: 300
Personal Computer Mfr
N.A.I.C.S.: 334111
Min Kim Young *(Pres)*

TRIGG MINERALS LIMITED
Suite 6 Level 1 389 Oxford Street Mount, Hawthorn, 6019, WA, Australia
Tel.: (61) 497203678 AU
Web Site: https://trigg.com.au
TMG—(ASX)
Rev.: $974,883
Assets: $1,165,075
Liabilities: $507,851
Net Worth: $657,224
Earnings: ($1,623,890)
Fiscal Year-end: 06/30/24
Metal Exploration Services
N.A.I.C.S.: 213114
Timothy Morrison *(Chm)*

TRIGGER COMMUNICATION & DESIGN LTD.
Suite 2000 222 3rd Avenue SW, Calgary, T2P 0B4, AB, Canada
Tel.: (403) 539-2000
Web Site: http://www.trgr.ca
Year Founded: 1980

Sales Range: $10-24.9 Million
Emp.: 40
Marketing Consulting Services
N.A.I.C.S.: 541613
Larry Bannerman *(Pres)*

TRIGIANT GROUP LIMITED
No 1 Junzhi Rd, Industry Park for Environmental Protection Science and Technology, Yixing, 214206, Jiangsu, China
Tel.: (86) 51080711111 Ky
Web Site: http://www.trigiant.com.hk
Year Founded: 2007
1300—(HKG)
Rev.: $369,297,770
Assets: $756,726,516
Liabilities: $259,088,965
Net Worth: $497,637,551
Earnings: ($7,913,225)
Emp.: 748
Fiscal Year-end: 12/31/22
RF Coaxial Cables & Other Electronic Components Mfr
N.A.I.C.S.: 334220
Lirong Qian *(Chm & CEO)*

Subsidiaries:

Jiangsu Trigiant Technology Co., Ltd. (1)
No 1 Junzhi Road, Environmental Protection Science Technology Industrial Park, Yixing, 214206, Jiangsu, China
Tel.: (86) 5108 071 1111
Web Site: https://www.trigiant.com.cn
Cable & Connector Mfr
N.A.I.C.S.: 335929

TRIGINTA CAPITAL
Kreuzstrasse 34, 40210, Dusseldorf, Germany
Tel.: (49) 211862890
Web Site: http://www.triginta-capital.com
Sales Range: $25-49.9 Million
Emp.: 20
Privater Equity Firm
N.A.I.C.S.: 523999
Peter Folle *(Mng Partner)*

Subsidiaries:

Berlin Capital Fund GmbH (1)
Markgrafenstr 33, 10717, Berlin, Germany
Tel.: (49) 306692063040
Web Site: http://www.berlin-capitalfund.de
Commercial Banking Services
N.A.I.C.S.: 522299

TRIGLAV OSIGURANJE, D.D.
Dolina 8, 71000, Sarajevo, Bosnia & Herzegovina
Tel.: (387) 33252110
Web Site: http://www.triglav.ba
BHOSPK2—(SARE)
Rev.: $23,879,909
Assets: $79,824,105
Liabilities: $56,209,054
Net Worth: $23,615,051
Earnings: $1,572,798
Emp.: 255
Fiscal Year-end: 12/31/20
General Insurance Services
N.A.I.C.S.: 524210

TRIGLAV OSIGURUVANE AD
8th Septemvri Blvd No 16, 1000, Skopje, North Macedonia
Tel.: (389) 25102222
Web Site: https://www.triglav.mk
VROS—(MAC)
Rev.: $26,483,539
Assets: $54,830,355
Liabilities: $39,099,762
Net Worth: $15,730,593
Earnings: $850,271
Fiscal Year-end: 12/31/23
Insurance Services
N.A.I.C.S.: 524210

TRIGLAV OSIGURUVANE AD

Triglav Osiguruvane AD—(Continued)
Tedo Djekanovic (Pres)

TRIGOLD HOLDINGS LTD.
22F No 189 Jingmao 2nd Rd, Nangang Dist, Taipei, 115, Taiwan
Tel.: (886) 223162888
3709—(TPE)
Rev.: $637,287,778
Assets: $250,106,119
Liabilities: $184,744,489
Net Worth: $65,361,630
Earnings: $5,538,348
Emp.: 514
Fiscal Year-end: 12/31/22
Investment Management Service
N.A.I.C.S.: 523940
Huang Wei Hsiang (Chm)

TRIGON METALS, INC.
658 Lansdowne Avenue, Toronto, M6H 3Y8, ON, Canada
Tel.: (647) 276-6002   Ca
Web Site:
  https://www.trigonmetals.com
Year Founded: 1997
PNTZF—(OTCQB)
Rev.: $949,194
Assets: $35,672,049
Liabilities: $42,578,783
Net Worth: ($6,906,734)
Earnings: ($18,214,284)
Fiscal Year-end: 03/31/23
Copper Mining & Exploration Services
N.A.I.C.S.: 212230
Fanie Muller (VP-Ops & Country Mgr)

Subsidiaries:

Safi Silver Corp.   (1)

Technomine Africa Sarl   (1)

TRIGON PROPERTY DEVELOPMENT AS
Parnu Mnt 18, 10141, Tallinn, 10141, Estonia
Tel.: (372) 6679200
Web Site:
  https://www.trigonproperty.com
TPD1T—(RSE)
Rev.: $29,341
Assets: $1,885,931
Liabilities: $23,291
Net Worth: $1,862,640
Earnings: ($35,779)
Fiscal Year-end: 12/31/23
Real Estate Development Services
N.A.I.C.S.: 531390
Joakim Johan Helenius (Chm-Supervisory Bd)

TRIGYN TECHNOLOGIES LIMITED
27 SDF-1 SEEPZ, Andheri East, Mumbai, 400 096, India
Tel.: (91) 2261400909
Web Site: https://www.trigyn.com
Year Founded: 1998
TRIGYN—(BOM)
Rev.: $153,373,886
Assets: $102,641,652
Liabilities: $20,992,303
Net Worth: $81,649,350
Earnings: $4,157,688
Emp.: 851
Fiscal Year-end: 03/31/23
Software Development Services
N.A.I.C.S.: 541511
R. Ganapathi (Chm)

Subsidiaries:

Trigyn Technologies, Inc.   (1)
100 Metroplex Dr, Edison, NJ 08817
Tel.: (732) 777-4600
Information Technology Services

N.A.I.C.S.: 541511
Thomas Gordon (Sr VP)

Trigyn Technologies, Inc.   (1)
2300 Yonge Street Suite 1600, Toronto, M4P 1E4, ON, Canada
Tel.: (732) 777-0050
Information Technology Services
N.A.I.C.S.: 541511

TRIIS, INC.
New Otani Garden Court 8F 4-1 Kioichon, Chiyoda-ku, Tokyo, 102-8578, Japan
Tel.: (81) 332210211
Web Site: https://www.triis.co.jp
Year Founded: 1995
4840—(TKS)
Rev.: $4,509,240
Assets: $39,704,000
Liabilities: $3,197,590
Net Worth: $36,506,410
Earnings: $723,180
Emp.: 25
Fiscal Year-end: 12/31/23
Management Holding Services
N.A.I.C.S.: 551112
Hitoshi Ikeda (CEO)

Subsidiaries:

Hamano Leather Crafts Co., Ltd.   (1)
4-1 Kioicho New Otani Garden Court 8th floor, Chiyoda-Ku, Tokyo, 112-8578, Japan
Tel.: (81) 36 691 8123
Web Site: https://www.hamanobag.com
Leather Product Mfr & Distr
N.A.I.C.S.: 316110

TRIiS International Co., Ltd.   (1)
9F-2 No 318 Songjiang Rd, Zhongshan Dist, Taipei, Taiwan
Tel.: (886) 227407146
Web Site: http://www.triis.co.jp
Apparel Distr
N.A.I.C.S.: 424350

TRIKOTAZA PELISTER AD
Devejani 13, 7000, Bitola, North Macedonia
Tel.: (389) 47 202 195
Year Founded: 1923
Sales Range: $1-9.9 Million
Knitted Wear Mfr
N.A.I.C.S.: 315120
Roza Vasilevska (Chm)

TRILIANCE POLYMERS LTD
14th Floor 1420 B B C Wing C/66 G Block One BKC Opp Bank of Baroda, Bandra E, Mumbai, 400051, India
Tel.: (91) 9099019355
Web Site:
  http://www.leenaconsultancy.in
509046—(BOM)
Rev.: $8,364
Assets: $27,781
Liabilities: $10,040
Net Worth: $17,741
Earnings: ($3,300)
Emp.: 3
Fiscal Year-end: 03/31/21
Financial Advisory Services
N.A.I.C.S.: 523940
Bhairavi Kadakia (Compliance Officer & Sec)

TRILLION ENERGY INTERNATIONAL INC.
Bulvari Park Oran Ofis Plaza, 180-y Daire 45 Kat 14 Oran Cankaya, 06450, Ankara, Turkiye
Tel.: (90) 7788198503   BC
Web Site: http://trillionenergy.com
Year Founded: 2015
TCF—(CNSX)
Rev.: $9,375,029
Assets: $37,018,219
Liabilities: $16,392,288
Net Worth: $20,625,931

Earnings: ($6,121,754)
Emp.: 17
Fiscal Year-end: 12/31/22
Holding Company
N.A.I.C.S.: 551112
David Michael Thompson (CFO)

TRILLIUM ACQUISITION CORP.
231 Wedgewood Drive, Oakville, L6J 4R6, ON, Canada
Tel.: (416) 505-0429
Year Founded: 2019
TCK.P—(TSXV)
Rev.: $19,584
Assets: $460,081
Liabilities: $85,329
Net Worth: $374,752
Earnings: ($108,234)
Fiscal Year-end: 12/31/23
Asset Management Services
N.A.I.C.S.: 523940

TRILOGIQ SA
5 rue Saint Simon Vert Galant Business Park, CS 70001 Saint-Ouen-l Aumne, 95046, Cergy-Pontoise, Cedex, France
Tel.: (33) 134307474   FR
Web Site: https://www.trilogiq.com
Year Founded: 1992
ALTRI—(EUR)
Sales Range: $25-49.9 Million
Metal Products Mfr
N.A.I.C.S.: 332999
Olivier Langrand (CFO)

Subsidiaries:

THE TUBE AND BRACKET COMPANY   (1)
Main Road Middleton Cheney, Banbury, OX17 2PW, Oxon, United Kingdom
Tel.: (44) 1295 277791
Web Site: http://www.tubeandbracket.com
Fabricated Structural Metal Mfr
N.A.I.C.S.: 332312

TRILOGIQ BENELUX BVBA   (1)
Avenue Charles-Quint 584, 1082, Brussels, Belgium
Tel.: (32) 490111547
Web Site: http://www.trilogiq.be
Fabricated Structural Metal Mfr
N.A.I.C.S.: 332312

TRILOGIQ DO BRASIL LTDA   (1)
Rua Dr Adhemar de Barros 201 - CEP, Valinhos, Sao Paulo, 13270-600, Brazil
Tel.: (55) 1938717705
Web Site: http://www.trilogiq.com.br
Industrial Metal Products Mfr
N.A.I.C.S.: 332999

TRILOGIQ Deutschland GmbH   (1)
Benzstr 5, 84051, Altheim, Germany
Tel.: (49) 8703 905758
Web Site: http://www.trilogiq.de
Fabricated Structural Metal Mfr
N.A.I.C.S.: 332312

TRILOGIQ Hungaria Kft.   (1)
Naplas ut 16, 2142, Nagytarcsa, Hungary
Tel.: (36) 20 3203146
Web Site: http://www.trilogiq.hu
Metal Product Distr
N.A.I.C.S.: 423510

TRILOGIQ ITALIA SRL   (1)
Via G Oberdan 13, Gorgonzola, 20064, Milan, Italy
Tel.: (39) 02 95784121
Web Site: http://www.trilogiq.com
Metal Product Distr
N.A.I.C.S.: 423510

TRILOGIQ India Modular System Private Limited   (1)
18/1B Anumepalli Agraharam Begapalli Road, Zuzuvadi, Hosur, 635 126, Tamil Nadu, India
Tel.: (91) 4344 31 3005
Metal Product Distr
N.A.I.C.S.: 423510

INTERNATIONAL PUBLIC

TRILOGIQ MAROC   (1)
131 bd Abdelmoumen 4e etage N17, 20000, Casablanca, Morocco
Tel.: (212) 5 22 22 54 09
Metal Product Distr
N.A.I.C.S.: 423510

TRILOGIQ MEXICO, S.A de C.V   (1)
Anillo Vial II 201 Int 8 y 9 Parque Industrial Quadrum, El Marques, 76246, Queretaro, Mexico
Tel.: (52) 4424300857
Web Site: http://www.trilogiqmexico.com.mx
Metal Products Mfr
N.A.I.C.S.: 332999

TRILOGIQ Poland Sp. Z o.o   (1)
ul Rogowska 117F, 54-440, Wroclaw, Poland
Tel.: (48) 22 243 21 67
Web Site: http://www.trilogiq.pl
Metal Product Distr
N.A.I.C.S.: 423510

TRILOGIQ RUSSIA   (1)
Maxim Zalyvsky Trifonovskaya 16-b, Kaluga, 248008, Russia
Tel.: (7) 920 094 7000
Web Site: http://www.trilogiq-russia.ru
Fabricated Structural Metal Mfr
N.A.I.C.S.: 332312

TRILOGIQ Romania srl   (1)
Strada Gavana Nr 2 Bl A27 Sc B Ap 11, 110305, Arges, Romania
Tel.: (40) 371 003 328
Industrial Metal Product Distr
N.A.I.C.S.: 423830

TRILOGIQ SA Ltd   (1)
Hunters Retreat Old Pick n Pay Building 677 Cape Road End, Parsonsvlei, Port Elizabeth, 6001, South Africa
Tel.: (27) 41 484 1523
Web Site: http://www.trilogiq.co.za
Fabricated Structural Metal Mfr
N.A.I.C.S.: 332312
Leslie Scanlen (Mng Dir)

TRILOGIQ SLOVAKIA s.r.o   (1)
Robotnicka 1, 036 01, Martin, Slovakia
Tel.: (421) 43 32 41 040
Web Site: http://www.trilogiq.sk
Fabricated Structural Metal Mfr
N.A.I.C.S.: 332312

TRILOGIQ SWEDEN AB   (1)
25654 Ramlosa Gravorgatan 1, 253 60, Helsingborg, Sweden
Tel.: (46) 42 300 9460
Web Site: http://www.trilogiq.se
Fabricated Structural Metal Mfr
N.A.I.C.S.: 332999
Christian Aslund (Mgr-Lean)

TRILOQ Turquie METAL VE KINYA   (1)
Grup center Kule is Mrk N 5-171/6, Pendik, 34912, Istanbul, Turkiye
Tel.: (90) 216 482 20 07
Metal Product Distr
N.A.I.C.S.: 423510

Trilogiq Australia Pty Ltd   (1)
Unit 15 209 Liverpool Road, Kilsyth, 3137, VIC, Australia
Tel.: (61) 3 9728 6500
Web Site: http://www.leantek.com.au
Fabricated Structural Metal Mfr
N.A.I.C.S.: 332312

Trilogiq CZ s.r.o   (1)
Jestrebicka 14, 181 00, Prague, Czech Republic
Tel.: (420) 233 550 629
Web Site: http://www.trilogiq.cz
Metal Product Distr
N.A.I.C.S.: 423510
Bedrich Dolezal (Mng Dir)

Trilogiq Iberia SL   (1)
Carretera Santiga 70 Nave B, Ripollet, 08291, Barcelona, Spain
Tel.: (34) 93 594 91 80
Web Site: http://www.trilogiq.es
Fabricated Structural Metal Mfr
N.A.I.C.S.: 332312
Xavier Forns (Country Mgr)

Trilogiq USA Corp.   (1)
31805 Glendale St, Livonia, MI 48150

Tel.: (734) 464-7430
Web Site: http://www.trilogiqusa.com
Industrial Metal Product Distr
N.A.I.C.S.: 423830

TRILOGY AI CORP.
6th Floor-905 West Pender Street,
Vancouver, V6C 1L6, BC, Canada
Tel.: (604) 229-9772 BC
Web Site:
 https://www.ambaribeauty.com
Year Founded: 2019
AMBBF—(OTCQB)
Rev.: $151,918
Assets: $806,137
Liabilities: $174,659
Net Worth: $631,479
Earnings: ($982,786)
Fiscal Year-end: 12/31/22
Skin Care Product Retailer
N.A.I.C.S.: 456199
Nisha Grewal *(CEO)*

TRILOGY METALS INC.
510 Burrard Street Suite 901, Vancouver, V6C 3A8, BC, Canada
Tel.: (604) 638-8088 BC
Web Site:
 https://www.trilogymetals.com
Year Founded: 2011
TMQ—NYSEAMEX)
Rev.: $120,000
Assets: $138,020,000
Liabilities: $465,000
Net Worth: $137,555,000
Earnings: ($14,951,000)
Emp.: 5
Fiscal Year-end: 11/30/23
Copper Exploration & Mining
N.A.I.C.S.: 212230
Tony Serafino Giardini *(Pres & CEO)*

TRILOGY RETAIL ENTERPRISES L.P.
161 Bay Street 49th Floor, Toronto,
M5J 2S1, ON, Canada
Tel.: (416) 364-4499
Year Founded: 2000
Rev.: $1,003,600,000
Emp.: 6
Book Retailer
N.A.I.C.S.: 459210

Subsidiaries:

Indigo Books & Music, Inc. (1)
620 King Street West Suite 400, Toronto,
M5V 1M6, ON, Canada **(60.6%)**
Tel.: (416) 364-4499
Web Site: http://www.chapters.indigo.ca
Rev.: $830,976,930
Assets: $633,151,617
Liabilities: $611,388,587
Net Worth: $21,763,030
Earnings: $2,554,144
Emp.: 5,000
Fiscal Year-end: 04/02/2022
Book & Specialty Stores
N.A.I.C.S.: 459210
Heather M. Reisman *(Founder & Chm)*

TRILUX FRANCE SAS
2 Rue Denis Papin, 67120, Duttlenheim, Bas Rhin, France
Tel.: (33) 388495780
Web Site: http://www.trilux.de
Rev.: $25,800,000
Emp.: 50
Electrical Appliances, Television & Rad
N.A.I.C.S.: 423620
Claude Jannot *(Dir)*

TRIMAC TRANSPORTATION LTD.
3215 12 St NE, Calgary, T2E 7S9,
AB, Canada
Tel.: (403) 298-5100
Web Site: http://www.trimac.com
Year Founded: 1945
Sales Range: $250-299.9 Million
Emp.: 1,774
Bulk Trucking Services
N.A.I.C.S.: 484121
Jeffrey J. McCaig *(Chm & Chm)*

Subsidiaries:

AIP Logistics, Inc. (1)
300 Industrial Dr, Wapakoneta, OH 45895
Tel.: (419) 738-9211
Web Site: http://www.aiplogistics.com
Sales Range: $1-9.9 Million
Emp.: 13
Commercial & Institutional Building Construction
N.A.I.C.S.: 236220
Charles Kantner *(Founder)*

Trimac Transportation Services Inc. (1)
700-II 326 11 Ave SW, PO Box 3500, Calgary, T2E 7S9, AB, Canada **(100%)**
Tel.: (403) 298-5100
Web Site: http://www.trimac.com
Sales Range: $50-74.9 Million
Emp.: 150
Bulk Trucking Services
N.A.I.C.S.: 484121

Division (Non-US):

Bulk Plus Logistics (2)
Web Site: http://www.bulkplus.com
Logistics Consulting Servies
N.A.I.C.S.: 541614

Division (Domestic):

National Tank Services (2)
474 Southdown Rd, Mississauga, L5J 2Y4,
ON, Canada
Tel.: (905) 822-4322
Web Site:
 http://www.nationaltankservices.com
Tank Cleaning & Maintenance Services
N.A.I.C.S.: 488490
Trevor Tiffany *(Dir-Washrack Svcs)*

Subsidiary (US):

Trimac Transportation Inc. (2)
15333 JFK Blvd Ste 800, Houston, TX 77032
Tel.: (281) 985-0000
Web Site: http://www.trimac.com
Sales Range: $25-49.9 Million
Emp.: 50
Transportation Services to Chemical Manufacturers & Distributors of Liquid Chemical, Petroleum & Dry Bulk Products
N.A.I.C.S.: 484121
Tim Machbank *(Pres & COO-US)*

Affiliate (Domestic):

Harris Transportation Company, LLC (3)
3077 NW Saint Helens Rd, Portland, OR 97210 **(100%)**
Tel.: (503) 552-5800
Web Site: http://www.htc-llc.com
Petroleum Transportation Services
N.A.I.C.S.: 484230

Subsidiary (Domestic):

Trimac Transportation Central Inc. (3)
3600 Universal Dr, Rapid City, SD 57702
Tel.: (605) 348-1071
Web Site: http://www.trimac.com
Sales Range: $25-49.9 Million
Long Distance Trucking Services
N.A.I.C.S.: 484121
Francis Hamm *(Branch Mgr)*

Trimac Transportation East Inc. (3)
3710 Cane Run Rd, Louisville, KY 40211
Tel.: (502) 775-8278
Web Site: http://www.trimac.com
Sales Range: $50-74.9 Million
Emp.: 20
Long Distance Bulk Trucking Services
N.A.I.C.S.: 484220

Trimac Transportation Services (3)
13550 Toepperwein Rd, San Antonio, TX 78233-4021
Tel.: (210) 654-1666
Long Distance Trucking Services
N.A.I.C.S.: 484121

Trimac Transportation Services (Western), Inc. (3)
3751 Breakwater Ave, Hayward, CA 94545-3220
Tel.: (510) 293-6838
Web Site: http://www.trimac.com
Long Distance Trucking Services
N.A.I.C.S.: 484110

Trimac Transportation South Inc. (3)
15333 John F Kennedy Blvd, Houston, TX 77032
Tel.: (281) 985-0000
Web Site: http://www.trimac.com
Sales Range: $25-49.9 Million
Bulk Trucking Services
N.A.I.C.S.: 484121
Jess McCaig *(CEO)*

TRIMAX STEEL INC.
1440 3rd Avenue East Industrial
Park, Sainte-Marie-Beauce, G6E 3T9,
QC, Canada
Tel.: (418) 387-7798
Web Site: http://www.trimaxsteel.com
Year Founded: 1992
Rev.: $13,204,979
Emp.: 65
Structural Steel Mfr
N.A.I.C.S.: 238120
Even Audet *(Mgr-Sls)*

TRIMET ALUMINIUM SE
Aluminiumallee 1, 45356, Essen, Germany
Tel.: (49) 2013660
Web Site: http://www.trimet.de
Year Founded: 1985
Sales Range: $500-549.9 Million
Emp.: 3,000
Aluminium Processing
N.A.I.C.S.: 331313
Thomas Ludwig *(Chm-Supervisory Bd)*

Subsidiaries:

Bohai Trimet Automotive Holding GmbH (1)
Aluminiumallee 1, 06493, Harzgerode, Germany
Tel.: (49) 39484500
Web Site: http://www.bohai-trimet.com
Aluminum Die-Cast Component Mfr
N.A.I.C.S.: 331523
Andreas Kiebel *(Mng Dir)*

Hamburger Aluminium-Werk GmbH (1)
Dradenauer Hauptdeich 15 Aluminium St 121129, Postfach 95 01 70 02 52, 21112, Hamburg, Germany
Tel.: (49) 407401101
Web Site: http://www.hydoaluminium.de
Sales Range: $200-249.9 Million
Emp.: 551
Mfr of Primary Aluminum
N.A.I.C.S.: 331313

Harzgerode Guss GmbH (1)
Aluminiumallee 1, 06493, Harzgerode, Germany
Tel.: (49) 39484500
Light-Metal Product Mfr & Distr
N.A.I.C.S.: 332999

TRIMET Automotive Sommerda GmbH & Co. KG (1)
Rheinmetall Strasse 24, 99610, Sommerda, Germany
Tel.: (49) 3634 3330
Aluminium Die Casting Products Mfr
N.A.I.C.S.: 331523

TRIMET France SAS (1)
Rue Henri Sainte Claire Deville, 73300, Saint-Jean-de-Maurienne, France
Tel.: (33) 4 79201010
Industrial Supplies Whslr
N.A.I.C.S.: 423840

TRIMET Italia s.r.l. (1)
Piazza Europa 7, 10044, Pianezza, Torino,
Italy
Tel.: (39) 011 9677472
Industrial Supplies Whslr
N.A.I.C.S.: 423840

TRIMIN CAPITAL CORP.
2 Bloor St W Ste 3400, Toronto,
M4W 3E2, ON, Canada
Tel.: (416) 963-8880 Ca
Year Founded: 1998
Sales Range: $25-49.9 Million
Emp.: 2
Investment Services
N.A.I.C.S.: 523999
James D. Meekison *(Chmn)*

TRIMPROOF LIMITED
Trim Co, Meath, Ireland
Tel.: (353) 469431396
Web Site:
 http://www.chieftainfabrics.com
Year Founded: 1946
Sales Range: $25-49.9 Million
Emp.: 15
Contract Furnishing
N.A.I.C.S.: 337127
Dearbhla Kinsella *(Dir-Fin)*

TRIMSEAL PLASTICS LTD.
3511 Jacombs Rd, Richmond, V6V 1Z8, BC, Canada
Tel.: (604) 278-3803
Web Site: https://www.trimseal.com
Year Founded: 1968
Sales Range: $10-24.9 Million
Emp.: 260
Plastic Binder Mfr
N.A.I.C.S.: 339940
Dan Siemens *(Pres)*

Subsidiaries:

Trimseal USA Inc. (1)
17371 NE 67th Ct Ste A2, Redmond, WA 98052
Tel.: (425) 867-1522
Web Site: http://trimseal.com
Sales Range: $10-24.9 Million
Blankbook Looseleaf Binders & Devices Mfr
N.A.I.C.S.: 339940

TRIMUDA NUANSA CITRA PT
Wisma Intra Asia Ground Floor Jl
Prof Dr Supomo SH No 58, Jakarta
Selatan, 12870, Indonesia
Tel.: (62) 2183703700
TNCA—(INDO)
Rev.: $7,308,378
Assets: $5,395,219
Liabilities: $1,066,390
Net Worth: $4,328,829
Earnings: $73,608
Emp.: 39
Fiscal Year-end: 12/31/22
Transport Services
N.A.I.C.S.: 485999
Ari Widiatmoko *(Dir)*

Subsidiaries:

P.T. GED Lintas Indonesia (1)
Jl Prof Dr Soepomo SH No 58 RT 5/1 Kel Menteng Dalam Kec Tebet, Jakarta Selatan, 12870, Indonesia
Tel.: (62) 2183703700
Web Site: https://ged.co.id
Garuda Express Delivery Services
N.A.I.C.S.: 492110

TRIMURTHI LIMITED
5-8-3541106 Office No 1106 Ratna
Block Raghav Ratna Towers, Chirag
Ali Lane, Hyderabad, 500001, India
Tel.: (91) 9121330909
Web Site:
 https://www.trimurthidrugs.com
Year Founded: 1994
536565—(BOM)
Rev.: $230,238

TRIMURTHI LIMITED

Trimurthi Limited—(Continued)
Assets: $870,062
Liabilities: $7,391
Net Worth: $862,672
Earnings: ($7,185)
Emp.: 7
Fiscal Year-end: 03/31/23
Pharmaceuticals Mfr
N.A.I.C.S.: 424210
Arun Kumar Bhangadia *(Chm)*

TRINA SOLAR LIMITED
No 2 Tian He Road, Trina Photovoltaic Industrial Park Xinbei District, Changzhou, 213031, Jiangsu, China
Tel.: (86) 51985482008   Ky
Web Site: http://www.trinasolar.com
Year Founded: 1997
688999—(SHG)
Rev.: $15,700,014,206
Assets: $16,658,214,236
Liabilities: $11,598,342,033
Net Worth: $5,059,872,203
Earnings: $765,853,733
Emp.: 50,000
Fiscal Year-end: 12/31/23
Holding Company; Integrated Solar-Power Products Mfr
N.A.I.C.S.: 551112
Stephanie Shao *(Chief HR Officer)*

Subsidiaries:

Changzhou Trina Solar Energy Co., Ltd. (1)
No 2 Tianhe Rd Trina Photovoltaic Industrial Park, New District, Changzhou, 213031, China
Tel.: (86) 51 9854 82008
Solar Cell Mfr
N.A.I.C.S.: 334413

Trina Solar (Australia) Pty Ltd. (1)
Level 35 60 Margaret Street, Sydney, 2000, NSW, Australia
Tel.: (61) 2 9199 8500
Web Site: http://www.trinasolar.com
Integrated Solar Powered Products Mfr
N.A.I.C.S.: 335999

Trina Solar (Changzhou) Science and Technology Co., Ltd. (1)
No 2 Tianhe Road Trina PV Industrial Park New District, Changzhou, 213031, China
Tel.: (86) 51989824000
Web Site: http://www.trinasolar.com
Solar Power Products Mfr
N.A.I.C.S.: 333414

Trina Solar (Germany) GmbH (1)
Einsteinring 26, Aschheim, 85609, Munich, Germany
Tel.: (49) 89122849250
Web Site: http://www.trinasolar.com
Emp.: 15
Photovoltaic Module Mfr
N.A.I.C.S.: 334413
Ulrich Mamat *(Mng Dir)*

Trina Solar (Italy) S.R.L (1)
Via Santa Maria Valle 3, Milan, 20124, Italy
Tel.: (39) 0200681521
Sales Range: $25-49.9 Million
Emp.: 20
Solar Power Products Mfr
N.A.I.C.S.: 333414

Trina Solar (Japan) Limited (1)
World Trade Ctr Bldg 25th Fl 2-chome Hamaama Ticho MinaToku, Hamamatsu-cho Minato-ku, Tokyo, 105-6121, Japan
Tel.: (81) 334377000
Web Site: http://www.trinasolar.com
Emp.: 25
Photovoltaic Module Mfr
N.A.I.C.S.: 335999
Ye Chen *(Gen Mgr)*

Trina Solar (Schweiz) AG (1)
Birkenweg 4, 8304, Wallisellen, Switzerland
Tel.: (41) 43 299 68 00
Web Site: http://www.trinasolar.com
Emp.: 40
Photovoltaic Module Mfr & Distr

N.A.I.C.S.: 334413

Trina Solar (Spain) S.L.U. (1)
C/Caleruega 79 3 A, 28033, Madrid, Spain
Tel.: (34) 911 335 935
Sales Range: $25-49.9 Million
Emp.: 9
Photovoltaic Module Mfr & Distr
N.A.I.C.S.: 334413
Alvaro Garcia-Maltras *(Dir-Sls)*

Trina Solar (Switzerland) Ltd (1)
Richtistrasse 11, Wallisellen, 8403, Switzerland
Tel.: (41) 432996800
Web Site: http://www.trinasolar.com
Photovoltaic Module Mfr
N.A.I.C.S.: 334413

Trina Solar (U.S.) Inc. (1)
100 Century Center Ct 340, San Jose, CA 95110-4512
Tel.: (800) 696-7114
Web Site: http://www.trisolar.com
Emp.: 30
Solar Powered Products Distr
N.A.I.C.S.: 423720
Jeff Dorety *(Pres-Americas)*

Subsidiary (Domestic):

Placer Solar, LLC (2)
115 W Canon Perdido St, Santa Barbara, CA 93101-3210
Tel.: (805) 284-9026
Photovoltaic Module Mfr & Distr
N.A.I.C.S.: 334413

Trina Solar Energy (Shanghai) Co., Ltd. (1)
Rooms 1704-1706 CCIG International Plaza, No 333 North Caoxi Road, Shanghai, 200030, China
Tel.: (86) 21 6057 5310
Photovoltaic Module Mfr
N.A.I.C.S.: 335999

TRINETHRA INFRA VENTURES LIMITED
210 Aditya Trade Center 2nd Floor, Ameerpet, Hyderabad, 500 016, India
Tel.: (91) 40 30724581
Web Site: http://www.trinethrainfra.com
Sales Range: $10-24.9 Million
Highway Construction Engineering Services
N.A.I.C.S.: 237310

TRINFICO INVESTMENT GROUP
5 Botanichesky Lane, 129090, Moscow, Russia
Tel.: (7) 4957252500
Web Site: http://www.trinfico.ru
Year Founded: 1993
Sales Range: Less than $1 Million
Investment & Asset Management Services
N.A.I.C.S.: 523940
Oleg Belay *(Chm-Mgmt Bd)*

TRINIDAD & TOBAGO STOCK EXCHANGE LIMITED
10th Floor Nicholas Tower 63-65 Independence Square, 63-65 Indepence Square, Port of Spain, Trinidad & Tobago
Tel.: (868) 6255107
Web Site: http://www.stockex.co.tt
Sales Range: $1-9.9 Million
Emp.: 27
Stock Exchange Services
N.A.I.C.S.: 523210
Ray A. Sumairsingh *(Chm)*

TRINITAS PRIVATE EQUITY (PROPRIETARY) LIMITED
1 Melrose Boulevard Suite 2 Ground Floor, Melrose Arch, Johannesburg, 2196, South Africa
Tel.: (27) 119949700   ZA

Web Site: http://www.trinitaspe.co.za
Year Founded: 2008
Privater Equity Firm
N.A.I.C.S.: 523999
Andrew Hall *(Founder)*

TRINITY ACQUISITION CORPORATION
Unit 1903-4 303 Hennessy Road, Wanchai, China (Hong Kong)
Tel.: (852) 28348000   Ky
Year Founded: 2021
Investment Services
N.A.I.C.S.: 523999
Li Ning *(Chm)*

TRINITY BIOTECH PLC
IDA Business Park, Bray, Co Wicklow, Ireland
Tel.: (353) 12769800   IE
Web Site:
https://www.trinitybiotech.com
Year Founded: 1992
TRIB—(NASDAQ)
Rev.: $92,965,000
Assets: $118,895,000
Liabilities: $119,214,000
Net Worth: ($319,000)
Earnings: $875,000
Emp.: 477
Fiscal Year-end: 12/31/21
Biopharmaceutical Product Mfr
N.A.I.C.S.: 325413
Ronan O'Caoimh *(Co-Founder, Chm & CEO)*

Subsidiaries:

IMMCO Diagnostics, Inc. (1)
60 Pineview Dr, Buffalo, NY 14228
Tel.: (716) 691-0091
Web Site: http://www.immcodiagnostics.com
Sales Range: $10-24.9 Million
Emp.: 90
Autoimmune Disease Diagnostics, Research & Medical Device Mfr
N.A.I.C.S.: 621511

Nova Century Scientific, Inc. (1)
An Immco Diagnostics Company 5022 South Service Road, Burlington, L7L 5Y7, ON, Canada
Electromedical Product Mfr
N.A.I.C.S.: 334510

Primus Corp. (1)
4231 E 75th Ter, Kansas City, MO 64132
Tel.: (816) 523-7491
Sales Range: $25-49.9 Million
Emp.: 24
Diagnostic Test Kit & Instrument Mfr
N.A.I.C.S.: 334516

TRINITY INDUSTRIAL CORPORATION
1-9 Kakimoto-cho, Toyota, 471-0855, Aichi, Japan
Tel.: (81) 565244800
Web Site: https://www.trinityind.co.jp
Year Founded: 1946
6382—(TKS)
Rev.: $244,517,120
Assets: $295,909,870
Liabilities: $90,887,500
Net Worth: $205,022,370
Earnings: $13,603,380
Emp.: 957
Fiscal Year-end: 03/31/24
Industrial Machinery Mfr
N.A.I.C.S.: 333248
Koji Noriyasu *(Mng Dir & Exec VP)*

Subsidiaries:

Mesac Corporation (1)
139 Iino Itakura-cho, Ora-gun, Gunma, 374-0123, Gunma Prefecture, Japan
Tel.: (81) 276822206
Emp.: 30
Industrial Equipment Mfr
N.A.I.C.S.: 333248

INTERNATIONAL PUBLIC

Taiwan Trinity Industrial Corp. (1)
22F-2B No 11 Sec 2 Huan-Nan Rd Pingchen, Taoyuan, Taiwan
Tel.: (886) 32810921
Industrial Machinery Distr
N.A.I.C.S.: 423830

Thai Trinity Co, Ltd. (1)
No 1 Md Tower Unit 10B 10th Floor Soi Bangna-Trad 25 Debaratana Road, Kwaeng Bangna Nua, Bangkok, 10260, khet bangna, Thailand
Tel.: (66) 23618138
Industrial Machinery Distr
N.A.I.C.S.: 423830

Trinity (Philippines) Corporation (1)
27th Flr Pacific Star Bldg Makati Ave Corner Sen Gilpuyat Ave, Makati, Metro Manila, Philippines
Tel.: (63) 28930091
Industrial Machinery Distr
N.A.I.C.S.: 423830

Trinity Coating Systems (Shanghai) Co., ltd. (1)
Room 9L Huamin Empire Plaza No 726 Yan'an West Road, Shanghai, 200050, China
Tel.: (86) 2162127833
Industrial Machinery Distr
N.A.I.C.S.: 423830

Trinity Industrial Corporation - Miyoshi Plant (1)
5-1-11 Neuramachi, Miyoshi, 470-0217, Aichi, Japan
Tel.: (81) 561330730
Industrial Machinery Mfr
N.A.I.C.S.: 333248

Trinity Industrial Corporation - Toyota Plant (1)
12-1 Shirawase, Katsurano-cho, Toyota, 444-2214, Aichi, Japan
Tel.: (81) 565582380
Industrial Machinery Mfr
N.A.I.C.S.: 333248

TRINITY LEAGUE INDIA LIMITED
A - 23 Mandakini Enclave Alaknanda Greater Kailash - II, New Delhi, 110019, India
Tel.: (91) 1206923902   In
Web Site: http://www.trinityasia.in
Year Founded: 1988
531846—(BOM)
Rev.: $415,023
Assets: $719
Liabilities: $17
Net Worth: $702
Earnings: $4,916
Emp.: 2
Fiscal Year-end: 03/31/23
Financial & Investment Advisory Services
N.A.I.C.S.: 523940
Devinder Kumar Jain *(Chm & Mng Dir)*

TRINITY LIMITED
39/F Dorset House Taikoo Place 979 Kings Road, Quarry Bay, China (Hong Kong)
Tel.: (852) 2 342 1151   BM
Web Site: http://www.trinitygroup.com
Year Founded: 1969
Rev.: $251,969,441
Assets: $766,635,308
Liabilities: $252,769,435
Net Worth: $513,865,873
Earnings: $6,465,829
Emp.: 1,599
Fiscal Year-end: 12/31/19
Menswear Retailer
N.A.I.C.S.: 315250
Agnes Shen *(COO)*

Subsidiaries:

Cerruti 1881 SAS (1)
3 Place de la Madeleine, Paris, 75008, France

Tel.: (33) 153301881
Garment Distr
N.A.I.C.S.: 424350
Laurent Grosgogeat *(Exec VP)*

Gieves Limited (1)
No 1 Savile Row, London, United Kingdom
Tel.: (44) 2074326403
Web Site: http://www.gievesandhawkes.com
Men Wear Distr
N.A.I.C.S.: 424350

Trinity Brands UK Limited (1)
22 King Street St James, London, SW1Y 6QY, United Kingdom
Tel.: (44) 2077342436
Web Site: http://www.trinitygroup.com
Emp.: 150
Garment Distr
N.A.I.C.S.: 424350
Ray Clacher *(Exec VP)*

TRINITY PRECISION TECHNOLOGY CO., LTD.
20 Lane 487 Chunghua Rd, Maoli, Toufen, Taiwan
Tel.: (886) 37626123
Web Site: https://www.trinity-ptc.com
Year Founded: 1993
4534—(TPE)
Rev.: $27,282,181
Assets: $46,836,632
Liabilities: $21,799,237
Net Worth: $25,037,395
Earnings: ($4,636,150)
Fiscal Year-end: 12/31/22
Automotive Gear & Equipment Mfr
N.A.I.C.S.: 333612
Kuang-Pin Wang *(Chm)*

TRINITY TRADELINK LIMITED
16 & 17 Washington Plaza Dispensary Road, Goregaon West, Mumbai, 400 062, India
Tel.: (91) 2228730274
Web Site: http://www.trinitytrade.in
Year Founded: 1985
Wholesale Trade Broker
N.A.I.C.S.: 425120

TRINITY WATTHANA PUBLIC COMPANY LIMITED
1 Park Silom 22nd Floor and Unit 2301 23rd Floor Convent Road, Silom, Bangkok, 10500, Thailand
Tel.: (66) 28019100
Web Site: http://www.trinitythai.com
Year Founded: 2001
TNITY—(THA)
Rev.: $8,828,467
Assets: $160,764,485
Liabilities: $120,297,171
Net Worth: $40,467,314
Earnings: ($10,316,419)
Fiscal Year-end: 12/31/23
Investment Banking Services
N.A.I.C.S.: 523150
Pakhawat Kovithvathanaphong *(Chm)*

TRIO INDUSTRIAL ELECTRONICS GROUP LIMITED
5J Phase 2 Kaiser Estate 51 Man Yue St Hung Hom, Kowloon, China (Hong Kong)
Tel.: (852) 27658787 HK
Web Site: https://www.trio-ieg.com
Year Founded: 1983
1710—(HKG)
Rev.: $124,708,133
Assets: $92,248,290
Liabilities: $43,305,503
Net Worth: $48,942,788
Earnings: $5,790,795
Emp.: 1,600
Fiscal Year-end: 12/31/22
Electronic Component Mfr & Distr
N.A.I.C.S.: 334419
Leung Lam Tai *(CEO & Exec Dir)*

Subsidiaries:

Panyu Trio Microtronics Co., Ltd. (1)
Nansha, Guangzhou, 511453, Guangdong, China
Tel.: (86) 2084902933
Electronic Components Distr
N.A.I.C.S.: 423690

Professional Electronics Manufacturing Solutions Limited (1)
5J Phase 2 Kaiser Estate 51 Man Yue St, Hung Hom, Kowloon, China (Hong Kong)
Tel.: (852) 2 355 9910
Web Site: https://www.pems.com.hk
Electronic Product Mfr & Distr
N.A.I.C.S.: 334419

Subsidiary (Non-US):

Professional Electronics Manufacturing Solutions (Guangzhou) Limited (2)
Shiji Industrial Estate, Dongyong Nansha, Guangzhou, Guangdong, China
Tel.: (86) 208 490 9980
Web Site: https://www.pems.com.hk
Emp.: 20
Electronic Equipment Whslr
N.A.I.C.S.: 423690

Trio Engineering Company Limited (1)
5J Phase 2 Kaiser Estate 51 Man Yue Street Hung Hom, Kowloon, China (Hong Kong)
Tel.: (852) 27658787
Web Site: https://www.triohk.com.hk
Semiconductor & Related Device Mfr
N.A.I.C.S.: 334418

Trio Engineering GmbH (1)
Max-Planck-Strasse 4, Aschheim-Dornach, 85609, Munich, Germany
Tel.: (49) 8921538523
Electronic Components Distr
N.A.I.C.S.: 423690

Trio-Tronics (Thailand) Limited (1)
7/295 Mu 6, Map Yang Phon Sub-District Pluak Daeng District, Rayong, Thailand
Tel.: (66) 33017808
Electronic Components Mfr
N.A.I.C.S.: 334419

Trio-tronics Manufacturing Global Limited (1)
Unit 11E Six Cross Roads Business Park, Carriganard, Waterford, X91 X851, Ireland
Tel.: (353) 15390606
Web Site: https://trio-engineering.com
Electronic Components Distr
N.A.I.C.S.: 423690

TRIO MERCANTILE & TRADING LIMITED
613/B Mangal Aarambh Nr M C Donalds Kora Kendra Off S V Road, Borivali West, Mumbai, 400092, India
Tel.: (91) 2228335999
Web Site: https://www.triomercantile.com
Year Founded: 2002
534755—(BOM)
Rev.: $550,839
Assets: $3,292,616
Liabilities: $391,533
Net Worth: $2,901,083
Earnings: ($12,015)
Emp.: 2
Fiscal Year-end: 03/31/23
Financial Investment Services
N.A.I.C.S.: 523999
Hiren S. Kothari *(CFO)*

TRIO RESOURCES, INC.
100 King Street West Suite 5600, Toronto, M5X 1C9, ON, Canada
Tel.: (647) 701-8013
Year Founded: 2011
Engineeering Services
N.A.I.C.S.: 541330
J. Duncan Reid *(Chm & CEO)*

TRIO-TECH INTERNATIONAL
Block 1008 Toa Payoh North 0309, Singapore, 318996, Singapore
Tel.: (65) 62653300 CA
Web Site: https://www.triotech.com
Year Founded: 1958
TRT—(NYSEAMEX)
Rev.: $42,312,000
Assets: $42,540,000
Liabilities: $10,962,000
Net Worth: $31,578,000
Earnings: $1,142,000
Emp.: 673
Fiscal Year-end: 06/30/24
Semiconductor & Test Equipment Mfr
N.A.I.C.S.: 333242
Siew Wai Yong *(Pres & CEO)*

Subsidiaries:

Trio-Tech (SIP) Co., Ltd. (1)
No 5 Xing Han Street Block A 04-13/16, Suzhou Industrial Park, Suzhou, 215021, China
Tel.: (86) 51267613481
Semiconductor Devices Mfr
N.A.I.C.S.: 334413

Trio-Tech (Tianjin) Co., Ltd. (1)
B7-2 XEDA International Industrial City, Xiqing Economic Development Area, Tianjin, 300385, China
Tel.: (86) 2223828118
Semiconductor Devices Mfr
N.A.I.C.S.: 334413
Yeun Heng Chan *(Production Mgr)*

Trio-Tech International - Singapore Facility (1)
Block 1004 Toa Payoh North 07-01/07, Singapore, 318996, Singapore
Tel.: (65) 62540255
Semiconductor Devices Mfr
N.A.I.C.S.: 334413

Trio-Tech International Pte., Ltd. (1) (100%)
Tel.: (65) 62653300
Web Site: http://www.triotech.com
Sales Range: $125-149.9 Million
Emp.: 280
Equipment & Systems for Production & Testing of Semiconductors
N.A.I.C.S.: 333310

Subsidiary (Non-US):

Trio-Tech (Chongqing) Co., Ltd. (2)
27-05 Huang Jin Fu Pan Building 26 HuangJinQiao Street, HeChuan District, Chongqing, 401520, China
Tel.: (86) 2342884933
Equipment & Systems for Production & Testing of Semiconductors
N.A.I.C.S.: 333242

Trio-Tech (Malaysia) Sdn. Bhd. (2) (55%)
Web Site: http://www.triotech.com
Sales Range: $10-24.9 Million
Emp.: 500
Equipment & Systems for Production & Testing of Semiconductors & Wafer Fabrication
N.A.I.C.S.: 334118

Trio-Tech Bangkok Co., Ltd. (2)
327 Chalongkrung Road, Lamplathew Lat Krabang, Bangkok, 10520, Thailand (100%)
Tel.: (66) 23260847
Sales Range: $10-24.9 Million
Emp.: 20
Semiconductor Mfr
N.A.I.C.S.: 334413
S. W. Wong *(Mng Dir)*

Universal (Far East) Pte. Ltd. (2)
Block 1008 Toa Payoh North 03-09, Singapore, 318996, Singapore (100%)
Tel.: (65) 63549738
Sales Range: $100-124.9 Million
Emp.: 275
Distr of Test & Manufacturing Equipment Used in Semiconductor, Electrical, Electronics, Manufacturing & Aerospace Industries
N.A.I.C.S.: 333242

TRIOCEAN INDUSTRIAL CORPORATION CO., LTD.
No 360 Jiabao Road, Dashe Dist, Kaohsiung, 815006, Taiwan
Tel.: (886) 73560666
Web Site: http://www.triocean.com.tw
1472—(TAI)
Rev.: $63,688,542
Assets: $87,178,224
Liabilities: $40,626,278
Net Worth: $46,551,946
Earnings: $4,643,056
Emp.: 32
Fiscal Year-end: 12/31/23
Textile Mfr
N.A.I.C.S.: 313310
Yu-Lien Chiang *(Chm)*

Subsidiaries:

EVALON TEXTILE (Thailand) CO., LTD. (1)
335/1 Moo 11 Tambon Nonglalok, Amphur Bankhai, Rayong, 21120, Thailand
Tel.: (66) 38892285
Web Site: http://www.triocean.com.tw
Sales Range: $25-49.9 Million
Emp.: 70
Nylon Spun Yarns Mfr
N.A.I.C.S.: 313110

EVALON TEXTILE CO., LTD. (1)
3 Kuan-Hsi 1 Road Chung-Hsin Industrial Park, Shen Kang Hsiang, Taichung, 429, Taiwan
Tel.: (886) 47991695
Web Site: http://www.evalon.com.tw
Sales Range: $25-49.9 Million
Emp.: 140
Yarn Mfr
N.A.I.C.S.: 313110

TRIOCHEM PRODUCTS LIMITED
4th Floor Sambava Chambers Sir P M Road, Fort, Mumbai, 400 001, India
Tel.: (91) 2222663150
Web Site: https://www.triochemproducts.com
Year Founded: 1972
512101—(BOM)
Rev.: $33,271
Assets: $1,419,052
Liabilities: $28,583
Net Worth: $1,390,468
Earnings: ($106,121)
Emp.: 10
Fiscal Year-end: 03/31/23
Pharmaceutical Product Mfr & Whslr
N.A.I.C.S.: 325412
Ramu S. Deora *(CEO & Compliance Officer)*

TRIODOS BANK N.V.
Tel.: (31) 306936500
Web Site: http://www.triodos.com
Year Founded: 1980
Rev.: $327,069,671
Assets: $13,505,845,318
Liabilities: $12,162,526,214
Net Worth: $1,343,319,104
Earnings: $43,395,695
Emp.: 1,493
Fiscal Year-end: 12/31/19
Banking Services
N.A.I.C.S.: 522110
Jeroen Rijpkema *(CEO & Member-Exec Bd)*

TRIP HOLDINGS, INC.
Sanwa Aoyama Bldg 6th Fl 2-22-19 Minami Aoyama, Minato-ku, Tokyo, 107-0062, Japan
Tel.: (81) 354128411 JP
Year Founded: 2006
Investment Holding Company
N.A.I.C.S.: 551112
Takumi Kobayashi *(CEO)*

TRIP HOLDINGS, INC.

TRIP Holdings, Inc.—(Continued)

Subsidiaries:

Orizzonti Co., Ltd. (1)
Yotsubashi Bldg 11th Floor 1-13-3 Shin-machi, Nishi-ku, Osaka, 550-0013, Japan
Tel.: (81) 665436281
Web Site: http://www.orizzonti.co.jp
Sales Range: $150-199.9 Million
Emp.: 343
Women's & Men's Fashion Apparel Designer, Marketer & Retailer
N.A.I.C.S.: 458110

TRIP.COM GROUP LTD.

968 JinZhong Road, Changning District, Shanghai, 20033, China
Tel.: (86) 2134064880   Ky
Web Site: https://group.trip.com
Year Founded: 1999
TCOM—(NASDAQ)
Rev.: $2,909,000,000
Assets: $27,793,000,000
Liabilities: $11,407,000,000
Net Worth: $16,386,000,000
Earnings: $201,000,000
Emp.: 32,202
Fiscal Year-end: 12/31/22
Travel Agencies Services
N.A.I.C.S.: 561510
James Jianzhang Liang *(Co-Founder & Chm)*

Subsidiaries:

Ctrip Computer Technology (Shanghai) Co., Ltd. (1)
No 99 Fuquan Rd, Shanghai, 200335, China
Tel.: (86) 2134064880
Information Technology Consulting Services
N.A.I.C.S.: 541512

Ctrip Travel Information Technology (Shanghai) Co., Ltd. (1)
No 99 Fuquan Rd, Changning Dist, Shanghai, 200335, China
Tel.: (86) 2134064880
Online Travel Booking Services
N.A.I.C.S.: 561599

Ctrip.com (Hong Kong) Limited (1)
Tel.: (852) 21690911
Web Site: http://www.english.ctrip.com
Sales Range: $25-49.9 Million
Emp.: 8
Travel & Lodging Consolidator
N.A.I.C.S.: 561599

Ctrip.com Beijing (1)
Tel.: (86) 1064181616
Web Site: http://pages.english.ctrip.com
Travel & Lodging Consolidator
N.A.I.C.S.: 561599

Ctrip.com Guangzhou (1)
9th Floor China Railway Nord Building No 477 Hanxi Avenue East, Panyu District, Guangzhou, 511400, China
Tel.: (86) 2083936393
Travel & Lodging Consolidator
N.A.I.C.S.: 561599

Ctrip.com Shenzhen (1)
20F Tower A Honglong Century Plz 3001 Heping Rd, Luohu District, Shenzhen, 518001, China
Tel.: (86) 75525981699
Travel & Lodging Consolidator
N.A.I.C.S.: 561599

MakeMyTrip Limited (1)
19th Floor Tower A B & C Epitome Building No 5, DLF Cyber City, Gurgaon, 122002, India   (53.5%)
Tel.: (91) 1244395000
Web Site: https://www.makemytrip.com
Rev.: $782,524,000
Assets: $1,660,077,000
Liabilities: $543,659,000
Net Worth: $1,116,418,000
Earnings: $216,743,000
Emp.: 4,576
Fiscal Year-end: 03/31/2024
Internet Travel Services
N.A.I.C.S.: 561599
Deep Kalra *(Co-Founder & Chm)*

Subsidiary (Domestic):

MakeMyTrip (India) Private Limited
DLF Building No 5 Tower B DLF Cyber City
DLF Phase 2 Sector 25, Gurgaon, 122002, Haryana, India
Tel.: (91) 1244628747
Web Site: https://www.makemytrip.com
Travel Ticket Booking Agencies
N.A.I.C.S.: 561510

Subsidiary (US):

MakeMyTrip.com Inc. (2)
60 E 42 St Ste 411, New York, NY 10165
Tel.: (212) 760-1511
Web Site: http://www.us.makemytrip.com
Sales Range: $25-49.9 Million
Emp.: 3
Online Travel Ticketing Agencies
N.A.I.C.S.: 561599

Qunar Cayman Islands Limited (1)
17th Floor Viva Plaza Building 18 Yard 29 Suzhou Street, Haidian District, Beijing, 100080, China   (45%)
Tel.: (86) 1089676966
Web Site: http://www.qunar.com
Internet Travel Search Services
N.A.I.C.S.: 561599
Haijun Yang *(Pres)*

Shanghai Ctrip Commerce Co., Ltd. (1)
3F Ctrip Building No 99 Fu Quan Road, Shanghai, 200335, China
Tel.: (86) 2134064880
Tour Operating Services
N.A.I.C.S.: 561520

Shanghai Huacheng Southwest Travel Agency Co., Ltd. (1)
No 99 Fuquan Rd, Shanghai, 200335, China
Tel.: (86) 2134064880
Tour Operating Services
N.A.I.C.S.: 561520

Skyscanner Limited (1)
Quartermile One 15 Lauriston Place, Edinburgh, EH3 9EN, United Kingdom
Tel.: (44) 1312525533
Web Site: https://www.skyscanner.co.in
Emp.: 900
Online Flight Comparison Services
N.A.I.C.S.: 519290
Joanna Lord *(CMO)*

Travix International B.V. (1)
Piet Heinkade 55, 1019 GM, Amsterdam, Netherlands
Tel.: (31) 20 702 7200
Web Site: http://www.travix.com
Travel Ticket Booking Services
N.A.I.C.S.: 561599

eLong, Inc. (1)
3rd Floor Tower B Xingke Building 10 Middle Jiuxianqiao Road, Chaoyang District, Beijing, 100015, China
Tel.: (86) 10 64367570
Web Site: http://www.elong.net
Rev.: $165,465,654
Assets: $341,720,791
Liabilities: $187,306,250
Net Worth: $154,414,541
Earnings: ($161,400,078)
Emp.: 4,222
Fiscal Year-end: 12/31/2015
Online Travel Services
N.A.I.C.S.: 561599

Branch (Domestic):

eLong, Inc. - Chengdu (2)
Unit 5-6 9F Huamin Empire Plaza No 1 Fuxing Street, Chengdu, 610016, China
Tel.: (86) 2886703358
Web Site: http://www.elong.net
Online Travel Services
N.A.I.C.S.: 481212

eLong, Inc. - Guangzhou (2)
Rm 1305-1306 Block B No 242 Fengxing Plaza Tianhe Road, Tianhe District, Guangzhou, China
Tel.: (86) 2085509255
Online Travel Services
N.A.I.C.S.: 481212

eLong, Inc. - Hangzhou (2)
10F Block E&F Zhijun Mansion 96 Fengqi Road, Hangzhou, China
Tel.: (86) 57185802110
Web Site: http://www.elong.net
Online Travel Services
N.A.I.C.S.: 481212

eLong, Inc. - Nanjing (2)
Room 403 Building No 2 Junlin International Building, 5 Guangzhou Road, Nanjing, China
Tel.: (86) 2552481038
Online Travel Services
N.A.I.C.S.: 561599

eLong, Inc. - Shanghai Office (2)
2F No 10 Multimedia Valley Road 777, Guangzhong West Road, Shanghai, China
Tel.: (86) 2161071417
Online Travel Services
N.A.I.C.S.: 481212

eLong, Inc. - Shenzhen (2)
News Building No 1002 Shennan Middle Road, Shenzhen, China
Tel.: (86) 75588263290
Online Travel Services
N.A.I.C.S.: 481212

eLong, Inc. - Wuhan (2)
Room 4101 World Trade Center Jiefang Avenue 686, Jianghan District, Wuhan, Jianghan, China
Tel.: (86) 2785449265
Web Site: http://www.elong.net
Online Travel Services
N.A.I.C.S.: 481212

TRIPLE ENERGY LIMITED

Unit 24 589 Stirling Highway, Cottesloe, 6011, WA, Australia
Tel.: (61) 8 9382 2322
Web Site: http://www.tripleenergy.net
Rev.: $1,694
Assets: $233,889
Liabilities: $595,490
Net Worth: ($361,601)
Earnings: ($487,462)
Fiscal Year-end: 03/31/18
Oil & Gas Exploration Services
N.A.I.C.S.: 213112
Alex Neuling *(Sec)*

TRIPLE FLAG PRECIOUS METALS CORP.

161 Bay Street Suite 4535, Toronto, M5J 2S1, ON, Canada
Tel.: (416) 304-9741
Web Site: https://tripleflagpm.com
Year Founded: 2016
TFPM—(NYSE)
Rev.: $151,885,000
Assets: $1,337,031,000
Liabilities: $18,552,000
Net Worth: $1,318,479,000
Earnings: $55,086,000
Emp.: 15
Fiscal Year-end: 12/31/22
Metal & Mining Industry
N.A.I.C.S.: 212290
C. Warren Beil *(Gen Counsel)*

Subsidiaries:

Maverix Metals, Inc. (1)
Suite 575 510 Burrard Street, Vancouver, V6C 3A8, BC, Canada
Tel.: (604) 449-9290
Web Site: http://www.maverixmetals.com
Rev.: $57,532,000
Assets: $392,535,000
Liabilities: $20,721,000
Net Worth: $371,814,000
Earnings: $24,072,000
Emp.: 1
Fiscal Year-end: 12/31/2021
Metal Ore Mining
N.A.I.C.S.: 212290
Geoff Burns *(Co-Founder & Chm)*

TRIPLE G CONSTRUCTION INC.

PO Box 695, Grande Prairie, T8V 3A8, AB, Canada
Tel.: (780) 532-9134
Web Site: http://www.triplegconstruction.ca
Rev.: $15,390,171
Emp.: 50
Logging & Timber Supplier
N.A.I.C.S.: 423390
Gervin Antypowich *(Owner)*

TRIPLE I LOGISTICS PUBLIC COMPANY LIMITED

628 Triple i Building 3rd Floor Soi Klab Chom Nonsee Road, Chongnonsee Yannawa, Bangkok, 10120, Thailand
Tel.: (66) 26818700   TH
Web Site: https://investor.iii-logistics.com
Year Founded: 2008
III—(THA)
Rev.: $51,026,677
Assets: $135,482,986
Liabilities: $25,644,885
Net Worth: $109,838,101
Earnings: $25,286,613
Emp.: 518
Fiscal Year-end: 12/31/23
Logistic Services
N.A.I.C.S.: 541614
Tipp Dalal *(CEO)*

Subsidiaries:

Asia Ground Service Co., Ltd. (1)
628 Triple i Building 6th Floor Soi Klab Chom Nonsee Road, Chongnonsee Yannawa, Bangkok, 10120, Thailand
Tel.: (66) 26815888
Oil Transportation Services
N.A.I.C.S.: 481112

Asia Network International Co., Ltd. (1)
628 Triple i Building 6th Floor Soi Klab Chom Nonsee Road, Chongnonsee Yannawa, Bangkok, 10120, Thailand
Tel.: (66) 2681314950
Freight Forwarding Services
N.A.I.C.S.: 488510

DG Packaging (Thailand) Co., Ltd. (1)
628 4th Floor Triple i Building Soi Klab Chom Nonsee Road Chongnonsee, Yannawa, Bangkok, 10120, Thailand
Tel.: (66) 26818122
Web Site: https://www.dg-packaging.co.th
Packaging & Logistics Consulting Services
N.A.I.C.S.: 561910

HazChem Logistics Management Co., Ltd. (1)
628 4th Floor Triple i Building Soi Klab Chom Nonsee Road, Chongnonsee Yannawa, Bangkok, 10120, Thailand
Tel.: (66) 26818000
Web Site: http://www.hazchemlogistics.com
Oil Transportation Services
N.A.I.C.S.: 481112
Tipp Dala *(CEO)*

HazChem Trans Management Co., Ltd. (1)
628 Triple i Building 4th Floor Soi Klab Chom Nonsee Road, Chongnonsee Yannawa, Bangkok, 10120, Thailand
Tel.: (66) 26818000
Web Site: https://www.hazchemlogistics.com
Logistics Consulting Servies
N.A.I.C.S.: 541614
Tipp Dala *(CEO)*

TSL Logistics Co., Ltd. (1)
3364/7 Rama IV Road Klongton, Klongtoey, Bangkok, 10110, Thailand
Tel.: (66) 2249809899
Air Freight Forwarding Services
N.A.I.C.S.: 541614

Triple i Asia Cargo Co., Ltd. (1)
628 Triple i Building 6th Floor Soi Klab Chom Nonsee Road, Chongnonsee Yan-

AND PRIVATE COMPANIES

nawa, Bangkok, 10120, Thailand
Tel.: (66) 26817900
Oil Transportation Services
N.A.I.C.S.: 481112

Triple i Maritime Agencies Co., Ltd. (1)
628 Triple i Building 2nd Floor Soi Klab Chom Nonsee Road, Chongnonsee Yannawa, Bangkok, 10120, Thailand
Tel.: (66) 26818988
Marine Transportation Services
N.A.I.C.S.: 488510

Triple i Supplychain Co., Ltd. (1)
628 Triple i Building 6th Floor Soi Klab Chom Nonsee Road, Chongnonsee Yannawa, Bangkok, 10120, Thailand
Tel.: (66) 26813722
Web Site: http://www.iii-supplychain.com
Logistic Services
N.A.I.C.S.: 541614

TRIPLE P N.V.
Nevelgaarde 60, 3436 ZZ, Nieuwegein, Netherlands
Tel.: (31) 880332500
Web Site: https://www.triple-p.nl
Year Founded: 1995
TPPPF—(OTCIQ)
Emp.: 299
Computer & Network Services
N.A.I.C.S.: 541512
Bert A. Bouwhuis (CTO)

TRIPLE POINT ENERGY TRANSITION PLC
The Scalpel 52 Lime Street 18th Floor, London, EC3M 7AF, United Kingdom
Tel.: (44) 2072018989   UK
Web Site: https://www.tpenergytransition.com
Year Founded: 2020
TENT—(LSE)
Rev.: $9,349,912
Assets: $110,388,791
Liabilities: $975,764
Net Worth: $109,413,027
Earnings: ($9,179,500)
Fiscal Year-end: 03/31/24
Asset Management Services
N.A.I.C.S.: 523999
John Roberts (Chm)

Subsidiaries:

Elementary Energy Limited (1)
124 City Road, London, EC1V 2NX, United Kingdom
Tel.: (44) 1483389481
Web Site: https://www.elemental-energies.com
Renewable Energy Consulting Services
N.A.I.C.S.: 541690

TEEC Holdings Limited (1)
10/11 West Mills Yard Kennet Road, Newbury, RG14 5LP, Berkshire, United Kingdom
Tel.: (44) 1635282361
Web Site: https://www.teec.co.uk
Software Solutions Services
N.A.I.C.S.: 541511

TRIPLE POINT INCOME VCT PLC
1 King William Street, London, EC4N 7AF, United Kingdom
Tel.: (44) 207 201 8989   UK
Web Site: http://www.triplepoint.co.uk
Year Founded: 2007
TPVC—(LSE)
Rev.: $2,020,287
Assets: $33,522,107
Liabilities: $351,649
Net Worth: $33,170,457
Earnings: $236,243
Emp.: 3
Fiscal Year-end: 03/31/22
Investment Management Service
N.A.I.C.S.: 523940

David Frank (Chm)

TRIPLE POINT SOCIAL HOUSING REIT PLC
The Scalpel 52 Lime Street 18th Floor, London, EC3M 7AF, United Kingdom
Tel.: (44) 2072018989   UK
Web Site: https://www.triplepointreit.com
Year Founded: 2004
SOHO—(LSE)
Rev.: $42,567,030
Assets: $849,184,545
Liabilities: $320,059,740
Net Worth: $529,124,805
Earnings: $29,992,050
Fiscal Year-end: 12/31/22
Real Estate Investment Trust Services
N.A.I.C.S.: 523940
Chris Phillips (Chm)

TRIPLE POINT VCT 2011 PLC
4-5 Grosvenor Place, London, SW1X 7HJ, United Kingdom
Tel.: (44) 2072018989   UK
Web Site: http://www.triplepoint.co.uk
Year Founded: 2010
TPOB—(LSE)
Rev.: $9,857,047
Assets: $49,563,569
Liabilities: $1,737,882
Net Worth: $47,825,687
Earnings: $6,656,901
Fiscal Year-end: 02/28/22
Investment Management Trust Services
N.A.I.C.S.: 523940

TRIPLE SEVEN CHRYSLER
700 Broad Street, Regina, S4R8H7, SK, Canada
Tel.: (306) 522-2222
Web Site: http://www.triplesevenchrysler.ca
New & Used Car Sales & Service
N.A.I.C.S.: 441110
Rob Fellner (Mgr-Parts)

TRIPOD TECHNOLOGY CORPORATION
No 21 Kuang-Yeh 5th Rd Ping-jen Industrial Park, Ping-jen District, Taoyuan, Taiwan
Tel.: (886) 34195678
Web Site: http://www.tripod-tech.com
3044—(TAI)
Rev.: $1,924,919,120
Assets: $2,496,626,905
Liabilities: $1,072,363,804
Net Worth: $1,424,263,101
Earnings: $198,237,312
Emp.: 26,334
Fiscal Year-end: 12/31/23
Printed Circuit Board Mfr
N.A.I.C.S.: 334412
Ching-Hsiu Hu (Vice Chm)

Subsidiaries:

Tripod Technology Corporation - Taiwan Plant (1)
21 Kung-Yeh 5th Road Ping-Jen Industrial Park, Taoyuan, Taiwan
Tel.: (886) 34195678
Web Site: http://www.tripod-tech.com
Printed Circuit Board Mfr
N.A.I.C.S.: 334412

Trison Technology Corporation (1)
De Boomgaard 9-13, 1243 HV, 's-Graveland, Netherlands
Tel.: (31) 356922312
Web Site: https://www.trison-technology.com
Radio Broadcasting Services
N.A.I.C.S.: 516110

TRIPPLE GEE & COMPANY PLC.
Plot 9 Kareem Giwa Street Abule Oshun Opposite, Inter'l Trade Fair Complex KM11 Badagry Express Way Abule Oshun, Lagos, Nigeria
Tel.: (234) 8055190713   NG
Web Site: http://www.tripplegee.com
Year Founded: 1980
TRIPPLEG—(NIGE)
Rev.: $1,630,429
Assets: $4,694,489
Liabilities: $4,098,162
Net Worth: $596,327
Earnings: $5,181
Emp.: 107
Fiscal Year-end: 03/31/24
Paper Packaging Product Mfr
N.A.I.C.S.: 326112
Samuel Idowu Ayininuola (Chm)

TRIPSITTER CLINIC LIMITED
77 King Street West-Suite 700, Toronto, M5K 1G8, ON, Canada
Tel.: (416) 462-1353   BC
Web Site: https://www.tripsitter.clinic
Year Founded: 2021
KETA—(CNSX)
Rev.: $10,553
Assets: $2,133
Liabilities: $551,661
Net Worth: ($549,528)
Earnings: ($230,207)
Fiscal Year-end: 01/31/24
Health Care Srvices
N.A.I.C.S.: 621610
Daniel Hanono (Chief Medical Officer)

TRISHAKTI INDUSTRIES LTD.
Godrej Genesis Salt lake City Sector V 10th Floor Unit No 1007, Kolkata, 700 091, India
Tel.: (91) 3340082489   In
Web Site: https://www.trishakti.com
Year Founded: 1985
531279—(BOM)
Rev.: $2,350,974
Assets: $1,374,858
Liabilities: $124,789
Net Worth: $1,250,069
Earnings: $61,423
Emp.: 18
Fiscal Year-end: 03/31/23
Industrial Electronic Products Mfr
N.A.I.C.S.: 333248
Ramesh Jhanwar (Exec Dir)

TRISLOT N.V.
Roterijstraat 134, 8790, Waregem, Belgium
Tel.: (32) 56627222
Web Site: http://www.trislot.be
Year Founded: 1975
Sales Range: $10-24.9 Million
Emp.: 100
Wedge Wire Filtering & Separation Products for Food & Beverage Industries Mfr
N.A.I.C.S.: 332618
Vanessa Haeck (Mgr-Fin)

TRISPAN LLP
39 Sloane Street, London, SW1X 9LP, United Kingdom
Tel.: (44) 2030562900
Web Site: http://www.trispanllp.com
Privater Equity Firm
N.A.I.C.S.: 523940
Fady Michel Abouchalache (Co-Founder)

Subsidiaries:

Allied Dental Practices of New Jersey, LLC (1)

TRISTEL PLC

1144 Hooper Ave Ste 201B, Toms River, NJ 08753
Tel.: (610) 250-7118
Web Site: http://www.allieddental.com
Offices of Dentists
N.A.I.C.S.: 621210
Edward Poller (Pres & CEO)

Prestige Employee Administrators, LLC (1)
538 Broadhollow Rd Ste 311, Melville, NY 11747
Tel.: (516) 692-8505
Web Site: http://www.prestigeemployee.com
Sales Range: $350-399.9 Million
Emp.: 7,000
Employee Benefit Programs & Insurance Services
N.A.I.C.S.: 524298
Allan Coopbrberg (Pres)

TRISTAR ACQUISITION GROUP
4 Via Federico Zuccari, 00153, Rome, Italy
Tel.: (39) 0657288176
Building Construction Services
N.A.I.C.S.: 236210
Manfredi Mazziotti Di Celso (Pres, CEO, CFO, Treas & Sec)

TRISTATE HOLDINGS LIMITED
5/F 66-72 Lei Muk Road, Kwai Chung, New Territories, China (Hong Kong)
Tel.: (852) 22793888
Web Site: https://www.tristateww.com
0458—(HKG)
Rev.: $475,727,235
Assets: $392,216,648
Liabilities: $259,683,203
Net Worth: $132,533,445
Earnings: $5,077,560
Emp.: 6,360
Fiscal Year-end: 12/31/22
Athletic Clothing Exporter
N.A.I.C.S.: 315120
Peter Kin Chung Wang (Chm & CEO)

Subsidiaries:

Hefei Tristate Garment Manufacturing Company Limited (1)
The Cross of Zipeng Rd and Tianmen, Hefei, 230601, China
Tel.: (86) 55163845588
Garments Mfr
N.A.I.C.S.: 315250

Shanghai Tristate Enterprises Co., Ltd. (1)
162 Zhen Ning Road Jing An District, Shanghai, 200000, China
Tel.: (86) 2122180000
Apparel Product Distr
N.A.I.C.S.: 424310

Tristate US Inc. (1)
285 W Broadway Ste 620, New York, NY 10013
Tel.: (646) 682-9099
Garment Distr
N.A.I.C.S.: 424350

TRISTEL PLC
Unit 1B Fordham Road, Lynx Business Park, Cambridge, CB8 7NY, United Kingdom
Tel.: (44) 1638721500
Web Site: https://www.tristel.com
TSTL—(AIM)
Rev.: $52,999,242
Assets: $55,749,494
Liabilities: $14,786,400
Net Worth: $40,963,094
Earnings: $8,201,466
Emp.: 250
Fiscal Year-end: 06/30/24
Pharmaceutical Industry
N.A.I.C.S.: 325412
Paul C. Swinney (CEO)

TRISTEL PLC

TRISTEL PLC—(Continued)

Subsidiaries:

Stella Performance Limited (1)
AS 10 12 Jean Batten Dr, Mount Maunganui, 3116, New Zealand
Tel.: (64) 75753730
Disinfection Instruments Sales
N.A.I.C.S.: 423450

Tristel GmbH (1)
Karl-Marx-Allee 90A, 10243, Berlin, Germany
Tel.: (49) 3054844226
Medical Device Mfr & Distr
N.A.I.C.S.: 339112

Tristel Italia Srl. (1)
Via Edoardo Collamarini 14, 40138, Bologna, BO, Italy
Tel.: (39) 0510014912
Web Site: https://www.tristel.it
Medical Device Distr
N.A.I.C.S.: 423450

Tristel New Zealand Ltd. (1)
23 Birch Avenue, Tauranga, 3110, Judea Bay Of Plenty, New Zealand
Tel.: (64) 75771560
Web Site: https://tristel.com
Medical Device Mfr & Distr
N.A.I.C.S.: 339112
Justine Beale (Mng Dir)

Tristel Pty. Ltd. (1)
40/328 Reserve Road, Cheltenham, 3192, VIC, Australia
Tel.: (61) 395836181
Web Site: https://tristel.com
Medical Device Mfr & Distr
N.A.I.C.S.: 339112
Ash McMaster (Mng Dir)

Tristel SaS (1)
130 Boulevard de la Liberte, 59000, Lille, France
Tel.: (33) 366880184
Web Site: https://tristel.com
Electromedical Product Mfr
N.A.I.C.S.: 334510

Tristel Solutions Limited (1)
Unit 1B Lynx Business Park Fordham Road, Snailwell, Cambridge, CB8 7NY, Cambridgeshire, United Kingdom
Tel.: (44) 1638721500
Web Site: http://www.tristel.com
Sales Range: $25-49.9 Million
Emp.: 60
Infection Control Products Supplier
N.A.I.C.S.: 424210

TRISUL S.A.
Avenida Paulista no 37 15th floor, Sao Paulo, 01311-902, SP, Brazil
Tel.: (55) 1130039285
Web Site: https://www.trisul-sa.com.br
Year Founded: 2007
TRIS3—(BRAZ)
Rev.: $187,106,053
Assets: $492,972,583
Liabilities: $244,307,389
Net Worth: $248,665,194
Earnings: $23,273,627
Fiscal Year-end: 12/31/23
Real Estate Development Services
N.A.I.C.S.: 531390
Jorge Cury Neto (VP)

TRISURA GROUP LTD.
333 Bay Street Suite 1610, PO Box 22, Toronto, M5H 2R2, ON, Canada
Tel.: (416) 214-2555
Web Site: https://www.trisura.com
TSU—(TSX)
Rev.: $1,222,864,790
Assets: $2,347,116,927
Liabilities: $2,066,443,468
Net Worth: $280,673,459
Earnings: $48,938,655
Emp.: 248
Fiscal Year-end: 12/31/21
General Insurance Services
N.A.I.C.S.: 524210
David Clare (Pres & CEO)

Subsidiaries:

Trisura Guarantee Insurance Company (1)
Bay Adelaide Centre 333 Bay Street Suite 1610, Toronto, M5H 2R2, ON, Canada
Tel.: (416) 214-2555
Web Site: https://www.trisura.com
Insurance Services
N.A.I.C.S.: 524210
Mark Murski (Founder)

TRITAX BIG BOX REIT PLC
72 Broadwick Street, London, W1F 9QZ, United Kingdom
Tel.: (44) 2072901616   UK
Web Site: https://www.tritaxbigbox.co.uk
Year Founded: 2013
BBOX—(LSE)
Rev.: $255,956,250
Assets: $6,209,317,950
Liabilities: $2,193,514,950
Net Worth: $4,015,803,000
Earnings: ($722,579,550)
Emp.: 31
Fiscal Year-end: 12/31/22
Real Estate Investment Trust Services
N.A.I.C.S.: 523940
Richard Jewson (Chm)

Subsidiaries:

UK Commercial Property REIT Limited (1)
Trafalgar Court Les Banques, PO Box 255, Saint Peter Port, GY1 3QL, Guernsey
Tel.: (44) 1481745001
Web Site: http://www.ukcpreit.com
Rev.: $84,486,241
Assets: $1,715,626,105
Liabilities: $408,230,245
Net Worth: $1,307,395,860
Earnings: ($280,647,564)
Fiscal Year-end: 12/31/2022
Real Estate Investment Trust Services
N.A.I.C.S.: 523940
Andrew Wilson (Chm)

TRITAX EUROBOX PLC
72 Broadwick Street, London, W1F 9QZ, United Kingdom
Tel.: (44) 2072901616   UK
Web Site: https://www.tritaxeurobox.co.uk
Year Founded: 2018
EBOX—(LSE)
Rev.: $135,269,644
Assets: $1,194,074,008
Liabilities: $509,905,323
Net Worth: $684,168,685
Earnings: $60,812,279
Fiscal Year-end: 09/30/20
Real Estate Investment Trust Services
N.A.I.C.S.: 523940
Henry Franklin (COO)

TRITECH GROUP LIMITED
31 Changi South Ave 2, Singapore, 486478, Singapore
Tel.: (65) 68482567
Web Site: https://www.tritech.com.sg
5G9—(SES)
Rev.: $20,254,298
Assets: $20,348,447
Liabilities: $18,897,822
Net Worth: $1,450,625
Earnings: ($1,717,809)
Emp.: 300
Fiscal Year-end: 03/31/24
Engineering & Construction Services
N.A.I.C.S.: 237990
Jeffrey Wang (CEO & Mng Dir)

Subsidiaries:

Anhui Clean Environment Biotechnology Co., Ltd. (1)
4th Floor Block E Huayi Science Park Hightech Development Zone, Hefei, China
Tel.: (86) 5516 539 2726
Web Site: https://www.ahclean.com
Emp.: 80
Construction Material Mfr & Distr
N.A.I.C.S.: 327120

Geosoft Pte Ltd (1)
31 Changi South Ave 2, Singapore, 486478, Singapore
Tel.: (65) 62420953
Web Site: https://www.geosoft.sg
Geotechnical Development Services
N.A.I.C.S.: 541380

SysEng (S) Pte Ltd (1)
2 Kaki Bukit Pl 05-00 Tritech Bldg, Singapore, 416180, Singapore
Tel.: (65) 62875710
Web Site: http://www.syseng.com.sg
Sales Range: $25-49.9 Million
Emp.: 24
Civil & Geotechnical Engineering Services
N.A.I.C.S.: 541330
Poh Ye Kong (Dir-Tech)

Terra Tritech Engineering (M) Sdn Bhd (1)
No 25-1 Jalan Puteri 5/10 Bandar Puteri, 47100, Puchong, Selangor Darul Ehsan, Malaysia
Tel.: (60) 380612665
Engineering & Construction Services
N.A.I.C.S.: 237990

TriTech Water Technologies Pte Ltd (1)
31 Changi South Avenue 2 Tritech Building 03-02, Singapore, 486478, Singapore
Tel.: (65) 68482567
Web Site: https://www.tritechwater.com.sg
Waste Treatment Services
N.A.I.C.S.: 221310
Jeffrey Wang (Mng Dir)

Tritech Consultants Pte Ltd (1)
31 Changi South Avenue 2, Singapore, 486478, Singapore
Tel.: (65) 67428096
Emp.: 200
Civil & Geotechnical Consulting Services
N.A.I.C.S.: 541618
Jeffrey Wang (Mng Dir)

Tritech Engineering & Testing (Singapore) Pte Ltd (1)
31 Changi South Avenue 2 Tritech Building 03-00, Singapore, 486478, Singapore
Tel.: (65) 68482567
Civil Engineering Services
N.A.I.C.S.: 541330
Stanley Chan (Project Mgr & Sr Engr-Instrumentation)

Tritech Geotechnic Pte Ltd (1)
31 Changi South Avenue 2, Singapore, 486478, Singapore
Tel.: (65) 65429315
Web Site: http://www.tritech.com.sg
Sales Range: $25-49.9 Million
Emp.: 20
Ground Engineering Design Services
N.A.I.C.S.: 541330

Tritech Vavie (Singapore) Pte. Ltd. (1)
31 Changi South Avenue 2, Singapore, 486478, Singapore
Tel.: (65) 68482567
Web Site: https://www.vavie.com.sg
Fresh & Healthy Water Services
N.A.I.C.S.: 924110

Tritech-Geokon Singapore Pte Ltd (1)
2 Kaki Bukit Pl Tritech Bldg, Singapore, 416180, Singapore
Tel.: (65) 68482567
Web Site: http://www.tritech.com.sg
Emp.: 100
Geotechnical Instruments Mfr
N.A.I.C.S.: 334519
Scott Cheng (Gen Mgr)

TRITENT INTERNATIONAL, CORP.
126 Simcoe St Unit 2706, Toronto, M5H 4E9, ON, Canada   NV

INTERNATIONAL PUBLIC

Web Site: https://tritentintlcorp.com
TICJ—(OTCIQ)
Rev.: $1,347,269,000
Assets: $9,642,633,000
Liabilities: $7,110,396,000
Net Worth: $2,532,237,000
Earnings: $353,279,000
Fiscal Year-end: 12/31/19
Petroleum Product Distr
N.A.I.C.S.: 424720
Nathaniel A. Hsieh (Pres)

TRITERRAS, INC.
7500A Beach Road 13-308 The Plaza, Singapore, 199591, Singapore
Tel.: (65) 66619240   Ky
Web Site: https://www.triterras.com
Year Founded: 2020
TRIRF—(OTCEM)
Rev.: $56,679,753
Assets: $170,760,100
Liabilities: $26,421,457
Net Worth: $144,338,643
Earnings: $33,423,529
Emp.: 49
Fiscal Year-end: 02/28/22
Financial Technology Platform Developer & Operator
N.A.I.C.S.: 541511
Srinivas Koneru (Founder, Chm & CEO)

TRITON ADVISERS LIMITED
5/6 Esplanade 1st Floor, Saint Helier, JE2 3QA, Jersey
Tel.: (44) 1534709400   JE
Web Site: http://www.triton-partners.com
Year Founded: 1997
Emp.: 106,000
Privater Equity Firm
N.A.I.C.S.: 523999
Beata Gawarecka-Green (COO & Head-HR)

Subsidiaries:

ARVOS Holding GmbH (1)
Ellenbacher Strasse 10, 34123, Kassel, Germany
Tel.: (49) 6221 7532 100
Holding Company; Thermal Industrial Equipment Mfr & Whslr
N.A.I.C.S.: 551112
Ludger Heuberg (CFO)

Subsidiary (Domestic):

ARVOS GmbH (2)
Ellenbacher Strasse 10, 34123, Kassel, Germany
Tel.: (49) 56195270
Web Site: http://www.arvos-group.com
Sales Range: $25-49.9 Million
Industrial Process Heat Transfer Equipment Designer, Mfr & Whslr
N.A.I.C.S.: 332410
Karsten Stuckrath (Pres)

Branch (Domestic):

ARVOS GmbH - Dusseldorf (3)
Parsevalstrasse 9A, 40468, Dusseldorf, Germany
Tel.: (49) 21147260
Web Site: http://www.arvos-group.com
Emp.: 70
Industrial Process Heat Transfer Equipment Whslr
N.A.I.C.S.: 423830

Alimak Group AB (1)
Blekholmstorget 30, SE-111 64, Stockholm, Sweden
Tel.: (46) 84021440
Web Site: https://www.alimakgroup.com
Rev.: $455,089,824
Assets: $720,479,536
Liabilities: $251,643,504
Net Worth: $468,836,032
Earnings: $37,539,600
Emp.: 2,057
Fiscal Year-end: 12/31/2021
Industrial Hoist & Elevator Equipment Mfr

AND PRIVATE COMPANIES — TRITON ADVISERS LIMITED

N.A.I.C.S.: 333923
Charlotte Brogren *(CTO)*

Subsidiary (Domestic):

Alimak Hek AB (2)
Alimakvagen 1, PO Box 720, Skelleftea, 931 42, Sweden **(100%)**
Tel.: (46) 91087000
Web Site: http://www.alimak.com
Sales Range: $50-74.9 Million
Emp.: 200
Industrial Hoist & Elevator Equipment Mfr
N.A.I.C.S.: 333923
Rolf Persson *(Mng Dir)*

Subsidiary (US):

Alimak Hek Inc. (2)
12552 Galveston Rd Ste A 160, Webster, TX 77598
Tel.: (713) 640-8500
Web Site: http://www.alimakhek.us
Sales Range: $25-49.9 Million
Emp.: 74
Industrial Hoist & Elevator Equipment Mfr
N.A.I.C.S.: 333923
Ed Gibbs *(VP-Construction Products)*

Subsidiary (Non-US):

Alimak Hek Ltd. (2)
Northampton Road, Rushden, NN10 6BW, United Kingdom
Tel.: (44) 1933 354700
Web Site: http://www.alimakhek.co.uk
Emp.: 50
Industrial Hoist & Elevator Equipment Mfr
N.A.I.C.S.: 333923
Russell Bates *(Dir)*

Alimak Hek Pty. Ltd. (2)
2 Ausco Place, Dandenong South, Melbourne, 3175, VIC, Australia
Tel.: (61) 3 8795 6789
Web Site: http://www.alimakhek.com
Emp.: 40
Industrial Hoist & Elevator Equipment Mfr
N.A.I.C.S.: 333923
Keith Carroll *(Mng Dir)*

All4Labels Group GmbH (1)
Mollner Landstrasse 15, D-22969, Witzhave, Germany
Tel.: (49) 4104 6930
Web Site: http://all4labels.com
Emp.: 3,000
Packaging & Labeling Services
N.A.I.C.S.: 561910
Tim Fiedler *(Mng Dir)*

Subsidiary (Domestic):

RAKO ETIKETTEN GmbH & Co. KG (2)
Mollner Landstrasse 15, 22969, Witzhave, Germany
Tel.: (49) 4104 693 0
Web Site: http://www.rako-etiketten.com
Self-Adhesive Labels & Flexible Packaging Material Mfr
N.A.I.C.S.: 326112
Matthias Kurtz *(Mng Dir)*

Subsidiary (Domestic):

All4Labels Kassel GmbH (3)
Vor der Hecke 5, 34355, Staufenberg, Germany
Tel.: (49) 55 43 94 34 0
Web Site: http://www.etibana.de
Self Adhesive Labels Mfr
N.A.I.C.S.: 326112
Andreas Boehm *(Mng Dir)*

Subsidiary (Non-US):

All4Labels Scheiz AG (3)
Martinsbruggstrasse 85, Saint Gallen, 9016, Switzerland
Tel.: (41) 71 228 43 83
Web Site: http://www.omnipack.ch
Adhesive Labels, Tags & Tickets Mfr
N.A.I.C.S.: 326112
Elisabeth Fehr *(Mgr)*

Subsidiary (Domestic):

Folienprint-RAKO GmbH (3)
Neu-Galliner Ring 26, 19258, Gallin, Germany
Tel.: (49) 38851 330 0
Web Site: http://www.folienprint.de
Flexible Packaging & Shrink-Sleeves Mfr
N.A.I.C.S.: 326112
Doris Erhardt-Freitag *(Mng Dir)*

Graphische Betriebe STAATS GmbH (3)
Rossfeld 8, 59557, Lippstadt, Germany
Tel.: (49) 29 41 29 03 0
Web Site: http://www.staats.de
Self Adhesive Labels Mfr
N.A.I.C.S.: 326112
Gabriele Staats *(Mng Dir)*

Ritter Haftetiketten GmbH & Co. KG (3)
Wertherstrasse 46-52, 32130, Enger, Germany
Tel.: (49) 52 24 9 70 6
Web Site: http://www.ritterhaftetiketten.de
Self Adhesive Labels Mfr
N.A.I.C.S.: 326112
Olaf Grass *(Mng Dir)*

Ambea AB (1)
Vretenvagen 13, 171 54, Solna, Sweden
Tel.: (46) 8578 700 00
Web Site: http://www.ambea.com
Holding Company; Social Care Services
N.A.I.C.S.: 551112
Fredrik Gren *(Pres & CEO)*

Subsidiary (Domestic):

Nytida AB (2)
Vretenvagen 13, 171 54, Solna, Sweden
Tel.: (46) 8578 700 00
Web Site: http://www.nytida.se
Emp.: 7,000
Disability & Social Disorder Care Services
N.A.I.C.S.: 623210
Fredrik Gren *(CEO)*

DSI International Luxembourg SARL (1)
26 B Boulevard Royal, 2449, Luxembourg, Luxembourg
Tel.: (352) 272 055 11
Web Site: http://www.dywidag-systems.com
Sales Range: $650-699.9 Million
Emp.: 2,200
Mining & Construction Post-Tensioning, Geotechnical & Underground Support Equipment Mfr
N.A.I.C.S.: 238120
Matti Kuivalainen *(CEO)*

Subsidiary (Non-US):

DSI Holding GmbH (2)
Destouchesstrasse 68, 80796, Munich, Germany
Tel.: (49) 89309050200
Web Site: http://www.dywidag-systems.com
Sales Range: $650-699.9 Million
Emp.: 2,200
Post-Tensioning Geotechnical & Underground Support Product Mfr
N.A.I.C.S.: 238120

Subsidiary (US):

DSI Underground Systems, Inc. (3)
9786 S Prosperity Rd, West Jordan, UT 84081
Tel.: (801) 973-7169
Web Site: http://www.dsiunderground.com
Mining & Tunneling Industry Hardware & Resin Products Mfr
N.A.I.C.S.: 332722
Roland Walker *(Dir-Engrg)*

Unit (Domestic):

DSI Underground Systems, Inc. - Cambridge (4)
9344 Sunrise Rd, Cambridge, OH 43725
Tel.: (740) 432-7302
Web Site: http://www.dsiunderground.com
Sales Range: $75-99.9 Million
Emp.: 31
Mining & Tunneling Industry Hardware & Resin Products Mfr
N.A.I.C.S.: 332722
Theodore Allen *(Gen Mgr)*

DSI Underground Systems, Inc. - Martinsburg (4)
447 Dupont Rd, Martinsburg, WV 25401-6550
Tel.: (304) 274-2121
Sales Range: $125-149.9 Million
Emp.: 105
Mining & Tunneling Industry Hardware & Resin Products Mfr
N.A.I.C.S.: 332722

Subsidiary (Non-US):

DYWIDAG-Systems International GmbH (3)
Alfred-Wagner-Strasse 1, Pasching, 4061, Austria
Tel.: (43) 7229 610 49 0
Web Site: http://www.dywidag-systems.at
Sales Range: $25-49.9 Million
Emp.: 10
Post-Tensioning Systems Mfr
N.A.I.C.S.: 238120
Gerhard Filas *(Gen Mgr)*

Subsidiary (Domestic):

DYWIDAG-Systems International GmbH (3)
Siemensstrasse 8, 85716, Unterschleissheim, Germany
Tel.: (49) 89309050100
Web Site: http://www.dywidag-systems.com
Sales Range: $10-24.9 Million
Emp.: 50
Post-Tensioning Systems Mfr
N.A.I.C.S.: 238120
Patrik Nolaker *(CEO)*

Subsidiary (Non-US):

DYWIDAG-Systems International A/S (4)
Industrieveien 7A, 1483, Skytta, Norway
Tel.: (47) 67061560
Web Site: http://www.dywidag-systems.com
Post-Tensioning Systems Mfr
N.A.I.C.S.: 238120

DYWIDAG-Systems International B.V. (4)
Veilingweg 2, 5301 KM, Zaltbommel, Netherlands
Tel.: (31) 418578922
Web Site: http://www.dywidag-systems.com
Emp.: 20
Post-Tensioning Systems Mfr
N.A.I.C.S.: 238120
J. Balkende *(Gen Mgr)*

DYWIDAG-Systems International Ltd. (4)
Northfield Road, Southam, CV47 OFG, United Kingdom
Tel.: (44) 1926813980
Web Site: http://www.dywidag.co.uk
Post-Tensioning Systems Mfr
N.A.I.C.S.: 238120
Ian Jarvis *(Dir-Comml)*

DYWIDAG-Systems International N.V. (4)
Industrieweg 25, 3190, Boortmeerbeek, Belgium
Tel.: (32) 16607760
Web Site: http://www.dywidag.be
Post-Tensioning Systems Mfr
N.A.I.C.S.: 238120

DYWIT S.p.A. (4)
Viale Europa 72 Strada A 7/9, 20090, Cusago, Italy
Tel.: (39) 02 901 65 71
Web Site: http://www.dywit.it
Concrete Post-Tensioning Systems & Construction Materials Mfr
N.A.I.C.S.: 238120

SpannStahl AG (4)
Wasseristrasse 29, 8340, Hinwil, Switzerland
Tel.: (41) 9389797
Web Site: http://www.spannstahl.ch
Post-Tensioning Systems Mfr
N.A.I.C.S.: 238120
Fredy Saxer *(Mng Dir)*

Subsidiary (Non-US):

DYWIDAG-Systems International Pty. Ltd. (3)
25 Pacific Highway, Bennetts Green, 2290, NSW, Australia
Tel.: (61) 249489099
Web Site: http://www.dsiminingproducts.com
Sales Range: $75-99.9 Million
Emp.: 300
Structural Support Products for the Mining & Tunneling Industries
N.A.I.C.S.: 238120
Derek Hird *(CEO)*

Subsidiary (Non-US):

DYWIDAG-Systems International Far East Ltd. (4)
Unit 905-907 Prosperity Millennia Plaza 663 King's Road North Point, 302-308 Hennessy Road, Hong Kong, China (Hong Kong)
Tel.: (852) 28331913
Web Site: http://www.dywidag-systems.com
Sales Range: $75-99.9 Million
Emp.: 10
Post-Tensioning Systems Mfr
N.A.I.C.S.: 238120
Alex Ho *(Asst Gen Mgr)*

DYWIDAG-Systems Korea Co. Ltd (4)
5th Floor Spring Morning B/D, 249-2 Yangjae-Dong Seocho-ku, Seoul, 137 894, Korea (South)
Tel.: (82) 234720141
Web Site: http://www.dsikorea.co.kr
Sales Range: $75-99.9 Million
Emp.: 11
Post-Tensioning Systems Mfr
N.A.I.C.S.: 238120
S. C. Jang *(Mgr)*

DYWITECH Co. Ltd. (4)
13th Fl No 3-163 Sec 1 Keelung Road, Taipei, 110, Taiwan
Tel.: (886) 227481076
Web Site: http://www.dywidag-systems.com
Post-Tensioning Systems Mfr
N.A.I.C.S.: 238120

Subsidiary (US):

DYWIDAG-Systems International USA, Inc. (3)
320 Marmon Dr, Bolingbrook, IL 60440-3078
Tel.: (630) 739-1100
Web Site: http://www.dsiamerica.com
Sales Range: $10-24.9 Million
Emp.: 50
Concrete Post-Tensioning System & Construction Material Mfr
N.A.I.C.S.: 238120

Unit (Non-US):

DYWIDAG-Systems International Canada Ltd. - Eastern Division (4)
37 Cardico Dr, Gormley, L0H 1G0, ON, Canada
Tel.: (905) 888-8988
Web Site: http://www.dsicanada.ca
Post-Tensioning Systems Mfr
N.A.I.C.S.: 238120

DYWIDAG-Systems International Canada Ltd. - Western Division (4)
19433 96th Avenue Suite 103, Surrey, V4N 4C4, BC, Canada
Tel.: (604) 888-8818
Web Site: http://www.dsicanada.ca
Emp.: 19
Post-Tensioning Systems Mfr
N.A.I.C.S.: 238120
Don Singer *(Branch Mgr)*

Subsidiary (Domestic):

DYWIDAG-Systems International USA, Inc. - Long Beach (4)
2154 South St, Long Beach, CA 90805
Tel.: (562) 531-6161
Web Site: http://www.dsiamerica.com
Concrete Post-Tensioning System & Construction Material Mfr
N.A.I.C.S.: 238120
Patrick Nolaker *(Grp CEO)*

DYWIDAG-Systems International USA, Inc. - Tucker (4)
5139 S Royal Atlanta Dr, Tucker, GA 30084
Tel.: (770) 491-3790
Web Site: http://www.dywidag-systems.com

TRITON ADVISERS LIMITED

Triton Advisers Limited—(Continued)
Concrete Post-Tensioning Systems & Construction Materials Mfr
N.A.I.C.S.: 238120

DeepOcean Group Holding AS (1)
Karmsundsgt 74, Haugesund, 5504, Norway
Tel.: (47) 52 70 04 00
Web Site: http://www.deepoceangroup.com
Subsea Construction & Engineering Services
N.A.I.C.S.: 541330
Ottar Maeland (COO)

Subsidiary (Domestic):

DeepOcean AS (2)
Karmsundgt 74, 5529, Haugesund, Norway (100%)
Tel.: (47) 52 70 04 00
Web Site: http://www.deepoceangroup.com
Marine Services
N.A.I.C.S.: 488320

Subsidiary (Non-US):

DeepOcean B.V. (2)
Nijverheidskade 2, Den Helder, 1785 AB, Netherlands
Tel.: (31) 223684156
Web Site: http://www.deepoceangroup.com
Construction Engineering Services
N.A.I.C.S.: 541330

DeepOcean Ghana Limited (2)
4th Floor The Grand Oyeeman #9 Airport Commercial Centre, South Liberation Road, Accra, Ghana
Tel.: (233) 303 969 019
Web Site: http://deepoceangroup.com
Construction Engineering Services
N.A.I.C.S.: 541330

DeepOcean Group Holding BV. (2)
Herengracht 433, 1017 BR, Amsterdam, Netherlands
Tel.: (31) 202 625110
Web Site: http://www.deepoceangroup.com
Subsea Construction & Engineering Services
N.A.I.C.S.: 541330

DeepOcean UK Ltd. (2)
29 Abercrombie Court Arnhall Business Park, West Hill, Aberdeen, AB32 6FE, United Kingdom (100%)
Tel.: (44) 1224 568450
Web Site: http://www.deepoceangroup.com
Marine Services
N.A.I.C.S.: 488510

DeepOcean de Mexico S. de R.L. de C.V (2)
Av Paseo del Mar Punta Norte Torre 7 Piso 6, Ciudad del Carmen, 24114, Campeche, Mexico
Tel.: (52) 9381381600
Web Site: http://www.deepoceangroup.com
Construction Engineering Services
N.A.I.C.S.: 541330

ENEXIO Management GmbH (1)
Dorstener Strasse 18-29, 44651, Herne, Germany
Tel.: (49) 234 980 2000
Web Site: http://www.enexio.com
Holding Company; Power Cooling & Water Treatment Equipment Mfr & Whslr
N.A.I.C.S.: 551112
Joseph A. Zwetolitz (Chm-Mgmt Bd)

Subsidiary (Domestic):

ENEXIO Germany GmbH (2)
Dorstener Strasse 18-29, 44654, Herne, Germany
Tel.: (49) 234 980 2611
Web Site: http://www.enexio.com
Cooling Systems & Equipment Mfr & Whslr
N.A.I.C.S.: 333415
Jorg Marzi (Grp CEO & Mng Dir)

Subsidiary (Non-US):

Beijing GEA Energietechnik Co., Ltd. (3)
Unit 2008 Tower 2 Landmark Towers No 8 Dongsanhuan Beilu, Beijing, 100004, China
Tel.: (86) 10 6590 7049
Cooling Systems & Equipment Mfr
N.A.I.C.S.: 333415

EGI Cooling Systems Trading (Beijing) Co. (3)
Unit 716 Tower 2 Londmark Towers No 8 Dongsanhuan Beilu, 100004, Beijing, China
Tel.: (86) 10 6590 7558
Cooling Systems & Equipment Whslr
N.A.I.C.S.: 423730

GEA Power Cooling Technology (China) Ltd. (3)
10 Baihe Road Langfeng Economic & Technical Development Zone, Langfang, 065001, Hebei, China
Tel.: (86) 21 6196 0742
Industrial Air Cooling Equipment Mfr
N.A.I.C.S.: 333415
Tanaka Kiyoshi (Gen Mgr)

GEA Saudi Arabia LLC (3)
Al Salah Tower M-Floor Prince Faisal Bin Fahd Road, Al Khobar, 31952, Saudi Arabia
Tel.: (966) 3 8675754
Cooling Systems & Equipment Whslr
N.A.I.C.S.: 423730

Subsidiary (Non-US):

ENEXIO UK Ltd. (2)
5 Sketty Close Brackmills Industrial Estate, Northampton, NN4 7PL, United Kingdom
Tel.: (44) 845 0039114
Cooling Tower, Water Purification & Wastewater Treatment Component Whslr; Dry Cooling Equipment Whslr
N.A.I.C.S.: 423840

Subsidiary (US):

ENEXIO US LLC (2)
300 Union Blvd Ste 350, Lakewood, CO 80228-1553
Tel.: (303) 987-0123
Web Site: http://www.enexio.com
Power Cooling Equipment Whslr
N.A.I.C.S.: 423730

Subsidiary (Domestic):

ENEXIO Water Technologies GmbH (2)
Dieselweg 5, 48493, Wettringen, Germany
Tel.: (49) 2557 9390 0
Web Site: http://www.enexio.com
Cooling Tower, Water Purification & Wastewater Treatment Component Mfr & Whslr
N.A.I.C.S.: 326199
Mario Dienstbier (CEO)

Subsidiary (Non-US):

ENEXIO Water Technologies Sp. z o.o. (3)
Ul mjr H Dobrzanskiego-Hubala 150, 41-218, Sosnowiec, Poland
Tel.: (48) 32 289 95 90
Web Site: http://www.enexio2h.pl
Cooling Tower, Water Purification & Wastewater Treatment Component Whslr
N.A.I.C.S.: 423840

ENEXIO Water Technologies s.r.o. (3)
Teplicka 22, 407 01, Jilove, Czech Republic
Tel.: (420) 412 545 465
Web Site: http://www.enexio.com
Cooling Tower Water Purification & Wastewater Treatment Component Whslr
N.A.I.C.S.: 423840
Pavla Hronova Hadrbolcova (Mng Dir)

FlaktGroup Holding GmbH (1)
Neue Hofe Herne Bahnhofstrasse 65-71, 44623, Herne, Germany
Tel.: (49) 2323623600
Web Site: https://www.flaktgroup.com
Emp.: 3,600
Holding Company; Energy Efficient Air Technology Solutions
N.A.I.C.S.: 551112
Omer Tuzer (Chief Sls Officer-Turkey & Middle East)

Subsidiary (Non-US):

CS Klimateknik ApS (2)
Orkebyvej 6, 5450, Otterup, Denmark
Tel.: (45) 3888 7070
Web Site: http://www.cs-klimateknik.dk

Air Conditioning, Treatment & Filtration Equipment Whslr
N.A.I.C.S.: 423730
Carsten Schjoldager (Mng Dir)

DencoHappel Austria GmbH (2)
Obeltshamerstrasse 12, 4673, Gaspoltshofen, Austria
Tel.: (43) 7735 8000 0
Web Site: http://www.dencohappel.at
Air Conditioning, Treatment & Filtration Equipment Distr
N.A.I.C.S.: 423730
Walter Stumpfl (Head-Customer Svc)

DencoHappel Baltics UAB (2)
Vingriu Str 13-40, 01141, Vilnius, Lithuania
Tel.: (370) 5 210 6060
Air Conditioning, Treatment & Filtration Equipment Distr
N.A.I.C.S.: 423730
Kastytis Sviderskis (Mgr)

DencoHappel Belgium N.V. (2)
Dobbelenbergstraat 7, 1130, Brussels, Belgium
Tel.: (32) 2 240 61 61
Web Site: http://www.dencohappel.be
Emp.: 43
Air Conditioning, Treatment & Filtration Equipment Distr
N.A.I.C.S.: 423730
Yves Vanpoucke (Mng Dir & Grp Head-Belgium & Luxembourg)

DencoHappel Klima Sanayi A.S. (2)
Barbaros Bulvari Bulvar Apt No 70/8, Balmumcu Besiktas, 34349, Istanbul, Türkiye
Tel.: (90) 212 275 7170
Air Conditioning, Treatment & Filtration Equipment Distr
N.A.I.C.S.: 423730
Zeynep Kose (Mgr-Sls)

DencoHappel Nederland B.V. (2)
Rivium Oostlaan 11, 2909 LL, Capelle aan den IJssel, Netherlands
Tel.: (31) 10 235 06 06
Web Site: http://www.dencohappel.nl
Emp.: 35
Air Conditioning, Treatment & Filtration Equipment Distr
N.A.I.C.S.: 423730
Edwin Izelaar (Mgr-IT)

DencoHappel S.A.S. (2)
1-3 rue des Campanules, ZAC du Mandinet, 77815, Lognes, France
Tel.: (33) 160043355
Web Site: http://www.dencohappel.fr
Air Filter Mfr
N.A.I.C.S.: 333413

DencoHappel UK Limited (2)
Moreton Business Park, Moreton-on-Lugg, Hereford, HR4 8DS, United Kingdom
Tel.: (44) 1432 27 7277
Web Site: http://www.dencohappel.com
Air Conditioning, Treatment & Filtration Equipment Distr
N.A.I.C.S.: 423730
Ian Howard (Controller-Comml & Compliance Officer)

FlaktGroup Deutschland GmbH (2)
Web Site: https://www.flaktgroup.com
Air Conditioning, Treatment & Filtration Equipment Mfr & Distr
N.A.I.C.S.: 333413
Trevor Young (CEO)

Subsidiary (Domestic):

FlaktGroup Wurzen GmbH (2)
Luptitzer Strasse 39, 04808, Wurzen, Germany
Tel.: (49) 3425 982 3980
Air Treatment & Filtration Equipment Mfr & Distr
N.A.I.C.S.: 333413

Subsidiary (Non-US):

FlaktGroup Switzerland AG (2)
18 Ave Louis Casai, 1209, Geneva, Switzerland
Tel.: (41) 432883800
Air Handling Processes, Ventilation & Air Conditioning Products & Services Developer & Mfr
N.A.I.C.S.: 238220

INTERNATIONAL PUBLIC

Subsidiary (Non-US):

Flakt OU (3)
Parnu mnt 105, 11313, Tallinn, Estonia
Tel.: (372) 506 6251
Air Conditioning Equipment Installation Services
N.A.I.C.S.: 238220

Flakt Woods (Ireland) Ltd (3)
Unit 1 Broomhill Business Park, Tallaght, Dublin, Ireland
Tel.: (353) 1 463 4600
Air Conditioning Equipment Installation Services
N.A.I.C.S.: 238220

Flakt Woods (L.L.C.) (3)
Office #2206 22nd Floor Exchange Tower, Business Bay, Dubai, United Arab Emirates
Tel.: (971) 4 421 7909
Air Conditioning Equipment Installation Services
N.A.I.C.S.: 238220
Mazin Ghannam (Mng Dir-Middle East Reg)

Flakt Woods AS (3)
Odalsgata 25, 2003, Lillestrom, Norway
Tel.: (47) 22 07 45 50
Air Conditioning Equipment Whslr
N.A.I.C.S.: 423730

Flakt Woods GmbH (3)
Schorbachstrasse 9, 35510, Butzbach, Germany
Tel.: (49) 6033 7 46 26 0
Air Conditioning Equipment Whslr
N.A.I.C.S.: 423730

Flakt Woods Ltd. (3)
Axial Way, Colchester, CO4 5ZD, United Kingdom
Tel.: (44) 1206222555
Web Site: https://www.woodsairmovement.com
Ventilation Equipment Mfr
N.A.I.C.S.: 333912

Flakt Woods Oy (3)
Rydonnotko 1, 20360, Turku, Finland
Tel.: (358) 20 442 3000
Air Conditioning Equipment Whslr
N.A.I.C.S.: 423730

Flakt Woods SAS (3)
4 Avenue Laurent Cely, 92600, Asnieres-sur-Seine, France
Tel.: (33) 1 80 21 07 00
Air Conditioning Equipment Whslr
N.A.I.C.S.: 423730

FlaktGroup Baltics UAB (3)
Olimpieciu Strasse 3E-117, 09235, Vilnius, Lithuania
Tel.: (370) 5 210 6061
Air Conditioning Equipment Whslr
N.A.I.C.S.: 423730
Vitalija Inte (Project Mgr)

FlaktGroup India Private Limited (3)
3B Ecotech-II Udyog Vihar, Greater Noida Dist GB Nagar, Noida, 201306, India
Tel.: (91) 120 498 2050
Air Conditioning Equipment Whslr
N.A.I.C.S.: 423730

FlaktGroup Italy SpA (3)
Viale della Repubblica 81/A, 20835, Muggio, MB, Italy
Tel.: (39) 039 936 0270
Air Conditioning Equipment Whslr
N.A.I.C.S.: 423730

FlaktGroup Poland Sp. z o.o. (3)
Ul Posag 7 Panien 1, 02-495, Warsaw, Poland
Tel.: (48) 22 392 43 43
Air Conditioning Equipment Installation Services
N.A.I.C.S.: 238220
Michal Kwiatkowski (Mgr-Global Product-Comml HVAC Air Diffusers)

FlaktGroup Singapore Pte. Ltd. (3)
178 Clemenceau Avenue 05-01 Haw Par Glass Tower, Singapore, 239926, Singapore
Tel.: (65) 6854 6060
Air Conditioning Equipment Installation Services
N.A.I.C.S.: 238220

AND PRIVATE COMPANIES

FlaktGroup Sweden AB (3)
Flaktgatan 1, 551 84, Jonkoping, Sweden
Tel.: (46) 771 26 26 26
Air Conditioning Equipment Installation Services
N.A.I.C.S.: 238220

Flaktgroup Latvija SIA (3)
Dommo Business Park B Entrance, 2127, Olaine, Latvia
Tel.: (371) 6780 7733
Air Conditioning Equipment Whslr
N.A.I.C.S.: 423730

Subsidiary (Non-US):

TOV GEA-Ukrayina (2)
Pavlivska Str 29, 01135, Kiev, Ukraine
Tel.: (380) 44 461 9356
Air Conditioning, Treatment & Filtration Equipment Distr
N.A.I.C.S.: 423730
Ievgen Davydenko *(Mng Dir)*

Glamox AS (1)
Hoffsveien 1C, N-0275, Oslo, Norway (76.16%)
Tel.: (47) 22021100
Web Site: http://www.glamox.com
Rev.: $317,642,574
Assets: $189,889,959
Liabilities: $109,877,016
Net Worth: $80,012,943
Earnings: $24,360,497
Emp.: 1,300
Fiscal Year-end: 12/31/2018
Land Based, Marine & Offshore Lighting Solutions Mfr
N.A.I.C.S.: 335132
Thomas Lindberg *(CFO & Sr VP)*

Subsidiary (Non-US):

AS Glamox HE (2)
Keki 2, 76606, Keila, Estonia (100%)
Tel.: (372) 671 2300
Web Site: http://www.glamox.ee
Lighting Product Mfr & Distr
N.A.I.C.S.: 335139
Valdo Ruul *(Dir-Sls)*

ES-SYSTEM S.A. (2)
Ul Przemyslowa 2, 30-701, Krakow, Poland
Tel.: (48) 126563633
Web Site: http://www.essystem.pl
Lighting Equipment Mfr
N.A.I.C.S.: 335131

Subsidiary (Domestic):

ES-SYSTEM NT Sp. z o.o. (3)
ul Jagiellonska 51, 32-410, Dobczyce, Poland
Tel.: (48) 12 397 89 00
Lighting Equipment Mfr
N.A.I.C.S.: 335139

ES-SYSTEM Rzeszow sp. z o.o. (3)
Spichlerzowa 42, Rzeszow, 35-322, Subcarpathia, Poland
Tel.: (48) 178508230
Sales Range: $25-49.9 Million
Emp.: 76
Lighting Equipment Mfr
N.A.I.C.S.: 335131
Jerzy Dyrda *(Pres)*

Division (Domestic):

ES-SYSTEM S.A. - Gdansk Division (3)
ul Biala 1, 80-435, Gdansk, Poland
Tel.: (48) 58 345 23 45
Lighting Equipment Mfr
N.A.I.C.S.: 335139

ES-SYSTEM S.A. - Krakow Centrala Division (3)
ul Przemyslowa 2, 30-701, Krakow, Poland
Tel.: (48) 12 656 36 33
Lighting Equipment Mfr
N.A.I.C.S.: 335139

ES-SYSTEM S.A. - Lodz Division (3)
ul Legionow 93/95, 91-072, Lodz, Poland
Tel.: (48) 42 633 60 13
Lighting Equipment Mfr
N.A.I.C.S.: 335139

ES-SYSTEM S.A. - Mazury Division (3)
ul Olsztynska 2, 11-500, Gizycko, Poland
Tel.: (48) 87 429 96 30
Lighting Equipment Mfr
N.A.I.C.S.: 335139

ES-SYSTEM S.A. - Poznan Division (3)
ul Niezlomnych 1a, 61-894, Poznan, Poland
Tel.: (48) 61 851 80 89
Lighting Equipment Mfr
N.A.I.C.S.: 335139

ES-SYSTEM S.A. - Slask Division (3)
ul Wincentego Pola 16, 44-100, Gliwice, Poland
Tel.: (48) 32 339 31 56
Lighting Equipment Mfr
N.A.I.C.S.: 335139

ES-SYSTEM S.A. - Warszawa Division (3)
ul Jagiellonska 78, 03-301, Warsaw, Poland
Tel.: (48) 22 334 63 30
Lighting Equipment Mfr
N.A.I.C.S.: 335139

ES-SYSTEM S.A. - Wroclaw Division (3)
ul Kobierzycka 18, 52-315, Wroclaw, Poland
Tel.: (48) 71 782 82 98
Lighting Equipment Mfr
N.A.I.C.S.: 335139

Subsidiary (Non-US):

ES-SYSTEM Scandinavia A.B. (3)
Klarabergsviadukten 92, 111 64, Stockholm, Sweden
Tel.: (46) 858500035
Web Site: http://www.essystem.se
Sales Range: $25-49.9 Million
Emp.: 4
Lighting Equipment Mfr
N.A.I.C.S.: 335139

Subsidiary (Domestic):

ES-SYSTEM Wilkasy sp. z o.o. (3)
Wilkasy Ul Olsztynska 2, Gizycko, 11 500, Poland
Tel.: (48) 874299600
Web Site: http://www.essystem.pl
Sales Range: $100-124.9 Million
Lighting Equipment Mfr
N.A.I.C.S.: 335132
Jozef Mikulski *(Gen Mgr)*

Subsidiary (Non-US):

Glamox (Suzhou) Lighting Co. Ltd (2)
No 228 Tongyuan Road Suzhou Industrial Park, Suzhou, 215006, Yiangsu, China (100%)
Tel.: (86) 512 62 52 21 89
Lighting Product Mfr
N.A.I.C.S.: 335132

Glamox A/S (2)
Spotorno All 8, 2630, Taastrup, Denmark (100%)
Tel.: (45) 70 100 304
Web Site: http://www.glamox.com
Lighting Product Mfr
N.A.I.C.S.: 335132
Henriette Jensen *(Controller)*

Glamox AB (2)
Gardveda, 570 82, Malilla, Sweden (100%)
Tel.: (46) 49 524 99 00
Lighting Product Mfr
N.A.I.C.S.: 335132
Joakim Andersson *(Country Mgr)*

Subsidiary (US):

Glamox Aqua Signal Corporation (2)
1125 Alexander Ct, Cary, IL 60013 (100%)
Tel.: (847) 639-6412
Lighting Product Distr
N.A.I.C.S.: 423610
Greg Gibson *(Mgr-Pur)*

Subsidiary (Non-US):

Glamox Canada Inc. (2)
117 Glencoe Dr, Mount Pearl, A1N 4S7, NL, Canada (100%)
Tel.: (709) 753-2373
Lighting Product Distr
N.A.I.C.S.: 423610

Glamox GmbH (2)
Daimlerring 25, 31135, Hildesheim, Germany (100%)
Tel.: (49) 512 170 600
Web Site: http://glamox.com
Lighting Product Mfr
N.A.I.C.S.: 335132
Thomas Zahl *(Mng Dir)*

Glamox Ireland Ltd. (2)
Unit C12 The Exchange Calmount Park, Ballymount, Dublin, Ireland (100%)
Tel.: (353) 1 4500755
Web Site: http://www.glamox.com
Lighting Product Distr
N.A.I.C.S.: 423610
Donna Kerfoot *(Controller-Fin)*

Glamox Ltd. (2)
Unit 3 Capital Business Park Manor Way, Borehamwood, WD6 1GW, Herts, United Kingdom (100%)
Tel.: (44) 208 9530540
Web Site: http://glamox.com
Lighting Product Mfr
N.A.I.C.S.: 335132
Liz Clarke *(Sls Mgr-Area)*

Glamox Oy (2)
Karhumaenkuja 2, 01530, Vantaa, Finland (100%)
Tel.: (358) 1 0841 0440
Web Site: http://www.glamox.com
Lighting Product Mfr
N.A.I.C.S.: 335132
Jon Backman *(Sls Mgr-Area)*

IFCO Systems N.V. (1)
Evert van de Beekstraat 310, 1118 CX, Schiphol, Netherlands
Tel.: (31) 206541854
Web Site: http://www.ifcosystems.de
Sales Range: $750-799.9 Million
Emp.: 3,849
Logistics Systems; Pallets & Round-Trip Container Pools Mfr
N.A.I.C.S.: 541614
Wolfgang Orgeldinger *(CEO)*

Infratek ASA (1)
Breivollveien 31, 0668, Oslo, Norway
Tel.: (47) 2312 8800
Web Site: http://www.infratekgroup.com
Rev.: $376,001,790
Assets: $205,714,170
Liabilities: $154,435,740
Net Worth: $51,278,430
Earnings: $19,934,940
Emp.: 1,317
Fiscal Year-end: 12/31/2016
Holding Company; Energy, Communication & Railway Infrastructure Construction, Maintenance & Contingency Support Services; Security Systems Services
N.A.I.C.S.: 551112
Lars Bangen *(CEO)*

Subsidiary (Domestic):

Infratek Elsikkerhet AS (2)
Innspurten 15, 0668, Oslo, Norway (100%)
Tel.: (47) 23128850
Web Site: http://www.infratek.no
Electrical Safety Services
N.A.I.C.S.: 238210
Lars Erik Finne *(Mng Dir)*

Subsidiary (Non-US):

Infratek Finland Oy (2)
Muuntotie 5, PL 261, 01531, Vantaa, Finland (100%)
Tel.: (358) 2032 0030
Web Site: http://www.infratek.fi
Sales Range: $25-49.9 Million
Emp.: 129
Energy, Communication & Railway Infrastucture Construction, Maintenance & Contingency Support Services; Security Systems Services
N.A.I.C.S.: 541330

Subsidiary (Domestic):

Infratek Security Finland Oy (3)

TRITON ADVISERS LIMITED

Muuntotie 5, PL 261, 01531, Vantaa, Finland (100%)
Tel.: (358) 2032 0030
Web Site: http://www.infratek.fi
Security System Services
N.A.I.C.S.: 561621

Subsidiary (Domestic):

Infratek Installasjon AS (2)
Breivollveien 31, 0668, Oslo, Norway
Tel.: (47) 21036000
Electrical System Installation Services
N.A.I.C.S.: 238210

Infratek Sikkerhet AS (2)
Breivollveien 31, 0668, Oslo, Norway
Tel.: (47) 2312 8800
Web Site: http://www.infratek.no
Sales Range: $25-49.9 Million
Security System Services
N.A.I.C.S.: 561621
Lars Bangen *(Mng Dir)*

Subsidiary (Non-US):

Infratek Sverige AB (2)
Vastberga Alle 36 B, Hagersten, Stockholm, 12612, Sweden (100%)
Tel.: (46) 771 22 2324
Web Site: http://www.infratek.se
Sales Range: $200-249.9 Million
Emp.: 826
Energy, Communication & Railway Infrastructure Construction, Maintenance & Contingency Support Services
N.A.I.C.S.: 541330

Subsidiary (Domestic):

Veka Entreprenad AB (3)
Falkenbergsvagen 55, 311 50, Falkenberg, Sweden
Tel.: (46) 34657930
Web Site: http://www.vekaentreprenad.se
Sales Range: $1-9.9 Million
Emp.: 30
Buried-Cable Network Infrastructure Services
N.A.I.C.S.: 237130

Kalte Eckert GmbH (1)
Maulbronner Weg 39, 71706, Markgroningen, Germany
Tel.: (49) 714596000
Web Site: http://www.kaelte-eckert.de
Emp.: 100
Air Conditioning Repair Services
N.A.I.C.S.: 238220

Kelvion Holding GmbH (1)
Dorstener Strasse 484, 44809, Bochum, Germany
Tel.: (49) 234 980 0
Web Site: http://www.kelvion.com
Emp.: 7,115
Holding Company; Heat Exchanger Mfr & Whslr
N.A.I.C.S.: 551112
Christoph Hirschmann *(Chief Compliance Officer)*

Subsidiary (Non-US):

GEA Ecoflex China Co., Ltd. (2)
No 218 Lane 1409 Ji Di Road Hua Cao Township, Minhang District, Shanghai, 201107, China
Tel.: (86) 21 6296 0872
Web Site: http://www.kelvion.com
Heat Exchanger Mfr & Whslr
N.A.I.C.S.: 332410
V.T. Lau *(Mng Dir)*

Kelvion AB (2)
Storgatan 28, 392 32, Kalmar, Sweden
Tel.: (46) 10 209 1900
Web Site: http://www.kelvion.com
Plate Heat Exchanger Whslr
N.A.I.C.S.: 423830

Kelvion BVBA (2)
Warandstraat 1, 9240, Zele, Belgium
Tel.: (32) 524 56600
Heat Exchanger Whslr
N.A.I.C.S.: 423830
Peter van Parys *(Gen Mgr)*

Subsidiary (Domestic):

Kelvion Brazed PHE GmbH (2)

TRITON ADVISERS LIMITED

Triton Advisers Limited—(Continued)
Remsaer Strasse 2a, 04603, Nobitz, Germany
Tel.: (49) 3447 55 39 0
Web Site: http://www.kelvion.com
Brazed Plate Heat Exchanger Mfr & Whslr
N.A.I.C.S.: 332410

Subsidiary (Non-US):

Kelvion FZE (2)
AC-03 South Zone 2, PO Box 18097, Jebel Ali Free Zone, Dubai, United Arab Emirates
Tel.: (971) 4 886 2100
Web Site: http://www.kelvion.com
Heat Exchanger Whslr
N.A.I.C.S.: 423730
Niels Bak *(Gen Mgr)*

Subsidiary (Domestic):

Kelvion GmbH (2)
Dorstener Strasse 484, 44809, Bochum, Germany
Tel.: (49) 234 980 1961
Web Site: http://www.kelvion.com
Industrial Heat Exchanger & Air-Cooling Equipment Mfr & Whslr
N.A.I.C.S.: 332410
Manuel Sanchez Bravo *(CEO & Chm-Mgmt Bd)*

Subsidiary (Non-US):

Kelvion Holding B.V. (2)
Nijverheidsweg 6, 4695 RC, Saint Maartensdijk, Netherlands
Tel.: (31) 166665665
Web Site: http://www.kelvion.com
Emp.: 200
Holding Company; Heat Exchanger & Refrigeration Equipment Mfr & Whslr
N.A.I.C.S.: 551112
Hans Traas *(Mgr)*

Subsidiary (Domestic):

Kelvion B.V. (3)
Vlijtstraat 25, 7005 BN, Doetinchem, Netherlands
Tel.: (31) 314 371414
Web Site: http://www.kelvion.com
Sales Range: $25-49.9 Million
Emp.: 60
Cooling Tower Designer, Mfr & Whslr
N.A.I.C.S.: 333415
Harold A. W. Medze *(CEO)*

Kelvion Machine Cooling B.V. (3)
Draaibrugweg 15, 1332 AB, Almere, Netherlands
Tel.: (31) 36 549 23 00
Web Site: http://www.kelvisers.com
Heat Exchanger Mfr
N.A.I.C.S.: 332410
Henk Reijn *(Mgr-Svc Dept)*

Kelvion PHE B.V. (3)
Craenakker 21, 5951 CC, Belfeld, Netherlands
Tel.: (31) 77 4759900
Web Site: http://www.kelvion.com
Plate Heat Exchanger Parts Sales & Services
N.A.I.C.S.: 811310

Kelvion Refrigeration B.V. (3)
Nijverheidsweg 6, 4695 RC, Saint Maartensdijk, Netherlands
Tel.: (31) 166 665 665
Web Site: http://www.kelvion.com
Industrial Air Cooler & Condenser Mfr & Whslr
N.A.I.C.S.: 333415
Hans Traas *(Mng Dir)*

Subsidiary (Non-US):

Kelvion India Pvt. Ltd. (2)
Road No 9, Wagle Indl Estate, Mumbai, 400604, India
Tel.: (91) 22 6193 2700
Web Site: http://www.kelvion.com
Plate Heat Exchanger Mfr & Whslr
N.A.I.C.S.: 332410
Rohidas Gorde *(Gen Mgr)*

Kelvion Intercambiadores Ltda. (2)
Estrada SP 354 Km 43.5 Serra dos Cristais, Caixa Postal 520, Franco da Rocha,
07803-970, Sao Paulo, Brazil
Tel.: (55) 11 4447 8800
Web Site: http://www.kelvion.com
Heat Exchanger Designer, Mfr & Whslr
N.A.I.C.S.: 332410

Kelvion Limited (2)
20 Davis Way Newgate Lane, Fareham, PO14 1AR, Hants, United Kingdom
Tel.: (44) 1329 823344
Web Site: http://www.kelvion.com
Emp.: 300
Heat Exchanger & Air Conditioning Equipment Mfr & Whslr
N.A.I.C.S.: 332410
Mark Knapman *(Dir-Sls & Engrg-Searle Div)*

Division (Domestic):

Kelvion Limited - PHE Systems (3)
Unit 3 Maybrook Business Park, Minworth, Birmingham, B76 1AL, W Midlands, United Kingdom
Tel.: (44) 121 765 5900
Web Site: http://www.kelvion.com
Plate Heat Exchanger Parts Sales & Services
N.A.I.C.S.: 811310

Kelvion Limited - Searle Systems (3)
20 Davis Way Newgate Lane, Fareham, PO14 1AR, Hants, United Kingdom
Tel.: (44) 1329 823344
Web Site: http://www.searle.co.uk
Air Conditioning Equipment Mfr & Distr
N.A.I.C.S.: 333415
Mark Knapman *(Dir-Sls & Engrg)*

Subsidiary (Domestic):

Kelvion Machine Cooling GmbH (2)
Sudstrasse 48, 44625, Herne, Germany
Tel.: (49) 2325 468 801
Web Site: http://www.kelvion.com
Thermotechnical Component & Cooling System Mfr & Whslr
N.A.I.C.S.: 332410
Axel Berger *(Member-Mgmt Bd)*

Subsidiary (Non-US):

Kelvion Mashimpeks LLC (2)
Malaya Pochtovaya str 12, 105082, Moscow, Russia
Tel.: (7) 4952349503
Web Site: http://www.kelvion.com
Plate Heat Exchanger Mfr
N.A.I.C.S.: 332410

Kelvion OU (2)
Moisa Tn 4, 13522, Tallinn, Estonia
Tel.: (372) 6502812
Heat Exchanger Mfr
N.A.I.C.S.: 332410

Subsidiary (Domestic):

Kelvion PHE GmbH (2)
Karl-Schiller-Strasse 1-3, 31157, Sarstedt, Germany
Tel.: (49) 5066 601 0
Web Site: http://www.kelvion.com
Plate Heat Exchanger Mfr & Whslr
N.A.I.C.S.: 332410
Lars Klinkebiel *(Head-Project Mgmt)*

Subsidiary (Non-US):

Kelvion Pte. Ltd. (2)
26 Soon Lee Road, Singapore, 628086, Singapore
Tel.: (65) 66640430
Web Site: http://www.kelvion.com
Emp.: 25
Heat Exchanger Distr
N.A.I.C.S.: 423720

Subsidiary (Domestic):

Kelvion Radiator GmbH (2)
Friedensstrasse 3a, 08491, Netzschkau, Germany
Tel.: (49) 3765 492 0
Web Site: http://www.kelvion.com
Emp.: 165
Energy Modular Radiator & Other Air-Cooled Heat Exchanger Mfr & Whslr
N.A.I.C.S.: 332410
Sven Krausse *(Member-Mgmt Bd)*

Kelvion Refrigeration GmbH (2)
Kuhler Weg 1, 82065, Baierbrunn, Germany
Tel.: (49) 89 744730
Web Site: http://www.kelvion.com
Industrial Air Cooler & Condenser Mfr & Distr
N.A.I.C.S.: 333415
Reinhard Kindler *(Mng Dir & Member-Mgmt Bd)*

Subsidiary (Non-US):

Kelvion S.A.S. (2)
2 Rue de l'Electrolyse, BP 66, ZA des Ateliers Centraux, 62410, Wingles, France
Tel.: (33) 3 2169 8900
Web Site: http://www.kelvion.com
Emp.: 185
Heat Exchanger Mfr & Whslr
N.A.I.C.S.: 332410
Christian Fromentin *(Dir Gen)*

Kelvion S.r.l. (2)
Via G Ferraris 3, 21020, Monvalle, VA, Italy
Tel.: (39) 0332799534
Web Site: http://www.kelvion.com
Emp.: 25
Heat Exchanger Mfr & Whslr
N.A.I.C.S.: 332410
Clius Wyrreas *(Mng Dir)*

Unit (Domestic):

Kelvion S.r.l. - PHE Systems (3)
Via Maria Da Erba Edoari 29/A, 43123, Parma, Italy
Tel.: (39) 0521 247 311
Plate Heat Exchanger Mfr
N.A.I.C.S.: 332410

Subsidiary (Domestic):

Kelvion Safety Heat Exchangers GmbH (2)
Industriestrasse 6, 55569, Monzingen, Germany
Tel.: (49) 6751 93 03 0
Web Site: http://www.kelvion.com
Heat Exchanger Mfr & Whslr
N.A.I.C.S.: 332410
Marwin Christ *(Member-Mgmt Bd)*

Subsidiary (Non-US):

Kelvion Sp. z o.o. (2)
Kobaltowa 2, 45-641, Opole, Poland
Tel.: (48) 77 402 0050
Web Site: http://www.kelvion.com
Heat Exchanger Mfr & Whslr
N.A.I.C.S.: 332410
Monika Blazejewska-Grudniok *(Mng Dir)*

Subsidiary (Domestic):

Kelvion Machine Cooling Sp. z o.o. (3)
ul Sikorskiego 38, 58-160, Swiebodzice, Poland
Tel.: (48) 748500800
Web Site: http://www.kelvion.com
Heat Exchanger Whslr
N.A.I.C.S.: 423730

Subsidiary (Non-US):

Kelvion Thermal Solutions (Pty) Ltd. (2)
Aberdein Street, Roodekop, Germiston, 1401, Gauteng, South Africa
Tel.: (27) 118664000
Web Site: http://www.kelvion.com
Heat Exchanger Mfr & Whslr
N.A.I.C.S.: 332410
Alex Dreyer *(Dir-Sls & Mktg)*

Subsidiary (Domestic):

Kelvion Services (Pty) Ltd. (3)
Aberdein Street, Roodekop, Germiston, 1401, Gauteng, South Africa
Tel.: (27) 11 866 4000
Web Site: http://www.kelvion.com
Heat Exchanger Support Services
N.A.I.C.S.: 811310
Pieter Herbst *(Gen Mgr)*

Subsidiary (Non-US):

Kelvion Thermal Solutions S.A.S. (2)
25 rue du Ranzai, 44300, Nantes, France
Tel.: (33) 2 40 68 24 24
Web Site: http://www.kelvion.com
Heat Exchanger Mfr & Whslr

INTERNATIONAL PUBLIC

N.A.I.C.S.: 332410
Emmanuel Renevot *(Dir Gen)*

Subsidiary (Non-US):

GEA Batignolles Thermal Technologies (Changshu) Co., Ltd. (3)
66 Xin An Jiang Road, Changshu Southeast Development Zone, Changshu, 215504, Jiangsu, China
Tel.: (86) 512 5230 6118
Web Site: http://www.kelvion.com
Air Cooled Heat Exchanger Mfr.
N.A.I.C.S.: 332410
Lawrence Cao *(Project Dir)*

Subsidiary (Domestic):

Kelvion Thermal Services S.A.S. (3)
25 Rue de Ranzai, 44300, Nantes, France
Tel.: (33) 2 72 74 00 93
Web Site: http://www.kelvion.com
Air Cooler & Condenser Technical Support Services
N.A.I.C.S.: 541990
Loic Michaud *(Dir Gen)*

Subsidiary (Non-US):

Kelvion Thermal Solutions W.L.L. (3)
Road L New Salwa Industrial Area, PO Box 23794, Doha, Qatar
Tel.: (974) 4411 4982
Heat Exchanger Mfr
N.A.I.C.S.: 332410

Subsidiary (Non-US):

Kelvion Thermal Solutions S.A.U. (2)
Barrio de San Juan 28, 48140, Igorre, Spain
Tel.: (34) 94 631 50 00
Web Site: http://www.kelvion.com
Heat Exchanger Mfr
N.A.I.C.S.: 332410
Oscar Cubero *(CEO)*

Kelvion s.r.o. (2)
Kostomlatecka 180, 288 26, Nymburk, Czech Republic
Tel.: (420) 325 519 951
Industrial Air Conditioning Equipment Mfr & Whslr
N.A.I.C.S.: 333415
Jozef Kralik *(Plant Mgr)*

Subsidiary (US):

Kelvion, Inc. (2)
100 Gea Dr, York, PA 17406
Web Site: http://us.kelvion.com
Heat Exchanger Equipment Mfr & Whslr
N.A.I.C.S.: 332410
Neil Swift *(Exec VP-North America)*

Division (Domestic):

Kelvion, Inc. - PHE Systems (3)
100 GEA Dr, York, PA 17406
Tel.: (717) 855-0145
Web Site: http://www.kelvion.com
Plate Heat Exchanger Mfr & Distr
N.A.I.C.S.: 332410
Rene Langley *(Office Mgr)*

Kelvion, Inc. - Thermal Solutions (3)
5202 W Channel Rd, Catoosa, OK 74015-3017
Tel.: (918) 266-3060
Web Site: http://www.kelvion.com
Emp.: 245
Air Cooled Heat Exchanger Mfr
N.A.I.C.S.: 332410

LOGSTOR A/S (1)
Danmarksvej 11, DK-9670, Logstor, Denmark (100%)
Tel.: (45) 99661000
Web Site: http://www.logstor.com
Emp.: 1,200
Pre-Insulated Pipe Systems Mfr & Distr
N.A.I.C.S.: 332996
Kim Christensen *(Pres & CEO)*

Subsidiary (Non-US):

Logstor AB (2)
Fridhemsgatan 2, 702 32, Orebro, Sweden (100%)
Tel.: (46) 19208100

AND PRIVATE COMPANIES

Web Site: http://www.logstor.com
Prefabricated Pipe Systems Mfr
N.A.I.C.S.: 332996
Kim Christensen (Pres & CEO)

Leadec Holding BV & Co. KG (1)
Meitnerstrasse 11, 70563, Stuttgart, Germany
Tel.: (49) 711 7841 0
Web Site: http://www.leadec-services.com
Holding Company; Industrial Process & Facility Planning, Engineering & Maintenance Services
N.A.I.C.S.: 551112
Markus Glaser-Gallion (Chm-Mgmt Bd)

Subsidiary (US):

Diversified Automation, Inc. (2)
1914 Stanley Gault Pkwy, Louisville, KY 40223
Tel.: (502) 634-1285
Web Site: http://www.diversified-automation.com
Rev.: $3,100,000
Emp.: 30
Industrial Automation System Solution Services
N.A.I.C.S.: 541330
Anthony Young (Pres)

Subsidiary (Domestic):

Leadec BV & Co. KG (2)
Hauptstrasse 45-47, 85614, Kirchseeon, Germany
Tel.: (49) 8091 520
Geotechnical Engineering Services
N.A.I.C.S.: 541330
Markus Glaser Gallion (CEO)

Subsidiary (US):

Leadec Corp. (2)
9395 Kenwood Rd Ste 200, Cincinnati, OH 45242 (100%)
Tel.: (513) 731-3590
Web Site: http://www.leadec-services.com
Industrial Production, Facility & Supply Chain Services
N.A.I.C.S.: 541990

Subsidiary (Domestic):

Leadec FM BV & Co. KG (2)
Meitnerstrasse 11, 70563, Stuttgart, Germany
Tel.: (49) 711 7841 0
Geotechnical Engineering Services
N.A.I.C.S.: 541330

Subsidiary (Non-US):

Leadec India Pvt. Ltd. (2)
201 & 206 2nd Floor Godrej Millennium 9 Koregaon Park Road, Pune, 411 001, India
Tel.: (91) 2041401000
Web Site: http://www.leadec-services.com
Industrial Production & Supply Chain Services
N.A.I.C.S.: 541990

Leadec Kft. (2)
Csipkegyari ut 2-4, 9025, Gyor, Hungary
Tel.: (36) 96550640
Web Site: http://www.leadec-services.com
Emp.: 728
Industrial Production, Facility & Supply Chain Services
N.A.I.C.S.: 541990
Ferenc Dakai (Mng Dir)

Leadec Limited (2)
Leadec House 2 Academy Drive, Warwick, CV34 6QZ, United Kingdom
Tel.: (44) 1926623550
Web Site: http://www.leadec-services.com
Industrial Production, Facility & Supply Chain Services
N.A.I.C.S.: 541990
Maralyn Kitchingman (Dir-HR)

Leadec Mexico S. de R.L. de C.V. (2)
Bldv Venustiano Carranza 3206, Colonia Jardin, CP 25240, Saltillo, Coahuila, Mexico
Tel.: (52) 8444168687
Web Site: http://www.leadec-services.com
Industrial Production, Facility & Supply Chain Services
N.A.I.C.S.: 541990

Leadec Osterreich GmbH (2)
Betriebspark 21, 4400, Steyr, Austria
Tel.: (43) 725241600
Industrial Production, Facility & Supply Chain Services
N.A.I.C.S.: 541990

Leadec Sp. z o.o. (2)
ul Toszecka 101, 44-100, Gliwice, Poland
Tel.: (48) 323385470
Web Site: http://www.leadec-services.com
Industrial Production, Facility & Supply Chain Services
N.A.I.C.S.: 541990
Przemyslaw Pendrowski (Mng Dir)

Leadec do Brasil Ltda. (2)
Avenida das Nacoes Unidas 22 833 Torre Ibirapuera 17 andar, Unidade 172 Jd Dom Basco, 04757-025, Sao Paulo, SP, Brazil
Tel.: (55) 11 5683 4444
Web Site: http://www.leadec-services.com
Emp.: 2,500
Industrial Production & Facility Services
N.A.I.C.S.: 541990
Joao Ricciarelli (CEO)

Leadec s.r.o. (2)
Debrska 378, 293 06, Kosmonosy, Czech Republic
Tel.: (420) 326733645
Web Site: http://www.leadec-services.com
Electrical Engineering & Automation Services
N.A.I.C.S.: 541990

Leadec s.r.o. (2)
Drobneho 27, 841 02, Bratislava, Slovakia
Tel.: (421) 260103901
Web Site: http://www.leadec-services.com
Industrial Production, Facility & Supply Chain Services
N.A.I.C.S.: 541990

NVS AS (1)
Teglverksvelen 1, 3400, Lier, Norway
Tel.: (47) 32276060
Web Site: http://www.nvs.no
Sales Range: $200-249.9 Million
Emp.: 60
Electronic Component Installation Services
N.A.I.C.S.: 238210
Elisabeth Mattisson (CFO)

Subsidiary (Non-US):

Assemblin Ventilation AB (2)
Stenyxegatan 25A, Box 20034, 200 74, Malmo, Sweden
Tel.: (46) 40 32 48 40
Web Site: http://www.assemblin.com
Heating & Ventilation Equipment Installation Services
N.A.I.C.S.: 238220
Sofia Blom (Branch Mgr)

NVS Installation AB (2)
Singelgatan 12, PO Box 384, SE 201 23, Malmo, Sweden
Tel.: (46) 40287700
Web Site: http://www.nvs.se
Sales Range: $500-549.9 Million
Emp.: 2,300
Heating, Cooling, Fire Protection & Sanitation Equipment Installation Services
N.A.I.C.S.: 238220

Polygon AB (1)
Sveagagen 9 3rd floor, 111 57, Stockholm, Sweden
Tel.: (46) 8 750 33 00
Web Site: http://www.polygongroup.com
Rev.: $68,905,505
Assets: $47,520,969
Liabilities: $39,121,085
Net Worth: $8,399,884
Earnings: $723,589
Emp.: 3,810
Fiscal Year-end: 12/31/2018
Property Damage Restoration Services
N.A.I.C.S.: 236118
Axel Granitz (Pres & CEO)

Subsidiary (Non-US):

Polygon AS (2)
Enebakkveien 307, N 1188, Oslo, Norway (100%)
Tel.: (47) 22 28 31 10
Web Site: http://www.polygongroup.com

Sales Range: $75-99.9 Million
Emp.: 120
Property Damage Restoration Services
N.A.I.C.S.: 236118
Atle Sjursen (CEO)

Subsidiary (US):

Polygon US Corporation (2)
15 Sharpners Pond Rd Bldg F N, Andover, MA 01845
Tel.: (800) 422-6379
Web Site: http://www.polygongroup.us
Temporary Climate Solutions, Document Recovery Services & Emergency Drying Services
N.A.I.C.S.: 561210

Subsidiary (Domestic):

Amrestore Inc. (3)
796 Cromwell Park Dr Ste R, Glen Burnie, MD 21061-2536
Web Site: http://www.amrestore.com
Residential Remodeler
N.A.I.C.S.: 236118

RGS Nordic A/S (1)
Selinevej 4, Copenhagen, 23000, Denmark
Tel.: (45) 88779000
Web Site: http://www.rgsnordic.com
Environmental Services
N.A.I.C.S.: 813312
Mark Holroyd (Sls Mgr)

Scandinavian Business Seating AS (1)
Fridtjof Nansens vei 12, N 0301, Oslo, Norway
Tel.: (47) 22 59 59 00
Web Site: http://www.sbseating.com
Sales Range: $150-199.9 Million
Emp.: 470
Furniture Mfr
N.A.I.C.S.: 337214
Lars Roiri (CEO)

Subsidiary (Non-US):

Flokk Holding AS (2)
Vallgatan 1, Box 294, 571 23, Nassjo, Sweden
Tel.: (46) 380555300
Web Site: https://www.flokk.com
Investment Management Service
N.A.I.C.S.: 523940
Johanna Hedstrom (Country Mgr)

Subsidiary (Domestic):

Flokk AS (3)
Vallgatan 1, Box 294, 571 23, Nassjo, Sweden
Tel.: (46) 380555300
Web Site: https://www.flokk.com
Emp.: 100
Office Furniture Mfr
N.A.I.C.S.: 337214
Berndt Axelson (Gen Mgr)

Subsidiary (Non-US):

Scandinavian Business Seating A/S (2)
Kajakvej 2, 2770, Kastrup, Denmark
Tel.: (45) 99 50 55 00
Web Site: http://www.sbseating.dk
Sales Range: $25-49.9 Million
Emp.: 15
Office Furniture Mfr
N.A.I.C.S.: 337214

Scandinavian Business Seating GmbH (2)
Kaistrasse 6, 40221, Dusseldorf, Germany
Tel.: (49) 2131 1510 0
Web Site: http://www.sbseating.de
Office Furniture Mfr
N.A.I.C.S.: 337214
Rene Sitter (Mng Dir)

Scandinavian Business Seating SARL (2)
Central Parc 1 Allee de Sanglier, 93421, Villepinte, France
Tel.: (33) 1 48 61 99 12
Web Site: http://www.sbseating.fr
Emp.: 7
Office Furniture Mfr
N.A.I.C.S.: 337214

Olgica Pezin (Dir-Sls)

TRITON ADVISERS LIMITED

Stabilus S.A. (1)
2 Rue Albert Borschette, L-1246, Luxembourg, Luxembourg
Tel.: (352) 2867701
Web Site: http://www.stabilus.com
Rev.: $1,341,488,023
Assets: $1,472,905,398
Liabilities: $686,945,579
Net Worth: $785,959,819
Earnings: $114,044,597
Emp.: 7,426
Fiscal Year-end: 09/30/2023
Holding Company
N.A.I.C.S.: 551112
Mark Wilhelms (CFO & Member-Mgmt Bd)

Subsidiary (Non-US):

Stabilus GmbH (2)
Wallersheimer Weg 100, 56070, Koblenz, Germany (100%)
Tel.: (49) 26189000
Web Site: http://www.stabilus.com
Automotive Hydraulics & Door Systems Mfr
N.A.I.C.S.: 336390
Mark Wilhelms (Mng Dir, CFO & Member-Mgmt Bd)

Subsidiary (Domestic):

HAHN Gasfedern GmbH (3)
Waldstrasse 39-43, 73773, Esslingen, Germany
Tel.: (49) 711 936 705 0
Web Site: http://www.hahn-gasfedern.de
Emp.: 250
Stainless Steel Gas Springs Designer, Mfr & Whslr
N.A.I.C.S.: 332613
Michael Demuth (Mng Dir)

Subsidiary (Non-US):

Stabilus (JiangSu) Ltd. (3)
No 8 Long Xiang Road, Wujin High-Tech Industrial Zone, Changzhou, 213164, JiangSu, China
Tel.: (86) 519 8662 3500
Web Site: http://www.stabilus.com
Automotive Hydraulics & Door Systems Mfr
N.A.I.C.S.: 336390

Stabilus Co. Ltd., Korea (3)
1493-1 Song Jeong-dong, GangSeo-gu, Busan, 618-270, Korea (South)
Tel.: (82) 519791500
Web Site: http://www.stabilus.com
Sales Range: $25-49.9 Million
Emp.: 43
Automotive Hydraulics & Door Systems Mfr
N.A.I.C.S.: 336390
Lee Joongho (CEO)

Subsidiary (US):

Stabilus Inc. (3)
1201 Tulip Dr, Gastonia, NC 28052-1898 (100%)
Tel.: (704) 865-7444
Web Site: http://www.stabilus.com
Automobile Parts Mfr
N.A.I.C.S.: 336390
Tom Napoli (VP-North American Ops)

Subsidiary (Domestic):

ACE Controls, Inc. (4)
23435 Industrial Park Dr, Farmington Hills, MI 48335 (100%)
Tel.: (248) 476-0213
Web Site: http://www.acecontrols.com
Fluid Power Cylinders & Actuators Mfr
N.A.I.C.S.: 333995
Keith Szukalowski (VP-Global Ops)

Unit (Non-US):

ACE Controls International - UK (5)
Unit 404 Easter Park, Haydock, WA11 9TH, United Kingdom
Tel.: (44) 1942727440
Web Site: http://www.acecontrols.co.uk
Automation & Motion Control Equipment Mfr
N.A.I.C.S.: 335314

Subsidiary (Non-US):

ACE Controls Japan, LLC (5)
224-0037 Chigasaki-Minami Japan City

TRITON ADVISERS LIMITED

Triton Advisers Limited—(Continued)
Center Building 2F, Tsuzuki-ku, Yokohama, 224-0037, Japan **(100%)**
Tel.: (81) 459450123
Web Site: http://www.acecontrols.co.jp
Automation & Motion Control Equipment Mfr
N.A.I.C.S.: 335314

Subsidiary (Domestic):

Fabreeka International Holdings, Inc. **(4)**
1023 Tpke St, Stoughton, MA 02072 **(100%)**
Tel.: (781) 341-3655
Web Site: http://www.fabreeka.com
Holding Company; Vibration-Isolation & Shock-Control Products Mfr & Distr
N.A.I.C.S.: 551112
David Meyer *(Gen Mgr)*

Subsidiary (Domestic):

Fabreeka International, Inc. **(5)**
1023 Tpke St, Stoughton, MA 02072 **(100%)**
Tel.: (781) 341-3655
Web Site: http://www.fabreeka.com
Vibration-Isolation & Shock-Control Products Mfr & Distr
N.A.I.C.S.: 326291

Subsidiary (Non-US):

Stabilus Japan Corporation **(3)**
Toshin 24 Kasa Bldg 8, 2-3-8 Shin-Yokohama Kohoku-ku, 222-0033, Yokohama, Japan
Tel.: (81) 454712970
Web Site: http://www.stabilus.co.jp
Automotive Hydraulics & Door Systems Mfr
N.A.I.C.S.: 336390
Hinck Michael *(Pres)*

Stabilus Ltd. **(3)**
Unit 4 Canada Close, Canada Close, Banbury, OX16 2RT, Oxon, United Kingdom
Tel.: (44) 1295700100
Web Site: http://www.stabilus.com
Sales Range: $25-49.9 Million
Emp.: 5
Gas Springs & Vibration Dampers
N.A.I.C.S.: 336390
Brian Ayliff *(Gen Mgr)*

Stabilus Ltda. **(3)**
Av Pres Tancredo, de Almeida Neves 1-2, 37 504 066, Itajuba, Brazil
Tel.: (55) 3536295000
Web Site: http://www.stabilus.com
Automotive Hydraulics & Door Systems Mfr
N.A.I.C.S.: 336390

Stabilus Pty. Ltd. **(3)**
65 Redwood Drive, Dingley, 3172, VIC, Australia
Tel.: (61) 395521400
Web Site: http://www.stabilus.com.au
Sales Range: $25-49.9 Million
Emp.: 35
Automotive Hydraulics & Door Systems Mfr
N.A.I.C.S.: 336390
Ruben Moses *(Mng Dir)*

Stabilus S. R. L. Romania **(3)**
5-900 Soseaua Brasov-Harman, 507190, Brasov, Romania
Tel.: (40) 372384100
Web Site: http://www.stabilus.com
Sales Range: $100-124.9 Million
Emp.: 800
Automotive Hydraulics & Door Systems Mfr
N.A.I.C.S.: 336390

Stabilus S.r.l. **(3)**
Via Nationale 209, 10069, Villar Perosa, Italy
Tel.: (39) 0121 316 711
Sales Range: $25-49.9 Million
Emp.: 85
Automotive Hydraulics & Door Systems Mfr
N.A.I.C.S.: 336390

Stabilus, S.A. de C.V. **(3)**
Industria Metalurgica No 1010, Parque Industrial Ramos Arizpe, 25900, Ramos Arizpe, Mexico
Tel.: (52) 844 411 0707
Web Site: http://www.stabilus.com
Automotive Hydraulics & Door Systems Mfr

N.A.I.C.S.: 336390

TALIS Management Holding GmbH **(1)**
Senefelder Strasse 2-3, 63110, Rodgau, Germany
Tel.: (49) 6106 6998 0
Web Site: http://www.talis-group.com
Sales Range: $350-399.9 Million
Emp.: 1,500
Holding Company
N.A.I.C.S.: 551112
Ansgar Nonn *(CEO)*

Subsidiary (Non-US):

Atlantic Plastics Ltd. **(2)**
Brackla Industrial Estate, Bridgend, CF31 2AX, United Kingdom
Tel.: (44) 1675 437 900
Emp.: 150
Mfr & Supplier of Valves & Fittings
N.A.I.C.S.: 332911
Mark Hodgens *(Mng Dir)*

Unit (Domestic):

Edward Barber & Company Limited **(3)**
Edison Road Hams Hall Distribution Park, Coleshill, Birmingham, B46 1AB, United Kingdom **(100%)**
Tel.: (44) 1675 437 900
Sales Range: $25-49.9 Million
Emp.: 22
Flow Control Products Mfr
N.A.I.C.S.: 332912
Saul Godfrey *(Mng Dir)*

Subsidiary (Non-US):

Bayard **(2)**
ZI 4 avenue Lionel Terray, BP 47, Meyzieu, 69881, France
Tel.: (33) 4 37 44 24 24
Web Site: http://www.bayard.fr
Valves, Fire Hydrants, Pipe Connections & Other Fluid Control Products Mfr
N.A.I.C.S.: 332912

Belgicast Internacional, S.L. **(2)**
B Zabalondo 31, Munguia, 48100, Bizkaia, Spain
Tel.: (34) 94 488 91 00
Web Site: http://www.belgicast.eu
Emp.: 140
Valves, Flanges, Couplings & Other Water Related Piping Products Mfr
N.A.I.C.S.: 332911
Ignacio Ispizua *(Gen Mgr)*

Subsidiary (Non-US):

Belgicast Italia, S.R.L. **(3)**
Via Lambro 7/7, Peschiera Borromeo, 20068, Milan, Italy
Tel.: (39) 02 55 30 11 90
Web Site: http://www.talis-group.com
Valve Mfr
N.A.I.C.S.: 332911

Subsidiary (Non-US):

INDUSTRA - Comercio de Equipamentos Industriais, S.A. **(2)**
5 Centro Empr Sintra-Estoril Bloco A4, Estrada de Albarraque Linho, 2710 297, Sintra, Portugal
Tel.: (351) 219109500
Valves & Pipe Fittings Sales & Service
N.A.I.C.S.: 423830

LLC TALIS **(2)**
Prishvina Str 8 Korpus 2, 127549, Moscow, Russia
Tel.: (7) 4 95 64 63 49 5
Web Site: http://www.talis-group.com
Emp.: 4
Technical Consulting & Business Development for TALIS Equipment
N.A.I.C.S.: 541690
Svetlana Zaytseva *(Mng Dir)*

Raphael Valves Industries Ltd. **(2)**
Northern Industrial Zone, PO Box 555, Or Akiva, 30600, Israel
Tel.: (972) 4 6263555
Web Site: http://www.raphael-valves.com
Valves Mfr & Distr
N.A.I.C.S.: 332911
Arnon Klein *(Gen Mgr)*

Subsidiary (Domestic):

TALIS Deutschland GmbH & Co. KG **(2)**
Meeboldstrasse 22, Heidenheim, 89518, Germany
Tel.: (49) 73 21 320 0
Web Site: http://www.talis-deutschland.com
Emp.: 250
Holding Company
N.A.I.C.S.: 551112
Serge Bertrand *(Mng Dir)*

Subsidiary (Domestic):

Erhard GmbH & Co. KG **(3)**
Meeboldstrasse 22, 89522, Heidenheim, Germany
Tel.: (49) 7321 320 0
Web Site: http://www.erhard.de
Water Valves Mfr
N.A.I.C.S.: 332911

Ludwig Frischhut GmbH & Co. KG **(3)**
Franz Stelzenberger Strasse 9-17, Pfarrkirchen, 84347, Germany
Tel.: (49) 85 61 3008 0
Web Site: http://www.frischhut.de
Mfr of Fittings for Supply of Potable Water
N.A.I.C.S.: 332919
Rainer Inkoferer *(Mng Dir)*

Schmieding Armaturen GmbH **(3)**
Friedrich-Ebert-Str 58, 59425, Unna, Germany
Tel.: (49) 2303936110
Web Site: http://www.schmieding.de
Valves for Municipal Gas & Water Supply Mfr
N.A.I.C.S.: 332911

Strate Technologie fur Abwasser GmbH **(3)**
Im Kirchenfelde 9, D 31157, Sarstedt, Germany
Tel.: (49) 50 66 988 0
Web Site: http://www.strate.com
Sewage Pumping Systems Mfr
N.A.I.C.S.: 333248

Subsidiary (Non-US):

TALIS Polska Sp. z.o.o. **(2)**
ul Plebiscytowa 3, Swietochlowice, 41-600, Poland
Tel.: (48) 32 770 50 00
Web Site: http://www.talis.com.pl
Emp.: 62
Mfr & Marketer of Valves for Water Supply & Disposal & Gas Supply
N.A.I.C.S.: 332912
Stanislawa Sztaba *(Mgr-Acctg)*

Uni Joint B.V. **(2)**
Rozenobel 15, Beringe, 5986, Netherlands
Tel.: (31) 77 3078200
Web Site: http://www.talis-benelux.com
Steel Couplings, Flange Adapters & Dismantling Joints Mfr
N.A.I.C.S.: 332911

Triton Advisers (Shanghai) Co. Ltd **(1)**
W18 22/F Tower 3 1228 Yan An Zhong Road, Jing An Kerry Center, Shanghai, 200040, China
Tel.: (86) 21 60627278
Industrial Business Services
N.A.I.C.S.: 561110

Triton Advisers (Sweden) AB **(1)**
Kungstradgardsgatan 20 7th Floor, 111 47, Stockholm, Sweden
Tel.: (46) 8 5055 9600
Web Site: http://www.triton-partners.com
Emp.: 40
Privater Equity Firm
N.A.I.C.S.: 523999

Triton Advisers (UK) Ltd. **(1)**
9 South Street 3rd Floor, London, W1K 2XA, United Kingdom
Tel.: (44) 207 297 6150
Privater Equity Firm
N.A.I.C.S.: 523999
Bjorn Nilsson *(Partner)*

Triton Advisers S.a.r.l. **(1)**
26-28 rue Edward Steichen, 2540, Luxem-

INTERNATIONAL PUBLIC

bourg, Luxembourg
Tel.: (352) 26 753 0
Web Site: http://www.triton-partners.com
Privater Equity Firm
N.A.I.C.S.: 523999

Triton Beteiligungsberatung GmbH **(1)**
Schillerstrasse 20, 60313, Frankfurt, Germany
Tel.: (49) 69 92102 0
Web Site: http://www.triton-partners.com
Sales Range: $50-74.9 Million
Privater Equity Firm
N.A.I.C.S.: 523999

Triton Investment Management Limited **(1)**
Charter Place 1st Floor 23-27 Seaton Place, Saint Helier, JE2 3QL, Jersey
Tel.: (44) 1534 709 400
Web Site: http://www.triton-partners.com
Investment Fund Management Services
N.A.I.C.S.: 523940
Mats Eklund *(CFO & COO)*

Subsidiary (Non-US):

Bormioli Pharma S.p.A. **(2)**
Via Torrente Bratica, Parma, 43124, Italy
Tel.: (39) 0521362620
Plastic & Glass Primary Packaging Materials Mfr
N.A.I.C.S.: 326160
Andrea Lodetti *(CEO)*

Subsidiary (Non-US):

Remy & Geiser GmbH **(3)**
Remy and Geiser Strasse 1 OT Hinternah, 98553, Schleusingen, Germany
Tel.: (49) 2639 9311 0
Web Site: http://www.remy-geiser.com
Plastic Glass & Elastomer Packaging Product Mfr
N.A.I.C.S.: 326199
Christoph Hanschke *(CEO)*

Subsidiary (Non-US):

Caverion Oyj **(2)**
Torpantie 2, 01650, Vantaa, Finland
Tel.: (358) 104071
Web Site: http://www.caverion.com
Rev: $2,631,258,552
Assets: $1,621,276,800
Liabilities: $1,373,909,264
Net Worth: $247,367,536
Earnings: $30,828,824
Emp.: 14,298
Fiscal Year-end: 12/31/2021
Building Systems Design, Construction & Maintenance Services
N.A.I.C.S.: 238990
Sakari Toikkanen *(Member-Mgmt Bd & Head-Div-Industrial Solutions)*

Subsidiary (Non-US):

Caverion Asia Pte. Ltd. **(3)**
20 Science Park Rd No 02-27 Teletech Park, Singapore, 117674, Singapore
Tel.: (65) 67782093
Web Site: http://www.caverion.com
Sales Range: $25-49.9 Million
Emp.: 15
Building Systems Design, Construction & Maintenance Services
N.A.I.C.S.: 238990

Caverion Central Europe GmbH **(3)**
Riesstr 25, Munich, 80992, Germany
Tel.: (49) 89374288500
Emp.: 15
Construction Engineering Services
N.A.I.C.S.: 541330
Karl-Walter Schuster *(Gen Mgr)*

Subsidiary (Non-US):

Caverion Industria Sverige AB **(4)**
Armegatan 40, 171 71, Solna, Sweden
Tel.: (46) 8 7053200
Emp.: 500
Construction Engineering Services
N.A.I.C.S.: 541330
Henrik Gyllenhammar *(CEO)*

Caverion Osterreich GmbH **(4)**
Bergerbrauhofstr 33, 5020, Salzburg, Austria

AND PRIVATE COMPANIES — TRITON HOLDING PUBLIC COMPANY LIMITED

Tel.: (43) 5 0606 3609
Construction Engineering Services
N.A.I.C.S.: 541330

SC Caverion Building Services S.R.L. (4)
Str Sibiului 2 Selimbar, Sibiu, Romania
Tel.: (40) 746055771
Construction Engineering Services
N.A.I.C.S.: 541330

Subsidiary (Non-US):

Caverion Danmark A/S (3)
Vejlevej 123, 7000, Fredericia, Denmark
Tel.: (45) 7623 2323
Web Site: http://www.caverion.dk
Emp.: 1,000
Industrial Building Construction & Maintenance Services
N.A.I.C.S.: 236210
Knut Gaaserud (Exec VP-Norway)

Caverion Deutschland GmbH (3)
Gstocketwiesenstrasse 9, Deggendorf, 94469, Germany
Tel.: (49) 89 374288 500
Web Site: http://www.yit.de
Sales Range: $75-99.9 Million
Emp.: 500
Facility Management, Construction & Industrial Services
N.A.I.C.S.: 561210

Caverion Eesti AS (3)
Madara 27, 10612, Tallinn, Estonia
Tel.: (372) 641 3115
Web Site: http://www.caverion.ee
Emp.: 60
Construction Engineering Services
N.A.I.C.S.: 541330

Caverion Latvija SIA (3)
Zane Dancauska Deju 4, 1004, Riga, Latvia
Tel.: (371) 67408630
Web Site: http://www.caverion.lv
Industrial Building Construction & Maintenance Services
N.A.I.C.S.: 236210
Aleksandrs Petruss (Dir)

Caverion Norge AS (3)
Ole Deviks vei 10, 0666, Oslo, Norway
Tel.: (47) 22 87 40 00
Web Site: http://www.caverion.no
Industrial Building Construction & Maintenance Services
N.A.I.C.S.: 236210

Caverion Sverige AB (3)
Lindhagensgatan 126, 112 51, Stockholm, Sweden (100%)
Tel.: (46) 87053200
Web Site: http://www.caverion.se
Construction Engineering Services
N.A.I.C.S.: 541330
Class Tocklin (VP, Head-Managed Svcs & Reg Mgr-Svc)

MISAB Sprinkler & VVS AB (3)
Skruvvagen 6, 451 75, Uddevalla, Sweden
Tel.: (46) 522 65 32 50
Web Site: http://www.misabsprinkler.se
Sprinkler System Installation Services
N.A.I.C.S.: 238220

Subsidiary (Domestic):

Maintpartner Group Oy (3)
Ahventie 4 B, Espoo, 2170, Finland
Tel.: (358) 923115000
Web Site: http://www.maintpartner.com
Sales Range: $200-249.9 Million
Emp.: 200
Industrial Maintenance & Operation Services
N.A.I.C.S.: 213112

Subsidiary (Non-US):

Maintpartner ASI Sp. z o.o. (4)
ul Jana Galla 29A, 41-800, Zabrze, Poland
Tel.: (48) 322313265
Web Site: http://www.maintpartner.com
Sales Range: $1-9.9 Million
Emp.: 300
Electrical Equipments Maintenance & Services
N.A.I.C.S.: 238210

Subsidiary (Non-US):

OOO Caverion Elmek (3)
5th Donskoy Proezd Building 15, 119991, Moscow, Russia (100%)
Tel.: (7) 495 955 5505
Web Site: http://www.caverion.ru
Industrial Building Construction Services
N.A.I.C.S.: 236220
Ekaterina Lipatnikova (Head-Procurement Dept)

Porreal GmbH (3)
Lehrbachgasse 2, 1120, Vienna, Austria
Tel.: (43) 506266538
Web Site: http://www.porreal.com
Emp.: 380
Real Estate Services
N.A.I.C.S.: 531390
Eva Cabela (Chm)

UAB Caverion Lietuva (3)
Skersines g 9, 08449, Vilnius, Lithuania
Tel.: (370) 52738200
Web Site: http://www.caverion.lt
Industrial Building Construction & Maintenance Services
N.A.I.C.S.: 236210
Giedre Surviliene (Mgr-Sls)

Subsidiary (Non-US):

Clinigen Group plc (2)
Pitcairn House Crown Square First Ave, Burton-on-Trent, DE14 2WW, Staffordshire, United Kingdom
Tel.: (44) 1283495010
Web Site: http://www.clinigengroup.com
Rev.: $710,902,192
Assets: $1,446,786,432
Liabilities: $839,885,592
Net Worth: $606,900,840
Earnings: $41,138,916
Emp.: 1,013
Fiscal Year-end: 06/30/2021
Pharmaceutical Mfr & Distr
N.A.I.C.S.: 325412
Shaun Chilton (CEO)

RENK Aktiengesellschaft (2)
Goegginger Strasse 73, 86159, Augsburg, Germany (100%)
Tel.: (49) 8215700681
Web Site: http://www.renk.eu
Vehicle Transmissions, Control & Testing Systems Mfr
N.A.I.C.S.: 336350

Subsidiary (US):

RENK Systems Corporation (3)
8880 Union Mills Dr, Camby, IN 46113-9705
Tel.: (317) 455-1367
Web Site: http://www.renksystems.com
Automotive, Truck, Helicopter, Railway & Power Industries Test Systems Whslr & Distr
N.A.I.C.S.: 423830

Subsidiary (Non-US):

Royal Reesink B.V. (2)
Ecofactorij 20, NL-7325 WC, Apeldoorn, Netherlands
Tel.: (31) 575 599 300
Web Site: http://www.reesink.com
Industrial Machinery & Equipment Merchant Whslr
N.A.I.C.S.: 423830
Gerrit Van Der Scheer (CEO)

Unica Groep B.V. (1)
De Wel 15, 3871 MT, Hoevelaken, Netherlands
Tel.: (31) 33 247 8080
Web Site: http://www.unica.nl
Holding Company; Technical Services
N.A.I.C.S.: 551112
Bert Moser (CFO & Member-Mgmt Bd)

Subsidiary (Domestic):

Nsecure B.V. (2)
Lubeck 1, 2993 LK, Barendrecht, Netherlands
Tel.: (31) 0881239000
Web Site: http://www.nsecure.nl
Protection & Security Services
N.A.I.C.S.: 561612
Hans Driel (Mng Dir)

Unica Energy Solutions B.V. (2)
De Wel 15, 3871 MT, Hoevelaken, Netherlands
Tel.: (31) 33 247 8080
Energy Industry Technical Services
N.A.I.C.S.: 541990
Arjen Leenhouts (CEO)

Subsidiary (Domestic):

Hellemans Consultancy B.V. (3)
De Beek 18-b, 3871 MS, Hoevelaken, Netherlands
Tel.: (31) 30 2255011
Web Site: http://www.hellemansconsultancy.nl
Energy Management & Procurement Services
N.A.I.C.S.: 541990
Arjen Leenhouts (CEO)

Subsidiary (Domestic):

Unica Industry Solutions B.V. (2)
De Wel 15, 3871 MT, Hoevelaken, Netherlands
Tel.: (31) 33 247 8080
Web Site: http://www.unica.nl
Industrial Technical Services
N.A.I.C.S.: 541990
Arjen Bos (Mng Dir)

Unica Installatietechniek B.V. (2)
De Wel 15, 3871 MT, Hoevelaken, Netherlands
Tel.: (31) 33 247 8080
Web Site: http://www.unica.nl
Technical Services
N.A.I.C.S.: 541990
Herbert Rabelink (Mng Dir)

Werner Co. (1)
93 Werner Rd, Greenville, PA 16125-9434
Tel.: (724) 588-8600
Web Site: http://www.wernerco.com
Aluminum Climbing Equipment, Fall Protection Products, Racks & Ramps Mfr
N.A.I.C.S.: 331318
Bob Zierk (Exec VP-HR-Global)

Unit (Non-US):

Bailey Ladders (2)
PO Box 197, Browns Plains, Logan, 4118, QLD, Australia
Tel.: (61) 1300760717
Web Site: http://baileyladders.com.au
Aluminum Ladder Mfr & Distr
N.A.I.C.S.: 331318

Unit (Domestic):

Green Bull (2)
11225 Bluegrass Pkwy, Louisville, KY 40299-2319
Tel.: (888) 523-3371
Web Site: http://www.greenbullladder.com
Wood, Aluminum & Fiberglass Ladders Mfr
N.A.I.C.S.: 332999

Subsidiary (Domestic):

Knaack LLC (2)
420 E Terra Cotta Ave, Crystal Lake, IL 60014-3611 (100%)
Tel.: (815) 459-6020
Web Site: http://www.knaack.com
Jobsite Storage Equipment, Including Storage Chests, Workstations, Rolling Workbenches & Hand Tool Boxes Mfr
N.A.I.C.S.: 332999

Subsidiary (Non-US):

ZARGES GmbH (2)
Zargesstrasse 7, PO Box 1630, 82362, Weilheim, Germany
Tel.: (49) 881 687 0
Web Site: http://www.zarges.com
Sales Range: $125-149.9 Million
Emp.: 800
Aluminum Products Mfr & Whslr
N.A.I.C.S.: 331318
Tom Kaiser (Mng Dir)

Subsidiary (US):

ZARGES Inc. (3)
1440 Center Park Dr, Charlotte, NC 28217
Tel.: (704) 357-6285
Web Site: http://www.zargescases.com

Aluminum Products Whslr
N.A.I.C.S.: 423990
Tracy Johnson (Natl Mgr-Sls & Mktg)

TRITON CONSTRUCTION LIMITED
Hare Park Mills Hare Park Lane, Hightown, Liversedge, WF15 8EP, W Yorkshire, United Kingdom
Tel.: (44) 1274 874772
Web Site: http://www.tritonconstruction.co.uk
Sales Range: $10-24.9 Million
Emp.: 30
General Contractors
N.A.I.C.S.: 236220
Michael J. Parkinson (Mng Dir)

TRITON CORP. LTD.
R-4 First Floor Khirki Extention Main Raod, Malviya Nagar, New Delhi, 110 017, India
Tel.: (91) 1149096562
Web Site: https://ww.tritoncorp.in
Year Founded: 1990
Rev.: $1,162
Assets: $1,465,548
Liabilities: $823,475
Net Worth: $642,074
Earnings: ($1,441,270)
Fiscal Year-end: 03/31/19
Information Technology & IT Enabled Services
N.A.I.C.S.: 541519
Sheetal Jain (Exec Dir)

TRITON DEVELOPMENT S.A.
ul Krolowej Aldony 21, 03-928, Warsaw, Poland
Tel.: (48) 223936220
Web Site: https://www.tritondevelopment.pl
Year Founded: 1992
TRI—(WAR)
Rev.: $3,842,226
Assets: $33,338,923
Liabilities: $12,843,242
Net Worth: $20,495,681
Earnings: ($1,081,555)
Fiscal Year-end: 12/31/23
Real Estate Development Services
N.A.I.C.S.: 531390
Magdalena Szmagalska (Chm-Mgmt Bd & Pres)

TRITON EMISSION SOLUTIONS INC.
1130 West Pender Street Unit 820, Vancouver, V6E 4A4, BC, CanadaDE
Web Site: http://www.tritoninc.com
Year Founded: 2002
DSOX—(OTCIQ)
Sales Range: Less than $1 Million
Emission Abatement Technologies for Marine Industry
N.A.I.C.S.: 333248
Robert C. Kopple (Chm)

TRITON HOLDING PUBLIC COMPANY LIMITED
60 Soi Praditmanutham 19 Praditmanutham Rd, Kwang Ladprao Khet Ladprao, Bangkok, 10230, Thailand
Tel.: (66) 25535000
Web Site: https://www.triton.co.th
Year Founded: 1987
TRITN—(THA)
Rev.: $21,659,654
Assets: $77,659,434
Liabilities: $44,400,902
Net Worth: $33,258,532
Earnings: ($8,185,518)
Emp.: 500
Fiscal Year-end: 12/31/23
Television Broadcasting Services
N.A.I.C.S.: 516120

TRITON HOLDING PUBLIC COMPANY LIMITED

Triton Holding Public Company Limited—(Continued)

Lertrat Ratanavanich *(Chm)*

Subsidiaries:

Strega Company Limited (1)
8/58 Moo 8 Bungkamproi, Lamlukka, Pathumthani, 12150, Thailand
Tel.: (66) 2 987 9667
Web Site: http://www.strega.co.th
Horizontal Drilling Services
N.A.I.C.S.: 237990

TRITON VALVES LTD.
Sunrise Chambers 22 Ulsoor Road, Bengaluru, 560042, Karnataka, India
Tel.: (91) 8025588965
Web Site:
https://www.tritonvalves.com
Year Founded: 1976
505978—(BOM)
Rev.: $31,613,455
Assets: $29,365,764
Liabilities: $17,676,491
Net Worth: $11,689,273
Earnings: $1,064,946
Emp.: 279
Fiscal Year-end: 03/31/21
Auto Parts & Equipment Mfr
N.A.I.C.S.: 336390
Shrikant Kamalakant Welling *(Chm)*

TRITON WATER AG
Werkstrasse 2b, 22844, Norderstedt, Germany
Tel.: (49) 40 413 6155 0 De
Web Site: http://www.tritonwater.com
Year Founded: 1851
Waste Water Treatment Plant Design & Construction Services
N.A.I.C.S.: 237110
Helge Schaare *(CEO)*

TRIUMPH CORPORATION, LTD.
18th Floor Sumitomo Real Estate Nishi-Shinjuku Building 7-20-1, Nishi-Shinjuku Shinjuku-ku, Tokyo, 160-0023, Japan
Tel.: (81) 3 5332 6751 JP
Web Site: http://www.uet.jp
Year Founded: 1998
Rev.: $21,667,200
Assets: $32,234,400
Liabilities: $28,895,520
Net Worth: $3,338,880
Earnings: $53,280
Emp.: 274
Fiscal Year-end: 09/30/18
Information Technology Consulting Services
N.A.I.C.S.: 541512
Masaru Ozawa *(Founder, Pres & CEO)*

TRIUMPH GOLD CORP.
1100 - 1111 Melville St, Vancouver, V6E 3V6, BC, Canada
Tel.: (604) 893-8757
Web Site:
https://www.triumphgoldcorp.com
Year Founded: 2006
8N6—(DEU)
Rev.: $5,540
Assets: $2,970,061
Liabilities: $227,753
Net Worth: $2,742,308
Earnings: $(882,122)
Fiscal Year-end: 12/31/23
Mineral Exploration Services
N.A.I.C.S.: 213114
John David Anderson *(Chm & Interim CEO)*

Subsidiaries:

Bushmaster Exploration Services (2007) Ltd. (1)
52A Powell Street Ste 200, Vancouver, V6A 1E7, BC, Canada
Tel.: (604) 893-8757
Emp.: 3
Metal Mining Services
N.A.I.C.S.: 213114
Paul Reynolds *(CEO)*

TRIUMPH INTERNATIONAL AG
Marsstrasse 40, 80323, Munich, Germany
Tel.: (49) 89511180 De
Web Site: http://www.triumph.com
Year Founded: 1891
Sales Range: $350-399.9 Million
Emp.: 60,000
Women's Intimate Apparel Mfr
N.A.I.C.S.: 315250
Wolfgang Spiesshofer *(Chm-Supervisory Bd)*

Subsidiaries:

Triumph International (1)
Apartado 15, 2686 952, Sacavem, Portugal
Tel.: (351) 219426000
Sales Range: $100-124.9 Million
Emp.: 500
Women's Intimate Apparel Whslr
N.A.I.C.S.: 424350

Triumph International India (Pvt) LTD (1)
No 240 B Sengundram Village, SingaperumalKoil Kanchipuram, Chennai, 603204, India
Tel.: (91) 4467414573
Womens' Intimate Apparel Distr
N.A.I.C.S.: 424350

TRIUMPH INTERNATIONAL FINANCE INDIA LTD.
Oxford Center 10 Shroff Lane Colaba Causeway, Colaba, Mumbai, 400005, Maharashtra, India
Tel.: (91) 2222826710
Web Site: https://tifil.in
532131—(BOM)
Financial Services
N.A.I.C.S.: 523999
Jatin Sarvaiya *(Mng Dir)*

TRIUMPH MOTORCYCLES LIMITED
Normandy Way, Hinckley, LE10 3BZ, Leicestershire, United Kingdom
Tel.: (44) 1455251700
Web Site: http://www.triumph.co.uk
Sales Range: $125-149.9 Million
Emp.: 980
Motorcycle Mfr
N.A.I.C.S.: 336991
John S. Bloor *(Owner)*

Subsidiaries:

Dublin Triumph (1)
Red Cow Naas Road, Dublin, Ireland
Tel.: (353) 14642211
Web Site: http://www.triumph.ie
Motor Cycle Distr
N.A.I.C.S.: 423110
Jeff Murphy *(Principal)*

PT. Triumph Motorcycles Indonesia (1)
Menara DEA Tower II 7th Floor Unit 3 Jl Mega Kuningan Barat, Kav E4 3 No 1-2, Jakarta, 12950, Indonesia
Tel.: (62) 215762672
Web Site:
http://www.triumphmotorcycles.co.id
Motorcycle Parts Mfr
N.A.I.C.S.: 336991

TRIUMPH MOTORCYCLES SLOVAKIA s.r.o. (1)
Roznavsk 4380/2 Areal NAD, 821 01, Bratislava, Slovakia
Tel.: (421) 220620707
Web Site: http://www.triumph-motorcycles.sk
Motor Cycle Distr
N.A.I.C.S.: 423110

TRIUMPH RUSSIA (1)
4 Krulatskay Str, Moscow, 121552, Russia
Tel.: (7) 4991493697
Web Site: http://www.triumph.granmoto.ru
Motor Cycle Distr
N.A.I.C.S.: 423110

Triumph Budapest (1)
Damjanich u 11-15, Ligetvaros, 1071, Budapest, Hungary
Tel.: (36) 13212609
Web Site: http://www.triumphbudapest.hu
Motorcycle Parts Mfr
N.A.I.C.S.: 336991

Triumph Buenos Aires (1)
Av del Libertador 520, Vicente Lopez, Buenos Aires, Argentina
Tel.: (54) 1147960838
Web Site:
http://www.argentina.triumph.co.uk
Motorcycle Parts Mfr
N.A.I.C.S.: 336991

Triumph Colombia S.A.S. (1)
Calle 127 No 7C - 09, Barrio Santa Barbara, Bogota, Colombia
Tel.: (57) 7022099
Web Site: http://www.triumphcolombia.com
Motor Cycle Distr
N.A.I.C.S.: 423110

Triumph Costa Rica (1)
Costado Sur la Ladrillera LA, San Jose, Costa Rica
Tel.: (506) 22574247
Web Site: http://www.triumphmotorcycles.cr
Motorcycle Parts Mfr
N.A.I.C.S.: 336991

Triumph France SA (1)
19 Bld Georges Bidault Bat G1, 77183, Croissy-Beaubourg, France
Tel.: (33) 164623838
Web Site: http://www.triumphmotorcycles.fr
Motorcycle Parts Mfr
N.A.I.C.S.: 336991

Triumph Guatemala (1)
Boulevard Los Proceres 22-69 zona 10, Guatemala, Guatemala
Tel.: (502) 23371550
Web Site:
http://www.triumphmotorcycles.com.gt
Motorcycle Parts Mfr
N.A.I.C.S.: 336991

Triumph Motocicletas Espana S. L. (1)
c/Cabo Rufino Lazaro 14 - Nave E, Las Rozas, 28232, Madrid, Spain
Tel.: (34) 902103823
Web Site: http://www.triumphmotorcycles.es
Motor Cycle Distr
N.A.I.C.S.: 423110

Triumph Motorcycles (India) Private Limited (1)
2nd Floor Wing-A Commercial Plaza Radisson Hotel NH-8, Mahipalpur, New Delhi, India
Tel.: (91) 1145031451
Web Site: http://www.triumphmotorcycles.in
Motorcycle Parts Mfr
N.A.I.C.S.: 336991

Triumph Motorcycles AB (1)
Staffans Vag 6B, 192 78, Sollentuna, Sweden
Tel.: (46) 86800725
Web Site: http://www.triumphmotorcycles.se
Motorcycle Parts Mfr
N.A.I.C.S.: 336991

Triumph Motorcycles Benelux B.V. (1)
Opaalstraat 16, 1812 RH, Alkmaar, Netherlands
Tel.: (31) 725410311
Web Site: http://www.triumphmotorcycles.nl
Motorcycle Parts Mfr
N.A.I.C.S.: 336991

Triumph Motorcycles South Africa (1)
PO Box 76770, Wendywood, 2144, South Africa
Tel.: (27) 115660333
Web Site:
http://www.triumphmotorcycles.co.za

INTERNATIONAL PUBLIC

Motorcycle Parts Mfr
N.A.I.C.S.: 336991

Triumph Motorcycles Srl (1)
Viale delle industrie 10/18, 20020, Arese, Milan, Italy
Tel.: (39) 029345451
Web Site: http://www.triumphmotorcycles.it
Motor Cycle Distr
N.A.I.C.S.: 423110

Triumph Motorrad Deutschland GmbH (1)
Raiffeisenstr 1, 61191, Rosbach vor der Hohe, Germany
Tel.: (49) 6003829090
Web Site: http://www.triumphmotorcycles.de
Motorcycle Parts Mfr
N.A.I.C.S.: 336991
Andre Veith *(Head-After Sls)*

Triumph Polska (1)
ul Gdanska 15, 05-152, Czosnow, Poland
Tel.: (48) 227141710
Web Site: http://www.triumph.net.pl
Motor Cycle Distr
N.A.I.C.S.: 423110

Triumph S.A.S. (1)
Succursale Suisse Rue des Bugnons 4, 1217, Meyrin, Switzerland
Tel.: (41) 227827350
Web Site: http://www.triumphmotorcycles.ch
Motor Cycle Distr
N.A.I.C.S.: 423110

TRIUMPH SCIENCE & TECHNOLOGY CO., LTD.
No 8009 Huangshan Avenue, Bengbu, 233010, Anhui, China
Tel.: (86) 5524968040
Web Site: https://www.triumphltd.cn
Year Founded: 2000
600552—(SHG)
Rev.: $649,091,622
Assets: $1,351,495,272
Liabilities: $724,315,485
Net Worth: $627,179,787
Earnings: $19,701,363
Fiscal Year-end: 12/31/22
Glass Product Mfr & Distr
N.A.I.C.S.: 327215

TRIUMPHAL ASSOCIATES BHD.
24 Persiaran Industri Bandar Sri Damansara, 52200, Kuala Lumpur, Malaysia
Tel.: (60) 362873888
Web Site:
http://www.triumphal.com.my
Sales Range: $50-74.9 Million
Construction Equipment Mfr & Distr
N.A.I.C.S.: 532412

Subsidiaries:

Triumphal Equipment Spare Parts Sdn. Bhd. (1)
Lot 635 Jalan Krokop, 98000, Miri, Sarawak, Malaysia
Tel.: (60) 85433366
Web Site: http://www.triumphal.com.my
Sales Range: $25-49.9 Million
Emp.: 20
Machinery Spare Parts Distr
N.A.I.C.S.: 423830
Yeoh Lean Hai *(Mng Dir)*

Triumphal Machinery Supply Sdn. Bhd. (1)
TB 5437 Jalan Apas Batu 2 1/2, 91000, Tawau, Sabah, Malaysia
Tel.: (60) 89763650
Web Site: http://www.triumphal.biz
Sales Range: $25-49.9 Million
Emp.: 11
Machinery Spare Parts Whslr & Retailer
N.A.I.C.S.: 423830

USG Far East International Trading (Shanghai) Ltd. (1)
No 318 Three-Gorge Business Building No A11 Jiuxianqiao Road, Chaoyang District, Beijing, 100016, China **(100%)**

Tel.: (86) 1064370270
Automobile Parts Distr
N.A.I.C.S.: 423110

USG Products (F.E.) Pte. Ltd. (1)
23B Sungei Kadut Street 1, Singapore, 729325, Singapore
Tel.: (65) 63686106
Web Site: http://www.usg.com.sg
Sales Range: $25-49.9 Million
Emp.: 34
Automotive Products Mfr & Whslr
N.A.I.C.S.: 336390
Toh Chee Lit (Mng Dir)

USG Products Sdn. Bhd. (1)
Lot No 728 Jalan Kapar KU 6, Taman Klang Utama, 42100, Kelang, Selangor, Malaysia
Tel.: (60) 332907886
Web Site: http://www.triumphal.biz
Sales Range: $25-49.9 Million
Emp.: 40
Machinery Spare Parts Distr
N.A.I.C.S.: 423830
Vivian Chooi (Sec)

TRIVAGO N.V.
Kesselstrasse 5 - 7, 40221, Dusseldorf, Germany
Tel.: (49) 2113876840000 NL
Web Site: https://www.trivago.com
Year Founded: 2016
TRVG—(NASDAQ)
Rev.: $657,113,313
Assets: $849,440,958
Liabilities: $159,494,333
Net Worth: $689,946,625
Earnings: ($156,254,236)
Emp.: 709
Fiscal Year-end: 12/31/22
Holding Company; Online Travel Pricing Comparison & Arrangement Services
N.A.I.C.S.: 551112
James Carter (Mng Dir & Chief Product & Tech Officer)

TRIVE PROPERTY GROUP BERHAD
Tel.: (60) 44031828 MY
Web Site:
   https://www.trivegroup.com.my
Year Founded: 2002
TRIVE—(KLS)
Rev.: $1,935,275
Assets: $26,651,928
Liabilities: $1,461,905
Net Worth: $25,190,023
Earnings: ($4,001,334)
Fiscal Year-end: 07/31/23
Energy Storage Device Mfr & Distr
N.A.I.C.S.: 335910
Khai Shyuan Kua (Exec Dir)

TRIVENI ENGINEERING & INDUSTRIES LTD
8th Floor Express Trade Towers Plot No 15 & 16 Sector 16-A, Noida, 201301, Uttar Pradesh, India
Tel.: (91) 1204308000
Web Site:
   https://www.trivenigroup.com
TRIVENI—(NSE)
Rev.: $646,156,848
Assets: $494,123,434
Liabilities: $281,773,933
Net Worth: $212,349,501
Earnings: $40,213,269
Emp.: 3,872
Fiscal Year-end: 03/31/21
Sugar Production, Gears & Gear Boxes Mfr, Water & Wastewater Treatment Services
N.A.I.C.S.: 311314
C. N. Narayanan (VP-Grp-IR & Bus Dev)

Subsidiaries:

Triveni Turbine Limited (1)
Express Trade Towers 8th Floor 15-16 Sector 16 A, Noida, 201 301, Uttar Pradesh, India
Tel.: (91) 4308000
Web Site: https://www.triveniturbines.com
Rev.: $120,355,053
Assets: $182,203,203
Liabilities: $65,170,287
Net Worth: $117,032,916
Earnings: $36,881,754
Emp.: 621
Fiscal Year-end: 03/31/2022
Steam Turbine Mfr
N.A.I.C.S.: 333611
Arun Prabhakar Mote (Exec Dir)

TRIVENI ENTERPRISES LIMITED
Office No 24 Bldg No 2 C N G Park S V Road, Rawalpada Dahisar, Mumbai, 400068, India
Tel.: (91) 9718980141
Web Site: https://trivenisteel.com
Year Founded: 1984
538569—(BOM)
Rev.: $1,085,083
Assets: $1,673,261
Liabilities: $429,401
Net Worth: $1,243,860
Earnings: $38,518
Fiscal Year-end: 03/31/23
Textile Product Whslr
N.A.I.C.S.: 424990
Bhavin Hemendra Nagda (Exec Dir)

TRIVENI GLASS LIMITED
I Kanpur Road, Allahabad, 211001, Uttar Pradesh, India
Tel.: (91) 5322407325
Web Site:
   https://www.triveniglassltd.com
Year Founded: 1971
502281—(BOM)
Rev.: $532,354
Assets: $690,186
Liabilities: $2,800,048
Net Worth: $(2,109,862)
Earnings: $200,096
Fiscal Year-end: 03/31/23
Figured & Float Glass Mfr
N.A.I.C.S.: 327212
Jitendra Kumar Agrawal (Mng Dir)

TRIVIT MLIN A.D.
Kulski put bb, Vrbas, Serbia
Tel.: (381) 21706421
Web Site: https://trivit.rs
Year Founded: 1992
TRVM—(BEL)
Rev.: $134,454
Assets: $846,710
Liabilities: $4,759
Net Worth: $841,950
Earnings: $45,123
Emp.: 9
Fiscal Year-end: 12/31/23
Grain Mill Product Mfr
N.A.I.C.S.: 311230
Vesna Vujovic (Gen Dir)

TRIVIT PEK A.D.
Kulski put bb, Vrbas, Serbia
Tel.: (381) 21700310
Web Site: https://www.trivitpek.com
Year Founded: 1991
TRVP—(BEL)
Rev.: $397,201
Assets: $1,557,429
Liabilities: $1,091,253
Net Worth: $466,176
Earnings: $24,694
Emp.: 17
Fiscal Year-end: 12/31/23
Bakery Products Mfr
N.A.I.C.S.: 311813
Vera Scepanovic (Gen Dir)

TRIWEST CAPITAL MANAGEMENT CORP.
4600 400 3rd Ave SW, Calgary, T2P 4H2, AB, Canada
Tel.: (403) 225-1144
Web Site: https://www.triwest.ca
Year Founded: 1998
Privater Equity Firm
N.A.I.C.S.: 523999
Ron Jackson (Co-Founder)

Subsidiaries:

Innova Global Limited (1)
4000 4th Street SE Suite 222, Calgary, T2G 2W3, AB, Canada
Tel.: (403) 292-7804
Web Site: http://www.innova-gl.com
Buildings & Acoustic Barriers Mfr
N.A.I.C.S.: 333413
Denise LeClaire (Dir-Bus Dev)

Subsidiary (US):

Braden Manufacturing, LLC (2)
5199 N Mingo Rd, Tulsa, OK 74117
Tel.: (800) 272-3360
Web Site: http://www.braden.com
Structural Steel Fabricator & Auxiliary Power Components Supplier
N.A.I.C.S.: 332312
Gene F. Schockemoehl (Pres)

Subsidiary (Non-US):

Braden-Europe B.V. (3)
Nieuw Eyckholt 290H, 6419 DJ, Heerlen, Limburg, Netherlands
Tel.: (31) 455615420
Web Site: http://bradeneurope.nl
Power Generation Design, Manufacture, Installation & Auxilliary Gas Turbine Equipments Retrofitting
N.A.I.C.S.: 333611
Gelu Dragan (Mgr-Quality & Retrofitting Services)

Division (Domestic):

Consolidated Fabricators, Inc. (3)
17 Saint Mark St Fairfax Industrial Park, Auburn, MA 01501
Tel.: (508) 797-8000
Web Site:
   http://www.consolidatedfabricators.com
Complex Mechanical & Fluid Systems Mfr
N.A.I.C.S.: 332999

Monarch Industries Limited (1)
51 Burmac Rd, Winnipeg, R2J 4J3, MB, Canada
Tel.: (204) 786-7921
Web Site:
   http://www.monarchindustries.com
Hydraulic Cylinders & Metal Casting Mfr
N.A.I.C.S.: 333517
Roy Cook (Pres & CEO)

NCSG Crane & Heavy Haul Corporation (1)
28765 Acheson Road, Acheson, T7X 6A8, AB, Canada
Tel.: (780) 960-6300
Web Site: http://www.ncsg.com
Emp.: 1,000
Crane & Heavy Haul Services
N.A.I.C.S.: 532412
Andy Popko (VP-Indigenous Rels & Major Accts)

Subsidiary (US):

Energy Transportation Inc. (2)
6301 Zero Rd, Casper, WY 82604
Tel.: (307) 266-3890
Web Site: http://www.energytran.com
Heavy Machinery Transport
N.A.I.C.S.: 484230
Donnie Masters (Mgr-Field)

NCSG Crane & Heavy Haul Services Ltd. (2)
1115 Smelter Ave, Black Eagle, MT 59414-1076
Tel.: (406) 452-4614
Web Site: http://www.ncsg.com
Crane Rental Services
N.A.I.C.S.: 532412

NCSG Crane & Heavy Haul Services, Inc. (2)
701 N Hooper Ave, Soda Springs, ID 83276

Tel.: (208) 547-4775
Web Site: http://www.mullencrane.com
Crane Rental Services
N.A.I.C.S.: 532412
Guy Wright (Branch Mgr)

Snowcrest Foods Ltd. (1)
1925 Riverside Rd, Abbotsford, V2S 4J8, BC, Canada
Tel.: (604) 859-4881
Web Site: http://www.snowcrest.ca
Distr of Frozen Produce
N.A.I.C.S.: 424420
Ray Biln (Pres)

TRIYARDS HOLDINGS LIMITED
51 Shipyard Road, Singapore, 628139, Singapore
Tel.: (65) 63498535
Web Site: https://www.triyards.com
Year Founded: 2012
RC5—(SES)
Sales Range: $300-349.9 Million
Ship Construction Services
N.A.I.C.S.: 336611
Eng Yew Chan (CEO)

Subsidiaries:

Strategic Marine (S) Pte. Ltd. (1)
51 Shipyard Road, Singapore, 628139, Singapore
Tel.: (65) 69329904
Web Site: http://www.strategicmarine.com
Logistic Services
N.A.I.C.S.: 488510
Wong Chai Vei (CFO)

Strategic Marine (V) Co., Ltd. (1)
12 Dong Xuyen, Industrial Zone Rach Dua Ward, Vung Tau, Ba Ria-Vung Tau, Vietnam
Tel.: (2) 2543615225
Logistic Services
N.A.I.C.S.: 488510
Truong Van Phuong (Sr Project Mgr)

TROAX GROUP AB
Tyngel, PO Box 89, 335 04, Hillerstorp, Sweden
Tel.: (46) 269563860 SE
Web Site: https://www.troax.com
TROAX—(OMX)
Rev.: $306,584,287
Assets: $314,134,470
Liabilities: $146,991,150
Net Worth: $167,143,320
Earnings: $39,708,612
Emp.: 1,144
Fiscal Year-end: 12/31/22
Holding Company; Mesh Panels, Machine Guarding Systems & Industrial Partition Solutions Mfr
N.A.I.C.S.: 551112
Thomas Widstrand (Pres & CEO)

Subsidiaries:

Lagermix Rullportar AB (1)
Tre Hjartans Vag 4, 302 41, Halmstad, Sweden
Tel.: (46) 35102949
Web Site: https://lagermix.se
Burglar Alarm Product Distr
N.A.I.C.S.: 423690

Natom Logistic Sp. z o.o. (1)
Ul Zakladowa 4, 63-000, Sroda Wielkopolska, Poland
Tel.: (48) 612819170
Web Site: https://natom.pl
Warehousing Logistic Services
N.A.I.C.S.: 493110

Satech K.K (1)
3-20-12 Shin-Yokohama, Kohoku-ku, Yokohama, 222-0033, Japan
Tel.: (81) 454768088
Modular Machine Guard Mfr
N.A.I.C.S.: 333998

Satech Safety Technology GmbH (1)
Steinmasch 4, Rahden, 32369, Espelkamp, Germany
Tel.: (49) 5771913900
Modular Machine Guard Mfr

TROAX GROUP AB

Troax Group AB—(Continued)
N.A.I.C.S.: 333998
Javier Garcia Morales *(Mng Dir)*

Satech Safety Technology SPA (1)
Via Conte Taverna 1, Bulciago, 23892, San Donato Milanese, LC, Italy
Tel.: (39) 031862301
Web Site: https://www.satech.it
Modular Machine Guard Mfr & Distr
N.A.I.C.S.: 333998

Satech Safety Technology Sarl (1)
29 Rue Maurice Flandin, 69003, Lyon, France
Tel.: (33) 487650650
Modular Machine Guard Mfr
N.A.I.C.S.: 333998

Troax AB (1)
Tyngel 34, 335 74, Hillerstorp, Sweden
Tel.: (46) 37082800
Web Site: https://www.troax.com
Mesh Panels, Machine Guarding Systems & Industrial Partition Solutions, Mfr & Whslr
N.A.I.C.S.: 332999
Thomas Widstrand *(Pres & CEO)*

Troax BV (1)
Heereweg 331, 2161 BL, Lisse, Netherlands
Tel.: (31) 252370154
Web Site: https://www.troax.com
Modular Machine Guard Mfr & Distr
N.A.I.C.S.: 333998

Troax Denmark A/S (1)
Elektronvej 6, Greve, 2670, Denmark
Tel.: (45) 43710233
Web Site: https://www.troax.com
Modular Machine Guard Mfr & Distr
N.A.I.C.S.: 333998

Troax GmbH (1)
Otto-Hahn-Strasse 9, Bad Camberg, 65520, Idstein, Germany
Tel.: (49) 643490900
Web Site: https://www.troax.com
Modular Machine Guard Mfr & Distr
N.A.I.C.S.: 333998

Troax Guvenlik Sistemleri Hiz. ve Tic. Ltd.Sti. (1)
Aydinli Mahallesi Yanyol Cad Melodi Sk, S S Bilmo Sanayi Sitesi No 2/24 Tuzla, 34953, Istanbul, Turkiye
Tel.: (90) 2163442000
Web Site: https://www.troax.com
Modular Machine Guard Mfr & Distr
N.A.I.C.S.: 333998

Troax Lee Manufacturing Ltd. (1)
Building 52 Third Avenue Pensnett Trading Estate, Kingswinford, DY6 7XF, West Midlands, United Kingdom
Tel.: (44) 1384277441
Modular Machine Guard Mfr & Distr
N.A.I.C.S.: 333998
Geoff McBride *(Natl Sls Mgr)*

Troax Nordic AB (1)
Tyngel 34, Box 89, 335 74, Hillerstorp, Sweden
Tel.: (46) 37082800
Web Site: https://www.troax.com
Modular Machine Guard Mfr & Distr
N.A.I.C.S.: 332999
Anders Eklof *(CFO)*

Troax Nordic AS (1)
Professor Birkelands Vei 26 B, 1081, Oslo, Norway
Tel.: (47) 22804200
Web Site: https://www.troax.com
Modular Machine Guard Mfr & Distr
N.A.I.C.S.: 333998

Troax SA (1)
Savoie Hexapole Rue Maurice Herzog Actipole 2, Viviers-du-Lac, Chambery, France
Tel.: (33) 479522670
Web Site: https://www.troax.com
Modular Machine Guard Mfr & Distr
N.A.I.C.S.: 333998

Troax Safety Systems Co., Ltd. (1)
Monopoly Building 6f 5-chome-26-30, Minato-ku, Tokyo, 108-0014, Japan
Tel.: (81) 364503848
Web Site: https://www.troax.com

Modular Machine Guard Mfr & Distr
N.A.I.C.S.: 333998

Troax Safety Systems India Private Limited (1)
Plot No 323-Part A Bommasandra Jigani Link Road, Industrial Area Anekal Taluk, Bengaluru, 560105, Karnataka, India
Tel.: (91) 29600249
Web Site: https://www.troax.com
Modular Machine Guard Mfr & Distr
N.A.I.C.S.: 333998
A. S. Vidyasagar Ganesh *(Sls Mgr)*

Troax Safety Systems Poland Sp.z.o.o (1)
Ul Kazimierza Wielkiego 86, 66-440, Gorzow Wielkopolski, Poland
Tel.: (48) 953070430
Web Site: https://www.troax.com
Modular Machine Guard Mfr & Distr
N.A.I.C.S.: 333998
Sebastian Chrzanowski-Sawicki *(Sls Mgr)*

Troax Safety Systems Pty Ltd. (1)
Unit 17 148 James Ruse Drive, Rosehill, Parramatta, 2142, NSW, Australia
Tel.: (61) 426508725
Web Site: https://www.troax.com
Modular Machine Guard Mfr & Distr
N.A.I.C.S.: 333998

Troax Schweiz AG (1)
Vogelhalde 23, Warth, 8853, Schwyz, Switzerland
Tel.: (41) 527400336
Web Site: https://www.troax.com
Modular Machine Guard Mfr & Distr
N.A.I.C.S.: 333998

Troax Shanghai Safety System Co., Ltd. (1)
Suite 1705 Building H Daning Music Plaz 777 WanRong Road, Shanghai, 200949, China
Tel.: (86) 2166278808
Web Site: https://www.troax.com
Modular Machine Guard Mfr & Distr
N.A.I.C.S.: 333998

Troax System SL (1)
C/ Vilar d Abdela n 5 Nave 7, Poligono Industrial Can Parellada Montornes del Valles, 08170, Barcelona, Spain
Tel.: (34) 935684000
Web Site: https://www.troax.com
Modular Machine Guard Mfr & Distr
N.A.I.C.S.: 333998

Troax UK Ltd. (1)
Enterprise House Murdock Road Dorcan, Swindon, SN3 5HY, Wiltshire, United Kingdom
Tel.: (44) 1793542000
Web Site: https://www.troax.com
Modular Machine Guard Mfr & Distr
N.A.I.C.S.: 333998

Troax, Inc. (1)
1410 Donelson Pike Ste B20, Nashville, TN 37217
Tel.: (615) 730-7581
Web Site: http://www.troax.com
Mesh Panels, Machine Guarding Systems & Industrial Partition Solutions Mfr & Whslr
N.A.I.C.S.: 332999
Thomas Sareyko *(Reg Dir-North America)*

Subsidiary (Domestic):

Folding Guard, Inc. (2)
5858 W 73rd St, Bedford Park, IL 60638
Tel.: (708) 325-0400
Web Site: http://www.foldingguard.com
All Other Plastics Product Mfr
N.A.I.C.S.: 326199

TROC DE L ILE SA
Quartier de Dinarelle 2 rue des Alizes, 30133, Les Angles, France
Tel.: (33) 490151413
Web Site: http://www.troc.com
MLTRO—(EUR)
Sales Range: $1-9.9 Million
Durable Goods Merchant Whslr
N.A.I.C.S.: 423990
Fabrice Baj *(Chm & CEO)*

TRODAT GMBH
Linzerstr 156, 4600, Wels, Austria
Tel.: (43) 7242 239 0
Web Site: http://www.trodat.net
Year Founded: 1912
Emp.: 1,500
Rubber Stamp Mfr
N.A.I.C.S.: 423990
Norbert Schrufer *(CEO)*

TROILUS GOLD CORP.
36 Lombard Street Floor 4, Toronto, M5C 2X3, ON, Canada
Tel.: (647) 276-0050
Web Site: https://www.troilusgold.com
Year Founded: 1985
TLG—(TSX)
Rev.: $331,297
Assets: $18,226,297
Liabilities: $6,829,390
Net Worth: $11,396,907
Earnings: ($25,051,749)
Emp.: 35
Fiscal Year-end: 07/31/24
Mineral Exploration Services
N.A.I.C.S.: 212290
Justin Reid *(Pres & CEO)*

Subsidiaries:

Signet Minerals Inc. (1)
1963 Comox Avenue, Comox, V9M 3M4, BC, Canada
Tel.: (250) 890-0607
Gold Exploration Services
N.A.I.C.S.: 212220

UrbanGold Minerals Inc. (1)
3208 Richmond Road, Ottawa, K2H 5B6, ON, Canada
Web Site: http://www.urbangoldminerals.com
Sales Range: Less than $1 Million
Mineral Exploration Services
N.A.I.C.S.: 213115

TROILUS GOLD CORP.
800-65 Queen Street W, Toronto, M5H 2M5, ON, Canada
Tel.: (416) 861-5805
Web Site: http://www.troilusgold.com
Mining Services
N.A.I.C.S.: 212220
Ian Pritchard *(Sr VP-Tech Svcs)*

TROJAN GOLD INC.
82 Richmond St E Suite 401, Toronto, M5C 1P1, ON, Canada
Tel.: (416) 315-6490
Web Site: https://www.trojangold.com
Year Founded: 2012
TRJGF—(OTCQB)
Rev.: $278
Assets: $753,186
Liabilities: $75,795
Net Worth: $677,391
Earnings: ($359,985)
Fiscal Year-end: 12/31/22
Mineral Exploration Services
N.A.I.C.S.: 213115
Jon Li *(CFO)*

TROJAN HOLDINGS LTD.
121 Gorge Road, PO Box 60, Queenstown, New Zealand
Tel.: (64) 34413620
Web Site: http://www.nsth.co.nz
Holding Company
N.A.I.C.S.: 551112
John Davies *(Chm)*

Subsidiaries:

Cromwell Transport Company (1)
147 McNulty Road, PO Box 25, Cromwell, New Zealand
Tel.: (64) 34450824
Web Site: http://www.cromtrans.co.nz
Freight Transportation Services
N.A.I.C.S.: 484220

INTERNATIONAL PUBLIC

Peter Carnahan *(CEO)*

Northern Southland Transport (1)
Level 2 The Station Building Cnr Camp and Shotover Streets, PO Box 956, Queenstown, New Zealand
Tel.: (64) 29 232 4565
Web Site: http://www.nsth.co.nz
Freight Trucking Services
N.A.I.C.S.: 484110
Peter Carnahan *(CEO)*

Otago Southland Waste Services Ltd (1)
PO Box 84, Queenstown, Queenstown, New Zealand (50%)
Tel.: (64) 34510106
Sales Range: $25-49.9 Million
Emp.: 6
Waste Collection & Deposit Svcs
N.A.I.C.S.: 562119

TROKOST GMBH
Heidenackerstrasse 17, 69207, Sandhausen, Germany
Tel.: (49) 622493010
Web Site: http://www.tro-kost.de
Year Founded: 1984
Rev.: $18,120,402
Emp.: 76
Dried Food Product Mfr
N.A.I.C.S.: 311423
Wolfgang Kocher *(Founder & Mng Dir)*

TROMBO EXTRACTIONS LIMITED
18-C Tejpur Bridge, AB Road, Indore, 452 001, Madhya Pradesh, India
Tel.: (91) 9302537000
Web Site: http://tromboextractions.com
Rev.: $7,858
Assets: $71,358
Liabilities: $17,412
Net Worth: $53,947
Earnings: $965
Fiscal Year-end: 03/31/18
Oilseed Processing Services
N.A.I.C.S.: 311224
Jawahar Kanhaiyalal Rajani *(Chm, CEO, Mng Dir & Compliance Officer)*

TRON GROUP INC.
K-2-8 2nd Floor Kuchai Business Park, Jalan 1/127 off Jalan Kuchai Lama, 58200, Kuala Lumpur, Malaysia
Tel.: (60) 379878688
Year Founded: 2015
TGRP—(OTCIQ)
Assets: $983,000
Liabilities: $1,087,000
Net Worth: ($104,000)
Earnings: ($56,000)
Emp.: 3
Fiscal Year-end: 12/31/21
Investment Services
N.A.I.C.S.: 523999

TRONY SOLAR HOLDINGS COMPANY LIMITED
Room 1403 Building A4 Kexing Science Park, Keyuan Road Middle District of Science Park, Shenzhen, 518057, China
Tel.: (86) 755 3398 7669
Web Site: http://www.trony.com
Year Founded: 1993
Thin Film Solar Products & Solutions
N.A.I.C.S.: 326113
Ying Yu *(Exec Dir)*

Subsidiaries:

Trony East Africa Limited (1)
Unit 7C TRV Office Plaza 58 Muthithi Road, Westlands, Nairobi, Kenya
Tel.: (254) 20 8023118
Solar Film Mfr

N.A.I.C.S.: 326113

Trony Solar Holdings (Hong Kong) Limited (1)
Unit 713 7/F Lakeside 1, 8 Science Park Avenue West, Hong Kong Science Park, Sha Tin, NT, China (Hong Kong)
Tel.: (852) 2603 5882
Solar Film Mfr
N.A.I.C.S.: 326113

TROOPS, INC.
Unit A 18/F 8 Fui Yiu Kok Street, Tsuen Wan, New Territories, China (Hong Kong)
Tel.: (852) 23863328   Ky
Web Site:
  http://www.sgocogroup.com
Year Founded: 2007
TROO—(NASDAQ)
Rev.: $3,875,000
Assets: $69,686,000
Liabilities: $7,482,000
Net Worth: $62,204,000
Earnings: ($346,000)
Emp.: 19
Fiscal Year-end: 12/31/22
LCD Products Mfr
N.A.I.C.S.: 334419
Tony Zhong *(VP-Fin)*

TROPIC AIR
Pescado Drive, PO Box 20, San Pedro, 20, Belize
Tel.: (501) 2262012
Web Site: http://www.tropicair.com
Year Founded: 1979
Sales Range: $25-49.9 Million
Emp.: 200
Oil Transportation Services
N.A.I.C.S.: 481111
Steve Schulte *(CEO)*

TROPICAL CANNING (THAILAND) PUBLIC COMPANY LIMITED
1/1 Karnjanavanich Road M 2 Thungyai, PO Box 44, Hatyai, Songkhla, 90110, Thailand
Tel.: (66) 74273600   TH
Web Site: https://www.tropical.co.th
Year Founded: 1979
TC—(THA)
Rev.: $144,394,658
Assets: $101,342,474
Liabilities: $31,548,367
Net Worth: $69,794,107
Earnings: $1,269,334
Fiscal Year-end: 12/31/23
Seafood Product Mfr
N.A.I.C.S.: 311710
Kampol Watcharanimit *(Mng Dir)*

Subsidiaries:

Elowfar Co., Ltd. (1)
10/F SV City Office Tower 2 898/15 Rama 3 Road, Bang Pongpang Yannawa, Bangkok, 10120, Thailand
Tel.: (66) 2 682 5482
Canned Food Mfr
N.A.I.C.S.: 311514

TC BOY Marketing Sdn. Bhd. (1)
Lot141-D Jalan Utas 15/7 Seksyen 15, 40200, Shah Alam, Selangor, Malaysia
Tel.: (60) 355130933
Web Site: https://www.tcboy.com
Canned Food Whslr
N.A.I.C.S.: 424450

TROPICAL FOOD MANUFACTURING (NINGBO) CO LTD (1)
78 Binjiang Zhilu, Xiaogang, Ningbo, 315803, Zhejiang, China
Tel.: (86) 57487132041
Web Site: https://www.tropical-food.com
Emp.: 700
Canned Food Mfr
N.A.I.C.S.: 311514
M. A. Oyma *(Vice Gen Mgr)*

Tropical Corporation (1)
Garden Square Buliding 9F 11-1 Koya Machi Aoi Ku, Shizuoka, 420-0852, Japan
Tel.: (81) 54 653 8870
Canned Food Whslr
N.A.I.C.S.: 424450

TROPICAL SKY LTD.
Kings House First Floor North 13/21 Cantelupe Road, East Grinstead, RH19 3BE, West Sussex, United Kingdom
Tel.: (44) 843 249 5276
Web Site:
  http://www.tropicalsky.co.uk
Year Founded: 2005
Sales Range: $50-74.9 Million
Emp.: 65
Tour Operator
N.A.I.C.S.: 561520
David Hennessy *(Mng Dir)*

TROPICANA CORPORATION BERHAD
Unit 1301 Level 13 Tropicana Gardens Office Tower, No 2A Persiaran Surian Tropicana Indah, 47810, Petaling Jaya, Selangor Darul Ehsan, Malaysia
Tel.: (60) 376636888
Web Site:
  http://www.tropicanacorp.com.my
TROP—(KLS)
Rev.: $199,482,963
Assets: $2,598,809,101
Liabilities: $1,380,817,354
Net Worth: $1,217,991,746
Earnings: ($86,898,836)
Emp.: 772
Fiscal Year-end: 12/31/22
Property & Resort Development Services
N.A.I.C.S.: 531312
Yong Chien Dion Tan *(Mng Dir-Grp)*

Subsidiaries:

Dijaya Development Sdn. Bhd. (1)
Level 10-12 Tropicana City Office Tower No 3 Jln Ss 20/27, 47400, Petaling Jaya, Selangor Darul Ehsan, Malaysia
Tel.: (60) 377101018
Property Development Services
N.A.I.C.S.: 531390

Dijaya Management Services Sdn. Bhd. (1)
328 3rd Floor Block A Damansara Intan No 1 Jalan SS 20/27, 47400, Petaling Jaya, Selangor, Malaysia
Tel.: (60) 371183111
Sales Range: $50-74.9 Million
Emp.: 20
Residential Property Management Services
N.A.I.C.S.: 531311
Ho Hon Chiap *(Deputy Gen Mgr)*

Irama Sejati Sdn. Bhd. (1)
A-G-10 Jalan Megah 37A Taman Megah, 43200, Cheras, Selangor, Malaysia
Tel.: (60) 390761315
Investment Management Service
N.A.I.C.S.: 523999

Tropicana Cheras Sdn. Bhd. (1)
Off Jalan P6/2, Kajang, 43500, Semenyih, Selangor, Malaysia
Tel.: (60) 376638888
Web Site:
  https://www.tropicanacorp.com.my
Real Estate Services
N.A.I.C.S.: 531390

Tropicana City Management Sdn. Bhd. (1)
Lot B1-01 Basement 1 Tropicana City Mall No 3 Jalan SS 20/27, Petaling Jaya, 47400, Selangor, Malaysia
Tel.: (60) 377101818
Web Site: https://www.tropicanacitymall.com
Sales Range: $25-49.9 Million
Emp.: 60
Shopping Mall Construction & Management Services

N.A.I.C.S.: 236220
Mabel Tan *(Deputy Gen Mgr)*

Tropicana Danga Bay Sdn. Bhd. (1)
Lot Ptb 22902 Teluk Danga Persiaran Abu Bakar Sultan, 80200, Johor Bahru, Johor, Malaysia
Tel.: (60) 72341585
Web Site:
  https://www.tropicanadangabay.com.my
Real Estate Services
N.A.I.C.S.: 531390
Russell K. K. Lim *(Deputy Gen Mgr)*

Tropicana GP Views Sdn Bhd (1)
Lot PTD 15346, Jalan Tanjung Kupang, 81550, Gelang Patah, Johor, Malaysia
Tel.: (60) 75103838
Web Site:
  https://www.tropicanauplands.com.my
Property Management Services
N.A.I.C.S.: 531312

Tropicana Golf & Country Resort Berhad (1)
Jalan Kelab Tropicana, 47410, Petaling Jaya, Selangor, Malaysia
Tel.: (60) 37 804 8888
Web Site:
  https://www.tropicanacorp.com.my
Golf Club & Resort Management Services
N.A.I.C.S.: 721110

Subsidiary (Domestic):

Nadi Jelita Sdn. Bhd. (2)
Level 10 Tropicana City Office Tower No 3 Jalan Ss 20/27, Petaling Jaya, 47400, Selangor Darul Ehsan, Malaysia
Tel.: (60) 377101018
Web Site: http://www.tropicanacorp.com.my
Sales Range: $50-74.9 Million
Emp.: 100
Property Development Services
N.A.I.C.S.: 531311

Tropicana Indah Sdn. Bhd. (1)
Level G Tropicana Gardens Mall No 2A Persiaran Surian, Tropicana Indah, 47810, Petaling Jaya, Selangor, Malaysia
Tel.: (60) 163670707
Web Site:
  https://www.tropicanagardens.com.my
Real Estate Services
N.A.I.C.S.: 531390
David Chee *(Mgr-Project)*

Tropicana Landmark Sdn. Bhd. (1)
Level 4 Penampang Point Mile 4 Jalan Penampang, 88200, Kota Kinabalu, Sabah, Malaysia
Tel.: (60) 88723322
Web Site:
  https://www.tropicanametropark.com.my
Real Estate Services
N.A.I.C.S.: 531390

TROTTER & MORTON LTD.
5711 1 Street SE, Calgary, T2H 1H9, AB, Canada
Tel.: (403) 255-7535
Web Site:
  https://www.trotterandmorton.com
Year Founded: 1927
Sales Range: $25-49.9 Million
Emp.: 3,000
Construction, Building Technologies & Facilities Services
N.A.I.C.S.: 236220
Steve Salt *(Gen Mgr)*

Subsidiaries:

Bluebird Contracting Services (1)
321 Ellis Dr, Acheson, T7X 5A7, AB, Canada
Tel.: (780) 777-7099
Web Site: http://www.trotterandmorton.com
Building Construction Services
N.A.I.C.S.: 236220

Rambler Fabrication Inc. (1)
285097 Bluegrass Dr, Rocky View, T1X 0P5, AB, Canada
Tel.: (403) 233-8345
Web Site: http://www.ramblerfabrication.com
Fabricated Metal Products Mfr
N.A.I.C.S.: 332999

Mark Clowry *(Gen Mgr)*

Trotter & Morton Building Technologies Inc (1)
200 5151 Canada Way, Burnaby, V5E 3N1, BC, Canada
Tel.: (604) 525-4499
Mechanical Installation Services
N.A.I.C.S.: 238220

Whaler Industrial Contracting Inc. (1)
5799 3rd Street SE, Calgary, T2H 1K1, AB, Canada
Tel.: (403) 255-7535
Industrial Building Construction Services
N.A.I.C.S.: 236210

TROTTHOLMEN AB
Strandvagen 7, SE-114 56, Stockholm, Sweden
Tel.: (46) 703166010
Web Site: http://www.trottholmen.se
Year Founded: 2004
Venture Capital & Private Equity
N.A.I.C.S.: 523999
Henrik Kvick *(Owner)*

Subsidiaries:

NetJobs Group AB (1)
Artillerigatan 42, 114 45, Stockholm, Sweden   (77.32%)
Tel.: (46) 86787420
Web Site: https://netjobsgroup.com
Rev.: $2,150,477
Assets: $981,577
Liabilities: $957,225
Net Worth: $24,352
Earnings: $61,817
Emp.: 17
Fiscal Year-end: 12/31/2022
Media Advertising Services
N.A.I.C.S.: 541840
Lena Strauss *(CFO)*

TROUBADOUR RESOURCES, INC.
6th Floor 905 West Pender Street, Vancouver, V6C 1L6, BC, Canada
Tel.: (604) 968-4844
Web Site:
  https://www.troubadourresource.com
TROUF—(OTCIQ)
Rev.: $2,393
Assets: $934,684
Liabilities: $53,242
Net Worth: $881,442
Earnings: ($378,132)
Fiscal Year-end: 12/31/19
Metal Exploration Services
N.A.I.C.S.: 213114
Gary Schellenberg *(CEO)*

Subsidiaries:

Greenflame Metals Inc. (1)

TROUILLET CARROSSIER CONSTRUCTEUR
Zone Artisanale, 1340, Attignat, Ain, France
Tel.: (33) 474251096
Web Site: http://www.carrosserie-trouillet.com
Sales Range: $75-99.9 Million
Emp.: 160
Motor Vehicles & Car Bodies
N.A.I.C.S.: 336110
Jean-Pierre Robinet *(Dir)*

TROY INFORMATION TECHNOLOGY CO., LTD.
No 28 Xixin Avenue, West Hi-Tech District, Chengdu, 611731, Sichuan, China
Tel.: (86) 2887825555
Web Site: https://www.sc-troy.com
Year Founded: 1996
300366—(CHIN)
Rev.: $307,784,880
Assets: $547,519,284

TROY INFORMATION TECHNOLOGY CO., LTD.

Troy Information Technology Co., Ltd.—(Continued)
Liabilities: $234,108,576
Net Worth: $313,410,708
Earnings: ($5,472,792)
Emp.: 190
Fiscal Year-end: 12/31/22
Data Network Integration Systems & Services
N.A.I.C.S.: 541512
Wenbin Lu (Chm & Gen Mgr)

Subsidiaries:

Shanghai Grid Electric Technology Co., Ltd. (1)
3F No 8 3601 Dongfang Road, Pudong New Area, Shanghai, 200125, China
Tel.: (86) 213 872 6853
Web Site: https://www.grid-elec.com
Software Development Services
N.A.I.C.S.: 513210

Subsidiary (Non-US):

Grid Investment (Cambodia) Co., Ltd. (2)
2 Level 5 Vattanac Capital Tower St 102, Phnom Penh, Cambodia
Tel.: (855) 10291818
Computer System Design Services
N.A.I.C.S.: 541512

Subsidiary (Domestic):

Xi'an Grid Electric Power Co., Ltd. (2)
7F North Area Zhongqing Building 42 Gaoxinliu Road, Xi'an, 710015, Shaanxi, China
Tel.: (86) 2984504010
Computer System Design Services
N.A.I.C.S.: 541512

Xi'an Tongyuan Intelligent Electric Co., Ltd. (2)
7F South west Area Zhongqing Building 42 Gaoxinliu Road, Xi'an, 710015, Shaanxi, China
Tel.: (86) 2988608561
Computer System Design Services
N.A.I.C.S.: 541512

Zhengzhou Grid Electric Intelligent Technology Company (2)
Room 1626 block A Shenglong 27 center nautical Road, Xinghua South Street Erqi District, Zhengzhou, 450015, Henan, China
Tel.: (86) 37165343568
Computer System Design Services
N.A.I.C.S.: 541512

TROY MINERALS INC.
1200-750 W Pender Street, Vancouver, V6C 2T8, BC, Canada
Tel.: (604) 218-4766   BC
Web Site:
  https://www.troyminerals.com
Year Founded: 2018
TROY—(CNSX)
Assets: $478,972
Liabilities: $15,262
Net Worth: $463,711
Earnings: ($92,558)
Fiscal Year-end: 05/31/22
Mineral Exploration Services
N.A.I.C.S.: 213115

TROY RESOURCES LIMITED
Level 2 5 Ord Street, West Perth, 6005, WA, Australia
Tel.: (61) 894811277   AU
Web Site: http://www.troyres.com.au
Rev: $72,868,360
Assets: $51,932,094
Liabilities: $24,559,959
Net Worth: $27,372,135
Earnings: ($32,229,979)
Emp.: 376
Fiscal Year-end: 06/30/19
Gold Exploration & Mining Services
N.A.I.C.S.: 212220
Ken K. Nilsson (CEO & Mng Dir)

Subsidiaries:

Reinarda Mineracao Ltda. (1)
Rua Nove 442 Centro, Rio Maria, CEP 68530-000, PA, Brazil
Tel.: (55) 94 3428 1621
Gold Mining Services
N.A.I.C.S.: 212220

Troy Resources Argentina Ltd. (1)
Fray Mamerto Esquiu 304 Oeste, San Juan, J540 2BGH, Argentina
Tel.: (54) 264 427 7035
Gold Mining Services
N.A.I.C.S.: 212220

TRP BAU GMBH
Stahnsdorfer Strasse 107, Teltow, 14513, Germany
Tel.: (49) 332960440
Web Site: http://www.trp-bau.de
Year Founded: 1997
Rev: $29,424,405
Emp.: 220
Civil Engineering & Pipeline Construction Services
N.A.I.C.S.: 237990
Wolfgang Frey (Mng Dir-Berlin)

TRSB GROUPE SA
11 rue Kepler, 75116, Paris, France
Tel.: (33) 156525200
Web Site: http://www.trsb.net
Sales Range: $10-24.9 Million
Information Technology Services
N.A.I.C.S.: 541519
Philippe Guinchard (Dir-Publication)

Subsidiaries:

Easy Field Services S.A. (1)
85 avenue de la Plaine ZI Rousset Peynier, 13790, Rousset, France
Tel.: (33) 811130014
Web Site: http://www.easy-field.fr
Sales Range: $10-24.9 Million
Emp.: 360
Computer Services
N.A.I.C.S.: 541519

TRU PRECIOUS METALS CORP.
70 Trius Drive, PO Box 1385, Fredericton, E3B 5E3, NB, Canada
Tel.: (647) 880-6414   AB
Web Site:
  https://www.trupreciousmetals.com
Year Founded: 1996
TRU—(OTCIQ)
Rev: $79,168
Assets: $1,142,499
Liabilities: $160,440
Net Worth: $982,059
Earnings: ($2,195,779)
Fiscal Year-end: 12/31/20
Investment Services
N.A.I.C.S.: 523999

TRU-TEST GROUP
25 Carbine Road, Mount Wellington, Auckland, 1060, New Zealand
Tel.: (64) 95748888
Web Site: http://www.tru-test.com
Sales Range: $75-99.9 Million
Mfr & Supplier of Livestock Scales, Milk Metering Equipment, Electric Fences, Fence Tools & Shearing Equipment
N.A.I.C.S.: 115210
John Loughlin (Chm)

Subsidiaries:

Fearing International (Stock Aids) Limited (1)
Creaton Road, Brixworth, Northampton, NN6 9BW, United Kingdom
Tel.: (44) 8456009070
Web Site: http://www.fearing.co.uk
Sales Range: $25-49.9 Million
Emp.: 12
Agricultural Products Supplier

N.A.I.C.S.: 424910
Lisa Harris (Mgr-Sls)

Tru-Test Brasil S.A. (1)
Av Ceara 965, Porto Alegre, 90240-511, Brazil
Tel.: (55) 5133379470
Web Site: http://www.trutest.com.br
Agricultural Products Supplier & Livestock Management
N.A.I.C.S.: 424910

Tru-Test Limited (1)
25 Carbine Road, Mount Wellington, Auckland, 1060, New Zealand
Tel.: (64) 95748888
Web Site: http://www.tru-test.com
Mfr & Whslr of Livestock Weighing & Milk Metering Equipment
N.A.I.C.S.: 333111
George Yerkovich (Mgr-Sls-Auckland Area)

Subsidiary (Non-US):

Ritchey Ltd (2)
Fearby Road, Masham, Ripon, HG4 4ES, North Yorkshire, United Kingdom
Tel.: (44) 1765 689541
Web Site: http://www.ritchey.co.uk
Emp.: 50
Mfr, Distr & Supplier of Animal Husbandry Products
N.A.I.C.S.: 115210
Ashley Musgrave (Dir-Comml)

Subsidiary (US):

Tru-Test, Inc. (2)
528 Grant Rd, Mineral Wells, TX 76067
Tel.: (940) 327-8020
Web Site: http://www.tru-test.com
Sales Range: $1-9.9 Million
Emp.: 15
Farm & Garden Machinery & Equipment Merchant Whslr
N.A.I.C.S.: 423820

Tru-Test Pty Limited (1)
12 Joseph Baldwin Place, Shepparton, 3630, VIC, Australia
Tel.: (61) 3 5820 1800
Electronic Equipment Distr
N.A.I.C.S.: 423690
Neil Silvester (Acct Mgr & Mgr-Natl Mktg)

TRUCKNET ENTERPRISE LTD.
Hasartat 1/Ha-Burseka i St 26, Eilat, Israel
Tel.: (972) 779709090
Web Site: https://www.trucknet.io
Year Founded: 2016
TRAN—(TAE)
Rev: $182,898
Assets: $284,017
Liabilities: $1,708,800
Net Worth: ($1,424,782)
Earnings: ($1,975,411)
Fiscal Year-end: 12/31/23
Software Development Services
N.A.I.C.S.: 541511
Ronen Chen (CTO)

TRUE DATA INC.
Shibadaimon Center Building 4F 1-10-11 Shibadaimon, Minato-ku, Tokyo, 105-0012, Japan
Tel.: (81) 364300721
Web Site: https://www.truedata.co.jp
Year Founded: 2000
4416—(TKS)
Data Processing Services
N.A.I.C.S.: 518210

TRUE ENERGY
Level 33 385 Bourke Street, Melbourne, 3000, VIC, Australia
Tel.: (61) 386281000
Web Site:
  http://www.energyaustralia.com.au
Sales Range: $300-349.9 Million
Emp.: 1,000
Electricity & Energy Supplier
N.A.I.C.S.: 221122
Catherine Tanna (Mng Dir)

INTERNATIONAL PUBLIC

TRUE GREEN ENERGY GROUP CORP.
Unit 5,7 & 8 BUsiness Arcade 1, Philexcel Park M. Roxas Hwy, Clark Freeport Zone, Pampanga, 2009, Philippines
Tel.: (63) 45 4991306
Green Energy Services
N.A.I.C.S.: 213112
Irish Mendoza (PR Officer)

TRUE NORTH FORD
10102 - 97 Street, High Level, T0H 1Z0, AB, Canada
Tel.: (877) 693-2992
Web Site:
  http://www.truenorthford.com
Car Dealership
N.A.I.C.S.: 441110
Davy Peters (Gen Mgr)

TRUE NORTH GEMS INC.
Suite 700 595 Howe St, Vancouver, V6C 2T5, BC, Canada
Tel.: (604) 687-8055
Web Site:
  https://www.truenorthgems.com
TGX—(TSXV)
Assets: $66,990
Liabilities: $5,133,784
Net Worth: ($5,066,793)
Earnings: ($151,044)
Fiscal Year-end: 12/31/23
Mineral Mining Exploration Service
N.A.I.C.S.: 213114
Andrew Lee Smith (CEO-Interim)

TRUE NORTH MANAGERS LLP
Suite F9C Grand Hyatt Plaza, Santacruz East, Mumbai, 400 055, Maharashtra, India
Tel.: (91) 2266824888
Web Site: http://www.truenorth.co.in
Privater Equity Firm
N.A.I.C.S.: 523999
Akash Malik (CEO-Cloudnine)

Subsidiaries:

Shree Digvijay Cement Co. Ltd. (1)
P O Digvijaygram, 361140, Jamnagar, 361140, Gujarat, India
Tel.: (91) 2882344272
Web Site: https://www.digvijaycement.com
Rev: $69,498,197
Assets: $58,924,088
Liabilities: $16,469,107
Net Worth: $42,454,981
Earnings: $7,365,526
Emp.: 273
Fiscal Year-end: 03/31/2021
Cement Mfr
N.A.I.C.S.: 327310
P. R. Singh (VP-Mktg)

TRUE NORTH NUTRITION LTD.
88 E Beaver Creek Rd Bldg A Unit 1, Richmond Hill, L4B 4A8, ON, Canada
Tel.: (905) 762-7070
Web Site:
  http://www.truenorthnutrition.com
Year Founded: 1997
Sales Range: $10-24.9 Million
Emp.: 50
Health Supplements Sales, Marketing & Distribution
N.A.I.C.S.: 424210
Sam DeSimone (CFO)

TRUE NORTH SPORTS & ENTERTAINMENT LIMITED
600-223 Carlton Street, Winnipeg, R3C 0V4, MB, Canada
Tel.: (204) 987-7825
Web Site: https://www.tnse.com
Year Founded: 2003

Holding Company; Sports & Entertainment Arena & Professional Hockey Team Owner & Operator
N.A.I.C.S.: 551112

Subsidiaries:

St. John's IceCaps Hockey Club (1)
Suite 801 Cabot Place 100 New Grower Street, Saint John's, A1C 6K3, NL, Canada
Tel.: (709) 576-2277
Web Site: http://www.stjohnsicecaps.com
Sales Range: $50-74.9 Million
Emp.: 12
Professional Hockey Club
N.A.I.C.S.: 711211
Danny Williams (Pres & CEO)

St. John's Sports & Entertainment (1)
50 New Gower Street, Saint John's, A1C 1J3, NL, Canada
Tel.: (709) 758-1111
Web Site: http://www.mileonecentre.com
Sports & Entertainment Arena & Convention Hall Owner & Operator
N.A.I.C.S.: 711310

The Winnipeg Jets Hockey Club LP (1)
345 Graham Ave, Winnipeg, R3C 5S6, MB, Canada
Tel.: (204) 987-7825
Web Site: http://www.winnipegjets.com
Sales Range: $50-74.9 Million
Professional Hockey Team
N.A.I.C.S.: 711211
Robert Thorsten (VP-People & Patron Svcs)

True North Entertainment Complex LP (1)
345 Graham Ave, Winnipeg, R3C 5S6, MB, Canada
Tel.: (204) 987-7825
Web Site: http://www.mtscentre.ca
Emp.: 200
Sports & Entertainment Arena Operator
N.A.I.C.S.: 711310
Kim Boulet (Dir-Event Mgmt & Security)

TRUE PARTNER CAPITAL HOLDING LIMITED
Suite 2902-03 29/F The Gateway Tower 2 Harbour City 25 Canton Road, Tsim Sha Tsui, Kowloon, China (Hong Kong)
Tel.: (852) 38455900   Ky
Web Site: http://www.truepartnercapital.com
Year Founded: 2010
8657—(HKG)
Holding Company
N.A.I.C.S.: 551112
Ralph Paul Joha Van Put (Chm)

Subsidiaries:

Capital True Partner Technology Co., Ltd. (1)
Room 408-410 4F Poly Center Tower C No 1 Jinxiu Road, Wuhou District, Chengdu, 610041, China   (51%)
Tel.: (86) 2865552888
Business Management Consulting Services
N.A.I.C.S.: 541611

T8 Software Consulting Limited (1)
Suite 2902-03 29/F The Gateway Tower 2 Harbour City 25 Canton Road, Tsim Sha Tsui, Kowloon, China (Hong Kong)
Tel.: (852) 38455900
Web Site: http://www.t8software.com.hk
Software Consulting Services
N.A.I.C.S.: 541512

True Partner Advisor Hong Kong Limited (1)
Suite 2902-03 29/F The Gateway Tower 2 Harbour City 25 Canton Road, Tsim Sha Tsui, Kowloon, China (Hong Kong)
Tel.: (852) 38455900
Web Site: http://www.truepartnercapitaladvisor.com
Investment Management Service
N.A.I.C.S.: 523940

True Partner Capital USA Holding, Inc. (1)
111 W Jackson Blvd Ste 1700, Chicago, IL 60604
Tel.: (312) 675-6128
Web Site: http://www.truepartnercapital.com
Investment Management Service
N.A.I.C.S.: 523940

True Partner China Holding Limited (1)
Suite 2902-03 29/F The Gateway Tower 2 Harbour City 25 Canton Road, Kowloon, China (Hong Kong)
Tel.: (852) 38455900
Investment Holding & Management Services
N.A.I.C.S.: 523999

TRUE SECURITIZADORA S.A.
Av Santo Amaro 48 1 Andar-Cj 12, Itaim Bibi, Sao Paulo, 04506-000, Brazil
Tel.: (55) 1130714475
Web Site: http://www.truesecuritizadora.com.br
Emp.: 100
Financial Investment Services
N.A.I.C.S.: 523940
Bruno Mancini Rovella (Mgr-Legal)

TRUECLAIM EXPLORATION INC.
999 Canada Place Suite 404, Vancouver, V6C 3E2, BC, Canada
Tel.: (604) 657-7004
Web Site: http://www.trmexploration.com
TRM—(TSXV)
Sales Range: Less than $1 Million
Metal Exploration Services
N.A.I.C.S.: 213114
Byron K. Coulthard (Pres & CEO)

TRUELIGHT CORPORATION
I Hsinchu Science Pk 21 Prosperity Rd, Hsin-chu, 300, Taiwan
Tel.: (886) 35780080
Web Site: http://www.truelight.com.tw
Year Founded: 1997
Sales Range: $25-49.9 Million
Emp.: 300
Optical Component Mfr
N.A.I.C.S.: 334419
Pinglin Chen (CFO)

TRUEN CO., LTD.
28 Digital-ro 33-gil, Guro-gu, Seoul, 1309, Korea (South)
Tel.: (82) 267386000
Web Site: https://truen.co.kr
Year Founded: 2005
417790—(KRS)
Broadcasting Equipment Mfr
N.A.I.C.S.: 334220

TRUFFLE ASSET MANAGEMENT (PTY) LTD.
Ground Floor, Lancaster Gate Bldg Hyde Park Lane Business Complex Corner William Nicol & Jan Smuts Hyde Park,, Gauteng, 2196, South Africa
Tel.: (27) 113250030
Web Site: https://truffle.co.za
Year Founded: 2008
Financial Services
N.A.I.C.S.: 523940
Iain Power (Chief Investment Officer & Dir)

TRUFFLE CAPITAL SAS
5 Rue de la Baume, 75008, Paris, France
Tel.: (33) 182284600   FR
Web Site: http://www.truffle.com
Year Founded: 2001
Sales Range: $650-699.9 Million
Emp.: 15
Privater Equity Firm
N.A.I.C.S.: 523999
Henri Moulard (Founder)

TRUFIN PLC
120 Regent Street, London, W1B 5FE, United Kingdom
Tel.: (44) 2037431340   JE
Web Site: https://www.trufin.com
Year Founded: 2017
TRU—(AIM)
Rev.: $20,347,135
Assets: $82,671,043
Liabilities: $32,047,463
Net Worth: $50,623,580
Earnings: ($8,591,265)
Emp.: 149
Fiscal Year-end: 12/31/22
Financial Management Services
N.A.I.C.S.: 541611
Henry Kenner (CEO & Chm)

Subsidiaries:

Magic Fuel Inc. (1)
19528 Ventura Blvd 135, Tarzana, CA 91356
Tel.: (818) 897-5312
Web Site: https://www.fuelmagicinc.com
Fuel Additive Services
N.A.I.C.S.: 541990

Oxygen Finance Limited (1)
Cathedral Place 42-44 Waterloo Street, Birmingham, B2 5QB, United Kingdom
Tel.: (44) 1212954038
Web Site: https://www.oxygen-finance.com
Financial Payment Services
N.A.I.C.S.: 522320
Andrew Price (CFO)

Subsidiary (US):

Oxygen Finance Americas, Inc. (2)
9901 Brodie Ln Ste 160 304, Austin, TX 78748
Financial Payment Services
N.A.I.C.S.: 522320

PlayIgnite Ltd. (1)
56A Poland Street, London, W1F 7NN, United Kingdom
Tel.: (44) 2071181668
Web Site: https://www.playignite.co.uk
Financial Services
N.A.I.C.S.: 523999
Harvey Elliott (CEO)

Porge Ltd. (1)
4th Floor Cathedral Place 42-44 Waterloo Street, Birmingham, B2 5QB, United Kingdom
Tel.: (44) 1242525321
Web Site: http://www.porge.co.uk
Financial Payment Services
N.A.I.C.S.: 522320

Satago Financial Solutions Limited (1)
4th Floor 120 Regent Street, London, W1B 5FE, United Kingdom
Tel.: (44) 2080503015
Web Site: https://www.satago.com
Financial Institution Services
N.A.I.C.S.: 522110

TRUKING TECHNOLOGY LIMITED
No 1 Xinkang Road, Yutan Town Ningxiang, Changsha, 410600, Hunan, China
Tel.: (86) 73187938293
Web Site: https://www.truking.cn
Year Founded: 2000
300358—(CHIN)
Rev.: $904,955,220
Assets: $1,551,070,404
Liabilities: $947,906,388
Net Worth: $603,164,016
Earnings: $79,669,980
Emp.: 6,500
Fiscal Year-end: 12/31/22
Medical Packaging Machinery Mfr
N.A.I.C.S.: 333993
Tang Yue (Chm, Pres & CEO)

Subsidiaries:

Romaco Holding GmbH (1)
Am Heegwald 11, 76227, Karlsruhe, Germany
Tel.: (49) 72148040
Pharmaceutical Product Mfr & Distr
N.A.I.C.S.: 325412

Romaco Pharmatechnik GmbH (1)
Am Heegwald 11, 76227, Karlsruhe, Germany   (75.1%)
Tel.: (49) 7 214 8040
Web Site: http://www.romaco.com
Pharmaceutical Packaging Services
N.A.I.C.S.: 333993
Markus Regner (Mng Dir)

Subsidiary (Non-US):

Romaco France S.A.S. (2)
5 Allee d'Helsinki, 67300, Schiltigheim, France
Tel.: (33) 55 399 7427
Web Site: http://www.romaco.com
Pharmaceutical Packaging & Processing Technologies Whslr
N.A.I.C.S.: 423830

Romaco S.r.L. (2)
Via del Savena 22 Pianoro, 40065, Bologna, Italy
Tel.: (39) 0516202411
Web Site: http://www.romaco.com
Printing, Packaging & Filling Services for the Pharmaceutical Industry
N.A.I.C.S.: 333993

Romaco do Brasil, Ltda. (2)
Rua da Paz 1275, Sao Paulo, 04713-001, SP, Brazil
Tel.: (55) 113 168 7992
Web Site: http://www.romaco.com
Pharmaceutical Packaging Machinery Sales & Service
N.A.I.C.S.: 423830

Sichuan Pharmaceutical Inc. (1)
Bai Ye Road No 18, High-tech zone, Chengdu, 611731, Sichuan, China
Tel.: (86) 2862808625
Web Site: https://www.sczyzj.com
Pharmaceuticals Product Mfr
N.A.I.C.S.: 325412

Truking Feiyun Pharmaceutical Equipment (Changsha) Limited (1)
No 197 Jinzhou Avenue, Ningxiang Economic-Technological Development Zone, Changsha, Hunan, China
Tel.: (86) 73187938258
Web Site: https://www.trukingfeiyun.com
Pharmaceutical Equipment Mfr
N.A.I.C.S.: 325412
Ye Dajin (Chm)

TRULIFE LIMITED
3013 Lake Drive City West Business Campus, 24, Dublin, Ireland
Tel.: (353) 4511755   IE
Web Site: http://trulife.com
Health Care Products Mfr
N.A.I.C.S.: 339999
Noel J. Murphy (Grp CEO)

Subsidiaries:

Trulife Limited (1)
41 Amos Road Meadowhall, Sheffield, S9 1BX, United Kingdom
Tel.: (44) 114 26 18100
Healthcare Products Mfr & Distr
N.A.I.C.S.: 339999

Branch (Domestic):

Trulife Limited-Birmingham (2)
30 Soverign Road, Kings Norton Business Centre, Birmingham, B30 3HN, United Kingdom
Tel.: (44) 121 4513 016
Healthcare Products Mfr & Distr
N.A.I.C.S.: 339999

Trulife Limited-Cork (1)
Kilbarry Business Park, Dublin Hill, Cork, Ireland

TRULIFE LIMITED

Trulife Limited—(Continued)
Tel.: (353) 214654012
Health Care Products Mfr
N.A.I.C.S.: 339999

Trulife, Inc. (1)
2010 High St, Jackson, MI 49203
Tel.: (800) 492-1088
Web Site: http://www.trulife.com
Sales Range: $1-9.9 Million
Emp.: 30
Surgical Appliance & Supplies Mfr
N.A.I.C.S.: 339113
Noel J. Murphy *(CEO)*

Subsidiary (Domestic):

Pro CNC, Inc. (2)
445 Sequoia Dr Ste 113, Bellingham, WA 98226
Tel.: (360) 714-9000
Web Site: http://www.procnc.com
Sales Range: $1-9.9 Million
Machine Shops
N.A.I.C.S.: 332710
Paul Van Metre *(Pres & VP-Sls & Mktg)*

TRULY INTERNATIONAL HOLDINGS LIMITED

2nd Floor Zhongxin Knitting Centre
1-3 Wing Yip Street, Kwai Chung,
New Territories, China (Hong Kong)
Tel.: (852) 24879803
Web Site: https://www.truly.com.hk
0732—(OTCIQ)
Rev.: $2,464,942,298
Assets: $3,385,576,827
Liabilities: $2,064,516,211
Net Worth: $1,321,060,616
Earnings: $40,794,024
Emp.: 14,000
Fiscal Year-end: 12/31/22
Electric Equipment Mfr
N.A.I.C.S.: 334416
James Pong Chun Wong *(COO)*

Subsidiaries:

Truly (USA) Inc. (1)
2620 Concord Ave Ste 106, Alhambra, CA 91803-1235
Tel.: (626) 284-3033
Web Site: https://www.trulyusa.com
Touch Display Mfr & Distr
N.A.I.C.S.: 334419

Truly Electrical Products Company Limited (1)
2F Chung Shun Knitting Ctr 1-3 Wing Yip St, Kwai Chung, New Territories, China (Hong Kong)
Tel.: (852) 24879803
Web Site: http://www.truly.com
Electric Motor Mfr
N.A.I.C.S.: 423610
Fred Canter *(Gen Mgr)*

Truly Electronics Manufacturing Limited (1)
2/F Chung Shun Knitting Centre 1-3 Wing Yip Street, Kwai Chung, New Territories, China (Hong Kong)
Tel.: (852) 2 487 9803
Web Site: https://www.trulypcb.com
Music Player & Calculator Mfr
N.A.I.C.S.: 333310

Subsidiary (Domestic):

Truly Industrial Limited (2)
2F Chung Shun Knitting Ctr 1-3 Wing Yip St, Kwai Chung, New Territories, China (Hong Kong)
Tel.: (852) 24879803
Web Site: http://www.truly.com.hk
Emp.: 100
Printed Circuit Board Panels Mfr
N.A.I.C.S.: 334412

Truly Instrument Limited (2)
2/F Chung Shun Knitting Centre 1-3 Wing Yip Street, Kwai Chung, New Territories, China (Hong Kong)
Tel.: (852) 24879803
Web Site: https://www.trulyinstrument.com

Sales Range: $50-74.9 Million
Emp.: 110
Diagnostic Devices Mfr & Distr
N.A.I.C.S.: 334510

Truly International Holdings Limited - Shanwei Factory (1)
North of The Dong Chong Road Truly IndustrialArea, Shanwei, Guangdong, China
Tel.: (86) 6603372777
Touch Display Mfr & Distr
N.A.I.C.S.: 334419

Truly Opto-Electronics Limited (1)
Xinli Industrial City Industrial Avenue, Shanwei, Guangdong, China (84.25%)
Tel.: (86) 6603823333
Web Site: https://www.trulyopto.com
Touch Display Mfr & Distr
N.A.I.C.S.: 334419

Truly Semiconductors (Singapore) Pte. Ltd. (1)
19 Keppel Road 06-05 Jit Poh Building, Singapore, 89058, Singapore
Tel.: (65) 65344119
Touch Display Distr
N.A.I.C.S.: 423690

Truly Semiconductors Limited (1)
North Section of Dongchong Road, Truly Electronic Industrial City, Shanwei, 516600, Guangdong, China
Tel.: (86) 660 337 2777
Web Site: https://www.trulysemi.com
Flat Panel Displays Mfr
N.A.I.C.S.: 334118

Subsidiary (Domestic):

Lightning Digital Technology Co., Ltd (2)
Units 2203 22nd Floor SEG Plaza Huaqiang Road North, Futian District, Shenzhen, 518000, Guangdong, China
Tel.: (86) 75583666639
Flat Panel Displays Mfr
N.A.I.C.S.: 334118

Truly Semiconductors Limited (1)
2/F Chung Shun Knitting Centre 1-3 Wing Yip Street, Kwai Chung, New Territories, China (Hong Kong)
Tel.: (852) 2 487 9803
Web Site: https://www.trulysemi.com
Automobile Parts Mfr
N.A.I.C.S.: 336211

TRUMPF SE + CO. KG

Johann-Maus-Strasse 2, 71254, Ditzingen, Germany
Tel.: (49) 71563030 De
Web Site: http://www.trumpf.com
Year Founded: 1923
Rev.: $4,237,561,439
Assets: $4,411,335,714
Liabilities: $2,145,713,352
Net Worth: $2,265,622,362
Earnings: $235,363,216
Emp.: 14,490
Fiscal Year-end: 06/30/19
Holding Company; Machine Tools, Power Tools, Laser Technologies, Electronics & Medical Technologies Mfr
N.A.I.C.S.: 551112
Peter Leibinger *(Vice Chm-Mgmt Bd & CTO)*

Subsidiaries:

Access Laser (Shenzhen) Co., Ltd. (1)
0903A Building C6 Hengfeng Industrial City 739 Zhoushi Road, Baoan District, Shenzhen, 518126, Guangdong, China
Tel.: (86) 75588866783
Web Site: http://www.accesslaser.cn
Photonic Equipment Mfr
N.A.I.C.S.: 333310

Amphos GmbH (1)
Kaiserstrasse 100, 52134, Herzogenrath, Germany
Tel.: (49) 24156529210
Web Site: http://www.amphos.de
Industrial Equipment Distr

N.A.I.C.S.: 423840
Jan Dolkemeyer *(Mng Dir)*

Auroma Technologies Co. Dba Access Laser Company (1)
2211 W Casino Rd Unit A1, Everett, WA 98204
Tel.: (425) 582-8674
Web Site: http://www.accesslaser.com
Photonic Equipment Mfr
N.A.I.C.S.: 333310
Ben Fisher *(Engr-Applications & Sls)*

BeSpoon SAS (1)
17 rue du lac Saint-Andre - Savoie Technolac, BP 10402, 73372, Le Bourget du Lac, France
Tel.: (33) 458828888
Web Site: http://www.bespoon.xyz
Tracking Services
N.A.I.C.S.: 517810
Jean Marie Andre *(Co-Founder & CEO)*

Bruma Machinehandel B.V. (1)
Edyweg 17, 6956 BA, Spankeren, Netherlands
Tel.: (31) 313490200
Web Site: http://www.en.bruma.nl
Metal Cutting Machinery Mfr
N.A.I.C.S.: 333517

FA Service Corporation (1)
4F MetLife Shin-Yokohama Building 3-8-11, Shin-Yokohama Kohoku-ku, Yokohama, 222-0033, Kanagawa, Japan
Tel.: (81) 454708851
Web Site: http://www.faservice.co.jp
3D CAD & CAM Product Mfr
N.A.I.C.S.: 333248

Huettinger Electronic GmbH & Co. KG (1)
Botzinger Strasse 80, Postfach 600 263, 79111, Freiburg, Germany
Tel.: (49) 76189710
Web Site: http://www.huettinger.com
Sales Range: $75-99.9 Million
Emp.: 500
Plasma Applications
N.A.I.C.S.: 335999

Jiangsu Jinfangyuan CNC Machine Co., Ltd. (1)
19 of Yinbai Road, Hanjiang Industry Park, Yangzhou, 225127, Jiangsu, China
Tel.: (86) 51480522468
Web Site: http://www.jfymachine.com
Machine Tools Mfr
N.A.I.C.S.: 333517

One Click Metal GmbH (1)
Carl-Benz-Str 2, 71732, Tamm, Germany
Tel.: (49) 1794142058
Web Site: http://www.oneclickmetal.com
Metal Additive Mfr
N.A.I.C.S.: 333248
Julia Neufer *(Mgr-HR & Bus Ops)*

PT TRUMPF Indonesia (1)
German Centre 4th floor suite 4260-4290 Jl Kapt, Subijanto Dj Block COA No 1, 15321, Tangerang, Indonesia
Tel.: (62) 21 2565 0016
Machine Tools Mfr
N.A.I.C.S.: 333517
Christian Handojo *(Engr-Svc)*

Q.ant GmbH (1)
Handwerkstr 29, 70565, Stuttgart, Germany
Tel.: (49) 71145969613
Web Site: http://www.qant.de
Engineering Services
N.A.I.C.S.: 541330
Helge Hattermann *(Product Dir-Quantum Sensors)*

SPI Lasers Korea Ltd. (1)
A-1201 Daebang Triplaon Business Tower 1682, Jungsan-dong Ilsandong-gu, Goyang, Korea (South)
Tel.: (82) 319267580
Fiber Optic Cable Mfr & Retailer
N.A.I.C.S.: 335921

SPI Lasers LLC (1)
4000 Burton Dr, Santa Clara, CA 95054
Tel.: (408) 454-1170
Electrical & Electronic Product Mfr
N.A.I.C.S.: 335999

SPI Lasers plc (1)

INTERNATIONAL PUBLIC

6 Wellington Park Tollbar Way, Hedge End, Southampton, SO30 2QU, United Kingdom
Tel.: (44) 1489779696
Web Site: http://www.spilasers.com
Emp.: 350
Fiber Optic Cable Mfr & Retailer
N.A.I.C.S.: 335921
Mark Greenwood *(CEO)*

TPT Maquinas-Ferramentas e Laser, Unipessoal, Lda. (1)
Lagoas Park Edificio 11 Piso 1, 2740-270, Porto Salvo, Portugal
Tel.: (351) 211964570
Power Supply Product Mfr
N.A.I.C.S.: 335999

TRUMPF (China) Co., Ltd. (1)
1/F Block A1 Jinghai Industrial Park No 156 Jinghai 4th Road, 100176, Beijing, China
Tel.: (86) 10 5920 9710
Machine Tools Mfr
N.A.I.C.S.: 333517

TRUMPF (India) Pvt. Ltd. (1)
Raisoni Industrial Park S No 276 Hissa No 1, Village Mann Taluka Mulshi, 411 057, Pune, India
Tel.: (91) 20 66759800
Machine Tools Mfr
N.A.I.C.S.: 333517
Soumitra Joshi *(Mng Dir)*

TRUMPF (Pte.) Ltd. (1)
25 International Business Park 02-28/29 German Centre, Singapore, 609916, Singapore
Tel.: (65) 65718000
Web Site: http://www.sg.trumpf.com
Machine Tools Mfr
N.A.I.C.S.: 333517
Hans-Peter Laubscher *(Mng Dir)*

TRUMPF AMSA SAS (1)
146 Bd Charcot, BP 477, 63013, Clermont-Ferrand, France
Tel.: (33) 473195050
Emp.: 30
Medical Equipment Mfr
N.A.I.C.S.: 334510
Jean Heinrich *(Gen Dir)*

TRUMPF Bulgaria Ltd. (1)
140 Mimi Balkanska St, 1540, Sofia, Bulgaria
Tel.: (359) 28601492
Power Supply Product Mfr
N.A.I.C.S.: 335999
Nikolai Georgiev *(Sls Mgr)*

TRUMPF Canada, Inc. (1)
3755 Laird Road Unit 1, Mississauga, L5L 0B3, ON, Canada
Tel.: (905) 363-3529
Web Site: http://www.us.trumpf.com
Emp.: 20
Machine Tools Mfr
N.A.I.C.S.: 333517
Tobias Kuehnle *(Mng Dir)*

TRUMPF China (Hong Kong) Ltd. (1)
23/F Tower A Southmark 11 Yip Hing Street, Hong Kong, China (Hong Kong)
Tel.: (852) 2880 9808
Machine Tools Mfr
N.A.I.C.S.: 333517

TRUMPF Corporation (1)
1-18-2 Hakusan, Midori-ku, Yokohama, 226-0006, Japan
Tel.: (81) 45 9315710
Machine Tools Mfr
N.A.I.C.S.: 333517

TRUMPF Engineering Services Italy s.r.l (1)
Via Alessandria 41/a, 10098, Rivoli, Italy
Tel.: (39) 011 5840010
Machine Tools Mfr
N.A.I.C.S.: 333517
Giovanni Vidotto *(Mng Dir)*

TRUMPF Finance (Schweiz) AG (1)
Ruessenstrasse 8, 6340, Baar, Switzerland
Tel.: (41) 41 769 6226
Machine Tools Mfr
N.A.I.C.S.: 333517

TRUMPF Financial Services GmbH (1)

Johann-Maus-Strasse 2, 71254, Ditzingen, Germany
Tel.: (49) 71563030
Power Supply Product Mfr
N.A.I.C.S.: 335999
Lars Grunert *(Chm)*

TRUMPF Grusch AG (1)
Strasse 8, 7214, Grusch, Switzerland
Tel.: (41) 81 3076161
Power Tool Mfr
N.A.I.C.S.: 333991
Marta Wandraschek *(Mgr-Matl)*

TRUMPF HUETTINGER Electronic K.K. (1)
3-22-13 Shin-Yokohama, Ko-hoku-ku, Yokohama, 222-0033, Japan
Tel.: (81) 45 470 3761
Electric Equipment Mfr
N.A.I.C.S.: 334419

TRUMPF Homberger S.r.l. (1)
Via del Commercio 6, 20090, Buccinasco, Italy
Tel.: (39) 02 484891
Machine Tools Mfr
N.A.I.C.S.: 333517
Fabio Cervo *(Mgr-Sls-Order Processing)*

TRUMPF Huettinger K.K. (1)
2-6-22 Kurigi, Asaou-ku, Kawasaki, 215-0033, Japan
Tel.: (81) 442813007
Power Supply Product Mfr
N.A.I.C.S.: 335999

TRUMPF Huettinger Sp. z o. o. (1)
Marecka 47, 05-220, Zielonka, Poland
Tel.: (48) 22 7613800
Electric Equipment Mfr
N.A.I.C.S.: 334419
Piotr Swiatkiewicz *(VP-Production)*

TRUMPF Huettinger, Inc. (1)
4000 Burton Dr, Santa Clara, CA 95054
Tel.: (408) 454-1180
Electric Equipment Mfr
N.A.I.C.S.: 334419
Pawel Grabowski *(Pres)*

TRUMPF Hungary Kft. (1)
Szallito u 6 III em, 1211, Budapest, Hungary
Tel.: (36) 1 2781600
Machine Tools Mfr
N.A.I.C.S.: 333517

TRUMPF Huttinger (Shanghai) Co., Ltd. (1)
Room 634 6F Shanghai Central Plaza No 381 Huaihai Zhong Road, 200020, Shanghai, China
Tel.: (86) 21 6171 9140
Electric Equipment Mfr
N.A.I.C.S.: 334419

TRUMPF Huttinger GmbH + Co. KG (1)
Botzinger Strasse 80, 79111, Freiburg, Germany
Tel.: (49) 76189710
Power Supply Product Mfr
N.A.I.C.S.: 335999
Christian Casar *(Head-Global Svcs)*

TRUMPF Inc. (1)
111 Hyde Rd, Farmington, CT 06032
Tel.: (860) 255-6000
Web Site: http://www.us.trumpf.com
Sales Range: $125-149.9 Million
Emp.: 700
Metal Fabrication Machinery Mfr & Laser Technology
N.A.I.C.S.: 333517
Doug Devnew *(VP-Fin & Admin)*

TRUMPF Korea Co., Ltd. (1)
7th Fl TRUTEC Building Sangam-dong 12 Worldcupbuk-ro 56-gil, Mapo-gu, Seoul, 121-835, Korea (South)
Tel.: (82) 2 60962510
Web Site: http://www.fr.trumpf.com
Emp.: 150
Machine Tools Mfr
N.A.I.C.S.: 333517
Jinyeung Bae *(CEO)*

TRUMPF Laser GmbH (1)
Aichhalder Strasse 39, 78713, Schramberg, Germany

Tel.: (49) 7422 515 0
Machine Tools Mfr
N.A.I.C.S.: 333517

TRUMPF Liberec, spol. s.r.o. (1)
Amperova 483, 46218, Liberec, Czech Republic
Tel.: (420) 482 365800
Machine Tools Mfr
N.A.I.C.S.: 333517
Radek Tybl *(Mgr)*

TRUMPF Ltd. (1)
President Way Airport Executive Park, Luton, LU2 9NL, Bedfordshire, United Kingdom
Tel.: (44) 1582 725335
Emp.: 80
N.A.I.C.S.: 333517
Gavin McNab *(Area Mgr-Sls)*

TRUMPF Ltd. (1)
19 21 Motorway Road Klongsongtonnoon, Lat Krabang, 10520, Bangkok, Thailand
Tel.: (66) 20327888
Power Supply Product Mfr
N.A.I.C.S.: 335999
Somchai Chakornsiri *(Gen Mgr)*

TRUMPF MIDDLE EAST (1)
10 Nehru street Roxy Heliopolis, 11341, Cairo, Egypt
Tel.: (20) 2 451 9974
Power Tool Mfr
N.A.I.C.S.: 333991

TRUMPF Macchine Italia S.r.l. (1)
Via E Fermi 17, 36045, Lonigo, Italy
Tel.: (39) 0444432811
Machine Tools Mfr
N.A.I.C.S.: 333517
Andrea Ramin *(Production Mgr)*

TRUMPF Machines SARL (1)
12 Chemin de la Sandlach, 67500, Haguenau, France
Tel.: (33) 390 552255
Machine Tools Mfr
N.A.I.C.S.: 333517

TRUMPF Makina Sanayii A.S. (1)
Serifali Mah Kutup Sok TRUMPF Plaza No 22, Umbraniye, 34775, Istanbul, Türkiye
Tel.: (90) 2165704500
Power Supply Product Mfr
N.A.I.C.S.: 335999

TRUMPF Malaysia Sdn. Bhd. (1)
No 41-8 8th Level Block SC The Boulevard Mid Valley City, Lingkaran Syed Putra, 59200, Kuala Lumpur, Malaysia
Tel.: (60) 3 20815 788
Machine Tools Mfr
N.A.I.C.S.: 333517
Dylan Siauw *(Asst Mgr-Sls)*

TRUMPF Maquinaria S.A. (1)
Valportillo Primera no 1, 28108, Alcobendas, Spain
Tel.: (34) 91 6573662
Machine Tools Mfr
N.A.I.C.S.: 333517

TRUMPF Maquinas Ind. E. Com. Ltda. (1)
Avenida Jurua 150 - Alphaville, Barueri, 06455-10, Sao Paulo, Brazil
Tel.: (55) 11 41333560
Machine Tools Mfr
N.A.I.C.S.: 333517
Sergio Carvalho *(Treas)*

TRUMPF Maschinen Austria GmbH + Co. KG (1)
Industriepark 24, 4061, Pasching, Austria
Tel.: (43) 7221 6030
Web Site: http://www.at.trumpf.com
Emp.: 550
Machine Tools Mfr
N.A.I.C.S.: 333517
Amin Rau *(Gen Mgr)*

TRUMPF Maskin AB (1)
Aleforsvaegen 5, 44139, Alingsas, Sweden
Tel.: (46) 322 669700
Machine Tools Mfr
N.A.I.C.S.: 333517

TRUMPF Mexico S. de R.L. de C.V. (1)
Blvd Apodaca No 201 Apodaca Technology Park, 66627, Apodaca, Nuevo Leon, Mexico
Tel.: (52) 81 81312100
Machine Tools Mfr
N.A.I.C.S.: 333517

TRUMPF Nederland B.V. (1)
John Maynard Keynesstraat 301, 7559 SV, Hengelo, Netherlands
Tel.: (31) 88 4002400
Machine Tools Mfr
N.A.I.C.S.: 333517

TRUMPF OOO (1)
1-j Proezd Perova Polja 9 Building 4, 111141, Moscow, Russia (100%)
Tel.: (7) 4952345713
Web Site: http://www.trumpf-powertools.com
Machine Tooling
N.A.I.C.S.: 333517

TRUMPF Philippines Inc. (1)
Unit 5S 26th Floor Twenty-Four Seven Mc-Kinley, 24th Street corner 7th Avenue Bonifacio Global City, Taguig, Philippines
Tel.: (63) 28644100
Power Supply Product Mfr
N.A.I.C.S.: 335999

TRUMPF Photonics, Inc. (1)
2601 US Route 130S, Cranbury, NJ 08512
Tel.: (609) 925-8200
Water Equipment Mfr
N.A.I.C.S.: 334510

TRUMPF Polska Sp. z o.o. (1)
ul Polczynska 111, 01-303, Warsaw, Poland
Tel.: (48) 22 5753900
Machine Tools Mfr
N.A.I.C.S.: 333517

TRUMPF Praha, spol. s.r.o. (1)
K Hajum 1355/2a, 15500, Prague, Czech Republic
Tel.: (420) 251 106200
Machine Tools Mfr
N.A.I.C.S.: 333517
Jiri Varenka *(Mgr-Svc)*

TRUMPF SAS (1)
ZI Paris Nord 2 86 Allee des Erables CS 52239, Villepinte, 95956, Roissy-en-France, Cedex, France
Tel.: (33) 1 48178040
Machine Tools Mfr
N.A.I.C.S.: 333517

TRUMPF Sachsen GmbH (1)
Leibingerstrasse 13, 01904, Neukirch, Germany
Tel.: (49) 35951 80
Machine Tools Mfr
N.A.I.C.S.: 333517

TRUMPF Scientific Lasers GmbH + Co. KG (1)
Feringastr 10a, 85774, Munich, Germany
Tel.: (49) 7156 303 0
Water Equipment Mfr
N.A.I.C.S.: 334510

TRUMPF Sheet Metal Products (Dongguan) Co., Ltd. (1)
4th North Industry Road North Industry Park Songshan Lake, Sci & Tech Industry Park, Dongguan, 523808, China
Tel.: (86) 769 2289 8088
Machine Tools Mfr
N.A.I.C.S.: 333517

TRUMPF Slovakia, s.r.o. (1)
Rozvojova 2, 04011, Kosice, Slovakia
Tel.: (421) 55 728091
Machine Tools Mfr
N.A.I.C.S.: 333517

TRUMPF Taiwan Industries Co., Ltd. (1)
No 28 Huaya 1st Rd Gueishan Shiang, 33383, Taoyuan, Taiwan
Tel.: (886) 3 2708000
Web Site: http://www.trumpf.com
Emp.: 43
Machine Tools Mfr
N.A.I.C.S.: 333517
Tseng James *(Mgr-Svc-Laser Tech)*

TRUMPF Vietnam PTE LTD (1)
Suite 238 3rd Floor No 33A Pham Ngu Lao Street, Hoan Kiem District, Hanoi, Vietnam
Tel.: (84) 4 3933 6155
Machine Tools Mfr

N.A.I.C.S.: 333517
Tong Kim *(Sr Engr-Svc)*

TRUMPF Werkzeugmaschinen GmbH + Co. KG (1)
Osikova 24, 637 00, Brno Jundrov, Czech Republic
Tel.: (420) 5 41238186
Web Site: http://www.trumpf.cz
Emp.: 70
Water Equipment Mfr
N.A.I.C.S.: 334510

TRUMPF Werkzeugmaschinen Teningen GmbH (1)
Emmendinger Strasse 21, 79331, Teningen, Germany
Tel.: (49) 764146090
Power Supply Product Mfr
N.A.I.C.S.: 335999

XETICS GmbH (1)
Mittlerer Pfad 4/2, 70499, Stuttgart, Germany
Tel.: (49) 71125252950
Web Site: http://www.xetics.com
Software Installation Services
N.A.I.C.S.: 541519
Philipp Dreiss *(Mng Dir)*

c-labs Corporation (1)
11819 268th Dr NE, Duvall, WA 98019
Tel.: (425) 999-3295
Web Site: http://www.c-labs.com
Mobile & Cloud Integration Services
N.A.I.C.S.: 541512
Chris M. Muench *(CEO)*

TRUNG AN HI-TECH FARMING JOINT STOCK COMPANY

No 649A national road No 91 Quy Thanh 1 Trung Kien, Thot Not, Can Tho, Vietnam
Tel.: (84) 2923857336
TAR—(HNX)
Rev.: $379,802,000
Assets: $279,313,300
Liabilities: $158,886,800
Net Worth: $120,426,500
Earnings: $6,820,100
Fiscal Year-end: 12/31/22
Agricultural Chemical Mfr
N.A.I.C.S.: 325320
Nguyen Le Bao Trang *(Gen Mgr)*

TRUNKBOW INTERNATIONAL HOLDINGS LIMITED

Unit 1217-1218 12F of Tower B Gemdale Plaza No 91 Jianguo Road, Chaoyang District, Beijing, 100022, China
Tel.: (86) 10 85712518 NV
Web Site: http://www.trunkbow.com
Year Founded: 2001
Sales Range: $10-24.9 Million
Emp.: 194
Holding Company; Mobile Platform Application Software Developer & Publisher
N.A.I.C.S.: 551112
Wanchun Hou *(Chm)*

Subsidiaries:

Trunkbow Asia Pacific (Shandong) Co., Ltd. (1)
6/F Main Bldg Shanda Technology Industrial Park Yingxiu Road, High-tech District, Jinan, 250101, Shandong, China (100%)
Tel.: (86) 531 8970 6000
Web Site: http://www.trunkbow.com
Mobile Platform Application Software Developer & Publisher
N.A.I.C.S.: 513210
Qiang Li *(CEO)*

Trunkbow Asia Pacific (Shenzhen) Co., Ltd. (1)
Room D 5/F Noble Center No 1006 Fuzhong San Road, Futian District, Shenzhen, 518026, Guangdong, China (100%)
Tel.: (86) 755 8202 8890
Web Site: http://www.trunkbow.com
Mobile Platform Application Software Developer & Publisher

TRUNKBOW INTERNATIONAL HOLDINGS LIMITED

Trunkbow International Holdings
Limited—(Continued)
N.A.I.C.S.: 513210
Qiang Li *(CEO)*

TRUONG HAI AUTO CORPORATION
01 H Slot Dien Bien Phu St, Ward 25, Biinh Thanh District, Ho Chi Minh City, Vietnam
Tel.: (84) 8 35126991
Web Site:
http://www.truonghaiauto.com.vn
Sales Range: $250-299.9 Million
Emp.: 2,500
Automobile Mfr
N.A.I.C.S.: 336110
Duong Ba Tran *(Chm)*

TRUONG LONG ENGINEERING & AUTO JOINT STOCK COMPANY
Lo 46 Duong so 3 Khu cong nghiep Tan Tao, Quan Binh Tan, Ho Chi Minh City, Vietnam
Tel.: (84) 0906720101
Web Site:
https://www.truonglong.com
HTL—(HOSE)
Rev.: $27,090,030
Assets: $18,465,634
Liabilities: $7,805,093
Net Worth: $10,660,541
Earnings: $1,578,908
Fiscal Year-end: 12/31/23
Motor Vehicle Maintenance Services
N.A.I.C.S.: 811114
Truong Son La Van *(Founder)*

TRUONG THANH FURNITURE CORPORATION
DT 747 Street Quarter 7, Uyen Hung Ward Tan Uyen District, Thuan An, Binh Duong, Vietnam
Tel.: (84) 2743642004   VN
Web Site:
https://www.truongthanh.com
Year Founded: 1993
TTF—(HOSE)
Rev.: $64,291,405
Assets: $117,438,993
Liabilities: $106,433,237
Net Worth: $11,005,756
Earnings: ($5,942,976)
Emp.: 1,179
Fiscal Year-end: 12/31/23
Wood Products Mfr
N.A.I.C.S.: 321999
Truong Thanh Vo *(Chm)*

TRUONG TIEN GROUP JSC
Truong An Industrial Group, An Khanh Commune Hoai Duc District, Hanoi, Vietnam
Tel.: (84) 433650853
Rev.: $6,539,117
Assets: $8,919,821
Liabilities: $1,339,433
Net Worth: $7,580,388
Earnings: $98,814
Fiscal Year-end: 12/31/19
Apparel Accessory Mfr
N.A.I.C.S.: 315990

TRUPHONE LIMITED
4 Royal Mint Court, London, EC3N 4HJ, United Kingdom
Tel.: (44) 20 7961 0880
Web Site: http://www.truphone.com
Year Founded: 2006
Sales Range: $75-99.9 Million
Emp.: 300
Mobile Telecommunications Services
N.A.I.C.S.: 517112
Steve Robertson *(Chm & CEO-Strategic Partnerships)*

Subsidiaries:

SCN Truphone SL (1)
Via de las Dos Castillas 33 Ed Atica III 1 planta, Pozuelo de Alarcon, 28224, Madrid, Spain
Tel.: (34) 913513426
Web Site: http://www.truphone.com
Wireless Telecommunication Services
N.A.I.C.S.: 517112

Truphone Australia Pty Ltd (1)
100 Walker Street, North Sydney, 2060, NSW, Australia
Tel.: (61) 289994206
Web Site: http://www.truphone.com
Wireless Telecommunication Services
N.A.I.C.S.: 517112

Truphone BV (1)
Rembrandtlaan 1a, 3723 BG, Bilthoven, Netherlands
Tel.: (31) 307600556
Web Site: http://www.truphone.com
Corn Syrup, Dried Or Unmixed
N.A.I.C.S.: 311221

Truphone GmbH (1)
An der Herrenmuehle 7 - 9, 61440, Oberursel, Germany
Tel.: (49) 61718976510
Web Site: http://www.truphone.com
Wireless Telecommunication Services
N.A.I.C.S.: 517112

Truphone Hong Kong Limited (1)
Level 15 Langham Place 8 Argyle Street, Mong Kok, Kowloon, China (Hong Kong)
Tel.: (852) 81012102
Web Site: http://www.truphone.com
Wireless Telecommunication Services
N.A.I.C.S.: 517112

Truphone Polska SP Z.o.o. (1)
ul Ilzecka 26, 02-135, Warsaw, Poland
Tel.: (48) 732400907
Web Site: http://www.truphone.com
Wireless Telecommunication Services
N.A.I.C.S.: 517112
Joanna Pedzinska *(Dir-Mktg)*

Truphone, Inc. (1)
4309 Emperor Blvd Ste 325 Research Triangle Park, Durham, NC 27703
Tel.: (888) 996-6245
Wireless Telecommunication Services
N.A.I.C.S.: 517112

TRUS Y 7 REIT CO., LTD.
923-12 Mok-dong, Yangcheon-gu, Seoul, 07995, Korea (South)
Tel.: (82) 27858920
Year Founded: 2011
Rev.: $3,043,513
Assets: $96,472,559
Liabilities: $55,862,936
Net Worth: $40,609,623
Earnings: $238,312
Fiscal Year-end: 12/31/17
Real Estate Related Services
N.A.I.C.S.: 531390

TRUSCO NAKAYAMA CORPORATION
TRUSCO Central Building 2-5 Honmachi 4-chome, Chuo-ku, Osaka, 541-0053, Japan
Tel.: (81) 662439830
Web Site: https://www.trusco.co.jp
9830—(TKS)
Rev.: $1,901,211,860
Assets: $1,736,185,020
Liabilities: $596,708,580
Net Worth: $1,139,476,440
Earnings: $86,980,120
Emp.: 3,043
Fiscal Year-end: 12/31/23
Machine & Mechanical Tools Whslr
N.A.I.C.S.: 423830
Tetsuya Nakayama *(Pres)*

Subsidiaries:

PT. Trusco Nakayama Indonesia (1)
Jl Kenari Raya No 36 Delta SiliconVI, Jayamukti Cikarang Pusat, Bekasi, 17815, Indonesia
Tel.: (62) 2189911276
Emp.: 20
Special Tool Mfr
N.A.I.C.S.: 333514

Trusco Nakayama Corporation (Thailand) Limited (1)
TIP7 789/8 Moo9, Bangpla Bangplee, Samut Prakan, 10540, Thailand
Tel.: (66) 213670458
Emp.: 22
Metal Product Whslr
N.A.I.C.S.: 423510

TRUSCOTT MINING CORPORATION LIMITED
Web Site:
http://www.truscottmining.com.au
TRM—(ASX)
Rev.: $632
Assets: $1,967,703
Liabilities: $1,283,821
Net Worth: $683,882
Earnings: ($349,717)
Fiscal Year-end: 06/30/24
Gold Metal Exploration
N.A.I.C.S.: 213114
Peter N. Smith *(Chm & Chm)*

TRUSCREEN GROUP LIMITED
Level 6 Equitable House 57 Symonds Street, Grafton, Auckland, 1010, New Zealand
Tel.: (64) 449115065
Web Site: https://www.truscreen.com
Year Founded: 2013
TRU—(NZX)
Rev.: $994,389
Assets: $2,075,468
Liabilities: $555,119
Net Worth: $1,520,349
Earnings: ($1,436,507)
Emp.: 13
Fiscal Year-end: 03/31/23
Medical Equipment Mfr
N.A.I.C.S.: 339112
Guy Robertson *(CFO)*

TRUST ALLIANCE INFORMATION DEVELOPMENT INC. LTD.
Building 11 No 879 Zhongjiang Road, Shanghai, 200333, China
Tel.: (86) 2151077666
Web Site:
https://www.cesgroup.com.cn
300469—(CHIN)
Rev.: $34,717,201
Assets: $189,550,409
Liabilities: $88,894,421
Net Worth: $100,655,988
Earnings: ($26,040,841)
Emp.: 800
Fiscal Year-end: 12/31/23
Information Management Services
N.A.I.C.S.: 519290

TRUST BANK LIMITED
3-4 ECOWAS Avenue, PO Box 1018, Banjul, Gambia
Tel.: (220) 4225777   GM
Web Site:
https://trustbankgambia.com
Year Founded: 1997
TBL—(GHA)
Rev.: $11,893,105
Assets: $170,290,661
Liabilities: $154,400,968
Net Worth: $15,889,693
Earnings: $2,109,126
Emp.: 348
Fiscal Year-end: 12/31/20
Banking Services
N.A.I.C.S.: 522110
Franklin A. Hayford *(Co-Chm)*

INTERNATIONAL PUBLIC

Subsidiaries:

Bayba Financial Service Limited (1)
West Field Junction West Field, Serrekunda, Gambia
Tel.: (220) 4394505
Money Transfer Services
N.A.I.C.S.: 522320

Home Finance Company Gambia Ltd. (1)
2nd Floor Bayba Financial Services Building Westfield Junction, PO Box SK/2362, Serrekunda, Gambia
Tel.: (220) 4380806
Mortgage Services
N.A.I.C.S.: 522310

Trust Axiata Digital Limited (1)
57 & 57/A Uday Tower 17th Floor Gulshan Avenue Gulshan - 1, Dhaka, 1212, Bangladesh
Tel.: (880) 9612201201
Web Site: https://www.trustaxiatapay.com
Mobile Financial Services
N.A.I.C.S.: 522320

TRUST FINANCE INDONESIA TBK
Gd Artha Graha Lt 12 Jl Jend Sudirman Kav 52-53, Jakarta Selatan, 12190, Indonesia
Tel.: (62) 215155477
Web Site:
https://www.trustfinance.com
TRUS—(INDO)
Rev.: $3,580,795
Assets: $27,764,028
Liabilities: $3,265,179
Net Worth: $24,498,849
Earnings: $1,688,060
Emp.: 64
Fiscal Year-end: 12/31/23
Investment Management Service
N.A.I.C.S.: 525990
Suparman Sulina *(Chm)*

TRUST HOLDINGS INC.
5-15-18 Hakataekiminami, Hakata-Ku, Fukuoka, 812-0016, Japan
Tel.: (81) 924378911
Web Site: https://www.trustpark.co.jp
3286—(FKA)
Rev.: $85,176,680
Assets: $54,966,140
Liabilities: $49,274,840
Net Worth: $5,691,300
Earnings: $2,102,360
Emp.: 461
Fiscal Year-end: 06/30/24
Holding Company; Parking Lots, Real Estate & Security Services
N.A.I.C.S.: 551112
Yasushi Watanabe *(Chm)*

TRUST INTERNATIONAL INSURANCE COMPANY E.C.
Trust Tower Bldg 125 Rd 1702, PO Box 10002, Diplomatic Area Block 317, Manama, Bahrain
Tel.: (973) 17532425
Web Site: http://www.trustgroup.net
Sales Range: $10-24.9 Million
Emp.: 300
Provider of Insurance & Reinsurance Services
N.A.I.C.S.: 524130
Ghazi Kamel Abu Nahl *(Chm)*

Subsidiaries:

Compass Insurance Co. S.A.L. (1)
Ivoire Ctr 8th Fl Commodore St, Beirut, 1136025, Lebanon   (100%)
Tel.: (961) 346441
Web Site: http://www.trustlebanon.com
Provider of Insurance Services
N.A.I.C.S.: 524128

Spielbank Berlin Gustav Jaenecke GmbH & Co. KG (1)

Marlene-Dietrich-Platz 1, 10785, Berlin, Germany
Tel.: (49) 30 255 99 0
Web Site: http://www.spielbank-berlin.de
Gaming Concession Management Services
N.A.I.C.S.: 713290

Trust Algeria Assurances Reassurance (1)
70 Chemin Larbi Allik, Hydra, Algeria
Tel.: (213) 21547483
Provider of Insurance Services
N.A.I.C.S.: 524128

Trust Compass Insurance Co. S.A.L. (1)
Hamra Commodore Str Ivoir Center, PO Box 113-6025, Beirut, Lebanon
Tel.: (961) 1346345
Web Site: http://www.trustlebanon.com
General Insurance Services
N.A.I.C.S.: 524210
Ahmad Tabaja (Chm & Gen Mgr)

Trust International Insurance Company (Cyprus) Ltd (1)
79 Limassol Avenue 1&3 Kosti Palama Corner, PO Box 20344, 2121, Aglandjia, Cyprus
Tel.: (357) 22050100
Web Site: http://www.trustcyprusinsurance.com
General Insurance Services
N.A.I.C.S.: 524210
Christos Christodoulou (CEO)

Trust International Insurance Company P.L.C (1)
Jerusalem St Trust Bldg, PO Box 1860, Ramallah, Palestine (55%)
Tel.: (970) 2 242 5735
Web Site: http://www.trustpalestine.com
Sales Range: $1-9.9 Million
Emp.: 100
Insurance Services
N.A.I.C.S.: 524128
Damal Hood (Mng Dir)

Trust Re (1)
Building 125 Road 1702, PO Box 10002, Diplomatic Area 317, Manama, Bahrain
Tel.: (973) 17517171
Web Site: http://www.trustre.com
General Insurance Services
N.A.I.C.S.: 524210
Kamal Tabaja (COO)

Trust Underwriting Limited (1)
PO Box 831409, Amman, 11183, Jordan
Tel.: (962) 65542025
Web Site: http://www.arabinsuranceinstitute.com
General Insurance Services
N.A.I.C.S.: 524210

Trust Yemen Insurance & Reinsurance Company (1)
Hadda Street Villa 143, PO Box 18392, Sana'a, Yemen
Tel.: (967) 1264263
Provider of Insurance Services
N.A.I.C.S.: 524128

TRUST INVESTMENT BANK LIMITED
6th Floor MM Tower 28 A/K Gulberg II, Lahore, Pakistan
Tel.: (92) 4235758285
Web Site: https://www.trustbank.com.pk
Year Founded: 1992
TRIBL—(PSX)
Sales Range: $1-9.9 Million
Emp.: 33
Non Banking Services
N.A.I.C.S.: 522291
Ahsan Rafique (Pres & CEO)

TRUST MODARABA
104-106 Kassam Court BC-9 Block 5, Clifton, Karachi, 75600, Pakistan
Tel.: (92) 35873369
Web Site: https://www.trustmodaraba.com
Year Founded: 1991

TRSM—(PSX)
Rev.: $148,114
Assets: $1,398,555
Liabilities: $247,336
Net Worth: $1,151,219
Earnings: ($263)
Emp.: 17
Fiscal Year-end: 06/30/23
Financial Investment Services
N.A.I.C.S.: 523999
Basheer A. Chowdry (CEO)

TRUST SECURITIES & BROKERAGE LIMITED
2nd Floor Associated House Building No 1 & 2 7-Kashmir Road, Lahore, Pakistan
Tel.: (92) 426373041
Web Site: https://www.tsbl.com.pk
Year Founded: 1993
TSBL—(PSX)
Rev.: $510,140
Assets: $1,777,875
Liabilities: $773,531
Net Worth: $1,004,344
Earnings: ($36,942)
Emp.: 74
Fiscal Year-end: 06/30/23
Corporate Brokerage Services
N.A.I.C.S.: 523940
Muhammad Ahmed (CFO)

TRUST-SEARCH CORP., LTD.
No 280 Sec 1 Nanshan Rd, Luzhu Dist, Taoyuan, 338, Taiwan
Tel.: (886) 228816777
Web Site: http://www.tscl.com.tw
3115—(TPE)
Rev.: $1,795,923
Assets: $7,922,709
Liabilities: $601,101
Net Worth: $7,321,608
Earnings: ($461,401)
Fiscal Year-end: 12/31/22
Electronic Parts Mfr & Distr
N.A.I.C.S.: 334419
Chia Hsien Chang (Chm & CEO)

TRUSTBIX, INC.
Unit 137 9650 20 Avenue NW, Edmonton, T6N 1G1, AB, Canada
Tel.: (780) 456-2207
Web Site: http://www.trustbix.com
TBIXF—(OTCQB)
Rev.: $1,696,631
Assets: $967,094
Liabilities: $1,132,867
Net Worth: ($165,773)
Earnings: ($1,751,806)
Fiscal Year-end: 09/30/21
Software Development Services
N.A.I.C.S.: 541511
Hubert Lau (CEO)

Subsidiaries:

ViewTrak Technologies Inc. (1)
200 10607 - 82 Street, Edmonton, T6A 3N2, AB, Canada
Information Technology Services
N.A.I.C.S.: 541511

TRUSTBRIDGE PARTNERS
Unit 1206 One Lujiazui No 68 Yincheng Road, Shanghai, 200120, China
Tel.: (86) 21 5100 6188
Investment Services
N.A.I.C.S.: 523999
Shujun Li (Mng Partner)

TRUSTCO GROUP HOLDINGS LIMITED
2 Keller Street Trustco House, PO Box 11363, 11363, Windhoek, 11363, Namibia
Tel.: (264) 612754000
Web Site: https://www.tgh.na

Year Founded: 1992
TTO—(JSE)
Rev.: $1,356,680
Assets: $226,461,200
Liabilities: $130,763,080
Net Worth: $95,698,120
Earnings: $74,982,660
Emp.: 567
Fiscal Year-end: 03/31/22
Insurance & Financial Services
N.A.I.C.S.: 524298
Raymond Heathcote (Chm)

Subsidiaries:

Covest Wealth Managers (Pty) Ltd. (1)
Trustco House 2 Keller Street, Windhoek, Namibia
Tel.: (264) 612754146
Web Site: https://covestwealth30.na
Investment Finance Services
N.A.I.C.S.: 524298

Trustco Financial Services (Pty) Ltd (1)
The Isle Of Houghton 11 Boundary Road Old Trafford 1, PO Box 6984, Houghton Estate, Johannesburg, 2198, South Africa
Tel.: (27) 11 644 6622
Financial Management Services
N.A.I.C.S.: 523940

Trustco Insurance Ltd (1)
2 Keller Street, Windhoek, Khomas, Namibia
Tel.: (264) 612754199
Web Site: https://www.legalshield.na
General Insurance Services
N.A.I.C.S.: 524210

TRUSTED BRAND 2016, INC.
805-1st St Sw Stu 200, Calgary, T2P 7N2, AB, Canada
Tel.: (403) 561-3355
HAH.P—(TSXV)
Assets: $167,514
Liabilities: $14,540
Net Worth: $152,975
Earnings: ($94,373)
Fiscal Year-end: 12/31/19
Asset Management Services
N.A.I.C.S.: 523940
Ted Geier (CEO)

TRUSTED NOVUS BANK LIMITED
76 Main St, PO Box 143, Gibraltar, Gibraltar
Tel.: (350) 20072782
Web Site: http://trustednovusbank.gi
Sales Range: $50-74.9 Million
Emp.: 100
Financial Investment Activities
N.A.I.C.S.: 523999
Christian Bjorlow (CEO)

TRUSTPILOT GROUP PLC
Pilestraede 58, 1112, Copenhagen, Denmark
Tel.: (45) 32759914
Web Site: https://www.trustpilot.com
Year Founded: 2007
TRST—(LSE)
Rev.: $148,932,000
Assets: $124,783,000
Liabilities: $78,947,000
Net Worth: $45,836,000
Earnings: ($14,644,000)
Emp.: 900
Fiscal Year-end: 12/31/22
Holding Company
N.A.I.C.S.: 551112
Angela Seymour-Jackson (Sr Dir)

Subsidiaries:

Trustpilot A/S (1)
Pilestraede 58, 1112, Copenhagen, Denmark
Tel.: (45) 89888472
Web Site: https://dk.trustpilot.com

Emp.: 850
Online Platform Development Services
N.A.I.C.S.: 561320

Trustpilot Ltd. (1)
5th Floor The Minster Building 21 Mincing Lane, London, EC3R 7AG, United Kingdom
Tel.: (44) 2045345222
Online Platform Development Services
N.A.I.C.S.: 561320

Trustpilot S.r.l. (1)
1st Floor Talent Garden Milan Calabiana Via Arcivescovo Calabiana 6, 20139, Milan, Italy
Tel.: (39) 0230562023
Online Platform Development Services
N.A.I.C.S.: 561320

Trustpilot UAB (1)
3rd Floor Vito Gerulaicio g 1, 08200, Vilnius, Lithuania
Tel.: (370) 4589888472
Digital Platform Operator
N.A.I.C.S.: 518210

TRUSVAL TECHNOLOGY CO., LTD.
No 66 Youyi Rd, Jhunan Township, Miao-li, 350-59, Taiwan
Tel.: (886) 37580791
Web Site: https://www.trusval.com.tw
Year Founded: 1995
6667—(TPE)
Rev.: $77,141,137
Assets: $98,909,452
Liabilities: $55,567,833
Net Worth: $43,341,619
Earnings: $6,590,376
Fiscal Year-end: 12/31/22
Water Supply Services
N.A.I.C.S.: 221310
Shih-Pao Chien (Chm & Pres)

TRUTRACE TECHNOLOGIES INC.
2303 4th Street SW, Calgary, T2S 2S7, AB, Canada BC
Web Site: https://www.trutrace.co
Year Founded: 2011
TTT—(CNSX)
Rev.: $127,121
Assets: $1,117,614
Liabilities: $1,503,261
Net Worth: ($385,646)
Earnings: ($1,267,994)
Fiscal Year-end: 04/30/21
Investment Services
N.A.I.C.S.: 523999
Robert Galarza (CEO)

TRUTZSCHLER GMBH & CO. KG
Duvenstrasse 82-92, 41199, Monchengladbach, Germany
Tel.: (49) 21666070
Web Site: http://www.truetzschler.com
Year Founded: 1888
Sales Range: $250-299.9 Million
Emp.: 2,200
Textile Machinery Mfr
N.A.I.C.S.: 333248
Heinrich Trutzschler (Mng Partner)

Subsidiaries:

American Trutzschler Inc (1)
PO Box 669228, Charlotte, NC 28266 (100%)
Tel.: (704) 399-4521
Web Site: http://www.truetzschler.com
Sales Range: $25-49.9 Million
Emp.: 100
Textile Machinery Mfr
N.A.I.C.S.: 333248

Truetzschler Card Clothing GmbH (1)
Rosenstrasse 7, 75387, Neubulach, Germany
Tel.: (49) 7053 68 0

TRUTZSCHLER GMBH & CO. KG

Trutzschler GmbH & Co. KG—(Continued)
Web Site: http://www.truetzschler-cardclothing.com
Textile Machinery Mfr
N.A.I.C.S.: 333248

Truetzschler India Private Limited (1)
N I D C Estate Near Lambha Village Post
Narol, Ahmedabad, 382 405, India
Tel.: (91) 79 25710608
Web Site: http://www.truetzschler.in
Textile Machinery Mfr & Distr
N.A.I.C.S.: 333248
Joseph Thomson *(Co-Mng Dir)*

Truetzschler Tekstil Makinalari Ticaret Ltd. (1)
1 Organize Sanayi Bolgesi Nolu Cadde No 13, Baspinar, 83104, Gaziantep, Turkiye
Tel.: (90) 342 337 43 55
Textile Machinery Distr
N.A.I.C.S.: 423830

Truetzschler Textile Machinery (Shanghai) Co., Ltd. (1)
Qingpu Industrial Zone, Shanghai, China
Tel.: (86) 21 39 20 33 00
Textile Machinery Distr
N.A.I.C.S.: 423830
Jungnickl Juergen *(Mgr-Assembling)*

Truetzschler de Mexico, S.A. de C.V. (1)
Ayuntamiento 136-B Col Centro Tlalnepantla, Tlalnepantla, 54000, Mexico
Tel.: (52) 55 5565 6600
Textile Machinery Distr
N.A.I.C.S.: 423830

Trutzschler Industria e Comercio de Maquinas Ltda (1)
Rua Joao Chede 941, Curitiba, Brazil
Tel.: (55) 41 3316 1200
Textile Machinery Distr
N.A.I.C.S.: 423830
MacHiel Zan Dein Doldil *(Mgr-Mktg)*

Trutzschler Nonwovens & Man-Made Fibers GmbH (1)
Wolfsgartenstrasse 6, 63329, Egelsbach, Germany
Tel.: (49) 61034010
Textile Machinery Mfr
N.A.I.C.S.: 333248
Ralf Napiwotzki *(Mng Dir & CFO)*

Trutzschler Nonwovens GmbH (1)
Wolfsgartenstrasse 6, Egelsbach, 63329, Germany
Tel.: (49) 61034010
Web Site: http://www.truetzschler-nonwovens.de
Sales Range: $50-74.9 Million
Emp.: 290
Continuous Finishing Plants for Separate Machines for Woven & Knitted Goods, Carpet Manufacturing, Nonwovens, Wool, Man-Made Fiber Manufacturing
N.A.I.C.S.: 333310
Marc Wolpers *(Mng Dir)*

Trutzschler Switzerland AG (1)
Schlosstalstrasse 45, 8406, Winterthur, Switzerland
Tel.: (41) 52 268 6969
Textile Machinery Distr
N.A.I.C.S.: 423830
Andreas Beutel *(Sr Mgr-Procurement)*

TRUWIN CO., LTD.

385 Expo-ro, Yuseong-gu, Daejeon, 306-230, Korea (South)
Tel.: (82) 426125000
Web Site: https://www.truwin.co.kr
Year Founded: 2006
105550—(KRS)
Rev.: $27,613,019
Assets: $87,565,003
Liabilities: $35,334,367
Net Worth: $52,230,637
Earnings: ($4,155,126)
Emp.: 98
Fiscal Year-end: 12/31/22
Motor Vehicle Parts & Accessories Mfr
N.A.I.C.S.: 336390
Yong Nam *(CEO)*

TRUWORTHS INTERNATIONAL LIMITED

1 Mostert Street, Cape Town, 8001, South Africa
Tel.: (27) 214607911
Web Site: http://www.truworths.co.za
TRW—(NAM)
Rev.: $1,147,762,480
Assets: $841,981,270
Liabilities: $442,519,010
Net Worth: $399,462,260
Earnings: $171,600,720
Emp.: 5,243
Fiscal Year-end: 07/02/23
Apparel & Accessories Retailers
N.A.I.C.S.: 458110
Michael Mark *(Chm & CEO)*

Subsidiaries:

Identity Retailing (Pty) Limited (1)
No 1 Mostert Street, Cape Town, 8001, Western Cape, South Africa
Tel.: (27) 214602400
Web Site: https://www.identity.co.za
Fashion Designing Services
N.A.I.C.S.: 541490

Young Designers Emporium (Pty) Limited (1)
No 1 Mostert Street, Cape Town, 8001, Western Cape, South Africa
Tel.: (27) 214602500
Web Site: https://www.yde.co.za
Fashion Designing Services
N.A.I.C.S.: 541490

TRUWORTHS LIMITED

4 Conald Road Granitesite, Hatfield, Harare, Zimbabwe
Tel.: (263) 783508479
Web Site: https://www.truworths.co.zw
Year Founded: 1957
TRUW—(ZIM)
Rev.: $3,099,088
Assets: $2,580,040
Liabilities: $1,495,447
Net Worth: $1,084,592
Earnings: ($102,498)
Emp.: 12,515
Fiscal Year-end: 07/10/22
Textile Product Whslr
N.A.I.C.S.: 424350
Bekithemba Ndebele *(CEO)*

TRX GOLD CORPORATION

Suite 403 277 Lakeshore Road East, Oakville, L6J 1H9, ON, Canada   AB
Web Site: https://trxgold.com
Year Founded: 1990
TRX—(NYSEAMEX)
Rev.: $41,158,000
Assets: $98,860,000
Liabilities: $32,821,000
Net Worth: $66,039,000
Earnings: $3,510,000
Emp.: 250
Fiscal Year-end: 08/31/24
Mineral Exploration & Mining Services
N.A.I.C.S.: 212390
Donna M. Moroney *(Sec)*

TRYG A/S

Klausdalsbrovej 601, 2750, Ballerup, Denmark
Tel.: (45) 70112020   DK
Web Site: https://www.tryg.com
Year Founded: 2002
TRYG—(CSE)
Rev.: $5,661,327,430
Assets: $16,341,826,916
Liabilities: $10,064,678,561
Net Worth: $6,277,148,356
Earnings: $557,219,545
Emp.: 6,805
Fiscal Year-end: 12/31/23
Financial Investment Services
N.A.I.C.S.: 523999
Torben Nielsen *(Deputy Chm-Supervisory Bd)*

Subsidiaries:

Moderna Forsakringar Sak AB (1)
Sveavagen 167, PO Box 7830, SE-103 98, Stockholm, Sweden
Tel.: (46) 86960555
Web Site: http://www.modernaforsakringar.se
Sales Range: $150-199.9 Million
Emp.: 166
Personal & Commercial Insurance Services
N.A.I.C.S.: 524210

RSA Insurance Group plc (1)
20 Fenchurch Street, London, EC3M 3AU, United Kingdom
Tel.: (44) 1403232323
Web Site: http://www.rsagroup.com
Rev.: $9,785,847,600
Assets: $26,182,159,200
Liabilities: $20,487,192,000
Net Worth: $5,694,967,200
Earnings: $502,342,800
Emp.: 12,378
Fiscal Year-end: 12/31/2019
Holding Company; Property, Casualty, Motor Vehicle & Household Insurance Products & Services
N.A.I.C.S.: 551112
William McDonnell *(Chief Risk Officer)*

Subsidiary (Non-US):

123 Money Limited (2)
RSA House Sandyford Rd, PO Box 12123, Dundrum, Dublin, D16 FC92, Ireland
Tel.: (353) 1 518 1434
Web Site: https://www.123.ie
Insurance Management Services
N.A.I.C.S.: 524298

Al Ahlia Insurance Company SAOG (2)
PO Box 1463, 112, Ruwi, Oman
Tel.: (968) 2 476 6800
Web Site: https://www.alahliarsa.com
Non-Life Insurance Services
N.A.I.C.S.: 524128

Subsidiary (Domestic):

British Aviation Insurance Company Limited (2)
Fitzwilliam House 10 St Mary Axe, London, EC3A 8EQ, United Kingdom
Tel.: (44) 2073692244
Web Site: http://www.baic.co.uk
Insurance Management Services
N.A.I.C.S.: 524298

Subsidiary (Non-US):

Coast Underwriters Limited (2)
Suite 2690 650 West Georgia Street, PO Box 11519, Vancouver, V6B 4N7, BC, Canada
Tel.: (604) 683-5631
Web Site: https://www.coastunderwriters.ca
Marine Insurance Claims Services
N.A.I.C.S.: 524126
Kevan Gielty *(Pres & CEO)*

Codan A/S (2)
GI Kongevej 60, 1790, Copenhagen, Denmark
Tel.: (45) 33555555
Web Site: http://www.codan.dk
Sales Range: $1-4.9 Billion
Emp.: 6,416
Holding Company; Insurance Products & Services
N.A.I.C.S.: 551112

Subsidiary (Domestic):

Codan Forsikring A/S (3)
Gammel Kongevej 60, 1790, Copenhagen, Denmark
Tel.: (45) 33555555
Web Site: http://www.codan.dk
Insurance Products & Services
N.A.I.C.S.: 524126

INTERNATIONAL PUBLIC

Subsidiary (Non-US):

Trygg-Hansa Forsakring AB (3)
Flemminggatan 18, 106 26, Stockholm, Sweden
Tel.: (46) 752431000
Web Site: http://www.rsagroup.com
Sales Range: $700-749.9 Million
Insurance Services
N.A.I.C.S.: 522299

Subsidiary (Non-US):

D.L. Deeks Insurance Services Inc. (2)
400 - 2255 Sheppard Avenue East, North York, M2J 4Y1, ON, Canada
Web Site: https://www.deeksinsurance.ca
Business Insurance Services
N.A.I.C.S.: 524128
Serge LaPalme *(Chm & CEO)*

Duborgh Skadeforsikring A/S (2)
Kongsgard Alle 53 A, 4632, Kristiansand, Norway
Tel.: (47) 38 09 31 60
Web Site: http://www.duborgh.no
Insurance Brokerage Services
N.A.I.C.S.: 524210

Forsikringsselskabet Privatsikring A/S (2)
Gammel Kongevej 60, 1790, Copenhagen, Denmark
Tel.: (45) 70111707
Web Site: http://www.privatsikring.dk
All Insurance Coverage Services
N.A.I.C.S.: 524114

Insurance Corporation of the Channel Islands Limited (2)
Dixcart House Sir William Place, PO Box 160, Saint Peter Port, GY1 4EY, Guernsey
Tel.: (44) 148 171 3322
Web Site: https://www.insurancecorporation.com
Emp.: 30
Insurance Management Services
N.A.I.C.S.: 524298
Paul Masterton *(Chm)*

L'Union Canadienne, Compagnie D'Assurances (2)
2475 Laurier Blvd, Quebec, G1T 1C4, QC, Canada
Tel.: (418) 622-2040
Web Site: http://www.unioncanadienne.com
Sales Range: $100-124.9 Million
Emp.: 250
Personal & Commercial Insurance Products
N.A.I.C.S.: 524113

Subsidiary (Domestic):

Noble Marine (Insurance Brokers) Limited (2)
Clinton House Lombard Street, Newark, NG24 1XB, Nottinghamshire, United Kingdom
Tel.: (44) 1636707606
Marine Insurance Claims Services
N.A.I.C.S.: 524126
Phil Kilburn *(Gen Mgr & Mgr-Claims)*

Noble Marine (Underwriting Agencies) Limited (2)
Clinton House Lombard Street, Newark, NG24 1XB, Nottinghamshire, United Kingdom
Tel.: (44) 1636707606
Marine Insurance Claims Services
N.A.I.C.S.: 524126

Subsidiary (Non-US):

RSA Actuarial Services (India) Private Limited (2)
1st Floor Building 10C Cyber City Complex DLF Phase II, Gurgaon, 122002, India
Tel.: (91) 1243863000
Household Insurance Product & Services
N.A.I.C.S.: 524126
Devika Sethi *(Mgr)*

RSA Insurance Ireland Limited (2)
Tel.: (353) 1 290 1000
Web Site: https://www.rsagroup.ie
Sales Range: $200-249.9 Million
Emp.: 500
Provision of insurance services

AND PRIVATE COMPANIES

N.A.I.C.S.: 525190

Subsidiary (Domestic):

Roins Financial Services Limited (2)
18 York St Ste 800, Toronto, M5J 2T8, ON, Canada
Tel.: (416) 366-7511
Web Site: http://www.rsagroup.ca
Emp.: 700
Insurance Holding Company
N.A.I.C.S.: 551112

Subsidiary (Domestic):

Royal & Sun Alliance Insurance Company of Canada (3)
700 University Ave Suite 1500A, Toronto, M5G 0A1, ON, Canada
Tel.: (416) 366-7511
Web Site: http://www.rsagroup.ca
Property & Casualty Insurance, Title Insurance & Reinsurance Products & Services
N.A.I.C.S.: 524126

Subsidiary (Domestic):

Canadian Northern Shield Insurance Company (4)
1900-555 West Hastings Street, Vancouver, V6B 4N6, BC, Canada
Tel.: (604) 662-2900
Web Site: http://www.cns.ca
Sales Range: $150-199.9 Million
Casualty & Property Insurance Services
N.A.I.C.S.: 524298

Compagnie d'Assurance du Quebec (4)
1001 de Maisonneuve Boulevard West Suite 1400, Montreal, H3A 3C8, QC, Canada
Tel.: (514) 844-1116
Web Site: http://www.rsagroup.ca
Sales Range: $200-249.9 Million
Emp.: 500
Property & Casualty Insurance Products & Services
N.A.I.C.S.: 524126

Johnson Inc. (4)
10 Factory Lane, PO Box 12049, Saint John's, A1B 1R7, NL, Canada
Tel.: (709) 737-1500
Web Site: http://www.johnson.ca
Sales Range: $900-999.9 Million
Home & Automotive Insurance Products & Services
N.A.I.C.S.: 524126

Western Assurance Company (4)
100 - 2 Prologis Blvd, Mississauga, L5W 0G8, ON, Canada
Tel.: (905) 403-3318
Web Site: https://www.rsagroup.ca
Sales Range: $50-74.9 Million
Emp.: 100
Insurance Services
N.A.I.C.S.: 524128

Subsidiary (Domestic):

Royal & Sun Alliance Insurance plc (2)
St Marks Court Chart Way, Horsham, RH12 1XL, West Sussex, United Kingdom
Tel.: (44) 140 323 2233
Web Site: https://www.rsagroup.com
Sales Range: $900-999.9 Million
Emp.: 2,500
Property & Casualty Insurance & Pension Products & Services
N.A.I.C.S.: 524126

Subsidiary (Non-US):

The Johnson Corporation (2)
10 Factory Ln, Saint John's, A1B 1R7, NL, Canada
Tel.: (709) 737-1500
Investment Management Service

N.A.I.C.S.: 523999

Tower Insurance Company Limited (2)
Jubilee Buildings 1 Victoria street, IM99 1BF, Douglas, Isle of Man
Tel.: (44) 162 464 5900
Web Site: https://www.towerinsurance.co.im
Sales Range: $50-74.9 Million
Emp.: 30
Insurance Services
N.A.I.C.S.: 524298
Emmet McQuillan (Mng Dir)

Tryg Forsikring A/S (1)
Kvalitet 5F1 Folke Bernadottesvei 50, PO Box 7070, 5020, Bergen, Norway
Tel.: (47) 55171000
Web Site: https://www.tryg.no
Sales Range: $350-399.9 Million
Emp.: 850
Property & Casualty Insurance Products
N.A.I.C.S.: 524126
Morten Hubbe (CEO)

TRYGHEDSGRUPPEN SMBA

Hummeltoftevej 49, 2830, Virum, Denmark
Tel.: (45) 260826
Web Site: http://www.tryghedsgruppen.dk
Investment Management Service
N.A.I.C.S.: 523940
Heidi Scheffler (Project Mgr)

TRYT INC.

Art Village Osaki Central Tower 17F 1-2-2 Osaki, Shinagawa-ku, Tokyo, 141-0032, Japan
Tel.: (81) 354367670
Web Site: https://tryt-group.co.jp
Year Founded: 2004
9164—(TKS)
Rev.: $374,118,030
Assets: $566,824,230
Liabilities: $383,001,800
Net Worth: $183,822,430
Earnings: $34,748,090
Emp.: 7,512
Fiscal Year-end: 12/31/23
Human Resource Consulting Services
N.A.I.C.S.: 541612
Hidetaka Sasai (Pres)

TRZNICA A.D.

Matije Gubca 50, 24000, Subotica, Serbia
Tel.: (381) 24555377
Web Site: https://www.subotickatrznica.rs
Year Founded: 1991
TZSU—(BEL)
Rev.: $1,568,238
Assets: $2,173,599
Liabilities: $236,818
Net Worth: $1,936,782
Earnings: $13,949
Emp.: 46
Fiscal Year-end: 12/31/23
Real Estate Manangement Services
N.A.I.C.S.: 531390
Kljajic Milos (Chm-Supervisory Bd)

TS CORPORATION

299 Olympic-ro, Songpa-gu, Seoul, Korea (South)
Tel.: (82) 24106000
Web Site: https://www.ts.co.kr
Year Founded: 1956
001790—(KRS)
Rev.: $1,056,983,923
Assets: $935,330,649
Liabilities: $522,900,366
Net Worth: $412,430,283
Earnings: $19,591,821
Emp.: 300
Fiscal Year-end: 12/31/22
Food Products
N.A.I.C.S.: 236210

Ki Young Kim (CEO)

Subsidiaries:

TS Corporation - Feed Division (1)
18-3 Ugori Kwangjukmyeon, Yangju, Gyeonggi, Korea (South)
Tel.: (82) 31 837 1300
Animal Feed Mfr
N.A.I.C.S.: 311119

TS Corporation - Oxan Plant (1)
359-1 Osanri Oxanmyun Cheongwongun, Cheongwon, Chungbuk, Korea (South)
Tel.: (82) 432694368
Refined Sugar Mfr
N.A.I.C.S.: 311314

TS Corporation - Sugar & Foodstuff Division (1)
299 Olympic-ro, Songpa-gu, Seoul, Korea (South)
Tel.: (82) 24106183
Sugar & Food Products Mfr
N.A.I.C.S.: 311314

TS Credit & Investment Corp. (1)
Songpa 7-23 15 Story Bldg, Seoul, 138-726, Korea (South)
Tel.: (82) 22039986
Web Site: http://www.tscni.co.kr
Sales Range: $50-74.9 Million
Emp.: 5
Investment Management & Consulting Services
N.A.I.C.S.: 523940

TS Wooin Co., Ltd (1)
6F Plz 654 B D 654-3 Yeoksam-Dong, Kangnam, Seoul, Korea (South)
Tel.: (82) 56462971
Sales Range: $25-49.9 Million
Emp.: 250
Sugar & Food Products Mfr
N.A.I.C.S.: 311314

TS GROUP GMBH

Gruner Winkel 10, 52070, Aachen, Germany
Tel.: (49) 241 91612521   De
Web Site: http://www.ts-group.org
Year Founded: 1933
Sales Range: Less than $1 Million
Holding Company
N.A.I.C.S.: 551112
Stephan Koehne (Mng Dir)

Subsidiaries:

Calyxo GmbH (1)
OT Thalheim Sonnenallee 1a, 06766, Bitterfeld-Wolfen, Germany
Tel.: (49) 3494 3689 800
Web Site: http://calyxo.com
Emp.: 175
Thin Film Solar Modules Mfr
N.A.I.C.S.: 334413
Michael Bauer (COO & CTO)

TS INVESTMENT CORP

3F 531 Seolleung-ro, Gangnam-gu, Seoul, 06149, Korea (South)
Tel.: (82) 262505700
Web Site: https://www.tsinvestment.co.kr
Year Founded: 2008
246690—(KRS)
Rev.: $21,528,785
Assets: $77,994,217
Liabilities: $19,873,312
Net Worth: $58,120,905
Earnings: $6,693,557
Emp.: 20
Fiscal Year-end: 12/31/22
Venture Capital Investment Services
N.A.I.C.S.: 523910
Kim Woong (Co-CEO)

TS LAW HOLDING SDN. BHD.

No 47 Jalan Kuchai Maju Kuchai Entrepreneurs Park, Off Jalan Kuchai Lama, 58200, Kuala Lumpur, Malaysia
Tel.: (60) 3 7987 2323   MY

TS TECH CO LTD

Web Site: http://www.tslaw.com.my
Year Founded: 2001
Holding Company
N.A.I.C.S.: 551112
David Law Tien Seng (Founder & Chm)

TS NEXGEN CO., LTD.

611 503 Teheran-ro, Gangnam-gu, Seoul, Korea (South)
Tel.: (82) 2544343301
Web Site: https://hlbpower.co.kr
Year Founded: 2002
043220—(KRS)
Rev.: $19,560,452
Assets: $57,203,602
Liabilities: $20,562,205
Net Worth: $36,641,397
Earnings: ($7,424,398)
Emp.: 102
Fiscal Year-end: 12/31/22
Wireless Communication Equipment Mfr
N.A.I.C.S.: 334220
Suk Chung (CEO)

TS TECH CO LTD

3-7-27 Sakae-cho Asaka-shi, Saitama, 351-0012, Japan
Tel.: (81) 484621121
Web Site: https://www.tstech.co.jp
7313—(TKS)
Rev.: $2,919,722,930
Assets: $2,949,474,540
Liabilities: $644,547,710
Net Worth: $2,304,926,830
Earnings: $67,514,540
Emp.: 14,719
Fiscal Year-end: 03/31/24
Automobile Parts Mfr
N.A.I.C.S.: 336360
Masanari Yasuda (Pres)

Subsidiaries:

C-Presto Co., Ltd. (1)
802-1 Koh Kamihonai, Sanjo, 955-0022, Niigata, Japan
Tel.: (81) 25 638 4669
Press Die Mfr
N.A.I.C.S.: 333514

Daiyu Co., Ltd. (1)
711-170 Fukudayama Fukuda, Sanjo, 996-0053, Yamagata, Japan
Tel.: (81) 23 323 1101
Trim Covers Mfr
N.A.I.C.S.: 332913

Guangzhou TS Automotive Interior Systems Co., Ltd. (1)
No 173 Chuangqiang Road Yongning Street, Zengcheng, Guangzhou, Guangdong, China
Tel.: (86) 208 270 4792
Automobile Mfr
N.A.I.C.S.: 336110

Guangzhou TS Tech Automotive Interior Research & Development Co., Ltd. (1)
106-110 Building 5 No 8 Qiyun Road, Huangpu District, Guangzhou, China
Tel.: (86) 203 880 8533
Research & Development Services
N.A.I.C.S.: 541714

Honda Cars Satiamakita Co., Ltd. (1)
479-1 Hirose, Kumagaya, 360-0833, Saitama, Japan
Tel.: (81) 485251412
Automobile Interior Component Distr
N.A.I.C.S.: 441110

INDUSTRIAS TRI-CON DE MEXICO S.A. DE C.V. (1)
Anzures 930 Fraccionamiento, Los Fresnos, Nuevo Laredo, Tamaulipas, Mexico
Tel.: (52) 8677111420
Sales Range: $200-249.9 Million
Emp.: 600
Trim Covers Mfr
N.A.I.C.S.: 336360

TS TECH CO LTD

TS Tech Co Ltd—(Continued)

KYUSYU TS CO., LTD. (1)
1890 Akahoshi, Kikuchi, 861-1311, Kumamoto, Japan
Tel.: (81) 968254195
Web Site: https://www.kyushu-ts.co.jp
Sales Range: $100-124.9 Million
Emp.: 231
Motor Vehicle Seats Mfr
N.A.I.C.S.: 336360

Kyushu Ts Co., Ltd. (1)
1890 Akahoshi, Kikuchi, 861-1311, Kumamoto, Japan
Tel.: (81) 968254195
Seats For Motorcycle Mfr
N.A.I.C.S.: 336991

Ningbo EPZ TS Trimont Automotive Interior Inc. (1)
5 Tianshan Rd Ningbo Processing Zone, Ningbo, 315806, China
Tel.: (86) 57426877577
Trim Covers Mfr
N.A.I.C.S.: 336360

PT. TS Tech Indonesia (1)
Kawasan Kota Bukit Indah - Blok AII No 3, Bungursari, Purwakarta, 41181, West Java, Indonesia
Tel.: (62) 264350560
Web Site: http://www.tstechindoneasia.co.id
Sales Range: $400-449.9 Million
Emp.: 1,300
Automobile Seats Mfr
N.A.I.C.S.: 336360

SOWA TECHNO CO., LTD. (1)
3-16-8 Kujominami, Nishi-ku, Osaka, 550-0025, Japan
Tel.: (81) 665836091
Web Site: http://www.swf.co.jp
Emp.: 9
Metal Framed Seats Mfr
N.A.I.C.S.: 336360
Miyoshi Takuto (Pres)

Sowa Sangyo Co., Ltd. (1)
83-3 Shitami, Kazo, 347-0042, Saitama, Japan
Tel.: (81) 480641611
Web Site: https://sowasangyo.com
Emp.: 103
Automobile Seats & Resin Products Mfr
N.A.I.C.S.: 336360

Sun Chemical Industry Co., Ltd. (1)
4-4-6 Shinmiyakoda, Kita-Ku, Hamamatsu, 431-2103, Shizuoka, Japan
Tel.: (81) 534285131
Web Site: https://www.tstech.co.jp
Rubber & Resin Products Whslr
N.A.I.C.S.: 424690

TRIMONT MFG. INC. (1)
115 Milner Avenue, Scarborough, M1S 4L7, ON, Canada
Tel.: (416) 640-2045
Sales Range: $50-74.9 Million
Emp.: 150
Door & Roof Trims Mfr
N.A.I.C.S.: 332913

TS CORPORATION Co., LTD. (1)
43-2 Tsukure Kikuyoumachi, Kikuchi-gun, Kumamoto, 869-1101, Japan
Tel.: (81) 962327333
Web Site: http://tscorp.info
Truck Whslr
N.A.I.C.S.: 423110

TS De San Pedro Industries, S. de R.L. de C.V. (1)
Carr San Pedro La Cuchilla Km 2 894 San Pedro, Coahuila, Mexico
Tel.: (52) 872 762 6300
Trim Covers Mfr
N.A.I.C.S.: 336360

TS Insurance Service Co., Ltd. (1)
3F Komazawa News 4 4 2 Kamiuma, Setagaya-ku, Tokyo, 154-0011, Japan
Tel.: (81) 334148948
Insurance Agencies
N.A.I.C.S.: 524210

TS Logistics Co., Ltd. (1)
Sales Range: $25-49.9 Million
Emp.: 100
Logistic Services

N.A.I.C.S.: 541614

TS Press Engineering Co., Ltd. (1)
802-1 Kamihonai-ko, Sanjo, 955-0022, Niigata, Japan
Tel.: (81) 256384669
Design & Press Dies Mfr
N.A.I.C.S.: 333511

TS Tech (Hong Kong) Co., Ltd. (1)
Suites 1709-11 17/F Tower 2 The Gateway Harbour City 25 Canton Road, Tsimshatsui, Kowloon, China (Hong Kong)
Tel.: (852) 23779502
Web Site: https://www.tstech.co.jp
Automobile Seats Mfr
N.A.I.C.S.: 336360

TS Tech (Mandal) Private Limited (1)
Plot no- 21 and 22 Japanese Industrial Park G I D C V and P Vithlapur, Tal Mandal District, Ahmedabad, 382130, Gujarat, India
Tel.: (91) 796 134 2525
Motorcycle Mfr
N.A.I.C.S.: 336991

TS Tech (Thailand) Co., Ltd. (1)
88 Moo 6 Hemaraj Saraburi Industrial Land Nong Pla Kradi Road, Nong Pla Moh Subdistrict Nong Khae District, Saraburi, 18140, Thailand
Tel.: (66) 3 631 3888
Automobile & Door Trim Mfr
N.A.I.C.S.: 336360

TS Tech Alabama LLC (1)
1685 N Main St, Boaz, AL 35957
Tel.: (256) 593-9399
Web Site: https://www.tstech.com
Sales Range: $200-249.9 Million
Emp.: 700
Automobile Seats Mfr
N.A.I.C.S.: 336360

TS Tech Business Services Philippines, Inc. (1)
6F 6780 Ayala Avenue, Makati, 1226, Philippines
Automotive Components Mfr
N.A.I.C.S.: 336390

TS Tech Canada Inc. (1)
17855 Leslie Street, Newmarket, L3Y 3E3, ON, Canada
Tel.: (905) 953-0098
Web Site: http://www.tstechcanada.com
Automobile Seats Mfr
N.A.I.C.S.: 336360

TS Tech Co., Ltd. - Hamamatsu Plant (1)
358 Zenji, Hamakita-ku, Hamamatsu, 434-0025, Shizuoka, Japan
Tel.: (81) 535870611
Web Site: https://www.tstech.co.jp
Automobile Seats Mfr
N.A.I.C.S.: 336360

TS Tech Co., Ltd. - Saitama Plant (Gyoda) (1)
3600 No, Gyoda, 361-0026, Saitama, Japan
Tel.: (81) 485591321
Web Site: http://www.tstech.co.jp
Automobile Seats Mfr
N.A.I.C.S.: 336360

TS Tech Co., Ltd. - Saitama Plant (Kawagoe) (1)
3600 No, Gyoda, 361-0026, Saitama, Japan
Tel.: (81) 485591321
Web Site: https://www.tstech.co.jp
Door Trim Mfr
N.A.I.C.S.: 321911

TS Tech Co., Ltd. - Saitama Plant (Konosu) (1)
3452 Minoda, Konosu, 365-0062, Saitama, Japan
Tel.: (81) 48 596 0669
Medical Equipment Mfr
N.A.I.C.S.: 339112

TS Tech Co., Ltd. - Saitama Plant (Sayama) (1)
1-10-2 Minamidai, Kawagoe, 350-1165, Saitama, Japan

Tel.: (81) 492431555
Web Site: http://www.tstech.co.jp
Door & Roof Trim Mfr
N.A.I.C.S.: 321911

TS Tech Co., Ltd. - Suzuka Plant (1)
60 Kida-cho, Suzuka, 513-0015, Mie, Japan
Tel.: (81) 593821331
Web Site: http://www.tstech.jp
Automobile Seats Mfr
N.A.I.C.S.: 336360

TS Tech Deutschland GmbH (1)
Peter-Hurst-Strasse 1b, 38444, Wolfsburg, Germany
Tel.: (49) 530 852 0430
Automobile Seat Mfr & Distr
N.A.I.C.S.: 336360

TS Tech Do Brasil Ltda. (1)
Rua 27 de Outubro 400, Distrito Industrial Paulo Kinock Leme, Sao Paulo, 13610-000, Brazil
Tel.: (55) 193 572 9110
Automobile & Door Trim Mfr
N.A.I.C.S.: 336360

TS Tech Hungary Kft. (1)
Iparos U 2, 2440, Szazhalombatta, Hungary
Tel.: (36) 2 354 4310
Automobile Mfr
N.A.I.C.S.: 336110

TS Tech Indiana, LLC (1)
3800 Brooks Dr, New Castle, IN 47362
Tel.: (765) 593-2300
Automobile Mfr & Distr
N.A.I.C.S.: 336110

TS Tech North America Inc. (1)
8458 E Broad St, Reynoldsburg, OH 43068
Tel.: (614) 575-4100
Web Site: http://www.tstech.com
Sales Range: $25-49.9 Million
Emp.: 330
Research & Development Services
N.A.I.C.S.: 541715
Akihiko Hayashi (Pres)

TS Tech Poland Sp, z o.o. (1)
Ul Legionow 202/210, 42-200, Czestochowa, Poland
Tel.: (48) 34 377 5100
Automobile Mfr
N.A.I.C.S.: 336110

TS Tech Sun (India) Limited (1)
SP4-885 RIICO Industrial Area, Pathredi Bhiwadi Dist, Alwar, 301019, Rajasthan, India
Tel.: (91) 7568008001
Sales Range: $100-124.9 Million
Emp.: 300
Automobile Seats & Door Trim Mfr
N.A.I.C.S.: 336360

TS Tech Sun Rajasthan Private Limited (1)
SP2 5 and 6 NIC Majrakath, Neemrana District, Alwar, 301705, Rajasthan, India
Tel.: (91) 149 467 8800
Automobile Mfr
N.A.I.C.S.: 336110

TS Tech Trim Philippines, Inc. (1)
02 Technology Ave Laguna Technopark, Special Export Processing Zone, Binan, Laguna, Philippines
Tel.: (63) 49 541 2841
Door Trim & Trim Cover Mfr
N.A.I.C.S.: 332321

TS Tech UK Ltd. (1)
Blackworth Indust Estate, Highworth, Swindon, SN6 7NA, Wiltshire, United Kingdom
Tel.: (44) 1793767060
Web Site: http://www.tstech.co.uk
Sales Range: $100-124.9 Million
Emp.: 410
Automobile Seats Mfr
N.A.I.C.S.: 336360
Ryuichi Kanamori (Mng Dir)

TS Tech USA Corporation (1)
8400 E Broad St, Reynoldsburg, OH 43068
Tel.: (614) 577-1088
Automobile Seats Mfr
N.A.I.C.S.: 336360

TS Trim Brasil S.A. (1)
Rua Angelina Rezende de Almeida n 400

Jardim Patricia Ouro Fino, Gerais, 570-000, Minas Gerais, Brazil
Tel.: (55) 353 441 4364
Trim Covers Mfr
N.A.I.C.S.: 336360

TS Trim Industries Inc. (1)
6380 Canal St, Canal Winchester, OH 43110-9640
Tel.: (614) 837-4114
Sales Range: $100-124.9 Million
Emp.: 500
Door & Roof Trims Mfr
N.A.I.C.S.: 332913
Phil Rody (Pres)

TSML Innovations, LLC (1)
401 E Olmos Ave, Hidalgo, TX 78557
Tel.: (956) 217-0173
Trim Covers & Other Automotive Interior Component Mfr
N.A.I.C.S.: 327212

TSt Manufacturing De Mexico, S. de R.L. de C.V. (1)
Rio Ota 978 Parque Tecnoindustrial Castro Del Rio Irapuato, 36815, Mexico, Guanajuato, Mexico
Tel.: (52) 462 478 3500
Automotive Products Mfr
N.A.I.C.S.: 336360

Tech Toei Co., Ltd. (1)
80 Kida-cho, Suzuka, 513-0015, Mie, Japan
Tel.: (81) 59 382 1172
Seat Frame Mfr
N.A.I.C.S.: 336360

Tri-Con Industries Ltd. (1)
4000 NW 44th St, Lincoln, NE 68524
Tel.: (402) 470-3311
Web Site: https://www.tstech.com
Automobile Seats & Seat Parts Mfr
N.A.I.C.S.: 336360

TriMold LLC (1)
200 Pittsburgh Rd, Circleville, OH 43113
Tel.: (740) 474-7591
Automobile Resin Products Mfr
N.A.I.C.S.: 325211

Wuhan Sowa Auto Parts Co., Ltd. (1)
No 200 Xing 3 Road Shamao Street, Wuhan, Hannan, China
Tel.: (86) 203 222 3258
Headrest Mfr
N.A.I.C.S.: 336360

Wuhan TS-GSK Auto Parts Co., Ltd. (1)
No 187 Wanjiahu Road Wuhan Economic and Technology Development Zone, Wuhan, 430056, Hubei, China
Tel.: (86) 2784236388
Web Site: https://www.tstech.co.jp
Sales Range: $200-249.9 Million
Automobile Seats & Door Trim Mfr
N.A.I.C.S.: 336360

TS TRILLION CO., LTD.

TS Building 8F 6F 1F Yangpyeongdong 4sa-ga 96 Yangpyeong-ro, Yeongdeungpo-gu, Seoul, Korea (South)
Tel.: (82) 27858296
Web Site: https://tstrillion.com
Year Founded: 2019
317240—(KRS)
Rev.: $48,263,775
Assets: $52,398,852
Liabilities: $39,026,822
Net Worth: $13,372,031
Earnings: ($7,810,796)
Emp.: 49
Fiscal Year-end: 12/31/22
Cosmetic Product Mfr & Distr
N.A.I.C.S.: 325620
Kim Yong-Chae (CEO)

TS WONDERS HOLDING LIMITED

255 Pandan Loop, Singapore, 128433, Singapore
Tel.: (65) 8408412569
Web Site: https://www.taisun.com.sg

Year Founded: 1966
1767—(HKG)
Rev.: $56,471,530
Assets: $60,930,499
Liabilities: $9,290,335
Net Worth: $51,640,163
Earnings: $4,390,351
Emp.: 311
Fiscal Year-end: 12/31/22
Holding Company
N.A.I.C.S.: 551112
Sandy Seow Yen Lim *(Chm)*

Subsidiaries:

TSS Global Pte. Ltd. (1)
CT Hub 2 Kallang Avenue 07-31, Singapore, 339407, Singapore
Tel.: (65) 83829120
Web Site:
https://www.tssglobalsingapore.com
Corporate Management Services
N.A.I.C.S.: 561110

TS3
62 Boulevard Pereire 20 treilhare
75008, 75017, Paris, France
Tel.: (33) 142122626
Web Site: http://www.tsprod.com
Sales Range: $25-49.9 Million
Emp.: 10
Tour Production Service
N.A.I.C.S.: 711320
Thierry Suc *(Founder & Pres)*

TSA INDUSTRIES SDN. BHD.
Lot 3998 Jalan 6/2A, Taman Industri Selesa Jaya, 43300, Balakong, Selangor Darul Ehsan, Malaysia
Tel.: (60) 3 8962 2888
Web Site: http://www.tsa.com.my
Year Founded: 1993
Sales Range: $50-74.9 Million
Emp.: 300
Ferrous & Non Ferrous Metal Whslr
N.A.I.C.S.: 423510
Chew Kuan Fah *(Mng Dir)*

Subsidiaries:

Mitra Bintang Sdn. Bhd. (1)
Lot 3998 Jalan 6/2A Taman Industri Selesa Jaya, Balakong, 43300, Selangor Darul Ehsan, Malaysia
Tel.: (60) 389622888
Web Site: http://www.atis.com.my
Sales Range: $75-99.9 Million
Industrial Electronic & Electrical Products Distr
N.A.I.C.S.: 423690
Kuan Fah Chew *(Mng Dir)*

TSA INDUSTRIES (SEA) PTE LTD (1)
10 Admiralty Street 06-50 Northlink Building, Singapore, 757695, Singapore
Tel.: (65) 6483 8308
Metal Cutting Machinery Distr
N.A.I.C.S.: 423830

TSA Industries (Ipoh) Sdn. Bhd. (1)
No 2 Persiaran Perusahaan Kledang Utara 1/2 Kawasan Perindustrian, Chandan Raya, Menglembu, 31450, Perak Darul Ridzuan, Malaysia
Tel.: (60) 52816688
Web Site: http://www.tsa.com.my
Non Ferrous Metal & Industrial Hardware Products Distr
N.A.I.C.S.: 423510

TSA Industries (Johor) Sdn. Bhd. (1)
No 26 Jalan Gemilang 1, Taman Perindustrian Cemerlang, 81800, Ulu Tiram, Johor Darul Takzim, Malaysia
Tel.: (60) 78683888
Web Site: http://www.tsa.com.my
Sales Range: $25-49.9 Million
Emp.: 20
Nonferrous Metal Product Distr
N.A.I.C.S.: 423510
S. D. Lim *(Mgr)*

TSA Industries (Penang) Sdn. Bhd. (1)
No 517 Jalan Perusahaan Baru, Prai Industrial Estate, Prai, 13600, Penang, Malaysia
Tel.: (60) 43898988
Web Site: http://www.tsa.com.my
Sales Range: $25-49.9 Million
Emp.: 20
Nonferrous Metal Product Distr
N.A.I.C.S.: 423510

TSA Industries Sdn. Bhd. - Sabah (1)
Jalan Tuaran, 84380, Kota Kinabalu, Sabah, Malaysia
Tel.: (60) 88 388855
Web Site: http://www.tsa.com.my
Stainless Steel Products Distr
N.A.I.C.S.: 423510

TSA Pipes Manufacturing Sdn. Bhd. (1)
Lot 3998 Jalan 6/2A Taman Industri Selesa Jaya, Balakong, 43300, Selangor, Malaysia
Tel.: (60) 389622888
Web Site: http://www.tsa.com.my
Sales Range: $25-49.9 Million
Emp.: 200
Steel Pipes & Tubes Mfr
N.A.I.C.S.: 331210
Chew Kankuan *(Mng Dir)*

TSAKER NEW ENERGY TECH CO., LIMITED
Building No 10 109 Jinghaisanlu, Economic-Technological Development Area, Beijing, China
Tel.: (86) 1059796688
Web Site: http://www.tsaker.com
Year Founded: 1997
1986—(HKG)
Rev.: $297,973,447
Assets: $448,611,556
Liabilities: $153,777,312
Net Worth: $294,834,244
Earnings: $35,694,173
Emp.: 1,947
Fiscal Year-end: 12/31/22
Chemical Product Mfr & Distr
N.A.I.C.S.: 325199
Yi Ge *(Chm & CEO)*

Subsidiaries:

Camp three signs (Yingkou) Fine Chemical Co., Ltd. (1)
Xii Village Lu Nan Laobian, Yingkou, 115018, Liaoning, China
Tel.: (86) 4173607018
Web Site: http://www.ykysfc.com
Emp.: 700
Chemical Product Mfr & Distr
N.A.I.C.S.: 325199

TSAKOS ENERGY NAVIGATION LIMITED
367 Syngrou Avenue, Palaio Faliro, 175 64, Athens, Greece
Tel.: (30) 2109407710
Web Site: https://www.tenn.gr
Year Founded: 1993
TEN—(NYSE)
Rev.: $860,400,000
Assets: $3,308,575,000
Liabilities: $1,785,656,000
Net Worth: $1,522,919,000
Earnings: $204,234,000
Emp.: 1,364
Fiscal Year-end: 12/31/22
Crude Oil & Petroleum Marine Transportation Services
N.A.I.C.S.: 483111
Nikolas P. Tsakos *(Co-Founder, Pres & CEO)*

TSANG YOW INDUSTRIAL CO., LTD.
No 18 Chung Shan Rd, Min-Hsiung Industrial Park, Chiayi, 62154, Taiwan
Tel.: (886) 52200888
Web Site:
https://www.tsangyow.com.tw
Year Founded: 1985
1568—(TAI)
Rev.: $39,016,186
Assets: $85,780,304
Liabilities: $25,928,708
Net Worth: $59,851,595
Earnings: $6,428,987
Emp.: 216
Fiscal Year-end: 12/31/23
OEM Transmission Systems Mfr
N.A.I.C.S.: 336350
Ryan Teng *(Founder)*

Subsidiaries:

Wuxi Tsang Yow Auto Parts Co., Ltd. (1)
No 69 Ximei Road High-tech Development Zone, Wuxi, Jiangsu, China
Tel.: (86) 51088156188
Web Site: http://www.tsangyow.com.cn
Automobile Parts Mfr & Distr
N.A.I.C.S.: 336110

TSANN KUEN (CHINA) ENTERPRISE CO., LTD.
No 88 Xinglong Road, Huli Industrial Zone, Xiamen, 363107, Fujian, China
Tel.: (86) 5925600887
Web Site: http://www.eupa.cn
Year Founded: 1993
200512—(SSE)
Rev.: $222,431,157
Assets: $366,098,742
Liabilities: $156,929,601
Net Worth: $209,169,141
Earnings: $13,267,375
Emp.: 9,100
Fiscal Year-end: 12/31/22
Electric Appliances Mfr
N.A.I.C.S.: 423620
Cai Yuansong *(Chm & Gen Mgr)*

TSANN KUEN ENTERPRISE CO., LTD.
No 331 Sec 1 Tiding Blvd, Neihu Dist, Taipei, 114, Taiwan
Tel.: (886) 277203999
Web Site: https://www.tk3c.com.tw
Year Founded: 1978
2430—(TAI)
Rev.: $653,549,241
Assets: $463,111,726
Liabilities: $314,182,924
Net Worth: $148,928,802
Earnings: $9,115,275
Emp.: 1,948
Fiscal Year-end: 12/31/23
Electronic Product Whslr
N.A.I.C.S.: 423620
Wang Yu-Liang *(CFO & Asst VP)*

TSC AUTO ID TECHNOLOGY CO., LTD.
9F No 95 Minquan Rd, Xindian Dist, New Taipei City, 231, Taiwan
Tel.: (886) 222186789
Web Site:
https://usca.tscprinters.com
3611—(TPE)
Rev.: $249,098,521
Assets: $259,349,311
Liabilities: $110,810,243
Net Worth: $148,539,068
Earnings: $30,169,434
Fiscal Year-end: 12/31/22
Thermal Bar Code & Label Printer Mfr
N.A.I.C.S.: 323111
Ming-I Chen *(Exec VP)*

Subsidiaries:

TSC Auto ID Technology America Inc. (1)
3040 Saturn St Ste 200, Brea, CA 92821
Tel.: (657) 258-0808
Electronic Products Mfr
N.A.I.C.S.: 334111
Kevin Aie *(CEO-Americas)*

TSC Auto ID Technology EMEA GmbH (1)
Tel.: (7) 4956463538
Electronic Products Mfr
N.A.I.C.S.: 334111

TSC Auto ID Technology EMEA GmbH (1)
Georg-Wimmer-Ring 8b, 85604, Zorneding, Germany
Tel.: (49) 637979000
Electronic Products Mfr
N.A.I.C.S.: 334111

TSC Auto ID Technology ME Ltd. (1)
Building 7WA/ West Wing Office Number - G050, PO Box No 293673, Dubai, United Arab Emirates
Tel.: (971) 42533069
Electronic Products Mfr
N.A.I.C.S.: 334111

Tianjin TSC Auto ID Technology Co., Ltd. (1)
2nd Floor Workshop Rongda Building No 51 the 9th Avenue, Tianjin Economic-Technologic Development Area, Tianjin, 300457, China
Tel.: (86) 2259816661
Electronic Products Mfr
N.A.I.C.S.: 334111

TSE CO., LTD.
189 Gunsu 1-gil Jiksan-eup, Gangnam-gu, Cheonan, 31032, Chungcheongnam-do, Korea (South)
Tel.: (82) 415819955
Web Site: https://www.tse21.com
Year Founded: 1994
131290—(KRS)
Rev.: $260,215,618
Assets: $334,286,088
Liabilities: $80,581,108
Net Worth: $253,704,981
Earnings: $38,211,487
Emp.: 637
Fiscal Year-end: 12/31/22
Semiconductor Testing Equipment Mfr
N.A.I.C.S.: 334413
Tak Jung *(Mng Dir)*

Subsidiaries:

GMTEST Co., Ltd. (1)
19 Gunseo 1-gil, Jiksan-eup Seobuk-gu, Cheonan, Chungcheongnam-do, Korea (South)
Tel.: (82) 414102600
Web Site: https://www.gmtest.com
Emp.: 147
Semiconductor Testing Services
N.A.I.C.S.: 334515

MegaSen Co., Ltd. (1)
7 Pungsesandan-ro Pungse-myeon, Dongnam-gu, Cheonan, 31217, Chungcheongnam-do, Korea (South)
Tel.: (82) 414117100
Web Site: https://megasen.co.kr
Display & Semiconductor Equipment Mfr
N.A.I.C.S.: 333242

Megatouch Co., Ltd. (1)
710 Baekseok-dong 42 3gongdan 2-ro, Seobuk-gu, Cheonan, 31093, Chungnam, Korea (South)
Tel.: (82) 414127100
Web Site: https://www.megatouch.co.kr
Mechanical & Rubber Contact Solution Services
N.A.I.C.S.: 811310

TSE STEEL LTD.
4436-90 Avenue SE, Calgary, T2C 2S7, AB, Canada
Tel.: (403) 279-6060
Web Site: https://www.tsesteel.com
Year Founded: 1968
Rev.: $10,860,520
Emp.: 50
Steel Foundries
N.A.I.C.S.: 331513
Troy Branch *(Gen Mgr)*

TSE SUI LUEN JEWELLERY (INTERNATIONAL) LIMITED

TSE SUI LUEN JEWELLERY (INTERNATIONAL) LIMITED
Ground Floor Block B Summit Building 30 Man Yue Street, Hunghom, Kowloon, China (Hong Kong)
Tel.: (852) 2 333 4221
Web Site: http://www.tslj.com
0417—(HKG)
Rev.: $356,989,296
Assets: $349,170,400
Liabilities: $213,993,556
Net Worth: $135,176,844
Earnings: $1,988,098
Emp.: 2,400
Fiscal Year-end: 03/31/22
Jewelry Product Mfr
N.A.I.C.S.: 339910
Annie On Yee Yau *(Chm & CEO)*

Subsidiaries:

Guangzhou Tai Yi Trading Company Limited (1)
Rm 1809 Bank of America Plz 555 Ren Min Zhong Rd, Guangzhou, 510145, Guangdong, China
Tel.: (86) 2081300498
Jewelry Retailer
N.A.I.C.S.: 423940

TSL Jewellery (Export) Company Limited (1)
Ground Fl Summit Bldg Block B 30 Man Yue St, Hung Hom, Kowloon, China (Hong Kong)
Tel.: (852) 23334221
Web Site: http://www.tslj.com
Jewelry Export Services
N.A.I.C.S.: 423940

TSL Jewellery (H.K.) Co. Limited (1)
G/F Summit Bldg 30 Man Yue St, Hung Hom, Kowloon, China (Hong Kong)
Tel.: (852) 23334221
Web Site: http://www.tslj.com
Jewelry Retailer
N.A.I.C.S.: 423940

TSL Jewellery (Macau) Limited (1)
The Grand Canal Shoppes No 2022 The Venetian Resort-Hotel, Macau, China (Macau)
Tel.: (853) 28576282
Sales Range: $25-49.9 Million
Emp.: 10
Jewelry Retailer
N.A.I.C.S.: 423940
Patrick Poon *(Gen Mgr)*

Tse Sui Luen Jewellery Company Limited (1)
Ground Fl Summit Bldg Block B 30 Man Yue St, Hung Hom, Kowloon, China (Hong Kong)
Tel.: (852) 23334228
Jewelry Retailer
N.A.I.C.S.: 423940
Annie Yau *(CEO)*

TSEC CORPORATION

8F No 225 Sec 3 Beixin Rd Xindian Dist, New Taipei City, 23143, Taiwan
Tel.: (886) 229122199
Web Site: https://www.tsecpv.com
Year Founded: 2010
6443—(TAI)
Rev.: $270,150,976
Assets: $394,606,447
Liabilities: $144,466,720
Net Worth: $250,139,727
Earnings: $17,242,617
Emp.: 1,745
Fiscal Year-end: 12/31/23
Solar Cell Mfr & Distr
N.A.I.C.S.: 335999
Ellick K. J. Liao *(Chm & CEO)*

Subsidiaries:

TSEC America Inc. (1)
1235 N Harbor Blvd Ste 240, Fullerton, CA 92832
Tel.: (714) 449-0966
Solar Cell Distr
N.A.I.C.S.: 423690

TSEC Corporation - Hsinchu Plant (1)
No 85 Guangfu N Rd Hukou Township, Hsinchu, 30351, Taiwan
Tel.: (886) 3696707
Solar Cell Mfr
N.A.I.C.S.: 334413

TSEC Corporation - Pingtung Plant (1)
No 335-12 Daxi Rd, Ping-tung, 90093, Pingtung, Taiwan
Tel.: (886) 87536899
Solar Cell Mfr
N.A.I.C.S.: 334413

TSG INTERNATIONAL AG

Bulachstrasse 5, 8057, Zurich, Switzerland
Tel.: (41) 43 960 1751   CH
Web Site: http://www.ridetsg.com
Year Founded: 1988
Sales Range: $10-24.9 Million
Emp.: 10
Skateboard, Ski, Bike, Snowboard & Wakeboard Safety Gear Developer & Distr
N.A.I.C.S.: 423910
Marcel Korner *(CEO)*

TSH BIOPHARM CORP LTD.

F-1 No 3-1 Yuanyuan Street, Nangang District, Taipei, Taiwan
Tel.: (886) 226558525
Web Site: https://www.tshbiopharm.com
8432—(TPE)
Rev.: $14,519,526
Assets: $36,094,957
Liabilities: $2,722,009
Net Worth: $33,372,948
Earnings: $1,935,091
Fiscal Year-end: 12/31/22
Pharmaceutical Product Mfr & Distr
N.A.I.C.S.: 325412
Chih-Meng Chang *(Chm)*

TSH CORPORATION LIMITED

51 Changi Business Park Central 2 The Signature 04-05, Singapore, 486066, Singapore
Tel.: (65) 6701 8696
Web Site: http://www.tshcorp.com.sg
Sales Range: Less than $1 Million
Electronic Products Mfr & Whslr
N.A.I.C.S.: 334419
Khoon Hui Chua *(CEO)*

Subsidiaries:

The Other Roof Pte. Ltd. (1)
28 Ann Siang Road, Singapore, 069708, Singapore
Tel.: (65) 61002882
Web Site: http://www.theotherroof.com
Alcoholic Beverages Services
N.A.I.C.S.: 722410

The Other Room Pte. Ltd. (1)
320 Orchard Road 01-05, Singapore, 238865, Singapore
Tel.: (65) 61007778
Web Site: http://www.theotherroom.com.sg
Alcoholic Beverages Services
N.A.I.C.S.: 722410

TSH RESOURCES BERHAD

Level 10 Menara TSH No 8 Jalan Semantan Damansara Heights, 50490, Kuala Lumpur, Malaysia
Tel.: (60) 320840888
Web Site: https://www.tsh.com.my
TSH—(KLS)
Rev.: $294,257,453
Assets: $818,738,910
Liabilities: $369,875,880
Net Worth: $448,863,030
Earnings: $49,998,218
Emp.: 7,216
Fiscal Year-end: 12/31/21
Holding Company; Wood-Based Products, Agroforestry, Palm Oil, Vegetable Fats & Cocoa Products
N.A.I.C.S.: 551112
Kelvin Aik Pen Tan *(Chm)*

Subsidiaries:

CocoaHouse Industries Sdn. Bhd. (1)
Lot 6 Jalan Sultan Hishamuddin 1-20, Kawasan Perusahaan Selat Klang, 42000, Port Klang, Selangor, Malaysia (100%)
Tel.: (60) 331763010
Web Site: http://www.tsh.com
Sales Range: $25-49.9 Million
Emp.: 60
Frozen Cakes Pies & Pastries Mfr
N.A.I.C.S.: 311813

CocoaHouse Sdn. Bhd. (1)
Lot 17 Jalan Sultan Mohamed 5 Kawasan 20 Selat Klang Utara, Bandar Sultan Suleiman, 42000, Port Klang, Selangor, Malaysia
Tel.: (60) 331763010
Cocoa Product Mfr & Retailer
N.A.I.C.S.: 311351

Ekowood (USA) Inc. (1)
32840 9th St Winchesto, Riverside, CA 92590
Tel.: (951) 926-1109
Sales Range: $25-49.9 Million
Emp.: 1
Wood Products Mfr
N.A.I.C.S.: 321999
Barbara Stevens *(Mgr)*

Ekowood Iberica SL (1)
Pol Ind Apatta- Erreka c/ Belabieta 4 Pab 3, Guipuzcoa, Spain
Tel.: (34) 943333700
Web Site: http://www.ekowood.com
Emp.: 5
Brick Stone & Related Construction Material Whslr
N.A.I.C.S.: 423320

Ekowood International Berhad (1)
Lot 1-12 Jalan Industri 2/1 Kawasan Perindustrian Gopeng KM 15, Jalan Gopeng, 31600, Gopeng, Perak, Malaysia
Tel.: (60) 53572020
Web Site: https://www.ekowood.com
Sales Range: $150-199.9 Million
Emp.: 300
Lumber Plywood Millwork & Wood Panel Whslr
N.A.I.C.S.: 423310

Ekowood Malaysia Sdn. Bhd. (1)
Menara TSH 8 Jalan Semantan Damansara Heights, 50490, Kuala Lumpur, Malaysia
Tel.: (60) 320840888
Investment Holding Services
N.A.I.C.S.: 551112

TSH Agri Pte. Ltd. (1)
15-07 TripleOne Somerset 111 Somerset Road, Singapore, 238164, Singapore
Tel.: (65) 63693008
Web Site: http://www.ekowood.com.sg
Investment Holding Services
N.A.I.C.S.: 551112
Matthias Jash Ng *(Mgr-Sls)*

TSH Plantation Sdn. Bhd (1)
TSH Resources Berhad Bangunan TSH TB 9 M 7 Aasp Rd, 91000, Tawau, Malaysia
Tel.: (60) 89912020
Web Site: https://www.tsh.com.my
Crude Oil & Petroleum Mfr
Emp.: 100
N.A.I.C.S.: 213112

TSH Products Sdn. Bhd. (1)
Lot 1-12 Jalan Industri 2-1, Kawasan Perindustrian Gopeng, 31600, Perak, Gopeng, Malaysia
Tel.: (60) 53572020
Web Site: http://www.ekowood.com
Sales Range: $75-99.9 Million
Emp.: 250
Lumber Plywood Millwork & Wood Panel Whslr
N.A.I.C.S.: 423310

TSI CO., LTD.

702-66 Baran-Ro Sujik-Ri Hyangnam-Eup, Hwaseong, Gyeonggi-do, Korea (South)
Tel.: (82) 316672623
Web Site: http://www.eng.taesungind.co.kr
Year Founded: 2011
277880—(KRS)
Rev.: $114,116,609
Assets: $178,646,142
Liabilities: $144,048,834
Net Worth: $34,597,308
Earnings: $2,396,560
Emp.: 215
Fiscal Year-end: 12/31/22
General Purpose Machinery Mfr
N.A.I.C.S.: 333998
In-Sik Pyo *(CEO)*

TSI HOLDINGS CO., LTD.

5-7-1 Koujimachi, Chiyoda-ku, Tokyo, 102-0083, Japan
Tel.: (81) 352135511   JP
Web Site: http://www.tsi-holdings.com
Year Founded: 2011
TSIHF—(OTCIQ)
Rev.: $1,101,665,470
Assets: $946,259,760
Liabilities: $255,537,780
Net Worth: $690,721,980
Earnings: $34,379,410
Fiscal Year-end: 02/29/24
Holding Company
N.A.I.C.S.: 551112
Masahiko Miyake *(Chm & Pres)*

Subsidiaries:

Anadis Co., Ltd. (1)
Avenueside Daikanyama II 2nd Floor, Sarugakucho Shibuya-ku, Tokyo, 150-0033, Japan
Tel.: (81) 354560567
Web Site: https://www.dunadix.co.jp
Emp.: 31
Clothing Product Mfr & Distr
N.A.I.C.S.: 315990

Anglobal Ltd. (1)
2-1-1 Shibuya, Shibuya-ku, Tokyo, 150-0002, Japan
Tel.: (81) 354677811
Web Site: http://www.anglobal.co.jp
Clothing Product Mfr & Distr
N.A.I.C.S.: 315990

Nano Universe Co., Ltd. (1)
1-6-3 Jinnan, Shibuya-ku, Tokyo, 150-0041, Japan
Tel.: (81) 354569972
Web Site: http://www.nanounverse.jp
Clothing Product Mfr & Distr
N.A.I.C.S.: 315990

Rosebud Co., Ltd. (1)
6-25-16 Jingumae Ichigo Jingumae Building 4th Floor, Shibuya-ku, Tokyo, Japan
Tel.: (81) 5058402525
Web Site: http://www.rosebud-web.com
Clothing Product Mfr & Distr
N.A.I.C.S.: 315990

Sanei BD Co., Ltd. (1)
1-1-1 Minami Aoyama, Minato-ku, Tokyo, 107-8578, Japan
Tel.: (81) 5058402525
Web Site: http://www.saneibd.com
Clothing Product Mfr & Distr
N.A.I.C.S.: 315990

Sanei International Co., Ltd. (1)
Aoyama Building 4F 1-2-3 Kita, Minato-ku, Tokyo, 107-0061, Japan
Tel.: (81) 367480222
Web Site: http://www.sanei.net
Clothing Product Mfr & Distr
N.A.I.C.S.: 315990

TSI EC Strategy Co., Ltd. (1)
Aoyama Building 6F 1-2-3 Kitaaoyama, Minato-ku, Tokyo, 107-0061, Japan
Tel.: (81) 367480254
Web Site: https://en-www.tsi-ec.com
Electronic Commerce Services

AND PRIVATE COMPANIES — TSINGHUA TONGFANG CO., LTD.

N.A.I.C.S.: 541612
Takahiko Miyake *(CEO)*

TSI Production Network Co., Ltd. (1)
1-1-1 Minami Aoyama, Minato-ku, Tokyo, Japan
Tel.: (81) 367480270
Web Site: https://www.tsipn.com
Clothing & Apparel Accessory Mfr
N.A.I.C.S.: 315990

Tokyo Style Co., LTD. (1)
Sumitomo Fudosan Harajuku Bldg 2-34-17 Jingumae, Shibuya-ku, Tokyo, 150-0001, Japan
Tel.: (81) 3 6836 1888
Web Site: http://www.tokyostyle.co.jp
Online Shopping Services
N.A.I.C.S.: 458110

Ueno Shokai Co., Ltd. (1)
Odakyu Southern Tower 6F 2-2-1, Yoyogi Shibuya-ku, Tokyo, 151-8583, Japan
Tel.: (81) 353520710
Web Site: http://www.uenoshokai.com
Emp.: 500
Men & Women Clothing Mfr & Distr
N.A.I.C.S.: 315250
Fumihiko Hasegawa *(CEO)*

Unit & Guest Co., Ltd. (1)
4F 6F 1-25-1 Ebisu Minami, Shibuya-ku, Tokyo, 150-0022, Japan
Tel.: (81) 337103107
Web Site: http://www.unit-and-guest.com
Clothing Product Mfr & Distr
N.A.I.C.S.: 315990
Takenari Sato *(Pres)*

TSIM SHA TSUI PROPERTIES LIMITED

12th Floor Tsim Sha Tsui Centre Salisbury Road, Tsim Sha Tsui, Kowloon, China (Hong Kong)
Tel.: (852) 2 721 8388
Web Site: http://www.sino.com
0247—(OTCIQ)
Rev.: $3,170,992,881
Assets: $23,559,958,745
Liabilities: $3,398,033,726
Net Worth: $20,161,925,019
Earnings: $1,350,786,728
Fiscal Year-end: 06/30/21
Property Investment Services
N.A.I.C.S.: 525990
Daryl Win Kong Ng *(Deputy Chm)*

Subsidiaries:

Acclaim Investment Limited (1)
12 Fl Tsim Sha Tsui Ctr, E Wing Tsim Sha Tsui, Kowloon, China (Hong Kong)
Tel.: (852) 27218388
Web Site: http://www.fino.com
Emp.: 1,000
Investment Management Service
N.A.I.C.S.: 523940

Sino Land Company Limited (1)
12/F Tsim Sha Tsui Centre Salisbury Road Tsimshatsui, Tsim Sha Tsui, Kowloon, China (Hong Kong)
Tel.: (852) 27218388
Web Site: http://www.sino.com
Rev.: $2,006,177,436
Assets: $23,085,340,300
Liabilities: $2,677,026,375
Net Worth: $20,408,313,925
Earnings: $769,328,208
Emp.: 7,000
Fiscal Year-end: 06/30/2022
Residential, Nonresidential & Hotels Developer & Manager
N.A.I.C.S.: 531311
Velencia Lee *(CFO & Sec)*

Subsidiary (Domestic):

Best Result Cleaning Services Limited (2)
Suite 1906-1908 19/F Skyline Tower 39 Wang Kwong Road Kowloon Bay, Kowloon, China (Hong Kong)
Tel.: (852) 31127282
Sales Range: $25-49.9 Million
Emp.: 55
Buildings & Dwellings Services
N.A.I.C.S.: 561790

Sino Hotels (Holdings) Limited (2)
12th Floor Tsim Sha Tsui Center, Tsim Sha Tsui, Kowloon, China (Hong Kong)
Tel.: (852) 27218388
Web Site: http://www.sino-hotels.com
Hotels & Motels
N.A.I.C.S.: 721110
Giovanni Viterale *(Exec Dir)*

Sino Security Services Limited (2)
Suite 1909 19/F Skyline Tower 39 Wang Kwong Road Kowloon Bay, Tsim Sha Tsui, Kowloon, China (Hong Kong)
Tel.: (852) 31127600
Security System Services
N.A.I.C.S.: 561621

TSINGHUA HOLDINGS CO., LTD.

25F Science Park Tower A Tsinghua University Science Park No 1, Zhongguancun East Road Haidian District, Beijing, 100084, China
Tel.: (86) 1082150983 **CN**
Web Site:
http://www.thholding.com.cn
Year Founded: 2003
Sales Range: $1-4.9 Billion
Holding Company
N.A.I.C.S.: 551112
Liye Zhou *(Pres)*

Subsidiaries:

Tsinghua Unigroup Ltd. (1)
10/F Unis Plaza Tsinghua Science Park, Haidian District, Beijing, 100084, China (51%)
Tel.: (86) 10 8215 9955
Web Site: http://www.unigroup.com.cn
Holding Company; Information Technologies & Biopharmaceuticals Developer & Mfr; Industrial Real Estate Investment; Urban Infrastructure Developer
N.A.I.C.S.: 551112
Weiguo Zhao *(Chm & CEO)*

Subsidiary (Domestic):

New H3C Technologies Co., Ltd. (2)
466 Changhe Road, Binjiang District, Hangzhou, 310052, China (51%)
Tel.: (86) 57186760000
Web Site: http://www.h3c.com
Computer System Design Services
N.A.I.C.S.: 541512

RDA Microelectronics, Inc. (2)
6/F Building 4 690 Bibo Road, Pudong District, Shanghai, 201203, China
Tel.: (86) 21 5027 1108
Web Site: http://www.rdamicro.com
Sales Range: $300-349.9 Million
Fabless Semiconductor Device Mfr
N.A.I.C.S.: 334413
Shuran Wei *(CTO)*

Spreadtrum Communications, Inc. (2)
Building 1 Spreadtrum Center 2288 Zuchongzhi Road, Zhangjiang High-Tech Park, Pudong District, Shanghai, 201203, China
Tel.: (86) 21 2036 0600
Web Site: http://www.spreadtrum.com
Sales Range: $700-749.9 Million
Emp.: 1,506
Fabless Semiconductor Designer, Mfr & Marketer
N.A.I.C.S.: 334413
Leo Li *(Chm, Pres & CEO)*

Subsidiary (Domestic):

Beijing Spreadtrum High-Tech Communications Technology Co., Ltd. (3)
9F Block D Tsinghua Tongfang Hi-tech Plaza No 1 Wangzhuang Rd, Haidian District, Beijing, 100083, China (100%)
Tel.: (86) 10 5785 0888
Web Site: http://www.spreadtrum.com
Fabless Semiconductor Mfr
N.A.I.C.S.: 334413

Spreadtrum Communications (Shanghai) Co., Ltd. (3)
Building 1 Spreadtrum Centre No 2288 Zuchongzhi Rd Zhangjiang, High-Tech Park, Pudong District, Shanghai, 201203, China (100%)
Tel.: (86) 21 2036 0600
Web Site: http://www.spreadtrum.com.cn
Fabless Semiconductor Mfr
N.A.I.C.S.: 334413
Leo Li *(Chm, Pres & CEO)*

Spreadtrum Communications (Tianjin) Co., Ltd. (3)
5F Gate 3 Building No 2 Ronghe Plaza No 168 West Fourth Avenue, Airport Economic Area, Tianjin, 300300, China
Tel.: (86) 22 84841399
Web Site: http://www.spreadtrum.com
Sales Range: $25-49.9 Million
Emp.: 18
Wireless Communication Equipment Mfr
N.A.I.C.S.: 334220

Subsidiary (US):

Spreadtrum Communications USA Inc. (3)
5960 Cornerstone Ct Ste 200, San Diego, CA 92121
Tel.: (858) 546-0895
Web Site: http://www.spreadtrum.com
Sales Range: $25-49.9 Million
Emp.: 48
Communication Transceiver Equipment Mfr
N.A.I.C.S.: 334220
Lon Christensen *(Gen Mgr)*

Tus-Holdings Co., Ltd. (1)
14-17/F Block A Tsinghua University Science Park Innovation Plaza, Beijing, 100084, China
Tel.: (86) 10 6278 5888
Web Site: http://www.tusholdings.com
Holding Company
N.A.I.C.S.: 551112
Wei Yuan *(Pres)*

Holding (Non-US):

Biorem Inc. (2)
7496 Wellington Road 34, Puslinch, Guelph, N0B 2J0, ON, Canada (65.6%)
Tel.: (519) 767-9100
Web Site: https://www.biorem.biz
Rev.: $19,002,933
Assets: $18,180,278
Liabilities: $13,106,034
Net Worth: $5,074,244
Earnings: $1,645,698
Fiscal Year-end: 12/31/2023
Air Pollution Control Systems Mfr
N.A.I.C.S.: 334519
Derek S. Webb *(Pres & CEO)*

Subsidiary (US):

Biorem Environmental Inc. (3)
100 Rawson Rd Ste 230, Victor, NY 14564
Tel.: (585) 924-2220
Web Site: http://www.biorem.biz
Emp.: 7
Pollution Control Services
N.A.I.C.S.: 334512
Shaun Keebler *(Plant Mgr)*

Subsidiary (Domestic):

Biorem Technologies Inc. (3)
7496 Wellington Road 34, Puslinch, N0B 2J0, ON, Canada
Tel.: (519) 767-9100
Web Site: http://www.biorem.biz
Sales Range: $25-49.9 Million
Pollution Control Services
N.A.I.C.S.: 334512

Holding (Domestic):

Tus Pharmaceutical Group Co., Ltd. (2)
No 33 Yangliu Road Hi-tech Zone, Zhengxiang District, Hengyang, 421001, Hunan, China
Tel.: (86) 7348239335
Web Site: http://www.guhan.com
Rev.: $49,214,145
Assets: $163,812,248
Liabilities: $65,182,104
Net Worth: $98,630,144
Earnings: $2,547,684
Fiscal Year-end: 12/31/2022
Pharmaceuticals Mfr
N.A.I.C.S.: 325412

Jiao Qisen *(Chm)*

VNET Group, Inc. (2)
Guanjie Building Southeast 1st Floor 10 Suite Jiuxianqiao East Road, Chaoyang District, Beijing, 100016, China (51%)
Tel.: (86) 1084562121
Web Site: http://www.21vianet.com
Rev.: $1,082,464,195
Assets: $4,128,765,130
Liabilities: $3,059,074,972
Net Worth: $1,069,690,158
Earnings: ($118,883,606)
Emp.: 3,293
Fiscal Year-end: 12/31/2022
Internet Data Center Services
N.A.I.C.S.: 518210
Joshua Sheng Chen *(Founder & Chm)*

Subsidiary (Non-US):

21ViaNet Group Limited (3)
Unit 716 7/F 12W Hong Kong Science Park Pak Shek Kok, Sha Tin, New Territories, China (Hong Kong)
Tel.: (852) 3565 4902
Holding Company
N.A.I.C.S.: 551112
Ho Yuen Kei *(Sr Mgr)*

Diyixian.com Limited (3)
Unit 2501 Global Gateway HK 168 Yeung Uk Road, Tsuen Wan, China (Hong Kong)
Tel.: (852) 2187 7600
Internet Service Provider
N.A.I.C.S.: 517112

TSINGHUA TONGFANG CO., LTD.

1 Wangzhuang Road Tsinghua Tongfang Hi-tech Plaza, Haidian District, Beijing, 100 083, China
Tel.: (86) 1082399888 **CN**
Web Site: https://www.thtf.com.cn
Year Founded: 1997
600100—(SHG)
Rev.: $3,336,093,343
Assets: $7,600,575,453
Liabilities: $4,797,136,544
Net Worth: $2,803,438,909
Earnings: ($108,322,615)
Fiscal Year-end: 12/31/22
Information, Energy & Environment Technologies Mfr & Services
N.A.I.C.S.: 339999
Liu Weidong *(CFO & VP)*

Subsidiaries:

Neo-Neon Holdings Limited (1)
15th Floor Allied Kajima Building, 138 Gloucester Road, Wanchai, China (Hong Kong) (69.68%)
Tel.: (852) 27862133
Web Site: http://www.neo-neon.com
Rev.: $130,221,842
Assets: $242,729,838
Liabilities: $34,638,505
Net Worth: $208,091,333
Earnings: $7,003,433
Emp.: 557
Fiscal Year-end: 12/31/2022
Holding Company
N.A.I.C.S.: 551112
Lok Wai Leung *(Sec)*

Subsidiary (US):

American Lighting, Inc (2)
1825 N Eastman Rd, Kingsport, TN 37664
Tel.: (423) 246-4281
Web Site:
http://www.americanlightingfixture.com
Electrical Apparatus & Equipment, Wiring Supplies & Related Equipment Merchant Whslr
N.A.I.C.S.: 423610

Subsidiary (Domestic):

Novelty Lights, Inc. (3)
9800 E Easter Ave Ste 160, Centennial, CO 80112 (80%)
Tel.: (303) 727-9000
Web Site: http://www.noveltylights.com
Sales Range: $10-24.9 Million
Emp.: 7
Holiday, Novelty & Rope Lighting

TSINGHUA TONGFANG CO., LTD.

Tsinghua Tongfang Co., Ltd.—(Continued)
N.A.I.C.S.: 335139
Tres Coors *(Pres & Mgr-Ops)*

Nuctech Company Limited (1)
2/F Block A Tongfang Building, Shuangqinglu Haidian District, Beijing, 100084, China
Tel.: (86) 1062780909
Web Site: https://www.nuctech.com
Radiation Imaging Equipment Mfr & Distr
N.A.I.C.S.: 334517

TSINGSHAN HOLDING GROUP CO., LTD.
Tsingshan Building A No 2666 Longxiang Road, Longwan District, Wenzhou, Zhejiang, China
Tel.: (86) 57786628888
Web Site: http://www.tssgroup.com.cn
Year Founded: 2003
Sales Range: Less than $1 Million
Stainless Steel Product Mfr & Distr
N.A.I.C.S.: 331110

TSINGTAO BREWERY GROUP COMPANY LTD.
Qingdao Brewery Building Wusi Square Hong Kong Middle Road, Qingdao, 266071, Shandong, China
Tel.: (86) 4006800899 CN
Web Site: https://www.tsingtao.com.cn
Year Founded: 1903
0168—(HKG)
Rev.: $4,698,787,486
Assets: $6,819,895,236
Liabilities: $2,907,795,771
Net Worth: $3,912,099,465
Earnings: $602,043,493
Emp.: 30,687
Fiscal Year-end: 12/31/23
Beer Distr
N.A.I.C.S.: 312120
Kexing Huang *(Chm)*

Subsidiaries:

Qingdao Tsingtao Beer & Asahi Beverage Co., Ltd. (1)
Wusi Square Hong Kong Middle Road, Qingdao Brewery Building, Qingdao, 266071, Shandong, China
Tel.: (86) 8008600899
Beer Whslr
N.A.I.C.S.: 424810

Tsingtao Brewery Company Limited (1)
Qingdao Brewery Building Wusi Square Hong Kong Middle Road, Qingdao, 266071, Shandong, China
Tel.: (86) 4006800899
Web Site: https://www.tsingtao.com.cn
Rev.: $4,516,887,810
Assets: $7,063,762,652
Liabilities: $3,375,129,977
Net Worth: $3,688,632,675
Earnings: $520,972,255
Emp.: 39,320
Fiscal Year-end: 12/31/2022
Liquor Product Mfr & Distr
N.A.I.C.S.: 312120
Huang Kexing *(Chm)*

TSIT WING INTERNATIONAL HOLDINGS LIMITED
Flats F-J 11/F Block 1 Kwai Tak Ind Centre Kwai Tak St, Kwai Chung, NT, China (Hong Kong)
Tel.: (852) 24290585
Web Site: http://www.twcoffee.com
2119—(HKG)
Sales Range: $75-99.9 Million
Grocery Product Distr
N.A.I.C.S.: 492210
Samuel Sum Yu Chan *(Gen Mgr-Supply Chain)*

TSK ELECTRONICA Y ELECTRICIDAD, S.A.
Parque Cientifico Tecnologico C/ Ada Byron 220, 33203, Gijon, Spain
Tel.: (34) 985 134 171 ES
Web Site: http://www.grupotsk.com
Year Founded: 1986
Sales Range: $600-649.9 Million
Emp.: 772
Industrial Engineering & Construction Services
N.A.I.C.S.: 237990
Santiago del Valle *(Mng Dir-Sls)*

Subsidiaries:

TSK Flagsol Engineering GmbH (1)
Agrippinawerft 26, 50678, Cologne, Germany (100%)
Tel.: (49) 221 925 970 0
Web Site: http://www.flagsol.com
Sales Range: $25-49.9 Million
Solar Thermal Power Plant Construction & Maintenance Services
N.A.I.C.S.: 236210
Oliver Baudson *(Head-Sls & Mktg)*

TSL INDUSTRIES LIMITED
P-50 2nd Floor Princess Street, Kolkata, 700 072, West Bengal, India
Tel.: (91) 33 25702006
Web Site: http://www.tslindustriesltd.com
Year Founded: 1994
Investment Management Service
N.A.I.C.S.: 523940
Dolly Shah *(Chm)*

Subsidiaries:

Titatgarh Steel Ltd. (1)
113 10th Floor Block A Park Street, Podar Point beside Kohinoor Street, Kolkata, 700016, West Bengal, India
Tel.: (91) 33 2226 0078
Steel Mfrs
N.A.I.C.S.: 332111

TSL LIMITED
28 Simon Mazorodze Road, Southerton, Harare, Zimbabwe
Tel.: (263) 772131302
Web Site: https://www.tsl.co.zw
Year Founded: 1957
TSL—(ZIM)
Rev.: $10,556,633
Assets: $25,461,131
Liabilities: $6,395,956
Net Worth: $19,065,175
Earnings: $1,707,455
Emp.: 337
Fiscal Year-end: 10/31/21
Tobacco Mfr
N.A.I.C.S.: 312230
A. S. Mandiwanza *(Chm)*

Subsidiaries:

Bak Logistics (Private) Limited (1)
106 Dartford Road, Willowvale, Harare, Zimbabwe
Tel.: (263) 24620070
Web Site: https://www.baklogistics.com
Emp.: 400
Logistic Services
N.A.I.C.S.: 541614
Patrick Devenish *(CEO)*

Key Logistics (Private) Limited (1)
106 Dartford Road, Willowvale, Harare, Zimbabwe
Tel.: (263) 242620600
Web Site: http://www.keylogistics.co.zw
Logistic Services
N.A.I.C.S.: 541614

Propak Hessian (Private) Limited (1)
18-20 Nuffield Road, Harare, Zimbabwe
Tel.: (263) 2426203945
Web Site: http://www.propakafrica.com
Emp.: 200
Agro Packaging Product Mfr
N.A.I.C.S.: 326112

TSM GLOBAL BERHAD
12 Lorong Medan Tuanku Satu, 50300, Kuala Lumpur, Malaysia
Tel.: (60) 326922923
Web Site: http://www.tsm-global.com.my
Sales Range: $75-99.9 Million
Emp.: 50
Wire Harnesses Mfr
N.A.I.C.S.: 336320
Min Er Chee *(Sec)*

Subsidiaries:

TSM Wellness Sdn. Bhd. (1)
No 60 Ground Floor Plaza Damas Blok L Jln Sri Hartamas 1, 50480, Kuala Lumpur, Malaysia
Tel.: (60) 362018333
Web Site: http://www.tsm-energy.com
Sales Range: $10-24.9 Million
Emp.: 4
Yoga Training Services
N.A.I.C.S.: 611699

TSODILO RESOURCES LIMITED
1 King Street West Suite 4800, PO Box 508, Toronto, M5H 1A1, ON, Canada
Tel.: (416) 800-4214
Web Site: https://www.tsodiloresources.com
TZO—(DEU)
Rev.: $64,882
Assets: $5,595,833
Liabilities: $3,282,477
Net Worth: $2,313,356
Earnings: ($1,151,356)
Emp.: 16
Fiscal Year-end: 12/31/23
Mineral Exploration Services
N.A.I.C.S.: 213114
James M. Bruchs *(Chm & CEO)*

TSON CO., LTD.
3-13-26 Meieki, Nakamura-ku, Nagoya, 450-0002, Japan
Tel.: (81) 525896055
Web Site: http://www.tson.co.jp
34560—(TKS)
Real Estate Related Services
N.A.I.C.S.: 531390
Akira Momose *(Pres)*

TSR CAPITAL BERHAD
Level 16 Menara TSR No 12 Jalan PJU 7/3 Mutiara Damansara, 47810, Petaling Jaya, Selangor Darul Ehsan, Malaysia
Tel.: (60) 377177717
Web Site: https://tsrcap.com.my
Year Founded: 1991
TSRCAP—(KLS)
Rev.: $11,227,302
Assets: $52,079,365
Liabilities: $23,239,788
Net Worth: $28,839,577
Earnings: $289,101
Emp.: 98
Fiscal Year-end: 06/30/23
Construction & Property Development Services
N.A.I.C.S.: 236220
Kim Keong Ng *(Co-Sec)*

Subsidiaries:

BHUB Holdings Sdn. Bhd. (1)
Level 17 Menara TSR No 12 Jalan PJU 7/3, Mutiara Damansara, 47810, Petaling Jaya, Selangor Darul Ehsan, Malaysia
Tel.: (60) 377177737
Web Site: https://bhubholdings.com
Honey Distr
N.A.I.C.S.: 424490

TSR Bina Sdn. Bhd. (1)
No 2-2 Jalan 4/62D Medan Putra Business Centre Bandar Manjalara, Off Jalan Damansara, Kuala Lumpur, Wilayah Persekutuan, Malaysia
Tel.: (60) 362778135

INTERNATIONAL PUBLIC

Sales Range: $25-49.9 Million
Emp.: 50
Civil Engineering Services
N.A.I.C.S.: 541330

TSR Concrete Products Sdn. Bhd. (1)
No 2-2 Jalan 4/62D Medan Putra Business Centre Bandar Manjalara, Off Jalan Damansara, 52200, Kuala Lumpur, Federal Territory, Malaysia
Tel.: (60) 362745942
Web Site: http://www.tsrconcrete.com.my
Precast Concrete Products Mfr & Distr
N.A.I.C.S.: 327390

Plant (Domestic):

TSR Concrete Products Sdn. Bhd. - Sepang Factory (2)
Lot PT33 Kampung LBJ Bandar Enstek, 71900, Labu, Negeri Sembilan, Malaysia
Tel.: (60) 362745942
Precast Concrete Products Mfr
N.A.I.C.S.: 327390

TSR Concrete Products Sdn. Bhd. - Terengganu Factory (2)
Lot PT1316 Kawasan Perindustrian Ceneh Baru 4KM Jalan Cerul, 24000, Kemaman, Terengganu, Malaysia
Tel.: (60) 9 8732 508
Precast Concrete Products Mfr
N.A.I.C.S.: 327390

TSRC CORPORATION
No 2 Singgong Rd, Dashe Dist, Kaohsiung, 815, Taiwan
Tel.: (886) 73513811
Web Site: https://www.tsrc.com.tw
Year Founded: 1973
2103—(TAI)
Rev.: $1,027,727,781
Assets: $1,242,302,743
Liabilities: $562,038,731
Net Worth: $680,264,012
Earnings: $31,620,621
Emp.: 898
Fiscal Year-end: 12/31/23
Synthetic Rubber Mfr
N.A.I.C.S.: 316210
Kevin Liu *(VP-Synthetic Rubber)*

Subsidiaries:

Dexco Polymers, L.P. (1)
12012 Wickchester Ln Ste 280, Houston, TX 77079
Tel.: (281) 754-5800
Web Site: http://www.dexcopolymers.com
Sales Range: $10-24.9 Million
Emp.: 15
Plastics Materials & Resins Mfr
N.A.I.C.S.: 325211

Polybus Corporation Pte. Ltd. (1)
9-16 100 Peck Seah St, Singapore, 079333, Singapore
Tel.: (65) 62276488
Synthetic Rubber Materials Distr
N.A.I.C.S.: 424690

Subsidiary (Non-US):

TSRC-UBE (Nantong) Chemical Industries Limited Corporation (2)
No 22 TongWang Road, Nantong, 226017, Jiangsu, China
Tel.: (86) 51385999966
Sales Range: $50-74.9 Million
Emp.: 140
Synthetic Rubber Mfr
N.A.I.C.S.: 325212

Shen Hua Chemical Industrial Co., Ltd. (1)
No 1 Shen Hua Road Nantong Economic Technological Development Zone, Nantong, 226009, Jiangsu, China
Tel.: (86) 51383592662
Web Site: http://www.shen-hua.com
Emp.: 290
Synthetic Rubber Mfr
N.A.I.C.S.: 325212

TSRC (Jinan) Industries Ltd. (1)
No 666 LinGang Street YaoQiang Town Li-

Cheng Zone, Jinan, 250100, Shandong, China
Tel.: (86) 53188746666
Synthetic Rubber Mfr
N.A.I.C.S.: 325212

TSRC (Lux.) Corporation S.a r.l. (1)
39-43 avenue de la Liberte, 1931, Luxembourg, Luxembourg
Tel.: (352) 262972
Synthetic Rubber Mfr & Distr
N.A.I.C.S.: 325212

TSRC (Nantong) Industries Ltd. (1)
No 22 TongWang Road, Nantong Economic and Technological Development Zone, Nantong, 226017, Jiangsu, China
Tel.: (86) 51385999966
Synthetic Rubber Mfr & Distr
N.A.I.C.S.: 325212

TSRC (Shanghai) Industries Ltd. (1)
1046 Yu-Shu Road Songjiang Zone, Shanghai, 201600, China
Tel.: (86) 2157734333
Sales Range: $25-49.9 Million
Emp.: 100
Thermoplastic Elastomer Products Mfr
N.A.I.C.S.: 325212
Tu Wei-Hua *(Pres & CEO-TSRC Corp)*

TSRC (Vietnam) Co., Ltd. (1)
No 8 VSIP II-A Street 31, Vietnam Singapore Industrial Park II-A, Binh Dong, Vietnam
Tel.: (84) 2742222233
Synthetic Rubber Mfr & Distr
N.A.I.C.S.: 325212

TSRC Corporation - Gangshan Factory (1)
39 Bengong 1st Road, Gangshan, Kaohsiung, 820, Taiwan
Tel.: (886) 7 623 3005
Web Site: http://www.tsrctexco.com
Sales Range: $25-49.9 Million
Emp.: 500
Synthetic Rubber Mfr
N.A.I.C.S.: 325212

TSRC Corporation - Kaohsiung Factory (1)
2 Singgong Road, Dashe Township, Kaohsiung, 815, Taiwan
Tel.: (886) 73513812
Sales Range: $125-149.9 Million
Emp.: 500
Synthetic Rubber Mfr
N.A.I.C.S.: 325212

TSSI SYSTEMS LTD
Rutland House Hargreaves Road, Groundwell Industrial Estate, Swindon, SN25 5AZ, United Kingdom
Tel.: (44) 1793747700   UK
Web Site: http://www.tssi-magnetics-and-coatings.com
Sales Range: $10-24.9 Million
Emp.: 25
Security Product Mfr
N.A.I.C.S.: 334290
Danny Chapchal *(Chm)*

TSUBAKIMOTO CHAIN CO.
Nakanoshima Mitsui Building 6F
3-3-3 Nakanoshima, Kita-ku, Osaka, 530-0005, Japan
Tel.: (81) 664410011   JP
Web Site:
  https://www.tsubakimoto.com
Year Founded: 1917
6371—(TKS)
Rev.: $1,763,627,320
Assets: $2,586,479,780
Liabilities: $864,184,790
Net Worth: $1,722,294,990
Earnings: $122,622,110
Emp.: 8,750
Fiscal Year-end: 03/31/24
Industrial Chains, Conveyors & Speed Change/Reduction Gears Mfr
N.A.I.C.S.: 333612
Isamu Osa *(Chm & CEO)*

Subsidiaries:

Ballantine, Inc. (1)
840 McKinley St, Anoka, MN 55303-1162
Tel.: (763) 427-3959
Web Site: http://www.ballantineinc.com
Sales Range: $25-49.9 Million
Emp.: 40
Sales of Trencher Parts
N.A.I.C.S.: 423810

Kabelschlepp China Co., Ltd. (1)
Plant No 2 of Germany Industry Park No 508 Heng Guan Jing Road, Zhangpu Town, Kunshan, 215321, China
Tel.: (86) 51257293500
Power Transistor Product Mfr
N.A.I.C.S.: 334413

Kabelschlepp GmbH (1)
Wielandstrasse 1 Hunsborn, 57482, Wenden, Germany
Tel.: (49) 276297420
Automobile Parts Mfr
N.A.I.C.S.: 336390

Korea Conveyor Ind. Co., Ltd. (1)
627-3 Gojan-dong 68B 7L, Namdong Industrial Estate, Incheon, 405 817, Korea (South)
Tel.: (82) 328170160
Web Site: http://www.conveyor.co.kr
Sales Range: $25-49.9 Million
Emp.: 78
Mfr & Seller of Materials Handling Systems
N.A.I.C.S.: 333922
Kwang Soon Kim *(CEO)*

Mahindra Tsubaki Conveyor Systems Private Limited (1)
Gat No 316-319 Ambadvet Pune-Paud Road Near Pirangut, Pune, 412 108, Maharashtra, India
Tel.: (91) 2067928400
Web Site: https://tsubaki-conveyor.in
Automobile Parts Distr
N.A.I.C.S.: 423120
Ravindra Vaidya *(Mng Dir)*

Mayfran France S.A.R.L. (1)
Val de Fontenay Business Centre Le Perigares A 201 rue Carnot, CS 80033, 94127, Fontenay-sous-Bois, Cedex, France
Tel.: (33) 173434399
Automobile Parts Mfr
N.A.I.C.S.: 336390

Mayfran GmbH (1)
Krantzstrasse 7, 52070, Aachen, Germany
Tel.: (49) 241938720
Web Site: https://www.mayfran.de
Automobile Parts Mfr
N.A.I.C.S.: 336390

Mayfran Limburg B.V. (1)
Edisonstraat 7, PB 31032, 6370 AA, Landgraaf, Netherlands
Tel.: (31) 455329292
Automobile Parts Mfr
N.A.I.C.S.: 336390

Mayfran U.K. Limited (1)
Unit 38 Bradley Fold Trading Estate Bradley Fold Road, Radcliffe, Bury, BL2 6RT, United Kingdom
Tel.: (44) 1204366469
Web Site: http://www.mayfran.co.uk
Automobile Parts Mfr
N.A.I.C.S.: 336390

OOO Tsubaki Kabelschlepp (1)
Prospekt Andropova 18 Building 6, 115432, Moscow, Russia
Tel.: (7) 4994180212
Web Site: http://www.kabelschlepp.ru
Cable Chain Product Mfr
N.A.I.C.S.: 335921

PT. Tsubaki Indonesia Manufacturing (1)
Jl Harapan VIII Lot LL-13 Parungmulya, Kawasan Karawang International Industrial City Ciampel, Karawang, 41361, Indonesia
Tel.: (62) 2129259975
Industrial Parts Mfr
N.A.I.C.S.: 336390

PT. Tsubaki Indonesia Trading (1)
Graha Bulevar Blok GB/B17 Jl Bulevar Ahmad Yani, Kelurahan Harapan Mulya Kecamatan Medan Satria Kota, Bekasi, 17143, Jawa Barat, Indonesia
Tel.: (62) 2189458898
Web Site: http://www.tsubakimoto.co.id
Industrial Parts Distr
N.A.I.C.S.: 423840

Schmidberger Gmbh (1)
Linzerstr 56, Kematen, 4531, Krems, Austria
Tel.: (43) 722864360
Web Site: https://www.schmidberger.co.at
Emp.: 32
Automobile & Car Parts Distr
N.A.I.C.S.: 423110

TSUBAKI BRASIL EQUIPAMENTOS INDUSTRIAIS LTDA (1)
Rua Dom Bernardo Nogueira 55, Jardim Paulista, Sao Paulo, 04134-000, Brazil
Tel.: (55) 1132535656
Web Site: https://www.tsubaki.ind.br
Emp.: 5
Power Transmission Equipment Mfr
N.A.I.C.S.: 333613

TSUBAKI YAMAKYU CHAIN CO (1)
2-15-16 Takanawa, Minato-ku, Tokyo, 108-0074, Japan
Tel.: (81) 334458516
Web Site: https://www.tsubaki-yamakyu.co.jp
Sales Range: $50-74.9 Million
Emp.: 150
Industrial Machinery Mfr
N.A.I.C.S.: 333248
Ken Omori *(Pres)*

TSUBAKIMOTO (THAILAND) CO., LTD (1)
388 Exchange Tower 19th Floor Unit 1902 Sukhumvit Road, Klongtoey, Bangkok, 10110, Thailand
Tel.: (66) 22620667
Power Transmission Component Distr
N.A.I.C.S.: 423830

TSUBAKIMOTO AUTOMOTIVE (SHANGHAI) CO., LTD (1)
Building 4 No 1151 Xingxian Road, North Industrial District Jiading, Shanghai, 201815, China
Tel.: (86) 2159968555
Web Site: https://www.tsubaki-auto.com.cn
Sales Range: $50-74.9 Million
Emp.: 361
Automotive Timing Drive System Mfr & Distr
N.A.I.C.S.: 336390
Wada Kenichi *(Mng Dir)*

TSUBAKIMOTO AUTOMOTIVE (THAILAND) CO., LTD. (1)
700-467 Moo 7 Amata Nakorn Industrial Estate Tambol, Don Hua Roh Amphur Muang, Chon Buri, 20000, Thailand
Tel.: (66) 38454021
Power Transmission Equipment Mfr & Distr
N.A.I.C.S.: 333613

TSUBAKIMOTO AUTOMOTIVE KOREA CO., LTD. (1)
15 Namyeong-ro, Jinhae-gu, Changwon, 51617, Gyeongsangnam-do, Korea (South)
Tel.: (82) 557148114
Sales Range: $25-49.9 Million
Emp.: 39
Automotive Chain Mfr
N.A.I.C.S.: 336390

TSUBAKIMOTO BULK SYSTEMS CORP (1)
4-1 Terauchi 2-Chome, Toyonaka, 561-0872, Osaka, Japan
Tel.: (81) 668622331
Web Site: https://www.tsubakimoto.com
Emp.: 176
Conveying Equipment Mfr
N.A.I.C.S.: 333922

TSUBAKIMOTO CHAIN TRADING (SHANGHAI) CO., LTD. (1)
Rm 1703 Aetna Tower 107 Zunyi Road, Huangpu District, Shanghai, 200051, China
Tel.: (86) 2153966651
Sales Range: $50-74.9 Million
Emp.: 6
Power Transmission Device Distr
N.A.I.C.S.: 423830

TSUBAKIMOTO IRON CASTING CO., LTD (1)
20 Shinko, Hanno, 357-0022, Saitama, Japan
Tel.: (81) 429738031
Web Site: https://tsubakimoto.com
Emp.: 68
Iron Casting Products Mfr & Distr
N.A.I.C.S.: 331511

TSUBAKIMOTO MACHINERY CO (1)
Kanden Fudosan Nishihonmachi Building 1-3-15 Awaza, Nishi-ku, Osaka, 550-0011, Japan
Tel.: (81) 643900050
Web Site: https://www.tsubakimoto.com
Sales Range: $75-99.9 Million
Emp.: 217
Power Transmission Products Distr
N.A.I.C.S.: 423830

TSUBAKIMOTO MAYFRAN CONVEYOR (SHANGHAI) CO., LTD (1)
Building 2 No 1300 Bei He Road, Jiading Industry Zone, Shanghai, 201807, China
Tel.: (86) 2139538656
Web Site: http://tsubaki.cn
Emp.: 38
Conveyor Chain Mfr
N.A.I.C.S.: 333922

TSUBAKIMOTO SPROCKET CO (1)
28-1 Ichida-Ichinotsubo Kumiyama-cho, Kuse-gun, Kyoto, 613-0022, Japan
Tel.: (81) 774434333
Web Site: https://tsubakimoto.com
Sales Range: $50-74.9 Million
Emp.: 159
Sprocket Mfr
N.A.I.C.S.: 333613

Taiwan Tsubakimoto Company (1)
No 33 Lane 17 Zihciang N Road, Kueishan District, Taoyuan, 33347, Taiwan
Tel.: (886) 33293827
Web Site: https://tsubakimoto.tw
Sales Range: $25-49.9 Million
Emp.: 100
Power Transmission Products Mfr & Distr
N.A.I.C.S.: 333613

Tsubaki Australia Pte. Limited (1)
95 101 Silverwater Road, Silverwater, Sydney, 2128, NSW, Australia   (100%)
Tel.: (61) 297042500
Web Site: https://www.tsubaki.com.au
Sales Range: $25-49.9 Million
Emp.: 30
Sales of Power Transmission Products
N.A.I.C.S.: 423840

Tsubaki Automotive Czech Republic S.R.O. (1)
Ovcary 295, 280 02, Kolin, Czech Republic
Tel.: (420) 311549300
Web Site: http://www.tsubaki.cz
Automobile Parts Mfr.
N.A.I.C.S.: 336390

Tsubaki Capt Power Transmission (Shijiazhuang) Co., Ltd. (1)
No 1 Guoxing Street, New Area Of Gao Cheng District, Shijiazhuang, 052160, Hebei, China
Tel.: (86) 31168018066
Web Site: http://www.en.chssb.com
Emp.: 780
Power Transistor Product Distr
N.A.I.C.S.: 423690

Tsubaki Deutschland GmbH (1)
Oskar-Messter-Strasse 33, 85737, Ismaning, Germany
Tel.: (49) 89200013380
Emp.: 700
Automotive Components Mfr
N.A.I.C.S.: 336390
Ralf Kronawitter *(Gen Mgr)*

Tsubaki Everbest Gear (Tianjin) Co., Ltd. (1)
135 Dongting Road Teda, Tianjin, 300457, China
Tel.: (86) 2225327078
Web Site: https://teg.com.cn
Worm Gear Reducer Distr
N.A.I.C.S.: 423840

Tsubaki Iberica Power Transmission S.L. (1)

TSUBAKIMOTO CHAIN CO.

Tsubakimoto Chain Co.—(Continued)
Calle de Juan de la Cierva 28, 28823, Coslada, Madrid, Spain
Tel.: (34) 911873450
Automobile Parts Mfr
N.A.I.C.S.: 336390

Tsubaki KabelSchlepp GmbH (1)
Daimlerstrasse 2, Gerlingen, 57482, Wenden, Germany
Tel.: (49) 276240030
Web Site: https://tsubaki-kabelschlepp.com
Sales Range: $25-49.9 Million
Emp.: 200
Cable Carrier & Conveyor Systems Mfr
N.A.I.C.S.: 333922

Subsidiary (Non-US):

KabelSchlepp France S.a.r.l. (2)
4 Rue Hippolyte Mege Mouries, 78120, Rambouillet, France (100%)
Tel.: (33) 134846365
Web Site: http://www.kabelschlepp.fr
Sales Range: $25-49.9 Million
Emp.: 10
Cable Carrier & Conveyor Systems Mfr
N.A.I.C.S.: 333922

KabelSchlepp India Pvt. Ltd. (2)
B-14 ITI Ancillary Industrial Estate Mahadevapura Post, Bengaluru, 560 048, India
Tel.: (91) 8041158997
Sales Range: $25-49.9 Million
Emp.: 35
Cable Carrier & Conveyor Systems Mfr
N.A.I.C.S.: 333922
Senthil Ganesan (Gen Mgr)

KabelSchlepp Italia S.r.l. (2)
Via Massari Marzoli 9, 21052, Busto Arsizio, VA, Italy (100%)
Tel.: (39) 0331350962
Web Site: https://tsubaki-kabelschlepp.com
Cable Carrier & Conveyor Systems Mfr
N.A.I.C.S.: 333922

KabelSchlepp Sp. z.o.o (2)
ul Piekna 13, 85-303, Bydgoszcz, Poland
Tel.: (48) 523487710
Web Site: https://kabelschlepp.pl
Emp.: 9
Cable Carrier & Conveyor Systems Mfr
N.A.I.C.S.: 333922

KabelSchlepp Systemtechnik spol. s.r.o. (2)
Povazska 67, 940 67, Nove Zamky, Slovakia (100%)
Tel.: (421) 356923200
Web Site: https://tsubaki-kabelschlepp.com
Emp.: 200
Cable Carrier & Conveyor Systems Mfr
N.A.I.C.S.: 333922

Metool Products Ltd. (2)
Osier Drive Sherwood Park, Annesley, NG15 0DX, United Kingdom (100%)
Tel.: (44) 1159225931
Web Site: https://tsubaki-kabelschlepp.com
Sales Range: $25-49.9 Million
Emp.: 15
Cable Carrier & Conveyor Systems Mfr
N.A.I.C.S.: 333922
Ben Arnz (Mng Dir)

Porta Cabos Industria e Comercio Ltda. (2)
Rua Francisco Visentainer 875, Sao Bernardo do Campo, 09861-630, SP, Brazil (100%)
Tel.: (55) 1140722217
Web Site: https://portacabos.com.br
Sales Range: $1-9.9 Million
Emp.: 80
Cable Carrier & Conveyor Systems Mfr
N.A.I.C.S.: 333922

Tsubaki KabelSchlepp Shanghai Co., Ltd. (2)
Rm 701 Tomsom Financial Building, No 710 Dong Fang Rd Pudong, Shanghai, 200122, China
Tel.: (86) 2168670511
Web Site: http://www.tsubaki-sh.cn
Emp.: 83
Cable Wire Mfr
N.A.I.C.S.: 335921

Takatoshi Kimura (Pres & Gen Mgr)
Tsubaki Motion Control (Shanghai) Co., Ltd. (1)
No 5 Building No 1151 Xingxian Rd, North Jiading Industrial Area, Shanghai, 201815, China
Tel.: (86) 2139538188
Power Transistor Product Mfr
N.A.I.C.S.: 334413

Tsubaki Motion Control (Thailand) Co., Ltd. (1)
700/914 Moo 3 Tambol Nongkakha Amphur, Panthong, Chon Buri, 20160, Thailand
Tel.: (66) 38212220
Automobile Parts Mfr
N.A.I.C.S.: 336390

Tsubaki Power Transmission (Malaysia) Sdn. Bhd. (1)
No 8 Jalan Utarid U5/16 Section U5, Mah Sing Integrated Industrial Park, 40150, Shah Alam, Selangor, Malaysia
Tel.: (60) 389662020
Industrial Parts Distr
N.A.I.C.S.: 423840

Tsubaki Support Center Co. (1)
1-1-3 Kannabidai, Kyotanabe, 610-0380, Kyoto, Japan
Tel.: (81) 774645101
Web Site: https://www.tsubakimoto.com
Emp.: 108
Back Office Administration Services
N.A.I.C.S.: 561110

Tsubaki of Canada Limited (1)
1630 Drew Road, Mississauga, L5S 1J6, ON, Canada (100%)
Tel.: (905) 676-0400
Web Site: http://www.tsubaki.ca
Sales Range: $25-49.9 Million
Emp.: 90
Mfr & Distributor of Power Transmission Products
N.A.I.C.S.: 333613

Tsubakimoto Automotive Mexico S.A. De C.V. (1)
Col Nuevo Cto San Roque Pte, Guanajuato, 36270, Mexico, Mexico
Tel.: (52) 4727489312
Web Site: https://www.tsubakimoto.com.mx
Automotive Parts Mfr & Distr
N.A.I.C.S.: 336390

Tsubakimoto Bulk Systems (Shanghai) Corp. (1)
Building A Rm 306-308 Shanghai MixC City 1799 WuZhong Road, Minhang District, Shanghai, 201103, China
Tel.: (86) 2160712120
Power Transistor Product Distr
N.A.I.C.S.: 423690

Tsubakimoto Chain (Shanghai) Co., Ltd. (1)
Building A Rm 306-308 Shanghai MixC City 1799 WuZhong Road, Minhang District, Shanghai, 201103, China
Tel.: (86) 2153966651
Web Site: https://tsubaki-sh.cn
Emp.: 86
Power Transistor Product Mfr
N.A.I.C.S.: 334413

Tsubakimoto Chain (Tianjin) Co., Ltd. (1)
No 22 Road 8 North District Economic Development Zone of Jinghai, Tianjin, 301617, China
Tel.: (86) 2268299509
Power Transistor Product Mfr
N.A.I.C.S.: 334413

Tsubakimoto Chain Co. (1)
1-1 Kotari Kuresumi, Nagaokakyo, Kyoto, 617-0833, Japan (100%)
Tel.: (81) 759560200
Web Site: https://www.tsubakimoto.com
Sales Range: $100-124.9 Million
Emp.: 500
Power Transmission Units & Components
N.A.I.C.S.: 333613

Tsubakimoto Chain Co. (1)
Nakanoshima Mitsui Building 6F 3-3-3 Nakanoshima, Kita-ku, Osaka, 530-0005, Japan (100%)

Tel.: (81) 664410011
Web Site: https://www.tsubakimoto.com
Emp.: 8,566
Power Transmission Chains & Conveyor Chains
N.A.I.C.S.: 333613
Tadasu Suzuki (Sr Mng Exec Officer)

Tsubakimoto Chain Co. (1)
1-1-3 Kannabidai, Kyotanabe, Kyoto, 610-0380, Japan (100%)
Tel.: (81) 774645001
Web Site: http://www.tsubakimoto.jp
Sales Range: Less than $1 Million
Emp.: 1,000
Automotive Parts & Materials Handling Systems
N.A.I.C.S.: 441330

Tsubakimoto Chain Co. - Hyogo Plant (1)
1140 Asazuma-cho, Kasai Industrial Park, Kasai, 679-0181, Hyogo, Japan
Tel.: (81) 790471515
Automotive Gear Drive Mfr
N.A.I.C.S.: 336350

Tsubakimoto Chain Co. - Saitama Plant (1)
20 Shinko, Hanno, 357-8510, Saitama, Japan
Tel.: (81) 429731131
Web Site: http://www.tsubakimoto.com
Automotive Gear Chain Mfr
N.A.I.C.S.: 336350

Tsubakimoto Chain Engineering (Shanghai) Co., Ltd. (1)
Building A Rm 303 305 Shanghai MixC City 1799 WuZhong Road, Minhang District, Shanghai, 201103, China
Tel.: (86) 2164183839
Power Transistor Product Distr
N.A.I.C.S.: 423690

Tsubakimoto Custom Chain Co. (1)
2-3-1 Goryo, Daito, 574-0064, Osaka, Japan
Tel.: (81) 728731881
Web Site: https://www.tsubakimoto.com
Emp.: 223
Power Transmission Equipment Mfr
N.A.I.C.S.: 333613

Tsubakimoto Europe B.V. (1)
Aventurijn 1200, 3316 LB, Dordrecht, Netherlands (100%)
Tel.: (31) 786204000
Web Site: http://www.tsubaki.eu
Sales Range: $50-74.9 Million
Emp.: 70
Sales of Power Transmission Products
N.A.I.C.S.: 423840

Tsubakimoto Korea Co., Ltd. (1)
25th Floor 97 Saemal-ro Center Point West, Guro-gu, Seoul, Guro-dong, Korea (South)
Tel.: (82) 221830311
Web Site: https://www.tsubakimoto-tck.co.kr
Industrial Parts Distr
N.A.I.C.S.: 423840

Tsubakimoto Mayfran Inc. (1)
5001 Ohno Tsuchiyama-cho, Koka, 528-0235, Shiga, Japan
Tel.: (81) 748671001
Emp.: 121
Coolant Processing System Mfr & Distr
N.A.I.C.S.: 333922

Tsubakimoto Philippines Corporation (1)
Unit 2404-A West Tower Philippine Stock Exchange Centre Exchange Road, Ortigas Center Metropolitan Manila, Pasig, 1605, Philippines
Tel.: (63) 288247519
Industrial Parts Distr
N.A.I.C.S.: 423840

Tsubakimoto Singapore Pte., Ltd. (1)
25 Gul Ln, Jurong, 629419, Singapore (100%)
Tel.: (65) 68610422
Web Site: http://www.tsubaki.sg
Sales Range: $25-49.9 Million
Emp.: 25
Manufacture & Sales of Power Transmission Products
N.A.I.C.S.: 333613

Subsidiary (Non-US):

Tsubaki India Power Transmission Private Limited (2)
Shri Kailash Logicity No 165 Walajabad Road, Venbakkam Village Panruti Post Kancheepuram District, Oragadam, 631604, Tamil Nadu, India
Tel.: (91) 4471012000
Web Site: http://www.tsubaki.in
Emp.: 1
Power Transmission Equipment Mfr
N.A.I.C.S.: 333613

Tsubakimoto UK Ltd. (2)
Osier Drive Sherwood Park, Annesley, Nottingham, NG15 0DX, Notts, United Kingdom (100%)
Tel.: (44) 1623688700
Web Site: http://tsubaki.eu
Sales Range: $50-74.9 Million
Emp.: 60
Sales & Maintenance of Materials Handling Systems
N.A.I.C.S.: 423830

Tsubakimoto Vietnam Co., Ltd. (1)
Unit 202 2nd Floor DMC Tower No 535 Kim Ma, Ngoc Khanh Ward Ba Dinh District, Hanoi, Vietnam
Tel.: (84) 2462741449
Automobile Parts Mfr
N.A.I.C.S.: 336390

U.S. Tsubaki Automotive, LLC (1)
106 Lonczak Dr, Chicopee, MA 01022
Tel.: (413) 593-1100
Web Site: https://www.ustsubaki.com
Automotive Parts Mfr & Distr
N.A.I.C.S.: 336390

U.S. Tsubaki Holdings, Inc. (1)
301 E Marquardt Dr, Wheeling, IL 60090
Tel.: (847) 459-9500
Web Site: http://www.ustsubaki.com
Holding Company
N.A.I.C.S.: 551112

Subsidiary (Domestic):

Central Conveyor Company, LLC (2)
52800 Pontiac Trail, Wixom, MI 48393
Tel.: (248) 446-0118
Web Site: http://www.centralconveyor.com
Conveyors & Conveying Equipment
N.A.I.C.S.: 333922
Mark Lemons (Mgr-Sls)

Subsidiary (Domestic):

Central Process Engineering, LLC (3)
52800 Pontiac Trl, Wixom, MI 48393
Tel.: (248) 446-9990
Industrial Material Handling System Mfr
N.A.I.C.S.: 333310

ELECTRICAL INSIGHTS LLC (3)
PO Box 313, Howell, MI 48844
Tel.: (248) 446-9967
Material Handling System & Conveyor Mfr
N.A.I.C.S.: 333922

Subsidiary (Domestic):

U.S. Tsubaki Power Transmission, LLC (2)
301 E Marquardt Dr, Wheeling, IL 60090-6431
Tel.: (847) 459-9500
Web Site: http://www.ustsubaki.com
Sales Range: $300-349.9 Million
Emp.: 1,000
Mfr of Drive Chains, Attachment Chains, Engineering Class Chains, Sprockets & Power Transmission Components
N.A.I.C.S.: 333613
Yoshi Kiteyama (Pres)

Branch (Domestic):

U.S. Tsubaki - Detroit Engineering Office (3)
560 Kirts Blvd Ste 109, Troy, MI 48084-4141
Tel.: (248) 362-5052
Sales Range: $25-49.9 Million
Emp.: 12
Speed Drive Developer
N.A.I.C.S.: 333612

AND PRIVATE COMPANIES

Plant (Domestic):

U.S. Tsubaki - Engineering Chain Division Sandusky Plant (3)
1010 Edgewater Dr, Sandusky, OH 44870-0651
Tel.: (419) 626-4560
Web Site: http://www.ustsubaki.com
Sales Range: $75-99.9 Million
Emp.: 155
Mfr of Industrial Equipments
N.A.I.C.S.: 423840

U.S. Tsubaki - Roller Chain Division Holyoke Plant (3)
821 Main St, Holyoke, MA 01040-5312
Tel.: (413) 536-1576
Web Site: http://www.ustsubaki.com
Sales Range: $50-74.9 Million
Emp.: 190
Mfr of Roller Chain
N.A.I.C.S.: 333613

Division (Domestic):

U.S. Tsubaki Power Transmission, LLC - KabelSchlepp Division (3)
7100 W Marcia Rd, Milwaukee, WI 53223-3363 (100%)
Tel.: (414) 354-1994
Web Site: http://www.ustsubaki.com
Sales Range: $25-49.9 Million
Emp.: 50
Cable Carrier & Conveyor Systems Mfr
N.A.I.C.S.: 333922

TSUBAKIMOTO KOGYO CO., LTD.
Meiji Yasuda Life Osaka Umeda Building 3-3-20 Umeda, Kita-ku, Osaka, 530-0001, Japan
Tel.: (81) 647958800
Web Site: https://www.tsubaki.co.jp
Year Founded: 1916
8052—(TKS)
Rev.: $750,254,830
Assets: $626,337,160
Liabilities: $359,445,190
Net Worth: $266,891,970
Earnings: $26,440,000
Emp.: 757
Fiscal Year-end: 03/31/24
Electric Equipment Mfr
N.A.I.C.S.: 334413
Masashi Koda *(Pres & CEO)*

Subsidiaries:

PT. Tsubaco Indonesia (1)
Wisma Nusantara Lt 24 Jl MH Thamrin No 59, Gondangdia Menteng, Jakarta, 10350, Indonesia
Tel.: (62) 2139838326
Web Site: https://www.tsubaco.co.id
Emp.: 9
Electronic Equipment Distr
N.A.I.C.S.: 423690

ShangHai TSUBACO Co., Ltd. (1)
Room 2005-07 Antai Building No 107 Zunyi Road, Changning District, Shanghai, 200051, China
Tel.: (86) 2162375577
Web Site: https://www.sh-tsubaco.cn
Electronic Equipment Distr
N.A.I.C.S.: 423690

TSUBACO (HONG KONG) CO., LTD. (1)
Flat 2202 22/F Paul Y Centre 51 Hung To Road, Kwun Tong, Kowloon, China (Hong Kong)
Tel.: (852) 27939220
Electronic Equipment Distr
N.A.I.C.S.: 423690

TSUBACO KOREA CO., LTD. (1)
Room 633 634 The Sky Valley 416 Hwagok-ro, Gangseo-gu, Seoul, 150-836, Korea (South)
Tel.: (82) 226728731
Web Site: https://m.tsubaki.co.kr
Electronic Equipment Distr
N.A.I.C.S.: 423690

TSUBACO KTE CO., LTD. (1)
952 Ramaland Bldg 17th Floor Rama 4 Road, Suriyawong Bangrak, Bangkok, 10500, Thailand
Tel.: (66) 26329466
Web Site: https://www.tsubaco.co.th
Electronic Equipment Distr
N.A.I.C.S.: 423690

Tsubaco Singapore Pte Ltd (1)
10 Toh Guan Rd 02-02/03, TT International Tradepark, Singapore, 608838, Singapore
Tel.: (65) 68626800
Web Site: https://www.tsubacosin.info
Power Transmission Equipment Distr
N.A.I.C.S.: 423840

TSUBOI INDUSTRIAL CO., LTD.
2-9-17 Ginza, Chuo-ku, Tokyo, 104 0061, Japan
Tel.: (81) 3 3563 1301
Web Site: http://www.tuboi.co.jp
Emp.: 230
Construction & Real Estate Leasing & Management Services
N.A.I.C.S.: 541330
Harumasa Tsuboi *(Pres)*

TSUBURAYA FIELDS HOLDINGS INC.
Shibuya Garden Tower 16-17 Nanpeidai-cho, Shibuya-ku, Tokyo, 150-0036, Japan
Tel.: (81) 357842111 JP
Web Site: https://www.fields.biz
Year Founded: 1988
2767—(TKS)
Rev.: $938,111,030
Assets: $649,630,800
Liabilities: $279,563,340
Net Worth: $370,067,460
Earnings: $76,352,110
Emp.: 1,542
Fiscal Year-end: 03/31/24
Holding Company; Gaming & Entertainment Products & Services
N.A.I.C.S.: 551112
Hidetoshi Yamamoto *(Chm, Pres & CEO-Grp)*

Subsidiaries:

Digital Frontier Inc (1)
3F KN Shibuya 3rd Bldg 9-8 Sakuragaoka-cho, Shibuya-ku, Tokyo, 150-0031, Japan
Tel.: (81) 368557821
Sales Range: $25-49.9 Million
Emp.: 250
Video Game Development Services
N.A.I.C.S.: 541511
Hidenori Ueki *(CEO)*

Japan Sports Marketing Inc. (1)
01-01-2013 Urbannet Uchisaiwaicho Building 3F, Minato-ku, Tokyo, 105-0004, Japan
Tel.: (81) 368073989
Web Site: https://www.j-sm.jp
Emp.: 18
Sports Marketing & Sponsorship Services
N.A.I.C.S.: 541613

Kadokawa Haruki Corporation (1)
Italian Cultural Center Building 5F 2-1-30, Kudanminami Chiyoda-ku, Tokyo, 102-0074, Japan
Tel.: (81) 332635167
Web Site: https://www.kadokawaharuki.co.jp
Sales Range: $25-49.9 Million
Emp.: 86
Books Publishing Services
N.A.I.C.S.: 513130

Lucent Pictures Entertainment, Inc. (1)
Nampeidai cho 16-17 Shibuya ku Shibuya Garden Tower 23 Fl, Shibuya-ku, Tokyo, 150-0036, Japan
Tel.: (81) 357842727
Web Site: http://www.lpei.co.jp
Sales Range: $25-49.9 Million
Emp.: 15
Animated Motion Picture Production & Distribution
N.A.I.C.S.: 512110
Eiichi Kamagata *(Pres)*

Shin-Nichi Technology Co., Ltd. (1)
1-21-4 Taito Tokyo Mishin Kaikan Building 6f, Taito-Ku, Tokyo, 110-0016, Japan
Tel.: (81) 338321580
Amusement Machines Mfr
N.A.I.C.S.: 339999

Total Workout Premium Management Inc. (1)
16-17 Nanpeidai-cho, Shibuya-ku, Tokyo, 150-0036, Japan
Tel.: (81) 35 784 4497
Web Site: https://www.totalworkout.jp
Personal Training Gym Services
N.A.I.C.S.: 713940

Tsuburaya Productions Co., Ltd. (1)
16-17 Nanpeidai-cho, Shibuya-ku, Tokyo, 150-0036, Japan (51%)
Tel.: (81) 354897860
Web Site: https://tsuburaya-prod.com
Sales Range: $25-49.9 Million
Emp.: 90
Television Show & Movie Production Services
N.A.I.C.S.: 512110

TSUCHIYA HOLDINGS CO., LTD.
Tsuchiya Home Sapporo Kitakujo Building 7-3-7 Kita 9-jo Nishi, Kita-ku, Sapporo, 060-0809, Hakodate, Japan
Tel.: (81) 117175553
Web Site: https://www.tsuchiya.co.jp
Year Founded: 1976
1840—(TKS)
Rev.: $243,917,270
Assets: $177,023,120
Liabilities: $89,539,610
Net Worth: $87,483,510
Earnings: $1,651,970
Emp.: 757
Fiscal Year-end: 10/31/23
Holding Company
N.A.I.C.S.: 551112
Shozo Tsuchiya *(Pres)*

TSUDAKOMA CORPORATION
18-18 Nomachi 5-chome, Kanazawa, 921-8650, Japan
Tel.: (81) 762421114
Web Site: https://www.tsudakoma.co.jp
Year Founded: 1909
6217—(TKS)
Rev.: $278,481,020
Assets: $222,158,060
Liabilities: $207,162,710
Net Worth: $14,995,350
Earnings: ($8,834,140)
Emp.: 775
Fiscal Year-end: 11/30/23
Textile Machinery & Machine Tool Attachments Mfr
N.A.I.C.S.: 333248
Nobuhiro Takano *(Chm & Pres)*

Subsidiaries:

Tsudakoma Shanghai Co Ltd (1)
17F No 66 Everbright Convention & Exhibition Ctr Caobao Road, Bo 86 Caobao Rd, Shanghai, 200050, China
Tel.: (86) 2164326538
Sales Range: $25-49.9 Million
Emp.: 18
Textile Machinery Mfr
N.A.I.C.S.: 333248

TSUGAMI CORPORATION
12-20 Tomizawa-cho Nihonbashi, Chuo-ku, Tokyo, 103-0006, Japan
Tel.: (81) 338081711
Web Site: http://www.tsugami.co.jp
6101—(TKS)
Rev.: $554,764,080
Assets: $778,089,540
Liabilities: $299,783,330
Net Worth: $478,306,210
Earnings: $35,535,360
Emp.: 3,063

TSUKADA GLOBAL HOLDINGS INC.

Fiscal Year-end: 03/31/24
Machine & Precision Tools Mfr
N.A.I.C.S.: 332216
Tomoko Takahashi *(Chief HR Officer)*

Subsidiaries:

Precision Tsugami (China) Corporation (1)
2001 Pingcheng Rd Pinghu Economic-Technological Development Zone, Pinghu, Zhejiang, China
Tel.: (86) 57385268718
Web Site: https://www.tsugami.com.cn
Precision Machine Tools Mfr
N.A.I.C.S.: 333517

Shinagawa Precision Machinery (Zhejiang) Co., Ltd. (1)
No 2088 Pingcheng Road, Economic and Technological Development Zone, Pinghu, 314200, Zhejiang, China
Tel.: (86) 5738 598 2088
Automated Machine Tool Mfr
N.A.I.C.S.: 333517

Tsugami (Thai) Co., Ltd. (1)
23/20-21 Sorachai Bldg 12th Floor Soi Sukhumvit 63 Sukhumvit Rd, Kwaeng Klongton Nua Khet Wattana, Bangkok, 10110, Thailand
Tel.: (66) 2 714 3022
Machine Tools Mfr
N.A.I.C.S.: 333517

Tsugami Corporation - Nagaoka Factory (1)
1-1 Higashizao 1-chome, Nagaoka, 940-8630, Niigata, Japan
Tel.: (81) 258350850
Precision Machine Tools Mfr
N.A.I.C.S.: 332216

Tsugami General Service Co., Ltd. (1)
1-1 Higashizao 1-chome, Nagaoka, 940-0029, Niigata, Japan
Tel.: (81) 25 836 8903
Automated Machine Tool Mfr
N.A.I.C.S.: 333517

Tsugami GmbH (1)
Trakehner Str 5, 60487, Frankfurt am Main, Germany
Tel.: (49) 6915408900
Sales Range: $25-49.9 Million
Emp.: 3
Industrial Machine Tool Mfr
N.A.I.C.S.: 333310

TSUI WAH HOLDINGS LIMITED
Unit 1606-1608 16/F Riley House 88 Lei Muk Road, Kwai Chung, New Territories, China (Hong Kong)
Tel.: (852) 2 541 2255
Web Site: http://www.tsuiwah.com
Year Founded: 1967
1314—(HKG)
Rev.: $128,118,930
Assets: $163,536,064
Liabilities: $98,127,597
Net Worth: $65,408,467
Earnings: ($15,999,840)
Emp.: 2,020
Fiscal Year-end: 03/31/22
Restaurant Owner & Operator; Catering Services
N.A.I.C.S.: 722511
Yuen Hong Lee *(Founder & Chm)*

TSUKADA GLOBAL HOLDINGS INC.
New Pier Takeshiba South Tower 1-16-1 Kaigan, Minato-ku, Tokyo, 105-0022, Japan
Tel.: (81) 354640081
Web Site: https://www.tsukada-global.holdings
Year Founded: 1995
2418—(TKS)
Rev.: $407,490,660
Assets: $660,461,860
Liabilities: $465,997,340

TSUKADA GLOBAL HOLDINGS INC.

Tsukada Global Holdings Inc.—(Continued)

Net Worth: $194,464,520
Earnings: $33,535,700
Emp.: 2,424
Fiscal Year-end: 12/31/23
Wedding Venues, Services & Sales
N.A.I.C.S.: 812990
Masayuki Tsukada *(Pres & CEO)*

Subsidiaries:

Best Bridal Hawaii, Inc. (1)
2055 Kalakaua Ave, Honolulu, HI 96815
Web Site: https://www.bestbridalhawaii.com
Wedding Chapel Operator
N.A.I.C.S.: 812990
Karen Mukai *(VP)*

Best Bridal Inc. (1)
12th floor New Pier Takeshiba South Tower 1-16-1 Kaigan, Minato-ku, Tokyo, 105-0022, Japan
Tel.: (81) 354640174
Web Site: https://www.bestbridal.co.jp
Event Management Services
N.A.I.C.S.: 561920
Masayuki Tsukada *(Pres & CEO)*

Best Bridal Korea Inc. (1)
3F Baeksong Bldg 14-2 Nonhyun-dog, Gangnam-gu, Seoul, 135-010, Korea (South)
Tel.: (82) 25179593
Event Management Services
N.A.I.C.S.: 561920

Best Bridal Singapore Pte. Ltd. (1)
1 Fullerton Square 01-08 The Fullerton Hotel, Singapore, 049178, Singapore
Tel.: (65) 65570820
Event Management Services
N.A.I.C.S.: 561920

Best Global, Inc. (1)
26-32F Shinagawa East One Tower 2-16-1 Konan, Minato-ku, Tokyo, 108-8282, Japan
Tel.: (81) 357831111
Web Site: https://intercontinental-strings.jp
Event Management Services
N.A.I.C.S.: 561920

Best Hospitality Network Corporation (1)
1-16-2 Kaigan, Minato-Ku, Tokyo, 105-8576, Japan
Tel.: (81) 354042222
Web Site: https://www.interconti-tokyo.com
Event Management Services
N.A.I.C.S.: 561920

Best Life Style Inc. (1)
3 Chome-4-7 Nishishinjuku, Shinjuku City, Tokyo, 160-0023, Japan
Tel.: (81) 120056658
Web Site: https://www.kimptonshinjuku.com
Hotel & Restaurant Services
N.A.I.C.S.: 721110

Best Planning, Inc. (1)
6-23-12 Higashi Kashiwagaya, Shibuya-ku, Ebina, 243-0401, Japan
Tel.: (81) 46 234 2206
Web Site: https://www.b-planning.co.jp
Sales Range: $10-24.9 Million
Emp.: 4
Services, Including Food & Beverage Supply, for Wedding Receptions & Other Events
N.A.I.C.S.: 561990
Mikio Takahashi *(Pres)*

Subsidiary (Domestic):

Hospitality Network Corporation (2)
1-16-2 Kaigan, Minato-ku, Tokyo, 105-8576, Japan
Tel.: (81) 3 5404 2222
Web Site: http://www.interconti-tokyo.com
Emp.: 287
Home Management Services

Best-Anniversary Inc. (1)
New Pier Takeshiba South Tower 1-16-1 Kaigan, Minato-ku, Tokyo, 105-0022, Japan
Tel.: (81) 354677877
Web Site: https://www.best-anniversary.co.jp
Event Management Services
N.A.I.C.S.: 561920
Masayuki Tsukada *(Chm)*

Ecpark Pte. Ltd. (1)
21 Lewin Terrace Singapore, Singapore, 179290, Singapore
Tel.: (65) 63339905
Event Management Services
N.A.I.C.S.: 561920

PT Tirtha Bridal (1)
Tel.: (62) 3618471151
Web Site: http://www.tirthabridal.com
Emp.: 100
Wedding Organizing Services
N.A.I.C.S.: 812990

Subsidiary (Non-US):

Tirtha Co., Ltd (2)
6-8F 6-29-6 Shinjuku, Shinjuku-ku, Tokyo, Japan
Tel.: (81) 3 5447 2540
Wedding Organizing Services
N.A.I.C.S.: 812990

TSUKAMOTO CORPORATION CO., LTD.

1-6-5 Nihonbashi Honcho, Chuo-ku, Tokyo, 103-0023, Japan
Tel.: (81) 332791330
Web Site: https://www.tsukamoto.co.jp
Year Founded: 1920
8025—(TKS)
Rev.: $64,764,780
Assets: $186,236,750
Liabilities: $95,507,890
Net Worth: $90,728,860
Earnings: $1,150,140
Fiscal Year-end: 03/31/24
Western Clothing Whslr
N.A.I.C.S.: 424350

Subsidiaries:

TSUKAMOTO ICHIDA Co., Ltd. (1)
Tsukamoto Building 1F 1-6-5 Nihonbashi, Honcho Chuo-ku, Tokyo, 103-0023, Japan
Tel.: (81) 362252990
Web Site: https://www.tsukamoto-ichida.co.jp
Emp.: 68
Traditional Garment Mfr
N.A.I.C.S.: 321999

TSUKASA CHEMICAL INDUSTRY CO. LTD.

Akihabara Business Center 3rd Floor 1-1 Akihabara, Taito-ku, Tokyo, 110-0006, Japan
Tel.: (81) 332580761
Web Site: http://www.tksc.com
Year Founded: 1968
Sales Range: $150-199.9 Million
Emp.: 103
Packaging Material & Machinery Mfr & Distr
N.A.I.C.S.: 333993
Kenichi Suzuki *(CEO)*

Subsidiaries:

Tsukasa Chemical Industry Co. Ltd. - Fukuoka Branch (1)
4-10-1 Hakozaki Higashiku Fukuokashi, Fukuokaken, Fukuoka, Japan
Tel.: (81) 926439591
Web Site: http://www.tksc.com
Industrial Packaging Materials & Machinery
N.A.I.C.S.: 333993

Tsukasa Chemical Industry Co. Ltd. - Kokubu Plant (1)
1-24-70 Kokubuhirose, Kagoshima, Kirishima, 899-4321, Japan
Tel.: (81) 995464900
Packaging Rope Mfr
N.A.I.C.S.: 314994

Tsukasa Chemical Industry Co. Ltd. - Osaka Branch (1)
6F Shinoosaka Marubiru Bekkan 1-18-22 Higashinakajima, Higashi Yodogawaku Oosakashi, Osaka, Japan
Tel.: (81) 663299833
Web Site: http://www.tksc.com
Industrial Packaging Materials & Machinery

N.A.I.C.S.: 333993

Tsukasa Chemical Industry Co. Ltd. - Sapporo Branch (1)
7F Sapporo Kuresutobiru 4-4-3 Kita 7, Jyousai Kitaku, Sapporo, Japan
Tel.: (81) 117071151
Web Site: http://www.tksc.com
Industrial Packaging Materials & Machinery
N.A.I.C.S.: 333993

Tsukasa Chemical Industry Co. Ltd. - Tsukuba Plant (1)
479-14 Nobori, Ibaraki, 300-2311, Tsukubamirai, Japan
Tel.: (81) 297581821
Adhesive Tape Mfr
N.A.I.C.S.: 325520

TSUKIJI UOICHIBA CO., LTD.

6-6-2 Toyosu, Koto-ku, Tokyo, 135-8114, Japan
Tel.: (81) 366333500
Web Site: https://www.tsukiji-uoichiba.co.jp
Year Founded: 1948
8039—(TKS)
Rev.: $388,013,610
Assets: $113,573,020
Liabilities: $71,163,260
Net Worth: $42,409,760
Earnings: $1,348,440
Emp.: 169
Fiscal Year-end: 03/31/24
Fish & Seafood Whslr
N.A.I.C.S.: 424460
Takeshi Yoshida *(Pres)*

Subsidiaries:

Kitashoku Co., Ltd. (1)
715-1 Shinkou Minami 2-chome, Ishikari, 061-3244, Hokkaido, Japan
Tel.: (81) 133648881
Marine Product Retailer
N.A.I.C.S.: 423860

Kyodosuisan Co., Ltd. (1)
5-3 Toyosu 6-chome, Koto-ku, Tokyo, 135-0061, Japan
Tel.: (81) 366330520
All Grocery Product Retailer
N.A.I.C.S.: 445110

Toichi Logistics Co., Ltd. (1)
5-3 Toyosu 6-chome, Koto-ku, Tokyo, 135-0061, Japan
Tel.: (81) 366333900
Cold Storage Services
N.A.I.C.S.: 493120

Toichi Tsukiji Fish (Shanghai) Co., Ltd. (1)
No 1-2 Building 3 No 2855 Jungong Road, Yangpu District, Shanghai, China
Tel.: (86) 2133816332
Marine Product Whslr
N.A.I.C.S.: 423860

Toyomi Toichi Reizo Co., Ltd. (1)
12-6 Toyomi-cho, Chou-ku, Tokyo, 104-0055, Japan
Tel.: (81) 335335441
Cold Storage Services
N.A.I.C.S.: 493120

Tsukiji Ichikawa Suisan Co., Ltd. (1)
5-1 Toyosu 6-chome, Koto-ku, Tokyo, 135-0061, Japan
Tel.: (81) 366335545
Marine Product Whslr
N.A.I.C.S.: 423860

Tsukiji Kigyo Co., Ltd. (1)
5-3 Toyosu 6-chome, Koto-ku, Tokyo, 135-0061, Japan
Tel.: (81) 366333999
Cargo Cleaning Services
N.A.I.C.S.: 561720

TSUKISHIMA HOLDINGS CO., LTD.

3-5-1 Harumi, Chuo-ku, Tokyo, 104-0053, Japan
Tel.: (81) 355606511
Web Site: https://www.tsk-g.co.jp

INTERNATIONAL PUBLIC

Year Founded: 1905
6332—(TKS)
Rev.: $820,995,050
Assets: $1,374,972,540
Liabilities: $677,366,360
Net Worth: $697,606,180
Earnings: $17,681,750
Emp.: 775
Fiscal Year-end: 03/31/24
Industrial Machines & Systems Mfr
N.A.I.C.S.: 811310
Yusaku Kuroita *(Mng Exec Officer)*

Subsidiaries:

Bokela GmbH (1)
Tullastr 64, 76131, Karlsruhe, Germany
Tel.: (49) 72 196 4560
Web Site: https://www.bokela.com
Industrial Automation Equipments Mfr
N.A.I.C.S.: 333248
Reiner Weidner *(Co-CEO)*

Samukawa Water Service Co., Ltd. (1)
4058-6 Miyayama, Samukawa-machi, Koza, 253-0106, Kanagawa, Japan
Tel.: (81) 355606540
Waste Treatment Services
N.A.I.C.S.: 221320

Sun Eco Thermal Co., Ltd. (1)
737-55 Shimoishikawa, Kanuma, 322-0017, Tochigi, Japan
Tel.: (81) 289720371
Web Site: https://www.set-g.co.jp
Emp.: 47
Industrial & Non Industrial Waste Treatment Services
N.A.I.C.S.: 562219

TSK Engineering Taiwan Co., Ltd. (1)
6th Floor No 24 Minsheng West Road, Zhongshan District, Taipei, Taiwan
Tel.: (886) 225236975
Web Site: https://www.tsktpe.com.tw
Industrial Wastes Treatment Services
N.A.I.C.S.: 562211

TSK Engineering Thailand Co., Ltd. (1)
14th Floor Room No 1404 United Center Building 323 Silom Road, Bangrak, Bangkok, 10500, Thailand
Tel.: (66) 22311726
Web Site: https://tsk.co.th
Emp.: 76
Industrial Equipment Mfr & Distr
N.A.I.C.S.: 333248
Kota Ogiwara *(Gen Mgr)*

Tsukishima Business Support Co., Ltd. (1)
3-5-1 Harumi, Chuo-ku, Tokyo, 104-0051, Japan
Tel.: (81) 335334824
Land Subdivision & Real Estate Management Services
N.A.I.C.S.: 531390

Tsukishima Engineering Malaysia Sdn. Bhd. (1)
Suite 16 04-05 16th Floor Wisma MCA 163, Jalan Ampang, 50450, Kuala Lumpur, Malaysia
Tel.: (60) 321628679
Sales Range: $25-49.9 Million
Emp.: 6
Industrial Equipment Mfr & Distr
N.A.I.C.S.: 333248
Takayuki Noguchi *(Mng Dir)*

Tsukishima Kankyo Engineering, Ltd. (1)
3-5-1 Harumi, Chuo-ku, Tokyo, 104-0053, Japan
Tel.: (81) 367582323
Web Site: https://www.tske.co.jp
Sales Range: $50-74.9 Million
Emp.: 181
Industrial Equipment Mfr & Distr
N.A.I.C.S.: 333248
Kikuo Makishima *(Chm)*

Tsukishima Kikai Co., Ltd. - Ichikawa Factory (1)
1-12 Shiohama Ichikawa Factory and

AND PRIVATE COMPANIES

Ichikawa R&D Center, Ichikawa, 272-0127, Chiba, Japan
Tel.: (81) 473591651
Web Site: http://www.tsk-g.co.jp
Emp.: 100
Industrial Machinery Design & Mfr
N.A.I.C.S.: 333248

Tsukishima Machine Sales Co., Ltd. (1)
3-5-1 Harumi Tsukishima Machinery Headquarters Building 3rd Floor, Chuo-ku, Tokyo, 104-0053, Japan
Tel.: (81) 35 560 6561
Web Site: https://www.tsms-g.co.jp
Industrial Machine Mfr & Distr
N.A.I.C.S.: 333248

Tsukishima Technology Maintenance Service Co., Ltd. (1)
Tsukishima Holdings Eitai Building 1-3-7 Saga, Koto-ku, Tokyo, 135-0031, Japan
Tel.: (81) 352457150
Web Site: https://www.t-tms.co.jp
Sales Range: $350-399.9 Million
Emp.: 1,456
Environmental Management Services
N.A.I.C.S.: 541620

TSUKUBA BANK, LTD.
1-7 Takezono, Tsuchiura, 305-0032, Ibaraki, Japan
Tel.: (81) 298598111
Web Site: https://www.tsukubabank.co.jp
Year Founded: 1952
8338—(TKS)
Rev.: $271,618,120
Assets: $18,865,561,340
Liabilities: $18,223,439,500
Net Worth: $642,121,840
Earnings: $33,050
Fiscal Year-end: 03/31/24
Banking Services
N.A.I.C.S.: 522110

TSUKUBA SEIKO CO., LTD.
216810 Ganjoji Kamigamo Kamisuwamachi, Kawauchi-gun, Fukushima, 329-0617, Tochigi prefecture, Japan
Tel.: (81) 285550081
Web Site: https://www.tsukubaseiko.co.jp
Year Founded: 1985
6596—(TKS)
Sales Range: Less than $1 Million
Electrostatic Equipment Mfr & Distr
N.A.I.C.S.: 325992
Fow-Lai Poh *(Pres)*

TSUKUI CORPORATION
6-1 Kamiooka-nishi 1-chome, Konan-ku, Yokohama, 233-0002, Kanagawa, Japan
Tel.: (81) 458424115
Web Site: http://www.tsukui.net
Year Founded: 1969
Rev.: $782,322,991
Assets: $684,829,210
Liabilities: $464,012,484
Net Worth: $220,816,725
Earnings: $19,649,817
Emp.: 21,300
Fiscal Year-end: 03/31/19
Nursing Home & Home Healthcare Services; Healthcare Employment Services
N.A.I.C.S.: 623110
Hiroshi Tsukui *(Chm)*

TSUKURUBA, INC.
Daini Ikura Building 2nd Floor 1-1-5 Kamimeguro, Meguro-ku, Tokyo, 153-0051, Japan
Tel.: (81) 344002946
Web Site: https://www.tsukuruba.com
Year Founded: 2011
2978—(TKS)
Rev.: $34,104,260
Assets: $26,254,620
Liabilities: $15,058,620
Net Worth: $11,196,000
Earnings: $1,337,300
Emp.: 135
Fiscal Year-end: 07/31/24
Software Development Services
N.A.I.C.S.: 541511
Hiroshi Kitahara *(COO)*

TSUMURA & CO.
2-17-11 Akasaka, Minato-ku, Tokyo, 107-8521, Japan
Tel.: (81) 363617101
Web Site: https://www.tsumura.co.jp
Year Founded: 1893
4540—(TKS)
Rev.: $997,085,450
Assets: $2,830,758,940
Liabilities: $878,402,900
Net Worth: $1,952,356,040
Earnings: $110,433,270
Emp.: 4,138
Fiscal Year-end: 03/31/24
Herbal Medicine Mfr
N.A.I.C.S.: 325411
Terukazu Kato *(Pres & CEO)*

Subsidiaries:

Logitem Tsumura Co., Ltd. (1)
157-1 Yainaba Yanagitsubo, Fujieda, 426-0083, Shizuoka, Japan
Tel.: (81) 546433886
Web Site: http://www.logitem-tsumura.co.jp
Sales Range: $75-99.9 Million
Emp.: 318
Truck Utility Trailer & RV Rental & Leasing
N.A.I.C.S.: 532120

Shanghai Tsumura Pharmaceuticals Co., Ltd. (1)
No 276 Guoshoujing Road, Pilot Free Trade Zone, Shanghai, 201203, China
Tel.: (86) 2150808866
Web Site: http://www.shtsumura-p.com
Drugs & Druggists Sundries Merchant Whslr
N.A.I.C.S.: 424210

Tsumura USA, Inc. (1)
1700 Rockville Pike, Rockville, MD 20852-1631
Tel.: (301) 468-1030
Sales Range: $50-74.9 Million
Emp.: 2
Drugs & Druggists Sundries Merchant Whslr
N.A.I.C.S.: 424210

TSUNAGU GROUP HOLDINGS INC.
7-3-5 Ginza, Chuo-ku, Tokyo, 104-0061, Japan
Tel.: (81) 5038165566
Web Site: https://www.tsunagu.co.jp
Year Founded: 2007
6551—(TKS)
Rev.: $106,541,430
Assets: $32,287,860
Liabilities: $20,709,890
Net Worth: $11,577,970
Earnings: $935,880
Emp.: 537
Fiscal Year-end: 09/30/23
Human Resource Consulting Services
N.A.I.C.S.: 541612
Masao Miyahara *(Auditor)*

Subsidiaries:

Asegonia Co., Ltd. (1)
2-2-1 Yurakucho, Chiyoda-ku, Tokyo, 100-0006, Japan
Tel.: (81) 335692791
Web Site: http://asegonia.com
Temporary Staffing Services
N.A.I.C.S.: 561320
Yoshinobu Inoue *(CEO)*

Indival, Inc. (1)
2-7-17 Shiba Sumitomo Shiba Park Building, Minato-ku, Tokyo, 105-0014, Japan
Tel.: (81) 368582104
Web Site: http://www.indival.co.jp
Emp.: 97
Temporary Staffing Services
N.A.I.C.S.: 561320

Star Planning Co., Ltd. (1)
3-72 Narumi, Koriyama, 963-0207, Fukushima, Japan
Tel.: (81) 249545910
Web Site: http://www.star-planning.co.jp
Temporary Staffing Services
N.A.I.C.S.: 561320

TSUNE SEIKI CO., LTD.
852 Takahizuki Fuchu-Machi, Toyama, 939-2613, Japan
Tel.: (81) 76 469 3330
Web Site: http://www.tsune.co.jp
Emp.: 100
Metal Cutting Machinery Mfr
N.A.I.C.S.: 333515
Yoshitaka Tsune *(Chm)*

Subsidiaries:

TSUNE SEIKI (THAILAND) CO., LTD. (1)
65/31 Moo 4Tambol Don Hua Lor, Amphur Muang, Chon Buri, 20000, Thailand
Tel.: (66) 38149594
Metal Cutting Machinery Mfr
N.A.I.C.S.: 333515

TSUNE WAGNER CARBIDE Co., LTD. (1)
8881 Uwano, Nyuzen Shimoniikawa, Toyama, 939-0642, Japan
Tel.: (81) 765723033
Saw Blades Mfr
N.A.I.C.S.: 332216

Tsune America LLC (1)
12550 N Presidential Way, Edinburgh, IN 46124-9039
Tel.: (812) 378-9875
Web Site: http://www.tsuneamerica.com
Sales Range: $1-9.9 Million
Emp.: 20
Metal Cutting Machinery Mfr
N.A.I.C.S.: 333515
Tom Billington *(Mgr-Sls)*

Tsune Europa GmbH (1)
Ringstrasse 41, 52078, Aachen, Germany
Tel.: (49) 24192787863
Web Site: http://www.tsune.eu
Metal Cutting Machinery Mfr
N.A.I.C.S.: 333515
Marc Hoffmann *(Co-CEO)*

Tsune Seiki Co., Ltd. - Nyuzen Factory (1)
1230 Aoki, Nyuzen Shimoniikawa, Toyama, 939-0643, Japan
Tel.: (81) 765720397
Saw Blades Mfr
N.A.I.C.S.: 332216

Tsune Seiki Co., Ltd. - Osawano Factory (1)
171 Takauchi, Toyama, Toyama, 939-2254, Japan
Tel.: (81) 764672351
Metal Cutting Machinery Mfr
N.A.I.C.S.: 333515

Tsune Seiki Co., Ltd. - Yatsuo Factory (1)
3-3 Yasuuchi Yatsuo Central Industrial Estate, Yatsuo, Toyama, 939-2366, Japan
Tel.: (81) 764553705
Metal Cutting Machinery Mfr
N.A.I.C.S.: 333515

TSUNEISHI HOLDINGS CORPORATION
1083 Tsuneishi Numakuma-cho, Fukuyama, 720-0393, Japan
Tel.: (81) 84 987 4915
Web Site: http://www.tsuneishi.co.jp
Year Founded: 1942
Ship Building & Repair Services
N.A.I.C.S.: 336611
Yasuharu Fushimi *(Chm & Pres)*

Subsidiaries:

TSUNEISHI GROUP (ZHOUSHAN) SHIPBUILDING Inc. (1)
Retiao Village, Daishan, Zhoushan, Zhejiang, China
Tel.: (86) 5804730099
Web Site: http://www.tsuneishi-zs.com
Ship Building Services
N.A.I.C.S.: 336611
Sachio Okumura *(Pres)*

TSUNEISHI HEAVY INDUSTRIES (CEBU) Inc. (1)
West Cebu Industrial Park Sez Buanoy Balamban, PO Box 08, Cebu, 6041, Philippines
Tel.: (63) 322308400
Web Site: http://www.thici.com
Ship Building & Repair Services
N.A.I.C.S.: 336611
Lionel Bitera *(Gen Mgr)*

TSUNO FOOD INDUSTRIAL CO., LTD.
94 Shinden Katsuragi-cho, Ito-gun, Wakayama, 649-7194, Japan
Tel.: (81) 736220061
Web Site: http://www.tsuno.co.jp
Year Founded: 1947
Sales Range: $25-49.9 Million
Emp.: 200
Rice Bran Product Mfr & Distr
N.A.I.C.S.: 311212
Fumi Tsuno *(Pres)*

Subsidiaries:

Tsuno Food Industrial Co., Ltd. - Osaka Tsuno Factory (1)
370 Imai Mihara-cho Sakai-shi, Osaka, 587-0061, Japan
Tel.: (81) 723 61 5121
Oil Extraction Services
N.A.I.C.S.: 311224

Tsuno Food Industrial Co., Ltd. - Takarazuka Tsuno Factory (1)
38-3 Suenari-cho, Takarazuka, 665-0044, Hyogo, Japan
Tel.: (81) 797 72 6324
Rice Bran Oil Mfr
N.A.I.C.S.: 311212

Tsuno Food Industrial Co., Ltd. - Yashiro Factory (1)
1029 Nishikose Kato-shi, Hyogo, 673-1425, Japan
Tel.: (81) 795 42 4861
Web Site: http://www.tsuno.co.jp
Dimer Acid Mfr
N.A.I.C.S.: 325199

Tsuno Rice Fine Chemicals Co., Ltd. (1)
2283 Chonomachi Katsuragi Cho, Ito Gun, Wakayama, 649 7194, Japan
Tel.: (81) 736228000
Web Site: http://www.tsuno.co.jp
Sales Range: $100-124.9 Million
Producer of Pharmaceuticals, Food & Feed Additives
N.A.I.C.S.: 311423
Sumi Fumitsuno *(Pres)*

Tsuno Transportation Co., Ltd. (1)
2222-1 Chonomachi, Katsuragi Cho Ito Gun, Wakayama, 649 7194, Japan (100%)
Tel.: (81) 736226727
Web Site: http://www.tsuno.co.jp
Sales Range: $75-99.9 Million
Transportation of Products, Refuelling & Raw Materials
N.A.I.C.S.: 488999

TSURUHA HOLDINGS INC.
20-1-21 Kita 24 Johigashi, Higashi-ku, Sapporo, 065-0024, Hokkaido, Japan
Tel.: (81) 117832755
Web Site: https://www.tsuruha-hd.co.jp
Year Founded: 1929
3391—(TKS)
Rev.: $6,791,523,820

TSURUHA HOLDINGS INC.

Tsuruha Holdings Inc.—(Continued)
Assets: $3,630,344,200
Liabilities: $1,596,162,970
Net Worth: $2,034,181,230
Earnings: $159,334,050
Emp.: 11,298
Fiscal Year-end: 05/31/24
Holding Company
N.A.I.C.S.: 551112
Tatsuru Tsuruha *(Chm)*

Subsidiaries:

Kusurinofukutaro Co., Ltd. (1)
2-8-17 Shinkamagaya F Tower 8th floor, Kamagaya, 273-0107, Japan
Tel.: (81) 474441111
Pharmaceutical Products Distr
N.A.I.C.S.: 424210

TSURUMI MANUFACTURING CO., LTD.
4-16-40 Tsurumi, Tsurumi-ku, Osaka, 538-8585, Japan
Tel.: (81) 669117011
Web Site: https://www.tsurumipump.co.jp
Year Founded: 1948
6351—(TKS)
Rev.: $413,977,690
Assets: $762,470,110
Liabilities: $166,281,160
Net Worth: $596,188,950
Earnings: $54,783,680
Emp.: 537
Fiscal Year-end: 03/31/24
Pump Mfr & Whslr
N.A.I.C.S.: 333914
Osamu Tsujimoto *(Pres)*

Subsidiaries:

H&E TSURUMI PUMP CO., LTD. (1)
Unit 2503-5 25/F Ocean Building 80 Shanghai St, Kowloon, China (Hong Kong)
Tel.: (852) 27307208
Industrial Pump Distr
N.A.I.C.S.: 423830

HANGZHOU CNP-TSURUMI PUMP CO., LTD. (1)
Xiaogucheng Village Jingshan Town, Yuhang District, Hangzhou, Zhejiang, China
Tel.: (86) 57188517209
Industrial Pump Distr
N.A.I.C.S.: 423830

PT. Tsurumi Pompa Indonesia (1)
Komplek Ruko Glodok Plaza Blok F 119 Jl Mangga Besar 1, Jakarta Barat, 11180, Indonesia
Tel.: (62) 216599749
Web Site: https://www.tsurumipump.co.id
Industrial Pump Distr
N.A.I.C.S.: 423830
Willianto Suwandibut *(Country Mgr)*

SHANGHAI TSURUMI PUMP CO., LTD. (1)
2nd Floor Building 3 No 386 Hangyi Road, Fengxian, Shanghai, 201499, China
Tel.: (86) 2164326010
Industrial Pump Distr
N.A.I.C.S.: 423830

TSURUMI (AMERICA), INC. (1)
1625 Fullerton Ct, Glendale Heights, IL 60139
Tel.: (630) 793-0127
Industrial Pump Distr
N.A.I.C.S.: 423830
Glenn Wiezzorek *(Gen Mgr)*

TSURUMI PUMP (THAILAND) CO., LTD. (1)
587/3 Rama 3 Road Bang Phongphang, Yannawa, Bangkok, 10120, Thailand
Tel.: (66) 22942886
Web Site: https://www.tsurumipump.co.th
Industrial Pump Distr
N.A.I.C.S.: 423830

TSURUMI PUMP KOREA CO., LTD. (1)
Rm728 PoongLim Building 127 Mapo-Daero, Mapo-Gu, Seoul, 4144, Korea (South)
Tel.: (82) 27016356
Industrial Pump Distr
N.A.I.C.S.: 423830

Plant (Domestic):

TSURUMI PUMP KOREA CO., LTD. - CHUNGJU PLANT (2)
108-16 Chungjusandan 1-ro, Chungju, Chungcheongbuk-do, Korea (South)
Tel.: (82) 43 857 8990
Industrial Pump Mfr
N.A.I.C.S.: 333996

TSURUMI PUMP TAIWAN CO., LTD. (1)
No 118 Lane 1191 Donglong Street, Pingzhen, Taoyuan, 32466, Taiwan
Tel.: (886) 34501335
Industrial Pump Distr
N.A.I.C.S.: 423830

Tsurumi (Europe) GmbH (1)
Wahlerstr 10, 40472, Dusseldorf, Germany
Tel.: (49) 2114179373
Industrial Pump Distr
N.A.I.C.S.: 423830

Tsurumi (Singapore) Pte Ltd (1)
No 37 Tampines Industrial Avenue 5 T5, Tampines, Singapore, 528628, Singapore
Tel.: (65) 67608338
Industrial Pump Distr
N.A.I.C.S.: 423830

Tsurumi Manufacturing Co., Ltd. - Kyoto Plant (1)
Tel.: (81) 759710831
Industrial Pump Mfr
N.A.I.C.S.: 333996

Tsurumi Manufacturing Co., Ltd. - Yonago Plant (1)
2700 Yomi-cho, Yonago, 683-0851, Tottori, Japan
Tel.: (81) 859290811
Industrial Pump Mfr
N.A.I.C.S.: 333996

Tsurumi Vacuum Engineering (Shanghai) Co., Ltd. (1)
No 2000 East Weiqing Road, Jinshanzui Industrial Park Jinshan District, Shanghai, 201508, China
Tel.: (86) 2157242030
Web Site: https://www.tsurumi.com.cn
Industrial Pump Distr
N.A.I.C.S.: 423830

TSURUYA CO., LTD.
2-12 Suno-saki-cho, Handa, 475-8528, Aichi, Japan
Tel.: (81) 569297311
Web Site: https://www.try110.com
Year Founded: 1887
5386—(TKS)
Sales Range: Less than $1 Million
Emp.: 473
Roof Tile Mfr
N.A.I.C.S.: 327390
Satoru Tsurumi *(CEO)*

TSUTSUMI JEWELRY CO., LTD.
4-24-26 Chuo, Warabi, 335-0004, Saitama, Japan
Tel.: (81) 484412500
Web Site: https://www.tsutsumi.co.jp
Year Founded: 1962
7937—(TKS)
Sales Range: $200-249.9 Million
Emp.: 924
Jewelry Mfr & Whslr
N.A.I.C.S.: 339910
Satoshi Tagai *(Pres)*

TSUZUKI DENKI CO., LTD.
Tokyo Art Club Building 6-19-15 Shinbashi, Minato-ku, Tokyo, 105-8665, Japan
Tel.: (81) 368337777
Web Site: https://www.tsuzuki.co.jp
Year Founded: 1932
8157—(TKS)
Rev.: $825,298,160
Assets: $535,846,260
Liabilities: $265,735,220
Net Worth: $270,111,040
Earnings: $36,202,970
Emp.: 1,239
Fiscal Year-end: 03/31/24
Electronic Parts Whslr
N.A.I.C.S.: 423690
Kazunori Yoshii *(Exec VP)*

Subsidiaries:

ComDesign Inc. (1)
3rd floor Sabo Kaikan Main Building 2-7-5 Hirakawacho, Chiyoda-ku, Tokyo, 102-0093, Japan
Tel.: (81) 5058085500
Web Site: https://comdesign.co.jp
Business Networking Services
N.A.I.C.S.: 561499

Next vision Co., Ltd. (1)
412 Azabu Gardenia 5-12-11 Roppongi, Minato-ku, Tokyo, 106-0032, Japan
Tel.: (81) 342831150
Web Site: https://www.next-vision.co.jp
Emp.: 5
Video Production Services
N.A.I.C.S.: 512110

Touto Systems, Ltd. (1)
7F Shin-Okayama Building 1-9-40 Nakasange, Kita-ku, Okayama, 700-0821, Japan
Tel.: (81) 862312511
Software Development Services
N.A.I.C.S.: 541511

Tsuzuki Densan Hong Kong Co., Ltd. (1)
Unit4012 Tower2 Metroplaza 223 Hing Fong Road, Kwai Chung, New Territories, China (Hong Kong)
Tel.: (852) 23143548
Emp.: 6
Electronic Components Distr
N.A.I.C.S.: 449210

Tsuzuki Densan Singapore Pte. Ltd. (1)
60 Paya Lebar Road 11-38 Paya Lebar Square, Singapore, 409051, Singapore
Tel.: (65) 63232262
Emp.: 3
Electronic Components Distr
N.A.I.C.S.: 449210

Tsuzuki Densan Trading (Shanghai) Co., Ltd. (1)
Room 3902 United Plaza No1468 Nanjing Road W, Shanghai, 200040, China
Tel.: (86) 2162896668
Emp.: 4
Electronic Components Distr
N.A.I.C.S.: 449210

Tsuzuki Embedded Solutions Co.,Ltd. (1)
2-5-3 Nishi-Shimbashi, Minato-ku, Tokyo, 105-8420, Japan
Tel.: (81) 335022521
Web Site: https://tsuzuki-es.co.jp
Emp.: 178
Electronic Device & Electronic Component Distr
N.A.I.C.S.: 423690

Tsuzuki Info-Techno East Japan Co., Ltd. (1)
1F Tsuzuki Koyamadai Building 1-20-20 Koyamadai, Shinagawa-ku, Tokyo, 142-0061, Japan
Tel.: (81) 357212551
Electrical Installation Services
N.A.I.C.S.: 238210

Tsuzuki Info-Techno West Japan Co., Ltd. (1)
7F Senba Grand Building 3-4-30 Kyutaromachi, Chuo-ku, Osaka, 541-0056, Japan
Tel.: (81) 662513229
Communication Network Design Services
N.A.I.C.S.: 541512

INTERNATIONAL PUBLIC

Tsuzuki Software Co., Ltd. (1)
2F Tsuzuki Koyamadai Building 1-20-20 Koyamadai, Shinagawa-ku, Tokyo, 142-0061, Japan
Tel.: (81) 357212411
Software Application Services
N.A.I.C.S.: 541511

Tsuzuki Techno Service Co., Ltd. (1)
23F New Pier Takeshiba North Tower 1-11-1 Kaigan, Minato-ku, Tokyo, 105-0022, Japan
Tel.: (81) 334373911
Computer & Network System LCM Services
N.A.I.C.S.: 541512

Tsuzuki Xross Support Co., Ltd. (1)
1-20-20 Koyamadai, Shinagawa-ku Tsuzuki Koyamadai Building, Tokyo, 142-0061, Japan
Tel.: (81) 357212551
Emp.: 162
Telecommunication Engineering Services
N.A.I.C.S.: 541330

TT ELECTRONICS PLC
Aspect House Spencer Road, Lancing, BN99 6DA, West Sussex, United Kingdom
Tel.: (44) 1932825300   UK
Web Site: https://www.ttelectronics.com
Year Founded: 1906
TTG—(LSE)
Rev.: $743,176,500
Assets: $851,822,400
Liabilities: $494,085,900
Net Worth: $357,736,500
Earnings: ($15,899,400)
Fiscal Year-end: 12/31/22
Electrical & Industrial Components Mfr
N.A.I.C.S.: 335999
Lynton Boardman *(Gen Counsel & Sec)*

Subsidiaries:

AB Connectors Limited (1)
Abercynon, Mountain Ash, CF45 4SF, Rhondda Cynon Taff, United Kingdom (100%)
Tel.: (44) 01443740331
Web Site: http://www.ttabconnectors.com
Sales Range: $50-74.9 Million
Emp.: 250
Connectors for Industrial, Transportation & Telecommunication Applications
N.A.I.C.S.: 335931

AB Elektronik GmbH (1)
Feldmark 50, 59368, Werne, Germany (100%)
Tel.: (49) 23897880
Web Site: http://www.abelektronik.de
Sales Range: $200-249.9 Million
Emp.: 550
Sensors, Potentiometers, Switches & Electronic Assemblies Mfr
N.A.I.C.S.: 334413

AB Elektronik Sachsen GmbH (1)
Salzstrasse 3, 01774, Klingenberg, Germany (100%)
Tel.: (49) 352025730
Web Site: http://www.ab-sachsen.de
Sales Range: $25-49.9 Million
Temperature Sensors, Pressure Sensors & Fuel Level Sensors Mfr
N.A.I.C.S.: 334513

AB Test Limited (1)
Tregwilym Industrial Estate Rogerstone, Newport, NP10 9YA, Gwent, United Kingdom (100%)
Tel.: (44) 1443290020
Web Site: http://www.abtest.com
Sales Range: $25-49.9 Million
Emp.: 10
Test Services to National & International Specifications
N.A.I.C.S.: 541380

BI Technologies Corporation Sdn Bhd (1)
A 1445 Jalan Tanjung Api, 25050, Kuantan, Pahang Darul Makmur, Malaysia (100%)

Tel.: (60) 95658888
Web Site: http://www.bitechnologies.com
Sales Range: $100-124.9 Million
Emp.: 332
Resistors Mfr
N.A.I.C.S.: 334416

BI Technologies ECD (1)
4200 Bonita Pl, Fullerton, CA
92835 **(100%)**
Tel.: (714) 447-2300
Web Site: http://www.bitechnologies.com
Sales Range: $25-49.9 Million
Emp.: 150
Automotive Sensors Mfr
N.A.I.C.S.: 334419

BI Technologies Japan Ltd (1)
Kakumaru Bldg 4 F 7-1-10, Tokyo, Koto-Ku,
Japan **(100%)**
Tel.: (81) 336151811
Web Site: http://www.bitechnologies.co.jp
Sales Range: $25-49.9 Million
Emp.: 20
Resistors Mfr
N.A.I.C.S.: 334416

BI Technologies Ltd (1)
Telford Rd Eastfield Industrial Est, Glenrothes, KY7 4NX, Fife, United
Kingdom **(100%)**
Tel.: (44) 01592662200
Web Site: http://www.bitechnologies.com
Sales Range: $25-49.9 Million
Emp.: 14
Resistors Mfr
N.A.I.C.S.: 334416

BI Technologies MCD (1)
4200 Bonita Pl, Fullerton, CA
92835 **(100%)**
Tel.: (714) 447-2300
Web Site: http://www.bitechnologies.com
Sales Range: $25-49.9 Million
Emp.: 100
Automotive Sensors Mfr
N.A.I.C.S.: 334419

BI Technologies Pte Ltd (1)
514 Chai Chee Ln, 02 01 Bedok Industrial
Est, 469029, Singapore,
Singapore **(100%)**
Tel.: (65) 64455166
Web Site: http://www.bitechnologies.com
Sales Range: $25-49.9 Million
Emp.: 20
Resistors Mfr
N.A.I.C.S.: 334416

Dale Power Systems plc (1)
Salter Road Eastfield Industrial Estate,
Scarborough, YO11 3DU, United
Kingdom **(100%)**
Tel.: (44) 3309993000
Web Site:
 http://www.dalepowersolutions.com
Sales Range: $50-74.9 Million
Emp.: 200
Diesel & Gas Powered Generators
N.A.I.C.S.: 333611

Erskine Systems Limited (1)
Salter Road, Eastfield Industrial Est, Scarborough, YO11 3DU, Yorkshire, United
Kingdom **(100%)**
Tel.: (44) 723583511
Sales Range: $50-74.9 Million
Emp.: 150
Power Supply Systems Mfr
N.A.I.C.S.: 332410

IRC Inc Advanced Film Division (1)
4222 S Staples St, Corpus Christi, TX
78401-3331 **(100%)**
Tel.: (361) 992-7900
Web Site: http://www.irctt.com
Electronic Resistor Mfr
N.A.I.C.S.: 334416

**IRC Inc Wire and Film
Technology** (1)
736 Greenway Rd, Boone, NC
28607-1860 **(100%)**
Tel.: (828) 264-8861
Web Site: http://www.irctt.com
Sales Range: $50-74.9 Million
Emp.: 200
Electronic Resistor Mfr
N.A.I.C.S.: 334416
Jack Hart *(Mgr-Product Line-Thin Film)*

**International Resistive Company,
Inc.** (1)
4222 S Staples St, Corpus Christi, TX
78411
Tel.: (361) 992-7900
Web Site: http://www.irctt.com
Resistive Component Mfr
N.A.I.C.S.: 335999
Jack Hart *(Mgr-Product Line)*

MMG North America Inc. (1)
Ste H214 271 Us Highway 46, Fairfield, NJ
07004-2458 **(100%)**
Tel.: (973) 345-8900
Web Site: http://www.mmgna.com
Sales Range: $25-49.9 Million
Emp.: 25
Electronic Components Mfr
N.A.I.C.S.: 327110

Midland Tool & Design Limited (1)
Barnfield Road, Tipton, DY4 9DF, West Midlands, United Kingdom **(100%)**
Tel.: (44) 1215201171
Web Site: http://www.mtdltd.co.uk
Sales Range: $25-49.9 Million
Emp.: 40
Progressive Stamping Die Tool Maker
N.A.I.C.S.: 333514

Neosid Australia Pty. Limited (1)
23 25 Percival St, Lilyfield, Sydney, 2040,
NSW, Australia **(100%)**
Tel.: (61) 296604566
Web Site: http://www.neosid.com.au
Sales Range: $25-49.9 Million
Emp.: 32
Soft Ferrite & Magnetic Components
N.A.I.C.S.: 327110

New Chapel Electronics Limited (1)
London Road, Fairford, GL7 4DS, Gloucestershire, United Kingdom
Tel.: (44) 1285 712144
Web Site: http://www.ttelectronics.com
Emp.: 80
Electronic Component Mfr & Whslr
N.A.I.C.S.: 334419
Andy Tubbs *(Dir-Site)*

OPTEK Technology Inc (1)
1645 Wallace Dr Ste 130, Carrollton, TX
75006 **(100%)**
Tel.: (972) 323-2200
Web Site: http://www.optekinc.com
Sales Range: $25-49.9 Million
Emp.: 43
Semiconductor Mfr
N.A.I.C.S.: 334413

Precision, Inc. (1)
1700 Fwy Blvd, Minneapolis, MN 55430
Tel.: (763) 561-6880
Web Site: http://www.ttelectronics.com
Emp.: 160
Precision Electromagnetic Products Design
& Mfr
N.A.I.C.S.: 334416

**Roxspur Measurement & Control
Ltd.** (1)
2 Downgate Drive, Sheffield, S4 8BT, South
Yorkshire, United Kingdom
Tel.: (44) 1142442521
Web Site: http://www.roxspur.com
Sales Range: $10-24.9 Million
Emp.: 150
Measurement & Control Instrumentation
Systems Mfr & Distr
N.A.I.C.S.: 334519

Semelab Limited (1)
Coventry Road, Lutterworth, LE17 4JB, Leicestershire, United Kingdom
Tel.: (44) 1455556565
Web Site: http://www.semelab.com
Sales Range: $50-74.9 Million
Emp.: 20
Semiconductor Device Mfr & Whslr
N.A.I.C.S.: 334413

Stontronics Limited (1)
Tofts Farm East Brenda Road, Cleveland,
Hartlepool, TS25 2BQ, United Kingdom
Tel.: (44) 1429852500
Web Site: http://www.stontronics.com
Electrical Equipment Mfr & Distr
N.A.I.C.S.: 335999

**TT Automotive Electronics (Suzhou)
Co Ltd** (1)
158 - 29 Hua Shan Road Feng Qiao Industrial Park, Suzhou New District, Suzhou,
215129, Jiangsu, China
Tel.: (86) 512 66611004
Web Site: http://www.ttelectronics.com
Automobile Parts Mfr
N.A.I.C.S.: 336390

TT Electronics Integrated Manufacturing Services Limited (1)
Tregwilym Industrial Estate, Rogerstone,
Newport, NP10 9YA, United
Kingdom **(100%)**
Tel.: (44) 1633892345
Web Site: http://www.ttelectronics-ims.com
Sales Range: $100-124.9 Million
Emp.: 320
Contract Electronic Systems, Sub-Systems
& Printed Circuit Board Assemblies
N.A.I.C.S.: 334418

TT electronics GmbH (1)
Max Lehner Street 31, 85354, Freising, Bavaria, Germany **(100%)**
Tel.: (49) 816149080
Web Site: http://www.tt-electronics.de
Sales Range: $25-49.9 Million
Emp.: 10
Resistors Mfr
N.A.I.C.S.: 334416
Klaus Zwerschina *(Mng Dir)*

TT electronics Srl (1)
Via Arese 12, 20159, Milan, Italy **(100%)**
Tel.: (39) 026888951
Web Site: http://www.ttelectronics.it
Sales Range: $25-49.9 Million
Emp.: 10
Resistors Mfr
N.A.I.C.S.: 334416

TT electronics integrated manufacturing services (Suzhou) Co Ltd (1)
158 - 29 Hua Shan Road Feng Qiao Industrial Park, Suzhou New District, Suzhou,
215129, Jiangsu, China
Tel.: (86) 512 66611004
Web Site: http://www.ttelectronics-ims.com
Emp.: 1,000
Electronic Components Mfr
N.A.I.C.S.: 334419

Torotel, Inc. (1)
520 N Rogers Rd, Olathe, KS 66062
Tel.: (913) 747-6111
Web Site: http://www.torotelinc.com
Rev.: $26,133,000
Assets: $13,380,000
Liabilities: $7,952,000
Net Worth: $5,428,000
Earnings: $714,000
Emp.: 170
Fiscal Year-end: 04/30/2020
Magnetic Components, Transformers,
Chokes, Toroidal Coils, Magnetic Amplifier,
High Power Switching Power Supplies Mfr
& Marketer
N.A.I.C.S.: 334416
Heath Carlton Hancock *(CFO)*

Subsidiary (Domestic):

Torotel Products, Inc. (2)
520 Rogers Rd, Olathe, KS 66062 **(100%)**
Tel.: (913) 747-6111
Web Site: http://www.torotelprod.com
Sales Range: $75-99.9 Million
Emp.: 160
Mfr of Electronic Components & Transformers
N.A.I.C.S.: 441110
Herb Sizemore *(Chm, Pres & CEO)*

**Twine & Cordage Manufacturing Co.
(PVT) Limited** (1)
48 Plymouth Road Southerton, PO Box
181, Harare, Zimbabwe **(100%)**
Tel.: (263) 46212827
Web Site:
 http://www.twineandcordage.co.zw
Sales Range: $50-74.9 Million
Emp.: 200
Twines, Threads & Plastic Strapping
N.A.I.C.S.: 326199

W.T. Henley Limited (1)
Unit 4A London Medway Commercial Park
James Swallow Way, Hoo, Rochester, ME3
9GX, United Kingdom **(100%)**
Tel.: (44) 1322444500

Web Site: http://www.wt-henley.com
Sales Range: $50-74.9 Million
Emp.: 200
Power Cable Mfr
N.A.I.C.S.: 237130

Welwyn Components Limited (1)
Welwyn Electronics Park, Bedlington, NE22
7AA, Northumberland, United
Kingdom **(100%)**
Tel.: (44) 1670822181
Web Site: http://www.welwyntt.com
Sales Range: $50-74.9 Million
Emp.: 220
Electronic Resistor Mfr
N.A.I.C.S.: 334416

TT GROUP LTD.
1806 Wharncliffe Rd S, PO Box 580,
London, N6L 1K1, ON, Canada
Tel.: (519) 652-0080
Web Site:
 http://www.tendertootsies.com
Year Founded: 1946
Sales Range: $50-74.9 Million
Emp.: 400
Mfr of Shoes
N.A.I.C.S.: 316210
James Perivolaris *(Pres & CEO)*

Subsidiaries:

TT Group, Inc. (1)
702 S Carnation Dr, Aurora, MO 65605
Tel.: (417) 678-2181
Web Site: http://skyler.tt-group.com
Sales Range: $50-74.9 Million
Emp.: 115
Misses & Junior Shoes Mfr & Distr
N.A.I.C.S.: 316210
David McAllister *(Controller & Office Mgr)*

TT INTERNATIONAL LIMITED
49 Sungei Kadut Avenue No 03-01,
Singapore, 729673, Singapore
Tel.: (65) 67930110   SG
Web Site: https://www.tt-intl.com
Year Founded: 1984
Rev.: $99,057,808
Assets: $192,446,636
Liabilities: $462,504,711
Net Worth: ($270,058,075)
Earnings: $23,833,580
Fiscal Year-end: 03/31/19
Consumer Electronics Distr
N.A.I.C.S.: 423620
Sze Hiang Sng *(Co-Founder, Chm & CEO)*

Subsidiaries:

**Aki Habara Electric Corporation Pte.
Ltd.** (1)
1 Venture Avenue, Singapore, 608521,
Singapore **(100%)**
Tel.: (65) 67930110
Investment Management Service
N.A.I.C.S.: 523999

Akira Corporation Pte. Ltd. (1)
47 Sungei Kadut Ave, Singapore, 729670,
Singapore **(100%)**
Tel.: (65) 67930110
Web Site: http://www.myakira.com
Consumer Electronics Distr
N.A.I.C.S.: 423620

Subsidiary (Domestic):

Akira International Pte. Ltd. (2)
47 Sungei Kadut Ave, Singapore, 729670,
Singapore
Tel.: (65) 67930110
Emp.: 100
Electric Appliances Mfr
N.A.I.C.S.: 335220
Tay Kia Lai *(Gen Mgr)*

Subsidiary (Non-US):

**Akira Electronics Hong Kong
Limited** (3)
Units E F G 14 F Gemstar Tower 23 Man
Lok Street, PO Box 4223, Hung Hom, Kowloon, China (Hong Kong)
Tel.: (852) 2333 1386

TT INTERNATIONAL LIMITED

TT International Limited—(Continued)
Web Site: http://www.myakira.com
Sales Range: $25-49.9 Million
Emp.: 12
Consumer Electronics Distr
N.A.I.C.S.: 423620

Akira Middle East L.L.C (3)
Office 701/702 Shaikha Mariam Building
P114 Al Maktom Street, PO Box 17258,
Dubai, United Arab Emirates
Tel.: (971) 42213320
Consumer Electronic Products Distr
N.A.I.C.S.: 423620

Akira West Africa Company Limited (3)
322 Capital Building Idiroko Bus Stop Ikorodu Road, Ikeja, Lagos, Nigeria
Tel.: (234) 8058501360
Sales Range: $25-49.9 Million
Emp.: 10
Consumer Electronics Distr
N.A.I.C.S.: 423620

Subsidiary (Domestic):

Akira Singapore Pte Ltd (2)
1 Venture Avenue 0707 Big Box, Singapore, 608521, Singapore
Tel.: (65) 67930110
Electric Appliances Mfr
N.A.I.C.S.: 335220

Ambur International Pte. Ltd. (1)
47 Sungeikadu Avenue, Singapore, 729670, Singapore
Tel.: (65) 67930110
Electrical & Electronics Products Distr
N.A.I.C.S.: 423620

Castilla Design Pte. Ltd. (1)
Pk Mall 9 Penang Rd 03-08/09, Singapore, 238459, Singapore (100%)
Tel.: (65) 63376433
Web Site: http://www.castilla.com.sg
Sales Range: $25-49.9 Million
Emp.: 7
Furniture Retailer
N.A.I.C.S.: 449110

First Omni Sdn. Bhd. (1)
First Omni Building 1 Sri Kemajuan Industrial Centre 10.5 Km, Jalan Tuaran, 89350, Kota Kinabalu, Sabah, Malaysia
Tel.: (60) 88433360
Web Site: http://www.myakira.com
Sales Range: $25-49.9 Million
Emp.: 20
Electrical & Electronics Appliances Distr
N.A.I.C.S.: 423620
Chong Yin Chye (Gen Mgr)

Furniture & Furnishings Pte. Ltd. (1)
1 Venture Avenue 07-07 Big Box, Singapore, 608521, Singapore
Tel.: (65) 67930110
Web Site: http://www.furn2.com
Furniture Whslr
N.A.I.C.S.: 449110
Susan Sng (Mgr-Sls & Ops)

IT-Kauppa Oy (1)
Hietasentie 14, Kotka, 48200, Finland
Tel.: (358) 5 2276276
Logistic Services
N.A.I.C.S.: 541614

Intracorp (B) Sdn. Bhd. (1)
No 13-17 Block B Lot No 39178 Spg 607-22 Kg Beribi, Muara, BE1118, Brunei Darussalam
Tel.: (673) 2793111
Electrical & Electronics Products Distr
N.A.I.C.S.: 423620

Mod.Living Pte. Ltd. (1)
215 Upper Bukit Timah Rd 02-00, Singapore, 588184, Singapore
Tel.: (65) 63362286
Web Site: http://www.modliving.com.sg
Sales Range: $25-49.9 Million
Emp.: 15
Furniture Retailer
N.A.I.C.S.: 449110

T. T. International Tradepark Pte. Ltd. (1)
47 Sungei Kadut Ave, Singapore, 729670, Singapore

Tel.: (65) 67930110
Web Site: http://www.tt-intl.com
Warehousing & Logistics Services
N.A.I.C.S.: 493110

TT Middle East FZE (1)
Shed MO02 6th Roundabout Jebel Ali Free Zone, PO Box 18115, Jebel Ali, Dubai, 18115, United Arab Emirates (100%)
Tel.: (971) 48872881
Web Site: http://www.ttint.com
Emp.: 10
Consumer Electronics Distr
N.A.I.C.S.: 423610
Sng Sze Hiang (Mng Dir)

TTA Holdings Limited (1)
Unit 59 7 Dalton Road, Thomastown, 3074, VIC, Australia (100%)
Tel.: (61) 392802333
Rev.: $700,527
Assets: $1,209,108
Liabilities: $485,923
Net Worth: $723,185
Earnings: ($836,880)
Fiscal Year-end: 03/31/2023
Investment Management Service
N.A.I.C.S.: 523999
Sng Sze Hiang (Chm)

TTC Sales and Marketing (SA) (Proprietary) Limited (1)
21, Kings Rd, Germiston, 1401, Gauteng, South Africa
Tel.: (27) 114550300
Sales Range: $50-74.9 Million
Emp.: 3
Consumer Electronics Distr
N.A.I.C.S.: 423620
Dean Fu (Mng Dir)

Tainahong Trading Limited (1)
Units E F G 13A/F Gemstar Tower 23 Man Lok Street, Hung Hom, Kowloon, China (Hong Kong) (100%)
Tel.: (852) 2333 1386
Web Site: http://www.tainahong.com.hk
Emp.: 20
Consumer Electronics Distr
N.A.I.C.S.: 423620
Baiju Sujanani (Gen Mgr)

The White Collection Pte. Ltd. (1)
47 Sungei Kadut Avenue, 729670, Singapore, Singapore
Tel.: (65) 67633233
Office Furniture Whslr
N.A.I.C.S.: 423210

TT LTD
879 Master Prithvi Nath Marg Opp Ajmal Khan Park Karol Bagh, New Delhi, 110005, India
Tel.: (91) 1145060708
Web Site: https://www.tttextiles.com
514142—(BOM)
Rev.: $53,901,434
Assets: $48,911,745
Liabilities: $39,610,935
Net Worth: $9,300,810
Earnings: ($1,036,895)
Emp.: 650
Fiscal Year-end: 03/31/21
Garments Mfr
N.A.I.C.S.: 315250
Sunil Mahnot (CFO & Dir-Fin)

Subsidiaries:

T.T.Limited - Tirupathi Spinning Mill (1)
305 1-A Tirupathi Thottam Thevampalayam Palangiri Vlg, Avinashi Taluk, Tirupur, 641654, Tamil Nadu, India
Tel.: (91) 4296272711
Web Site: http://www.tttextiles.com
Sales Range: $25-49.9 Million
Emp.: 150
Yarn Mfr
N.A.I.C.S.: 313110

T.T.Limited - Tirupur Unit (1)
305/1 Padmavati Garden Avinashi Dist, Tirupur, 641654, Tamil Nadu, India
Tel.: (91) 11 45060708
Web Site: http://www.tttextiles.com
Garments Mfr

N.A.I.C.S.: 315120
Manoj Tandon (VP-Garments)

TT VISION HOLDINGS BERHAD
Plot 106 Hilir Sungai Keluang 5 Bayan Lepas Phase 4, 11900, Penang, Malaysia
Tel.: (60) 46456294
Web Site: https://www.ttvision-tech.com
TTVHB—(KLS)
Rev.: $12,666,602
Assets: $30,058,473
Liabilities: $7,844,860
Net Worth: $22,213,614
Earnings: $2,334,999
Fiscal Year-end: 12/31/23
Holding Company
N.A.I.C.S.: 551112

TT&T PUBLIC COMPANY LIMITED
252/30 24th Fl Muang Thai-Phatra Complex Tower 1 Rachadapisek Rd, Huaykwang, Bangkok, 10320, Thailand
Tel.: (66) 2693 2100
Web Site: http://www.ttt.co.th
Year Founded: 1992
Sales Range: $50-74.9 Million
Information & Communication Services
N.A.I.C.S.: 517810
Sasiprin Chandratat (CEO)

TTBIO CORP.
2F No 07 6th Road Industry Park, Taichung, 40755, Taiwan
Tel.: (886) 423595958
Web Site: https://www.ttbio.com
Year Founded: 2012
6493—(TAI)
Medical Equipment Mfr
N.A.I.C.S.: 339112
Chou-Chang Huang (VP)

TTET UNION CORP
No 32 Gongye West Road Erzhenli, Guantian District, T'ainan, 72048, Taiwan
Tel.: (886) 66984500
Web Site: https://www.ttet.com.tw
1232—(TAI)
Rev.: $770,474,708
Assets: $267,514,330
Liabilities: $85,924,259
Net Worth: $181,590,071
Earnings: $41,000,064
Emp.: 145
Fiscal Year-end: 12/31/23
Canola Oil Mfr
N.A.I.C.S.: 311225
Chih-Hsien Lo (Chm)

TTFB CO., LTD.
7F -1 No 176 Jian 1st Rd, Zhonghe Dist, New Taipei City, 235, Taiwan
Tel.: (886) 282271280
Year Founded: 1990
2729—(TPE)
Rev.: $141,919,989
Assets: $136,008,223
Liabilities: $68,012,194
Net Worth: $67,996,029
Earnings: $3,462,402
Fiscal Year-end: 12/31/22
Restaurant Operators
N.A.I.C.S.: 722511
Cheng-I Hsu (Chm & Pres)

TTG GLOBAL GROUP LIMITED
Field House Uttoxeter Old Road, Derby, DE1 1NH, United Kingdom
Tel.: (44) 1332 375 596 UK
Web Site: http://www.ttg-group.com

INTERNATIONAL PUBLIC

Holding Company; Telecommunications Services
N.A.I.C.S.: 551112
Peter Burridge (Chm)

TTI ENTERPRISE LIMITED
No-822 8th Floor 4 Synagogue, Kolkata, 700 001, India
Tel.: (91) 3340679020
Web Site: https://www.ttienterprises.com
Year Founded: 1981
538597—(BOM)
Rev.: $1,307,135
Assets: $3,650,420
Liabilities: $1,826
Net Worth: $3,648,594
Earnings: $21,928
Emp.: 3
Fiscal Year-end: 03/31/21
Financial Services
N.A.I.C.S.: 523999
Binjal Mehta (Exec Dir)

TTJ HOLDINGS LIMITED
No 57 Pioneer Road, Singapore, 628508, Singapore
Tel.: (65) 68622126
Web Site: http://www.ttj.com.sg
K1Q—(SES)
Rev.: $56,920,208
Assets: $123,926,061
Liabilities: $26,018,531
Net Worth: $97,907,529
Earnings: $2,397,030
Emp.: 5,300
Fiscal Year-end: 07/31/21
Structural Steel Mfr & Engineering Services
N.A.I.C.S.: 332312
Hock Chwee Teo (Founder, Chm & Mng Dir)

Subsidiaries:

T T J Design & Engineering (India) Private Limited (1)
House No 8 56 & 8 56 1 Isnapur Cross Roads, Isnapur Patancheru Mandal, Medak, 502307, Andhra Pradesh, India
Tel.: (91) 8455226006
Construction Services
N.A.I.C.S.: 236220

TTJ Design and Engineering Pte Ltd (1)
57 Pioneer Road, Singapore, 628508, Singapore
Tel.: (65) 68622126
Structured Steel Products Mfr
N.A.I.C.S.: 331110

TTK BANK AD SKOPJE
19a Naroden Front St, 1000, Skopje, North Macedonia
Tel.: (389) 23247000
Web Site: http://www.ttk.com.mk
Year Founded: 2006
TTK—(MAC)
Rev.: $10,484,039
Assets: $180,180,886
Liabilities: $158,889,065
Net Worth: $21,291,821
Earnings: $878,253
Emp.: 278
Fiscal Year-end: 12/31/21
Banking Services
N.A.I.C.S.: 522110
Gligorie Gogovski (Chm-Supervisory Bd)

TTK HEALTHCARE LTD
6 Cathedral Road, Chennai, 600086, India
Tel.: (91) 4428116106
Web Site: https://www.ttkhealthcare.com
Year Founded: 1928

TTKHEALTH—(NSE)
Rev.: $88,251,072
Assets: $67,468,073
Liabilities: $27,248,840
Net Worth: $40,219,234
Earnings: $6,339,210
Emp.: 2,485
Fiscal Year-end: 03/31/21
Consumer Products MFR
N.A.I.C.S.: 424350
S. Kalyanaraman (Sec)

TTK PRESTIGE LIMITED
Nagarjana Castle No 1/1 & 1/2 Wood Street Ashok Nagar Richmond Town, Bengaluru, 560025, Karnataka, India
Tel.: (91) 8022217438
Web Site: https://www.ttkprestige.com
517506—(BOM)
Rev.: $376,398,750
Assets: $329,577,885
Liabilities: $93,491,580
Net Worth: $236,086,305
Earnings: $41,691,195
Emp.: 1,418
Fiscal Year-end: 03/31/22
Kitchen Product Mfr
N.A.I.C.S.: 332215
T. T. Jagannathan (Chm)

Subsidiaries:

Cigna TTK Limited (1)
401/402 Raheja Titanium Western Express Highway, Goregaon East, Mumbai, 400063, India
Tel.: (91) 2249854100
Web Site: http://www.manipalcigna.com
Health Insurance Services
N.A.I.C.S.: 524114
Luis Miranda (Chm)

Horwood Homewares Limited (1)
Avonmouth Way, Avonmouth, Bristol, BS11, United Kingdom
Tel.: (44) 1179400000
Web Site: https://www.horwood.co.uk
Kitchen Accessory Mfr
N.A.I.C.S.: 332215

TTK Protective Devices Limited (1)
No 6 Cathedral Road, Chennai, 600 086, India
Tel.: (91) 4428115800
Web Site: http://www.skorecondoms.com
Condom Mfr
N.A.I.C.S.: 326299

Ultrafresh Modular Solutions Limited (1)
C 35 1st Floor RDC Raj Nagar, Ghaziabad, 201002, Uttar Pradesh, India
Tel.: (91) 1800226900
Web Site: https://ultrafreshindia.com
Kitchen Appliance Distr
N.A.I.C.S.: 423620

TTL BETEILIGUNGS UND GRUNDBESITZ AG
Maximilianstrasse 35C, 80539, Munich, Germany
Tel.: (49) 893816110
Web Site: https://www.ttl-ag.de
TTO—(DEU)
Rev.: $1,423,998
Assets: $103,587,592
Liabilities: $82,073,077
Net Worth: $21,514,516
Earnings: $(16,613,313)
Emp.: 2
Fiscal Year-end: 12/31/23
Information Technology Services
N.A.I.C.S.: 541512
Klaus Kirchberger (Deputy Chm-Supervisory Bd)

TTL ENTERPRISES LIMITED
1118 Fortune Business Hub Nr Satyamev Elysiym Science City Road Sola, Navrangpura, Ahmedabad, 380060, India
Tel.: (91) 9998952293
Web Site: https://www.ttlent.com
Year Founded: 1988
514236—(BOM)
Rev.: $1,401,905
Assets: $836,949
Liabilities: $907,337
Net Worth: $(70,388)
Earnings: $38,849
Fiscal Year-end: 03/31/23
Textile Product Mfr & Distr
N.A.I.C.S.: 313240
Malay Desai (Compliance Officer & Sec)

TTL INDUSTRIES PUBLIC COMPANY LIMITED
Lumpini Tower Building 18th Floor 1168/47 Rama IV Road Thungmahamek, Sathorn, Bangkok, 10120, Thailand
Tel.: (66) 2679 9727
Web Site: http://www.ttl.co.th
Year Founded: 1965
Sales Range: Less than $1 Million
Emp.: 5
Yarn Mfr & Whslr
N.A.I.C.S.: 313110
Pongpol Adireksarn (Chm & Pres)

TTM RESOURCES INC.
Suite 202 750 West Pender Street, Vancouver, V6C 2T7, BC, Canada
Tel.: (604) 685-1144
Web Site: http://ttmresources.ca
Year Founded: 2004
Sales Range: Less than $1 Million
Mineral Exploration Services
N.A.I.C.S.: 213114
W. K. Crichton Clarke (Pres & CEO)

TTP GMBH
Bahnhofstrasse 15, 83022, Rosenheim, Germany
Tel.: (49) 8031 282000
Web Site: http://www.ttp-group.eu
Holding Company
N.A.I.C.S.: 551112
Andreas Bonhoff (CEO)

Subsidiaries:

Triplan GmbH (1)
Siemensstrasse 21, Bad Homburg, 61352, Germany
Tel.: (49) 619660920
Web Site: http://www.triplan.com
Engineering Services
N.A.I.C.S.: 541330

Subsidiary (Non-US):

Triplan Gebaudetechnik AG (2)
Kagenstrasse 18, 4153, Reinach, Switzerland
Tel.: (41) 589116600
Web Site: http://www.rmb.ch
Engineeering Services
N.A.I.C.S.: 541330

Triplan India Pvt. Ltd. (2)
A - South Wing 1st Floor Manikchand Icon Dhole Patil Road, Pune, 411001, Maharashtra, India
Tel.: (91) 2067080300
Web Site: http://www.triplan.in
Engineeering Services
N.A.I.C.S.: 541330

Triplan Ingenieur AG (2)
Kagenstrasse 18, 4153, Reinach, Switzerland
Tel.: (41) 613383232
Web Site: http://www.triplanag.ch
Engineeering Services
N.A.I.C.S.: 541330
C. Eifler (Mng Dir)

TTT MONEYCORP LIMITED
Zig Zag Building 70 Victoria Street, London, SW1E 6SQ, United Kingdom
Tel.: (44) 207 589 3000
Web Site: http://www.moneycorp.com
Year Founded: 1962
Foreign Exchange & Payment Services
N.A.I.C.S.: 523160
Michael Low (Mgr-Bus Dev)

Subsidiaries:

Moneycorp US Inc. (1)
Corporate International Payments Businesses
N.A.I.C.S.: 523160

TTV, S.A.
Calle de Severo Ochoa 11, Poligono Ind Ntra Sra De Butarque, 28914, Leganes, Madrid, Spain
Tel.: (34) 916 857 365
Web Site: http://en.ttv.es
Year Founded: 1982
Industrial Valve Mfr
N.A.I.C.S.: 332911
Cesar Abarca (Gen Mgr-TTV-JC)

Subsidiaries:

JC Fabrica de Valvulas S.A.U. (1)
c/ Cantabria 2, Poligono Industrial Les Salines, 08830, Sant Boi de Llobregat, Barcelona, Spain
Tel.: (34) 93 654 86 86
Web Site: http://www.jc-vlaves.com
Industrial Valve Mfr
N.A.I.C.S.: 332911
Antonio Da Gama (Dir-Sls)

Subsidiary (Non-US):

JC Flow Controls Pte. Ltd. (2)
133 Cecil Street 16-01 Keck Seng Tower, Singapore, 069535, Singapore (100%)
Tel.: (65) 6862 4662
Web Site: http://en.jc-valves.com
Industrial Valves Mfr & Distr
N.A.I.C.S.: 332911
Bernard Wong (Mng Dir)

TTW PUBLIC COMPANY LIMITED
30/130 Moo 12 Phuttamonthon Sai 5 Rd, Rai Khing Samphran, Nagorn Pathom, 73210, Thailand
Tel.: (66) 20199490
Web Site: https://www.ttwplc.com
TTAPY—(OTCIQ)
Rev.: $170,724,355
Assets: $591,936,107
Liabilities: $145,828,626
Net Worth: $446,107,482
Earnings: $86,008,098
Emp.: 322
Fiscal Year-end: 12/31/23
Tap Water Production & Distribution Services
N.A.I.C.S.: 221310
Hongthong Artit (Dir-Bus Dev)

Subsidiaries:

Pathum Thani Water Company Limited (1)
43 Moo 3 Chiang Rak Noi - Bang Sai Rd Ban Pathum, Sam Khok, Pathumthani, 12160, Thailand
Tel.: (66) 297 988 0103
Web Site: http://www.ptw.co.th
Tap Water Production & Distribution Services
N.A.I.C.S.: 221310

Thai Water Operations Company Limited (1)
30/10 Moo 12 Phuttamonthon Sai 5 Rd Raiking, Samphran, Nakhon Pathom, 73210, Thailand
Tel.: (66) 20 199 4903
Web Site: https://www.ttwplc.com
Water Distribution Services
N.A.I.C.S.: 221310

Plant (Domestic):

Thai Water Operations Company Limited - Bang Len Water Treatment Plant (2)
67-68 Moo 9 Tambon Bangrakam, Bang Len, Nakhon Pathom, 73130, Thailand
Tel.: (66) 34 276805 7
Water Distribution Services
N.A.I.C.S.: 221310

TTY BIOPHARM CO., LTD.
3F No 3-1 Park St, Nangang, Taipei, 11503, Taiwan
Tel.: (886) 26525999
Web Site: https://www.eng.tty.com.tw
Year Founded: 1960
4105—(TPE)
Rev.: $158,259,263
Assets: $300,179,314
Liabilities: $105,285,746
Net Worth: $194,893,568
Earnings: $34,489,885
Emp.: 524
Fiscal Year-end: 12/31/22
Pharmaceuticals Product Mfr
N.A.I.C.S.: 325412
Lin Chuan (Chm)

TU LIEM URBAN DEVELOPMENT JOINT STOCK COMPANY
No 08 Hoang Tang Bi Street, Dong Ngac Ward Bac Tu Liem District, Hanoi, Vietnam
Tel.: (84) 22213518
Web Site: https://www.lideco.vn
Year Founded: 1974
NTL—(HOSE)
Rev.: $37,657,789
Assets: $83,855,802
Liabilities: $23,613,986
Net Worth: $60,241,816
Earnings: $15,004,628
Emp.: 103
Fiscal Year-end: 12/31/23
Real Estate Development Services
N.A.I.C.S.: 531390

TU YI HOLDING COMPANY LIMITED
Room 813 8/F Block 4 Hai No 1288 Wenyi West Road, Chuang Technology Centre Canggian Sub-Yuhang, Hangzhou, Zhejiang, China
Tel.: (86) 57185285222
Web Site: http://www.tuyigroup.com
Year Founded: 2008
1701—(HKG)
Rev.: $3,691,537
Assets: $29,589,440
Liabilities: $11,575,559
Net Worth: $18,013,882
Earnings: $(2,598,523)
Emp.: 75
Fiscal Year-end: 12/31/22
Holding Company
N.A.I.C.S.: 551112
Dingxin Yu (Co-Founder & Chm)

TUAN SING HOLDINGS LIMITED
9 Oxley Rise No 03-02 The Oxley, Singapore, 238697, Singapore
Tel.: (65) 62237211
Web Site: https://www.tuansing.com
T24—(SES)
Rev.: $230,038,627
Assets: $1,983,918,048
Liabilities: $1,053,783,231
Net Worth: $930,134,817
Earnings: $4,097,554
Emp.: 777
Fiscal Year-end: 12/31/23
Holding Company
N.A.I.C.S.: 551112
Nick Choong How Ng (Sr VP-Bus Dev)

TUAN SING HOLDINGS LIMITED

Tuan Sing Holdings Limited—(Continued)

Subsidiaries:

Grand Hotel Group - Grand Hotel Company Pty Limited (1)
Level 7 Professional Suites 123 Collins Street, Melbourne, 3000, VIC, Australia
Tel.: (61) 396678888
Web Site: https://grandhotelgroup.com.au
Property Investment Services
N.A.I.C.S.: 531390
Mishca Davis *(CFO & Sec)*

Hypak Sdn. Berhad (1)
Lot 24 Jalan Usaha 8 Air Keroh Industrial Estate, 75450, Melaka, Malaysia (100%)
Tel.: (60) 62327822
Web Site: http://www.tuansing.com
Sales Range: $50-74.9 Million
Emp.: 200
Packaging Materials Mfr
N.A.I.C.S.: 326112

Maylands Investment Pte Ltd (1)
9 Oxley Rise 03-02 The Oxley, Singapore, 238697, Singapore
Tel.: (65) 62237211
Web Site: http://www.tuansing.com
Sales Range: $50-74.9 Million
Emp.: 40
Property Investment Services
N.A.I.C.S.: 523999
William Liem *(CEO)*

Oxley Development Pte Ltd (1)
9 Oxley Rise 03-02 The Oxley, Singapore, 238697, Singapore
Tel.: (65) 62237211
Sales Range: $50-74.9 Million
Emp.: 40
Real Estate Investment Services
N.A.I.C.S.: 523999
Peter Kock *(VP-Property Mgmt)*

Pan-West (Private) Limited (1)
16 New Industrial Road 01-03/04 Hudson TechnoCentre, Singapore, 536204, Singapore
Tel.: (65) 6 356 5553
Web Site: https://www.pan-west.com
Golf Product Retailer
N.A.I.C.S.: 459110
Joey Gan *(Ops Mgr)*

SP Corporation Limited (1)
896 Dunearn Road 03-11 Link 896, Singapore, 589472, Singapore (100%)
Tel.: (65) 66453260
Web Site: http://www.spcorp.com.sg
Rev.: $22,220,277
Assets: $48,740,108
Liabilities: $5,907,640
Net Worth: $42,832,468
Earnings: $1,053,183
Fiscal Year-end: 12/31/2020
Holding Company; Tire & Auto Products Mfr
N.A.I.C.S.: 551112
Jason Kay Chen Lee *(Sr Mgr-Dev)*

Subsidiary (Domestic):

Globaltraco International Pte. Ltd. (2)
6 Shenton Way OUE Downtown 1 #41-03, Singapore, 068809, Singapore
Tel.: (65) 6645 3260
Tire & Auto Products Mfr & Sales
N.A.I.C.S.: 326211

Subsidiary (Non-US):

PT. SP Mining & Engineering (2)
15th Floor Wisma Sudirman Suite 01 Jl Jend Sudirman Kav 34, Jakarta, 10220, Indonesia
Tel.: (62) 21 570 8588
Geotechnical & Soil Investigation Services
N.A.I.C.S.: 541360

Performance Retreads Sdn. Bhd. (2)
53 Jalan Cemerlang Taman Perindustrian Cemerlang, 81800, Ulu Tiram, Johor Darul Takzim, Malaysia
Tel.: (60) 7 861 7671
Retreaded Tire Mfr & Sales
N.A.I.C.S.: 326212

Subsidiary (Domestic):

SP Global International Pte. Ltd. (2)
896 Dunearn Road 03-11, Singapore, 589472, Singapore
Tel.: (65) 6 645 3260
Web Site: https://www.spcorp.com.sg
Commodities Trading Services
N.A.I.C.S.: 425120

SP Resources International Pte. Ltd. (2)
6 Shenton Way OUE Downtown 1, Singapore, 068809, Singapore
Tel.: (65) 6645 3260
Web Site: http://www.spglobal-sin.com
Emp.: 15
Commodities Trading Services
N.A.I.C.S.: 425120
Jason Lee *(Sr Mgr-Ops)*

Soil & Foundation (Pte) Limited (2)
59 Jalan Pemimpin #05-01 L&Y Building, Singapore, 577218, Singapore
Tel.: (65) 6281 7622
Geotechnical & Soil Investigation Services
N.A.I.C.S.: 541360

TS Planet Sports Pte. Ltd. (1)
30 Robinson Rd 12-01, Singapore, 048546, Singapore
Tel.: (65) 62237211
Golf Equipment Retailer
N.A.I.C.S.: 423910

Yewglade Pte Ltd (1)
9 Oxley Rise 03-02, Singapore, 238697, Singapore
Tel.: (65) 62237211
Web Site: http://www.tuansing.com
Emp.: 40
Residential Property Development Services
N.A.I.C.S.: 236115

Subsidiary (Domestic):

Habitat Properties (Shanghai) Ltd. (2)
9 Oxley Rise 01-02 The Oxley, Singapore, 238697, Singapore (91%)
Tel.: (65) 67380866
Emp.: 5
Residential Real Estate Management Services
N.A.I.C.S.: 531311

TUANCHE LIMITED

9F Ruihai Building No 21 Yangfangdian Road, Haidian District, Beijing, 100038, China
Tel.: (86) 1063976232 Ky
Web Site: https://www.tuanche.com
Year Founded: 2012
TC—(NASDAQ)
Rev.: $22,481,031
Assets: $16,524,701
Liabilities: $13,826,983
Net Worth: $2,697,718
Earnings: ($11,488,010)
Emp.: 324
Fiscal Year-end: 12/31/23
Automobile Dealing & Distr
N.A.I.C.S.: 423110
Wei Wen *(Co-Founder, Chm, CEO & Acting CFO)*

TUAS LTD.

C/- Suite 1 12 Lyonpark Road, Sutherland, Macquarie Park, 2113, NSW, Australia
Tel.: (61) 280260886 AU
Web Site: https://www.tuas.com.au
Year Founded: 2020
TUA—(ASX)
Rev.: $63,799,185
Assets: $346,949,240
Liabilities: $20,735,828
Net Worth: $326,213,412
Earnings: ($11,340,496)
Emp.: 150
Fiscal Year-end: 07/31/23
Telecommunication Servicesb
N.A.I.C.S.: 517810
David Teoh *(Chm)*

TUBA CITY GOLD CORP.

250 King Street West, Dundas, L9H 1V9, ON, Canada
Tel.: (905) 628-6000 NV
Year Founded: 2012
Gold Mining
N.A.I.C.S.: 212220
Braden Klumpp *(Pres, CEO, CFO, Treas & Sec)*

TUBACEX S.A.

Tres Cruces 8, PO Box 22, 1400, Llodio, Alava, Spain
Tel.: (34) 946719300
Web Site: https://www.tubacex.com
Year Founded: 1963
TUB—(MAD)
Rev.: $940,933,878
Assets: $1,337,295,507
Liabilities: $1,013,158,185
Net Worth: $324,137,322
Earnings: $47,263,495
Emp.: 2,513
Fiscal Year-end: 12/31/23
Stainless Steel Tube Mfr
N.A.I.C.S.: 331210
Alvaro Videgain Muro *(Chm)*

Subsidiaries:

Aceria de Alava S.A. (1)
Poligono Industrial de Saratxo, 01470, Amurrio, Alava, Spain
Tel.: (34) 945891461
Web Site: https://aceralava.com
Steel Products Mfr
N.A.I.C.S.: 332999

Metaux Inox Services, S.A.S. (1)
Z A C des Chesnes Nord rue des Combes, 38290, Satolas-et-Bonce, France
Tel.: (33) 474 94 00 64
Steel Tube Mfr & Distr
N.A.I.C.S.: 331210
Alvaro Videgain *(Pres)*

Salem Tube Inc. (1)
485 Nickel St, Greenville, PA 16125
Tel.: (724) 286-4900
Web Site: http://www.salemtube.com
Emp.: 128
Stainless Steel Products Mfr
N.A.I.C.S.: 331210

Schoeller - Bleckman Edelstahlrohr, GmbH (1)
Rohrstrasse 1, 2630, Ternitz, Austria
Tel.: (43) 2630 316 0
Web Site: http://ns1.sber.co.at
Emp.: 550
Stainless Tube Product Mfr & Distr
N.A.I.C.S.: 331210

Subsidiary (Non-US):

Schoeller - Bleckman AS (2)
Pod Parukakrou 12, 130 00, Prague, Czech Republic
Tel.: (420) 2 7100 1193
Steel Tube Distr
N.A.I.C.S.: 423510

Schoeller - Bleckman Edelstahlrohr Deutschland, GmbH (2)
Heinrichstrasse 169B, 40239, Dusseldorf, Germany
Tel.: (49) 211 6165 9 0
Steel Tube Distr
N.A.I.C.S.: 423510

Schoeller - Bleckman Edelstahlrohr Phonix Kft (2)
Bokor utca 15-19, 1036, Budapest, Hungary
Tel.: (36) 1 250 2342
Steel Tube Distr
N.A.I.C.S.: 423510

Schoeller - Bleckman Tube France (2)
9 Rue du 11 Novembre, 93600, Paris, Aulnay-Sous-Bois, France
Tel.: (33) 1 48 79 30 50
Steel Tube Distr
N.A.I.C.S.: 423510

TTI- Tubacex Tubos Inoxidables S.A.U. (1)
Tres Cruces 8, PO Box 22, Llodio, 01400,
Alava, Spain
Tel.: (34) 94 671 9300
Mining Services
N.A.I.C.S.: 212290

Tubacex & Cotubes Canada, Inc. (1)
4580 Eastgate Pkwy, Mississauga, L4W 4K4, ON, Canada
Tel.: (905) 629-2011
Emp.: 2
Steel Tube Distr
N.A.I.C.S.: 423510
Steve Rumble *(Gen Mgr)*

Tubacex America Inc. (1)
15990 N Barkers Landing Rd Ste 175, Houston, TX 77079
Tel.: (713) 856-2700
Web Site: https://tubacexamerica.com
Steel Tube Distr
N.A.I.C.S.: 423510

Tubacex Awaji (Thailand) Ltd. (1)
10/20 Moo 8 Tambon Tai-Ban Mai, Amphur Muang, 10280, Samutprakarn, Thailand
Tel.: (66) 27015069
Mining Services
N.A.I.C.S.: 212290

Tubacex Distribucao de Acos, Ltda. (1)
Rod Anhanguera S/N Km 15 - Modulo 31 Sala 01, Parque Sao Domingos, Sao Paulo, 05112-000, Brazil
Tel.: (55) 11 3622 4860
Steel Tube Mfr
N.A.I.C.S.: 331210

Tubacex India Pvt Ltd. (1)
402-A Platina G- Block Bandra Kurla Complex Bandra East, Mumbai, 400 051, India
Tel.: (91) 2240015300
Web Site: https://www.tubacexindia.com
Stainless Steel Mfr
N.A.I.C.S.: 331110

Tubacex Taylor Accesorios, S.A. (1)
Barrio Arenaza 10, Artziniega, 01474, Alava, Spain
Tel.: (34) 945396030
Emp.: 30
Stainless Steel Products Mfr
N.A.I.C.S.: 331210
Eguzkine Paz Aretxabala *(Asst Mgr-Sls)*

Tubacoat S.L. (1)
Parque Cientifico y Tecnologico de Bizkaia Ibaizabal bidea Edificio702, 48160, Derio, Bizkaia, Spain
Tel.: (34) 946719300
Web Site: https://www.tubacoat.com
Power Generation Services
N.A.I.C.S.: 221118

Tubos Mecanicos S.A. (1)
C/ Hostal del Pi 14 Poligono Industrial Barcelones, Abrera, 08630, Barcelona, Alava, Spain
Tel.: (34) 93 770 33 33
Web Site: http://www.tubosmecanicos.es
Steel Tube Mfr
N.A.I.C.S.: 331210

Subsidiary (Domestic):

Tubos Mecanicos Norte, S.A. (2)
Pol Ind Ayala S/N, Aiara, 01479, Alava, Spain
Tel.: (34) 945399800
Steel Tube Distr
N.A.I.C.S.: 423510

TUBE-MAC INDUSTRIES LTD.

853 Arvin Ave, Stoney Creek, L8E 5N8, ON, Canada
Tel.: (905) 643-8823
Web Site: http://www.tube-mac.com
Year Founded: 1977
Rev.: $16,987,772
Emp.: 100
Piping & Tubing Systems Mfr
N.A.I.C.S.: 326122
Gary Mackay *(Pres)*

TUBESOLAR AG

Berliner Allee 65, 86153, Augsburg, Germany

Tel.: (49) 82132910900
Web Site: https://www.tubesolar.de
Year Founded: 2019
9TS—(DEU)
Emp.: 140
Semiconductor Devices Mfr
N.A.I.C.S.: 334413

TUBOS REUNIDOS, S.A.
Barrio de Sagarribai 2, 01470, Alava, Spain
Tel.: (34) 945897100
Web Site:
   https://www.tubosreunidos.com
Year Founded: 1892
TRG—(MAD)
Rev.: $581,715,329
Assets: $568,875,054
Liabilities: $564,090,812
Net Worth: $4,784,242
Earnings: $60,697,724
Emp.: 1,376
Fiscal Year-end: 12/31/23
Seamless Steel Tubular Products Mfr & Distr
N.A.I.C.S.: 331210
Emilio Ybarra Aznar (Vice Chm)

Subsidiaries:

Aceros Calibrados, S.A. (1)
Pol Ind Agustinos C/G Parc B4-B5, 31013, Pamplona, Spain
Tel.: (34) 948 30 91 10
Steel Pole Mfr
N.A.I.C.S.: 331210

Productos Tubulares, S.A. (1)
Carretera Galindo a Ugarte s/n, 48510, Valle de Trapaga, Biscay, Spain
Tel.: (34) 944 95 50 11
Web Site:
   http://www.productostubulares.com
Steel Pole Mfr
N.A.I.C.S.: 331210

Rotary Drilling Tools USA, LLC (1)
9022 Vincik Ehlert, Beasley, TX 77417
Tel.: (979) 387-3223
Web Site: http://www.rdt-usa.com
Water & Sewer Line & Related Structures Construction Services
N.A.I.C.S.: 237110
Enrique Arriola (Mng Dir)

Tubos Reunidos America, Inc. (1)
550 Post Oak Blvd Ste 460, Houston, TX 77027
Tel.: (713) 960-1014
Steel Pole Mfr
N.A.I.C.S.: 331210
John Cary (Pres)

Tubos Reunidos Industrial, S.L. (1)
Barrio Sagarribai 2, 01470, Amurrio, Alava, Spain
Tel.: (34) 945 89 71 00
Web Site:
   http://www.tubosreunidosindustrial.com
Steel Pole Mfr
N.A.I.C.S.: 331210

TUC BRANDS LTD.
One Hines Road Suite 301, Ottawa, K2K 3C7, ON, Canada
Tel.: (613) 591-9800
Web Site: http://www.tucbrands.com
Year Founded: 2011
Sales Range: $10-24.9 Million
Holding Company; Managed Information Technology Industry Software & Support Services
N.A.I.C.S.: 551112
Mark Scott (Founder & CEO)

TUCOWS, INC.
96 Mowat Avenue, Toronto, M6K 3M1, ON, Canada
Tel.: (416) 535-0123   PA
Web Site: https://www.tucows.com
Year Founded: 1993
TCX—(NASDAQ)
Rev.: $321,142,000
Assets: $664,747,000
Liabilities: $568,090,000
Net Worth: $96,657,000
Earnings: ($27,571,000)
Emp.: 1,020
Fiscal Year-end: 12/31/22
Internet Services to ISP's & Web Hosting Companies; Software Downloads
N.A.I.C.S.: 518210
Elliot Noss (Pres & CEO)

Subsidiaries:

Ascio Technologies Inc. (1)
Tel.: (45) 33886100
Web Site: https://www.ascio.com
Web Hosting & Internet Domain Managing Services
N.A.I.C.S.: 518210
Jorgen Christensen (Mng Dir)

EPAG Domainservices GmbH (1)
Niebuhrstr 16b, 53113, Bonn, Germany
Tel.: (49) 2283296849
Web Site: http://www.epag.de
Sales Range: $1-9.9 Million
Emp.: 8
Domain Registration Services
N.A.I.C.S.: 513199
Ashley La Bolle (Mng Dir)

Enom, LLC (1)
5808 Lake Washington Blvd NE Ste 201, Kirkland, WA 98033
Tel.: (425) 274-4500
Web Site: http://www.enom.com
Internet Domain Names Management Services
N.A.I.C.S.: 517810

Tucows.com Co. (1)
96 Mowat Avenue, Toronto, M6K 3M1, ON, Canada
Tel.: (416) 535-0123
Web Site: https://www.tucowsdomains.com
Domain Names & Other Internet Services Whslr
N.A.I.C.S.: 518210
Elliot Noss (Pres)

TUDELEY HOLDINGS LIMITED
Tudeley Hall Hartlake Road, Tudeley, Tonbridge, TN11 0PQ, Kent, United Kingdom
Tel.: (44) 1732 770 817   UK
Year Founded: 1980
Holding Company
N.A.I.C.S.: 551112
Konrad P. Legg (Owner)

Subsidiaries:

New Coburg Limited (1)
Tudeley Hall Hartlake Road, Tudeley, Tonbridge, TN11 0PQ, Kent, United Kingdom
Tel.: (44) 1732 770 817
Production of Coffee & Coffee Substitutes
N.A.I.C.S.: 311920
Konrad P. Legg (Owner)

Subsidiary (Domestic):

Coburg Coffee Company Ltd. (2)
3 Harrington Way Warspite Road, Woolwich, London, SE18 5NU, United Kingdom
Tel.: (44) 8453553388
Web Site:
   http://www.coburgcoffeecompany.co.uk
Sales Range: $1-9.9 Million
Roasting & Blending Coffee Mfr
N.A.I.C.S.: 311920

Subsidiary (Domestic):

CK Coffee Ltd. (3)
3 Harrington Way Warspite Road, Woolwich, London, SE18 5NU, United Kingdom
Tel.: (44) 800 783 5397
Web Site: http://www.cafedor.co.uk
Emp.: 12
Supplies Coffee, Tea & Other Beverages to Offices, Cafes, Hotels & Restaurants
N.A.I.C.S.: 311920

TUDOR GOLD CORP.
999 West Hastings Street Suite 789, Vancouver, V6C 2W2, BC, Canada
Tel.: (604) 559-8092
Web Site: https://www.tudor-gold.com
TDRRF—(OTCIQ)
Rev.: $24,198
Assets: $79,085,479
Liabilities: $7,932,096
Net Worth: $71,153,383
Earnings: ($3,277,551)
Emp.: 2
Fiscal Year-end: 03/31/23
Metal Product Distr
N.A.I.C.S.: 423510
Kenneth J. Konkin (Pres)

Subsidiaries:

Tudor Gold Service Corporation (1)

TUFF GROUP AG
Marienplatz 2, 80331, Munich, Germany
Tel.: (49) 6998972350   De
Web Site: https://www.tuffgroup.com
Year Founded: 2005
TUF—(MUN)
Rev.: $106,620
Assets: $202,578
Liabilities: $181,254
Net Worth: $21,324
Earnings: ($53,310)
Fiscal Year-end: 12/31/22
Oil & Gas Field Engineering Services
N.A.I.C.S.: 213112
Natarajan Paulraj (Chm)

TUFFIEH FUNDS SICAV PLC
Central North Business Centre Level 1 Sqaq il-Fawwara, Sliema, SLM 1670, Malta
Tel.: (356) 2131 2880
Web Site: http://www.tuffieh.com
Year Founded: 2011
Investment Management Service
N.A.I.C.S.: 523940

Subsidiaries:

Euroclinicum AS (1)
Na Pankraci 1658/121, 14021, Prague, Czech Republic
Tel.: (420) 261 223 300,
Holding Company
N.A.I.C.S.: 523999
Vaclav Vachta Vaclav Vachta (Gen Dir)

TUFTON OCEANIC ASSETS LIMITED
3rd Floor 1 Le Truchot, Saint Peter Port, GY1 1WD, Guernsey   GY
Web Site:
   https://www.tuftonoceanicasset.com
Year Founded: 2017
SHIP—(LSE)
Rev.: $3,646
Assets: $413,917,616
Liabilities: $1,144,523
Net Worth: $412,773,093
Earnings: ($2,473,359)
Emp.: 780
Fiscal Year-end: 06/30/23
Asset Management Services
N.A.I.C.S.: 523999

TUGA INNOVATIONS, INC.
409 Granville Street Suite 1000, Vancouver, V6C 1T2, BC, Canada
Tel.: (415) 799-7911   BC
Web Site:
   https://www.tugainnovations.com
Year Founded: 2021
TUGAF—(OTCIQ)
Assets: $749,702
Liabilities: $105,669
Net Worth: $644,033
Earnings: ($4,334,580)
Fiscal Year-end: 07/31/22
Electric Vehicle Mfr
N.A.I.C.S.: 336320
Cesar Barbosa (VP)

TUGCELIK ALUMINYUM VE METAL MAMULLERI SANAYI VE TIC. A.S.
NATO Road No 282, Sancaktepe, Istanbul, Turkiye
Tel.: (90) 2164152457
Web Site: https://www.tugcelik.com.tr
TUCLK—(IST)
Rev.: $5,802,540
Assets: $10,388,505
Liabilities: $7,038,509
Net Worth: $3,349,997
Earnings: $214,200
Emp.: 130
Fiscal Year-end: 12/31/20
Aluminum Die Casting & Distr
N.A.I.C.S.: 331523

TUHAMA FOR FINANCIAL INVESTMENT P.L.C
PO Box 5821, Amman, 11953, Jordan
Tel.: (962) 65542137
Year Founded: 2007
THMA—(AMM)
Assets: $5,516,678
Liabilities: $1,191,401
Net Worth: $4,325,276
Earnings: ($58,090)
Emp.: 10
Fiscal Year-end: 12/31/20
Financial Investment & Advisory Services
N.A.I.C.S.: 523999

TUI AG
Karl-Wiechert-Allee 23, I D-30625, Hannover, Germany
Tel.: (49) 51156600   De
Web Site: https://www.tuigroup.com
Year Founded: 1923
TUI1—(DEU)
Rev.: $21,196,822,066
Assets: $18,221,130,074
Liabilities: $13,556,577,216
Net Worth: $4,664,552,858
Earnings: $466,085,732
Emp.: 71,473
Fiscal Year-end: 09/30/19
Holding Company; Travel & Tour Services
N.A.I.C.S.: 551112
Frank Jakobi (Vice Chm-Supervisory Bd)

Subsidiaries:

ATC African Travel Concept Proprietary Limited (1)
5th Floor Graphic Centre 199 Loop Street Vlaeberg, PO Box 15974, Cape Town, 8018, South Africa
Tel.: (27) 214260032
Web Site:
   https://www.africantravelconcept.com
Travel Management Services
N.A.I.C.S.: 561510

Acampora Travel S.r.l. (1)
Piazza Tasso 18, 80067, Sorrento, Italy
Tel.: (39) 08118658558
Web Site: https://www.acamporatravel.it
Sales Range: $25-49.9 Million
Emp.: 3
Tour Operating & Hotel Management Services
N.A.I.C.S.: 561520

Adventure Tours Australia Group Pty Ltd (1)
Level 13 600-602 St Kilda Road, Melbourne, 3004, VIC, Australia
Tel.: (61) 391253630
Web Site:
   https://www.adventuretours.com.au
Sales Range: $25-49.9 Million
Emp.: 230
Tour Operating Services

TUI AG

INTERNATIONAL PUBLIC

TUI AG—(Continued)
N.A.I.C.S.: 561520

Adventures Worldwide Limited (1)
1 Cross & Pillory House Cross & Pillory Lane, Alton, GU34 1HL, Hampshire, United Kingdom
Tel.: (44) 8454505310
Web Site: http://www.adventurecompany.co.uk
Sales Range: $25-49.9 Million
Emp.: 4
Tour & Travel Operating Services
N.A.I.C.S.: 561520
Claire Wilson (Mng Dir)

African Travel Concept Pty. Ltd. (1)
5th Floor Graphic Centre 199 Loop Street, Cape Town, 8018, South Africa
Tel.: (27) 214260032
Web Site: https://www.africantravelconcept.com
Sales Range: $10-24.9 Million
Emp.: 3
Tour Operating Services
N.A.I.C.S.: 561520

Ambassador Tours S.A (1)
Calle Diputacio 238 - 244, Barcelona, 8007, Spain
Tel.: (34) 934827100
Tour Operating Services
N.A.I.C.S.: 561520

American Holidays (NI) Limited (1)
9 Lombard Street, Belfast, BT1 1RB, United Kingdom
Tel.: (44) 2890511800
Tour & Travel Management Services
N.A.I.C.S.: 561520

Atlantica Hellas S.A. (1)
Ialyssos Beach, Rhodes, Dodekanissos, Greece (50%)
Tel.: (30) 2241093308
Web Site: http://www.atlanticahotel.com
Hotel
N.A.I.C.S.: 721110

Audio Tours and Travel Hong Kong Limited (1)
Rm 2606 26/F Peninsula Twr 538 Castle Peak Rd, Cheung Sha Wan, Hong Kong, China (Hong Kong)
Tel.: (852) 23701933
Travel & Tour Operating Services
N.A.I.C.S.: 561510
Francine Cheung (Gen Mgr)

Australian Sports Tours Pty Ltd (1)
1114 Botany Road, Botany, 2019, NSW, Australia
Tel.: (61) 290714540
Web Site: https://www.astsports.com.au
Emp.: 12
Sports Tour Operating Services
N.A.I.C.S.: 561520

BDS Destination Services Company (1)
El Qanonein Tower Corniche El Nil Corniche El Maadi, Cairo, 11728, Egypt
Tel.: (20) 2 25260440
Web Site: http://www.bdsegypt.net
Emp.: 8
Tour Operating Services
N.A.I.C.S.: 561520
Marcella Zunini (Mng Dir)

Bergbau Goslar GmbH (1)
Bergtal 18, 38640, Goslar, Germany
Tel.: (49) 53217010
Web Site: https://www.bgg-bergbau.de
Mining Services
N.A.I.C.S.: 212290

Boomerang Reisen - Pacific Tours AG (1)
Zweierstrasse 35, 8004, Zurich, Switzerland
Tel.: (41) 442988000
Web Site: https://www.boomerang-reisen.ch
Travel Agency Services
N.A.I.C.S.: 561510

Boomerang-Reisen GmbH (1)
Biewerer Str 15, 54293, Trier, Germany
Tel.: (49) 651966808360
Web Site: http://www.boomerang-reisen.de
Travel & Tour Services
N.A.I.C.S.: 561520

Sabine Schamburger (Product Mgr)

Brightspark Travel (1)
8750 W Bryn Mawr Ave Ste 450e, Chicago, IL 60631
Tel.: (847) 509-0011
Web Site: http://www.brightsparktravel.com
Student Travel Services
N.A.I.C.S.: 561510
Christine Raffa (Mng Dir)

Division (Domestic):

Brightspark Travel (2)
8750 W Bryn Mawr Ave Ste 450 E, Chicago, IL 60631
Tel.: (801) 495-9118
Web Site: https://www.brightsparktravel.com
Tour Operating Services
N.A.I.C.S.: 561520

Caradonna Dive Adventures, Inc. (1)
280 Wekiva Springs Rd Ste 1060, Longwood, FL 32779
Tel.: (407) 937-0733
Web Site: http://www.caradonna.com
Tour Operating Services
N.A.I.C.S.: 561520

Connoisseur Belgium BVBA (1)
Brugsevaart 48, 8620, Nieuwpoort, Belgium
Tel.: (32) 58236623
Sales Range: $25-49.9 Million
Emp.: 5
Tour Operating Services
N.A.I.C.S.: 561520
Powell Cheryl (Gen Mgr)

Country Walkers, Inc. (1)
426 Industrial Ave Ste 120, Williston, VT 05495
Tel.: (802) 244-1387
Web Site: http://www.countrywalkers.com
Sales Range: $25-49.9 Million
Emp.: 20
Tour Operating Services
N.A.I.C.S.: 561520
Jamen Yeaton-Masi (VP-Worldwide Product & Ops)

Crown Blue Line Limited (1)
The Port House, Port Solent, Portsmouth, PO6 4TH, United Kingdom
Tel.: (44) 844 463 2389
Web Site: http://www.crownblueline.co.uk
Sales Range: $25-49.9 Million
Emp.: 4
Boating Excursion Services
N.A.I.C.S.: 487210
Danie O'Conell (Gen Mgr)

Cruisetour AG (1)
Friesenbergstrasse 75, 8055, Zurich, Switzerland
Tel.: (41) 442898181
Web Site: https://www.cruisetour.ch
Travel & Tour Services
N.A.I.C.S.: 561520

Destination Services Greece Travel & Tourism SA (1)
364 Mesogeion Avenue, Agia Paraskevi, 15341, Athens, Greece
Tel.: (30) 2146871100
Travel & Tour Services
N.A.I.C.S.: 561520

Destination Services Morocco SA (1)
35 Avenue Moulay Hassan I, BP 272, Dakhla, 80000, Agadir, Morocco
Tel.: (212) 528829000
Travel & Tour Services
N.A.I.C.S.: 561520

Destination Services Singapore Pte Limited (1)
101 Thomson Road 26-02 United Square, Singapore, 307591, Singapore
Tel.: (65) 63306863
Travel & Tour Services
N.A.I.C.S.: 561520
Adrian Wong (Mgr-Destination)

Disma Reizen Eindhoven B.V. (1)
Elzentlaan 139, 5611 LL, Eindhoven, Netherlands
Tel.: (31) 402146300
Travel & Tour Services
N.A.I.C.S.: 561520
Liesbeth Verhoeven (Office Mgr)

Disma Reizen Oosterhout/Beins Travel B.V. (1)
De Hovel 46, 5051 NR, Goirle, Netherlands
Tel.: (31) 135300377
Travel & Tour Services
N.A.I.C.S.: 561520

Dorfhotel GesmbH (1)
Dorfstrasse 26, 9582, Oberaichwald, Karnten, Austria
Tel.: (43) 42542384
Web Site: http://www.schoenleitn.at
Emp.: 10
Restaurant Operating Services
N.A.I.C.S.: 722511
Mihaly Manasses (Mng Dir)

Easy Market S.p.A. (1)
Via Consular 51/c, 47924, Rimini, RN, Italy
Tel.: (39) 05411610200
Web Site: https://www.easymarket.travel
Travel Agency Booking Software Development Services
N.A.I.C.S.: 541511

Emerald Star Limited (1)
The Marina Carrick-on-Shannon Co, Leitrim, Ireland
Tel.: (353) 719627633
Web Site: https://www.emeraldstar.ie
Boat Rental & Leasing Services
N.A.I.C.S.: 532411

Events International (Sports Travel) Limited (1)
Ground Floor Ashvale 2 Ashchurch Business Centre Alexandra Way, Tewkesbury, GL20 8NB, United Kingdom
Tel.: (44) 1432 263 263
Web Site: http://www.eventsinternational.co.uk
Sales Range: $25-49.9 Million
Emp.: 9
Sports Tour Operating Services
N.A.I.C.S.: 561520
Richard Moss (Mng Dir)

Events International Limited (1)
Ground Floor Ashvale 2 Ashchurch Business Centre Alexandra Way, Tewkesbury, GL20 8NB, United Kingdom
Tel.: (44) 143 226 3263
Web Site: https://www.eventsinternational.co.uk
Sales Range: $50-74.9 Million
Emp.: 10
Sports Team Hospitality Services
N.A.I.C.S.: 711320
Maureen Walsh (Mng Dir)

Exodus Travels Limited (1)
Grange Mills Weir Road, London, SW12 0NE, United Kingdom
Tel.: (44) 20 8675 5550
Web Site: http://www.exodus.co.uk
Sales Range: $25-49.9 Million
Emp.: 100
Travel Agency Services
N.A.I.C.S.: 561510
Andy Ross (Head-Product)

FIRST Travel GmbH (1)
Markgrafenstrasse 46, 10117, Berlin, Germany
Tel.: (49) 3020058550
Web Site: https://www.tui-berlin.de
Travel Agency Services
N.A.I.C.S.: 561510
Beate Arnold (Mng Dir)

FOX-TOURS Reisen GmbH (1)
Andreestrasse 27, 56578, Rengsdorf, Germany
Tel.: (49) 26346500
Web Site: http://www.foxtours.de
Travel & Tourism Services
N.A.I.C.S.: 561520
Thomas Klein (Mng Dir)

Fanatics Sports & Party Tours UK LIMITED (1)
Dst House St Marks Hill, Surbiton, KT6 4BH, United Kingdom
Tel.: (44) 207 240 3223
Web Site: http://www.thefanatics.com
Emp.: 3
Sports Tour Operating Services
N.A.I.C.S.: 561520
Ben Parker (Office Mgr)

Fanatics Sports and Party Tours PTY LIMITED (1)
1114 Botany Road, Botany, 2019, NSW, Australia
Tel.: (61) 290714541
Web Site: https://www.thefanatics.com
Emp.: 14
Sports & Party Tour Operating Services
N.A.I.C.S.: 561520

First Choice Holidays Limited (1)
Wigmore House Wigmore Lane, Luton, LU2 9TN, Bedfordshire, United Kingdom
Tel.: (44) 2034512690
Web Site: https://www.firstchoice.co.uk
Tourism Services
N.A.I.C.S.: 561520

First Choice Leisure Limited (1)
266-268 Whitchurch Road, Cardiff, CF14 3ND, South Glamorgan, United Kingdom
Tel.: (44) 2920522889
Tour Operating Services
N.A.I.C.S.: 561520

First Choice Lyon SAS (1)
42 Rue De L Universite, 69007, Lyon, France
Tel.: (33) 4 72 00 88 89
Tour Operating Services
N.A.I.C.S.: 561520

First Choice Tour Operations Limited. (1)
120 London Road North, Lowestoft, NR32 1HB, Suffolkshire, United Kingdom
Tel.: (44) 1502 588333
Web Site: http://www.firstchoice.co.uk
Sales Range: $25-49.9 Million
Emp.: 6
Travel Agency Services
N.A.I.C.S.: 561510
Jamie-Lea Cassidy (Gen Mgr)

Fritidsresor AB (1)
Soder Malarstrand 27, 117 85, Stockholm, Sweden
Tel.: (46) 87207200
Web Site: http://www.fritidsresor.se
Sales Range: $75-99.9 Million
Emp.: 35
Tour Operating Services
N.A.I.C.S.: 561520
Christian Clemens (CEO)

Fritidsresor Holding Spain S.A.U. (1)
Ctra Comarcal 812 44, 35290, San Bartolome de Tirajana, Las Palmas, Spain
Tel.: (34) 928157170
Investment Management Service
N.A.I.C.S.: 523999

GEAFOND Numero Dos Fuerteventura S.A. (1)
Avenida Grandes Playas Hotel Oliva Beach S/N, La Oliva, Las Palmas, 35660, Spain
Tel.: (34) 971743030
Tour Operating Services
N.A.I.C.S.: 561520

GeBeCo Gesellschaft fur internationale Begegnung und Cooperation mbH & Co. KG (1)
Holzkoppelweg 19, 24118, Kiel, Germany
Tel.: (49) 43154460
Tour Operating Services
N.A.I.C.S.: 561520

Groupe Marmara SAS (1)
81 Rue Saint Lazare, 75009, Paris, France
Tel.: (33) 144636300
Tour & Travel Operating Services
N.A.I.C.S.: 561510

Groupe Nouvelles Frontieres S.A.S. (1)
74 Rue De Lagny, Montreuil, France
Tel.: (33) 145687038
Web Site: http://www.nouvelles-frontieres.fr
Travel Agency & Tour Operator
N.A.I.C.S.: 561520

Gulliver Travel d.o.o. (1)
Obala Stjepana Radica 25, 20000, Dubrovnik, Croatia
Tel.: (385) 20410888
Web Site: https://www.gulliver.hr
Sales Range: $10-24.9 Million
Emp.: 74
Tour Operating Services

AND PRIVATE COMPANIES — TUI AG

N.A.I.C.S.: 561520

Gullivers Sports Travel Limited (1)
Ashchurch Business Centre Alexandra Way, Tewkesbury, GL20 8NB, Gloucestershire, United Kingdom
Tel.: (44) 1684878683
Web Site: http://www.gulliverstravel.co.uk
Emp.: 5
Sports Tour Operating Services
N.A.I.C.S.: 561520
Neil Salmon (Mng Dir)

Hapag-Lloyd Executive GmbH (1)
Benkendorffstr 22B, 30855, Langenhagen, Germany
Tel.: (49) 21142165050
Web Site: http://www.hl-executive.com
Aircraft Management Services
N.A.I.C.S.: 488190
Friedrich Keppler (Co-Mng Dir)

Headwater Holidays Limited (1)
Old School House Chester Road, Northwich, CW8 1LE, United Kingdom
Tel.: (44) 1606369409
Web Site: http://www.headwater.com
Sales Range: $25-49.9 Million
Emp.: 24
Travel & Tour Operating Services
N.A.I.C.S.: 561510
Clare Redhead (Mgr-Ops)

Hellenic Sailing Holidays SA (1)
17 Nireos Str, P Phaliro, 17561, Athens, Greece
Tel.: (30) 2109885889
Web Site: https://hellenicsailingcruises.com
Emp.: 5
Tour Operating Services
N.A.I.C.S.: 561520

Holiday Center S.A. (1)
C/ Ramon de Moncada 40, Mallorca, 07180, Calvia, Spain
Tel.: (34) 971691461
Web Site: https://www.holidaycenter.es
Travel & Tourism Services
N.A.I.C.S.: 561520

I TO I INTERNATIONAL PROJECTS LTD (1)
4th Floor Wilson House Lorne Park Road, Bournemouth, BH1 1JN, United Kingdom
Tel.: (44) 1132054610
Web Site: https://www.i-to-i.com
Emp.: 3
Tour Operating Services
N.A.I.C.S.: 561520

I Viaggi des Turchese S.r.l. (1)
Viale Martiri Della Liberta 29, 43036, Fidenza, Parma, Italy
Tel.: (39) 0524 526180
Tour Operating Services
N.A.I.C.S.: 561520

I'tur GmbH (1)
Karlsruher Str 22, 76437, Rastatt, Germany
Tel.: (49) 761557557
Web Site: http://www.ltur.com
Travel & Tourism Services
N.A.I.C.S.: 561510
Marco Rauer (Partner & Head-Online-Mktg)

Iberotel Otelcilik A.S (1)
Inonu Cad Gumussu Palas No 18-8, Gumussuyu, 34437, Istanbul, Turkiye
Tel.: (90) 2122525452
Web Site: http://www.3-blue.com
Emp.: 8
Restaurant Operating Services
N.A.I.C.S.: 722511

International Expeditions, Inc. (1)
1 Environs Park, Helena, AL 35080
Tel.: (205) 428-1700
Web Site: http://www.ietravel.com
Emp.: 25
Tour & Travel Operating Services
N.A.I.C.S.: 561520

Jandia Playa S.A. (1)
Avenida del Saladar 6, Jandia, 35626, Pajara, Spain
Tel.: (34) 928169100
Emp.: 250
Restaurant Operating Services
N.A.I.C.S.: 722511
Tom Peck (Gen Mgr)

Jaz Hotel Group S.A.E. (1)
Corridor Sheikh Zayed, 12588, Giza, Egypt
Tel.: (20) 238541111
Web Site: https://www.jazhotels.com
Travel Management Services
N.A.I.C.S.: 561510

Jetair N.V. (1)
Gistelsesteenweg 1, B-8400, Oostende, Belgium
Tel.: (32) 59565611
Web Site: http://www.jetair.be
Sales Range: $100-124.9 Million
Emp.: 450
Travel Agency & Tour Operator
N.A.I.C.S.: 561510
Elie Bruyninckx (Gen Mgr)

Jetair Travel Distribution N.V. (1)
Gistelsesteenweg 1, Oostende, 8400, Belgium
Tel.: (32) 59565611
Web Site: http://www.jetair.be
Emp.: 572
Travel Agency Services
N.A.I.C.S.: 561510
Tracy Mellor (CEO)

Jetaircenter N.V. (1)
Stationstraat 102, 2800, Mechelen, Belgium
Tel.: (32) 70 222 346
Travel Agency Services
N.A.I.C.S.: 561510

Kras B.V. (1)
Bernseweg 22a, 5324 JW, Ammerzoden, Netherlands
Tel.: (31) 880885886
Web Site: http://www.kras.nl
Sales Range: $25-49.9 Million
Emp.: 20
Travel Agency Services
N.A.I.C.S.: 561510
Romijn Nick (Gen Mgr)

Kurt Safari (Pty) Ltd. (1)
68 Korhaan Street, Hazyview, Mpumalanga, 1242, South Africa
Tel.: (27) 637185590
Web Site: https://www.kurtsafari.com
Travel & Tourism Services
N.A.I.C.S.: 561520

Le Passage to India Tours & Travels Pvt Ltd (1)
Plot No B-152 4th Floor Sector 6, Noida, 201301, Uttar Pradesh, India
Tel.: (91) 1203823500
Web Site: https://www.lepassagetoindia.com
Travel & Tourism Services
N.A.I.C.S.: 561520
Piyush Upadhyay (Gen Mgr)

Les Tours Jumpstreet Tours, Inc. (1)
780 Brewster suite 02-300, Montreal, H4C 2K1, QC, Canada
Tel.: (514) 954-9990
Web Site: https://www.jumpstreet.com
Emp.: 30
Educational Tour Operating Services
N.A.I.C.S.: 561520
Mark Clark (Founder)

Lima Tours S.A.C. (1)
Av Juan de Arona 755 Piso 3, San Isidro, Lima, Peru
Tel.: (51) 16196900
Web Site: https://www.limatours.com.pe
Travel & Tourism Services
N.A.I.C.S.: 561520
Jose Pedraza (Mng Dir)

Loc Vacances SARL (1)
2 avenue de la Marionnais, 35131, Chartres-de-Bretagne, France
Tel.: (33) 299774587
Web Site: https://www.locvacances.fr
Real Estate Services
N.A.I.C.S.: 531390

Lodges & Mountain Hotels SARL (1)
144 Rue Emile Allais, Jardin Alpin Courchevel, 73120, Saint-Bon-Tarentaise, France
Tel.: (33) 479080201
Web Site: http://www.lodges-mountain-hotels.com
Hospitality Services
N.A.I.C.S.: 721110
Sophie Roskam (Mng Dir-Grp)

Lunn Poly (Jersey) Ltd. (1)
55 King Street, Saint Helier, JE2 4WE, Jersey
Tel.: (44) 1534888428
Travel Agency Services
N.A.I.C.S.: 561510

Lunn Poly Ltd. (1)
29 Almondvale South, West Lothian, Livingston, EH54 6NB, United Kingdom
Tel.: (44) 1506430101
Sales Range: $25-49.9 Million
Emp.: 11
Travel Agency Services
N.A.I.C.S.: 561510
Edward Devine (Gen Mgr)

Luxury Mountain Hotels SARL (1)
Rue Bellecote, 73120, Saint-Bon-Tarentaise, France
Tel.: (33) 4 79 08 03 77
Home Management Services
N.A.I.C.S.: 721110

MAGIC LIFE DER CLUB INTERNATIONAL Turizm Hizmetleri A.S (1)
1 Kat 7 Kisikli Caddesi, Istanbul, 34662, Turkiye
Tel.: (90) 2423104000
Tour Operating Services
N.A.I.C.S.: 561520

Magic Hotels SA (1)
Route touristique merezka, 8050, Hammamet, Tunisia
Tel.: (216) 72322333
Web Site: https://www.magichotelsandresorts.com
Hotel Operator
N.A.I.C.S.: 721110

Magic Life Egypt for Hotels LLC (1)
Club Sharm el Sheikh, Nabq Bay, Sharm el-Sheikh, Egypt
Tel.: (20) 693710050
Hospitality Services
N.A.I.C.S.: 721110
Sayed Gamal (Asst Mgr-Restaurant)

Magic Life International Hotelbetriebs GmbH & Co. KG (1)
Landstrasser Hauptstrasse 153-155, A-1030, Vienna, Austria (100%)
Tel.: (43) 0187802777
Web Site: http://www.magiclife.com
Sales Range: $10-24.9 Million
Emp.: 50
All-Inclusive Hotel & Resort Operator
N.A.I.C.S.: 721110

Manchester Academy Teacher Training (UK) Limited (1)
St Margarets Chambers 5 Newton Street, Piccadilly, Manchester, M1 1HL, United Kingdom
Tel.: (44) 161 237 5619
Web Site: http://www.experienceenglish.com
Sales Range: $10-24.9 Million
Emp.: 30
Educational Support Services
N.A.I.C.S.: 611710
Karen Pate (Gen Mgr)

Manchester Academy of English (1)
2nd Floor Royal Buildings 2 Mosley Street, Manchester, M2 3AN, United Kingdom
Tel.: (44) 1612367575
Web Site: https://themcacademy.co.uk
Educational Language School
N.A.I.C.S.: 611630
Karen Page (Gen Mgr)

Mariner Travel GmbH (1)
Theodor-Heuss-Str 53-63, 61118, Bad Vilbel, Germany
Tel.: (49) 610155791522
Travel Agency Services
N.A.I.C.S.: 561510

Meetings & Events UK Limited (1)
54 St Winifred's Road, Harrogate, HG2 8LR, North Yorkshire, United Kingdom
Tel.: (44) 1423888889
Web Site: https://www.meetingsandevents.co.uk
Hotel & Resort Services
N.A.I.C.S.: 721110

Molay Travel SARL (1)
Le Chateau, 14330, Le Molay-Littry, France
Tel.: (33) 231214551

Tour & Travel Arrangement Services
N.A.I.C.S.: 561599

Moorings Mexico SA de CV (1)
Costa Baja Resort and Marina KM 75 Carretera a Pichilingue, Baja California Sur, 23019, La Paz, Mexico
Tel.: (52) 612 1067141
Web Site: http://www.mymoorings.com
Sales Range: $25-49.9 Million
Emp.: 8
Tour Operating Services
N.A.I.C.S.: 561520
Harry Mountain (Reg Dir)

Moorings Yachting SAS (1)
10-12 Quai Papacino, 6300, Nice, France
Tel.: (33) 492000901
Ship Chartering Services
N.A.I.C.S.: 483212

Musement S.p.A. (1)
Via Polesine 13, 20139, Milan, Italy
Tel.: (39) 0281480473
Web Site: https://www.musement.com
Tourism Services
N.A.I.C.S.: 561520

MyPlanet International A/S (1)
Soren Frichs Vej 38K 1, Aabyhoi, 8230, Arhus, Denmark
Tel.: (45) 70125011
Web Site: https://www.myplanet.dk
Emp.: 28
Travel Agency Services
N.A.I.C.S.: 561510
Andre Bonnet (COO)

MyPlanet Sweden AB (1)
Datavagen 14A 1 tr, Sisjon, 436 32, Gothenburg, Sweden
Tel.: (46) 775888088
Web Site: https://www.myplanet.se
Travel Agency Services
N.A.I.C.S.: 561510

Nazar Nordic AB (1)
Oresundshuset Hans Michelsensgatan 9, 211 20, Malmo, Sweden
Tel.: (46) 770777888
Web Site: https://www.nazar.se
Tour Operating Services
N.A.I.C.S.: 561520

Nordotel S.A.U. (1)
Carretera General del Sur Km 44, 35100, San Bartolome de Tirajana, Gran Canaria, Spain
Tel.: (34) 928 157 170
Web Site: http://www.nordotel.es
Sales Range: $150-199.9 Million
Emp.: 69
Tour Operating Services
N.A.I.C.S.: 561520

Nouvelles Frontieres Distribution S.A. (1)
74 rue de Lagny, 93107, Montreuil, France
Tel.: (33) 148518000
Travel Agency Services
N.A.I.C.S.: 561510

Nouvelles Frontieres Senegal S.R.L. (1)
Route des Almadies Lot no 1 Mamelles Aviation, BP 145, Dakar, Senegal
Tel.: (221) 338594447
Web Site: https://www.nfsenegal.com
Tourism Services
N.A.I.C.S.: 561520

Ocean College LLC (1)
South Sinai, Sharm el-Sheikh, DOX120, Egypt
Tel.: (20) 128075516
Web Site: http://www.ocean-college.com
Tour Operating Services
N.A.I.C.S.: 561520

Oy Finnmatkat AB (1)
Porkkalankatu 20 A, Helsinki, 00180, Finland
Tel.: (358) 303 60300
Web Site: http://www.finnmatkat.fi
Sales Range: $25-49.9 Million
Emp.: 50
Travel & Tour Operating Services
N.A.I.C.S.: 561510
Peik Martin (CIO)

PATS N.V. (1)

TUI AG

TUI AG—(Continued)
Gistelsesteenweg 1, Oostende, 8400, Belgium
Tel.: (32) 59565611
Web Site: http://www.jetair.be
Emp.: 570
Travel & Tour Operating Services
N.A.I.C.S.: 561520

PT. Pacific World Nusantara (1)
Jln By Pass Ngurah Rai 15 Padang Galak-Sanur, PO Box 3291, Bali, Indonesia
Tel.: (62) 361282474
Travel Agency Services
N.A.I.C.S.: 561510

Pacific World (Beijing) Travel Agency Co., Ltd. (1)
Room 301 Sunjoy Mansion No 6 Ritan Road, Chao Yang District, Beijing, 100020, China
Tel.: (86) 1065923511
Destination & Event Management Services
N.A.I.C.S.: 561510

Pacific World (Shanghai) Travel Agency Co. Limited (1)
Room 705 No 1277 Bei Jing Xi Road, Shanghai, 200040, China
Tel.: (86) 2162895559
Travel Agency Services
N.A.I.C.S.: 561510

Pacific World Destination East Sdn. Bhd. (1)
Suite 12 03 Level 12 Centrepoint South Mid Valley City, Lingkaran Syed Putra, 59200, Kuala Lumpur, Malaysia
Tel.: (60) 322799722
Travel Agency Services
N.A.I.C.S.: 561510

Pacific World Meetings & Events Hellas Travel Limited (1)
Karyatidon 16, Kifisia, 14564, Athens, Greece
Tel.: (30) 2146871186
Travel Agency Services
N.A.I.C.S.: 561510

Pacific World Meetings & Events Hong Kong, Limited (1)
Suites 2603-05 26th Floor Peninsula Tower 538 Castle Peak Road, Kowloon, China (Hong Kong)
Tel.: (852) 23701888
Travel Agency Services
N.A.I.C.S.: 561510
Sharon Goi *(Mgr-Destination)*

Pacific World Meetings & Events SAM (1)
Palais de la Scala 1 Avenue Henry Dunant, Monte Carlo, 98000, Monaco
Tel.: (377) 97970170
Travel Agency Services
N.A.I.C.S.: 561510

Pacific World Meetings & Events Singapore Pte. Ltd. (1)
Rex House Suite 03-01 73 Bukit Timah Road, Singapore, 229832, Singapore
Tel.: (65) 63306768
Travel Agency Services
N.A.I.C.S.: 561510

Peregrine Adventures Pty Ltd (1)
Level 7 567 Collins Street, Melbourne, 3000, VIC, Australia
Tel.: (61) 385943902
Web Site: https://www.peregrineadventures.com
Tour & Travel Operating Services
N.A.I.C.S.: 561520

Porter and Haylett Limited (1)
Viaduct Works, Wroxham, NR12 8RX, United Kingdom
Tel.: (44) 1603782472
River Boat Operating Services
N.A.I.C.S.: 713210

ProTel Gesellschaft fur Kommunikation mbH (1)
Romergraben 5, 56579, Rengsdorf, Rheinland-Pfalz, Germany
Tel.: (49) 26346500
Communication Service
N.A.I.C.S.: 517810

Quark Expeditions, Inc. (1)
3131 Elliot Ave Ste 250, Seattle, WA 98121
Tel.: (203) 803-2888
Web Site: http://www.quarkexpeditions.com
Travel Agencies
N.A.I.C.S.: 561510
Andrew White *(Pres)*

RIUSA II S.A. (1)
C/ Llaud, Playa de Palma, 07610, Mallorca, Spain (49.8%)
Tel.: (34) 971743030
Web Site: https://www.riu.com
Sales Range: $25-49.9 Million
Emp.: 25
Travel Agency
N.A.I.C.S.: 561510

ROBINSON AUSTRIA Clubhotel GmbH (1)
Ossiachersee Suduferstrasse 69, 9523, Landskron, Austria
Tel.: (43) 4242423460
Web Site: http://www.robinson.de
Restaurant Operating Services
N.A.I.C.S.: 722511

Real Travel Ltd (1)
1 Meadow Road, Tunbridge Wells, TN1 2YG, Kent, United Kingdom
Tel.: (44) 1892 516164
Web Site: http://www.realgap.co.uk
Educational Support Services
N.A.I.C.S.: 611710

Robinson Club (Schweiz) AG (1)
Hubelstrasse 56, 7050, Arosa, Graubuenden, Switzerland
Tel.: (41) 813785800
Web Site: http://www.robinson-schweiz.ch
Sales Range: $25-49.9 Million
Emp.: 15
Casino Hotel & Club Operating Services
N.A.I.C.S.: 721120

Robinson Club GmbH (1)
Karl-Wiechert-Allee 23, 30625, Hannover, Germany (99.6%)
Tel.: (49) 5119555736
Web Site: https://www.robinson.com
Sales Range: $25-49.9 Million
Emp.: 45
Provider of Development, Construction & Operation of Resorts & Hotels
N.A.I.C.S.: 236220

Robinson Club Italia S.p.A. (1)
Localita Fontanelle, Apulia, 73059, Ugento, LE, Italy
Tel.: (39) 0833934111
Web Site: https://www.robinson.com
Sales Range: $25-49.9 Million
Emp.: 12
Restaurant Operating Services
N.A.I.C.S.: 722511
Mario Mauro *(Gen Mgr)*

Robinson Club Maldives Private Limited (1)
Ameer Ahmed Magu H Maaram Building 5th Floor, Male, MV-20077, Maldives
Tel.: (960) 6820000
Web Site: https://www.robinson-maldives.com
Sales Range: $75-99.9 Million
Emp.: 20
Club Operating Services
N.A.I.C.S.: 711211

Robinson Hotels Portugal SA (1)
Quinta Da Ria, Algarve, 8900-057, Vila Nova de Cacela, Portugal
Tel.: (351) 281959000
Web Site: http://www.robinson-ep.com
Emp.: 15
Restaurant Operating Services
N.A.I.C.S.: 722511

Robinson Otelcilik A.S. (1)
Inonu Cad Gumussu Palas No 18/8, Beyoglu, 34437, Istanbul, Turkiye
Tel.: (90) 2122525452
Restaurant Operating Services
N.A.I.C.S.: 722511

Royal Vacaciones SA (1)
Calle de Mesena 22 2nd floor, Madrid, 28033, Spain
Tel.: (34) 917 59 71 25
Web Site: http://www.tuispain.com

Sales Range: $10-24.9 Million
Emp.: 70
Tour Operating Services
N.A.I.C.S.: 561520
Stephen Dapper *(Gen Mgr)*

Sawadee Amsterdam BV (1)
Sarphatistraat 650, 1018 AV, Amsterdam, Netherlands
Tel.: (31) 204202220
Web Site: https://www.sawadee.nl
Sales Range: $25-49.9 Million
Emp.: 45
Travel Agencies Services
N.A.I.C.S.: 561510

Schwerin Plus Touristik-Service GmbH (1)
Mecklenburgstr 85, 19053, Schwerin, Germany
Tel.: (49) 38 555 8020
Web Site: https://www.von-schloss-zu-schloss.de
Tourism Services
N.A.I.C.S.: 561520
Karsten Levermann *(Gen Mgr)*

Simply Travel Ltd. (1)
Wigmore House Wigmore Lane, Luton, LU2 9TN, United Kingdom
Tel.: (44) 8712314050
Web Site: http://www.simplytravel.co.uk
Tour & Travel Agency Services
N.A.I.C.S.: 561520

Skibound France SARL (1)
95 Rue Derobert, 73400, Ugine, France
Tel.: (33) 479104189
Emp.: 9
Educational Tour Operating Services
N.A.I.C.S.: 561520
Ben Shinn *(Gen Mgr)*

Societe Marocaine pour le Developpement des Transports Touristiques S.A (1)
Rue du Souk, 80000, Agadir, Morocco
Tel.: (212) 528821361
Tour Operating Services
N.A.I.C.S.: 561520

SplashLine Event und Vermarktungs GmbH (1)
Knollgasse 15, Vienna, 1100, Austria
Tel.: (43) 1 504 68 68 60
Web Site: http://www.splashline.com
Travel Agency Services
N.A.I.C.S.: 561510
Tidi Tunkel *(Mgr)*

Sport Abroad (UK) Limited (1)
Thomson Sport London Office 27-37 Saint George's Road, London, SW19 4EU, United Kingdom
Tel.: (44) 8456803086
Web Site: http://www.sportabroad.co.uk
Sales Range: $25-49.9 Million
Emp.: 2
Sports Tour Operating Services
N.A.I.C.S.: 561520

Sportsworld Hospitality Limited (1)
Wind Rush Cord Blacklan way, Abingdon, OX141SY, Oxfordshire, United Kingdom
Tel.: (44) 1235554844
Sales Range: $50-74.9 Million
Emp.: 2
Sports Event Organizing Services
N.A.I.C.S.: 711310

Sportsworld Travel Limited (1)
Windrush Court Blacklands Way, Abingdon, OX14 1SY, Oxfordshire, United Kingdom
Tel.: (44) 1235554844
Sports Tour Operating Services
N.A.I.C.S.: 561520

Star Tour A/S (1)
Gl Koge Landevej 22, 2500, Valby, Denmark
Tel.: (45) 33 47 90 00
Web Site: http://www.startour.dk
Sales Range: $10-24.9 Million
Emp.: 30
Holiday Travel Packaging Services
N.A.I.C.S.: 561510
Birthe Madsen *(Mng Dir)*

Star Tour Holding A/S (1)
Kirsten Walthers Vej 9, Valby, 2500, Denmark

Tel.: (45) 33 47 90 00
Web Site: http://www.startour.dk
Investment Management Service
N.A.I.C.S.: 523999

Startour-Stjernereiser AS (1)
Professor Kohts vei 108, PO Box 10, Stabekk, Norway
Tel.: (47) 67 11 51 00
Tour Operating Services
N.A.I.C.S.: 561520
Christian Lunde *(Gen Mgr)*

Summer Times Ltd. (1)
Tel.: (230) 4271111
Web Site: https://www.summer-times.com
Travel Agency Services
N.A.I.C.S.: 561510
Philippe Hitie *(Founder, Chm & Mng Dir)*

Summertime International Ltd. (1)
5 Avenue Bernardin De Saint Pierre, Quatre Bornes, Mauritius
Tel.: (230) 4271111
Web Site: https://summer-times.com
Travel Management Services
N.A.I.C.S.: 561510

Sunsail Hellas MEPE (1)
12 Apollonos, Palaio Faliro, Athens, Greece
Tel.: (30) 2109819024
Tour Operating Services
N.A.I.C.S.: 561520

Sunsail International B.V. (1)
Hoogstraat 97, 3011 PK, Rotterdam, Netherlands
Tel.: (31) 104115454
Web Site: https://www.sunsail.nl
Sales Range: $25-49.9 Million
Emp.: 7
Yacht Chartering Services
N.A.I.C.S.: 487210

Sunsail SAS (1)
8 Avenue de Verdun, 06000, Nice, France
Tel.: (33) 142616111
Web Site: https://www.sunsail.fr
Boating Excursion & Sailing Services
N.A.I.C.S.: 488390

Sunsail Worldwide Sailing Limited (1)
Platinum House St Marks Hill, Surbiton, KT6 4BH, Surrey, United Kingdom
Tel.: (44) 3303321172
Web Site: https://www.sunsail.co.uk
Amusement & Recreation Services
N.A.I.C.S.: 713990

THG Holidays Limited (1)
Suite 3 RVB House New Mill Court, Llansamlet, Swansea, SA7 9FG, United Kingdom
Tel.: (44) 1792482432
Web Site: https://www.thgholidays.co.uk
Tour Operating Services
N.A.I.C.S.: 561520

TLT Urlaubsreisen GmbH (1)
Karl-Wiechert-Allee 23, 30625, Hannover, Germany
Tel.: (49) 51189880410
Web Site: https://reiseberatung.de
Travel Consulting Services
N.A.I.C.S.: 561599
Andre Repschinski *(Mng Dir)*

TRAVCOA Corporation (1)
3131 Elliott Ave Ste 250, Seattle, WA 98121
Tel.: (310) 649-7104
Web Site: http://www.travcoa.com
Escorted & Custom Journey Operating Services
N.A.I.C.S.: 812990

TT Hotels Croatia d.o.o. (1)
Nova ves 17, 10000, Zagreb, Croatia
Tel.: (385) 12002001
Web Site: https://tthotels-croatia.com
Emp.: 500
Hotel & Tourist Resort Operator
N.A.I.C.S.: 721120

TT Hotels Turkey Otel Hizmetleri Turizm ve ticaret AS (1)
Guzeloba Mah Havaalani Street No 64 Plaza Batuhan B 6-7, Muratpasa, Antalya, Turkiye
Tel.: (90) 2423104000
Web Site: https://www.tthotels.com

AND PRIVATE COMPANIES — TUI AG

Hotel & Resort Services
N.A.I.C.S.: 721110
Ozlem Gok *(Mgr-Pub Rels)*

TUI (Suisse) AG (1)
Friesenbergstrasse 75, 8036, Zurich, Switzerland
Tel.: (41) 444554444
Web Site: https://www.tui.ch
Tour Operating Services
N.A.I.C.S.: 561520

TUI 4 U GmbH (1)
Otto-Lilienthal-Str 17, 28199, Bremen, Germany
Tel.: (49) 4215250102
Web Site: https://www.tui4u.de
Emp.: 150
Travel Agencies Business Process Outsourcing Services
N.A.I.C.S.: 561499
Florian Fleischer-Bthe *(Mng Dir)*

TUI Airlines Belgium N.V. (1)
Luchthaven Nationaal 40, P Box 1, 1930, Zaventem, Belgium
Tel.: (32) 27178661
Web Site: https://www.tuifly.be
Oil Transportation Services
N.A.I.C.S.: 481111

TUI Airlines Nederland B.V. (1)
Tel.: (31) 884416000
Web Site: https://www.tui.nl
Sales Range: $200-249.9 Million
Emp.: 600
Oil Transportation Services
N.A.I.C.S.: 488190
Hans Fianvelde *(Gen Mgr)*

TUI Ambassador Tours Unipessoal Lda (1)
Avenida Conselheiro Fernando Sousa 25A, 1070-026, Lisbon, Portugal
Tel.: (351) 213124727
Web Site: https://pt.tui.com
Tourism Services
N.A.I.C.S.: 561520

TUI Austria Holding GmbH (1)
Heiligenstadter Strasse 31, A - 1190, Vienna, Austria
Tel.: (43) 508840
Web Site: https://www.tui.at
Travel Agency Services
N.A.I.C.S.: 561510

TUI BLUE DE GmbH (1)
Karl-Wiechert-Allee 23, 30625, Hannover, Germany
Tel.: (49) 5115662500
Home Management Services
N.A.I.C.S.: 561110

TUI Belgium Retail N.V. (1)
National Airport 40, P Box 4, 1930, Zaventem, Belgium
Tel.: (32) 59565611
Web Site: https://www.tuiticketshop.be
Travel Agency Services
N.A.I.C.S.: 561510
Anne Vanhie *(Mgr-Retail Strategy & Innovation)*

TUI Beteiligungs GmbH (1)
Karl-Wiechert-Allee 4, Hannover, Germany
Tel.: (49) 5115660
Web Site: http://www.tui-group.com
Holding Company
N.A.I.C.S.: 551112

TUI Bulgaria EOOD (1)
113 General Kolev Bvld 10th Floor, 9002, Varna, Bulgaria
Tel.: (359) 52382525
Web Site: https://www.tui.bg
Tourism Services
N.A.I.C.S.: 561520

TUI Business Services GmbH (1)
Karl-Wiechert-Allee 4, 30625, Hannover, Germany
Tel.: (49) 5115661338
Web Site: http://www.tui-business-services.com
Financial Services
N.A.I.C.S.: 523999
Tim Lassig *(Head-Payroll)*

TUI China Travel CO. Ltd. (1)
Bright China Chang An Building, Tower 2 Unit 921-926 7 Jianguomen Nei Avenue, Beijing, 100005, China
Tel.: (86) 1085198800
Web Site: https://www.tui.cn
Tourism Services
N.A.I.C.S.: 561520
Guido Brettschneider *(CEO)*

TUI Consulting & Services GmbH (1)
Karl-Wiechert-Allee 4, 30625, Hannover, Germany
Tel.: (49) 511 566 2181
Sales Range: $25-49.9 Million
Emp.: 15
Management Consulting Services
N.A.I.C.S.: 541611
Hans-Joergen Beck *(Gen Mgr)*

TUI Cruises GmbH (1)
Heidenkampsweg 58, 20097, Hamburg, Germany
Tel.: (49) 40600015000
Web Site: https://www.meinschiff.com
Cruise Line & Tour Operator
N.A.I.C.S.: 561520
Wybcke Meier *(Chm)*

Subsidiary (Domestic):

Hapag-Lloyd Kreuzfahrten GmbH (2)
Ballindamm 25, 20095, Hamburg, Germany
Tel.: (49) 403070300
Web Site: http://www.hl-cruises.com
Ship Chartering Services
N.A.I.C.S.: 483112

TUI Danmark A/S (1)
Gammel Kongevej 60, 1850, Frederiksberg, Denmark
Tel.: (45) 70101050
Web Site: https://www.tui.dk
Tourism Services
N.A.I.C.S.: 561520

TUI Deutschland GmbH (1)
Karl-Wiechert-Allee 23, 30625, Hannover, Germany
Tel.: (49) 5115678600
Web Site: https://www.tui.com
Sales Range: $350-399.9 Million
Emp.: 1,700
Travel Agency & Tour Operator
N.A.I.C.S.: 561520

Unit (Domestic):

First Reiseburo (2)
Bertoldstrasse 16, 79098, Freiburg, Germany
Tel.: (49) 7613686222
Web Site: http://www.first-reiseburo.de
Internet Travel Agency & Tour Marketing & Sales Services
N.A.I.C.S.: 561510
Volker Bottcher *(CEO)*

Subsidiary (Domestic):

TUIfly.com (2)
Benkendorffstr 22b, 30855, Langenhagen, Germany
Tel.: (49) 2070480143
Web Site: http://www.tuifly.com
Sales Range: $500-549.9 Million
Emp.: 1,600
Passenger Air Transpotation Services
N.A.I.C.S.: 481111

Division (Domestic):

Hapag-Lloyd Fluggesellschaft mbH (3)
Flughafenstrasse 10, D 30855, Hannover, Germany
Tel.: (49) 51197270
Web Site: http://www.tuifly.com
Sales Range: $700-749.9 Million
Passenger Air Transportation Operations
N.A.I.C.S.: 481111

TUI Espana Turismo S.A (1)
Cami Vell de Bunyola 43 Edificio Rotonda Local 22, 7009, Palma de Mallorca, Spain
Tel.: (34) 971766400
Tour Operating Services
N.A.I.C.S.: 561520

TUI Finland Oy Ab (1)
Konepajankuja 3, 00510, Helsinki, Finland Tel.: (358) 923100010
Web Site: https://www.tui.fi
Tourism Services
N.A.I.C.S.: 561520

TUI Finland Oy Ab (1)
Konepajankuja 3, 00510, Helsinki, Finland
Tel.: (358) 923100010
Web Site: https://www.tui.fi
Tourism Services
N.A.I.C.S.: 561520

TUI Finland Oy Ab (1)
Konepajankuja 3, 00510, Helsinki, Finland
Tel.: (358) 923100010
Web Site: https://www.tui.fi
Tourism Services
N.A.I.C.S.: 561520

TUI Finland Oy Ab (1)
Konepajankuja 3, 00510, Helsinki, Finland
Tel.: (358) 923100010
Web Site: https://www.tui.fi
Tourism Services
N.A.I.C.S.: 561520

TUI France SA (1)
107 rue Henri Barbusse, 92110, Clichy, France
Tel.: (33) 825000825
Web Site: https://www.tui.fr
Tourism Services
N.A.I.C.S.: 561520
Audrey Durousseau *(Head-Paid Traffic)*

TUI Hellas S.A. (1)
Kartiyadon 16, Kato Kifissia, 14564, Athens, Greece
Tel.: (30) 210 350 2000
Web Site: http://www.tui.gr
Sales Range: $100-124.9 Million
Travel Agency & Tour Operator
N.A.I.C.S.: 561520

TUI Holidays Ireland Limited (1)
One Spencer Dock North Wall Quay, Dublin, 1, Ireland
Tel.: (353) 16937700
Web Site: https://www.tuiholidays.ie
Travel Management Services
N.A.I.C.S.: 561510

TUI Hotel Betriebsgesellschaft mbH (1)
Karl-Wiechert-Allee 4, 30625, Hannover, Germany
Tel.: (49) 5662500
Web Site: https://www.tui-blue.com
Hotel & Resort Services
N.A.I.C.S.: 721110
Artur Gerber *(Mng Dir)*

TUI India Private Limited (1)
Soulstice Plot No 52 4th Floor Sector 44, Gurgaon, 122003, India
Tel.: (91) 1800112737
Web Site: http://www.tui.in
Tourism Services
N.A.I.C.S.: 561520
Pervez Ahmad *(Gen Mgr)*

TUI InfoTec GmbH (1)
Karl-Wiechert-Allee 23, 30625, Hannover, Germany
Tel.: (49) 5115679000
Web Site: http://www.tui-tech.com
Sales Range: $150-199.9 Million
Emp.: 420
Information Technology Services
N.A.I.C.S.: 518210

TUI International Holiday (Malaysia) Sdn. Bhd. (1)
B1-26-6 SOHO Suites KLCC No 20 Jalan Perak Wilayah Persekutuan, 50450, Kuala Lumpur, Malaysia
Tel.: (60) 1546000044
Tourism Services
N.A.I.C.S.: 561520

TUI Ireland Limited (1)
One Spencer Dock North Wall Quay, Dublin, D04 K7H2, Ireland
Tel.: (353) 19635304
Web Site: https://www.tuiholidays.ie
Tourism Services
N.A.I.C.S.: 561520
Charlotte Brenner *(Mktg Mgr)*

TUI Leisure Travel Service GmbH (1)
Hellersbergstr 4, Neuss, 41460, Germany
Tel.: (49) 213112130
Travel Agency Services
N.A.I.C.S.: 561510

TUI Leisure Travel Special Tours GmbH (1)
Wachtstr 17, 30625, Bremen, Germany
Tel.: (49) 4213226880
Travel Agency Services
N.A.I.C.S.: 561510

TUI Magic Life GmbH (1)
Karl-Wiechert-Allee 4, 30625, Hannover, Germany
Tel.: (49) 511 567 8670
Web Site: https://www.magiclife.com
Hotel & Resort Services
N.A.I.C.S.: 721110
Andreas Pospiech *(CEO)*

TUI Magyarorszag Utazasi Iroda Kft. (1)
Raday U 58, 1092, Budapest, Hungary
Tel.: (36) 1 463 0800
Web Site: https://www.tui.hu
Travel Agency Services
N.A.I.C.S.: 561510
Tamas Taskar *(Sls Mgr)*

TUI Nederland Holding N.V. (1)
Volmerlaan 3, Rijswijk, 2288 GC, Netherlands
Tel.: (31) 703266000
Web Site: http://www.arke.nl
Sales Range: $200-249.9 Million
Emp.: 45
Investment Management Service
N.A.I.C.S.: 523999
Elie . Bruyninckx *(CEO)*

TUI Nederland N.V. (1)
Volmerlaan 3, 2288 GC, Rijswijk, Netherlands (100%)
Tel.: (31) 880885885
Web Site: https://www.tui.nl
Sales Range: $650-699.9 Million
Emp.: 2,000
Tour Operator
N.A.I.C.S.: 561520

TUI Nordic Holding AB (1)
Soder Malarstrand 27, Stockholm, 11785, Sweden
Tel.: (46) 87207200
Web Site: http://www.fritidsresor.se
Investment Management Service
N.A.I.C.S.: 523999
Himrek Norlem *(Gen Mgr)*

TUI Norge AS (1)
Lille Grensen 7, 0159, Oslo, Norway
Tel.: (47) 67115000
Web Site: https://www.tui.no
Tourism Services
N.A.I.C.S.: 561520

TUI Northern Europe Ltd. (1)
Wigmore House, Wigmore Place, Wigmore Lane, Luton, LU2 9TN, United Kingdom
Tel.: (44) 2034512688
Web Site: https://www.tui.co.uk
Travel Agency & Tour Operator
N.A.I.C.S.: 561520

Subsidiary (Domestic):

TUI Travel Aviation Finance Limited (2)
Tui Travel House Fleming Way, Crawley, RH10 9QL, W Sussex, United Kingdom
Tel.: (44) 1293645700
Web Site: http://www.tuitravelplc.com
Emp.: 100
Financial Management Services
N.A.I.C.S.: 523999

TUI Travel Healthcare Limited (2)
Crawley Business Quarter Fleming Way, Crawley, RH10 9QL, West Sussex, United Kingdom
Tel.: (44) 1293645700
Web Site: http://www.extranet.axappphealthcare.com
Sales Range: $50-74.9 Million
Emp.: 300
Health Care Srvices
N.A.I.C.S.: 621610

TUI UK Ltd. (2)
Wigmore House Wigmore Lane, Luton, LU2

TUI AG

TUI AG—(Continued)
9TN, Bedfordshire, United Kingdom
Tel.: (44) 2034512699
Web Site: http://www.tui-uk.co.uk
Sales Range: $200-249.9 Million
Emp.: 1,000
Travel Agency & Tour Operator
N.A.I.C.S.: 561520
Jeremy Osborne (Dir-Strategic Bus Change & Innovation)

Subsidiary (Domestic):

Citalia Holidays Limited (3)
Origin One 108 High Street, Crawley, RH10 1BD, West Sussex, United Kingdom
Tel.: (44) 1293765055
Web Site: https://www.citalia.com
Tour Operating Services
N.A.I.C.S.: 561520

First Choice Holidays & Flights Limited (3)
Jetset House Church Road, Crawley, RH11 0PQ, West Sussex, United Kingdom
Tel.: (44) 1293816265
Tour Operating Services
N.A.I.C.S.: 561520

First Choice Retail (Management Services) Limited (3)
International House Parkway 100 Worle, Weston-super-Mare, BS22 6WA, United Kingdom
Tel.: (44) 1934523319
Business Management Consulting Services
N.A.I.C.S.: 541611

Hayes & Jarvis (Travel) Limited (3)
Origin One 108 High Street, Crawley, RH10 1BD, West Sussex, United Kingdom
Tel.: (44) 2081062403
Web Site: https://www.hayesandjarvis.co.uk
Tour Operating Services
N.A.I.C.S.: 561520

I Love Tour Limited (3)
Origin One 108 High Street, Crawley, RH10 1BD, West Sussex, United Kingdom
Tel.: (44) 203 617 7978
Web Site: http://www.ilovetour.co.uk
Emp.: 15
Tour Operating Services
N.A.I.C.S.: 561520
Matt Wildridge (Mgr-Sls)

Platinum Event Travel Limited (3)
53 Saint Owen Street, Hereford, HR1 2JQ, United Kingdom
Tel.: (44) 1432263263
Sales Range: $25-49.9 Million
Emp.: 9
Sports Tour Operating Services
N.A.I.C.S.: 561520
Paul Terry (Mng Dir)

STUDENT SKIING LIMITED (3)
1 Ogden Street, Didsbury, Manchester, M20 6DN, United Kingdom
Tel.: (44) 845 680 1503
Web Site: http://www.studentskiing.com
Sales Range: $10-24.9 Million
Emp.: 13
Educational Support Services
N.A.I.C.S.: 611710
Luke Taylor (Coord-Groups)

Ski Alpine Limited (3)
University Travel Team 1 Union Street, Kingston upon Thames, KT1 1BL, United Kingdom
Tel.: (44) 8455333184
Web Site: http://www.ski-alpine.co.uk
Tour Operating Services
N.A.I.C.S.: 561520
Lynsey Devon (Mgr-PR-Specialist & Activity Sector)

Skibound Holidays Limited (3)
Olivier House 18 Marine Parade, Brighton, BN2 1TL, East Sussex, United Kingdom
Tel.: (44) 1273244514
Web Site: https://www.skiboundholidays.co.uk
Tour Operating Services
N.A.I.C.S.: 561520

Sovereign Tour Operations Limited (3)
The Atrium London Road, Crawley, RH10 9SR, West Sussex, United Kingdom
Tel.: (44) 2073857090
Web Site: http://www.sovereign.com
Tour Operating Services
N.A.I.C.S.: 561520

Sportsworld Group Limited (3)
Causeway House 13 The Causeway Teddington, London, TW11 0JR, United Kingdom
Tel.: (44) 2033148255
Web Site: https://www.sportsworld.co.uk
Sales Range: $25-49.9 Million
Emp.: 2
Event Management Services
N.A.I.C.S.: 711310

Sunsail Limited (3)
Platinum House St Marks Hill, Surbiton, KT6 4BH, Surrey, United Kingdom
Tel.: (44) 3303321172
Web Site: https://www.sunsail.co.uk
Boating Excursion & Sailing Services
N.A.I.C.S.: 487210

TTSS Limited (3)
The Fens 7 Brooklyn Crescent, Cheadle, SK8 1DX, Cheshire, United Kingdom
Tel.: (44) 1614916969
Web Site: http://www.edwindoran.com
Sports Tour Operating Services
N.A.I.C.S.: 561520
Andrew Loughlin (Mgr-Sales)

Thomson Fly (3)
Culumbus House Westwood Business Park Coventry, Luton, CV4 8TT, Bedfordshire, United Kingdom
Tel.: (44) 2476282828
Web Site: http://www.thomsonfly.com
Sales Range: $350-399.9 Million
Charter Airline
N.A.I.C.S.: 481111

Thomson Sport (UK) Limited (3)
4th Floor Tuition House 27-37 St Georges Road, Wimbledon, London, SW19 4EU, United Kingdom
Tel.: (44) 8450042060
Web Site: http://www.thomsonsport.com
Sports Tour Operating Services
N.A.I.C.S.: 561520

Travel Class Limited (3)
Olivier House 18 Marine Parade, Brighton, BN2 1TL, East Sussex, United Kingdom
Tel.: (44) 1273647200
Web Site: https://www.jca-adventure.co.uk
Emp.: 2
Educational Tour Operating Services
N.A.I.C.S.: 561520

World Challenge Expeditions Limited (3)
17-21 Queens Road, High Wycombe, HP13 6AQ, Buckinghamshire, United Kingdom
Tel.: (44) 1494427600
Web Site: https://weareworldchallenge.com
Educational Tour Operating Services
N.A.I.C.S.: 561520

TUI PORTUGAL - Agencia de Viagens e Turismo S.A. (1)
Urbanizacao Monte Ria Edificio Tui-Lote 2 Montenegro, 8005-237, Faro, Portugal
Tel.: (351) 289001600
Web Site: http://www.tuiviagens.pt
Tour Operating Services
N.A.I.C.S.: 561520
Feona Downie (Gen Mgr)

TUI Poland Sp. z o.o. (1)
ul Woloska 22a, 02-675, Warsaw, Poland
Tel.: (48) 222703120
Web Site: https://www.tui.pl
Emp.: 500
Tourism Services
N.A.I.C.S.: 561520

TUI ReiseCenter Slovensko s.r.o. (1)
Panska 10, 811 01, Bratislava, Slovakia
Tel.: (421) 254434042
Web Site: https://www.tui-reisecenter.sk
Travel Agency Services
N.A.I.C.S.: 561510

TUI Service AG (1)
Tiergartenstrasse 1, 8852, Altendorf, 8852, Switzerland
Tel.: (41) 554516737
Web Site: http://www.tui-service.ch
Sales Range: $10-24.9 Million
Emp.: 50
Tour Operating Services
N.A.I.C.S.: 561520
Andra Illmer (CEO)

TUI Spain, SLU (1)
Mesena 22 2nd Floor, 28033, Madrid, Spain
Tel.: (34) 917582828
Web Site: https://www.es.tui.com
Tourism Services
N.A.I.C.S.: 561520
Eduardo Carranza Simon (Mktg Dir)

TUI Suisse Retail AG (1)
Friesenbergstrasse 75, PO Box 9180, 8036, Zurich, Switzerland
Tel.: (41) 444554444
Web Site: http://www.tui-suisse.com
Emp.: 180
Tour Operating Services
N.A.I.C.S.: 561520

TUI Sverige AB (1)
Soder Malarstrand 27, Stockholm, Sweden
Tel.: (46) 771840100
Web Site: https://www.tui.se
Tourism Services
N.A.I.C.S.: 561520
Jessica Enbacka (Mng Dir)

TUI UK Transport Ltd. (1)
Wigmore House Wigmore Lane Wigmore Place, Luton, LU2 9TN, Bedfordshire, United Kingdom
Tel.: (44) 2476282828
Travel Agency Services
N.A.I.C.S.: 561510

TUIfly GmbH (1)
Flughafenstrasse 10, 30855, Langenhagen, Germany
Tel.: (49) 51122004321
Web Site: http://www.tuifly.com
Oil Transportation Services
N.A.I.C.S.: 481111
Henrik Homann (Co-Chm)

TUIfly Nordic AB (1)
Soder Malarstrand 27, 118 25, Stockholm, 118 25, Sweden
Tel.: (46) 771840100
Web Site: https://www.tuiflynordic.se
Emp.: 450
Tour Operating Services
N.A.I.C.S.: 561520
Alexander Huber (CEO)

TUIfly Vermarktungs GmbH (1)
Karl-Wiechert-Allee 23, 30625, Hannover, Germany
Tel.: (49) 8706060519
Oil Transportation Services
N.A.I.C.S.: 481111
Olaf Petersenn (Mng Dir)

Tantur Turizm Seyahat Ltd. (1)
Mueyyedzade Mah Yuksekkaldirim Cad Terim Is Hani No 43 K 2, Karakoy-Beyoglu, Istanbul, Turkiye
Tel.: (90) 2423103000
Web Site: https://tui.com.tr
Sales Range: $10-24.9 Million
Emp.: 25
Tourism Management Services
N.A.I.C.S.: 561520

Tenuta di Castelfalfi S.p.A. (1)
Localita Castelfalfi, Firenze, 50050, Montaione, Italy
Tel.: (39) 0571892000
Web Site: http://www.castelfalfi.it
Emp.: 100
Home Management Services
N.A.I.C.S.: 721110
Stefan Neuhaus (Mng Dir)

The Moorings Limited (1)
93 N Park Pl Blvd, Clearwater, FL 33759
Tel.: (727) 437-5112
Web Site: http://www.moorings.com
Sales Range: $25-49.9 Million
Yacht Chartering & Vacation Services
N.A.I.C.S.: 488390

Thomson Airways Limited (1)
Wigmore House Wigmore Lane, Luton, LU2 9TN, United Kingdom
Tel.: (44) 2476 282 828
Web Site: http://www.thomsonfly.com
Sales Range: $1-4.9 Billion
Emp.: 1,800
Oil Transportation Services
N.A.I.C.S.: 488190
Jill Carter (Dir-Customer Delivery)

Subsidiary (Domestic):

Thomson Airways (Services) Limited (2)
Jetset House Church Rd, Crawley, RH11 0PQ, West Sussex, United Kingdom
Tel.: (44) 1293 816000
Web Site: http://www.thomson.co.uk
Sales Range: $50-74.9 Million
Emp.: 200
Oil Transportation Services
N.A.I.C.S.: 488190
Peter Davies (Mgr-Facility)

Touraventure S.A. (1)
74 Rue de Lagny, F-93100, Montreuil, France
Tel.: (33) 148518000
Web Site: http://www.nouvelles-frontieres.fr
Sales Range: $150-199.9 Million
Emp.: 650
Travel Services
N.A.I.C.S.: 561599
Jeinmarc Seiano (Pres)

Transfar - Agencia de Viagens e Turismo Lda. (1)
Rua Tome Da Costa 6, Loja, Faro, Portugal
Tel.: (351) 289001710
Travel Agency Services
N.A.I.C.S.: 561510

Travel Partner Bulgaria EOOD (1)
113 General Kolev Blvd 10th Floor, 9002, Varna, Bulgaria
Tel.: (359) 52 382525
Web Site: http://www.tpb.bg
Sales Range: $25-49.9 Million
Emp.: 16
Tour Operating Services
N.A.I.C.S.: 561520
Plamen Katzarov (CEO)

Travel Sense A/S (1)
Amager Strandvej 390 1 sal, 2770, Kastrup, Denmark
Tel.: (45) 70 23 06 44
Web Site: http://www.travelsense.dk
Emp.: 10
Travel Agency Services
N.A.I.C.S.: 561510
Camilla Andersen (Founder)

Travel Services Europe Spain SL (1)
Ronda San Antonio 36-38 3-2, 08001, Barcelona, Spain
Tel.: (34) 933568292
Web Site: https://www.travelse.co.uk
Sales Range: $25-49.9 Million
Emp.: 12
Tour Operating Services
N.A.I.C.S.: 561520

Travel Turf, Inc. (1)
7540 Windsor Dr Ste 202, Allentown, PA 18195
Tel.: (610) 391-9094
Web Site: http://www.wcv.com
Emp.: 20
Travel & Tour Operating Agencies
N.A.I.C.S.: 561510
Matt Schaeffer (Dir-Events)

Travelbound European Tours Limited (1)
Olivier House 18 Marine Parade, Brighton, BN2 1TL, East Sussex, United Kingdom
Tel.: (44) 1273265265
Web Site: http://www.travelbound.co.uk
Sales Range: $10-24.9 Million
Emp.: 5
Tour Operating Services
N.A.I.C.S.: 561520
Ali Clark (Coord-Tour)

Trek America Travel Limited (1)
DST House St Marks Hill, Surbiton, KT6 4BH, Surrey, United Kingdom
Tel.: (44) 2039784871
Web Site: https://www.trekamerica.com
Tour Operating Services

AND PRIVATE COMPANIES

Trek International Travel Corp (1)
353 S 20th Ave, Brighton, CO 80301
Tel.: (303) 655-9439
Web Site: http://www.trektravel.com
Travel Agency Services
N.A.I.C.S.: 561510

Tunisie Voyages S.A. (1)
Boulevard de la Terre B2 Ground Floor of Pavilion B, The Sana Business Center Residence Center Urbain Nord, 1082, Tunis, Tunisia
Tel.: (216) 71805805
Web Site: http://www.tunisie-voyages.com
Travel Agency Services
N.A.I.C.S.: 561510

Turcotel Turizm A.S. (1)
No 7 Kisikli Caddesi, Istanbul, Turkiye
Tel.: (90) 2165542400
Web Site: http://www.tui.com
Sales Range: $25-49.9 Million
Emp.: 9
Tour Operator
N.A.I.C.S.: 561520

Turismo Asia Company Ltd. (1)
511 Soi 6 Sri-Ayuthaya Road, Rajthevee, Bangkok, 10400, Thailand
Tel.: (66) 2 245 1551
Web Site: http://www.turismoasia.com
Travel & Tour Operating Services
N.A.I.C.S.: 561510

Ultra Montes C.V. (1)
Rue Archimede 1, 1000, Brussels, Belgium
Tel.: (32) 22305820
Web Site: http://www.jetair.be
Sales Range: $25-49.9 Million
Emp.: 4
Travel Agency Services
N.A.I.C.S.: 561510
Joelle Hellemans *(Mng Dir)*

Ultramar Express Transport S.A. (1)
Carretera Bika Llucmajor, 7009, Palma de Mallorca, Spain
Tel.: (34) 971494045
Web Site: http://www.ultramartransport.com
Tour Operating Services
N.A.I.C.S.: 561520
Francisco Tome *(Gen Mgr)*

Viajes Verger SA (1)
Suipacha 570 Pisos 8 y 9, Buenos Aires, 1008, Argentina
Tel.: (54) 11 4316 5200
Web Site: http://www.barceloviajes.com.ar
Travel Agencies
N.A.I.C.S.: 561510

WAG Salzgitter Wohnungs-GmbH (1)
Chemnitzer Strasse 90 - 94, 38226, Salzgitter, Germany
Tel.: (49) 534185980
Web Site: https://wag-salzgitter.de
Real Estate Development Services
N.A.I.C.S.: 531390

WE LOVE RUGBY PTY LIMITED (1)
1114 Botany Road, Botany, 2019, NSW, Australia
Tel.: (61) 290714542
Web Site: https://www.weloverugby.com
Tour Operating Services
N.A.I.C.S.: 561520

Wolters Reisen GmbH (1)
Bremer Str 61, 28816, Stuhr, Germany
Tel.: (49) 211668878800
Web Site: http://www.tuivillas.com
Tourism Services
N.A.I.C.S.: 561520
Matthias Gieschen *(Fin Dir)*

WonderCruises AB (1)
Soder Malarstrand 27, Stockholm, 11785, Sweden
Tel.: (46) 7 71 34 50 00
Tour Operating Services
N.A.I.C.S.: 561520

World Challenge (Dubai) Limited (1)
17-21 Queens Road, High Wycombe, HP13 6AQ, Birminghamshire, United Kingdom
Tel.: (44) 1494427600
Web Site: http://weareworldchallenge.com
Emp.: 70
Tour Operating Services
N.A.I.C.S.: 561520

World Challenge (Hong Kong) Limited (1)
17-21 Queens Road, High Wycombe, HP13 6AQ, Buckinghamshire, United Kingdom
Tel.: (44) 1494427600
Sales Range: $25-49.9 Million
Emp.: 70
Tour Operating Services
N.A.I.C.S.: 561520
Matt Eastlake *(Mng Dir)*

World Challenge Expeditions Pty Ltd (1)
Level 5 163 Eastern Road, Melbourne, 3205, VIC, Australia
Tel.: (61) 1300728568
Web Site: http://www.worldchallenge.com.au
Sales Range: $10-24.9 Million
Emp.: 30
Educational Support Services
N.A.I.C.S.: 611710
Peter Fletcher *(Grp Mng Dir)*

World Challenge Expeditions, Inc. (1)
8 Essex Ctr Dr, Peabody, MA 01960
Web Site: http://weareworldchallenge.com
Sales Range: $25-49.9 Million
Emp.: 7
Tour Operating Services
N.A.I.C.S.: 561520
Pete Fletcher *(Mng Dir-Grp)*

Zegrahm Expeditions, Inc. (1)
3131 Elliott Ave Ste 250, Seattle, WA 98121
Tel.: (206) 285-4000
Web Site: http://www.zegrahm.com
Sales Range: $10-24.9 Million
Emp.: 30
Travel Agencies
N.A.I.C.S.: 561510

i-To-i UK Limited (1)
Woodside House 261 Low Lane, Leeds, LS18 5NY, United Kingdom
Tel.: (44) 1132054602
Web Site: https://www.i-to-i.com
Travel Agency Services
N.A.I.C.S.: 561510

travel-Ba.Sys GmbH & Co KG (1)
Alexanderstrasse 38, 45472, Mulheim an der Ruhr, Germany
Tel.: (49) 20830672500
Web Site: https://www.travelbasys.de
Software Solutions Services
N.A.I.C.S.: 541511

TUKA TRANSPORTATION CO.
Next to Foulad Mobarakeh, Mobarakeh, Isfahan, Iran
Tel.: (98) 335543 2270
Web Site: http://www.tukatrans.com
HTOK—(THE)
Land Transportation Services
N.A.I.C.S.: 484121

TUKAS GIDA SANAYI VE TICARET A.S.
Caybasi Mah Aydin Cad No 51, Torbali, 35880, Izmir, Turkiye
Tel.: (90) 2328651555
Web Site: https://www.tukas.com.tr
Year Founded: 1962
TUKAS—(IST)
Rev.: $123,415,853
Assets: $122,781,862
Liabilities: $57,640,732
Net Worth: $65,141,129
Earnings: $42,436,911
Fiscal Year-end: 12/31/22
Frozen Food Distr
N.A.I.C.S.: 424420
Cem Okulla *(Chm)*

TULASEE BIO-ETHANOL LIMITED
Plot No 41/3 & 41/5 Lohop Chowk Road Village Lohop, Raigad, Khalapur, 410202, Maharashtra, India
Tel.: (91) 2225203161 In
Web Site: https://www.tulaseebio-ethanolltd.com
Year Founded: 1988
524514—(BOM)
Assets: $1,005,401
Liabilities: $890,199
Net Worth: $115,202
Earnings: ($15,296)
Fiscal Year-end: 03/31/23
Alcohol Ethanol Mfr
N.A.I.C.S.: 325193
Kapil Lalitkumar Nagpal *(Mng Dir)*

TULIKIVI CORPORATION
Kuhnustantie 10, 83900, Juuka, Finland
Tel.: (358) 403063100
Web Site: https://warm.tulikivi.fi
TULAV—(HEL)
Rev.: $47,795,165
Assets: $42,394,777
Liabilities: $26,801,209
Net Worth: $15,593,568
Earnings: $5,211,526
Emp.: 242
Fiscal Year-end: 12/31/22
Soapstone Fireplace Marketer
N.A.I.C.S.: 423320
Heikki Vauhkonen *(Mng Dir)*

Subsidiaries:

ARMAKA AG (1)
Dugginestrasse 10, CH 4153, Reinach, Switzerland
Tel.: (41) 617159911
Web Site: http://www.armaka.ch
Sales Range: $25-49.9 Million
Emp.: 10
Stone Fireplaces Mfr
N.A.I.C.S.: 335139

Baltic TK (1)
Pihlaka 1A, 11216, Tallinn, Estonia
Tel.: (372) 6555486
Web Site: http://www.tulikivi.ee
Sales Range: $50-74.9 Million
Emp.: 2
Fireplaces Mfr
N.A.I.C.S.: 922160

Contemperary Fire Inc. (1)
78 Centennial Rd Unit 11, Orangeville, L9W 1P9, ON, Canada
Tel.: (519) 938-9166
Machine Tool Mfr & Distr
N.A.I.C.S.: 333515

Eurotrias S.R.L. (1)
Via Max Planck 13, 39100, Bolzano, BZ, Italy
Tel.: (39) 0471201616
Web Site: https://eurotrias.it
Furniture Distr
N.A.I.C.S.: 423210

Feuer im Stein GmbH & Co KG (1)
Gewerbepark 1, A-4861, Schorfling am Attersee, Austria
Tel.: (43) 766229061
Web Site: https://www.feuerimstein.at
Ventilating & Air Conditioning Services
N.A.I.C.S.: 238220

Horizont DOM, d.o.o. (1)
Presernova 10a, 1000, Ljubljana, Slovenia
Tel.: (386) 12516600
Web Site: http://www.honka.com
Sales Range: $50-74.9 Million
Emp.: 3
Stone Fireplaces Mfr
N.A.I.C.S.: 922160

Kad Nebutu Salta, UAB (1)
Liepu g 54, LT-92106, Klaipeda, Lithuania
Tel.: (370) 61141399
Web Site: https://www.kadnebutusalta.lt
Heating Equipment Mfr
N.A.I.C.S.: 333414

Komiexpert s r.o. (1)
Ceskomoravska 2255/12a, 190 00, Prague, 9, Czech Republic
Tel.: (420) 734202584
Web Site: https://www.komiexpert.cz

Chimney Liner Installation Services
N.A.I.C.S.: 238220

OOO Tulikivi (1)
Bersenevskiy lane 3/10 bld 7, Moscow, 119072, Russia
Tel.: (7) 4994448418
Web Site: https://www.tulikivi.com
Fireplace & Stove Sales
N.A.I.C.S.: 423320

TALC s.r.o. (1)
Stiavnicka 673/77, 976 81, Podbrezova, Slovakia
Tel.: (421) 904945888
Web Site: https://www.talc.sk
Storage Furnace Distr
N.A.I.C.S.: 423730

Tiba AG (1)
Hammerstrasse 26, 4410, Liestal, Switzerland
Tel.: (41) 619351710
Web Site: https://tiba.ch
Stove & Oven Distr
N.A.I.C.S.: 333414

Tulikivi UK Limited (1)
Unit 14 Elliott Road Love Lane Industrial Estate, Cirencester, GL7 1YS, United Kingdom
Tel.: (44) 1285650633
Fireplace & Stove Sales
N.A.I.C.S.: 423320

Tulikivi US Inc. (1)
199 Spotnap Rd - Ste 5, Charlottesville, VA 22911
Web Site: https://www.tulikivi.com
Stone Fireplaces & Masonry
N.A.I.C.S.: 238140

TULIP STAR HOTELS LTD.
Indra Palace Building H-Block Middle Circle Connaught Circus, New Delhi, 110001, India
Tel.: (91) 11 23738811 In
Web Site: http://www.tulipstarhotel.com
Year Founded: 1987
Rev.: $72
Assets: $8,976,078
Liabilities: $11,512,005
Net Worth: ($2,535,927)
Earnings: ($1,139,498)
Emp.: 5
Fiscal Year-end: 03/31/19
Hotel Operator
N.A.I.C.S.: 721120
Ajit Baburao Kerkar *(Mng Dir)*

TULIVE DEVELOPERS LIMITED
No 5 1st Street Subba Rao Avenue, Chennai, 600006, Tamil Nadu, India
Tel.: (91) 4428230223
Web Site: https://www.tulivedevelopers.com
505285—(BOM)
Rev.: $83,412
Assets: $5,886,026
Liabilities: $2,446
Net Worth: $5,883,580
Earnings: $151,322
Fiscal Year-end: 03/31/23
Housing Project Development Services
N.A.I.C.S.: 236117
Ramana Shetty Venkata Krishna *(Chm)*

TULLOW OIL PLC
9 Chiswick Park 566 Chiswick High Road, London, W4 5XT, United Kingdom
Tel.: (44) 2032499000
Web Site: https://www.tullowoil.com
TLWL—(GHA)
Rev.: $1,273,200,000
Assets: $5,540,600,000
Liabilities: $6,006,700,000
Net Worth: ($466,100,000)

TULLOW OIL PLC

Tullow Oil plc—(Continued)
Earnings: ($80,700,000)
Emp.: 378
Fiscal Year-end: 12/31/21
Crude Petroleum Extraction Services
N.A.I.C.S.: 211120
Les Wood (CFO)

Subsidiaries:

Tullow Cote d'Ivoire Limited (1)
3rd Fl Bldg 11 Chiswick Park, 566 Chiswick High Road, London, W4 5YS, United Kingdom
Tel.: (44) 20 89961000
Web Site: http://www.tullowoil.ie
Crude Petroleum & Natural Gas Extraction
N.A.I.C.S.: 211120

Tullow Ghana Limited (1)
Plot No 70 George Walker Bush Highway, North Dzorwulu, Accra, Ghana
Tel.: (233) 302742200
Web Site: http://www.tullowoil.com
Oil & Gas Exploration Services
N.A.I.C.S.: 213112

Tullow Hardman Holdings B.V. (1)
Scheveningseweg, Hague, 2517KW, Netherlands
Tel.: (31) 703387546
Investment Management Service
N.A.I.C.S.: 523999

Tullow Kenya B.V. (1)
Scheveningseweg 58, Hague, 2517 KW, Zuid-Holland, Netherlands
Tel.: (31) 703387546
Oil & Gas Exploration Services
N.A.I.C.S.: 213112

Tullow Madagascar Limited (1)
c/o Tullow South Africa, Convention Tower, 11th Fl cnr Heerengracht St, & Coen Steyler Ave, Cape Town, 8001, Foreshore, South Africa (100%)
Tel.: (27) 21 400 7600
Web Site: http://www.tullowoil.com
Oil & Gas Field Machinery & Equipment Mfr
N.A.I.C.S.: 333132

Tullow Oil Gabon SA (1)
Quartier Tahiti Immeuble Narval, BP 9773, Libreville, Gabon
Tel.: (241) 732640
Drilling Oil & Gas Wells
N.A.I.C.S.: 213111

Tullow Oil Limited (1)
(100%)
Tel.: (353) 12137300
Sales Range: $50-74.9 Million
Emp.: 70
Drilling Oil & Gas Wells
N.A.I.C.S.: 213111

Tullow Oil SK Limited (1)
9 Chiswick Park 566 Chiswick High Road, London, W4 5XT, United Kingdom (100%)
Tel.: (44) 2089961000
Web Site: http://www.tullowoil.com
Sales Range: $200-249.9 Million
Emp.: 300
Crude Petroleum & Natural Gas Extraction
N.A.I.C.S.: 211120

Tullow Oil SPE Limited (1)
(100%)
Tel.: (44) 2089961000
Web Site: http://www.tullowoil.com
Sales Range: $200-249.9 Million
Emp.: 300
Support Activities for Oil & Gas Operations
N.A.I.C.S.: 213112

Tullow Oil UK Limited (1)
3rd Floor Building 11 Chiswick Park, 566 Chiswick High Road, W45YS, London, United Kingdom (100%)
Tel.: (44) 2089961000
Sales Range: $200-249.9 Million
Emp.: 350
Drilling Oil & Gas Wells
N.A.I.C.S.: 213111

Tullow Overseas Holdings B.V. (1)
Scheveningseweg 58, Hague, 2517 KW, Netherlands (100%)
Tel.: (31) 703387546
Web Site: http://www.tullowoil.com

Sales Range: $25-49.9 Million
Emp.: 3
Oil & Gas Field Machinery & Equipment Mfr
N.A.I.C.S.: 333132

Tullow South Africa (Pty) Ltd (1)
(100%)
Tel.: (27) 214007600
Web Site: http://www.tullowoil.com
Sales Range: $25-49.9 Million
Emp.: 100
Oil & Gas Field Machinery & Equipment Mfr
N.A.I.C.S.: 333132

Tullow Tanzania B.V. (1)
Scheveningseweg 58, Hague, 2517 KW, Zuid-Holland, Netherlands
Tel.: (31) 703387546
Oil & Gas Exploration Services
N.A.I.C.S.: 213112

Tullow Uganda Operations Pty Ltd (1)
2nd Floor Lotis Towers Plot 16 Mackinnon Road, PO Box 16644, Kampala, Uganda
Tel.: (256) 312564000
Oil & Gas Exploration Services
N.A.I.C.S.: 213112

TULPAR JOINT STOCK COMPANY

2nd Bag Ulgii Soum, Olgii, Mongolia
Tel.: (976) 99422199
TLP—(MONG)
Rev.: $10,260
Assets: $10,119
Liabilities: $232
Net Worth: $9,887
Earnings: ($376)
Fiscal Year-end: 12/31/20
Transportation Services
N.A.I.C.S.: 488999

TULSI EXTRUSIONS LIMITED

N-99/100 M I D C Area, Jalgaon, 425 003, India
Tel.: (91) 8530069505
Web Site: https://www.tulsipipes.in
Year Founded: 1994
Polyvinyl Chloride, Soil Waste, Rain Water, PVC Casing, Screen Pipes, High Density Polyethylene & Linear Low Density Polyethylene Pipes & Fittings
N.A.I.C.S.: 332996

Subsidiaries:

Tulsi Extrusions Limited, Unit -I (1)
Plot No N-99 100 109 M I D C Area, Jalgaon, 425 003, Maharashtra, India
Tel.: (91) 2572272732
Emp.: 400
Pipes Mfr
N.A.I.C.S.: 327332
Sanjay Kumar Taparia (CEO)

Tulsi Extrusions Limited, Unit -II (1)
Plot No H 16 M I D C Area, Jalgaon, 425 003, India
Tel.: (91) 2572271265
Pipes Mfr
N.A.I.C.S.: 486990

Tulsi Extrusions Limited, Unit -III (1)
Plot No G-51 52 M I D C Area, Jalgaon, 425 003, Maharashtra, India
Tel.: (91) 257 2210792
Pipes Mfr
N.A.I.C.S.: 327332

TULSYAN NEC LIMITED

Apex Plaza 1st Floor 3 Nungambakkam, Chennai, 600 034, India
Tel.: (91) 4439181060
Web Site: http://www.tulsyannec.co.in
Year Founded: 1947
Rev.: $116,030,556
Assets: $127,566,362
Liabilities: $107,944,705
Net Worth: $19,621,657
Earnings: $107,953,086
Emp.: 555
Fiscal Year-end: 03/31/22

Steel Tube Mfr
N.A.I.C.S.: 331210
Lalit Kumar Tulsyan (Chm)

Subsidiaries:

Chitrakoot Steel & Power Pvt. Ltd. (1)
Survey No 77 Thandalacherry Road New Gummidipoondi, Thiruvallur, Chennai, India
Tel.: (91) 44 27921541
Sales Range: $25-49.9 Million
Emp.: 80
Sponge Iron Mfr
N.A.I.C.S.: 331110

Cosmic Global Ltd (1)
3 Apex Plaza First Floor Nungambakkam High Road, Chennai, 600 034, Tamil Nadu, India
Tel.: (91) 44 39181080
Web Site: http://www.cosmicgloballimited.com
Emp.: 110
Business Process Outsourcing Services
N.A.I.C.S.: 561499
Priya Tulsyan (Exec Dir)

TUM FINANCE PLC

Tum Invest Mdina Road, Qormi, QRM 9010, Malta
Tel.: (356) 23850100
Web Site: http://www.tumfinance.com
Year Founded: 2015
TM29A—(MAL)
Rev.: $4,076,333
Assets: $82,888,533
Liabilities: $37,195,418
Net Worth: $45,693,115
Earnings: $1,878,586
Emp.: 9
Fiscal Year-end: 12/31/23
Real Estate Investment Services
N.A.I.C.S.: 531390
Anthony Fenech (Exec Dir)

Subsidiaries:

San Gwakkin Limited (1)

TUMOSAN MOTOR VE TRAKTOR SANAYI A.S.

Maltepe Mahallesi Londra Asfalti Cad No 28/1 Topkapi, Zeytinburnu, 34010, Istanbul, Turkiye
Tel.: (90) 2124676700
Web Site: https://www.tumosan.com.tr
Year Founded: 1976
TMSN—(IST)
Rev.: $114,948,287
Assets: $101,990,414
Liabilities: $51,893,207
Net Worth: $50,097,207
Earnings: $17,835,922
Emp.: 627
Fiscal Year-end: 12/31/22
Tractor Mfr
N.A.I.C.S.: 333111

Subsidiaries:

Tumosan Dokum A.S. (1)
Maltepe Mahallesi Londra Asfalti Caddesi No 28/1 Topkapi, Zeytinburnu, 34010, Istanbul, Turkiye
Tel.: (90) 2124681900
Web Site: https://www.tumosandokum.com.tr
Gary Casting Iron Mfr
N.A.I.C.S.: 331511

TUMRIIN ZAVOD JOINT STOCK COMPANY

3rd Khoroo Osg, Bayangol District, Ulaanbaatar, Mongolia
Tel.: (976) 1 134 4747
Rev.: $3,455
Assets: $53,358
Liabilities: $372,191
Net Worth: ($318,833)
Earnings: ($153,069)

Fiscal Year-end: 12/31/18
Iron Forging Services
N.A.I.C.S.: 332111

TUNE PROTECT GROUP BERHAD

Tel.: (60) 320566200
Web Site: https://www.tuneprotect.com
Year Founded: 2011
TUNEPRO—(KLS)
Rev.: $112,065,397
Assets: $343,990,053
Liabilities: $222,468,571
Net Worth: $121,521,481
Earnings: ($7,229,841)
Emp.: 484
Fiscal Year-end: 12/31/22
Holding Company; Insurance Services
N.A.I.C.S.: 551112
Ng Siek Chuan (Chm)

Subsidiaries:

Tune Insurance Malaysia Berhad (1)
Level 8 Wisma Capital A 19 Lorong Dungun, Damansara Heights, 50490, Kuala Lumpur, Malaysia
Tel.: (60) 340654244
Web Site: https://www.tuneprotect.com
Insurance Services
N.A.I.C.S.: 524298
N.G. Soon Lai (Chm)

TUNG HO STEEL ENTERPRISE CORPORATION

6F No 9 Sec 1 Chang-an E Rd, Taipei, 10441, Taiwan
Tel.: (886) 225511100
Web Site: https://www.tunghosteel.com
Year Founded: 1962
TNGHS—(LUX)
Rev.: $1,993,587,289
Assets: $1,843,712,282
Liabilities: $824,673,830
Net Worth: $1,019,038,452
Earnings: $153,998,653
Emp.: 3,107
Fiscal Year-end: 12/31/23
Steel Products Mfr
N.A.I.C.S.: 331110
Henry C. T. Ho (Chm & CEO)

Subsidiaries:

Fujian Tung Kang Steel Co., Ltd. (1)
No 5 Yanxi Road, Hongkuan Industrial Village Yangxia Town, Fuqing, 350323, Fujian, China
Tel.: (86) 59185295118
Iron & Steel Forging Product Mfr
N.A.I.C.S.: 332111

Katec Creative Resources Corporation (1)
NO 231 Huanke Rd Park, Guanyin Township, Taoyuan, 32841, Taiwan
Tel.: (886) 34738898
Web Site: https://www.kcr-metal.com.tw
Iron & Steel Forging Product Mfr
N.A.I.C.S.: 332111

Tung Ho Steel Enterprise Corporation - Kaohsiung Works (1)
No 8 Jiaxing St, Xiaogang Dist, Kaohsiung, 81257, Taiwan
Tel.: (886) 78023131
Web Site: http://www.tunghosteel.com
Reinforcing Bars & Rolling Iron Products Mfr
N.A.I.C.S.: 331110
Tsung-Yu Wang (Gen Mgr)

Tung Ho Steel Enterprise Corporation - Miaoli Works (1)
No 22 Pingding Erhu Village, Sihu Township, Miao-li, 36842, Taiwan
Tel.: (886) 37923333
Sales Range: $100-124.9 Million
Emp.: 500
Iron Slab & Billets Mfr

N.A.I.C.S.: 331110
Lu Ming Zong (Gen Mgr)

Tung Ho Steel Enterprise Corporation - Taoyuan Works (1)
No 116 Neighbor 8 Baojhang Village, Guanyin Township, Taoyuan, 32851, Taiwan
Tel.: (886) 34761151
Sales Range: $125-149.9 Million
Emp.: 300
Reinforcing Bars & Iron Billets Mfr
N.A.I.C.S.: 331110

Tung Ho Steel Vietnam Corporation Limited (1)
Phu My II Industrial Zone, Phu My Ward, Phu My, Ba Ria Vung Tau, Vietnam
Tel.: (84) 2543924461
Web Site: https://www.thsvc.com.vn
Iron & Steel Forging Product Mfr
N.A.I.C.S.: 332111

Tung Kang Steel Structure Corp. (1)
6 Fl 9Chang An E Road Sec 1, Taipei, 104, Taiwan
Tel.: (886) 225511100
Iron & Steel Forging Product Mfr
N.A.I.C.S.: 332111

Subsidiary (Domestic):

Tung Kang Engineering & Construction Corp. (2)
No 116 Caota Neighbor 8, Baozhang Vil Guanyin Dist, Taoyuan, 32847, Taiwan
Tel.: (886) 34761889
Iron & Steel Forging Product Mfr
N.A.I.C.S.: 332111

Tung Kang Wind Power Corp. (1)
9 Fl 9Chang An E Road Sec 1, Taipei, 104, Taiwan
Tel.: (886) 37923333
Iron & Steel Forging Product Mfr
N.A.I.C.S.: 332111

TUNG HO TEXTILE CO., LTD.
No 227 Industrial Road, Madou Dist, T'ainan, 721, Taiwan
Tel.: (886) 65703211
Web Site: https://www.tungho.com.tw
Year Founded: 1959
1414—(TAI)
Rev.: $18,531,017
Assets: $146,870,265
Liabilities: $44,405,669
Net Worth: $102,464,596
Earnings: $1,074,234
Emp.: 200
Fiscal Year-end: 12/31/23
Textile Products Mfr
N.A.I.C.S.: 314999

TUNG LOK RESTAURANTS (2000) LTD
26 Tai Seng Street 02-01, Singapore, 534057, Singapore
Tel.: (65) 62707998
Web Site: https://www.tunglok.com
540—(CAT)
Rev.: $63,869,806
Assets: $35,601,720
Liabilities: $24,434,848
Net Worth: $11,166,871
Earnings: $3,982,219
Emp.: 501
Fiscal Year-end: 03/31/23
Restaurant Services
N.A.I.C.S.: 722511
Poh York Chua (Sr VP-Ops)

Subsidiaries:

Garuda Padang Restaurant (Singapore) Pte Ltd (1)
1 HarbourFront Walk B2-28 Vivo City, Singapore, 098585, Singapore
Tel.: (65) 63769595
Restaurant Services
N.A.I.C.S.: 722511

My Humble House in Beijing (Restaurant) Company Ltd (1)
Oriental Plaza Podium Level W3 Office Towers Unit 01-07 No 1, East Chang An Avenue, Beijing, 100738, China
Tel.: (86) 1085188811
Web Site: http://www.tunglk.com
Restaurant Services
N.A.I.C.S.: 722511

Olde Peking Dining Hall Pte Ltd (1)
02-11/12 238 Thomson Road, Singapore, 307683, Singapore
Tel.: (65) 63584466
Web Site: http://www.laobeijing.com.sg
Sales Range: $10-24.9 Million
Emp.: 14
Restaurant Operating Services
N.A.I.C.S.: 722511
Jason Li (Mgr)

Shin Yeh Restaurant Pte Ltd (1)
177 River Valley Rd Liang Ct Shopping Ctr 02-19, Singapore, 179030, Singapore
Tel.: (65) 63387337
Web Site: http://www.shinyeh.com.sg
Emp.: 18
Restaurant Operating Services
N.A.I.C.S.: 722511

Slappy Cakes (Singapore) Pte. Ltd. (1)
The Grandstand 200 Turf Club Road Old Turf Club in Bt Timah 01-20/21, Singapore, 287994, Singapore
Tel.: (65) 64651814
Web Site: http://www.slappycakes.com.sg
Restaurant Services
N.A.I.C.S.: 722511

Tong Le Private Dining Pte. Ltd. (1)
OUE Tower Level 10 60 Collyer Quay, Singapore, 049322, Singapore
Tel.: (65) 66343233
Web Site: https://www.tong-le.com.sg
Restaurant Services
N.A.I.C.S.: 722511

Tung Lok Arena Pte Ltd (1)
511 Up Jurong Road, Singapore, 638366, Singapore
Tel.: (65) 62626996
Sales Range: $10-24.9 Million
Emp.: 30
Restaurant Operating Services
N.A.I.C.S.: 722511

Tung Lok Millennium Pte Ltd (1)
26 Tai Seng Street Unit 02- 01, Singapore, 534057, Singapore
Tel.: (65) 62707998
Web Site: http://www.tunglok.com
Emp.: 600
Restaurant Operating Services
N.A.I.C.S.: 722511
Andrew Tjioe (Exec Chm)

Subsidiary (Domestic):

Tung Lok Central Restaurant Pte Ltd (2)
6 Eu Tong Sen St Ste 02-88, Singapore, 059817, Singapore
Tel.: (65) 63366022
Web Site: http://www.tunglok.com
Emp.: 200
Restaurant Services
N.A.I.C.S.: 722511
Esther Hu (Mgr)

Tung Lok Signatures Pte Ltd (1)
Orchard Rendezvous Hotel 02-18 1 Tanglin Road, Singapore, 247905, Singapore
Tel.: (65) 68340660
Web Site: http://www.tungloksignatures.com
Sales Range: $10-24.9 Million
Emp.: 30
Restaurant Services
N.A.I.C.S.: 722511
Emily Loh (Gen Mgr)

TUNG THIH ELECTRONIC CO., LTD.
No 9 Ln 1156 Nanqing Rd, Luzhu Dist, Taoyuan, 338015, Taiwan
Tel.: (886) 33222902
Web Site: https://tungthih.com.tw
Year Founded: 1979
3552—(TPE)
Rev.: $297,134,228
Assets: $318,936,341
Liabilities: $184,327,236
Net Worth: $134,609,105
Earnings: $19,315,980
Emp.: 2,142
Fiscal Year-end: 12/31/22
Automobile Part Mfr & Distr
N.A.I.C.S.: 336390
Scott Chen (Chm & CEO)

TUNG-JETEK CO., LTD.
6F 3 No 94 Bau Chung Rd, Hsin Tien City, Taipei, 104, Hsien, Taiwan
Tel.: (886) 229162199
Web Site: http://www.tung-jetek.com.tw
Sales Range: $25-49.9 Million
Emp.: 10
Semiconductor Assembly & Packaging Products
N.A.I.C.S.: 326199
Jun Cheng Liu (Pres)

Subsidiaries:

Magajine Sapurai Malaysia Sdn Bhd (1)
PLO 439, Off Jalan Besi, Kawasan Perindustrian, Pasir Gudang, 81700, Johor, Pasir Gudang, Malaysia
Tel.: (60) 7 252 8929
Semiconductor Assembly & Packaging Products
N.A.I.C.S.: 326199

Magazine Supply Co., Ltd. (1)
608-1 Kodama Kodama-cho, Honjo City, Saitama, 367-0212, Japan
Tel.: (81) 495726567
Web Site: http://www.tanehashi.co.jp
Semiconductor Assembly & Packaging Products
N.A.I.C.S.: 326199

TR Tech Co., Ltd. (1)
2-23-3 Sengoku, Bunkyo-ku, Tokyo, 112-0011, Japan
Tel.: (81) 3 3944 3581
Semiconductor Assembly & Packaging Products
N.A.I.C.S.: 326199

TUNGHSU AZURE RENEWABLE ENERGY CO., LTD.
1 Caiyuan Street, Xicheng District, Beijing, 100000, Guangdong, China
Tel.: (86) 1083978866
Web Site: https://www.dongxulantian.com
Year Founded: 1994
000040—(SSE)
Rev.: $426,283,575
Assets: $3,576,487,052
Liabilities: $1,995,341,943
Net Worth: $1,581,145,109
Earnings: $43,422,112
Emp.: 1,735
Fiscal Year-end: 12/31/22
Investment Services
N.A.I.C.S.: 523999
Zhao Yanjun (Chm & Gen Mgr)

TUNGKONG CO., LTD.
No 23 Shanda Northern Rd, Jinan, 250100, Shandong, China
Tel.: (86) 4006185968
Web Site: https://www.tungkong.com.cn
Year Founded: 1996
002117—(SSE)
Rev.: $149,522,195
Assets: $314,665,758
Liabilities: $96,508,475
Net Worth: $218,157,283
Earnings: $18,899,441
Emp.: 1,400
Fiscal Year-end: 12/31/22
Printing Services
N.A.I.C.S.: 323120
Wang Aixian (Chm)

Subsidiaries:

Tung Kong Security Printing Co., Ltd. - Beijing Factory (1)
No 139 Jinghai Fourth Road, Beijing Economic & Technological Development Zone, Beijing, China
Tel.: (86) 1080806101
Ticket & Security Printing Services
N.A.I.C.S.: 323120

Tung Kong Security Printing Co., Ltd. - Chengdu Factory (1)
No 163 Qingjiang Road Shuangliu Industrial Park, Chengdu, Sichuan, China
Tel.: (86) 2885737535
Ticket & Security Printing Services
N.A.I.C.S.: 323120

Tung Kong Security Printing Co., Ltd. - Guangzhou Factory (1)
No 5 Nanyun Fifth Road Science City, Guangzhou, Guangdong, China
Tel.: (86) 2028398111
Ticket & Security Printing Services
N.A.I.C.S.: 323120

Tung Kong Security Printing Co., Ltd. - Qinghai Factory (1)
No 22 Jingsi Road, Xining, Qinghai, China
Tel.: (86) 9718062051
Ticket & Security Printing Services
N.A.I.C.S.: 323120

Tung Kong Security Printing Co., Ltd. - Shanghai Factory (1)
No 597 Yuandian Road Minhang Development Zone, Shanghai, China
Tel.: (86) 2151591718
Ticket & Security Printing Services
N.A.I.C.S.: 323120

Tung Kong Security Printing Co., Ltd. - Xinjiang Factory (1)
No 3 the second Xiamen Street, Urumchi Economic & Technological Development Zone, Xinjiang, China
Tel.: (86) 9913780301
Ticket & Security Printing Services
N.A.I.C.S.: 323120

Tung Kong Security Printing Co., Ltd. - Zhengzhou Factory (1)
No 11 Guohuai Street High-tech Development Zone, Zhengzhou, Henan, China
Tel.: (86) 37167995187
Ticket & Security Printing Services
N.A.I.C.S.: 323120

TUNGKUANG INDUSTRIAL JOINT STOCK COMPANY
No 3 Road 2A Bien Hoa II Industrial Park Long Binh Tan Ward, Bien Hoa, Dong Nai, Vietnam
Tel.: (84) 2513836688
Web Site: https://www.tungkuang.com.vn
Year Founded: 1989
TKU—(HNX)
Rev.: $119,463,900
Assets: $115,108,800
Liabilities: $57,742,200
Net Worth: $57,366,600
Earnings: $6,726,500
Fiscal Year-end: 12/31/22
Aluminium Products Mfr
N.A.I.C.S.: 331315

Subsidiaries:

TungKuang Industrial Joint Stock Company - HAI DUONG FACTORY (1)
Road No 5 Cau Ghe Cam Phuc Comute, Cam Giang District, Hai Duong, Vietnam
Tel.: (84) 320 3630888
Web Site: http://www.tungkuang.com.vn
Emp.: 100
Aluminium Products Mfr
N.A.I.C.S.: 331315
Fung Nguyen (CEO)

TungKuang Industrial Joint Stock Company - NHON TRACH FACTORY (1)
No 25B Road Nhon Trach I Industrial Park,

TUNGKUANG INDUSTRIAL JOINT STOCK COMPANY

TungKuang Industrial Joint Stock Company—(Continued)
Nhon Trach District, Nhon Trach, Dong Nai, Vietnam
Tel.: (84) 61 3569569
Aluminium Products Mfr
N.A.I.C.S.: 331315

TUNGRAY TECHNOLOGIES INC.
02-01 31 Mandai Estate Innovation Place Tower 4, Singapore, 729933, Singapore
Tel.: (65) 66369820 Ky
Web Site: https://www.tungray.com
Year Founded: 2022
TRSG—(NASDAQ)
Rev.: $14,362,502
Assets: $26,869,174
Liabilities: $10,649,306
Net Worth: $16,219,868
Earnings: $915,422
Emp.: 170
Fiscal Year-end: 12/31/23
Industrial Machinery Mfr
N.A.I.C.S.: 333248

TUNGSTEN MINING NL
Level 4 46 Colin Street, West Perth, 6005, WA, Australia
Tel.: (61) 894868492
Web Site:
  https://www.tungstenmining.com
TGN—(ASX)
Rev.: $852,740
Assets: $19,933,793
Liabilities: $1,654,213
Net Worth: $18,279,579
Earnings: ($3,414,113)
Fiscal Year-end: 06/30/24
Tungsten Mining
N.A.I.C.S.: 212290
Craig Ferrier (CEO)

TUNGSTEN WEST PLC
Hemerdon Mine Drakelands, Plympton, PL7 5BW, Devon, United Kingdom
Tel.: (44) 1752278500 UK
Web Site:
  https://www.tungstenwest.com
Year Founded: 2019
TUN—(AIM)
Rev.: $777,938
Assets: $52,677,986
Liabilities: $14,205,169
Net Worth: $38,472,817
Earnings: ($12,772,453)
Emp.: 81
Fiscal Year-end: 03/31/23
Mining Services
N.A.I.C.S.: 212390
David Connal Cather (Chm)

TUNGTEX (HOLDINGS) CO. LTD.
Office A 26th Floor EGL Tower No 83 Hung To Road, Kwun Tong, Kowloon, China (Hong Kong)
Tel.: (852) 27977000
Web Site: https://www.tungtex.com
Year Founded: 1977
0518—(HKG)
Rev.: $75,874,936
Assets: $80,100,707
Liabilities: $29,271,624
Net Worth: $50,829,083
Earnings: ($3,443,379)
Emp.: 1,200
Fiscal Year-end: 03/31/22
Women's Clothing Mfr
N.A.I.C.S.: 315220
Dickson Pui Ki Chu (Sec)

Subsidiaries:

Do Do Fashion Limited (1)
4/F Tungtex Building, 203 Wai Yip Street Kwun Tong, Kowloon, China (Hong Kong) (100%)
Tel.: (852) 27977770
Emp.: 100
Clothing & Furnishings Whslr
N.A.I.C.S.: 424350
Edmund Lan (Mng Dir)

Guangzhou Panyu Golden Fountain Ind., Ltd. (1)
67 Shi Xin Road South Nan Village Panyu, Guangzhou, 511442, China
Tel.: (86) 20 2288 7333
Web Site: http://www.tungtex.com
Fashion Apparels Mfr
N.A.I.C.S.: 315250

Sing Yang Services Limited (1)
8 11th Floor Tungtex Building, 203 Wai Yip St Kwun Tong, Kowloon, China (Hong Kong) (100%)
Tel.: (852) 27977900
Sales Range: $25-49.9 Million
Emp.: 11
Childrens & Infants Clothing & Accessories Whslr
N.A.I.C.S.: 424350

Sing Yang Trading Limited (1)
12/F Tungtex Building 203 Wai Yip St, Kowloon, China (Hong Kong) (100%)
Tel.: (852) 27977770
Web Site: http://www.tungtex.com
Childrens & Infants Clothing & Accessories Whslr
N.A.I.C.S.: 424350

THL Inc. (1)
499 Fashion Ave Fl 19 S, New York, NY 10018-6853
Tel.: (212) 764-0020
Web Site: http://www.thl.com
Women's Clothing Store
N.A.I.C.S.: 458110

Tung Thai Fashions Limited (1)
587 Moo 6 Taiboon Rd Soi Tessaban Bangpoo 21, Tambol Taibann Amphur Muang, 10280, Bangkok, Samutprakarn, Thailand (100%)
Tel.: (66) 27034810
Web Site: http://www.tungtex.com
Sales Range: $250-299.9 Million
Emp.: 1,000
Childrens & Infants Clothing & Accessories Whslr
N.A.I.C.S.: 424350

Tungtex (UK) Limited (1)
74 New Bond St, 1st & 2nd Floor, London, W1S 1RT, United Kingdom (100%)
Tel.: (44) 2074090080
Web Site: http://www.tungtex.com
Sales Range: $50-74.9 Million
Emp.: 5
Childrens & Infants Clothing & Accessories Whslr
N.A.I.C.S.: 424350
David Chan (Dir-UK)

Tungtex Fashions (Vietnam) Limited (1)
Lot A2 Road No 2, Thuan Dao Industrial Park, Ben Luc, Long An, Vietnam
Tel.: (84) 72 363 7808
Lady Apparel Mfr & Distr
N.A.I.C.S.: 315250

Tungtex International Limited (1)
12/F Tungtex Building 203 Wai Yip Street, Kwun Tong, Kowloon, China (Hong Kong)
Tel.: (852) 2 797 7070
Web Site: https://www.tungtexint.com
Lady Apparel Mfr & Distr
N.A.I.C.S.: 315250

Tungtex Trading Company Limited (1)
12/F Tungtex Building 203 Wai Yip Street, Kwun Tong, Kowloon, China (Hong Kong) (100%)
Tel.: (852) 27977070
Web Site: http://www.tungtex.com
Emp.: 2,000
Children's & Infants' Clothing & Accessories Whslr
N.A.I.C.S.: 424350

West Pacific Enterprises Corporation (1)
530 7th Ave Ste 907, New York, NY 10018
Tel.: (212) 564-6800
Web Site: http://www.tungtex.com
Sales Range: $25-49.9 Million
Emp.: 3
Apparel & Accessories Mfr
N.A.I.C.S.: 315990
Daniel Kwok (VP)

Winnertex Fashions Limited (1)
4th Floor Tungtex Bldg, 203 Wai Yip St Kwun Tong, Kowloon, China (Hong Kong) (75%)
Tel.: (852) 27977822
Childrens & Infants Clothing & Accessories Whslr
N.A.I.C.S.: 424350

Yellow River, Inc. (1)
499 7th Ave 39th St S Tower, New York, NY 10018
Tel.: (212) 764-1775
Emp.: 10
Childrens & Infants Clothing & Accessories Whslr
N.A.I.C.S.: 424350
Peter Mui (Pres)

TUNI TEXTILE MILLS LIMITED
Unit No 207 2nd Floor Building No 3A Mittal Industrial Estate, Andheri Kurla Road Andheri E, Mumbai, 400 059, India
Tel.: (91) 2249700409
Web Site:
  https://www.tunitextiles.com
Year Founded: 1987
531411—(BOM)
Rev.: $5,221,965
Assets: $4,009,184
Liabilities: $2,450,980
Net Worth: $1,558,204
Earnings: $30,646
Emp.: 72
Fiscal Year-end: 03/31/23
Textile Products Mfr
N.A.I.C.S.: 313310
Narendra Kumar Sureka (Co-Founder, Chm & Mng Dir)

TUNISIE TELECOM
Jardins du Lac II, Tunis, 1053, Tunisia
Tel.: (216) 71 901 717
Web Site:
  http://www.tunisietelecom.tn
Telecommunication Servicesb
N.A.I.C.S.: 517810
Philippe Montourcier (CFO)

Subsidiaries:

GO p.l.c. (1)
Triq Fra Diegu, Marsa, MRS 1501, Malta (65.42%)
Tel.: (356) 80072121
Web Site: https://www.go.com.mt
Rev.: $227,436,886
Assets: $438,932,444
Liabilities: $283,730,809
Net Worth: $155,201,635
Earnings: $17,270,283
Emp.: 1,213
Fiscal Year-end: 12/31/2020
Telcommunications Services
N.A.I.C.S.: 517112
Francis Galea Salomone (Sec)

Subsidiary (Domestic):

BMIT Technologies PLC (2)
SCM02 Level 2 SmartCity Malta, Kalkara, SCM1001, Malta
Tel.: (356) 22588200
Web Site: https://www.bmit.com.mt
Rev.: $27,823,225
Assets: $27,509,173
Liabilities: $15,575,221
Net Worth: $11,933,952
Earnings: $5,779,193
Emp.: 59
Fiscal Year-end: 12/31/2022
Information Technology Services
N.A.I.C.S.: 541512
Christian Sammut (CEO)

INTERNATIONAL PUBLIC

TUNIU CORPORATION
Tuniu Building No 699-32 Xuanwu-dadao, Xuanwu District, Nanjing, 210042, Jiangsu, China
Tel.: (86) 2586853969 Ky
Web Site: https://www.tuniu.com
Year Founded: 2006
TOUR—(NASDAQ)
Rev.: $28,132,420
Assets: $287,717,655
Liabilities: $129,735,777
Net Worth: $157,981,879
Earnings: ($29,628,056)
Emp.: 896
Fiscal Year-end: 12/31/22
Online Travel Services
N.A.I.C.S.: 561599
Donald Dunde Yu (Co-Founder, Chm & CEO)

TUNSTALL GROUP LIMITED
Whitley Lodge Whitley Bridge, Doncaster, DN14 0HR, Yorkshire, United Kingdom
Tel.: (44) 1977 66 1234 UK
Web Site: http://www.uk.tunstall.com
Year Founded: 1957
Sales Range: $150-199.9 Million
Emp.: 2,000
Holding Company; Telehealthcare Solutions
N.A.I.C.S.: 551112
Steve Sadler (CTO)

Subsidiaries:

Tunstall A/S (1)
Niels Bohrs Vej 42 Stilling, 8660, Skanderborg, Denmark
Tel.: (45) 87 93 50 00
Healtcare Services
N.A.I.C.S.: 622110
Niels Ole Andersen (Dir-Quality Assurance & Regulatory Compliance)

Tunstall AB (1)
Agnesfridsvagen 113 A, 212 37, Malmo, Sweden
Tel.: (46) 40 625 25 00
Web Site: http://www.tunstallnordic.com
Safety Equipment Mfr
N.A.I.C.S.: 561621
Anna Skogh (Mgr-Alarm Central)

Tunstall AG (1)
Atte Lysstrasse 12, 3270, Bern, Switzerland
Tel.: (41) 264 93 43 46
Web Site: http://www.tunstall.ch
Safety Equipment Mfr
N.A.I.C.S.: 561621

Tunstall Australasia Pty Ltd (1)
Unit 1 56 Lavarack Ave, Eagle Farm, 4009, QLD, Australia
Tel.: (61) 7 3637 2200
Web Site:
  http://www.tunstallhealthcare.com.au
Healtcare Services
N.A.I.C.S.: 622110
Geoff Feakes (CIO)

Tunstall B.V. (1)
Oslo 26-28, 2993 LD, Barendrecht, Netherlands
Tel.: (31) 180 696 696
Web Site: http://www.tunstall.de
Healtcare Services
N.A.I.C.S.: 622110
Florian Lupfer-Kusenberg (Mng Dir)

Tunstall Canada Inc (1)
111 Zenway Blvd Unit 6A, Woodbridge, L4H 3H9, ON, Canada
Tel.: (905) 677-1144
Web Site: https://canada.tunstall.com
Healtcare Services
N.A.I.C.S.: 622110
Stan Albert (Gen Mgr)

Tunstall Emergency Response Ltd. (1)
Ryland Road Bunclody, Enniscorthy, Co Wexford, Ireland
Tel.: (353) 53 937 6400

AND PRIVATE COMPANIES — TURBON AG

Web Site: http://www.emergencyresponse.ie
Healtcare Services
N.A.I.C.S.: 622110
James Doyle *(Mng Dir)*

Tunstall GmbH (1)
Orkotten 66, 48291, Telgte, Germany
Tel.: (49) 2504 7010
Web Site: http://www.tunstall.de
Healtcare Services
N.A.I.C.S.: 622110
Stefan Goehler *(Mgr-Sls)*

Tunstall Healthcare Group Limited (1)
Whitley Lodge Whitley Bridge, Goole, DN14 0HR, North Yorkshire, United Kingdom
Tel.: (44) 1977661234
Web Site: http://www.tunstallhealth.com
Emp.: 400
Holding Company; Telehealthcare Products & Services
N.A.I.C.S.: 551112
Steve Sadler *(CTO)*

Subsidiary (US):

American Medical Alert Corp. (2)
3265 Lawson Blvd, Oceanside, NY 11572-3723
Tel.: (516) 536-5850
Web Site: http://www.amacalert.com
Sales Range: $25-49.9 Million
Healthcare Communication Appliances Mfr
N.A.I.C.S.: 423450

Subsidiary (Domestic):

Tunstall Healthcare (UK) Limited (2)
Whitley Lodge Whitley Bridge, Doncaster, DN14 0HR, Yorkshire, United Kingdom
Tel.: (44) 1977 66 1234
Web Site: http://www.tunstallhealthcare.com
Sales Range: $100-124.9 Million
Emp.: 400
Telehealthcare Products & Services
N.A.I.C.S.: 561990
Simon Arnold *(Mng Dir)*

Subsidiary (Non-US):

Tunstall Healthcare A/S (2)
Stroemmen 6, DK-9400, Norresundby, Denmark
Tel.: (45) 7210 0163
Web Site: http://www.tunstallhealth.com
Telehealthcare Products & Services
N.A.I.C.S.: 561990

Tunstall Iberica, S.A. (1)
Avda de Castilla 2 Parque Empresarial San Fernando Edificio Munich 2 P, San Fernando de Henares, 28830, Madrid, Spain
Tel.: (34) 91 655 58 30
Healtcare Services
N.A.I.C.S.: 622110

Tunstall New Zealand Limited (1)
2 65 Chaple Street, PO Box 13153, Tauranga, 3110, New Zealand
Tel.: (64) 7 571 2680
Web Site: http://www.tunstall.co.nz
Health Care Srvices
N.A.I.C.S.: 622110

Tunstall Oy (1)
Ayritie 22, Vantaa, Finland
Tel.: (358) 10 320 1690
Healtcare Services
N.A.I.C.S.: 622110
Kim Ek *(Country Mgr)*

Tunstall S.A./N.V. (1)
Rue De Naples 18, 1050, Brussels, Belgium
Tel.: (32) 2 51 000 70
Web Site: http://www.tunstall.be
Healtcare Services
N.A.I.C.S.: 622110

Tunstall Technologies S.A. (1)
140 Avenue Jean Lolive, 93500, Pantin, France
Tel.: (33) 810 00 55 63
Web Site: http://www.tunstall.fr
Healtcare Services
N.A.I.C.S.: 622110
Alain Monteux *(Dir-Publ)*

TUNTEX DISTINCT CORP.
Tower C 16FL No 90 Sec 1 Hsin-Tai 5th Rd, Hsichih, Taipei, 221, Taiwan
Tel.: (886) 226961000
Web Site: http://www.tdc.com.tw
Year Founded: 1972
Sales Range: $350-399.9 Million
Emp.: 1,970
Polyester Products Mfr; Real Estate Services
N.A.I.C.S.: 313230
Jeffrey Huang *(Mgr)*

Subsidiaries:

Tuntex (Thailand) Public Company Limited (1)
Tower C 16FL No 90 Sec 1 Hsin-Tai 5th Rd, Hsichih, Taipei, Taiwan
Tel.: (886) 226961000
Web Site: http://www.tdc.com.tw
Broadwoven Fabric Mills
N.A.I.C.S.: 313210

Tuntex Incorporation (1)
23rd Floor 90 Hsin Tai 5th Rd, Sec 1, Taipei, Taiwan
Tel.: (886) 226969933
Web Site: http://www.tuntexinc.com
Yarn Texturizing Throwing & Twisting Mills
N.A.I.C.S.: 313110

TUOXIN PHARMACEUTICAL GROUP CO., LTD.
No 515 Kelong Avenue, Hongqi District, Xinxiang, 453000, Henan, China
Tel.: (86) 3736351918
Web Site: https://www.tuoxinpharm.com
Year Founded: 2001
301089—(CHIN)
Rev.: $110,174,688
Assets: $258,793,704
Liabilities: $65,551,356
Net Worth: $193,242,348
Earnings: $40,230,216
Fiscal Year-end: 12/31/22
Pharmaceutical Product Mfr & Distr
N.A.I.C.S.: 325412
Yang Yuhua *(Sec)*

TUPPER, INC.
5 Ipil Street Project 3, Quezon City, 1102, Philippines
Tel.: (63) 9153711115   NV
Year Founded: 2008
Pig Watering Troughs Developer, Mfr & Sales
N.A.I.C.S.: 333111
David Ring *(Pres, CEO, CFO, Chief Acctg Officer, Treas & Sec)*

TUPY S.A.
Rua Albano Schmidt 3400, Joinville, 89205 100, SC, Brazil
Tel.: (55) 4740098181   BR
Web Site: https://www.tupy.com.br
Year Founded: 1938
TUPY3—(BRAZ)
Rev.: $1,278,400,374
Assets: $1,268,641,266
Liabilities: $677,568,031
Net Worth: $591,073,235
Earnings: $69,057,985
Emp.: 12,000
Fiscal Year-end: 12/31/19
Iron & Steel Products & Automotive Parts Mfr
N.A.I.C.S.: 331511
Fernando Cestari De Rizzo *(CEO)*

Subsidiaries:

TUPY Europe GmbH (1)
Am Hochacker 2, D-85630, Grasbrunn, Germany
Tel.: (49) 8994548430
Web Site: http://www.tupy-europe.de
Emp.: 10
Automotive Parts Mfr & Distr
N.A.I.C.S.: 441330

Technocast, S.A. de C.V. (1)
Rodovia Monterrey-Saltillo Km 21 5, Ramos Arizpe, 25900, Coahuila, Mexico
Tel.: (52) 844 866 0600
Web Site: http://www.tupy.com.br
Engine Blocks & Heads Mfr
N.A.I.C.S.: 333618

Tupy American Foundry Corp (1)
Tel.: (248) 324-0167
Sales Range: $50-74.9 Million
Emp.: 10
Iron & Steel Castings
N.A.I.C.S.: 423510

Tupy Mexico Saltillo, S.A. de C.V. (1)
Rua Isidro Lopez Zertuche 4003 Zona Industrial, Saltillo, 25230, Coahuila, Mexico (100%)
Tel.: (52) 844 411 2000
Web Site: http://www.tupy.com.br
Engine Equipment Mfr
N.A.I.C.S.: 333618

TURACO GOLD LIMITED
Level 1 50 Ord Street, Mount Hawthorn, West Perth, 6005, WA, Australia
Tel.: (61) 894800402   AU
Web Site: https://turacogold.com.au
TCG—(ASX)
Rev.: $84,991
Assets: $3,673,798
Liabilities: $1,003,606
Net Worth: $2,670,192
Earnings: ($7,097,724)
Emp.: 2
Fiscal Year-end: 12/31/22
Gold Exploration & Mining Services
N.A.I.C.S.: 212220
Justin Tremain *(CEO & Mng Dir)*

TURANBANK OJSC
I Gutgashinli Str 85, Yasamal District, AZ1073, Baku, Azerbaijan
Tel.: (994) 125107911
Web Site: http://www.turanbank.az
Year Founded: 1992
TURB2—(BAK)
Rev.: $35,560,068
Assets: $469,048,208
Liabilities: $431,322,032
Net Worth: $37,726,176
Earnings: $4,013,185
Fiscal Year-end: 12/31/22
Commercial Banking Services
N.A.I.C.S.: 522110
Fazail Musayev *(Chm-Mgmt Bd)*

TURBO POWER SYSTEMS INC.
1 Queens Park Queensway North, Team Valley Trading Estate, Gateshead, NE11 0QD, United Kingdom
Tel.: (44) 191 482 9200   YT
Web Site: http://www.turbopowersystems.com
Year Founded: 1986
Sales Range: $10-24.9 Million
Emp.: 112
Electric Motors, Generators, Drives & Power Electronics Mfr
N.A.I.C.S.: 335312
Carlos Neves *(CEO)*

TURBO-MECH BERHAD
39-5 Jalan PJU 1/41 Dataran Prima, 47301, Petaling Jaya, Selangor Darul Ehsan, Malaysia
Tel.: (60) 378055592
Web Site: https://www.turbomech.com.my
TURBO—(KLS)
Rev.: $10,422,404
Assets: $27,648,672
Liabilities: $2,452,753
Net Worth: $25,195,920
Earnings: $371,092
Emp.: 31

Fiscal Year-end: 12/31/22
Pumps, Gas Compressors & Turbine Mfr
N.A.I.C.S.: 333914
Kok Ten Gan *(Chm & CFO)*

Subsidiaries:

Bayu Manufacturing Sdn. Bhd. (1)
No 33 Jalan Johan 2/6 Kawasan Perindustrian, Pengkalan II Lahat, 31500, Perak, Malaysia
Tel.: (60) 53662800
Web Site: https://bayupurnama.com.my
Oil & Gas Well Drilling Services
N.A.I.C.S.: 213111

Turbo-Mech (Thailand) Co. Ltd. (1)
5th Floor Samaphan Building 180/1-2 Sukhumvit Rd, Cherngnern Muang, Rayong, 21000, Thailand
Tel.: (66) 38619309
Web Site: https://www.turbo-mech.co.th
Pump Equipment Mfr & Distr
N.A.I.C.S.: 333996

Turbo-Mech Asia Pte. Ltd. (1)
22 Joo Koon Circle, Singapore, 629054, Singapore
Tel.: (65) 62506047
Web Site: https://www.turbo-mech.com.sg
Oil & Gas Field Machinery Mfr & Distr
N.A.I.C.S.: 333914

Subsidiary (Non-US):

Turbo-Mech (Thail) Co. Ltd. (2)
5th Floor Samaphan Building 180/1-2 Sukhumvit Rd Cherngnern, Muang, Rayong, 21000, Thailand
Tel.: (66) 3 861 9309
Web Site: https://www.turbo-mech.co.th
Oil & Gas Field Machinery Mfr & Distr
N.A.I.C.S.: 333914

TURBOATOM JSC
199 Moskovsky Avenue, Kharkiv, 61037, Ukraine
Tel.: (380) 573492450
Web Site: http://www.turboatom.com.ua
Year Founded: 1934
Sales Range: Less than $1 Million
Emp.: 3,488
Turbine Equipment Mfr
N.A.I.C.S.: 333611
Subotin Victor *(Gen Dir)*

TURBOGEN LTD.
Ef'Al St 22, Petach Tikva, Israel
Tel.: (972) 35795452
Web Site: https://www.turbogenchp.com
TURB—(TAE)
Assets: $1,184,141
Liabilities: $6,797,071
Net Worth: ($5,612,930)
Earnings: ($5,210,112)
Fiscal Year-end: 12/31/23
Turbine Mfr & Distr
N.A.I.C.S.: 333611
Yaron Gilboa *(CEO)*

TURBOMECANICA S.A.
244 Iuliu Blvd, Maniu District 6, 61126, Bucharest, Romania
Tel.: (40) 214343206
Web Site: https://www.turbomecanica.ro
TBM—(BUC)
Rev.: $30,225,583
Assets: $39,404,865
Liabilities: $12,743,567
Net Worth: $26,661,298
Earnings: $2,647,454
Emp.: 461
Fiscal Year-end: 12/31/22
Aircraft Part Mfr
N.A.I.C.S.: 334519
Radu Viehmann *(Chm & CEO)*

TURBON AG

TURBON AG

Turbon AG—(Continued)

Zum Ludwigstal 14-16, 45527, Hattingen, Germany
Tel.: (49) 23249772340
Web Site: https://www.turbon.de
TUR—(MUN)
Rev.: $63,527,718
Assets: $50,358,549
Liabilities: $30,135,651
Net Worth: $20,222,898
Earnings: ($242,851)
Emp.: 541
Fiscal Year-end: 12/31/23
Toner Cartridge Mfr & Whslr
N.A.I.C.S.: 325910
Simon John McCouaig (Member-Mgmt Bd)

Subsidiaries:

Clarity Imaging Technologies, Inc.
Park 80 W 250 Pehle Ave Ste 402, Saddle Brook, NJ 07663
Tel.: (781) 890-1890
Web Site: http://www.clarityimaging.com
Sales Range: $10-24.9 Million
Laser Printer Toner Cartridges Mfr
N.A.I.C.S.: 325910

Plant (Domestic):

Clarity Imaging Technologies, Inc. (2)
75 Cadwell Dr Ste A, Springfield, MA 01104
Tel.: (413) 693-1234
Web Site: http://www.clarityimaging.com
Sales Range: $25-49.9 Million
Emp.: 5
Laser Printer Toner Cartridges Mfr
N.A.I.C.S.: 325910
Denise Tilelli (Mgr-HR)

Turbon (Thailand) Co. Ltd. (1)
651 Mu 4 Pattana 1 Road T Pracksa Bangpoo Ind-Est, EPZ A Muang, Samut Prakan, 10280, Thailand
Tel.: (66) 2 7106633
Web Site: http://www.turbon.co.th
Emp.: 500
Toner Cartridge Mfr
N.A.I.C.S.: 333310
Nitikorn Srikhirin (Mng Dir)

Turbon USA, Inc. (1)
4350 Haddonfield Rd Ste 300, Pennsauken, NJ 08109
Tel.: (856) 665-6650
Web Site: http://www.turbongroup.com
Toner Cartridge Mfr & Whslr
N.A.I.C.S.: 325910
Chris Cooper (Mgr-Channel)

TURCAS PETROL A.S.

Eski Buyukdere Cad No 14 Park Plaza Kat 4, 34398, Istanbul, Turkiye
Tel.: (90) 2123656200
Web Site: https://www.turcas.com.tr
Year Founded: 1931
TRCAS—(IST)
Assets: $247,201,856
Liabilities: $14,331,778
Net Worth: $232,870,078
Earnings: $27,986,120
Fiscal Year-end: 12/31/23
Oil & Petroleum Products Mfr & Distr
N.A.I.C.S.: 324110
Arkin Akbay (COO)

TURCK HOLDING GMBH

Witzlebenstrasse 7, 45472, Mulheim an der Ruhr, Germany
Tel.: (49) 20849520
Web Site: http://www.turck.de
Sales Range: $50-74.9 Million
Emp.: 4,800
Holding Company; Process Automation Sensor, Fieldbus, Interface & Connectivity Products Developer, Mfr & Distr
N.A.I.C.S.: 551112
Christian Wolf (Mng Dir)

Subsidiaries:

Hans Turck GmbH & Co. KG (1)
Witzlebenstrasse 7, 45472, Mulheim an der Ruhr, Germany
Tel.: (49) 20849520
Web Site: http://www.turck.de
Sales Range: $50-74.9 Million
Emp.: 200
Process Automation Sensor, Fieldbus, Interface & Connectivity Products Developer, Mfr & Distr
N.A.I.C.S.: 334513
Ulrich Turck (Owner)

Subsidiary (Domestic):

TURCK Electronics GmbH (2)
Gildestrasse 5, 32760, Detmold, Germany
Tel.: (49) 5231 948 0
Web Site: http://www.mt-x.de
Sales Range: $100-124.9 Million
Electronic Testing Equipment & Software Developer & Mfr
N.A.I.C.S.: 334515
Guido Frohnhaus (Mng Dir)

TURCK (Tianjin) Sensor Co. Ltd. (1)
18 4th Xinghuazhi Road, Xiqing Economic Development Area, Tianjin, 300381, China
Tel.: (86) 22 83988188
Web Site: http://www.turck.com.cn
Electronic Equipment Distr
N.A.I.C.S.: 423610

TURCK Automation Romania SRL
Str Siriului nr 6-8 Sector 1, 014354, Bucharest, Romania
Tel.: (40) 21 230 02 79
Web Site: http://www.turck.ro
Electronic Equipment Distr
N.A.I.C.S.: 423610

TURCK B.V. (1)
Ruiterlaan 7, 8019 BN, Zwolle, Netherlands
Tel.: (31) 38 422 77 50
Web Site: http://www.turck.nl
Electronic Equipment Distr
N.A.I.C.S.: 423610

TURCK BANNER S.A.S. (1)
11 rue de Courtalin - Bat C, 77703, Marne-la-Vallee, Cedex, Magny-le-Hongre, France
Tel.: (33) 1 60 43 60 70
Web Site: http://www.turckbanner.fr
Electronic Equipment Distr
N.A.I.C.S.: 423610

TURCK BANNER S.R.L. (1)
Via San Domenico 5, Bareggio, 20010, Milan, Italy
Tel.: (39) 0 2 90 36 42 91
Web Site: http://www.turckbanner.it
Electronic Equipment Distr
N.A.I.C.S.: 423610

TURCK GmbH (1)
Graumanngasse 7/A5-1, 1150, Vienna, Austria
Tel.: (43) 1 486 15 87
Web Site: http://www.turck.at
Emp.: 12
Electronic Equipment Distr
N.A.I.C.S.: 423610

TURCK Hungary kft. (1)
Neumann Janos u 1/E Infopark, 1117, Budapest, Hungary
Tel.: (36) 6 1 477 0740
Web Site: http://www.turck.hu
Electronic Equipment Distr
N.A.I.C.S.: 423610

TURCK India Automation Pvt. Ltd. (1)
401-403 Aurum Avenue Survey No 109/4 Baner - Balewadi Link Road, Near Cummins Complex, Pune, 411045, Maharashtra, India
Tel.: (91) 77 68 93 30 05
Web Site: http://www.turck.co.in
Electronic Equipment Distr
N.A.I.C.S.: 423610

TURCK Japan Corporation (1)
Syuuhou Bldg 6F 2-13-12, Kanda-Sudacho Chiyoda-ku, Tokyo, 101-0041, Japan
Tel.: (81) 3 5298 2128
Web Site: http://www.turck.jp

Electronic Equipment Distr
N.A.I.C.S.: 423610

TURCK RUS OOO (1)
Nizhnjaya Pervomajskaya bld 43A fl 4 of 48, Vn Ter G Munitsipalniy okrug Vostochnoe Izmailovo, 105203, Moscow, Russia
Tel.: (7) 4952342661
Web Site: http://www.turck.ru
Electronic Equipment Distr
N.A.I.C.S.: 423610

TURCK Singapore Pte. Ltd. (1)
25 International Business Park 03-22/23 German Centre, 609916, Singapore, Singapore
Tel.: (65) 6562 8716
Web Site: http://www.turck.sg
Electronic Equipment Distr
N.A.I.C.S.: 423610
Matthias Turck (Mng Dir)

TURCK s.r.o. (1)
Na Brne 2065, 500 06, Hradec Kralove, Czech Republic
Tel.: (420) 495 518 766
Web Site: http://www.turck.cz
Electronic Equipment Distr
N.A.I.C.S.: 423610

TURCK sp.z.o.o. (1)
Wroclawska 115, 45-836, Opole, Poland
Tel.: (48) 77 443 4800
Web Site: http://www.turck.pl
Electronic Equipment Distr
N.A.I.C.S.: 423610

Turck Australia Pty. Ltd. (1)
Units 5-7 Gilda Court, Mulgrave, 3170, VIC, Australia
Tel.: (61) 1300 132 566
Web Site: http://www.turck.com.au
Electronic Equipment Distr
N.A.I.C.S.: 423610
Cameron Dwyer (Mng Dir)

Turck Chartwell Canada Inc. (1)
140 Duffield Drive, Markham, L6G 1B5, ON, Canada
Tel.: (905) 513-7100
Web Site: https://www.turck.ca
Emp.: 25
Electronic Equipment Distr
N.A.I.C.S.: 423610
Mark Boehmer (Pres)

Turck Korea Co, Ltd. (1)
B-509 Gwangmyeong Technopark 60 Haanro, Gwangmyeong, 423-795, Gyeonggi-Do, Korea (South)
Tel.: (82) 2 2068 1630
Web Site: http://www.turok.co.kr
Electronic Equipment Distr
N.A.I.C.S.: 423610

Turck Middle East S.P.C. (1)
Unit No 2105 Building No 2648 Road No 5720 Block No 257, The lagoon Amwaj Island, Muharraq, Bahrain
Tel.: (973) 160 306 46
Electronic Equipment Distr
N.A.I.C.S.: 423610

Turck Otomasyon Ticaret Limited Sirketi
Inonu Mah Kayisdagi c Yesil Konak Evleri No 178 A Blok D 4, Kadikoy, 34755, Istanbul, Turkiye
Tel.: (90) 216 572 21 77
Web Site: http://www.turck.com.br
Electronic Equipment Distr
N.A.I.C.S.: 423610

Turck do Brasil Automacao Ltda. (1)
Rua Anjo Custodio Nr 42, Jardim Analia Franco, 03358-040, Sao Paulo, Brazil
Tel.: (55) 11 2676 9600
Web Site: http://www.turck.com.br
Electronic Equipment Distr
N.A.I.C.S.: 423610

TURDAPAN SA

str Rosiori nr1, Cluj, 401176, Turda, Romania
Tel.: (40) 264 315 124
Web Site:
http://www.turdapan.wordpress.com
Sales Range: Less than $1 Million
Emp.: 8

INTERNATIONAL PUBLIC

Real Estate Prorperty Leasing Services
N.A.I.C.S.: 531190

TURENNE CAPITAL PARTENAIRES SAS

9 rue de Teheran, 75008, Paris, France
Tel.: (33) 1 5343 0303 FR
Web Site:
http://www.turennecapital.com
Year Founded: 1999
Rev.: $727,423,200
Emp.: 43
Investment Management & Private Equity Firm
N.A.I.C.S.: 523940
Francois Lombard (Founder)

TURIS BEST D.D. KONJIC

ul Donje Polje br 42, 88400, Konjic, Bosnia & Herzegovina
Tel.: (387) 36735160
UISHRK1—(SARE)
Rev.: $2,009
Assets: $964,090
Liabilities: $915,688
Net Worth: $48,402
Earnings: ($17,934)
Emp.: 1
Fiscal Year-end: 12/31/21
Restaurant Operators
N.A.I.C.S.: 311999

TURIYA BERHAD

Suite 7 3 7th Floor Wisma Chase Perdana Changkat Semantan, Damansara Heights, 50490, Kuala Lumpur, Malaysia
Tel.: (60) 327183800 MY
Web Site: https://www.turiya.com.my
Year Founded: 1961
TURIYA—(KLS)
Rev.: $5,909,251
Assets: $36,770,365
Liabilities: $9,462,902
Net Worth: $27,307,463
Earnings: $864,438
Fiscal Year-end: 03/31/23
Investment Holding Company
N.A.I.C.S.: 551112
Youn Kim Wong (Sec)

Subsidiaries:

Pyramid Manufacturing Industries Pte. Ltd. (1)
No 87 Tuas Avenue 1, Singapore, 639519, Singapore
Tel.: (65) 68621900
Web Site:
https://www.pyramidchemicals.com.sg
Chemical Products Mfr
N.A.I.C.S.: 325998

TURK HAVA YOLLARI ANONIM ORTAKLIGI

Turk Hava Yollari Genel Yonetim Binasi Ataturk Havalimani, Yesilkoy, 34149, Istanbul, Turkiye
Tel.: (90) 2124636363
Web Site: http://p.turkishairlines.com
Year Founded: 1933
THYAO—(IST)
Rev.: $21,840,433,400
Assets: $45,468,940,300
Liabilities: $25,675,990,700
Net Worth: $19,792,949,600
Earnings: $7,057,813,400
Fiscal Year-end: 12/31/23
Oil Transportation Services
N.A.I.C.S.: 481111
Ilker Ayci (Chm)

Subsidiaries:

Cornea Havacilik (1)
E Gate, Pendik, 34912, Istanbul, Turkiye
Tel.: (90) 2165859833

Web Site: http://www.cornea.aero
Internet System Services
N.A.I.C.S.: 517810
Mustafa Iceloglu (Gen Mgr)

THY Teknik A.S. (1)
Sanayi Havaalani Ic Yolu Caddesi Sabiha
Gokcen Havaalani E Kapisi No 3, Pendik,
34906, Istanbul, Turkiye
Tel.: (90) 2165859800
Aircraft Maintenance Services
N.A.I.C.S.: 488190
Ahmet Karaman (Gen Mgr)

TURK ILAC VE SERUM SANAYI A.S.
Tel.: (90) 3128376767
Web Site: https://www.turkilac.com.tr
TRILC—(IST)
Pharmaceutical Product Mfr & Distr
N.A.I.C.S.: 325412
Mehmet Berat Battal (Chm)

TURK TUBORG BIRA VE MALT SANAYII A.S.
Kemalpasa Street No 258/9, Isikkent-Bornova, 35070, Izmir, Turkiye
Tel.: (90) 2323992000
Web Site:
 https://www.turktuborg.com.tr
Year Founded: 1969
TBORG—(IST)
Rev.: $351,011,066
Assets: $469,062,846
Liabilities: $220,902,910
Net Worth: $248,159,936
Earnings: $71,218,175
Emp.: 1,474
Fiscal Year-end: 12/31/20
Beer Mfr
N.A.I.C.S.: 312120
Aran Ernest Oelsner (Chm)

Subsidiaries:

Tuborg Pazarlama A.S. (1)
KemalPasa Cad No 52, 35070, Izmir, Turkiye
Tel.: (90) 232 399 2000
Web Site:
 https://www.tuborgpazarlama.com.tr
Beer & Ale Distr
N.A.I.C.S.: 424810

TURKCELL FINANSMAN A.S.
Mesrutiyet Cad No 71 Turkcell Plaza, Tepebasi Beyoglu, Istanbul, Turkiye
Tel.: (90) 8502011111
Web Site: http://www.financell.com.tr
FNCLL—(IST)
Rev.: $29,907,832
Assets: $161,522,756
Liabilities: $110,372,164
Net Worth: $51,150,592
Earnings: $17,256,166
Fiscal Year-end: 12/31/22
Financial Investment Services
N.A.I.C.S.: 523999
Murat Erkan (Chm)

TURKCELL ILETISIM HIZMETLERI A.S.
Turkcell Kucukyal Plaza Aydnevler Mahallesi Inonu Caddesi, No 20 Kucukyali Ofispark Maltepe, Istanbul, Turkiye
Tel.: (90) 2123131000 TR
Web Site: https://www.turkcell.com.tr
TKC—(NYSE)
Rev.: $3,308,556,903
Assets: $7,631,799,509
Liabilities: $3,856,263,533
Net Worth: $3,775,535,976
Earnings: $387,090,423
Emp.: 24,352
Fiscal Year-end: 12/31/23
Communication Service
N.A.I.C.S.: 517111
Aziz Gediz Sezgin (Exec VP-Network Technologies)

TURKER PROJE GAYRIMENKUL VE YATIRIM GELISTIRME AS
Akasya Ac4 25/32 badem Housing Compl Urban, Stage A Blk D 222 Ac4 25/32b, Istanbul, Turkiye
Tel.: (90) 2163041298
Web Site: https://www.turker-gg.com
TURGG—(IST)
Sales Range: Less than $1 Million
Real Estate Brokerage Services
N.A.I.C.S.: 531210
Attila Turker (Chm)

TURKISH BANK A.S.
Valikonagi cad No 1, Nisantasi, 34371, Istanbul, Turkiye
Tel.: (90) 2123737114
Web Site:
 http://www.turkishbank.com
Year Founded: 1982
TRKSH—(IST)
Rev.: $2,732,529
Assets: $91,767,880
Liabilities: $84,167,781
Net Worth: $7,600,099
Earnings: $742,382
Fiscal Year-end: 12/31/22
Banking & Investment Services
N.A.I.C.S.: 523150
I. Haken Bortecene (Chm)

Subsidiaries:

Allied Turkish Bank IBU Ltd. (1)
182 Kyrenia Ave Nicosia Trnc, Mersin, Turkiye
Tel.: (90) 3926003388
Web Site: http://www.atbibu.com
Commercial Banking Services
N.A.I.C.S.: 522110
Tanju Ozyol (Pres)

Turk Bankasi Ltd. (1)
Valikonagi Cad No 1, Nisantasi, 34371, Istanbul, Turkiye
Tel.: (90) 2123736373
Commercial Banking Services
N.A.I.C.S.: 522110

Turkish Bilgi Islem Hizmetleri A.S. (1)
Esentepe Mah Ali Kaya Sok Polat Plaza A Blok 1A/52, Sisli, Turkiye
Tel.: (90) 2123737305
Commercial Banking Services
N.A.I.C.S.: 522110

Turkish Investment Securities Inc. (1)
Esentepe Mahallesi Ali Kaya Sokak No 1A/52 Polat Plaza A Blok Kat 4, Sisli, Istanbul, Turkiye
Tel.: (90) 2123151000
Commercial Banking Services
N.A.I.C.S.: 522110

Turkish Yatirim A.S. (1)
1 Interior Door No 62, Sisli, Istanbul, Turkiye
Tel.: (90) 2123151000
Web Site: https://www.turkishyatirim.com
Financial Brokerage Services
N.A.I.C.S.: 523150

TURKIYE CUMHURIYET MERKEZ BANKASI
Istiklal Cad 10 Ulus, Ankara, 06100, Turkiye
Tel.: (90) 3123103646
Web Site: http://www.tcmb.gov.tr
Sales Range: $1-4.9 Billion
Central Bank
N.A.I.C.S.: 521110
Erdem Basci (Governor)

TURKIYE CUMHURIYETI ZIRAAT BANKASI A.S.
Haci Bayram Mahallesi Ataturk Bulvari No 8, Altindag, 06050, Ankara, Turkiye
Tel.: (90) 3125842000
Web Site: http://www.ziraat.com.tr
Sales Range: $5-14.9 Billion
Emp.: 21,299
Banking Services
N.A.I.C.S.: 522110
Ahmet Genc (Chm)

Subsidiaries:

Fintek Finansal Teknoloji Hizmetleri A.S. (1)
C2 Blok Yildiz Teknik Universitesi Davutpasa Kampusu Teknopark, 34220, Istanbul, Turkiye
Tel.: (90) 212 484 6000
Web Site: http://www.ziraatteknoloji.com
Emp.: 800
Information Technology Development Services
N.A.I.C.S.: 541511

Kazakhstan Ziraat International Bank (1)
Klockova Street No 132, Almaty, Kazakhstan
Tel.: (7) 727 250 60 80
Web Site: http://www.kzibank.kz
Commercial Banking Services
N.A.I.C.S.: 522110
Masenova Galia Bagasharovna (Deputy Chm-Exec Bd)

Turkish Ziraat Bank Bosnia dd (1)
Dzenetica Cikma 2/1, Sarajevo, Bosnia & Herzegovina
Tel.: (387) 33564120
Web Site: http://www.ziraatbank.ba
Emp.: 229
Commercial Banking Services
N.A.I.C.S.: 522110
Ali Riza Akbas (Gen Mgr)

Ziraat Bank (Moscow) CJSC (1)
Marksistskaya Str 16, Moscow, 109147, Russia
Tel.: (7) 4952326737
Web Site: https://www.ziraatbank.ru
Commercial Banking Services
N.A.I.C.S.: 522110
Avni Demirci (CEO)

Ziraat Bank International A.G. (1)
Myliusstr 14, 60323, Frankfurt, Germany
Tel.: (49) 6929805777
Web Site: https://www.ziraatbank.de
Emp.: 134
Commercial Banking Services
N.A.I.C.S.: 522110
Ayten Turkmen (Chm-Mgmt Bd & CEO)

Ziraat Finansal Kiralama A.S. (1)
Mecidiyekoy Mah Buyukdere Cad No 83, Sisli, 34387, Istanbul, Turkiye
Tel.: (90) 212 459 88 00
Web Site: http://www.ziraatleasing.com.tr
Financial Lending Services
N.A.I.C.S.: 523999

Ziraat Portfoy Yonetimi A.S. (1)
Istanbul Finance Center Finance Street B Block No 44B, Inside Door No 13 Financekent District Umraniye, 34398, Istanbul, Turkiye
Tel.: (90) 2165901600
Web Site: https://www.ziraatportfoy.com.tr
Financial Investment Services
N.A.I.C.S.: 523999
Hakan Eryilmaz (Gen Mgr)

Ziraat Yatirim Menkul Degerler A.S. (1)
Finans Street B Block No 44/B Interior Door No 15 Umraniye, Finanskent District, 34330, Istanbul, Turkiye
Tel.: (90) 8502222979
Web Site: https://www.ziraatyatirim.com
Investment Banking & Financial Service
N.A.I.C.S.: 523150

TURKIYE GARANTI BANKASI A.S.
Nispetiye Mah Aytar Cad No 2, Levent Besiktas, 34340, Istanbul, Turkiye
Tel.: (90) 2123181818
Web Site:
 https://www.garantibbva.com.tr
Year Founded: 1946
GARAN—(IST)
Rev.: $7,066,187,737
Assets: $72,022,810,113
Liabilities: $62,939,041,572
Net Worth: $9,083,768,541
Earnings: $1,048,928,003
Emp.: 18,784
Fiscal Year-end: 12/31/19
Retail & Wholesale Banking Services
N.A.I.C.S.: 522110
Suleyman Sozen (Chm)

Subsidiaries:

Garanti Faktoring A.S. (1)
Tersane Street No 15, Camcesme District, 34899, Istanbul, Turkiye
Tel.: (90) 2166254000
Web Site:
 https://www.garantibbvafactoring.com
Rev.: $41,631,481
Assets: $298,684,314
Liabilities: $277,307,841
Net Worth: $21,376,473
Earnings: $10,833,562
Emp.: 123
Fiscal Year-end: 12/31/2022
Factoring, Financing & Collection Services
N.A.I.C.S.: 523999
Ali Temel (Vice Chm)

Garanti Konut Finansmani Danismanlik Hizmetleri A.S. (1)
Bilinmiyor, Levent, Istanbul, Turkiye (100%)
Tel.: (90) 2123181980
Mortgage Services
N.A.I.C.S.: 522310

Garanti Portfoy Yonetimi AS (1)
Levent Nispetiye Mah Aytar Cad No 2, Besiktas, Istanbul, 34340, Turkiye
Tel.: (90) 212 384 1300
Web Site:
 https://www.garantibbvaportoy.com.tr
Asset Management Services
N.A.I.C.S.: 523940
Maria De La Paloma Piqueras Hernandez (Chm)

Garanti Yatirim Menkul Kiymetler AS (1)
Etiler Mahallesi Tepecik Yolu Demirkent Sok No 1, Besiktas, Istanbul, 34337, Turkiye
Tel.: (90) 212 384 1010
Web Site:
 https://www.garantibbvayatirim.com
Financial Brokerage Services
N.A.I.C.S.: 523150
Recep Bastug (Chm)

GarantiBank International N.V. (1)
Keizersgracht 569-575, 1017 DR, Amsterdam, Netherlands (100%)
Tel.: (31) 205539741
Web Site: http://www.garantibank.nl
Sales Range: $100-124.9 Million
Emp.: 150
Banking Services
N.A.I.C.S.: 522110

GarantiBank Moscow (1)
4th Lesnoy pereulok 8th Fl, Capital Plaza Business Centre, Moscow, 125047, Russia (100%)
Tel.: (7) 4959612500
Web Site: http://www.gbm.ru
Sales Range: $50-74.9 Million
Emp.: 85
Banking Services
N.A.I.C.S.: 522110
A. Niyazi Gurcan (CEO & Gen Mgr)

TURKIYE HALK BANKASI A.S.
Finanskent Mahallesi Finans Caddesi No 42/1, Umraniye, 34760, Istanbul, Turkiye
Tel.: (90) 2165038601
Web Site:
 https://www.halkbank.com.tr
Year Founded: 1933
HALKB—(IST)
Rev.: $9,630,101,404
Assets: $7,094,903,708
Liabilities: $2,680,610,709
Net Worth: $4,414,292,999

TURKIYE HALK BANKASI A.S.

Turkiye Halk Bankasi A.S.—(Continued)
Earnings: $548,354,126
Emp.: 22,219
Fiscal Year-end: 12/31/23
Commercial Banking Services
N.A.I.C.S.: 522110
Osman Arslan (Gen Mgr)

Subsidiaries:

Halk Faktoring A.S. (1)
Tel.: (90) 2123933232
Web Site: https://www.halkfaktoring.com.tr
Financial Services
N.A.I.C.S.: 523999

Halk Osiguruvanje A.D. (1)
Ul Mother Teresa No 1 Entrance 2, Skopje, 1000, North Macedonia
Tel.: (389) 2 312 2385
Web Site: https://www.halkinsurance.com.mk
Property Liability Insurance Services
N.A.I.C.S.: 524126

Halk Yatirim Menkul Degerler A.S. (1)
Barbaros Mah Mor Sumbul Sk WBC Business Center Blok No 9, Interior Door No 21 Atasehir, Istanbul, 34707, Turkiye
Tel.: (90) 216 285 0900
Web Site: https://www.halkyatirim.com.tr
Financial Brokerage Services
N.A.I.C.S.: 523150

Halkbank AD (1)
Sv Kiril i Metodij no 54, 1000, Skopje, North Macedonia
Tel.: (389) 23240800
Web Site: http://www.halkbank.com.mk
Sales Range: $10-24.9 Million
Banking Services
N.A.I.C.S.: 522110
Bilal Sucubasi (CEO)

TURKIYE IHRACAT KREDI BANKASI A.S.

Saray Mah Ahmet Tevfik Ileri Cad No 19, Umraniye, 34768, Istanbul, Turkiye
Tel.: (90) 2166665500
Web Site: http://www.eximbank.gov.tr
Year Founded: 1987
EXIMB—(IST)
Rev.: $974,848,486
Assets: $43,414,754,594
Liabilities: $41,442,060,069
Net Worth: $1,972,694,525
Earnings: $421,150,510
Emp.: 734
Fiscal Year-end: 12/31/21
Banking Services
N.A.I.C.S.: 522110
Riza Tuna Turagay (Vice Chm)

TURKIYE IS BANKASI A.S.

Is Kuleleri, Levent, 34330, Istanbul, Turkiye
Tel.: (90) 2123160000   TR
Year Founded: 1924
ISCTR—(IST)
Rev.: $4,342,542,138
Assets: $52,985,484,981
Liabilities: $46,497,471,112
Net Worth: $6,488,013,869
Earnings: $2,133,022,872
Emp.: 23,148
Fiscal Year-end: 12/31/22
Commercial Banking Services
N.A.I.C.S.: 522110
Fusun Tumsavas (Chm)

Subsidiaries:

Anadolu Hayat Emeklilik A.S. (1)
Anadolu Hayat Emeklilik A S Is Kuleleri, Tower 2 Floor 17-20, 34330, Istanbul, Turkiye
Tel.: (90) 2123177070
Web Site: www.anadoluhayat.com.tr
Rev.: $295,527,123
Assets: $4,892,416,620
Liabilities: $4,675,247,937
Net Worth: $217,168,683
Earnings: $44,414,486
Emp.: 1,051
Fiscal Year-end: 12/31/2020
Life Insurance & Pension Services
N.A.I.C.S.: 524113
N. Cem Ozcan (Deputy CEO & Member-Exec Bd)

Bayek Tedavi Saglik Hizmetleri ve Isletmeciligi A.S. (1)
1443 Avenue No 17, Sogutozu Kizilirmak District, Ankara, Turkiye
Tel.: (90) 312 287 9000
Web Site: https://www.bayindirhospitals.com
Healthcare Services
N.A.I.C.S.: 621610

Covision Medical Technologies Limited (1)
Lawn Road, Carlton-in-Lindrick, Worksop, S81 9LB, Nottinghamshire, United Kingdom
Tel.: (44) 190 973 3737
Web Site: https://www.covision-medical.co.uk
Orthopedic Surgery Device Mfr & Distr
N.A.I.C.S.: 339113

Efes Varlik Yonetim A.S. (1)
Icerenkoy Mahallesi Karaman Ciftligi Yolu Cad No 47 Kar Plaza Floor 4, Atasehir, Istanbul, Turkiye
Tel.: (90) 21 653 8410
Web Site: https://www.efesvarlik.com.tr
Financial Services
N.A.I.C.S.: 523999

Erisim Musteri Hizmetleri A.S. (1)
Icerenkoy Mah Degirmenyolu Cad No 6-8, Atasehir, 34752, Istanbul, Turkiye
Tel.: (90) 216 655 5757
Web Site: https://www.iserisim.com.tr
Financial Services
N.A.I.C.S.: 523999

Is Finansal Kiralama A.S. (1)
Is Kuleleri Kule 1 Kat 6 4 Levent, 34330, Istanbul, Turkiye
Tel.: (90) 2123507400
Web Site: https://www.isleasing.com.tr
Rev.: $106,117,404
Assets: $1,122,147,272
Liabilities: $1,006,502,880
Net Worth: $115,644,392
Earnings: $25,536,779
Emp.: 262
Fiscal Year-end: 12/31/2022
Financial Lending Services
N.A.I.C.S.: 522291
Murat Bilgic (Chm)

Is Merkezleri Yonetim ve Isletim A.S. (1)
Levent Mah Meltem Sk No 14/1 Is Kuleleri Tower 3 Mezzanine Floor, Besiktas, Istanbul, 34330, Turkiye
Tel.: (90) 21231 649 9899
Web Site: https://www.ismer.com.tr
Facility Management Services
N.A.I.C.S.: 561210

Is Net Elektronik Bilgi Uret. Dag. Tic. ve Ilet. Hizm. A.S. (1)
Icmeler Mah Piri Reis Cd No 62 Turkiye Is, Bankasi Tuzla Technology and Operations Center D Block Tuzla, Istanbul, 34947, Turkiye
Tel.: (90) 850 290 0290
Web Site: https://www.isnet.net.tr
Information Technology Services
N.A.I.C.S.: 541511

Is Yatirim Menkul Degerler A.S. (1)
Meltem Sokak Is Kuleleri Kule-2 Kat 13 No 10/14, Levent Mahallesi, 34330, Istanbul, Turkiye
Tel.: (90) 2123502000
Web Site: https://www.isyatirim.com
Rev.: $6,924,392,570
Assets: $1,106,071,036
Liabilities: $881,589,942
Net Worth: $224,481,094
Earnings: $139,908,474
Emp.: 468
Fiscal Year-end: 12/31/2022
Financial Investment Services
N.A.I.C.S.: 523999
Isil Dadayli (Vice Chm)

Isbank AG (1)
Zeil 123, 60313, Frankfurt am Main, Germany
Tel.: (49) 6 929 9010
Web Site: https://www.isbank.de
Financial Services
N.A.I.C.S.: 523999
Unal Tolga Esgin (CEO)

JSC Isbank Georgia (1)
Ilia Chavchavadze ave No 72a 10th Floor Vake Plaza Business Center, 0162, Tbilisi, Georgia
Tel.: (995) 32 244 2244
Web Site: https://www.isbank.ge
Banking Services
N.A.I.C.S.: 522110
Ozan Gur (CEO)

Kasaba Gayrimenkul Insaat Taahhut ve Ticaret A.S. (1)
Omerli Mah Kasaba Sitesi Ayvali Ciftligi Caddesi No 80 D 1 Kat 2, Cekmekoy, Istanbul, Turkiye
Tel.: (90) 216 435 8435
Web Site: https://www.kasabaomerli.com
Real Estate Services
N.A.I.C.S.: 531390

Livewell Giyilebilir Saglik Urun Hizm. A.S. (1)
Sanayi Mahallesi Teknopark Bulvari Teknopark 4A Apt No 1 4A /309, Pendik, Istanbul, Turkiye
Tel.: (90) 216 504 5240
Web Site: https://www.livewell.com.tr
Information Technology Services
N.A.I.C.S.: 541511

Maxis Girisim Sermayesi Portfoy Yonetimi A.S. (1)
Is Towers Tower 2 Floor 2, Levent, Istanbul, 34330, Turkiye
Tel.: (90) 212 283 5113
Web Site: https://www.maxisgirisimpys.com.tr
Portfolio Management Services
N.A.I.C.S.: 523940

Maxis Investments Ltd. (1)
7 Princes Street 1st Floor, London, EC2R 8AQ, United Kingdom
Tel.: (44) 207 726 3310
Web Site: https://www.maxisinvestments.co.uk
Investment Advisory Services
N.A.I.C.S.: 523940

Miltas Turizm Insaat Ticaret A.S. (1)
Suadiye Ulus Sok No 10, Kadikoy, Istanbul, Turkiye
Tel.: (90) 216 373 8011
Web Site: https://www.miltasturizm.com.tr
Sports Facility Services
N.A.I.C.S.: 713940

Nevotek Middle East FZ Limited Liability Company (1)
Building 14 Office 217 2nd Floor Al Falak Street, Dubai Internet City, Dubai, United Arab Emirates
Tel.: (971) 4 365 4245
Web Site: https://nevotek-middle-east-fz-llc.business.site
Software Development Services
N.A.I.C.S.: 541511

Ortopro Tibbi Aletler San. Tic. A.S. (1)
Ayrancilar Mahallesi 67 Sokak No 52/B, Torbali, Izmir, Turkiye
Tel.: (90) 2328548550
Web Site: https://www.ortopro.com.tr
Emp.: 110
Medical Device Mfr & Distr
N.A.I.C.S.: 339112

Sisecam Chemicals Resources LLC (1)
5 Concourse Pkwy, Ste 2500, Atlanta, GA 30328
Tel.: (770) 375-2300
Web Site: https://www.sisecamusa.com
Concrete Mfr
N.A.I.C.S.: 327390

Subsidiary (Domestic):

Sisecam Resources LP (2)
5 Concourse Pkwy Ste 2500, Atlanta, GA 30328
Tel.: (770) 375-2300
Web Site: http://www.ciner.us.com
Rev.: $720,100,000
Assets: $671,900,000
Liabilities: $255,900,000
Net Worth: $416,000,000
Earnings: $63,300,000
Emp.: 503
Fiscal Year-end: 12/31/2022
Trona Ore Mining & Processing
N.A.I.C.S.: 212290

TSKB Gayrimenkul Degerleme A.S. (1)
Omer Avni Mah Karun-Cikmazi Sok No 2/1, Beyoglu, 34427, Istanbul, Turkiye
Tel.: (90) 2123345054
Web Site: https://www.tskbgd.com.tr
Real Estate Services
N.A.I.C.S.: 531390
Makbule Yonel Maya (Gen Mgr)

TSKB Surdurulebilirlik Danismanligi A.S. (1)
Meclisi Mebusan Cad Omer Avni Mah Karun Cikmazi Sok No 2, Beyoglu, 34427, Istanbul, Turkiye
Tel.: (90) 2123345460
Web Site: https://www.escarus.com
Management Consulting Services
N.A.I.C.S.: 541618
Cigdem Icel (Chm)

Toksoz Spor Malzemeleri Tic. A.S. (1)
Namik Kemal Mah Adile Nasit Bulvari No 32/A Haramidere, Esenyurt, 34567, Istanbul, Turkiye
Tel.: (90) 850 221 2300
Web Site: https://www.sportive.com.tr
Sport Equipment Distr
N.A.I.C.S.: 423910

Topkapi Danismanlik Elektronik Hizmetler Pazarlama ve Ticaret A.S. (1)
Levent Mahallesi Meltem Sokak Isbankasi Towers Block No 10, Inner Door No 4 Besiktas, Istanbul, Turkiye
Tel.: (90) 850 722 3000
Web Site: https://www.topkapidanismanlik.com.tr
Financial Payment Services
N.A.I.C.S.: 522320

Turkiye Sise ve Cam Fabrikalan A.S. (1)
Iclemer Mahallesi Karayolu Caddesi No 44/A, 34947, Istanbul, Turkiye
Tel.: (90) 8502065050
Rev.: $5,147,453,868
Assets: $9,862,226,869
Liabilities: $4,202,289,406
Net Worth: $5,659,937,463
Earnings: $642,711,138
Emp.: 25,000
Fiscal Year-end: 12/31/2023
Glass Mfr
N.A.I.C.S.: 327215
Adnan Bali (Chm)

Subsidiary (Domestic):

Trakya Cam Sanayii A.S. (2)
Saadetdere Mahallesi 122 Sokak No 27/12 Esenyurt, Haramidere, Istanbul, Turkiye (71.79%)
Tel.: (90) 2126903191
Web Site: http://www.trakya-cam.com.tr
Sales Range: $1-4.9 Billion
Flat Glass Mfr
N.A.I.C.S.: 327211

Subsidiary (Non-US):

Richard Fritz GmbH & Co. KG (3)
Gottlieb-Daimler-Strasse 4, D-74354, Besigheim, Germany
Tel.: (49) 71433790
Web Site: http://www.fritz-group.com
Sales Range: $400-449.9 Million
Emp.: 1,420
Automotive Glass & Plastic Components Mfr & Distr
N.A.I.C.S.: 327211
Thomas Duckers (Mng Dir)

TURKIYE KALKINMA VE YATIRIM BANKASI AS

Dr Adnan Buyukdeniz St No 10 Umraniye, Inkilap District, 34768, Istanbul, Turkiye
Tel.: (90) 2166368700
Web Site:
https://www.kalkinma.com.tr
KLNMA—(IST)
Rev.: $547,916,877
Assets: $4,595,627,278
Liabilities: $4,227,072,967
Net Worth: $368,554,311
Earnings: $254,843,227
Emp.: 331
Fiscal Year-end: 12/31/23
Investment Banking Services
N.A.I.C.S.: 523150
Raci Kaya *(Chm)*

TURKIYE SINAI KALKINMA BANKASI A.S.
Meclisi Mebusan Cad 81 Findikli, 34427, Istanbul, Turkiye
Tel.: (90) 2123345050
Web Site: https://www.tskb.com.tr
Year Founded: 1950
TSKB—(IST)
Rev.: $362,667,458
Assets: $6,126,857,458
Liabilities: $5,387,726,755
Net Worth: $739,130,703
Earnings: $242,140,538
Emp.: 779
Fiscal Year-end: 12/31/23
Investment Banking Services
N.A.I.C.S.: 523150
Hakan Aygen *(Exec VP-Corp Fin, Loans Allocation & Loan Analysis)*

Subsidiaries:

TSKB Gayrimenkul Yatirim Ortakligi A.S. (1)
Omer Avni Mah Karun Cikmazi Sok No 2, Findikli, 34427, Istanbul, Turkiye
Tel.: (90) 2123345020
Web Site: https://www.tskbgyo.com
Rev.: $3,133,234
Assets: $81,755,441
Liabilities: $18,764,371
Net Worth: $62,991,070
Earnings: ($6,206,560)
Emp.: 11
Fiscal Year-end: 12/31/2020
Real Estate Investment Services
N.A.I.C.S.: 523999
Cengaver Yildizgoz *(Deputy Gen Mgr)*

TSKB Surdurulebirlik Danismanligi A.S. (1)
Meclisi Mebusan Cad Omer Avni Mah Karun Cikmazi Sok No 2, Findikli Beyoglu, 34427, Istanbul, Turkiye
Tel.: (90) 2123345460
Web Site: https://www.escarus.com
Business Consulting Services
N.A.I.C.S.: 541611
Meral Murathan *(Chm)*

TURKIYE SISE VE CAM FABRIKALARI A.S.
Icmeler Mah D100 Karayolu Cad No 44A, 34947, Istanbul, Turkiye
Tel.: (90) 8502065050
Web Site:
https://www.sisecam.com.tr
Year Founded: 1935
SISE—(IST)
Rev.: $5,147,453,868
Assets: $9,862,226,869
Liabilities: $4,202,289,406
Net Worth: $5,659,937,463
Earnings: $798,900,818
Emp.: 25,000
Fiscal Year-end: 12/31/23
Glass & Chemical Mfr
N.A.I.C.S.: 327211
Ahmet Kirman *(Vice Chm, CEO & Member-Exec Bd)*

Subsidiaries:

AC Glass Holding B.V. (1)
Karspeldreef GB, 1101 CJ, Amsterdam, Netherlands
Tel.: (31) 208908645
Glass Packaging Product Mfr & Distr
N.A.I.C.S.: 327212

Anadolu Cam Eskisehir Sanayi A.S. (1)
Organize Sanayi Bolgesi 1203 Sokak 15 Cadde No 6, Odunpazari, Eskisehir, Turkiye
Tel.: (90) 8502065200
Glass Packaging Product Mfr & Distr
N.A.I.C.S.: 327212

Anadolu Cam Yenisehir Sanayi A.S. (1)
Toroslar Mah Tekke Cad No 1 33100, Yeni Taskent Kasabasi, 33100, Mersin, Turkiye
Tel.: (90) 3242417070
Glass Packaging Product Mfr & Distr
N.A.I.C.S.: 327212

CJSC Brewery Pivdenna (1)
Tairove 5 Pyvovarna Str, Ovidiopol Dist, 65496, Odessa, Ukraine
Tel.: (380) 80487167979
Glass Packaging Product Mfr & Distr
N.A.I.C.S.: 327212

Cam Elyaf Sanayii A.S. (1)
Sisecam Yolu Sok No7, Cumhuriyet Mahallesi Gebze, Izmit, 41400, Kocaeli, Turkiye
Tel.: (90) 2626781583
Chemical Product Mfr & Distr
N.A.I.C.S.: 325199
Cansu Altan *(Mgr-Quality)*

Camis Ambalaj Sanayi A.S. (1)
istasyon Mh Sehitler Cd No 139, Tuzla, 34940, Istanbul, Turkiye
Tel.: (90) 2165812727
Web Site: https://www.camisambalaj.com.tr
Packaging Product Mfr & Distr
N.A.I.C.S.: 326112

Plant (Domestic):

Camis Ambalaj Sanayi A.S. - Eskisehir Plant (2)
Organize San Bolgesi Mumtaz Zeytinoglu Bulvari, 26110, Eskisehir, Turkiye
Tel.: (90) 2163952794
Packaging Products Mfr
N.A.I.C.S.: 326112

Camis Egypt Mining Ltd. Co. (1)
Corner Road 254-206, Digla-Maadi, Cairo, Egypt
Tel.: (20) 25198237
Chemical Product Mfr & Distr
N.A.I.C.S.: 325199

Camis Limited (1)
4/Watt House/Dudley Innovation Centre/Second Av, Kingswinford, DY6 7YD, United Kingdom
Tel.: (44) 1384286969
Flat Glass Mfr & Distr
N.A.I.C.S.: 327211

Cromital S.p.A (1)
Strada 4 - Palazzo A7, 20090, Assago, MI, Italy
Tel.: (39) 028688601
Web Site: https://www.cromital.eu
Chemical Product Mfr & Distr
N.A.I.C.S.: 325199

Plant (Domestic):

Cromital S.p.A - Ostellato Plant (2)
Via Giotto 4-Localita Sipro San Giovanni, 44020, Ostellato, Italy
Tel.: (39) 053357548
Glass Packaging Product Mfr & Distr
N.A.I.C.S.: 327212

JSC Mina (1)
Tel.: (995) 5322449981
Glass Packaging Product Mfr & Distr
N.A.I.C.S.: 327212

Merefa Glass Company Ltd. (1)
84-A Leonivska Str, 62472, Merefa, Kharkiv, Ukraine
Tel.: (380) 577298506
Web Site: http://www.msk.net.ua
Glass Packaging Product Mfr & Distr
N.A.I.C.S.: 327212

OOO Posuda Limited (1)
Tel.: (7) 8315976408
Glassware Product Mfr & Distr
N.A.I.C.S.: 327215

OOO Ruscam (1)
84 Gagarin Str, Gorokhovets, 601481, Russia
Tel.: (7) 8613124052
Glass Packaging Product Mfr & Distr
N.A.I.C.S.: 327212

OOO Ruscam Glass (1)
Krasnodar Kurgannaya Str 1A, Krymsk, Russia
Tel.: (7) 4923824003
Glass Packaging Product Mfr & Distr
N.A.I.C.S.: 327212

OOO Ruscam Glass Packaging Holding (1)
Tel.: (7) 3472924053
Glass Packaging Product Mfr & Distr
N.A.I.C.S.: 327212

Plant (Domestic):

OOO Ruscam Glass Packaging Holding - Kirishi Plant (2)
Volkhov Highway 11, 187110, Kirishi, Leningradskaya, Russia
Tel.: (7) 8136896903
Glass Packaging Product Mfr
N.A.I.C.S.: 327212

OOO Ruscam Management Company (1)
Tel.: (7) 4956627000
Web Site: http://www.ruscam.ru
Emp.: 5,000
Glass Container Product Mfr & Distr
N.A.I.C.S.: 327213

PAO Ruscam Pokrovsky (1)
Sovetskaya Street 96, Vologda, Chagodashensky, Russia
Tel.: (7) 8174131140
Glass Packaging Product Mfr & Distr
N.A.I.C.S.: 327212

Pasabahce Glass GmbH (1)
Rheinstrasse 2A, 56068, Koblenz, Germany
Tel.: (49) 261303740
Glass Packaging Product Mfr & Distr
N.A.I.C.S.: 327212

Pasabahce Investment B.V. (1)
Strawinskylaan 1265 World Trade Center Amsterdam D Tower Level 12, 1077 XX, Amsterdam, Netherlands
Tel.: (31) 208201120
Glassware Product Mfr & Distr
N.A.I.C.S.: 327215

Pasabahce Magazalari A.S. (1)
Icmeler Mahallesi D-100 Karayolu Caddesi No 44A, Tuzla, 34947, Istanbul, Turkiye
Tel.: (90) 8502065050
Glassware Product Mfr & Distr
N.A.I.C.S.: 327215

Pasabahce USA Inc. (1)
41 Madison Ave 7th Fl, New York, NY 10010
Tel.: (212) 683-1600
Glass Packaging Product Mfr & Distr
N.A.I.C.S.: 327212

Sisecam Automotive Hungary Kft. (1)
Pesti Ut 19/A, 2170, Aszod, Hungary
Tel.: (36) 28501100
Glass Encapsulation Mfr & Distr
N.A.I.C.S.: 327215

Sisecam Automotive Romania SA (1)
Aleea Industriilor No 1BIS, 120068, Buzau, Romania
Tel.: (40) 238710552
Flat Glass Mfr & Distr
N.A.I.C.S.: 327211

Sisecam Bulgaria EOOD (1)
27 Bratya Miladinovi str FL 4 Apt 14, 9002, Varna, Bulgaria
Tel.: (359) 52608963
Emp.: 3
Glass Packaging Product Mfr & Distr
N.A.I.C.S.: 327212

Sisecam Shanghai Trade Co., Ltd. (1)
93 Huaihai Zhong Road Shanghai Times Square Office Tower 1106, 200021, Shanghai, China
Tel.: (86) 2163910352
Glass Packaging Product Distr
N.A.I.C.S.: 423840

Sisecam Sigorta Aracilik Hizmetleri A.S (1)
Sisecam Operasyon Merkezi Yayla Mah D-100 Karayolu Cad No 70/C Kat 2, Tuzla, 34944, Istanbul, Turkiye
Tel.: (90) 8502063980
General Insurance Services
N.A.I.C.S.: 524210

Sisecam Soda Lukavac D.O.O. (1)
Prva Ulica br1, 75300, Lukavac, Bosnia & Herzegovina
Tel.: (387) 35552323
Chemical Product Mfr & Distr
N.A.I.C.S.: 325199

Trakya Glass Bulgaria EAD (1)
Industrial Area, District Vabel, 7700, Targovishte, Bulgaria
Tel.: (359) 60147801
Flat Glass Mfr
N.A.I.C.S.: 327211

Trakya Glass Rus AO (1)
Sh-2 Street Building 12/7 Office 4002, Alabuga Special Ekonomic Zone Elabuga Municipal District, Yelabuga, 423600, Tatarstan, Russia
Tel.: (7) 8555753301
Flat Glass Mfr & Distr
N.A.I.C.S.: 327211
Beytullah Sahin *(Gen Mgr)*

Trakya Polatli Cam Sanayii A.S. (1)
Polatli Organize Sanayii Bolgesi, Polatli, 06900, Ankara, Turkiye
Tel.: (90) 8502062322
Flat Glass Mfr
N.A.I.C.S.: 327211

Trakya Yenisehir Cam Sanayii A.S. (1)
Icmeler Mah D-100 Karayolu Cad No 44A, Yenisehir, 34947, Bursa, Turkiye
Tel.: (90) 8502065050
Web Site: http://www.sisecam.com.tr
Flat Glass Mfr
N.A.I.C.S.: 327211
Gul Gunay *(Mgr-HR)*

TURKIYE VAKIFLAR BANKASI T.A.O.
Saray Mahallesi Dr Adnan Buyukdeniz Cad A1 Blok No 7A Umraniye, Istanbul, Turkiye
Tel.: (90) 2167241000 TR
Web Site:
http://www.vakifbank.com.tr
Year Founded: 1954
TKYVY—(OTCEM)
Rev.: $2,755,517,867
Assets: $139,488,121,856
Liabilities: $132,140,224,060
Net Worth: $7,347,897,796
Earnings: $700,335,098
Emp.: 16,835
Fiscal Year-end: 12/31/21
Commercial Banking Services
N.A.I.C.S.: 522110
Metin Recep Zafer *(Exec VP-Information Technologies & Operational Transactions)*

Subsidiaries:

Gunes Sigorta AS (1)
Gunes Plaza 110 Buyukdere, Istanbul, 34330, Turkiye
Tel.: (90) 2123556565
Web Site: http://www.gunessigorta.com.tr
Sales Range: $350-399.9 Million
Emp.: 600
Insurance Services
N.A.I.C.S.: 524298
Serhat Sureyya Cetin *(Gen Mgr)*

Taksim Otelcilik AS (1)

TURKIYE VAKIFLAR BANKASI T.A.O.

Turkiye Vakiflar Bankasi T.A.O.—(Continued)
19 Mayis Caddesi Golden Plaza No 3 Kat 3, Sisli, Istanbul, Turkiye
Tel.: (90) 2122321606
Web Site: https://www.taksimotelcilik.com.tr
Sales Range: $10-24.9 Million
Emp.: 23
Home Management Services
N.A.I.C.S.: 721110

Vakif Enerji ve Madencilik AS (1)
Sancak Mah 507 Sok No 9 D 4, Cankaya, Ankara, Turkiye
Tel.: (90) 3124417367
Electric & Heat Energy Generation Services
N.A.I.C.S.: 221111

Vakif Finans Factoring Hizmetleri AS (1)
Yazarlar Sok No 10, Esentepe, 34394, Istanbul, Turkiye
Tel.: (90) 2123555555
Web Site: http://www.vakiffactoring.com.tr
Domestic & International Factoring Services
N.A.I.C.S.: 525990

Vakif Finansal Kiralama AS (1)
Gazeteciler Sitesi 13 Buyukdere, Caddesi Matbuat Sokak, Istanbul, 34394, Turkiye
Tel.: (90) 2123376767
Web Site: http://www.vakifleasing.com.tr
Financial Lending Services
N.A.I.C.S.: 532490
Seref Aksac *(Gen Mgr)*

Vakif Gayrimenkul Degerleme AS (1)
Eti Mahallesi Ali Suavi Sok No 11, Maltepe, Ankara, Turkiye
Tel.: (90) 3122313737
Web Site: http://www.vakifekspertiz.com.tr
Sales Range: $50-74.9 Million
Emp.: 100
Real Estate Property Development Services
N.A.I.C.S.: 531390
Kerim Karakaya *(Gen Mgr)*

Vakif Menkul Kiymet Yatirim Ortakligi A.S. (1)
Inkilap Mah Dr Adnan Buyukdeniz Cad No 7A Interior Door No 21, Umraniye, Istanbul, Turkiye
Tel.: (90) 2162859545
Web Site: https://www.vkfyo.com.tr
Sales Range: Less than $1 Million
Investment Management Service
N.A.I.C.S.: 523940
Ozturk Oran *(Chm)*

Vakif Portfoy Yonetimi AS (1)
Nisbetiye Mahallesi Nisbetiye Caddesi Ayyildiz Is Merkezi, No:4/1 Besiktas Sisli, 34340, Istanbul, Turkiye
Tel.: (90) 2122754303
Web Site: http://www.vakifportfoy.com.tr
Sales Range: $50-74.9 Million
Emp.: 16
Portfolio Management Services
N.A.I.C.S.: 523940
Numan Tanriover *(Gen Mgr)*

Vakif Yatirim Menkul Degerler AS (1)
Akat Mah Ebulula Mardin Cad No 18 Park Maya Sitesi F-2/A Blok, Besiktas, 34335, Istanbul, Turkiye
Tel.: (90) 2123523577
Web Site: http://www.vakifyatirim.com.tr
Emp.: 50
Brokerage Services
N.A.I.C.S.: 523150

VakifBank International Wien AG (1)
Prinz-Eugen-Strasse 8-10 / 8 OG / Top 17, 1040, Vienna, Austria
Tel.: (43) 015123520
Web Site: http://www.vakifbank.at
Sales Range: $50-74.9 Million
Emp.: 35
Commercial Bank
N.A.I.C.S.: 522110

TURKIYE VARLIK FONU YONETIMI AS

Ortakoy Muallim Naci Cd No 22, Besiktas, 34347, Istanbul, Turkiye
Tel.: (90) 2123712200
Web Site:
 http://www.turkiyevarlikfonu.com.tr

Asset & Fund Management
N.A.I.C.S.: 523999
Tayyip Erdogan *(Chm)*

Subsidiaries:

Halk Sigorta A.S. (1)
Halide Edip Adivar Mah Darulaceze Cad No 23 Sisli, Istanbul, Turkiye **(89.18%)**
Tel.: (90) 212 314 73 73
Web Site: http://www.halksigorta.org
Sales Range: $50-74.9 Million
Emp.: 180
Insurance Services
N.A.I.C.S.: 524298
Bulent Karan *(Gen Mgr)*

Vakif Emeklilik AS (1)
Levent Mah Cayir Cimen Sokak No 7, Levent - Besiktas, 34330, Istanbul, Turkiye
Tel.: (90) 2123103724
Web Site: http://www.vakifemeklilik.com.tr
Sales Range: $100-124.9 Million
Emp.: 150
Fire Insurance Services
N.A.I.C.S.: 524113
Serdar Cam *(Vice Chm)*

Ziraat Hayat ve Emeklilik A.S. (1)
Turgut Ozal Millet Cad No 7, Aksaray, 34096, Istanbul, Turkiye
Tel.: (90) 212 459 85 85
Web Site: http://www.ziraatemeklilik.com.tr
Fire Insurance Services
N.A.I.C.S.: 524113

TURKVEN PRIVATE EQUITY

Muallim Naci Cad No 40, Ortakoy,, Istanbul, 34347, Turkiye
Tel.: (90) 212 3268400
Web Site: http://www.turkven.com
Year Founded: 2000
Privater Equity Firm
N.A.I.C.S.: 523999
Seymur Tari *(Mng Dir)*

TURMALINA METALS CORP.

Suite 488-1090 W Georgia St, Vancouver, V6E 3V7, BC, Canada
Tel.: (604) 802-4447
Web Site:
 https://www.turmalinametals.com
TBX—(TSXV)
Rev.: $46,817
Assets: $1,448,039
Liabilities: $398,715
Net Worth: $1,049,323
Earnings: ($4,137,521)
Fiscal Year-end: 12/31/23
Metal Exploration Services
N.A.I.C.S.: 213114
Bryan Slusarchuk *(Pres)*

TURNALL HOLDINGS LIMITED

5 Glasgow Rd Southerton, Harare, Zimbabwe
Tel.: (263) 74546259
Web Site: https://www.turnall.co.zw
Year Founded: 1943
TURN—(ZIM)
Rev.: $232,546,055
Assets: $472,474,722
Liabilities: $127,744,909
Net Worth: $344,729,814
Earnings: $355,420
Emp.: 91
Fiscal Year-end: 12/31/23
Pipes & Cement Mfr
N.A.I.C.S.: 332996
Zvidzayi Bikwa *(Mng Dir)*

TURNER & CO. (GLASGOW) LIMITED

65 Craigton Road, Glasgow, G51 3EQ, Scotland, United Kingdom
Tel.: (44) 141 440 0666
Web Site: http://www.turner.co.uk
Year Founded: 1912
Sales Range: $300-349.9 Million
Emp.: 2,000
Investment Management Service

N.A.I.C.S.: 523940
Alan Turner *(Grp Chm)*

Subsidiaries:

Blue Cube Portable Cold Stores Limited (1)
8 Parker Court, Staffordshire Technology Park Beaconside, Stafford, ST18 0FX, Staffordshire, United Kingdom
Tel.: (44) 3333202620
Web Site: http://www.bluecubepcs.co.uk
Refrigeration System Distr
N.A.I.C.S.: 423740
Mark Giles *(Mgr-Fleet)*

Exsel Pumps Limited (1)
Unit G5 Fort Wallington Industrial Estate Military Rd, Fareham, PO16 8TT, Hampshire, United Kingdom
Tel.: (44) 1329 229 800
Web Site: http://www.exselpumps.co.uk
Emp.: 10
Pump Distr
N.A.I.C.S.: 423830
Steve Handy *(Gen Mgr)*

Iceni Marine Services Ltd (1)
2 Battery Green Road, Lowestoft, NR32 1DH, Suffolk, United Kingdom
Tel.: (44) 1502 290030
Web Site: http://www.icenimarine.co.uk
Marine Support Services
N.A.I.C.S.: 488390
Owen Nutt *(Mgr-Ops)*

Mitchell Diesel Limited - Central Diesel Division (1)
Unit 18 Erdington Industrial Park Off Chester Road, Erdington, Birmingham, B24 0RD, United Kingdom
Tel.: (44) 121 386 1700
Web Site: http://www.central-diesel.co.uk
Industrial Engine Distr
N.A.I.C.S.: 423120

Mitchell Diesel Limited - Central Driveline Division (1)
Fulwood Road South, Sutton in Ashfield, NG17 2JZ, United Kingdom
Tel.: (44) 1773 605 444
Axle Product Distr
N.A.I.C.S.: 423830

Mitchell Powersystems Ltd (1)
Fulwood Road South, Sutton in Ashfield, NG17 2JZ, Nottinghamshire, United Kingdom
Tel.: (44) 1623 550 550
Web Site: http://www.mitchells.co.uk
Diesel Engine Distr
N.A.I.C.S.: 423830

Northburn Industrial Services Ltd (1)
70 Northburn Road, Coatbridge, ML5 2HY, Lanarkshire, United Kingdom
Tel.: (44) 1236 427514
Web Site: http://www.northburn.co.uk
Waste Management & Recycling Services
N.A.I.C.S.: 562219

Optimum Technical Services Ltd. (1)
Unit 1 Abbey Mill Business Centre, Seedhill, Paisley, PA1 1TJ, Renfrewshire, United Kingdom
Tel.: (44) 845 433 3394
Web Site:
 http://www.optimumtechservices.com
Gas Auditing Services
N.A.I.C.S.: 561990

PE Generators Ltd (1)
Central Fulfilment Hub Brook Farm Thrapston Road, Ellington, Huntingdon, PE28 0AE, Cambridge, United Kingdom
Tel.: (44) 844 824 1007
Web Site: http://www.pe-generators.com
Generator Rental Services
N.A.I.C.S.: 532490

Powerplant Stamford Ltd (1)
Wakerley Works Bourne Road, Essendine, Stamford, PE9 4LT, Lincolnshire, United Kingdom
Tel.: (44) 1780 766017
Web Site:
 http://www.powerplantstamford.co.uk
Generator Mfr & Distr
N.A.I.C.S.: 335312

INTERNATIONAL PUBLIC

Stamford Van & Car Hire Ltd (1)
Hartington House Hartington Road, Altrincham, WA14 5LY, United Kingdom
Tel.: (44) 161 969 1015
Car Rental Services
N.A.I.C.S.: 532111
Deborah Johnson *(Branch Mgr)*

TCL Tanker Rental Ltd (1)
Lotherton Way, Garforth, Leeds, LS25 2JY, West Yorkshire, United Kingdom
Tel.: (44) 113 286 3322
Web Site: http://www.tcl-tankers.com
Emp.: 18
Steel Tanker Rental & Leasing Services
N.A.I.C.S.: 532411
Stuart Blacoe *(Mgr-Technical Sls)*

Turner Aviation Ltd (1)
Spiersbridge Terrace Thornliebank Industrial Estate, Thornliebank, Glasgow, G46 8JQ, United Kingdom
Tel.: (44) 141 638 2265
Web Site: http://www.turner-aviation.co.uk
Aircraft Assembly Mfr
N.A.I.C.S.: 336413
Douglas Muirhead *(Mng Dir)*

Turner Engine Control Solutions BV (1)
Hoofdweg 601, 2131 BA, Hoofddorp, Netherlands
Tel.: (31) 23 566 23 72
Web Site: http://www.turner-enginecontrols.com
Turbine & Diesel Engine Distr
N.A.I.C.S.: 423860
Allison Searle *(Coord-Field Svc & Trng)*

Subsidiary (Non-US):

Turner MCS S.r.l. (2)
Viale Monza 128, 20127, Milan, Italy
Tel.: (39) 022 829 932
Diesel Engine & Turbine Distr
N.A.I.C.S.: 423830

Turner Engine Powered Services Limited (1)
Unit 1a Dyce Industrial Park, Dyce, Aberdeen, AB21 7EZ, United Kingdom
Tel.: (44) 1224 723 925
Web Site: http://www.turner-eps.co.uk
Marine Engine & Turbine Distr
N.A.I.C.S.: 423860

Turner Engine Powered Solutions Ltd. (1)
Unit 1 Millennium Way High Carr Business Park, Newcastle-under-Lyme, ST5 7XE, United Kingdom
Tel.: (44) 1782569190
Web Site: http://www.turner-eps.co.uk
Emp.: 60
Power Generator Distr
N.A.I.C.S.: 423610
Steve Faulkner *(Mng Dir)*

Turner Fabrication Ltd (1)
Foss Way Walkerville Industrial Estate, Catterick Garrison, DL9 4SA, North Yorkshire, United Kingdom
Tel.: (44) 1748 835276
Web Site:
 http://www.turnersfabrications.com
Storage Tank Distr
N.A.I.C.S.: 423510
Peter Turner *(Co-Founder)*

Turner Groundscare (1)
Lansdown Road - Stamford Bridge, Tarvin, Chester, CH3 8EL, United Kingdom
Tel.: (44) 1829 741797
Web Site:
 http://www.turnergroundscare.co.uk
Farm Equipment Distr
N.A.I.C.S.: 423820

TURNER INDUSTRIES LTD.

City Centre Old No 186 New No 232 Purasawalkam High Road, B-28 Basement Kilpauk, Chennai, 600 010, India
Tel.: (91) 4426426440
Web Site:
 https://www.laserdiamonds.co.in
Year Founded: 1995
531164—(BOM)

AND PRIVATE COMPANIES

Assets: $59,327
Liabilities: $31,826
Net Worth: $27,501
Earnings: ($6,164)
Fiscal Year-end: 03/31/22
Jewelry Mfr & Whslr
N.A.I.C.S.: 339910
Lalit Kumar Samdaria *(Officer-Compliance)*

TURNERS (SOHAM) LTD
Fordham Road, Newmarket, CB8 7NR, Suffolk, United Kingdom
Tel.: (44) 1638720335
Web Site: http://www.turners-distribution.com
Year Founded: 1930
Rev.: $473,512,560
Emp.: 2,000
Transport & Warehousing Services
N.A.I.C.S.: 493110
Kevin Rampley *(Mgr-Trailer & Refrigeration)*

TURNERS AUCTIONS LIMITED
1st Floor Turners Auction Buildings Cnr Penrose & Leonard Road, PO Box 112022, Auckland, 1640, New Zealand
Tel.: (64) 95809360
Web Site: http://www.turners.co.nz
TUA—(NZX)
Sales Range: $50-74.9 Million
Emp.: 320
House Auction Services
N.A.I.C.S.: 333120
Shane Prince *(Gen Mgr-Ops-North Island)*

Subsidiaries:

Smart Group Services Ltd (1)
68 Gavin Street, Penrose, Auckland, New Zealand
Tel.: (64) 95809386
Sales Range: $25-49.9 Million
Emp.: 20
Automobile Auction Services
N.A.I.C.S.: 561990

Turners Auctions Limited - Damaged Vehicles Trucks and Mobile Plant (1)
120 Hutt Pk Rd, PO Box 38738, Seaview, Wellington, 5010, New Zealand
Tel.: (64) 45871470
Web Site: http://www.turners.co.nz
Sales Range: $25-49.9 Million
Emp.: 52
Automobile Auction Services
N.A.I.C.S.: 561990

Turners Fleet Ltd. (1)
Corner Penrose & Leonard Roads, Penrose, 1023, Auckland, New Zealand
Tel.: (64) 95251920
Motor Vehicle Auction Services
N.A.I.C.S.: 425120

TURNERS AUTOMOTIVE GROUP LIMITED
Level 5 70 Shortland Street, PO Box 1232, Auckland, 1140, New Zealand
Tel.: (64) 800100601 NZ
Web Site: https://www.turnersautogroup.co.nz
Year Founded: 1984
TRA—(NZX)
Rev.: $232,671,651
Assets: $509,534,091
Liabilities: $346,705,144
Net Worth: $162,828,947
Earnings: $19,477,273
Emp.: 627
Fiscal Year-end: 03/31/23
Financial Services
N.A.I.C.S.: 523999
Grant Baker *(Chm)*

Subsidiaries:

EC Credit Control (Aust) Pty Limited (1)
PO Box 248, Botany, 2019, NSW, Australia
Tel.: (61) 1300361070
Web Site: https://www.eccreditcontrol.com.au
Debt Collection Services
N.A.I.C.S.: 561440

EC Credit Control (NZ) Limited (1)
Tel.: (64) 68351800
Web Site: https://www.eccreditcontrol.co.nz
Debt Collection Services
N.A.I.C.S.: 561440

Turners Group NZ Limited (1)
Level 1 Building 8 Central Park 660-670 Great South Road, Ellerslie, Auckland, 1051, New Zealand
Tel.: (64) 95251920
Web Site: https://www.turners.co.nz
Financial Services
N.A.I.C.S.: 523999
Sean Wiggans *(Gen Mgr)*

Turners Group NZ Limited (1)
Level 1 Building 8 Central Park 660-670 Great South Road, Ellerslie, Auckland, 1051, New Zealand
Tel.: (64) 95251920
Web Site: https://www.turners.co.nz
Financial Services
N.A.I.C.S.: 523999
Sean Wiggans *(Gen Mgr)*

Turners Group NZ Limited (1)
Level 1 Building 8 Central Park 660-670 Great South Road, Ellerslie, Auckland, 1051, New Zealand
Tel.: (64) 95251920
Web Site: https://www.turners.co.nz
Financial Services
N.A.I.C.S.: 523999
Sean Wiggans *(Gen Mgr)*

Turners Group NZ Limited (1)
Level 1 Building 8 Central Park 660-670 Great South Road, Ellerslie, Auckland, 1051, New Zealand
Tel.: (64) 95251920
Web Site: https://www.turners.co.nz
Financial Services
N.A.I.C.S.: 523999
Sean Wiggans *(Gen Mgr)*

TURPAZ INDUSTRIES LTD
Halahav 2, Holon, 5885708, Israel
Tel.: (972) 35598211
Web Site: https://www.turpaz.co.il
TRPZ—(TAE)
Rev.: $127,355,000
Assets: $222,028,000
Liabilities: $104,701,000
Net Worth: $117,327,000
Earnings: $12,894,000
Emp.: 466
Fiscal Year-end: 12/31/23
Chemical Products Mfr
N.A.I.C.S.: 325199
Keren Cohen Khazon *(Chm & CEO)*

Subsidiaries:

Pollena Aroma Sp. z o.o. (1)
Ul Przemyslowa 14, 05-100, Nowy Dwor Mazowiecki, Poland
Tel.: (48) 225041740
Web Site: https://pollenaaroma.pl
Perfume Mfr
N.A.I.C.S.: 325620

TURVO INTERNATIONAL CO., LTD.
No 59 Jing 2 Rd, Taichung Harbor Export Processing Zone Wuci Dist, Taichung, 435, Taiwan
Tel.: (886) 426575790
Web Site: http://www.turvo.com.tw
2233—(TAI)
Rev.: $109,143,035
Assets: $168,974,878
Liabilities: $51,784,066
Net Worth: $117,190,813
Earnings: $17,329,866
Emp.: 531
Fiscal Year-end: 12/31/23
Automobile Component Mfr & Distr

N.A.I.C.S.: 336390
Chun-Chang Liu *(Chm)*

TUS ENVIRONMENTAL SCIENCE AND TECHNOLOGY DEVELOPMENT CO., LTD.
11/F Block A Science and Technology Building Tsighua Science Park, Haidian District, Beijing, China
Tel.: (86) 1082152400
Web Site: https://www.tus-est.com
Year Founded: 1993
000826—(SSE)
Rev.: $996,784,725
Assets: $3,738,715,138
Liabilities: $2,283,564,736
Net Worth: $1,455,150,402
Earnings: ($135,301,206)
Fiscal Year-end: 12/31/22
Water Supply Services
N.A.I.C.S.: 488390
Wang Chao *(Deputy Chm)*

TUS-DESIGN GROUP CO., LTD.
No 9 Wangmao Street, Suzhou Industrial Park, Suizhou, 215028, Jiangsu, China
Tel.: (86) 51269564641
Web Site: http://www.siad-c.com
Year Founded: 1988
300500—(CHIN)
Rev.: $224,882,476
Assets: $484,258,540
Liabilities: $306,917,812
Net Worth: $177,340,728
Earnings: ($46,589,546)
Fiscal Year-end: 12/31/23
Residential Building Construction Services
N.A.I.C.S.: 236115
Zha Jinrong *(Chm)*

TUSCAN VENTURES PVT. LTD.
Unit No 2 Level 1 Phoenix Market City, Kurla West, Mumbai, 400 070, India
Tel.: (91) 2261801800
Web Site: http://www.tuscanventures.com
Year Founded: 2007
Investment Firm
N.A.I.C.S.: 523999
Shagun Kapur Gogia *(Co-Founder & Dir)*

TUSCANY HOLDINGS GP, LLC
Calle 113 No 7-80 Torre AR Piso 14, Bogota, Colombia
Tel.: (57) 1 600 0006 DE
Web Site: http://www.tuscanydrilling.com
Year Founded: 2010
Sales Range: $150-199.9 Million
Emp.: 1,490
Oil & Gas Exploration & Drilling Services
N.A.I.C.S.: 211120
Aramis Guerra *(CEO)*

Subsidiaries:

Tuscany Holdings - Bogota (1)
Calle 113 No 7-80 Torre AR Centro Empresarial Santa Barbara, Piso 14, Bogota, Colombia
Tel.: (57) 1 600 0006
Web Site: http://www.tuscanydrilling.com
Oil & Natural Gas Drilling Wells
N.A.I.C.S.: 213111
Spyridon Christophides *(VP-Ops)*

Tuscany Holdings - Quito (1)
Av 12 de Octubre N 24-660 Calle Francisco Salazar Edificio Concorde, Piso 10B y 10C, Quito, Ecuador
Tel.: (593) 3 2 381 6330
Web Site: http://www.tuscanydrilling.com
Oil & Natural Gas Wells Drilling

N.A.I.C.S.: 213111
Spyridon Christophides *(VP-Ops)*

TUTICORIN ALKALI CHEMICALS & FERTILISERS LTD.
SPIC House 88 Mount Road, Guindy, Chennai, 600 032, India
Tel.: (91) 4422352513
Web Site: https://www.tacfert.in
Year Founded: 1981
506808—(BOM)
Rev.: $61,757,592
Assets: $64,533,673
Liabilities: $63,374,186
Net Worth: $1,159,487
Earnings: $12,131,023
Emp.: 252
Fiscal Year-end: 03/31/23
Chemical Products Mfr
N.A.I.C.S.: 325998
G. Ramachandran *(Mng Dir)*

TUV NORD AG
Am TUV 1, 30519, Hannover, Germany
Tel.: (49) 5119980 De
Web Site: http://www.tuev-nord.de
Year Founded: 1869
Sales Range: $1-4.9 Billion
Emp.: 10,000
Diversified Technical, Engineering & Consulting Services
N.A.I.C.S.: 541990
Georg Schoning *(Chm-Supervisory Bd)*

Subsidiaries:

ALTER TECHNOLOGY TUV NORD S.A.U. (1)
C/ Majada 3, Tres Cantos, 28760, Madrid, Spain
Tel.: (34) 91 804 1893
Web Site: http://www.altertechnology.com
Emp.: 150
Engineering Consulting Services
N.A.I.C.S.: 541330
Luis Gomez *(Mng Dir)*

Subsidiary (Non-US):

ALTER TECHNOLOGY China (2)
15F Sail Tower No 266 Han Kou Rd, Huangpu District, 200001, Shanghai, China
Tel.: (86) 21 53855353
Engineering Consulting Services
N.A.I.C.S.: 541330

ALTER TECHNOLOGY RUSSIA (2)
PO 25, Saint Petersburg, 197375, Russia
Tel.: (7) 812 943 14 52
Engineering Consulting Services
N.A.I.C.S.: 541330

ALTER TECHNOLOGY UK (2)
Regus Building 1000 Western Road, Lakeside North Harbour, Portsmouth, PO6 3EZ, United Kingdom
Tel.: (44) 23 9270 4240
Engineering Consulting Services
N.A.I.C.S.: 541330

Optocap Limited (2)
5 Bain Square, Livingston, EH54 7DQ, Scotland, United Kingdom
Tel.: (44) 1506403550
Web Site: http://www.optocap.com
Emp.: 30
Microelectronic & Optoelectronic Device Packaging Design & Assembly Services
N.A.I.C.S.: 561910
David Ruxton *(CEO)*

Asesoria y Control en Proteccion Radiologica. S.L. (1)
C/ Rafael Batlle 24, 08017, Barcelona, Spain
Tel.: (34) 93 204 16 80
Web Site: http://www.acpro.es
Medical Equipment Mfr
N.A.I.C.S.: 334519

BRTUV AVALIACOES DA QUALIDADE S.A. (1)
Alameda Madeira 222 - 3 andar - Cj 31 -

TUV NORD AG

TUV NORD AG—(Continued)
Alphaville, Barueri, 06454-010, Sao Paulo, Brazil
Tel.: (55) 11 4689 9400
Web Site: http://www.brtuv.com.br
Emp.: 40
Certification & Inspection Services
N.A.I.C.S.: 541690
Fernando Suarez *(Coord-Technical)*

Cualicontrol-ACI S.A.U. (1)
Calle Caleruega 67 - Planta 1, 28033, Madrid, Spain
Tel.: (34) 91 766 31 33
Certification & Inspection Services
N.A.I.C.S.: 541690

DMT GmbH & Co. KG (1)
Am Technologiepark 1, 45307, Essen, Germany
Tel.: (49) 201 172 01
Web Site: http://www.dmt.de
Engineering Consulting Services
N.A.I.C.S.: 541330
Carsten Kohn *(Deputy Chm-Supervisory Bd)*

Subsidiary (Non-US):

DMT Consulting Limited (2)
Lake View Drive, Sherwood Park, Nottingham, NG15 0DT, United Kingdom
Tel.: (44) 1623 726166
Web Site: http://www.imcgcl.com
Engineering Consultancy Services
N.A.I.C.S.: 541330

DMT Consulting Private Limited (2)
Unit No-ESNT3B0203 Block 3B Ecospace Business Park Premises No-IIF/11, Action Area II New Town Rajarhat, Kolkata, 700156, India
Tel.: (91) 33 2324 0096
Web Site: http://www.dmt-group.com
Emp.: 35
Engineering Consultancy Services
N.A.I.C.S.: 541330
Pankaj Kumar Sinha *(Mng Dir)*

DMT GEOSCIENCES LTD. (2)
Suite 415 708 - 11th Avenue SW, Calgary, T2R 0E4, AB, Canada
Tel.: (403) 264-9496
Web Site: http://www.dmtgeosciences.ca
Emp.: 20
Engineering Consulting Services
N.A.I.C.S.: 541330
Keith McCandlish *(Mng Dir)*

DMT Geosurvey spol. s.r.o. (2)
Na Porici 1079/3a, 11000, Prague, Czech Republic
Tel.: (420) 519 322 126
Oil & Gas Exploration Services
N.A.I.C.S.: 213112

Subsidiary (Domestic):

DMT Petrologic GmbH (2)
Karl-Wiechert-Allee 76, 30625, Hannover, Germany
Tel.: (49) 511 5413917
Web Site: http://www.petrologic.dmt.de
Emp.: 20
Geophysical Surveying Services
N.A.I.C.S.: 541360
Franco Rost *(Mgr-Bus)*

DMT Verwaltungsgesellschaft mbH (2)
Woldeforster Str 5, Demmin, Germany
Tel.: (49) 3998 4350
Engineering Consulting Services
N.A.I.C.S.: 541330

Subsidiary (Non-US):

DMT-Kai Batla Pty, Ltd. (2)
26 Republic Road Randburg, Bordeaux, 2194, Johannesburg, South Africa
Tel.: (27) 11 781 4548
Emp.: 20
Engineering Consulting Services
N.A.I.C.S.: 541330

Subsidiary (Domestic):

Hontzsch GmbH (2)
Gottlieb-Daimler-Str 37, 71334, Waiblingen, Germany
Tel.: (49) 7151 1716 66
Web Site: http://www.hoentzsch.com
Emp.: 45
Measuring Equipment Mfr & Distr
N.A.I.C.S.: 334519

Subsidiary (Non-US):

PT. DMT Exploration Engineering Consulting Indonesia (2)
Aldevco Octagon Building Jl Warung Jati Barat Raya No 75, Jakarta, 12740, Indonesia
Tel.: (62) 21 798 1987
Web Site: http://www.dmt-indonesia.co.id
Emp.: 1,000
Engineering Consulting Services
N.A.I.C.S.: 541330

ENCOS GmbH Engineering + Construction + Service (1)
Buxtehuder Strasse 29, 21073, Hamburg, Germany
Tel.: (49) 40 751158 0
Web Site: http://www.encos.de
Emp.: 50
Engineering Consulting Services
N.A.I.C.S.: 541330
Virginia Green *(Mng Dir)*

FORMATION SaarLor FSL EURL (1)
4 rue Jules Verne, 57600, Forbach, France
Tel.: (33) 3 57 55 10 00
Industrial Training Services
N.A.I.C.S.: 611430

FS FAHRZEUG-SERVICE GmbH & Co. KG (1)
Am TUV 1, 30519, Hannover, Germany
Tel.: (49) 511 9986 2250
Web Site: http://www.fs-fahrzeugservice.com
Automotive Inspection Services
N.A.I.C.S.: 811198

GWQ Gesellschaft fur Werkstoffprufung und Qualitatssicherung mbH (1)
Am Schurmannshutt 30s, 47441, Moers, Germany
Tel.: (49) 2841 1707 5154
Web Site: http://www.gwq-ndt.de
Testing Services
N.A.I.C.S.: 541380
Frank Kuske *(Mng Dir)*

Guangzhou TUV Industrial Technical Services Co., Ltd. (1)
Room 604 Tai Koo Hui Tower 1 385 Tianhe Road, Tianhe District, 510620, Guangzhou, China
Tel.: (86) 20 3891 1187
Web Site: http://www.tuv-nord.de
Emp.: 20
Engineering Consulting Services
N.A.I.C.S.: 541330
Ran Jun *(CEO)*

HIREX ENGINEERING SAS (1)
Parc Technologique du Canal 2 rue des Satellites, 31520, Ramonville-Saint-Agne, France
Tel.: (33) 5 62 47 56 90
Web Site: http://www.hirex.fr
Emp.: 48
Semiconductor Devices Mfr
N.A.I.C.S.: 334413
Guirre S. X. *(Mgr-Comml)*

Hundt & Partner Ingenieurgesellschaft mbH & Co. KG (1)
Lister Strasse 11, 30163, Hannover, Germany
Tel.: (49) 511 39781 0
Web Site: http://www.hundt-partner.de
Elevator Mfr
N.A.I.C.S.: 333921

IGN Ingenieurgesellschaft Nord mbH & Co. KG (1)
An den Wurthen 28, 17489, Greifswald, Germany
Tel.: (49) 3834 88 65 0
Engineering Consulting Services
N.A.I.C.S.: 541330

LLC IMC Montan (1)
second floor 22 building 4 Chayanova Str,
125047, Moscow, Russia
Tel.: (7) 4952506717
Web Site: http://www.imcmontan.ru
Emp.: 50
Engineering Consulting Services
N.A.I.C.S.: 541330

Nord-Kurs GmbH & Co. KG (1)
Lilienstrasse 15, 20095, Hamburg, Germany
Tel.: (49) 40 4293012 42
Web Site: http://www.nord-kurs.de
Automobile Maintenance Services
N.A.I.C.S.: 811198

Nord-Kurs Verwaltungsgesellschaft mbH (1)
Kattrepel 10, 20095, Hamburg, Germany
Tel.: (49) 40 42930120
Automobile Maintenance Services
N.A.I.C.S.: 811198

PT. TUV NORD Indonesia (1)
Perkantoran Hijau Arkadia Tower F 7th Floor Suite 706 Jl TB, Simatupang Kav 88 Pasar Minggu, Jakarta, Indonesia
Tel.: (62) 21 78837338
Technical Services
N.A.I.C.S.: 541690
Robert Napitupulu *(Pres)*

RWTUV Akademie GmbH (1)
Frohnhauser Str 65, 45127, Essen, Germany
Tel.: (49) 2 01 7 26 77 84
Technical Services
N.A.I.C.S.: 541690

THE INSPECTION COMPANY OF KOREA (1)
20 Dogok-ro 3-gil, Yeoksam-dong Gangnam-gu, Seoul, 135-937, Korea (South)
Tel.: (82) 2 2188 0011
Emp.: 170
Technical Services
N.A.I.C.S.: 541690

TOP REL S.R.L. (1)
Via Cardinal Lambruschini 3, Fiumicino, 00054, Rome, Italy
Tel.: (39) 06 4548 1019
Engineering Consulting Services
N.A.I.C.S.: 541330

TU Service Ingenieurgesellschaft mbH & Co. KG (1)
Potsdamer Str 38, 14469, Potsdam, Germany
Tel.: (49) 331 58499 0
Web Site: http://www.tue-service.de
Automobile Maintenance Services
N.A.I.C.S.: 811198

TU-Service Anlagentechnik GmbH & Co. KG (1)
Cicerostrasse 22, 10709, Berlin, Germany
Tel.: (49) 30 89 000 61 0
Web Site: http://www.tue-service-at.de
Environmental Consulting Services
N.A.I.C.S.: 541620

TUV ASIA PACIFIC LTD (1)
Unit 01-03 26th Floor Tower 1 Millennium City 1 388 Kwun Tong Road, Kwun Tong, Kowloon, China (Hong Kong)
Tel.: (852) 2376 0783
Web Site: http://www.tuv-nord.com
Technical Services
N.A.I.C.S.: 541690
Lex Boon *(CEO)*

TUV CYPRUS LTD. (1)
Corner No 2 Grammou Str & Acropoleos Av, Strovolos, 2006, Nicosia, Cyprus
Tel.: (357) 22442840
Web Site: http://www.tuv-nord.com
Technical Consulting Services
N.A.I.C.S.: 541690
Dimos Dimosthenous *(Gen Mgr)*

TUV Croatia d.o.o. (1)
Savska 41, 10 000, Zagreb, Croatia
Tel.: (385) 1 3668 307
Technical Services
N.A.I.C.S.: 541690

TUV Eesti OU (1)
Vana-Narva mnt 24B, 74114, Maardu, Estonia
Tel.: (372) 6075 918
Technical Services

INTERNATIONAL PUBLIC

N.A.I.C.S.: 541690
Tatjana Veske *(Mng Dir)*

TUV HELLAS S.A. (1)
282 Mesogeion Av, 155 62, Athens, Greece
Tel.: (30) 215 215 7400
Technical Services
N.A.I.C.S.: 541690
Ahmed Marei *(Gen Mgr)*

TUV India Pvt Limited (1)
801 Raheja Plaza-1 L B S Marg, Ghatkopar W, Mumbai, 400 086, India
Tel.: (91) 2266477000
Ship Building & Repair Services
N.A.I.C.S.: 541990
Geeta Kamath *(Mgr-HR)*

TUV Informationstechnik GmbH (1)
Langemarckstrasse 20, 45141, Essen, Germany
Tel.: (49) 201 8999 9
Web Site: http://www.tuvit.de
Technical Services
N.A.I.C.S.: 541690
Dirk Kretzschmar *(Mng Dir)*

TUV NORD (Malaysia) SDN. BHD. (1)
20 Jalan Tiara 3 Tiara Square Taman Perindustrian UEP, 47600, Subang Jaya, Selangor, Malaysia
Tel.: (60) 3 8023 2124
Technical Services
N.A.I.C.S.: 541690
Bill Kong *(CEO)*

TUV NORD (Thailand) Ltd. (1)
1858/75-76 16th Floor TCIF Tower Bangna-Trad Rd, Whaeng Bangna Khet Bangna, Bangkok, 10260, Thailand
Tel.: (66) 2 751 4050
Emp.: 50
Technical Services
N.A.I.C.S.: 541690

TUV NORD ARGENTINA S.A. (1)
Av Leandro N Alem 762 3 Piso Oficina 7, C1001AAP, Buenos Aires, Argentina
Tel.: (54) 11 4311 3032
Technical Services
N.A.I.C.S.: 541690

TUV NORD AUTO GmbH (1)
Frillendorfer Str 139, 45139, Essen, Germany
Tel.: (49) 201 8250
Technical Services
N.A.I.C.S.: 541690

TUV NORD Akademie GmbH & Co. KG (1)
TUV NORD Akademie GmbH & Co. KG, 22525, Hamburg, Germany
Tel.: (49) 40 85 57 22 90
Professional & Management Training Services
N.A.I.C.S.: 611430
Bob Gong *(Gen Mgr)*

TUV NORD Austria GmbH (1)
Diefenbachgasse 35, 1150, Vienna, Austria
Tel.: (43) 1 8932015 0
Technical Services
N.A.I.C.S.: 541690

TUV NORD Bildung GmbH & Co. KG (1)
Am Technologiepark 1, 45307, Essen, Germany
Tel.: (49) 2018929832
Web Site: http://www.tuev-nord-bildung.de
Sales Range: $125-149.9 Million
Emp.: 1,500
Vocational Training Services
N.A.I.C.S.: 611519

TUV NORD Bildung Saar GmbH (1)
Saarbrucker Strasse 131, 66333, Volklingen, Germany
Tel.: (49) 6898 566280
Professional Development Training Services
N.A.I.C.S.: 611430

TUV NORD Bulgarien GmbH (1)
Naiden Gerov Str 13, 4000, Plovdiv, Bulgaria
Tel.: (359) 32 624243
Web Site: http://www.tuev-nord.bg
Emp.: 20
Technical Services

TUV NORD Certification (Tianjin) Co., Ltd. (1)
Room 2603 Asia Pacific Tower No 35 Nanjing Rd, Hexi Dist, Tianjin, 300200, China
Tel.: (86) 22 2314 0018
Technical Services
N.A.I.C.S.: 541690

TUV NORD Czech s.r.o. (1)
Pod Hajkem 406/1, 180 00, Prague, Czech Republic
Tel.: (420) 296 587 201 209
Technical Services
N.A.I.C.S.: 541690

TUV NORD EGYPT S.A.E. (1)
34 Al Riyadh St off Shehab st, El Mohandissen Ground Floor, Giza, Egypt
Tel.: (20) 2 330 51 948
Technical Services
N.A.I.C.S.: 541690

TUV NORD Finland Oy (1)
Tillinmaentie 3, Tillinmaentie 3, 02330, Espoo, Finland
Tel.: (358) 9 2900175
Technical Services
N.A.I.C.S.: 541690

TUV NORD France S.A.S. (1)
26 Avenue des Fleurs, 59110, La Madeleine, France
Tel.: (33) 3 2076 6275
Web Site: http://www.tuev-nord.fr
Emp.: 3
Diversified Technical, Engineering & Consulting Services
N.A.I.C.S.: 541990
Philippe Bohm (Chm)

TUV NORD INTEGRA BVBA (1)
Statiestraat 164, 2600, Berchem, Belgium
Tel.: (32) 3 287 37 60
Web Site: http://www.tuv-nord-integra.com
Emp.: 50
Technical Services
N.A.I.C.S.: 541690

TUV NORD ITALIA S.r.l. (1)
Via Filippo Turati 70, Cerro Maggiore, 20023, Milan, Italy
Tel.: (39) 0331 541488
Web Site: http://www.tuev-nord.it
Technical Services
N.A.I.C.S.: 541690

TUV NORD Iran PJS (1)
Apt 2 4th Floor Firoozeh Building 22Firoozeh St North Sohrevardi St, PO Box 14185, Tehran, Iran
Tel.: (98) 2188749544
Ship Building & Repair Services
N.A.I.C.S.: 541990

TUV NORD Kft. (1)
Than Karoly u 3, 1119, Budapest, Hungary
Tel.: (36) 1 371 5943
Technical Services
N.A.I.C.S.: 541690

TUV NORD Luxembourg s.a.r.l. (1)
124 bld de la Petrusse, 2330, Luxembourg, Luxembourg
Tel.: (352) 27 177 220
Technical Consulting Services
N.A.I.C.S.: 541690

TUV NORD MEXICO S.A. DE C.V. (1)
Blvd Bernardo Quintana 7001 Tower 2 Suite 1012, Centro Sur, 76090, Queretaro, Mexico
Tel.: (52) 1 44 2199 5135
Technical Services
N.A.I.C.S.: 541690

TUV NORD MPA Gesellschaft fur Materialprufung und Anlagensicherheit mbH & Co. KG (1)
Am Haupttor Bau 4305, 6237, Leuna, Germany
Tel.: (49) 34 61 43 44 77
Web Site: http://www.tuev-nord-mpa.de
Technical Services
N.A.I.C.S.: 541690

TUV NORD Material Testing GmbH (1)
Bliersheimer Str 338, 47229, Duisburg, Germany
Tel.: (49) 2065 96168 0
Technical Services
N.A.I.C.S.: 541690
Dominik Spahn (CEO)

TUV NORD Mobilitat Immobilien GmbH (1)
Rudolf-Diesel-Str 5, 48157, Munster, Germany
Tel.: (49) 251 141220
Technical Services
N.A.I.C.S.: 541690

TUV NORD Philippines. Inc. (1)
Unit 406-407 Common Goal Tower Finance cor Industry Sts, Madrigal Business Park Ayala-Alabang, 1780, Muntinlupa, Philippines
Tel.: (63) 2 807 6317
Technical Services
N.A.I.C.S.: 541690

TUV NORD Polska Sp. z o.o. (1)
Mickiewicza 29, 40-085, Katowice, Poland
Tel.: (48) 32 786 46 46
Technical Services
N.A.I.C.S.: 541690
Agata Godula (Mgr-Dev)

TUV NORD ROMANIA S.R.L. (1)
34-36 Carol I Bd, 20922, Bucharest, Romania
Tel.: (40) 21 3150303
Technical Services
N.A.I.C.S.: 541690
Gabriel Spita (Mng Dir)

TUV NORD SLOVAKIA. s.r.o. (1)
Mliekarenska c 8, 821 09, Bratislava, Slovakia
Tel.: (421) 2 5341 6380
Technical Services
N.A.I.C.S.: 541690
Jan Weinfurt (Mng Dir)

TUV NORD SOUTHERN AFRICA (PTY) LTD. (1)
Unit G3 & G4 Bayside Office Park 41/43 Erica Road, Table View, 7443, South Africa
Tel.: (27) 21 521 6800
Web Site: http://www.tuv-nord.com
Emp.: 13
Technical Services
N.A.I.C.S.: 541690
Lars Sitzki (Mng Dir)

TUV NORD Sweden AB (1)
Gasebacksvagen 20, 252 27, Helsingborg, Sweden
Tel.: (46) 10 474 99 00
Technical Services
N.A.I.C.S.: 541690
Anders Egerbo (Mng Dir)

TUV NORD SysTec GmbH & Co. KG (1)
Halderstrasse 27, 86150, Augsburg, Germany
Tel.: (49) 40 8557 2139
Engineering Consulting Services
N.A.I.C.S.: 541330

TUV NORD Systems GmbH & Co. KG (1)
Grosse Bahnstrasse 31, 22525, Hamburg, Germany
Tel.: (49) 40 8557 2368
Web Site: http://www.tuev-nord.de
Technical Services
N.A.I.C.S.: 541690
Rudolf Wieland (Gen Mgr)

TUV NORD Technisches Schulungszentrum GmbH & Co. KG (1)
Ruwoldtweg 12, 22309, Hamburg, Germany
Tel.: (49) 40 740416018
Professional Development Training Services
N.A.I.C.S.: 611430

TUV NORD Transfer GmbH (1)
Am Technologiepark 28, 45307, Essen, Germany
Tel.: (49) 201 8929 542
Employment Placement Services
N.A.I.C.S.: 561311

TUV NORD Ukraina GmbH (1)
Mira Avenue 15 off 63, 83015, Donetsk, Ukraine
Tel.: (380) 62 343 4069
Web Site: http://www.tuev-nord.com.ua
Emp.: 70
Technical Services
N.A.I.C.S.: 541690
Galina Shpak-Levenberg (Gen Dir)

TUV NORD VIETNAM LTD. (1)
Room 803 8th Floor Thang Long Building 105 Lang Ha Street, Hanoi, Vietnam
Tel.: (84) 4 3772 2892
Technical Services
N.A.I.C.S.: 541690

TUV Nederland QA B.V. (1)
De Waal 21 C, 5684 PH, Best, Netherlands
Tel.: (31) 499 339 500
Web Site: http://www.tuv.nl
Emp.: 45
Technical Services
N.A.I.C.S.: 541690
Edwin Franken (Gen Mgr)

TUV Nord Baltik SIA (1)
Klijanu iela 23, Riga, 1012, Latvia
Tel.: (371) 67370391
Technical Services
N.A.I.C.S.: 541690

TUV Nord Danmark ApS (1)
Staktoften 20, 2950, Vedbaek, Denmark
Tel.: (45) 7026 8800
Web Site: http://www.tuv-nord.com
Emp.: 4
Technical Services
N.A.I.C.S.: 541690

TUV Teknik Kontrol ve Belgelendirme A.S. (1)
Ayazmadere Cad Pazar Sok No 2-4 Bareli Plaza Kat 4, Gayrettepe Besiktas, 34349, Istanbul, Turkiye
Tel.: (90) 212 293 2642
Web Site: http://www.tuv-nord.com
Emp.: 30
Technical Services
N.A.I.C.S.: 541690
Riza Baskan (Gen Mgr)

TUV Thuringen Anlagentechnik GmbH & Co. KG (1)
Melchendorfer Str 64, 99096, Erfurt, Germany
Tel.: (49) 361 4283 0
Web Site: http://www.tuev-thueringen.de
Emp.: 600
Technical Services
N.A.I.C.S.: 541690
Volker Hohnisch (CEO)

TUV UK Ltd. (1)
AMP House Suites 27 - 29 Fifth Floor Dingwall Road, Croydon, CR0 2LX, United Kingdom
Tel.: (44) 20 8680 7711
Web Site: http://www.tuv-uk.com
Technical Services
N.A.I.C.S.: 541690

TUV USA. Inc. (1)
215 Main St Ste 3, Salem, NH 03079
Tel.: (603) 870-8023
Technical Services
N.A.I.C.S.: 541690

Verebus Engineering B.V. (1)
Handelskade 49, 2288 BA, Rijswijk, Netherlands
Tel.: (31) 70 3528200
Web Site: http://www.verebus.nl
Emp.: 150
Engineering Consulting Services
N.A.I.C.S.: 541330
Kees Aling (Mng Dir)

adapt engineering GmbH & Co. KG (1)
Motorenstrasse 1a, 99734, Nordhausen, Germany
Tel.: (49) 3631 6054 0
Emp.: 35
Engine Mfr
N.A.I.C.S.: 333618
Leif-Erik Schulte (CEO)

TUV RHEINLAND BERLIN-BRANDENBURG PFALZ E.V.
Am Grauen Stein, 51105, Cologne, Germany
Tel.: (49) 2218060
Web Site: http://www.tuv.com
Year Founded: 1872
Sales Range: $1-4.9 Billion
Emp.: 17,950
Technical Inspections Organization
N.A.I.C.S.: 926150
Bruno O. Braun (Chm-Mgmt Bd)

Subsidiaries:

TUV Rheinland AG (1)
Am Grauen Stein, 51105, Cologne, Germany (100%)
Tel.: (49) 2218060
Web Site: https://www.tuv.com
Rev.: $2,334,918
Assets: $2,373,511,914
Liabilities: $1,905,944,607
Net Worth: $467,567,307
Earnings: $85,979,491
Emp.: 21,441
Fiscal Year-end: 12/31/2019
Holding Company; Technical Inspection Services
N.A.I.C.S.: 551112
Andreas Hofer (Exec VP-Asia Pacific, India, Middle-East & Africa)

Subsidiary (Domestic):

AMD TUV Arbeits-medizinische Dienste GmbH (2)
Alboinstr 56, 12103, Berlin, Germany
Tel.: (49) 30 7562 1710
Technical Services
N.A.I.C.S.: 541690

Subsidiary (Non-US):

AUTESTS SIA (2)
Magonu 25, Cesis, 4101, Latvia
Tel.: (371) 64122056
Technical Services
N.A.I.C.S.: 541690

Subsidiary (Domestic):

BNDT Pruftechnik GmbH (2)
Werkstrasse 20, 04564, Bohlen, Germany
Tel.: (49) 34206 684430
Web Site: http://www.bndt-prueftechnik.de
Inspection Equipment Mfr
N.A.I.C.S.: 334519

Subsidiary (Non-US):

Benelux NDT & Inspection Supplies B.V (2)
Elschot 30, 4905 AZ, Oosterhout, Netherlands
Tel.: (31) 162 421624
Web Site: http://www.benelux-ndt.com
Emp.: 3
Inspection Equipment Mfr
N.A.I.C.S.: 334519
David De Vos (Sr Acct Mgr)

Subsidiary (Domestic):

DIN GOST TUV Berlin Brandenburg Gesellschaft fur Zertifizierung in Europa mbH (2)
Budapester Strasse 31, 10787, Berlin, Germany
Tel.: (49) 30 2601 2110
Web Site: http://www.din-gost.de
Technical Services
N.A.I.C.S.: 541690
Petra Wernke (Head-Certification)

Subsidiary (Non-US):

DUCTOR Implantacao de PROJETOS Ltda. (2)
Av Queiroz Filho 767, 05319-000, Sao Paulo, Brazil
Tel.: (55) 11 3837 4800
Web Site: http://www.ductor.com.br
Engineering Consulting Services
N.A.I.C.S.: 541330

Subsidiary (Domestic):

FSP-Fahrzeug-Sicherheitsprufung Geschaftsfuhrungs-GmbH (2)
Zur Bergmeierei 1, 14548, Berlin, Germany
Tel.: (49) 3327 5998110
Technical Consulting Services
N.A.I.C.S.: 541690

TUV RHEINLAND BERLIN-BRANDENBURG PFALZ E.V.

TUV Rheinland Berlin-Brandenburg Pfalz e.V.—(Continued)

FSP-Fahrzeug-Sicherheitsprufung Leitung und Service GmbH (2)
Mittelhauser Str 76, 99089, Erfurt, Germany
Tel.: (49) 361 740150
Technical Services
N.A.I.C.S.: 541690

Subsidiary (Non-US):

GERIS Engenharia e Servicos Ltda. (2)
Rua Libero Badro 293-cj 18 C/D, Centro, Sao Paulo, 01009-907, Brazil
Tel.: (55) 11 3116 3333
Web Site: http://www.gerisengenharia.com.br
Technical Services
N.A.I.C.S.: 541690

LC LUXCONTROL asbl (2)
1 avenue des Terres Rouges, BP 349, 4004, Esch-sur-Alzette, Luxembourg
Tel.: (352) 54 77 11 1
Web Site: http://www.luxcontrol.com
Emp.: 230
Technical Services
N.A.I.C.S.: 541690

Subsidiary (Domestic):

LGA InterCert Zertifizierungsgesellschaft mbH (2)
Tillystrasse 2, 90431, Nuremberg, Germany
Tel.: (49) 800 888 2378
Web Site: http://www.lga-intercert.com
Technical Services
N.A.I.C.S.: 541690

Subsidiary (Non-US):

LRTDEA - TUV Rheinland Grupa, SIA (2)
Ieriku Street 3/C 2, Riga, 1084, Latvia
Tel.: (371) 67568607
Web Site: http://www.tuv.lv
Emp.: 30
Technical Services
N.A.I.C.S.: 541690

Subsidiary (Domestic):

Luxcontrol GmbH (2)
Sternstrasse 108, 20357, Hamburg, Germany
Tel.: (49) 40 378671 0
Web Site: http://www.luxcontrol.de
Technical Services
N.A.I.C.S.: 541690

Subsidiary (Non-US):

Luxcontrol Nederland B.V. (2)
Artauer Fun Schender Straat 600, 3511 MJ, Utrecht, Netherlands
Tel.: (31) 30 298 2121
Web Site: http://www.luxcontrol-nl.com
Technical Services
N.A.I.C.S.: 541690
Jens Wolff (Head-Certification)

MINELL Kft. (2)
Sajoszigeti ut 1, Miskolc, 3527, Hungary
Tel.: (36) 23 397 111
Web Site: http://www.minell.hu
Testing Services
N.A.I.C.S.: 541380

PT TUV Rheinland Indonesia (2)
Menara Karya 10th Floor Jl H R Rasuna Said Block X-5 Kav 1 - 2, Jakarta, 12950, Indonesia
Tel.: (62) 21 579 44 579
Certification & Inspection Services
N.A.I.C.S.: 541690

Risktec Solutions DMCC (2)
Office 3006 Liwa Heights, PO Box 450113, Jumeirah Lakes Towers, Dubai, United Arab Emirates
Tel.: (971) 4 446 2788
Risk Management Consulting Services
N.A.I.C.S.: 541618

SECTA S.A. (2)
20 ter rue de bezons CS 60030, 92415, Courbevoie, Cedex, France
Tel.: (33) 1 49041500
Technical Services
N.A.I.C.S.: 541690

TUV Akademia Polska Sp. z o.o (2)
ul Wolnosci 327, 41-800, Zabrze, Poland
Tel.: (48) 32 271 64 89
Technical Services
N.A.I.C.S.: 541690

Subsidiary (Domestic):

TUV Berlin Brandenburg Verwaltungs-GmbH (2)
Magirusstrasse 5, 12103, Berlin, Germany
Tel.: (49) 30 75620
Technical Services
N.A.I.C.S.: 541690

Subsidiary (Non-US):

TUV DCTA SAS (2)
76 rue Carnot, 59150, Wattrelos, France
Tel.: (33) 3 20 02 41 61
Technical Services
N.A.I.C.S.: 541690

TUV FRANCE SAS-GROUPE TUV RHEINLAND (2)
62 Bis Avenue Henri Ginoux, Montrouge, France
Tel.: (33) 1 40 92 23 00
Technical Services
N.A.I.C.S.: 541690

TUV International RUS OOO (2)
80/16 Leningradsky prospect Porch 3 Second floor, 125190, Moscow, Russia
Tel.: (7) 4956600889
Technical Services
N.A.I.C.S.: 541690
Denis Medvedev (Gen Mgr)

Subsidiary (Domestic):

TUV Pfalz Anlagen und Betriebstechnik GmbH (2)
Merkurstr 45, 67663, Kaiserslautern, Germany
Tel.: (49) 1806 252535 6600
Technical Services
N.A.I.C.S.: 541690

Subsidiary (US):

OpenSky Corporation (3)
One Technology Dr, Tolland, CT 06084
Web Site: http://www.openskycorp.com
IT Services
N.A.I.C.S.: 541512
Roger Levasseur (Chief Customer Officer)

Subsidiary (Non-US):

Risktec Solutions Ltd. (3)
Wilderspool Park Greenall's Avenue, Warrington, WA4 6HL, Cheshire, United Kingdom
Tel.: (44) 1925 611200
Web Site: http://www.risktec.co.uk
Emp.: 230
Risk Management Consulting & Training
N.A.I.C.S.: 541618
Alan Hoy (Mng Dir)

Subsidiary (Non-US):

Risktec Solutions Canada Ltd. (4)
Suite 1000 Bankers Hall West 888 3rd Street SW, Calgary, T2P 5C5, AB, Canada
Tel.: (403) 269-2106
Risk Management Consulting & Training
N.A.I.C.S.: 541618

Risktec Solutions Ltd (4)
Office 3006 Liwa Heights Jumeirah Lakes Towers, PO Box 450113, Dubai, United Arab Emirates
Tel.: (971) 4 446 2788
Web Site: http://www.risktec.com
Risk Management Consulting & Training
N.A.I.C.S.: 541618

Risktec Solutions Ltd (4)
PO Box 788, 116, Muscat, Oman
Tel.: (968) 24403712
Web Site: http://www.risktec.com
Emp.: 20
Risk Management Consulting & Training
N.A.I.C.S.: 541618

Division (Domestic):

Risktec Solutions Ltd. - Aberdeen (4)
Riverside House Riverside Drive, Aberdeen, AB11 7LH, United Kingdom
Tel.: (44) 1224 224454
Web Site: http://www.risktec.com
Risk Management Consulting & Training
N.A.I.C.S.: 541618

Risktec Solutions Ltd. - Alderley Edge (4)
10 George Street, Alderley Edge, SK9 7EJ, Cheshire, United Kingdom
Tel.: (44) 1625 590008
Web Site: http://www.astecservices.com
Emp.: 10
Risk Management Consulting & Training
N.A.I.C.S.: 541618
Andy Thompson (Gen Mgr)

Risktec Solutions Ltd. - Ashford (4)
Unit 5 Belmont Farm Business Centre, Bethersden, Ashford, TN26 3DY, Kent, United Kingdom
Tel.: (44) 1233 820784
Risk Management Consulting & Training
N.A.I.C.S.: 541618

Risktec Solutions Ltd. - Crawley (4)
Pinnacle Station Way, Crawley, RH10 1JH, United Kingdom
Tel.: (44) 1293229790
Risk Management Consulting & Training
N.A.I.C.S.: 541618

Risktec Solutions Ltd. - Edinburgh (4)
Regus House 10 Lochside Place, Edinburgh Park, Edinburgh, EH12 9RG, United Kingdom
Tel.: (44) 131 2010 190
Risk Management Consulting & Training
N.A.I.C.S.: 541618

Risktec Solutions Ltd. - Glasgow (4)
Unit 21-22 The Technology Centre Scottish Enterprise Technology Park, East Kilbride, Glasgow, G75 0QD, United Kingdom
Tel.: (44) 1355 340200
Web Site: http://www.risktec.co.uk
Emp.: 30
Risk Management Consulting & Training
N.A.I.C.S.: 541618

Risktec Solutions Ltd. - London (4)
1st Floor 3 More London Riverside, London, SE1 2RE, United Kingdom
Tel.: (44) 20 7357 9942
Web Site: http://www.risktec.co.uk
Risk Management Consulting & Training
N.A.I.C.S.: 541618

Subsidiary (US):

Risktec Solutions, Inc. (4)
1110 NASA Pkwy Ste 203, Houston, TX 77058
Tel.: (281) 333-5080
Web Site: http://www.risktec.com
Emp.: 30
Risk Management Consulting & Training
N.A.I.C.S.: 541618
Kris Smith (Pres)

Subsidiary (Non-US):

TUV International s.r.o. (3)
Washingtonova Str 5, 110 00, Prague, 1, Czech Republic
Tel.: (420) 224 210 608
Technical Services
N.A.I.C.S.: 541690

Subsidiary (US):

TUV Rheinland AIA Services, LLC (3)
15915 Katy Freeway Ste 215, Houston, TX 77094
Tel.: (281) 579-1320
Web Site: http://www.tuvaia.com
Emp.: 15
Inspection Services
N.A.I.C.S.: 541350
Kim Gates (Mgr-Ops)

Subsidiary (Non-US):

TUV Rheinland China Ltd. (3)
Unit 707 AVIC Building No 10B Central Road East 3rd Ring Road, Chaoyang District, Beijing, 100022, China
Tel.: (86) 10 65666660

INTERNATIONAL PUBLIC

Technical Services
N.A.I.C.S.: 541690
Ralf Scheller (Pres & CEO)

TUV Rheinland Japan Ltd. (3)
Shin Yokohama Daini Center Bldg 3-19-5 Shin Yokohama, Kohoku-ku, Yokohama, 222-0033, Japan
Tel.: (81) 45 4701860
Web Site: http://www.tuv.com
Emp.: 400
Technical Services
N.A.I.C.S.: 541990
Holger Kunz (Pres & CEO)

TUV Rheinland Middle East LLC (3)
Office no 2702 Shining Towers Mubarak Bin Mohammed St, PO Box 27483, Khalidiyah, Abu Dhabi, United Arab Emirates
Tel.: (971) 2 659 1500
Technical Services
N.A.I.C.S.: 541614

TUV Rheinland do Brasil Ltda. (3)
Av Netuno 32 2 andar, Santana de Parnaiba, CEP 06541, Sao Paulo, Brazil
Tel.: (55) 1 3638 5700
Technical Services
N.A.I.C.S.: 541690

Subsidiary (Non-US):

TUV Quality Control Ltd. (2)
Building 11B Road, 206 Maadi Degla, Cairo, Egypt
Tel.: (20) 2 2516 6297
Technical Services
N.A.I.C.S.: 541690

TUV RHEINLAND ARGENTINA S.A. (2)
San Jose 83-7, C1076AAA, Buenos Aires, Argentina
Tel.: (54) 11 4372 5033
Web Site: http://www.tuv.com.ar
Emp.: 150
Technical Services
N.A.I.C.S.: 541690
Pablo Gilardoni (Mgr)

TUV RHEINLAND BELGIUM A.S.B.L. (2)
Weiveldlaan 41, Bus 1, 1930, Brussels, Belgium
Tel.: (32) 2 725 73 10
Technical Services
N.A.I.C.S.: 541690

TUV RHEINLAND COLOMBIA S.A.S. (2)
Calle 108 45 - 27, Bogota, Colombia
Tel.: (57) 1 7460980
Technical Services
N.A.I.C.S.: 541690
Cilene Zarate Ardila (Mgr-Bus Field)

TUV RHEINLAND DE MEXICO S.A. DE C.V. (2)
Av Santa Fe No 170 Oficina 2-4-12 Col Lomas de Santa Fe Del, Alvaro Obregon, Mexico, 01210, Mexico
Tel.: (52) 55 8503 9940
Technical Services
N.A.I.C.S.: 541690
Bernd Indlekofer (Dir Gen)

TUV RHEINLAND HONG KONG LIMITED (2)
8-10F Goldin Financial Global Square 7 Wang Tai Street, Kowloon Bay, Kowloon, China (Hong Kong)
Tel.: (852) 21921000
Technical Services
N.A.I.C.S.: 541690
Chris Ho (Gen Mgr)

TUV RHEINLAND IBERICA, S.A. (2)
Avenida de Burgos 114-3a, 28050, Madrid, Spain
Tel.: (34) 91 7444500
Technical Services
N.A.I.C.S.: 541690

TUV RHEINLAND NAVARRA SA (2)
c/Soto de Aizoain s/n Mercairuna, 31013, Pamplona, Spain
Tel.: (34) 948 303586
Technical Services
N.A.I.C.S.: 541690

TUV RHEINLAND SINGAPORE PTE. LTD. (2)
25 International Business Park 05-105 German Centre, Singapore, 609916, Singapore
Tel.: (65) 6562 8750
Technical Services
N.A.I.C.S.: 541690
Than Soe *(Mgr)*

TUV RHEINLAND TAIWAN LTD. (2)
11F No 758 Sec 4 Bade Rd, Songshan Dist, Taipei, 00105, Taiwan
Tel.: (886) 2 21727000
Technical Services
N.A.I.C.S.: 541690
Bodo Kretzschmar *(COO)*

TUV RHEINLAND VISTORIAS LTDA. (2)
Av Netuno 32 - 2 Andar - Alphaville - Centro de Apoio 1, 06541-015, Santana de Parnaiba, Sao Paulo, Brazil
Tel.: (55) 11 2424 2600
Web Site: http://www.tuvvistorias.com.br
Certification & Inspection Services
N.A.I.C.S.: 541690

TUV Rheinland (Guangdong) Ltd. (2)
Unit 101 201 301 401 501 601 No 199 Kezhu Road, Guangzhou Science City, Guangzhou, 510663, China
Tel.: (86) 20 28391888
Web Site: http://www.tuv.com
Emp.: 400
Technical Services
N.A.I.C.S.: 541690
Yushun Wong *(Mng Dir)*

TUV Rheinland (Hainan) Co., Ltd. (2)
1 & 5F Food Development Center Building Guilinyang Linggui Road, Luoniushan Agricultural Industrial Meilan, Haikou, 571127, China
Tel.: (86) 898 36657588
Technical Services
N.A.I.C.S.: 541690

TUV Rheinland (India) Private Ltd. (2)
82/A West Wing 3rd Main Road, Electronics City Phase 1, Bengaluru, 560100, India
Tel.: (91) 80 6723 3500
Emp.: 250
Technical Services
N.A.I.C.S.: 541690
Raghavendra Kulkarni *(Mgr-Wireless Product Testing & Certification)*

TUV Rheinland (Shanghai) Co., Ltd. (2)
No 177 Lane 777 West Guangzhong Road, Shanghai, 200072, China
Tel.: (86) 21 61081188
Technical Services
N.A.I.C.S.: 541690
Ying Zhang *(Sr Mgr)*

TUV Rheinland (Shenzhen) Co., Ltd. (2)
1F East & 2-4 F Cybio Technology Building No 1 Langshan No 2 Road, 5th Industrial Area High-Tech Industry Park North Nanshan, 518057, Shenzhen, China
Tel.: (86) 755 82681188
Web Site: http://www.tuv.com
Emp.: 500
Technical Services
N.A.I.C.S.: 541690
Peter Ambrus *(Gen Mgr)*

TUV Rheinland (Wuxi) Automotive Testing Co., Ltd. (2)
No 18 East Gaolang Road, Wuxi, 214028, China
Tel.: (86) 510 85269201
Technical Services
N.A.I.C.S.: 541690

TUV Rheinland - KTI Kft. (2)
Than Karoly U 3-5, 1119, Budapest, Hungary
Tel.: (36) 6 1 371 5948
Web Site: http://www.tuvkti.hu
Technical Services
N.A.I.C.S.: 541690
Finszter Ferenc *(Mng Dir)*

TUV Rheinland / CCIC (Qingdao) Co., Ltd. (2)
6F No 2 Bldg No 175 Zhuzhou Rd, Qingdao, 266101, China
Tel.: (86) 532 88706655
Technical Services
N.A.I.C.S.: 541690
Nancy Shen *(Sr Mgr-Quality)*

TUV Rheinland AIMEX Ltd. (2)
8F No 758 Sec 4 Bade Rd, Songshan Dist, Taipei, 10567, Taiwan
Tel.: (886) 2 2172 7000
Web Site: http://www.aimex.tw
Laboratory Testing Services
N.A.I.C.S.: 541380
Samuel Chang *(Engr-Sls)*

TUV Rheinland Akademie Chile Ltda. (2)
Av Holanda 100 Piso 6, Santiago, Providencia, Chile
Tel.: (56) 22 235242 00
Technical Services
N.A.I.C.S.: 541690

TUV Rheinland Arabia LLC (2)
Al Andalus Street, PO Box 11488, Al Ruwais Dist, Jeddah, 21453, Saudi Arabia
Tel.: (966) 1 2 6571416
Technical Services
N.A.I.C.S.: 541690
Sameer Nagi *(Project Mgr)*

TUV Rheinland Australia Pty. Ltd. (2)
182 Dougharty Road, PO Box 5050, Heidelberg, 3081, VIC, Australia
Tel.: (61) 3 9450 1400
Technical Services
N.A.I.C.S.: 541690
Parveen Akther *(Mng Dir)*

TUV Rheinland Bangladesh Pvt. Ltd. (2)
Road 113 A Plot 17 Alauddin Tower 6th to 8th Floor Gulshan 2, Dhaka, 1212, Bangladesh
Tel.: (880) 2 9894904
Technical Services
N.A.I.C.S.: 541690
Shanmuga Sundaram *(Mng Dir)*

TUV Rheinland Belgium NV (2)
Korte Lozanastraat 20, 2018, Antwerp, Belgium
Tel.: (32) 3 2167020
Technical Services
N.A.I.C.S.: 541690
Stefan Lauwers *(Mng Dir)*

TUV Rheinland Cambodia Co., Ltd. (2)
SSN Center 4th Floor No 66 Norodom Blvd, Phnom Penh, Cambodia
Tel.: (855) 23 212 209
Technical Services
N.A.I.C.S.: 541690
Thanaporn Nuengtong Grimaud *(Mgr-Bus Stream)*

TUV Rheinland Canada Inc. (2)
251 Consumers Rd Ste 1200, Toronto, M2J 4R3, ON, Canada
Tel.: (416) 733-3677
Web Site: http://www.tuv.com
Technical Services
N.A.I.C.S.: 541690

Subsidiary (Domestic):

TUV Rheinland Grebner Ruchay Consulting GmbH (2)
Kennedyallee 97, 60596, Frankfurt am Main, Germany
Tel.: (49) 69 963657 0
Web Site: http://www.grebner-ruchay.de
Technical Services
N.A.I.C.S.: 541690

TUV Rheinland Grundstucksgesellschaft mbH & Co. KG (2)
Tolzer Strasse 15, 82031, Grunwald, Germany
Tel.: (49) 89 641430
Technical Services
N.A.I.C.S.: 541690

Subsidiary (Non-US):

TUV Rheinland Iberica Inspection Certification & Testing S.A. (2)
Parc de Negocis Mas Blau Edifici Oceano, Garrotxa 10-12, 08820, El Prat de Llobregat, Spain
Tel.: (34) 93 478 11 31
Technical Services
N.A.I.C.S.: 541690

TUV Rheinland InterCert d.o.o. (2)
Kosovska 10, 11000, Belgrade, Serbia
Tel.: (381) 11 3616 156
Web Site: http://www.tuvrheinland.rs
Emp.: 20
Technical Services
N.A.I.C.S.: 541690
Vladimir Todorovic *(Gen Mgr)*

TUV Rheinland Italia S.r.l. (2)
Via Mattei 3, 20010, Pogliano Milanese, Milan, Italy
Tel.: (39) 02 939 687 1
Technical Services
N.A.I.C.S.: 541690
Andrea Lovati *(Product Mgr)*

TUV Rheinland Korea Ltd. (2)
E & C Venture Dream Tower 6 197-28, Guro-gu, Seoul, 152-719, Guro-dong, Korea (South)
Tel.: (82) 2 860 9860
Technical Services
N.A.I.C.S.: 541690
Kwang-woo Lee *(Mgr)*

Subsidiary (Domestic):

TUV Rheinland Lichttechnik GmbH (2)
Rhinstr 46, 12681, Berlin, Germany
Tel.: (49) 30 641972 30
Technical Services
N.A.I.C.S.: 541690

Subsidiary (Non-US):

TUV Rheinland Luxemburg GmbH (2)
2a Kalchesbruck, 1852, Luxembourg, Luxembourg
Tel.: (352) 52 2909
Technical Services
N.A.I.C.S.: 541690

TUV Rheinland Malaysia SDN BHD (2)
No 27 Jalan Para U8/103 Metropolitan Business Park, Seksyen U8, 40150, Shah Alam, Selangor, Malaysia
Tel.: (60) 3 7859 8023
Technical Services
N.A.I.C.S.: 541690

TUV Rheinland Mandy Ltd. (2)
Room 201 No 16 Baihuazhou Rd, Cangshan District, Fuzhou, 350000, China
Tel.: (86) 591 87505076
Technical Services
N.A.I.C.S.: 541690

TUV Rheinland Middle East FZE (2)
Jafza View 18 Office No 904, PO Box 293542, Jebel Ali Free Zone, Dubai, United Arab Emirates
Tel.: (971) 4 8800669
Technical Services
N.A.I.C.S.: 541690

Subsidiary (US):

TUV Rheinland Mobility, Inc. (2)
1901 Montreal Rd Ste 126, Tucker, GA 30084
Tel.: (404) 294-5300
Emp.: 70
Technical Services
N.A.I.C.S.: 541690
Sebastian Oertel *(COO)*

Subsidiary (Non-US):

TUV Rheinland NIFE Academy Private Ltd. (2)
No 1346 2nd Floor South End Road, Jayanagar 9th Block, Bengaluru, 560069, India
Tel.: (91) 80 65981183
Web Site: http://www.nifeindia.com
Educational Support Services
N.A.I.C.S.: 611710

TUV Rheinland Nederland B.V. (2)
Boogschutterstraat 11A, 7324 AE, Apeldoorn, Netherlands
Tel.: (31) 88 8887888
Technical Services
N.A.I.C.S.: 541690
Henk van Ginkel *(Mgr-Bus Field)*

Subsidiary (US):

TUV Rheinland North America Holding, Inc. (2)
1300 Massachusetts Ave Ste 103, Boxborough, MA 01719
Tel.: (978) 266-9500
Technical Services
N.A.I.C.S.: 541690
Luebken Gerhard *(Pres & CEO)*

TUV Rheinland PTL LLC (2)
2210 S Roosevelt St, Tempe, AZ 85282
Tel.: (480) 966-1700
Testing Services
N.A.I.C.S.: 541380
Christopher Karpurk *(Project Engr)*

Subsidiary (Non-US):

TUV Rheinland Peru S.A.C. (2)
Avenida Camino Real 348 Torre El Pilar - Oficina 606, San Isidro, Lima, Peru
Tel.: (51) 1 221 5990
Technical Services
N.A.I.C.S.: 541690

TUV Rheinland Philippines, Inc. (2)
2241 Don Chino Roces Avenue G/F La Fuerza Building 1, Makati, 1231, Philippines
Tel.: (63) 2 812 8887
Emp.: 100
Technical Services
N.A.I.C.S.: 541690
Tristan Arwen Loveres *(Mng Dir)*

TUV Rheinland Polska Sp. z o.o. (2)
ul 17 Stycznia 56, 02-146, Warsaw, Poland
Tel.: (48) 22 846 79 99
Technical Services
N.A.I.C.S.: 541690

TUV Rheinland Portugal Inspeccoes Tecnicas, Lda. (2)
Arquiparque - Edificio Zenith R Dr Antonio Loureiro Borges 9 3, 1495-131, Alges, Portugal
Tel.: (351) 21 413 70 40
Technical Services
N.A.I.C.S.: 541690

TUV Rheinland Romania S.R.L. (2)
Calea Dorobantilor Nr 103-105 Sector 1, 010561, Bucharest, Romania
Tel.: (40) 21 318 8834
Web Site: http://www.tuv.com
Emp.: 30
Technical Services
N.A.I.C.S.: 541690
Valentina Berariu *(Mgr-Fin)*

Subsidiary (Domestic):

TUV Rheinland STEP International GmbH (2)
Julius-Vosseler-Str 42, Hamburg, 22527, Germany
Tel.: (49) 63135450
Technical Services
N.A.I.C.S.: 541690

TUV Rheinland Schniering GmbH (2)
Heegstr 60, 45356, Essen, Germany
Tel.: (49) 201 86139 0
Web Site: http://www.schniering.com
Inspection Equipment Mfr
N.A.I.C.S.: 334519
Volker Jakobi *(Mng Dir)*

Subsidiary (Non-US):

TUV Rheinland Slovensko s.r.o. (2)
Racianska 22/A, 83154, Bratislava, Slovakia
Tel.: (421) 910 868 690
Technical Services
N.A.I.C.S.: 541690

TUV Rheinland TUrkiye A. S. (2)
Kozyatagi Mah Saniye Ermutlu Sok No 12, Kadikoy, Istanbul, Turkiye
Tel.: (90) 216 665 32 00
Technical Services
N.A.I.C.S.: 541690
Demet Kopuz *(Engr-Indus Svc)*

TUV RHEINLAND BERLIN-BRANDENBURG PFALZ E.V.

TUV Rheinland Berlin-Brandenburg Pfalz e.V.—(Continued)

TUV Rheinland Thailand Ltd. (2)
18 F Tararom Business Tower 2445/36-38
New Petchburi Road, Bangkapi Huay
Kwang, Bangkok, 10320, Thailand
Tel.: (66) 2 314 2071
Technical Services
N.A.I.C.S.: 541690
Stefan Heuer (Mng Dir)

TUV Rheinland UK Ltd. (2)
Vienna House International Square Birmingham International Park, Bickenhill Lane, Solihull, B37 7GN, West Midlands, United Kingdom
Tel.: (44) 121 767 1399
Technical Services
N.A.I.C.S.: 541690
Linda Rhodes (Mgr-HR)

TUV Rheinland Ukraine GmbH (2)
25A Dneprovskaya Naberejnaya Str, 02081, Kiev, Ukraine
Tel.: (380) 44 220 1427
Technical Services
N.A.I.C.S.: 541690
Alexander Andreev (Mng Dir)

TUV Rheinland Vietnam Co. Ltd. (2)
Unit 805-806 Centre Point Building 106
Nguyen Van Troi St, Ward 8 Phu Nhuan
Dist, Ho Chi Minh City, Vietnam
Tel.: (84) 8 3842 0600
Laboratory Testing Services
N.A.I.C.S.: 541380
Frank Juettner (Gen Dir)

Subsidiary (Domestic):

ifes GmbH (2)
Am Wassermann 36, 50829, Cologne, Germany
Tel.: (49) 221 801099 0
Web Site: http://www.ifes-koeln.de
Engineering Consulting Services
N.A.I.C.S.: 541330

TUV SUD AG
Westendstrasse 199, 80686, Munich, Germany
Tel.: (49) 8957910 De
Web Site: http://www.tuev-sued.de
Year Founded: 1866
Rev.: $2,900,549,386
Assets: $2,732,682,372
Liabilities: $1,717,193,324
Net Worth: $1,015,489,048
Earnings: $148,493,436
Emp.: 23,024
Fiscal Year-end: 12/31/19
Holding Company; Technical Consulting, Testing, Certification & Training Services
N.A.I.C.S.: 551112
Axel Stepken (Chm-Mgmt Bd)

Subsidiaries:

APZ Auto-Pflege-Zentrum GmbH (1)
Otto-Rohm-Strasse 66, 64293, Darmstadt, Germany
Tel.: (49) 61 51 66 75 2 0
Web Site: http://www.apz-carmotion.de
Vehicle Valeting Services
N.A.I.C.S.: 811192

ARISE Boiler Inspection and Insurance Company Risk Retention Group (1)
PO Box 23790, Louisville, KY 40223-0790
Tel.: (800) 608-1340
General Insurance Services
N.A.I.C.S.: 524210

ARMAT GmbH & Co. KG (1)
Emil-Riedl-Weg 6, 82049, Pullach, Germany
Tel.: (49) 8157 93410
Real Estate Development Services
N.A.I.C.S.: 531210

Arise, Inc. (1)
Grand Bay 7000 S Edgerton Rd Ste 100, Brecksville, OH 44141
Tel.: (440) 746-8860
Web Site: http://www.ariseinc.com

Boiler & Pressure Vessel Inspection Services
N.A.I.C.S.: 541990
Tom Kovach (Mgr-Sls & Mktg)

Bureau de Projetos e Consultoria Ltda. (1)
Rua Girassol 1033, 05433-002, Sao Paulo, Brazil
Tel.: (55) 11 3817 0200
Web Site: http://www.tuv-sud.com.br
Engineering Consulting Services
N.A.I.C.S.: 541330

EMI-TUV SUD Kft. (1)
Dozsa Gyorgy ut 26, 2000, Szentendre, Hungary
Tel.: (36) 26501120
Web Site: http://www.tuvsud.com
Training Development Services
N.A.I.C.S.: 611430
Tamas Karsai (Project Mgr)

FLTL, Logistics Portugal, unipessoal Lda. (1)
Av da Republica 52, 1000, Lisbon, Portugal
Tel.: (351) 808 202 964
Fleet Management Services
N.A.I.C.S.: 485310

Fleet Logistics International NV (1)
Luchthavenlaan 25B, 1800, Vilvoorde, Belgium
Tel.: (32) 2 600 72 22
Web Site: http://www.fleetlogistics.com
Fleet Management Services
N.A.I.C.S.: 485310
Andreas Roterberg (CFO)

Subsidiary (Non-US):

Fleet Logistics Austria GmbH (2)
Arsenal Objekt 207, 1030, Vienna, Austria
Tel.: (43) 1 8900 628 64
Fleet Management Services
N.A.I.C.S.: 485310

Fleet Logistics Finland Oy (2)
Kuortaneenkatu 7, 00520, Helsinki, Finland
Tel.: (358) 9 7562 0400
Fleet Management Services
N.A.I.C.S.: 485310
Sari Vepsalainen (Head-Country)

Fleet Logistics France S.A.S (2)
159 rue de Silly, 92641, Boulogne-Billancourt, Cedex, France
Tel.: (33) 1 41 10 12 40
Web Site: http://www.fleetlogistics.com
Fleet Management Services
N.A.I.C.S.: 485310

Fleet Logistics Hungary Kft (2)
Kerepesi ut 27/A, 1087, Budapest, Hungary
Tel.: (36) 19 50 06 03
Fleet Management Services
N.A.I.C.S.: 485310

Fleet Logistics Italia S.r.l. (2)
Via Ripamonti 89, 20141, Milan, Italy
Tel.: (39) 0257371400
Web Site: http://www.fleetlogistics.com
Fleet Management Services
N.A.I.C.S.: 485310

Fleet Logistics Netherlands B.V. (2)
Hoevestein 36A, 4903 SC, Oosterhout, Netherlands
Tel.: (31) 162 447 766
Fleet Management Services
N.A.I.C.S.: 485310

Fleet Logistics Nordic AB (2)
Djaknegatan 31, 211 35, Malmo, Sweden
Tel.: (46) 40 33 04 60
Fleet Management Services
N.A.I.C.S.: 485310
Katharina Muller (Head-Ops-Fleet Acctg & Reporting)

Fleet Logistics Poland Sp. z o.o. (2)
Walicow 9-11, 00-851, Warsaw, Poland
Tel.: (48) 22 206 84 11
Fleet Management Services
N.A.I.C.S.: 485310
Krzysztof Dzietczenia (Mgr-Ops)

Fleet Logistics Portugal Unipessoal Lda (2)
Taguspark - Parque de Ciencia e Tecnologia Nucleo Central Sala 232, 2740-122, Oeiras, Portugal
Tel.: (351) 211 926 240
Web Site: http://www.fleetlogistics.com
Emp.: 1,000
Fleet Management Services
N.A.I.C.S.: 485310

Fleet Logistics Romania (2)
Banul Udrea 9-11 Sect 3, Bucharest, Romania
Tel.: (40) 745043408
Fleet Management Services
N.A.I.C.S.: 485310

Fleet Logistics Russia (2)
of 232 bld19 2/4 Luzhnetskaya nab, 119270, Moscow, Russia
Tel.: (7) 916 351 9461
Fleet Management Services
N.A.I.C.S.: 485310

Fleet Logistics Spain S.A.U. (2)
c/Chile 10, Las Matas, 28290, Madrid, Spain
Tel.: (34) 91 630 8210
Fleet Management Services
N.A.I.C.S.: 485310

Fleet Logistics UK Limited (2)
3500 Parkside Birmingham Business Park, Solihull, B37 7YG, United Kingdom
Tel.: (44) 121 717 1060
Fleet Management Services
N.A.I.C.S.: 485310
Madelaine Webster (Mgr-Bus Dev)

Joint Venture (Non-US):

FleetCompany GmbH (2)
Keltenring 13, 82041, Oberhaching, Germany (40%)
Tel.: (49) 89 63 89 82 0
Web Site: http://www.fleetlogistics.de
Fleet Management Services
N.A.I.C.S.: 485310
Arnd K. Martin (Mng Dir)

GRC Merlin Holdings, Inc. (1)
100 Walnut Ave, Clark, NJ 07066-1253
Tel.: (732) 827-4400
Holding Company
N.A.I.C.S.: 551112

Global Risk Consultants (Australia) Pty Ltd (1)
L 2 31 QUEEN ST, Melbourne, 3000, VIC, Australia
Tel.: (61) 3 96137999
Technical Consulting Services
N.A.I.C.S.: 541990

Global Risk Consultants (Malaysia) Sdn. Bhd. (1)
Suite 25-03 25th Floor Menara Keck Seng 203 Jalan Bukit Bintang, 55100, Kuala Lumpur, Malaysia
Tel.: (60) 3 2143 1510
Technical Consulting Services
N.A.I.C.S.: 541990

Global Risk Consultants (Singapore) Pte. Ltd. (1)
1 Science Park Drive, Singapore, 118221, Singapore
Tel.: (65) 68851724
Web Site: http://www.globalriskconsultants.com
Emp.: 7
Technical Consulting Services
N.A.I.C.S.: 541990

Global Risk Consultants, Inc. (1)
West Byfleet, London, KT14 6LB, United Kingdom
Tel.: (44) 1932358660
Web Site: http://www.globalriskconsultants.com
Technical Consulting Services
N.A.I.C.S.: 541990

Jiangsu TUV Product Service Limited (1)
3-13 No 151 Heng Tong Road, Shanghai, 200 070, China
Tel.: (86) 21 6141 0123
Web Site: http://www.tuv-sud.cn
Emp.: 1,300
Laboratory Testing Services
N.A.I.C.S.: 541380
Dirk von Wahl (Pres & CEO)

INTERNATIONAL PUBLIC

K + S Haustechnik Planungsgesellschaft mbH (1)
Egermannstrasse 7, 53359, Rheinbach, Germany
Tel.: (49) 2226 8080 0
Web Site: http://www.k-s-haustechnik.com
Construction Engineering Services
N.A.I.C.S.: 541330
Arthur Kramp (Mng Dir)

National Association of Boiler and Pressure Vessel Owners and Operators, Inc. (1)
1700 Eastpoint Pkwy, Louisville, KY 40223
Tel.: (800) 989-7475
Pressure Vessel Inspection Services
N.A.I.C.S.: 541990

OOO TUV SUD RUS (1)
20/2 Verkhnyaya Maslovka str, 127083, Moscow, Russia
Tel.: (7) 495 221 18 04
Web Site: http://www.tuev-sued.ru
Technical Consulting Services
N.A.I.C.S.: 541690
Olga Gaiderova (Project Mgr)

PIMA-MPU GmbH (1)
Sendlinger Str 24, 80331, Munich, Germany
Tel.: (49) 89 32 16 67 60
Web Site: http://www.pima-mpu.de
Automobile Driving Training Services
N.A.I.C.S.: 611692

PSB Management Consulting (Shanghai) Co. Ltd. (1)
369 Jiangsu Road 5th Floor Unit E Zaofeng World Trade Building, Shanghai, 200050, China
Tel.: (86) 21 5237 9031
Management Consulting Services
N.A.I.C.S.: 541611

Product Safety Engineering Inc. (1)
12955 Bellamy Brothers Blvd, Dade City, FL 33525
Tel.: (352) 588-2209
Web Site: http://www.pseinc.com
Rev.: $1,428,000
Emp.: 14
Testing Laboratories
N.A.I.C.S.: 541380
Herb Watkins (Owner)

SFDK Laboratorio de Analise de Produtos Ltda. (1)
Av Aratas 754, Moema, Sao Paulo, 04081 004, Brazil
Tel.: (55) 11 5097 7888
Web Site: http://www.sfdk.com.br
Laboratory Testing Services
N.A.I.C.S.: 541380

SIGNON Deutschland GmbH (1)
Schutzenstrasse 15-17, 10117, Berlin, Germany
Tel.: (49) 30 247387 13
Web Site: http://www.signon-group.com
Information Technology Consulting Services
N.A.I.C.S.: 541512
Gerd Hubner (CFO)

SIGNON Osterreich GmbH (1)
Marxergasse 1B/Top 6, 1030, Vienna, Austria
Tel.: (43) 1 5811454
Web Site: http://www.signongroup.com
Software Development & Information Technology Consulting Services
N.A.I.C.S.: 541511
Paul Kleinrath (CEO)

SIGNON Schweiz AG (1)
Aargauerstrasse 250, 8048, Zurich, Switzerland
Tel.: (41) 44 43537 00
Software Development Services
N.A.I.C.S.: 541511
C. H. Stefan Bauer (Member-Exec Bd & Project Mgr)

SWISSI Process Safety GmbH (1)
Mattenstrasse 24a, 4002, Basel, Switzerland
Tel.: (41) 61 696 80 50
Technical Consulting Services
N.A.I.C.S.: 541690
Andreas Gitzi (Engr-Safety)

TUV Hessen Mobilitat und Beratung GmbH (1)

AND PRIVATE COMPANIES — TUV SUD AG

Rudesheimer Strasse 119, 64285, Darmstadt, Germany
Tel.: (49) 6172 21114
Technical Consulting Services
N.A.I.C.S.: 541990

TUV Italia S.r.l. (1)
Via Carducci 125 pal 23, Sesto San Giovanni, 20099, Milan, Italy
Tel.: (39) 0224130 1
Web Site: http://www.tuv.it
Emp.: 470
Inspection Services
N.A.I.C.S.: 541990

Subsidiary (Domestic):

Bytest S.r.l. (2)
Via Pisa 12-14-16, 10088, Volpiano, Turin, Italy
Tel.: (39) 0 11 037221
Laboratory Testing Services
N.A.I.C.S.: 541380

P.H. S.r.l. (2)
Via Bramante 10/12, Loc Sambuca, 50028, Rome, Florence, Italy
Tel.: (39) 055 80677
Laboratory Testing Services
N.A.I.C.S.: 541380

TUV SUD Advimo GmbH (1)
Grillparzerstrasse 12a, Munich, Germany
Tel.: (49) 8941109680
Training Development Services
N.A.I.C.S.: 611430
Philippe Habermeyer *(Mgr-Strategic Acct & Head-Sls)*

TUV SUD Akademie GmbH (1)
Westendstr 160, 80339, Munich, Germany
Tel.: (49) 8957912388
Web Site: http://www.tuev-sued.de
Sales Range: $50-74.9 Million
Training & Personnel Certification Services
N.A.I.C.S.: 611430

TUV SUD America Inc. (1)
10 Centennial Dr, Peabody, MA 01960
Tel.: (978) 573-2500
Holding Company; Regional Managing Office; Business-to-Business Engineering Services
N.A.I.C.S.: 551112
Christoph Weimer *(CFO)*

Subsidiary (Domestic):

Global Risk Consultants Corp. (2)
100 Walnut Ave Ste 501, Clark, NJ 07066-1247
Tel.: (732) 827-4400
Web Site: http://www.globalriskconsultants.com
Emp.: 40
Loss Prevention & Control Engineering & Consulting Services
N.A.I.C.S.: 541330
James J. Marsh *(CEO)*

RCI Consultants, Inc. (2)
17314 Hwy 249 Ste 350, Houston, TX 77064
Tel.: (281) 970-4221
Web Site: http://www.rcigroup.us
Rev.: $21,800,000
Emp.: 76
Energy Project Management & Support Services
N.A.I.C.S.: 541690
Brant Le Blanc *(Founder, CEO & Sr Mgr-Consulting)*

Subsidiary (Non-US):

TUV SUD Canada Inc. (2)
1229 Ringwell Dr, Newmarket, L3Y 8T8, ON, Canada
Tel.: (905) 715-7991
Web Site: http://www.tuv-sud.ca
Laboratory Testing Services
N.A.I.C.S.: 541380

TUV SUD America de Mexico S.A. de C.V. (1)
Ave Juarez 898 PH Colonia Centro San Pedro Garza Garcia, 66200, Monterrey, Nuevo Leon, Mexico
Tel.: (52) 81 8221 3530
Web Site: http://www.tuv-sud.mx
Inspection Services
N.A.I.C.S.: 541990

TUV SUD Asia Pacific Pte. Ltd. (1)
04-01/05 The Franklin 3 Science Park Drive, 118223, Singapore, Singapore
Tel.: (65) 6427 4700
Technical Consulting Services
N.A.I.C.S.: 541690
Yin Wang *(Asst Mgr-Technical)*

TUV SUD Auto Partner GmbH (1)
Trankestr 11, 70597, Stuttgart, Germany
Tel.: (49) 711 72 20 84 71
Automotive Repair Services
N.A.I.C.S.: 811111

TUV SUD Auto Plus GmbH (1)
Gutenbergstr 13, 70771, Leinfelden-Echterdingen, Germany
Tel.: (49) 711 7220 840
Automotive Inspection Services
N.A.I.C.S.: 811198
Patrick Fruth *(Mng Dir)*

TUV SUD Auto Service GmbH (1)
Westendstr 199, 80686, Munich, Germany
Tel.: (49) 89 5791 0
Web Site: http://www.tuev-sued.de
Automotive Diagnostic Testing
N.A.I.C.S.: 811198

Subsidiary (Domestic):

TUV Hanse GmbH (2)
Ausschlager Weg 100, 20537, Hamburg, Germany
Tel.: (49) 40 42858 5004
Environmental Consulting Services
N.A.I.C.S.: 541620
Hero Wilters *(Mng Dir)*

TUV SUD Automotive GmbH (1)
Daimlerstr 11, 85748, Garching, Germany
Tel.: (49) 89 32950 620
Automotive Repair & Maintenance Services
N.A.I.C.S.: 811198

TUV SUD Bangladesh (Pvt.) Ltd. (1)
Level 7 8 & 14 Update Tower 01 Shahjalal Avenue Sector - 06, Uttara Model Town, Dhaka, 1230, Bangladesh
Tel.: (880) 258954115
Web Site: http://www.tuv-sud.com.bd
Emp.: 110
Laboratory Testing Services
N.A.I.C.S.: 541380
Ezhilan Neelan *(Country Dir)*

TUV SUD Battery Testing GmbH (1)
Daimlerstr 15, 85748, Garching, Germany
Tel.: (49) 89 32950 710
Battery Testing Services
N.A.I.C.S.: 334515
Christian Theeck *(Mng Dir)*

TUV SUD Benelux B.V.B.A. (1)
Leuvensesteenweg 350, 3190, Boortmeerbeek, Belgium
Tel.: (32) 15509630
Web Site: http://www.tuv-sud.be
Engineeering Services
N.A.I.C.S.: 541330
Filip Michiels *(Mng Dir & Member-Mgmt Bd)*

TUV SUD Brasil Engenharia e Consultoria Ltda. (1)
Rua do Tesouro 23-12o Andar-Centro, Sao Paulo, 01013-020, Brazil
Tel.: (55) 1150977888
Web Site: http://www.tuv-sud.com.br
Training Development Services
N.A.I.C.S.: 611430

TUV SUD Bursa Tasit Muayene Istasyonlari Isletim A.S. (1)
Kukurtlu Mah Oulu Cad Oylum Cigdem Sitesi A Blok K 1 D 4 PK, Osmangazi, 16080, Bursa, Turkiye
Tel.: (90) 224 211 39 25
Technical Consulting Services
N.A.I.C.S.: 541690

TUV SUD Central Eastern Europe s.r.o. (1)
Novodvorska 994/138, 142 21, Prague, Czech Republic
Tel.: (420) 239 046 700
Web Site: http://www.tuv-sud.cz
Inspection Services
N.A.I.C.S.: 541990
Petr Janas *(Controller-Reg Fin)*

TUV SUD Certification and Testing (China) Co., Ltd. (1)
No 10 Huaxia Road M Dongting, Wuxi, 214100, Jiangsu, China
Tel.: (86) 510 8820 3737
Web Site: http://www.tuvsud.com
Emp.: 3,000
Testing Services
N.A.I.C.S.: 541380

TUV SUD Chemie Service GmbH (1)
Kaiser-Wilhelm-Allee Gebaude B 407, 51368, Leverkusen, Germany
Tel.: (49) 214 30 62653
Chemical Testing Services
N.A.I.C.S.: 541380
Hans-Nicolaus Rindfleisch *(Mng Dir)*

TUV SUD Danmark ApS (1)
Strandvejen 125, 2900, Hellerup, Denmark
Tel.: (45) 44770010
Web Site: http://www.tuv-sud.dk
Emp.: 15
Technical Consulting Services
N.A.I.C.S.: 541690
Lars Brockhoff *(Gen Mgr)*

TUV SUD ELAB GmbH (1)
Birlenbacher Strasse 14, 57078, Siegen, Germany
Tel.: (49) 271 77 50 3
Laboratory Testing Services
N.A.I.C.S.: 541380
Bernd Roesner *(Mng Dir)*

TUV SUD Energietechnik GmbH Baden-Wurttemberg (1)
Gottlieb-Daimler-Strasse 7, 70794, Filderstadt, Germany
Tel.: (49) 711 7005 800
Web Site: http://www.tuev-sued.de
Emp.: 200
Energy Consulting Services
N.A.I.C.S.: 541690

TUV SUD Food Safety Institute GmbH (1)
Martin-Behaim-Strasse 22, 63263, Neu-Isenburg, Germany
Tel.: (49) 6102 8138 0
Technical Consulting Services
N.A.I.C.S.: 541690
Frank Altmann *(Mng Dir)*

TUV SUD France S.A.S. (1)
Le Norly 42 Chemin du Moulin Carron, 69130, Ecully, France
Tel.: (33) 4 72 18 90 00
Web Site: http://www.tuv-sud.fr
Inspection Services
N.A.I.C.S.: 541990

TUV SUD Global Inspection Limited (1)
3/F West Wing Lakeside 2 10 Science Park West Avenue Science Park, Sha Tin, China (Hong Kong)
Tel.: (852) 3728 6230
Web Site: http://www.sercura.com
Inspection Services
N.A.I.C.S.: 541990

TUV SUD Industrie Service GmbH (1)
Westendstrasse 199, 80686, Munich, Germany
Tel.: (49) 8957910
Sales Range: $1-4.9 Billion
Emp.: 16,000
Safety Training & Consulting
N.A.I.C.S.: 541614

Subsidiary (Domestic):

TUV SUD ImmoWert GmbH (2)
Westendstr 199, 80686, Munich, Germany
Tel.: (49) 8957912080
Web Site: http://www.tuev-sued.de
Sales Range: $25-49.9 Million
Real Estate Appraisal Services
N.A.I.C.S.: 531320
Krlotz Ulrich *(Mng Dir)*

TUV SUD Industry Service, Inc. (1)
6200 Klines Dr, Girard, OH 44420
Tel.: (330) 539-5169
Inspection Services
N.A.I.C.S.: 541990

TUV SUD Japan Ltd. (1)
Sumitomo Fudosan Nishi-shinjuku Bldg No 4 8F 4-33-4 Nishi-Shinjuku, Tokyo, 160-0023, Japan
Tel.: (81) 3 3372 4970
Web Site: http://www.tuv-sud.jp
Chemical Testing Services
N.A.I.C.S.: 541380

TUV SUD KOCEN Ltd. (1)
13F Kranz-Techno Bldg 5442-1 Sangdaewon-dong, Seongnam, 462-729, Gyeonggi, Korea (South)
Tel.: (82) 31 777 8500
Web Site: http://www.tuv-sud-kocen.kr
Emp.: 207
Equipment Inspection Services
N.A.I.C.S.: 926130
Ki Sung Jung *(Deputy Gen Mgr)*

TUV SUD Korea Ltd. (1)
29th floor Two IFC 10 Gukjeokhan-ro, Youngdeungpo-Gu, Seoul, 07326, Korea (South)
Tel.: (82) 2 3215 1100
Web Site: http://www.tuv-sud.kr
Technical Consulting Services
N.A.I.C.S.: 541690
Stefan Rentsch *(Pres & CEO)*

TUV SUD Landesgesellschaft Osterreich GmbH (1)
Tiwagstrasse 7, 6200, Jenbach, Austria
Tel.: (43) 505284050
Web Site: http://www.tuvsud.com
Engineeering Services
N.A.I.C.S.: 541330

TUV SUD Life Service GmbH (1)
Westendstrasse 199, Munich, 80686, Germany
Tel.: (49) 8957912904
Sales Range: $25-49.9 Million
Emp.: 15
Medical & Psychological Testing Services
N.A.I.C.S.: 541690

TUV SUD Management Service GmbH (1)
Ridlerstrasse 65, D-80339, Munich, Germany
Tel.: (49) 59 5791 2500
Quality Control Services; Auditing, Surveillances & Validation
N.A.I.C.S.: 561499

Subsidiary (Domestic):

LSG-Hygiene Institute GmbH (2)
Dornhofstrasse 40, 63263, Neu-Isenburg, Germany (75%)
Tel.: (49) 6102240467
Web Site: http://www.lsg-skychefs.com
Food Safety Testing
N.A.I.C.S.: 541380

TUV SUD Sec-IT GmbH (2)
Ridlerstrasse 65, 80339, Munich, Germany
Tel.: (49) 8950084747
Web Site: http://www.safer-shopping.com
Information Technology Consulting Services
N.A.I.C.S.: 541512

TUV SUD Middle East LLC (1)
Villa No 676 Al Azaiba P C 130 Way No 6808 Street 68, PO Box 1621, Muscat, Oman
Tel.: (968) 2449 3451
Inspection Services
N.A.I.C.S.: 541990

TUV SUD Middle East LLC (1)
Plot No 129 SR Ahl Al'Ilm Street ICAD III Mussafah, PO Box 45117, Abu Dhabi, United Arab Emirates
Tel.: (971) 2 676 7600
Web Site: http://www.tuv-sud.ae
Inspection Services
N.A.I.C.S.: 541990
Salah Safah *(CEO & Mng Dir)*

TUV SUD Middle East LLC (1)
Office No-Sy36-C101 1st Floor Block 36 Building Type-Sayer, PO Box 24240, Barwa Commercial Avenue, Doha, Qatar
Tel.: (974) 4005 2000
Inspection Services
N.A.I.C.S.: 541990
Mohammad Farook Mohammad Fiham *(Sec)*

TUV SUD AG

TUV SUD AG—(Continued)

TUV SUD NEL LIMITED (1)
Scottish Enterprise Technology Park, East Kilbride, Glasgow, G75 0QF, United Kingdom
Tel.: (44) 1355 220222
Web Site: http://www.tuvnel.com
Technical Consulting Services
N.A.I.C.S.: 541690
Brian Millington *(Mng Dir)*

TUV SUD Nuclear Technologies plc (1)
Avionics House Quedgeley Enterprise Centre, Gloucester, GL2 2SN, Gloucestershire, United Kingdom
Tel.: (44) 1452 720760
Technical Consulting Services
N.A.I.C.S.: 541690

TUV SUD PMSS (1)
590 Madison Ave 18th Fl, New York, NY 10022
Tel.: (212) 521-4161
Renewable Energy Consulting Services
N.A.I.C.S.: 541690
Sebastian Chivers *(Pres)*

TUV SUD PMSS Ltd. (1)
8 Latimer Walk, Romsey, SO51 8LA, Hampshire, United Kingdom
Tel.: (44) 1794 527 500
Renewable Energy Consulting Services
N.A.I.C.S.: 541690

TUV SUD PSB (Thailand) Ltd. (1)
111 Moo 9 Phaholyothin road Khlong Nueng, Khlong Luang, 12120, Pathum Thani, Thailand
Tel.: (66) 2 564 8041
Web Site: http://www.tuv-sud.co.th
Emp.: 80
Laboratory Testing Services
N.A.I.C.S.: 541380
Chatvitai Tantraporn *(Gen Mgr)*

TUV SUD PSB Indonesia, PT. (1)
Dipo Tower 9th floor suite C-D Dipo Business Centre Jalan Gatot, Subroto Kav 51-52 Petamburan Tanah Abang, Jakarta, 10260, Indonesia
Tel.: (62) 21 2986 5795
Web Site: http://www.tuv-sud.co.id
Laboratory Testing Services
N.A.I.C.S.: 541380
Eric Paulsen *(Gen Mgr)*

TUV SUD PSB Philippines Inc. (1)
Unit 1808 The Orient Square Building F Ortigas Jr Road Ortigas Center, Pasig, 1605, Metro Manila, Philippines
Tel.: (63) 286875673
Web Site: http://www.tuvsud.com
Emp.: 50
Laboratory Testing Services
N.A.I.C.S.: 541380
Klaus Langner *(Member-Mgmt Bd)*

TUV SUD PSB Products Testing (Shanghai) Co., Ltd. (1)
B-3/4 No 1999 Du Hui Road, Minhang District, Shanghai, 201108, China
Tel.: (86) 21 6037 6375
Web Site: http://www.tuv-sud.cn
Laboratory Testing Services
N.A.I.C.S.: 541380

TUV SUD PSB Pte. Ltd. (1)
15 International Business Park, Singapore, 609937, Singapore
Tel.: (65) 67787777
Web Site: http://www.tuv-sud-psb.sg
Emp.: 600
Laboratory Testing Services
N.A.I.C.S.: 541380
Niranjan Nadkarni *(Member-Mgmt Bd)*

TUV SUD PSB Vietnam Co. Ltd. (1)
Lot III-26 Road 19/5A Industrial Group III, Tan Binh Industrial Park, Tay Thanh Ward Tan Phu District, Ho Chi Minh City, Vietnam
Tel.: (84) 8 6267 8507
Web Site: http://www.tuv-sud.vn
Emp.: 100
Technical Consulting Services
N.A.I.C.S.: 541690
Sathish Kumar Somuraj *(Gen Dir)*

TUV SUD Pluspunkt GmbH (1)
Ridlerstrasse 57, D-80339, Munich, Germany
Tel.: (49) 8951903472
Drivers Training
N.A.I.C.S.: 611430

TUV SUD Polska Sp. z.o.o. (1)
ul Podwale 17, 00-252, Warsaw, Poland
Tel.: (48) 22 696 43 96
Web Site: http://www.tuv-sud.pl
Technical Consulting Services
N.A.I.C.S.: 541690

TUV SUD Process Safety (1)
C/ Lope de Vega 22-24, 08005, Barcelona, Spain
Tel.: (34) 34 93 303 66 12
Web Site: http://www.swissips.es
Chemical Consulting Services
N.A.I.C.S.: 541690
Alex Arevalo *(Mgr-Operational)*

Subsidiary (Non-US):

TUV SUD PSB (Malaysia) Sdn. Bhd. (2)
18 Jalan Astaka U8/82, Bukit Jelutong, 40150, Shah Alam, Selangor, Malaysia
Tel.: (60) 378598822
Web Site: http://www.tuv-sud.my
Laboratory Testing Services
N.A.I.C.S.: 541380
Klaus Langner *(Member-Mgmt Bd)*

TUV SUD Product Service GmbH (1)
Ridlerstr 65, 80339, Munich, Germany
Tel.: (49) 89 5008 40
Technical Consulting Services
N.A.I.C.S.: 541690
K. Michael *(Acct Mgr)*

TUV SUD Rail GmbH (1)
Barthstrasse 16, 80339, Munich, Germany
Tel.: (49) 89 5791 1473
Web Site: http://www.tuev-sued.de
Emp.: 100
Railway Construction Services
N.A.I.C.S.: 236220
Klaus-Michael Bosch *(Mng Dir)*

Subsidiary (Non-US):

Railcert B.V. (2)
Horaplantsoen 18, 6717 LT, Ede, Netherlands
Tel.: (31) 318 860 300
Web Site: http://www.railcert.com
Inspection Services
N.A.I.C.S.: 541690
D. Mohr *(Mgr-Technical Certifier-RST)*

TUV SUD Romania S.R.L. (1)
Calea Victoriei 155, Bucharest, 010073, Romania
Tel.: (40) 21 330 6600
Web Site: http://www.tuv-sud.ro
Emp.: 38
Technical Consulting Services
N.A.I.C.S.: 541690

TUV SUD SENTON GmbH (1)
Aussere Fruhlingstrasse 45, 94315, Straubing, Germany
Tel.: (49) 9421 5522 0
Technical Consulting Services
N.A.I.C.S.: 541690

TUV SUD Sava d.o.o. (1)
Stozenska ulica 2, 1000, Ljubljana, Slovenia
Tel.: (386) 1 300 61 30
Web Site: http://www.tuv-sud.si
Laboratory Testing Services
N.A.I.C.S.: 541380

TUV SUD Services (UK) Limited (1)
Octagon House Concorde Way Segensworth North, Fareham, PO15 5RL, Hampshire, United Kingdom
Tel.: (44) 1489 558100
Web Site: http://www.tuv-sud.co.uk
Sales Range: $25-49.9 Million
Emp.: 180
Laboratory Testing Services
N.A.I.C.S.: 541380

TUV SUD Slovakia s.r.o. (1)
Jasikova 6, 821 03, Bratislava, Slovakia
Tel.: (421) 850221200
Web Site: http://www.tuv-sud.sk

Inspection Services
N.A.I.C.S.: 541990

TUV SUD South Africa (Pty) Ltd. (1)
Boston Circle Airport Industria, Cape Town, 7490, South Africa
Tel.: (27) 21 935 7960
Web Site: http://www.tuv-sud.co.za
Technical Consulting Services
N.A.I.C.S.: 541690

TUV SUD South Africa Pro-Tec (Pty) Ltd. (1)
17 Spring Street, Middelburg, 1050, Mpumalanga, South Africa
Tel.: (27) 13 244 1330
Inspection & Testing Services
N.A.I.C.S.: 541990

TUV SUD South Africa Real Estate Services (Pty) Ltd. (1)
179 Blaauwberg Road, Table View, 7441, Cape Town, South Africa
Tel.: (27) 21 557 7438
Technical Consulting Services
N.A.I.C.S.: 541690

TUV SUD TGK Ltd. Sti. (1)
Ayazaga Mahallesi Mimar Sinan Sokak No 21 Seba ofis Bulvar B Blok, Sariyer, 34396, Istanbul, Turkiye
Tel.: (90) 212 347 98 10
Web Site: http://www.tuv-sud.com.tr
Food Inspection Services
N.A.I.C.S.: 926140

TUV SUD Wallace Whittle Ltd. (1)
166 Great Western Road, Aberdeen, AB10 6QE, United Kingdom
Tel.: (44) 1224285300
Emp.: 20
Engineeering Services
N.A.I.C.S.: 541330

TUV SUD do Brasil Ltda. (1)
Av Brigadeiro Faria Lima 1188 - 8 andar - conj 83, Pinheiros, 01451-001, Sao Paulo, Brazil
Tel.: (55) 11 2395 6000
Emp.: 400
Technical Consulting Services
N.A.I.C.S.: 541690

TUV SUD Iberia, S.L.U. (1)
C/ Frederic Mompou 4 A 1 4, San Just Desvern, 08960, Barcelona, Spain
Tel.: (34) 93490 2220
Web Site: http://www.tuv-sud.es
Inspection Services
N.A.I.C.S.: 541990

TUVTURK A.S. (1)
Ayazaga Mahallesi Mimar Sinan Sokak No 21 Seba Ofis Bulvar B Blok, Sariyer, 34396, Istanbul, Turkiye
Tel.: (90) 2123658700
Web Site: http://www.tuvturk.com.tr
Training Development Services
N.A.I.C.S.: 611430
Erman Yerdelen *(Chm)*

ZWP - Zerstorungsfreie Werkstoffprufung GmbH (1)
Einzingergasse 4, 1210, Vienna, Austria
Tel.: (43) 1 271 74 05
Laboratory Testing Services
N.A.I.C.S.: 541380

TUV US JOINT STOCK COMPANY
5th Group Zuun Mod, Zuunmod, Tov, Mongolia
Tel.: (976) 1272 23857
Water & Sewage Treatement Services
N.A.I.C.S.: 221320

TUYA INC.
901 Building 1 Huace Center, Xihu District, Hangzhou, 310012, Zhejiang, China
Tel.: (86) 8446725646
Web Site: https://tuya.com
Year Founded: 2014
TUYA—(NYSE)
Rev.: $208,172,000
Assets: $1,056,139,000

INTERNATIONAL PUBLIC

Liabilities: $93,972,000
Net Worth: $962,167,000
Earnings: ($146,175,000)
Emp.: 1,835
Fiscal Year-end: 12/31/22
Holding Company
N.A.I.C.S.: 551112
Xueji Wang *(Founder & CEO)*

TUZLA-REMONT D.D. TUZLA
Armije Bih 8, Tuzla, Bosnia & Herzegovina
Tel.: (387) 35 251 084
Rev.: $57,445
Assets: $2,279,791
Liabilities: $242,904
Net Worth: $2,036,888
Earnings: ($915,971)
Emp.: 3
Fiscal Year-end: 12/31/17
Automotive Services
N.A.I.C.S.: 811198

TV ASAHI HOLDINGS CORPORATION
6-9-1 Roppongi, Minato-ku, Tokyo, 106-8001, Japan
Tel.: (81) 364061115
Web Site: https://www.tv-asahihd.co.jp
Year Founded: 1957
9409—(TKS)
Rev.: $2,035,205,780
Assets: $3,440,055,520
Liabilities: $640,211,550
Net Worth: $2,799,843,970
Earnings: $113,282,180
Fiscal Year-end: 03/31/24
Television Broadcasting Services
N.A.I.C.S.: 516120

Subsidiaries:

AbemaProduction, Inc. (1)
Esla Harajuku Building 6F 3-25-14, Jingumae Shibuya-ku, Tokyo, 150-0001, Japan
Tel.: (81) 354135561
Web Site: https://www.abemapro.co.jp
Mobile Phone Mfr & Distr
N.A.I.C.S.: 321991

Bunkakobo, Inc. (1)
Bunka Kobo Building 5-10-31, Roppongi Minato-ku, Tokyo, 106-0032, Japan
Tel.: (81) 357707111
Web Site: https://www.bun.co.jp
Emp.: 219
Television Broadcasting Services
N.A.I.C.S.: 561492

CS One Ten, Ltd. (1)
6-9-1 Roppongi, Minato-ku, Tokyo, 106-8001, Japan
Tel.: (81) 357723110
Web Site: https://www.cs110.co.jp
Satellite Broadcasting Services
N.A.I.C.S.: 517410

Itty, Inc. (1)
8F Aioi Nissay Dowa Insurance Shibuya Building 2-14-18 Shibuya, Shibuya-ku, Tokyo, 150-0002, Japan
Tel.: (81) 120974875
Web Site: https://itty.co.jp
Emp.: 37
Cosmetics & Health Food Distr
N.A.I.C.S.: 424420

Japan Cable Television, Ltd. (1)
1-1-1 Roppongi, Minato-ku, Tokyo, 106-0032, Japan
Tel.: (81) 335688221
Web Site: https://www.jctv.co.jp
Emp.: 80
Convolution Neural Network Program Services
N.A.I.C.S.: 541511

Media Mix Japan Co., Ltd. (1)
HI Gotanda Bldg 2-11-17, Nishi Gotand Shinagawa-ku, Tokyo, 141-0031, Japan
Tel.: (81) 357408188
Software Development Services
N.A.I.C.S.: 541714

AND PRIVATE COMPANIES

ROPPING LIFE Co., Ltd. (1)
1-2-9 Nishi-Azabu EX Tower 5F, Minato-ku, Tokyo, 106-0031, Japan
Tel.: (81) 357722100
Web Site: https://www.roppinglife.co.jp
Television Broadcasting Operator
N.A.I.C.S.: 561492

TV Asahi ASK Co., Ltd. (1)
Ex Roppongi Building 6F 7-18-23, Roppongi Minato-ku, Tokyo, 106-0032, Japan
Tel.: (81) 334011010
Web Site: https://www.tv-asahi-ask.co.jp
Emp.: 12
Television Broadcasting Services
N.A.I.C.S.: 561492

TV Asahi BEST Co., Ltd. (1)
Sk Roppongi Heim 6F 6-8-21, Roppongi Minato-ku, Tokyo, 106-0032, Japan
Tel.: (81) 364062901
Web Site: https://www.tv-asahi-best.co.jp
Emp.: 44
Building & Facility Management Operator
N.A.I.C.S.: 541618

TV Asahi Create Corporation (1)
1-2-9 Nishi-Azabu, Minato-ku, Tokyo, 106-0031, Japan
Tel.: (81) 357756021
Web Site: https://www.tv-asahi-create.co.jp
Emp.: 227
Television Broadcasting Services
N.A.I.C.S.: 561492

TV Asahi Music Co., Ltd. (1)
Roppongi Hills North Tower 12F 6-2-31, Roppongi Minato-ku, Tokyo, 106-8552, Japan
Tel.: (81) 337967500
Web Site: https://www.tv-asahi-music.co.jp
Emp.: 103
Television Broadcasting Services
N.A.I.C.S.: 561492

TV Asahi Productions Co., Ltd. (1)
2-2-10 Sekimachikita, Nerima-ku, Tokyo, 177-0051, Japan
Tel.: (81) 359275133
Web Site: https://www.asahi-pro.co.jp
Emp.: 165
Television Broadcasting Services
N.A.I.C.S.: 561492

TV Asahi mediaplex corporation (1)
7F EX Tower 1-2-9 Nishiazabu, Minato-ku, Tokyo, 106-0031, Japan
Tel.: (81) 354136111
Web Site: https://www.mediaplex.co.jp
Digital Marketing Services
N.A.I.C.S.: 541613

Takesystems Co., Ltd. (1)
Rahmhofstrasse 4 3 Og, 60313, Frankfurt am Main, Germany
Tel.: (49) 69222213800
Web Site: https://www.teksystems.com
Television Broadcasting Services
N.A.I.C.S.: 561492

Tokyo Sound Production Inc. (1)
Azabu West Building 2-24-11, Nishi-Azabu Minato-ku, Tokyo, 106-0031, Japan
Tel.: (81) 354665640
Web Site: https://tsp.co.jp
Emp.: 411
Television Broadcasting Services
N.A.I.C.S.: 561492

UltraImpression Inc. (1)
6-9-1 Roppongi, Minato-ku, Tokyo, Japan
Tel.: (81) 354134890
Web Site: https://ultraimpression.co.jp
Digital Video Advertisement Distribution Platform Services
N.A.I.C.S.: 541870

TV DIRECT PUBLIC COMPANY LIMITED
25 Watcharaphon Road Tarang, Bangkhen, Bangkok, 10230, Thailand
Tel.: (66) 26660122
Web Site: https://www.tvdirect.tv
TVDH—(THA)
Rev.: $51,902,929
Assets: $43,181,872
Liabilities: $24,461,370
Net Worth: $18,720,503
Earnings: ($12,801,740)
Emp.: 762
Fiscal Year-end: 12/31/23
TV & Online Direct Marketing
N.A.I.C.S.: 541613

TV SUNDRAM IYENGAR & SONS LIMITED
7-B West Veli Street, Madurai, 625 001, India
Tel.: (91) 4524356400 In
Web Site: http://www.tvsiyengar.com
Year Founded: 1911
Sales Range: $1-4.9 Billion
Emp.: 5,000
Holding Company; Automobile Distr
N.A.I.C.S.: 551112
Suresh Krishna (Chm)

Subsidiaries:

Sundaram Motors Pvt. Ltd. (1)
180 Anna Salai, Chennai, 600006, India
Tel.: (91) 44 28579300
Web Site: http://www.sundarammotors.com
Car Dealer
N.A.I.C.S.: 441110

Sundram Fasteners Ltd. (1)
98 - A VII Floor Dr Radhakrishnan Salai Mylapore, Chennai, 600004, India
Tel.: (91) 4428478500
Web Site: https://www.sundram.com
Rev.: $674,501,100
Assets: $584,789,205
Liabilities: $224,947,905
Net Worth: $359,841,300
Earnings: $63,039,795
Emp.: 2,937
Fiscal Year-end: 03/31/2022
Mfr of High-Tensile Fasteners, Powder Metal Components, Cold Extruded Parts, Hot Forged Components, Radiator Caps, Automotive Pumps, Gear Shifters & Couplings
N.A.I.C.S.: 332722
S. Meenakshisundaram (CFO)

Subsidiary (Non-US):

Peiner Umformtechnik GmbH (2)
Woltorfer Strasse 20-24, Peine, 31224, Germany
Tel.: (49) 51715450
Web Site: http://www.peiner-ut.com
Sales Range: $50-74.9 Million
Emp.: 250
Fastening Product Mfr
N.A.I.C.S.: 332722
Srancesco Bruno (Gen Mgr)

TV THUNDER PUBLIC COMPANY LIMITED
1213/309 - 310 Ladprao 94 Panjamitr Sriwara Road, Phlapphla, Phlapphla Wangthonglang, Bangkok, 10310, Thailand
Tel.: (66) 25590022
Web Site: https://www.tvthunder.co.th
Year Founded: 1993
TVT—(THA)
Rev.: $5,608,137
Assets: $19,229,253
Liabilities: $1,438,800
Net Worth: $17,790,452
Earnings: ($98,747)
Emp.: 67
Fiscal Year-end: 12/31/23
Television Production
N.A.I.C.S.: 512110

Subsidiaries:

Creatist Media Co., Ltd. (1)
527/12 Soi Lardprao 94 Panjamit Srivara Road, Phlapphla Wangthonglang, Bangkok, 10310, Thailand
Tel.: (66) 25590022
Television Production Services
N.A.I.C.S.: 512110

TV TODAY NETWORK LIMITED
F-26 First Floor Connaught Circus, New Delhi, 110 001, India
Tel.: (91) 1204807100 In
Web Site: https://www.indiatodaygroup.com
Year Founded: 1999
532515—(BOM)
Rev: $111,945,015
Assets: $164,939,775
Liabilities: $29,735,160
Net Worth: $135,204,615
Earnings: $17,949,750
Emp.: 1,822
Fiscal Year-end: 03/31/21
Television Broadcasting Services
N.A.I.C.S.: 516120
Aroon Purie (Chm)

TV TOKYO HOLDINGS CORPORATION

Roppongi Grand Tower 3-2-1, Roppongi Minato-ku, Tokyo, 106-0087, Japan
Tel.: (81) 366351771
Web Site: https://www.txhd.co.jp
Year Founded: 2010
9413—(TKS)
Rev.: $982,160,070
Assets: $972,291,340
Liabilities: $316,129,860
Net Worth: $656,161,480
Earnings: $44,524,960
Fiscal Year-end: 03/31/24
Television Broadcasting
N.A.I.C.S.: 516120
Shigeru Komago (Chm)

Subsidiaries:

BS Japan Corporation (1)
Roppongi Grand Tower 3-2-1 Roppongi, Minato-ku, Tokyo, 106-8107, Japan
Tel.: (81) 366350700
Web Site: https://www.bs-tvtokyo.co.jp
Television Broadcasting
N.A.I.C.S.: 516120

Bs Tv Tokyo Corporation (1)
Roppongi Grand Tower 3-2-1 Roppongi, Minato-ku, Tokyo, 106-8107, Japan
Tel.: (81) 366350700
Web Site: https://www.bs-tvtokyo.co.jp
Television Broadcasting Services
N.A.I.C.S.: 516120

Nikkei CNBC Japan Inc. (1)
1-3-7 Otemachi Nihon Keizai Shimbun Inc, Chiyoda-ku, Tokyo, 100-8066, Japan
Tel.: (81) 366367908
Web Site: https://www.nikkei-cnbc.co.jp
Television Broadcasting Services
N.A.I.C.S.: 561492

Real Max Co., Ltd. (1)
1-7-12 Yagi, Asaminami-ku, Hiroshima, 731-0101, Japan
Tel.: (81) 822097716
Web Site: https://www.realmax.co.jp
Golf Training Services
N.A.I.C.S.: 611620

TV TOKYO Communications Corporation (1)
Sumitomo Shin-Toranomon Building 4F 4-3-9 Toranomon, Minato ku, Tokyo, 105-0001, Japan
Tel.: (81) 357333888
Web Site: https://txcom.jp
Emp.: 85
Digital Media & Digital Content for Television Characters & Multi-Screen Businesses
N.A.I.C.S.: 516120

TV TOKYO Corporation (1)
Roppongi Grand Tower 3-2-1 Roppongi, Minato-ku, Tokyo, 106-8007, Japan
Tel.: (81) 366327777
Web Site: https://www.tv-tokyo.co.jp
Sales Range: $1-4.9 Billion
Emp.: 768
Broadcasting Services
N.A.I.C.S.: 516120

Subsidiary (Domestic):

TV TOKYO Art, Inc. (2)
8F TV Tokyo Tennozu Studio 1-3-3 Higashi-Shinagawa, Shinagawa-ku, Tokyo, 140-0002, Japan
Tel.: (81) 364330986
Web Site: https://tx-art.co.jp
Sales Range: $25-49.9 Million
Emp.: 99
Studio Sets & Lighting Mfr
N.A.I.C.S.: 334220
Shuichi Yokosen (Pres)

TV TOKYO Building, Inc. (2)
3-3 Higashi-Shinagawa 1-Chome, Shinagawa-ku, Tokyo, 140-0002, Japan
Tel.: (81) 354621012
Studio Leasing & Management Services
N.A.I.C.S.: 531120
Masayuki Shimada (Pres)

TV TOKYO Commercial, Inc. (2)
Sumitomo Shintoranomon Building 5F 4-3-9, Toranomon Minato-ku, Tokyo, 105-0001, Japan
Tel.: (81) 334321231
Web Site: http://www.tv-tokyo-cm.co.jp
Sales Range: $50-74.9 Million
Emp.: 140
Television Commercials Production Services
N.A.I.C.S.: 516120

TV TOKYO Direct, Inc. (2)
Nikkei Toranomon Annex 3F 4-3-12 Toranomon, Minato-ku, Tokyo, 105-0001, Japan
Tel.: (81) 354010220
Web Site: https://www.tx-direct.co.jp
Sales Range: $25-49.9 Million
Emp.: 20
Advertising Services
N.A.I.C.S.: 541890

TV TOKYO Human, Inc. (2)
Roppongi Grand Tower 14F 3-2-1, Roppongi Minato-ku, Tokyo, 106-8007, Japan
Tel.: (81) 334364801
Web Site: http://www.tx-human.com
Sales Range: $50-74.9 Million
Emp.: 132
Television Broadcasting Services
N.A.I.C.S.: 516120

TV TOKYO Medianet Inc. (2)
5F Sumitomo Shin-Toranomon Building 4-3-9 Toranomon, Minato-ku, Tokyo, 105-0001, Japan
Tel.: (81) 334321288
Web Site: https://www.medianet.co.jp
Sales Range: $25-49.9 Million
Emp.: 52
Television Program Production Services
N.A.I.C.S.: 512110

TV TOKYO Music, Inc. (2)
Nikkei Toranomon Annex 2F 4-3-12 Toranomon, Minato-ku, Tokyo, 105-0001, Japan
Tel.: (81) 334321260
Web Site: https://www.ttmnet.co.jp
Sales Range: $25-49.9 Million
Emp.: 20
Music Production & Broadcasting Services
N.A.I.C.S.: 512230

TV TOKYO Production, Inc. (2)
Nikkei Toranomon Annex 4F 4-3-12 Toranomon, Minatoku, Tokyo, 105-0001, Japan
Tel.: (81) 357775101
Web Site: https://www.protx.co.jp
Emp.: 71
Television Program Production Services
N.A.I.C.S.: 512110

TV TOKYO Systems, Inc. (2)
1-3-3 TV Tokyo Tennozu Studio 6F Higashi-Shinagawa, Shinagawa-ku, Tokyo, 140-0002, Japan
Tel.: (81) 357833107
Web Site: https://www.systx.co.jp
Emp.: 32
Computer Systems Planning & Management & Development Services
N.A.I.C.S.: 541512

Technomax, Inc. (2)
TV Tokyo Tennozu Studio 5F 1-3-3 Higashi-Shinagawa, Shinagawa-ku, Tokyo, 140-0002, Japan
Tel.: (81) 354621200
Web Site: https://www.t-max.co.jp
Sales Range: $50-74.9 Million
Emp.: 233
Television Program Production Services
N.A.I.C.S.: 512110

TV TOKYO Mediaworks, Inc. (1)

TV TOKYO HOLDINGS CORPORATION

TV TOKYO Holdings Corporation—(Continued)
Sumitomo Shintoranomon Building 5F 4-3-9 Toranomon, Minato-ku, Tokyo, 105-0001, Japan
Tel.: (81) 334321231
Web Site: https://www.tv-tokyo-mw.co.jp
Emp.: 235
Television Broadcasting Services
N.A.I.C.S.: 561492

TV TOKYO Technomax, Inc. (1)
TV Tokyo Tennozu Studio 5th Fl 1-3-3 Higashishinagawa, Shinagawa-ku, Tokyo, 140-0002, Japan
Tel.: (81) 354621200
Television Broadcasting Services
N.A.I.C.S.: 561492

Tv Tokyo America, Inc. (1)
1325 Ave of the Americas Ste 2402, New York, NY 10019
Tel.: (212) 261-6430
Television Broadcasting Services
N.A.I.C.S.: 516120

Tv Tokyo Business Service, Inc. (1)
8F TV Tokyo Tennozu Studio 1-3-3 Higashi-Shinagawa, Shinagawa-ku, Tokyo, 140-0002, Japan
Tel.: (81) 354621012
Web Site: https://www.tx-biz.co.jp
Television Broadcasting Services
N.A.I.C.S.: 516120

TV VISION LIMITED
4th Floor Adhikari Chambers Oberoi Complex Andheri West, Mumbai, 400 053, India
Tel.: (91) 2240230000
Web Site: https://www.tvvision.in
Year Founded: 2007
TVVISION—(NSE)
Rev.: $9,292,044
Assets: $19,823,443
Liabilities: $25,994,343
Net Worth: ($6,170,900)
Earnings: ($7,229,786)
Emp.: 93
Fiscal Year-end: 03/31/21
Television Broadcasting Services
N.A.I.C.S.: 516120
Markand Adhikari (Mng Dir)

TV2U INTERNATIONAL LIMITED
Level 2 35 Outram Street, West Perth, 6005, WA, Australia
Tel.: (61) 8 6555 9500   AU
Web Site: http://www.tv2u.com
Rev.: $7,995
Assets: $783,226
Liabilities: $1,492,241
Net Worth: ($709,016)
Earnings: ($7,359,952)
Fiscal Year-end: 06/30/17
Holding Company; Television Content Online Streaming Services
N.A.I.C.S.: 551112
Nick Fitzgerald (Founder & CEO)

Subsidiaries:

tv2u Pty. Ltd. (1)
Level 2 35 Outram Street, West Perth, 6005, WA, Australia
Tel.: (61) 8 6555 9500
Web Site: http://www.tv2u.com
Television Content Streaming Services
N.A.I.C.S.: 518210
Nick Fitzgerald (Founder & Chm)

TVC HOLDINGS PLC
Block 2A Richview Office Park, Clonskeagh, Dublin, Ireland
Tel.: (353) 12057700
Web Site: http://www.tvc.com
Year Founded: 2007
Sales Range: $25-49.9 Million
Investment Holding Company
N.A.I.C.S.: 551112
Shane Reihill (Chm)

Subsidiaries:

Trinity Venture Capital Nominees Limited (1)
2A Richview Office Park Clonskeagh, Dublin, 14, Ireland
Tel.: (353) 12057700
Investment Management Service
N.A.I.C.S.: 523999

TVE CO., LTD.
5-12-1 Nishitachibana-cho, Amagasaki, 660-0054, Hyogo, Japan
Tel.: (81) 664168865
Web Site: https://www.toavalve.co.jp
6466—(TKS)
Rev.: $66,617,640
Assets: $99,720,850
Liabilities: $29,069,000
Net Worth: $70,651,850
Earnings: $3,084,150
Fiscal Year-end: 09/30/23
Industrial Valve Mfr
N.A.I.C.S.: 332911

Subsidiaries:

TVE Global Asia Pacific Pte. Ltd. (1)
12J Enterprise Road Enterprise 10, Singapore, 627689, Singapore
Tel.: (65) 63550027
Automotive Valve & Spare Part Distr
N.A.I.C.S.: 441330

TVE Refining Metal Co., Ltd. (1)
2-4 Aza Nishizato-ga-mae 119 Hongo Oicho, Oi-gun, Fukui, 919-2111, Japan
Tel.: (81) 770775097
Metal Recycling Services
N.A.I.C.S.: 562920

Toa Create Co., Ltd. (1)
4th Fl Iwaki New Town Center Building 4-2-4 Chuodai Iino, Iwaki, 970-8044, Fukushima, Japan
Tel.: (81) 246845322
Staffing Services
N.A.I.C.S.: 561311

Toa Service Co., Ltd. (1)
5-12-1 Nishitachibana-cho, Amagasaki, 660-0054, Hyogo, Japan
Tel.: (81) 664165233
Staffing Services
N.A.I.C.S.: 561311

TVG CAPITAL PARTNERS LIMITED
Unit A 8th Fl World Trust Twr, 50 Stanley St, Central, China (Hong Kong)
Tel.: (852) 21472080
Web Site: http://www.tvgfunds.com
Sales Range: $25-49.9 Million
Emp.: 20
Private Equity Services
N.A.I.C.S.: 525910
Varun Bery (Co-Founder & Mng Dir)

Subsidiaries:

Claude Neon Pty Ltd (1)
Level 5 657 Pacific Hwy, Saint Leonards, 2065, NSW, Australia
Tel.: (61) 2 9315 2777
Web Site: http://www.claudeneon.com.au
Outdoor Advertising Services
N.A.I.C.S.: 541850
Nick Rigney (Gen Mgr-Sls & Ops)

Claude Outdoor Pty Ltd (1)
Unit 11 23 Ashtan Place, Brisbane, 4014, QLD, Australia
Tel.: (61) 7 3113 4300
Web Site: http://www.claudeoutdoor.com.au
Outdoor Advertising Services
N.A.I.C.S.: 541850

Neighbourhood Cable Limited (1)
10 Neerim Crescent, Mitchell Park, Ballarat, 3355, VIC, Australia
Tel.: (61) 353390500
Web Site: http://www.neighborhoodcable.com.au
Cable Services
N.A.I.C.S.: 516210

TorchMedia Pty Ltd (1)
Level 1 46 Rouse Street, Port Melbourne, 3207, VIC, Australia
Tel.: (61) 3 8618 7400
Web Site: http://www.torchmedia.com.au
Outdoor Advertising Services
N.A.I.C.S.: 541850

TVI PACIFIC INC.
Suite 600 505 - 2nd Street SW, Calgary, T2P 1N8, AB, Canada
Tel.: (403) 265-4356   AB
Web Site: https://www.tvipacific.com
TVIPF—(OTCIQ)
Rev.: $2,223,962
Assets: $14,706,827
Liabilities: $1,999,828
Net Worth: $12,706,999
Earnings: $1,011,551
Emp.: 2
Fiscal Year-end: 12/31/20
Metal Mining Services
N.A.I.C.S.: 212290
Clifford M. James (Chm, Pres & CEO)

Subsidiaries:

Exploration Drilling Corporation (1)
Philipines beijing Motor Corp Conpound 88 Iabogon Rd, 6014, Mandaue, Cebu, Philippines
Tel.: (63) 323451305
Sales Range: $50-74.9 Million
Emp.: 8
Oil Drilling Services
N.A.I.C.S.: 213111

TVN S.A.
Ul Wiertnicza 166, 02-952, Warsaw, Poland
Tel.: (48) 22 856 60 60
Web Site: http://www.tvn.pl
Television Broadcasting Services
N.A.I.C.S.: 516120

TVNZ
100 Victoria St W, PO Box 3819, Auckland, New Zealand
Tel.: (64) 99167000
Web Site: http://www.tvnz.co.nz
Sales Range: $250-299.9 Million
Emp.: 1,000
Television Station Owner & Operator
N.A.I.C.S.: 516120
Kevin Kenrick (CEO)

Subsidiaries:

TVNZ Satellite Services Limited (1)
100 Victoria Street West, PO Box 3819, Auckland, New Zealand
Tel.: (64) 9 916 7708
Digital Satellite Operator
N.A.I.C.S.: 517410

nzoom Limited (1)
Level 6 23-26 Albert Street, PO Box 91-209, Auckland, New Zealand
Tel.: (64) 9 916 7000
Internet Portal Operator
N.A.I.C.S.: 519290

TVORNICA CARAPA KLJUC D.D.
Trampina 4, 71 000, Sarajevo, Bosnia & Herzegovina
Tel.: (387) 33664560
KLUCR—(SARE)
Rev.: $278,067
Assets: $1,984,737
Liabilities: $1,405,736
Net Worth: $579,001
Earnings: ($31,105)
Emp.: 18
Fiscal Year-end: 12/31/22
Clothing Apparel Mfr
N.A.I.C.S.: 314999

TVORNICA CEMENTA KAKANJ D.D.

INTERNATIONAL PUBLIC

Selima ef Merdanovica 146, 72 240, Kakanj, Bosnia & Herzegovina
Tel.: (387) 32557500
Web Site: http://www.kakanjcement.ba
TCMKR—(SARE)
Rev.: $56,928,215
Assets: $106,486,374
Liabilities: $9,224,153
Net Worth: $97,262,221
Earnings: $14,785,012
Emp.: 202
Fiscal Year-end: 12/31/20
Cement Mfr
N.A.I.C.S.: 327310

TVORNICA ELEKTRO OPREME D.D. SARAJEVO
Bosnia Herzegovina, Sarajevo, 71240, Hadzici, Bosnia & Herzegovina
Tel.: (387) 33 517 164
Web Site: http://www.teo-sarajevo.com
Year Founded: 1976
TELPRK1—(SARE)
Sales Range: $1-9.9 Million
Electrical Equipment Mfr & Distr
N.A.I.C.S.: 335999

TVORNICA STOCNE HRANE D.D.
Dr Ivana Novaka 11, 40000, Cakovec, Croatia
Tel.: (385) 40329160
Web Site: http://www.tsh-cakovec.hr
Animal Feed Mfr
N.A.I.C.S.: 311119
Zoran Deban (Pur & Mgr)

TVORNICA ZA OBRADU METALA EKSPLOZIJOM A.D.
Drage Lukica Bb, 79000, Prijedor, Bosnia & Herzegovina
Tel.: (387) 52360036
TOME-R-A—(BANJ)
Rev.: $46,243
Assets: $681,405
Liabilities: $29,161
Net Worth: $652,244
Earnings: ($7,002)
Emp.: 4
Fiscal Year-end: 12/31/12
Metal Plating Services
N.A.I.C.S.: 332812
Milutin Kos (Chm)

TVS AUTOMOBILE SOLUTIONS PVT. LTD.
No. 10 Jawahar Road, Madurai, 625 002, India
Tel.: (91) 8002660301
Web Site: http://www.tvsautomobiles.com
Automobile Equipment & Maintemnce Sevices
N.A.I.C.S.: 811198
Sanjay Nigam (CEO)

Subsidiaries:

Mahindra First Choice Services Limited (1)
Mahindra & Mahindra Automotive Sector Behind SSBU Bldg Akurli Rd, Kandivali East, Mumbai, 400101, Maharashtra, India
Tel.: (91) 2226879869
Web Site: http://www.mahindrafirstchoiceservice.com
Sales Range: $25-49.9 Million
Emp.: 30
Car Repair & Maintenance Services
N.A.I.C.S.: 811111

TVS ELECTRONICS LIMITED
Arihant E-Park No 117/1 9th Floor, L B Road Adyar, Chennai, 600020, India

AND PRIVATE COMPANIES

Tel.: (91) 4442005200
Web Site: https://www.tvs-e.in
Year Founded: 1995
532513—(BOM)
Rev.: $42,565,793
Assets: $26,524,789
Liabilities: $14,319,285
Net Worth: $12,205,503
Earnings: $1,141,418
Emp.: 604
Fiscal Year-end: 03/31/23
Computer Peripherals Mfr
N.A.I.C.S.: 334118
S. Santosh *(Compliance Officer & Sec)*

Subsidiaries:

Harita Techserv Private Limited (1)
8th Floor No 117 Arihant E Park 1 LB Rd,
Adyar, Chennai, 600020, India
Tel.: (91) 4442928500
Web Site: http://www.harita.in
Engineeering Services
N.A.I.C.S.: 541330

International Money Matters Pvt
Ltd (1)
18 3rd B Cross Domlur II Stage, Bengaluru,
560071, Karnataka, India
Tel.: (91) 8040493939
Web Site: http://www.immpl.com
Emp.: 55
Financial Planning Services
N.A.I.C.S.: 523940
Lovaii Navlakhi *(Founder, CEO & Mng Dir)*

Sundaram Industries Private
Limited (1)
Kochadai, Madurai, 625 016, Tamil Nadu,
India
Tel.: (91) 4524348888
Web Site: http://www.tvsrubber.com
Molded Rubber Product Mfr
N.A.I.C.S.: 326299

TVS Capital Funds Private
Limited (1)
249 A Ambujammal Street Off TTK Road
Near Alwarpet Post Office, Chennai,
600018, India
Tel.: (91) 7667016666
Web Site: http://www.tvscapital.in
Investment Fund Services
N.A.I.C.S.: 525910
Gopal Srinivasan *(Chm & Mng Dir)*

TVS Credit Services Limited (1)
Jayalakshmi Estates 29 Haddows Road,
Nungambakkam, Chennai, 600006, India
Tel.: (91) 4428277155
Web Site: https://www.tvscredit.com
Vehicle Loan Services
N.A.I.C.S.: 522291
Shelvin Mathews *(Chief Risk Officer)*

TVS Upasna Limited (1)
98 A Dr Radhakrishnan Salai 3rd Floor, My-
lapore, Chennai, 600 004, India
Tel.: (91) 4428478500
Web Site: http://www.uel.in
Spoke & Nipple Product Mfr
N.A.I.C.S.: 326299

TVS LOGISTICS SERVICES LTD.
58 Eldams Road TK Kumarasamy
Towers, Teynampet, Chennai, 600
018, India
Tel.: (91) 44 66793222
Web Site:
   http://www.tvslogisticsservices.com
Year Founded: 2004
Supply Chain Solutions & Logistics
Services
N.A.I.C.S.: 541614
R. Dinesh *(Mng Dir)*

Subsidiaries:

Drive India Enterprise Solutions
Limited (1)
7th Floor Kamla Executive Park Andheri
East, 400 059, Mumbai, India
Tel.: (91) 22 6777 9000
Web Site: http://www.diesl.in

Freight Forwarding Services
N.A.I.C.S.: 488510
Ranjish Kumar Dugar *(Head-Sourcing & Distr)*

Flexlol Packaging (I) Limited (1)
52 Eldams Road, Teynampet, Chennai, 600
018, Tamil Nadu, India
Tel.: (91) 4466793222
Web Site: http://www.flexol.in
Logistics Consulting Servies
N.A.I.C.S.: 541614
Mukundan Seshadri *(CEO)*

Manufacturers Equipment and Supply
Company (1)
2401 Lapeer Rd, Flint, MI 48503
Tel.: (810) 239-2173
Web Site: http://www.mescosolutions.com
Logistics Consulting Servies
N.A.I.C.S.: 541614

Rico Logistics Ltd (1)
886 Plymouth Road, Slough, SL1 4LP,
United Kingdom
Tel.: (44) 441753567313
Web Site: http://www.ricogroup.co.uk
Logistics Consulting Servies
N.A.I.C.S.: 541614
George Kyriatzis *(Head-IT)*

TVS Dynamic Global Freight Services
Limited (1)
No 18-A First Street Kamdar Nagar, Nun-
gambakkam, Chennai, 600 034, India
Tel.: (91) 4442678900
Web Site: http://www.tvsdynamic.com
Logistics Consulting Servies
N.A.I.C.S.: 541614
Shankar Tekale *(Mgr-Bus Dev)*

TVS SCS Limited (1)
Logistics House Buckshaw Avenue, Buck-
shaw Village, Chorley, PR6 7AJ, Lan-
cashire, United Kingdom
Tel.: (44) 1257265531
Web Site: http://www.tvsscs.com
Logistics Consulting Servies
N.A.I.C.S.: 541614
Mark Watson *(Dir-Supply Chain)*

TVS Supply Chain Solutions Ltd. (1)
Logistics House, Buckshaw, Chorley, PR6
7AJ, Lancashire, United Kingdom
Tel.: (44) 1257265531
Web Site: http://www.tvsscs.com
Sales Range: $100-124.9 Million
Emp.: 15,000
Supply Chain Solutions & Logistics Services
N.A.I.C.S.: 541614
Richard Slee *(CEO-Europe)*

Wainwright Industries,
Incorporated (1)
101 Interstate Dr, Wentzville, MO 63385
Tel.: (636) 327-8292
Web Site:
   http://www.wainwrightindustries.com
Sales Range: $10-24.9 Million
Third-Party Logistics Services
N.A.I.C.S.: 488510
David A. Robbins *(Pres)*

TVS MOTOR COMPANY LTD.
Post Box No 4 Harita, Hosur, 635
109, India
Tel.: (91) 4344276780
Web Site: https://www.tvsmotor.com
TVSMOTOR—(NSE)
Rev.: $3,850,127,690
Assets: $4,224,316,288
Liabilities: $3,515,743,660
Net Worth: $708,572,628
Earnings: $159,303,399
Emp.: 5,459
Fiscal Year-end: 03/31/23
Bike Mfr
N.A.I.C.S.: 441227
K. S. Srinivasan *(Compliance Officer & Sec)*

Subsidiaries:

Colag E-Mobility GmbH (1)
Regensburger Str 40-46, 90478, Nurem-
berg, Germany
Tel.: (49) 91113137544

Web Site: https://colag-deutschland.de
Emp.: 20
Trading Services
N.A.I.C.S.: 523999

EGO Movement Stuttgart, GmbH (1)
Kronenstr 7, D-70173, Stuttgart, Germany
Tel.: (49) 41445153586
Web Site: https://egomovement.de
LED Light Mfr
N.A.I.C.S.: 335131

Sundaram Auto Components
Limited (1)
Hosur- Thally road Belagondapalli,
krishnagiri district, Hosur, 635 114, India
Tel.: (91) 4347233445
Web Site:
   https://www.sundaramcomponents.com
Automobile Component Mfr & Distr
N.A.I.C.S.: 336110

Swiss E-Mobility Group (Schweiz)
AG (1)
Raffelstrasse 25, 8045, Zurich, Switzerland
Tel.: (41) 432557797
Web Site: https://www.semg.ch
Financial Services
N.A.I.C.S.: 523999

TVS Digital Pte. Limited (1)
1 Kim Seng Promenade 10-7 Great World
City West Tower, Singapore, 237994, Sin-
gapore
Tel.: (65) 63519797
Web Site: https://www.tvsd.ai
Financial Services
N.A.I.C.S.: 523999

TVS SRICHAKRA LTD
TVS Building 7-B West Veli Street,
Madurai, 625 001, India
Tel.: (91) 4522420461
Web Site: https://www.tvstyres.com
Year Founded: 1982
509243—(BOM)
Rev.: $351,622,337
Assets: $323,331,932
Liabilities: $190,067,878
Net Worth: $133,264,054
Earnings: $12,920,424
Emp.: 2,762
Fiscal Year-end: 03/31/24
Tiles Mfr
N.A.I.C.S.: 326211
R. Naresh *(Vice Chm)*

Subsidiaries:

Fiber Optic Sensing Solutions Private
Limited (1)
503-A Bhumiraj Costarica Sector-18, San-
pada, Navi Mumbai, 400705, India
Tel.: (91) 2249793916
Web Site: https://tvsss-foss.com
Automotive Components Mfr
N.A.I.C.S.: 336110

Super Grip Corporation (1)
513 Sportsman Dock Rd, Piney Flats, TN
37686
Tel.: (423) 538-8605
Web Site: http://www.supergrip.net
Sales Range: $250-299.9 Million
Emp.: 3,200
Provider of Motor Vehicle Services
N.A.I.C.S.: 326211

TVS Sensing Solutions Private
Limited (1)
Madurai-Melur Road, Vellaripatti, Madurai,
625122, Tamil Nadu, India
Tel.: (91) 4522911444
Web Site: https://tvsss.co.in
Automotive Component Whslr
N.A.I.C.S.: 441330

TVT MEDIA
540 Chiswick High Rd, London,
United Kingdom
Tel.: (91) 2033553355
Web Site: http://www.tvt.media
Broadcasting Services
N.A.I.C.S.: 516120
Rain Lau *(Head-Localization Ops)*

TWC ENTERPRISE LIMITED

Subsidiaries:

Digital Media Centre B.V. (1)
Kon Wilhelminaplein 2-4, Amsterdam, 1062
HK, Netherlands
Tel.: (31) 207788733
Web Site:
   http://www.digitalmediacentre.com
Cable & Other Subscription Programming
Services
N.A.I.C.S.: 516210
Jon Try *(VP-Strategy & Innovation)*

Subsidiary (Non-US):

AMC Networks International-Central
Europe (2)
Lomb U 23-27, Budapest, 1139, Hungary
Tel.: (36) 12369100
Web Site: http://www.amctvce.com
Thematic Programming, Cable & Subscrip-
tion Services
N.A.I.C.S.: 516210
Patrick Connolly *(Sr VP-Programming & Mktg)*

Subsidiary (Domestic):

At Media Hungary Kft (3)
Dunvirag u 2-6 Tower I-II floor, 1138, Buda-
pest, Hungary
Tel.: (36) 1 799 2653
Web Site: http://www.atmedia.hu
Television Broadcasting Services
N.A.I.C.S.: 516120
Csaba Guttengeber *(Mng Dir)*

Subsidiary (US):

AMC Networks Latin America
LLC (2)
2020 Ponce De Leon Blvd Ste 800, Coral
Gables, FL 33134
Tel.: (305) 445-4350
Web Site:
   http://www.amcnetworkslatam.com
Cable Television Programming & Distribu-
tion Services
N.A.I.C.S.: 517111
Hector Costa *(Sr VP-Adv Sls)*

TVZONE MEDIA CO., LTD.
101 Tennis Club New Century Sports
and Culture Center, No 188 Furong
Middle Road 2nd Section Tianxin Dis-
trict, Changsha, 410005, Hunan,
China
Tel.: (86) 73188745233
Web Site: http://www.tvzone.cn
Year Founded: 2007
603721—(SHG)
Rev.: $29,798,285
Assets: $131,560,121
Liabilities: $49,530,382
Net Worth: $82,029,739
Earnings: $2,209,629
Fiscal Year-end: 12/31/22
Entertainment Services
N.A.I.C.S.: 516210
Peng Yong *(Chm)*

TWAY HOLDINGS CO LTD
10th floor Yelim Publishing Culture
Center, 153 Achasan-ro, Seoul, 133
120, Seongdong, Korea (South)
Tel.: (82) 220569800
Web Site:
   https://www.twayholdings.com
Year Founded: 1945
004870—(KRS)
Rev.: $8,797,767
Assets: $161,620,842
Liabilities: $35,272,325
Net Worth: $126,348,516
Earnings: $58,527,008
Emp.: 20
Fiscal Year-end: 12/31/22
Holding Company
N.A.I.C.S.: 551112
Jeong-Hyun Hwang *(CEO)*

TWC ENTERPRISE LIMITED

TWC ENTERPRISE LIMITED

TWC Enterprise Limited—(Continued)
15675 Dufferin Street, King City, L7B 1K5, ON, Canada
Tel.: (905) 841-5372
Web Site:
https://www.twcenterprises.ca
Year Founded: 1997
4TW—(DEU)
Rev.: $174,030,809
Assets: $530,148,758
Liabilities: $124,208,261
Net Worth: $405,940,497
Earnings: $7,179,642
Emp.: 649
Fiscal Year-end: 12/31/23
Holding Company; Golf Club Owner; Railway Operator
N.A.I.C.S.: 551112
K. Rai Sahi *(Chm & CEO)*

Subsidiaries:

ClubLink Corporation (1)
15675 Dufferin Street, King City, L7B 1K5, ON, Canada (100%)
Tel.: (905) 841-3730
Web Site: https://www.clublink.ca
Sales Range: $125-149.9 Million
Emp.: 3,500
Golf Clubs & Resorts
N.A.I.C.S.: 713910

TWENTY SEVEN CO. LIMITED
Suite 17 Chelsea Village 145 Stirling Hwy, Nedlands, 6009, Western Australia, Australia
Tel.: (61) 8 9385 6911   AU
Web Site:
http://www.twentysevenco.com.au
TSC—(ASX)
Rev.: $13,349
Assets: $6,425,416
Liabilities: $84,429
Net Worth: $6,340,988
Earnings: ($2,595,440)
Fiscal Year-end: 06/30/21
Cobalt Exploration Services
N.A.I.C.S.: 212290
Damien Connor *(CFO & Sec)*

Subsidiaries:

Gingertom Resources Pty. Ltd. (1)
32 Beulah Rd, Norwood, 5067, South Australia, Australia
Tel.: (61) 881320577
Sales Range: $50-74.9 Million
Emp.: 7
Mineral Exploration Services
N.A.I.C.S.: 212390
David Paterson *(CEO)*

TWENTY-FOUR CON & SUPPLY PUBLIC COMPANY LIMITED
89 AIA Capital Center 9th Floor Unit 901 Ratchadaphisek Road, Din Daeng, Bangkok, 10400, Thailand
Tel.: (66) 22481948
Web Site: https://www.24con-supply.com
Year Founded: 2013
24CS—(THA)
Rev.: $19,894,176
Assets: $22,127,700
Liabilities: $5,663,461
Net Worth: $16,464,239
Earnings: ($1,315,713)
Emp.: 81
Fiscal Year-end: 12/31/23
Engineeering Services
N.A.I.C.S.: 541330
Yodsawee Wattanateerakitja *(CEO)*

TWENTYCI HOLDINGS LIMITED
8 Whittle Court Knowlhill, Milton Keynes, MK5 8FT, United Kingdom
Tel.: (44) 1908 829300   UK
Web Site: http://www.twentyci.co.uk
Sales Range: $50-74.9 Million
Emp.: 200
Holding Company: Marketing Services
N.A.I.C.S.: 551112
Ian M. Lancaster *(CEO)*

Subsidiaries:

Dataforce Limited (1)
6th Fl 1 London Wall Buildings, London, EC2M 5PP, United Kingdom
Tel.: (44) 8448156188
Web Site: http://www.dataforce.co.uk
Database Management & Marketing Services
N.A.I.C.S.: 541613

Twenty Web Limited (1)
6 Whittle Court Knowlhill, Milton Keynes, MK5 8FT, Bucks, United Kingdom
Tel.; (44) 1908829380
Web Site: http://www.twentyci.co.uk
Sales Range: $25-49.9 Million
Emp.: 30
E-Commerce Solutions & Business Support Services
N.A.I.C.S.: 561439
Ian Lancaster *(Mng Dir)*

TWENTYFIRST CENTURY MANAGEMENT SERVICES LTD.
NEW67 OLD NO28A Eldams Road, Alwarpet, Chennai, 600 018, TamilNadu, India
Tel.: (91) 4424330006
Web Site: https://www.tcms.bz
21STCENMGM—(NSE)
Rev.: $153,034
Assets: $3,974,040
Liabilities: $1,411,578
Net Worth: $2,562,462
Earnings: ($4,491,480)
Emp.: 9
Fiscal Year-end: 03/31/20
Financial Services
N.A.I.C.S.: 523999
Sundar Iyer *(Chm & CEO)*

TWENTYFOUR INCOME FUND LTD.
Trafalgar Court Les Banques St, PO Box 255, Saint Peter Port, GY13QL, Guernsey
Tel.: (44) 2070158900
TFIF—(LSE)
Rev.: $81,472,768
Assets: $979,397,335
Liabilities: $64,246,159
Net Worth: $915,151,176
Earnings: ($28,522,273)
Fiscal Year-end: 03/31/23
Investment Management Service
N.A.I.C.S.: 525990

TWENTYFOUR SELECT MONTHLY INCOME FUND LTD.
Trafalga Court Les Banques, PO Box 255, Saint Peter Port, GY1 3QL, Guernsey
Tel.: (44) 2070158900
SMIF—(LSE)
Rev.: $36,769,510
Assets: $234,915,785
Liabilities: $5,568,348
Net Worth: $229,347,438
Earnings: $34,008,632
Fiscal Year-end: 09/30/23
Investment Management Service
N.A.I.C.S.: 525990

TWEPPY S.P.A.
Via Foro Buonaparte 59, 20121, Milan, Italy
Tel.: (39) 0800708224
Web Site: https://tweppy.it
Year Founded: 2018

TWEP—(EUR)
Software Devolopment
N.A.I.C.S.: 513210
Omero Narducci *(Head-IR)*

TWIG COM LTD.
Lairolantie 14, 24910, Salo, Finland
Tel.: (358) 40 5105058
Web Site: http://www.twigcom.com
Sales Range: $10-24.9 Million
Emp.: 100
Mobile Telematics Software & Solutions
N.A.I.C.S.: 334210
Tomi Raita *(Co-Mng Dir)*

TWIM CORP.
seokwoodong 1914 74 Samsung 1ro 4gil, Hwaseong, 18449, Gyeonggi-do, Korea (South)
Tel.: (82) 3180558455
Web Site: https://www.twim21.com
Year Founded: 2010
290090—(KRS)
Rev.: $15,003,760
Assets: $56,191,423
Liabilities: $5,579,411
Net Worth: $50,612,012
Earnings: ($4,088,926)
Emp.: 152
Fiscal Year-end: 12/31/22
Software Development Services
N.A.I.C.S.: 541511

TWIN HILLS FORD LINCOLN
10801 Yonge Street, Richmond Hill, L4C 3E3, ON, Canada
Tel.: (905) 884-4441
Web Site:
http://www.twinhillsford.com
Rev.: $23,735,971
Emp.: 50
New & Used Car Dealers
N.A.I.C.S.: 441110
Ninetta Panetta *(Pres)*

TWIN ROSES TRADES & AGENCIES LTD.
147 14th Floor Atlanta Nariman Point, Mumbai, 400 021, India
Tel.: (91) 2222800131
Web Site: https://www.trtal.org.in
Rev.: $28,653
Assets: $450,689
Liabilities: $12,103
Net Worth: $438,586
Earnings: $1,700
Fiscal Year-end: 03/31/19
Financial Investment Services
N.A.I.C.S.: 523999
Bhavin Mehta *(Sec)*

TWIN TOWNS SERVICES CLUB LIMITED
1 Wharf Street, Tweed Heads, 2485, NSW, Australia
Tel.: (61) 755362277   AU
Web Site:
http://www.twintowns.com.au
Sales Range: $50-74.9 Million
Emp.: 461
Holding Company; Hotels, Clubs & Resorts Owner & Operator
N.A.I.C.S.: 551112
Rob L. Smith *(CEO)*

TWINBIRD CORPORATION
2084-2 Yoshida Nishiota, Tsubame, 959-0292, Niigata, Japan
Tel.: (81) 256926160
Web Site: https://store.twinbird.jp
Year Founded: 1962
6897—(TKS)
Rev.: $83,614,500
Assets: $85,190,400
Liabilities: $21,726,000

INTERNATIONAL PUBLIC

Net Worth: $63,464,400
Earnings: $527,850
Emp.: 303
Fiscal Year-end: 02/28/23
Home Electric Appliance Mfr & Whslr
N.A.I.C.S.: 335220
Shigeaki Nomizu *(Pres)*

Subsidiaries:

Twinbird Electrical Appliance (Shenzhen) Co., Ltd. (1)
Room 1106 11F 1st Building Guangchang Dasha Baoming Road East, Xinan Sub-District Baoan District, Shenzhen, China
Tel.: (86) 75529636045
Home Electric Appliance Distr
N.A.I.C.S.: 423620

TWINHEAD INTERNATIONAL CORP.
9F No 550 Ruiguang Rd, Neihu, Taipei, 11492, Taiwan
Tel.: (886) 255899999
Web Site:
https://www.twinhead.com.tw
Year Founded: 1984
2364—(TAI)
Rev.: $35,338,597
Assets: $42,741,128
Liabilities: $28,737,041
Net Worth: $14,004,087
Earnings: $3,380,980
Emp.: 192
Fiscal Year-end: 12/31/23
Computer & Peripheral Equipment Mfr
N.A.I.C.S.: 334111
Yu- Jen Kao *(Chm & Pres)*

Subsidiaries:

Durabook Americas Inc. (1)
48329 Fremont Blvd, Fremont, CA 94538
Tel.: (510) 492-0828
Computer Hardware Parts Mfr & Distr
N.A.I.C.S.: 334111

Gammatech Computer Corporation (1)
48329 Fremont Blvd, Fremont, CA 94538
Tel.: (800) 995-8946
Embedded Design Services
N.A.I.C.S.: 541420

Kunshan Lun Teng System Co., Ltd. (1)
Room 406 floor 4 Yuda Commercial Plaza No 6 Leshan Road, Yushan Town, Kunshan, Jiangsu, China
Tel.: (86) 51255113799
Computer & Digital Camera Services
N.A.I.C.S.: 811210

TWINSTAR INDUSTRIES LIMITED
Plot No EL-178 TTC Ind Area MIDC, Mahape, Navi Mumbai, 400701, Maharashtra, India
Tel.: (91) 2228263462
Web Site: http://www.twinstar.in
Year Founded: 1994
531917—(BOM)
Rev.: $137
Assets: $8,559,396
Liabilities: $5,853,175
Net Worth: $2,706,222
Earnings: ($461,916)
Emp.: 5
Fiscal Year-end: 03/31/21
Software Development Services
N.A.I.C.S.: 541511
Daulat Samirmal Mehta *(Mng Dir)*

TWINTEK INVESTMENT HOLDINGS LIMITED
Room 806 8/F Eastern Centre 1065 King's Road, Quarry Bay, China (Hong Kong)
Tel.: (852) 2 541 8090   Ky

Web Site:
http://www.kwantaieng.com
6182—(HKG)
Rev.: $40,210,031
Assets: $30,094,516
Liabilities: $9,903,084
Net Worth: $20,191,432
Earnings: $1,457,474
Emp.: 34
Fiscal Year-end: 03/31/21
Construction Management Services
N.A.I.C.S.: 238310

TWL HOLDINGS BHD
T3-13A-20 Level 13A Menara 3 3
Towers, Jalan Ampang, 50450, Kuala
Lumpur, Malaysia
Tel.: (60) 327330038
Web Site:
https://www.tigersynergy.my
Year Founded: 1994
TWL—(KLS)
Rev.: $5,437,282
Assets: $102,550,071
Liabilities: $6,650,233
Net Worth: $95,899,838
Earnings: ($662,340)
Fiscal Year-end: 06/30/23
Holding Company
N.A.I.C.S.: 551112
Tan Chin Lee *(Deputy Chm & Mng Dir)*

Subsidiaries:

Minply Construction & Engineering
Sdn. Bhd. (1)
No 482 Ground Fl, 70200, Seremban, Negeri Sembilan, Malaysia
Tel.: (60) 67679418
Construction & Engineering Services
N.A.I.C.S.: 237990

TWO HANDS CORPORATION
1035 Queensway East, Mississauga,
L4Y 4C1, ON, Canada
Tel.: (416) 357-0399 DE
Web Site:
http://www.twohandsapp.com
Year Founded: 2009
TWOH—(CNSX)
Rev.: $731,302
Assets: $230,202
Liabilities: $4,868,410
Net Worth: ($4,638,208)
Earnings: ($21,693,111)
Fiscal Year-end: 12/31/22
Application Software Development Services
N.A.I.C.S.: 541511
Nadav Elituv *(Chm, Pres, CEO, Treas & Sec)*

TWO SHIELDS INVESTMENTS PLC
Hyde Park House 5 Manfred Road,
London, SW15 2RS, United Kingdom
Tel.: (44) 207 2361177
Web Site: http://twoshields.co.uk
Year Founded: 1994
TSI—(LSE)
Investment Company
N.A.I.C.S.: 523940
Charlie Wood *(Chm)*

TWT GROUP LIMITED
Umbrella District Songxia, Shangyu,
Zhejiang, China
Tel.: (86) 575 2065005
Web Site: http://www.twtoutdoor.com
Sales Range: $10-24.9 Million
Outdoor Furniture Mfr
N.A.I.C.S.: 321912
Brad Borgman *(VP-Engrg)*

TWX GROUP HOLDING LIMITED

1 Scarsdale Road, Toronto, M3B
2R2, ON, Canada
Tel.: (647) 556-3478
Web Site: http://eaedu.ca
Year Founded: 1995
Sales Range: $1-9.9 Million
Education Services
N.A.I.C.S.: 611710
Simon S. Ma *(CFO)*

TWX GROUP HOLDING LIMITED
200 Consumers Road Suite 702, Toronto, M2J 4R4, ON, Canada
Tel.: (647) 556-3478
Assets: $431,716
Liabilities: $107,615
Net Worth: $324,101
Earnings: ($336,646)
Holding Company
N.A.I.C.S.: 551112
Kevin Beaulieu *(CEO)*

TWYFORD VENTURES INC.
404-999 Canada Place Business
Centre, Vancouver, V6C 3E2, BC,
Canada
Tel.: (778) 835-2551 BC
Year Founded: 2010
TWY—(TSXV)
Assets: $10,490
Liabilities: $153,125
Net Worth: ($142,635)
Earnings: ($103,475)
Fiscal Year-end: 12/31/23
Investment Services
N.A.I.C.S.: 523999
Alnesh Mohan *(CFO)*

TWZ CORPORATION PUBLIC COMPANY LIMITED
269 Ratchadapisek Rd, Ratchadaphisek Subdistrict Din Daeng District,
Bangkok, 10400, Thailand
Tel.: (66) 22759789
Web Site: https://www.twz.co.th
Year Founded: 1993
TWZ—(THA)
Rev.: $105,295,077
Assets: $180,735,911
Liabilities: $60,692,038
Net Worth: $120,043,873
Earnings: $687,356
Emp.: 273
Fiscal Year-end: 12/31/23
Telecommunication Product Whslr
N.A.I.C.S.: 517121

TX GROUP AG
Werdstrasse 21, CH-8021, Zurich,
Switzerland
Tel.: (41) 442484111 CH
Web Site: https://www.tamedia.ch
Year Founded: 1970
TXGN—(SWX)
Rev.: $1,167,696,701
Assets: $4,075,469,473
Liabilities: $1,013,192,303
Net Worth: $3,062,277,170
Earnings: $71,785,120
Emp.: 3,529
Fiscal Year-end: 12/31/23
Multimedia Holding Company
N.A.I.C.S.: 551112
Pietro Supino *(Chm)*

Subsidiaries:

20 Minuten AG (1)
Werdstrasse 21, 8004, Zurich,
Switzerland (100%)
Tel.: (41) 442486820
Web Site: http://www.20min.ch
Sales Range: $50-74.9 Million
Emp.: 200
Newspaper Publishers
N.A.I.C.S.: 513110

Unit (Domestic):

20 Minutes SA (2)
Avenue de la Gare 33, PO Box 1170, 1001,
Lausanne, Switzerland
Tel.: (41) 216218787
Web Site: http://www.20min.ch
Emp.: 80
Newspaper Publishers
N.A.I.C.S.: 513110

Subsidiary (Non-US):

MetroXpress Denmark A/S (2)
Bygmestervej 61, 2400, Copenhagen, NV,
Denmark (51%)
Tel.: (45) 77305757
Web Site: http://www.mx.dk
Sales Range: $25-49.9 Million
Emp.: 80
Newspaper Publishing Services
N.A.I.C.S.: 513110
Marius Hagger *(Mng Dir)*

Annabelle AG (1)
Werdstrasse 21, 8021, Zurich,
Switzerland (100%)
Tel.: (41) 442486333
Web Site: http://www.annabelle.ch
Sales Range: $400-449.9 Million
Emp.: 1,200
Newspaper Publishers
N.A.I.C.S.: 513110
Pietro Supino *(Chm)*

Basler Zeitung AG (1)
Aeschenplatz 7, PO Box 2250, 4002, Basel,
Switzerland
Tel.: (41) 616911111
Web Site: http://www.bazonline.ch
Newspaper Publishing Services
N.A.I.C.S.: 513110

DZB Druckzentrum Bern AG (1)
Zentweg 7, 3006, Bern, Switzerland
Tel.: (41) 313494142
Newspaper Printing Services
N.A.I.C.S.: 513110

Das Magazin AG (1)
Werdstrasse 21, 8021, Zurich,
Switzerland (100%)
Tel.: (41) 442484501
Web Site: http://www.dasmagazin.ch
Sales Range: $400-449.9 Million
Emp.: 20
Newspaper Publishers
N.A.I.C.S.: 513110
Pietro Supino *(Publr)*

Edita SA (1)
115a rue Emile Mark, 4620, Differdange,
Luxembourg
Tel.: (352) 2658661
Newspaper Publishing Services
N.A.I.C.S.: 513110
Elisa Spada *(Mgr-Community)*

Espace Media Groupe AG (1)
Dammweg 9, Bern, 3001, Switzerland
Tel.: (41) 31 330 33 10
Web Site: http://www.tamedia.ch
Newspaper Publishing Services
N.A.I.C.S.: 513110

Subsidiary (Domestic):

Buchler Grafino AG (2)
Zentweg 7, 3006, Bern, Switzerland
Tel.: (41) 31 349 41 47
Newspaper Printing Services
N.A.I.C.S.: 323111

Espace Media AG (2)
Dammweg 9, 3001, Bern, Switzerland
Tel.: (41) 31 330 33 10
Web Site: http://www.tamedia.ch
Sales Range: $150-199.9 Million
Emp.: 800
Newspaper Publishing Services
N.A.I.C.S.: 513110

Subsidiary (Domestic):

BZ Langenthaler Tagblatt (3)
Schulhausstrasse 2a, CH-4900, Langenthal,
Switzerland
Tel.: (41) 629195023
Emp.: 11
Newspaper Publishers
N.A.I.C.S.: 513110

Theodor Eckert *(Editor-in-Chief)*

Subsidiary (Domestic):

FMM Fachmedien Mobil AG (2)
Dammweg 9, Bern, 3001, Switzerland
Tel.: (41) 31 330 30 30
Magazine Publishing Services
N.A.I.C.S.: 513120

Schaer Thun AG (2)
Seestrasse 26, 3600, Thun, Switzerland
Tel.: (41) 332251533
Web Site: http://www.schaerthun.ch
Newspaper Printing & Publishing Services
N.A.I.C.S.: 323111

Finanz und Wirtschaft AG (1)
Werdstrasse 21, 8021, Zurich, Switzerland
Tel.: (41) 442485800
Web Site: http://www.fuw.ch
Sales Range: $25-49.9 Million
Emp.: 15
Newspaper Publishers
N.A.I.C.S.: 513110

Goldbach Austria GmbH (1)
Laimgrubengasse 14, 1060, Vienna, Austria
Tel.: (43) 13708808
Web Site: https://goldbach.com
Marketing & Advertising Services
N.A.I.C.S.: 541810
Birgit Maier *(Mgr-Mktg)*

Goldbach Germany GmbH (1)
Feringastrasse 12b, 85774, Unterfohring,
Germany
Tel.: (49) 89614240400
Web Site: https://goldbach.com
Marketing & Advertising Services
N.A.I.C.S.: 541810

Goldbach Group AG (1)
Seestrasse 39, 8700, Kusnacht, Zurich,
Switzerland
Tel.: (41) 449149100
Web Site: https://goldbach.com
Electronic & Mobile Media Marketing Services
N.A.I.C.S.: 541519
Michi Frank *(Co-CEO)*

Subsidiary (Non-US):

Goldbach Audience (Slovenia)
d.o.o. (2)
Litostrojska Cesta 44e, 1000, Ljubljana,
Slovenia
Tel.: (386) 1 56 56 006
Web Site:
http://www.goldbachaudience.com
Online Marketing Services
N.A.I.C.S.: 541810

Subsidiary (Domestic):

Goldbach Audience (Switzerland)
AG (2)
Seestrasse 39, CH 8700, Kusnacht, Switzerland
Tel.: (41) 449149270
Online, Internet TV, Mobile & In-Game Marketing & Advertising Services
N.A.I.C.S.: 541519
Alexander Horrolt *(Mng Dir)*

Subsidiary (Non-US):

Goldbach Audience Austria
GmbH (2)
Laimgrubengasse 14, 1060, Vienna, Austria
Tel.: (43) 13708808
Web Site:
https://www.goldbachaudience.com
Emp.: 50
Online Marketing Services
N.A.I.C.S.: 541810
Maurizio Berlini *(Co-Mng Dir)*

Goldbach Audience Romania
SRL (2)
Bd Luliu Maniu Nr 7 Corp A Intrarea 3 Etaj
3 Sector 6, Bucharest, 061072, Romania
Tel.: (40) 372 111 777
Web Site:
http://www.goldbachaudience.com
Online Marketing Services
N.A.I.C.S.: 541810
Ana Maria Diaconu *(Mgr-Sls)*

TX GROUP AG

TX Group AG—(Continued)

Holding (Non-US):

Goldbach Holding (Poland) Sp.z.o.o. (2)
Ul Altowa 2, 02386, Warsaw, Poland
Tel.: (48) 225924500
Web Site: http://www.goldbachpoland.pl
Holding Company
N.A.I.C.S.: 551112

Subsidiary (Non-US):

Goldbach Interactive (Austria) AG (2)
Nuestiftgasse 73-75, 1070, Vienna, Austria
Tel.: (43) 1 370 880 80
Web Site:
http://www.goldbachinteractive.com
Digital Marketing Services
N.A.I.C.S.: 541519

Goldbach Interactive (Germany) AG (2)
Bleicherstrasse 10-14, 78467, Konstanz, Germany
Tel.: (49) 7531 89207 0
Web Site:
http://www.goldbachinteractive.com
Radio Broadcasting Services
Emp.: 40
Digital Marketing Services
N.A.I.C.S.: 541519
Macus Koch (Mgr)

Subsidiary (Domestic):

Goldbach Interactive (Switzerland) AG (2)
Mattenstrasse 90, 2503, Biel, Switzerland
Tel.: (41) 32 366 01 00
Web Site:
http://www.goldbachinteractive.com
Sales Range: $50-74.9 Million
Emp.: 200
Digital Marketing Services
N.A.I.C.S.: 541519
Andreas Roth (CTO)

Subsidiary (Non-US):

Goldbach Interactive Poland Sp. Z.o.o. (2)
Ul Altowa 4, PL 02 386, Warsaw, Poland
Tel.: (48) 22 592 49 50
Web Site:
http://www.goldbachinteractive.com
Digital Marketing Services
N.A.I.C.S.: 541519

Subsidiary (Domestic):

Goldbach Management AG (2)
Seestrasse 39, 8700, Zurich, Switzerland
Tel.: (41) 44 485 55 00
Mobile Media Marketing Services
N.A.I.C.S.: 541890

Goldbach Media (Switzerland) AG (2)
Seestrasse 39, CH 8700, Kusnacht, Switzerland (54%)
Tel.: (41) 449149100
Web Site: http://www.goldbachmedia.com
Marketing & Advertising Services
N.A.I.C.S.: 541613
Alexander Duphorn (CEO)

Goldbach Mobile AG (2)
Eichstrasse 25, CH 8045, Zurich, Switzerland
Tel.: (41) 44 454 10 80
Web Site:
http://www.goldbachinteractive.com
Sales Range: $25-49.9 Million
Emp.: 19
Mobile Communications Solutions
N.A.I.C.S.: 517810

Goldbach Neo OOH AG (2)
Raffelstrasse 26, 8045, Zurich, Switzerland
Tel.: (41) 584555500
Web Site: http://www.clearchannel.ch
Sales Range: $50-74.9 Million
Emp.: 200
Outdoor Advertising Services
N.A.I.C.S.: 541850
Roberto Credaro (Head-Ops)

Subsidiary (Domestic):

Clear Channel AIDA GmbH (3)
Rothusstrasse 2B, 6331, Hunenberg, Switzerland
Tel.: (41) 417845400
Radio Broadcasting Services
N.A.I.C.S.: 516210

Clear Channel AWI AG (3)
Rothusstrasse 2, 6331, Hunenberg, Zug, Switzerland
Tel.: (41) 58 455 57 00
Radio Broadcasting Services
N.A.I.C.S.: 516210

Clear Channel Interpubli AG (3)
Rothusstrasse 2 B, 6331, Hunenberg, Switzerland
Tel.: (41) 313521313
Outdoor Advertising Services
N.A.I.C.S.: 541850

Clear Channel Plakatron AG (3)
Chrummacherstrasse 2, 8954, Geroldswil, Switzerland
Tel.: (41) 448305050
Web Site: http://www.clearchannel.ch
Sales Range: $25-49.9 Million
Emp.: 70
Radio Broadcasting Services
N.A.I.C.S.: 516210
Oliver Bruhlmann (Sr Mgr-Key Acct)

Affiliate (Non-US):

Renderspace d.o.o. (2)
Trubarjeva cesta 79, 1000, Ljubljana, Slovenia (51%)
Tel.: (386) 1 2391 390
Web Site: http://www.renderspace.si
Sales Range: $25-49.9 Million
Emp.: 37
Digital Advertising & Marketing Services
N.A.I.C.S.: 541613
Primoz Pusar (CEO)

Goldbach Media Austria GmbH (1)
Laimgrubengasse 14, 1060, Vienna, Austria
Tel.: (43) 137088080
Marketing & Advertising Services
N.A.I.C.S.: 541810
Alexandra Tratnig Frankl (Acct Mgr)

Homegate AG (1)
Werdstrasse 21, 8004, Zurich, Switzerland
Tel.: (41) 447118614
Web Site: http://www.homegate.ch
Real Estate Marketing Services
N.A.I.C.S.: 531390

ImmoStreet.ch SA (1)
Avenue de la Gare 33, 1003, Lausanne, Switzerland
Tel.: (41) 848100200
Web Site: http://www.immostreet.ch
Real Estate Marketing Services
N.A.I.C.S.: 531390

Jaduda GmbH (1)
Kortestr 10, 10967, Berlin, Germany
Tel.: (49) 3060940280
Web Site: https://www.jaduda.com
Mobile Marketing Services
N.A.I.C.S.: 541613

Jobwinner AG (1)
Jobupat Werdstrasse 21, Zurich, 8032, Switzerland
Tel.: (41) 442481010
Web Site: http://www.jobwinner.ch
Sales Range: $25-49.9 Million
Emp.: 100
Newspaper Publishers
N.A.I.C.S.: 513110

Olmero AG (1)
Europa-Strasse 30, 8152, Glattbrugg, Switzerland
Tel.: (41) 848656376
Web Site: https://www.olmero.ch
Construction Platform Services
N.A.I.C.S.: 236220
Markus Schulte (CEO)

PartnerWinner AG (1)
Werdstrasse 21, 8021, Zurich, Switzerland (100%)
Tel.: (41) 442484411
Web Site: http://www.partnerwinner.ch

Sales Range: $400-449.9 Million
Emp.: 1,200
Newspaper Publishers
N.A.I.C.S.: 513110
Pietro Supino (Chm)

Piazza AG (1)
Werdstrasse 21, 8004, Zurich, Switzerland
Tel.: (41) 844 441 441
Web Site: http://www.piazza.ch
Sales Range: $400-449.9 Million
Emp.: 1,200
Newspaper Publishers
N.A.I.C.S.: 513110

Schweizer Familie AG (1)
Werdstrasse 21, 8021, Zurich, Switzerland (100%)
Tel.: (41) 442486106
Web Site: http://www.schweizerfamilie.ch
Sales Range: $400-449.9 Million
Emp.: 1,200
Newspaper Publishers
N.A.I.C.S.: 513110

Schweizer Mediendatenbank (SMD) AG (1)
Badenerstrasse 119, 8036, Zurich, Switzerland
Tel.: (41) 443156080
Web Site: http://www.smd.ch
Sales Range: $1-9.9 Million
Emp.: 20
Online Operator & Services
N.A.I.C.S.: 812990
Mumprecht Jurg (Gen Mgr)

SonntagsZeitung AG (1)
Werdstrasse 21, 8021, Zurich, Switzerland (100%)
Tel.: (41) 442484040
Web Site:
http://www.abo.sonntagszeitung.ch
Sales Range: $400-449.9 Million
Emp.: 1,250
Newspaper Publishers
N.A.I.C.S.: 513110

TVtaglich AG (1)
Werdstrasse 21, 8021, Zurich, Switzerland (100%)
Tel.: (41) 442484411
Web Site: http://www.tvtaeglich.ch
Sales Range: $400-449.9 Million
Emp.: 1,200
Newspaper Publishers
N.A.I.C.S.: 513110

Tagblatt der Stadt Zurich AG (1)
Werdstrasse 21, 8021, Zurich, Switzerland (65%)
Tel.: (41) 442486510
Web Site: http://www.tagblattzuerich.ch
Sales Range: $400-449.9 Million
Emp.: 1,200
Newspaper Publishers
N.A.I.C.S.: 513110

Tamedia Publications romandes SA (1)
Avenue de la Gare 33, 1001, Lausanne, Switzerland (100%)
Tel.: (41) 213494545
Web Site: http://www.tamedia.ch
Holding company; Newspaper & Magazine Publisher; Commercial Printing Services
N.A.I.C.S.: 551112

Affiliate (Domestic):

Societe de Publications Nouvelles SPN SA (2)
Avenue du Mail 22, 1205, Geneva, Switzerland (50%)
Tel.: (41) 228072211
Holding Company; Newspaper Publisher
N.A.I.C.S.: 551112
Jean-Marc Velleman (Dir Gen)

Subsidiary (Domestic):

LC Lausanne cites S.A. (3)
Avenue d Echallens 17, 1004, Lausanne, Switzerland
Tel.: (41) 215550505
Web Site: http://www.lausannecites.ch
Sales Range: $10-24.9 Million
Newspaper Publishers
N.A.I.C.S.: 513110
Pascal Fleury (Dir)

Tilllate Schweiz AG (1)
Werdstrasse 21, PO Box 8021, Zurich, Switzerland
Tel.: (41) 44 248 41 11
Web Site: http://ch.tilllate.com
Nightlife Internet Portal Operation Services
N.A.I.C.S.: 519290
Rita Meyer (Mgr)

Verlag Finanz und Wirtschaft AG (1)
Hallwylstrasse 71, Zurich, 8004, Switzerland
Tel.: (41) 44 404 65 55
Sales Range: $25-49.9 Million
Emp.: 50
Economic Newspaper Publishing Services
N.A.I.C.S.: 513110

Zurcher Unterland Medien AG (1)
Schulstrasse 12, 8157, Dielsdorf, Switzerland
Tel.: (41) 44 854 82 82
Newspaper Publishing Services
N.A.I.C.S.: 513110

Zuritipp AG (1)
Werdstrasse 21, 8021, Zurich, Switzerland (100%)
Tel.: (41) 442484411
Web Site: http://www.tamedia.ch
Sales Range: $400-449.9 Million
Emp.: 1,200
Newspaper Publishers
N.A.I.C.S.: 513110

dreifive (Switzerland) AG (1)
Feldstrasse 42, Wollishofen, 8004, Zurich, Switzerland
Tel.: (41) 444855533
Digital Agency Services
N.A.I.C.S.: 541613
Marcel Oppliger (Mng Dir)

dreifive AG (1)
Bleicherstrasse 10, 78467, Konstanz, Germany
Tel.: (49) 7531892070
Web Site: https://www.dreifive.com
Digital Agency Services
N.A.I.C.S.: 541613

dreifive GmbH (1)
Laimgrubengasse 14, 1060, Vienna, Austria
Tel.: (43) 13800550
Digital Agency Services
N.A.I.C.S.: 541613
Zeynep Atesman (Head-Digital Mktg)

ricardo.ch AG (1)
Theilerstrasse 1a, PO Box 1160, 6301, Zug, Switzerland
Tel.: (41) 900950950
Web Site: http://www.help.ricardo.ch
Online Shopping Services
N.A.I.C.S.: 541219
Rafael Martini (Mgr-Product)

TXC CORPORATION

No 4 Gongye 6th Road, Pingzhen District, Taoyuan, 324403, Taiwan
Tel.: (886) 34698121
Web Site: https://www.txccorp.com
3042—(TAI)
Rev: $354,831,799
Assets: $615,532,761
Liabilities: $227,239,633
Net Worth: $388,293,128
Earnings: $56,041,791
Emp.: 3,375
Fiscal Year-end: 12/31/23
Quartz Crystal Mfr
N.A.I.C.S.: 334419
Linda Lin (VP-Supply Chain Center)

Subsidiaries:

TXC (Chongqing) Corporation (1)
22 Fung Sheng Rd, Jiulongpo District, Chongqing, 401329, China
Tel.: (86) 2361511888
Frequency Control & Sensor Product Mfr & Distr
N.A.I.C.S.: 334511

TXC (Ningbo) Corporation (1)
189 Huangshan West Road, Beilun District, Ningbo, 315800, China
Tel.: (86) 57486874666

AND PRIVATE COMPANIES

Frequency Control & Sensor Product Mfr & Distr
N.A.I.C.S.: 334511

TXC Corporation - Ningbo Factory (1)
No 189 Huangshan West Road, Beilun District, Ningbo, 315800, Zhejiang, China
Tel.: (86) 57486874666
Web Site: http://www.txc.com.tw
Emp.: 1,000
Electronic Components Mfr
N.A.I.C.S.: 334416

TXC Europe GmbH (1)
Sebastian-Kneipp-Strasse 41, 60439, Frankfurt am Main, Germany
Tel.: (49) 69505064272
Frequency Control & Sensor Product Mfr & Distr
N.A.I.C.S.: 334511

TXC JAPAN CORPORATION (1)
Urban Square 1-3-1 Shin-yokohama, Kohoku-ku, Yokohama, 222-0033, Kanagawa, Japan
Tel.: (81) 454775305
Web Site: http://www.txccorp.com
Sales Range: $25-49.9 Million
Emp.: 7
Electronic Components Mfr
N.A.I.C.S.: 334419

TXC Technology Inc. (1)
451 West Lambert Rd Ste 201, Brea, CA 92821
Tel.: (714) 990-5510
Web Site: http://www.txccorp.com
Sales Range: $25-49.9 Million
Emp.: 13
Frequency Control Components Mfr & Distr
N.A.I.C.S.: 334515

TXCOM S.A.
10 Avenue Descartes, ZI du Petit Clamart, 92350, Le Plessis-Robinson, France
Tel.: (33) 146010506
Web Site: http://www.txcom.com
ALTXC—(EUR)
Sales Range: $10-24.9 Million
Emp.: 50
Logistics Software & Hardware Designer & Mfr
N.A.I.C.S.: 334610
Phillippe Clavery (Chm & CEO)

Subsidiaries:

ATTEL Ingenierie-SATCO (1)
Parc d Affaires Noveos 10 Ave Descartes, 92350, Le Plessis-Robinson, France
Tel.: (33) 146303610
Web Site: http://www.satco.fr
Sales Range: $25-49.9 Million
Emp.: 35
Projectors & Television Sets Mfr
N.A.I.C.S.: 321999

Axiohm S.A.S. (1)
1 Rue D Arcueil, 92542, Montrouge, Hauts De Seine, France
Tel.: (33) 158071717
Web Site: http://www.axiohm.com
Sales Range: $25-49.9 Million
Thermal Printer Mfr
N.A.I.C.S.: 333248

Subsidiary (US):

Axiohm USA LLC (2)
2411 N Oak St - Ste 203 C, Myrtle Beach, SC 29577
Tel.: (843) 443-3155
Web Site: http://www.axiohm.com
Thermal Printer Distr
N.A.I.C.S.: 423430

Deal Tag S.A. (1)
NOVEOS Business Park 10 avenue, Descartes, 92350, Le Plessis-Robinson, France
Tel.: (33) 146010506
Web Site: http://www.dealtag.fr
Electronic Parts Distr
N.A.I.C.S.: 423690

ISIS S.A.S. (1)
19 chemin sous les Saules, 01700, Neyron, France

Tel.: (33) 478550435
Web Site: http://www.isis-outillages.com
Emp.: 22
Alloy Steel Tool Mfr
N.A.I.C.S.: 331110

Maintag SAS (1)
Parc d'affaire NOVEOS 10 avenue, Descartes, 92350, Le Plessis-Robinson, France
Tel.: (33) 146010506
Web Site: http://www.maintag.com
Aerospace Parts Mfr
N.A.I.C.S.: 336413

TXO PLC
Office No 5 37 Billing Road, Northampton, NN1 5DQ, United Kingdom
Tel.: (44) 20 7518 4300   UK
Web Site: http://www.txoplc.co.uk
Sales Range: Less than $1 Million
Emp.: 4
Oil Well Refurbisher; Oil & Gas Exploration Services
N.A.I.C.S.: 213111
Geoffrey Harris (Sec)

TXT E-SOLUTIONS S.P.A.
Via Frigia 27, 20126, Milan, Italy
Tel.: (39) 02257711
Web Site: https://www.txtgroup.com
Year Founded: 1989
TXT—(ITA)
Sales Range: $25-49.9 Million
Emp.: 481
Software Solutions for Chain Management
N.A.I.C.S.: 513210
Marco Edoardo Guida (Co-CEO)

Subsidiaries:

AssioPay S.r.l. (1)
Via Rimembranze, Cesano Boscone, 20090, Milan, Italy
Tel.: (39) 024 505 5810
Web Site: https://www.assiopay.it
Aircraft & System Design Services
N.A.I.C.S.: 541512

Butterfly S.R.L. (1)
Via Zona Artigianale 3/A, Quero Vas, 32038, Belluno, Italy
Tel.: (39) 0439787942
Web Site: https://llelu.com
Optical Product Mfr
N.A.I.C.S.: 327215

Cheleo S.r.l. (1)
Via Benaco 115/A, 25081, Bedizzole, BS, Italy
Tel.: (39) 030 687 1793
Web Site: https://cheleo.txtgroup.com
Aircraft & System Design Services
N.A.I.C.S.: 541512
Alessandro Angelini (CEO)

HSPI S.p.A. (1)
Viale Aldo Moro 16, 40127, Bologna, Italy
Tel.: (39) 051 001 6400
Web Site: https://www.hspi.it
Management Consulting Services
N.A.I.C.S.: 541611

Mac Solutions S.A. (1)
Via V D'Alberti 1, 6830, Chiasso, Switzerland
Tel.: (41) 91 695 1630
Web Site: https://macsol.txtgroup.com
Information Technology Services
N.A.I.C.S.: 541519

PGMD Consulting S.R.L. (1)
Via Milano 150, 20093, Cologno Monzese, MI, Italy
Tel.: (39) 02257711
Web Site: https://www.pgmd.it
Information Technology Services
N.A.I.C.S.: 541519

Pace GmbH (1)
Am Bahnhof Westend 13, 14059, Berlin, Germany
Tel.: (49) 3 029 3620
Web Site: https://pace.txtgroup.com
Aircraft & System Design Services
N.A.I.C.S.: 541512

Frank Ehlermann (Mng Dir)

Soluzioni Prodotti Sistemi S.R.L. (1)
Via Cornelia 498, 00166, Rome, Italy
Tel.: (39) 066243509
Web Site: https://spsistemi.net
Information Technology Services
N.A.I.C.S.: 541519

TLOGOS S.R.L. (1)
Via Francesco Gentile 135, 00173, Rome, Italy
Tel.: (39) 065012811
Web Site: https://tlogos.txtgroup.com
Information Technology Consulting Services
N.A.I.C.S.: 541519

TXT Novigo S.R.L. (1)
Borgo Pietro Wuhrer 137, 25123, Brescia, BS, Italy
Tel.: (39) 0307776657
Web Site: https://novigo.txtgroup.com
Information Technology Consulting Services
N.A.I.C.S.: 541519

TXT Quence S.R.L. (1)
Via Milano 150, 20093, Cologno Monzese, MI, Italy
Tel.: (39) 02257711
Web Site: https://quence.txtgroup.com
Information Technology Services
N.A.I.C.S.: 541519

TXT e-Solutions GmbH (1)
Mansfelder Strasse 48, 6108, Halle, Germany   (100%)
Tel.: (49) 345555840
Web Site: http://www.txtgroup.com
Sales Range: $25-49.9 Million
Emp.: 50
Software Solutions
N.A.I.C.S.: 513210
Holger Klappstein (Mng Dir)

TXT e-Solutions Ltd. (1)
5 Chapell Lane Wynyard Park Business Village Wynyard, Billingham, TS22 5FG, Cleveland, United Kingdom
Tel.: (44) 1740 768360
Sales Range: $50-74.9 Million
Emp.: 8
Software Solutions
N.A.I.C.S.: 423430
Andrea Cencini (Dir)

TXT e-Solutions S.L. (1)
Av Diagonal 463 bis 3rd Fl 1a, Barcelona, 08036, Spain   (100%)
Tel.: (34) 933634040
Sales Range: $25-49.9 Million
Emp.: 10
Software Solutions
N.A.I.C.S.: 513210

TXT e-Solutions SarL (1)
9 rue Notre Dame des Victoires, 75002, Paris, France   (100%)
Tel.: (33) 155807940
Web Site: http://www.txt.fr
Sales Range: $25-49.9 Million
Emp.: 16
Software Solutions
N.A.I.C.S.: 513210

TXT e-Tech S.R.L. (1)
Via Milano 150, 20093, Cologno Monzese, MI, Italy
Tel.: (39) 02257711
Information Technology Services
N.A.I.C.S.: 541519

TXT e-solutions S.A.G.L. (1)
35 Corso San Gottardo, 6830, Chiasso, Switzerland
Tel.: (41) 77 969 3928
Aircraft & System Design Services
N.A.I.C.S.: 541512

Tecno Team Srl (1)
Via San Giuseppe 16, 43039, Salsomaggiore Terme, Ponte Ghiara, Italy
Tel.: (39) 0524585140
Web Site: https://www.tecnoteamsrl.com
Food Packaging Equipment Mfr
N.A.I.C.S.: 333993

TeraTron GmbH (1)
Gewerbegebiet Sonnenberg Martin-Siebert-Str 5, 51647, Gummersbach, Germany
Tel.: (49) 226180820
Web Site: https://teratron.txtgroup.com

Emp.: 50
Electronic Component Mfr
N.A.I.C.S.: 334419

TY HOLDINGS CO. LTD.
10F 111 Yeouigongwon-ro, Yeongdeungpo-gu, Seoul, Korea (South)
Tel.: (82) 220906620
Web Site: https://www.ty-holdings.co.kr
363280—(KRS)
Rev.: $262,773,043
Assets: $1,803,540,820
Liabilities: $581,913,053
Net Worth: $1,221,627,767
Earnings: $74,969,980
Emp.: 24
Fiscal Year-end: 12/31/22
Holding Company; Construction, Broadcasting, Environment, Logistics & Leisure
N.A.I.C.S.: 551112
Jong Yeon Yoo (CEO)

Subsidiaries:

SBS Media Holdings Co., Ltd. (1)
920 Mok-dong, Yangcheon-ku, Seoul, 158-725, Korea (South)   (61.22%)
Tel.: (82) 221135599
Web Site: http://www.sbsmedia.co.kr
Rev.: $126,830,107
Assets: $549,399,800
Liabilities: $148,604,783
Net Worth: $400,795,018
Earnings: ($51,082,857)
Emp.: 7
Fiscal Year-end: 12/31/2022
Holding Company
N.A.I.C.S.: 551112
Kyung-Ryul Shin (Pres & CEO)

Subsidiary (Domestic):

Seoul Broadcasting System (2)
161 Mokdongseo-ro, Yangcheon-gu, Seoul, Korea (South)
Tel.: (82) 220610006
Web Site: http://www.sbs.co.kr
Rev.: $900,290,473
Assets: $1,079,850,630
Liabilities: $410,047,521
Net Worth: $669,803,110
Earnings: $120,077,812
Emp.: 1,038
Fiscal Year-end: 12/31/2022
Television Broadcasting Services
N.A.I.C.S.: 516120
Min Insik (Dir-Bus Admin)

Subsidiary (Domestic):

SBS Contents Hub Co., Ltd. (3)
15F/16F SBS Prism Tower 82 Sangamsan-ro, Mapo-gu, Seoul, Korea (South)   (64.96%)
Tel.: (82) 220016600
Web Site: http://www.sbscontentshub.co.kr
Rev.: $151,590,154
Assets: $190,504,332
Liabilities: $55,811,123
Net Worth: $134,693,209
Earnings: $7,380,470
Emp.: 53
Fiscal Year-end: 12/31/2022
Multimedia Broadcasting Services
N.A.I.C.S.: 516120
Hwi-Jin Kim (CEO)

TYC BROTHER INDUSTRIAL CO., LTD.
No 72-2 Sin-le Rd, An-Ping Industrial Park, T'ainan, 70248, Taiwan
Tel.: (886) 62658781
Web Site: https://www.tyc.com.tw
1522—(TAI)
Rev.: $630,417,747
Assets: $844,719,580
Liabilities: $533,570,764
Net Worth: $311,148,816
Earnings: $37,815,787
Emp.: 1,639
Fiscal Year-end: 12/31/23
Motorcycle Lamps Mfr

TYC BROTHER INDUSTRIAL CO., LTD.

TYC Brother Industrial Co., Ltd.—(Continued)
N.A.I.C.S.: 335139
Yi-Feng Weng *(Deputy Gen Mgr)*

Subsidiaries:

Chang Chun Sparx Auto Lamps Co., Ltd. (1)
No 2528 Chuang Shin Road Hi-New Technology Development District, Changchun, 130012, Jilin, China
Tel.: (86) 43185881855
Sales Range: $25-49.9 Million
Emp.: 18
Automobile Lamp Mfr
N.A.I.C.S.: 335139

Changzhou Tamou Precision Industrial Co., Ltd. (1)
No 99 Taishan Road, Changzhou New District, Jiangsu, 213022, China
Tel.: (86) 51985126080
Web Site: https://www.dmprs.cn
Plastic Mold Mfr
N.A.I.C.S.: 333511

DBM Reflex of Taiwan Co., Ltd. (1)
54 Shing-Leh Road, Tainan City, 702, Taiwan
Tel.: (886) 62646618
Web Site: https://www.dbmreflex.com.tw
Emp.: 80
Real Estate Development Services
N.A.I.C.S.: 531390

Genera Corporation (1)
2800 Saturn St, Brea, CA 92821
Tel.: (714) 203-0800
Web Site: http://www.genera.com
Automobile Parts Distr
N.A.I.C.S.: 423120

JUOKU Technology Co., Ltd. (1)
No 25 Gongye 3rd Rd, Tainan Technology Industrial Park Annan Dist, Tainan City, 70955, Taiwan
Tel.: (886) 63845888
Web Site: https://www.juoku.com.tw
Core Reflector Mfr
N.A.I.C.S.: 335139

Kun Shan TYC High Performance Lighting Tech Co., Ltd. (1)
No 99 Lighthouse Road, Yushan Town, Kunshan, China
Tel.: (86) 51257286286
Automobile Component Distr
N.A.I.C.S.: 423120

TIT International Co., Ltd. (1)
119 Moo 3 Bankhai Nonglalok Road, Tambon Bankhai, Rayong, 21120, Thailand
Tel.: (66) 38892295
Automotive Lighting Mfr
N.A.I.C.S.: 335139

TYC Americas Inc. (1)
2800 Saturn St, Brea, CA 92821
Tel.: (714) 203-0800
Web Site: https://www.tycusa.com
Automobile Component Mfr & Distr
N.A.I.C.S.: 336390

TYC Baltic UAB (1)
A Juozapavicius Avenue 7K, 45251, Kaunas, Lithuania
Tel.: (370) 37400149
Sales Range: $50-74.9 Million
Emp.: 5
Automotive Lights Distr
N.A.I.C.S.: 423610

TYC Europe B.V. (1)
Rondebeltweg 92, 1329 BG, Almere, Netherlands
Tel.: (31) 365307188
Web Site: https://www.tyceurope.com
Sales Range: $25-49.9 Million
Emp.: 40
Automobile Parts Distr
N.A.I.C.S.: 423120

Varroc TYC Auto Lamps Co., Ltd. (1)
No 228 Taishan Road New Zone, Changzhou, 213022, Jiangsu, China
Tel.: (86) 51985111180
Automotive Product Mfr & Distr
N.A.I.C.S.: 336390
Nicole Feng *(Gen Mgr)*

TYCHE INDUSTRIES LTD
C21/A Road No-9 Film Nagar Jubilee Hills, Hyderabad, 500 096, Telangana, India
Tel.: (91) 4023541688
Web Site: https://www.tycheindustries.net
Year Founded: 1998
532384—(BOM)
Rev.: $9,617,313
Assets: $16,919,621
Liabilities: $2,921,156
Net Worth: $13,998,465
Earnings: $1,699,119
Emp.: 166
Fiscal Year-end: 03/31/23
Pharmaceuticals Product Mfr
N.A.I.C.S.: 325412
Ganesh Kumar G. *(Chm & Mng Dir)*

TYCOON GROUP HOLDINGS LIMITED
Room 14 8/F Wah Wai Centre 38-40 Au Pui Wan Street, Shatin, Hong Kong, China (Hong Kong)
Tel.: (852) 26616727   Ky
Web Site:
   https://www.tycoongroup.com.hk
Year Founded: 2015
3390—(HKG)
Holding Company
N.A.I.C.S.: 551112
Michael Wong Ka Chun *(Chm & CEO)*

TYCOONS GROUP ENTERPRISE CO., LTD.
No 79-1 Xinle St, Gangshan Dist, Kaohsiung, 820, Taiwan
Tel.: (886) 76212191
Web Site: https://www.tycons.com.tw
Year Founded: 1980
2022—(TAI)
Rev.: $275,355,397
Assets: $291,411,873
Liabilities: $65,611,070
Net Worth: $225,800,802
Earnings: $11,219,595
Fiscal Year-end: 12/31/23
Hardware Mfr
N.A.I.C.S.: 332722
Yen-Chuan Lu *(Chm)*

Subsidiaries:

Huanghua Jujin Hardware Products Co., Ltd. (1)
Baizhuang, Jiucheng Town, Huanghua, 061100, Hebei, China
Tel.: (86) 3175656601
Web Site: https://www.jujinwj.com
Screw Mfr
N.A.I.C.S.: 332722

Tycoons Worldwide Group (Thailand) Public Co., Ltd. (1)
99 Moo 1 Nikhom Phatthana, Amphur Nikompattana, Rayong, 21180, Thailand (76.31%)
Tel.: (66) 33658558
Web Site: https://www.tycons.com
Rev.: $259,072,717
Assets: $172,005,729
Liabilities: $47,720,650
Net Worth: $124,285,079
Earnings: $4,444,287
Emp.: 874
Fiscal Year-end: 12/31/2022
Wirerods, Annealed Wire & Screws Mfr
N.A.I.C.S.: 332618
Yen-Chuan Lu *(Chm)*

TYCROP MANUFACTURING LTD.
9880 McGrath Road, Rosedale, V0X 1X0, BC, Canada
Tel.: (604) 794-7078
Web Site: https://www.tycrop.com
Year Founded: 1978
Farm Equipment Mfr

N.A.I.C.S.: 333111
Murray Sasyniuk *(VP-Fin)*

TYE SOON LIMITED
3C Toh Guan Road East, Singapore, 608832, Singapore
Tel.: (65) 65678601
Web Site: https://www.tyesoon.com
Year Founded: 1933
BFU—(SES)
Rev.: $192,683,481
Assets: $136,363,705
Liabilities: $89,638,718
Net Worth: $46,724,987
Earnings: $3,271,984
Emp.: 3,000
Fiscal Year-end: 12/31/23
Spare Parts Mfr
N.A.I.C.S.: 336330
Evelyn Kim Lin Wee *(Sec)*

Subsidiaries:

Imparts Automotive Pty Ltd (1)
726 High Street, Kew, 3102, VIC, Australia
Tel.: (61) 1300467278
Web Site: https://www.imparts.com.au
Motor Vehicle Parts Distr
N.A.I.C.S.: 423140

TYHEE GOLD CORP.
Suite 401 - 675 West Hastings Street, Vancouver, V6B 1N2, BC, Canada
Tel.: (604) 681-2877
Web Site: http://tyhee.com
Mineral Exploration Services
N.A.I.C.S.: 213114
Harjinder S. Gill *(CFO)*

TYK CORPORATION
Shinagawa City Bldg 2-11-1 Konan, Minato-ku, Tokyo, 108-0075, Japan
Tel.: (81) 364332888
Web Site: https://www.tyk.co.jp
Year Founded: 1947
5363—(TKS)
Rev.: $198,372,710
Assets: $376,115,610
Liabilities: $77,574,960
Net Worth: $298,540,650
Earnings: $15,718,580
Emp.: 397
Fiscal Year-end: 03/31/24
Refractories Mfr for the Steel Industry
N.A.I.C.S.: 327120
Nobutaka Ushigome *(Pres)*

Subsidiaries:

TYK America, Inc. (1)
301 Brickyard Rd, Clairton, PA 15025-3650 (100%)
Tel.: (412) 384-4259
Web Site: http://www.tykamerica.com
Sales Range: $25-49.9 Million
Emp.: 35
Mfr of Refractories for the Steel Industry
N.A.I.C.S.: 327120
James Karamanos *(Exec VP & Gen Mgr-Sls)*

TYM CORPORATION
Dae Yong B/D 7 Eonju-ro 133-gil, Gangnam-Gu, Seoul, Korea (South)
Tel.: (82) 230142800
Web Site: http://www.tym.co.kr
Year Founded: 1951
002900—(KRS)
Rev.: $894,428,434
Assets: $599,892,503
Liabilities: $343,359,973
Net Worth: $256,532,530
Earnings: $75,308,747
Emp.: 620
Fiscal Year-end: 12/31/22
Agricultural Machinery Mfr & Distr
N.A.I.C.S.: 333111
Jin-Sung Choi *(Mgr-Acctg Team)*

INTERNATIONAL PUBLIC

Subsidiaries:

Aflvelar Ehf. (1)
Vesturhraun 3 210, Gardabaer Gagnheidi 35 800 Selfoss, 603, Akureyri, Iceland
Tel.: (354) 4800000
Web Site: https://aflvelar.is
Agricultural Equipment Mfr
N.A.I.C.S.: 333111

Agricortes.Com Maq. E Equip. S.A. (1)
Avenida Do Lis-Cortes, 2410-501, Leiria, Portugal
Tel.: (351) 244819110
Web Site: https://agricortes.com
Agriculture Equipment Mfr & Distr
N.A.I.C.S.: 333111

Agriexport Industry Ltd. (1)
B Industrial S Varavara Area, Paphos, Cyprus
Tel.: (357) 26949898
Agricultural Machinery & Equipment Mfr
N.A.I.C.S.: 333111

Anderson Enterprises & Equipment, LLC (1)
505 S E St, Annawan, IL 61234
Tel.: (309) 935-6700
Web Site:
   https://www.andersonenterpriseseq.com
Emp.: 8
Lawn & Garden Equipment Distr
N.A.I.C.S.: 423820

Arizona's Best Equipment Inc. (1)
3455 S 36th St, Phoenix, AZ 85040
Tel.: (602) 437-2345
Web Site:
   https://www.arizonasbestequipment.com
Tractor & Forklift Distr
N.A.I.C.S.: 423820

Ausra Equipment & Supply Company Inc. (1)
30155 Yaw St, Dowagiac, MI 49047
Tel.: (269) 782-7178
Web Site: https://www.ausraequipment.com
Farm Equipment Distr
N.A.I.C.S.: 423820

Bell Creek Equipment LLC (1)
21927 Dover Bridge Rd, Preston, MD 21655
Tel.: (410) 673-2700
Web Site:
   https://www.bellcreekequipment.net
Lawn & Garden Equipment Distr
N.A.I.C.S.: 423820

Branson Tractors Limited (1)
Bidford-On-Avon, Alcester, B50 4JH, United Kingdom
Tel.: (44) 1789774089
Web Site: https://www.bransontractor.co.uk
Tractor Equipment Mfr & Distr
N.A.I.C.S.: 333112

Cape Fear Tractor and Saw LLC (1)
4616 Coddington Loop, Wilmington, NC 28405
Tel.: (910) 769-4137
Web Site:
   https://www.capefeartractorandsaw.com
Tractor & Lawn Mower Distr
N.A.I.C.S.: 423820

Contractor Equipment Rental & Supply LLC (1)
15620 Hwy 107, Jacksonville, AR 72076
Tel.: (501) 833-2300
Agricultural Machinery Mfr
N.A.I.C.S.: 333111

Elite Lift Truck Inc. (1)
7575 Hwy 10 NW, Ramsey, MN 55303
Tel.: (763) 421-9081
Web Site: https://elitelift.com
Heli Forklift & Dock Equipment Distr
N.A.I.C.S.: 423830

Georgia Land Equipment LLC (1)
5695 GA-400, Cumming, GA 30028
Tel.: (470) 839-9119
Web Site: https://georgialandequipment.com
Tractor Implement & Equipment Trailer Distr
N.A.I.C.S.: 423830

Harkness Jim Equipment Ltd. (1)

5808 Highway 9, Harriston, N0G 1Z0, ON, Canada
Tel.: (519) 338-3946
Web Site: https://harknessequipment.ca
Agricultural Equipment Retailer
N.A.I.C.S.: 444230

Helms TMT-Centret A/S (1)
Tavlundvej 4-6, Lind, 7400, Herning, Denmark
Tel.: (45) 99282930
Web Site: https://www.helmstmt.com
Emp.: 45
Agricultural Equipment Mfr
N.A.I.C.S.: 333111

Henson Farm Supply Inc. (1)
1415 HC 1, Greenville, MO 63944
Tel.: (573) 224-5400
Web Site:
  https://www.hensonfarmsupply.com
Agricultural Equipment & Lawn Mower Mfr
N.A.I.C.S.: 333111

Holtry's LLC (1)
10948 Roxbury Rd, Roxbury, PA 17251
Tel.: (717) 532-7261
Web Site: https://deutzboyz.com
Agricultural Tractor Distr
N.A.I.C.S.: 423820

Horn's Outdoor Inc. (1)
3034 Albert Pike Rd, Hot Springs, AR 71913
Tel.: (501) 767-9000
Web Site: https://www.hornsoutdoor.net
Motor Vehicles & Parts Distr
N.A.I.C.S.: 423690

Jiangsu Tong Yang Machinery Co., Ltd. (1)
No889 Jianbao Road, Jianhu County, Yancheng, Jiangsu, China
Tel.: (86) 51586119009
Tractor Mfr
N.A.I.C.S.: 333924

Johnson Equipment & Cattle LLC (1)
3 Loys Johnson Rd, Newbern, TN 38059
Tel.: (731) 643-6749
Farm Equipment & Tractors Maintenance Services
N.A.I.C.S.: 811411

Merchant logo Goldoni Keestrack S.R.L. (1)
Via Canale 3, Migliarina di Carpi, 41012, Modena, Italy
Tel.: (39) 0522640111
Web Site: https://www.goldoni.com
Tractor Equipment Retailer
N.A.I.C.S.: 423820

Motor Power Finland OY (1)
Keskuojankatu 12, 33900, Tampere, Finland
Tel.: (358) 105489900
Web Site: https://motorpower.fi
Automotive Vehicle Mfr & Distr
N.A.I.C.S.: 336390

New Frontier Equipment Sales & Rental Corp. (1)
7213 Line 86, Wallenstein, N0B 2S0, ON, Canada
Tel.: (519) 669-8709
Web Site: https://frontierequipsales.com
Farm Equipment Repair & Maintenance Services
N.A.I.C.S.: 811310

Nordmax Equipment Inc. (1)
2711 Route 111 Est, Amos, J9T 3A1, QC, Canada
Tel.: (819) 732-6296
Web Site:
  https://en.equipementsnordmax.com
Forestry Machine & Equipment Services
N.A.I.C.S.: 532412

Northern Michigan Tractor & Equipment, LLC (1)
10997 Hetherton Rd, Johannesburg, MI 49751
Tel.: (989) 731-1818
Web Site:
  https://northernmichigantractor.com
Tractor & Equipment Distr
N.A.I.C.S.: 423820

O'Bryan's Farm Equipment LLC (1)
1545 New Haven Rd, Bardstown, KY 40001
Tel.: (502) 249-8520
Web Site:
  https://www.obryansequipment.com
Farm Equipment Distr
N.A.I.C.S.: 423820

Persha Equipment Sales Inc. (1)
W2911 WI-33, Mayville, WI 53050
Tel.: (920) 387-5320
Web Site:
  https://www.pershaequipment.com
Mower & Chainsaw Distr
N.A.I.C.S.: 423820

Rjm Equipment Sales LLC (1)
14 Hwy W, Wright City, MO 63390
Tel.: (636) 295-0495
Web Site:
  https://www.rjmequipmentsales.com
Branson Tractor Distr
N.A.I.C.S.: 423820

Roger Fowler Sales & Service, Inc. (1)
8648 Whaleyville Blvd, Suffolk, VA 23438
Tel.: (757) 986-2441
Web Site:
  https://www.rogerfowlerssalesservice.com
Lawn Equipment Rental Services
N.A.I.C.S.: 532210

Schnoebelen, Inc. (1)
450 E 4th St, Riverside, IA 52327
Tel.: (319) 648-2481
Web Site: https://www.schnoebelen.com
Mower & Compact Tractor Maintenance Services
N.A.I.C.S.: 811411

Swantak Inc. (1)
6325 State Hwy 28 S, Oneonta, NY 13820
Tel.: (607) 432-0891
Web Site: https://www.swantak.com
Tractor & Lawn Mower Distr
N.A.I.C.S.: 423820

Szal-Agro Kft. (1)
Sajo Ut 4, 3527, Miskolc, Hungary
Tel.: (36) 46505624
Web Site: https://www.szalagro.hu
Agriculture Machine & Equipment Distr
N.A.I.C.S.: 423820

TYM-USA Inc. (1)
Potato House Ct, Wilson, NC 27893
Tel.: (252) 293-1224
Tractor Mfr
N.A.I.C.S.: 333924

Team Tractor and Equipment Corp. (1)
1100 W Happy Valley Rd, Phoenix, AZ 85085
Tel.: (602) 734-9944
Web Site: https://www.teamtractor.com
Tractor & Farm Equipment Distr
N.A.I.C.S.: 423820

Tym Central Europe S.r.o. (1)
Holzova 9 Lisen, 628 00, Brno, Czech Republic
Tel.: (420) 725337656
Web Site: https://tymtractors.cz
Agricultural Tractor Distr
N.A.I.C.S.: 423820

Wakarusa AG LLC (1)
711 E Waterford St, Wakarusa, IN 46573
Tel.: (574) 862-1163
Web Site: https://wakarusaag.com
Farm & Construction Equipment Maintenance Services
N.A.I.C.S.: 811411

Waldo Implement Inc. (1)
1200 W 1st St, Waldo, WI 53093
Tel.: (920) 528-8631
Agricultural Machinery Mfr
N.A.I.C.S.: 333111

Weber Gerate GmbH (1)
Alte Eisenstrasse 27-29, 57258, Freudenberg, Germany
Tel.: (49) 2734434280
Tractor Equipment Distr
N.A.I.C.S.: 423820

Weiser Tractor & Feed, LLC (1)
605 US-95, Weiser, ID 83672
Tel.: (208) 414-4111
Web Site: https://weisertractorandfeed.com
Farm Equipment & Tractors Maintenance Services
N.A.I.C.S.: 811411

Young Ford, Inc. (1)
570 E 525 N, Morgan, UT 84050
Tel.: (801) 821-4415
Web Site:
  https://www.youngfordbrigham.com
Car & Truck Distr
N.A.I.C.S.: 484230

TYMBAL RESOURCES LTD.
600-850 West Hastings Street Suite 401, Vancouver, V6C 1E1, BC, Canada
Tel.: (604) 662-8130
Year Founded: 1980
NTBRF—(OTCIQ)
Assets: $244,386
Liabilities: $3,494,610
Net Worth: ($3,250,225)
Earnings: ($459,582)
Fiscal Year-end: 01/31/24
Mineral Exploration Services
N.A.I.C.S.: 212390
Sammy Cheng (Pres & CEO)

TYMLEZ GROUP LTD.
c/o Moray and Agnew Level 6 505 Little Collins Street, Melbourne, 3000, VIC, Australia
Tel.: (61) 383955446
Web Site: http://www.tymlez.com
Year Founded: 2016
NVQ—(ASX)
Rev.: $533,235
Assets: $444,729
Liabilities: $484,128
Net Worth: ($39,399)
Earnings: ($2,008,693)
Fiscal Year-end: 12/31/23
Software Development Services
N.A.I.C.S.: 541511
Dan Voyce (CTO)

TYNER RESOURCES LTD.
Suite 615 -800 West Pender Street, Vancouver, V6C 2V6, BC, Canada
Tel.: (604) 728-4080 BC
Year Founded: 1978
TIP—(TSXV)
Assets: $1,217
Liabilities: $64,551
Net Worth: ($63,334)
Earnings: ($49,981)
Emp.: 3
Fiscal Year-end: 03/31/23
Oil & Gas Exploration Services
N.A.I.C.S.: 211120
Jonathan Younie (CFO)

TYNTEK CORPORATION
No 15 Kejung Rd Chunan Science Park, Chunan, 350, Miaoli County, Taiwan
Tel.: (886) 37582997
Web Site: https://www.tyntek.com.tw
Year Founded: 1987
2426—(TAI)
Rev.: $74,156,673
Assets: $174,975,598
Liabilities: $48,064,749
Net Worth: $126,910,849
Earnings: ($4,437,522)
Emp.: 780
Fiscal Year-end: 12/31/23
Semiconductor Mfr
N.A.I.C.S.: 334413

Subsidiaries:

Keeper Technology Co., Ltd. (1)
No 29 Wuquan 7th Rd Wugu Dist, New Taipei City, 24890, Taiwan
Tel.: (886) 222997233
Web Site: http://www.keepertech.com.tw
Chip Mfr
N.A.I.C.S.: 334413

Tynrich Technology Corporation (1)
5F No 6 Ln 24 Heiping Rd, Banqiao Dist, New Taipei City, 220, Taiwan
Tel.: (886) 229621801
Web Site: http://www.tynrich.net
Emp.: 15
LED Mfr
N.A.I.C.S.: 334413

Tynsolar Corporation (1)
No 620 Sec 6 Jhonghua Rd, Siangshan District, Hsinchu, 300, Taiwan
Tel.: (886) 35181686
Web Site: http://www.tynsolar.com.tw
Chip Mfr
N.A.I.C.S.: 334413

TYPHOON FINANCIAL SERVICES LTD.
35 Omkar House Near Swastik Cross Roads C G Road, Navrangpura, Ahmedabad, 380009, Gujarat, India
Tel.: (91) 7926449515
Web Site:
  https://www.typhoonfinancial.com
Year Founded: 1990
539468—(BOM)
Rev.: $72,946
Assets: $658,067
Liabilities: $165,998
Net Worth: $492,069
Earnings: $1,092
Emp.: 3
Fiscal Year-end: 03/31/21
Finance Services
N.A.I.C.S.: 523150
Ashok R. Chhajer (Mng Dir)

TYRANNA RESOURCES LIMITED
L3 101 St Georges Terrace, Perth, 6000, WA, Australia
Tel.: (61) 865580886 AU
Web Site:
  https://www.tyrannaresources.com
TYX—(ASX)
Rev.: $40,739
Assets: $5,411,195
Liabilities: $113,977
Net Worth: $5,297,218
Earnings: ($28,611,951)
Fiscal Year-end: 06/30/24
Minerals Exploration
N.A.I.C.S.: 213114
Yugi Gouw (Sec)

TYRENS AB
Peter Myndes Backe 16, 118 86, Stockholm, Sweden
Tel.: (46) 10 452 20 00
Web Site: http://www.tyrens.se
Emp.: 1,300
Urban Planning & Infrastructure Solutions
N.A.I.C.S.: 541330
Ulrika Francke (Pres & CEO)

Subsidiaries:

Tyrens UK Limited (1)
100 St John Street, London, EC1M 4EH, United Kingdom
Tel.: (44) 20 7250 7666
Web Site: http://www.tyrens.se
Urban Planning & Consulting Services
N.A.I.C.S.: 541330
David Hampton (Dir-Technical)

TYRO PAYMENTS LIMITED
Level 18 55 Market Street, Sydney, 2000, NSW, Australia
Tel.: (61) 283114889 AU
Web Site: https://www.tyro.com
Year Founded: 2003
TYR—(ASX)
Rev.: $332,344,214
Assets: $301,456,565
Liabilities: $162,784,328

Tyro Payments Limited—(Continued)

Net Worth: $138,672,237
Earnings: $17,164,257
Emp.: 584
Fiscal Year-end: 06/30/24
Credit Card Issuer
N.A.I.C.S.: 522210
Steve Chapman *(Head-Internal Audit)*

TYROL EQUITY AG
Kaiserjagerstrasse 30, 6020, Innsbruck, Austria
Tel.: (43) 512 58 01 58 0
Web Site: http://www.tyrolequity.com
Year Founded: 2007
Emp.: 11
Privater Equity Firm
N.A.I.C.S.: 523999
Christoph Gerin-Swarovski *(Founder)*

Subsidiaries:
EISBAR SPORTMODEN GMBH (1)
Hauptstrasse 15, 4101, Feldkirchen an der Donau, Austria
Web Site: http://www.eisbaer.info
Emp.: 55
Sports Cap Mfr
N.A.I.C.S.: 315120

RSN SIHN GMBH (1)
Werk Muhlacker In den Waldackern 23, 75417, Muhlacker, Germany
Tel.: (49) 704181074100
Web Site: http://www.rsn-sihn.de
Mechanical Component Mfr
N.A.I.C.S.: 332912
John Frances *(CEO)*

SAV Workholding and Automation GmbH. (1)
Schiessplatzstrasse 36/38a, 90469, Nuremberg, Germany
Tel.: (49) 91194830
Web Site: http://www.en.sav-spanntechnik.de
Emp.: 200
Hydraulic Components Mfr
N.A.I.C.S.: 333998
Stefan Hamm *(CEO)*

TYROON TEA COMPANY LIMITED
McLeod House 3 Netaji Subhas Road, Kolkata, 700001, India
Tel.: (91) 3322483236
Web Site: https://www.tyroontea.com
Year Founded: 1890
526945—(BOM)
Rev.: $5,245,609
Assets: $6,626,413
Liabilities: $2,500,306
Net Worth: $4,126,108
Earnings: $421,569
Emp.: 1,366
Fiscal Year-end: 03/31/23
Tea Mfr
N.A.I.C.S.: 311920
Keshab Chandra Mishra *(CFO & Sec)*

TYSNES SPAREBANK
Teiglandsvegen 2, Tysnes, 5680, Hordaland, Norway
Tel.: (47) 53430300
Web Site: https://www.tysnes-sparebank.no
Year Founded: 1863
TYSB—(EUR)
Commercial Banking Services
N.A.I.C.S.: 522110
Hilde Lill Harrison *(Mgr-Insurance)*

TZ LIMITED
Level 2 40 Gloucester Street, The Rocks, Sydney, 2000, NSW, Australia
Tel.: (61) 90536753
Web Site: https://www.tz.net
TZL—(ASX)
Rev.: $9,306,511
Assets: $4,638,235
Liabilities: $7,002,402
Net Worth: ($2,364,167)
Earnings: $66,341
Fiscal Year-end: 06/30/24
Software Technology Services
N.A.I.C.S.: 513210
John Wilson *(CEO & Mng Dir)*

Subsidiaries:
Product Development Technologies, Inc. (1)
3 Ashurst Court London Rd, Wheatley, OX33 1AR, Oxfordshire, United Kingdom
Tel.: (44) 1844278000
Web Site: http://www.pdt.com
Sales Range: $25-49.9 Million
Product Development Services
N.A.I.C.S.: 523999
Mark Schwartz *(Founder & CEO)*

TZI Australia Pty Limited (1)
Level 2 40 Gloucester Street, The Rocks, Sydney, 2000, NSW, Australia
Tel.: (61) 291377300
Software Development Services
N.A.I.C.S.: 518210

TZI Singapore Pte Ltd. (1)
Suntec Tower 2 9 Temasek Boulevard 29-01, Singapore, 038989, Singapore
Tel.: (65) 31573108
Software Development Services
N.A.I.C.S.: 518210

TZI UK Limited (1)
Oxford Centre for Innovation New Road, Oxford, OX1 1BY, United Kingdom
Tel.: (44) 1865546611
Software Development Services
N.A.I.C.S.: 518210

Telezygology, Inc. (1)
999 E Touhy Ave Ste 460, Des Plaines, IL 60018
Tel.: (650) 644-4470
Web Site: https://tz.net
Sales Range: $25-49.9 Million
Emp.: 5
Security Solutions
N.A.I.C.S.: 561621

TZE SHIN INTERNATIONAL CO., LTD.
12F No 33 Sec 2 Jianguo N Rd, Zhongshan Dist, Taipei, 104482, Taiwan
Tel.: (886) 225090036
Web Site: https://www.tsgroup.com.tw
Year Founded: 1973
2611—(TAI)
Rev.: $20,187,939
Assets: $137,332,053
Liabilities: $31,408,874
Net Worth: $105,923,179
Earnings: $15,560,711
Emp.: 245
Fiscal Year-end: 12/31/23
Construction Services
N.A.I.C.S.: 236118
Chun-Fa Huang *(Chm)*

U AND I GROUP PLC
7a Howick Place, London, SW1P 1DZ, United Kingdom
Tel.: (44) 2078284777
Web Site: http://www.uandiplc.com
UAI—(LSE)
Rev.: $62,174,072
Assets: $579,743,725
Liabilities: $304,222,963
Net Worth: $275,520,762
Earnings: ($118,838,516)
Emp.: 120
Fiscal Year-end: 03/31/21
Commercial Real Estate Development & Investment
N.A.I.C.S.: 531390
Marcus Shepherd *(CFO)*

Subsidiaries:
DS Property Developments Limited (1)
140 Nottingham Rd Burton Joyce, Nottingham, NG14 5AU, United Kingdom
Tel.: (44) 7973 897933
Roofing Services
N.A.I.C.S.: 332322

Development Securities (Investments) PLC (1)
Portland House Bressenden Place, London, SW1E 5DS, United Kingdom
Tel.: (44) 2078284777
Web Site: http://www.developmentsecurities.com
Sales Range: $10-24.9 Million
Emp.: 40
Management & Investment Services
N.A.I.C.S.: 561110
Debby Wedstone *(Office Mgr)*

Development Securities (Paddington) Limited (1)
Portland House Bressenden Pl, London, SW1E 5DS, United Kingdom
Tel.: (44) 2078284777
Web Site: http://www.developmentsecurities.co.uk
Sales Range: $50-74.9 Million
Emp.: 40
Investment Services
N.A.I.C.S.: 523999
Mathew Wenier *(Mng Dir)*

Development Securities (Southampton A) Limited (1)
Portland House Bressenden Pl, London, SW1E 5DS, United Kingdom
Tel.: (44) 2078284777
Web Site: http://www.developmentsecurities.co.uk
Investment Services
N.A.I.C.S.: 523150
Matthew Weiner *(CEO)*

Development Securities Estates PLC (1)
Portland House Bressenden Place, London, SW1E 5DS, United Kingdom
Tel.: (44) 2078284777
Web Site: http://www.developmentsecurities.co.uk
Sales Range: $10-24.9 Million
Emp.: 45
Management & Investment Services
N.A.I.C.S.: 561110
David Jenkins *(Chm)*

U CITY PUBLIC COMPANY LIMITED
21 TST Tower 20th Floor Soi Choei Phuang Vibhavadi-Rangsit Road, Chomphon Chatuchak, Bangkok, 10900, Thailand
Tel.: (66) 22738838
Web Site: http://www.ucity.co.th
RABBIT—(THA)
Rev.: $154,232,362
Assets: $1,825,787,104
Liabilities: $844,007,618
Net Worth: $981,779,486
Earnings: ($126,720,039)
Emp.: 153
Fiscal Year-end: 12/31/23
Real Estate Development Services
N.A.I.C.S.: 531110
Nuttapun Giramethakul *(VP-Acctg Dept)*

Subsidiaries:
59 Club Asia Co., Ltd. (1)
1091/343 4th Floor New Petchburi Road, Makkasan Rajthevee, Bangkok, 10400, Thailand
Tel.: (66) 98 280 4055
Web Site: https://www.59clubasia.com
Sports Club Operator
N.A.I.C.S.: 711211
Araya Singhsuwan *(Dir-Operations)*

Absolute Design Services Co., Ltd. (1)
1091/343 4th Floor New Petchburi Road, Makkasan Rajthevee, Bangkok, 10400, Thailand
Tel.: (66) 2 255 9247
Web Site: https://www.absolutedesignservices.com
Interior Design Services
N.A.I.C.S.: 541410
Jonathan Wigley *(CEO)*

Andel's Berlin Hotelbetriebs GmbH (1)
Landsberger Allee 106, 10369, Berlin, Germany
Tel.: (49) 30 453 0530
Hotel & Motel Operator
N.A.I.C.S.: 721110

Lombard Estate Holdings Limited (1)
8th Floor Chung Nam House 59 Des Voeux Road, Central, China (Hong Kong)
Tel.: (852) 2 877 2008
Web Site: https://www.leh.hk
Real Estate Investment Services
N.A.I.C.S.: 531390

UOB Apartment Property Fund One (1)
Bangkok City Tower Fl 5 179 6-10 S Sathorn Rd, Thungmahamek Sathon, Bangkok, 10120, Thailand
Tel.: (66) 26767100
Asset & Investment Management Services
N.A.I.C.S.: 533110

VH Amber Baltic Sp. z o.o. (1)
ul Promenada Gwiazd 1, 72-500, Miedzyzdroje, Poland
Tel.: (48) 91 322 8500
Hotel & Motel Operator
N.A.I.C.S.: 721110

VH Andel's Lodz Sp. z o.o. (1)
ul Ogrodowa 17, 91-065, Lodz, Poland
Tel.: (48) 42 279 1000
Hotel & Motel Operator
N.A.I.C.S.: 721110

VH Kronberg Hotelbetriebs GmbH (1)
Bahnhofstrasse 38, 61476, Kronberg, Germany
Tel.: (49) 617 396 9940
Hotel & Motel Operator
N.A.I.C.S.: 721110

VHE Berlin Hotelbetriebs GmbH (1)
Storkower Str 162, 10407, Berlin, Germany
Tel.: (49) 30 666 4440
Hotel & Motel Operator
N.A.I.C.S.: 721110

VHE Bratislava s.r.o. (1)
Galvaniho ul 28, 82104, Bratislava, Slovakia
Tel.: (421) 23 229 9100
Hotel & Motel Operator
N.A.I.C.S.: 721110
Johanna Weichselbaumer *(CFO)*

VHE Leipzig Hotelbetriebs GmbH (1)
Goethestr 11, 04109, Leipzig, Germany
Tel.: (49) 341 991 5390
Hotel & Motel Operator
N.A.I.C.S.: 721110

Vienna House Andel's Cracow Sp. z o.o. (1)
ul Pawia 3, 31-154, Krakow, Poland
Tel.: (48) 12 660 0100
Hotel & Motel Operator
N.A.I.C.S.: 721110

Vienna House Easy Bremen GmbH (1)
Breitenweg 28, 28195, Bremen, Germany
Tel.: (49) 421 877 4360
Hotel & Motel Operator
N.A.I.C.S.: 721110

Vienna House Easy Cracow RE Sp. z o.o. (1)
ul Przy Rondzie 2, 31-547, Krakow, Poland
Tel.: (48) 12 299 0000
Hotel & Motel Operator
N.A.I.C.S.: 721110

Vienna House Easy Katowice Sp. z o.o. (1)
ul Sokolska 24, 40-086, Katowice, Poland
Tel.: (48) 32 783 8100

AND PRIVATE COMPANIES

Hotel & Motel Operator
N.A.I.C.S.: 721110

Vienna House Easy Munchen GmbH (1)
Nymphenburger Strasse 136, 80636, Munich, Germany
Tel.: (49) 89 540 2270
Hotel & Motel Operator
N.A.I.C.S.: 721110

Vienna House Easy Pilsen s.r.o. (1)
U Prazdroje 6, 301 00, Plzen, Czech Republic
Tel.: (420) 37 801 6111
Hotel & Motel Operator
N.A.I.C.S.: 721110

Vienna House Easy Potsdam GmbH (1)
Zeppelinstrasse 136, 14471, Potsdam, Germany
Tel.: (49) 3 319 8150
Hotel & Motel Operator
N.A.I.C.S.: 721110

Vienna House Eisenach GmbH (1)
Karlsplatz 11, 99817, Eisenach, Germany
Tel.: (49) 369 1280
Hotel & Motel Operator
N.A.I.C.S.: 721110

Vienna House Rostock GmbH (1)
Neuer Markt 2, 18055, Rostock, Germany
Tel.: (49) 3 814 9730
Hotel & Motel Operator
N.A.I.C.S.: 721110

Vienna House Stralsund GmbH (1)
Frankendamm 22, 18439, Stralsund, Germany
Tel.: (49) 3 831 2040
Hotel & Motel Operator
N.A.I.C.S.: 721110

Vienna International Asset GmbH (1)
Leuchtenbergring 20, 81677, Munich, Germany
Tel.: (49) 7 132 9100
Hotel & Motel Operator
N.A.I.C.S.: 721110

U POWER LIMITED
West 4th Floor No 88 Qinjiang Road, Xuhui District, Shanghai, China
Tel.: (86) 2168593598 Ky
Web Site: https://upower.com
Year Founded: 2013
UCAR—(NASDAQ)
Rev.: $2,736,486
Assets: $59,396,876
Liabilities: $11,681,436
Net Worth: $47,715,441
Earnings: ($3,525,975)
Emp.: 77
Fiscal Year-end: 12/31/23
Software Development Services
N.A.I.C.S.: 541511
Bingyi Zhao (CFO)

U&D COAL LIMITED
Suite A Level 4 Rowes Building 235 Edward St, Brisbane, 4000, QLD, Australia
Tel.: (61) 7 3188 9101 AU
Web Site: http://www.udcoal.com.au
Year Founded: 2014
Sales Range: Less than $1 Million
Coal Exploration & Mining Services
N.A.I.C.S.: 212115
Peter Edwards (CFO)

Subsidiaries:

U&D Mining Industry (Australia) Pty. Ltd. (1)
Level 1 37 Brandl Street, Eight Mile Plains, 4113, QLD, Australia (100%)
Tel.: (61) 731889101
Web Site: http://www.udmining.com.au
Coal Mining Exploration
N.A.I.C.S.: 213113
Peter Edwards (CFO & Sec)

U&I LEARNING NV
Ottergemsesteenweg Zuid 808, 9032, Gent, Belgium
Tel.: (32) 92657474
Web Site: http://www.uni-learning.com
Year Founded: 1997
FLSP—(EUR)
Rev.: $10,407,568
Assets: $12,635,048
Liabilities: $5,570,227
Net Worth: $7,064,821
Earnings: $1,208,087
Emp.: 60
Fiscal Year-end: 12/31/23
Online Education Services
N.A.I.C.S.: 611710
Guy Herregodts (CEO)

U-BIX CORPORATION
U-BIX Bldg Angono St, corner JP Rizal, 1344, Makati, Philippines
Tel.: (63) 28976819
Web Site: http://www.ubix.com.ph
Year Founded: 1974
Sales Range: $75-99.9 Million
Emp.: 400
Office Equipment Distr
N.A.I.C.S.: 423420
Edilberto B. Bravo (Chm & CEO)

U-BLOX HOLDING AG
Zuercherstrasse 68, 8800, Thalwil, Switzerland
Tel.: (41) 447227444
Web Site: https://www.u-blox.com
Year Founded: 1997
UBXN—(SWX)
Rev.: $685,654,864
Assets: $704,903,735
Liabilities: $227,294,986
Net Worth: $477,608,749
Earnings: ($10,257,904)
Emp.: 1,400
Fiscal Year-end: 12/31/23
Electronic & Precision Equipment Repair & Maintenance
N.A.I.C.S.: 811210
Jean-Pierre Wyss (Co-Founder & Head-Production & Logistics)

Subsidiaries:

u-blox AG (1)
Tel.: (41) 415602930
Sales Range: $25-49.9 Million
Emp.: 100
Wireless Communication Solutions
N.A.I.C.S.: 517112
Peter Zimmermann (VP-Pur & Logistics)

Subsidiary (US):

u-blox America Inc. (2)
1900 Campus Commons Dr Ste 401, Reston, VA 20191-1563
Tel.: (703) 483-3180
Sales Range: $25-49.9 Million
Emp.: 10
Global Positioning System Software Development Services
N.A.I.C.S.: 541511
Nikolaos Papadopoulos (Sr VP-Strategy)

Subsidiary (Non-US):

u-blox Japan K.K. (2)
VPO Akasaka 6F 7-9-1 Akasaka, Minato-ku, Tokyo, 107-0052, Japan
Tel.: (81) 357755720
Web Site: https://www.u-blox.com
Sales Range: $25-49.9 Million
Emp.: 10
Global Positioning System Modules Mfr
N.A.I.C.S.: 333248
Tesshu Naka (Country Mgr)

u-blox Malmo AB (2)
Ostra Varvsgatan 4, 211 75, Malmo, Sweden
Tel.: (46) 406307100
Sales Range: $10-24.9 Million
Emp.: 37

Wireless Telecommunications Equipment Mfr
N.A.I.C.S.: 334220
Rolf Nilsson (Mng Dir)

u-blox Singapore Pte. Ltd. (2)
435 Orchard Road 22-02/03 Wisma Atria, Singapore, 238877, Singapore
Tel.: (65) 67343811
Sales Range: $25-49.9 Million
Emp.: 6
Global Positioning System Software Development Services
N.A.I.C.S.: 541511

u-blox UK Ltd. (2)
Suite 8 Second Floor Pilgrims Court 15-17 West Street, Reigate, RH2 9BL, Surrey, United Kingdom
Tel.: (44) 1737944487
Sales Range: $25-49.9 Million
Emp.: 25
Wireless Communication Software Development Services
N.A.I.C.S.: 541511
Michelle West (Gen Mgr)

u-blox Berlin GmbH (1)
Am Studio 26, 12489, Berlin, Germany
Tel.: (49) 3055573100
Wireless Semiconductor Mfr
N.A.I.C.S.: 334413

u-blox Cork Ltd. (1)
1A First Floor 6 Lapps Quay, Cork, T12 E273, Ireland
Tel.: (353) 212067815
Wireless Semiconductor Mfr
N.A.I.C.S.: 334413

u-blox Espoo Oy (1)
Itsehallintokuja 6 Polaris Business Park Capella Building, 02600, Espoo, Finland
Tel.: (358) 4247331
Wireless Semiconductor Mfr
N.A.I.C.S.: 334413

u-blox Italia S.p.A. (1)
Via Stazione di Prosecco 15, 34010, Sgonico, TS, Italy
Tel.: (39) 0409790200
Wireless Semiconductor Mfr
N.A.I.C.S.: 334413

u-blox Lahore (Private) Ltd. (1)
16th Floor, Arfa Software Technology Park 346-B Ferozepur Road, Lahore, 54600, Pakistan
Tel.: (92) 4235972110
Wireless Semiconductor Mfr
N.A.I.C.S.: 334413

U-BTECH SOLUTIONS LTD.
Hagavish Street 10, Netanya, Israel
Tel.: (972) 77 5455028 Il
Web Site: http://www.u-btech.com
Year Founded: 2007
Information Technology Integration, Consulting & Support Services
N.A.I.C.S.: 541519
Tzachi Asif (CEO & Partner)

U-BX TECHNOLOGY LTD.
Zhongguan Science and Technology Park No 1 Linkong Er Road, Shunyi District, Beijing, China
Tel.: (86) 10065120297 Ky
Web Site: https://www.u-bx.com
Year Founded: 2021
UBXG—(NASDAQ)
Rev.: $51,600,106
Assets: $16,794,398
Liabilities: $2,920,400
Net Worth: $13,873,998
Earnings: ($748,542)
Emp.: 17
Fiscal Year-end: 06/30/24
Holding Company
N.A.I.C.S.: 551112
Mingfei Liu (COO)

U-MING MARINE TRANSPORT CORP.
29th Fl Taipei Metro Tower No 207 Tun Hwa S Rd, Taipei, 106, Taiwan

Tel.: (886) 227338000
Web Site: https://www.uming.com.tw
2606—(TAI)
Rev.: $470,109,306
Assets: $2,636,905,653
Liabilities: $1,530,814,979
Net Worth: $1,106,090,674
Earnings: $87,277,867
Emp.: 1,158
Fiscal Year-end: 12/31/23
Marine Transportation Services
N.A.I.C.S.: 488320
Choo-Kiat Ong (Pres)

Subsidiaries:

U-Ming Marine Transport (Singapore) Pte. Ltd. (1)
5 Little Road 08-01 Cemtex Industrial Building, Singapore, 536983, Singapore
Tel.: (65) 62899397
Web Site: http://www.uming.com.tw
Emp.: 17
Marine Transportation Services
N.A.I.C.S.: 483113
Benson Chen (Mgr-Ops)

U-NEXT HOLDINGS CO.,LTD
Meguro Central Square 1-1 Kami-Osaki 3-chome, Shinagawa-ku, Tokyo, Japan
Tel.: (81) 120117440 JP
Web Site: https://www.unext-hd.co.jp
Year Founded: 2009
9418—(TKS)
Rev.: $2,032,409,880
Assets: $1,424,143,640
Liabilities: $851,698,380
Net Worth: $572,445,260
Earnings: $95,520,540
Emp.: 303
Fiscal Year-end: 08/31/24
Holding Company; Digital Content Delivery Services
N.A.I.C.S.: 551112
Yasuhide Uno (Pres, CEO & Dir-Rep)

Subsidiaries:

USEN Corporation (1)
3-1-1 Kamiosaki Meguro Central Square, Shinagawa-ku, Tokyo, 141-0021, Japan
Tel.: (81) 368237111
Web Site: https://www.usen.com
Holding Company; Broadcasting, Business Systems, Broadband & Telecommunications, Media Content, Recruitment Consulting & Services
N.A.I.C.S.: 517112
Yasuhide Uno (Chm)

Subsidiary (Domestic):

ALMEX Inc. (2)
MEGURO CENTRAL SQUARE 3-1-1 Kamiosaki, Shinagawa-ku, Tokyo, 141-0021, Japan
Tel.: (81) 368201411
Web Site: https://www.almex.jp
Emp.: 700
Hospital, Hotel & Golf Course Electronic Billing Systems Mfr & Whslr
N.A.I.C.S.: 333310
Yasuhide Uno (Chm)

U's Music Co., Ltd. (2)
9-8 Shinsencho, Shibuya-ku, Tokyo, 150-0045, Japan (100%)
Tel.: (81) 368239300
Web Site: https://www.usmusic.co.jp
Compact Disc & DVD Production & Music Licensing Services
N.A.I.C.S.: 334610
Yutaka Inaba (Dir)

U-TECH MEDIA CORPORATION
No 222 Hwa-Ya 2 Rd, Guishan Dist, Taoyuan, 333, Taiwan
Tel.: (886) 33961111
Web Site: https://www.utechmedia.com.tw
Year Founded: 1999

U-TECH MEDIA CORPORATION

U-TECH Media Corporation—(Continued)
3050—(TAI)
Rev.: $37,163,902
Assets: $164,371,131
Liabilities: $75,638,180
Net Worth: $88,732,951
Earnings: $2,944,668
Emp.: 130
Fiscal Year-end: 12/31/23
Compact Disc Mfr
N.A.I.C.S.: 334610
Yang Wei-Fen *(Chm)*

Subsidiaries:

U-Tech Media Korea Co., Ltd. (1)
Ochang Industrial Complex Namchon-ri 1111-7 Oksan-myeon, Cheongwon, Chungcheongbuk-do, Korea (South)
Tel.: (82) 432193965
Compact Disc Mfr & Distr
N.A.I.C.S.: 334610

U. Y. FINCORP LIMITED
Vaman Techno Centre A-Wing 7th Floor, Marol Naka Makwana Road, Mumbai, 400059, Andheri, India
Tel.: (91) 2242300800
Web Site: https://uyfincorp.com
Year Founded: 1993
530579—(BOM)
Rev.: $2,050,216
Assets: $38,162,670
Liabilities: $5,717,111
Net Worth: $32,445,559
Earnings: $1,459,267
Emp.: 9
Fiscal Year-end: 03/31/21
Financial Management Services
N.A.I.C.S.: 523999
Amrita Mohta Kothari *(Compliance Officer & Sec)*

Subsidiaries:

Aristro Capital Markets Limited (1)
24 Park Street Magma House 10th Floor, Kolkata, 700 016, India
Tel.: (91) 334 017 0500
Web Site: https://www.aristrocapital.com
Stock Brokerage Services
N.A.I.C.S.: 523150

U.C.A. AG
Stefan-George-Ring 29, 81929, Munich, Germany
Tel.: (49) 899931940
Web Site: https://www.uca.de
Year Founded: 1989
UCA1—(DEU)
Assets: $12,871,178
Liabilities: $1,677,889
Net Worth: $11,193,288
Earnings: $1,435,037
Fiscal Year-end: 12/31/23
Management Consulting Services
N.A.I.C.S.: 541611

Subsidiaries:

Pflegia AG (1)
Chausseestrasse 19, D-10115, Berlin, Germany
Tel.: (49) 1624791364
Web Site: https://www.pflegia.de
Emp.: 5,000
Nursing Homes Services
N.A.I.C.S.: 621399

U.C.M. RESITA S.A.
1 Golului Street No 1, 320053, Resita, Romania
Tel.: (40) 255217111
Sales Range: $50-74.9 Million
Emp.: 2,500
Hydraulic Engines & Turbines Mfr
N.A.I.C.S.: 332912
Cosmin Ursoniu *(Gen Dir)*

U.H. ZAVERI LIMITED
Shop No 1-2 Manish Complex Indrajit Tenament Nikol Gam Rd, Opp Diamond Mill Bapunagar, Ahmedabad, 382350, Gujarat, India
Tel.: (91) 9016910100
Web Site: https://www.uhzaveri.in
Year Founded: 1999
541338—(BOM)
Rev.: $1,771,366
Assets: $1,816,634
Liabilities: $83,449
Net Worth: $1,733,185
Earnings: $99,654
Fiscal Year-end: 03/31/23
Jewellery Distr
N.A.I.C.S.: 458310
Hitesh Mahendrakumar Shah *(Mng Dir)*

U.I. DISPLAY CO., LTD.
174 Daesin-ro 146beon-gil, Heungdeok-gu, Cheongju, Chungcheongbuk-do, Korea (South)
Tel.: (82) 432119064
Web Site: http://www.uidkorea.co.kr
Year Founded: 1990
069330—(KRS)
Rev.: $47,925,838
Assets: $28,447,741
Liabilities: $10,925,953
Net Worth: $17,521,787
Earnings: $2,891,295
Emp.: 67
Fiscal Year-end: 12/31/22
Display Electronics Components Mfr
N.A.I.C.S.: 334419
Park Jongsoo *(CEO)*

U.K. SPAC PLC
3rd Floor 80 Cheapside, London, EC2V 6EE, United Kingdom
Tel.: (44) 1268561516
Web Site: http://www.ukspacplc.com
Year Founded: 2007
SPC—(AIM)
Assets: $3,929,774
Liabilities: $175,257
Net Worth: $3,754,517
Earnings: ($9,344,060)
Fiscal Year-end: 03/31/21
Building & Construction Services
N.A.I.C.S.: 236220
Peter Harry Jay *(Chm & Sec)*

Subsidiaries:

Connaught Access Flooring Ltd (1)
Unit 1 Hill Farm Church Lane Ford End, Chelmsford, CM3 1LH, Essex, United Kingdom
Tel.: (44) 1245237527
Web Site: http://www.connaughtfloors.com
Sales Range: $25-49.9 Million
Emp.: 10
Access Flooring Services
N.A.I.C.S.: 238330
Andy Collins *(Mng Dir)*

Mountfield Building Group Ltd (1)
Unit 9 Hurricane Close, Wickford Business Park, Wickford, SS11 8YR, Essex, United Kingdom
Tel.: (44) 1268561516
Web Site: http://www.mountfieldbg.com
Sales Range: $25-49.9 Million
Emp.: 22
Industrial Building Mfr
N.A.I.C.S.: 236210

U.P. HOTELS LIMITED
1101 Surya Kiran 19 Kasturba Gandhi Marg, New Delhi, 110001, India
Tel.: (91) 1123312367
Web Site: https://www.hotelclarks.com
509960—(BOM)
Sales Range: $10-24.9 Million
Emp.: 735
Hotel Operator
N.A.I.C.S.: 721110

Apurv Kumar *(Co-Mng Dir & Co-CFO)*

U10 CORP SA
1 Place Verrazzano, CP 610, 69258, Lyon, cedex 09, France
Tel.: (33) 474138682
Web Site: http://www.u10.com
Year Founded: 1994
ALU10—(EUR)
Rev.: $176,686,805
Assets: $145,523,844
Liabilities: $97,132,411
Net Worth: $48,391,433
Earnings: ($3,227,228)
Emp.: 304
Fiscal Year-end: 12/31/20
Home Furnishing Product Mfr & Distr
N.A.I.C.S.: 314120
Thierry Lievre *(Founder, Chm & CEO)*

Subsidiaries:

LONGFIELD LIMITED (1)
525 Zhenning Road 4F, Shanghai, 200050, China
Tel.: (86) 21 6120 1220
Household Furniture Distr
N.A.I.C.S.: 423210

La Nouba Sarl (1)
Route d'Avallon, Sainte, 89440, Colombe, France
Tel.: (33) 386338809
Web Site: http://www.lanouba.fr
Event Management Services
N.A.I.C.S.: 561920

Smerwick Taiwan Branch Limited (1)
9F-4 No1 FuXing North Road, Taipei, 105, Taiwan
Tel.: (886) 287710007
Web Site: http://sos.smerwick.com.tw
Information Technology Services
N.A.I.C.S.: 541511
Jean-Pascal Rignault *(Acct Mgr)*

U2BIO CO., LTD.
4th floor 489 Ogeum-ro, Songpa-gu, Seoul, 138-818, Korea (South)
Tel.: (82) 16444450
Web Site: https://it.u2bio.com
Medical Research & Development Services
N.A.I.C.S.: 541714
Kim Jin-Tae *(CEO)*

U3O8 HOLDINGS PLC
3 Jane Forby Close, Wretton, King's Lynn, PE33 9QE, United Kingdom
Tel.: (44) 1366 500722
Web Site:
http://www.U3O8Holdings.com
Uranium Mining
N.A.I.C.S.: 212290
Conrad Windham *(CEO)*

UAB BALTIC ENGINEERS
Savanoriu pr 28, LT-03116, Vilnius, Lithuania
Tel.: (370) 5 2334 112
Web Site:
http://www.balticengineers.com
Year Founded: 2011
Emp.: 27
Property Planning, Architectural Designing, Project Management & Engineering Consultancy Services
N.A.I.C.S.: 541310
Darius Kvedaras *(Mng Dir)*

UAB GARSU PASAULIS
Salomejos Neries 69, Vilnius, 6304, Lithuania
Tel.: (370) 52499900
Web Site: http://www.gp.lt
Year Founded: 1994
Sales Range: $75-99.9 Million
Emp.: 300

INTERNATIONAL PUBLIC

Scanning, Layouts, Color Sparation & Films & Color Proofs Mfr
N.A.I.C.S.: 323111
Simonas Naujikas *(Head-Comml Printing)*

UAB IGNITIS GRUPE
Juozapaviciaus St 13, 09311, Vilnius, Lithuania
Tel.: (370) 2782082
Web Site: http://www.ignitisgrupe.lt
Sales Range: $300-349.9 Million
Emp.: 1,140
Electronic Services
N.A.I.C.S.: 221122
Henrikas Bernatavicius *(Chm-Mgmt Bd)*

Subsidiaries:

AB LESTO (1)
Zveju g 14, 09310, Vilnius, Lithuania
Tel.: (370) 5 277 75 24
Web Site: http://www.lesto.lt
Electric Power Supply Services
N.A.I.C.S.: 221122
Aidas Ignatavicius *(CEO)*

Subsidiary (Domestic):

NT Valdos, UAB (2)
Baznycios g 21, 15172, Nemencine, Lithuania
Tel.: (370) 5 210 6539
Web Site: http://www.valdos.eu
Real Estate Services
N.A.I.C.S.: 531210

UAB ELEKTROS TINKLO PASLAUGOS (2)
Motoru st 2, 2190, Vilnius, Lithuania
Tel.: (370) 5 210 6809
Web Site: http://www.enepro.lt
Electricity Network Construction Services
N.A.I.C.S.: 237130

Energijos Skirstymo Operatorius AB (1)
Aguonu g 24, Vilnius, 03212, Lithuania (97.66%)
Tel.: (370) 852777524
Web Site: http://www.eso.lt
Rev.: $462,663,440
Assets: $1,911,159,795
Liabilities: $1,167,665,704
Net Worth: $743,494,092
Earnings: $38,425,756
Emp.: 2,374
Fiscal Year-end: 12/31/2019
Electric & Natural Gas Distribution Services
N.A.I.C.S.: 221122
Mindaugas Keizeris *(Chm)*

Energijos tiekimas SIA (1)
Elizabetes iela 45-47, 1010, Riga, Latvia
Tel.: (371) 677 98006
Electric Power Supply Services
N.A.I.C.S.: 221122

Energijos tiekimas UAB (1)
P Luksio g 1, 08221, Vilnius, Lithuania
Tel.: (370) 700 55088
Web Site: http://www.etiekimas.lt
Electric Power Supply Services
N.A.I.C.S.: 221122

Subsidiary (Non-US):

Geton Energy SIA (2)
Bezdeligu str 12, 1048, Riga, Latvia
Tel.: (371) 2844 0040
Web Site: http://www.geton.lv
Electric Power Supply Services
N.A.I.C.S.: 221122

UAB Energetikos Pajegos (1)
T Masiulio Str 16d, Kaunas, Lithuania (100%)
Tel.: (370) 37309897
Sales Range: $25-49.9 Million
Emp.: 50
Specialized Design Services
N.A.I.C.S.: 541490

UAB Kauno Energetikos Remontas (1)
Chemijos Str 17, Kaunas, 51331, Lithuania (100%)

Tel.: (370) 37456598
Web Site: http://www.ker.lt
Sales Range: $75-99.9 Million
Emp.: 300
Electronic & Precision Equipment Repair & Maintenance
N.A.I.C.S.: 811210

Subsidiary (Domestic):

Gotlitas UAB (2)
R Kalantos g 119, Kaunas, 52311, Lithuania
Tel.: (370) 8 37 370390
Web Site: http://www.gotlitas.lt
Hotel Operator
N.A.I.C.S.: 721110

Vsi Respublikinis energetiku mokymo centras (1)
Jeruzales g 21, 08420, Vilnius, Lithuania
Tel.: (370) 8 5 237 4577
Web Site: http://www.remc.lt
Industrial Training Services
N.A.I.C.S.: 611519

UAB KONCERNAS SBA
Laisves pr 3, 04215, Vilnius, Lithuania
Tel.: (370) 5 210 16 81
Web Site: http://www.sba.lt
Year Founded: 1990
Sales Range: $300-349.9 Million
Emp.: 5,000
Furniture Product Mfr & Distr
N.A.I.C.S.: 337127
Arunas Martinkevicius *(Chm)*

Subsidiaries:

Utenos Trikotazas AB (1)
J Basanaviciaus Str 122, LT-28214, Utena, Lithuania   (92.31%)
Tel.: (370) 389 63 009
Web Site: http://www.ut.lt
Rev.: $34,836,412
Assets: $25,408,151
Liabilities: $12,642,311
Net Worth: $12,765,840
Earnings: $1,305,064
Emp.: 1,159
Fiscal Year-end: 12/31/2018
Men & Women's Clothing, Underwear & Hosiery Mfr
N.A.I.C.S.: 313310
Andrej Grobov *(CFO)*

UAB MEGRAME
Zirmunu 68, 09108, Vilnius, Lithuania
Tel.: (370) 52737014
Web Site: http://www.megrame.lt
Sales Range: $50-74.9 Million
Emp.: 1,500
PVC, Wooden, Glass & Aluminum Windows, Doors & Other Constructions Mfr & Installer
N.A.I.C.S.: 321911
Juozas Magelinskas *(Pres)*

UAB PRICEWATERHOUSECOOPERS
J Jasinskio 16B, 03163, Vilnius, Lithuania
Tel.: (370) 5 239 2300   LT
Web Site: http://www.pwc.com
Emp.: 150
Accounting & Business Consulting Services
N.A.I.C.S.: 541211
Audrius Cesiulis *(Dir-Mgmt Consulting)*

UAB VALBRA
Vytenio St 13, Vilnius, 03112, Lithuania
Tel.: (370) 52603601   LT
Web Site: http://www.valbra.lt
Year Founded: 1993
Kitchen Furniture
N.A.I.C.S.: 337110

UAC ENERGY HOLDINGS PTY. LTD.
Suite 2 Level 2 15 Castray Esplanade, Battery Point, 7004, TAS, Australia
Web Site: http://www.uacenergy.com.au
Investment Holding Company & Energy Provider
N.A.I.C.S.: 551112
Bardin Davis *(CEO)*

UAC GLOBAL PUBLIC COMPANY LIMITED
1 TPT Tower 19th Soi Vibhavadirangsit 19 Vibhavadirangsit Road, Chatuchak, Bangkok, 10900, Thailand
Tel.: (66) 29361701
Web Site: https://www.uac.co.th
UAC—(THA)
Rev.: $51,441,865
Assets: $106,196,099
Liabilities: $52,012,035
Net Worth: $54,184,063
Earnings: $7,321,861
Emp.: 155
Fiscal Year-end: 12/31/23
Chemicals Mfr
N.A.I.C.S.: 325998
Kitti Jivacate *(CEO)*

Subsidiaries:

UAC Advance Polymer & Chemicals Co., Ltd. (1)
1 TP&T Tower 21st floor Vibhavadirangsit 19, Vibhavadirangsit Chatuchak, Bangkok, 10900, Thailand
Tel.: (66) 25379016
Web Site: http://www.uapc.co.th
Emp.: 90
Chemicals Mfr
N.A.I.C.S.: 325199

UAC OF NIGERIA PLC
1-5 Odunlami St Lagos Island, Lagos, Nigeria
Tel.: (234) 17624331
Web Site: http://www.uacnplc.com
Holding Company
N.A.I.C.S.: 551112
Folasope Aiyesimoju *(CEO & Mng Dir)*

Subsidiaries:

Portland Paints & Products Nigeria PLC (1)
Sandtex House 105 Adeniyi Jones Avenue, PO Box 21782, Ikeja, Lagos, Nigeria
Tel.: (234) 8133599428
Rev.: $4,411,913
Assets: $4,904,733
Liabilities: $1,592,873
Net Worth: $3,311,860
Earnings: ($817,692)
Emp.: 55
Fiscal Year-end: 12/31/2020
Paint & Coating Mfr
N.A.I.C.S.: 325510

UACJ CORPORATION
Tokyo Sankei Bldg Otemachi 1-7-2, Chiyoda-ku, Tokyo, 100-0004, Japan
Tel.: (81) 362022600   JP
Web Site: https://www.uacj.co.jp
Year Founded: 1964
5741—(TKS)
Rev.: $5,901,282,410
Assets: $6,044,382,300
Liabilities: $4,047,858,240
Net Worth: $1,996,524,060
Earnings: $91,601,380
Emp.: 10,460
Fiscal Year-end: 03/31/24
Aluminum, Copper & Other Non-Ferrous Metal Alloy Products Mfr & Distr
N.A.I.C.S.: 331524
Miyuki Ishihara *(Chm & Pres)*

Subsidiaries:

Izumi Metal Corporation (1)
2-10-8 Ryogoku Sumitomo Real Estate Ryogoku Building, Sumida-ku, Tokyo, 130-0026, Japan
Tel.: (81) 35 600 1430
Web Site: https://www.izumi-metal.co.jp
Aluminum & Copper Material Mfr
N.A.I.C.S.: 332999

Kamakura Industry Co., Ltd. (1)
4391-1 Kawashiri Yoshida-cho, Haibara-gun, Shizuoka, 421-0302, Japan
Tel.: (81) 54 832 8020
Aluminum & Copper Material Mfr
N.A.I.C.S.: 332999

Nalco Koriyama Co., Ltd. (1)
1-22 Machiikedai inside Koriyama West, No 2 Industrial Park, Koriyama, 963-0215, Fukushima, Japan
Tel.: (81) 24 959 3800
Web Site: https://www.kry.nalcoiwai.co.jp
Aluminum Panel Mfr
N.A.I.C.S.: 331315

Nihon Cooler Co., Ltd. (1)
3-21 Tsutoogocho, Nishinomiya, 663-8243, Hyogo, Japan
Tel.: (81) 79 833 0513
Web Site: https://www.nihon-cooler.ecnet.jp
Aluminum Pipe Material Mfr
N.A.I.C.S.: 332999

Nikkin Co., Ltd. (1)
6-5 Nihonbashi Kabutocho, Chuo-ku, Tokyo, 103-0026, Japan
Tel.: (81) 35 847 2860
Aluminium Products Mfr
N.A.I.C.S.: 331315

P.T. Yan Jin Indonesia (1)
Plot 8 H, East Jakarta Industrial Park Cikarang Selatan, Bekasi, 17550, Indonesia
Tel.: (62) 21 897 0187
Web Site: https://www.uacj-yanjin.com
Emp.: 186
Metal Component Product Mfr
N.A.I.C.S.: 332999
Yutaka Nomura *(Pres)*

PT. Furukawa Indal Aluminum (1)
Block L3 Kawasan Industri Maspion Desa Sukomulyo Kecamatan Manyar, Kabupaten, Gresik, 61151, Jawa Timur, Indonesia
Tel.: (62) 313953769
Web Site: http://www.indelcorp.com
Sales Range: $100-124.9 Million
Emp.: 300
Extruded Aluminum Products Mfr
N.A.I.C.S.: 331318
Fumihiko Sato *(Pres & Dir)*

Siam UACJ Trading Co., Ltd. (1)
2525 FYI Center Building Tower One 5th Floor Unit1/510 Rama4 Road, Klongtoei District, Bangkok, 10110, Thailand
Tel.: (66) 2 090 2211
Aluminium Products Mfr
N.A.I.C.S.: 331315

Tri-Arrows Aluminum Inc. (1)
12501 Plantside Dr, Louisville, KY 40299
Tel.: (502) 566-5700
Web Site: https://www.triaa.com
Aluminum Rolled Sheet Distr
N.A.I.C.S.: 423510
Henry Gordinier *(Pres & CEO)*

UACJ (Thailand) Co., Ltd. (1)
Amata City Industrial Estate 7/352 Moo 6 Tambol Mabyang porn, Pluak Daeng, 21140, Rayong, Thailand
Tel.: (66) 3 802 7360
Web Site: https://www.uath.uacj-group.com
Emp.: 700
Aluminum Product Mfr & Distr
N.A.I.C.S.: 331315
Hironori Tsuchiya *(Pres)*

UACJ Automotive Whitehall Industries, Inc. (1)
5175 W 6th St, Ludington, MI 49431
Tel.: (231) 845-5101
Web Site: https://www.whitehallindustries.com
Automotive Components Mfr
N.A.I.C.S.: 336390
David Cooper *(Pres & COO)*

UACJ Extrusion Czech s.r.o. (1)
Prumyslova 1010, 294 71, Benatky nad Jizerou, Czech Republic
Tel.: (420) 32 657 0410
Web Site: https://www.uacj.cz
Emp.: 195
Automobile Parts Mfr
N.A.I.C.S.: 336390
Miroslav Koci *(Mng Dir)*

UACJ Foil Corporation (1)
6-5 Nihonbashi Kabutocho, Chuo-ku, Tokyo, 103-0026, Japan
Tel.: (81) 35847 2800
Web Site: http://ufo.uacj-group.com
Rolled Products (in aluminum, copper, tin, lead & other metals) Mfr & Sls
N.A.I.C.S.: 332999
Akito Imaizumi *(Pres)*

Plant (Domestic):

Nippon Foil Mfg. Co., Ltd. - Nogi Plant (2)
55 Wakabayashi Nogi-machi, Shimotsuga-gun, Tochigi, 329-0103, Japan
Tel.: (81) 280 56 2315
Web Site: http://www.nihonseihaku.co.jp
Aluminum Foil Mfr
N.A.I.C.S.: 331315
Shunji Kokubo *(Pres)*

Nippon Foil Mfg. Co., Ltd. - Shiga Plant (2)
61-8 Sasatani Yamadera-cho, Kusatsu, 525-0042, Shiga, Japan
Tel.: (81) 77 565 3331
Metal Foil Mfr
N.A.I.C.S.: 331315

UACJ Foil Malaysia Sdn. Bhd. (1)
Lot 4 Jalan Besar Pasir Gudang Industrial Estate, 81700, Pasir Gudang, Johor, Malaysia
Tel.: (60) 7 254 1913
Aluminum Foil Mfr
N.A.I.C.S.: 331315

UACJ Foil Sangyo Corporation (1)
61-8 Sasatani Yamaderacho, Kusatsu, 525-0042, Shiga, Japan
Tel.: (81) 77 565 2800
Aluminium Products Mfr
N.A.I.C.S.: 331315

UACJ Foil Service Corporation (1)
1670 Kasukawacho, Isesaki, 372-0023, Gunma, Japan
Tel.: (81) 27 023 7100
Aluminium Products Mfr
N.A.I.C.S.: 331315

UACJ Foundry & Forging (Vietnam) Co., Ltd. (1)
Road No 16 Tan Thuan Export Processing Zone, Tan Thuan Dong Ward District 7, Ho Chi Minh City, Vietnam
Tel.: (84) 83 770 0560
Emp.: 630
Aluminum Product Mfr & Distr
N.A.I.C.S.: 331315
Hiroshi Akimoto *(Pres)*

UACJ Foundry & Forging Corporation (1)
Tokyo Sankei Bldg 1-7-2 Otemachi, Chiyoda-ku, Tokyo, 100-0004, Japan
Tel.: (81) 36 202 2638
Web Site: https://uff.uacj-group.com
Emp.: 200
Aluminium Products Mfr
N.A.I.C.S.: 331315
Akinori Yoshida *(Pres)*

UACJ MH (Thailand) Co., Ltd. (1)
689 Sukhumvit Road Soi 35, Klongton Nuea Vadhana, Bangkok, 10110, Thailand
Tel.: (66) 21 688 6856
Aluminum Product Mfr & Distr
N.A.I.C.S.: 331315

UACJ Marketing & Processing America, Inc. (1)
166 McQuiston Dr, Battle Creek, MI 49037
Tel.: (269) 719-8030
Web Site: https://www.ump-america.com
Emp.: 10
Aluminium Products Mfr
N.A.I.C.S.: 331315
Masaki Yoshitake *(Pres)*

UACJ CORPORATION

UACJ Corporation—(Continued)

UACJ Marketing & Processing Corporation (1)
89-8 Hoden Nodera-cho, Anjo, 444-1165, Aichi, Japan
Tel.: (81) 56 699 3705
Web Site: https://www.umpj.co.jp
Emp.: 122
Metal Product Distr
N.A.I.C.S.: 423510
Yukihiro Kuwamoto *(Pres & CEO)*

UACJ Metal Components Central Mexico, S.A. de C.V. (1)
Av Tabias Hagenmeyer Manzana M Late 1C, Col Parque Tecno Industrial Castro del Rio, 36810, Irapuato, Mexico
Tel.: (52) 462 622 8700
Automobile Parts Mfr & Distr
N.A.I.C.S.: 336110

UACJ Metal Components Mexico, S.A. de C.V. (1)
Blvd Pacifico No 9871 Industrial Pacifico II, 22644, Tijuana, Baja California, Mexico
Tel.: (52) 664 211 6800
Automobile Parts Mfr & Distr
N.A.I.C.S.: 336110

UACJ Metal Components North America, Inc. (1)
106 Kuder Dr, Greenville, PA 16125
Tel.: (724) 646-4250
Web Site: https://www.umcna.uacj-group.com
Automobile Parts Mfr & Distr
N.A.I.C.S.: 336110

UACJ Trading (Kunshan) Metal Products Co., Ltd. (1)
No 99 Shaojing Road, KunShan Economical Technology Development Zone, Kunshan, 215300, Jiangsu, China
Tel.: (86) 5128 617 6853
Web Site: https://www.utrks.uacj-group.com
Emp.: 40
Aluminium Products Mfr
N.A.I.C.S.: 331315
Yasuo Takahashi *(Chm)*

UACJ Trading (Shanghai) Co., Ltd. (1)
Room11B 16th Floor International Trading Mansion No 118 Xin Ling Lu, Pilot Free Trade Zone, Shanghai, 200131, China
Aluminium Products Mfr
N.A.I.C.S.: 331315

UACJ Trading (Thailand) Co., Ltd. (1)
689 Sukhumvit Road Soi 35, Klongton Nuea Vadhana, Bangkok, 10110, Thailand
Tel.: (66) 2 664 3821
Aluminum Product Mfr & Distr
N.A.I.C.S.: 331315

UACJ Trading Corporation (1)
Sumitomo-Building 4-7-28 Kitahama, chuoku, Osaka, 541-0041, Japan
Tel.: (81) 66 201 1430
Web Site: https://www.utr.uacj-group.com
Emp.: 103
Aluminum & Copper Material Mfr
N.A.I.C.S.: 332999
Masahiro Teshima *(Pres)*

UAE OIL SERVICES PLC
Unit 2 Level currency House 1 DIFC, Dubai, 121208, United Arab Emirates
Year Founded: 2018
UOS—(LSE)
Oil & Gas Generation Services
N.A.I.C.S.: 213112

UALA SRL
Via Fabio Filzi 25, 20124, Milan, Italy
Tel.: (39) 0256566170
Web Site: http://www.uala.it
Online Booking for Beauty Products & Services
N.A.I.C.S.: 456120
Simone Alberio *(Acct Mgr-Sls)*

UAMT S.A.
Uzinelor 8, 410605, Oradea, Romania
Tel.: (40) 259451026
Web Site: http://www.uamt.ro
UAM—(BUC)
Rev.: $17,704,802
Assets: $20,735,626
Liabilities: $6,011,393
Net Worth: $14,724,232
Earnings: $65,496
Emp.: 550
Fiscal Year-end: 12/31/22
Motor Vehicle Parts Mfr
N.A.I.C.S.: 336390

UANGEL CORPORATION
13595 Hyundai Office Bldg 10F Hwangsaeul-ro 240, Bundang-gu, Seongnam, Gyeonggi-do, Korea (South)
Tel.: (82) 317106200
Web Site: https://www.uangel.com
Year Founded: 1999
072130—(KRS)
Rev.: $23,044,440
Assets: $46,805,125
Liabilities: $5,555,300
Net Worth: $41,249,825
Earnings: $1,693,046
Emp.: 200
Fiscal Year-end: 12/31/22
Telecommunication Servicesb
N.A.I.C.S.: 517810

Subsidiaries:

PT Uangel Indonesia (1)
Gandaria City office tower 10th floor Jl sultan iskandar muda, Jakarta Selatan, Jakarta, 12240, Indonesia
Tel.: (62) 21 2903 6388
Emp.: 12
Telecommunication Servicesb
N.A.I.C.S.: 517810

UANGEL Brazil (1)
Rua Jardim Botanico 674/123, Rio de Janeiro, Brazil
Tel.: (55) 2121796060
Telecommunication Servicesb
N.A.I.C.S.: 517810

UANGEL Italy (1)
Via Rasella 155, 00187, Rome, Italy
Tel.: (39) 06 4201 2025
Telecommunication Servicesb
N.A.I.C.S.: 517810

UANGEL Korea (1)
10F Hyundai Office Bldg 3 Hwangsaeul-ro 240beon-gil, Bundang-gu, Seongnam, Gyeonggi-do, Korea (South)
Tel.: (82) 31 710 6200
Web Site: http://www.uangel.com
Telecommunication Servicesb
N.A.I.C.S.: 517810

UANGEL U.S.A (1)
3070 Bristol St Ste 160, Costa Mesa, CA 92626
Tel.: (714) 241-4660
Telecommunication Servicesb
N.A.I.C.S.: 517810

Uangel Thailand Co., Ltd. (1)
Unit 10/113-114 Level9 The Trendy Office Building Sukhumvit Soi 13, Klongtoey-Nua Wattana, Bangkok, 10110, Thailand
Tel.: (66) 2 168 6030
Telecommunication Servicesb
N.A.I.C.S.: 517810

UAP AUSTRALIA PTY LTD
41 Holland Street Northgate, Brisbane, 4013, QLD, Australia
Tel.: (61) 7 3630 6300
Web Site: http://www.uapcompany.com
Year Founded: 1993
Public Art Strategies & Masterplans
N.A.I.C.S.: 711410
Matthew Tobin *(Mng Dir)*

UBA INVESTMENTS LIMITED
Flat B 16th Floor Wah Kit Commercial Centre 300 Des Voeux Road, Central, China (Hong Kong)
Tel.: (852) 35759396
Web Site: http://www.uba.com.hk
0768—(HKG)
Rev.: $584,460
Assets: $11,532,248
Liabilities: $41,438
Net Worth: $11,490,810
Earnings: ($1,840,208)
Emp.: 4
Fiscal Year-end: 03/31/23
Securities
N.A.I.C.S.: 551112
Andrew Wai Lun Cheng *(Mng Dir)*

UBE CORPORATION
1978-96 Kogushi, Ube, 755-8633, Yamaguchi, Japan
Tel.: (81) 354196112   JP
Web Site: https://ube.co.jp
Year Founded: 1942
UBEOF—(OTCIQ)
Rev.: $6,342,965,200
Assets: $8,111,394,720
Liabilities: $4,297,135,920
Net Worth: $3,814,258,800
Earnings: $237,160,000
Emp.: 9,849
Fiscal Year-end: 03/31/22
Holding Company; Chemicals, Construction Materials, Plastics & Metal Products Mfr & Distr
N.A.I.C.S.: 551112
Yuzuru Yamamoto *(Chm)*

Subsidiaries:

ANA Hotel Ube Ltd. (1)
8-1 Aioi-cho, Ube, 755-8588, Yamaguchi, Japan
Tel.: (81) 836 32 1112
Web Site: http://www.anahotelube.co.jp
Sales Range: $10-24.9 Million
Emp.: 100
Restaurant Management Services
N.A.I.C.S.: 722511
Norio Kawato *(Gen Mgr)*

API Corporation (1)
The Kaiteki Building 13-4 Uchikanda 1-chome, Chiyodu-ku, Tokyo, 101-0047, Japan
Tel.: (81) 352177170
Web Site: http://www.api-corp.co.jp
Sales Range: $250-299.9 Million
Emp.: 516
Mfr of Active Pharmaceutical Ingredients & Intermediates & Other Industrial Chemicals
N.A.I.C.S.: 325412
Seiichi Kiso *(Dir)*

Plant (Domestic):

API Corporation - Fukuroi Plant (2)
3056 Kuno, Fukuroi, 437-0061, Shizuoka, Japan
Tel.: (81) 538 42 6211
Industrial Chemicals Mfr
N.A.I.C.S.: 325998

API Corporation - Iwaki Plant (2)
1-2 Keiseisaku Jobanmisawamachi, Iwaki, 971-8136, Fukushima, Japan
Tel.: (81) 246 44 5411
Web Site: http://www.api-corp.co.jp
Specialty Chemicals Mfr
N.A.I.C.S.: 325998

API Corporation - Yoshitomi Plant (2)
955 Oaza-Koiwai, Yoshitomi-cho Chikujo-gun, Fukuoka, 871-0801, Japan
Tel.: (81) 979 23 8911
Industrial Chemicals Mfr
N.A.I.C.S.: 325998

Unit (Domestic):

API Research Laboratories (2)
955 Oaza Koiwai Yoshitomi cho, Chikujo-gun, Fukuoka, 871-0801, Japan
Tel.: (81) 979238913

INTERNATIONAL PUBLIC

Sales Range: $125-149.9 Million
Emp.: 400
Provider of Pharmaceutical Development Services
N.A.I.C.S.: 325412

Bekkai Ube Concrete Co., Ltd. (1)
1-24 Tottori-Minami 5-Chome, Kushiro, 084-0905, Hokkaido, Japan
Tel.: (81) 154 51 2101
Ready Mixed Concrete Mfr & Distr
N.A.I.C.S.: 423320

Chiba Butadiene Industry Company, Limited (1)
2-1-1 Irifune, Chuo-ku, Tokyo, 104-0042, Japan
Tel.: (81) 33 552 9373
Butadiene Mfr
N.A.I.C.S.: 325211

Chiba Riverment and Cement Corporation (1)
1 Kawasaki-cho, Chuo-ku, Chiba, 260-0835, Japan
Tel.: (81) 432622162
Web Site: http://www.ube-ind.co.jp
Micro Slag Powder Mfr & Distr
N.A.I.C.S.: 331420

Chiba Ube Concrete Co., Ltd. (1)
220-10 Shinminato, Chiba, 261-0002, Japan
Tel.: (81) 43 243 1845
Web Site: https://www.ube-ind.co.jp
Readymix Concrete Mfr
N.A.I.C.S.: 327320

Chushikoku Ube Concrete Co., Ltd. (1)
3-2 Minamimyoujin-machi, Kaita-cho Akigun, Hiroshima, 736-0055, Japan
Tel.: (81) 82 822 2125
Web Site: https://www.ube-ind.co.jp
Readymix Concrete Mfr
N.A.I.C.S.: 327320

EMS-UBE Ltd. (1)
1978-96 Kogushi, Ube, 755-8633, Yamaguchi, Japan   (33%)
Tel.: (81) 83 631 0213
Web Site: http://www.ube-ind.co.jp
Sales Range: $50-74.9 Million
Emp.: 23
N.A.I.C.S.: 212114

Fukusei Tech Co., Ltd. (1)
9-80 Mikawa Kita-machi, Fukushima, 960-8054, Japan
Tel.: (81) 24 534 3144
Dynamo Mfr & Distr
N.A.I.C.S.: 335312

Fukusei vender service Co., Ltd. (1)
1-14 Shishida Okajima, Fukushima, 960-8201, Japan
Tel.: (81) 24 531 8762
Web Site: http://www.ube-ind.co.jp
Vending Machine Whslr & Repair Services
N.A.I.C.S.: 811310

Hagimori Industries, Ltd. (1)
525 Oklube, Ube, 755-0001, Yamaguchi, Japan
Tel.: (81) 83 631 1678
Web Site: https://www.hagimori.co.jp
Ready Mixed Concrete Mfr & Distr
N.A.I.C.S.: 325998
Seishi Murata *(Pres & CEO)*

Hagimori Logistics, Ltd. (1)
3926-5 Higasisue, Ube, 755-0206, Yamaguchi, Japan
Tel.: (81) 83 641 7546
Web Site: https://www.ube-ind.co.jp
Marine Cargo Handling Services
N.A.I.C.S.: 488320

Hokkaido Ube Co., Ltd. (1)
1-2-37 Higashi-naeho 1-jou, Higashi-ku, Sapporo, 065-0801, Hokkaido, Japan
Tel.: (81) 11 781 2030
Ready Mixed Concrete Mfr & Distr
N.A.I.C.S.: 327320

Hokuriku Ube Concrete Co., Ltd. (1)
932 Washizuka, Imizu, 939-0305, Toyama, Japan
Tel.: (81) 76 655 2755
Web Site: http://www.ube-ind.co.jp

AND PRIVATE COMPANIES — UBE CORPORATION

Ready Mixed Concrete Mfr & Distr
N.A.I.C.S.: 327320

Ichinoseki Remicon Co., Ltd. (1)
64-1 Iwanosawa Mashiba, Ichinoseki, 021-0901, Iwate, Japan
Tel.: (81) 19 126 2275
Web Site: http://www.ube-ind.co.jp
Ready Mixed Concrete Mfr & Distr
N.A.I.C.S.: 327320

Kano Ube Concrete Co., Ltd. (1)
1-2697 Kano-shimo, Kano-cho, Shunan, 745-0304, Yamaguchi, Japan
Tel.: (81) 834 68 2638
Ready Mixed Concrete Mfr & Sales
N.A.I.C.S.: 327320

Kansai Ube Co., Ltd. (1)
4-2-23 Kaigan-dori, Minato-ku, Osaka, 552-0022, Japan
Tel.: (81) 64 395 9300
Web Site: http://www.ube-ind.co.jp
Ready Mixed Concrete Mfr & Sales
N.A.I.C.S.: 327320

Kanto Ready-mixed Concrete Transportation Co., Ltd. (1)
1-1-1 Jyonanjima, Ota-ku, Tokyo, 143-0002, Japan
Tel.: (81) 33 790 2388
Web Site: https://www.ube-ind.co.jp
Ready Mixed Concrete Transportation & Flooring Materials Whslr
N.A.I.C.S.: 444180

Kanto Ube Concrete Co., Ltd. (1)
6F Estage Osaki Building 3-5-2 Osaki, Shinagawa-ku, Tokyo, 141-0032, Japan
Tel.: (81) 35 759 7696
Web Site: https://www.ube-ind.co.jp
Ready Mixed Concrete Mfr & Distr
N.A.I.C.S.: 327320

Kanto Ube Holdings Co., Ltd. (1)
6F Estage Osaki Building 3-5-2 Osaki, Shinagawa-ku, Tokyo, 141-0032, Japan
Tel.: (81) 35 759 7715
Web Site: https://www.ube-ind.co.jp
Cement Distr
N.A.I.C.S.: 423320

Kitakyushu Ube Concrete Co., Ltd. (1)
69-2 Nishiminatomachi, Kokurakita-ku, Kitakyushu, 803-0801, Fukuoka, Japan
Tel.: (81) 93 561 4331
Ready Mixed Concrete Mfr & Distr
N.A.I.C.S.: 327320

Kushiro Ube Co., Ltd. (1)
5-1-24 Tottoriminami, Kushiro, 084-0905, Hokkaido, Japan
Tel.: (81) 15 451 2101
Web Site: http://www.ube-ind.co.jp
Ready Mixed Concrete & Cement Mfr & Distr
N.A.I.C.S.: 327320

LOTTE UBE Synthetic Rubber Sdn. Bhd. (1)
Plo 8 Jalan Nibong, Tanjung Langsat Industrial Estate, 81700, Pasir Gudang, Johor, Malaysia
Tel.: (60) 7 253 7111
Butadiene Mfr
N.A.I.C.S.: 325211

Libertas Ube, Ltd. (1)
525-110 Higashimisome-cho, Ube, 755-0009, Yamaguchi, Japan
Tel.: (81) 83 635 7878
Web Site: https://www.ube-ind.co.jp
Printing, Book Binding & Document Preparation Services
N.A.I.C.S.: 323117

Nishiharima Ube Co., Ltd (1)
3059-13 Nakajima, Shikama-ku, Himeji, 672-8035, Hyogo, Japan
Tel.: (81) 792 35 4156
Readymix Concrete Mfr
N.A.I.C.S.: 327320

Ozawa Corporation (1)
2-4-1 Nishihongo-dori, Seki, 501-3803, Gifu, Japan
Tel.: (81) 57 524 2244
Web Site: https://www.ozawa-cop.co.jp
Roofing Installation Services
N.A.I.C.S.: 238160

R-Koma Ltd. (1)
9-1 Iwakura Kurikoma Iwagasaki, Kurihara, 989-5301, Miyagi, Japan
Tel.: (81) 22 845 5771
Web Site: http://www.ube-ind.co.jp
Ready Mixed Concrete Mfr & Distr
N.A.I.C.S.: 327320

Rayong Fertilizer Trading Co., Ltd. (1)
87/2 CRC Tower All Seasons Place 9th Floor Wireless Road Lumpini, Pathumwan, Bangkok, 10330, Thailand
Tel.: (66) 2 263 6600
Fertilizer Whslr
N.A.I.C.S.: 424190

SUMaterials Co., Ltd. (1)
150 Myungam-ri Tangjeung-myeon, Asan, Chungcheongnam-do, Korea (South)
Tel.: (82) 41 623 8300
Polyimide Mfr
N.A.I.C.S.: 325211

Samekawa Ready-mixed Concrete Co., Ltd. (1)
26-1 Eguri-omachi Nishiki-cho, Iwaki, 974-8232, Fukushima, Japan
Tel.: (81) 246 63 5371
Web Site: http://www.ube-ind.co.jp
Ready Mixed Concrete Mfr & Distr
N.A.I.C.S.: 327320

Sanshin Tsusho Co., Ltd. (1)
2-12-8 RBM lawn Park Building 3F, Shibadaimon Minato-ku, Tokyo, 105-0012, Japan
Tel.: (81) 33 434 0821
Building Materials Distr
N.A.I.C.S.: 444180

Sanyo Ube Co., Ltd. (1)
1091-1 Asada, Yamaguchi, 753-0871, Japan
Tel.: (81) 83 922 3511
Ready Mixed Concrete Mfr & Sales
N.A.I.C.S.: 327320

Shinko Transportation and Warehouse Co., Ltd. (1)
3-30-1 Kaigan, Minato-ku, Tokyo, 108-0022, Japan
Tel.: (81) 33 453 6001
Web Site: https://www.shinko-tw.co.jp
Emp.: 90
Chemical Products Storage Services
N.A.I.C.S.: 493110

Thai Synthetic Rubbers Co., Ltd. (1)
Factory 140/9 Moo 4 Tapong, Mueang Rayong, Rayong, 21000, Thailand
Tel.: (66) 3 892 8700
Web Site: https://www.ube.co.th
Sales Range: $100-124.9 Million
Emp.: 150
N.A.I.C.S.: 212114

UBE Asset & Insurance, Ltd. (1)
Seavance N Building 1-2-1 Shibaura, Minato-ku, Tokyo, 105-6791, Japan (100%)
Tel.: (81) 35 419 6321
Web Site: https://www.ube-ind.co.jp
Emp.: 43
Insurance & Real Estate Management Services
N.A.I.C.S.: 524210
Matsumura Tayo (Pres)

UBE Construction Materials Co., Ltd. (1)
1-2-1 Shibaura Seavans North Building, Minato-ku, Tokyo, 105-0023, Japan
Tel.: (81) 35 419 6206
Web Site: http://www.ube-ind.co.jp
Building Materials Mfr
N.A.I.C.S.: 327120
Masatake Okazaki (Pres)

UBE Elastomer Co., Ltd. (1)
Seavance North Building 1-2-1 Shibaura, Minato-ku, Tokyo, 105-6791, Japan
Tel.: (81) 354196167
Emp.: 270
Synthetic Rubber Mfr & Distr
N.A.I.C.S.: 325212

UBE Mexico S. de R.L. de C.V. (1)
Av Insurgentes Sur 859 S 282 P 2 Col Napoles, Benito Juarez, CP 03810, Mexico, Mexico

Tel.: (52) 5541220002
Pharmaceutical Chemical Product Mfr & Distr
N.A.I.C.S.: 325412

UBE-MC Hydrogen Peroxide Ltd. (1)
20F Seavance North Building 1-2-1 Shibaura, Minato-ku, Tokyo, 105-6791, Japan (51%)
Tel.: (81) 354196340
Web Site: http://www.ube-ind.co.jp
Sales Range: Less than $1 Million
Emp.: 30
Hydrogen Peroxide Mfr & Distr
N.A.I.C.S.: 325998

UBE-Mitsubishi Cement Corporation (1)
Iino Building 2-1-1 Uchisaiwaich, Chiyoda-ku, Tokyo, 1010062, Japan (50%)
Tel.: (81) 36 275 0330
Web Site: https://www.mu-cc.com
Emp.: 8,000
Cement Mfr
N.A.I.C.S.: 327310

UMG ABS, Ltd. (1)
Shiodome Sumitomo Bldg 22F 1-9-2 Higashi-Shimbashi, Minato-ku, Tokyo, 105-0021, Japan (50%)
Tel.: (81) 3 6218 3880
Web Site: http://www.umgabs.co.jp
Holding Company; Resins Mfr
N.A.I.C.S.: 551112

Joint Venture (Domestic):

Techno-UMG Co., Ltd. (2)
Shiodome Sumitomo Building 22F 1-9-2 Higashi-Shimbashi, Minato, Tokyo, 105-0021, Japan (49%)
Tel.: (81) 362183880
Web Site: https://www.t-umg.com
Styrene Resin Mfr & Whslr
N.A.I.C.S.: 325211
Masaaki Mori (Exec VP)

Subsidiary (Non-US):

Techno-UMG (Shanghai) Co., Ltd. (3)
Room 2507-08 The Place Tower A 100 Zunyi Road, Shanghai, 200051, China
Tel.: (86) 2162953327
Web Site: http://www.t-umg.com
Synthetic Resin Sales
N.A.I.C.S.: 424690

Subsidiary (US):

Techno-UMG America, Inc. (3)
5405 Dupont Cir Ste E, Milford, OH 45150
Tel.: (513) 248-2033
Web Site: http://www.t-umg.com
Plastics Sales & Services
N.A.I.C.S.: 424610

Subsidiary (Non-US):

Techno-UMG Asia Co., Ltd. (3)
968 28th Floor U-Chuliang Foundation Building Rama 4 Road silom, Bangrak, Bangkok, 10500, Thailand
Tel.: (66) 26367569
Web Site: http://www.t-umg.com
Sales Range: $25-49.9 Million
Emp.: 20
Synthetic Resin Sales
N.A.I.C.S.: 424690
Takao Nagai (Mng Dir)

Techno-UMG Hong Kong Co., Ltd. (3)
Room 1002 10/F Tower 2 Lippo Centre 89 Queensway, Admiralty, Kowloon, China (Hong Kong)
Tel.: (852) 25217622
Web Site: http://www.t-umg.com
Chemical & Allied Products Merchant Whslr
N.A.I.C.S.: 424690
Louis Lo (Mng Dir)

Techno-UMG Shanghai Technical Center Co., Ltd. (3)
207 Zhongqing Road Maqiao, Minhang, Shanghai, 201111, China
Tel.: (86) 21 5457 3262
Synthetic Resin Research & Development
N.A.I.C.S.: 541715

Ube (Hong Kong) Ltd. (1)

Rm 1001 12 Sun Hung Kai Ctr 30 Harbour Rd, Hong Kong, China (Hong Kong) (100%)
Tel.: (852) 28771628
Web Site: http://www.ube-ind.co.jp
Sales Range: $25-49.9 Million
Emp.: 7
N.A.I.C.S.: 212114
Matsuti Nasahiro (Mng Dir)

Ube (Shanghai) Ltd. (1)
Room 2403 Shanghai International Trade Centre Yan'an West Road 2201, Changning District, Shanghai, 200336, China (100%)
Tel.: (86) 216 273 2288
Web Site: http://www.ube-ind.co.jp
Sales Range: $25-49.9 Million
Emp.: 10
Chemicals Mfr
N.A.I.C.S.: 325180

Ube Aluminum Wheels Ltd. (1)
2575-62 Fujimagari, Ube, 755-0057, Yamaguchi, Japan
Tel.: (81) 836 35 5401
Web Site: http://www.ube-ind.co.jp
Aluminum Wheel Mfr & Distr
N.A.I.C.S.: 327910

Ube America Inc. (1)
38777 Six Mile Rd Ste 400, Livonia, MI 48152
Tel.: (248) 869-0050
Web Site: https://www.northamerica.ube.com
Chemical Products & Materials
N.A.I.C.S.: 325999
Frank Hormann (Pres & CEO)

Unit (Domestic):

Ube Automotive (2)
39555 Orchard Hill Pl Ste 240, Novi, MI 48375-5345
Tel.: (513) 459-1760
Sales Range: $125-149.9 Million
Emp.: 400
Mfr of Aluminum Wheels
N.A.I.C.S.: 423120

Ube Ammonia Industry, Ltd. (1)
2575 Fujimagari, Ube, 755-0057, Yamaguchi, Japan
Tel.: (81) 836315858
Web Site: http://www.ube-ind.co.jp
Pharmaceutical Products Mfr & Distr
N.A.I.C.S.: 325412

Ube Board Co., Ltd. (1)
525-125 Okinoyama, Okiube, Ube, 755-0001, Yamaguchi, Japan
Tel.: (81) 836 22 0251
Web Site: http://www.ube-ind.co.jp
Corrugated Sheet & Board Mfr
N.A.I.C.S.: 322211

Ube Chemicals (Asia) Public Co., Ltd. (1)
140/6 Moo 4 Tambol Tapong, Muang Rayong District, Rayong, 21000, Thailand
Tel.: (66) 3 892 8700
Web Site: https://www.ube.co.th
Sales Range: $250-299.9 Million
Emp.: 600
Nylon Resin Mfr & Whslr
N.A.I.C.S.: 325211
Pirulh Laothanasin (Mgr-Mktg)

Ube Concrete Industry Co., Ltd. (1)
15-2 Ishizu Nishi-cho, Nishi-ku, Sakai, 592-8332, Osaka, Japan
Tel.: (81) 72 241 5252
Web Site: http://www.ubecon.co.jp
Concrete Pile Mfr & Distr
N.A.I.C.S.: 327390
Norihiko Sawabe (Pres)

Ube Construction Materials Sales Co., Ltd. (1)
1-6-34 Konan Shinagawa East 6th floor, Minato-ku, Tokyo, 108-0075, Japan
Tel.: (81) 35 781 7510
Web Site: http://www.ube-ind.co.jp
Building Materials Distr
N.A.I.C.S.: 423320

Ube Corporation Europe, S.A. (1)
Poligono Industrial El Serrallo s/n, Grao de Castellon, 12100, Castellon de la Plana, Spain (100%)

UBE CORPORATION

UBE Corporation—(Continued)
Tel.: (34) 96 473 8000
Web Site: https://www.ube.es
Sales Range: $150-199.9 Million
Emp.: 280
Holding Company
N.A.I.C.S.: 551112

Division (Domestic):

Ube Chemical Europe, S.A. (2)
Poligono El Serrallo, Grao de Castellon,
ES-12080, Castellon de la Plana, Spain
Tel.: (34) 964738000
Web Site: http://www.ube.es
Sales Range: $100-124.9 Million
Emp.: 250
Chemicals Mfr
N.A.I.C.S.: 325998
Raeasdo Lopez (Mng Dir)

Ube Electronics (Wuxi) Co., Ltd. (2)
52 Block 27 B Wuix State High New Technology Industry Development Zone, Wuxi,
214028, Jiangsu, China
Tel.: (86) 510 8521 1117
Sales Range: $100-124.9 Million
Emp.: 400
Electronic Components Mfr
N.A.I.C.S.: 334419
Motoharu Hanaki (Pres)

Ube Electronics, Ltd. (1)
2023-2 Aza Mugigawa Okubun Omine-cho,
Mine, 759-2214, Yamaguchi, Japan
Tel.: (81) 837 52 2900
Web Site: http://www.uel.co.jp
Telecommunication Electronic Device Mfr
N.A.I.C.S.: 334419

Ube Engineering Plastics, S.A. (1)
Poligono El Serrallo Grao de Castellon,
12100, Castellon de la Plana, Spain
Tel.: (34) 964738000
Nylon Products Mfr & Distr
N.A.I.C.S.: 325211

Ube Europe GmbH (1)
Immermannstrasse 65B, 40210, Dusseldorf,
Germany (100%)
Tel.: (49) 211178830
Web Site: https://www.ube.es
Sales Range: $100-124.9 Million
Emp.: 25
Chemical Production
N.A.I.C.S.: 212114

Ube Exsymo Co., Ltd. (1)
9-19 Nihonbashitomizawacho, Sumitomo
Life Nihonbashi Tomizawacho Building
Chuo-ku, Tokyo, 103-0006, Japan
Tel.: (81) 36 667 2411
Web Site: https://www.ube-exsymo.co.jp
Emp.: 535
Resin Products, Synthetic Fibers & Fine
Ceramics Mfr
N.A.I.C.S.: 325211
Toshimitsu Takahashi (Pres)

Ube Fine Chemicals (Asia) Co., Ltd. (1)
140/6 Moo 4 Tambol Tapong, Muang Rayong District, Rayong, 21000, Thailand
Tel.: (66) 3 892 8700
Web Site: https://www.ube.co.th
Specialty Chemicals Mfr
N.A.I.C.S.: 325998

Ube Industries Total Service Co., Ltd. (1)
8-1 Aioi-cho, Ube, 755-8577, Yamaguchi,
Japan
Tel.: (81) 83 634 5430
Web Site: http://www.ube-ind.co.jp
Building Management & Welfare Facilities
Operation Services
N.A.I.C.S.: 561790

Ube Industries, Ltd. - Chiba Petrochemical Factory (1)
8-1 Goi-Minamikaigan, Ichihara, 290-8550,
Chiba, Japan
Tel.: (81) 43 623 5111
Web Site: http://www.ube-ind.co.jp
Petrochemical Mfr
N.A.I.C.S.: 325110

Ube Industries, Ltd. - Isa Cement Factory (1)
4768 Isa Isa-cho, Mine, 759-2222, Yamaguchi, Japan
Tel.: (81) 83 752 1212
Web Site: http://www.ube-ind.co.jp
Cement Mfr
N.A.I.C.S.: 327310

Ube Industries, Ltd. - Kanda Cement Factory (1)
7 Nagahama-machi Kanda-cho, Miyakogun, Fukuoka, 800-0311, Japan
Tel.: (81) 93 434 2111
Emp.: 120
Cement Mfr
N.A.I.C.S.: 327310
Yasuhiro Mihara (Gen Mgr)

Ube Industries, Ltd. - Sakai Factory (1)
3-1 Chikko-Shinmachi, Nishi-ku, Sakai, 592-8543, Osaka, Japan
Tel.: (81) 72 243 5100
Web Site: https://www.ube-ind.co.jp
Chemical Products Mfr
N.A.I.C.S.: 325998

Ube Industries, Ltd. - Ube Cement Factory (1)
1978-10 Kogushi, Ube, 755-8633, Yamaguchi, Japan
Tel.: (81) 83 631 0111
Web Site: http://www.ube-ind.co.jp
Cement Mfr
N.A.I.C.S.: 327310

Ube Industries, Ltd. - Ube Chemical Factory (1)
1978-10 Kogushi, Ube, 755-8633, Yamaguchi, Japan
Tel.: (81) 83 631 2112
Web Site: https://www.ube-ind.co.jp
Chemical Products Mfr
N.A.I.C.S.: 325998

Ube Information Systems Inc. (1)
8-1 Aioi-cho, Ube, 755-8622, Yamaguchi,
Japan
Tel.: (81) 83 622 0111
Web Site: http://www.ube-ind.co.jp
Information Processing & Fiduciary Services
N.A.I.C.S.: 519290

Ube Korea Co., Ltd. (1)
2nd Floor Donghoon Tower 702-19
Yeoksam-dong, Gangnam-gu, Seoul, 135-513, Korea (South)
Tel.: (82) 2 557 7590
Chemical Product Whslr
N.A.I.C.S.: 424690

Ube Latin America Servicos Ltda. (1)
Rua Iguatemi 192 - 13 andar cj 134, Itaim Bibi, Sao Paulo, 01451-010, Brazil
Tel.: (55) 1130785424
Web Site: http://www.ube.ind.br
Emp.: 10
Chemical Product Whslr
N.A.I.C.S.: 424690

Ube Machinery Corporation, Ltd. (1)
1980 Okinoyama Kogushi, Ube, 755-8633,
Yamaguchi, Japan
Tel.: (81) 83 622 0072
Web Site: https://www.ubemachinery.co.jp
Emp.: 1,030
Injection Molding Machine Mfr & Distr
N.A.I.C.S.: 333248
Hironori Miyauchi (Pres)

Subsidiary (Domestic):

FUKUSHIMA, Ltd. (2)
9-80 Mikawa Kitamachi, Fukushima, 960-8054, Japan
Tel.: (81) 24 534 3146
Web Site: https://fukusei.co.jp
Emp.: 180
Industrial Machinery Mfr & Distr
N.A.I.C.S.: 333248

T&U Electronics, Co., Ltd. (2)
203-143 Ushiake Yoshiwa, Ube, 759-0134,
Yamaguchi, Japan
Tel.: (81) 836 62 1151
Emp.: 100
Electronic Control Equipment Mfr & Distr
N.A.I.C.S.: 334513
Shimichi Tomita (Pres)

U-MHI Platech Co., Ltd. (2)
1 Takamichi Iwatsuka-cho, Nakamura-ku,
Nagoya, 453-0862, Aichi, Japan (85%)
Tel.: (81) 52 412 1111
Web Site: http://www.u-mhipt.co.jp
Sales Range: $75-99.9 Million
Emp.: 139
Injection Molding Machinery Design & Mfr
N.A.I.C.S.: 333248
Koji Kubota (Pres)

Subsidiary (Non-US):

Ube Machinery (Shanghai) Ltd. (2)
No 91 Fute North Road, Waigaoqiao Free
Trade Zone Pudong, Shanghai, 200131,
China
Tel.: (86) 215 868 1633
Web Site: https://www.ubesh.com
Emp.: 70
Industrial Machinery Mfr & Distr
N.A.I.C.S.: 333248
Lin Zhijian (Gen Mgr)

Subsidiary (US):

Ube Machinery Inc. (2)
5700 S State Rd, Ann Arbor, MI 48108
Tel.: (734) 741-7000
Web Site: http://www.ubemachinery.com
Emp.: 70
Injection Molding Machinery Whslr
N.A.I.C.S.: 423830
Yasuo Honda (Pres)

Subsidiary (Domestic):

Ube Steel Co., Ltd. (2)
1978-19 Okinoyama Kogushi, Ube, 755-0067, Yamaguchi, Japan
Tel.: (81) 836 35 1300
Steel Billets Mfr & Distr
N.A.I.C.S.: 331110

Ube Techno Eng Co., Ltd. (2)
1980 Okinoyama Kogushi, Ube, 755-8633,
Yamaguchi, Japan
Tel.: (81) 836 34 5080
Industrial Machinery Maintenance Services
N.A.I.C.S.: 811310

Ube Material Industries, Ltd. (1)
8-1 Aioi-Chou, Ube, 755-0043, Yamaguchi,
Japan (100%)
Tel.: (81) 83 631 0156
Web Site: https://www.ubematerial.com
Sales Range: $300-349.9 Million
Emp.: 700
Chemical Product Mfr & Whslr
N.A.I.C.S.: 325998
Masataka Ichikawa (Pres)

Ube Nisshin Lime Co., Ltd. (1)
11-1 Showa-machi, Kure, 737-0027, Hiroshima, Japan
Tel.: (81) 823 23 0920
Web Site: http://www.ube-ind.co.jp
Dephosphorization Agents & Quicklime Mfr
N.A.I.C.S.: 327410

Ube Nylon (Thailand) Limited (1)
87/2 CRC Tower All Seasons Place 9th
Floor, Wireless Road Lumpini, Pathumwan,
Bangkok, 10330, Thailand
Tel.: (66) 22636600
Web Site: http://www.ube.co.th
Bituminous Coal Mining
N.A.I.C.S.: 212114

Ube Realty & Development Co., Ltd. (1)
2423-1 Ajisu, Yamaguchi, 754-1277, Japan
Tel.: (81) 836 65 3211
Web Site: http://www.ube-ind.co.jp
Home Management Services
N.A.I.C.S.: 721110

Ube Sand Co., Ltd. (1)
332-9 Okubun Omine-cho, Mine, 759-2214,
Yamaguchi, Japan
Tel.: (81) 837 52 1321
Silica Mfr & Distr
N.A.I.C.S.: 325180

Ube Scientific Analysis Laboratory, Inc. (1)
2-20-15 Shinbashi Shinbashi Ekimae Building No 1 Building Room 501, Minato-ku,
Tokyo, 105-0004, Japan
Tel.: (81) 36 280 6981
Web Site: https://www.ube-ind.co.jp

Emp.: 135
Compound Chemicals Research & Development Services
N.A.I.C.S.: 541715
Hideki Asada (Pres)

Ube Shipping & Logistics, Ltd. (1)
1-5-5 Minato-machi, Ube, 755-0027, Yamaguchi, Japan (100%)
Tel.: (81) 83 634 1181
Web Site: http://www.ube-ind.co.jp
Harbor Transportation Services
N.A.I.C.S.: 488310

Ube Singapore Pte. Ltd. (1)
150 Beach Road 20-05 Gateway West, Singapore, 189720, Singapore (100%)
Tel.: (65) 62919363
Web Site: http://www.ube-ind.co.jp
Emp.: 8
N.A.I.C.S.: 212114
Masahiko Ota (Mng Dir)

Ube Technical Center (Asia) Limited (1)
140/8 Moo4 Tambol Tapong, Mueang Rayong, Rayong, 21000, Thailand
Tel.: (66) 3 892 8700
Nylon Compound Testing Services
N.A.I.C.S.: 541380

Ube-C&A Co., Ltd. (1)
Seavans North Bldg 1-2-1 Shibaura,
Minato-ku, Tokyo, 105 8449, Japan
Tel.: (81) 354196331
Web Site: http://www.ube-ind.co.jp
Sales Range: $50-74.9 Million
Emp.: 2
N.A.I.C.S.: 212114
Kurauchi Takafumi (Gen Mgr)

Urayasu Concrete Co., Ltd. (1)
10-23 Kitasakae 4-chome, Urayasu, 279-0002, Chiba, Japan
Tel.: (81) 47 352 5184
Web Site: http://www.ube-ind.co.jp
Ready Mixed Concrete Mfr & Sales
N.A.I.C.S.: 327320

Yamaguchi Eco-tech Corporation (1)
7-46 Harumi-cho, Shunan, 745-0024,
Yamaguchi, Japan
Tel.: (81) 83 434 2935
Web Site: https://www.y-eco.co.jp
Cement Raw Material Mfr
N.A.I.C.S.: 339999

Yamaishi Metal Co., Ltd. (1)
791 Kimagase, Noda, 270-0222, Chiba,
Japan
Tel.: (81) 4 7198 0151
Web Site: http://www.yamaishimetal.co.jp
Aluminum Metal Powder Mfr & Distr
N.A.I.C.S.: 331314

Yamayo Trading Co., Ltd. (1)
311-5 Okubun Omine-cho, Mine, 759-2214,
Yamaguchi, Japan
Tel.: (81) 83 752 0660
Web Site: http://www.ube-ind.co.jp
Coal & Household Fuel Whslr
N.A.I.C.S.: 423520

UBERALL GMBH

Hussitenstrasse 32 33, 13355, Berlin,
Germany
Tel.: (49) 90 208479320
Web Site: http://www.uberall.com
Online Marketing & Advertising
N.A.I.C.S.: 541890
David Federhen (Member-Mgmt Bd)

Subsidiaries:

MomentFeed, Inc. (1)
1540 2nd St 3rd Fl, Santa Monica, CA
90401
Tel.: (424) 322-5300
Web Site: http://www.momentfeed.com
Sales Range: $10-24.9 Million
Emp.: 100
Software Development Services
N.A.I.C.S.: 541511
Robert Blatt (Chm)

SweetIQ Analytics Corp. (1)
1100 Avenue des Canadiens-de-Montreal
Suite 150, Montreal, H3B 2S2, QC, Canada
Tel.: (514) 461-3527

AND PRIVATE COMPANIES

Web Site: http://www.sweetiq.com
Marketing & Advertising Services
N.A.I.C.S.: 541810
Michael Mire *(Founder & Chief Revenue Officer)*

UBI BLOCKCHAIN INTERNET, LTD.
Unit 03 Level 9 Core F Smart Space Block 3 100 Cyberport Rd, Hong Kong, China (Hong Kong)
Tel.: (852) 3618 6110   DE
Web Site: http://www.globalubi.com
Year Founded: 2010
Assets: $694,704
Liabilities: $2,075,004
Net Worth: ($1,380,300)
Earnings: ($3,104,366)
Emp.: 18
Fiscal Year-end: 08/31/18
Investment Services
N.A.I.C.S.: 523999
Tony Liu *(CEO)*

UBICOM HOLDINGS, INC.
7F Ichibancho Tokyu Building 21 Ichibancho, Chiyoda-ku, Tokyo, 102-0082, Japan
Tel.: (81) 358037339
Web Site: https://www.ubicom-hd.com
Year Founded: 2005
3937—(TKS)
Rev.: $39,276,620
Assets: $45,466,630
Liabilities: $14,304,040
Net Worth: $31,192,590
Earnings: $3,476,860
Emp.: 1,088
Fiscal Year-end: 03/31/24
Software Development Services
N.A.I.C.S.: 541511
Masayuki Aoki *(Pres & CEO)*

Subsidiaries:

AIS, Co., Ltd.   (1)
1-3-9 Kandasudacho PMO Kanda Manseibashi 9F, Chiyoda-ku, Tokyo, 101-0041, Japan
Tel.: (81) 362608858
Web Site: https://www.a-i-s.co.jp
Emp.: 48
Software Development Services
N.A.I.C.S.: 513210

AWS (Beijing), Ltd.   (1)
Office 559 5/F South Block Raycom Info Tech Park, No 2 Kexueyuan South Road Zhongguancun, Beijing, 100190, China
Tel.: (86) 1059822174
Software Development Services
N.A.I.C.S.: 513210

AWS (Kunshan), Ltd.   (1)
Room 2104 Block A Modern Plaza, Kunshan, Jiangsu, China
Tel.: (86) 51250331032
Software Development Services
N.A.I.C.S.: 513210

UBION CO., LTD.
Daeryungpost III 6F 34Gil 27 Digital-ro, Guro-gu, Seoul, 08378, Korea (South)
Tel.: (82) 216000052
Web Site: https://www.ubion.co.kr
Year Founded: 2000
Emp.: 130
Software Applications
N.A.I.C.S.: 513210
Lee Yong Jong *(CFO)*

UBIQUE MINERALS LTD.
100 King Street West Suite 5700, Toronto, M5X 1C7, ON, Canada
Tel.: (416) 232-9114
Web Site: https://www.ubiqueminerals.com
UBQ—(CNSX)
Rev.: $1,341
Assets: $1,681,713
Liabilities: $503,056
Net Worth: $1,178,657
Earnings: ($1,383,414)
Fiscal Year-end: 07/31/23
Mineral Exploration Services
N.A.I.C.S.: 213114
Vilhjalmur Thor Vilhjalmsson *(CEO)*

UBIQUITOUS AI CORPORATION
Shinjuku First West 17F 1-23-7 Nishi-Shinjuku, Shinjuku-ku, Tokyo, 160-0023, Japan
Tel.: (81) 359083451
Web Site: https://www.ubiquitous-ai.com
Year Founded: 2001
3858—(TKS)
Rev.: $22,989,580
Assets: $24,668,520
Liabilities: $9,247,390
Net Worth: $15,421,130
Earnings: $211,520
Fiscal Year-end: 03/31/24
Semiconductor Software & Hardware Products Mfr
N.A.I.C.S.: 541512
Satoshi Hasegawa *(Pres)*

UBIQUOSS HOLDINGS INC.
68 Pangyo-ro 255 beon-gil, Bundang-gu, Seongnam, 463-400, Gyeonggi-do, Korea (South)
Tel.: (82) 7048650500
Web Site: https://www.ubiquoss.com
Year Founded: 2000
078070—(KRS)
Rev.: $116,264,342
Assets: $279,889,873
Liabilities: $31,751,000
Net Worth: $248,138,874
Earnings: $11,192,148
Emp.: 17
Fiscal Year-end: 12/31/22
Holding Company; Wired Telecommunication Equipment Mfr
N.A.I.C.S.: 551112
Se-Woong Moon *(CTO & Sr VP)*

Subsidiaries:

Ubiquoss Japan, Inc.   (1)
3-7-1 Nishi Shinjuku, Shinjuku-ku, Tokyo, 163-1030, Japan
Tel.: (81) 353263052
Infrastructure Management Software Development Services
N.A.I.C.S.: 541511

UBIS (ASIA) PUBLIC CO., LTD.
238 15th Floor Unit 4-6 TRR Tower, Bangkok, 10120, Thailand
Tel.: (66) 26830008
Web Site: https://www.ubisasia.com
Year Founded: 1997
UBIS—(THA)
Rev.: $25,931,081
Assets: $30,125,179
Liabilities: $11,802,168
Net Worth: $18,323,011
Earnings: ($2,160,235)
Emp.: 178
Fiscal Year-end: 12/31/23
Can Coatings & Closure Sealants Mfr & Distr
N.A.I.C.S.: 325510
Nawat Triyapongpattana *(Deputy CEO)*

Subsidiaries:

Ubis Primatech Company Limited   (1)
807/1 6th Floor Rama 3 Road Bangpongpang, Yannawa, Bangkok, 10120, Thailand
Tel.: (66) 26830008
Paint & Coating Mfr
N.A.I.C.S.: 325510

UBISENSE LIMITED
St Andrews House St Andrews Road, Chesterton, Cambridge, CB4 1DL, United Kingdom
Tel.: (44) 1223535170   UK
Web Site: http://www.ubisense.com
Software Development Services
N.A.I.C.S.: 541511
Clare Colhoun *(CEO)*

UBISOFT ENTERTAINMENT S.A.
2 Rue du Chene Heleuc, 56910, Montreuil-sous-Bois, Cedex 2, Carentoir, France
Tel.: (33) 148185000   FR
Web Site: http://www.ubisoft.com
Year Founded: 1986
UBI—(EUR)
Rev.: $1,958,018,562
Assets: $5,040,794,302
Liabilities: $3,440,751,133
Net Worth: $1,600,043,169
Earnings: ($533,887,330)
Emp.: 20,133
Fiscal Year-end: 03/31/23
Interactive Entertainment Products Developer, Publisher & Distr
N.A.I.C.S.: 513210
Yves Guillemot *(Chm & CEO)*

Subsidiaries:

Blue Byte GmbH   (1)
Luise-Rainer-Strasse 7, 40235, Dusseldorf, Germany
Tel.: (49) 21154089580
Entertainment Software Development Services
N.A.I.C.S.: 541511
Karsten Lehmann *(Mgr-Pub Affairs)*

Blue Byte GmbH   (1)
Romerpassage 1, D-55116, Mainz, Germany
Tel.: (49) 6131 55447 0
Web Site: http://www.bluebyte.com
Entertainment Software Development Services
N.A.I.C.S.: 541511
Yves Guillemot *(CEO)*

Chengdu Ubi Computer Sofware Co. Ltd.   (1)
2F Building B2 TianFu Software Park TianFu Main Road High Tech Zone, Chengdu, 610041, China
Tel.: (86) 2885333228
Software Publisher
N.A.I.C.S.: 513210
Jean-Francois Vallee *(Mgr-Studio)*

Hybride Technologies Inc.   (1)
111 Chemin De La Gare, Piedmont, J0R 1K0, QC, Canada
Tel.: (450) 227-4245
Web Site: https://www.hybride.com
Emp.: 100
Digital Imagery & Stereoscopic Services
N.A.I.C.S.: 512191
Michel Murdock *(Pres)*

Owlient SAS   (1)
261 rue de Paris, 93100, Montreuil, France
Tel.: (33) 155765620
Software Publisher
N.A.I.C.S.: 541511

Quazel Technologies Inc.   (1)
555 Rene-Levesque Ouest Ste 1800, Montreal, H2Z 1B1, QC, Canada
Tel.: (514) 395-4646
Web Site: http://www.quazal.com
Gaming Software Development Services
N.A.I.C.S.: 541511

Red Storm Entertainment Inc.   (1)
3001 Weston Pkwy, Cary, NC 27513
Tel.: (919) 460-1776
Web Site: https://www.redstorm.com
Emp.: 135
Video Game Publisher
N.A.I.C.S.: 541511

RedLynx Oy   (1)
Kumpulantie 3, 00520, Helsinki, Finland
Tel.: (358) 207641860
Web Site: https://www.redlynx.com
Software Publisher
N.A.I.C.S.: 513210

Shanghai Ubi Computer Software Co. Ltd   (1)
3rd Floor 7 Gaoqing, Shanghai, 200031, China
Tel.: (86) 2154674545
Sales Range: $100-124.9 Million
Emp.: 400
Software Publishing Services
N.A.I.C.S.: 513210

SmartDC BV   (1)
Van Nelleweg 1, 3044 BC, Rotterdam, Netherlands
Tel.: (31) 108900048
Web Site: https://www.smartdc.net
Information Technology Services
N.A.I.C.S.: 541519

SmartDC Heerlen BV   (1)
Kloosterweg 1, 6412 CN, Heerlen, Netherlands
Tel.: (31) 8900048
Information Technology Services
N.A.I.C.S.: 541519

Ubi Games SA   (1)
Chemin d'Entre-Bois 31, 1018, Lausanne, Switzerland
Tel.: (41) 216416868
Web Site: http://www.ubisoftgroup.com
Sales Range: $50-74.9 Million
Emp.: 8
Interactive Entertainment Products Developer, Publisher & Distr
N.A.I.C.S.: 513210

Ubi Studios SL   (1)
Ausias March 1 4th Floor, Sant Cugat del Valles, 8195, Spain
Tel.: (34) 935441500
Sales Range: $25-49.9 Million
Emp.: 5
Photo Studio Operating Services
N.A.I.C.S.: 541921
Maria Teresa Cordon *(Mgr-HR)*

Ubisoft Annecy SAS   (1)
6 Rue Andre Fumex, 74000, Annecy, France
Tel.: (33) 450109340
Web Site: https://www.ubisoft.com
Software Publisher
N.A.I.C.S.: 513210

Ubisoft BV   (1)
Rijnzathe 7A4, De Meern, 3454 PV, Netherlands
Tel.: (31) 306629110
Web Site: http://www.ubisoft.nl
Sales Range: $50-74.9 Million
Emp.: 25
Interactive Entertainment Products Distr
N.A.I.C.S.: 423430
Edwin Groeneveld *(Mng Dir)*

Ubisoft Barcelona Mobile SL   (1)
Placa d'Ernest Lluch i Martin 5 Planta 9, 08019, Barcelona, Spain
Tel.: (34) 933151602
Software Publisher
N.A.I.C.S.: 513210

Ubisoft Blue Byte GmbH   (1)
Luise-Rainer-Strasse 7, 40235, Dusseldorf, Germany
Tel.: (49) 21154089580
Web Site: https://bluebyte.ubisoft.com
Software Publisher
N.A.I.C.S.: 513210

Ubisoft Canada Inc.   (1)
5505 Blvd St-Laurent, Montreal, H2T 1S6, QC, Canada
Tel.: (514) 490-2000
Web Site: http://montreal.ubisoft.com
Sales Range: $400-449.9 Million
Emp.: 3,000
Interactive Entertainment Products Developer, Publisher & Distr
N.A.I.C.S.: 513210
Olivier Ernst *(Mng Dir)*

Ubisoft Emea SARL   (1)

UBISOFT ENTERTAINMENT S.A.

Ubisoft Entertainment S.A.—(Continued)
28 Rue Armand Carrel, 93100, Montreuil, France
Tel.: (33) 148185000
Web Site: http://www.ubisoftgroup.com
Emp.: 100
Video Game Software Publishing Services
N.A.I.C.S.: 513210

Ubisoft Entertainment (1)
3F Building 3 No 3 Gui Qing Road entrance on Quan Zhou Road, Shanghai, 200233, China
Tel.: (86) 2154674545
Web Site: http://www.ubisoft.com.cn
Interactive Entertainment Products Developer, Publisher & Distr
N.A.I.C.S.: 513210

Ubisoft Entertainment India Private Ltd (1)
B3-5th floor Behind Gold Adlabs Kalyaninagar, Kumar Cerebrum IT Park, Pune, 411014, Maharashtra, India
Tel.: (91) 2066424500
Sales Range: $50-74.9 Million
Emp.: 1,200
Video Production Services
N.A.I.C.S.: 512110

Ubisoft Entertainment Ltd. (1)
1st Floor Chertsey Gate East London Street, Chertsey, KT16 8AP, Surrey, United Kingdom
Tel.: (44) 1932578000
Web Site: http://www.ubi.com
Video Games Distr
N.A.I.C.S.: 423430

Ubisoft Entertainment Sweden AB (1)
Barkgatan 5, 214 22, Malmo, Sweden
Tel.: (46) 406001000
Web Site: http://www.massive.se
Emp.: 650
Computer Gaming Software Publishing Services
N.A.I.C.S.: 513210

Ubisoft Eood (1)
47A Tsarigradsko Shose blvd Polygraphia Office Center 5th floor, 1124, Sofia, Bulgaria
Tel.: (359) 24894606
Software Publisher
N.A.I.C.S.: 513210
Ivan Balabanov *(Mng Dir)*

Ubisoft Finland Oy (1)
World Trade Center Helsinki, PO Box 800, Aleksanterinkatu 17, 00101, Helsinki, Finland
Tel.: (358) 969694180
Web Site: http://www.ubisoftgroup.com
Sales Range: $50-74.9 Million
Emp.: 20
Interactive Entertainment Products Distr
N.A.I.C.S.: 423430

Ubisoft France SAS (1)
40 rue Armand Carrel, Lenoir, 93100, Montreuil, France
Tel.: (33) 1 48 18 50 00
Web Site: http://www.ubi.com
Emp.: 6
Gambling Software Distr
N.A.I.C.S.: 423430

Ubisoft GmbH (1)
Luise-Rainer-Strasse 7, 40235, Dusseldorf, Germany
Tel.: (49) 21154089580
Web Site: http://www.ubi.com
Interactive Entertainment Products Developer, Publisher & Distr
N.A.I.C.S.: 513210

Branch (Non-US):

Ubisoft GmbH (2)
Goldschlagstrasse 172, 1120, Vienna, Austria
Tel.: (43) 18032121
Web Site: http://www.ubi.com
Sales Range: $50-74.9 Million
Emp.: 5
Interactive Entertainment Products Distr
N.A.I.C.S.: 423430
Eugen Knippel *(Mgr-PR & Mktg)*

Ubisoft Inc. (1)
300 Mission St 20th Fl, San Francisco, CA 94105
Tel.: (415) 547-4000
Web Site: http://www.ubi.com
Interactive Entertainment Products Developer, Publisher & Distr
N.A.I.C.S.: 513210

Ubisoft KK (1)
KDX Ebisu Bldg 2F 4-3-8 Ebisu, Shibuya-Ku, Tokyo, 150-0013, Japan
Tel.: (81) 332808780
Web Site: https://www.ubisoft.com
Sales Range: $50-74.9 Million
Emp.: 18
Interactive Entertainment Products Developer, Publisher & Distr
N.A.I.C.S.: 513210

Ubisoft Limited (1)
Unit C 17/F Yardley Commercial Building 3 Connaught Road West, Sheung Wan, China (Hong Kong)
Tel.: (852) 35201102
Web Site: http://www.ubisoftgroup.com
Sales Range: $25-49.9 Million
Emp.: 6
Interactive Entertainment Products Developer, Publisher & Distr
N.A.I.C.S.: 513210
Kif Chen *(Mng Dir)*

Ubisoft Ltd (1)
3rd Fl Ranger House, London Street Walnut Tree Close, Guildford, GU1 4UL, Surrey, United Kingdom
Tel.: (44) 1932578000
Web Site: http://www.ubi.com
Sales Range: $25-49.9 Million
Emp.: 50
Interactive Entertainment Products Developer, Publisher & Distr
N.A.I.C.S.: 513210
Rob Copper *(Mng Dir)*

Ubisoft Manufacturing & Administration SARL (1)
28 Rue Armand Carrel, 93100, Montreuil, France
Tel.: (33) 148185000
Gaming Software Development Services
N.A.I.C.S.: 541511

Ubisoft Marketing France SARL (1)
173-179 Rue Du Chevaleret, 75013, Paris, France
Tel.: (33) 148185000
Sales Range: $25-49.9 Million
Emp.: 5
Entertainment Software Publishing Services
N.A.I.C.S.: 513210
John Parkes *(Gen Mgr)*

Ubisoft Mobile Games SARL (1)
28 rue Armand Carrel, Montreuil, Cedex, France
Tel.: (33) 148185000
Software Publisher
N.A.I.C.S.: 513210

Ubisoft Montpellier SAS (1)
Z A Jean Mermoz 85 rue Didier Daurat, 34170, Castelnau-le-Lez, France
Tel.: (33) 499528590
Software Publisher
N.A.I.C.S.: 513210

Ubisoft Montreal (1)
5505 St-Laurent Boulevard 2000, Montreal, H2T 1S6, QC, Canada
Tel.: (514) 490-2000
Web Site: http://montreal.ubisoft.com
Emp.: 2,700
Entertainment Products Developer, Publisher & Distr
N.A.I.C.S.: 513210
Yannis Mallat *(CEO)*

Ubisoft Nordic AS (1)
Borupvang 2B 1 tv, 2750, Ballerup, Denmark
Tel.: (45) 38320300
Web Site: http://www.ubisoft.com
Sales Range: $50-74.9 Million
Emp.: 20
Interactive Entertainment Products Distr
N.A.I.C.S.: 423430
Peter Weile *(Mng Dir)*

Ubisoft Osaka KK (1)
Nakatsu Center Building 3F 1-11-1 Nakatsu, Kita-ku, Osaka, 531-0071, Japan
Tel.: (81) 332808780
Software Publisher
N.A.I.C.S.: 513210

Ubisoft Production France SAS (1)
28 rue Armand Carrel, 93100, Montreuil, France
Tel.: (33) 148185000
Motion Picture Production Services
N.A.I.C.S.: 512110

Ubisoft Pty Ltd (1)
Level 1 2-14 Mountain Street, Ultimo, 2007, NSW, Australia
Tel.: (61) 285871800
Web Site: http://www.ubi.com
Interactive Entertainment Products Developer, Publisher & Distr
N.A.I.C.S.: 513210

Ubisoft SA (1)
C/ Rozabella n 2 Planta 2 Zona A Edificio Berlin, Complejo Europa Empresarial, 28230, Las Rozas, Spain
Tel.: (34) 916404600
Entertainment Services
N.A.I.C.S.: 711130
Antonio Temprano *(Mng Dir)*

Ubisoft Simulations SAS (1)
6 Rue Fumax, 74000, Annecy, France
Tel.: (33) 450109340
Sales Range: $25-49.9 Million
Emp.: 100
Video Games Production Services
N.A.I.C.S.: 512110
Rebecka Coutaz *(Gen Mgr)*

Ubisoft Singapore Pte Ltd (1)
1 Fusionopolis Walk 04-01 Solaris, Singapore, 138628, Singapore
Tel.: (65) 64083000
Video Games Production Services
N.A.I.C.S.: 512110

Ubisoft SpA (1)
Via Enrico Fermi 10/2, Buccinasco, 20090, Milan, Italy
Tel.: (39) 024886711
Web Site: http://www.ubi.com
Sales Range: $25-49.9 Million
Emp.: 30
Interactive Entertainment Products Developer, Publisher & Distr
N.A.I.C.S.: 513210

Ubisoft Srl (1)
Jiului 8 street, Sector 1, Bucharest, Romania
Tel.: (40) 310403000
Web Site: http://www.ubisoft.com
Sales Range: $300-349.9 Million
Emp.: 1,800
Production, Marketing & Sales of Software Engines, Multimedia Production Tools & Computer Hardware Accessories
N.A.I.C.S.: 423430

Ubisoft Studios Srl (1)
Via Del Bosco Rinnovato 6 EdificioU7 Centro Direzionale, Assago, 20057, Milan, Italy
Tel.: (39) 0248867121
Video Production Services
N.A.I.C.S.: 512110

Ubisoft Toronto Inc. (1)
224 Wallace Ave Ste 200, Toronto, M6H 1V7, ON, Canada
Tel.: (416) 840-1240
Web Site: https://www.toronto.ubisoft.com
Emp.: 500
Video Game Development Services
N.A.I.C.S.: 541511

Ubisoft Winnipeg Inc. (1)
250 McDermot Ave Unit 204, Winnipeg, R3B 0S5, MB, Canada
Tel.: (204) 815-5717
Software Publisher
N.A.I.C.S.: 513210
Ashley Smith *(Mgr-HR)*

i3D.net BV (1)
Rivium 1e straat 1, 2909 LE, Capelle aan den IJssel, Netherlands
Tel.: (31) 108900070
Information Technology Services
N.A.I.C.S.: 541519

INTERNATIONAL PUBLIC

i3D.net LLC (1)
7 N Fair Oaks Ave, Pasadena, CA 91103
Web Site: https://www.i3d.net
Information Technology Services
N.A.I.C.S.: 513210
Stijn Koster *(Founder)*

UBIVELOX CO., LTD.
L Building-16 Floor Daeryung Post Tower 8th 43 Digital-ro 26-gil, Guro-gu, Seoul, 08380, Korea (South)
Tel.: (82) 25973023
Web Site: https://www.ubivelox.com
Year Founded: 2000
089850—(KRS)
Rev.: $344,637,829
Assets: $339,605,821
Liabilities: $175,576,476
Net Worth: $164,029,346
Earnings: $2,030,598
Emp.: 300
Fiscal Year-end: 12/31/22
System Software Development Services
N.A.I.C.S.: 541511
Alex Lee *(Co-CEO)*

Subsidiaries:

Healthnbio, Inc. (1)
9th Floor 20 Banpo-daero, Seocho-gu, Seoul, Korea (South)
Tel.: (82) 7050155028
Web Site: https://www.carepod.co.kr
Household Product Retailer
N.A.I.C.S.: 423620

INAVI Systems Inc. (1)
A-8 Floor 240, Pangyoyeok-ro Bundang-gu, Seongnam, Gyeonggi, Korea (South)
Tel.: (82) 25899610
Web Site: https://inavisys.com
Surveying & Mapping Services
N.A.I.C.S.: 541370

Inavi Mobility Inc. (1)
9th Floor Samhwan Hipex Building A, 240 Pangyoyeok-ro Bundang-gu Sampyeong-dong, Seongnam, Gyeonggi, Korea (South)
Tel.: (82) 18334242
Web Site: https://www.inavimobility.com
Call Center Services
N.A.I.C.S.: 561422

Mondo Systems Inc. (1)
3/F Dongyang Bldg 128 - 5 Cheongpa-Dong 3-Ga, Yongsan-Gu, Seoul, 140133, Korea (South)
Tel.: (82) 24493084
Web Site: http://www.mondosystem.com
Sales Range: $25-49.9 Million
Emp.: 15
Household Electronic Appliance Distr
N.A.I.C.S.: 423620

Thinkware Japan Co., Ltd. (1)
3-9-9 Iwamotocho First Seno Building 2F, Chiyoda-ku, Tokyo, 101-0032, Japan
Tel.: (81) 355774311
Web Site: https://www.thinkware.co.jp
Automotive Device Mfr
N.A.I.C.S.: 336320

Ubivelox Mobile Corp. (1)
5F Ace Techno Tower 1, 38-9 Digital-ro 31-gil Guro-gu, Seoul, 152-050, Korea (South)
Tel.: (82) 28652416
Web Site: https://www.ubiveloxmobile.com
Mobile Communications Services
N.A.I.C.S.: 517112

UBM HOLDING PUBLIC COMPANY LIMITED
Kisvasut Utca 1, 2085, Pilisvorosvar, Hungary
Tel.: (36) 26530540
Web Site: https://www.ubm.hu
UBM—(BUD)
Rev.: $634,692,727
Assets: $172,723,460
Liabilities: $138,683,986
Net Worth: $34,039,474
Earnings: $2,502,225
Emp.: 394
Fiscal Year-end: 06/30/23

AND PRIVATE COMPANIES — UBS GROUP AG

Holding Company
N.A.I.C.S.: 551112
Varga Akos (Chm-Mgmt Bd)

Subsidiaries:

OOO UBM RUS (1)
Frezer Str 5/1 of 1/12, 109202, Moscow, Russia
Tel.: (7) 9639314738
Web Site: http://www.ubmrus.ru
Animal Feed Mfr
N.A.I.C.S.: 311119

UBM Agri Trade SRL (1)
4 Tablitei Street Floor 1-2, 1st District, Bucharest, Romania
Tel.: (40) 771307519
Web Site: http://www.ubmagri.ro
Animal Food Distr
N.A.I.C.S.: 424910

UBM Agro Slovakia s.r.o. (1)
Zeleznicna 2, Cana, Slovakia
Tel.: (421) 908603601
Animal Feed Mfr
N.A.I.C.S.: 311119

UBM Feed Romania SRL (1)
Sanpaul nr 6A, Targu Mures, Mures, Romania
Tel.: (40) 372903358
Web Site: http://www.ubmfeed.ro
Animal Feed Mfr
N.A.I.C.S.: 311119

UBOUR LOGISTICS SERVICES P.L.C.
PO Box 940071, Amman, 11194, Jordan
Tel.: (962) 65623062
Year Founded: 2009
TRUK—(AMM)
Rev.: $74,795
Assets: $547,122
Liabilities: $86,894
Net Worth: $460,229
Earnings: $63,036
Fiscal Year-end: 12/31/23
Transportation Related Services
N.A.I.C.S.: 488999

UBS GLOBAL ALLOCATION TRUST
161 Bay Street Suite 3900, Toronto, M5J 2S1, ON, Canada
Tel.: (416) 681-5121 ON
Year Founded: 2004
Sales Range: Less than $1 Million
Financial Investment Services
N.A.I.C.S.: 523999
Shawn K. Lytle (Chm)

UBS GROUP AG
Bahnhofstrasse 45, CH-8001, Zurich, Switzerland
Tel.: (41) 442341111 CH
Web Site: https://www.ubs.com
Year Founded: 2014
UBS—(NYSE)
Rev.: $40,834,000,000
Assets: $1,717,246,000,000
Liabilities: $1,630,607,000,000
Net Worth: $86,639,000,000
Earnings: $27,849,000,000
Emp.: 112,842
Fiscal Year-end: 12/31/23
Financial Investment Services
N.A.I.C.S.: 551112
Christian Bluhm (Chief Risk Officer & Member-Exec Bd)

Subsidiaries:

Credit Suisse Group AG (1)
Paradeplatz 8, Postfach 100, 8001, Zurich, Switzerland
Tel.: (41) 443339911
Web Site: https://www.credit-suisse.com
Rev.: $16,542,128,603
Assets: $589,088,691,796
Liabilities: $538,832,594,235
Net Worth: $50,256,097,561
Earnings: ($8,085,365,854)
Emp.: 50,480
Fiscal Year-end: 12/31/2022
Financial Investment Services
N.A.I.C.S.: 551112
Lukas Gahwiler (Executives)

Subsidiary (Domestic):

BANK-now AG (2)
Neugasse 18, Postfach 852, 8810, Horgen, Switzerland
Tel.: (41) 589005166
Web Site: https://www.credit-now.ch
Financial Management Services
N.A.I.C.S.: 523999

Credit Suisse AG (2)
Paradeplatz 8, 8001, Zurich, CH, Switzerland (100%)
Tel.: (41) 443331111
Rev.: $18,894,678,492
Assets: $501,670,731,707
Liabilities: $459,413,525,499
Net Worth: $42,257,206,208
Earnings: ($4,560,975,610)
Emp.: 28,840
Fiscal Year-end: 12/31/2023
Private Banking, Investment Banking & Asset Management Services
N.A.I.C.S.: 523150
Jeremy Anderson (Vice Chm)

Subsidiary (Non-US):

AXA penzijni spolecnost A.S. (3)
Uzka 488/8, Brno, 60200, Czech Republic
Tel.: (420) 292292292
Web Site: http://www.axa.cz
Insurance Carrier
N.A.I.C.S.: 524128

Banco Credit Suisse (Mexico), S.A. (3)
Paseo de la Reforma 115 - Piso 26 Colonia Lomas de Chapultepec, 11000, Mexico, Mexico
Tel.: (52) 55 5283 8900
Web Site: http://www.credit-suisse.com
Financial Management Services
N.A.I.C.S.: 523999

C.S. Consultaciones y Servicios S.A (3)
Av Luis Alberto de Herrera 1248 Torre B Piso 9, 11300, Montevideo, Uruguay
Tel.: (598) 2 622 9393
Web Site: http://www.credit-suisse.com
Financial Management Services
N.A.I.C.S.: 523999

CJSC Bank Credit Suisse (3)
4 Romanov Pereulok Bldg 2 Fl 6, Moscow, 125009, Russia
Tel.: (7) 495 967 8200
Web Site: http://www.credit-suisse.com
Commercial Banking Services
N.A.I.C.S.: 522110

Casa de Bolsa Credit Suisse (Mexico), S.A. de C.V. (3)
Paseo de la Reforma No 115 Piso 25, Col Lomas de Chapultepec, 11000, Mexico, Mexico
Tel.: (52) 5552838900
Web Site: https://www.credit-suisse.com
Sales Range: $1-9.9 Million
Emp.: 190
Financial Planning Services
N.A.I.C.S.: 523940

Subsidiary (US):

Column Financial, Inc. (3)
201 Spear St Ste 1850, San Francisco, CA 94105
Tel.: (415) 836-8600
Banking Services
N.A.I.C.S.: 522110

Subsidiary (Non-US):

Corner Bank Ltd. (3)
(100%)
Tel.: (41) 918005111
Banking Services
N.A.I.C.S.: 522299

Credit Suisse (Bahamas) Ltd. (3)
4th Floor The Bahamas Financial Centre Shirley and Charlotte Streets, Nassau, Bahamas (100%)
Tel.: (242) 3568100
Sales Range: $50-74.9 Million
Emp.: 65
Investment & Private Banking Services
N.A.I.C.S.: 523150

Credit Suisse (Guernsey) Ltd. (3)
Helvetia Court, PO Box 368, South Esplanade, Saint Peter Port, GY1 3YJ, Guernsey (100%)
Tel.: (44) 1481719000
Web Site: http://www.credit-suisse.com
Sales Range: $75-99.9 Million
Emp.: 250
Investment Banking Services
N.A.I.C.S.: 523150

Subsidiary (Domestic):

Credit Suisse Finance (Guernsey) Limited (4)
Helvetia Court South Esplanade, Saint Peter Port, GY1 3YJ, Guernsey
Tel.: (44) 1481 719 000
Web Site: http://www.credit-suisse.com
Financial Management Services
N.A.I.C.S.: 523999

Credit Suisse Group Finance (Guernsey) Limited (4)
Helvetia Court, PO Box 413, Saint Peter Port, GY1 3YJ, Guernsey
Tel.: (44) 1481724568
Financial Planning Services
N.A.I.C.S.: 523940

Credit Suisse Trust Holdings Ltd. (4)
Mill Court, Saint Peter Port, GY1 6A, Guernsey (100%)
Tel.: (44) 1481719100
Sales Range: $50-74.9 Million
Emp.: 80
International Financial Services Company; Provider of Institutional Asset Management & Corporate Investment Banking Services
N.A.I.C.S.: 523150
Andy Veron (Mng Dir)

Subsidiary (Non-US):

Credit Suisse (Hong Kong) Ltd. (3)
Level 88 One Austin Road West, Kowloon, China (Hong Kong) (100%)
Tel.: (852) 21016000
Sales Range: $50-74.9 Million
Emp.: 20
Investment Banking Services
N.A.I.C.S.: 523150

Subsidiary (Domestic):

Credit Suisse (International) Holding AG (4)
Bahnhofstrasse 17, Zurich, 6300, Switzerland
Tel.: (41) 44 212 16 16
Investment Management Service
N.A.I.C.S.: 523940

Subsidiary (Non-US):

Credit Suisse (Investment Banking) (3)
Avenida Ricardo Rivera Navarrete 501, Office B 7th Floor, 27, Lima, Peru
Tel.: (51) 14220500
Investment Banking Services
N.A.I.C.S.: 523150

Credit Suisse (Italy) S.p.A. (3)
Via Santa Margherita 3, 20121, Milan, Italy (100%)
Tel.: (39) 0288550471
Sales Range: $75-99.9 Million
Emp.: 200
Investment & Private Banking Services
N.A.I.C.S.: 523150

Credit Suisse (Lebanon) Finance S.A.L. (3)
Park Avenue BCD Berytus Park Mina'a el Hosn Bloc B 6th Floor, PO Box 11-966, Beirut, 2060, Lebanon
Tel.: (961) 1 95 66 00
Web Site: http://www.credit-suisse.com
Financial Management Services
N.A.I.C.S.: 523999

Credit Suisse (Luxembourg) S.A. (3)
5 Rue Jean Monnet, 2180, Luxembourg, Luxembourg (100%)
Tel.: (352) 4361611
Sales Range: Less than $1 Million
Emp.: 200
Private Banking Services
N.A.I.C.S.: 522180

Subsidiary (Domestic):

Credit Suisse Equity Fund Management Company SA (4)
5 Rue Jean Monnet, Luxembourg, 2180, Luxembourg (100%)
Tel.: (352) 4361611
Web Site: http://www.creditsussie.com
Sales Range: $1-9.9 Million
Emp.: 100
N.A.I.C.S.: 522299

Subsidiary (Non-US):

Credit Suisse Fund Management S.A. (4)
Tel.: (352) 4361611
Web Site: http://www.credit-suisse.com
Emp.: 15
Fund Management Services
N.A.I.C.S.: 523940

Subsidiary (Domestic):

Credit Suisse Fund Services (Luxembourg) S.A. (4)
5 Rue Jean Monnet, PO Box 369, 2013, Luxembourg, Luxembourg
Web Site: http://www.credit-suisse.com
Sales Range: $100-124.9 Million
Financial Management Services
N.A.I.C.S.: 523999

Subsidiary (Non-US):

Credit Suisse (Singapore) Limited (3)
One Raffles Link 03-01, Singapore, 039393, Singapore
Tel.: (65) 62126000
Provider of Investment Banking Services
N.A.I.C.S.: 523150

Credit Suisse (UK) Limited (3)
Five Cabot Square, London, E14 4QR, United Kingdom
Tel.: (44) 2078888000
Web Site: https://www.credit-suisse.com
Financial Planning Services
N.A.I.C.S.: 523940

Subsidiary (Domestic):

Credit Suisse Asset Management Ltd. (4)
One Cabot Square, London, E14 4QJ, United Kingdom (100%)
Tel.: (44) 2078888912
Sales Range: $150-199.9 Million
Emp.: 400
Investment Banking
N.A.I.C.S.: 523150

Credit Suisse International (4)
One Cabot Square, London, E14 4QJ, United Kingdom
Tel.: (44) 2078888888
Emp.: 7,000
Investment Banking
N.A.I.C.S.: 523150
Jerome Renard (Mng Dir)

Credit Suisse Securities Ltd. (4)
One Cabot Square, London, E144QJ, United Kingdom (100%)
Tel.: (44) 2078888888
Sales Range: $50-74.9 Million
Emp.: 100
International Financial Services Company; Provider of Institutional Asset Management & Corporate/Investment Banking Services
N.A.I.C.S.: 523940

Subsidiary (US):

Credit Suisse (USA), Inc. (3)
11 Madison Ave, New York, NY 10010-3629 (100%)
Tel.: (212) 325-2000

UBS GROUP AG

UBS Group AG—(Continued)
Sales Range: $1-4.9 Billion
Emp.: 10,465
Investment & Merchant Banking Services
N.A.I.C.S.: 523150
Lara J. Warner *(Member-Exec Bd)*

Branch (Domestic):

Credit Suisse (4)
11 Madison Ave, New York, NY 10010-3629
Tel.: (212) 325-2000
Rev.: $3,500,000
Emp.: 40
Security Brokers & Dealers
N.A.I.C.S.: 518210
Jose A. Figueroa *(Asst VP-Equities United States)*

Subsidiary (Domestic):

Credit Suisse Asset Management, LLC (4)
11 Madison Ave, New York, NY 10010-3629 **(100%)**
Tel.: (212) 325-2000
Sales Range: $150-199.9 Million
Emp.: 400
Asset Management for Institutional & Individual Investors
N.A.I.C.S.: 523940

Credit Suisse First Boston Mortgage Capital LLC (4)
11 Madison Ave, New York, NY 10010
Tel.: (212) 325-2000
Mortgage Loan Brokerage Services
N.A.I.C.S.: 522310

Credit Suisse Holdings (USA), Inc. (4)
11 Madison Ave, New York, NY 10010-3629
Tel.: (212) 325-2000
Investment Management Service
N.A.I.C.S.: 523940
Eric M. Varvel *(Pres & CEO)*

Credit Suisse Management LLC (4)
1 Madison Ave Ste 450, New York, NY 10010
Tel.: (212) 538-6320
Financial Planning Services
N.A.I.C.S.: 523940

Credit Suisse Private Equity, LLC (4)
11 Madison Ave, New York, NY 10010
Tel.: (212) 325-2000
Web Site: http://www.creditsuisse.com
Private Equity Investment Services
N.A.I.C.S.: 523999

Credit Suisse Securities (USA) LLC (4)
11 Madison Ave, New York, NY 10010 **(100%)**
Tel.: (212) 325-2000
Web Site: http://www.credit-suisse.com
Emp.: 9,050
Investment & Merchant Banking Services
N.A.I.C.S.: 523150

Subsidiary (Domestic):

Special Situations Holdings, Inc. Westbridge (5)
11 Madison Ave, New York, NY 10010
Tel.: (212) 325-2000
Holding Company
N.A.I.C.S.: 551112

Subsidiary (Domestic):

USHEALTH Group, Inc. (6)
300 Burnett St Ste200, Fort Worth, TX 76102-2734
Tel.: (817) 878-3300
Web Site: https://www.ushealthgroup.com
Sales Range: $200-249.9 Million
Emp.: 213
Insurance Services
N.A.I.C.S.: 524127
Bill Shelton *(Sr VP-Mktg)*

Subsidiary (Domestic):

Freedom Life Insurance Company (7)
300 Burnett St Ste 200, Fort Worth, TX 76102-7025 **(100%)**
Tel.: (817) 878-3303
Web Site: http://www.ushealthgroup.com
Sales Range: $25-49.9 Million
Emp.: 145
Health Insurance Services
N.A.I.C.S.: 524113

USHEALTH Career (7)
3100 Burnett Plz 801 Cherry St Unit 33, Fort Worth, TX 76102 **(100%)**
Tel.: (817) 878-3300
Web Site: http://www.ushealthgroup.com
Insurance Marketing Services
N.A.I.C.S.: 524298

Subsidiary (Domestic):

LifeStyles Marketing Group, Inc. (8)
3100 Burnett Plz 801 Cherry St Unit 33, Fort Worth, TX 76102 **(100%)**
Tel.: (817) 878-3300
Insurance Marketing Services
N.A.I.C.S.: 524298

Precision Dialing Services, Inc. (8)
1100 E Campbell Rd Ste 150, Richardson, TX 75081 **(100%)**
Tel.: (214) 343-7374
Emp.: 100
Telemarketing Services
N.A.I.C.S.: 561422

Subsidiary (Domestic):

Sprout Group (5)
11 Madison Ave 13th Fl, New York, NY 10010
Tel.: (212) 538-3600
Web Site: http://www.sproutgroup.com
Sales Range: $25-49.9 Million
Emp.: 36
Open-End Management Investment Services
N.A.I.C.S.: 525910

Stewart Stamping Corp. (5)
45 Old Waterbury Rd, Thomaston, CT 06787-1903
Tel.: (914) 965-0816
Web Site: http://www.insilco.com
Metal Stamping & Formed Wire Products
N.A.I.C.S.: 332119

Subsidiary (Non-US):

Credit Suisse Asesoria (Panama) S.A. (3)
Calle 50 con Calle Santo Domingo, Piso 39, Panama, Panama
Tel.: (507) 2941200
Web Site: http://www.credit-suisse.com
Financial Planning Services
N.A.I.C.S.: 523940

Credit Suisse Asia International (Cayman) Limited (3)
6/F No 109 Min-Sheng East Road Section 3, Taipei, Taiwan
Tel.: (886) 225445288
Financial Management Services
N.A.I.C.S.: 523999

Subsidiary (Domestic):

Credit Suisse Asset Management (3)
Gieshubelstrasse 40, 8045, Zurich, Switzerland **(100%)**
Tel.: (41) 3351111
Web Site: http://www.csam.com
Sales Range: $300-349.9 Million
Emp.: 600
Provider of Investment Services
N.A.I.C.S.: 523940

Credit Suisse Asset Management International Holding Ltd (3)
Schutzengasse 14, 8001, Zurich, Switzerland
Tel.: (41) 443331111
Emp.: 5,000
Investment Management Service
N.A.I.C.S.: 523940

Credit Suisse Bank (3)
St Alban-Graben 1-3, 4051, Basel, Switzerland **(100%)**
Tel.: (41) 612667711
Sales Range: $25-49.9 Million
Emp.: 50
Mortgage Banking Services
N.A.I.C.S.: 522292

Credit Suisse Bank (3)
Uetlibergstrasse 231, PO Box 700, 8070, Zurich, Switzerland **(100%)**
Tel.: (41) 443331111
N.A.I.C.S.: 522390

Subsidiary (Non-US):

Credit Suisse Brasil S.A. (3)
Avenida Brigadeiro Faria Lima 3064 13 andar, Itaim Bibi, 01451 000, Sao Paulo, Brazil **(100%)**
Tel.: (55) 1138416800
Web Site: https://www.credit-suisse.com
Sales Range: $150-199.9 Million
Emp.: 300
Investment Banking Services
N.A.I.C.S.: 523150

Subsidiary (Domestic):

Banco Credit Suisse (Brasil) S.A. (4)
Av Brigadeiro Faria Lima 3064 - 13 Andar Parte, Jardim Paulistano, Sao Paulo, 01451-000, Brazil
Tel.: (55) 1138416000
Web Site: http://www.credit-suisse.com
Financial Planning Services
N.A.I.C.S.: 523940

Credit Suisse (Brasil) Distribuidora de Titulos e Valores Mobiliarios S.A. (4)
Avenida Brigadeiro Faria Lima 3064 - 13 andar, Sao Paulo, 01451-000, Brazil
Tel.: (55) 1138416800
Financial Planning Services
N.A.I.C.S.: 523940

Credit Suisse (Brasil) S.A. Corretora de Titulos e Valores Mobiliarios (4)
Av Brig Faria Lima 3064 - 13 floor, Sao Paulo, 01451-000, Brazil
Tel.: (55) 1138416000
Financial Planning Services
N.A.I.C.S.: 523940

Subsidiary (Non-US):

Credit Suisse Consultaciones y Servicios S.A. (3)
Av Luis Alberto de Herrera 1248 Torre B Piso 9, 11300, Montevideo, Uruguay **(19%)**
Tel.: (598) 2 622 9393
Web Site: http://www.creditsuisse.com
Sales Range: $75-99.9 Million
Emp.: 6
Private Banking Services
N.A.I.C.S.: 522299

Subsidiary (Domestic):

Credit Suisse Entrepreneur Capital AG
Uetlibergstrasse 231, 8070, Zurich, Switzerland
Banking Services
N.A.I.C.S.: 522110

Subsidiary (Non-US):

Credit Suisse Equities (Australia) Limited (3)
L 31 Gateway 1 Macquarie Pl, Sydney, 2000, NSW, Australia
Tel.: (61) 282054400
Web Site: http://www.credit-suisse.com
Financial Planning Services
N.A.I.C.S.: 523940

Credit Suisse Founder Securities Limited (3)
15/F South Tower Financial Street Centre No A9 Financial Street, Xi Cheng District, Beijing, 100033, China
Tel.: (86) 1066538666
Web Site: http://www.csfounder.com
Security Services
N.A.I.C.S.: 561621

Credit Suisse France (3)
25 Ave Kleber, 75009, Paris, France **(100%)**
Tel.: (33) 149705800
Web Site: http://www.credit-suisse.com
Sales Range: $75-99.9 Million
Emp.: 120
Investment & Private Banking Services
N.A.I.C.S.: 523150

Credit Suisse Hedging-Griffo Corretora de Valores S.A. (3)
Rua Leopoldo Couto de Magalhaes Jr 700 11 andar, Itaim Bibi, Sao Paulo, 04542-000, SP, Brazil
Tel.: (55) 1137018669
Banking Services
N.A.I.C.S.: 522110

Credit Suisse Holdings (Australia) Limited (3)
1 Macquarie Place Level 31, Sydney, 2000, NSW, Australia
Tel.: (61) 282054400
Investment Management Service
N.A.I.C.S.: 523940
Rob Stewart *(CEO)*

Subsidiary (Domestic):

Credit Suisse IT Services AG (3)
Zurichstrasse 8, 8600, Dubendorf, Switzerland **(100%)**
Tel.: (41) 448029292
Web Site: http://www.credit-suisse.com
Sales Range: $50-74.9 Million
Emp.: 120
IT Services
N.A.I.C.S.: 519290

Subsidiary (Non-US):

Credit Suisse Investment Services (Cayman) (3)
802 West Bay Road, PO Box KY1-1104, Georgetown, Grand Cayman, Cayman Islands
Tel.: (345) 949 7942
Web Site: http://www.credit-suisse.com
Investment Banking Services
N.A.I.C.S.: 523150

Credit Suisse Istanbul Menkul Degerler A.S. (3)
Levazim Mahallesi Koru Sokak No 2 Zorlu Center Terasevler No 61, Besiktas, 34340, Istanbul, Turkiye
Tel.: (90) 2123490400
Banking Services
N.A.I.C.S.: 522110

Subsidiary (Domestic):

Credit Suisse Leasing AG (3)
Thurgauerstrasse 56, Zurich, 8070, Switzerland **(100%)**
Tel.: (41) 13342800
Web Site: http://www.creditsuisse.com
Sales Range: $125-149.9 Million
Emp.: 130
N.A.I.C.S.: 532210

Subsidiary (Non-US):

Credit Suisse Life & Pensions (3)
Rakoczi UT 70 72, Budapest, 1074, Hungary **(65%)**
Tel.: (36) 014135100
Web Site: http://www.axa.hu
Insurance Provider
N.A.I.C.S.: 524128

Credit Suisse Life & Pensions AG (3)
Pradafant 21, 9490, Vaduz, Liechtenstein
Tel.: (423) 230 17 60
Web Site: http://www.credit-suisse.com
General Insurance Services
N.A.I.C.S.: 524210

Credit Suisse Life (Bermuda) Ltd. (3)
5 Park Road, Hamilton, HM 09, Bermuda
Tel.: (441) 3330369
Financial Management Services
N.A.I.C.S.: 523999

Credit Suisse Saudi Arabia (3)
Tel.: (966) 12039700
Web Site: http://www.credit-suisse.com
Financial Management Services
N.A.I.C.S.: 523999

Credit Suisse Securities (Canada), Inc. (3)
1 First Canadian Place 100 King Street West Suite 2900, Toronto, M5X 1C9, ON, Canada

AND PRIVATE COMPANIES

Tel.: (416) 352-4500
Web Site: http://www.credit-suisse.com
Securities Brokerage Services
N.A.I.C.S.: 523150

Credit Suisse Securities (Hong Kong) Limited (3)
Level 88 One Austin Road West, Kowloon, China (Hong Kong)
Tel.: (852) 21016000
Investment Banking Services
N.A.I.C.S.: 523150

Credit Suisse Securities (India) Private Limited (3)
9 Floor Ceejay House Plot F Shivsagar Estate, Dr Annie Besant Road Worli, Mumbai, 400018, India
Tel.: (91) 2267773777
Securities Brokerage Services
N.A.I.C.S.: 523150

Credit Suisse Securities (Japan) Limited (3)
24th floor Izumi Garden Tower 1-6-1 Roppongi, Minato-ku, Tokyo, 106-6024, Japan
Tel.: (81) 345509000
Web Site: https://www.credit-suisse.com
Investment Banking
N.A.I.C.S.: 523150

Credit Suisse Securities (Johannesburg) (Proprietary) Limited (3)
2nd Floor Building 3 Inanda Greens 54 Wierda Road, Wierda Valley, Sandton, 2146, South Africa
Tel.: (27) 110128000
Financial Investment Services
N.A.I.C.S.: 523999

Credit Suisse Securities (Thailand) Limited (3)
Tel.: (66) 26146000
Web Site: http://www.credit-suisse.com
Sales Range: $50-74.9 Million
Emp.: 32
Financial Management Services
N.A.I.C.S.: 523999

Credit Suisse Services (India) Private Limited (3)
9 Floor Ceejay House Plot F Shivsagar Estate Dr Annie Besant Road, Mumbai, 400 018, India
Tel.: (91) 2267773777
Banking Services
N.A.I.C.S.: 522110

LLC Credit Suisse Securities (3)
Romanov pereulok 4 Building 2, 125009, Moscow, Russia
Tel.: (7) 495 967 8200
Web Site: http://www.credit-suisse-securities-moscow.ru
Sales Range: $200-249.9 Million
Emp.: 300
Securities Trading Services
N.A.I.C.S.: 523150

Limited Liability Partnership "Credit Suisse (Kazakhstan)" (3)
77/7 Al-Farabi Avenue Esentai Towers Building Centre 8th Floor, 050040, Almaty, Kazakhstan
Tel.: (7) 727 356 2727
Web Site: http://www.credit-suisse.com
Securities Trading Services
N.A.I.C.S.: 523150

Affiliate (Non-US):

McLarens Young International Panama (3)
(12%)
Web Site: http://www.mclarensyoung.com
Sales Range: $50-74.9 Million
Emp.: 12
Financial Services
N.A.I.C.S.: 523999

Representative Office (Non-US):

Oficina de Representacion de Credit Suisse AG (3)
Avda Francisco de Miranda Edificio Cavendes Los Palos, Grandes Office 1401 Piso 14, Caracas, 1060, Venezuela
Tel.: (58) 21 2283 6422
Financial Management Services
N.A.I.C.S.: 523999

Subsidiary (Non-US):

PT Credit Suisse Securities Indonesia (3)
Gedung Sampoerna Strategic Square South Tower 23rd floor, Jalan Jenderal Sudirman Kav45, Jakarta, 12930, Indonesia
Tel.: (62) 2125537900
Web Site: https://www.credit-suisse.com
Financial Planning Services
N.A.I.C.S.: 523940

Subsidiary (Domestic):

Credit Suisse Funds AG (2)
Sihlcity Kalandergasse 4, 8045, Zurich, Switzerland
Tel.: (41) 2123252000
Rev.: $20,255,526,591
Assets: $537,802,474,393
Liabilities: $492,501,784,870
Net Worth: $45,300,689,523
Earnings: ($488,946,995)
Emp.: 28,840
Fiscal Year-end: 12/31/2023
Investment Management Service
N.A.I.C.S.: 523999

Fides Treasury Services Ltd. (2)
Raeffelstrasse 28, 8045, Zurich, Switzerland (100%)
Tel.: (41) 442986566
Web Site: https://www.fides.ch
Sales Range: $25-49.9 Million
Emp.: 45
Financial Services & Software
N.A.I.C.S.: 334610
Andreas Lutz *(CEO)*

Neue Aargauer Bank (2)
Bahnhofstrasse 49, 5001, Aarau, Switzerland (98%)
Tel.: (41) 564627100
Web Site: http://www.nab.ch
Sales Range: $350-399.9 Million
Emp.: 900
Full Banking Services
N.A.I.C.S.: 522320

Savoy Hotel Baur en Ville AG (2)
Paradeplatz, Zurich, 8022, Switzerland
Tel.: (41) 44 215 25 25
Web Site: http://www.savoy-baurenville.ch
Home Management Services
N.A.I.C.S.: 721110

Joint Venture (Domestic):

Swisscard AECS AG (2)
Neugasse 18, 8810, Horgen, Switzerland
Tel.: (41) 446596492
Web Site: https://www.swisscard.ch
Sales Range: $150-199.9 Million
Emp.: 400
Credit Cards
N.A.I.C.S.: 522210

Swisscard AECS GmbH (1)
Neugasse 18, 8810, Horgen, Switzerland (50%)
Tel.: (41) 446596492
Web Site: https://www.swisscard.ch
Emp.: 700
Credit Card Providers
N.A.I.C.S.: 522210
Florence Schnydrig Moser *(CEO)*

UBS AG (1)
Bahnhofstrasse 45, 8001, Zurich, Switzerland
Tel.: (41) 442341111
Rev.: $34,915,000,000
Assets: $1,105,436,000,000
Liabilities: $1,048,496,000,000
Net Worth: $56,940,000,000
Earnings: $7,084,000,000
Emp.: 47,628
Fiscal Year-end: 12/31/2022
Investment Banking, Asset & Wealth Management Services
N.A.I.C.S.: 523150
Markus U. Diethelm *(Member-Exec Bd & Gen Counsel)*

Subsidiary (Domestic):

Aventic Partners AG (2)
Giesshubelstrasse 4, CH 8027, Zurich, Switzerland (100%)
Tel.: (41) 12851585
Web Site: http://www.aventic.ch

Sales Range: $50-74.9 Million
Emp.: 4
Provider of Individual & Corporate Banking Services
N.A.I.C.S.: 522320

Subsidiary (Non-US):

CCR Asset Management S.A. (2)
44 rue Washington, 75008, Paris, France
Tel.: (33) 1 49 53 21 40
Web Site: http://www.ccr-am.com
Sales Range: $50-74.9 Million
Emp.: 80
Asset Management Services
N.A.I.C.S.: 523940

Caisse Centrale de Reescompte, S.A. (2)
Tel.: (33) 149532000
Sales Range: $75-99.9 Million
Emp.: 100
Asset Management Services
N.A.I.C.S.: 523999

Subsidiary (Non-US):

CCR Actions S.A. (3)
Tel.: (33) 149532000
Asset Management Services
N.A.I.C.S.: 523999

CCR Gestion S.A. (3)
Tel.: (33) 149532000
Asset Management Services
N.A.I.C.S.: 523999

Subsidiary (Domestic):

Factors AG (2)
Weberstrasse 5, Zurich, 8036, Switzerland (100%)
Tel.: (41) 442983262
Web Site: http://www.factors.ch
Sales Range: $1-9.9 Million
Emp.: 65
Individual & Corporate Banking Services
N.A.I.C.S.: 522320

Subsidiary (Non-US):

OOO UBS Bank (2)
2/2 Paveletskaya Ploshchad, 115054, Moscow, Russia
Tel.: (7) 4956482000
Web Site: http://www.ubs.com
Investment Banking Services
N.A.I.C.S.: 523940
Dufur Natalia Georgievna *(Deputy Chm-Exec Bd & Member-Mgmt Bd)*

Affiliate (Non-US):

Swiss Advisory Group S.A. (2)
Edificio Laminar Calle Ing Butty No 240 Piso 18, C1001AFB, Buenos Aires, Argentina (100%)
Tel.: (54) 11 4316 0200
Web Site: http://www.ubs.com.ar
Sales Range: $50-74.9 Million
Emp.: 20
Private Equity Services
N.A.I.C.S.: 523999

Subsidiary (Domestic):

Topcard Service AG (2)
Flughofstrasse 35, 8152, Glattbrugg, CH, Switzerland
Tel.: (41) 225937365
Web Site: https://www.topcard.ch
Financial Planning Services
N.A.I.C.S.: 523940

Subsidiary (Non-US):

UBS (Bahamas) Ltd. (2)
1st Floor East Bay Street, PO Box N-7757, 00000, Nassau, Bahamas
Tel.: (242) 3949300
Private Banking Services
N.A.I.C.S.: 523150

UBS (France) SA (2)
69 Boulevard Haussmann, 75008, Paris, France (100%)
Tel.: (33) 144564545
Sales Range: $100-124.9 Million
Emp.: 200
Provider of Private Banking Services
N.A.I.C.S.: 522180

UBS GROUP AG

Subsidiary (Non-US):

UBS La Maison de Gestion SAS (3)
Tel.: (33) 153052800
Web Site: http://www.lamaisondegestion.com
Commercial Banking Services
N.A.I.C.S.: 522110

Subsidiary (Non-US):

UBS (India) Private Ltd (2)
2/F 3 North Avenue Bandra- Kurla Complex, Bandra East, Mumbai, 400 051, India
Tel.: (91) 2261556000
Investment Banking Services
N.A.I.C.S.: 523150

UBS (Italia) S.p.A. (2)
Via Del Vecchio Politecnico 3, 20121, Milan, Italy (100%)
Tel.: (39) 02762651
Web Site: https://www.ubs.com
Sales Range: $100-124.9 Million
Emp.: 250
Provider of Private Banking Services
N.A.I.C.S.: 522180

Subsidiary (Domestic):

UBS Italia SIM S.p.A. (3)
Via Santa Margherita 16, 21100, Milan, Italy
Tel.: (39) 02721001
Web Site: http://www.ubs.com
Sales Range: $25-49.9 Million
Emp.: 50
Securities Brokerage & Dealing Services
N.A.I.C.S.: 523150

Subsidiary (Non-US):

UBS (Luxembourg) S.A. (2)
33A avenue J F Kennedy, 1855, Luxembourg, Luxembourg (100%)
Tel.: (352) 451211
Sales Range: $200-249.9 Million
Emp.: 400
Provider of Private Banking Services
N.A.I.C.S.: 522180

UBS (Monaco) SA (2)
2 Ave De Grande Bretagne, MC 98000, Monaco, Cedex, Monaco (100%)
Tel.: (377) 93155815
Web Site: http://www.ubs.com
Sales Range: $100-124.9 Million
Emp.: 135
Provider of Private Banking Services
N.A.I.C.S.: 522180

UBS (Trust & Banking) Limited (2)
E Tower Otemachi 1 Sq 5-1 Otemachi 1-Chome, Tokyo, 100 0004, Japan
Tel.: (81) 352933500
Web Site: http://www.ubs.com
Provider of Asset Management Services
N.A.I.C.S.: 531390

UBS (Uruguay) Ltda. (2)
Calle 27 Los Muergos, Punta del Este, Uruguay
Tel.: (598) 42 44 2582
Financial Planning Services
N.A.I.C.S.: 523940

Representative Office (Non-US):

UBS AG - Hong Kong (2)
2 International Finance Centre, 52/F 8 Finance Street, Central, China (Hong Kong) (100%)
Tel.: (852) 29718888
Web Site: http://www.ubs.com
Sales Range: $1-4.9 Billion
Emp.: 2,000
Commercial, Private & Investment Banking Services
N.A.I.C.S.: 522110

UBS AG - Singapore (2)
One Raffles Quay, #50-01 North Tower, Singapore, 48583, Singapore
Tel.: (65) 64958000
Web Site: http://www.ubs.com
Sales Range: $1-4.9 Billion
Emp.: 1,500
Commercial, Private & Investment Banking Services
N.A.I.C.S.: 522110

UBS GROUP AG — INTERNATIONAL PUBLIC

UBS Group AG—(Continued)

Branch (US):

UBS AG Miami Agency (2)
701 Brickell Ave Ste 3250, Miami, FL 33131-2847 **(100%)**
Tel.: (305) 375-0110
Web Site: http://www.ubs.com
Sales Range: $50-74.9 Million
Emp.: 65
Provider of Private Banking Services
N.A.I.C.S.: 523150

Subsidiary (Non-US):

UBS Asesores S.A. (2)
(100%)
Tel.: (507) 2067000
Banking Services
N.A.I.C.S.: 522299

UBS Asia Equities Limited (2)
Two International Finance Cent 8 Finance Street, Central, 518000, China (Hong Kong)
Tel.: (852) 29718888
Financial Planning Services
N.A.I.C.S.: 523940

UBS Asset Management (Singapore) Ltd. (2)
9 Penang Rd, 18 00 Suntec Tower 5, Singapore, 238459, Singapore **(100%)**
Tel.: (65) 6564958000
Sales Range: $25-49.9 Million
Emp.: 15
Asset Management
N.A.I.C.S.: 531890
Rene Buehlmann (Head-Asia Pacific)

UBS Australia Ltd. (2)
(100%)
Tel.: (61) 293242000
Web Site: http://www.apps1.ubs.com
Sales Range: $700-749.9 Million
Emp.: 1,500
Banking
N.A.I.C.S.: 522299

Subsidiary (Non-US):

UBS Global Asset Management (Australia) Ltd. (3)
Tel.: (61) 392426500
Sales Range: $150-199.9 Million
Emp.: 300
Provider of Asset Management Services
N.A.I.C.S.: 531390

Subsidiary (Non-US):

UBS Bank (Canada) (2)
154 University Ave Suite 800, Toronto, M5H 3Z4, ON, Canada **(100%)**
Tel.: (416) 345-7099
Web Site: http://www.ubs.com
Sales Range: $50-74.9 Million
Emp.: 90
Investment Banking Services
N.A.I.C.S.: 523150
Ricardo Gonzalez (Chm)

Subsidiary (Domestic):

UBS Bank (3)
154 University Avenue Suite 800, Toronto, M5H 3Z4, ON, Canada **(100%)**
Tel.: (416) 343-1800
Web Site: http://www.ubs.ca
Sales Range: $75-99.9 Million
Emp.: 85
Commericial Banking
N.A.I.C.S.: 522299

UBS Securities (Canada), Inc. (3)
161 Bay Street Suite 4000 Brookfield Place Canada Trust Tower, Toronto, M5J 2S1, ON, Canada **(100%)**
Tel.: (416) 364-3293
Web Site: http://www.ubs.ca
Sales Range: $75-99.9 Million
Emp.: 110
Private Banking Services
N.A.I.C.S.: 523150

Subsidiary (Non-US):

UBS Bank (Netherlands) B.V. (2)
Amstelplein 1 18th Floor, Amstelplein, 1096 HA, Amsterdam, Netherlands
Tel.: (31) 205510100

Financial Planning Services
N.A.I.C.S.: 523940

UBS Bank USA (2)
Tel.: (801) 741-0310
Web Site: http://www.ubs.com
Commercial Banking Services
N.A.I.C.S.: 522110
Andreas Wyler (Mng Dir & Chief Risk Officer)

UBS Capital Asia Pacific (HK) Ltd. (2)
52nd Fl 2 International Finance Ctr, 8 Connaught Pl, Central, China (Hong Kong) **(100%)**
Tel.: (852) 29718887
Provider of Private Equity Services
N.A.I.C.S.: 522299

UBS Capital GmbH (2)
Europaplatz 1, Munich, 81675, Germany **(100%)**
Tel.: (49) 6921790
Web Site: http://www.ubs.com
Sales Range: $50-74.9 Million
Emp.: 45
Provider of Private Equity Services
N.A.I.C.S.: 522299

Subsidiary (US):

UBS Capital LLC (2)
299 Park Ave 26th Fl, New York, NY 10171-0002
Tel.: (212) 821-3000
Sales Range: $50-74.9 Million
Emp.: 15
Private Equity Services
N.A.I.C.S.: 522220

Subsidiary (Non-US):

UBS Capital S.p.A. (2)
Via Santa Margherita 16, I 20121, Milan, Italy **(100%)**
Tel.: (39) 02721001
Web Site: http://www.ibb.ubs.com
Sales Range: $50-74.9 Million
Emp.: 15
Private Equity Services
N.A.I.C.S.: 522180

UBS Capital Securities (Jersey) Limited (2)
1 IFC, Saint Helier, JE2 3BX, Jersey
Tel.: (44) 1534701000
Security Brokerage Services
N.A.I.C.S.: 523150

Subsidiary (Domestic):

UBS Card Center AG (2)
Flughofstrasse 35, CH 8152, Glattbrugg, Switzerland **(100%)**
Tel.: (41) 18283135
Web Site: http://www.cardcenter.ch
Sales Range: $50-74.9 Million
Emp.: 12
N.A.I.C.S.: 522299

Subsidiary (Non-US):

UBS Derivatives Hong Kong Limited (2)
2 International Finance 52 Floor Centre 8 Finance Street, Central, China (Hong Kong)
Tel.: (852) 2971 8888
Web Site: http://www.ubs.com
Financial Planning Services
N.A.I.C.S.: 523940

UBS Espana, S.A. (2)
Maria de Molina 4, E 28006, Madrid, Spain **(100%)**
Tel.: (34) 917457000
Web Site: http://www.ubs.com
Sales Range: $200-249.9 Million
Emp.: 400
Private Banking Services
N.A.I.C.S.: 523150

UBS Fiduciaria S.p.A. (2)
Via del Vecchio Politecnico 3, 20121, Milan, Italy
Tel.: (39) 0276398128
Financial Management Services
N.A.I.C.S.: 523999

Subsidiary (US):

UBS Financial Services Inc. (2)

1285 Ave of the Americas, New York, NY 10019
Tel.: (212) 649-8000
Sales Range: $1-4.9 Billion
Emp.: 16,000
Holding Company; Investment Advisory Services, Securities Brokerage Services, Investment Banking & Related Services
N.A.I.C.S.: 523150

Subsidiary (Domestic):

Financial Counselors Inc. (3)
5901 College Blvd Str 100, Kansas City, MO 66211
Tel.: (816) 329-1500
Sales Range: $50-74.9 Million
Emp.: 25
Investment Advisory Services
N.A.I.C.S.: 523940
Robert T. Hunter (Pres & CEO)

UBS Capital Markets (3)
1000 Harbor Blvd, Weehawken, NJ 07086
Tel.: (201) 352-3000
Web Site: http://www.ubs.com
Sales Range: $25-49.9 Million
Emp.: 220
Internet Investment Banking & Brokerage
N.A.I.C.S.: 541611

UBS Financial Services Inc. (3)
299 Park Ave 8th 9th 11th fl, New York, NY 10171-0002
Tel.: (212) 821-7000
Provider of Corporate & Institutional Banking Services
N.A.I.C.S.: 522110
Abby Vaughn (VP-Wealth Mgmt-Lexington)

UBS Financial Services Inc. (3)
1000 Main St Ste 2600, Houston, TX 77002-2548
Tel.: (713) 654-0200
Sales Range: $50-74.9 Million
Emp.: 100
Dealers, Security
N.A.I.C.S.: 523150

UBS Securities, LLC (3)
1285 Avenue of the Americas, Boston, NY 10019
Tel.: (212) 713-2000
Web Site: http://www.ubs.com
Brokerage Services
N.A.I.C.S.: 523150

Subsidiary (US):

UBS Fund Advisor, L.L.C. (2)
51 W 52nd St, New York, NY 10019-6119
Tel.: (212) 713-2000
Financial Management Services
N.A.I.C.S.: 523999

Subsidiary (Non-US):

UBS Fund Services (Cayman) Ltd. (2)
UBS House 227 Elgin Ave, Georgetown, KY1 1103, Grand Cayman, Cayman Islands
Tel.: (345) 9141000
Web Site: http://www.ubs.com
Sales Range: $100-124.9 Million
Emp.: 160
Fund Administration
N.A.I.C.S.: 525910

UBS Fund Services (Ireland) Limited (2)
Web Site: http://www.ubs.com
Sales Range: $50-74.9 Million
Emp.: 80
Fund Management Services
N.A.I.C.S.: 523940

Subsidiary (US):

UBS Global Asset Management (Americas) Inc. (2)
1 N Wacker Dr, Chicago, IL 60606
Tel.: (312) 525-7100
Sales Range: $100-124.9 Million
Emp.: 250
Provider of Asset Management Services
N.A.I.C.S.: 523150
Federico Kaune (Mng Dir & Head-Emerging Markets Debt)

Subsidiary (Non-US):

UBS Global Asset Management (Canada) Co. (3)

161 Bay Street Suite 400, PO Box 617, Toronto, M5J 2S1, ON, Canada **(100%)**
Tel.: (416) 681-5200
Sales Range: $50-74.9 Million
Emp.: 75
Investment Services
N.A.I.C.S.: 523940

Subsidiary (Domestic):

UBS Global Asset Management (US) Inc. (3)
51 W 52nd St, New York, NY 10019 **(100%)**
Tel.: (212) 882-5000
Web Site: http://www.ubs.com
Sales Range: $75-99.9 Million
Emp.: 181
Provides Investment Advisory & Portfolio Management Services To Domestic & Foreign Institutions, Individuals & Mutual & Money Market Funds
N.A.I.C.S.: 523150

Unit (Domestic):

UBS Infrastructure Asset Management (4)
51 W 52nd St, New York, NY 10019.
Tel.: (212) 882-5000
Web Site: http://www.ubs.com
Investment Services
N.A.I.C.S.: 523999

Joint Venture (Domestic):

Northern Star Generation Services Company LLC (5)
2929 Allen Pkwy Ste 3275, Houston, TX 77019
Tel.: (713) 580-6300
Web Site: https://northernstargeneration.com
Emp.: 30
Power Generation Services
N.A.I.C.S.: 324199
Joe M. Stevens Jr. (VP-HR & Dev)

Subsidiary (Domestic):

Cambria Cogen Inc. (6)
243 Rubisch Rd, Ebensburg, PA 15931-4500
Tel.: (814) 472-1120
Web Site: http://www.northernstargeneration.com
Rev: $310,000
Emp.: 45
Electric Power Generation
N.A.I.C.S.: 221118
David Simms (Co-Pres)

Subsidiary (Non-US):

UBS Global Asset Management (Deutschland) GmbH (2)
Bockenheimer Landstrasse 2-4, 60306, Frankfurt am Main, Germany **(100%)**
Tel.: (49) 6913695300
Sales Range: $50-74.9 Million
Emp.: 4
Provider of Asset Management Services
N.A.I.C.S.: 531390

UBS Global Asset Management (France) SA (2)
69 Blvd Haussmann, Paris, 75008, France **(100%)**
Tel.: (33) 144564545
Web Site: http://www.ubs.com
Sales Range: $25-49.9 Million
Emp.: 200
Asset Management Services
N.A.I.C.S.: 523999

UBS Global Asset Management (Hong Kong) Limited (2)
52/F Two International Finance Centre 8 Finance Street, Central, China (Hong Kong)
Tel.: (852) 02971 8888
Web Site: http://www.ubs.com
Financial Management Services
N.A.I.C.S.: 523999

UBS Global Asset Management (Japan) Limited (2)
E Tower Otemachi 1st Square, Chiyoda Ku, Tokyo, 1000004, Japan **(100%)**
Tel.: (81) 352933700
Web Site: http://www.ubsglobal.com

AND PRIVATE COMPANIES   UBS GROUP AG

Provider of Asset Management Services
N.A.I.C.S.: 531390

UBS Global Asset Management (Singapore) Ltd (2)
One Raffles Quay 50-01 North Tower, Singapore, 048583, Singapore
Tel.: (65) 64958000
Investment Management Service
N.A.I.C.S.: 523940

UBS Global Asset Management (Taiwan) Ltd (2)
Web Site: http://www.ubs.com
Private Banking Services
N.A.I.C.S.: 522110

UBS Global Asset Management (UK) Ltd. (2)
5 Broadgate, London, EC2M 2QS, United Kingdom (100%)
Tel.: (44) 2075678000
Sales Range: $250-299.9 Million
Emp.: 750
Provider of Asset Management Services
N.A.I.C.S.: 531390
Graham Kane *(Head-Retail-UK)*

UBS Global Asset Management Funds Ltd (2)
5 Broadgate, London, EC2M 2QS, United Kingdom
Tel.: (44) 2075678000
Asset Management Services
N.A.I.C.S.: 523940

UBS Global Asset Management Holding Ltd (2)
5 Broadgate, London, EC2M 2QS, United Kingdom
Tel.: (44) 2075678000
Asset Management Services
N.A.I.C.S.: 523940
Oliver Bilal *(Head-EMEA)*

UBS Global Trust Corporation (2)
161 Bay St Ste 4100, Toronto, M5J 2S1, ON, Canada
Tel.: (416) 364-3293
Financial Management Services
N.A.I.C.S.: 523999

UBS Hong Kong Nominees Ltd. (2)
2 International Finance Centre 52/F 8 Finance Street, Central, China (Hong Kong)
Tel.: (852) 2971 8888
Web Site: http://www.ubs.com
Financial Planning & Bank Investment Services
N.A.I.C.S.: 523940

UBS International Holdings B.V. (2)
Amstelplein 1 18th Floor Rembrandt Tower, 1096 HA, Amsterdam, Netherlands
Tel.: (31) 205510100
Emp.: 30
Financial Management Services
N.A.I.C.S.: 523999

UBS Invest Kapitalanlagegesellschaft mbH (2)
Bockenheimer Landstrasse 2-4, 60306, Frankfurt am Main, Germany (100%)
Tel.: (49) 6921790
Sales Range: $25-49.9 Million
Emp.: 50
Provider of Asset Management Services
N.A.I.C.S.: 531390

Division (Domestic):

UBS Investment Bank (2)
PO Box AG, CH-8098, Zurich, Switzerland
Tel.: (41) 442341111
Web Site: http://www.ibb.ubs.com
Investment Banking & Securities Brokerage Services
N.A.I.C.S.: 523150

Subsidiary (Non-US):

PT UBS Securities Indonesia (3) (100%)
Sales Range: $25-49.9 Million
Emp.: 20
Corporate & Institutional Banking Services
N.A.I.C.S.: 236220

UBS (South Africa) (Pty) Ltd. (3)
64 Wierda Rd E, Sandton, 2196, ZA, South Africa
Tel.: (27) 13227000
Web Site: http://www.ubswarburg.com
Sales Range: $50-74.9 Million
Emp.: 90
Provider of Banking Services
N.A.I.C.S.: 522320

Subsidiary (US):

UBS Investment Bank (3)
1 N Wacker Dr Fl 31, Chicago, IL 60606
Tel.: (312) 525-5000
Web Site: http://www.ubs.com
Sales Range: $5-14.9 Billion
Emp.: 66,000
Provider of Corporate & Institutional Banking Services
N.A.I.C.S.: 523150

Subsidiary (Non-US):

UBS Investment Bank AG (3)
Bockenheimer Landstrasse 224, Frankfurt am Main, 60306, Germany (100%)
Tel.: (49) 6913690
Web Site: http://www.ubs.com
Sales Range: $600-649.9 Million
Emp.: 1,200
Provider of Corporate & Institutional Banking Services
N.A.I.C.S.: 523150

UBS Investment Bank UK (3)
1 Finsbury Ave, London, EC2M 2PP, United Kingdom (100%)
Tel.: (44) 2075678000
Web Site: http://www.ubs.com
Sales Range: $600-649.9 Million
Emp.: 1,956
Asset Management & Banking Services
N.A.I.C.S.: 522320

UBS New Zealand Ltd. (3)
HSBC Tower 188 Quay Street, PO Box 45, Auckland, 1010, New Zealand (100%)
Tel.: (64) 99134800
Web Site: https://www.ubs.com
Sales Range: $25-49.9 Million
Emp.: 26
Provider of Corporate & Institutional Banking Services
N.A.I.C.S.: 236220

UBS Securites India Private Ltd. (3) (100%)
Web Site: http://www.ubswarburg.com
Sales Range: $25-49.9 Million
Emp.: 50
Provider of Corporate & Institutional Banking Services
N.A.I.C.S.: 522299

UBS Securities (Espana) S.V., S.A. (3)
Maria De Molina 4, 28006, Madrid, Spain (100%)
Tel.: (34) 914369000
Web Site: http://www.ubswarburg.com
Sales Range: $25-49.9 Million
Emp.: 60
Provider of Corporate & Institutional Banking Services
N.A.I.C.S.: 236220

UBS Securities Australia Ltd. (3) (100%)
Tel.: (61) 293242000
Web Site: http://www.ubs.com
Sales Range: $350-399.9 Million
Emp.: 1,700
Provider of Corporate & Institutional Banking Services
N.A.I.C.S.: 236220

Branch (Domestic):

UBS Securities Australia Ltd. - Melbourne (4)
Level 16 8 Exhibition St, Melbourne, 3000, VIC, Australia
Tel.: (61) 392426100
Web Site: http://www.ubs.com
Sales Range: $100-124.9 Million
Emp.: 400
Provider of Corporate & Institutional Banking Services
N.A.I.C.S.: 236220

Subsidiary (Non-US):

UBS Securities CJSC (3)
2/2 Paveletskaya Ploshchad, Moscow, 115054, Russia
Tel.: (7) 4956 48 20 00
Securities Brokerage Services
N.A.I.C.S.: 523150

Affiliate (Non-US):

UBS Securities Canada, Inc (3)
161 Bay Street Suite 400, PO Box 617, Toronto, M5J 2S1, ON, Canada (51%)
Tel.: (416) 364-3293
Web Site: http://www.ubsw.com
Sales Range: $75-99.9 Million
Emp.: 150
Provider of Corporate Financial Services
N.A.I.C.S.: 523940

Subsidiary (Domestic):

UBS Securities Canada, Inc. (4)
161 Bay Street Suite 4000 Brookfield Place Canada Trust Tower, PO Box 617, Toronto, M5J 2S1, ON, Canada (100%)
Tel.: (416) 364-3293
Sales Range: $75-99.9 Million
Emp.: 120
Provider of Investment Banking Services
N.A.I.C.S.: 522320

Subsidiary (Non-US):

UBS Securities France S.A. (3) (100%)
Tel.: (33) 48883030
Web Site: http://www.ubswarburg.com
Sales Range: $100-124.9 Million
Emp.: 114
Provider of Corporate & Institutional Banking Services
N.A.I.C.S.: 236220

UBS Securities India Private Limited (3)
2/F 3 North Avenue Maker Maxity, Bandra East, Mumbai, 400051, India
Tel.: (91) 2261556000
Financial Advisory Services
N.A.I.C.S.: 523940

UBS Securities Israel Ltd. (3)
8 Hachoshlim St 7th Floor, Herzliya Pituach, 4672408, Israel (100%)
Tel.: (972) 98789100
Sales Range: $50-74.9 Million
Emp.: 20
Banking Services
N.A.I.C.S.: 522320

UBS Securities Japan Preparation Co., Ltd. (3)
Otemachi One Tower 23F-24F 2-1 Otemachi 1-chome, Chiyoda-ku, Tokyo, 100-0004, Japan
Tel.: (81) 352086000
Financial Management Services
N.A.I.C.S.: 523999

UBS Securities Ltd. (3)
9F Centropolis B 26 Ujeongguk-ro, Gongpyeong-dong, Seoul, 03161, Korea (South) (100%)
Tel.: (82) 237028888
Sales Range: $25-49.9 Million
Emp.: 80
Provider of Corporate & Institutional Banking Services
N.A.I.C.S.: 236220
Jae Hong Lee *(Gen Mgr)*

UBS Securities Malaysia Sdn. Bhd. (3) (100%)
Tel.: (60) 327811100
Web Site: http://www.apps2.ubs.com
Sales Range: $25-49.9 Million
Emp.: 30
Provider of Corporate & Institutional Banking Services
N.A.I.C.S.: 522299

UBS Securities Philippines, Inc. (3)
Tower One Ayala Triangle - UB 19/F Tower One Ayala Ave, Makati, 1226, Philippines (99%)
Tel.: (63) 27848888
Sales Range: Less than $1 Million
Emp.: 50
Provider of Corporate & Institutional Banking Services
N.A.I.C.S.: 522320

UBS Securities Thailand Co., Ltd. (3)
GPF Witthayu - UBSS Withayu Road 93/1, Bangkok, 10330, Thailand (100%)
Tel.: (66) 26135700
Sales Range: $25-49.9 Million
Emp.: 27
Provider of Corporate & Institutional Banking Services
N.A.I.C.S.: 236220

Subsidiary (US):

UBS Securities, LLC (3)
677 Washington Blvd, Stamford, CT 06901
Tel.: (203) 719-3000
Web Site: http://www.ubs.com
Sales Range: $200-249.9 Million
Emp.: 400
Corporate & Institutional Banking Services
N.A.I.C.S.: 523150

Subsidiary (Domestic):

UBS Asset Management New York (4)
51 W 52nd St, New York, NY 10109
Tel.: (212) 821-3000
Web Site: http://www.ubs.com
Rev.: $21,700,000
Emp.: 145
Investment Advisory Services
N.A.I.C.S.: 531210
Perry Offutt *(Mng Dir & Head-Infrastructure)*

Division (Domestic):

UBS Financial Services Inc (4)
600 Washington Blvd, Stamford, CT 06901-3707
Tel.: (203) 357-0700
Investment Firm & General Brokerage
N.A.I.C.S.: 523150
Jeremy Wallace *(First VP-Wealth Mgmt)*

Subsidiary (Non-US):

UBS Investment Bank Nederland B.V. (2)
Amstelplein 1 18th Floor, 1096 HA, Amsterdam, Netherlands
Tel.: (31) 205510100
Emp.: 30
Financial Management Services
N.A.I.C.S.: 523999

UBS Investment Management Canada Inc. (2)
154 University Avenue 8th Fl, Toronto, M5H 3Y9, ON, Canada
Tel.: (416) 343-1800
Investment Management Service
N.A.I.C.S.: 523940

UBS Investments Ltd. (2)
2 International Finance Centre 52/F 8 Finance Street, Central, China (Hong Kong)
Tel.: (852) 2971 8888
Web Site: http://www.ubs.com
Financial Planning Services
N.A.I.C.S.: 523940

UBS Investments Philippines, Inc. (2)
19th Floor Ayala Triangle Ayala Avenue, Makati, 1226, Manila, Philippines
Tel.: (63) 27848888
Financial Management Services
N.A.I.C.S.: 523999

Subsidiary (Domestic):

UBS Leasing AG (2)
Badenerstrasse 13, CH 5201, Brugg, Switzerland (100%)
Tel.: (41) 564625555
Web Site: http://www.ubsleasing.ch
Sales Range: $50-74.9 Million
Emp.: 35
Credit & Leasing Services
N.A.I.C.S.: 522299

Subsidiary (Non-US):

UBS New Zealand Holdings Ltd. (2)
HSBC Tower 188 Quay Street, Level 17, Auckland, 1010, New Zealand
Tel.: (64) 99134800
Investment Management Service

UBS GROUP AG

UBS Group AG—(Continued)
N.A.I.C.S.: 523940

Subsidiary (US):

UBS O'Connor LLC (2)
1 N Whacker Dr, Chicago, IL 60606
Tel.: (312) 525-4100
Sales Range: $50-74.9 Million
Emp.: 100
Financial Management Services
N.A.I.C.S.: 523999

Subsidiary (Non-US):

UBS O'Connor Limited (2)
5 Broadgate, London, EC2M 2QS, United Kingdom
Tel.: (44) 2075678000
Financial Management Services
N.A.I.C.S.: 523999

Subsidiary (US):

UBS Preferred Funding Company LLC IV (2)
1209 Orange St, Wilmington, DE 19801
Tel.: (302) 658-7581
Financial Planning Services
N.A.I.C.S.: 523940

Subsidiary (Non-US):

UBS Principal Capital Asia Ltd. (2)
9 Penang Road, Singapore, 238459, Singapore
Tel.: (65) 64958000
Financial Planning Services
N.A.I.C.S.: 523940

Division (Domestic):

UBS Private Banking (2)
Paradeplatz 6, 8001, Zurich, Switzerland (100%)
Tel.: (41) 442341111
Sales Range: $1-4.9 Billion
Emp.: 7,000
Provider of Banking Services
N.A.I.C.S.: 522320

Subsidiary (Non-US):

UBS AG Jersey (3)
1 IFC, PO Box 350, Saint Helier, JE2 3BX, Jersey (100%)
Tel.: (44) 1534701000
Sales Range: $75-99.9 Million
Emp.: 200
Wealth Management Services
N.A.I.C.S.: 523999
Tom Hill (CEO)

Subsidiary (Non-US):

UBS Private Banking (Duetschland) AG (2)
Bockenheimer Landstrasse 2-4, 60306, Frankfurt am Main, Germany (100%)
Tel.: (49) 06921790
Sales Range: $200-249.9 Million
Emp.: 400
Provider of Private Banking Services
N.A.I.C.S.: 522180

UBS Real Estate GmbH (2)
Tel.: (49) 892060950
Web Site: http://www.ubs.com
Real Estate Investment Services
N.A.I.C.S.: 523940

Subsidiary (US):

UBS Real Estate Securities Inc (2)
1285 Avenue of the Americas, New York, NY 10019
Tel.: (212) 713-2000
Real Estate Manangement Services
N.A.I.C.S.: 531390

UBS Realty Investors LLC (2)
10 State House Sq, Hartford, CT 06103-3604
Tel.: (860) 616-9000
Financial Planning Services
N.A.I.C.S.: 523940
Peter Shaplin (Dir-Asset Mgmt)

Subsidiary (Non-US):

UBS Saudi Arabia Company (2)
Tower 4 Tatweer Towers, Riyadh, 11588, Saudi Arabia
Tel.: (966) 112038000
Financial Investment Services
N.A.I.C.S.: 523999

UBS Securities Asia Limited (2)
Two International Finance Cent 8 Finance Street, Central, 518000, China (Hong Kong)
Tel.: (852) 29718888
Security Brokerage Services
N.A.I.C.S.: 523150
David Chin (Co-Head-Investment Banking)

UBS Securities Hong Kong Limited (2)
2 International Finance Centre 52/F 8 Finance Street, Central, China (Hong Kong)
Tel.: (852) 2971 8888
Web Site: http://www.ubs.com
Security & Investment Services
N.A.I.C.S.: 523150

UBS Securities Pte. Ltd. (2)
9 Penang Road, Singapore, 238459, Singapore
Tel.: (65) 64958000
Security Brokerage Services
N.A.I.C.S.: 523150

UBS Trustee Company Limited (2)
1 Finsbury Avenue, London, EC2M 2AN, United Kingdom
Tel.: (44) 2075678000
Web Site: http://apps1.ubs.com
Business Management Services
N.A.I.C.S.: 561499

UBS Trustees (Bahamas) Ltd. (2)
1st Floor East Bay Street, PO Box N-7757, Nassau, Bahamas
Tel.: (242) 3949300
Trust & Fudiciary Services
N.A.I.C.S.: 523991
Beat Paoletto (Mng Dir)

UBS Trustees (Cayman) Ltd (2)
Cayman Corporate Centre 27 Hospital Road, Georgetown, KY1 1106, Cayman Islands
Tel.: (345) 9146000
Trust Management Services
N.A.I.C.S.: 523991

UBS Trustees (Channel Islands) Ltd.
1 IFC, Saint Helier, JE2 3BX, Jersey (100%)
Tel.: (44) 534701600
Sales Range: $100-124.9 Million
Emp.: 250
International Trust Service
N.A.I.C.S.: 523991

UBS Trustees (Jersey) Ltd. (2)
2nd Floor 5 Castle Street, Saint Helier, JE2 3BT, Jersey
Tel.: (44) 1534716530
Trust Management Services
N.A.I.C.S.: 523991
Alan Butel (Mng Dir)

UBS Trustees (Singapore) Ltd. (2)
9 Penang Road, Singapore, 238459, Singapore (100%)
Tel.: (65) 64958000
Sales Range: $350-399.9 Million
Emp.: 1,000
Trust & Banking Services
N.A.I.C.S.: 523991

UBS Wealth Management Israel Ltd (2)
8 Hachoshlim St 7th Floor, Herzliya Pituach, 4672408, Israel
Tel.: (972) 98789100
Financial Management Services
N.A.I.C.S.: 523999

UBS Asset Management (UK) Ltd. (1)
5 Broadgate, London, EC2M 2QS, United Kingdom
Tel.: (44) 207 567 8000
Asset Management Services
N.A.I.C.S.: 523940
Francesca Guagnini (Head-EMEA)

UBS Asset Management Switzerland AG (1)
Bahnhofstrasse 45, 8001, Zurich, Switzerland
Tel.: (41) 44 234 9080
Asset Management Services
N.A.I.C.S.: 523940
Stefan Richner (Head)

UBS Europe SE (1)
Bockenheimer Landstrasse 2-4, 60306, Frankfurt am Main, Germany
Tel.: (49) 692 1790
Asset Management Services
N.A.I.C.S.: 523940
Martin C. Wittig (Chm-Supervisory Bd)

UBS SuMi TRUST Wealth Management Co., Ltd. (1)
Marunouchi Eiraku Building 1-4-1 Marunouchi, Chiyoda-ku, Tokyo, Japan
Tel.: (81) 352933100
Web Site: https://www.ubs-sumitrust.com
Business Management Services
N.A.I.C.S.: 541611

UBUBELE HOLDINGS LIMITED

Ground Floor Acorn House East Wing Old Oak Office Park, Cnr Old Oak & Durban Roads, Bellville, 7530, South Africa
Tel.: (27) 219143553   ZA
Web Site: http://www.ububele.co.za
Year Founded: 2002
Sales Range: $50-74.9 Million
Financial Management Services
N.A.I.C.S.: 523940
Elana Kruger (Dir-Fin)

UCAL LTD.

Tel.: (91) 4442208100
Web Site: https://www.ucal.com
500464—(BOM)
Rev.: $99,764,466
Assets: $93,802,734
Liabilities: $46,642,695
Net Worth: $47,160,038
Earnings: $102,212
Emp.: 728
Fiscal Year-end: 03/31/23
Automotive Product Mfr
N.A.I.C.S.: 339999
Jayakar Krishnamurthy (Chm & Mng Dir)

Subsidiaries:

Amtec Moulded Products Inc. (1)
1355 Holmes Rd Unit A, Elgin, IL 60123-1298
Tel.: (815) 226-0187
Web Site: https://www.amtecmolded.com
Mold Product Mfr
N.A.I.C.S.: 333511

UCAL Systems Inc. (1)
1875 Holmes Rd, Elgin, IL 60123
Tel.: (847) 695-8030
Web Site: https://ucalsystems.com
Precision Metal Components Mfr
N.A.I.C.S.: 332322

Ucal Polymer Industries Limited (1)
B114-116 PIPDIC Industrial Estate Mettupalayam, Pondicherry, 605009, India
Tel.: (91) 4132276264
Web Site: https://www.ucalpolymer.com
Rubber & Plastic Product Mfr
N.A.I.C.S.: 326220

UCAP CLOUD INFORMATION TECHNOLOGY CO., LTD.

33F Block 9B Kaixuan Building Huanyu Huijin Center No 428, Dongguan Avenue Nancheng District, Dongguan, 523300, Guangdong, China
Tel.: (86) 76986115656
Web Site: http://www.kaipuyun.cn
Year Founded: 2000
688228—(SHG)
Rev.: $77,913,323
Assets: $259,079,966
Liabilities: $64,308,788
Net Worth: $194,771,178

Earnings: $13,763,398
Fiscal Year-end: 12/31/22
Information Technology Services
N.A.I.C.S.: 541512
Min Wang (Chm & Gen Mgr)

UCAPITAL GLOBAL PLC

12 Old Bond Street 1st Floor, London, W1S 4PW, United Kingdom
Tel.: (44) 2080791355   UK
Web Site: https://www.alephgroup.io
Year Founded: 2008
MLALE—(EUR)
Rev.: $2,327,858
Assets: $4,648,738
Liabilities: $7,122,146
Net Worth: ($2,473,408)
Earnings: $37,754
Emp.: 5
Fiscal Year-end: 12/31/22
Investment Management Service
N.A.I.C.S.: 523999

UCAPITAL24 S.P.A.

Via dei Piatti 11, 20123, Milan, Italy
Tel.: (39) 0245377149
Web Site: https://www.ucapital24.com
Year Founded: 2017
U24—(ITA)
Sales Range: Less than $1 Million
Financial Investment Services
N.A.I.C.S.: 523940
Giovanni Raffa (CFO)

UCAR SA

10 rue Louis Pasteur, FR-92100, Boulogne-Billancourt, France
Tel.: (33) 170956000
Web Site: http://www.ucar.fr
ALUCR—(EUR)
Sales Range: $25-49.9 Million
Car Rental & Utility Vehicle Leasing Services
N.A.I.C.S.: 532111
Jean-Claude Puerto-Salavert (Chm & CEO)

UCB NOVOBANK PJSC

D 11 Nab Reki Gzen, Velikiy Novgorod, 173003, Russia
Tel.: (7) 88162501101
Web Site: http://www.novobank.ru
Sales Range: Less than $1 Million
Commercial Banking Services
N.A.I.C.S.: 522110

UCB S.A.

Allee de la Recherche 60, B-1070, Brussels, Belgium
Tel.: (32) 25599999
Web Site: https://www.ucb.com
Year Founded: 1928
UCBJF—(OTCIQ)
Rev.: $5,668,033,671
Assets: $16,769,911,504
Liabilities: $7,083,962,875
Net Worth: $9,685,948,629
Earnings: $370,170,516
Emp.: 9,083
Fiscal Year-end: 12/31/23
Chemical Products Mfr
N.A.I.C.S.: 325998
Isabelle Ghellynck (Assoc Dir-Investor Relations)

Subsidiaries:

Celltech Ltd (1)
208 Bath Road, Slough, SL1 3WE, Berkshire, United Kingdom
Tel.: (44) 1753 534655
Web Site: http://www.ucb.com
Emp.: 30
Pharmaceutical Products Research & Development Services
N.A.I.C.S.: 541715

AND PRIVATE COMPANIES — UCB S.A.

Subsidiary (Domestic):

Celltech Japan Ltd (2)
208 Bath Road, Slough, SL1 3WE, United Kingdom
Tel.: (44) 1753534655
Web Site: http://www.ucbpharma.co.uk
Pharmaceuticals Product Mfr
N.A.I.C.S.: 325412

Subsidiary (Non-US):

Celltech R&D Ltd (2)
208 Bath Rd, SL1 3WE, Slough, United Kingdom - England
Tel.: (44) 1753 534655
Pharmaceutical Products Research & Development Services
N.A.I.C.S.: 541715

Korea UCB Co Ltd. (1)
369 Gangnam-Daero A Plus Asset Tower 4th Floor, Seocho-gu, Seoul, Korea (South)
Tel.: (82) 2 534 3580
Web Site: https://www.ucbkorea.co.kr
Pharmaceuticals Product Mfr
N.A.I.C.S.: 325412

Ra Pharmaceuticals, Inc. (1)
87 Cambridge Park Dr, Cambridge, MA 02140
Tel.: (617) 401-4060
Web Site: http://www.rapharma.com
Rev: $3,000,000
Assets: $284,152,000
Liabilities: $22,038,000
Net Worth: $262,114,000
Earnings: ($102,688,000)
Emp.: 89
Fiscal Year-end: 12/31/2019
Biopharmaceutical Research & Development
N.A.I.C.S.: 541715
Douglas A. Treco *(Pres & CEO)*

UCB (Investments) Ltd (1)
208 Bath Road, Slough, SL1 3WE, Berkshire, United Kingdom
Tel.: (44) 1753 534655
Web Site: http://www.ucb.com
Emp.: 45
Investment Management Service
N.A.I.C.S.: 523999

UCB (Pharma) Ireland Ltd (1)
United Drug House Magna Drive City West Road, Dublin, D24 X0CT, Ireland
Tel.: (353) 1 463 7395
Web Site: https://www.ucb.com
Sales Range: $50-74.9 Million
Emp.: 10
Pharmaceutical Products Distr
N.A.I.C.S.: 424210

UCB A.E. (1)
Agiou Dimitriou 63, Alimos, 17456, Alimos, Greece
Tel.: (30) 210 997 4000
Web Site: https://www.ucbpharma.gr
Sales Range: $25-49.9 Million
Emp.: 10
Pharmaceuticals Product Mfr
N.A.I.C.S.: 325412

UCB Australia Pty. Ltd. (1)
Level 1 1155 Malvern Road, PO Box 158, Malvern, 3144, VIC, Australia
Tel.: (61) 39 828 1800
Web Site: https://ucbaustralia.com.au
Emp.: 50
Pharmaceuticals Product Mfr
N.A.I.C.S.: 325412

UCB Belgium S.A. (1)
Allee de la Recherche 60, 1070, Brussels, Belgium
Tel.: (32) 2 559 9999
Web Site: http://www.ucb.com
Sales Range: $125-149.9 Million
Emp.: 50
Pharmaceuticals Product Mfr
N.A.I.C.S.: 325412

UCB BioSciences GmbH (1)
Alfred-Nobel-Strasse 10, 40789, Monheim, Germany
Tel.: (49) 2173 48 0
Pharmaceuticals Product Mfr
N.A.I.C.S.: 325412

UCB Biopharma Ltda. (1)
Av Presidente Juscelino Kubitschek N 1 327 5 Andar, Condominio Edificio Internacional Plaza II, Sao Paulo, 04543-011, Brazil
Tel.: (55) 1138471700
Web Site: http://www.ucb-biopharma.com.br
Biopharmaceutical & Therapeutic Services
N.A.I.C.S.: 621340

UCB Bulgaria EOOD (1)
2B Srebarna Str 9th floor office 8B, Lozenets quarter, 1407, Sofia, Bulgaria
Tel.: (359) 29623049
Web Site: https://www.ucb.bg
Emp.: 10
Pharmaceuticals Product Mfr
N.A.I.C.S.: 325412

UCB Canada Inc. (1)
2201 Bristol Circle Suite 602, Oakville, L6H 0J8, ON, Canada
Tel.: (905) 287-5129
Web Site: https://www.ucb-canada.ca
Emp.: 6
Pharmaceuticals Product Mfr
N.A.I.C.S.: 325412

UCB Farchim S.A. (1)
Zone Industrielle de Planchy d'Avau Chemin de Croix-Blanche 10, 1630, Bulle, Switzerland
Tel.: (41) 58 822 3200
Web Site: https://www.ucb.com
Emp.: 400
Pharmaceuticals Product Mfr
N.A.I.C.S.: 325412

UCB Finance N.V. (1)
Lage Mosten 33, 4822 NK, Breda, Netherlands
Tel.: (31) 765731140
Web Site: http://www.ucbpharma.nl
Emp.: 28
Financial Management Services
N.A.I.C.S.: 523999

Subsidiary (Non-US):

UCB GmbH (2)
Alfred-Nobel-Strasse 10, 40789, Monheim am Rhein, Germany
Tel.: (49) 2173 48 0
Pharmaceuticals Product Mfr
N.A.I.C.S.: 325412
Willy Cnops *(Gen Mgr)*

Subsidiary (Non-US):

UCB Pharma GmbH (3)
Vienna Twin Tower Wienerbergstrasse 11/12A, 1110, Vienna, Austria
Tel.: (43) 12918000
Sales Range: $25-49.9 Million
Emp.: 15
Pharmaceuticals Product Mfr
N.A.I.C.S.: 325412
Margot Writzel *(Gen Mgr)*

Subsidiary (Non-US):

UCB Pharma (Zhuhai) Company Ltd. (4)
Section A No 3 Science and Technology 5th Road Innovation Coast, National Hi-Tech Industrial Development Zone, Zhuhai, 519085, Guangdong, China
Tel.: (86) 7563673688
Pharmaceuticals Product Mfr
N.A.I.C.S.: 325412

Subsidiary (Non-US):

UCB Investissements S.A. (2)
Chemin De Croix Blanche 10, Bulle, 1630, Switzerland
Tel.: (41) 269190278
Investment Management Service
N.A.I.C.S.: 523999

Subsidiary (Domestic):

Doutors Reassurance S.A. (3)
Chemin de Croix-Blanche 10 Z I de Planchy, 1630, Bulle, Switzerland
Tel.: (41) 26 919 02 79
Insurance Brokerage Services
N.A.I.C.S.: 524210

UCB Medical Devices SA (3)
Planchy d Avau Industrial Zone Chemin de Croix-Blanche 10, 1630, Bulle, Switzerland
Tel.: (41) 588223200
Pharmaceuticals Product Mfr
N.A.I.C.S.: 325412

Subsidiary (Non-US):

UCB Pharma AB (2)
Master Samuelsgatan 60, 111 21, Stockholm, Sweden
Tel.: (46) 4 029 4900
Web Site: http://www.ucb.com
Pharmaceuticals Product Mfr
N.A.I.C.S.: 325412

Subsidiary (Domestic):

UCB Pharma B.V. (2)
Lage Mosten 33, 4822 NK, Breda, Netherlands
Tel.: (31) 765731140
Sales Range: $25-49.9 Million
Emp.: 25
Pharmaceuticals Product Mfr
N.A.I.C.S.: 325412

Subsidiary (Non-US):

UCB Pharma Gesellschaft m.b.H. (2)
Business Park Vienna Vienna Twin Tower Wienerbergstrasse 11/12a, Tower A 13th floor, 1100, Vienna, Austria
Tel.: (43) 1 291 8000
Web Site: https://www.ucbpharma.at
Sales Range: $25-49.9 Million
Emp.: 25
Pharmaceuticals Product Mfr
N.A.I.C.S.: 325412

UCB Pharma Oy (2)
Bertel Jungin Aukio 5 6th floor, 02600, Espoo, Finland
Tel.: (358) 92 514 4221
Web Site: http://www.ucb.com
Sales Range: $25-49.9 Million
Emp.: 20
Pharmaceuticals Product Mfr
N.A.I.C.S.: 325412

UCB Hungary Ltd (1)
Obuda Gate Building Arpad Fejedelem Utja 26-28, 1023, Budapest, Hungary
Tel.: (36) 1 391 0060
Sales Range: $25-49.9 Million
Emp.: 22
Pharmaceuticals Product Mfr
N.A.I.C.S.: 325412
Melitts Gellos *(Gen Mgr)*

UCB India Private Ltd (1)
Building No P3 Unit No 103 1st Floor Prithvi Complex Kalher Pipe Line, Kalher Bhiwandi, Thane, 421302, MH, India
Tel.: (91) 226 700 4911
Web Site: https://www.ucb.com
Sales Range: $125-149.9 Million
Emp.: 450
Pharmaceuticals Product Mfr
N.A.I.C.S.: 325412

UCB Japan Co. Ltd. (1)
8-17-1 Nishi-Shinjuku Shinjuku Grand Tower 13F, Shinjuku-ku, Tokyo, 160-0023, Japan (100%)
Tel.: (81) 36 864 7500
Web Site: https://www.ucbjapan.com
Emp.: 554
Sales of Industrial Films
N.A.I.C.S.: 423410

UCB Korea Co., Ltd. (1)
4FL A Plus Tower 369 Gangnam-Daero, Seocho-gu, Seoul, 06621, Korea (South)
Tel.: (82) 25343580
Pharmaceuticals Product Mfr
N.A.I.C.S.: 325412

UCB Lux S.A. (1)
12 Rue Eugene Ruppert, Luxembourg, 2453, Luxembourg
Tel.: (352) 26 48 27 13
Web Site: http://www.ucb.com
Emp.: 5
Pharmaceuticals Product Mfr
N.A.I.C.S.: 325412

UCB Manufacturing Ireland Ltd (1)
Shannon Industrial Estate, Shannon, V14F X09, Ireland
Tel.: (353) 61 714 100
Emp.: 13
Pharmaceuticals Product Mfr
N.A.I.C.S.: 325412
Brener Kunz *(Mng Dir)*

UCB Nordic AS (1)
Arne Jacobsens Alle 15, 2300, Copenhagen, Denmark
Tel.: (45) 32462400
Emp.: 35
Pharmaceuticals Product Mfr
N.A.I.C.S.: 325412
Fleming Anderson *(Gen Mgr)*

UCB Pharma (Hong Kong) Ltd (1)
Rooms 156 And 157 20/F Cityplaza Three 14 Taikoo Wan Road, Taikoo, Hong Kong, China (Hong Kong)
Tel.: (852) 2 854 9333
Web Site: http://www.ucb.com
Pharmaceuticals Product Mfr
N.A.I.C.S.: 325412

UCB Pharma (Produtos Farmaceuticos) Lda (1)
Rua do Silval n 37 piso 1 S1 3, 2780-373, Oeiras, Portugal
Tel.: (351) 21 302 5300
Web Site: http://www.ucb.com
Sales Range: $25-49.9 Million
Emp.: 15
Pharmaceuticals Product Mfr
N.A.I.C.S.: 325412

UCB Pharma (Produtos Farmaceuticos) Lda. (1)
Rua do Silval n 37 piso 1 S1 3, 2780-373, Oeiras, Portugal
Tel.: (351) 21 302 5300
Web Site: http://www.ucb.com
Pharmaceuticals Product Mfr
N.A.I.C.S.: 325412

UCB Pharma A.S. (1)
Grini Naeringspark 8 B, 1361, Osteras, Norway
Tel.: (47) 67 16 5880
Sales Range: $25-49.9 Million
Emp.: 35
Pharmaceuticals Product Mfr
N.A.I.C.S.: 325412
Flemming Andersen *(Gen Mgr)*

UCB Pharma A.S. (1)
Palladium Tower Barbaros Mah Kardelen Sok No 2 Kat 24/80 34746, Atasehir, 34746, Istanbul, Turkiye
Tel.: (90) 216 538 0000
Web Site: https://www.ucb.com.tr
Pharmaceuticals Product Mfr
N.A.I.C.S.: 325412
Seda Levent Baykara *(Mgr-Mktg)*

UCB Pharma Ireland Ltd. (1)
United Drug House Magna Drive Magna Business Park, City West Road, Dublin, 24, Ireland
Tel.: (353) 14637395
Sales Range: $25-49.9 Million
Emp.: 11
Biotechnology Research & Development of New Pharmaceuticals
N.A.I.C.S.: 541714
Allison Melichar *(Office Mgr)*

UCB Pharma LLC (1)
1st Krasnogvardeyskiy proezd 15 flour 13, 123100, Moscow, Russia
Tel.: (7) 4956443322
Web Site: http://www.ucbrussia.ru
Emp.: 230
Pharmaceuticals Product Mfr
N.A.I.C.S.: 325412

UCB Pharma Romania S.R.L. (1)
40-44 Banu Antonache-4th Floor, District 1, 011665, Bucharest, Romania
Tel.: (40) 213001907
Pharmaceuticals Product Mfr
N.A.I.C.S.: 325412

UCB Pharma S.A. (1)
Allee de la Recherche 60, 1070, Brussels, Belgium (100%)
Tel.: (32) 25599999
Web Site: http://www.ucb.be
Sales Range: $125-149.9 Million
Emp.: 500
Provider of Pharmaceuticals
N.A.I.C.S.: 325412

UCB Pharma S.A. (1)

UCB S.A.

UCB S.A.—(Continued)
6 Pl Boulnois, 75017, Paris, France
Tel.: (33) 47660000
Pharmaceutical Research & Development
N.A.I.C.S.: 541715

UCB Pharma S.A. (1)
Plaza de Manuel Gomez Moreno s/n Edificio Bronce 5th floor, 28020, Madrid, Spain
Tel.: (34) 91 570 3444
Web Site: https://www.ucb.com
Sales Range: $25-49.9 Million
Emp.: 150
Pharmaceutical Research & Development
N.A.I.C.S.: 541715

UCB Pharma Sp. z.o.o. (1)
ul L Kruczkowskiego 8, 00-380, Warsaw, Poland
Tel.: (48) 22 696 9920
Web Site: https://www.ucb.pl
Sales Range: $50-74.9 Million
Emp.: 120
Pharmaceuticals Product Mfr
N.A.I.C.S.: 325412

UCB Pharmaceuticals (Taiwan) Ltd. (1)
12th Floor-2 No 88 Dunhua North Road, Songshan District, Taipei, 105-51, Taiwan
Tel.: (886) 289796177
Pharmaceuticals Product Mfr
N.A.I.C.S.: 325412

UCB S.R.O. (1)
Jankovcova 1518/2, 170 00, Prague, Czech Republic
Tel.: (420) 22 177 3411
Web Site: https://www.ucb.cz
Sales Range: $25-49.9 Million
Emp.: 20
Pharmaceuticals Product Mfr
N.A.I.C.S.: 325412

UCB Trading (Shanghai) Co Ltd (1)
Room 2802 Office Building Raffles City No 268 Tibet Middle Road, Shanghai, 200001, China
Tel.: (86) 212 321 0288
Web Site: https://www.ucbchina.com
Sales Range: $50-74.9 Million
Emp.: 88
Pharmaceutical Products Distr
N.A.I.C.S.: 424210

UCB Watford Ltd (1)
U C B House George St, Watford, WD18 0BX, Hertfordshire, United Kingdom
Tel.: (44) 1753 534 655
Pharmaceuticals Product Mfr
N.A.I.C.S.: 325412

UCB de Mexico S.A. de C.V. (1)
Homero 440 7th Floor Col Chapultepec Morales, Seccion Miguel Hidalgo, Mexico, 11570, Mexico
Tel.: (52) 55 9159 6868
Pharmaceuticals Product Mfr
N.A.I.C.S.: 325412

UCB, Inc. (1)
1950 Lake Park Dr, Smyrna, GA 30080
Tel.: (770) 970-7500
Web Site: https://www.ucb-usa.com
Holding Company; Chemical & Pharmaceutical Mfr
N.A.I.C.S.: 551112
Duane Barnes (Pres & Head)

Subsidiary (Domestic):

Schwarz Pharma Manufacturing, Inc. (2)
1101 C Ave W, Seymour, IN 47274-1635
Tel.: (812) 523-3457
Sales Range: $100-124.9 Million
Emp.: 400
Pharmaceuticals Mfr
N.A.I.C.S.: 325412
Holly Kleman (Dir-QC)

Subsidiary (Non-US):

UCB Biosciences, Inc. (2)
Tel.: (919) 767-2555
Web Site: http://www.ucb.com
Sales Range: $75-99.9 Million
Emp.: 350
Pharmaceutical Research & Development Services

N.A.I.C.S.: 541715

Subsidiary (Domestic):

Upstate Pharma LLC (2)
1950 Lk Pkwy Dr Se, Smyrna, GA 30080
Pharmaceuticals Product Mfr
N.A.I.C.S.: 325412

UCB-Bioproducts S.A. (1)
Allee de la Recherche 60, 1070, Brussels, Belgium (100%)
Tel.: (32) 25599999
Web Site: http://www.ucb.com
Sales Range: $125-149.9 Million
Emp.: 300
Pharmaceutical Manufacturing
N.A.I.C.S.: 325412

UCB-Pharma AG (1)
Zone Industrielle de Planchy d'Avau Chemin de Croix Blanche 10, 1630, Bulle, Switzerland
Tel.: (41) 26 919 0180
Emp.: 400
Pharmaceuticals Product Mfr
N.A.I.C.S.: 325412
Nicolas Hug (Dir)

Vedim Pharma SA (1)
Plaza De Manuel Gomez Moreno s/n Edificio Bronce 5th floor, 28020, Madrid, Spain
Tel.: (34) 91 570 3444
Web Site: https://www.ucb.com
Emp.: 100
Pharmaceuticals Whslr
N.A.I.C.S.: 456110

Vedim SA de C.V. (1)
Mariano Escobedo 595 piso 3 Colonia Bosque de Chapultepec I Seccion, Miguel Hidalgo, 11580, Mexico, Mexico
Tel.: (52) 559 159 6868
Web Site: http://www.ucb.com.mx
Pharmaceuticals Product Mfr
N.A.I.C.S.: 325412

Vedim Sp. z.o.o. (1)
ul L Kruczkowskiego 8, 00-380, Warsaw, Poland
Tel.: (48) 22 696 9920
Web Site: https://www.ucb.pl
Pharmaceuticals Product Mfr
N.A.I.C.S.: 325412

Zhuhai Schwarz Pharma Company Ltd (1)
Section A No 3 Science and Technology 5th Road Innovation Coast, National Hi-Tech Industrial Development Zone, Zhuhai, 519085, Guangdong, China
Tel.: (86) 7563673633
Web Site: http://www.ucb.com
Pharmaceuticals Product Mfr
N.A.I.C.S.: 325412

Zogenix, Inc. (1)
5959 Horton St Ste 500, Emeryville, CA 94608
Tel.: (510) 550-8300
Web Site: http://www.zogenix.com
Rev.: $13,643,000
Assets: $651,130,000
Liabilities: $281,461,000
Net Worth: $369,669,000
Earnings: ($209,383,000)
Emp.: 218
Fiscal Year-end: 12/31/2020
Pharmaceuticals Mfr
N.A.I.C.S.: 325412
Cam L. Garner (Co-Founder & Chm)

Subsidiary (Domestic):

Modis Therapeutics, Inc. (2)
409 13th St Ste 700, Oakland, CA 94612
Tel.: (510) 806-8562
Web Site: http://www.modistx.com
Biopharmaceutical Development Services
N.A.I.C.S.: 541714

Subsidiary (Non-US):

Zogenix International Limited (2)
The Pearce Building West Street, Maidenhead, SL6 1RL, Berkshire, United Kingdom
Tel.: (44) 1628244050
Biopharmaceutical Development Services
N.A.I.C.S.: 541714

UCHI TECHNOLOGIES BERHAD

3097 Tingkat Perusahaan 4A Free Trade Zone, 13600, Prai, Malaysia
Tel.: (60) 43990035
Web Site: https://www.uchi.net
UCHITEC—(KLS)
Rev.: $52,789,675
Assets: $52,833,144
Liabilities: $8,740,572
Net Worth: $44,092,572
Earnings: $29,436,445
Emp.: 235
Fiscal Year-end: 12/31/23
Weighing Scale Mfr
N.A.I.C.S.: 811210
Ted De-Tsan Kao (Exec Dir)

Subsidiaries:

Uchi Optoelectronic (M) Sdn. Bhd. (1)
3097 Tingkat Perusahaan 4A, Free Trade Zone, 13600, Prai, Penang, Malaysia
Tel.: (60) 4 399 0035
Web Site: https://www.uchi.net
Emp.: 300
Electronic Control System Mfr
N.A.I.C.S.: 334513

UCHIDA YOKO CO., LTD.

4-7 Shinkawa 2-Chome, Chuo-ku, Tokyo, 104-8282, Japan
Tel.: (81) 335554072
Web Site: https://www.uchida.co.jp
Year Founded: 1910
8057—(TKS)
Rev.: $1,728,786,800
Assets: $937,005,680
Liabilities: $536,288,400
Net Worth: $400,717,280
Earnings: $43,515,120
Emp.: 3,248
Fiscal Year-end: 07/31/24
Educational Material Distr
N.A.I.C.S.: 513130
Noboru Okubo (Pres & CEO)

Subsidiaries:

ATR-Learning Technology Corporation (1)
2-2-2 Hikaridai, Seika-cho Soraku-gun, Kyoto, 619-0288, Japan
Tel.: (81) 77 495 2502
Web Site: https://www.atr-lt.jp
Learning Technology Services
N.A.I.C.S.: 611710

CBN Inc. (1)
5th floor Sumio Kowa Toyo Building 2-3-25 Toyo, Koto-ku, Tokyo, 135-0016, Japan
Tel.: (81) 36 222 8648
Web Site: https://www.cbn-inc.co.jp
Hardware & Software Development Services
N.A.I.C.S.: 541511

Edosaki Kyoei Industries Co., Ltd. (1)
2100 Sakura, Inashiki, Ibaraki Prefecture, Japan
Tel.: (81) 298923551
Web Site: http://www.edosaki-kye.co.jp
Steel Furniture Mfr
N.A.I.C.S.: 337126

Hundred System Co., Ltd. (1)
Sumisekowa Toyocho Building 2-3-25 Toyo, Koto-ku, Tokyo, 135-0016, Japan
Tel.: (81) 356346690
Web Site: https://www.uchida.co.jp
Software Development Services
N.A.I.C.S.: 541511

Infosign Inc. (1)
NDK Ikenohata Building 4F 1-2-18 Ikenohata, Taito-ku, Tokyo, 110-0008, Japan
Tel.: (81) 358325580
Web Site: https://www.infosign.co.jp
Emp.: 17
Software Development Services
N.A.I.C.S.: 541511

Kondoh Shokai Co., Ltd. (1)
4-1-7 Kita 6 Johigashi deAUNE Sapporo 11th Floor, Higashi-ku, Sapporo, 060-0906, Japan

INTERNATIONAL PUBLIC

Tel.: (81) 11 721 2411
Web Site: https://www.s-kondoh.co.jp
Emp.: 21
Office Relocation Support Services
N.A.I.C.S.: 484210

Marvy Corporation (1)
5th floor Hulic Hatchobori Building 2-12-15 Shinkawa, Chuo-ku, Tokyo, 104-0033, Japan
Tel.: (81) 36 222 2256
Web Site: https://www.marvy.jp
Emp.: 80
Stationery Product Mfr
N.A.I.C.S.: 322230

Nakashima Uchida Corporation (1)
5322 Haga Okayama Research Park, Kitaku, Okayama, 701-1221, Japan
Tel.: (81) 86 286 9500
Web Site: https://www.nuc-ok.co.jp
Office Furniture Mfr
N.A.I.C.S.: 337214

Nishinihon Officemation Co., Ltd. (1)
3-5-16 Commerce and Industry Center, Nishi-ku, Hiroshima, 733-0833, Yamaguchi, Japan
Tel.: (81) 82 270 3811
Web Site: http://hiroshima.nom.co.jp
Software Development Services
N.A.I.C.S.: 541511

Ousystem Co., Ltd. (1)
839-1 Natsukawa, Kita-ku, Okayama, 701-0164, Japan
Tel.: (81) 86 293 2755
Web Site: https://www.ous.co.jp
Emp.: 80
Software Development Services
N.A.I.C.S.: 541511

Powerplace Inc. (1)
2-4-7 Shinkawa, Chuo-ku, Tokyo, 104-0033, Japan
Tel.: (81) 33 555 4435
Web Site: https://www.powerplace.co.jp
Interior Design Services
N.A.I.C.S.: 541410

Sakura Seiki Co., Ltd. (1)
2-61 Kusune-cho, Yao, 581-0814, Osaka, Japan
Tel.: (81) 729965528
Web Site: https://www.sakura-seiki.co.jp
Emp.: 70
Office Equipments Mfr
N.A.I.C.S.: 337214

Smart Insight, Corporation (1)
2nd Floor Iwamotocho 2-chome Building Iwamotocho 2-11-2, Chiyoda-ku, Tokyo, 101-0032, Japan
Tel.: (81) 358234601
Web Site: http://www.smartinsight.jp
Software Development Services
N.A.I.C.S.: 541511

Taiyougiken Co., Ltd. (1)
385-1 Omama-cho, Midori, 376-0101, Gunma, Japan
Tel.: (81) 277733111
Web Site: http://www.taiyougiken.com
Office Equipments Mfr
N.A.I.C.S.: 337214

Toyox Software Co., Ltd. (1)
5 of 277 Taieshin, Kuroishi, 938-0045, Toyama, Japan
Tel.: (81) 76 554 1121
Web Site: https://www.toyoxsw.co.jp
Emp.: 16
System Development Services
N.A.I.C.S.: 541511

Uchida Business Solutions Co., Ltd. (1)
3-4-34 Nionohama, Otsu, 520-0801, Shiga, Japan
Tel.: (81) 77 522 7575
Web Site: https://www.uchida-bs.co.jp
Office Supply & Furniture Distr
N.A.I.C.S.: 459410

Uchida Esco Co., Ltd. (1)
5-8-40 Kiba, Koto-ku, Tokyo, Japan (98.28%)
Tel.: (81) 356392221
Web Site: http://www.esco.co.jp
Rev.: $204,296,400
Assets: $166,747,680

Liabilities: $85,648,640
Net Worth: $81,099,040
Earnings: $19,582,640
Emp.: 667
Fiscal Year-end: 07/31/2021
Software Development Services
N.A.I.C.S.: 541511
Masaru Fukui *(Auditor)*

Subsidiary (Domestic):

UI Techno Service Co., Ltd. (2)
1-10-4 Hokuei, Urayasu, 279-0002, Chiba, Japan
Tel.: (81) 473058551
Web Site: https://www.utsnet.co.jp
Emp.: 31
Software Development Services
N.A.I.C.S.: 541511

Uchida Human Development Co., Ltd. (1)
1-6-1 Yokoami International Fashion Center Building 7F 8F 9F, Sumida-ku, Tokyo, 130-0015, Japan
Tel.: (81) 36 658 5260
Web Site: http://www.uhd.co.jp
Employment Placement Services
N.A.I.C.S.: 561311

Uchida MK Sdn. Bhd. (1)
Lot 719 Persiaran Kuala Selangor Section 26, HICOM Industrial Area, 40400, Shah Alam, Selangor, Malaysia
Tel.: (60) 35 191 2322
Web Site: https://www.uchidamk.com.my
Office Furniture Mfr
N.A.I.C.S.: 337214
Tomotsugu Okada *(Chm & Mng Dir)*

Uchida Spectrum Inc. (1)
1-16-14 Shinkawa Across Shinkawa Building Annex, Chuo-ku, Tokyo, 104-0033, Japan
Tel.: (81) 355436800
Web Site: https://www.spectrum.co.jp
Software Development Services
N.A.I.C.S.: 541511

Uchida Systems Co., Ltd. (1)
Kayabacho Tower 14F 1-21-2 Shinkawa, Chuo-ku, Tokyo, 104-0033, Japan
Tel.: (81) 33 537 0888
Web Site: https://www.uchida-systems.co.jp
Emp.: 253
Office Equipment Distr
N.A.I.C.S.: 423420

Uchida Techno Co., Ltd. (1)
1-10-14 Shinkawa Forecast Kayabacho 2F, Chuo-ku, Tokyo, 104-0033, Japan
Tel.: (81) 35 657 4070
Web Site: https://www.utecs.co.jp
Office Equipment Mfr & Distr
N.A.I.C.S.: 337214

Uchida Yoko Business Expert Co., Ltd. (1)
2-4-7 Shinkawa, Chuo-ku, Tokyo, 104-8282, Japan
Tel.: (81) 33 555 4805
Web Site: https://www.ubx.uchida.co.jp
Emp.: 258
Human Resource & General Affair Services
N.A.I.C.S.: 541612

Uchida Yoko Global Limited (1)
Unit Unit 06B 25/F Nanyang Plaza 57 Hung To Road, Kwun Tong, Kowloon, China (Hong Kong)
Tel.: (852) 2 877 3663
Web Site: https://www.uchidayoko.com
Stationery Product Mfr
N.A.I.C.S.: 322230
Toshiji Hayashi *(Pres)*

Uchida Yoko IT Solutions Co., Ltd. (1)
6-1-11 Shinbashi Daiwa Onarimon Building, Minato-ku, Tokyo, 105-0004, Japan
Tel.: (81) 35 777 6621
Web Site: https://www.uchida-it.co.jp
Emp.: 634
Software Development Services
N.A.I.C.S.: 541511

Uchida Yoko Office Facilities (Shanghai) Co., Ltd. (1)
Room 2902-1 No 580 West Nanjing Road, Jing An District, Shanghai, 200041, China

Tel.: (86) 215 235 2233
Web Site: https://www.uchidayoko.cn
Office Furniture Mfr
N.A.I.C.S.: 337214

Uchida of America, Corp. (1)
3535 Del Amo Blvd, Torrance, CA 90503
Tel.: (310) 793-2200
Web Site: http://www.uchida.com
Emp.: 20
Art & Craft Product Distr
N.A.I.C.S.: 459999

Yoko Corporation (1)
17th floor Nakanoshima Intes 6-2-40 Nakanoshima, Kita-ku, Osaka, 530-0005, Japan
Tel.: (81) 664597603
Web Site: https://www.l-yoko.co.jp
Emp.: 158
General Freight Transportation Services
N.A.I.C.S.: 484230

UCHIHASHI ESTEC CO., LTD.
Room 407 12-1 Minami-Ikebukuro 2-chome, Toshima-ku, Tokyo, 171-0022, Japan
Tel.: (81) 6 6962 6666 JP
Web Site: http://www.uchihashi.co.jp
Year Founded: 1918
Sales Range: $1-9.9 Million
Emp.: 42
Solder & Related Products Mfr & Whslr
N.A.I.C.S.: 331491
Akimitsu Fujii *(Pres)*

UCHIYAMA HOLDINGS CO., LTD.
1F Uchiyama 20 Building 2-10-10 Kumamoto, Kokurakita-ku, Kitakyushu, 802-0044, Japan
Tel.: (81) 935510002
Web Site: https://www.uchiyama-gr.jp
Year Founded: 2006
6059—(TKS)
Rev.: $190,645,620
Assets: $205,723,030
Liabilities: $123,977,160
Net Worth: $81,745,870
Earnings: $1,407,930
Emp.: 2,270
Fiscal Year-end: 03/31/24
Management Services
N.A.I.C.S.: 541611
Fumiharu Uchiyama *(Co-Chm, Pres & Dir-Rep)*

Subsidiaries:

Bonheure Co., Ltd. (1)
2-10-10 Kumamoto Uchiyama 20th Building 1F, Kokurakita-ku, Kitakyushu, 802-0044, Japan
Tel.: (81) 935510008
Web Site: https://www.uchiyama-bld.com
Real Estate Services
N.A.I.C.S.: 531210
Shimami Ueno *(CEO)*

UCHUMI SUPERMARKETS LIMITED
Langata Hyper Complex Off Langata Road, PO Box 73167, 00200, Nairobi, Kenya
Tel.: (254) 2080200801
Web Site: https://www.uchumimarkets.co.ke
Year Founded: 1976
UCHM—(NAI)
Sales Range: $50-74.9 Million
Emp.: 2,317
Supermarket Operator
N.A.I.C.S.: 445110
John Peter Kariuki *(Chm & Mgr-Security Svcs)*

UCI CO., LTD.
604 Daeryung Post Tower 7 48 Digital-ro 33-gil, Guro-gu, Seoul, Korea (South)

Tel.: (82) 234386912
Web Site: https://www.m-it.co.kr
Year Founded: 1967
038340—(KRS)
Rev.: $2,543,349
Assets: $13,005,433
Liabilities: $9,021,060
Net Worth: $3,984,373
Earnings: ($2,963,424)
Fiscal Year-end: 12/31/22
Gas Station Operator
N.A.I.C.S.: 457110
Kim Hwan *(CEO)*

UCLOUD TECHNOLOGY CO., LTD.
Block B Building 10 Urban Concept Creative Park No 619 Longchang Road, Yangpu, Shanghai, 200090, China
Tel.: (86) 2155509888
Web Site: https://www.ucloud.cn
Year Founded: 2012
688158—(SHG)
Rev.: $276,899,505
Assets: $572,396,198
Liabilities: $154,049,183
Net Worth: $418,347,016
Earnings: ($58,029,300)
Emp.: 1,000
Fiscal Year-end: 12/31/22
Information Technology Services
N.A.I.C.S.: 541512
Xinhua Ji *(Chm, Pres & CEO)*

UCLOUDLINK GROUP, INC.
Unit 2214-Rm1 22/F Mira Place Tower A 132 Nathan Road, Tsim Sha Tsui, Kowloon, China (Hong Kong)
Tel.: (852) 21806111 Ky
Web Site: https://www.ucloudlink.com
Year Founded: 2014
UCL—(NASDAQ)
Rev.: $85,576,000
Assets: $56,607,000
Liabilities: $40,554,000
Net Worth: $16,053,000
Earnings: $2,811,000
Emp.: 393
Fiscal Year-end: 12/31/23
Holding Company
N.A.I.C.S.: 551112
Chaohui Chen *(Co-Founder & CEO)*

UCO BANK LIMITED
10 B T M Sarani, Kolkata, 700 001, West Bengal, India
Tel.: (91) 3344557227
Web Site: https://www.ucobank.com
Year Founded: 1943
UCOBANK—(NSE)
Rev.: $2,479,715,634
Assets: $34,580,378,906
Liabilities: $33,226,525,414
Net Worth: $1,353,853,492
Earnings: $22,800,141
Emp.: 22,012
Fiscal Year-end: 03/31/21
International Banking Services
N.A.I.C.S.: 522110
Sanjay Kumar *(Gen Mgr-Credit Monitoring)*

UCORE RARE METALS INC.
106-210 Waterfront Drive, Halifax, B4A 0H3, NS, Canada
Tel.: (902) 482-5214 AB
Web Site: https://www.ucore.com
Year Founded: 2006
UCU—(OTCIQ)
Rev.: $162,084
Assets: $38,678,916
Liabilities: $2,672,326
Net Worth: $36,006,590
Earnings: ($4,310,947)
Emp.: 7
Fiscal Year-end: 12/31/21

Metal Ore Mining Services
N.A.I.C.S.: 212290
Peter Manuel *(CFO, Sec & VP)*

UCR SA
SOS Panduri 71 S5, Bucharest, Romania
Tel.: (40) 21 4100810
Footwear Mfr
N.A.I.C.S.: 316210

UCREST BERHAD
Lot 6 04 Level 6 KPMG Tower 8 First Avenue Bandar Utama, 47800, Petaling Jaya, Selangor, Malaysia
Tel.: (60) 377289880 MY
Web Site: https://www.ucrest.net
UCREST—(KLS)
Rev.: $2,869,285
Assets: $10,007,400
Liabilities: $3,136,506
Net Worth: $6,870,894
Earnings: $21,355
Emp.: 11
Fiscal Year-end: 05/31/23
Information Technology Services
N.A.I.C.S.: 541512
Eg Kah Yee *(Founder, Chm & Mng Dir)*

UCW LIMITED
Level 1 333 Kent Street, Sydney, 2000, NSW, Australia
Tel.: (61) 291124540
Web Site: http://www.ucwlimited.com.au
EDU—(ASX)
Rev.: $14,449,281
Assets: $22,682,935
Liabilities: $15,543,652
Net Worth: $7,139,283
Earnings: ($1,918,761)
Fiscal Year-end: 12/31/23
Investment Services
N.A.I.C.S.: 523999
Adam Davis *(CEO & Mng Dir)*

Subsidiaries:

Australian Learning Group Pty. Limited (1)
Building 5B Level 3 1-59 Quay Street, Haymarket, Sydney, 2000, NSW, Australia
Tel.: (61) 244046255
Web Site: https://www.alg.edu.au
Educational Support Services
N.A.I.C.S.: 611710

UDAIPUR CEMENT WORKS LIMITED
Shripati Nagar CFA P O Dabok, Udaipur, 313 022, Rajasthan, India
Tel.: (91) 2942655076
Web Site: https://udaipurcement.com
Year Founded: 1993
530131—(BOM)
Rev.: $123,764,762
Assets: $215,255,680
Liabilities: $173,794,137
Net Worth: $41,461,543
Earnings: $4,299,502
Emp.: 340
Fiscal Year-end: 03/31/23
Cement Mfr & Distr
N.A.I.C.S.: 327310
Naveen Kumar Sharma *(Exec Dir)*

UDARNIK D.D. BREZA
Dzemala Bijedica 2, 71370, Breza, Bosnia & Herzegovina
Tel.: (387) 32784736
UDRNRK2—(SARE)
Rev.: $8,138
Assets: $1,207,675
Liabilities: $10,484
Net Worth: $1,197,191
Earnings: ($37,379)
Emp.: 1

UDARNIK D.D. BREZA

Udarnik d.d. Breza—(Continued)
Fiscal Year-end: 12/31/21
Food & Beverage Dist
N.A.I.C.S.: 445298

UDAY JEWELLERY INDUSTRIES LTD.
2nd Floor 3-6-307/1 3-6-307/2 3-6-308/1 Hyderguda Main Road, Simple Natural Systems Basheer Bagh, Hyderabad, 500004, Telangana, India
Tel.: (91) 4048506411
Web Site:
https://www.udayjewellery.com
Year Founded: 1999
539518—(BOM)
Rev.: $21,375,385
Assets: $12,705,749
Liabilities: $4,549,679
Net Worth: $8,156,070
Earnings: $1,139,248
Emp.: 93
Fiscal Year-end: 03/31/23
Jewelry Mfr & Distr
N.A.I.C.S.: 339910
Ritesh Kumar Sanghi (Mng Dir)

UDAYSHIVAKUMAR INFRA LTD.
1924A/196 Banashankari Badavane Near NH-4 Bypass, Davangere, Davanagere, 577005, India
Tel.: (91) 8192297009
Web Site: https://uskinfra.com
Year Founded: 2002
USK—(NSE)
Engineering Construction Services
N.A.I.C.S.: 237990
Sanjeevani Shivaji Redekar (Officer)

Subsidiaries:

Kevadiya Construction Private Limited (1)
5th & 7th Floor Sanskruti Building B/h Rajpath Club, Opp Astral Pipe House Sindhu Bhavan Road Bodakdev, Ahmedabad, 380054, Gujarat, India
Tel.: (91) 9016584176
Web Site:
https://www.kevadiyaconstruction.co.in
Civil Engineering Services
N.A.I.C.S.: 541330

UDEA B.V.
Doornhoek 4040, 5465 TD, Veghel, Netherlands
Tel.: (31) 413 256 700
Web Site: http://www.udea.nl
Year Founded: 1999
Organic Food Whslr
N.A.I.C.S.: 311999
Jeroen Nooijen (Mgr-HR)

Subsidiaries:

Hagor NV (1)
Remylaan 4 C Bus 9, 3018, Wijgmaal, Belgium
Tel.: (32) 16 629 667
Web Site: http://www.hagor.be
Sales Range: $25-49.9 Million
Emp.: 16
Food Products Mfr & Distr
N.A.I.C.S.: 311999
Wim Kestens (Product Mgr)

Natudis Nederland B.V. (1)
Daltonstraat 38, PO Box 376, Harderwijk, 3846 BX, Netherlands
Tel.: (31) 341464211
Web Site: http://www.natudis.nl
Dry Grocery Products Distr
N.A.I.C.S.: 424410
Yvonne Witpaard (Area Mgr-Sls)

UDENNA CORPORATION
Stella Hizon Reyes Rd Bo Pampanga, Davao, 8000, Philippines
Tel.: (63) 82 235 8888   PH
Web Site: http://www.udenna.ph

Year Founded: 2002
Holding Company; Investment Services
N.A.I.C.S.: 551112
Dennis A. Uy (Chm & CEO)

Subsidiaries:

UC Malampaya Philippines Pte. Ltd. (1)
350 Orchard Road #17-05/06 Shaw House, Singapore, 238868, Singapore
Tel.: (65) 6360 0780
Investment Services
N.A.I.C.S.: 523999

Subsidiary (Non-US):

Chevron Malampaya LLC (2)
5/F 6750 Ayala Avenue, Makati, 1226, Philippines
Tel.: (63) 28458400
Oil & Gas Support Services
N.A.I.C.S.: 213112

UDP TECHNOLOGY LTD.
4F Woolim Blue 9 Building 240-21 Yeomchang-Dong, Gangseo-Gu, Seoul, 157-861, Korea (South)
Tel.: (82) 2 2605 1486
Web Site:
http://www.udptechnology.com
Year Founded: 2000
Sales Range: $10-24.9 Million
Emp.: 100
Video Security Equipment, Hardware & Software
N.A.I.C.S.: 334310

UE FURNITURE CO., LTD.
No 1 YongYi West Road, Lingfeng Subdistrict Anji County, Huzhou, 313300, Zhejiang, China
Tel.: (86) 5725137669
Web Site: http://www.uechairs.com
Year Founded: 2001
603600—(SHG)
Rev.: $569,361,424
Assets: $419,394,217
Liabilities: $170,363,578
Net Worth: $249,030,639
Earnings: $47,064,060
Emp.: 4,300
Fiscal Year-end: 12/31/22
Office Chair Mfr & Distr
N.A.I.C.S.: 337214
Xi Chen (VP & Deputy Gen Mgr)

UEC GROUP LTD.
UEC Plaza Building 106 A10 Jiuxianqiao North Road, Chaoyang District, Beijing, China
Tel.: (86) 1062602000
Web Site: http://www.ronglian.com
002642—(SSE)
Rev.: $524,921,104
Assets: $447,595,804
Liabilities: $235,323,317
Net Worth: $212,272,487
Earnings: $1,712,866
Emp.: 800
Fiscal Year-end: 12/31/22
IT Services
N.A.I.C.S.: 541519
Donghui Wang (Chm)

Subsidiaries:

Unlimited Express (Guangzhou) Corp. (1)
A1-6 Nanxi Cargo Area Dongjun Commercial Street, Huadong Town Huadu District, Guangzhou, China
Tel.: (86) 13088880033
Customs Brokerage Services
N.A.I.C.S.: 541614

Unlimited Express (Jakarta) Corp. (1)
Rukan Puri Niaga III Block M8-3F Jl Puri Kencana, Kembangan, Jakarta, 11610, Indonesia

Tel.: (62) 2158302280
Web Site: https://www.yudhanusa.co.id
Air Freight Services
N.A.I.C.S.: 926120

Unlimited Express (Myanmar) Corp. (1)
Rm-1003 10TH Floor Yuzana Condo Tower No 69 Shwe Gone Daing Road, Bahan T/S, Yangon, Myanmar
Tel.: (95) 15586602
Air & Sea Port Transportation Services
N.A.I.C.S.: 926120

Unlimited Express (Semarang) Corp. (1)
JL Puri Anjasmoro Blok F No 11A, Semarang, 50144, Indonesia
Tel.: (62) 247617488
Customs Brokerage Services
N.A.I.C.S.: 541614

Unlimited Express (Shenzhen) Corp. (1)
The Sky Castle B-28D No 77 Jingtian Road, Futian District, Shenzhen, 518034, China
Tel.: (86) 75583056659
Customs Brokerage Services
N.A.I.C.S.: 541614

Unlimited Express (Taiwan) Corp. (1)
5F-2 No 76 Nanjing W Rd, Tatung District, Taipei, Taiwan
Tel.: (886) 225589323
Customs Brokerage Services
N.A.I.C.S.: 541614

Unlimited Express (Thailand) Corp. (1)
No 23/17-18 12th Floor Sorachai Building Soi Sukhumvit 63, Sukhumvit Road North Klongton Wattana, Bangkok, 10110, Thailand
Tel.: (66) 23817575
Customs Brokerage Services
N.A.I.C.S.: 541614

Unlimited Express (USA) Corp. (1)
147-39 175th St Ste 103, Jamaica, NY 11434
Tel.: (718) 656-1888
Air & Sea Port Transportation Services
N.A.I.C.S.: 926120

Unlimited Worldwide Logistics Corp. (1)
930 W Hyde Park Blvd Unit B, Inglewood, CA 90302
Tel.: (310) 215-9268
Air & Sea Port Transportation Services
N.A.I.C.S.: 926120

UEG-GREEN ENERGY SOLUTIONS/ALBERTA, INC.
2 Bloor Street West Suite 735, Toronto, M4W 3R1, ON, Canada
Tel.: (416) 972-5068   NV
Year Founded: 2011
Wind Energy
N.A.I.C.S.: 221118
Kyle E. Barnette (Treas & Sec)

UEHARA SEI SHOJI CO., LTD.
2-6-5 Tani-machi Chuo-ku, Nakagyo-ku, Kyoto, 604-8580, Japan
Tel.: (81) 75 2126000
Web Site: http://www.ueharasei.co.jp
Year Founded: 1948
Sales Range: $650-699.9 Million
Emp.: 277
Petroleum Product & Construction Material Distr
N.A.I.C.S.: 424720
Daisaku Uehara (Pres)

UEKI CORPORATION
1545 Ekimae, Kashiwazaki, 945-8540, Niigata, Japan
Tel.: (81) 257232200
Web Site: https://www.uekigumi.co.jp
Year Founded: 1948

1867—(TKS)
Rev.: $369,565,100
Assets: $332,483,000
Liabilities: $152,063,050
Net Worth: $180,419,950
Earnings: $12,406,970
Emp.: 670
Fiscal Year-end: 03/31/24
Construction & Real Estate Services
N.A.I.C.S.: 541330
Yoshiaki Ueki (Mng Dir)

Subsidiaries:

Ueki Real Estate Co., Ltd. (1)
3-9 Shinbashi, Kashiwazaki, 945-0056, Niigata, Japan
Tel.: (81) 257245506
Real Estate Services
N.A.I.C.S.: 531390

UEMATSU SHOKAI CO., LTD.
3-7-5 Oroshi-machi, Wakabayashi-ku, Sendai, 984-0015, Miyagi, Japan
Tel.: (81) 222325171
Web Site: https://uematsushokai.jp
Year Founded: 1955
9914—(TKS)
Sales Range: Less than $1 Million
Industrial Machinery Whslr
N.A.I.C.S.: 423830
Seiichiro Uematsu (Pres & CEO)

UENO FINE CHEMICALS INDUSTRY, LTD.
2-4-8 Koraibashi 2-Chome, Chuo-Ku, Osaka, 541 8543, Japan
Tel.: (81) 662030761
Web Site: http://www.ueno-fc.co.jp
Year Founded: 1945
Sales Range: $200-249.9 Million
Emp.: 417
Producer of Chemicals
N.A.I.C.S.: 325998
Ryuzo Ueno (Chm)

Subsidiaries:

Ueno Fine Chemicals Industries USA (1)
420 Lexington Ave Rm 2832, New York, NY 10170
Tel.: (212) 953-8920
Rev.: $30,000,000
Emp.: 5
Producer of Chemicals & Allied Products
N.A.I.C.S.: 424690
T. Ohashi (Gen Mgr)

UES HOLDINGS PTE. LTD.
12 Ang Mo Kio Street 64 03A-14 UE BizHub Central, Singapore, 569088, Singapore
Tel.: (65) 68188188   SG
Web Site: http://www.uesh.sg
Electrical Engineering Services
N.A.I.C.S.: 541330
Yujie Liu (CEO)

UESA GMBH
Gewerbepark-Nord 7, 04938, Uebigau-Wahrenbruck, Germany
Tel.: (49) 35365490
Web Site: http://www.uesa.de
Year Founded: 1990
Rev.: $67,874,739
Emp.: 291
Electric Equipment Mfr
N.A.I.C.S.: 335999
Helmut Hoffmann (Mgr)

Subsidiaries:

Kunststoffverarbeitung Uebigau GmbH (1)
Doberluger Str 52, 4938, Uebigau-Wahrenbruck, Germany
Tel.: (49) 3536549140
Plastics Product Mfr
N.A.I.C.S.: 326112

metec GmbH (1)

AND PRIVATE COMPANIES

Max-Beckmann-Str 7, 73257, Kongen, Germany
Tel.: (49) 70248689190
Web Site: http://www.metec-gmbh.com
Copper Product Mfr
N.A.I.C.S.: 331523
Joachim Peter *(CEO)*

uemet GmbH (1)
Gewerbepark-Nord 9, 4938, Uebigau-Wahrenbruck, Germany
Tel.: (49) 3536544990
Sheet Metal Mfr
N.A.I.C.S.: 332114

uesatrans GmbH (1)
Elsterwerdaer Str 31 a, Berlin, 4932, Germany
Tel.: (49) 353348190
Trucks Mfr
N.A.I.C.S.: 336212

UESTRA HANNOVERSCHE VERKEHRSBETRIEBE AG
Am Hohen Ufer 6, 30159, Hannover, 30159, Germany
Tel.: (49) 51116680
Web Site: https://www.uestra.de
HVB—(BER)
Sales Range: Less than $1 Million
Transportation Services
N.A.I.C.S.: 485999
Andre Neiss *(Chm-Mgmt Bd)*

UET UNITED ELECTRONIC TECHNOLOGY AG
Frankfurter Strasse 80-82, D-65760, Eschborn, Germany
Tel.: (49) 61967777550 De
Web Site: https://www.uet-group.com
Year Founded: 2006
CFC—(MUN)
Rev.: $80,295,504
Assets: $59,465,477
Liabilities: $57,886,943
Net Worth: $1,578,534
Earnings: ($1,280,489)
Emp.: 252
Fiscal Year-end: 12/31/23
Investment Holding Company
N.A.I.C.S.: 551112
Werner Neubauer *(CEO & Member-Mgmt Bd)*

Subsidiaries:

Albis-Elcon System Germany GmbH (1)
Obere Hauptstrasse 10, Hartmannsdorf, 09232, Eschborn, Germany
Tel.: (49) 372273510
Web Site: https://www.albis-elcon.com
Emp.: 250
Security System Services
N.A.I.C.S.: 561621

UEX, LTD.
Tennoz Central Tower 2-2-24 Higashi Shinagawa Shinagawa Ward, Tokyo, 140-8630, Japan
Tel.: (81) 354606528
Web Site: http://www.uex-ltd.co.jp
Year Founded: 1955
9888—(TKS)
Rev.: $344,466,930
Assets: $343,561,360
Liabilities: $223,695,620
Net Worth: $119,865,740
Earnings: $8,566,560
Emp.: 288
Fiscal Year-end: 03/31/24
Metallic Machinery Product Mfr & Distr
N.A.I.C.S.: 332999
Noriyuki Kishimoto *(Pres)*

Subsidiaries:

Reiwa Specialty Steel Corporation (1)
1-2-2 Hitotsubashi, Chiyoda-ku, Tokyo, 100-0003, Japan
Tel.: (81) 352192525
Web Site: http://www.sumitoku.co.jp
Emp.: 84
Steel Stocking, Processing & Sales
N.A.I.C.S.: 423510
Kenji Yamamoto *(CEO)*

UFI CHARITABLE TRUST
26 Red Lion Square, London, WC1R 4AG, United Kingdom
Tel.: (44) 203 086 7974
Web Site: http://www.ufi.co.uk
Education Services
N.A.I.C.S.: 624310

UFLEX LTD
A-107-108 Sector-IV, Noida, 201 301, UP, India
Tel.: (91) 1204012345
Web Site: https://www.uflexltd.com
500148—(NSE)
Rev.: $1,772,612,817
Assets: $1,970,826,461
Liabilities: $1,070,938,901
Net Worth: $899,887,561
Earnings: $57,632,456
Emp.: 7,194
Fiscal Year-end: 03/31/23
Polyester Chip Mfr
N.A.I.C.S.: 326113
Ajay Krishna *(Compliance Officer, Sec & Sr VP-Legal)*

Subsidiaries:

Flex Americas S.A. de C.V. (1)
Boulevard de los Rios 5680, Zona Puerto Industrial, CP 89603, Altamira, Tamaulipas, Mexico
Tel.: (52) 8332608100
Polymeric Film Mfr
N.A.I.C.S.: 325211

Flex Films (USA) Inc. (1)
1221 N Black Branch Rd, Elizabethtown, KY 42701
Tel.: (270) 982-3456
Polymeric Film Mfr
N.A.I.C.S.: 325211

Flex Films Europa Korlatolt Felelossegu Tarsasag (1)
Ipari Park 7, 2651, Retsag, Hungary
Tel.: (36) 213000113
Polymeric Film Mfr
N.A.I.C.S.: 325211

Flex Films Europa Sp. z o.o. (1)
Ul Gen Wladyslawa Sikorskiego 48, PO Box 62 300, Wrzesnia, Poland
Tel.: (48) 616701000
Polymeric Film Mfr
N.A.I.C.S.: 325211

Flex Films RUS LLC (1)
Tel.: (7) 4956431194
Polymeric Film Mfr
N.A.I.C.S.: 325211
Junaid Iqbal Khan *(Gen Dir)*

Flex Foods Ltd. (1)
Lal Tappar Industrial Area Haridwar Road, PO Resham Majri, Resham Majri, Dehradun, 248140, Uttarakhand, India
Tel.: (91) 1352499262
Web Site: https://www.flexfoodsltd.com
Rev.: $14,136,958
Assets: $45,432,312
Liabilities: $33,200,336
Net Worth: $12,231,977
Earnings: ($1,270,619)
Emp.: 478
Fiscal Year-end: 03/31/2023
Food Products & Vegetable Mfr
N.A.I.C.S.: 311411
Madan Mohan Varshney *(Exec Dir)*

Flex Middle East FZE (1)
Jebel Ali Free Zone, PO Box 17930, Dubai, United Arab Emirates
Tel.: (971) 48102300
Web Site: http://www.flexflim.com
Sales Range: $50-74.9 Million
Emp.: 200
Plastics Films Mfr
N.A.I.C.S.: 322220

Flex P. Films (Egypt) S.A.E. (1)
Plot No R2 in Engineering Square e2 Plot No 3 in, North Extensions Of Industrial Zones, 6th of October City, Egypt
Tel.: (20) 238283000
Polymeric Film Mfr
N.A.I.C.S.: 325211

Uflex Europe Limited (1)
Tel.: (44) 2074875777
Polymeric Film Mfr
N.A.I.C.S.: 325211

Uflex Packaging Inc. (1)
Tel.: (201) 947-3539
Web Site: http://www.uflexpackaging.com
Emp.: 6
Packaging Services
N.A.I.C.S.: 561910

UFO MOVIEZ INDIA LTD
Valuable Techno Park Plot No 53/1 Road No 7, MIDC Marol Andheri E, Mumbai, 400093, India
Tel.: (91) 2240305060
Web Site: https://www.ufomoviez.com
UFO—(NSE)
Rev.: $12,380,632
Assets: $71,002,372
Liabilities: $34,868,898
Net Worth: $36,133,475
Earnings: ($16,052,400)
Emp.: 480
Fiscal Year-end: 03/31/21
Digital Cinema Distribution Network & In-Cinema Advertising Platform
N.A.I.C.S.: 512120
Sanjeev Aga *(Chm)*

Subsidiaries:

Nova Cinemaz Private Limited (1)
Valuable Techno Park Plot No 53/1 Road No 7 MIDC, Andheri East, Mumbai, 400 093, Maharashtra, India
Tel.: (91) 9619125770
Digital Cinema Network Services
N.A.I.C.S.: 512120

Scrabble Digital Limited (1)
501 Janaki Centre 5th Floor Off Veera Desai Road Andheri West, Mumbai, 400 053, India
Tel.: (91) 2261038000
Web Site: https://www.scrabbledigital.com
Digital Marketing Services
N.A.I.C.S.: 541613

Scrabble Entertainment Limited (1)
3rd Floor Valuable Techno Park Plot No 53/1 Road No 7 MIDC, Andheri East, Mumbai, 400093, India
Tel.: (91) 2240305060
Web Site: http://www.scrabbleentertainment.com
Entertainment Services
N.A.I.C.S.: 711130

UFO Lanka Private Limited (1)
CBM House 2A 2/1 Lake Drive, 08, Colombo, Sri Lanka
Tel.: (94) 117707777
Web Site: https://www.ufo.lk
Logistic Services
N.A.I.C.S.: 488510

UFUK YATIRIM YONETIM VE GAYRIMENKUL AS
Kisikli Mah Cesme Dead End Street No 6/1, Uskudar, Istanbul, Turkiye
Tel.: (90) 2165252500
Web Site: https://www.ufukyyg.com.tr
Year Founded: 1995
UFUK—(IST)
Sales Range: Less than $1 Million
Bank Financing Services
N.A.I.C.S.: 522299
Huseyin Avni Metinkale *(Vice Chm)*

UG HEALTHCARE CORPORATION LIMITED
Lot 62-63 Lorong Senawang 3/2 Senawang Industrial Estate, 70450, Seremban, Negeri Sembilan, Malaysia
Tel.: (60) 66772751
Web Site: https://www.ughealthcarecorp.com
Year Founded: 1989
8K7—(CAT)
Rev.: $74,941,089
Assets: $170,430,530
Liabilities: $36,165,987
Net Worth: $134,264,542
Earnings: ($19,979,993)
Emp.: 1,054
Fiscal Year-end: 06/30/23
Latex & Nitrile Examination Glove Mfr & Distr; Other Medical Gloves & Ancillary Products Distr
N.A.I.C.S.: 339112
Keck Keong Lee *(CEO)*

UGANDA CLAYS LTD.
14 Km Entebbe Road, PO Box 3188, Kajjansi, Kampala, Uganda
Tel.: (256) 312305403
Web Site: http://www.ugandaclays.co.ug
Year Founded: 1950
UCL—(UGAN)
Rev.: $8,055,201
Assets: $20,327,651
Liabilities: $8,889,836
Net Worth: $11,437,815
Earnings: ($754,270)
Emp.: 237
Fiscal Year-end: 12/31/23
Clay Building Material & Refractories Manufacturing
N.A.I.C.S.: 327120
Patrick Mukasa *(Head-Internal Audit)*

UGANDA SECURITIES EXCHANGE LTD.
Plot 2 Pilkington Rd Workers House 2nd Fl Northern Wing, PO Box 23552, Kampala, Uganda
Tel.: (256) 41343297
Web Site: http://www.use.or.ug
Sales Range: $1-9.9 Million
Emp.: 13
Stock Exchange Services
N.A.I.C.S.: 523210
Paul Bwiso *(CEO)*

UGM HOLDINGS PTY LTD.
91 York Street, Teralba, 2284, NSW, Australia
Tel.: (61) 2 4941 7500
Web Site: http://www.ugm.com.au
Year Founded: 1997
Emp.: 100
Mining Support Services
N.A.I.C.S.: 213113
Paul Hartcher *(Mng Dir)*

Subsidiaries:

ADDCAR Systems LLC (1)
No 1 HWM Dr, Ashland, KY 41102
Tel.: (606) 928-7244
Web Site: http://www.addcarsystems.com
Mining Equipment Mfr
N.A.I.C.S.: 333131
Johnny Sturgill *(Pres)*

UGOPROM A.D.
Zarka Zrenjanina 12, 23330, Novi Knezevac, Serbia
Tel.: (381) 23081202
Web Site: http://www.ugoprom.co.rs
Year Founded: 1991
UGPR—(BEL)
Sales Range: Less than $1 Million
Emp.: 1
Home Management Services
N.A.I.C.S.: 721110
Radomir Elezovic *(CEO)*

UGOTURS A.D.

Ugoprom a.d.—(Continued)

UGOTURS A.D.
I Krajiskog Prolet Bataljona Bb, 78240, Celinac, Bosnia & Herzegovina
Tel.: (387) 51 851 093
UGOT—(BANJ)
Sales Range: Less than $1 Million
Home Management Services
N.A.I.C.S.: 721110
Zeljko Cvijanovic (Chm-Mgmt Bd)

UGRO CAPITAL LIMITED
Equinox Business Park Tower 3 4th Floor LBS Road, Mumbai, 400070, India
Tel.: (91) 2248918686
Web Site: https://www.ugrocapital.com
UGROCAP—(NSE)
Rev.: $42,781,270
Assets: $389,601,794
Liabilities: $257,665,918
Net Worth: $131,935,877
Earnings: $1,986,157
Emp.: 1,111
Fiscal Year-end: 03/31/22
Merchant Banking, Mutual Fund, Debt Market Operations, Insurance & Depository Services
N.A.I.C.S.: 524210
Amit Gupta (CFO & Chief Treasury Officer)

UHINENUD AJAKIRJAD OU
Liivalaia 13/15, 10118, Tallinn, Estonia
Tel.: (372) 610 4000 EE
Web Site: http://www.ajakirjad.ee
Year Founded: 1998
Magazine Publisher
N.A.I.C.S.: 513120

UIE PLC
Blue Harbour Business Centre Level 1 Sector L, Ta' Xbiex Yacht Marina, XBX 1027, Ta' Xbiex, XBX 1027, Malta
Tel.: (356) 33933330 BS
Web Site: https://uie.dk
Year Founded: 1982
UIE—(CSE)
Rev.: $573,271,000
Assets: $1,123,049,000
Liabilities: $107,190,000
Net Worth: $1,015,859,000
Earnings: $48,928,000
Emp.: 6,386
Fiscal Year-end: 12/31/22
Commodity Goods Mfr
N.A.I.C.S.: 523160
Carl Bek-Nielsen (Chm)

Subsidiaries:

International Plantation Services Limited (1)
Plantations House 49 H C Andersens Boulevard, 1553, Copenhagen, 1553, Denmark
Tel.: (45) 33933330
Web Site: http://www.uie.dk
Sales Range: $25-49.9 Million
Emp.: 6
Palm Oil Processing Services
N.A.I.C.S.: 311224

UIE Services A/S (1)
Vandtarnsvej 83A, 2860, Soborg, Denmark
Tel.: (45) 33933330
Financial Services
N.A.I.C.S.: 523940

UIL CO., LTD.
869-26 Bokwong-ro Gwangtanmyeon, P'aju, 413-851, Gyeonggi-do, Korea (South)
Tel.: (82) 319481234
Web Site: https://www.e-uil.com
Year Founded: 1982

049520—(KRS)
Rev.: $255,358,200
Assets: $160,390,807
Liabilities: $46,600,333
Net Worth: $113,790,474
Earnings: $5,239,903
Emp.: 143
Fiscal Year-end: 12/31/22
Electronic Components Mfr
N.A.I.C.S.: 334419
Kim Si Gyoon (CEO)

Subsidiaries:

India Corporation (1)
51 Bibijan Street Office no- 18, Mumbai, 400003, India
Tel.: (91) 2223450519
Web Site: https://indiacorporation.net
Gas Cutting Equipment Distr
N.A.I.C.S.: 423840

UIL ENERGY LTD.
Level 9 1 Eagle Street, Brisbane, 4000, QLD, Australia
Tel.: (61) 730079600 AU
Web Site: http://www.uilenergy.com.au
Year Founded: 2011
Rev.: $14,416
Assets: $8,213,708
Liabilities: $183,300
Net Worth: $8,030,408
Earnings: ($811,716)
Fiscal Year-end: 06/30/18
Oil & Gas Exploration Services
N.A.I.C.S.: 213112
John de Stefani (CEO & Mng Dir)

UIL FINANCE LIMITED
Clarendon House 2 Church Street, Hamilton, HM 11, Bermuda BM
Web Site: https://www.uil.limited
Year Founded: 2007
UTLG—(LSE)
Rev.: $12,912,143
Assets: $396,052,764
Liabilities: $184,514,012
Net Worth: $211,538,753
Earnings: ($56,110,831)
Fiscal Year-end: 06/30/23
Investment Management Service
N.A.I.C.S.: 523999
Peter Burrows AO (Chm)

UJAAS ENERGY LIMITED
Survey No 211/1 Opp Sector C and Metalman Sanwer Road Industrial Area, Indore, 452015, Madhya Pradesh, India
Tel.: (91) 7312721672
Web Site: https://www.ujaas.com
Year Founded: 1979
UEL—(NSE)
Rev.: $5,041,395
Assets: $43,123,353
Liabilities: $18,873,405
Net Worth: $24,249,948
Earnings: ($4,153,845)
Emp.: 105
Fiscal Year-end: 03/31/21
Switchgear & Transformer Mfr
N.A.I.C.S.: 335313
Shyam Sunder Mundra (Chm & Co-Mng Dir)

UJJIVAN FINANCIAL SERVICES LTD.
Grape Garden 3rd A Cross 18th Main 6th Block, Koramangala, Bengaluru, 560 095, India
Tel.: (91) 804 071 2121
Web Site: http://www.ujjivan.com
Year Founded: 2005
539874—(NSE)
Rev.: $434,205,886
Assets: $2,758,215,642
Liabilities: $2,395,292,786

Net Worth: $362,922,856
Earnings: ($32,638,106)
Emp.: 16,571
Fiscal Year-end: 03/31/21
Financial Support Services
N.A.I.C.S.: 523999
Ittira Davis (CEO & Mng Dir)

Subsidiaries:

Ujjivan Small Finance Bank Limited (1)
Grape Garden No 27 3rd A Cross 18th Main 6th Block, Koramangala, Bengaluru, 560 095, Karnataka, India
Tel.: (91) 8040712121
Web Site: https://www.ujjivansfb.in
Emp.: 17,018
Financial Services
N.A.I.C.S.: 541611
Ittira Davis (CEO)

UJU ELECTRONICS CO., LTD.
3F 7 Daehak 3-ro, Yeongtong-gu, Suwon, Gyeonggi-do, Korea (South)
Tel.: (82) 312123701
Web Site: https://www.uju.com
Year Founded: 1993
065680—(KRS)
Rev.: $143,586,618
Assets: $224,658,330
Liabilities: $51,672,520
Net Worth: $172,985,810
Earnings: $9,372,247
Emp.: 374
Fiscal Year-end: 12/31/22
Electronic Connector Mfr
N.A.I.C.S.: 334417

Subsidiaries:

Electronics Co., Ltd. (1)
Scripture Industrial Park, Chengyang District, Qingdao, Shandong, China
Tel.: (86) 532 8908 3700
Electronic Components Mfr
N.A.I.C.S.: 334419

UJU HOLDING LIMITED
4/F Building G Dongfengdebi WE AI Innovative Park, 8 Dongfeng South Road Chaoyang District, Beijing, 100050, China
Tel.: (86) 1064642557 Ky
Web Site: https://www.ujumedia.com
Year Founded: 2020
1948—(HKG)
Rev.: $979,729,868
Assets: $476,491,056
Liabilities: $284,604,702
Net Worth: $191,886,354
Earnings: $12,595,813
Emp.: 576
Fiscal Year-end: 12/31/23
Holding Company
N.A.I.C.S.: 523999
Kam Le Hong (Sec)

UK ARSAGERA OAO
Renaissance Plaza Build 26 A Shatelena str, Saint Petersburg, 194021, Russia
Tel.: (7) 8123130530 RU
ARSA—(MOEX)
Sales Range: Less than $1 Million
Emp.: 28
Asset Management Services
N.A.I.C.S.: 531390
Vasily E. Solovev (Chm-Mgmt Bd & Dir-Investments)

UK FLOORING DIRECT LTD.
Key Park Zone 1A Bayton Road Industrial Estate Exhall, Coventry, CV7 9EL, West Midlands, United Kingdom
Tel.: (44) 844 234 0084
Web Site: http://www.ukflooringdirect.co.uk
Year Founded: 2004
Sales Range: $10-24.9 Million

Emp.: 37
Electronic Shopping Services
N.A.I.C.S.: 449121
Jason Ashby (CEO)

UK OIL & GAS PLC
8th Floor The Broadgate Tower 20 Primrose Street, London, EC2A 2EW, United Kingdom
Tel.: (44) 1483941493 UK
Web Site: https://www.ukogplc.com
Year Founded: 2013
UKOG—(AIM)
Rev.: $2,015,316
Assets: $46,725,894
Liabilities: $4,902,426
Net Worth: $41,823,468
Earnings: ($6,362,964)
Fiscal Year-end: 09/30/22
Oil & Gas Investment Services
N.A.I.C.S.: 213112
Stephen Sanderson (CEO)

Subsidiaries:

Horse Hill Developments Ltd. (1)
The Broadgate Tower 8th Floor 20 Primrose Street, London, EC2A 2EW, United Kingdom
Tel.: (44) 1483362483
Web Site: https://horsehilldevelopments.co.uk
Oil Exploration Services
N.A.I.C.S.: 213112
Stephen Sanderson (Chm)

UK PACKAGING SUPPLIES LIMITED
100 Brantwood Road Tottenham, London, N17 0XY, United Kingdom
Tel.: (44) 2088018144
Web Site: http://www.ukplc.co.uk
Year Founded: 1984
Rev.: $23,105,687
Emp.: 58
Packaging Material Distr
N.A.I.C.S.: 423840
Tony Dark (Chm)

UK WISDOM LTD.
Floor 8 Tower D No 2 Guang Hua Road, Chaoyang District, Beijing, 100026, China
Tel.: (86) 10 6506 7789 Ky
Year Founded: 2021
UKWI—(NASDAQ)
Investment Services
N.A.I.C.S.: 523999
Xuefei Xiao (CEO)

UKAI CO., LTD.
2-14-16 Akatsuki-cho, Hachioji, 192-0043, Tokyo, Japan
Tel.: (81) 426261166
Web Site: https://www.ukai.co.jp
Year Founded: 1982
76210—(TKS)
Sales Range: Less than $1 Million
Restaurant Operators
N.A.I.C.S.: 722511

UKC SYSTEMS LTD.
St George's House 19 Church Street, Uttoxeter, ST14 8AG, Staffordshire, United Kingdom
Tel.: (44) 8708 636 187
Web Site: http://www.topcashback.co.uk
Year Founded: 2005
Sales Range: $25-49.9 Million
Emp.: 47
Cashback Website Operator
N.A.I.C.S.: 513199

UKFAST.NET LTD.
City Tower Piccadilly Plaza, Manchester, M1 4BT, United Kingdom
Tel.: (44) 8004584545

Web Site: http://www.ukfast.co.uk
Year Founded: 1999
Sales Range: $10-24.9 Million
Emp.: 250
Internet Hosting Services
N.A.I.C.S.: 517810
Lawrence Jones *(Co-Founder & CEO)*

UKRAINIAN STOCK EXCHANGE
10 Rylskyy provulok, 01025, Kiev, Ukraine
Tel.: (380) 00442794158
Web Site: http://www.ukrse.kiev.ua
Sales Range: $250-299.9 Million
Stock Exchange Services
N.A.I.C.S.: 523210
Valentyn Oskolskyy *(Chm)*

UKRAS A.D.
Kolubarska 29, 74101, Doboj, Bosnia & Herzegovina
Tel.: (387) 65636361
UKRD-R-A—(BANJ)
Sales Range: Less than $1 Million
Emp.: 33
Painting & Glazing Services
N.A.I.C.S.: 238320
Marina Cvijanovic *(Exec Dir)*

UKRAS A.D.
Rudera Boskovica 3, Novi Pazar, Serbia
Tel.: (381) 20385109
Year Founded: 1953
UKNP—(BEL)
Sales Range: Less than $1 Million
Emp.: 70
Construction Stone Product Mfr
N.A.I.C.S.: 327991
Hajriz Nicevic *(Board of Directors & Exec Dir)*

UKRGAZBANK, PJSC
19 21 23 Staronavodnytska St, 01015, Kiev, Ukraine
Tel.: (380) 986202020
Web Site: https://www.ukrgasbank.com
Year Founded: 1993
Rev.: $131,805,780
Assets: $1,979,425,860
Liabilities: $1,784,886,752
Net Worth: $194,539,108
Earnings: $10,611,897
Emp.: 3,447
Fiscal Year-end: 12/31/16
Commercial Banking Services
N.A.I.C.S.: 522110
Nataliia Vasylets *(Deputy Chm-Mgmt Bd)*

UKRPRODUCT GROUP LTD
26 New Street, Saint Helier, JE2 3RA, Jersey
Tel.: (44) 1534507000
Web Site: https://www.ukrproduct.com
Year Founded: 2004
UKR—(AIM)
Rev.: $47,093,571
Assets: $21,371,101
Liabilities: $15,598,982
Net Worth: $5,772,120
Earnings: $496,499
Emp.: 813
Fiscal Year-end: 12/31/23
Food Industry
N.A.I.C.S.: 311512
Alexander Slipchuk *(Founder & CEO)*

Subsidiaries:

Ukrproduct Group CJSC (1)
4th Floor 8 Sikorsky St, Kiev, 4112, Ukraine
Tel.: (380) 442329602
Web Site: http://www.ukrproduct.com

Sales Range: $25-49.9 Million
Emp.: 80
Dairy Products Mfr & Distr
N.A.I.C.S.: 311514

UKRTELECOM JSC
18 Tarasa Shevchenka Blvd, Kiev, 01030, Ukraine
Tel.: (380) 44 230 9011
Web Site: http://www.ukrtelecom.ua
Year Founded: 1993
Sales Range: Less than $1 Million
Telecommunication Servicesb
N.A.I.C.S.: 517810

UKUS A.D.
Slobodana Bajica 12, Pecinci, Serbia
Tel.: (381) 22436600
Web Site: http://www.ukus.co.rs
Year Founded: 1956
UKUS—(BEL)
Sales Range: $1-9.9 Million
Emp.: 34
Food Product Retailer
N.A.I.C.S.: 445298
Aleksandar Jovicic *(CEO)*

ULAANBAATAR KHIVS JOINT STOCK COMPANY
Chinggis Avenue-36, Ulaanbaatar, Mongolia
Tel.: (976) 11342559
Web Site: http://www.mongolia-carpet.mn
Year Founded: 1971
Rev.: $1,408,570
Assets: $3,499,253
Liabilities: $1,031,247
Net Worth: $2,468,006
Earnings: $89,542
Fiscal Year-end: 12/31/18
Textile Products Mfr
N.A.I.C.S.: 314999

ULASLAR TURIZM YATIRIMLARI VE DAYANIKLI TUKETIM MALLARI TICARET PAZARLAMA A.S.
Asagi Ovecler Mah 1042 Cadde 1330 Sokak No 3 4, Cankaya, Ankara, Turkiye
Tel.: (90) 312 474 04 90
Web Site: http://www.ulaslar.com.tr
Tourism Activities
N.A.I.C.S.: 721199
Yilmaz Ulas *(Chm)*

ULFERTS INTERNATIONAL LIMITED
Room 1905-07 19/F Emperor Group Centre 288 Hennessy Road, Wanchai, China (Hong Kong)
Tel.: (852) 21568866
Web Site: https://www.ulfertsintl.com
Year Founded: 1975
1711—(HKG)
Rev.: $27,558,870
Assets: $25,027,740
Liabilities: $13,588,823
Net Worth: $11,438,918
Earnings: ($2,679,668)
Emp.: 133
Fiscal Year-end: 03/31/23
Furniture Retailer
N.A.I.C.S.: 449110
Chi Fai Wong *(Chm & Exec Dir)*

Subsidiaries:

Ulferts of Sweden (Far East) Limited (1)
Room 1905-1907 19/F Emperor Group Centre 288 Hennessy Road, Wanchai, China (Hong Kong)
Tel.: (852) 21568866
Web Site: http://www.ulferts.com.hk
Household Furniture Retailer
N.A.I.C.S.: 449110

ULISSE BIOMED S.P.A.
Via Cavour 20, 33100, Udine, Italy
Tel.: (39) 0403757540
Web Site: https://www.ulissebiomed.com
Year Founded: 2015
UBM—(EUR)
Biotechnology Research & Development Services
N.A.I.C.S.: 541714
Matteo Petti *(CFO)*

ULMA CONSTRUCCION POLSKA S.A.
Koszajec 50, Brwinow, 05-840, Warsaw, Poland
Tel.: (48) 225067000
Web Site: https://www.ulmaconstruction.pl
ULM—(WAR)
Rev.: $51,759,400
Assets: $100,562,500
Liabilities: $15,265,244
Net Worth: $85,297,256
Earnings: $5,196,646
Emp.: 2,142
Fiscal Year-end: 12/31/23
Formwork & Scaffolding Systems Mfr
N.A.I.C.S.: 238190
Jose Irizar Lasa *(Member-Mgmt Bd)*

ULRIC DE VARENS S.A.
6 rue de Berri, 750008, Paris, France
Tel.: (33) 156903232
Web Site: http://www.ulric-de-varens.com
Sales Range: $25-49.9 Million
Emp.: 80
Perfume Mfr
N.A.I.C.S.: 325620

ULRICH ALBER GMBH
Vor dem Weissen Stein 21, Albstadt, 72461, Germany
Tel.: (49) 743220060
Web Site: http://www.alber.de
Year Founded: 1986
Rev.: $64,831,800
Emp.: 250
Medical Equipment Mfr
N.A.I.C.S.: 423450
Ralf Ledda *(Mng Dir)*

ULS GROUP, INC.
14th Floor Triton Square Tower X 1-8-10 Harumi, Chuo-ku, Tokyo, 104-6014, Japan
Tel.: (81) 368901600
Web Site: https://www.ulsgroup.co.jp
Year Founded: 2000
3798—(TKS)
Rev.: $68,625,020
Assets: $72,776,100
Liabilities: $14,323,870
Net Worth: $58,452,230
Earnings: $7,475,910
Fiscal Year-end: 03/31/24
Consulting Services
N.A.I.C.S.: 541618
Shigeru Urushibara *(Pres & CEO)*

ULS TECHNOLOGY PLC
The Old Grammar School Church Road, Thame, OX9 3AJ, Oxfordshire, United Kingdom
Web Site: http://www.ulstechnology.com
Year Founded: 2003
ULS—(AIM)
Rev.: $22,980,769
Assets: $47,205,209
Liabilities: $6,589,015
Net Worth: $40,616,194
Earnings: ($3,243,593)
Emp.: 97
Fiscal Year-end: 03/31/21

Software Publisher
N.A.I.C.S.: 513210
John Sinclair Williams *(CFO)*

Subsidiaries:

Legal-Eye Limited (1)
Masters Court Church Road, Thame, OX9 3FA, Oxfordshire, United Kingdom
Tel.: (44) 2030512049
Web Site: https://www.legal-eye.co.uk
Risk Management & Compliance Services
N.A.I.C.S.: 541611
Paul Saunders *(Mng Dir)*

ULTIMA UNITED LIMITED
Suite 14 11 Preston Street, Como, 6152, WA, Australia
Tel.: (61) 864361888
Web Site: http://ultimaunited.com
UUL—(ASX)
Rev.: $757,211
Assets: $3,159,068
Liabilities: $1,974,772
Net Worth: $1,184,296
Earnings: ($205,368)
Fiscal Year-end: 06/30/20
Property Development
N.A.I.C.S.: 236115
Eric Hon Yap Kong *(Exec Dir)*

ULTIMATE FINANCE HOLDINGS LIMITED
Unit 1 Westpoint Court Great Park Road, Bradley Stoke, Bristol, BS32 4PY, United Kingdom
Tel.: (44) 845 251 30655
Sales Range: $10-24.9 Million
Holding Company; Corporate Financial & Lending Services
N.A.I.C.S.: 551112
Neil McMyn *(CFO)*

Subsidiaries:

Ultimate Finance Group Limited (1)
Unit 1 Westpoint Court Great Park Road, Bradley Stoke, Bristol, BS32 4PY, United Kingdom
Tel.: (44) 8452513030
Web Site: http://www.ultimatefinance.co.uk
Emp.: 200
Holding Company; Financial Services
N.A.I.C.S.: 551112
Claire Lewis *(Dir-Ops)*

Subsidiary (Domestic):

Ultimate Invoice Finance Limited (2)
First Floor Unit 1 Westpoint Court Great Park Road, Bradley Stoke, Bristol, BS32 0PS, United Kingdom
Tel.: (44) 8452513030
Web Site: http://www.ultimatefinance.co.uk
Invoice Discounting & Debt Factoring Services
N.A.I.C.S.: 522299
Bryn Ible *(Reg Dir)*

ULTIMATE GAMES SA
Marszalkowska 87/102, 00-683, Warsaw, Poland
Tel.: (48) 508379738
Web Site: https://ultimate-publishing.com
Year Founded: 2018
ULG—(WAR)
Rev.: $5,851,626
Assets: $7,309,959
Liabilities: $1,279,726
Net Worth: $6,030,234
Earnings: ($971,291)
Emp.: 10
Fiscal Year-end: 12/31/23
Computer Game Development Services
N.A.I.C.S.: 541511
Mateusz Lukasz Zawadzki *(Founder, Chm-Mgmt Bd & CEO)*

ULTIMATE HOLDINGS GROUP, INC.

Ultimate Games SA—(Continued)

ULTIMATE HOLDINGS GROUP, INC.
2-18-23 Nishiwaseda, Shinjuku, Tokyo, 162-0051, Japan
Tel.: (81) 366701692 NV
Year Founded: 2021
UHGI—(OTCIQ)
Assets: $9,101
Liabilities: $258,674
Net Worth: ($249,573)
Earnings: ($245,274)
Emp.: 1
Fiscal Year-end: 07/31/24
Holding Company
N.A.I.C.S.: 551112

Subsidiaries:

Luboa Group, Inc. (1)
Room 202-1 Building 21 of Intelligence and Wealth Center, Jiaxing, 314000, Zhejiang, China (100%)
Tel.: (86) 53782239727
Web Site: http://www.tw-luboa-group.com
Rev.: $11,567
Assets: $617,761
Liabilities: $1,388,978
Net Worth: ($771,217)
Earnings: ($1,607,997)
Emp.: 25
Fiscal Year-end: 12/31/2019
Holding Company; Specialty Agricultural Products & Carbon Emissions Platform Developer
N.A.I.C.S.: 551112
Xianyi Hao (Chm, Pres, CEO & CFO)

ULTIMOVACS ASA
Ullernchausseen 64, 0379, Oslo, Norway
Tel.: (47) 41380080
Web Site: https://www.ultimovacs.com
Year Founded: 2011
ULTIMO—(OSL)
Rev.: $2,913,767
Assets: $34,312,356
Liabilities: $6,846,762
Net Worth: $27,465,594
Earnings: ($18,603,182)
Emp.: 25
Fiscal Year-end: 12/31/23
Pharmaceutical Product Mfr & Distr
N.A.I.C.S.: 325412
Jens Bjorheim (Chief Medical Officer)

ULTRA BRANDS LTD.
106-1641 Lonsdale Avenue, North Vancouver, V7M 2J5, BC, Canada
Web Site: http://www.nhsindustries.ca
ULTA—(CNSX)
Assets: $158,097
Liabilities: $577,874
Net Worth: ($419,777)
Earnings: ($335,538)
Fiscal Year-end: 12/31/23
Fabrics Mfr
N.A.I.C.S.: 314999

ULTRA EQUITY INVESTMENTS LTD.
Zabotinski 7, Ramat Gan, 52520, Israel
Tel.: (972) 36127778
Year Founded: 1991
Assets: $231,127
Liabilities: $520,684
Net Worth: ($289,557)
Earnings: ($285,815)
Fiscal Year-end: 12/31/17
Investment Management Service
N.A.I.C.S.: 523999

ULTRA LITHIUM INC.
1120 - 789 West Pender Street, Vancouver, V6C 1H2, BC, Canada
Tel.: (778) 968-1176 BC
Web Site: https://ultraresourcesinc.com
Year Founded: 2004
ULTXF—(OTCQB)
Rev.: $34,691
Assets: $10,364,611
Liabilities: $2,260,783
Net Worth: $8,103,828
Earnings: ($1,977,484)
Emp.: 5
Fiscal Year-end: 10/31/23
Nonmetallic Mineral Services
N.A.I.C.S.: 213115
Weiguo Lang (CEO)

ULTRA WIRING CONNECTIVITY SYSTEM LTD.
Plot No 287-A and B Sector-59, HSIDC Industrial Estate Ballabgarh, Faridabad, 121004, Haryana, India
Tel.: (91) 9312327007
Web Site: https://www.ultrawiring.com
Year Founded: 1991
UWCSL—(NSE)
Rev.: $5,328,082
Assets: $4,306,309
Liabilities: $2,235,056
Net Worth: $2,071,253
Earnings: $266,796
Emp.: 176
Fiscal Year-end: 03/31/23
Electrical Equipment & Component Mfr
N.A.I.C.S.: 335999
Sanjay Mathur (Mng Dir)

ULTRA-BRAG AG
Sudquaistrasse 55, 4057, Basel, Switzerland
Tel.: (41) 616397200
Web Site: http://www.ultra-brag.ch
Sales Range: $50-74.9 Million
Emp.: 150
River Transportation & Logistics Services
N.A.I.C.S.: 488999
Christoph Adam (Chief Compliance Officer)

ULTRACAB (INDIA) LIMITED
Sr No 262 B/h Galaxy Bearings Ltd, Shapar Veraval, Rajkot, 360024, Gujarat, India
Tel.: (91) 2827253122
Web Site: https://www.ultracabwires.com
Year Founded: 2007
538706—(BOM)
Rev.: $12,909,526
Assets: $10,602,314
Liabilities: $6,767,580
Net Worth: $3,834,734
Earnings: $697,440
Emp.: 75
Fiscal Year-end: 03/31/23
Electric Wire & Cable Mfr & Exporter
N.A.I.C.S.: 335929
Nitesh Parshottambhai Vaghasiya (Chm & Mng Dir)

ULTRACHARGE LTD
Level 6 105 St Georges Terrace, Perth, 6000, WA, Australia
Tel.: (61) 0865580886 AU
Web Site: http://www.ultra-charge.net
Year Founded: 2009
Rev.: $5,567
Assets: $4,514,288
Liabilities: $203,315
Net Worth: $4,310,973
Earnings: ($2,855,311)
Fiscal Year-end: 06/30/17
Battery Technology Mfr
N.A.I.C.S.: 335910

ULTRACHIP INC.
4F 618 Recom Road, Neihu, 114, Taipei, Taiwan
Tel.: (886) 287978947
Web Site: http://www.ultrachip.com
Year Founded: 1999
Sales Range: $10-24.9 Million
Emp.: 100
Semiconductor Research & Development
N.A.I.C.S.: 334413

ULTRAHAPTICS LTD.
The West Wing Glass Wharf, Bristol, BS2 0EL, United Kingdom
Tel.: (44) 117 325 9002
Web Site: http://www.ultrahaptics.com
Year Founded: 2013
Mid-air Haptics Technology; Tactile Feedback & Consumer Electronics
N.A.I.C.S.: 334419
Steve Cliffe (Pres & CEO)

Subsidiaries:

Leap Motion, Inc. (1)
321 11th St Ste #LL150, San Francisco, CA 94103
Tel.: (415) 689-5212
Web Site: http://www.leapmotion.com
Virtual Reality & Software Publisher
N.A.I.C.S.: 513210
David Holz (Co-Founder & CTO)

ULTRAMAR LTDA.
Avenida El Bosque Norte No 500 piso 18, Vitacura, Santiago, 7550092, Chile
Tel.: (56) 226301000 CL
Web Site: http://www.ultramar.cl
Emp.: 600
Holding Company; Freight Shipping, Cargo Handling, Port Operations, Towing & Salvage Services
N.A.I.C.S.: 551112
Dag von Appen (Mng Dir)

Subsidiaries:

AGENCIA MARITIMA SUDOCEAN SRL (1)
25 de Mayo 555 - 19 Piso, C1002ABK, Buenos Aires, Argentina
Tel.: (54) 11 4310 2300
Web Site: http://www.sudocean.com
Cost Management Services
N.A.I.C.S.: 488320

Agencia Maritima Internacional S.A. (1)
25 de Mayo 555 20th Floor, C10002ABK, Buenos Aires, Argentina
Tel.: (54) 11 4310 2400
Web Site: http://www.amisa.com
Cost Management Services
N.A.I.C.S.: 488320
Fernando Verziera (Mgr-Ops)

Antares Naviera S.A. (1)
Bouchard 547 Piso 21, C1106ABG, Buenos Aires, Argentina
Tel.: (54) 11 4317 8400
Web Site: http://www.antaresnaviera.com
Freight Transportation Services
N.A.I.C.S.: 483111
Jorge Martinez Klein (Mgr-Offshore)

FULL-PAK PERU BULK CONTAINERS S.A. (1)
Av El Bosque 500 Piso 14, Las Condes, Santiago, Chile
Tel.: (56) 2 26301250
Web Site: http://www.fullpak.com
Container Trucking Services
N.A.I.C.S.: 484121
Matias Bauza (Gen Mgr)

Humboldt Marine Training Ltda. (1)
Avda Blanco 725 3er Piso, Valparaiso, Chile
Tel.: (56) 32 202660
Web Site: http://www.marinetraining.cl
Educational Support Services
N.A.I.C.S.: 611710

Humboldt Shipmanagement Co. (1)
Blanco 737, Valparaiso, Chile
Tel.: (56) 32 2202699
Web Site: http://www.humboldt.cl
Freight Transportation Services
N.A.I.C.S.: 483111

Inversiones Neltume Ltda. (1)
El Bosque Norte #500 Piso 18, Las Condes, Santiago, Chile
Tel.: (56) 2 2630 1881
Web Site: http://neltumeports.cl
Cost Management Services
N.A.I.C.S.: 488310

Joint Venture (Domestic):

Terminal Puerto Arica S.A. (2)
Av Maximo Lira 389, Arica, Chile (50%)
Tel.: (56) 58 2 202000
Web Site: http://www.tpa.cl
Cost Management Services
N.A.I.C.S.: 488320
Diego Bulnes (Gen Mgr)

Mercotrade Agencia Maritima Ltda. (1)
Avenida Ibirapuera 2033 - Cjs 91/94, Moema, Sao Paulo, 04029-100, Brazil
Tel.: (55) 11 3383 4450
Web Site: http://www.mercotrade.com.br
Freight Forwarding Services
N.A.I.C.S.: 488510
Miguel Ribeiro (Mgr-Comml)

Montecon S.A. (1)
Rincon 500, 11600, Montevideo, Uruguay
Tel.: (598) 2915 0404
Emp.: 40
Cost Management Services
N.A.I.C.S.: 488320
Juan Olascoaga (Gen Mgr)

Naviera Ultranav Limitada (1)
El Bosque Norte 500 piso 19-20, 7550092, Las Condes, Santiago, Chile
Tel.: (56) 2 2630 1100
Web Site: http://www.ultranav.cl
Freight Shipping Services
N.A.I.C.S.: 483111
Per Lange (CEO-Ultrabulk)

Subsidiary (Non-US):

Ultrabulk Shipping A/S (2)
Smakkedalen 6, 2820, Gentofte, Denmark (100%)
Tel.: (45) 3997 0400
Web Site: http://www.ultrabulk.com
Emp.: 97
Dry Bulk Freight Shipping Services
N.A.I.C.S.: 483111
Per Lange (CEO)

Subsidiary (Non-US):

Ultrabulk (Germany) GmbH (3)
Grosse Elbstrasse 145 E Im Elbkaihaus, 22767, Hamburg, Germany
Tel.: (49) 40 3802390
Freight Transportation Services
N.A.I.C.S.: 483111
Philip Matthiesen (Sr Mgr-Chartering)

Ultrabulk (Hong Kong) Limited (3)
303 Hennessy Road, Wanchai, China (Hong Kong)
Tel.: (852) 2877 7875
Freight Transportation Services
N.A.I.C.S.: 483111

Ultrabulk (Singapore) Pte Ltd. (3)
1 Harbourfront Avenue #15-08 Keppel Bay Tower, Singapore, 098632, Singapore
Tel.: (65) 6325 5777
Web Site: http://www.ultrabulk.com
Freight Transportation Services
N.A.I.C.S.: 483111
Kaare Grenness (Sr VP & Head-Asia)

Subsidiary (US):

Ultrabulk (USA) Inc (3)
1055 Washington Blvd Ste 420, Stamford, CT 06901
Tel.: (203) 964-2121
Freight Transportation Services
N.A.I.C.S.: 483111
Guy G. Smith (Head-North America & Sr Mgr)

AND PRIVATE COMPANIES

Subsidiary (Non-US):

Ultrabulk do Brasil Ltda. (3)
Atlantica Business Center Av Atlantica 1130 12th floor, Rio de Janeiro, 22021-000, Brazil
Tel.: (55) 21 3873 8681
Freight Transportation Services
N.A.I.C.S.: 483111
Thomas Ingerslev *(Gen Mgr)*

Oceano Agencia Maritima SA (1)
Jr Talara N 140 2 Piso, Callao, Lima, Peru
Tel.: (51) 1 2196930
Web Site: http://www.moceano.com
Shipping Agency Services
N.A.I.C.S.: 488510
Augusto Ganoza *(Exec Mgr-Country Ops)*

Petrolera Transoceanica S.A (1)
Manuel Olguin 501 Ave - 12th Floor, Lima, Peru
Tel.: (51) 1 513 9300
Web Site: http://www.petranso.com
Freight Transportation Services
N.A.I.C.S.: 483111

Puerto Angamos (1)
Avenida Longitudinal N 5500 Barrio Industrial, Mejillones, Antofagasta, Chile
Tel.: (56) 55 2357000
Web Site: http://www.puertoangamos.cl
Cost Management Services
N.A.I.C.S.: 488320

Puerto de Coronel S.A. (1)
Av Carlos Prats N 40, VIII Region, Coronel, Chile
Tel.: (56) 41 2727200
Web Site: http://www.puertodecoronel.cl
Cargo Handling Services
N.A.I.C.S.: 488320

Puerto de Mejillones S.A. (1)
Av Costanera Norte 2800, Mejillones, Chile
Tel.: (56) 55 2883600
Web Site: http://www.puertomejillones.cl
Cargo Handling Services
N.A.I.C.S.: 488320
Cristobal Ugalde Rother *(Mgr-Ops)*

Sitrans Ltda. (1)
Avda Jorge Alessandri Rondriguez 10700, Barrio Industrial Lo chena, Santiago, Chile
Tel.: (56) 2 540 2100
Web Site: http://www.sitrans.cl
Container Trucking Services
N.A.I.C.S.: 484121
Alvaro Calbacho *(Gen Mgr)*

Sociedad Minera Isla Riesco S.A. (1)
El Bosque Norte 500 Piso 23, Las Condes, Santiago, Chile
Tel.: (56) 2 429 6300
Web Site: http://www.minainvierno.cl
Coal Mining
N.A.I.C.S.: 212115

Terminal Graneles del Norte S.A. (1)
Calle Puerto Uno N 7100 Barrio Industrial, Mejillones, Antofagasta, Chile
Tel.: (56) 55 2883700
Web Site: http://www.puertotgn.cl
Cost Management Services
N.A.I.C.S.: 488320
Andres Elgueta Galmez *(Chm)*

Terminal Pacifico Sur Valparaiso S.A. (1)
Antonio Varas 2, Valparaiso, Chile
Tel.: (56) 32 2275800
Web Site: http://www.portal.tps.cl
Cost Management Services
N.A.I.C.S.: 488320

ULTRAMAR NETWORK BRAZIL (1)
Avenida Sao Francisco no 65 cj 48 Centro, Santos, Brazil
Tel.: (55) 13 21026644
Cost Management Services
N.A.I.C.S.: 488320
Elder Justo *(Branch Mgr)*

ULTRAMAR NETWORK ECUADOR REMAR (1)
10 de Agosto 103 y Malecon Edificio Valra Piso 9, Guayaquil, Ecuador
Tel.: (593) 4 2322111
Cost Management Services
N.A.I.C.S.: 488320
Andres Hurel *(Mgr-Ops)*

ULTRAMAR NETWORK URUGUAY SCHANDY (1)
Avenida Sarmiento 2265, Montevideo, 11300, Uruguay
Tel.: (598) 2 711 6050
Cost Management Services
N.A.I.C.S.: 488320
Derek Larbalestier *(Mgr)*

Ultramar Network Colombia (1)
Carrera 12 no79 - 32 piso 4, Bogota, Colombia
Tel.: (57) 1 3172400
Cost Management Services
N.A.I.C.S.: 488320
Andres Carvajal *(Mgr-Ops)*

Ultramara Agencia Maritima Ltda. (1)
Avenida El Bosque Norte No 500 piso 18, Vitacura, Santiago, Chile
Tel.: (56) 2 2630 1000
Web Site: http://www.ultramar.cl
Shipping Arrangement, Port Operations & Other Shipping Support Services
N.A.I.C.S.: 488510
Julio Ramirez *(Gen Mgr-Chile)*

Ultraport Ltda. (1)
Blanco 853, Valparaiso, Chile
Tel.: (56) 32 2202900
Web Site: http://www.ultraport.cl
Cost Management Services
N.A.I.C.S.: 488320

ULTRAPAR PARTICIPACOES S.A.
Av Brigadeiro Luis Antonio 1 343, Sao Paulo, 01317-910, SP, Brazil
Tel.: (55) 1131777014 BR
Web Site: https://www.ultra.com.br
Year Founded: 1937
UGP—(NYSE)
Rev.: $27,613,772,613
Assets: $7,005,782,827
Liabilities: $4,665,145,229
Net Worth: $2,340,637,598
Earnings: $353,753,265
Emp.: 9,778
Fiscal Year-end: 12/31/22
Chemicals & Petrochemicals Producer & Distr
N.A.I.C.S.: 325110
Pedro Wongtschowski *(Chm)*

Subsidiaries:

Distribuidora de Produtos de Petroleo Ipiranga S.A. (1)
Rua Dolores Acaraz Caldas 90, Praia de Belas, Porto Alegre, 90110-180, RS, Brazil
Tel.: (55) 51 3216 4411
Web Site: http://www.ipiranga.com.br
Sales Range: $5-14.9 Billion
Emp.: 360
Gasoline & Petroleum Distr
N.A.I.C.S.: 221210

Empresa Carioca de Produtos Quimicos S.A. (1)
Rua Eteno - 3189, Camacari, 42810-000, Bahia, Brazil
Tel.: (55) 7136347000
Sales Range: $25-49.9 Million
Emp.: 50
Chemical Products Mfr
N.A.I.C.S.: 325998

Ipiranga Produtos de Petroleo S.A. (1)
Francisco Eugenio 329, Rio de Janeiro, 20941-900, Brazil
Tel.: (55) 2125745858
Web Site: http://www.ipiranga.com.br
Petroleum Product Whslr
N.A.I.C.S.: 424720

Subsidiary (Domestic):

Companhia Ultragaz S.A. (2)
Avenida Brigadeiro Luis Antonio 1 343, Bela Vista, Sao Paulo, 01317-001, Brazil
Tel.: (55) 40030123
Web Site: https://www.ultragaz.com.br
Liquefied Petroleum Gas Distr
N.A.I.C.S.: 424720

Imaven Imoveis Ltda. (2)
Brg Luis Antonio 1343, Sao Paulo, 01317-910, Brazil
Tel.: (55) 1131776884
Real Estate Development Services
N.A.I.C.S.: 531390

Ipiranga Imobiliaria Ltda. (2)
Francisco Eugenio 329, Rio de Janeiro, 20941-900, Brazil
Tel.: (55) 2125745470
Real Estate Development Services
N.A.I.C.S.: 531390

Oil Trading Importadora e Exportadora Ltda. (2)
Doutor Alberto Schwedtzer 600, Santos, 11095-520, Sao Paulo, Brazil
Tel.: (55) 2125745932
Petroleum Product Distr
N.A.I.C.S.: 424720

Tropical Transportes Ipiranga Ltda. (2)
Rua Francisco Eugenio 329 - Sao Cristovao, Rio de Janeiro, 20941-900, Brazil
Tel.: (55) 5332313234
Fuel Distr
N.A.I.C.S.: 457210

Utingas Armazenadora S.A. (2)
Rod BR 476 S/N Km 16, Araucaria, Parana, Brazil
Tel.: (55) 4136432001
General Warehousing Services
N.A.I.C.S.: 493110

Oleoquimica Industria e Comercio de Produtos Quimicos Ltda. (2)
Rua Amonia S/No, Camacari, 42810-340, Bahia, Brazil
Tel.: (55) 7136347744
Chemical Product Whslr
N.A.I.C.S.: 424690

Oxiteno Andina, C.A. (1)
Calle Guaicaipuro Con Mohedano Torre Hener Piso 3-B El Rosal, Caracas, 1060, Venezuela
Tel.: (58) 2127408222
Chemical Products Mfr
N.A.I.C.S.: 325998

Oxiteno Colombia S.A.S (1)
Tel.: (57) 16585859
Web Site: http://www.oxiteno.com.br
Chemical Products Mfr
N.A.I.C.S.: 325998

Oxiteno Europe SPRL (1)
Tel.: (32) 27610360
Sales Range: $25-49.9 Million
Emp.: 4
Chemical Products Mfr
N.A.I.C.S.: 325998

Oxiteno Mexico S.A. de C.V. (1)
Insurgentes Sur 1685 Piso 11 Col Guadalupe Inn, 01020, Mexico, Mexico
Tel.: (55) 5322 0560
Chemical Products Mfr
N.A.I.C.S.: 325998

Subsidiary (Domestic):

Oxiteno Servicios Corporativos S.A. de C.V. (2)
Insurgentes Sur No 1685 Piso 11, Mexico, 01020, Mexico
Tel.: (52) 5553220600
Business Management Consulting Services
N.A.I.C.S.: 541611

Subsidiary (US):

Oxiteno USA LLC (2)
1730 Park St Ste 202, Naperville, IL 60563
Tel.: (630) 364-5100
Web Site: http://www.oxiteno.com.br
Sales Range: $25-49.9 Million
Emp.: 50
Specialty Chemicals Mfr
N.A.I.C.S.: 325998

Oxiteno Nordeste S.A. Industria e Comercio (1)
Rua Benzano 1065 Polo Petroquimico, Camacari, 42810-000, Bahia, Brazil
Tel.: (55) 7136347777
Petrochemical Mfr & Distr
N.A.I.C.S.: 325110

Refinaria de Petroleo Riograndense S.A. (1)
Rua Eng Heitor Amaro Barcellos 551, Rio Grande, 96202-900, Rio Grande do Sul, Brazil
Tel.: (55) 5332338000
Web Site: http://www.refinariariograndense.com.br
Oil Refinery Mfr
N.A.I.C.S.: 311225

Terminal Quimico de Aratu S.A. - Tequimar (1)
Via Matoim S/N Porto de Aratu, Candeias, 43810-000, Bahia, Brazil
Tel.: (55) 7136026424
General Warehousing & Storage Services
N.A.I.C.S.: 493110

Uniao Vopak - Armazens Gerais Ltda. (1)
Uniao/Vopak Armazens Gerais Rua Cel Santa Rita s/n Rocio Paranagua, Parana, 83221-340, Brazil
Tel.: (55) 1332951000
Vegetable Oil & Chemical Mfr
N.A.I.C.S.: 311225

ULTRASONIC AG
c/o BPG mbH Graf-Adolf-Platz 12, 40213, Dusseldorf, Germany
Tel.: (49) 211 1 72 980 De
Web Site: http://www.ultrasonic-ag.de
Year Founded: 2011
US5—(DEU)
Sales Range: $200-249.9 Million
Emp.: 1,415
Holding Company; Footwear
N.A.I.C.S.: 551112
Clifford Chi Kwong Chan *(CFO & Member-Mgmt Bd)*

ULURU CO., LTD.
KDX Harumi Building 9F 3-12-1 Harumi, Chuo-ku, Tokyo, 104-0053, Japan
Tel.: (81) 362213069
Web Site: https://www.uluru.biz
3979—(TKS)
Rev.: $39,243,570
Assets: $39,997,110
Liabilities: $21,416,400
Net Worth: $18,580,710
Earnings: $4,759,200
Emp.: 638
Fiscal Year-end: 03/31/24
Business Process Outsourcing Services
N.A.I.C.S.: 561110
Tomoya Hoshi *(Chm & Pres)*

ULUSAL FAKTORING A.S.
Maslak Mah Sumer Sok No 3 Ayazaga Ticaret Merkezi B Blok Kat 10, Sariyer, 34485, Istanbul, Turkiye
Tel.: (90) 2123461111
Web Site: http://www.ulusalfaktoring.com
ULSFA—(IST)
Sales Range: Less than $1 Million
Financial Investment Services
N.A.I.C.S.: 523940
Kurt Korkut Jolker *(Chm)*

ULUSOY UN SANAYI VE TICARET A.S.
42 Interior Door No 1, Atakum, Samsun, Turkiye
Tel.: (90) 3622669090
Web Site:
https://www.ulusoyflour.com
ULUUN—(IST)
Rev.: $1,343,155,146
Assets: $695,185,194
Liabilities: $455,706,111
Net Worth: $239,479,083

ULUSOY UN SANAYI VE TICARET A.S.

Ulusoy Un Sanayi ve Ticaret A.S.—(Continued)
Earnings: ($22,648,970)
Emp.: 1,000
Fiscal Year-end: 12/31/23
Flour Mfr
N.A.I.C.S.: 311211
Gunhan Ulusoy *(Chm)*

ULVAC, INC.
2500 Hagisono, Chigasaki, 253 8543, Kanagawa, Japan
Tel.: (81) 467892033
Web Site: https://www.ulvac.co.jp
Year Founded: 1952
6728—(TKS)
Rev.: $1,624,135,300
Assets: $2,417,421,660
Liabilities: $1,000,959,720
Net Worth: $1,416,461,940
Earnings: $125,849,260
Emp.: 6,234
Fiscal Year-end: 06/30/24
Semiconductor Vacuum Technology Solutions
N.A.I.C.S.: 334413
Mitsuru Motoyoshi *(Exec VP)*

Subsidiaries:

Advance Riko, Inc. (1)
4388 Ikonobe-cho, Tsuzuki-ku, Yokohama, 224-0053, Kanagawa, Japan
Tel.: (81) 459312221
Web Site: https://advance-riko.com
Sales Range: $10-24.9 Million
Emp.: 82
Analytical & Test Instruments Mfr
N.A.I.C.S.: 334515
Katsumi Tsuda *(Mgr-Sls)*

Ampersand Inc. (1)
No 1189 Baicao Road Hi-Tech West Zone Chengdu, Sichuan, 611731, China
Tel.: (86) 2887980138
Metal Forming Machine Mfr
N.A.I.C.S.: 333519

FINE SURFACE TECHNOLOGY CO., LTD. (1)
2804 Terao, Chichibu, 368-0056, Saitama, Japan
Tel.: (81) 49 424 6590
Web Site: http://www.fst-corp.co.jp
Emp.: 85
Precision Polishing Equipment Mfr
N.A.I.C.S.: 332216
Hiroyuki Nawa *(Pres)*

Hong Kong ULVAC Co., Ltd. (1)
Flat 8C Summit Building 30 Man Yue Street, Hunghom, Kowloon, China (Hong Kong)
Tel.: (852) 2 627 0200
Web Site: https://www.hkulvac.com
Emp.: 24
Vacuum Equipment Whslr
N.A.I.C.S.: 423620

Initium,Inc. - Chigasaki Factory (1)
2500 Hagizono, Chigasaki, 253-8543, Kanagawa, Japan
Tel.: (81) 467 89 2491
Web Site: http://www.initium2000.com
Molecular Interaction Analyzer Mfr
N.A.I.C.S.: 334513

LVAC Research Center SUZHOU Co., Ltd. (1)
No7 Suhong East Road, Suzhou Industrial Park, Suzhou, 215026, China
Tel.: (86) 51289179801
Vacuum Equipment Mfr
N.A.I.C.S.: 333120

NISSIN SEIGYO Co., LTD. (1)
1160-33 Hagisono, Chigasaki, 253-0071, Kanagawa, Japan
Tel.: (81) 467584525
Vacuum Equipment & Sell Automatic Control Panel Mfr
N.A.I.C.S.: 335313

Pure Surface Technology, Ltd. (1)
456-1 Hyeongok-Ri Chungbuk-Myeon, Pyeongtaek, 451-831, Geyonggi-Do, Korea (South)
Tel.: (82) 2 324 1617
Surface Treatment Services
N.A.I.C.S.: 561499

RAS Co., Ltd (1)
2-23-4 Sachiura, Kanazawa-Ku, Yokohama, 236-0003, Kanagawa, Japan
Tel.: (81) 457883851
Sales Range: $25-49.9 Million
Emp.: 70
Electronic Components Mfr
N.A.I.C.S.: 334419
Tatsuo Sato *(Pres)*

Sanko ULVAC Co., Ltd. (1)
544 Takamacho, Meito-ku, Nagoya, 465-0081, Japan
Tel.: (81) 52 702 6811
Web Site: http://www.sanko-ulvac.co.jp
Vacuum Equipment Whslr
N.A.I.C.S.: 423830

Tigold Corporation (1)
2500 Hagisono, Chigasaki, 253-8543, Kanagawa, Japan
Tel.: (81) 46 789 2198
Web Site: https://www.tigold.co.jp
Sales Range: $10-24.9 Million
Emp.: 70
Depostion Coating Services
N.A.I.C.S.: 332812

Plant (Domestic):

Tigold Corporation - Chiba Plant (2)
516 Yokota Sammu, Chiba, 289-1226, Japan
Tel.: (81) 475 89 1581
Web Site: http://www.tigold.co.jp
Emp.: 70
Optical Thin Film Coatings Mfr
N.A.I.C.S.: 333310

UF TECH, Ltd. (1)
115-8 Gwangsung-gil, Cheongbuk-Myeon, Pyeongtaek, 17811, Gyeonggi-Do, Korea (South)
Tel.: (82) 31 683 9283
Web Site: http://www.ulvac.co.jp
Industrial Machinery Whslr
N.A.I.C.S.: 423830

ULTRA CLEAN PRECISION TECHNOLOGIES CORP. (1)
No 27 Section 1 Huandong Road, Southern Science Park Xincheng District, Tainan City, 744092, Taiwan
Tel.: (886) 6 505 8888
Web Site: https://www.ucpt.com.tw
Vaccum Pump Mfr
N.A.I.C.S.: 335210

ULVAC (China) Holding Co., Ltd. (1)
No 1000 Qixin Road, Minhang District, Shanghai, 201199, China
Tel.: (86) 216 127 6610
Web Site: https://www.ulvac-china.com
Emp.: 30
Investment Management Service
N.A.I.C.S.: 523999

ULVAC (SHANGHAI) Trading Co., Ltd.
No 1000 Qixin Road, Minhang, Shanghai, 201199, China (100%)
Tel.: (86) 216 217 6618
Web Site: http://www.ulvac-shanghai.com
Vacuum Equipment Distr & Maintenance Services
N.A.I.C.S.: 811310

ULVAC (SUZHOU) Co., Ltd. (1)
No 277 Suhong East Road Suzhou Industrial Park, Suzhou, 215026, Jiangsu, China
Tel.: (86) 51286669111
Electronic Component Mfr & Whslr
N.A.I.C.S.: 334419

ULVAC (Shenyang) Co., Ltd. (1)
No 12A Lantai Road, Hunnan District, Shenyang, 110171, China
Tel.: (86) 2423812999
Vacuum Equipment Mfr
N.A.I.C.S.: 333120

ULVAC AUTOMATION TAIWAN INC. (1)
3rd Floor No 149 Wugong Road, Wugu District, New Taipei City, 24886, Taiwan
Tel.: (886) 22 298 9957
Web Site: https://www.ulvac-auto.tw

Control Panel Mfr & Whslr
N.A.I.C.S.: 334513

ULVAC Automation Technology (Shanghai) Corporation (1)
No198 East Huancheng Road, FengXian District, Shanghai, 201401, China
Tel.: (86) 2137565599
Electrical Control Panel & Automatic Control Solution
N.A.I.C.S.: 335313

ULVAC COATING CORPORATION (1)
2804 Terao, Chichibu, 368-0056, Saitama, Japan
Tel.: (81) 49 424 6511
Web Site: https://www.ulcoat.co.jp
Emp.: 207
Photomask Blanks Mfr
N.A.I.C.S.: 327212
Yoshinori Gonokami *(Pres & CEO)*

Subsidiary (Non-US):

ULCOAT TAIWAN, Inc. (2)
No 60 Industry III Road, An-nan Distract, Tainan City, 709, Taiwan
Tel.: (886) 6 384 0736
Web Site: http://www.ulcoat.com.tw
Sales Range: $25-49.9 Million
Emp.: 10
Hard Mask Blank Mfr
N.A.I.C.S.: 334413

ULVAC Coating Technology (HEFEI) Co., Ltd. (1)
No 358 Ming Zhu road, Hi-Tech District, Hefei, Anhui, China
Tel.: (86) 55165665280
Flat Panel Displays Mfr
N.A.I.C.S.: 334118

ULVAC Corporation (1)
2-3-1 Yaesu Chuo-ku, Tokyo, 104-0028, Japan
Tel.: (81) 352186070
Web Site: http://www.ulvac-uc.co.jp
Sales Range: $25-49.9 Million
Emp.: 26
Management & Administration Services
N.A.I.C.S.: 541611

ULVAC Cryogenics, Inc. (1)
1222-1 Yabata, Chigasaki, 253-0085, Kanagawa, Japan
Tel.: (81) 46 785 9366
Web Site: https://www.ulvac-cryo.com
Sales Range: $25-49.9 Million
Emp.: 80
Cryopump Mfr
N.A.I.C.S.: 333996
Takeshi Haginouchi *(Pres)*

ULVAC EQUIPMENT SALES, Inc. (1)
2-3-13 Konan Shinagawa Front Building 5F, Minato- ku, Tokyo, 108-0075, Japan
Tel.: (81) 35 769 5511
Web Site: https://www.ulvac-es.co.jp
Emp.: 121
Vacuum Pump Whslr
N.A.I.C.S.: 423830

ULVAC GmbH (1)
Klausnerring 4, Kirchheim b Munchen, 85551, Munich, Germany
Tel.: (49) 89 960 9090
Web Site: https://www.ulvac.eu
Sales Range: $25-49.9 Million
Emp.: 15
Vacuum Equipment Mfr
N.A.I.C.S.: 333310
Takaaki Yamaguchi *(Co-CEO & Mng Dir)*

ULVAC KIKO, Inc. (1)
291-7 Chausubaru, Saito, 881-0037, Miyazaki, Japan
Tel.: (81) 983 42 1411
Web Site: http://www.ulvac-kiko.com
Sales Range: $125-149.9 Million
Emp.: 200
Vacuum Pump Mfr, Developer & Whslr
N.A.I.C.S.: 333914
Yuusuke Terashita *(Sr Mng Dir)*

Division (Domestic):

ULVAC KIKO, Inc. - Overseas Division (2)

INTERNATIONAL PUBLIC

2500 Hagisono, Kohoku-ku, Chigasaki, 253-8543, Kanagawa, Japan
Tel.: (81) 467892261
Web Site: https://ulvac-kiko.com
Sales Range: $25-49.9 Million
Emp.: 200
Vaccum Pump Mfr
N.A.I.C.S.: 333912
Seiji Horikoshi *(Pres)*

ULVAC Korea Precision Co., Ltd. (1)
60 Hyeongoksandan-Ro 93beon-Gil, Cheongbuk-Myeon, Pyeongtaek, 17812, Gyeonggi-Do, Korea (South)
Tel.: (82) 31 617 9600
Web Site: https://www.ukpkorea.co.kr
Sales Range: $25-49.9 Million
Emp.: 22
Vacuum Equipment Parts Mfr
N.A.I.C.S.: 333248

ULVAC Korea, Ltd. (1)
5 Hansan-Gil Cheongbuk-Myeon, Pyeongtaek, Gyeonggi-Do, Korea (South)
Tel.: (82) 316832922
Web Site: http://www.ulvackorea.co.kr
Sales Range: $100-124.9 Million
Emp.: 400
Display Monitor & Components Mfr
N.A.I.C.S.: 334513

ULVAC Kyushu Corporation (1)
3313-1 Kamino Yokogawa-chou, Yokogawa, Kirishima, 899-6301, Kagoshima, Japan
Tel.: (81) 99 572 1114
Web Site: http://www.ulvac-kyushu.com
Sales Range: $100-124.9 Million
Emp.: 417
Vacuum Systems Mfr
N.A.I.C.S.: 333248

ULVAC MALAYSIA SDN. BHD. (1)
No 8 Jalan Gitar 33/3 Elite Industrial Estate Jalan Bukit, Kemuning, 40350, Shah Alam, Selangor, Malaysia
Tel.: (60) 162285299
Web Site: https://www.ulvac.com.my
Vacuum Equipment Whslr
N.A.I.C.S.: 423620
Masaki Yamaguchi *(Mng Dir)*

ULVAC Materials (Suzhou) Co., Ltd. (1)
No 55 Pingsheng Road, Suzhou Industrial Park, Jiangsu, 215126, China
Tel.: (86) 512 8777 0123
Web Site: http://ulvac-umz.com
Sputtering Targets Whslr
N.A.I.C.S.: 423840

ULVAC Materials Korea, Ltd. (1)
51 Dangdong 2-ro, Munsan-Eup, P'aju, 10816, Gyeonggi-Do, Korea (South)
Tel.: (82) 31 937 2900
Web Site: http://www.ulvac.com
Sputtering Target Bonding Services
N.A.I.C.S.: 561499

ULVAC Materials Taiwan, Inc. (1)
No 37 Keya Road, Daya District, Taichung, 42881, Taiwan
Tel.: (886) 425658299
Flat Panel Displays Mfr
N.A.I.C.S.: 334118

ULVAC SINGAPORE PTE LTD (1)
11 Tampines Street 92, Tampines Biz-Hub 02-08, Singapore, 528872, Singapore
Tel.: (65) 65422700
Web Site: https://www.ulvac.com.sg
Vacuum Equipment Maintenance Services
N.A.I.C.S.: 811310

ULVAC SOFTWARE CREATIVE TECHNOLOGY, Co., Ltd. (1)
23F No 27-9 Sec 2 Zhongzheng E Rd, Tamsui Danshuei Dist, New Taipei City, 25170, Taiwan
Tel.: (886) 28 809 2259
Web Site: https://www.usct.com.tw
Vacuum Equipment Software Development Services
N.A.I.C.S.: 541511
Chih-Chung Huang *(Gen Mgr)*

ULVAC TAIWAN INC. (1)
8th Floor No 5 Keji Road Hsinchu Science Park, Hsinchu Science Park, Hsinchu, 300092, Taiwan
Tel.: (886) 3 579 5688

Web Site: https://www.ulvac.com.tw
Sales Range: $25-49.9 Million
Emp.: 60
Vacuum Equipment Sales & Maintenance Services
N.A.I.C.S.: 423620

ULVAC Techno, Ltd. (1)
2609-5 Hagisono, Chigasaki, 253-8555, Kanagawa, Japan
Tel.: (81) 46 787 1046
Web Site: https://www.ulvac-techno.co.jp
Emp.: 956
Technical Support & Maintenance Services
N.A.I.C.S.: 811310

ULVAC Technologies, Inc. (1)
401 Griffin Brook Dr, Methuen, MA 01844
Tel.: (978) 686-7550
Web Site: http://www.ulvac.com
Sales Range: $25-49.9 Million
Emp.: 50
Vacuum Technology Solutions for the Semiconductor Industry
N.A.I.C.S.: 334419

ULVAC Tianma Electric (Jingjiang) Co., Ltd. (1)
No 18 Xinzhou Road, Jingjiang, 214500, China
Tel.: (86) 52382926099
Vacuum Pump Parts Mfr
N.A.I.C.S.: 333914

ULVAC Tohoku, Inc. (1)
6-1-16 Kita Inter Kogyo Danchi, Hachinohe, 039-2245, Aomori, Japan
Tel.: (81) 178287733
Web Site: http://www.ulvac-tohoku.com
Sales Range: $200-249.9 Million
Emp.: 320
Vacuum Systems Mfr for the Semiconductor Industry
N.A.I.C.S.: 333248
Takeo Kato (Pres)

ULVAC Vacuum Furnace (Shenyang) Co., Ltd. (1)
No 10 Huiquandong Road, Hunnan New District, Shenyang, 110168, China
Tel.: (86) 242 381 2999
Web Site: http://www.ulvac-usy.com
Emp.: 300
Vacuum Heat Treatment Furnaces Mfr & Whslr
N.A.I.C.S.: 333415

ULVAC, Inc. - Chiba Tomisato Plant (1)
10-1 Misawa, Tomisato, 286-0225, Chiba, Japan
Tel.: (81) 476906111
Vaccum Pump Mfr
N.A.I.C.S.: 333912

ULVAC, Inc. - Fuji Susono Plant (1)
1220-14 Suyama, Susono, 410-1231, Shizuoka, Japan
Tel.: (81) 55 998 1711
Web Site: http://www.ulvac.co.jp
Semiconductor Devices Mfr
N.A.I.C.S.: 334413

ULVAC, Inc. - Kagoshima Plant (1)
3313-1 Kamino Yokogawa-cho, Kirishima, 899-6301, Kagoshima, Japan
Tel.: (81) 995 72 1115
Vacuum Equipment Mfr
N.A.I.C.S.: 333912

ULVAC-PHI, Inc. (1)
2500 Hagisono, Chigasaki, 253-8522, Kanagawa, Japan
Tel.: (81) 46 785 6522
Web Site: http://www.ulvac-phi.com
Sales Range: $50-74.9 Million
Emp.: 140
Surface Analysis Equipment & Component Mfr
N.A.I.C.S.: 334515
Ichiro Kimura (Pres)

Division (Non-US):

Physical Electronics GmbH (2)
Salzstrasse 8, Feldkirchen, 85622, Munich, Germany
Tel.: (49) 8 996 2750
Web Site: https://www.phi-gmbh.eu

Surface Analysis Equipment & Component Mfr
N.A.I.C.S.: 334515
Thomas Gross (Mng Dir)

Division (US):

Physical Electronics Inc. (2)
18725 Lake Dr E, Chanhassen, MN 55317-3307
Tel.: (952) 828-6100
Web Site: http://www.phi.com
Sales Range: $25-49.9 Million
Emp.: 80
Surface Analysis & Materials Characterization
N.A.I.C.S.: 334516

Ulvac (Ningbo) Co., Ltd. (1)
No 888 Tonghui Road, Jiangbei, Ningbo, 315040, China
Tel.: (86) 57487905551
Web Site: https://www.ulvac.com.cn
Vacuum Pump Mfr & Distr
N.A.I.C.S.: 333912

Ulvac (Thailand) Ltd. (1)
110/6 Moo 13 Soi 25/2 Kingkaew Rd, Rachathewa Bangplee, Samut Prakan, 10540, Thailand
Tel.: (66) 27388883
Web Site: https://www.ulvac.co.th
Emp.: 55
Vacuum Equipment Mfr & Distr
N.A.I.C.S.: 333112

Ulvac Orient Test And Measurement Technology (Chengdu) Co., Ltd. (1)
No 1189 Baicao Road, Hi-Tech West Zone, Chengdu, 611731, China
Tel.: (86) 2887980138
Leak Test Equipment & Component Mfr
N.A.I.C.S.: 334519

Ulvac Vacuum Equipment (Shanghai) Co., Ltd. (1)
Room 331 3/F No 8 Huajing Road, Shanghai Free Trade Pilot Zone, Shanghai, 200131, China
Tel.: (86) 2161276618
Vacuum Equipment & Component Mfr
N.A.I.C.S.: 333120

UMA EXPORTS LIMITED
Suite No161st FloorGanga Jamuna Building281 Shakespeare Sarani, Kolkata, 700017, West Bengal, India
Tel.: (91) 3322811396
Web Site: https://www.umaexports.net
Year Founded: 1988
UMAEXPORTS—(NSE)
Agriculture Product Distr
N.A.I.C.S.: 423820
Rakesh Khemka (Mng Dir)

UMALIS GROUP SA
10 Pentiver Street, 75008, Paris, France
Tel.: (33) 184604444
Web Site: https://www.umalis.fr
Year Founded: 2008
MLUMG—(EUR)
Sales Range: $1-9.9 Million
Wage Portage Services
N.A.I.C.S.: 813930
Christian Person (Chm & CEO)

UMARO S.A.
Mihai Viteazul Street No 5, Roman, 611118, Neamt, Romania
Tel.: (40) 233741354   RO
Web Site: http://www.umaro.ro
Year Founded: 1916
Sales Range: $1-9.9 Million
Emp.: 181
Lathes & Woodworking Machines Mfr
N.A.I.C.S.: 333243
Claudiu-Florin Tampu (CEO & Member-Mgmt Bd)

UMATRIN HOLDING LIMITED
32 Jalan Radin Bagus 3 Bandar Baru, Seri Petaling, Kuala Lumpur, 57000, Malaysia
Tel.: (60) 1700818988   DE
Year Founded: 2005
UMHL—(OTCBB)
Rev.: $3,681,484
Assets: $1,556,752
Liabilities: $1,447,289
Net Worth: $109,463
Earnings: $375,714
Emp.: 22
Fiscal Year-end: 12/31/20
Financial Advisory & Consulting Services
N.A.I.C.S.: 523940
Warren Hin Chai Eu (Chm, Pres, CEO & CFO)

UMBRAGROUP S.P.A.
Via V Baldaccini 1, 06034, Foligno, Italy
Tel.: (39) 0742 3481
Web Site: http://www.umbragroup.com
Ball Screws & High Precision Components Mfr
N.A.I.C.S.: 334511
Antonio Baldaccini (CEO)

Subsidiaries:

Linear Motion LLC (1)
628 N Hamilton St, Saginaw, MI 48602
Tel.: (989) 759-8372
Web Site: http://www.umbragroup.com
Ball Screw Mfr
N.A.I.C.S.: 336413

UMBRELLA SOLAR INVESTMENT SA
Plaza de America 2 4 piso puerta AB, 46004, Valencia, Spain
Tel.: (34) 961196250
Web Site: https://www.umbrellasolarinvest.com
Year Founded: 2018
USI—(MAD)
Investment Management Service
N.A.I.C.S.: 523999
Enrique Selva Bellvs (CEO)

UMC ELECTRONICS CO., LTD.
721 Kawarabuki, Ageo, 362-0022, Saitama, Japan
Tel.: (81) 487240001   JP
Web Site: https://www.umc.co.jp
Year Founded: 1968
6615—(TKS)
Rev.: $867,820,290
Assets: $522,289,150
Liabilities: $391,959,780
Net Worth: $130,329,370
Earnings: $6,748,810
Emp.: 7,211
Fiscal Year-end: 03/31/24
Electric Equipment Mfr
N.A.I.C.S.: 335999
Kota Otoshi (Pres)

Subsidiaries:

UMC Electronics (Dongguan) Co., Ltd. (1)
Yuquan Industrial Zone Floor Space, Fenggang Town, Dongguan, Guangdong, China
Tel.: (86) 7698 786 2222
Electronic Product Mfr & Distr
N.A.I.C.S.: 334419

UMC Electronics (Thailand) Limited (1)
TFD Industrial Estate 1/23 Moo 5 Tambol Tha Sa-an Amphar, Bang Pakong, 24130, Chachoengsao, Thailand
Tel.: (66) 38989828
Industrial Equipment Mfr & Distr
N.A.I.C.S.: 336320

UMC Electronics Europe GmbH (1)
Landsberger Strasse 302, 80687, Munich, Germany

Tel.: (49) 8990405425
Industrial Equipment Distr
N.A.I.C.S.: 423120

UMC Electronics Hong Kong Ltd. (1)
Unit B 20/F Reason Group Tower 403-413 Castle Peak Road, New Territories, Kwai Chung, China (Hong Kong)
Tel.: (852) 26205797
Industrial Equipment Distr
N.A.I.C.S.: 423120

UMC Electronics Manufacturing (Dongguan) Co., Ltd. (1)
20 Yanhe Industrial Zone, Liwu Village Qiaotou Town, Dongguan, Guangdong, China
Tel.: (86) 76981024999
Industrial Equipment Mfr & Distr
N.A.I.C.S.: 336320

UMC Electronics Mexico, S.A. de C.V. (1)
Parque Industrial Colinas de Lagos, Lagos de Moreno, 47515, Jalisco, Mexico
Tel.: (52) 4741166055
Industrial Equipment Mfr & Distr
N.A.I.C.S.: 336320

UMC Electronics Products (Dongguan) Co., Ltd. (1)
Yuquan Industrial Zone Fenggang Town, Dongguan, Guangdong, China
Tel.: (86) 76987862222
Industrial Equipment Mfr & Distr
N.A.I.C.S.: 336320

UMC Electronics Vietnam Limited (1)
Tan Truong Industrial Zone, Cam Giang Dist, Hai Duong, Vietnam
Tel.: (84) 2203570001
Industrial Equipment Mfr & Distr
N.A.I.C.S.: 336320

UMC H Electoronics Co., Ltd. (1)
1 Horiyamashita, Hadano, 259-1304, Kanagawa, Japan
Tel.: (81) 46 388 8007
Web Site: https://www.umc.co.jp
Electronic Product Mfr & Distr
N.A.I.C.S.: 334419

UMC Just In Staff Co., Ltd. (1)
TAK Building 4F 5-44-1 Higashi Omiya, Minuma-ku, Saitama, 337-0051, Japan
Tel.: (81) 486822100
Industrial Equipment Mfr & Distr
N.A.I.C.S.: 336320

UMCOR AG
Steinstrasse 21, 8003, Zurich, Switzerland
Tel.: (41) 43 960 7979   CH
Web Site: http://www.umcor.ch
Year Founded: 2003
Sales Range: $1-4.9 Billion
Metal Wholesale Trade Distr
N.A.I.C.S.: 425120
Michael Grunstein (CEO)

Subsidiaries:

Gindre Duchavany S.A. (1)
31 rue Giffard, BP 23, 38230, Pont-de-Cheruy, France
Tel.: (33) 4 72 46 09 01
Web Site: http://www.gindre.com
Copper Product Mfr
N.A.I.C.S.: 331420
Francois Luneau (Gen Mgr)

Subsidiary (Domestic):

Gindre Composant S.A. (2)
7 Route de Loyettes Chavanoz, 38230, Pont-de-Cheruy, France
Tel.: (33) 4 72 46 09 01
Copper Mfr
N.A.I.C.S.: 331420

Subsidiary (US):

Gindre Copper Inc. (2)
202 Lee St, Greenwood, SC 29646
Tel.: (864) 227-5262
Web Site: http://www.gindrecopper.com
Emp.: 5
Copper Product Mfr

UMCOR AG

Umcor AG—(Continued)
N.A.I.C.S.: 331420
Daniel Brendel (Gen Mgr)

Subsidiary (Non-US):

Gindre Torns S.L. (2)
C/ Londres 29 Pol Ind Cova Solera, Rubi,
08191, Barcelona, Spain
Tel.: (34) 93 588 95 42
Web Site: http://www.gindretorns.com
Copper Components Distr
N.A.I.C.S.: 423510
Massimiliano Sabella (Dir-Comml)

Kupferrheydt GmbH (2)
Nobelstasse 18, 41189, Monchengladbach,
Germany
Tel.: (49) 2166 956 0
Web Site: http://www.kupferrheydt.de
Emp.: 60
Copper Product Mfr
N.A.I.C.S.: 331420
Daniel Brendel (Mng Dir)

Metelec Ltd (2)
Vulcan Industrial Estate Leamore Lane,
Walsall, WS2 7BZ, West Midlands, United
Kingdom
Tel.: (44) 1922 712665
Web Site: http://www.metelec.co.uk
Emp.: 28
Copper Product Distr
N.A.I.C.S.: 423510
Paul Bird (Mng Dir)

Montanwerke Brixlegg AG (1)
Werkstrasse 1, Brixlegg, 6230, Austria
Tel.: (43) 5337 6151
Web Site: http://www.montanwerke-brixlegg.com
Sales Range: $125-149.9 Million
Emp.: 280
Copper & Other Metal Recovery
N.A.I.C.S.: 331410
Gabriele Punz-Praxmarer (CFO)

Subsidiary (Non-US):

KOVUHUTY, a.s. (2)
Polianky 5, 841 01, Bratislava, Slovakia
Tel.: (421) 53 4161 104
Web Site: http://www.kovuhuty.sk
Copper Product Mfr
N.A.I.C.S.: 331420

UMDASCH GROUP AG

Josef Umdasch Platz 1, 3300, Amstetten, Austria
Tel.: (43) 74726050   AT
Web Site: http://www.umdasch.com
Year Founded: 1868
Sales Range: $1-4.9 Billion
Emp.: 7,641
Holding Company; Retail Store Design & Marketing Services; Construction Formworks Mfr
N.A.I.C.S.: 551112
Andreas J. Ludwig (CEO)

Subsidiaries:

Doka GmbH (1)
Josef Umdasch Platz 1, 3300, Amstetten, Austria
Tel.: (43) 74726050
Web Site: http://www.doka.com
Sales Range: $1-4.9 Billion
Emp.: 2,000
Construction Formworks Mfr & Whslr
N.A.I.C.S.: 332311
Ludwig Pekarek (Member-Exec Bd)

Subsidiary (Non-US):

Ceska Doka spol s r.o. (2)
Za Avii 868, Cakovice, 196 00, Prague,
Czech Republic
Tel.: (420) 284 001 311
Web Site: http://www.doka.cz
Construction Materials Whslr
N.A.I.C.S.: 423390
Martin Misar (Bus Mgr)

Deutsche Doka Schalungstechnik GmbH (2)
Frauenstrasse 35, PO Box 115, 82216,
Maisach, Germany
Tel.: (49) 8141 394 0
Web Site: http://www.doka.de
Construction Materials Whslr
N.A.I.C.S.: 423390
Georg Will (Mgr-Sls)

Doka Algerie SARL (2)
Route de Dar El Beida Domaine Bakalem,
16017, Rouiba, Algeria
Tel.: (213) 770 112 540
Construction Materials Whslr
N.A.I.C.S.: 423390

Doka Belform IOOO (2)
ul Ponomarenko 43A Office 304, 220015,
Minsk, Belarus
Tel.: (375) 17 213 0014
Web Site: http://www.doka.by
Construction Materials Whslr
N.A.I.C.S.: 423390

Doka Brasil Ltda. (2)
Rua Guilherme Lino dos Santos 756,
Jardim Flor do Campo, 07190-010, Guarulhos, Sao Paulo, Brazil
Tel.: (55) 11 2088 5777
Web Site: http://www.doka.com
Construction Materials Whslr
N.A.I.C.S.: 423390

Doka Bulgaria EOOD (2)
12 Rozova Gradina str, Krivina, 1588, Sofia, Bulgaria
Tel.: (359) 2 41 990 00
Web Site: http://www.doka.com
Emp.: 40
Construction Materials Whslr
N.A.I.C.S.: 423390

Doka Canada Ltd. (2)
6921 - 107th Ave S E, PO Box AB, Calgary,
T2C 5N6, AB, Canada
Tel.: (403) 243-6629
Web Site: http://www.doka.ca
Emp.: 40
Construction Materials Whslr
N.A.I.C.S.: 423390
Gunnar Falke (Area Mgr)

Doka Chile Limitada (2)
Santa Isabel 1697, Lampa, Santiago, Chile
Tel.: (56) 2 4131 600
Construction Materials Whslr
N.A.I.C.S.: 423390

Doka China Ltd. (2)
22-24 Prat Avenue Tsim Sha Tsui Room A2
16/F, Valiant Commercial Building, Kowloon,
China (Hong Kong)
Tel.: (852) 2739 9311
Construction Materials Whslr
N.A.I.C.S.: 423390
Rodolfo Estrada (Sr Engr-Plng)

Doka Danmark ApS (2)
Egegaardsvej 11, Gadstrup, 4621, Roskilde, Denmark
Tel.: (45) 46 56 32 00
Web Site: http://www.doka-danmark.dk
Construction Materials Whslr
N.A.I.C.S.: 423390
Hans Henrik Norskov Mikkelsen (Mgr-Sls)

Doka Drevo s.r.o. (2)
Cesta k Smrecine 11, 974 01, Banska
Bystrica, Slovakia
Tel.: (421) 48 4360 401
Web Site: http://www.doka-drevo.sk
Construction Materials Whslr
N.A.I.C.S.: 423390
Robert Fusko (Mgr-Production)

Doka Eesti OU. (2)
Gaasi 6a, 11415, Tallinn, Estonia
Tel.: (372) 603 0650
Web Site: http://www.dokaeesti.ee
Construction Materials Whslr
N.A.I.C.S.: 423390

Doka Emirates LLC (2)
Sharjah Buheirah Corniche Road Al Durrah
Tower, PO Box 3658, Sharjah, United Arab Emirates
Tel.: (971) 6 556 2801
Construction Materials Whslr
N.A.I.C.S.: 423390
Shabeer Udyavar (Coord-Comml)

Doka Espana S.A. (2)
Central Madrid Acero 4 - P I Aimayr, 28330,
San Martin de la Vega, Spain
Tel.: (34) 91 685 75 00
Web Site: http://www.doka.es
Construction Materials Whslr
N.A.I.C.S.: 423390
Noemi Mendez (Dir-Fin & HR)

Doka Finland OY (2)
Selintie 542, 03320, Vihti, Finland
Tel.: (358) 9 224 264 0
Web Site: http://www.doka.fi
Emp.: 16
Construction Materials Whslr
N.A.I.C.S.: 423390
Tony Rehn (Head-Ops)

Doka Formwork (Shanghai) Co., Ltd. (2)
Building 2 No 3883 Yuanjiang Road,
201109, Shanghai, China
Tel.: (86) 21 6090 0899
Web Site: http://www.doka.cn
Construction Materials Whslr
N.A.I.C.S.: 423390

Doka Formwork Australia Pty Ltd. (2)
52 Airds Rd, Minto, 2566, NSW, Australia
Tel.: (61) 2 8796 0500
Construction Materials Whslr
N.A.I.C.S.: 423390
Reiner Schwarz (Mng Dir)

Doka Formwork Malaysia Snd. Bhd. (2)
Lot 9 Jalan TUDM Subang New Village,
40150, Shah Alam, Selangor, Malaysia
Tel.: (60) 3 7844 5588
Construction Materials Whslr
N.A.I.C.S.: 423390

Doka Formwork Nigeria Ltd. (2)
Block 101 Plot 21 Adewunmi Adebimpe
drive Off Marua Bus Stop, Lekki Phase 1,
Lagos, Nigeria
Tel.: (234) 806 484 04 08
Construction Materials Whslr
N.A.I.C.S.: 423390
Joy Anuli Okechukwu (Project Engr)

Doka Formwork Pte. Ltd. (2)
9 Gul Circle 02-01 to 07, Singapore,
629565, Singapore
Tel.: (65) 6897 7737
Construction Materials Whslr
N.A.I.C.S.: 423390

Doka France SAS (2)
3 chemin des Iles Zone Industrielle du,
Chemin Vert, 78610, Le Perray-en-Yvelines,
France
Tel.: (33) 1 34 84 27 27
Web Site: http://www.doka.fr
Construction Materials Whslr
N.A.I.C.S.: 423390
Arnaud Carree (Mgr-Ops)

Doka Gulf FZE (2)
Jebel Ali Free Zone, Dubai, United Arab Emirates
Tel.: (971) 4 870 8700
Construction Materials Whslr
N.A.I.C.S.: 423390
Michael Arnold (Mng Dir)

Doka Hellas A.E. (2)
5 Agiou Athanasiou str, 15351, Pallini, Greece
Tel.: (30) 210 66 69 211
Web Site: http://www.doka.com
Emp.: 15
Construction Materials Whslr
N.A.I.C.S.: 423390
Vassilios Maniatakos (Mng Dir)

Doka Hrvatska d.o.o. (2)
Radnicka cesta 173/g, 10000, Zagreb, Croatia
Tel.: (385) 1 2480 020
Construction Materials Whslr
N.A.I.C.S.: 423390
Darija Malnar (Gen Mgr)

Doka India Pvt. Ltd. (2)
Plot No 26 A Sector-7 Kharghar Mahavir
Landmark, Bldg 601 to 606 6th Floor,
410210, Navi Mumbai, India
Tel.: (91) 22 2774 6452
Construction Materials Whslr
N.A.I.C.S.: 423390
Anupam Sharma (Mng Dir)

INTERNATIONAL PUBLIC

Subsidiary (Domestic):

Doka Industrie GmbH (2)
ILOC Doka Park 1, 3304, Sankt Georgen
am Ybbsfelde, Austria
Tel.: (43) 7472 605 74001
Construction Materials Whslr
N.A.I.C.S.: 423390

Subsidiary (Non-US):

Doka Ireland Ltd. (2)
Tinure Industrial Complex, Monasterboice,
Drogheda, Louth, Ireland
Tel.: (353) 41 686 1620
Web Site: http://www.doka.com
Emp.: 5
Construction Materials Whslr
N.A.I.C.S.: 423390
Luis Morral (Mng Dir)

Doka Israel Ltd. (2)
Tnuport Area, PO Box 581, 40201, Kfar Vitkin, Israel
Tel.: (972) 9 89000 00
Web Site: http://www.doka.com
Emp.: 30
Construction Materials Whslr
N.A.I.C.S.: 423390
Avai Koren (Mng Dir)

Doka Italia S.p.A. (2)
Strada Provinciale Cerca 23, 20060, Colturano, Milan, Italy
Tel.: (39) 02 98 27 61
Web Site: http://www.doka.it
Construction Materials Whslr
N.A.I.C.S.: 423390

Doka Japan K.K. (2)
Miwanoyama 744-6, Nagareyama, 270-0175, Chiba, Japan
Tel.: (81) 4 7178 8808
Web Site: http://www.dokajapan.co.jp
Construction Materials Whslr
N.A.I.C.S.: 423390

Doka Jordan LLC (2)
Al Madina Al Munawara Street Al Haitham
Center Bldg No 156, PO Box 3856, 1st
Floor 101, 11953, Amman, Jordan
Tel.: (962) 6 554 5586
Construction Materials Whslr
N.A.I.C.S.: 423390

Doka Kalip-Iskele A.S. (2)
Inonu Mahallesi Nazarbayev Sok No 19,
41400, Gebze, Kocaeli, Turkiye
Tel.: (90) 262 751 50 66
Web Site: http://www.dokakalipiskele.com
Emp.: 15
Construction Materials Whslr
N.A.I.C.S.: 423390
Ender Ozatay (Gen Mgr)

Doka Korea Ltd. (2)
444-1 Yongdoo-ri Gongdo-eup, Anseong,
456-821, Gyeonggi-Do, Korea (South)
Tel.: (82) 31 8053 0700
Web Site: http://www.dokakorea.co.kr
Construction Materials Whslr
N.A.I.C.S.: 423390

Doka Latvia SIA (2)
Henrihi Marupes novads, Rigas rajons,
2167, Marupe, Latvia
Tel.: (371) 67 02 97 00
Construction Materials Whslr
N.A.I.C.S.: 423390

Doka Lietuva UAB (2)
Visoriu g 27, 08300, Vilnius, Lithuania
Tel.: (370) 5 278 0678
Web Site: http://www.doka.lt
Construction Materials Whslr
N.A.I.C.S.: 423390
Leokadia Rakovska (CFO)

Doka Maroc SARL AU (2)
La commune Rurale SEBBAH, BP 4439,
Skhirat, Rabat, Morocco
Tel.: (212) 538 004090
Construction Materials Whslr
N.A.I.C.S.: 423390

Doka Mexico S. de R.L. de C.V. (2)
Carr Cuautitla - Teoloyucan Km 24 5 Col
San Lorenzo Rio Tenco, 54713, Cuautitlan
Izcalli, Mexico, Mexico
Tel.: (52) 55 16677553
Web Site: http://www.doka.com.mx

AND PRIVATE COMPANIES

Construction Materials Whslr
N.A.I.C.S.: 423390

Doka Mocambique Ltd. (2)
Rua dos Elefantes Talhao B Parcela 730,
Cidade Da Matola, Maputo, Mozambique
Tel.: (258) 84 831 34 56
Construction Materials Whslr
N.A.I.C.S.: 423390

Doka Muscat LLC (2)
MSQ, PO Box 562, 115, Muscat, Oman
Tel.: (968) 244 844 45
Web Site: http://www.doka-me.com
Construction Materials Whslr
N.A.I.C.S.: 423390
Harald Hartung (Mng Dir & Engr-Civil)

Doka N.V. (2)
Handelsstraat 3, 1740, Ternat, Belgium
Tel.: (32) 2 582 02 70
Web Site: http://www.dokabekisting.be
Construction Materials Whslr
N.A.I.C.S.: 423390

Doka Nederland BV (2)
Longobardenweg 11, PO Box 399, 5342
PL, Oss, Netherlands
Tel.: (31) 412 65 30 30
Web Site: http://www.doka-nederland.nl
Construction Materials Whslr
N.A.I.C.S.: 423390
Alex Volders (Mgr-Ops)

Doka Norge AS (2)
Vekstveien 19, Aros, 3474, Royken, Norway
Tel.: (47) 31 00 50 70
Web Site: http://www.doka.no
Construction Materials Whslr
N.A.I.C.S.: 423390
Stig Haglund (Mgr-Sls)

Doka Panama S.A. (2)
Arnulfo Arias Avenue Diablo Ancon Building
42D & 42G, PO Box 0833, 02577, Panama,
Panama
Tel.: (507) 316 8150
Web Site: http://www.doka.com.pa
Construction Materials Whslr
N.A.I.C.S.: 423390

Doka Peru S.A.C. (2)
Predio Rural Huarangal UC N 10688, Lima,
Peru
Tel.: (51) 1 748 0400
Web Site: http://www.doka.com.pe
Construction Materials Whslr
N.A.I.C.S.: 423390

Doka Polska Sp. z.o.o. (2)
ul Bankowa 32, 05-220, Zielonka, Poland
Tel.: (48) 22 771 08 00
Web Site: http://www.doka.pl
Construction Materials Whslr
N.A.I.C.S.: 423390
Gomisz Konzuk (Mng Dir)

Doka Portugal Lda. (2)
Santa Maria e S Miguel Estrada Real no 41
- Recta da Granja, 2710-450, Sintra, Portugal
Tel.: (351) 21 911 26 60
Web Site: http://www.doka.pt
Construction Materials Whslr
N.A.I.C.S.: 423390

Doka Qatar LLC (2)
2nd Gate Light Industries Area, Mesaieed,
Qatar
Tel.: (974) 4 4500 628
Construction Materials Whslr
N.A.I.C.S.: 423390
Carla Mamede (Mgr-HR & Admin)

Doka Romania S.R.L. (2)
Soseaua de Centura 34, Tunari, 077180,
Bucharest, Ilfov, Romania
Tel.: (40) 21 206 49 50
Construction Materials Whslr
N.A.I.C.S.: 423390

Doka Rus OOO (2)
st Zolotaya 11 BC "Gold" of 10A20,
105094, Moscow, Russia
Tel.: (7) 4952490304
Web Site: https://www.doka.com
Construction Materials Whslr
N.A.I.C.S.: 423390

Doka Saudi Arabia Company LLC (2)

Prince Sultan Rd Rm 908 Zahran Business
Center, PO Box 18882, Salama District,
21425, Jeddah, Saudi Arabia
Tel.: (966) 12 669 1008
Construction Materials Whslr
N.A.I.C.S.: 423390

Doka Schweiz AG (2)
Mandachstrasse 50, 8155, Niederhasli,
Switzerland
Tel.: (41) 43 411 20 40
Web Site: http://www.doka-schweiz.ch
Construction Materials Whslr
N.A.I.C.S.: 423390
Roger Doka Bachmann (Mgr-Ops)

Doka Serb d.o.o. (2)
Svetogorska 4, 22310, Simanovci, Serbia
Tel.: (381) 22 400 100
Web Site: http://www.doka.rs
Construction Materials Whslr
N.A.I.C.S.: 423390
Radovan Zivanovic (Mgr-Fin & Controlling)

Doka Slovakia s.r.o. (2)
Ivanska cesta 28, PO Box 39, 82104, Bratislava, Slovakia
Tel.: (421) 2 43 42 14 26
Web Site: http://www.doka.sk
Construction Materials Distr
N.A.I.C.S.: 423390

Doka Slovenija d.o.o. (2)
Spodnji Plavz 14 d, 4270, Jesenice, Slovenia
Tel.: (386) 4 5834 400
Web Site: http://www.doka.si
Construction Materials Whslr
N.A.I.C.S.: 423390
Erik Zupancic (Gen Mgr)

Doka South Africa (Pty) Ltd. (2)
2 Sibasa Road Chloorkop Extension 10,
1619, Kempton Park, South Africa
Tel.: (27) 11 310 9709
Web Site: http://www.doka.co.za
Emp.: 33
Construction Materials Whslr
N.A.I.C.S.: 423390
David King (Reg Mgr-Sls)

Doka Sverige AB (2)
Kurodsvagen 20, 45155, Uddevalla, Sweden
Tel.: (46) 10 45 16 300
Web Site: http://www.doka.se
Construction Materials Whslr
N.A.I.C.S.: 423390
Mikael Jagroth (Mgr-Logistic)

Doka Tunisia Ltd. (2)
Rue de l'usine Le Kram Zone Industrielle,
2015, Tunis, Tunisia
Tel.: (216) 71 977 350
Construction Materials Whslr
N.A.I.C.S.: 423390
Nadia Rezgui (Mgr-Fin & Gen Admin)

Doka UK Ltd. (2)
Boughton Monchelsea Heath Road Monchelsea Farm, Maidstone, ME17 4JD, Kent,
United Kingdom
Tel.: (44) 1622 749050
Web Site: http://www.doka-formwork.co.uk
Construction Materials Whslr
N.A.I.C.S.: 423390
Joseph Affinito (Mng Dir)

Subsidiary (US):

Doka USA Ltd. (2)
214 Gates Rd, Little Ferry, NJ 07643
Tel.: (201) 641-6500
Web Site: http://www.dokausa.com
Construction Formworks Whslr
N.A.I.C.S.: 423810

Subsidiary (Non-US):

Magyar Doka Kft. (2)
Torokko u 5-7, 1037, Budapest, Hungary
Tel.: (36) 1 436 7373
Web Site: http://www.doka.hu
Construction Materials Whslr
N.A.I.C.S.: 423390
Daniel Gyenese (Mgr-Ops)

Franz Jonas GmbH & Co. KG (1)
Lessingstrasse 18, 46140, Oberhausen,
Germany
Tel.: (49) 208 62 18 0

Web Site: http://www.jonas-shop.de
Apparel Accessory Mfr
N.A.I.C.S.: 315990
Gerhard Schwers (Mng Dir)

Goeva N.V. (1)
Bevrijdingslaan 17, 8700, Tielt, Belgium
Tel.: (32) 51 40 42 75
Construction Materials Whslr
N.A.I.C.S.: 423390

Umdasch Shopfitting Group GmbH (1)
Josef Umdasch Platz 1, Amstetten, 3300,
Austria
Tel.: (43) 74726050
Web Site: http://www.umdasch-shopfitting.com
Sales Range: $300-349.9 Million
Emp.: 300
Retail Store Design, Shop-Fitting & Marketing Services
N.A.I.C.S.: 541490
Silvio Kirchmair (CEO)

Subsidiary (Domestic):

ShopConsult by Umdasch GmbH (2)
Josef Umdasch Platz 1, 3300, Amstetten,
Austria
Tel.: (43) 74726052281
Web Site: http://www.shopconsult.at
Sales Range: $25-49.9 Million
Emp.: 20
Retail Store Brand Strategy & Design Services
N.A.I.C.S.: 541490
Max Woss (Head-Brand Strategy Div)

Subsidiary (Non-US):

Umdasch Shop-Concept AG (2)
Suhrerstrasse 57, CH-5036, Oberentfelden,
Switzerland
Tel.: (41) 627372525
Web Site: http://www.umdaschshop-concept.com
Retail Store Design, Shop-Fitting & Marketing Services
N.A.I.C.S.: 541490

Umdasch Shop-Concept spol. s.r.o. (2)
Rudolfovska 204, CZ-37001, Ceske Budejovice, Czech Republic
Tel.: (420) 387022011
Web Site: http://www.umdasch-shop-concept.com
Retail Store Design, Shop-Fitting & Marketing Services
N.A.I.C.S.: 541490

Umdasch Shopfitting AG (2)
Suhrerstrasse 57, 5036, Oberentfelden,
Switzerland
Tel.: (41) 62 737 25
Apparel Accessory Mfr
N.A.I.C.S.: 315990
Martin Hoffinger (Mng Dir)

Subsidiary (Domestic):

Umdasch Shopfitting GmbH (2)
Ottokar-Kernstock-Gasse 16, 8430,
Leibnitz, Austria
Tel.: (43) 3452 700 0
Travel Agency Services
N.A.I.C.S.: 561510
Markus Thallinger (Mng Dir)

Subsidiary (Non-US):

Umdasch Shopfitting GmbH (2)
Josef-Umdasch-Strasse 5-7, 74933, Neidenstein, Germany
Tel.: (49) 7263 401 0
Apparel Accessory Mfr
N.A.I.C.S.: 315990
Helmut Neher (Mng Dir)

Umdasch Shopfitting GmbH (2)
Josef-Umdasch-Strasse 5-7, Neidenstein,
D-74933, Heidelberg, Germany
Tel.: (49) 72634010
Web Site: http://www.umdaschshopfitting.com
Sales Range: $25-49.9 Million
Emp.: 150
Retail Store Design, Shop-Fitting & Marketing Services
N.A.I.C.S.: 541490

Helmut Neher (Mng Dir)

Umdasch Shopfitting LLC (2)
22nd Street Al Quoz Industrial Area 3, PO
Box 182774, Dubai, United Arab Emirates
Tel.: (971) 4 341 77 15
Travel Agency Services
N.A.I.C.S.: 561510

Umdasch Shopfitting Limited (2)
4 The Gallery 54 Marston Street, Oxford,
OX4 1LF, United Kingdom
Tel.: (44) 1865207800
Web Site: http://www.umdasch-shop-concept.com
Sales Range: $25-49.9 Million
Emp.: 8
Retail Store Design, Shop-Fitting & Marketing Services
N.A.I.C.S.: 541490
Roman Fussthaler (Mng Dir & Dir-Sls)

Umdasch Shopfitting Ltd. (2)
Tinure Industrial Complex Monasterboice,
Drogheda, ox4 1lf, Louth, Ireland
Tel.: (353) 1 490 99 41
Web Site: http://www.umdasch.com
Emp.: 20
Apparel Accessory Mfr
N.A.I.C.S.: 315990
Roman Fussthaler (Mng Dir & Head-Premium & Travel Retail Div)

Umdasch Shopfitting S.r.l. (2)
Via Galvani 40/c, Bolzano, Italy
Tel.: (39) 0 471 95 87 00
Apparel Accessory Mfr
N.A.I.C.S.: 315990
Markus Rothbock (Mng Dir)

Umdasch Shopfitting SAS (2)
7 Rue du Chemin Blanc, Champlan, 91160,
Paris, France
Tel.: (33) 1 60 49 18 40
Travel Agency Services
N.A.I.C.S.: 561510
Emmanuel Tricot (Mng Dir & Mgr-Sls)

UMEDIC GROUP BERHAD
PMT 790 Jalan Cassia Selatan 5/2
Taman Perindustrian Batu Kawan,
Bandar Cassia, 14110, Penang, Malaysia
Tel.: (60) 45899676
Web Site:
https://www.umedic.com.my
Year Founded: 2002
UMC—(KLS)
Rev.: $9,867,925
Assets: $15,918,966
Liabilities: $2,131,911
Net Worth: $13,787,055
Earnings: $2,250,979
Emp.: 100
Fiscal Year-end: 06/30/23
Medical Device Distr
N.A.I.C.S.: 423450
Taw Seong Lim (CEO)

UMENOHANA CO., LTD.
146 Tenjin-cho, Kurume, 830-0033,
Fukuoka, Japan
Tel.: (81) 942383440
Web Site:
http://www.umenohana.co.jp
Year Founded: 1990
7604—(TKS)
Rev.: $197,083,760
Assets: $165,977,100
Liabilities: $143,641,910
Net Worth: $22,335,190
Earnings: $6,742,200
Emp.: 421
Fiscal Year-end: 04/30/24
Restaurant Operators
N.A.I.C.S.: 722511
Shigetoshi Umeno (Chm & CEO)

UMETNOST A.D.
Bulevar Despota Stefana 5, 21000,
Novi Sad, Serbia
Tel.: (381) 21 636 9467
Year Founded: 1965

UMETNOST A.D.

Umetnost a.d.—(Continued)

Emp.: 11
Wood Products Mfr
N.A.I.C.S.: 321999

UMICORE S.A./N.V.
Broekstraat 31/Rue du Marais,
B-1000, Brussels, Belgium
Tel.: (32) 22277068 BE
Web Site: https://www.umicore.com
Year Founded: 1805
UMICY—(OTCIQ)
Rev.: $25,535,991,476
Assets: $10,244,618,418
Liabilities: $7,024,350,005
Net Worth: $3,220,268,413
Earnings: $166,950,978
Emp.: 10,859
Fiscal Year-end: 12/31/20
Metal Products Mfr
N.A.I.C.S.: 551112
Stephan Csoma (Member-Exec Bd & Exec VP)

Subsidiaries:

Allgemeine Gold- Und Silberscheideanstalt AG (1)
Kanzlerstr 17, 75175, Pforzheim, Germany (91.21%)
Tel.: (49) 72319600
Web Site: http://www.agosi.de
Jeweler & Watch Mfr
N.A.I.C.S.: 339910
Franz-Josef Kron (Chm)

Allgemeine Suisse SA
Rue Galilee 15 Umicore Algemeine Suisse, Yverdon-les-Bains, 1400, Switzerland
Tel.: (41) 24246111
Fabricated Metal & Hardware Mfr
N.A.I.C.S.: 332510

Coimpa Industrial Ltda. (1)
Rodrigo Otavio 3 047, Manaus, 69077-000, Amazonas, Brazil
Tel.: (55) 926147500
Precious Metals Refining Services
N.A.I.C.S.: 331410

Italbras S.p.A. (1)
Strada del Balsego 6, 36100, Vicenza, Italy
Tel.: (39) 0444347500
Web Site: https://www.italbras.it
Emp.: 50
Brazing Alloys Mfr
N.A.I.C.S.: 332811
Stefania Dalla Rosa (Sls Mgr)

Oegussa GmbH (1)
Liesinger-Flur-Gasse 4, 1230, Vienna, Austria
Tel.: (43) 186646
Web Site: https://www.oegussa.at
Emp.: 130
Precious Metal Distr
N.A.I.C.S.: 423940
Walz Reinhard (Head-Sls & Mktg)

Schone Edelmetaal BV (1)
Scannerstraat 29, 1033 RV, Amsterdam, Netherlands
Tel.: (31) 204350222
Web Site: https://schone.umicore.com
Sales Range: $50-74.9 Million
Emp.: 60
Precious Metal Distr
N.A.I.C.S.: 423940

Todini & Co. S.P.A. (1)
Corso Milano 46 Umicore/Todini Chemicals, 20900, Monza, Italy
Tel.: (39) 0392302495
Fabricated Metal & Hardware Mfr
N.A.I.C.S.: 332510

Todini Deutschland GmbH (1)
Kastanienallee 95,, Essen, 45127, Germany
Tel.: (49) 201836050
Precious Metals Refining Services
N.A.I.C.S.: 331410

Todini Metals and Chemicals India Private Limited (1)
Plot No18 And 19 sector 15 A-1004 And A-1005 Shelton Sapphire, Palm Beach Road Navi Mumbai, Thane, Maharashtra, India
Tel.: (91) 8048952331
Web Site: https://www.todinimetals.co.in
Emp.: 10
Nickel Chemical Mfr & Distr
N.A.I.C.S.: 325130

Todini Quimica Iberica, S.L. (1)
C/ Rosellon 188 2A Umicore/Todini Quimica Iberica null, Barcelona, 08008, Spain
Tel.: (34) 933689467
Fabricated Metal & Hardware Mfr
N.A.I.C.S.: 332510

Umicore AG & Co. KG (1)
Rodenbacher Chaussee 4, Wolfgang, 63457, Hanau, Germany
Tel.: (49) 6 181 5902
Web Site: https://www.umicore.de
Sales Range: $200-249.9 Million
Emp.: 1,700
Precious Metals Refining Services
N.A.I.C.S.: 331410

Umicore Abrasives S.A (1)
Rue Du Marais 31, Brussels, 1000, Belgium
Tel.: (32) 22277111
Web Site: http://www.umicore.com
Sales Range: $800-899.9 Million
Emp.: 3,000
Fabricated Metal Products Mfr
N.A.I.C.S.: 332312

Umicore Argentina S.A. (1)
Calle 14 nr 229 Parque Industrial de Pilar, B1629MXA, Buenos Aires, Argentina
Tel.: (54) 2304529468
Web Site: http://www.pmc.umicore.com
Platinum Products Mfr
N.A.I.C.S.: 332999

Umicore Australia Ltd. (1)
414 Somerville Rd, Tottenham, 3012, VIC, Australia
Tel.: (61) 395141100
Inorganic Pigments Mfr
N.A.I.C.S.: 325130

Umicore Autocat (China) Co. Ltd. (1)
398 East Su Hong Road, Industrial Park Suzhou Catalyst plant, Jiangsu, 215026, China
Tel.: (86) 51262751361
Fabricated Metal & Hardware Mfr
N.A.I.C.S.: 332510

Umicore Autocat (Thailand) Co., Ltd. (1)
359 Moo 3 Ban Khai-Nong La Lok Road, Hemaraj Rayong Industrial Land Ban Khai District, Rayong, 21120, Thailand
Tel.: (66) 66683910
Fabricated Metal & Hardware Mfr
N.A.I.C.S.: 332510

Umicore Autocat Canada Corp (1)
4261 Mainway Drive, PO Box 509, Burlington, L7R 3Y8, ON, Canada
Tel.: (905) 336-5503
Catalytic Converters Mfr & Distr
N.A.I.C.S.: 336390

Umicore Autocat France S.A.S. (1)
Rue Lavoisier z i Ste-Agathe, 57190, Florange, France
Tel.: (33) 382822863
Fabricated Metal & Hardware Mfr
N.A.I.C.S.: 332510

Umicore Autocat India Pvt. Ltd. (1)
Plot No 03 Survey No 1295 1296 1122B 129B 1140, Village Mauje Shirwal Shirwal, 412 801, Pune, Maharashtra, India
Tel.: (91) 2266275656
Fabricated Metal & Hardware Mfr
N.A.I.C.S.: 332510

Umicore Autocat Luxembourg SA (1)
Zone Industrielle Bommelscheuer, Hautcharage, Bascharagé, 4940, Capellen, Luxembourg
Tel.: (352) 2665741
Sales Range: $25-49.9 Million
Emp.: 8
Fabricated Metal Products Mfr
N.A.I.C.S.: 332312
Soran Dominic (Mng Dir)

Umicore Autocat Poland Sp. z o.o. (1)
Ul Slupiecka 31, Nowa Ruda, 57-402, Warsaw, Poland
Tel.: (48) 746674200
Fabricated Metal & Hardware Mfr
N.A.I.C.S.: 332510

Umicore Autocat South Africa (Pty) Ltd. (1)
John Tallant Road, PO Box 11250, Algoa Park, Port Elizabeth, 6012, Eastern Cape, South Africa
Tel.: (27) 414043800
Web Site: http://www.umicore.com
Zinc Refining Services
N.A.I.C.S.: 331410

Umicore Autocat Sweden AB (1)
Hangarvagen 24, 691 35, Karlskoga, Sweden
Tel.: (46) 586721550
Catalytic Conductors Mfr
N.A.I.C.S.: 339999

Umicore Autocatalyst Recycling Belgium N.V. (1)
Adolf Greinerstraat 14, Hoboken, Antwerp, 2660, Belgium
Tel.: (32) 38217111
Web Site: http://www.preciousmetals.umicore.com
Sales Range: $400-449.9 Million
Emp.: 1,500
Fabricated Metal Products Mfr
N.A.I.C.S.: 332312

Umicore Bausysteme GmbH (1)
Gladbecker Street 413, Essen, 45326, Nordrhein-Westfalen, Germany
Tel.: (49) 201836060
Web Site: http://www.vmzinc.de
Sales Range: $25-49.9 Million
Emp.: 50
Zinc Products Mfr
N.A.I.C.S.: 332999
Lehmann Halph (Mgr)

Umicore Brazil Ltda. (1)
Barao do Rio Branco 368, Guarulhos, 07042-010, SP, Brazil
Tel.: (55) 1124211313
Web Site: http://www.umicore.com.br
Sales Range: $75-99.9 Million
Emp.: 400
Global Materials Technologies
N.A.I.C.S.: 541690

Umicore Catalisadores Ltda. (1)
Rua Dona Francisca 8300 - Bloco C2/C3, Perini Business Park - Distrito Industrial Norte, Joinville, Brazil
Tel.: (55) 4734893660
Fabricated Metal & Hardware Mfr
N.A.I.C.S.: 332510

Umicore Catalysis Korea Co.,Ltd. (1)
331 Songdogukje-daero, Yeonsu-gu, Incheon, 21990, Korea (South)
Tel.: (82) 324542707
Fabricated Metal & Hardware Mfr
N.A.I.C.S.: 332510

Umicore Catalyst (China) Co., Ltd. (1)
No 69 Chuangye Road East, Nangang Industrial Zone Economic-Technological Development Area, Tianjin, China
Tel.: (86) 15122567886
Fabricated Metal & Hardware Mfr
N.A.I.C.S.: 332510

Umicore Catalyst South Africa (Pty) Ltd. (1)
217 Archie Place, Young Park, Port Elizabeth, 6001, Eastern Cape, South Africa
Tel.: (27) 414017411
Web Site: http://www.umicore.com
Emp.: 270
Catalytic Conductors Mfr
N.A.I.C.S.: 339999

Umicore Catalyst USA, LLC (1)
9900 Bayport Blvd, Pasadena, TX 77507-1416
Tel.: (832) 261-3775
Automotive Catalyst Mfr
N.A.I.C.S.: 336390

Umicore Climeta S.A.S. (1)
1 Rue Edouard Branly, 68740, Colmar, Haut-Rhin, France
Tel.: (33) 3 89 48 69 12
Web Site: http://www.climeta.com
Sales Range: $50-74.9 Million
Emp.: 10
Copper Anodes & Chemicals Mfr
N.A.I.C.S.: 325180

Umicore Coating Services Ltd. (1)
Kinnoull Street, Dundee, DD2 3ED, United Kingdom
Tel.: (44) 138 283 3022
Web Site: http://www.coatingservices.umicore.com
Sales Range: $25-49.9 Million
Emp.: 20
Technical Coating Services
N.A.I.C.S.: 332812
Mark Naples (Mng Dir)

Umicore Financial Services NV/SA (1)
Rue De Marais 31, Brussels, 1000, Belgium
Tel.: (32) 22277111
Web Site: http://www.umicore.com
Sales Range: $400-449.9 Million
Emp.: 200
Fabricated Metal Products Mfr
N.A.I.C.S.: 332312

Umicore Galvanotechnik GmbH (1)
Klarenbergstrasse 53 - 79, Schwaebisch Gmuend, 73525, Stuttgart, Germany
Tel.: (49) 717160701
Fabricated Metal & Hardware Mfr
N.A.I.C.S.: 332510
Markus Legeler (Mgr-Sls Intl)

Umicore Hunan Fuhong Zinc Chemicals Co., Ltd.
Xingcheng Town, Wangcheng County, Changsha, Hunan, China
Tel.: (86) 731 8838 0156
Web Site: http://www.umicore.com
Sales Range: $50-74.9 Million
Emp.: 160
Zinc Powder Mfr
N.A.I.C.S.: 325130

Umicore IR Glass S.A.S. (1)
ZA du Boulais Umicore IR Glass Acigne null, Acigne, 35690, Dol-de-Bretagne, France
Tel.: (33) 299043226
Electro-Optic Material Mfr
N.A.I.C.S.: 335921

Umicore Japan KK (1)
Ark Mori Building 26th Floor 1-12-32 Akasaka, Minato-ku, Tokyo, 107-6026, Japan
Tel.: (81) 36 685 3106
Web Site: https://www.umicore.jp
Catalysts & Specialty Materials Developer, Mfr & Recycler
N.A.I.C.S.: 339999

Plant (Domestic):

Umicore Japan KK - Tsukuba Tech. Center/Plant (2)
21 Kasumi-no-sato Ami-Machi, Inashiki-gun, Tsukuba, 300-0315, Ibaraki, Japan
Tel.: (81) 2 98 89 28 19
Web Site: http://www.umicore.com
Sales Range: $25-49.9 Million
Emp.: 17
Fabricated Metal Products Mfr
N.A.I.C.S.: 332312

Umicore Jubo Thin Film Products (Beijing) Co., Ltd. (1)
No 5 Xingguang the 4th Street Tongzhou Park ZhongGuan Cun Science Park, Tonghzou District, Beijing, 101111, China
Tel.: (86) 1081508360
Fabricated Metal & Hardware Mfr
N.A.I.C.S.: 332510

Umicore Korea Ltd (1)
410 Chaam-Dong, Seobuk-Gu, Cheonan, Chungchongnam-Do, Korea (South)
Tel.: (82) 416200200
Sales Range: $50-74.9 Million
Emp.: 200
Fabricated Metal Products Mfr
N.A.I.C.S.: 332312
Frank Streignart (Gen Mgr)

Umicore Malaysia Sdn Bhd (1)
Plot 376 Jalan Perak 4, Pasir Gudang,

AND PRIVATE COMPANIES

81700, Johor, Malaysia
Tel.: (60) 72524431
Metal Fabricated Products Mfr
N.A.I.C.S.: 332312

Umicore Marketing Services (Hong Kong) Ltd. (1)
Room A & B 19F Manulife Tower 169 Electric Road, North Point, China (Hong Kong)
Tel.: (852) 27002230
Sales Range: $25-49.9 Million
Emp.: 40
Precious Metal Distr
N.A.I.C.S.: 423940
Gary Lee Richard (Mgr)

Umicore Marketing Services (Shanghai) Co., Ltd. (1)
1800 Zhongshan Road W Zao Feng Universe Bldg Unit A1 18th Floor, Shanghai, 200235, China
Tel.: (86) 2124116838
Web Site: http://www.ums.umicore.com
Precious Metal Distr
N.A.I.C.S.: 423940

Umicore Marketing Services Africa (Pty) Ltd. (1)
Tel.: (27) 11 697 0626
Web Site: https://www.brazetec.com
Emp.: 5
Seal Products Distr
N.A.I.C.S.: 423510

Umicore Marketing Services Australia Pty. Ltd. (1)
Level 5 606 Saint Kilda Rd, Melbourne, 3004, VIC, Australia
Tel.: (61) 395141100
Sales Range: $50-74.9 Million
Emp.: 5
Seal Products Distr
N.A.I.C.S.: 423840

Umicore Marketing Services Belgium S.A./NV (1)
Broekstraat 31 Rue du Marais, Brussels, 1000, Belgium
Tel.: (32) 22277111
Web Site: http://www.umicore.com
Sales Range: $400-449.9 Million
Emp.: 250
Fabricated Metal Products Mfr
N.A.I.C.S.: 332312

Umicore Marketing Services France S.A.S. (1)
Les Mercuriales-Tour du Ponant-40 rue Jean Jaures, 93176, Bagnolet, Cedex, France
Tel.: (33) 14 972 4242
Web Site: http://www.ums.umicore.com
Fabricated Metal Products Mfr
N.A.I.C.S.: 332312

Umicore Marketing Services Korea Co., Ltd. (1)
3rd Floor Ebenezer B D 1564-12 Seocho-Dong, Seocho-Gu, 137-874, Seoul, Korea (South)
Tel.: (82) 25222246
Web Site: http://www.technicalmaterials.umicore.com
Fabricated Metal Products Mfr
N.A.I.C.S.: 332312

Umicore Marketing Services Lusitana Metais, Lda. (1)
Rua do Caulino 374 4445 Valongo, Alfena, 445 259, Portugal
Tel.: (351) 229998950
Web Site: http://www.lusitanaumicore.com
Sales Range: $25-49.9 Million
Emp.: 4
Precious Metals Refining Services
N.A.I.C.S.: 331410
Maria-Teresa Madureira (Gen Mgr)

Umicore Marketing Services UK Ltd. (1)
Collier House Mead Lane, Hertford, SG13 7AX, Hertfordshire, United Kingdom
Tel.: (44) 203 445 5640
Web Site: http://www.vmzinc.co.uk
Sales Range: $25-49.9 Million
Emp.: 21
Zinc Products Whslr
N.A.I.C.S.: 423520

Umicore Materials AG (1)
Alte Landstrasse 8, PO Box 364, Balzers, 9496, Liechtenstein
Tel.: (423) 3887300
Web Site: http://www.thinfilmproducts.umicore.com
Emp.: 85
Coating Material Mfr
N.A.I.C.S.: 324122
Rene Buhler (Gen Mgr & Mgr-Optics & Electronics)

Umicore Norway AS (1)
Hoffs Gate 10, 3262, Larvik, Norway
Tel.: (47) 33180950
Web Site: http://www.umicore.com
Sales Range: $25-49.9 Million
Emp.: 55
Zinc Products Mfr
N.A.I.C.S.: 339999

Umicore Oxyde Belgium NV (1)
Industrieweg 16, 3550, Heusden, North Brabant, Belgium
Tel.: (32) 13530370
Web Site: http://www.umicore.com
Emp.: 32
Fabricated Metal Products Mfr
N.A.I.C.S.: 332312

Umicore Portugal S.A. (1)
Travessa do Padrao, Perafita, 4455-524, Matosinhos, Portugal
Tel.: (351) 229950076
Web Site: http://www.asturianadasminas.pt
Zinc Refining Services
N.A.I.C.S.: 331410

Umicore Precious Metals Canada Inc. (1)
451 Denison Street, Markham, L3R 1B7, ON, Canada
Tel.: (905) 475-9566
Web Site: https://jim-ca.umicore.com
Sales Range: $25-49.9 Million
Emp.: 60
Precious Metal Smelting & Refining Services
N.A.I.C.S.: 331410

Umicore Precious Metals USA Inc. (1)
300 Wampanoag Trl, Riverside, RI 02915
Tel.: (401) 450-0907
Electro-Optic Material Mfr
N.A.I.C.S.: 335921

Umicore Shanghai Co., Ltd. (1)
No 235 Changshi Road, Shanghai, 201600, China
Tel.: (86) 2157843961
Web Site: http://www.umicore.com
Emp.: 90
Cobalt & Zinc Powders Mfr
N.A.I.C.S.: 331221

Umicore Shokubai (China) Co., Ltd. (1)
398 East Su Hong Road, Industrial Park Suzhou Catalyst plant, Jiangsu, 215026, China
Tel.: (86) 51262751769
Fabricated Metal & Hardware Mfr
N.A.I.C.S.: 332510

Umicore Shokubai (Thailand) Co., Ltd. (1)
359 Moo 3 Ban Khai-Nong La Lok Road, Hemaraj Rayong Industrial Land Ban Khai District, Rayong, 21120, Thailand
Tel.: (66) 33683982
Fabricated Metal & Hardware Mfr
N.A.I.C.S.: 332510

Umicore Shokubai Brasil Industrial Ltda (1)
Av Sao Jeronimo 5000 Caixa Postal 1013, Americana, Sao Paulo, Brazil
Tel.: (55) 1934714141
Fabricated Metal & Hardware Mfr
N.A.I.C.S.: 332510

Umicore Shokubai Germany GmbH (1)
Rodenbacher Chaussee 4, PO Box 1351, Hanau-Wolfgang, 63457, Hessen, Germany
Tel.: (49) 6181596217
Fabricated Metal & Hardware Mfr
N.A.I.C.S.: 332510

Umicore Shokubai Japan Co., Ltd. (1)
992-1 Aza-Nishioki Okihama ku Aboshiku Tsuichiba, Himeji, 671-1292, Hyogo-ken, Japan
Tel.: (81) 366853199
Fabricated Metal & Hardware Mfr
N.A.I.C.S.: 332510

Umicore Shokubai USA Inc. (1)
2347 Commercial Dr, Auburn Hills, MI 48326
Tel.: (248) 340-1040
Fabricated Metal & Hardware Mfr
N.A.I.C.S.: 332510

Umicore South Africa (Pty) Ltd (1)
8 Penny Road, Roodepoort, 1724, Gauteng, South Africa
Tel.: (27) 117614801
Fabricated Metal Products Mfr
N.A.I.C.S.: 332312

Umicore Specialty Chemicals Subic Inc. (1)
1044 Sitio Malinta Asinan Proper Subic Shipyard Economic Zone, Subic, 2209, Zambales, Philippines
Tel.: (63) 472323218
Web Site: http://www.csm.umicore.com
Sales Range: $25-49.9 Million
Emp.: 82
Chemicals Mfr
N.A.I.C.S.: 325998

Umicore Specialty Materials Brugge NV (1)
Kleine Pathoekeweg 82, Brugge, 8000, West-Vlaanderen, Belgium
Tel.: (32) 50320720
Web Site: http://www.usnb.be
Emp.: 90
Chemicals Mfr
N.A.I.C.S.: 325180
Kathy Devos (Coord-R&D)

Umicore Specialty Materials Recycling, LLC (1)
28960 Lakeland Blvd, Wickliffe, OH 44092
Tel.: (440) 833-3000
Fabricated Metal & Hardware Mfr.
N.A.I.C.S.: 332510

Umicore Specialty Powders France S.A.S. (1)
9 Rue Andre Sibellas Umicore Specialty Powders Null, 38100, Grenoble, France
Tel.: (33) 476705454
Fabricated Metal & Hardware Mfr
N.A.I.C.S.: 332510

Umicore Strub AG (1)
Hauptstrasse 48, Postfach 40, CH 3250, Lyss, Wiler, Switzerland
Tel.: (41) 32 3879797
Web Site: http://www.strubline.com
Sales Range: $25-49.9 Million
Emp.: 20
Building Materials Distr
N.A.I.C.S.: 444180

Umicore Technical Materials (Suzhou) Co., Ltd. (1)
No 508-2 Zhujiang Road Hi Tech Industrial Development Zone, Suzhou, 215300, Jiangsu, China
Tel.: (86) 51266670800
Web Site: http://www.technicalmaterials.umicore.com
Fabricated Metal Products Mfr
N.A.I.C.S.: 332312

Umicore Thin Film Products AG (1)
Alte Landstrasse 8, 9496, Balzers, Liechtenstein
Tel.: (423) 3887300
Fabricated Metal & Hardware Mfr
N.A.I.C.S.: 332510

Umicore Thin Film Products Taiwan Co., Ltd. (1)
No 22 Aly 4 Ln 711 Bo ai street Umicore Thin Film Products, Hsinchu Hsien Hsinchu County, Zhubei, 302, Taiwan
Tel.: (886) 35532999
Electro-Optic Material Mfr
N.A.I.C.S.: 335921

Umicore USA Inc. (1)
3600 Glenwood Ave Ste 250, Raleigh, NC 27612-4945
Tel.: (919) 874-7171

UMIYA TUBES LIMITED

Web Site: http://www.umicore.com
Holding Company; Regional Managing Office
N.A.I.C.S.: 551112

Subsidiary (Domestic):

Palm Commodities International, LLC (2)
1717 JP Hennessy Dr, La Vergne, TN 37086
Tel.: (615) 641-1200
Web Site: https://www.palminc.com
Sales Range: $75-99.9 Million
Emp.: 52
Specialty Chemicals & Metal Compound Products Mfr & Whslr
N.A.I.C.S.: 325180

Umicore Autocat USA Inc. (2)
1301 W Main Pkwy, Catoosa, OK 74015-2560
Tel.: (918) 266-1400
Automobile Parts Distr
N.A.I.C.S.: 423120

Unit (Domestic):

Umicore Indium Products (2)
50 Sims Ave, Providence, RI 02909-1023
Tel.: (401) 456-0800
Web Site: http://www.umicore.com
Sales Range: $25-49.9 Million
Emp.: 40
Mfr of Indium Alloys
N.A.I.C.S.: 331491

Subsidiary (Domestic):

Umicore Marketing Services USA Inc. (2)
3600 Glenwood Ave Ste 250, Raleigh, NC 27612
Tel.: (919) 874-7173
Web Site: https://www.umicore.com
Sales Range: $25-49.9 Million
Emp.: 30
Precious Metal Products Whslr
N.A.I.C.S.: 423510

Umicore Optical Materials Inc. (2)
PO Box 737, Quapaw, OK 74363
Tel.: (918) 673-1650
Web Site: http://www.umicore.com
Emp.: 100
Germanium Wafer Mfr
N.A.I.C.S.: 339999

Umicore Precious Metals NJ LLC (2)
3950 S Clinton Ave, South Plainfield, NJ 07080
Tel.: (908) 222-5007
Sales Range: $25-49.9 Million
Emp.: 30
Precious Metal Product Mfr
N.A.I.C.S.: 331410

UMIDA GROUP AB
Humlegardsgatan 13, 114 46, Stockholm, Sweden
Tel.: (46) 511773200
Web Site: https://umidagroup.com
Alcoholic Beverages Mfr
N.A.I.C.S.: 445320
Katarina Nielsen (CEO)

UMIYA TUBES LIMITED
208 2nd Floor Suman Tower Sector-11, Gandhinagar, 382 011, Gujarat, India
Tel.: (91) 7923242052
Web Site: http://www.umiyatubes.com
Year Founded: 2013
539798—(BOM)
Rev.: $865,404
Assets: $2,967,232
Liabilities: $1,287,213
Net Worth: $1,680,019
Earnings: ($488,316)
Emp.: 1
Fiscal Year-end: 03/31/23
Stainless Steel Tube Mfr
N.A.I.C.S.: 331210

UMIYA TUBES LIMITED

Umiya Tubes Limited—(Continued)

Saurabhkumar Rameshchandra Patel (*Co-Mng Dir*)

UMM AL QAIWAIN GENERAL INVESTMENTS P.S.C.
Tel.: (971) 67681999   AE
Web Site: https://www.qic-uaq.ae
Year Founded: 1982
QIC—(EMI)
Rev.: $7,360,724
Assets: $188,253,373
Liabilities: $12,941,497
Net Worth: $175,311,877
Earnings: $6,151,775
Fiscal Year-end: 12/31/19
Cement Mfr & Whslr
N.A.I.C.S.: 327310
Nasser Rashid Al Moalla (*Vice Chm*)

UMM AL-QURA CEMENT COMPANY
King Abdulaziz Road AlSahafa District, PO Box 10182, Riyadh, 11433, Saudi Arabia
Tel.: (966) 114874477
Web Site: https://www.uacc.com.sa
3005—(SAU)
Rev.: $58,983,293
Assets: $314,684,771
Liabilities: $111,474,097
Net Worth: $203,210,674
Earnings: $6,129,035
Emp.: 63
Fiscal Year-end: 12/31/22
Cement Mfr
N.A.I.C.S.: 327310
Abdulaziz Omran Al-Omran (*Chm*)

UMN PHARMA INC.
Nisso17 Bldg 8F 2-14-30 Shin-Yokohama, Kohoku-ku, Yokohama, 222-0033, Kanagawa, Japan
Tel.: (81) 45 595 9840
Web Site:
   http://www.umnpharma.com
Year Founded: 2004
4585—(TKS)
Sales Range: Less than $1 Million
Emp.: 96
Pharmaceuticals Mfr
N.A.I.C.S.: 325412
Tatsuyoshi Hirano (*Chm & CEO*)

UMOE GRUPPEN AS
Fornebuveien 84, 1366, Lysaker, Norway
Tel.: (47) 94860000   NO
Web Site: http://www.umoe.com
Year Founded: 1984
Sales Range: $900-999.9 Million
Emp.: 5,443
Investment Holding Company
N.A.I.C.S.: 551112
Jens Dag Ulltveit-Moe (*Founder & CEO*)

Subsidiaries:

American Bistro Sweden AB   (1)
Skeppsbron 46, 111 30, Stockholm, Sweden
Tel.: (46) 8 611 31 31
Restaurant Operators
N.A.I.C.S.: 722511
Therese Anvelius (*Gen Mgr*)

Blender AS   (1)
Lysaker Torg 35, 1366, Lysaker, Norway
Tel.: (47) 67555555
Web Site: http://www.blender.no
Restaurant Operators
N.A.I.C.S.: 722511

Kagra IX AS   (1)
Industriveien 1, 8907, Bronnoysund, Norway
Tel.: (47) 75 02 35 90
Restaurant Operators
N.A.I.C.S.: 722511

Sonnico AS   (1)
Hans Moller Gasmanns vei 9, 0598, Oslo, Norway
Tel.: (47) 993 21 973
Web Site: http://www.sonnico.no
Emp.: 400
Electrical Equipment Installation Services
N.A.I.C.S.: 238210
Anders Hauglie-Hanssen (*CEO & Dir-Admin*)

Umoe Advanced Composites AS   (1)
Vige Havnevei 64, 4633, Kristiansand, Norway
Tel.: (47) 3827 9200
Web Site: http://www.uac.no
Emp.: 20
Pressure Vessel Mfr
N.A.I.C.S.: 332420
Oyvind Hamre (*Mng Dir*)

Umoe Bioenergy S.A   (1)
Fazenda Taquarussu s/n - Zona Rural, Sandovalina, Sao Paulo, 19250-000, Brazil
Tel.: (55) 18 3277 9900
Bioethanol Mfr
N.A.I.C.S.: 325193
Knut Arne Karlsen (*Pres*)

Umoe Consulting AS   (1)
Nygardsgaten 15, 5008, Bergen, Norway
Tel.: (47) 980 48 000
Web Site: http://www.umoeconsulting.no
Emp.: 40
Information Technology Consulting Services
N.A.I.C.S.: 541512
Jan Helge Meland (*Mgr-IT*)

Umoe Mandal Inc.   (1)
1101 30th St NW Ste 500, Washington, DC 20007
Tel.: (202) 683-0939
Ship Building Services
N.A.I.C.S.: 336611
Tracy Wacker (*VP-Mktg*)

Umoe Restaurant Group AS   (1)
Lysaker Torg 35, 1336, Lysaker, Norway   **(90.1%)**
Tel.: (47) 94860000
Web Site: http://www.umoe.com
Sales Range: $400-449.9 Million
Emp.: 110
Holding Company; Restaurants Owner & Operator
N.A.I.C.S.: 551112
Ranghlid Wederrg (*Exec Dir-HR*)

Umoe Schat-Harding Group AS   (1)
Seimsvegen 116, 5470, Rosendal, Norway   **(99.82%)**
Tel.: (47) 53483600
Web Site: http://www.schat-harding.com
Sales Range: $400-449.9 Million
Emp.: 800
Holding Company; Rescue Boat & Lifeboat Systems Designer, Mfr, Whslr & Maintenance Services
N.A.I.C.S.: 551112
Jarle Kjell Roth (*Chm & CEO*)

Subsidiary (Domestic):

Umoe Schat-Harding Equipment AS   (2)
Seimsvegen 116, Rosendal, 5472, Norway   **(100%)**
Tel.: (47) 53483600
Web Site: http://www.harding.no
Rescue Boat & Lifeboat Systems Designer, Mfr & Whslr
N.A.I.C.S.: 336612
Styrk Bekkenes (*CEO*)

Umoe Schat-Harding Services AS   (2)
Fornebuveien 84, NO-1366, Lysaker, Norway   **(100%)**
Tel.: (47) 9486 0000
Web Site: http://www.schat-harding.com
Rescue Boat & Lifeboat Systems Repair & Maintenance Services
N.A.I.C.S.: 336611

Subsidiary (US):

Umoe Schat-Harding, Inc.   (2)
912 Hwy 90 E, New Iberia, LA 70560-8764   **(100%)**

Tel.: (337) 365-5451
Web Site: http://www.schat-harding.com
Rescue Boat & Lifeboat Systems Whslr & Maintenance Services
N.A.I.C.S.: 423860

UMP HEALTHCARE HOLDINGS LTD.
14/F Wing On House, 71 Des Voeux Road Central, Hong Kong, China (Hong Kong)
Tel.: (852) 2 824 0231   Ky
Web Site: http://www2.ump.com.hk
Year Founded: 1990
0722—(HKG)
Rev.: $80,324,230
Assets: $125,107,633
Liabilities: $35,717,271
Net Worth: $89,390,363
Earnings: $4,067,642
Emp.: 519
Fiscal Year-end: 06/30/21
Holding Company
N.A.I.C.S.: 551112
Kwong Yiu Sun (*Founder, Chm & CEO*)

Subsidiaries:

Procare Physiotherapy & Rehabilitation Centre Limited   (1)
Room 1601 16/F Wing On House 71 Des Voeux Road, Central, China (Hong Kong)
Tel.: (852) 25072655
Medical Physiotherapy Services
N.A.I.C.S.: 621340

UMPAS HOLDING A.S.
Kome Mahallesi Taslak Sokak No 9/A, Merkez, 64200, Usak, Turkiye
Tel.: (90) 8524147
Web Site:
   https://www.umpasholding.com.tr
UMPAS—(IST)
Rev.: $1,273,147
Assets: $13,156,900
Liabilities: $7,833,642
Net Worth: $5,323,259
Earnings: ($585,810)
Fiscal Year-end: 12/31/22
Ceramic Tile Mfr
N.A.I.C.S.: 327120
Huseyin Karakas (*Chm*)

UMPO JSC
Ferin str 2, 450039, Ufa, Russia
Tel.: (7) 347 238 33 66
Web Site: http://www.umpo.ru
Year Founded: 1931
Emp.: 20,000
Aircraft Engine Mfr
N.A.I.C.S.: 336412
Yury Lastochkin (*Chm*)

UMS HOLDINGS BERHAD
No 2 Jalan Segambut Pusat, Segambut, 51200, Kuala Lumpur, Malaysia
Tel.: (60) 362587211
Web Site: https://www.umsh.com
UMS—(KLS)
Rev.: $15,000,667
Assets: $37,051,558
Liabilities: $1,352,702
Net Worth: $35,698,856
Earnings: $888,550
Fiscal Year-end: 09/30/23
Industrial Spare Parts Distr
N.A.I.C.S.: 336510
Fong Ying Tam (*Co-Sec*)

Subsidiaries:

UMS (Kuantan) Sdn. Bhd.   (1)
No 6 8 Jalan Industri 9/3 Cocopalm Industrial Park, Semambu, 25350, Kuantan, Pahang Darul Makmur, Malaysia
Tel.: (60) 95663124
Industrial Spare Parts Mfr
N.A.I.C.S.: 336510

INTERNATIONAL PUBLIC

UMS Corporation Sdn. Bhd.   (1)
No 2 Jalan Segambut Pusat, Segambut, 51200, Kuala Lumpur, Federal Territory, Malaysia
Tel.: (60) 362587211
Web Site: https://www.umsh.com
Sales Range: $75-99.9 Million
Emp.: 120
Material Handling Machinery Distr
N.A.I.C.S.: 423830

Subsidiary (Domestic):

UMS (JB) Sdn. Bhd.   (2)
No 10 Jalan Dewani 4 Kawasan Perindustrian Dewani, Kawasan Perindustrian Dewani, 81100, Johor Bahru, Johor Darul Takzim, Malaysia
Tel.: (60) 73327998
Web Site: http://www.umsh.com
Sales Range: $25-49.9 Million
Emp.: 20
Material Handling Machinery Distr
N.A.I.C.S.: 423830

UMS (Penang) Sdn. Bhd.   (2)
No 1 & 3 Lorong Perusahaan Maju 12, Perai, 13600, Penang, Malaysia
Tel.: (60) 45070822
Web Site: http://www.umsh.com
Sales Range: $25-49.9 Million
Emp.: 13
Material Handling Equipment Distr
N.A.I.C.S.: 423830

UMS (Sarawak) Sdn. Bhd.   (2)
44 45 Yoshi Square Jalan Pelabuhan, 93450, Kuching, Sarawak, Malaysia
Tel.: (60) 82341722
Emp.: 20
Material Handling Machinery Distr
N.A.I.C.S.: 423830
Chong Liew (*Branch Mgr*)

UMS Engineering (S) Pte. Ltd.   (1)
8 Kaki Bukit Avenue 4 Premier Kaki Bukit 06-06/06-07, Singapore, 415875, Singapore
Tel.: (65) 67472506
Web Site: https://www.umse.com
Industrial Spare Parts Mfr
N.A.I.C.S.: 336510

UMS HOLDINGS LIMITED
23 Changi North Crescent Changi North Industrial Estate, Singapore, 499616, Singapore
Tel.: (65) 65432272
Web Site:
   https://www.umsgroup.com.sg
Year Founded: 2001
558—(SES)
Rev.: $227,150,647
Assets: $368,980,535
Liabilities: $75,921,381
Net Worth: $293,059,153
Earnings: $46,343,255
Emp.: 838
Fiscal Year-end: 12/31/23
Semiconductor Devices Mfr
N.A.I.C.S.: 334413
Andy Luong (*Founder, Chm & CEO*)

Subsidiaries:

Integrated Manufacturing Technologies, Inc.   (1)
1477 N Milpitas Blvd, Milpitas, CA 95035
Tel.: (510) 659-9770
Web Site: https://www.imt-intl.com
Stainless Steel Gasline Mfr
N.A.I.C.S.: 331210

JEP Holdings Ltd.   (1)
16 Seletar Aerospace Crescent, Singapore, 797567, Singapore   **(38.8%)**
Tel.: (65) 65454222
Web Site: https://www.jep-holdings.com
Rev.: $44,039,991
Assets: $89,302,431
Liabilities: $31,381,504
Net Worth: $57,920,927
Earnings: $1,268,651
Emp.: 193
Fiscal Year-end: 12/31/2023
Precision Machining & Contract Equipment Manufacturing Services
N.A.I.C.S.: 333248

Andy Luong *(Chm & CEO)*

Subsidiary (Domestic):

Dolphin Engineering Pte. Ltd. (2)
2 Loyang Way 4, Singapore, 507098, Singapore
Tel.: (65) 67415556
Web Site: https://www.dolphin.com.sg
Fabricated Metal Mfr
N.A.I.C.S.: 332312

JEP Industrades Pte.Ltd. (2)
No 16 Seletar Aerospace Crescent, Singapore, 797567, Singapore
Tel.: (65) 62412522
Web Site: https://jep.com.sg
Hardware Distr
N.A.I.C.S.: 423710

Kalf Engineering Pte. Ltd. (1)
23 Changi North Crescent, Changi North Industrial Estate, Singapore, 499616, Singapore
Tel.: (65) 64491677
Web Site: https://www.kalf.sg
Water Treatment Equipment Mfr & Distr
N.A.I.C.S.: 334512

Starke Singapore Pte Ltd. (1)
34 Gul Lane, Singapore, 629428, Singapore
Tel.: (65) 6 863 1630
Web Site: https://www.starke.com.sg
Aluminum Sheet & Roll Distr
N.A.I.C.S.: 423510
Luah Damien *(Sls Dir)*

Subsidiary (Non-US):

Starke Asia Sdn. Bhd. (2)
Lot 1436 1437 Jalan Kebun Baru Juru Estate, Taman Perindustrian Ringan Juru, 14100, Simpang Empat, Pulau Pinang, Malaysia
Tel.: (60) 45020933
Aluminum Sheet & Roll Distr
N.A.I.C.S.: 423510

UMS Pte Ltd (1)
23 Changi North Crescent, Changi North Industrial Estate, Singapore, 499616, Singapore
Tel.: (65) 65432272
Semiconductor Components Mfr
N.A.I.C.S.: 334413

Ultimate Machining Solutions (M) Sdn. Bhd. (1)
1058 Jalan Kebun Baru, Juru Simpang Ampat, 14100, Seberang Perai Tengah, Pulau Penang, Malaysia
Tel.: (60) 45073000
Semiconductor Components Mfr
N.A.I.C.S.: 334413
Edwin Yap *(Mgr-QA)*

UMS TECHNOLOGIES LIMITED
Gopal Bagh 1062 Avinashi Road, Coimbatore, 641 018, TamilNadu, India
Tel.: (91) 422 2243439
Web Site: http://www.umstech.in
Year Founded: 1957
Sales Range: $1-9.9 Million
Aerospace Component Mfr
N.A.I.C.S.: 334511
G. D. Gopal *(Chm)*

UMS-NEIKEN GROUP BERHAD
Tel.: (60) 360914146
Web Site: https://www.ums-neiken.com
UMSNGB—(KLS)
Rev.: $14,287,549
Assets: $28,754,027
Liabilities: $1,805,181
Net Worth: $26,948,846
Earnings: $1,090,118
Emp.: 279
Fiscal Year-end: 12/31/23
Electrical Wire Mfr
N.A.I.C.S.: 333248
Kok Yong Dee *(Exec Dir)*

Subsidiaries:

United MS Electrical Mfg (M) Sdn. Bhd. (1)
Lot 48 Jalan Industry 2/1 Rawang Integrated Industrial Park, 48000, Rawang, Selangor, Malaysia
Tel.: (60) 360912626
Electrical Wiring Accessory Mfr
N.A.I.C.S.: 335931

UMT UNITED MOBILITY TECHNOLOGY AG
Brienner Strasse 7, 80333, Munich, Germany
Tel.: (49) 8920500680
Web Site: https://www.umt.ag
Year Founded: 1989
UMDK—(DEU)
Rev.: $242,852
Assets: $12,054,311
Liabilities: $4,106,414
Net Worth: $7,947,897
Earnings: ($34,749,972)
Emp.: 1
Fiscal Year-end: 12/30/23
Asset Management Services
N.A.I.C.S.: 523999

UMWELTBANK AG
Laufertorgraben 6, 90489, Nuremberg, Germany
Tel.: (49) 91153082020
Web Site: https://www.umweltbank.de
UBK—(DEU)
Assets: $6,284,358,098
Liabilities: $6,009,327,741
Net Worth: $275,030,357
Earnings: $838,945
Emp.: 354
Fiscal Year-end: 12/31/23
Commercial Banking Services
N.A.I.C.S.: 522110
Juergen Koppmann *(Chm-Mgmt Bd & CEO)*

UN TOIT POUR TOI SA
10 Rue de Penthievre, 75008, Paris, France
Tel.: (33) 143354985
Web Site: http://www.untoitpourtoi.fr
Residential Real Estate Management Services
N.A.I.C.S.: 531311
Jean-Noel Medus *(Chm, CEO & VP-IR)*

UNBANKED INC.
Ebisu First Square 9F1-18-14 Ebisu, Shibuya-Ku, Tokyo, 150-0013, Japan
Tel.: (81) 364562667
Web Site: https://unbanked.jp
Year Founded: 1972
87460—(TKS)
Sales Range: Less than $1 Million
Commodity Trading Services
N.A.I.C.S.: 523160
Yoshitaka Okada *(Chm & Pres)*

UNECO CO., LTD.
117 Jeongseojiin-ro, Seo-gu, Incheon, Korea (South)
Tel.: (82) 325760501
Web Site: http://www.ecomaister.com
Year Founded: 1999
064510—(KRS)
Rev.: $14,812
Assets: $45,699,515
Liabilities: $42,985,686
Net Worth: $2,713,829
Earnings: ($26,191,298)
Emp.: 87
Fiscal Year-end: 12/31/20
Industrial Machinery Mfr
N.A.I.C.S.: 333248
Sang-Yoon Oh *(CEO)*

UNEEDKOREA
500-35 Bukyang-Dong, Hwaseong, 445-040, Korea (South)
Tel.: (82) 31 3554087
Web Site: http://www.uneedkorea.co.kr
Sales Range: $1-9.9 Million
Emp.: 40
Liquid Crystal Display (LCD) Equipment Mfr
N.A.I.C.S.: 334419
Won Jae Lee *(CEO)*

UNEEK CLOTHING COMPANY LTD.
Unit 1 and 2 Wellesley Court Apsley Way Neasden, London, NW2 7HF, United Kingdom
Tel.: (44) 845 871 8711
Web Site: http://www.uneekclothing.com
Year Founded: 1996
Sales Range: $25-49.9 Million
Emp.: 75
Men & Women Apparel Mfr
N.A.I.C.S.: 315250
Mehul Sheth *(Controller-Fin)*

UNET CREDIT FINANCE SERVICES LTD.
The Craft 6, Holon, Israel
Tel.: (972) 35638200
Web Site: https://www.unet.co.il
UNCR—(TAE)
Rev.: $10,483,155
Assets: $63,723,051
Liabilities: $39,590,368
Net Worth: $24,132,683
Earnings: ($2,029,248)
Fiscal Year-end: 12/31/21
Investment Management Service
N.A.I.C.S.: 523999

UNEVIT D.D.
Kolonija br 8, 88 400, Konjic, Bosnia & Herzegovina
Tel.: (387) 36726625
UNEVR—(SARE)
Rev.: $169,066
Assets: $2,355,359
Liabilities: $4,321
Net Worth: $2,351,038
Earnings: ($147,423)
Emp.: 6
Fiscal Year-end: 12/31/20
Real Estate Manangement Services
N.A.I.C.S.: 531210

UNEX GROUP
Ilica 26, 10000, Zagreb, Croatia
Tel.: (385) 1 4888 800
Web Site: http://www.unex.hr
Year Founded: 1992
Sales Range: $25-49.9 Million
Emp.: 85
Advertising Services
N.A.I.C.S.: 541810
Andrea Sumanovac *(Mng Dir)*

UNEXO SAS
7bis Boulevard Tour d'Auvergne, CS 86505, Rennes, Cedex, France
Tel.: (33) 2 99 67 20 14
Web Site: http://www.unexo.fr
Privater Equity Firm
N.A.I.C.S.: 523999
Jean-Luc Creach *(Gen Mgr)*

UNFOLD.VC ASI S.A.
plac Powstancow Slaskich 17a/225, 53-329, Wroclaw, Poland
Tel.: (48) 518860217
Web Site: https://unfold.vc
Year Founded: 2008
UNF—(WAR)
Rev.: $2,439,787

Assets: $17,472,815
Liabilities: $83,333
Net Worth: $17,389,482
Earnings: ($3,282,774)
Fiscal Year-end: 12/31/23
Investment Services
N.A.I.C.S.: 523940
Karina Glinska-Tkocz *(COO)*

UNGA GROUP PLC
Commercial Street Industrial Area Ngano House, PO Box 30386, Nairobi, Kenya
Tel.: (254) 207603000
Web Site: https://www.unga-group.com
Year Founded: 1908
UNGA—(NAI)
Rev.: $182,786,320
Assets: $87,444,908
Liabilities: $43,552,303
Net Worth: $43,892,605
Earnings: ($7,291,237)
Emp.: 298
Fiscal Year-end: 06/30/23
Holding Company
N.A.I.C.S.: 551112
Nicholas C. Hutchinson *(Exec Dir)*

Subsidiaries:

Ennsvalley Bakery Limited (1)
Enterprise Road, Industrial Area, Nairobi, Kenya
Tel.: (254) 202090920
Web Site: http://www.ennsvalleybakery.com
Bakery Food Products Mfr
N.A.I.C.S.: 311919

UNI ABEX ALLOY PRODUCTS LTD.
Liberty Building Sir Vithaldas Thackersey Marg, Mumbai, 400 020, Maharashtra, India
Tel.: (91) 2222032797
Web Site: https://www.uniabex.com
Year Founded: 1972
504605—(BOM)
Rev.: $19,927,342
Assets: $15,156,801
Liabilities: $5,375,061
Net Worth: $9,781,740
Earnings: $2,221,617
Emp.: 95
Fiscal Year-end: 03/31/23
Alloy Metal Casting & Mfr
N.A.I.C.S.: 331523
Milind S. Ashar *(Officer-Compliance & Sec)*

UNI CHEM CO., LTD.
38 Haebong-ro, Danwon-gu, Ansan, Gyeonggi-do, Korea (South)
Tel.: (82) 314913751
Web Site: https://uni-chem.net
Year Founded: 1979
011330—(KRS)
Rev.: $92,381,043
Assets: $333,551,603
Liabilities: $226,809,648
Net Worth: $106,741,955
Earnings: $994,371
Emp.: 280
Fiscal Year-end: 12/31/22
Leather Mfr
N.A.I.C.S.: 316110

UNI CORE HOLDINGS CORPORATION
World Financial Center Room 721 Shennan East Road, Shenzhen, Guangdong, China
Tel.: (86) 75582233721
Year Founded: 2003
Data Hosting & Maintenance Services
N.A.I.C.S.: 518210
I-Hsiu Peng *(CEO)*

UNI LAND S.P.A.

Uni Core Holdings Corporation—(Continued)

UNI LAND S.P.A.
Via Vittorio Emanuele II No 84,
40063, Monghidoro, BO, Italy
Tel.: (39) 0516554549   IT
Year Founded: 1959
Sales Range: $10-24.9 Million
Emp.: 41
Land Purchaser; Building & Home Construction Services
N.A.I.C.S.: 237210
Vincenzo Borgogna *(CEO)*

Subsidiaries:

House Building SpA   (1)
Via Selice 90, Imola, 40016, Bologna, Italy   **(89%)**
Tel.: (39) 0542647000
Sales Range: $10-24.9 Million
Residential Building & Construction Services
N.A.I.C.S.: 236117
Maurizio Zuffa *(CEO)*

UNI TREND TECHNOLOGY CHINA CO., LTD.
No 6 Industrial North 1st Road, Songshan Lake High-tech Industrial Development Zone, Dongguan, 523808, Guangdong, China
Tel.: (86) 76985729808
Web Site: https://instruments.uni-trend.com
Year Founded: 2003
688628—(SHG)
Rev.: $125,155,551
Assets: $170,958,579
Liabilities: $22,263,663
Net Worth: $148,694,916
Earnings: $16,484,013
Fiscal Year-end: 12/31/22
Measuring Instruments Mfr
N.A.I.C.S.: 334513
Shaojun Hong *(Chm & Gen Mgr)*

UNI-ASIA GROUP LIMITED
30/F Prosperity Millennia Plaza No 663 King's Road, North Point, China (Hong Kong)
Tel.: (852) 25285016   SG
Web Site: https://www.uni-asia.com
Year Founded: 1997
CHJ—(SES)
Rev.: $69,435,000
Assets: $230,736,000
Liabilities: $98,162,000
Net Worth: $132,574,000
Earnings: $18,045,000
Emp.: 70
Fiscal Year-end: 12/31/21
Financial Services
N.A.I.C.S.: 522220
Matthew Wai Keung Yuen *(Mng Dir & Head-Maritime Asset Mgmt Dept)*

Subsidiaries:

Uni-Asia Capital (Japan) Ltd.   (1)
5F Hulic Kandabashi Building 1-21-1, Kanda Nishikicho Chiyoda-ku, Tokyo, 104-0061, Japan
Tel.: (81) 335189220
Web Site: https://uni-asia.co.jp
Sales Range: $50-74.9 Million
Emp.: 30
Investment Management Service
N.A.I.C.S.: 523999

Subsidiary (Domestic):

Vista Hotel Management Co., Ltd.   (2)
7-13-10 Ginza Nihonkoaginza Building 3F, Chuo-ku, Tokyo, 104-0061, Japan
Tel.: (81) 351486600
Web Site: http://www.hotel-vista.jp
Sales Range: $25-49.9 Million
Emp.: 7
Home Management Services
N.A.I.C.S.: 561110

Uni-Asia Shipping Limited   (1)
30th Floor Prosperity Millennia Plaza No663 King's Road, North Point, China (Hong Kong)
Tel.: (852) 25285016
Web Site: http://www.uniasiashipping.com
Navigation & Shippin Services
N.A.I.C.S.: 488330
Michio Tanamoto *(Chm)*

Subsidiary (Non-US):

Hope Bulkship S.A.   (2)
MD Kanda Building 7F 9-1 Kanda Mitoshirocho Chiyoda-ku, Tokyo, 101-0053, Japan   **(100%)**
Tel.: (81) 3 3518 9255
Marine Shipping Services
N.A.I.C.S.: 483111

UNI-BIO SCIENCE GROUP LTD
Unit 502 5/F No 20 Science Park East Avenue Hong Kong Science Park, Sha Tin, New Territories, China (Hong Kong)
Tel.: (852) 31023232
Web Site: http://www.uni-bioscience.com
0690—(HKG)
Rev.: $56,140,290
Assets: $37,290,053
Liabilities: $12,459,938
Net Worth: $24,830,115
Earnings: $4,910,280
Emp.: 370
Fiscal Year-end: 12/31/22
Pharmaceuticals Mfr
N.A.I.C.S.: 325412
Kingsley Leung *(Chm)*

Subsidiaries:

Beijing Genetech Pharmaceutical Co., Limited   (1)
No 7 Xinghuo Street Changping Sector of Zhongguancun Science Park, Changping District, Beijing, 102299, China
Tel.: (86) 1080117799
Health Care Product Whslr
N.A.I.C.S.: 423450

Guizhou Tongren Parkson Retail Co., Ltd.   (1)
Parkson Commercial Plaza No 270 Jinlin Avenue, Wanshan District, Tongren, 554300, China
Tel.: (86) 8568658606
Grocery Products Retailer
N.A.I.C.S.: 455219

Uni-Bio Science Healthcare (Beijing) Co. Limited   (1)
1105 10th floor building 3 yard 93 Jianguo Road, Chaoyang District, Beijing, 100025, China
Tel.: (86) 1080117799
Health Care Product Whslr
N.A.I.C.S.: 423450

UNI-PRESIDENT CHINA HOLDINGS LTD
No 131 Linhong Road Shanghai Hongqiao Linkong Economic Park, Changning District, Shanghai, 200335, China
Tel.: (86) 2122158888
Web Site: http://www.uni-president.com.cn
0220—(OTCIQ)
Rev.: $3,487,338,749
Assets: $3,386,610,681
Liabilities: $1,259,054,960
Net Worth: $2,127,555,721
Earnings: $249,073,957
Emp.: 30,430
Fiscal Year-end: 12/31/20
Beverage & Noodles Mfr
N.A.I.C.S.: 311824
Chih-Hsien Lo *(Chm)*

UNI-PRESIDENT ENTERPRISES CORPORATION
No 301 Zhongzheng Rd, Yongkang Dist, T'ainan, 710401, Taiwan
Tel.: (886) 62532121
Web Site: https://www.uni-president.com
Year Founded: 1967
1216—(TAI)
Rev.: $16,842,454,366
Assets: $18,284,389,639
Liabilities: $11,846,442,129
Net Worth: $6,437,947,510
Earnings: $1,024,287,770
Emp.: 88,354
Fiscal Year-end: 12/31/21
Food Products Mfr
N.A.I.C.S.: 311423
Chih-Hsien Lo *(Chm & Chief Strategy Officer-Grp)*

Subsidiaries:

Beijing Ton Yi Industrial Co., Ltd.   (1)
C Building, Fule Industrial Zone Huairou District, Beijing, 101400, China
Tel.: (86) 1089681966
Beverage Product Mfr
N.A.I.C.S.: 312111

Cayman Ton Yi Industrial Holdings Ltd.   (1)
Intersection of Meiyu Road and Xinhong, Wuxi, 214028, Jiangsu, China
Tel.: (86) 51085214650
Beverage Product Mfr
N.A.I.C.S.: 327910

Subsidiary (Domestic):

Wuxi Tonyi Daiwa Industrial Co., Ltd.   (2)
Intersection of Meiyu Road and Xinhong Road, Xinwu, Wuxi, 214000, Jiangsu, China
Tel.: (86) 51081157888
Bottle Can Mfr
N.A.I.C.S.: 326160

Changsha Ton Yi Industrial Co., Ltd.   (1)
Chigang Road No 188, Wangcheng Economic Development Zone, Changsha, 410200, Hunan, China
Tel.: (86) 73188720702
Beverage Product Mfr
N.A.I.C.S.: 312111

Chendu Ton Yi Industrial Packing Co., Ltd.   (1)
No 58 Guihu East Road, Xindu Town Xindu District, Chengdu, 610500, Sichuan, China
Tel.: (86) 2883966885
Beverage Product Mfr
N.A.I.C.S.: 312111

Fujian Ton Yi Tinplate Co., Ltd.   (1)
Wengjiao Road No 160, Zhangzhou Taiwanese Investment Zone Fulong Industrial Park, Xiamen, 363107, Fujian, China
Tel.: (86) 5966766266
Beverage Product Mfr
N.A.I.C.S.: 312111

Huizhou Ton Yi Industrial Co., Ltd.   (1)
Banqiao Industry Industrial Park, Taimei Town Boluo County, Huizhou, 516166, Guangzhou, China
Tel.: (86) 7526509038
Beverage Product Mfr
N.A.I.C.S.: 312111

Jiangsu Ton Yi Tinplate Co., Ltd.   (1)
Intersection of Meiyu Road and Xinhong, Xinwu, Wuxi, 214028, Jiangsu, China
Tel.: (86) 51085215096
Beverage Product Mfr
N.A.I.C.S.: 312111

Kunshan Ton Yi Industrial Co., Ltd.   (1)
301 Qingyang South RD, Kunshan, 215300, Jiangsu, China
Tel.: (86) 51257880998
Beverage Product Mfr
N.A.I.C.S.: 312111

Nanlien International Corp.   (1)
12 F 560 Chung Hsiao E Road Sec 4, Taipei, 11071, Taiwan

INTERNATIONAL PUBLIC

Web Site: http://www.nic.com.tw
Professional Investment Services
N.A.I.C.S.: 523940

Presicarre Corp.   (1)
6th Fl 1 137 Nanking East Rd Section 2, Taipei, 106, ROC, Taiwan   **(60%)**
Tel.: (886) 225063400
Sales Range: $50-74.9 Million
Emp.: 100
Grocery Store Operator; Joint Venture of Carrefour SA & Uni-President Enterprises Corp.
N.A.I.C.S.: 457110

President Chain Store Corp.   (1)
2F 65 Tung Hsing Rd, Taipei, 105, Taiwan
Tel.: (886) 227478711
Web Site: https://www.7-11.com.tw
Rev.: $9,912,824,125
Assets: $8,046,539,474
Liabilities: $6,550,513,460
Net Worth: $1,496,026,014
Earnings: $395,870,650
Emp.: 36,189
Fiscal Year-end: 12/31/2023
Grocery Retailer
N.A.I.C.S.: 445131
Wen-Chi Wu *(CFO)*

Subsidiary (Domestic):

Books.com Co., Ltd.   (2)
8F No 8 Dongsing Road, Songshan, Taipei, 10565, Taiwan
Tel.: (886) 227821100
Web Site: http://www.books.com.tw
Online Book Retailer
N.A.I.C.S.: 424920

Cold Stone Creamery Taiwan Ltd.   (2)
7F 69 Tung Hsing Rd, Taipei, 11070, Taiwan
Tel.: (886) 227478711
Web Site: http://www.coldstone.com.tw
Ice Cream Mfr & Sales
N.A.I.C.S.: 311520

Duskin Serve Taiwan Co.   (2)
43 Wu Chuan 3rd Road Wuku Industrial Park, Wuku Hsiang, Taipei, 24891, Taiwan
Tel.: (886) 222996760
Cleaning Instruments Distr
N.A.I.C.S.: 449210

President Collect Services Co. Ltd.   (2)
8F No. 8 Tung Hsing Rd., Songhan District, Taipei, Taiwan   **(70%)**
Tel.: (886) 227889588
Rev.: $15,236,939
Assets: $50,082,816
Liabilities: $47,388,329
Net Worth: $2,694,487
Earnings: $1,996,999
Fiscal Year-end: 12/31/2015
Bill Collection Services
N.A.I.C.S.: 561440
Chieh-Shan Chen *(Pres)*

President Musashino Corp.   (2)
No 301 Zhongzheng Road Yongkang District, T'ainan, 71001, R.O.C., Taiwan
Tel.: (886) 6 2532121
Web Site: http://www.uni-president.com
Convenience Foods Mfr
N.A.I.C.S.: 311999

President Pharmaceutical Corp.   (2)
No 126 Section 4 Nanjing East Road 105 6 building, Songshan District, Taipei, 10570, Taiwan
Tel.: (886) 226590419
Web Site: https://www.ppc-life.com.tw
Sales Range: $50-74.9 Million
Emp.: 70
Pharmaceutical Products Distr
N.A.I.C.S.: 423450

President Transnet Corp.   (2)
4F 200 Chongyang Road, Taipei, 11573, Taiwan
Tel.: (886) 227887887
Web Site: http://www.t-cat.com.tw
Sales Range: $50-74.9 Million
Emp.: 200
Food Products Distr
N.A.I.C.S.: 445298

President YiLan Art and Culture Corp.   (2)

AND PRIVATE COMPANIES

201 Wu Ping Road Sec 2, Wujie, 26841, Yilan, Taiwan
Tel.: (886) 39507711
Art & Cultural Exhibition Organizing Services
N.A.I.C.S.: 561920

Q-Ware Systems & Services Corp. (2)
5th Floor No 61 Dongxing Road, Xinyi District, Taipei, 110, Taiwan
Tel.: (886) 287523999
Web Site: https://www.qware.com.tw
Software Development Services
N.A.I.C.S.: 541511

Uni-President Cold-Chain Corp. (2)
7 Ta Yin Village, Hsin Shih, 744 7, Tainan, Taiwan
Tel.: (886) 65898966
Web Site: http://www.upcc.com.tw
Refrigerated Warehousing & Logistics Services
N.A.I.C.S.: 493120

Uni-President Department Store Corp. (2)
789 Chung Hua 5th Rd, Kaohsiung, 80661, Taiwan
Tel.: (886) 78233689
Web Site: http://www.uni-hankyu.com.tw
Department Stores Operation Services
N.A.I.C.S.: 455110

Wisdom Distribution Service Corp. (2)
No 70-1 Section 2 Jiayuan Road, Shulin, 238, Taipei, Taiwan
Tel.: (886) 226687071
Web Site: https://www.wds.com.tw
Emp.: 400
Books & Magazines Distr
N.A.I.C.S.: 424920

President Global Corporation (1)
6965 Aragon Cir, Buena Park, CA 90620
Tel.: (714) 994-2990
Web Site: https://www.presidentglobal.com
Sales Range: $50-74.9 Million
Emp.: 70
Mfr of Convenient Foods
N.A.I.C.S.: 424490
Ping C. Wu (Owner, Pres & CEO)

Subsidiary (Domestic):

Ameripec Inc. (2)
6965 Aragon Cir, Buena Park, CA 90620
Tel.: (714) 994-2990
Web Site: http://www.ameripec.com
Juice & Soft Drink Mfr
N.A.I.C.S.: 312111

Affiliate (Domestic):

Pung Pec, Inc. (2)
6905 Aragon Cir, Buena Park, CA 90620 (50%)
Tel.: (714) 562-0848
Sales Range: $25-49.9 Million
Emp.: 3
Import & Wholesale of Canned & Frozen Food to Institutions, Restaurants
N.A.I.C.S.: 332322
Frank Liu (Pres & Gen Mgr)

President International Development Corp (1)
10F No 11 Sonaggo Rd, Taipei, 110, Taiwan
Tel.: (886) 223458680
Web Site: http://www.pidc.com.tw
Investment Holding Services
N.A.I.C.S.: 551112

President Natural Industrial Corp. (1)
7F No 560 Section 4 Zhongxiao East Road, Taipei, 110, Taiwan
Tel.: (886) 227582880
Web Site: http://www.pnic.com.tw
Food Products Mfr
N.A.I.C.S.: 311999

President Packaging Industrial Corp. (1)
No 465 Mayou Rd, Madou District, Tainan City, 721, Taiwan
Tel.: (886) 65704066
Web Site: http://www.ppi.com.tw
Packaging Services

N.A.I.C.S.: 561910

President Tokyo Corp. (1)
8th Floor No 85 and 87 Section 2 Nanjing East Road, Zhongshan District, Taipei, 104489, Taiwan
Tel.: (886) 227478188
Auto Leasing Services
N.A.I.C.S.: 532112

Qingdao President Feed & Livestock Co., Ltd. (1)
No 1 Qingquan Road, Zhangge Town Pingdu, Qingdao, 266738, Shandong, China
Tel.: (86) 53284318527
Web Site: http://www.qdpec.cn
Aquatic Feed Mfr
N.A.I.C.S.: 311119

Sichuan Ton Yi Industrial Co., Ltd. (1)
No 18 North Section RongTai Avenue, Cross-strait Science and Technology Industrial Park Wenjiang District, Chengdu, 611137, Sichuan, China
Tel.: (86) 2882630888
Beverage Product Mfr
N.A.I.C.S.: 312111

Taizhou Ton Yi Industrial Co., Ltd. (1)
No 301 Zhenxing Road, Gaogang Science and Technology Innovation Park Gaogang District, Taizhou, 225324, Jiangsu, China
Tel.: (86) 52389500500
Beverage Product Mfr
N.A.I.C.S.: 312111

Tian Jin Ton Yi Industrial Co., Ltd. (1)
Tianjin Airport Economic Zone Jinglu 269B, Tianjin, 101400, China
Tel.: (86) 1089681966
Beverage Product Mfr
N.A.I.C.S.: 312111

Ton Yi Industrial Corp. (1)
No 837 Zhongzheng N Rd, YongKang District, T'ainan, 71042, Taiwan
Tel.: (886) 62531131
Web Site: https://www.tonyi.com.tw
Rev.: $1,152,431,429
Assets: $1,065,202,877
Liabilities: $413,375,438
Net Worth: $651,827,439
Earnings: $19,454,527
Emp.: 1,112
Fiscal Year-end: 12/31/2023
Packaging Products Mfr
N.A.I.C.S.: 326112
Shing-Chi Liang (Mng Dir)

Tong-Sheng Finance Leasing Co., Ltd. (1)
Room 1602 Building 1 Harmony Xingzuo Business Plaza No 269 Wangdun Rd, Industrial Park, Suzhou, 215028, Jiangsu, China
Tel.: (86) 51286867128
Equipment Leasing Services
N.A.I.C.S.: 532490

Uni-President (Philippines) Corp. (1)
Ground Floor Topys Place Bldg Cor, Economia and Industria Streets Bagumbayan, Quezon City, Philippines
Tel.: (63) 86873020
Web Site: http://www.uni-president.com.ph
Food Products Mfr
N.A.I.C.S.: 311999

Uni-President (Thailand) Ltd. (1)
253 18th Floor Soi Asoke Sukhumvit 21 Road, Khlong Toei Nuea Wattana, Bangkok, 10110, Thailand
Tel.: (66) 26651900
Food Product Mfr & Distr
N.A.I.C.S.: 311999

Subsidiary (Domestic):

Uni-President Marketing Co., Ltd. (2)
Building 253 19th Floor Soi Asoke Sukhumvit 21 Road, Khlong Toei Nuea Wattana, Bangkok, 10110, Thailand
Tel.: (66) 226207849
Food Product Mfr & Distr

N.A.I.C.S.: 311999

Uni-President (Vietnam) Co., Ltd. (1)
No 16-18-20 DT 743 Road, Industrial Zone Song Than 2 Di An Ward, Di An, Binh Duong, Vietnam
Tel.: (84) 27437908116
Web Site: http://www.uni-president.com.vn
Food Products Mfr
N.A.I.C.S.: 311999

Subsidiary (Domestic):

Tribeco Binh Duong Co., Ltd. (2)
No 8 Street 11 Viet Nam - Singapore Industrial Park, Thuan An, Binh Duong, Vietnam
Tel.: (84) 2743768780
Web Site: https://www.tribeco.com.vn
Soft Drinks Mfr
N.A.I.C.S.: 312111
Duc Nguyen Hoang (Mgr-QA)

Uni-President Vietnam Aquatic Breeding Co., Ltd. (2)
Manufacturing and Inspection Aquatic Product Zone, An Hai Commune Ninh Phuoc District, Ho Chi Minh City, Ninh Thuan, Vietnam
Tel.: (84) 683668166
Aquatic Product Mfr
N.A.I.C.S.: 311710

Uni-President Glass Industrial Co., Ltd. (1)
No 36 Singong Rd, Sinying, Tainan City, 73054, Taiwan
Tel.: (886) 66536281
Web Site: https://www.upgi.com.tw
Glass Bottle Mfr
N.A.I.C.S.: 327213

Zhangzhou Ton Yi Industrial Co., Ltd. (1)
Zhangzhou Taiwanese Investment Zone, Feng Shan Industrial Park, Zhangzhou, 363107, Fujian, China
Tel.: (86) 5966766288
Beverage Product Mfr
N.A.I.C.S.: 312111

ZhanjiangTon Yi Industrial Co., Ltd. (1)
1 Henger Rd, Lingbei Industrial Bases Suixi County, Zhanjiang, 524338, Guangdong, China
Tel.: (86) 7598218288
Beverage Product Mfr
N.A.I.C.S.: 312111

Zhongshan President Enterprises Co., Ltd. (1)
No 83 Funan Rd, Fusha Town, Zhongshan, Guangdong, China
Tel.: (86) 76023452191
Aquatic Feed Mfr & Distr
N.A.I.C.S.: 311119

UNIA SP. Z O.O.
ul Szosa Torunska 32/38, 86-300, Grudziadz, Poland
Tel.: (48) 564510500
Web Site: http://www.uniamachines.com
Emp.: 1,000
Farm Machinery Mfr
N.A.I.C.S.: 333111

Subsidiaries:

Agrisem International SAS (1)
Le Petit Beauce, 439 rue de l'etang, 44850, Ligne, France
Tel.: (33) 2 40 77 40 48
Web Site: http://www.agrisem.com
Sales Range: $10-24.9 Million
Emp.: 60
Agricultural Equipment & Machinery Mfr & Sales
N.A.I.C.S.: 423820

UNIAQUE SPA
Via delle Canovine 21, 24126, Bergamo, Italy
Tel.: (39) 0353070111
Web Site: http://www.uniacque.bg.it
Year Founded: 2006
Integrated Water Services

N.A.I.C.S.: 924110
Luca Serughetti (Pres)

UNIBAIL-RODAMCO-WESTFIELD SE
7 place du Chancelier Adenauer, CS 31622, 75772, Paris, Cedex 16, France
Tel.: (33) 153437437   FR
Web Site: https://www.urw.com
Year Founded: 2018
URW—(ASX)
Rev.: $2,506,043,600
Assets: $57,822,253,400
Liabilities: $35,409,885,603
Net Worth: $22,412,367,796
Earnings: ($1,919,598,532)
Emp.: 2,531
Fiscal Year-end: 12/31/22
Real Estate Manangement Services
N.A.I.C.S.: 531390
Michel Dessolain (COO-Europe)

Subsidiaries:

Centrum Cerny Most as (1)
Chlumecka 765/6, 198 19, Prague, Czech Republic
Tel.: (420) 28 191 8100
Web Site: https://www.centrumcernymost.cz
Shopping Center Operation Services
N.A.I.C.S.: 531120

DX Donauplex Betriebsges.mbH (1)
Wagramerstreet 81, 1220, Vienna, Austria
Tel.: (43) 120347220
Commercial Property Leasing Services
N.A.I.C.S.: 531120

Donau Zentrum Betriebsfuhrungsges.m.b.H. (1)
Wagramerstrasse 81 Stiege 2/3 Stock, Vienna, 1220, Austria
Tel.: (43) 120347220
Web Site: http://www.donauzentrum.at
Sales Range: $75-99.9 Million
Emp.: 150
Shopping Center Operation Services
N.A.I.C.S.: 531120
Michael Male (Mng Dir)

Donauzentrum Besitz- u. Vermietungs GmbH (1)
Donaustadtstrasse 1/6 OG, 1220, Vienna, Austria
Tel.: (43) 1203 472 2177
Web Site: http://www.donauzentrum.at
Emp.: 35
Commercial Property Leasing Services
N.A.I.C.S.: 531120
Arnaud Burlin (Gen Mgr)

Espace Expansion (1)
7 Place du Chancelier Adenauer CS 31622, 75772, Paris, Cedex 16, France (100%)
Tel.: (33) 153437437
Web Site: http://www.unibail-rodamco.com
Sales Range: $150-199.9 Million
Emp.: 400
Shopping Centre Development & Management
N.A.I.C.S.: 531120

Promociones Unibail-Rodamco Generales SLU (1)
Calle Jose Abascal 56, Madrid, 28003, Spain
Tel.: (34) 917006500
Web Site: http://www.unibail-rodamco.com
Emp.: 100
Property Management Services
N.A.I.C.S.: 531312
Simon Orchard (Gen Mgr)

Rodamco Ceska Republica sro (1)
Panorama Centrum Skretova 490/12, CZ-12000, Prague, 2, Czech Republic
Tel.: (420) 221 442 220
Web Site: http://www.unibail-rodamco.com
Property Management Services
N.A.I.C.S.: 531312

Rodamco Eneby AB (1)
Attundafaltet 6, 183 34, Taby, Sweden
Tel.: (46) 858623000
Web Site: http://www.unibail-rodamco.com

UNIBAIL-RODAMCO-WESTFIELD SE

Unibail-Rodamco-Westfield SE—(Continued)
Sales Range: $25-49.9 Million
Emp.: 50
Commercial Property Leasing Services
N.A.I.C.S.: 531120

Rodamco Europe N.V. (1)
World Trade Center Tower H Schiphol Boulevard 371, 1118 BJ, Schiphol, Netherlands
Tel.: (31) 206582500
Web Site: http://www.rodamco.com
Real Estate Property Investment Services
N.A.I.C.S.: 531390
Peter M. van Rossum *(Mng Dir)*

Rodamco Nederland Winkels BV (1)
Schiphol Boulevard 371 Wtc Toren H, Luchthaven Schiphol, 1118 BJ, Schiphol, Noord-Holland, Netherlands
Tel.: (31) 302394195
Commercial Property Leasing Services
N.A.I.C.S.: 531120

Rodamco Tyreso Centrum AB (1)
Bollmoravagen 24 F, 135 40, Tyreso, Sodermanland, Sweden
Tel.: (46) 858623000
Commercial Property Management Services
N.A.I.C.S.: 531312

Rodamco Vasby Centrum AB (1)
Dragonvagen 86 Upplands Vasby, 10398, Stockholm, Sweden
Tel.: (46) 858623000
Web Site: http://www.inibail-rodamco.com
Sales Range: $25-49.9 Million
Emp.: 40
Commercial Property Management Services
N.A.I.C.S.: 531312
Lena Rune *(Mgr)*

SA Rodamco France (1)
7 Place Du Chancelier Adenauer, 75116, Paris, France
Tel.: (33) 140709781
Property Management Services
N.A.I.C.S.: 531312

SARL Espace Expansion Immobiliere (1)
7 Place du Chancelier Adenauer, CS 31622, 75772, Paris, Cedex 16, France
Tel.: (33) 15 343 7313
Web Site: http://www.unibail-rodamco.com
Sales Range: $150-199.9 Million
Emp.: 450
Real Estate Manangement Services
N.A.I.C.S.: 531210

SAS La Toison d'Or (1)
84 Avenue De La Vallee Des Baux, 13520, Maussane-les-Alpilles, Bouches Du Rhone, France (100%)
Tel.: (33) 490543285
Property Management Services
N.A.I.C.S.: 531312

SAS SFAM (1)
30 Rue Jean Charcot, Aulnay-sous-Bois, 93600, Seine-Saint-Denis, France
Tel.: (33) 148693854
Property Management Services
N.A.I.C.S.: 531312

SAS Societe de Lancement de Magasins a l'Usine (1)
228 Avenue Alfred Motte, 59100, Roubaix, Nord, France
Tel.: (33) 320831620
Commercial Property Leasing Services
N.A.I.C.S.: 531130

SAS Viparis - Nord Villepinte (1)
2 Place de la Porte Maillot, 75853, Paris, France
Tel.: (33) 140682222
Exhibition Hall Leasing Services
N.A.I.C.S.: 531120
Renaud Hamaide *(Pres)*

SCS Liegenschaftsverwertung GmbH (1)
Bureau Center B4, Voesendorf, 2334, Lower Austria, Austria
Tel.: (43) 169939690
Web Site: http://www.scs.at
Sales Range: $1-4.9 Billion
Property Management Services
N.A.I.C.S.: 531311
Anton Cech *(Gen Mgr)*

SCS Motor City Sud Errichtungsges.mbH (1)
Shopping City Sud, Vosendorf, Voesendorf, 2334, Niederosterreich, Austria
Tel.: (43) 169939690
Web Site: http://www.scs.at
Emp.: 16
Property Management Services
N.A.I.C.S.: 531311
Anton Cech *(Mgr)*

SNC Capital 8 (1)
32 Street Monceau, 75008, Paris, France
Tel.: (33) 140741010
Commercial Property Leasing & Real Estate Services
N.A.I.C.S.: 531120

Sas Iseult (1)
7 Place du Chancelier Adenauer, 75016, Paris, France
Tel.: (33) 153437167
Web Site: http://www.immeuble-shift.com
Interior Design Services
N.A.I.C.S.: 541410

Shopping Center Planungs- und Entwicklungsgesellschaft mbH (1)
Dr -Adolf-Scharf-Platz 4/4/3, 1220, Vienna, Austria
Tel.: (43) 16 993 9690
Web Site: https://at.westfield.com
Sales Range: $50-74.9 Million
Emp.: 13
Commercial Property Leasing Services
N.A.I.C.S.: 531120
Anton Cech *(Gen Mgr)*

Shopping Center Planungs- und Entwicklungsgesellschaft mbH & Co. Werbeberatung KG (1)
Dr-Adolf-Scharf-Platz 4/4/3, Vienna, 1220, Austria
Tel.: (43) 169939690
Emp.: 50
Commercial Property Leasing Services
N.A.I.C.S.: 531120
Anton Cech *(Gen Mgr)*

Shopping Center Vosendorf Verwaltungsgesellschaft mbH (1)
Shopping City Sud Burocenter, Voesendorf, 2334, Lower Austria, Austria
Tel.: (43) 16993969
Property Management Services
N.A.I.C.S.: 531311

Societe de Tayninh SA (1)
7 place du Chancelier Adenauer, 75772, Paris, Cedex 16, France
Tel.: (33) 153437437
Web Site: https://www.tayninh.fr
Sales Range: Less than $1 Million
Holding Company
N.A.I.C.S.: 551112
Astrid Panosyan *(Chm & CEO)*

Sudpark Holding GmbH (1)
Drive-Adolf-Scharf-Platz 4/4/3, 1220, Vienna, Austria
Tel.: (43) 120347220
Web Site: http://www.unibail-rodamco.com
Sales Range: $25-49.9 Million
Emp.: 35
Property Holding Services
N.A.I.C.S.: 531312

Trinity Defense LLC (1)
PO Box 31, Pansey, AL 36370
Tel.: (334) 726-3080
Web Site: https://www.trinitydefensellc.com
Firearm Training Services
N.A.I.C.S.: 611699

U&R Management BV (1)
World Trade Center Schiphol Tower H Schiphol Boulevard 371, 1118 BJ, Schiphol, Netherlands
Tel.: (31) 206582500
Commercial Real Estate Services
N.A.I.C.S.: 531210

Unibail-Rodamco Beteiligungsverwaltung GmbH (1)
Drive-Adolf-Scharf-Platz 4/4/3, Vienna, 1220, Austria
Tel.: (43) 1202320011
Web Site: http://www.unibail-rodamco.com
Emp.: 35
Commercial Property Leasing Services
N.A.I.C.S.: 531120
Thomas Heidenhofer *(Mng Dir)*

Unibail-Rodamco Development Nederland BV (1)
Schiphol Boulevard 371, Luchthaven Schiphol, 1118 BJ, Schiphol, Netherlands
Tel.: (31) 206582500
Web Site: http://www.unibailrodamco.com
Sales Range: $50-74.9 Million
Emp.: 75
Property Management Services
N.A.I.C.S.: 531312
John Van Haaren *(Mng Dir)*

Unibail-Rodamco Invest GmbH (1)
Drive-Adolf-Scharf-Platz 4/4/3, Vienna, 1220, Austria
Tel.: (43) 12023200
Commercial Property Leasing Services
N.A.I.C.S.: 531120

Unibail-Rodamco Liegenschaftserwerbs GmbH (1)
Dr-Adolf-Scharf-Platz 4/4/3, 1220, Vienna, Austria
Tel.: (43) 12023200
Web Site: http://www.unibail-rodamco.com
Sales Range: $25-49.9 Million
Emp.: 50
Real Estate Property Investment Services
N.A.I.C.S.: 531210
Heiden Hofer *(Gen Mgr)*

Unibail-Rodamco Nederland Winkels BV (1)
Schiphol Blvd 371, 1118 BJ, Schiphol, Noord-Holland, Netherlands
Tel.: (31) 203120120
Sales Range: $50-74.9 Million
Emp.: 100
Commercial Property Leasing Services
N.A.I.C.S.: 531120

Unibail-Rodamco Polska Sp zoo (1)
Skylight Office Building 22nd floor Ul Zlota 59, 00-120, Warsaw, Poland
Tel.: (48) 223463600
Web Site: http://www.rodamco.pl
Emp.: 60
Commercial Building Construction Services
N.A.I.C.S.: 236220
Magdalena Klin *(Mgr-HR)*

Unibail-Rodamco Spain SA (1)
Calle Jose Abascal 56 Cuarta Plt, Madrid, 28003, Spain
Tel.: (34) 917006500
Property Management Services
N.A.I.C.S.: 531312

Unibail-Rodamco-Westfield Germany GmbH (1)
Klaus-Bungert-Str 1, 40468, Dusseldorf, Germany
Tel.: (49) 21 130 2310
Web Site: https://www.unibail-rodamco-westfield.de
Emp.: 450
Commercial Real Estate Services
N.A.I.C.S.: 531210
Christoph Berentzen *(Mgr)*

Univail-Rodamco as (1)
Skretova 490/12, CZ-12000, Prague, Czech Republic
Tel.: (420) 221442220
Web Site: http://www.unibail-rodamco.com
Property Management Services
N.A.I.C.S.: 531312

Westfield Europe Limited (1)
4th Floor 1 Ariel Way, London, W12 7SL, United Kingdom
Tel.: (44) 20 7061 1400
Web Site: http://uk.westfield.com
Retail Shopping Center Property Investment, Development & Management
N.A.I.C.S.: 531390

UNIBAN CANADA, INC.
2115 des Laurentides Blvd, Laval, H7M 4M2, QC, Canada
Tel.: (450) 663-2555 ON
Web Site: http://www.unibancanada.ca
Sales Range: $1-9.9 Million
Emp.: 20

INTERNATIONAL PUBLIC

Holding Company; Auto Glass Repair, Replacement & Protection Franchises
N.A.I.C.S.: 551112
James F. Levagood *(VP-IT)*

UNIBANK CJSC
St Charents 12 Number 53 1-5, 0025, Yerevan, Armenia
Tel.: (374) 10592259
Web Site: http://www.unibank.am
UNIBB7—(ARM)
Rev.: $50,817,933
Assets: $813,899,026
Liabilities: $727,142,866
Net Worth: $86,756,160
Earnings: $11,181,246
Emp.: 819
Fiscal Year-end: 12/31/22
Commercial Banking Services
N.A.I.C.S.: 522110
Gagik Zakaryan *(Co-Founder & Chm)*

UNIBANK COMMERCIAL BANK OJSC
55 Rashid Behbudov Street, Baku, AZ1014, Azerbaijan
Tel.: (994) 124982244 Az
Web Site: http://www.unibank.az
Year Founded: 1992
UNBNK—(BAK)
Rev.: $93,989,640
Assets: $822,629,937
Liabilities: $755,246,336
Net Worth: $67,383,601
Earnings: ($2,978,398)
Fiscal Year-end: 12/31/22
Commercial Banking Services
N.A.I.C.S.: 522110
Faig Huseynov *(Chm-Mgmt Bd)*

UNIBANK S.A.
157 rue Faubert Petion-Ville, 6140, Port-au-Prince, Haiti
Tel.: (509) 22992050
Web Site: http://www.unibankhaiti.com
Sales Range: $200-249.9 Million
Emp.: 750
Banking Services
N.A.I.C.S.: 522110
Carl Braun *(Pres)*

Subsidiaries:

Immobilier S.A. (1)
67 Public s Plaza Canape Vert Bureaux 2324, Port-au-Prince, Haiti
Tel.: (509) 2459616
Real Estate Management Services
N.A.I.C.S.: 531210

International Sunrise Partners LLC (1)
2455 E Sunrise Blvd, Fort Lauderdale, FL 33304-3118
Tel.: (954) 564-6312
Commercial Banking Services
N.A.I.C.S.: 522110

Micro Credit National S.A. (1)
27 'ruelle Jeremie, Port-au-Prince, Haiti
Tel.: (509) 25109807
Web Site: http://www.mcn.ht
Financial Services
N.A.I.C.S.: 523940

UniAssurances S.A. (1)
Angle des rues Clerveaux et Lambert, postale 46, 6140, Petion Ville, Haiti
Tel.: (509) 22992413
Financial Services
N.A.I.C.S.: 523940
George Sander *(Gen Mgr)*

Unitransfer international Ltd. (1)
901 S State Rd 7 Ste 215, Hollywood, FL 33023
Tel.: (954) 628-0022
Web Site: http://www.unitransfer.com
Commercial Banking Services
N.A.I.C.S.: 522110
Adrien Castera *(Pres)*

AND PRIVATE COMPANIES

UNIBANK, S.A.
Building Grand Bay Tower, Plantaja Baja, Panama, Panama
Tel.: (507) 2976000
Web Site: http://www.unibank.com.pa
UNIB—(PAN)
Rev.: $28,112,827
Assets: $548,077,216
Liabilities: $477,120,298
Net Worth: $70,956,918
Earnings: $1,541,359
Emp.: 119
Fiscal Year-end: 12/31/20
Commercial Banking Services
N.A.I.C.S.: 522110
Daniel S. Levy (Sec)

UNIBANKA AD
Tel.: (389) 23111111
Year Founded: 1993
UNI—(MAC)
Rev.: $36,752,542
Assets: $505,420,910
Liabilities: $436,356,856
Net Worth: $69,064,054
Earnings: $8,569,432
Fiscal Year-end: 12/31/23
Banking Services
N.A.I.C.S.: 522110

UNIBAP AB
Vastra Agatan 16 5 tr, 753 22, Uppsala, Sweden
Tel.: (46) 18320330
Web Site: https://www.unibap.com
UNIBAP—(OMX)
Rev.: $1,192,316
Assets: $6,158,270
Liabilities: $1,367,464
Net Worth: $4,790,806
Earnings: ($2,401,491)
Emp.: 36
Fiscal Year-end: 06/30/21
Hardware Product Mfr
N.A.I.C.S.: 332510
Fredrik Bruhn (CEO)

UNIBEL SA
2 Allee de Longchamp, BP 431, 92150, Suresnes, Cedex 08, France
Tel.: (33) 552002578
Web Site: https://www.unibel.fr
UNBL—(EUR)
Sales Range: $1-4.9 Billion
Holding Company; Cheese Mfr
N.A.I.C.S.: 551112
Antoine Fievet (Chm-Exec Bd)

Subsidiaries:

Fromageries Bel S.A. (1)
2 Allee de Longchamp, 92150, Suresnes, France **(67.8%)**
Tel.: (33) 140077250
Web Site: http://www.bel-group.com
Rev.: $4,023,512,530
Assets: $4,617,397,064
Liabilities: $2,933,436,362
Net Worth: $1,683,960,702
Earnings: $78,375,097
Emp.: 10,902
Fiscal Year-end: 12/31/2023
Cheese Producer
N.A.I.C.S.: 311513
Antoine Fievet (Chm & CEO)

Subsidiary (US):

Bel Brands USA (2)
25 NW Point Blvd Ste 1000, Elk Grove Village, IL 60007
Tel.: (847) 879-1900
Web Site: http://www.kaukauna.com
Sales Range: $75-99.9 Million
Emp.: 400
Cheese Products Mfr & Producer
N.A.I.C.S.: 311513

Subsidiary (Non-US):

Bel Deutschland GmbH (2)
Werner-von-Siemens-Ring 12, Grasbrunn, 82024, Germany
Tel.: (49) 89666960
Web Site: http://www.bel-deutschland.de
Sales Range: $25-49.9 Million
Emp.: 200
Cheese Producer
N.A.I.C.S.: 311513

Bel UK Ltd. (2)
160 London Road, Sevenoaks, TN13 1BT, Kent, United Kingdom
Tel.: (44) 1622 774800
Web Site: http://www.bel-uk.co.uk
Sales Range: $25-49.9 Million
Emp.: 40
Cheese Sales
N.A.I.C.S.: 424490

Subsidiary (Domestic):

Materne S.A.S. (2)
45 Chemin des Peupliers, 69570, Dardilly, France
Tel.: (33) 478663232
Web Site: http://www.materne.fr
Preserves, Compotes & Jams Mfr & Whslr
N.A.I.C.S.: 311421
Michel Larroche (Pres & CEO)

Unit (Domestic):

Materne Industries (3)
Place Andre Venet, F-02450, Boue, France
Tel.: (33) 3 2360 3361
Web Site: http://www.materneindustries.com
Commercial-Use Jam & Preserves Mfr
N.A.I.C.S.: 311421
Patrick Pawlak (Sls Dir & Engr-Agro-food)

Subsidiary (Domestic):

Mont Blanc S.A.S. (3)
2 rue Rex Combs, F-50480, Chef-du-Pont, France
Tel.: (33) 233217171
Web Site: http://www.desserts-montblanc.fr
Pudding & Dairy Dessert Products Mfr & Whslr
N.A.I.C.S.: 311999
Michel Larroche (Pres & CEO)

UNIBEP S.A.
ul 3 Maja 19, 17-100, Bielsk Podlaski, Poland
Tel.: (48) 857318000
Web Site: https://www.unibep.pl
Year Founded: 1950
UNI—(WAR)
Rev.: $617,319,104
Assets: $459,176,066
Liabilities: $405,028,200
Net Worth: $54,147,866
Earnings: ($39,757,622)
Emp.: 1,778
Fiscal Year-end: 12/31/23
Construction Engineering Services
N.A.I.C.S.: 237990
Slawomir Kiszycki (Vice Chm-Mgmt Bd & CFO)

Subsidiaries:

Budrex Sp. z o.o. (1)
ul Hetmanska 92, 15-727, Bialystok, Poland
Tel.: (48) 856529100
Construction Services
N.A.I.C.S.: 236220

Unidevelopment SA (1)
ul Kondratowicza 37, 03-285, Warsaw, Poland
Tel.: (48) 222989896
Web Site: https://www.unidevelopment.pl
Real Estate Development Services
N.A.I.C.S.: 531390

Unihouse SA (1)
ul Rejonowa 5, 17-100, Bielsk Podlaski, Poland
Tel.: (48) 857303477
Web Site: https://www.unihouse.pl
Construction Services
N.A.I.C.S.: 236220
Slawomir Kiszycki (Pres)

UNIBIOS HOLDINGS S.A.
1st and 18th Street, Ano Liosia, 13341, Athens, Greece
Tel.: (30) 2106037030
Web Site: https://www.unibios.gr
Year Founded: 1940
0RMW—(LSE)
Sales Range: Less than $1 Million
Emp.: 72
Heating, Ventilation & Air Conditioning Unit Mfr
N.A.I.C.S.: 333415
George Efthimiou Papathanasiou (Bd of Dirs & VP)

Subsidiaries:

BIOSSOL CONSTRUCTION TOOLS S.A. (1)
19th Km Leoforos Marathonos, Palini, 15351, Athens, Greece
Tel.: (30) 210 6633366
Web Site: http://www.biossol-c-t.gr
Construction Engineering Services
N.A.I.C.S.: 541330

UNICAFE INC.
8-5-26 Akasaka, Minato-ku, Tokyo, 107-0052, Japan
Tel.: (81) 354005444
Web Site: https://www.unicafe.com
Year Founded: 1972
2597—(TKS)
Rev.: $87,611,130
Assets: $98,685,710
Liabilities: $55,004,220
Net Worth: $43,681,490
Earnings: $3,133,780
Emp.: 175
Fiscal Year-end: 12/31/23
Coffee Product & Pulp Mold Mfr
N.A.I.C.S.: 311920
Hiroshi Shibatani (Pres)

Subsidiaries:

Unicafe Inc. - Kanagawa General Factory (1)
4026-9 Nakatsu Sakuradai Aikawa, Aiko, 243-0303, Kanagawa, Japan
Tel.: (81) 462843466
Coffee Product Mfr
N.A.I.C.S.: 311920

UNICAJA BANCO, S.A.
Avenida de Andalucia 10-12, 29007, Malaga, Spain
Tel.: (34) 952076263 ES
Web Site: https://www.unicajabanco.es
Year Founded: 2011
UNI—(MAD)
Rev.: $2,531,733,218
Assets: $104,848,532,269
Liabilities: $97,676,012,303
Net Worth: $7,172,519,965
Earnings: $287,645,154
Emp.: 8,000
Fiscal Year-end: 12/31/23
Commercial Banking Services
N.A.I.C.S.: 522110
Manuel Azuaga Moreno (Chm)

UNICAP INVESTMENT & FINANCE COMPANY K.S.C.P.
Murgab - Block 3 - Omar Ben Al Khattab St - KBT Tower - 10th Floor, PO Box 2290, Safat, Kuwait, 13021, Kuwait
Tel.: (965) 22261444
Web Site: http://unicap.com.kw
Year Founded: 2002
UNICAP—(KUW)
Rev.: $20,976,363
Assets: $186,160,008
Liabilities: $111,332,871
Net Worth: $74,827,138
Earnings: ($4,440,817)
Emp.: 31
Fiscal Year-end: 08/31/23
Investment & Financial Real Estate Services
N.A.I.C.S.: 523999
Abdullah Jaber Al Ahmad Al Sabah (Chm)

UNICAP MODARABA
104-106 Kassam Court BC-9 Block-5, Clifton, Karachi, Pakistan
Tel.: (92) 3000434434
Web Site: https://unicapmodaraba.com
Year Founded: 1991
Financial Services
N.A.I.C.S.: 523999

UNICAPITAL, INC.
3/F Majalco Building Benavidez cor Trasierra St, Makati, Philippines
Tel.: (63) 288920991
Web Site: http://www.unicapital-inc.com
Year Founded: 1994
Investment Banking Services
N.A.I.C.S.: 523150
Felipe S. Yalong (Vice Chm)

UNICASA INDUSTRIA DE MOVEIS S.A.
Rodovia Federal BR 470 KM 212 930, PO Box 2505, 95707-540, Bento Goncalves, RS, Brazil
Tel.: (55) 5434554444
Web Site: http://www.unicasamoveis.com.br
Year Founded: 1985
UCAS3—(BRAZ)
Rev.: $43,353,674
Assets: $69,634,261
Liabilities: $31,745,139
Net Worth: $37,889,122
Earnings: $3,024,629
Emp.: 532
Fiscal Year-end: 12/31/23
Household Furniture Mfr
N.A.I.C.S.: 337122
Gelson Luis Rostirolla (Chm)

UNICEP COMMERCE A.D.
Veselina Maslese 1, 78000, Banja Luka, Bosnia & Herzegovina
Tel.: (387) 51335522
UNCC-R-A—(BANJ)
Assets: $330,123
Liabilities: $91,285
Net Worth: $238,838
Earnings: ($14,977)
Emp.: 1
Fiscal Year-end: 12/31/13
Computer Data Management Services
N.A.I.C.S.: 518210
Mira Ninic (Chm)

UNICEP COMPANY A.D.
Svetozar Markovica 15, 78000, Banja Luka, Bosnia & Herzegovina
Tel.: (387) 63892050
UNCM—(BANJ)
Sales Range: Less than $1 Million
Emp.: 2
Real Estate Property Rental Services
N.A.I.C.S.: 531190
Dragan Cerovac (Pres)

UNICER - BEBIDAS DE PORTUGAL, SGPS, SA
Via Norte Leca do Balio, Matosinhos Apartado 1044, Mamede de Infesta, 446, Codex, Portugal
Tel.: (351) 229052100
Web Site: http://www.unicer.pt
Year Founded: 1977
Sales Range: $450-499.9 Million
Emp.: 1,200

UNICER - BEBIDAS DE PORTUGAL, SGPS, SA

Unicer - Bebidas de Portugal, SGPS, SA—(Continued)

Beer, Malt, Soft Drinks, Bottled Water, Wine & Coffee Producer & Marketer
N.A.I.C.S.: 312120
Juan Abecasis *(CEO)*

Subsidiaries:

Quinta da Pedra - Sociedade Vinicola de Moncao Lda. (1)
Quinta Da Pedra, Troviscoso, Viana do Castelo, Portugal **(100%)**
Tel.: (351) 251652775
Wine & Distilled Alcoholic Beverage Whslr
N.A.I.C.S.: 424810

Unicer - Aguas S.A. (1)
Via Norte, Leca Do Bailio, Porto, 4465703, Portugal **(100%)**
Tel.: (351) 229052100
Web Site: http://www.unicer.pt
Sales Range: $150-199.9 Million
Emp.: 800
Bottled Water Mfr
N.A.I.C.S.: 312112

Unicer - Bebidas, SA (1)
Apartado 1044, Leca Do Bailio, Matosinhos, Portugal **(100%)**
Tel.: (351) 229052100
Web Site: http://www.unicer.pt
Wine & Distilled Alcoholic Beverage Whslr
N.A.I.C.S.: 424810
Antonio Pires de Lima *(CEO)*

Unicer - Cervejas SA (1)
Via Norte Apartado, Leca Do Bailio, Porto, 1044, Portugal **(100%)**
Tel.: (351) 229052100
Web Site: http://www.unicer.pt
Sales Range: $150-199.9 Million
Emp.: 1,000
Malt Mfr
N.A.I.C.S.: 311213
Antonio Pires de Lima *(CEO)*

Unicer - Distribuicao de Bebidas S.A. (1)
Via Norte Apartado 1044, Leca Do Bailio, Porto, 44657U3, Portugal **(100%)**
Tel.: (351) 229052100
Web Site: http://www.unicer.pt
Sales Range: $250-299.9 Million
Emp.: 800
Beer & Ale Whslr
N.A.I.C.S.: 424810

Unicer - Servicos de Gestao Empresarial S.A. (1)
Via Norte, Leca Do Bailio, Porto, 4466966, Portugal **(100%)**
Tel.: (351) 229052100
Web Site: http://www.unicer.pt
Sales Range: $150-199.9 Million
Emp.: 1,000
Business Support Services
N.A.I.C.S.: 561499
Antonio Pires de Lima *(CEO)*

Unicer - Sumos e Refrigerantes S.A. (1)
Via Norte, Leca Do Bailio, Porto, Portugal **(100%)**
Tel.: (351) 243359300
Web Site: http://www.unicer.pt
Bottled Water Mfr
N.A.I.C.S.: 312112
Antonio Pires de Lima *(CEO)*

Unicer - Vinhos S.A. (1)
Via Norte, Leca Do Bailio, Porto, Portugal **(100%)**
Tel.: (351) 229052100
Web Site: http://www.unicer.pt
Sales Range: $250-299.9 Million
Emp.: 1,000
Wine & Distilled Alcoholic Beverage Whslr
N.A.I.C.S.: 424810
Antonio Pires de Lima *(CEO)*

Unicer Internacional - Exportacao e Importacao de Bebidas S.A. (1)
Via Norte, Porto, Portugal **(100%)**
Tel.: (351) 229052100
Web Site: http://www.unicer.pt
Beer & Ale Whslr
N.A.I.C.S.: 424810

Joao Abecasis *(Pres)*

Unicer.Com - Tecnologias de Informacao S.A. (1)
Via Norte Apartado 1044 S Mamede de Infesta, Porto, 4466-955, Portugal **(100%)**
Tel.: (351) 229052569
Data Processing Services
N.A.I.C.S.: 518210
Antonio Pires de Lima *(CEO)*

Unicergeste - Gestao de Servicos de Distribuicao S.A. (1)
Via Norte, Porto, Portugal **(100%)**
Tel.: (351) 229052100
Web Site: http://www.unicer.pt
Sales Range: $200-249.9 Million
Emp.: 1,000
Beer Wine & Liquor Stores
N.A.I.C.S.: 445320
Antonio Pires de Lima *(CEO)*

UNICHARM CORPORATION

Sumitomo Fudosan Tokyo Mita Garden Tower 3-5-19 Mita, Minato-ku, Tokyo, 108-8575, Japan
Tel.: (81) 334515111
Web Site: https://www.unicharm.co.jp
Year Founded: 1961
8113—(TKS)
Rev.: $6,222,596,630
Assets: $7,490,102,412
Liabilities: $2,281,975,553
Net Worth: $5,208,126,858
Earnings: $647,386,852
Emp.: 16,206
Fiscal Year-end: 12/31/23
Baby Care Product Mfr
N.A.I.C.S.: 322291
Takahisa Takahara *(Pres & CEO)*

Subsidiaries:

Diana Unicharm Joint Stock Company (1)
Vinh Tuy Linh Nam Industrial Zones, Hoang Mai, Hanoi, Vietnam
Tel.: (84) 2436445758
Web Site: http://www.unicharm.vn
Diaper & Childcare Product Mfr
N.A.I.C.S.: 322291

Disposable Soft Goods (Zhongshan) Limited (1)
Jinchang Industrial Road, Shalang, Zhongshan, 528411, Guangdong, China **(100%)**
Tel.: (86) 76088550004
Web Site: http://www.fitti.com
Sales Range: $50-74.9 Million
Emp.: 200
N.A.I.C.S.: 322291
Ambrose Chan *(Gen Mgr)*

LG Unicharm Co., Ltd. (1)
155 Gongdan-dong, Kumi, 730-030, Kyongsangbuk-do, Korea (South)
Tel.: (82) 547123600
Web Site: http://www.lgunicharm.co.kr
Sanitary Napkins Mfr & Whslr
N.A.I.C.S.: 322291

Mieux Products Co., Ltd. (1)
1349 Tokunomori, Ozu, 795-0061, Ehime, Japan
Tel.: (81) 893252611
Web Site: http://www.unicharm.co.jp
Sanitary Products Mfr
N.A.I.C.S.: 322291

Mycare Unicharm.Co., Ltd. (1)
No 8 MyaYa Mone 8 Street Kyi Pwar Yay North Quarter Thingankyung, Yangon, Myanmar
Tel.: (95) 565823
Web Site: http://www.unicharm.com.mm
Diaper & Childcare Product Mfr
N.A.I.C.S.: 322291
Hein Kyaw *(Asst Mgr)*

PT Uni-Charm Indonesia (1)
Jl Permata Raya Plot D-2B Karawang International Industrial City, Karawang, 41361, West Java, Indonesia
Tel.: (62) 218904607
Sanitary Paper Napkins Mfr & Distr
N.A.I.C.S.: 322120

Peparlet Co., Ltd. (1)
422 Shimodoma, Fujieda, 426-0003, Shizuoka-Ken, Japan
Tel.: (81) 546432943
Web Site: http://www.peparlet.com
Label & Litter Mfr
N.A.I.C.S.: 322299
Shotaro Otoguro *(Pres)*

The Hartz Mountain Corporation (1)
400 Plz Dr, Secaucus, NJ 07094-3605 **(51%)**
Tel.: (201) 271-4800
Web Site: https://www.hartz.com
Sales Range: $125-149.9 Million
Pet Care Products & Accessories Mfr & Distr
N.A.I.C.S.: 311111
Vitor Oliveira *(Engr-Pkg)*

Uni-Charm (Thailand) Co., Ltd. (1)
105 Moo 9 Wellgrow Industrial Estate, Bang Pakong, 24180, Chachoengsao, Thailand
Tel.: (66) 38570900
Web Site: http://www.unicharm.co.th
Sanitary Paper Products Mfr & Whslr
N.A.I.C.S.: 322120

Uni-Charm Corporation Sdn. Bhd. (1)
19-03 19-04 Level 19 Imazium No 8 Jalan SS21/37, Damansara Uptown, 47400, Petaling Jaya, Selangor, Malaysia
Tel.: (60) 377317720
Web Site: https://www.unicharm.com.my
Personal Care Services
N.A.I.C.S.: 812990
Takahisa Takahara *(Pres & CEO)*

Uni-Charm Molnlycke B.V. (1)
Abramskade 6, 9600 AB, Hoogezand, Netherlands
Tel.: (31) 598312911
Web Site: http://www.seapersonalcare.com
Emp.: 400
Sanitary Products Distr
N.A.I.C.S.: 424130

Uni.Charm Molnlycke Baby B.V. (1)
Abramskade 6, 9601 KM, Hoogezand, Groningen, Netherlands
Tel.: (31) 598312911
Sales Range: $250-299.9 Million
Emp.: 150
Baby Diapers Distr
N.A.I.C.S.: 424350
Richard Fernhout *(Gen Mgr)*

Uni.Charm Molnlycke Incontinence B.V. (1)
Abramskade 6, Hoogezand, 9601 KM, Groningen, Netherlands
Tel.: (31) 598 312911
Web Site: http://www.soapersonalcare.com
Emp.: 400
Adult Incontinence Products Distr
N.A.I.C.S.: 424350

Unicharm Australasia Pty. Ltd. (1)
3 Lake Drive, Dingley, 3172, VIC, Australia
Tel.: (61) 395521222
Web Site: http://www.unicharm.com.au
Sales Range: $75-99.9 Million
Emp.: 100
Baby Diapers & Adult Incontinence Pads Mfr
N.A.I.C.S.: 322291

Unicharm Consumer Products (China) Co., Ltd. (1)
22F Donghai Business Center No 618 Yanan East Road, Huangpu, Shanghai, China
Tel.: (86) 2169768666
Sanitary Napkins & Diapers Mfr
N.A.I.C.S.: 322291

Unicharm Humancare Corporation (1)
3-25-23 Takanawa, Minato-ku, Tokyo, 108-0074, Japan
Tel.: (81) 334493596
Web Site: http://www.humany.jp
Adult Incontinence Products Mfr
N.A.I.C.S.: 322291

Unicharm India Private Ltd. (1)
Unit No 501 to 508 510 to 518 5th Floor, Centrum Plaza Building Golf Course Road Sector-53, Gurgaon, 122002, Haryana, India

INTERNATIONAL PUBLIC

Tel.: (91) 1244351300
Web Site: https://www.unicharm.co.in
Sales Range: $25-49.9 Million
Emp.: 38
Baby Care Products Whslr
N.A.I.C.S.: 424490

Unicharm Kokko Nonwoven Co., Ltd. (1)
1531-15 Toyohama-cho Wadahama, Kanonji, 769-1602, Kagawa, Japan
Tel.: (81) 875526111
Web Site: http://www.unicharm.co.jp
Emp.: 300
Nonwoven Fabric Mfr
N.A.I.C.S.: 313230
Toshihite Nakaya *(Gen Mgr)*

Unicharm Middle East & North Africa Hygienic Industries Company S.A.E. (1)
Al Tajamouat Industrial Park Zezenia Area, 10th of Ramadan City, Egypt
Tel.: (20) 55 433 4040
Baby Health Care Product Mfr & Distr
N.A.I.C.S.: 311514
Takahisa Takahara *(Pres & CEO)*

Unicharm Middle East & North Africa Industries Company S.A.E. (1)
Al Tajamouat Industrial Park Zezenia Area, 10th of Ramadan City, Egypt
Tel.: (20) 554334040
Web Site: http://www.eng.unicharm.com.eg
Feminine Care & Healthcare Product Mfr
N.A.I.C.S.: 322291

Unicharm Molnlycke K.K. (1)
1-5-12 Moto Akasaka, Minato-ku, Tokyo, 107-0051, Japan
Tel.: (81) 357720190
Web Site: http://www.tena.co.jp
Sales Range: $75-99.9 Million
Emp.: 130
Adult Incontinence Care Products Distr
N.A.I.C.S.: 424130
Toru Morita *(Pres)*

United Charm Co., Ltd. (1)
3F 77 Chung Hua Road Section 1, Taipei, Taiwan
Tel.: (886) 2 2382 5678
Web Site: http://www.ucc.com.tw
Sanitary Paper Products Mfr & Whslr
N.A.I.C.S.: 322120

UNICK CORPORATION

90 Seobu-ro 179 Beon-gil Jinyeong-eup, Gimhae, 621-801, Gyeongsahngnam-do, Korea (South)
Tel.: (82) 553402000
Web Site: http://www.unick.co.kr
011320—(KRS)
Rev.: $217,888,517
Assets: $187,032,676
Liabilities: $100,674,309
Net Worth: $86,358,367
Earnings: $2,719,978
Emp.: 609
Fiscal Year-end: 12/31/22
Automobile Parts Mfr
N.A.I.C.S.: 336330
Ahn Young Koo *(Chm)*

Subsidiaries:

Qingdao Unick Co. Ltd. (1)
No 1 Shenyang Rd, Laixi, Qingdao, Shandong, China
Tel.: (86) 53287412000
Sales Range: $50-74.9 Million
Emp.: 214
Automotive Product Mfr
N.A.I.C.S.: 336110

Unick Corporation - Asan Plant (1)
No 1-4 Sinnam-ri, Dunpo-myeon, Asan, 336873, Chungcheongnam-do, Korea (South)
Tel.: (82) 415419691
Automotive Product Mfr
N.A.I.C.S.: 336110

Unick Corporation - Gimhae 1st Plant (1)
90 Seobu-ro 179beon-gil, Jinyeong-eup,

Kimhae, 621801, Gyeongsangnam-do, Korea (South)
Tel.: (82) 553402000
Web Site: http://www.unick.co.kr
Sales Range: $100-124.9 Million
Emp.: 400
Automotive Product Mfr
N.A.I.C.S.: 336110
Sang Yun Lee (Mgr-Sls)

UNICK FIX-A-FORM & PRINTERS LTD.
472 Tajpur Road Ahmedabad - Rajkot Highway Changodhar, Ahmedabad, 382213, Gujarat, India
Tel.: (91) 9687643935
Web Site: https://www.unickfix-a-form.com
Year Founded: 1993
541503—(BOM)
Rev.: $7,995,023
Assets: $8,457,848
Liabilities: $4,909,779
Net Worth: $3,548,070
Earnings: $268,742
Emp.: 255
Fiscal Year-end: 03/31/23
Printing & Labeling Product Mfr
N.A.I.C.S.: 323111

UNICO SILVER LIMITED
Level 4 100 Albert Road, South Melbourne, 3205, VIC, Australia
Tel.: (61) 396927222   AU
Web Site: https://www.e2metals.com.au
Year Founded: 2005
USL—(ASX)
Rev.: $634,857
Assets: $4,489,056
Liabilities: $1,775,996
Net Worth: $2,713,061
Earnings: ($1,921,738)
Fiscal Year-end: 06/30/24
Mineral Exploration Services
N.A.I.C.S.: 213115
Melanie Leydin (Chm & Co-Sec)

Subsidiaries:
Fisher Resources Pty Limited   (1)
20 Flinders Street, Melbourne, 3042, VIC, Australia
Tel.: (61) 396927222
Metal Exploration Services
N.A.I.C.S.: 213114

UNICOBE CORP.
Serdike 17A ap 37, 1000, Sofia, Bulgaria
Tel.: (359) 7028506585   NV
Web Site: http://www.unicobecorp.com
Year Founded: 2014
Rev.: $20,189
Assets: $18,465
Liabilities: $30,267
Net Worth: ($11,802)
Earnings: ($5,030)
Emp.: 1
Fiscal Year-end: 06/30/18
Glass Laser Engravings Services
N.A.I.C.S.: 327215
Anatoliy Kanev (Pres, CEO, CFO, Chief Acctg Officer, Treas & Sec)

UNICON OPTICAL CO., LTD.
No 16 Gongye East 9th Road Hsinchu Science Park, Baoshan Township Hsinchu County, Zhubei, 30075, Taiwan
Tel.: (886) 35775586
Web Site: https://www.uniconvision.com.tw
Year Founded: 1992
4150—(TAI)
Contact Lens Mfr
N.A.I.C.S.: 339115
Hsi-Ho Liu (Chm)

UNICOOP COOPERATIVE AGRICOLE
108 Principale Rue, Sainte-Henedine, G0S2R0, QC, Canada
Tel.: (418) 935-3651
Web Site: http://www.unicoop.qc.ca
Rev.: $78,521,956
Emp.: 241
Garden Machinery & Flour Mills Equipment Supplies
N.A.I.C.S.: 423820
Alain Larochelle (Pres & CEO)

UNICORD PUBLIC CO. LTD.
404 Phaya Thai Rd, Patumwan, Bangkok, 10330, Thailand
Tel.: (66) 34424437
Web Site: http://www.unicord.net
Year Founded: 1978
Sales Range: $800-899.9 Million
Emp.: 7,500
Mfr of Canned & Frozen Products; Tuna, Sardines, Pet Food, Frozen Tuna Loins, Frozen Shrimp
N.A.I.C.S.: 311710

Subsidiaries:
Unicord Public Co. Ltd. - Plant 1   (1)
56/5 Moo 8 Setthakij 1 Road Thasai, Muang, Samut Sakhon, 74000, Thailand
Tel.: (66) 3442443742
Pet Food Mfr
N.A.I.C.S.: 311111

Unicord Public Co. Ltd. - Plant 2   (1)
39/3 Moo 8 Setthakij 1 Road Thasai, Muang, Samut Sakhon, 74000, Thailand
Tel.: (66) 3483121920
Pet Food Mfr
N.A.I.C.S.: 311111

UNICORN AIM VCT PLC
120 Cannon Street, London, EC4N 6AS, United Kingdom
Tel.: (44) 1392487056
Web Site: https://www.unicornaimvct.co.uk
Year Founded: 2001
UAV—(LSE)
Assets: $252,265,482
Liabilities: $26,482,158
Net Worth: $225,783,324
Earnings: $713,286
Fiscal Year-end: 09/30/22
Business Services
N.A.I.C.S.: 561499
Tim Woodcock (Chm)

UNICORN CAPITAL PARTNERS LIMITED
First Floor Building 8 Inanda Greens Office Park Wierda Road West, Wierda Valley, Sandton, 2196, South Africa
Tel.: (27) 116561303   ZA
Web Site: http://www.unicorncapital.co.za
Year Founded: 1993
UCP—(JSE)
Rev.: $51,929,762
Assets: $95,767,774
Liabilities: $65,192,930
Net Worth: $30,574,844
Earnings: $17,929,565
Emp.: 1,253
Fiscal Year-end: 06/30/19
Coal Mining Services
N.A.I.C.S.: 212115
Johann C. Lemmer (CFO & Fin Dir)

Subsidiaries:
Benicon Opencast Mining (Proprietary) Limited   (1)
Plot 26 Naauwpoort Bethal Rd, PO Box 2244, Witbank, 1035, Mpumalanga, South Africa
Tel.: (27) 13 691 1144
Web Site: http://www.benicon.co.za
Emp.: 40
Mining Support Services
N.A.I.C.S.: 541330
Philip Vanvuuren (CEO)

Geosearch South Africa (Proprietary) Limited   (1)
10 Derrick Rd, Spartan, 1620, Johannesburg, Gauteng, South Africa
Tel.: (27) 119703200
Web Site: http://www.geosearch.co.za
Sales Range: $750-799.9 Million
Emp.: 1,100
Exploration Drilling Services
N.A.I.C.S.: 213115
Mike Fitzgerald (CEO)

Megacube Mining (Proprietary) Limited   (1)
28 Patrick Rd, Boksburg, 1469, Gauteng, South Africa
Tel.: (27) 113973870
Earthmoving Services
N.A.I.C.S.: 238910

Ritchie Crane Hire (Proprietary) Limited   (1)
44 Impala Rd, Witbank, 1034, Mpumalanga, South Africa
Tel.: (27) 136975111
Emp.: 60
Crane Rental Services
N.A.I.C.S.: 238990

UNICORN MINERAL RESOURCES PLC
39 Castleyard 20/21 St Patrick's Road, Dalkey, Dublin, Ireland   IE
Web Site: https://www.unicornminerals.com
Year Founded: 2010
UMR—(LSE)
Assets: $1,185,263
Liabilities: $524,153
Net Worth: $661,111
Earnings: ($544,881)
Fiscal Year-end: 03/31/24
Mineral Exploration Services
N.A.I.C.S.: 213115
David Blaney (COO)

UNICORP TOWER PLAZA, S.A.
Punta Pacifica Tower of the Americas Blvd Tower C Floor 30, PO Box 0832-00396, Panama, Panama
Tel.: (507) 303 1900
Year Founded: 2012
UNIC—(PAN)
Sales Range: Less than $1 Million
Real Estate Investment Services
N.A.I.C.S.: 531390
Juan Carlos Fabrega (Pres)

UNICREDIT S.P.A.
Piazza Gae Aulenti 3 - Tower A, 20154, Milan, Italy
Tel.: (39) 0288621   IT
Web Site: https://www.unicreditgroup.eu
Year Founded: 1998
UNCFF—(OTCIQ)
Rev.: $20,316,500,120
Assets: $958,204,849,420
Liabilities: $876,629,767,580
Net Worth: $81,575,081,840
Earnings: $3,777,287,780
Emp.: 84,245
Fiscal Year-end: 12/31/19
Financial Investment Services
N.A.I.C.S.: 551111
Lamberto Andreotti (Deputy Chm & Deputy Vice Chm)

Subsidiaries:
Bank Austria Real Invest Immobilienmanagement Gmbh   (1)
Rothschildplatz 1, 1020, Vienna, Austria
Tel.: (43) 1331710
Web Site: https://www.realinvest.at
Finance Services
N.A.I.C.S.: 921130

Bank Austria Wohnbaubank AG   (1)
Rothschildplatz 1, A-1020, Vienna, Austria
Tel.: (43) 5050540304
Housing Construction Financial Services
N.A.I.C.S.: 522292

Structured Invest Societe Anonyme   (1)
8-10 Rue Jean Monnet, L-2180, Luxembourg, Luxembourg
Tel.: (352) 24824800
Web Site: https://www.structuredinvest.lu
Investment Financing Services
N.A.I.C.S.: 541611

UniCredit Bank Czech Republic & Slovakia AS   (1)
Zeletavska 1525/1, Michle, 140 92, Prague, Czech Republic
Tel.: (420) 95 591 1111
Web Site: https://www.unicreditbank.cz
Banking Services
N.A.I.C.S.: 522110
Jakub Dusilek (Co-Chm)

UniCredit Bank SA   (1)
1F Blvd Expozitiei, 012101, Bucharest, Romania
Tel.: (40) 21 200 2000
Banking Services
N.A.I.C.S.: 522110

Subsidiary (Domestic):
Alpha Bank Romania S.A.   (2)
Calea Dorobantilor 237 B Sector 1, 010566, Bucharest, Romania   (90.1%)
Tel.: (40) 212092100
Banking Services
N.A.I.C.S.: 522110
Antoaneta Curteanu (Pres)

UniCredit Services GmbH   (1)
Str Fabrica de Glucoza nr 5 Novo Park Cladirea G, 020331, Bucharest, Romania
Tel.: (40) 21 209 7205
Banking Services
N.A.I.C.S.: 522110

UniCredit Services GmbH   (1)
Rothschildplatz 4, 1020, Vienna, Austria
Tel.: (43) 171 7300
Information Technology Services
N.A.I.C.S.: 541519

UniCredito Italiano S.p.A.   (1)
Piazza Cordusio, 20123, Milan, Italy
Tel.: (39) 0288621
International Banking Services
N.A.I.C.S.: 921140

Subsidiary (Non-US):
ACIS IMMOBILIEN- UND PROJEKTENTWICKLUNGS GMBH   (2)
Otto-Heilmann-Str 17, 82031, Grunwald, Germany
Tel.: (49) 89 44990
Real Estate Manangement Services
N.A.I.C.S.: 531390

ARRONDA IMMOBILIENVERWALTUNGS GMBH   (2)
Am Eisbach 3, 80538, Munich, Germany
Tel.: (49) 892 12 38 80
Real Estate Manangement Services
N.A.I.C.S.: 531390

AUSTRIA LEASING GMBH   (2)
Tel.: (49) 6192200770
Web Site: https://www.austria-leasing.de
Sales Range: $50-74.9 Million
Emp.: 5
Real Estate Lending Services
N.A.I.C.S.: 531190

Subsidiary (Non-US):
Raifeisen Leasing d.o.o.   (3)
Zmaja od Bosne bb, 71 000, Sarajevo, Bosnia & Herzegovina
Tel.: (387) 33254367
Web Site: http://www.rlbh.ba
Automotive Financial Leasing Services
N.A.I.C.S.: 522220

Raiffeisen Corporate Lizing Zrt.   (3)
(100%)
Tel.: (36) 614865177
Web Site: https://www.raiffeisen.hu
Automobile Leasing Services

UNICREDIT S.P.A.

UniCredit S.p.A.—(Continued)
N.A.I.C.S.: 532112
Andreas Gschwenter (Chm)

Raiffeisen Leasing IFN S.A. (3)
Tel.: (40) 213064444
Web Site: https://www.raiffeisen-leasing.ro
Automotive Financial Leasing Services
N.A.I.C.S.: 522220

Raiffeisen Leasing Kazakhstan LLP (3)
146 Shevchenko str office 1 1st floor, Almaty, 50008, Kazakhstan
Tel.: (7) 27 378 54 30
Web Site: http://www.raiffeisen-leasing.at
Sales Range: $50-74.9 Million
Financial Lending Services
N.A.I.C.S.: 522220

Raiffeisen Leasing d.o.o. (3)
Letaliska cesta 29a, 1000, Ljubljana, Slovenia
Tel.: (386) 82816200
Web Site: https://www.rl-sl.si
Financial Lending Services
N.A.I.C.S.: 522220

Raiffeisen-Leasing GmbH (2)
Mooslackengasse 12, 1190, Vienna, Austria
Tel.: (43) 1716010
Web Site: http://www.raiffeisen-leasing.at
Automobile & Real Estate Leasing Services
N.A.I.C.S.: 532112
Alexander Schmidecker (CEO)

Subsidiary (Non-US):

Raiffeisen Leasing Sh.A. (4)
Tish Daija Street Haxhiu Complex Building 1 7th floor, Tirana, Albania
Tel.: (355) 42274920
Web Site: https://raiffeisen-leasing.al
Sales Range: $25-49.9 Million
Emp.: 18
Financial Lending Services
N.A.I.C.S.: 522220

Subsidiary (Non-US):

B.I. INTERNATIONAL LIMITED (2)
Falcon Mill Handel St Off Halliwell Rd, Bolton, BL1 8BL, United Kingdom
Tel.: (44) 1204 846404
Web Site: http://www.biinternational.co.uk
Emp.: 4
Kitchenware Product Mfr & Distr
N.A.I.C.S.: 337126

BA-CA INFRASTRUCTURE FINANCE ADVISORY GMBH (2)
Renngasse 2, 1010, Vienna, Austria
Tel.: (43) 1588080
Financial Management Services
N.A.I.C.S.: 523999

BA/CA-LEASING BETEILIGUNGEN GMBH (2)
Operng 21, 1040, Vienna, Austria
Tel.: (43) 1 58808 0
Financial Management Services
N.A.I.C.S.: 523999

BACA CHEOPS LEASING GMBH (2)
Operngasse 21, 1040, Vienna, Austria
Tel.: (43) 158808 0
Financial Management Services
N.A.I.C.S.: 523999

BAL HORUS IMMOBILIEN LEASING GMBH (2)
Operngasse 21, 1040, Vienna, Austria
Tel.: (43) 1 58808
Real Estate Manangement Services
N.A.I.C.S.: 531390

BAL HYPNOS IMMOBILIEN LEASING GMBH (2)
Operngasse 21, 1040, Vienna, Austria
Tel.: (43) 1 71192 0
Real Estate Manangement Services
N.A.I.C.S.: 531390

BIL IMMOBILIEN FONDS GMBH (2)
Am Tucherpark 16, 80538, Munich, Bavaria, Germany
Tel.: (49) 89 44990
Real Estate Manangement Services
N.A.I.C.S.: 531390

BV GRUNDSTUCKSENTWICKLUNGSGMBH & CO. SCHLOSSBERGPROJEKTEN TWICKLUNGS-KG (2)
Isartorplatz 8, 80331, Munich, Germany
Tel.: (49) 892123980
Real Estate Development Services
N.A.I.C.S.: 531390

Division (Domestic):

Banca di Roma S.p.A. (2)
Viale Umberto Tupini 180, 00144, Rome, Italy (100%)
Tel.: (39) 0233408967
Web Site: http://www.unicredit.it
Banking Services
N.A.I.C.S.: 522180
Antonio Longo (Deputy Chm)

Banco di Sicilia S.p.A. (2)
Via Generale Vincenzo Magliocco 1, 90141, Palermo, Italy (100%)
Tel.: (39) 0916081111
Web Site: http://www.bancodisicilia.it
Commercial Bank
N.A.I.C.S.: 522180
Giuseppe Reina (VP)

Subsidiary (Non-US):

CA IB Corporate Finance Ltd. (2)
Nagymezo u 44 7th Floor, Budapest, 1065, Hungary
Tel.: (36) 1 301 5155
Web Site: http://www.unicreditgroup.eu
Emp.: 1,700
Commercial Banking Services
N.A.I.C.S.: 522110

CALG 451 GRUNDSTUCKVERWALTUNG GMBH (2)
Operngasse 21, 1040, Vienna, Austria
Tel.: (43) 1 58808 0
Real Estate Manangement Services
N.A.I.C.S.: 531390

CALG ALPHA GRUNDSTUCKVERWALTUNG GMBH (2)
Operngasse 21, 1040, Vienna, Austria
Tel.: (43) 1 58808 0
Real Estate Manangement Services
N.A.I.C.S.: 531390

Subsidiary (Non-US):

CARLO ERBA REAGENTI SPA (2)
Viale Luraghi Snc, 20020, Arese, Italy
Tel.: (39) 02 95325 357
Laboratory Reagent Mfr
N.A.I.C.S.: 325998

Subsidiary (Non-US):

CHRISTOPH REISEGGER GESELLSCHAFT M.B.H. (2)
Schottengasse 6 - 8, 1010, Vienna, Austria
Tel.: (43) 133171
Real Estate Development Services
N.A.I.C.S.: 531390

Subsidiary (Domestic):

COMPAGNIA ITALPETROLI S.P.A. (2)
via Aurelia Nord 8, 53, Civitavecchia, Italy (100%)
Tel.: (39) 076625884
Petroleum Product Storage & Refining Services
N.A.I.C.S.: 324110

Subsidiary (Domestic):

ROMA 2000 SRL (3)
Via Sante Bargellini 80, Rome, 00157, Italy
Tel.: (39) 0641732387
Sporting Goods Distr
N.A.I.C.S.: 459110

SOCIETA DEPOSITI COSTIERI SO.DE.CO. SRL (3)
Via Vigna Turci, 00053, Civitavecchia, Italy
Tel.: (39) 076629 881
Petroleum Refining Services
N.A.I.C.S.: 324110

Subsidiary (Domestic):

COM.P.I.S. - COMPAGNIA PETROLIFERA ITALIA SUD SOCI-

ETA A RESPONSABILITA LIMITATA (4)
Via Aurelia 294, 00165, Rome, Italy
Tel.: (39) 064825901
Investment Management Service
N.A.I.C.S.: 523999

Subsidiary (Domestic):

CRIVELLI SRL (2)
24 Viale Alighieri Dante, 15048, Valenza, Italy
Tel.: (39) 0131950 313
Gold & Silver Article Mfr
N.A.I.C.S.: 339910

Creditras Previdenza SIM S.p.A. (2)
Via San Protaso 1/3, 20121, Milan, Italy
Tel.: (39) 0288621
Management of Pension Funds
N.A.I.C.S.: 525110

ENTASI SRL (2)
Via Barberini 47, 00187, Rome, Italy
Tel.: (39) 06 6977571
Web Site: http://www.entasi.eu
Investment Management Service
N.A.I.C.S.: 523940

Subsidiary (Non-US):

ERSTE ONSHORE WINDKRAFT BETEILIGUNGSGESELLSCHAFT MBH & CO. WINDPARK KRAHENBERG KG (2)
Staulinie 14, 26122, Oldenburg, Lower Saxony, Germany
Tel.: (49) 2119946100
Financial Management Services
N.A.I.C.S.: 523999

ERSTE ONSHORE WINDKRAFT BETEILIGUNGSGESELLSCHAFT MBH & CO. WINDPARK MOSE KG (2)
Staulinie 14, 26122, Oldenburg, Germany
Tel.: (49) 441 2170890
Electric Power Generation Services
N.A.I.C.S.: 221118

Europa Facility Management Ltd. (2)
Sandgate Car Park, Newcastle upon Tyne, NE1 2NG, Tyne & Wear, United Kingdom
Tel.: (44) 1912211363
Financial Management Services
N.A.I.C.S.: 523999

Subsidiary (Domestic):

FINECO LEASING S.P.A. (2)
Via Marsala 42/A, Brescia, 25122, Italy
Tel.: (39) 03 037681
Web Site: http://www.finecoleasing.it
Financial Lending Services
N.A.I.C.S.: 522220

Subsidiary (Non-US):

GOLF- UND COUNTRY CLUB SEDDINER SEE IMMOBILIEN GMBH (2)
Rotherstrasse 16, 10245, Berlin, Germany
Tel.: (49) 30 5388190
Golf Course & Country Club Operator
N.A.I.C.S.: 713910

H.F.S. IMMOBILIENFONDS EUROPA 2 BETEILIGUNGS GMBH (2)
Arabellastrasse 14, 81925, Munich, Germany
Tel.: (49) 896782050
Web Site: http://www.wealthcap.com
Emp.: 250
Real Estate Manangement Services
N.A.I.C.S.: 531390

HVB AUTO LEASING EOOD (2)
40 Tzarigradsko Shosse blvd, Mladost, 1750, Sofia, Bulgaria
Tel.: (359) 29765100
Automobile Leasing Services
N.A.I.C.S.: 532112

HVB Profil GmbH (2)
Grillparzerstrasse 12 a, 81675, Munich, Germany
Tel.: (49) 89 378 24065
Web Site: http://www.hvbprofil.de
Personnel Management Consulting Services

INTERNATIONAL PUBLIC

N.A.I.C.S.: 541612

HVB-LEASING ATLANTIS INGATLANHASZNOSITO KORLATOLT FELELOSSEGU TARSASAG (2)
Hegyalja Ut 7-13, 1016, Budapest, Hungary
Tel.: (36) 14896040
Sales Range: $50-74.9 Million
Emp.: 100
Financial Management Services
N.A.I.C.S.: 522320

HVZ GmbH & Co. Objekt KG (2)
Am Tucherpark 16, 80538, Munich, Bavaria, Germany
Tel.: (49) 89 37 80
Real Estate Manangement Services
N.A.I.C.S.: 522292

Subsidiary (Domestic):

I-FABER SPA (2)
Via Livio Cambi 1, 20151, Milan, Italy
Tel.: (39) 02 8683 8410
Web Site: http://www.i-faber.com
Online Procurement Services
N.A.I.C.S.: 513199
Attilio Leonardo Lentati (Chm)

Subsidiary (Domestic):

JOINET SRL (3)
Via Giuseppe Brini 45, 40128, Bologna, Italy
Tel.: (39) 051 42 17 511
Web Site: http://www.joinet.eu
Sales Range: $25-49.9 Million
Emp.: 10
Information Technology Consulting Services
N.A.I.C.S.: 541612
Bruno Mussini (Mng Dir)

Subsidiary (Domestic):

I.M.E.S. - INDUSTRIA MECCANICA E STAMPAGGIO SPA (2)
Via Sandroni 46, Varese, 21040, Italy
Tel.: (39) 0331988503
Web Site: http://www.imes-spa.com
Emp.: 120
Metal Forging Mfr
N.A.I.C.S.: 331110

INDUSTRIA LIBRARIA TIPOGRAFICA EDITRICE SPA (2)
Via F Postiglione 14, Moncalieri, 10024, Italy
Tel.: (39) 011 6475111
Commercial Printing Services
N.A.I.C.S.: 323111

Subsidiary (Non-US):

INTRO LEASING GESELLSCHAFT M.B.H. (2)
Operngasse 21, 1040, Vienna, Austria
Tel.: (43) 158 8080
Financial Management Services
N.A.I.C.S.: 523999

Subsidiary (Domestic):

IRFIS - FINANZIARIA PER LO SVILUPPO DELLA SICILIA S.P.A. (2)
via Giovanni Bonanno 47, Palermo, 90143, Italy
Tel.: (39) 091 7821219
Web Site: http://www.irfis.it
Financial Management Services
N.A.I.C.S.: 523999

Subsidiary (Non-US):

JOHA GEBAEUDE- ERRICHTUNGS- UND VERMIETUNGS- GESELLSCHAFT M.B.H. (2)
Im Backerfeld 1, Leonding, 4060, Austria
Tel.: (43) 732 677475 10
Sales Range: $50-74.9 Million
Emp.: 5
Real Estate Development Services
N.A.I.C.S.: 531390
Andrea Altenberger (Gen Mgr)

KSG KARTEN-VERRECHNUNGS- UND SERVICEGESELLSCHAFT M.B.H. (2)
Lassalle St No 3, 1020, Vienna, Austria
Tel.: (43) 1 713 556 60

AND PRIVATE COMPANIES — UNICREDIT S.P.A.

Sales Range: $50-74.9 Million
Emp.: 2
Credit Card Issuing Services
N.A.I.C.S.: 522210
Martin Hofmarcher *(Mng Dir)*

Subsidiary (Domestic):

DC ELEKTRONISCHE ZAHLUNGS-SYSTEME GMBH (3)
Invalidenstrasse 3, Vienna, 1030, Austria
Tel.: (43) 1 7133500
Credit Card Issuing Services
N.A.I.C.S.: 522210
Erwin Urbitsch *(Gen Mgr)*

Subsidiary (Non-US):

LARGO LEASING GESELLSCHAFT M.B.H. (2)
Operngasse 21, 1040, Vienna, Austria
Tel.: (43) 158 80 80
Financial Management Services
N.A.I.C.S.: 523999

LEASFINANZ GMBH (2)
Operngasse 21, 1040, Vienna, Austria
Tel.: (43) 5 05 88 0
Web Site: http://www.leasfinanz.at
Financial Management Services
N.A.I.C.S.: 523999

Subsidiary (Domestic):

Locat S.p.A. (2)
Viale Banca Maria 4, 20129, Milan, Italy
Tel.: (39) 0255681
Web Site: http://www.unicreditleasing.it
Sales Range: $150-199.9 Million
Automobile, Property & Equipment Lessor for Industries & Small Businesses
N.A.I.C.S.: 531190

Mediocredito Centrale S.p.A. (2)
Viale America 351, 00187, Rome, Italy (100%)
Tel.: (39) 0647911
Web Site: http://www.mcc.it
Investment Banking
N.A.I.C.S.: 523150

Subsidiary (Non-US):

NATA IMMOBILIEN-LEASING GESELLSCHAFT M.B.H. (2)
Hollandstr 11-13, 1020, Vienna, Austria
Tel.: (43) 1 71601
Real Estate Lending Services
N.A.I.C.S.: 531190

Subsidiary (Domestic):

PARMACOTTO SPA (2)
Via Felice da Mareto Padre Molga 2A, 43123, Parma, Italy
Tel.: (39) 0521700111
Web Site: http://www.parmacotto.com
Meat Product Distr
N.A.I.C.S.: 424470
Marco Rosi *(Founder)*

Subsidiary (Non-US):

PUBLIC JOINT STOCK COMPANY UNICREDIT BANK (2)
29 Kovpaka Street, 03150, Kiev, Ukraine
Tel.: (380) 44 230 32 99
Web Site: http://www.unicredit.com.ua
Sales Range: $1-4.9 Billion
Emp.: 9,000
Commercial Banking Services
N.A.I.C.S.: 522110
Willibald Cernko *(Chm-Supervisory Bd)*

Pioneer Asset Management S.A. (2)
8-10 Rue Jean Monnet, Luxembourg, L-2180, Luxembourg
Tel.: (352) 421201
Web Site: http://www.pioneerinvestments.com
Emp.: 45
Financial Management Services
N.A.I.C.S.: 523999

Pioneer Investments (2)
Zeletavska 1525/1, Prague, 140 00, Czech Republic
Tel.: (420) 296354111
Web Site: http://www.pioneerinvestments.cz
Financial Management Services
N.A.I.C.S.: 523999

Roman Dvorak *(Mgr)*

Subsidiary (Domestic):

Quercia Software Spa (2)
Via Monte Bianco 18, 37132, Verona, Italy
Tel.: (39) 0458954900
Web Site: http://www.quercia.com
Banking Software Development Services
N.A.I.C.S.: 541512

Subsidiary (Non-US):

REAL INVEST IMMOBILIEN GMBH (2)
Lassallestrasse 5, 1020, Vienna, Austria
Tel.: (43) 1 331 71 0
Real Estate Development Services
N.A.I.C.S.: 531390

Subsidiary (Domestic):

ROME 2000 SRL (2)
Via Sante Bargellini 80, Rome, 00157, Italy
Tel.: (39) 0641 73 23 87
Investment Management Service
N.A.I.C.S.: 523999

Subsidiary (Non-US):

RONCASA IMMOBILIEN-VERWALTUNGS GMBH (2)
Am Eisbach 3, 80538, Munich, Bavaria, Germany
Tel.: (49) 89 44990
Real Estate Manangement Services
N.A.I.C.S.: 531390

RONDO LEASING GMBH (2)
Operngasse 21, 1040, Vienna, Austria
Tel.: (43) 1588080
Financial Management Services
N.A.I.C.S.: 523999

Subsidiary (Domestic):

BANK AUSTRIA LEASING ARGO IMMOBILIEN LEASING GMBH (3)
Operngasse 21, 1040, Vienna, Austria
Tel.: (43) 1 71192 0
Real Estate Manangement Services
N.A.I.C.S.: 531390

Subsidiary (Domestic):

Z LEASING PERSEUS IMMOBILIEN LEASING GESELLSCHAFT M.B.H. (4)
Operngasse 21, 1040, Vienna, Austria
Tel.: (43) 171192 0
Real Estate Lending Services
N.A.I.C.S.: 531390

Subsidiary (Non-US):

SALVATORPLATZ-GRUNDSTUCKSGESELLSCHAFT MBH (2)
Sederanger 5, 80538, Munich, Bavaria, Germany
Tel.: (49) 89 4 49 90
Real Estate Manangement Services
N.A.I.C.S.: 531390

SALVATORPLATZ-GRUNDSTUCKSGESELLSCHAFT MBH & CO. OHG SAARLAND (2)
Am Tucherpark 16, 80538, Munich, Germany
Tel.: (49) 89 37 84 93 05
Real Estate Development Services
N.A.I.C.S.: 531390

SCHLOSSBERGPROJEKTENTWICKLUNGS-GMBH & CO 683 KG (2)
Am Tucherpark 16, 80538, Munich, Bavaria, Germany
Tel.: (49) 89 290760
Financial Management Services
N.A.I.C.S.: 523999

SECA-LEASING GESELLSCHAFT M.B.H. (2)
Operngasse 21, 1040, Vienna, Austria
Tel.: (43) 1 58808
Financial Management Services
N.A.I.C.S.: 523999

SEXT Z IMMOBILIEN LEASING GESELLSCHAFT M.B.H (2)
Operngasse 21, 1040, Vienna, Austria
Tel.: (43) 1 58808 0
Real Estate Lending Services
N.A.I.C.S.: 531390

SFS FINANCIAL SERVICES GMBH (2)
Lassallestrasse 5, 1020, Vienna, Austria
Tel.: (43) 1 33171 0
Financial Management Services
N.A.I.C.S.: 523999

Subsidiary (Domestic):

SICILIA CONVENTION BUREAU SRL (2)
Piazza Ludovico Ariosto 3, 95127, Catania, Italy
Tel.: (39) 0952276420
Web Site: http://www.siciliaconvention.com
Emp.: 5
Meeting & Event Organizer
N.A.I.C.S.: 711310
Daniela Marino *(Dir-Ops)*

Subsidiary (Non-US):

SIRIUS IMMOBILIEN- UND PROJEKTENTWICKLUNGS GMBH (2)
Die Haftung weg, 80538, Munich, Germany
Tel.: (49) 89 4499 0
Real Estate Manangement Services
N.A.I.C.S.: 531390

Subsidiary (Domestic):

SOFIPA SOCIETA DI GESTIONE DEL RISPARMIO (SGR) S.P.A. (2)
40 Via Manzoni Alessandro, 20121, Milan, Italy
Tel.: (39) 027 259 271
Financial Management Services
N.A.I.C.S.: 523999

Societa Veronese Gestione Compravendita Immobili A.R.L. (2)
Via Emilia 47, Rome, 00187, Italy
Tel.: (39) 064825977
Facility Management Services
N.A.I.C.S.: 561210

Subsidiary (Non-US):

Solaris Verwaltungsgesellschaft mbH & Co. Vermietungs KG (2)
Am Eisbach 3, 80538, Munich, Bavaria, Germany
Tel.: (49) 89 44990
Investment Management Service
N.A.I.C.S.: 523999

T & P VASTGOED STUTTGART B.V. (2)
Evert van de Beekstraat 310, 1118 CX, Schiphol, Netherlands
Tel.: (31) 20 4064444
Real Estate Manangement Services
N.A.I.C.S.: 531390

Subsidiary (Non-US):

OTHMARSCHEN PARK HAMBURG GMBH & CO. CENTERPARK KG (3)
Am Eisbach 3, 80538, Munich, Bavaria, Germany
Tel.: (49) 89 44990
Real Estate Manangement Services
N.A.I.C.S.: 531390

OTHMARSCHEN PARK HAMBURG GMBH & CO. GEWERBEPARK KG (3)
Am Eisbach 3, 80538, Munich, Bavaria, Germany
Tel.: (49) 89 3780
Real Estate Manangement Services
N.A.I.C.S.: 531390

Subsidiary (Non-US):

TC-TERTIA PROJEKTVERWALTUNGSGESELLSCHAFT MBH (2)
Lassallestrasse 5, 1020, Vienna, Austria
Tel.: (43) 1 711920
Financial Management Services
N.A.I.C.S.: 523999

Tivoli Grundstucks-Aktiengesellschaft (2)
Am Eisbach 3, 80538, Munich, Germany
Tel.: (49) 894 49 90
Real Estate Manangement Services
N.A.I.C.S.: 531390

UBIS Solutions Information Technology GmbH (2)
Nordbergstr 13, 1090, Vienna, Austria
Tel.: (43) 1 71730 0
Web Site: http://www.unicreditgroup.eu
Information Technology Consulting Services
N.A.I.C.S.: 541512

Subsidiary (Domestic):

UNICREDIT BPC MORTGAGE S.R.L. (2)
Piazzetta Monte 1, Verona, 37121, Italy
Tel.: (39) 0458678711
Real Estate Manangement Services
N.A.I.C.S.: 531390

UNICREDIT BUSINESS PARTNER SOCIETA CONSORTILE PER AZIONI (2)
Via Volta 1, Cologno Monzese, 20093, Milan, Italy
Tel.: (39) 02 26731
Web Site: http://www.upa.unicredit.it
Accounting Services
N.A.I.C.S.: 541219

Subsidiary (Non-US):

UNICREDIT CONSUMER FINANCING IFN S.A. (2)
Gheatare Street 2325 District 1, Bucharest, 14106, Romania
Tel.: (40) 21 200 9700
Sales Range: $75-99.9 Million
Emp.: 135
Commercial Banking Services
N.A.I.C.S.: 522110

UNICREDIT FUGGETLEN BIZTOSITASKOZVETITO KFT (2)
Hegyalja ut 7-13, 1016, Budapest, Hungary
Tel.: (36) 1 301 12 71
Insurance Brokerage Services
N.A.I.C.S.: 524210

Subsidiary (Domestic):

UNICREDIT GLOBAL INFORMATION SERVICES SOCIETA CONSORTILE PER AZIONI (2)
71 Via Gentilin Monsignor Giacomo, 37132, Verona, Italy
Tel.: (39) 0458 093 311
Investment Banking Services
N.A.I.C.S.: 523150

Subsidiary (Non-US):

UNICREDIT INTERNATIONAL BANK (LUXEMBOURG) SA (2)
8-10 rue Jean Monnet, 2180, Luxembourg, Luxembourg
Tel.: (352) 22 08 42 1
Commercial Banking Services
N.A.I.C.S.: 522110

Subsidiary (Domestic):

UNICREDIT LUXEMBOURG FINANCE SA (3)
8 10 rue Jean Monnet, Luxembourg, 2180, Luxembourg
Tel.: (352) 26 47 82 84
Emp.: 3
Commercial Banking Services
N.A.I.C.S.: 522110
Carlo Gastaldi *(Mgr)*

Subsidiary (Non-US):

UNICREDIT LEASING FINANCE GMBH (2)
Heidenkampsweg 75, Hammerbrook, 20097, Hamburg, Germany
Tel.: (49) 40 23643 100
Financial Lending Services
N.A.I.C.S.: 522220

UNICREDIT LEASING FUHRPARK-MANAGEMENT GMBH (2)

UNICREDIT S.P.A.

UniCredit S.p.A.—(Continued)
Shuttleworthstrasse 17, 1210, Vienna, Austria
Tel.: (43) 1711925550
Web Site: http://www.unicreditleasing-gebrauchtwagen.at
Sales Range: $25-49.9 Million
Emp.: 40
Automobile Leasing Services
N.A.I.C.S.: 532112

UNICREDIT LEASING HUNGARY ZRT (2)
Hegyalja ut 7-13, 1016, Budapest, Hungary
Tel.: (36) 1 489 7800
Sales Range: $50-74.9 Million
Emp.: 100
Financial Management Services
N.A.I.C.S.: 522320

Subsidiary (Domestic):

UNICREDIT LEASING S.P.A. (2)
Viale Bianca Maria 4, 20129, Milan, Italy
Tel.: (39) 02 5568 1
Web Site: http://www.unicreditleasing.it
Automobile & Industrial Equipment Leasing Services
N.A.I.C.S.: 532490

Subsidiary (Non-US):

ALLIB LEASING S.R.O. (3)
Zeletavska 1525/1, Prague, 140 10, Czech Republic
Tel.: (420) 257 091 111
Financial Management Services
N.A.I.C.S.: 523999

ALLIB NEKRETNINE D.O.O. ZA POSLOVANJE NEKRETNINAMA (3)
Heinzelova 33, Zagreb, Croatia
Tel.: (385) 1 4877100
Real Estate Manangement Services
N.A.I.C.S.: 531390

ANI LEASING IFN S.A. (3)
Str Nicolae Caramfil nr 25 Sector 1, Bucharest, Romania
Tel.: (40) 21 2007777
Financial Management Services
N.A.I.C.S.: 523999

BACAL ALPHA DOO ZA POSLOVANJE NEKRETNINAMA (3)
Heinzelova 33, 10000, Zagreb, Croatia
Tel.: (385) 1 2447294
Real Estate Manangement Services
N.A.I.C.S.: 531390

CA-LEASING YPSILON INGATLAN-HASZNOSITO KORLATOLT FELELOSSEGU TARSASAG (3)
Hegyalja ut 7-13, Budapest, Hungary
Tel.: (36) 14896040
Financial Management Services
N.A.I.C.S.: 523999

Citadele Leasing (3)
Republikas 2A, Riga, 1004, Latvia
Tel.: (371) 67010000
Web Site: https://www.citadeleleasing.lv
Emp.: 50
Management Consulting Services
N.A.I.C.S.: 541618

Subsidiary (Domestic):

SIA UNICREDIT INSURANCE BROKER (4)
Mukusalas Iela 41, Riga, 1004, Latvia
Tel.: (371) 67502204
Insurance Brokerage Services
N.A.I.C.S.: 524210

Subsidiary (Non-US):

HVB-LEASING SPORT INGATLAN-HASZNOSITO KOLATPOT FEOEOASSEGU TARSASAG (3)
Hegyalja Ut 7-13, Budapest, Hungary
Tel.: (36) 14897800
Property Management Services
N.A.I.C.S.: 531312

LOCAT CROATIA DOO (3)
Heinzelova 33, 10000, Zagreb, Croatia
Tel.: (385) 12 447 100
Financial Management Services
N.A.I.C.S.: 523999

OOO UNICREDIT LEASING (3)
Butikovskiy pereulok 9, 119034, Moscow, Russia
Tel.: (7) 4952873150
Web Site: http://www.unicreditleasing.ru
Financial Lending Services
N.A.I.C.S.: 522220

REAL ESTATE MANAGEMENT POLAND SP. Z O.O. (3)
ul Bonifraterska 17, 00-203, Warsaw, Poland
Tel.: (48) 222460100
Real Estate Manangement Services
N.A.I.C.S.: 531390

UNICREDIT GLOBAL LEASING PARTICIPATION MANAGEMENT GMBH (3)
Operngasse 21, 1040, Vienna, Austria
Tel.: (43) 1 588 08 0
Financial Management Services
N.A.I.C.S.: 523999

Subsidiary (Domestic):

UNICREDIT GLOBAL LEASING EXPORT GMBH (4)
Operng 21, 1040, Vienna, Austria
Tel.: (43) 1 58808 0
Financial Management Services
N.A.I.C.S.: 523999

Subsidiary (Non-US):

UNICREDIT GLOBAL LEASING VERSICHERUNGSSERVICE GMBH (3)
Operngasse 21, 1040, Vienna, Austria
Tel.: (43) 1 588 08
Financial Management Services
N.A.I.C.S.: 523999

UNICREDIT LEASING AD (3)
40 Tzarigradsko Shose Boulevard 1 Floor, 1750, Sofia, Bulgaria
Tel.: (359) 2 9765 100
Web Site: http://www.unicreditleasing.bg
Financial Management Services
N.A.I.C.S.: 523999
Dimitar Lichev *(Chief Risk Officer & Member-Mgmt Bd)*

UNICREDIT LEASING CORPORATION IFN S.A. (3)
23-25 Ghetarilor Street, 014106, Bucharest, Romania
Tel.: (40) 212007777
Web Site: http://www.unicreditleasing.ro
Financial Management Services
N.A.I.C.S.: 523999

UNICREDIT LEASING CROATIA d.o.o. (3)
Bundek Center dc Garana 17, Zagreb, 10000, Croatia
Tel.: (385) 1 2447 100
Web Site: http://www.unicreditleasing.hr
Financial Lending Services
N.A.I.C.S.: 522220
Eugen Paic-Karega *(Chm)*

UNICREDIT LEASING D.O.O. (3)
Dzemala Bijedica 2, 71000, Sarajevo, Bosnia & Herzegovina
Tel.: (387) 33 721 750
Web Site: http://www.unicreditleasing.ba
Emp.: 30
Financial Management Services
N.A.I.C.S.: 523999
Izmilia Alicic Tuka *(CEO)*

UNICREDIT LEASING REAL ESTATE S.R.O. (3)
Plynarenska 7/A, 821 09, Bratislava, Slovakia
Tel.: (421) 2 59 27 12 80
Web Site: http://www.unicreditleasing.sk
Real Estate Manangement Services
N.A.I.C.S.: 531390

UNICREDIT LEASING TOB (3)
Illinskaya 8, Kiev, Ukraine
Tel.: (380) 44 590 1496
Financial Management Services
N.A.I.C.S.: 523999

UniCredit Leasing (Austria) GmbH (3)
Operngasse 21, A-1040, Vienna, Austria

Tel.: (43) 05 05 88 0
Web Site: http://www.unicreditleasing.at
Financial Management Services
N.A.I.C.S.: 523999
Gunter Populorum *(Mng Dir)*

Subsidiary (Domestic):

BA CA SECUND LEASING GMBH (4)
Operngasse 21, 1040, Vienna, Austria
Tel.: (43) 1 58808 0
Financial Management Services
N.A.I.C.S.: 523999

BA EUROLEASE BETEILIGUNGSGESELLSCHAFT M.B.H. (4)
Operngasse 21, 1040, Vienna, Austria
Tel.: (43) 1 711920
Financial Management Services
N.A.I.C.S.: 523999

Subsidiary (Domestic):

BA/CA-LEASING FINANZIERUNG GMBH (5)
Operngasse 21, 1040, Vienna, Austria
Tel.: (43) 158808
Financial Management Services
N.A.I.C.S.: 523999

Z LEASING CORVUS IMMOBILIEN LEASING GESELLSCHAFT M.B.H. (5)
Operngasse 21, 1040, Vienna, Austria
Tel.: (43) 1 71192 0
Real Estate Lending Services
N.A.I.C.S.: 531390

Z LEASING TAURUS IMMOBILIEN LEASING GESELLSCHAFT M.B.H. (5)
Operngasse 21, 1040, Vienna, Austria
Tel.: (43) 17135516
Real Estate Lending Services
N.A.I.C.S.: 531390

Subsidiary (Domestic):

BA-CA ANDANTE LEASING GMBH (4)
Operngasse 21, 1040, Vienna, Austria
Tel.: (43) 1 588 08 0
Financial Management Services
N.A.I.C.S.: 523999

BA-CA LEASING MAR IMMOBILIEN LEASING GMBH (4)
Operngasse 21, 1040, Vienna, Austria
Tel.: (43) 158 8080
Real Estate Manangement Services
N.A.I.C.S.: 531390

BA-CA LEASING VERSICHERUNGSSERVICE GMBH (4)
Operngasse 21, 1040, Vienna, Austria
Tel.: (43) 1588083344
Financial Management Services
N.A.I.C.S.: 523999

BA-CA PRESTO LEASING GMBH (4)
Operngasse 21, Vienna, 1040, Austria
Tel.: (43) 1 588 08 0
Web Site: http://www.unicredit.at
Financial Management Services
N.A.I.C.S.: 523999

BACA HYDRA LEASING GESELLSCHAFT M.B.H. (4)
Operngasse 21, 1040, Vienna, Austria
Tel.: (43) 1 58808 0
Financial Management Services
N.A.I.C.S.: 523999

BACA KOMMUNALLEASING GMBH (4)
Operngasse 21, 1040, Vienna, Austria
Tel.: (43) 1 588 08 0
Financial Management Services
N.A.I.C.S.: 523999

BAL CARINA IMMOBILIEN LEASING GMBH (4)
Operngasse 21, 1040, Vienna, Austria
Tel.: (43) 158808 0
Real Estate Manangement Services
N.A.I.C.S.: 531390

INTERNATIONAL PUBLIC

BAL HESTIA IMMOBILIEN LEASING GMBH (4)
Operng 21, 1040, Vienna, Austria
Tel.: (43) 1 58808 0
Real Estate Manangement Services
N.A.I.C.S.: 531390

BANK AUSTRIA LEASING IKARUS IMMOBILIEN LEASING GESELLSCHAFT M.B.H. (4)
Operngasse 21, 1040, Vienna, Austria
Tel.: (43) 1 588 080
Real Estate Manangement Services
N.A.I.C.S.: 531390

BETEILIGUNGSVERWALTUNGSGESELLSCHAFT DER BANK AUSTRIA CREDITANSTALT LEASING GMBH (4)
Operngasse 21, 1040, Vienna, Austria
Tel.: (43) 158808
Financial Management Services
N.A.I.C.S.: 523999

Subsidiary (Domestic):

CA-LEASING SENIOREN PARK GMBH (5)
Operngasse 21, 1040, Vienna, Austria
Tel.: (43) 1 588 08 0
Financial Management Services
N.A.I.C.S.: 523999

CALG 307 MOBILIEN LEASING GMBH (5)
Operngasse 21, 1040, Vienna, Austria
Tel.: (43) 158808
Commercial Equipment Leasing Services
N.A.I.C.S.: 532490

CALG 443 GRUNDSTUCKVERWALTUNG GMBH (5)
Operng 21, 1040, Vienna, Austria
Tel.: (43) 1 588080
Real Estate Manangement Services
N.A.I.C.S.: 327910

CHARADE LEASING GESELLSCHAFT M.B.H. (5)
Operngasse 21, 1040, Vienna, Austria
Tel.: (43) 1 58808 0
Financial Management Services
N.A.I.C.S.: 523999

FOLIA LEASING GESELLSCHAFT M.B.H. (5)
Operngasse 21, 1040, Vienna, Austria
Tel.: (43) 158808
Financial Management Services
N.A.I.C.S.: 523999

FUGATO LEASING GESELLSCHAFT M.B.H. (5)
Operngasse 21, 1040, Vienna, Austria
Tel.: (43) 158808
Financial Management Services
N.A.I.C.S.: 523999

GEBAUDELEASING GRUNDSTUCKSVERWALTUNGSGESELLSCHAFT M.B.H. (5)
Operngasse 21, 1040, Vienna, Austria
Tel.: (43) 158 80 80
Real Estate Manangement Services
N.A.I.C.S.: 531390

Honeu Leasing Gesellschaft m.b.H (5)
Operngasse 21, 1040, Vienna, Austria
Tel.: (43) 158808
Financial Management Services
N.A.I.C.S.: 523999

LIPARK LEASING GESELLSCHAFT M.B.H. (5)
Operngasse 21, 1040, Vienna, Austria
Tel.: (43) 158808
Financial Management Services
N.A.I.C.S.: 523999

Legato Leasing Gmbh (5)
Operngasse 21, 1040, Vienna, Austria
Tel.: (43) 158808
Financial Management Services
N.A.I.C.S.: 523999

POSATO LEASING GESELLSCHAFT M.B.H. (5)
Operngasse 21, 1040, Vienna, Austria

Tel.: (43) 15 88 08
Financial Management Services
N.A.I.C.S.: 523999

UNICREDIT TECHRENT LEASING GMBH (5)
Operngasse 21, 1040, Vienna, Austria
Tel.: (43) 1 588 08 0
Financial Management Services
N.A.I.C.S.: 523999

Subsidiary (Domestic):

Baca Cena Immobilien Leasing Gmbh (4)
Operngasse 21, 1040, Vienna, Austria
Tel.: (43) 1 588 08 0
Real Estate Manangement Services
N.A.I.C.S.: 531390

Baca Leasing Carmen Gmbh (4)
Operngasse 21, 1040, Vienna, Austria
Tel.: (43) 1 588 08 0
Financial Management Services
N.A.I.C.S.: 523999

CALG ANLAGEN LEASING GMBH (4)
Opera Gasse 21, 1040, Vienna, Austria
Tel.: (43) 1 58808
Financial Management Services
N.A.I.C.S.: 523999

Subsidiary (Domestic):

CALG IMMOBILIEN LEASING GMBH (5)
Opera Gasse 21, 1040, Vienna, Austria
Tel.: (43) 1 58808 0
Real Estate Lending Services
N.A.I.C.S.: 531190

Subsidiary (Domestic):

BAULANDENTWICKLUNG GDST 1682/8 GMBH & CO OEG (6)
Operngasse 21, 1040, Vienna, Austria
Tel.: (43) 1 588 08 0
Banking Services
N.A.I.C.S.: 522110

CALG 445 GRUNDSTUCKVERWALTUNG GMBH (6)
Operngasse 21, 1040, Vienna, Austria
Tel.: (43) 158 8080
Real Estate Manangement Services
N.A.I.C.S.: 531390

CALG GAMMA GRUNDSTUCKVERWALTUNG GMBH (6)
Operngasse 21, 1040, Vienna, Austria
Tel.: (43) 1588080
Real Estate Development Services
N.A.I.C.S.: 531390

CALG GRUNDSTUCKVERWALTUNG GMBH (6)
Operngasse 21, 1040, Vienna, Austria
Tel.: (43) 158 8080
Real Estate Development Services
N.A.I.C.S.: 531390

CALG IMMOBILIEN LEASING GMBH & CO 1050 WIEN, SIEBENBRUNNENGASSE 10-21 OG (6)
Operngasse 21, 1040, Vienna, Austria
Tel.: (43) 152145
Real Estate Lending Services
N.A.I.C.S.: 531190

CALG IMMOBILIEN LEASING GMBH & CO 1120 WIEN, SCHONBRUNNER SCHLOSS-STRASSE 38-42 OG (6)
Operngasse 21, 1040, Vienna, Austria
Tel.: (43) 1 588 08 0
Real Estate Lending Services
N.A.I.C.S.: 531190

CALG IMMOBILIEN LEASING GMBH & CO PROJEKT VIER OG (6)
Operngasse 21, 1040, Vienna, Austria
Tel.: (43) 158808
Real Estate Lending Services
N.A.I.C.S.: 531190

RSB ANLAGENVERMIETUNG GESELLSCHAFT M.B.H. (6)
Operngasse 21, 1040, Vienna, Austria
Tel.: (43) 158808 0
Investment Management Service
N.A.I.C.S.: 523999

UNICREDIT PEGASUS LEASING GMBH (6)
Operngasse 21, 1040, Vienna, Austria
Tel.: (43) 1 58808 0
Financial Management Services
N.A.I.C.S.: 523999

Subsidiary (Domestic):

QUART Z IMMOBILIEN LEASING GESELLSCHAFT M.B.H. (5)
Operngasse 21, 1040, Vienna, Austria
Tel.: (43) 158808 0
Real Estate Lending Services
N.A.I.C.S.: 531390

Subsidiary (Domestic):

CIVITAS Immobilien Leasing Gesellschaft m.b.H. (4)
Operngasse 21, Vienna, 1040, Austria
Tel.: (43) 1588080
Real Estate Lending Services
N.A.I.C.S.: 531190

DLV IMMOBILIEN LEASING GESELLSCHAFT M.B.H. (4)
Operngasse 21, Vienna, 1040, Austria
Tel.: (43) 505050
Real Estate Lending Services
N.A.I.C.S.: 531190

DUODEC Z IMMOBILIEN LEASING GESELLSCHAFT M.B.H. (4)
Operngasse 21, 1040, Vienna, Austria
Tel.: (43) 1 711920
Real Estate Lending Services
N.A.I.C.S.: 531190

EUROLEASE AMUN IMMOBILIEN LEASING GESELLSCHAFT M.B.H. (4)
Opera Gasse 21, 1040, Vienna, Austria
Tel.: (43) 1 711920
Real Estate Lending Services
N.A.I.C.S.: 531190

EUROLEASE ANUBIS IMMOBILIEN LEASING GESELLSCHAFT M.B.H. (4)
Operngasse 21, 1040, Vienna, Austria
Tel.: (43) 158808 0
Real Estate Lending Services
N.A.I.C.S.: 531190

EUROLEASE ISIS IMMOBILIEN LEASING GESELLSCHAFT M.B.H. (4)
Opera Gasse 21, 1040, Vienna, Austria
Tel.: (43) 1 711920
Real Estate Lending Services
N.A.I.C.S.: 531190

EUROLEASE RAMSES IMMOBILIEN LEASING GESELLSCHAFT M.B.H. (4)
Operngasse 21, 1040, Vienna, Austria
Tel.: (43) 1 71 192
Real Estate Lending Services
N.A.I.C.S.: 531190

Subsidiary (Domestic):

UNICREDIT GARAGEN ERRICHTUNG UND VERWERTUNG GMBH (5)
Operngasse 21, 1040, Vienna, Austria
Tel.: (43) 1 71192 0
Real Estate Manangement Services
N.A.I.C.S.: 531390

Subsidiary (Domestic):

BAL DEMETER IMMOBILIEN LEASING GMBH (6)
Operngasse 21, 1040, Vienna, Austria
Tel.: (43) 1 71192 0
Real Estate Manangement Services
N.A.I.C.S.: 531390

BAL SOBEK IMMOBILIEN LEASING GMBH (6)
Operngasse 21, Vienna, 1040, Austria
Tel.: (43) 1 588 080
Real Estate Manangement Services
N.A.I.C.S.: 531390

BANK AUSTRIA LEASING HERA IMMOBILIEN LEASING GMBH (6)
Operngasse 21, 1040, Vienna, Austria
Tel.: (43) 1 58808 0
Real Estate Manangement Services
N.A.I.C.S.: 531390

LIVA IMMOBILIEN LEASING GESELLSCHAFT M.B.H. (6)
Operngasse 21, 1040, Vienna, Austria
Tel.: (43) 1 588 08 0
Real Estate Lending Services
N.A.I.C.S.: 531390

MM OMEGA PROJEKTENTWICKLUNGS GMBH (6)
Operngasse 21, 1040, Vienna, Austria
Tel.: (43) 463 50 36 36 0
Financial Management Services
N.A.I.C.S.: 523999

NAGE LOKALVERMIETUNGSGESELLSCHAFT M.B.H. (6)
Operngasse 21, 1040, Vienna, Austria
Tel.: (43) 158808
Real Estate Manangement Services
N.A.I.C.S.: 531390

REAL-LEASE GRUNDSTUCKSVERWALTUNGSGESELLSCHAFT M.B.H. (6)
Operng 21, 1010, Vienna, Austria
Tel.: (43) 1 58808 0
Real Estate Lending Services
N.A.I.C.S.: 531390

TERZ Z IMMOBILIEN LEASING GESELLSCHAFT M.B.H. (6)
Operngasse 21, 1040, Vienna, Austria
Tel.: (43) 1 58808
Real Estate Lending Services
N.A.I.C.S.: 531390

TREDEC Z IMMOBILIEN LEASING GESELLSCHAFT M.B.H. (6)
Operngasse 21, 1040, Vienna, Austria
Tel.: (43) 171 1920
Real Estate Lending Services
N.A.I.C.S.: 531390

Z LEASING AURIGA IMMOBILIEN LEASING GESELLSCHAFT M.B.H. (6)
Operngasse 21, 1040, Vienna, Austria
Tel.: (43) 1 58808 0
Real Estate Lending Services
N.A.I.C.S.: 531390

Z LEASING GEMINI IMMOBILIEN LEASING GESELLSCHAFT M.B.H. (6)
Operngasse 21, 1040, Vienna, Austria
Tel.: (43) 1 58808 0
Real Estate Lending Services
N.A.I.C.S.: 531390

Z LEASING HERCULES IMMOBILIEN LEASING GESELLSCHAFT M.B.H. (6)
Operngasse 21, 1040, Vienna, Austria
Tel.: (43) 171 1920
Real Estate Lending Services
N.A.I.C.S.: 531390

Subsidiary (Domestic):

EXPANDA IMMOBILIEN LEASING GESELLSCHAFT M.B.H. (4)
Operngasse 21, 1040, Vienna, Austria
Tel.: (43) 158808 0
Real Estate Lending Services
N.A.I.C.S.: 531190

GRUNDSTUCKSVERWALTUNG LINZ-MITTE GMBH (4)
Operngasse 21, 1040, Vienna, Austria
Tel.: (43) 1 588 08 0
Real Estate Manangement Services
N.A.I.C.S.: 531390

Kunsthaus Leasing GmbH (4)
Operngasse 21, 1040, Vienna, Austria
Tel.: (43) 1 58808
Financial Management Services
N.A.I.C.S.: 523999

LAGERMAX LEASING GMBH (4)
Operngasse 21, 1040, Vienna, Austria
Tel.: (43) 158808

Financial Management Services
N.A.I.C.S.: 523999

LAGEV IMMOBILIEN LEASING GESELLSCHAFT M.B.H. (4)
Operngasse 21, 1040, Vienna, Austria
Tel.: (43) 1 71192 0
Real Estate Lending Services
N.A.I.C.S.: 531190

LINO HOTEL-LEASING GMBH (4)
Opera Gasse 21, 1040, Vienna, Austria
Tel.: (43) 1 588 08 0
Home Leasing Services
N.A.I.C.S.: 531120

MBC IMMOBILIEN LEASING GESELLSCHAFT M.B.H. (4)
Operngasse 21, 1040, Vienna, Austria
Tel.: (43) 158808 0
Real Estate Lending Services
N.A.I.C.S.: 531390

MENUETT GRUNDSTUCKSVERWALTUNGSGESELLSCHAFT M.B.H. (4)
Operngasse 21, 1040, Vienna, Austria
Tel.: (43) 158 8080
Real Estate Manangement Services
N.A.I.C.S.: 531390

PIANA LEASING GESELLSCHAFT M.B.H. (4)
Operngasse 21, 1040, Vienna, Austria
Tel.: (43) 158808 0
Banking Services
N.A.I.C.S.: 522110

PRIM Z IMMOBILIEN LEASING GESELLSCHAFT M.B.H. (4)
Operngasse 21, 1040, Vienna, Austria
Tel.: (43) 158808 0
Real Estate Lending Services
N.A.I.C.S.: 531390

Quadec Z Immobilien Leasing Gesellschaft m.b.H. (4)
Operngasse 21, 1040, Vienna, Austria
Tel.: (43) 5 588 0
Real Estate Lending Services
N.A.I.C.S.: 531390

Quint Z Immobilien Leasing Gesellschaft m.b.H. (4)
Operngasse 21, 1040, Vienna, Austria
Tel.: (43) 1 58808 0
Real Estate Lending Services
N.A.I.C.S.: 531390

SONATA LEASING-GESELLSCHAFT M.B.H. (4)
Operngasse 21, 1040, Vienna, Austria
Tel.: (43) 1 588080
Financial Management Services
N.A.I.C.S.: 523999

UFFICIUM IMMOBILIEN LEASING GESELLSCHAFT M.B.H. (4)
Operng 21, 1040, Vienna, Austria
Tel.: (43) 1 71192
Real Estate Lending Services
N.A.I.C.S.: 531390

UNICOM Immobilien Leasing Gesellschaft m.b.H. (4)
Operngasse 21, 1040, Vienna, Austria
Tel.: (43) 1 71192
Real Estate Lending Services
N.A.I.C.S.: 531390

UNICREDIT AURORA LEASING GMBH (4)
Operngasse 21, 1040, Vienna, Austria
Tel.: (43) 158808 0
Real Estate Manangement Services
N.A.I.C.S.: 531390

UNICREDIT LEASING BAUTRAGER GMBH (4)
Operngasse 21, 1040, Vienna, Austria
Tel.: (43) 158808 0
Financial Management Services
N.A.I.C.S.: 523999

UNICREDIT LEASING VERSICHERUNGSSERVICE GMBH & CO KG (4)
Operngasse 21, 1040, Vienna, Austria
Tel.: (43) 1 588 08 0
Financial Management Services

UNICREDIT S.P.A.

UniCredit S.p.A.—(Continued)
N.A.I.C.S.: 523999

UNICREDIT LUNA LEASING GMBH (4)
Operngasse 21, 1040, Vienna, Austria
Tel.: (43) 1 58 808
Financial Management Services
N.A.I.C.S.: 523999

UNICREDIT POLARIS LEASING GMBH (4)
Operngasse 21, 1040, Vienna, Austria
Tel.: (43) 1 58 808
Financial Management Services
N.A.I.C.S.: 523999

Subsidiary (Non-US):

UNICREDIT RENT D.O.O. BEOGRAD (4)
Bulevar Umetnosti 2-A, 11000, Belgrade, Serbia
Tel.: (381) 11 3093500
Financial Management Services
N.A.I.C.S.: 523999

UniCredit Leasing CZ a.s. (4)
Radlicka 14/3201, 15000, Prague, Czech Republic
Tel.: (420) 257091111
Web Site: http://www.unicreditleasing.cz
Sales Range: $400-449.9 Million
Emp.: 282
Equipment Leasing Services
N.A.I.C.S.: 532490
Jaroslav Jaromersky (Vice Chm)

Affiliate (Domestic):

Renault Leasing CZ, s.r.o. (5)
IBC Pobrezni 3, 180 00, Prague, 8, Czech Republic
Tel.: (420) 257 091 449
Web Site: http://www.renaultleasing.cz
Financing of Renault Automobiles
N.A.I.C.S.: 525990

Subsidiary (Domestic):

UniCredit Fleet Management, s.r.o. (5)
zeledavska brague 4 St 1525, 140 92, Prague, Czech Republic (100%)
Tel.: (420) 257091190
Web Site: http://www.unicreditleasing.cz
Car Fleet Leasing Services
N.A.I.C.S.: 532112

UniCredit pojist'ovaci maklerska spol. s.r.o. (5)
Radlicka 14/3201, 150 00, Prague, Czech Republic (100%)
Tel.: (420) 257091111
Web Site: http://www.unicreditleasing.cz
Insurance Brokers
N.A.I.C.S.: 524210

Subsidiary (Domestic):

Z LEASING ALFA IMMOBILIEN LEASING GESELLSCHAFT M.B.H. (4)
Operng 21, 1040, Vienna, Austria
Tel.: (43) 1 58808
Real Estate Lending Services
N.A.I.C.S.: 531390

Z LEASING ARKTUR IMMOBILIEN LEASING GESELLSCHAFT M.B.H. (4)
Operngasse 21, 1040, Vienna, Austria
Tel.: (43) 1 71570350
Real Estate Lending Services
N.A.I.C.S.: 531390

Z LEASING GAMA IMMOBILIEN LEASING GESELLSCHAFT M.B.H. (4)
Operngasse 21, 1040, Vienna, Austria
Tel.: (43) 1 711920
Real Estate Lending Services
N.A.I.C.S.: 531390

Z LEASING KALLISTO IMMOBILIEN LEASING GESELLSCHAFT M.B.H. (4)
Operngasse 21, 1040, Vienna, Austria
Tel.: (43) 1 588 08
Real Estate Lending Services
N.A.I.C.S.: 531390

Z LEASING NEREIDE IMMOBILIEN LEASING GESELLSCHAFT M.B.H. (4)
Operngasse 21, 1040, Vienna, Austria
Tel.: (43) 158808 0
Real Estate Lending Services
N.A.I.C.S.: 531390

Z LEASING VENUS IMMOBILIEN LEASING GESELLSCHAFT M.B.H. (4)
Opera Gasse 21, 1040, Vienna, Austria
Tel.: (43) 1 58808 0
Real Estate Lending Services
N.A.I.C.S.: 531390

Z LEASING VOLANS IMMOBILIEN LEASING GESELLSCHAFT M.B.H. (4)
Operngasse 21, 1040, Vienna, Austria
Tel.: (43) 158808 0
Real Estate Lending Services
N.A.I.C.S.: 531390

Subsidiary (Non-US):

Unicredit Leasing, d.o.o. (3)
Smartinska cesta 140, 1000, Ljubljana, Slovenia
Tel.: (386) 1 5206 000
Web Site: http://www.unicreditleasing.si
Financial Lending Services
N.A.I.C.S.: 522220

Subsidiary (Non-US):

UNICREDIT LEASING TECHNIKUM GMBH (2)
Operngasse 21, 1040, Vienna, Austria
Tel.: (43) 1 588 08 0
Financial Management Services
N.A.I.C.S.: 523999

UNICREDIT MOBILIEN LEASING GMBH (2)
Operngasse 21, 1040, Vienna, Austria
Tel.: (43) 1588080
Real Estate Lending Services
N.A.I.C.S.: 531390

Subsidiary (Domestic):

M. A. V. 7., BANK AUSTRIA LEASING BAUTRAGER GMBH & CO.OHG. (3)
Operngasse 21, 1040, Vienna, Austria
Tel.: (43) 158 80 80
Real Estate Manangement Services
N.A.I.C.S.: 531390

Subsidiary (Non-US):

UNICREDIT PARTNER D.O.O (2)
Heinzelova 33, 10000, Zagreb, Croatia
Tel.: (385) 1 24 47 100
Financial Management Services
N.A.I.C.S.: 523999

Subsidiary (Domestic):

UNICREDIT REAL ESTATE SOCIETA CONSORTILE PER AZIONI (2)
Via Dante 1, 16121, Genoa, Italy
Tel.: (39) 02 37721
Web Site: http://www.unicreditrealestate.it
Real Estate Manangement Services
N.A.I.C.S.: 531390

Subsidiary (Non-US):

UNICREDIT TURN-AROUND MANAGEMENT CEE GMBH (2)
Lassallestrasse 5, 1020, Vienna, Austria
Tel.: (43) 5 05 05 56456
Financial Management Services
N.A.I.C.S.: 523999
Robert Zadrazil (CEO)

UNO-EINKAUFSZENTRUM-VERWALTUNGSGESELLSCHAFT MBH (2)
Im Backerfeld 1, Leonding, 4060, Austria
Tel.: (43) 732 67 74 75
Web Site: http://www.uno-shopping.at
Emp.: 5
Shopping Mall Operator
N.A.I.C.S.: 531120

Roland Pinz (Gen Mgr)

Division (Domestic):

UniCredit Banca S.p.A. (2)
Milan Branch Piazza Gae Aulenti 4 Tower C, 20154, Milan, Italy (100%)
Tel.: (39) 0516408478
Web Site: http://www.unicredit.it
Sales Range: $300-349.9 Million
Provider of Banking Services
N.A.I.C.S.: 522320

Group (Non-US):

UniCredit Bank Aktiengesellschaft (2)
Kardinal Faulhaber Strasse 1, D 80333, Munich, Germany
Tel.: (49) 893780
Web Site: http://www.hypovereinsbank.de
Sales Range: $5-14.9 Billion
Emp.: 19,247
Bank Holding Company
N.A.I.C.S.: 551111
Federico Ghizzoni (Chm-Supervisory Bd)

Subsidiary (Non-US):

AWT International Trade AG (3)
Hohenstaufengasse 6, 1010, Vienna, Austria
Tel.: (43) 50543250
Web Site: http://www.ba-ca.com
International Trade Financing
N.A.I.C.S.: 522299

Subsidiary (Domestic):

BD INDUSTRIEBETEILIGUNGSGESELLSCHAFT MBH (3)
Am Tucherpark 1, 80538, Munich, Germany
Tel.: (49) 893780
Investment Management Service
N.A.I.C.S.: 523999

BFL BETEILIGUNGSGESELLSCHAFT FUR FLUGZEUG-LEASING MBH (3)
Am Tucherpark 12, 80538, Munich, Germany
Tel.: (49) 89 21326417
Aircraft Leasing Services
N.A.I.C.S.: 532411

Bankhaus Neelmeyer AG (3)
Am Markt 14 16, 28195, Bremen, Germany
Tel.: (49) 42136030
Web Site: http://www.neelmeyer.de
Sales Range: $150-199.9 Million
Emp.: 320
Bank
N.A.I.C.S.: 522299

Subsidiary (Domestic):

BONUM ANLAGE-UND BETEILIGUNGSGESELLSCHAFT MBH (4)
Schwachhauser Heerstrasse 193, 28211, Bremen, Germany
Tel.: (49) 421 44 41 91
Web Site: http://www.bonum-bremen.de
Real Estate Manangement Services
N.A.I.C.S.: 531390

Subsidiary (Domestic):

Bayerische Beteiligungsgesellschaft mbH (3)
Koniginstrasse 23, 80539, Munich, Germany
Tel.: (49) 89122280100
Assets: $293,432,766
Fiscal Year-end: 09/30/2004
Investment Company
Peter Pauli (Co-Mng Dir)

FOOD & MORE GMBH (3)
Buchungsservice Tucherpark 16, 80538, Munich, Germany
Tel.: (49) 89 37829800
Web Site: http://www.erholung-in-der-natur.de
Restaurant Management Services
N.A.I.C.S.: 722511

Subsidiary (US):

HVB Capital Markets, Inc. (3)
150 E 42nd St, New York, NY 10017-5612
Tel.: (212) 672-6000

Web Site: http://www.hvb.com
Sales Range: $75-99.9 Million
Emp.: 200
Brokerage Firm
N.A.I.C.S.: 523150

Subsidiary (Domestic):

HVB EXPORT LEASING GMBH (3)
Am Eisbach 4, 80538, Munich, Bavaria, Germany
Tel.: (49) 89 37826281
Financial Management Services
N.A.I.C.S.: 523999

HVB GESELLSCHAFT FUR GEBAUDE BETEILIGUNGS GMBH (3)
Am Eisbach 3, 80538, Munich, Germany
Tel.: (49) 89 378 0
Investment Management Service
N.A.I.C.S.: 523999

HVB Immobilien AG (3)
Am Eisbach 3, D-80538, Munich, Germany
Tel.: (49) 8937864374
Web Site: http://www.hvbimmobilien-ag.de
Sales Range: $150-199.9 Million
Emp.: 370
Real Estate Services
N.A.I.C.S.: 531190
Peter Weidenhofer (Chm, CEO & Member-Mgmt Bd)

Subsidiary (Domestic):

HVB TECTA GMBH (4)
Am Tucherpark 16, Munich, 80538, Bavaria, Germany
Tel.: (49) 89 37 84 93 78
Financial Management Services
N.A.I.C.S.: 523999
Rolf Kroener (Mgr)

Subsidiary (Domestic):

TERRENO GRUNDSTUCKSVERWALTUNG GMBH (5)
Am Tucherpark 16, 80538, Munich, Germany
Tel.: (49) 89 378 49320
Real Estate Manangement Services
N.A.I.C.S.: 531390

Subsidiary (Domestic):

MILLETERRA GESELLSCHAFT FUR IMMOBILIENVERWALTUNG MBH (4)
Am Tucherpark 16, 80538, Munich, Bavaria, Germany
Tel.: (49) 89 3780
Real Estate Manangement Services
N.A.I.C.S.: 531390

Subsidiary (Domestic):

NF OBJEKT FFM GMBH (4)
Am Tucherpark 16, 80538, Munich, Bavaria, Germany
Tel.: (49) 8937849378
Financial Management Services
N.A.I.C.S.: 523999

NF OBJEKT MUNCHEN GMBH (4)
Am Tucherpark 16, 80538, Munich, Bavaria, Germany
Tel.: (49) 89 37849378
Financial Management Services
N.A.I.C.S.: 523999

NF OBJEKTE BERLIN GMBH (4)
Am Tucherpark 16, 80538, Munich, Bavaria, Germany
Tel.: (49) 89 37849378
Financial Management Services
N.A.I.C.S.: 523999

RHOTERRA GESELLSCHAFT FUR IMMOBILIENVERWALTUNG MBH (4)
Am Tucherpark 16, 80538, Munich, Germany
Tel.: (49) 89 44990
Real Estate Manangement Services
N.A.I.C.S.: 531390

Subsidiary (Domestic):

HVB Leasing Gmbh (3)
Heidenkampsweg 75, 20097, Hamburg, Germany
Tel.: (49) 40236430
Web Site: http://www.hvbleasing.de

AND PRIVATE COMPANIES — UNICREDIT S.P.A.

Sales Range: $150-199.9 Million
Emp.: 260
Leasing Services
N.A.I.C.S.: 533110

HVB PROFIL GESELLSCHAFT FUR PERSONALMANAGEMENT MBH (3)
Grillparzerstrabe, 81675, Munich, Germany
Tel.: (49) 89 378 25417
Financial Management Services
N.A.I.C.S.: 522320

HVB TRUST PENSIONSFONDS AG (3)
Arabellastr 12, 81925, Munich, Bavaria, Germany
Tel.: (49) 89 3 78 0
Financial Management Services
N.A.I.C.S.: 523999

Subsidiary (Non-US):

Industrie-Immobilien-Verwaltung GmbH (3)
Herrengasse 17, 1010, Vienna, Austria
International Financial Services
N.A.I.C.S.: 522299

Subsidiary (Domestic):

PLANETHOME AG (3)
Apianstrasse 8, Unterfohring, 85774, Munich, Germany
Tel.: (49) 89 76774 0
Web Site: http://www.planethome.de
Real Estate Manangement Services
N.A.I.C.S.: 531390
Ludwig Wiesbauer (Mng Dir)

Subsidiary (Non-US):

BANK AUSTRIA IMMOBILIENSERVICE GMBH (4)
Lassallestrasse 1, 1020, Vienna, Austria
Tel.: (43) 1 5137477 0
Web Site: http://www.ba-is.at
Sales Range: $25-49.9 Million
Emp.: 50
Real Estate Consulting Service
N.A.I.C.S.: 531390
Daniel Maxian (Mng Dir)

Subsidiary (Domestic):

ENDERLEIN & CO. GMBH (4)
Neumarkt 11-13, 33602, Bielefeld, Germany
Tel.: (49) 521 5800 40
Web Site: http://www.enderlein.com
Emp.: 24
Real Estate Manangement Services
N.A.I.C.S.: 531390

PLANETHOME GMBH (4)
Janderstr 5, Mannheim, 68199, Baden-Wurttemberg, Germany
Tel.: (49) 621 87559980
Financial Management Services
N.A.I.C.S.: 523999

Subsidiary (Non-US):

Redstone Mortgages Limited (3)
Gateway House Gargrave Road, Skipton, BD23 2HL, N Yorkshire, United Kingdom
Tel.: (44) 844 892 2730
Web Site: http://www.redstonemortgages.com
Financial Management Services
N.A.I.C.S.: 523999

Subsidiary (Domestic):

STATUS VERMOGENSVERWALTUNG GMBH (3)
Schleifmuhlenweg 9, 19061, Schwerin, Germany
Tel.: (49) 385 521 47 55
Web Site: http://www.status-gmbh.de
Asset Management Services
N.A.I.C.S.: 523940

UNICREDIT BETEILIGUNGS GMBH (3)
Arabellastr 14, 81925, Munich, Bavaria, Germany
Tel.: (49) 89 37825963
Financial Management Services
N.A.I.C.S.: 523999

UNICREDIT DIRECT SERVICES GMBH (3)
Heinrich-Wieland-Strasse 170, 81735, Munich, Germany
Tel.: (49) 89 55877 0
Web Site: http://www.directservices.unicredit.eu
Business Management Consulting Services
N.A.I.C.S.: 541618

UNICREDIT GLOBAL BUSINESS SERVICES GMBH (3)
Jahnstr 3, 40215, Dusseldorf, Germany
Tel.: (49) 211 8986 644
Financial Management Services
N.A.I.C.S.: 523999

UNICREDIT LEASING GMBH (3)
Nagelsweg 53, 20097, Hamburg, Germany
Tel.: (49) 40236430
Financial Management Services
N.A.I.C.S.: 523999

Subsidiary (Domestic):

BALEA SOFT VERWALTUNGSGESELLSCHAFT MBH (4)
Heidenkampsweg 75, Hamburg, 20097, Germany
Tel.: (49) 40236430
Financial Management Services
N.A.I.C.S.: 523999

Subsidiary (Domestic):

UniCredit Bank AG (3)
Kardinal Faulhaber Strasse 1, 80333, Munich, Germany
Tel.: (49) 89 37 80
Web Site: http://www.unicreditgroup.eu
Banking Services
N.A.I.C.S.: 522110

Subsidiary (Domestic):

BAYERISCHE WOHNUNGSGESELLSCHAFT FUR HANDEL UND INDUSTRIE, GESELLSCHAFT MIT BESCHRKTER HAFTUNG (4)
Am Tucherpark 16, 80538, Munich, Bavaria, Germany
Tel.: (49) 89 378 0
Financial Management Services
N.A.I.C.S.: 523999

GRUNDSTUCKSGESELLSCHAFT SIMON BESCHRANKT HAFTENDE KOMMANDITGESELLSCHAF (4)
Am Tucherpark 16, 80538, Munich, Bavaria, Germany
Tel.: (49) 89 37849305
Real Estate Manangement Services
N.A.I.C.S.: 531390

H & B IMMOBILIEN GMBH & CO. OBJEKTE KG (4)
Am Tucherpark 16, 80538, Munich, Bavaria, Germany
Tel.: (49) 8944990
Real Estate Manangement Services
N.A.I.C.S.: 531390

Subsidiary (Non-US):

UniCredit Bank Austria AG (3)
Schottengasse 628, 1010, Vienna, Austria
Tel.: (43) 5050525
Web Site: http://www.bankaustria.at
Sales Range: $1-4.9 Billion
Banking Services
N.A.I.C.S.: 522299
Robert Zadrazil (CEO)

Subsidiary (Non-US):

ATFBank JSC (4)
100 Furmanov Str, 050000, Almaty, Kazakhstan
Tel.: (7) 727 258 3016
Web Site: http://www.atfbank.kz
Sales Range: Less than $1 Million
Commercial Banking Services
N.A.I.C.S.: 522110
Galimzhan Yessenov (Chm-Supervisory Bd)

Subsidiary (Non-US):

ATF CAPITAL B.V. (5)
Schouwburgplein 30 34 West Blaak, Rotterdam, Netherlands
Tel.: (31) 102245333
Financial Management Services
N.A.I.C.S.: 523999

UNICREDIT BANK OJSC (5)
D Galitsky st 14, Volynska Region, 43016, Lutsk, Ukraine
Tel.: (380) 33 277 62 10
Web Site: http://www.en.unicreditbank.com.ua
Commercial Banking Services
N.A.I.C.S.: 522110

Subsidiary (Domestic):

B & C Industrieholding GmbH (4)
Am Graben 19 12, A1010, Vienna, Austria
Tel.: (43) 153325330
Web Site: http://bcgruppe.at
Holding Company
N.A.I.C.S.: 551112
Wolfgang Hofer (Chm-Supervisory Bd)

B&C Privatstiftung (4)
Universitatsring 14, 1010, Vienna, Austria
Tel.: (43) 1531010
Web Site: http://bcgruppe.at
Asset Management Services
N.A.I.C.S.: 523999
Erich Hampel (Chm)

Subsidiary (Domestic):

Schur Flexibles Holding GesmbH (5)
IZ No Sud Strasse 1 Objekt 50 Haus C, 2351, Wiener Neudorf, Austria
Tel.: (43) 2252 266014
Web Site: http://www.schurflexibles.com
Emp.: 1,750
Holding Company Flexible Packaging Solutions Systems & Services
N.A.I.C.S.: 551112
Friedrich Humer (Chief Sls Officer)

Subsidiary (Non-US):

Alfa Beta Roto S.A. (6)
Kapsorahi 2, 12241, Athens, Greece
Tel.: (30) 210 3456 454
Web Site: http://www.alfabetaroto.com
Flexible Packaging Products Mfr
N.A.I.C.S.: 326112

Plant (Domestic):

Alfa Beta Roto S.A. (7)
Komotini Industrial Area, 69100, Komotini, Greece
Tel.: (30) 2531038691
Web Site: http://www.alfabetaroto.com
Flexible Packaging Products Mfr
N.A.I.C.S.: 326112

Subsidiary (Non-US):

Danapak Flexibles A/S (6)
Strudsbergsvej 3, DK-4200, Slagelse, Denmark (100%)
Tel.: (45) 65480000
Web Site: http://www.danapakflex.com
Emp.: 190
Flexible Packaging Products Mfr
N.A.I.C.S.: 322220
Lars Wiggers Hyldgaard (Mng Dir)

Schur Flexibles Benelux B.V. (6)
Zernikelaan 4, 9351 VA, Leek, Netherlands
Tel.: (31) 594 513 010
Web Site: http://www.schurflexibles.com
Flexible Packaging Products Mfr
N.A.I.C.S.: 326112

Schur Flexibles Denmark A/S (6)
Gammel Skartved 11, 6091, Bjert, Denmark
Tel.: (45) 76 32 32 32
Web Site: http://www.schurflexibles.com
Emp.: 40
Flexible Packaging Products Mfr
N.A.I.C.S.: 326112

Schur Flexibles Dixie GmbH (6)
Roemerstrasse 12, 87437, Kempten, Germany
Tel.: (49) 831 5616 0
Web Site: http://www.schurflexibles.com
Emp.: 100
Flexible Packaging Products Mfr
N.A.I.C.S.: 326111

Schur Flexibles Finland Oy (6)
Jakobsgatan 53, 68601, Jakobstad, Finland
Tel.: (358) 20 768 6111

Web Site: http://www.schurflexibles.com
Flexible Packaging Products Mfr
N.A.I.C.S.: 326111

Schur Flexibles Germany GmbH (6)
Leibigstrasse 7, 24941, Flensburg, Germany
Tel.: (49) 461 505 640 0
Web Site: http://www.schurflexibles.com
Flexible Packaging Products Mfr
N.A.I.C.S.: 326111

Schur Flexibles Moneta (6)
Cukrovarska 8/32, 075 01, Trebisov, Slovakia
Tel.: (421) 566684218
Web Site: http://www.schurflexibles.com
Flexible Packaging Products Mfr
N.A.I.C.S.: 326112

Schur Flexibles Poland Sp. z o.o. (6)
Ul Pilotow 12, Bogucin, 62 006, Poznan, Poland
Tel.: (48) 61 8151 600
Web Site: http://www.schurflexibles.com
Flexible Packaging Products Mfr
N.A.I.C.S.: 326112

Schur Flexibles Vacufol GmbH (6)
Hinter den Garten 10, 87730, Bad Gronenbach, Germany
Tel.: (49) 8334 2590 0
Web Site: http://www.schurflexibles.com
Emp.: 125
Flexible Packaging Products Mfr
N.A.I.C.S.: 326112

Subsidiary (Domestic):

BA GVG-HOLDING GMBH (4)
Schottengasse 6-8, 1010, Vienna, Austria
Tel.: (43) 505050
Investment Management Service
N.A.I.C.S.: 523999

BA-CA WIEN MITTE HOLDING GMBH (4)
Renngasse 2, 1010, Vienna, Austria
Tel.: (43) 50 5050
Investment Management Service
N.A.I.C.S.: 523999

BANK AUSTRIA CREDITANSTALT LEASING IMMOBILIENANLAGEN GMBH (4)
Operngasse 21, 1040, Vienna, Austria
Tel.: (43) 1588080
Real Estate Manangement Services
N.A.I.C.S.: 531190

Subsidiary (Non-US):

Bank Austria Creditanstalt d.d. Ljubljana (4)
Smartinska 140, 1000, Ljubljana, Slovenia
Tel.: (386) 15876600
Web Site: http://www.unicreditogroup.si
Sales Range: $50-74.9 Million
Emp.: 550
Private & Retail Banking Services
N.A.I.C.S.: 522320
Helmut Bernkopf (Chm)

Subsidiary (Domestic):

Bank Austria Finanzservice GmbH (4)
Lassallestrasse 5 4 Stock A-1020 Wien, Vienna, 1020, Austria
Tel.: (43) 5050553000
Web Site: http://www.bacaf.at
Sales Range: $50-74.9 Million
Emp.: 66
Financial Services
N.A.I.C.S.: 522299
Arrey Mayoor (Mng Dir)

Bank Austria Private Banking AG (4)
Hohenstaufengasse 6, Vienna, 1010, Austria
Tel.: (43) 5 05 05 46000
Web Site: http://www.bankaustria.at
Commercial Banking Services
N.A.I.C.S.: 522110
Ruth Iwonski-Bozo (Gen Mgr)

Bank Austria Real Invest GmbH (4)
Lassallestrasse 5, A-1020, Vienna, Austria
Tel.: (43) 133171

UNICREDIT S.P.A.

UniCredit S.p.A.—(Continued)
Web Site: http://www.bacat.at
Sales Range: $25-49.9 Million
Emp.: 40
Finance Consultation
N.A.I.C.S.: 523940

Subsidiary (Domestic):

BANK AUSTRIA REAL INVEST ASSET MANAGEMENT GMBH (5)
Lassallestrasse 5, 1020, Vienna, Austria
Tel.: (43) 1 331 71 0
Sales Range: $125-149.9 Million
Real Estate Development Services
N.A.I.C.S.: 531390
Harald Heinzl *(Mng Dir)*

BANK AUSTRIA REAL INVEST CLIENT INVESTMENT GMBH (5)
Lassallestrasse 5, 1020, Vienna, Austria
Tel.: (43) 1 331 71 0
Web Site: http://www.realinvest.at
Real Estate Investment Services
N.A.I.C.S.: 523940

BANK AUSTRIA REAL INVEST IMMOBILIEN-KAPITALANLAGE GMBH (5)
Lassallestrasse 5, Vienna, 1020, Austria
Tel.: (43) 1 331 71 0
Web Site: http://www.realinvest.at
Real Estate Manangement Services
N.A.I.C.S.: 531390

PROMETHEUS IMMOBILIENERRICHTUNGS-UND-BETEILIGUNGS GMBH (5)
Lassallestr 5, 1020, Vienna, Austria
Tel.: (43) 133171
Real Estate Manangement Services
N.A.I.C.S.: 531390

TREUCONSULT BETEILIGUNGSGESELLSCHAFT M.B.H. (5)
Lassallestr 5, 1020, Vienna, Austria
Tel.: (43) 133171
Investment Management Service
N.A.I.C.S.: 523999

Subsidiary (Domestic):

TREUCONSULT PROPERTY BETA GMBH (6)
Lassallestrasse 5, 1020, Vienna, Austria
Tel.: (43) 1 331 71 0
Real Estate Manangement Services
N.A.I.C.S.: 531390

TREUCONSULT PROPERTY EPSILON GMBH (6)
Lassallestrasse 5, 1020, Vienna, Austria
Tel.: (43) 1 331 71 0
Real Estate Manangement Services
N.A.I.C.S.: 531390

Subsidiary (Domestic):

CARD COMPLETE SERVICE BANK AG (4)
Lassallestrasse 3, 1020, Vienna, Austria
Tel.: (43) 1 711 11 0
Web Site: http://www.cardcomplete.com
Emp.: 400
Commercial Banking Services
N.A.I.C.S.: 522110

CARDS & SYSTEMS EDV-DIENSTLEISTUNGS GMBH (4)
Landstrasser Hauptstrasse 5, 1030, Vienna, Austria
Tel.: (43) 1790230
Web Site: http://www.cardsys.at
Emp.: 35
Credit Card Issuing Services
N.A.I.C.S.: 522210
Florian Neudecker *(CTO)*

DOMUS CLEAN REINIGUNGS GMBH (4)
Althanstrasse 21-25, 1090, Vienna, Austria
Tel.: (43) 1 254 00 53516
Janitorial Services
N.A.I.C.S.: 561720

DOMUS FACILITY MANAGEMENT GMBH (4)
Althanstrasse 21-25, 1090, Vienna, Austria
Tel.: (43) 1 25400 0
Web Site: http://www.domus-fm.at
Facility Management Services
N.A.I.C.S.: 561210

FactorBank Aktiengesellschaft (4)
Floragasse 7, 1040, Vienna, Austria
Tel.: (43) 1506780
Web Site: http://www.factorbank.com
Sales Range: $1-9.9 Million
Emp.: 40
Factoring & Debtor Services
N.A.I.C.S.: 522299

MEZZANIN FINANZIERUNGS AG (4)
Operngasse 6, 1010, Vienna, Austria
Tel.: (43) 1 513 41 97 21
Web Site: http://www.mezz.at
Financial Management Services
N.A.I.C.S.: 523999

POLLUX IMMOBILIEN GMBH (4)
Marzstr 45, 1150, Vienna, Austria
Tel.: (43) 1 786 54 21
Real Estate Manangement Services
N.A.I.C.S.: 531390

RAMSES IMMOBILIEN LEASING GESELLSCHAFT MBH & CO OG (4)
Althanstrasse 21-25, 1090, Vienna, Austria
Tel.: (43) 5 05 05 0
Real Estate Lending Services
N.A.I.C.S.: 531390

RAMSES-IMMOBILIENHOLDING GMBH (4)
Althanstrasse 21-25, 1090, Vienna, Austria
Tel.: (43) 5 05 05 0
Financial Management Services
N.A.I.C.S.: 523999

Subsidiary (Non-US):

SINERA AG (4)
Baarerstrasse 43, 6304, Zug, Switzerland
Tel.: (41) 417117876
Investment Management Service
N.A.I.C.S.: 523999

Subsidiary (Domestic):

Schoellerbank Aktiengesellschaft (4)
Palais Rothschild Renngasse 3, 1010, Vienna, Austria
Tel.: (43) 1534710
Web Site: http://www.skwbschoellerbank.at
Sales Range: $10-24.9 Million
Private Banking Services
N.A.I.C.S.: 522299

Subsidiary (Domestic):

CAFU VERMOEGENSVERWALTUNG GMBH & CO OG (5)
Renngasse 3, 1010, Vienna, Austria
Tel.: (43) 1 313 32 0
Asset Management Services
N.A.I.C.S.: 523940

SCHOELLERBANK INVEST AG (5)
Sterneckstrasse 5, 5024, Salzburg, Austria
Tel.: (43) 662885511
Investment Management Service
N.A.I.C.S.: 523999

Division (Domestic):

UNICREDIT BANK AUSTRIA AG - Global Securities Services Division (4)
Julius Tandler Platz 3, 1090, Vienna, Austria
Tel.: (43) 50505 57311
Web Site: http://www.unicreditgroup.eu
Commercial Banking Services
N.A.I.C.S.: 522110

Subsidiary (Non-US):

UNICREDIT BANK SERBIA JSC (4)
Rajiceva 27-29, 11000, Belgrade, Serbia
Tel.: (381) 11 3777 888
Web Site: http://www.unicreditbank.rs
Commercial Banking Services
N.A.I.C.S.: 522110

UNICREDIT CAIB CZECH REPUBLIC A.S. (4)
BB Centrum-Filadelfie 12th floor Zeletavska 1525/1, 140 00, Prague, Czech Republic
Tel.: (420) 241 095 611
Management Consulting Services
N.A.I.C.S.: 541618

UNICREDIT CAIB ROMANIA SRL (4)
Str Grigore Mora 37, Bucharest, Romania
Tel.: (40) 723776291
Financial Management Services
N.A.I.C.S.: 523999

UNICREDIT CAIB SLOVENIJA, D.O.O. (4)
Dvorakova ulica 3, 1000, Ljubljana, Slovenia
Tel.: (386) 1 234 00 00
Financial Management Services
N.A.I.C.S.: 523999

Subsidiary (Domestic):

UNIVERSALE INTERNATIONAL REALITAETEN GMBH (4)
Leopold Moses-Gasse 4/2/2B, Vienna, 1021, Austria
Tel.: (43) 1 513 9727 0
Web Site: http://www.universale-int.com
Sales Range: $25-49.9 Million
Emp.: 10
Real Estate Manangement Services
N.A.I.C.S.: 531390
Gerhard Engelsberger *(Mng Dir)*

Subsidiary (Domestic):

DIRANA LIEGENSCHAFTSVERWERTUNGSGESELLSCHAFT M.B.H. (5)
Leopold-Moses-Gasse 4 Stiege 2 Top 2b, Vienna, 1020, Austria
Tel.: (43) 1 513 97 27 0
Real Estate Manangement Services
N.A.I.C.S.: 531390

Subsidiary (Non-US):

ISB UNIVERSALE BAU GMBH (5)
Judith-Auer-Strasse 2a, 10369, Berlin, Germany
Tel.: (49) 30 97602204
Real Estate Development Services
N.A.I.C.S.: 531390

Subsidiary (Domestic):

RANA-LIEGENSCHAFTSVERWERTUNG GMBH (5)
Leopold-Moses-Gasse 4 Stiege 2 Top 2b, 1020, Vienna, Austria
Tel.: (43) 151397270
Real Estate Manangement Services
N.A.I.C.S.: 531390

Subsidiary (Non-US):

UniCredit Bank Czech Republic a.s. (4)
Nam Republiky 3 A, 110 00, Prague, Czech Republic
Tel.: (420) 221119611
Web Site: http://www.unicreditbank.cz
Sales Range: $250-299.9 Million
Emp.: 1,000
Private Banking Services
N.A.I.C.S.: 522299
Jiri Kunert *(Chm-Supervisory Bd)*

UniCredit Bank Hungary Zrt. (4)
Szabadsag place 5 6, 1054, Budapest, Hungary
Tel.: (36) 3253200
Web Site: http://www.unicreditbank.hu
Sales Range: $100-124.9 Million
Emp.: 1,100
Retail & Corporate Banking Services
N.A.I.C.S.: 522110
Silvano Silvestri *(Chm-Supervisory Bd)*

UniCredit Bank SA (4)
Sector 1 Bd Expozitiei No 1F, 12101, Bucharest, Romania
Tel.: (40) 212002000
Web Site: https://www.unicredit.ro
Commercial Banking Services
N.A.I.C.S.: 522110

UniCredit Bank a.d. (4)
Marije Bursac 7, 78000, Banja Luka, Bosnia & Herzegovina **(90.92%)**
Tel.: (387) 51243200
Web Site: https://www.unicreditbank-bl.ba
Rev.: $37,309,296
Assets: $700,206,344
Liabilities: $564,511,030
Net Worth: $135,695,313
Earnings: $12,498,628
Emp.: 386
Fiscal Year-end: 12/31/2023
Banking Services
N.A.I.C.S.: 522110
Sinisa Adzic *(Exec Officer-Corp Investment Banking)*

ZAO UNICREDIT BANK (4)
9 Prechistenskaya emb, 119034, Moscow, Russia
Tel.: (7) 4952587200
Web Site: http://www.unicreditbank.ru
Sales Range: $1-4.9 Billion
Emp.: 3,666
Commercial Banking Services
N.A.I.C.S.: 522110
Dmitry Mokhnachev *(Member-Mgmt Bd)*

Zagreb nekretnine doo (4)
Nova Ves 17, 10000, Zagreb, Croatia **(100%)**
Tel.: (385) 14860111
Web Site: http://www.zane.hr
Sales Range: $100-124.9 Million
Emp.: 45
Commericial Banking
N.A.I.C.S.: 522110

Subsidiary (Non-US):

ZANE BH DOO (5)
Branilaca Sarajeva 20, Sarajevo, 71000, Bosnia & Herzegovina
Tel.: (387) 33 211 667
Commercial Banking Services
N.A.I.C.S.: 522110

Subsidiary (Non-US):

Zagrebacka banka dd (4)
Trg bana Josipa Jelacica 10, 10000, Zagreb, Croatia **(84.21%)**
Tel.: (385) 13773333
Web Site: https://www.zaba.hr
Rev.: $897,450,050
Assets: $27,146,484,163
Liabilities: $24,186,996,361
Net Worth: $2,959,487,803
Earnings: $561,872,171
Emp.: 4,611
Fiscal Year-end: 12/31/2023
Commericial Banking
N.A.I.C.S.: 522110
Dalibor Cubela *(Vice Chm-Mgmt Bd & Gen Mgr)*

Subsidiary (Domestic):

Centar Kaptol doo (5)
Nova Ves 17, Zagreb, 10000, Croatia **(100%)**
Tel.: (385) 14860241
Web Site: http://www.centarkaptol.hr
Sales Range: $50-74.9 Million
Emp.: 13
Shopping Stores
N.A.I.C.S.: 561439

POMINVEST DD (5)
Ulica Ivana Gundulica 26/A, Split, Croatia
Tel.: (385) 21390301
Real Estate Development Services
N.A.I.C.S.: 531390

PRVA STAMBENA STEDIONICA DD (5)
Savska 60 Centrala, Zagreb, 10000, Croatia
Tel.: (385) 1 6065 111
Web Site: http://www.prva-stambena.hr
Commercial Banking Services
N.A.I.C.S.: 522110

Subsidiary (Non-US):

UniCredit Bank d.d. (5)
Kardinala Stepinca b b, 88000, Mostar, Bosnia & Herzegovina
Tel.: (387) 36312112
Web Site: https://www.unicreditbank.ba
Rev.: $123,433,232
Assets: $4,044,389,903
Liabilities: $3,546,727,637
Net Worth: $497,662,267
Earnings: $91,426,798

AND PRIVATE COMPANIES

UNICREDIT S.P.A.

Emp.: 1,157
Fiscal Year-end: 12/31/2023
Commercial Banking Services
N.A.I.C.S.: 522110
Igor Bilandzija *(Member-Mgmt Bd)*

Subsidiary (Domestic):

ZB INVEST DOO (5)
Ivana Lucica 2A Eurotower, Zagreb, 10000, Croatia
Tel.: (385) 1 4803 399
Web Site: http://www.zbi.hr
Sales Range: $125-149.9 Million
Emp.: 24
Investment Management Service
N.A.I.C.S.: 523999
Hrvoje Krstulovic *(Pres)*

Subsidiary (Non-US):

UniCredit Luxembourg S.A (3)
10 rue Jean Monnet, 2180, Luxembourg, Luxembourg
Tel.: (352) 4272 1
Web Site: http://www.unicreditbank.lu
Sales Range: $75-99.9 Million
Emp.: 200
Investment Banking Services
N.A.I.C.S.: 523999
Theodor Weimer *(Chm-Supervisory Bd)*

Subsidiary (Domestic):

VERBA VERWALTUNGSGESELL-SCHAFT MBH (3)
Am Tucherpark 14, 80538, Munich, Germany
Tel.: (49) 893780
Investment Management Service
N.A.I.C.S.: 523999

VERWALTUNGSGESELLSCHAFT KATHARINENHOF MBH (3)
Nagelsweg 49 St Georg, 20097, Hamburg, Germany
Tel.: (49) 40369201
Investment Management Service
N.A.I.C.S.: 523999

WEALTH MANAGEMENT CAPITAL HOLDING GMBH (3)
Am Eisbach 3, Munich, 80538, Germany
Tel.: (49) 89 678 205 500
Web Site: http://www.wealthcap.com
Emp.: 253
Investment Management Service
N.A.I.C.S.: 523940

Subsidiary (Domestic):

H.F.S. HYPO-FONDSBETEILIGUNGEN FUR SACHWERTE GMBH (4)
Arabellastrasse 14, 81925, Munich, Germany
Tel.: (49) 89 6782050
Financial Management Services
N.A.I.C.S.: 523999

Subsidiary (Domestic):

H.F.S. ZWEITMARKTFONDS DEUTSCHLAND 4 GMBH & CO. KG (5)
Am Eisbach 3, Munich, 80538, Germany
Tel.: (49) 896782050
Emp.: 253
Financial Management Services
N.A.I.C.S.: 523999
Rainer Krutten *(Gen Mgr)*

Subsidiary (Domestic):

WEALTHCAP PEIA MANAGEMENT GMBH (4)
Am Eisbach 3, 80538, Munich, Bavaria, Germany
Tel.: (49) 89 678205 0
Web Site: http://www.wealthcap.com
Emp.: 250
Financial Management Services
N.A.I.C.S.: 523999
Gabriele Volz *(Gen Mgr)*

Subsidiary (Non-US):

UniCredit Bulbank Inc. (2)
7 Sveta Nedelya Square, Sofia, 1000, Bulgaria
Tel.: (359) 29232111
Web Site: http://www.unicreditbulbank.bg
Sales Range: $250-299.9 Million
Emp.: 4,000
Banking Services
N.A.I.C.S.: 522110
Alberto Devoto *(Chm-Supervisory Bd)*

Subsidiary (Domestic):

HYPOVEREINS IMMOBILIEN EOOD (3)
1 Ivan Vazov Str, Sofia, 1000, Bulgaria
Tel.: (359) 2 809 974
Real Estate Management Services
N.A.I.C.S.: 531390

Division (Domestic):

UniCredit Corporate Banking Services S.p.A. (2)
Piazza Cordusio, 20123, Milan, Italy (100%)
Tel.: (39) 0288621
Web Site: http://www.unicredit.it
Sales Range: $150-199.9 Million
Emp.: 300
Corporate Banking Services
N.A.I.C.S.: 522110

Subsidiary (Domestic):

UniCredit Factoring S.p.A. (3)
Via Calabria 31, 20158, Milan, Italy
Tel.: (39) 0237731
Web Site: http://www.credfact.it
Sales Range: $50-74.9 Million
Emp.: 80
Factoring Services
N.A.I.C.S.: 522299

Subsidiary (Non-US):

UniCredit Family Financing Bank S.p.A (2)
Eisbach 4, 80538, Munich, Germany
Tel.: (49) 89 389979 0
Web Site: http://www.ucfin.de
Financial Management Services
N.A.I.C.S.: 523999
Markus Kilb *(Gen Mgr)*

Division (Domestic):

UniCredit Private Banking S.p.A. (2)
Via Arsenale 21, 10121, Turin, Italy
Tel.: (39) 0115605502
Web Site: http://www.unicreditprivate.it
Sales Range: $700-749.9 Million
Private Banking & Wealth Management Services
N.A.I.C.S.: 523991
Cesare Bisoni *(VP)*

Subsidiary (Domestic):

Cordusio Societa Fiduciaria per Azioni (3)
Via Dante 4, Milan, 20121, Italy
Tel.: (39) 027259111
Web Site: http://www.cordusio.fiduciaria.it
Sales Range: $50-74.9 Million
Emp.: 40
Fiduciary Administration
N.A.I.C.S.: 523991

Subsidiary (Domestic):

CORDUSIO SIM - ADVISORY & FAMILY OFFICE SPA (4)
Via Dante 4, 20121, Milan, Italy
Tel.: (39) 0272591181
Financial Advisory Services
N.A.I.C.S.: 523940

Subsidiary (Domestic):

FinecoBank S.p.A. (3)
Via Revolution dOttobre 16, 42123, Reggio Emilia, Italy (80%)
Tel.: (39) 0228872023
Web Site: https://it.finecobank.com
Rev.: $840,061,515
Assets: $35,954,780,919
Liabilities: $35,297,430,391
Net Worth: $657,350,529
Earnings: $657,350,529
Emp.: 1,384
Fiscal Year-end: 12/31/2023
Commercial Banking Services
N.A.I.C.S.: 522110

Alessandro Foti *(CEO & Gen Mgr)*

Subsidiary (Domestic):

UniCredit Services S.C.p.A (2)
Via Livio Cambi 1, 20151, Milan, Italy
Tel.: (39) 02 88 621
Software Development Services
N.A.I.C.S.: 541511
Paolo Cederle *(CEO)*

Subsidiary (Non-US):

UniCredito Italiano Bank (Ireland) p.l.c. (2)
La Touche House IFSC, Dublin, Ireland
Tel.: (353) 1 670 2000
Web Site: http://www.unicreditgroup.ie
Sales Range: $25-49.9 Million
Emp.: 30
Commercial Banking Services
N.A.I.C.S.: 522110

Subsidiary (Domestic):

V. QUATTRO SPA (2)
Piazzale Leonardo Da Vinci 8/A, Venice, 30172, Italy
Tel.: (39) 0413969100
Financial Management Services
N.A.I.C.S.: 523999

VIRGINIA SRL (2)
Via Rua Muro 62, 41100, Modena, Italy
Tel.: (39) 059341945
Financial Management Services
N.A.I.C.S.: 523999

Subsidiary (Non-US):

WCREM CANADIAN MANAGEMENT INC. (2)
1 Toronto St, Toronto, M5C 2V6, ON, Canada
Tel.: (416) 861-9200
Investment Management Service
N.A.I.C.S.: 523999

Subsidiary (US):

WEALTH CAPITAL INVESTMENT INC. (2)
3344 Peachtree Rd NE, Atlanta, GA 30326-4801
Tel.: (678) 383-4101
Investment Management Service
N.A.I.C.S.: 523999

Subsidiary (Domestic):

WEALTH CAPITAL MANAGEMENT INC. (3)
3399 Peachtree Rd NE Ste 400, Atlanta, GA 30326
Tel.: (678) 383-4101
Web Site: http://www.wealthcap.com
Emp.: 3
Property Management Services
N.A.I.C.S.: 531312

Subsidiary (Non-US):

WEALTHCAP FONDS GMBH (2)
Am Eisbach 3, 80538, Munich, Bavaria, Germany
Tel.: (49) 89 678205 500
Web Site: http://www.wealthcap.com
Emp.: 215
Financial Management Services
N.A.I.C.S.: 523999

Subsidiary (Domestic):

BLUE CAPITAL EUROPA IMMOBILIEN GMBH & CO. ACHTE OBJEKTE GROBRITANNIEN KG (3)
Nagelsweg 49, 20097, Hamburg, Germany
Tel.: (49) 40 369201
Real Estate Management Services
N.A.I.C.S.: 531390

Subsidiary (Non-US):

WEALTHCAP IMMOBILIENFONDS DEUTSCHLAND 35 GMBH & CO. KG (2)
Am Eisbach 3, Munich, 80538, Bavaria, Germany
Tel.: (49) 89678205500
Web Site: http://www.wealthcap.com
Real Estate Development Services

N.A.I.C.S.: 531390

WEALTHCAP IMMOBILIENFONDS EUROPA 11 GMBH & CO. KG (2)
Am Eisbach 3, 80538, Munich, Bavaria, Germany
Tel.: (49) 896782050
Web Site: http://www.wealthcap.com
Emp.: 250
Real Estate Management Services
N.A.I.C.S.: 531390
Gabriele Volz *(Mgr)*

WEALTHCAP INVESTORENBETREUUNG GMBH (2)
Am Eisbach 3, 80538, Munich, Bavaria, Germany
Tel.: (49) 89 678205 0
Investment Management Service
N.A.I.C.S.: 523999

Subsidiary (Domestic):

WEALTHCAP FLUGZEUG PORTFOLIO 25 GMBH & CO. KG (3)
Bavariafilmplatz 3, Grunwald, 82031, Bavaria, Germany
Tel.: (49) 896782050
Portfolio Management Services
N.A.I.C.S.: 523940

WEALTHCAP IMMOBILIENFONDS DEUTSCHLAND 34 GMBH & CO. KG (3)
Am Eisbach 3, Munich, 80538, Bavaria, Germany
Tel.: (49) 89678205500
Web Site: http://www.wealthcap.com
Emp.: 250
Real Estate Management Services
N.A.I.C.S.: 531390

WEALTHCAP LEBENSWERT 3 GMBH & CO. KG (3)
Bavariafilmplatz 3, Grunwald, 82031, Bavaria, Germany
Tel.: (49) 896782050
Financial Management Services
N.A.I.C.S.: 523999

WEALTHCAP PHOTOVOLTAIK 2 GMBH & CO. KG (3)
Bavariafilmplatz 3, Grunwald, 82031, Bavaria, Germany
Tel.: (49) 896782050
Web Site: http://www.wealthcap.com
Financial Management Services
N.A.I.C.S.: 523999
Rainer Krutten *(CEO)*

WEALTHCAP PHOTOVOLTAIK 3 GMBH & CO. KG (3)
Bavariafilmplatz 3, Grunwald, 82031, Bavaria, Germany
Tel.: (49) 8212992796
Financial Management Services
N.A.I.C.S.: 523999

Subsidiary (Non-US):

WEALTHCAP PEIA SEKUNDAR GMBH (2)
Arabellastrasse 14, 81925, Munich, Germany
Tel.: (49) 89 6782050
Emp.: 250
Financial Management Services
N.A.I.C.S.: 523999
Raina Kruetten *(Gen Mgr)*

WEALTHCAP PRIVATE EQUITY GMBH (2)
Eisbach 3, 80538, Munich, Germany
Tel.: (49) 89 678205 0
Financial Management Services
N.A.I.C.S.: 523999

WEALTHCAP REAL ESTATE KOMPLEMENTAR GMBH (2)
Am Eisbach 3, 80538, Munich, Bavaria, Germany
Tel.: (49) 89 678205 0
Web Site: http://www.wealthcap.com
Emp.: 214
Real Estate Manangement Services
N.A.I.C.S.: 531390
Frou Falls *(Gen Mgr)*

WEALTHCAP REAL ESTATE SEKUNDAR GMBH (2)

UNICREDIT S.P.A.

UniCredit S.p.A.—(Continued)

Am Eisbach 3, Munich, 80538, Germany
Tel.: (49) 89 6782050
Web Site: http://www.wealthcap.com
Real Estate Manangement Services
N.A.I.C.S.: 531390

Wiener-Kuhlhaus Frigoscandia GmbH (2)
Franzosen Traven 20, A 1031, Vienna, Austria **(100%)**
Tel.: (43) 001797950
Web Site: http://www.wkf.at
Sales Range: $25-49.9 Million
Emp.: 70
Freezing & Storage of Foodstuffs
N.A.I.C.S.: 493120

Joint Venture (Non-US):

Yapi Kredi Bank Nederland N.V. (2)
Amstelplein 1 Rembrandt Tower, 1096 HA, Amsterdam, Netherlands
Tel.: (31) 204624444
Web Site: http://www.yapikredi.nl
Rev.: $144,294,827
Assets: $2,249,426,597
Liabilities: $1,829,025,439
Net Worth: $420,401,158
Earnings: $31,653,244
Emp.: 55
Fiscal Year-end: 12/31/2018
Commercial Banking Services
N.A.I.C.S.: 522110
Semih Ulugol (CEO & Member-Mgmt Bd)

Subsidiary (Non-US):

Z LEASING ITA IMMOBILIEN LEASING GESELLSCHAFT M.B.H. (2)
Operngasse 21, 1040, Vienna, Austria
Tel.: (43) 1 71192 0
Real Estate Lending Services
N.A.I.C.S.: 531390

Z LEASING KAPA IMMOBILIEN LEASING GESELLSCHAFT M.B.H. (2)
Operngasse 21, 1040, Vienna, Austria
Tel.: (43) 158808 0
Real Estate Lending Services
N.A.I.C.S.: 531390

Z LEASING OMEGA IMMOBILIEN LEASING GESELLSCHAFT M.B.H. (2)
Operngasse 21, 1040, Vienna, Austria
Tel.: (43) 1 58808 0
Real Estate Lending Services
N.A.I.C.S.: 531390

Unicredit Center Am Kaiserwasser Gmbh (1)
Eiswerkstrasse 20, 1220, Vienna, Austria
Tel.: (43) 5050557520
Web Site:
   https://kaiserwasser.unicreditcenter.at
Conference Centre Operator
N.A.I.C.S.: 561920

Unicredit Factoring Czech Republic AndSlovakia, A.S. (1)
BB Centrum - Budova Filadelfie Zeletavska 1525/1, Michle, 14010, Prague, Czech Republic
Tel.: (420) 602169100
Web Site: https://www.unicreditfactoring.cz
Finance Services
N.A.I.C.S.: 921130

Unicredit Insurance Broker Srl (1)
Sector 1 Bulevardul Expozitiei Nr 1F Etajul 8, Bucharest, Romania
Tel.: (40) 212007777
Web Site: https://www.unicreditinsurancebroker.ro
Insurance Brokerage Services
N.A.I.C.S.: 524210

Unicredit Jelzalogbank Zrt. (1)
Szabadsag ter 5-6, 1054, Budapest, Hungary
Tel.: (36) 3015500
Web Site: https://www.jelzalogbank.hu
Finance Services
N.A.I.C.S.: 921130

Unicredit Leased Asset Management Spa (1)
Via Livio Cambi 5, 20151, Milan, Italy

Tel.: (39) 03666974022
Web Site: https://www.unicredituclam.it
Real Estate Asset Management Services
N.A.I.C.S.: 531390

Wealthcap Kapitalverwaltungsgesellschaft Mbh (1)
Bavariafilmplatz 8, D-82031, Grunwald, Germany
Tel.: (49) 89678205500
Web Site: https://www.wealthcap.com
Emp.: 240
Strategic Consulting Services
N.A.I.C.S.: 541611

UNID BTPLUS CO., LTD.

6F Central Place Bldg 50 Seosomunro, jung-gu, Seoul, Korea (South)
Tel.: (82) 237096600
Web Site:
   https://www.unidbtplus.co.kr
Year Founded: 2022
446070—(KRS)
Wood Product Mfr & Distr
N.A.I.C.S.: 321999
Sangjun Han (Chm & CEO)

UNID CO., LTD.

17th Fl Ferrum Tower No 19 Eulji-ro 5-gil Suha-dong, Jung-gu, Seoul, Korea (South)
Tel.: (82) 237099500
Web Site: https://www.unid.co.kr
Year Founded: 1980
014830—(KRS)
Rev.: $1,077,560,188
Assets: $1,142,266,008
Liabilities: $450,775,497
Net Worth: $691,490,511
Earnings: $97,217,571
Emp.: 229
Fiscal Year-end: 12/31/22
Chemical Products Mfr
N.A.I.C.S.: 424690
Eui Seung Chung (Pres)

Subsidiaries:

UNID Jiangsu Chemical Co., Ltd. (1)
81 Songlinshan Road New Zone, Zhenjiang, China
Tel.: (86) 51183365700
Chemical Product Mfr & Distr
N.A.I.C.S.: 325998

UNIDAS LOCADORA DE VEICULOS LTDA.

R Cincinato Braga 388, 01333-010, Sao Paulo, Brazil
Tel.: (55) 8007715158
Web Site: http://www.unidas.com.br
Year Founded: 1985
Car Rental Services
N.A.I.C.S.: 532111
Pedro Roque de Pinho de Almeida (Chm)

UNIDATA S.P.A.

Viale A G Eiffel 100 Commercity M25-M26, 00148, Rome, Italy
Tel.: (39) 06404041
Web Site: http://www.unidata.it
Year Founded: 1985
Telecommunication Servicesb
N.A.I.C.S.: 517810
Renato Brunetti (Chrm)

UNIDEN HOLDINGS CORPORATION

2-12-7 Hatchobori Chuo-ku, Tokyo, 104-8512, Japan
Tel.: (81) 35 543 2800 JP
Web Site: http://www.uniden.co.jp
Year Founded: 1966
6815—(TKS)
Rev.: $124,746,160
Assets: $420,218,480
Liabilities: $93,412,000
Net Worth: $326,806,480

Earnings: $17,298,160
Emp.: 833
Fiscal Year-end: 03/31/22
Electronics Mfr
N.A.I.C.S.: 532210
Takeyuki Nishikawa (Pres)

Subsidiaries:

Uniden America Corporation (1)
4700 Amon Carter Blvd, Fort Worth, TX 76155-2207
Tel.: (817) 858-3300
Web Site: http://www.uniden.com
Sales Range: $75-99.9 Million
Emp.: 200
Mfr of Consumer & Commercial Electronics Specializing in Radio Communication Equipment
N.A.I.C.S.: 423690
Franklin Raines (Natl Acct Mgr)

Division (Domestic):

Uniden Corporation-Marine Communications Div. (2)
4700 Amon Carter Blvd, Fort Worth, TX 76155-2207
Tel.: (817) 858-3300
Web Site: http://www.uniden.com
Sales Range: $50-74.9 Million
Emp.: 210
Wireless Marine Products
N.A.I.C.S.: 423690

Uniden Australia Proprietary Limited (1)
73 Alfred Road, Chipping Norton, 2170, NSW, Australia
Tel.: (61) 295993355
Electronic Device Mfr & Distr
N.A.I.C.S.: 335931

Uniden Australia Pty. Limited (1)
73 Alfred Road Chipping Northern, Rockvale, Sydney, 2170, NSW, Australia
Tel.: (61) 295993355
Web Site: http://www.uniden.com.au
Sales Range: $25-49.9 Million
Emp.: 50
Telecommunications Mfr
N.A.I.C.S.: 334220

Uniden Honk Kong Ltd. (1)
Units 8-9 5th Floor 113 Argyle Street, Mongkok, Kowloon, China (Hong Kong)
Tel.: (852) 27230113
Web Site: http://www.uniden.com
Wireless Electronic Devices Mfr
N.A.I.C.S.: 334220

Uniden New Zealand Ltd. (1)
150 Harris Rd, East Tamaki, Auckland, 2145, New Zealand
Tel.: (64) 92738383
Web Site: http://www.uniden.co.nz
Sales Range: $25-49.9 Million
Emp.: 17
Wireless Telecommunication Equipments Distr
N.A.I.C.S.: 423690
Vic Sacco (Mng Dir)

UNIDEVICE AG

Mittelstrasse 7, 12529, Schonefeld, Germany
Tel.: (49) 3063415600
Web Site: https://www.unidevice.de
Year Founded: 2014
UDC—(MUN)
Rev.: $491,006,424
Assets: $42,882,564
Liabilities: $17,570,976
Net Worth: $25,311,588
Earnings: $3,091,980
Fiscal Year-end: 12/31/22
Electronic Equipment Distr
N.A.I.C.S.: 423690
Christian Pahl (CEO)

UNIDOC HEALTH CORP.

893 250-997 Seymour St, Vancouver, V6B 3M1, BC, Canada
Tel.: (778) 383-6731 BC
Web Site: https://www.unidoctor.com
Year Founded: 2021

INTERNATIONAL PUBLIC

UDOCF—(OTCIQ)
Assets: $239,068
Liabilities: $911,056
Net Worth: ($671,988)
Earnings: ($1,012,370)
Fiscal Year-end: 03/31/23
Health Care Srvices
N.A.I.C.S.: 621610
Antonio Baldassarre (CEO)

UNIEQUIP LABORGERATEBAU- UND VERTRIEBS GMBH

Fraunhoferstr 11, 82152, Planegg, Germany
Tel.: (49) 898575200
Web Site: http://www.uniequip.com
Year Founded: 1975
Rev.: $19,311,600
Emp.: 200
Laboratory Equipment Mfr
N.A.I.C.S.: 334516
A. N. Kraupa (Mng Dir)

UNIFARM AD

Cara Dusana 264, 11080, Zemun, Serbia
Tel.: (381) 11 261 87 99
Web Site: http://www.unifarmad.co.rs
Year Founded: 1948
UNFZ—(BEL)
Sales Range: $1-9.9 Million
Emp.: 30
Pharmaceutical Product Whslr
N.A.I.C.S.: 424210
Dusan Zivkovic (CEO)

UNIFAST FINANCE & INVESTMENT PLC

23 Themistokli Dervi Avenue S.TA.D.Y.L. Building, 1066, Nicosia, Cyprus
Tel.: (357) 22150000
Web Site: http://www.pharmakas.com
UFI—(CYP)
Sales Range: Less than $1 Million
Financial Investment Management Services
N.A.I.C.S.: 523940
Stavros Theodosiou (Chm)

UNIFIED TRANSPORT & LOGISTICS CO

PO Box 925218, Amman, 11192, Jordan
Tel.: (962) 64714716
Web Site: http://www.unified.com.jo
Sales Range: $1-9.9 Million
Emp.: 154
Transportation Services
N.A.I.C.S.: 488999
Saeed Al Dashti (Chm)

UNIFIED VALVE LTD

3815 - 32 St NE, Calgary, T1Y 7C1, AB, Canada
Tel.: (403) 215-7800
Web Site:
   https://www.unifiedvalve.com
Year Founded: 1994
Rev.: $18,787,614
Emp.: 68
Valve Repair Services & Distr
N.A.I.C.S.: 811210
Keith LeVoir (Founder)

UNIFIEDPOST GROUP SA

Avenue Reine Astrid 92A, 1310, La Hulpe, Belgium
Tel.: (32) 26340628 BE
Web Site:
   https://www.unifiedpostgroup.com
Year Founded: 2001
UPG—(EUR)
Rev.: $147,436,866
Assets: $299,997,842

Liabilities: $218,074,682
Net Worth: $81,923,160
Earnings: ($89,732,355)
Emp.: 829
Fiscal Year-end: 12/31/23
Software Development Services
N.A.I.C.S.: 541511
Geert De Herdt *(CIO)*

Subsidiaries:

21 Grams AB (1)
Lumaparksvagen 9, 120 31, Stockholm, Sweden
Tel.: (46) 86003721
Web Site: https://www.21grams.se
Postal Management Services
N.A.I.C.S.: 541618

21 Grams AS (1)
Sven Oftedals vei 8A, 0950, Oslo, Norway
Tel.: (47) 23653530
Web Site: https://www.21grams.no
Postal Management Services
N.A.I.C.S.: 541618

Addoro AB (1)
Lumaparksvagen 9, 120 31, Stockholm, Sweden
Tel.: (46) 86003721
Web Site: https://www.addoro.com
Communication Software Development Services
N.A.I.C.S.: 541511

Crossinx GmbH (1)
Hanauer Landstr 291A, 60314, Frankfurt am Main, Germany
Tel.: (49) 694800651
Web Site: https://www.crossinx.com
Emp.: 200
Electronic Invoice Management Services
N.A.I.C.S.: 541420

Digithera S.r.l. (1)
Via Paleocapa 1, 20121, Milan, Italy
Tel.: (39) 0598638663
Web Site: https://www.digithera.it
Electronic Invoice Consulting Services
N.A.I.C.S.: 541420

Europe Post ApS (1)
Hedelykken 2-4, 2640, Hedehusene, Denmark
Tel.: (45) 42700866
Web Site: https://www.europepost.eu
E-Commerce & Mail Distribution Services
N.A.I.C.S.: 491110

First Business Post Kft. (1)
Aliz utca 3 Office Garden IV, 1117, Budapest, Hungary
Tel.: (36) 16961202
Financial Services
N.A.I.C.S.: 522320

Mailworld AB (1)
Lumaparksvagen 9, 120 31, Stockholm, Sweden
Tel.: (46) 87916600
Web Site: https://www.mailworld.se
International Postal Services
N.A.I.C.S.: 541618

Sistema Efactura S.L. (1)
Calle Musgo 3, 28023, Madrid, Spain
Tel.: (34) 917082161
Web Site: https://www.sistemaefactura.com
Electronic Invoice Management Services
N.A.I.C.S.: 541420

Tehnobiro d.o.o. (1)
Varvarinska 14, 11000, Belgrade, Serbia
Tel.: (381) 117442078
Web Site: https://www.tehnobiro.com
Emp.: 23
Offset & Digital Printing Services
N.A.I.C.S.: 561439

Unifiedpost AG (1)
Seefeldstrasse 69, 8008, Zurich, Switzerland
Tel.: (41) 432161768
Financial Services
N.A.I.C.S.: 522320

Unifiedpost AS (1)
Delu Iela 4, Riga, LV-1004, Latvia
Tel.: (371) 67066500
Financial Services
N.A.I.C.S.: 522320

Unifiedpost Limited (1)
Unit 3 Park Seventeen Moss Lane, Manchester, M45 8FJ, United Kingdom
Tel.: (44) 1617665544
Financial Services
N.A.I.C.S.: 522320

Unifiedpost Limited Liability Company (1)
Oreskoviceva street 6N/2, 10010, Zagreb, Croatia
Tel.: (385) 13141500
Financial Services
N.A.I.C.S.: 522320

Unifiedpost Solutions d.o.o. (1)
Tosin Bunar 185, 11070, New Belgrade, Serbia
Tel.: (381) 117150748
Web Site: https://www.unifiedpost.rs
Emp.: 150
Electric Appliances Mfr
N.A.I.C.S.: 334416

Unifiedpost UAB (1)
Senasis Ukmerges kel 2 Uzubaliai, LT-14302, Vilnius, Lithuania
Tel.: (370) 52780330
Financial Services
N.A.I.C.S.: 522320

Unifiedpost d.o.o. (1)
Tosin Bunar 185, 11070, Belgrade, Serbia
Tel.: (381) 117150748
Financial Services
N.A.I.C.S.: 522320

Unifiedpost s.r.o. (1)
Roztylska 1860/1, Chodov, 148 00, Prague, Czech Republic
Tel.: (420) 911869777
Financial Services
N.A.I.C.S.: 522320

Unifiedpost, Unipessoal LDA. (1)
Avenida da Liberdade 110-10 Andar, 1269-046, Lisbon, Portugal
Tel.: (351) 213404527
Financial Services
N.A.I.C.S.: 522320

UNIFIN FINANCIERA, S.A.B. DE C.V., SOFOM, E.N.R.
111 Presidente Masaryk, Polanco, 11560, Mexico, 11560, Mexico
Tel.: (52) 52495800
Web Site: https://www.unifin.com.mx
UNIFIN—(MEX)
Rev.: $359,918,013
Assets: $3,998,340,248
Liabilities: $3,996,932,694
Net Worth: $1,407,554
Earnings: $237,837,517
Emp.: 377
Fiscal Year-end: 12/31/23
Financial Support Services
N.A.I.C.S.: 541611
Rodrigo Lebois Mateos *(Chm)*

UNIFINZ CAPITAL INDIA LIMITED
Chawla House 3 floor 19 Nehru Place, DDA Community Center, New Delhi, 110 019, India
Tel.: (91) 7373737316
Web Site: https://www.unifinz.in
Year Founded: 1982
541358—(BOM)
Rev.: $161,673
Assets: $915,049
Liabilities: $813,617
Net Worth: $101,432
Earnings: $66,332
Emp.: 2
Fiscal Year-end: 03/31/21
Commercial Banking Services
N.A.I.C.S.: 522110
Nidhi Marwaha *(CEO)*

UNIFLEX TECHNOLOGY INC.
No 38 Xingbang Rd, Taoyuan Dist, Taoyuan, 330, Taiwan
Tel.: (886) 32150198
Web Site: https://www.uniflex.com.tw
Year Founded: 1990
3321—(TAI)
Rev.: $50,400,992
Assets: $63,405,145
Liabilities: $42,080,773
Net Worth: $21,324,372
Earnings: ($8,861,800)
Fiscal Year-end: 12/31/23
Printed Circuit Board Mfr & Distr
N.A.I.C.S.: 334412
Tzyy-Jang Tseng *(Chm)*

Subsidiaries:

Uniflex Technology Inc. - Taichung Chingnian Plant (1)
No 123 Qingnian Rd Dajia Dist, Taichung, 43768, Taiwan
Tel.: (886) 426817070
Printed Circuit Board Mfr
N.A.I.C.S.: 334412

Uniflex Technology Inc. - Yangzhou Plant (1)
No 77 Hua Yang West Rd, Yangzhou, 225009, Jiangsu, China
Tel.: (86) 51487960000
Printed Circuit Board Mfr
N.A.I.C.S.: 334412

UNIFORM INDUSTRIAL CORPORATION
1F No 1 Ln 15 Ziqiang St, Tucheng Dist, New Taipei City, 236, Taiwan
Tel.: (886) 222687075
Web Site: http://www.uicworld.com
2482—(TAI)
Rev.: $47,105,430
Assets: $56,185,517
Liabilities: $12,411,851
Net Worth: $43,773,667
Earnings: $6,108,113
Fiscal Year-end: 12/31/23
Personal Digital Assistance & Palmtop Computers Mfr
N.A.I.C.S.: 334111
Attlee Ba Lo *(Chm & Gen Mgr)*

Subsidiaries:

Uniform Industrial Corp.USA (1)
47341 Bayside Pkwy, Fremont, CA 94538
Tel.: (510) 438-6799
Web Site: http://www.uicusa.com
Sales Range: $25-49.9 Million
Emp.: 25
Electronic Components Mfr
N.A.I.C.S.: 334419

UNIFORM NEXT CO., LTD.
25-81 Yaemakicho, Fukui, 910-0123, Japan
Tel.: (81) 776431890
Web Site: https://uniformnext.co.jp
Year Founded: 1994
3566—(TKS)
Sales Range: Less than $1 Million
Online Uniform Apparel Distr
N.A.I.C.S.: 458110
Yasutaka Yokoi *(Chm, Pres, CEO & Dir-Rep)*

UNIFOSA CORP.
3F-6 No 5 Alley 22 Lane 513 Jui Kuang Rd, Nei-Hu, Taipei, 11492, Taiwan
Tel.: (886) 287971108
Web Site: https://www.unifosa.com.tw
Year Founded: 1994
Computer Storage Device Mfr
N.A.I.C.S.: 334112
Ching-Jong Chen *(Chm & Gen Mgr)*

UNIFREIGHT AFRICA LIMITED
Cnr Orme Willow Road Ardbennie, Harare, Zimbabwe
Tel.: (263) 4621015
Web Site: http://www.unifreight.co.zw
Year Founded: 1946
UNIF—(ZIM)
Rev.: $556,669,895
Assets: $986,308,221
Liabilities: $328,458,367
Net Worth: $657,849,854
Earnings: $390,004,250
Emp.: 803
Fiscal Year-end: 12/31/23
Transport & Logistics Solutions
N.A.I.C.S.: 488510
Robert Edward Kuipers *(CEO-Grp & Exec Dir)*

UNIFUNDS LIMITED
65/10-12 Floor 1 Chamnan Phenjati Business Centre Building, Rama IX Road Huai Khwang, Bangkok, Thailand
Tel.: (66) 852 3106 3133   NV
Year Founded: 2005
Assets: $6,666
Liabilities: $367,352
Net Worth: ($360,686)
Earnings: ($83,133)
Fiscal Year-end: 01/31/18
Investment Services
N.A.I.C.S.: 523999
Prom Vuoch *(CEO)*

UNIGEL GROUP PLC
Unigel House 7 Park View Alder Close, Eastbourne, BN23 6QE, East Sussex, United Kingdom
Tel.: (44) 1273612122
Web Site: https://www.unigel.com
Year Founded: 2022
GX7—(DEU)
All Other Telecommunications
N.A.I.C.S.: 517810
Ben Harber *(Sec)*

UNIGLOBE ADVANCE TRAVEL LTD
300 1444 Alberni St, Vancouver, V6G 2Z4, BC, Canada
Tel.: (604) 688-3551
Web Site: http://www.uniglobetravel.com
Rev.: $11,579,118
Emp.: 34
Travel Agencies
N.A.I.C.S.: 561510
Irv Wight *(Pres)*

UNIGOLD INC.
Ste 2704- 401 Bay St, PO Box 4, Toronto, M5H 2Y4, ON, Canada
Tel.: (416) 866-8157   ON
Web Site: https://www.unigoldinc.com
Year Founded: 1990
UGD—(OTCIQ)
Rev.: $7,691
Assets: $4,134,495
Liabilities: $83,957
Net Worth: $4,050,538
Earnings: ($3,988,020)
Emp.: 84
Fiscal Year-end: 12/31/20
Gold Mining & Exploration Services
N.A.I.C.S.: 212220
Joseph Andrew Hamilton *(Chm & CEO)*

UNIGRADNJA DD SARAJEVO
Mula Mustafe Baseskije 10, 71000, Sarajevo, Bosnia & Herzegovina
Tel.: (387) 3 325 3300
Web Site: http://www.unigradnja.ba
Year Founded: 1973
UGRDRK3—(SARE)
Rev.: $6,392,069
Assets: $14,466,223
Liabilities: $2,918,734
Net Worth: $11,547,489
Earnings: $915,457
Emp.: 147

UNIGRADNJA DD SARAJEVO

UNIGRADNJA dd Sarajevo—(Continued)
Fiscal Year-end: 12/31/20
Building Construction Services
N.A.I.C.S.: 236210

UNIGRAINS
23 avenue de Neuilly, 75116, Paris, France
Tel.: (33) 1 44 31 10 00
Web Site: http://www.unigrains.fr
Year Founded: 1963
Private Equity Investor
N.A.I.C.S.: 551112
Didier Bosc *(Head-Investments & Dev)*

UNIGROUP GUOXIN MICRO-ELECTRONICS CO., LTD.
No 3129 Wuzhong West Street, Yutian County, Hebei, 064100, China
Tel.: (86) 3156198161
Web Site: http://www.gosinoic.com
Year Founded: 2001
002049—(SSE)
Rev.: $999,634,690
Assets: $2,152,157,076
Liabilities: $779,725,356
Net Worth: $1,372,431,720
Earnings: $369,517,539
Emp.: 1,948
Fiscal Year-end: 12/31/22
Integrated Circuits Mfr
N.A.I.C.S.: 334413
Qiuping Yang *(CFO)*

UNIGROWTH INVESTMENTS PUBLIC LTD
Archbishop Makarios Avenue 40, Peristerona, Nicosia, Cyprus
Tel.: (357) 22673666
Year Founded: 1999
UNI—(CYP)
Sales Range: Less than $1 Million
Financial Services
N.A.I.C.S.: 523999
Zenios Demetriou *(Bd of Dirs & Chm)*

UNIHEALTH CONSULTANCY LIMITED
H-13/14 Everest 156 Tardeo Road, Mumbai, 400034, Maharashtra, India
Tel.: (91) 2223544625
Web Site:
https://www.unihealthonline.com
Year Founded: 2010
UNIHEALTH—(NSE)
Information Technology Services
N.A.I.C.S.: 541512

UNIHOLDINGS INC.
Chemphil Building 851 Antonio S Arnaiz Avenue Legaspi Village, Makati, 1229, Philippines
Tel.: (63) 8188711 **PH**
Web Site:
http://www.chemphil.com.ph
Year Founded: 1959
UNH—(PHI)
Industrial Chemicals Mfr
N.A.I.C.S.: 325180
Chi Thing Co *(Chm)*

Subsidiaries:

CAWC, Inc (1)
Chemphil Building 851 Antonio S Arnaiz Avenue, Legaspi Village, Makati, 1229, Philippines
Tel.: (63) 28188711
Emp.: 30
Sodium Polyphosphate Mfr
N.A.I.C.S.: 325180

UNIINFO TELECOM SERVICES LIMITED
403 Chetak Centre 12/2 R N T Marg, Indore, 452001, Madhya Pradesh, India
Tel.: (91) 7314208091
Web Site: https://www.uni-info.co.in
Year Founded: 2010
UNIINFO—(NSE)
Rev.: $5,576,386
Assets: $6,113,415
Liabilities: $1,337,179
Net Worth: $4,776,236
Earnings: ($473,950)
Emp.: 572
Fiscal Year-end: 03/12/21
Telecommunication Servicesb
N.A.I.C.S.: 517810
Kishore Bhuradia *(Chm & Mng Dir)*

UNIKAI FOODS P.J.S.C.
Al Quoz Industrial Area, PO Box 6424, Dubai, United Arab Emirates
Tel.: (971) 800864524
Web Site: https://www.unikai.com
Year Founded: 1977
UNIKAI—(DFM)
Rev.: $96,038,991
Assets: $68,333,697
Liabilities: $51,341,756
Net Worth: $16,991,941
Earnings: $5,542,910
Emp.: 624
Fiscal Year-end: 12/31/23
Dairy Products Mfr
N.A.I.C.S.: 311514
Neeraj Vohra *(CEO)*

Subsidiaries:

Unikai & Company LLC (1)
PO Box 670, Wadi Kabir, 117, Muscat, Oman
Tel.: (968) 24856200
Dairy Products Mfr
N.A.I.C.S.: 311514

UNILEVER PLC
100 Victoria Embankment, London, EC4Y 0DY, United Kingdom
Tel.: (44) 2074382800 **UK**
Web Site: https://www.unilever.com
Year Founded: 1872
UL—(NYSE)
Rev.: $75,333,670,240
Assets: $95,128,917,929
Liabilities: $68,885,237,491
Net Worth: $26,243,680,439
Earnings: $9,024,266,920
Emp.: 128,000
Fiscal Year-end: 12/31/23
Holding Company; Food, Beverage, Home & Personal Care Products Mfr & Distr
N.A.I.C.S.: 551112
Andrea Jung *(Vice Chm)*

Subsidiaries:

Binzagr Unilever Co. (1)
Al Malik Road East Al Musaad Petrol Station, Jeddah, 21462, Saudi Arabia
Tel.: (966) 26226777
Sales Range: $25-49.9 Million
Emp.: 200
Oil-Based Food Product Mfr & Marketer
N.A.I.C.S.: 311999

Blueair AB (1)
Karlavagen 108, 115 26, Stockholm, Sweden
Tel.: (46) 8 679 4500
Web Site: https://www.blueair.com
Air Purification Equipment Mfr & Distr
N.A.I.C.S.: 333413

Blueair Asia Limited (1)
Suite 1106-8 11/F Tai Yau Building 181 Johnston Road, Kwun Tong, Wanchai, China (Hong Kong)
Tel.: (852) 23458988
Air Purification Equipment Mfr & Distr
N.A.I.C.S.: 333413

Blueair India Pvt. Limited (1)
S-327 Greater Kailash - II, New Delhi, 110048, Delhi, India
Tel.: (91) 8860606505
Air Purification Equipment Mfr & Distr
N.A.I.C.S.: 333413

Blueair Shanghai Sales Co. Limited (1)
Room 1001 No 398 Caoxi Road, Xuhui Dist, Shanghai, 200030, China
Tel.: (86) 2160910981
Air Purifier Product Mfr
N.A.I.C.S.: 333413

Corporativo Unilever de Mexico, S. de R.L. de C.V. (1)
Paseo De Los Tamarindos No 150 Bosques De Las Lomas, Mexico, 05120, Mexico
Tel.: (52) 55 1105 4000
Cosmetics Products Mfr
N.A.I.C.S.: 325620

DU Gesellschaft fur Arbeitnehmeruberlassung mbH (1)
Sohlbacher Strasse 32, Geisweid, 57078, Siegen, Germany
Tel.: (49) 271880190
Web Site: https://www.dilba.de
Employment Services
N.A.I.C.S.: 561311

Delico Handels GmbH (1)
Dresdnerstrasse 82, 1200, Vienna, Austria
Tel.: (43) 1331790
Web Site: https://www.delico-eskimo.at
Food Service
N.A.I.C.S.: 722310

Dermalogica GmbH (1)
Wiesenstr 21, 40549, Dusseldorf, Germany
Tel.: (49) 2115504650
Web Site: https://www.dermalogica.de
Cosmetic Product Distr
N.A.I.C.S.: 456120

Doma B.V. (1)
Newtonstraat 14C, 2665 JL, Numansdorp, Netherlands
Tel.: (31) 104125822
Web Site: https://www.doma.nl
Electronic Product Distr
N.A.I.C.S.: 423690

Elais Unilever Hellas SA (1)
Kymis & Seneka Ave 10, Kifisia, 145 64, Athens, Greece
Tel.: (30) 2102215000
Web Site: https://www.unilever.gr
Cosmetic Product Distr
N.A.I.C.S.: 424210

Equilibra S.R.L. (1)
Via Plava 74, 10135, Turin, TO, Italy
Tel.: (39) 0116279775
Web Site: https://www.equilibra.it
Personal Care Product Mfr & Distr
N.A.I.C.S.: 325620

Fima/VG Distribuicao de Produtos Alimentares, Lda. (1)
Largo Monterroio Mascarenhas 1, 1070-184, Lisbon, Portugal
Tel.: (351) 213892000
Web Site: http://www.unilever.com
Sales Range: $100-124.9 Million
Emp.: 500
Food & Personal Care Product Mfr
N.A.I.C.S.: 311999

Hindustan Unilever Ltd. (1)
Unilever House B D Sawant Marg Chakala, Andheri E, Mumbai, 400099, India
Tel.: (91) 2250432792
Web Site: https://www.hul.co.in
Rev.: $7,194,096,000
Assets: $9,625,570,500
Liabilities: $2,925,195,000
Net Worth: $6,700,375,500
Earnings: $1,213,758,000
Emp.: 8,480
Fiscal Year-end: 03/31/2022
Food & Personal Care Products Mfr
N.A.I.C.S.: 311999
Dev Bajpai *(Sec & Exec Dir-Legal & Corp Affairs)*

Subsidiary (Non-US):

GlaxoSmithKline Bangladesh Ltd. (2)

INTERNATIONAL PUBLIC

Fouzderhat Industrial Area, Dhaka Trunk Rd N Kattali, Chittagong, 4217, Bangladesh (100%)
Tel.: (880) 317520718
Pharmaceutical Mfr & Distr
N.A.I.C.S.: 325412

Subsidiary (Domestic):

GlaxoSmithKline Consumer Healthcare Ltd. (2)
24-25 Floor 1 Horizon Center Golf Course Road, DLF Phase 5, Gurgaon, 122002, India
Tel.: (91) 1244336500
Web Site:
http://www.india-consumer.gsk.com
Rev.: $747,775,088
Assets: $870,164,006
Liabilities: $282,982,018
Net Worth: $587,181,988
Earnings: $140,934,094
Emp.: 3,844
Fiscal Year-end: 03/31/2019
Nutritional & Over-the-Counter Pharmaceutical Products Mfr & Distr
N.A.I.C.S.: 325412
Navneet Saluja *(Mng Dir)*

Jamnagar Properties Private Limited (1)
Unilever House B D, Chakala Andheri, Mumbai, 400099, Gujarat, India
Tel.: (91) 2882540046
Commercial Building Rental Services
N.A.I.C.S.: 531120

Knorr Alimentaria, S.A. (1)
Calle C #6 Zona Industrial Herrera, Apartado Postal 623-2, Santo Domingo, Dominican Republic
Tel.: (809) 5307611
Sales Range: $50-74.9 Million
Emp.: 160
Soups, Bouillons, Seasonings, Corn Starch, Oats, Mayonaise & Mustard
N.A.I.C.S.: 424490

Laboratoire Garancia SAS (1)
42 Rue Jean de la Fontaine, 75016, Paris, France
Tel.: (33) 145207365
Web Site: https://www.garancia-beauty.com
Cosmetic Product Distr
N.A.I.C.S.: 456120
Eric Coste *(Dir & Mgr-Editorial)*

Levers Associated Trust Limited (1)
Unilever House B D, Chakala Andheri, Mumbai, 400099, Maharashtra, India
Tel.: (91) 2239830000
Financial Management Services
N.A.I.C.S.: 523999

OJSC Concern Kalina (1)
80 Komsomolskaya St, Ekaterinburg, 620138, Russia (100%)
Tel.: (7) 3433658338
Web Site: http://www.kalina.org
Sales Range: $400-449.9 Million
Emp.: 2,000
Cosmetics, Fragrances, Household & Personal Care Products Mfr
N.A.I.C.S.: 325620
Andrzej Zoledziowski *(Gen Mgr-Logistic & Production)*

Subsidiary (Domestic):

Glavskazka International LLC (2)
80 Komsomolskaya Street, Yekaterinburg, 620138, Sverdlovsk, Russia
Tel.: (7) 3433658303
Web Site: http://www.glavskazka.ru
Sales Range: $25-49.9 Million
Emp.: 50
Cosmetics Mfr
N.A.I.C.S.: 325620

Pond's Exports Limited (1)
Unilever House B D, Chakala Andheri, Mumbai, 400099, India
Tel.: (91) 4428345505
Perfume & Cosmetic Product Distr
N.A.I.C.S.: 424210

Rafra Japan K.K. (1)
22F Nakameguro GT Tower 2-1-1 Kamimeguro, Meguro-ku, Tokyo, 153-0051, Japan
Tel.: (81) 367727710

AND PRIVATE COMPANIES

Web Site: https://www.rafra-japan.com
Cosmetic Product Distr
N.A.I.C.S.: 456120
Jun Matsuoka *(Founder & Chm)*

SachaJuan Haircare AB (1)
Tel.: (46) 8369805
Haircare Product Mfr & Distr
N.A.I.C.S.: 325620

TIGI Haircare GmbH (1)
Rotebuhlplatz 21, 70178, Stuttgart, Germany
Tel.: (49) 711699490
Web Site: https://www.tigi.com
Barber Shop Services
N.A.I.C.S.: 812111

UNUS Holding B.V. (1)
Weena 455, 3013 AL, Rotterdam, Zuid-Holland, Netherlands
Tel.: (31) 102174000
Investment Management Service
N.A.I.C.S.: 523940

Unilever (Malaysia) Holdings Sdn Bhd (1)
Suite 2-1 Level 2 & Suite 3-1 Level 3 Vertical Corporate Tower B, Avenue 10 The Vertical Bangsar South City No 8 Jalan Kerinchi, 59200, Kuala Lumpur, Malaysia
Tel.: (60) 322462188
Web Site: https://www.unilever.com.my
Sales Range: $150-199.9 Million
Emp.: 520
Food & Personal Care Product Mfr
N.A.I.C.S.: 311999

Subsidiary (Non-US):

Unilever Singapore Pte. Ltd. (2)
18 Nepal Park, Singapore, 139407, Singapore
Tel.: (65) 66434800
Web Site: https://www.unilever.com.sg
Food & Personal Care Product Mfr
N.A.I.C.S.: 311999
Sudipto Roy *(Mng Dir-Asia Pacific, Africa, Middle East, Turkey & Russia)*

Unilever Algerie SPA (1)
ZI Hassi Ameur commune de Hassi Bounif Daira de Bir Eldjir, BP 7272, 31025, Oran, Algeria
Tel.: (213) 321793720
Cosmetic & Nutrition Product Mfr
N.A.I.C.S.: 325620

Unilever Andina Bolivia S.A. (1)
Av Blanco Galindo Km 10 1/2, Cochabamba, Bolivia
Tel.: (591) 800100057
Web Site: http://www.unilever.bo
Sales Range: $100-124.9 Million
Emp.: 300
Cosmetics Products Mfr
N.A.I.C.S.: 325620

Unilever Andina Colombia Ltda. (1)
Avenida Carrera 45 Torre 3 Piso 5Y 6, Barrio Puente Aranda, 108-27, Bogota, DC, Colombia
Tel.: (57) 14239700
Sales Range: $200-249.9 Million
Emp.: 700
Producer of Margarine, Fats, Oils, Detergents & Toilet Preparations
N.A.I.C.S.: 325611

Unilever Andina Peru S.A. (1)
Av Paseo de la Republica 5895 OF 402, Miraflores, 18, Lima, Peru
Tel.: (51) 14111600
Web Site: http://www.unilever.com.pe
Sales Range: $50-74.9 Million
Emp.: 120
Cosmetics & Toiletries Mfr
N.A.I.C.S.: 325620

Unilever Andina Venezuela S.A. (1)
Av Blandin, Caracas, Venezuela
Tel.: (58) 2458507211
Consumer Products Distr
N.A.I.C.S.: 424490

Unilever Australia Ltd. (1)
219 North Rocks Rd, North Rocks, 2151, NSW, Australia
Tel.: (61) 800888449
Web Site: https://www.unilever.com.au
Sales Range: $25-49.9 Million
Emp.: 500
Personal Care Products Whslr
N.A.I.C.S.: 456199

Subsidiary (Domestic):

Streets Ice Cream Pty. Ltd. (2)
20-22 Cambridge St, PO Box 2, Epping, 1710, NSW, Australia
Tel.: (61) 298696400
Web Site: http://www.unilever.com.au
Sales Range: $75-99.9 Million
Emp.: 400
Ice Cream Mfr
N.A.I.C.S.: 311520

Subsidiary (Non-US):

Unilever New Zealand Ltd. (2)
Level 4 103 Carlton Gore Rd, Newmarket, Auckland, 1023, New Zealand
Tel.: (64) 800900028
Sales Range: $25-49.9 Million
Emp.: 50
Foods, Detergents & Personal Products Mfr
N.A.I.C.S.: 325611

Unilever Austria GmbH (1)
Jakov-Lind-Strasse 5, A - 1020, Vienna, Austria
Tel.: (43) 1605350
Web Site: https://www.unileverfoodsolutions.at
Sales Range: $25-49.9 Million
Emp.: 200
Food Products Mfr
N.A.I.C.S.: 311423

Unilever Bangladesh Limited (1)
hanta Forum Level 11 - 15 187-188/B, Bir Uttam Mir Shawkat Sarak, Dhaka, 1208, Bangladesh
Tel.: (880) 9610999190
Web Site: https://www.unilever.com.bd
Sales Range: $1-4.9 Billion
Emp.: 300
Foods, Detergents, Personal Products, Chemicals
N.A.I.C.S.: 325611

Unilever Belgium BVBA (1)
Industrielaan 9, 1070, Brussels, Belgium
Tel.: (32) 23336666
Web Site: https://www.unilever.be
Sales Range: $100-124.9 Million
Emp.: 400
Detergents Mfr
N.A.I.C.S.: 325611
Chris Poollet *(CEO)*

Unilever Bestfoods Brasil Ltda (1)
Paulista Ave 2300 4 Andar, Sao Paulo, 01310-300, Brazil
Tel.: (55) 11 3138 1400
Web Site: http://www.unilever.com.br
Sales Range: $75-99.9 Million
Emp.: 500
Margarine, Fats, Oils & Foods Mfr
N.A.I.C.S.: 311224

Unilever Bestfoods HK Ltd. (1)
6 Dai Fu Street, Tai Po Industrial Estate, Tai Po, China (Hong Kong)
Tel.: (852) 26642011
Food Products Mfr
N.A.I.C.S.: 311423

Unilever Brasil Ltda. (1)
Av Nacoes Unidas 14261, Jardim Sao Luiz, Sao Paulo, CEP 04794-000, Brazil
Tel.: (55) 1137414323
Web Site: https://www.unilever.com.br
Sales Range: $750-799.9 Million
Emp.: 5,000
Food & Personal Care Product Mfr
N.A.I.C.S.: 311999

Unilever CR spol. s r. o. (1)
Voctarova 2497/18, 180 00, Prague, Czech Republic
Tel.: (420) 844222844
Web Site: https://www.unilever.cz
Sales Range: $100-124.9 Million
Emp.: 330
Cosmetics Products Mfr
N.A.I.C.S.: 325620

Unilever Canada Inc. (1)
160 Bloor Street East Suite 1400, Toronto, M4W 3R2, ON, Canada
Tel.: (416) 415-3000
Web Site: https://www.unilever.ca
Sales Range: $1-4.9 Billion
Emp.: 450
Production of Food Products
N.A.I.C.S.: 311999

Unilever Caribbean Limited (1)
Eastern Main Rd, PO Box 295, Champs Fleurs, Trinidad & Tobago
Tel.: (868) 6631787
Web Site: https://www.unilevercaribbean.com
Sales Range: $100-124.9 Million
Emp.: 400
Tea, Margarine, Detergents & Personal Products Mfr & Distr
N.A.I.C.S.: 311225

Unilever Chile SA (1)
Carrascal Ave 3551 Quinta Normal, Santiago, 64 D, Chile
Tel.: (56) 26812511
Web Site: http://www.lever.cl
Sales Range: $50-74.9 Million
Emp.: 200
Toilet Preparations
N.A.I.C.S.: 325611

Unilever Cote D'Ivoire SA (1)
Boulevard De Vridi Site Unilever, BP 1751, Abidjan, Cote d'Ivoire
Tel.: (225) 21754400
Web Site: http://www.unilever-fwa.com
Soap & Detergent Mfr
N.A.I.C.S.: 325611

Unilever Danmark A/S (1)
Orestads Boulevard 73, 2300, Copenhagen, Denmark
Tel.: (45) 43284100
Web Site: http://www.unilever.dk
Cosmetic Product Mfr & Distr
N.A.I.C.S.: 325620

Unilever Deutschland Holding GmbH (1)
Neue Burg 1, 20457, Hamburg, Germany
Tel.: (49) 4034930
Sales Range: $150-199.9 Million
Emp.: 1,000
Holding Company; Food, Home & Personal Care Products Mfr & Distr
N.A.I.C.S.: 551112

Subsidiary (Domestic):

Unilever Deutschland GmbH (2)
Neue Burg 1, 20457, Hamburg, Germany
Tel.: (49) 40696392000
Food, Home & Personal Care Products Mfr & Distr
N.A.I.C.S.: 339999

Subsidiary (Domestic):

Pfanni GmbH & Co. OHG (3)
Schultetusstrasse 37, Stavenhagen, 17153, Germany
Tel.: (49) 39954 330
Emp.: 250
Nutritional Product Mfr
N.A.I.C.S.: 311999

Subsidiary (Domestic):

Pfanni Werke Grundstucksverwaltung GmbH & Co. OHG (4)
Schultetusstrasse 37, Stavenhagen, 17153, Germany
Tel.: (49) 39954 330
Property Management Services
N.A.I.C.S.: 531312

Subsidiary (Domestic):

Unilever Deutschland Immobilien Leasing GmbH & Co. OHG (3)
Schultetusstr 37, 17153, Stavenhagen, Germany
Tel.: (49) 39954 330
Industrial Real Estate Investment, Development & Property Management Services
N.A.I.C.S.: 531390

Unilever Deutschland Produktions GmbH & Co. OHG (3)
Neue Burg 1, 20457, Hamburg, Germany
Tel.: (49) 4034930
Food & Personal Care Products Manufacturing Plant Management Services

UNILEVER PLC

N.A.I.C.S.: 561110

Plant (Domestic):

Unilever Deutschland Produktions GmbH & Co. OHG - Werk Auerbach (4)
Dr Wilhelm-Kutz-Strasse 21, 08209, Auerbach, Germany
Tel.: (49) 3744 257 0
Web Site: http://www.unilever.de
Instant Soups, Croutons, Convenience & Customized Food Products Mfr
N.A.I.C.S.: 311999

Unilever Deutschland Produktions GmbH & Co. OHG - Werk Buxtehude (4)
Alter Postweg 25, 21614, Buxtehude, Germany
Tel.: (49) 4161 702 0
Web Site: http://www.unilever.de
Soap & Other Personal Care Products Mfr
N.A.I.C.S.: 325611

Unilever Deutschland Produktions GmbH & Co. OHG - Werk Heilbronn (4)
Knorrstrasse 1, 74074, Heilbronn, Germany
Tel.: (49) 7131 501 1
Web Site: http://www.unilever.de
Soups, Sauces, Salad Dressing & Other Food Products Mfr
N.A.I.C.S.: 311941

Unilever Deutschland Produktions GmbH & Co. OHG - Werk Heppenheim (4)
Langnesestrasse 1, 64646, Heppenheim, Germany
Tel.: (49) 6252 707 01
Web Site: http://www.unilever.de
Ice Cream Mfr
N.A.I.C.S.: 311520

Unilever Deutschland Produktions GmbH & Co. OHG - Werk Kleve (4)
Van-den-Bergh-Strasse 35, 47533, Kleve, Germany
Tel.: (49) 2821 997 90 0
Web Site: http://www.unilever.de
Spice Mfr
N.A.I.C.S.: 311941

Unilever Deutschland Produktions GmbH & Co. OHG - Werk Mannheim (4)
Rhenaniastrasse 76-102, 68219, Mannheim, Germany
Tel.: (49) 621 8049 0
Web Site: http://www.unilever.de
Soap & Other Personal Care Products Mfr
N.A.I.C.S.: 325611

Unilever Deutschland Produktions GmbH & Co. OHG - Werk Pratau (4)
Thedinghauser Strasse 3, 06888, Lutherstadt Wittenberg, Germany
Tel.: (49) 3491 4530
Web Site: http://www.unilever.de
Margarine Mfr
N.A.I.C.S.: 311225

Unilever Deutschland Supply Chain Services GmbH (1)
Neue Burg 1, 20457, Hamburg, Germany
Tel.: (49) 40696392000
Web Site: https://www.unileverlogistik.de
Consumer Products Distr
N.A.I.C.S.: 424490

Unilever Espana, S.A. (1)
Calle de la Tecnologia n 19, Business Park, 08840, Viladecans, Barcelona, Spain
Tel.: (34) 936812200
Web Site: https://www.unilever.es
Sales Range: $150-199.9 Million
Emp.: 589
Food Products Mfr
N.A.I.C.S.: 311423

Unilever Finland Oy (1)
Verkkosaarenkatu 5, PL 254, 00580, Helsinki, Finland
Tel.: (358) 1075901
Web Site: https://www.unilever.fi
Sales Range: $25-49.9 Million
Emp.: 150
Cleaning, Hygiene & Food Products Mfr

UNILEVER PLC

Unilever PLC—(Continued)
N.A.I.C.S.: 311999

Unilever France SAS (1)
20 Rue Des Deux Gares, CS 90056,
92842, Rueil-Malmaison, Cedex, France
Tel.: (33) 141966200
Web Site: https://www.unilever.fr
Sales Range: $150-199.9 Million
Emp.: 1,000
Food & Personal Care Products Mfr
N.A.I.C.S.: 311999

Division (Domestic):

Unilever France (2)
7 Rue Emmy Noether, 93484, Saint-Ouen,
Cedex 17, France
Tel.: (33) 1 58 79 30 00
Web Site: http://www.unilever.com
Perfumes & Toiletries Mfr
N.A.I.C.S.: 325620

Unilever Ghana PLC (1)
Heavy Industrial Area, PO Box 721, Tema,
Ghana
Tel.: (233) 303218247
Web Site: https://www.unileverghana.com
Rev.: $89,580,309
Assets: $65,035,795
Liabilities: $58,783,848
Net Worth: $6,251,948
Earnings: $59,504
Emp.: 252
Fiscal Year-end: 12/31/2021
Food & Personal Care Products Mfr
N.A.I.C.S.: 325611
Edward Effah *(Chm)*

Unilever Hong Kong Ltd. (1)
6 Dai Fu St Tai Po Industrial Estate, Hong
Kong, New Territories, China (Hong Kong)
Tel.: (852) 28923110
Web Site: https://www.unilever.com.hk
Fast Moving Consumer Goods Mfr & Distr
N.A.I.C.S.: 325620

Unilever Hrvatska d.o.o. (1)
Strojarska Ulica 20, 10000, Zagreb, Croatia
Tel.: (385) 16311401
Web Site:
https://www.unileverfoodsolutions.hr
Food Service
N.A.I.C.S.: 722310

Unilever Iran P.J.S.C (1)
No 23 corner of 33 St Zagros St Argentina
Square, 1516683111, Tehran, Iran
Tel.: (98) 2187719000
Web Site: https://unilever.ir
Sales Range: $125-149.9 Million
Emp.: 300
Home & Personal Care Product Distr
N.A.I.C.S.: 424210

Unilever Israel Marketing Ltd (1)
52 Julius Simon Street, PO Box 208, Haifa,
3296279, Israel
Tel.: (972) 39729222
Fast Moving Consumer Goods Distr
N.A.I.C.S.: 424210

Unilever Italia Srl (1)
Ufficio Relazioni Esterne, Via Paolo di Dono
3/A, 00142, Rome, Italy
Tel.: (39) 0654491
Web Site: http://www.unileveritalia.it
Sales Range: $750-799.9 Million
Emp.: 5,000
Food & Personal Care Product Mfr & Marketer
N.A.I.C.S.: 311999

Unilever Italy Holdings S.R.L. (1)
Via Paolo Di Dono 3/A, 00142, Rome, Italy
Tel.: (39) 0800800121
Web Site: https://www.unilever.it
Consumer Products Distr
N.A.I.C.S.: 424210

Unilever Japan Holdings K.K. (1)
2-1-1 Kamimeguro, Meguro-ku, Tokyo, 153-8578, Japan
Tel.: (81) 120500513
Web Site: https://www.unilever.co.jp
Consumer Products Distr
N.A.I.C.S.: 424210

Unilever Japan KK
Nakameguro GT Tower 2-1-1 Kamimeguro,
Meguro-ku, Tokyo, 153-8578, Japan
Tel.: (81) 120500513
Web Site: https://www.unilever.co.jp
Sales Range: $200-249.9 Million
Emp.: 400
Margarine, Fats, Oils, Detergents, Personal
Products & Food Products Mfr & Distr
N.A.I.C.S.: 311224

Unilever Kenya Ltd. (1)
Commercial Street, PO Box 30062, Nairobi,
Kenya
Tel.: (254) 206922000
Web Site: http://www.unilever.co.ke
Sales Range: $150-199.9 Million
Emp.: 800
Margarine, Fats, Oils, Detergents & Toilet
Preparations Mfr
N.A.I.C.S.: 311224

Unilever Korea Ltd. (1)
Appletree Tower Bldg 6/7F Teheran-ro
Samseong-dong, Gangnam-gu, 135-877,
Seoul, Korea (South)
Tel.: (82) 2 709 1900
Web Site: http://www.unilever.co.kr
Cosmetic Product Distr
N.A.I.C.S.: 424210

Unilever Maghreb Export SA (1)
Megrine Riadh Z4 Voie Z4, Tunis, Tunisia
Tel.: (216) 71425505
Cosmetic Product Distr
N.A.I.C.S.: 424210

Unilever Maghreb S.A. (1)
km10 route Cotiere, Ain Sebaa, 20252,
Casablanca, Morocco
Tel.: (212) 522345000
Consumer Products Distr
N.A.I.C.S.: 424490

Unilever Magyarorszag Kft. (1)
Vaci ut 121-127 Building D, 1138, Budapest, Hungary
Tel.: (36) 80180144
Web Site: https://www.unilever.hu
Sales Range: $150-199.9 Million
Emp.: 1,300
Food & Personal Care Products Mfr
N.A.I.C.S.: 311999

**Unilever Market Development (Pty)
Ltd** (1)
No 15 Northern Crescent Armstrong Ave,
La Lucia, Durban, 4051, South Africa
Tel.: (27) 31 571 9600
Sales Range: $450-499.9 Million
Emp.: 2,500
Cosmetic & Nutrition Product Mfr
N.A.I.C.S.: 325620

Unilever Mocambique Limitada (1)
Avenida 24 de Julho Edificio 24 n 1097 4
andar, Maputo, Mozambique
Tel.: (258) 21720082
Cosmetic Product Distr
N.A.I.C.S.: 424210

Unilever Nederland B.V. (1)
Hofplein 19, 3032 AC, Rotterdam,
Netherlands (16%)
Tel.: (31) 8000991197
Food Product Product Mfr
N.A.I.C.S.: 311999

Subsidiary (Domestic):

Marga BV (2)
Weena 455, 3000 DK, Rotterdam, Netherlands
Tel.: (31) 102174000
Holding Company
N.A.I.C.S.: 551112

**Unilever Nederland Holdings
B.V.** (2)
Weena 455, 3013 AL, Rotterdam, Netherlands
Tel.: (31) 102174000
Web Site: http://www.unilever.nl
Holding Company
N.A.I.C.S.: 551112

Holding (Non-US):

P.T. Unilever Indonesia Tbk (3)
Jl BSD Boulevard Barat Green Office Park
Kavling 3, BSD City, Tangerang, 15245,
Indonesia
Tel.: (62) 2180827000
Web Site: https://www.unilever.co.id
Sales: $2,507,424,381
Assets: $1,082,165,745
Liabilities: $862,588,149
Net Worth: $219,577,596
Earnings: $311,773,044
Emp.: 4,573
Fiscal Year-end: 12/31/2023
Food & Personal Care Product Mfr
N.A.I.C.S.: 311999
Enny Hartati Sampurno *(Dir-Customer Dev)*

Unilever Nigeria Plc (1)
1 Billings Way, PO Box 1063, Oregun Ikeja,
Lagos, Nigeria
Tel.: (234) 12240332
Web Site: https://www.unilevernigeria.com
Emp.: 944
Food, Home & Personal Care Products Mfr
N.A.I.C.S.: 325611
Adesola Sotande-Peters *(Acting Mng Dir)*

Unilever Pakistan Ltd. (1)
Avari Plaza Fatima Jinnah Road Saddar,
Karachi, 75500, Pakistan
Tel.: (92) 2135671705
Web Site: http://www.unilever.pk
Rev.: $777,746,642
Assets: $322,372,034
Liabilities: $295,747,303
Net Worth: $26,624,730
Earnings: $118,864,290
Emp.: 1,670
Fiscal Year-end: 12/31/2017
Food, Detergent & Personal Care Products
Mfr
N.A.I.C.S.: 311999
Shazia Syed *(Exec VP-Tea Bus-Global)*

Unilever Peru S.A (1)
Francisco Grana 155 Urb, Santa Catalina,
Lima, Peru
Tel.: (51) 14111600
Web Site: http://www.unilever.com.pe
Home & Personal Care Product Mfr
N.A.I.C.S.: 325620

Unilever Philippines Inc. (1)
7F Bonifacio Stopover Corporate Center
31st St Cor 2nd Avenue, Bonifacio Global
City Fort Bonifacio, Taguig, 1630, Philippines
Tel.: (63) 285888800
Web Site: https://www.unilever.com.ph
Sales Range: $350-399.9 Million
Emp.: 2,000
Margarine, Fats, Oils, Foods, Detergents,
Personal Products
N.A.I.C.S.: 311224

Unilever Polska S.A. (1)
Al Jerozolimskie 134, PO Box 41, 02-305,
Warsaw, Poland
Tel.: (48) 695188005
Web Site: https://www.unilever.pl
Sales Range: $75-99.9 Million
Emp.: 302
Food Products Mfr
N.A.I.C.S.: 311423

Unilever Romania S.A. (1)
Str Barbu Vacarescu 301 - 311 etaj 8 Afi
Lakeview Sector 2, 020276, Bucharest,
Romania
Tel.: (40) 213034800
Web Site: https://www.unilever.ro
Consumer Products Distr
N.A.I.C.S.: 424490

Unilever Russia (1)
Sergey Makeev St 13, Moscow, 123022,
Russia (77%)
Tel.: (7) 4957457500
Web Site: https://www.unilever.ru
Sales Range: $200-249.9 Million
Emp.: 3,000
Cosmetics Mfr
N.A.I.C.S.: 325620

Unilever Sanayi ve Turk A.S. (1)
84 Degirmenyolu Caddesi, Huzor Hoca
Sokak, 81120, Istanbul, Turkiye
Tel.: (90) 2164639000
Web Site: http://www.unilever.com.tr
Food & Personal Care Product Mfr
N.A.I.C.S.: 311999
Ozgur Kolukfaki *(VP-Food & Beverage)*

Unilever Schweiz GmbH (1)
Bahnhofstrasse 19, CH-8240, Thayngen,
Switzerland

INTERNATIONAL PUBLIC

Tel.: (41) 526456666
Web Site: http://www.unilever.ch
Sales Range: $100-124.9 Million
Emp.: 400
Food & Personal Care Products Mfr
N.A.I.C.S.: 311999

**Unilever Services (Hei Fei) Co.
Limited** (1)
88 Jinxiu Avenue Hefei Economic and Technology Development Zone, Anhui, 230601,
China
Tel.: (86) 5513856000
Sales Range: $25-49.9 Million
Emp.: 170
Food & Personal Care Products Mfr
N.A.I.C.S.: 311423

Unilever Slovensko, spol. s r.o. (1)
Karadzicova 10, 821 08, Bratislava, Slovakia
Tel.: (421) 850123850
Web Site: https://www.unilever.sk
Cosmetic Product & Nutritional Food Mfr
N.A.I.C.S.: 325620

Unilever South Africa (Pty) Ltd. (1)
15 Nollsworth Crescent Nollsworth Park, La
Lucia Ridge, Durban, 4051, South
Africa (74.25%)
Tel.: (27) 313441706
Web Site: https://www.unilever.co.za
Sales Range: $125-149.9 Million
Emp.: 3,000
Food & Personal Care Product Mfr
N.A.I.C.S.: 311999

**Unilever South Central Europe
SA** (1)
Ploiesti 291 Republicii Avenue, Bldg B 4th
Fl, 720089, Bucharest, Prahova, Romania
Tel.: (40) 213034800
Detergents Mfr
N.A.I.C.S.: 325611

Unilever South East Africa Ltd (1)
2 Sterling Rd, Workington, Harare, Zimbabwe
Tel.: (263) 4753700
Sales Range: $75-99.9 Million
Emp.: 400
Food Products Mfr
N.A.I.C.S.: 311999

Unilever Sri Lanka Limited (1)
258 M Vincent Perera Mawatha, Colombo,
Sri Lanka
Tel.: (94) 777002700
Web Site: https://www.unilever.com.lk
Consumer Products Distr
N.A.I.C.S.: 424490

**Unilever Supply Chain Company
AG** (1)
Spitalstrasse 5, 8200, Schaffhausen, Switzerland
Tel.: (41) 526315002
Consumer Products Distr
N.A.I.C.S.: 424490
Neil Humphrey *(Chm)*

Unilever Sverige AB (1)
Tel.: (46) 86199500
Web Site: https://www.unilever.se
Sales Range: $350-399.9 Million
Emp.: 1,210
Food & Personal Care Product Mfr
N.A.I.C.S.: 311999

Subsidiary (Non-US):

Unilever Norge AS (2)
Martin Linges vei 25, Postbox 1, 1331,
Fornebu, Norway
Tel.: (47) 66776100
Sales Range: $25-49.9 Million
Emp.: 40
Food & Personal Care Product Mfr
N.A.I.C.S.: 311999
Lars Aaseby *(Gen Mgr)*

Unilever Tanzania Limited (1)
Plot 4A Nyerere Road, PO Box 40383, Dar
es Salaam, Tanzania
Tel.: (255) 789041005
Consumer Products Distr
N.A.I.C.S.: 424490

Unilever Tea Rwanda Limited (1)
2nd Floor Sanlam Towers, PO Box 973,
Kigali, Rwanda

AND PRIVATE COMPANIES — UNILEVER PLC

Tel.: (250) 78 046 8939
Web Site: https://www.unilever-ewa.com
Consumer Products Distr
N.A.I.C.S.: 424490

Unilever Thai Trading Limited (1)
161 Rama 9 Road, Huay Kwang, Bangkok, 10310, Thailand
Tel.: (66) 25542000
Web Site: http://www.unilever.co.th
Sales Range: $350-399.9 Million
Emp.: 2,000
Food & Personal Care Product Mfr & Marketer
N.A.I.C.S.: 311999

Unilever Tunisia S.A. (1)
Megrine Riadh Z4 Voie Z4, Tunis, Tunisia
Tel.: (216) 71425505
Web Site: https://www.unilevermaghreb.com
Consumer Products Distr
N.A.I.C.S.: 424490

Unilever UK Ltd. (1)
Unilever House Springfield Drive, Leatherhead, KT22 7GR, Surrey, United Kingdom (81%)
Tel.: (44) 1372945000
Web Site: http://www.unilever.co.uk
Sales Range: $350-399.9 Million
Emp.: 1,400
Food & Personal Care Product Mfr & Marketer
N.A.I.C.S.: 311999

Subsidiary (Domestic):

REN Limited (2)
Union House 182-194 Union Street, London, SE1 0LH, United Kingdom
Tel.: (44) 2077242900
Web Site: https://www.renskincare.com
Health & Personal Care Product Distr
N.A.I.C.S.: 456199

Simple Health & Beauty Limited (2)
Unilever House Springfield Drive, Leatherhead, KT22 7GR, Surrey, United Kingdom
Tel.: (44) 1372945000
Web Site: http://www.simple.co.uk
Sales Range: $150-199.9 Million
Emp.: 50
Health & Beauty Products Mfr & Distr
N.A.I.C.S.: 325620

Subsidiary (Domestic):

Simple Toiletries Limited (3)
Unilever House Springfield Drive, Leatherhead, KT22 7GR, Surrey, United Kingdom (100%)
Tel.: (44) 1372945000
Web Site: http://www.simple.co.uk
Toiletries Whslr
N.A.I.C.S.: 424210

Subsidiary (Non-US):

Unilever Ireland Ltd. (2)
20 River Walk National Digital Pk, Citywest Bus Campus, Dublin, 24, Ireland
Tel.: (353) 12914000
Web Site: http://www.unilever.ie
Sales Range: $125-149.9 Million
Emp.: 360
Food & Personal Care Products Mfr
N.A.I.C.S.: 325611
Emily Pittman (VP & Gen Mgr)

Subsidiary (Domestic):

Unilever UK & CN Holdings Limited (2)
Unilever House 100 Victoria Embankment, London, EC4Y 0DY, United Kingdom
Tel.: (44) 1495248555
Food Products Mfr
N.A.I.C.S.: 311999

Unilever UK Holdings Ltd. (2)
5 Temple Square Temple Street, Liverpool, L2 5RH, Surrey, United Kingdom
Tel.: (44) 2078225252
Investment Management Service
N.A.I.C.S.: 523940

Unilever Uganda Limited (1)
5th Floor DFCU Towers Kyadondo Road, PO Box 3515, Kampala, Uganda
Tel.: (256) 312226100
Consumer Products Distr

N.A.I.C.S.: 424490

Unilever Ukraine LLC (1)
St Velika Vasylkivska 139, 03150, Kiev, Ukraine
Tel.: (380) 444905846
Web Site: https://www.unilever.ua
Consumer Products Distr
N.A.I.C.S.: 424490

Unilever United States, Inc. (1)
800 Sylvan Ave, Englewood Cliffs, NJ 07632-3113
Tel.: (201) 894-4000
Web Site: https://www.unileverusa.com
Sales Range: $1-4.9 Billion
Emp.: 14,000
Food, Home & Personal Care Products Mfr
N.A.I.C.S.: 311941
Esi Eggleston Bracey (Pres & CEO-Personal Care-North America)

Subsidiary (Domestic):

Conopco, Inc. (2)
2815 Forbs Ave Ste 107, Hoffman Estates, IL 60192
Tel.: (847) 645-5000
Web Site: https://www.conopco.com
Home & Personal Care Product Mfr
N.A.I.C.S.: 311999

Subsidiary (Domestic):

Ben & Jerry's Homemade, Inc. (3)
530 Community Dr Ste 1, South Burlington, VT 05403
Tel.: (802) 992-2600
Web Site: https://www.benjerry.com
Sales Range: $250-299.9 Million
Emp.: 115
Homemade Ice Cream & Frozen Yogurt Mfr & Retailer; Ice Cream Parlor Franchises Owner
N.A.I.C.S.: 311520
Ben R. Cohen (Founder)

Plant (Domestic):

Ben & Jerry's Homemade (4)
1281 Waterbury Stowe Rd, Waterbury, VT 05676
Tel.: (802) 882-1240
Web Site: http://www.benjerry.com
Sales Range: $75-99.9 Million
Ice Cream Mfr
N.A.I.C.S.: 722513

Subsidiary (Non-US):

Ben & Jerry's Homemade Ltd. (4)
1st Floor Goswell House, Windsor, SL4 1DS, Berks, United Kingdom
Tel.: (44) 1753834034
Web Site: http://www.benjerry.co.uk
Sales Range: $50-74.9 Million
Emp.: 15
Ice Cream Distr
N.A.I.C.S.: 311520

Plant (Domestic):

Conopco (3)
19161 E Walnut Dr N, City of Industry, CA 91748-1429
Tel.: (626) 854-5000
Sales Range: $25-49.9 Million
Emp.: 250
Hair Shampoos & Conditioners Mfr
N.A.I.C.S.: 325620

Conopco (3)
1100 Frederick St, Hagerstown, MD 21740-6867
Tel.: (301) 797-9603
Web Site: http://www.icecreamusa.com
Sales Range: $50-74.9 Million
Emp.: 480
Ice Cream Mfr
N.A.I.C.S.: 311520

Conopco (3)
255 Saddleback Dr, Loveland, OH 45140-8780
Tel.: (513) 683-5925
Sales Range: $25-49.9 Million
Emp.: 1
Ice Cream Mfr
N.A.I.C.S.: 311520

Conopco (3)

100 Faberge Blvd, Raeford, NC 28376
Tel.: (910) 875-4121
Sales Range: $75-99.9 Million
Emp.: 400
Personal Care Product Mfr
N.A.I.C.S.: 325611

Conopco (3)
1001 Olsen St, Henderson, NV 89015-3006
Tel.: (702) 564-0020
Web Site: http://www.icecreamusa.com
Sales Range: $50-74.9 Million
Emp.: 400
Ice Cream Mfr
N.A.I.C.S.: 311520

Conopco (3)
523 S 17th St, Harrisburg, PA 17104-2220
Tel.: (717) 234-6215
Sales Range: $10-24.9 Million
Emp.: 50
Mfr of Macaroni & Spaghetti
N.A.I.C.S.: 311824

Conopco (3)
5448 Prairie Stone Parkway, Hoffman Estates, IL 60192
Tel.: (847) 645-5000
Web Site: http://www.conopco.com
Sales Range: $25-49.9 Million
Emp.: 250
Mfr of Consumer Products
N.A.I.C.S.: 325620
William G. Conopeotis (Pres)

Conopco (3)
13000 E 35th St, Independence, MO 64055-2423
Tel.: (816) 833-1700
Sales Range: $25-49.9 Million
Emp.: 220
Food Products Mfr
N.A.I.C.S.: 311999

Conopco (3)
490 Old Connecticut Path, Framingham, MA 01701-4577
Tel.: (508) 620-4300
Web Site: http://www.icecreamusa.com
Sales Range: $25-49.9 Million
Emp.: 250
Ice Cream & Frozen Deserts Mfr
N.A.I.C.S.: 311520

Conopco (3)
27080 W 159th St, New Century, KS 66031-0032
Tel.: (913) 782-7171
Web Site: http://www.bestfoods.com
Sales Range: $25-49.9 Million
Emp.: 210
Production of Food Products
N.A.I.C.S.: 311225

Conopco (3)
1591 Murphy Ave SW, Atlanta, GA 30310-4505
Tel.: (404) 758-4531
Web Site: http://www.conopco.com
Sales Range: $25-49.9 Million
Emp.: 175
Food Products Mfr
N.A.I.C.S.: 311999

Conopco (3)
2900 W Truman Blvd, Jefferson City, MO 65109
Tel.: (573) 893-3040
Web Site: http://www.unilever.com
Sales Range: $25-49.9 Million
Emp.: 450
Cosmetic & Toiletries Mfr
N.A.I.C.S.: 325620

Division (Domestic):

Unilever Food Solutions (3)
2200 Cabot Dr, Lisle, IL 60532
Tel.: (630) 505-5300
Web Site: http://www.unileverfoodsolutions.us
Sales Range: $25-49.9 Million
Emp.: 250
Food Preparation & Support Services
N.A.I.C.S.: 311999

Plant (Domestic):

Unilever (4)
2816 S Kilbourn Ave, Chicago, IL 60623
Tel.: (773) 247-5800

Web Site: http://www.unileverusa.com
Food Products Mfr
N.A.I.C.S.: 311225

Unilever Food Solutions - Little Rock (4)
8201 Frazier Pike, Little Rock, AR 72206-3871
Tel.: (501) 490-1441
Web Site: http://www.unileverfoodsolutions.us
Sales Range: $100-124.9 Million
Emp.: 125
Food Products Mfr
N.A.I.C.S.: 311999

Unilever Food Solutions - Milwaukee (4)
8622 N 87th St, Milwaukee, WI 53224
Tel.: (414) 365-5720
Web Site: http://www.unileverfoodsolutions.com
Sales Range: $100-124.9 Million
Emp.: 240
Dressings Raw & Cooked Salads
N.A.I.C.S.: 311941

Plant (Domestic):

Unilever Home & Personal Care USA (3)
75 Merritt Blvd, Trumbull, CT 06611
Tel.: (203) 377-8300
Web Site: http://www.unilever.com
Sales Range: $25-49.9 Million
Emp.: 1,000
Home & Personal Care Products Research & Development
N.A.I.C.S.: 541715

Unilever Home & Personal Care USA (3)
1 John St, Clinton, CT 06413-1753
Tel.: (860) 669-8601
Web Site: http://www.unilever.com
Sales Range: $75-99.9 Million
Emp.: 500
Cosmetics Mfr
N.A.I.C.S.: 325620

Subsidiary (Non-US):

Unilever Pakistan Foods Limited (3)
Avari Plaza Fatima Jinnah Road, Karachi, 75530, Pakistan
Tel.: (92) 2135660062
Web Site: https://www.unilever.pk
Rev.: $85,596,771
Assets: $45,652,085
Liabilities: $30,813,056
Net Worth: $14,839,029
Earnings: $15,796,921
Emp.: 251
Fiscal Year-end: 12/31/2019
Food Products Mfr
N.A.I.C.S.: 311999
Kamran Y. Mirza (Chm)

Unit (Domestic):

Unilever Research & Development Co. (3)
40 Merritt Blvd, Trumbull, CT 06611-5413
Tel.: (203) 381-4108
Sales Range: $50-74.9 Million
Emp.: 350
Research & Development Services
N.A.I.C.S.: 541715

Subsidiary (Domestic):

Dermalogica, Inc. (2)
1535 Beachey Pl, Carson, CA 90746
Tel.: (310) 900-4000
Web Site: http://www.dermalogica.com
Sales Range: $200-249.9 Million
Skin Care Product Mfr
N.A.I.C.S.: 325620
Jane Wurwand (Founder)

Dollar Shave Club, Inc. (2)
PO Box 5688, Santa Monica, CA 90499
Tel.: (310) 975-8528
Web Site: http://www.dollarshaveclub.com
Personal Grooming Product Distr
N.A.I.C.S.: 424210
Jason Goldberger (CEO)

Living Proof, Inc. (2)
301 Binney St 1st Fl, Cambridge, MA 02142

UNILEVER PLC

Unilever PLC—(Continued)
Tel.: (617) 621-1800
Web Site: https://www.livingproof.com
Hair Care Product Mfr & Distr
N.A.I.C.S.: 325620
Robert S. Langer *(Co-Founder)*

Olly Public Benefit Corporation (2)
415 Jackson St Fl 2, San Francisco, CA 94111
Web Site: https://www.olly.com
Nutritional & Supplement Product Distr
N.A.I.C.S.: 456191

Royal Estates Tea Company (2)
800 Sylvan Ave, Englewood Cliffs, NJ 07632
Tel.: (201) 567-8000
Tea Mfr
N.A.I.C.S.: 311920

Seventh Generation, Inc. (2)
60 Lake St, Burlington, VT 05401
Tel.: (802) 658-3773
Web Site:
 http://www.seventhgeneration.com
Environmentally Safe Cleaning Products Mfr
N.A.I.C.S.: 424990
Alison Whritenour *(CEO)*

St. Ives Laboratories, Inc. (2)
1655 Waters Ridge, Lewisville, TX 75057
Tel.: (818) 998-3511
Web Site: https://www.stives.com
Rev.: $59,000,000
Emp.: 150
Perfumes Cosmetics & Other Toilet Preparations
N.A.I.C.S.: 325620

Sundial Brands LLC (2)
11 Ranick Dr S, Amityville, NY 11701
Web Site: https://www.sheamoisture.com
Cosmetic Product Distr
N.A.I.C.S.: 456120

TATCHA, LLC (2)
208 Utah Ste 400, San Francisco, CA 94103
Web Site: https://www.tatcha.com
Sales Range: $10-24.9 Million
Emp.: 50
Cosmetic Product Distr
N.A.I.C.S.: 456120
Vicky Tsai *(Founder)*

Tazo Tea Company (2)
301 SE 2nd Ave, Portland, OR 97214
Web Site: http://www.tazo.com
Tea Retailers
N.A.I.C.S.: 311920

Plant (Domestic):

Unilever - Covington (2)
2000 Hwy 51 N, Covington, TN 38019-2361
Tel.: (901) 475-5141
Sales Range: $200-249.9 Million
Emp.: 400
Food Supplement Mfr
N.A.I.C.S.: 311999

Subsidiary (Domestic):

Unilever Capital Corporation (2)
700 Sylvan Ave, Englewood Cliffs, NJ 07632
Tel.: (201) 894-7135
Investment & Management Services
N.A.I.C.S.: 523999

Unilever HPC USA, Inc. (2)
2900 W Truman Blvd, Jefferson City, MO 65109
Tel.: (573) 893-3040
Web Site: http://www.unilever.com
Cosmetics Products Mfr
N.A.I.C.S.: 325620

Unit (Domestic):

Unilever US Government & Public Affairs (2)
816 Connecticut Ave NW 7th Fl, Washington, DC 20006-2705
Tel.: (202) 828-1010
Sales Range: $25-49.9 Million
Emp.: 4
Business Support Services
N.A.I.C.S.: 561499

Unilever Vietnam International Company Limited (1)
156 Nguyen Luong Bang Avenue, Tan Phu Ward District 7, Ho Chi Minh City, 70000, Vietnam
Tel.: (84) 2854135686
Web Site: https://www.unilever.com.vn
Sales Range: $200-249.9 Million
Emp.: 700
Consumer Goods Mfr & Distr
N.A.I.C.S.: 311999

Unilever Zimbabwe Pvt Ltd (1)
2 Stirling Rd, PO Box 950, Workington, Harare, Zimbabwe
Tel.: (263) 4753700
Soap & Detergent Mfr
N.A.I.C.S.: 325611

Unilever de Argentina SA (1)
Alf H Bouchard 4191, Vicente Lopez District, B1605BNA, Buenos Aires, Argentina
Tel.: (54) 8008886666
Web Site: http://www.unilever.com.ar
Sales Range: $200-249.9 Million
Emp.: 1,000
Home & Personal Care Products Mfr, Marketer & Distr
N.A.I.C.S.: 325620

Unilever de Mexico S de RL de CV (1)
Paseo de Tamarindos 150, Cuajimalpa, DFCP 05120, Mexico, Mexico
Tel.: (52) 5511054002
Web Site: http://www.unilever.com.mx
Sales Range: $450-499.9 Million
Emp.: 2,500
Marketer of Margarine, Shortening, Pancake/Cake Mixes, Gelatins, Salad Dressings & Peanut Butter Products; Producer of Chocolates, Lollipops & Candies
N.A.I.C.S.: 424490

UNILOCK CAPITAL CORP.
905-1030 West Georgia Street, Vancouver, V6E 2Y3, BC, Canada
Tel.: (604) 689-2646
UUU.P—(TSXV)
Assets: $200,074
Liabilities: $8,348
Net Worth: $191,726
Earnings: ($88,215)
Fiscal Year-end: 02/29/20
Asset Management Services
N.A.I.C.S.: 523940
Harry Chew *(Pres, CEO & CFO)*

UNILUMIN GROUP CO., LTD.
112 Yongfu Rd, Qiaotou Village Baoan District, Shenzhen, 518103, China
Tel.: (86) 75529918999
Web Site: https://www.unilumin.com
Year Founded: 2004
300232—(CHIN)
Rev.: $993,463,380
Assets: $1,383,928,416
Liabilities: $738,414,144
Net Worth: $645,514,272
Earnings: $8,933,652
Emp.: 5,000
Fiscal Year-end: 12/31/22
LED Displays, Screens & Lighting Mfr
N.A.I.C.S.: 334413
Mingfeng Lin *(Founder, Chm & Gen Mgr)*

Subsidiaries:

ROE Visual Co., Ltd. (1)
Bldg 7 ZhongYuntai Technology Industrial Park, Baoan, Shenzhen, 518108, China
Tel.: (86) 7558 392 4892
Web Site: https://www.roevisual.com
Semiconductor & Related Device Mfr
N.A.I.C.S.: 334413
Grace Kuo *(Dir-Overseas Sls)*

Unilumin Group Co., Ltd. (1)
1F 6-104 Aioicho, Naka-ku, Yokohama, 231-0012, Kanagawa, Japan
Tel.: (81) 803 731 1696
Light Emitting Diode Product Mfr & Distr

N.A.I.C.S.: 334413

Unilumin Australia Pty. Ltd. (1)
Unit 2 7 Anzed Court, Mulgrave, 3170, VIC, Australia
Tel.: (61) 39 006 8960
Light Emitting Diode Product Mfr & Distr
N.A.I.C.S.: 334413

Unilumin Germany GmbH (1)
Robert-Bosch-Strasse 4, 72622, Nurtingen, Germany
Tel.: (49) 7022 306 0521
Web Site: https://www.de.unilumin.com
Light Emitting Diode Product Mfr & Distr
N.A.I.C.S.: 334413

Unilumin LED Europe BV (1)
Parellaan 28, 2132 WS, Hoofddorp, Netherlands
Tel.: (31) 20 214 9657
Light Emitting Diode Product Mfr & Distr
N.A.I.C.S.: 334413

Unilumin Middle East DMCC (1)
Suite 1702 Reef Tower Cluster O Jumeriah Lake Towers, Dubai, United Arab Emirates
Tel.: (971) 4 427 0171
Light Emitting Diode Product Mfr & Distr
N.A.I.C.S.: 334413

Unilumin Saudi Arabia LLC (1)
3731 Abi Al Fath Al Ansari Al Manar, Riyadh, Saudi Arabia
Tel.: (966) 508786186
LED Display Product Mfr
N.A.I.C.S.: 334419

Unilumin South Korea Ltd. (1)
Room 321 3F B-dong Munjeong Station Terra Tower 651, Munjeong-dong Songpa-gu, Seoul, Korea (South)
Tel.: (82) 1046170852
LED Display Product Mfr
N.A.I.C.S.: 334419

Unilumin Technologies Pte. Ltd. (1)
10 Ubi Crescent 07-36 Lobby C Ubi Techpark, Singapore, 408564, Singapore
Tel.: (65) 6 622 2288
Light Emitting Diode Product Mfr & Distr
N.A.I.C.S.: 334413

Unilumin Thailand Limited (1)
21st Floor TST Tower No 21 Viphawadi-Rangsit Road, Chomphon Chatuchak, Bangkok, 10900, Thailand
Tel.: (66) 200199002
LED Display Product Mfr
N.A.I.C.S.: 334419

Unilumin UK Co., Ltd. (1)
Profile West 950 Great West Road, Brentford, London, TW8 9ES, United Kingdom
Tel.: (44) 208 568 6333
Light Emitting Diode Product Mfr & Distr
N.A.I.C.S.: 334413

Unilumin USA LLC (1)
254W 31st St 12th Fl, New York, NY 10001
Web Site: https://www.unilumin-usa.com
Light Emitting Diode Product Mfr & Distr
N.A.I.C.S.: 334413

UNIMA 2000 SYSTEMY TELEINFORMATYCZNE S.A.
ul Skarzynskiego 14, 31-866, Krakow, Poland
Tel.: (48) 122980511
Web Site:
 http://www.unima2000.com.pl
Year Founded: 1992
YARRL—(WAR)
Rev.: $7,802,846
Assets: $11,322,154
Liabilities: $4,112,043
Net Worth: $7,210,112
Earnings: $358,486
Emp.: 400
Fiscal Year-end: 12/31/23
Telecommunications & Data Communications Services
N.A.I.C.S.: 561422
Grzegorz Pardela *(CEO)*

Subsidiaries:

IQnet Sp. z o.o. (1)

INTERNATIONAL PUBLIC

ul Jasnogorska 44, 31-358, Krakow, Poland
Tel.: (48) 609687408
Web Site: http://www.iqnet.pl
Business Management Services
N.A.I.C.S.: 561499

Teleinvention Sp. z o.o. (1)
ul Skarzynskiego 14, 31-866, Krakow, Poland
Tel.: (48) 122980760
Web Site: http://www.teleinvention.pl
Professional & Outsourcing Services
N.A.I.C.S.: 561110

UNIMAT LIFE CORPORATION
2-12-14 Minami Aoyama Unimat Aoyama Building, Minato-ku, Tokyo, 107-0062, Japan
Tel.: (81) 357701661
Web Site: http://www.unimat-life.co.jp
Year Founded: 1958
Coffee, Tea & Soft Drink Mfr
N.A.I.C.S.: 311920
Takahito Sugata *(Pres & CEO)*

Subsidiaries:

CASSINA IXC. Ltd. (1)
2-13-10 Minami-aoyama, Minato-ku, Tokyo, Japan
Tel.: (81) 364391360
Web Site: http://www.cassina-ixc.jp
Rev.: $110,932,800
Assets: $88,523,600
Liabilities: $33,589,600
Net Worth: $54,934,000
Earnings: $9,525,120
Fiscal Year-end: 12/31/2021
Furniture Store Operator
N.A.I.C.S.: 449110
Yoji Takahashi *(Chm)*

Subsidiary (Domestic):

Conran Shop Japan Limited (2)
3-7-1 Nishi-Shinjuku Shinjuku Park Tower 3F, Shinjuku-ku, Tokyo, Japan
Tel.: (81) 36 632 8500
Web Site: https://www.conranshop.jp
Household Good & Furniture Whslr
N.A.I.C.S.: 423210

UNIMECH GROUP BERHAD
Wisma Unimech 4934 Jalan Chain Ferry, 12100, Butterworth, Malaysia
Tel.: (60) 43328821
Web Site:
 https://www.unimechgroup.com
UNIMECH—(KLS)
Rev.: $70,521,008
Assets: $107,559,289
Liabilities: $30,572,191
Net Worth: $76,987,098
Earnings: $7,531,665
Fiscal Year-end: 12/31/22
Industrial Valve Mfr
N.A.I.C.S.: 332911
Angelina Gaik Suan Cheah *(Co-Sec)*

Subsidiaries:

Arita Engineering Sdn. Bhd. (1)
No 9 Jalan PJU 1A/18 TPJ 7, Taman Perindustrian Jaya, 47200, Subang Jaya, Selangor, Malaysia
Tel.: (60) 37 845 1989
Web Site: https://arita.com.my
Sales Range: $25-49.9 Million
Emp.: 12
Industrial Heating Equipments Installation & Maintenance Services
N.A.I.C.S.: 238220

Subsidiary (Non-US):

PT. Arita Prima Indonesia Tbk. (2)
Jalan Danau Sunter Utara Rukan Sunter Permai, Block C No 9 Sunter, Jakarta Utara, 14350, Kode Pos, Indonesia
Tel.: (62) 216519188
Web Site: https://www.arita.co.id
Rev.: $19,424,262
Assets: $39,011,883
Liabilities: $12,357,436
Net Worth: $26,654,447
Earnings: $1,990,505

AND PRIVATE COMPANIES

Emp.: 251
Fiscal Year-end: 12/31/2023
Valves, Fittings & Other Industrial Equipment Distr
N.A.I.C.S.: 423720

Subsidiary (Domestic):

PT. Arita Prima Teknindo (3)
Komplek Pertokoan Rungkut Megah Raya Blok E-27 Jl Raya Kali Rungkut 5, Surabaya, 60293, East Java, Indonesia
Tel.: (62) 318795656
Emp.: 17
Industrial Valve Distr
N.A.I.C.S.: 423840
Yew Lean Low *(Mng Dir)*

Arita Flanges Industries Sdn. Bhd. (1)
Lot 414 Off Lorong Perusahaan 8C, Seberang Perai, 13600, Prai, Penang, Malaysia
Tel.: (60) 43973388
Emp.: 8
Industrial Flanges Mfr
N.A.I.C.S.: 332919

Arita Valve Mfg. (M) Sdn. Bhd. (1)
Lot 414 Lorong Perusahaan 8C, Prai Industrial Estate, 13700, Prai, Penang, Malaysia
Tel.: (60) 43973388
Web Site: https://www.aritavalve.com
Sales Range: $25-49.9 Million
Emp.: 20
Valves & Pipe Fittings Mfr
N.A.I.C.S.: 332919
J. L. Lim *(Gen Mgr)*

Bells Marketing Sdn. Bhd. (1)
No 1 Jalan Perunding U1/17 Glenmarie Industrial Park, 40150, Shah Alam, Selangor Darul Ehsan, Malaysia
Tel.: (60) 355693838
Sales Range: $50-74.9 Million
Emp.: 20
Insulation Materials & Valves Installation & Distr
N.A.I.C.S.: 423330
Kai Fun Loh *(Mgr)*

Griferia Sanitario (M) Sdn. Bhd. (1)
Wisma Arita 1033 Jalan Chain Ferry, Perai, 13600, Penang, Malaysia
Tel.: (60) 4 3993241
Web Site: http://www.sanitario.com.my
Emp.: 10
Bathroom Fixtures Distr
N.A.I.C.S.: 423720

Icontronic Technology Sdn. Bhd. (1)
No 10 Lorong Usahajaya 1 and Kawasan Perindustrian Usahajaya, Permatang Tinggi, 14000, Bukit Mertajam, Penang, Malaysia (60%)
Tel.: (60) 4 588 5336
Web Site: https://www.icontronic.com
Sales Range: $25-49.9 Million
Emp.: 10
Industrial Electronic Automation Control Systems Mfr
N.A.I.C.S.: 334513

M.E.T. Motion (Alor Star) Sdn. Bhd. (1)
No 31 Kompleks Perniagaan Gangsa Jalan Gangsa 1, 05150, Alor Setar, Kedah, Malaysia
Tel.: (60) 47311223
Pump Distr
N.A.I.C.S.: 423840

M.E.T. Motion (KL) Sdn. Bhd. (1)
No 12G Jalan Tandang Seksyen 51, 46050, Petaling Jaya, Selangor, Malaysia
Tel.: (60) 124942293
Water Pumping Services
N.A.I.C.S.: 237110

Multiplex Control & Engineering Services Pte. Ltd. (1)
87 Second Lok Yang Rd, Singapore, 628163, Singapore
Tel.: (65) 6 862 1922
Web Site: https://www.multiplexcontrol.com
Sales Range: $25-49.9 Million
Emp.: 8
Industrial Control Accessories Mfr
N.A.I.C.S.: 335314

P.T. Artha Mulia Nusantar (1)
Green Sedayu Bizpark No 1, Jakarta Timur, 13910, Indonesia
Tel.: (62) 2122469702
Web Site: https://arthamulia-nusantara.co.id
Nonferrous Metal Product Distr
N.A.I.C.S.: 423510

P.T. Bont Technologies Nusantara (1)
Komplek Rukan Sunter Permai Blok C No 9 Jl Danau, Sunter Utara Raya, Jakarta Utara, 14350, Indonesia
Tel.: (62) 216519188
Web Site: https://bont-technus.com
Security System Services
N.A.I.C.S.: 561612

P.T. Internasional Asia Pasifik Sinergi (1)
Komplek Rukan Sunter Permai Blok C No 15 Jl Danau Sunter Utara Sunter, Jakarta Utara, 14350, Indonesia
Tel.: (62) 21652680
Web Site: https://www.iaps-marine.com
Marine Shipping Services
N.A.I.C.S.: 541990

P.T. Internasional Asia Prima Sukses (1)
Komplek Union Industrial Park Blok H No 12A Batu Ampar, Riau Archipelago, Batam, Indonesia
Tel.: (62) 778458583
Web Site: https://www.iaps-kepri.com
Ship & Port Management Services
N.A.I.C.S.: 541990

P.T. Makmur Abadi Valve (1)
Komplek rukan sunter permai blok C No 9 Jl Danau sunter utara Kel, Sunter Agung Kec Tanjung Priok, Jakarta Utara, 14350, Indonesia
Tel.: (62) 2648641149
Web Site: https://mav.co.id
Engineering Research & Development Services
N.A.I.C.S.: 541715

Q-Flex Industries (M) Sdn. Bhd. (1)
17-23 Persiaran Kilang Pengkalan 28, Kawasan Pengkalan Maju Industrial Estate, 31500, Ipoh, Perak, Malaysia
Tel.: (60) 5 322 8268
Web Site: https://www.q-flex.com.my
Sales Range: $25-49.9 Million
Emp.: 50
Industrial Joints Mfr
N.A.I.C.S.: 332312

Sumitech Engineering Solutions Ltd. (1)
RM 103 Bld A No 4 Shichang Alley 2nd of XiaoBian Industrial Zone, ChangAn Town, Dongguan, China
Tel.: (86) 76982285118
Precision Machining & Modular Assembly Mfr
N.A.I.C.S.: 332721

TM Unimech Co. Ltd. (1)
68/60 Moo 5 Kingkaew Road T Rachatewa, Bang Phli, 10540, Samutprakar, Thailand
Tel.: (66) 273886406
Industrial Valve & Related Product Distr
N.A.I.C.S.: 423840

Unijin Instruments Industries Sdn. Bhd. (1)
46 Lengkok Kapal Taman Industry Chain Ferry, 12100, Butterworth, Penang, Malaysia
Tel.: (60) 43248788
Web Site: https://www.unijin.my
Sales Range: $25-49.9 Million
Emp.: 20
Field Instrument & Pressure Gauges Mfr
N.A.I.C.S.: 334513
Chee Leong Kam *(Mgr-Factory)*

Unimax Sanitario (M) Sdn. Bhd. (1)
Wisma Arita 1033 Jalan Chain Ferry, 13600, Perai, Malaysia
Tel.: (60) 43993241
Web Site: https://www.sanitario.com.my
Industrial Equipment Mfr
N.A.I.C.S.: 333415

Unimech (Asia Pacific) Pty. Ltd. (1)
Unit 9 30 Heathcote Road, Moorebank, 2170, NSW, Australia
Tel.: (61) 29 600 7179
Web Site: https://www.unimech.com.au
Emp.: 1,000
Industrial Valve & Fitting Mfr
N.A.I.C.S.: 332911

Unimech Engineering (JB) Sdn. Bhd. (1)
No 18 Jalan Rosmerah Satu 3 Taman Johor Jaya, 81100, Johor Bahru, Johor, Malaysia
Tel.: (60) 73557261
Sales Range: $25-49.9 Million
Emp.: 17
Industrial Heating Equipments Installation & Maintenance Services
N.A.I.C.S.: 238220
Mun Kuan Han *(Mng Dir)*

Subsidiary (Domestic):

Unimech Engineering (Kuantan) Sdn. Bhd. (2)
B364 Jalan Air Putih, 25300, Kuantan, Pahang Darul Makmul, Malaysia
Tel.: (60) 9 567 3812
Web Site: http://www.unimechgroup.com
Industrial Heating Equipments Installation & Maintenance Services
N.A.I.C.S.: 238220

Unimech Engineering (KL) Sdn. Bhd. (1)
12G Jalan Tandang 204A Seksyen 51, 46050, Petaling Jaya, Selangor Darul Ehsan, Malaysia
Tel.: (60) 37 783 5688
Web Site: https://www.unimechkl.com
Sales Range: $25-49.9 Million
Emp.: 15
Industrial Heating Equipments Installation & Maintenance Services
N.A.I.C.S.: 238220

Subsidiary (Domestic):

TCE Casting Sdn. Bhd. (2)
Plot 10 15 & 10 16 Jalan PKNK 1/2 Kawasan Perusahaan, 08000, Sungai Petani, Selangor Darul Ehsan, Malaysia
Tel.: (60) 44427677
Web Site: https://tcecasting.com.my
Sales Range: $25-49.9 Million
Metal Stampings & Die Castings Mfr
N.A.I.C.S.: 331523

Unimech Engineering (M) Sdn. Bhd. (1)
Wisma Unimech No 4934 Jalan Chain Ferry, 12100, Butterworth, Penang, Malaysia
Tel.: (60) 4 332 8823
Web Site: https://unimechengineering.com.my
Sales Range: $25-49.9 Million
Emp.: 30
Industrial Heating Equipments Installation & Maintenance Services
N.A.I.C.S.: 238220

Subsidiary (Domestic):

Inventive Potentials Sdn. Bhd. (2)
Lot 519 Lencongan Timur, Kawasan Perusahaan Cendana, 08000, Sungai Petani, Kedah, Malaysia
Tel.: (60) 4 431 8810
Web Site: https://www.inventive.my
Sales Range: $25-49.9 Million
Emp.: 30
Metal Stampings & Die Castings Mfr
N.A.I.C.S.: 332119

UME Service & Trading Sdn. Bhd. (2)
59 Lebuh Raya Kapal, 12100, Butterworth, Penang, Malaysia
Tel.: (60) 43328823
Emp.: 10
Burners Service & Distr
N.A.I.C.S.: 423720

Subsidiary (Non-US):

Unimech Engineering (Aust) Pty. Ltd. (2)
Unit 9 30 Heathcote Road, Moorebank, 2170, NSW, Australia
Tel.: (61) 296007179
Web Site: https://www.unimech.com.au

UNIMED LABORATORIES

Sales Range: $25-49.9 Million
Emp.: 8
Valves & Industrial Fittings Distr
N.A.I.C.S.: 423840

Subsidiary (Domestic):

Unimech International Sdn. Bhd. (2)
Wisma Unimech 4934 Jalan Chain Ferry, 12100, Butterworth, Penang, Malaysia
Tel.: (60) 4 332 8823
Web Site: https://unimech.my
Sales Range: $25-49.9 Million
Industrial Heating Equipments Installation & Maintenance Services
N.A.I.C.S.: 238220

Unimech Marine & Sanitary Equipment Sdn. Bhd. (2)
1033 Jalan Chain Ferry, 13600, Prai, Malaysia
Tel.: (60) 43328823
Sales Range: $100-124.9 Million
Marine & Sanitary Equipments Sales & Installation Services
N.A.I.C.S.: 423440

Unimech Valve Technology Sdn. Bhd. (2)
26-G & 26-1 Jalan LJ 4 Taman Industri Lembah Jaya, 68000, Ampang, Selangor Darul Ehsan, Malaysia
Tel.: (60) 3 4270 9181
Industrial Valve Distr
N.A.I.C.S.: 423830

Unimech Flow System Sdn. Bhd. (1)
No 7976 Lot 2016, Nyigu Light Industrial Estate Jalan Sungai Nyigu, 97000, Bintulu, Sarawak, Malaysia
Tel.: (60) 86338830
Sales Range: $25-49.9 Million
Emp.: 7
Industrial Heating Equipments Installation & Maintenance Services
N.A.I.C.S.: 238220
Alan Teoh *(Mgr)*

Unimech Instruments & Control Sdn. Bhd. (1)
50 Lengkok Kapal Taman Industry Chain Ferry, 12100, Butterworth, Penang, Malaysia
Tel.: (60) 43248788
Web Site: https://www.myuic.com.my
Fluid Control Equipments & Instruments Distr
N.A.I.C.S.: 423830
C. L. Kam *(Mgr)*

Unimech Marine Equipment Sdn. Bhd. (1)
Wisma Arita Lot 1033 Jalan Chain Ferry, Prai, 13600, Prai, Pulau Pinang, Malaysia
Tel.: (60) 4 399 3229
Web Site: https://unimechmarine.com
Marine Equipment Mfr
N.A.I.C.S.: 333618

Unimech Vietnam Co. Ltd. (1)
34/6E Dinh Tien Hoang, Ward 1 Binh Thanh District, Ho Chi Minh City, Vietnam
Tel.: (84) 1228738284
Industrial Valve & Related Product Distr
N.A.I.C.S.: 423840

Unimech Worldwide (Shanghai) Sdn. Bhd. (1)
Wisma Unimech 4934 Jalan Chain Ferry, 12100, Butterworth, Penang, Malaysia
Tel.: (60) 43328823
Sales Range: $25-49.9 Million
Emp.: 30
Fluid Control System Installation & Maintenance Services
N.A.I.C.S.: 334513

Valtrox Sanitary Equipment Sdn. Bhd. (1)
No 8 Jalan BJ2-7A Kawasan Perindustrian Belakong Jaya 2, Seri Kembangan, 43300, Selangor, Malaysia
Tel.: (60) 389640033
Web Site: http://www.valtrox.com
Sanitary Equipment Distr
N.A.I.C.S.: 423720

UNIMED LABORATORIES
Tel.: (216) 70029501

UNIMED LABORATORIES

Unimed laboratories—(Continued)
Web Site: https://www.unimed.com.tn
Year Founded: 1989
UMED—(BVT)
Emp.: 750
Pharmaceuticals Product Mfr
N.A.I.C.S.: 325412
Ridha Charfeddine *(CEO)*

UNIMER GROUP
15 Rue Jabal Saghrou - CIL, Bernoussi QI, 20252, Casablanca, Morocco
Tel.: (212) 522791480
Web Site:
 https://www.unimergroup.com
Year Founded: 1973
UMR—(CAS)
Sales Range: $125-149.9 Million
Food Products Mfr
N.A.I.C.S.: 311999
Said Alj *(Chm & Mng Dir)*

UNIMET GMBH
Aggensteinstrasse 8-10, Rieden, 87669, Germany
Tel.: (49) 836291220
Web Site: http://www.unimet-group.de
Year Founded: 1970
Rev.: $19,784,022
Emp.: 220
Industrial Tools Mfr
N.A.I.C.S.: 333517
Rudi Kolb *(Mng Partner)*

UNIMICRON TECHNOLOGY CORPORATION
No 173/179 Shanying Road Guishan Ind Park, Taoyuan, Taiwan
Tel.: (886) 33500386
Web Site: https://www.unimicron.com
Year Founded: 1990
3037—(TAI)
Rev.: $3,402,208,937
Assets: $7,063,851,723
Liabilities: $3,915,138,902
Net Worth: $3,148,712,821
Earnings: $399,787,486
Emp.: 28,499
Fiscal Year-end: 12/31/23
Printed Circuit Board Mfr
N.A.I.C.S.: 334412
Tzyy-Jang Tseng *(Chm)*

Subsidiaries:

Apm Communication Inc. (1)
No 2 RandD Rd VI, Science-Based Industrial Park, Hsinchu, 30076, Taiwan
Tel.: (886) 3 666 8315
Web Site: https://www.apmcomm.com
Software Development Services
N.A.I.C.S.: 541511

Asia Pacific Microsystems, Inc. (1)
No 2 R D 6th Road, Hsinchu Science Park, Hsinchu, 308, Taiwan
Tel.: (886) 36661188
Web Site: https://www.apmsinc.com
Electronic Components Mfr
N.A.I.C.S.: 334419
T. J. Tseng *(Co-Chm)*

Clover Electronics Industries Co., Ltd. (1)
573-19 Toiso, Eniwa, 061 1405, Hokkaido, Japan
Tel.: (81) 1 2334 5001
Web Site: http://www.clover-e.co.jp
Sales Range: $25-49.9 Million
Emp.: 210
Printed Circuit Board Mfr
N.A.I.C.S.: 334412
Ishii Masami *(Pres)*

Neoconix, Inc. (1)
4020 Moorpark Ave Ste 108, San Jose, CA 95117 **(75.42%)**
Tel.: (408) 530-9393
Web Site: https://www.neoconix.com

Sales Range: $1-9.9 Million
Emp.: 30
Electronic Connector Mfr
N.A.I.C.S.: 334417
Woody Maynard *(Dir-Product Mktg)*

RUWEL International GmbH (1)
Am Hollander See 70, 47608, Geldern, Germany
Tel.: (49) 28 31 3 94 0
Web Site: http://www.ruwel.com
Emp.: 220
Circuit Board Mfr
N.A.I.C.S.: 334418
Gerard van Dierendonck *(Mng Dir)*

UniSense Technology Co., Ltd. (1)
9F No 1 Jinshan 7th St, Hsinchu, 30080, Taiwan
Tel.: (886) 3 668 6778
Web Site: https://www.unisense.com.tw
Medical Device Mfr
N.A.I.C.S.: 339112

Unimicron Germany GmbH (1)
Am Hollander See 70, 47608, Geldern, Germany
Tel.: (49) 28313940
Web Site: https://unimicron-germany.de
Emp.: 350
Electronic Component Mfr & Distr
N.A.I.C.S.: 334419

Unimicron JAPAN Co., Ltd. (1)
573-19 Toiso, Hokkaido, Eniwa, 061-1405, Japan
Tel.: (81) 123345001
Web Site: https://www.unimicron-j.co.jp
Emp.: 135
Printed Circuit Board Mfr & Distr
N.A.I.C.S.: 334412

Unimicron Management (Kunshan) Co., Ltd. (1)
No 168 Xiaolin Road, Kunshan, Jiangsu, 215316, China
Tel.: (86) 51257799168
Printed Circuit Board Mfr & Distr
N.A.I.C.S.: 334412

Unimicron Technology (ShenZhen) Corp. (1)
Building B-D Environment Protection Ind Zone, Shayi Village Shajing Town Baoan District, Shenzhen, 518104, Guangdong, China
Tel.: (86) 75527245188
Web Site: http://www.unimicron-sz.com.cn
Electronic Component Mfr & Distr
N.A.I.C.S.: 334419

Unimicron Technology (Suzhou) Corp. (1)
No 160 Fengli Street, Suzhou, China
Tel.: (86) 51262996168
Web Site: http://www.unimicron-suz.com.cn
Electronic Component Mfr & Distr
N.A.I.C.S.: 334419

Unimicroncarrier Technology (Huangshi) Inc. (1)
No 168 East of Daqi Avenue, Economic and Technological Development Zone, Huangshi, 435000, Hubei, China
Tel.: (86) 7143268168
Printed Circuit Board Mfr & Distr
N.A.I.C.S.: 334412

UNIMIN INDIA LTD
Village Kadaiya Daman Industrial Estate, Bhimpore, Daman, 396210, India
Tel.: (91) 260 2221557
Web Site:
 http://www.uniminindia.com
Nonwoven Fabric Mfr
N.A.I.C.S.: 313230
J. K. Bakshi *(Co-Chm & Co-Mng Dir)*

UNIMIT ENGINEERING PUBLIC COMPANY LIMITED
109/92-95 Mu 19 Soi Suksawat 66 Suksawat Road, Phra Pradaeng, Bangkok, 10130, Thailand
Tel.: (66) 24630100
Web Site: https://www.unimit.com
Year Founded: 1982

UEC—(THA)
Rev.: $15,803,675
Assets: $46,698,869
Liabilities: $3,509,914
Net Worth: $43,188,954
Earnings: $455,347
Emp.: 557
Fiscal Year-end: 12/31/21
Oil Refinery Field Construction Services
N.A.I.C.S.: 333132
Phaibul Chalermsaphayakorn *(Chm)*

UNIMODE OVERSEAS LIMITED
C-18 Shivaji Park, Punjabi Bagh, New Delhi, 110026, India
Tel.: (91) 8447976925   In
Web Site:
 https://www.unimodeoverseas.in
Year Founded: 1992
512595—(BOM)
Rev: $12,136
Assets: $10,492
Liabilities: $40,994
Net Worth: ($30,502)
Earnings: ($1,615)
Fiscal Year-end: 03/31/21
Fabrics Whslr
N.A.I.C.S.: 424310
D. K. Mahawar *(CEO)*

UNIMOT SA
ul Swierklanska 2 a, Zawadzkie, 47-120, Opole, Poland
Tel.: (48) 774616548
Web Site: https://www.unimot.pl
UNT—(WAR)
Rev.: $3,274,133,376
Assets: $797,061,228
Liabilities: $523,211,635
Net Worth: $273,849,593
Earnings: $124,113,821
Fiscal Year-end: 12/31/23
Petroleum Mfr
N.A.I.C.S.: 324110
Andreas Golombek *(Chm-Supervisory Bd)*

Subsidiaries:

Blue LNG Sp. z o.o (1)
Al Jerozolimskie 142A West Station Building I 12th Floor, 02-305, Warsaw, Poland
Tel.: (48) 51 717 0269
Web Site: https://www.bluelng.pl
Natural Gas Distribution Services
N.A.I.C.S.: 221210

Unimot Energia i Gaz Sp. z o.o. (1)
Ul Cyprian Kamil Norwid 2, 80-280, Gdansk, Poland
Tel.: (48) 50 910 9999
Web Site: https://www.unimot-eig.pl
Natural Gas Distribution Services
N.A.I.C.S.: 221210

Unimot Energy LLC (1)
4 Mykoly Hrinchenko Street Office 142, 03038, Kiev, Ukraine
Tel.: (380) 50 053 2351
Web Site: https://www.unimot-energy.com.ua
Electricity Distribution Services
N.A.I.C.S.: 221122

UNIO SA SATU MARE
35 Lucian Blaga Blvd, 440227, Satu-Mare, Romania
Tel.: (40) 261 705500
Web Site: http://www.unio.ro
Year Founded: 2000
Emp.: 1,200
Conveyer Mfr
N.A.I.C.S.: 339999

UNIOIL RESOURCES & HOLDINGS COMPANY INC.
6th Floor Sagittarius Building 111 HV

INTERNATIONAL PUBLIC

dela Costa Street, Salcedo Village, Makati, Philippines
Tel.: (63) 892 7002
Year Founded: 1987
UNI—(PHI)
Sales Range: $150-199.9 Million
Holding Company
N.A.I.C.S.: 551112
Rolando A. Castro *(Treas)*

UNION AGRICULTURE GROUP CORP.
Plaza Independencia 737, 11000, Montevideo, Uruguay
Tel.: (598) 2900 0000   UY
Web Site:
 http://www.unionagrogroup.com
Year Founded: 2008
Agricultural Products Mfr & Distr
N.A.I.C.S.: 111998
Juan Sartori *(Founder & Exec Chm)*

UNION ANDINA DE CEMENTOS S.A.A.
Av Atocongo 2440 Villa Maria del Triunfo, Lima, Peru
Tel.: (51) 12170200   Pe
Web Site: https://unacem.pe
Year Founded: 1967
Rev.: $1,056,737,301
Assets: $3,189,887,786
Liabilities: $1,953,577,994
Net Worth: $1,236,309,792
Earnings: $29,795,696
Emp.: 4,058
Fiscal Year-end: 12/31/16
Holding Company; Cement & Ready-Mix Concrete Mfr, Precast Concrete Products Mfr & Electric Power Generation
N.A.I.C.S.: 551112
Alfredo Gastaneta Alayza *(Vice Chm)*

Subsidiaries:

Compania Electrica el Platanal S.A. (1)
Avenida Carlos Villaran 514, La Victoria, Lima, Peru **(90%)**
Tel.: (51) 1 619 2800
Web Site: http://www.celepsa.com
Hydroelectric & Geothermal Power Plants Operator
N.A.I.C.S.: 221111
Ricardo Ugas Delgado de la Piedra *(Chm)*

Drake Cement, LLC (1)
5745 N Scottsdale Rd Ste B-135, Scottsdale, AZ 85250 **(94.1%)**
Tel.: (480) 219-6670
Web Site: http://www.drakecement.com
Cement Mfr
N.A.I.C.S.: 327310
Marco Gomez *(Pres & CEO)*

Subsidiary (Domestic):

Sunshine Concrete & Materials, Inc. (2)
5745 N Scottsdale Rd Ste B-110, Scottsdale, AZ 85250
Tel.: (480) 607-3999
Web Site: http://www.drakematerials.com
Sales Range: $25-49.9 Million
Emp.: 131
Readymix Concrete Mfr
N.A.I.C.S.: 327320
Marco Gomez *(CEO)*

Union de Concreteras S.A. (1)
Panamericana Sur Km 11 400, San Juan de Miraflores, Lima, 29, Peru
Tel.: (51) 1 215 4600
Web Site: http://www.unicon.com.pe
Readymix Concrete Mfr
N.A.I.C.S.: 327320
Miguel Velasco de la Cotera *(Gen Mgr)*

UNION ASSET MANAGEMENT HOLDING AG
Wiesenhuttenstr 10, 60329, Frankfurt am Main, Germany

Tel.: (49) 180 3 959501
Web Site: http://www.union-investment.de
Sales Range: $400-449.9 Million
Emp.: 2,267
Holding Company; Investment & Real Estate Asset Management Services
N.A.I.C.S.: 551112
Alexander Schindler (Member-Mgmt Bd)

Subsidiaries:

Quoniam Asset Management GmbH (1)
Westhafen Tower Westhafenplatz 1, 60327, Frankfurt am Main, Germany
Tel.: (49) 69743840
Web Site: http://www.quoniam.com.de
Sales Range: $10-24.9 Million
Emp.: 125
Asset Management Services
N.A.I.C.S.: 533110
Helmut Paulus (Dir-Fixed Income & Asset Allocation)

UNION AUCTION PUBLIC COMPANY LIMITED
518/28 Ramkhamheng 39 tepleela 1, Wangthonglang, Bangkok, 10310, Thailand
Tel.: (66) 20336555
Web Site: https://www.auct.co.th
Year Founded: 1991
AUCT—(THA)
Rev.: $36,215,986
Assets: $57,778,948
Liabilities: $40,518,769
Net Worth: $17,260,179
Earnings: $10,156,667
Emp.: 446
Fiscal Year-end: 12/31/23
Auctions
N.A.I.C.S.: 455219
Suvit Yoadjarust (Chm-Exec Bd & Vice Chm)

UNION BANCAIRE PRIVEE, UBP SA
96-98 rue du Rhone, PO Box 1320, CH-1211, Geneva, Switzerland
Tel.: (41) 58 819 2111   CH
Web Site: http://www.ubp.com
Year Founded: 1969
Rev.: $1,099,125,663
Assets: $33,730,406,656
Liabilities: $31,305,091,190
Net Worth: $2,425,315,466
Earnings: $193,357,005
Emp.: 1,743
Fiscal Year-end: 12/31/19
Private Banking Services
N.A.I.C.S.: 522110
Marcel Rohner (Vice Chm)

Subsidiaries:

UBP Asset Management (Europe) S.A. (1)
Taunustor 1 Buro Nr 18 21, 60311, Frankfurt am Main, Germany
Tel.: (49) 695050604140
Investment Advisory Services
N.A.I.C.S.: 523940
Peter Richters (Head-Institutional Bus)

UBP Asset Management (Europe) S.A. (1)
287-289 route d'Arlon, PO Box 79, 1150, Luxembourg, Luxembourg
Tel.: (352) 2280071
Investment Advisory Services
N.A.I.C.S.: 523940

UBP Asset Management Asia Limited (1)
Level 20 101 Collins Street, Melbourne, 3000, VIC, Australia
Tel.: (61) 386376021
Investment Advisory Services
N.A.I.C.S.: 523940

UBP Asset Management Asia Ltd. (1)
Level 26 AIA Central 1 Connaught Road, Central, China (Hong Kong)
Tel.: (852) 37131111
Investment Advisory Services
N.A.I.C.S.: 523940

UBP Asset Management LLC (1)
116 avenue des Champs-Elysees, 75008, Paris, France
Tel.: (33) 175778080
Investment Advisory Services
N.A.I.C.S.: 523940

UBP Asset Management Taiwan Ltd. (1)
10F-E No 1 Song Zhi Road, Xin Yi District, Taipei, 11047, Taiwan
Tel.: (886) 227236258
Web Site: http://www.ubp.com.tw
Investment Advisory Services
N.A.I.C.S.: 523940

UBP Gestion Institucional S.A.U. (1)
Calle Ortega y Gasset n 22-24 5 planta, 28006, Madrid, Spain
Tel.: (34) 910472011
Emp.: 3
Investment Advisory Services
N.A.I.C.S.: 523940
Felipe Leria (Head-Iberia)

UBP Investment Management (Shanghai) Ltd. (1)
Room 1205 12 FBank of East Asia Finance Tower 66, Hua Yuan Shi Qiao Road Pudong, Shanghai, China
Tel.: (86) 2120629980
Investment Advisory Services
N.A.I.C.S.: 523940

UBP Investment Management (Zhejiang) Ltd. (1)
Room 1207 12 FBank of East Asia Finance Tower, 66 Hua Yuan Shi Qiao Road Pudong, Shanghai, China
Tel.: (86) 2120629980
Investment Advisory Services
N.A.I.C.S.: 523940

UBP Investment Services Ltd. (1)
28 Ha'Arbaah Street, Tel Aviv, 6473925, Israel
Tel.: (972) 36915626
Investment Advisory Services
N.A.I.C.S.: 523940

UBP Investments Co., Ltd. (1)
1-9-1 Yurakucho Hibiya Sankei Building 11th Floor, Chiyoda-ku, Tokyo, Japan
Tel.: (81) 352202111
Investment Advisory Services
N.A.I.C.S.: 523940

Union Bancaire Asset Management (Jersey) Ltd. (1)
40 Esplanade, PO Box 526, Saint Helier, JE4 5UH, Jersey
Tel.: (44) 1534514672
Emp.: 20
Investment Advisory Services
N.A.I.C.S.: 523940

Union Bancaire Privee (Europe) SA (1)
Via Brera 5, 20121, Milan, Italy
Tel.: (39) 0287338500
Investment Advisory Services
N.A.I.C.S.: 523940

Union Bancaire Privee Asset Management (Bermuda) Ltd. (1)
Cumberland House 4th floor 1 Victoria Street, PO Box HM 2572, HM 11, Hamilton, Bermuda
Tel.: (441) 2958339
Investment Advisory Services
N.A.I.C.S.: 523940

Union Bancaire Privee Asset Management LLC (1)
540 Madison Ave 29th Fl, New York, NY 10022
Tel.: (212) 317-6700
Web Site: http://www.ubpny.com
Investment Advisory Services
N.A.I.C.S.: 523940

UNION BANK OF COLOMBO LIMITED
64 Galle Road, Colombo, 03, Sri Lanka
Tel.: (94) 112374100
Web Site: http://www.unionb.com
Year Founded: 1995
Sales Range: $50-74.9 Million
Emp.: 180
Banking Services
N.A.I.C.S.: 522110
Nirosha Kannangara (Sec)

Subsidiaries:

UB Finance Company Limited (1)
No 10 Daisy Villa Avenue, 04, Colombo, Sri Lanka
Tel.: (94) 112168888
Web Site: https://www.ubf.lk
Financial Investment Services
N.A.I.C.S.: 523940
Alexis Indrajit Lovell (Chm)

UNION BANK OF INDIA
Union Bank Bhavan 239 Vidhan Bhavan Marg, Nariman Point, Mumbai, 400 021, Maharashtra, India
Tel.: (91) 2222892000   In
Web Site: https://www.unionbankofindia.co.in
Year Founded: 2020
532477—(BOM)
Commercial Bank; Loan Services
N.A.I.C.S.: 522110
Nitesh Ranjan (Gen Mgr)

Subsidiaries:

Andhra Bank (1)
5-9-11 Dr Pattabhi Bhavan Secretariat Road, Saifabad, Hyderabad, 500 004, Telangana, India
Tel.: (91) 4023252000
Web Site: http://www.andhrabank.in
Rev.: $3,196,525,586
Assets: $36,429,906,890
Liabilities: $34,518,137,568
Net Worth: $1,911,769,322
Earnings: $(393,202,528)
Emp.: 20,346
Fiscal Year-end: 03/31/2019
Banking Services
N.A.I.C.S.: 522110
M. Babu Rajendra Prasad (CFO & Gen Mgr)

Corporation Bank (1)
Mangaladevi Temple Road, Pandeshwar, Mangalore, 575 001, Karnataka, India
Tel.: (91) 8242861888
Web Site: http://www.corpbank.com
Rev.: $3,103,815,860
Assets: $34,531,713,561
Liabilities: $32,837,568,956
Net Worth: $1,694,144,605
Earnings: $(630,169,404)
Emp.: 19,419
Fiscal Year-end: 03/31/2018
Banking Services
N.A.I.C.S.: 522110
Yerrapati Lakshminarayana (Deputy Gen Mgr)

Subsidiary (Domestic):

Corp Bank Securities Ltd (2)
21 Mezzanine Floor Dalal Street Fort, Veena Chambers, Mumbai, 400 023, Maharashtra, India
Tel.: (91) 2222670146
Web Site: http://corpsecu.com
Securities Trading & Related Services
N.A.I.C.S.: 523150

UBI Services Ltd. (1)
504-506 5th Floor Centrum S G Barve Road Wagle Estate MIDC W, Thane, 400 604, India
Tel.: (91) 222 081 4363
Web Site: https://www.ubisl.co.in
Banking Services
N.A.I.C.S.: 522110
Rajkiran Rai G. (Chm)

Union Bank of India UK Limited (1)
12 Arthur Street, London, EC4R 9AB, United Kingdom
Tel.: (44) 2073324250
Web Site: https://www.unionbankofindiauk.co.uk
Retail & Commercial Banking Services
N.A.I.C.S.: 522110

UNION BANK OF IRAQ
Iraq - Baghdad Alkarada -Al Masbah int, Al-Karada, Baghdad, Iraq
Tel.: (964) 47717505580
Web Site: https://www.ub-iq.com
Year Founded: 2002
Commercial Banking Services
N.A.I.C.S.: 522110
Ali Muftin Khafif (Chm & Chm)

UNION BANK OF NIGERIA PLC.
Stallion Plaza 36 Marina, PMB 2027, Lagos, Nigeria
Tel.: (234) 1 2716816   NG
Web Site: http://www.unionbankng.com
Year Founded: 1917
UBN—(NIGE)
Rev.: $295,339,770
Assets: $5,718,577,860
Liabilities: $5,028,707,880
Net Worth: $689,869,980
Earnings: $48,733,920
Emp.: 2,342
Fiscal Year-end: 12/31/20
Commercial Banking Services
N.A.I.C.S.: 522110
Emeka Emuwa (CEO)

Subsidiaries:

Union Homes Savings & Loans Plc. (1)
153 Ikorodu Road, PMB 041, Onipanu Shomolu, Lagos, Nigeria
Tel.: (234) 8090710061
Web Site: https://unionhomesplc.com
Loan Mortgage Services
N.A.I.C.S.: 522310
Olutoyin Okeowo (Chm)

UNION BANK OF TAIWAN
3F No 109 Sec 3 Minsheng E Rd, Songshan District, Taipei, 105, Taiwan
Tel.: (886) 227180001
Web Site: https://www.ubot.com.tw
Year Founded: 1991
2838—(TAI)
Rev.: $653,063,908
Assets: $30,712,155,712
Liabilities: $28,401,993,433
Net Worth: $2,310,162,279
Earnings: $141,295,655
Emp.: 3,935
Fiscal Year-end: 12/31/23
Banking Services
N.A.I.C.S.: 522110
Jiang Zhen-Xong (Mng Dir)

Subsidiaries:

Union Information Technology Corporation (1)
399 Ruiguang Road, 114, Taipei, Taiwan
Tel.: (886) 266012888
Printed Circuit Board Mfr
N.A.I.C.S.: 333248

UNION BANKA D.D. SARAJEVO
Hamdije Kresevljakovica 19, 71000, Sarajevo, Bosnia & Herzegovina
Tel.: (387) 33561000
Web Site: http://www.unionbank.ba
Year Founded: 1955
UNIBR—(SARE)
Rev.: $12,034
Assets: $628,524
Liabilities: $557,921
Net Worth: $70,603
Earnings: $3,020
Emp.: 201
Fiscal Year-end: 12/31/23

UNION BANKA D.D. SARAJEVO

Union Banka d.d. Sarajevo—(Continued)
Commercial Banking Services
N.A.I.C.S.: 522110
Vedran Hadziahmetovic *(Chm-Mgmt Bd)*

UNION BEARINGS (INDIA) LTD.
123 Mangal Moorty Ashram Road, Ahmedabad, 380009, Gujarat, India
Tel.: (91) 7926580809
522271—(BOM)
Bearing Mfr
N.A.I.C.S.: 332991
Madhusoodan N. Kakkad *(Chm)*

UNION BRIDGE HOLDINGS LIMITED
Suite 4801 48/F Central Plaza 18 Harbour Road, Wanchai, China (Hong Kong)
Tel.: (852) 24683103   NV
Web Site: http://www.ughl-us.com
Year Founded: 2014
UGHL—(OTCBB)
Rev.: $86,939
Assets: $188,166
Liabilities: $1,482,463
Net Worth: ($1,294,297)
Earnings: ($912,099)
Emp.: 13
Fiscal Year-end: 12/31/19
Holding Company; Environmental, Biotechnology & Healthcare Products & Services
N.A.I.C.S.: 551112
Joseph Ho *(Pres & CEO)*

UNION CAPITAL LIMITED
bti Landmark Level- 8 Plot- 16 Gulshan Avenue, Gulshan- 1, Dhaka, 1212, Bangladesh
Tel.: (880) 226601505
Web Site: https://www.unicap-bd.com
UNIONCAP—(CHT)
Rev.: $3,815,921
Assets: $150,633,922
Liabilities: $175,593,968
Net Worth: ($24,960,046)
Earnings: ($18,811,914)
Emp.: 155
Fiscal Year-end: 12/31/22
Investment Banking Services
N.A.I.C.S.: 523150
Chowdhury Tanzim Karim *(Chm)*

Subsidiaries:

SES Company Limited   (1)
Sonartori Tower 14th Floor 12 Sonargaon Road, Dhaka, Bangladesh
Tel.: (880) 2 8616878
Securities Brokerage Services
N.A.I.C.S.: 523150

UniCap Securities Limited   (1)
A-A Bhaban 9th Floor 23, Motijheel, Dhaka, 1000, Bangladesh
Tel.: (880) 2951595155
Web Site: https://unicap-securities.com
Brokerage & Security Services
N.A.I.C.S.: 523150

UNION CATALANA DE VALORES SA
Via Laietana 45 7 2a, 08003, Barcelona, Spain
Tel.: (34) 933014085
Web Site: https://www.uncavasa.com
UNC—(MAD)
Sales Range: Less than $1 Million
Real Estate Manangement Services
N.A.I.C.S.: 531390
Enrique Gomis Pinto *(Chm & CEO)*

UNION CHEMICALS LANKA PLC
5th Floor No 4 Tickell Road, 08, Colombo, Sri Lanka
Tel.: (94) 112472921
Web Site: https://www.ucll.lk
Year Founded: 1984
UCAR.N0000—(COL)
Rev.: $5,584,847
Assets: $4,478,123
Liabilities: $1,453,563
Net Worth: $3,024,560
Earnings: $538,401
Emp.: 40
Fiscal Year-end: 12/25/22
Paint Product Mfr & Distr
N.A.I.C.S.: 325510
Azeez M. Mubarak *(Chm)*

UNION CONSTRUCTION AND INVESTMENT
17 Nizar Qabani Street Masyoun Heights, PO Box 4029, West Bank, Ramallah, Palestine
Tel.: (970) 22974992
Web Site: https://www.uci.ps
Year Founded: 2005
UCI—(PAL)
Rev.: $2,615,310
Assets: $63,464,109
Liabilities: $22,358,506
Net Worth: $41,105,603
Earnings: $1,172,862
Emp.: 237
Fiscal Year-end: 12/31/21
Real Estate Development & Investment Services
N.A.I.C.S.: 525990
Mohamed M. Al Sabawi *(Chm)*

UNION CORPORATION
13th Fl OCI Bldg 94 Sogong-ro, Jung-gu, Seoul, 04532, Korea (South)
Tel.: (82) 27573801
Web Site: https://www.unioncement.com
Year Founded: 1964
000910—(KRS)
Rev.: $180,230,563
Assets: $288,477,692
Liabilities: $154,591,095
Net Worth: $133,886,597
Earnings: $7,755,363
Emp.: 237
Fiscal Year-end: 12/31/22
Construction Material Mfr & Whslr
N.A.I.C.S.: 327120
Geonyoung Lee *(CEO)*

Subsidiaries:

Union Materials Corp.   (1)
1-85 Wolarm-dong, Dalseo-gu, Taegu, 704-320, Korea (South)
Tel.: (82) 535804340
Web Site: https://www.unionmaterials.com
Rev.: $96,754,624
Assets: $156,594,390
Liabilities: $92,303,577
Net Worth: $64,290,813
Earnings: ($164,895)
Emp.: 307
Fiscal Year-end: 12/31/2022
Ferrite Magnet & Fine Ceramic Product Mfr
N.A.I.C.S.: 327110
Jin Young Kim *(Pres & CEO)*

UNION DIAGNOSTIC & CLINICAL SERVICES PLC.
5 Eletu Ogabi Street Off Adeola Odeku Street V/I, Shomolu, Lagos, Nigeria
Tel.: (234) 8074516930
Web Site: http://www.uniondiagnostic.com.ng
UNIONDAC—(NIGE)
Rev.: $3,696,721
Assets: $12,757,210
Liabilities: $324,096
Net Worth: $12,433,114
Earnings: $170,428
Emp.: 500
Fiscal Year-end: 12/31/19
Diagnostic Testing Lab Services
N.A.I.C.S.: 621512
Bariyu A. Adeyemi *(Chm)*

UNION DICON SALT PLC.
Phase 2 Kirikiri Lighter Terminal, Kirikiri, Apapa, Nigeria
Tel.: (234) 9060305130
Web Site: https://uniondiconsaltplc.com
UNIONDICON—(NIGE)
Rev.: $312,499
Assets: $429,652
Liabilities: $3,519,665
Net Worth: ($3,090,013)
Earnings: ($25,502)
Fiscal Year-end: 12/31/22
Spice & Extract Manufacturing
N.A.I.C.S.: 311942
Bekuochi Nwawudu *(Deputy Mng Dir)*

UNION EL GOLF S.A.
Golf Avenue 50, Las Condes, Santiago, Chile
Tel.: (56) 9258400
Web Site: http://www.clubelgolf50.cl
UNION.GOLF—(SGO)
Sales Range: Less than $1 Million
Recreational Activity Services
N.A.I.C.S.: 611620
Herman Chadwick Pinera *(Chm)*

UNION EUROPEA DE INVERSIONES, S.A.
Jose Ortega y Gasset 29, Madrid, 28006, Spain
Tel.: (34) 91 576 59 20
Web Site: http://www.europeainversiones.com
Investment Management Service
N.A.I.C.S.: 523940
Jose Antonio Guzman Gonzalez *(CEO)*

UNION GAS HOLDINGS LIMITED
3 Lorong Bakar Batu 07-04 Union Industrial Center, Singapore, 348741, Singapore
Tel.: (65) 63166666
Web Site: https://www.uniongas.com.sg
Year Founded: 1974
1F2—(SES)
Rev.: $97,592,214
Assets: $109,809,892
Liabilities: $57,867,909
Net Worth: $51,941,983
Earnings: $9,257,744
Emp.: 385
Fiscal Year-end: 12/31/23
Fuel Product Distr
N.A.I.C.S.: 457210
Kiang Ang Teo *(Founder)*

UNION GROUP
Prince Shaker Ben Zeid St, Amman, 11180, Jordan
Tel.: (962) 65607011
Web Site: http://www.uniongroupjo.com
Holding Company
N.A.I.C.S.: 551112
Issam H. Salfiti *(Chm)*

Subsidiaries:

Bank al Etihad PSC   (1)
Shmeisani, PO Box 35104, Amman, 11180, Jordan
Tel.: (962) 65607011
Web Site: https://www.bankaletihad.com
Rev.: $357,540,967
Assets: $7,438,244,475
Liabilities: $6,723,992,945
Net Worth: $714,251,530

INTERNATIONAL PUBLIC

Earnings: $42,375,321
Emp.: 1,215
Fiscal Year-end: 12/31/2020
Banking Services
N.A.I.C.S.: 522110
Issam Halim Salfiti *(Chm)*

Union Advanced Industries Co. plc   (1)
Hanena industrial area, PO Box 94, 09625, Madaba, Jordan
Tel.: (962) 53241130
Web Site: http://www.unionadvance.com
Rev.: $6,000,000
Emp.: 90
Commercial Gravure Printing
N.A.I.C.S.: 323111
Mohammed Alshawawreh *(Gen Mgr)*

Union Chemical & Vegetable Oil Industries Co. plc   (1)
PO Box 15362, Amman, 11134, Jordan
Tel.: (962) 64460567
Edible Oil Mfr
N.A.I.C.S.: 311224

Union Marketing Group   (1)
Princess Hala Bint Hashem Street, Al Qastal, Jordan
Tel.: (962) 6 47 90 600
Web Site: http://www.umg.jo
Alcoholic Beverage Distr
N.A.I.C.S.: 424820

Union Tobacco & Cigarette Industries Co. plc   (1)
PO Box 851015, Amman, 11185, Jordan
Tel.: (962) 64460300
Web Site: http://www.uniontobacco.com
Sales Range: $100-124.9 Million
Emp.: 400
Cigarette Mfr
N.A.I.C.S.: 312230
Samer Shawawreh *(CEO)*

UNION INMOBILIARIA S.A.
Av Libertador Bernardo O Higgins N 1091 - 4 Piso, PO Box 89-D, Santiago, Chile
Tel.: (56) 224284625
Web Site: https://www.unioninmobiliaria.cl
CLUBUNION—(SGO)
Sales Range: Less than $1 Million
Asset Management Services
N.A.I.C.S.: 531312

UNION INSURANCE COMPANY P.S.C.
Single Business Tower Sheikh Zayed Road, PO Box 119227, Dubai, United Arab Emirates
Tel.: (971) 43787777
Web Site: https://www.unioninsurance.ae
Year Founded: 1998
UNION—(ABU)
Rev.: $172,494,285
Assets: $410,264,382
Liabilities: $354,441,575
Net Worth: $55,822,806
Earnings: ($674,962)
Emp.: 260
Fiscal Year-end: 12/31/23
Insurance Services
N.A.I.C.S.: 524298
Abdul Muttaleb M. Al Jaedi *(CEO & Mng Dir)*

UNION INVESTMENT CORPORATION
Um Uthaynah Eriteria St Nebal Bldg No 6 2nd floor, PO Box 144064, Amman, 11814, Jordan
Tel.: (962) 65514757
Web Site: http://www.unioninvestco.com
UINV—(AMM)
Rev.: $13,269,867
Assets: $186,397,560
Liabilities: $127,080,754
Net Worth: $59,316,806

Earnings: ($13,635,264)
Emp.: 7
Fiscal Year-end: 12/31/20
Investment Management Service
N.A.I.C.S.: 523940

UNION INVIVO - UNION DE COOPERATIVES AGRICOLES
83 avenue de la Grande Armee, 75782, Paris, France
Tel.: (33) 1 40 66 22 22
Web Site: http://www.invivo-group.com
Sales Range: $5-14.9 Billion
Emp.: 201
Holding Company; Agricultural Cooperative
N.A.I.C.S.: 551112
Thierry Blandinieres *(Gen Mgr)*

Subsidiaries:

Baarsma Wine Group Holding B.V. (1)
Rontgenlaan 3, 2719 DX, Zoetermeer, Netherlands
Tel.: (31) 513469469
Web Site: http://baarsmawines.com
Holding Company; Wine Distr
N.A.I.C.S.: 551112
Tjeerd C. van der Hoek *(CFO)*

Subsidiary (Non-US):

Baarsma South Africa Pty. Ltd. (2)
Blaauwklip Office Park Blaauwklip Offices nr 1, Webersvallei Road, Stellenbosch, South Africa
Tel.: (27) 218801221
Web Site: http://www.baarsma.co.za
Winery & Wine Distr
N.A.I.C.S.: 312130
Chris Rabie *(Mng Dir)*

Subsidiary (Domestic):

Baarsma Wines BV (2)
Rontgenlaan 3, 2719 DX, Zoetermeer, Netherlands (100%)
Tel.: (31) 513469469
Web Site: http://baarsmawines.com
Wine Distr
N.A.I.C.S.: 424820
Bert Meerstadt *(CEO)*

De Wijnbeurs (2)
Oude Enghweg 8, 1217 JC, Hilversum, Netherlands (100%)
Tel.: (31) 294 788 103
Web Site: http://www.wijnbeurs.nl
Direct Mail Wine Distr
N.A.I.C.S.: 424820

Wijnhandel Leon Colaris B.V. (2)
Franklinstraat 1, 6003 DK, Weert, Netherlands
Tel.: (31) 495532462
Web Site: http://www.colaris.nl
Wine Distr
N.A.I.C.S.: 424820
Ruud Heuvelmans *(Mng Dir)*

Wine Excel BV (2)
Hoofdtocht 3, 1507 CJ, Zaandam, Netherlands (100%)
Tel.: (31) 756429930
Web Site: http://www.wine-excel.com
Wine Bottler & Distr
N.A.I.C.S.: 424820

Gamm Vert SA (1)
83-85 avenue of the Grande Armee, 75116, Paris, Cedex 16, France
Tel.: (33) 892 16 40 50
Web Site: http://www.gammvert.fr
Garden & Pet Stores
N.A.I.C.S.: 444240

Subsidiary (Domestic):

Jardiland Enseignes SAS (2)
1 quai Gabriel Peri, Joinville-le-Pont, 94340, France
Tel.: (33) 974595974
Web Site: http://www.jardiland.com
Gardening & Pet Products Mfr
N.A.I.C.S.: 444240

UNION JACK OIL PLC
6 Charlotte Street, Bath, BA1 2NE, United Kingdom
Tel.: (44) 1225428139
Web Site: https://www.unionjackoil.com
Year Founded: 2011
UJO—(AIM)
Rev.: $10,738,513
Assets: $33,276,113
Liabilities: $4,236,438
Net Worth: $29,039,676
Earnings: $4,552,669
Emp.: 4
Fiscal Year-end: 12/31/22
Crude Petroleum Extraction Services
N.A.I.C.S.: 211120
David Bramhill *(Chm)*

UNION KOREA PHARM CO., LTD.
417 Samwhan Hipex A 240 Pangyoyeok-Ro, Bundang-Gu, Seongnam, Gyeonggi-do, Korea (South)
Tel.: (82) 24893611
Web Site: https://www.ukp.co.kr
Year Founded: 1985
080720—(KRS)
Rev.: $47,012,107
Assets: $86,304,960
Liabilities: $49,019,335
Net Worth: $37,285,624
Earnings: ($714,861)
Emp.: 218
Fiscal Year-end: 12/31/22
Pharmaceutical & Medicine Mfr
N.A.I.C.S.: 325412
Back Bying Ha *(Pres & CEO)*

UNION LAND DEVELOPMENT
PO Box 926648, Amman, 11192, Jordan
Tel.: (962) 64641868
Web Site: http://www.uld.jo
Year Founded: 1995
ULDC—(AMM)
Rev.: $4,858,590
Assets: $94,969,467
Liabilities: $22,922,669
Net Worth: $72,046,798
Earnings: $824,591
Emp.: 79
Fiscal Year-end: 12/31/22
Real Estate Development Services
N.A.I.C.S.: 531390
Muath Mustafa Enayah *(Gen Mgr)*

UNION METALLURGIQUE DE LA HAUTE SEINE SA
49 RN6, BP 6, 77002, Melun, Cedex, France
Tel.: (33) 160567777
Web Site: http://www.umhs.fr
MLUMH—(EUR)
Sales Range: $50-74.9 Million
Industrial Machinery & Equipment Merchant Whslr
N.A.I.C.S.: 423830
Olivier Scialom *(Chm & CEO)*

UNION N.V.
Rondebeltweg 31, 1329 BN, Almere, Netherlands
Tel.: (31) 885016712
Web Site: http://www.union.nl
Sales Range: $10-24.9 Million
Emp.: 56
Bicycle Mfr
N.A.I.C.S.: 336991

UNION NACIONAL DE EMPRESAS, S.A.
SUCASA Building Via Espana and Calle 50, Apartado 8001, 7, Panama, Panama
Tel.: (507) 3025464
Web Site: https://www.unesa.com
UNEM—(PAN)
Sales Range: $75-99.9 Million
Emp.: 638
Holding Company; Real Estate & Construction Services; Hotel Owner & Operator; Restaurant Franchise Owner & Operator
N.A.I.C.S.: 551112
Raul Orillac *(Vice Chm)*

UNION OPTECH CO., LTD.
No 10 yiwei Road M Torch Development Zone, Zhongshan, Guangdong, China
Tel.: (86) 76086138999
Web Site: https://www.union-optech.com
Year Founded: 2005
300691—(CHIN)
Rev.: $231,990,612
Assets: $367,709,588
Liabilities: $136,833,338
Net Worth: $230,876,249
Earnings: $9,055,627
Fiscal Year-end: 12/31/23
Electronic Parts Mfr & Distr
N.A.I.C.S.: 333310

UNION ORTHOPEDIC CORP.
12F No 80 Sec 1 Chenggong Rd, Yonghe Dist, New Taipei City, 234634, Taiwan
Tel.: (886) 229294567
Web Site: https://unitedorthopedic.com
Year Founded: 1993
4129—(TPE)
Rev.: $99,073,883
Assets: $175,578,370
Liabilities: $78,968,421
Net Worth: $96,609,949
Earnings: $6,990,620
Emp.: 761
Fiscal Year-end: 12/31/22
Orthopedic Surgery Product Mfr
N.A.I.C.S.: 339113
Yan-Shen Lin *(Chm & Pres)*

UNION PETROCHEMICAL PUBLIC COMPANY LIMITED
728 Union House Bldg Boromratchonnani Rd Bang Bamru, Bang Phlad, Bangkok, 10700, Thailand
Tel.: (66) 28818288
Web Site: https://www.unionpetrochemical.com
Year Founded: 1981
UKEM—(THA)
Rev.: $83,875,258
Assets: $49,171,138
Liabilities: $25,224,572
Net Worth: $23,946,566
Earnings: $270,744
Emp.: 127
Fiscal Year-end: 12/31/23
Petrochemical Mfr & Distr
N.A.I.C.S.: 325110
Wirat Suwannaphasri *(Mng Dir)*

UNION PIONEER PUBLIC COMPANY LIMITED
No 1 Soi Serithai 62 Khwaeng Minburi, Khet Minburi, Bangkok, 10510, Thailand
Tel.: (66) 251701058
Web Site: https://www.unionpioneer.co.th
Year Founded: 1973
UPF—(THA)
Rev.: $16,309,775
Assets: $13,906,638
Liabilities: $3,678,408
Net Worth: $10,228,230
Earnings: $190,471
Emp.: 512
Fiscal Year-end: 12/31/23
Rubber Thread, Rubber Tape, Elastic Braiding & Elastic Webbing Products Mfr
N.A.I.C.S.: 326299
Chadaporn Jiemsakultip *(Chief Compliance Officer & Sec)*

UNION QUALITY PLASTICS LIMITED
209/A Shyam Kamal B CHS LTD Agarwal Market, Tejpal Road Ville Parle East, Mumbai, 400057, Maharashtra, India
Tel.: (91) 9848098088
Web Site: https://uqpl.org
Year Founded: 1981
526799—(BOM)
Rev.: $2,267,374
Assets: $3,118,989
Liabilities: $2,834,893
Net Worth: $284,096
Earnings: ($32,352)
Emp.: 225
Fiscal Year-end: 03/31/21
Plastics Product Mfr
N.A.I.C.S.: 326199
Rajesh Singh Javvar Kapish *(Mng Dir)*

UNION REAL ESTATE COMPANY K.S.C.C.
Shaab Ghazwa Building Ground Floor, PO Box 24080, Safat, Kuwait, 13101, Kuwait
Tel.: (965) 22623176
Web Site: http://www.urckw.com
Year Founded: 1975
Sales Range: $1-9.9 Million
Emp.: 25
Real Estate Services
N.A.I.C.S.: 531390

UNION STEEL HOLDINGS LIMITED
33 Pioneer Road North, Singapore, 628474, Singapore
Tel.: (65) 68619833
Web Site: https://www.unionsteel.com.sg
Year Founded: 1984
ZB9—(SES)
Rev.: $79,507,966
Assets: $116,420,156
Liabilities: $58,883,290
Net Worth: $57,536,866
Earnings: $8,256,391
Emp.: 549
Fiscal Year-end: 06/30/23
Steel Mfrs
N.A.I.C.S.: 331110
Yu Seng Ang *(Co-Founder, Chm & CEO)*

Subsidiaries:

Gee Sheng Machinery & Engineering Pte. Ltd. (1)
2 Kranji Link, Singapore, 728648, Singapore
Tel.: (65) 65431626
Web Site: https://www.geesheng.com.sg
Gasoline Product Mfr
N.A.I.C.S.: 324110
Rachel Chong *(Engr-Sls)*

Hock Ann Metal Scaffolding Pte. Ltd. (1)
10 Bukit Batok Crescent 04-01 The Spire, Singapore, 658079, Singapore
Tel.: (65) 68422808
Web Site: https://www.hock-ann.com.sg
Scaffolding Rental Services
N.A.I.C.S.: 532490

Megafab Engineering Pte. Ltd. (1)
7 Gul Road, Singapore, 629364, Singapore
Tel.: (65) 6 898 1055
Web Site: https://www.megafab.com.sg

UNION STEEL HOLDINGS LIMITED

Union Steel Holdings Limited—(Continued)
Material Handling Equipment Distr
N.A.I.C.S.: 423830
Sebastian Low *(Gen Mgr)*

Transvictory Winch System Pte. Ltd. (1)
20 Third Chin Bee Road, Singapore, 618693, Singapore
Tel.: (65) 67743127
Web Site:
 https://www.transvictorywinch.com
Wrench & Crane Mfr
N.A.I.C.S.: 333923
Ang Jun Long *(Gen Mgr)*

Union Steel Pte. Ltd. (1)
33 Pioneer Road North, Singapore, 628474, Singapore
Tel.: (65) 68619833
Emp.: 50
Steel Products Mfr
N.A.I.C.S.: 331110

YLS Steel Pte Ltd (1)
33 Pioneer Road North, Singapore, 628474, Singapore
Tel.: (65) 68619833
Web Site: https://www.ylssteel.com.sg
Steel Product Distr
N.A.I.C.S.: 423510

Yew Lee Seng Metal Pte Ltd (1)
14 Defu Lane 11, Singapore, 539170, Singapore
Tel.: (65) 63820576
Demolition Contractor
N.A.I.C.S.: 238910

UNION TECHNIQUE DE L'AUTOMOBILE, DU MOTOCYCLE ET DU SASU
Autodrome de Linas-Montlhery Avenue Georges Boillot, 91310, Linas, France
Tel.: (33) 1 69 80 17 00
Web Site: http://www.utacceram.com
Vehicle & Equipment Testing Services
N.A.I.C.S.: 334515
Laurent Benoit *(Pres)*

Subsidiaries:

Millbrook Proving Ground Limited (1)
Proving Ground, Millbrook, Bedford, MK45 2JQ, United Kingdom
Tel.: (44) 1525404242
Web Site: http://www.millbrook.co.uk
Vehicle Test & Validation Services
N.A.I.C.S.: 541380

Subsidiary (US):

Millbrook Revolutionary Engineering Inc. (2)
36865 Schoolcraft Rd, Livonia, MI 48150
Tel.: (734) 432-9334
Web Site: http://www.millbrook.us
Dynamometer-based Testing Solutions
N.A.I.C.S.: 541330
Robert Camp *(Mgr-Engrg)*

UNION TECHNOLOGIES INFORMATIQUE GROUP SA
68 rue de Villiers, 92300, Levallois-Perret, France
Tel.: (33) 141490510
Web Site: https://www.uti-group.com
Year Founded: 1986
FPG—(EUR)
Sales Range: $10-24.9 Million
Management Consulting Services
N.A.I.C.S.: 541618
Christian Aumard *(Chm, CEO & Dir-IR)*

UNION TOOL CO.
6-17-1 Minami-ohi, Shinagawa-ku, Tokyo, 140-0013, Japan
Tel.: (81) 354931001
Web Site: https://www.uniontool.co.jp
Year Founded: 1960
6278—(TKS)
Rev.: $179,646,420
Assets: $500,589,450
Liabilities: $23,581,340
Net Worth: $477,008,110
Earnings: $21,815,930
Emp.: 1,450
Fiscal Year-end: 12/31/23
Cutting Tool Mfr
N.A.I.C.S.: 333515
Akira Sato *(Mng Exec Officer)*

Subsidiaries:

Dongguan Union Tool Ltd. (1)
No 5 Hong Jin Road, Hongmei Town, Dongguan, 523160, Guangdong, China
Tel.: (86) 76988848901
Web Site: http://www.dguniontool.com.cn
Sales Range: $50-74.9 Million
Emp.: 200
Cutting Tools Mfr & Supplier
N.A.I.C.S.: 333517

Taiwan Union Tool Corp. (1)
No 180 Zhong-Zun Street 14 Neighborhood Bin-Hai Vil, Lu-Zhu Dist, Taoyuan, 338, Taiwan
Tel.: (886) 33543111
Web Site: https://www.uniontool.com.tw
Emp.: 160
Machine Tools Mfr
N.A.I.C.S.: 333517

US Union Tool Inc. (1)
1260 N Fee Ana St, Anaheim, CA 92807-1817
Tel.: (714) 521-6242
Sales Range: $25-49.9 Million
Emp.: 58
Cutting Tools Mfr & Distr
N.A.I.C.S.: 333517

Union Engineering Co., Ltd. (1)
3-1-1 KCC Bldg 4F Kaigan-dori, Chuo-ku, Kobe, 650-0024, Hyogo, Japan
Tel.: (81) 783323381
Sales Range: $25-49.9 Million
Emp.: 6
Measuring Instruments Mfr
N.A.I.C.S.: 334519
Michael Mortensen *(CEO)*

Union Tool (Shanghai) Co., Ltd. (1)
Tel.: (86) 2157628588
Sales Range: $50-74.9 Million
Emp.: 250
Cutting Tools Mfr & Whslr
N.A.I.C.S.: 333517

Union Tool (Thailand) Co., Ltd. (1)
55/73 Moo 15, Bangsaothong Sub-District Bangsaothong District, Samut Prakan, 10570, Thailand
Tel.: (66) 21300908
Cutting Tool Distr
N.A.I.C.S.: 423830

Union Tool (Waigaoqiao Shanghai) Co., Ltd. (1)
No 6 Lane 385 Gaoji Road, Sijing High New Technology Development Zone Songjiang District, Shanghai, 2011601, China
Tel.: (86) 2157628588
Web Site: http://www.uniontool.co.jp
Cutting Tool Mfr
N.A.I.C.S.: 333517

Union Tool Co. - Mitsuke Plant (1)
3-1 Shinko-Cho, Mitsuke, 954-0076, Japan
Tel.: (81) 25 866 0800
Web Site: http://www.uniontool.co.jp
Sales Range: $25-49.9 Million
Emp.: 100
Industrial Instrument Mfr
N.A.I.C.S.: 541330

Union Tool Co. - Nagaoka Plant (1)
2706-6 Togawa Settaya-machi, Nagaoka, 940-1104, Niigata Pref, Japan
Tel.: (81) 25 822 2620
Web Site: http://www.uniontool.jp
Industrial Measuring Instruments Mfr
N.A.I.C.S.: 334519

Union Tool Europe S.A. (1)
Ave Des Champs-Montants 14a, 2074, Marin, Neuchatel, Switzerland
Tel.: (41) 327566633
Web Site: http://www.uniontool.com
Sales Range: $25-49.9 Million
Emp.: 11
Cutting Tools & Linear Motion Guides Distr
N.A.I.C.S.: 334519
Christopher Serre *(Pres)*

Union Tool Hong Kong Ltd. (1)
Tel.: (852) 23703012
Web Site: http://www.uniontool.hk
Sales Range: $25-49.9 Million
Emp.: 6
Industrial Instrument Mfr
N.A.I.C.S.: 332999

Union Tool Singapore Pte., Ltd. (1)
140 Paya Lebar Road 08-17 AZ, Paya Lebar, Singapore, 409015, Singapore
Tel.: (65) 68469309
Sales Range: $25-49.9 Million
Emp.: 6
Cutting Tools Mfr & Supplier
N.A.I.C.S.: 333517
Miyama Takanori *(Dir)*

UNION TRACTOR LTD.
6210 75th Street, Edmonton, T6E 2W6, AB, Canada
Tel.: (780) 468-8600 Ca
Web Site:
 http://www.uniontractor.com
Year Founded: 1927
Construction Equipment Parts Distr
N.A.I.C.S.: 423830

UNION VERSICHERUNGS-AKTIENGESELLSCHAFT
ERGO Center Businesspark Marximum / Objekt 3 0, Modecenterstrase 17, 1110, Vienna, Austria
Tel.: (43) 1313830
Web Site: http://www.ba-v.at
Year Founded: 1911
Sales Range: $50-74.9 Million
Emp.: 115
Life Insurance Carrier
N.A.I.C.S.: 524113
Tosef Adelmann *(Gen Dir)*

UNIONBANK OF THE PHILIPPINES
UnionBank Plaza Meralco Avenue Cor Onyx & Sapphire Roads, Ortigas Center, Pasig, 1605, Philippines
Tel.: (63) 9178250273 PH
Web Site:
 https://www.unionbankph.com
Year Founded: 1968
UBP—(PHI)
Rev.: $755,613,435
Assets: $17,286,785,589
Liabilities: $14,952,750,446
Net Worth: $2,334,035,142
Earnings: $260,527,821
Emp.: 3,506
Fiscal Year-end: 12/31/21
Banking Services
N.A.I.C.S.: 522110
Edwin R. Bautista *(Pres & CEO)*

Subsidiaries:

First Union Direct (1)
Unionbank Plaza Bldg Meralco Ave Corner Onyx St, West Tower Tektite Bldg, Pasig, 1605, Philippines (100%)
Tel.: (63) 88418600
Web Site: http://www.unionbankph.com
Sales Range: $50-74.9 Million
Emp.: 2
Financial Services Marketing
N.A.I.C.S.: 523999

First Union Plans (1)
SSS Makati Building, Ayala Avenue, Manila, Makati, Philippines (100%)
Tel.: (63) 28134620
Web Site: http://www.unionbankph.com
Pension Plan
N.A.I.C.S.: 525110

UBP Capital Corporation (1)
SSS Makati Building, Ayala Avenue, Manila,

INTERNATIONAL PUBLIC

Makati, Philippines (100%)
Tel.: (63) 28134620
Web Site: http://www.unionbankph.com
Investment Services
N.A.I.C.S.: 523940

Subsidiary (Domestic):

Union Properties, Inc. (2)
SSS Makati Building, Ayala Avenue, Manila, Makati, Philippines (100%)
Tel.: (63) 28134620
Real Property Development & Marketing
N.A.I.C.S.: 531390

UNIONELEKTRO A.D.
Milutina Milankovica 34, Beograd-Novi, Belgrade, Serbia
Tel.: (381) 11 6130 524
Year Founded: 1978
Sales Range: Less than $1 Million
Electrical Installation Services
N.A.I.C.S.: 238210

UNIONINVEST D.D.
Grbavicka 4, 71000, Sarajevo, Bosnia & Herzegovina
Tel.: (387) 33 214 535
Web Site: http://www.unioninvest.net
Year Founded: 1949
Construction Equipment Mfr
N.A.I.C.S.: 339999
Zlatko Cengic *(Chm-Supervisory Bd)*

UNIONINVEST INZENJERING I PROJEKTOVANJE A.D.
Milutina Milankovica 34, Novi Beograd, Serbia
Tel.: (381) 11 2054 059
Year Founded: 1950
UNIP—(BEL)
Sales Range: Less than $1 Million
Emp.: 4
Engineering & Technical Consulting Services
N.A.I.C.S.: 541330
Slobodan Curcic *(Dir)*

UNIONINVEST PLASTIKA D.D. SEMIZOVAC
Semizovac bb, Vogosca, 71320, Semizovac, Bosnia & Herzegovina
Tel.: (387) 33475250
Web Site:
 http://unioninvestplastika.ba
UNPLR—(SARE)
Rev.: $5,870,456
Assets: $7,561,570
Liabilities: $4,538,369
Net Worth: $3,023,201
Earnings: $57,703
Emp.: 103
Fiscal Year-end: 12/31/21
Plastic Production Services
N.A.I.C.S.: 326199

UNIONIZGRADNJA SIP D.D. SARAJEVO
Aleja Lipa 56, 71000, Sarajevo, Bosnia & Herzegovina
Tel.: (387) 33 643 757
Sales Range: Less than $1 Million
Emp.: 2
Architectural Services
N.A.I.C.S.: 541310

UNIONMAN TECHNOLOGY CO., LTD.
No 5 Huitai Road Huinan High-tech Industrial Park Huiao Avenue, Huizhou, 516025, Guangdong, China
Tel.: (86) 7525853999
Web Site:
 https://www.unionman.com.cn
Year Founded: 2001
688609—(SHG)
Rev.: $337,345,538
Assets: $395,868,597

AND PRIVATE COMPANIES

Liabilities: $215,231,810
Net Worth: $180,636,787
Earnings: $8,471,006
Emp.: 1,400
Fiscal Year-end: 12/31/22
Communication Equipment Mfr
N.A.I.C.S.: 334290
Qijun Zhan *(Chm & Gen Mgr)*

UNIOR COMPONENTS A.D.
Kosovska 4, 34 000, Kragujevac, Serbia
Tel.: (381) 34 306300
Web Site: http://www.unior-components.com
Year Founded: 1953
Emp.: 160
Machine Tool, Hand Tools & Heating Treatments
N.A.I.C.S.: 333517
Milan Marjanovic *(Mgr-Broaching Tools Programme)*

UNIOR KOVASKA INDUSTRIJA D.D.
Kovaska cesta 10, 3214, Zrece, Slovenia
Tel.: (386) 37578100
Web Site: https://www.unior.com
Year Founded: 1919
UKIG—(LJU)
Rev.: $324,800,367
Assets: $431,403,298
Liabilities: $225,561,038
Net Worth: $205,842,261
Earnings: $5,449,350
Emp.: 2,812
Fiscal Year-end: 12/31/23
Machine Tools Mfr
N.A.I.C.S.: 333517
Robert Ribic *(Mgr-Forge Programme)*
Subsidiaries:

Ningbo Unior Forging, Co. Ltd. (1)
Dongwu Village, Moushan Town, Yuyao, Zhejiang, China
Tel.: (86) 57462496927
Web Site: https://www.unior.cn
Emp.: 441
Hot Forging Parts Mfr
N.A.I.C.S.: 332111

Rekreacijsko turisticni center Krvavec, d.d. (1)
Grad 76, 4207, Cerklje na Gorenjskem, Slovenia
Tel.: (386) 42525930
Web Site: https://www.rtc-krvavec.si
Emp.: 70
Ski Resort Operator
N.A.I.C.S.: 721110

SPITT d.o.o. (1)
Vojkova Cesta 19, Solkan, 5250, Nova Gorica, Slovenia
Tel.: (386) 53305100
Web Site: https://www.spit.si
Civil Engineering Services
N.A.I.C.S.: 541330
Miran Lozej *(Gen Mgr)*

UNIOR IN d.o.o. (1)
Kovaska cesta 10, 3214, Zrece, Slovenia
Tel.: (386) 37578100
Emp.: 26
Metal & Sintered Product Mfr
N.A.I.C.S.: 332999

Unidal d.o.o. (1)
Ulica Kneza Mislava 42, 32100, Vinkovci, Croatia
Tel.: (385) 32 323 999
Emp.: 129
Hand Tool Mfr
N.A.I.C.S.: 332216

Unior - North America Inc. (1)
28213 Carlton Way Dr, Novi, MI 48377
Tel.: (248) 730-0060
Light Emitting Diode Product Mfr & Distr
N.A.I.C.S.: 334413

Unior Bionic, d.o.o. (1)
Kovaska Cesta 10, 3214, Zrece, Slovenia
Tel.: (386) 3 757 81 00
Web Site: http://www.unior.com
Emp.: 1
Hand Tool Whslr
N.A.I.C.S.: 423830
Robert Ribic *(Dir-Forging)*

Unior Bulgaria, Ltd. (1)
str Atanas Hranov bl 71, PO Box 168, 1309, Sofia, Bulgaria
Tel.: (359) 29559233
Web Site: https://www.unior.bg
Emp.: 8
Hand Tools Distr
N.A.I.C.S.: 423830

Unior Coframa sp. z o.o. (1)
Obornicka 227, 61-005, Poznan, Poland
Tel.: (48) 618770506
Web Site: http://www.unior.pl
Emp.: 14
Hand Tool Whslr
N.A.I.C.S.: 423120

Unior Deutschland GmbH (1)
Am oberen Schlossberg 5, 71686, Remseck am Neckar, Germany
Tel.: (49) 714628500
Web Site: http://www.unior.com
Emp.: 4
Hand Tool Whslr
N.A.I.C.S.: 423710
Bogdan Kukovic *(Gen Mgr)*

Unior Espana, S.L. (1)
Poligon Sargaitz 2 Nave A5, Uharte-Arakil, 31840, Navarra, Spain
Tel.: (34) 948567113
Web Site: https://www.unior.es
Emp.: 2
Hand Tool Whslr
N.A.I.C.S.: 423830
Xabi de Xerica *(Mgr)*

Unior Hungaria Kft. (1)
Napfeny utca 1, 8756, Nagyrecse, Hungary
Tel.: (36) 93 571 070
Hand Tool Whslr
N.A.I.C.S.: 423710

Unior Italia S.R.L. (1)
Via Caserta 8, 20812, Limbiate, MB, Italy
Tel.: (39) 03484827894
Web Site: https://uniortools.com
Emp.: 5
Hand Tool Whslr
N.A.I.C.S.: 423830
Alessandro Cavallari *(Mng Dir)*

Unior Professional Tools, Ltd. (1)
Tel.: (7) 8124498350
Web Site: https://www.unior.ru
Emp.: 30
Hand Tool Mfr
N.A.I.C.S.: 333517

Unior Savjetovanje i trgovina d.o.o. (1)
Dr Silve Rizvanbegovic b b, 71000, Sarajevo, Bosnia & Herzegovina
Tel.: (387) 33 80 91 32
Hand Tool Whslr
N.A.I.C.S.: 423830

Unior Vinkovci d.o.o. (1)
Kneza Mislava 27, 32100, Vinkovci, Croatia
Tel.: (385) 32637468
Steel Products Mfr
N.A.I.C.S.: 332999

UNIPAR CARBOCLORO S.A.
Avenida Presidente Juscelino Kubitschek 1327 - 22 andar, Sao Paulo, 04534-011, SP, Brazil
Tel.: (55) 1137044200
Web Site: https://unipar.com
Year Founded: 1969
UNIP3—(BRAZ)
Rev.: $875,438,028
Assets: $1,143,435,196
Liabilities: $705,857,760
Net Worth: $437,577,436
Earnings: $141,447,772
Emp.: 1,400
Fiscal Year-end: 12/31/23
Petrochemicals Mfr & Distr
N.A.I.C.S.: 325110

Frank Geyer Abubakir *(Chm)*
Subsidiaries:

Unipar Indupa S.A.I.C. (1)
Av Del Desarrollo Pte Fronizi 2450, B8101XAD, Bahia Blanca, Buenos Aires, Argentina (100%)
Tel.: (54) 2914593000
Web Site: http://www.uniparindupa.com
Plastics & Chemicals Mfr
N.A.I.C.S.: 325998

UNIPART GROUP OF COMPANIES LIMITED
Unipart House Garsington Road, Cowley, OX4 2PG, Oxford, United Kingdom
Tel.: (44) 1865778966
Web Site: http://www.unipart.com
Year Founded: 1987
Sales Range: $1-4.9 Billion
Emp.: 10,000
Logistic Services
N.A.I.C.S.: 541614
John M. Neill *(Chm & Grp CEO)*
Subsidiaries:

Intertruck Benelux B.V. (1)
Koddeweg 10, Hoogvliet, 3194 DH, Rotterdam, Netherlands
Tel.: (31) 10 50 34 444
Web Site: http://www.intertruck.nl
Emp.: 60
Freight Forwarding Services
N.A.I.C.S.: 488510
Marcel van Eeuwen *(CEO)*

Intertruck Deutschland GMBH (1)
Siemensstrasse 31, 47533, Kleve, Germany
Tel.: (49) 2821 7193563
Web Site: http://www.intertruck.com
Freight Forwarding Services
N.A.I.C.S.: 488510
Marcel van Eeuwen *(CEO)*

Serck Services (Gulf) Limited (1)
PO Box 5834, Sharjah, United Arab Emirates
Tel.: (971) 6 5086600
Web Site: http://www.serckgulf.com
Emp.: 400
Automotive Components Mfr
N.A.I.C.S.: 336390
Billy Tyrrell *(Dir-Ops-Radiator)*

Serck Services (Oman) LLC (1)
Behind Shansarry, PO Box 1056, Ruwi, 112, Muscat, Oman
Tel.: (968) 24697785
Web Site: http://www.serckgulf.com
Automotive Components Mfr
N.A.I.C.S.: 336390

Serck Services Co. (LLC) (1)
PO Box 4439, Abu Dhabi, United Arab Emirates
Tel.: (971) 2 5553108
Web Site: http://www.serckgulf.com
Emp.: 84
Automotive Components Mfr
N.A.I.C.S.: 336390
Mark Sanhope *(Mng Dir)*

Serck Services, Inc. (1)
5501 Pearl St, Denver, CO 80216
Tel.: (303) 295-1379
Web Site: http://www.serckservices.com
Sales Range: $25-49.9 Million
Emp.: 45
Radiators, Oil Coolers, Fuel Tanks, Heater Cores & Heat Exchangers Supplier & Services
N.A.I.C.S.: 811198
Peter Young *(Mng Dir)*

TTC Air Brake Centre Ltd (1)
3 Sadler Road, Lincoln, LN6 3RS, United Kingdom
Tel.: (44) 844 264 2388
Automobile Component Distr
N.A.I.C.S.: 423120

Unipart Polymer and Composite Solutions (1)
Dakota Business Park Downley Road, Havant, PO9 2NJ, Hampshire, United Kingdom
Tel.: (44) 2392499276
Web Site: http://www.formaplex.com
Sales Range: $25-49.9 Million
Emp.: 124
Injection Mould Tool Mfr
N.A.I.C.S.: 333991
Angela Tomkins *(Mgr-HR)*

Unipart Rail (1)
Jupiter Building First Point Balby Carr Bank, Doncaster, DN4 5JQ, S Yorkshire, United Kingdom
Tel.: (44) 1302 731400
Web Site: http://www.unipartrail.com
Sales Range: $75-99.9 Million
Emp.: 250
Rail Components Supplier
N.A.I.C.S.: 423860
John Clayton *(CEO)*

Unipart Security Solutions Ltd (1)
Cavalry Hill Industrial Park, Weedon, Northamptonshire, United Kingdom
Tel.: (44) 1327 344055
Web Site: http://www.unipartsecurity.co.uk
Security Services
N.A.I.C.S.: 561612
Colin Moore *(Mng Dir)*

Unipart Services America Inc. (1)
555 MacArthur Blvd, Mahwah, NJ 07430
Tel.: (201) 818-8318
Automotive Parts Supplier
N.A.I.C.S.: 423120

Unipart Services India Private Limited (1)
Office No 224 & 225 Sector 30A Platinum Techno Park Vashi, Navi Mumbai, 400 703, India
Tel.: (91) 22 66099370
Emp.: 383
Freight Forwarding Services
N.A.I.C.S.: 488510
Jonathan Horton *(Gen Mgr)*

Van Wezel Autoparts GMBH (1)
Schlossmuhlstrasse 15b, 2320, Schwechat, Austria
Tel.: (43) 1 760 28 0
Web Site: http://www.vanwezel.be
Automobile Component Distr
N.A.I.C.S.: 423120

Van Wezel GMBH (1)
Sudfeld 7a, 59174, Kamen, Germany
Tel.: (49) 23 07 94 77 0
Web Site: http://www.vanwezel.de
Automobile Component Distr
N.A.I.C.S.: 423120

Van Wezel NV (1)
Soldatenplein Z2 Industriepark 33, 3300, Tienen, Belgium
Tel.: (32) 16 82 01 01
Web Site: http://www.vanwezel.be
Emp.: 200
Automotive Component Mfr & Distr
N.A.I.C.S.: 336390

UNIPARTS INDIA LIMITED
Gripwel House Block 5 C6 & 7 Vasant Kun, New Delhi, 110070, India
Tel.: (91) 1126137979
Web Site: https://www.unipartsgroup.com
Year Founded: 1994
543689—(BOM)
Rev.: $168,036,824
Assets: $140,756,480
Liabilities: $47,221,629
Net Worth: $93,534,851
Earnings: $23,038,470
Fiscal Year-end: 03/31/22
Hydraulic Components Mfr
N.A.I.C.S.: 333996
Subsidiaries:

Uniparts India GmBH (1)
Reutherstr 3, 53773, Hennef, Germany
Tel.: (49) 2242933940
Automotive Component Mfr & Distr
N.A.I.C.S.: 336390

UNIPHAR PLC
4045 Kingswood Rd Citywest Busi-

UNIPHAR PLC

Uniphar Plc—(Continued)
ness Park, D24 VO6K, Dublin, Ireland
Tel.: (353) 1 428 7777
Web Site: http://www.uniphar.ie
Year Founded: 1967
Healthcare & Pharmacy Services
N.A.I.C.S.: 456110
Maurice Pratt *(Chm)*

Subsidiaries:

Cahill May Roberts Ltd. (1)
Pharmapark Chapelizod, PO Box 601, Dublin, 20, Ireland (100%)
Tel.: (353) 16305555
Web Site: http://www.cmrg.ie
Sales Range: $50-74.9 Million
Emp.: 200
Pharmaceutical Preparations
N.A.I.C.S.: 325412
Donal O'Sullivan *(Dir-Ops)*

Durbin plc (1)
Durbin House Unit 5, Swallowfield Wy Hayes, Middlesex, UB3 1DQ, United Kingdom
Tel.: (44) 2088696500
Web Site: http://www.durbin.co.uk
Pharmaceutical Product Whslr
N.A.I.C.S.: 424210

UNIPLY DECOR LIMITED

309 L/3 The Summit Business Bay, St. Janabai Road, Mumbai, 400 057, Vile Parle East, India
Tel.: (91) 22 2610 0647 In
Web Site:
  http://www.uniplydecor.com
Year Founded: 1996
526957—(BOM)
Plywood Mfr & Whslr
N.A.I.C.S.: 321211
Keshav Kantamneni *(Chm)*

UNIPLY INDUSTRIES LIMITED

No 572 Anna Salai Teynampet, Chennai, 600 018, India
Tel.: (91) 4424362019 In
Web Site: http://www.uniply.in
Year Founded: 1996
Rev.: $72,388,797
Assets: $153,944,270
Liabilities: $60,981,961
Net Worth: $92,962,309
Earnings: $5,664,882
Emp.: 12
Fiscal Year-end: 03/31/19
Plywood Mfr
N.A.I.C.S.: 321211
Raghuram Nath *(Officer-Compliance & Sec)*

Subsidiaries:

Uniply Blaze Private Limited (1)
No 204 Level-2 The Summit Business Bay St Janabai Road, Near Western Express Highway Vile Parle-East, Mumbai, 400 057, India
Tel.: (91) 2226100647
Web Site: http://www.uniplyblaze.com
Internet Services
N.A.I.C.S.: 517810

UNIPOINT CORP.

7F 8F Building D Gwacheon Pentawon 117 Gwacheon-daero, Mapo-gu, Seoul, 121-836, Korea (South)
Tel.: (82) 266765500
Web Site: https://www.unipoint.co.kr
Year Founded: 1996
Computer Programming Services
N.A.I.C.S.: 541511
Eun Young Kwon *(CEO)*

UNIPOL GRUPPO S.P.A.

Via Stalingrado 45, 40128, Bologna, Italy
Tel.: (39) 0515076111
Web Site: https://www.unipol.it IT
UNI—(ITA)
Rev.: $19,017,910,464
Assets: $85,223,473,734
Liabilities: $75,923,484,378
Net Worth: $9,299,989,356
Earnings: $1,216,839,876
Emp.: 12,337
Fiscal Year-end: 12/31/19
Financial Investment Services
N.A.I.C.S.: 551111
Matteo Laterza *(CEO)*

Subsidiaries:

Ambra Property S.r.l (1)
Via del Colle 95, 50041, Calenzano, Florence, Italy
Tel.: (39) 05588881
Web Site: http://www.unawayhotels.it
Home Management Services
N.A.I.C.S.: 721110

Arca Vita S.p.A (1)
Via San Marco 48, Verona, 37138, Italy
Tel.: (39) 0458182111
Web Site: http://www.arcassicura.com
General Insurance Services
N.A.I.C.S.: 524210

Subsidiary (Domestic):

Arca Assicurazioni S.p.A. (2)
Via San Marco 48, 37138, Verona, Italy
Tel.: (39) 0458182111
Web Site: http://www.arcassicura.com
Fire Insurance Services
N.A.I.C.S.: 524113

Compagnia Assicuratrice Linear S.p.A. (1)
Via Larga 8, 40138, Bologna, Italy
Tel.: (39) 0516378111
Web Site: http://www.linear.it
General Insurance Services
N.A.I.C.S.: 524210
Federico Corradini *(Pres)*

Midi S.r.l (1)
Via Stalingrado 45, 40128, Bologna, Italy
Tel.: (39) 0516097111
General Insurance Services
N.A.I.C.S.: 524210

UniSalute S.p.A. (1)
Via Larga 8, 40138, Bologna,
Italy (98.53%)
Tel.: (39) 051 6386111
Web Site: http://www.unisalute.it
Health Insurance Products & Services
N.A.I.C.S.: 524114

Subsidiary (Domestic):

Centri Medici Unisalute S.r.l. (2)
Via Larga 8, 40138, Bologna, Italy
Tel.: (39) 051 6386503
Health Insurance Claims Adjusting Services
N.A.I.C.S.: 524291

UnipolSai Assicurazioni S.p.A. (1)
Via Stalingrado 45, 40128, Bologna,
Italy (63.4%)
Tel.: (39) 0515077111
Web Site: https://www.unipolsai.com
Rev.: $18,326,569,040
Assets: $93,910,370,632
Liabilities: $83,797,288,120
Net Worth: $10,113,082,512
Earnings: $89,907,168
Emp.: 11,881
Fiscal Year-end: 12/31/2021
Holding Company; Insurance, Real Estate Investment & Financial Services
N.A.I.C.S.: 551112
Fabio Cerchiai *(Deputy Chm)*

Subsidiary (Non-US):

Banca Gesfid SA (2)
Via Adamini 10 A, CH-6900, Lugano, Switzerland
Tel.: (41) 919857400
Web Site: http://www.bancagesfid.com
Sales Range: $50-74.9 Million
Emp.: 75
Banking Services
N.A.I.C.S.: 522110

Subsidiary (Domestic):

BancaSAI S.p.A. (2)
Corso Vittorio Emanuele, Turin, Italy
Tel.: (39) 0116915111
Web Site: http://www.bancasai.it
Commercial Bank
N.A.I.C.S.: 522110

SAI Investimenti SGR S.p.A. (2)
Via Carlo Marenco 25, 10126, Turin, Italy
Tel.: (39) 0116657111
Web Site: http://www.saiinvestimenti.it
Investment Management
N.A.I.C.S.: 523999

UNIPRES CORPORATION

Sun Hamada Bldg 5F 1-19-20 Shin-Yokohama, Kohoku-ku, Yokohama, 222-0033, Kanagawa, Japan
Tel.: (81) 454708250
Web Site: https://www.unipres.co.jp
Year Founded: 1945
5949—(TKS)
Rev.: $2,214,872,190
Assets: $2,225,844,790
Liabilities: $1,071,249,650
Net Worth: $1,154,595,140
Earnings: $34,742,160
Emp.: 7,984
Fiscal Year-end: 03/31/24
Automobile Parts Mfr & Whslr
N.A.I.C.S.: 336390
Nobuya Uranishi *(Pres & Pres)*

Subsidiaries:

Dongfeng Unipres Hot Stamping Corporation (1)
Building A-1 77 The West Side of Hua Gang Road, Haudu District, Guangzhou, 510800, Guangdong, China
Tel.: (86) 2036866999
Auto Body Parts Mfr
N.A.I.C.S.: 336211

MA Automotive Brazil Ltd. (1)
Avenida Renato Monteiro 6200 A Tecnopolo 1-Porto Real, Rio de Janeiro, Brazil
Tel.: (55) 2433588077
Auto Body Parts Mfr
N.A.I.C.S.: 336211

PT. Unipres Indonesia (1)
Kawasan Industri Kota Bukit Indah Blok D-IV, Purwakarta, 41183, Jawa Barat, Indonesia
Tel.: (62) 2648371280
Emp.: 150
Automobile Spare Parts Mfr & Distr
N.A.I.C.S.: 336390
Kenji Miura *(Pres)*

San-Esu Co., Ltd. (1)
1200 Okabe, Okabe-cho, Fujieda, 421-1121, Shizuoka, Japan
Tel.: (81) 546673011
Automobile Body Parts Mfr
N.A.I.C.S.: 336370

UM Corporation, SAS (1)
3 Rue Pasteur, BP59, 62118, Biache-Saint-Vaast, France
Tel.: (33) 321608200
Auto Body Parts Mfr
N.A.I.C.S.: 336211

Unipres (China) Corporation (1)
Building C 77 The West Side of Hua Gang Road, Huadu District, Guangzhou, 510800, Guangdong, China
Tel.: (86) 2036867888
Auto Body Parts Mfr
N.A.I.C.S.: 336211

Unipres (Thailand) Co., LTD. (1)
159/18 Serm-Mit Tower 11th Floor Unit 1111 Sukhumvit 21 Asoke Road, Khwaeng Klongtoey Nua Khet Wattana, Bangkok, 10110, Thailand
Tel.: (66) 22617690
Emp.: 27
Automobile Spare Parts Mfr & Distr
N.A.I.C.S.: 336390
Masayuki Hirose *(Pres)*

Unipres (UK) Limited (1)
Cherry Blossom Way, Sunderland, SR5 3NT, United Kingdom
Tel.: (44) 1914182000
Web Site: https://unipres.co.uk

INTERNATIONAL PUBLIC

Automobile Parts Mfr
N.A.I.C.S.: 336390
Gary Graham *(Mng Dir)*

Unipres Alabama, Inc. (1)
990 Duncan Farms Rd, Steele, AL 35987
Tel.: (256) 538-1974
Auto Body Parts Mfr
N.A.I.C.S.: 336211
Sandy Satterfield *(Reg Mgr-HR)*

Unipres Butsuryu Co., Ltd. (1)
3-6-37 Chuo-rinkan-nishi, Yamato, 242-0008, Kanagawa, Japan
Tel.: (81) 462748808
Emp.: 256
Automotive Spare Parts Distr
N.A.I.C.S.: 423120
Tatsuro Kogawa *(Pres)*

Unipres Corporation - Tochigi Plant (1)
7 Matsuyama-cho, Moka, 321-4346, Tochigi, Japan
Tel.: (81) 285837000
Automobile Spare Parts Mfr
N.A.I.C.S.: 336390

Unipres Corporation - Tool & Die Plant (1)
6-1-1 Chuo-rinkan-nishi, Yamato, 242-0008, Kanagawa, Japan
Tel.: (81) 462737632
Machine Tools Mfr
N.A.I.C.S.: 333517

Unipres Europe, SAS (1)
Cherry Blossom Way, Sunderland, SR5 3NT, Tyne & Wear, United Kingdom
Tel.: (44) 1914182030
Emp.: 9
Automotive Spare Parts Distr
N.A.I.C.S.: 423120
Masahide Masuda *(Pres)*

Unipres Guangzhou Corporation (1)
77 The west side of Hua Gang Road, Huadu District, Guangzhou, 510800, Guangdong, China
Tel.: (86) 2036806888
Emp.: 755
Automobile Spare Parts Mfr & Distr
N.A.I.C.S.: 336390
Zhibin Xiong *(Pres)*

Unipres India Private Limited (1)
RNS-6 Sipcot Industrial Growth Centre, Oragadam Vadakupattu Post Sriperumbudur Taluk, Kanchipuram, 603 204, Tamil Nadu, India
Tel.: (91) 4437176000
Emp.: 350
Automobile Spare Parts Mfr & Distr
N.A.I.C.S.: 336390
Takayuki Miura *(Pres)*

Unipres Kyushu Corporation (1)
507 Katsuyama-Matsuda, Miyako-machi, Miyako, 824-0802, Fukuoka, Japan
Tel.: (81) 930324051
Automotive Spare Parts Distr
N.A.I.C.S.: 423120

Unipres Mexicana, S.A. de C.V. (1)
Avenida Japon No 128 Parque Industrial De San Francisco, 20355, San Francisco de los Romo, Aguascalientes, Mexico
Tel.: (52) 4499103000
Emp.: 921
Automobile Spare Parts Mfr & Distr
N.A.I.C.S.: 336390
Toshiaki Takahashi *(Pres)*

Unipres Mold Corporation (1)
2608-73 Nakazato, Fuji, 417-0826, Shizuoka, Japan
Tel.: (81) 545322098
Emp.: 113
Automobile Spare Parts Mfr
N.A.I.C.S.: 336390
Nobuaki Takagi *(Pres)*

Unipres North America, Inc. (1)
575 Sage Rd N Ste 200, White House, TN 37188
Tel.: (615) 745-5800
Emp.: 33
Automotive Spare Parts Distr
N.A.I.C.S.: 423120
Tetsuo Uotsu *(Pres)*

AND PRIVATE COMPANIES

Unipres Precision Corporation (1)
2608-25 Nakazato, Fuji, 419-0021, Shizuoka, Japan
Tel.: (81) 545322125
Emp.: 209
Automobile Spare Parts Mfr
N.A.I.C.S.: 336390

Unipres Precision Guangzhou Corporation
Building A 77 The West Side of Hua Gang Road, Huadu District, Guangzhou, 510800, Guangdong, China
Tel.: (86) 2036866668
Auto Body Parts Mfr
N.A.I.C.S.: 336211

Unipres R & D Co., Ltd.
LIVMO Rising Building 3-19-1 Shin-Yokohama, Kohoku-ku, Yokohama, 222-0033, Kanagawa, Japan
Tel.: (81) 454759256
Emp.: 356
Automobile Spare Parts Mfr & Distr
N.A.I.C.S.: 336390
Masanobu Yoshizawa *(Pres)*

Unipres Service Corporation (1)
19-1 Aoba-cho, Fuji, 416-8510, Shizuoka, Japan
Tel.: (81) 545632780
Emp.: 22
Real Estate Development Services
N.A.I.C.S.: 531210
Yoshio Ito *(Pres)*

Unipres Southeast U.S.A., Inc. (1)
1001 Fountain Dr, Forest, MS 39074
Tel.: (601) 469-0234
Emp.: 146
Automobile Spare Parts Mfr & Distr
N.A.I.C.S.: 336390
Kevin R. Logan *(Pres)*

Unipres Sunrise Corporation (1)
No 178 Haiming Road The Free Trade Zone, Dalian, 116600, China
Tel.: (86) 41139274061
Auto Body Parts Mfr
N.A.I.C.S.: 336211

Unipres U.S.A., Inc. (1)
201 Kirby Dr, Portland, TN 37148
Tel.: (615) 325-7311
Emp.: 975
Automobile Spare Parts Mfr & Distr
N.A.I.C.S.: 336390
Takeo Sato *(Pres)*

Unipres Wuhan Corporation (1)
No 1 Jiukang Avenue Changfu Industrial Park, Caidian, Wuhan, 430100, China
Tel.: (86) 2783337888
Car Body Press Part Development Services
N.A.I.C.S.: 811121

Unipres Zhengzhou Corporation (1)
No 10 of No 21st Street Zhengzhou, Economic and Technological Development Zone, Henan, 450016, China
Tel.: (86) 37155006888
Emp.: 209
Automobile Spare Parts Mfr & Distr
N.A.I.C.S.: 336390
Kazushi Sakuma *(Pres)*

Yamakawa Transportations Co., Ltd. (1)
218-8 Tadehara, Fuji, 416-0931, Shizuoka, Japan
Tel.: (81) 545610486
Freight & Cargo Services
N.A.I.C.S.: 541614

UNIPRO TECHNOLOGIES LIMITED
503B Maheswari Chambers Somajiguda, Hyderabad, 500 034, India
Tel.: (91) 9494351116
Web Site: http://www.uniproltd.com
Rev.: $487,565
Assets: $1,125,029
Liabilities: $565,555
Net Worth: $559,474
Earnings: $30,804
Emp.: 2
Fiscal Year-end: 03/31/17
Website Development Services
N.A.I.C.S.: 541511

UNIPROF REAL ESTATE HOLDING AG
Zettachring 10, Stuttgart, 70567, Germany
Tel.: (49) 711900620
UPR—(DEU)
Sales Range: Less than $1 Million
Holding Company
N.A.I.C.S.: 551112
Oliver Heller *(Chm-Mgmt Bd & CEO)*

UNIPROM A.D.
Stevana Nemanje 14, Novi Pazar, Serbia
Tel.: (381) 20 337 040
Year Founded: 1997
UNPR—(BEL)
Sales Range: Less than $1 Million
Emp.: 33
Food Product Retailer
N.A.I.C.S.: 445298
Dzafer Hajrovic *(Exec Dir)*

UNIPROMET D.D.
Bulevar Oslobodilaca 92A, 32000, Cacak, Serbia
Tel.: (381) 32357040
Web Site: http://www.unipromet.co.rs
Year Founded: 1990
Metal Road Restraint Systems Mfr
N.A.I.C.S.: 332999
Dejan Ciric *(Exec Dir-Legal & HR)*

Subsidiaries:

MS & Wood d.d. Sarajevo (1)
Dzemala Bijedica 160, 71000, Sarajevo, Bosnia & Herzegovina (67%)
Tel.: (387) 33 775 100
Web Site: http://www.mswood.ba
Rev.: $12,035,170
Assets: $30,719,823
Liabilities: $20,915,095
Net Worth: $9,804,728
Earnings: $55,027
Emp.: 302
Fiscal Year-end: 12/31/2017
Steel Pole Mfr
N.A.I.C.S.: 331222

UNIPULSE CORPORATION
9-11 Nihonbashi Hisamatsucho, Chuo-ku, Tokyo, 103-0005, Japan
Tel.: (81) 3 3639 6120
Web Site: http://www.unipulse.com
Year Founded: 1970
Sales Range: $50-74.9 Million
Emp.: 150
Electronic Device Mfr & Whslr
N.A.I.C.S.: 334419
Takami Yoshimoto *(Pres & Gen Mgr-Technical)*

Subsidiaries:

Shoei Densetsu Corporarion (1)
116-5 Kobuke-cho, Inage-ku, Chiba, 263-0003, Japan
Tel.: (81) 434217550
Electronic Devices Mfr & Distr
N.A.I.C.S.: 334413

Unipulse Asia Pacific Pte. Ltd. (1)
1 Kaki Bukit Ave 3 10-10 KB-1 Bldg, Singapore, 416 087, Singapore
Tel.: (65) 68445951
Electronic Device Distr
N.A.I.C.S.: 423620
Medhi Koh *(Mgr-Sls)*

Unipulse Instruments Pvt. Ltd. (1)
Level 9 Spaze I-Tech Park A1 Tower Sector - 49 Sohna Road, Gurgaon, 122018, India
Tel.: (91) 1246769140
Electronic Device Distr
N.A.I.C.S.: 423620
Chander Sethi *(CEO)*

Unipulse Instruments Thailand Co., Ltd. (1)
118/152 153 M 6 T Donhuaroh, Amphur Muang, 20000, Chonburi, Thailand
Tel.: (66) 38110038
Electronic Device Distr
N.A.I.C.S.: 423620

Unipulse Trading (Wuxi) Co., Ltd. (1)
Rm 25-DE DongFang GuangChang A Bldg No 343 ZhongShan-Road, Wuxi, 214001, JiangSu, China
Tel.: (86) 51082720324
Electronic Device Distr
N.A.I.C.S.: 423620

UNIQA INSURANCE GROUP AG
Untere Donaustrase 21, A-1029, Vienna, Austria
Tel.: (43) 50677670 AT
Web Site: https://www.uniqagroup.com
Year Founded: 1811
UQA—(VIE)
Rev.: $6,699,169,005
Assets: $30,429,692,424
Liabilities: $28,214,726,959
Net Worth: $2,214,965,465
Earnings: $413,347,723
Emp.: 21,200
Fiscal Year-end: 12/31/22
Insurance Holding Company
N.A.I.C.S.: 551112
Walter Rothensteiner *(Chm-Supervisory Bd)*

Subsidiaries:

AUSTRIA Hotels Liegenschaftsbesitz AG (1)
Hebgasse 7, Vienna, 1010, Austria
Tel.: (43) 1316650
Web Site: http://www.gerstner.at
Sales Range: $50-74.9 Million
Emp.: 50
Home Management Services
N.A.I.C.S.: 721110

AVE-PLAZA LLC (1)
Sumskaya str 10, Kharkivs'ka oblast, 61000, Kharkiv, Ukraine
Tel.: (380) 577544034
Web Site: https://www.aveplaza.com.ua
Shopping Mall Management Services
N.A.I.C.S.: 812990

Agenta Risiko- und Finanzierungsberatung Gesellschaft m.b.H. (1)
Untere Donaustrasse 47, 1020, Vienna, Austria
Tel.: (43) 15331323
Sales Range: $50-74.9 Million
Emp.: 1
General Insurance Services
N.A.I.C.S.: 524210

Agenta-Consulting Kft. (1)
Konyves Kalman krt 11 C Epulet 7 Emelet, 1097, Budapest, Hungary
Tel.: (36) 1 236 3400
Web Site: http://www.agenta.hu
Sales Range: $100-124.9 Million
Emp.: 7
Insurance Brokerage Services
N.A.I.C.S.: 524210

Allfinanz Versicherungs- und Finanzservice GmbH (1)
Untere Donaustrasse 21, Vienna, 1029, Austria
Tel.: (43) 121175
General Insurance Services
N.A.I.C.S.: 524210

Ambulatorien Betriebsgesellschaft m.b.H. (1)
Heiligenstadter Strabe 46-48/10, Vienna, 1190, Austria
Tel.: (43) 1360665000
Sales Range: $10-24.9 Million
Emp.: 5
Hospital & Medical Services
N.A.I.C.S.: 622110
Christian Kainz *(Dir-Medical)*

Austria Hotels Betriebs CZ s.r.o. (1)
Kralodvorska 4, 110 00, Prague, Czech Republic
Tel.: (420) 234 608 111
Web Site: http://www.granthotelbohemia.cz
Home Management Services
N.A.I.C.S.: 721110
Gerd Wessels *(Gen Mgr)*

Austria Hotels Liegenschaftsbesitz CZ s.r.o. (1)
Kralodvorska 4, 110 00, Prague, Czech Republic
Tel.: (420) 542518111
Home Management Services
N.A.I.C.S.: 721110

CALL DIRECT Versicherungen AG (1)
Untere Donaustrasse 21, 1029, Vienna, Austria (100%)
Tel.: (43) 1211092858
Web Site: http://www.calldirect.at
Sales Range: $50-74.9 Million
Emp.: 30
Life & Health Insurance Carrier
N.A.I.C.S.: 524113
Andreas Brandsdesdder *(CEO)*

Dekra Expert Muszaki Szakertoi Kft. (1)
Robert Karoly Krt 70-74, 1134, Budapest, Hungary
Tel.: (36) 1 453 6100
Web Site: http://www.dekra.hu
Automotive Repair & Maintenance Services
N.A.I.C.S.: 811198

Dr. E. Hackhofer EDV-Softwareberatung Gesellschaft m.b.H. (1)
Schrankgasse 16 A, 1070, Vienna, Austria
Tel.: (43) 1 403 10 94
Web Site: http://www.hackhofer.at
Sales Range: $25-49.9 Million
Insurance Software Development Services
N.A.I.C.S.: 541511
Erich Hackhofer *(Founder & Mng Dir)*

FL-Vertriebs- und Service GmbH (1)
Innsbrucker Bundesstrabe 136, 5020, Salzburg, Austria
Tel.: (43) 66222528120
Web Site: http://www.fl-service.de
Emp.: 3
Investment Management Service
N.A.I.C.S.: 523999
Juan Mattl *(Gen Mgr)*

FinanceLife Lebensversicherung AG (1)
Untere Donaustrasse 21, A 1029, Vienna, Austria
Tel.: (43) 121454010
Web Site: http://www.financelife.com
Sales Range: $50-74.9 Million
Emp.: 50
Life Insurance Carrier
N.A.I.C.S.: 524113

GSM Gesellschaft fur Service Management mbH (1)
Johannes-Brahms-Platz 1, 20355, Hamburg, Germany
Tel.: (49) 40 309 678 0
Web Site: http://www.gsm-hh.de
Sales Range: $50-74.9 Million
Emp.: 4
General Insurance Services
N.A.I.C.S.: 524210

Insdata spol s.r.o. (1)
Palarikova 3, 949 01, Nitra, Slovakia
Tel.: (421) 37 7760 100
Web Site: http://www.insdata.sk
Sales Range: $75-99.9 Million
Emp.: 40
Insurance Software Development Services
N.A.I.C.S.: 541511
Reinhard Bock *(Head-Cross-Border Svc Section)*

Insurance company UNIQA (1)
Tel.: (380) 442256000
Web Site: https://uniqa.ua
Insurance Services
N.A.I.C.S.: 524210
Uljee Elena Vladimirovna *(CEO)*

MV Augustaanlage GmbH & Co. KG (1)
Augustaanlage 66, Mannheim, 68165, Germany

UNIQA INSURANCE GROUP AG

UNIQA Insurance Group AG—(Continued)
Tel.: (49) 18022024
Insurance Services
N.A.I.C.S.: 524210

Mamax Lebensversicherung AG (1)
Augustaanlage 66, 68165, Mannheim, Germany
Tel.: (49) 6214574995
Web Site: http://www.mamax.com
Life Insurance Carrier
N.A.I.C.S.: 524113

Mannheimer Service und Vermogensverwaltungs GmbH (1)
Augustaanlage 66, 68165, Mannheim, Germany
Tel.: (49) 6 21 4 57 80 00
General Insurance Services
N.A.I.C.S.: 524210

Passauerhof Betriebs-Ges.m.b.H. (1)
Hessgasse 7, Vienna, 1190, Austria
Tel.: (43) 13206345
Emp.: 25
Real Estate Manangement Services
N.A.I.C.S.: 531390
Oliver Braun *(Owner & Gen Mgr)*

Praterstrasse Eins Hotelbetriebs GmbH (1)
Praterstrasse 1 1020 Wien, Vienna, 1029, Austria
Tel.: (43) 1906160
Web Site: http://www.sofitel-vienna-stephansdom.com
Sales Range: $25-49.9 Million
Emp.: 200
Home Management Services
N.A.I.C.S.: 721110

PremiQaMed Holding GmbH (1)
Tel.: (43) 5862840
Web Site: https://www.premiqamed.at
Health Care Services
N.A.I.C.S.: 621999
Martin Fuchs *(Chm)*

PremiQaMed Management GmbH (1)
Heiligenstadter Strabe 46-48, 1190, Vienna, Austria
Tel.: (43) 158628400
Web Site: http://www.premiqamed.com
Emp.: 1,200
Hospital Management Services
N.A.I.C.S.: 622110

PremiaFIT Facility und IT Management u. Service GmbH (1)
Heiligenstadter Strasse 46-48, 1190, Vienna, Austria
Tel.: (43) 720333100
Web Site: http://www.premiafit.at
Information Technology Services
N.A.I.C.S.: 519290

PremiaFIT GmbH (1)
Rothschildplatz 4/6 Stock, 1020, Vienna, Austria
Tel.: (43) 720333100
Information Technology Services
N.A.I.C.S.: 541519

Privatklinik Dobling GmbH (1)
Heiligenstadter Strasse 57-63, Vienna, Austria
Tel.: (43) 1 360 66 0
Web Site: http://www.privatklinik-doebling.at
Hospital Management Services
N.A.I.C.S.: 622110

Privatklinik Graz Ragnitz GmbH (1)
Berthold-Linder-Weg 15, 8047, Graz, Austria
Tel.: (43) 316 596 0
Web Site: http://www.privatklinik-graz-ragnitz.at
Hospital Management Services
N.A.I.C.S.: 622110
Michael Hessinger *(Dir-Medical)*

Privatklinik Josefstadt GmbH (1)
Skodagasse 32, Vienna, 1180, Austria
Tel.: (43) 1 401 14 0
Web Site: http://www.confraternitaet.at
Hospital Operation Services
N.A.I.C.S.: 622110

Privatklinik Wehrle GmbH (1)
Haydnstrasse 18, Salzburg, 5020, Austria
Tel.: (43) 662 90509 0
Web Site: http://www.pkwd.at
Emp.: 100
Medical & Surgical Hospital Services
N.A.I.C.S.: 622110

RSG - Risiko Service und Sachverstandigen GmbH (1)
Untere Donaustrabe 21, Vienna, 1029, Austria
Tel.: (43) 121600523590
Web Site: http://www.rsg.at
Insurance Brokerage Services
N.A.I.C.S.: 524210
Leopold Kramer *(Gen Mgr)*

Raiffeisen Life Insurance Company LLC (1)
1st Nagatinskiy Proezd 10 Bld 1, 115230, Moscow, Russia (75%)
Tel.: (7) 4957717118
Web Site: http://www.raiffeisen-life.ru
Emp.: 5
Insurance Services
N.A.I.C.S.: 524210
Maxim Chumachenko *(Gen Mgr)*

Raiffeisen Versicherung AG (1)
Untere Donaustrabe 21, 1029, Vienna, Austria
Tel.: (43) 12025588
Web Site: http://www.raiffeisen-versicherung.at
Sales Range: $200-249.9 Million
Emp.: 500
General Insurance Services
N.A.I.C.S.: 524126

Real Versicherungs-Makler GmbH (1)
Untere Donaustrabe 47, 1020, Vienna, Austria
Tel.: (43) 1 269 73 63
Insurance Brokerage Services
N.A.I.C.S.: 524210

SIGAL LIFE UNIQA Group AUSTRIA Sh.A. (1)
Tel.: (355) 42233308
Web Site: http://www.sigal.com.al
General Insurance Services
N.A.I.C.S.: 524210

SIGAL UNIQA Group AUSTRIA Sh.A. (1)
Tel.: (355) 42233308
Web Site: http://sigal.com.al
Insurance Management Services
N.A.I.C.S.: 524298
Avni Ponari *(CEO)*

SIGAL UNIQA Group AUSTRIA, Rr. (1)
Str Vaso Pasha p n Pejton, 10000, Pristina, Kosovo, Serbia
Tel.: (381) 38 240 241
Sales Range: $50-74.9 Million
Emp.: 10
Insurance Brokerage Services
N.A.I.C.S.: 524210
Sofo Limaj *(Gen Mgr)*

Salzburger Landes-Versicherung AG (1)
Auerspergstrasse 9, A 5021, Salzburg, Austria (100%)
Tel.: (43) 66286890
Web Site: http://www.salzburger.biz
Emp.: 300
Property & Casualty Insurance Carrier
N.A.I.C.S.: 524126
Reinhold Kelderer *(Mng Dir)*

UNIQA A.D. Skopje (1)
Boulevard VMRO 3, 1000, Skopje, North Macedonia
Tel.: (389) 2 3125 920
Sales Range: $100-124.9 Million
Emp.: 18
Insurance Services
N.A.I.C.S.: 524210
Saimir Dhamo *(CEO)*

UNIQA Alternative Investments GmbH (1)
Untere Donaustrabe 21, Vienna, 1020, Austria

Tel.: (43) 1213620
Investment Management Service
N.A.I.C.S.: 523999

UNIQA Asigurari S.A. (1)
Str Nicolae Caramfil nr 25 parter sector 1, Bucharest, Romania
Tel.: (40) 212120882
Web Site: https://www.uniqa.ro
Insurance Services
N.A.I.C.S.: 524210

UNIQA Asigurari de viata (1)
Str Nicolae Caramfil no 25 floor 5 sector 1, Bucharest, Romania
Tel.: (40) 213137993
Web Site: https://www.uniqa.ro
Fire Insurance Services
N.A.I.C.S.: 524210
Radu Bragarea *(VP)*

UNIQA Assurances S.A. (1)
Rue Des Eaux-Vives 94, 1207, Geneva, Switzerland
Tel.: (41) 227186300
Web Site: http://www.uniqa.ch
Sales Range: $50-74.9 Million
Emp.: 15
Health Insurance Carrier
N.A.I.C.S.: 524114
Nadine Burcher Grainville *(Mng Dir)*

UNIQA Beteiligungs-Holding GmbH (1)
Untere Donaustrabe 21, Vienna, 1029, Austria
Tel.: (43) 1211750
Investment Management Service
N.A.I.C.S.: 523999

UNIQA Biztosito Zrt. (1)
Robert Karoly krt 70-74, H-1134, Budapest, Hungary
Tel.: (36) 15445555
Web Site: https://www.uniqa.hu
Property, Life & Health Insurance Carrier
N.A.I.C.S.: 524210
Krisztian Kurtisz *(CEO & Member-Mgmt Bd)*

UNIQA Erwerb von Beteiligungen Gesellschaft m.b.H. (1)
Untere Donaustrabe 21, Vienna, 1029, Austria
Tel.: (43) 1211750
Investment Management Service
N.A.I.C.S.: 523999

UNIQA Finanz-Service GmbH (1)
Untere Donaustrabe 21, Vienna, 1020, Austria
Tel.: (43) 1211750
Management Consulting Services
N.A.I.C.S.: 541618

UNIQA GlobalCare SA (1)
Tel.: (41) 227186300
Web Site: https://www.uniqa.ch
Insurance Services
N.A.I.C.S.: 524210

UNIQA Immobilien-Service GmbH (1)
Untere Donaustrabe 21, Vienna, 1029, Austria
Tel.: (43) 1 214 24 22
Real Estate Manangement Services
N.A.I.C.S.: 531390

UNIQA Insurance plc (1)
18 Todor Alexandrov Blvd, 1000, Sofia, Bulgaria (62.5%)
Tel.: (359) 70011150
Web Site: https://www.uniqa.bg
Sales Range: $200-249.9 Million
Emp.: 350
Property & Casualty Insurance Products & Services
N.A.I.C.S.: 524126

UNIQA International Versicherungs-Holding GmbH (1)
Untere Donaustr 47, 1020, Vienna, Austria
Tel.: (43) 1211750
Web Site: http://www.uniqa.at
Investment Management Service
N.A.I.C.S.: 523999

UNIQA Lebensversicherung AG (1)
Austrasse 46, Vaduz, 9490, Liechtenstein
Tel.: (423) 2375010
Web Site: http://www.uniqa.li

INTERNATIONAL PUBLIC

Emp.: 10
Life Insurance Products & Services
N.A.I.C.S.: 524113

UNIQA Life Insurance Company (1)
70-A Saksaganskogo Street, 01601, Kiev, Ukraine
Tel.: (380) 442256000
Web Site: http://www.uniqa.ua
Health, Property & Casualty Insurance Carrier
N.A.I.C.S.: 524114
Vladimir Simonchuk *(CEO & Member-Mgmt Bd)*

UNIQA Life Insurance plc (1)
(99.7%)
Tel.: (359) 885011150
Web Site: https://www.uniqa.bg
Emp.: 269
Life Insurance Carrier
N.A.I.C.S.: 524113
Dimitar Tonev *(Member-Mgmt Bd)*

UNIQA Life Private Joint Stock Company (1)
Tel.: (380) 971700373
Web Site: https://uniqa.ua
Insurance Services
N.A.I.C.S.: 524210
Teymur Bagirov *(Chm)*

UNIQA Life ad-Skopje (1)
Tel.: (389) 23288820
Web Site: https://uniqa.mk
Insurance Agency Services
N.A.I.C.S.: 524210

UNIQA Nezivotno Osiguranje A.D. (1)
Bulevar Dzordza Vasingtona 98/4, 81000, Podgorica, Montenegro
Tel.: (382) 20444700
Web Site: https://www.uniqa.me
Emp.: 108
Insurance Services
N.A.I.C.S.: 524210

UNIQA Osiguranje d.d. (1)
Obala Kulina Bana 19, 71000, Sarajevo, Bosnia & Herzegovina
Tel.: (387) 33289000
Web Site: https://www.uniqa.ba
Emp.: 228
Life, Health & General Insurance Services
N.A.I.C.S.: 524113

UNIQA Osterreich Versicherungen AG (1)
Untere Donaustrasse 21, 1029, Vienna, Austria (100%)
Tel.: (43) 50677670
Web Site: https://www.uniqa.at
Insurance Management Services
N.A.I.C.S.: 524210
Kurt Svoboda *(CEO, CFO, Chief Risk Officer & Member-Mgmt Bd)*

UNIQA Personenversicherung AG (1)
Untere Donaustrasse 21, 1029, Vienna, Austria (63.4%)
Tel.: (43) 50677670
Web Site: http://www.uniqa.at
Sales Range: $700-749.9 Million
Emp.: 1,600
Health Insurance Services
N.A.I.C.S.: 524114

UNIQA Raiffeisen Software Service Kft. (1)
Tel.: (36) 17665100
Web Site: https://urss.hu
Insurance Services
N.A.I.C.S.: 524210

UNIQA Raiffeisen Software Service S.R.L. (1)
Tel.: (40) 742084897
Web Site: https://www.uniqasoftware.ro
Sales Range: $25-49.9 Million
Emp.: 90
Software Consulting & Development Services
N.A.I.C.S.: 513210

UNIQA Re AG (1)
Tel.: (41) 433444130
Web Site: https://www.uniqa.com

AND PRIVATE COMPANIES

Sales Range: $50-74.9 Million
Emp.: 18
Property, Casualty & Reinsurance Carrier
N.A.I.C.S.: 524130
Ivana Stark *(CEO)*

UNIQA Real Estate AG (1)
Untere Donaustrasse 21, 1029, Vienna, Austria
Tel.: (43) 121241710
Web Site: http://www.uniqa-realestate.at
Sales Range: $25-49.9 Million
Emp.: 40
Real Estate Manangement Services
N.A.I.C.S.: 531390
Christein Traunsellner *(Gen Mgr)*

UNIQA Real Estate BH nekretnine, d.o.o. (1)
Obala Kulina Bana 19, Sarajevo, 71000, Bosnia & Herzegovina
Tel.: (387) 33557711
Real Estate Development Services
N.A.I.C.S.: 531390

UNIQA Real Estate Dritte Beteiligungsverwaltung GmbH (1)
Untere Donaustrabe 25, 1029, Vienna, Austria
Tel.: (43) 1 212 41 71
Web Site: http://www.rem.at
Emp.: 59
Real Estate Development Services
N.A.I.C.S.: 531390
Ernst Kirisits *(Mgr)*

UNIQA Real Estate Holding GmbH (1)
Untere Donaustrabe 21, Vienna, 1029, Austria
Tel.: (43) 1 212 41 71
Emp.: 10
Investment Management Service
N.A.I.C.S.: 523999

UNIQA Real Estate Management GmbH (1)
Untere Donaustrasse 47/B09, 1029, Vienna, Austria
Tel.: (43) 12142422
Web Site: https://www.uniqa-rem.at
Insurance Services
N.A.I.C.S.: 524210

UNIQA Real Estate Vierte Beteiligungsverwaltung GmbH (1)
Untere Donaustrasse 21, 1020, Vienna, Austria
Tel.: (43) 12124171
Sales Range: $50-74.9 Million
Emp.: 2
Real Estate Manangement Services
N.A.I.C.S.: 531390

UNIQA Sachversicherung AG (1)
Untere Donaustrasse 21, 1029, Vienna, Austria
Tel.: (43) 50677670
Web Site: http://www.uniqa.at
Sales Range: $700-749.9 Million
Emp.: 1,200
Personal Property Insurers
N.A.I.C.S.: 524126

UNIQA Software Service Bulgaria OOD (1)
R-N Tsentralen 55 Str Slavyanska, Plovdiv, 4000, Bulgaria
Tel.: (359) 32626291
Software Development Services
N.A.I.C.S.: 541511

UNIQA Software Service Kft. (1)
Szep strasse utca 2, 1134, Budapest, Hungary
Tel.: (36) 1 7665 100
Web Site: http://www.uss.hu
Sales Range: $25-49.9 Million
Emp.: 65
Information Technology Services
N.A.I.C.S.: 519290
Michael Girke *(Co-Mng Dir)*

UNIQA Software Service d.o.o. (1)
Savska Cesta 41, Zagreb, Croatia
Tel.: (385) 16178887
Computer Programming Services
N.A.I.C.S.: 541511

UNIQA Software-Service GmbH (1)

Untere Donaustrabe 21, Vienna, 1029, Austria
Tel.: (43) 121366
Web Site: http://www.uniqa.com
Emp.: 2,500
Information Technology Consulting Services
N.A.I.C.S.: 541618
Alexander Bockelmann *(Mng Dir)*

UNIQA TA na Zycie S.A. (1)
ul Gdanska 132, 90-520, Lodz, Poland
Tel.: (48) 426666500
Web Site: http://www.uniqa.pl
Life Insurance Carrier
N.A.I.C.S.: 524113

UNIQA TU S.A. (1)
ul Gdanska 132, 90-520, Lodz, Poland
Tel.: (48) 426666500
Web Site: http://www.uniqa.pl
Sales Range: $100-124.9 Million
Emp.: 200
Property Insurance Carrier
N.A.I.C.S.: 524126

Subsidiary (Domestic):

TU Filar S.A. (2)
ul. Zubrow 3, 71617, Szczecin, Poland (90%)
Tel.: (48) 914254510
Web Site: http://www.filar.pl
Insurance Sales & Claims Management
N.A.I.C.S.: 524210

UNIQA Ventures GmbH (1)
Untere Donaustrasse 21, 1029, Vienna, Austria
Tel.: (43) 50677670
Web Site: https://www.uniqaventures.com
Venture Capital Services
N.A.I.C.S.: 523999

UNIQA Versicherung AG (1)
Austrasse 46, LI - 9490, Vaduz, Liechtenstein
Tel.: (423) 2375011
Web Site: http://www.uniqa.li
Sales Range: $50-74.9 Million
Emp.: 10
Property & Casualty Insurance Carrier
N.A.I.C.S.: 524126
Carsten Abraham *(CFO)*

UNIQA a.d.o. (1)
Milutina Milankovica 134 G, SRB-11070, Belgrade, Serbia
Tel.: (381) 112024100
Life Insurance Carrier
N.A.I.C.S.: 524113

Subsidiary (Domestic):

Basler osiguranja - Serbia (2)
Resavska 29, 11 000, Belgrade, Serbia
Tel.: (381) 113247716
Web Site: http://www.basler.rs
Sales Range: $50-74.9 Million
Emp.: 442
Insurance Products & Services
N.A.I.C.S.: 524298

Subsidiary (Domestic):

Nezivotno osiguranje Basler a.d.o. (3)
Resavska 29, 11000, Belgrade, Serbia
Tel.: (381) 11 2222 800
Web Site: http://www.basler.rs
Sales Range: $50-74.9 Million
Emp.: 10
Non-Life Insurance Products & Services
N.A.I.C.S.: 524298
Vladimir Radic *(Gen Mgr)*

UNIQA investicni spolecnost, a.s. (1)
Evropska 136, 160 12, Prague, Czech Republic
Tel.: (420) 225393111
Insurance Services
N.A.I.C.S.: 524210

UNIQA nezivotno osiguranje a.d.o. (1)
Milutina Milankovica 134 G, 11070, Belgrade, Serbia
Tel.: (381) 112024100
Web Site: https://www.uniqa.rs
Sales Range: $50-74.9 Million
Emp.: 568
General Insurance Services

N.A.I.C.S.: 524210

UNIQA osiguranje d.d. (1)
Tel.: (385) 16324200
Web Site: https://www.uniqa.hr
Emp.: 503
Property & Casualty Insurance Carrier
N.A.I.C.S.: 524126

Subsidiary (Domestic):

Basler osiguranje Zagreb d.d (2)
Radnicka Cesta 37b, 10000, Zagreb, Croatia
Tel.: (385) 1 640 5000
Sales Range: $350-399.9 Million
Emp.: 500
Insurance Products & Services
N.A.I.C.S.: 524298
Ralph Peterson *(Gen Mgr)*

UNIQA poistovna a.s. (1)
Krasovskeho 15, PO Box 232, 850 00, Bratislava, Slovakia
Tel.: (421) 232600100
Web Site: http://www.uniqa.sk
Property, Casualty & Life Insurance Carrier
N.A.I.C.S.: 524113
Martin Zacek *(Chm & CEO)*

UNIQA pojistovna a.s. (1)
Evropska 136, CZ - 160 12, Prague, 6, Czech Republic
Tel.: (420) 488125125
Web Site: https://www.uniqa.cz
Emp.: 919
Property & Casualty Insurance Carrier
N.A.I.C.S.: 524126

UNIQA poslovni centar Korzo d.o.o. (1)
Korzo 11, Rijeka, 51000, Croatia
Tel.: (385) 51580999
Insurance Management Services
N.A.I.C.S.: 524210
Zoran Visnjic *(Mgr-Property)*

UNIQA zivotno osiguranje a.d. (1)
Tel.: (381) 112024100
Sales Range: $50-74.9 Million
Fire Insurance Services
N.A.I.C.S.: 524126
Gordana Bukumiric *(CEO)*

UNIQA zivotno osiguranje a.d. (1)
Tel.: (382) 20444700
Web Site: http://www.uniqa.me
Sales Range: $100-124.9 Million
Fire Insurance Services
N.A.I.C.S.: 524126
Gordana Bukumiric *(Chm)*

Versicherungsagentur Wilhelm Steiner GmbH (1)
Liechtenwerder Platz 4, 1190, Vienna, Austria
Tel.: (43) 13 693 4340
Insurance Management Services
N.A.I.C.S.: 524210

Versicherungsmarkt-Servicegesellschaft m.b.H. (1)
Untere Donaustrasse 47, 1020, Vienna, Austria
Tel.: (43) 1599630
Web Site: https://www.vms.at
Automobile Insurance Services
N.A.I.C.S.: 524126

Wehring & Wolfes GmbH (1)
Kurze Muhren 6, 20095, Hamburg, Germany
Tel.: (49) 40 87 97 96 95
Web Site: http://www.wehring-wolfes.de
Sales Range: $50-74.9 Million
Emp.: 40
Yacht & Boat Insurance Services
N.A.I.C.S.: 524210

UNIQUE BROADBAND SYSTEMS LTD.
400 Spinnaker Way Unit 1-10, Vaughan, L4K 5Y9, ON, Canada
Tel.: (905) 669-8533 ON
Web Site: http://www.uniquesys.com
Year Founded: 1990
Rev.: $14,869,630
Emp.: 85

UNIQUE ORGANICS LIMITED

Wireless Fixed, Mobile Digital Television & Radio Broadcasting Services
N.A.I.C.S.: 334220
David Dane *(Pres & CEO)*

UNIQUE ENGINEERING AND CONSTRUCTION PUBLIC COMPANY LIMITED
200 Jasmine International Tower 15th Floor Moo 4 Changwattana Rd, Pak Kret, Nonthaburi, 11120, Thailand
Tel.: (66) 25821888
Web Site: https://www.unique.co.th
Year Founded: 1994
UNIQ—(THA)
Rev.: $304,276,953
Assets: $1,330,295,004
Liabilities: $1,089,719,017
Net Worth: $240,575,987
Earnings: $3,708,548
Fiscal Year-end: 12/31/23
Construction Services
N.A.I.C.S.: 236210
Prasong Suvivattanachai *(Chm & CEO)*

UNIQUE FIRE HOLDINGS BERHAD
9 Jalan Anggerik Mokara 3155 Kota Kemuning, 40460, Shah Alam, Selangor, Malaysia
Tel.: (60) 351311226
Web Site: https://www.uniquefire.com
Year Founded: 1997
UNIQUE—(KLS)
Rev.: $22,155,385
Assets: $21,804,057
Liabilities: $4,249,209
Net Worth: $17,554,848
Earnings: $1,721,226
Emp.: 178
Fiscal Year-end: 03/31/24
Holding Company
N.A.I.C.S.: 551112
Sze Min Yeow *(Sec)*

UNIQUE FURNITURE A/S
Petersbjerggard 10 1 th, 6000, Kolding, Denmark
Tel.: (45) 7027 6799 DK
Web Site: http://www.uniquefurniture.dk
Furniture Mfr
N.A.I.C.S.: 423210

Subsidiaries:

Jesper Office, LLC (1)
745 Route 202/206 S Ste 300, Bridgewater, NJ 08807
Tel.: (908) 218-4200
Web Site: http://www.jesperoffice.com
Sales Range: $1-9.9 Million
Emp.: 20
Furniture Merchant Whslr
N.A.I.C.S.: 423210
Torben Corneliussen *(Mgr-Sls-Natl)*

UNIQUE HOTEL & RESORTS LIMITED
Borak Mehnur Level-13 51/B Kemal Ataturk Avenue, Banani, Dhaka, 1213, Bangladesh
Tel.: (880) 29885116
Web Site: https://www.uhrlbd.com
UNIQUEHRL—(CHT)
Rev.: $27,171,666
Assets: $405,824,336
Liabilities: $164,597,150
Net Worth: $241,227,186
Earnings: $17,842,131
Emp.: 687
Fiscal Year-end: 06/30/23
Hotel Operator
N.A.I.C.S.: 721110
Mohammed Noor Ali *(Mng Dir)*

UNIQUE ORGANICS LIMITED

UNIQUE ORGANICS LIMITED

Unique Organics Limited—(Continued)
E-521 Sitapura Industrial Area,
Jaipur, 302 022, Rajasthan, India
Tel.: (91) 1412770315
Web Site:
  https://www.uniqueorganics.com
Year Founded: 1993
530997—(BOM)
Rev.: $22,220,381
Assets: $3,784,638
Liabilities: $1,841,233
Net Worth: $1,943,405
Earnings: $458,933
Emp.: 34
Fiscal Year-end: 03/31/23
Animal Feed Mfr & Distr
N.A.I.C.S.: 311119
Jyoti Prakash Kanodia *(Mng Dir)*

UNIQUEST CORPORATION
Uniquest Building 314 Hwangsaeul-ro
Bundang-gu, Seongnam, 13591,
Gyeonggi-do, Korea (South)
Tel.: (82) 317089988
Web Site: http://www.uniquest.co.kr
077500—(KRS)
Rev.: $567,165,665
Assets: $468,424,862
Liabilities: $201,630,674
Net Worth: $266,794,188
Earnings: $33,811,672
Emp.: 218
Fiscal Year-end: 12/31/22
IT Solutions Marketing Provider
N.A.I.C.S.: 541613
Andrew Kim *(Pres & CEO)*

Subsidiaries:

Uniquest America Inc. (1)
1035 Live Oak Dr, Santa Clara, CA 95051
Tel.: (408) 432-8805
Web Site: http://www.uqc.com
Sales Range: $50-74.9 Million
Emp.: 2
Semiconductor Whslr
N.A.I.C.S.: 423690

Uniquest Hong Kong (1)
1901 19th floor Tower 1 China Hong Kong
City 33 Canton Road, Tsim Sha Tsui, Kowloon, China (Hong Kong)
Tel.: (852) 27369008
Semiconductor Whslr
N.A.I.C.S.: 423690

Uniquest Korea Inc. (1)
Uniquest Buliding 314 Hwangsaeul-ro,
Bundang-gu, Seongnam, 13591, Gyeonggi-
Do, Korea (South)
Tel.: (82) 317089988
Web Site: https://www.uniquest.co.kr
Sales Range: $75-99.9 Million
Emp.: 150
Semiconductor Whslr
N.A.I.C.S.: 423690

UNIREA SA
P-ta 1 Mai 1-2, Cluj, Cluj-Napoca,
Romania
Tel.: (40) 264425861
Web Site: https://www.unirea-cluj.ro
UNIR—(BUC)
Rev.: $1,040,177
Assets: $5,748,322
Liabilities: $2,243,464
Net Worth: $3,504,858
Earnings: $106,115
Emp.: 13
Fiscal Year-end: 12/31/22
Metal Forming Machinery Mfr
N.A.I.C.S.: 333517

UNIRITA INC.
Shinagawa Intercity A-29 2-15-1 Kounan, Minato-ku, Tokyo, 108-6029,
Japan
Tel.: (81) 354636381
Web Site: https://www.unirita.co.jp
Year Founded: 1982
3800—(TKS)
Rev.: $79,201,020
Assets: $104,193,430
Liabilities: $26,691,180
Net Worth: $77,502,250
Earnings: $5,387,150
Emp.: 668
Fiscal Year-end: 03/31/24
Information Technology Services
N.A.I.C.S.: 519290
Hiroki Takefuji *(Chm)*

Subsidiaries:

BSP (Shanghai) Inc. (1)
Room 2001-2002 Sheng Kang Liao Shi
Building 738 Shang Cheng Road, PuDong
New District, Shanghai, China
Tel.: (86) 21 5058 8268
Web Site: http://www.bsp-sh.cn
Emp.: 28
Software Development Services
N.A.I.C.S.: 541511
Hiroki Takefuji *(Chm)*

UNIROYAL INDUSTRIES LTD.
Plot No 365 Phase-II Industrial Estate, Panchkula, 134113, Haryana,
India
Tel.: (91) 1725066531
Web Site:
  https://www.uniroyalgroup.com
521226—(BOM)
Rev.: $9,189,929
Assets: $6,937,455
Liabilities: $4,581,114
Net Worth: $2,356,341
Earnings: ($123,489)
Fiscal Year-end: 03/31/21
Computerized Labeling Services
N.A.I.C.S.: 561910
Arvind Mahajan *(Chm & Mng Dir)*

UNIROYAL MARINE EXPORTS LIMITED
Vengalam PO, Kozhikode, 673 303,
Kerala, India
Tel.: (91) 4962633781
Web Site: https://uniroyalmarine.com
526113—(BOM)
Rev.: $3,462,346
Assets: $2,329,872
Liabilities: $1,955,183
Net Worth: $374,690
Earnings: ($62,898)
Emp.: 58
Fiscal Year-end: 03/31/23
Seafood Distr
N.A.I.C.S.: 424460

UNIS - UDRUZENA METALNA INDUSTRIJA D.D.
Envera Sehovica 54, 71000, Sarajevo, Bosnia & Herzegovina
Tel.: (387) 33725360 BA
Web Site: http://www.unis.ba
Year Founded: 1968
UMISRK2—(SARE)
Rev.: $680,076
Assets: $24,854,797
Liabilities: $3,097,619
Net Worth: $21,757,178
Earnings: $627,425
Emp.: 10
Fiscal Year-end: 12/31/21
Holding Company; Gas Measurement
& Control Equipment Mfr; Real Estate
& Investment Services
N.A.I.C.S.: 551112

UNIS FABRIKA CIJEVI A.D.
Derventa Dubicka 50, 74400, Derventa, Bosnia & Herzegovina
Tel.: (387) 53333347
Web Site: https://www.unis.rs.ba
Steel Welded Pipe & Precision Tube
Mfr
N.A.I.C.S.: 331410

Subsidiaries:

UAB UNIS Steel Baltija (1)
Pramones str 8, Klaipeda, 94102, Lithuania
Tel.: (370) 46416262
Web Site: http://www.unis-steel.lt
Emp.: 30
Seal Products Distr
N.A.I.C.S.: 423510
Martynas Balskus *(CFO)*

UNIS GINEX D.D. GORAZDE
Visegradska bb, 73000, Gorazde,
Bosnia & Herzegovina
Tel.: (387) 3 822 1251
Web Site: http://www.ginex.com.ba
Year Founded: 1951
GINXR—(SARE)
Rev.: $21,942,839
Assets: $44,746,837
Liabilities: $3,579,514
Net Worth: $41,167,323
Earnings: $3,160,138
Emp.: 634
Fiscal Year-end: 12/31/20
Plastic Production Services
N.A.I.C.S.: 326199

UNIS KOMERC D.D. SARAJEVO
Azici br 20 Sarajevo, 71210, Ilidza,
Bosnia & Herzegovina
Tel.: (387) 33 776 830
Web Site: http://www.unis-komerc.com
Year Founded: 1968
UKMCRK1—(SARE)
Rev.: $364,747
Assets: $5,555,831
Liabilities: $2,557,994
Net Worth: $2,997,837
Earnings: ($3,963)
Emp.: 12
Fiscal Year-end: 12/31/19
Automotive Parts & Machinery Equipment Distr
N.A.I.C.S.: 423120

UNIS STEEL DISTRIBUTION ROMANIA SRL
Turnu Magurele 270D, Sector 4, Bucharest, 041713, Romania
Tel.: (40) 216830935
Sales Range: $25-49.9 Million
Emp.: 20
Seal Products Distr
N.A.I.C.S.: 423510

UNIS TAS A.D.
Put Pavlovica most bb Popovi,
76300, Bijeljina, Bosnia & Herzegovina
Tel.: (387) 55355212
UTAS-R-A—(BANJ)
Rev.: $7,243
Assets: $692,311
Liabilities: $116,361
Net Worth: $575,950
Earnings: ($15,165)
Emp.: 1
Fiscal Year-end: 12/31/12
Motor Vehicles Mfr
N.A.I.C.S.: 336110
Petar Mitrovic *(Chm)*

UNIS TELEKOM D.D.
Dr Ante Starcevica 50, 88000, Mostar, Bosnia & Herzegovina
Tel.: (387) 36445300
Web Site: http://www.unistelekom.ba
Year Founded: 1977
UTLKRK1—(SARE)
Rev.: $6,436,258
Assets: $4,356,228
Liabilities: $1,509,612
Net Worth: $2,846,616
Earnings: $26,185

INTERNATIONAL PUBLIC

Emp.: 43
Fiscal Year-end: 12/31/21
Communication Equipment Mfr
N.A.I.C.S.: 334290

UNIS USHA A.D. VISEGRAD
Gavrila Principa 26, 73240, Visegrad,
Bosnia & Herzegovina
Tel.: (387) 58620851
Web Site: https://www.unisusha.com
Year Founded: 1982
USHA—(BANJ)
Sales Range: $1-9.9 Million
Emp.: 60
Steel Wire Rope Mfr
N.A.I.C.S.: 314994
Miodrag Kacarevic *(Head-Technical Dept)*

Subsidiaries:

Unis-Usha d.o.o. (1)
Koce Popovica 9, Savski Venac, 11000,
Belgrade, Serbia
Tel.: (381) 112182280
Steel Wire Rope Mfr
N.A.I.C.S.: 314994

UNIS VALJCICI D.D.
Hadzica Polje bb, 88400, Konjic, Bosnia & Herzegovina
Tel.: (387) 36 72 34 57
Web Site: http://www.rfk-valjcici.com
Emp.: 179
Gear & Power Transmission Equipment Mfr
N.A.I.C.S.: 333613

UNIS-FEROS A.D.
Tel.: (387) 65309930
Year Founded: 2001
UFRS-R-A—(BANJ)
Emp.: 33
Nonmetallic Mineral Product Mfr
N.A.I.C.S.: 327999
Radenko Kocevic *(Chm-Mgmt Bd)*

UNIS-PRETIS NIS D.D. VOGOSCA
ul Lgmanska bb, 71320, Vogosca,
Bosnia & Herzegovina
Tel.: (387) 33475650
UNPRRK1—(SARE)
Rev.: $27,011,553
Assets: $196,382,315
Liabilities: $158,955,125
Net Worth: $37,427,190
Earnings: $5,476,432
Emp.: 339
Fiscal Year-end: 12/31/19
Aerospace Equipment Mfr
N.A.I.C.S.: 334511

UNISEM CO., LTD.
10-7 Jangjinam-gil, Hwaseong,
18510, Gyeonggi-do, Korea (South)
Tel.: (82) 313795800
Web Site: https://www.unisem.co.kr
Year Founded: 1988
036200—(KRS)
Rev.: $194,226,709
Assets: $180,035,863
Liabilities: $27,068,189
Net Worth: $152,967,675
Earnings: $15,024,691
Emp.: 818
Fiscal Year-end: 12/31/22
Semiconductor Equipment Mfr
N.A.I.C.S.: 333242
Hyung-gyoon Kim *(CEO)*

UNISEM SA
Splaiul Unirii nr 16 Etaj 3 cam 313
sector 4, Bucharest, Romania
Tel.: (40) 725554307
Web Site:
  https://www.unisemromania.ro
Year Founded: 1949

AND PRIVATE COMPANIES

UNISEM—(BUC)
Rev.: $2,636,413
Assets: $12,772,998
Liabilities: $968,285
Net Worth: $11,804,713
Earnings: $301,048
Emp.: 4
Fiscal Year-end: 12/31/23
Seed Whslr
N.A.I.C.S.: 424910

UNISERVE COMMUNICATIONS CORPORATION
209 - 333 Terminal Ave, Vancouver, V6A 4C1, BC, Canada
Tel.: (604) 395-3900
Web Site: https://home.uniserve.com
Year Founded: 2003
USSHF—(OTCIQ)
Rev.: $4,756,756
Assets: $2,401,747
Liabilities: $1,917,052
Net Worth: $484,696
Earnings: ($141,170)
Fiscal Year-end: 05/31/24
Telecommunication & Information Technology Services
N.A.I.C.S.: 517810
Walter Schultz (Chm)

Subsidiaries:

Jolt Health Inc. (1)
1780 - 355 Burrard Street, Vancouver, V6C 2G8, BC, Canada (81.93%)
Tel.: (604) 343-2977
Web Site: https://love-pharma.com
Assets: $1,421,411
Liabilities: $474,150
Net Worth: $947,261
Earnings: $7,448,209)
Fiscal Year-end: 12/31/2021
Information Technology Services
N.A.I.C.S.: 541511
Tatiana Kovaleva (CFO)

UNISHIRE URBAN INFRA LTD
13/1A Government Place East Top Floor, Kolkata, 700069, India
Tel.: (91) 3325349061
Web Site: https://www.uuil.co.in
Year Founded: 1987
537582—(BOM)
Rev.: $158,528
Assets: $2,497
Liabilities: $18
Net Worth: $2,479
Earnings: ($40,010)
Emp.: 4
Fiscal Year-end: 03/31/23
Communities Developer
N.A.I.C.S.: 237210
Kirti Kantilal Mehta (Chm)

UNISON CAPITAL, INC.
The New Otani Garden Court 9F 4-1 Kioicho, Chiyoda-ku, Tokyo, 102-0094, Japan
Tel.: (81) 335113900
Web Site: http://www.unisoncap.com
Sales Range: $25-49.9 Million
Emp.: 40
Investment
N.A.I.C.S.: 523940
Hitoshi Yamaguchi (CEO)

Subsidiaries:

Kyowa Pharmaceutical Industry Co., Ltd. (1)
5-13-9 Nishinakajima, Yodogawa-ku, Osaka, 532-0011, Japan (99.82%)
Tel.: (81) 6 6308 3320
Web Site: http://www.kyowayakuhin.co.jp
Pharmaceutical Product Mfr & Distr
N.A.I.C.S.: 325412
Fabrice Egros (Chm)

N Field Co., Ltd. (1)
Aqua Dojima Higashikan 1-4-4 Dojimahama Kita-ku, Osaka-shi, Osaka, 530-0004, Japan (85.3%)
Tel.: (81) 6 6343 0600
Web Site: http://www.nfield.co.jp
Home Nursing Care Services
N.A.I.C.S.: 621610

Osstem Implant Co., Ltd. (1)
3 Magokjungang 12-ro, Gangseo-gu, Seoul, 153-759, Korea (South)
Tel.: (82) 220167000
Web Site: http://www.osstem.com
Rev.: $808,013,209
Assets: $1,052,570,092
Liabilities: $774,497,883
Net Worth: $278,072,209
Earnings: $105,950,894
Emp.: 2,143
Fiscal Year-end: 12/31/2022
Medical Appliances & Instruments Mfr
N.A.I.C.S.: 339113
Tae Kwan Uhm (CEO)

Subsidiary (Non-US):

Deutsche Osstem GmbH (2)
Mergenthalerallee 35-37, 65760, Eschborn, Germany
Tel.: (49) 61967775500
Dental Equipment & Device Mfr
N.A.I.C.S.: 339114

HIOSSEN Implant Canada Inc. (2)
122-8337 Eastlake Drive, Burnaby, V5A 4W2, BC, Canada
Tel.: (604) 324-0112
Web Site: https://www.hiossenimplantcanada.ca
Dental Equipment & Device Mfr
N.A.I.C.S.: 339114

Subsidiary (US):

HIOSSEN Inc. (2)
85 Ben Fairless Dr, Fairless Hills, PA 19030
Dental Equipment & Device Mfr
N.A.I.C.S.: 339114

Subsidiary (Non-US):

HIOSSEN de Mexico, S.A. de C.V. (2)
Chimalhuacan 3574-3B Edificio Torrvan Col Ciudad del Sol, 45050, Zapopan, Jalisco, Mexico
Tel.: (52) 3331215663
Dental Equipment & Device Mfr
N.A.I.C.S.: 339114

Hiossen Chile SpA (2)
Avda Providencia 2008 Oficina C, Santiago de, Providencia, Chile
Tel.: (56) 232451457
Dental Surgical Instruments Mfr & Distr
N.A.I.C.S.: 339114

Hiossen China Co., Ltd. (2)
Room 1-1403/1404 No 65 Dagu North Road Xiaobailou Street, Heping, Tianjin, China
Tel.: (86) 2227165021
Dental Surgical Instruments Mfr & Distr
N.A.I.C.S.: 339114

OSSTEM Philippines Inc. (2)
unit 203 2nd Floor Penensula Court Bldg 8735 Paceo de Roxas, Makati, Philippines
Tel.: (63) 9171283000
Web Site: http://www.ph.osstem.com
Dental Equipment & Device Mfr
N.A.I.C.S.: 339114
Christian Hizon (Mgr-Product)

Osstem Autralia Pty. Ltd. (2)
6A / 5 Talavera Road, Macquarie Park, 2113, NSW, Australia
Tel.: (61) 298892675
Web Site: http://au.osstem.com
Dental Equipment & Device Mfr
N.A.I.C.S.: 339114

Osstem Bangladesh Ltd. (2)
5FL House-13 Road-34 Gulshan-1, Dhaka, 1212, Bangladesh
Tel.: (880) 29898098
Web Site: http://bd.osstem.com
Dental Equipment & Device Distr
N.A.I.C.S.: 423450
Zillur Rahman (Mgr-Sls)

Osstem China Co., Ltd. (2)
Room 708-1B Zhubang 2000 No 100 Balizhuangxili, Chaoyang District, Beijing, 100025, China
Tel.: (86) 1085868702
Dental Equipment & Device Mfr
N.A.I.C.S.: 339114
Michael Lee (Mgr-Mktg)

Osstem Co., Ltd. (2)
3850/2 Theptarin Hospital 2 Bld 16FL Rama 4 Rd, phrakanong Klongtoey, Bangkok, 10110, Thailand
Tel.: (66) 26717988
Web Site: http://www.th.osstem.com
Dental Equipment & Device Mfr
N.A.I.C.S.: 339114

Osstem Corporation (2)
5F-2 No 131 Sec3 E Rd Nanjing E Rd, Jhongshan District, Taipei, Taiwan
Tel.: (886) 225471082
Web Site: http://www.tw.osstem.com
Dental Equipment & Device Mfr
N.A.I.C.S.: 339114

Osstem Hong Kong Ltd. (2)
Rm 2404 24/F Windsor House 311 Gloucester Road, Causeway Bay, China (Hong Kong)
Tel.: (852) 31129416
Web Site: http://www.hk.osstem.com
Dental Equipment & Device Mfr
N.A.I.C.S.: 339114

Osstem Implant Brasil Ltda. (2)
Rua Dr Rafael de Barros 210 - sala 81 e 82- Paraiso, Sao Paulo, 04003-041, SP, Brazil
Tel.: (55) 1132073107
Dental Equipment Mfr & Distr
N.A.I.C.S.: 339114

Osstem Implant LLP (2)
Office 808 Section-2 Abay Street 150/230 Bostandykskiy Region, Almaty, Kazakhstan
Tel.: (7) 87273115253
Dental Equipment & Device Mfr
N.A.I.C.S.: 339114

Osstem Implant Spain S.L. (2)
Avenida de Manoteras 32 Bloque B Primero B, 28050, Madrid, Spain
Tel.: (34) 910136949
Dental Equipment Mfr & Distr
N.A.I.C.S.: 339114

Osstem Implant Vina Co., Ltd. (2)
2nd Floor B14 C4-1 Hoang Van Thai Street Center of International, Trade Finance Phu My Hung Tan Phu Ward District 7, Ho Chi Minh City, Vietnam
Tel.: (84) 854130009
Web Site: http://vn.osstem.com
Dental Equipment & Device Mfr
N.A.I.C.S.: 339114

Osstem Implant dis Tic. A.S. (2)
Esentepe Mah Buyukdere Cd No 111 TEV Kocabas Ishani K 2, Sisli, 34394, Istanbul, Turkiye
Tel.: (90) 2123472097
Web Site: http://www.tr.osstem.com
Dental Equipment & Device Mfr
N.A.I.C.S.: 339114
Jeongwon Kim (Mgr-HR & Fin)

Osstem Implant india Pvt. Ltd. (2)
Office No 306 3rd Floor A Wing Sagar Tech Plaza Sakinaka Andheri Kurla, Road Andheri East, Mumbai, 400072, Maharashtra, India
Tel.: (91) 2267257111
Web Site: http://www.in.osstem.com
Dental Equipment & Device Mfr
N.A.I.C.S.: 339114
Mangesh Saroj (Mgr-Product Trng)

Osstem Japan Corp. (2)
B1F 4-5-37 Kamiosaki, Shinagawa-ku, Tokyo, 141-0021, Japan
Tel.: (81) 357479441
Dental Equipment & Device Mfr
N.A.I.C.S.: 339114

Osstem LLC (2)
8th Fl Ofc 1 Nagatino i-land 18/7 Andropova Prospect, 115432, Moscow, Russia
Tel.: (7) 4957399925
Web Site: http://www.osstem.ru
Dental Equipment & Device Mfr
N.A.I.C.S.: 339114

Osstem Malaysia Sdn. Bhd. (2)
B-07-12 Gateway Kiaramas Corporate Suite No 1 Jalan Desa Kiara, Mpnt kiara, 50480, Kuala Lumpur, Malaysia
Tel.: (60) 362110585
Web Site: http://my.osstem.com
Dental Equipment & Device Mfr
N.A.I.C.S.: 339114

Osstem Middle East FZCO (2)
Unit G23 inside Dubai Airport Free Zone, PO Box 371629, Dubai, United Arab Emirates
Tel.: (971) 43491922
Dental Equipment Mfr & Distr
N.A.I.C.S.: 339114

Osstem Mongol LLC (2)
201 Barilga MN Office 13th Microdistrict 6th Horoo 13373 Street 24-1, Bayanzurkh District, Ulaanbaatar, Mongolia
Tel.: (976) 70161599
Dental Equipment & Device Mfr
N.A.I.C.S.: 339114

Osstem New Zealand Limited (2)
Unit 10/6 Omega Street, Rosedale, Auckland, New Zealand
Tel.: (64) 96001500
Web Site: https://osstem.co.nz
Dental Equipment Mfr & Distr
N.A.I.C.S.: 339114

Osstem Singapore Pte. Ltd. (2)
Pico Creative Centre Level 3 PT 20 Kallang Avenue, Singapore, 339411, Singapore
Tel.: (65) 62701840
Web Site: https://www.sg.osstem.com
Dental Equipment & Device Mfr
N.A.I.C.S.: 339114
Tim T. H. Lee (Mng Dir)

Osstem South China Co., Ltd. (2)
Rm 01B 05-06 25F Centralcon Tower Jintian Road 3088, Futian District, Shenzhen, China
Tel.: (86) 75582046986
Dental Equipment & Device Mfr
N.A.I.C.S.: 339114

Osstem uah LLC (2)
Sumska str 1 office 903, 03022, Kiev, Ukraine
Tel.: (380) 675166500
Dental Equipment Mfr & Distr
N.A.I.C.S.: 339114

PT. Osstem Implant (2)
K-Link Office Tower 27 Jl Jend Gatot Subroto No 59A Kuningan Timur, Setiabudi Jakarta Selatan, Jakarta, 12950, Indonesia
Tel.: (62) 81113305574
Web Site: http://www.id.osstem.com
Dental Equipment & Device Mfr
N.A.I.C.S.: 339114

UNISON CO., LTD.
513 Haeansaneop-Ro Sanam-Myeon, Sacheon, 52535, Gyeongsangnam-Do, Korea (South)
Tel.: (82) 558518777
Web Site: https://www.unison.co.kr
Year Founded: 1984
018000—(KRS)
Rev.: $183,450,305
Assets: $200,958,867
Liabilities: $149,410,683
Net Worth: $51,548,184
Earnings: ($10,041,217)
Emp.: 211
Fiscal Year-end: 12/31/22
Wind Powered Turbines Mfr
N.A.I.C.S.: 333611
Hwa Do Heo (CEO)

Subsidiaries:

Unison E&C Co., Ltd. (1)
83-6 Jangsan-Ri Soosin-Myun, Cheonan, Choongnam-Do, Korea (South)
Tel.: (82) 25288777
Web Site: http://www.unisoneandc.co.kr
Sales Range: $25-49.9 Million
Emp.: 63
Construction Materials Mfr
N.A.I.C.S.: 333120

UNISON METALS LTD.

Unison Co., Ltd.—(Continued)

UNISON METALS LTD.
Plot No 5015 Phase-IV Ramol Char Rasta GIDC Estate Vatva, Ahmedabad, 382 445, Gujarat, India
Tel.: (91) 7925841512
Web Site:
https://www.unisongroup.net
Year Founded: 1990
538610—(BOM)
Rev.: $19,543,101
Assets: $17,197,772
Liabilities: $13,595,414
Net Worth: $3,602,358
Earnings: $239,667
Emp.: 31
Fiscal Year-end: 03/31/21
Stainless Steel Metal Distr
N.A.I.C.S.: 423510
Hans V. Mittal *(Chm)*

UNISPLENDOUR CORPORATION LIMITED
Ziguang Building outside the East Gate of Tsinghua University, Haidian District, Beijing, 100084, China
Tel.: (86) 62789898
Web Site: http://www.thunis.com
Year Founded: 1988
000938—(SSE)
Rev.: $10,703,894,938
Assets: $12,082,478,207
Liabilities: $6,538,245,846
Net Worth: $5,544,232,360
Earnings: $291,179,843
Fiscal Year-end: 12/31/23
Electronic Products Mfr
N.A.I.C.S.: 334419

UNISTAR MULTIMEDIA LIMITED
901/902 Atlanta Centre Sonawala Lane Opp Udyog Bhavan Goregoan E, Mumbai, 400063, India
Tel.: (91) 2243211800
Web Site:
http://www.unistarmultimedia.com
Year Founded: 1991
532035—(BOM)
Rev.: $17,927
Assets: $1,156,032
Liabilities: $592
Net Worth: $1,155,440
Earnings: ($4,667,093)
Emp.: 2
Fiscal Year-end: 03/31/21
Securities Dealing Services
N.A.I.C.S.: 523150
Suresh B. Bafna *(Chm)*

UNISTER HOLDING GMBH
Barfussgasschen 11, 04109, Leipzig, Germany
Tel.: (49) 341 650 500
Web Site: http://www.unister.de
Year Founded: 2002
Emp.: 1,800
Holding Company; Online Marketing & Publishing Services
N.A.I.C.S.: 551112
Thomas Wagner *(Founder & CEO)*

Subsidiaries:

Travel Viva GmbH (1)
Luitpoldstrasse 9, 63739, Aschaffenburg, Germany
Tel.: (49) 6021454820
Web Site: http://www.travelviva.de
Sales Range: $10-24.9 Million
Online Ticket Booking Services
N.A.I.C.S.: 561599
Oliver Trompke *(CEO)*

Subsidiary (Domestic):

ASNM New Media AG (2)
Boppstrasse 10, 10967, Berlin, Germany
(95%)
Tel.: (49) 30 698 02 110
Web Site: http://www.asnm.de
Online Marketing Services for Flight & Travel Portals
N.A.I.C.S.: 541519
Michael Schwarz *(Member-Mgmt Bd)*

Affiliate (Domestic):

Maxviva Technologies AG (2)
Luitpoldstrasse 9, 63739, Aschaffenburg, Germany
(49.5%)
Tel.: (49) 6021456670
Web Site: http://www.maxviva.com
Online Airline Ticket Booking Services
N.A.I.C.S.: 561599
Oliver Trompke *(Mng Dir)*

UNISTER TRAVEL RETAIL GmbH & Co. KG (1)
Barfussgasschen 12, 04109, Leipzig, Germany
Tel.: (49) 3413557585560
Web Site: http://www.fly.co.uk
Tour Operator
N.A.I.C.S.: 561520
Thomas Wagner *(Mng Dir)*

UNISTREAM COMMERCIAL BANK OJSC
20 Verhnyaya Maslovka Str Bldg 2, 127083, Moscow, Russia
Tel.: (7) 4957445555
Web Site: http://www.unistream.ru
Sales Range: Less than $1 Million
Financial Transaction Services
N.A.I.C.S.: 522320
Nadegda Kibalnik *(Chm-Mgmt Bd)*

UNISYNC CORP.
6695 Airport Road, Mississauga, L4V 1Y4, ON, Canada
Web Site:
https://www.unisyncgroup.com
Year Founded: 1940
UNI—(TSXV)
Rev.: $78,230,289
Assets: $82,625,813
Liabilities: $68,266,595
Net Worth: $14,359,218
Earnings: ($6,935,148)
Emp.: 303
Fiscal Year-end: 09/30/23
Garment Leather Mfr & Sales
N.A.I.C.S.: 315250
Douglas F. Good *(CEO)*

Subsidiaries:

Peerless Garments Inc. (1)
515 Notre Dame Avenue, Winnipeg, R3B 1R9, MB, Canada
Tel.: (204) 774-5428
Emp.: 100
Fur & Leather Apparel Mfr
N.A.I.C.S.: 315250

Peerless Garments LP (1)
515 Notre Dame, Winnipeg, R3B 1R9, MB, Canada
(90%)
Tel.: (204) 774-5428
Web Site: http://www.peerless.mb.ca
Emp.: 110
Leather Garment Mfr & Distr
N.A.I.C.S.: 315250
Albert El Tassi *(Pres)*

Red The Uniform Tailor Inc. (1)
475 Oberlin Ave S, Lakewood, NJ 08701
Tel.: (848) 299-0148
Web Site: http://www.rtut.com
Mfr of Made-To-Measure Uniforms for the Law Enforcement Industry: Military Goods & Regalia
N.A.I.C.S.: 458110
Tracy Gluck *(VP-Sls)*

Utility Garments Inc. (1)
666 Montee-de-Liesse, Saint Laurent, H4T 1P2, QC, Canada
Web Site: https://www.utilitygarments.ca
Uniform Apparel Mfr
N.A.I.C.S.: 315990

UNISYS SOFTWARES & HOLDING INDUSTRIES LIMITED
75C Park Street, Kolkata, 700 016, India
Tel.: (91) 33 22295359
Web Site:
http://www.unisyssoftwares.com
Rev.: $39,690,775
Assets: $9,856,039
Liabilities: $5,181,167
Net Worth: $4,674,872
Earnings: ($4,545,809)
Fiscal Year-end: 03/31/18
Holding Company
N.A.I.C.S.: 551112
Jagdish Prasad Purohit *(Chm & Mng Dir)*

UNISYST ENGINEERING PLC
No 400 Deans Road, 10, Colombo, Sri Lanka
Tel.: (94) 114347987
Web Site: https://www.unisystplc.com
ALUF—(COL)
Rev.: $2,609,472
Assets: $2,621,249
Liabilities: $3,019,821
Net Worth: ($398,572)
Earnings: ($580,829)
Emp.: 57
Fiscal Year-end: 03/31/23
Aluminum Facade Product Mfr
N.A.I.C.S.: 332323

UNIT4 N.V.
Stationspark 1000, 3364 DA, Sliedrecht, Netherlands
Tel.: (31) 882471777   NI
Web Site: http://www.unit4.com
Sales Range: $650-699.9 Million
Emp.: 3,000
Business Software Mfr
N.A.I.C.S.: 513210
Jeremy Roche *(Exec Dir)*

Subsidiaries:

Agresso France S.A. (1)
63 Av Du General Leclerc Le Centralis, Bourg-la-Reine, 92340, Hauts-de-Seine, France
Tel.: (33) 141872600
Web Site: http://www.agresso.fr
Enterprise Resource Planning Software Development Services
N.A.I.C.S.: 541511

CODA Group International Ltd. (1)
Saint Georges Hall Easton in Gordano, Bristol, BS20 0PX, United Kingdom
Tel.: (44) 1249461313
Sales Range: $25-49.9 Million
Emp.: 200
Financial Software Development Services
N.A.I.C.S.: 541511

FinancialForce Inc. (1)
900 Concar Dr, San Mateo, CA 94402
Tel.: (866) 743-2220
Web Site: http://www.financialforce.com
Financial Management Software Development Services
N.A.I.C.S.: 541511
Jeremy Roche *(Founder)*

Foundation ICT Solutions B.V. (1)
Kobaltweg 44, 3542 CE, Utrecht, Netherlands
Tel.: (31) 302489600
Web Site: http://www.unit4.nl
Business Administration Software Development Services
N.A.I.C.S.: 541511

UNIT4 Agresso GmbH (1)
Marcel Breuer Strasse 22, 80807, Munich, Bavaria, Germany
Tel.: (49) 893236300
Web Site: http://www.unit4agresso.de
Emp.: 40
Business Administration Software Development Services

INTERNATIONAL PUBLIC

N.A.I.C.S.: 541511
Gorg Tung *(Gen Mgr)*

UNIT4 Asia Pacific Pte Ltd. (1)
24 Raffles Pl 25-05, Singapore, 048621, Singapore
Tel.: (65) 63382811
Sales Range: $25-49.9 Million
Emp.: 12
Business Software Development Services
N.A.I.C.S.: 541511
Jack van der Velde *(Mng Dir)*

UNIT4 Business Software Benelux B.V. (1)
Stationspark 1000, Sliedrecht, 3364 DA, South Holland, Netherlands
Tel.: (31) 184444444
Web Site: http://www.unit4.nl
Emp.: 600
Enterprise Resource Planning Software Development Services
N.A.I.C.S.: 541511
Aande Randekark *(Mgr-HR)*

Subsidiary (Domestic):

UNIT4 Accountancy B.V. (2)
De Schutterij 27, Veenendaal, 3905 PK, Utrecht, Netherlands
Tel.: (31) 8581600
Web Site: http://www.unit4.nl
Sales Range: $25-49.9 Million
Emp.: 140
Accounting Software Development Services
N.A.I.C.S.: 541511
Herman DeJonge *(Dir-Veenendaal)*

UNIT4 Business Software B.V. (2)
Stationspark 1000, Sliedrecht, 3364 DA, South Holland, Netherlands
Tel.: (31) 184444444
Web Site: http://www.unit4.nl
Enterprise Resource Planning Software Development Services
N.A.I.C.S.: 541511

UNIT4 Consist B.V. (2)
Papendorpseweg 100, Post Bus 500, Utrecht, Netherlands
Tel.: (31) 306026666
Web Site: http://www.unit4consist.nl
Sales Range: $25-49.9 Million
Emp.: 130
Business Administration Software Development Services
N.A.I.C.S.: 541511
Scott Kamieneski *(Mng Dir-North America)*

UNIT4 Financiele Intermediairs B.V. (2)
Boerhaavelaan 15-17, 2713 HA, Zoetermeer, South Holland, Netherlands
Tel.: (31) 793292300
Web Site: http://www.unit4.com
Sales Range: $25-49.9 Million
Emp.: 100
Financial Software Development Services
N.A.I.C.S.: 541511

UNIT4 IT Solutions B.V. (2)
Papendorpseweg 100, Utrecht, 3528 BJ, South Holland, Netherlands
Tel.: (31) 102580444
Web Site: http://www.unit4.nl
Enterprise Resource Planning Software Development Services
N.A.I.C.S.: 541511

UNIT4 Oost Nederland B.V (2)
Jan Tinbergenstraat 172, 7559 SP, Hengelo, Netherlands
Tel.: (31) 742455444
Web Site: http://www.unit4.com
Enterprise Resource Planning Software Development Services
N.A.I.C.S.: 541511
Jan Pol *(Gen Mgr)*

Subsidiary (Non-US):

UNIT4 R&D AS (2)
Gjerdrums V 4, PO Box 4244, 0484, Oslo, Norway
Tel.: (47) 22588500
Web Site: http://www.unit4.com
Sales Range: $25-49.9 Million
Emp.: 150
Business Administration Software Development Services

AND PRIVATE COMPANIES

N.A.I.C.S.: 541511
Herbert Van zijl *(Mng Dir)*

Subsidiary (Domestic):

UNIT4 Software B.V. (2)
Stationspark 1000, 3364, Sliedrecht, Netherlands
Tel.: (31) 184444444
Web Site: http://www.unit4.com
Emp.: 600
Enterprise Resource Planning Software Development Services
N.A.I.C.S.: 541511

UNIT4 Business Software Holding B.V. (1)
Stationspark 1000, Sliedrecht, 3364, Netherlands
Tel.: (31) 184444444
Web Site: http://www.unit4.nl
Sales Range: $350-399.9 Million
Emp.: 2,000
Business Administration Software Development Services
N.A.I.C.S.: 541511
Chris Ouwinga *(Pres & CEO)*

Subsidiary (Non-US):

Agresso Travel Industry Solutions Ltd. (2)
Terminal House Station Approach, Shepperton, TW17 8AS, Middlesex, United Kingdom
Tel.: (44) 2070792770
Web Site: http://www.unit4.com
Travel Management Software Development Services
N.A.I.C.S.: 541511

UNIT4 Agresso AB (2)
Gustav IIIs Boulevard 18, PO Box 705, Solna, 16927, Sweden
Tel.: (46) 8 55333100
Web Site: http://www.agresso.se
Emp.: 300
Enterprise Resource Planning Software Development Services
N.A.I.C.S.: 541511
Jeremias Jansson *(Gen Mgr)*

Subsidiary (Domestic):

UNIT4 MAP AB (3)
Box 295, 851 05, Sundsvall, Sweden
Tel.: (46) 60 66 30 90
Web Site: http://www.unit4map.com
Business Software Development Services
N.A.I.C.S.: 541511

Subsidiary (Non-US):

UNIT4 Agresso AS (2)
Gjerdrums Vei 4, PO Box 4244, Nydalen, 0484, Oslo, Norway
Tel.: (47) 22588500
Web Site: http://www.unit4.com
Sales Range: $25-49.9 Million
Emp.: 130
Business Administration Software Development Services
N.A.I.C.S.: 541511
Helge Strypet *(Mng Dir)*

UNIT4 Business Software Ltd. (2)
Suite 201 100 Longwater Avenue Green Park, Reading, RG2 6GP, Berkshire, United Kingdom
Tel.: (44) 1423537837
Web Site: http://www.unit4.com
Sales Range: $150-199.9 Million
Business Software Development Services
N.A.I.C.S.: 541511

Subsidiary (Domestic):

UNIT4 Business Software Ltd. (3)
Riverside House Normandy Road, Swansea, SA1 2JA, West Glamorgan, United Kingdom
Tel.: (44) 1792524524
Web Site: http://www.unit4software.co.uk
Business Software Development Services
N.A.I.C.S.: 513210

UNIT4 Business Software Ltd. (3)
Suite 201 100 Longwater Avenue Green Park, Reading, RG2 6GP, Berkshire, United Kingdom
Tel.: (44) 1182076767
Web Site: http://www.unit4.com

Sales Range: $10-24.9 Million
Emp.: 50
Business Software Development Services
N.A.I.C.S.: 513210

UNIT4 Business Software Ltd. (3)
Cardale Park Beckwith Head Road, Harrogate, HG3 1RY, North Yorkshire, United Kingdom
Tel.: (44) 1423 509999
Web Site: http://www.unit4software.co.uk
Business Software Development Services
N.A.I.C.S.: 513210

Subsidiary (Non-US):

UNIT4 Portugal LDA (2)
Rua Dr Antonio Loureiro Borges N 9 - 11 Edificio Zenith, Miraflores, 1495-131, Lisbon, Portugal
Tel.: (351) 214460090
Web Site: http://www.unit4.com
Sales Range: $25-49.9 Million
Emp.: 16
Business Administration Software Development Services
N.A.I.C.S.: 541511
Goao Capitoleno *(Mng Dir)*

UNIT4 Business Software Inc. (1)
201-4420 Chatterton Way, Victoria, V8X 5J2, BC, Canada
Tel.: (250) 704-4450
Web Site: http://www.unit4software.com
Sales Range: $25-49.9 Million
Emp.: 60
Business Management Software Publisher
N.A.I.C.S.: 513210
Jim Millard *(VP-Sls & Strategic Alliances)*

Subsidiary (US):

UNIT4 Coda Inc (2)
1000 Elm St Ste 801, Manchester, NH 03101
Tel.: (603) 471-1700
Web Site: http://www.unit4coda.com
Sales Range: $10-24.9 Million
Emp.: 30
Software Development Services
N.A.I.C.S.: 541511
Michele Zangri *(VP-Pro Svcs)*

UNIT4 Business Software N.V. (1)
Meir 24, Antwerp, 2000, Belgium
Tel.: (32) 324022
Web Site: http://www.unit4.be
Sales Range: $25-49.9 Million
Emp.: 40
Business Administration Software Development Services
N.A.I.C.S.: 541511
Roel Caers *(Gen Mgr)*

UNIT4 Business Software Srl (1)
Via Torino 61, 20123, Milan, Italy
Tel.: (39) 0287166643
Web Site: http://www.unit4.it
Enterprise Resource Planning Software Development Services
N.A.I.C.S.: 541511

UNIT4 C-Logic N.V. (1)
Rijselstraat 247, 8200, Brugge, West Flanders, Belgium
Tel.: (32) 50391336
Web Site: http://www.unit4-c-logic.be
Sales Range: $25-49.9 Million
Emp.: 13
Business Administration Software Development Services
N.A.I.C.S.: 541511
Rudy Steyaert *(Gen Mgr)*

UNIT4 Coda Czech s.r.o (1)
Na Strzi 1702/65, Prague, 140 00, Czech Republic
Tel.: (420) 222191560
Web Site: http://www.unit4.cz
Business Administration Software Development Services
N.A.I.C.S.: 541511

UNIT4 Current Software AS (1)
Kjoita 18, 4630, Kristiansand, Norway
Tel.: (47) 40006744
Web Site: http://www.current.no
Sales Range: $25-49.9 Million
Emp.: 28
Travel Management Software Development Services

N.A.I.C.S.: 541511

UNIT4 Eesti OU (1)
Parnu Maantee 141, Tallinn, 11314, Estonia
Tel.: (372) 6617980
Web Site: http://www.unit4.com
Emp.: 7
Business Administration Software Development Services
N.A.I.C.S.: 541511
Alar Lange *(Gen Mgr)*

UNIT4 Ocra AB (1)
Gustav IIIs Boulevard 18, PO Box 705, 169 27, Solna, Sweden
Tel.: (46) 86788766
Web Site: http://www.unit4ocra.com
Business Software Development Services
N.A.I.C.S.: 541511

UNIT4 TETA S.A. (1)
Al Wisniowa 1, Wroclaw, 53-137, Lower Silesia, Poland
Tel.: (48) 71 323 4000
Web Site: http://www.teta.com.pl
Business Administration Software Development Services
N.A.I.C.S.: 541511

Subsidiary (Domestic):

TETA BI Center Sp. z o.o. (2)
Al Wisniowa 1, 53 137, Wroclaw, Lower Silesia, Poland
Tel.: (48) 713234000
Web Site: http://www.tetabic.pl
Business Administration Software Development Services
N.A.I.C.S.: 541511

TETA HR Center Sp. z o.o. (2)
ul sw Mikolaja 8/11, 50-125, Wroclaw, Lower Silesia, Poland
Tel.: (48) 713362070
Web Site: http://www.unit4teta.pl
Emp.: 500
Human Resource Management Software Development Services
N.A.I.C.S.: 541511
Artur Sawicki *(CEO)*

UNIT4 Software Engineering sp. z o.o. (2)
ul Kobierzycka 3, 52-315, Wroclaw, Poland
Tel.: (48) 717905665
Web Site: http://www.unit4se.pl
Information Technology Consulting Services
N.A.I.C.S.: 541512

VT-SOFT Software Kft. (1)
7 Zahony Street, Budapest, 1031, Hungary
Tel.: (36) 1 436 0540
Web Site: http://www.vtsoft.hu
Sales Range: $25-49.9 Million
Emp.: 50
Human Resource Management Software Development Services
N.A.I.C.S.: 541511
Tamas Wehring *(Mng Dir)*

UNITAINER TRADING GMBH
Schluisgrove 1, 21107, Hamburg, Germany
Tel.: (49) 403008980
Web Site: http://www.unitainer.de
Year Founded: 1990
Rev.: $16,552,800
Emp.: 7
Container Leasing Service & Mfr
N.A.I.C.S.: 332439
Dirk Hoffmann *(Founder & Mng Dir)*

Subsidiaries:

CDS Container Depot Stuttgart GmbH (1)
Dammstr 5, 71384, Weinstadt, Germany
Tel.: (49) 7151277560
Web Site: http://www.con-tainer.de
Container Distr
N.A.I.C.S.: 423510

UNITAINER Trading (UAE) FZE (1)
Sharjah Al Hamriyah Free Zone, PO Box 42208, Sharjah, United Arab Emirates
Tel.: (971) 65261412
Container Distr
N.A.I.C.S.: 423510

UNITE & GROW, INC.

UNITAS CAPITAL PTE. LTD.
29th Floor 2 Chinachem Central 26 Des Voeux Road Central, 1 Harbour View Street, Central, China (Hong Kong)
Tel.: (852) 25331818
Web Site: http://www.unitascapital.com
Year Founded: 1999
Rev.: $4,000,000,000
Emp.: 20
Investment Management Service
N.A.I.C.S.: 523940
Andrew Liu *(Chm)*

Subsidiaries:

Air International Thermal (Australia) Pty Ltd. (1)
80 Turner Street, Port Melbourne, 3207, VIC, Australia
Tel.: (61) 3 9644 4281
Web Site: http://www.ai-thermal.com
Emp.: 1,500
Heating & Ventilation System Whslr
N.A.I.C.S.: 423730
Todd P. Sheppelman *(CEO)*

Subsidiary (Non-US):

Air International (Shanghai) Co., Ltd (2)
No 108 Chun Guang Road Xinzhung Industrial Zone, Shanghai, 201108, China
Tel.: (86) 21 5483 1800
Heating & Ventilation System Whslr
N.A.I.C.S.: 423730

Godfreys Group Limited (1)
Building 2 Level 1 Brandon Business Park, 530-540 Springvale Road, Glen Waverley, 3150, VIC, Australia
Tel.: (61) 3 8542 2110
Web Site: http://www.godfreys.com.au
Vacuums & Cleaning Products Whslr
N.A.I.C.S.: 449210
Rod Walker *(Chm)*

Unitas Capital Investment Consulting (Shanghai) Co. Ltd. (1)
Suite 3804 K Wah Centre 1010 Huai Hai Zhong Road, Shanghai, 200031, China
Tel.: (86) 21 6103 2688
Financial Investment Management Services
N.A.I.C.S.: 523999

Unitas Capital Yuhan Hoesa (1)
21F Seoul Finance Centre 84 Taepyungro 1-ga, Jung-gu, Seoul, 100-768, Korea (South)
Tel.: (82) 2 3198600
Financial Investment Management Services
N.A.I.C.S.: 523999

UNITAS HOLDINGS LIMITED
Flat C 16/F MG Tower 133 Hoi Bun Road, Kwun Tong, Hong Kong, China (Hong Kong)
Tel.: (852) 21589999 Ky
Web Site: http://www.chanceton.com
8020—(HKG)
Investment Holding Company; Corporate Finance Advisory Services
N.A.I.C.S.: 551112
Ling Tak Lau *(Exec Dir)*

Subsidiaries:

Chanceton Capital Partners Limited (1)
Units A 23/F CMA Building 64-66 Connaught Road, Central, China (Hong Kong)
Tel.: (852) 2158 9999
Web Site: http://www.chanceton.com
Corporate Financial Advisory Services
N.A.I.C.S.: 523940
Kam Wah Wong *(Founder & CEO)*

UNITE & GROW, INC.
Shin-Ochanomizu Bldg 3F 4-3 Kanda-Surugadai, Chiyoda-ku, Tokyo, 101-0062, Japan
Tel.: (81) 355772092
Web Site: https://www.ug-inc.net
Year Founded: 2005

UNITE & GROW, INC.

Unite & Grow, Inc.—(Continued)
4486—(TKS)
Rev.: $18,909,030
Assets: $18,519,080
Liabilities: $5,430,940
Net Worth: $13,088,140
Earnings: $2,162,450
Emp.: 292
Fiscal Year-end: 12/31/23
Information Technology Services
N.A.I.C.S.: 541512
Kiichiro Suda *(Pres & CEO)*

UNITECH COMPUTER CO., LTD.
3Fl No 236 Shinhu 2nd Rd Neihu Chiu, Taipei, 114, Taiwan
Tel.: (886) 227962345
Web Site: http://www.unitech.com.tw
Year Founded: 1979
2414—(TAI)
Rev.: $756,086,272
Assets: $266,893,414
Liabilities: $131,800,643
Net Worth: $135,092,771
Earnings: $13,391,608
Emp.: 406
Fiscal Year-end: 12/31/23
Computer & Peripheral Devices Whslr
N.A.I.C.S.: 423430
K. C. Yeh *(Bd of Dirs & Chm)*

Subsidiaries:

Unique Technology Europe B.V. (1)
Kapitein Hatterasstraat 19, 5015 BB, Tilburg, Netherlands
Tel.: (31) 134609292
Automatic Data Capture Product Distr
N.A.I.C.S.: 423430

Unitech Japan Co., Ltd. (1)
798-1 Kamikasuya, Isehara, 259-1141, Kanagawa, Japan
Tel.: (81) 463961132
Web Site: https://unitech-net.jp
Emp.: 98
Optical Connector Core Pin Mfr & Distr
N.A.I.C.S.: 334417

Xiamen Unitech Computer Co., Ltd. (1)
Room401C 4F Rihua International Mansion Xinfeng 3nd Road, Huoju Hi-tech District, Xiamen, Fujan, China
Tel.: (86) 5923109966
Automatic Data Capture Product Distr
N.A.I.C.S.: 423430

UNITECH ELECTRICAL CONTRACTING INC.
700 58 Ave SE Unit 11, Calgary, T2H 2E2, AB, Canada
Tel.: (403) 255-2277
Rev.: $14,519,807
Emp.: 120
Electrical Work
N.A.I.C.S.: 238210

UNITECH INTERNATIONAL LIMITED
D/714 7th Floor D-Wing Nilkant Business Park Vidhyavihar West, Kirol Village, Mumbai, 400 086, Maharashtra, India
Tel.: (91) 2266667004
Web Site: http://www.unitechinternational.in
531867—(BOM)
Rev.: $2,788,226
Assets: $4,712,655
Liabilities: $4,619,675
Net Worth: $92,980
Earnings: ($1,396,187)
Fiscal Year-end: 03/31/23
Ferrour & Non Ferrous Product Mfr
N.A.I.C.S.: 332111
Joseph Mathoor *(CFO)*

UNITECH LIMITED
1306-1308 13th Floor Tower B Signature Towers, South City-1, Gurgaon, 122007, India
Tel.: (91) 1244726860
Web Site: https://www.unitechgroup.com
UNITECH—(NSE)
Rev.: $76,597,821
Assets: $3,532,578,340
Liabilities: $3,112,130,617
Net Worth: $420,447,723
Earnings: ($217,603,577)
Emp.: 249
Fiscal Year-end: 03/31/21
Real Estate Services
N.A.I.C.S.: 237210
Ajay Chandra *(Mng Dir)*

Subsidiaries:

New India Construction Co. Limited (1)
201/A Vertex Vikas Sir M V Road Andheri East, Mumbai, 400069, Maharashtra, India
Tel.: (91) 2226821767
Web Site: https://nicco.co.in
Construction Planning & Execution Services
N.A.I.C.S.: 541330

Unitech Power Transmission Limited (1)
3rd Floor Unitech House L Block South City 1 Sector 41, Gurgaon, 122 016, Haryana, India
Tel.: (91) 8046048090
Web Site: https://www.unitech-power.com
Mechanical Power Transmission Equipment Mfr
N.A.I.C.S.: 333613

UNITECH PRINTED CIRCUIT BOARD CORP.
No 3 Lane 4 Chung-Shan Road, Tucheng Dist, New Taipei City, Taiwan
Tel.: (886) 222685071
Web Site: https://www.pcbut.com.tw
Year Founded: 1984
2367—(TAI)
Rev.: $489,251,494
Assets: $700,845,292
Liabilities: $379,579,010
Net Worth: $321,266,282
Earnings: ($11,257,431)
Emp.: 3,439
Fiscal Year-end: 12/31/23
Printed Circuit Board Mfr
N.A.I.C.S.: 334412
Chang Yuan-Min *(Chm & Chief Strategy Officer)*

Subsidiaries:

Unitech Printed Circuit Board Corp. - Factory No. 2 (1)
No 3 Lane 4 Chung-Shan Road, Tucheng, 236, Taipei, Taiwan
Tel.: (886) 222685071
Sales Range: $800-899.9 Million
Emp.: 3,000
Printed Circuit Board Mfr
N.A.I.C.S.: 334412
John Kavin *(Mgr-HR)*

Unitech Printed Circuit Board Corp. - Factory No. 3 (1)
No 12 Datong Street, Tucheng, 236, Taiwan
Tel.: (886) 222680580
Printed Circuit Board Mfr
N.A.I.C.S.: 334412

Unitech Printed Circuit Board Corp. - Plant II (1)
No 3 Lane 4 Chung-Shan Road, Tucheng, 23680, Taiwan
Tel.: (886) 222685071
Sales Range: $800-899.9 Million
Emp.: 3,000
Printed Circuit Board Mfr
N.A.I.C.S.: 334412

UNITED & COLLECTIVE CO., LTD.
1-12-32 Akasaka Minato-Ku, Tokyo, 107-6023, Japan
Tel.: (81) 362778088
Web Site: http://www.united-collective.co.jp
3557—(TKS)
Sales Range: Less than $1 Million
Restaurant Management Services
N.A.I.C.S.: 722511
Hideya Sakai *(Pres & CEO)*

UNITED AIRWAYS (BD) LTD.
House 7 Dolon Chapa 2nd floor Road 12 Sector 1, Uttara Model Town, Dhaka, 1230, Bangladesh
Tel.: (880) 28932338
Web Site: http://www.uabdl.com
Year Founded: 2005
Passenger Air Transportation Services
N.A.I.C.S.: 481111
Tasbirul Ahmed Choudhury *(Founder, Chm & Mng Dir)*

UNITED AIRWAYS BANGLADESH LTD.
1 Jasimuddin Avenue Uttara Tower 5th Floor, Uttara, Dhaka, 1230, Bangladesh
Tel.: (880) 28932338
Web Site: http://www.uabdl.com
Year Founded: 2005
Sales Range: $75-99.9 Million
Emp.: 472
Airline
N.A.I.C.S.: 481111
Tasbirul Ahmed Choudhury *(Chm & Mng Dir)*

UNITED AJOD INSURANCE LIMITED
CTC Mall 7th Floor, Bagdurbar Marga, Sundhara,, Kathmandu, Nepal
Tel.: (977) 015343072
Web Site: https://unitedajodinsurance.com
Year Founded: 2023
UAIL—(NEP)
Insurance Services
N.A.I.C.S.: 524298

UNITED ARAB BANK PJSC
UAB Tower Al Majaz Street Buhaira Corniche, PO Box 25022, Sharjah, United Arab Emirates
Tel.: (971) 65075222
Web Site: https://www.uab.ae
Year Founded: 1975
UAB—(ABU)
Rev.: $250,914,783
Assets: $4,804,750,329
Liabilities: $4,181,351,202
Net Worth: $623,399,127
Earnings: $69,509,665
Emp.: 392
Fiscal Year-end: 12/31/23
Banking Services
N.A.I.C.S.: 522110
Faisal Salem Al Qassimi *(Chm)*

UNITED ARAB EMIRATES LPT (FZC)
Executive Suite X4-37, PO Box 9304, Saif Zone Airprt International, Sharjah, 9304, United Arab Emirates
Tel.: (971) 65573205
Web Site: http://www.lenze.com
Sales Range: $50-74.9 Million
Emp.: 5
Holding Company
N.A.I.C.S.: 551112
Reza Sarraf *(Gen Mgr)*

UNITED ARROWS LTD.
Nihonseimei Akasaka Bldg 8-1-19

INTERNATIONAL PUBLIC

Akasaka, Minata-ku, Tokyo, 107-0052, Japan
Tel.: (81) 357856325
Web Site: https://www.united-arrows.co.jp
Year Founded: 1989
7606—(TKS)
Rev.: $887,518,090
Assets: $397,948,440
Liabilities: $166,400,140
Net Worth: $231,548,300
Earnings: $32,230,360
Emp.: 258
Fiscal Year-end: 03/31/24
Men's Clothing Stores
N.A.I.C.S.: 458110
Hiroyuki Higashi *(Chief Human Officer & Mng Exec Officer)*

Subsidiaries:

Chrome Hearts JP, Gk (1)
6-3-14 Minami-Aoyama, Minato-ku, Tokyo, 107-0062, Japan
Tel.: (81) 357661081
Web Site: https://www.chromehearts.com
Fashion Accessory Mfr & Distr
N.A.I.C.S.: 315990

Coen Co., Ltd. (1)
Nippon Life Akasaka Building 8-1-19 Akasaka, Minato-ku, Tokyo, 107-0052, Japan
Tel.: (81) 368947720
Web Site: https://www.coen.co.jp
Emp.: 790
Dress Mfr
N.A.I.C.S.: 311941

Figo Co., Ltd. (1)
7-1-5 Minami Aoyama Column Minami Aoyama 7F, Minato-ku, Tokyo, 107-0052, Japan
Tel.: (81) 364272907
Web Site: http://www.figo.co.jp
Sales Range: $25-49.9 Million
Emp.: 15
Clothing Retailer
N.A.I.C.S.: 458110

UNITED AUTOMOTIVE DISTRIBUTORS LTD
5340 Lougheed Hwy, Burnaby, V5B 2Z8, BC, Canada
Tel.: (604) 291-8611
Rev.: $21,400,000
Emp.: 155
New & Used Car Dealers
N.A.I.C.S.: 441110
Douglas Reid *(Pres)*

UNITED BANK FOR AFRICA PLC
UBA House 57 Marina, PO Box 2406, Lagos, Nigeria
Tel.: (234) 12808822
Web Site: http://www.ubagroup.com
Year Founded: 1949
UBA—(NIGE)
Rev.: $1,216,733,624
Assets: $23,368,679,342
Liabilities: $21,071,554,303
Net Worth: $2,297,125,039
Earnings: $687,595,870
Emp.: 10,007
Fiscal Year-end: 12/31/23
Financial Holding Company
N.A.I.C.S.: 551111
Tony O. Elumelu *(Chm)*

Subsidiaries:

UBA Chad S.A (1)
Avenue Charles de Gaulle, BP 1148, N'djamena, Chad
Tel.: (235) 62821717
Web Site: http://www.ubachad.com
Banking Services
N.A.I.C.S.: 522110

UBA Congo Brazzaville SA (1)
37 Avenue William Guynet opposite Rondpoint City Center, Brazzaville, Congo, Republic of

Tel.: (242) 66972331
Web Site:
   http://www.ubacongobrazzaville.com
Banking Services
N.A.I.C.S.: 522110

UBA Congo DRC SA (1)
N 1853 Avenue de la Liberation, Kinshasa, Congo, Democratic Republic of
Tel.: (243) 996020064
Web Site: http://www.ubardc.com
Banking Services
N.A.I.C.S.: 522110
Herve Otschudi *(Deputy Mng Dir)*

UBA Ghana Limited (1)
Heritage Tower Ambassadorial Enclave Off Liberia Road, Ridge Accra P M B 29 Ministries, Accra, Ghana
Tel.: (233) 302634060
Web Site: http://www.ubaghana.com
Banking Services
N.A.I.C.S.: 522110
Kweku Andoh Awotwi *(Chm)*

UBA Guinea SA (1)
Rue du Chateau d'Eau Marche Niger, Conakry, Kaloum, Guinea
Tel.: (224) 629463696
Web Site: http://www.ubaguinea.com
Banking Services
N.A.I.C.S.: 522110

UBA Liberia Limited (1)
Broad Nelson Street, Monrovia, Liberia
Tel.: (231) 880560509
Web Site: http://www.ubaliberia.com
Banking Services
N.A.I.C.S.: 522110
Eugene Shanon *(Chm)*

UBA Mozambique SA (1)
Square 16 June Malanga 312, Maputo, Mozambique
Tel.: (258) 43008601
Web Site: http://www.ubamozambique.com
Banking Services
N.A.I.C.S.: 522110

UBA Senegal SA (1)
Route des Almadies Zone 12 Lot D Peytavin, BP 11 4776, Dakar, Senegal
Tel.: (221) 338595100
Web Site: http://www.ubasenegal.com
Banking Services
N.A.I.C.S.: 522110

UBA Tanzania Limited (1)
30 C 30 D Nyerere Road, PO Box 80514, Dar es Salaam, Tanzania
Tel.: (255) 22284468
Web Site: http://www.ubatanzania.co.tz
Banking Services
N.A.I.C.S.: 522110
Tuvako Manongi *(Chm)*

UBA UK Limited (1)
36 Queen Street, London, EC4R 1BN, United Kingdom
Tel.: (44) 2077664600
Web Site: http://www.ubauk.com
Banking Services
N.A.I.C.S.: 522110
Patrick Gutmann *(CEO & Exec Dir)*

UBA Uganda Limited (1)
Plot 2 Jinja Road, Kampala, Uganda
Tel.: (256) 417715100
Web Site: http://www.ubauganda.com
Banking Services
N.A.I.C.S.: 522110
Chioma A. Mang *(CEO & Mng Dir)*

UNITED BANKERS PLC
Aleksanterinkatu 21 A, 00100, Helsinki, Finland
Tel.: (358) 925380300
Web Site:
   https://www.unitedbankers.fi
Year Founded: 1986
UNITED—(HEL)
Rev.: $52,408,806
Assets: $77,237,211
Liabilities: $25,374,487
Net Worth: $51,862,724
Earnings: $13,890,568
Emp.: 156
Fiscal Year-end: 12/31/22
Investment Banking
N.A.I.C.S.: 523150
Patrick Anderson *(CEO)*
Subsidiaries:

UB Yritysrahoitus Oy (1)
Aleksanterinkatu 21 A, 00100, Helsinki, Finland
Tel.: (358) 5244520
Web Site: https://www.ubrahoitus.fi
Portfolio Management Services
N.A.I.C.S.: 525110

UNITED BASALT PRODUCTS LIMITED
Trianon, Quatre Bornes, Mauritius
Tel.: (230) 4541964
Web Site: https://www.ubp.mu
Year Founded: 1953
UBP—(MAU)
Rev.: $71,029,987
Assets: $137,235,855
Liabilities: $56,405,315
Net Worth: $80,830,540
Earnings: $539,286
Emp.: 1,399
Fiscal Year-end: 06/30/20
Concrete Block Mfr & Whslr
N.A.I.C.S.: 327331
Christophe Quevauvilliers *(Mgr-Grp Fin)*
Subsidiaries:

Drymix Ltd. (1)
Geoffroy Branch Road, Bambous, Mauritius
Tel.: (230) 4520103
Web Site: https://www.drymix.mu
Ready Mix Bag Mortar Mfr
N.A.I.C.S.: 327320
Jonas Robert *(Sls Mgr)*

Espace Maison Ltee (1)
Trianon, Quatre Bornes, Mauritius
Tel.: (230) 4608585
Web Site: https://www.espacemaison.mu
Wireless Power Tool Retailer
N.A.I.C.S.: 423690

UNITED BEVERAGES S.A.
Ul Plaska 24-36, 87100, Torun, Poland
Tel.: (48) 695875919
Web Site:
   http://www.unitedbeverages.pl
Emp.: 750
Alcoholic Drinks Whslr & Distr
N.A.I.C.S.: 424820
William Carey *(Chm-Mgmt Bd & CEO)*
Subsidiaries:

Sobieski Trade Sp. z.o.o. (1)
Kolaczkowo 9, 62-230, Witkowo, Wielkopolska, Poland
Tel.: (48) 614778212
Web Site: https://www.sobieskitrade.com.pl
Alcoholic Beverages Mfr
N.A.I.C.S.: 312120

UNITED BRANDS LIMITED
1st Floor One IBL Center Block No 7 & 8 Delhi Mercantile Muslim, Cooperative Housing Society Main Shahrah-e-Faisal, Karachi, Pakistan
Tel.: (92) 2137170176
Web Site: https://www.ubrands.biz
Year Founded: 1965
Household Appliances Mfr
N.A.I.C.S.: 335220
Arshad Anis *(CEO)*

UNITED BREWERIES (HOLDINGS) LTD.
UB Towers, 24 Vittal Mallya Road, Bengaluru, 560001, India
Tel.: (91) 8022293333
Web Site:
   https://www.unitedbreweries.com
Year Founded: 1915
532478—(BOM)
Holding Company; Beer Brewing, Liquor Distillation & Other Alcoholic Beverages Mfr & Distr
N.A.I.C.S.: 551112
Vijay Mallya *(Chm)*
Subsidiaries:

UBICS, Inc. (1)
333 Technology Dr Ste 210, Canonsburg, PA 15317-9513
Tel.: (724) 746-6001
Web Site: http://www.ubics.com
Sales Range: $25-49.9 Million
Emp.: 200
Information Technology Services
N.A.I.C.S.: 541511
Vijay Mallya *(Chm & CEO)*

UNITED BUS SERVICE LTD.
Les Cassis, Port Louis, Mauritius
Tel.: (230) 2122026
Web Site: https://www.ubsgroup.mu
Year Founded: 1954
UBS—(MAU)
Rev.: $19,734,507
Assets: $35,102,290
Liabilities: $18,951,185
Net Worth: $16,151,105
Earnings: $1,359,453
Emp.: 1,300
Fiscal Year-end: 06/30/23
Transportation Services
N.A.I.C.S.: 488490
M. Yacoob Ramtoola *(Chm)*

UNITED CABLE INDUSTRIES COMPANY
PO Box 4970, Amman, 11953, Jordan
Tel.: (962) 65549292
Web Site:
   https://www.uciccables.com
UCIC—(AMM)
Rev.: $13,269,867
Assets: $186,397,560
Liabilities: $127,080,754
Net Worth: $59,316,806
Earnings: ($13,635,264)
Emp.: 185
Fiscal Year-end: 12/31/20
Cable Mfr
N.A.I.C.S.: 332618

UNITED CANADIAN MALT LIMITED
843 Park St S, Peterborough, K9J 3V1, ON, Canada
Tel.: (705) 876-9110
Web Site:
   http://www.unitedcanadianmalt.ca
Year Founded: 1929
Sales Range: $10-24.9 Million
Emp.: 10
Brewer's Malt Extracts, Custom Brewing & Specialty Products Mfr
N.A.I.C.S.: 312120
L. Pecoskie *(Mgr-Production & Distr-Sls, Ops & Plant)*

UNITED CAPITAL BANK
Plot 411 Square 65 Mamoun Beheiry St, Khartoum East, Khartoum, Sudan
Tel.: (249) 183 247700
Web Site: http://www.bankalmal.net
Year Founded: 2005
UCBA—(KHAR)
Rev.: $13,230,586
Assets: $168,130,335
Liabilities: $74,030,465
Net Worth: $94,099,870
Earnings: $3,598,875
Emp.: 160
Fiscal Year-end: 12/31/19
Banking Services
N.A.I.C.S.: 522110
Mansour Qaiser Bteish *(Vice Chm)*

UNITED CAPITAL PARTNERS ADVISORY LLC
2 Paveletskaya Square Bldg 2, 115054, Moscow, Russia
Tel.: (7) 4956431100   RU
Web Site: http://ucpadvisory.ru
Year Founded: 2006
Privater Equity Firm
N.A.I.C.S.: 523999
Ilya Sherbovich *(Pres & Mng Partner)*
Subsidiaries:

Nayara Energy Limited (1)
5th Floor Jet Airways Godrej BKC Plot No C-68 G Block, Bandra East Kurla Complex, Mumbai, 400 051, Maharashtra, India   (24.5%)
Tel.: (91) 2833661444
Web Site: http://www.nayaraenergy.com
Rev.: $14,384,912,880
Assets: $10,700,264,220
Liabilities: $7,944,618,120
Net Worth: $2,755,646,100
Earnings: $98,730,900
Fiscal Year-end: 03/31/2019
Oil & Gas Exploration, Production & Marketing Services
N.A.I.C.S.: 211120
Chakrapany Manoharan *(Dir-Refinery)*

UNITED CARPETS GROUP PLC
Moorhead House Moorhead Way, Bramley, Rotherham, S66 1YY, S Yorkshire, United Kingdom
Tel.: (44) 1709 732 666   UK
Web Site:
   http://www.unitedcarpetsandbeds.net
Sales Range: $25-49.9 Million
Emp.: 164
Holding Company; Carpet, Wood Flooring & Bed Stores Owner, Franchisor & Operator
N.A.I.C.S.: 551112
Deborah Grayson *(Dir-Comml)*
Subsidiaries:

Unit L Trident Pkhalton Lea (1)
Unit L Trident Pkhalton Lea, Runcorn, WA7 2FQ, Cheshire, United Kingdom
Tel.: (44) 1928714658
Web Site:
   http://www.unitedcarpetsgroup.com
Sales Range: $50-74.9 Million
Emp.: 3
Carpet Retailer
N.A.I.C.S.: 423220

United Carpets (Northern) Limited (1)
17 Great Portwood St City Ctr, Stockport, SK1 2DW, Cheshire, United Kingdom
Tel.: (44) 1614764200
Web Site: http://www.unitedcarpets.com
Sales Range: $50-74.9 Million
Emp.: 5
Carpet Distr
N.A.I.C.S.: 423220

UNITED COAL HOLDINGS LTD.
3467 Commercial Street, Vancouver, V5N 4E8, BC, Canada
Tel.: (604) 871-9930
Web Site: http://www.unitedcoal.ca
Year Founded: 1958
Sales Range: Less than $1 Million
Mineral Exploration Services
N.A.I.C.S.: 213114
Simon Ma *(CFO)*

UNITED COMMERCIAL BANK LIMITED
Bulus Center Plot-CWS-A-1 Road No-34 Gulshan Avenue, Dhaka, 1212, Bangladesh
Tel.: (880) 255668070
Web Site: https://www.ucbl.com.bd
Year Founded: 1983

UNITED COMMERCIAL BANK LIMITED

United Commercial Bank Limited—(Continued)
UCB—(CHT)
Rev.: $352,234,738
Assets: $6,285,963,913
Liabilities: $5,905,834,806
Net Worth: $380,129,108
Earnings: $20,092,050
Emp.: 5,749
Fiscal Year-end: 12/31/23
Banking Services
N.A.I.C.S.: 522110
Rukhmila Zaman (Chm)

Subsidiaries:

UCB Fintech Company Limited (1)
Plot CWS A -1 Road 34 Gulshan Avenue, Dhaka, Bangladesh
Tel.: (880) 9612316268
Web Site: https://www.upaybd.com
Mobile Financial Services
N.A.I.C.S.: 522320

UCB Stock Brokerage Limited (1)
6 Dilkusha C/A 1 st Floor, Dhaka, 1000, Bangladesh
Tel.: (880) 29558481
Web Site: https://ucbstock.com.bd
Stock Broker Services
N.A.I.C.S.: 523150
Syed Adnan Huda (COO)

UNITED COMPANY RUSAL PLC
Vasilisa Kozhina St 1, Moscow, 121096, Russia
Tel.: (7) 4957205170
Web Site: https://www.rusal.ru
Year Founded: 2000
RUAL—(MOEX)
Rev.: $11,994,000,000
Assets: $20,906,000,000
Liabilities: $10,382,000,000
Net Worth: $10,524,000,000
Earnings: $3,225,000,000
Fiscal Year-end: 12/31/21
Aluminum Production
N.A.I.C.S.: 331313
Evgenii Nikitin (CEO)

Subsidiaries:

Alumina Partners of Jamaica (1)
Spur Tree Post Office, Manchester, Jamaica
Tel.: (876) 9623251
Alumina, Bauxite
N.A.I.C.S.: 331313

Aughinish Alumina Limited (1)
Aughinish Island Area 71, Askeaton, Co Limerick, Ireland
Tel.: (353) 61604000
Web Site: http://www.rusalaughinish.com
Sales Range: $100-124.9 Million
Emp.: 430
Provider of Aluminum Refining
N.A.I.C.S.: 331313
Sean Garland (Mng Dir)

Columbia Falls Aluminum Company LLC (1)
2000 Aluminum Dr, Columbia Falls, MT 59912
Tel.: (406) 892-8400
Web Site: http://www.cfaluminum.com
Sales Range: $50-74.9 Million
Emp.: 250
Aluminum Mfr
N.A.I.C.S.: 331313

Eurallumina SpA (1)
Casella postale 64, Portoscuso, Italy
Tel.: (39) 07815001
Aluminium Product Distr
N.A.I.C.S.: 423510
Evgeniy Zenkin (Mng Dir)

JSC RUSAL Sayanogorsk (1)
Promploshchadka, Sayanogorsk, 655600, Russia
Tel.: (7) 39042211011
Emp.: 2,736
Aluminium Product Distr
N.A.I.C.S.: 423510

Evgeniy Popov (Mng Dir)

Kubikenborg Aluminium AB (1)
Landsvagsallen 79, 852 29, Sundsvall, 852 29, Sweden
Tel.: (46) 60166100
Emp.: 450
Aluminium Products Mfr
N.A.I.C.S.: 332999
Javier Navia (Mng Dir)

OJSC RUSAL Achinsk (1)
RUSAl Alumina Compound, Krasnoyarsk, 662100, Russia
Tel.: (7) 3915 13 50 00
Emp.: 2,950
Aluminium Products Mfr
N.A.I.C.S.: 331313
Evgeny Zhukov (Mng Dir)

OJSC RUSAL Novokuznetsk (1)
D 7 Prospekt Ferrosplavny, Novokuznetsk, Russia
Tel.: (7) 3843397322
Emp.: 2,074
Aluminium Products Mfr
N.A.I.C.S.: 332999
Victor Zhirnakov (Mng Dir)

Rusal America Corp. (1)
800 Westchester Ave Ste S308, Rye Brook, NY 10573-1330
Tel.: (914) 670-5771
Web Site: http://www.rusalamerica.com
Aluminum Mfr
N.A.I.C.S.: 331318

Rusal Marketing GmbH (1)
Baarerstrasse 22, 6300, Zug, Switzerland
Tel.: (41) 415609800
Web Site: https://allow.rusal.com
Aluminum Extruder Distr
N.A.I.C.S.: 423830

West Indies Alumina Company (1)
Kirkvine Post Office, Manchester, Jamaica
Tel.: (876) 9623141
Web Site: http://www.windalco.com
Sales Range: $100-124.9 Million
Emp.: 350
Bauxite & Alumina
N.A.I.C.S.: 331313

UNITED COOPERATIVE ASSURANCE COMPANY
1st & 4th Floors Al Mukmal Centre Prince Saud Al Faisal Street, PO Box 5019, Al Khalidiyah District, Jeddah, 21422, Saudi Arabia
Tel.: (966) 122609200
Web Site: http://www.uca.com.sa
Year Founded: 2008
8190—(SAU)
Rev.: $82,896,947
Assets: $282,866,818
Liabilities: $228,038,662
Net Worth: $54,828,156
Earnings: ($11,428,076)
Emp.: 205
Fiscal Year-end: 12/31/22
Insurance Management Services
N.A.I.C.S.: 524298
Khalid Hussein Ali Reza (Chm)

UNITED CORPORATIONS LTD.
Tenth Floor 165 University Avenue, Toronto, M5H 3B8, ON, Canada
Tel.: (416) 947-2578
Web Site: https://www.ucorp.ca
Year Founded: 1929
UNC—(TSX)
Rev.: $17,472,224
Assets: $1,604,823,952
Liabilities: $25,557,870
Net Worth: $1,579,266,082
Earnings: ($18,064,410)
Emp.: 3
Fiscal Year-end: 03/31/22
Investment Services
N.A.I.C.S.: 523999
Duncan N. R. Jackman (Chm & Pres)

UNITED CREDIT LTD

27B Camac Street 8th Floor, Kolkata, 700 016, India
Tel.: (91) 3322879359
Web Site: https://www.unitedcreditltd.com
Year Founded: 1970
531091—(BOM)
Rev.: $414,385
Assets: $3,756,602
Liabilities: $258,707
Net Worth: $3,497,895
Earnings: $125,301
Emp.: 11
Fiscal Year-end: 03/31/20
Financial Services
N.A.I.C.S.: 522291
Ashok Kumar Dabriwala (Chm & Mng Dir)

Subsidiaries:

United Nanotechnologies Private Limited (1)
103 Park St, Kolkata, 700 016, West Bengal, India
Tel.: (91) 3322872525
Web Site: http://www.uncpl.com
Sales Range: $25-49.9 Million
Scientific Engineering Services
N.A.I.C.S.: 541330

UNITED CREDIT SYSTEMS OAO
Petrovka street building 27 premises 1 room 8 floor 2, Moscow, 107031, Russia
Tel.: (7) 4959330193
Web Site: https://www.ucsys.ru
UCSS—(MOEX)
Sales Range: Less than $1 Million
Investment Management & Consulting Services
N.A.I.C.S.: 523940
Aleksey A. Korzun (CEO)

UNITED DEVELOPMENT COMPANY PSC
Alfardan Towers Dafna Area 24th Floor, PO Box 7256, Doha, Qatar
Tel.: (974) 44098374
Web Site: https://www.udcqatar.com
Year Founded: 1999
UDCD—(QE)
Rev.: $555,430,589
Assets: $5,450,091,554
Liabilities: $2,432,537,952
Net Worth: $3,017,553,602
Earnings: $96,897,703
Emp.: 145
Fiscal Year-end: 12/31/21
Property Management Services
N.A.I.C.S.: 531390
Abdulrahman Abdullah Abdulghani Nasser Al Abdulghani (Vice Chm)

Subsidiaries:

Ronautica Middle East O.M.C. (1)
Retail Units 30 & 42 Parcel 1 The Pearl - Qatar, Doha, 7256, Qatar
Tel.: (974) 44095279
Web Site: http://ronauticame.com
Marine Management Services
N.A.I.C.S.: 488510

Scoop Media and Communication Company O.M.C. (1)
Al Fardan Tower 22nd Floor West Bay Area, PO Box 7256, Doha, Qatar
Tel.: (974) 44098526
Web Site: http://www.scoop-me.com
Advertising Services
N.A.I.C.S.: 541810

United Facilities Management Company O.M.C (1)
PO Box 26665, Doha, Qatar
Tel.: (974) 44 96 17 07
Web Site: http://www.glitterqatar.com
Emp.: 230
Home Management Services
N.A.I.C.S.: 561790

INTERNATIONAL PUBLIC

John Jones (Gen Mgr)

UNITED DOCKS LTD
United Docks Business Park Caudan, Port Louis, Mauritius
Tel.: (230) 2123261
Web Site: https://www.uniteddocks.com
Year Founded: 1991
UTDL—(MAU)
Rev.: $1,501,466
Assets: $78,223,350
Liabilities: $19,245,344
Net Worth: $58,978,006
Earnings: $47,215
Emp.: 23
Fiscal Year-end: 06/30/21
Real Estate Development Services
N.A.I.C.S.: 531390
Nitin Pandea (CEO)

UNITED DRILLING TOOLS LTD.
26th Floor Astralis Tower Supernova Complex Sector-94, Dist-Gautam Budh Nagar, Noida, 201301, UP, India
Tel.: (91) 1204221777
Web Site: https://www.udtltd.com
Year Founded: 1985
UNIDT—(NSE)
Rev.: $19,997,318
Assets: $31,917,181
Liabilities: $5,472,722
Net Worth: $26,444,459
Earnings: $4,463,318
Emp.: 206
Fiscal Year-end: 03/31/21
Handling Tools Mfr
N.A.I.C.S.: 332216
Pramod Kumar Ojha (Compliance Officer & Co-Sec)

UNITED DRYWALL LTD.
4339-14th St NE, Calgary, T2E 7A9, AB, Canada
Tel.: (403) 291-4835
Web Site: https://www.uniteddrywall.com
Year Founded: 1962
Sales Range: $10-24.9 Million
Drywall Contractor
N.A.I.C.S.: 238510
Colin Steele (Pres)

UNITED ELECTRONICS COMPANY KSA
PO Box 76688, Al Khobar, 31952, Saudi Arabia
Tel.: (966) 920004123
Web Site: http://www.extrastores.com
Sales Range: $350-399.9 Million
Emp.: 1,800
Electronics & Appliances Retailer
N.A.I.C.S.: 449210
Abdullah Abdulatif Al Forzan (Chm)

Subsidiaries:

United Electronics Company-Extra L.L.C. (1)
2421-2421 Way3703 - Block 237, Al Gubrah Al Janubia, Muscat, Oman
Tel.: (968) 8001240900
Web Site: http://www.extrastores.com
Electronic Product Distr
N.A.I.C.S.: 423620

UNITED ENERGY GROUP LIMITED
Room 2505 25F Two Pacific Place 88 Queensway, Hong Kong, China (Hong Kong)
Tel.: (852) 25228287
Web Site: https://www.uegl.com.hk
UNEGF—(OTCIQ)
Rev.: $1,374,332,946
Assets: $3,504,267,767

Liabilities: $1,484,021,624
Net Worth: $2,020,246,144
Earnings: $332,427,569
Emp.: 2,183
Fiscal Year-end: 12/31/22
Oil & Gas Exploration & Production Services
N.A.I.C.S.: 211120
Meiying Zhang (Exec Dir)

Subsidiaries:

United Energy Pakistan Limited (1)
Tel.: (92) 2135611194
Web Site: https://uep.com.pk
Petroleum & Gas Exploration, Development & Production
N.A.I.C.S.: 211120

Unit (Domestic):

OMV (Pakistan) Exploration GmbH (2)
ISE Towers Floor 19 55-B Jinnah Avenue, PO Box 2653, Islamabad, Pakistan
Tel.: (92) 51 2089 480
Oil & Gas Production & Exploration
N.A.I.C.S.: 211130

UNITED FAITH AUTO ENGINEERING CO., LTD.
North Side of Checheng Avenue, Auto City Huadu, Guangzhou, 510800, Guangdong, China
Tel.: (86) 2088581807
Web Site: https://www.uf.com.cn
Year Founded: 2005
301112—(SSE)
Rev.: $77,196,399
Assets: $230,634,546
Liabilities: $59,946,237
Net Worth: $170,688,309
Earnings: $9,134,564
Fiscal Year-end: 12/31/22
Industrial Automation Equipment Mfr & Distr
N.A.I.C.S.: 333248
Li Gang (Chm)

UNITED FARMERS OF ALBERTA CO-OPERATIVE LIMITED
Suite 700 4838 Richard Rd SW, Calgary, T3E 6L1, AB, Canada
Tel.: (403) 570-4500
Web Site: https://www.ufa.com
Year Founded: 1909
Sales Range: $1-4.9 Billion
Emp.: 400
Farm Supply & Petroleum Product Whslr
N.A.I.C.S.: 424910
Bob Fink (Chief Corp Affairs Officer)

UNITED FIBER OPTIC COMMUNICATION, INC.
No 12 Creation 4th Road Science-Based Industrial Park, Hsinchu, 300, Taiwan
Tel.: (886) 35779211
Web Site: https://www.ufoc.com.tw
Year Founded: 1984
4903—(TPE)
Rev.: $25,609,918
Assets: $35,657,474
Liabilities: $15,783,354
Net Worth: $19,874,121
Earnings: ($2,937,748)
Fiscal Year-end: 12/31/22
Fiber Optic Electrical Equipment Mfr
N.A.I.C.S.: 335921
Hui Chun Lin (Chm)

UNITED FIDELITY INSURANCE CO PSC
The Opus Tower Block B Office B703 Business Bay, Post Box 1888, Dubai, United Arab Emirates
Tel.: (971) 42502501
Web Site: https://fidelityunited.ae
Year Founded: 1976
UIC—(ABU)
Rev.: $114,934,647
Assets: $219,049,411
Liabilities: $180,894,652
Net Worth: $38,154,760
Earnings: $186,046
Fiscal Year-end: 12/31/22
General Insurance Services
N.A.I.C.S.: 524114
Bilal Adhami (CEO)

UNITED FINANCE COMPANY SAOG
PO Box 3652, 112, Ruwi, Oman
Tel.: (968) 24577300
Web Site: https://www.ufcoman.com
Year Founded: 1997
UFCI—(MUS)
Rev.: $22,969,789
Assets: $269,561,684
Liabilities: $142,616,151
Net Worth: $126,945,533
Earnings: $4,650,381
Emp.: 135
Fiscal Year-end: 12/31/23
Financial Services
N.A.I.C.S.: 523999
K. T. Ramasamy (Asst Gen Mgr-Fin & IT)

UNITED FINANCE LIMITED
IJ Plaza Durwar Marga, PO Box 12311, Kathmandu, Nepal
Tel.: (977) 14241648
Year Founded: 1992
UFL—(NEP)
Rev.: $27,829,181
Assets: $251,414,099
Liabilities: $214,655,936
Net Worth: $36,758,164
Earnings: $2,830,859
Emp.: 882
Fiscal Year-end: 12/31/19
Financial Services
N.A.I.C.S.: 523999
Sunanda B. Shrestha (CEO)

UNITED FINANCE PLC
G B Buildings Second Floor Triq il-Watar, Ta' Xbiex, XBX 1301, Malta
Tel.: (356) 23388000
Web Site: http://www.unitedgroup.com.mt
Year Founded: 1926
UF23A—(MAL)
Rev.: $699,856
Assets: $10,684,402
Liabilities: $1,013,357
Net Worth: $9,671,045
Earnings: $908,489
Fiscal Year-end: 12/31/23
Financial Investment Services
N.A.I.C.S.: 523940
Carmen Gatt Baldacchino (Chm)

UNITED FOOD HOLDINGS LIMITED
16F The Hong Kong Club Building 3A Chater Road, Central, China (Hong Kong)
Tel.: (852) 2 851 6688   BM
Web Site: http://www.unitedfood.com.sg
AZR—(SES)
Rev.: $1,488,129
Assets: $28,765,637
Liabilities: $9,715,659
Net Worth: $19,049,978
Earnings: ($10,409,241)
Emp.: 922
Fiscal Year-end: 03/31/21
Soybean & Animal Feed Mfr
N.A.I.C.S.: 111110
Wai Ming Chiang (Sec)

UNITED FOODS COMPANY (PSC)
Al Quoz 1, PO Box 5836, Dubai, United Arab Emirates
Tel.: (971) 45063800
Web Site: https://www.unitedfoods.ae
Year Founded: 1976
UFC—(DFM)
Rev.: $160,466,605
Assets: $112,870,535
Liabilities: $22,562,520
Net Worth: $90,308,015
Earnings: $8,346,208
Emp.: 503
Fiscal Year-end: 12/31/23
Food Products Mfr
N.A.I.C.S.: 311999
Ali Humaid Al Owais (Chm)

Subsidiaries:

United Foods Company (PSC) - Jabel Ali Plant (1)
PO Box 5836, Dubai, United Arab Emirates
Tel.: (971) 4 8802990
Edible Oil Mfr
N.A.I.C.S.: 311225

UNITED FOODSTUFF INDUSTRIES GROUP CO. K.S.C.C.
Area-8, Street -81 Subhan, PO Box 170, Salmiya, Kuwait, 22002, Kuwait
Tel.: (965) 1822226
Web Site: http://www.ufigkw.com
Year Founded: 1992
Sales Range: $25-49.9 Million
Emp.: 650
Desserts, Chocolates, Sweets & Pastries Producer & Caterer
N.A.I.C.S.: 311813

UNITED GLOBAL LIMITED
14 Tuas Drive 2, Singapore, 638647, Singapore
Tel.: (65) 68611157   SG
Web Site: http://www.unitedgloballimited.com
Year Founded: 1999
43P—(SES)
Rev.: $175,000
Assets: $102,666,000
Liabilities: $2,943,000
Net Worth: $99,723,000
Earnings: $3,240,000
Emp.: 199
Fiscal Year-end: 12/31/20
Lubricant Mfr & Distr
N.A.I.C.S.: 324191
Jacky Thuan Hor Tan (Founder & CEO)

Subsidiaries:

PT. Pacific Lubritama Indonesia (1)
Jalan Raya Bojonegara km 6 Bojonegara Cilegon Serang, Banten, Indonesia
Tel.: (62) 2545750555
Web Site: http://www.pli-corp.com
Lubricant Product Mfr
N.A.I.C.S.: 324191

UNITED GRAIN COMPANY JSC
Orlikov lane 3 building 1, 107140, Moscow, Russia
Tel.: (7) 4956473992
Web Site: http://ozk-group.ru
Year Founded: 2007
Sales Range: Less than $1 Million
Grain Storage Services
N.A.I.C.S.: 493130
Vitaly Yu. Sergeychuk (Deputy Head-Client Rels Dept-Market Reg)

UNITED GRINDING GROUP AG
Jubilaumsstrasse 95, 3005, Bern, Switzerland
Tel.: (41) 31 3560111   CH
Web Site: http://www.grinding.ch

Holding Company; Industrial Machinery Mfr
N.A.I.C.S.: 551112
Stephan Nell (CEO)

Subsidiaries:

Blohm Jung GmbH (1)
Kurt A Korber Chaussee 63-71, 21033, Hamburg, Germany
Tel.: (49) 40 33461 2000
Web Site: http://www.blohmgmbh.com
Grinding Machine Mfr
N.A.I.C.S.: 333519

Ewag AG (1)
Industriestrasse 4, 4554, Etziken, Switzerland
Tel.: (41) 32 613 3131
Web Site: http://www.ewag.com
Industrial Machinery Mfr
N.A.I.C.S.: 333248

Fritz Studer AG (1)
Thunstrasse 15, 3612, Steffisburg, Switzerland
Tel.: (41) 33 4391 111
Web Site: http://www.studer.com
Industrial Machinery Mfr
N.A.I.C.S.: 333248

Korber Schleifring Machinery (Shanghai) Co. Ltd. (1)
1128 Tai Shun Road Anting Town, Jiading District, Shanghai, 201814, China
Tel.: (86) 21 3958 7333
Web Site: http://www.grinding.cn
Industrial Machinery Mfr
N.A.I.C.S.: 333248

Magerle AG Maschinenfabrik (1)
Allmendstrasse 50, Postfach 123, 8320, Fehraltorf, Switzerland
Tel.: (41) 43 3556 600
Web Site: http://www.maegerle.com
Industrial Machinery Mfr
N.A.I.C.S.: 333248

United Grinding North America, Inc. (1)
510 Earl Blvd, Miamisburg, OH 45342-6411
Tel.: (937) 859-1975
Web Site: http://www.grinding.com
Industrial Machinery Distr
N.A.I.C.S.: 423830
Michael Gebhardt (VP-Ops)

Subsidiary (Non-US):

StuderTEC K.K. (2)
Matsumoto insatsu Bldg 2F 4-10-8, Omorikita, Ota, 143-0016, Tokyo, Japan
Tel.: (81) 3 68016140
Web Site: http://www.studer.com
Industrial Equipment Distr
N.A.I.C.S.: 423830

Walter Maschinenbau GmbH (1)
Jopestrasse 5, 72072, Tubingen, Germany
Tel.: (49) 7071 93930
Web Site: http://www.walter-machines.de
Grinding Machine Mfr
N.A.I.C.S.: 333998

Walter s.r.o. (1)
Blanenska 1289, 66434, Kurim, Czech Republic
Tel.: (420) 541 426611
Web Site: http://www.walter-machines.com
Industrial Machinery Mfr
N.A.I.C.S.: 333248

Subsidiary (Non-US):

Walter Ewag Asia Pacific Pte. Ltd. (2)
25 International Business Park, #01-53/56 German Centre, Singapore, 609916, Singapore
Tel.: (65) 6562 8101
Web Site: http://www.walter-machines.com
Industrial Machinery Sales
N.A.I.C.S.: 423830

Walter Ewag Italia S.r.l. (2)
Via G Garibaldi 42, 22070, Bregnano, Como, Italy
Tel.: (39) 031 770898
Machine Tool Distr
N.A.I.C.S.: 423830

UNITED GRINDING GROUP AG

United Grinding Group AG—(Continued)

Walter Ewag Japan K.K. (2)
MA Park Building 1-10-14 Mikawaanjo-cho,
Anjo, 446-0056, Aichi, Japan
Tel.: (81) 566 711 666
Industrial Machinery & Tool Distr
N.A.I.C.S.: 423830

Walter Ewag UK Ltd. (2)
2 St George's Business Park Lower Cape,
Warwick, CV34 5DR, United Kingdom
Tel.: (44) 1926 485047
Web Site: http://www.walter-machines.com
Industrial Machinery & Tool Distr
N.A.I.C.S.: 423830
Neil Whittingham *(Gen Mgr)*

UNITED GROUP FOR PUBLISHING ADVERTISING & MARKETING
Al Eskenderia Street - AlHouda Building, PO Box 2000, Damascus, Syria
Tel.: (963) 116129877
Year Founded: 2002
Advertising Services
N.A.I.C.S.: 541890

UNITED GULF HOLDING COMPANY BSC
Diplomatic Area UGB Tower, PO Box 5565, Manama, Bahrain
Tel.: (973) 17533233
Web Site: https://www.ughbh.com
UGH—(BAH)
Rev.: $186,741,000
Assets: $3,163,874,000
Liabilities: $2,763,649,000
Net Worth: $400,225,000
Earnings: ($21,293,000)
Fiscal Year-end: 12/31/22
Commercial Banking Services
N.A.I.C.S.: 522110
Masaud M. J. Hayat *(Chm)*

Subsidiaries:

United Gulf Financial Services
Company (1)
Rue Du Lac Biwa- Immeuble Fraj - Etg 2
1053 Les Berges du Lac, Tunis, Tunisia
Tel.: (216) 71167500
Web Site:
https://www.ugfsnorthafrica.com.tn
Asset Management Financial Services
N.A.I.C.S.: 541611

United Gulf Financial Services-North
Africa SA (1)
Rue du Lac Biwa- Immeuble Fraj - Etg 2,
Les berges du lac, 1053, Tunis, Tunisia
Tel.: (216) 71167500
Web Site: http://www.ugfsnorthafrica.com.tn
Asset Management Services
N.A.I.C.S.: 523940
Mohamed Salah Frad *(Gen Mgr)*

UNITED GULF INVESTMENT CORPORATION B.S.C.
32nd Floor Almoayyed Tower, PO
Box 10177, Seef District, Manama,
Bahrain
Tel.: (973) 17581654
Web Site: https://www.ugiccorp.com
Year Founded: 1991
UGIC—(BAH)
Rev.: $140,362,547
Assets: $168,886,939
Liabilities: $70,483,910
Net Worth: $98,403,029
Earnings: $9,305,774
Emp.: 7
Fiscal Year-end: 12/31/22
Portfolio Investment Services
N.A.I.C.S.: 523940
Rashed Al Abdulla Al Suwaiket Al
Hajri *(Chm)*

Subsidiaries:

Gulf Ferro Alloys Company (Sabayek)
W.L.L. (1)

Tel.: (966) 133584444
Web Site: https://www.sabayek.com
Ferroalloy Product Mfr
N.A.I.C.S.: 331110
Hamdan Abdullah Al-Samreen *(Chm)*

United Gulf Trading S.P.C. (1)
P2-Hamriyah Business Centre, Hamriyah
Free Zone, Sharjah, United Arab Emirates
Tel.: (971) 504729799
Web Site: http://www.unitedgulf-trading.com
Oil & Gas Power Services
N.A.I.C.S.: 221112

UNITED HAMPSHIRE US REAL ESTATE INVESTMENT TRUST
80 Raffles Place 28-21 UOB Plaza 2,
Singapore, 048624, Singapore
Tel.: (65) 67979010   SG
Web Site: https://www.uhreit.com
ODBU—(SES)
Rev.: $72,229,000
Assets: $808,758,000
Liabilities: $374,624,000
Net Worth: $434,134,000
Earnings: $32,991,000
Emp.: 13
Fiscal Year-end: 12/31/23
Real Estate Investment Services
N.A.I.C.S.: 531190
Robert Totten Schmitt *(CEO)*

UNITED HUNTER OIL & GAS CORP.
20 Adelaide Street East Suite 200,
Toronto, M5C 2T6, ON, Canada
Tel.: (832) 487-0813   Ca
Web Site:
http://www.unitedhunteroil.com
Year Founded: 2008
UHO—(DEU)
Assets: $17,479
Liabilities: $266,735
Net Worth: ($249,256)
Earnings: ($242,999)
Fiscal Year-end: 12/31/19
Oil & Gas Exploration Services
N.A.I.C.S.: 213112
Timothy J. Turner *(Pres & CEO)*

UNITED INSURANCE COMPANY LTD.
Camellia House 22 Kazi Nazrul Islam
Avenue, Dhaka, 1000, Bangladesh
Tel.: (880) 258611720
Web Site:
https://www.unitedinsurance.com.bd
Year Founded: 1985
UNITEDINS—(DHA)
Rev.: $1,773,523
Assets: $19,020,530
Liabilities: $6,239,596
Net Worth: $12,780,934
Earnings: $1,147,327
Emp.: 150
Fiscal Year-end: 12/31/23
Insurance Services
N.A.I.C.S.: 524298
Aziz Ahmad *(Chm)*

UNITED INSURANCE LIMITED
188 Zahran Street 6th Circle, PO Box
7521, Amman, 11118, Jordan
Tel.: (962) 62003333
Web Site: https://www.unitedjo.com
Year Founded: 1972
UNIN—(AMM)
Rev.: $31,722,200
Assets: $56,987,524
Liabilities: $33,691,358
Net Worth: $23,296,166
Earnings: $1,864,806
Emp.: 70
Fiscal Year-end: 12/31/21
Insurance Services
N.A.I.C.S.: 524298
Emad Al-hajeh *(Gen Mgr)*

UNITED INTEGRATED SERVICES CO., LTD.
5F No 3 Ln 7 Baogao Rd, Xindian
Dist, New Taipei City, 23144, Taiwan
Tel.: (886) 229174060
Web Site: https://www.uisco.com.tw
Year Founded: 1982
2404—(TAI)
Rev.: $2,252,842,716
Assets: $1,519,488,088
Liabilities: $1,113,042,503
Net Worth: $406,445,585
Earnings: $158,523,752
Emp.: 700
Fiscal Year-end: 12/31/23
Engineeering Services
N.A.I.C.S.: 334514
Belle Lee *(Chm)*

UNITED INTERNATIONAL HOLDINGS B.V.
Strawinskylaan 411, WTC Tower A
4th Floor, 1077 XX, Amsterdam,
Netherlands
Tel.: (31) 20 575 2727   NI
Web Site: http://www.uibt.com
Year Founded: 2006
Bank Holding Company; Commercial
Banking & Trust Services
N.A.I.C.S.: 551111
Robert Stroeve *(CEO)*

Subsidiaries:

The United Trust Company N.V. (1)
Landhuis Joonchi Kaya Richard J Beaujón
z/n, PO Box 837, Willemstad, Curaçao
Tel.: (599) 9 736 6277
Trust Services
N.A.I.C.S.: 523991

United International Bank N.V. (1)
Landhuis Joonchi II Kaya Richard J Beaujon z/n, PO Box 152, Willemstad, Curaçao
Tel.: (599) 9 733 1888
Web Site: http://www.united-ibank.com
Commericial Banking
N.A.I.C.S.: 522110
Christian van Dijk *(CTO)*

United International Management
B.V. (1)
Strawinskylaan 411, WTC Tower A 4th
Floor, Amsterdam, 1077 XX, Netherlands
Tel.: (31) 20 575 2727
Web Site: http://www.united-itrust.com
Trust Services
N.A.I.C.S.: 523991
Igmar den Heijer *(Exec Dir)*

United International Management
Ltd (1)
1st Floor 32 Wigmore Street, London, W1U
2RP, United Kingdom
Tel.: (44) 20 7535 1070
Financial Consulting Services
N.A.I.C.S.: 523940
Alex Smotlak *(Mng Dir)*

United International Management
S.A. (1)
Avenue Gaston Diderich 5, Luxembourg,
L-1420, Luxembourg
Tel.: (352) 2744 81
Emp.: 34
Trust Services
N.A.I.C.S.: 523991
Gerard Matheis *(Mng Dir)*

United Trust (Anguilla) Limited (1)
Babrow Building, Po Box PW 5334, The
Valley, Anguilla
Tel.: (264) 498 4224
Financial Consulting Services
N.A.I.C.S.: 523940
Gregory Elias *(Chm)*

United Trust Management (Aruba)
UTM N.V. (1)
Lloyd G Smith Boulevard 62, Miramar building suite 301, Oranjestad, Aruba
Tel.: (297) 582 3301
Financial Consulting Services
N.A.I.C.S.: 523940

INTERNATIONAL PUBLIC

UNITED INTERNATIONAL TRANSPORTATION COMPANY
Tel.: (966) 26927070
Web Site:
http://www.budgetsaudi.com
Year Founded: 1978
4260—(SAU)
Rev.: $273,340,088
Assets: $671,938,941
Liabilities: $212,123,184
Net Worth: $459,815,758
Earnings: $67,193,441
Emp.: 1,100
Fiscal Year-end: 12/31/22
Car Rental Services
N.A.I.C.S.: 532111

UNITED INTERNET AG
Elgendorfer Strasse 57, 56410, Montabaur, Germany
Tel.: (49) 2602961100   De
Web Site: https://www.united-internet.de
Year Founded: 1998
UTDI—(DEU)
Rev.: $6,858,587,161
Assets: $12,413,713,588
Liabilities: $7,006,936,251
Net Worth: $5,406,777,337
Earnings: $256,892,626
Emp.: 10,962
Fiscal Year-end: 12/31/23
Holding Company; Telecommunications & Data Hosting Services
N.A.I.C.S.: 551112
Ralph Dommermuth *(CEO & Member-Mgmt Bd)*

Subsidiaries:

1&1 AG (1)
Wilhelm Rontgen Strasse 1-5, 63477, Maintal, Germany   **(73.29%)**
Tel.: (49) 61814123
Web Site: https://www.1und1-drillisch.de
Rev.: $4,522,224,229
Assets: $8,544,296,000
Liabilities: $2,045,736,039
Net Worth: $6,498,559,961
Earnings: $347,663,856
Emp.: 3,320
Fiscal Year-end: 12/31/2023
Holding Company; Telecommunication Services
N.A.I.C.S.: 551112
Ralph Dommermuth *(CEO & Member-Exec Bd)*

Subsidiary (Domestic):

1&1 Telecommunication SE (2)
Elgendorfer Strasse 57, 56410, Montabaur,
Germany   **(100%)**
Tel.: (49) 7219605743
Web Site: https://www.1und1.de
Holding Company; Telecommunication
Products & Services
N.A.I.C.S.: 551112

Subsidiary (Domestic):

1&1 Internet SE (3)
Elgendorfer Strasse 57, 56410, Montabaur,
Germany
Tel.: (49) 721 96 00
Web Site: http://www.1und1.de
Holding Company; Internet Domain Registration & Web Hosting Services
N.A.I.C.S.: 551112
Hans-Henning Kettler *(Member-Mgmt Bd-Tech & Dev)*

Subsidiary (Non-US):

1&1 Internet (Philippines) Inc. (4)
15 & 16 F i3 Building Asianown IT Park
Salinas Drive, Lahug, Cebu, 6000, Philippines
Tel.: (63) 324158747
Web Site: http://unternehmen.1und1.de
Web Hosting Services
N.A.I.C.S.: 518210

1&1 Internet Development SRL (4)
Skyflower Building 16th Floor Calea Florea-

AND PRIVATE COMPANIES

sca 246C 1st District, 14476, Bucharest, Romania
Tel.: (40) 312239152
Web Site: https://www.1and1.ro
Web Hosting Services
N.A.I.C.S.: 518210

1&1 Internet Ltd (4)
Discovery House 154 Southgate Street, Gloucester, GL1 2EX, United Kingdom
Tel.: (44) 1452541285
Web Site: http://www.order.1and1.co.uk
Web Hosting Services
N.A.I.C.S.: 518210

1&1 Internet SARL (4)
7 place de la Gare, 57200, Sarreguemines, France
Tel.: (33) 970808911
Web Site: http://www.1and1.fr
Web Hosting Services
N.A.I.C.S.: 518210

Subsidiary (US):

IONOS (4)
701 Lee Rd Ste 300, Chesterbrook, PA 19087
Tel.: (484) 254-5555
Web Site: https://www.ionos.com
Internet & Web Hosting Services
N.A.I.C.S.: 517810

Subsidiary (Domestic):

1&1 Versatel GmbH (3)
Aroser Allee 78, 13407, Berlin, Germany
Tel.: (49) 30 81 88 10 00
Web Site: http://www.versatel.de
Emp.: 1,000
Telecommunications & Internet Services
N.A.I.C.S.: 517111
Walter Denk (CEO)

Subsidiary (Domestic):

Drillisch Logistik GmbH (2)
Munsterstr 109, 48155, Munster, Germany
Tel.: (49) 7074070
Web Site: https://www.drillisch-logistik.de
Mobile Communication Contract Services
N.A.I.C.S.: 517112

Drillisch Online GmbH (2)
Wilhelm-Rontgen-Strasse 1-5, D-63477, Maintal, Germany
Tel.: (49) 61817074070
Web Site: https://www.drillisch-online.de
Mobile Communication Operator
N.A.I.C.S.: 517121

Subsidiary (Domestic):

Mobile Ventures GmbH (3)
Wilhelm-Rontgen-Str 1-5, 63477, Maintal, Germany
Tel.: (49) 6181412400
Web Site: http://www.mobile-ventures.com
Mobile Communication Contract Services
N.A.I.C.S.: 517112
Andre Driesen (CEO)

Subsidiary (Domestic):

Drillisch Telecom GmbH (2)
Wilhelm Rontgen St 1-5, 63477, Maintal, Germany
Tel.: (49) 1805221416
Wireless Telecommunications Service Provider
N.A.I.C.S.: 517112

IQ-Optimize Software AG (2)
Robert-Bosch-Strasse 8, 63477, Maintal, Germany
Tel.: (49) 6181180540
Web Site: https://www.iq-optimize.de
Sales Range: $25-49.9 Million
Emp.: 140
Wireless Telecommunication Software Services
N.A.I.C.S.: 513210
Wolgang Egert (Mng Dir)

1&1 IONOS Cloud Inc. (1)
200 Continental Dr Ste 40, Newark, DE 19713
Tel.: (267) 481-7983
Internet & Web Hosting Services
N.A.I.C.S.: 517810

1&1 Mail & Media GmbH (1)
Brauerstrasse 48, 76135, Karlsruhe, Germany
Tel.: (49) 7219609740
Web Site: https://www.web.de
Web Search Portal Publisher & Operator
N.A.I.C.S.: 518210
Thomas Ludwig (Mng Dir)

Arsys Internet S.L. (1)
C/Madre de Dios n 21, 26004, Logrono, La Rioja, Spain
Tel.: (34) 941620100
Web Site: https://www.arsys.net
Emp.: 300
Internet & Web Hosting Services
N.A.I.C.S.: 517810

Fasthosts Internet Ltd. (1)
Discovery House 154 Southgate Street, Gloucester, GL1 2EX, United Kingdom
Tel.: (44) 1452541285
Web Site: https://www.fasthosts.co.uk
Web Hosting Services
N.A.I.C.S.: 518210

GMX GmbH (1)
Frankfurter Ring 129, 80807, Munich, Bavaria, Germany
Tel.: (49) 89143390
Web Site: http://www.gmx.de
Web Hosting Services
N.A.I.C.S.: 518210

Subsidiary (Domestic):

GMX Internet Services GmbH (2)
Frankfurter Ri North G 129, 80807, Munich, Bavaria, Germany
Tel.: (49) 2602961100
Web Hosting Services
N.A.I.C.S.: 518210

Immobilienverwaltung AB GmbH (1)
Elgendorfer Strasse 57, Rhineland-Palatinate, 56410, Montabaur, Germany
Tel.: (49) 2602961100
Web Hosting Services
N.A.I.C.S.: 518210

InterNetX GmbH (1)
Johanna-Dachs-Str 55, 93055, Regensburg, Germany
Tel.: (49) 941595590
Web Site: https://www.internetx.com
Emp.: 110
Web Hosting Services
N.A.I.C.S.: 518210
Thomas Morz (CEO)

Subsidiary (Non-US):

Domain Robot Enterprises Inc. (2)
1100-1200 West 73rd Avenue, Vancouver, V6P 6G5, BC, Canada
Tel.: (604) 267-7091
Web Site: https://www.domainrobot.ca
Domain Registration Services
N.A.I.C.S.: 518210

Subsidiary (US):

InterNetX Corp. (2)
1001 Brickell Bay Dr Ste 2700 Q-2, Miami, FL 33131
Tel.: (786) 476-2862
Web Site: https://www.internetx.info
Domain Registration Services
N.A.I.C.S.: 518210
Stephanie Ospin (Dir-Registry Ops)

PSI-USA Inc (1)
3960 Howard Hughes Pkwy Ste 500, Las Vegas, NV 89169
Tel.: (702) 990-3672
Web Site: http://www.psi-usa.info
Web Hosting Services
N.A.I.C.S.: 518210
Robert F. Connelly (Founder)

Subsidiary (Domestic):

Schlund Technologies GmbH (2)
Johanna-Dachs-Str 55, 93055, Regensburg, Germany
Tel.: (49) 94163086420
Web Site: https://www.schlundtech.com
Domain Registration Services
N.A.I.C.S.: 518210

MIP Multimedia Internet Park GmbH (1)
Prager Ring 4-12, 66482, Zweibrucken, Rhineland-Palatinate, Germany
Tel.: (49) 63327901
Web Site: http://www.mipz.de
Sales Range: $350-399.9 Million
Emp.: 1,300
Online Marketing Services
N.A.I.C.S.: 541613

STRATO AG (1)
Otto-Ostrowski-Strasse 7, 10249, Berlin, Germany (100%)
Tel.: (49) 303001460
Web Site: https://www.strato.de
Web Hosting Services
N.A.I.C.S.: 541512
Christian Boing (Chm, Co-CEO & Member-Mgmt Bd)

Subsidiary (Domestic):

Cronon AG (2)
Otto-Ostrowski-Strasse 7, 10249, Berlin, Germany
Tel.: (49) 30398020
Web Site: https://www.cronon.net
Internet & Web Hosting Services
N.A.I.C.S.: 517810
Nils Jeppe (Sr Mgr-Svc)

Sedo Holding AG (1)
Im Mediapark 6b, 50670, Cologne, Germany (96.05%)
Tel.: (49) 221 34030 560
Web Site: http://www.sedoholding.com
Sales Range: $150-199.9 Million
Emp.: 332
Holding Company; Online Marketing Services
N.A.I.C.S.: 551112

Subsidiary (Domestic):

Sedo GmbH (2)
Im Mediapark 6B, Nordrhein-Westfalen, 50670, Cologne, Germany
Tel.: (49) 221340300
Web Site: http://www.sedo.de
Sales Range: $50-74.9 Million
Emp.: 150
Web Hosting Services
N.A.I.C.S.: 518210

Subsidiary (Domestic):

DomCollect International GmbH (3)
Im Mediapark 6b, 50670, Cologne, Germany
Tel.: (49) 2219955530
Web Site: https://www.domcollect.com
Domain Registration Services
N.A.I.C.S.: 518210

Subsidiary (Non-US):

DomCollect Worldwide Intellectual Property AG (3)
Zeughausgasse 9a, 6300, Zug, Switzerland
Tel.: (41) 41 710 93 64
Web Site: http://www.domcollect.com
Sales Range: $25-49.9 Million
Emp.: 10
Web Hosting Services
N.A.I.C.S.: 518210

Subsidiary (US):

Sedo.com LLC (3)
625 Massachusetts Ave 2nd Fl, Cambridge, MA 02139
Tel.: (617) 499-7200
Web Site: https://sedo.com
Emp.: 20
Web Hosting Services
N.A.I.C.S.: 518210

United Internet Beteiligungen GmbH (1)
Elgendorfer Strasse 57, 56410, Montabaur, Germany
Tel.: (49) 2602 96 1100
Investment Holding Company
N.A.I.C.S.: 551112

United Internet Media AG (1)
Elgendorfer Strasse 57, 56410, Montabaur, Germany
Tel.: (49) 721913741717
Web Site: http://www.united-internet-media.de

UNITED INVESTMENTS LTD.

Sales Range: $800-899.9 Million
Emp.: 5,000
Internet Service Provider
N.A.I.C.S.: 517810

United Internet Media Austria GmbH (1)
Opernring 23/8, 1010, Vienna, Austria
Tel.: (43) 158814200
Internet & Web Hosting Services
N.A.I.C.S.: 517810

United-Domains AG (1)
Gautinger Strasse 10, Bavaria, 82319, Starnberg, Germany
Tel.: (49) 8151368670
Web Site: https://www.uniteddomains.com
Sales Range: $25-49.9 Million
Emp.: 65
Web Hosting Services
N.A.I.C.S.: 518210

Subsidiary (US):

United Domains, Inc. (2)
161 1st St 4th Fl, Cambridge, MA 02142
Tel.: (781) 285-1851
Web Site: http://www.uniteddomains.com
Web Hosting Services
N.A.I.C.S.: 518210

Subsidiary (Domestic):

united-domains Reselling GmbH (2)
Gautinger Str 10, D-82319, Starnberg, Germany
Tel.: (49) 81513686730
Web Site: https://www.ud-reselling.com
Web Hosting Services
N.A.I.C.S.: 518210

World4You Internet Services GmbH (1)
Hafenstrasse 35, 4020, Linz, Germany
Tel.: (49) 73293035
Web Site: https://www.world4you.com
Domain Registration Services
N.A.I.C.S.: 518210
Johannes Kuhrer (CEO)

home.pl S.A. (1)
ul Zbozowa 4, 70-653, Szczecin, Poland
Tel.: (48) 504502500
Web Site: https://www.pomoc.home.pl
Broadcasting & Web Hosting Services
N.A.I.C.S.: 518210

Subsidiary (Domestic):

AZ.pl Sp. z o.o. (2)
ul Zbozowa 4, 70-653, Szczecin, Poland
Tel.: (48) 570510570
Web Site: https://www.pomoc.az.pl
Broadcasting & Web Hosting Services
N.A.I.C.S.: 516210

Premium.pl Sp. z o.o. (2)
Zbozowa 4, 70-653, Szczecin, Poland
Tel.: (48) 801066444
Web Site: https://www.premium.pl
Domain Registration Services
N.A.I.C.S.: 518210

UNITED INVESTMENTS LTD.
6th Floor Dias Pier Building, Le Caudan Waterfront Caudan, Port Louis, Mauritius
Tel.: (230) 4054000
Web Site: https://www.uil.mu
UTIN—(MAU)
Rev.: $579,940
Assets: $36,317,953
Liabilities: $321,988
Net Worth: $35,995,965
Earnings: $5,346,063
Fiscal Year-end: 06/30/22
Investment Management Service
N.A.I.C.S.: 523999
Didier Merven (Chm)

Subsidiaries:

AXIOM (Mauritius) Equity Fund Ltd. (1)
6th Floor Dias Pier Building Le Caudan Waterfront, Port Louis, 11307, Mauritius
Tel.: (230) 4054000
Web Site: http://www.axiom.mu

UNITED INVESTMENTS LTD.

United Investments Ltd.—(Continued)
Investment Services
N.A.I.C.S.: 523999

AXYS Group Ltd. (1)
6th Floor Dias Pier Building Le Caudan Waterfront Caudan, 11307, Port Louis, Mauritius
Tel.: (230) 4054000
Web Site: https://axys.mu
Financial Services
N.A.I.C.S.: 523999
Didier Merven (Founder)

AXYS Investment Partners Ltd. (1)
6/7th Floor Dias Pier Building Le Caudan Waterfront, Port Louis, 11307, Mauritius
Tel.: (230) 4054000
Web Site:
http://www.axysinvestmentpartners.com
Investment Services
N.A.I.C.S.: 523999
Constantin De Grivel (Mng Dir)

AXYS Stockbroking Ltd. (1)
6/7th Floor Dias Pier Building Le Caudan Waterfront, Port Louis, 11307, Mauritius
Tel.: (230) 4054000
Web Site: http://www.axysstockbroking.com
Financial Services
N.A.I.C.S.: 523999
Melvyn Chung Kaito (Mng Dir)

Mechanization Company Limited (1)
Mecom building Grande Riviere Nord d'Ouest, Port Louis, Mauritius
Tel.: (230) 2084873
Web Site: https://www.mecom.mu
Crane Mfr
N.A.I.C.S.: 333923
Denis Lagesse (Mng Dir)

Megabyte Ltd. (1)
F4 The Technopark, Mosta, MST 3000, Malta
Tel.: (356) 21421600
Web Site: https://www.megabyte.net
Information Technology Consulting Services
N.A.I.C.S.: 541512
Jonathan Briffa (CFO)

NW Trust (Switzerland) SA (1)
8-10 Rue Muzy, 1207, Geneva, Switzerland
Tel.: (41) 223177373
Fund Services
N.A.I.C.S.: 523940

NWT Holding (HK) Limited (1)
15/f 100 Queen's Road, Central, China (Hong Kong)
Tel.: (852) 31809253
Fund Services
N.A.I.C.S.: 523940

SPICE Finance Ltd. (1)
6th Floor Dias Pier Building Le Caudan Waterfront, 11307, Port Louis, 11307, Mauritius
Tel.: (230) 4054050
Web Site: https://www.spicefinance.mu
Fixed Deposit Services
N.A.I.C.S.: 522180
Vikash Tulsidas (CEO)

UNITED LABELS AG

Gildenstrasse 6, 48157, Munster, Germany
Tel.: (49) 25132210
Web Site:
https://www.unitedlabels.com
Year Founded: 1991
ULC—(DEU)
Rev.: $27,398,053
Assets: $23,126,076
Liabilities: $20,167,705
Net Worth: $2,958,372
Earnings: $695,438
Emp.: 59
Fiscal Year-end: 12/31/23
Comic Ware Products Producer
N.A.I.C.S.: 513120
Peter Boder (CEO & Member-Mgmt Bd)

Subsidiaries:

Colombine B.V.B.A. (1)
Birgit Vandenheede Pathoekeweg 48, 8000, Brugge, West Flanders, Belgium
Tel.: (32) 50456960
Sales Range: $25-49.9 Million
Emp.: 3
Gifts Whslr
N.A.I.C.S.: 459420

Subsidiary (Non-US):

UNITEDLABELS France S.A.S. (2)
435 Rue de Marquette St, 59118, Wambrechies, Nord, France
Tel.: (33) 328334401
Sales Range: $25-49.9 Million
Emp.: 2
Comic Labels Mfr & Sales
N.A.I.C.S.: 322220

Elfen Service GmbH (1)
Gildenstr 6, 48157, Munster, Germany
Tel.: (49) 2513221626
Web Site: https://www.elfen-service.de
Ecommerce Services
N.A.I.C.S.: 541511

UNITEDLABELS Belgium N.V. (1)
Colombine bvba Pathoekeweg 48, 8000, Brugge, West Flanders, Belgium
Tel.: (32) 50456960
Sales Range: $25-49.9 Million
Emp.: 3
Licensed Comicware Labels Mfr & Marketing Services
N.A.I.C.S.: 322220

UNITEDLABELS Iberica S.A. (1)
Av de la Generalitat 29E Pol Ind Fontsana, 8970, Sant Joan Despi, Barcelona, Spain
Tel.: (34) 934771363
Web Site: http://www.unitedlabelsnews.es
Sales Range: $25-49.9 Million
Emp.: 60
Media Entertainment Services
N.A.I.C.S.: 541840
Peter Matthias Boder (CEO)

Subsidiary (Non-US):

UNITEDLABELS Italia S.R.L. (2)
Via Fra Paolo Sarpi 5d, 50136, Florence, Italy
Tel.: (39) 0556120350
Sales Range: $25-49.9 Million
Emp.: 4
Comic Labels Mfr & Sales
N.A.I.C.S.: 322220

UNITED LEASING & INDUSTRIES LIMITED

D-41 South Extension Part-II, New Delhi, 110 049, India
Tel.: (91) 1141644996
Web Site: https://www.ulilltd.com
Year Founded: 1983
507808—(BOM)
Rev.: $629,836
Assets: $1,524,071
Liabilities: $774,725
Net Worth: $749,346
Earnings: $67,852
Fiscal Year-end: 03/31/22
Financial Lending Services
N.A.I.C.S.: 522220
Aditya Khanna (Mng Dir)

UNITED LEGAL SERVICES LTD.

The Old Grammar School Church Road, Thame, OX9 3AJ, Oxfordshire, United Kingdom
Tel.: (44) 1844 262392
Web Site:
http://www.econveyancer.com
Year Founded: 2000
Sales Range: $10-24.9 Million
Emp.: 60
Software Development Services
N.A.I.C.S.: 541511
Nigel Hoath (Mng Dir)

UNITED LITHIUM CORP.

Suite 710 1030 West Georgia Street, Vancouver, V6E 2Y3, BC, Canada
Tel.: (604) 336-6128
Web Site: https://unitedlithium.com
ULTH—(CNSX)
Assets: $9,831,440
Liabilities: $357,045
Net Worth: $9,474,395
Earnings: $8,310,571
Fiscal Year-end: 07/31/23
Metal Exploration Services
N.A.I.C.S.: 213114
Cathy Fitzgerald (Exec VP-Exploration)

UNITED MALACCA BERHAD

6th Floor No 61 Jalan Melaka Raya 8 Taman Melaka Raya, 75000, Melaka, Malaysia
Tel.: (60) 62823700
Web Site:
http://www.unitedmalacca.com.my
UMCCA—(KLS)
Rev.: $126,061,375
Assets: $391,265,182
Liabilities: $77,760,846
Net Worth: $313,504,336
Earnings: $10,109,630
Emp.: 583
Fiscal Year-end: 04/30/24
Palm Oil Mills
N.A.I.C.S.: 311224
Yoke Hiong Yong (Co-Sec & Head-Grp Admin & Corp Affairs)

Subsidiaries:

Leong Hin San Sdn. Bhd. (1)
Ladang Leong Hin San, 71200, Rantau, Negeri Sembilan, Malaysia
Tel.: (60) 66941248
Sales Range: $10-24.9 Million
Emp.: 29
Oil Palm Cultivation Services
N.A.I.C.S.: 115112

Syarikat Penanaman Bukit Senorang Sdn. Bhd. (1)
6th Floor No 61 Jalan Melaka Raya 8, Taman Melaka Raya, 75000, Melaka, Malaysia
Tel.: (60) 62823700
Web Site:
https://www.unitedmalacca.com.my
Emp.: 70
Palm Oil Mfr
N.A.I.C.S.: 311225

UNITED MARITIME CORPORATION

154 Vouliagmenis Avenue, 166 74, Glyfada, Greece
Tel.: (30) 2130181507   MH
Web Site:
https://www.unitedmaritime.gr
Year Founded: 2022
USEA—(NASDAQ)
Emp.: 3
Transportation Services
N.A.I.C.S.: 488330
Stamatios Tsantanis (Chm)

UNITED MEDIA HOLDING

Kyrilliska St 104A, Kiev, 4080, Ukraine
Tel.: (380) 442054300
Sales Range: $150-199.9 Million
Emp.: 300
Media Holding Company; Television, Radio, Internet, Publishing, Printing, Mail Order & Advertising Related Services
N.A.I.C.S.: 551112
Boris Lozhkin (Pres)

Subsidiaries:

United Media Holding Russia (1)
13 Leningradsky Avenue, Moscow, 125040, Russia
Tel.: (7) 495 645 21 81
Web Site: http://www.umh-russia.ru
Magazine Publisher
N.A.I.C.S.: 513120

INTERNATIONAL PUBLIC

UNITED MICROELECTRONICS CORPORATION

No 3 Li-Hsin 2nd Road, Hsinchu Science Park, Hsin-chu, Taiwan
Tel.: (886) 35782258   TW
Web Site: https://www.umc.com
Year Founded: 1980
UMC—(NYSE)
Rev.: $6,957,852,609
Assets: $17,089,604,853
Liabilities: $6,342,740,331
Net Worth: $10,746,864,522
Earnings: $1,880,346,872
Emp.: 19,833
Fiscal Year-end: 12/31/23
Mfr of Semiconductors
N.A.I.C.S.: 334413
Jason S. Wang (Co-Pres)

Subsidiaries:

Fortune Venture Capital Corp. (1)
Li-Hsin 2nd Rd Hsinchu Science Park No 3, Hsin-chu, Taiwan
Tel.: (886) 35782258
Venture Capital Funding Services
N.A.I.C.S.: 523910

Tera Energy Development Co., Ltd. (1)
No 3 Li-Hsin Rd II Hsinchu Science Park, Hsin-chu, 300, Taiwan
Tel.: (886) 35782258
Web Site: http://www.tera-solardevelop.com
Solar Product Mfr
N.A.I.C.S.: 334413

Topcell Solar International Co. Ltd. (1)
No 1560 Sec 1 Zhongshan Rd, Taoyuan, Taoyuan, 328, Taiwan
Tel.: (886) 3 473 8199
Web Site: http://www.topcell-solar.com
Eletric Power Generation Services
N.A.I.C.S.: 221118

UMC Capital (U.S.A) (1)
488 De Guigne Dr, Sunnyvale, CA 94085
Tel.: (408) 523-7800
Venture Capital Services
N.A.I.C.S.: 523910

UMC Group (USA) (1)
488 De Guigne Dr, Sunnyvale, CA 94085
Tel.: (408) 523-7800
Semiconductor Distr
N.A.I.C.S.: 423690
Wei-Ling Huang (Mgr-HR)

UMC USA (1)
488 De Guigne Dr, Sunnyvale, CA 94085 (100%)
Tel.: (408) 523-7800
Sales Range: $25-49.9 Million
Emp.: 100
Sales & Marketing of Semiconductors
N.A.I.C.S.: 334112

UMC-SG (1)
No 3 Pasir Ris Drive 12, Singapore, 519528, Singapore
Tel.: (65) 62130018
Sales Range: $400-449.9 Million
Emp.: 1,600
Semiconductor Mfr & Distr
N.A.I.C.S.: 334413

Unistars Corp. (1)
1f 669 Chung Hsing Rd Sec 4 Chutung Chen, Hsin-chu, 31061, Taiwan
Tel.: (886) 35823711
Solar Product Mfr
N.A.I.C.S.: 334413

United Lighting Opto-Electronic Inc. (1)
2F No 1 Jinshan 8th Street, Hsin-chu, 300, Taiwan
Tel.: (886) 3 5630598
Web Site: http://www.u-lighting.com
Lighting Equipment Mfr
N.A.I.C.S.: 335139

United Microelectronics (Europe) B.V. (1)
De entree 77, 1101 BH, Amsterdam, Netherlands
Tel.: (31) 205640950

AND PRIVATE COMPANIES

Semiconductor Mfr & Distr
N.A.I.C.S.: 334413

Wavetek Microelectronics Corporation (1)
No 10 Innovation 1st Rd, Hsinchu Science Park, Hsin-chu, Hsinchu County, Taiwan
Tel.: (886) 35781259
Web Site: https://www.wtkmicro.com
Semiconductor Devices Mfr
N.A.I.C.S.: 334413

UNITED MOTORS LANKA PLC
Tel.: (94) 112448112
Web Site:
  https://www.unitedmotors.lk
UML—(COL)
Rev.: $68,544,205
Assets: $108,521,717
Liabilities: $34,683,937
Net Worth: $73,837,780
Earnings: $1,675,896
Emp.: 963
Fiscal Year-end: 03/31/22
Motor Vehicles Parts & Accessories Distribution Services
N.A.I.C.S.: 423120
Buddhika Singhage *(Gen Mgr-Technical, Parts & Accessories)*

Subsidiaries:

Dutch Lanka Trailer Manufacturers Ltd (1)
32 Wijerama Rd Gonawala, Kelaniya, Sri Lanka
Tel.: (94) 114973901
Web Site: http://www.dutchlankatrailers.lk
Trailer Mfr
N.A.I.C.S.: 336212

Orient Motor Company Limited (1)
100 Hyde Park Corner, PO Box 697, Colombo, 2, Western Province, Sri Lanka
Tel.: (94) 112448112
Emp.: 35
Fleet Operation Services
N.A.I.C.S.: 532112
G. C. B. Ranasinghe *(CEO)*

Unimo Enterprises Limited (1)
100 Hyde Park Corner, PO Box 697, 00200, Colombo, Sri Lanka
Tel.: (94) 114797225
Automobile Dealers
N.A.I.C.S.: 441110
Devaka Cooray *(Chm)*

UNITED OIL & GAS PLC
2nd Floor 38 - 43 Lincoln's Inn Fields, London, WC2A 3PE, United Kingdom
Tel.: (44) 2075397272   UK
Web Site: https://www.uogplc.com
Year Founded: 2015
UOG—(AIM)
Rev.: $15,831,237
Assets: $33,957,608
Liabilities: $6,998,863
Net Worth: $26,958,745
Earnings: $2,348,777
Emp.: 7
Fiscal Year-end: 12/31/22
Oil & Gas Exploration Services
N.A.I.C.S.: 213111
Brian Larkin *(CEO)*

UNITED OVERSEAS AUSTRALIA LTD
Suite 51/11 Tanunda Drive, Rivervale, 6103, WA, Australia
Tel.: (61) 893680336
Web Site: https://www.uoa.com.my
UOS—(ASX)
Rev.: $94,618,214
Assets: $2,036,910,973
Liabilities: $329,399,223
Net Worth: $1,707,511,750
Earnings: $81,059,192
Emp.: 1,372
Fiscal Year-end: 12/31/23
Land & Buildings Resales

N.A.I.C.S.: 236118
Alan Charles Winduss *(Sec)*

Subsidiaries:

LTG Development Sdn Bhd (1)
Wisma UOA Bangsar S, Tower 1 Ave 3 Bangsar S, 59200 KL, Kuala Lumpur, Malaysia
Tel.: (60) 322459188
Sales Range: $75-99.9 Million
Emp.: 200
Property Development Services
N.A.I.C.S.: 531312
Cecelie Chan *(Mgr)*

Peninsular Home Sdn Bhd (1)
No 2 Bangsar S Jalan 1 112 H Off Jalan Kerinchi, Bangsar, 59200, Kuala Lumpur, Malaysia
Tel.: (60) 322829993
Residential Building Construction Services
N.A.I.C.S.: 236116

UOA (Singapore) Pte Ltd (1)
Property Gallery 7Temasek Boulevard 18-02 Suntec Tower One, Singapore, 038987, Singapore
Tel.: (65) 6 333 9383
Investment Management Service
N.A.I.C.S.: 523940

UOA Asset Management Sdn Bhd (1)
UOA Corporate Tower Lobby A Avenue 10 The Vertical Bangsar South City, No 8 Jalan Kerinchi, 59200, Kuala Lumpur, Malaysia
Tel.: (60) 32 245 9192
Web Site: https://www.uoareit.com.my
Real Estate Services
N.A.I.C.S.: 531390

UOA Holdings Sdn Bhd (1)
Suite G-1 Vertical Corporate Tower BAvenue 10, No 8 Jalan Kerinchi, 59200, Kuala Lumpur, Malaysia
Tel.: (60) 322829993
Web Site: http://www.uoa.com.my
Emp.: 1,000
Property Management Services
N.A.I.C.S.: 531311

Subsidiary (Domestic):

UOA Development Bhd. (2)
Suite G1 Vertical Corporate Tower B Avenue 10, The Vertical Bangsar South City No 8 Jalan Kerinchi, 59200, Kuala Lumpur, Malaysia
Tel.: (60) 322459188
Web Site: https://www.uoa.com.my
Rev.: $95,587,937
Assets: $1,365,838,519
Liabilities: $113,548,783
Net Worth: $1,252,289,735
Earnings: $47,144,974
Emp.: 1,193
Fiscal Year-end: 12/31/2022
Investment Management Service
N.A.I.C.S.: 523940
Kong Chong Soon *(Mng Dir)*

UOA Hospitality Sdn Bhd (1)
UOA Corporate Tower Lobby A Level 33 No 8 Jalan Kerinchi, 59200, Kuala Lumpur, Malaysia
Tel.: (60) 32 245 9188
Web Site:
  https://www.uoahospitality.com.my
Hospital Services
N.A.I.C.S.: 622110
Dickson Kong *(Head)*

UOA Property Gallery - The Village (1)
Suite G-1 Vertical Corporate Tower B Avenue 10, The Vertical Bangsar South City No 8 Jalan Kerinchi, 59200, Kuala Lumpur, Malaysia
Tel.: (60) 322829993
Property Management Services
N.A.I.C.S.: 531312

United Carparks Sdn Bhd (1)
Carpark Office Basement 1 Tower B The Vertical Bangsar South No 8, Jalan Kerinchi, 59200, Kuala Lumpur, Malaysia
Tel.: (60) 32 241 2988
Web Site: https://www.unitedcarparks.com
Commercial Parking Management Services

N.A.I.C.S.: 812930

UNITED OVERSEAS BANK LIMITED
80 Raffles Place UOB Plaza Robinson Road, PO Box 1688, Singapore, 048624, Singapore
Tel.: (65) 62222121   SG
Web Site: https://www.uobgroup.com
Year Founded: 1935
U11—(OTCIQ)
Rev.: $8,577,250,834
Assets: $373,664,320,119
Liabilities: $341,351,611,708
Net Worth: $32,312,708,411
Earnings: $3,396,072,619
Emp.: 28,659
Fiscal Year-end: 12/31/22
Retail, Commercial & Investment Banking Services
N.A.I.C.S.: 522110
Kok Seong Chan *(Chief Risk Officer)*

Subsidiaries:

Innoven Capital India Private Limited (1)
12th Floor Express Towers Nariman Point, Nariman Point, Mumbai, 400 021, India
Tel.: (91) 2267446500
Web Site: http://www.svb.com
Investment Management Service
N.A.I.C.S.: 523940
Anshu Prasher *(Assoc Dir)*

Innoven Capital Singapore Pte. Ltd. (1)
138 Market Street CapitaGreen 27-01, Singapore, 48946, Singapore
Tel.: (65) 65322416
Web Site: http://www.innovencapital.com
Investment Management Service
N.A.I.C.S.: 523940
Darren Chuah *(Dir-Governance Risk & Compliance)*

P.T. Avatec Services Indonesia (1)
Mayapada Tower 11th Floor Jl Jend Sudirman Kav 28, Jakarta, 12920, Indonesia
Tel.: (62) 2152897338
Corporate Banking Services
N.A.I.C.S.: 523999

P.T. Saat Keuangan Indonesia (1)
Mayapada Tower 11th Floor Jl Jend Sudirman Kav 28, Jakarta, 12920, Indonesia
Tel.: (62) 2152897338
Corporate Banking Services
N.A.I.C.S.: 523999

P.T. UOB Asset Management Indonesia (1)
Uob Plaza Lantai 42 Unit 2 Jl M H Thamrin No 10, Jakarta, 10230, Indonesia
Tel.: (62) 2129290889
Web Site: https://www.uobam.co.id
Emp.: 12
Asset Management Banking Services
N.A.I.C.S.: 523999

PT Bank UOB Buana (1)
Jalan MH Thamrin No 10, Jakarta, 10230, Indonesia (99%)
Tel.: (62) 2123506000
Web Site: http://www.uobbuana.com
Retail & Commercial Banking
N.A.I.C.S.: 522110

PT Bank UOB Indonesia (1)
Jl M H Thamrin No 10, Jakarta Pusat, 10230, Indonesia
Tel.: (62) 2123506000
Web Site: https://www.uob.co.id
Commercial Banking Services
N.A.I.C.S.: 522110
Melissa Haris *(Mgr-Rels)*

UOB Alternative Investment Management Pte. Ltd. (1)
80 Raffles Place 16-21 UOB Plaza 2, Singapore, 048624, Singapore
Tel.: (65) 65392492
Commercial Banking Services
N.A.I.C.S.: 522110
Low Hen Seng *(CEO)*

UNITED OVERSEAS BANK LIMITED

UOB Asset Management (B) Sdn. Bhd. (1)
Unit Ff03-Ff05 1st Floor The Centrepoint Hotel Jalan Gadong, BE3519, Bandar Seri Begawan, Brunei Darussalam
Tel.: (673) 2424806
Asset Management Services
N.A.I.C.S.: 531390

UOB Asset Management (Japan) Ltd. (1)
13F Sanno Park Tower 2-11-1 Nagatacho, Chiyoda-ku, Tokyo, 100-6113, Japan
Tel.: (81) 335005981
Asset Management Banking Services
N.A.I.C.S.: 523999

UOB Asset Management (Malaysia) Berhad (1)
Level 22 Vista Tower The Intermark 348 Jalan Tun Razak, 50400, Kuala Lumpur, Malaysia
Tel.: (60) 32 732 1181
Web Site: https://www.uobam.com.my
Asset Management Services
N.A.I.C.S.: 523940
Lim Suet Ling *(CEO & Exec Dir)*

UOB Asset Management (Taiwan) Co., Ltd. (1)
16th Floor No 109 Section 3 Minsheng East Road, Taipei, Taiwan
Tel.: (886) 227197005
Web Site: https://www.uobam.com.tw
Asset Management Banking Services
N.A.I.C.S.: 523999

UOB Asset Management Ltd. (1)
80 Raffles Place 03-00 UOB Plaza 2, Singapore, 048624, Singapore
Tel.: (65) 6 532 7988
Web Site: https://www.uobam.com.sg
Emp.: 200
Asset Management Services
N.A.I.C.S.: 523940
Thio Boon Kiat *(CEO)*

Subsidiary (Non-US):

UOB Asset Management (Thai) Co., Ltd. (2)
23A 25th Floor Asia Centre Building 173/27-30 32-33 South Sathon Road, Thungmahamek Sathon, Bangkok, 10120, Thailand
Tel.: (66) 27862000
Asset Management Services
N.A.I.C.S.: 523940
Vana Bulbon *(CEO)*

Subsidiary (Domestic):

UOB Asset Management (Thailand) Co., Ltd. (3)
15-17th Floors Sindhoorn Tower III 130-132 Wireless Road, Lumpini Pathumwan, Bangkok, 10330, Thailand
Tel.: (66) 2 688 7777
Web Site: http://www.uobamth.co.th
Asset Management Services
N.A.I.C.S.: 523940

UOB Australia Limited (1)
32 Martin Place Level 9 United Overseas Bank Building, Sydney, 2000, NSW, Australia
Tel.: (61) 292211924
Commercial Banking Services
N.A.I.C.S.: 522110
John Liles *(Head-Country)*

UOB Bullion & Futures Limited (1)
80 Raffles Place 5th Floor UOB Plaza 1, Singapore, 048624, Singapore
Tel.: (65) 67098806
Commercial Banking Services
N.A.I.C.S.: 522110
Adi Ng Lai Wah *(CEO)*

UOB Global Capital LLC (1)
592 Fifth Avenue Suite 602, New York, NY 10036
Tel.: (212) 398-6633
Banking Services
N.A.I.C.S.: 522110
David Goss *(Mng Dir)*

UOB Islamic Asset Management Sdn. Bhd. (1)
Level 20 UOB Plaza 1 7 Jalan Raja Laut,

UNITED OVERSEAS BANK LIMITED

United Overseas Bank Limited—(Continued)
50350, Kuala Lumpur, Malaysia
Tel.: (60) 327321181
Asset Management Services
N.A.I.C.S.: 531390

UOB Travel Planners Pte. Ltd. (1)
480 Lorong 6 Toa Payoh 20-01 HDB Hub East Wing, Singapore, 310480, Singapore
Tel.: (65) 6 252 2322
Web Site: https://www.uobtravel.com
Travel Agency Services
N.A.I.C.S.: 561510
Cindy Yeap *(Head-MICE)*

UOB Venture Management (Shanghai) Co., Ltd. (1)
1468 Nanjing Road West Room 3307 United Plaza, Shanghai, 200040, China
Tel.: (86) 2180280999
Commercial Banking Services
N.A.I.C.S.: 522110
Seah Kian Wee *(Mng Dir)*

UOB Venture Management Private Limited (1)
80 Raffles Place 30-20 UOB Plaza 2, Singapore, 048624, Singapore
Tel.: (65) 65393044
Web Site: http://www.uobvm.com.sg
Emp.: 1,800
Asset Management Services
N.A.I.C.S.: 523940
Kian-Wee Seah *(CEO & Mng Dir)*

United Overseas Bank (China) Limited (1)
116 128 Yincheng Road, Pudong New Area, Shanghai, 200120, China **(100%)**
Tel.: (86) 216 061 8888
Web Site: https://www.uobchina.com.cn
Retail & Commercial Banking
N.A.I.C.S.: 522110
Peter Foo Moo Tan *(Pres & CEO)*

United Overseas Bank (Malaysia) Bhd. (1)
Menara UOB Jalan Raja Laut, PO Box 11212, Kuala Lumpur, 50738, Malaysia **(100%)**
Tel.: (60) 326927722
Web Site: http://www.uob.com.my
Retail & Commercial Banking
N.A.I.C.S.: 522110
Kim Choong Wong *(CEO)*

United Overseas Bank (Thai) Public Company Limited (1)
191 South Sathon Road, Bangkok, 10120, Thailand **(99.7%)**
Tel.: (66) 23433000
Web Site: http://www.uob.co.th
Rev.: $789,428,561
Assets: $18,830,705,373
Liabilities: $16,834,609,201
Net Worth: $1,996,096,173
Earnings: $151,785,236
Emp.: 4,906
Fiscal Year-end: 12/31/2019
Retail & Commercial Banking
N.A.I.C.S.: 522110
Ee Cheong Wee *(Deputy Chm)*

United Overseas Bank (Vietnam) Limited (1)
Ground Floor Central Plaza Office Building 17 Le Duan Boulevard, District 1, Ho Chi Minh City, Vietnam
Tel.: (84) 2838989999
Web Site: http://www.uob.com.vn
Commercial Banking Services
N.A.I.C.S.: 522110
Fred Lim *(Head-Retail Banking)*

UNITED PALM OIL INDUSTRY PUBLIC COMPANY LIMITED
64 Soi Bangna-Trad 25 Khwaeng Bangna Nuea, Khet Bangna, Bangkok, 10260, Thailand
Tel.: (66) 27441046
Web Site: https://www.upoic.co.th
Year Founded: 1978
UPOIC—(THA)
Rev.: $44,905,384
Assets: $53,792,834
Liabilities: $7,508,728
Net Worth: $46,284,106
Earnings: $5,940,789
Emp.: 284
Fiscal Year-end: 12/31/23
Palm Seed Oil Mfr
N.A.I.C.S.: 311224
Thira Wipuchanin *(Chm)*

Subsidiaries:

Phansri Co., Ltd. (1)
98 Moo 6 Nuaklong-Khao Phanom Road, Huayyoong Sub-District Nuaklong District, Krabi, 81130, Thailand
Tel.: (66) 75666075
Oilseed & Palm Oil Mfr
N.A.I.C.S.: 311224

UNITED PAPER INDUSTRIES BSC
PO Box 2004, Manama, Bahrain
Tel.: (973) 17732626
Web Site: http://www.bahrainpack.com
Year Founded: 1993
UPI—(BAH)
Sales Range: $25-49.9 Million
Emp.: 152
Carton Product Mfr
N.A.I.C.S.: 322212
Adbulla Hasan Abdulla Buhindi *(Chm)*

UNITED PAPER PUBLIC COMPANY LIMITED
113-115 Rimklongprapa Road, Bang Sue, Bangkok, 10800, Thailand
Tel.: (66) 29102700
Web Site: https://www.unitedpaper.co.th
Year Founded: 1990
UTP—(THA)
Rev.: $122,368,068
Assets: $147,348,804
Liabilities: $12,919,490
Net Worth: $134,429,314
Earnings: $25,582,383
Fiscal Year-end: 12/31/23
Paper Product Mfr & Distr
N.A.I.C.S.: 322299
Mongkol Mangkornkanok *(Chm, Pres & Mng Dir)*

Subsidiaries:

United Paper Public Company Limited - Muang Factory (1)
61 Moo 8 Watboth, Mueang District, Prachin Buri, 25000, Thailand
Tel.: (66) 748296674
Kraft Paper Mfr & Distr
N.A.I.C.S.: 322120

UNITED PARAGON MINING CORPORATION
5th Floor Quad Alpha Centrum Building 125 Pioneer Street, Mandaluyong, 1550, Philippines
Tel.: (63) 6315139
Web Site: https://www.unitedparagon.com
UPM—(PHI)
Assets: $19,968,249
Liabilities: $27,074,255
Net Worth: ($7,106,006)
Earnings: $1,924,744
Emp.: 8
Fiscal Year-end: 12/31/23
Gold Mining Services
N.A.I.C.S.: 212220
Adrian Paulino S. Serrano *(Treas & VP)*

UNITED PETROLEUM PTY. LTD.
600 Glenferrie Rd, Hawthorn, 3122, VIC, Australia
Tel.: (61) 3 9413 1400 AU
Web Site: http://www.unitedpetroleum.com.au
Year Founded: 1981
Sales Range: $10-24.9 Million
Emp.: 200
Petroleum Retail; Gasoline Service Stations & Convenience Stores
N.A.I.C.S.: 457110

UNITED PLANTATIONS BERHAD
Jendarata Estate, 36009, Teluk Intan, Perak Darul Ridzuan, Malaysia
Tel.: (60) 56411411
Web Site: https://www.unitedplantations.com
Year Founded: 1906
UTDPLT—(KLS)
Rev.: $508,761,495
Assets: $780,403,140
Liabilities: $115,748,573
Net Worth: $664,654,568
Earnings: $129,255,143
Emp.: 5,735
Fiscal Year-end: 12/31/21
Oil Palm & Other Plantation Crops
N.A.I.C.S.: 111998
Carl Bek-Nielsen *(Vice Chm)*

Subsidiaries:

Bernam Advisory Services Sdn. Bhd. (1)
Unit 3 2 3rd Floor Wisma Concorde No 2, Jalan Sultan Ismail, 50250, Kuala Lumpur, Malaysia **(100%)**
Tel.: (60) 320267220
Web Site: https://www.unitedplantations.com
Sales Range: $75-99.9 Million
Emp.: 4
Engineeering Services
N.A.I.C.S.: 541330

Bernam Agencies Sdn. Bhd. (1)
4536 Deep Water Wharf, 12100, Butterworth, Malaysia
Tel.: (60) 43231709
Cooking Edible Oil Product Mfr & Distr
N.A.I.C.S.: 311225
Soo Yook Kee *(Sr Mgr)*

Bernam Bakery Sdn Bhd (1)
Ladang Jendarata Teluk Intan, Perak, 36009, Malaysia **(100%)**
Tel.: (60) 56411336
Sales Range: $25-49.9 Million
Emp.: 8
Retail Bakeries
N.A.I.C.S.: 311811
D. Shashidharan *(Mgr)*

Berta Services Sdn. Bhd. (1)
Unit 5 03 Plaza 138 138 Jalan Ampang, 50250, Kuala Lumpur, Malaysia
Tel.: (60) 321612363
Web Site: https://www.unitedplantations.com
Emp.: 3
Oil Palm & Coconut Cultivation Services
N.A.I.C.S.: 115112

Butterworth Bulking Installation Sdn. Bhd. (1)
4536 Deep Water Wharf, Butterworth, 12100, Malaysia **(100%)**
Tel.: (60) 43231709
Sales Range: $25-49.9 Million
Emp.: 15
Oilseed Farming
N.A.I.C.S.: 111120
Soo Yook Kee *(Mgr)*

Unitata Berhad (1)
Jendarata Estate, Teluk Intan, 36009, Perak, Darul Ridzuan, Malaysia **(100%)**
Tel.: (60) 56411511
Web Site: https://www.unitata.com
Sales Range: $100-124.9 Million
Emp.: 300
Fats & Oils Refining & Blending
N.A.I.C.S.: 311225
Allan Loh Teik Boon *(Mgr-Commerce)*

United International Enterprises (M) Sdn. Bhd. (1)
Jendarata Estate, 36009, Teluk Intan, Perak Darul Ridzuan, Malaysia **(100%)**
Tel.: (60) 56411411
Web Site: https://www.unitedplantations.com

INTERNATIONAL PUBLIC

Emp.: 30
Palm Oil Production; Soil Preparation Planting & Cultivating
N.A.I.C.S.: 115112
Geoffrey Cooper *(Grp Mgr)*

UNITED POLYFAB GUJARAT LTD.
Survey No 238 239 Shahwadi Opp New Aarvee Denim Narol-Sarkhej Highway, Ahmedabad, 382405, India
Tel.: (91) 9925232824
Web Site: https://www.upgl.in
UNITEDPOLY—(NSE)
Rev.: $78,353,048
Assets: $23,718,038
Liabilities: $16,081,782
Net Worth: $7,636,257
Earnings: $656,783
Emp.: 435
Fiscal Year-end: 03/31/23
Textile Products Mfr
N.A.I.C.S.: 314999
Gagan Mittal *(Mng Dir)*

UNITED POWER GENERATION & DISTRIBUTION CO., LTD.
Gulshan Centre Point H 23-26 R 90 Gulshan - 2, Dhaka, 1212, Bangladesh
Tel.: (880) 9666700900
Web Site: https://www.unitedpowerbd.com
Year Founded: 2007
UPGDCL—(DHA)
Rev.: $573,447,894
Assets: $1,000,040,108
Liabilities: $614,947,005
Net Worth: $385,093,103
Earnings: $117,801,438
Emp.: 493
Fiscal Year-end: 06/30/22
Electric Power Distribution Services
N.A.I.C.S.: 221122
Moinuddin Hasan Rashid *(Mng Dir)*

UNITED POWER OF ASIA PUBLIC COMPANY LIMITED
1 Q-House Lumpini Building Floor 11 Room 1103 South Sathon Road, Thung Maha Mek Sathon, Bangkok, Thailand
Tel.: (66) 26777151
Web Site: https://greentechventures.co.th
Year Founded: 2000
GTV—(THA)
Rev.: $19,782,876
Assets: $162,299,998
Liabilities: $82,660,366
Net Worth: $79,639,632
Earnings: ($40,371,057)
Fiscal Year-end: 12/31/23
Property Developer
N.A.I.C.S.: 237210
Tirawat Sucharitakul *(Chm)*

UNITED POWER TECHNOLOGY AG
Mergenthalerallee 10-12, 65760, Eschborn, Germany
Tel.: (49) 6371350
Web Site: https://www.unitedpower.de.com
UP7—(DEU)
Sales Range: $100-124.9 Million
Emp.: 586
Holding Company; Generators, Engines & Other Power Equipment Developer, Mfr & Distr
N.A.I.C.S.: 551112
Zhong Dong Huang *(Founder, Deputy Chm-Mgmt Bd & Co-CEO)*

UNITED PROPERTIES REIT
Al Zhendov 6, Sofia, 1113, Bulgaria

Tel.: (359) 29713545
Real Estate Investment Services
N.A.I.C.S.: 531210

UNITED RADIANT TECHNOLOGY CORPORATION
NO 2 Fu-Shing Road Taichung Tanzi Technology Industrial Park Tanzi, Taichung, Taiwan
Tel.: (886) 4253142779
Web Site: https://www.urt.com.tw
Year Founded: 1990
5315—(TPE)
Rev.: $60,928,650
Assets: $63,656,974
Liabilities: $13,747,116
Net Worth: $49,909,858
Earnings: $7,913,235
Fiscal Year-end: 12/31/22
Industrial Electronic Product Mfr
N.A.I.C.S.: 335132
Chih-Hua Han *(Chm)*

Subsidiaries:

U.R.T Europe ApS (1)
Rugmarken 23 1 byg 2, 3520, Farum, Denmark
Tel.: (45) 48161200
LCD Panel & Module Mfr
N.A.I.C.S.: 334419

UNITED RENEWABLE ENERGY CO., LTD.
No 7 Li-Hsin 3rd Rd Hsinchu Science Park, Hsin-chu, 30078, Taiwan
Tel.: (886) 35780011
Web Site: https://www.nsp.com
Year Founded: 2005
3576—(TAI)
Rev.: $409,307,908
Assets: $939,856,533
Liabilities: $511,285,634
Net Worth: $428,570,898
Earnings: ($128,027,661)
Emp.: 1,246
Fiscal Year-end: 12/31/23
Photovoltaic Cell & Module Developer & Mfr
N.A.I.C.S.: 334413
Sam Hong *(Chm)*

Subsidiaries:

Clean Focus Renewables Inc. (1)
150 Mathilda Pl Ste 206, Sunnyvale, CA 94086
Tel.: (408) 329-9280
Solar Cell & Module Mfr
N.A.I.C.S.: 334413

DSS-USF PHX LLC (1)
46101 Fremont Blvd, Fremont, CA 94538
Tel.: (510) 668-5100
Solar Cell & Module Mfr
N.A.I.C.S.: 334413

General Energy Solutions Inc. (1)
No 18-1Guangfu n Rd, Hukou, 30351, Hsin-chu, Taiwan (75.89%)
Tel.: (886) 3 5972899
Web Site: http://www.gesyw.com
Electronic Component Mfr & Distr
N.A.I.C.S.: 334419

Subsidiary (Non-US):

General Energy Solutions UK Limited (2)
City View House 5 Union Street, Manchester, M12 4JD, United Kingdom
Tel.: (44) 1612 777640
Investment Management Service
N.A.I.C.S.: 523940

Subsidiary (Non-US):

GES Japan Corporation (3)
JBC 14 World Business Garden Nakase 2-6-1, Mihama-ku, Chiba, 261-7114, Japan
Tel.: (81) 434458567
Web Site: http://www.geservs.com
Investment Management Service
N.A.I.C.S.: 523940

Subsidiary (Non-US):

Yong Shun Ltd. (2)
1 2/46 Garema Circuit, Kingsgrove, 2208, NSW, Australia
Tel.: (61) 297580203
Solar Cell & Module Mfr
N.A.I.C.S.: 334413

Hillsboro Town Solar, LLC (1)
22 Rosemary Ln, Durham, NH 03824
Tel.: (603) 397-5245
Electronic Services
N.A.I.C.S.: 811210

Prime Energy Corp. (1)
9821 Katy Fwy Ste 1050, Houston, TX 77024-1218
Tel.: (203) 358-5700
Electronic Component Mfr & Distr
N.A.I.C.S.: 334419

UNITED STEELWORKERS OF AMERICA
234 Eglinton Ave. E., 8th Fl., Toronto, M4P 1K7, ON, Canada
Tel.: (412) 562-2400
Web Site: https://www.m.usw.org
Year Founded: 1942
Rubber Products Mfr
N.A.I.C.S.: 326299

UNITED STRENGTH POWER HOLDINGS LIMITED
Room 2101 Unit 1 Building 23 G District Blue Harbor Phase II, Erdao District, Changchun, Jilin, China
Tel.: (86) 43182996088
Web Site: http://www.united-strength.com
Year Founded: 1997
2337—(HKG)
Rev.: $854,946,986
Assets: $218,385,742
Liabilities: $152,731,332
Net Worth: $65,654,410
Earnings: $2,660,720
Emp.: 1,620
Fiscal Year-end: 12/31/22
Petroleum Product Distr
N.A.I.C.S.: 221210
Jinmin Zhao *(Co-Founder & Co-Chm)*

UNITED TEXTILES LIMITED
7th KM Stone Barwala Road, Hisar, 125001, Haryana, India
Tel.: (91) 1662276182
Web Site: https://www.unitedtextileslimited.com
Year Founded: 1993
521188—(BOM)
Rev.: $1,988,766
Assets: $2,721,480
Liabilities: $1,467,502
Net Worth: $1,253,978
Earnings: $3,633
Emp.: 19
Fiscal Year-end: 03/31/23
Cotton Yarn Mfr & Whslr
N.A.I.C.S.: 313110
Sunder Singh *(Compliance Officer)*

UNITED U-LI CORPORATION BERHAD
33 Jalan Kartunis U1/47 Temasya Industrial Park Seksyen U1, 40150, Shah Alam, Selangor Darul Ehsan, Malaysia
Tel.: (60) 355695999
Web Site: http://www.uli.com.my
ULICORP—(KLS)
Rev.: $54,544,141
Assets: $84,197,302
Liabilities: $9,925,347
Net Worth: $74,271,956
Earnings: $8,311,315
Emp.: 1,000
Fiscal Year-end: 12/31/22
Light Fittings Products Distr

N.A.I.C.S.: 423610
Li Ling Foo *(Co-Sec)*

Subsidiaries:

United U-LI Goodlite Sdn. Bhd. (1)
Lot 44 Jalan Cetak Tasek Industrial Estate, 31400, Ipoh, Perak, Malaysia
Tel.: (60) 55451411
Web Site: https://www.goodlite.com.my
Sales Range: $25-49.9 Million
Emp.: 100
Light Fitting Systems Mfr
N.A.I.C.S.: 335131

UNITED URBAN INVESTMENT CORPORATION
Shiroyama Trust Tower 18F 4-3-1 Toranomon, Minato-ku, Tokyo, 105-6018, Japan
Tel.: (81) 354023680
Web Site: https://www.united-reit.co.jp
Year Founded: 2003
8960—(TKS)
Sales Range: $150-199.9 Million
Real Estate Investment Services
N.A.I.C.S.: 523999
Masakazu Watase *(Supervisory Officer)*

UNITED UTILITIES GROUP PLC
Haweswater House Lingley Mere Business Park Lingley Green Avenue, Great Sankey, Warrington, WA5 3LP, Cheshire, United Kingdom
Tel.: (44) 1925237000
Web Site: http://www.unitedutilities.com
Year Founded: 1994
UU—(LSE)
Rev.: $2,302,953,800
Assets: $18,337,793,486
Liabilities: $15,171,042,666
Net Worth: $3,166,750,820
Earnings: $258,646,806
Emp.: 5,975
Fiscal Year-end: 03/31/23
Holding Company; Water Supply & Treatment Services
N.A.I.C.S.: 551112
Philip Aspin *(CFO)*

Subsidiaries:

United Utilities International Ltd. (1)
Lingley Business Park Lingley Green Avenue Great Sankey, Warrington, WA5 3LP, Cheshire, United Kingdom
Tel.: (44) 1925234000
Web Site: http://corporate.unitedutilities.com
Project Management & Consulting Services
N.A.I.C.S.: 541611
Steven Lewis Mogford *(CEO)*

UNITED VAN DER HORST LTD.
E-29 30 MIDC Taloja, Raigad Dist, Navi Mumbai, 410208, Maharashtra, India
Tel.: (91) 2227412728
Web Site: https://www.uvdhl.com
Year Founded: 1987
522091—(BOM)
Rev.: $2,070,547
Assets: $8,805,767
Liabilities: $4,623,428
Net Worth: $4,182,339
Earnings: $280,415
Emp.: 21
Fiscal Year-end: 03/31/23
Hydraulic Cylinder Mfr
N.A.I.C.S.: 333995
Kalpesh Kantilal Shah *(CFO)*

UNITED VERTICAL MEDIA GMBH
Pretzfelder Strasse 7-11, D-90425, Nuremberg, Germany

Tel.: (49) 91137750299
Web Site: http://www.unitedverticalmedia.de
Online Search Platform
N.A.I.C.S.: 519290
Jurgen Renghart *(Mng Dir)*

Subsidiaries:

11880 Solutions AG (1)
Fraunhoferstr 12a, 82152, Martinsried, Munich, Germany (100%)
Tel.: (49) 8989540
Web Site: http://unternehmen.11880.com
Rev.: $49,433,286
Assets: $31,319,248
Liabilities: $14,606,705
Net Worth: $16,712,543
Earnings: ($11,540,183)
Emp.: 624
Fiscal Year-end: 12/31/2017
Telecommunication Services, Directory Assistance & News & Weather Information & Call Center Services
N.A.I.C.S.: 517111
Ralf Grusshaber *(Vice Chm-Supervisory Bd)*

Subsidiary (Domestic):

11880 Internet Services AG (2)
Kruppstrasse 74, Essen, 45145, Germany (100%)
Tel.: (49) 201 8099 0
Web Site: http://unternehmen.11880.com
Directory Information Services
N.A.I.C.S.: 519290
Jurgen Krieger *(Chm)*

UNITED WAGON COMPANY RESEARCH & PRODUCTION CORPORATION PJSC
Arbat st 10, Moscow, 119002, Russia
Tel.: (7) 4999991520
Web Site: https://www.uniwagon.com
Year Founded: 2004
UWGN—(MOEX)
Sales Range: $800-899.9 Million
Construction Management Services
N.A.I.C.S.: 237990
Timofey Khryapov *(CEO)*

Subsidiaries:

TyazhMash Joint Stock Company (1)
13 Hydroturbine St, Syzran, 446010, Samara, Russia
Tel.: (7) 8464378109
Web Site: http://www.tyazhmash.com
Conveyor & Conveying Equipment Mfr
N.A.I.C.S.: 333922

UNITED WHOLESALE (SCOTLAND) LTD.
110 Easter Queenslie Road, Glasgow, G33 4UL, United Kingdom
Tel.: (44) 1417816600
Web Site: http://www.joinday-today.co.uk
Year Founded: 2001
Sales Range: $250-299.9 Million
Emp.: 187
Grocery Store Operator
N.A.I.C.S.: 445110
Asim Sarwar *(Mng Dir)*

UNITED WIRE FACTORIES COMPANY
Al Kharj Road Second New Industrial City, Riyadh, Saudi Arabia
Tel.: (966) 112655556
Web Site: https://unitedwires.com.sa
Year Founded: 1990
1301—(SAU)
Rev.: $273,660,203
Assets: $153,217,084
Liabilities: $33,355,254
Net Worth: $119,861,830
Earnings: $15,111,406
Emp.: 630
Fiscal Year-end: 12/31/22

United Wire Factories Company—(Continued)
Steel Wire Mfr & Whslr
N.A.I.C.S.: 331222
Khaled Saad Abdul Rahman Al-kanhal *(Chm)*

UNITED WORLD HOLDING GROUP LTD. VG
Year Founded: 2018
UWHGF—(OTCIQ)
Rev.: $375,912
Assets: $482,658
Liabilities: $1,160,344
Net Worth: ($677,686)
Earnings: ($3,864,310)
Emp.: 13
Fiscal Year-end: 12/31/21
Holding Company
N.A.I.C.S.: 551112

UNITED, INC.
MFPR Shibuya Bldg B1F 10F 1-2-5 Shibuya, Shibuyaku, Tokyo, 150-0002, Japan
Tel.: (81) 368210000 JP
Web Site: https://www.united.jp
Year Founded: 1998
2497—(TKS)
Rev.: $83,107,530
Assets: $176,784,450
Liabilities: $21,185,050
Net Worth: $155,599,400
Earnings: $15,639,260
Emp.: 337
Fiscal Year-end: 03/31/24
Internet & Mobile Platform Media Software Publisher, Sales & Support Services
N.A.I.C.S.: 513210
Yozo Kaneko *(Pres & COO)*

UNITEKNO CO.,LTD.
140 Sinsan-ro, Sahagu, Busan, Korea (South)
Tel.: (82) 512035460
Web Site: https://www.unitekno.co.kr
Year Founded: 1993
241690—(KRS)
Rev.: $63,179,498
Assets: $119,272,659
Liabilities: $29,557,840
Net Worth: $89,714,819
Earnings: $3,743,201
Emp.: 228
Fiscal Year-end: 12/31/22
Automotive Parts Mfr & Distr
N.A.I.C.S.: 336320
Jwoa Young Lee *(Board of Directors & CEO)*

Subsidiaries:

UNITEKNO Co., Ltd. - Aaan Factory (1)
48-16 Dogomyeon-ro Dogo-myeon, Asan, Chungcheongnam-do, Korea (South)
Tel.: (82) 415381800
Automobile Parts Mfr
N.A.I.C.S.: 336390

UNITEL HIGH TECHNOLOGY CORP.
No 10 89 lane Sec 3 Chung-yang, Tu Cheng District, Taipei, Hsien, Taiwan
Tel.: (886) 222678151
Rubber Compression Product Mfr
N.A.I.C.S.: 326291
Liao Chung-Hsiung *(Chm)*

UNITEL S.A.
Rua Marechal Broz Tito 77/79, Ingombotas, Luanda, Angola
Tel.: (244) 923 199100
Web Site: http://www.unitel.ao
Year Founded: 2001
Telecommunication Services
N.A.I.C.S.: 517111

Amilcar Safeca *(CTO)*

Subsidiaries:

Banco de Fomento Angola (1)
Rua Amilcar Cabral n 58 Maianga, Luanda, Angola (51.9%)
Tel.: (244) 222638900
Web Site: http://www.bfa.ao
Rev.: $388,874,512
Assets: $4,499,868,974
Liabilities: $3,552,346,875
Net Worth: $947,522,099
Earnings: $245,877,394
Emp.: 2,724
Fiscal Year-end: 12/31/2019
Commercial Banking
N.A.I.C.S.: 522110
Tidiane de Sousa Mendes dos Santos *(Sec)*

UNITEST INC.
155-1 Hagal-dong Gigok-ro, Giheung-gu, Yongin, Gyeonggi-do, Korea (South)
Tel.: (82) 315470300
Web Site: https://www.uni-test.com
Year Founded: 2000
086390—(KRS)
Rev.: $94,939,234
Assets: $145,501,801
Liabilities: $35,705,068
Net Worth: $109,796,733
Earnings: ($4,765,993)
Emp.: 220
Fiscal Year-end: 12/31/22
Semiconductor Testing Equipment Mfr
N.A.I.C.S.: 334515
Jong Hyeon Kim *(CEO)*

Subsidiaries:

Daeyangets Co., Ltd. (1)
16 Goji 5-Gil Jeongnam-Myeon, Hwaseong, Gyeonggi-do, Korea (South)
Tel.: (82) 313517023
Web Site: https://www.daeyangets.com
Air Purifier & Heater Recovery Ventilator Mfr
N.A.I.C.S.: 333415

Testian, Inc. (1)
Unit No 2208 Building A Heungdeok IT Valley Heungdeok-1-ro 13, Giheung-gu, Yongin, Gyeonggi-do, Korea (South)
Tel.: (82) 312167500
Semiconductor Memory Device Mfr & Distr
N.A.I.C.S.: 334413

UniFusion Inc. (1)
Ra-207 Cheomdan Building 530 Daedeok-Daero, Yuseong-gu, Daejeon, 34121, Korea (South)
Tel.: (82) 428627510
Web Site: https://www.uni-fusion.com
Innovative Technology & Unique Design Services
N.A.I.C.S.: 541512

UNITH LTD
202/37 Barrack St, Perth, 6000, WA, Australia
Tel.: (61) 1300034045 AU
Web Site: https://www.unith.ai
UNT—(ASX)
Rev.: $3,017,558
Assets: $9,154,249
Liabilities: $1,225,591
Net Worth: $7,928,658
Earnings: ($1,277,585)
Fiscal Year-end: 06/30/24
Mobile Applications
N.A.I.C.S.: 513210
Sytze Voulon *(Chm)*

Subsidiaries:

Track Online B.V. (1)
Papsouwselaan 119T, 2624 AK, Delft, Netherlands
Tel.: (31) 15 750 1050
Web Site: https://trackonline.com
Packaging & Labeling Services
N.A.I.C.S.: 561910

Danny Van Kampen *(Co-Founder)*

UNITI SA
73 Boulevard Haussmann, 75008, Paris, France
Tel.: (33) 467996947
Web Site: https://www.uniti-habitat.fr
ALUNT—(EUR)
Sales Range: $75-99.9 Million
Residential Communities Development Including Retirement Homes, Student Campus Housing & Social Rental Housing
N.A.I.C.S.: 623311
Stephane Oria *(Chm & CEO)*

UNITIKA LTD.
Osaka Center Bldg 4-1-3 Kyutaro-machi, Chuo-ku, Osaka, 541-8566, Japan
Tel.: (81) 662815533
Web Site: https://www.unitika.co.jp
Year Founded: 1889
3103—(TKS)
Rev.: $782,234,010
Assets: $1,231,661,130
Liabilities: $978,848,460
Net Worth: $252,812,670
Earnings: ($35,978,230)
Fiscal Year-end: 03/31/24
Synthetic & Natural Fibers Mfr; Engineering, Construction & Real Estate Services
N.A.I.C.S.: 325220
Hiroyuki Shime *(Chm)*

Subsidiaries:

AD'ALL Co., Ltd. (1)
5 Uji Tonouchi, Uji, 611-0021, Japan
Tel.: (81) 774252274
Web Site: https://www.adall.co.jp
Emp.: 30
Activated Carbon Fibers Mfr
N.A.I.C.S.: 325220
Kusunoki Mykio *(Chm)*

Brazcot Ltda. (1)
Rua Senador Paulo Egidio 72-10 Andar-Sala 1010, Sao Paulo, 01006-010, Brazil
Tel.: (55) 113 104 7141
Rubber Products Mfr
N.A.I.C.S.: 326299

COSOF Co., Ltd. (1)
331 Sayama-Shinkaichi Kumiyama-Cho, Kyoto, 613-0034, Japan
Tel.: (81) 774451201
Plastic Resins Encapsulation Molding Services
N.A.I.C.S.: 325991

Daisen Kosan Co., Ltd. (1)
2-1-1 Yamazaki Shimamoto-cho, Mishima-gun, Osaka, 618-0001, Japan
Tel.: (81) 759623282
Woven Fabrics Warehousing Services
N.A.I.C.S.: 493110

I-TEX Co., Ltd. (1)
377-6 Ka Minatomachi, Hakusan, 929-0217, Ishikawa, Japan
Tel.: (81) 762783211
Web Site: http://www.unitika.co.jp
Woven Fabrics Finishing & Dyeing Services
N.A.I.C.S.: 313310

Kamijyo Seiki Co., Ltd. (1)
26 Ichibanwari, Gokasho, Uji, 611-0011, Kyoto, Japan
Tel.: (81) 774328352
Spinning Sleeves Mfr & Sales
N.A.I.C.S.: 339999

Nippon Ester Co., Ltd. (1)
1-3 4- chome Kutaro-cho, Chuo-ku, Osaka, 541-0056, Japan
Tel.: (81) 662815520
Web Site: https://www.nippon-ester.co.jp
Polyester Fibers Mfr & Sales
N.A.I.C.S.: 325220

P.T. Emblem Asia (1)
MM 2100 Industrial Town BlokT-3, Cikarang Barat, Bekasi, 17520, Jawa Barat, Indonesia

Tel.: (62) 21 898 0318
Web Site: https://emblem-asia.com
Nylon Film Mfr & Distr
N.A.I.C.S.: 326113

P.T.ENBLEM ASIA (1)
MM2100 Industrial Town Blok T-3, Cikarang Barat, Bekasi, 17520, Jawa Barat, Indonesia
Tel.: (62) 218980318
Nylon Film Mfr & Sales
N.A.I.C.S.: 325220

PT Unitex Tbk (1)
Jl Raya Tajur No 1, Bogor, 16001, Indonesia
Tel.: (62) 2518311309
Web Site: https://www.unitex.co.id
Sales Range: $10-24.9 Million
Emp.: 1,022
Textile Products Mfr
N.A.I.C.S.: 314999

PT. Unitika Trading Indonesia (1)
Ratu Plaza Office Tower Lt30 Jl Jend Sudirman Kav 9, Jakarta, 10270, Indonesia
Tel.: (62) 212 904 4180
Nylon Film Mfr & Distr
N.A.I.C.S.: 326113

Terabo Co., Ltd. (1)
28-55 Tsudaminami-cho, Kaizuka, 597-8511, Osaka, Japan
Tel.: (81) 72 431 2424
Web Site: https://www.terabo.co.jp
Emp.: 84
Synthetic Resin Mfr
N.A.I.C.S.: 325211

Thai Nylon Co., Ltd. (1)
No 91 Opposite Royal Thai Naval Academy Sukhumvit Road, Samut Prakan, 10270, Thailand
Tel.: (66) 23942596
Web Site: http://www.nittoseimo.co.jp
Emp.: 200
Nylon Fishing Net Mfr & Sales
N.A.I.C.S.: 314999
Somma Masa Yuki *(Mgr)*

Thai Unitika Spunbond Co., Ltd. (1)
1/1 Moo-3 Phahonyothin Rd KM 35, Klong-nueng Klongluang, Pathumthani, 12120, Thailand
Tel.: (66) 25 162 8856
Web Site: https://www.tusco.co.th
Polyester Spunbond Mfr & Distr
N.A.I.C.S.: 313230

U.C.S. Co., Ltd. (1)
1 Amaike, Gotanda-cho, Inazawa, 221-0000, Aichi, Japan
Tel.: (81) 453451100
Web Site: https://www.ucscard.co.jp
Polyester & Nylon Films Slitting Services
N.A.I.C.S.: 561990

Unimore Ltd. (1)
Osaka Ctr Bldg 4-1-3 Kyutaro-machi, Chuo-ku, Osaka, 541-0056, Japan
Tel.: (81) 662815631
Web Site: http://www.unitika.co.jp
Finance & Factoring Services
N.A.I.C.S.: 522291

Union Co., Ltd. (1)
Kobe Miyuki Bldg 7F 44 Akashi-cho, Chuo-ku, Kobe, 650-0037, Osaka, Japan
Tel.: (81) 783924930
Web Site: https://union-will.jp
Sales Range: $25-49.9 Million
Emp.: 105
Glass Micro Spheres Mfr
N.A.I.C.S.: 313310
Yasuo Takemura *(Pres)*

Union Kosan Co., Ltd. (1)
8-3 Doyama Higashimachi, Hirakata, 573-0006, Osaka, Japan
Tel.: (81) 728495211
Web Site: http://www.unitika.co.jp
Reflective Road Sign Mfr & Sales
N.A.I.C.S.: 339950
Nunomura Hideo *(Pres)*

Unitika (Beijing) Trading Co., Ltd. (1)
Room 1010 East Ocean Centre No 24A Jianguomen Wai St, Chao Yang District, Beijing, China
Tel.: (86) 106 515 5673
Industrial Machinery & Equipment Whslr

N.A.I.C.S.: 423830

Unitika (Hong Kong) Ltd. (1)
Unit No 261926/F The Metropolis Tower No 10 Metropolis Drive, Hunghom, Kowloon, China (Hong Kong) **(100%)**
Tel.: (852) 27368923
Sales Range: $50-74.9 Million
Emp.: 7
N.A.I.C.S.: 333120

Unitika (Shanghai) Ltd. (1)
Room 1403 New Town Center No 83 Loushanguan Road, Changning District, Shanghai, 200336, China
Tel.: (86) 2161268585
Web Site: http://www.unitika.co.jp
Polymer Products Import & Distr
N.A.I.C.S.: 424610

Unitika America Corporation (1)
3300 Great American Tower 301 E 4th St, Cincinnati, OH 45202
Tel.: (212) 765-3760
Resin & Plastic Mfr
N.A.I.C.S.: 325211

Unitika Emblem China Ltd. (1)
No 6 Xinhua Road, Wuxi, Jiangsu, China
Tel.: (86) 51085345920
Web Site: http://www.unitika.co.jp
Nylon Film Mfr & Whslr
N.A.I.C.S.: 325220

Unitika Estate Co., Ltd. (1)
1F Shinkawaramachi Building 2-4-7 Kawara-machi, Chuo-ku, Osaka, 541-0048, Japan
Tel.: (81) 662040124
Web Site: http://www.unitikaestate.co.jp
Real Estate Management Services
N.A.I.C.S.: 531390

Unitika Europe GmbH (1)
Steinstrasse 31, 40210, Dusseldorf, Germany
Tel.: (49) 211 323 0296
Nylon Film Mfr & Distr
N.A.I.C.S.: 326113

Unitika Garments Technology & Research Laboratorise Ltd. (1)
28-55 Tsuda-minami-cho, Kaizuka, 597-0014, Osaka, Japan
Tel.: (81) 72 437 0055
Consulting Advisor Services
N.A.I.C.S.: 523999

Unitika Glass Fiber Co., Ltd. (1)
45-2 Uji-Kozakura, Chuo-ku, Uji, 611-0021, Kyoto, Japan
Tel.: (81) 774252361
Web Site: http://www.ugf.co.jp
Glass Fibers Mfr & Sales
N.A.I.C.S.: 327212

Unitika Golfing Tarui Co., Ltd. (1)
2210 Tarui-cho, Fuwa-gun, Gifu, 503-2121, Japan
Tel.: (81) 584222754
Web Site: http://www.unitika.co.jp
Golf Training Course Operation Services
N.A.I.C.S.: 713910

Unitika Logistics Co., Ltd. (1)
Osaka Ctr Bldg 1-3 Kyutaro-machi, Chuo-ku, Osaka, 541-8566, Japan
Tel.: (81) 662815589
Web Site: http://www.unitika.co.jp
Logistics & Warehousing Services
N.A.I.C.S.: 493110

Unitika Ltd. - Advanced Materials Division (1)
Osaka Center Bldg 4-1-3 Kyutaro-machi, Chuo-ku, Osaka, 541-8566, Japan
Tel.: (81) 662815288
Web Site: http://www.unitika.co.jp
Timber Product Mfr
N.A.I.C.S.: 322219

Unitika Ltd. - Environment & Engineering Division (1)
Osaka Center Building 4-1-3 Kyutaro-machi, Chuo-ku, Osaka, 541-8566, Japan
Tel.: (81) 6 6281 5312
Environmental Engineering Services
N.A.I.C.S.: 541330

Unitika Ltd. - Film Division (1)
Osaka Center Bldg 4-1-3 Kyutaro-machi, Chuo-ku, Osaka, 541-8566, Japan
Tel.: (81) 662815553
Web Site: http://www.unitika.co.jp
Packaging Film Mfr
N.A.I.C.S.: 326112

Unitika Ltd. - Health & Amenity Division (1)
Osaka Center Building 4-1-3 Kyutaro-machi, Chuo-ku, Osaka, 541-8566, Japan
Tel.: (81) 662815036
Sales Range: $450-499.9 Million
Emp.: 2,000
Dietary Supplements Mfr
N.A.I.C.S.: 325412

Unitika Ltd. - Nonwoven Division (1)
Osaka Center Bldg 4-1-3 Kyutaro-machi, Chuo-ku, Osaka, 541-8566, Japan
Tel.: (81) 662815362
Web Site: https://www.unitika.co.jp
Nonwoven Fabric Mfr
N.A.I.C.S.: 313230

Unitika Ltd. - Okazaki Plant (1)
4-1 Hinakita-machi, Okazaki, 444-8511, Aichi, Japan
Tel.: (81) 564232311
Nonwoven Fabric Mfr
N.A.I.C.S.: 313230

Unitika Ltd. - Plastics Division (1)
Osaka Center Bldg 4-1-3 Kyutaro-machi, Chuo-ku, Osaka, 541-8566, Japan
Tel.: (81) 662815816
Web Site: https://www.unitika.co.jp
Plastics Product Mfr
N.A.I.C.S.: 325211

Unitika Ltd. - Sakoshi Plant (1)
846 Takano, Ako, 678-0171, Hyogo, Japan
Tel.: (81) 791488185
Polyvinyl Alcohol Fibers Mfr
N.A.I.C.S.: 325220

Unitika Ltd. - Tarui Plant (1)
2210 Tarui-cho, Fuwa-gun, Gifu, 503-2121, Japan
Tel.: (81) 584221201
Glass Cloth & Cotton Nonwoven Fabrics Mfr
N.A.I.C.S.: 313220

Unitika Ltd. - Tokiwa Mill (1)
88 Nakahara, Soja, 719-1195, Okayama, Japan
Tel.: (81) 866931251
Web Site: http://www.unitika.co.jp
Natural Fibers Mfr
N.A.I.C.S.: 325220

Unitika Ltd. - Toyohashi Plant (1)
101 Matsunami Akebono-cho, Toyohashi, 441-8527, Aichi, Japan
Tel.: (81) 532 45 6221
Web Site: http://www.unitika.co.jp
Nonwoven Fabric Mfr
N.A.I.C.S.: 313230

Unitika Ltd. - U Imide Division (1)
23 Uji-Kozakura, Uji, 611-0021, Kyoto, Japan
Tel.: (81) 662815034
Aromatic Polyimide Mfr
N.A.I.C.S.: 326140

Unitika Ltd. - Uji Plant (1)
5 Uji-Tonouchi, Uji, 611-8555, Kyoto, Japan
Tel.: (81) 774252029
Industrial Chemicals Mfr
N.A.I.C.S.: 325411

Unitika Mate Co., Ltd. (1)
3-1-4 Motomachi, Naniwa-ku, Osaka, 556-0016, Japan **(100%)**
Tel.: (81) 647059141
Web Site: https://unitikamate.co.jp
Sales Range: $1-4.9 Billion
Emp.: 33
Sports Garments Mfr
N.A.I.C.S.: 315210

Unitika NP Cloth Co., Ltd. (1)
2210 Tarui-cho, Fuwa-gun, Gifu, 503-2121, Japan
Tel.: (81) 584231501
Web Site: http://www.unitika.co.jp
Nonwoven Fabric Mfr & Sales
N.A.I.C.S.: 313230

Unitika Nariwa Co., Ltd. (1)
2371 Nariwa Nariwa-cho, Takahashi, 716-0121, Okayama, Japan
Tel.: (81) 866422122
Web Site: http://www.unitika.co.jp
Sewing Thread Mfr
N.A.I.C.S.: 313110

Unitika Plant Engineering Co., Ltd. (1)
5 Uji-Tonouchi, Uji, 611-8555, Kyoto, Japan
Tel.: (81) 774252074
Plant Engineering & Construction Services
N.A.I.C.S.: 236210

Unitika Sparklite Ltd. (1)
13-8 Ikagahera Goma, Hiyoshi-Cho, Nantan, 629-0311, Kyoto, Japan
Tel.: (81) 771741075
Web Site: https://www.unitika.co.jp
Sales Range: $25-49.9 Million
Emp.: 50
Retroreflective Materials Mfr
N.A.I.C.S.: 326199

Unitika Technos Co., Ltd. (1)
19 Uji Yaochi, Uji, 611-0021, Kyoto, Japan
Tel.: (81) 774238088
Web Site: https://www.unitika.co.jp
Emp.: 17
Resins & Synthetic Fibers Whslr
N.A.I.C.S.: 325220

Unitika Trading Co., Ltd. (1)
MetLife Honmachi Square 2-5-7 Honmachi, Chuo-ku, Osaka, 541-0053, Japan
Tel.: (81) 647059011
Web Site: https://www.unitrade.co.jp
Sales Range: $200-249.9 Million
Emp.: 215
Household & Industrial Products Import & Distr
N.A.I.C.S.: 423620

Subsidiary (Non-US):

Beijing Unitika Textiles Trading Co., Ltd. (1)
Room 1010 East Ocean Centre No 24A Jianguomen Wai Street, Chao Yang District, Beijing, China
Tel.: (86) 1065157817
Web Site: http://www.unitika.co.jp
Fiber & Sewing Products Whslr
N.A.I.C.S.: 424310

Subsidiary (Domestic):

Nikko Textiles Ltd. (2)
Shinkawaramachi Building 2-4-7 Kawaramachi, Chuo-ku, Osaka, 541-0048, Japan
Tel.: (81) 662280881
Web Site: http://www.unitika.co.jp
Uniform Whslr
N.A.I.C.S.: 423910

Unitika do Brasil Industia Textil Limitade (1)
Via Anhanguera Km 125, Americana, Sao Paulo, 13474-000, Brazil
Tel.: (55) 1934789888
Web Site: http://www.unitika.com.br
Cotton Yarn Mfr
N.A.I.C.S.: 313110

UNITRADE INDUSTRIES BERHAD
No 2 Jalan Astaka U8/87 Seksyen U8 Bukit Jelutong, 40150, Shah Alam, Selangor, Malaysia
Tel.: (60) 378432828
Web Site:
  https://www.unitrade.com.my
Year Founded: 1979
UNITRAD—(KLS)
Rev.: $310,474,209
Assets: $211,608,950
Liabilities: $156,177,044
Net Worth: $55,431,905
Earnings: $10,411,530
Emp.: 189
Fiscal Year-end: 03/31/22
Construction Materials Distr
N.A.I.C.S.: 423390
Keng Chor Sim *(Vice Chm & Exe)*

UNITRANS SA
Sos Buc Ploiesti Km 57 Comuna Barcanesti, Prahova, Tatarani, Romania
Tel.: (40) 244277002
Web Site: http://www.unitrans-sa.ro
TRCE—(BUC)
Rev.: $166,826
Assets: $2,036,022
Liabilities: $18,315
Net Worth: $2,017,707
Earnings: ($22,154)
Emp.: 3
Fiscal Year-end: 12/31/19
Grocery Store Operator
N.A.I.C.S.: 445110

UNITRONICS (1989) (R"G) LTD.
Ben Gurion, PO Box 300, Airport City, 70100, Israel
Tel.: (972) 39778888
Web Site:
  https://www.unitronicsplc.com
Year Founded: 1989
UNIT—(TAE)
Rev.: $58,480,728
Assets: $41,812,128
Liabilities: $22,477,966
Net Worth: $19,334,162
Earnings: $11,386,379
Emp.: 163
Fiscal Year-end: 12/31/23
Other Electronic Component Manufacturing
N.A.I.C.S.: 334419
Haim Shani *(Co-Chm & CEO)*

Subsidiaries:

U-tron Systems Inc. (1)
401 Hackensack Ave Ste 505, Hackensack, NJ 07601
Tel.: (201) 592-1444
Electronic Components Mfr
N.A.I.C.S.: 334419

Unitronics Inc. (1)
1 Batterymarch Park, Quincy, MA 02169
Tel.: (617) 657-6596
Web Site: http://www.unitronics.com
Emp.: 200
Electronic Components Mfr
N.A.I.C.S.: 334419
Yair Goldberg *(CEO & Exec VP-Sls & Mktg)*

UNITRONIX CORP.
Ben Gurion Airport, PO Box 300, Airport City, 7019900, Israel
Tel.: (972) 39778888
Web Site: https://www.unitronics.com
Year Founded: 1989
UTRX—(OTCIQ)
Rev.: $39,678,982
Assets: $42,566,955
Liabilities: $26,251,103
Net Worth: $16,315,852
Earnings: $758,702
Emp.: 157
Fiscal Year-end: 12/31/19
Software Development Services
N.A.I.C.S.: 541511
Haim Shani *(Chm)*

UNITTEC CO., LTD.
The 10Th Floor of No 4 Building No 1785 Jianghan Road, Binjiang District, Hangzhou, 310051, Zhejiang, China
Tel.: (86) 57187959000
Web Site:
  https://www.unitedmne.com
Year Founded: 1999
000925—(SSE)
Rev.: $359,362,477
Assets: $1,025,778,616
Liabilities: $599,480,215
Net Worth: $426,298,401
Earnings: $7,917,675
Emp.: 1,441
Fiscal Year-end: 12/31/22

UNITTEC CO., LTD.

UniTTEC Co., Ltd.—(Continued)
Flue Gas Desulfurization, Rail Transit & Semiconductor Products
N.A.I.C.S.: 488210
Lichun Pan *(Chm & CEO)*

UNITY BANK PLC.
Plot 42 Ahmed Onibudo Street Victoria island, Lagos, Nigeria
Tel.: (234) 7080666000   NG
Web Site:
  https://www.unitybankng.com
Year Founded: 2006
UNITYBNK—(NIGE)
Rev.: $36,262,917
Assets: $377,607,502
Liabilities: $581,123,566
Net Worth: ($203,516,064)
Earnings: $696,804
Emp.: 1,301
Fiscal Year-end: 12/31/22
Commercial Banking Services
N.A.I.C.S.: 522110
Aminu Babangida *(Chm)*

Subsidiaries:

Veritas Kapital Assurance Plc   (1)
Plot 497 Abogo Largema Street off Constitution Avenue, Central Business District, Abuja, Federal Capital Terr, Nigeria
Tel.: (234) 94619900
Web Site: https://www.veritaskapital.com
Rev.: $3,456,844
Assets: $12,961,710
Liabilities: $3,591,047
Net Worth: $9,370,664
Earnings: $513,162
Emp.: 86
Fiscal Year-end: 12/31/2022
Insurance Management Services
N.A.I.C.S.: 524298
Aisha Garba *(Head-Corp Scvs)*

UNITY ENTERPRISE HOLDINGS LIMITED
Unit 1002 10/F Billion Trade Centre 31 Hung To Road, Kwun Tong, Kowloon, China (Hong Kong)
Tel.: (852) 25290928   Ky
Web Site:
  https://www.hongdau.com.hk
Year Founded: 1999
2195—(HKG)
Rev.: $13,695,999
Assets: $32,822,830
Liabilities: $12,793,139
Net Worth: $20,029,691
Earnings: ($955,613)
Emp.: 23
Fiscal Year-end: 12/31/22
Holding Company
N.A.I.C.S.: 551112

UNITY GROUP HOLDINGS INTERNATIONAL LIMITED
15/F Chinachem Century Tower 178 Gloucester Road, Wanchai, China (Hong Kong)
Tel.: (852) 21218033   Ky
Web Site: https://www.unitygroup.eco
Year Founded: 2008
1539—(HKG)
Rev.: $5,935,125
Assets: $47,638,845
Liabilities: $31,490,715
Net Worth: $16,148,130
Earnings: ($3,061,785)
Emp.: 57
Fiscal Year-end: 03/31/23
Holding Company; Eco-Friendly Products & Solutions
N.A.I.C.S.: 551112
Mansfield Man Fai Wong *(Founder, Chm, Chm & CEO)*

Subsidiaries:

Synergy ESCO (Malaysia) Sdn. Bhd.   (1)
Lot No B-2-2 Level 2 The Ascent Paradigm No 1 Jalan SS7/26A, Kelana Jaya, 47301, Petaling Jaya, Selangor, Malaysia
Tel.: (60) 378901188
Renewable Energy Services
N.A.I.C.S.: 221114

UNITY OPTO TECHNOLOGY CO., LTD.
10F No 88-8 Sec 1 Guangfu Rd, Sanchong Dist, Taipei, 241, Taiwan
Tel.: (886) 229993988
Web Site:
  http://www.unityopto.com.tw
Year Founded: 1993
2499—(TAI)
Sales Range: $125-149.9 Million
Emp.: 1,300
Light Emitting Diode (LED) & Other Lightng Products Mfr
N.A.I.C.S.: 333310
C. H. Wu *(Chm)*

Subsidiaries:

Duraled Lighting Technologies Corp.   (1)
4989 Santa Anita Ave, Temple City, CA 91780-3657
Tel.: (714) 893-0162
Web Site: http://www.duraled.com
Sales Range: $25-49.9 Million
Emp.: 18
Neon Lighting Products Mfr
N.A.I.C.S.: 335132

Unity Microelectronics, Inc.   (1)
1501 Summit Ave Ste 10, Plano, TX 75074-8176
Tel.: (972) 312-0702
Web Site: http://www.unity.com
Sales Range: $25-49.9 Million
Emp.: 5
Electronic Components
N.A.I.C.S.: 334419

UNITY PACIFIC GROUP
Suite 1 6 Chambers Level 1 308 Queen Street, Brisbane, 4000, QLD, Australia
Tel.: (61) 733704800   AU
Web Site:
  http://www.unitypacific.com.au
Sales Range: $1-9.9 Million
Real Estate Investment Services
N.A.I.C.S.: 523940
Christopher Morton *(Mng Dir)*

Subsidiaries:

Trinity Funds Management Limited   (1)
Mezzanine Level The Tower, Trinity Pl 88 Creek St, Brisbane, 4000, Queensland, Australia   **(50%)**
Tel.: (61) 730024200
Web Site: http://www.trinity.com.au
Sales Range: $25-49.9 Million
Emp.: 40
Fund Management Services
N.A.I.C.S.: 541618

UNITY4 HOLDINGS PTY LTD
Level 2 410 Crown Street, Surry Hills, 2010, NSW, Australia
Tel.: (61) 300886489
Web Site: http://www.unity4.com
Year Founded: 2000
Emp.: 850
Holding Company
N.A.I.C.S.: 551112
Daniel Turner *(Chm)*

Subsidiaries:

Cohort Australia Pty Ltd   (1)
Level 2/410 Crown St, Surry Hills, 2010, NSW, Australia
Tel.: (61) 1300886489
Web Site: http://www.cohort.com.au
Digital Marketing Services
N.A.I.C.S.: 541613

UNIVA FOODS LIMITED
2 Ground Floor 9 Dev Bhuvan Gazdar Street Chira Bazar Kalbadevi, Churchgate, Mumbai, 400002, India
Tel.: (91) 2267470380
Web Site: http://www.hotelrugby.in
Year Founded: 1991
UNIVAFOODS—(NSE)
Rev.: $9,883
Assets: $64,756
Liabilities: $4,027
Net Worth: $60,729
Earnings: ($734,834)
Fiscal Year-end: 03/31/22
Catering & Hotel Management Services
N.A.I.C.S.: 561110
Mahendra R. Thacker *(Chm, CEO & COO)*

UNIVA OAK HOLDINGS LIMITED
Tokyo Toranomon Global Square 17F 1-3-1 Toranomon, Minato-ku, Tokyo, Japan
Tel.: (81) 366829884
Web Site: https://univahld.com
Year Founded: 1868
3113—(TKS)
Rev.: $33,281,350
Assets: $39,950,840
Liabilities: $22,222,820
Net Worth: $17,728,020
Earnings: ($9,439,080)
Fiscal Year-end: 03/31/24
Investment Banking, Financial Advisory & Venture Capital Services
N.A.I.C.S.: 523150
Tsutomu Akita *(Head-Admin & Control Div)*

Subsidiaries:

BSL Insurance Corporation   (1)
6th floor Kita-Aoyama Building 1-4-4 Kita-Aoyama, Minato-ku, Tokyo, 107-0061, Japan
Tel.: (81) 357860040
Web Site: https://www.bsl-ins.com
Sales Range: $50-74.9 Million
Emp.: 7
Insurance Agencies
N.A.I.C.S.: 524210
Katsushi Tanaka *(Pres)*

UNIVACCO TECHNOLOGY, INC.
No 1-13 Makou Vil, Madou Dist, Tainan City, 72154, Taiwan
Tel.: (886) 65703853
Web Site: https://www.univacco.com
3303—(TPE)
Rev.: $87,804,646
Assets: $97,853,391
Liabilities: $36,702,123
Net Worth: $61,151,268
Earnings: $8,579,245
Emp.: 600
Fiscal Year-end: 12/31/22
Fabricated Metal Products Mfr
N.A.I.C.S.: 332999
Bruce Lee *(CEO)*

UNIVANCE CORPORATION
2418 Washizu, Kosai, 431-0494, Shizuoka, Japan
Tel.: (81) 535761311
Web Site: https://www.uvc.co.jp
Year Founded: 1937
7254—(TKS)
Rev.: $348,816,310
Assets: $306,452,820
Liabilities: $143,423,780
Net Worth: $163,029,040
Earnings: $11,719,530
Emp.: 308
Fiscal Year-end: 03/31/24
Automobile Parts Mfr

INTERNATIONAL PUBLIC

N.A.I.C.S.: 336390
Iwao Suzuki *(Chm)*

Subsidiaries:

PT. Univance Indonesia   (1)
Kota Bukit Indah Blok D-II No 16 17 18 19 Bungursari, Purwakarta, 41181, Jawa Barat, Indonesia
Tel.: (62) 264351128
Emp.: 362
Transportation Machinery & Equipment Distr
N.A.I.C.S.: 423860

UNIVANCE (Thailand) Co., Ltd.   (1)
221/14 Moo 6 Tambon Bueng, Amphur, Si Racha, 20230, Chonburi, Thailand
Tel.: (66) 38109430
Emp.: 447
Transportation Machinery & Equipment Distr
N.A.I.C.S.: 423860

Univance Corporation - Hamamatsu Plant   (1)
8 Kozawatari-cho, Minami-ku, Hamamatsu, 432-8063, Shizuoka, Japan
Tel.: (81) 535761311
Automobile Parts Mfr
N.A.I.C.S.: 336390

Univance Corporation - Kosai Plant   (1)
28-1 Komi, Kosai, 431-0442, Shizuoka, Japan
Tel.: (81) 535761891
Automobile Parts Mfr
N.A.I.C.S.: 336390

Univance Inc.   (1)
3400 Corporate Dr, Winchester, KY 40391
Tel.: (859) 737-2306
Emp.: 167
Transportation Machinery & Equipment Distr
N.A.I.C.S.: 423860
Lynsey Witt *(Mgr-HR & Gen Affairs)*

West Lake Co., Ltd.   (1)
2418 Washizu, Kosai, 431-0494, Shizuoka, Japan
Tel.: (81) 535750148
Web Site: https://www.westlake-s.com
Emp.: 54
Container Cleaning & Management Services
N.A.I.C.S.: 562998

UNIVANICH PALM OIL PUBLIC COMPANY LIMITED
258 Aoluk-Laemsak Road, PO Box 8-9, Krabi, 81110, Thailand
Tel.: (66) 75681116
Web Site: https://www.univanich.com
Year Founded: 1995
UVPOF—(OTCIQ)
Rev.: $537,718,550
Assets: $152,492,584
Liabilities: $18,786,201
Net Worth: $133,706,383
Earnings: $43,553,484
Emp.: 1,295
Fiscal Year-end: 12/31/22
Crude Palm Oil Mfr
N.A.I.C.S.: 325194
Apirag Vanich *(Chm)*

UNIVASTU INDIA LTD.
Bunglow No 36/B Madhav Baug Shivtirth Nagar Kothrud Paud Road, Pune, 411 038, India
Tel.: (91) 2025434617
Web Site: https://www.univastu.com
Year Founded: 2009
UNIVASTU—(NSE)
Rev.: $10,472,741
Assets: $14,908,519
Liabilities: $9,473,125
Net Worth: $5,435,394
Earnings: $796,427
Emp.: 75
Fiscal Year-end: 03/31/23
Building Construction Services

N.A.I.C.S.: 236210
Pradeep Khandagale *(Chm & Mng Dir)*

Subsidiaries:

Univastu HVAC India Private
Limited (1)
Bunglow No 36/B Madhav Baug Shivtirth
Nagar Paud Road, Kothrud, Pune, 411038,
India
Tel.: (91) 2025434617
Web Site: http://www.univastu.com
Construction Services
N.A.I.C.S.: 236220
Prashant Akashe *(Gen Mgr)*

UNIVENTURES PUBLIC COMPANY LIMITED

22nd Floor Park Ventures Ecoplex 57
Wireless Road Lumpini Patumwan,
Bangkok, 10330, Thailand
Tel.: (66) 26437100
Web Site:
   https://www.univentures.co.th
UV—(THA)
Rev.: $485,997,030
Assets: $1,128,029,866
Liabilities: $820,368,231
Net Worth: $307,661,634
Earnings: $14,185,848
Emp.: 655
Fiscal Year-end: 09/30/23
Investment Services; Zinc Oxide Importer & Exporter; Time Recorders, Car Parking Systems & Access Control Systems Distr
N.A.I.C.S.: 523999
Panote Sirivadhanabhakdi *(Vice Chm)*

Subsidiaries:

Ahead All Company Limited (1)
2526/18 Krungthep-Nonthaburi Rd, Wongsawang Bangsue, Bangkok, 10800, Thailand
Tel.: (66) 29223467
Web Site: https://www.aheadall.co.th
Electronic Product Distr
N.A.I.C.S.: 423690

Connextion Company Limited (1)
22nd Floor Park Ventures Ecoplex 57 Wireless Road, Lumpini Patumwan, Bangkok, 10330, Thailand
Tel.: (66) 26437100
Portfolio Management Services
N.A.I.C.S.: 523150

ESCO Ventures Co., Ltd. (1)
2nd Floor Mahatun Plaza Building, 888/210 - 212 Ploenchit Road, Lumpini Patumwan, Bangkok, 10330, Thailand (60%)
Tel.: (66) 22559401
Web Site: http://www.univentures.co.th
Energy Investment Services
N.A.I.C.S.: 523999

Forward System Co., Ltd. (1)
888/222-224 Mahatun Plaza 2nd Floor Ploenchit Road, Lumpini Patumwan, Bangkok, 10330, Thailand (100%)
Tel.: (66) 26437222
Web Site: https://www.forwardsystem.co.th
Sales Range: $25-49.9 Million
Emp.: 26
Time Recorders, Car Parking Systems & Access Control Systems Distr
N.A.I.C.S.: 423620

Grand Unity Development Company
Limited (1)
900 7th Floor Tonson Tower Ploenchit Road, Lumpini Patumwan, Bangkok, 10330, Thailand
Tel.: (66) 26524000
Web Site: https://grandunity.co.th
Real Estate Development Services
N.A.I.C.S.: 531390

Patana Intercool Co., Ltd. (1)
119/8-119/9 Moo 10, Khlong Nueng Khlong Luang, Pathumthani, 12120, Thailand
Tel.: (66) 202639668
Web Site: https://www.patanaintercool.com
Commercial Freezer Mfr & Distr
N.A.I.C.S.: 333415

Senses Property Management Company Limited (1)
6th Floor Tonson Tower 900 Ploenchit Road, Lumpini Patumwan, Bangkok, 10330, Thailand
Tel.: (66) 26437595
Web Site: https://www.senses.co.th
Property Development Services
N.A.I.C.S.: 531390

Thai-Lysaght Co., Ltd. (1)
Rojana Industrial Park 3 54 Moo 3, Sam Bundit U-Thai, Ayutthaya, 13210, Thailand
Tel.: (66) 26437111
Web Site: https://www.thai-lysaght.co.th
Zinc Oxide Distr
N.A.I.C.S.: 424690

Thai-Zinc Oxide Company
Limited (1)
Rojana Industrial Park 3 54 Moo 3, Phra Nakhon Si Ayutthaya, 13210, Thailand
Tel.: (66) 26437111
Web Site: https://www.univentures.co.th
Real Estate Development Services
N.A.I.C.S.: 531390

Univentures Consulting Co., Ltd. (1)
22nd Floor Park Ventures Ecoplex 57 Wireless Road Lumpini, Patumwan, Bangkok, 10330, Thailand (100%)
Tel.: (66) 26437100
Web Site: http://www.univentures.co.th
Financial Advisory & Investment Banking Services
N.A.I.C.S.: 523940

UNIVER CAPITAL LLC

8/1 Presnenskaya Embankment Moscow Tower Northern Block 4th floor, Capital City, Moscow, 123112, Russia
Tel.: (7) 4957925550
Web Site: http://www.univer.ru
Emp.: 100
Financial Investment Services
N.A.I.C.S.: 523940
Askhat Sagdiev *(CEO)*

UNIVERMA AG

Beimoorkamp 6, 22926, Ahrensburg, Germany
Tel.: (49) 4102 98765 70
Investment & Portfolio Management Services
N.A.I.C.S.: 523940
Kai Hoffmann *(Chm-Mgmt Bd)*

UNIVERSAL ADVANCED SYSTEMS

31 Manshiet El-Bakry Street, Heliopolis West, Cairo, 11341, Egypt
Tel.: (20) 24556744
Web Site: http://www.uas.com.eg
Year Founded: 1994
Sales Range: $1-9.9 Million
Emp.: 25
Computer & Telecommunications Equipment Distr
N.A.I.C.S.: 423430

UNIVERSAL ARTS LIMITED

Plot No 45 First Floor Ganapati Bhavan M G Road, Goregoan West, Mumbai, 400062, Maharashtra, India
Tel.: (91) 2228749001
Web Site: https://www.universal-arts.in
Year Founded: 1995
532378—(BOM)
Rev.: $15,639
Assets: $803,990
Liabilities: $3,891
Net Worth: $800,099
Earnings: ($23,500)
Emp.: 3
Fiscal Year-end: 03/31/23
Video Distribution Services
N.A.I.C.S.: 512120
Manish Girish Shah *(Mng Dir)*

Subsidiaries:

Bama Infotech Pvt. Ltd. (1)
14-D Kitchlu Nagar Opp Lions Club, Ludhiana, 141 001, Punjab, India
Tel.: (91) 1612305300
Web Site: https://www.bama.in
Information Technology Services
N.A.I.C.S.: 541519

UNIVERSAL AUTOFOUNDRY LIMITED

B-307 Road No 16 VKI Area, Jaipur, 302 013, India
Tel.: (91) 1414109598
Web Site: https://www.ufindia.com
Year Founded: 2009
539314—(BOM)
Rev.: $17,505,035
Assets: $12,014,936
Liabilities: $8,629,323
Net Worth: $3,385,614
Earnings: $281,172
Emp.: 90
Fiscal Year-end: 03/31/21
Iron Casting Component Mfr
N.A.I.C.S.: 331511
Vimal Chand Jain *(Mng Dir)*

UNIVERSAL BIOSENSORS, INC.

1 Corporate Avenue, Rowville, 3178, VIC, Australia
Tel.: (61) 392139000 DE
Web Site:
   https://www.universalbiosensor.com
UBI—(ASX)
Rev.: $4,324,730
Assets: $19,542,851
Liabilities: $6,823,409
Net Worth: $12,719,443
Earnings: ($4,395,621)
Emp.: 80
Fiscal Year-end: 12/31/23
Holding Company; In-Vitro Diagnostic Test Devices Mfr
N.A.I.C.S.: 551112
Nick Bliesner *(Head-Operations)*

Subsidiaries:

Hemostasis Reference Laboratory
Inc. (1)
44 Frid Street Suite 103, Hamilton, ON, Canada
Tel.: (289) 919-1375
Electrochemical Product Mfr
N.A.I.C.S.: 335999

Universal Biosensors Pty. Ltd. (1)
1 Corporate Ave, Rowville, 3178, VIC, Australia
Tel.: (61) 392139000
Web Site:
   https://www.universalbiosensors.com
Sales Range: $25-49.9 Million
In-Vitro Diagnostic Test Devices Mfr
N.A.I.C.S.: 339112

UNIVERSAL CABLES LIMITED

PO Birla Vikas, Satna, 485 005, Madhya Pradesh, India
Tel.: (91) 7672257121
Web Site: https://www.unistar.co.in
Year Founded: 1962
UNIVCABLES—(NSE)
Rev.: $176,649,591
Assets: $320,867,370
Liabilities: $165,848,333
Net Worth: $155,019,037
Earnings: $9,176,404
Emp.: 961
Fiscal Year-end: 03/31/21
Power Cable Mfr
N.A.I.C.S.: 335999
Sudeep Jain *(Compliance Officer & Sec)*

UNIVERSAL CARGO LOGISTICS HOLDING B.V.

Strawinskylaan 3051, 1077 ZX, Amsterdam, Netherlands
Tel.: (31) 203012186 NI
Web Site: http://www.uclholding.com
Year Founded: 2007
Sales Range: $1-4.9 Billion
Emp.: 17,700
Holding Company; Water Freight, Railway Freight & Inland Water Passenger Transportation Services
N.A.I.C.S.: 551112
Igor P. Feodorov *(Gen Dir)*

Subsidiaries:

CJSC Container Terminal
Saint-Petersburg (1)
Elevator site 22 Coal Harbor, 198096, Saint Petersburg, Russia
Tel.: (7) 8123357111
Web Site: http://www.terminalspb.ru
Container Transportation Services
N.A.I.C.S.: 484110
Alexand Foley *(CFO)*

Independent Transportation Company
LLC (1)
Stabutmaniya St 12 bldg, 119991, Moscow, Russia
Tel.: (7) 4957265926
Web Site: http://www.ntcorp.ru
Railway Freight Transportation Services
N.A.I.C.S.: 482111

Subsidiary (Domestic):

OJSC Freight One (2)
Staraya Basmannaya St 12 Bldg 1, 105064, Moscow, Russia (100%)
Tel.: (7) 4956630101
Web Site: http://www.pgkweb.ru
Sales Range: $1-4.9 Billion
Emp.: 3,800
Rail Cargo Operator
N.A.I.C.S.: 488210
Tavrovskaya Elena Alexandrovna *(Head-Corp Fin Dept)*

JSC North-Western Shipping
Company (1)
37 Bolshaya Morskaya ulitsa, Saint Petersburg, 190000, Russia
Tel.: (7) 812 380 23 98
Web Site: http://www.nwship.com
Marine Transportation Services
N.A.I.C.S.: 483111
Albert Vygovsky *(Mng Dir)*

JSC OKA Shipyard (1)
Proezhaya Str 4, 607100, Navashino, Nizhny Novgorod, Russia
Tel.: (7) 83175 575 46
Web Site: http://www.osy.ru
Ship Building Services
N.A.I.C.S.: 336611
Vladimir P. Kulikov *(Gen Dir)*

LLC Multipurpose Reloading
Complex (1)
Dvinskaya str 6, Saint Petersburg, 198035, Russia
Tel.: (7) 812 680 2985
Web Site: http://www.upk-terminal.ru
Cargo Transportation Services
N.A.I.C.S.: 488490
Yaroslavtsev Andrey Nikolaevich *(Mng Dir)*

OJSC Sea Port of
Saint-Petersburg (1)
5 Mezhevoy kanal, 198035, Saint Petersburg, Russia
Tel.: (7) 8127149927
Web Site: http://www.seaport.spb.ru
Cargo Transportation Services
N.A.I.C.S.: 488490

OJSC Taganrog Sea Commercial
Port (1)
2 Komsomolskiy spusk, Taganrog, 347900, Russia
Tel.: (7) 8634 319 566
Web Site: http://www.seaport.ru
Railway Transportation Services
N.A.I.C.S.: 482112
Sergey V. Naryshkin *(Mng Dir)*

OJSC Tuapse Sea Commercial
Port (1)

UNIVERSAL CARGO LOGISTICS HOLDING B.V.

Universal Cargo Logistics Holding B.V.—(Continued)
Morskoy Bulvar str 2, Tuapse, 352800, Krasnodar, Russia
Tel.: (7) 8616771030
Web Site: http://www.tmtp.ru
Oil & Gas Transportation Services
N.A.I.C.S.: 486210
Yuriy V. Matvienko *(Mng Dir)*

Universal Forwarder LLC **(1)**
st Staraya Basmannaya 12 building 1, 105064, Moscow, Russia
Tel.: (7) 4957753607
Web Site: http://www.unfc.ru
Cargo Transportation Services
N.A.I.C.S.: 484230
Irina E. Davidyan *(Gen Dir)*

Vodohod Cruise Company **(1)**
Skakovaya alleya 11, Moscow, 125284, Russia
Tel.: (7) 495 223 96 04
Web Site: http://www.bestrussiancruises.com
Tour Operator
N.A.I.C.S.: 561520
Alexander Trofimov *(Mng Dir)*

Volga Shipping Company **(1)**
15A Markin square, 603001, Nizhniy Novgorod, Russia
Tel.: (7) 8312960101
Web Site: http://www.volgaflot.com
Cargo Transportation Services
N.A.I.C.S.: 488490
Alexander Alekseevich Shishkin *(Chm)*

UNIVERSAL CEMENT CORPORATION
10th Floor No 125 Section 2 Nanjing East Road, Zhongshan District, Taipei, 10485, Taiwan
Tel.: (886) 225077801
Web Site: https://www.ucctw.com
Year Founded: 1960
1104—(TAI)
Rev.: $255,154,247
Assets: $921,860,065
Liabilities: $180,235,645
Net Worth: $741,624,420
Earnings: $76,760,257
Emp.: 473
Fiscal Year-end: 12/31/23
Cement Mfr
N.A.I.C.S.: 327310
Hou Boyi *(Chm)*

Subsidiaries:

Huanchun Cement International Corporation Ltd. **(1)**
10th Floor 125 Sec 2 Nan King East Road, Taipei, Taiwan
Tel.: (886) 2 25077801
Concrete & Cement Mfr
N.A.I.C.S.: 327320

Kiriu Lioho Co.,Ltd. **(1)**
8 Dongfeng Road, Huadu, 510800, Guangzhou, Guangdong, China
Tel.: (86) 2086733000
Iron Casting & Machinery Parts Mfr
N.A.I.C.S.: 331511

Lio-Ho Machine Works Ltd. **(1)**
No 334 Sec 2 Xinsheng Road, Zhongli Dist, Taoyuan, 32056, Taiwan
Tel.: (886) 34532131
Web Site: http://www.lioho.com
Automobile Casting Parts Mfr
N.A.I.C.S.: 336370

Subsidiary (Domestic):

Chiuo Ho Automotive Sales Co.,Ltd. **(2)**
12th Floor 40 Cheng Teh Road Sec 1, Taipei, 10355, Taiwan
Tel.: (886) 225559211
Emp.: 100
Automobile Dealers
N.A.I.C.S.: 441110

Subsidiary (Non-US):

Fuzhou Ibara Lioho Machinery Co.,Ltd. **(2)**
BaiShui Road QingKou, MinHou County, Fuzhou, 350119, Fujian, China
Tel.: (86) 59122772231
Automobile Metal Stamping Parts Mfr
N.A.I.C.S.: 332119

Fuzhou King Duan Industrial Co., Ltd. **(2)**
Meixi Road Qingkou Investment Zone, Minhou County, Fuzhou, 350119, Fujian, China
Tel.: (86) 59122778822
Web Site: http://www.kingduan.ch
Sales Range: $75-99.9 Million
Emp.: 270
Automobile Forging Parts Mfr
N.A.I.C.S.: 331110

Fuzhou Lioho Machinery Co.,Ltd. **(2)**
Baishui Road QingKou, Minhou County, Fuzhou, 350119, Fujian, China
Tel.: (86) 59122772231
Web Site: http://www.flm.com.cn
Iron Casting Machinery Parts Mfr
N.A.I.C.S.: 331511

Subsidiary (Domestic):

King Duan Industrial Co.,Ltd. **(2)**
4-4 Nei Chung Fu Road, Wanli Hsiang, 207, Taipei, Taiwan
Tel.: (886) 224925366
Iron Forging Parts Mfr
N.A.I.C.S.: 332111
Henchung Chiang *(Gen Mgr)*

Subsidiary (Non-US):

Kunshan Tonghe Toyota Service Co.,Ltd. **(2)**
No 105 Changjiang Middle Road, Kunshan, Jiangsu, China
Tel.: (86) 51257327777
Automobile Casting Parts Mfr
N.A.I.C.S.: 336370

Lioho Machinery Industry (Hianan) Co.,Ltd. **(2)**
M 28 Ii Item Haima Industry Park High New Zone, 570216, Haikou, Hainan, China
Tel.: (86) 89866961133
Automobile Casting Parts Mfr
N.A.I.C.S.: 336370

Subsidiary (Domestic):

San Ho Automotive Sales Co.,Ltd. **(2)**
12FL No 40 Sec 1 Cheng Teh Road, 103, Taipei, Taiwan
Tel.: (886) 225594010
Automobile Dealers
N.A.I.C.S.: 441110

Takaoka Lioho Industry Co.,Ltd. **(1)**
No 37 Gaoxin Avenue Jinwei Highway East Beichen Technology In, 300409, Tianjin, China
Tel.: (86) 2286995950
Iron Casting & Machinery Parts Mfr
N.A.I.C.S.: 331511

Toyota Industry (Kunshan) Co.,Ltd. **(1)**
18 Zhonghuayuan Road, Kunshan, Jiangsu, China
Tel.: (86) 51257303182
Automobile Casting Parts Mfr & Sales
N.A.I.C.S.: 331511

Toyota Industry Automobile (Kunshan) Parts Co.,Ltd. **(1)**
408 San Xiang Road Kunshan E & T Development Zone, Kunshan, Jiangsu, China
Tel.: (86) 51257303182
Web Site: http://www.toyota-industries.com
Automobile Casting Parts Mfr & Sales
N.A.I.C.S.: 441330

Uneo Incorporated **(1)**
8F No 6 Jiankang Road, Zhonghe, New Taipei City, 235, Taiwan
Tel.: (886) 222252018
Web Site: https://www.uneotech.com
Electronic Technology Services
N.A.I.C.S.: 541512

UNIVERSAL CREDIT & SECURITIES LIMITED
Block No B-5 Mira Co Op HSG Society B H Mothers School, Makrand Desai Road, Vadodara, 390015, India
Tel.: (91) 265 2363678
Web Site: http://www.universalcreditltd.com
Year Founded: 1994
Rev.: $459,646
Assets: $1,227,403
Liabilities: $341,607
Net Worth: $885,796
Earnings: ($181)
Fiscal Year-end: 03/31/18
Financial Services
N.A.I.C.S.: 523999
Narendra R. Shah *(Compliance Officer)*

UNIVERSAL DRUM RECONDITIONING COMPANY
2460 Royal Windsor Drive, Mississauga, L5J 1K7, ON, Canada
Tel.: (905) 822-3280
Web Site: https://www.universaldrum.com
Rev.: $31,126,292
Emp.: 100
Steel & Plastic Drums Mfr
N.A.I.C.S.: 423840
Angelo Petrucci *(Pres)*

UNIVERSAL ENGEISHA CO., LTD.
193-2 Saho Ibaraki-shi, Osaka, 568-0095, Japan
Tel.: (81) 726492266
Web Site: https://www.uni-green.co.jp
Year Founded: 1974
6061—(TKS)
Rev.: $104,862,980
Assets: $95,284,180
Liabilities: $20,252,320
Net Worth: $75,031,860
Earnings: $10,175,920
Emp.: 1,445
Fiscal Year-end: 06/30/24
Lawn & Garden Products
N.A.I.C.S.: 424930
Takumi Morisaka *(Pres)*

Subsidiaries:

Rolling Greens, Inc. **(1)**
7801 Old Branch Ave Ste 404, Clinton, MD 20735-1766
Tel.: (301) 868-0800
Web Site: https://rollinggreensinc.com
Sales Range: $1-9.9 Million
Emp.: 75
Landscaping Services
N.A.I.C.S.: 561730
Takumi Morisaka *(Founder)*

UNIVERSAL ENTERTAINMENT CORPORATION
Ariake Frontier Building A 3-7-26 Ariake, Koto-ku, Tokyo, 135-0063, Japan
Tel.: (81) 355303055
Web Site: https://www.universal-777.com
Year Founded: 1969
6425—(TKS)
Rev.: $1,269,074,550
Assets: $4,452,562,540
Liabilities: $1,698,891,620
Net Worth: $2,753,670,920
Earnings: $201,632,510
Emp.: 6,983
Fiscal Year-end: 12/31/23
Peripheral Devices Mfr & Distr
N.A.I.C.S.: 334118
Jun Fujimoto *(Pres)*

Subsidiaries:

Aruze USA, Inc. **(1)**
745 Grier Dr, Las Vegas, NV 89119-3703
Tel.: (702) 361-3166

INTERNATIONAL PUBLIC

Investment Management Service
N.A.I.C.S.: 523940

Asiabest Group International Inc. **(1)**
8th Floor Chatham House Building Valero Cor Rufino Sts, Salcedo Village, Makati, Philippines **(66.6%)**
Tel.: (63) 28443819
Web Site: http://www.asiabestgroup.com
Rev.: $120,548
Assets: $4,637,620
Liabilities: $90,627
Net Worth: $4,546,993
Earnings: ($40,202)
Fiscal Year-end: 12/31/2023
Investment Management Service
N.A.I.C.S.: 523940
Manuel M. Lazaro *(Chm)*

UNIVERSAL GOLF ENTERPRISES PLC
Universal Tower 85 Dhigenis Akritas Avenue, Nicosia, Cyprus
Tel.: (357) 22882222
Year Founded: 2011
Assets: $48,181,063
Liabilities: $9,836,262
Net Worth: $38,344,800
Earnings: ($903,375)
Building Construction Services
N.A.I.C.S.: 236220

UNIVERSAL HEALTH INTERNATIONAL GROUP HOLDING LIMITED
No 14-1 Bei Yi Zhong Road, Tiexi District, Shenyang, Liaoning, China
Web Site: https://www.uhighl.com
Year Founded: 1998
2211—(HKG)
Rev.: $195,123,966
Assets: $128,554,834
Liabilities: $65,936,375
Net Worth: $62,618,459
Earnings: ($28,805,472)
Emp.: 3,396
Fiscal Year-end: 06/30/22
Health Care Srvices
N.A.I.C.S.: 621610
Dongkun Jin *(Vice Chm)*

UNIVERSAL HYDRAULIK GMBH
Siemensstr 33, 61267, Neu-Anspach, Germany
Tel.: (49) 608194180
Web Site: http://www.universalhydraulik.com
Year Founded: 1983
Rev.: $15,173,400
Emp.: 70
Heating Equipment Supplier
N.A.I.C.S.: 423720
Ralf Uhl *(Mng Dir)*

UNIVERSAL INCORPORATION
10F 372 Linsen N Rd, Taipei, 104, Taiwan
Tel.: (886) 225119161
Web Site: https://www.uk.com.tw
Year Founded: 1962
1325—(TAI)
Rev.: $13,269,335
Assets: $97,189,734
Liabilities: $3,667,680
Net Worth: $93,522,054
Earnings: $416,593
Emp.: 145
Fiscal Year-end: 12/31/23
Nonwoven Fabric Mfr
N.A.I.C.S.: 313230

UNIVERSAL INVESTMENT BANK AD SKOPJE
Maksim Gorki 6, 1000, Skopje, North Macedonia
Tel.: (389) 23111111

AND PRIVATE COMPANIES

Web Site:
http://www.unibank.com.mk
Year Founded: 1993
Sales Range: $10-24.9 Million
Banking Services
N.A.I.C.S.: 522110
Kosta Mitrovski *(Chm-Mgmt Bd)*

UNIVERSAL LOGISTICS INC.
125 Commerce Valley Drive West Suite 750, Thornhill, L3T 7W4, ON, Canada
Tel.: (905) 882-4880
Web Site:
http://www.universallogistics.ca
Year Founded: 1949
Rev.: $18,498,230
Emp.: 50
Logistics Services Provider
N.A.I.C.S.: 488510
Chris Barnard *(VP)*

UNIVERSAL MICROELECTRONICS CO., LTD.
No 3 27th Rd Taichung Industrial Park, Taichung, Taiwan
Tel.: (886) 423590096
Web Site: http://www.umec-web.net
2413—(TAI)
Rev.: $150,553,675
Assets: $158,573,165
Liabilities: $92,558,713
Net Worth: $66,014,452
Earnings: $3,467,935
Emp.: 3,250
Fiscal Year-end: 12/31/23
Power Supplies Mfr
N.A.I.C.S.: 335313

Subsidiaries:

UMEC Co.,Ltd. (1)
832-7 Yeoksam-Dong, Gangnam-Ku, Seoul, Korea (South)
Tel.: (82) 5 228 0 668
Electrical Components Mfr & Sales
N.A.I.C.S.: 423690

UMEC USA Inc. (1)
720 W Cheyenne Ave Ste 150, North Las Vegas, NV 89030
Tel.: (702) 722-6028
Web Site: http://www.umec-usa.com
Sales Range: $25-49.9 Million
Emp.: 2,300
Electrical Component Mfr
N.A.I.C.S.: 335999

UNIVERSAL MODERN INDUSTRIES CO. PLC
Zarqa - Free Zone Area, PO Box 927139, Amman, 1119, Jordan
Tel.: (962) 65055711
Web Site: https://www.umic.jo
Year Founded: 1986
UMIC—(AMM)
Rev.: $18,022,030
Assets: $15,716,998
Liabilities: $1,624,203
Net Worth: $14,092,795
Earnings: $788,257
Emp.: 97
Fiscal Year-end: 12/31/20
Vegetable Oil Refining Services
N.A.I.C.S.: 311225
Nader Sindaha *(CEO)*

UNIVERSAL MOVERS CORPORATION
125 Beech Hall Road, London, E4 9NN, United Kingdom
Tel.: (44) 20 3734 7531   NV
Year Founded: 2013
Moving & Storage
N.A.I.C.S.: 484210
Shahzad Ahmed *(Pres, CEO, Treas & Sec)*

UNIVERSAL MUSIC GROUP N.V.
Gravelandseweg 80, 1217 EW, Hilversum, Netherlands
Tel.: (31) 357994200   NI
Web Site:
https://www.universalmusic.com
UMG—(EUR)
Rev.: $11,987,912,799
Assets: $14,127,994,820
Liabilities: $10,908,698,468
Net Worth: $3,219,296,352
Earnings: $1,363,047,701
Emp.: 9,972
Fiscal Year-end: 12/31/23
Advertising Media Services
N.A.I.C.S.: 541840
Sir Lucian Grainge *(CEO)*

Subsidiaries:

Universal Music Group, Inc. (1)
2200 Colorado Ave, Santa Monica, CA 90404
Tel.: (310) 865-5000
Web Site: http://www.umusic.com
Sales Range: $5-14.9 Billion
Emp.: 1,000
Holding Company; Music Recording, Publishing, Production & Distribution Services
N.A.I.C.S.: 551112
Sunny Chang *(Chm/CEO-Greater China)*

Subsidiary (Domestic):

GRP Records (2)
1755 Broadway, New York, NY 10019
Tel.: (212) 331-2000
Record Company
N.A.I.C.S.: 423990

Subsidiary (Non-US):

IMC MP d.o.o (2)
Pod Hribom 23A, 1235, Radomlje, Slovenia
Tel.: (386) 41726836
Web Site: http://www.umpg.com
Music Publishers
N.A.I.C.S.: 512230

Subsidiary (Domestic):

Interscope Geffen & A&M Records (2)
2220 Colorado Ave, Santa Monica, CA 90404
Tel.: (310) 865-1000
Web Site: http://www.interscope.com
Sales Range: $100-124.9 Million
Recorded Music & Video Mfr & Distr
N.A.I.C.S.: 512250
Steve Berman *(Vice Chm)*

Unit (Domestic):

Geffen Records (3)
2220 Colorado Ave, Santa Monica, CA 90404
Tel.: (310) 865-4500
Web Site: http://www.geffen.com
Music Record Production
N.A.I.C.S.: 512250
Aaron Sherrod *(Pres-Urban A&R)*

Interscope Records (3)
2220 Colorado Ave, Santa Monica, CA 90404-3574
Tel.: (310) 865-1000
Web Site: http://www.interscope.com
Sales Range: $25-49.9 Million
Emp.: 200
Music Record Production
N.A.I.C.S.: 512250

Subsidiary (Non-US):

Koch Musikverlage GmbH (2)
Ganghoferstrasse 66, 80339, Munich, Germany
Tel.: (49) 89857953227
Web Site: http://www.kochmusikverlage.com
Music Publishers
N.A.I.C.S.: 512230

Media Men Group Israel LTD (2)
8 Ben Zakai Street, Tel Aviv, 61005, Israel
Tel.: (972) 35603656
Web Site: http://www.mmgmusic.com

Music Publishers
N.A.I.C.S.: 512230
Ran Geffen-Lifshit *(CEO)*

Subsidiary (Domestic):

Rondor Music International, Inc. (2)
2110 Colorado Ave Ste 100, Santa Monica, CA 90404
Tel.: (310) 235-4800
Sales Range: $25-49.9 Million
Emp.: 90
Music Publishers
N.A.I.C.S.: 512230

Group (Domestic):

The Capitol Music Group (2)
1750 Vine St, Hollywood, CA 90028-5209
Tel.: (323) 462-6252
Music Publisher & Distr
N.A.I.C.S.: 512230
Michelle Jubelirer *(Chm & CEO)*

Subsidiary (Domestic):

Capitol Christian Music Group (3)
101 Winners Cir, Brentwood, TN 37027-5017
Tel.: (615) 371-4300
Web Site:
http://www.capitolchristianmusicgroup.com
Music Publishing & Distr
N.A.I.C.S.: 334610
Chris Koon *(CFO)*

Subsidiary (Domestic):

Motown Gospel (4)
PO Box 5085, Brentwood, TN 37024
Tel.: (615) 371-6800
Web Site: http://www.motowngospel.com
Music Publisher & Distr
N.A.I.C.S.: 512230
Monica Coates *(VP-A&R & Creative)*

Tooth & Nail, LLC (4)
3522 W Government Way, Seattle, WA 98199
Tel.: (206) 691-9782
Web Site: http://www.toothandnail.com
Sales Range: $1-9.9 Million
Emp.: 15
Music Publisher & Distr
N.A.I.C.S.: 512250
Brandon Ebel *(Founder)*

Subsidiary (Domestic):

Capitol Records, Inc. (3)
1750 Vine St, Hollywood, CA 90028-5209
Tel.: (323) 462-6252
Web Site: http://www.capitolrecords.com
Music Publisher & Distr
N.A.I.C.S.: 512230
Jeff Vaughn *(Pres)*

The Blue Note Label Group (3)
150 5th Ave, New York, NY 10011
Tel.: (212) 786-8700
Web Site: http://www.bluenote.com
Jazz Music Publisher & Distr
N.A.I.C.S.: 512230

Virgin Records America, Inc. (3)
150 5th Ave, New York, NY 10011
Tel.: (212) 786-8200
Web Site: http://www.virginrecords.com
Record Publisher & Distr
N.A.I.C.S.: 512230
David Wolter *(Exec VP-Hollywood)*

Subsidiary (Domestic):

UMG Recordings, Inc. (2)
2220 Colorado Ave, Santa Monica, CA 90404
Tel.: (310) 865-5000
Web Site:
http://www.universalmusicgroup.com
Music Publishers
N.A.I.C.S.: 512230

Subsidiary (Non-US):

Ukrainian Music PC (2)
18/24 Dmitrievskaya 12 Flr, 01054, Kiev, Ukraine
Tel.: (380) 443615869
Web Site: http://www.umpg.com
Music Publishers
N.A.I.C.S.: 512230

UNIVERSAL MUSIC GROUP N.V.

Subsidiary (Domestic):

Universal Classics, Inc. (2)
825 8th Ave Fl 19, New York, NY 10019-7416
Tel.: (212) 333-8000
Web Site: http://www.iclassics.com
Mfr & Distribuiton of Records, Cassettes & CDs
N.A.I.C.S.: 512110
Graham Parker *(Pres-Music)*

Subsidiary (Non-US):

Universal Entertainment GmbH (2)
Stralauer Allee 1, 10245, Berlin, Germany
Tel.: (49) 305200701
Web Site: http://www.universal-music.de
Sales Range: $100-124.9 Million
Music Publishers
N.A.I.C.S.: 512230

Subsidiary (Domestic):

Universal Motown Records (2)
1755 Broadway, New York, NY 10019
Tel.: (212) 841-8000
Web Site: http://www.universalmotown.com
Mfr & Marketer of Records
N.A.I.C.S.: 449210
Ethiopia Habtemariam *(Chm & CEO)*

Subsidiary (Non-US):

Universal Music Canada Inc. (2)
2450 Victoria Park Ave Ste 1, Toronto, M2J 5H3, ON, Canada
Tel.: (416) 718-4177
Web Site: http://www.umusic.ca
Sales Range: $50-74.9 Million
Music Record Production & Distribution
N.A.I.C.S.: 512250

Universal Music Colombia S.A. (2)
103 No 19-60 Piso 3, Bogota, Colombia
Tel.: (57) 12185114
Web Site:
http://www.universalmusicandina.com
Music Publishers
N.A.I.C.S.: 512230

Branch (Domestic):

Universal Music Group (2)
825 8th Ave, New York, NY 10019-7416
Tel.: (212) 333-8000
Production of Recorded Music; Manufacture & Distribution of Records, Audio-Tapes & CD's
N.A.I.C.S.: 334610

Universal Music Group (2)
1755 Broadway, New York, NY 10019
Tel.: (212) 841-8000
Web Site: http://www.universalmusic.com
Sales Range: $25-49.9 Million
Emp.: 100
Music Publishing & Licensing
N.A.I.C.S.: 512230
Darcus Beese *(Pres-Island Records)*

Subsidiary (Non-US):

Universal Music Group International Ltd. (2)
364-366 Kensington High Street, London, W14 8NS, United Kingdom
Tel.: (44) 2077474000
Web Site: http://www.umusic.com
Holding Company; Music Record Production & Distribution
N.A.I.C.S.: 551112
Dickon Stainer *(Pres/CEO-Global Classics & Jazz)*

Subsidiary (Non-US):

Britannia Music Company Ltd. (3)
Osprey House 5 7 Old St, PO Box 739, Saint Helier, JE4 0QW, Jersey
Tel.: (44) 8712221133
Web Site: http://www.bclub.co.uk
Sales Range: $75-99.9 Million
Emp.: 500
CDs, Videos & DVDs Whslr
N.A.I.C.S.: 449210

Subsidiary (Domestic):

Decca Music Group Ltd. (3)
Bond House 347-353 Chiwick High Rd,

8079

UNIVERSAL MUSIC GROUP N.V.

Universal Music Group N.V.—(Continued)
London, W4 4HS, United Kingdom **(100%)**
Tel.: (44) 2074715000
Web Site: http://www.umusic.co.uk
Sales Range: $75-99.9 Million
Emp.: 500
Music Record Production & Distribution
N.A.I.C.S.: 512250

Subsidiary (Non-US):

Deutsche Grammophon GmbH (3)
Baumwall 3, 20459, Hamburg,
Germany **(100%)**
Tel.: (49) 40441810
Web Site:
http://www.deutschegrammophon.com
Sales Range: $10-24.9 Million
Emp.: 40
Production of Recorded Music; Manufactrer of Records, Audio-Tapes & CD's
N.A.I.C.S.: 512250
Clemens Trautmann *(Pres-Berlin)*

Universal International Music B.V. (3)
Gerrit van der Veenlaan 4, 3743 DN, Baarn, Netherlands **(100%)**
Tel.: (31) 356261500
Web Site: http://www.universalmusic.nl
Sales Range: $25-49.9 Million
Emp.: 100
Music Record Production & Distribution
N.A.I.C.S.: 512250

Universal Music (Austria) GmbH (3)
Schwarzenbergplatz 2, 1010, Vienna, Austria
Tel.: (43) 1811210
Web Site: http://universalmusic.at
Sales Range: $10-24.9 Million
Emp.: 50
Music Record Production & Distribution
N.A.I.C.S.: 512250
Martin Haider *(Mgr-Digital)*

Universal Music (Japan) K.K. (3)
8-5-30 Akasaka, Minato-ku, Tokyo, 107-8583, Japan
Tel.: (81) 364063001
Web Site: http://www.universal-music.co.jp
Sales Range: $75-99.9 Million
Emp.: 450
Music Record Production & Distribution
N.A.I.C.S.: 512250
George Ash *(Pres-Asia Pacific)*

Universal Music AB (3)
Banergatan 16, 114 83, Stockholm, Sweden **(100%)**
Tel.: (46) 86295300
Web Site: http://www.universalmusic.se
Sales Range: $25-49.9 Million
Emp.: 16
Music Record Production & Distribution
N.A.I.C.S.: 512250
Per Sundin *(Mng Dir)*

Universal Music Australia Pty. Ltd. (3)
150 William St, Sydney, 2011, NSW, Australia
Tel.: (61) 292070500
Web Site: http://www.umusic.com.au
Sales Range: $25-49.9 Million
Emp.: 120
Music Record Production & Distribution
N.A.I.C.S.: 512250
Adam Ireland *(Gen Mgr-Music & Brands)*

Universal Music Entertainment GmbH (3)
Stralauer Allee 1, 10245, Berlin, Germany
Tel.: (49) 305200701
Web Site: http://www.universal-music.de
Sales Range: $75-99.9 Million
Emp.: 400
Music Record Production & Distribution
N.A.I.C.S.: 512250

Division (Domestic):

Universal Music Domestic Division (4)
Stralauer Allee 1, 10245, Berlin, Germany
Tel.: (49) 305200701
Music Record Production
N.A.I.C.S.: 512250

Subsidiary (Non-US):

Universal Music France (3)
20 Rue Des Fosses Saint Jacques, PO Box 05, 75005, Paris, France **(99.99%)**
Tel.: (33) 144419191
Web Site: http://www.universalmusic.com
Sales Range: $75-99.9 Million
Emp.: 500
Music Record Production & Distribution
N.A.I.C.S.: 512250
Olivier Nusse *(CEO)*

Universal Music Italia Srl (3)
via Benigno Crespi 19, IT-20159, Milan, Italy
Tel.: (39) 0267961
Web Site: http://www.universalmusic.it
Music Record Production & Distribution
N.A.I.C.S.: 512250

Universal Music NZ Ltd. (3)
Site 3 Stables Building 30 St Benedicts Street, Newton, Auckland, 1010, New Zealand
Tel.: (64) 98888750
Web Site: http://www.universalmusic.co.nz
Sales Range: $10-24.9 Million
Emp.: 20
Music Record Production & Distribution
N.A.I.C.S.: 512250

Universal Music Oy (3)
Merimiehenkatu 36 D, Helsinki, Finland
Tel.: (358) 96154677
Web Site: https://universalmusic.fi
Music Label Services
N.A.I.C.S.: 711130
Jarkko Nordlund *(Mng Dir)*

Subsidiary (Domestic):

Poko Rekords (4)
Kyttalankatu 6, PO Box 483, 33101, Tampere, Finland
Tel.: (358) 32136800
Web Site: http://www.pokorekords.fi
Music Publisher & Distr
N.A.I.C.S.: 512230

Subsidiary (Non-US):

Universal Music Spain S.L. (3)
C Torrelaguna 64, 28043, Madrid, Spain **(100%)**
Tel.: (34) 917745600
Web Site: http://www.universalmusic.es
Music Record Production & Distribution
N.A.I.C.S.: 512250
Fabrice Benoit *(Mng Dir)*

Universal Music Switzerland GmbH (3)
Hardturmstrasse 130, 8021, Zurich, Switzerland **(100%)**
Tel.: (41) 434444111
Web Site: http://www.universalmusic.ch
Sales Range: $10-24.9 Million
Emp.: 45
Music Record Production & Distribution
N.A.I.C.S.: 512250
Ivo M. Sacchi *(Mng Dir)*

Subsidiary (Domestic):

Universal Music UK Ltd. (3)
4 Pancras Square, London, N1C 4AG, United Kingdom
Tel.: (44) 2039326000
Web Site: http://www.umusic.co.uk
Sales Range: $75-99.9 Million
Emp.: 300
Music Record Production & Distribution
N.A.I.C.S.: 512250
Selina Webb *(Exec VP)*

Subsidiary (Domestic):

Mercury Records Ltd. (3)
364366 Kensington High St, London, W14 8NS, United Kingdom **(100%)**
Tel.: (44) 2077475000
Web Site: http://www.mercuryrecords.co.uk
Sales Range: $75-99.9 Million
Emp.: 100
Music Record Production
N.A.I.C.S.: 512250

Polydor Ltd. (4)
364 366 Kensington High St, London, W14 8NS, United Kingdom **(100%)**
Tel.: (44) 2074715400
Web Site: http://www.polydor.co.uk
Production of Recorded Music; Manufacture & Distribution of Records, Audio-Tapes & CDs
N.A.I.C.S.: 512250

Unit (Domestic):

Universal Music Group Nashville (2)
401 Commerce St, Nashville, TN 37219
Tel.: (615) 524-7500
Web Site: http://www.umgnashville.com
Sales Range: $25-49.9 Million
Emp.: 60
Recorded Music Mfr
N.A.I.C.S.: 334610
Cindy Mabe *(Pres)*

Subsidiary (Non-US):

Universal Music Holdings Limited (2)
364-366 Kensington High Street, London, W14 8NS, United Kingdom
Tel.: (44) 2074715300
Web Site: http://www.umusic.co.uk
Investment Management Service
N.A.I.C.S.: 523999

Division (Domestic):

Universal Music Latin America (2)
404 Washington Ave, Miami Beach, FL 33139
Tel.: (305) 604-1300
Web Site: http://www.umusic.com
Music Record Production & Distribution
N.A.I.C.S.: 512250

Division (Domestic):

Universal Music Latin Entertainment (3)
5820 Canoga Ave Ste 300, Woodland Hills, CA 91367
Tel.: (818) 577-4700
Web Site: http://www.universalmusic.com
Sales Range: $25-49.9 Million
Music Record Production & Distribution
N.A.I.C.S.: 512250

Subsidiary (Non-US):

Universal Music Mexico, SA de CV (3)
Hegel 721 Col Bosques De Chapultepec, Mexico, 11580, Mexico **(100%)**
Tel.: (52) 5525816600
Web Site: http://www.universal.com.mx
Sales Range: $25-49.9 Million
Emp.: 15
Music Record Production & Distribution
N.A.I.C.S.: 512250

Subsidiary (Non-US):

Universal Music Oy (2)
Merimiehenkatu 36D, 00150, Helsinki, Finland
Tel.: (358) 96154677
Web Site: http://www.universalmusic.fi
Emp.: 100
Music Publishers
N.A.I.C.S.: 512230

Universal Music Portugal S.A. (2)
Rua Prof Reinaldo dos Santos 12-D, 1549-006, Lisbon, Portugal
Tel.: (351) 217710410
Web Site: http://www.universalmusic.pt
Emp.: 22
Music Publishers
N.A.I.C.S.: 512230
Jesus Lopez *(Chm & CEO-Iberian Peninsula)*

Group (Domestic):

Universal Music Publishing Group (2)
2100 Colorado Ave, Santa Monica, CA 90404
Tel.: (310) 235-4892
Web Site: http://www.umusicpub.com
Sales Range: $25-49.9 Million
Emp.: 100
Music Publishers
N.A.I.C.S.: 512230
Marc Cimino *(COO)*

INTERNATIONAL PUBLIC

Subsidiary (Non-US):

PT. Suara Publisindo (3)
Prince Centre Building 14th Floor Room 1401, Jl Jendral Sudirman Kav 3-4, Jakarta, 10220, Indonesia
Tel.: (62) 215734566
Web Site: http://www.umpg.com
Music Publishers
N.A.I.C.S.: 512230

RICoM Publishing DOO (3)
Kapetan Misina 16, 11000, Belgrade, Serbia
Tel.: (381) 113283148
Web Site: http://www.ricompublishing.com
Music Publishers
N.A.I.C.S.: 512230

Universal Music Publishing (Pty) Ltd. (3)
Ground Floor Building B Sandton Place 68 Wierda Road East, Wierda Valley, 2196, South Africa
Tel.: (27) 117220571
Web Site: http://www.umpg.com
Music Publishers
N.A.I.C.S.: 512230

Unit (Non-US):

Universal Music Publishing Group Canada (3)
2450 Victoria Park Avenue Suite 1, Toronto, M2J 5H3, ON, Canada **(100%)**
Tel.: (416) 718-4177
Web Site: http://www.umusicpub.com
Sales Range: $25-49.9 Million
Music Publishers
N.A.I.C.S.: 512230

Subsidiary (Non-US):

Universal Music Publishing Group Denmark (3)
PO Box 55755, 114 83, Stockholm, Sweden
Tel.: (46) 86295385
Web Site: http://www.umusicpub.com
Music Publishers
N.A.I.C.S.: 512230

Unit (Domestic):

Universal Music Publishing Group Latin America (3)
1425 Collins Ave, Miami Beach, FL 33139
Tel.: (305) 604-1380
Web Site: http://www.umpglatin.com
Sales Range: $25-49.9 Million
Emp.: 4
Music Publishers
N.A.I.C.S.: 512230

Subsidiary (Non-US):

Universal Music Publishing S.A. (4)
Juramento 1775 Pisos 12/13, C1428DNA, Buenos Aires, Argentina
Tel.: (54) 1148148600
Web Site: http://www.universal.com
Sales Range: $75-99.9 Million
Music Publishers
N.A.I.C.S.: 512230

Unit (Domestic):

Universal Music Publishing Group Nashville (3)
1904 Adelicia St, Nashville, TN 37212
Tel.: (615) 340-5400
Web Site: http://www.umusicpub.com
Sales Range: $25-49.9 Million
Emp.: 12
Music Publishers
N.A.I.C.S.: 512230
Cyndi Forman *(Sr VP-A&R)*

Subsidiary (Non-US):

Universal Music Publishing Group Thailand (3)
Unit 2903 Level 29 Millennium City 6 392 Kwun Tong Road, Kwun Tong, Kowloon, China (Hong Kong)
Tel.: (852) 23015675
Web Site: http://www.umpg.com
Emp.: 15
Music Publishers
N.A.I.C.S.: 512230

AND PRIVATE COMPANIES

UNIVERSAL MUSIC GROUP N.V.

Division (Non-US):

Universal Music Publishing International Ltd. (3)
Bond House, 347-353 Chiswick High Rd, London, W4 4HS, United Kingdom **(100%)**
Tel.: (44) 2087425600
Web Site: http://www.universalmusicpublishing.com
Sales Range: $25-49.9 Million
Emp.: 70
Holding Company; Music Publisher
N.A.I.C.S.: 551112
Mike McCormack *(Mng Dir)*

Subsidiary (Non-US):

BMG Music Publishing (4)
Neumarkter Str 28, 81673, Munich, Germany
Tel.: (49) 8941360
Web Site: http://www.bmg.com
Music Publishers
N.A.I.C.S.: 512230

Subsidiary (US):

Ariola Eurodisc Inc. (5)
1540 Broadway Fl 24, New York, NY 10036-4039
Tel.: (212) 782-1000
Web Site: http://www.bmgmusic.com
Sales Range: $200-249.9 Million
Emp.: 3,000
Multimedia Company
N.A.I.C.S.: 334610

Subsidiary (Non-US):

BMG Ariola Music Ltda. (5)
Rua Dona Veridiana, 203, 5th Flr. CEP, 01238, Sao Paulo, Brazil
Web Site: http://www.bmg.com.br
Mfr of Phonograph Records, Picture Tubes & Solid State Devices; Manufacturer Telesystems
N.A.I.C.S.: 512250

BMG Ariola Musica S.p.A. (5)
Via di San Alessandro 7, 00131, Rome, Italy
Tel.: (39) 0641995308
Mfr of Phonograph Records & Tapes & Solid State Products
N.A.I.C.S.: 512250

BMG Ariola, S.A. (5)
Avda de los Madronos, 27, 28043, Madrid, Spain
Tel.: (34) 913884910
Music Production & Distribution Services
N.A.I.C.S.: 512230

BMG Music Publishing Ltd. (5)
Bedford House 69-79 Fulham High Street, London, SW6 3JW, United Kingdom
Tel.: (44) 2073847600
Web Site: http://www.bmgmusicsearch.com
Sales Range: $25-49.9 Million
Emp.: 350
Music Publishing
N.A.I.C.S.: 512230

Subsidiary (US):

BMG US - New York (5)
1 Park Ave, New York, NY 10016
Tel.: (212) 561-3000
Web Site: http://www.bmg.com
Sheet Music Publisher
N.A.I.C.S.: 512230
Hartwig Masuch *(CEO)*

BMG/Music (5)
1540 Broadway, New York, NY 10036-4039 **(100%)**
Tel.: (212) 930-4939
Web Site: http://www.bmg.com
Sales Range: $250-299.9 Million
Emp.: 4,500
International Manufacturing & Marketing of Records & Tapes, Record & Tape Club
N.A.I.C.S.: 334610
Keith Hauprich *(Gen Counsel/Sr VP-Bus & Legal Affairs-North America)*

Subsidiary (Non-US):

Universal Music Publishing (Austria) GmbH (4)
Schwarzenbergplatz 1, 6604, Hoefen, Austria **(100%)**
Tel.: (43) 56726060
Web Site: http://www.universalmusicpublishing.com
Sales Range: $50-74.9 Million
Emp.: 50
Music Publishers
N.A.I.C.S.: 512230

Universal Music Publishing AB (4)
Banergatan 16, PO Box 55777, 114 83, Stockholm, Sweden **(100%)**
Tel.: (46) 86295300
Web Site: http://www.umusicpub.com
Sales Range: $50-74.9 Million
Emp.: 50
Music Publishers
N.A.I.C.S.: 512230
Martin Ingestrom *(Pres & Sr VP-Nordic Reg)*

Universal Music Publishing GmbH (4)
Stralauer Allee 1, 10245, Berlin, Germany **(100%)**
Tel.: (49) 305200701
Web Site: http://www.umusicpub.com
Music Publishers
N.A.I.C.S.: 512230

Universal Music Publishing LLC (4)
8-5-30 Akasaka, Minato-ku, Tokyo, 107-0052, Japan **(100%)**
Tel.: (81) 364063070
Web Site: http://www.universalmusicpublishing.com
Sales Range: $75-99.9 Million
Emp.: 8
Music Publishers
N.A.I.C.S.: 512230

Subsidiary (Domestic):

Universal Music Publishing Ltd (4)
4 Pancras Square Kings Cross, London, N1C 4AG, United Kingdom **(100%)**
Tel.: (44) 2039326565
Web Site: http://www.umusicpub.com
Sales Range: $75-99.9 Million
Emp.: 100
Music Publishers
N.A.I.C.S.: 512230

Subsidiary (Non-US):

Universal Music Publishing Pty. Ltd. (4)
4th Floor 150 William Street, PO Box 17, Woolloomooloo, 2011, NSW, Australia
Tel.: (61) 292070500
Web Site: http://www.umusicpub.com
Sales Range: $50-74.9 Million
Emp.: 50
Music Publishers
N.A.I.C.S.: 512230

Universal Music Publishing S.A. (4)
Calle Torrelaguna n 64 4 Planta F, 28043, Madrid, Spain **(100%)**
Tel.: (34) 917445656
Web Site: http://www.umusicpub.com
Sales Range: $50-74.9 Million
Emp.: 13
Music Publishers
N.A.I.C.S.: 512230

Universal Music Publishing S.A. (4)
16 Rue des Fosses St Jacques, 75005, Paris, France
Tel.: (33) 144419400
Web Site: http://www.umusicpub.com
Music Publishers
N.A.I.C.S.: 512230

Unit (Domestic):

Editions Durand-Salabert-Eschig (5)
16 rue des Fosses Saint Jacques, F-75005, Paris, Cedex, France
Tel.: (33) 144415090
Web Site: http://www.salabert.fr
Emp.: 50
Classical Music Publisher
N.A.I.C.S.: 512230

Subsidiary (Non-US):

Universal Music Publishing Kft. (3)
Victor Hugo U 11-15 5th Floor, Budapest, 1132, Hungary
Tel.: (36) 12361100
Web Site: http://www.umpg.com
Music Publishers
N.A.I.C.S.: 512230

Universal Music Publishing LTD. (3)
3F 2 Min Shen East Road Section 3, Taipei, Taiwan
Tel.: (886) 225024546
Web Site: http://www.umpg.com
Music Publishers
N.A.I.C.S.: 512230

Universal Music Publishing Ltd. (3)
Nonhyeon 1-dong 130-29 ana building 3rd Fl, Kangnam-Gu, Seoul, 135824, Korea (South)
Tel.: (82) 221062050
Web Site: http://www.umpg.com
Emp.: 500
Music Publishers
N.A.I.C.S.: 512230

Universal Music Publishing Ltda (3)
Apoquindo 4775 of 501, Las Condes, Santiago, Chile
Tel.: (56) 22632001
Web Site: http://www.umpg.com
Sales Range: $25-49.9 Million
Emp.: 4
Music Publishers
N.A.I.C.S.: 512230

Universal Music Publishing Ltda. (3)
Ave Das Americas 3500 - Bloco 1 - Loja A - Condominio Le Monde, Barra De Tijuca, 22640-102, Rio de Janeiro, Brazil
Tel.: (55) 2121087667
Sales Range: $25-49.9 Million
Emp.: 20
Music Publishers
N.A.I.C.S.: 512230
Marcelo Falcao *(Mng Dir)*

Universal Music Publishing S.R.O. (3)
Velvarska 7, Prague, 160 00, Czech Republic
Tel.: (420) 233029902
Web Site: http://www.umusic.cz
Emp.: 30
Music Publishers
N.A.I.C.S.: 512230

Universal Music Publishing SRL (3)
Via Crespi N 19 - Mac 4, 20159, Milan, Italy
Tel.: (39) 0280282811
Web Site: http://www.umpg.com
Sales Range: $25-49.9 Million
Emp.: 34
Music Publishers
N.A.I.C.S.: 512230

Universal Music Publishing Sdn Bhd (3)
G 01 Ground Floor Wisma Academy 4A Jalan 19/1, Petaling Jaya, 46300, Selangor Darul Ehsan, Malaysia
Tel.: (60) 376201194
Web Site: http://www.umusicpub.com
Sales Range: $25-49.9 Million
Emp.: 5
Music Publishers
N.A.I.C.S.: 512230

Universal Music Publishing Sp. Z.O.O. (3)
Ul Wlodarzewska 69, 02-384, Warsaw, Poland
Tel.: (48) 225928246
Web Site: http://www.umpg.com
Music Publishers
N.A.I.C.S.: 512230

Universal Music Publishing, B.V. (3)
Gerrit van der Veenlaan 4, 3743 DN, Baarn, Netherlands
Tel.: (31) 356261646
Web Site: http://www.umpg.com
Sales Range: $50-74.9 Million
Emp.: 15
Music Publishers
N.A.I.C.S.: 512230
Mark Bremer *(Mng Dir)*

Virginia Publishing OOD (3)
9 Pop Bogomil Street, 1202, Sofia, Bulgaria
Tel.: (359) 29833581
Web Site: http://www.umpg.com
Sales Range: $25-49.9 Million
Emp.: 20
Music Publishers
N.A.I.C.S.: 512230

Subsidiary (Non-US):

Universal Music Romania Srl (2)
Strada General C Nicolae Dona nr 16 Corp A Sector 1, Bucharest, 010782, Romania
Tel.: (40) 213130803
Web Site: http://www.umusic.ro
Emp.: 16
Music Publishers
N.A.I.C.S.: 512230

Universal Music Taxim Edition (2)
Arnavutkoy Mahallesi Kamaci Sokak No 10, Arnavutkoy Besiktas, 34345, Istanbul, Turkiye
Tel.: (90) 2123581700
Web Site: http://www.umusictaxim.com
Music Publishers
N.A.I.C.S.: 512230

Joint Venture (Domestic):

VEVO LLC (2)
825 8th Ave 23rd Fl, New York, NY 10019
Tel.: (212) 331-1357
Web Site: http://www.vevo.com
Music Video Website Operator
N.A.I.C.S.: 516210
Alan Price *(CEO)*

Subsidiary (Non-US):

Virgin EMI Records (2)
364-366 Kensington High Street, London, W14 8NS, United Kingdom
Tel.: (44) 2074715000
Web Site: http://www.virginemirecords.com
Music Publishing
N.A.I.C.S.: 512230
Janie Orr *(CFO)*

Subsidiary (Domestic):

Abbey Road Studios Ltd. (3)
3 Abbey Road, St Johns Wood, London, NW8 9AY, United Kingdom
Tel.: (44) 2072667000
Web Site: http://www.abbeyroad.com
Sales Range: $50-74.9 Million
Emp.: 50
Recording Studio
N.A.I.C.S.: 512250

Subsidiary (US):

EMI Recorded Music North America (3)
150 5th Ave, New York, NY 10011
Tel.: (212) 786-8200
Music Publisher & Distr
N.A.I.C.S.: 512230

Subsidiary (Domestic):

EMI Latin America Inc. (4)
404 Washington Ave Ste 700, Miami Beach, FL 33139-6606
Tel.: (305) 674-7529
Sales Range: $50-74.9 Million
Emp.: 40
Music Publisher & Distr
N.A.I.C.S.: 512230

Subsidiary (Non-US):

EMI Recorded Music Australia Pty. Ltd. (4)
98 100 Glover St, 2090, Cremorne, NSW, Australia
Tel.: (61) 299080777
Web Site: http://www.musichead.com.au
Sales Range: $25-49.9 Million
Emp.: 70
Music Publisher & Distr
N.A.I.C.S.: 512250

EMI Records (Ireland) Ltd. (4)
9 Whitefriars, Aungier Street, Dublin, 2, Ireland
Tel.: (353) 12039900
Web Site: http://www.emimusic.com
Sales Range: $75-99.9 Million
Emp.: 13
Music Publisher & Distr
N.A.I.C.S.: 512250

Universal Music GmbH (4)
Stralauer Allee 1, 10245, Berlin, Germany
Tel.: (49) 305000000

UNIVERSAL MUSIC GROUP N.V.

Universal Music Group N.V.—(Continued)
Sales Range: $25-49.9 Million
Emp.: 150
Music Publishing & Distr
N.A.I.C.S.: 512230

UNIVERSAL OFFICE AUTOMATION LIMITED
806 Siddharth 96 Nehru Place, New Delhi, 110019, India
Tel.: (91) 1126444812
Web Site: https://www.uniofficeautomation.com
Year Founded: 1991
523519—(BOM)
Rev.: $12,337
Assets: $257,515
Liabilities: $2,050
Net Worth: $255,464
Earnings: ($3,273)
Fiscal Year-end: 03/31/23
Electronic Components Mfr
N.A.I.C.S.: 334419
Naina Luthra (Compliance Officer & Sec)

UNIVERSAL OUTDOOR GROUP PLC
44-46 Whitfield Street, London, W1T 2RJ, United Kingdom
Tel.: (44) 207 754 0459
Web Site: http://www.universaloutdoor.co.uk
Year Founded: 2008
Outdoor Advertising Services
N.A.I.C.S.: 541850
Dominic Berger (Dir-Comml)

UNIVERSAL PARTNERS LIMITED
Level 3 Alexander House 35 Cybercity, 72201, Ebene, 72201, Mauritius
Tel.: (230) 2600451 MU
Web Site: https://www.universalpartners.mu
Year Founded: 2016
UPL—(JSE)
Rev.: $2,610,536
Assets: $134,646,495
Liabilities: $17,365,171
Net Worth: $117,281,324
Earnings: ($3,802,605)
Emp.: 4,000
Fiscal Year-end: 06/30/23
Investment Management Service
N.A.I.C.S.: 523999
Pierre Joubert (CEO)

UNIVERSAL POLICY INVESTMENT VEHICLE LTD.
60 Street Market Square, Belize, Belize
Tel.: (501) 5073601200
UPIV—(PAN)
Sales Range: Less than $1 Million
Automobile Finance Services
N.A.I.C.S.: 522220
Juan C. Pastor (Pres)

UNIVERSAL POSTAL UNION
Weltpoststrasse 4 International Bureau, Bern, 3000, Switzerland
Tel.: (41) 313503111
Web Site: http://www.upu.int
Sales Range: $25-49.9 Million
Emp.: 250
Postal Agency Services
N.A.I.C.S.: 491110
Bishar Hussein (Gen Dir)

UNIVERSAL PRIME ALUMINIUM LIMITED
Century Bhavan 1st Floor 771 Dr Annie Besant Road, Worli, Mumbai, 400 030, India
Tel.: (91) 22 24304198
Web Site: http://www.universalprime.in
Rev.: $115,357
Assets: $1,002,589
Liabilities: $76,387
Net Worth: $926,202
Earnings: $2,495
Fiscal Year-end: 03/31/19
Aluminium Products Mfr
N.A.I.C.S.: 331210
B. L. Bagaria (CFO)

UNIVERSAL PROPTECH INC.
1 Royal Gate Blvd Suite D, Vaughan, L4L 8Z7, ON, Canada
Tel.: (905) 850-8686
Web Site: https://universalproptech.com
UPIPF—(OTCQB)
Rev.: $6,897,889
Assets: $4,793,137
Liabilities: $1,999,378
Net Worth: $2,793,759
Earnings: ($852,980)
Fiscal Year-end: 08/31/21
Building Materials Mfr
N.A.I.C.S.: 333415
Chris Hazelton (CEO)

UNIVERSAL RESOURCE & SERVICES LIMITED
10 Collyer Quay No 10-01, Ocean Financial Centre, Singapore, 049315, Singapore
Tel.: (65) 63893000
Year Founded: 1995
BGO—(SES)
Sales Range: $1-9.9 Million
Oil Industry Services
N.A.I.C.S.: 213112
Chen Chuanjian Jason (Sec)

UNIVERSAL STARCH-CHEM ALLIED LIMITED
Mhatre Pen Building B Wing 2nd Floor Senapati Bapat Marg, Dadar West, Mumbai, 400 028, India
Tel.: (91) 2224362210
Web Site: https://www.universalstarch.com
Year Founded: 1973
524408—(BOM)
Rev.: $62,192,550
Assets: $24,500,103
Liabilities: $17,516,499
Net Worth: $6,983,604
Earnings: $707,628
Emp.: 375
Fiscal Year-end: 03/31/23
Maize Starch Mfr
N.A.I.C.S.: 311221
Jitendrasinh Jaysinh Rawal (Chm & Mng Dir)

Subsidiaries:
Unique Sugars Limited (1)
Rawal Industrial Estate, Dhule, 425 408, Maharashtra, India
Tel.: (91) 2566244152
Emp.: 1,000
Maize Starch Mfr
N.A.I.C.S.: 311221
G.P. Chaudhary (Gen Mgr)

UNIVERSAL STORE HOLDINGS LIMITED
42A William Farrior Place, Eagle Farm, 4009, QLD, Australia
Tel.: (61) 733686500 AU
Web Site: https://www.universalstore.com
Year Founded: 1999
UNI—(ASX)
Rev.: $101,278,607
Assets: $172,683,706
Liabilities: $83,720,415
Net Worth: $88,963,291
Earnings: $15,368,716
Fiscal Year-end: 06/30/23
Holding Company
N.A.I.C.S.: 551112
Alice Barbery (CEO)

Subsidiaries:
Cheap Thrills Cycles Pty. Ltd. (1)
9-11 Centennial Circuit, Byron Bay, 2481, NSW, Australia
Tel.: (61) 478782335
Web Site: https://thrills.co
Apparel Mfr & Distr
N.A.I.C.S.: 314999

UNIVERSAL SYSTEM GROUP SA
27 rue Nicolo, 75116, Paris, France
Tel.: (33) 170613522
Web Site: http://www.u-systemgroup.com
Solar Panel Mfr & Distr
N.A.I.C.S.: 333414
Maurice Fitoussi (Chm & CEO)

UNIVERSAL TECHNOLOGIES HOLDINGS LIMITED
Room A B2 11/F Guangdong Investment Tower No 148 Connaught Road, Sheung Wan, China (Hong Kong)
Tel.: (852) 21864500 Ky
Web Site: http://www.uth.com.hk
Year Founded: 2001
1026—(HKG)
Rev.: $44,497,500
Assets: $321,576,293
Liabilities: $183,219,030
Net Worth: $138,357,263
Earnings: ($20,853,390)
Emp.: 405
Fiscal Year-end: 12/31/22
Real Estate Investing Management System
N.A.I.C.S.: 523999
Chi Wai Tang (Sec & Controller-Fin)

Subsidiaries:
Hooray Securities Limited (1)
Room A & B2 11/F Guangdong Investment Tower, 148 Connaught Road Central, Hong Kong, China (Hong Kong)
Tel.: (852) 21594500
Web Site: https://hooraysec.com.hk
Investment Banking & Financial Services
N.A.I.C.S.: 522320

International Payment Solutions (Hong Kong) Limited (1)
Room 231- 233 Building 2 Phase 1 1 Science Park West Avenue, Hong Kong Science Park, Hong Kong, China (Hong Kong)
Tel.: (852) 2 649 6133
Web Site: https://www.ips.com.hk
Sales Range: $700-749.9 Million
Emp.: 204
Online Payment Processing Services
N.A.I.C.S.: 522320

UNIVERSAL TEXTILE CO., LTD.
7/F 62-5 Hsi-Ning North Road, Taipei, 105, Taiwan
Tel.: (886) 225523977
Web Site: https://www.universal-tex.com
Year Founded: 1969
1445—(TAI)
Rev.: $45,185,191
Assets: $101,523,852
Liabilities: $13,432,028
Net Worth: $88,091,824
Earnings: $32,976,257
Fiscal Year-end: 12/31/23
Textile Products Mfr
N.A.I.C.S.: 313310
Chen Yao -Ming (Chm)

INTERNATIONAL PUBLIC

Subsidiaries:
Universal Textile Co., Ltd. - Spinning Factory, Changbin (1)
No 6 Gongye W 6th, Lugang Township, Lukang, 505, Changhua, Taiwan
Tel.: (886) 47810150
Professional Fabric Mfr
N.A.I.C.S.: 314999

Universal Textile Co., Ltd. - Weaving Factory, Luzhu (1)
No 417 Dazhu N Rd, Luzhu Township, Taoyuan, 338, Taiwan
Tel.: (886) 3 323 2393
Professional Fabric Mfr
N.A.I.C.S.: 314999

Universal Textile Co., Ltd. - Weaving Factory, Taoyuan (1)
No 42 Xingbang Rd, Taoyuan, 330, Taiwan
Tel.: (886) 33615514
Professional Fabric Mfr
N.A.I.C.S.: 314999

UNIVERSAL TRANSPORT KANN GMBH
Auf Der Kaiserbitz 3, 51147, Cologne, Germany
Tel.: (49) 22039229110
Year Founded: 1994
Freight Forwarding Services
N.A.I.C.S.: 488510
Heinz Jurgen Kann (Mng Dir)

UNIVERSAL TRAVEL GROUP
9F Building A Rongchao Marina Bay Center No 2021 Haixiu Road, Baoan District, Shenzhen, 518133, China
Tel.: (86) 75583668489 NV
Web Site: http://www.us.cnutg.com
Sales Range: $125-149.9 Million
Emp.: 771
Airline Ticketing, Cargo Transportation, Hotel Reservation, Packaged Tours & Air Delivery Services
N.A.I.C.S.: 488999
Jing Xie (Interim CFO & VP)

UNIVERSAL VISION BIOTECHNOLOGY CO., LTD.
4F No 3-1 Yuanqu St, Nangang Dist, Taipei, 115, Taiwan
Tel.: (886) 226558000
Web Site: https://uvb.com.tw
Year Founded: 1994
3218—(TPE)
Rev.: $109,247,319
Assets: $140,393,053
Liabilities: $51,967,139
Net Worth: $88,425,914
Earnings: $27,136,573
Emp.: 665
Fiscal Year-end: 12/31/22
Biotechnology Research & Development Services
N.A.I.C.S.: 541714
Ou Shu-Fang (Chm)

UNIVERSE ENTERTAINMENT AND CULTURE GROUP COMPANY LIMITED
Tel.: (852) 24163008 BM
Web Site: http://www.uih.com.hk
1046—(HKG)
Rev.: $77,723,348
Assets: $135,657,553
Liabilities: $70,462,419
Net Worth: $65,195,134
Earnings: $19,665,581
Emp.: 139
Fiscal Year-end: 06/30/21
Holding Company; Financial Services
N.A.I.C.S.: 551112
Daneil Shiu Ming Lam (Chm & Exec Dir)

Subsidiaries:
Formex Financial Press Limited (1)

12/F One Lyndhurst Tower No 1 Lyndhurst Terrace, Central, China (Hong Kong)
Tel.: (852) 28539530
Web Site: https://www.formex.hk
Financial Marketing Services
N.A.I.C.S.: 541611
Hermia Hung (Mgr-Bus Dev)

Universe Optical Company Limited (1)
18/F Wyler Centre II 192-200 Tai Lin Pai Road, Kwai Chung, China (Hong Kong)
Tel.: (852) 26689960
Web Site:
  https://www.universeoptical.com.hk
Optical Product Mfr & Distr
N.A.I.C.S.: 339115

UNIVERSE PHARMACEUTICALS INC.
265 Jingjiu Avenue, Economic & Technological Development Zone, Jian, Jiangxi, China
Tel.: (86) 57187555823 Ky
Web Site: https://universe-pharmacy.com
Year Founded: 2019
UPC—(NASDAQ)
Rev.: $32,308,735
Assets: $53,287,032
Liabilities: $13,754,331
Net Worth: $39,532,701
Earnings: ($6,163,061)
Emp.: 225
Fiscal Year-end: 09/30/23
Holding Company
N.A.I.C.S.: 551112
Gang Lai (Chm & CEO)

UNIVERSE PRINTSHOP HOLDINGS LTD.
Office F 12/F Legend Tower 7 Shing Yip Street, Kwun Tong, China (Hong Kong)
Tel.: (852) 35654707 Ky
Web Site: http://www.uprintshop.hk
Year Founded: 2001
8448—(HKG)
Rev.: $12,172,920
Assets: $4,183,789
Liabilities: $4,270,593
Net Worth: ($86,804)
Earnings: ($2,614,108)
Emp.: 69
Fiscal Year-end: 03/31/23
Digital Printing Services
N.A.I.C.S.: 561439
Man Keung Chau (Co-Founder, Chm & Compliance Officer)

UNIVERSIDAD CNCI, S.A. DE C.V.
Batallon de San Patricio 109 Valle Oriente, 66280, Garza Garcia, NL, Mexico
Tel.: (52) 8182328000
Web Site: http://www.cnci.com.mx
Sales Range: $10-24.9 Million
Emp.: 1,375
Colleges & Technical Schools
N.A.I.C.S.: 611710
Alberto Hinojosa-Canales (Vice Chm & CEO)

UNIVERSITIES SUPERANNUATION SCHEME LIMITED
Royal Liver Building, Liverpool, L3 1PY, United Kingdom
Tel.: (44) 333 300 1043
Web Site: http://www.uss.co.uk
Year Founded: 1974
Financial Services
N.A.I.C.S.: 523999
Graham Betts (Head-Ops)

UNIVERSITY PLUMBING & HEATING LTD
3655 Keele Street, Toronto, M3J 1M8, ON, Canada
Tel.: (416) 630-6010
Web Site:
  https://www.universityplumbing.ca
Year Founded: 1995
Rev.: $22,906,400
Emp.: 180
Plumbing Contractor
N.A.I.C.S.: 238220

UNIVERSITY PRESS PLC
Three Crowns Building Jericho, PMB 5095, Ibadan, Oyo, Nigeria
Tel.: (234) 8110713098
Web Site:
  https://www.universitypressplc.com
Year Founded: 1949
UPL—(NIGE)
Rev.: $1,948,378
Assets: $3,783,582
Liabilities: $1,510,715
Net Worth: $2,272,867
Earnings: ($116,747)
Emp.: 229
Fiscal Year-end: 03/31/24
Periodical & Book Publisher
N.A.I.C.S.: 513130
Samuel Kolawole (Mng Dir)

UNIVERSO ONLINE S.A
Av Brig Faria Lima 1384 Jardim Paulistano, Sao Paulo, 01451-001, Brazil
Tel.: (55) 8007033000
Web Site: http://www.uol.com.br
Year Founded: 1996
Journalism, Information, Entertainment & Content Services
N.A.I.C.S.: 513199

Subsidiaries:

Compass UOL (1)
Alameda Barao de Limeira 425 Santa Cecilia, Sao Paulo, 01202-900, Brazil
Tel.: (55) 1155014655
Web Site: https://compass.uol
Emp.: 100
IT Services & IT Consulting Services
N.A.I.C.S.: 561499
Alexis Rockenbach (CEO)

Subsidiary (US):

Avenue Code LLC (2)
26 O'Farrell St Ste 600, San Francisco, CA 94108
Tel.: (415) 766-4178
Web Site: http://www.avenuecode.com
Software Development Services
N.A.I.C.S.: 541511
David Bealby (VP-Global Svcs)

UNIVERUS SOFTWARE, INC.
130 Brew Street Suite 401, Port Moody, V3H 0E3, BC, Canada
Tel.: (604) 757-1326
Web Site: https://univerus.com
Year Founded: 2019
Emp.: 150
Software Devolepment
N.A.I.C.S.: 513210

Subsidiaries:

Accent Business Services, Inc. (1)
7710 NE Greenwood Dr Ste 210, Vancouver, WA 98682
Tel.: (360) 882-4002
Web Site: https://www.varasset.com
Emp.: 100
Management Consulting Services
N.A.I.C.S.: 541618
Jeff Tompkins (Pres)

UNIVERZAL A.D.
Suboticki put 50, 24420, Kanjiza, 24420, Vojvodina, Serbia
Tel.: (381) 24874876
Web Site: https://www.univerzal-kanjiza.com
Year Founded: 1991

UNVK—(BEL)
Rev.: $345,525
Assets: $3,191,063
Liabilities: $327,530
Net Worth: $2,863,532
Earnings: $13,519
Emp.: 8
Fiscal Year-end: 12/31/22
Real Estate Manangement Services
N.A.I.C.S.: 531390
Dorde Loncar (Dir)

UNIVERZAL BANKA A.D. BEOGRAD
Francuska 29, 11000, Belgrade, Serbia
Tel.: (381) 112022720
Web Site: https://www.ubbad.rs
Sales Range: $25-49.9 Million
Emp.: 448
Banking Services
N.A.I.C.S.: 522180

UNIVERZALPROMET D.D. TUZLA
Ulica Mitra Trifunovica Uce br 7, Tuzla, Bosnia & Herzegovina
Tel.: (387) 35280525
Web Site:
  http://www.univerzalpromet.ba
Year Founded: 1946
UVZPR—(SARE)
Sales Range: Less than $1 Million
Non-Durable Goods Whslr
N.A.I.C.S.: 424990
Miralem Nuhanovic (Dir)

UNIVID ASA
Grundingen 2, 0250, Oslo, Norway
Tel.: (47) 93480010 NO
Web Site: https://www.univid.no
Year Founded: 1996
UNIV—(EUR)
Rev.: $1,966,000
Assets: $38,930,000
Liabilities: $34,880,000
Net Worth: $4,050,000
Earnings: $37,232,000
Fiscal Year-end: 12/31/22
Investment Management Service
N.A.I.C.S.: 523999
James Haft (Chm)

UNIVISION ENGINEERING LIMITED
Unit 201 2/F Sunbeam Centre 27 Shing Yip Street, Kwun Tong, Kowloon, China (Hong Kong)
Tel.: (852) 23893256
Web Site: http://www.uvel.com
UVEL—(LSE)
Rev.: $14,860,635
Assets: $21,629,566
Liabilities: $10,550,719
Net Worth: $11,078,847
Earnings: $764,877
Emp.: 79
Fiscal Year-end: 03/31/21
Surveillance System Installation & Maintenance Services
N.A.I.C.S.: 561621
Stephen Sin Mo Koo (Chm)

UNIVO PHARMACEUTICALS LTD.
Haaraba 30, Post Box 78, IL-6473926, Tel Aviv, Israel
Tel.: (972) 89448585
Web Site:
  https://www.univopharma.com
Year Founded: 1993
UNVO.M—(TAE)
Rev.: $11,187,442
Assets: $26,792,423
Liabilities: $14,517,949
Net Worth: $12,274,473

Earnings: ($1,140,813)
Fiscal Year-end: 12/31/21
Pharmaceutical Preparation Mfr
N.A.I.C.S.: 325412
Golan Bitton (Founder & CEO)

UNIWHEELS MANAGEMENT (SWITZERLAND) AG
Bosch 45, Hunenberg, 6331, Switzerland
Tel.: (41) 7845300
Web Site: http://www.uniwheels.com
Sales Range: $400-449.9 Million
Emp.: 1,300
Light Alloy Wheel Mfr
N.A.I.C.S.: 336390
Heike Pfleger (Mng Dir)

Subsidiaries:

ALUTEC Leichtmetallfelgen GmbH (1)
Industriestrasse 17, 67136, Fussgonheim, Germany
Tel.: (49) 623797690
Web Site: http://www.alutec.de
Sales Range: $25-49.9 Million
Emp.: 20
Light Alloy Wheel Mfr
N.A.I.C.S.: 336390

ANZIO Wheels Poland Sp. z.o.o. (1)
Ul Ignacego Moscickiego 2, 37 450, Stalowa Wola, Poland
Tel.: (48) 158782541
Web Site: http://www.anziowheels.com
Sales Range: $25-49.9 Million
Emp.: 10
Light Alloy Wheel Mfr
N.A.I.C.S.: 336390

ATS Leichtmetallrader GmbH (1)
Bruchstrasse 34, 67098, Bad Durkheim, Germany
Tel.: (49) 6322 9899 6500
Web Site: http://www.ats-wheels.com
Light Alloy Wheel Mfr
N.A.I.C.S.: 336390
Peter Bodenschatz (Mgr-Sls)

Subsidiary (Domestic):

ATS Stahlschmidt & Maiworm GmbH (2)
In der Lacke 7 9, 58791, Werdohl, Germany
Tel.: (49) 23 92 5 04 1 78
Light Alloy Wheel Mfr
N.A.I.C.S.: 336390

Subsidiary (Non-US):

ATS Stahlschmidt & Maiworm Sp. z o.o. (2)
Kazimierza Mireckiego, Stalowa Wola, Poland
Tel.: (48) 158772222
Web Site: http://www.ats-company.com
Sales Range: $150-199.9 Million
Emp.: 800
Light Alloy Wheel Mfr
N.A.I.C.S.: 336390

RIAL Leichtmetallfelgen GmbH (1)
Industriestrasse 11, 67136, Fussgonheim, Germany
Tel.: (49) 6237402260
Web Site: http://www.rial.de
Light Alloy Wheel Mfr
N.A.I.C.S.: 336390

UNIWIDE HOLDINGS INC.
Upper Ground Floor Pearl Plaza Buiding, 165 Quirino Ave Barangay Tambo Paranaque, Manila, Philippines
Tel.: (63) 633 5951
Year Founded: 1994
Holding Company
N.A.I.C.S.: 551112
Jimmy N. Gow (Chm & CEO)

UNIWORTH INTERNATIONAL LTD.
Rawdon Chambers 11A Sarojini

UNIWORTH INTERNATIONAL LTD.

Uniworth International Ltd.—(Continued)
Naidu Sarani 4th Floor Unit 4B, Kolkata, 700 017, India
Tel.: (91) 3340061301
Web Site:
 https://www.uniworthnational.com
Textile Products Mfr
N.A.I.C.S.: 314999

UNIWORTH TEXTILES LTD.

Rawdon Chambers 11A Sarojini Naidu Sarani 4th Floor Unit 4B, Kolkata, 700 017, India
Tel.: (91) 40003100
Web Site:
 http://www.uniworthtextiles.com
Textile Products Mfr
N.A.I.C.S.: 314999
Priti Mohta *(Compliance Officer)*

UNIZO HOLDINGS COMPANY LIMITED

2-10-9 Hatchobori, Chuo-ku, Tokyo, 104-0032, Japan
Tel.: (81) 335237531
Web Site: http://www.unizo-hd.co.jp
Year Founded: 1959
3258—(TKS)
Rev.: $507,840,180
Assets: $6,283,581,120
Liabilities: $5,258,342,460
Net Worth: $1,025,238,660
Earnings: $107,841,180
Emp.: 386
Fiscal Year-end: 03/31/19
Holding Company; Real Estate Services Including Office Building & Hotel Owner & Operator
N.A.I.C.S.: 551112
Takao Suzuki *(Chm)*

UNIZYX HOLDING CORPORATION

No 6 Innovation Rd II Science Park, Hsin-chu, Taiwan
Tel.: (886) 35788838
Web Site: http://www.unizyx.com.tw
3704—(TAI)
Rev.: $993,491,640
Assets: $714,629,523
Liabilities: $351,112,351
Net Worth: $363,517,171
Earnings: $44,330,814
Emp.: 3,145
Fiscal Year-end: 12/31/23
Holding Company
N.A.I.C.S.: 551112
Shun-I Chu *(Chm)*

Subsidiaries:

MitraStar Technology Corporation (1)
No 6 Innovation Road II Hsinchu Science Park, Hsinchu, 300, Taiwan
Tel.: (886) 35777998
Web Site: https://www.mitrastar.com
Information Technology Services
N.A.I.C.S.: 541519

Wuxi Genezys Technology Ltd. (1)
No 1-1 Minshan Road, Xin Wu District, Wuxi, Jiangsu, China
Tel.: (86) 51088080888
Networking Product Mfr
N.A.I.C.S.: 334111

ZyXEL Communications Corporation (1)
No 2 Industry East RD IX Hsinchu Science Park, Hsin-chu, 30075, Taiwan
Tel.: (886) 35783942
Web Site: http://www.zyxel.com
Sales Range: $450-499.9 Million
Emp.: 3,200
Broadband Access Products & Services
N.A.I.C.S.: 334220
Shun-I Chu *(Founder)*

Subsidiary (Non-US):

ZyXEL Communications UK Ltd. (2)
2 Old Row Court Rose Street, Wokingham, RG40 1XZ, United Kingdom
Tel.: (44) 1189121700
Web Site: http://www.zyxel.co.uk
Sales Range: $25-49.9 Million
Emp.: 40
Broadband Access Products & Services
N.A.I.C.S.: 334220

Subsidiary (US):

ZyXEL Communications, Inc. (2)
1130 N Miller St, Anaheim, CA 92806-2001
Tel.: (714) 632-0882
Web Site: http://www.zyxel.com
Sales Range: $25-49.9 Million
Emp.: 100
Broadband Access Products & Services
N.A.I.C.S.: 334220
David Soares *(VP-Sls-North America)*

Zyxel (Thailand) Company Ltd. (1)
1/1 Moo 2 Ratchaphruk Road, Bangrak-Noi Muang, Nonthaburi, 11000, Thailand
Tel.: (66) 28315315
Wireless Local Area Network Services
N.A.I.C.S.: 517112

Zyxel Communication (ShangHai) Co., Ltd. (1)
2602 Building 2 No 750 Zhongshan West Road, Changning District, Shanghai, China
Tel.: (86) 2152069033
Software Development Services
N.A.I.C.S.: 541511

Zyxel Communications A/S (1)
Gladsaxevej 378 2 th, 2860, Soborg, Denmark
Tel.: (45) 39550700
Wireless Local Area Network Services
N.A.I.C.S.: 517112

Zyxel Communications B.V. (1)
Binnenweg 4, 2132CT, Hoofddorp, Netherlands
Tel.: (31) 235553689
Wireless Local Area Network Services
N.A.I.C.S.: 517112

Zyxel Communications Do Brasil, Ltda. (1)
Rua Urussui 300 - Conjs 12 e 13, Itaim Bibi, Sao Paulo, 04542-903, SP, Brazil
Tel.: (55) 1130782345
Wireless Local Area Network Services
N.A.I.C.S.: 517112

Zyxel Communications Italy S.r.l. (1)
Via Umbria 27/B, 10099, Settimo Torinese, Italy
Tel.: (39) 0113028500
Wireless Local Area Network Services
N.A.I.C.S.: 517112

Zyxel Communications RU LLC (1)
Trubnaya St 12, Moscow, Russia
Tel.: (7) 4997056106
Information Technology Services
N.A.I.C.S.: 541519

Zyxel Deutschland GmbH (1)
Sirius Europark Adenauerstr 20 entrance A3/3OG, 52146, Wurselen, Germany
Tel.: (49) 240569090
Emp.: 700
Wireless Local Area Network Services
N.A.I.C.S.: 517112

Zyxel France SASU (1)
1 Rue des Vergers, 69760, Limonest, France
Tel.: (33) 472529797
Wireless Local Area Network Services
N.A.I.C.S.: 517112

Zyxel Iletisim Teknolojileri A.S. (1)
Kaptanpasa Mah Piyalepasa Bulvari Ortadogu Plaza N 73 K 6, Okmeydani-Sisli, 34484, Istanbul, Turkiye
Tel.: (90) 2123141800
Wireless Local Area Network Services
N.A.I.C.S.: 517112

Zyxel Korea Co., Ltd. (1)
Room 809 Building A 33 Gwacheon-daero 7-gil, Gwacheon, Gyeonggi, Korea (South)
Tel.: (82) 262435533

Web Site: http://www.zyxel.kr
Wireless Local Area Network Services
N.A.I.C.S.: 517112

Zyxel Networks Corporation (1)
No 2 Industry East RD IX Hsinchu Science Park, Hsinchu, 30076, Taiwan
Tel.: (886) 35783942
Web Site: https://www.zyxel.com
Wireless Local Area Network Services
N.A.I.C.S.: 517112

Zyxel Technology India Pvt Ltd. (1)
1624D Floor-16th Max Towers DND Flyway Sector-16B, Noida, 201301, Uttar Pradesh, India
Tel.: (91) 1147608800
Wireless Local Area Network Services
N.A.I.C.S.: 517112

UNJHA FORMULATIONS LIMITED

Khali Char Rasta State Highway, Siddhapur, 384151, Gujarat, India
Tel.: (91) 2767282395
Web Site:
 https://www.unjhaformulations.com
531762—(BOM)
Rev.: $1,580,769
Assets: $408,836
Liabilities: $114,681
Net Worth: $294,155
Earnings: $33,871
Emp.: 17
Fiscal Year-end: 03/31/23
Pharmaceutical Products Distr
N.A.I.C.S.: 325412
Mayankkumar Shambhubhai Patel *(Chm, CEO & Mng Dir)*

Subsidiaries:

Radiant Nutraceuticals Limited (1)
SKS Tower 7th Floor 7 VIP Road Mohakhali, Dhaka, 1206, Bangladesh
Tel.: (880) 29835717
Web Site: https://www.radiantnutrabd.com
Herbal Medicine Mfr & Distr
N.A.I.C.S.: 325412

UNLU MENKUL DEGERLER A.S.

Ahi Evran Cad No 21 Kat 1 Polaris Plaza, Maslak, Istanbul, Turkiye
Tel.: (90) 2123673636
Web Site:
 http://www.unlumenkul.com
Year Founded: 1996
UNLUS—(IST)
Assets: $102,978,050
Liabilities: $96,205,610
Net Worth: $6,772,440
Earnings: $2,964,738
Emp.: 450
Fiscal Year-end: 12/31/22
Investment Management Service
N.A.I.C.S.: 523940
Mahmut L. Unlu *(Chm)*

UNM PHARMA INC.

4-2-3 Gosyonoyumoto, Akita, 010-1415, Japan
Tel.: (81) 18 892 7411
Web Site:
 http://www.umnpharma.com
Year Founded: 2004
Sales Range: $10-24.9 Million
Emp.: 20
Pharmaceuticals Mfr
N.A.I.C.S.: 325412
Tatsuyoshi Hirano *(Chm & CEO)*

UNNO INDUSTRIES LTD.

Laxmi Plaza 6th Floor Room 60 New link Road, Mumbai, 400053, India
Tel.: (91) 2266989401
Financial Investment Services
N.A.I.C.S.: 523999
Prafulchandra Gordhandas Zaveri *(Mng Dir)*

INTERNATIONAL PUBLIC

UNO MINDA LIMITED

Tel.: (91) 1242290693
Web Site: http://www.unominda.com
532539—(BOM)
Rev.: $712,903,184
Assets: $523,611,116
Liabilities: $274,230,996
Net Worth: $249,380,120
Earnings: $51,481,816
Emp.: 3,417
Fiscal Year-end: 03/31/18
Auto Electrical Parts Mfr
N.A.I.C.S.: 335910
Nirmal Kumar Minda *(Chm & Mng Dir)*

Subsidiaries:

Delvis GmbH (1)
Prinz-Ludwig-Strasse 11, 93055, Regensburg, Germany
Tel.: (49) 94160095800
Web Site: http://www.delvis.de
Emp.: 170
Automobile Parts Mfr
N.A.I.C.S.: 336390

Harita Fehrer Limited (1)
Survey No 29 30 31 Vellanthangal Village 55 Thandalam Group, Irrungattukottai Sriperumbudur Kancheepuram Dist, Chennai, 602105, Tamil Nadu, India (51%)
Tel.: (91) 4347233445
Web Site: http://www.haritafehrer.co.in
Automotive Interior Component Mfr
N.A.I.C.S.: 336390

Harita Seating Systems Limited (1)
Jayalakshmi Estates Vth Floor 8 Haddows Road, Chennai, 600016, India
Tel.: (91) 4428272233
Web Site: http://www.haritaseating.com
Rev.: $141,179,609
Assets: $75,682,634
Liabilities: $39,196,798
Net Worth: $36,485,836
Earnings: $5,768,423
Emp.: 358
Fiscal Year-end: 03/31/2019
Motor Vehicle Seating Mfr
N.A.I.C.S.: 336360
A. G. Giridharan *(CEO)*

Minda Rinder Private Limited (1)
Gat No 148 Mhalunge Ingale Off Chakan Talegaon Road, Tal-Khed Chakan Dist, Pune, 410501, India
Tel.: (91) 2030616100
Web Site: http://www.rinder.in
Automobile Parts Mfr
N.A.I.C.S.: 336390

iSYS RTS GmbH (1)
Moosacher Str 88, 80809, Munich, Germany
Tel.: (49) 8944230680
Web Site: http://www.isys-rts.de
Information Technology Services
N.A.I.C.S.: 541511

UNOFI PATRIMOINE

7 B Rue Galvani, 75017, Paris, France
Tel.: (33) 144093870
Web Site: http://www.unofi.fr
Emp.: 310
Real Estate Agents & Brokers
N.A.I.C.S.: 531210

UNOZAWA-GUMI IRON WORKS, LTD.

2-36-40 Shimomaruko, Ota-ku, Tokyo, 146-0092, Japan
Tel.: (81) 337594191
Web Site: https://www.unozawa.co.jp
Year Founded: 1899
6396—(TKS)
Sales Range: Less than $1 Million
Emp.: 197
Pumps Mfr
N.A.I.C.S.: 333914
Torao Unozawa *(Chm)*

UNQ HOLDINGS LIMITED

AND PRIVATE COMPANIES

Room 2505 Guohua Life Finance Tower No 288 Xiangcheng Road, Pudong New Area, Shanghai, China Ky
Year Founded: 2019
2177—(HKG)
Rev.: $364,488,735
Assets: $270,502,826
Liabilities: $153,583,220
Net Worth: $116,919,607
Earnings: ($17,900,903)
Emp.: 421
Fiscal Year-end: 12/31/22
Holding Company
N.A.I.C.S.: 551112
Yong Wang (Chm)

UNTERNEHMENS INVEST AG
Am Hof 4, 1010, Vienna, Austria
Tel.: (43) 140597710 AT
Web Site: http://www.uiag.at
UIV—(VIE)
Rev.: $574,333,622
Assets: $640,831,764
Liabilities: $415,390,768
Net Worth: $225,440,996
Earnings: ($12,423,648)
Emp.: 2,631
Fiscal Year-end: 09/30/20
Investment Services
N.A.I.C.S.: 523999
Rudolf Knunz (Chm-Mgmt Bd)

Subsidiaries:

All for One Group SE (1)
Rita-Maiburg-Strasse 40, Bernhausen, 70794, Filderstadt, Germany
Tel.: (49) 711788070
Web Site: https://www.all-for-one.com
Emp.: 2,800
Information Technology Consulting Services
N.A.I.C.S.: 541512

All for One Steeb AG (1)
Rita-Maiburg-Strasse 40, Filderstadt, 70794, Stuttgart, Germany (50.14%)
Tel.: (49) 711788070
Web Site: http://www.all-for-one.com
Rev.: $463,209,836
Assets: $325,418,503
Liabilities: $213,122,977
Net Worth: $112,295,527
Earnings: $16,599,664
Emp.: 1,710
Fiscal Year-end: 09/30/2021
Data Processing Systems, Applications & Products
N.A.I.C.S.: 518210
Josef Blazicek (Chm-Supervisory Bd)

Subsidiary (Domestic):

Steeb Anwendungssysteme GmbH (2)
Heilbronner Strasse 4, 74232, Abstatt, Germany
Tel.: (49) 70626730
Sales Range: $75-99.9 Million
Emp.: 220
Computer Related Services
N.A.I.C.S.: 541511

Begalom Guss GmbH (1)
Grossalmstrasse 5, 4813, Altmunster, Austria
Tel.: (43) 761 287 8080
Web Site: https://www.begalom.at
Automobile Parts Mfr
N.A.I.C.S.: 336390
Benjamin Behr (Mng Dir)

Pongratz Trailer-Group GmbH (1)
An der Bundesstrasse 34, Traboch, 8772, Leoben, Austria
Tel.: (43) 3843260330
Web Site: http://www.pongratztrailers.com
Vehicle Trailer Mfr
N.A.I.C.S.: 336212

UNTERNEHMENSGRUPPE THEO MULLER S.E.C.S.
2 b rue Albert Borschette, 1246, Luxembourg, Luxembourg
Tel.: (352) 266 309 10 LU
Web Site: http://www.muellergroup.com
Year Founded: 1971
Dairy & Food Services
N.A.I.C.S.: 112120
Dirk Barnard (Mng Dir)

Subsidiaries:

Culina Group Limited (1)
Shrewsbury Road, Market Drayton, TF9 3SQ, Salop, United Kingdom
Tel.: (44) 1630 695 000
Web Site: http://www.culina.co.uk
Warehousing, Distribution & Sales Order Management Services
N.A.I.C.S.: 541614
Chris Price (Fin Dir)

Subsidiary (Domestic):

Fowler Welch Limited (2)
West Marsh Road, Spalding, PE11 2BB, Lincolnshire, United Kingdom
Tel.: (44) 8705882288
Web Site: http://www.fowlerwelch.co.uk
Sales Range: $200-249.9 Million
Emp.: 800
Food Transport & Distribution Services
N.A.I.C.S.: 488510

Mlekarna Pragolaktos a.s. (1)
Ceskobrodska 1174, Kyje, 198 00, Prague, Czech Republic
Tel.: (420) 23 410 6411
Web Site: http://www.mlekarnapragolaktos.cz
Dairy Products Mfr
N.A.I.C.S.: 311514
Vladimir Kadlec (Gen Mgr)

Molkerei Alois Muller GmbH & Co. KG (1)
Zollerstrasse 7, 86850, Berlin, Germany
Tel.: (49) 8236 999 0
Web Site: http://www.muellermilch.de
Dairy Products Mfr
N.A.I.C.S.: 311514

Molkerei Weihenstephan GmbH & Co. KG (1)
Milchstrasse 1, 85354, Freising, Germany
Tel.: (49) 8161 172 222
Web Site: http://www.molkerei-weihenstephan.de
Dairy Products Mfr
N.A.I.C.S.: 311514

Muller Dairy (UK) Limited (1)
Shrewsbury Road, Market Drayton, TF9 3SQ, Shropshire, United Kingdom
Tel.: (44) 1630 692000
Dairy Products Mfr
N.A.I.C.S.: 424430

Subsidiary (Domestic):

Muller Wiseman Dairies Limited (2)
159 Glasgow Road, East Kilbride, Glasgow, G74 4PA, United Kingdom
Tel.: (44) 1355244261
Web Site: http://www.muller-wiseman.co.uk
Sales Range: $1-4.9 Billion
Emp.: 150
Milk Processing Services
N.A.I.C.S.: 112120
Martyn Mulcahy (Dir-Ops)

Muller International Ltd (1)
Genesis House 17 Godliman Street, London, EC4V 5BD, United Kingdom
Tel.: (44) 207 448 1160
Web Site: http://www.muller-london.com
Financial Investment Services
N.A.I.C.S.: 523940
Peter Shapeero (Mng Dir-Investment)

Sachsenmilch Leppersdorf GmbH (1)
An den Breiten, Wachau, 1454, Berlin, Germany (100%)
Tel.: (49) 35 28 4 34 0
Web Site: http://www.sachsenmilch-ingredients.com
Dairy Products Mfr
N.A.I.C.S.: 311514
Jeroen Derks (Mng Dir)

TM Telford Dairy Ltd. (1)
Shrewsbury Road, Market Drayton, TF9 3SQ, Shropshire, United Kingdom
Tel.: (44) 1630 69 2000
Web Site: http://www.muller.co.uk
Dairy Products Mfr
N.A.I.C.S.: 311514

UNYE CIMENTO SANAYI VE TICARET A.S.
Gunpinari Mah Bogazagzi Sok No 2 PK 31, Unye, 52300, Ordu, Turkiye
Tel.: (90) 4523211100
Web Site: http://www.unyecimento.com.tr
Year Founded: 1969
Cement Mfr
N.A.I.C.S.: 327310
Safak Karakoc (Vice Chm)

UOA REAL ESTATE INVESTMENT TRUST
No 9 Jalan Indah 16 Taman Cheras Indah, 56100, Kuala Lumpur, Malaysia
Tel.: (60) 392871000 MY
Web Site: https://www.uoareit.com.my
Year Founded: 2005
UOAREIT—(KLS)
Rev.: $18,767,156
Assets: $365,947,052
Liabilities: $155,225,041
Net Worth: $210,722,010
Earnings: $12,883,105
Fiscal Year-end: 12/31/22
Trust Management Services
N.A.I.C.S.: 523940
Alan Charles Winduss (Chm)

UOB-KAY HIAN HOLDINGS LIMITED
8 Anthony Road 01-01, Singapore, 229957, Singapore
Tel.: (65) 65356868
Web Site: https://www.uobkayhian.com
U10—(SES)
Rev.: $448,006,310
Assets: $3,024,925,774
Liabilities: $1,576,736,283
Net Worth: $1,448,189,490
Earnings: $129,348,808
Emp.: 3,200
Fiscal Year-end: 12/31/23
Holding Company; Securities Trading & Investment Banking Services
N.A.I.C.S.: 551112
Ee-Chao Wee (Chm & Mng Dir)

Subsidiaries:

UOB Kay Hian (Malaysia) Holdings Sdn. Bhd. (1)
Suite 19 01 Menara Keck Seng 203 Jalan Bukit Bintang, 55100, Kuala Lumpur, Malaysia
Tel.: (60) 321471888
Security Broking Services
N.A.I.C.S.: 523150

UOB Kay Hian Private Ltd. (1)
8 Anthony Road 01-01, Singapore, 229957, Singapore (100%)
Tel.: (65) 65356868
Sales Range: $350-399.9 Million
Emp.: 800
Securities Trading & Investment Banking
N.A.I.C.S.: 523150
Ee-Chao Wee (Chm & Mng Dir)

Subsidiary (Non-US):

PT UOB Kay Hian Securities (2)
UOB Plaza Thamrin Nine Fl 36 Jl MH Thamrin Kav 8 - 10, Jakarta, 10230, Indonesia
Tel.: (62) 2129933888
Web Site: https://www.uobkayhian.co.id
Sales Range: $50-74.9 Million
Emp.: 100
Securities Trading Services
N.A.I.C.S.: 523150

UOB-KAY HIAN HOLDINGS LIMITED

Subsidiary (Domestic):

Trans-Pacific Credit Private Limited (2)
8 Anthony Road Suite 01-01, Singapore, 229957, Singapore
Tel.: (65) 65356868
Web Site: http://www.uobkayhian.com.sg
Sales Range: $600-649.9 Million
Emp.: 1,000
Securities Brokerage Services
N.A.I.C.S.: 523150
Tan Chek Teck (Exec Dir)

Subsidiary (Non-US):

UOB Kay Hian (Hong Kong) Limited (2)
6/F Harcourt House 39 Gloucester Road, Central, China (Hong Kong)
Tel.: (852) 21361818
Web Site: https://www.uobkayhian.com.hk
Emp.: 400
Securities Brokerage Services
N.A.I.C.S.: 523150

UOB Kay Hian (U.K.) Limited (2)
1st Floor 14 Austin Friars, London, EC2N 2HE, United Kingdom
Emp.: 4
Securities Trading Services
N.A.I.C.S.: 523999
Simon Dickson (Gen Mgr)

Subsidiary (US):

UOB Kay Hian (U.S.) Inc. (2)
592 5th Ave 48th St 6th Fl, New York, NY 10036
Tel.: (212) 840-1301
Web Site: http://us.uobkayhian.com
Securities Brokerage Services
N.A.I.C.S.: 523150

Subsidiary (Domestic):

UOB Kay Hian Credit Pte Ltd (2)
8 Anthony Rd 01-01, Singapore, 229957, Singapore
Tel.: (65) 65356868
Web Site: http://www.uobkayhian.com
Sales Range: $300-349.9 Million
Emp.: 1,000
Securities Brokerage Services
N.A.I.C.S.: 523150

Subsidiary (Non-US):

UOB Kay Hian Investment Consulting (Shanghai) Company Limited (2)
Tel.: (86) 2154047225
Sales Range: $50-74.9 Million
Emp.: 20
Investment Consulting Services
N.A.I.C.S.: 523940

UOB Kay Hian Securities (Philippines), Inc. (2)
Unit 4B Level 18 Tower 2 The Enterprise Center, 6766 Ayala Avenue corner Paseo De Roxas, Makati, 1226, Philippines
Tel.: (63) 28877972
Securities Trading Services
N.A.I.C.S.: 523150

UOB Kay Hian Securities (M) Sdn. Bhd. (1)
Ground 19th 23rd Floor Menara Keck Seng 203 Jalan Bukit Bintang, 55100, Kuala Lumpur, Malaysia
Tel.: (60) 32 147 1888
Web Site: https://www.utrade.com.my
Financial Institution Services
N.A.I.C.S.: 522110

UOB Kay Hian Securities (Thailand) Public Company Limited (1)
130-132 Sindhorn Tower I at 2nd and 3rd floor Wireless Road, Lumpini Pathumwan, Bangkok, 10330, Thailand (88.68%)
Tel.: (66) 26598000
Web Site: https://www.utrade.co.th
Rev.: $33,381,870
Assets: $193,717,139
Liabilities: $71,140,111
Net Worth: $122,577,028
Earnings: $2,652,381
Emp.: 642
Fiscal Year-end: 12/31/2023
Securities Brokerage Services

UOB-KAY HIAN HOLDINGS LIMITED

UOB-Kay Hian Holdings Limited—(Continued)
N.A.I.C.S.: 523150
Usa Sangcham *(Sr Mng Dir-Retail 8)*

UTrade (1)
1st Floor Bangunan Heng Guan 171 Jalan Burmah, 171 Jalan Burmah, 10050, George Town, Pulau Pinang, Malaysia
Tel.: (60) 4 229 9318
Web Site: http://www.aaasec.com.my
Sales Range: $50-74.9 Million
Emp.: 100
Securities Broking Services
N.A.I.C.S.: 523150

Zenworld Holdings Bhd (1)
MyKRIS Avenue C 1 G The Link 2 Jalan Jalil Perkasa 1, Bukit Jalil, 57000, Kuala Lumpur, Malaysia
Tel.: (60) 378903833
Web Site: http://www.mykris.net
Rev.: $11,059,383
Assets: $14,208,722
Liabilities: $3,212,842
Net Worth: $10,995,880
Earnings: $2,590,291
Fiscal Year-end: 03/31/2020
Broadband Services
N.A.I.C.S.: 517810
Chew Choo Soon *(Mng Dir)*

Subsidiary (Domestic):

Mykris Asia Sdn Bhd (2)
MyKRIS Avenue C-1-G The Link 2 Jalan Jalil Perkasa 1, Bukit Jalil, 57000, Kuala Lumpur, Malaysia
Tel.: (60) 378903833
Web Site: http://www.mykris.net
Internet Providing Services
N.A.I.C.S.: 517121
Ivan Khor *(Sr Acct Mgr)*

UOKI CO., LTD.
2-10-5 Shonandai, Fujisawa, 252-0804, Kanagawa, Japan
Tel.: (81) 466459282
Web Site: https://www.uoki.co.jp
Year Founded: 1968
2683—(TKS)
Rev.: $69,871,950
Assets: $15,257,680
Liabilities: $9,181,550
Net Worth: $6,076,130
Earnings: $297,780
Emp.: 322
Fiscal Year-end: 02/29/24
Fish Distr
N.A.I.C.S.: 424460

UOL GROUP LIMITED
101 Thomson Road 33 00 United Square, Singapore, 307591, Singapore
Tel.: (65) 62550233 SG
Web Site: https://www.uol.com.sg
Year Founded: 1963
U14—(SES)
Rev.: $2,031,130,045
Assets: $16,813,584,025
Liabilities: $4,846,815,873
Net Worth: $11,966,768,153
Earnings: $653,240,172
Emp.: 1,900
Fiscal Year-end: 12/31/23
Holding Company; Property Development & Investment
N.A.I.C.S.: 551112
Cho Yaw Wee *(Chm)*

Subsidiaries:

Pan Pacific Hotels & Resorts Seattle Limited Liability Co. (1)
2125 Terry Ave, Seattle, WA 98121
Tel.: (206) 264-8111
Web Site: https://www.panpacificseattle.com
Hotel & Resort Operator
N.A.I.C.S.: 721110

Pan Pacific Hotels Group (1)
101 Thomson Road 33-00 United Square, Singapore, 307591, Singapore
Tel.: (65) 8008526885

Web Site: https://www.panpacific.com
Hotel & Resort Rental Services
N.A.I.C.S.: 721110

Pan Pacific Hotels Group Ltd. (1)
96 Somerset Road, Singapore, 238163, Singapore (98.2%)
Tel.: (65) 6 884 5222
Web Site: http://www.pphg.com
Sales Range: $300-349.9 Million
Hotel Operator
N.A.I.C.S.: 721110
Soon Hup Neo *(COO)*

Unit (Non-US):

The Sari Pan Pacific Jakarta (2)
Jl M H Thamrin No 6, Jakarta, 10340, Indonesia
Tel.: (62) 212 993 2888
Web Site: https://www.saripacificjakarta.com
Sales Range: $50-74.9 Million
Emp.: 400
Hotel Management
N.A.I.C.S.: 721110

Promatik Emas Sdn. Bhd. (1)
President House Suite 3018 3Rd Floor Jalan Sultan Ismail, 50250, Kuala Lumpur, Malaysia
Tel.: (60) 321410059
Real Estate Services
N.A.I.C.S.: 531390

St Gregory Spa Pte Ltd (1)
6 Raffles Boulevard Level 5, Singapore, 039594, Singapore
Tel.: (65) 68451156
Web Site: https://www.stgregoryspa.com
Spa Operator
N.A.I.C.S.: 812199
Luise Cheng *(Dir-Spa)*

UOMO MEDIA INC.
157 Adelaide Street West Suite 616, Toronto, M5H 4E7, ON, Canada
Tel.: (416) 368-4400 NV
Web Site: http://www.uomomedia.com
Year Founded: 2004
Sales Range: Less than $1 Million
Music Producer, Publisher & Distr;
Digital Music Services; Talent Management Services
N.A.I.C.S.: 512250

Subsidiaries:

GetTickets E Solutions Inc. (1)
105 Balmoral Ave, Toronto, M4V 1J5, ON, Canada
Tel.: (416) 960-8499
Web Site: http://www.gettickets.ca
Emp.: 5
Online Ticketing Services
N.A.I.C.S.: 561599

The NE Inc. (1)
235 Carlaw Avenue Suite 106 - Side Entrance, Toronto, M4M 2S1, ON, Canada
Tel.: (647) 895-7767
Web Site: http://www.thene.ca
Sales Range: $25-49.9 Million
Emp.: 2
Motion Picture & Video Production Services
N.A.I.C.S.: 512110

UORIKI CO., LTD.
2-8-3 Akebonocho, Tachikawa, 190-0012, Tokyo, Japan
Tel.: (81) 425255600
Web Site: https://www.uoriki.co.jp
Year Founded: 1974
7596—(TKS)
Rev.: $240,233,840
Assets: $141,440,780
Liabilities: $27,418,280
Net Worth: $114,022,500
Earnings: $8,996,210
Emp.: 26
Fiscal Year-end: 03/31/24
Fish Products Whslr
N.A.I.C.S.: 424460
Takahide Kurokawa *(Pres & CEO)*

UP ENERGY DEVELOPMENT GROUP LIMITED
Room 3201 32/F Tower 1 Admiralty Centre, 18 Harcourt Road Admiralty, Hong Kong, China (Hong Kong)
Tel.: (852) 29729900 BM
Web Site: http://www.upenergy.com
Sales Range: $25-49.9 Million
Emp.: 641
Coal Mining Services
N.A.I.C.S.: 213113
Jun Qin *(Chm & CEO)*

UP FINTECH HOLDING LIMITED
18/F Grandyvic Building No 1 Building No 16 Taiyanggong Middle Road, Chaoyang District, Beijing, 100020, China
Tel.: (86) 1056216660 Ky
Web Site: http://www.itiger.com
Year Founded: 2018
TIGR—(NASDAQ)
Rev.: $225,365,547
Assets: $3,797,360,388
Liabilities: $3,350,373,496
Net Worth: $446,986,892
Earnings: ($2,186,441)
Emp.: 1,040
Fiscal Year-end: 12/31/22
Holding Company; Securities Brokerage & Dealing Services
N.A.I.C.S.: 551112
Tianhua Wu *(Founder & CEO)*

Subsidiaries:

Tradeup Securities Inc. (1)
101 Eisenhower Pkwy, Roseland, NJ 07068
Tel.: (973) 228-2886
Web Site: https://www.tradeup.com
Security Brokerage & Dealing Services
N.A.I.C.S.: 523150

UP GLOBAL SOURCING HOLDINGS PLC
Ultimate Products Victoria Street Manor Mill, Chadderton, Manchester, OL9 0DD, United Kingdom
Tel.: (44) 1616271400 UK
Web Site: https://www.upgs.com
Year Founded: 1997
UPGS—(LSE)
Rev.: $185,148,203
Assets: $124,156,705
Liabilities: $80,634,991
Net Worth: $43,521,715
Earnings: $9,929,006
Emp.: 295
Fiscal Year-end: 07/31/21
Household Appliance Retailer
N.A.I.C.S.: 423620
Simon Showman *(CEO)*

Subsidiaries:

UP Global Sourcing Hong Kong Limited (1)
Unit B 13/F Yun Tat Commercial Building 70-74 Wuhu Street, Hung Hom, Kowloon, China (Hong Kong)
Tel.: (852) 39063906
Household Appliance Retailer
N.A.I.C.S.: 449210

UP INVEST OU
Ravala puiestee 4 Laagri Business House Vae 16, Laagri Harjumaa, 10143, Tallinn, Estonia
Tel.: (372) 666 3450 EE
Web Site: http://www.upi.ee
Year Founded: 2012
Sales Range: $450-499.9 Million
Investment Holding Services
N.A.I.C.S.: 551112
Marko Virkebau *(Fin Dir & Member-Mgmt Bd)*

INTERNATIONAL PUBLIC

Subsidiaries:

AS Postimees Grupp (1)
Tartu maantee 80, 10112, Tallinn, Estonia (100%)
Tel.: (372) 666 2350
Web Site: http://www.postimeesgrupp.ee
Sales Range: $100-124.9 Million
Emp.: 1,100
Newspapers, Magazines & Television Broadcasting Services
N.A.I.C.S.: 513110
Andrus Raudsalu *(CTO)*

Subsidiary (Domestic):

AS Kanal 2 (2)
Maakri 23 A, 10145, Tallinn, Estonia (100%)
Tel.: (372) 6662450
Web Site: http://www.kanal2.ee
Sales Range: $25-49.9 Million
Emp.: 60
Television Broadcasting Services
N.A.I.C.S.: 516120

AS Kroonpress (2)
133 Tahe St, 51013, Tartu, Estonia
Tel.: (372) 730 5100
Web Site: http://www.kroonpress.eu
Sales Range: $25-49.9 Million
Emp.: 250
Newspaper & Magazine Printing Services
N.A.I.C.S.: 323111
Cerli Noormaegi *(Sec)*

AS Postimees (2)
Gildi 1 E-R 9-17, Tartu, 50095, Estonia
Tel.: (372) 7 390 300
Web Site: http://www.postimees.ee
Sales Range: $25-49.9 Million
Emp.: 10
Newspaper Publishing Services
N.A.I.C.S.: 513110
Mart Luik *(CEO)*

Unit (Domestic):

Parnu Postimees (3)
Ruutli 14, 80010, Parnu, Estonia
Tel.: (372) 4477077
Web Site: http://www.parnupostimees.ee
Newspaper Publishers
N.A.I.C.S.: 513110
Peep Kala *(Chm & CEO)*

Tartu Postimees (3)
Gildi 1, Tartu, 51007, Estonia
Tel.: (372) 7390300
Emp.: 7
IT & Administrative Services
N.A.I.C.S.: 561499
Andres Ratassepp *(Gen Mgr)*

Subsidiary (Domestic):

Balti Uudistetalituse AS (2)
Parnu mnt 158/1, Tallinn, 15043, Estonia
Tel.: (372) 6108800
Web Site: http://www.bns.ee
Sales Range: $1-9.9 Million
Emp.: 100
Holding Company; News Syndicate
N.A.I.C.S.: 551112
Triin Vasserman *(CFO)*

Subsidiary (Domestic):

BNS Eesti OU (3)
Maakri 23A, EE-15043, Tallinn, Estonia (100%)
Tel.: (372) 6108800
Web Site: http://www.news.bns.ee
News Syndicates
N.A.I.C.S.: 516210
Kalev Korv *(Chief Editor)*

Subsidiary (Non-US):

BNS UAB (3)
Saltoniskiu g 9B, 08105, Vilnius, Lithuania (99.95%)
Tel.: (370) 852058501
Web Site: http://www.bns.lt
Emp.: 100
News Agency Services
N.A.I.C.S.: 516210

Subsidiary (Domestic):

OU Scanpix Baltics (2)

Gildi 1, Tartu, 51007, Estonia
Tel.: (372) 6662335
Web Site: http://www.scanpix.ee
Newspaper Publishers
N.A.I.C.S.: 516210
Art Soonets (CEO)

Soov OU (2)
Maakri 23a, Tallinn, 10145, Estonia
Tel.: (372) 6662001
Web Site: http://www.soov.ee
Sales Range: $25-49.9 Million
Emp.: 20
Online Classified Advertising & Publishing Services
N.A.I.C.S.: 541810

Subsidiary (Non-US):

TVNET, SIA (2)
Marijas iela 2, Riga, 1050, Latvia
Tel.: (371) 64904868
Web Site: http://www.tvnet.lv
Sales Range: $25-49.9 Million
Emp.: 4
Online News Publishing Services
N.A.I.C.S.: 513110
Ivars Bauls (CEO)

Balti Meediamonitooringu Grupp OU (1)
Parnu mnt 158/1, 15043, Tallinn, Estonia **(82.4%)**
Tel.: (372) 6536688
Holding Company; Media Monitoring & Analysis Services
N.A.I.C.S.: 551112
Sven-Erik Heinsoo (CEO & Member-Mgmt Bd)

Subsidiary (Non-US):

Mediaskopas, UAB (2)
Jogailos St 9/1, 01116, Vilnius, Lithuania
Tel.: (370) 5 213 59 50
Web Site: http://www.mediaskopas.lt
Emp.: 47
Media Monitoring & Analysis Services
N.A.I.C.S.: 541910
Akvile Katiliene (Head-Analysis)

Subsidiary (Domestic):

OU Meedia Monitooring (2)
Parnu mnt 158/1, 15043, Tallinn, Estonia
Tel.: (372) 6108865
Web Site: http://www.monitooring.ee
Sales Range: $1-9.9 Million
Media Monitoring & Analysis Services
N.A.I.C.S.: 541910
Ursula Nuutmann (Mktg Mgr)

UP MADERA A.D.
Mihajla Pupina 10b, Belgrade, Serbia
Tel.: (381) 11 301 5387
Web Site: http://www.madera.rs
Year Founded: 1951
MDRA—(BEL)
Sales Range: Less than $1 Million
Emp.: 14
Restaurant & Mobile Food Services
N.A.I.C.S.: 722511
Jelena Sarenac-Delic (Exec Dir)

UP SCIENTECH MATERIALS CORP.
No 5-1 Jianguo Rd, Guayin Dist, Taoyuan, Taiwan
Tel.: (886) 3 483 3690
Web Site: http://www.upplate.com
Wear Plate Mfr
N.A.I.C.S.: 332313
Chen Chien-Hsin (Chm)

Subsidiaries:

VAUTID GmbH (1)
Brunnwiesenstrasse 5, Ostfildern, 73760, Stuttgart, Germany
Tel.: (49) 711 44040
Web Site: http://www.vautidgroup.com
Industrial Machinery & Equipment Mfr
N.A.I.C.S.: 333248
Hans Wahl (Founder)

UP TO ELEVEN DIGITAL SO-LUTIONS GMBH
Munzgrabenstrasse 92/4, 8010, Graz, Austria
Tel.: (43) 316 22 84 09
Web Site: http://www.ut11.net
Year Founded: 2012
Sales Range: $1-9.9 Million
Emp.: 3
Digital Software Designer, Developer & Marketer
N.A.I.C.S.: 513210
Martin Pansy (Co-Founder & Mng Dir)

UPA CORPORATION BERHAD
Lot 8228 Batu 6 1/2 Jalan Kuchai Lama, 58200, Kuala Lumpur, Malaysia
Tel.: (60) 379823888 MY
Web Site: https://www.upa.com.my
Year Founded: 1975
UPA—(KLS)
Rev.: $33,712,169
Assets: $65,453,545
Liabilities: $7,155,767
Net Worth: $58,297,778
Earnings: $2,254,815
Emp.: 600
Fiscal Year-end: 12/31/22
Management Services
N.A.I.C.S.: 551114
Kam Moi Kok (Co-Founder & Mng Dir)

Subsidiaries:

Macro Plastic Sdn. Bhd. (1)
Lot 3 Jalan 6/1, Seri Kembangan Industrial Area, 43300, Seri Kembangan, Selangor Darul Ehsan, Malaysia
Tel.: (60) 389458700
Web Site: https://www.macroplastic.com
Plastic Film & Sheet Mfr
N.A.I.C.S.: 326112

Macroplas Industries Co., Ltd. (1)
23/5 Moo 11 Latbualuang-Sainoi Road Sai-yai Sainoi, Nonthaburi, 11150, Thailand
Tel.: (66) 29855937
Web Site: https://www.macroplasindustries.com
Plastic Product Mfr & Distr
N.A.I.C.S.: 326199

UPA Machinery Sdn. Bhd. (1)
Lot 9 Jalan 6/1 Seri Kembangan Industrial Area, 43300, Seri Kembangan, Selangor Darul Ehsan, Malaysia
Tel.: (60) 389499928
Printing Machinery Distr
N.A.I.C.S.: 423830

UPA Press Sdn. Bhd. (1)
Lot 8228 Batu 6 1/2 Jalan Kuchai Lama, 58200, Kuala Lumpur, Malaysia
Tel.: (60) 379823888
Dairy Products Mfr
N.A.I.C.S.: 323111

UPBEST GROUP LIMITED
2/F Wah Kit Commercial Centre 300 Des Voeux Road, Central, China (Hong Kong)
Tel.: (852) 2 545 3298 Ky
Web Site: http://www.upbest.com
Year Founded: 1988
0335—(HKG)
Rev.: $16,381,879
Assets: $424,727,916
Liabilities: $74,095,657
Net Worth: $350,632,259
Earnings: $11,220,357
Emp.: 40
Fiscal Year-end: 03/31/22
Financial Services Including Stock Broking, Margin Financing, Corporate Finance Advisory, Futures Broking, Asset Management & Property Investment & Holding
N.A.I.C.S.: 523150
Annie Wai Ling Cheng (CEO)

Subsidiaries:

Upbest Assets Management Limited (1)
2 F Wah Kit Commercial Centre, 302 Des Voeux Road, Central, China (Hong Kong) **(100%)**
Tel.: (852) 25453298
Web Site: http://www.upbest.com
Emp.: 110
Asset Management Services
N.A.I.C.S.: 523999

Upbest Bullion Company Limited (1)
7/F Wah Kit Commercial Centre, 302 Des Voeux Road, Central, China (Hong Kong) **(100%)**
Tel.: (852) 25453298
Bullion Dealing
N.A.I.C.S.: 523160

Upbest Commodities Company Limited (1)
2 F Wah Kit Commercial Centre, 302 Des Voeux Road, Central, China (Hong Kong) **(100%)**
Tel.: (852) 25453298
Futures Broking & Dealing
N.A.I.C.S.: 523160
Helen Choy (Mgr)

Upbest Cyber Trade Company Limited (1)
2/F Wah Kit Commercial Centre, 302 Des Voeux Road, Central, China (Hong Kong) **(100%)**
Tel.: (852) 2545
IT Services
N.A.I.C.S.: 541519

Upbest Finance Company Limited (1)
2 F Wah Kit Commercial Centre, 302 Des Voeux Road, Central, China (Hong Kong) **(100%)**
Tel.: (852) 25453298
Money Lending Services
N.A.I.C.S.: 522291

Upbest Financial Services Limited (1)
2/F Wah Kit Commercial Centre, 302 Des Voeux Road, Central, China (Hong Kong) **(50%)**
Tel.: (852) 25453298
Financial Services
N.A.I.C.S.: 525990

Upbest Investment Company Limited (1)
2/F Wah Kit Commercial Ctr, 302 Des Voeux Rd, Central, China (Hong Kong) **(100%)**
Tel.: (852) 25453298
Sales Range: $75-99.9 Million
Emp.: 100
Securities Margin Financing Services
N.A.I.C.S.: 525990

Upbest Securities Company Limited (1)
2/F Wah Kit Commercial Centre, 302 Des Voeux Road, Central, China (Hong Kong)
Tel.: (852) 25453298
Securities Dealing & Broking
N.A.I.C.S.: 523150

UPC LTD.
20-11 Gamgok 1-gil, Bujeok-Myeon, Nonsan, 32916, Chungcheongnam-do, Korea (South)
Tel.: (82) 417336922 KS
Web Site: http://www.upc.co.kr
Year Founded: 1990
Sales Range: $10-24.9 Million
Emp.: 70
Disposable Sanitary Product & Plastic Mfr
N.A.I.C.S.: 325211

UPD STARI GRAD A.D.
Terazije 25, Belgrade, Serbia
Tel.: (381) 11 377 81 13
Web Site: http://www.stari-grad.rs
Year Founded: 1951
Sales Range: $1-9.9 Million
Emp.: 184
Home Management Services
N.A.I.C.S.: 721110

UPDATER SERVICES LIMITED
1st Floor No 42 Gandhi Mandapam Road, Chennai, 600085, Tamil Nadu, India
Tel.: (91) 7305092137
Web Site: https://www.uds.in
Year Founded: 1990
543996—(BOM)
Rev.: $256,830,144
Assets: $147,980,755
Liabilities: $100,822,938
Net Worth: $47,157,818
Earnings: $4,351,578
Emp.: 57,000
Fiscal Year-end: 03/31/23
Management Consulting Services
N.A.I.C.S.: 541618
Balaji Swaminathan (CFO)

Subsidiaries:

Avon Solutions & Logistics Private Limited (1)
NO-33 Balammal Building 1st Floor Burkit Road, T Nagar, Chennai, 600017, Tamilnadu, India
Tel.: (91) 4428345611
Web Site: https://www.avonsolutions.com
Emp.: 800
Logistics Management Services
N.A.I.C.S.: 541614

Denave (M) Sdn. Bhd. (1)
Suite 17-09 Level 17 Gtower 199, Jalan Tun Razak, 50400, Kuala Lumpur, Malaysia
Tel.: (60) 321681913
Information Technology Services
N.A.I.C.S.: 541519

Denave India Private Limited (1)
A154A 2nd Floor Sector - 63, Noida, 201307, Uttar-Pradesh, India
Tel.: (91) 1203875100
Web Site: https://www.denave.com
Information Technology Services
N.A.I.C.S.: 541519

Denave SG Pte. Ltd. (1)
11 Collyer Quay The Arcade 17-14/19, Singapore, 049317, Singapore
Tel.: (65) 68361762
Information Technology Services
N.A.I.C.S.: 541519

Fusion Foods & Catering Private Limited (1)
First Floor Sai Tech Park 105 Anna Salai Little Mount, Guindy, Chennai, 600032, Tamilnadu, India
Tel.: (91) 9841396365
Web Site: https://fusionfoods.co
Restaurant Management Services
N.A.I.C.S.: 722513

Global Flight Handling Services Private Limited (1)
No 158 Rayala Towers Tower 2 1ST floor Mount Road Anna Salai, Chennai, 600002, India
Tel.: (91) 9445099956
Web Site: https://www.globalflighthandling.com
Logistics Handling Services
N.A.I.C.S.: 541614

Matrix Business Services India Private Limited (1)
Sree Mahamadhi Towers No 17 Arulambal Street, T Nagar, Chennai, 600 017, India
Tel.: (91) 4440107200
Web Site: https://www.matrixbsindia.com
Emp.: 1,400
Automation Parts Mfr & Distr
N.A.I.C.S.: 336390

Washroom Hygiene Concepts Private Limited (1)
4D Gopala Tower Rajendra Place, New Delhi, 110008, India
Tel.: (91) 9818099459
Web Site: https://washroomhygiene.co.in
Washroom Environment Consulting Services

UPDATER SERVICES LIMITED

Updater Services Limited—(Continued)
N.A.I.C.S.: 541620

UPERGY
314 Allee des noisetiers, BP 10020, 69760, Limonest, Cedex, France
Tel.: (33) 472524900
Web Site: https://www.upergy.com
Year Founded: 1996
ALVDIPA—(EUR)
Sales Range: $50-74.9 Million
Emp.: 266
Battery & Medical Product Distr
N.A.I.C.S.: 335910
David Buffelard (CEO)

UPET S.A.
Str Arsenalului nr 14, Targoviste, Romania
Tel.: (40) 245 616514
Web Site: http://www.upetgroup.ro
Year Founded: 1872
Sales Range: $25-49.9 Million
Emp.: 656
Oil & Gas Drilling Rigs Mfr
N.A.I.C.S.: 333132

UPL LIMITED
UPL House 610 B/2 Bandra Village, Off Western Express Highway Bandra East, Mumbai, 400 051, India
Tel.: (91) 2271528000
Web Site: https://www.upl-ltd.com
Year Founded: 1969
512070—(BOM)
Rev.: $6,350,116,500
Assets: $11,285,683,500
Liabilities: $7,285,141,500
Net Worth: $4,000,542,000
Earnings: $605,650,500
Emp.: 5,456
Fiscal Year-end: 03/31/22
Holding Company; Crop Protection Products Mfr
N.A.I.C.S.: 551112
Rajnikant Devidas Shroff (Mng Dir & Chm)

Subsidiaries:

Advanta Enterprises Limited (1)
c/o UPL Limited - 3-11 GIDC Vapi, Valsad, 396195, Gujarat, India **(86.67%)**
Tel.: (91) 2602432716
Rev.: $127,927,200
Emp.: 1,200
Fiscal Year-end: 03/31/2023
Holding Company; Seed Production
N.A.I.C.S.: 551112

Subsidiary (Non-US):

Advanta Seeds Pty. Ltd. (2)
268 Anzac Avenue, PO Box 337, Toowoomba, 4350, QLD, Australia
Tel.: (61) 746902666
Web Site: https://www.pacificseeds.com.au
Emp.: 100
Agricultural Crop & Plant Seeds Developer & Distr
N.A.I.C.S.: 115112
Rob McCarron (Mgr-Hunter Valley, South Coast, and Central West NSW)

Advanta Semillas S.A.I.C. (2)
Dr Nicolas Repetto 3656 - 2do piso, Olivos, CP 1636, Buenos Aires, Argentina
Tel.: (54) 1121525199
Web Site: http://www.advantasemillas.com.ar
Agricultural Crop & Plant Seeds Developer & Distr
N.A.I.C.S.: 115112

Advanta US, LLC (2)
Tel.: (806) 364-0560
Web Site: https://www.advantaus.com
Agricultural Research & Development Services
N.A.I.C.S.: 541715

Pacific Seeds (Thai) Ltd. (2)
1 Moo 13 Phaholyothin Road Phraphuttabat, PO Box 15, Phraputtabat, Saraburi, 18120, Thailand
Tel.: (66) 36266316
Web Site: http://www.advantaseedsth.com
Agricultural Crop & Plant Seeds Developer & Distr
N.A.I.C.S.: 115112
Pachok Pongpanich (Mng Dir)

Advanta Mauritius Limited (1)
Level 3 Alexander House 35 Cybercity, Ebene, Mauritius
Tel.: (230) 4026893
Cultivating Seed Mfr
N.A.I.C.S.: 311224

Advanta Seeds Romania S.R.L. (1)
Str Izvor no 92-96 Building A Floor 3 Sector 5, Bucharest, Romania
Tel.: (40) 723456322
Web Site: https://ro.altaseeds.com
Cultivating Seed Mfr
N.A.I.C.S.: 311224

Agrodan ApS (1)
Ramskovvej 11 Sorvad, Ringkobing, 7550, Denmark
Tel.: (45) 76660300
Web Site: http://www.upleurope.com
Sales Range: $50-74.9 Million
Emp.: 1
Agriculture Chemicals Mfr & Sales
N.A.I.C.S.: 325320
Niels Jensen (Mgr)

Arysta LifeScience Inc. (1)
15401 Weston Pkwy Ste 150, Cary, NC 27513-8640
Tel.: (919) 678-4948
Web Site: http://www.arystalifescience.com
Holding Company; Crop Protection & Life Science Products Mfr & Distr
N.A.I.C.S.: 551112
Diego Lopez Casanello (Pres)

Subsidiary (Non-US):

Arysta Agroquimicos y Fertilzantes Uruguay SA (2)
Luis A de Herrera 1248 Torre B piso 17, Montevideo, Montevideo, Uruguay
Tel.: (598) 98638425
Agricultural Chemical Product Mfr
N.A.I.C.S.: 325320

Arysta Health and Nutrition Sciences Corporation (2)
Tel.: (81) 352039410
Web Site: https://ahns.arysta-hns.jp
Emp.: 25
Pharmaceutical Product Mfr & Distr
N.A.I.C.S.: 325412
Keisuke Sugai (CEO)

Arysta LifeScience Benelux SRL (2)
Rue de Renory 26/1, 4102, Ougree, Belgium
Tel.: (32) 43859711
Web Site: http://www.agriphar.com
Agricultural Chemical Product Mfr
N.A.I.C.S.: 325320
Marc Bonnet (Mgr-Product Dev-Herbicides-Global)

Arysta LifeScience Corporation (2)
Tel.: (81) 352039350
Web Site: https://www.arystalifescience.jp
Sales Range: $150-199.9 Million
Emp.: 97
Agrochemicals, Pharmaceuticals & Veterinary Medicines Processing, Mfr & Sales
N.A.I.C.S.: 325412
Daniel Kenji Kano (Co-CEO)

Arysta LifeScience Europe Sarl (2)
Tour Crystal 7-11 Quai Andre Citroen 24 etage, 75740, Paris, Cedex 15, France
Tel.: (33) 140644915
Web Site: http://www.arystalifescience.fr
Agricultural Research & Development Services
N.A.I.C.S.: 541715
Jose Nobre (Pres & CEO)

Arysta LifeScience France SAS (2)
Tour Cristal 7-11 Quai Andre Citroen 24 etage, 75740, Paris, Cedex 15, France
Tel.: (33) 140644930
Web Site: http://www.arystalifescience.fr
Emp.: 45

Agricultural Chemical Product Mfr
N.A.I.C.S.: 325320
Vivien Rousselin (Comml Dir & Sls Dir-South)

Arysta LifeScience Iberia SLU (2)
Josep Pla 2 planta 12 torre B-2, 08019, Barcelona, Catalonia, Spain
Tel.: (34) 90 190 0040
Web Site: http://www.arystalifescience.es
Agricultural Chemical Product Mfr
N.A.I.C.S.: 325320
Jose Buendia (Mgr-Sls-Iberia)

Arysta LifeScience Italia S.rl (2)
Centro Direzionale Colleoni Palazzo Liicorno VIa Paracelso 2, 20864, Agrate Brianza, MB, Italy
Tel.: (39) 0399300418
Web Site: http://www.arystalifescience.it
Agricultural Chemical Product Mfr
N.A.I.C.S.: 325320
Giovanni Malaguti (CEO)

Arysta LifeScience RUS LLC (2)
st Bolshaya Tatarskaya 9, 115184, Moscow, Russia
Tel.: (7) 495 580 7775
Web Site: http://www.arystalifescience.ru
Crop Planting & Protection Services
N.A.I.C.S.: 115112

Arysta LifeScience Vostok LLC (2)
40/12 Korp 2 Ul Nizhnyaya Krasnos, Moscow, 105066, Russia
Tel.: (7) 9859971904
Chemical Products Distr
N.A.I.C.S.: 423490

Arysta Lifescience (Shanghai) Co Ltd (2)
Room 1001 Harbour Ring Plaza No 1, Shanghai, 200001, China
Tel.: (86) 2152411285
Web Site: http://www.arystalifescience.com
Farm Supply Whslr
N.A.I.C.S.: 424910
Prashant Kharwadkar (Head-North Asia)

Arysta Lifescience Argentina SA (2)
Av de Los Lagos 6855-Edificio Puerta Norte II Piso 5to Oficina 522, Nordelta Partido Tigre-Pcia, B-1670, Buenos Aires, Argentina
Tel.: (54) 1152441555
Web Site: http://www.arysta.com.ar
Emp.: 890
Agricultural Chemical Product Mfr & Distr
N.A.I.C.S.: 325320

Arysta Lifescience CentroAmerica SA (2)
5a Avenida 16-62 Zona 10 Torre Platina Nivel 6 Oficina 602, Guatemala, Guatemala
Tel.: (502) 25037200
Web Site: http://www.arystalifesciencecayc.com
Emp.: 1,700
Agricultural Chemical Distr
N.A.I.C.S.: 424910

Arysta Lifescience Chile SA (2)
Calle el Rosal 4610, Huechuraba, Santiago, Chile
Tel.: (56) 225604500
Web Site: http://www.arysta.cl
Agricultural Chemical Product Mfr
N.A.I.C.S.: 325320

Arysta Lifescience Colombia SA (2)
Oficina Bogota Calle 127 A No 53 A - 45 Torre 2 Piso 5 Of 501, Bogota, Colombia
Tel.: (57) 15111888
Web Site: http://www.arysta.com.co
Agricultural Chemical Mfr & Distr
N.A.I.C.S.: 325320

Arysta Lifescience Espana SA (2)
Paseo Castellana 177 - Septimo D 1, 28046, Madrid, Spain
Tel.: (34) 915718191
Agricultural Chemical Mfr & Distr
N.A.I.C.S.: 325320

Arysta Lifescience Finechemical Europe GmbH (2)
Elisabethstrasse 44-46, 40217, Dusseldorf, Germany
Tel.: (49) 2113013050
Chemical & Allied Product Whslr
N.A.I.C.S.: 424690

INTERNATIONAL PUBLIC

Arysta Lifescience Holdings France SAS (2)
Route D Artix, 64150, Nogueres, France
Tel.: (33) 559609292
Holding Company
N.A.I.C.S.: 551112

Arysta Lifescience India Limited (2)
A 301 Kanakia Zillion 3rd Floor LBS Marg, Kurla W, Mumbai, 400 070, India
Tel.: (91) 2261843333
Web Site: http://www.arystalifescienceindia.com
Agricultural Chemical Product Mfr & Distr
N.A.I.C.S.: 325320
S. Ganeshkumar (Mng Dir)

Arysta Lifescience Kenya Ltd (2)
Tulip House 5th Floor Mombasa Road, PO Box 30335, 00100, Nairobi, Kenya
Tel.: (254) 717432174
Web Site: http://www.arystalifescience.co.ke
Agricultural Chemical Product Mfr
N.A.I.C.S.: 325320

Arysta Lifescience Magyarorszag Kft (2)
Tomori utca 34, 1138, Budapest, Hungary
Tel.: (36) 13352100
Web Site: http://www.arystalifescience.hu
Chemical & Allied Product Whslr
N.A.I.C.S.: 424690
Sandor Herpai (Mng Dir)

Arysta Lifescience Pakistan (Pvt) Ltd (2)
3rd Floor Building 5/A P E C H S Block-6 Shahrah-e-Faisal, Shahrah-e-Faisal, Karachi, 75350, Pakistan
Tel.: (92) 213 452 2611
Web Site: https://www.upl-ltd.bOM
Pesticide Mfr
N.A.I.C.S.: 325320
Amir Jafri (CEO)

Arysta Lifescience Polska Sp zoo (2)
ul Przasnyska 6 b, 01-756, Warsaw, Poland
Tel.: (48) 228664180
Web Site: http://www.arysta.pl
Emp.: 40
Crop Protection Product Whslr
N.A.I.C.S.: 423820
Tomasz Stadnikiewicz (Dir-Sls)

Arysta Lifescience Slovakia Sro (2)
Komarnanska ul 16, 940 76, Nove Zamky, Slovakia
Tel.: (421) 91 750 7071
Web Site: http://www.arysta.sk
Crop Planting & Protection Services
N.A.I.C.S.: 115112
Jan Benovsky (Dir-Sls)

Arysta Lifescience South Africa (Pty) Ltd (2)
7 Sunbury Office Park Douglas Saunders Drive La Lucia Ridge, PO Box 1726, Mount Edgecombe, 4300, South Africa
Tel.: (27) 315145600
Web Site: http://www.arystalifescience.co.za
Crop Protection Product Whslr
N.A.I.C.S.: 423820
Marcel Dreyer (CEO)

Arysta Lifescience UK Ltd (2)
Suite G8 Evans Business Centre Monckton Road, Wakefield, WF2 7AS, West Yorkshire, United Kingdom
Tel.: (44) 7795572037
Web Site: http://www.agriphar.co.uk
Agrochemical Mfr
N.A.I.C.S.: 325320

Arysta Lifescience Ukraine LLC (2)
Okhtyrsky lane building 7 building 4 office 4-201, 03066, Kiev, Ukraine
Tel.: (380) 44 490 9590
Web Site: http://www.arystalifescience.ua
Agricultural Chemical Product Mfr
N.A.I.C.S.: 325320

Arysta Lifescience Vietnam Co Ltd (2)
Room 4 6 4th Floor ETown Building No 364, Cong Hoa Ward 13 Tan Binh District, Ho Chi Minh City, Vietnam
Tel.: (84) 838122463
Web Site: http://www.arysta.vn
Agricultural Chemical Product Mfr & Distr-

AND PRIVATE COMPANIES UPL LIMITED

N.A.I.C.S.: 325320

Myanmar Arysta Lifescience Co Ltd (2)
95 Padonmar St Pyay Ward, Dagon, Yangon, Myanmar
Tel.: (95) 1395318
Agricultural Chemical Product Mfr
N.A.I.C.S.: 325320
Zaw Win *(Mgr-Regulatory Affairs)*

UPL Hellas S.A. (2)
Rizariou 16, Chalandri, 15233, Athens, Greece
Tel.: (30) 2105578777
Web Site: http://www.arystalifescience.gr
Chemical & Allied Product Whslr
N.A.I.C.S.: 424690

Cropserve Zambia Limited (1)
Plot No 5055 Mungwi Road Industrial Area Manda Hill, 10101, Lusaka, Zambia
Tel.: (260) 211212513
Agricultural Chemical Mfr
N.A.I.C.S.: 325320

Decco Italia SRL (1)
Tel.: (39) 0957131903
Web Site: https://www.deccopostharvest.com
Mechanized Farming Services
N.A.I.C.S.: 115113

PT Catur Agrodaya Mandiri (1)
AIA Central Lt 27 Jl Gen Sudirman Kav 48A, Jakarta, 12930, Indonesia
Tel.: (62) 212521318
Web Site: https://www.upl-ltd.com
Crop Protection Services
N.A.I.C.S.: 111419

Riceco International Bangladesh Ltd. (1)
Paragon House 7th Floor 5 Mohakhali C/A, Dhaka, 1212, Bangladesh
Tel.: (880) 488 108 6465
Web Site: https://www.upl-ltd.com
Mechanized Farming Services
N.A.I.C.S.: 115113

SWAL Corporation Limited (1)
UPL House 4th Floor CTS No 610B/2 Bandra Village Off, Western Express Highway Behind Teachers Colony Bandra East, Mumbai, 400 051, India
Tel.: (91) 2271528000
Web Site: https://www.swal.in
Crop Protection Services
N.A.I.C.S.: 115113

Samma International S.R.L. (1)
Via Mongibello 186, 95032, Belpasso, Catania, Italy
Tel.: (39) 095391181
Web Site: http://www.sammaproget.it
Agricultural Machinery Mfr
N.A.I.C.S.: 333111

UPL Agricultural Solutions Romania S.R.L. (1)
Strada Izvor 92-96 Forum III building 4th floor office A sector 5, Bucharest, Romania
Tel.: (40) 215295544
Crop Protection Product Mfr
N.A.I.C.S.: 325320

UPL Agrosolutions Canada Inc. (1)
2-400 Michener Rd, Guelph, N1K 1E4, ON, Canada
Tel.: (519) 822-3790
Crop Protection Product Mfr
N.A.I.C.S.: 325320

UPL Argentina S.A. (1)
Tel.: (54) 1121525199
Web Site: https://www.upl-ltd.com
Mechanized Farming Services
N.A.I.C.S.: 115113

UPL Australia Pty. Limited (1)
Level 3 70 Hindmarsh Square, Adelaide, 5000, SA, Australia
Tel.: (61) 1800078007
Crop Protection Product Mfr
N.A.I.C.S.: 325320

UPL Benelux B.V. (1)
Claudius Prinsenlaan 144 a Blok A, 4818 CP, Breda, Netherlands
Tel.: (31) 850712300
Web Site: https://www.upl-ltd.com

Mechanized Farming Services
N.A.I.C.S.: 115113

UPL Bulgaria EOOD (1)
12 Chiprovtsi St, Sofia, Bulgaria
Tel.: (359) 29434761
Crop Protection Product Mfr
N.A.I.C.S.: 325320

UPL Colombia SAS (1)
Tel.: (57) 16012626
Web Site: http://www.evofarms.com
Agricultural Chemical Product Mfr
N.A.I.C.S.: 325998

UPL Czech s.r.o. (1)
Novodvorska 803/82, Lhotka, 14200, Prague, Czech Republic
Tel.: (420) 724207143
Crop Protection Product Mfr
N.A.I.C.S.: 325320

UPL Deutschland GmbH (1)
An der Hasenkaule 10 / Building 8, 50354, Hurth, Germany
Tel.: (49) 22327012555
Web Site: https://de.upl-ltd.com
Sugar Beet Farming Services
N.A.I.C.S.: 111991

UPL Europe Limited (1)
Engine Rooms Birchwood Park, Warrington, WA3 6YN, Cheshire, United Kingdom
Tel.: (44) 192 581 9999
Web Site: https://www.upl-ltd.com
Mechanized Farming Services
N.A.I.C.S.: 115113

UPL France SAS (1)
1 Place des Degres, 92800, Puteaux, France
Tel.: (33) 146359200
Web Site: https://www.upl-ltd.com
Mechanized Farming Services
N.A.I.C.S.: 115113

UPL Holdings SA (Pty.) Ltd. (1)
21 Repens Street, Heriotdale, Johannesburg, 2094, South Africa
Tel.: (27) 116262600
Web Site: https://www.upl.co.za
Crop Protection Product Mfr
N.A.I.C.S.: 325320

UPL Hungary Kereskedelmi es Szolgaltato Korlatolt Felelossegu Tarsasag (1)
Tomori Street 34, Budapest, Hungary
Tel.: (36) 13352100
Crop Protection Product Mfr
N.A.I.C.S.: 325320

UPL Iberia S.A. (1)
Josep Pla 2 planta 12 torre B-2, 08019, Barcelona, Catalonia, Spain
Tel.: (34) 901900040
Web Site: http://www.upliberia.com
Chemical Products Mfr
N.A.I.C.S.: 325320
Ganesh Yanadi *(Mng Dir)*

Subsidiary (Domestic):

Agrindustrial S.A. (2)
Josep Tarradellas 20 4th floor, Barcelona, 08029, Spain
Tel.: (34) 932402127
Web Site: http://www.uplonline.com
Sales Range: $25-49.9 Million
Emp.: 18
Agricultural Chemicals Mfr & Distr
N.A.I.C.S.: 325320
Ganesh Janadi *(Office Mgr)*

Phosfonia, S.L. (2)
Avenida Josep Tarradellas 20 4th floor, Barcelona, 08029, Spain
Tel.: (34) 932402127
Web Site: http://www.ublonline.com
Agricultural Chemicals Mfr & Distr
N.A.I.C.S.: 325320
Ganesh Yanadi *(Gen Mgr)*

UPL Paraguay S.A. (1)
Itaipu Superhighway North Head of the Costa Cavalcanti Bridge, Paraqvaria I Building 5th Floor Alto Parana, Hernandarias, CP 7220, Paraguay
Tel.: (595) 213389100
Web Site: https://www.upl-ltd.com
Mechanized Farming Services
N.A.I.C.S.: 115113

UPL Polska Sp. z o.o. (1)
Ul Stawki 40, 01-040, Warsaw, Poland
Tel.: (48) 224340090
Web Site: https://www.upl-ltd.com
Sugar Beet Farming Services
N.A.I.C.S.: 111991

UPL Slovakia s.r.o. (1)
Komarnanska ul 16, 94076, Nove Zamky, Slovakia
Tel.: (421) 917507071
Web Site: https://www.upl-ltd.com
Sugar Beet Farming Services
N.A.I.C.S.: 111991

UPL South Africa (Pty.) Ltd. (1)
7 Sunbury Office Park Douglas Saunders Drive, PO Box 1726, La Lucia Ridge, Mount Edgecombe, 4300, South Africa
Tel.: (27) 315145600
Web Site: https://www.upl-ltd.com
Sugar Beet Farming Services
N.A.I.C.S.: 111991

UPL Ukraine LLC (1)
Okhtyrskyi lane building 7 building 4 office 4-201, Kiev, Ukraine
Tel.: (380) 444909590
Crop Protection Product Mfr
N.A.I.C.S.: 325320

UPL Ziraat Ve Kimya Sanayi Ve Ticaret Limited Sirketi (1)
Justice Mah Manas Blv Folkart Towers No 47/BA Tower Floor 31 No 3107, Bayrakli, 35530, Izmir, Turkiye
Tel.: (90) 2324465789
Web Site: https://www.upl-ltd.com
Mechanized Farming Services
N.A.I.C.S.: 115113

United Phosphorus (Korea) Ltd. (1)
813 Bizcenter SK Technopark 190-1 Sangdaewon-dong, Jungwon-gu, Seongnam, 462-120, Kyunggi-do, Korea (South)
Tel.: (82) 31 776 4110
Web Site: http://www.my.uplonline.com
Sales Range: $50-74.9 Million
Emp.: 4
Agricultural Chemicals Whslr
N.A.I.C.S.: 424690

United Phosphorus (Taiwan) Limited. (1)
9F No 1027 Sec 3 Wenxin Rd, Beitun Dist, Taichung, 40667, Taiwan
Tel.: (886) 422932121
Web Site: http://www.uplonline.com
Sales Range: $50-74.9 Million
Emp.: 5
Agricultural Chemicals Mfr & Distr
N.A.I.C.S.: 325320

United Phosphorus Holdings Cooperatief U.A. (1)
Tankhoofd 10, PO Box 6030, Amsterdam, Netherlands
Tel.: (31) 104725100
Web Site: http://www.uponline.com
Agricultural Chemicals Mfr & Distr
N.A.I.C.S.: 325320

Subsidiary (Domestic):

United Phosphorus Holdings B.V. (2)
Tankhoofd 10, 3196 KE, Vondelingenplaat, South Holland, Netherlands
Tel.: (31) 104725221
Web Site: http://www.uplonline.com
Agricultural Chemical Products Mfr & Distr
N.A.I.C.S.: 325320
Orange Field *(Mng Dir)*

Subsidiary (Domestic):

Cerexagri BV (3)
Tankhoofd 10, Vondelingenplaat, 3196 KE, Rotterdam, Netherlands
Tel.: (31) 104725100
Web Site: http://www.cerexagri.nl
Sales Range: $25-49.9 Million
Emp.: 100
Agricultural Chemical Mfr
N.A.I.C.S.: 325320

Subsidiary (Non-US):

Cerexagri Ziraat ve Kimya Sanayi ve Ticaret Limited Sirketi (4)
Erbay Is Hani K 8 D 802 82, Cumhuriyet Bulvari, Izmir, Turkiye
Tel.: (90) 2324465789
Sales Range: $50-74.9 Million
Emp.: 7
Agricultural Chemicals Mfr & Distr
N.A.I.C.S.: 325320
Korkmaz Ertan *(Gen Mgr)*

Subsidiary (Non-US):

Decco Iberica Post Cosecha, S.A. (3)
Villa de Madrid 54 Pl Fuente del Jarro Paterna, 46988, Valencia, Spain
Tel.: (34) 961 344 011
Web Site: http://www.deccoiberica.es
Emp.: 40
Agricultural Chemicals Mfr & Distr
N.A.I.C.S.: 325320
Michel Sanchez *(Gen Mgr)*

Subsidiary (Non-US):

Anning Decco Fine Chemical Co.,Limited. (4)
Xijiaochangpo, 650301, Anning, Yunnan, China
Tel.: (86) 8718614861
Agricultural Chemicals Mfr & Distr
N.A.I.C.S.: 325320

Citrashine (Pty) Ltd (4)
75 2nd Street Booysens Reserve, Johannesburg, 2016, Gauteng, South Africa
Tel.: (27) 118352646
Web Site: http://www.citrashine.co.za
Emp.: 100
Fruit Coatings Mfr
N.A.I.C.S.: 325320

Subsidiary (Domestic):

DECCO IBERICA Post Cosecha S.A.U. (4)
Calle Villa De Madrid 54, 46988, Paterna, Valencia, Spain
Tel.: (34) 961344011
Web Site: http://www.decco-web.com
Fruit Coatings Mfr
N.A.I.C.S.: 325320
Daniel Aalbadi *(Gen Mgr)*

Subsidiary (US):

DECCO US Post-Harvest, Inc. (4)
1713 S California Ave, Monrovia, CA 91016
Tel.: (800) 221-0925
Web Site: http://www.deccous.com
Postharvest Protection Products Mfr
N.A.I.C.S.: 325320
Jim Sargent *(Gen Mgr)*

Subsidiary (Non-US):

SAFEPACK PRODUCTS Ltd. (4)
Meir Astoria 7, 44100, Hadera, Israel
Tel.: (972) 732555666
Web Site: http://www.decco-safepack.com
Industrial Brushes Mfr & Distr
N.A.I.C.S.: 339994

United Phosphorus Limited, Japan (1)
30F Ark Mori Bldg Nippon 1-12-32 Akasaka, Minato-ku, 107-6030, Tokyo, Japan
Tel.: (81) 362301071
Web Site: http://www.upl-japan.co.jp
Rev: $48,960,000
Pesticides Mfr & Distr
N.A.I.C.S.: 325320
Osamu Noda *(Pres & VP-Bus Strategy)*

United Phosphorus Ltd. Australia (1)
Suite 416 Level 4 14 Lexington Drive Norwest Business Park, Bella Vista, 2153, NSW, Australia
Tel.: (61) 288247277
Web Site: http://au.uplonline.com
Sales Range: $1-9.9 Million
Emp.: 9
Crop & Lawn Protection Products & Industrial Chemicals Mfr
N.A.I.C.S.: 325320

United Phosphorus Ltd. Hong Kong (1)
Units 803-5 8/F Nan Fung Tower, 173 Des Voeux Road, Central, Hong Kong, China (Hong Kong)

UPL LIMITED

UPL Limited—(Continued)
Tel.: (852) 28542268
Web Site: http://www.uplonline.com
Sales Range: $10-24.9 Million
Crop & Lawn Protection Products & Industrial Chemicals Mfr
N.A.I.C.S.: 325320

Subsidiary (Non-US):

United Phosphorus (Shanghai) Company Limited. (2)
3001 30th Floor Modern Plaza Tower 1 369 XianXia Road, Changning, 200336, Shanghai, China
Tel.: (86) 21 61921195
Agricultural Chemicals Mfr & Distr
N.A.I.C.S.: 325320

United Phosphorus Ltd. UK (1)
The Centre, Birchwood Park, Warrington, WA3 6YN, Cheshire, United Kingdom
Tel.: (44) 1925819999
Web Site: http://www.upleurope.com
Sales Range: $50-74.9 Million
Emp.: 150
Crop & Lawn Protection Products & Industrial Chemicals Mfr
N.A.I.C.S.: 325320
Mark Thomson (Office Mgr)

Subsidiary (Non-US):

Cerexagri S.A.S. (2)
1 Rue Des Freres Lumieres, 78370, Plaisir, France
Tel.: (33) 130817300
Web Site: http://www.uplonline.com
Agriculture Chemicals Mfr & Sales
N.A.I.C.S.: 325320

United Phosphorus Polska Sp.z.o.o (1)
Na Przelaj 8, Warsaw, 02092, Masovian, Poland
Tel.: (48) 226140045
Sales Range: $25-49.9 Million
Emp.: 1
Agricultural Chemical Mfr
N.A.I.C.S.: 325320
Maciej Karolczak (Gen Mgr)

United Phosphorus, Inc. (1)
630 Freedom Business Ctr Ste 402, King of Prussia, PA 19406 (100%)
Tel.: (610) 491-2800
Web Site: https://www.upl-ltd.com
Sales Range: $100-124.9 Million
Emp.: 72
Crop & Lawn Protection Products & Industrial Chemicals Mfr
N.A.I.C.S.: 325320
Gerald Adrian (Bus Mgr)

Subsidiary (Domestic):

RiceCo LLC (2)
5100 Poplar Ave Ste 2428, Memphis, TN 38137
Tel.: (901) 260-5401
Web Site: http://www.ricecollc.com
Sales Range: $25-49.9 Million
Emp.: 15
Crop Protection Products Distr
N.A.I.C.S.: 424910
Jim Hines (CEO)

Vetophama S.A.S. (1)
12-14 rue de la Croix Martre, 91120, Palaiseau, France
Tel.: (33) 169188480
Web Site: https://www.veto-pharma.com
Emp.: 80
Crops & Fertilizer Mfr
N.A.I.C.S.: 325320

UPLAND RESOURCES LIMITED

3rd Floor 44 Esplanade, Saint Helier, JE4 9WG, Jersey
Tel.: (44) 7891677441 VG
Web Site: https://upland.energy
Year Founded: 2012
UPL—(LSE)
Assets: $424,574
Liabilities: $775,481
Net Worth: ($350,907)
Earnings: ($671,114)
Fiscal Year-end: 06/30/22
Oil & Gas Exploration Services
N.A.I.C.S.: 213112
Bolhassan Di (Chm, CEO & CEO)

UPLINK DIGITAL GMBH

Heerdter Sandberg 32, D-40549, Dusseldorf, Germany
Tel.: (49) 211417401
Web Site: https://www.uplink-digital.de
Emp.: 100
Software Publr
N.A.I.C.S.: 513210

Subsidiaries:

nacamar GmbH (1)
Prinzenallee 11, 40549, Dusseldorf, Germany
Tel.: (49) 21155007170
Web Site: https://www.nacamar.de
Business-to-Business Telecommunications Services
N.A.I.C.S.: 517121

UPM-KYMMENE CORPORATION

Alvar Aallon katu 1, FI-00100, Helsinki, Finland
Tel.: (358) 20415111 FI
Web Site: https://www.upm.com
Year Founded: 1995
UPMKF—(OTCIQ)
Rev.: $10,538,299,200
Assets: $18,249,189,920
Liabilities: $6,564,942,800
Net Worth: $11,684,247,120
Earnings: $697,640,320
Emp.: 18,557
Fiscal Year-end: 12/31/20
Holding Company; Paper, Pulp, Plywood & Lumber Mfr & Distr; Hydroelectric Power Generation
N.A.I.C.S.: 551112
Pirkko Harrela (Exec VP-Stakeholders Rels)

Subsidiaries:

Forestal Oriental S.A. (1)
Tel.: (598) 26046660
Eucalyptus Forest Plantation Services
N.A.I.C.S.: 111421

Kymi Paper Oy (1)
Serluntie 1, Kuusankoski, 45700, Finland
Tel.: (358) 20415121
Web Site: http://www.upm.com
Sales Range: $200-249.9 Million
Emp.: 900
Mfr of Coated & Uncoated Fine Papers
N.A.I.C.S.: 322120

Outokumpu Metals Off-Take Oy (1)
Riihitontuntie 7 C, 02200, Espoo, Finland
Tel.: (358) 9 4211
Stainless Steel Mfr
N.A.I.C.S.: 331221

SunCoal Industries GmbH (1)
Rudolf-Diesel-Strasse 15, 14974, Ludwigsfelde, Germany
Tel.: (49) 33788812210
Web Site: https://www.suncoal.com
Chemical & Biofuel Carbon Mfr
N.A.I.C.S.: 325180

UPM Asia Pacific Pte. Ltd (1)
Tel.: (65) 69627387
Emp.: 10
Paper Products Mfr
N.A.I.C.S.: 322299

Subsidiary (Non-US):

UPM (China) Co., Ltd. (2)
Tel.: (86) 2162881919
Pulp Distr
N.A.I.C.S.: 424990

Plant (Domestic):

UPM (China) Co., Ltd. - Changshu Paper Mill #2 (3)
Xinye Road Changshu Economic & Technological Development Zone, Changshu, 215536, Jiangsu, China
Tel.: (86) 512 5265 1818
Sales Range: $200-249.9 Million
Emp.: 700
Paper Mills
N.A.I.C.S.: 322120

Subsidiary (Domestic):

UPM-Kymmene (S) Pte. Ltd. (2)
501 Orchard Road, 515 Wheeloc Pl, Singapore, 238880, Singapore (100%)
Tel.: (65) 67359511
Web Site: http://www.upmkymmene.com
Sales Range: $25-49.9 Million
Emp.: 25
Marketing & Sales of Paper
N.A.I.C.S.: 424130

UPM Biochemicals GmbH (1)
Am Haupttor Bau 4614, 06237, Leuna, Germany
Tel.: (49) 34615195001
Biochemical Mfr
N.A.I.C.S.: 325199

UPM Energy (1)
Alvar Aallon katu 1, FI-00100, Helsinki, Finland
Tel.: (358) 20415111
Web Site: https://www.upmenergy.com
Emp.: 79
Hydroelectric Power Generation & Transmission
N.A.I.C.S.: 221111

UPM Forest (1)
Akerlundinkatu 11 B, PO Box 32, Tampere, 33101, Finland
Tel.: (358) 2041 6121
Sales Range: $25-49.9 Million
Emp.: 100
Forestry Support Services
N.A.I.C.S.: 115310
Sauli Brander (Mng Dir)

UPM France S.A.S. (1)
134 rue Danton, F-92593, Levallois-Perret, Cedex, France
Tel.: (33) 146393000
Holding Company; Paper Mills & Wood Planing; Paper & Wood Products Distr
N.A.I.C.S.: 551112

Plant (Domestic):

UPM France S.A.S. - Aigrefeuille Further Processing Mill (2)
Avenue de la Gare, 17290, Aigrefeuille-d'Aunis, France
Tel.: (33) 5 46 35 02 60
Sales Range: $25-49.9 Million
Emp.: 40
Wood Planing & Processing
N.A.I.C.S.: 321912

UPM France S.A.S. - Chapelle Darblay Paper Mill (2)
Usine de Grand Couronne, PO Box 1 - CD 3, Grand Couronne, 76530, France
Tel.: (33) 2 3518 4000
Sales Range: $200-249.9 Million
Emp.: 420
Newsprint Mill
N.A.I.C.S.: 322120

UPM France S.A.S. - Docelles Paper Mill (2)
1 Rue du Grand Meix, 88460, Docelles, France
Tel.: (33) 3 2933 8100
Sales Range: $50-74.9 Million
Emp.: 180
Printing, Copying & Specialty Paper Mill
N.A.I.C.S.: 322120

UPM France S.A.S. - Stracel Paper Mill (2)
4 rue Charles Friedel Port du Rhin, PO Box 79, F 67016, Strasbourg, France
Tel.: (33) 388417541
Sales Range: $100-124.9 Million
Emp.: 310
Paper Mills
N.A.I.C.S.: 322120

UPM Fray Bentos S.A. (1)
Ruta Vladimir Roslik Km 307, 65000, Fray Bentos, Uruguay
Tel.: (598) 45620100
Emp.: 200
Eucalyptus Hardwood Pulp Mfr
N.A.I.C.S.: 325998

UPM GmbH (1)
Georg-Haindl-Strasse 5, 86153, Augsburg, Germany
Tel.: (49) 82131090
Web Site: https://www.upm.com
Sales Range: $200-249.9 Million
Emp.: 700
Paper Products Mfr
N.A.I.C.S.: 322120

Subsidiary (Non-US):

Gebruder Lang GmbH Papierfabrik (1)
Tel.: (49) 82498020
Emp.: 250
Printing Paper Mfr
N.A.I.C.S.: 322120

Subsidiary (Domestic):

Lignis GmbH & Co. KG (1)
Stadtbachstrasse 9, 86153, Augsburg, Germany
Tel.: (49) 821 31 09 79 00
Web Site: http://www.lignis.com
Timber Harvesting Services
N.A.I.C.S.: 115310

NorService GmbH (1)
Industriestrasse 32, 26892, Dorpen, Germany
Tel.: (49) 496391070
Web Site: http://w3.norservice.upm.com
Sales Range: $25-49.9 Million
Emp.: 100
Converted Paper Product Mfr
N.A.I.C.S.: 322299

Nordland Papier GmbH (2)
Nordlandallee 1, PO Box 1160, 26892, Dorpen, Germany
Tel.: (49) 496340100
Web Site: http://www.nordlandpapier.de
Emp.: 1,500
Mfr of Fine Paper
N.A.I.C.S.: 322120

Plant (Domestic):

UPM GmbH - Ettringen Paper Mill (2)
Fabrikstrasse 4, 86833, Ettringen, Germany
Tel.: (49) 8249 802 0
Web Site: http://www.upm.com
Sales Range: $200-249.9 Million
Newsprint Mill
N.A.I.C.S.: 322120

UPM GmbH - Hurth Paper Mill (2)
Bertramsjagdweg 12, PO Box 1564, 50354, Hurth, Germany
Tel.: (49) 2233 200 6100
Web Site: http://www.upmpaper.com
Sales Range: $25-49.9 Million
Emp.: 120
Newsprint Mill
N.A.I.C.S.: 322120

UPM GmbH - Plattling Paper Mill (2)
Nicolausstrasse 7, 94447, Plattling, Germany
Tel.: (49) 9931 5020
Web Site: http://www.upmpaper.com
Sales Range: $100-124.9 Million
Emp.: 590
Paper Mills
N.A.I.C.S.: 322120

UPM GmbH - Schongau Paper Mill (2)
Friedrich-haindl-strasse lo, 86956, Schongau, Germany
Tel.: (49) 8861 213 0
Web Site: http://www.upmpaper.com
Sales Range: $200-249.9 Million
Emp.: 540
Paper Mills
N.A.I.C.S.: 322120

UPM GmbH - Schwedt Paper Mill (2)
Kuhheide 1, 16303, Schwedt an der Oder, Germany

AND PRIVATE COMPANIES — UPM-KYMMENE CORPORATION

Tel.: (49) 3332 281 0
Web Site: http://www.upm.com
Sales Range: $50-74.9 Million
Emp.: 250
Paper Mills
N.A.I.C.S.: 322120

Subsidiary (Domestic):

UPM Sales GmbH (2)
Georg-Haindl-Strasse 5, D-86153, Augsburg, Germany **(100%)**
Tel.: (49) 82131090
Web Site: https://www.upm.com
Sales Range: $25-49.9 Million
Emp.: 50
Paper & Wood Product Sales
N.A.I.C.S.: 424110

UPM Kymmene Lda. (1)
Av Eng Duarte Pacheco Torre 1 4 Sala 1, 1070 101, Lisbon, Portugal **(100%)**
Tel.: (351) 213815710
Web Site: http://www.upm.com
Sales Range: $50-74.9 Million
Emp.: 7
Marketing & Sales of Paper
N.A.I.C.S.: 424130

UPM ProFi (1)
Niemenkatu 16, PO Box 203, 15140, Lahti, Finland
Tel.: (358) 2 041 5113
Web Site: https://www.upmprofi.com
Wood-Plastic Composite Products Mfr
N.A.I.C.S.: 321999

Plant (Non-US):

UPM ProFi - Bruchsal (2)
Industriestrasse 78, 76646, Bruchsal, Germany
Tel.: (49) 7251 505 1400
Web Site: http://www.upmprofi.com
Sales Range: $25-49.9 Million
Emp.: 40
Wood-Plastic Composite Products Mfr
N.A.I.C.S.: 321999

UPM Pulp Sales Oy (1)
Alvar Aallon katu 1, PO Box 380, FI-00101, Helsinki, Finland
Tel.: (358) 20415111
Web Site: https://www.upmpulp.com
Wood Pulp Mfr
N.A.I.C.S.: 322110

UPM Raflatac Chile SpA (1)
Camino Lo Boza 9590 Modulo 32, Pudahuel, Santiago, Chile
Tel.: (56) 994035333
Paper Products Mfr
N.A.I.C.S.: 322120

UPM Raflatac Oy (1)
Tesomankatu 31, PO Box 53, 33101, Tampere, Finland **(100%)**
Tel.: (358) 20416143
Emp.: 400
Mfr of Self-Adhesive Labels
N.A.I.C.S.: 322220

Subsidiary (Non-US):

Gascogne Laminates Switzerland SA (2)
Rue des Finettes 110, PO Box 807, Martigny, Switzerland
Tel.: (41) 27 721 30 10
Sales Range: $50-74.9 Million
Emp.: 11
Adhesive Product Mfr
N.A.I.C.S.: 325520

PT. UPM Raflatac Indonesia (2)
Delta Silicon 1 Jalan Meranti Blok L-2-8, Lippo Cikarang, Bekasi, 17550, Jakarta, Indonesia
Tel.: (62) 2189906866
Web Site: https://www.upmraflatac.com
Sales Range: $10-24.9 Million
Emp.: 25
Label Mfr
N.A.I.C.S.: 561910

Raflatac Canada, Inc. (2)
1100 Ave Beaumont Ste 305, Mount-Royal, H3P 3H5, QC, Canada **(100%)**
Tel.: (514) 849-1303
Web Site: http://www.upmraflatac.com

Sales Range: $25-49.9 Million
Emp.: 10
Paper Sales
N.A.I.C.S.: 459410

UPM Raflatac (2)
Universitetsparken 2, DK-4000, Roskilde, Denmark
Tel.: (45) 43 712022
Web Site: http://www.upmraflatac.com
Sales Range: $25-49.9 Million
Emp.: 2,900
Distr & Supplier of Pressure Sensitive Labeling Solutions
N.A.I.C.S.: 561910
Jan-Erik Forsstrom (VP-Global R&D)

UPM Raflatac (Beijing) Co., Ltd (2)
Room 906 Tower C Oriental Media Centre 4 Guonghua Lu, Beijing, 100026, China
Tel.: (86) 1085570866
Web Site: http://www.upmraflatac.com
Paper Products Mfr
N.A.I.C.S.: 322120

UPM Raflatac (Changshu) Co., Ltd (2)
No 88 Tong Gang Road Changshu Economic Development Zone, Tonggang Industrial Park, Changshu, 215536, Jiangsu, China
Tel.: (86) 512 5229 9588
Web Site: http://www.upmraflatac.com
Paperboard Mfr
N.A.I.C.S.: 322130

UPM Raflatac Brazil (2)
Av Vicenzo Grannghelli 856-3A Joao Aldo Nassif, 13820-000, Jaguariuna, Sao Paulo, Brazil
Tel.: (55) 19 3837 9570
Sales Range: $25-49.9 Million
Emp.: 40
Packaging Paper Products Mfr
N.A.I.C.S.: 322120
Mauricio Medici (Gen Mgr)

UPM Raflatac Co., Ltd (2)
470 Moo 5 T Phraeksamai, A Muang-Samutprakarn, Bangkok, 10280, Samut Prakarn, Thailand
Tel.: (66) 23465325
Emp.: 30
Label Material Distr
N.A.I.C.S.: 424310

UPM Raflatac Iberica S.A. (2)
Pintor Fortuny 17, Polinya, 08213, Barcelona, Spain
Tel.: (34) 937131900
Emp.: 70
Packaging Paper Products Mfr
N.A.I.C.S.: 322299

Subsidiary (US):

UPM Raflatac Inc. (2)
101 E Corporate Dr, Dixon, IL 61021
Label Material Mfr
N.A.I.C.S.: 322220

Plant (Domestic):

UPM Raflatac Inc. - Illinois Labelstock Factory (3)
101 E Corporate Dr, Dixon, IL 61021
Packaging Paper Products Mfr
N.A.I.C.S.: 322220

Subsidiary (Non-US):

UPM Raflatac Limited (2)
Wareham Road, Eastfield, Scarborough, YO11 3DX, N Yorks, United Kingdom **(100%)**
Tel.: (44) 172 358 3661
Web Site: https://www.upmraflatac.com
Sales Range: $200-249.9 Million
Emp.: 190
Self Adhesive Labels Mfr
N.A.I.C.S.: 325520

UPM Raflatac Ltd. (2)
211a Premier Business Centre 3013 Lake Drive, Citywest, Dublin, Ireland
Tel.: (353) 1 469 3123
Web Site: https://www.upmraflatac.com
Emp.: 2
Packaging Paper Products Mfr
N.A.I.C.S.: 322120

UPM Raflatac Mexico S.A. de C.V. (2)
Avenida Olivo S/N Col San Francisco Chilpan, Tultitlan de Mariano Escobedo, CP 54940, Mexico, Mexico
Tel.: (52) 5554438672
Web Site: https://www.upmraflatac.com
Packaging Paper Products Mfr
N.A.I.C.S.: 322120

UPM Raflatac NZ Limited (2)
Tel.: (64) 95736003
Sales Range: $25-49.9 Million
Emp.: 8
Packaging Paper Products Mfr
N.A.I.C.S.: 322120

UPM Raflatac Pty Ltd (2)
Tel.: (61) 387727000
Packaging Paper Products Mfr
N.A.I.C.S.: 322120

UPM Raflatac Pvt. Ltd. (2)
C-45/1 T T C Industrial Area Pawane Off Thane-Belapur Road, Turbhe Dist-Thane, Navi Mumbai, 400705, India
Tel.: (91) 223 025 9000
Web Site: https://www.upmraflatac.com
Emp.: 40
Packaging Paper Products Mfr
N.A.I.C.S.: 322220

UPM Raflatac RFID (Guangzhou) Co. Ltd (2)
67 HongJing Road Eastern Section of GETDD, 510530, Guangzhou, China
Tel.: (86) 20 82020126
Packaging Paper Products Mfr
N.A.I.C.S.: 322220

UPM Raflatac S.A.S. (2)
ZI Pompey Industries 1 rue du jet, Pompey, F-54340, Nancy, France **(100%)**
Tel.: (33) 383925959
Sales Range: $50-74.9 Million
Emp.: 200
Mfr of Self-Adhesive Labels
N.A.I.C.S.: 322220

UPM Raflatac Sdn. Bhd. (2)
Plo 434 Jalan Perak 4, Pasir Gudang Industrial Estate, 81700, Johor, Malaysia **(100%)**
Tel.: (60) 7 255 1510
Web Site: https://www.upmraflatac.com
Emp.: 170
Mfr of Self-Adhesive Labels
N.A.I.C.S.: 322220

UPM Raflatac Sdn. Bhd. (2)
Plo 434 Jalan Perak 4 Kawasan Perindustrian, Pasir Gudang, 81700, Johor, Malaysia
Tel.: (60) 72551510
Packaging Paper Products Mfr
N.A.I.C.S.: 322220

UPM Raflatac Sp. z o.o. (2)
Tel.: (48) 717765000
Packaging Paper Products Mfr
N.A.I.C.S.: 322220

UPM Raflatac s.r.l. (2)
Tel.: (54) 1145899710
Labelstock Product Mfr
N.A.I.C.S.: 322220

UPM Romania S.R.L. (1)
1 Arh Louis Blank Louis Blank Business Offices Floor 2 Office Nr 2, 1st District, 011751, Bucharest, Romania
Tel.: (40) 21 231 7600
Paper Products Mfr
N.A.I.C.S.: 322120

UPM Sahkonsiirto Oy (1)
Akerlundinkatu 11, Tampere, 33100, Finland
Tel.: (358) 20416111
Web Site: http://www.upm.com
Hydroelectric Power Generation & Transmission
N.A.I.C.S.: 221121

UPM Silvesta Oy (1)
Akerlundinkatu 11 B, PO Box 85, 33101, Tampere, Finland
Tel.: (358) 20415111
Web Site: http://www.upmsilvesta.fi
Forestry Support Services
N.A.I.C.S.: 115310

UPM Timber (1)
Peltokatu 26 C, PO Box 203, 33101, Tampere, Finland
Tel.: (358) 2 041 5113
Web Site: https://www.upmtimber.com
Emp.: 410
Lumber Mfr & Distr
N.A.I.C.S.: 423310

UPM-Kymmene (Belgium) S.A./N.V. (1)
Rue De La Charite 17, 1210, Brussels, Belgium **(100%)**
Tel.: (32) 22094211
Web Site: http://www.upm_kymmene.com
Sales Range: $50-74.9 Million
Emp.: 18
N.A.I.C.S.: 322120
Ivan Bouchart (Mng Dir)

UPM-Kymmene (UK) Holdings Limited (1)
Station House Stamford New Road, Altrincham, WA14 1EP, Cheshire, United Kingdom **(100%)**
Tel.: (44) 8706000876
Web Site: http://www.upm.com
Sales Range: $50-74.9 Million
Emp.: 60
Marketing & Sales of Paper
N.A.I.C.S.: 424130

Subsidiary (Domestic):

Shotton Paper Company PLC (2)
Weighbridge Rd, Deeside, Shotton, CH5 2LL, Frint Shire, United Kingdom **(100%)**
Tel.: (44) 244280000
N.A.I.C.S.: 322120

Sterling-Lohja Ltd. (2)
Victoria House 55 Queen St, Maidenhead, SL6 1LT, Berkshire, United Kingdom
Tel.: (44) 870 6000875
Web Site: http://w3.upm-kymmene.com
Mfr of Release Paper
N.A.I.C.S.: 322299

UPM Tilhill Forestry Ltd (2)
Kings Park House Laurelhill, Stirling, FK7 9NS, United Kingdom
Tel.: (44) 1786 435000
Web Site: http://www.tilhill.com
Emp.: 8
Timber Harvesting Services
N.A.I.C.S.: 111421
Rob Dillon (CFO)

Subsidiary (Non-US):

UPM-Kymmene (UK) Limited (2) **(100%)**
Tel.: (44) 1294312020
Sales Range: $100-124.9 Million
Emp.: 270
Paper Manufacturing
N.A.I.C.S.: 322120

Plant (Domestic):

UPM-Kymmene (UK) Limited - Shotton Paper Mill (3)
Weighbridge Road Shotton, Deeside, CH5 2LL, Flintshire, United Kingdom
Tel.: (44) 1244 280 000
Sales Range: $125-149.9 Million
Emp.: 400
Paper Products Mfr
N.A.I.C.S.: 322120
Tomi Hyton (Gen Mgr)

UPM-Kymmene A/S (1)
Station Parken 24, DK 2600, Glostrup, Denmark **(100%)**
Tel.: (45) 33481800
Web Site: http://www.upmKymmene.com
Sales Range: $25-49.9 Million
Emp.: 18
Marketing & Sales of Paper
N.A.I.C.S.: 459410

UPM-Kymmene AB (1)
Ralambsvagen 17 7th floor, PO Box 34113, Stockholm, 112 59, Sweden
Tel.: (46) 8 440 36 00
Paper Product Distr
N.A.I.C.S.: 424110

UPM-Kymmene AG (1)
Claridenstrasse 25, 8002, Zurich, Switzerland **(100%)**
Tel.: (41) 445785353

UPM-KYMMENE CORPORATION

UPM-Kymmene Corporation—(Continued)
Web Site: http://www.upmraflatac.com
Sales Range: $25-49.9 Million
Emp.: 16
Marketing & Sales of Paper
N.A.I.C.S.: 424130

UPM-Kymmene AS (1)
Joe 3 4th Fl, Tallinn, 10151,
Estonia (100%)
Tel.: (372) 6261030
Web Site: http://www.upm.com
Sales Range: $50-74.9 Million
Emp.: 8
Marketing & Sales of Paper
N.A.I.C.S.: 424130

UPM-Kymmene B.V. (1)
World Trade Ctr Amsterdam Strawinskylaan
857, NL 1077 XX, Amsterdam,
Netherlands (100%)
Tel.: (31) 205775451
Web Site: http://www.upm.com
Sales Range: $25-49.9 Million
Emp.: 12
Marketing & Sales of Paper
N.A.I.C.S.: 424130

UPM-Kymmene Corp. - Alholma Sawmill (1)
Laukontie 6, 68600, Pietarsaari, Finland
Tel.: (358) 2041 4143
Sales Range: $25-49.9 Million
Emp.: 80
Sawmills
N.A.I.C.S.: 321113

UPM-Kymmene Corp. - Fray Bentos Pulp Mill (1)
Ruta Puente Puerto Km 307, 65000, Fray Bentos, Uruguay
Tel.: (598) 456 20 100
Sales Range: $50-74.9 Million
Emp.: 200
Pulp Mill
N.A.I.C.S.: 322110
Matias Martinez *(Mgr-Comm)*

UPM-Kymmene Corp. - Jamsankoski Paper Mill (1)
Tiilikantie 17, PO Box 35, 42301, Jamsankoski, Finland
Tel.: (358) 20416161
Web Site: http://www.upm.com
Emp.: 380
Uncoated Magazine, Label & Packaging Paper Mill
N.A.I.C.S.: 322120
Ari Karaila *(Mgr-Fin)*

UPM-Kymmene Corp. - Kaipola Paper Mill (1)
Tehtaankatu 1, Kaipola, 42220, Finland
Tel.: (358) 2041 6161
Sales Range: $150-199.9 Million
Emp.: 400
Magazine Paper & Newsprint Mill
N.A.I.C.S.: 322120
Markku Taavitsainen *(Mgr)*

UPM-Kymmene Corp. - Kaukas Paper/Pulp Mill (1)
Kaukaankatu 16, Lappeenranta, 53200, Finland
Tel.: (358) 2041 5161
Sales Range: $250-299.5 Million
Emp.: 600
Newsprint & Chemical Pulp Mill
N.A.I.C.S.: 322120
Teuvo Solismaa *(Gen Dir)*

UPM-Kymmene Corp. - Kaukas Sawmill (1)
Kaukaantie 16, 53200, Lappeenranta, Finland
Tel.: (358) 2 041 4139
Web Site: http://www.upmtimber.com
Emp.: 100
Sawmills
N.A.I.C.S.: 321113
Antti Waajakoski *(Dir-Mill)*

UPM-Kymmene Corp. - Korkeakoski Sawmill (1)
Sahantie 10, PO Box 25, 35501, Korkeakoski, Finland
Tel.: (358) 2 041 4149
Web Site: http://www.upmtimber.com
Sales Range: $25-49.9 Million
Emp.: 70
Sawmills
N.A.I.C.S.: 321113

UPM-Kymmene Corp. - Kymi Paper/Pulp Mill (1)
Selluntie 1, 45700, Kuusankoski, Finland
Tel.: (358) 204 15 121
Sales Range: $300-349.9 Million
Emp.: 620
Newsprint, Specialty Paper & Pulp Mill
N.A.I.C.S.: 322120

UPM-Kymmene Corp. - Pietarsaari Pulp Mill (1)
Luodontie 149, PL 42, Pietarsaari, 68601, Finland
Tel.: (358) 20416113
Sales Range: $125-149.9 Million
Emp.: 300
Chemical Pulp Mill
N.A.I.C.S.: 322110
Simon Fagerudd *(Gen Mgr)*

UPM-Kymmene Corp. - Rauma Paper Mill (1)
Tikkalantie 1, PL 95, Rauma, 26100, Finland
Tel.: (358) 20414101
Sales Range: $200-249.9 Million
Emp.: 690
Magazine Paper Mill
N.A.I.C.S.: 322120
Kari Pasanen *(Dir-Maintenance)*

UPM-Kymmene Corp. - Seikku Sawmill (1)
Aittaluoto, 28101, Pori, Finland
Tel.: (358) 2 041 4153
Web Site: https://www.upmtimber.com
Emp.: 75
Sawmills
N.A.I.C.S.: 321113

UPM-Kymmene Corp. - Tervasaari Paper Mill (1)
Tehtaankatu 7, Valkeakoski, 37600, Finland
Tel.: (358) 204 16 111
Sales Range: $125-149.9 Million
Emp.: 330
Label Base Paper Mill
N.A.I.C.S.: 322120
Jari Gamminen *(Dir-Growth Projects)*

UPM-Kymmene Hellas Ltd (1)
41 Laodikis Str, Athens, Glyfada, 16674, Greece
Tel.: (30) 210 9680610
Sales Range: $25-49.9 Million
Emp.: 5
Paper Products Mfr
N.A.I.C.S.: 322120
George Filis *(Gen Mgr)*

UPM-Kymmene Inc. (1)
Tel.: (630) 922-2500
Web Site: http://w3.upm.com
Sales Range: $50-74.9 Million
Emp.: 100
Paper Product Distr
N.A.I.C.S.: 424110

Subsidiary (Domestic):

Blandin Paper Co. (2)
115 SW 1st St, Grand Rapids, MN 55744-3699
Tel.: (218) 327-6200
Web Site: http://www.upm-kymmene.com
Emp.: 230
Mfr of Light Weight Coated Paper
N.A.I.C.S.: 322120

UPM-Kymmene India PVT Ltd (1)
Tel.: (91) 2230259007
Emp.: 18
Labelstock Product Mfr
N.A.I.C.S.: 322220

UPM-Kymmene Japan K.K. (1)
Tel.: (81) 362058130
Web Site: https://www.upm.com
Paper & Pulp Mfr
N.A.I.C.S.: 322120

UPM-Kymmene Kagit Urunleri Sanayi ve Ticaret Ltd. Sti. (1)
Tel.: (90) 2162173400
Emp.: 37

Paper Products Mfr
N.A.I.C.S.: 322120

UPM-Kymmene Kagit Urunleri Sanoy ve Ticaret Ltd. Sti (1)
Nidakule Goztepe Is Merkezi Bora Sokak No 1 Kat 10 D 35 36 Merdiven, Istanbul, 34732, Turkiye
Tel.: (90) 216 464 5364
Paper Products Mfr
N.A.I.C.S.: 322120

UPM-Kymmene Keresbedelmi Kft. (1)
MOM Park Centrum, 1123, Budapest, Hungary (100%)
Tel.: (36) 1 224 7970
Web Site: http://www.upmraflatac.com
Sales Range: $50-74.9 Million
Emp.: 10
Newsprint Mill Services
N.A.I.C.S.: 322120

UPM-Kymmene Pty. Ltd. (1)
Level 13 124 Walkers Street, Sydney, 2060, NSW, Australia (100%)
Tel.: (61) 293345000
Web Site: http://www.upm-kymmene.com.au
Sales Range: $1-9.9 Million
Emp.: 12
Paper Products Mfr
N.A.I.C.S.: 322120

UPM-Kymmene S.A. (1)
Caleruega 102-104, Edificio Ofipinar, Madrid, 28033, Spain (100%)
Tel.: (34) 913609500
Web Site: http://www.upm-kymmene.com
Sales Range: $25-49.9 Million
Emp.: 40
Marketing & Sales of Paper
N.A.I.C.S.: 424130

UPM-Kymmene S.r.l. (1)
Via Martiri della Liberazione 12, I-23875, Osnago, LC, Italy
Tel.: (39) 039952211
Emp.: 25
Paper Products Mfr
N.A.I.C.S.: 322120

UPM-Kymmene Seven Seas Oy (1)
Porkkalankatu 24, 00180, Helsinki, Finland
Tel.: (358) 20415111
Paper Products Mfr
N.A.I.C.S.: 322120

UPM-Kymmene Wood Oy (1)
Niemenkatu 16, 15140, Lahti, Finland (100%)
Tel.: (358) 20415113
Web Site: http://www.upmwood.com
Sales Range: $500-549.9 Million
Emp.: 2,600
Plywood & Veneer Products Mfr & Distr
N.A.I.C.S.: 321211

Subsidiary (Non-US):

OOO UPM-Kymmene Chudovo (2)
Ul Derzhavin, 174210, Chudovo, Russia (100%)
Tel.: (7) 8123268494
Plywood & Veneer Mill
N.A.I.C.S.: 321211

UPM-Kymmene Otepaa AS (2)
Tel.: (372) 7679100
Web Site: https://www.wisaplywood.com
Sales Range: $50-74.9 Million
Emp.: 265
Plywood Mfr
N.A.I.C.S.: 321211

Plant (Domestic):

UPM-Kymmene Wood Oy - Joensuu Plywood Mill (2)
Sirkkalantie 17, 80100, Joensuu, Finland
Tel.: (358) 2041 5133
Web Site: http://www.wisaplywood.com
Sales Range: $50-74.9 Million
Plywood Mfr
N.A.I.C.S.: 321211

UPM-Kymmene Wood Oy - Jyvaskyla Plywood Mill (2)
Puutie 2, 40900, Saynatsalo, Finland
Tel.: (358) 2041 5143
Web Site: http://www.wisaplywood.com

Sales Range: $100-124.9 Million
Emp.: 200
Plywood Mfr
N.A.I.C.S.: 321211

UPM-Kymmene Wood Oy - Kalso Veneer Mill (2)
Siikakoskentie 88, 47900, Vuohijarvi, Finland
Tel.: (358) 2 041 5117
Web Site: https://www.wisaplywood.com
Sales Range: $50-74.9 Million
Emp.: 120
Veneer Mill
N.A.I.C.S.: 321211

UPM-Kymmene Wood Oy - Pellos Plywood Mill (2)
UPM Pellos Plywood Mills, 52420, Pellosniemi, Finland
Tel.: (358) 2 041 5173
Web Site: https://www.wisaplywood.com
Emp.: 580
Plywood Mill
N.A.I.C.S.: 321211

UPM-Kymmene Wood Oy - Savonlinna Plywood Mill (2)
Schaumanintie 1, 57200, Savonlinna, Finland
Tel.: (358) 2 041 5183
Web Site: https://www.wisaplywood.com
Sales Range: $100-124.9 Million
Emp.: 280
Plywood Mill
N.A.I.C.S.: 321211

UPM-Kymmene s.r.o. (1)
Vaclavske Nam 56, 110 00, Prague, Czech Republic
Tel.: (420) 222090933
Web Site: http://www.upm.com
Emp.: 12
Paper Product Distr
N.A.I.C.S.: 322120

UPMARITIME LONDON LTD.
1146 High Road Whetstone, London, N20 0RA, United Kingdom
Tel.: (44) 2033182345
Web Site:
 http://www.upm2.webnode.com
Year Founded: 2009
Financial Investment Services
N.A.I.C.S.: 523940
Theodore Chouliaras *(Pres)*

UPPER CANYON MINERALS CORP.
808 Nelson Street Suite 407, Box 12129, Vancouver, V6Z 2H2, BC, Canada
Tel.: (604) 628-1767
Mineral Mining Services
N.A.I.C.S.: 213114
Jatinder Singh Bal *(Pres & CEO)*

UPPER EGYPT CONTRACTING
26th of July Street 11th Floor, P.O. Box 89, Cairo, Egypt
Tel.: (20) 25901186
Web Site: https://www.elsaeed-contracting.com
Year Founded: 1964
Construction Engineering Services
N.A.I.C.S.: 236220
Ahmed Mohamed Mustafa Suleiman Al-Qadri *(Chm)*

UPPER EGYPT FLOUR MILLS
Jerjaoah St, Sohag, Egypt
Tel.: (20) 932350010
Web Site:
 http://www.upperegyptmills.org
Year Founded: 1965
UEFM.CA—(EGX)
Sales Range: Less than $1 Million
Flour Milling Services
N.A.I.C.S.: 311211
Rabiea Qulaiee Mohammed Hussein *(Chm & CEO)*

UPPER LAKES GROUP INC.
49 Jackes Ave, Toronto, M4T 1E2, ON, Canada
Tel.: (416) 920-7610
Year Founded: 1932
Sales Range: $200-249.9 Million
Holding Company; Great Lakes Freight Transportation, Shipbuilding & Repair, Port Facility Services & Other Marine & Industrial Services
N.A.I.C.S.: 813410
John D. Leitch *(Chm)*

Subsidiaries:

Allied Marine & Industrial Inc. (1)
1 Lake Road, Port Colborne, L3K 1A2, ON, Canada
Tel.: (905) 834-8275
Web Site: http://www.allmind.com
Sales Range: $25-49.9 Million
Emp.: 60
Commercial Ship Building & Repair Services
N.A.I.C.S.: 336611
A. E. Mitchell *(Pres)*

Canal Marine & Industrial Inc. (1)
155 Cushman Rd, Saint Catharines, L2M 6T4, ON, Canada
Tel.: (905) 685-9293
Web Site: http://www.canal.ca
Sales Range: $50-74.9 Million
Emp.: 50
Industrial, Commercial & Marine Electrical, Mechanical & Engineering Contractor Services
N.A.I.C.S.: 238990

Heritage Pointe Properties Inc. (1)
Suite 1 Heritage Pointe Drive, Heritage Pointe, De Winton, T1S 4H1, AB, Canada
Tel.: (403) 256-2002
Web Site: http://www.heritagepointe.com
Emp.: 130
Golf Course Provider
N.A.I.C.S.: 611620
Carol Oxtoby *(Pres & CEO)*

Lakehead Marine & Industrial Inc. (1)
401 Shipyard Drive, Thunder Bay, P7A 7T8, ON, Canada
Tel.: (807) 683-6261
Commercial Ship Building & Repair Services
N.A.I.C.S.: 336611

Lansdowne Technologies Inc. (1)
275 Slater Street Suite 203, Ottawa, K1P 5H9, ON, Canada
Tel.: (613) 236-3333
Web Site: http://www.lansdowne.com
Sales Range: $25-49.9 Million
Emp.: 50
Technical & Management Consulting Services
N.A.I.C.S.: 541990
Diane MacInnes *(Controller)*

Seaway Marine & Industrial Inc. (1)
340 Lakeshore Rd E, Saint Catharines, L2M 0A2, ON, Canada
Tel.: (905) 934-7759
Web Site: http://www.seamind.ca
Sales Range: $75-99.9 Million
Emp.: 400
Commercial Ship Building & Repair Services
N.A.I.C.S.: 336611

UPR CORPORATION
Uchisaiwaicho Tokyu Building 12F
1-3-2 Uchisaiwaicho, Chiyoda-Ku, Tokyo, 100-0011, Japan
Tel.: (81) 335931730
Web Site: https://www.upr-net.co.jp
Year Founded: 1979
7065—(TKS)
Rev.: $96,179,860
Assets: $133,543,400
Liabilities: $77,407,900
Net Worth: $56,135,500
Earnings: $3,713,340
Emp.: 228
Fiscal Year-end: 08/31/24

Logistic Equipment Distribution Services
N.A.I.C.S.: 541614
Yoshiya Sakata *(Chm, Pres & CEO)*

Subsidiaries:

UPR (Thailand) Co., Ltd. (1)
Exchange Tower Room No 2001-2 20 Floor No 388 Sukhumvit Road, Klongtoey, Bangkok, 10110, Thailand
Tel.: (66) 2 672 5100
Web Site: https://www.upr-thailand.co.th
Pallet Distr
N.A.I.C.S.: 423830
Hiromichi Sasaki *(Mng Dir)*

UPR Singapore Pte. Ltd. (1)
24 Raffles Place 20-01 Clifford Centre, Singapore, 048621, Singapore
Tel.: (65) 6 533 6141
Web Site: https://www.upr-singapore.sg
Pallet Distr
N.A.I.C.S.: 423830
Shin Matsubara *(Mng Dir)*

UPR Solution (Malaysia) Sdn. Bhd. (1)
Lot 18 Jalan Sementa 27/91 Seksyen 27, 40400, Shah Alam, Selangor, Malaysia
Tel.: (60) 35 614 3219
Web Site: https://www.upr-malaysia.my
Pallet Distr
N.A.I.C.S.: 423830

UPR Vietnam Co., Ltd. (1)
5th floor Miss Aodai Building 21 Nguyen Trung Ngan St, Ben Nghe Ward District 1, Ho Chi Minh City, Vietnam
Tel.: (84) 2862752201
Web Site: https://www.upr-vietnam.vn
Pallet Equipment Rental Services
N.A.I.C.S.: 532490

UPSELLON BRANDS HOLDINGS LTD.
Ha-Yetsira St 3 8th Floor, Ramat Gan, 5252141, Israel
Tel.: (972) 509200194
Web Site: http://www.upsellon.com
Year Founded: 2019
UPSL—(TAE)
Rev.: $15,288,000
Assets: $8,158,000
Liabilities: $1,515,000
Net Worth: $6,643,000
Earnings: ($3,963,000)
Fiscal Year-end: 06/30/23
Holding Company
N.A.I.C.S.: 551112
Amitay Weiss *(Chm)*

UPSIDE ENGINEERING LTD.
409 10th Avenue SE, Calgary, T2G 0W3, AB, Canada
Tel.: (403) 290-4650
Web Site: http://www.upsideeng.com
Year Founded: 1989
Sales Range: $10-24.9 Million
Engineering & Consulting Services
N.A.I.C.S.: 541330
Rod P. Evans *(Founder)*

UPSNAP, INC.
100 Consilium Placee Suite 200, Toronto, M1H 3E3, ON, Canada
Tel.: (416) 619-3900 Ca
Web Site: http://www.upsnap.com
Year Founded: 2000
CEENF—(OTCIQ)
Rev.: $689,222
Assets: $267,415
Liabilities: $3,070,104
Net Worth: ($2,802,689)
Earnings: ($487,553)
Emp.: 34
Fiscal Year-end: 12/31/22
Mobile Local Search & Advertising Solutions
N.A.I.C.S.: 541890
A. Alex Pekurar *(CFO)*

UPSON INTERNATIONAL CORPORATION
Unit 2308 23/F Capital House Tower 1 9th Avenue Corner 34th Street, Bonifacio Global City, Taguig, Philippines
Tel.: (63) 285267152
Web Site: https://www.upson.com.ph
Year Founded: 1995
UPSON—(PHI)
Rev.: $180,741,327
Assets: $112,425,801
Liabilities: $61,834,390
Net Worth: $50,591,411
Earnings: $8,381,165
Emp.: 795
Fiscal Year-end: 12/31/23
Information Technology Services
N.A.I.C.S.: 541512
Lawrence O. Lee *(Chm)*

UPSURGE INVESTMENT & FINANCE LTD.
Office No 303 Morya Landmark- I Behind Crystal Plaza Off New Link Road, Andheri West, Mumbai, 400 053, India
Tel.: (91) 2267425441
Web Site: https://www.upsurgeinvestment.com
Year Founded: 1994
531390—(BOM)
Rev.: $3,913,558
Assets: $5,019,215
Liabilities: $560,198
Net Worth: $4,459,016
Earnings: $60,311
Emp.: 8
Fiscal Year-end: 03/31/23
Financial Services
N.A.I.C.S.: 522320
Daya Krishna Goyal *(Founder & Mng Dir)*

UR HOLDING S.P.A
Viale Edison 44 Trezzano, 20090, Milan, Italy
Tel.: (39) 02 4840 1580
Web Site: http://www.ur-group.com
Sales Range: $25-49.9 Million
Emp.: 31
Computer System Design Services
N.A.I.C.S.: 541512
Giovanbattista Laghezza *(Pres & CEO)*

Subsidiaries:

UR A.B. (1)
Brunnsgatan 3 1tr, Sundbyberg, 172 68, Sweden
Tel.: (46) 8 564720 60
Web Site: http://www.urgroup.se
Emp.: 4
Business Support Services
N.A.I.C.S.: 561499
Mekeel Rosvall *(Gen Mgr)*

UR GmbH (1)
Fahrenheitstrasse 1, 28359, Bremen, Germany
Tel.: (49) 421 2208 270
Sales Range: $25-49.9 Million
Emp.: 5
Business Support Services
N.A.I.C.S.: 561499

UR GmbH (1)
Gewerbestrasse 6, 3304, Sankt Georgen am Ybbsfelde, Austria
Tel.: (43) 7472 666 6012
Web Site: http://www.urgroup.com
Sales Range: $25-49.9 Million
Emp.: 5
Business Support Services
N.A.I.C.S.: 561499
Stefan Haas *(Gen Mgr)*

UR Group Inc. (1)
Wyatt Dr Ste 6, Santa Clara, CA 95054
Tel.: (508) 739-2010

Web Site: http://www.ur-group.com
Emp.: 10
Electronic Components Distr
N.A.I.C.S.: 423690
Joe Matano *(Pres)*

UR Ltd. (1)
105 Faraday Park Dorcan, Swindon, SN3 5JF, Wiltshire, United Kingdom
Tel.: (44) 1793 756980
Web Site: http://www.ur-group.com
Sales Range: $25-49.9 Million
Emp.: 22
Business Support Services
N.A.I.C.S.: 561499
Roy Tuff *(Mgr-Mktg)*

UR S.A. (1)
Plaza de Vallvidrera n 7 C-2, 08017, Barcelona, Spain
Tel.: (34) 93 406 9119
Business Support Services
N.A.I.C.S.: 561499

UR S.A.R.L. (1)
6 Allee De Londres, 91140, Villejust, France
Tel.: (33) 9 80 81 77 34
Web Site: http://www.ur-group.com
Sales Range: $25-49.9 Million
Emp.: 4
Business Support Services
N.A.I.C.S.: 561499
Yzea Colliea *(Gen Mgr)*

UR-Israel Ltd. (1)
Poleg Business Park, 42505, Netanya, Israel
Tel.: (972) 9 885 866 8
Sales Range: $25-49.9 Million
Emp.: 1
Business Support Services
N.A.I.C.S.: 561499

UR SUGAR INDUSTRIES LTD.
UR Building Basweshwar Circle Bellad Bagewadi, Tal Hukerri District, Belgaum, 591305, Karnataka, India
Tel.: (91) 9686195430
Web Site: https://www.ursugar.co.in
Year Founded: 2010
539097—(BOM)
Rev.: $935,680
Assets: $2,506,850
Liabilities: $40,718
Net Worth: $2,466,132
Earnings: $201,187
Emp.: 2
Fiscal Year-end: 03/31/22
Computer Products, Steel & Fabric Products Distr
N.A.I.C.S.: 423430
Rajeev Gupta *(Mng Dir)*

URA HOLDINGS PLC
6th Floor 60 Gracechurch Street, London, EC3V 0HR, United Kingdom
Tel.: (44) 2079203150 UK
Web Site: http://www.uraholdingsplc.co.uk
Year Founded: 2005
Assets: $1,637,832
Liabilities: $2,714,429
Net Worth: ($1,076,598)
Earnings: ($2,155,894)
Emp.: 7
Fiscal Year-end: 06/30/17
Mineral Exploration Services
N.A.I.C.S.: 212390
Peter Redmond *(Chm)*

URAI CO., LTD.
498 Niwatoriboko-cho Muromachidori-Ayanokojiagaru, Shimogyo-ku, Kyoto, 600-8491, Japan
Tel.: (81) 75 3610330
Web Site: http://www.urai.co.jp
Year Founded: 1951
Kimono, Jewelry & Fashion Related Products Retailer
N.A.I.C.S.: 459999

URAL AIRLINES JSC

URAL AIRLINES JSC

Ural Airlines JSC—(Continued)
per Utrenniy 1G SITA SVXTOU6,
620025, Yekaterinburg, Russia
Tel.: (7) 4951394101 RU
Web Site: http://www.uralairlines.ru
Year Founded: 1993
Sales Range: $300-349.9 Million
Emp.: 1,600
Oil Transportation Services
N.A.I.C.S.: 481111
Sergey Skuratov (Gen Dir)

URALCHEM OJSC
6/2 Presnenskaya Embankment,
123112, Moscow, Russia
Tel.: (7) 4957218989 RU
Web Site: http://www.uralchem.com
Year Founded: 2007
Sales Range: $450-499.9 Million
Nitrogen & Phosphate Fertilizers Mfr
N.A.I.C.S.: 325311
Dmitry A. Mazepin (Chm)

Subsidiaries:

SIA Uralchem Trading (1)
Krisjan Valdemara 6, Riga, Latvia
Tel.: (371) 673 88 100
Web Site: http://www.uralchem.com
Chemical Products Distr
N.A.I.C.S.: 424690
Olga Velikanova (Mgr-Export Sls)

Uralchem Trading do Brasil Ltda. (1)
120 Rua Samuel Morse 2 anadar conjunto 21, Brooklin, Sao Paulo, 04576-060, Brazil
Tel.: (55) 11 5102 2584
Web Site: http://www.uralchem.com.br
Mineral Fertilizer Mfr
N.A.I.C.S.: 212390

Uralchem-Trans LLC (1)
6/2 Presnenskaya Naberezhnaya, 123112, Moscow, Russia
Tel.: (7) 4957218989
Logistics Consulting Servies
N.A.I.C.S.: 541614

URALS ENERGY PUBLIC COMPANY LIMITED
Glafkos Tower Office 501 5th Floor 3 Menandrou Street, 1066, Nicosia, Cyprus
Tel.: (357) 22451686
Web Site:
    http://www.uralsenergy.com
Rev.: $44,179,000
Assets: $105,469,000
Liabilities: $28,384,000
Net Worth: $77,085,000
Earnings: $14,048,000
Emp.: 461
Fiscal Year-end: 12/31/17
Oil & Gas Exploration & Production Services
N.A.I.C.S.: 211120
Leonid Y. Dyachenko (CEO)

Subsidiaries:

ZAO Arcticneft (1)
ul Osennaya 11, Moscow, 121609, Russia
Tel.: (7) 495 795 0300
Web Site: http://www.uralsenergy.com
Oil Refining & Gas Production Services
N.A.I.C.S.: 324110

URAN BARILGA JOINT STOCK COMPANY
18th Khoroo, Bayangol District,
Ulaanbaatar, Mongolia
Tel.: (976) 11 360135
Rev.: $1,408,570
Assets: $3,499,253
Liabilities: $1,031,247
Net Worth: $2,468,006
Earnings: $89,542
Fiscal Year-end: 12/31/18
Building Construction Services
N.A.I.C.S.: 236220

URANIUM ENERGY CORP.
1830 1188 West Georgia Street, Vancouver, V6E 4A2, BC, Canada
Tel.: (604) 682-9775 NV
Web Site:
    https://www.uraniumenergy.com
Year Founded: 2003
UEC—(NYSEAMEX)
Uranium Exploration & Mining Development Services
N.A.I.C.S.: 213114
Craig Wall (VP-Environmental, Health, and Safety)

Subsidiaries:

South Texas Mining Venture, L.L.P. (1)
500 N Shoreline Blvd Ste 800, Corpus Christi, TX 78471
Tel.: (361) 888-8235
Uranium-Radium-Vanadium Ore Mining Services
N.A.I.C.S.: 212290

UEC Resources Ltd. (1)
320 1111 W Hastings St, Vancouver, V6E 2J3, BC, Canada
Tel.: (604) 682-9775
Metal Mining Services
N.A.I.C.S.: 213114

UEX Corporation (1)
Unit 200 - 3530 Millar Avenue, Saskatoon, S7P 0B6, SK, Canada
Tel.: (306) 979-3849
Web Site: http://www.uexcorp.com
Rev.: $97,166
Assets: $11,705,076
Liabilities: $811,676
Net Worth: $10,893,400
Earnings: ($6,981,846)
Emp.: 10
Fiscal Year-end: 12/31/2019
Uranium Mining Services
N.A.I.C.S.: 212290
Graham C. Thody (Chm)

Subsidiary (Domestic):

CoEX Metals Corporation (2)
Unit 200-3530 Millar Ave, Saskatoon, S7P 0B6, SK, Canada
Tel.: (306) 979-3849
Web Site: http://www.coexmetals.com
Uranium Exploration Services
N.A.I.C.S.: 212290
Roger Lemaitre (Pres & CEO)

Uranium Energy Corp. - Corporate Office (1)
500 N Shoreline Ste 800N, Corpus Christi, TX 78401
Tel.: (361) 888-8235
Web Site: http://www.uraniumenergy.com
Emp.: 16
Corporate Office; Uranium Exploration & Mining Development
N.A.I.C.S.: 551114

URANIUM PARTICIPATION CORPORATION
1100 - 40 University Avenue, Toronto,
M5J 1T1, ON, Canada
Tel.: (416) 979-1991 ON
Web Site:
    http://www.uraniumparticipation.com
Year Founded: 2005
U—(TSX)
Sales Range: Less than $1 Million
Emp.: 1
Holding Company; Uranium Investments
N.A.I.C.S.: 551112
Jeff Kennedy (Chm)

URANIUM ROYALTY CORP.
1188 West Georgia Street Suite 1830, Vancouver, V6E 4A2, BC, Canada
Tel.: (604) 396-8222
Web Site:
    https://www.uraniumroyalty.com

UROY—(NASDAQ)
Rev.: $31,547,610
Assets: $205,882,396
Liabilities: $2,152,619
Net Worth: $203,729,777
Earnings: $7,224,644
Emp.: 14
Fiscal Year-end: 04/30/24
Financial Investment Services
N.A.I.C.S.: 523999
Amir Adnani (Chm)

URAVAN MINERALS INC.
Suite 1117 204-70 Shawville Blvd SE,
Calgary, T2Y 2Z3, AB, Canada
Tel.: (403) 607-5908 AB
Web Site:
    http://www.uravanminerals.com
Year Founded: 1997
UVN—(TSXV)
Rev.: $588
Assets: $42,760
Liabilities: $18,725
Net Worth: $24,035
Earnings: ($804,007)
Fiscal Year-end: 12/31/19
Uranium, Nickel, Copper & Platinum Exploration & Development Services
N.A.I.C.S.: 212230
Larry Lahusen (CEO)

Subsidiaries:

Prime Fuels Corp. (1)
Unit 403 Reef Tower Cluster O, PO Box 123691, Dubai, United Arab Emirates
Tel.: (971) 44390436
Web Site: https://primefuels.com
Emp.: 1,000
Transport & Logistics Services
N.A.I.C.S.: 541614

URAVI T & WEDGE LAMPS LTD.
Q-6 RajLaxmi Techno Park Sonale Village NH3 - Nashik Bhiwandi Bypass, Bhiwandi Dist, Thane, 421 302, India
Tel.: (91) 8087726000
Web Site:
    https://www.uravilamps.com
Year Founded: 2004
543930—(BOM)
Rev.: $4,150,902
Assets: $6,181,284
Liabilities: $3,372,400
Net Worth: $2,808,884
Earnings: $104,035
Emp.: 96
Fiscal Year-end: 03/31/23
Light Mfr
N.A.I.C.S.: 335139
Niraj D. Gada (Chm)

URBAN BARNS FOODS INC.
13000 Chemin Belanger, Mirabel, J7J 2N8, QC, Canada
Tel.: (450) 434-4344 NV
Year Founded: 2009
Fruits & Vegetables Producer & Supplier
N.A.I.C.S.: 311411
J. Robyn Jackson (Pres, CEO, Treas & Sec)

URBAN DEVELOPMENT & CONSTRUCTION CORPORATION
No 37 3/2 Street, Ward 8, Vung Tau,
Ba Ria-Vung Tau, Vietnam
Tel.: (84) 2543859617
Web Site: http://www.udec.com.vn
Year Founded: 1995
UDC—(HOSE)
Rev.: $3,955,571
Assets: $35,828,880
Liabilities: $25,502,429
Net Worth: $10,326,450

INTERNATIONAL PUBLIC

Earnings: ($3,269,508)
Fiscal Year-end: 12/31/23
Building Construction Services
N.A.I.C.S.: 236220
Tran Thai Hoa (Chm)

URBAN LOGISTICS REIT PLC
65 Gresham Street 6th Floor, London, EC2V 7NQ, United Kingdom
Tel.: (44) 2075911600 UK
Web Site:
    https://www.urbanlogisticsreit.com
Year Founded: 2016
SHED—(LSE)
Rev.: $75,675,484
Assets: $1,449,056,141
Liabilities: $491,404,660
Net Worth: $957,651,482
Earnings: $31,229,549
Fiscal Year-end: 03/31/24
Real Estate Investment Trust Services
N.A.I.C.S.: 531190
Richard Moffitt (CEO)

URBANA CORPORATION
150 King St W Ste 1702, Toronto,
M5H 1J9, ON, Canada
Tel.: (416) 595-9106
Web Site:
    https://www.urbanacorp.com
Year Founded: 1947
URB—(CNSX)
Rev.: $24,023,667
Assets: $271,201,928
Liabilities: $42,493,804
Net Worth: $228,708,124
Earnings: $13,974,350
Emp.: 2
Fiscal Year-end: 12/31/22
Mining Industry
N.A.I.C.S.: 213115
Harry K. Liu (Gen Counsel & Sec)

URBANET CORPORATION CO., LTD.
13th floor Tri-Edge Ochanomizu 4-2-5 Kanda Surugadai, Chiyoda-Ku, Tokyo, 101-0062, Japan
Tel.: (81) 366303050
Web Site: https://www.urbanet.jp
Year Founded: 1997
3242—(TKS)
Rev.: $173,942,300
Assets: $292,165,840
Liabilities: $198,467,760
Net Worth: $93,698,080
Earnings: $10,580,220
Emp.: 85
Fiscal Year-end: 06/30/24
Real Estate Development Services
N.A.I.C.S.: 531110
Shinji Hattori (Pres)

URBANEX SA
Str Marasesti 45, Neamt, Piatra
Neamt, Romania
Tel.: (40) 233 213757
Sales Range: $1-9.9 Million
Emp.: 49
Building Construction Services
N.A.I.C.S.: 236116

URBANFUND CORP.
35 Lesmill Road, Toronto, M3B 2T3,
ON, Canada
Tel.: (905) 940-6011
Year Founded: 1997
UFC—(TSXV)
Rev.: $6,523,048
Assets: $117,351,100
Liabilities: $58,664,186
Net Worth: $58,686,914
Earnings: $5,127,212
Fiscal Year-end: 12/31/23
Investment Banking Services
N.A.I.C.S.: 523150

Ronald S. Kimel (Chm)

URBANIMMERSIVE, INC.
3135 Boulevard Moise-Vincent, Longueuil, J3Z 0G7, QC, Canada
Web Site:
https://www.urbanimmersive.com
UBMRF—(OTCIQ)
Rev.: $3,408,593
Assets: $5,576,904
Liabilities: $4,120,168
Net Worth: $1,456,736
Earnings: $1,485,990
Emp.: 16
Fiscal Year-end: 09/30/19
Real Estate Manangement Services
N.A.I.C.S.: 531390
Ghislain Lemire (Founder)

Subsidiaries:

HomeVisit, LLC (1)
14100 Parke-Long Ct Ste G, Chantilly, VA 20151
Tel.: (703) 953-3866
Web Site: http://www.homevisit.com
Real Estate Agent & Broker Services
N.A.I.C.S.: 531210

URBANISE.COM LIMITED
Level 1 201 Miller Street, North Sydney, 2060, NSW, Australia
Tel.: (61) 412292977 AU
Web Site: https://www.urbanise.com
Year Founded: 2001
UBN—(ASX)
Rev.: $8,724,145
Assets: $9,351,711
Liabilities: $5,897,052
Net Worth: $3,454,659
Earnings: ($2,313,246)
Fiscal Year-end: 06/30/24
Cloud Software Development Services
N.A.I.C.S.: 541511
Almero Strauss (Bd of Dirs & Chm)

URBAR INGENIEROS, S.A.
Ctra Villabona-Asteasu km 3 Apartado 247, E-20159, Asteasu, Spain
Tel.: (34) 916695022
Web Site: https://www.urbar.com
Year Founded: 1953
UIN—(MAD)
Vibrating Equipment Mfr
N.A.I.C.S.: 333248
Francisco Martin Morales de Castilla (Pres)

URBAS GRUPO FINANCIERO S.A.
C/Gobelas 15, 28023, Madrid, Spain
Tel.: (34) 918615896
Web Site:
https://www.grupourbas.com
Year Founded: 1944
UBS—(MAD)
Rev.: $227,632,829
Assets: $1,322,299,261
Liabilities: $659,048,947
Net Worth: $663,250,315
Earnings: $73,273,213
Emp.: 840
Fiscal Year-end: 12/31/21
Real Estate Investment & Financial Services
N.A.I.C.S.: 525990
Juan Antonio Acedo Fernandez (Pres & CEO)

URBI, DESARROLLOS URBANOS, S.A. B. DE C. V.
Av Alvaro Obregon 1137 Nueva, 21100, Mexicali, Mexico
Tel.: (52) 6865238620
Web Site: http://www.pixelsiete.com
Year Founded: 1981
URBI—(MEX)
Rev.: $6,570,470
Assets: $131,955,467
Liabilities: $111,640,476
Net Worth: $20,314,991
Earnings: $3,572,119
Emp.: 80
Fiscal Year-end: 12/31/23
Housing Development Services
N.A.I.C.S.: 236117
Domingo Javier Moreno Gamez (Dir-Technical)

URBIS ARMATURI SANITARE SA
B-Dul Theodor Pallady Nr 57 Hala Con-Dem Parter Sl Etaj Sect 3, Bucharest, Romania
Tel.: (40) 213453613
Other Tap & Valve Mfr
N.A.I.C.S.: 332919

URBISINVEST A.D.
Bulevar cara Lazara 3/III, 21000, Novi Sad, Serbia
Tel.: (381) 21 450 377
Year Founded: 1982
Emp.: 11
Management Consulting Services
N.A.I.C.S.: 541618

URBISPROJEKT A.D.
Bulevar cara Lazara 3, 21000, Novi Sad, Serbia
Tel.: (381) 21 450 422
Web Site:
http://www.urbisprojekt.co.rs
Year Founded: 1953
Sales Range: Less than $1 Million
Emp.: 30
Architectural Designing Services
N.A.I.C.S.: 541310

URC SA
Str Argesului Nr 13, Vascau, Bihor, Romania
Tel.: (40) 744284457
Sales Range: Less than $1 Million
Emp.: 5
Mining Machinery Mfr
N.A.I.C.S.: 333131

URENCO LIMITED
18 Oxford Rd, Marlow, SL7 2NL, United Kingdom
Tel.: (44) 1628486941 UK
Web Site: http://www.urenco.com
Year Founded: 1970
Sales Range: $800-899.9 Million
Emp.: 825
Holding Company; Uranium Production
N.A.I.C.S.: 551112
Marcel Niggebrugge (CFO)

Subsidiaries:

URENCO ChemPlants Limited (1)
Capenhurst, Chester, CH1 6ER, United Kingdom
Tel.: (44) 151 473 7400
Uranium Mfr
N.A.I.C.S.: 325180
Helmut Engelbrecht (Chm)

Urenco Deutschland GmbH (1)
Rontgenstrasse 4, Postfach 19 20, 48599, Gronau, Germany (100%)
Tel.: (49) 25627110
Web Site: http://www.urenco.com
Sales Range: $100-124.9 Million
Emp.: 250
Enriched Uranium Production Services
N.A.I.C.S.: 212290
Joachim Ohnemus (Mng Dir)

Urenco Nederland B.V. (1)
Drienemansweg 1, PO Box 158, 7600 AD, Almelo, Netherlands
Tel.: (31) 5 46 54 54 54

Emp.: 300
Uranium Distr
N.A.I.C.S.: 424690
Arjan Bos (Head-Stable Isotopes)

Urenco, Inc. (1)
1560 Wilson Blvd Ste 300, Arlington, VA 22209-2463
Tel.: (703) 465-8110
Web Site: http://www.urenco.com
Sales Range: $25-49.9 Million
Emp.: 6
Production, Marketing & Sales of Uranium Enrichment Services
N.A.I.C.S.: 541910
Kirk S. Schnoebelen (Pres & CEO)

URGO GROUP SAS
42 rue de Longvic, 21300, Chenove, France
Tel.: (33) 3 80 54 50 00
Web Site: http://www.urgo-group.com
Year Founded: 1880
Advanced Wound Care & Selfcare Management & Neurotechnologies
N.A.I.C.S.: 812199
Edouard de Tinguy (Head-Comm & Pub Affairs)

Subsidiaries:

Urgo Medical North America (1)
3801 Hulen St Ste 251, Fort Worth, TX 76107-7289
Tel.: (855) 888-8273
Web Site: http://www.steadmed.com
Medical Devices & Products Supplier
N.A.I.C.S.: 339112
Michael Steadman (CEO & Pres)

URIEL GAS HOLDINGS CORP.
PO Box 15030 RPO Aspenwoods, Calgary, T3H 0N8, AB, Canada
Tel.: (403) 536-4140
Web Site: https://www.urielgas.com
Year Founded: 2021
UGH—(CNSX)
Holding Company
N.A.I.C.S.: 551112
Greg Kaiser (CEO)

URJA GLOBAL LTD.
487/ 63 1st Floor National Market Peeragarhi, New Delhi, 110 087, India
Tel.: (91) 1145588275
Web Site: https://www.urjaglobal.in
Year Founded: 1992
526987—(BOM)
Rev.: $20,723,361
Assets: $72,252,000
Liabilities: $48,755,746
Net Worth: $23,496,254
Earnings: $236,996
Emp.: 27
Fiscal Year-end: 03/31/21
Electric Power Distribution Services
N.A.I.C.S.: 221118
Neha Shukla (Sec)

Subsidiaries:

Urja Batteries Limited (1)
Plot No 11 Sec 16, HSIIDC Industrial Complex Distt Jhajjar, Bahadurgarh, 124507, Haryana, India
Tel.: (91) 1125279143
Web Site: https://www.urjabatteries.in
Solar Battery Mfr
N.A.I.C.S.: 335910

URMET FRANCE CAPTIV
1 Rue Edouard Branly, 93600, Paris, France
Tel.: (33) 148198400
Web Site: http://www.urmet-captiv.fr
Rev.: $24,800,000
Emp.: 64
Electronic Parts & Equipment Whslr
N.A.I.C.S.: 423690
Olivier Nougaret (Dir)

URMIA CEMENT COMPANY LLP
35 km Road, Mahabad, Urmia, Iran
Tel.: (98) 44212238082
Web Site:
http://www.urmiacement.com
Sales Range: $25-49.9 Million
Cement Mfr
N.A.I.C.S.: 327310
Hedayat Mostafai (Mgr-Mechanics)

UROICA PRECISION INFORMATION ENGINEERING CO., LTD.
Fengxiang Road, High-Tech Zone in Southern Shandong, Tai'an, 271000, China
Tel.: (86) 5388926152
Web Site: https://www.uroica.com.cn
Year Founded: 1998
300099—(CHIN)
Rev.: $94,084,504
Assets: $371,655,613
Liabilities: $43,427,154
Net Worth: $328,228,459
Earnings: $18,629,891
Fiscal Year-end: 12/31/23
Mine Safety Controlling Equipment Mfr
N.A.I.C.S.: 213115
Ziwei Huang (Chm & Gen Mgr)

URSUS S.A.
Ul Frezerow 7, 20-952, Lublin, Poland
Tel.: (48) 22 266 0 266
Web Site: http://en.ursus.com.pl
WFM—(WAR)
Sales Range: $50-74.9 Million
Emp.: 654
Agricultural Machinery Mfr
N.A.I.C.S.: 333111
Jan Andrzej Wielgus (Member-Mgmt Bd)

URSUS TRANSPORT INC.
85 Vulcan Street, Etobicoke, M9W 1L4, ON, Canada
Tel.: (416) 243-8780
Web Site:
http://www.ursustransport.com
Year Founded: 1997
Rev.: $10,463,245
Emp.: 16
Transportation Services
N.A.I.C.S.: 488510
John Poreba (Pres)

URTHECAST CORP.
Suite 33 1055 Canada Place, Vancouver, V6C 0C3, BC, Canada
Tel.: (604) 669-1788 ON
Web Site: http://www.urthecast.com
Year Founded: 2004
Rev.: $11,976,730
Assets: $83,293,978
Liabilities: $66,809,483
Net Worth: $16,484,495
Earnings: ($61,021,218)
Emp.: 224
Fiscal Year-end: 12/31/18
Orbital Camera Technologies Developer & Mfr
N.A.I.C.S.: 334310
George Tyc (Co-Founder & CTO)

Subsidiaries:

Deimos Imaging S.L.U. (1)
Ronda de Poniente 19 1 2 planta, 28760, Tres Cantos, Madrid, Spain
Tel.: (34) 910289897
Web Site: http://www.deimos-imaging.com
Software Development Services
N.A.I.C.S.: 513210

Urthecast Imaging.S.L.U. (1)
Ronda de Poniente 19, 28760, Tres Can-

URTHECAST CORP.

UrtheCast Corp.—(Continued)
tos, Madrid, Spain
Tel.: (34) 918063450
Software Development Services
N.A.I.C.S.: 513210

Urthecast USA, Inc. (1)
111 W Port Plz Ste 300, Saint Louis, MO 63146
Tel.: (314) 227-0370
Emp.: 20
Software Development Services
N.A.I.C.S.: 513210

URU METALS LIMITED
4 King St West Suite 401, Toronto, M5H 1B6, ON, Canada
Tel.: (416) 504-3978
Web Site: https://www.urumetals.com
Year Founded: 2007
URU—(AIM)
Rev.: $67,000
Assets: $291,000
Liabilities: $3,555,000
Net Worth: ($3,264,000)
Earnings: ($5,940,000)
Fiscal Year-end: 03/31/24
Mineral Exploration Services
N.A.I.C.S.: 213114
John Zorbas *(CEO)*

Subsidiaries:

Zeb Nickel Company (Pty.) Ltd. (1)

US COPPER CORP.
217 Queen Street West Suite 401, Toronto, M5V 0R2, ON, Canada
Tel.: (416) 361-2827
Web Site: https://uscoppercorp.com
USCU—(OTCIQ)
Assets: $1,282,448
Liabilities: $52,166
Net Worth: $1,230,282
Earnings: ($423,631)
Fiscal Year-end: 12/31/20
Gold Mining Services
N.A.I.C.S.: 212220
Johnny Oliveira *(Office Mgr)*

US CRITICAL METALS CORP.
550 Burrard St 2300, Vancouver, V6C 2B5, BC, Canada
Tel.: (786) 633-1756
Web Site: https://www.uscmcorp.com
USCM—(DEU)
Assets: $202,266
Liabilities: $11,540
Net Worth: $190,726
Earnings: ($60,759)
Fiscal Year-end: 09/30/21
Business Consulting Services
N.A.I.C.S.: 522299
Joel Freudman *(CEO)*

US MASTERS RESIDENTIAL PROPERTY FUND
Level 32 1 OConnell Street, Sydney, 2000, NSW, Australia
Tel.: (61) 396916110
Web Site: https://www.mastersresidential.com
Year Founded: 2011
URF—(ASX)
Rev.: $29,378,965
Assets: $637,940,371
Liabilities: $351,010,171
Net Worth: $286,930,200
Earnings: ($12,973,390)
Fiscal Year-end: 12/31/23
Investment Management Service
N.A.I.C.S.: 525990
Stuart Nisbett *(Chm)*

US OIL SANDS INC.
Suite 1600 521-3rd Avenue SW, Calgary, T2P 3T3, AB, Canada
Tel.: (403) 233-9366
Web Site: http://www.usoilsandsinc.com
USO—(TSXV)
Sales Range: Less than $1 Million
Mineral Exploration Services
N.A.I.C.S.: 213114
Cameron M. Todd *(CEO)*

US STUDENT HOUSING REIT
Level 1 575 Bourke Street, PO Box 2307, Melbourne, 3000, VIC, Australia
Tel.: (61) 1300133472
Web Site: https://www.usq-reit.com
Year Founded: 2021
USQ—(ASX)
Rev.: $5,918,000
Assets: $58,828,000
Liabilities: $107,000
Net Worth: $58,721,000
Earnings: $4,368,000
Fiscal Year-end: 06/30/23
Property Management Services
N.A.I.C.S.: 531311

US VR GLOBAL.COM, INC.
Lot A-2-10 Galeria Hartamas Jalan, 26A/70A Desa Sri Hartam, Kuala Lumpur, 50480, Malaysia
Tel.: (60) 362010069
Year Founded: 2003
Software Development Services
N.A.I.C.S.: 541511
Andrzej Jonczyk *(CEO)*

USA REAL ESTATE HOLDING COMPANY
9-7125 Pacific Circle, Mississauga, L5T2A5, ON, Canada
Tel.: (866) 557-5745
Web Site: http://usarealestateholding.com
Year Founded: 2009
USTC—(OTCIQ)
Sales Range: Less than $1 Million
Commercial Property Purchasing & Leasing Services
N.A.I.C.S.: 531390

USAK SERAMIK SANAYI A.S.
Degirmenler Sokak No 100, Dilek Mahallesi Banaz, 64500, Usak, Turkiye
Tel.: (90) 2763262010
Web Site: https://www.usakseramik.com
Year Founded: 1972
USAK—(IST)
Ceramic Tile Mfr
N.A.I.C.S.: 327120

USCE BOSNE VP A.D.
Kralja Aleksandra I Karadordevica 69, 76230, Samac, Bosnia & Herzegovina
Tel.: (387) 54612489
USBS—(BANJ)
Sales Range: $1-9.9 Million
Emp.: 22
Sand & Gravel Mining Services
N.A.I.C.S.: 212321
Tatjana Gavric *(Chm & Pres)*

USCOM LIMITED
Level 8 66 Clarence Street, Sydney, 2000, NSW, Australia
Tel.: (61) 292474144
Web Site: https://www.uscom.com.au
UCM—(ASX)
Rev.: $2,813,492
Assets: $3,428,594
Liabilities: $1,384,609
Net Worth: $2,043,986
Earnings: ($1,385,393)
Fiscal Year-end: 06/30/24
Cardiac Monitoring Devices Mfr
N.A.I.C.S.: 334510
Robert Allan Phillips *(CEO, Founder & Chm)*

Subsidiaries:

Beijing Uscom Consulting Co. Ltd. (1)
Room 632 East Wing of Building 2 Zhubang 2000 Business Center, Chaoyang District, Beijing, China
Tel.: (86) 18911053205
Respiratory Device Retailer
N.A.I.C.S.: 423450

Uscom Kft (1)
Boglarka utca 17, 1119, Budapest, Hungary
Tel.: (36) 205837564
Respiratory Device Mfr
N.A.I.C.S.: 334510

USER LOCAL, INC.
Osaki With Tower 4th floor 2-11-1 Osaki, Shinagawa-ku, Tokyo, 141-0032, Japan
Tel.: (81) 364352167
Web Site: https://www.userlocal.jp
3984—(TKS)
Sales Range: Less than $1 Million
Emp.: 69
Software Development Services
N.A.I.C.S.: 541511
Masao Ito *(CEO)*

USER TREND LTD.
HAIYARKON 23, Bnei Brak, 52573, Israel
Tel.: (972) 8 8526010
Assets: $46,958
Liabilities: $81,712
Net Worth: ($34,754)
Earnings: ($171,118)
Fiscal Year-end: 12/31/18
Web Designing Services
N.A.I.C.S.: 541511
Michael Friedman *(CEO)*

USERJOY TECHNOLOGY CO., LTD.
17F - 8 No 2 Chien-Pa Rd Chung-Ho Hsien 235, Taipei, Taiwan
Tel.: (886) 282269989
Web Site: http://www.userjoy.tw
3546—(TPE)
Rev.: $49,517,494
Assets: $59,949,629
Liabilities: $12,642,185
Net Worth: $47,307,445
Earnings: $10,119,376
Emp.: 500
Fiscal Year-end: 12/31/22
Software Development Services
N.A.I.C.S.: 541511
Hsin Liu *(Chm)*

USEWALTER INC.
2954 Laurier Blvd Suite 560, Quebec, G1V 4T2, QC, Canada
Tel.: (514) 380-2700
Web Site: https://usewalter.com
WLTR—(TSXV)
Rev.: $70,258
Assets: $6,969,476
Liabilities: $1,842,669
Net Worth: $5,126,807
Earnings: ($9,672,122)
Fiscal Year-end: 12/31/20
Mobile Application Development Services
N.A.I.C.S.: 541511

USG TECH SOLUTIONS LIMITED
HIG Vasista Bhavan 4th Floor APHB Colony, Indira Nagar, Hyderabad, 500 032, Telangana, India
Tel.: (91) 4040339668
Web Site: https://www.usgtechsolutions.com

532402—(BOM)
Rev.: $458,271
Assets: $5,807,802
Liabilities: $644,635
Net Worth: $5,163,167
Earnings: ($681,135)
Emp.: 2
Fiscal Year-end: 03/31/21
Software Development Services
N.A.I.C.S.: 541511
Servesh Gupta *(Chm & Mng Dir)*

USHA MARTIN EDUCATION & SOLUTIONS LTD.
Godrej Waterside Tower-2 12th Floor Unit No. 1206 Block-DP Sector V, Salt Lake City, Kolkata, 700 091, West Bengal, India
Tel.: (91) 3333223700
Web Site: http://www.umesl.co.in
UMESL—(NSE)
Rev.: $97,195
Assets: $2,205,087
Liabilities: $511,764
Net Worth: $1,693,323
Earnings: $7,587
Fiscal Year-end: 03/31/23
Computer Services
N.A.I.C.S.: 541519
Vinay Kumar Gupta *(Exec Dir)*

Subsidiaries:

Usha Martin Technologies Limited (1)
Godrej Waterside Tower 2 Unit No 1206 12th Floor DP - 5 Sector - V, Saltlake City, Kolkata, 700091, West Bengal, India
Tel.: (91) 3340853700
Telecom Billing Services
N.A.I.C.S.: 541219

USHA MARTIN LIMITED
2A Shakespeare Sarani Mangal Kalash, Kolkata, 700 071, India
Tel.: (91) 3371006300
Web Site: https://www.ushamartin.com
517146—(NSE)
Rev.: $290,825,535
Assets: $355,622,085
Liabilities: $163,557,030
Net Worth: $192,065,055
Earnings: $20,679,750
Emp.: 2,271
Fiscal Year-end: 03/31/21
Specialty Steel & Wire Rope Mfr
N.A.I.C.S.: 332111
Shampa Ghosh Ray *(Sec)*

Subsidiaries:

Brunton Shaw UK Limited (1)
Sandy Lane, Worksop, S80 3ES, Nottinghamshire, United Kingdom
Tel.: (44) 1909537600
Web Site: https://www.brunton-shaw.com
Sales Range: $25-49.9 Million
Wire Ropes Mfr
N.A.I.C.S.: 331110

Brunton Wire Ropes FZCO. (1)
Jebel Ali Free Zone, PO Box 17491, Dubai, United Arab Emirates
Tel.: (971) 48838151
Web Site: https://bruntonwire.com
Steel Wire Rope Mfr & Distr
N.A.I.C.S.: 314994

De Ruiter Staalkabel BV (1)
Kerkeplaat 10, 3313 LC, Dordrecht, Netherlands
Tel.: (31) 788200600
Web Site: https://www.deruiterstaalkabel.nl
Sales Range: $25-49.9 Million
Wire Ropes Mfr
N.A.I.C.S.: 331110

European Management and Marine Corporation Limited (1)
Howe Moss Place Kirkhill Industrial Estate Dyce, Aberdeen, AB21 0GS, United Kingdom

AND PRIVATE COMPANIES

Tel.: (44) 1224775151
Web Site: http://www.emmcorp.com
Wire Ropes Mfr
N.A.I.C.S.: 331222

PT Usha Martin Indonesia (1)
Tel.: (62) 2142870794
Fiber Optic Cable Mfr
N.A.I.C.S.: 335921

Peng Usha Martin Pvt. Ltd. (1)
Tatisilwai, Ranchi, 835103, India
Tel.: (91) 651 3053900
Wire Product Mfr
N.A.I.C.S.: 332618

U M Cables Limited (1)
Survey No 1/1/3 Chinchpada Jogeshwari East, Dadra and Nagar Haveli, Silvassa, 396230, India
Tel.: (91) 8048075865
Web Site: http://www.umcablesltd.com
Emp.: 500
Telecommunication Cable Mfr
N.A.I.C.S.: 517111
Phanindra Kumar (Mgr-Mktg)

Usha Martin Americas Inc. (1)
701 Plastics Ave, Houston, TX 77020
Tel.: (713) 676-1800
Sales Range: $25-49.9 Million
Copper & Fiber Wire Ropes Mfr
N.A.I.C.S.: 331420

Usha Martin Australia Pty Limited (1)
Tel.: (61) 296094971
Wire Ropes Mfr & Distr
N.A.I.C.S.: 332618

Usha Martin Europe B.V. (1)
Kerkeplaat 10, 3133 LC, Dordrecht, Netherlands
Tel.: (31) 180745099
Web Site: https://www.ushamartineurope.com
Steel Wire Rope Mfr
N.A.I.C.S.: 314994

Usha Martin International Limited (1)
Unit 4 Blair Court Clyde Bank Business Park, Clydebank, G81 2LA, United Kingdom
Tel.: (44) 1419518801
Web Site: http://www.ushamartin.com
Emp.: 6
Fiber Optic Wires Mfr
N.A.I.C.S.: 335921
Shyam Jodhawat (CEO)

Usha Martin Italia S.R.L. (1)
Via Antonio Segni 6, 25062, Concesio, BS, Italy
Tel.: (39) 03385379230
Steel Wire Rope Mfr
N.A.I.C.S.: 314994

Usha Martin Singapore Pte. Limited (1)
91 Tuas Bay Drive Usha Martin Building, Singapore, 637307, Singapore
Tel.: (65) 62657756
Sales Range: $25-49.9 Million
Wire Ropes Mfr
N.A.I.C.S.: 331110

Usha Martin UK Ltd. (1)
Tasman House Mariner Court, Clydebank, Glasgow, G81 2NR, United Kingdom
Tel.: (44) 1419518801
Web Site: http://www.ushamartin.com
Sales Range: $25-49.9 Million
Wire Rope & Chords Mfr
N.A.I.C.S.: 331110

Usha Martin Vietnam Company Limited (1)
Tel.: (84) 2835122209
Fiber & Copper Wire Ropes Mfr
N.A.I.C.S.: 331420

Usha Siam Steel Industries Public Company Limited (1)
66 Q House Asoke Building 12TH Floor Unit 1207 Sukhumvit 21 road, North Klongtoey Wattana, Bangkok, 10110, Thailand
Tel.: (66) 22617361
Web Site: https://www.ushasiam.com
Sales Range: $100-124.9 Million
Steel Pole Mfr
N.A.I.C.S.: 331110

USHA RESOURCES LTD.
1575 Kamloops Street, Vancouver, V5K 3W1, BC, Canada
Tel.: (604) 251-6320
Year Founded: 2018
JO00—(DEU)
Rev: $12,378
Assets: $5,180,352
Liabilities: $75,810
Net Worth: $5,104,542
Earnings: ($2,221,305)
Fiscal Year-end: 03/31/23
Asset Management Services
N.A.I.C.S.: 523940
Deepak Varshney (CEO)

USHAKIRAN FINANCE LIMITED
405 Raghava Ratna Towers Chirag Ali Lane, Hyderabad, 500 001, India
Tel.: (91) 4023201073
Web Site: https://www.uflfinance.com
Year Founded: 1986
511507—(BOM)
Rev.: $48,270
Assets: $1,398,357
Liabilities: $2,098
Net Worth: $1,396,259
Earnings: $16,222
Emp.: 3
Fiscal Year-end: 03/31/23
Financial Services
N.A.I.C.S.: 523999
Tunuguntla Adinarayana (Chm)

USHANTI COLOUR CHEM LIMITED
88/6 88/7 88/8 Phase-1 Gidc Vatwa, Ahmedabad, 382445, India
Tel.: (91) 7925894903
Web Site: https://www.ushanti.com
UCL—(NSE)
Rev: $5,660,644
Assets: $12,015,647
Liabilities: $6,427,157
Net Worth: $5,588,490
Earnings: $117,475
Emp.: 56
Fiscal Year-end: 03/31/23
Dyestuff Product Mfr & Distr
N.A.I.C.S.: 325130
Shantilal Bhailal Gandhi (Chm)

USHDEV INTERNATIONAL LIMITED
Appejay House 6th Floor 130 Mumbai Samachar Marg, Fort, Mumbai, 400023, India
Tel.: (91) 2261948888
Web Site: https://www.ushdev.com
Year Founded: 1994
511736—(BOM)
Rev.: $1,872,538
Assets: $14,946,934
Liabilities: $396,371,261
Net Worth: ($381,424,327)
Earnings: ($5,550,902)
Emp.: 10
Fiscal Year-end: 03/31/23
Metals & Power Generation
N.A.I.C.S.: 221122
Prateek Gupta (Vice Chm)

USHER AGRO LTD.
422-424 Laxmi Plaza Laxmi Industrial Estate New Link Road, Andheri W, Mumbai, 400 053, India
Tel.: (91) 2239381100
Web Site: http://www.usheragro.com
Sales Range: $150-199.9 Million
Emp.: 15
Agribusiness
N.A.I.C.S.: 115115
Vinod Kumar Chaturvedi (Mng Dir)

USHINE PHOTONICS CORP.
No 199 Section 3 Huanbei Road, Hsinchu County, Zhubei, 302, Taiwan
Tel.: (886) 36561668
Web Site: https://www.ushine.com.tw
Year Founded: 2001
3678—(TAI)
Flexible Plastic Substrate Product Mfr
N.A.I.C.S.: 326112
Chun-Kuang Lai (Chm & Pres)

USHIO, INC.
1-6-5 Marunouchi, Chiyoda-ku, Tokyo, 100-8150, Japan
Tel.: (81) 356571000
Web Site: https://www.ushio.co.jp
Year Founded: 1964
6925—(TKS)
Rev.: $1,185,966,200
Assets: $2,231,179,060
Liabilities: $664,774,310
Net Worth: $1,566,404,750
Earnings: $71,288,850
Emp.: 1,713
Fiscal Year-end: 03/31/24
Light Units & Lighting Systems
N.A.I.C.S.: 335139
Koji Naito (Pres & CEO)

Subsidiaries:

ADTEC Engineering Co., Ltd. (1)
Toranomon 2-chome Tower 8F 2-3-17 Toranomon, Minato-ku, Tokyo, 105-0001, Japan (100%)
Tel.: (81) 363699800
Web Site: https://www.adtec.com
Emp.: 348
Industrial Machinery Manufacturing
N.A.I.C.S.: 333248
Keizo Tokuhiro (Chm)

BLV Licht-und Vakuumtechnik GmbH (1)
Munchener Strasse 10, Steinhoring, 85643, Ebersberg, Germany (100%)
Tel.: (49) 80949060
Web Site: https://www.blv-licht.de
Sales Range: $50-74.9 Million
Emp.: 125
Developer of Light Units & Systems
N.A.I.C.S.: 332613
Wilhelmus de Koning (Mng Dir)

Christie Digital Systems (India) Private Limited (1)
Unit No S30 & S31 Lower Ground floor Creator Building Concourse, International Technology Park Whitefield Road, Bengaluru, 560 066, India
Tel.: (91) 8067089999
Laser Projector Mfr & Distr
N.A.I.C.S.: 333310

Christie Digital Systems, Inc. (1)
Ariake-Frontier Bldg A-2F 3-7-26 Ariake, Koto-ku, Tokyo, 135-0063, Japan
Tel.: (81) 335997481
Projection System Distr
N.A.I.C.S.: 423410
Mamoru Hanzawa (Branch Mgr)

Subsidiary (Non-US):

CHRISTIE DIGITAL SYSTEMS (Shanghai), Co., Ltd. (2)
Floor 11 Building K No 26 Lane 168 Daduhe Road, Putuo District, Shanghai, 200062, China
Tel.: (86) 2160300500
Digital Movie Projection System Mfr
N.A.I.C.S.: 334310

CHRISTIE DIGITAL SYSTEMS (Shenzhen) Co., Ltd. (2)
3rd 4th floor Building AD GaoxinqiIndustrial Park Liuxian 1st Road, District 67 Bao'an District, Shenzhen, 518101, Guangdon, China
Tel.: (86) 75536807000
Digital Movie Projection System Mfr
N.A.I.C.S.: 334310

Christie Digital Systems Canada Inc. (2)
809 Wellington St N, Kitchener, N2G 4Y7, ON, Canada

Tel.: (519) 744-8005
Web Site: http://www.chrisdigital.com
Sales Range: $100-124.9 Million
Emp.: 700
Developer of Light Units & Systems
N.A.I.C.S.: 335139
Greg Shepherd (VP & Assoc Gen Counsel)

Subsidiary (US):

Christie Digital Systems USA, Inc. (2)
10550 Camden Dr, Cypress, CA 90630-4600
Tel.: (714) 236-8610
Web Site: http://www.christiedigital.com
Sales Range: $125-149.9 Million
Mfr & Developer of Projection Light & Theatre Projection Equipment
N.A.I.C.S.: 423410
Brian Gifford (Exec VP-HR-Global)

Dipl.-Ing.Reinhold Eggers GmbH (1)
Burgau 17, 88525, Durmentingen, Germany
Tel.: (49) 737195180
Web Site: http://www.egger-gmbh.com
Sales Range: $25-49.9 Million
Emp.: 5
Lamp Coil Mfr
N.A.I.C.S.: 334416
Thomas Eggers (Mng Dir)

EPITEX INC. (1)
66-3 Minamikawabe-cho Higashi-Kujyo, Minami-Ku, Kyoto, 601-8034, Japan
Tel.: (81) 756822338
Web Site: http://www.epitex.com
Sales Range: $25-49.9 Million
Emp.: 21
Light Emitting Diode Mfr
N.A.I.C.S.: 334413

Event Audio Visual Group, Inc. (1)
50888 Century Ct, Wixom, MI 48393
Web Site: http://www.nationwidevideo.com
Audio & Video Equipment Rental Services
N.A.I.C.S.: 532490

Necsel Intellectual Property, Inc. (1)
801 Ames Ave, Milpitas, CA 95035
Tel.: (408) 940-0751
High Powered Visible Laser Product Mfr
N.A.I.C.S.: 334516

Protosera Inc. (1)
Kento Innovation Park NK Building 3-17 Senrioka Shinmachi, Settsu City, Osaka, 566-0002, Japan
Tel.: (81) 663185471
Web Site: https://www.protosera.co.jp
Emp.: 18
Pharmaceuticals Product Mfr
N.A.I.C.S.: 325412

TAIWAN USHIO LIGHTING, INC. (1)
82 Taiho Road Taiho-Li, Jhubei, 30267, Hsinchu Hsien, Taiwan
Tel.: (886) 35513207
Web Site: http://www.ushio.com
Electric Lamp Mfr
N.A.I.C.S.: 335139

USHIO (SUZHOU) CO., LTD. (1)
6 Yuyang Street, Suzhou New District, Suzhou, 215011, China
Tel.: (86) 51268076628
Electric Lamp Mfr
N.A.I.C.S.: 335139

USHIO SHANGHAI, INC (1)
02 03 Unit 30F New Bund Center NO 555 West Haiyang Road, NO 588 Dongyu Road Pudong, Shanghai, 200126, China
Tel.: (86) 2168411135
Web Site: http://www.ushio.com.cn
Lamp & Lighting Equipment Mfr
N.A.I.C.S.: 335139

USHIO SHENZHEN, INC. (1)
Unit 08 52/F A Block Kingkey 100 Building, No 5016 Shennan East Road Luohu District, Shenzhen, China
Tel.: (86) 75582070162
Optical Goods Mfr.
N.A.I.C.S.: 333310
Murakami Masalotu (Mgr-Sls)

Ushio (Shaoguan) Co., Ltd. (1)
A2 Workshop No 9 Fuqiang Road, Muxi Industrial Park 2nd Road Wujiang District,

USHIO, INC.

Ushio, Inc.—(Continued)
Shaoguan, 512029, Guangdong, China
Tel.: (86) 7518173833
Halogen Lamp Mfr & Whslr
N.A.I.C.S.: 335139

Ushio America, Inc. (1)
5440 Cerritos Ave, Cypress, CA 90630-4567 **(100%)**
Tel.: (714) 236-8600
Web Site: http://www.ushio.com
Sales Range: $50-74.9 Million
Emp.: 100
Developer of Light Units & Systems
N.A.I.C.S.: 423610
William F. Mackenzie (Pres & CEO)

Branch (Domestic):

Ushio America, Central Regional Office (2)
14795 W 101st Ave Ste B, Dyer, IN 46311-3025
Tel.: (866) 383-8836
Web Site: http://www.ushio.com
Emp.: 8
Mfr of Light Units & Systems
N.A.I.C.S.: 541613
Shinji Kameda (Pres & CEO)

Ushio America, Eastern Division Branch Office (2)
30-B Pennington-Hopewell Rd, Pennington, NJ 08534
Tel.: (609) 564-7900
Web Site: http://www.ushio.com
Sales Range: $25-49.9 Million
Emp.: 6
Developer of Light Units & Systems
N.A.I.C.S.: 423610

Ushio Asia Pacific (Thailand) Ltd. (1)
202 Le Concorde Tower 12th Floor Room No 1206 Ratchadapisek Road, Huaykwang, Bangkok, 10310, Thailand
Tel.: (66) 26941441
UV Lamp Whslr
N.A.I.C.S.: 423610

Ushio Asia Pacific Pte. Ltd. (1)
28 Genting Lane 05-05 Platinum 28, Singapore, 349585, Singapore
Tel.: (65) 62745311
Web Site: http://www.ushioasiapacific.com
UV Lamp Whslr
N.A.I.C.S.: 423610

Ushio Asia Pacific Vietnam Co., Ltd. (1)
Suite No 301 Floor 3 Empire Tower Building 26-28 Ham Nghi Street, Ben Nghe Ward District 1, Ho Chi Minh City, Vietnam
Tel.: (84) 2835218648
UV Lamp Whslr
N.A.I.C.S.: 423610

Ushio Asia Trading Ltd. (1)
Suites 3113-14 31/F Tower 6 The Gateway 9 Canton Road, Tsim Sha Tsui, Kowloon, China (Hong Kong)
Tel.: (852) 82070162
Light Source & Component Distr
N.A.I.C.S.: 423610

Ushio Deutschland GmbH (1)
Munchener Strasse 10, Steinhoering, 85643, Ebersberg, Germany **(100%)**
Tel.: (49) 80949060
Web Site: https://www.ushio.eu
Developer of Light Units & Systems
N.A.I.C.S.: 332613

Ushio Europe B.V. (1)
Breguetlaan 53, 1438 BD, Oude Meer, Netherlands **(100%)**
Tel.: (31) 204469333
Web Site: http://www.ushio.eu
Sales Range: $25-49.9 Million
Emp.: 15
Developer of Light Units & Systems
N.A.I.C.S.: 423610
Wilhelmus de Koning (Exec VP)

Ushio France S.a.r.l. (1)
20 rue Lavoisier, PO Box 77043, Saint Ouen l'Aumone, 95300, Pontoise, Cedex, France **(100%)**
Tel.: (33) 134649494
Web Site: http://www.ushio.eu
Emp.: 4

Developer of Light Units & Systems
N.A.I.C.S.: 332613

Ushio Hong Kong Ltd. (1)
Suites 3113-14 31/F Tower 6 The Gateway 9 Canton Road, Tsim Sha Tsui, Kowloon, China (Hong Kong) **(100%)**
Tel.: (852) 27567880
Web Site: https://www.ushio.com.hk
Sales Range: $50-74.9 Million
Emp.: 88
Developer of Light Units & Systems
N.A.I.C.S.: 332613

Ushio Inc., Osaka Branch (1)
Shin-Osaka Prime Tower 12F 6-1-1 Nishi-Nakajima, Yodogawa-ku, Osaka, 532-0011, Japan **(100%)**
Tel.: (81) 663065711
Web Site: http://www.ushio.co.jp
Sales Range: $25-49.9 Million
Emp.: 20
Developer of Light Units & Systems
N.A.I.C.S.: 332613

Ushio Korea, Inc. (1)
388 Gangnam-daero Gangnam Center Building 17th floor, Gangnam-gu, Seoul, 06232, Korea (South) **(100%)**
Tel.: (82) 5871115
Web Site: https://www.ushio.co.jp
Sales Range: Less than $1 Million
Emp.: 49
Developer of Light Units & Systems
N.A.I.C.S.: 332613

Ushio Lighting, Inc. (1)
860-22 Saiji Fukusaki-cho, Kanzaki-Gun, Hyogo, 679-2215, Japan **(100%)**
Tel.: (81) 790226371
Web Site: http://www.ushiolighting.co.jp
Sales Range: $100-124.9 Million
Emp.: 350
Developer of Light Units & Systems
N.A.I.C.S.: 332613
Gen Kato (Mng Exec Officer)

Ushio Lighting, Inc. (1)
2-9-1 Hatchobori, Chuo-ku, Tokyo, 104-0032, Japan **(100%)**
Tel.: (81) 335528261
Web Site: https://www.ushiolighting.com
Sales Range: $10-24.9 Million
Emp.: 300
Developer of Light Units & Systems
N.A.I.C.S.: 332613

Division (Domestic):

Ushio Lighting, Inc. - Fukusaki Division (2)
860-22 Nishiji, Kanzaki-gun, Fukusaki, 679-2215, Hyogo, Japan
Tel.: (81) 790226371
Lamp Mfr
N.A.I.C.S.: 335139

Ushio Lighting, Inc. - Tsukuba Division (2)
5-4-2 Tokodai, Ibaraki, Tsukuba, 300-2635, Japan
Tel.: (81) 298477421
Sales Range: $25-49.9 Million
Emp.: 60
Lamps & Lighting Systems Mfr & Distr
N.A.I.C.S.: 335139

Ushio Lighting, Inc. - Yokohama Division (2)
6409 Moto-Ishikawa-cho, Aoba-ku, Yokohama, 225-0004, Kanagawa, Japan
Tel.: (81) 459012571
Lamp Mfr
N.A.I.C.S.: 335139

Ushio Philippines, Inc. (1)
Blk 2 Lot 7 8 Phase 3, First Cavite Industrial Estate Brgy Langkaan II, Dasmarinas, 4126, Cavite, Philippines **(100%)**
Tel.: (63) 464021422
Web Site: https://www.ushio.com.ph
Sales Range: $100-124.9 Million
Emp.: 672
Developer of Light Units & Systems
N.A.I.C.S.: 332613

Ushio Poland Sp. z o.o. (1)
Pass Ul Stefana Batorego 17, Pass, 05-870, Blonie, Poland
Tel.: (48) 227311368

Web Site: http://www.natrium.com.pl
Lamp Mfr & Whslr
N.A.I.C.S.: 335139

Ushio Singapore Pte. Ltd. (1)
28 Genting Lane 05-05 Platinum 28, Singapore, 349585, Singapore **(100%)**
Tel.: (65) 62745311
Web Site: http://www.ushioasiapacific.com
Sales Range: $25-49.9 Million
Emp.: 11
Developer of Light Units & Systems
N.A.I.C.S.: 332613
Katherine Kwan (Office Mgr)

Ushio Spax, Inc. (1)
1 20 19 Horikiri, Tokyo, 124 0006, Japan
Tel.: (81) 356727711
Sales Range: $25-49.9 Million
Emp.: 100
Developer of Light Units & Systems
N.A.I.C.S.: 332613

Plant (Domestic):

Ushio Spax, Inc. - Horikiri Plant (2)
1-20-19 Horikiri, Katsushika-ku, Tokyo, 124-0006, Japan
Tel.: (81) 3 5672 7711
Web Site: http://www.ushio.co.jp
Sales Range: $25-49.9 Million
Emp.: 10
Lamp Coil Mfr
N.A.I.C.S.: 334416
Nobuhiko Terumichi (Pres)

Ushio Taiwan, Inc. (1)
8th Floor No 4 Section 1 Zhongxiao West Road, Zhongzheng District, Taipei, 100405, Taiwan **(100%)**
Tel.: (886) 223123358
Web Site: https://www.ushio.com.tw
Sales Range: $25-49.9 Million
Emp.: 50
Developer of Light Units & Systems
N.A.I.C.S.: 332613

Ushio U.K., Ltd. (1)
Argyll house Quarrywood Court, Industrial Estate, Livingston, EH54 6AX, West Lothian, United Kingdom **(100%)**
Tel.: (44) 1296256067
Web Site: http://www.ushio.eu
Sales Range: $25-49.9 Million
Emp.: 3
Developer of Light Units & Systems
N.A.I.C.S.: 332613

Ushio, Inc. (1)
1-90 Komakado, Gotenba, Shizuoka, 412-0038, Japan **(100%)**
Tel.: (81) 550873000
Web Site: https://www.ushio.co.jp
Sales Range: $50-74.9 Million
Emp.: 150
Institute for the Development of Light Units & Systems
N.A.I.C.S.: 332613

Ushio, Inc. - System Sales Division (2)
6409 Moto-Ishikawa-cho, Aoba Ku, Yokohama, 225-0004, Kanagawa, Japan
Tel.: (81) 459012571
Web Site: http://www.ushio.co.jp
Sales Range: $25-49.9 Million
Emp.: 100
Retailer of Light Units & Systems
N.A.I.C.S.: 332613

Ushio, Inc., Gotemba Division (1)
1-90 Komakado, Gotenba, 412-0038, Shizuoka, Japan **(100%)**
Tel.: (81) 550873000
Web Site: http://www.ushio.co.jp
Sales Range: $25-49.9 Million
Emp.: 280
Developer of Light Units & Systems
N.A.I.C.S.: 332613

Ushio, Inc., Harima Division (1)
1194 Sazuchi Bessho-cho, Himeji, Hyogo, 671-0224, Japan **(100%)**
Tel.: (81) 792524381
Web Site: http://www.ushio.co.jp
Emp.: 1,000
Developer of Light Units & Systems
N.A.I.C.S.: 332613

Ushio, Inc., Tokyo Sales Headquarters (1)

INTERNATIONAL PUBLIC

Asahi Tokai Bldg 6 1 Otemachi 2 Chome, Chiyoda Ku, Tokyo, 100 0004, Japan **(100%)**
Tel.: (81) 332425610
Web Site: http://www.ushio.co.jp
Sales Range: $25-49.9 Million
Emp.: 100
Developer of Light Units & Systems
N.A.I.C.S.: 332613
Shiro Sugata (Pres)

Ushio, Inc., Yokohama Division (1)
6409 Moto-Ishikawa-cho, Aoba-ku, Yokohama, 225-0004, Kanagawa, Japan **(100%)**
Tel.: (81) 459012571
Web Site: http://www.ushio.co.jp
Sales Range: $100-124.9 Million
Emp.: 300
Developer of Light Units & Systems
N.A.I.C.S.: 332613
Sugata Shiro (Pres)

Xebex, Inc. (1)
Nishino Kinryo Building 4-9-4 Hatchobori, Chuo-ku, Tokyo, 104-0032, Japan **(100%)**
Tel.: (81) 355669100
Web Site: https://www.xebex.co.jp
Emp.: 71
Developer of Light Units & Systems
N.A.I.C.S.: 335139
Yosato Nejima (Acct Mgr)

XtreMe Technologies GmbH (1)
Munchener Strasse 10, Steinhoring, 85643, Aachen, Germany
Tel.: (49) 8094 906 120
Web Site: http://www.xtremetec.de
Sales Range: $50-74.9 Million
Emp.: 200
Laser Assisted Discharge Plasma Mfr
N.A.I.C.S.: 334413
Hiroshi Watanabe (Mng Dir)

USHKUY JSC

150 6 Promzona 4th floor, Promzona district, 130000, Aktau, Mangistau, Kazakhstan
Tel.: (7) 292525560
ANSA—(KAZ)
Sales Range: Less than $1 Million
Hydrocarbon Exploration & Production Services
N.A.I.C.S.: 211130
Kaniev Bolat (CEO & Gen Dir)

USI CORPORATION

No 330 Fengren Rd, Nei-Hu District, Taipei, 114, Taiwan
Tel.: (886) 287516888
Web Site: https://www.usife.com
Year Founded: 1965
1304—(TAI)
Rev.: $1,709,171,655
Assets: $2,422,342,202
Liabilities: $867,553,027
Net Worth: $1,554,789,176
Earnings: ($62,351,350)
Emp.: 4,909
Fiscal Year-end: 12/31/23
Polyethylene Resins Mfr
N.A.I.C.S.: 325211
Quintin Wu (Chm)

Subsidiaries:

Chong Loong Trading Co., Ltd. (1)
No 37 and 39 Ji-Hu Rd, Nei Hu Dist, Taipei, 114, Taiwan
Tel.: (886) 287516888
Soft Magnet & Iron Oxide Model Equipment Mfr
N.A.I.C.S.: 332999

Dynamic Ever Investments Limited (1)
114 4th Floor No 39 Jihu Road, Neihu District, Taipei, Taiwan
Tel.: (886) 287516888
Web Site: http://www.dynamicever.com
Petrochemical Plastic Mfr
N.A.I.C.S.: 325211

INOMA Corporation (1)
4th Floor No 39 Ji-Hu Rd, Nei Hu Dist, Taipei, 11492, Taiwan

Tel.: (886) 226503768
Web Site: http://www.inoma.com.tw
Glass & Fireproof Material Services
N.A.I.C.S.: 238190

Taiwan United Venture Capital Corp. (1)
No 37 and 39 Ji-Hu Rd, Nei Hu Dist, Taipei, 114, Taiwan
Tel.: (886) 287516888
Financial Investment Services
N.A.I.C.S.: 523999

USI Investment Co., Ltd. (1)
No 37 & 39 Ji-Hu Rd, Nei Hu, Taipei, 114, Taiwan
Tel.: (886) 287516888
Web Site: https://www.usig.com
Software & Hardware Development Services
N.A.I.C.S.: 541511

USI Management Consulting Corp. (1)
No 37 and 39 Ji-Hu Dist, Nei Hu Dist, Taipei, 114, Taiwan
Tel.: (886) 287516888
Financial Investment Services
N.A.I.C.S.: 523999

USI Optronics Corporation (1)
12th Floor No 37 Ji-Hu Rd, Nei Hu Dist, Taipei, Taiwan
Tel.: (886) 37630168
Web Site: https://www.usio.com.tw
Ingot & Substrate Product Mfr
N.A.I.C.S.: 333511
Quintin Wu *(Chm)*

USI Trading(Shanghai) Co., Ltd. (1)
6A Yinglong Bldg No 1358 Yan-an West Road, Shanghai, 200052, China
Tel.: (86) 21 5258 1258
Web Site: http://www.usife.com
Polyethylene Resins Distr
N.A.I.C.S.: 424610

USIG (Shanghai) Co., Ltd. (1)
No 169 Sheng Xia Road Zhangjiang High-Tech Park, Pudong New Area, Shanghai, 201203, China
Tel.: (86) 2158966996
Electronic Device Mfr & Distr
N.A.I.C.S.: 334419

USLUZNE DJELATNOSTI A.D.
Karadordeva 2, 78000, Banja Luka, Bosnia & Herzegovina
Tel.: (387) 51316577
USLD—(BANJ)
Restaurant Management Services
N.A.I.C.S.: 722511
Romeo Valjevac *(Chm & Pres)*

USMANIA GLASS SHEET FACTORY LIMITED
Kalurghat Heavy I/A, Chandgaon, Chittagong, 4212, Bangladesh
Tel.: (880) 31670430
Web Site: https://www.ugsflbd.com
Year Founded: 1959
USMANIAGL—(DHA)
Rev.: $2,747,394
Assets: $21,702,343
Liabilities: $9,477,869
Net Worth: $12,224,474
Earnings: ($942,885)
Emp.: 111
Fiscal Year-end: 06/30/23
Glass Products Mfr
N.A.I.C.S.: 327212
Amin Ul Ahsan *(Dir-Comml)*

USP GROUP LIMITED
1 Harbourfront Avenue 14-07 Keppel Bay Tower, Singapore, 098632, Singapore
Tel.: (65) 65343533 SG
Web Site: http://www.uspgroup.com.sg
Year Founded: 2004
BRS—(SES)
Rev.: $25,727,113
Assets: $54,316,317

Liabilities: $37,633,745
Net Worth: $16,682,572
Earnings: ($958,057)
Emp.: 162
Fiscal Year-end: 03/31/21
Oil Blending & Distr; Property Development
N.A.I.C.S.: 311225
Tanoto Sau Ian *(CEO)*

Subsidiaries:

Biofuel Research Pte Ltd (1)
2 Tuas South Street Suite 15, Singapore, 637079, Singapore
Tel.: (65) 6515 6268
Biodiesel Mfr
N.A.I.C.S.: 324110

Liuzhou Union Zinc Industry Co., Ltd. (1)
17 Baiyun Road, Liuzhou, 545005, Guangxi, China
Tel.: (86) 7722623058
Web Site: http://www.unionmet.com.sg
Nonferrous Metal Mfr & Distr
N.A.I.C.S.: 331410

USS CO., LTD.
507-20 Shinpo-Machi, Tokai, 476-0005, Aichi, Japan
Tel.: (81) 526891111 JP
Web Site: https://www.ussnet.co.jp
Year Founded: 1980
4732—(TKS)
Rev.: $644,902,363
Assets: $1,794,231,410
Liabilities: $479,259,859
Net Worth: $1,314,971,551
Earnings: $217,416,523
Emp.: 1,161
Fiscal Year-end: 03/31/24
Automobile Auctions & Services
N.A.I.C.S.: 423110
Yukihiro Ando *(Chm & CEO)*

Subsidiaries:

ARBIZ Co., Ltd. (1)
14-24 Showa-cho, Minato-ku, Nagoya, 455-0026, Aichi, Japan
Tel.: (81) 526196600
Web Site: https://www.arbiz.co.jp
Emp.: 165
Scrap Vehicle Recycling Services
N.A.I.C.S.: 423930
Dai Seta *(CEO)*

Japan Bike Auction Co., Ltd. (1)
9-17-2 Daikoku-cho, Tsurumi-ku, Yokohama, 230-0053, Kanagawa, Japan
Tel.: (81) 45 507 0819
Web Site: http://www.j-ba.co.jp
Motorcycle Auction Services
N.A.I.C.S.: 425120

Rabbit Car Network Co., Ltd. (1)
Web Site: https://www.e-rabbit.jp
Automotive Distr
N.A.I.C.S.: 423110

Reproworld Co., Ltd. (1)
1830 Funakata, Noda, Chiba, Japan
Tel.: (81) 471291111
Web Site: http://www.world-com.co.jp
Automotive Distr
N.A.I.C.S.: 423110
Eiichi Arai *(CEO)*

USS Logistics International Service Co., Ltd. (1)
9-19 daikokucyo Tsurumiku, Yokohama, Japan
Tel.: (81) 455087025
Used Car Distr
N.A.I.C.S.: 423110
Masayuki Akase *(Pres)*

UST TECHNOLOGY PTE. LTD.
998 Toa Payoh North 05-25, Singapore, 318993, Singapore
Tel.: (65) 252 2272 SG
Web Site: http://www.ust.com.sg
Semiconductor Equipment Trading & Distr
N.A.I.C.S.: 423690

UST-KAMENOGORSK POULTRY PLANT JSC
Building 1 Accounting quarter 033 Kasym Kaisenov village, Ulan district, Ust'-Kamenogorsk, 071600, Kazakhstan
Tel.: (7) 23 249 2295
UKPF—(KAZ)
Rev.: $39,652,899
Assets: $79,354,383
Liabilities: $12,028,053
Net Worth: $67,326,330
Earnings: $15,577,060
Fiscal Year-end: 12/31/20
Chicken Product Mfr
N.A.I.C.S.: 112320

UST-KAMENOGORSK TITANIUM MAGNESIUM PLANT JSC
Ust-Kamenogorsk Bagdat Shayakhmetov st building 1/1, East-Kazakhstan, 070017, Oskemen, Kazakhstan
Tel.: (7) 87232233148
Web Site: https://www.uktmp.kz
Year Founded: 1954
UTMK—(KAZ)
Rev.: $169,103,488
Assets: $404,267,604
Liabilities: $297,209,490
Net Worth: $107,058,115
Earnings: $15,073,434
Fiscal Year-end: 12/31/22
Nonferrous Metal Mfr & Distr
N.A.I.C.S.: 331491
Asem Mamutova *(Pres)*

USU SOFTWARE AG
Spitalhof, D-71696, Moglingen, Germany
Tel.: (49) 714148670 De
Web Site: https://www.usu.com
OSP2—(MUN)
Rev.: $136,544,356
Assets: $121,928,556
Liabilities: $60,462,983
Net Worth: $61,465,573
Earnings: $8,182,603
Emp.: 225
Fiscal Year-end: 12/31/22
Software & Solutions Provider
N.A.I.C.S.: 513210
Bernhard Oberschmidt *(Chm-Mgmt Bd & CEO)*

Subsidiaries:

Aspera GmbH (1)
Charlottenburger Allee 60, 52068, Aachen, Germany
Tel.: (49) 2419278700
Software Asset Management Services
N.A.I.C.S.: 541511

LeuTek GmbH (1)
Stadionstrasse 4-6, 70771, Leinfelden-Echterdingen, Germany
Tel.: (49) 711947070
Web Site: http://www.leutek.com
Emp.: 75
Cloud Monitoring & System Monitoring Services
N.A.I.C.S.: 561621
Holger Sampel *(Mng Dir)*

Omega Software GmbH (1)
Schloss Weiler - Herrengasse 2, 74182, Obersulm, Germany
Tel.: (49) 7130400619
Web Site: https://www.omegasoft.de
Software Publishing Services
N.A.I.C.S.: 513210

USU GmbH (1)
Spitalhof, 71696, Moglingen, Germany
Tel.: (49) 714148670
Software Publishing Services
N.A.I.C.S.: 513210

Subsidiary (Non-US):

USU Software s.r.o. (2)
Bezrucova 17a, 602 00, Brno, Czech Republic
Tel.: (420) 530350511
IT Software Management Services
N.A.I.C.S.: 541511

USU SAS (1)
Tour Nova 71 Boulevard National, 92250, La Garenne-Colombes, France
Tel.: (33) 155681010
Software Publishing Services
N.A.I.C.S.: 513210
Maxime Pawlak *(Mng Dir)*

USU Technologies Inc. (1)
119 Braintree St Ste 602, Boston, MA 02134
Tel.: (617) 307-7733
Web Site: https://www.usu.com
Software Asset Management Services
N.A.I.C.S.: 541511

USUM INVESTMENT GROUP CO., LTD.
33th Floor Tower A Fortune Center No 2 Fortune Avenue, Liangjiang New Area, Chongqing, 401121, China
Tel.: (86) 23 63076116
Web Site: http://en.usum.com.cn
Year Founded: 2013
Investment Firm Services
N.A.I.C.S.: 551112
Jianhua Tu *(Chm)*

Subsidiaries:

Chiho Environment Group Limited (1)
48 Wang Lok Street Yuen Long Industrial Estate, Hong Kong, China (Hong Kong) (63%)
Tel.: (852) 25877700
Web Site: http://www.chihogroup.com
Rev.: $2,495,723,250
Assets: $1,093,057,500
Liabilities: $483,518,250
Net Worth: $609,539,250
Earnings: $30,268,500
Emp.: 2,748
Fiscal Year-end: 12/31/2022
Metal Scrap Recycling Services
N.A.I.C.S.: 423510
Jianhua Tu *(Exec Dir)*

USUN TECHNOLOGY CO., LTD.
337 No 68 Shengde North Road Xihai, Dayuan, Taoyuan, Taiwan
Tel.: (886) 32707100
Web Site: https://www.usuntek.com
3498—(TPE)
Rev.: $54,429,197
Assets: $119,558,078
Liabilities: $45,027,327
Net Worth: $74,530,751
Earnings: $3,185,880
Fiscal Year-end: 12/31/22
Electromechanical Equipment Mfr & Distr
N.A.I.C.S.: 333310
Chiu-Fong Huang *(Chm & Pres)*

Subsidiaries:

Usun (Foshan) Technology Co., Ltd. (1)
1 Lexin Road, Leping Town Sanshui District, Foshan, Guangdong, China
Tel.: (86) 75787393266
Flat Panel Display Equipment Mfr
N.A.I.C.S.: 334118

USV PVT LTD.
Arvind Vithal Gandhi Chowk BSD Marg, Station Road Govandi East, Mumbai, 400088, India
Tel.: (91) 22 25564048
Web Site: http://www.usvindia.com
Pharmaceuticals Mfr
N.A.I.C.S.: 325412
Leena Gandhi Tewari *(Chm)*

USV PVT LTD.

USV Pvt Ltd.—(Continued)

Subsidiaries:

Juta Pharma GmbH (1)
Gutenbergstrasse 13, 24941, Flensburg, Germany
Tel.: (49) 4619957990
Web Site: http://www.jutapharma.de
Generic Pharmaceutical Mfr
N.A.I.C.S.: 325412

UT BANK LIMITED

25B Manet Towers Airport City, PO Box CT 1778, Cantonments, Accra, Ghana
Tel.: (233) 302740740
Web Site:
http://www.utbankghana.com
Year Founded: 1996
UTB—(GHA)
Sales Range: $50-74.9 Million
Banking Services
N.A.I.C.S.: 522110
Joseph Nsonamoah (Chm)

UT GROUP CO., LTD.

Denpa Bldg 6F 1-11-15 Higashi-Gotanda, Shinagawa-ku, Tokyo, 141-0022, Japan
Tel.: (81) 354471711
Web Site: https://www.ut-g.co.jp
Year Founded: 2007
2146—(TKS)
Rev.: $1,104,068,300
Assets: $452,494,160
Liabilities: $224,825,930
Net Worth: $227,668,230
Earnings: $42,046,210
Fiscal Year-end: 03/31/24
Semiconductor Mfr
N.A.I.C.S.: 334413
Yoichi Wakayama (Pres & CEO)

Subsidiaries:

Fujitsu UT Co., Ltd. (1)
1-11-15 Higashigotanda, Shinagawa-ku, Tokyo, 141-0022, Japan
Tel.: (81) 35 447 1720
Web Site: https://www.ut-g.co.jp
Semiconductor & Electronic Component Mfr
N.A.I.C.S.: 334413

Support System Co., Ltd. (1)
5-14 Jumonji, Shirakawa, 961-0027, Fukushima, Japan
Tel.: (81) 24 821 2345
Web Site: https://www.haken-support.co.jp
Temporary Employment Services
N.A.I.C.S.: 561320
Tamiko Mizoi (Pres)

UT Aim Co., Ltd. (1)
1-11-15 Higashigotanda 6th Floor Denpa Building, Shinagawa-ku, Tokyo, 141-0022, Japan
Tel.: (81) 35 447 1715
Web Site: https://www.ut-g.co.jp
Semiconductor & Electronic Component Mfr
N.A.I.C.S.: 334413

UT Connect Co., Ltd. (1)
6th Floor Dempa Building 1-11-15 Higashigotanda, Shinagawa-ku, Tokyo, 141-0022, Japan
Tel.: (81) 354477368
Contract Manpower Services
N.A.I.C.S.: 561320

UT Construction Co., Ltd. (1)
6th floor Denpa Building 1-11-15 Higashi-Gotanda, Shinagawa-ku, Tokyo, 141-0022, Japan
Tel.: (81) 362771862
Web Site: https://www.ut-g.co.jp
Construction Contractor Services
N.A.I.C.S.: 236220

UT Pabec Co., Ltd. (1)
1-1 Matsushita-cho, Moriguchi, 570-0052, Osaka, Japan
Tel.: (81) 669944374
Web Site: http://www.ut-pabec.co.jp
Battery Mfr
N.A.I.C.S.: 335910

Koji Morikawa (Pres)

UT Suri-Emu Co., Ltd. (1)
16-1 Furo Harisaki-cho, Okazaki, 444-0827, Aichi, Japan
Tel.: (81) 56 455 6433
Web Site: https://www.ut-g.co.jp
On-Site Contracting Services
N.A.I.C.S.: 236220

UTAC HOLDINGS LTD.

22 Ang Mo Kio Industrial Park 2, Singapore, 569506, Singapore
Tel.: (65) 64818811   SG
Web Site: http://www.utacgroup.com
Year Founded: 1997
Sales Range: $800-899.9 Million
Holding Company; Semiconductor Testing & Assembly Services
N.A.I.C.S.: 551112
John Nelson (CEO)

Subsidiaries:

PT. UTAC Manufacturing Services Indonesia (1)
Jl Maligi I Lot A1-4 Kawasan Industri KIIC Sukaluyu, Teluk Jambe Timur, Karawang, 41361, West Java, Indonesia
Tel.: (62) 2189111119
Electric Device Mfr
N.A.I.C.S.: 334413
Muhammad Hasan (Sr Mgr-Customer Engrg)

UGS America Sales Inc. (1)
161 Mission Falls Ln Ste 200, Fremont, CA 94539
Tel.: (510) 490-8870
Electrical Device Distr
N.A.I.C.S.: 423690

UGS China Sales Ltd (1)
1088 Pudong South Road Unit 1308 Room C, Shanghai, 200120, China
Tel.: (86) 13817578606
Electrical Device Distr
N.A.I.C.S.: 423690

UGS Europe LLC (1)
Voie du Chariot 3, 1003, Lausanne, Switzerland
Tel.: (41) 215605551
Electrical Device Distr
N.A.I.C.S.: 423690

UGS Europe Sales SrL (1)
25 via Ettore Maiorana, Basta Umbra, 06083, Perugia, Italy
Tel.: (39) 0758005185
Electrical Device Distr
N.A.I.C.S.: 423690

UTAC (Shanghai) Company, Ltd (1)
South Part of 55 Building No 273 De Bao Road Pilot Free Trade Zone, Shanghai, 200131, China
Tel.: (86) 2150483333
Electric Device Mfr
N.A.I.C.S.: 334413

UTAC Dongguan Limited (1)
Zhen An Hi-Tech Industrial Park Zhen An Road, Chang An Town, Dongguan, 523850, Guangdong, China (100%)
Tel.: (86) 76985647688
Web Site: http://www.utacgroup.com
Semiconductor Assembly & Test Facilities
N.A.I.C.S.: 334413
Jeff Kam (Gen Mgr)

UTAC Japan Co., Ltd (1)
1 Kotari-yakemachi, Nagaokakyo, Kyoto, 617-8520, Japan
Tel.: (81) 759636250
Electrical Device Distr
N.A.I.C.S.: 423690

UTAC Manufacturing Services Malaysia Sdn Bhd (1)
Lot 26 & 27 Batu Berendam FTZ III, 75350, Melaka, Malaysia
Tel.: (60) 6 284 3676
Semiconductor Devices Mfr
N.A.I.C.S.: 334413

UTAC Taiwan Corporation (1)
2 Li Hsin Road 3 Science Based Industrial Park, Hsin-chu, Taiwan

Tel.: (886) 35788780
Electric Device Mfr
N.A.I.C.S.: 334413

UTAC Thai Ltd (1)
237 Lasalle Road Sukhumvit 105, Bang Na, Bangkok, 10260, Thailand
Tel.: (66) 27491680
Electric Device Mfr
N.A.I.C.S.: 334413
Thanarkhom Chavasiri (Gen Mgr)

United Test & Assembly Center Ltd. (1)
5 Serangoon North Avenue 5, Singapore, 554916, Singapore
Tel.: (65) 6481 0033
Web Site: http://www.utacgroup.com
Sales Range: $1-4.9 Billion
Emp.: 2,000
Semiconductor Testing & Assembly Services
N.A.I.C.S.: 334413
Douglas J. Devine (CFO)

UTECH ELECTRONICS

5250 Finch Avenue East Unit 1, Scarborough, M1S 5A4, ON, Canada
Tel.: (416) 609-2900
Web Site: http://www.utech.ca
Year Founded: 1991
Rev.: $12,636,000
Emp.: 30
Electronic Products Mfr
N.A.I.C.S.: 532210
Jason Riley (Mgr-Sls)

UTECHZONE CO., LTD.

Rm 1 10F No 268 Liancheng Rd, Jhonghe, New Taipei City, 23553, Taiwan
Tel.: (886) 282262088
Web Site:
https://www.utechzone.com.tw
3455—(TPE)
Rev.: $98,470,969
Assets: $157,544,289
Liabilities: $68,505,081
Net Worth: $89,039,208
Earnings: $23,476,503
Emp.: 329
Fiscal Year-end: 12/31/22
Optical Component Mfr
N.A.I.C.S.: 333310
Joseph Tzou (Chm)

UTEX HOLDING PLC

70-72 Cherni vrah Blvd, Sofia, 1407, Bulgaria
Tel.: (359) 29624445
Web Site:
http://www.utexholding.com
Year Founded: 1996
5Y1—(BUL)
Holding Company
N.A.I.C.S.: 551112
Andrey Davidov (Chm & CEO)

UTEXBEL N.V.

Cesar Snoecklaan Avenue Cesar Snoeck 30, Rainx, 9600, Ronse, Belgium
Tel.: (32) 55231211
Web Site: http://www.utexbel.com
Year Founded: 1929
Fabric Product Mfr
N.A.I.C.S.: 313320
Jean-Francois Pierre Gribomont (Chm)

UTI ASSET MANAGEMENT CO. LTD.

Uti Tower Gn Block Bandra-Kurla Complex, Bandra-East, Mumbai, 400051, India
Tel.: (91) 2266786079
Web Site: https://www.utimf.com
Year Founded: 2002

543238—(BOM)
Rev.: $163,612,995
Assets: $500,252,025
Liabilities: $58,405,620
Net Worth: $441,846,405
Earnings: $67,450,110
Emp.: 1,474
Fiscal Year-end: 03/31/21
Financial Services
N.A.I.C.S.: 523999
Imtaiyazur Rahman (CEO)

UTI GROUP LTD.

UTI Business Center 31 Vasile Lascar St, 020492, Bucharest, Romania
Tel.: (40) 314138001
Web Site: http://www.uti.ro
Sales Range: $50-74.9 Million
Emp.: 655
Information Technology, Communications, Engineering & Security Products Mfr & Distr
N.A.I.C.S.: 541519
Lucia Urdareanu (VP)

Subsidiaries:

UTI & Maintenance Services S.A. (1)
107A Oltentei Rd 4th Fl Corp cam 11 Sect 4, Bucharest, 70000, Romania
Tel.: (40) 241 601 3122
Web Site: http://www.utisp.ro
Sales Range: $25-49.9 Million
Emp.: 50
Facility Management & Perimeter Security Services for Port Operations
N.A.I.C.S.: 488310
Mihai Popescu (Gen Mgr)

UTI INSTAL CONSTRUCT Inc (1)
27B Cernauti Street, Bucharest, 022183, Romania
Tel.: (40) 21 20 13 601
Electrical Engineering Services
N.A.I.C.S.: 541330

UTI SECURITY & FIRE SOLUTIONS (1)
UTI Business Center 4th Floor 31 Vasile Lascar St, 020492, Bucharest, Romania
Tel.: (40) 31 40 57 101
Security & Fire Safety System Installation Services
N.A.I.C.S.: 238210

UTI Systems S.A. (1)
27C Cernauti Street, 022183, Bucharest, Romania
Tel.: (40) 31 10 11 884
Web Site: http://www.uti.eu.com
Information Technology Consulting Services
N.A.I.C.S.: 541512

UTIME LIMITED

7th Floor Building 5A Shenzhen Software Industry Base, Nanshan District, Shenzhen, 518061, China
Tel.: (86) 75586512266   Ky
Year Founded: 2008
WTO—(NASDAQ)
Rev.: $23,836,398
Assets: $89,990,446
Liabilities: $39,784,559
Net Worth: $50,205,887
Earnings: ($8,613,203)
Emp.: 172
Fiscal Year-end: 03/31/24
Holding Company
N.A.I.C.S.: 551112

UTIQUE ENTERPRISES LTD.

603 Lodha Supremus 453 Senapati Bapat Marg Lower Parel, Mumbai, 400 013, India
Tel.: (91) 2246198172
Web Site: https://www.utique.in
500014—(BOM)
Rev.: $838,514
Assets: $5,428,488
Liabilities: $2,333,941
Net Worth: $3,094,547

Earnings: $333,527
Emp.: 4
Fiscal Year-end: 03/31/21
Financial Services
N.A.I.C.S.: 523999
P. B. Deshpande *(Officer-Compliance, Sec & Mgr)*

UTKARSH SMALL FINANCE BANK LIMITED
Utkarsh Tower NH-31 Airport Road, Sehmalpur Kazi Sarai Harhua, Varanasi, 221105, Uttar Pradesh, India
Tel.: (91) 5422500596 In
Web Site: https://www.utkarsh.bank
Year Founded: 2016
UTKARSH—(NSE)
Rev.: $339,879,463
Assets: $2,317,046,030
Liabilities: $2,074,607,173
Net Worth: $242,438,857
Earnings: $49,025,630
Emp.: 15,424
Fiscal Year-end: 03/31/23
Commercial Banking Services
N.A.I.C.S.: 522110
Abhijeet Bhattacharjee *(CIO)*

UTL INDUSTRIES LIMITED
607 World Trade Center, Sayajigunj, Vadodara, 390 005, Gujarat, India
Tel.: (91) 7433973999 In
Web Site:
    https://www.utlindustries.com
Year Founded: 1989
500426—(BOM)
Rev.: $8,752
Assets: $747,547
Liabilities: $216,357
Net Worth: $531,190
Earnings: ($11,607)
Emp.: 10
Fiscal Year-end: 03/31/23
Metal Product Distr
N.A.I.C.S.: 423510
Parimal Rameshbhai Shah *(Chm & Mng Dir)*

UTMOST INTERNATIONAL GROUP HOLDINGS LIMITED
1st and 2nf Floors Elizabeth House Les Ruettes Brayes, Saint Peter Port, GY1 1EW, Guernsey
Tel.: (44) 2038614343 GY
Web Site:
    http://www.utmostgroup.co.uk
Year Founded: 2013
Rev.: $1,506,327
Assets: $31,858,906,997
Liabilities: $31,327,079,750
Net Worth: $531,827,247
Earnings: $85,047,182
Fiscal Year-end: 12/31/18
Holding Company
N.A.I.C.S.: 551112
Paul Thompson *(Co-Founder & CEO)*

Subsidiaries:

LCCG UK Limited (1)
Tallis House 2 Tallis Street, London, EC4Y 0AB, United Kingdom
Tel.: (44) 20 3666 5163
Web Site: http://www.lccgl.co.uk
Holding Company
N.A.I.C.S.: 551112

Subsidiary (Non-US):

Generali Worldwide Insurance Company Limited (2)
Hirzel St, PO Box 613, Saint Peter Port, GY1 4PA, Guernsey (100%)
Tel.: (44) 1481715400
Web Site: http://www.generali-guernsey.com
Sales Range: $10-24.9 Million
Emp.: 100
Provider of Assurance & Investement Products
N.A.I.C.S.: 611430

Subsidiary (Domestic):

Generali International Limited (3)
Hirzel St, PO Box 613, South Esplanade, Saint Peter Port, GY1 4PA, Guernsey (100%)
Tel.: (44) 1481714108
Web Site: http://www.generali-guernsey.com
Assurance & Investment Products
N.A.I.C.S.: 524128

Generali Portfolio Management (Ci) Limited (3)
Hirzel Street, Saint Peter Port, GY1 4PA, Guernsey
Tel.: (44) 1481 703000
Sales Range: $50-74.9 Million
Emp.: 5
Portfolio Management Services
N.A.I.C.S.: 523940

Subsidiary (Non-US):

Utmost Limited (2)
Royal House Walpole Avenue, Douglas, IM1 2SL, Isle of Man
Tel.: (44) 1624 643 345
Web Site: http://www.utmostwealth.com
Investment Services
N.A.I.C.S.: 523940

Utmost PanEurope (1)
Navan Business Park, Navan, County Meath, Ireland
Tel.: (353) 46 9099 700
Web Site: http://www.utmost.ie
Wealth Management Services
N.A.I.C.S.: 523940
Paul Gillett *(CEO)*

UTON S.A.
Str Uzinei nr 16, 601123, Onesti, Romania
Tel.: (40) 234 324222
Web Site: http://www.uton.ro
Year Founded: 1973
Emp.: 700
Industrial Equipment Mfr
N.A.I.C.S.: 333248
Octavian Iancu *(Gen Mgr)*

UTOUR GROUP CO., LTD.
No 8 Chaoyang Park Road, Chaoyang District, Beijing, 100125, China
Tel.: (86) 1064489696
Web Site: https://uzai.com
Year Founded: 1995
002707—(SSE)
Rev.: $71,181,564
Assets: $302,138,582
Liabilities: $233,760,047
Net Worth: $68,378,535
Earnings: ($31,080,081)
Emp.: 1,060
Fiscal Year-end: 12/31/22
Travel Services
N.A.I.C.S.: 561599
Feng Bin *(Chm & Pres)*

UTP BELA CRKVA A.D.
Kozaracka 1, Bela Crkva, Serbia
Tel.: (381) 13 851 812
Year Founded: 2003
Sales Range: Less than $1 Million
Emp.: 2
Mobile Food Services
N.A.I.C.S.: 722330

UTP KASTEL AD
Novosadska 7, 23203, Ecka, Serbia
Tel.: (381) 23 554 800
Web Site: http://www.kastelecka.com
Year Founded: 1820
Sales Range: Less than $1 Million
Emp.: 31
Home Management Services
N.A.I.C.S.: 721110

UTS MARKETING SOLUTIONS HOLDINGS LIMITED
Tingkat 10 Bangunan KWSP No 3 Changkat Raja Chulan, Kuala Lumpur, 50200, Malaysia
Tel.: (60) 320366888 Ky
Web Site:
    http://www.unitedteleservice.com
Year Founded: 2007
6113—(HKG)
Rev.: $20,557,031
Assets: $16,104,049
Liabilities: $5,448,193
Net Worth: $10,655,856
Earnings: $2,243,143
Emp.: 1,412
Fiscal Year-end: 12/31/23
Call Center Services
N.A.I.C.S.: 561422
Chee Wai Wai Ng *(Chm)*

Subsidiaries:

UTS Marketing Solutions Sdn. Bhd. (1)
23rd Floor Plaza See Hoy Chan Jalan Raja Chulan, 50200, Kuala Lumpur, Malaysia
Tel.: (60) 320366888
Web Site: https://unitedteleservice.com
Telemarketing Services
N.A.I.C.S.: 561422

UTSTARCOM HOLDINGS CORP.
4th Floor South Wing 368 Liuhe Road, Binjiang District, Hangzhou, China
Tel.: (86) 57181928888 DE
Web Site: https://www.utstar.com
Year Founded: 1991
UTSI—(NASDAQ)
Rev.: $14,052,000
Assets: $89,230,000
Liabilities: $31,766,000
Net Worth: $57,464,000
Earnings: ($5,002,000)
Emp.: 241
Fiscal Year-end: 12/31/22
Networking & Telecommunications Equipment Mfr
N.A.I.C.S.: 334210
Ellen Chen *(VP-Admin & HR-Global-UTStarcom Incorporated)*

Subsidiaries:

UTStarcom (1)
Rua James Watt 142-7o, Andar Edificio Century Plaza, Sao Paulo, Brazil (100%)
Tel.: (55) 1151122466
Sales Range: $25-49.9 Million
Emp.: 100
Telecommunication Systems Mfr & Service
N.A.I.C.S.: 517112

UTStarcom (Beijing) Technologies Co., Ltd. (1)
20F Tower E1 The Towers Oriental Plaza No 1 East Chang An Avenue, Dong Cheng District, Beijing, 100738, China
Tel.: (86) 1085205588
Telecommunications Equipment Mfr
N.A.I.C.S.: 334290

UTStarcom (China) Ltd. (1)
20F Tower E1 Oriental Plaza No1 East Chang an Avenue, DongCheng District, Beijing, 100738, China
Tel.: (86) 1085205588
Sales Range: $75-99.9 Million
Emp.: 100
Telecommunication Systems Manufacture & Service
N.A.I.C.S.: 517112

UTStarcom (Thailand) Limited (1)
252/98 Ratchadapisek Huaykwang, Huaykwang Distr, Bangkok, Thailand
Tel.: (66) 2 693 2550
Telecommunications Equipment Mfr
N.A.I.C.S.: 334290

UTStarcom Inc. (1)
1275 Harbor Bay Pkwy, Alameda, CA 94502
Tel.: (510) 864-8800
Web Site: http://www.utstar.com
Networking & Telecommunications Equipment Mfr
N.A.I.C.S.: 334210

UTStarcom India Telecom Pvt. Ltd. (1)
1st Floor Ravshan building 7 Ashley Road, Bengaluru, 560025, Karnataka, India
Tel.: (91) 8030787777
Sales Range: $25-49.9 Million
Emp.: 1
Telecommunications Equipment Mfr
N.A.I.C.S.: 334290

UTStarcom Japan KK (1)
18F The Front Tower Shiba Koen 2-6-3 Shiba Koen, Minato-Ku, Tokyo, 105-0011, Japan
Tel.: (81) 364308600
Telecommunications Equipment Mfr
N.A.I.C.S.: 334290

UTStarcom Korea Limited (1)
275-7 YangjaeDong, Seocho-gu, Seoul, Korea (South)
Tel.: (82) 2 368 8900
Telecommunications Equipment Mfr
N.A.I.C.S.: 334290

UTStarcom Taiwan Ltd (1)
14F No 51 Sec 3 Minsheng E Rd, Taipei, 10478, Taiwan
Tel.: (886) 2 25053963
Emp.: 100
Telecommunications Equipment Mfr
N.A.I.C.S.: 334290

UTStarcom Telecom Co., Ltd. (1)
4th Floor South Wing 368 Liuhe Road, Binjiang District, Hangzhou, 310053, China
Tel.: (86) 57181928888
Mobile Network Services
N.A.I.C.S.: 517112

uSTAR Technologies Limited (1)
4th Floor South Wing 368 Liuhe Road, Binjiang District, Hangzhou, 310053, China
Tel.: (86) 57187156669
Mobile Network Services
N.A.I.C.S.: 517112

UTTAM GALVA STEELS LIMITED
Uttam House 69 P D'Mello Road, Mumbai, 400 009, India
Tel.: (91) 2266563500
Web Site: http://www.uttamgalva.com
Year Founded: 1985
UTTAMSTL—(BOM)
Rev.: $91,483,665
Assets: $836,716,335
Liabilities: $1,356,860,505
Net Worth: ($520,144,170)
Earnings: ($32,096,610)
Emp.: 820
Fiscal Year-end: 03/31/21
Steel Products Mfr
N.A.I.C.S.: 331221
Anuj R. Miglani *(CEO & Mng Dir)*

Subsidiaries:

Atlantis International Service Company Ltd. (1)
Schalienhoevedreef No 20H, 2800, Mechelen, Belgium
Tel.: (32) 3 828 8400
Web Site: https://www.atlantis-international.net
Marine Products Distr
N.A.I.C.S.: 423910
Wilfried Vangompel *(Gen Mgr)*

Uttam Galva International, FZE (1)
Office No Lb03016 Jebel Ali Free Zone, Dubai, United Arab Emirates
Tel.: (971) 509857064
Metal Mining Services
N.A.I.C.S.: 213114

Uttam Galva North America, INC (1)
1500 Broadway, New York, NY 10036
Tel.: (917) 722-8177
Metal Mining Services
N.A.I.C.S.: 213114

UTTAM SUGAR MILLS LIMITED

UTTAM SUGAR MILLS LIMITED

Uttam Sugar Mills Limited—(Continued)
A-2E 3rd Floor C M A Tower Sector-24, Noida, 201301, Uttar Pradesh, India
Tel.: (91) 1204525000
Web Site: https://www.uttamsugar.in
Year Founded: 1993
532729—(BOM)
Rev.: $247,907,967
Assets: $194,499,478
Liabilities: $125,388,094
Net Worth: $69,111,384
Earnings: $14,821,821
Emp.: 744
Fiscal Year-end: 03/31/23
Sugar Mfr
N.A.I.C.S.: 311313
Raj Kumar Adlakha *(Mng Dir)*

UTTARA BANK PLC

47 Shahid Bir Uttam Asfaqus Samad Sarak, PO Box No 9551162, Dhaka, 1000, Bangladesh
Tel.: (880) 2223381164
Web Site: https://www.uttarabank-bd.com
UTTARABANK—(CHT)
Rev.: $117,501,205
Assets: $2,245,253,157
Liabilities: $2,058,574,505
Net Worth: $186,678,653
Earnings: $24,687,156
Emp.: 4,003
Fiscal Year-end: 12/31/22
Commercial Banking Services
N.A.I.C.S.: 522110
Iftekharul Islam *(Vice Chm)*

UTTARA FINANCE AND INVESTMENTS LIMITED

Uttara Centre 11th Floor 102 S, Shahid Tajuddin Ahmed Sarani Tejgaon, Dhaka, 1208, Bangladesh
Tel.: (880) 24102509397
Web Site: https://uttarafinance.com
Year Founded: 1995
UTTARAFIN—(DHA)
Sales Range: $50-74.9 Million
Financial Services
N.A.I.C.S.: 523999
Matiur Rahman *(Vice Chm)*

UTUSAN MELAYU (MALAYSIA) BERHAD

No 44 Jalan Utusan Off Jalan Chan Sow Lin, 55200, Kuala Lumpur, Malaysia
Tel.: (60) 392322600
Web Site:
   http://www.utusangroup.com.my
Rev.: $54,416,053
Assets: $70,852,848
Liabilities: $92,137,136
Net Worth: ($21,284,288)
Earnings: ($44,299,944)
Emp.: 1,630
Fiscal Year-end: 12/31/18
Newspaper Services
N.A.I.C.S.: 513110
Abd Aziz Fadzir *(Chm)*

Subsidiaries:

Karya Outdoor Sdn Bhd (1)
No 11-1 Level 1 The Right Angle Jalan 14/22, 46100, Petaling Jaya, Selangor, Malaysia
Tel.: (60) 379563355
Newspaper Printing & Publishing Services
N.A.I.C.S.: 513110
Mohd Yazid Ahmad *(Exec Dir)*

Sibermedia Sdn Bhd (1)
Unit 209 Blok A Level 2 Kelana Business Centre 97 Jalan SS7/2, Kelana Jaya, 47301, Petaling Jaya, Selangor, Malaysia
Tel.: (60) 378879787
Newspaper Printing & Publishing Services
N.A.I.C.S.: 513110

Tintarona Publications Sdn Bhd (1)
No 1 dan 3 Jalan 3/91A, Taman Shamelin Perkasa, 56100, Kuala Lumpur, Malaysia
Tel.: (60) 392856577
Newspaper Printing & Publishing Services
N.A.I.C.S.: 513110

Utusan Airtime Sdn Bhd (1)
No 11A-2 The Right Angle Jalan 14/22, 46100, Petaling Jaya, Selangor, Malaysia
Tel.: (60) 379588787
Television & Radio Advertising Marketing Services
N.A.I.C.S.: 541810
Shan Kanniah *(Sr Mgr-Sls)*

Utusan Karya Sdn Bhd (1)
Lot 6 Jalan P/10 Kawasan Perusahaan Bangi Seksyen 10, 43650, Bandar Baru Bangi, Selangor, Malaysia
Tel.: (60) 389262999
Newspaper Printing & Publishing Services
N.A.I.C.S.: 513110
Arffin Nordin *(Exec Dir)*

Utusan Melayu (Malaysia) Berhad - Bandar Baru Bangi Plant (1)
Lot 6 Jalan P/10 Kawasan Perindustrian Bangi Seksyen 10, Bandar Baru Bangi, 43650, Selangor, Malaysia
Tel.: (60) 389243888
Newspaper Printing & Publishing Services
N.A.I.C.S.: 513110

Utusan Printcorp Sdn Bhd (1)
Kompleks Sri Utusan Lot 6 Jalan P/10 Kawasan Perusahaan Bangi, Kawasan Perusahaan Bangi Seksyen 10, 43650, Bandar Baru Bangi, Malaysia
Tel.: (60) 3 8926 4141
Commercial Printing Services
N.A.I.C.S.: 323111

Utusan Publications & Distributors Sdn Bhd (1)
No 1 & 3 Jalan 3/91A, Taman Shamelin Perkasa, 56100, Kuala Lumpur, Malaysia
Tel.: (60) 392856577
Newspaper Printing & Publishing Services
N.A.I.C.S.: 513110
Rozita Yusoff *(Exec Dir)*

UTV SOFTWARE COMMUNICATIONS LIMITED

1st Floor Building No 14 Solitaire Corporate Park, Guru Hargovindji Marg Chakala Andheri, Mumbai, 400 093, India
Tel.: (91) 2261091000
Web Site: http://www.utvgroup.com
Sales Range: $200-249.9 Million
Emp.: 887
Integrated Media & Entertainment Services
N.A.I.C.S.: 516120
Mahesh Samat *(Mng Dir)*

Subsidiaries:

Indiagames Ltd. (1)
Vishwaroop IT Park Vashi International Infotech Pk 11th Fl Plot No 34, 35/38 Sector 30 A CIDCO Vashi, Mumbai, 400 705, Navi, India
Tel.: (91) 2267710700
Web Site: http://www.indiagames.com
Video Games
N.A.I.C.S.: 339930

UTVA PROING A.D.

Utve Zlatokrile 9, Pancevo, Serbia
Tel.: (381) 13 342 787
Year Founded: 1989
UTPR—(BEL)
Sales Range: Less than $1 Million
Emp.: 18
Metal Structure & Part Mfr
N.A.I.C.S.: 332312
Slavko Jelic *(Exec Dir)*

UTVA SILOSI A.D. KOVIN

Dunavska 46, 26220, Kovin, Serbia
Tel.: (381) 13741484
Web Site: https://www.utva.rs
Year Founded: 1979
Sales Range: Less than $1 Million
Tube & Silo Producer
N.A.I.C.S.: 339999
Vesna Jovanovic *(CEO & Exec Director, Legal, Gen Affairs, and Human Resources-Economic)*

UUV AQUABOTIX LTD

suite 5 CPC 145s Stirling Highway, Nedlands, 6009, WA, Australia
Tel.: (61) 893893160
Web Site: http://www.aquabotix.com
Year Founded: 2011
UUV—(ASX)
Rev.: $350,736
Assets: $726,799
Liabilities: $173,306
Net Worth: $553,493
Earnings: ($1,032,280)
Fiscal Year-end: 12/31/20
Underwater Vehicle Mfr & Distr
N.A.I.C.S.: 336612
Durval Tavares *(Founder)*

Subsidiaries:

Aquabotix Technology Corporation (1)
21 Father Devalles Blvd Ste 106, Fall River, MA 02723
Tel.: (508) 676-1000
Underwater Vehicle Mfr
N.A.I.C.S.: 336612
Derek Daly *(COO)*

UV GERMI SA

ZAC de la Nau, Saint-Viance, 19240, Brive-la-Gaillarde, France
Tel.: (33) 555881888
Web Site: https://www.uvgermi.fr
Year Founded: 1979
ALUVI—(EUR)
Sales Range: $1-9.9 Million
Polyethylene Device Mfr
N.A.I.C.S.: 336612
Andrea Bordas *(Founder, Chm & CEO)*

UVAT TECHNOLOGY CO., LTD.

6F No 51 Housheng Rd, Luzhu, Taoyuan, 338, Taiwan
Tel.: (886) 32126201
Web Site: http://www.uvat.com
Year Founded: 2002
3580—(TPE)
Rev.: $32,469,656
Assets: $71,244,411
Liabilities: $41,128,131
Net Worth: $30,116,281
Earnings: $7,732,201
Fiscal Year-end: 12/31/22
Electric Equipment Mfr
N.A.I.C.S.: 335999
Chung-Chiung Liu *(VP)*

UVEX WINTER HOLDING GMBH & CO KG

Wurzburger Str 181, 90766, Furth, Germany
Tel.: (49) 911 9736 0
Web Site: http://www.uvex-group.com
Holding Company
N.A.I.C.S.: 551112
Georg Hofler *(CFO)*

Subsidiaries:

UVEX Safety Group GmbH & Co. KG (1)
Wurzburger Str 181, 90766, Furth, Germany
Tel.: (49) 8006644891
Personal Protective Equipment Mfr
N.A.I.C.S.: 423450
Stefan Bruck *(CEO)*

Subsidiary (US):

Performance Fabrics, Inc. (2)
640 Leffingwell Ave NE, Grand Rapids, MI 49505

INTERNATIONAL PUBLIC

Tel.: (616) 459-4144
Web Site: http://www.hexarmor.com
Personal Protective Equipment
N.A.I.C.S.: 423450
Steven R. VanErmen *(Co-Founder)*

UVRE LIMITED

1202 Hay Street, West Perth, 6005, WA, Australia
Tel.: (61) 893227600   AU
Web Site:
   https://www.uvrelimited.com
Year Founded: 2021
UVA—(ASX)
Exploration & Mining Services
N.A.I.C.S.: 213115
Peter Woods *(Mng Dir)*

UWC BERHAD

PMT 744-745 Jalan Cassia Selatan 5/1 Taman Perindustrian Batu Kawan, Bandar Cassia, 14110, Pulau Penang, Malaysia
Tel.: (60) 45556937   MY
Web Site:
   https://www.uwcberhad.com.my
UWC—(KLS)
Rev.: $57,511,987
Assets: $98,178,213
Liabilities: $8,815,012
Net Worth: $89,363,201
Earnings: $11,391,777
Emp.: 435
Fiscal Year-end: 07/31/23
Engineeering Services
N.A.I.C.S.: 541330
Ng Chai Eng *(Co-Founder & CEO)*

UXA RESOURCES LIMITED

43a Fullarton Road, Kent Town, 5067, SA, Australia
Tel.: (61) 883637970   AU
Web Site: http://www.uxa.com.au
Sales Range: $1-9.9 Million
Emp.: 15
Base Metals, Coal & Uranium Exploration Services
N.A.I.C.S.: 212290
Andrew White *(CFO)*

Subsidiaries:

Geoscience Associates Australia Pty. Ltd. (1)
20 Oborn Rd, Mount Barker, 5251, SA, Australia
Tel.: (61) 883930900
Web Site: http://www.gaawireline.com
Logging Systems Design & Mfr
N.A.I.C.S.: 423810

UXIN LIMITED

1-3/F No 12 Beitucheng East Road, Chaoyang District, Beijing, 100029, China
Tel.: (86) 1056916765   Ky
Web Site: http://www.xin.com
Year Founded: 2011
UXIN—(NASDAQ)
Rev.: $190,342,407
Assets: $289,121,206
Liabilities: $308,933,318
Net Worth: ($19,812,112)
Earnings: ($51,166,094)
Emp.: 846
Fiscal Year-end: 03/31/24
Online Shopping Services
N.A.I.C.S.: 423110
Kun Dai *(Founder, Chm & CEO)*

UXN CO., LTD.

C-506 145 Gwanggyo-Ro, Yeongtong-Gu, Suwon, Gyeonggi-do, Korea (South)
Tel.: (82) 28580931
Web Site: http://www.uxn.co.kr
337840—(KRS)

AND PRIVATE COMPANIES

Medical Device Equipment Mfr & Distr
N.A.I.C.S.: 339112
Sejin Park *(CEO)*

UYENO KOSAN LTD.
46 Yamashita-cho, Naka-ku, Yokohama, 2310023, Kanagawa, Japan
Tel.: (81) 456814689 JP
Web Site: http://www.uyeno-group.co.jp
Year Founded: 1963
Real Estate, Property Management & Consulting Services
N.A.I.C.S.: 531390
Takashi Ueno *(Chm, Pres, CEO & COO)*

Subsidiaries:

Oxalis Chemicals Ltd. (1)
13 F Daiba Frontier Building, 2 3 2 Daiba Minato ku, Tokyo, 135-0091, Japan
Tel.: (81) 355003014
Web Site: http://www.oxachem.com
Petrochemical Mfr
N.A.I.C.S.: 325110
Gen Uyeno *(Chm)*

UZABASE, INC.
Level 13 7-7-7 Roppongi, Minato-ku, Tokyo, 106-0032, Japan
Tel.: (81) 345746552
Web Site: http://www.uzabase.com
Year Founded: 2008
3966—(TKS)
Rev.: $133,671,120
Assets: $154,057,200
Liabilities: $85,145,280
Net Worth: $68,911,920
Earnings: ($62,648,960)
Fiscal Year-end: 12/31/20
Business Consulting Services
N.A.I.C.S.: 541611
Yusuke Inagaki *(COO)*

Subsidiaries:

FORCAS, Inc. (1)
Tri-Seven Roppongi 13F 7-7-7 Roppongi, Minato-ku, Tokyo, 106-0032, Japan
Tel.: (81) 343568998
Web Site: http://www.forcas.com
Management Consulting Services
N.A.I.C.S.: 541618
H. Sakuma *(CEO)*

Mimir, Inc. (1)
1-1-6 Uchisaiwaicho, Chiyoda-ku, Tokyo, 100-0011, Japan
Tel.: (81) 344002904
Web Site: http://www.mimir-inc.biz
Market Research & Various Advisory Services
N.A.I.C.S.: 541910
Shoji Kawaguchi *(Pres)*

Uzabase Asia Pacific Pte. Ltd. (1)
Twenty Anson 11-01 20 Anson Rd, Singapore, 079912, Singapore
Tel.: (65) 6 303 5206
Web Site: http://www.uzabase.com
Business Management Services
N.A.I.C.S.: 561110
Naito Yasunori *(Dir)*

Uzabase China Limited (1)
606 No 1440 Yan An Rd M, Shanghai, China
Tel.: (86) 2161031677
Business Management Services
N.A.I.C.S.: 561110

Uzabase Hong Kong Limited (1)
30/F Entertainment Building 30 Queens Road Central, Central, China (Hong Kong)
Tel.: (852) 58083148
Business Management Services
N.A.I.C.S.: 561110

UZARIJA A.D.
Njegoseva 14, 76230, Samac, Bosnia & Herzegovina
Tel.: (387) 54611422

UZAR-R-A—(BANJ)
Rev.: $1,141
Assets: $331,400
Liabilities: $128,754
Net Worth: $202,646
Earnings: ($15,980)
Emp.: 1
Fiscal Year-end: 12/31/12
Rope & Cordage Mfr
N.A.I.C.S.: 314994
Savo Vujicic *(Chm)*

UZEL MAKINA SANAYI A.S.
Topcular Kisla Caddesi 5 Rami, 34147, Istanbul, Turkiye
Tel.: (90) 2125670841
Web Site: http://www.uzel.com.tr
Sales Range: $500-549.9 Million
Emp.: 939
Tractor & Truck Mfr; Automotive Parts Mfr & Distr
N.A.I.C.S.: 333924
E.I. Onder Uzel *(Chm & Pres)*

Subsidiaries:

Agrel Dis Ticaret A.S. (1)
Kisla Cad No 5 Rami, Istanbul, Turkiye
Tel.: (90) 2125670841
Sales Range: $50-74.9 Million
Emp.: 100
Industrial Supplies Whslr
N.A.I.C.S.: 423840

Uzel Deutz Motor Sanayi ve Ticaret A.S. (1)
Fatih Mah Malkocoglu Cad No 10 Kartal, Istanbul, Turkiye
Tel.: (90) 2125670841
Industrial Supplies Whslr
N.A.I.C.S.: 423840

Uzel Emlak Hizmetleri A.S. (1)
Visnezade Mah Bayildim Cad No 6 Besiktas, Istanbul, Turkiye
Tel.: (90) 2122609923
Web Site: http://www.century21.com.tr
Real Estate Agency
N.A.I.C.S.: 531210

Uzel Lojistik ve Satinalma Hizmetleri A.S. (1)
Kisla Cad No 5 Rami, Istanbul, Turkiye
Tel.: (90) 2165616820
Holding Company
N.A.I.C.S.: 551112

Uzel Park Danismanlik ve Ticaret A.S. (1)
Kisla Cad No 5 Rami, Istanbul, Turkiye
Tel.: (90) 2125670841
Farm Labor Contractors & Crew Leaders
N.A.I.C.S.: 115115

Uzel Sigorta Aracilik Hizmetleri A.S. (1)
Kisla Cad No 5 Rami, Istanbul, Turkiye
Tel.: (90) 2125670841
Commericial Banking
N.A.I.C.S.: 522110

Uzel Sinai Yatirim A.S. (1)
Kisla Cad No 5 Rami, Istanbul, Turkiye
Tel.: (90) 2125670841
Management Consulting Services
N.A.I.C.S.: 541618

Uzel Sistem A.S. (1)
Kisla Cad No 5 Rami, Istanbul, Turkiye
Tel.: (90) 2125670841
Sales Range: $50-74.9 Million
Emp.: 120
Data Processing Services
N.A.I.C.S.: 518210

Uzel Tarim Makinalari ve Parca Sanayi ve Ticaret A.S. (1)
Fatih Mah Malkocoglu Cad No 10 Kartal, Istanbul, Turkiye
Tel.: (90) 2165616820
Farm & Garden Machinery & Equipment Whslr
N.A.I.C.S.: 423840

Uzel Tuketici Finansmani ve Kart Hizmetleri A.S. (1)
Kisla Cad No 5 Rami, Istanbul, Turkiye

Tel.: (90) 2125670841
Sales Range: $100-124.9 Million
Emp.: 150
Commericial Banking
N.A.I.C.S.: 522110

UZERTAS BOYA SANAYI TICARET VE YATIRIM AS
Aydinli Mah Birlik Osb Bati Ca 1, Tuzla, Istanbul, 34953, Turkiye
Tel.: (90) 2165930203
Web Site: http://www.uzertas.com.tr
UZERB—(IST)
Sales Range: Less than $1 Million
Sell Paint Mfr & Distr
N.A.I.C.S.: 325510
Ilham Erem *(Chm)*

UZIN UTZ AG
Dieselstrasse 3, 89079, Ulm, Germany
Tel.: (49) 73140970
Web Site: https://de.uzin.com
UZU—(STU)
Rev.: $529,129,046
Assets: $463,625,400
Liabilities: $179,798,346
Net Worth: $283,827,054
Earnings: $24,925,385
Emp.: 1,480
Fiscal Year-end: 12/31/23
Flooring Installations Services
N.A.I.C.S.: 321114
Heinz Werner Utz *(Chm-Supervisory Bd)*

Subsidiaries:

Hermann Frank GmbH & Co. KG. (1)
Ostliche Bahnhofstrasse 8, 75038, Oberderdingen, Baden-Wurttemberg, Germany
Tel.: (49) 725860880
Sales Range: $25-49.9 Million
Emp.: 10
Wood Flooring Machines Mfr & Sales
N.A.I.C.S.: 333998

INTR. B.V. (1)
Hamburgweg 8, 7418 ES, Deventer, Netherlands
Tel.: (31) 880204000
Web Site: https://www.intr.nl
Flooring Product Whlsr
N.A.I.C.S.: 423220

Neopur GmbH (1)
Dieselstrasse 3, 89079, Ulm, Germany
Tel.: (49) 60639109010
Web Site: https://www.neopur.de
Flooring Product Mfr
N.A.I.C.S.: 321918
Wolf Schindler *(Sls Dir)*

Pallmann GmbH (1)
Im Kreuz 6, D-97076, Wurzburg, Germany
Tel.: (49) 931279640
Web Site: https://www.pallmann.net
Wood Varnishes Mfr
N.A.I.C.S.: 325510
Stefan Alois Neuberger *(Chm-Exec Bd)*

RZ Chemie GmbH. (1)
Muhlgrabenstr 13, Meckenheim, 53340, Nordrhein-Westfalen, Germany
Tel.: (49) 222594460
Sales Range: $25-49.9 Million
Emp.: 40
Floor Cleaning Solutions Mfr
N.A.I.C.S.: 325612

Servo 360 GmbH (1)
Dieselstrasse 3, 89079, Ulm, Germany
Tel.: (49) 73140974757
Web Site: http://www.servo360.de
Technical Consulting Services
N.A.I.C.S.: 541690

Sifloor AG (1)
Allmendstrasse 26, 6210, Sursee, Switzerland
Tel.: (41) 419222121
Web Site: https://www.sifloor.ch
Dry Adhesives Mfr
N.A.I.C.S.: 325520
Heinz Leibundgut *(Mng Dir)*

UZIN UTZ North America Inc. (1)
14509 E 33rd Pl Unit G, Aurora, CO 80011-1612
Tel.: (720) 374-4810
Web Site: https://us.uzin.com
Sales Range: $50-74.9 Million
Emp.: 35
Synthetic Resin Adhesives & Flooring Installation Products Mfr
N.A.I.C.S.: 321918
Matthias Liebert *(Pres)*

Unipro B.V. (1)
Industriestraat 15, 7482 EW, Haaksbergen, Netherlands
Tel.: (31) 535737373
Web Site: http://www.unipro.nl
Sales Range: $25-49.9 Million
Emp.: 65
Flooring Installation Services
N.A.I.C.S.: 238330
Gerben Bouwmeester *(Co-Mng Dir)*

Unipro-Belgie N.V. (1)
Poortakkerstraat 41 A, 9051, Gent, Belgium
Tel.: (32) 92225848
Web Site: http://www.unipro.be
Sales Range: $25-49.9 Million
Emp.: 15
Flooring Installation Services
N.A.I.C.S.: 238330
Marc Nelen *(Mng Dir)*

Uzin France SAS. (1)
6 Ave Du Professure Andre Lemierre, 75020, Paris, France
Tel.: (33) 141632720
Web Site: http://www.uzin.fr
Industrial Chemical Whslr
N.A.I.C.S.: 424690

Uzin Limited (1)
Tachbrook Park Dr Tachbrook Park, Leamington Spa, CV34 6RH, Warwickshire, United Kingdom
Tel.: (44) 1926436700
Web Site: http://www.uzin.co.uk
Sales Range: $50-74.9 Million
Emp.: 5
Floor Covering Adhesives & Accessories Mfr & Supplier
N.A.I.C.S.: 325520
Gary Onate *(Mgr-Midwest)*

Uzin Tyro AG. (1)
Ennetburgerstrasse 47, 6374, Buochs, Nidwalden, Switzerland
Tel.: (41) 416244888
Web Site: http://www.uzin-tyro.ch
Flooring Installation Services
N.A.I.C.S.: 238330

Subsidiary (Domestic):

DS Derendinger AG. (2)
Freiburgstrasse 830 A, Case Postale 41, 3174, Thorishaus, Switzerland
Tel.: (41) 318881200
Web Site: http://www.ds-derendinger.ch
Sales Range: $25-49.9 Million
Emp.: 20
Flooring Machines & Accessories Mfr & Supplier
N.A.I.C.S.: 321918
Vitus Meier *(Mng Dir)*

Uzin Utz Belgie N.V (1)
Poortakkerstraat 37/0102, 9051, Gent, Belgium
Tel.: (32) 92225848
Web Site: https://be.uzin-utz.com
Chemical Products Distr
N.A.I.C.S.: 424690
Marc Nelen *(Mng Dir)*

Uzin Utz Ceska republika s.r.o. (1)
Ceskomoravska 12a, 190 00, Prague, Czech Republic
Tel.: (420) 283083314
Web Site: https://cz.wolff-tools.com
Professional Machine & Tool Mfr
N.A.I.C.S.: 333517

Uzin Utz Denmark ApS (1)
Kongelundsvej 294, 2770, Kastrup, Denmark
Tel.: (45) 25848003
Emp.: 8
Chemical Products Mfr
N.A.I.C.S.: 325998

UZIN UTZ AG

Uzin Utz AG—(Continued)
Jens Schimmel *(Mng Dir)*

Uzin Utz France SAS (1)
6 Avenue du Professeur Andre Lemierre,
75980, Paris, Cedex, France
Tel.: (33) 141632720
Web Site: https://fr.uzin-utz.com
Emp.: 51
Chemical Products Mfr
N.A.I.C.S.: 325998
Stephane Tavano *(Mng Dir)*

Uzin Utz Hrvatska d.o.o. (1)
Trgovacka 6, 10000, Zagreb, Croatia
Tel.: (385) 12498214
Web Site: https://www.uzin.hr
Technical Support Services
N.A.I.C.S.: 561210

Uzin Utz Magyarorszag Kft. (1)
Tel.: (36) 14319422
Web Site: https://www.ufloor-systems.hu
Sales Range: $25-49.9 Million
Emp.: 3
Floor Covering Installation Services
N.A.I.C.S.: 238330
Istvan Boeszoermenyi *(Mng Dir)*

Uzin Utz Nederland B.V. (1)
Bouwstraat 18, 7483 PA, Haaksbergen,
Netherlands
Tel.: (31) 535737373
Web Site: https://nl.uzin-utz.com
Chemical Products Mfr
N.A.I.C.S.: 325998
Rene Keemers *(Mgr-Comml)*

Uzin Utz Norge AS (1)
Elveveien 34 - Building 4, Larvik, Norway
Tel.: (47) 35506400
Web Site: http://www.uzin.no
Chemical Products Mfr
N.A.I.C.S.: 325998

Uzin Utz North America, Inc. (1)
14509 E 33rd Pl Unit G, Aurora, CO 80011
Tel.: (720) 374-4810
Web Site: https://us.uzin-utz.com
Emp.: 1,300
Flooring & Machinery Installation Product
Mfr
N.A.I.C.S.: 333120

Uzin Utz Polska Sp. Z o. o. (1)
ul Jaworzynska 287, 59-220, Legnica, Poland
Tel.: (48) 767239150
Web Site: https://pl.uzin.com
Flooring Product Mfr
N.A.I.C.S.: 321918

Uzin Utz Schweiz AG (1)
Ennetburgerstrasse 47, 6374, Buochs, Switzerland
Tel.: (41) 416244888
Web Site: https://ch.uzin-utz.com
Chemical Products Mfr
N.A.I.C.S.: 325998
Simon Odermatt *(Head-Mktg)*

Uzin Utz Singapore Pte. Ltd. (1)
25 International Business Park 03-12 German Centre, Singapore, 609916, Singapore
Tel.: (65) 62662330
Web Site: https://sg.uzin.com
Flooring Product Mfr
N.A.I.C.S.: 321918
Joel Ng *(Mgr-Bus Dev)*

Uzin Utz Slovenija d.o.o. (1)
Kajakaska Cesta 30, Smartno, 1211, Ljubljana, Slovenia
Tel.: (386) 15110200
Web Site: https://www.uzin.si
Technical Support Services
N.A.I.C.S.: 561210

Uzin Utz South Pacific Ltd. (1)
5 Clayden, PO Box 426, Whangaparaoa,
Auckland, 0943, New Zealand
Tel.: (64) 21933780
Web Site: https://www.uzin.co.nz
Flooring Product Mfr
N.A.I.C.S.: 321918
Tony King *(Natl Sls Mgr)*

Uzin Utz Srbija d.o.o. (1)
Bulevar Peke Dapcevica 43, 11041, Novi
Beograd, Serbia
Tel.: (381) 113989044
Emp.: 5
Chemical Products Distr
N.A.I.C.S.: 424690
Heinz Leibundgut *(Mng Dir)*

Uzin Utz Sverige AB (1)
Dieselstrasse 3, Ulm, 89079, Stockholm,
Sweden
Tel.: (46) 25848003
Chemical Products Mfr
N.A.I.C.S.: 325998

Uzin Utz Tools Verwaltungs GmbH (1)
Ungerhalde 1, 74360, Ilsfeld, Germany
Tel.: (49) 7062915560
Web Site: https://de.wolff-tools.com
Machine Tools Mfr
N.A.I.C.S.: 333517

Uzin Utz United Kingdom Ltd. (1)
Unit 2 Mitchell Court Central Park, Rugby,
CV23 0UY, Warwickshire, United Kingdom
Tel.: (44) 1788530080
Web Site: https://uk.uzin.com
Construction Services
N.A.I.C.S.: 236220
Daniel Leeson *(Mktg Mgr)*

Uzin s.r.o. (1)
Ceskomoravska 12a, 190 00, Prague, 9,
Czech Republic
Tel.: (420) 2 83 08 33 14
Web Site: http://www.uzin.cz
Sales Range: $25-49.9 Million
Emp.: 20
Floor Covering Adhesives & Accessories
Mfr & Distr
N.A.I.C.S.: 238330
Michal Belohlavek *(Mng Dir)*

WOLFF GmbH & Co. KG (1)
Schonebergstr 7a, 52068, Aachen, Germany
Tel.: (49) 241968130
Web Site: http://www.wolff-aachen.de
Chemical Products Mfr
N.A.I.C.S.: 325998

codex GmbH & Co. KG (1)
Heuweg 5/1, D-89079, Ulm, Germany
Tel.: (49) 7319270930
Web Site: https://int.codex-x.com
Flooring Product Mfr
N.A.I.C.S.: 321918

UZINEXPORT S.A.
8 Iancu de Hunedoara Blvd Sect 1,
011742, Bucharest, Romania
Tel.: (40) 213185757
Web Site: https://www.uzinexport.ro
UZIN—(BUC)
Rev.: $639,950
Assets: $14,123,737
Liabilities: $1,891,198
Net Worth: $12,232,539
Earnings: ($264,026)
Emp.: 8
Fiscal Year-end: 12/31/23
Cement & Engineering Plants Construction Services
N.A.I.C.S.: 236210
Matache Nicolaide *(Chm & Mng Dir)*

Subsidiaries:

Commet S.A. Tecuci (1)
144 1 Decembrie 1918 Str, Tecuci, Galati,
Romania
Tel.: (40) 236820035
Structured Steel Fabrication Mfr & Distr
N.A.I.C.S.: 332312

UZINSIDER ENGINEERING S.A.
Sos Smardan nr 2, 800701, Galati,
Romania
Tel.: (40) 236 449 016
Web Site: http://www.uzineng.ro
Year Founded: 1999
Sales Range: $1-9.9 Million
Emp.: 78
Engineering Consulting Services
N.A.I.C.S.: 541330

UZLOMAC A.D.
Cara Dusana 48, 78220, Kotor Varos,
Bosnia & Herzegovina
Tel.: (387) 51880143
UZLM-R-A—(BANJ)
Assets: $384,476
Liabilities: $144,384
Net Worth: $240,092
Earnings: ($34,060)
Emp.: 1
Fiscal Year-end: 12/31/12
Logging Services
N.A.I.C.S.: 113310
Nevenka Acimovic *(Chm-Supervisory Bd)*

UZMA BERHAD
Uzma Tower No 2 Jalan PJU 8/8A,
Damansara Perdana, 47820, Petaling
Jaya, Selangor Darul Ehsan, Malaysia
Tel.: (60) 376114000
Web Site:
https://www.uzmagroup.com
Year Founded: 2000
UZMA—(KLS)
Rev.: $93,538,913
Assets: $311,850,743
Liabilities: $182,006,303
Net Worth: $129,844,440
Earnings: $1,628,550
Emp.: 748
Fiscal Year-end: 06/30/22
Oil & Gas Geoscience, Reservoir Engineering, Drilling & Project Operation
Services
N.A.I.C.S.: 211120
Kamarul Redzuan Muhamed *(CEO & Mng Dir)*

Subsidiaries:

Malaysian Energy Chemical & Services Sdn. Bhd. (1)
7th Floor Uzma Tower No 2 Jalan PJU
8/8A, Damansara Perdana, 47820, Petaling
Jaya, Malaysia
Tel.: (60) 376114000
Field Chemical Products Mfr & Distr
N.A.I.C.S.: 325998

Setegap Ventures Petroleum Sdn. Bhd. (1)
No 68 and 70 Fraser Business Park Jalan
Metro Pudu 2, 55200, Kuala Lumpur, Malaysia
Tel.: (60) 392326200
Web Site: https://www.svpetroleum.com.my
Oil & Gas Upstream Services
N.A.I.C.S.: 213112

UZTEL SA
243 Mihai Bravu street, Prahova,
Ploiesti, Romania
Tel.: (40) 244541399
Web Site: https://www.uztel.ro
Year Founded: 1856
UZT—(BUC)
Rev.: $8,605,393
Assets: $19,878,957
Liabilities: $7,492,902
Net Worth: $12,386,054
Earnings: ($2,925,446)
Emp.: 400
Fiscal Year-end: 12/31/20
Oil Field Machinery Mfr
N.A.I.C.S.: 333132
George Anghel *(Gen Mgr)*

V R FILMS & STUDIOS LIMITED
107 Abhishek Bldg Dalia Industrial
Estate Off New Link Road Andheri W,
Mumbai, 400068, Maharashtra, India
Tel.: (91) 2267024280
Web Site: https://www.vrfilms.in
Year Founded: 2007
542654—(BOM)
Rev.: $1,424,639

INTERNATIONAL PUBLIC

Assets: $2,709,933
Liabilities: $1,249,026
Net Worth: $1,460,908
Earnings: $98,591
Emp.: 37
Fiscal Year-end: 03/31/23
Entertainment Services
N.A.I.C.S.: 512110
Manish Dutt *(Mng Dir)*

V V FOOD & BEVERAGE CO., LTD.
No 300 Weiwei Avenue, Xuzhou,
221111, Jiangsu, China
Tel.: (86) 51683290169
Web Site: http://www.vvgroup.com
Year Founded: 2000
600300—(SHG)
Rev.: $592,800,867
Assets: $700,533,325
Liabilities: $262,452,051
Net Worth: $438,081,275
Earnings: $13,378,632
Fiscal Year-end: 12/31/22
Food & Beverage Mfr & Distr
N.A.I.C.S.: 311999
Ren Dong *(Chm)*

V-CUBE, INC.
NBF Platinum Tower 1-17-3 Shirokane, Minato-ku, Tokyo, 108-0072,
Japan
Tel.: (81) 54757250
Web Site: https://www.vcube.com
Year Founded: 1998
3681—(TKS)
Rev.: $78,585,560
Assets: $87,412,610
Liabilities: $82,123,470
Net Worth: $5,289,140
Earnings: ($39,867,070)
Emp.: 473
Fiscal Year-end: 12/31/23
Visual Communication Platform
N.A.I.C.S.: 513210
Naoaki Mashita *(Founder, Pres & CEO)*

Subsidiaries:

Kushim Inc. (1)
3rd floor VORT Minamiaoyama I 6-7-2 Minamiaoyama, Minato-ku, Tokyo,
Japan (41.13%)
Tel.: (81) 364277380
Web Site: https://www.kushim.co.jp
Rev.: $2,793,460
Assets: $437,176,490
Liabilities: $408,603,790
Net Worth: $28,572,700
Earnings: ($11,755,220)
Emp.: 5,439
Fiscal Year-end: 10/31/2023
Online Learning Services
N.A.I.C.S.: 513199
Fujiko Uchiyama *(Mng Exec Officer)*

Telecube, Inc. (1)
1-5-1 Marunouchi Shin Marunouchi Building
10F EGG, Chiyoda-ku, Tokyo, Japan
Tel.: (81) 363865319
Web Site: http://www.telecube.co.jp
Telecube Planning Development & Provision Services
N.A.I.C.S.: 541330
Hiroyuki Mashita *(Pres)*

V-cube (Thailand) Co., Ltd. (1)
622 Emporium Tower Room No 114 Floor
10/18 Sukhumvit Road, Klongton Klongtoey, Bangkok, 10110, Thailand
Tel.: (66) 97 019 3190
Web Site: https://www.v-cube.co.th
Telecube Planning Development & Provision Services
N.A.I.C.S.: 541330
Naoaki Mashita *(Pres & CEO)*

V-cube USA, Inc. (1)
13950 Milton Ave Ste 305, Westminster, CA
92683
Tel.: (310) 329-5959
Web Site: http://vcubewebcasting.com

AND PRIVATE COMPANIES

Video Recording & Live Streaming Services
N.A.I.C.S.: 518210
Raheem Maddox *(Dir-Video)*

V-GUARD INDUSTRIES LTD.
42/962 Vennala High School Road,
Vennala, Cochin, 682028, India
Tel.: (91) 4843005000
Web Site: https://www.vguard.in
532953—(BOM)
Rev.: $353,930,402
Assets: $203,685,734
Liabilities: $63,813,638
Net Worth: $139,872,096
Earnings: $26,355,504
Emp.: 2,302
Fiscal Year-end: 03/31/20
Electronic Voltage Stabilizers, PVC Wiring Cables, Pumps, Motors, Fans, Power Cables, Electric & Solar Water Heaters Mfr
N.A.I.C.S.: 335999
Kochouseph Chittilappilly *(Founder)*

Subsidiaries:

Sunflame Enterprises Private Limited (1)
58 Sector 27C Mathura Road, Faridabad, 121003, Haryana, India
Tel.: (91) 1294266999
Web Site: https://www.sunflame.com
Kitchen Product Mfr
N.A.I.C.S.: 332215

V-star Creations Pvt. Ltd. (1)
V-Star Tower VI/963 AB Model Engineering College Road, Thrikkakara Ernakulam, Cochin, 682 021, Kerala, India
Tel.: (91) 4842759999
Web Site: http://www.vstar.in
Sales Range: $25-49.9 Million
Garments Production Services
N.A.I.C.S.: 315210

V-MARC INDIA LIMITED
Plot No 3 4 18 & 20 Sector-IIDC SIDCUL, Haridwar, 249403, Uttarakhand, India
Tel.: (91) 1334239638
Web Site: https://www.v-marc.com
Year Founded: 1996
VMARCIND—(NSE)
Rev.: $24,708,861
Assets: $26,304,806
Liabilities: $16,842,544
Net Worth: $9,462,262
Earnings: $681,435
Fiscal Year-end: 03/31/22
Electrical Wire & Cable Mfr
N.A.I.C.S.: 336320

V-MART RETAIL LTD
610-611 Guru Ram Dass Nagar Main Market, Opp SBI Bank Laxmi Nagar, New Delhi, 110092, India
Tel.: (91) 4640030
Web Site: https://www.vmart.co.in
Year Founded: 2003
534976—(BOM)
Rev.: $149,672,305
Assets: $222,022,819
Liabilities: $109,379,375
Net Worth: $112,643,445
Earnings: ($846,709)
Emp.: 7,026
Fiscal Year-end: 03/31/21
Clothing Stores
N.A.I.C.S.: 458110
Lalit Agarwal *(Mng Dir)*

V-ONE TECH CO., LTD.
A-710 Sampyeong-Dong Uspace1 660 Daewangpangyo-Ro, Bundang-Gu, Seongnam, 13494, Gyeonggi-do, Korea (South)
Tel.: (82) 316075540
Web Site: https://www.v-one.co.kr
Year Founded: 2006

251630—(KRS)
Rev.: $45,853,688
Assets: $134,542,070
Liabilities: $59,955,335
Net Worth: $74,586,735
Earnings: ($503,503)
Emp.: 117
Fiscal Year-end: 12/31/22
Display Component Mfr
N.A.I.C.S.: 334419
Sun Joong Kim *(CEO)*

Subsidiaries:

TMS Europe B.V. (1)
Hurksestraat 43 Begane Grond, 5652 AH, Eindhoven, Netherlands
Tel.: (31) 404021122
Electronic Device Equipment Mfr & Distr
N.A.I.C.S.: 335999

V-TAC TECHNOLOGY CO., LTD.
31F-12 No 99 Sec 1 Xintai 5th Rd, Xizhi Dist, New Taipei City, Taiwan
Tel.: (886) 226971318
Web Site: https://www.vtac.com.tw
Year Founded: 1992
6229—(TPE)
Rev.: $35,999,050
Assets: $40,448,411
Liabilities: $19,543,510
Net Worth: $20,904,901
Earnings: $63,083
Fiscal Year-end: 12/31/23
Semiconductor Product Mfr
N.A.I.C.S.: 334413
Joe Hsu *(Founder & Pres)*

Subsidiaries:

A'Tech Enterprises Int'l Ltd. (1)
Unit G 18/F World Tech Centre 95 How Ming Street, kwun Tong, Kowloon, China (Hong Kong)
Tel.: (852) 2 754 9344
Micro Control Unit Product Mfr
N.A.I.C.S.: 334111

Jet Capital Technology (SZ) Limited (1)
Rm B 2/F T2-A Bldg Shenzhen Software Park Gaoxin Ave 7 S, Nanshan District, Shenzhen, China
Tel.: (86) 75526551055
Electronic Equipment Whslr
N.A.I.C.S.: 423690

Jet Captial Technology (SZ) Limited (1)
Rm B 2/F T2-A Bldg Gaoxin Ave 7 S, Shenzhen Software Park Nanshan District, Shenzhen, China
Tel.: (86) 7552 655 1055
Micro Control Unit Product Mfr
N.A.I.C.S.: 334111

V-TECHNOLOGY CO., LTD.
Yokohama Business Park YBP East Tower 9F 134 Godo-cho, Hodogaya-ku Kanagawa, Yokohama, 240-0005, Japan
Tel.: (81) 453381980
Web Site: https://www.vtec.co.jp
Year Founded: 1997
7717—(TKS)
Rev.: $246,784,350
Assets: $499,755,660
Liabilities: $270,791,870
Net Worth: $228,963,790
Earnings: $5,142,580
Emp.: 924
Fiscal Year-end: 03/31/24
Flat Panel Display System Mfr & Whslr
N.A.I.C.S.: 334419
Shigeto Sugimoto *(Pres & CEO)*

Subsidiaries:

Lumiotec Inc. (1)
4149-8 Hachimanpara 5-chome, Yonezawa, 992-1128, Yamagata, Japan

Tel.: (81) 238 29 0725
Web Site: http://www.lumiotec.com
Panel Lighting Equipment Mfr & Distr
N.A.I.C.S.: 335139
Futoshi Inoue *(Pres & CEO)*

Shanghai V Technology Co., Ltd. (1)
Unit 301 Block G Hongqiao Green Valley Plaza No 69 Yonghong Road, Minhang District, Shanghai, China
Tel.: (86) 2162172455
Flat Panel System Mfr & Distr
N.A.I.C.S.: 334419

V Technology Korea Co., Ltd. (1)
60 Beakseokgongdan 2-Gil, Seobuk-gu, Cheonan, 330-220, Chungcheongnam-Do, Korea (South)
Tel.: (82) 415646181
Flat Panel System Mfr & Distr
N.A.I.C.S.: 334419

V-TEC Co., Ltd. (1)
10F-2 No 660 Sec 3 Taiwan Blvd, Xitun Dist, Taichung, Taiwan
Tel.: (886) 427080505
Flat Panel System Mfr & Distr
N.A.I.C.S.: 334419

V-ZUG HOLDING AG
Industriestrasse 66, 6302, Zug, Switzerland
Tel.: (41) 587676767
Web Site: https://www.vzug.com
Year Founded: 1913
VZUG—(SWX)
Rev.: $724,900,222
Assets: $672,771,619
Liabilities: $169,650,776
Net Worth: $503,120,843
Earnings: $8,800,443
Emp.: 2,193
Fiscal Year-end: 12/31/22
Holding Company
N.A.I.C.S.: 551112

V. B. DESAI FINANCIAL SERVICES LIMITED.
Cama Building 1st Floor 24/26 Dalal Street, Fort, Mumbai, 400 001, India
Tel.: (91) 2240770777
Web Site: https://www.vbdesai.com
511110—(BOM)
Rev.: $332,018
Assets: $1,388,442
Liabilities: $67,082
Net Worth: $1,321,360
Earnings: $37,132
Emp.: 5
Fiscal Year-end: 03/31/23
Banking & Corporate Advisory Services
N.A.I.C.S.: 523150
Pradip Ratilal Shroff *(Mng Dir)*

V. MANE FILS SA
620 route de Grasse, Le Bar sur Loup, 06620, Paris, France
Tel.: (33) 4 93 09 70 00   FR
Web Site: http://www.mane.com
Year Founded: 1871
Fragrance & Flavor Mfr
N.A.I.C.S.: 311930
Jean M. Mane *(Pres & CEO)*

Subsidiaries:

BANAWI MANE FLAVORS Co., Ltd. (1)
South Industrial Area - Phase 2 Street 11, 22423, Jeddah, Saudi Arabia
Tel.: (966) 26082529
Food Ingredient Mfr
N.A.I.C.S.: 311230
Abdul Saboor *(Reg Mgr-Sls)*

Kancor Ingredients Ltd. (1)
Kancor House 814/C Seaport Airport Rd, Thrikkakara PO, Kerala, 682 021, Ernakulam, India
Tel.: (91) 484 3051 100
Web Site: http://www.kancor.in
Food & Pharmaceutical Additives Mfr

N.A.I.C.S.: 311942
Geemon Korah *(CEO)*

Subsidiary (Domestic):

OmniActive Health Technologies, Inc. (2)
Phoenix House T- 8 A Wing 462 Senapati Bapat Marg Lower Parel, Mumbai, 400 013, India
Tel.: (91) 22 24970003
Web Site: http://www.omniactives.com
Flavor Extract Mfr
N.A.I.C.S.: 311942
Sanjaya Mariwala *(Mng Dir)*

Subsidiary (US):

OmniActive Health Technologies, Inc. (2)
67 E Park Pl Ste 500, Morristown, NJ 07960
Tel.: (866) 588-3629
Flavor Extract Mfr
N.A.I.C.S.: 311942

Plant (Domestic):

OmniActive Health Technologies, Inc. - Pune Plant (2)
Plot No 38 & 39 Phase-II, Hinjewadi, Pune, 411 057, Maharashtra, India
Tel.: (91) 20 66742700
Flavor Extract Mfr
N.A.I.C.S.: 311942

MANE AUSTRIA GmbH (1)
Landstrasser Hauptstrasse 97-99/3/1, 1030, Vienna, Austria
Tel.: (43) 18900941
Food Ingredient Mfr
N.A.I.C.S.: 311230
Andreas Reichenbach *(Gen Mgr)*

MANE CHILE, S.A. (1)
Alcalde Guzman 1450, 8700216, Santiago, Quilicura, Chile
Tel.: (56) 29253600
Food Ingredient Mfr
N.A.I.C.S.: 311230
Patricio Astudillo *(Acct Mgr-Flavors)*

MANE DEUTSCHLAND GmbH (1)
Mittelweg 41b, 20148, Hamburg, Germany
Tel.: (49) 404147770
Food Ingredient Mfr
N.A.I.C.S.: 311230
Martina Klein *(Product Mgr-Mktg)*

MANE INDIA Private Limited (1)
Survey No 586-587 Quthbullapur Mandal, Dundigal village R R district, Hyderabad, Andhra Pradesh, India
Tel.: (91) 8418339000
Food Ingredient Mfr
N.A.I.C.S.: 311230
Nadiminti Sekhar *(Deputy Mgr-Regulatory Affairs & Product Safety)*

MANE ITALIA s.r.l. (1)
Via Adamello 5/7, 20010, Bareggio, Italy
Tel.: (39) 023313315
Food Ingredient Mfr
N.A.I.C.S.: 311230

MANE Iberica S.A. (1)
Ctra Molins de Rei a Sabadell KM 13 3, 08191, Rubi, Spain
Tel.: (34) 935881221
Food Ingredient Mfr
N.A.I.C.S.: 311230
Joaquim Vives *(Gen Mgr)*

MANE Inc. (1)
999 Tech Dr, Milford, OH 45150
Tel.: (513) 248-9876
Food Ingredient Mfr
N.A.I.C.S.: 311230

MANE Ltd. (1)
Unit 23 Pullman Business Park 4 Mallard Way Pride Park, Derby, DE24 8GX, Derbyshire, United Kingdom
Tel.: (44) 1332221742
Food Ingredient Mfr
N.A.I.C.S.: 311230
Bryn Williams *(Dir-Flavours)*

MANE MEXICO, S.A. DE C.V. (1)
Av La Paz No 1690-304 Col Americana, 44160, Guadalajara, Jalisco, Mexico

V. MANE FILS SA

V. Mane Fils SA—(Continued)
Tel.: (52) 3338270068
Food Ingredient Mfr
N.A.I.C.S.: 311230

MANE POLSKA Sp. z o.o. (1)
Ul Taneczna 18, 02-892, Warsaw, Poland
Tel.: (48) 224671813
Food Ingredient Mfr
N.A.I.C.S.: 311230
Krystyna Jaskolska *(Mgr-Comml)*

MANE SA (PTY) LTD (1)
Unit 1 Bertie Park 12 Bertie Avenue Epping Industria 2, 7460, Cape Town, South Africa
Tel.: (27) 215344422
Food Ingredient Mfr
N.A.I.C.S.: 311230

MANE SHANGHAI CO., Ltd. (1)
Rm 06 23F D Block Royal Harbour Building No 37, Zhujiang Xincheng Linjiang Dadao Tianhe District, 510620, Guangzhou, China
Tel.: (86) 2038665596
Food Ingredient Mfr
N.A.I.C.S.: 311230

MANE TAIWAN Fragrances and Flavours Co., Ltd
1F No 6 Ln 92 Sec 1 Jianguo N Rd, Zhongshan Dist, 10491, Taipei, Taiwan
Tel.: (886) 225033325
Food Ingredient Mfr
N.A.I.C.S.: 311230

Mane Aroma ve Esans San. ve Tic. Ltd. Sti
Girne Mah Irmak Sok Kucukyali Is Merkezi B Blok No 3, 34852, Istanbul, Turkiye
Tel.: (90) 2164659700
Food Ingredient Mfr
N.A.I.C.S.: 311230
Merve Budak *(Acct Mgr)*

Mane SA
Route de I Industrie 21, CP 176, 1896, Monthey, Switzerland
Tel.: (41) 244811681
Food Ingredient Mfr
N.A.I.C.S.: 311230

Mane Vostok LLC (1)
65 Kashirskoe shosse, 115583, Moscow, Russia
Tel.: (7) 4959358939
Food Ingredient Mfr
N.A.I.C.S.: 311230

Mane do Brasil Industria E Comercio Ltda (1)
Estrada de Guerengue 1421, Jacarepagua, 22713-001, Rio de Janeiro, Brazil
Tel.: (55) 2121961500
Food Ingredient Mfr
N.A.I.C.S.: 311230
Tania Fazzi *(Mgr-Tech & Innovation)*

PT. MANE INDONESIA (1)
Jl Jababeka XVI Blok V-66 Cikarang Industrial Estate, Cikarang, 17530, Bekasi, Indonesia
Tel.: (62) 218937640
Food Ingredient Mfr
N.A.I.C.S.: 311230

V MANE FILS Ghana (PTY) LTD (1)
Oaklands 26 Mensah Wood Street Next to Ghana Link East Lagon, PO Box 8483, Accra, Ghana
Tel.: (233) 302541934
Food Ingredient Mfr
N.A.I.C.S.: 311230

V. MANE FILS JAPAN, Ltd. (1)
1-7-16 Sendagaya, Shibuya-Ku, Tokyo, 151-0051, Japan
Tel.: (81) 357711871
Food Ingredient Mfr
N.A.I.C.S.: 311230

V. MANE FILS NIGERIA LTD (1)
3 Ijora Causeway-Ijora, Lagos, Nigeria
Tel.: (234) 9038358559
Food Ingredient Mfr
N.A.I.C.S.: 311230

V. MANE Fils (Thailand) Co., LTD (1)
No 520 5th Floor Unit 5 A Kabaraye Pagoda Road, Ko Min ko Chin Quarter Bahan Township, Yangon, Myanmar
Tel.: (95) 1552943
Food Ingredient Mfr
N.A.I.C.S.: 311230
Nicolas Bres *(Mng Dir)*

V. R. WOODART LIMITED
1-2 Shiv Smriti Chambers 49-A Dr Annie Besant Road, Worli, Mumbai, 400018, Maharashtra, India
Tel.: (91) 22 4351 4444
Web Site: http://www.vrwoodart.com
Sales Range: Less than $1 Million
Wood Product Mfr & Whslr
N.A.I.C.S.: 321999
Anwar Shaikh *(CFO)*

V.A. TRANSPORT INC.
600 Louis Pasteur St, Boucherville, J4B 7Z1, QC, Canada
Tel.: (450) 641-0082
Web Site: http://www.vatransport.com
Year Founded: 1978
Rev.: $12,743,710
Emp.: 58
Transportation Services
N.A.I.C.S.: 485999
Viateur Audet *(Pres & Gen Mgr)*

Subsidiaries:

V.A. Transport Inc. - Warehousing Division (1)
265 chemin du Tremblay, Boucherville, J4B 7M1, QC, Canada
Tel.: (450) 641-0082
General Warehousing & Storage Services
N.A.I.C.S.: 493110

V.I.P SALES LTD
30270 Automall Dr, Abbotsford, V2T 5M1, BC, Canada
Tel.: (604) 857-1600
Web Site: http://www.vipmazda.com
Year Founded: 1954
Rev.: $11,646,759
Emp.: 26
New & Used Car Dealers
N.A.I.C.S.: 441110
Crystal Warkentin *(Controller-Fin)*

V.I.P. COMPUTER CENTRE LIMITED
VIP House Unit 4 Hardwick Grange, Woolston, Warrington, WA1 4RF, Cheshire, United Kingdom
Tel.: (44) 1925 286 900
Web Site: http://www.vip-computers.com
Year Founded: 1990
Sales Range: $250-299.9 Million
Computer Components, Peripherals & Associated Products Distr
N.A.I.C.S.: 423430
Jatti Sahni *(Owner)*

Subsidiaries:

Ergo Computing UK Limited (1)
Ergo House Mere Way Ruddington Fields Business Park, Nottingham, NG11 6JS, United Kingdom
Tel.: (44) 115 914 4144
Web Site: http://www.ergo.co.uk
Emp.: 20
Computer Peripheral Equipment Distr
N.A.I.C.S.: 423430
Anna Johnston *(Mgr-Pur)*

VIP Computers BV (1)
Bliek 12, 4941 SG, Raamsdonksveer, Netherlands
Tel.: (31) 162 581440
Web Site: http://www.vip-computers.com
Computer Peripheral Equipment Distr
N.A.I.C.S.: 423430

VIP Computers LLC (1)
2555 NW 102nd Ave Ste 205, Miami, FL 33172
Tel.: (305) 809-8823
Web Site: http://www.vip-computers.com
Computer Peripheral Equipment Distr
N.A.I.C.S.: 423430

Viridian Reverse Logistics, LLC (1)
2555 NW 102 Ave Ste 208, Miami, FL 33172
Tel.: (305) 873-6277
Web Site: http://www.viridianrl.com
Data Security Services
N.A.I.C.S.: 541519

V.L. ENTERPRISE PUBLIC COMPANY LIMITED
41 Asoke-Dindaeng Road, Makkasan Ratchathewi, Bangkok, 10400, Thailand
Tel.: (66) 22546604
Web Site: https://www.vlenterprise.co.th
Year Founded: 1991
VL—(THA)
Rev.: $22,058,620
Assets: $55,470,289
Liabilities: $25,646,897
Net Worth: $29,823,392
Earnings: $904,659
Fiscal Year-end: 12/31/23
Petroleum Product Distr
N.A.I.C.S.: 486910
Chutipa Klinsuwan *(Co-Chm & CEO)*

V.S. INDUSTRY BERHAD
88 Lot 65 Jalan I-Park SAC 5 Taman Perindustrian I-Park SAC, 81400, Senai, Johor Darul Takzim, Malaysia
Tel.: (60) 75973399
Web Site: https://www.vs-i.com
VS—(KLS)
Rev.: $974,438,307
Assets: $855,563,810
Liabilities: $373,266,455
Net Worth: $482,297,354
Earnings: $35,834,709
Emp.: 11,755
Fiscal Year-end: 07/31/23
Plastic Injection Machinery Mfr
N.A.I.C.S.: 333248
Mui Kiow Ang *(Co-Sec)*

Subsidiaries:

Guardian South East Asia Pte. Ltd. (1)
Vision Exchange 2 Venture Drive 13-08, Singapore, 608526, Singapore
Tel.: (65) 68988998
Web Site: https://www.guardiansea.com
Driver Safety Services
N.A.I.C.S.: 611699

PT. V.S. Technology Indonesia (1)
Kawasan Industri Delta Silicon III Jl Cendana Raya Blok F10 No 06B, Desa Serang Kec Cikarang Selatan Lippo Cikarang, 17550, Bekasi, West Java, Indonesia
Tel.: (62) 2129288998
Web Site: https://www.vstechnology.co.id
Emp.: 1,200
Plastic Mold Mfr
N.A.I.C.S.: 333511
Mohamad Yusof *(Pres)*

V.S. Integrated Management Sdn. Bhd. (1)
Unit 901 Level 9 City Plaza 21 Jalan Tebrau, 80300, Johor Bahru, Malaysia
Tel.: (60) 73331898
Hostel Management Services
N.A.I.C.S.: 721199

V.S. International Group Limited (1)
40th Floor Jardine House 1 Connaught Place, Central, China (Hong Kong)
Tel.: (852) 25119002
Web Site: http://www.vs-ig.com
Rev.: $18,599,847
Assets: $56,463,401
Liabilities: $10,200,875
Net Worth: $46,262,526
Earnings: ($7,391,923)
Emp.: 253
Fiscal Year-end: 07/31/2022
Plastic Product Mfr & Whslr
N.A.I.C.S.: 326199
Kim Ling Beh *(Chm)*

INTERNATIONAL PUBLIC

V.S. Technology Sdn. Bhd. (1)
PLO 7 Jalan Perindustrian Senai Industrial Estate, 81400, Senai, Johor, Malaysia
Tel.: (60) 75995050
Plastic Mold Mfr
N.A.I.C.S.: 333511

V.S.T TILLERS TRACTORS LIMITED
Plot No-1 Dyavasandra Indl Layout Whitefield Road Mahadevapura Post, Bengaluru, 560 048, India
Tel.: (91) 8067141111
Web Site: https://www.vsttractors.com
VSTTILLERS—(NSE)
Rev.: $77,431,036
Assets: $99,459,584
Liabilities: $20,711,519
Net Worth: $78,748,065
Earnings: $2,457,806
Emp.: 758
Fiscal Year-end: 03/31/21
Power Tillers, Tractors & Other Agricultural Equipment Mfr
N.A.I.C.S.: 333111
V. K. Surendra *(Chm)*

V2 RETAIL LIMITED
Khasra No 928 Extended Lal Dora Abadi Village Kapashera Border, Tehsil Vasant Vihar, New Delhi, 110 037, India
Tel.: (91) 1141771850
Web Site: https://www.v2retail.com
Year Founded: 2001
532867—(BOM)
Rev.: $76,660,147
Assets: $110,969,914
Liabilities: $74,293,101
Net Worth: $36,676,813
Earnings: ($1,753,029)
Emp.: 2,799
Fiscal Year-end: 03/31/21
Garments Whslr
N.A.I.C.S.: 424350
Ram Chandra Agarwal *(Chm & Mng Dir)*

V2Y CORPORATION LTD.
16 Raffles Quay 17-03 Hong Leong Building, Singapore, 048581, Singapore
Tel.: (65) 67451668
Web Site: https://v2y.si
Year Founded: 2015
E-commerce Services, Warehousing & Logistics
N.A.I.C.S.: 493110
Shen Chieh Ong *(CEO & Exec Dir)*

VA AUTOMOTIVE AB
Frykholmsgatan 11, Box 34, 281 21, Hasslehom, Sweden
Tel.: (46) 451 425 00
Web Site: http://www.va-automotive.com
Automotive Components Mfr
N.A.I.C.S.: 336390
Lars Thunberg *(CEO)*

VA TECH WABAG LIMITED
WABAG House No 17 200 Feet Thoraipakkam Pallavaram Main Road Sunnambu, Kolathur, Chennai, 600 117, India
Tel.: (91) 4461232323
Web Site: https://www.wabag.com
533269—(NSE)
Rev.: $388,028,550
Assets: $568,006,530
Liabilities: $377,406,120
Net Worth: $190,600,410
Earnings: $13,761,930
Emp.: 1,065
Fiscal Year-end: 03/31/21

Drinking Water & Wastewater Plant Construction Services
N.A.I.C.S.: 237990
Rajiv D. Mittal *(Grp CEO & Mng Dir)*

Subsidiaries:

Beijing VA TECH WABAG Water Treatment Technology Co., Ltd. (1)
Rm 1113 Tower B Fullink Plaza, No 18 Chaoyangmenwai Street, Chaoyang District, 100020, Beijing, China
Tel.: (86) 10 6588 6300
Water Treatment Plant Construction Services
N.A.I.C.S.: 221310

VA TECH WABAG (Hong Kong) Limited (1)
Room 1902 19th Fl Asia Oliean tower 23, Wan Chai, Hong Kong, China (Hong Kong)
Tel.: (852) 24266426
Drinking & Waste Water Management Services
N.A.I.C.S.: 221310

VA TECH WABAG (SPAIN) S.L. (1)
Zurbano 76 4, 28010, Madrid, Spain
Tel.: (34) 917901133
Waste Treatment Services
N.A.I.C.S.: 221310

VA TECH WABAG Algerie S.A.R.L. (1)
2 rue Bois des Pin Kouba, 16050, Algiers, Algeria
Tel.: (213) 21 68 9315
Water Treatment Plant Construction Services
N.A.I.C.S.: 221310

VA TECH WABAG Deutschland GmbH (1)
Barmeisterallee 13-15, 04442, Zwenkau, Germany
Tel.: (49) 3420343546
Water Treatment Plant Construction Services
N.A.I.C.S.: 221310

VA TECH WABAG Egypt LLC (1)
El Gehaz Street Villa No 49 Cairo, Fifth District-Region 6-district 4, New Cairo, Egypt
Tel.: (20) 1227706675
Web Site: http://www.wabag.com
Water Treatment Plant Construction Services
N.A.I.C.S.: 221310

VA TECH WABAG GmbH (1)
Dresdner Str 87-91, 1200, Vienna, Austria
Tel.: (43) 1251050
Web Site: http://www.wabag.com
Emp.: 8
Water Treatment Plant Construction Services
N.A.I.C.S.: 221310

VA TECH WABAG Muscat LLC (1)
Flat No 32 Building No P/22 Azaiba, PO Box 997, 116, Muscat, Oman
Tel.: (968) 22005390
Water Treatment Plant Construction Services
N.A.I.C.S.: 221310

VA TECH WABAG Su Teknolojisi Ve Tycaret Lymyted Sirket (1)
Oruc Reis Mah Tekstilkent Cad Koza Plaza No 12 A-Blok Kat 8 D 29-32, Esenler, 34235, Istanbul, Turkiye
Tel.: (90) 2124381226
Water Treatment Plant Construction Services
N.A.I.C.S.: 221310

VA TECH WABAG Tunisie S.A.R.L. (1)
21 rue Abdelaziz Mastouri El Menzah 9, Ariana, 1013, Tunis, Tunisia
Tel.: (216) 71883433
Water Treatment Plant Construction Services
N.A.I.C.S.: 221310

VA Tech Wabag (Philippines) Inc. (1)
7/F Peninsula Court Building 8735, Paseo de Roxas, Makati, 1226, Philippines
Tel.: (63) 24798100

Drinking & Waste Water Plant Consturction Services
N.A.I.C.S.: 237990

WABAG Wassertechnik AG (1)
Burglistrasse 31, 8401, Winterthur, Switzerland
Tel.: (41) 52 262 4343
Water Treatment Plant Construction Services
N.A.I.C.S.: 221310

WABAG Water Services (Macao) Ltd. (1)
Coloane ETAR Estrada Seac Pai Van S/N, Etar de Coloane, Coloane, China (Macau)
Tel.: (853) 3 28882080
Water Treatment Plant Construction Services
N.A.I.C.S.: 221310

Wabag Muhibbah JV SDN. BHD. (1)
12th Floor Menara Symphony No 5 Jalan Prof Khoo Kaykim Seksyen 13, 46000, Petaling Jaya, Selangor, Malaysia
Tel.: (60) 333424323
Environmental Consulting Services
N.A.I.C.S.: 541620

VA-Q-TEC AG

AlfredNobelStr 33, 97080, Wurzburg, Germany
Tel.: (49) 931359420
Web Site: https://www.va-q-tec.com
Year Founded: 2001
VQT—(DEU)
Rev.: $127,814,339
Assets: $178,297,460
Liabilities: $114,862,548
Net Worth: $63,434,911
Earnings: $2,655,455
Emp.: 625
Fiscal Year-end: 12/31/21
Insulation Panel Mfr & Distr
N.A.I.C.S.: 326140
Joachim Kuhn *(Founder, CEO & Member-Mgmt Bd)*

Subsidiaries:

va-Q-tec India Ltd. (1)
606 B-Wing Satellite Gazebo Near Solitaire park Guru Hargovindji Road, Chakala Andheri East, Mumbai, 400 093, India
Tel.: (91) 2246028035
Metal Container Mfr & Distr
N.A.I.C.S.: 332439

va-Q-tec Japan G.K. (1)
5-13-1 Toranomon Minatoku 7F Toranomon 40MT Building, Tokyo, 105-0001, Japan
Tel.: (81) 8059564808
Building Materials Distr
N.A.I.C.S.: 423330

va-Q-tec Korea Ltd. (1)
1706ho 2dong Ace High-tech City B/D Gyeongin-ro 775, Yeongdungpo-gu, Seoul, 07299, Korea (South)
Tel.: (82) 263098989
Building Materials Distr
N.A.I.C.S.: 423330

va-Q-tec Limited (1)
105 Laker Road, Rochester Airport Industrial Estate, Rochester, ME1 3QX, Kent, United Kingdom
Tel.: (44) 1634868618
Building Materials Distr
N.A.I.C.S.: 423330

va-Q-tec SG Pte. Ltd. (1)
11 Changi South Street 3 B1-01, Singapore, 486122, Singapore
Tel.: (65) 68176767
Building Materials Distr
N.A.I.C.S.: 423330

va-Q-tec USA Inc. (1)
2221 Cabot Blvd W, Langhorne, PA 19047
Tel.: (267) 512-6913
Building Materials Distr
N.A.I.C.S.: 423330

va-Q-tec Uruguay S.A. (1)
Zonamerica Business & Technology Park Edificio, Celebra-Oficina 103 Ruta 8 Km 17 500, 91600, Montevideo, Uruguay

Tel.: (598) 25182997
Building Materials Distr
N.A.I.C.S.: 423330

VAARAD VENTURES LIMITED

Flat No 5 Sannidhan Plot No 145 Indulal D Bhuva Marg Wadala, Mumbai, 400031, Maharashtra, India
Tel.: (91) 2224117080
Web Site: http://www.vaaradventures.com
532320—(BOM)
Assets: $3,423,428
Liabilities: $692,057
Net Worth: $2,731,371
Earnings: ($27,085)
Fiscal Year-end: 03/31/23
Portfolio Management Services
N.A.I.C.S.: 523940
Leena V. Doshi *(Mng Dir)*

VADILAL ENTERPRISES LTD

Vadilal House Nr Navrangpura Rly Crossing, Navangapura, Ahmedabad, 9, Gujarat, India
Tel.: (91) 7926564018
Web Site: https://www.vadilalgroup.com
Year Founded: 1985
519152—(BOM)
Rev.: $46,946,472
Assets: $19,636,658
Liabilities: $19,147,128
Net Worth: $489,530
Earnings: $116,530
Emp.: 566
Fiscal Year-end: 03/31/21
Frozen Food Products
N.A.I.C.S.: 424420
Rajesh Bhagat *(CFO)*

Subsidiaries:

Vadilal Enterprises Ltd - Forex Division (1)
Nr Navarangpura Railway Crossing, Ahmedabad, 380009, Gujarat, India
Tel.: (91) 7926564025
Web Site: http://www.vadilalmarkets.com
Sales Range: $25-49.9 Million
Emp.: 40
Marketing Services
N.A.I.C.S.: 541613
Hemandra Bhatia *(Deputy Gen Mgr)*

Vadilal Enterprises Ltd - Ice-cream Division (1)
Vadilal House Nr Navrangpura Rly Crossing Navangapura, Ahmedabad, 380009, Gujarat, India
Tel.: (91) 7926564018
Web Site: http://www.vadilalgroup.com
Sales Range: $75-99.9 Million
Emp.: 150
Ice Cream Suppliers
N.A.I.C.S.: 424430

Vadilal Enterprises Ltd - Processed Food Division (1)
Vadilal House Nr Navrangpura Rly Crossing, 53 Srimali Society, Ahmedabad, 380009, Gujarat, India
Tel.: (91) 7926564019
Web Site: http://www.vadilalgroup.com
Sales Range: $25-49.9 Million
Emp.: 40
Processed Food Suppliers
N.A.I.C.S.: 445298

Vadilal Enterprises Ltd - Real Estate Division (1)
Nr Navarangpura Railway Crossing, Ahmedabad, 380009, Gujarat, India
Tel.: (91) 7926564019
Web Site: http://www.vadilalgroup.com
Sales Range: $150-199.9 Million
Real Estate Managemnt Services
N.A.I.C.S.: 531390
Vishal Shruthi *(Mgr-Mktg)*

VADILAL INDUSTRIES LIMITED

Vadilal House Shrimali Society Nr Navrangpura Rly Crossing Navangapura, Ahmedabad, 380 009, Gujarat, India
Tel.: (91) 7926564019
Web Site: https://www.vadilalgroup.com
Year Founded: 1907
519156—(BOM)
Rev.: $128,485,043
Assets: $100,461,735
Liabilities: $52,830,322
Net Worth: $47,631,413
Earnings: $11,545,519
Emp.: 638
Fiscal Year-end: 03/31/23
Ice Cream Mfr & Whslr
N.A.I.C.S.: 311520
Kalpit R. Gandhi *(CFO)*

VADIVARHE SPECIALITY CHEMICALS LIMITED

1st Floor K K Chambers Sir P T Road Fort, Mumbai, 400001, Maharashtra, India
Tel.: (91) 2261872121
Web Site: https://www.vscl.in
Year Founded: 2009
VSCL—(NSE)
Chemical Products Mfr
N.A.I.C.S.: 325199

VADO CORP.

Dlha 816/9, Nitra, 94901, Slovakia
Tel.: (421) 372302900 NV
Year Founded: 2017
VADP—(OTCIQ)
Assets: $48,154
Liabilities: $10,354
Net Worth: $37,800
Earnings: ($34,956)
Fiscal Year-end: 11/30/22
Embroidery Services
N.A.I.C.S.: 333248

VAESSEN INDUSTRIES NV

Kruishoefstraat 50, Dilsen, 3650, Belgium
Tel.: (32) 89790542
Web Site: http://www.vaessenindustries.com
Year Founded: 1975
Emp.: 1,250
Holding Company; Heating, Lighting & Metal Products Mfr
N.A.I.C.S.: 551112

Subsidiaries:

VASCO GMBH (1)
Flugplatz 21, 44319, Dortmund, Germany
Tel.: (49) 2314773150
Web Site: http://www.vasco.eu
Heating Equipment Distr
N.A.I.C.S.: 423720

VASCO GROUP SRL (1)
Via Murialdo 15, 31046, Oderzo, Treviso, Italy
Tel.: (39) 0422714905
Web Site: http://www.vasco.eu
Heating Equipment Distr
N.A.I.C.S.: 423720

VASCO GROUP Sarl (1)
1/5 Rue Jean Monnet, 94130, Nogent-sur-Marne, France
Tel.: (33) 148720341
Web Site: https://www.vasco.eu
Heating Equipment Distr
N.A.I.C.S.: 423720

VASCO Ltd (1)
11 Winward Close, Lower Darwen, Darwen, BB3 0SE, Lancashire, United Kingdom
Tel.: (44) 1254704420
Web Site: http://www.vasco.eu
Heating Equipment Distr
N.A.I.C.S.: 423720
Dave Thornback *(Mgr-Sls)*

Vasco Group NV (1)

VAESSEN INDUSTRIES NV

Vaessen Industries nv—(Continued)
Kruishoefstraat 50, B-3650, Dilsen, Belgium
Tel.: (32) 89790411
Heating & Ventilation Equipment Mfr
N.A.I.C.S.: 333415
Patrick Nijs *(CEO)*

Subsidiary (Non-US):

Brugman International B.V. (2)
Boskampstraat 26, NL-7651 AM, Tubbergen, Netherlands
Tel.: (31) 546629320
Web Site: http://www.brugman.net
Sales Range: $50-74.9 Million
Emp.: 83
Holding Company; Industrial Heating Equipment Mfr
N.A.I.C.S.: 551112

Subsidiary (Non-US):

Brugman Fabryka Grzejnikow Sp. z o.o. (3)
Ul Jaworzynska 295, 59-220, Legnica, Poland
Tel.: (48) 768508300
Web Site: https://brugman.eu
Emp.: 83
Industrial Heating Equipment Mfr
N.A.I.C.S.: 333415

Subsidiary (Domestic):

Brugman Radiatorenfabriek B.V. (3)
Boskampstraat 26, NL-7651 AM, Tubbergen, Netherlands
Tel.: (31) 546629320
Web Site: https://brugman.eu
Sales Range: $50-74.9 Million
Industrial Heating Equipment Mfr
N.A.I.C.S.: 333415

Subsidiary (Domestic):

Superia Radiatoren, N.V. (2)
Remi Claeysstraat 66, 8210, Zedelgem, Belgium
Tel.: (32) 50209461
Web Site: http://www.superia.be
Sales Range: $25-49.9 Million
Emp.: 90
Standard Plate Radiator Mfr
N.A.I.C.S.: 333414
Bart Berton *(Mgr-Sls)*

Subsidiary (Non-US):

The Heating Company Denmark A/S (2)
Ambolten 14, 6000, Kolding, Denmark
Tel.: (45) 44857466
Web Site: http://www.thor-radiatorer.dk
Sales Range: $25-49.9 Million
Emp.: 1
Heating Equipment Distr
N.A.I.C.S.: 423730
Hans Eric Hanson *(Mgr-Ops)*

The Heating Company France SARL (2)
35th Ave de Belgique, 68110, Illzach, France
Tel.: (33) 389818090
Web Site: http://www.theheatingcompany.com
Sales Range: $25-49.9 Million
Emp.: 20
Heating Equipment Distr
N.A.I.C.S.: 423730

The Heating Company Germany GmbH (2)
Offenbergweg 5, 48432, Rheine, Germany
Tel.: (49) 597197470
Web Site: http://www.brugman.de
Heating Equipment Distr
N.A.I.C.S.: 423730

Subsidiary (Domestic):

VASCO bvba (2)
Kruishoefstraat 50, 3650, Dilsen, Belgium
Tel.: (32) 89790411
Sales Range: $50-74.9 Million
Heating Equipment Mfr & Distr
N.A.I.C.S.: 333415
Patrick Nigs *(Gen Mgr)*

VAGAR A.D.
Temerinska 47, Novi Sad, Serbia
Tel.: (381) 21 895389
Web Site: http://www.vagarns.com
Year Founded: 2005
VGAR—(BEL)
Sales Range: $1-9.9 Million
Emp.: 60
Industrial Machinery Mfr
N.A.I.C.S.: 333998
Milos Vlajkov *(Dir)*

VAGHANI TECHNO-BUILD LIMITED
D-Wing Karma Sankalp Corner of 6th & 7th Road Of Rajawadi, Ghatkopar East, Mumbai, 400 077, India
Tel.: (91) 2225018800   In
Web Site: https://www.vaghanitechnobuild.com
Year Founded: 1994
531676—(BOM)
Rev.: $19,172
Assets: $878,820
Liabilities: $7,913
Net Worth: $870,907
Earnings: $7,146
Emp.: 1
Fiscal Year-end: 03/31/23
TDR Trading Services
N.A.I.C.S.: 523160
Kantilal Manilal Savla *(Chm)*

VAIBHAV GLOBAL LIMITED
K-6B Adarsh Nagar Fateh Tiba, Jaipur, 302 004, Rajasthan, India
Tel.: (91) 1412601020   In
Web Site: https://www.vaibhavglobal.com
Year Founded: 1989
532156—(BOM)
Rev.: $325,944,668
Assets: $214,437,324
Liabilities: $70,201,451
Net Worth: $144,235,873
Earnings: $12,605,683
Emp.: 1,199
Fiscal Year-end: 03/31/23
Online Jewelry & Accessories Retailer
N.A.I.C.S.: 458310
R. Rahimullah *(Exec Dir)*

Subsidiaries:

Encase Packaging Private Limited (1)
1200 Thespia Dr, Sri City, 517541, Andhra Pradesh, India
Tel.: (91) 8712609173
Web Site: https://www.encasepackaging.com
Packaging Products Mfr
N.A.I.C.S.: 333993

P.T. STS Bali (1)
Jln Sekar Tunjung 6A, Gatot Subrato Timur, Denpasar, 80237, Bali, Indonesia
Tel.: (62) 361290366
Jewelry Whslr
N.A.I.C.S.: 423940

STS Jewels Inc. (1)
100 Michael Angelo Way Ste 400D, Austin, TX 78728
Tel.: (512) 852-7080
Web Site: https://www.stsjewels.com
Sales Range: $25-49.9 Million
Online Jewelry Sales
N.A.I.C.S.: 423940
Sunil Agrawal *(CEO)*

Subsidiary (Non-US):

STS Gems Japan Limited (2)
401 Wada Building 1-13-10 Higashi Ueno, Taito-Ku, Tokyo, 110-0015, Japan
Tel.: (81) 3 3831 2270
Platinum Jewelry Distr
N.A.I.C.S.: 423940

STS Gems Limited (2)
Unit-614 6/F Heng Ngai Jewellery Cente 4 Hok Yuen Street, East Hung Hom, Kowloon, China (Hong Kong)
Tel.: (852) 23675066
Gemstone & Jewelry Mfr
N.A.I.C.S.: 339910

STS Gems Thai Limited (2)
919/478-479 Jewelery Trade Center BLDG 40th Floor Silom Road, Bangrak, 10500, Bangkok, Thailand
Tel.: (66) 223 757 2224
Web Site: https://www.stsgemsthai.com
Jewelry Product Mfr & Distr
N.A.I.C.S.: 339910
Anshu Abhishek *(Mgr-Mdsg)*

Unit (Domestic):

Shop LC (2)
100 Michael Angelo Way Ste 300D, Austin, TX 78728
Tel.: (512) 852-7017
Web Site: https://www.shoplc.com
Online Jewelry Sales
N.A.I.C.S.: 458310
Kevin Lyons *(Pres)*

Shop LC Global Inc. (1)
100 Michael Angelo Way Bldg D Ste 200, Austin, TX 78728
Web Site: https://www.shoplc.com
Fashion Product Distr
N.A.I.C.S.: 424350

The Jewellery Channel Limited (2)
Surrey House Plane Tree Crescent, Feltham, TW13 7HF, Mddx, United Kingdom
Tel.: (44) 844 375 2525
Web Site: http://www.thejewellerychannel.tv
Television Jewelry Sales
N.A.I.C.S.: 458310
Colin Wegstaffe *(Mng Dir)*

VAIDYA SANE AYURVED LABORATORIES LTD.
701 Ishan Arcade Tower No 2 Gokhale Road Naupada, Thane, 400602, Maharashtra, India
Tel.: (91) 9595079808
Web Site: https://madhavbaug.org
Year Founded: 1999
MADHAVBAUG—(NSE)
Rev.: $12,053,210
Assets: $6,580,397
Liabilities: $1,730,052
Net Worth: $4,850,345
Earnings: $579,390
Emp.: 632
Fiscal Year-end: 03/31/23
Medical Laboratory Services
N.A.I.C.S.: 621511

Subsidiaries:

F-Health Accelerators Private Limited (1)
21 B Bhoomi Velocity Above ICICI Bank Road No 23 Wagle Estate, Thane, 400604, Maharashtra, India
Tel.: (91) 2248933666
Web Site: https://fhealth.in
Healthcare Ecosystem Services
N.A.I.C.S.: 923120

VAILLANT GMBH
Berghauser Strasse 40, Remscheid, 42859, Germany
Tel.: (49) 2191180
Web Site: http://www.vaillant-group.com
Sales Range: $1-4.9 Billion
Emp.: 12,000
Mfr of Refrigeration & Heating Equipment
N.A.I.C.S.: 333415
Norbert Schiedeck *(Mng Dir-Tech)*

Subsidiaries:

VAILLANT GROUP France SA (1)
8 Avenue Pablo Picasso, 94120, Fontenay-sous-Bois, Cedex, France
Tel.: (33) 9 74 75 74 75
Web Site: http://www.vaillant.fr

INTERNATIONAL PUBLIC

Heating & Ventilation System Mfr & Distr
N.A.I.C.S.: 333415

VAILLANT, S.L.U. (1)
La Granja 26 Poligono Industrial Apartado 1 143, Alcobendas, 28108, Spain
Tel.: (34) 91 657 20 91
Web Site: http://www.vaillant.es
Heating & Ventilation System Mfr & Distr
N.A.I.C.S.: 333415
Inigo Aldecoa-Otalora *(Product Dir)*

Vaillant A/S (1)
Drejergangen 3A, 2690, Karlslunde, Denmark
Tel.: (45) 46 16 02 00
Web Site: http://www.vaillant.dk
Heating & Ventilation System Distr
N.A.I.C.S.: 423730

Vaillant Corp (1)
PO Box 95, Palmyra, NJ 08065
Tel.: (856) 786-2000
Web Site: http://www.vaillant.com
Heating & Ventilation System Distr
N.A.I.C.S.: 423730

Vaillant Group Austria GmbH (1)
Forchheimergasse 7, 1230, Vienna, Austria
Tel.: (43) 5 7050 0
Web Site: http://www.vaillant.at
Heating & Ventilation System Mfr & Distr
N.A.I.C.S.: 333415

Vaillant Group Czech s.r.o. (1)
Chrastany 188, 252 19, Chrastany, Czech Republic
Tel.: (420) 281 028 011
Web Site: http://www.vaillant.cz
Heating & Ventilation System Distr
N.A.I.C.S.: 423730

Vaillant Group Gaseres AB (1)
Norra Ellenborgsgatan 4, 233 51, Svedala, Sweden
Tel.: (46) 40 803 30
Web Site: http://www.vaillant.se
Heating & Ventilation System Distr
N.A.I.C.S.: 423730

Vaillant Group Italia SpA (1)
Via Benigno Crespi 70, 20159, Milan, Italy
Tel.: (39) 02 697121
Web Site: http://www.vaillant.it
Heating & Ventilation System Distr
N.A.I.C.S.: 423730
Francesco Galante *(Mgr-Credit)*

Vaillant Group Norge A/S (1)
Stottumveien 7, 1540, Vestby, Norway
Tel.: (47) 64 95 99 00
Web Site: http://www.vaillant.no
Heating & Ventilation System Distr
N.A.I.C.S.: 423730

Vaillant Group Slovakia, s.r.o. (1)
Pplk Pljusta 45, 909 01, Skalica, Slovakia
Tel.: (421) 34 6966 101
Web Site: http://www.vaillant.sk
Heating & Ventilation System Distr
N.A.I.C.S.: 423730
Jarmila Klatilova *(Mgr-Mktg)*

Vaillant Group UK Ltd (1)
Ground Floor 7400 Building Cambridge Research Park, Cambridge, CB25 9TL, United Kingdom
Tel.: (44) 845 601 8885
Web Site: http://www.vaillant.co.uk
Heating & Ventilation System Mfr & Distr
N.A.I.C.S.: 333415
Jim Moore *(Mng Dir)*

Vaillant Limited (1)
Vaillant House Trident Close, Medway City Estate, Rochester, ME2 4EZ, Kent, United Kingdom
Tel.: (44) 1634292300
Web Site: http://www.vaillant.co.uk
Sales Range: $50-74.9 Million
Emp.: 200
Heating Equipment Mfr
N.A.I.C.S.: 333414
Jim Moore *(Mng Dir)*

Division (Domestic):

Vaillant Limited (2)
Westbrook House, Sharrowvale Rd, Sheffield, S11 8YZ, S Yorkshire, United Kingdom
(100%)

Tel.: (44) 142515400
Sales Range: $25-49.9 Million
Emp.: 15
Clay, Concrete & Plastic Pipe Systems, Refractories, Industrial Sands & Minerals, Foundry Resins & Equipment, Domestic Heating Appliances, Garage Doors & Security Systems, Access Equipment
N.A.I.C.S.: 327120

Subsidiary (Non-US):

Saunier Duval Eau Chaude Chauffage SA (3)
Le Technipole 8 Ave Pablo Picasso, 94132, Fontenay-sous-Bois, France (99.5%)
Tel.: (33) 149741111
Web Site: http://www.saunierduval.com
Sales Range: $25-49.9 Million
Gas Boilers & Water Heaters Mfr
N.A.I.C.S.: 332410

Subsidiary (Non-US):

Saunier Duval Belgique S.A. (4)
Chaussee De Mons 1425, 1070, Brussels, Belgium (100%)
Tel.: (32) 25551313
Web Site: http://www.bulex.be
Sales Range: $25-49.9 Million
Boiler Mfr
N.A.I.C.S.: 332410

Vaillant Saunier Duval Kft. (1)
Hunyadi J ut 1, 1116, Budapest, Hungary
Tel.: (36) 1 464 7800
Web Site: http://www.vaillant.hu
Heating & Ventilation System Distr
N.A.I.C.S.: 423730
Fodor Istvan (Mgr-Svc)

Vaillant d.o.o. (1)
Dolenjska 242B, 1000, Ljubljana, Slovenia
Tel.: (386) 1 280 93 40
Web Site: http://www.vaillant.si
Heating & Ventilation System Distr
N.A.I.C.S.: 423730

Vaillant s.a. (1)
rue Golden Hope 15, 1620, Drogenbos, Belgium
Tel.: (32) 2 334 93 00
Web Site: http://www.vaillant.be
Heating & Ventilation System Distr
N.A.I.C.S.: 423730

VAISALA OYJ

Vanha Nurmijarventie 21, 01670, Vantaa, Finland
Tel.: (358) 358989491
Web Site: https://www.vaisala.com
VAIAS—(HEL)
Rev.: $537,846,296
Assets: $501,121,920
Liabilities: $218,258,248
Net Worth: $282,863,672
Earnings: $48,515,480
Emp.: 1,979
Fiscal Year-end: 12/31/21
Electronic Measurement Systems & Equipment For Meteorology
N.A.I.C.S.: 334512
Raimo Voipio (Chm)

Subsidiaries:

Vaisala Canada Inc. (1)
200-15225 104 Avenue, Surrey, V3R 6Y8, BC, Canada
Industrial Measurement Product Mfr & Distr
N.A.I.C.S.: 334513

Vaisala China Ltd. (1)
Floor 36 Block B'Guorui Plaza No 1 Ronghua South Road, Beijing Economic and Technological Development Area, Beijing, 100176, China
Tel.: (86) 1058274100
Industrial Measurement Product Mfr & Distr
N.A.I.C.S.: 334513

Vaisala East Africa Limited (1)
Nairobi Laiboni Centre 4th floor Lenana Road, PO Box 100798-00101, Kilimani, Nairobi, Kenya
Tel.: (254) 204938324
Industrial Measurement Product Mfr & Distr
N.A.I.C.S.: 334513

Vaisala France SAS (1)
Tech Park 6A Rue Rene Razel, 91400, Saclay, France
Tel.: (33) 130572728
Industrial Measurement Product Mfr & Distr
N.A.I.C.S.: 334513

Vaisala GmbH (1)
Notkestrasse 11, D-22607, Hamburg, Germany
Tel.: (49) 40839030
Industrial Measurement Product Mfr & Distr
N.A.I.C.S.: 334513

Vaisala Inc. (1)
10 D Gill St, Woburn, MA 01801 (100%)
Tel.: (781) 933-4500
Web Site: https://www.vaisala.com
Sales Range: $25-49.9 Million
Emp.: 50
Mfr & Retail of Weather Measuring & Controlling Devices
N.A.I.C.S.: 334512

Division (Domestic):

Vaisala Inc. (2)
194 S Taylor Ave, Louisville, CO 80027 (100%)
Tel.: (303) 499-1701
Web Site: http://www.vintura.vaisala.com
Sales Range: $25-49.9 Million
Mfr of Meteorology & Hydrology Monitoring Systems
N.A.I.C.S.: 334519
Phil Allegretti (Bus Mgr-Technical)

Subsidiary (Domestic):

Vaisala Inc. (2)
2001 6th Ave Ste 2100, Seattle, WA 98121
Tel.: (206) 325-1573
Web Site: http://www.vaisala.com
Custom Computer Programming Services
N.A.I.C.S.: 541511

Division (Domestic):

Vaisala Inc. (2)
2705 E Medina Rd, Tucson, AZ 85706-7147 (100%)
Tel.: (520) 806-7300
Web Site: http://www.vaisala.com
Sales Range: $25-49.9 Million
Mfr of Lightning Surge Protection Devices
N.A.I.C.S.: 334511

Vaisala Limited (1)
6230 Bishops Court Solihull Parkway, Birmingham Business Park, Birmingham, B37 7YB, United Kingdom
Tel.: (44) 1216835620
Industrial Measurement Product Mfr & Distr
N.A.I.C.S.: 334513

Vaisala Mexico Limited, S. de R. L. de C.V. (1)
Socrates 140 Col Polanco Seccion II, Del Miguel Hidalgo, CP 11540, Mexico, CDMX, Mexico
Tel.: (52) 5555573917
Industrial Measurement Product Mfr & Distr
N.A.I.C.S.: 334513

Vaisala Pty. Ltd. (1)
3 Guest Street, Hawthorn, 3122, VIC, Australia
Tel.: (61) 398156700
Industrial Measurement Product Mfr & Distr
N.A.I.C.S.: 334513

Vaisala Sdn. Bhd. (1)
W11-A0 Level 11 West Block Wisma Golden Eagle Realty, 142-C Jalan Ampang, Kuala Lumpur, Malaysia
Tel.: (60) 321633363
Industrial Measurement Product Mfr & Distr
N.A.I.C.S.: 334513

Vaisala Servicos De Marketing Ltda. (1)
Avenida Presidente Antonio Carlos 54 Sala 901 Centro, Rio de Janeiro, 20020-010, Brazil
Tel.: (55) 2122633006
Industrial Measurement Product Mfr & Distr
N.A.I.C.S.: 334513

Vaisala Shanghai Sensors Ltd. (1)
Room D 12F Meihuan Building No 107 Zhongshan 2nd Road Southern, Xuhui District, Shanghai, 200032, China
Tel.: (86) 4008100126
Industrial Measurement Product Mfr & Distr
N.A.I.C.S.: 334513

VAISHALI PHARMA LTD.

706-709 Aravalli Business Center RC Patel Road Sodawala Lane, Borivali West, Mumbai, 400092, India
Tel.: (91) 2242171819
Web Site: https://www.vaishalipharma.com
Year Founded: 1989
VAISHALI—(NSE)
Rev.: $8,619,567
Assets: $9,459,625
Liabilities: $4,599,976
Net Worth: $4,859,649
Earnings: $791,739
Emp.: 27
Fiscal Year-end: 03/31/23
Pharmaceuticals Product Mfr
N.A.I.C.S.: 325412
Ratnesh Singh (CFO)

VAISHNAVI CORPORATE COMMUNICATIONS PVT. LTD.

5th Floor Dr Gopal Das Bhawan, 28 Barakhamba Road, New Delhi, 110001, India
Tel.: (91) 011 423 93500
Web Site: http://www.vccpl.com
Emp.: 150
Advertising Services
N.A.I.C.S.: 541810
Rohit Dubey (CEO)

VAISHNAVI GOLD LIMITED

1-206 Divya Shakthi Complex Green Lands Ameerpet, Hyderabad, 500016, India
Tel.: (91) 40 3298 2353
Web Site: http://www.vaishnavigold.com
Jewelry Whslr
N.A.I.C.S.: 423940
K. Narsi Reddy (Compliance Officer)

VAIV COMPANY INC.

97 Dokseodang-Ro, Yongsan-Gu, Seoul, 04419, Korea (South)
Tel.: (82) 25650531
Web Site: https://www.vaiv.kr
Year Founded: 2000
301300—(KRS)
Rev.: $28,056,010
Assets: $72,634,935
Liabilities: $62,817,153
Net Worth: $9,817,782
Earnings: ($17,565,929)
Emp.: 269
Fiscal Year-end: 12/31/22
Software Development Services
N.A.I.C.S.: 541511

VAKIF FAKTORING A.S.

Serifali Mahallesi Bayraktar Bulvari No 62, Umraniye, 34775, Istanbul, Turkiye
Tel.: (90) 2166001616
Web Site: http://www.vakiffaktoring.com.tr
Year Founded: 1998
VAKFA—(IST)
Rev.: $293,642,365
Assets: $1,294,906,189
Liabilities: $1,204,366,263
Net Worth: $90,539,926
Earnings: $50,959,630
Emp.: 59
Fiscal Year-end: 12/31/23
Financial Management Services
N.A.I.C.S.: 551112
Muhammet Lutfu Celebi (Chm)

VAKIF GAYRIMENKUL YATIRIM ORTAKLIGI AS

inkilap Mahallesi Dr Adnan Buyukdeniz Caddesi No 7/A is Kapi No 28, Umraniye, Istanbul, Turkiye
Tel.: (90) 2162859400
Web Site: https://www.vakifgyo.com.tr
Year Founded: 1996
VKGYO—(IST)
Rev.: $48,028,115
Assets: $505,900,920
Liabilities: $139,991,324
Net Worth: $365,909,596
Earnings: $45,230,666
Emp.: 41
Fiscal Year-end: 12/31/23
Financial Support Services
N.A.I.C.S.: 541611
Mikail Hidir (Chm)

VAKIF VARLIK KIRALAMA A.S.

Saray Mah Dr Adnan Buyukdeniz Cad No 10, Umraniye, 34768, Istanbul, Turkiye
Tel.: (90) 2168003571
Web Site: http://www.vakifvarlikkiralama.com.tr
VAKVK—(IST)
Sales Range: Less than $1 Million
Financial Lending Services
N.A.I.C.S.: 533110
Ibrahim Bilgic (Asst Gen Mgr)

VAKKO TEKSTIL VE HAZIR GIYIM SANAYI ISLETMELERI A.S.

Altunizade Mah Kusbakisi St No 35, Uskudar Istanbul Uskudar, 34117, Istanbul, Turkiye
Tel.: (90) 2164540800
Web Site: https://vakko.com
VAKKO—(IST)
Rev.: $130,899,294
Assets: $120,576,780
Liabilities: $62,393,857
Net Worth: $58,182,924
Earnings: $33,397,943
Fiscal Year-end: 12/31/22
Clothing Apparel Mfr & Distr
N.A.I.C.S.: 315120

VAKRANGEE LIMITED

Vakrangee Corporate House Plot No 93 Road No 16, M I D C Marol Andheri East, Mumbai, 400093, Maharashtra, India
Tel.: (91) 2228504028
Web Site: https://www.vakrangee.in
Year Founded: 1990
VAKRANGEE—(NSE)
Rev.: $52,409,352
Assets: $392,523,986
Liabilities: $28,877,012
Net Worth: $363,646,975
Earnings: $8,571,012
Emp.: 800
Fiscal Year-end: 03/31/21
Software Publisher
N.A.I.C.S.: 513210
Nishikant Hayatnagarkar (Exec Dir-R&D)

VAL-D'OR MINING CORPORATION

2864 Chemin Sullivan, Val d'Or, J9P 0B9, QC, Canada
Tel.: (819) 824-2808 BC
Web Site: https://www.valdormining.com
Year Founded: 2010
VZZ—(TSXV)
Rev.: $270,198
Assets: $3,523,573
Liabilities: $273,759
Net Worth: $3,249,814
Earnings: ($816,014)
Fiscal Year-end: 12/31/23

VAL-D'OR MINING CORPORATION

Val-d'Or Mining Corporation—(Continued)

Nickel Mining Services
N.A.I.C.S.: 212230
C. Jens Zinke (COO)

Subsidiaries:

Juno Corp. (1)
Old Paarl Road, Klapmuts, Stellenbosch, 7625, South Africa
Tel.: (27) 21 380 4740
Web Site: https://www.junocrp.co.za
Hazardous Waste Transportation Services
N.A.I.C.S.: 562112

Progenitor Metals Corp. (1)
595 Howe St 1100, Vancouver, V6C 2T5, BC, Canada
Tel.: (604) 929-1234
Web Site: http://www.progenitormetals.com
Mineral Exploration Services
N.A.I.C.S.: 213114
Michael Collins (Pres & CEO)

VALAMAR RIVIERA D.D.

Stancija Kaligari 1, 52440, Poric, Croatia
Tel.: (385) 52408000
Web Site: https://www.valamar-riviera.com
Year Founded: 1953
RIVP—(ZAG)
Rev.: $403,707,915
Assets: $912,033,337
Liabilities: $418,798,984
Net Worth: $493,234,353
Earnings: $37,165,250
Emp.: 2,520
Fiscal Year-end: 12/31/23
Hotels (except Casino Hotels) & Motels
N.A.I.C.S.: 721110
Zeljko Kukurin (Pres & CEO)

VALARIS LIMITED

Clarendon House 2 Church Street, Hamilton, HM 11, Bermuda
Tel.: (441) 7137891400   BM
Web Site: https://www.valaris.com
Year Founded: 2021
VAL—(NYSE)
Rev.: $1,784,200,000
Assets: $4,322,200,000
Liabilities: $2,325,200,000
Net Worth: $1,997,000,000
Earnings: $865,400,000
Emp.: 4,261
Fiscal Year-end: 12/31/23
Holding Company; Offshore Drilling Services
N.A.I.C.S.: 551112
Christopher T. Weber (CFO & Sr VP)

Subsidiaries:

Valaris plc (1)
78 Cannon Street Cannon Place, London, EC4N 6AF, United Kingdom
Tel.: (44) 2076594660
Web Site: http://www.valaris.com
Rev.: $1,427,200,000
Assets: $12,873,200,000
Liabilities: $8,502,900,000
Net Worth: $4,370,300,000
Earnings: ($4,855,500,000)
Emp.: 4,500
Fiscal Year-end: 12/31/2020
Holding Company; Offshore Drilling Services
N.A.I.C.S.: 551112
Christopher T. Weber (CFO & Sr VP)

Subsidiary (US):

Atwood Oceanics, Inc. (2)
15011 Katy Fwy Ste 800, Houston, TX 77094
Tel.: (281) 749-7800
Sales Range: $1-4.9 Billion
Emp.: 938
International Offshore Drilling of Exploratory & Developmental Oil & Gas Wells & Related Support, Management & Consulting Services
N.A.I.C.S.: 213112
Alik Fedorenko (Dir-Engrg)

Subsidiary (Non-US):

Atwood Australian Waters Drilling Pty. Ltd. (3)
35 Peel Road, Canberra, O'Connor, 6163, ACT, Australia
Tel.: (61) 893312099
Water Drilling Services
N.A.I.C.S.: 213111

Subsidiary (Domestic):

Atwood Deep Seas, Ltd. (3)
5847 San Felipe Ste 3300, Houston, TX 77057
Tel.: (713) 789-1400
Drilling Management Services
N.A.I.C.S.: 213111

Atwood Drilling, Inc. (3)
5847 San Felipe Ste 3300, Houston, TX 77057
Tel.: (713) 789-1400
Oil & Gas Drilling
N.A.I.C.S.: 236118
Elizabeth Gallimore (VP)

Atwood Hunter Co. (3)
5847 San Felipe Ste 3300, Houston, TX 77057
Tel.: (713) 789-1400
Offshore Drilling
N.A.I.C.S.: 213111
Coleen Grable (VP)

Subsidiary (Non-US):

Atwood Oceanics Australia Pty. Ltd. (3)
35 Peel Road, O'Connor, 6163, WA, Australia
Tel.: (61) 8 9331 2099
Sales Range: $150-199.9 Million
Offshore Oil Drilling Operations
N.A.I.C.S.: 213111

Subsidiary (Domestic):

Atwood Oceanics Management, LP (3)
15011 Katy Freeway Ste 800, Houston, TX 77094 (100%)
Tel.: (281) 749-7800
Web Site: http://www.atwd.com
Sales Range: $75-99.9 Million
Emp.: 100
Drilling Management
N.A.I.C.S.: 213111
Rob Saltieo (Pres & CEO)

Subsidiary (Non-US):

ENSCO Asia Pacific (Singapore) Pte. Ltd. (2)
300 Beach Rd Ste 10 01 03, The Concourse, Singapore, 199555, Singapore (100%)
Tel.: (65) 63943100
Sales Range: $25-49.9 Million
Emp.: 11
Provider of Oil & Gas Drilling & Marine Transportation
N.A.I.C.S.: 213111

ENSCO Asia Pacific Pte. Limited (2)
5 Temasek Boulevard 11-07 Suntec Tower 5, Singapore, 038985, Singapore
Tel.: (65) 66228900
Coal Mining Services
N.A.I.C.S.: 213113
Tom Morin (VP-APR)

ENSCO Australia Pty. Ltd. (2)
10 Kings Pk Rd, West Perth, 6005, WA, Australia (100%)
Tel.: (61) 892113388
Web Site: http://www.enscous.com.au
Sales Range: $50-74.9 Million
Emp.: 10
Oil & Gas Drilling Transportation Services
N.A.I.C.S.: 213111

ENSCO Drilling (Venezuela), S.A. (2)
Muelle Terminales Maracaibo, Los Morochas, 4019, Edo Zulia, Venezuela (100%)
Tel.: (58) 2656312287

Sales Range: $150-199.9 Million
Oil & Gas Drilling
N.A.I.C.S.: 213111

ENSCO Drilling Company (Nigeria) Ltd. (2)
Plot 184C Trans Amadi Industrial Layout, Port Harcourt, Nigeria (99%)
Tel.: (234) 8423-1322
Sales Range: $250-299.9 Million
Petroleum & Natural Gas Drilling & Extraction
N.A.I.C.S.: 213111

ENSCO Gerudi (M) Sdn. Bhd. (2)
5th Flr Angkasa Raya Bldg, Jalan Ambang, 50450, Kuala Lumpur, Malaysia (49%)
Tel.: (60) 321402205
Sales Range: $10-24.9 Million
Emp.: 7
Provider of Oil & Gas Drilling Transportation
N.A.I.C.S.: 213111

Subsidiary (US):

ENSCO Incorporated (2)
3 Holiday Hl, Endicott, NY 13760
Tel.: (607) 786-9000
Drilling Oil & Gas Well Contract Services
N.A.I.C.S.: 213111

ENSCO Offshore LLC (2)
620 Moulin Rd, Broussard, LA 70518
Tel.: (337) 837-8500
Web Site: http://www.enscoplc.com
Sales Range: $50-74.9 Million
Emp.: 75
Oil & Gas Drilling Services
N.A.I.C.S.: 213111

Unit (Domestic):

ENSCO Offshore Company - Marketing & Contracts (3)
16340 Park Ten Pl Ste 350, Houston, TX 77084-5147
Tel.: (281) 920-6440
Web Site: http://www.enscous.com
Sales Range: $10-24.9 Million
Emp.: 5
Contract Drilling Services
N.A.I.C.S.: 213112

Subsidiary (Domestic):

ENSCO Offshore UK Ltd. (2)
Badentoy Avenue Badentoy Industrial Estate, Aberdeen, AB12 4YB, Portlethen, United Kingdom (100%)
Tel.: (44) 1224780400
Sales Range: $50-74.9 Million
Emp.: 50
Provider of Oil & Gas Drilling & Marine Transportation
N.A.I.C.S.: 213111

ENSCO Services Limited (2)
Gateway Cresent Gateway Business Park, Aberdeen, AB12 3GA, United Kingdom
Tel.: (44) 1224780400
Web Site: http://www.enscoplc.com
Emp.: 100
Offshore Drilling Services
N.A.I.C.S.: 213111

Division (US):

Ensco (2)
5847 San Felipe St Ste 3300, Houston, TX 77057-3195
Tel.: (713) 789-1400
Web Site: http://www.enscoplc.com
Sales Range: $1-4.9 Billion
Emp.: 3,900
International Oil & Gas Contract Drilling Services
N.A.I.C.S.: 211120

Subsidiary (Domestic):

Larcom Insurance, Ltd. (3)
5847 San Felipe St Ste 3300, Houston, TX 77057-3195 (100%)
Tel.: (713) 789-1400
Sales Range: $250-299.9 Million
Insurance Services
N.A.I.C.S.: 524298

Subsidiary (Non-US):

Pride Forasol-Foramer S.A. (3)

INTERNATIONAL PUBLIC

16 bis rue Grange Dame Rose, PO Box 100, Velizy-Villacoublay, 78143, Paris, France (100%)
Tel.: (33) 130705807
Sales Range: $50-74.9 Million
Emp.: 60
Drillings & Ancillary Services for Oil Industry
N.A.I.C.S.: 213111

Subsidiary (Non-US):

Forwest de Venezuela SA (2)
Santa Rosalia, Distrito Capital, Caracas, Venezuela
Tel.: (58) 2125764937
Oil & Gas Field Drilling Services
N.A.I.C.S.: 213111

P.T. ENSCO Sarida Offshore (2)
Jl Warung Buncit Raya 2 Ged Wahana Graha Lt 3, Durentiga Pancoran, Jakarta, 12790, Indonesia
Tel.: (62) 217989080
Sales Range: $50-74.9 Million
Emp.: 20
Offshore Drilling Services
N.A.I.C.S.: 213111
Raymond Pachtiar (Dir)

Pride Forasol S.A.S. (2)
7 Ave du Vert Galant, 64230, Lescar, France
Tel.: (33) 130705858
Oil & Gas Field Drilling Services
N.A.I.C.S.: 213111

Subsidiary (US):

Pride International, Inc. (2)
2200 Broening Hwy Ste 230, Baltimore, MD 21224
Tel.: (410) 633-0033
Web Site: http://www.pridebaltimore.com
Emp.: 3,900
Oil & Gas Field Drilling Services
N.A.I.C.S.: 213111
Luanne M. Ciaccio (VP)

Rowan Companies plc (2)
2800 Post Oak Blvd Ste 5450, Houston, TX 77056-6189
Tel.: (713) 621-7800
Web Site: http://www.rowan.com
Rev.: $824,800,000
Assets: $8,117,700,000
Liabilities: $3,082,700,000
Net Worth: $5,035,000,000
Earnings: ($347,400,000)
Fiscal Year-end: 12/31/2018
Offshore & Land Drilling Services
N.A.I.C.S.: 483113
Kelly McHenry (CEO-ARO Drilling)

Subsidiary (Domestic):

Atlantic Maritime Services LLC (3)
2800 Post Oak Blvd Ste 5450, Houston, TX 77056
Tel.: (713) 621-7800
Emp.: 30
Offshore Oil & Gas Drilling Services
N.A.I.C.S.: 213111

Subsidiary (Non-US):

RD International Services Pte Ltd. (3)
6 Raffles Quay 10-05/06, Singapore, 48580, Singapore
Tel.: (65) 64384498
Web Site: http://www.rdinternational.com
Offshore Drilling Services
N.A.I.C.S.: 213111

RDC Holdings Luxembourg S.a r.l. (3)
8-10 Avenue de la Gare, Luxembourg, L-1610, Luxembourg
Tel.: (352) 661169633
Offshore Drilling Services
N.A.I.C.S.: 213111

Holding (Non-US):

Rowan Drilling (U.K.) Limited (3)
Rowan House Peterseat Drive Altens Industrial Estate AB12 3HT, Aberdeen, AB12 3HT, United Kingdom (100%)
Tel.: (44) 1224 216550
Web Site: http://www.rowancompanies.com
Offshore & Land Drilling Services

AND PRIVATE COMPANIES — VALE S.A.

N.A.I.C.S.: 213111

Subsidiary (Non-US):

Rowan Drilling Mexico, S. de R.L. de C.V. (3)
Av Paseo de las Palmas, Del Miguel Hidalgo, 11000, Mexico, Mexico
Tel.: (52) 15552636000
Offshore Oil & Gas Drilling Services
N.A.I.C.S.: 213111

Subsidiary (Domestic):

Rowan International, Inc. (3)
2800 Post Oak Blvd Ste 5450, Houston, TX 77056-6127 **(100%)**
Tel.: (713) 621-7800
Web Site: http://www.rowancompanies.com
Sales Range: $25-49.9 Million
Emp.: 25
Offshore & Land Drilling Services
N.A.I.C.S.: 213111

Subsidiary (Non-US):

Rowan Norway Limited (3)
Koppholen 20, 4313, Sandnes, Norway
Tel.: (47) 51829600
Web Site: http://www.rowancompanies.com
Emp.: 11
Offshore Drilling Services
N.A.I.C.S.: 213111

Subsidiary (Domestic):

Rowandrill, Inc. (3)
2800 Post Oak Blvd Ste 5450, Houston, TX 77056
Tel.: (713) 960-7588
Oil Well Drilling Services
N.A.I.C.S.: 213111

VALARTIS GROUP AG
Rue de Romont 29/31, 1700, Fribourg, FR, Switzerland
Tel.: (41) 585016220
Web Site: https://www.valartisgroup.ch
Year Founded: 2005
VLRT—(SWX)
Rev.: $22,830,377
Assets: $226,491,131
Liabilities: $86,756,098
Net Worth: $139,735,033
Earnings: $7,965,632
Emp.: 67
Fiscal Year-end: 12/31/22
Commercial Banking Services
N.A.I.C.S.: 522110

Subsidiaries:

Bendura Fund Management Alpha AG (1)
Schaaner Strasse 27, 9487, Gamprin, Furstentum, Liechtenstein
Tel.: (423) 3881000
Web Site: https://www.bendurafunds-alpha.li
Emp.: 10
Investment Services
N.A.I.C.S.: 523940

MCT Luxembourg Management S.a.r.l. (1)
23 Rue des Jardiniers, 1835, Luxembourg, Luxembourg
Tel.: (352) 26202594
Financial Management Services
N.A.I.C.S.: 523940

VLR Germany GmbH (1)
Zeil 127, 60313, Frankfurt am Main, Germany
Tel.: (49) 6987009590
Web Site: https://vlrgermany.de
Asset Management Services
N.A.I.C.S.: 523940
Fariborz Ehtesham (Mng Dir)

Valartis Advisory Services SA (1)
rue du Rhone 118, 1204, Geneva, Switzerland
Tel.: (41) 227161000
Web Site: http://www.valartisfunds.ch
Financial Management Services
N.A.I.C.S.: 523940

Valartis Financial Advisory Pte. Ltd. (1)
50 Raffles Place #42-05 Singapore Land Tower, Singapore, Singapore
Tel.: (65) 64230783
Investment Services
N.A.I.C.S.: 523940

Valartis International Ltd. (1)
Petrovka Street 5, 107031, Moscow, Russia
Tel.: (7) 4957303525
Financial Services
N.A.I.C.S.: 522110
Alexander Nikolaev (Head-Ops)

VALAYA LUXURY HOLDINGS PTY. LTD.
No 123 Pace City 2 Udyog Vihar Phase 6 Sector 37, Gurgaon, 122 001, Haryana, India
Tel.: (91) 1244539444
Web Site: http://www.valaya.com
Year Founded: 1992
Sales Range: $100-124.9 Million
Emp.: 250
Clothing, Accessories & Furniture Designer, Mfr & Retailer
N.A.I.C.S.: 315250
J. J. Valaya (Co-Founder)

VALBIOTIS SA
ZI des Quatre Chevaliers - Batiment 12F - Rue Paul Vatine, Perigiry, 17180, La Rochelle, France
Tel.: (33) 546286258
Web Site: https://www.valbiotis.com
ALVAL—(EUR)
Sales Range: $1-9.9 Million
Healtcare Services
N.A.I.C.S.: 423450
Sebastien Peltier (Co-Founder, Chm & CEO)

VALCO GROUP AS
Luramyrveien 40, N 4313, Sandnes, Norway
Tel.: (47) 52 97 77 60
Web Site: http://www.valcogroup.no
Rev.: $100,000,000
Industrial Valve Mfr
N.A.I.C.S.: 332911
Oddbjorn Kopperstad (CEO)

Subsidiaries:

Westad Industri A/S (1)
Heggenveien 530, 3360, Geithus, Norway **(100%)**
Tel.: (47) 32789500
Web Site: http://www.westad.com
Sales Range: $25-49.9 Million
Emp.: 80
Industrial Valve Mfr
N.A.I.C.S.: 332911
Jorn-Inge Throndsen (Mng Dir)

VALCO SRL
Via dell'Industria 27-29, 36063, Marostica, VE, Italy
Tel.: (39) 0424 77847 IT
Web Site: http://www.valco.eu
Year Founded: 1976
Fluid Pump, Motor & Control Mfr
N.A.I.C.S.: 333996
Valerio Costenaro (Founder)

VALCORP FINE FOODS PTY. LTD.
Level 3 624 Johnston Street, Abbotsford, 3067, VIC, Australia
Tel.: (61) 392241900
Web Site: http://www.valcorp.com.au
Year Founded: 1954
Emp.: 100
Food Products Distr
N.A.I.C.S.: 424490
Gary Crawford (Gen Mgr)

VALDOR TECHNOLOGY INTERNATIONAL INC.
Suite 450 - 789 West Pender St, Vancouver, V6C 1H2, BC, Canada
Tel.: (604) 687-3775
Web Site: https://www.valdor.com
VTI—(CNSX)
Rev.: $227,134
Assets: $43,965
Liabilities: $1,642,937
Net Worth: ($1,598,972)
Earnings: ($61,081)
Fiscal Year-end: 12/31/20
Fibre Products Mfr
N.A.I.C.S.: 334210
Brian Findlay (CFO)

Subsidiaries:

Valdor Fiber Optics, Inc. (1)
3116 Diablo Ave, Hayward, CA 94545
Tel.: (510) 293-1212
Sales Range: $25-49.9 Million
Emp.: 5
Fiber Optic Cable & Connector Mfr
N.A.I.C.S.: 334417
Las Yabut (Dir-Ops)

VALE BROTHERS HOLDINGS LIMITED
Unit 2 75 Midland Road, Walsall, London, WS1 3QQ, United Kingdom
Tel.: (44) 1922 64 2222
Holding Company
N.A.I.C.S.: 551112

Subsidiaries:

Davies Odell Ltd. (1)
Davies Odell Ltd, Rushden, NN10 0DJ, Northamptonshire, United Kingdom
Tel.: (44) 1933410818
Web Site: http://www.daviesodell.com
Sales Range: $25-49.9 Million
Emp.: 25
Body Armour & Matting & Footwear Products Mfr & Distr
N.A.I.C.S.: 316210

Vale Brothers Limited (1)
Unit 2 75 Midland Road, Walsall, London, United Kingdom
Tel.: (44) 1922 642222
Web Site: http://www.valebrothers.co.uk
Leisure Bags, Whips & Horse Rugs Mfr & Sales
N.A.I.C.S.: 314999

VALE S.A.
Praia de Botafogo 186 Rooms 1801 to 2001, Rio de Janeiro, 22250-145, RJ, Brazil
Tel.: (55) 2134853900 BR
Web Site: https://www.vale.com
Year Founded: 1942
VALE—(NYSE)
Rev.: $41,784,000,000
Assets: $94,186,000,000
Liabilities: $53,205,000,000
Net Worth: $40,981,000,000
Earnings: $8,105,000,000
Emp.: 66,807
Fiscal Year-end: 12/31/23
Ferrous & Non-Ferrous Metal Ore, Anthracite Coal & Mineral Mining, Processing & Logistics Services
N.A.I.C.S.: 213114
Luciano Siani Pires (CFO & Exec Dir-Fin & IR)

Subsidiaries:

ALBRAS - Aluminio Brasileiro S.A. (1)
Rodovia Pa-483 Km 21 Area 711 Distrito Murucupi, Barcarena, Para, CEP 68447 000, Brazil
Tel.: (55) 9137546000
Web Site: http://www.albras.net
Rev.: $1,100,000,000
Emp.: 1,200
Aluminum Processing Services
N.A.I.C.S.: 331314

Biopalma da Amazonia S.A - Reflorestamento, Industria e Comercio (1)
Tv Angustura 1967 Sl 2, Pedreira, Belem, Para, Brazil
Tel.: (55) 91 3276 4607
Palm Oil Production Services
N.A.I.C.S.: 311225

CENIBRA_Cellulose Nipo Brasileiro S.A. (1)
Avenida Afonso Pena 1964 7th floor, Employee, Belo Horizonte, 30130-005, Brazil **(100%)**
Tel.: (55) 3132354041
Web Site: https://www.cenibra.com.br
Sales Range: $50-74.9 Million
Emp.: 18
N.A.I.C.S.: 212230

CPP Participacoes S.A. (1)
Av Graca Aranha 26 80th Floor, Rio de Janeiro, 20030-900, Brazil
Tel.: (55) 2138144755
Transportation Services
N.A.I.C.S.: 488999

Companhia Nipo-Brasileira de Pelotizacao-NIBRASCO (1)
Ponta Do Tubarao, PO Box 334, 29090-900, Vitoria, Espirito Santo, Brazil
Tel.: (55) 2733335179
Web Site: http://www.cale.com
Iron Ore Pellet Manufacturer
N.A.I.C.S.: 212210

Compania Minera Miski Mayo S.Ac. (1)
Av Victor A Belaunde 147 701 B 3 Edificio Torre Real Tres, San Isidro, Lima, Peru
Tel.: (51) 17160010
Web Site: http://www.vale.com
Sales Range: $200-249.9 Million
Emp.: 50
Mineral Exploration Services
N.A.I.C.S.: 212390

Corredor do Desenvolvimento do Norte S.a.r.L (1)
Rua Do Porto St Zona Portuaria Porto De Nacala Area, Nacala, Mozambique
Tel.: (258) 26 52 6216
Transportation Services
N.A.I.C.S.: 488999

Florestas Rio Doce S.A. (1)
Rodovia Coronel Orlando De Paiva Almeida, Bairro Bebedouro, Linhares, Espirito Santo, Brazil
Tel.: (55) 2733710227
Chocolate Product Mfr
N.A.I.C.S.: 311351

Integra Coal Operations Pty Ltd. (1)
653 Bridgman Rd, Singleton, 2330, NSW, Australia
Tel.: (61) 265702111
Web Site: http://www.integra.valeaustralia.com.au
Coal Mining Services
N.A.I.C.S.: 213113

KOBRASCO (1)
Av Dante Michelini No 5500 Jardim Camburi, Ponta do Tubarao, Vitoria, 29090-900, ES, Brazil **(50%)**
Tel.: (55) 2733335164
Web Site: http://www.posco.com
Metal Pellet Mfr & Distr
N.A.I.C.S.: 332991

Mineracoes Brasileiras Reunidas S.A. (1)
Avenida de Ligacao 3580, Nova Lima, 34000-000, Brazil
Tel.: (55) 21 3814 4477
Iron Ore Mining Services
N.A.I.C.S.: 212210

PT Vale Eksplorasi Indonesia (1)
Jl Cilandak KKO Kawasan Komersial Cilandak 111 M-2, Cilandak Timur Pasar Min, Jakarta, 12560, Indonesia
Tel.: (62) 21 7802109
Nickel Mining Services
N.A.I.C.S.: 212230

Sociedad Portuaria Rio Cordoba S.A. (1)

VALE S.A.

Vale S.A.—(Continued)
Km 67 Via Troncal del Caribe, Cienaga, Colombia
Tel.: (57) 5 361 9379
Coal Mining Services
N.A.I.C.S.: 213113

Taiwan Nickel Refining Corporation (1)
40 Hsing Yeh Road Ta-Fa Industrial District, Kaohsiung, 83162, Taiwan (49.9%)
Tel.: (886) 77870320
Web Site: http://www.vale.com
Sales Range: $50-74.9 Million
Emp.: 3
Nickel Refining Services & Mfr
N.A.I.C.S.: 212230

Tethys Mining LLC (1)
St 501 Bodi Tower Sukhbaatar Sq, Ulaanbaatar, Mongolia
Tel.: (976) 11 330281
Sales Range: $50-74.9 Million
Emp.: 20
Coal Mining Services
N.A.I.C.S.: 213113

VBG - Vale BSGR Guinea Limitad (1)
Cite Chemin De Fer Immeuble Pita 5eme Et 6eme Etages, Conakry, Papua New Guinea
Tel.: (675) 65676502
Transportation Services
N.A.I.C.S.: 488999

VLI Multimodal S.A. (1)
Av Graca Aranha, Rio de Janeiro, Brazil
Tel.: (55) 31 3279 4307
Mineral Mining Services
N.A.I.C.S.: 212390

Vale Energia Limpa S.A. (1)
Praia de Botafogo 186 Salas 501 a 1901, Botafogo, Rio de Janeiro, 22250-145, Brazil
Tel.: (55) 2134853900
Mineral Mining Services
N.A.I.C.S.: 212390

Vale Exploration Peru SAC (1)
Av Belaunde N 147 Torre Real 3 Of 701 B, San Isidro, Lima, 27, Peru
Tel.: (51) 1 4211673
Web Site: http://www.vale.com
Sales Range: $200-249.9 Million
Emp.: 50
Mineral Mining Services
N.A.I.C.S.: 212390

Vale Exploration Philippines Inc (1)
23F Tower 2 The Enterprise Ctr 6676 Ayala Ave, Metro Manila, Makati, 1200, Philippines
Tel.: (63) 2 856 7931
Web Site: http://www.vale.com
Sales Range: $50-74.9 Million
Emp.: 2
Gold & Copper Exploration Services
N.A.I.C.S.: 212230

Vale Holdings AG (1)
Sterneckstr 11, 5020, Salzburg, Austria
Tel.: (43) 662 870554
Web Site: http://www.vale.com
Iron Producer
N.A.I.C.S.: 331511

Vale International S.A. (1)
Rte de Pallatex 29, 1162, Saint Prex, Switzerland
Tel.: (41) 218060555
Metal Product Whslr
N.A.I.C.S.: 423510

Vale International Singapore (1)
1 Temasek Avenue 39-01 Millennia Tower, Singapore, 039192, Singapore
Tel.: (65) 65001800
Sales Range: $50-74.9 Million
Emp.: 7
Metal Mining Services
N.A.I.C.S.: 213114

Vale Japan Limited (1)
Atago Green Hills Mori Tower 25F, 5-1 Atago 2-chome, Minato Ku, Tokyo, 105 6225, Japan (100%)
Tel.: (81) 354012971
Web Site: http://www.vale.com

Sales Range: $50-74.9 Million
Emp.: 7
Producer of Intermediate & Refined Nickel Products from Indonesian Ore
N.A.I.C.S.: 212230

Vale Malaysia Minerals SDN. BHD. (1)
Level 17 Pbs 2 Ipoh Tower Tower Regency Jalan Dato Seri Ahmad Said, Lingkaran Syed Putra, Ipoh, 30450, Malaysia
Tel.: (60) 524005003
Mineral Mining Services
N.A.I.C.S.: 212290

Vale Minerals China Co. Ltd (1)
50f Intercontinental Business Ctr 100 Yu Tong Rd Zhabei Di, Shanghai, 200131, China
Tel.: (86) 2122150200
Mineral Mining Services
N.A.I.C.S.: 212390

Vale Mocambique Ltda. (1)
Centro Cimpor Avenida 24 De Julho No 7, Maputo, Mozambique
Tel.: (258) 21489900
Coal Mining Services
N.A.I.C.S.: 213113

Vale Nouvelle Caledonie S.A.S. (1)
Malawi Building-52 Avenue Foch, BP 218, 98845, Noumea, New Caledonia
Tel.: (687) 235000
Web Site: http://www.vale.nc
Mineral Mining Services
N.A.I.C.S.: 213114
Jennifer Maki (Exec Dir-Base Metals)

Vale Oman Pelletizing Company LLC (1)
PO Box 208, Falaj Al Qabail, 322, Sohar, Oman
Tel.: (968) 26759600
Mineral Mining Services
N.A.I.C.S.: 213114

Vale Technology Development (Canada) Limited (1)
2060 Flavelle Blvd, Mississauga, L5K 1Z9, ON, Canada
Tel.: (905) 403-2400
Metal Mining Services
N.A.I.C.S.: 212290

Vale Trading (Shanghai) Co., Ltd (1)
No 100 Yutong Rd, Shanghai, 200070, China
Tel.: (86) 2122150200
Web Site: http://www.vale.com
Emp.: 10
Nickel Product Distr
N.A.I.C.S.: 327910

Vale do Rio Doce Aluminio S.A. (1)
Praia de Botafogo 186 Salas 501 a 1901, Botafogo, Rio de Janeiro, Brazil (100%)
Tel.: (55) 2134853900
Sales Range: $100-124.9 Million
Emp.: 500
N.A.I.C.S.: 331524

ValeServe Malaysia Sdn. Bhd. (1)
Suite 16 01 & 16 02 Level 16 No1 First Avenue Bandar Utama, Petaling Jaya, 47800, Malaysia
Tel.: (60) 378622200
Coal Mining Services
N.A.I.C.S.: 213113

Valesul Aluminio S.A. (1)
Estr Do Aterrado Do Leme 1225, Santa Cruz, Rio de Janeiro, 23575-330, Brazil
Tel.: (55) 21 3305 8383
Web Site: http://www.valesul.com.br
Aluminum & Alloys Mfr
N.A.I.C.S.: 331313

VALEDO PARTNERS AB

Kungsbron 1 F7, 111 22, Stockholm, Sweden
Tel.: (46) 8 678 08 50
Web Site:
http://www.valedopartners.com
Privater Equity Firm
N.A.I.C.S.: 523999
Per Forsber (Partner)

Subsidiaries:

Aditro Logistics AB (1)
Gustavslundsvagen 137 4 trappa, Bromma, Stockholm, 165 51, Sweden
Tel.: (46) 771883800
Web Site: http://www.aditrologistics.eu
Logistics Consulting Servies
N.A.I.C.S.: 541614
Zdenko Topolovec (CEO)

Best Transport AB (1)
Finspangsgatan 31, 16308, Spanga, Sweden
Tel.: (46) 87337700
Logistics Consulting Servies
N.A.I.C.S.: 541614

VALENCIA CAPITAL, INC.

1111 Melville Street Suite 620, Vancouver, V6E 3V6, BC, Canada
Tel.: (604) 250-4376
Year Founded: 2019
VAL.P—(TSXV)
Assets: $338,818
Liabilities: $6,123
Net Worth: $332,695
Earnings: ($80,874)
Fiscal Year-end: 06/30/24
Asset Management Services
N.A.I.C.S.: 523940
MacPhail John (CEO)

VALENCIA NUTRITION LIMITED

601 A wing Neelkanth Business Park Vidyavihar West, Vidyavihar, Mumbai, 400086, Maharashtra, India
Tel.: (91) 8928056974
Web Site:
https://valencianutrition.com
Year Founded: 2013
542910—(BOM)
Beverage Product Distr
N.A.I.C.S.: 424820
Jay Jatin Shah (CFO)

VALENS SEMICONDUCTOR LTD.

8 Hanagar St. POB 7152,, Hod Hasharon, 4501309, Israel
Tel.: (972) 97626900
Web Site: https://www.valens.com
VLN—(NYSE)
Rev.: $84,161,000
Assets: $180,558,000
Liabilities: $16,254,000
Net Worth: $164,304,000
Earnings: ($19,679,000)
Fiscal Year-end: 12/31/23
Semiconductor Mfr
N.A.I.C.S.: 333242

Subsidiaries:

Acroname Inc. (1)
4822 Sterling Dr, Boulder, CO 80301
Tel.: (720) 564-0373
Web Site: http://www.acroname.com
Rev.: $1,238,500
Emp.: 6
Custom Computer Programming Services
N.A.I.C.S.: 541511
Jeremiah Sullenger (Dir-Software Engrg)

VALEO PHARMA, INC.

16667 Hymus Blvd, Kirkland, H9H 4R9, QC, Canada
Tel.: (514) 694-0150
Web Site:
https://www.valeopharma.com
Year Founded: 2003
VPHIF—(OTCQB)
Rev.: $21,704,359
Assets: $45,579,544
Liabilities: $59,541,678
Net Worth: ($13,962,133)
Earnings: ($20,140,581)
Emp.: 115
Fiscal Year-end: 10/31/22

INTERNATIONAL PUBLIC

Health Care Srvices
N.A.I.C.S.: 621999
Richard J. Mackay (Chm)

VALEO S.A.

100 rue de Courcelles, 75017, Paris, France
Tel.: (33) 140552020 FR
Web Site: https://www.valeoservice.fr
Year Founded: 1923
FR—(EUR)
Rev.: $21,201,878,880
Assets: $23,133,900,400
Liabilities: $17,617,874,560
Net Worth: $5,516,025,840
Earnings: $300,918,800
Emp.: 12,251
Fiscal Year-end: 12/31/21
Automobile Parts Mfr
N.A.I.C.S.: 336390
Hans-Peter Kunze (Exec VP-Sls & Bus Dev)

Subsidiaries:

Cibie Argentina, SA (1)
Boulevard De Los Polacos 7649, Barrio Los Boulevares, Cordoba, 5022, Argentina
Tel.: (54) 3514165100
Motor Vehicle Parts Mfr
N.A.I.C.S.: 336390

Connaught Electronics Limited (1)
Dunmore Rd, County Galway, Tuam, Ireland
Tel.: (353) 9325128
Web Site: https://cel-europe.com
Sales Range: $125-149.9 Million
Electrical Equipment Mfr & Distr
N.A.I.C.S.: 336320

DAV S.A. (1)
2 Voie Andre Boulle, BP 150, Creteil, 94017, France
Tel.: (33) 450954000
Automobile Parts Mfr
N.A.I.C.S.: 336390

DAV Tunisie SA (1)
Rue des Metaux Zone Industrielle, Ben Arous, 2013, Tunisia
Tel.: (216) 79100100
Electronic Components Mfr
N.A.I.C.S.: 334419

Dae Myong Precision Corporation (1)
1124-1 Shiengil-dong, Danwon-gu, 425120, Ansan, Kyonggi, Korea (South)
Tel.: (82) 31 4919841
Web Site: http://www.valeo.com
Sales Range: $25-49.9 Million
Emp.: 74
Automobile Parts Mfr
N.A.I.C.S.: 336390

FTE automotive Czechia s.r.o. (1)
Hlubany 124, 441 01, Podborany, Czech Republic
Tel.: (420) 415232111
Emp.: 600
Hydraulic Actuator Mfr
N.A.I.C.S.: 333995
Vladimir Kolba (Supvr)

FTE automotive GmbH (1)
Andreas-Humann-Str 2, Ebern, 96106, Coburg, Germany
Tel.: (49) 9531810
Web Site: https://ww.fte.de
Emp.: 1,100
Automotive Component Mfr & Distr
N.A.I.C.S.: 336390

Foshan Ichikoh Valeo Auto Lighting Systems Co., Ltd. (1)
No 7 Huabaonan Road Chengxi Industrial Park Foshan National, Hi-Tech Industry Zone Changcheng District, Foshan, 528000, Guangdong, China (85%)
Tel.: (86) 75788011170
Vehicular Lighting Equipment Mfr
N.A.I.C.S.: 336320

Hubei Valeo Autolighting Company Ltd (1)
6 Yaohualu ETDZ Hubei, Wuhan, 430056,

AND PRIVATE COMPANIES — VALEO S.A.

Hubei, China
Tel.: (86) 27 59408208
Emp.: 1,350
Lighting Equipment Mfr
N.A.I.C.S.: 335139
Larry Chen (Gen Mgr)

Ichikoh (Wuxi) Automotive Parts Co., Ltd. (1)
No 69 Xue Dian North Road, New Wu District, Wuxi, Jiangsu, China
Tel.: (86) 51085330855
Automotive Lamp & Mirror Mfr
N.A.I.C.S.: 335139
Huan Zhou (Plant Mgr)

Ichikoh Industries (Thailand) Co. Ltd. (1)
7/346 Moo 6 Amata City T Mabyangporn, Industrial Estate A Pluakdaeng, Rayong, 21140, Thailand
Tel.: (66) 38929700
Automotive Lamp & Mirror Mfr
N.A.I.C.S.: 335139
Kridsada Pathaninthanatul (Project Mgr-Mgmt)

Ichikoh Industries, Ltd. (1)
80 Itado, Isehara, 259-1192, Kanagawa, Japan (55.1%)
Tel.: (81) 463961451
Web Site: https://www.ichikoh.com
Rev.: $1,034,409,730
Assets: $917,566,530
Liabilities: $458,630,830
Net Worth: $458,935,700
Earnings: $55,571,420
Emp.: 4,913
Fiscal Year-end: 12/31/2023
Electrical Motor Vehicle Components Mfr & Whslr
N.A.I.C.S.: 336320
Hideo Nakano (Sr Mng Exec Officer & Dir-Mirror PL)

Subsidiary (Non-US):

Ichikoh (Malaysia) Sdn. Bhd. (2)
Lot PT 627 Nilai Industrial Estate Mukim Setul, 71800, Nilai, Negari Sembilan, Malaysia (70%)
Tel.: (60) 67992443
Web Site: http://www.ichikoh.com
Vehicular Lighting Equipment Mfr

Plant (Domestic):

Ichikoh Industries, Ltd - Mirror Plant (2)
1360 Fujioka, Fujioka, 375-8507, Gunma, Japan
Tel.: (81) 27 423 2121
Web Site: https://www.ichikoh.com
Automobile Parts Mfr
N.A.I.C.S.: 336110
Hideo Nakano (Dir)

Ichikoh Industries, Ltd. - Fujioka Plant (2)
1467 Higashi-Hirai, Fujioka, 375-8508, Gunma, Japan
Tel.: (81) 274232211
Web Site: http://www.ichikoh.com
Automobile Parts Mfr
N.A.I.C.S.: 336110

Ichikoh Industries, Ltd. - Isehara Plant (2)
80 Itado, Isehara, 259-1192, Kanagawa, Japan
Tel.: (81) 46 396 1451
Web Site: https://www.ichikoh.com
Automobile Parts Mfr
N.A.I.C.S.: 336110

Subsidiary (Domestic):

Life Elex Inc. (2)
971 Shinozuka Orama-cho, Oraku-gun, Gunma, 370-0615, Japan (59.1%)
Tel.: (81) 27 688 3911
Web Site: https://www.lifeelex.co.jp
Emp.: 50
Electric Lamp Bulb & Part Mfr
N.A.I.C.S.: 335139
Masayoshi Owada (Pres)

Subsidiary (US):

PIAA Corporation (2)
3004 NE 181st Ave, Portland, OR 97230
Web Site: http://www.piaa.com
Motor Vehicles Mfr
N.A.I.C.S.: 336310

Subsidiary (Non-US):

PT. Ichikoh Indonesia (2)
MM2100 Industrial Town Blok LL-1 West Cikarang, Bekasi, 17520, West Java, Indonesia (100%)
Tel.: (62) 218981201
Web Site: https://www.ichikoh.com
Vehicular Lighting Equipment Mfr
N.A.I.C.S.: 336320

SC2N SA (1)
45 Rue Charles De Coulomb, 14125, Mondeville, France
Tel.: (33) 231523200
Sales Range: $150-199.9 Million
Emp.: 40
Electronic Components Distr
N.A.I.C.S.: 423690

Telma Retarder Division (1)
28 Rue Paul Painleve, ZA Du Vert Galant, 95310, Saint-Ouen, L'Aumone, France
Tel.: (33) 134485400
Web Site: http://www.telma.com
Sales Range: $5-14.9 Billion
Emp.: 68,200
Electromagnetic Braking Systems Mfr for Enhancing Standard Industrial Vehicle Brakes
N.A.I.C.S.: 336390

Division (Non-US):

Telma Retarder Deutschland GmbH (2)
Sweewiensenstrasse 9, 74321, Bietigheim-Bissingen, Germany
Tel.: (49) 7142733668
Web Site: http://www.telma.co
Electromagnetic Braking Systems Mfr for Enhancing Standard Industrial Vehicle Brakes
N.A.I.C.S.: 336390

Telma Retarder Ltd. (2)
25 Clarke Road, Milton Keynes, MK1 1LG, Bucks, United Kingdom
Tel.: (44) 1908642822
Web Site: http://www.telma.co.uk
Sales Range: $25-49.9 Million
Emp.: 3
Assisted Braking Products Mfr
N.A.I.C.S.: 336340

Division (US):

Telma Retarder, Inc. (2)
1245 Humbracht Cir Ste B, Bartlett, IL 60103
Tel.: (847) 593-1098
Web Site: http://www.telmausa.com
Sales Range: $25-49.9 Million
Emp.: 18
Electro Magnetic Breaking System Distr
N.A.I.C.S.: 423120

VALEO S.p.A. (1)
89 Via Asti, Santena, 10026, Turin, Italy
Tel.: (39) 01 194951
Web Site: http://www.gallino.com
Motor Vehicle Parts Mfr & Distr
N.A.I.C.S.: 336390

Valeo Auto-Electric Hungary LLC (1)
Piramis utca 1, 8200, Veszprem, Hungary
Tel.: (36) 88205540
Web Site: https://www.valeo.hu
Motor Vehicle Parts Mfr
N.A.I.C.S.: 336390

Valeo Autoklimatizace K.S. (1)
Kustova 2596/II, 269 01, Rakovnik, Czech Republic
Tel.: (420) 313527111
Emp.: 1,300
Automotive Distr
N.A.I.C.S.: 423120
Gabriela Rakova (Partner-HR Bus)

Valeo Automotive (Thailand) Co. Ltd. (1)
Bangna-Trad Road KM 57 T Don Hua Lor, Muangchonburi, Chon Buri, 20000, Thailand
Tel.: (66) 38265600
Automotive Component Mfr & Distr
N.A.I.C.S.: 336390
Thanachai Mahdcha (Dir-HR)

Valeo Automotive Air Conditioning Hubei Co. Ltd (1)
No 123 DongFeng Avenue Economic Zone, Shashi District, Jingzhou, 434008, China
Tel.: (86) 7164089512
Automotive Air Conditioning System Mfr & Distr
N.A.I.C.S.: 336390

Valeo Automotive Security Systems (Wuxi) Co. Ltd (1)
No B1 Workshop Xixie Road High-Tech Industry Development Zone, Wuxi, 214112, Jiangsu, China
Tel.: (86) 51082993000
Motor Vehicle Parts Mfr
N.A.I.C.S.: 336390

Valeo Autosystemy Sp. z.o.o. (1)
Przemyslowa 3, Skawina, 32-050, Poland
Tel.: (48) 122771000
Emp.: 2,000
Automotive Electric Lamp Mfr
N.A.I.C.S.: 335139

Valeo Climate Control Limited (1)
Heming Road, Washford, Redditch, B98 0DZ, United Kingdom
Tel.: (44) 1527838300
Sales Range: $25-49.9 Million
Emp.: 90
Automotive Air Conditioning Equipment Mfr
N.A.I.C.S.: 333415

Valeo Climatizacion, S.A. (1)
Can Fenosa S/N Poligono Industrial 2, Martorell, 08107, Spain
Tel.: (34) 935655000
Web Site: http://www.valeo.com
Emp.: 200
Automobile Climate Control Equipment Mfr
N.A.I.C.S.: 336320
Luis Chica (Dir-Natl)

Valeo Compressor (Changchun) Co. Ltd. (1)
No 1243 Hai An Road Jingkai Zone, Changchun, 130000, Jilin, China
Tel.: (86) 43181866009
Air Conditioning Compressor Mfr
N.A.I.C.S.: 333912

Valeo Compressor (Thailand) Co. Ltd. (1)
55 Moo 4 T Pluak Daeng, 21140, Rayong, Thailand
Tel.: (66) 38954711
Web Site: http://www.valeo.com
Sales Range: $100-124.9 Million
Emp.: 400
Air Conditioning Mfr
N.A.I.C.S.: 333415

Valeo Compressor Clutch (Thailand) Co. Ltd (1)
55 Moo 4 T Pluak Daeng, 21140, Rayong, Thailand
Tel.: (66) 38 954 711
Web Site: http://www.valeo.com
Air Conditioning Equipment Mfr
N.A.I.C.S.: 333415

Valeo Compressor Europe S.r.o. (1)
Central Trade Park 1571, 396 01, Humpolec, Czech Republic
Tel.: (420) 565505111
Web Site: https://www.valeo.cz
Automotive Air Conditioning Component Mfr
N.A.I.C.S.: 336390

Valeo Embragues Argentina, SA (1)
Bv de los Polacos 7149, Cordoba, Argentina
Tel.: (54) 35434165100
Automotive
N.A.I.C.S.: 423120
Christian Fux (Controller)

Valeo Engine Cooling (Foshan) Co. Ltd. (1)
No 56 F1 B Area Center, Technology Industrial Zone Sanshui, Foshan, 528137, Guangdong, China
Tel.: (86) 75788302935
Automotive Component Mfr & Distr
N.A.I.C.S.: 336390
Shenglin Li (Mgr-R&D)

Valeo Equipement Electriques Moteur (1)
2 Rue Andre Boulle, BP 150, 94017, Creteil, France
Tel.: (33) 1 48 98 86 00
Sales Range: $150-199.9 Million
Emp.: 50
Electronic Components Distr
N.A.I.C.S.: 423690
Andrea Sargent (Gen Mgr)

Valeo Friction Materials India Ltd. (1)
No 16A Sengundram Industrial Area, Melrosapuram S P Koil Via Kancheepuram Dist, Kanchipuram, 603204, Tamil Nadu, India
Tel.: (91) 4447413474
Emp.: 500
Clutch Facing Product Mfr
N.A.I.C.S.: 336350
Suresh Kanniappan (Deputy Gen Mgr-Production)

Valeo GmbH (1)
Engstlatter Weg 18, Stuttgart, 70567, Germany
Tel.: (49) 7117870600
Automotive Parts Mfr & Distr
N.A.I.C.S.: 336390

Subsidiary (Domestic):

Valeo Auto-Electric GmbH (2)
Laeirnstrasse 12, 74321, Bietigheim-Bissingen, Germany
Tel.: (49) 71429160
Web Site: https://www.valeo.com
Automotive Parts Mfr & Distr
N.A.I.C.S.: 336390

Subsidiary (Non-US):

Valeo Klimasysteme GmbH (2)
Tel.: (49) 9564810
Web Site: https://www.valeo.de
Emp.: 700
Motor Vehicle Parts Mfr
N.A.I.C.S.: 336390

Subsidiary (Domestic):

Valeo Schalter und Sensoren GmbH (2)
Valeostrasse 1, 86650, Wemding, Germany
Tel.: (49) 90926030
Motor Vehicle Parts Mfr
N.A.I.C.S.: 336390

Valeo Service Deutschland GmbH (2)
Balcke-Durr-All 1, 40882, Ratingen, Germany
Tel.: (49) 8008692840
Web Site: https://www.valeoservice.de
Automobile Parts Distr
N.A.I.C.S.: 423120

Valeo Sicherheitssysteme GmbH (2)
Waldstr 2, Erdweg, 85253, Germany
Tel.: (49) 8138850
Automobile Parts Mfr & Distr
N.A.I.C.S.: 336390

Valeo Holding Netherlands B.V. (1)
Strawinslykaan 411 1077XX, 1043 BW, Amsterdam, Netherlands
Tel.: (31) 205752727
Investment Management Service
N.A.I.C.S.: 523999

Valeo Iluminacion, S.A. (1)
Pol Ind de Martos C Linares 15, Martos, 23600, Spain
Tel.: (34) 95 356 91 00
Motor Vehicle Lighting Equipment Mfr
N.A.I.C.S.: 336320

Valeo India Private Ltd (1)
CEE DEE YES IT Parks Block 1 No 63 Rajiv Gandhi Salai, Navalur, Chennai, 600 130, Tamilnadu, India
Tel.: (91) 4471027300
Industrial Machinery Mfr
N.A.I.C.S.: 333248

Valeo Interbranch Automotive Software Egypt (1)
Smart Village 22 F KM 28 Cairo-Alex Road, Giza, Cairo, 12577, Egypt
Tel.: (20) 235380500

VALEO S.A.

Valeo S.A.—(Continued)
Web Site: http://www.valeo.com
Sales Range: $150-199.9 Million
Emp.: 60
Powertrain System Research & Development Services
N.A.I.C.S.: 541715

Valeo Interior Controls (1)
Rue Jules Verne, 74106, Annemasse, France (100%)
Tel.: (33) 450954000
Sales Range: $100-124.9 Million
Emp.: 300
Electronic Components
N.A.I.C.S.: 334419

Valeo Interior Controls (Shenzhen) Co. Ltd (1)
North Junyi Industrial Zone Six Area Cuigang Fuyong Town Bao, Shenzhen, 518103, China
Tel.: (86) 75536885222
Sales Range: $200-249.9 Million
Emp.: 680
Electronic Components Mfr
N.A.I.C.S.: 334419

Valeo Lighting Hubei Technical Center Co. Ltd. (1)
B4 building Phase I South Taizi Lake Innoviation Valley, No 18 ShengLong street Wuhan Economic and Technology Development Zone, Wuhan, 430056, Hubei, China
Tel.: (86) 2759554712
Automotive Component Mfr & Distr
N.A.I.C.S.: 336390
Tingjun Duan (Mgr-Design Engrg)

Valeo Management (Beijing) Co. Ltd. (1)
7 Floor Innov Tower 1801 Hong Mei Road Caohejing Hi-Tech Park, Xuhui District, Shanghai, 200233, China
Tel.: (86) 2151752618
Automotive Component Mfr & Distr
N.A.I.C.S.: 336390

Valeo Management Services (1)
43 Rue Bayen, 75017, Paris, France
Tel.: (33) 140552020
Sales Range: $25-49.9 Million
Emp.: 20
Business Management Services
N.A.I.C.S.: 541611

Valeo Management Services UK Limited (1)
Heming Road, Washford, Redditch, B98 0DZ, Worcestershire, United Kingdom
Tel.: (44) 1527838300
Business Management Consulting Services
N.A.I.C.S.: 541611

Valeo Motherson Thermal Commercial Vehicles India Ltd. (1)
Plot No 75 A-1 Ecotech 12, Noida, 201310, Uttar Pradesh, India
Tel.: (91) 1206051100
Heating & Air Conditioning Equipment Mfr
N.A.I.C.S.: 333415
Prachi Singhal (Sr Mgr)

Valeo North America, Inc. (1)
150 Stephenson Hwy, Troy, MI 48083-1116
Tel.: (248) 619-8300
Web Site: http://www.valeo.us
Automobile Electrical Systems, Interior Controls, Engine Cooling & Wiper Systems Mfr
N.A.I.C.S.: 336320

Division (Domestic):

Valeo Electrical Systems, Inc. - Wiper Systems (2)
150 Stephenson Hwy, Troy, MI 48083 (100%)
Tel.: (248) 619-8300
Web Site: http://www.valeo.com
Sales Range: $25-49.9 Million
Emp.: 170
Mfr of Automotive Parts
N.A.I.C.S.: 336350

Valeo Otomotiv Sistemleri Endustrisi A.S. (1)
614 Demirtas Organize Sanayi Bolgesi Yeni Yalova Yolu Caddesi, Bursa, 16335, Turkiye
Tel.: (90) 2242700400

Motor Vehicle Parts Mfr
N.A.I.C.S.: 336390

Valeo Raytheon Systems, Inc. (1)
150 Stephenson Hwy, Troy, MI 48083
Tel.: (248) 619-8300
Sales Range: $300-349.9 Million
Emp.: 500
Radar-Based Automotive Blind-Spot Detections Systems Mfr; Owned by Raytheon Company & Valeo S.A.
N.A.I.C.S.: 336390
Howard Broughton (Mgr-Bus Dev)

Valeo Service Belgique SA (1)
Tel.: (32) 23551446
Motor Vehicle Parts Distr
N.A.I.C.S.: 423120

Valeo Service Benelux B.V. (1)
Heibloemweg 1, 5704 BS, Helmond, Netherlands
Tel.: (31) 492 580 894
Web Site: http://www.valeoservice.com
Sales Range: $50-74.9 Million
Emp.: 60
Automobile Parts Distr
N.A.I.C.S.: 423120

Valeo Service Eastern Europe Sp. z.o.o (1)
ul Marynarska 15, 02-674, Warsaw, Poland
Tel.: (48) 224405301
Web Site: https://www.valeoservice.pl
Sales Range: $550-599.9 Million
Emp.: 165
Automobile Parts Distr
N.A.I.C.S.: 423120

Valeo Service Espana, S.A. (1)
c/ Rio Almanzora 50, 28906, Getafe, Madrid, Spain
Tel.: (34) 914958500
Automobile Parts Distr
N.A.I.C.S.: 423120

Valeo Service Italia, S.p.A. (1)
Via Asti 89, 10026, Santena, Italy
Tel.: (39) 01194951
Web Site: https://www.valeoservice.it
Motor Vehicle Parts Mfr
N.A.I.C.S.: 423120

Valeo Service Limited Liability Company (1)
Rusakovskaya St 13 3rd Floor Office 6, 107140, Moscow, Russia
Tel.: (7) 4959810696
Automotive Component Mfr & Distr
N.A.I.C.S.: 336390

Valeo Service SAS (1)
70 Rue Pleyel, 93285, Saint Denis, Cedex, France
Tel.: (33) 149453232
Automobile Parts Mfr & Distr
N.A.I.C.S.: 336390

Valeo Service UK Limited (1)
Heming Road - Washford, Redditch, B98 0DZ, Worcestershire, United Kingdom
Tel.: (44) 1527838300
Sales Range: $300-349.9 Million
Emp.: 85
Motor Vehicle Parts Maintenance Services
N.A.I.C.S.: 811121

Valeo Shanghai Automotive Electric Motors & Wiper Systems Co., Ltd (1)
No 2281 Jianchuan Road, Minhang District, Shanghai, 200245, China
Tel.: (86) 6264626150
Motor Vehicle Parts Mfr & Distr
N.A.I.C.S.: 336390

Valeo Siam Thermal Systems Co. Ltd (1)
700-424 Moo 7 Armata Nakorn Industrial Estate Tombol Donhualor, Amphur Muang Chonburi, 20000, Chon Buri, Thailand
Tel.: (66) 38265600
Air Conditioning Equipment Mfr
N.A.I.C.S.: 333415

Valeo Sistemas Automotivos Ltda (1)
Rod Itatiba Braganca Paulista S/n Km 5, Itatiba, 13252-904, Brazil

Tel.: (55) 1145348500
Motor Vehicle Parts Mfr & Distr
N.A.I.C.S.: 336390
Mauro Gosdzinski (Dir-HR)

Valeo Sistemas Electricos Servicios S de RL de CV (1)
Ave Eje 130 S/n, San Luis Potosi, 78395, Mexico
Tel.: (52) 444 826 7000
Automotive Electronic Component Mfr
N.A.I.C.S.: 336320

Valeo Sistemas Electronicos, S de RL de CV (1)
Km 99 Carr Matamoros - Brecha 115 Celanese, 88920, Rio Bravo, Mexico
Tel.: (52) 8999322000
Web Site: https://www.valeo.com
Automotive Electronic Parts Mfr
N.A.I.C.S.: 336320

Valeo Sisteme Termice S.R.L. (1)
2b Str Uzinei, Mioveni, 115400, Romania
Tel.: (40) 248504679
Web Site: https://www.valeo.com
Sales Range: $25-49.9 Million
Emp.: 10
Vehicle Parts & Accessories Mfr
N.A.I.C.S.: 336390

Valeo Switches and Detection Systems, Inc. (1)
150 Stephenson Hwy, Troy, MI 48083-1116
Tel.: (248) 619-8300
Web Site: http://www.valeo.com
Sales Range: $50-74.9 Million
Motor Vehicle Parts Mfr
N.A.I.C.S.: 336390

Valeo Systemes Thermiques SAS (1)
8 Rue Louis Lormand, 78320, La Verriere, France
Tel.: (33) 134615700
Sales Range: $200-249.9 Million
Emp.: 800
Climate Control Equipment Mfr
N.A.I.C.S.: 334512

Valeo Systemes d'Essuyage SAS (1)
8 Rue Louis Lormand, 78320, La Verriere, France
Tel.: (33) 130696019
Windshield Wiper Blade & Rain Sensor Mfr
N.A.I.C.S.: 336390

Valeo Systemes de Controle Moteur SASU (1)
14 Avenue Des Beguines, 95800, Cergy, France
Tel.: (33) 134331300
Emp.: 800
Automobile Parts Mfr & Distr
N.A.I.C.S.: 336390
Vilchenon Franck (Gen Mgr)

Valeo Systems South Africa (Proprietary) Ltd. (1)
1 Fitzpatrick Street, PO Box 277, Niven Industrial Area, Uitenhage, 6230, Eastern Cape, South Africa
Tel.: (27) 419953052
Web Site: https://www.valeo.com
Emp.: 41
Motor Vehicle Parts Mfr
N.A.I.C.S.: 336390

Valeo Termico, S.A. (1)
Carretera de Logrono Km 8 9 Apartado de Correos N 615, 50011, Zaragoza, Spain
Tel.: (34) 976248700
Automotive Parts Mfr & Distr
N.A.I.C.S.: 336390

Valeo Thermal Commercial Vehicles Australia Pty. Ltd. (1)
15 Rodeo Drive, Dandenong South, 3175, VIC, Australia
Tel.: (61) 397000084
Heating & Air Conditioning Equipment Mfr
N.A.I.C.S.: 333415

Valeo Thermal Commercial Vehicles Finland Oy Ltd. (1)
Urusvuorenkatu 2, 20360, Turku, Finland
Tel.: (358) 24366000
Web Site: https://www.valeo-thermalbus.com

Commercial Vehicle Equipment Mfr
N.A.I.C.S.: 336110
Claudio Oddone (Mgr-Quality)

Valeo Thermal Commercial Vehicles Germany GmbH (1)
Friedrichshafener Str 7, 82205, Gilching, Germany
Tel.: (49) 810577210
Web Site: https://www.valeo-thermalbus.com
Heating & Air Conditioning Equipment Mfr
N.A.I.C.S.: 333415
Mark Sondermann (Gen Mgr)

Valeo Thermal Commercial Vehicles Mexico, SA de CV (1)
Blvd Miguel Aleman N 160 Local 17, Lerma, Edo de Mexico, Mexico
Tel.: (52) 5591994291
Heating & Air Conditioning Equipment Mfr
N.A.I.C.S.: 333415

Valeo Thermal Commercial Vehicles Middle East FZE (1)
Jafza One Tower A Office 1906, PO Box 17933, Dubai, United Arab Emirates
Tel.: (971) 48860664
Heating & Air Conditioning Equipment Mfr
N.A.I.C.S.: 333415
Mohammed Hashmi (Project Mgr)

Valeo Thermal Commercial Vehicles SA (Pty) Ltd. (1)
Unit 2 14 Ranworth Crescent and Laneshaw Street Longlakes, Modderfontein, Johannesburg, 1501, South Africa
Tel.: (27) 768344371
Heating & Air Conditioning Equipment Mfr
N.A.I.C.S.: 333415

Valeo Thermal Commercial Vehicles System (Suzhou) Co. Ltd. (1)
No 23 Building Export Processing Zone No 666 Jianlin Road, Sub-Industrial Park Suzhou New District, Suzhou, 215151, Jiangsu, China
Tel.: (86) 51266710766
Heating & Air Conditioning Equipment Mfr
N.A.I.C.S.: 333415
Patrick Misskampf (Dir-Sls-South East Asia)

Valeo Thermal Systems Japan Corporation (1)
6F Minamishinjuku Hoshino Bldg, Tokyo, 151 0051, Japan (100%)
Tel.: (81) 353684128
Sales Range: $1-4.9 Billion
Emp.: 3,376
Automobile Compressors & Air Conditioning Systems Mfr
N.A.I.C.S.: 333912

Valeo Thermal Systems Korea Co. Ltd (1)
19 Hwangseong-Dong, Kyongju, 780130, Korea (South)
Tel.: (82) 552878110
Automobile Parts Mfr
N.A.I.C.S.: 336390

Valeo Ticari Tasitlar Termo Sistemleri AS (1)
Koza Mah Evren Oto Sanayi Sitesi 1678 Sk No 17, Esenyurt, 34510, Istanbul, Turkiye
Tel.: (90) 2126721590
Heating & Air Conditioning Equipment Mfr
N.A.I.C.S.: 333415
Vedat Metin (Supvr-Maintenance)

Valeo Transmisiones Servicios de Mexico S. de R.L. de C.V. (1)
Av Central No 505, San Luis Potosi, 78395, Mexico
Tel.: (52) 4441374790
Automotive Transmission Equipment Mfr
N.A.I.C.S.: 336350

Valeo Vision Belgique SA (1)
Rue Du Parc Industrial 31, Meslin-l'Eveque, B-7822, Ath, Belgium
Tel.: (32) 68265211
Motor Vehicle Parts & Accessories Mfr
N.A.I.C.S.: 336390

Valeo Vision S.A.S. (1)
34 Rue Saint Andre, Bobigny, 93012, France
Tel.: (33) 149426262
Rev.: $1,470,080,600

Emp.: 800
Automotive Lighting Equipment Mfr
N.A.I.C.S.: 336320

Valeo Vymeniky Tepla s.r.o. (1)
Street Skandinavska 992, 267 53, Zebrak,
Czech Republic
Tel.: (420) 319800204
Emp.: 900
Heating & Air Conditioning Equipment Mfr
N.A.I.C.S.: 333415
Lucie Ortova *(Partner-HR Bus)*

Valeo climatizacao do Brasil - veiculos comerciais S/A (1)
Av Rio Branco 4688 - Bairro, Sao Cristovao, Caxias do Sul, 95060-145, RS, Brazil
Tel.: (55) 5421015701
Heating & Air Conditioning Equipment Mfr
N.A.I.C.S.: 333415

Valeo-Sylvania, LLC (1)
1231 A Ave N, Seymour, IN 47274 **(100%)**
Tel.: (812) 523-5200
Web Site: http://www.valeosylvania.com
Sales Range: $75-99.9 Million
Emp.: 1,000
Automotive Lighting Systems & Components Mfr
N.A.I.C.S.: 335139

ValeoThermal Commercial Vehicles North America, Inc. (1)
22150 Challenger Dr, Elkhart, IN 46514
Tel.: (574) 264-2190
Heating & Air Conditioning Equipment Mfr
N.A.I.C.S.: 333415

Wuhu Valeo Automotive Lighting Systems Co. Ltd. (1)
North Feng Ming Hu Road, Wuhu Economic Development Zone, Wuhu, Anhui, China
Tel.: (86) 5535613333
Emp.: 300
Automotive Component Mfr & Distr
N.A.I.C.S.: 336390
Hejing Qin *(Mgr-Pur)*

Wuxi Valeo Automotive Components & System Co. Ltd. (1)
No 28 East Chunhui Road Xishan Economic and Technological, Development Zone, Wuxi, Jiangsu, China
Tel.: (86) 51081132101
Automotive Component Mfr & Distr
N.A.I.C.S.: 336390
Qiaozhen Shu *(Engr-Quality-APU)*

gestigon GmbH (1)
Maria-Goeppert-Strasse 17, 23562, Lubeck, Germany
Tel.: (49) 45187929130
Web Site: https://www.gestigon.com
Software Development Services
N.A.I.C.S.: 513210
Frank Wippich *(CEO & Mng Dir)*

VALETRON S.A.
Av Presidente Wilson 231 - 28 Floor/parte, 20030021, Rio de Janeiro, Brazil
Tel.: (55) 21 3804 3700
Web Site: http://www.valetron.com.br
Year Founded: 1997
Investment Management Service
N.A.I.C.S.: 523999
Maria Amalia Delfim de Melo Coutrim *(Dir-IR)*

VALEURA ENERGY INC.
Bow Valley Square 1 Suite 1200 202 - 6th Avenue SW, Calgary, T2P 2R9, AB, Canada
Tel.: (403) 237-7102 **AB**
Web Site:
   http://www.valeuraenergy.com
VLERF—(OTCQX)
Rev.: $260,000
Assets: $64,010,000
Liabilities: $35,553,000
Net Worth: $28,457,000
Earnings: ($12,495,000)
Emp.: 5
Fiscal Year-end: 12/31/22
Oil & Gas Exploration

N.A.I.C.S.: 211120
Timothy R. Marchant *(Chm)*

Subsidiaries:

Valeura Energy Asia Pte. Ltd. (1)
111 Somerset Road No 09-31, Singapore, 238164, Singapore
Tel.: (65) 63736940
Oil Extraction Services
N.A.I.C.S.: 211120

VALGROUP PACKAGING SOLUTIONS
Rua Joaquim Floriano 1052 - 5 andar, 04534-004, Lorena, Sao Paulo, Brazil
Tel.: (55) 11 3706 9790
Web Site: http://www.valgroup.com.br
Year Founded: 1976
Emp.: 12
Holding Company; Flexible & Rigid Plastic Packaging Products Mfr & Whslr
N.A.I.C.S.: 551112
Carlo Bergamaschi *(Mng Dir-Valfilm)*

Subsidiaries:

ValGroup Packaging Solutions - Camacari Unit (1)
Avenida Leste s/n Quadra A Lotes 2 a 24 Poloplast, 42801-170, Camacari, Bahia, Brazil
Tel.: (55) 7136218800
Sheet Metal Distr
N.A.I.C.S.: 423330

ValGroup Packaging Solutions - Itamonte Unit (1)
Rua Leonardo Costa Goncalves 1010, Parque Monte Verde, 37466-000, Itamonte, Brazil
Tel.: (55) 3533639200
Sheet Metal Distr
N.A.I.C.S.: 423330

ValGroup Packaging Solutions - Lorena Unit (1)
Avenida A 21, Bairro Cecap - Lorena, 12610-195, Sao Paulo, Brazil
Tel.: (55) 1221244600
Sheet Metal Distr
N.A.I.C.S.: 423330

ValGroup Packaging Solutions - Manaus Unit (1)
Avenida Cupiuba nr 617, Distrito Industrial, 69075-060, Manaus, Amazonas, Brazil
Tel.: (55) 9231868900
Sheet Metal Distr
N.A.I.C.S.: 423330

Valfilm - MG Industria de Embalagens Ltda. (1)
Rodovia Presidente Dutra s/n km 55 Galpao 1 e 3 Cond Industrial, Bairro Mondesir, CEP 12605-530, Lorena, SP, Brazil
Tel.: (55) 12 2124 4400
Web Site: http://www.valfilm.com.br
Polyethylene Flexible Packaging Products Mfr & Whslr
N.A.I.C.S.: 326112
Carlo Bergamaschi *(Mng Dir)*

Subsidiary (US):

Valfilm North America, Inc. (2)
6945 Atlantic Ave, Long Beach, CA 90805
Tel.: (562) 790-8834
Polyethylene Flexible Packaging Products Mfr & Distr
N.A.I.C.S.: 424610
Julio Mercado *(Gen Mgr)*

Plant (Domestic):

Valfilm North America, Inc. - Findlay Plant (3)
3441 N Main St, Findlay, OH 45840
Tel.: (419) 423-6500
Polyolefin Films Mfr
N.A.I.C.S.: 326113
Joao Bosco Barros Filho *(Sls Mgr-North America)*

VALIANT CO., LTD.
No 11 Wuzhishan Rd Development Zone, Yantai, 264006, Shandong, China
Tel.: (86) 5356382740
Web Site: https://www.valiant-cn.com
Year Founded: 1992
002643—(SSE)
Rev.: $713,296,865
Assets: $1,300,066,569
Liabilities: $347,507,297
Net Worth: $952,559,272
Earnings: $101,272,626
Fiscal Year-end: 12/31/22
Liquid Crystal Material Mfr
N.A.I.C.S.: 325199
Huang Yiwu *(Chm)*

Subsidiaries:

Jiangsu Sunera Technology Co., Ltd. (1)
Xixian Road 129, Wuxi, Jiangsu, China
Tel.: (86) 51082106600
Web Site: https://www.sunera-cn.com
Electronic Functional Material Distr
N.A.I.C.S.: 423690

Yantai Gem Chemicals Co., Ltd. (1)
No 48 Chengdu Street Dajijia Industrial Park, Yantai, 264006, Shandong, China
Tel.: (86) 5356977329
Web Site: https://www.ytgemchem.com
Chemical Products Mfr
N.A.I.C.S.: 325998

Yantai Haichuan Chemicals Co., Ltd. (1)
23 Main Street, Yantai Economic and Technological Development Zone Industrial Park, Chengdu, 264006, Shandong, China
Tel.: (86) 5356975698
Web Site: https://www.hcchem.cn
Emp.: 182
Chemical Products Mfr
N.A.I.C.S.: 325998

VALIANT COMMUNICATIONS LIMITED
71-1 Shivaji Marg, New Delhi, 110 015, India
Tel.: (91) 1125928415
Web Site:
   https://www.valiantcom.com
Year Founded: 1994
526775—(BOM)
Rev.: $3,792,111
Assets: $4,797,758
Liabilities: $843,067
Net Worth: $3,954,691
Earnings: $201,571
Emp.: 70
Fiscal Year-end: 03/31/23
Telecom Transmission Equipment Mfr
N.A.I.C.S.: 517810
Inder Mohan Sood *(Chm, CEO & Mng Dir)*

VALIANT HOLDING AG
Pilatusstrasse 39, 6003, Lucerne, Switzerland
Tel.: (41) 313107744
Web Site: https://www.valiant.ch
Year Founded: 1824
VATN—(SWX)
Rev.: $753,980,274
Assets: $42,881,418,060
Liabilities: $39,820,432,784
Net Worth: $3,060,985,276
Earnings: $171,446,400
Emp.: 1,003
Fiscal Year-end: 12/31/23
Offices of Bank Holding Companies
N.A.I.C.S.: 551111
Jurg Bucher *(Chm)*

Subsidiaries:

Valiant Bank AG (1)
Bundesplatz 4, 3001, Bern, Switzerland
Tel.: (41) 313209111
Web Site: https://www.valiant.ch

Sales Range: $50-74.9 Million
Emp.: 50
Retail Banking Services
N.A.I.C.S.: 522110

Valiant Bank AG (1)
Bundesplatz 4, 3001, Bern, Switzerland
Tel.: (41) 313209111
Web Site: http://www.valiant.ch
Sales Range: $50-74.9 Million
Emp.: 100
Banking Services; Asset Management
N.A.I.C.S.: 522110

Valiant Mortgages Ltd. (1)
426 505 - 8840 210th Street, Langley, BC, Canada
Tel.: (604) 424-8904
Web Site: https://www.valiantmortgage.ca
Mortgage Services
N.A.I.C.S.: 522310

VALIANT LABORATORIES LIMITED
104 1st Floor Udyog Kshetra Above Krishna Motors Near D-mart, Mulund Goregaon Link Road Mulund West, Mumbai, 400080, India
Tel.: (91) 2249712001
Web Site: https://www.valiantlabs.in
Year Founded: 1980
543998—(BOM)
Rev.: $41,194,700
Assets: $25,896,629
Liabilities: $13,676,948
Net Worth: $12,219,681
Earnings: $3,526,193
Emp.: 91
Fiscal Year-end: 03/31/23
Pharmaceuticals Product Mfr
N.A.I.C.S.: 325412
Paresh S. Shah *(CFO)*

VALIANT ORGANICS LIMITED
109 Udyog Kshetra 1st Floor Mulund Goregaon Link Road Mulund W, Mumbai, 400 080, India
Tel.: (91) 2267976683
Web Site:
   https://www.valiantorganics.com
Year Founded: 1985
540145—(BOM)
Rev.: $127,071,207
Assets: $148,579,366
Liabilities: $59,848,211
Net Worth: $88,731,155
Earnings: $12,297,188
Emp.: 1,142
Fiscal Year-end: 03/31/23
Chemical Preparation Mfr & Distr
N.A.I.C.S.: 325199
Arvind Kanji Chheda *(Mng Dir)*

VALICA SPA
Via Arezzo 1, 00161, Rome, Italy
Tel.: (39) 069499884
Web Site: https://www.valica.it
Year Founded: 2016
VLC—(EUR)
Marketing Agent Services
N.A.I.C.S.: 541613
Andrea Mearelli *(CTO)*

VALID SOLUCOES S.A.
Alameda Rio Claro 241 Bela Vista, Sao Paulo, 01332-010, Brazil
Tel.: (55) 2121957200 **BR**
Web Site: https://valid.com
Year Founded: 1957
VSSPY—(OTCIQ)
Rev.: $403,194,426
Assets: $455,055,493
Liabilities: $217,078,166
Net Worth: $237,977,327
Earnings: $37,650,559
Fiscal Year-end: 12/31/23
Payment, Identification, Security & Telecommunications Card Printing Services

VALID SOLUCOES S.A.

Valid Solucoes S.A.—(Continued)
N.A.I.C.S.: 323111
Marcilio Marques Moreira *(Vice Chm)*

Subsidiaries:

Interprint S.A. (1)
Av Dr Rudge Ramos 1561 Bairro Rudge Ramos, Sao Bernardo do Campo, Sao Paulo, Brazil
Tel.: (55) 11 4367 7222
Payment & Identification Services
N.A.I.C.S.: 561499

Valid Asia Pte. Ltd. (1)
67 Ubi Ave 1 06-06 Starhub Green, Singapore, 408942, Singapore
Tel.: (65) 8001302206
Information Technology Services
N.A.I.C.S.: 541511

Valid Soluciones y Servicios de Seguridad en Medios de Pago e Identificacion S.A. (1)
Jose C Paz 3640, Buenos Aires, C1437IQP, Argentina (95.6%)
Tel.: (54) 1149124100
Web Site: http://www.valid.com
Payment, Identification, Security & Telecommunications Card Printing Services
N.A.I.C.S.: 323111

Subsidiary (Non-US):

CSB Transtex Chile S.A (2)
Guardia Vieja 255 of 1101, Santiago, Chile
Tel.: (56) 29463232
Sales Range: $25-49.9 Million
Emp.: 10
Commercial Printing Services
N.A.I.C.S.: 323111

Valid South Africa (Pty.) Ltd. (1)
Office No 3 1st Floor Block C Eagle Canyon Office Park, CNR Dolfyn & Jan Frederick Street Randparkridge, Randburg, 2169, South Africa
Tel.: (27) 800980477
Information Technology Services
N.A.I.C.S.: 541511

Valid USA Inc. (1)
1011 Warrenville Rd Ste 450, Lisle, IL 60532
Tel.: (630) 852-8200
Web Site: http://www.validusa.com
Sales Range: $50-74.9 Million
Emp.: 1,000
Data Base Management, Merge Purge Processing, Address Delivery Improvement, E-Marketing Forms, Printing Personalization, Demographics & Data Processing Services
N.A.I.C.S.: 518210

Subsidiary (Domestic):

Marketing Software Company LLC (2)
6200 Canoga Ave Ste 102, Woodland Hills, CA 91367-2429
Tel.: (818) 346-1600
Web Site: http://www.mscnet.com
Database Marketing Software Developer
N.A.I.C.S.: 513210
Bruce Morgan *(VP-SIs)*

VALIDIAN CORPORATION

6 Gurdwara Street Suite 205, Ottawa, K2E 8A3, ON, Canada
Tel.: (613) 224-3535 NV
Web Site: http://www.validian.com
VLDI—(OTCBB)
Sales Range: Less than $1 Million
Emp.: 10
Security Applications Software
N.A.I.C.S.: 513210
Bruce I. Benn *(Pres, CEO, CFO, Treas & Sec)*

VALIDSOFT UK LIMITED

25 Finsbury Circus, London, EC2M 7EE, United Kingdom
Tel.: (44) 2071646460 UK
Web Site: http://www.validsoft.com
Sales Range: $1-9.9 Million

Telecommunication Security Software Publisher
N.A.I.C.S.: 513210
Patrick M. Carroll *(Founder, Chm & CEO)*

VALIDUS AS

Vollsveien 13C, 1366, Lysaker, Norway
Tel.: (47) 32231100
Web Site: http://www.validus.no
Sales Range: $400-449.9 Million
Emp.: 3,000
Personal Care Products Mfr & Distr
N.A.I.C.S.: 325620
Per Christian Voss *(CEO)*

Subsidiaries:

Adam og Eva AS (1)
Schweigaards Gate 50, 191, Oslo, Norway
Tel.: (47) 22 17 99 61
Web Site: http://www.adamogeva.no
Beauty Salon Operator
N.A.I.C.S.: 812112

CM-gruppen AS (1)
Ranhammarsvagen 21, Bromma, 16111, Sweden
Tel.: (46) 8 50 59 33 00
Web Site: http://www.cm.se
Personal Care Product Distr
N.A.I.C.S.: 424210

Tendenz Harleie AS (1)
Drammensveien 35, 0271, Oslo, Norway
Tel.: (47) 22 92 50 00
Web Site: http://www.tendenz.net
Personal Care Product Distr
N.A.I.C.S.: 424210

Validus Butikkdrift AS (1)
Orkidehogda 3, Mjondalen, 3051, Norway
Tel.: (47) 32 23 11 00
Personal Care Product Distr
N.A.I.C.S.: 424210

Vita AS (1)
Haslevangen 15 3 etasje, 0579, Oslo, Norway
Tel.: (47) 22 57 69 50
Web Site: http://www.vita.no
Cosmetic Product Distr
N.A.I.C.S.: 456120

VALINGE INVEST AB

Prastavagen 513, SE 263 65, Viken, Sweden
Tel.: (46) 42 23 78 15
Web Site: http://www.valinge.se
Sales Range: $75-99.9 Million
Emp.: 60
Holding Company
N.A.I.C.S.: 551112
Anders Borg *(Chm)*

Subsidiaries:

Bjoorn Klickgolv pa Natet AB (1)
Grev Turegatan 11 B, 114 46, Stockholm, Sweden
Tel.: (46) 20 51 50 10
Web Site: http://www.bjoorn.se
Flooring System Distr
N.A.I.C.S.: 423310

Valinge Innovation AB (1)
Prastavagen 513, 263 65, Viken, Sweden
Tel.: (46) 42237815
Web Site: http://www.valinge.se
Sales Range: $75-99.9 Million
Emp.: 200
Flooring Systems Mfr
N.A.I.C.S.: 321211
Niclas Hakansson *(Co-CEO)*

VALIO LTD.

Meijeritie 6, 00370, Helsinki, Finland
Tel.: (358) 10381121 FI
Web Site: http://www.valio.com
Year Founded: 1905
Rev.: $2,000,660,126
Assets: $1,256,784,162
Liabilities: $656,729,579
Net Worth: $600,054,584

Earnings: $36,460,402
Emp.: 4,256
Fiscal Year-end: 12/31/19
Dairy Products Mfr & Distr
N.A.I.C.S.: 112120
Annikka Hurme *(CEO & Member-Exec Bd)*

Subsidiaries:

OOO Valio (1)
Primorsky pr Building 54 building 1 letter A, 197374, Saint Petersburg, Russia
Tel.: (7) 8123201221
Web Site: http://www.valio.ru
Sales Range: $400-449.9 Million
Dairy Products Mfr & Distr
N.A.I.C.S.: 311513

SIA Valio International (1)
A Briana 9A-2, Riga, 1001, Latvia
Tel.: (371) 67368650
Web Site: http://www.valio.lv
Cheese, Yogurt & Milk Products Mfr & Sales
N.A.I.C.S.: 311513

Syrian-Finnish Company for Dairy Products (1)
Sehnaya Daraa Highway, PO Box 11850, Damascus, Syria
Tel.: (963) 116711905
Web Site: http://www.sfcdp.com
Sales Range: $25-49.9 Million
Emp.: 75
Dairy Products Processor
N.A.I.C.S.: 112120
Mohamed Mokadem *(Gen Mgr)*

UAB Valio International (1)
Laisves al 2-1, 44215, Kaunas, Lithuania
Tel.: (370) 37202478
Web Site: http://www.valio.lt
Sales Range: $25-49.9 Million
Emp.: 3
Dairy Product Processor
N.A.I.C.S.: 112120

Valio - Vache Bleue S.A. (1)
552 Grand Route, 1428, Lillois-Witterzee, Belgium
Tel.: (32) 67894940
Web Site: http://www.vachebleue.com
Sales Range: $100-124.9 Million
Emp.: 149
Cheese Producer
N.A.I.C.S.: 311513

Valio Eesti AS (1)
Sopruse pst 145 B building, B Korpus, 13425, Tallinn, Estonia
Tel.: (372) 6285700
Web Site: http://www.valio.ee
Sales Range: $10-24.9 Million
Emp.: 135
Dairy Product Processor
N.A.I.C.S.: 112120
Maido Solovjov *(Mng Dir)*

Subsidiary (Domestic):

AS Voru Juust (2)
Pkk tn 23, 65604, Voru, Estonia
Tel.: (372) 7821028
Web Site: http://www.vjuust.ee
Sales Range: $10-24.9 Million
Emp.: 160
Cheese Mfr
N.A.I.C.S.: 311513

Valio Shanghai Ltd. (1)
Room 3102-3106 Office Building 1 Plaza 66 1266 West Nanjing Road, Jing an District, Shanghai, 200040, China
Tel.: (86) 2150584316
Web Site: http://www.valio.fi
Dairy Products Mfr & Distr
N.A.I.C.S.: 424430

Valio Sverige AB (1)
Lindhagensterrassen 1, PO Box 30065, 104 25, Stockholm, Globen, Sweden
Tel.: (46) 87255150
Web Site: http://www.valio.se
Sales Range: $25-49.9 Million
Emp.: 40
Cheese & Milk Products Mfr & Sales
N.A.I.C.S.: 311513

Valio USA, Inc. (1)

INTERNATIONAL PUBLIC

2001 Rte 46 Ste 303, Parsippany, NJ 07054
Tel.: (973) 316-6699
Web Site: http://www.valio.com
Sales Range: $50-74.9 Million
Dairy Products Mfr & Distr
N.A.I.C.S.: 424430

Subsidiary (Domestic):

Finlandia Cheese Co., Inc. (2)
2001 Rte 46 E Ste 303, Parsippany, NJ 07054
Tel.: (973) 316-6699
Web Site: http://www.finlandiacheese.com
Sales Range: $50-74.9 Million
Emp.: 15
Cheese Processor
N.A.I.C.S.: 311513

VALIRX PLC

MediCity Nottingham D6 Thane Road, Nottingham, NG90 6BH, United Kingdom
Tel.: (44) 1157840026
Web Site: https://www.valirx.com
VAL—(AIM)
Assets: $5,018,866
Liabilities: $188,898
Net Worth: $4,829,968
Earnings: ($2,987,236)
Emp.: 10
Fiscal Year-end: 12/31/22
Investment Company
N.A.I.C.S.: 523940
Gerry Desler *(CFO)*

Subsidiaries:

ValiPharma Ltd. (1)
24 Greville St, London, EC1N 8SS, United Kingdom
Tel.: (44) 2030084416
Oncology & Diagnostic Products Mfr
N.A.I.C.S.: 334510

VALJAONICA BAKRA SEVOJNO AD

Prvomajska bb, 31205, Sevojno, Serbia
Tel.: (381) 31 594 340
Web Site: http://www.coppersev.com
Year Founded: 1952
Copper Product Mfr
N.A.I.C.S.: 331420
Milija Bozovic *(Gen Mgr)*

VALLABH POLY PLAST INTERNATIONAL LIMITED

Raheja Point -1 3rd Floor A Wing Vakola Pipe Line, Santacruz East, Mumbai, 400 055, India
Tel.: (91) 22 3950 9900
Web Site: http://www.vppil.com
Year Founded: 1989
Assets: $57
Liabilities: $4,962
Net Worth: ($4,904)
Earnings: ($31,548)
Fiscal Year-end: 03/31/19
Plastics Bag Mfr
N.A.I.C.S.: 314910
Bhagwat Swarup Sharma *(Mng Dir)*

VALLABH STEELS LTD.

G T Road Village Pawa, Sahnewal, Ludhiana, 141 120, Punjab, India
Tel.: (91) 1612511413
Web Site: https://www.vallabhsteelsltd.in
Year Founded: 1980
513397—(BOM)
Rev.: $807,862
Assets: $6,456,218
Liabilities: $6,397,182
Net Worth: $59,036
Earnings: ($2,873,830)
Emp.: 46
Fiscal Year-end: 03/31/21
Iron & Steel Products Mfr

N.A.I.C.S.: 331210
Kapil Kumar Jain *(Chm & Mng Dir)*

VALLANCE CARRUTHERS COLEMAN PRIEST
Greencoat House 15 Francis St 5th Fl, Victoria, London, SW1P 1DH, United Kingdom
Tel.: (44) 207 592 9331
Web Site: http://www.vccp.com
Year Founded: 2002
Emp.: 260
N.A.I.C.S.: 541810
Charles Vallance *(Founding Partner)*

VALLEY MAGNESITE COMPANY LIMITED
A-402 Mangalam 24-26 Hemanta Basu Sarani, Kolkata, 700 001, India
Tel.: (91) 3322436243
Web Site: https://www.valleymagnesite.com
Rev.: $52,094
Assets: $922,318
Liabilities: $5,962
Net Worth: $916,356
Earnings: ($13,278)
Fiscal Year-end: 03/31/19
Financial Investment Services
N.A.I.C.S.: 523999
Arun Kumar Agarwalla *(Mng Dir)*

VALLIANZ HOLDINGS LIMITED
1 Harbourfront Avenue 06-08 Keppel Bay Tower, Singapore, 98632, Singapore
Tel.: (65) 69116200   SG
Web Site: https://www.vallianzholdings.com
WPC—(CAT)
Rev.: $149,174,000
Assets: $267,729,000
Liabilities: $268,347,000
Net Worth: ($618,000)
Earnings: ($11,276,000)
Fiscal Year-end: 03/31/23
Oil & Gas Support Services
N.A.I.C.S.: 213112
Darren Chee Neng Yeo *(Vice Chm)*

Subsidiaries:

Offshore Engineering Resources Pte. Ltd.   (1)
12 International Business Park 01-01/02, Singapore, 609920, Singapore
Tel.: (65) 65053870
Offshore Services
N.A.I.C.S.: 488390

Vallianz Offshore Capital Mexico, A. De C.V. SOFOM, E.N.R.   (1)
Calle 35-D S/N entre Gustavo Ferrer y Josefa Capdepon Fracc Malibran, 24197, Ciudad del Carmen, Campeche, Mexico
Tel.: (52) 9381312606
Web Site: http://www.vallianz.com.mx
Financial Lending Services
N.A.I.C.S.: 522220

Vallianz Samson Pte Ltd   (1)
Newcruz Offshore Marine Pt 03-02 12 International Business Park, Singapore, 609920, Singapore
Tel.: (65) 6505 0600
Inland Water Freight Transportation Services
N.A.I.C.S.: 483211

VALLIBEL POWER ERATHNA PLC
Tel.: (94) 112381111
Web Site: https://www.vallibel-hydro.com
VPEL—(COL)
Rev.: $3,736,790
Assets: $12,486,501
Liabilities: $1,338,829
Net Worth: $11,147,672
Earnings: $2,180,743
Emp.: 81
Fiscal Year-end: 03/31/23
Hydro Power Generation & Distribution
N.A.I.C.S.: 221111
K. D. Dhammika Perera *(Chm)*

VALLOUREC SA
12 rue de la Verrerie, 92190, Meudon, France
Tel.: (33) 149093500   FR
Web Site: https://www.vallourec.com
Year Founded: 1884
VLOUF—(OTCIQ)
Rev.: $5,004,967
Assets: $8,002,666,962
Liabilities: $1,458,783,530
Net Worth: $6,543,883,432
Earnings: $1,275,043,603
Emp.: 14,771
Fiscal Year-end: 12/31/23
Seamless Steel Tubing Mfr
N.A.I.C.S.: 331210
Philippe Guillemot *(Chm & CEO)*

Subsidiaries:

Ascoval S.A.S.   (1)
14 rue du Vieux Faubourg, 59042, Lille, Cedex, France
Tel.: (33) 327231340
Web Site: http://www.ascoval.fr
Emp.: 320
Steel Mfrs
N.A.I.C.S.: 331110

PT Citra Tubindo Tbk.   (1)
World Trade Centre 5 16th floor Jl Jendral Sudirman Kav 29-31, Jakarta, 12920, Indonesia
Tel.: (62) 215250609
Web Site: https://www.citratubindo.com
Rev.: $208,240,090
Assets: $171,146,562
Liabilities: $68,713,574
Net Worth: $102,432,988
Earnings: $18,660,279
Emp.: 370
Fiscal Year-end: 12/31/2023
Oil & Gas Steel Pipes & Tubes Mfr
N.A.I.C.S.: 331210
Didier Dubedout Laurent *(Dir-Comml)*

Seamless Tubes Asia Pacific Pte Ltd.   (1)
133 New Bridge Road 21-01 Chinatown Point, Singapore, 059413, Singapore
Tel.: (65) 673 34 778
Web Site: http://www.vamservices.com
Oil & Gas Field Equipment Mfr
N.A.I.C.S.: 333132

Serimax   (1)
8 rue Mercier, 77290, Mitry-Mory, France
Tel.: (33) 60216700
Web Site: http://www.serimax.com
Emp.: 20
Integrated Welding Services
N.A.I.C.S.: 331491

Serimax Do Brasil Servicos de Soldagem e Fabricacao Ltda.   (1)
Edificio Castelo Branco Avenida Republica do Chile 230 12 Andar, Centro, 20031-919, Rio de Janeiro, Brazil
Tel.: (55) 2138738370
Welding Services
N.A.I.C.S.: 811310

Serimax Field Joint Coating Ltd.   (1)
Unit 5 Greenbank Business Park Dyneley Road, Blackburn, BB1 3AB, Lancashire, United Kingdom
Tel.: (44) 1254264320
Web Site: http://www.serimaxfjc.com
Welding Services
N.A.I.C.S.: 811310
Humberto Schulte *(Project Mgr)*

Serimax Holdings S.A.S.   (1)
346 Rue de la Belle Etoile, CS 90023, Roissy en France, 95926, Charles de Gaulle, Cedex, France
Tel.: (33) 156489050
Web Site: http://www.serimax.com
Welding Services
N.A.I.C.S.: 811310

Serimax Ltd.   (1)
16 Airfield RoadÂ , Evanton Industrial EstateÂ Â , Evanton, IV16 9XJ, Ross-shire, United Kingdom
Tel.: (44) 1349831122
Welding Services
N.A.I.C.S.: 811310
Kelly O'Connor *(Mgr-IT & Ops-Grp)*

Serimax North America LLC   (1)
11315 W Little York Rd Bldg 3, Houston, TX 77041
Tel.: (832) 230-2700
Welding Services
N.A.I.C.S.: 811310
Cedric Chardenoux *(VP-North America)*

Serimax OOO   (1)
Mayakovskogo per 11, Moscow, 109044, Russia
Tel.: (7) 4959892364
Welding Services
N.A.I.C.S.: 811310

Serimax S.A.S.   (1)
ZI Mitry-Compans 8 rue Mercier, 77290, Mitry-Mory, France
Tel.: (33) 160216700
Welding Services
N.A.I.C.S.: 811310

Serimax Welding Services Malaysia Sdn. Bhd.   (1)
G Tower Suite 18-1 Level 18 199 Jalan Tun Razak, 50400, Kuala Lumpur, Malaysia
Tel.: (60) 326034555
Welding Services
N.A.I.C.S.: 811310
Vincent Raoult *(Project Mgr)*

Tubos Soldados Atlantico Ltda.   (1)
Rod Governador Mario Covas BR 101 - km 276 - Carapina, Polo Industrial de Piracema, 29161-064, Serra, Espirito Santo, Brazil
Tel.: (55) 2732124670
Seamless Steel Tube Mfr
N.A.I.C.S.: 331210
Cristiano Poloni *(Mgr-Production-TSA)*

V & M (Beijing) Co. Ltd.   (1)
Room 301 East Ocean Centre, 24A Jianguomenwai Avenue, Beijing, 100022, China
Tel.: (86) 1059233000
Web Site: http://www.vmtubes.com.cn
Sales Range: $25-49.9 Million
Emp.: 40
Oil & Gas Steel Pipes & Tubes Mfr
N.A.I.C.S.: 331210

V & M Changzhou Co. Ltd   (1)
No 88 Xinmin Road Weitang, Xinbei, Changzhou, 213033, Jiangsu, China
Tel.: (86) 51985171000
Web Site: http://www.vmtubes.com
Sales Range: $25-49.9 Million
Emp.: 100
Oil & Gas Steel Pipes & Tubes Mfr
N.A.I.C.S.: 331210

VAM Changzhou Oil & Gas Premium Equipments Co., Ltd.   (1)
N 18 Xin Min East Road, Changzhou, 213033, Jiangsu, China
Tel.: (86) 1059233000
Seamless Steel Tube Mfr
N.A.I.C.S.: 331210
Huang Jian *(Production Mgr)*

VAM Drilling Middle East FZE   (1)
Jebel Ali Free Zone, PO Box 261108, Dubai, United Arab Emirates
Tel.: (971) 4 883 5350
Web Site: http://www.vamservices.com
Sales Range: $25-49.9 Million
Emp.: 6
Oil & Gas Field Equipment Mfr
N.A.I.C.S.: 333132

VAM Far East Pte Ltd   (1)
51 Goldhill Plaza Unit 18-11/04, Singapore, 308900, Singapore
Tel.: (65) 67362372
Emp.: 10
Facility Management Services
N.A.I.C.S.: 561210
Shaun Blues *(Mng Dir)*

VAM Field Services Angola Lda.   (1)
Rua Amilcar Cabral N 211 Edificio IRCA Andar N 2, Luanda, Angola
Tel.: (244) 222399503
Electronic Accessory & Repair Retailer
N.A.I.C.S.: 449210
Charles Dubourg *(Mng Dir)*

Vallourec Deutschland GmbH   (1)
Theodorstrasse 109, 40472, Dusseldorf, Germany
Tel.: (49) 2119600
Web Site: http://www.vallourec.com
Steel Pipes & Tubes Mfr
N.A.I.C.S.: 331210

Vallourec Fittings SAS   (1)
Avenue Joseph Cugnot ZI de Grevaux-les-Guides, BP 10132, 59602, Maubeuge, Cedex, France
Tel.: (33) 3 2769 1100
Web Site: http://www.vallourec.com
Steel Fittings Mfr
N.A.I.C.S.: 332996

Vallourec Florestal Ltda.   (1)
Tel.: (55) 3837296050
Seamless Steel Tube Mfr
N.A.I.C.S.: 331210

Vallourec Italiana s.r.l.   (1)
Via Cimarosa 11, 20144, Milan, Italy
Tel.: (39) 024985441
Web Site: http://www.vmtubes.com.cn
Oil & Gas Steel Pipes & Tubes Mfr
N.A.I.C.S.: 331210

Vallourec Middle East FZE   (1)
Near R/A 7 Behind Bridgestone Jebel Ali Free Zone, PO Box 261108, Dubai, United Arab Emirates
Tel.: (971) 48150000
Electronic Accessory & Repair Retailer
N.A.I.C.S.: 449210
Bertrand de Rotalier *(Mng Dir-Middle East)*

Vallourec Mineracao Ltda.   (1)
Rod Br 040 -km 562 5-Mina Pau Branco, 35460-000, Brumadinho, Minas Gerais, Brazil
Tel.: (55) 3135719000
Seamless Steel Tube Mfr
N.A.I.C.S.: 331210
Marcelo Fontan *(Mgr-Maintenance)*

Vallourec Oil & Gas France   (1)
27 Avenue du General Leclerc, 92660, Boulogne-Billancourt, France
Tel.: (33) 1 49 09 37 31
Web Site: http://www.vamservices.com
Oil & Gas Steel Pipes & Tubes Mfr
N.A.I.C.S.: 331210

Plant (Domestic):

Vallourec Oil & Gas France - Aulnoye-Aymeries   (2)
54 rue Anatole France, BP 1, 59620, Aulnoye-Aymeries, Cedex, France
Tel.: (33) 327696600
Web Site: http://www.vamservices.com
Oil & Gas Steel Pipes & Tubes Mfr
N.A.I.C.S.: 331210

Vallourec Oil & Gas Mexico S.A. de C.V.   (1)
Av Framboyanes Lote 6 Manzana 5 Cd Ind Bruno Pagliai, Tejeria, Veracruz, 91697, Mexico
Tel.: (52) 229 989 8716
Web Site: http://www.vmtubes.com.cn
Oil & Gas Steel Pipes & Tubes Mfr & Distr
N.A.I.C.S.: 331210

Vallourec Oil & Gas Nederland B.V.   (1)
Kelvinstraat 8-16, 1704 RS, Heerhugowaard, Netherlands
Tel.: (31) 72 571 8255
Oil & Gas Field Equipment Mfr
N.A.I.C.S.: 333132

Vallourec Oil & Gas Nigeria Ltd.   (1)
15B Akanbi Danmola Street South West, Ikoyi, Lagos, Nigeria
Tel.: (234) 14630840
Electronic Accessory & Repair Retailer
N.A.I.C.S.: 449210

Vallourec Oil & Gas UK Ltd.   (1)
Clydesdale Works Clydesdale Road, Mossend, Bellshill, ML4 2RR, Lanarks, United Kingdom

VALLOUREC SA

Vallourec SA—(Continued)
Tel.: (44) 1698 742 300
Web Site: http://www.vmog.co.uk
Sales Range: $25-49.9 Million
Emp.: 50
Oil & Gas Steel Pipes & Tubes Mfr
N.A.I.C.S.: 331210
Alastair Clarke (Mgr-Sls)

Vallourec Tubes SAS (1)
27 avenue du General Leclerc, 92660, Boulogne-Billancourt, France (100%)
Tel.: (33) 149093679
Web Site: http://www.vmtubes.com
Sales Range: $50-74.9 Million
Emp.: 225
Steel Pipes & Tubes Mfr
N.A.I.C.S.: 331210

Subsidiary (Non-US):

Anhui Tianda Oil Pipe Company Limited (2)
Zhengxing Road, Tongcheng Town, Tianchang, 239311, Anhui, China (99.03%)
Tel.: (86) 550 3088388
Web Site: http://www.tiandapipe.com
Sales Range: $300-349.9 Million
Oil & Gas Pipe Mfr
N.A.I.C.S.: 332996
Pascal Braquehais (Mng Dir-Vallourec Northeast Asia)

Plant (Domestic):

Vallourec Tubes France - Aulnoye-Aymeries Mill (2)
64 Rue Anatole, BP 159, 59620, Aulnoye-Aymeries, France
Tel.: (33) 327696600
Steel Pipes & Tubes Mfr
N.A.I.C.S.: 331210

Vallourec Tubes France - Rouen Mill (2)
50 rue Laveissiere, BP 14, Deville-les-Rouen, 76250, Rouen, Cedex, France
Tel.: (33) 232822828
Sales Range: $75-99.9 Million
Steel Pipes & Tubes Mfr
N.A.I.C.S.: 331210

Vallourec Tubes France - Saint-Saulve Tube Mill (2)
Zone Industrielle No 4, BP 2, 59880, Saint-Saulve, Cedex, France
Tel.: (33) 327231301
Steel Pipes & Tubes Mfr
N.A.I.C.S.: 331210
Fishman Dertrang (Mgr)

Vallourec Tubos do Brasil S.A. (1)
Av. Olinto Meireles 65, Barreiro De Baixo, Belo Horizonte, 30640-010, Brazil (100%)
Tel.: (55) 3133282121
Seamless Steel Pipes & Tubes Mfr
N.A.I.C.S.: 331210
Alexandre Lyra (Mng Dir & Member-Exec Bd)

Subsidiary (Domestic):

V&M Florestal Ltda. (2)
rua Honduras 78, Curvelo, 35790-000, Brazil
Tel.: (55) 3837296050
Tree Planting & Charcoal Mfg
N.A.I.C.S.: 111421

V&M Mineracao Ltda. (2)
Mina Pau Branco Rodovia BR 040 Km 5625, 35460 000, Brumadinho, Brazil
Tel.: (55) 3135719000
Iron Ore Mining Production Services
N.A.I.C.S.: 212210

Vallourec USA Corporation (1)
2107 CityWest Blvd Ste 1300, Houston, TX 77042
Tel.: (713) 479-3200
Steel Tube & Pipe Mfr
N.A.I.C.S.: 331210

Subsidiary (Domestic):

VAM USA, LLC (2)
19210 E Hardy Rd, Houston, TX 77073
Tel.: (281) 821-5510
Web Site: https://www.vam-usa.com

Sales Range: $200-249.9 Million
Emp.: 300
Oil & Gas Field Consulting Services
N.A.I.C.S.: 213112
Eric Schuster (Pres)

Vallourec Star, LP (2)
2669 Martin Luther King Jr Blvd, Youngstown, OH 44510-1033
Tel.: (330) 742-6300
Sales Range: $75-99.9 Million
Mfr of Iron & Steel Fumeless Pipes
N.A.I.C.S.: 331210
Joel Mastervich (Pres & COO)

Unit (Domestic):

Vallourec Tube-Alloy, LLC - Houma (2)
1914 Grand Caillou Rd, Houma, LA 70363
Tel.: (985) 876-2886
Web Site: http://www.vallourec.com
Tubular Accessories Mfr & Distr
N.A.I.C.S.: 331210

Valtimet SAS (1)
27 avenue du general Leclerc, 92100, Boulogne, France
Tel.: (33) 149093981
Web Site: http://www.valtimet.com
Sales Range: $25-49.9 Million
Emp.: 15
Welded Tubing Mfr
N.A.I.C.S.: 331210

Subsidiary (Non-US):

CST Valinox Ltd. (2)
9-14 Isnapur Village IDE Pashmailarm, Patancheru Mandal, Medak, Secunderabad, 502 307, Andhra Pradesh, India
Tel.: (91) 8455224900
Web Site: http://www.cstvalinox.com
Sales Range: $25-49.9 Million
Steel Tube Mfr
N.A.I.C.S.: 331210

Subsidiary (US):

Neotiss, Inc. (2)
5501 Air Park Blvd, Morristown, TN 37813
Tel.: (423) 587-1888
Web Site: http://www.valtimet.com
Steel Tube Mfr
N.A.I.C.S.: 331210

Plant (Domestic):

Valtimet Inc. - Brunswick Plant (3)
4008 Community Rd, Brunswick, GA 31520
Tel.: (912) 264-4323
Web Site: http://www.valtimet.com
Sales Range: $25-49.9 Million
Emp.: 40
Steel Tube Mfr
N.A.I.C.S.: 331210

Joint Venture (Non-US):

Poongsan Valinox Corporation (2)
324-6 Hyosung-Dong, Keyang-Gu, Incheon, 407717, Korea (South)
Tel.: (82) 32 556 4424
Titanium & Steel Tube Mfr
N.A.I.C.S.: 331210
Jong Inn Ryu (Pres)

Subsidiary (Non-US):

Valtimet GmbH (2)
Dusselthaler Strasse 9, 40211, Dusseldorf, Germany
Tel.: (49) 2111723211
Web Site: http://www.valtimet.com
Sales Range: $25-49.9 Million
Emp.: 2
Welded Tubing Mfr
N.A.I.C.S.: 331210

Plant (Domestic):

Valtimet SAS - Les Laumes Plant (2)
Z I rue Marthe Paris, PO Box 30, 21150, Venarey-les-Laumes, France
Tel.: (33) 3 80 96 90 10
Web Site: http://www.neotiss.com
Sales Range: $25-49.9 Million
Steel Tube Mfr
N.A.I.C.S.: 331210

Vam Canada Inc - Newfoundland Plant (1)
10 Saint Anne's Crescent, Paradise, A1L 1K1, NL, Canada
Tel.: (709) 782-1450
Web Site: http://www.vam-usa.com
Sales Range: $25-49.9 Million
Emp.: 13
Oil Drilling Pipe Mfr
N.A.I.C.S.: 332996

VALMET AUTOMOTIVE OY

Autotehtaankatu 14, 23501, Uusikaupunki, Finland
Tel.: (358) 204848111   FI
Web Site: http://www.valmet-automotive.com
Year Founded: 1968
Rev.: $729,546,235
Assets: $614,698,993
Liabilities: $592,327,550
Net Worth: $22,371,443
Earnings: $1,871,286
Emp.: 4,812
Fiscal Year-end: 12/31/19
Motor Vehicle Engineering & Mfr
N.A.I.C.S.: 336110
Jarkko Sairanen (Chm)

Subsidiaries:

Valmet Automotive Engineering GmbH (1)
Bergrat-Bilfinger-Strasse 5, 74177, Bad Friedrichshall, Germany
Tel.: (49) 7136 999 0
Automotive Engineering Services
N.A.I.C.S.: 541330
Horst Bardehle (Mng Dir)

Subsidiary (Domestic):

Valmet Automotive Engineering GmbH (2)
Wolfsburger Landstrasse 22, DE-38442, Wolfsburg, Germany
Tel.: (49) 5362 17 0
Automotive Engineering Services
N.A.I.C.S.: 541330

Valmet Automotive GmbH (1)
Rudolph-Richter-Strasse 3, 49084, Osnabruck, Germany
Tel.: (49) 541 38059 0
Web Site: http://www.valmet-automotive.com
Sales Range: $75-99.9 Million
Emp.: 400
Automobile Parts Mfr
N.A.I.C.S.: 336390
Stefan Warneke (Gen Mgr)

Valmet Automotive Sp. z o.o. (1)
Ul Transportowa 1, 68-200, Zary, Poland
Tel.: (48) 68 459 6000
Web Site: http://www.valmet-automotive.com
Sales Range: $75-99.9 Million
Emp.: 400
Automobile Mfr
N.A.I.C.S.: 336110
Remigiusz Grzeskowiak (Mng Dir & Plant Mgr)

VALMET OYJ

Keilasatama 5, 02150, Espoo, Finland
Tel.: (358) 106720000   FI
Web Site: https://www.valmet.com
VALMT—(HEL)
Rev.: $4,833,124,400
Assets: $5,428,820,800
Liabilities: $3,792,805,120
Net Worth: $1,636,015,680
Earnings: $363,559,040
Emp.: 12,655
Fiscal Year-end: 12/31/21
Holding Company; Pulp, Paper & Power Solutions
N.A.I.C.S.: 322120
Pasi Laine (Pres & CEO)

Subsidiaries:

Enertechnix, Inc. (1)

INTERNATIONAL PUBLIC

9730B Lathrop Industrial Dr SW, Olympia, WA 98512
Tel.: (360) 753-8831
Web Site: http://www.enertechnix.com
Industrial Machinery & Equipment Merchant Whslr
N.A.I.C.S.: 423830
Christina Beason (CFO)

J&L Fiber Services, Inc. (1)
831 Progress Ave, Waukesha, WI 53186
Tel.: (262) 544-1890
Web Site: http://www.jlfiberservices.com
Emp.: 100
Refiner Plates, Screen Cylinders & Other Products for the Pulp & Paper Industry
N.A.I.C.S.: 331513
Shari Skopek (Mgr-HR)

Neles Oyj (1)
Toolonlahdenkatu 2, 00100, Helsinki, Finland
Tel.: (358) 20484100
Web Site: https://www.neles.com
Rev.: $4,076,528,560
Assets: $6,765,145,920
Liabilities: $4,259,536,320
Net Worth: $2,505,609,600
Earnings: $169,497,120
Emp.: 15,466
Fiscal Year-end: 12/31/2020
Holding Company; Automation, Power Transmission Equipment & Automobile Engineering & Technology Mfr
N.A.I.C.S.: 551112
Juha Rouhiainen (VP-IR)

Subsidiary (Non-US):

AB P.J. Jonsson Och Soner (2)
Krossvagen 14, Overhornas, 894 41, Ornskoldsvik, Sweden
Tel.: (46) 66073100
Web Site: https://www.pjjonsson.se
Automation Equipment Services
N.A.I.C.S.: 811310

Subsidiary (US):

Glens Falls Interweb Inc. (2)
PO Box 1347, South Glens Falls, NY 12803-1347
Tel.: (518) 793-6102
Web Site: http://www.gfinterweb.com
Engineering Services
N.A.I.C.S.: 541330
Jeffrey Riggi (Pres)

Subsidiary (Domestic):

Kaukotalo Oy (2)
c/o Metso Oyj--Fabianinkatu 9 A, 00130, Helsinki, Finland
Tel.: (358) 204 84100
Real Estate Management Services
N.A.I.C.S.: 531390
Turkka Makinen (Controller-Fin)

Subsidiary (Non-US):

McCloskey International Limited (2)
1 McCloskey Road, Keene, K9J 0G6, ON, Canada
Tel.: (705) 295-4925
Web Site: http://www.mccloskeyinternational.com
Rev.: $36,561,839
Emp.: 155
Machinery Mfr
N.A.I.C.S.: 333998
Paschal McCloskey (Founder & Pres)

Subsidiary (US):

Lippmann Milwaukee, Inc. (3)
3271 E Van Norman Ave, Cudahy, WI 53110
Tel.: (414) 744-2565
Web Site: http://www.lippmann-milwaukee.com
Sales Range: $10-24.9 Million
Emp.: 100
Mining Machinery
N.A.I.C.S.: 333131
Jeremy Kerber (Mgr-Field Svc & Warranty)

Subsidiary (Non-US):

Metso (Ukraine) LLC (2)
1/33 Kalinichenko Street, 50000, Krivoy Rog, Ukraine (100%)

AND PRIVATE COMPANIES   VALMET OYJ

Tel.: (380) 564938687
Web Site: http://www.metso.com
Mining & Construction Sales & Services
N.A.I.C.S.: 333131

Metso Automation Canada Ltd (2)
4716 Thimens Blvd, H4R 2B2, Saint Laurent, QC, Canada
Tel.: (514) 908-7045
Web Site: http://www.metso.com
Sales Range: $25-49.9 Million
Emp.: 5
Industrial Machinery & Equipment Distr
N.A.I.C.S.: 423830

Metso Automation Portugal Lda (2)
Rua Padre Americo Nr 7 B -1 Dt, Lisbon, 1600-548, Portugal
Tel.: (351) 21 711 0720
Sales Range: $25-49.9 Million
Emp.: 4
Industrial Machinery Whslr
N.A.I.C.S.: 423830
Laura Johanna Koskenranta *(Mgr)*

Metso Automation S.A./N.V. (2)
Koning Albert-I-laan 48, 1780, Wemmel, Belgium
Tel.: (32) 2 461 0227
Web Site: http://www.metso.com
Sales Range: $25-49.9 Million
Emp.: 4
Industrial Machinery Whslr
N.A.I.C.S.: 423830

Subsidiary (US):

Metso Automation USA Inc. (2)
44 Bowditch Dr, Shrewsbury, MA 01545
Tel.: (508) 852-0200
Valves & Process Systems Mfr
N.A.I.C.S.: 333248

Subsidiary (Non-US):

Metso Brasil Industria e Comercio Ltda. (2)
Rua Guarapari 634- Bairro Santa Amelia, 31560-300, Belo Horizonte, Minas Gerais, Brazil
Tel.: (55) 31 3055 2500
Web Site: http://www.metso.com
Mining Machinery & Equipment Mfr
N.A.I.C.S.: 333131

Subsidiary (Domestic):

Metso Capital Oy (2)
Fabianinkatu 9a, 130, Helsinki, Finland
Tel.: (358) 20484100
Financial Management Services
N.A.I.C.S.: 523999

Subsidiary (Non-US):

Metso Chile (2) **(100%)**
Tel.: (56) 222909600
Sales Range: $25-49.9 Million
Emp.: 25
N.A.I.C.S.: 236220

Unit (Domestic):

Metso Corporation Stock Preparation (2)
PO Box 34, 33841, Tampere, Finland **(100%)**
Tel.: (358) 20482120
Sales Range: $25-49.9 Million
Emp.: 80
Paper Machinery Manufacturing
N.A.I.C.S.: 333243

Subsidiary (Non-US):

Metso Denmark A/S (2)
Vejlevej 5, Horsens, 8700, Denmark
Tel.: (45) 76 26 64 00
Web Site: http://www.metso.com
Sales Range: $25-49.9 Million
Emp.: 100
Waste Shredders Mfr & Distr
N.A.I.C.S.: 333111

Joint Venture (Domestic):

Metso Endress+Hauser Oy (2)
Laippatie 4C, Helsinki, Finland
Tel.: (358) 20483160
Web Site: http://www.metsoendress.com

Sales Range: $50-74.9 Million
Emp.: 100
Electronic Parts & Equipment Whslr
N.A.I.C.S.: 423690
Tuomo Saukkonen *(Gen Mgr)*

Subsidiary (Non-US):

Metso FZE (Dubai) (2)
Jebel Ali Freezone, Dubai, 17175, United Arab Emirates
Tel.: (971) 4 8836 974
Emp.: 28
Industrial Machinery Distr
N.A.I.C.S.: 423830
Kalle Autto *(Mng Dir)*

Metso France SAS (2)
41 rue de la Republique, CS 61609, 71009, Macon, France
Tel.: (33) 385396200
Automobile Parts Mfr
N.A.I.C.S.: 336390

Metso India Pvt. Ltd. (2)
SKCL Design Square 3rd Floor S-11 & 12 Thiru-Vi-Ka Industrial Estate, Guindy, Chennai, 600 032, India
Tel.: (91) 44 40206500
Sales Range: $25-49.9 Million
Emp.: 136
Fabricated Plate Work Mfr
N.A.I.C.S.: 332313
Rakesh Thakur *(Mng Dir-Admin)*

Metso Mexico S.A. de C.V. (2)
Salamanca Ote Esq Celaya SN, Irapuato, 36541, Guanajuato, Mexico
Tel.: (52) 4626225190
Web Site: http://www.metso.com
Sales Range: $200-249.9 Million
Emp.: 300
Mining & Construction Operations
N.A.I.C.S.: 212290

Metso ND Engineering (Pty) Ltd (2)
MR385 ROAD Keystone Business Park, Cliffdale Hammarsdale, Durban, 3700, South Africa
Tel.: (27) 31 464 0510
Web Site: http://www.ndengineering.co.za
Sales Range: $25-49.9 Million
Emp.: 220
Industrial Engineering Services
N.A.I.C.S.: 541330

Metso Peru SA (2)
Avenida El Derby 055 Torre 1 Oficina 401 402, Lima, 3, Peru **(100%)**
Tel.: (51) 3134366
Sales Range: $75-99.9 Million
Emp.: 100
Mining & Construction
N.A.I.C.S.: 213114

Subsidiary (Domestic):

Metso Shared Services Oy (2)
Fabianinkatu 9 A, 130, Helsinki, Finland
Tel.: (358) 20484100
Office Administrative & IT Services
N.A.I.C.S.: 561110
Juha Seppala *(Sr VP)*

Subsidiary (Non-US):

Metso Svenska AB (2)
Axel Johnsons Vag 6, 652 21, Karlstad, Sweden **(100%)**
Tel.: (46) 16162500
Holding Company
N.A.I.C.S.: 551112

Metso Sweden AB (2)
Maskinvagen 11, SE-972 54, Lulea, Sweden
Tel.: (46) 920250680
Automobile Parts Mfr
N.A.I.C.S.: 336390

Metso Vietnam Co. Ltd (2)
Tel.: (84) 983222333
Emp.: 4
Mining Engineering Services
N.A.I.C.S.: 541330

Ou Noviter Eesti (2)
Vana-Posti 7, 10146, Tallinn, Estonia
Tel.: (372) 6 446 861
Sales Range: $75-99.9 Million
Emp.: 5
Electric Power Generation Services

N.A.I.C.S.: 221118

Przedstawicielstwo Metso (2)
Ul Jutrzenki 118, 02-230, Warsaw, Poland
Tel.: (48) 22 381 72 43
Pulp & Paper Industry Machinery Mfr
N.A.I.C.S.: 333243

Shaoguan City Shaorui Heavy Industries Co. Ltd. (2)
Industrial Park of Wujiang, Shaoguan, Guangdong, China
Tel.: (86) 7518136739
Web Site: http://www.shaoruiheavy.com
Industrial Equipment Mfr
N.A.I.C.S.: 333248

PMPKonmet Sp. z o.o. (1)
ul Wojewodzka 5, 58-560, Jelenia Gora, Poland
Tel.: (48) 75 755 2060
Web Site: https://www.pmpkonmet.pl
Construction Machinery Mfr
N.A.I.C.S.: 333120

Valmet Automation Oy (1)
Vanha Porvoontie 229, 01380, Vantaa, Finland
Tel.: (358) 106720000
Web Site: https://www.valmet.com
Sales Range: $750-799.9 Million
Emp.: 3,400
Installation of Industrial Machinery & Equipment
N.A.I.C.S.: 423830
Markku Simula *(Pres-Flow Control Bus Unit & VP)*

Subsidiary (Non-US):

PT Valmet Automation Indonesia (2)
Gedung Atria Sudirman 9th Floor Jl Jend Sudirman Kav 33-A, Jakarta, 10220, Indonesia
Tel.: (62) 215735034
Web Site: https://www.valmet.com
Industrial Machinery Sales
N.A.I.C.S.: 423830

Valmet Automacao Ltda. (2)
Av Independencia 2500 Bairro, Iporanga, Sorocaba, 18087-101, Sao Paulo, Brazil
Tel.: (55) 15 2102 9834
Industrial Machinery & Equipment Whslr
N.A.I.C.S.: 423830
Jonathan Bento *(Head-Ops, Svcs & Supply Chain-South America)*

Valmet Automation (Pty) Ltd (2)
Kingfisher Office Park 28 Siphosethu Road, Mount Edgecumbe, 4300, Durban, South Africa
Tel.: (27) 31 539 8640
Web Site: http://www.valmet.com
Sales Range: $25-49.9 Million
Emp.: 30
Industrial Machinery Whslr
N.A.I.C.S.: 423830
Steve Clark *(Country Mgr)*

Valmet Automation (Shanghai) Co., Ltd. (2)
688 Baofeng Road, Xuhang Town Jiading District, Shanghai, 201809, China
Tel.: (86) 2139975000
Web Site: https://www.valmet.com
Sales Range: $75-99.9 Million
Emp.: 500
Industrial Machinery Mfr, Sales & Service
N.A.I.C.S.: 333248

Valmet Automation A/S (2)
Teglverksveien 7, 3413, Lier, Norway
Tel.: (47) 32229550
Web Site: http://www.valmet.com
Industrial Machinery Distr
N.A.I.C.S.: 423830

Valmet Automation AB (2)
Axel Johnsons Vag 6, 652 21, Karlstad, Sweden
Tel.: (46) 54 171 000
Web Site: http://www.valmet.com
Industrial Machinery Whslr
N.A.I.C.S.: 423830

Valmet Automation B.V. (2)
Energieweg 13b, 3751 LT, Bunschoten, Netherlands
Tel.: (31) 33 25 44 600
Web Site: http://www.valmet.com

Industrial Automation Equipment Distr
N.A.I.C.S.: 423830

Valmet Automation Co., Ltd. (2)
Modernform Tower 2204 22nd Floor 699 Srinakarindr Road, Kweang Suangluang, Khet Suangluang, 10250, Bangkok, Thailand
Tel.: (66) 2 712 7241
Web Site: http://www.valmet.com
Industrial Machinery & Equipment Whslr
N.A.I.C.S.: 423830

Valmet Automation GesmbH (2)
Franzosengraben 12, 1030, Vienna, Austria
Tel.: (43) 1 79552 0
Web Site: http://www.valmet.com
Sales Range: $25-49.9 Million
Emp.: 50
Industrial Machinery Sales & Service
N.A.I.C.S.: 423830

Valmet Automation GmbH (2)
Marie-Curie-Strasse 10, 51377, Leverkusen, Germany
Tel.: (49) 214 2067 0
Web Site: http://www.valmet.com
Emp.: 49
Industrial Machinery Distr & Maintenance Services
N.A.I.C.S.: 423830
Michael Simon *(Mng Dir)*

Valmet Automation JSC (2)
Pulkovskoe Shosse 40 Build 4 A, 196158, Saint Petersburg, Russia
Tel.: (7) 8123334000
Web Site: http://www.valmet.com
Emp.: 52
Automation System Sales
N.A.I.C.S.: 423830
Leonid Mamontov *(Mng Dir)*

Valmet Automation KK (2)
4F 2-5-8 Higashi-Shinagawa, Shinagawa-ku, Tokyo, 140-0002, Japan
Tel.: (81) 3 6744 3001
Industrial Automation Equipment Distr
N.A.I.C.S.: 423830
Satoshi Mabuchi *(Controller)*

Valmet Automation Limited (2)
2 Lindenwood Crockford Lane, Chineham Business Park, Basingstoke, RG24 8QY, Hampshire, United Kingdom
Tel.: (44) 1256 376200
Web Site: http://www.valmet.com
Sales Range: $25-49.9 Million
Emp.: 26
Industrial Machinery Sales & Service
N.A.I.C.S.: 423830
Neil Buckland *(Dir-Sls)*

Valmet Automation Ltd (2)
SungOk Bldg 2nd Floor 262 Hwangsaeul-ro, Bundang-gu, Seongnam, 463-825, Gyeounggi-do, Korea (South)
Tel.: (82) 2 582 1517
Web Site: http://www.valmet.com
Emp.: 20
Industrial Machinery Sales & Service
N.A.I.C.S.: 423830
Soonho Lee *(Mgr)*

Unit (Domestic):

Valmet Automation Oy - Kajaani (2)
Kehraamontie 3, 87101, Kajaani, Finland
Tel.: (358) 10 672 0000
Sales Range: $25-49.9 Million
Emp.: 130
Mfr of Pulp & Paper Process Control Systems & Measurement Systems
N.A.I.C.S.: 333243
Juka Pirainen *(Product Mgr)*

Valmet Automation Oy - Tampere (2)
Lentokentankatu 11, 33900, Tampere, Finland
Tel.: (358) 10 672 0000
Sales Range: $150-199.9 Million
Emp.: 900
Mfr of Equipment for Monitoring Pressure, Differential Pressure, Pulp Consistancy, Temperature, Liquid Level, Flow & Liquid Density in the Papermaking Process
N.A.I.C.S.: 333243
Risto Lehtimaki *(Sr VP-Mktg & Comm)*

Subsidiary (Non-US):

Valmet Automation Polska Sp. z.o.o. (2)

VALMET OYJ

Valmet Oyj—(Continued)
ul Kosciuszki 1c, 44 100, Gliwice, Poland
Tel.: (48) 3240 00 900
Web Site: http://www.valmet.com
Emp.: 100
Industrial Machinery & Equipment Whslr
N.A.I.C.S.: 423830
Karolina Trznadel-Puzon *(Mgr-Supply Center)*

Valmet Automation Private Limited (2)
A-464 TTC Indl Area, Mahape, Navi Mumbai, 400 710, Maharashtra, India
Tel.: (91) 22 39130100
Web Site: http://www.valmet.com
Sales Range: $50-74.9 Million
Emp.: 110
Industrial Machinery Distr
N.A.I.C.S.: 423830
Karan Sitaraman *(Dir-Bus Controls)*

Valmet Automation Pte. Ltd. (2)
180 Clemenceau Avenue 06-01 Haw Par Centre, Singapore, 239922, Singapore
Tel.: (65) 11 1011
Web Site: http://www.valmet.com
Industrial Machinery & Equipment Sales
N.A.I.C.S.: 423830

Valmet Automation Pty. Ltd. (2)
173-181 Rooks Road, Vermont, 3133, VIC, Australia
Tel.: (61) 3 9872 0300
Web Site: http://www.valmet.com
Industrial Automation Equipment Distr
N.A.I.C.S.: 423830
Sandra Dent *(Acct Mgr)*

Valmet Automation S.A.S. (2)
Les Cinq Chemins 84 rue de Venteille, Bordeaux Technowest, 33187, Le Haillan, Cedex, France
Tel.: (33) 557921040
Web Site: https://www.valmet.com
Sales Range: $25-49.9 Million
Emp.: 20
Industrial Machinery Mfr & Distr
N.A.I.C.S.: 333248

Valmet Automation s.r.o. (2)
Zeleny pruh 95/97, 140 00, Prague, 4, Czech Republic
Tel.: (420) 2 27027360
Web Site: http://www.valmet.com
Industrial Machinery Whslr
N.A.I.C.S.: 423830

Valmet B.V. (1)
Databankweg 32, NL-3821 AL, Amersfoort, Netherlands
Tel.: (31) 854831870
Pulp & Paper Whslr
N.A.I.C.S.: 424130

Valmet Fabrics (China) Co., Ltd. (1)
No 1 Xi Er Dao Bonded area, Airport Free Trade Zone, Tianjin, C300308, China
Tel.: (86) 13651637651
Web Site: https://www.valmet.com
Mfr of Textiles for Feeders, Ironers & Folders in Commercial Laundries
N.A.I.C.S.: 314999

Valmet Fabrics Tecidos Tecnicos Ltda. (1)
Rod Anel Rodoviario Celso Mello, Azevedo 1300 - Olhos D'Agua, Belo Horizonte, 30390-085, Minas Gerais, Brazil (100%)
Tel.: (55) 3130731500
Web Site: https://www.valmet.com
Sales Range: $10-24.9 Million
Emp.: 34
Textile Product Mills
N.A.I.C.S.: 314999

Valmet Kauttua Oy (1)
Kauttuan Kyla Paperitehdas, PO Box 55, 27500, Kauttua, Finland
Tel.: (358) 103032265
Sales Range: $25-49.9 Million
Emp.: 36
Industrial Machinery Repair & Maintenance Services
N.A.I.C.S.: 811310
Kari Rantama *(Mng Dir)*

Valmet Seluloz Kagit ve Enerji Teknolojileri A.S. (1)
Akasya Acibadem Cecen Sk No 25 Kule Blok A Giris Kat 30/194, Uskudar, 34660, Istanbul, Turkiye
Tel.: (90) 2165042004
Pulp & Paper Whslr
N.A.I.C.S.: 424130

Valmet Technologies Oy (1)
Keilasatama 5, 02150, Espoo, Finland
Tel.: (358) 106720000
Paper Processing Machinery Mfr
N.A.I.C.S.: 333310
Pasi Laine *(Pres)*

Subsidiary (Non-US):

PT. Valmet (2)
9th Floor Jl Jend Sudirman Kav 33-A, Jakarta, 10220, Indonesia (100%)
Tel.: (62) 21 573 5034
Web Site: http://www.valmet.com
Pulp & Paper Industry Machinery Mfr
N.A.I.C.S.: 423830

Valmet (China) Co., Ltd. (2)
688 Baofeng Road Xuhang Town, Jiading District, Shanghai, 201809, Jiading, China
Tel.: (86) 21 3997 5000
Web Site: http://www.valmet.com
Emp.: 1,000
Paper Industry Machinery Mfr
N.A.I.C.S.: 333243
Zhenhua Wang *(Mgr-Foundry Dept & Dryer Line)*

Valmet AB (2)
Gustaf Gidlofs vag 4, 851 94, Sundsvall, Sweden
Tel.: (46) 107870000
Emp.: 1,500
Paper & Pulp Machinery Mfr & Distr
N.A.I.C.S.: 333243
Kristina Lindgren *(Sec)*

Branch (Domestic):

Valmet AB - Gavle (3)
Industrigatan 14, 802 83, Gavle, Sweden
Tel.: (46) 26 545 610
Web Site: http://www.valmet.com
Paper Industry Machinery Repair & Maintenance Services
N.A.I.C.S.: 811310
Mikael Nyman *(Dir-Svc Ops-Scandinavia)*

Valmet AB - Gothenburg (3)
Regnbagsgatan 6, 417 55, Gothenburg, Sweden
Tel.: (46) 31 50 10 00
Web Site: http://www.valmet.com
Emp.: 416
Paper & Pulp Industry Machinery Mfr
N.A.I.C.S.: 333243
Lina Elisabeth Stolpe *(Mng Dir)*

Plant (Domestic):

Valmet AB - Gothenburg Works (4)
Regnbagsgatan 6, 417 55, Gothenburg, Sweden
Tel.: (46) 31 50 10 00
Web Site: http://www.valmet.com
Emp.: 500
Paper Idustry Machinery Mfr
N.A.I.C.S.: 333243
Bo Lindqvist *(Mgr-Quality)*

Branch (Domestic):

Valmet AB - Hagfors (3)
Jarnverkets Industriomrade, PO Box 709, 683 29, Hagfors, Sweden
Tel.: (46) 563 255 00
Web Site: http://www.valmet.com
Processes & Equipment for Chemical & Mechanical Pulping, Fiberboard Production, Baling Systems & Hydrolysis Systems
N.A.I.C.S.: 333243
Lovisa Nilsson *(Mgr-Category)*

Valmet AB - Karlstad (3)
Axel Johnsons vag 6, 652 21, Karlstad, Sweden
Tel.: (46) 54171000
Web Site: http://www.valmet.com
Paper Machinery Mfr & Sales
N.A.I.C.S.: 333243
Malin Sandstrom *(Controller-Svc Dept)*

Subsidiary (Non-US):

Valmet Celulose, Papel e Energia Ltda. (2)
Rua Pedro de Alcantara Meira No 1 301 Bairro Fazenda Velha, Araucaria, 83704-530, Parana, Brazil (100%)
Tel.: (55) 4133414444
Web Site: https://www.valmet.com
Paper Industry Machinery Mfr & Distr
N.A.I.C.S.: 333243
Celso Tacla *(Pres-South America)*

Plant (Domestic):

Valmet Celulose Papel e Energia Ltda. - Sorocaba (3)
Av Independencia 2500 Bairro, Iporanga, Sorocaba, 18087-101, SP, Brazil
Tel.: (55) 1534140589
Web Site: http://www.valmet.com
Paper Industry Machinery Mfr & Distr
N.A.I.C.S.: 333243

Subsidiary (Non-US):

Valmet Chennai Pvt. Ltd. (2)
Central Square 1 Fourth Floor South Wing CIPET Road, Thiru-vi-ka Industrial Estate Guindy, Chennai, 600032, India
Tel.: (91) 44 30179300
Web Site: http://www.valmet.com
Pulp & Paper Machinery Whslr
N.A.I.C.S.: 423830
Radhakrishnan Melukote *(Gen Mgr-Tech Dev)*

Valmet Co., Ltd. (2)
49/24 Moo 5 Tambon Thoongsukla, Amphoe Sriracha, Chon Buri, 20230, Thailand (100%)
Tel.: (66) 38401100
Web Site: https://www.valmet.com
Paper Industry Machinery Sales
N.A.I.C.S.: 423830
Pornpracha Wattanakijsiri *(Mng Dir & Head-South East Asia)*

Valmet Deutschland GmbH (2)
Ostendstrasse 1, 64319, Pfungstadt, Hessen, Germany
Tel.: (49) 615794550
Web Site: http://www.valmet.com
Paper Machinery Sales & Service
N.A.I.C.S.: 423830

Valmet GesmbH (2)
Lassallestrasse 7a, 1020, Vienna, Austria
Tel.: (43) 1795520
Web Site: http://www.valmet.com
Paper Machinery Sales
N.A.I.C.S.: 423830
Markus Bolhar Nordenkampf *(Dir-Energy Sls & Svc Ops-Central Europe North & EMEA)*

Valmet GmbH (2)
Raiffeisenallee 5, 82041, Oberhaching, Germany (100%)
Tel.: (49) 896138080
Web Site: https://www.valmet.com
Sales & Distribution of Paper Machinery
N.A.I.C.S.: 423830

Valmet Inc. (2)
3rd Fl Shinyoung Bldg 74, Technojoongang-ro Yuseong-Gu, Daejeon, 34018, Korea (South)
Tel.: (82) 429364856
Web Site: https://www.valmet.com
Paper & Pulp Industry Machinery Sales & Service
N.A.I.C.S.: 811310
Kyoung-Seop Kim *(Gen Mgr)*

Valmet K.K. (2)
4F 2-5-8 Higashi-Shinagawa, Shinagawa-ku, Tokyo, 140-0002, Japan (100%)
Tel.: (81) 3 6744 3001
Web Site: http://www.valmet.com
Paper Industry Machinery Whslr
N.A.I.C.S.: 423830
Michio Imai *(Pres)*

Branch (Domestic):

Valmet K.K. (3)
3-10 Togiyacho, Kita-ku, Okayama, 700-0826, Japan
Tel.: (81) 86 212 3250
Web Site: http://www.valmet.com
Pulp & Paper Machinery Whslr & Service
N.A.I.C.S.: 423830

INTERNATIONAL PUBLIC

Subsidiary (Non-US):

Valmet Lda (2)
Estrada de Sao Joao 6, 3880-705, Ovar, Portugal (100%)
Tel.: (351) 256579579
Web Site: http://www.valmet.com
Pulp & Paper Machinery Mfr & Whslr
N.A.I.C.S.: 333243
Amadeu Santos *(Country Mgr)*

Valmet Limited (2)
Manchester Road, Haslingden, BB4 5SL, United Kingdom (100%)
Tel.: (44) 1706225521
Emp.: 150
Paper & Pulp Industry Machinery Mfr
N.A.I.C.S.: 333243
Vesa Simola *(Reg Pres-EMEA)*

Branch (Domestic):

Valmet Ltd (3)
Waterside Business Park Johnson Road, Eccleshill, Darwen, BB3 3BA, United Kingdom (100%)
Tel.: (44) 1254 819 050
Web Site: http://www.valmet.com
Emp.: 450
Pulp & Paper Machinery Sales & Service
N.A.I.C.S.: 423830
Tommy Kallerdahl *(Sls Mgr)*

Subsidiary (Non-US):

Valmet Ltd. (2)
8161 Keele Street, Vaughan, L4K 1Z3, ON, Canada (100%)
Tel.: (905) 532-2000
Web Site: http://www.valmet.com
Paper Machinery Sales
N.A.I.C.S.: 423830

Valmet Paper (Shanghai) Co., Ltd. (2)
Section B 168 Fute Road East No 1 Waigaoqiao Free Trade Zone, Waigaoqiao, Shanghai, 200131, China
Tel.: (86) 2139975000
Web Site: https://www.valmet.com
Paper Industry Machinery Sales & Service
N.A.I.C.S.: 423830
Steven Zhang *(Gen Mgr)*

Valmet Paper Technology (China) Co., Ltd. (2)
21F Wuxi IFS 99 Zhongshu Road, Liangxi District, Wuxi, 214000, Jiangsu, China
Tel.: (86) 51085225939
Web Site: https://www.valmet.com
Paper Machinery Mfr
N.A.I.C.S.: 333243

Valmet Paper Technology (Guangzhou) Co., Ltd. (2)
No 1 Mugu Road Yonghe Economic Zone Guangzhou, Economic & Technological Development District, Guangzhou, 511356, Guangdong, China
Tel.: (86) 2032225061
Paper Industry Machinery Mfr
N.A.I.C.S.: 333243

Valmet Paper Technology (Xi'an) Co., Ltd. (2)
No 4 4th A Fang Road, Xi'an, 710086, Shaanxi, China (75%)
Tel.: (86) 2984363226
Web Site: https://www.valmet.com
Pulp & Paper Machinery Mfr
N.A.I.C.S.: 333243

Valmet Plattling GmbH (2)
Nicolausstrasse 7, 94447, Plattling, Germany (100%)
Tel.: (49) 993189606801
Web Site: https://www.valmet.com
Industrial Machinery Repair & Maintenance Services
N.A.I.C.S.: 811310
Markus Weinzierl *(Mng Dir)*

Valmet Pty. Ltd. (2)
14-28 South Road, Braybrook, Melbourne, 3019, VIC, Australia (100%)
Tel.: (61) 393118133
Web Site: https://www.valmet.com
Emp.: 25
Paper Machinery Sales & Service
N.A.I.C.S.: 423830

AND PRIVATE COMPANIES — VALOE OYJ

Valmet S.p.A. (2)
Via A Gregorcic 46, 34170, Gorizia, Italy **(100%)**
Tel.: (39) 0481528311
Paper Machinery Sales & Production
N.A.I.C.S.: 333243

Branch (Domestic):

Valmet SpA (3)
Via G Leopardi 10, 22070, Grandate, Como, Italy
Tel.: (39) 031 4129452
Emp.: 25
Pulp & Paper Machinery Sales & Service
N.A.I.C.S.: 423830
Stefano Simionato *(Gen Mgr)*

Subsidiary (Non-US):

Valmet SA (2)
Ruta 150 km 6 3 calle 1 N 40 Fundo Landa, camino a Penco, Concepcion, Chile
Tel.: (56) 41 2851 160
Web Site: http://www.valmet.com
Emp.: 25
Pulp & Paper Product Whslr
N.A.I.C.S.: 424130

Branch (Domestic):

Valmet SA (3)
Av Alonso de Cordova 5670 Oficina 802, Las Condes, Santiago, Chile
Tel.: (56) 2 2 597 01 80
Web Site: http://www.valmet.com
Paper Industry Machinery Sales
N.A.I.C.S.: 423830
Diego Gonzalez Binimelis *(Mgr-Mill Sls)*

Subsidiary (Non-US):

Valmet SAS (2)
Bat E Axis Business Park 18, Avenue de Pythagore, 33700, Merignac, France
Tel.: (33) 557104010
Web Site: http://www.valmet.com
Paper Idustry Machinery Mfr
N.A.I.C.S.: 333243
Philippe Bentz *(VP-Sls-South Europe, Middle East & Africa)*

Branch (Domestic):

Valmet SAS (3)
5 rue de l'Industrie ZI EST, 68700, Cernay, France
Tel.: (33) 3 89 75 32 00
Web Site: http://www.valmet.com
Emp.: 125
Pulp & Paper Machinery Servicing
N.A.I.C.S.: 811310
Thierry Didierlaurent *(Sls Mgr-Product-Filtration Products)*

Subsidiary (Non-US):

Valmet South Africa (Pty) Ltd (2)
1st Floor Block 3 Nkwazi Office Park 3 Dumat Place, Mount Edgecombe, 4300, Durban, South Africa
Tel.: (27) 315398640
Web Site: https://www.valmet.com
Paper & Pulp Industry Machinery Whslr
N.A.I.C.S.: 423830

Valmet Technologies Co. Pvt Ltd (2)
UG Floor DLF Building No 10 Tower A DLF Cybercity DLF Phase II, Gurgaon, 122 002, Haryana, India
Tel.: (91) 124 3305800
Web Site: http://www.valmet.com
Paper & Pulp Mfr
N.A.I.C.S.: 322120

Valmet Technologies Ou (2)
Roosikrantsi 2 3rd floor, 10119, Tallinn, Estonia **(100%)**
Tel.: (372) 6 446 861
Web Site: http://www.valmet.com
Paper Machinery Sales
N.A.I.C.S.: 423830

Plant (Domestic):

Valmet Technologies Oy - Jarvenpaa (2)
Wartsilankatu 100, 04400, Jarvenpaa, Finland
Tel.: (358) 10 672 0000
Web Site: http://www.valmet.com
Mfr of Equipment for Coating Preparation, Impregnation of Pulp & Handling Paper Converting Chemicals
N.A.I.C.S.: 333243
Esa Ananin *(Sr Project Mgr)*

Valmet Technologies Oy - Jyvaskyla (2)
Rautpohjankatu, 40700, Jyvaskyla, Finland
Tel.: (358) 10 672 0000
Paper Making Machinery Mfr
N.A.I.C.S.: 333243
Ulla-Kaisa Aho *(Mgr-Mktg)*

Valmet Technologies Oy - Pori (2)
Karjarannantie 39, 28100, Pori, Finland
Tel.: (358) 10 672 0000
Web Site: http://www.valmet.com
Pulp Drying Technology
N.A.I.C.S.: 333243

Branch (Domestic):

Valmet Technologies Oy - Raisio (2)
Raisionkaari 60, 21200, Raisio, Finland
Tel.: (358) 10 672 0000
Web Site: http://www.valmet.com
Paper & Paperboard Production Machinery Sales
N.A.I.C.S.: 423830
Pasi Laine *(Pres)*

Subsidiary (Non-US):

Valmet Technologies SAU (2)
Parque Cientifico y Tecnologico de Bizkaia, Kanala Bidea Edificio 103, 48170, Zamudio, Biscay, Spain **(100%)**
Tel.: (34) 946477007
Web Site: http://www.valmet.com
Paper Industry Machinery Sales & Service
N.A.I.C.S.: 423830

Valmet Technologies Sp. z o.o. (2)
ul Jutrzenki 118, 02-230, Warsaw, Poland
Tel.: (48) 223817243
Web Site: http://www.valmet.com
Sales Range: $10-24.9 Million
Emp.: 40
Textile Mill
N.A.I.C.S.: 313310

Valmet Technologies Zaragoza, S.L. (2)
Poligono Malpica C/A 16-Dpdo, 50016, Zaragoza, Spain **(81%)**
Tel.: (34) 976572487
Emp.: 180
Industrial Machinery Repair & Maintenance Services
N.A.I.C.S.: 811310
Jose Luis Davila *(Gen Mgr)*

Valmet Technologies, SAU (2)
Parque Cientifico y Tecnologico de Bizkaia, Kanala Bidea Edificio 103, 48170, Zamudio, Spain
Tel.: (34) 946477007
Web Site: http://www.valmet.com
Pulp & Paper Product Whslr
N.A.I.C.S.: 424130

Valmet ZAO (2)
Business Center Senator Chapaeva Street 15 Letter G Office 4-303, 197101, Saint Petersburg, Russia
Tel.: (7) 8 123 323 650
Web Site: http://www.valmet.com
Paper Machinery Sales
N.A.I.C.S.: 423830
Ivan Gubin *(VP-Sls)*

Valmet s.r.o. (2)
Litomericka 272, CZ-41108, Steti, Czech Republic
Tel.: (420) 416803551
Paper Industry Machinery Servicing
N.A.I.C.S.: 811310

Valmet Technologies S. de R.L. de C.V. (1)
Avenida Jorge Jimenez Cantu no 6 Oficina 101, Colonia Fracc Plazas del Condado, 52930, Ciudad Lopez Mateos, Mexico
Tel.: (52) 555 308 5580
Pulp & Paper Whslr
N.A.I.C.S.: 424130

Valmet, Inc. (1)
2425 Commerce Ave Ste 100, Duluth, GA 30096
Tel.: (770) 263-7863
Web Site: http://www.valmet.com
Pulp & Paper Industry Manufacturing Equipment Mfr & Whslr
N.A.I.C.S.: 333243
Kari Lindberg *(Sr VP-Svcs-North America)*

Plant (Domestic):

Valmet, Inc. - Appleton (2)
2323 E Capitol Dr Ste 200, Appleton, WI 54911-8315
Tel.: (920) 733-7361
Web Site: http://www.valmet.com
Sales Range: $50-74.9 Million
Emp.: 100
Pulp & Paper Industry Manufacturing Equipment Mfr & Whslr
N.A.I.C.S.: 333243
Greg VanHandel *(Dir-Roll Svcs-North America)*

Valmet, Inc. - Beloit (2)
1280 Willowbrook Rd, Beloit, WI 53511
Tel.: (608) 365-3319
Web Site: http://www.valmet.com
Sales Range: $25-49.9 Million
Emp.: 97
Pulp & Paper Industry Manufacturing Equipment Servicing
N.A.I.C.S.: 811310

Valmet, Inc. - Biddeford (2)
516 Alfred St, Biddeford, ME 04005
Tel.: (207) 282-1521
Web Site: http://www.valmet.com
Sales Range: $50-74.9 Million
Emp.: 130
Pulp & Paper Industry Drying Equipment Mfr & Whslr
N.A.I.C.S.: 333243
Rick Fortier *(Mgr-Projects)*

Valmet, Inc. - Clarks Summit (2)
987 Griffin Pond Rd, Clarks Summit, PA 18411-9214
Tel.: (570) 587-5111
Web Site: http://www.valmet.com
Sales Range: $25-49.9 Million
Emp.: 35
Paper Industry Rubber Roll Covers Mfr & Whslr
N.A.I.C.S.: 326299
Sandra Delicati *(Mgr-Roll Project)*

VALNEVA SE
6 rue Alain Bombard, 44800, Saint-Herblain, France
Tel.: (33) 228073710
Web Site: https://www.valneva.com
Year Founded: 1999
VALN—(NASDAQ)
Rev.: $443,766,797
Assets: $763,159,555
Liabilities: $493,196,087
Net Worth: $269,963,467
Earnings: ($175,980,999)
Emp.: 719
Fiscal Year-end: 12/31/22
Biopharmaceutical Research & Development, Mfr & Distr
N.A.I.C.S.: 325412
Franck Grimaud *(Co-Pres, Chief Bus Officer & Member-Mgmt Bd)*

Subsidiaries:

Valneva Austria GmbH (1)
Campus Vienna Biocenter 3, 1030, Vienna, Austria
Tel.: (43) 120620
Web Site: https://www.valneva.at
Vaccines & Pre-clinical & Clinical Development Services
N.A.I.C.S.: 325414

Subsidiary (US):

Intercell USA, Inc. (2)
910 Clopper Rd Ste 160S, Gaithersburg, MD 20878
Tel.: (301) 556-4500
Web Site: http://www.valneva.com
Sales Range: $25-49.9 Million
Emp.: 6
Biopharmaceuticals Distr
N.A.I.C.S.: 424210

Subsidiary (Non-US):

Valneva Scotland Limited (2)
Oakbank Park Road, Livingston, EH53 0TG, United Kingdom
Tel.: (44) 1506446600
Sales Range: $25-49.9 Million
Emp.: 100
Vaccines Mfr
N.A.I.C.S.: 325414
Matt Henderson *(Mgr-Mfg Ops)*

Valneva Canada Inc. (1)
Commercial Operations 3535 Saint-Charles Blvd Suite 600, Kirkland, H9H 5B9, QC, Canada
Tel.: (514) 630-6999
Web Site: https://www.valneva.ca
Pharmaceutical Products Distr
N.A.I.C.S.: 424210

Valneva France SAS (1)
Ilot Saint-Joseph Bureaux Convergence Batiment A 12 ter quai Perrache, 69002, Lyon, France
Tel.: (33) 228073710
Web Site: https://www.valneva.fr
Pharmaceutical Products Distr
N.A.I.C.S.: 424210

Valneva Sweden AB (1)
Gunnar Asplunds alle 16, 171 69, Solna, Sweden
Tel.: (46) 87351000
Web Site: http://www.crucell.se
Emp.: 115
Pharmaceuticals Research, Development & Mfr
N.A.I.C.S.: 325412

Valneva UK Ltd. (1)
Commercial Operations Centaur House Ancells Business Park Ancells Road, Fleet, GU51 2UJ, Hampshire, United Kingdom
Tel.: (44) 1252761007
Web Site: https://www.valneva.co.uk
Pharmaceutical Products Distr
N.A.I.C.S.: 424210
Sean O'Reilly *(Head-Sls & Mktg)*

Valneva USA, Inc. (1)
4550 Montgomery Ave Ste 460, Bethesda, MD 20814
Tel.: (301) 556-4500
Pharmaceutical Products Distr
N.A.I.C.S.: 424210
Amy Jezek *(Mgr-Bus Ops)*

VALODE ET PISTRE
115 Rue Du Bac, 75007, Paris, France
Tel.: (33) 153634390
Web Site: http://www.v-p.com
Rev.: $22,300,000
Emp.: 143
Architectural Firm
N.A.I.C.S.: 541310
Denis Valode *(Co-Founder & Partner)*

VALOE OYJ
Insinoorinkatu 8, 50150, Mikkeli, Finland
Tel.: (358) 207747788
Web Site: https://www.valoe.com
VALOE—(HEL)
Rev.: $1,408,375
Assets: $16,672,782
Liabilities: $23,447,011
Net Worth: ($6,774,228)
Earnings: ($8,275,415)
Emp.: 58
Fiscal Year-end: 12/31/22
Automation Equipment Mfr
N.A.I.C.S.: 333248
Hannu Savisalo *(Chm)*

Subsidiaries:

Cencorp AS (1)
Mustamaee tee 44, Tallinn, 10621, Estonia
Tel.: (372) 6671710
Industrial Automation Equipment Distr
N.A.I.C.S.: 423830

Savcor Face (Beijing) Technologies Co., Ltd. (1)

VALOE OYJ

Valoe Oyj—(Continued)

No 18 Jinxiu Road Beijing Economic & Technological Development Area, Beijing, 100176, China
Tel.: (86) 10 6787 0011
Electromagnetic Shielding Mfr
N.A.I.C.S.: 334419

Savcor Face (Guangzhou) Technologies Co., Ltd. (1)
No 18 Jungong Road Eastern Section GETDD, Guangzhou, 510530, China
Tel.: (86) 20 8226 6811
Web Site: http://www.cencorp.com
Film Coating Mfr
N.A.I.C.S.: 322220

VALOR HOLDINGS CO., LTD.
661-1 Oharicho, Tajimi, Gifu, 507-0062, Japan
Tel.: (81) 572200860
Web Site:
https://www.valorholdings.co.jp
Year Founded: 1958
9956—(TKS)
Rev.: $5,339,524,950
Assets: $2,940,174,270
Liabilities: $1,754,816,190
Net Worth: $1,185,358,080
Earnings: $78,956,450
Emp.: 955
Fiscal Year-end: 03/31/24
Departmental Store Operator
N.A.I.C.S.: 445110
Masami Tashiro (Chm & CEO)

Subsidiaries:

Chubu Foods Co., Ltd. (1)
4-20 Takane-cho, Tajimi, Gifu, Japan
Tel.: (81) 572291610
Web Site: https://www.chubufoods.co.jp
Food Products Mfr
N.A.I.C.S.: 311999

First Co., Ltd. (1)
20F Chuo Odori FN Bldg 1-3-8 Tokiwamachi, Chuo-ku, Osaka, 540-0028, Japan
Tel.: (81) 676392020
Web Site: https://www.the-first.co.jp
Emp.: 200
Software Services
N.A.I.C.S.: 541511
Yoshinobu Oka (Chm)

Kohseiya Co., Ltd. (1)
873-10 Shinden, Ueno, 409-0113, Yamanashi, Japan
Tel.: (81) 554633367
Web Site: https://www.kohseiya.co.jp
Emp.: 525
Food Product Retailer
N.A.I.C.S.: 445110

Tachiya Co., Ltd. (1)
7th floor Shirakawa 8th Building 1-10-29 Marunouchi, Naka-ku, Nagoya, 460-0002, Japan
Tel.: (81) 522015155
Web Site: https://www.tachiya.co.jp
Emp.: 779
Food Product Retailer
N.A.I.C.S.: 445110

Time Co., Ltd. (1)
73-48 Obara, Nutanishi-cho, Mihara, 729-0473, Hiroshima, Japan
Tel.: (81) 848850666
Web Site: https://time-merit.com
Emp.: 55
Industrial Machinery Mfr
N.A.I.C.S.: 333242

VALOR PROPERTIES REIT
2 Enos Street 5th floor, Sofia, 1408, Bulgaria
Tel.: (359) 28106447
Web Site:
http://www.valorproperties.bg
VLRP—(BUL)
Sales Range: Less than $1 Million
Real Estate Investment Services
N.A.I.C.S.: 531210
Milena Vasileva (Chm)

VALOR RESOURCES LIMITED
22 Lindsay Street, Perth, 6000, WA, Australia
Tel.: (61) 892003467
Web Site:
http://www.valorresources.com.au
THB—(ASX)
Rev.: $739,881
Assets: $11,502,393
Liabilities: $1,655,575
Net Worth: $9,846,819
Earnings: ($333,770)
Fiscal Year-end: 06/30/24
Metal Mineral Mining Services
N.A.I.C.S.: 212290

VALORA EFFEKTEN HANDEL AG
Am Hardtwald 7, 76275, Ettlingen, Germany
Tel.: (49) 724390001
Web Site: https://www.veh.de
Year Founded: 1988
VEH—(MUN)
Assets: $1,942,811
Liabilities: $275,968
Net Worth: $1,666,844
Earnings: ($198,697)
Emp.: 5
Fiscal Year-end: 12/31/23
Financial Support Services
N.A.I.C.S.: 523940
Klaus Helffenstein (Member-Mgmt Bd)

VALORE METALS CORP.
Suite 1020-800 West Pender St, Vancouver, V6C 2V6, BC, Canada
Tel.: (778) 819-4484 BC
Web Site:
https://www.valoremetals.com
Year Founded: 2008
VO—(TSXV)
Rev.: $64,302
Assets: $7,779,987
Liabilities: $811,823
Net Worth: $6,968,164
Earnings: $18,119,514
Emp.: 22
Fiscal Year-end: 09/30/23
Uranium Exploration & Mining Services
N.A.I.C.S.: 213114
James R. Paterson (Chm & CEO)

VALOREM S.A.
Calle 75 No 5-59, Bogota, Colombia
Tel.: (57) 1 756 0809 Co
Web Site: http://www.valorem.com.co
Year Founded: 1998
Sales Range: $1-4.9 Billion
Investment Holding Company
N.A.I.C.S.: 551112
Carlos Arturo Londono Gutierrez (CEO)

VALORES SIMESA SA
Carrera 48 No 26-85 Piso 1 Torre Sur, 403, Medellin, Colombia
Tel.: (57) 6044447231
Web Site: https://valoressimesa.com
Year Founded: 2000
Real Estate Manangement Services
N.A.I.C.S.: 531390
Carlos Guillermo Posada Gonzalez (Acct Mgr)

VALORO RESOURCES INC.
Suite 501 570 Granville Street, Vancouver, V6C 1P1, BC, Canada
Tel.: (604) 694-1742 BC
Web Site: http://www.geologix.ca
Year Founded: 1996
Rev.: $893
Assets: $22,627,977
Liabilities: $1,835,217

Net Worth: $20,792,759
Earnings: ($1,010,078)
Emp.: 7
Fiscal Year-end: 12/31/17
Gold & Copper Exploration Services
N.A.I.C.S.: 212220

VALPARAISO SPORTING CLUB S.A.
Av Los Castanos 404, PO Box 297, Vina del Mar, Chile
Tel.: (56) 322655610
Web Site: https://www.sporting.cl
Year Founded: 1882
SPORTING—(SGO)
Sales Range: Less than $1 Million
Horse Racing Course Management Services
N.A.I.C.S.: 711219
Carlo Rossi Soffia (Chm)

VALQUA, LTD.
ThinkPark Tower 24F 2-1-1 OSAKI, Shinagawa-ku, Tokyo, 141-6024, Japan
Tel.: (81) 354347370
Web Site: https://www.valqua.com
Year Founded: 1927
7995—(TKS)
Rev.: $408,127,840
Assets: $492,359,070
Liabilities: $170,247,160
Net Worth: $322,111,910
Earnings: $32,448,490
Emp.: 1,682
Fiscal Year-end: 03/31/24
Fiber, Fluorocarbon Resin & High-functional Rubber Processing, Sale & Manufacturing
N.A.I.C.S.: 325211
Masahiro Imai (Exec Officer & Deputy Dir-H&S Sls Grp)

Subsidiaries:

Garlock Valqua Japan, Inc. (1)
ThinkPark Tower 24 Fl Osaki, Shinagawa-ku, Tokyo, 163-0427, Japan
Tel.: (81) 354347431
Web Site: http://www.garlock-valqua.co.jp
Sales Range: $25-49.9 Million
Emp.: 10
Semiconductor Mfr
N.A.I.C.S.: 334413

Taiwan Valqua Engineering International, Ltd. (1)
8F-3 336 Bo'ai 2nd Road, Zuoying District, Kaohsiung, 821, Taiwan
Tel.: (886) 75566644
Web Site: http://www.valqua.com.tw
Sales Range: $25-49.9 Million
Emp.: 60
Gaskets Whslr
N.A.I.C.S.: 423840
Toshikazu Takisawa (Pres)

Taiwan Valqua Industries Ltd. (1)
No 379 1 Chung Shan Rd Chutung Tsun Luchu Hsiang, Kaohsiung, 82152, Taiwan
Tel.: (886) 76962400
Emp.: 58
Gaskets Whslr
N.A.I.C.S.: 423840

Valqua (Shanghai) Trading Co., Ltd. (1)
Room 4807 Tower 1 Grand Gateway 66 No 1 Hongqiao Road, Xuhui District, Shanghai, 200040, China
Tel.: (86) 2153082468
Web Site: http://www.valqua-vsht.com
Gaskets Whslr
N.A.I.C.S.: 423840

Valqua America Inc. (1)
1130 Mountain View Alviso Rd, Sunnyvale, CA 94089
Tel.: (408) 962-5030
Sales Range: $25-49.9 Million
Emp.: 15
Semiconductor Device Suppliers
N.A.I.C.S.: 423690

INTERNATIONAL PUBLIC

Valqua Industries (Thailand) Ltd. (1)
538 Bangpoo Industrial Estate Soi 9B Moo4 Pattana2 Road, Praksa Muang Samutprakarn, Samut Prakan, 10280, Thailand
Tel.: (66) 23240400
Sales Range: $25-49.9 Million
Emp.: 99
Plant Equipment Products Mfr
N.A.I.C.S.: 334513

Valqua Korea Co., Ltd. (1)
10F O2 Tower 83 Uisadang-daero, Yeongdeungpo-Gu, Seoul, 07325, Korea (South)
Tel.: (82) 27866718
Web Site: http://www.valqua.co.kr
Sales Range: $25-49.9 Million
Emp.: 40
Gaskets Whslr
N.A.I.C.S.: 339991
Toshikazu Takisawa (Pres & CEO)

Valqua NGC, Inc. (1)
1717 Tidwell Rd, Houston, TX 77093
Tel.: (713) 691-1193
Specialty Trade Contractors
N.A.I.C.S.: 238990

Valqua Seal Products (Shanghai) Co., Ltd (1)
No 111 Nanle Rd, Songjiang Export Processing Zone, Shanghai, 201611, China
Tel.: (86) 2157749766
Web Site: http://www.valqua.com.jp
Sales Range: $100-124.9 Million
Emp.: 300
Gaskets Mfr
N.A.I.C.S.: 339991

Valqua Vietnam Co., Ltd. (1)
Tan Truong Industrial Zone, Cam Giang District, Hai Duong, 35000, Vietnam
Tel.: (84) 2203570078
Web Site: http://www.valquavietnam.com
Sales Range: $75-99.9 Million
Emp.: 150
Plant Equipment Products Mfr
N.A.I.C.S.: 423830

VALSEF GROUP
Suite 100 7405 Transcanadienne, Saint Laurent, H4T 1Z2, QC, Canada
Tel.: (514) 316-7647
Web Site:
http://www.valsefgroup.com
Investment Services
N.A.I.C.S.: 523999
Sam Youssef (Co-Founder & CEO)

Subsidiaries:

Valsoft Corporation Inc. (1)
7405 Rte Transcanadienne Suite 100, Montreal, H4T 1Z2, QC, Canada
Tel.: (514) 316-7647
Web Site: http://www.valsoftcorp.com
Holding Company; Vertical Market Software Companies
N.A.I.C.S.: 551112
Sam Youssef (Founder & CEO)

Subsidiary (Domestic):

ALDATA Software Management Inc. (2)
203-211 Pembina Avenue, Hinton, T7V 1G6, AB, Canada
Web Site: http://www.aldatasoftware.com
Logging Software Developer
N.A.I.C.S.: 513210
Mike Meagher (Pres)

Aspire Software (2)
7405 Rte Transcanadienne Suite 100, Monteal, QC H4T 1Z2, QC, Canada
Tel.: (514) 316-7647
Web Site: https://www.aspiresoftware.com
Portfolio Management: Software
N.A.I.C.S.: 523940

Holding (US):

Exuma Technologies, Inc. (3)
11940 US Highway 1, North Palm Beach, FL 33408
Tel.: (561) 969-2882
Web Site: http://www.dockmaster.com

Sales Range: $1-9.9 Million
Emp.: 32
Custom Computer Programming Services
N.A.I.C.S.: 541511

Subsidiary (US):

Aysling LLC (2)
1020 N Orlando Ave Ste 400, Maitland, FL 32751-4514
Tel.: (877) 297-5464
Web Site: https://www.aysling.com
Graphic Design Services
N.A.I.C.S.: 541430
Sheila Magie *(Pres)*

BEI Services, Inc. (2)
341 Trout Peak Dr, Cody, WY 82414
Tel.: (307) 587-8446
Web Site: http://www.beiservices.com
Data Processing, Hosting & Related Services
N.A.I.C.S.: 518210
Bud Karakey *(VP-Ops)*

Creative Information Systems, Inc. (2)
27 Lowell St Ste 403, Manchester, NH 03101-1646
Tel.: (603) 627-4144
Web Site: http://www.creativeinfo.net
Management Software Solutions
N.A.I.C.S.: 513210
Doug Manter *(Founder)*

DemandBridge LLC (2)
3500 Parkway Ln Ste 200, Norcross, GA 30092
Tel.: (770) 448-1484
Web Site: http://www.demandbridge.com
Software Development Services
N.A.I.C.S.: 513210
Michelle Bengermino *(VP-Product Mgmt)*

Subsidiary (Domestic):

Kramer-Smilko (3)
10830 Gilroy Rd, Cockeysville, MD 21031
Tel.: (410) 569-5725
Electronics Stores
N.A.I.C.S.: 449210
Richard Kramer *(Pres)*

e-Quantum (3)
1380 Greg St Ste 230, Sparks, NV 89431
Tel.: (775) 856-2800
Web Site: http://www.e-quantum.com
Computer & Computer Peripheral Equipment & Software Merchant Whslr
N.A.I.C.S.: 423430
Cori Jackson *(Mktg Dir)*

Subsidiary (US):

ICL Systems, Inc. (2)
445 S Livernois Ste 321, Rochester Hills, MI 48307
Tel.: (714) 885-8182
Web Site: http://www.iclsystems.com
Computer System Design Services
N.A.I.C.S.: 541512
Thomas Swennes *(VP-Strategic Plng & Admin)*

Innquest Software Corp. (2)
5300 W Cypress St Ste 160, Tampa, FL 33607
Tel.: (813) 288-4900
Web Site: http://www.innquest.com
Sales Range: $1-9.9 Million
Emp.: 15
Computer & Computer Peripheral Equipment & Software Merchant Whslr
N.A.I.C.S.: 423430

Keystone Information Systems (2)
1000 Lenola Rd, Maple Shade, NJ 08052
Tel.: (856) 722-0700
Web Site: http://www.keyinfosys.com
Sales Range: $10-24.9 Million
Emp.: 20
Computers & Accessories, Personal & Home Entertainment
N.A.I.C.S.: 423430
Stephen D. Juliana *(Sr VP-Product Dev)*

MacPractice, Inc. (2)
233 N 8th St Ste 300, Lincoln, NE 68508
Tel.: (402) 420-2430
Web Site: http://www.macpractice.com

Sales Range: $1-9.9 Million
Emp.: 20
Software Development Services
N.A.I.C.S.: 423430
Mark Hollis *(Pres)*

Professional Computing Resources, Inc. (2)
4635 N Breton Ct SE, Grand Rapids, MI 49508
Tel.: (616) 554-0000
Web Site: http://www.pcr.com
Sales Range: $1-9.9 Million
Emp.: 31
Computer Software Development
N.A.I.C.S.: 541511
Bob Glover *(Pres)*

Sam Asher Computing Services Inc. (2)
3300 Monroe Ave Ste 317, Rochester, NY 14618-4617
Tel.: (585) 586-0020
Web Site: http://www.ashergroup.com
Data Processing, Hosting & Related Services
N.A.I.C.S.: 518210
Russ Bell *(VP)*

Scholarchip Card, LLC (2)
6 Commercial St, Hicksville, NY 11801
Tel.: (800) 399-7340
Web Site: http://www.scholarchip.com
Sales Range: $1-9.9 Million
Emp.: 21
Computer System Design Services
N.A.I.C.S.: 541512
Maged Atiya *(Founder)*

Vertical Software, Inc. (2)
409 Keller St, Bartonville, IL 61607
Tel.: (309) 676-0700
Web Site: http://www.verticalsoftware.net
Software Publisher
N.A.I.C.S.: 513210
Alexis Michas *(Mng Partner)*

XLDent (2)
279 N Medina St, Loretto, MN 55357
Tel.: (763) 479-6166
Web Site: https://www.xldent.com
Sales Range: $1-9.9 Million
Emp.: 21
Dental Software Products & Services
N.A.I.C.S.: 423430

VALSOIA S.P.A.
Via Ilio Barontini 16/5, 40138, Bologna, Italy
Tel.: (39) 0516086800
Web Site: http://www.valsoia.it
Year Founded: 1990
VLS—(ITA)
Rev.: $102,509,575
Assets: $126,400,457
Liabilities: $34,268,155
Net Worth: $92,132,302
Earnings: $9,401,085
Emp.: 123
Fiscal Year-end: 12/31/20
Health Food Mfr & Whslr
N.A.I.C.S.: 311520
Lorenzo Sassoli De Bianchi *(Chm)*

VALSON INDUSTRIES LIMITED
Unit No 28 Building No 6 Gr Fl Mittal Industrial Estate, Sir M V Road, Mumbai, 400059, Maharashtra, India
Tel.: (91) 2240661000
Web Site:
  https://www.valsonindia.com
Year Founded: 1983
530459—(BOM)
Rev.: $15,701,960
Assets: $6,625,610
Liabilities: $3,523,985
Net Worth: $3,101,625
Earnings: $2,158
Emp.: 648
Fiscal Year-end: 03/31/23
Textile Products Mfr
N.A.I.C.S.: 314999
Suresh N. Mutreja *(Chm & Mng Dir)*

VALTECH SE
46 Colebrooke Row, London, N1 8AF, United Kingdom
Tel.: (44) 20 7014 0800 UK
Web Site: http://www.valtech.com
Year Founded: 1993
Rev.: $304,570,564
Assets: $263,238,771
Liabilities: $174,194,223
Net Worth: $89,044,548
Earnings: $11,827,961
Emp.: 2,591
Fiscal Year-end: 12/31/18
Digital Advertising Services
N.A.I.C.S.: 541850
Sebastian Lombardo *(Chm & CEO)*

Subsidiaries:

The Berndt Group Ltd. (1)
3618 Falls Rd Ste 300, Baltimore, MD 21211-1814
Tel.: (410) 889-5854
Web Site: http://www.berndtgroup.net
Custom Computer Programming Services
N.A.I.C.S.: 541511

VALTECNE S.P.A.
Via Al Campo Sportivo 277, Berbenno di Valtellin, 23010, Sondrio, Italy
Tel.: (39) 0342492382
Web Site: https://www.valtecne.com
Year Founded: 1983
VLT—(ITA)
Mechanical Product Mfr
N.A.I.C.S.: 333613
Paul Mainetti *(CEO)*

VALTERRA RESOURCE CORPORATION
Suite 1100-1199 West Hastings St, Vancouver, V6E 3T5, BC, Canada
Tel.: (604) 684-9384 YT
Web Site:
  https://www.valterraresource.com
Year Founded: 1997
VQA—(OTCIQ)
Assets: $75,932
Liabilities: $777,580
Net Worth: ($701,649)
Earnings: ($856,281)
Fiscal Year-end: 12/31/19
Metal Mining & Exploration Services
N.A.I.C.S.: 212290
Graham Thatcher *(CFO)*

VALTES CO., LTD.
8F KEPCO Fudosan Nishihonmachi Building 1-3-15 Awaza, Nishi-ku, Osaka, 550-0011, Japan
Tel.: (81) 665346561
Web Site: https://www.valtes.co.jp
Year Founded: 2004
4442—(TKS)
Rev.: $68,492,820
Assets: $35,667,560
Liabilities: $16,987,700
Net Worth: $18,679,860
Earnings: $3,423,980
Emp.: 9,518
Fiscal Year-end: 03/31/24
Software Development Services
N.A.I.C.S.: 541511
Shinji Tanaka *(Pres)*

Subsidiaries:

Real System Research Co., Ltd. (1)
Komatsu Building 2-7-7 Otemachi, Naka-ku, Hiroshima, 730-0051, Japan
Tel.: (81) 82 246 3400
Web Site: https://www.rsr.co.jp
Software Development Services
N.A.I.C.S.: 541511

VALTES Mobile Technology Co., Ltd. (1)
1-3-15 Awaza Kanden Real Estate Nishihonmachi Building 8F, Nishi-ku, Osaka,

550-0011, Japan
Tel.: (81) 66 534 6568
Web Site: https://www.valtes-mt.co.jp
Web System Development Services
N.A.I.C.S.: 541511

Valtes Advanced Technology, Inc. (1)
Unit 2A Trafalgar Plaza HV Dela Costa Street, Salcedo Village, Makati, 1227, Philippines
Tel.: (63) 2 823 8391
Web Site: https://www.valtes.com.ph
Software Development Services
N.A.I.C.S.: 541511
Shinji Tanaka *(Pres)*

VALUE CONVERGENCE HOLDINGS LIMITED
6th Floor Centre Point 181-185 Gloucester Road, Wanchai, China (Hong Kong)
Tel.: (852) 21018163
Web Site:
  https://www.vcgroup.com.hk
0821—(HKG)
Rev.: $9,343,328
Assets: $103,134,878
Liabilities: $7,809,503
Net Worth: $95,325,375
Earnings: ($22,706,730)
Emp.: 72
Fiscal Year-end: 12/31/22
Financial Investment Services
N.A.I.C.S.: 523150
Peter Yiu Man Fu *(Chm, CEO & Exec Dir)*

Subsidiaries:

VC Asset Management Ltd (1)
6th Floor Centre Point 181 - 185 Gloucester Road, Wanchai, China (Hong Kong)
Tel.: (852) 21018163
Financial Brokerage Services
N.A.I.C.S.: 523150

VC Brokerage Limited (1)
6th Floor Centre Point 181 - 185 Gloucester Road, Wanchai, China (Hong Kong)
Tel.: (852) 2 913 6332
Web Site: http://www.vcgroup.com.hk
Securities Brokerage Services
N.A.I.C.S.: 523150

VC Capital Limited (1)
6th Floor Centre Point 181 - 185 Gloucester Road, Wanchai, China (Hong Kong)
Tel.: (852) 3 151 3993
Web Site: http://www.vcgroup.com.hk
Sales Range: $25-49.9 Million
Emp.: 10
Financial Management Consulting Services
N.A.I.C.S.: 541611

VC Futures Limited (1)
28 F The Centrium 60 Wyndham St, Central, China (Hong Kong)
Tel.: (852) 29136332
Financial Brokerage Services
N.A.I.C.S.: 523150

VALUE CREATION INC.
1100 635 - 8th Avenue SW, Calgary, T2P 3M3, AB, Canada
Tel.: (403) 539-4500
Web Site: http://www.vctek.com
Year Founded: 1999
Crude Petroleum & Natural Gas Exploration
N.A.I.C.S.: 211120
Columba Yeung *(Founder, Chm & CEO)*

VALUE ENHANCEMENT PARTNERS B.V.
World Trade Center Amsterdam Tower G 3rd Floor Strawinskylaan 385, 1077 XX, Amsterdam, Netherlands
Tel.: (31) 205755090 NI
Web Site: http://www.vepartners.com
Year Founded: 1999

VALUE ENHANCEMENT PARTNERS B.V.

Value Enhancement Partners B.V.—(Continued)
Privater Equity Firm
N.A.I.C.S.: 327910
Kenneth Tjon (Co-Founder & Mng Partner)
Subsidiaries:

EQIN B.V. (1)
Theemsweg 2, 3197 KM, Rotterdam, Netherlands
Tel.: (31) 181296666
Web Site: http://en.eqin.eu
Industrial Equipment Distr
N.A.I.C.S.: 423830

Subsidiary (Non-US):
EQIN N.V. (2)
Oosterweelsteenweg 57 Havennummer 269, 2030, Antwerp, Belgium
Tel.: (32) 36094300
Engineeering Services
N.A.I.C.S.: 541330
Mark Duym (Mgr-Acct)

PSS Belgium NV
Hoogveld 50, 9200, Dendermonde, Belgium
Tel.: (32) 52261412
Web Site: https://www.premiumsoundsolutions.com
Audio Speaker Products Mfr
N.A.I.C.S.: 512290
Stijn Goeminne (CEO)

Subsidiary (Non-US):
Crown Million Industries (International) Limited (2)
Unit G 33/F COS Centre 56 Tsun Yip Street, Kwun Tong, Kowloon, China (Hong Kong)
Tel.: (852) 29505000
Speaker Mfr & Distr
N.A.I.C.S.: 334310

VALUE EXCHANGE INTERNATIONAL, INC.
10F FTLife Tower 18 Sheung Yuet Road Kowloon Bay Kowloon, 5-7 Yuen Shun Circuit Shatin N T, Hong Kong, China (Hong Kong)
Tel.: (852) 29504288 NV
Web Site: https://www.value-exch.com
Year Founded: 2007
VEII—(OTCQB)
Rev.: $10,924,330
Assets: $5,739,861
Liabilities: $3,485,118
Net Worth: $2,254,743
Earnings: $3,366
Emp.: 300
Fiscal Year-end: 12/31/22
Holding Company; Payment Processing Technologies & Services
N.A.I.C.S.: 551112
Channing Au (CFO & Treas)
Subsidiaries:

Value Exchange International Limited (1)
7/F Darton Tower 142 Wai Yip Street Kwun Tong, Kwun Tong, Kowloon, China (Hong Kong)
Tel.: (852) 2950 4288
Web Site: http://www.value-exch.com
Emp.: 20
eCommerce Technologies & Software Developer, Mfr & Data Services
N.A.I.C.S.: 335999
Benny Lee (Founder & Chm)

VALUE GOLF, INC.
First Okada Building 5F 3-5 Shiba 4-chome, Minato-ku, Tokyo, 108-0014, Japan
Tel.: (81) 354417390
Web Site: https://corp.valuegolf.co.jp
Year Founded: 2004
3931—(TKS)
Rev.: $25,921,040
Assets: $18,675,060
Liabilities: $10,429,390
Net Worth: $8,245,670
Earnings: $155,980
Emp.: 1,682
Fiscal Year-end: 01/31/24
Golf Advertising Services
N.A.I.C.S.: 541810
Michio Mizuguchi (Founder, Pres, CEO & Dir-Rep)

VALUE GROUP LIMITED
49 Brewery Road, PO Box 778, Isando, 1600, South Africa
Tel.: (27) 860100046 ZA
Web Site: http://www.value.co.za
Year Founded: 1981
VLE—(JSE)
Rev.: $204,790,040
Assets: $166,351,031
Liabilities: $109,585,394
Net Worth: $56,765,637
Earnings: $9,058,270
Emp.: 3,636
Fiscal Year-end: 02/29/20
Logistics & Freight Transportation Services
N.A.I.C.S.: 541614
Steven David Gottschalk (Founder & CEO)

VALUE HR CO., LTD.
Value HR Building Sendagaya 5-21-14, Shibuya-ku, Tokyo, 151-0051, Japan
Tel.: (81) 363801300
Web Site: https://www.valuehr.com
Year Founded: 2001
6078—(TKS)
Rev.: $50,339,000
Assets: $122,189,060
Liabilities: $77,380,260
Net Worth: $44,808,800
Earnings: $6,877,300
Emp.: 959
Fiscal Year-end: 12/31/23
Information Services
N.A.I.C.S.: 519290
Michio Fujita (Founder, Pres & Dir-Rep)

VALUE INDUSTRIES LIMITED
15 K M Stone Aurangabad Paithan Road, Village Chittegaon Taluka Paithan, Aurangabad, 431 105, Maharashtra, India
Tel.: (91) 2431252501
Web Site: https://www.valueind.in
Year Founded: 1988
500945—(BOM)
Consumer Electronics Mfr & Whslr
N.A.I.C.S.: 335220
Sumit Mishra (Officer-Compliance & Sec)

VALUE PARTNERS GROUP LIMITED
43rd Floor The Center 99 Queens Road, Central, China (Hong Kong)
Tel.: (852) 28809263
Web Site: http://www.valuepartners-group.com
0806—(HKG)
Rev.: $74,529,233
Assets: $605,351,768
Liabilities: $32,341,395
Net Worth: $573,010,373
Earnings: ($69,400,163)
Emp.: 205
Fiscal Year-end: 12/31/22
Investment Management Service
N.A.I.C.S.: 523940
Vivienne Lee (Chief Compliance Officer)
Subsidiaries:

Hong Kong Asset Management Group Limited (1)
Unit 02 40/F 118 Connaught Road West, Hong Kong, China (Hong Kong)
Tel.: (852) 39709595
Web Site: https://www.asset-mg.com
Investment Management Service
N.A.I.C.S.: 523940

Sensible Asset Management Limited (1)
9th Fl Nexxus Bldg 41 Connaught Rd, Central, China (Hong Kong)
Tel.: (852) 28686848
Web Site: http://www.samfund.com.hk
Asset Management Services
N.A.I.C.S.: 525920

Value Partners (UK) Limited (1)
City Tower 40 Basinghall Street, London, EC2V 5DE, United Kingdom
Tel.: (44) 2039073870
Investment Management Service
N.A.I.C.S.: 523940

Value Partners Asset Management Singapore Pte. Ltd. (1)
9 Raffles Place 13-04 Republic Plaza, Singapore, 048619, Singapore
Tel.: (65) 67180380
Investment Management Service
N.A.I.C.S.: 523940
King Lun Au (Chm & Dir)

Value Partners Fund Management (Shanghai) Limited (1)
701 Citigroup Tower 33 Hua Yuan Shi Qiao Road, Pudong New District, Shanghai, 200120, China
Tel.: (86) 2161871300
Investment Management Service
N.A.I.C.S.: 523940

Value Partners Index Services Limited (1)
9th Fl Nexxus Bldg 41 Connaught Rd, Central, China (Hong Kong)
Tel.: (852) 28809263
Web Site: http://www.valuepartners-index.com.hk
Sales Range: $50-74.9 Million
Emp.: 90
Investment Management Service
N.A.I.C.S.: 523999

Value Partners Investment Management (Shanghai) Limited (1)
702 Citigroup Tower 33 Hua Yuan Shi Qiao Road, Pudong New District, Shanghai, 200120, China
Tel.: (86) 2138186888
Investment Management Service
N.A.I.C.S.: 523940

VALUE VALVES CO., LTD.
No 9 Chung-Shan Rd, Tu-Chung Industrial District, New Taipei City, 236, Taiwan
Tel.: (886) 222698000
Web Site: https://www.valuevalves.com
Year Founded: 1980
4580—(TPE)
Rev.: $79,736,829
Assets: $109,755,714
Liabilities: $42,288,653
Net Worth: $67,467,061
Earnings: $10,411,750
Fiscal Year-end: 12/31/22
Industrial Valve Mfr & Distr
N.A.I.C.S.: 332911
Tai-Chung Yang (Chm)
Subsidiaries:

Kaho Valve Co., Ltd. (1)
No 9-1 Zhongshan Rd, Tucheng Dist, New Taipei City, Taiwan
Tel.: (886) 222679250
Web Site: http://www.kahovalve.com
Industrial Valve Mfr
N.A.I.C.S.: 332911

Value Valves (SuZhou) Ltd. (1)
No 2 WangShan Road Economic Development Zone, Photoelectricity Industrial Park WangShan, Suzhou, 215104, Jiangsu, China
Tel.: (86) 51266558783

INTERNATIONAL PUBLIC

Industrial Valve Mfr
N.A.I.C.S.: 332911

VALUE8 N.V.
Brediusweg 33, 1401 AB, Bussum, Netherlands
Tel.: (31) 357111387
Web Site: https://www.value8.com
VALUE—(EUR)
Rev.: $9,033,006
Assets: $120,007,727
Liabilities: $12,686,831
Net Worth: $107,320,896
Earnings: $6,424,550
Fiscal Year-end: 12/31/23
Investment Holding Company; Corporate Financing & Consulting Services
N.A.I.C.S.: 551112
Peter Paul de Vries (Chm-Mgmt Bd)
Subsidiaries:

NedSense enterprises N.V. (1)
Laanakkerweg 2b, 4131 PA, Vianen, Netherlands (58.3%)
Tel.: (31) 652000431
Web Site: http://www.nedsense.com
Holding Company; Fashion & Textile Industry Software Developer, Publisher, Distr & Other Services
N.A.I.C.S.: 551112
Gerben Hettinga (Co-Chm-Supervisory Bd)

Subsidiary (Domestic):
NedSense enterprises b.v. (2)
Laanakkerweg 2b, 4131 PA, Vianen, Netherlands (100%)
Tel.: (31) 652000431
Web Site: http://www.nedsense.nl
Holding Company
N.A.I.C.S.: 551112
Pieter A. J. J. Aarts (Mng Dir)

SnowWorld Leisure N.V. (1)
Buytenparklaan 30, 2717 AX, Zoetermeer, Netherlands
Tel.: (31) 79 3 202 302
Web Site: http://www.snowworld.com
Sales Range: $25-49.9 Million
Ski Resort
N.A.I.C.S.: 713920
J. H. M. Hendriks (CEO)

VALUEHD CORPORATION
2-3F No 2 Honghui Industrial Park, Xinan Subdistrict Baoan District, Shenzhen, 518101, Guangdong, China
Tel.: (86) 75584528267
Web Site: https://www.vhd.com.cn
Year Founded: 2008
301318—(CHIN)
Rev.: $68,741,000
Assets: $266,744,027
Liabilities: $19,197,944
Net Worth: $247,546,084
Earnings: $11,573,324
Fiscal Year-end: 12/31/23
Electronic Component Mfr & Distr
N.A.I.C.S.: 334419
Chen Tao (Gen Mgr)

VALUEMART INFO TECHNOLOGIES LIMITED
2 2nd Floor RR Chambers 11th Main Vasanthnagar Off Millers Road, Bengaluru, 560052, India
Tel.: (91) 80 26633272
Web Site: http://www.valuemartinfo.com
Year Founded: 1995
Sales Range: $1-9.9 Million
Software Development Services
N.A.I.C.S.: 541511
C. K. Vasudevan (Mng Dir)

VALUEMAX GROUP LIMITED
261 Waterloo Street 01-35 Waterloo Centre, Singapore, 180261, Singapore

AND PRIVATE COMPANIES

Tel.: (65) 64665500
Web Site:
https://www.valuemax.com.sg
Year Founded: 1988
T6I—(SES)
Rev.: $250,728,622
Assets: $815,415,435
Liabilities: $490,549,875
Net Worth: $324,865,561
Earnings: $40,540,786
Emp.: 300
Fiscal Year-end: 12/31/23
Pawn Shop Owner
N.A.I.C.S.: 522310
Hiang Nam Yeah *(CEO & Mng Dir)*

Subsidiaries:

VM Credit Pte. Ltd. (1)
261 Waterloo Street 01-31, Singapore, 180261, Singapore
Tel.: (65) 64811788
Mortgage & Nonmortgage Loan Brokering Services
N.A.I.C.S.: 522310

VM Money Pte. Ltd. (1)
261 Waterloo Street 01-35, Singapore, 180261, Singapore
Tel.: (65) 69931188
Corporate Investment Financial Services
N.A.I.C.S.: 541611

VM Worldwide Services Pte. Ltd. (1)
261 Waterloo Street 01-35 Waterloo Centre, Singapore, 180261, Singapore
Tel.: (65) 68178919
Pawn Broking Services
N.A.I.C.S.: 522291

ValueMax Pawnshop (CCK) Pte. Ltd. (1)
309 Choa Chu Kang Avenue 4 01-02, Choa Chu Kang Centre, Singapore, 680309, Singapore
Tel.: (65) 68172958
Mortgage & Nonmortgage Loan Brokering Services
N.A.I.C.S.: 522310

VALUENCE HOLDINGS, INC.
Shinagawa Season Terrace 28F 1-2-70, Minato-ku, Konan, 108-0075, Japan
Tel.: (81) 345809983
Web Site: https://www.valuence.inc
9270—(TKS)
Rev.: $506,730,960
Assets: $165,750,560
Liabilities: $123,112,460
Net Worth: $42,638,100
Earnings: ($10,629,980)
Emp.: 1,074
Fiscal Year-end: 08/31/24
Used Merchandise Retailer
N.A.I.C.S.: 459510
Shinsuke Sakimoto *(Founder, Pres & CEO)*

Subsidiaries:

Valuence International Limited (1)
7F and 8F 38 Hillwood Road, Tsim Sha Tsui, Kowloon, China (Hong Kong)
Tel.: (852) 38958100
Precious Metal Retailer
N.A.I.C.S.: 423940
Susumu Muguruma *(Mng Dir)*

Valuence Ventures Inc. (1)
MA5 5-6-19 Minamiaoyama, Minato-ku, Tokyo, 107-0062, Japan
Tel.: (81) 345809864
Venture Capital Investment Services
N.A.I.C.S.: 523999

Yone Automobile Co., Ltd. (1)
Azabu Showroom 1F Higashi-Azabu Annex Building 1-10-13, Higashi-Azabu Minato-ku, Tokyo, 106-0044, Japan
Tel.: (81) 364265903
Web Site: https://www.yonemotors.jp
New & Used Car Distr
N.A.I.C.S.: 441120

VALUENEX JAPAN, INC.
3F Twin Hills 4-5-16 Kohinata, Bunkyo-ku, Tokyo, 112-0006, Japan
Tel.: (81) 369029833
Web Site:
https://www.en.valuenex.com
Year Founded: 2006
4422—(TKS)
Rev.: $4,888,920
Assets: $6,263,540
Liabilities: $1,355,960
Net Worth: $4,907,580
Earnings: $18,660
Fiscal Year-end: 07/31/24
Software Development Services
N.A.I.C.S.: 541511
Tatsuo Nakamura *(Founder & CEO)*

VALUES CULTURAL INVESTMENT LIMITED
601 Tower C Oriental Media Center No 4 Guanghua Road, Chaoyang District, Beijing, China
Web Site:
https://www.yuanshimedia.com
Year Founded: 2013
1740—(HKG)
Rev.: $8,710,955
Assets: $28,328,533
Liabilities: $3,900,227
Net Worth: $24,428,306
Earnings: ($13,768,830)
Emp.: 22
Fiscal Year-end: 12/31/23
Investment Management Service
N.A.I.C.S.: 523999
Xiaoxin Cai *(CEO)*

VALUETRONICS HOLDINGS LIMITED
Unit 9-11 7/F Technology Park 18 On Lai Street, Sha Tin, New Territories, China (Hong Kong)
Tel.: (852) 27908278
Web Site:
https://www.valuetronics.com.hk
BN2—(SES)
Rev.: $261,497,405
Assets: $270,297,582
Liabilities: $93,775,167
Net Worth: $176,522,415
Earnings: $14,645,163
Fiscal Year-end: 03/31/22
Original Equipment Mfr
N.A.I.C.S.: 333519
Jian Yuan Huang *(VP-Ops)*

Subsidiaries:

Honor Tone Limited (1)
Unit 1-2 23/F CCT Telecom Building No 11 Wo Shing Street, Fotan, New Territories, China (Hong Kong)
Tel.: (852) 27908278
Electronic Components Mfr
N.A.I.C.S.: 334412

Valuetronics Holdings Limited - Manufacturing Facility (1)
Dong Er Road Science and Technology Park, Daya Bay Economy and Technology Western District Development District, Huizhou, 516081, Guangdong, China
Tel.: (86) 752 5378000
Web Site: http://www.valuetronics.com.hk
Printed Circuit Board Mfr
N.A.I.C.S.: 334418

VALVOSACCO S.P.A.
Via Solferino 2, Forette di Vigasio, 37068, Italy
Tel.: (39) 0456685257
Web Site: http://www.valvosacco.com
Sales Range: $25-49.9 Million
Emp.: 100
Paper Products Mfr
N.A.I.C.S.: 322220
Bruno Fabris *(Mng Dir)*

VAM INVESTMENTS SPAC B.V.
Via Manzoni 3, 20121, Milan, Italy
Tel.: (39) 0284138800
Web Site:
https://www.vaminvestments-spac.com
Year Founded: 2021
VAM—(EUR)
Rev.: $163,356
Assets: $263,159,018
Liabilities: $263,256,049
Net Worth: ($97,031)
Earnings: ($8,270,968)
Emp.: 2
Fiscal Year-end: 12/31/22
Investment Management Service
N.A.I.C.S.: 523999
Francesco Trapani *(Chm)*

VAMA INDUSTRIES LIMITED
Ground Floor 8-2-248/1/7/78/12 13 Block-A Lakshmi Towers, Nagarjuna Hills Punjagutta, Hyderabad, 500082, Telangana, India
Tel.: (91) 4066615534
Web Site: https://www.vamaind.com
Year Founded: 1985
512175—(BOM)
Rev.: $1,804,520
Assets: $3,624,687
Liabilities: $1,165,002
Net Worth: $2,459,685
Earnings: ($109,262)
Emp.: 30
Fiscal Year-end: 03/31/23
Software & Engineering Services
N.A.I.C.S.: 541330
Vegesna Rajam Raju *(Exec Dir)*

Subsidiaries:

Vama Technologies Pte. Ltd. (1)
10 Jalan Besar 10-10 Sim Lim Tower, Singapore, 208787, Singapore
Tel.: (65) 62938089
Software Development Services
N.A.I.C.S.: 541511

VAMA SUNDARI INVESTMENTS (DELHI) PRIVATE LIMITED
Plot No. A9, Sector 3, Noida, 201301, India
Tel.: (91) 1204306000
Web Site: https://vamadelhi.com
Year Founded: 2008
Private Limited Company
N.A.I.C.S.: 523999

Subsidiaries:

HDFC Education & Development Services Pvt. Ltd. (1)
Survey No 13 Nehru Nagar Shivanahalli Road Off Jakkur-Yelahanka Road, Bengaluru, 560 064, Karnataka, India (91%)
Tel.: (91) 802 972 0103
Web Site: https://www.thehdfcschool.com
Educational Support Services
N.A.I.C.S.: 611710
Parvathy Seshadri *(Principal)*

VAMSHI RUBBER LIMITED
Vamshi House Plot No 41Jayabheri Enclave, Gachibowli, Hyderabad, 500032, Telangana, India
Tel.: (91) 4029802533
Web Site:
https://www.vamshirubber.org
530369—(BOM)
Rev.: $9,629,111
Assets: $5,272,562
Liabilities: $3,725,568
Net Worth: $1,546,994
Earnings: $11,114
Emp.: 147
Fiscal Year-end: 03/31/23
Rubber Products Mfr
N.A.I.C.S.: 326299

VAN ELLE HOLDINGS PLC

M. Ramesh Reddy *(Chm & CFO)*

VAN DE VELDE N.V.
Lageweg 4, 9260, Schellebelle, Belgium
Tel.: (32) 93652100
Web Site: https://www.vandevelde.eu
VDEVF—(OTCIQ)
Rev.: $223,243,184
Assets: $250,196,490
Liabilities: $83,909,924
Net Worth: $166,286,566
Earnings: $41,159,068
Emp.: 1,558
Fiscal Year-end: 12/31/23
Lingerie Designer, Mfr & Retailer
N.A.I.C.S.: 315210
Herman Van de Velde *(Chm)*

Subsidiaries:

Eurocorset SA (1)
Calle Santa Eulalia 5, 08012, Barcelona, Spain
Tel.: (34) 932081460
Web Site: http://www.andressarda.com
Sales Range: $25-49.9 Million
Emp.: 60
Lingerie Mfr & Distr
N.A.I.C.S.: 315210

Intimacy Management Company LLC (1)
3500 Peachtree Rd NE, Atlanta, GA 30326 (85%)
Tel.: (404) 261-9333
Web Site: http://www.rigbyandpeller.com
Sales Range: $25-49.9 Million
Lingerie Retailer
N.A.I.C.S.: 458110

SU DISTRIBUIDORA SUL TU. CORPO, S.L. (1)
Santa Eulalia 5-7-9, 08012, Barcelona, Spain
Tel.: (34) 915781545
Lingerie Distr
N.A.I.C.S.: 424350

Van de Velde North America Inc. (1)
1252 Madison Ave, New York, NY 10128
Tel.: (212) 213-0587
Web Site: http://www.vandevelde.eu
Sales Range: $25-49.9 Million
Emp.: 10
Lingerie Mfr & Distr
N.A.I.C.S.: 315250

VAN DE WATER RAYMOND LTD
2300 Monterey, Laval, H7L 3H9, QC, Canada
Tel.: (450) 688-7580
Web Site:
http://www.vandewaterraymond.com
Year Founded: 1960
Rev.: $42,506,420
Emp.: 150
Warehousing Services
N.A.I.C.S.: 493110
Yves Raymond *(Pres)*

VAN DEN ENDE & DEITMERS B.V.
Johannes Vermeerstraat 23, 1071 DK, Amsterdam, Netherlands
Tel.: (31) 20 794 7777
Web Site: http://www.endeit.com
Year Founded: 2006
Emp.: 7
Venture Capital Firm
N.A.I.C.S.: 523999
Hubert Deitmers *(Co-Founder & Mng Partner)*

VAN ELLE HOLDINGS PLC
Summit Close, Kirkby in Ashfield, NG17 8GJ, Nottinghamshire, United Kingdom
Tel.: (44) 1773580580
Web Site: https://www.van-elle.co.uk

VAN ELLE HOLDINGS PLC

Van Elle Holdings PLC—(Continued)

Year Founded: 1984
VANL—(AIM)
Rev.: $184,588,803
Assets: $117,941,733
Liabilities: $55,849,500
Net Worth: $62,092,233
Earnings: $5,808,348
Fiscal Year-end: 04/30/23
Engineering Contractor Services
N.A.I.C.S.: 238910
Mark Cutler *(CEO)*

Subsidiaries:

Rock & Alluvium Limited (1)
4 Swan Court High Street, Leatherhead, KT22 8AH, Surrey, United Kingdom
Tel.: (44) 1372389333
Web Site: https://www.rockal.com
Sales Range: $25-49.9 Million
Emp.: 90
Heavy & Civil Engineering Construction Services
N.A.I.C.S.: 237990
Darren Brockett *(Mng Dir)*

ScrewFast Foundations Limited (1)
6th Floor Hampton by Hilton 42-50 Kimpton Road, Luton, LU2 0FP, United Kingdom
Tel.: (44) 1727735550
Web Site: https://www.screwfast.com
Telecommunication Tower Foundation Services
N.A.I.C.S.: 713990

VAN GENECHTEN PACKAGING N.V.

Raadsherenstraat 2, 2300, Turnhout, Belgium
Tel.: (32) 14 40 36 40
Web Site:
http://www.vangenechten.com
Sales Range: $350-399.9 Million
Emp.: 1,600
Playing Card & Paperboard Packaging Mfr
N.A.I.C.S.: 322212
Henk Rogiers *(CFO)*

Subsidiaries:

VG Angouleme S.A.S. (1)
146 bd Salvador Allende Z I No 3, PO Box 20609, Isle d'Espagnac, France
Tel.: (33) 545682322
Food Packaging Services
N.A.I.C.S.: 424420

VG Contours ZAO (1)
Chermyanskaya 1a, Moscow, 127081, Russia
Tel.: (7) 4993463930
Food Packaging Services
V.A.N.I.C.S.: 424420

VG Extrusion GmbH & Co. KG (1)
Ulmer Strasse 18, Allgau, 87437, Kempten, Germany
Tel.: (49) 831526110
Food Packaging Services
N.A.I.C.S.: 424420

VG KVADRA PAK JSC (1)
Vienibas gatve 11, Riga, 1004, Latvia
Tel.: (371) 67605064
Food Packaging Services
N.A.I.C.S.: 424420

VG Meyzieu S.A.S. (1)
124 rue de la Republique, PO Box 108, 69882, Meyzieu, France
Tel.: (33) 472027351
Food Packaging Services
N.A.I.C.S.: 424420

VG Nicolaus GmbH & Co. KG (1)
Gutenbergstr 1, 50259, Pulheim, Germany
Tel.: (49) 223480010
Food Packaging Services
N.A.I.C.S.: 424420

VG Ostprint, OOO (1)
Severnaya St 5, Podolino Village Solnechnogorskiy District, 141420, Moscow, Russia
Tel.: (7) 4996422610
Food Packaging Services

VG Polska Sp. z o.o. (1)
Pl Kilinskiego 1, 32-660, Chelmek, Poland
Tel.: (48) 338447070
Food Packaging Services
N.A.I.C.S.: 424420

VAN HEES GMBH

Kurt van Hees Str 1, Walluf, 65396, Germany
Tel.: (49) 61237080
Web Site: http://www.van-hees.com
Year Founded: 1947
Rev.: $38,300,200
Emp.: 237
Food Products Mfr
N.A.I.C.S.: 311999
Jurgen Georg Huniken *(Pres)*

Subsidiaries:

Eurospice Technologies and Additives (1)
Promyschlennyj Projezd 22 Derevnja Beljaninovo, Mytischinskij Region, 141032, Moscow, Russia
Tel.: (7) 4957442212
Food Products Distr
N.A.I.C.S.: 424420

VAN HEES GmbH - Halal Produktion Factory (1)
Beule 52, 42277, Wuppertal, Germany
Tel.: (49) 202266440
Food Products Mfr
N.A.I.C.S.: 311999

VAN HEES Inc. (1)
2500 Regency Pkwy, Cary, NC 27518
Tel.: (919) 654-6862
Food Products Distr
N.A.I.C.S.: 424420
W. D. Dave Pierce *(Pres)*

VAN HEES SARL (1)
Technopole de Forbach Sud, BP 122, 57600, Forbach, France
Tel.: (33) 387292701
Food Products Distr
N.A.I.C.S.: 424420

Van Hees AG (1)
Allmendstrasse 14 a, 5612, Villmergen, Switzerland
Tel.: (41) 566106307
Food Products Distr
N.A.I.C.S.: 424420

Van Hees Benelux BV (1)
Industriestrasse 27, 4700, Eupen, Belgium
Tel.: (32) 87560242
Food Products Distr
N.A.I.C.S.: 424420

VAN KEULEN INTERIEURBOUW BV

Van den Bergsweg 18, 7442 CK, Nijverdal, Netherlands
Tel.: (31) 548610555
Web Site: http://www.keulen.nl
Year Founded: 1944
Sales Range: $10-24.9 Million
Emp.: 500
Interior Design Services
N.A.I.C.S.: 541410
J. Van Keulen *(Chm)*

Subsidiaries:

Magista Netherlands (1)
James Wact Str 1, 7442 DC, Nijverdal, Netherlands (100%)
Tel.: (31) 505025500
Web Site: http://www.magista.nl
Commercial & Industrial Shelving & Racking Services
N.A.I.C.S.: 337215

VAN LANG TECHNOLOGY DEVELOPMENT AND INVESTMENT JOINT STOCK COMPANY

81 Tran Huang Dao, Hoan Kiem, Hanoi, Vietnam

Tel.: (84) 435121610
Web Site: https://www.vla.vn
Year Founded: 2007
VLA—(HNX)
Rev.: $1,098,700
Assets: $4,537,100
Liabilities: $181,800
Net Worth: $4,355,300
Earnings: $13,200
Fiscal Year-end: 12/31/23
Design Services, Website Building, Software & Consulting
N.A.I.C.S.: 541519

VAN LANSCHOT KEMPEN NV

Hooge Steenweg 29, 5211 JN, 's-Hertogenbosch, Netherlands
Tel.: (31) 203544590 NI
Web Site:
https://www.vanlanschotkempen.nd
Year Founded: 1737
VLK—(EUR)
Rev.: $738,902,749
Assets: $18,584,705,820
Liabilities: $17,095,825,149
Net Worth: $1,488,880,671
Earnings: $138,156,529
Emp.: 2,112
Fiscal Year-end: 12/31/23
Bank Holding Company
N.A.I.C.S.: 551111
Willy W. Duron *(Chm-Supervisory Bd)*

Subsidiaries:

F. van Lanschot Bankiers (Schweiz) AG (1)
Mittelstrasse 10, 8008, Zurich, Switzerland
Tel.: (41) 433771111
Web Site: https://www.vanlanschot.ch
Emp.: 25
Commercial Banking Services
N.A.I.C.S.: 522110

F. van Lanschot Bankiers NV (1)
29 Hoogesteenweg, 5211 JN, 's-Hertogenbosch, Netherlands
Tel.: (31) 735483548
Web Site:
https://www.vanlanschotkempen
Sales Range: $700-749.9 Million
Emp.: 1,500
Commericial Banking
N.A.I.C.S.: 522110

Subsidiary (Domestic):

F. van Lanschot Management BV (2)
Hooge Steenweg 29, 5211JN, 's-Hertogenbosch, Netherlands
Tel.: (31) 735483202
Web Site: http://www.vanlanschot.nl
Sales Range: $600-649.9 Million
Emp.: 2,000
Commericial Banking
N.A.I.C.S.: 522110

F. van Lanschot Participaties BV (2)
Hooge Steenweg 29, PO Box 10215200, 5211JN, 's-Hertogenbosch, Netherlands
Tel.: (31) 735483202
Web Site: http://www.vanlanschot.nl
Commericial Banking
N.A.I.C.S.: 522110

Hof Hoorneman Bankiers NV (1)
Oosthaven 52, 2801 PE, Gouda, Netherlands
Tel.: (31) 1 82 597 777
Web Site: http://www.hofhoorneman.nl
Sales Range: $1-4.9 Billion
Emp.: 55
Investment & Banking Services
N.A.I.C.S.: 523999
Fried van 't Hof *(Mng Dir)*

Kempen Capital Management BV (1)
Beethovenstraat 300, 1077 WZ, Amsterdam, Netherlands
Tel.: (31) 203488700
Investment Banking Services
N.A.I.C.S.: 523150

Kempen Finance BV (1)

INTERNATIONAL PUBLIC

Beethovenstraat 300, 1077 WZ, Amsterdam, Netherlands
Tel.: (31) 203488500
Web Site: https://www.kempen.com
Asset Management Services
N.A.I.C.S.: 523150

Van Lanschot Ars Mundi BV (1)
Nieuwe Uitleg 22, Den Haag, 2514BR, Hague, Netherlands
Tel.: (31) 703131967
Web Site: http://www.vanlanschot-arsmundi.com
Commerical Banking
N.A.I.C.S.: 522110

Van Lanschot Asset Management BV (1)
Hooge Steenweg 29, PO Box 1021, 5200 HC, 's-Hertogenbosch, Netherlands
Tel.: (31) 735488372
Web Site: http://www.vanlanschot.com
Sales Range: $200-249.9 Million
Emp.: 300
Commericial Banking
N.A.I.C.S.: 522110

Van Lanschot Assurantien BV (1)
Statenlaan 8, 's-Hertogenbosch, 5223 LA, Netherlands
Tel.: (31) 736924692
Web Site: http://www.vanlanschot-assurantien.com
Sales Range: $100-124.9 Million
Emp.: 160
Insurance Related Activities
N.A.I.C.S.: 524298
Lambo Molder *(Gen Mgr)*

Van Lanschot Bankiers (Curacao) NV (1)
Schottegatweg Oost 32, Willemstad, Curacao
Tel.: (599) 9 737 10 11
Sales Range: $50-74.9 Million
Emp.: 21
Commerical Banking Services
N.A.I.C.S.: 522110

Van Lanschot Bankiers Belgie NV (1)
Desguinlei 50, 2018, Antwerp, Belgium
Tel.: (32) 3 286 78 00
Web Site: http://www.vanlanschot.be
Emp.: 140
Commericial Banking Services
N.A.I.C.S.: 522110
Mitchell Buysschiaret *(Gen Mgr)*

VAN LEEUWEN PIPE & TUBE GROUP B.V.

Lindtsedijk 120, 3336 LE, Zwijndrecht, Netherlands
Tel.: (31) 786252525 NI
Web Site:
http://www.vanleeuwen.com
Year Founded: 1924
Rev.: $882,079,100
Assets: $915,285,095
Liabilities: $632,993,026
Net Worth: $282,292,069
Earnings: $11,270,271
Emp.: 2,619
Fiscal Year-end: 12/31/19
Pipe, Tubular Products & Fittings Mfr & Distr
N.A.I.C.S.: 331210
P. L. Rietberg *(Chm-Mgmt Bd)*

Subsidiaries:

Combulex B.V. (1)
Stuartweg 3, 4131 NH, Vianen, Netherlands
Tel.: (31) 347 361911
Web Site: http://www.combulex.com
Emp.: 40
Steel Pipe & Bar Steel Mfr
N.A.I.C.S.: 331210

NV Jean Wauters - Aciers Speciaux (1)
Liverpoolstraat 23, 1080, Brussels, Belgium
Tel.: (32) 2 5221850
Steel Pipe & Bar Steel Distr
N.A.I.C.S.: 423390
J. Elegheert *(Mng Dir)*

AND PRIVATE COMPANIES — VAN RIJN B.V.

P. Van Leeuwen Jr's Buizenhandel B.V. (1)
Lindtsedijk 120, 3336 LE, Zwijndrecht, Netherlands **(100%)**
Tel.: (31) 786252525
Web Site: http://www.vanleeuwen.com
Sales Range: $100-124.9 Million
Emp.: 300
Mfr & Distr of Pipes & Tubes, Bar Steel Valves & Beams
N.A.I.C.S.: 331210

Teuling Staal B.V. (1)
Lindtsedijk 120, Lindtsedijk 100, 3336 LE, Zwijndrecht, Netherlands
Tel.: (31) 786252525
Web Site: http://www.teulingstaal.nl
Sales Range: $25-49.9 Million
Emp.: 15
Steel Warehousing & Distr
N.A.I.C.S.: 423510

Van Leeuwen (Shanghai) Pipe and Tube Co., Ltd. (1)
Room 1708 You You International Plaza 76 Pu Jian Road, Pudong New District, Shanghai, China
Tel.: (86) 21 58311866
Emp.: 20
Steel Pipe & Bar Steel Distr
N.A.I.C.S.: 423390
D. Yap (Gen Mgr)

Van Leeuwen Boru Sanayi Ve Ticaret Ltd
Sirketi Inonu Caddesi Sumer Sokak Zitas Bloklari C2 Blok Kat 6 Daire 1, Istanbul, Turkiye
Tel.: (90) 216 3804525
Steel Pipe & Bar Steel Distr
N.A.I.C.S.: 423390

Van Leeuwen Buizen Belgium N.V. (1)
Schaarbeeklei 189, 1800, Vilvoorde, Belgium **(100%)**
Tel.: (32) 22554000
Web Site: http://www.vanleeuwen.be
Sales Range: $50-74.9 Million
Emp.: 90
Mfr & Distr of Pipes & Tubes, Bar Steel Valves & Beams
N.A.I.C.S.: 331210

Van Leeuwen Buizen Europa B.V. (1)
Lindtsedijk 120, 3336 LE, Zwijndrecht, Netherlands **(100%)**
Tel.: (31) 786252525
Web Site: http://www.vanleeuwen.com
Sales Range: $100-124.9 Million
Emp.: 300
Steel Pole Mfr
N.A.I.C.S.: 331210

Van Leeuwen Ltd (1)
Tullow Industrial Estate Bunclody Road, Co Carlow, Tullow, Ireland
Tel.: (353) 599181120
Steel Pipe & Bar Steel Distr
N.A.I.C.S.: 423390

Van Leeuwen Pipe & Tube (Canada) Inc. (1)
945 Ave 48 Southeast, Calgary, 2TG 2A7, AB, Canada **(100%)**
Tel.: (403) 569-0050
Web Site: http://www.vanleeuwen.com
Sales Range: $25-49.9 Million
Emp.: 15
Tube & Piping
N.A.I.C.S.: 331210

Van Leeuwen Pipe & Tube (Canada) Inc. (1)
2875 - 64th Avenue, Edmonton, T6P 1R1, AB, Canada **(100%)**
Tel.: (780) 469-7410
Sales Range: $25-49.9 Million
Emp.: 45
Distribution of Tube & Pipe
N.A.I.C.S.: 423510

Van Leeuwen Pipe & Tube (Malaysia) Sdn. Bhd. (1)
Suite 11-02 Level 11 Menara IGB The Boulevard, Lingkaran Syed Putra, 59200, Kuala Lumpur, Malaysia **(100%)**
Tel.: (60) 322873358
Web Site: http://www.vanleeuwen.com.sg
Sales Range: $1-9.9 Million
Emp.: 23
Mfr & Distr of Pipes & Tubes, Bar Steel Valves & Beams
N.A.I.C.S.: 331210

Van Leeuwen Pipe & Tube (Middle East) Ltd. (1)
ADDAX Commercial Tower Unit 1211 Al Reem Island, PO Box 47144, Hamdan St, Abu Dhabi, United Arab Emirates **(100%)**
Tel.: (971) 26271840
Web Site: http://www.vanleeuwen.ae
Sales Range: $25-49.9 Million
Emp.: 10
Steel Pole Mfr
N.A.I.C.S.: 331210

Van Leeuwen Pipe & Tube (Thailand) Ltd. (1)
B Grimm Alma Link Building 10th Floor 25 Soi Chidlom Ploenchit, Lumphini Park Patumwan, 10330, Bangkok, Thailand
Tel.: (66) 26551022
Web Site: http://www.vanleeuwen.com.sg
Sales Range: $25-49.9 Million
Emp.: 15
Mfr & Distr of Pipes & Tubes, Bar Steel Valves & Beams
N.A.I.C.S.: 331210

Plant (Domestic):

Van Leeuwen Pipe & Tube (Thailand) Ltd. (2)
Chonburi Industrial Estate Bo-Win 341 Moo 6 Highway no 331 KM 91, Bo-Win Amphur, Si Racha, 20230, Chonburi, Thailand
Tel.: (66) 38345765
Web Site: http://www.vanleeuwen.com.sg
Steel Pole Mfr
N.A.I.C.S.: 331210

Van Leeuwen Pipe & Tube Australia Pty. Ltd. (1)
95-113 Lee Holm Road St Mary s, Sydney, 2760, NSW, Australia **(100%)**
Tel.: (61) 298961111
Web Site: http://www.vanleeuwen.com.au
Sales Range: $25-49.9 Million
Emp.: 25
Mfr & Distr of Pipes & Tubes, Bar Steel Valves & Beams
N.A.I.C.S.: 331210

Division (Domestic):

Van Leeuwen Pipe & Tube Western Australia Pty. Ltd. (2)
31 - 35 Vulcan road, Canning Vale, 6155, WA, Australia **(100%)**
Tel.: (61) 894552882
Web Site: http://www.vanleeuwen.com.au
Sales Range: $25-49.9 Million
Emp.: 20
Mfr & Distr of Pipes & Tubes, Bar Steel Valves & Beams
N.A.I.C.S.: 331210

Van Leeuwen Pipe & Tube Indonesia Pte. Ltd. (1)
Wisma 46 Kota BNI 48th floor Jl Jend Sudirman Kav 1, Jakarta, 10220, Indonesia **(100%)**
Tel.: (62) 215748815
Web Site: http://www.vanleeuwen.com.sg
Sales Range: $25-49.9 Million
Emp.: 5
Mfr & Distr of Pipes & Tubes, Bar Steel Valves & Beams
N.A.I.C.S.: 331210

Van Leeuwen Pipe & Tube S.A. de C.V. (1)
Calle Eucken 8 Despacho 403, Colonia Anzures, 11590, Mexico, DF, Mexico
Tel.: (52) 5552544865
Sales Range: $25-49.9 Million
Emp.: 25
N.A.I.C.S.: 331210

Van Leeuwen Pipe & Tube Singapore Pte. Ltd. (1)
4 Pioneer Place, Singapore, 627893, Singapore **(100%)**
Tel.: (65) 68979301
Web Site: http://www.vanleeuwen.com.sg
Sales Range: $10-24.9 Million
Emp.: 60
Pipe & Tubes
N.A.I.C.S.: 331210

Van Leeuwen Pipe and Tube (1)
Naschokinskiy pereulok 12 build 2 office 318, 119019, Moscow, Russia
Tel.: (7) 495 695 07 64
Steel Pipe & Bar Steel Distr
N.A.I.C.S.: 423390

Van Leeuwen Pipe and Tube Gulf FZE (1)
OilFields Supply Center B11 Jebel Ali free zone, PO Box 261145, Dubai, 461145, United Arab Emirates
Tel.: (971) 4 8833872
Web Site: http://www.vanleeuwen.com
Emp.: 50
Steel Pipe & Bar Steel Distr
N.A.I.C.S.: 423390

Van Leeuwen Pipe and Tube LCC (1)
10235 W Little York Rd Ste 250, Houston, TX 77040
Tel.: (281) 582-3150
Emp.: 15
Steel Pipe & Bar Steel Distr
N.A.I.C.S.: 423390
J. de Vries (Gen Mgr)

Van Leeuwen Pipe and Tube s.r.o. (1)
Kratka 753 / 3b, 682 01, Vyskov, Czech Republic
Tel.: (420) 515 532 201
Web Site: http://www.vanleeuwen.cz
Emp.: 50
Steel Pipe & Bar Steel Distr
N.A.I.C.S.: 423390

Van Leeuwen Precision B.V. (1)
Hamburgweg 6, 7418 ES, Deventer, Netherlands **(100%)**
Tel.: (31) 570500700
Web Site: http://www.vanleeuwen.com
Sales Range: $25-49,9 Million
Emp.: 60
Mfr & Distr of Pipes & Tubes, Bar Steel Valves & Beams
N.A.I.C.S.: 331210

Van Leeuwen Rury Spolka z.o.o. (1)
Ul Spoleczna 8, 41-200, Sosnowiec, Poland
Tel.: (48) 32 294 4600
Web Site: http://www.vanleeuwen.pl
Steel Pipe & Bar Steel Distr
N.A.I.C.S.: 423390

Van Leeuwen Stainless (1)
Industrieweg 26, 4153 BW, Beesd, Netherlands **(100%)**
Tel.: (31) 345687777
Web Site: http://www.vanleeuwen.com
Sales Range: $25-49.9 Million
Emp.: 60
Mfr & Distr of Pipes & Tubes, Bar Steel Valves & Beams
N.A.I.C.S.: 331210

Van Leeuwen Tubes S.A. (1)
10 Bis Rue Nicephore, 45700, Montargis, France **(100%)**
Tel.: (33) 238281515
Web Site: http://www.vanleeuwen.fr
Sales Range: $25-49.9 Million
Emp.: 8
Mfr & Distr of Pipes & Tubes, Bar Steel Valves & Beams
N.A.I.C.S.: 331210

Van Leeuwen Wheeler - Sheffield (1)
Unit 1A Rotunda Business Center, Thorncliffe Park Chapletown, Sheffield, S35 2PG, United Kingdom **(100%)**
Tel.: (44) 1142577577
Web Site: http://www.vanleeuwen.com
Sales Range: $25-49.9 Million
Emp.: 8
Steel Pole Mfr
N.A.I.C.S.: 331210

Van Leeuwen s.r.o. (1)
Zamocka 3, 811 01, Bratislava, Slovakia
Tel.: (421) 532 123251
Steel Pipe & Bar Steel Distr
N.A.I.C.S.: 423390

H. Zondervan (Gen Mgr)

VAN OORD NV
Schaardijk 211, 3063 NH, Rotterdam, Netherlands
Tel.: (31) 88 826 0000   NI
Web Site: http://www.vanoord.com
Year Founded: 1868
Dredging & Reclamation Services
N.A.I.C.S.: 237990
Paul W. Verheul (COO & Member-Exec Bd)

Subsidiaries:

Van Oord Dredging and Marine Contractors B.V. (1)
20 Harbour Drive PSA Vista #07-02, 117612, Singapore, Singapore
Tel.: (65) 67736643
Web Site: http://www.vanoord.com
Dredging & Land Reclamation Services
N.A.I.C.S.: 541330

VAN PHAT HUNG CORPORATION
Floor 2 Tulip Tower 15 Hoang Quoc Viet Street, Phu Thuan Ward District 7, Ho Chi Minh City, Vietnam
Tel.: (84) 2837830011
Web Site:
   https://www.vanphathung.com
Year Founded: 1999
VPH—(HOSE)
Rev.: $3,013,492
Assets: $97,492,837
Liabilities: $55,451,698
Net Worth: $42,041,139
Earnings: ($33,866)
Emp.: 69
Fiscal Year-end: 12/31/23
Residential Building Construction Services
N.A.I.C.S.: 236116
Truong Thanh Nhan (CEO & Member-Mgmt Bd)

VAN PHU - INVEST INVESTMENT JOINT STOCK COMPANY
104 Thai Thinh, Trung Liet ward Dong Da district, Hanoi, Vietnam
Tel.: (84) 2462583535
Web Site: http://www.vanphu.vn
Year Founded: 2003
Rev.: $129,566,446
Assets: $358,893,804
Liabilities: $251,247,091
Net Worth: $107,646,713
Earnings: $20,435,416
Emp.: 483
Fiscal Year-end: 12/31/19
Real Estate Manangement Services
N.A.I.C.S.: 531390
To Nhu Toan (Chm)

VAN RAALTE DE VENEZUELA C.A.
Avenida Principal de la Yaguara, Urb la Yaguara, Caracas, DF, Venezuela
Tel.: (58) 2129446830
Year Founded: 1965
Sales Range: $125-149.9 Million
Emp.: 570
Women's Lingerie, Swimwear, Blouses & Dresses Mfr & Whslr
N.A.I.C.S.: 315210
Robert Frank (Pres)

VAN RIJN B.V.
ABC Westland 574, 2685 DG, Poeldijk, Netherlands
Tel.: (31) 174419400   NI
Web Site: http://www.van-rijn.nl
Year Founded: 1855
Sales Range: $350-399.9 Million
Emp.: 250

VAN RIJN B.V.

Van Rijn B.V.—(Continued)
Fruit & Vegetable Whslr
N.A.I.C.S.: 424480
Aad van der Windt (CEO)

VAN-WHOLE PRODUCE LTD.
830 Malkin Avenue, Vancouver, V6A 2K2, BC, Canada
Tel.: (604) 251-3330
Web Site: https://www.vanwhole-produce.com
Year Founded: 1984
Sales Range: $50-74.9 Million
Vegetables & Fruits Whslr
N.A.I.C.S.: 424480
Leonard Jang (VP & Gen Mgr)

VANACHAI GROUP PUBLIC COMPANY LIMITED
2/1 Wongsawang Road Wongsawang Bangsue, Bangkok, 10800, Thailand
Tel.: (66) 25854900
Web Site: https://www.vanachai.com
Year Founded: 1943
VNG—(THA)
Rev.: $413,013,395
Assets: $542,039,589
Liabilities: $327,930,644
Net Worth: $214,108,945
Earnings: $1,311,942
Emp.: 1,738
Fiscal Year-end: 12/31/23
Particle Board & Plywood Mfr & Distr
N.A.I.C.S.: 321219
Sompop Sahawat (Chm)

Subsidiaries:

Durospan Co., Ltd. (1)
2/1 Piboonsongkram Road, Bangsue, Bangkok, 10800, Thailand
Tel.: (66) 25854900
Reconstituted Wood Product Mfr
N.A.I.C.S.: 321219

Particle Planner Co., Ltd. (1)
2/1 Wongsawang Road, Bangsue, Bangkok, 10800, Thailand
Tel.: (66) 258549003
Sales Range: $75-99.9 Million
Emp.: 220
Plywood, Particle Board & Timber Products Mfr
N.A.I.C.S.: 321212

Vanachai Chemical Industries Co., Ltd. (1)
10 Soi G-14 Prakornsongkroaraj Road, Mabtapud Muang, Rayong, 21150, Thailand
Tel.: (66) 38685071
Sales Range: $25-49.9 Million
Emp.: 92
Glue & Adhesives Mfr
N.A.I.C.S.: 325520
Somporn Sahawat (Chm)

Vanachai Panel Industries Co., Ltd. (1)
2/1 Wongsawang Road, Bangsue, Bangkok, 10800, Thailand
Tel.: (66) 291321809
Web Site: http://www.vanachai.com
Emp.: 200
Reconstituted Wood Product Mfr
N.A.I.C.S.: 321219

Woodtex International Co., Ltd. (1)
2/1 Sunant Building, Piboonsongkram Road, Bangkok, 10800, Thailand
Tel.: (66) 25854900
Web Site: http://www.vanachai.com
Sales Range: $25-49.9 Million
Emp.: 100
Wood Furniture
N.A.I.C.S.: 337126

VANADIA UTAMA, PT
Pantai Indah Kapuk Blok G1 No 5, Komplek Sentra Industri Terpadu, Jakarta, 14470, Indonesia
Tel.: (62) 2156982988   Id
Web Site: http://www.vanadia.co.id
Laboratory Equipment Distr
N.A.I.C.S.: 423490

VANADIAN ENERGY CORPORATION
3123 - 595 Burrard Street, PO Box 49179, Bentall Three, Vancouver, V7X 1J1, BC, Canada
Tel.: (604) 506-6996   BC
Web Site: http://www.vanadianenergy.com
Year Founded: 1999
VEC—(TSXV)
Rev.: $67
Assets: $508,301
Liabilities: $1,029,975
Net Worth: ($521,674)
Earnings: ($145,584)
Fiscal Year-end: 07/31/22
Mineral Mining Services
N.A.I.C.S.: 212290
Marc Simpson (Pres & CEO)

VANADIUM RESOURCES LIMITED
Suite 7 63 Shepperton Road, Victoria Park, 6100, WA, Australia
Tel.: (61) 861589990   AU
Web Site: https://www.vr8.global
TR3—(DEU)
Rev.: $91,793
Assets: $20,186,727
Liabilities: $470,122
Net Worth: $19,716,605
Earnings: ($1,342,221)
Fiscal Year-end: 06/30/24
Mineral Exploration Services
N.A.I.C.S.: 213114
Eugene Nel (CEO)

VANADIUMCORP RESOURCE INC.
303 - 5455 West Boulevard West, Vancouver, V6M 3W5, BC, Canada
Tel.: (604) 282-3967   BC
Web Site: https://www.vanadiumcorp.com
Year Founded: 1980
VRBFF—(OTCIQ)
Assets: $5,536,210
Liabilities: $1,011,106
Net Worth: $4,525,104
Earnings: ($718,251)
Fiscal Year-end: 10/31/22
Mineral Exploration Services
N.A.I.C.S.: 213114
Adriaan Bakker (Pres & CEO)

VANCAMEL AG
c/o HRG Hansische Revisions-Gesellschaft mbH Wirts Ferdinandstrasse 25, 20095, Hamburg, Germany
Tel.: (49) 40 689999 0
Web Site: http://www.vancamel.de
Year Founded: 2005
Sales Range: $200-249.9 Million
Emp.: 208
Men's Clothing Mfr & Distr
N.A.I.C.S.: 315250
Xiaming Ke (Chm-Mgmt Bd & CEO)

VANCOUVER PORT AUTHORITY
100 The Pointe 999 Canada Place, Vancouver, V6C 3T4, BC, Canada
Tel.: (604) 665-9000
Web Site: http://www.portvancouver.com
Sales Range: $25-49.9 Million
Emp.: 200
Marine Cargo Handling Services
N.A.I.C.S.: 488320
Robin Silvester (Pres & CEO)

VANDANA KNITWEAR LIMITED
Bhandari Plaza 2nd Floor Opp Nagar Parishad, Rajendra Marg Road, Bhilwara, 311001, Rajasthan, India
Tel.: (91) 482297261
Web Site: https://vandanaknitwear.com
Year Founded: 1995
532090—(BOM)
Rev.: $465,402
Assets: $1,592,865
Liabilities: $235,701
Net Worth: $1,357,164
Earnings: $15,612
Fiscal Year-end: 03/31/23
Textile Product Mfr & Distr
N.A.I.C.S.: 314999
Naresh Kumar Gattani (Mng Dir)

VANDEMOORTELE N.V.
Ottergemsesteenweg-Zuid 816, 9000, Gent, Belgium
Tel.: (32) 92424512
Web Site: http://www.vandemoortele.com
Year Founded: 1899
Rev.: $1,549,964,630
Assets: $1,192,789,763
Liabilities: $741,285,728
Net Worth: $451,504,035
Earnings: $53,321,014
Emp.: 5,200
Fiscal Year-end: 12/31/19
Food Products, Margarines, Oils, Mayonnaise, Dressings & Soy Foods Producer
N.A.I.C.S.: 311224
Jean Vandemoortele (Chm)

Subsidiaries:

Cottes Usines SAS (1)
Z I La Mirande - 7 Avenue de l'Aerodrome, Saint-Esteve, 66240, France
Tel.: (33) 4 68 92 28 47
Bakery Product Mfr & Distr
N.A.I.C.S.: 311813

Croustifrance Benelux N.V. (1)
Ottergemsesteenweg Zuid 816, 9000, Gent, Belgium
Tel.: (32) 92429675
Web Site: http://www.croustico.com
Sales Range: $25-49.9 Million
Emp.: 40
Food Products, Margarines, Oils, Mayonnaise, Dressings, Frying Fats & Soy Foods Producer
N.A.I.C.S.: 311224

Croustifrance S.A. (1)
95 Allee de France ZI Artoipole, Arras, 62118, France
Tel.: (33) 321607080
Web Site: http://www.vandemoortele.com
Sales Range: $25-49.9 Million
Emp.: 100
Food Products, Margarines, Oils, Mayonnaise, Dressings, Frying Fats & Soy Foods Producer
N.A.I.C.S.: 311224

Croustifrance S.A. (1)
1 rue des Macecliers, Reims, 51689, France
Tel.: (33) 326859464
Food Products, Margarines, Oils, Mayonnaise, Dressings, Frying Fats & Soy Foods Producer
N.A.I.C.S.: 311224
Jean Vandemoortele (Gen Mgr)

Hobum Oele und Fette GmbH (1)
Seehafenstrasse 2, Postfach 90 04 52, 21079, Hamburg, Germany
Tel.: (49) 4077114290
Web Site: http://www.hobum-foodservice.de
Sales Range: $25-49.9 Million
Emp.: 15
Food Products, Margarines, Oils, Mayonnaise, Dressings, Frying Fats & Soy Foods Producer
N.A.I.C.S.: 311224

Incotra N.V. (1)
Prins Albertlaan 12, 8870, Izegem, Belgium
Tel.: (32) 51332211
Web Site: http://www.vandemoortele.com
Sales Range: $25-49.9 Million
Emp.: 100
Food Products, Margarines, Oils, Mayonnaise, Dressings, Frying Fats & Soy Foods Producer
N.A.I.C.S.: 311224

Metro N.V. (1)
Prins Albertlaan 12, 8870, Izegem, Belgium
Tel.: (32) 51332700
Web Site: http://www.metrotransport.be
Sales Range: $25-49.9 Million
Emp.: 70
Food Products, Margarines, Oils, Mayonnaise, Dressings, Frying Fats & Soy Foods Producer
N.A.I.C.S.: 311224

N.V. Vandemoortele (1)
Handelsweg 1, 3899 AA, Zeewolde, Netherlands
Tel.: (31) 36 5229700
Web Site: http://www.vandemoortele.com
Food Products, Margarines, Oils, Mayonnaise, Dressings, Frying Fats & Soy Foods Producer
N.A.I.C.S.: 311224

N.V. Vandemoortele Izegem (1)
Prins Albertlaan 12, 8870, Izegem, Belgium
Tel.: (32) 51332211
Web Site: http://www.vandemoortele.com
Sales Range: $100-124.9 Million
Emp.: 350
Food Products, Margarines, Oils, Mayonnaise, Dressings, Frying Fats & Soy Foods Producer
N.A.I.C.S.: 311224

Subsidiary (Non-US):

Vandemoortele Deutschland GmbH (2)
Pirnaer Landstrasse 194, 01257, Dresden, Germany
Tel.: (49) 351207740
Web Site: http://www.vandemoortele.com
Sales Range: $50-74.9 Million
Emp.: 80
Margarine Mfr
N.A.I.C.S.: 311512

Paindor Provence Frais SAS (1)
2 rue de Lisbonne, Vitrolles, 13127, France
Tel.: (33) 4 42 10 50 35
Bakery Product Mfr & Distr
N.A.I.C.S.: 311813

Paindor SAS (1)
Z I 14eme rue - 1ere Avenue, 06513, Carros, France
Tel.: (33) 4 92 08 51 15
Bakery Product Mfr & Distr
N.A.I.C.S.: 311813

Panarmen SAS (1)
ZA des Grouas, 72190, Neuville-sur-Sarthe, France
Tel.: (33) 2 43 51 11 50
Bakery Product Mfr & Distr
N.A.I.C.S.: 311813

Panavi SAS (1)
Z A Montigne Est, 35370, Torce, France
Tel.: (33) 2 99 75 72 00
Bakery Product Mfr & Distr
N.A.I.C.S.: 311813

Subsidiary (Domestic):

Panalog SAS (2)
La Chapellerie, 35210, Chatillon-en-Vendelais, France
Tel.: (33) 2 99 76 15 00
Bakery Product Mfr & Distr
N.A.I.C.S.: 311813

S.A. Vandemoortele (1)
Avenue des Artisans 47, 7822, Ghislenghien, Belgium
Tel.: (32) 68570800
Web Site: http://www.vandemoortele.com
Sales Range: $25-49.9 Million
Emp.: 45
Food Product Margarine Oil Mayonnaise Dressing Frying Fat & Soy Food Producer Mfr
N.A.I.C.S.: 311224

Safinco Nederland bv (1)
Molenvaart 12, 6442 PL, Brunssum, Netherlands
Tel.: (31) 45 527 7575
Bakery Product Mfr & Distr
N.A.I.C.S.: 311813

Teiglingswerk Dommitzsch GmbH (1)
Rudolf-Breitscheid-Strasse 10, Dommitzsch Saxony, 04880, Delitzsch, Germany
Tel.: (49) 3422341641
Food Products, Margarines, Oils, Mayonnaise, Dressings, Frying Fats & Soy Foods Producer
N.A.I.C.S.: 311224

Vamix CR (1)
Belohorska 95, 16900, Prague, 6, Czech Republic
Tel.: (420) 2243390959
Food Products, Margarines, Oils, Mayonnaise, Dressings, Frying Fats & Soy Foods Producer
N.A.I.C.S.: 311224

Vamix Slovenska Republika sro (1)
Karadzicova ulica 8/A, 821 08, Bratislava, Slovakia
Tel.: (421) 2 59 39 62 39
Bakery Product Mfr & Distr
N.A.I.C.S.: 311813

Vandemoortele (UK) Ltd. (1)
Charta House 30 - 38 Church Street, Staines-upon-Thames, TW18 4EP, Surrey, United Kingdom
Tel.: (44) 2088147830
Web Site: http://vandemoortele.com
Sales Range: $25-49.9 Million
Emp.: 30
Food Products, Margarines, Oils, Mayonnaise, Dressings, Frying Fats & Soy Foods Producer
N.A.I.C.S.: 311224

Vandemoortele Bakery Products Ghislenghien sa (1)
Avenue des Artisans 47, Ghislenghien, 7822, Belgium
Tel.: (32) 68 57 08 03
Bakery Product Mfr & Distr
N.A.I.C.S.: 311813
Gulas Noten (Mng Dir)

Vandemoortele Dommitzsch GmbH (1)
Rudolf-Breitscheid-Strasse 10, 04880, Dommitzsch, Germany
Tel.: (49) 34 223 46 30
Bakery Products Mfr
N.A.I.C.S.: 311813

Vandemoortele France (1)
30 rue des Peupliers, 92752, Nanterre, France
Tel.: (33) 146525600
Web Site: http://www.vandemoortele.com
Food Products, Margarines, Oils, Mayonnaise, Dressings, Frying Fats & Soy Foods Producer
N.A.I.C.S.: 311224

Vandemoortele Hungary Ltd. (1)
Kapolna u12, 6000, Kecskemet, Hungary
Tel.: (36) 76 505 027
Bakery Product Mfr & Distr
N.A.I.C.S.: 311813

Vandemoortele Iberica S.A. (1)
Calle Sant Marti de l'Erm n 1 planta 5a, 08960, Sant Just Desvern, Barcelona, Spain
Tel.: (34) 934999800
Web Site: http://vandemoortele.com
Sales Range: $25-49.9 Million
Emp.: 150
Food Products, Margarines, Oils, Mayonnaise, Dressings, Frying Fats & Soy Foods Producer
N.A.I.C.S.: 311224
Giorgio Benedetti (Dir-Comml-Southern Europe)

Vandemoortele Italia S.p.A. (1)
Via de Capitani 2, 20041, Agrate Brianza, Italy
Tel.: (39) 03964191
Sales Range: $25-49.9 Million
Emp.: 25

Food Products, Margarines, Oils, Mayonnaise, Dressings, Frying Fats & Soy Foods Producer
N.A.I.C.S.: 311224

Vandemoortele PPI UK (1)
The Plaza 11th Floor 100 Old Hall Street, Liverpool, L3 9QJ, United Kingdom
Tel.: (44) 1512420870
Food Products, Margarines, Oils, Mayonnaise, Dressings, Frying Fats & Soy Foods Producer
N.A.I.C.S.: 311224

Vandemoortele Polska sp.z.o.o. (1)
Tokarzewskiego 7-12, 91-842, Lodz, Poland
Tel.: (48) 42 617 10 70
Bakery Product Mfr & Distr
N.A.I.C.S.: 311813

Vandemoortele Ruckversicherung AG (1)
Schochenmuhlestrasse, 6340, Baar, Switzerland
Tel.: (41) 41 769 10 20
Bakery Product Mfr & Distr
N.A.I.C.S.: 311813

Vandemoortele Seneffe sa (1)
Rue Jules Bordet Zone C, 7180, Seneffe, Belgium
Tel.: (32) 64 31 05 50
Emp.: 170
Bakery Product Mfr & Distr
N.A.I.C.S.: 311813
Brice Gatez (Plant Mgr)

VANDEN BUSSCHE IRRIGATION & EQUIPMENT LIMITED
2515 Pinegrove Road, PO Box 304, Delhi, N4B 2X1, ON, Canada
Tel.: (519) 582-2380
Web Site: http://www.vandenbussche.com
Year Founded: 1954
Rev.: $21,563,015
Emp.: 85
Agricultural Services
N.A.I.C.S.: 423820
MarcVanden Bussche (Owner)

VANDERFIELD PTY LTD
Carrington Rd, PO Box 2010, Toowoomba, 4350, QLD, Australia
Tel.: (61) 746334822
Web Site: http://www.vanderfield.com.au
Year Founded: 1963
Sales Range: $25-49.9 Million
Emp.: 200
Farm Machinery & Truck Distr & Sales
N.A.I.C.S.: 423820
Bruce Vandersee (Mng Dir)

VANDERPOL'S EGGS LTD.
3911 Mt Lehman Road, Abbotsford, V2T 5W5, BC, Canada
Tel.: (604) 856-4127
Web Site: http://www.vanderpolseggs.com
Year Founded: 1959
Sales Range: $10-24.9 Million
Egg Products Mfr
N.A.I.C.S.: 311999
Henry Meerstra (Mgr-Sls)

VANDERWELL CONTRACTORS (1971) LTD
695 West Mitsue Industrial Rd, Slave Lake, T0G 2A0, AB, Canada
Tel.: (780) 849-3824
Web Site: http://www.vanderwell.com
Sales Range: $25-49.9 Million
Saw Mill & Lumber Whslr
N.A.I.C.S.: 321113
Faron B. (CFO)

VANDOR REAL ESTATE SOCIMI, S.A.U.
Beethoven 15 7th floor, 08021, Barcelona, Spain
Tel.: (34) 935952001 ES
Web Site: https://www.vandor.es
Year Founded: 2019
MLVRE—(EUR)
Rev.: $625,252
Assets: $43,352,283
Liabilities: $16,740,329
Net Worth: $26,611,954
Earnings: ($2,510,605)
Fiscal Year-end: 12/19/21
Real Estate Investment Services
N.A.I.C.S.: 531190
Pedro Luis Barcelo Bou (Chm & CEO)

VANEDGE CAPITAL PARTNERS LTD
1333 West Broadway Suite 750, Vancouver, V6H 4C1, BC, Canada
Tel.: (604) 569-3883
Web Site: https://www.vanedgecapital.com
Year Founded: 2010
Rev.: $296,000,000
Venture Capital & Private Equity Firm
N.A.I.C.S.: 523999
V. Paul Lee (Founder & Mng Partner)

VANET GIDA SANAYI IC VE DIS TICARET A.S.
Buyukdere Cad Metro City A Blok, 171 Kat 17 Levent, Istanbul, Turkiye
Tel.: (90) 2123192831
Web Site: http://www.vanet.com.tr
Sales Range: $10-24.9 Million
Emp.: 45
Veal Product Mfr
N.A.I.C.S.: 311612
Erdal Dolukeas (Chm)

VANEXPORT SA
Les Portes du Millenaire Bat C 4 496 route de la Pompignane, BP 45542, 34170, Castelnau-le-Lez, France
Tel.: (33) 899236713
Web Site: http://www.vanexport.fr
Telecommunication Products Mfr
N.A.I.C.S.: 517810
Pascal Vandromme (Chm & CEO)

VANFUND URBAN INVESTMENT&DEVELOPMENT CO., LTD.
12A Tower B China International Science and Technology Exhibition Cent, No 12 Yumin Road Chaoyang District, Beijing, 100029, China
Tel.: (86) 1064656161
Web Site: http://www.vanfund.cn
Year Founded: 1996
000638—(SSE)
Rev.: $22,142,189
Assets: $79,679,541
Liabilities: $47,617,980
Net Worth: $32,061,561
Earnings: $589,848
Fiscal Year-end: 12/31/22
Medical Equipment Distr
N.A.I.C.S.: 423450
Hui Zhang (Chm)

VANGUARD GREEN INVESTMENT LIMITED
Rm 5 7F No 296 Sec 4 Xinyi Rd, Daan District, Taipei, 106427, Taiwan
Tel.: (886) 905153139 NV
Web Site: https://www.vg-il.com
Year Founded: 2018
VGES—(OTCIQ)
Assets: $17,002
Liabilities: $664,802
Net Worth: ($647,800)
Earnings: ($26,035)
Emp.: 2

Fiscal Year-end: 07/31/24
Holding Company
N.A.I.C.S.: 551112
Niu Yen-Yen (Chm, Pres, CEO & CFO)

VANGUARD INTERNATIONAL SEMICONDUCTOR CORPORATION
No 123 Park Ave-3rd Hsinchu Science Park, Hsinchu, 300096, Taiwan
Tel.: (886) 35770355
Web Site: https://www.vis.com.tw
Year Founded: 1994
Semiconductor Mfr
N.A.I.C.S.: 334413
Leuh Fang (Chm & Chief Strategy Officer)

VANI COMMERCIALS LIMITED
162-A Second Floor Sector-7, New Delhi, 110045, India
Tel.: (91) 9560066230 In
Web Site: https://www.vanicommercials.com
Year Founded: 1988
538918—(BOM)
Rev.: $258,054
Assets: $2,766,285
Liabilities: $1,197,986
Net Worth: $1,568,299
Earnings: ($35,825)
Emp.: 20
Fiscal Year-end: 03/31/23
Consumer Lending Services
N.A.I.C.S.: 522291
Neha Ashish Karia (Mng Dir & CFO)

VANITY CAPITAL INC.
Suite 700 838 West Hastings Street, Vancouver, V6C 0A6, BC, Canada
Tel.: (604) 649-6916 BC
Web Site: http://vanitycapitalinc.com
Year Founded: 2008
VYC.H—(TSXV)
Rev.: $5,117
Assets: $140,759
Liabilities: $18,514
Net Worth: $122,245
Earnings: ($42,756)
Fiscal Year-end: 02/29/24
Investment Services
N.A.I.C.S.: 523999
Nicholas Segounis (Chm, Pres & CEO)

VANJEE TECHNOLOGY CO., LTD.
VanJee Space Building 12 Zhongguancun Software Park, Haidian District, Beijing, 100193, China
Tel.: (86) 1059766986
Web Site: https://www.vanjee.net
Year Founded: 1994
300552—(SSE)
Rev.: $122,580,853
Assets: $480,097,379
Liabilities: $101,165,613
Net Worth: $378,931,766
Earnings: ($4,069,929)
Fiscal Year-end: 12/31/22
Dynamic Weighing Product Mfr & Distr
N.A.I.C.S.: 333993
Zhai Jun (Chm & Gen Mgr)

VANOIL ENERGY LTD.
3595 Glenview Crescent, Vancouver, V7R 3E9, BC, Canada
Tel.: (604) 763-1229 BC
Year Founded: 2009
Oil & Gas Exploration Services
N.A.I.C.S.: 211120

VANOV HOLDINGS COMPANY LIMITED

VANOV HOLDINGS COMPANY LIMITED

Vanov Holdings Company Limited—(Continued)
No 519 Section 2 Xinhua Avenue, Chengdu Strait Science & Technology Industry Development Park Wenjiang, Chengdu, Sichuan, China　Ky
Web Site: https://www.vanov.cn
Year Founded: 2018
2260—(HKG)
Rev.: $32,865,806
Assets: $113,958,933
Liabilities: $57,328,312
Net Worth: $56,630,621
Earnings: $7,432,848
Emp.: 357
Fiscal Year-end: 12/31/23
Holding Company
N.A.I.C.S.: 551112
Genlian Shen (Chm)

VANQUIS BANKING GROUP PLC
No 1 Godwin Street, Bradford, BD1 2SU, United Kingdom
Tel.: (44) 1274351135　UK
Web Site: https://www.vanquisbanking.com
VANQ—(OTCIQ)
Rev.: $1,096,766,216
Assets: $4,179,197,932
Liabilities: $3,299,802,688
Net Worth: $879,395,244
Earnings: ($113,233,848)
Emp.: 4,865
Fiscal Year-end: 12/31/20
All Other Business Support Services
N.A.I.C.S.: 561499
Malcolm Le May (CEO)

Subsidiaries:

Cheque Exchange Limited　(1)
No 1 Godwin Street, Bradford, BD1 2SU, WEST YORKSHIRE, United Kingdom
Tel.: (44) 8001959530
Web Site: http://www.cashmycheques.co.uk
Check Cashing & Money Transfer Services
N.A.I.C.S.: 522320

Direct Auto Financial Services Limited　(1)
Springfield House, Springfield Rd, Horsham, RH12 2RG, West Sussex, United Kingdom　(100%)
Tel.: (44) 1403246300
Sales Range: $50-74.9 Million
Emp.: 5
Financial Investment Activities
N.A.I.C.S.: 523999

Greenwood Personal Credit Limited　(1)
Unit 11 Lister Close Plympton, Plymouth, 1752348562, United Kingdom　(100%)
Tel.: (44) 1752348562
Web Site: http://www.greenwoodpersonalcredit.com
Sales Range: $50-74.9 Million
Emp.: 20
Nondepository Credit Intermediation
N.A.I.C.S.: 522299

Moneybarn Limited　(1)
Athena House Bedford Road, Petersfield, GU32 3LJ, Hampshire, United Kingdom
Tel.: (44) 3305551230
Web Site: http://www.moneybarn.com
Car & Motorbike Financing Services
N.A.I.C.S.: 522220

Provident Financial S.r.o.　(1)
Mlynske Nivy 49, 82109, Bratislava, Slovakia　(100%)
Tel.: (421) 259800600
Web Site: http://www.provident.sk
Sales Range: $50-74.9 Million
Emp.: 80
Nondepository Credit Intermediation
N.A.I.C.S.: 522299
Evo Kalek (Mgr-Ops)

Provident Personal Credit Limited　(1)
Unit 2-4 Maxwell house Liverpool Innovation Park, Liverpool, L7 9NJ, United Kingdom　(100%)
Tel.: (44) 1512361669
Nondepository Credit Intermediation
N.A.I.C.S.: 522299

Provident Polska S.A.　(1)
ul Inflancka 4A, 00-189, Warsaw, Poland　(100%)
Tel.: (48) 224554933
Web Site: https://www.provident.pl
Credit Card Issuing
N.A.I.C.S.: 522210

Vanquis Bank Limited　(1)
20 Fenchurch Street, London, EC3M 3BY, United Kingdom　(100%)
Tel.: (44) 2073376300
Web Site: http://www.vanquisbank.co.uk
Sales Range: $200-249.9 Million
Emp.: 450
Depository Credit Intermediation
N.A.I.C.S.: 522180
Malcolm Le May (Interim Mng Dir)

VANTA BIOSCIENCE LTD.
NO 02/G/308/G NO 3/FF/SF/1-20-248 Umajay Complex Rasoolpura, Secunderabad, 500003, Telangana, India
Tel.: (91) 4066575454
Web Site: https://www.vantabio.com
Year Founded: 2016
540729—(BOM)
Rev.: $1,374,936
Assets: $9,504,386
Liabilities: $5,924,352
Net Worth: $3,580,034
Earnings: $61,363
Emp.: 56
Fiscal Year-end: 03/31/21
Biotechnology Research & Development Services
N.A.I.C.S.: 541714
Zoheb Sayani (Sec)

VANTAGE DRILLING INTERNATIONAL
Damac Executive Heights Barsha Heights Tecom Floor 18 Office 1809, PO Box 282292, Dubai, United Arab Emirates
Tel.: (971) 4 449 3400　Ky
Web Site: http://www.vantagedrilling.com
Year Founded: 2007
Rev.: $760,848,000
Assets: $1,090,737,000
Liabilities: $437,646,000
Net Worth: $653,091,000
Earnings: $456,475,000
Emp.: 425
Fiscal Year-end: 12/31/19
Offshore Drilling Contractor
N.A.I.C.S.: 488320
Ihab Toma (CEO)

Subsidiaries:

Manufacturas Zapaliname, S.A. de C.V.　(1)
Parque Industrial La Angostura Carretera Saltillo Zacatecas Km 4 5, 25086, Saltillo, Coahuila, Mexico
Tel.: (52) 4113855
Web Site: http://www.zapa.com.mx
Business Process Outsourcing Services
N.A.I.C.S.: 561499

VANTAGE EQUITIES, INC.
15th Floor Philippine Stock Exchange Tower 28th St Corner 5th Ave, Bonifacio Global City, Taguig, Philippines
Tel.: (63) 82508750　PH
Web Site: https://www.vantage.com.ph
Year Founded: 1992
V—(PHI)
Rev.: $20,516,138
Assets: $232,290,754
Liabilities: $10,491,958
Net Worth: $221,798,796
Earnings: $7,995,788
Emp.: 559
Fiscal Year-end: 12/31/20
Money Remittance & Internet Services
N.A.I.C.S.: 522390
Joseph L. Ong (Treas)

Subsidiaries:

Philequity Management, Inc.　(1)
15th Floor Philippine Stock Exchange Tower 5th Avenue Corner, 28th Street Bonifacio Global City, Taguig, 1634, Philippines
Tel.: (63) 282508700
Web Site: https://www.philequity.net
Emp.: 13
Investment Management Service
N.A.I.C.S.: 523940
Roberto Z. Lorayes (Chm)

VANTAGE GOLDFIELDS LIMITED
Level 7 99 Macquarie Street, Sydney, 2000, NSW, Australia
Tel.: (61) 2 82263323
Web Site: http://www.vantagegoldfields.com
Sales Range: Less than $1 Million
Gold Mining Services
N.A.I.C.S.: 212220
Michael McChesney (Founder & CEO)

Subsidiaries:

Eastern Goldfields Exploration (Pty) Ltd　(1)
Kpmg Forum 33 Van Rensburg Street, Nelspruit, 1200, Mpumalanga, South Africa
Tel.: (27) 137533046
Gold Ore Mining Services
N.A.I.C.S.: 212220

Makonjwaan Imperial Mining Company (Pty) Ltd　(1)
8 Streak Street, Nelspruit, 1201, Mpumalanga, South Africa
Tel.: (27) 137126808
Sales Range: $100-124.9 Million
Emp.: 232
Gold Ore Mining Services
N.A.I.C.S.: 212220

VANTAGE INTERNATIONAL (HOLDINGS) LIMITED
155 Waterloo Road, Kowloon Tong, Kowloon, China (Hong Kong)
Tel.: (852) 2796 0960　BM
Web Site: http://www.vantageholdings.com
Rev.: $452,599,631
Assets: $888,561,511
Liabilities: $309,656,167
Net Worth: $578,905,344
Earnings: $94,475,022
Emp.: 369
Fiscal Year-end: 03/31/19
Civil Engineering Services
N.A.I.C.S.: 541330
Chun Hung Ngai (Chm)

VANTEA SMART S.P.A.
Via Tiburtina 1231, Lazio, 00131, Rome, Italy
Tel.: (39) 0641990300
Web Site: https://www.vantea.com
Year Founded: 1993
VNT—(EUR)
Software Development Services
N.A.I.C.S.: 541511
Simone Veglioni (Chm)

VANTIVA SA
8-10 rue du Renard, 75004, Paris, France
Tel.: (33) 188243000　FR
Web Site: https://www.technicolor.com
Year Founded: 1915

INTERNATIONAL PUBLIC

VANTI—(EUR)
Rev.: $3,559,439,520
Assets: $3,683,491,760
Liabilities: $3,518,907,600
Net Worth: $164,584,160
Earnings: ($171,953,600)
Emp.: 16,676
Fiscal Year-end: 12/31/21
Digital Video Technologies, Systems & Services
N.A.I.C.S.: 334310
Ginny Davis (CIO & Chief Security Officer)

Subsidiaries:

CIRPACK　(1)
26-40 Rue d Oradour-sur-Glane, 75015, Paris, France
Tel.: (33) 183753800
Web Site: http://www.cirpack.com
Voice Switching Platform Developer
N.A.I.C.S.: 517112

Deutsche Thomson OHG　(1)
Karl-Wiechert-Allee 74, Hannover, 30625, Germany
Tel.: (49) 5114180
Web Site: http://www.technicolor.com
Optical Data Storage Services
N.A.I.C.S.: 518210

MPC (Shanghai) Digital Technology Co., Ltd.　(1)
A 1/F Building 4 No 727 Dingxi Road, Changning District, Shanghai, China
Tel.: (86) 2162820088
Visual Effect & Video Production Services
N.A.I.C.S.: 512110
Lily Li (Mng Dir)

Mikros Image S.A.　(1)
8-10 rue du Renard, 75004, Paris, France
Tel.: (33) 407754613
Web Site: http://www.mikrosimage.com
Motion Picture & Video Production
N.A.I.C.S.: 512110

Technicolor Creative Studios UK Ltd.　(1)
11-14 Windmill Street, London, W1T 2JG, United Kingdom
Tel.: (44) 2072874041
Web Site: https://www.themill.com
Media Advertising Services
N.A.I.C.S.: 541840

Technicolor Entertainment Services, S.L.　(1)
The Santa Leonor Street 65, Pozuelo de Alarcon, Madrid, 28037, Spain
Tel.: (34) 915122110
Web Site: http://www.technicolor.com
Emp.: 2
Communication Equipment Mfr
N.A.I.C.S.: 334290

Technicolor India Pvt Ltd.　(1)
Level 09-11 Navigator Building ITPL Whitefield Road, Bengaluru, 560066, India
Tel.: (91) 80 40461234
Web Site: http://www.technicolor.com
Emp.: 100
Animation Picture Production Services
N.A.I.C.S.: 512110

Technicolor International SAS　(1)
1-5 rue Jeanne d Arc, Issy-les-Moulineaux, 92130, France
Tel.: (33) 1 41 86 50 00
Electronic Appliance Distr
N.A.I.C.S.: 423620

Technicolor Japan KK　(1)
Omori Park Building 1-6-1 Omorihonmachi, Ota-ku, Tokyo, Japan
Tel.: (81) 366348710
Digital Broadcast Set Box Mfr
N.A.I.C.S.: 334220
Hiroaki Kurihara (Mgr)

Technicolor Limited　(1)
28-32 Lexington Street, Soho, London, W1F 0LF, United Kingdom
Tel.: (44) 207 319 4900
Web Site: http://www.technicolor.com
Film Processing & Recording Services
N.A.I.C.S.: 512110

AND PRIVATE COMPANIES / VAPO OY

Subsidiary (Domestic):

Technicolor Disc Services International Ltd. (2)
Building 1 3rd Floor Chiswick Park 566
Chiswick High Rd, London, W4 5BE, United Kingdom
Tel.: (44) 20 8100 1000
Video Production Services
N.A.I.C.S.: 512110

The Moving Picture Company Ltd. (2)
127 Wardour St, Soho, London, W1F 0NL, United Kingdom
Tel.: (44) 204343100
Web Site: http://www.moving-picture.com
Digital Picture Production Services
N.A.I.C.S.: 512110

Technicolor Mexicana, S de R.L. de C.V. (1)
Av Labna 1781 Col Jardines del Sol, Zapopan, Jalisco, Mexico
Tel.: (52) 3331344200
Web Site: http://www.technicolor-mexico.com.mx
Optical Disc Mfr
N.A.I.C.S.: 334610

Technicolor Polska. (1)
Julianowska 65a, Piaseczno, 05-500, Poland
Tel.: (48) 22 702 7530
Digital Video Disc Mfr
N.A.I.C.S.: 334310

Technicolor Pty Ltd. (1)
134-138 Euston Road, Alexandria, 2015, NSW, Australia
Tel.: (61) 2 9519 2677
Web Site: http://www.technicolor.com.au
Emp.: 30
Digital Video Disc Mfr
N.A.I.C.S.: 334310

Technicolor R&D France SNC (1)
1 Avenue Belle Fontaine CS 17616, 35576, Cesson Sevigne, France
Tel.: (33) 2 99 27 30 00
Video Production Research & Development Services
N.A.I.C.S.: 541715

Technicolor S.p.A. (1)
Via Tiburtina 1138, 00156, Rome, Italy
Tel.: (39) 06 41 888 256
Web Site: http://www.technicolor.com
Video Recorders & Equipment Distr
N.A.I.C.S.: 423410

Technicolor Trademark Management SASU (1)
1-5 rue Jeanne d Arc, Issy-les-Moulineaux, 92130, France
Tel.: (33) 1 41 86 50 00
Intellectual Property & Licensing Services
N.A.I.C.S.: 926150

Technicolor, Inc. (1)
3233 Mission Oaks Blvd, Camarillo, CA 93012-5047
Tel.: (805) 445-1122
Web Site: http://www.technicolor.com
Sales Range: $25-49.9 Million
Emp.: 130
Worldwide Color Processing & Special Services for the Motion Picture & Television Industry; Videocassette Duplication
N.A.I.C.S.: 334310
B. Quentin Lilly *(Head-Home Entertainment Svcs)*

Subsidiary (Non-US):

Technicolor Brasil Midia Eentretenimento Ltda. (2)
Av Max Teixeira 2319 - Col Santo Antonio, Manaus, 69093-770, Amazonas, Brazil
Tel.: (55) 92 36529000
Web Site: http://br.technicolor.com
Sales Range: $200-249.9 Million
Emp.: 800
Video Production Services
N.A.I.C.S.: 512110

Technicolor Canada Inc. (2)
3195 Bedford, Montreal, H3S 1G3, QC, Canada
Tel.: (514) 737-2777

Web Site: http://www.technicolor.com
Sales Range: $100-124.9 Million
Video Distribution Services
N.A.I.C.S.: 334610

Subsidiary (Domestic):

Technicolor Creative Services Canada Inc. (3)
2101 Saint Catherine Street West Suite 300, Montreal, H3H 1M6, QC, Canada (100%)
Tel.: (514) 939-5060
Web Site: http://www.technicolor.com
Emp.: 400
Technical Services for Cinema, Television & Advertising
N.A.I.C.S.: 512110

Branch (Domestic):

Technicolor Creative Services Canada Inc. - Toronto (4)
49 Ontario Street, Toronto, M5A 2V1, ON, Canada
Tel.: (416) 585-9995
Web Site: http://www.technicolor.com
Movie Post Production Services
N.A.I.C.S.: 512191

Subsidiary (Domestic):

Technicolor Laboratory Canada, Inc. (4)
10205 Cargo A-4, Mirabel, J7N 3C5, QC, Canada
Tel.: (450) 476-6800
Surgical Equipment Distr
N.A.I.C.S.: 423450

Subsidiary (Domestic):

Technicolor USA Inc. (2)
3233 Mission Oaks Blvd, Camarillo, CA 93012-5047
Tel.: (805) 445-1122
Web Site: http://www.technicolor.com
Emp.: 130
Holding Company; Regional Managing Office; Motion Picture Production & Distribution Services
N.A.I.C.S.: 551112
Quentin Lily *(CEO)*

Subsidiary (Domestic):

Technicolor Creative Services (3)
440 W Los Feliz Rd, Glendale, CA 91204
Tel.: (818) 500-9090
Web Site: http://www.technicolor.com
Provider of Digital Post-Production Film Services
N.A.I.C.S.: 334610

Technicolor Digital Cinema Inc. (3)
2233 N Ontario St Ste 300, Burbank, CA 91504-4500
Tel.: (818) 260-3600
Web Site: http://www.technicolor.com
Digital Video Production & Distribution Services
N.A.I.C.S.: 512110

Division (Domestic):

Technicolor Entertainment Services (3)
6040 Sunset Blvd, Hollywood, CA 90028
Tel.: (323) 817-6600
Web Site: http://www.technicolor.com
Worldwide Color Processing & Special Services for Motion Pictures & TV
N.A.I.C.S.: 522130
Sandra Carvalho *(CMO)*

Subsidiary (Domestic):

Technicolor Home Entertainment Services, Inc. (3)
3233 Mission Oaks Blvd, Camarillo, CA 93012-5097
Tel.: (805) 445-1122
Web Site: http://www.technicolor.com
Sales Range: $100-124.9 Million
Emp.: 400
Home Video Publisher
N.A.I.C.S.: 513199

Technicolor Videocassette of Michigan, Inc. (3)

36121 Schoolcraft Rd, Livonia, MI 48150-1216
Tel.: (734) 853-3800
Video Tape & Disk Reproduction Services
N.A.I.C.S.: 334310

Thomson Inc. (3)
101 W 103 St, Indianapolis, IN 46290-1024
Tel.: (317) 587-3000
Web Site: http://www.technicolor.net
Research, Distribution, Sales, Leasing & Service of Television Receivers, Home Video Cassette Recorders, Color Picture Tubes, Audio & Communications Equipment
N.A.I.C.S.: 334310

Holding (Domestic):

RCA Holdings Ltd. (4)
6363 Woodway Dr Ste 200, Houston, TX 77057-1757
Tel.: (713) 780-1997
Sales Range: $50-74.9 Million
Emp.: 200
Provider of Subdividing & Developing Services
N.A.I.C.S.: 237210

The Mill (Facility) Limited (1)
11-14 Windmill Street, London, W1T 2JG, United Kingdom
Tel.: (44) 2072874041
Web Site: http://www.themill.com
Motion Picture Production
N.A.I.C.S.: 512110

Subsidiary (US):

The Mill Group Inc. (2)
451 Broadway 6th Fl, New York, NY 10013
Tel.: (212) 337-3210
Web Site: http://www.themill.com
Sales Range: $25-49.9 Million
Motion Picture Production
N.A.I.C.S.: 512110

Branch (Domestic):

The Mill Group Inc. - Los Angeles (3)
3233 S La Cienega Blvd, Los Angeles, CA 90016
Tel.: (310) 566-3111
Web Site: http://www.themill.com
Motion Picture Production
N.A.I.C.S.: 512110
Ben Hampshire *(Mng Dir)*

Thomson Angers SAS (1)
1 Rue Jeanne D Arc, 92130, Issy-les-Moulineaux, France
Tel.: (33) 141865000
Video Production Services
N.A.I.C.S.: 512110

Thomson Licensing SAS (1)
1 Rue Jeanne d Arc, 92443, Issy-les-Moulineaux, France
Tel.: (33) 1 4186 5284
Electronic Industries Licensing Services
N.A.I.C.S.: 926150

Thomson Telecom SAS (1)
46 Quai Alphonse Le Gallo, Boulogne, 92648, France
Tel.: (33) 1 41 86 50 00
Web Site: http://www.myhometelephone.com
Cellular Telephones Distr
N.A.I.C.S.: 423690

Trace VFX LLC (1)
228 Park Ave S 26231, New York, NY 10003
Tel.: (212) 380-3047
Web Site: http://www.tracevfx.com
Emp.: 1,000
Visual Effect & Production Services
N.A.I.C.S.: 512191

VANTONE NEO DEVELOPMENT GROUP CO., LTD.
No 6 Chaowai Street, Chaoyang District, Beijing, 100020, China
Tel.: (86) 1059070710
Web Site: https://www.vantone.com
Year Founded: 1998
600246—(SHG)
Rev.: $59,269,762

Assets: $1,336,476,473
Liabilities: $439,514,506
Net Worth: $896,961,967
Earnings: ($45,364,265)
Emp.: 583
Fiscal Year-end: 12/31/22
Property Development Services
N.A.I.C.S.: 531311
Wang Yihui *(Chm)*

Subsidiaries:

Beijing Vantone Dingan Property Service Co. Ltd. (1)
2 Floor No 7 Building Shangdu Park, Tianjin, China
Tel.: (86) 2227255550
Real Estate Brokerage Services
N.A.I.C.S.: 531210

VAPEK ACLANICA LUTRA GROUP A.D.
Bircaninova 128, Valjevo, Serbia
Tel.: (381) 14 234 112
Web Site: http://www.vapek.com
Year Founded: 1952
VAPK—(BEL)
Sales Range: $1-9.9 Million
Emp.: 73
Bakery Products Mfr
N.A.I.C.S.: 311813
Ljubomir Dukic *(Exec Dir)*

VAPI ENTERPRISE LTD.
Plot No 298/299 GIDC 2nd Phase Industrial Area, Vapi, Wapi, 396195, Gujarat, India
Tel.: (91) 9820068363
Web Site: https://www.vapienterprise.com
Year Founded: 1980
502589—(BOM)
Rev.: $390,206
Assets: $467,292
Liabilities: $1,188,921
Net Worth: ($721,629)
Earnings: $42,285
Fiscal Year-end: 03/31/21
Paper Products Mfr
N.A.I.C.S.: 322299
Manoj Ramanbhai Patel *(Chm & Mng Dir)*

VAPIANO SE
Im Zollhafen 2-4, 50678, Cologne, Germany
Tel.: (49) 490228854670
Web Site: https://www.vapiano.com
Year Founded: 2002
VAO—(DEU)
Sales Range: $450-499.9 Million
Emp.: 7,225
Restaurant Operators
N.A.I.C.S.: 722511
Jochen Halfmann *(CEO)*

VAPO OY
Yrjonkatu 42, PO Box 22, FI-40101, Jyvaskyla, Finland
Tel.: (358) 207904000
Web Site: http://www.vapo.fi
Rev.: $527,089,314
Assets: $921,637,387
Liabilities: $459,569,103
Net Worth: $462,068,284
Earnings: $28,772,037
Emp.: 1,061
Fiscal Year-end: 04/30/19
Renewable Fuel, Bioelectricity & Bioheat Services
N.A.I.C.S.: 321999
Mia Suominen *(Dir-Bus Area-Ventures)*

Subsidiaries:

AS Tootsi Turvas (1)
Biroomaja 1 Papiniidu 5, Parnu, 80010, Estonia

VAPO OY

Vapo Oy—(Continued)
Tel.: (372) 44 71 530
Web Site: http://www.vapo.ee
Wood Chip Mfr
N.A.I.C.S.: 321113
Matti Puuronen (Chm & CEO)

Kekkila Oy (1)
Ayritie 8 D, 01510, Vantaa, Finland
Tel.: (358) 207904800
Web Site: http://www.kekkila.fi
Sales Range: $75-99.9 Million
Emp.: 251
Fertilizer Producer
N.A.I.C.S.: 325314
Mikael Johansson (Bus Dir)

Neova AB (1)
Sjotullsgatan 8, 824 50, Hudiksvall, Sweden
Tel.: (46) 77 198 00 00
Web Site: http://www.neova.se
Bioenergy Product Mfr
N.A.I.C.S.: 221117

VAPORJET LTD.

1 Hanit Kikos Street, PO Box 571,
Ofakim, 87514, Israel
Tel.: (972) 8 996 0880 IL
Web Site: http://www.vaporjet.co.il
Year Founded: 1995
Non-Woven Hydroentangled Spunlace Roll Good Mfr
N.A.I.C.S.: 313230
Shlomo Finkelstein (Ops Mgr)

Subsidiaries:

Novita S.A. (1)
ul Dekoracyjna 3, 65-722, Zielona Gora, Poland (63.17%)
Tel.: (48) 684561500
Web Site: https://teraz.novita.pl
Rev.: $46,975,356
Assets: $41,742,378
Liabilities: $8,582,063
Net Worth: $33,160,315
Earnings: $5,916,159
Emp.: 178
Fiscal Year-end: 12/31/2023
Carpet Mfr
N.A.I.C.S.: 314110
Eyal Maor (Chm)

VAPTSAROV JSC

17 Tsarigradsko Shossee Blvd, 1504,
Sofia, Bulgaria
Tel.: (359) 2 984 1600
Web Site: http://www.vaptech.bg
Year Founded: 1914
Heavy Machinery Mfr
N.A.I.C.S.: 333248
Svetlozar Venelinov Ivanov (Gen Mgr)

VAR RESOURCES CORP.

2489 Bellevue Avenue, West Vancouver, V7V 1E1, BC, Canada
Tel.: (604) 922-2030 BC
Web Site: http://canpharmacorp.ca
Year Founded: 1983
VAR—(TSXV)
Rev.: $52
Assets: $3,941
Liabilities: $279,715
Net Worth: ($275,774)
Earnings: ($65,819)
Fiscal Year-end: 10/31/20
Investment Services
N.A.I.C.S.: 523999

VARAAN B.V.

Waardsedijk Oost 1, 3417 XJ, Montfoort, Netherlands
Tel.: (31) 348479544 NL
Web Site: http://www.varaan.com
Sales Range: $10-24.9 Million
Emp.: 50
Direct Marketing & Fulfillment Services
N.A.I.C.S.: 541860

VARANGIS AVEPE S.A.

38 Kifisias Avenue, 15125, Maroussi, Greece
Tel.: (30) 210 61 54 800
Web Site: http://www.varangis.com.gr
Year Founded: 1990
Emp.: 53
Household Furniture Mfr
N.A.I.C.S.: 337121

Subsidiaries:

VARANGIS QATAR L.L.C (1)
Mohammed bin Thani St, PO Box 1399, Doha, 1399, Qatar
Tel.: (974) 4437 2226
Web Site: http://www.varangisqatar.com
Household Furniture Distr
N.A.I.C.S.: 423210

VARANGIS TURNKEY INTERIOR PROJECTS L.L.C (1)
Level 4 The Union National Bank Building Corniche Road West, PO Box 112 687, Abu Dhabi, United Arab Emirates
Tel.: (971) 2 6281600
Household Furniture Distr
N.A.I.C.S.: 423210
Pantelis Spagis (Area Mgr)

VARDHAMAN LABORATORIES LIMITED

1393 Peth Bhag, High School Road, Sangli, 416416, Maharashtra, India
Tel.: (91) 2332623886
Rev.: $5,509
Assets: $315,451
Liabilities: $4,499
Net Worth: $310,952
Earnings: ($6,233)
Fiscal Year-end: 03/31/18
Medical Instrument Mfr
N.A.I.C.S.: 339912
Sunil D. Shah (Mng Dir & Compliance Officer)

VARDHAN CAPITAL & FINANCE LTD.

113 Commerce House N M Marg
Fort, Mumbai, 400023, India
Tel.: (91) 2243226100
Web Site:
https://www.vardhancapital.com
542931—(BOM)
Financial Services
N.A.I.C.S.: 523150
Akash Rajesh Vardhan (Mng Dir)

VARDHMAN GROUP OF COMPANIES

Chandigarh Road, Ludhiana, 141010,
Punjab, India
Tel.: (91) 161 2228943
Web Site: http://www.vardhman.com
Sales Range: $1-4.9 Billion
Emp.: 300
Holding Company
N.A.I.C.S.: 551112
Paul Oswal (Chm & Mng Dir)

Subsidiaries:

Vardhman Acrylics Limited (1)
Chandigarh Road, Ludhiana, 141 010, Punjab, India
Tel.: (91) 1612228943
Web Site: https://www.vardhman.com
Rev.: $40,343,831
Assets: $66,218,006
Liabilities: $11,840,160
Net Worth: $54,377,846
Earnings: $5,858,116
Emp.: 315
Fiscal Year-end: 03/31/2021
Fiber Mfr
N.A.I.C.S.: 325220
Bal Krishan Choudhary (Mng Dir)

Vardhman Concrete Limited (1)
Survey No 35/10 Malóhop Village Khalapur Taluka, Raigad District, Thane, 410 220, India
Tel.: (91) 2192251069
Web Site:
http://www.vardhmandevelopers.com
Rev.: $3,546
Assets: $904,652
Liabilities: $1,909,216
Net Worth: ($1,004,564)
Earnings: ($48,507)
Emp.: 1
Fiscal Year-end: 03/31/2023
Civil Engineering Services
N.A.I.C.S.: 237990
Ramesh Babulal Vardhan (Chm-Grp)

Vardhman Holdings Limited (1)
Chandigarh Road, Ludhiana, 141010, Punjab, India
Tel.: (91) 161 222 8943
Web Site: http://www.vardhman.com
Rev.: $2,870,868
Assets: $314,951,719
Liabilities: $211,002
Net Worth: $314,740,717
Earnings: $17,678,320
Fiscal Year-end: 03/31/2021
Holding Company
N.A.I.C.S.: 551112
Shri Paul Oswal (Chm & Mng Dir)

Vardhman Polytex Limited (1)
Vardhman Park Chandigarh Road, Ludhiana, 141 123, India
Tel.: (91) 1612685301
Web Site: https://www.oswalgroup.com
Rev.: $69,768,003
Assets: $41,699,658
Liabilities: $89,268,243
Net Worth: ($47,568,585)
Earnings: ($7,739,100)
Emp.: 2,639
Fiscal Year-end: 03/31/2021
Yarn Mfr
N.A.I.C.S.: 313110
Adish Oswal (Chm, Mng Dir & COO)

Vardhman Textiles Limited (1)
Chandigarh Road, Ludhiana, 141010, Punjab, India
Tel.: (91) 1612228943
Web Site: https://www.vardhman.com
Rev.: $865,605,195
Assets: $1,314,082,770
Liabilities: $412,217,715
Net Worth: $901,865,055
Earnings: $57,667,155
Emp.: 20,916
Fiscal Year-end: 03/31/2021
Textile Products Mfr
N.A.I.C.S.: 339999
Shri Paul Oswal (Chm & Co-Mng Dir)

Subsidiary (Domestic):

Vardhman Special Steels Limited (2)
C-58 Focal Point, Ludhiana, 141 010, India
Tel.: (91) 1612670707
Web Site: https://www.vardhmansteel.com
Rev.: $212,666,507
Assets: $123,555,998
Liabilities: $46,556,537
Net Worth: $76,999,460
Earnings: $12,043,379
Emp.: 1,125
Fiscal Year-end: 03/31/2023
Alloy Steel Mfr
N.A.I.C.S.: 331110
Sachit Jain (Vice Chm & Mng Dir)

VARDHMAN INDUSTRIES LTD.

No 223 / G H 6 Meera Bagh, Paschim Vihar Paschim Vihar, New
Delhi, 110087, Delhi, India
Tel.: (91) 8048079342
Web Site: http://www.vardhman-industries.com
513534—(BOM)
Rev.: $10,695,848
Assets: $18,841,670
Liabilities: $19,683,643
Net Worth: ($841,973)
Earnings: ($921,345)
Emp.: 80
Fiscal Year-end: 03/31/19
Precision Steel Tube Mfr
N.A.I.C.S.: 331210
Rahul Jain (Mng Dir)

INTERNATIONAL PUBLIC

VARENGOLD BANK AG

Grosse Elbstrasse 39, 22767, Hamburg, Germany
Tel.: (49) 406686490
Web Site: https://www.varengold.de
Year Founded: 1995
VG8—(DEU)
Assets: $1,515,464,694
Liabilities: $1,446,278,976
Net Worth: $69,185,718
Earnings: $9,659,772
Emp.: 114
Fiscal Year-end: 12/31/22
Banking Services
N.A.I.C.S.: 523150
Bernhard Fuhrmann (Member-Mgmt Bd)

VARIA US PROPERTIES AG

Gubelstrasse 19, 6300, Zug, Switzerland
Tel.: (41) 225524030 CH
Web Site:
https://www.variausproperties.com
Year Founded: 2015
VARN—(SWX)
Rev.: $123,988,576
Assets: $1,366,868,902
Liabilities: $969,616,019
Net Worth: $397,252,883
Earnings: ($139,008,965)
Fiscal Year-end: 12/31/23
Offices of Real Estate Agents & Brokers
N.A.I.C.S.: 531210
Manuel Leuthold (Chm)

Subsidiaries:

PC Applewood LLC (1)
101 E New Hampshire Ave, Deland, FL 32724
Apartment Residential Building Services
N.A.I.C.S.: 531110

PC Avenue 8 Mesa LLC (1)
1050 W 8th Ave, Mesa, AZ 85210
Tel.: (480) 969-0839
Web Site: https://www.avenue8apts.com
Apartment Residential Building Services
N.A.I.C.S.: 531110

PC Devonshire Gardens LLC (1)
815 Erie Ave, Evansville, IN 47715
Tel.: (812) 624-7403
Web Site:
http://www.liveatdevonshiregardens.com
Apartment Residential Building Services
N.A.I.C.S.: 531110

PC Devonshire Place LLC (1)
1237 Devonshire Pl, Evansville, IN 47715
Tel.: (812) 465-2351
Web Site: http://www.devonshireplace-apartments.com
Apartment Residential Building Services
N.A.I.C.S.: 531110

PC Parkway Square LLC (1)
2855 Apalachee Pkwy, Tallahassee, FL 32301
Tel.: (850) 250-5737
Web Site:
http://www.liveatparkwaysquare.com
Apartment Residential Building Services
N.A.I.C.S.: 531110

PC Rolling Hills Louisville LLC (1)
9100 Rainbow Springs Ct, Louisville, KY 40241
Web Site:
http://www.rollinghillsapartmenthomes.com
Apartment Residential Building Services
N.A.I.C.S.: 531110

PC Tally Square LLC (1)
1112 S Magnolia Dr, Tallahassee, FL 32301
Tel.: (850) 250-4340
Web Site:
http://www.tallysquareapartments.com
Apartment Residential Building Services
N.A.I.C.S.: 531110

PC The Ridge on Spring Valley LLC (1)

5704 Spring Vly Rd, Dallas, TX 75254
Tel.: (972) 784-8095
Web Site:
https://www.ridgeonspringvalley.com
Apartment Residential Building Services
N.A.I.C.S.: 531110

PC Zona VillageTucson LLC (1)
2855 W Anklam Rd, Tucson, AZ 85745
Tel.: (520) 882-0363
Web Site: http://www.zonavillage.com
Apartment Residential Building Services
N.A.I.C.S.: 531110

Village at Mayfield LLC (1)
919 Aintree Park Dr, Mayfield Village, OH 44143
Tel.: (440) 568-5397
Web Site:
https://www.thevillageatmayfield.com
Apartment Residential Building Services
N.A.I.C.S.: 531110

VARIANT S.A.
Ul Czerwienskiego 3B, 31-319, Krakow, Poland
Tel.: (48) 12 636 99 44
Web Site: http://www.variant.pl
Automobile Parts Mfr
N.A.I.C.S.: 441330

VARIMAN GLOBAL ENTERPRISES LTD.
1-2-217/10/1 Street No 10 Lane No1 Near GHMC Muncipal Office, Domalguda Gagan Mahal, Hyderabad, 500029, India
Tel.: (91) 4066146198
Web Site:
https://www.varimanglobal.com
Year Founded: 1993
540570—(BOM)
Rev.: $14,396,787
Assets: $8,458,426
Liabilities: $4,741,574
Net Worth: $3,716,852
Earnings: $218,308
Emp.: 36
Fiscal Year-end: 03/31/23
Civil Engineering Services
N.A.I.C.S.: 541330
Dayata Sirish *(Mng Dir)*

Subsidiaries:

Straton Business Solutions Private Limited (1)
1-4-879/62 Bank Colony Gandhi Nagar, Hyderabad, 500 080, Telangana, India
Tel.: (91) 8096833300
Web Site: https://www.straton.co.in
Emp.: 50
Computer Equipment Whslr
N.A.I.C.S.: 423430

VARINDERA CONSTRUCTIONS LTD.
Plot no 65 Sector -18, Vill Sarhaul Opp, Gurugram, 122001, Haryana, India
Tel.: (91) 1244046363
Web Site: https://vclgroup.in
Emp.: 100
Real Estate Development & Construction Services
N.A.I.C.S.: 531390

Subsidiaries:

VA TECH WABAG Brno spol. s r.o. (1)
Zelezna 492/16, 619 00, Brno, Czech Republic
Tel.: (420) 545427711
Web Site: http://www.wabag.cz
Water Treatment Plant Construction Services
N.A.I.C.S.: 221310

VARIO SECURE, INC.
5F Sumitomo Corporation Nishikicho Building 1-6 Kanda Nishikicho, Chiyoda-ku, Tokyo, 101-0054, Japan
Tel.: (81) 357332090
Web Site:
https://www.variosecure.net
Year Founded: 2001
4494—(TKS)
Security Equipment Distr
N.A.I.C.S.: 459999
Yoshihiko Inami *(CEO)*

VARIOUS EATERIES PLC
20 St Thomas Street Runway East, London, SE1 9RS, United Kingdom UK
Web Site:
https://www.variouseateries.co.uk
Year Founded: 2014
VARE—(AIM)
Rev.: $55,214,399
Assets: $97,315,939
Liabilities: $72,947,580
Net Worth: $24,368,359
Earnings: ($9,795,950)
Emp.: 717
Fiscal Year-end: 10/02/22
Full-Service Restaurants
N.A.I.C.S.: 722511

Subsidiaries:

Coppa Club Limited (1)
3 Three Quays Walk Lower Thames Street, London, EC3R 6AH, United Kingdom
Tel.: (44) 2080169227
Web Site: https://www.coppaclub.co.uk
Restaurant Services
N.A.I.C.S.: 722511

VARIPERM (CANADA) LIMITED
7 3424 26th Street NE, Calgary, T1Y 4T7, AB, Canada
Tel.: (403) 250-7263
Web Site: http://www.variperm.com
Year Founded: 1969
Sales Range: $25-49.9 Million
Sand Control Products Mfr & Services
N.A.I.C.S.: 333132
James Nurcombe *(Pres)*

VARISCAN MINES LIMITED
Level 5/191 St Georges Terrace, Perth, 6000, WA, Australia
Tel.: (61) 893169100
Web Site:
https://www.variscan.com.au
VAR—(ASX)
Rev.: $7,036
Assets: $6,566,167
Liabilities: $340,292
Net Worth: $6,225,876
Earnings: ($434,212)
Fiscal Year-end: 06/30/24
Metal Mining & Exploration Services
N.A.I.C.S.: 212290
Stewart Dickson *(CEO & Mng Dir)*

VARNA PLOD AD
Street Academician Kurchatov 1, 9000, Varna, Bulgaria
Tel.: (359) 52747636
Web Site: https://www.varnaplod.bg
VPLD—(BUL)
Sales Range: Less than $1 Million
Commodity Exchange
N.A.I.C.S.: 523210
Andrei Nikolaev Vassilev *(CEO)*

VARNER-GRUPPEN AS
Nesoyveien 4, PO Box 124, Billingstad, 1376, Norway
Tel.: (47) 66773100
Web Site: http://www.varner.com
Sales Range: $1-4.9 Billion
Emp.: 12,000
Clothing Retailer
N.A.I.C.S.: 458110
Stein Marius Varner *(CEO)*

Subsidiaries:

Varner Polska Ltd. Sp.Z.o.o. (1)
Ul Okopowa St 58/72, 00-876, Warsaw, Poland
Tel.: (48) 225 314782
Clothing Retailer
N.A.I.C.S.: 458110

VARNOST FITEP A.D.
Gunduliceva 8-10, Zemun, 11080, Belgrade, Serbia
Tel.: (381) 11 2194 015
Web Site: http://www.varnost-fitep.rs
Year Founded: 1969
Sales Range: $1-9.9 Million
Emp.: 391
Physical Security Services
N.A.I.C.S.: 561612

VAROPAKORN PUBLIC CO., LTD.
181 Soi Amorn Nanglinchee Road Chongnonsri, Yanawa, Bangkok, 10120, Thailand
Tel.: (66) 22132514
Web Site:
https://www.varopakorn.com
Year Founded: 1979
VARO—(THA)
Rev.: $69,420,775
Assets: $57,725,044
Liabilities: $36,507,542
Net Worth: $21,217,502
Earnings: ($2,984,065)
Emp.: 90
Fiscal Year-end: 12/31/23
Aluminium Rolled Products Mfr
N.A.I.C.S.: 331221
Chaiyong Deephanphongs *(CEO)*

VAROVA BV
Maliebaan 27-1, 3581, Utrecht, Netherlands
Tel.: (31) 302305930
Investment Firm
N.A.I.C.S.: 523999

Subsidiaries:

Nordeon GmbH (1)
Rathenaustrasse 2-6, D-31832, Springe, Germany
Tel.: (49) 5041 750
Web Site: http://www.nordeon.com
Commercial & Industrial Lighting Equipment Mfr
N.A.I.C.S.: 335132

Vulkan Benelux BV (1)
Van Coulsterweg 3, 2952 CB, Alblasserdam, Netherlands
Tel.: (31) 786810780
Web Site: http://www.vulkan.com
Industrial Machinery & Equipment Distr
N.A.I.C.S.: 423830
Robert van Riemsdijk *(Mng Dir)*

VARROC ENGINEERING LTD.
L4 MIDCIndustrial Area Waluj Aurangabad, 431 136, Mumbai, 431 136, Maharashtra, India
Tel.: (91) 6653700
Web Site: https://www.varroc.com
541578—(BOM)
Rev.: $829,800,012
Assets: $554,031,773
Liabilities: $433,637,072
Net Worth: $120,394,701
Earnings: ($97,970,745)
Emp.: 3,669
Fiscal Year-end: 03/31/23
Automobile Equipment Mfr
N.A.I.C.S.: 336110
Naresh Chandra *(Chm)*

Subsidiaries:

Team Concepts Private Limited (1)
1A/07 East End Main Road Jayanagar 4th T Block 2nd Floor, Bengaluru, 560 041, Karnataka, India
Tel.: (91) 8026637922
Web Site: http://www.hikerindia.com
Automobile Parts Mfr
N.A.I.C.S.: 336390

Varroc Lighting Systems (India) Private Limited (1)
Survey No 279 Mann Hinjewadi, Taluka Mulshi, Pune, 411 057, India
Tel.: (91) 2066752100
Automobile Parts Distr
N.A.I.C.S.: 423120
Nagnath Todkari *(Project Mgr)*

Varroc Lighting Systems Bulgaria EOOD (1)
139 Haskovska str, village of Krepost PK municipality of Dimitrovgrad, 6410, Dimitrovgrad, Bulgaria
Tel.: (359) 38536080
Automobile Parts Distr
N.A.I.C.S.: 423120

Varroc Lighting Systems GmbH (1)
Toyota-Allee 7 Koln-Marsdorf, 50858, Cologne, Germany
Tel.: (49) 22349594333
Automobile Parts Distr
N.A.I.C.S.: 423120

Varroc Lighting Systems Inc. (1)
47828 Halyard Dr, Plymouth, MI 48170
Tel.: (734) 446-4400
Automobile Parts Distr
N.A.I.C.S.: 423120
Gary Tamer *(Sr Mgr-Engrg)*

Varroc Lighting Systems S de R.L. de C.V. (1)
Av Parque Industrial Monterrey 608, Apodaca, Nuevo Leon, Mexico
Tel.: (52) 8183692200
Automobile Parts Distr
N.A.I.C.S.: 423120

Varroc Lighting Systems SRO (1)
Suvorovova 195, Senov u Noveho Jicina, 742 42, Ostrava, Czech Republic
Tel.: (420) 556623111
Automobile Parts Distr
N.A.I.C.S.: 423120

Varroc Lighting Systems, Italy S.p.A. (1)
Via dei Prati 20, Cambiano, 10020, Turin, Italy
Tel.: (39) 0119457159
Automobile Parts Distr
N.A.I.C.S.: 423120

Varroc Polymers Private Limited (1)
Gut No 99 Village-Pharola, Paithan, Aurangabad, 431 105, Maharashtra, India
Tel.: (91) 9673001480
Automobile Parts Mfr
N.A.I.C.S.: 336390

VARSAV GAME STUDIOS SA
ul Aleje Jerozolimskie 123a, 02-017, Warsaw, Poland
Tel.: (48) 221004629
Web Site: https://www.varsav.com
Year Founded: 2016
Software Development Services
N.A.I.C.S.: 541511
Konrad Mroczek *(CEO)*

VARSHNEY CAPITAL CORP.
Suite 2050-1055 West Georgia St, PO Box 11121, 1055 West Georgia Street, Vancouver, V6E 3P3, BC, Canada
Tel.: (604) 684-2181 BC
Web Site:
https://www.varshneycapital.com
Sales Range: $10-24.9 Million
Emp.: 15
Merchant Banking, Venture Capital & Investment Advisory Services
N.A.I.C.S.: 523999
Hari B. Varshney *(Founder & Partner)*

Subsidiaries:

BetterU Education Corp. (1)
171 Slater Street 2nd Floor, Ottawa, K1P

VARSHNEY CAPITAL CORP.

Varshney Capital Corp.—(Continued)
5H7, ON, Canada
Tel.: (613) 695-4100
Web Site: http://readytogo.betteru.ca
Rev.: $1,295
Assets: $33,309
Liabilities: $4,444,941
Net Worth: ($4,411,632)
Earnings: ($2,090,415)
Fiscal Year-end: 03/31/2020
Online Education
N.A.I.C.S.: 923110
Jason Burke *(CFO)*

VARSITY TENTS INC
Downsview Park 40 Carl Hall Rd Box 5, Toronto, M3K 2C1, ON, Canada
Tel.: (416) 410-7370
Web Site:
  http://www.varsitytents.com
Year Founded: 1988
Rev.: $27,900,000
Emp.: 40
Tent Rental Services
N.A.I.C.S.: 532289
Graham Bauckham *(Pres & Gen Mgr)*

VARSTEEL LTD.
330-220 4th Street South, Lethbridge, T1J 4J7, AB, Canada
Tel.: (403) 320-1953
Web Site: http://www.varsteel.ca
Year Founded: 1953
Sales Range: $125-149.9 Million
Structural Steel Mfr
N.A.I.C.S.: 331210
Dave Hasley *(Mgr-HR)*

Subsidiaries:

Makin Metals Ltd. (1)
19433 96th Ave, Surrey, V4N 4C4, BC, Canada
Tel.: (604) 882-9344
Web Site: http://www.makinmetals.ca
Sales Range: $10-24.9 Million
Flat Rolled Sheet Products Mfr & Distr
N.A.I.C.S.: 332322
Gerald W. Varzari *(Pres & CEO)*

VARTEKS D.D.
Zagrebacka 94, 42000, Varazdin, Croatia
Tel.: (385) 42 377 105
Web Site: http://www.varteks.com
Year Founded: 1918
Sales Range: $25-49.9 Million
Emp.: 1,950
Apparel Product Mfr & Whslr
N.A.I.C.S.: 314999
Zoran Koscec *(Chm-Mgmt Bd & CEO)*

VARUN MERCANTILE LIMITED
147 14th Floor Atlanta Nariman Point, Mumbai, 400 021, India
Tel.: (91) 2222800131 In
Web Site: https://www.vml.org.in
512511—(BOM)
Rev.: $31,173
Assets: $619,879
Liabilities: $995
Net Worth: $618,884
Earnings: $8,489
Fiscal Year-end: 03/31/23
Household Product Whslr
N.A.I.C.S.: 423620
Forum J. Shah *(Sec)*

VARUN SHIPPING COMPANY LIMITED
Laxmi Building 6 Shoorji Vallabhdas Marg, Ballard Estate, Mumbai, 400001, India
Tel.: (91) 2266350100
Web Site: http://www.varunship.com
Sales Range: $25-49.9 Million
Shipping Services
N.A.I.C.S.: 488510

Yudhishthir D. Khatau *(Chm & Mng Dir)*

Subsidiaries:

VSC International Pte Ltd (1)
6 Shenton Way, #21-13 DBS Building Tower 2, 068809, Singapore, Singapore
Tel.: (65) 62211290
Web Site: http://www.varunship.com
Sales Range: $25-49.9 Million
Emp.: 2
Shipping Services
N.A.I.C.S.: 488320

VARVARESSOS S.A.
D D Stenimaxou, PO Box 16, Stenimachos, 592 00, Naousa, Greece
Tel.: (30) 2332052650
Web Site:
  https://www.varvaressos.eu
Year Founded: 1974
VARNH—(ATH)
Sales Range: Less than $1 Million
Emp.: 220
Fiber & Cotton Yarn Mfr
N.A.I.C.S.: 313110
Popee Serafim *(Mgr-HR)*

VAS INFRASTRUCTURE LIMITED
Jwala Estate Soniwadi S V Road Borivali W, Mumbai, 400092, India
Tel.: (91) 4843100900
Web Site:
  https://www.vasinfrastructureltd.com
Year Founded: 1994
531574—(BOM)
Rev.: $81,258
Assets: $20,538,732
Liabilities: $34,513,465
Net Worth: ($13,974,733)
Earnings: ($4,806,342)
Emp.: 4
Fiscal Year-end: 03/31/21
Real Estate Development Services
N.A.I.C.S.: 531390
H. K. Bijlani *(Compliance Officer & Compliance Officer)*

VASA RETAIL & OVERSEAS LTD.
23 Floor-5 Plot-76 Prabhat Bhulabhai Desai Road Cumballa Hill, Wadala Truck Terminal Wadala (E), Mumbai, 400026, India
Tel.: (91) 9324540058
Web Site: https://www.vasagroup.com
Year Founded: 2017
VASA—(NSE)
Assets: $698,975
Liabilities: $2,797,758
Net Worth: ($2,098,783)
Earnings: ($1,502,848)
Emp.: 2
Fiscal Year-end: 03/31/23
Stationery Product Mfr
N.A.I.C.S.: 322230
Priyansh Shah *(CFO)*

VASCON ENGINEERS LIMITED
Vascon Weikfield Chambers Behind Hotel Novotel Opposite Hyatt Hotel, Pune Nagar Road, Pune, 411 014, India
Tel.: (91) 2030562100
Web Site: https://www.vascon.com
Year Founded: 1986
533156—(BOM)
Rev.: $70,731,884
Assets: $180,175,441
Liabilities: $83,375,101
Net Worth: $96,800,340
Earnings: ($5,498,452)
Emp.: 632
Fiscal Year-end: 03/31/21
Engineering & Construction Services
N.A.I.C.S.: 237990

D. Santhanam *(CFO)*

VASCULAR BIOGENICS LTD.
8 HaSatat St, Modi'in-Maccabim-Re'ut, 7178106, Israel
Tel.: (972) 36346450
Web Site: https://www.vblrx.com
Year Founded: 2000
NTBL—(NASDAQ)
Rev.: $310,000
Assets: $19,541,000
Liabilities: $4,427,000
Net Worth: $15,114,000
Earnings: ($11,264,000)
Emp.: 16
Fiscal Year-end: 12/31/23
Biopharmaceutical Mfr
N.A.I.C.S.: 325412
Dror Harats *(Founder & CEO)*

VASHU BHAGNANI INDUSTRIES LIMITED
Pooja House 1st Floor CTS No 892-893 Juhu Tara Road, Opp J W Marriott Hotel Juhu, Mumbai, 400049, Maharashtra, India
Tel.: (91) 2226121613
Web Site:
  http://www.poojaentertainment.in
532011—(BOM)
Rev.: $5,590,432
Assets: $14,639,662
Liabilities: $9,555,854
Net Worth: $5,083,808
Earnings: $343,816
Emp.: 7
Fiscal Year-end: 03/31/23
Entertainment Related Services
N.A.I.C.S.: 512110
Puja Bhagnani *(Mng Dir)*

VASSALLO BUILDERS GROUP LIMITED
The Three Arches Valletta Road, Mosta, MST 9016, Malta
Tel.: (356) 21432333
Web Site:
  http://www.vassallogroupmalta.com
Year Founded: 1946
Sales Range: $150-199.9 Million
Emp.: 375
Building Construction, Civil Engineering, Property Management, Elderly Care & Hotel Management
N.A.I.C.S.: 236220
Nazzareno Vassallo *(Chm)*

Subsidiaries:

CareMalta Finance plc. (1)
St Dominic's Square, Rabat, RBT 06, Malta
Tel.: (356) 2143 4342
Venture Capital Services
N.A.I.C.S.: 523910

Makeezi Ltd. (1)
6PM Business Centre Triq it-Torri Swatar, Birkirkara, BKR 4012, Malta
Tel.: (356) 5622584951
Web Site: http://www.makeezi.com
Emp.: 3
Real Estate Manangement Services
N.A.I.C.S.: 531390
Edward Camielleri *(Gen Mgr)*

Vassallo Builders International DOO (1)
Dubrovacka ulica 14, Split, Croatia
Tel.: (385) 21 534 160
Real Estate Manangement Services
N.A.I.C.S.: 531390

Vassallo Builders Ltd. (1)
The Three Arches Valletta Road, Mosta, Malta
Tel.: (356) 21432333
Real Estate Manangement Services
N.A.I.C.S.: 531390

VASSILICO CEMENT WORKS PUBLIC COMPANY LTD

INTERNATIONAL PUBLIC

1A Kyriakos Matsis Avenue, PO Box 22281, CY-1519, Nicosia, Cyprus
Tel.: (357) 22458100
Web Site: https://www.vassiliko.com
Year Founded: 1963
VCW—(CYP)
Rev.: $153,961,796
Assets: $325,382,042
Liabilities: $57,157,349
Net Worth: $268,224,692
Earnings: $13,854,954
Emp.: 231
Fiscal Year-end: 12/31/22
Cement Whslr
N.A.I.C.S.: 423320
Antonios A. Antoniou *(Chm)*

VAST RESOURCES PLC
Nettlestead Place, Nettlestead, Maidstone, ME18 5HA, Kent, United Kingdom
Tel.: (44) 2078460974
Web Site: https://www.vastplc.com
VAST—(AIM)
Rev.: $3,720,000
Assets: $23,590,000
Liabilities: $21,050,000
Net Worth: $2,540,000
Earnings: ($10,510,000)
Fiscal Year-end: 04/30/23
Mineral Mining Services
N.A.I.C.S.: 212390
Roy Clifford Tucker *(Exec Dir)*

VASTA PLATFORM LIMITED
Av Paulista 901 5th Floor, Bela Vista, Sao Paulo, 01310-100, Brazil
Tel.: (55) 1131337311 Ky
Web Site:
  https://www.vastaedu.com.br
Year Founded: 2019
VSTA—(NASDAQ)
Rev.: $243,057,830
Assets: $1,445,833,620
Liabilities: $555,777,832
Net Worth: $890,055,788
Earnings: ($10,491,659)
Emp.: 1,926
Fiscal Year-end: 12/31/22
Holding Company
N.A.I.C.S.: 551112
Rodrigo Calvo Galindo *(Chm)*

VASTNED EMLAK YATIRIM VE INSAAT TICARET A.S.
Ust Zeren Sk NO 28 1 Levent, Besiktas, Istanbul, Turkiye
Tel.: (90) 2122704192
Real Estate Investment Services
N.A.I.C.S.: 531210

VASTNED RETAIL N.V.
Mercuriusplein 11, 2132 HA, Hoofddorp, Netherlands
Tel.: (31) 202424300 Nl
Web Site: https://www.vastned.com
Year Founded: 1986
VASTN—(EUR)
Rev.: $79,631,306
Assets: $1,544,051,220
Liabilities: $721,792,692
Net Worth: $822,258,528
Earnings: ($16,794,348)
Emp.: 25
Fiscal Year-end: 12/31/23
Real Estate Investment Trust
N.A.I.C.S.: 525990
Reinier Walta *(CEO-Interim, Mng Dir, CFO-Interim & Member-Exec Bd)*

Subsidiaries:

Plaisimmo S.A.R.L. (1)
718 Avenue Jean Jaures, 59790, Ronchin, France
Tel.: (33) 320908333
Real Estate Manangement Services

AND PRIVATE COMPANIES

VATIKA GROUP

N.A.I.C.S.: 531210

Vastned Management B.V. (1)
Mercuriusplein 11, 2132 HA, Hoofddorp, Netherlands
Tel.: (31) 102424300
Web Site: http://www.vastned.com
Real Estate Investment Management Services
N.A.I.C.S.: 531390
T. Degroot *(CEO)*

Vastned Retail Belgium NV (1)
Uitbreidingstraat 18, 2600, Berchem, Belgium
Tel.: (32) 3 287 67 81
Real Estate Investment Services
N.A.I.C.S.: 531210

VASTRA HAMNEN CORPORATE FINANCE AB
Stortorget 13 A, 211 22, Malmo, Sweden
Tel.: (46) 40200250
Web Site: https://www.vhcorp.se
Year Founded: 2005
NP8—(DEU)
Investment Management Service
N.A.I.C.S.: 523999
Bjorn Andersson *(CFO)*

VASUDHAGAMA ENTERPRISES LIMITED
G-04 Newyork Corner Building behind Kiran Motors, S G Highway Bodakdev, Ahmedabad, 380 054, India
Tel.: (91) 8149030844
Web Site:
 https://www.vasudhagama.com
Year Founded: 1989
539291—(BOM)
Rev.: $24
Assets: $774,510
Liabilities: $27,336
Net Worth: $747,173
Earnings: ($8,800)
Emp.: 3
Fiscal Year-end: 03/31/23
Commodity Trading Services
N.A.I.C.S.: 523160
Jayeshkumar Kantilal Patel *(Chm & Mng Dir)*

VASUNDHARA RASAYANS LIMITED
Shed No 42 Phase II IDA Mallapur, Hyderabad, 500 076, Andhra Pradesh, India
Tel.: (91) 4023437617
Web Site: https://www.vrlindia.in
Year Founded: 1990
538634—(BOM)
Rev.: $4,824,507
Assets: $4,138,853
Liabilities: $923,398
Net Worth: $3,215,455
Earnings: $670,344
Emp.: 37
Fiscal Year-end: 03/31/23
Pharmaceutical Preparation Mfr & Distr
N.A.I.C.S.: 325412
Rajesh Pokerna *(Mng Dir)*

VASWANI INDUSTRIES LIMITED
Phase - II Bahesar Road Siltara, Raipur, Chhattisgarh, India
Tel.: (91) 7713540202
Web Site:
 https://www.vaswaniindustries.com
Year Founded: 2003
VASWANI—(NSE)
Rev.: $42,970,611
Assets: $26,824,324
Liabilities: $12,851,760
Net Worth: $13,972,564

Earnings: $554,438
Emp.: 188
Fiscal Year-end: 03/31/21
Metal Products Mfr
N.A.I.C.S.: 332999
Ravi Vaswani *(Chm & Mng Dir)*

VAT GROUP AG
Seelistrasse 1, Haag, 9469, Sennwald, Switzerland
Tel.: (41) 817716161   CH
Web Site: https://www.vatvalve.com
Year Founded: 1965
VACN—(SWX)
Rev.: $1,269,932,373
Assets: $1,413,288,248
Liabilities: $548,188,470
Net Worth: $865,099,778
Earnings: $340,109,756
Emp.: 2,991
Fiscal Year-end: 12/31/22
Vacuum Valve Mfr & Distr
N.A.I.C.S.: 332911
Martin Komischke *(Chm)*

Subsidiaries:

VAT Deutschland GmbH (1)
Zur Wetterwarte 50 Haus 337/G, 01109, Dresden, Germany
Tel.: (49) 35150193400
Vacuum Valve Mfr
N.A.I.C.S.: 332919
Rainer Handke *(Sls Mgr-Area)*

VAT Korea Ltd. (1)
55-16 Mogok-gil, Pyeongtaek, 17747, Gyeonggi-do, Korea (South)
Tel.: (82) 316626856
Vacuum Valve Mfr
N.A.I.C.S.: 332919
Brian Jeon *(Gen Mgr)*

VAT Ltd. (1)
1f MFIP Haneda 10-11 Hanedaasahicho, Ota-ku, Tokyo, 144-0042, Japan
Tel.: (81) 366292121
Vacuum Valve Mfr
N.A.I.C.S.: 332919

VAT Romania S.R.L. (1)
Str I Nr 9, West Industrial Area, 310375, Arad, Romania
Tel.: (40) 257216911
Vacuum Valve Mfr
N.A.I.C.S.: 332919
Corneliu Ioan Gligor *(Gen Mgr)*

VAT SARL (1)
26 Avenue Jean Kuntzmann, 38330, Montbonnot-Saint-Martin, France
Tel.: (33) 456607395
Vacuum Valve Mfr
N.A.I.C.S.: 332919

VAT Singapore Pte. Ltd. (1)
2 Ang Mo Kio Street 64 01-01B, Econ Industrial Building, Singapore, 569084, Singapore
Tel.: (65) 62525121
Vacuum Valve Mfr
N.A.I.C.S.: 332919

VAT Taiwan Co. Ltd. (1)
10F No 6 Taiyuan 2nd St Zhubei City, Hsinchu, 302082, Taiwan
Tel.: (886) 35169088
Vacuum Valve Mfr
N.A.I.C.S.: 332919
Michael Young *(Gen Mgr)*

VAT Vacuum Products Ltd. (1)
Edmund House Rugby Road, Leamington Spa, CV32 6EL, Warwickshire, United Kingdom
Tel.: (44) 1926452753
Vacuum Valve Mfr
N.A.I.C.S.: 332919
John Dunbar *(Acct Mgr)*

VAT Vacuum Valves Shanghai Company Ltd. (1)
615 Ningqiao Rd Building 4 1st Floor, Pudong New District, Shanghai, 201206, China
Tel.: (86) 2150326658
Vacuum Valve Mfr

N.A.I.C.S.: 332919
Jerry Zhang *(Sls Mgr-South)*

VAT Vakuumventile AG (1)
Seelistrasse 1 Haag, 9469, Sennwald, Switzerland
Tel.: (41) 817716161
Vacuum Valve Mfr
N.A.I.C.S.: 332919

VATECH CO., LTD.
13 Samsung 1-ro 2-gil, Hwaseong, 18449, Gyeonggi, Korea (South)
Tel.: (82) 316792000
Web Site: https://www.vatech.co.kr
Year Founded: 1992
043150—(KRS)
Rev.: $303,007,948
Assets: $392,024,525
Liabilities: $113,271,044
Net Worth: $278,753,482
Earnings: $58,974,946
Emp.: 279
Fiscal Year-end: 12/31/22
Digital X-Ray Machine Mfr
N.A.I.C.S.: 334517
Kim Sunbum *(CEO)*

Subsidiaries:

Ewoosoft Co., Ltd. (1)
13 Samsung 1-ro 2-gil, Hwaseong, 18449, Gyeonggi-do, Korea (South)
Tel.: (82) 3180156164
Web Site: https://www.ewoosoft.com
Clinical Equipment Mfr
N.A.I.C.S.: 339112

LLC Vatech Corp. (1)
Nauchny pr-d 17 entrance 2, 117246, Moscow, Russia
Tel.: (7) 4959679044
Web Site: http://www.vatechrussia.com
Clinical Equipment Mfr
N.A.I.C.S.: 339112

Vatech America Inc. (1)
2200 Fletcher Ave Ste 705A, Fort Lee, NJ 07024
Tel.: (201) 210-5028
Web Site: http://www.vatechamerica.com
Clinical Equipment Mfr
N.A.I.C.S.: 339112
Brian Hwang *(Pres)*

Vatech Brasil Ltda. (1)
Rua Aureliano Guimaraes 172 - Conjunto 1010, Vila Andrade, Sao Paulo, 05727-160, Brazil
Tel.: (55) 1123657154
Web Site: https://www.vatechbrasil.com.br
Clinical Equipment Mfr
N.A.I.C.S.: 339112

Vatech China Co., Ltd. (1)
E-3 No 1618 Yishan Rd Caohejing Development Zone, Minhang Dist, Shanghai, 201103, China
Tel.: (86) 2161450398
Web Site: https://www.vatech-china.com
Clinical Equipment Mfr
N.A.I.C.S.: 339112

Vatech Dental Manufacturing Ltd. (1)
Chancery house St Nicholas way, Sutton, SM1 1JB, United Kingdom
Tel.: (44) 2086521900
Web Site: https://www.vatech.uk.com
Clinical Equipment Mfr
N.A.I.C.S.: 339112

Vatech France Co., Ltd. (1)
4/6 Allee Kepler, Champs sur Marne, 60528, Torcy, France
Tel.: (33) 164114330
Web Site: http://www.vatech-france.fr
Clinical Equipment Mfr
N.A.I.C.S.: 339112

Vatech Global (HK) Ltd. (1)
23/F 8 Commercial Tower 8 Sun Yip Street, Chai Wan, China (Hong Kong)
Tel.: (852) 54098552
Clinical Equipment Mfr
N.A.I.C.S.: 339112

Vatech Global Asia HQ Sdn. Bhd. (1)
41-2 Block D Jalan SS7/26, Zenith Corporate Park, 47301, Petaling Jaya, Selangor, Malaysia
Tel.: (60) 378876901
Web Site: https://vatechmalaysia.com
Clinical Equipment Mfr
N.A.I.C.S.: 339112
Kenneth Sow *(VP)*

Vatech Global Mexico S de RL de CV. (1)
Paseo de la Reforma 389 floor 16 Col, Cuauhtemoc Delegation, 06500, Cuauhtemoc, Mexico
Tel.: (52) 5565852395
Clinical Equipment Mfr
N.A.I.C.S.: 339112

Vatech India Pvt. Ltd. (1)
1016/2 2nd Floor S M Plaza Opp CISF Complex Mahipalpur Bypass, Mahipalpur, New Delhi, 110037, India
Tel.: (91) 9599812206
Web Site: https://www.vatechindia.in
Clinical Equipment Mfr
N.A.I.C.S.: 339112
George Shin *(Pres)*

Vatech Medical Pty. Ltd. (1)
Suite 5 04 Gateway Business Park 63 79 Parramatta Road, Silverwater, 2128, NSW, Australia
Tel.: (61) 296444866
Clinical Equipment Mfr
N.A.I.C.S.: 339112

Vatech Spain S.L. (1)
Volta Dels Garrofers 63, Vilassar de Mar, 08340, Barcelona, Spain
Tel.: (34) 937542620
Web Site: http://www.vatech.es
Clinical Equipment Mfr
N.A.I.C.S.: 339112

Vatech Vietnam Co., Ltd. (1)
Floor 4 TTC Building 19 Duy Tam Street, Dich Vong Hau Ward Cau Giay District, Hanoi, Vietnam
Tel.: (84) 2432262932
Clinical Equipment Mfr
N.A.I.C.S.: 339112

Woorien Co., Ltd. (1)
13 Samsung 1-ro 2-gil, Hwaseong, 18449, Gyeonggi-do, Korea (South)
Tel.: (82) 313238628
Web Site: https://www.woorien.com
Clinical Equipment Mfr
N.A.I.C.S.: 339112

VATIC VENTURES CORP.
1400 - 1040 West Georgia Street, Vancouver, V6E 4H1, BC, Canada
Tel.: (604) 757-9792
Web Site:
 https://www.vaticventures.com
V8V—(DEU)
Assets: $1,861,594
Liabilities: $331,738
Net Worth: $1,529,856
Earnings: ($962,154)
Fiscal Year-end: 02/28/23
Metal Mining Exploration Service
N.A.I.C.S.: 213114
Loren Currie *(CEO)*

Subsidiaries:

VV Mining Mexico S de R.L. de C.V. (1)

VATIKA GROUP
Vatika Triangle 7th Floor Sushant Lok-1 Block-A, Mehrauli-Gurgaon Road, Gurgaon, 122022, Haryana, India
Tel.: (91) 1244177777
Web Site: http://www.vatikagroup.com
Sales Range: $150-199.9 Million
Emp.: 300
Commercial, Residential & Industrial Real Estate

VATIKA GROUP

Vatika Group—(Continued)
N.A.I.C.S.: 531390
Anil Bhalla (Chm)

VATROSERVIS A.D.
Jovana Cvijica 7, Novi Sad, 21000, Serbia
Tel.: (381) 21 442 580
Web Site: http://www.vatroservis.co.rs
Year Founded: 1993
Sales Range: Less than $1 Million
Safety & Fire Protection Services
N.A.I.C.S.: 541618

VATROSPREM AD
Slobodana Jovica 3, Belgrade, Serbia
Tel.: (381) 113989227
Web Site: http://www.vatrosprem.rs
VTRS—(BEL)
Sales Range: Less than $1 Million
Fire Protection Services
N.A.I.C.S.: 115310

VATS LIQUOR CHAIN STORE MANAGEMENT JOINT STOCK CO., LTD.
5th Floor Jiahe Guoxin Building No 15 Baiqiao Street, Dongcheng District, Beijing, 100062, China
Tel.: (86) 1056969898
Web Site: https://www.vatsliquor.com
Year Founded: 2005
300755—(CHIN)
Rev.: $1,425,547,540
Assets: $1,021,372,057
Liabilities: $471,732,369
Net Worth: $549,639,687
Earnings: $33,137,934
Fiscal Year-end: 12/31/23
Liquor Store Operator
N.A.I.C.S.: 424820
Wu Xiangdong (Chm)

VATTENFALL AB
Evenemangsgatan 13C, SE-169 56, Solna, Sweden
Tel.: (46) 87395000   SE
Web Site: http://www.vattenfall.com
Year Founded: 1909
Rev.: $17,828,801,200
Assets: $48,310,092,600
Liabilities: $36,679,789,860
Net Worth: $11,630,302,740
Earnings: $1,411,750,410
Emp.: 19,815
Fiscal Year-end: 12/31/19
Electricity & Heat Production, Transmission & Distribution Services
N.A.I.C.S.: 221122
Karl Bergman (Head-R&D)

Subsidiaries:

Barseback Kraft AB (1)
PO Box 524, 246 25, Loddekopinge, Sweden
Tel.: (46) 771765765
Web Site: http://www.uniper.energy
Eletric Power Generation Services
N.A.I.C.S.: 221118

Boras Elhandel AB (1)
Vasterlangatan 6, 501 13, Boras, Sweden
Tel.: (46) 33206700
Web Site: http://www.boraselhandel.se
Electric Power Distribution Services
N.A.I.C.S.: 221122

Eclipse Energy UK Plc (1)
The Crewyards Cringle Road Stoke Rochford, Grantham, NG33 5EF, United Kingdom
Tel.: (44) 1476 530983
Eletric Power Generation Services
N.A.I.C.S.: 221118

Feenstra Isolatie B.V. (1)
Transportweg 33 Veendam, Groningen, 9645 KZ, Netherlands
Tel.: (31) 598666717
Electric Power Generation Services
N.A.I.C.S.: 221118

Feenstra N.V. (1)
Schepenbergweg 29, 1105 AS, Amsterdam, Netherlands
Tel.: (31) 888455000
Air Conditioning System Installation Services
N.A.I.C.S.: 238220

Forsmarks Kraftgrupp AB (1)
Forsmarks Kraftgrupp, 74203, Osthammar, Sweden (66%)
Tel.: (46) 17381268
Web Site: http://www.forsmark.com
Sales Range: $1-4.9 Billion
Emp.: 2,500
Nuclear Power Plant & Distr
N.A.I.C.S.: 221113

Gotlands Energi AB (1)
Tornekvior 4A, 621 43, Visby, Sweden
Tel.: (46) 498285000
Web Site: http://www.gotlandsenergi.se
Emp.: 142
Electric Power Distribution Services
N.A.I.C.S.: 221122

Subsidiary (Domestic):

Gotlands Energiverk AB (2)
Storgatan 95, Slite, 60230, Sweden (75%)
Tel.: (46) 0498285000
Web Site: http://www.gotlandsenergi.se
Sales Range: $150-199.9 Million
Emp.: 150
Electric Power Distr
N.A.I.C.S.: 221122

N.V. Nuon Energy (1)
Spaklerweg 20, 1096 BA, Amsterdam, Netherlands (49%)
Tel.: (31) 880980000
Web Site: http://www.nuon.com
Sales Range: $1-4.9 Billion
Emp.: 6,000
Energy Production & Supply Services
N.A.I.C.S.: 221112
Oystein Loseth (Chm-Supervisory Bd)

Subsidiary (Domestic):

N.V. Nuon Business (2)
Spaklerweg 20, 1096 BA, Amsterdam, Netherlands
Tel.: (31) 205972000
Web Site: http://www.nuon.com
Business Support Services
N.A.I.C.S.: 561499

Subsidiary (Domestic):

De Kleef B.V. (3)
Westervoortsedijk 73, 6827 AV, Arnhem, Netherlands
Tel.: (31) 263665367
Web Site: http://www.dken.nl
Sales Range: $75-99.9 Million
Emp.: 20
Electric Power Services
N.A.I.C.S.: 221122

Ingenieursbureau Ebatech B.V. (3)
Spaklerweg 20, 1096 BA, Amsterdam, Netherlands
Tel.: (31) 205971597
Web Site: http://www.ebatech.nl
Sales Range: $10-24.9 Million
Emp.: 50
Sustainable Energy & Facility Solutions & Services
N.A.I.C.S.: 561790

Subsidiary (Non-US):

Nuon Energie und Service GmbH (2)
Boos-Fremery-Strasse 62, 52525, Heinsberg, Germany
Tel.: (49) 245 2152440
Web Site: http://www.bizzpark-oberbruch.de
Emp.: 65
Park Operator
N.A.I.C.S.: 713110
Ivo R. Verdonkschot (CEO)

Subsidiary (Domestic):

Nuon Epe Gas Service B.V. (2)
Spaklerweg 20, 1096 BA, Amsterdam, Netherlands
Tel.: (31) 205972729
Web Site: http://www.nuon.com
Gas Utility Services
N.A.I.C.S.: 221210
Oystein Loseth (CEO)

Nuon Power Generation B.V. (2)
Atoomweg 7-9, 3542 AA, Utrecht, Netherlands
Tel.: (31) 302472234
Web Site: http://www.nuon.com
Sales Range: $100-124.9 Million
Emp.: 200
Electric Power Generation
N.A.I.C.S.: 221122

Nuon Retail B.V. (2)
Spaklerweg 20, 1096 BA, Amsterdam, Netherlands
Tel.: (31) 205971111
Sales Range: $100-124.9 Million
Emp.: 200
Electricity Distribution Services
N.A.I.C.S.: 221122

Subsidiary (Domestic):

Nuon Retail Beveiliging Service B.V. (3)
Lichtenhorststraat 17, 6942 GS, Didam, Netherlands
Tel.: (31) 316226800
Sales Range: $25-49.9 Million
Emp.: 100
Business Support Services
N.A.I.C.S.: 561499
P. Orsel (Mgr-Fin)

Nuon Retail Installatie Service B.V. (3)
Spaklerweg 20, 1096 BA, Amsterdam, Netherlands
Tel.: (31) 268450271
Retail Gas & Electric System Installation Services
N.A.I.C.S.: 237130

Subsidiary (Domestic):

Feenstra Verwarming B.V. (4)
Steenstraat 1, 8211 AG, Lelystad, Netherlands
Tel.: (31) 32023 2380
Sales Range: $300-349.9 Million
Emp.: 1,381
Plumbing, Heating & Air Conditioning Contractors
N.A.I.C.S.: 238220

Subsidiary (Domestic):

n.v. Nuon Customer Care Center (3)
Groningensingel 1, 6835 EA, Arnhem, Netherlands
Tel.: (31) 26324 3111
Electric Power Services
N.A.I.C.S.: 221122

Subsidiary (Domestic):

Nuon Storage B.V. (3)
PO Box 41920, 1009 DC, Amsterdam, Netherlands
Tel.: (31) 651 5947273
Natural Gas Distribution Services
N.A.I.C.S.: 221210

Nuon Zuidwending B.V. (2)
Spaklerweg 20, 1096 BA, Amsterdam, Netherlands
Tel.: (31) 205972000
Web Site: http://www.nuon.com
Sales Range: $200-249.9 Million
Emp.: 550
Pipeline Operator
N.A.I.C.S.: 486910

n.v. Nuon Energy Sourcing (2)
Spaklerweg 20, 1009 DC, Amsterdam, Netherlands
Tel.: (31) 205627418
Web Site: http://www.nuon.nl
Sales Range: $125-149.9 Million
Emp.: 276
Utility Services
N.A.I.C.S.: 926130

Subsidiary (Domestic):

N.V. Nuon Duurzame Energie (3)

INTERNATIONAL PUBLIC

Spaklerweg 20, 1096 BA, Amsterdam, Netherlands
Tel.: (31) 205972000
Web Site: http://www.nuon.com
Electric Power Services
N.A.I.C.S.: 221122

Nuon International Renewables Projects B.V. (3)
Utrechtseweg 68, 6812 AH, Arnhem, Netherlands
Tel.: (31) 268442442
Web Site: http://www.nuon.com
Energy Generation Projects
N.A.I.C.S.: 221118
Oystein Loseth (Dir)

Ringhals AB (1)
Evenemangsgatan 13C, 169 56, Solna, Sweden (75%)
Tel.: (46) 87395000
Web Site: http://www.group.vattenfall.com
Sales Range: $1-4.9 Billion
Emp.: 1,500
Nuclear Power Plant & Electric Power Distr
N.A.I.C.S.: 221122
Olof Froberg (CFO)

Svensk Karnbranslehantering AB (1)
Evenemangsgatan 13, 169 79, Solna, Sweden
Tel.: (46) 845 98400
Web Site: http://www.skb.se
Emp.: 500
Waste Management Services
N.A.I.C.S.: 562998
Johan Svenningsson (Vice Chm)

Vasterbergslagens Elnat AB (1)
Svetsaredagen 4, S 771 28, Ludvika, Sweden (100%)
Tel.: (46) 2408762000
Sales Range: $100-124.9 Million
Emp.: 60
Electric Power Distribution
N.A.I.C.S.: 221122

Vasterbergslagens Energi AB (1)
Sveavagen 20 B Fagersta, Box 860, 771 28, Ludvika, Dalarna, Sweden
Tel.: (46) 240 87600
Web Site: http://www.vbenergi.se
Electric Power Distribution Services
N.A.I.C.S.: 221122

Vattenfall (Sweden) AB (1)
Evenemangsgatan 13, 169 79, Solna, Sweden (100%)
Tel.: (46) 87395000
Web Site: http://www.vattenfall.se
Electric Power Distribution
N.A.I.C.S.: 221122

Vattenfall AB Vattenkraft (1)
Timmermansgatan 25, S 97177, Lulea, Sweden (100%)
Tel.: (46) 87395000
Web Site: http://www.vattenfall.com
Sales Range: $800-899.9 Million
Emp.: 200
Electric Power Distribution
N.A.I.C.S.: 221122

Vattenfall Bransle AB (1)
Jamtlandsgatan 99, S 162 87, Stockholm, Sweden (100%)
Tel.: (46) 87395000
Web Site: http://www.vattenfall.se
Sales Range: $100-124.9 Million
Emp.: 75
Electric Power Distr
N.A.I.C.S.: 221122

Vattenfall Business Services Nordic AB (1)
Osterbeiygatan 60, SE 461 88, Trollhattan, Sweden (100%)
Tel.: (46) 52088000
Web Site: http://www.vattenfall.com
Sales Range: $150-199.9 Million
Emp.: 200
Electric Power Distribution
N.A.I.C.S.: 221122

Vattenfall Eldistribution AB (1)
Timmermansgatan 25, Lulea, 97177, Sweden (100%)
Tel.: (46) 92077039
Sales Range: $350-399.9 Million
Emp.: 300
Electric Power Distribution

N.A.I.C.S.: 221122
Cathrina Jacobsson *(Dir-Mktg)*

Vattenfall Eldistribution AB (1)
Bygdevagen 18, SE 191 97, Sollentuna,
Sweden (100%)
Tel.: (46) 86232700
Sales Range: $350-399.9 Million
Emp.: 300
Electric Power Distr
N.A.I.C.S.: 221122

**Vattenfall Energy Solutions
GmbH** (1)
Uberseering 12, 22297, Hamburg, Germany
Tel.: (49) 3026710267
Web Site: https://warme.vattenfall.de
Heating & Cooling Supply Services
N.A.I.C.S.: 221330

Vattenfall Energy Trading A/S (1)
Oldenborggade 25-31, Fredericia, Vejle,
7000, Denmark
Tel.: (45) 88275000
Electric Power Distribution Services
N.A.I.C.S.: 221122

**Vattenfall Europe Nuclear Energy
GmbH** (1)
Uberseering 12, 22297, Hamburg, Germany
Tel.: (49) 4063963024
Web Site: https://perspektive-brunsbuettel.de
Nuclear Electric Power Generation Services
N.A.I.C.S.: 221113

Vattenfall GmbH (1)
Sellerstrasse 16, 13353, Berlin, Germany
Tel.: (49) 30818222
Web Site: http://www.vattenfall.de
Sales Range: $5-14.9 Billion
Emp.: 20,000
Heat & Electricity Generation & Distr
N.A.I.C.S.: 221122
Tuomo J. Hatakka *(Chm)*

Subsidiary (Domestic):

Fernheizwerk Neukolln AG (2)
Weigandufer 49, 12059, Berlin, Germany
Tel.: (49) 30 6 88 90 40
Web Site: http://www.fhw-neukoelln.de
Electric Power Distribution Services
N.A.I.C.S.: 221122

Joint Venture (Domestic):

GASAG AG (2)
Henriette-Herz-Platz 4, 10178, Berlin,
Germany (31.57%)
Tel.: (49) 3078723050
Web Site: http://www.gasag.de
Rev.: $1,401,660,451
Assets: $2,365,415,326
Liabilities: $1,610,674,481
Net Worth: $754,740,846
Earnings: $36,177,077
Emp.: 1,708
Fiscal Year-end: 12/31/2019
Liquid Natural Gas Distr
N.A.I.C.S.: 211120

Subsidiary (Domestic):

**BAS Kundenservice GmbH & Co.
KG** (2)
Euref-Campus 23-24, 10829, Berlin, Germany
Tel.: (49) 3078724444
Web Site: https://www.bas-kundenservice.de
Telephone Meter Reading, Billing & Collection Services
N.A.I.C.S.: 561990

**DSE Direkt-Service-Energie
GmbH** (3)
Henriette-Herz-Platz 4, 10178, Berlin, Germany
Tel.: (49) 3078721540
Web Site: http://www.dse-vertrieb.de
Energy Consulting Services
N.A.I.C.S.: 541690

GASAG Contracting GmbH (3)
Im Teelbruch 55, 45219, Essen, Germany
Tel.: (49) 20 54 96 954 0
Web Site: http://www.gasag-contracting.de
Sales Range: $25-49.9 Million
Emp.: 20
Energy Solutions & Contracting Projects

N.A.I.C.S.: 221118
Frank Mattat *(Mgr)*

GASAG Solution Plus GmbH (3)
Euref-Campus 23-24, 10829, Berlin, Germany
Tel.: (49) 3078724444
Web Site: https://www.gasag-solution.de
Sales Range: $25-49.9 Million
Emp.: 20
Electricity Meter Reading Services
N.A.I.C.S.: 561990

NBB Netz gesellschaft Berlin-Brandenburg mbH (3)
An der Spandauer Brucke 10, 10178, Berlin, Germany
Tel.: (49) 30 81876 0
Web Site: http://www.nbb-netzgesellschaft.de
Gas Supply & Meter Reading Services
N.A.I.C.S.: 221210

**SpreeGas Gesellschaft fur Gasversorgung und Energiedienstleistung
mbH** (3)
Nordparkstrasse 30, 03044, Cottbus, Germany
Tel.: (49) 35578220
Web Site: http://www.spreegas.de
Natural Gas Services
N.A.I.C.S.: 221210

Stadtwerke Forst GmbH (3)
Euloer Strasse 90, 03149, Forst, Germany
Tel.: (49) 35629500
Web Site: http://www.stadtwerke-forst.de
Electricity, Gas, Water & Heat Administration Services
N.A.I.C.S.: 926130

Joint Venture (Domestic):

KKK GmbH & Co OHV (2)
Elbuferstrasse 82, Geesthacht, 21502,
Germany (50%)
Tel.: (49) 4152150
Nuclear Electric Power Generation
N.A.I.C.S.: 221113
Torsten Fricke *(Plant Mgr)*

Subsidiary (Domestic):

Stromnetz Berlin GmbH (2)
Eichenstr 3a, 12435, Berlin, Germany
Tel.: (49) 304 920200
Web Site: http://www.stromnetz-berlin.de
Electric Power Distribution Services
N.A.I.C.S.: 221122
Thomas Schafer *(Chm-Mgmt Bd)*

Subsidiary (Non-US):

Vattenfall Danmark A/S (2)
Havneholmen 29 5th Fl, 1561, Copenhagen, Denmark
Tel.: (45) 88 27 50 00
Web Site: http://group.vattenfall.com
Sales Range: $400-449.9 Million
Emp.: 700
Energy Solutions Services
N.A.I.C.S.: 221122
Jorgen Nielsen *(CEO)*

Subsidiary (Domestic):

Vattenfall Vindkraft A/S (3)
Exnersgade 2, 6700, Esbjerg, Denmark
Tel.: (45) 88275000
Web Site: http://www.vattenfall.dk
Wind Electric Power Generation Services
N.A.I.C.S.: 221115

Subsidiary (Domestic):

Vattenfall Energy Trading GmbH (2)
Dammtorstrasse 29-32, 20354, Hamburg,
Germany
Tel.: (49) 24430972
Web Site: http://energysales.vattenfall.de
Emp.: 400
Electric Power Distribution Services
N.A.I.C.S.: 221122

Vattenfall Europe Sales GmbH (2)
Uberseering 12, 22297, Hamburg, Germany
Tel.: (49) 40180409092
Web Site: http://www.vattenfall.de
Sales Range: $400-449.9 Million
Generation, Transmission, Distribution &
Sale of Electricity & Heat

N.A.I.C.S.: 221122
Unit (Non-US):

Vattenfall European Affairs (2)
Rue de la Loi 223, 1040, Brussels,
Belgium (100%)
Tel.: (32) 27377380
Web Site: http://www.vattenfall.com
Sales Range: $100-124.9 Million
Emp.: 6
Electric Power Distr
N.A.I.C.S.: 221122

Subsidiary (Non-US):

Vattenfall Lithuania UAB (2)
13 A Juozapaviciaus Gatve, LT-2005, Vilnius, Lithuania
Tel.: (370) 2730956
Web Site: http://www.vattenfall.se
Electric Power Distr
N.A.I.C.S.: 221122

Vattenfall Poland Sp. z o.o. (2)
Zlopa 59, 00 120, Warsaw, Poland (100%)
Tel.: (48) 225875000
Web Site: http://www.vattenfall.pl
Sales Range: $75-99.9 Million
Emp.: 40
Energy Solutions Services
N.A.I.C.S.: 221122

Subsidiary (Domestic):

**Vattenfall IT Services Poland Sp. z
o.o** (3)
ul Gruszczynskiego 2-4, 44-100, Gliwice,
Poland
Tel.: (48) 32 33 28 501
Web Site: http://www.vattenfall.com
Emp.: 118
Information Technology Services
N.A.I.C.S.: 541512

Vattenfall Klantenservice N.V. (1)
Postbus 40021, 6803 HA, Arnhem, Netherlands
Tel.: (31) 208920255
Web Site: https://www.vattenfall.nl
Heating & Cooling Supply Services
N.A.I.C.S.: 221330

Vattenfall Mega Norge (1)
Arnstein Arnebergs vei 28, N 1366, Lysaker, Norway
Tel.: (47) 23891100
Web Site: http://www.vattenfall.no
Sales Range: $125-149.9 Million
Emp.: 2
Energy Solutions Services
N.A.I.C.S.: 221122

**Vattenfall Real Estate Energy Sales
GmbH** (1)
Hildegard-Knef-Platz 2, 10829, Berlin, Germany
Tel.: (49) 3052688311
Web Site: https://gewerbekunden.vattenfall.de
Heating & Cooling Supply Services
N.A.I.C.S.: 221330

Vattenfall Service Syd AB (1)
osterlangatan 60, Trollhattan, 461 88,
Sweden (100%)
Tel.: (46) 52088000
Web Site: http://www.vattenfall.com
Sales Range: $100-124.9 Million
Emp.: 15
Electric Power Distribution
N.A.I.C.S.: 221122

Vattenfall Services Nordic AB (1)
Stortorget 3, S 211 22, Malmo, Sweden
Tel.: (46) 406644600
Sales Range: $75-99.9 Million
Emp.: 30
Electric Power Distribution
N.A.I.C.S.: 221122

Vattenfall Smarter Living GmbH (1)
Hildegard-Knef-Platz 2, 10829, Berlin, Germany
Tel.: (49) 8002335335
Web Site: https://incharge.vattenfall.de
Economic Consulting Services
N.A.I.C.S.: 541690

Vattenfall Utveckling AB (1)

PO Box 534, S-814 26, Alvkarleby,
Sweden (100%)
Tel.: (46) 2683500
Web Site: http://www.vattenfall.com.se
Sales Range: $150-199.9 Million
Emp.: 185
Research & Development of Renewable
Energy, Nuclear Power & Carbon Capture
Storage (CCS) Technologies
N.A.I.C.S.: 221122
Niklas Dahlback *(Gen Mgr)*

Vattenfall Warme Berlin AG (1)
Hildegard-Knef-Platz 2, 10829, Berlin, Germany
Tel.: (49) 3026710267
Web Site: https://warme.vattenfall.de
Heating & Cooling Supply Services
N.A.I.C.S.: 221330

Vattenfall Wind Power Ltd (1)
Bridge End, Hexham, NE46 4NU, United
Kingdom
Tel.: (44) 1434 611300
Electric Power Generation Services
N.A.I.C.S.: 221118
Andrew Bennett *(Project Mgr)*

VATTI CORPORATION LIMITED
No 1 Nanhuayuan Road Gongye Avenue, Xiaolan Town, Zhongshan,
528416, Guangdong, China
Tel.: (86) 76022839177
Web Site: http://www.vatti-china.com
Year Founded: 1992
002035—(SSE)
Rev.: $816,918,888
Assets: $940,595,900
Liabilities: $462,587,533
Net Worth: $478,008,367
Earnings: $20,089,864
Emp.: 2,000
Fiscal Year-end: 12/31/22
Household Appliances Mfr
N.A.I.C.S.: 335220
Yejiang Pan *(Chm & Pres)*

VATUKOULA GOLD MINES
Tavua, Vatukoula, SW1Y 6DN, Fiji
Tel.: (679) 668 0630
Web Site: http://www.vgmplc.com
Sales Range: $50-74.9 Million
Emp.: 1,425
Mineral Exploration Services
N.A.I.C.S.: 213115
Yeung Ng *(Exec Dir)*

VAUDE SPORT GMBH & CO. KG
Vaude Strasse 2, Tettnang, 88069,
Germany
Tel.: (49) 754253060
Web Site: http://www.vaude.com
Sales Range: $250-299.9 Million
Emp.: 1,300
Outdoor Equipment Mfr
N.A.I.C.S.: 339920
Antje von Dewitz *(Mng Dir)*

VAUDOISE ASSURANCES HOLDING SA
Place de Milan, PO Box 120, 1001,
Lausanne, Switzerland
Tel.: (41) 216188080
Web Site: https://www.vaudoise.ch
VAHN—(SWX)
Sales Range: Less than $1 Million
Holding Company
N.A.I.C.S.: 551112
Philippe Hebeisen *(Chm)*

VAUEN VEREINIGTE PFEIFEN-FABRIKEN NURNBERG GMBH
Landgrabenstrasse 12, Nuremberg,
90443, Germany
Tel.: (49) 9114243680
Web Site: http://www.vauen.de
Year Founded: 1848
Rev.: $13,780,206
Emp.: 50

VAUEN VEREINIGTE PFEIFENFABRIKEN NURNBERG GMBH

VAUEN Vereinigte Pfeifenfabriken Nurnberg GmbH—(Continued)

Tobacco Pipe Mfr
N.A.I.C.S.: 339999
Alexander Eckert *(Partner & Mng Dir)*

VAX HOUSING FINANCE CORPORATION LIMITED
301 Simandhar Estate Nr Sakar III
Income Tax, Ahmedabad, 380 014,
Gujarat, India
Tel.: (91) 7966143941
531650—(BOM)
Rev.: $6,285
Assets: $5,934,579
Liabilities: $101,028
Net Worth: $5,833,551
Earnings: ($192)
Fiscal Year-end: 03/31/21
Housing Financial Services
N.A.I.C.S.: 523999
Vijay Nanusingh Rathore *(Chm, Mng Dir & Exec Dir)*

VAXCELL BIOTHERAPEUTICS CO., LTD.
3rd floor 234-2, Hwasun-eup, Hwasun, Jeollanam-do, Korea (South)
Tel.: (82) 613730046
Web Site: https://www.vaxcell-bio.com
Year Founded: 2010
323990—(KRS)
Rev.: $323,604
Assets: $18,533,056
Liabilities: $641,042
Net Worth: $17,892,014
Earnings: ($5,234,814)
Emp.: 51
Fiscal Year-end: 12/31/22
Research & Experimental Development Services
N.A.I.C.S.: 541715
Joon Haeng Rhee *(Co-CEO)*

VAXFAB ENTERPRISES LTD
F6-603 The Palace, Parvat Patia Choryasi, Surat, 395 010, Gujarat, India
Tel.: (91) 7428669284
Web Site:
  https://vaxfabenterprisesltd.in
Year Founded: 1983
542803—(BOM)
Investment Management Service
N.A.I.C.S.: 523940

VAXIL BIO LTD.
First Canadian Place 34th Floor 100 King Street W, Toronto, M2N 6N4, ON, Canada
Tel.: (416) 227-9667   BC
Web Site: https://vaxilbio.com
Year Founded: 2009
VXLLF—(OTCIQ)
Assets: $1,787,510
Liabilities: $457,634
Net Worth: $1,329,876
Earnings: ($771,328)
Fiscal Year-end: 12/31/21
Holding Company; Vaccine & Other Immunotherapeutic Products Developer
N.A.I.C.S.: 551112

Subsidiaries:

Vaxil Bio Ltd. (1)
B1 13A 13 Einstein St, Weizmann Science Park, Rehovot, 74036, Israel
Tel.: (972) 8 9396948
Web Site: http://www.vaxilbio.com
Holding Company; Vaccine & Other Immunotherapeutic Products Developer
N.A.I.C.S.: 551112
Lior Carmon *(Engr-Environmental)*

Subsidiary (Domestic):

Vaxil BioTherapeutics Ltd. (2)
B1 13A 13 Einstein St, Weizmann Science Park, Rehovot, 74036, Israel
Tel.: (972) 8 939 6948
Web Site: http://www.vaxilbio.com
Vaccine & Other Immunotherapeutic Products Developer
N.A.I.C.S.: 541715
Lior Carmon *(Founder & Head-Res)*

VAXTEX COTFAB LIMITED
Survey No 230 Ranipur Rd Opp Mariya Park, B/H Ranipur Village Saijpur-Gopal Narol, Ahmedabad, 382405, Gujarat, India
Tel.: (91) 9727123838
Web Site:
  https://www.vaxtexcotfabltd.com
VCL—(NSE)
Rev.: $9,173,719
Assets: $8,330,999
Liabilities: $5,515,533
Net Worth: $2,815,467
Earnings: $135,723
Fiscal Year-end: 03/31/23
Textile Product Mfr & Distr
N.A.I.C.S.: 314999
Kailash Gupta *(Mng Dir)*

VAZIVA S.A.
31-35 rue de la Federation carre suffren, 75015, Paris, France
Tel.: (33) 980808100
Web Site: https://www.vaziva.group
MLVAZ—(EUR)
Information Technology Services
N.A.I.C.S.: 541512

VB HOLDINGS LIMITED
366 Grantham Road, GPO Box 450, Suva, Fiji
Tel.: (679) 3381555   FJ
VBH—(SPSE)
Rev.: $1,391,158
Assets: $10,001,838
Liabilities: $1,100,781
Net Worth: $8,901,057
Earnings: $273,319
Fiscal Year-end: 12/31/23
Holding Company
N.A.I.C.S.: 551112

VB INDUSTRIES LTD.
P-27 Princep Street 3, Shubham Enclave Paschim Vihar, Kolkata, 700 072, India
Tel.: (91) 3322346715
Web Site:
  http://www.vbindustriesltd.in
539123—(BOM)
Rev.: $256,112
Assets: $12,327,606
Liabilities: $927,319
Net Worth: $11,400,288
Earnings: $13,668
Emp.: 10
Fiscal Year-end: 03/31/23
Financial Support Services
N.A.I.C.S.: 523999
Payal Bafna *(Compliance Officer & Sec)*

VBARE IBERIAN PROPERTIES SOCIMI SA
Calle de Jose Abascal 41, 28004, Madrid, Spain
Tel.: (34) 912777578
Web Site:
  https://www.vbarealestate.com
YVBA—(VAL)
Rev.: $2,516,834
Assets: $79,007,617
Liabilities: $27,888,288
Net Worth: $51,119,329
Earnings: $2,150,348
Fiscal Year-end: 12/31/23
Other Activities Related to Real Estate
N.A.I.C.S.: 531390
Fernando Acuna *(Chm)*

VBC FERRO ALLOYS LTD.
3rd Floor Progressive Towers 6-2-913/914 Khairatabad, Hyderabad, 500 004, Telangana, India
Tel.: (91) 4023301200
Web Site: http://www.vbcfal.in
513005—(BOM)
Rev.: $2,969,733
Assets: $33,303,154
Liabilities: $17,539,385
Net Worth: $15,763,769
Earnings: ($6,225,279)
Emp.: 20
Fiscal Year-end: 03/31/21
Ferro Metal Alloys Mfr
N.A.I.C.S.: 331110

VBG GROUP AB
Kungsgatan 57, SE-461 34, Trollhattan, Sweden
Tel.: (46) 521277700   SE
Web Site: https://www.vbggroup.com
Year Founded: 1951
VBG.B—(OMX)
Rev.: $440,858,226
Assets: $569,325,207
Liabilities: $228,288,745
Net Worth: $341,036,462
Earnings: $41,154,267
Emp.: 1,714
Fiscal Year-end: 12/31/21
Coupling Equipment, Anti-Skid Device, Dropside Pillars, Shaft-Hub Connection & Friction Springs Developer, Mfr & Marketer
N.A.I.C.S.: 333924
Bo Hedberg *(Sr VP-Bus Dev)*

Subsidiaries:

EDSCHA Automotive Kamenice s.r.o. (1)
Masarykova 701, 39470, Kamenice nad Lipou, Czech Republic
Tel.: (420) 56 542 4111
Web Site: https://www.edscha.com
Power Transmission Equipment Mfr
N.A.I.C.S.: 333613

European Trailer Systems S.R.O. (1)
Ke Gabrielce 786, CZ-39470, Kamenice nad Lipou, Czech Republic
Tel.: (420) 565422402
Web Site: https://www.vbggroup.cz
Industrial Truck Equipment Distr
N.A.I.C.S.: 423830

Mobile Climate Control Group Holding AB (1)
Kungsgatan 57, 461 34, Trollhattan, Sweden
Tel.: (46) 521277700
Web Site: https://www.mcc-hvac.com
Sales Range: $100-124.9 Million
Motor Vehicle HVAC System Mfr
N.A.I.C.S.: 336390
Clas Gunneberg *(Mgr-Div)*

Subsidiary (US):

Mobile Climate Control Corp. (2)
17103 State Rd 4, Goshen, IN 46528
Tel.: (574) 534-1516
Web Site: https://www.mcc-hvac.com
Sales Range: $25-49.9 Million
Emp.: 123
Automotive Heating & Air Conditioning Equipment Mfr
N.A.I.C.S.: 336390

Subsidiary (Non-US):

Mobile Climate Control GmbH (2)
Lehmingen 33, Oettingen, 86732, Germany
Tel.: (49) 9082 96109 0
Sales Range: $25-49.9 Million
Emp.: 12
Engineeering Services

INTERNATIONAL PUBLIC

N.A.I.C.S.: 541330

Mobile Climate Control Inc. (2)
7540 Jane St, Vaughan, L4K 0A6, ON, Canada
Tel.: (905) 482-2750
Web Site: https://www.mcc.com
Sales Range: $25-49.9 Million
Emp.: 300
Mobile Heating, Ventilating & Air Conditioning Systems Mfr for the Off-Road, Mass-Transit & Military Market Segments
N.A.I.C.S.: 333415

Subsidiary (US):

Mobile Climate Control York Corporation (2)
3189 Farmtrail Rd, York, PA 17406
Tel.: (717) 767-6531
Sales Range: $50-74.9 Million
Emp.: 50
Motor Vehicle Air-Conditioning System Mfr
N.A.I.C.S.: 336390
Robert Picker *(Mgr-Customer Svc)*

ONSPOT S.a.r.l. (1)
14 Route de Sarrebruck, 57645, Montoy-Flanville, France
Tel.: (33) 3 8776 3080
Web Site: http://www.onspot.com
Emp.: 4
Motor Vehicle Parts Mfr
N.A.I.C.S.: 336390
Eric Gulino *(Gen Mgr)*

ONSPOT of North America, Inc. (1)
1075 Rodgers Park Dr, North Vernon, IN 47265-5603
Tel.: (812) 346-1719
Web Site: https://www.onspot.com
Sales Range: $1-9.9 Million
Emp.: 30
Tire Chain System Mfr
N.A.I.C.S.: 332999
Ray Paul *(Reg Mgr-Western)*

RINGFEDER Power Transmission GmbH (1)
Werner-Heisenberg-Strasse 18, 64823, Gross-Umstadt, Germany (100%)
Tel.: (49) 60 789 3850
Web Site: https://www.ringfeder.com
Sales Range: $25-49.9 Million
Emp.: 55
Fiber Can Tube Drum & Similar Products Mfr
N.A.I.C.S.: 322219

Subsidiary (Non-US):

Kunshan RINGFEDER Power Transmission Co., Ltd. (2)
No 406 Jiande Road, Zhangpu Town, Kunshan, 215321, Jiangsu, China
Tel.: (86) 51257453960
Power Transmission Equipment Mfr
N.A.I.C.S.: 333613

Subsidiary (US):

RINGFEDER Power Transmission USA Corporation (2)
165 Carver Ave, Westwood, NJ 07675 (100%)
Tel.: (201) 666-3320
Web Site: http://www.ringfeder.com
Sales Range: $25-49.9 Million
Emp.: 20
Industrial Machinery & Equipment Whslr
N.A.I.C.S.: 423830

Subsidiary (Non-US):

RINGFEDER Power Transmission s.r.o. (2)
Oty Kovala 1172, CZ-33441, Dobrany, Czech Republic
Tel.: (420) 377201511
Power Transmission Component Mfr
N.A.I.C.S.: 333613

VBG Group Etes NV (1)
Industriezone Zuid 2 2 Lochtemanweg 50, 3580, Beringen, Belgium
Tel.: (32) 11 60 90 90
Motor Vehicle Parts Mfr
N.A.I.C.S.: 336390

VBG Group Sales A/S (1)

Industribuen 20-22, 5592, Ejby, Denmark **(100%)**
Tel.: (45) 64461919
Web Site: https://www.vbg.dk
Sales Range: $50-74.9 Million
Emp.: 6
Motor Vehicle Supplies & New Parts Merchant Whslr
N.A.I.C.S.: 423120

VBG Group Sales AS (1)
Karihaugveien 102, PO Box 94 Leirdal, PO Box 94 Leirdal, 1009, Oslo, Norway **(100%)**
Tel.: (47) 2 314 1660
Web Site: https://www.vbggroupsales.no
Sales Range: $75-99.9 Million
Emp.: 120
Motor Vehicle Supplies & New Parts Merchant Whslr
N.A.I.C.S.: 423120

VBG Group Sales Ltd (1)
Unit 9 Willow Court West Quay Road, Winwick Quay, Warrington, WA2 8UF, United Kingdom **(100%)**
Tel.: (44) 192 523 4111
Web Site: https://www.vbggroupsales.co.uk
Sales Range: $25-49.9 Million
Emp.: 6
Heavy Duty Truck Mfr
N.A.I.C.S.: 336120

VBG Group Truck Equipment AB (1)
Herman Kreftings gata 4, Box 1216, SE-462 28, Vanersborg, Sweden
Tel.: (46) 521277700
Web Site: https://www.vbg.com
Sales Range: $50-74.9 Million
Emp.: 170
Motor Vehicle Parts Mfr
N.A.I.C.S.: 336390
Anders Birgersson *(Gen Mgr)*

VBG Group Truck Equipment GmbH (1)
(100%)
Tel.: (49) 2 151 8350
Web Site: https://www.ringfeder-rf.com
Sales Range: $25-49.9 Million
Emp.: 21
All Other Miscellaneous Fabricated Metal Product Mfr
N.A.I.C.S.: 332999

VBG Group Truck Equipment NV (1)
Industrie Zuid Zone 2 2 Lochtemanweg 50, 3580, Beringen, Belgium
Tel.: (32) 1 160 9090
Web Site: https://www.vbggroup.com
Emp.: 17
Truck Distr
N.A.I.C.S.: 423110

VBG Produkter AB (1)
Box 1216, 462 28, Vanersborg, Sweden
Tel.: (46) 521 27 77 00
Web Site: http://www.vbggroup.com
Sales Range: $50-74.9 Million
Emp.: 175
Automobile Parts Mfr
N.A.I.C.S.: 336390

VBH HOLDING AG
Siemensstrasse 38, 70825, Korntal-Munchingen, Germany
Tel.: (49) 7150150
Web Site: http://www.vbh.de
Sales Range: $650-699.9 Million
Emp.: 2,369
Hardware Whslr
N.A.I.C.S.: 423710
Jurgen Kassel *(Member-Exec Bd)*

Subsidiaries:

Beijing VBH Construction Hardware Co. Ltd. (1)
Rm A 101 LanTao Ctr No 5 Wanhong Rd, Chaoyang Dist, Beijing, China
Tel.: (86) 1064379261
Web Site: http://www.vbh.com.cn
Sales Range: $25-49.9 Million
Emp.: 50
Construction Hardware Whslr
N.A.I.C.S.: 423710

ESCO RUS OOO (1)
Pryanishnikova 23A, 127550, Moscow, Russia
Tel.: (7) 4959379535
Web Site: http://www.esco-online.ru
Sales Range: $25-49.9 Million
Emp.: 10
Steel Door & Window Fittings Mfr & Sales
N.A.I.C.S.: 332321

Guangzhou VBH Construction Hardware Trading Co.,Ltd. (1)
13D Sanxin Plaza No 33 West Huangpu Avenue, Tianhe District, Guangzhou, 510620, Guangdong, China
Tel.: (86) 2038201185
Web Site: http://www.vbh.com.cn
Sales Range: $25-49.9 Million
Emp.: 13
Door & Window Hardware Whslr
N.A.I.C.S.: 423710
Jens Rothemund *(Gen Mgr)*

PJSC Brovary Plastics Plant (1)
53 Brovary Blvd 7th Fl8, 07400, Brovary, Ukraine
Tel.: (380) 444173560
Plastic Mfr
N.A.I.C.S.: 326199

Subsidiary (Non-US):

VBH-OFIR S.R.L. (2)
Str Mesager Nr 1 Bl Sc Et Ap 705 706, MD-2069, Chisinau, Moldova
Tel.: (373) 22 593370
Sales Range: $25-49.9 Million
Emp.: 5
Doors & Windows Hardware Whslr
N.A.I.C.S.: 423710

SC VBH Romcom SRL (1)
Str Principala nr 1P, Ungheni Mures, 547605, Iasi, Romania
Tel.: (40) 372340302
Web Site: http://www.vbh.ro
Window Door Production & Assembly Product Whslr
N.A.I.C.S.: 423310

SIA VBH Latvia Ltd. (1)
Ulbrokas 23, Riga, 1021, Latvia
Tel.: (371) 67381890
Web Site: http://www.vbh.lv
Sales Range: $25-49.9 Million
Emp.: 18
Door & Window Accessories Whslr
N.A.I.C.S.: 423310

Shanghai VBH Construction Hardware Co., Ltd. (1)
Rm 2004-2006 Zhongliang Bldg No 440 S 2nd Zhong Shan Rd, Shanghai, 200032, China
Tel.: (86) 2164436025
Web Site: http://www.vbh.com.cn
Sales Range: $25-49.9 Million
Emp.: 20
Doors & Windows Hardware Whslr
N.A.I.C.S.: 423710
Hong Gu *(Pres)*

TOO VBH
Kazibaeva Strasse 1, 050050, Almaty, Kazakhstan
Tel.: (7) 7273645026
Iron & Steel Product Whslr
N.A.I.C.S.: 423510

TOV VBH (1)
Promusel Brovarskij Zavod Plastmass 7 Etage, 07400, Brovary, Ukraine
Tel.: (380) 445371561
Window & Door Installation Mfr
N.A.I.C.S.: 321911

V.B.H. Trading (L.L.C.) (1)
Jebel Ali, PO Box 17994, Dubai, United Arab Emirates
Tel.: (971) 48870822
Sales Range: $25-49.9 Million
Emp.: 12
Doors & Windows Hardware Whslr
N.A.I.C.S.: 423710
Ahmet Abbat *(Mgr)*

VBH (GB) Ltd (1)
VBH House Bailey Drive Gillingham Business Park, Gillingham, ME8 0WG, Kent, United Kingdom
Tel.: (44) 1634263263
Web Site: http://www.vbhgb.com
Sales Range: $25-49.9 Million
Emp.: 30
Doors & Window Hardware Distr
N.A.I.C.S.: 423710
Simon Monks *(Mng Dir)*

VBH - Malum S.L. (1)
C Agricultura 37 E, Viladecans, 08840, Barcelona, Spain
Tel.: (34) 936473470
Web Site: http://www.vbh.com.es
Sales Range: $25-49.9 Million
Emp.: 35
Doors & Windows & Fittings Distr
N.A.I.C.S.: 423220

Subsidiary (Non-US):

VBH MEXICO S.A. de C.V. (2)
Blvd Carlos Camacho Espiritu 2469-C Lomas de Coatepeque, San Francisco Totimehuacan, Puebla, 72960, Mexico
Tel.: (52) 2221292300
Web Site: http://www.vbhmexico.com
Sales Range: $25-49.9 Million
Emp.: 10
Doors & Windows Hardware Distr
N.A.I.C.S.: 423710
Francisco Cecero *(Gen Mgr)*

VBH - SIB (1)
Gertsena Str 48 Gebaude 5 Office 406 Gebiet, 644007, Omsk, Russia
Tel.: (7) 3812356333
Window & Door Installation Mfr
N.A.I.C.S.: 321911

VBH - TBM UAB (1)
Dariaus ir Gireno g 81, LT-02189, Vilnius, Lithuania
Tel.: (370) 52788624
Web Site: http://www.vbh.lt
Construction Materials Whslr
N.A.I.C.S.: 423390
Kestutis Simkevicius *(Acct Mgr)*

VBH Belgium NV (1)
Koolmijnlaan 99, 3580, Beringen, Limburg, Belgium
Tel.: (32) 11458350
Web Site: http://www.vbh.be
Sales Range: $50-74.9 Million
Emp.: 90
Doors & Windows Fittings Sales
N.A.I.C.S.: 423710
Bart Bertrands *(Mng Dir)*

VBH Budapest Kft (1)
Lakatos u 38, 1184, Budapest, Hungary
Tel.: (36) 12971010
Web Site: http://www.vbh.hu
Sales Range: $25-49.9 Million
Emp.: 30
Doors & Windows Hardware Whslr
N.A.I.C.S.: 423710
Kotanyi Andras *(Mng Dir)*

VBH Bulgarien OOD (1)
Poruchik Nedelcho Bonchev Str 6, 1528, Sofia, Bulgaria
Tel.: (359) 29434617
Iron & Steel Product Whslr
N.A.I.C.S.: 423510

VBH Dems d.o.o. (1)
Pijacna 6, Ilidza, 71210, Sarajevo, Bosnia & Herzegovina
Tel.: (387) 33467177
Web Site: http://www.vbh.ba
Sales Range: $25-49.9 Million
Emp.: 12
Door & Window & Installation Mfr
N.A.I.C.S.: 332321

VBH Deutschland GmbH (1)
Siemensstr 38, 70825, Korntal-Munchingen, Germany
Tel.: (49) 7150150
Web Site: http://www.vbh.de
Sales Range: $50-74.9 Million
Emp.: 200
Door & Window Mfr
N.A.I.C.S.: 332321

VBH Estonia AS (1)
Laike Tee 12, Peetri, 75301, Harju, Estonia
Tel.: (372) 6401331
Web Site: http://www.vbh.ee
Sales Range: $25-49.9 Million
Emp.: 34
Window & Door Accessories Supplier
N.A.I.C.S.: 423310
Indrek Sauga *(Mng Dir)*

VBH Hellas S.A. (1)
Leoforos Stratou 155, Polichni, 56429, Thessaloniki, Greece
Tel.: (30) 2310604490
Web Site: http://www.vbh.com.gr
Doors & Windows Hardware Supplier
N.A.I.C.S.: 423710

VBH Hody Belgium SA (1)
Rue Du Parc Industriel 14, 6900, Marche-en-Famenne, Luxembourg, Belgium
Tel.: (32) 84321321
Web Site: http://www.vbh.be
Sales Range: $25-49.9 Million
Emp.: 70
Doors & Windows Fittings Sales
N.A.I.C.S.: 444180
Bart Bertrands *(Mng Dir)*

VBH Italia S.r.l. (1)
Via Macello 26 b, 39100, Bolzano, Italy
Tel.: (39) 0471305900
Web Site: http://www.vbh.it
Fabricated Metal Products Mfr
N.A.I.C.S.: 332999

VBH Kapi ve Pencere Sistemleri San. Ve Tic. A.S.
Mahmutbey Mh Kucuk Halkali Cd No 10/11, Bagcilar, 34218, Istanbul, Turkiye
Tel.: (90) 2126046060
Web Site: http://www.vbh.com.tr
Window & Door Installation Mfr
N.A.I.C.S.: 321911
Levent Onur *(Sls Mgr-Paint)*

VBH Kuwait for General Trading Co. (W.L.L) (1)
PO Box 66365, 43754, Kuwait, Kuwait
Tel.: (965) 2647044
Web Site: http://www.vbh.com.kw
Doors & Windows Hardware Whslr
N.A.I.C.S.: 423710

VBH Montenegro d.o.o. (1)
Bracana Bracanovica 49, 81000, Podgorica, Montenegro
Tel.: (382) 20624708
Web Site: http://www.vbh.co.me
Construction Materials Whslr
N.A.I.C.S.: 423390
Dusko Garcevic *(Gen Mgr)*

VBH Nederland BV (1)
Houtduifstraat 22, 4901 BP, Oosterhout, Netherlands
Tel.: (31) 162483400
Web Site: http://www.vbh-nl.com
Sales Range: $25-49.9 Million
Emp.: 45
Building Hardware Retailer
N.A.I.C.S.: 423710
John Smits *(Mng Dir)*

VBH O.O.O. (1)
Domostroitelnaja Str 4-E, 194292, Saint Petersburg, Russia
Tel.: (7) 8123253692
Window & Door Installation Mfr
N.A.I.C.S.: 321911

VBH OOO (St. Petersburg) (1)
Domostroitelnaja Str 4-E, 194292, Saint Petersburg, Russia
Tel.: (7) 8123253692
Web Site: http://www.vbh.ru
Sales Range: $50-74.9 Million
Emp.: 100
Doors & Windows Hardware Whslr
N.A.I.C.S.: 423710

VBH Okovi d.o.o. (1)
Industrijska 5, Novaki, 10431, Sveta Nedelja, Zagreb, Croatia
Tel.: (385) 16530750
Web Site: http://www.vbh.hr
Sales Range: $25-49.9 Million
Emp.: 14
Doors & Windows Hardware Whslr
N.A.I.C.S.: 423710
Drazen Drenski *(Mng Dir)*

VBH Polska Sp.z.o.o. (1)
Ul Chelmzynska 180, 04-464, Warsaw, Poland
Tel.: (48) 225152120
Web Site: http://www.vbh.pl

VBH HOLDING AG

VBH Holding AG—(Continued)
Sales Range: $50-74.9 Million
Emp.: 70
Building Hardware Distr
N.A.I.C.S.: 423710
Andrzej Wyszogrodzki *(Member-Mgmt Bd)*

VBH Singapore Pte. Ltd. (1)
No 31 Jurong Port Rd No 07-10, Jurong Logistic Hub, Singapore, 619115, Singapore
Tel.: (65) 62646616
Web Site: http://www.vbh.com.sg
Sales Range: $25-49.9 Million
Emp.: 34
Doors & Windows Hardware Whslr
N.A.I.C.S.: 423710

VBH Trgovina d.o.o. (1)
Kidriceva 75, 4220, Skofja Loka, Slovenia
Tel.: (386) 45023110
Web Site: http://www.vbhtrgovina.si
Sales Range: $25-49.9 Million
Emp.: 10
Doors & Windows Hardware Distr
N.A.I.C.S.: 423710
Slavko Zorc *(Mng Dir)*

VBH Vereinigter Baubeschlag- Handel spol. s r.o. (1)
Zitavskeho 496, 156 00, Prague, Czech Republic
Tel.: (420) 257922334
Web Site: http://www.vbh.cz
Construction Materials Whslr
N.A.I.C.S.: 423390

Vbh Holding India Private Limited (1)
Plot No 131 Sector-37 Pace City-i, Gurgaon, 122001, Haryana, India
Tel.: (91) 124 302 0895
Web Site: http://www.vbh.in
Sales Range: $25-49.9 Million
Emp.: 25
Hardware Components Distr
N.A.I.C.S.: 423710

esco Metallbausysteme GmbH (1)
Dieselstrasse 2, 71254, Ditzingen, Germany
Tel.: (49) 715630080
Web Site: http://www.esco-online.de
Sales Range: $50-74.9 Million
Emp.: 200
Metal Door & Window Fittings Mfr & Supplier
N.A.I.C.S.: 332321

Subsidiary (Non-US):

ESCO Polska Sp.z.o.o. (2)
ul Rzeczna 10, 03-794, Warsaw, Poland
Tel.: (48) 226792522
Web Site: http://www.esco.com.pl
Sales Range: $25-49.9 Million
Emp.: 40
Building Hardware & Accessories Whslr
N.A.I.C.S.: 423710

esco Metallbausysteme Austria GmbH (2)
Tewerte 14, 5301, Eugendorf, Austria
Tel.: (43) 622570030
Web Site: http://www.esco-austria.at
Sales Range: $25-49.9 Million
Emp.: 5
Metal Door & Window Fittings Mfr & Supplier
N.A.I.C.S.: 332321
Christoch Schill *(Mgr)*

VCI GLOBAL LIMITED
B03-C-8 Menara 3A KL Eco City No 3 Jalan Bangsar, 59200, Kuala Lumpur, Malaysia
Tel.: (60) 377173089
Web Site: https://v-capital.co
Year Founded: 2013
VCIG—(NASDAQ)
Rev.: $11,750,073
Assets: $10,918,414
Liabilities: $6,126,011
Net Worth: $4,792,403
Earnings: $4,934,610
Emp.: 43
Fiscal Year-end: 12/31/21
Management Consulting Services
N.A.I.C.S.: 541618
Zhi Feng Ang *(CFO)*

VCPLUS LIMITED
223 Mountbatten Road 03 09/10/08, Singapore, 398008, Singapore
Tel.: (65) 69925333
Web Site: https://www.vcplus.sg
Year Founded: 2015
43E—(CAT)
Rev.: $301,447
Assets: $2,870,560
Liabilities: $806,635
Net Worth: $2,063,925
Earnings: ($1,655,684)
Emp.: 29
Fiscal Year-end: 12/31/23
Gold Exploration, Mining & Production
N.A.I.C.S.: 212220
Ben Lim Beng Chew *(Exec Dir)*

VCREDIT HOLDINGS LIMITED
Suite 1918 19/F Two Pacific Place 88 Queensway, Hong Kong, China (Hong Kong)
Tel.: (852) 29185500
Web Site: https://www.vcredit.com
Year Founded: 2006
2003—(HKG)
Rev.: $477,905,042
Assets: $1,547,947,430
Liabilities: $961,805,651
Net Worth: $586,141,779
Earnings: $81,579,882
Emp.: 762
Fiscal Year-end: 12/31/22
Holding Company
N.A.I.C.S.: 551112
Stephen Sai Wang Liu *(CEO)*

Subsidiaries:

Guangdong Weishi Data Technology Co., Ltd. (1)
Room 1201 building 1 Xinghui center No 88 Sichuan North Road, Hongkou District, Shanghai, China
Tel.: (86) 13611637643
Web Site: https://www.weishi-data.com
Auto Parts Mfr & Distr
N.A.I.C.S.: 336390

VCREDIT Finance Limited (1)
Room 1904 19th Floor Bank of America Tower 12 Harcourt Road, Central, China (Hong Kong)
Tel.: (852) 63692338
Web Site: https://www.crefit.com
Money Lending Services
N.A.I.C.S.: 522291

VCU DATA MANAGEMENT LIMITED
303 3rd Floor Aaditya Arcade Topiwala Lane Grant Road, Mumbai, 400007, Maharashtra, India
Tel.: (91) 2240054245
Web Site: https://www.vcupack.com
536672—(BOM)
Rev.: $558,878
Assets: $4,820,484
Liabilities: $1,123,083
Net Worth: $3,697,401
Earnings: ($20,217)
Emp.: 10
Fiscal Year-end: 03/31/21
Wireless Video Communications
N.A.I.C.S.: 334220
Shripal Bafna *(Chm & Mng Dir)*

VDH MOERDIJK
Tradeboulevard 2, 4761 RL, Moerdijk, Netherlands
Tel.: (31) 168 745 701
Web Site: http://www.vdhcompany.com
Freight Management Services
N.A.I.C.S.: 488510

Subsidiaries:

VDH Dirksland (1)
Vlakbodem-3, 3247 CP, Dirksland, South Holland, Netherlands
Tel.: (31) 187 685 080
Web Site: http://www.vdhcompany.com
General Freight Trucking Services
N.A.I.C.S.: 484122

VDI VEREIN DEUTSCHER INGENIEURE E.V.
VDI-Platz 1, 40468, Dusseldorf, Germany
Tel.: (49) 211 6214 0
Web Site: http://www.vdi.de
Engineering Association
N.A.I.C.S.: 813910
Ralph C. Appel *(Exec Dir)*

Subsidiaries:

VDI Verlag GmbH (1)
VDI-Platz 1, 40468, Dusseldorf, Germany
Tel.: (49) 21161880
Web Site: http://www.vdi-verlag.de
Engineering Trade Journal Publisher
N.A.I.C.S.: 513120
Ken Fouhy *(Mng Dir)*

VDK BANK
Sint-Michielsplein 16, 9000, Gent, Belgium
Tel.: (32) 92673211
Web Site: http://www.vdk.be
Year Founded: 1926
Commercial Banking Services
N.A.I.C.S.: 522110
Leen Van den Neste *(CEO)*

VDL GROEP B.V.
Hoevenweg 1, 5652 AW, Eindhoven, Netherlands
Tel.: (31) 402925000
Web Site: http://www.vdlgroep.com
Year Founded: 1953
Sales Range: $1-4.9 Billion
Emp.: 9,216
Diversified Industrial Services, Including Metalworking, Vehicle Assembly, Plastics Processing & Surface Treatment
N.A.I.C.S.: 333248
Wim van der Leegte *(Pres & Member-Mgmt Bd)*

Subsidiaries:

APTS B.V. (1)
1 Steenovenweg, PO Box 1015, 5708 HN, Helmond, Netherlands (70%)
Tel.: (31) 492562013
Web Site: http://www.apts-phileas.com
Sales Range: $1-9.9 Million
Emp.: 20
Developer & Sales of Public Transport Systems
N.A.I.C.S.: 926120

Caja BV (1)
Steenbergstraat 25, 6465 AB, Kerkrade, Netherlands (100%)
Tel.: (31) 455436262
Web Site: http://www.vdlgroup.com
Sales Range: $25-49.9 Million
Emp.: 30
Mfr of Steel & Plastic Wheels for Pram, Buggy, Toy, Gardening & Automotive Industries
N.A.I.C.S.: 326199

Hapro Deutschland GmbH (1)
Sudring 30, 56412, Ruppach-Goldhausen, Germany (100%)
Tel.: (49) 260294000
Web Site: http://www.hapro.com
Sales Range: $25-49.9 Million
Emp.: 10
Mfr, Sales & Servicer of Professional Sun Beds & Accessories for Sun Tanning Market
N.A.I.C.S.: 449110

Hapro International BV (1)
Fleerbosseweg 33, Kapelle, 4421 RR, Netherlands

INTERNATIONAL PUBLIC

Tel.: (31) 113362362
Web Site: http://www.hapro.com
Sales Range: $25-49.9 Million
Emp.: 100
Mfr of Sun Beds for Consumer & Commercial Markets & Car Roof-Boxes
N.A.I.C.S.: 449110

Helmondse Metaal Industrie BV (1)
Kleibeemd 1, Helmond, 5705 DP, Netherlands (100%)
Tel.: (31) 492540800
Web Site: http://www.vdlgroup.com
Sales Range: $25-49.9 Million
Emp.: 100
Provider of Machining Work, Cutting, Sawing, Stamping, Setting, Welding, Construction, Assembly & Soldering
N.A.I.C.S.: 333310
Leegte Wim *(Owner)*

Industrial Modules (1)
Daalakkersweg 8, 5641 JA, Eindhoven, Netherlands (100%)
Tel.: (31) 402829500
Web Site: http://www.vdl-odms.com
Rev.: $48,292,400
Emp.: 40
Developer & Mfr of Optical Media Replication Equipment
N.A.I.C.S.: 334610

KTI Belgium N.V. (1)
Nijverheidsstraat 10, Mol, 2400, Belgium (100%)
Tel.: (32) 14346262
Web Site: http://www.vdlkti.be
Sales Range: $10-24.9 Million
Emp.: 130
Engineering & Manufacturing for Gas, Oil & Petrochemical Industries
N.A.I.C.S.: 325110
Luterst Venhoos *(Head-Accts)*

NSA Metaalindustrie BV (1)
De Run 4234, 5503 LL, Veldhoven, Netherlands (100%)
Tel.: (31) 402544565
Web Site: http://www.vdlgroup.com
Sales Range: $25-49.9 Million
Emp.: 70
Provider of Engineering Services for High-Grade Composite Products; Sheet Metal Machining
N.A.I.C.S.: 541330

PMB-UVA International bv (1)
Meerenakkerweg 32, Eindhoven, 5652 AV, Netherlands
Tel.: (31) 40 2825000
Web Site: http://www.pmb-uva.com
Packaging Machinery Mfr
N.A.I.C.S.: 333993
M. Tonten *(Pres)*

Postma Heerenveen BV (1)
Leeuwarderstraatweg 121 D, 8441 PK, Heerenveen, Netherlands (100%)
Tel.: (31) 513622536
Web Site: http://www.vdlgroap.com
Sales Range: $25-49.9 Million
Emp.: 42
Supplier of Sheet Metal & Pipes; Provider of Shearing, Squaring, Punching, Welding, Machining, Powder Coating & Chemical Pre-Treatment Services
N.A.I.C.S.: 332322
Johan Zwarts *(Mng Dir)*

RPI Componenten BV (1)
Nijverheidsweg 40, Hendrik-Ido-Ambacht, 3441 LJ, Hendrik Ido Ambacht, Netherlands (100%)
Tel.: (31) 786831800
Web Site: http://www.vdlgroep.com
Sales Range: $25-49.9 Million
Emp.: 50
Provider of Sheet Metal Services, Cutting, Sawing, CNC Punching, Pressing, Setting, Spot Welding & CO2 Welding
N.A.I.C.S.: 333331
Hims Debresser *(Gen Mgr)*

Staalservice Weert BV (1)
Celciusstraat 13, 6003 DG, Weert, Netherlands (100%)
Tel.: (31) 495540838
Web Site: http://www.vdl.nl
Sales Range: $25-49.9 Million
Emp.: 60

AND PRIVATE COMPANIES — VDL GROEP B.V.

Provider of CNC Torch & Laser Cutting, Punching & Aligning
N.A.I.C.S.: 333517

Steelweld (1)
Unit 10 Dunbeath Ct, Swindon, SN2 8QF, Wiltshire, United Kingdom (100%)
Tel.: (44) 1793420444
Designer of Turnkey Production Automation Systems
N.A.I.C.S.: 238210

TIM Hapert BV (1)
Energieweg 2, 5527 AH, Hapert, Netherlands (100%)
Tel.: (31) 497383805
Web Site: http://www.vdlgroep.com
Sales Range: $50-74.9 Million
Emp.: 120
Provider of Machining Operations, Drilling, Turning, Milling & CNC Milling Machines & Lathes
N.A.I.C.S.: 333310

Technische Industrie VDS BV (1)
Industrieweg 29, 5527 AJ, Hapert, Netherlands (100%)
Tel.: (31) 497383844
Sales Range: $75-99.9 Million
Emp.: 200
Provider of Sheet Metal Services
N.A.I.C.S.: 423510
Jos Van Meijl *(Dir)*

Truck & Trailer Industry AS (1)
Persveien 20, Oslo, 0581, Norway
Tel.: (47) 23 039600
Web Site: http://www.tti.no
Automobile Parts Distr
N.A.I.C.S.: 423120

VD Leegte Metaal B.V. (1)
Handelsweg 21, 5527 AL, Hapert, Netherlands (100%)
Tel.: (31) 497331100
Sales Range: $50-74.9 Million
Emp.: 120
Provider of Machining Services, Cutting, Setting, Punching, Deep Drawing, CNC Punching, Laser Cutting, Welding & Robot Welding
N.A.I.C.S.: 333310
Gos Bax *(Mng Dir)*

VDL Agrotech B.V. (1)
Hoevenweg 1, Eindhoven, 5652 AW, Netherlands (100%)
Tel.: (31) 402925500
Web Site: http://www.vdlagrotech.com
Sales Range: $25-49.9 Million
Emp.: 40
Mfr of Stalls & Stall Equipment for Intensive Livestock Keeping
N.A.I.C.S.: 333415
Brian van Hooff *(Mng Dir)*

VDL Apparatenbouw bv (1)
Sigarenmaker 8, 5521 DJ, Eersel, Netherlands (100%)
Tel.: (31) 497515150
Web Site: http://www.vdlapparatenbouw.com
Mechanical, Electronic Production & Assembly Technology Services
N.A.I.C.S.: 333310
Pieter Aarts *(Mng Dir)*

VDL Bus & Coach (Suisse) GmbH (1)
De Vest 7, Valkenswaard, 5555 XL, Netherlands
Tel.: (31) 40 2084400
Web Site: http://www.vdlbuscoach.com
Coach Mfr & Distr
N.A.I.C.S.: 336211

VDL Bus & Coach Czech Republic s.r.o. (1)
Hastalska 6/1072, 110 00, Prague, Czech Republic
Tel.: (420) 384420348
Web Site: http://www.vdlbuscoach.com
Bus Mfr & Distr
N.A.I.C.S.: 336350
Pavel Schlosser *(Mng Dir)*

VDL Bus & Coach Danmark A/S (1)
Naverland 21, Glostrup, 2600, Denmark
Tel.: (45) 70 23 83 23
Coach Distr
N.A.I.C.S.: 423120

VDL Bus & Coach Deutschland GmbH (1)
Oberer Westring 1 Industriegebiet West, Buren, 33142, Germany
Tel.: (49) 2951 6080
Coach Distr
N.A.I.C.S.: 423120

VDL Bus & Coach France sarl (1)
5 rue du Pont de la Breche Z A E Les Grandes Vignes, Goussainville, 95192, France
Tel.: (33) 1 34388940
Coach Distr
N.A.I.C.S.: 423120

VDL Bus & Coach Italia s.r.l. (1)
Piazza dei Beccadori 12, Spilamberto, Modena, 41057, Italy
Tel.: (39) 059 782931
Coach Distr
N.A.I.C.S.: 423120

VDL Bus & Coach Polska Sp. z o.o. (1)
Straszkow 121, Koscielec, 62-604, Poland
Tel.: (48) 63 2616091
Coach Distr
N.A.I.C.S.: 423120

VDL Bus & Coach Serbia d.o.o. (1)
Gandijeva 99d, Belgrade, 11070, Serbia
Tel.: (381) 11 2166 525
Emp.: 5
Coach Distr
N.A.I.C.S.: 423120
Branislav Radovanovic *(Mng Dir)*

VDL Bus & Coach South Africa Ltd (1)
Office Unit 1 Isando Business Park Corner Gewel & Hulley Streets, Isando, 1610, Gauteng, South Africa
Tel.: (27) 82 415 14 74
Coach Distr
N.A.I.C.S.: 423120

VDL Bus & Coach bv (1)
De Vest 7, 5555 XL, Valkenswaard, Netherlands
Tel.: (31) 40 208 44 00
Web Site: http://www.vdlbuscoach.com
Sales Range: $75-99.9 Million
Emp.: 200
Bus Mfr
N.A.I.C.S.: 336211

Holding (Domestic):

Berkhof Valkenswaard BV (2)
De Vest 55, 5555XB, Valkenswaard, Netherlands (51%)
Tel.: (31) 402082424
Web Site: http://www.vdlberkhof.com
Sales Range: $50-74.9 Million
Emp.: 200
Mfr of Coaches, Buses, Interurban Buses, VIP Coaches, School Buses & Double Deckers
N.A.I.C.S.: 485210

VDL Bus Heerenveen B.V. (2)
Wetterwille 12, 8447 GC, Heerenveen, Netherlands (100%)
Tel.: (31) 513618500
Web Site: http://www.vdlbuscoach.com
Sales Range: $1-9.9 Million
Emp.: 200
Bus Mfr
N.A.I.C.S.: 336211
Dennis Van Opzeeland *(Mng Dir)*

Holding (Non-US):

VDL Bus Roesalare nv (2)
Schoolstraat 50, B 8800, Roeselare, Belgium
Tel.: (32) 51232611
Web Site: http://www.vdlbuscoach.com
Sales Range: $100-124.9 Million
Buses, Coaches, VIP Coaches, School Buses & Double-Deckers Mfr
N.A.I.C.S.: 485210
Peter Wouters *(Mng Dir)*

VDL Bus Center bv (1)
De Run 4232, Veldhoven, 5503 LL, Netherlands
Tel.: (31) 40 2954635
Web Site: http://www.vdlbuscenter.nl
Emp.: 4
Coach Distr
N.A.I.C.S.: 423120
Paul Michim *(Gen Mgr)*

VDL Bus International B.V. (1)
Hoevenweg 1, Eindhoven, 5652 AW, Netherlands (81%)
Tel.: (31) 402500500
Web Site: http://www.vdlgroup.com
Sales Range: $50-74.9 Million
Emp.: 160
Mfr of Bus & Coach Underframes; Sales of Complete Vehicles
N.A.I.C.S.: 485210
Jan-Cees Santema *(Gen Mgr)*

VDL Bus Modules bv (1)
De Vest 55, Valkenswaard, 5555 XP, Netherlands
Tel.: (31) 40 2082424
Coach Distr
N.A.I.C.S.: 423120

VDL Bus Valkenswaard bv (1)
De Vest 9, Valkenswaard, 5555 XL, Netherlands
Tel.: (31) 40 2084611
Coach Distr
N.A.I.C.S.: 423120

VDL Bus Venlo bv (1)
Huiskensstraat 49, Venlo, 5916 PN, Netherlands
Tel.: (31) 77 3200080
Coach Distr
N.A.I.C.S.: 423120

VDL Busland bv (1)
De Vest 3, Valkenswaard, 5555 XL, Netherlands
Tel.: (31) 40 2084460
Coach Distr
N.A.I.C.S.: 423120

VDL Containersysteme GmbH (1)
Industrieweg 21, Hapert, 5527 AJ, Netherlands
Tel.: (31) 497 387050
Web Site: http://www.vdlcontainersyst.nl
Industrial Machinery Distr
N.A.I.C.S.: 423830

VDL Containersystemen B.V. (1)
Industrieweg 21, 5527 AJ, Hapert, Netherlands (100%)
Tel.: (31) 497387050
Web Site: http://www.vdlcontainerssystemen.com
Sales Range: $1-9.9 Million
Emp.: 80
Mfr of Hydraulic Containers & Handling Systems
N.A.I.C.S.: 332439

VDL Delmas GmbH (1)
Breitenbachstrabe 10, Berlin, 13509, Germany
Tel.: (49) 30 4380920
Heat Exchanger & Cooling Equipment Mfr & Distr
N.A.I.C.S.: 333415

VDL ETG Projects bv (1)
Wekkerstraat 1, 5652 AN, Eindhoven, Netherlands
Tel.: (31) 402923377
Web Site: http://www.vdletgprojects.com
Industrial Supplies Distr
N.A.I.C.S.: 423840

VDL ETG Research bv (1)
High Tech Campus 7, Eindhoven, 5656 AE, Netherlands
Tel.: (31) 40 274 8308
Mechanical Power Transmission Equipment Mfr
N.A.I.C.S.: 333613

VDL ETG Technology & Development bv (1)
Achtseweg Noord 5, Eindhoven, 5651 GG, Netherlands
Tel.: (31) 40 2638888
Mechanical Power Transmission Equipment Mfr
N.A.I.C.S.: 333613

VDL Enabling Technologies Group Eindhoven BV (1)
Achtseweg Noord 5, 5651 GG, Eindhoven, Netherlands
Tel.: (31) 402638888
Web Site: http://www.vdletg.com
Sales Range: $400-449.9 Million
Emp.: 800
Manufactures, Develops & Supplies Precision Components & Modules for Industrial Equipment
N.A.I.C.S.: 333248
Wil-Jan Schutte *(Mng Dir)*

Subsidiary (Domestic):

VDL Enabling Technologies Group Almelo BV (2)
Bornsestraat 345, PO Box 176, 7600 AD, Almelo, Netherlands
Tel.: (31) 546540000
Web Site: http://www.vdletg.com
Sales Range: $75-99.9 Million
Emp.: 400
System Integration of Mechatronic Sub Systems & Modules for OEMs in Equipment Industry
N.A.I.C.S.: 333248
Sander Verschoor *(Mng Dir)*

VDL Enabling Technologies Group Projects BV (2)
De Schakel 22, 5651 GH, Eindhoven, Netherlands
Tel.: (31) 402638666
Web Site: http://www.vdletg.com
Sales Range: $25-49.9 Million
Emp.: 150
Develops, Manufactures, Assembles & Installs Mass Production Equipment
N.A.I.C.S.: 333248
Arie Van Kraaij *(Mng Dir-Precision)*

VDL Enabling Technologies Group Research BV (2)
High Tech Campus 7, 5656 AE, Eindhoven, Netherlands
Tel.: (31) 40 274 83 08
Sales Range: $25-49.9 Million
Emp.: 80
Mfr of Parts & System Integration of Mechatronic Modules for OEMs in Equipment Industry
N.A.I.C.S.: 541715
Jadranko Dovic *(Mng Dir)*

Subsidiary (Non-US):

VDL Enabling Technologies Group Singapore Pte. Ltd. (2)
259 Jalan Ahmad Ibrahim, Singapore, 629148, Singapore
Tel.: (65) 65080320
Web Site: http://www.vdletg.com
Sales Range: $25-49.9 Million
Emp.: 250
System Integration of Mechatronic Subsystems & Modules for OEMs
N.A.I.C.S.: 333248
Yong Lin Wu *(Mng Dir)*

Subsidiary (US):

VDL Enabling Technologies Group USA - East Coast (2)
3 Hemlock Ct, Newfields, NH 03856
Tel.: (603) 778-7738
Sales Range: $25-49.9 Million
Emp.: 1
Precision Components & Modules for Industrial Equipment
N.A.I.C.S.: 423830
Michael McGrail *(Dir-Bus Dev)*

VDL Enabling Technologies Group USA - West Coast (2)
890 Hillview Ct Ste 260, Milpitas, CA 95035
Tel.: (408) 648-4630
Web Site: http://www.vdletg.com
Sales of Precision Components & Modules for Industrial Equipment
N.A.I.C.S.: 423830
Peter Severeijns *(Dir-Sls)*

Subsidiary (Non-US):

VDL Enabling Technologies Group of Suzhou Ltd. (2)
288 Su Hong Xi Road, Suzhou Industrial Park, Suzhou, 215021, Jiangsu, China
Tel.: (86) 51285188998

VDL GROEP B.V.

VDL Groep B.V.—(Continued)
Web Site: http://www.vdletg.com
Sales Range: $75-99.9 Million
Emp.: 365
System Integration of Mechatronic Sub Systems & Modules for OEMs
N.A.I.C.S.: 333248
Tom Dehaan (Mng Dir)

VDL Fibertech Industries bv (1)
Hallenweg 15, Best, 5683 CT, Netherlands
Tel.: (31) 499 36 76 76
Web Site:
http://www.vdlfibertechindustries.com
Commercial & Industrial Machinery Mfr
N.A.I.C.S.: 332999

VDL Gereedschapmakerij B.V. (1)
Industrieweg 29, 5527 AJ, Hapert, Netherlands (100%)
Tel.: (31) 497381062
Web Site: http://www.vdl.com
Sales Range: $25-49.9 Million
Emp.: 60
Mfr of Complex, High-Grade Tools
N.A.I.C.S.: 333310
Vaoof Manmaeijl (Mgr)

VDL Holding Belgium N.V. (1)
Antwerpsesteenweg 13, PO Box 4, Aartselaar, 2630, Belgium (100%)
Tel.: (32) 38705540
Web Site: http://www.vdlgroup.com
Sales Range: $50-74.9 Million
Emp.: 4
Holding Company
N.A.I.C.S.: 551112
Leen van Devoorde (Mng Dir)

Holding (Domestic):

VDL Belgium N.V. (2)
Industrielaan 15, Industriezone III, 9320, Erembodegem, Belgium (100%)
Tel.: (32) 53837090
Web Site: http://www.vdl-belgium.be
Sales Range: $25-49.9 Million
Emp.: 115
Provider of Machining Services
N.A.I.C.S.: 333310
Michael Van Tongeren (Gen Mgr)

VDL Industrial Modules BV (1)
Brandevoortse Dreef 4, Helmond, 5707 DG, Netherlands
Tel.: (31) 492505800
Web Site: http://www.vdlgroup.nl
Sales Range: $50-74.9 Million
Emp.: 150
Producer of Advanced Electronic & Mechanical Components & Systems
N.A.I.C.S.: 334419
Geroen Vendenhurk (Mng Dir)

VDL Industrial Products bv (1)
Hoevenweg 3, Eindhoven, 5652 AW, Netherlands
Tel.: (31) 40 2925580
Web Site:
http://www.vdlindustrialproducts.com
Conveyor Mfr
N.A.I.C.S.: 333922
Carloes Ooegen (Gen Mgr)

VDL KTI nv (1)
Nijverheidsstraat 10 Industrial Area II, Mol, 2400, Belgium
Tel.: (32) 14 346262
Web Site: http://www.vdlkti.be
Industrial Tool & Machinery Mfr
N.A.I.C.S.: 333998

VDL Klima B.V. (1)
Meerenakkerwag 30, 5652 AV, Eindhoven, Netherlands
Tel.: (31) 402981818
Web Site: http://www.vdlklima.com
Sales Range: $50-74.9 Million
Emp.: 200
Heat Exchange & Ventilation Technology Specialist Mfr
N.A.I.C.S.: 333415
Wim Jenniskens (Mng Dir)

Subsidiary (Non-US):

Klima Belgium NV (2)
Planet II Unit A 4 0 Leuvensesteenweg 542, B 1930, Zaventem, Belgium (95%)
Tel.: (32) 27206026
Web Site: http://www.klima.com
Sales Range: $25-49.9 Million
Emp.: 6
Sales of Heating & Cooling Products
N.A.I.C.S.: 333415
Wim Jenniskens (Mng Dir)

VDL Klima France S.A.R.L. (2)
Chateau Rouge 276 Ave De La Marne, 59708, Marcq-en-Baroeul, France (100%)
Tel.: (33) 320659165
Web Site: http://www.vdlklima.com
Sales Range: $1-9.9 Million
Emp.: 13
Heating & Cooling Products Mfr & Distr
N.A.I.C.S.: 333415
Pascal Pecuchet (Dir-France)

VDL Konings bv (1)
Bosstraat 93, Swalmen, 6071 XT, Netherlands
Tel.: (31) 475 500100
Web Site: http://www.vdlkonings.com
Industrial Machinery Mfr
N.A.I.C.S.: 333310

VDL Kunststoffen B.V. (1)
Industrieweg 107, 5591 JL, Heeze, Netherlands (100%)
Tel.: (31) 402241160
Web Site: http://www.vdlkunststoffen.com
Sales Range: $25-49.9 Million
Emp.: 50
Provider of Injection Moulding & Immersion Work for Plastics Processing
N.A.I.C.S.: 333248
Rick Van Haren (Mng Dir)

VDL Laktechniek B.V. (1)
Meerenakkenweg 20, 5652 AV, Eindhoven, Netherlands (100%)
Tel.: (31) 402501900
Web Site: http://www.vdlgroep.com
Sales Range: $25-49.9 Million
Emp.: 100
Provider of Powder Coating & Wet Coating
N.A.I.C.S.: 325510

VDL Lasindustrie B.V. (1)
Hoevenveg 3, 5652 AW, Eindhoven, Netherlands (100%)
Tel.: (31) 402512000
Web Site: http://www.vdl.nl
Sales Range: $25-49.9 Million
Emp.: 55
Provider of Machining Services, Cutting, Sawing, Stamping, Setting CO2 Welding, MIG/TIG Welding, CNC Punching & CNC Laser Cutting
N.A.I.C.S.: 333310
Bas van Der Leegte (Mng Dir)

VDL MPC bv (1)
Terminalweg 40, 3821 AJ, Amersfoort, Netherlands (100%)
Tel.: (31) 334542900
Web Site: http://www.vdlmpc.com
Sales Range: $25-49.9 Million
Emp.: 115
Producer & Assembler of High-Grade Technical Components
N.A.I.C.S.: 334419
Edwin Leenders (Mng Dir)

VDL MPC bv (1)
Terminalweg 40, Amersfoort, 3821 AJ, Netherlands
Tel.: (31) 33 4542900
Web Site: http://www.vdlmpc.com
Emp.: 100
Industrial Machinery Mfr
N.A.I.C.S.: 333310
Leo Spaan (Gen Mgr)

VDL Nedcar bv (1)
Dr Hub van Doorneweg 1, Born, 6121 RD, Netherlands
Tel.: (31) 46 489 4444
Web Site: http://www.vdlnedcar.nl
Emp.: 1,500
Car Mfr
N.A.I.C.S.: 336110
Paul Van Vuuren (CEO)

VDL Network Supplies bv (1)
Handelsweg 21, Hapert, 5527 AL, Netherlands
Tel.: (31) 497 331100
Web Site: http://www.vdlnetworksupplies.nl
Emp.: 200

Network Cable Mfr & Distr
N.A.I.C.S.: 335921
Jos Bax (Gen Mgr)

VDL Parree bv (1)
Spoorstraat 8, Sevenum, 5975 RK, Netherlands
Tel.: (31) 77 4677088
Web Site: http://www.vdlparree.com
Plastic Injection Molding Mfr
N.A.I.C.S.: 326199

VDL Parts bv (1)
De Run 5410, Veldhoven, 5504 DE, Netherlands
Tel.: (31) 40 2084100
Web Site: http://www.vdlparts.com
Emp.: 70
Coach Distr
N.A.I.C.S.: 423120
Peter Schellems (Gen Mgr)

VDL Postma bv (1)
Leeuwarderstraatweg 121d, Heerenveen, 8441 PK, Netherlands
Tel.: (31) 513 622536
Web Site: http://www.vdlpostma.nl
Emp.: 40
Industrial Tool & Machinery Mfr
N.A.I.C.S.: 333998
Johan Zwarts (Mng Dir)

VDL Rotech SRL (1)
Zona industriala NV str 1 nr 5, Arad, 310419, Romania
Tel.: (40) 257 256643
Sheet Metal Work & Metal Stamping Mfr
N.A.I.C.S.: 332322

VDL Staalservice bv (1)
Celsiusstraat 13, Weert, 6003 DG, Netherlands
Tel.: (31) 495 54 08 38
Web Site: http://www.vdlstaalservice.nl
Industrial Tool & Machinery Mfr
N.A.I.C.S.: 333998

VDL Steelweld bv (1)
Terheijdenseweg 169, 4825 BJ, Breda, Netherlands
Tel.: (31) 765792700
Web Site: http://www.vdlagrotech.com
Sales Range: $100-124.9 Million
Emp.: 500
Design & Installation of Turnkey Project in Automated Welding Hemming Glueing & Assembling Equipment for the Automotive Industry Vibrator Motor & Mfr
N.A.I.C.S.: 333992
Peter Dos (Mng Dir)

VDL Systems B.V. (1)
Erfstraat 3, 5405 AC, Uden, Netherlands (100%)
Tel.: (31) 413250505
Web Site: http://www.vdl.com
Sales Range: $25-49.9 Million
Emp.: 80
Mfr of Machinery & Internal Transport Systems for Food Processing Industry
N.A.I.C.S.: 333310

VDL TIM Hapert bv (1)
Energieweg 2, Hapert, 5527 AH, Netherlands
Tel.: (31) 497 383805
Web Site: http://www.vdltimhapert.nl
Industrial Mold Mfr
N.A.I.C.S.: 333511

VDL Technics BV (1)
korenmolen 2, Boxtel, 5281 PB, Netherlands (100%)
Tel.: (31) 411682980
Web Site: http://www.vdlgroup.com
Sales Range: $50-74.9 Million
Emp.: 90
Provider of Sheet Metal Services
N.A.I.C.S.: 423510
H. Sanders (CEO)

VDL Weweler Parts bv (1)
Minden 12, Apeldoorn, 7327 AW, Netherlands
Tel.: (31) 55 5380400
Web Site: http://www.vdlwewelerparts.nl
Motor Vehicle Spare Parts Distr
N.A.I.C.S.: 423120

VDL Weweler bv (1)

INTERNATIONAL PUBLIC

Ecofactorij 10, Apeldoorn, 7325 WC, Netherlands
Tel.: (31) 55 538 51 00
Web Site: http://www.vdweweler.nl
Vehicle Axle & Suspension System Mfr
N.A.I.C.S.: 336390

VDL Wientjes Emmen bv (1)
Phileas Foggstraat 30, Emmen, 7825 AK, Netherlands
Tel.: (31) 591 669666
Web Site: http://www.vdlgroep.com
Emp.: 90
Plastics Product Mfr
N.A.I.C.S.: 326199

VDL Wientjes Roden bv (1)
Ceintuurbaan Noord 130, Roden, 9301 ZS, Netherlands
Tel.: (31) 50 5024811
Web Site: http://www.vdlwientjesroden.nl
Emp.: 40
Plastic Injection Molding Mfr
N.A.I.C.S.: 326199

VDL-USA (1)
8111 Virginia Pine Ct, Richmond, VA 23237 (100%)
Tel.: (804) 275-8067
Web Site: http://www.vdlusa.com
Sales Range: $25-49.9 Million
Emp.: 12
Distr & Retailer of Media Replication Equipment Replacement Parts
N.A.I.C.S.: 423690

VDS Technische Industrie bv (1)
Industrieweg 29, Hapert, 5527 AJ, Netherlands
Tel.: (31) 497 383844
Web Site:
http://www.vdstechnischeindustrie.nl
Industrial Tool & Machinery Mfr
N.A.I.C.S.: 333998

Valiant Steelweld Deutschland GmbH (1)
Max Planck Strasse 39 C, 50858, Cologne, Germany (100%)
Tel.: (49) 223418810
Web Site: http://www.vdlsteelweld.com
Sales Range: $25-49.9 Million
Emp.: 5
Designer of Turnkey Production Automation Systems
N.A.I.C.S.: 238210
Joseph Schooesser (Mgr-Sls)

Weweler-Colaert nv (1)
Beneluxlaan 1-3, Poperinge, 8970, Belgium
Tel.: (32) 57 346205
Web Site: http://www.weweler.eu
Vehicle Axle & Suspension System Mfr
N.A.I.C.S.: 336390

VDM GROUP LIMITED

Suite 2 Level 2 123 Adelaide Terrace, Perth, 6004, WA, Australia
Tel.: (61) 861666126 **AU**
Web Site:
https://www.vdmgroup.com.au
VMG—(ASX)
Rev.: $668
Assets: $1,770,475
Liabilities: $11,586,198
Net Worth: ($9,815,723)
Earnings: ($951,998)
Fiscal Year-end: 06/30/23
Engineering & Construction Services
N.A.I.C.S.: 541330
Michael Fry (Sec)

Subsidiaries:

BCA Consultants Pty Ltd. (1)
Ste 59 City West Ctr Cnr Railway Pde & Plaistowe Mews, West Perth, 6872, WA, Australia
Tel.: (61) 893216255
Web Site: http://www.bcagroup.com.au
Sales Range: $25-49.9 Million
Emp.: 35
Building Consulting Services
N.A.I.C.S.: 236220
Tony Richards (Mng Dir & Gen Mgr)

VDM (QLD) Pty Ltd. (1)
Ste 10 & 11 121 Shute Harbour Rd, Can-

nonvale, 4802, QLD, Australia
Tel.: (61) 749463900
Web Site: http://www.vdmconsulting.com.au
Sales Range: $25-49.9 Million
Emp.: 6
Engineering Consulting Services
N.A.I.C.S.: 541330

VDM Construction (1)
310 Selby Street North, Osborne Park, 6017, WA, Australia
Tel.: (61) 892411800
Web Site: http://www.vdmgroup.com.au
Sales Range: $25-49.9 Million
Commercial Building Construction Services
N.A.I.C.S.: 236220

VDM Earthmoving Contractors Pty Ltd. (1)
16 Kalamunda Rd, Guildford, 6055, WA, Australia
Tel.: (61) 893506948
Sales Range: $25-49.9 Million
Emp.: 20
Earthmoving Contract Services
N.A.I.C.S.: 238910

Van Der Meer Consulting Vietnam Co Ltd. (1)
Ste 203 DMC Lake View Tower 535 Kim Ma St, Ba Dinh Dist, Hanoi, Vietnam
Tel.: (84) 422203196
Sales Range: $25-49.9 Million
Emp.: 20
Engineering Consulting Services
N.A.I.C.S.: 541330

VDS ALUMINIUM
Domaine Du Mafay, 35890, Rennes, France
Tel.: (33) 299424343
Web Site: http://www.seplaumic.com
Rev.: $21,700,000
Emp.: 35
N.A.I.C.S.: 423510
Jean-Louis Duribreux (Pres)

VE WONG CORPORATION
5th Fl No 79 Chungshan N Rd Sec 2, Taipei, Taiwan
Tel.: (886) 225717271
Web Site: http://www.vewong.com
1203—(TAI)
Rev.: $209,415,375
Assets: $330,698,408
Liabilities: $109,560,250
Net Worth: $221,138,158
Earnings: $21,508,812
Emp.: 1,754
Fiscal Year-end: 12/31/23
Canned Beverages Mfr
N.A.I.C.S.: 311421
Chen Ching-Fu (Chm)

Subsidiaries:

SAIGON VE WONG CO., LTD. (1)
1707 Hwy 1A An Phu Dong Ward, District 12, Ho Chi Minh City, Vietnam
Tel.: (84) 837195550
Web Site: http://www.aone.vn
Sales Range: $200-249.9 Million
Emp.: 900
Convenience Foods & Ingredients Mfr
N.A.I.C.S.: 311230
Egawa Taketada (Chm)

VEALLS LIMITED
1st Floor 484 Toorak Road, Toorak, 3142, VIC, Australia
Tel.: (61) 3 9827 4110 AU
Sales Range: $1-9.9 Million
Investment Management Service
N.A.I.C.S.: 523999
Martin Charles Veall (Exec Dir)

VEATIVE GROUP PLC
Ventura House Ventura Park Road, Tamworth, B78 3EL, United Kingdom
Tel.: (44) 1827930408
Web Site: http://www.devcleverholdings.com
Year Founded: 2013
DEV—(LSE)
Rev.: $9,986,643
Assets: $32,608,743
Liabilities: $3,469,761
Net Worth: $29,138,982
Earnings: ($3,434,049)
Emp.: 48
Fiscal Year-end: 10/31/21
Software Development Services
N.A.I.C.S.: 541511
Christopher Michael Jeffries (CEO)

Subsidiaries:

DevClever Limited (1)
1 Ninian Park Ninian Way, Wilnecote, Tamworth, B77 5ES, United Kingdom
Tel.: (44) 3300582922
Web Site: http://www.devclever.co.uk
Software Development Services
N.A.I.C.S.: 541511
Chris Jeffries (Mng Dir)

VEB.RF
Akademika Sakharova Prospekt 9, 107996, Moscow, Russia
Tel.: (7) 4956046363 RU
Web Site: http://www.veb.ru
Year Founded: 1924
Sales Range: $125-149.9 Million
Emp.: 1,200
Banking Services
N.A.I.C.S.: 522110
Dmitriev Vladimir Aleksandrovich (Chm)

Subsidiaries:

JSC Russian Agency for Export Credit and Investment Insurance (1)
12 Krasnopresnenskaya Embankment entrance 9, 123610, Moscow, Russia
Tel.: (7) 4957831188
Web Site: http://www.exiar.ru
General Insurance Services
N.A.I.C.S.: 524298
Alexey Tsovbun (Head-Rep Office)

Subsidiary (Domestic):

Eximbank of Russia (2)
12 Krasnopresnenskaya Embankment entrance 9, 123610, Moscow, Russia
Tel.: (7) 4959670767
Web Site: http://www.eximbank.ru
Financial Support Services
N.A.I.C.S.: 541611
Smagin Roman Yurievich (Chm-Acting)

LLC "VEB Engineering" (1)
Masha Poryvayeva Street 7 Bld 2, Moscow, 107078, Russia
Tel.: (7) 495 258 84 20
Web Site: http://vebeng.ru
Civil Engineering Services
N.A.I.C.S.: 541330

LLC "VEB-Capital" (1)
7a Mashi Poryvayevoi Str, Moscow, 107078, Russia
Tel.: (7) 495 662 1515
Web Site: http://www.vebcapital.ru
Sales Range: $50-74.9 Million
Emp.: 100
Real Estate Asset Management & Investment Services
N.A.I.C.S.: 531390
A. P. Udod (Dir-Fin)

Mutual Fund RDIF (1)
8 Presnenskaya Nab Building 1 Gorod Stolits South Tower 7th Floor, Moscow, 123317, Russia
Tel.: (7) 495 644 3414
Web Site: http://www.rdif.ru
Sales Range: $50-74.9 Million
Emp.: 100
Investment Management Service
N.A.I.C.S.: 523940
Kirill A. Dmitriev (CEO-Supervisory Bd)

OJSC "Belvnesheconombank" (1)
29 Pobediteley Ave 220004 Minsk, Myasnikova St 32, 220030, Minsk, Belarus
Tel.: (375) 17 209 29 44
Banking & Financial Services
N.A.I.C.S.: 521110

Subsidiary (Domestic):

Sivelga Associated Closed Joint Stock Company (2)
Korol Str 2, Minsk, 220004, Belarus
Tel.: (375) 17 226 59 90
Web Site: http://eng.sivelga.com
Footwear Mfr
N.A.I.C.S.: 316210

OJSC "Federal Center for Project Finance" (1)
Posledniy Pereulok 11 Bld 1, Moscow, Russia
Tel.: (7) 495 777 3993
Web Site: http://www.fcpf.ru
Sales Range: $50-74.9 Million
Emp.: 31
Banking & Financial Services
N.A.I.C.S.: 521110
Rauf Yabbarov (Deputy CEO)

OJSC "North Caucasus Development Corporation" (1)
Pyatigorskaya Str 139, Stavropol Territory, Yessentuki, 357625, Russia
Tel.: (7) 87934 4 28 30
Web Site: http://www.en.krskfo.ru
Sales Range: $50-74.9 Million
Emp.: 60
Investment Management Services523920
N.A.I.C.S.: 523940
Vladimir Aleksandrovich Dmitriev (Chm)

OJSC "SME Bank" (1)
79 Sadovnicheskaya Street, Moscow, 115035, Russia
Tel.: (7) 495 783 79 98
Web Site: http://mspbank.ru
Banking & Financial Services
N.A.I.C.S.: 521110
Sergei Pavlovich Krjukov (Chm)

OJSC "VEB-Leasing" (1)
str Vozdvizhenka 10, 119019, Moscow, Russia
Tel.: (7) 4959814240
Web Site: http://www.veb-leasing.ru
Aircraft Leasing Services
N.A.I.C.S.: 532411
Vitaly Vavilin (Chm & CEO)

PSC "Prominvestbank" (1)
12 Shevchenka Lane, Kiev, 01001, Ukraine
Tel.: (380) 44 279 51 61
Web Site: http://www.pib.com.ua
Banking & Financial Services
N.A.I.C.S.: 521110
Dmitriev Vladimir Alexandrovich (Chm-Supervisory Bd)

VECIMA NETWORKS, INC.
771 Vanalman Avenue, Victoria, V8Z 3B8, BC, Canada
Tel.: (250) 881-1982
Web Site: https://www.vecima.com
Year Founded: 1988
VCM—(TSX)
Rev.: $62,325,905
Assets: $147,158,387
Liabilities: $14,660,866
Net Worth: $132,497,521
Earnings: ($2,535,343)
Emp.: 364
Fiscal Year-end: 06/30/19
Telecommunication & Broadband Internet Products Mfr
N.A.I.C.S.: 334220
Surinder G. Kumar (Founder & Chm)

Subsidiaries:

Spectrum Signal Processing, Inc. (1)
300-2700 Production Way, Burnaby, V5A 4X1, BC, Canada
Tel.: (604) 676-6700
Web Site: http://www.spectrumsignal.com
Sales Range: $10-24.9 Million
Emp.: 81
Producers of High Density Signal Processing Solutions
N.A.I.C.S.: 334220
Mark Briggs (Gen Mgr)

Subsidiary (US):

Spectrum Signal Processing (USA), Inc. (2)
6630E Eli Whitney Dr, Columbia, MD 21046
Tel.: (410) 872-0202
Wireless Signal Solutions
N.A.I.C.S.: 334290

Vecima Telecom (P) Ltd., (1)
3rd Floor Airport Road Kavoor, Mangalore, 575015, Karnataka, India
Tel.: (91) 824 2483447
Sales Range: $25-49.9 Million
Emp.: 25
Software Development Services
N.A.I.C.S.: 541511
H. C. Guruprasad (Mgr)

VECTION TECHNOLOGIES LTD.
The Garden Office Park Building C Level 4 355 Scarborough Beach Road, Osborne Park, 6017, WA, Australia
Tel.: (61) 863807446 AU
Web Site: https://vection-technologies.com
VR1—(ASX)
Rev.: $21,920,569
Assets: $30,854,262
Liabilities: $24,473,339
Net Worth: $6,380,923
Earnings: ($6,676,732)
Emp.: 100
Fiscal Year-end: 06/30/24
Holding Company; Application Software Development Services
N.A.I.C.S.: 551112
Gianmarco Biagi (Mng Dir)

Subsidiaries:

Blank Canvas Studios (Aus) Pty Ltd. (1)
The Garden Office Park Level 4 Building C 355 Scarborough Beach Rd, Osborne Park, 6017, WA, Australia
Tel.: (61) 863114658
Web Site: https://blankcanvas.studio
Architectural Services
N.A.I.C.S.: 541310

JMC AMEA Ltd. (1)
Level 17 Office Tower The World Trade Center, Abu Dhabi, United Arab Emirates
Tel.: (971) 26544155
Computer System Design Services
N.A.I.C.S.: 541512

JMC Group SRL (1)
Via L da Vinci 155, Cassano d'Adda, 20062, Milan, Italy
Tel.: (39) 0283591103
Web Site: https://www.jmcgroup.it
Computer System Design Services
N.A.I.C.S.: 541512

Real Estate Agent Performance Pty Ltd (1)
20/30 Hasler Rd, Osborne Park, 6017, WA, Australia
Tel.: (61) 1300776812
Web Site: http://reaperformance.com.au
Administrative Services
N.A.I.C.S.: 561110

Vection Consulting Pty Ltd. (1)
PO Box 221, Melbourne, VIC, Australia
Tel.: (61) 412256004
Web Site: https://www.vector-consulting.com.au
Business Consulting Services
N.A.I.C.S.: 541611
Brad Davies (Founder & Mng Dir)

VECTOR CAPITAL PLC
6th Floor First Central 200 2 Lakeside Drive, London, NW10 7FQ, United Kingdom
Tel.: (44) 2081917615 UK
Web Site: https://www.vectorcapital.co.uk
Year Founded: 2019
VCAP—(AIM)
Rev.: $7,482,959
Assets: $69,030,548
Liabilities: $37,361,777

VECTOR CAPITAL PLC

Vector Capital Plc—(Continued)
Net Worth: $31,668,771
Earnings: $2,871,750
Emp.: 9
Fiscal Year-end: 12/31/22
Asset Management Services
N.A.I.C.S.: 523999

VECTOR CONSTRUCTION LTD.
474 Dovercourt Drive, Winnipeg, R3Y 1G4, MB, Canada
Tel.: (204) 489-6300
Web Site: http://www.vector-construction.com
Year Founded: 1968
Rev.: $18,638,977
Emp.: 150
Concrete Contractor services
N.A.I.C.S.: 327331

Subsidiaries:

Vector Construction Inc. (1)
3814 3rd Ave NW, Fargo, ND 58103
Tel.: (701) 280-9697
Construction Engineering Services
N.A.I.C.S.: 541330

Vector Corrosion Technologies Inc. (1)
3822 Turman Loop Ste 102, Wesley Chapel, FL 33544
Tel.: (813) 830-7566
Construction Engineering Services
N.A.I.C.S.: 541330

Vector Corrosion Technologies Ltd (1)
474B Dovercourt Drive, Winnipeg, R3Y 1G4, MB, Canada
Tel.: (204) 489-9611
Bricks Mfr
N.A.I.C.S.: 327331
David Macleod (Project Mgr)

VECTOR INC.
Akasaka Garden City 18th Floor
4-15-1 Akasaka, Minato-ku, Tokyo, 107-0052, Japan
Tel.: (81) 35 572 6080
Web Site: http://www.vectorinc.co.jp
Year Founded: 1989
6058—(TKS)
Rev.: $458,357,680
Assets: $305,646,000
Liabilities: $149,042,960
Net Worth: $156,603,040
Earnings: $20,047,280
Emp.: 1,303
Fiscal Year-end: 02/28/22
Public Relations
N.A.I.C.S.: 541820
Keiji Nishie (Founder & Chm)

Subsidiaries:

ANTIL Inc. (1)
Akasaka Garden City 18th Floor 4-15-1 Akasaka, Minato-ku, Tokyo, Japan
Tel.: (81) 355726060
Risk Managemeng Srvices
N.A.I.C.S.: 541611

AdInte Co., Ltd. (1)
347-1 Shijo-machi Shinmachi-dori Shijo-dori 7F CUBE Nishikarasuma, Shimogyo-ku, Kyoto, Japan
Tel.: (81) 753420255
Web Site: https://adinte.jp
Emp.: 123
Information Technology Services
N.A.I.C.S.: 541511

Allm Inc. (1)
Shibuya Mark City West 16F 1-12-1 Dogenzaka, Shibuya-ku, Tokyo, Japan
Tel.: (81) 343612650
Web Site: https://www.allm.net
Health Care Srvices
N.A.I.C.S.: 621610

Bears Co., Ltd. (1)
5-7F Tanabehamacho Building 2-1-1 Nihonbashihamacho, Chuo-ku, Tokyo, Japan
Tel.: (81) 356400211
Web Site: https://www.happy-bears.com
Emp.: 216
Housekeeping Services
N.A.I.C.S.: 561720

Brand Cloud.Inc. (1)
TODA BUILDING 4F 8-5-34 Akasaka, Minato-ku, Tokyo, Japan
Tel.: (81) 364472653
Web Site: https://brandcloud.co.jp
Management Consulting Services
N.A.I.C.S.: 541618

CHIKYUJIN.jp Co., Ltd. (1)
Taisei Hakataeki Higashi Building 6F 1-9-11 Hakataeki Higashi, Hakata-ku, Fukuoka, Japan
Tel.: (81) 924343135
Web Site: https://chikyujin.jp
Employee Placement Services
N.A.I.C.S.: 561311

CLOUD BEAUTY inc. (1)
6th floor Tatsuno Minamihonmachi Building 2-2-9 Minamihonmachi, Chuo-ku, Osaka, Japan
Tel.: (81) 662686884
Web Site: https://cloudbeauty.co.jp
Salon Services
N.A.I.C.S.: 812112

Cinnamon Inc. (1)
3-19-13 Toranomon 6F Spirit Building, Minato, Tokyo, Japan
Tel.: (81) 368074091
Web Site: https://cinnamon.ai
Artificial Intelligence Development Services
N.A.I.C.S.: 541715

FANTAS technology, Inc. (1)
5F KDX Ebisu Building 4-3-8 Ebisu, Shibuya-ku, Tokyo, Japan
Tel.: (81) 354241800
Web Site: https://fantas-tech.co.jp
Emp.: 138
Real Estate Services
N.A.I.C.S.: 531210

Hachimenroppi, Inc. (1)
4th floor Toyomi Distribution Center 6-8 Toyomi-cho, Chuo-ku, Tokyo, Japan
Tel.: (81) 362282795
Web Site: https://hachimenroppi.com
Fruit & Vegetable Whslr
N.A.I.C.S.: 424480

Hatch Work Co., Ltd. (1)
3rd floor DF Building 2-2-8 Minami-Aoyama, Minato-ku, Tokyo, Japan
Tel.: (81) 357723621
Web Site: https://hatchwork.co.jp
Parking Management Services
N.A.I.C.S.: 812930

INFLUENCER BANK,Inc. (1)
Akasaka Garden City 15th Floor 4-15-1 Akasaka, Minato-ku, Tokyo, Japan
Tel.: (81) 355727369
Digital Marketing Services
N.A.I.C.S.: 541613

IR Robotics Inc. (1)
Nittele Yotsuya Building 5-3-23 Kojimachi, Chiyoda-ku, Tokyo, Japan
Tel.: (81) 367728482
Web Site: https://ir-robotics.co.jp
Education Related Services
N.A.I.C.S.: 236220

Infratop Inc. (1)
23rd floor Sumitomo Fudosan Roppongi Grand Tower 3-2-1 Roppongi, Minato-ku, Tokyo, Japan
Tel.: (81) 368694700
Web Site: https://infratop.jp
Education Services
N.A.I.C.S.: 611710

Keyword Marketing Inc. (1)
The Terrace Tsukiji 2F 7-2-1 Tsukiji, Chuo-ku, Tokyo, Japan
Tel.: (81) 362265880
Web Site: https://www.kwm.co.jp
Emp.: 70
Advertising Services
N.A.I.C.S.: 541810

Last One Mile Co., Ltd. (1)
3rd floor Owl Tower 4-21-1 Higashiikebukuro, Toshima-ku, Tokyo, Japan
Tel.: (81) 5017810250
Web Site: https://lomgrp.co.jp
Emp.: 233
Information Technology Services
N.A.I.C.S.: 541519

Leading Mark, Inc. (1)
6th floor Hokkai Shiba Building 2-31-15 Shiba, Minato-ku, Tokyo, Japan
Tel.: (81) 367127431
Web Site: https://www.leadingmark.jp
Emp.: 96
Human Resouce Services
N.A.I.C.S.: 541612

Liveron Inc. (1)
3F NTT Toranomon Building 3-8-8 Toranomon, Minato-ku, Tokyo, Japan
Tel.: (81) 366360300
Web Site: https://www.livero.co.jp
Emp.: 279
Human Resouce Services
N.A.I.C.S.: 541612

Mental Health Technologies Co., Ltd. (1)
4F Tokai Akasaka Building 3-16-11 Akasaka, Minato-ku, Tokyo, Japan
Tel.: (81) 362776595
Web Site: https://mh-tec.co.jp
Mental Health Solution Services
N.A.I.C.S.: 621330

Metro Engines Co., Ltd. (1)
9th floor Nishigotanda 7-chome Building 25-5, Shinagawa-ku, Tokyo, Japan
Tel.: (81) 368223919
Web Site: https://info.metroengines.jp
Emp.: 80
Rental Car Related Services
N.A.I.C.S.: 532111

News Technology.Inc. (1)
Akasaka Garden City 13th Floor 4-15-1 Akasaka, Minato-ku, Tokyo, Japan
Tel.: (81) 355448775
Content Creation Services
N.A.I.C.S.: 541890

PR TIMES INC. (1)
Hulic Minami Aoyama Building 3F 2-27-25, Minami Aoyama Minato-ku, Tokyo, 107-0062, Japan
Tel.: (81) 364555463
Web Site: http://www.prtimes.co.jp
Online Publishing Services
N.A.I.C.S.: 513110

PROGRIT Inc. (1)
5F Tokyo Kotsu Kaikan 2-10-1 Yurakucho, Chiyoda-ku, Tokyo, Japan
Tel.: (81) 363817760
Web Site: https://www.progrit.co.jp
English Coaching Services
N.A.I.C.S.: 611710

PacRim Marketing Group Inc. (1)
1585 Kapiolani Blvd Ste 888, Honolulu, HI 96814-4522
Tel.: (808) 949-4592
Web Site: http://www.pacrimmarketing.com
Marketing & Advertising Services
N.A.I.C.S.: 541613
Jennifer Erwin (COO)

Public Affairs Japan Inc. (1)
Akasaka Garden City 17F 4-15-1 Akasaka, Minato-ku, Tokyo, Japan
Tel.: (81) 368253015
Web Site: https://www.pajapan.co.jp
Survey & Analysis Policy Services
N.A.I.C.S.: 541360

ROXX Inc. (1)
8th floor Shinjuku East Side Square 6-27-30 Shinjuku, Shinjuku-ku, Tokyo, Japan
Tel.: (81) 367777070
Web Site: https://roxx.co.jp
Emp.: 186
Banking Services
N.A.I.C.S.: 522110

Renoveru Co., Ltd. (1)
Tatsumura Aoyama Building 5-4-35 Minami-Aoyama, Minato-ku, Tokyo, Japan
Tel.: (81) 357662590
Web Site: https://renoveru.co.jp
Building Renovation Services
N.A.I.C.S.: 236118

Robot Payment Inc. (1)
15th Arai Building 4F 6-19-20, Jingumae Shibuya-ku, Tokyo, Japan
Tel.: (81) 354695780
Web Site: https://www.robotpayment.co.jp
Emp.: 96
Financial Services
N.A.I.C.S.: 921130

Secual, inc. (1)
2F Shibuya East Place 2-6-4 Shibuya, Shibuya-ku, Tokyo, Japan
Tel.: (81) 364275123
Web Site: https://secual-inc.com
Smart Home Security Services
N.A.I.C.S.: 561621

Vecks Inc. (1)
6th floor Leela Nogizaka 1-15-18 Minami Aoyama, Minato-ku, Tokyo, Japan
Tel.: (81) 354141633
Web Site: https://vecks.jp
Emp.: 40
Digital Marketing Services
N.A.I.C.S.: 486210

W TOKYO Inc. (1)
W Building 5-28-5 Jingumae, Shibuya-ku, Tokyo, Japan
Tel.: (81) 364197165
Web Site: https://w-tokyo.co.jp
Emp.: 44
Marketing Services
N.A.I.C.S.: 541613

Waqoo, Inc. (1)
Yokomizo Building 4F 2-14-1 Kamiuma, Setagaya-ku, Tokyo, Japan
Tel.: (81) 368054600
Web Site: https://waqoo.jp
Medical Support Services
N.A.I.C.S.: 621610

Willgate, Inc. (1)
Clover Minami-Aoyama 3F 3-8-38 Minami-Aoyama, Minato-ku, Tokyo, Japan
Tel.: (81) 368690631
Web Site: https://www.willgate.co.jp
Emp.: 191
Marketing Services
N.A.I.C.S.: 541613

VECTOR INFORMATIK GMBH
Holderackerstr 36, 70499, Stuttgart, Germany
Tel.: (49) 711 806700
Web Site: http://www.vector.com
Year Founded: 1988
Emp.: 2,000
Tools, Software Components, Hardware & Services
N.A.I.C.S.: 513210
Thomas Beck (Mgr)

Subsidiaries:

Squoring Technologies SAS (1)
9 Rue Matabiau, 31000, Toulouse, France
Tel.: (33) 170952200
Automobile Parts Mfr
N.A.I.C.S.: 336390
Helene Sardin (CFO)

VecScan AB (1)
Theres Svenssons Gata 9, 417 55, Gothenburg, Sweden
Tel.: (46) 317647600
Automobile Parts Mfr
N.A.I.C.S.: 336390
Karin Anjou (Sr Mgr-IT Project)

Vector Austria GmbH (1)
Millennium Tower Etage 41 Handelskai 94-96, Vienna, Austria
Tel.: (43) 1901600
Automobile Parts Mfr
N.A.I.C.S.: 336390
Thomas Geyer (Mng Dir)

Vector Automotive Technology (Shanghai) Co., Ltd. (1)
Sunyoung Center Room 1601-1603 No 398 Jiang Su Road, Changning District, Shanghai, 200050, China
Tel.: (86) 2122834688
Automobile Parts Mfr
N.A.I.C.S.: 336390
Rixin Zhang (Gen Mgr)

AND PRIVATE COMPANIES

VEDANTA RESOURCES LTD

Vector France S.A.S. (1)
106 avenue Marx Dormoy, 92120, Montrouge, France
Tel.: (33) 173284200
Automobile Parts Mfr
N.A.I.C.S.: 336390

Vector GB Ltd. (1)
2480 Regents Court The Crescent Business Park, Birmingham, B37 7YE, West Midlands, United Kingdom
Tel.: (44) 1217887900
Automobile Parts Mfr
N.A.I.C.S.: 336390
James Cooper *(Mng Dir)*

Vector Informatica Brasil Ltda. (1)
Rua Verbo Divino 1488 3 andar, Sao Paulo, 4719-904, Brazil
Tel.: (55) 1151802350
Automobile Parts Mfr
N.A.I.C.S.: 336390

Vector Informatik India Pvt. Ltd. (1)
No 11-14 6th Floor Tara Heights Old Mumbai Pune Road, Wakadewadi Shivaji Nagar, Pune, 411003, India
Tel.: (91) 2066346600
Automobile Parts Mfr
N.A.I.C.S.: 336390
Hemant Adhikari *(Mgr)*

Vector Italia s.r.l. (1)
Corso Sempione 68, 20154, Milan, Italy
Tel.: (39) 0267817110
Automobile Parts Mfr
N.A.I.C.S.: 336390

Vector Korea IT Inc. (1)
9F Yongsan Prugio Summit Office-dong 69 Hangang-daero, Yongsan-gu, Seoul, 04378, Korea (South)
Tel.: (82) 28070600
Automobile Parts Mfr
N.A.I.C.S.: 336390
Daehwan Kim *(Mgr-Bus Dev)*

Vector North America Inc. (1)
39500 Orchard Hill Pl, Novi, MI 48375
Tel.: (248) 449-9290
Web Site: http://www.vector.com
Automobile Parts Mfr
N.A.I.C.S.: 336390
Steven Werner *(Project Engr)*

Vector Software Inc. (1)
1351 S County Trl Ste 310, East Greenwich, RI 02818
Tel.: (401) 398-7185
Web Site: http://www.vectorcast.com
Software Development Services
N.A.I.C.S.: 541511

VECTOR LIMITED
101 Carlton Gore Road Newmarket, Auckland, 1023, New Zealand
Tel.: (64) 99787788 NZ
Web Site: http://www.vector.co.nz
VCT—(NZX)
Rev.: $713,098,086
Assets: $4,502,153,110
Liabilities: $2,134,928,230
Net Worth: $2,367,224,880
Earnings: $67,344,498
Emp.: 115
Fiscal Year-end: 06/30/23
Electric Power & Gas Distribution Services
N.A.I.C.S.: 221122
Alison Paterson *(Chm)*

Subsidiaries:

Liquigas Limited (1)
Hutchen Place, Level 3 New Plymouth District, New Plymouth, 4310, New Zealand
Tel.: (64) 67511823
Web Site: https://www.liquigas.co.nz
Emp.: 25
Liquefied Petroleum Gas Distr
N.A.I.C.S.: 424720
Albert De Geest *(CEO)*

Liquigas Limited (1)
Hutchen Place, Level 3 New Plymouth District, New Plymouth, 4310, New Zealand
Tel.: (64) 67511823
Web Site: https://www.liquigas.co.nz

Emp.: 25
Liquefied Petroleum Gas Distr
N.A.I.C.S.: 424720
Albert De Geest *(CEO)*

Liquigas Limited (1)
Hutchen Place, Level 3 New Plymouth District, New Plymouth, 4310, New Zealand
Tel.: (64) 67511823
Web Site: https://www.liquigas.co.nz
Emp.: 25
Liquefied Petroleum Gas Distr
N.A.I.C.S.: 424720
Albert De Geest *(CEO)*

Liquigas Limited (1)
Hutchen Place, Level 3 New Plymouth District, New Plymouth, 4310, New Zealand
Tel.: (64) 67511823
Web Site: https://www.liquigas.co.nz
Emp.: 25
Liquefied Petroleum Gas Distr
N.A.I.C.S.: 424720
Albert De Geest *(CEO)*

VECTOR RESOURCES LIMITED
Suite 16 83 Mill Point Road, South Perth, 6151, WA, Australia
Tel.: (61) 8 6188 7800 AU
Web Site:
http://www.vectorres.com.au
Rev.: $1,916
Assets: $9,051,200
Liabilities: $1,248,761
Net Worth: $7,802,439
Earnings: ($1,762,454)
Emp.: 15
Fiscal Year-end: 06/30/18
Exploration of Minerals Services
N.A.I.C.S.: 213115
Michael Hendriks *(Sec)*

VECTOR SOFTWARE SP. Z O. O.
ul Al Jerozolimskie 184B, 02-486, Warsaw, Poland
Tel.: (48) 22 489 89 00
Web Site: http://vectorsoft.pl
Software Publisher
N.A.I.C.S.: 513210
Marcin Adamiak *(Pres)*

Subsidiaries:

ASEC S.A. (1)
Ul Wadowicka 6, 30-415, Krakow, Poland
Tel.: (48) 122930200
Web Site: http://www.asec.com.pl
Sales Range: $25-49.9 Million
Emp.: 30
Smart Card Solutions
N.A.I.C.S.: 519290
Malgorzata Olszewska *(Fin Dir & VP)*

VECTRA S.A.
Aleja Zwyciestwa 253, 81-525, Gdynia, Poland
Tel.: (48) 58 624 83 52
Web Site: http://www.vectra.pl
Year Founded: 1991
Telecommunication Cable Operator
N.A.I.C.S.: 517410

Subsidiaries:

Multimedia Polska S.A. (1)
ul Tadeusza Wendy 7/9, Gdynia, Poland
Tel.: (48) 225538611
Web Site: http://www.multimedia.pl
Sales Range: $150-199.9 Million
Emp.: 1,879
Telecommunication Servicesb
N.A.I.C.S.: 517111
Tomasz Ulatowski *(Co-Chm-Supervisory Bd)*

Subsidiary (Domestic):

Telewizja Kablowa Brodnica Sp. z o.o. (2)
Tadeusza Wendy 7-9, Gdynia, 81-341, Pomeranian, Poland
Tel.: (48) 587110300

Sales Range: $200-249.9 Million
Emp.: 1,000
Cable Television Installation Services
N.A.I.C.S.: 516210

VECTUS BIOSYSTEMS LIMITED
Unit 5 Ground Floor 26-34 Dunning Avenue, Rosebery, 2018, NSW, Australia
Tel.: (61) 283441300
Web Site:
https://www.vectusbiosystems.com
Year Founded: 2005
VBS—(ASX)
Rev.: $760,338
Assets: $1,352,592
Liabilities: $360,087
Net Worth: $992,505
Earnings: ($1,561,259)
Fiscal Year-end: 06/30/24
Biotechnology Research & Development Services
N.A.I.C.S.: 541714
Karen Duggan *(Founder, Founder & CEO)*

VEDAN INTERNATIONAL (HOLDINGS) LTD.
Level 54 Hopewell Centre 183 Queens Road East, Hong Kong, China (Hong Kong)
Tel.: (852) 29801888
Web Site:
http://www.vedaninternational.com
2317—(HKG)
Rev.: $451,007,000
Assets: $405,972,000
Liabilities: $114,254,000
Net Worth: $291,718,000
Earnings: ($4,384,000)
Emp.: 3,855
Fiscal Year-end: 12/31/22
Conglomerates & Holding Companies
N.A.I.C.S.: 551112
Cheng Yang *(Exec Dir)*

Subsidiaries:

Shandong Vedan Snowflake Enterprise Co., Ltd. (1)
Xuehua Industry Park Wangyin Jining High-Tech Industrial Development, Zone, Jining, Shandong, China
Tel.: (86) 5373866566
Web Site:
http://www.vedaninternational.com
Monosodium Glutamate Mfr & Sales
N.A.I.C.S.: 325199

Vedan (Vietnam) Enterprise Corporation Limited (1)
6th Floor Eurowindow Building 27 Tran Duy Hung, Trung Hoa Ward Cau Giay District, Hanoi, Vietnam
Tel.: (84) 2437833721
Web Site: http://www.vedan.com.vn
Emp.: 3,000
Seasoning & Starch Product Mfr
N.A.I.C.S.: 311942
Ko Chung Chih *(VP)*

Xiamen Darong Import & Export Trade Co., Ltd. (1)
No 568 Tongji N Rd, Tong An Dist, Xiamen, 361100, Fujian, China
Tel.: (86) 5927364913
Cassava Starch Import & Distr
N.A.I.C.S.: 424690

VEDANT ASSET LIMITED
3rd Floor Gayways House P P Compound Main Road, Ranchi, 834001, Jharkhand, India
Tel.: (91) 9304955505
Web Site: https://vedantasset.com
Year Founded: 2002
543623—(BOM)
Rev.: $230,112
Assets: $346,505
Liabilities: $33,470

Net Worth: $313,035
Earnings: $21,035
Fiscal Year-end: 03/31/22
Investment Management Service
N.A.I.C.S.: 523999

VEDANT FASHIONS LIMITED
A501-A502 SDF-1 4th Floor Paridhan Garment Park 19 Canal South Road, Kolkata, 700 015, West Bengal, India
Tel.: (91) 9674373838
Web Site:
https://www.vedantfashions.com
Year Founded: 2002
MANYAVAR—(NSE)
Rev.: $167,276,662
Assets: $259,698,579
Liabilities: $91,857,323
Net Worth: $167,841,257
Earnings: $51,448,714
Emp.: 414
Fiscal Year-end: 03/31/23
Clothing Accessory Distr
N.A.I.C.S.: 458110
Navin Pareek *(Compliance Officer & Sec)*

Subsidiaries:

Manyavar Creations Private Limited (1)
1925 Chakragaria Metropolis Mall 1st Floor Shop No 016A, Kolkata, 700094, West Bengal, India
Tel.: (91) 9830742323
Fashion Wear Mfr & Distr
N.A.I.C.S.: 315990

VEDANTA RESOURCES LTD
4th Floor 30 Berkeley Square, London, W1J 6EX, United Kingdom
Tel.: (44) 2074995900 UK
Web Site:
https://www.vedantalimited.com
Year Founded: 2003
Rev.: $18,283,000,000
Assets: $23,430,000,000
Liabilities: $24,302,000,000
Net Worth: ($872,000,000)
Earnings: $838,000,000
Emp.: 87,500
Fiscal Year-end: 03/31/23
Mineral Mining Services
N.A.I.C.S.: 212290
Navin Agarwal *(Vice Chm)*

Subsidiaries:

Black Mountain Mining (Proprietary) Limited (1)
1 Penge Road, Springbok, 8893, Northern Cape, South Africa
Tel.: (27) 54 983 9202
Sales Range: $150-199.9 Million
Lead & Zinc Ore Mining Services
N.A.I.C.S.: 212230

Konkola Copper Mines Plc (1)
Stand M/1408 Fern Ave, Chingola, Zambia (79.4%)
Tel.: (260) 212350000
Web Site: http://www.kcm.co.zm
Copper Mining
N.A.I.C.S.: 212230
Tom Albanese *(Chm)*

Madras Aluminum Company Ltd. (1)
PO Box 4, Mettur Dam, 636 402, Salem, Tamil Nadu, India (80%)
Tel.: (91) 4298222061
Web Site: http://www.malco-india.com
Aluminum Mining, Refining & Smelting
N.A.I.C.S.: 331313
Navin Agarwal *(Chm)*

Vedanta Limited (1)
1st Floor C wing Unit 103 Corporate Avenue Atul Projects, Chakala Andheri East, Mumbai, 400 093, Maharashtra, India (50.1%)
Tel.: (91) 2266434500
Web Site: http://www.vedantalimited.com
Rev.: $18,003,596,907
Assets: $23,542,473,473

VEDANTA RESOURCES LTD

Vedanta Resources Ltd—(Continued)
Liabilities: $17,616,329,956
Net Worth: $5,926,143,517
Earnings: $1,738,864,576
Emp.: 12,064
Fiscal Year-end: 03/31/2023
Iron Ore Products Mfr
N.A.I.C.S.: 331210
Navin Agarwal (Vice Chm)

Subsidiary (Domestic):

Bharat Aluminium Company
Limited (2)
Scope Office Complex Core - 6, 2nd Floor
7 Lodi Road, 110003, New Delhi,
India (51%)
Tel.: (91) 1124360418
Web Site: http://www.balco.com
Aluminum Rolling & Drawing
N.A.I.C.S.: 331318
Ramesh Ramachandran Nair (CEO)

Cairn India Limited (2)
DLF Atria Phase 2, Gurgaon, 122002, India
Tel.: (91) 124 476 4000
Web Site: http://www.cairnindia.com
Sales Range: $1-4.9 Billion
Holding Company; Crude Oil & Natural Gas
Exploration & Production Services
N.A.I.C.S.: 551112
Sudhir Mathur (CEO)

Subsidiary (Non-US):

AvanStrate Inc. (3)
1-11-1 Nishi-Gotanda, Shinagawa-ku, To-
kyo, 141-0031, Japan (51.63%)
Tel.: (81) 357195883
Web Site: http://www.avanstrate.com
LCD Glass Substrate Mfr & Whslr
N.A.I.C.S.: 327215
Akarsh K. Hebbar (Mng Dir)

Cairn Energy Netherlands Holdings
B.V. (3)
Koninginnegracht 23, 2514 AB, Hague,
Netherlands
Tel.: (31) 703836561
Holding Company
N.A.I.C.S.: 551112

Subsidiary (Domestic):

Cairn Energy Group Holdings
B.V. (4)
Koninginnegracht 23 A, 2514 AB, Hague,
Netherlands (100%)
Tel.: (31) 703836531
Holding Company
N.A.I.C.S.: 551112

Subsidiary (Non-US):

Cairn Energy India Pty. Limited (5)
DLF Atria Building Jacaranda Marg - N
Block, DLF City Phase II, Gurgaon, 122
002, India (100%)
Tel.: (91) 124 459 3000
Sales Range: $600-649.9 Million
Emp.: 1,093
Oil & Gas Exploration & Production
N.A.I.C.S.: 211120
Mayank Ashar (CEO & Mng Dir)

Subsidiary (Non-US):

Copper Mines of Tasmania Pty
Limited (2)
Penghana Rd, Queenstown, Queenstown,
7467, TAS, Australia (100%)
Tel.: (61) 364711666
Web Site: http://www.cmt.com.au
Copper Ore & Nickel Ore Mining
N.A.I.C.S.: 212230

Subsidiary (Domestic):

ESL Steel Limited (2)
Lohanchal Colony Plot No 10 Sector 12,
Bokaro Steel City, Bokaro, 82 7013, India
Tel.: (91) 3371034400
Web Site: http://www.eslsteel.com
Iron Pipe Mfr
N.A.I.C.S.: 331210
Ashish Kumar Gupta (CEO)

Ferro Alloys Corporation Ltd. (2)
Factor House A-45 to 50 Sector 16, Disst
Gautam Budh Nagar, Noida, 201 301, Uttar
Pradesh, India
Tel.: (91) 1204171000
Web Site: http://www.facorgroup.in
Rev.: $83,187,874
Assets: $52,590,330
Liabilities: $19,851,909
Net Worth: $32,738,421
Earnings: $4,023,460
Emp.: 603
Fiscal Year-end: 03/31/2019
Ferro Alloys Distr
N.A.I.C.S.: 331110
R. K. Saraf (Chm & Mng Dir)

Ferro Alloys Corporation Ltd. -
Charge Chrome Plant (3)
D P Nagar, Randia, Bhadrak, 756 135, Odi-
sha, India
Tel.: (91) 6784 240320
Ferro Alloy Mfr
N.A.I.C.S.: 331110
B. B. Singh (Dir-Technical)

Subsidiary (Domestic):

Hindustan Zinc Limited (2)
Yashad Bhawan, Udaipur, 313004, Rajast-
han, India (64.92%)
Tel.: (91) 2946604000
Web Site: https://www.hzlindia.com
Rev.: $3,337,152,000
Assets: $6,241,735,500
Liabilities: $1,831,011,000
Net Worth: $4,410,724,500
Earnings: $1,089,270,000
Emp.: 3,719
Fiscal Year-end: 03/31/2021
Zinc Producer
N.A.I.C.S.: 212230
Rajendra Pandwal (Officer-Nodal & Sec)

Subsidiary (Non-US):

Monte Cello BV (2)
Leliegracht 10, Amsterdam,
Netherlands (100%)
Tel.: (31) 205502311
Metal Ore Mining
N.A.I.C.S.: 212290

Thalanga Copper Mines Pty
Limited (2)
Gregory Dev Rd, Reward-Highway Mine,
4820, Charters Towers, Australia (100%)
Tel.: (61) 747529700
Metal Ore Mining
N.A.I.C.S.: 212290

Vedanta Lisheen Mining Limited (1)
Killoran Moyne, Thurles, Tipperary,
Ireland (100%)
Tel.: (353) 50445600
Web Site: http://www.lisheenmine.ie
Sales Range: $300-349.9 Million
Emp.: 400
Zinc & Lead Mining
N.A.I.C.S.: 212230
Alan Buckley (Gen Mgr)

Vizag General Cargo Berth Pvt.
Ltd. (1)
Administrative Building Eastern Stack Yard
Visakhapatnam Port Trust, Visakhapatnam,
530 035, Andhra Pradesh, India
Tel.: (91) 8916654000
Web Site: http://www.vgcb.co.in
Rev.: $21,589,820
Assets: $88,932,321
Liabilities: $90,577,216
Net Worth: $(1,644,894)
Earnings: $(4,755,974)
Emp.: 29
Fiscal Year-end: 03/31/2019
Coal Mining Services
N.A.I.C.S.: 213113
Srikanth Gudivada (CFO & Head-Fin)

VEDAVAAG SYSTEMS LIMITED

103 West Block Siri Sai Orchid, Mad-
hapur Hitec City, Hyderabad, 500
081, Telangana, India
Tel.: (91) 4040188140
Web Site: http://www.vedavaag.com
Year Founded: 1998
533056—(BOM)
Rev.: $9,926,495
Assets: $18,884,595
Liabilities: $3,152,417
Net Worth: $15,732,178
Earnings: $955,746
Emp.: 159
Fiscal Year-end: 03/31/21
Software Development Services
N.A.I.C.S.: 541511
D. Himabindhu (Sec)

Subsidiaries:

VSL Data Systems Private
Limited (1)
H No 8-2-269/N/34 Sagar Society Road No
2 Banjara Hills, Hyderabad, 500 034, India
Tel.: (91) 4040272246
Web Site: http://www.vsldatasystems.com
Database Management Services
N.A.I.C.S.: 518210

VEDER DO BRASIL LTDA

Rua Secundino Domingues No 22
Jardim Independencia, Sao Paulo,
03223-110, SP, Brazil
Tel.: (55) 1123413132 BR
Motion Controller Mfr
N.A.I.C.S.: 335314

VEE TIME CORP.

15 Sec 4 Wen Sin Road, Dali City,
Taichung, Taiwan
Tel.: (886) 424069811 TW
Web Site: http://www.vee.com.tw
8307—(TAI)
Sales Range: $25-49.9 Million
Emp.: 253
Fiber Optic Broadband, Local Tele-
phone & Cable Television Services
N.A.I.C.S.: 517810
Fu-Yuan Lai (Chm)

Subsidiaries:

Tatung InfoComm Co., Ltd. (1)
No 495 Zhongxiao lst Rd, Sanmin Dist, Ka-
ohsiung, Taiwan
Tel.: (886) 7 236 0081
Web Site: http://www.tatung.net.tw
Wireless Telecommunication Services
N.A.I.C.S.: 517112

VEEFIN SOLUTIONS LIMITED

Off No-601 602 603 Neelkanth Cor-
porate IT Park Kirol Road, Vidyavihar
W, Mumbai, 400086, Maharashtra,
India
Tel.: (91) 9004917712
Web Site: https://www.veefin.com
Year Founded: 2010
543931—(BOM)
Rev.: $750,095
Assets: $1,880,709
Liabilities: $782,904
Net Worth: $1,097,805
Earnings: $67,145
Fiscal Year-end: 03/31/22
Software Development Services
N.A.I.C.S.: 541511
Gautam Udani (COO)

VEEJAY LAKSHMI ENGINEERING WORKS LTD

Sengalipalayam, NGGO Colony post,
Coimbatore, 641 022, Tamilnadu,
India
Tel.: (91) 7373045125
Web Site:
https://www.veejaylakshmi.com
Year Founded: 1974
522267—(BOM)
Rev.: $7,707,871
Assets: $8,000,935
Liabilities: $5,124,993
Net Worth: $2,875,943
Earnings: ($1,683,400)
Emp.: 500

INTERNATIONAL PUBLIC

Fiscal Year-end: 03/31/23
Automatic Cone Winders Mfrs
N.A.I.C.S.: 333248
J. Anand (Mng Dir)

VEEKO INTERNATIONAL HOLDINGS LTD.

10/F Wyler Centre Phase II 192-200
Tai Lin Pai Road, Kwai Chung, Hong
Kong, New Territories, China (Hong
Kong)
Tel.: (852) 28870888 Ky
Web Site: http://www.veeko.com.hk
Year Founded: 1984
1173—(HKG)
Rev.: $64,470,524
Assets: $97,953,861
Liabilities: $72,233,830
Net Worth: $25,720,031
Earnings: ($6,883,147)
Emp.: 950
Fiscal Year-end: 03/31/22
Holding Company
N.A.I.C.S.: 551112
Johnny Chung Man Cheng (Chm &
Exec Dir)

VEEM LTD

22 Baile Rd, Canning Vale, 6155,
WA, Australia
Tel.: (61) 894559355 AU
Web Site: https://www.veem.com.au
Year Founded: 1968
VEE—(ASX)
Rev.: $53,789,383
Assets: $62,744,813
Liabilities: $27,833,010
Net Worth: $34,911,803
Earnings: $4,664,709
Emp.: 200
Fiscal Year-end: 06/30/24
Propeller Mfr & Distr
N.A.I.C.S.: 332999
Mark David Miocevich (Mng Dir)

VEENHUIS MACHINES B.V.

Almelosestraat 54, 8102 HE, Raalte,
Netherlands
Tel.: (31) 572-35 21 45 NI
Web Site: http://www.veenhuis.com
Year Founded: 1938
Agricultural Machinery Mfr
N.A.I.C.S.: 333112
Walter Veenhuis (Mng Dir)

VEER ENERGY & INFRASTRUCTURE LTD.

629 / A Gazdar House 1st Floor Near
Kalbadevi Post Office, J Shankar
Sheth Marg, Mumbai, 400002, India
Tel.: (91) 2222072641
Web Site: https://www.veerenergy.net
Year Founded: 2006
503657—(BOM)
Rev.: $991,607
Assets: $7,911,804
Liabilities: $276,135
Net Worth: $7,635,669
Earnings: $6,402
Emp.: 4
Fiscal Year-end: 03/31/23
Infrastructure Development & Engi-
eering Services
N.A.I.C.S.: 541330
Yogesh Mahasuklal Shah (Chm &
Mng Dir)

Subsidiaries:

Veer Enterprise GmbH (1)
Wasen Str 11, 70327, Stuttgart, Germany
Tel.: (49) 176 70837 903
Sales Range: $25-49.9 Million
Emp.: 1
Solar Power Structure Installation Services
N.A.I.C.S.: 237130

VEER GLOBAL INFRACON-

STRUCTION LIMITED
Office 01 shalibhadra classic 100 feet link road, Nalasopara East, Palghar, 401209, Maharashtra, India
Tel.: (91) 8767747777
Web Site:
https://www.veerglobalitd.com
543241—(BOM)
Rev.: $1,372,532
Assets: $6,430,814
Liabilities: $2,697,069
Net Worth: $3,733,745
Earnings: $85,762
Emp.: 10
Fiscal Year-end: 03/31/23
Real Estate Services
N.A.I.C.S.: 531390
Deepali Chundawat *(Sec & Compliance Officer)*

VEERAM SECURITIES LIMITED
Ground and First Floor 7 Natvarshyam Co Op Ho S Ltd, Opp Orchid Park Ramdevnagar Road Satellite, Ahmedabad, 380051, India
Tel.: (91) 9925266150
Web Site:
https://www.veeramsecuritiesltd.com
Year Founded: 2011
540252—(BOM)
Rev.: $2,259,878
Assets: $2,440,016
Liabilities: $90,130
Net Worth: $2,349,887
Earnings: $278,042
Emp.: 8
Fiscal Year-end: 03/31/23
Jewellery Product Mfr & Distr
N.A.I.C.S.: 339910
Mahendra Ramniklal Shah *(Mng Dir & CFO)*

VEERHEALTH CARE LIMITED
629-A Gazdar House 1st Floor JSS Marg Near Kalbadevi Post Office, Mumbai, 400002, India
Tel.: (91) 2222018582
Web Site:
https://www.veerhealthcare.net
511523—(BOM)
Rev.: $1,740,028
Assets: $3,027,960
Liabilities: $458,246
Net Worth: $2,569,714
Earnings: $189,677
Emp.: 21
Fiscal Year-end: 03/31/23
Financial Investment Services
N.A.I.C.S.: 523999
Shruti Y. Shah *(Exec Dir)*

VEERKRUPA JEWELLERS LIMITED
Shop-7 Vrundavan Residency Near Satyam School, Near Dharmnath Prabhu Society Naroda, Ahmedabad, 382330, Gujarat, India
Tel.: (91) 7922981555
Web Site:
https://www.veerkrupajewellers.com
Year Founded: 2001
543545—(BOM)
Rev.: $2,253,924
Assets: $1,801,480
Liabilities: $235,847
Net Worth: $1,565,633
Earnings: $4,923
Fiscal Year-end: 03/31/23
Jewelry Product Distr
N.A.I.C.S.: 458310

VEF AS
Brivibas gatve 204a, Riga, LV-1039, Latvia
Tel.: (371) 67552331
Web Site: http://www.vef.lv
Year Founded: 1991
VEF1R—(RSE)
Sales Range: Less than $1 Million
Lighting Lamp Mfr
N.A.I.C.S.: 335132

VEF LTD.
Clarendon House 2 Church Street, Hamilton, HM 11, Bermuda
Tel.: (441) 46854501550
Web Site:
http://www.vostokemerging.com
0TX—(DEU)
Rev.: $410,000
Assets: $430,094,000
Liabilities: $48,263,000
Net Worth: $381,831,000
Earnings: ($377,359,000)
Emp.: 11
Fiscal Year-end: 12/31/22
Electronic Finance Services
N.A.I.C.S.: 522320
Lars O. Gronstedt *(Chm)*

VEF RADIOTEHNIKA RRR
Kurzemes pr 3, Riga, 1067, Latvia
Tel.: (371) 67852012
Web Site: http://www.rrr.lv
Year Founded: 1927
Audio Equipment Mfr
N.A.I.C.S.: 334310
Eriks Ertmanis *(Chm-Mgmt Bd)*

VEG-PAK PRODUCE LIMITED
165 The Queensway Suite 249, Toronto, M8Y 1H8, ON, Canada
Tel.: (416) 259-4686
Web Site:
http://www.vegpakproduce.com
Year Founded: 1943
Rev.: $19,513,494
Emp.: 60
Fresh Fruits & Vegetables Distr
N.A.I.C.S.: 424480
Vic Carnevale *(Owner & Pres)*

Subsidiaries:

Veg-Pak Produce Limited Warehouse & Production Facility (1)
25 Belvia Road, Toronto, M8W 3R2, ON, Canada
Tel.: (416) 255-7400
Food Products Mfr
N.A.I.C.S.: 311991

VEGA AD
Vit 1 p k 18, 5800, Pleven, 5800, Bulgaria
Tel.: (359) 64680781
Web Site:
http://www.vegapleven.com
VEGA—(BUL)
Sales Range: Less than $1 Million
Footwear Mfr
N.A.I.C.S.: 316210

VEGA CORPORATION CO., LTD.
4F Hakata Gion Center Place 7-20 Gion-machi, Hakata-ku, Fukuoka, 812 0038, Japan
Tel.: (81) 922813501
Web Site: https://www.vega-c.com
Year Founded: 2004
3542—(TKS)
Rev.: $124,436,900
Assets: $55,075,020
Liabilities: $21,072,660
Net Worth: $34,002,360
Earnings: $366,800
Emp.: 222
Fiscal Year-end: 03/31/20
Online Furniture Distr
N.A.I.C.S.: 423210
Tomokazu Ukishiro *(Pres & CEO)*

VEGANO FOODS INC.
1040 West Georgia Street Unit 415, Vancouver, V6E 4H1, BC, Canada
Tel.: (604) 259-0028 BC
Web Site:
https://www.veganofoods.com
Year Founded: 2020
VAGN—(CNSX)
Rev.: $148,510
Assets: $72,982
Liabilities: $528,372
Net Worth: ($455,390)
Earnings: ($4,068,517)
Fiscal Year-end: 03/31/23
Food Service Contracting Services
N.A.I.C.S.: 722310
Conor Power *(CEO)*

VEGANZ GROUP AG
An den Kiefern 7, Ludwigsfelde, 14974, Halle, Germany
Tel.: (49) 3029363780
Web Site: https://www.veganz.com
Year Founded: 2011
VEZ—(DEU)
Rev.: $17,720,699
Assets: $26,947,982
Liabilities: $19,922,297
Net Worth: $7,025,685
Earnings: ($10,263,328)
Emp.: 104
Fiscal Year-end: 12/31/23
Packaged Food Distr
N.A.I.C.S.: 424420
Jan Bredack *(Founder)*

VEGETABLE OIL PACKING JOINT STOCK COMPANY
Block 6-12 Tan Thoi Hiep Industrial, District 12, Ho Chi Minh City, Vietnam
Tel.: (84) 8 3597 4228
Web Site: http://www.vmpack.com
Year Founded: 2002
VPK—(HOSE)
Sales Range: $1-9.9 Million
Paper Packaging Product Mfr
N.A.I.C.S.: 322220
Le Hoang Vu *(CEO)*

VEGETABLE PRODUCTS LTD.
Old Nimta Road Nandan Nagar Belghoria, Kolkata, 700083, West Bengal, India
Tel.: (91) 3322315686
Web Site:
https://www.vegetableindia.com
Year Founded: 1953
539132—(BOM)
Rev.: $959,247
Assets: $18,648,043
Liabilities: $4,313,878
Net Worth: $14,334,165
Earnings: ($1,071,327)
Emp.: 153
Fiscal Year-end: 03/31/23
Edible Oil Mfr
N.A.I.C.S.: 213112
Tanmoy Mondal *(Mng Dir)*

VEGREVILLE FORD SALES & SERVICE INC
6106 50th Avenue, Vegreville, T9C 1N6, AB, Canada
Tel.: (780) 632-2060
Web Site: http://www.veg-ford.com
Year Founded: 1991
Rev.: $17,438,860
Emp.: 40
New & Used Car Dealers
N.A.I.C.S.: 441110
Eddy Sadlowski *(Mgr-Sls)*

VEHCO AB
Falkenbergsgatan 3, Gothenburg, Sweden
Tel.: (46) 31645100
Web Site: http://www.vehco.com
Fleet Management Services
N.A.I.C.S.: 561110
Anna Stoldt *(Dir-Corp)*

Subsidiaries:

Vehco NV (1)
Drukpersstraat 4, 1000, Brussels, Belgium
Tel.: (32) 32255393
Web Site: http://www.vehco.com
Transport Management Software Distr
N.A.I.C.S.: 423430
Johan Frilund *(Mng Dir)*

Subsidiary (Non-US):

Vehco BV (2)
Kleine Landtong 27, 4201 HL, Gorinchem, Netherlands
Tel.: (31) 183641400
Transport Management Software Distr
N.A.I.C.S.: 423430
Johan Frilund *(Mng Dir)*

Vehco France SAS (2)
53 Rue Antoine Condorcet, 38090, Vaulx-Milieu, France
Tel.: (33) 474999333
Transport Management Software Distr
N.A.I.C.S.: 423430
Johan Frilund *(Mng Dir)*

Vehco ICT GmbH (2)
Pliniusstrasse 8 Niedersachsen, 48488, Emsburen, Germany
Tel.: (49) 59032176870
Transport Management Software Distr
N.A.I.C.S.: 423430
Thomas Postges *(Mgr)*

VEHICLE AXLE MANUFACTURING CO.
Azadi Square Azadi Street Shahid Mirghasemi Alley No 32, 1341647547, Tehran, Iran
Tel.: (98) 2166024351
Web Site: https://www.vamco.ir
Year Founded: 1986
TMKH1—(THE)
Sales Range: Less than $1 Million
Automobile Equipment Mfr
N.A.I.C.S.: 811198

VEHO GROUP OY AB
Salomonkatu 17B, PO Box 158, FI 00101, Helsinki, Finland
Tel.: (358) 10569 12
Web Site: http://www.veho.fi
Year Founded: 1939
Sales Range: $1-4.9 Billion
Emp.: 2,244
Motor Vehicle Importer & Retailer
N.A.I.C.S.: 423110
Jan-Martin Borman *(Pres & CEO)*

VEHO OY AB
Makituvantie 3 G, Vantaa, 01510, Uusimaa, Finland
Tel.: (358) 1056912
Web Site: http://www.veho.fi
Automobiles
N.A.I.C.S.: 423110
Juha Ruotsalainen *(CEO)*

VEIDEKKE ASA
Skabos vei 4, 0278, Oslo, Norway
Tel.: (47) 21055000
Web Site: http://www.veidekke.no
VK4—(DEU)
Rev.: $3,570,847,959
Assets: $1,629,780,159
Liabilities: $1,353,131,350
Net Worth: $276,648,808
Earnings: $107,057,085
Emp.: 7,772
Fiscal Year-end: 12/31/22
Construction & Property Development Services
N.A.I.C.S.: 236220

VEIDEKKE ASA

Veidekke ASA—(Continued)

Hans Olav Sorlie (*Exec VP-Building Construction*)

Subsidiaries:

AS Noremco Construction (1)
Skabos vei 4, Skoyen, 0278, Oslo, Norway (100%)
Tel.: (47) 21055000
Building Construction Services
N.A.I.C.S.: 236116

Arcona AB (1)
Tulegatan 19 Across the Yard, 113 57, Stockholm, Sweden
Tel.: (46) 86012100
Web Site: https://www.arcona.se
Emp.: 275
Logistic Services
N.A.I.C.S.: 541614

BRA Bygg AB (1)
Alfagatan 7, 431 49, Molndal, Sweden
Tel.: (46) 3 189 4400
Web Site: https://www.bragroup.se
Emp.: 215
Building Construction Services
N.A.I.C.S.: 236220

BSK Arkitekter AB (1)
Rehnsgatan 11, PO Box 4020, 113 57, Stockholm, Sweden
Tel.: (46) 86011500
Web Site: https://www.bsk.se
Emp.: 40
Architectural Engineering Services
N.A.I.C.S.: 541310
Alena Zhuk (*CFO*)

Billstrom Riemer Andersson AB (1)
Alfagatan 7, 431 49, Molndal, Sweden
Tel.: (46) 3 189 4400
Web Site: https://www.bragroup.se
Commercial & Institutional Building Construction Services
N.A.I.C.S.: 236220

Brinkab AB (1)
Ullvagen 6a, 824 35, Hudiksvall, Sweden
Tel.: (46) 20779900
Web Site: https://brinkab.se
Building Construction Services
N.A.I.C.S.: 236220

Hande AS (1)
Kjelsasveien 174, 0884, Oslo, Norway
Tel.: (47) 23008480
Web Site: https://hande.no
Building Construction Services
N.A.I.C.S.: 236220

Hoffmann A/S (1)
Fabriksparken 66, 2600, Glostrup, Denmark
Tel.: (45) 43299000
Web Site: https://www.hoffmann.dk
Sales Range: $25-49.9 Million
Emp.: 500
Construction & Property Development Services
N.A.I.C.S.: 541330
Anne Mette (*Sec*)

Kolo Veidekke AS (1)
Skabos Vei 4 Pb 508 Skoyen, NO 0214, Oslo, Norway
Tel.: (47) 21055050
Web Site: http://www.veidekke.no
Sales Range: $400-449.9 Million
Emp.: 2,000
Building Contractors
N.A.I.C.S.: 236116

Leif Grimsrud AS (1)
Svinesrudveien 334, 1788, Halden, Norway
Tel.: (47) 69216420
Web Site: https://www.leifgrimsrud.no
Emp.: 236
Machinery Equipment Contract Services
N.A.I.C.S.: 811310

Ost AS (1)
Svinesundsveien 334, 1788, Halden, Norway
Tel.: (47) 69192508
Web Site: https://www.ost.as
Building Construction Services
N.A.I.C.S.: 236220

Sydbelaggningar AB (1)
Granitgatan 2, 25468, Helsingborg, Sweden
Tel.: (46) 4 352 1816
Web Site: https://sydbelaggningar.se
Road Construction Services
N.A.I.C.S.: 237310

Tautech AB (1)
Vastra Bjorrodsvagen 9, Landvetter, 438 93, Gothenburg, Sweden
Tel.: (46) 70 818 9255
Web Site: https://www.tautech.se
Building Construction Services
N.A.I.C.S.: 236220

Veidekke Eiendom AS (1)
Skabos Rd 4, PO Box 507, Skoyen, 0214, Oslo, Norway
Tel.: (47) 21055000
Web Site: http://www.veidekke.com
Building Contractors
N.A.I.C.S.: 236116

Veidekke Entreprenor AS (1)
Skoyen Skabos vei 4, 0278, Oslo, Norway
Tel.: (47) 21055000
Web Site: https://www.veidekke.no
Sales Range: $900-999.9 Million
Emp.: 7
Construction & Property Development Services
N.A.I.C.S.: 236116

Veidekke Logistikkbygg AS (1)
Faret 20, 3271, Larvik, Norway
Tel.: (47) 33291900
Web Site: https://www.veidekke.no
Commercial & Institutional Building Construction Services
N.A.I.C.S.: 236220

Veidekke Prefab AB (1)
Fridhemsgatan 17, 733 39, Sala, Sweden
Tel.: (46) 22418800
Web Site: https://www.vprefab.se
Fiber Concrete Mfr
N.A.I.C.S.: 327999

Veidekke Sverige AB (1)
Kalkstensvagen 2, Lund, 224 78, Sweden
Tel.: (46) 199400
Web Site: https://www.veidekke.se
Sales Range: $25-49.9 Million
Emp.: 100
Building Construction Services
N.A.I.C.S.: 236116
Erik Alteryd (*Mng Dir*)

Veitech AB (1)
Svetsarvagen 12, 171 41, Solna, Sweden
Tel.: (46) 86356100
Web Site: https://www.veitech.se
Building Construction Services
N.A.I.C.S.: 236220

VEKEN TECHNOLOGY CO., LTD.

Floor 20 Yuehu Jinhui Building No 225, Liuting Street Haishu District, Ningbo, 315010, Zhejiang, China
Tel.: (86) 57487206656
Web Site: https://www.veken-tech.com
Year Founded: 1993
600152—(SHG)
Rev.: $326,451,678
Assets: $490,261,960
Liabilities: $223,862,872
Net Worth: $266,399,088
Earnings: ($14,727,876)
Fiscal Year-end: 12/31/22
Textile Products Mfr
N.A.I.C.S.: 313210
Chen Liangqin (*Chm*)

Subsidiaries:

Dongguan City Yongwei Technology Co., Ltd. (1)
No 26-101 Xinfu Road, Lincun Village Tangxia Town, Dongguan, China
Tel.: (86) 76982167866
Battery Mfr
N.A.I.C.S.: 335910

Dongguan Veken Battery Co., Ltd. (1)
No 19 Xinghua Road, New City Industrial Zone Tiankeng Village Hengali Town, Dongguan, China
Tel.: (86) 76981019588
Battery Mfr
N.A.I.C.S.: 335910

Dongguan Veken New Energy Science & Technology Co., Ltd. (1)
No 19 Xinghua Road New City Industrial Zone, Tiankeng Village Hengli Town, Dongguan, China
Tel.: (86) 76982167866
Lithium Ion Battery Mfr & Distr
N.A.I.C.S.: 325180

Ningbo Veken Battery Co., Ltd. (1)
No 5 Gangxi Avenue, Bonded West Zone, Ningbo, China
Tel.: (86) 57486822355
Web Site: https://www.vekenbattery.com
Battery Mfr
N.A.I.C.S.: 335910

Ningbo Veken New Energy Science & Technology Co., Ltd. (1)
27 Weiwu Road, Beilun District, Ningbo, Zhejiang, China
Tel.: (86) 57486968675
Web Site: https://www.vekenner.com
Battery Mfr
N.A.I.C.S.: 335910

Shenzhen Veken New Energy Science & Technology Co., Ltd. (1)
Floor 2 Annex Building Of Mairui Building No 12 Keji South Road, High-Tech Industrial Zone Nansha, Shenzhen, China
Tel.: (86) 75586576627
Battery Mfr
N.A.I.C.S.: 335910

VEKOBS S.R.O.

U Plynarny 99, 101 00, Prague, Czech Republic
Tel.: (420) 725929976
Web Site: http://www.vekobs.cz
Emp.: 10
Electronic Product Repair & Maintenance Services
N.A.I.C.S.: 811210
Vaclav Civka (*Mgr*)

VEKTOR MANAGEMENT GMBH & CO ERSTE KG

Karntner Strasse 6, A-1010, Vienna, Austria
Tel.: (43) 1 908 9600
Web Site: http://www.vektor-industrie.com
Miscellaneous Financial Investment Services
N.A.I.C.S.: 523999
Klaus Sernetz (*Mng Partner*)

Subsidiaries:

Hinke Tankbau GmbH (1)
Frankenburger Strasse 2, Vocklamarkt, 4870, Austria (100%)
Tel.: (43) 76823660
Web Site: http://www.hinke.com
Sales Range: $25-49.9 Million
Emp.: 50
Industrial Machinery & Equipment Whslr
N.A.I.C.S.: 423830
Ernst Steiner (*Dir*)

VELA TECHNOLOGIES PLC

15 Victoria Mews Cottingley Business Park, Millfield Road, Bingley, BD16 1PY, United Kingdom
Tel.: (44) 2076539850
Web Site: http://www.velatechplc.com
Year Founded: 1999
VELA—(AIM)
Assets: $1,653,703
Liabilities: $820,063
Net Worth: $833,640
Earnings: ($1,917,101)
Emp.: 2
Fiscal Year-end: 03/31/20
Investment Services
N.A.I.C.S.: 523999

VELAN HOTELS LTD.

41 Kangayam Road, Tirupur, 641604, Tamilnadu, India
Tel.: (91) 4214311111
Web Site: https://www.velanhotels.com
Year Founded: 1990
526755—(BOM)
Rev.: $2,758
Assets: $7,785,624
Liabilities: $7,001,271
Net Worth: $784,353
Earnings: ($2,217,097)
Emp.: 56
Fiscal Year-end: 03/31/23
Hotel & Resort Operator
N.A.I.C.S.: 721120
Eswaramoorthy Venkatachalam
Muthukumara Ramalingam (*Mng Dir*)

VELAN INC.

7007 Cote De Liesse, Montreal, H4T 1G2, QC, Canada
Tel.: (514) 748-7743
Web Site: https://www.velan.com
Year Founded: 1952
VLN—(TSX)
Rev.: $411,242,000
Assets: $508,428,000
Liabilities: $242,918,000
Net Worth: $265,510,000
Earnings: ($10,255,000)
Emp.: 1,650
Fiscal Year-end: 02/28/22
Industrial Valve Mfr for the Pulp & Paper Industry
N.A.I.C.S.: 332911
G. Perez (*VP-Product Tech & Strategic Initiatives*)

Subsidiaries:

Velan GmbH (1)
Daimlerstrasse 8, D-47877, Willich, Germany (100%)
Tel.: (49) 2154493800
Web Site: http://www.velan.de
Sales Range: $25-49.9 Million
Emp.: 18
Industrial Valve Mfr & Sales
N.A.I.C.S.: 332911
Stefan Wemgrath (*Pres*)

Velan Gulf Manufacturing Co. Ltd.
7289 -77 3872 2nd Industrial City, Dammam, 34334, Saudi Arabia
Tel.: (966) 138300658
Industrial Valve Mfr & Distr
N.A.I.C.S.: 332911

Velan Ltd. (1)
89 Sinwon-ro, Danwon-gu, Ansan, 15409, Gyeonggi-do, Korea (South)
Tel.: (82) 314912811
Industrial Valve Mfr & Distr
N.A.I.C.S.: 332911

Velan S.A.S. (1)
90 rue Challemel Lacour, 69367, Lyon, Cedex 7, France (100%)
Tel.: (33) 478616700
Web Site: http://www.velan.fr
Sales Range: $50-74.9 Million
Emp.: 200
Industrial Valve Sales & Supplier
N.A.I.C.S.: 332911
Jean-Luc Mazel (*Mng Dir*)

Velan Valvac Manufacturing Co. Ltd. (1)

Velan Valve (Suzhou) Co. Ltd. (1)
6 Chaichang Road, Mudu Wuzhong District, Suzhou, 215101, Jiangsu, China
Tel.: (86) 51269213380
Industrial Valve Mfr & Distr
N.A.I.C.S.: 332911

Velan Valve Corp. (1)
94 Ave C, Williston, VT 05495 (100%)
Tel.: (802) 863-2562

Web Site: http://www.velan.com
Sales Range: $50-74.9 Million
Emp.: 202
Industrial Valve Mfr
N.A.I.C.S.: 332911
Dennis Lalancette *(Gen Mgr)*

Velan Valves Ltd. (1)
Unit 1 Lakeside Business Park, Pinfold Road, Thurmaston, LE4 8AS, Leics, United Kingdom **(100%)**
Tel.: (44) 1162695172
Web Site: http://www.velan.co.uk
Sales Range: $25-49.9 Million
Emp.: 30
Industrial Valve Mfr & Sales
N.A.I.C.S.: 332911
Rob Velan *(Sec)*

Velan Valvulas Industriais, Lda. (1)
Av Avry dos Santos, Famoes, 1689-018, Portugal **(100%)**
Tel.: (351) 219347800
Web Site: http://www.velan.pt
Sales Range: $25-49.9 Million
Emp.: 55
Industrial Valve Mfr
N.A.I.C.S.: 332911

VELANA DD
Smartinska 52, 1000, Ljubljana, Slovenia
Tel.: (386) 41656500
Web Site: http://www.velana.si
Year Founded: 1948
Curtain Fabrics & Textures Mfr
N.A.I.C.S.: 314120

VELBAZHD AD
Buzludzha 97, Kyustendil, 2500, Bulgaria
Tel.: (359) 78551320
Web Site: http://www.velbazhd.com
VELB—(BUL)
Sales Range: Less than $1 Million
Yarn Mfr
N.A.I.C.S.: 313110
Marijka Ivanova Vaseva *(Chm)*

VELCAN HOLDINGS SA
11 avenue Guillaume, L-1651, Luxembourg, Luxembourg
Tel.: (352) 142685108
Web Site: https://www.velcan.lu
Rev.: $3,727,740
Assets: $150,563,815
Liabilities: $3,478,585
Net Worth: $147,085,229
Earnings: ($4,981,900)
Emp.: 29
Fiscal Year-end: 12/31/17
Hydro Power Plants
N.A.I.C.S.: 221111
Philippe Pedrini *(Chm)*

VELCRO INDUSTRIES N.V.
22-24 Castorweg, Willemstad, Curacao
Tel.: (599) 94618199   NL
Web Site:
  http://www.velcroindustriesnv.com
Year Founded: 1940
Sales Range: $250-299.9 Million
Emp.: 2,856
Holding Company; Velcro Brand Fasteners Mfr
N.A.I.C.S.: 551112
Albert John Holton *(Deputy Chm)*

Subsidiaries:

Velcro Australia Pty. Ltd. (1)
5-11 David Lee Rd, Hallam, 3803, VIC, Australia **(100%)**
Tel.: (61) 397032466
Web Site: http://www.velcro.com.au
Sales Range: $25-49.9 Million
Emp.: 30
Marketing & Sales of Velcro Fasteners
N.A.I.C.S.: 424310
Ian Coleman *(Mng Dir)*

Velcro Canada, Inc. (1)
114 East Drive, Brampton, L6T 1C1, ON, Canada **(100%)**
Tel.: (905) 791-1630
Web Site: http://www.velcro.ca
Sales Range: $50-74.9 Million
Emp.: 220
Fastener Mfr
N.A.I.C.S.: 339993

Velcro Europe S.A. (1)
Carretera Mataro a Granollers Km 5 8, Argentona, E08310, Barcelona, Spain
Tel.: (34) 937023500
Web Site: http://www.velcro.es
Sales Range: $100-124.9 Million
Emp.: 300
Fastener Mfr
N.A.I.C.S.: 339993
Alain Zijlstra *(Mng Dir)*

Velcro GmbH (1)
Kleines Wegle 1, D 71691, Freiberg am Neckar, Germany
Tel.: (49) 141991190
Sales Range: $25-49.9 Million
Emp.: 20
Provider of Fastener Services
N.A.I.C.S.: 339993

Velcro Group Corporation (1)
95 Sun Dial Ave, Manchester, NH 03103 **(100%)**
Tel.: (603) 669-4880
Sales Range: $750-799.9 Million
Mfr of Laminated Velcro Products
N.A.I.C.S.: 313220
Scott Filion *(Pres-Americas)*

Velcro Holdings B.V. (1)
Coaude Debuffylaan 24, 1082 ND, Amsterdam, Netherlands **(100%)**
Tel.: (31) 206610090
Web Site: http://www.velcro.com
Provider of Fasteners
N.A.I.C.S.: 339993
Peter Bossam *(Mgr-Ops)*

Velcro Hong Kong Ltd. (1)
Ste 1-7 1st Fl Sino Industrial Plz, 9 Kai Cheung Road, Kowloon, China (Hong Kong) **(100%)**
Tel.: (852) 25703698
Web Site: http://www.velcro.com
Sales Range: $25-49.9 Million
Emp.: 23
Fasteners Mfr & Distr
N.A.I.C.S.: 339993
Joanna Cheng *(Gen Mgr)*

Velcro Industries B.V. (1)
15 Pietermaai, Willemstad, Curacao **(100%)**
Tel.: (599) 94335000
Sales Range: $25-49.9 Million
Emp.: 100
Mfr of Hook & Loop Fasteners
N.A.I.C.S.: 339993

Velcro Industries France S.A. (1)
Zone D Active Valnor 31-40 Rue Jacques Robert, PO Box 862, 95508, Le Thillay, Cedex, France **(100%)**
Tel.: (33) 134387888
Web Site: http://www.velcro.fr
Sales Range: $25-49.9 Million
Emp.: 11
Fastener Mfr
N.A.I.C.S.: 339993

Velcro Italia, S.R.L. (1)
Via Nazario Sauro 12, 20862, Arcore, MB, Italy
Tel.: (39) 039627001
Web Site: http://www.velcro.it
Sales Range: $25-49.9 Million
Emp.: 20
Fasteners Mfr & Distr
N.A.I.C.S.: 339993

Velcro Ltd. (1)
1 Aston Way, Middlewich Industrial Estate, Middlewich, CW10 0HS, Cheshire, United Kingdom **(100%)**
Tel.: (44) 1606738806
Web Site: http://www.velcro.co.uk
Sales Range: $25-49.9 Million
Emp.: 23
Fasteners Mfr & Distr
N.A.I.C.S.: 339993

Velcro USA Inc. (1)
95 Sundial Ave, Manchester, NH 03103-7202 **(100%)**
Tel.: (603) 669-4880
Web Site: http://www.velcro.com
Sales Range: $200-249.9 Million
Emp.: 650
Fastener & Related Product for Consumer & Industrial Use Mfr
N.A.I.C.S.: 339993
Mark Papantones *(Engr-Electrical Controls)*

Velcro de Mexico S.A. de C.V. (1)
Ave Industria No 102 Nave IV-A, Col Los Reyes Pueblo, Tlalnepantla, 54090, Mexico **(100%)**
Tel.: (52) 5550053300
Web Site: http://www.velcro.com
Sales Range: $25-49.9 Million
Emp.: 19
Fastener Mfr
N.A.I.C.S.: 339993

VELEPREHRANA A.D.
Dunavska 1c, 78000, Banja Luka, Bosnia & Herzegovina
Tel.: (387) 51309609
Web Site: https://veleprehrana.com
Year Founded: 1970
VLPH—(BANJ)
Sales Range: $1-9.9 Million
Emp.: 37
Grocery Product Whslr
N.A.I.C.S.: 445110
Miodrag Mijatovic *(Chm-Mgmt Bd & Pres)*

VELEPROMET-ZENICA D.D.
Stara Carsija bb, 72000, Zenica, Bosnia & Herzegovina
Tel.: (387) 32 246489
Emp.: 14
Food & Beverages Whslr
N.A.I.C.S.: 424820

VELES CAPITAL INVESTMENT COMPANY LLC
12 Krasnopresnenskaya quay entrance 7 floor 18, Moscow, 123610, Russia
Tel.: (7) 495 258 19 88
Web Site: http://www.veles-capital.ru
VELS—(SPBE)
Financial Investment Services
N.A.I.C.S.: 523999
Dmitry V. Bugaenko *(Mng Partner)*

VELESTO ENERGY BERHAD
Level 18 Block 3A Plaza Sentral Jalan Stesen Sentral 5, 50470, Kuala Lumpur, 50470, Malaysia
Tel.: (60) 320968788   MY
Web Site: https://www.velesto.com
5243—(KLS)
Rev.: $264,218,983
Assets: $676,457,340
Liabilities: $137,622,334
Net Worth: $538,835,006
Earnings: $21,664,127
Emp.: 171
Fiscal Year-end: 12/31/23
Holding Company; Offshore Drilling & Support Services
N.A.I.C.S.: 551112
Rohaizad Darus *(Pres)*

Subsidiaries:

Velesto Drilling Academy Sdn Bhd (1)
Suite 3B-20-3 Level 20 Block 3B Plaza Sentral Jalan Stesen Sentral 5, 50470, Kuala Lumpur, Malaysia
Tel.: (60) 32 742 6193
Oil & Gas Services
N.A.I.C.S.: 213112

Velesto Workover Sdn. Bhd. (1)
Suite 3A Level 18 Block 3A Plaza Sentral, Jalan Stesen Sentral 5, 50470, Kuala Lumpur, Malaysia
Tel.: (60) 320968788
Oil & Gas Support Services
N.A.I.C.S.: 213112

VELETRGOVINA A.D.
Srpska krila slobode A, 78400, Gradiska, Bosnia & Herzegovina
Tel.: (387) 51813461
VLTG—(BANJ)
Sales Range: Less than $1 Million
Emp.: 4
Food Product Retailer
N.A.I.C.S.: 445110
Drazen Markovic *(Pres)*

VELGRAF ASSET MANAGEMENT AD
1 Brussels Blvd, Sofia, Bulgaria
Tel.: (359) 29800028
Web Site: https://www.velgraf.com
VAM—(BUL)
Sales Range: Less than $1 Million
Real Estate Manangement Services
N.A.I.C.S.: 531390
Rumen Goranov Tsonkov *(Chm & CEO)*

VELINA AD-VELINGRAD
st Doctor Doshnikov 14, Velingrad, Bulgaria
Tel.: (359) 35953412
Web Site: http://www.velinahotel.com
4VE—(BUL)
Hotel Services
N.A.I.C.S.: 721110

VELIQ BV
Trondheim 6, Barendrecht, 2993LE, Netherlands
Tel.: (31) 10 20 60 20 8
Web Site: http://www.veliq.com
Sales Range: $25-49.9 Million
Emp.: 100
Enterprise Mobility Software Developer
N.A.I.C.S.: 513210
Alex Bausch *(Founder)*

VELJAN DENISON LIMITED
A18 & 19 APIE Balanagar, Begumpet, Hyderabad, 500037, Telangana, India
Tel.: (91) 4023772794
Web Site: https://www.veljan.in
Year Founded: 1973
505232—(BOM)
Rev.: $14,704,514
Assets: $26,967,268
Liabilities: $4,764,307
Net Worth: $22,202,961
Earnings: $1,921,204
Emp.: 293
Fiscal Year-end: 03/31/23
Hydraulic Pumps Mfr
N.A.I.C.S.: 333996
Janardan Rao Chandrasekhara Velamati *(Chm & Mng Dir)*

Subsidiaries:

Adan Limited (1)
Riverside Industrial Estate, Boston, PE21 7TN, Lincolnshire, United Kingdom
Tel.: (44) 1205311500
Web Site: https://www.adanltd.co.uk
Hydraulic Motor Mfr & Distr
N.A.I.C.S.: 333996

VELJAN DENISON LIMITED - Patancheru Factory (1)
Plot No 9 Phase-I IDA Industrial Development Area, Patancheru, 502 319, Andhra Pradesh, India
Tel.: (91) 8455 242013
Hydraulic Pumps Mfr
N.A.I.C.S.: 333996

VELLEMAN COMPONENTS S.A./NV
Legen Heirweg 33, Gavere, 9890, Belgium

VELLEMAN COMPONENTS S.A./NV

Velleman Components S.A./NV—(Continued)
Tel.: (32) 93843611
Web Site: http://www.velleman.eu
Sales Range: $50-74.9 Million
Emp.: 100
Electronic Kits, Test Equipment & Security Related Electronic Products Whslr
N.A.I.C.S.: 423690
Dirk Vlerick *(CEO)*

Subsidiaries:

Velleman, Inc. (1)
7354 Tower St, Fort Worth, TX 76118
Tel.: (817) 284-7785
Web Site: http://www.vellemanusa.com
Electronic Kits, Test Equipment, Security Related Products & Electronic Products Mfr
N.A.I.C.S.: 334419

VELLIV, PENSION & LIVSFORSIKRING A/S
Lautrupvang 10, 2750, Ballerup, Denmark
Tel.: (45) 43 33 99 99   DK
Web Site: http://www.velliv.dk
Pension Fund Management Services
N.A.I.C.S.: 523940
Stone Michael Erichsen *(Mng Dir)*

VELLNER LEISURE PRODUCTS
1890 49th Avenue, Red Deer, T4R 2N7, AB, Canada
Tel.: (403) 343-1464
Web Site: https://www.vellner.com
Year Founded: 1951
Sales Range: $10-24.9 Million
Recreational Vehicle Dealers
N.A.I.C.S.: 441210

VELMOS D.D. MOSTAR
Ul Rodoc bb, 88000, Mostar, Bosnia & Herzegovina
Tel.: (387) 3 635 0001
Web Site: http://www.velmos.com
VLMSRK1—(SARE)
Assets: $2,431,147
Liabilities: $433,564
Net Worth: $1,997,583
Earnings: ($10,067)
Emp.: 2
Fiscal Year-end: 12/31/20
Food & Beverage Whslr
N.A.I.C.S.: 424820

VELOCITY COMPOSITES PLC
AMS Technology Park, Burnley, BB11 5UB, Lancashire, United Kingdom
Tel.: (44) 1282577577   UK
Web Site: https://www.velocity-composites.com
Year Founded: 2007
VEL—(AIM)
Rev.: $16,236,973
Assets: $13,323,306
Liabilities: $8,707,058
Net Worth: $4,616,248
Earnings: ($1,815,272)
Emp.: 75
Fiscal Year-end: 10/31/22
Aerospace Composite Product Mfr & Distr
N.A.I.C.S.: 334511
Darren Ingram *(COO)*

VELOCITY DATA INC.
Suite 600 - 1285 West Broadway, Vancouver, V6H 3X8, BC, Canada
Tel.: (778) 371-3479   BC
Year Founded: 2011
EMRG—(CNSX)
Rev.: $1,925,778
Assets: $5,057,541
Liabilities: $2,239,781
Net Worth: $2,817,760
Earnings: ($282,640)
Fiscal Year-end: 10/31/21
Technology Products
N.A.I.C.S.: 541512

Subsidiaries:

Nubreed Nutrition Inc. (1)
318 John R Rd Ste 310, Troy, MI 48083
Web Site: https://www.nubreednutrition.com
Nutrition Supplement Distr
N.A.I.C.S.: 456191

VELOCITY MINERALS LTD.
890-999 West Hastings Street, Vancouver, V6C 2W2, BC, Canada
Tel.: (604) 484-1233   AB
Web Site: https://www.velocityminerals.com
VLC—(TSXV)
Rev.: $189,460
Assets: $22,550,300
Liabilities: $737,368
Net Worth: $21,812,932
Earnings: ($1,396,609)
Emp.: 25
Fiscal Year-end: 12/31/23
Molybdenum Mineral Mining Services
N.A.I.C.S.: 212230
Darren Morgans *(CFO)*

VELTI PLC
First Floor 28-32 Pembroke Street Upper, Dublin, 2, Ireland
Tel.: (353) 1234 2676   JE
Web Site: http://www.velti.com
Year Founded: 2000
Sales Range: $250-299.9 Million
Emp.: 1,135
Mobile Advertising & Marketing Services
N.A.I.C.S.: 541519

Subsidiaries:

Casee (Beijing) Information Technology Company Limited (1)
Ying Du Building A - 9B 48 Zhi Chun Road, Haidian District, Beijing, 100086, China
Tel.: (86) 10 5873 3380 112
Mobile Advertising & Marketing Services
N.A.I.C.S.: 541810

Mobile Interactive Group Blgm N.V. (1)
Kievitplein 20, 2018, Antwerp, Belgium
Tel.: (32) 3 304 95 35
Mobile Advertising & Marketing Services
N.A.I.C.S.: 541810

Velti FZ LLC (1)
Internet City Business Central Towers Tower A Office 2003a, PO Box 500663, Dubai, United Arab Emirates
Tel.: (971) 44574800
Mobile Advertising & Marketing Services
N.A.I.C.S.: 541810

Velti Istanbul Mobil Teknolojileri (1)
Levent No 193 Binasi Buyukdere cad No 193 K 2, Istanbul, 343944, Turkiye
Tel.: (90) 212 371 4648
Mobile Advertising & Marketing Services
N.A.I.C.S.: 541810

Velti Limited (1)
The Tower Building 10th Floor 11 York Road, London, SE1 7NX, United Kingdom
Tel.: (44) 207 633 5043
Investment Management Service
N.A.I.C.S.: 523940

Velti Mobile Marketing Technology LLC (1)
Bldg 14-2 Sadovnicheskaya Street, 115035, Moscow, Russia
Tel.: (7) 495 988 7703
Mobile Advertising & Marketing Services
N.A.I.C.S.: 541810

Velti Platforms and Services Limited (1)
Jacovides Tower 1st Floor 81-83 Grivas Digenis Avenue, Nicosia, 1080, Cyprus
Tel.: (357) 2250 3136

Mobile Advertising & Marketing Services
N.A.I.C.S.: 541810

Velti S.A. (1)
44 Kifissias Avenue, Marousi, Athens, 151 25, Greece
Tel.: (30) 210 637 8800
Web Site: http://www.velti.com
Emp.: 100
Mobile Advertising & Marketing Services
N.A.I.C.S.: 541810

Velti Ukraine Mobile Marketing Services LLC (1)
31 Bozhenka Street Office 303, Kiev, Ukraine
Tel.: (380) 442291916
Mobile Advertising & Marketing Services
N.A.I.C.S.: 541810

VELTRA CORP.
Nippon Life Nihonbashi Bldg 5F 2-13-12 Nihonbashi, Chuo-Ku, Tokyo, 103-0027, Japan
Tel.: (81) 368237990
Web Site: https://corp.veltra.com
Year Founded: 1991
7048—(TKS)
Rev.: $22,142,070
Assets: $45,843,940
Liabilities: $36,201,540
Net Worth: $9,642,400
Earnings: ($404,130)
Emp.: 235
Fiscal Year-end: 12/31/23
Travel Agency Services
N.A.I.C.S.: 561510
Wataru Futagi *(CEO)*

VENAC A.D.
Slobodana Bajica 12, Pecinci, Serbia
Tel.: (381) 22471024
Web Site: http://www.venacad.co.rs
Year Founded: 1993
VNAC—(BEL)
Rev.: $165,994
Assets: $2,319,338
Liabilities: $112,688
Net Worth: $2,206,650
Earnings: ($44,235)
Emp.: 1
Fiscal Year-end: 12/31/23
Grocery Store Operator
N.A.I.C.S.: 445110
Mira Jevremovic *(Exec Dir)*

VENCANNA VENTURES INC.
310 250-6th Avenue S W, Calgary, T2P 3H7, AB, Canada
Tel.: (403) 992-9676
Web Site: https://www.vencanna.com
VENI—(CNSX)
Rev.: $466,801
Assets: $7,830,403
Liabilities: $1,633,060
Net Worth: $6,197,343
Earnings: ($1,057,007)
Fiscal Year-end: 04/30/21
Petroleum & Natural Gas Extracting Services
N.A.I.C.S.: 211120
David McGorman *(CEO)*

VENDETTA MINING CORP.
Suite 1500 - 409 Granville Street, Vancouver, V6C 1T2, BC, Canada
Tel.: (604) 484-7855   BC
Web Site: https://www.vendettaminingcorp.com
Year Founded: 2009
5V8—(DEU)
Assets: $4,502,561
Liabilities: $651,589
Net Worth: $3,850,972
Earnings: ($492,130)
Fiscal Year-end: 05/31/24
Metal Mining Services
N.A.I.C.S.: 212290
Michael J. Williams *(Pres & CEO)*

INTERNATIONAL PUBLIC

VENERA D.O.O.
Blagoja Parovica bb, Banja Luka, Bosnia & Herzegovina
Tel.: (387) 51388972
Web Site: http://www.venera.ba
Year Founded: 1995
Emp.: 140
Logistic & Supply Chain Services
N.A.I.C.S.: 541614

VENERABLE VENTURES LTD.
595 Burrard Street Suite 3123, Vancouver, V7X 1J1, BC, Canada
Tel.: (604) 609-6103   BC
Web Site: https://www.venerableventures.com
Year Founded: 2010
VLV—(TSXV)
Assets: $3,555
Liabilities: $82,111
Net Worth: ($78,555)
Earnings: ($91,518)
Fiscal Year-end: 03/31/24
Investment Services
N.A.I.C.S.: 523999
Marilyn Miller *(CFO)*

VENKY'S (INDIA) LTD.
Venkateshwara House S No 114/A/2 Pune-Sinhagad Road, Viththalwadi, Pune, 411 030, Maharashtra, India
Tel.: (91) 2024251803
Web Site: https://www.venkys.com
Year Founded: 1976
VENKEYS—(NSE)
Rev.: $430,306,477
Assets: $244,288,454
Liabilities: $93,535,410
Net Worth: $150,753,043
Earnings: $36,546,237
Emp.: 5,346
Fiscal Year-end: 03/31/21
Poultry Hatcheries
N.A.I.C.S.: 112340
Anuradha J. Desai *(Chm)*

Subsidiaries:

Bala Industries and Entertainment pvt. ltd. (1)
Survey No 114/A/2 Pune-Sinhagad Road Jaydeo Nagar Hingne Khurd, Pune, 410030, Maharashtra, India
Tel.: (91) 9850099080
Web Site: https://www.bala-industries.com
Poultry Equipment Mfr
N.A.I.C.S.: 333241

VENLON ENTERPRISES LIMITED
26 P & Plot No 2 Belavadi Industrial Area Hunsur Road, Mysore, 570 018, Karnataka, India
Tel.: (91) 8212402530
Web Site: https://www.venlonenterprises.com
Year Founded: 1983
524038—(BOM)
Rev.: $365,314
Assets: $7,843,199
Liabilities: $17,266,747
Net Worth: ($9,423,548)
Earnings: ($3,974,018)
Emp.: 3
Fiscal Year-end: 03/31/23
Polyester Film Mfr
N.A.I.C.S.: 322220
Chand D. Datwani *(Chm & Mng Dir)*

VENSHORE MECHANICAL LTD.
1019 Northern Ave, Thunder Bay, P7C 5L6, ON, Canada
Tel.: (807) 623-6414
Web Site: http://www.venshore.com
Year Founded: 1987
Rev.: $13,537,159
Emp.: 50

AND PRIVATE COMPANIES / VENTURE CORPORATION LIMITED

Industrial & Pipe Fabrication Contractor
N.A.I.C.S.: 238220
John Jurcik *(Pres)*

VENTIA SERVICES GROUP LIMITED
Level 8 80 Pacific Highway, North Sydney, 2060, NSW, Australia
Tel.: (61) 1300836842 AU
Web Site: https://www.ventia.com
VNT—(NZX)
Rev.: $3,701,114,951
Assets: $1,912,759,992
Liabilities: $1,540,979,331
Net Worth: $371,780,661
Earnings: $123,753,016
Emp.: 35,000
Fiscal Year-end: 12/31/23
Asset Management Services
N.A.I.C.S.: 523999
David Moffatt *(Chm)*

Subsidiaries:

ChargePoint Pty. Limited (1)
236 East Boundary Road 2 North Drive Virginia Park, Bentleigh, 3165, VIC, Australia
Tel.: (61) 1300300885
Web Site: https://au.chargepoint.com
Electric Vehicle Charging Services
N.A.I.C.S.: 811211

Ventia NZ Limited (1)
501 Karangahape Road, Auckland, 1010, New Zealand
Tel.: (64) 800266417
Asset Management Services
N.A.I.C.S.: 531390

VENTOS S.A.
40 Rue Du Cure 2nd Floor, L-1255, Luxembourg, Luxembourg
Tel.: (352) 225902
Web Site: http://www.ventos.lu
Year Founded: 1994
Sales Range: $50-74.9 Million
Emp.: 50
Investment Holding Company
N.A.I.C.S.: 551112
Pere Portabella Rafols *(Chm & Pres)*

VENTRIPOINT DIAGNOSTICS LTD.
18 Hook Ave Unit 101, Toronto, M6P 1T4, ON, Canada
Tel.: (416) 848-4156 Ca
Web Site: https://www.ventripoint.com
Year Founded: 2005
5V7—(DEU)
Rev.: $25,008
Assets: $7,466,744
Liabilities: $947,213
Net Worth: $6,519,531
Earnings: ($3,036,052)
Emp.: 10
Fiscal Year-end: 12/31/21
Medical Diagnostic Imaging
N.A.I.C.S.: 339112
George Adams *(Chm & CEO)*

VENTURA BUS LINES PTY LTD
1037 Centre Road South, Oakleigh, 3167, Vic, Australia
Tel.: (61) 395754800
Web Site: http://www.venturabus.com
Sales Range: $75-99.9 Million
Emp.: 500
Bus Transportation Services
N.A.I.C.S.: 485510
Andrew Cornwall *(Mng Dir)*

Subsidiaries:

Ventura Bus Company Pty Ltd (1)
21 Scotchmer St, Fitzroy, 3068, Victoria, Australia (100%)
Tel.: (61) 394882100
Web Site: http://www.venturabus.com.au
Sales Range: $125-149.9 Million
Emp.: 433
Bus Services
N.A.I.C.S.: 485510

VENTURA GUARANTY LIMITED
I-Think Techno Campus B Wing 8th Floor Pokhran Road No 2, Off Eastern Express Highway, Thane, 400 607, Maharashtra, India
Tel.: (91) 22 67547000
Web Site: http://www.venturaguaranty.com
Rev.: $20,260,113
Assets: $62,053,397
Liabilities: $45,678,546
Net Worth: $16,374,851
Earnings: $2,505,021
Fiscal Year-end: 03/31/19
Non Banking Financial Services
N.A.I.C.S.: 523999
Hemant Majethia *(Exec Dir)*

Subsidiaries:

M/s Ventura Allied Services Private Limited (1)
A 163 13 14 1st Floor Navdeep House 0 Incimetex Char Rasta Navjivan, Ahmedabad, 380014, India
Tel.: (91) 9833476091
Financial Services
N.A.I.C.S.: 541611

M/s. Ventura Securities Limited (1)
C-112/116 1st Floor Building No 1 Kailash Industrial Complex, Vikhroli West, Mumbai, 400079, India
Tel.: (91) 2267547000
Web Site: http://www.ventura1.com
Financial Services
N.A.I.C.S.: 541611

VENTURA TEXTILES LIMITED
121 MIDAS Sahar Plaza J B Nagar, Andheri E, Mumbai, 400 059, India
Tel.: (91) 2228214225
Web Site: https://www.venturatextiles.com
Year Founded: 1970
516098—(BOM)
Rev.: $321,661
Assets: $2,636,943
Liabilities: $4,670,165
Net Worth: ($2,033,222)
Earnings: ($676,669)
Emp.: 5
Fiscal Year-end: 03/31/21
Textile Product Mfr & Distr
N.A.I.C.S.: 314999
Penugonda Mohan Rao *(Chm & Mng Dir)*

Subsidiaries:

Ventura Textiles Limited - Nashik Works (1)
NH-3 Village Gonde Wadivarhe, Igatpuri, Nashik, 422 403, India
Tel.: (91) 2553 225142
Textile Products Mfr
N.A.I.C.S.: 314999

VENTURE COMMUNICATIONS LTD.
411 11th Ave SE, Calgary, T2G 0Y5, AB, Canada
Tel.: (403) 237-2388
Year Founded: 1984
Sales Range: $10-24.9 Million
Emp.: 70
Full Service, Public Relations, Publicity/Promotions
N.A.I.C.S.: 541820
Paul Hains *(Chief Creative Officer)*

VENTURE CORPORATION LIMITED
5006 Ang Mo Kio Ave 5 05-01/12 Techplace II, Singapore, 569873, Singapore
Tel.: (65) 64821755 SG
Web Site: http://www.venture.com.sg
Year Founded: 1984
V03—(SES)
Rev.: $2,291,167,158
Assets: $2,692,405,513
Liabilities: $543,004,620
Net Worth: $2,149,400,893
Earnings: $205,049,610
Emp.: 11,180
Fiscal Year-end: 12/31/23
Electronics Holding Company
N.A.I.C.S.: 551112
Sita Lim *(Chief HR Officer)*

Subsidiaries:

Advanced Products Corporation Pte Ltd
5006 Ang Mo Kio Ave 5 05-01/12 TECH Place II, Singapore, 569873, Singapore
Tel.: (65) 64821755
Web Site: https://apc-vest.com
Emp.: 150
Electronic Products Mfr
N.A.I.C.S.: 334412

GES (Singapore) Pte. Ltd. (1)
28 Marsiling Lane, Singapore, 739152, Singapore
Tel.: (65) 67329898
Electronic Computer Mfr
N.A.I.C.S.: 334111

GES International Limited (1)
28 Marsiling Lane, Singapore, 739152, Singapore
Tel.: (65) 6 732 9898
Web Site: http://www.ges.com.sg
Sales Range: $400-449.9 Million
Emp.: 700
Electronics Mfr
N.A.I.C.S.: 334419

Subsidiary (Domestic):

GES Investment Pte. Ltd. (2)
28 Marsiling Lane, Singapore, 739152, Singapore (100%)
Tel.: (65) 6 732 9898
Web Site: http://www.venture.com.sg
Emp.: 400
Management Consulting Services
N.A.I.C.S.: 541618
Kris Altice *(Sr VP-Bus & Alliance Dev)*

Subsidiary (Non-US):

GES Manufacturing Services (M) Sdn Bhd (2)
PLO 34 FASA II Kawasan, Perindustrian Senai, Senai, 81400, Malaysia
Tel.: (60) 75992511
Web Site: http://www.venture.com.sg
Sales Range: $450-499.9 Million
Electronic Parts & Equipment Whslr
N.A.I.C.S.: 423690
Choo Wun On *(Gen Mgr)*

Subsidiary (US):

GES US (New England), Inc. (2)
121 Hale St 121 Hale St, Lowell, MA 01851
Tel.: (978) 459-4434
Emp.: 90
Electronic Components Mfr
N.A.I.C.S.: 334419

Subsidiary (Non-US):

Shanghai GES Information Technology Co., Ltd. (2)
668 Li Shi Zhen Road Shanghai Zhangjiang Hi-Tech Park, Shanghai, 201203, China
Tel.: (86) 2138984898
Web Site: http://www.venture.com.sg
Sales Range: $250-299.9 Million
Emp.: 600
Space Research & Technology
N.A.I.C.S.: 927110

Subsidiary (Domestic):

Venture GES Singapore Pte. Ltd. (2)
28 Marsiling Lane, Singapore, 739152, Singapore (100%)
Tel.: (65) 67329898
Web Site: http://www.venture.com.sg
Electronic Parts & Equipment Whslr
N.A.I.C.S.: 423690

Innovative Trek Technology Pte Ltd (1)
5006 Ang Mo Kio Avenue 5 05-01/12 TECHplace II, Singapore, 569873, Singapore
Tel.: (65) 6 482 1755
Web Site: http://www.venture.com.sg
Electronic Equipment Mfr & Whslr
N.A.I.C.S.: 334419

Multitech Systems Pte Ltd (1)
5006 Ang Mo Kio Avenue 5 05-01/12 TECHplace II, Singapore, 569873, Singapore
Tel.: (65) 6 482 1755
Web Site: http://www.venture.com.sg
Civil Engineering Services
N.A.I.C.S.: 541330

Pintarmas Sdn Bhd (1)
6 Jalan Kempas 5/2 Tampoi, 81200, Johor Bahru, Johor, Malaysia
Tel.: (60) 7 237-7201
Web Site: http://www.venture.com.sg
Computer Peripheral Distr
N.A.I.C.S.: 423430

Scinetic Engineering Pte Ltd (1)
5006 Ang Mo Kio Ave 5 05-01/12 TECH Pl II, Singapore, 569873, Singapore
Tel.: (65) 64821755
Web Site: http://www.venture.com.sg
Sales Range: $75-99.9 Million
Emp.: 500
Civil Engineering Services
N.A.I.C.S.: 541330

Technocom Systems Sdn Bhd (1)
2 Jalan Kempas 5/2 Tampoi, 81200, Johor Bahru, Johor, Malaysia
Tel.: (60) 72377201
Electronic Components Mfr
N.A.I.C.S.: 334419

Univac Design & Engineering Pte Ltd (1)
211 Woodlands Avenue 9 01-86, Singapore, 738960, Singapore
Tel.: (65) 68543333
Web Site: http://www.univacprecision.com
Sales Range: $125-149.9 Million
Emp.: 300
Injection Molded Plastic Products Mfr
N.A.I.C.S.: 326130
Amos Lung *(Pres & CEO)*

Univac Precision Engineering Pte Ltd (1)
211 Ulland Ave 9 01-86, Singapore, 738960, Singapore
Tel.: (65) 68543333
Sales Range: $125-149.9 Million
Emp.: 260
Injection Molded Plastic Products Mfr
N.A.I.C.S.: 326130
Amos Leong *(Pres & CEO)*

Subsidiary (Non-US):

Munivac Sdn. Bhd (2)
51 53 Jalan Riang 21 Taman Gembira, 81200, Johor Bahru, Johor, Malaysia
Tel.: (60) 7 335 6333
Web Site: http://www.venture.com.sg
Electronic Components Mfr
N.A.I.C.S.: 334416

Univac Precision Plastics (Shanghai) Co., Ltd (2)
308 Plant 11 Fen Ju Road Wai Gao Qiao Free Trade Zone, Pudong, Shanghai, 200131, China
Tel.: (86) 21 5048 1868
Web Site: http://tempunivac.tripod.com
Plastics Product Mfr
N.A.I.C.S.: 326130

Subsidiary (US):

Univac Precision, Inc (2)
6701 Mowry Ave, Newark, CA 94560
Tel.: (510) 744-1854
Electronic Equipment Whslr
N.A.I.C.S.: 423690

Univac Precision Plastics (Suzhou) Co., Ltd. (1)

VENTURE CORPORATION LIMITED

Venture Corporation Limited—(Continued)
2 3E No 18 Chunyao Road, Industrial Park Xiang Cheng District, Suzhou, 215131, Jiangsu, China
Tel.: (86) 51262828828
Electronic Computer Mfr
N.A.I.C.S.: 334111

V-Design Services (M) Sdn. Bhd. (1)
No 2 and 4 Jalan Kempas 5/2, Tampoi, 81200, Johor Bahru, Johor, Malaysia
Tel.: (60) 72312100
Electronic Computer Mfr
N.A.I.C.S.: 334111

VIPColor Technologies Pte Ltd (1)
5006 Ang Mo Kio Avenue 5 05-01/12 TECHplace II, Singapore, 569873, Singapore
Tel.: (65) 64821755
Web Site: https://vipcolor.com
Colour Imaging Products Mfr & Distr
N.A.I.C.S.: 327420

Subsidiary (US):

VIPColor Technologies USA, Inc (2)
1621 Barber Ln, Milpitas, CA 95035
Tel.: (408) 715-4080
Web Site: https://www.vipcolor.com
Printing Supplies Whslr
N.A.I.C.S.: 424110

Venture Electronics (Shanghai) Co., Ltd
1201 Gui Qiao Road T52/11 Jin Qiao Export Processing Zone, Pudong New Area, Shanghai, 201206, China
Tel.: (86) 21 5899 8086
Electronic Products Mfr
N.A.I.C.S.: 334515

Venture Electronics (Shenzhen) Co., Ltd (1)
3832 Chang Ping Business Building Shihua Road Free Trade Zone, Futian, Shenzhen, 518038, Guangdong, China
Tel.: (86) 7552 395 0126
Web Site: http://www.venture.com.sg
Electronic Products Mfr
N.A.I.C.S.: 334413

Venture Electronics Services (Malaysia) Sdn Bhd (1)
Plot 44 Bayan Lepas Industrial Pk IV, Bayan Lepas, 11900, Penang, Malaysia
Tel.: (60) 4 642 8000
Web Site: http://www.venture.com.sg
Software Development Services
N.A.I.C.S.: 541511

Venture Electronics Solutions Pte Ltd (1)
5006 Ang Mo Kio Avenue 5 05-01/12 TECHplace II, Singapore, 569873, Singapore
Tel.: (65) 6 482 1755
Web Site: http://www.venture.com.sg
Emp.: 250
Wireless Communication Devices Mfr & Distr
N.A.I.C.S.: 334210

Venture Electronics Spain S.L. (1)
Carrer Pagesia 22-24 1B, 08191, Rubi, Barcelona, Spain
Tel.: (34) 93 588 3018
Web Site: http://www.venture.com.sg
Sales Range: $25-49.9 Million
Emp.: 30
Electronic Engineering Services
N.A.I.C.S.: 541330
Roberto Guilen (Gen Mgr)

Venture Enterprise Innovation, Inc. (1)
6701 Mowry Ave, Newark, CA 94560
Tel.: (510) 744-3720
Electronic Computer Mfr
N.A.I.C.S.: 334111

VENTURE INCORPORATION PCL
544 Soi Ratchadapisak 26 Ratchadapisak Road Samsennok Huai Khwang, Bangkok, 10310, Thailand
Tel.: (66) 254141456

Web Site: http://www.ventureinc.co.th
Rev.: $677,444
Assets: $879,762
Liabilities: $1,557,129
Net Worth: ($677,367)
Earnings: ($343,103)
Fiscal Year-end: 12/31/19
Electric Equipment Mfr
N.A.I.C.S.: 334111
Sakkaphongs Boonmee (CEO)

VENTURE LIFE GROUP PLC
12 The Courtyard Eastern Road, Bracknell, RG12 2XB, Berkshire, United Kingdom
Tel.: (44) 1344578004   UK
Web Site: https://www.venture-life.com
Year Founded: 2010
VLG—(AIM)
Rev.: $40,834,787
Assets: $125,828,059
Liabilities: $27,924,227
Net Worth: $97,903,831
Earnings: $3,215,081
Emp.: 119
Fiscal Year-end: 12/31/20
Medical Devices, Food Supplements & Dermocosmetics Mfr
N.A.I.C.S.: 339112
Jerry Randall (CEO)

Subsidiaries:

Biokosmes Srl (1)
Via dei Livelli 1, Bosisio Parini, 23842, Lecco, Italy
Tel.: (39) 0313581085
Web Site: https://www.biokosmes.it
Beauty Parlour Retailer
N.A.I.C.S.: 456120

Lubatti Limited (1)
12 The Courtyard Eastern Road, Bracknell, RG12 2XB, United Kingdom
Tel.: (44) 1344578004
Web Site: http://www.lubatti.co.uk
Beauty Parlour Retailer
N.A.I.C.S.: 456120
Sharon Collins (Co-Founder)

VENTURE LIGHTING INDIA LTD.
Plot No A30 D5 Phase II Zone B MEPZ, 600045, Chennai, India
Tel.: (91) 4422625567
Web Site: http://www.venturelightingindia.com
Sales Range: $25-49.9 Million
Emp.: 900
Metal Halide Lighting Mfr
N.A.I.C.S.: 335131

VENTURE MINERALS LIMITED
Level 2 16 Altona Street, West Perth, 6005, WA, Australia
Tel.: (61) 862799428
Web Site: https://www.ventureminerals.com.au
CRI—(ASX)
Rev.: $1,128,899
Assets: $2,273,257
Liabilities: $1,698,328
Net Worth: $574,929
Earnings: ($4,042,744)
Fiscal Year-end: 06/30/24
Mineral Exploration Services
N.A.I.C.S.: 213115
Andrew Radonjic (Mng Dir)

VENTURE REPUBLIC INC.
Izumi Nishiazabu Building 4-3-11, Nishi-azabu, Tokyo, 106-0031, Minato-ku, Japan
Tel.: (81) 364192901
Web Site: http://www.vrg.jp
Year Founded: 2001
Sales Range: $10-24.9 Million
Emp.: 68

E-Commerce Portal Operator & Internet-Based Marketer & Sales Promotion Services
N.A.I.C.S.: 425120
Kei Shibata (Pres & CEO)

VENTURE REVITALIZE INVESTMENT, INC.
1-6-1 Roppongi, Minato-ku, Tokyo, 106-6017, Japan
Tel.: (81) 3 62290180
Web Site: http://www.v-revitalize.co.jp
Year Founded: 2002
Financial Investment Management Services
N.A.I.C.S.: 525990
Takeo Nishikawa (CIO)

VENTUREAXESS GROUP LIMITED
Level 7 160 Queen Street, Melbourne, 3000, VIC, Australia
Tel.: (61) 408 580 087
Year Founded: 2006
Investment & Fund Management Services
N.A.I.C.S.: 523999
David M. Hickie (Mng Dir)

VENTURI AUTOMOBILES S.A.M.
7 Rue du Gabian, Gildo Pastor Ctr Ground Fl, 98000, Monaco, Monaco
Tel.: (377) 99995200   MC
Web Site: http://www.venturi.com
Year Founded: 1984
Sales Range: $25-49.9 Million
Emp.: 50
Electric Powered Automobile Design, Engineering & Mfr
N.A.I.C.S.: 336110
Gildo Pallanca Pastor (Co-Owner)

Subsidiaries:

Voxan-SCCM S.A. (1)
17 avenue Jean Jaures, 63500, Paris, France
Tel.: (33) 473557171
Web Site: http://www.voxan.com
Sales Range: $1-9.9 Million
Emp.: 12
Motorcycle Mfr & Distr
N.A.I.C.S.: 336991

VENTUS VCT PLC
Berger House 36-38 Berkeley Square, London, W1J 5AE, United Kingdom
Tel.: (44) 5667210
Web Site: http://www.ventusvct.com
VENC—(LSE)
Rev.: $3,991,199
Assets: $47,090,375
Liabilities: $415,777
Net Worth: $46,674,598
Earnings: $726,626
Fiscal Year-end: 02/29/20
Investment Management Service
N.A.I.C.S.: 525990
Lloyd Chamberlain (Chm-Ventus 2 VCT)

VENUS CONCEPT INC.
235 Yorkland Blvd Suite 900, Toronto, M2J 4Y8, ON, Canada
Tel.: (888) 907-0115   DE
Web Site: http://www.venusconcept.com
Year Founded: 2002
VERO—(NASDAQ)
Rev.: $99,497,000
Assets: $125,378,000
Liabilities: $117,285,000
Net Worth: $8,093,000
Earnings: ($43,700,000)
Emp.: 384
Fiscal Year-end: 12/31/22

INTERNATIONAL PUBLIC

Hair Restoration Services
N.A.I.C.S.: 812199
Hemanth Varghese (Pres & COO)

Subsidiaries:

Venus Concept Argentina SA (1)
Galicia 1627, C1406, Buenos Aires, Argentina
Tel.: (54) 91168059398
Medical Equipment Distr
N.A.I.C.S.: 423450

Venus Concept Korea Ltd. (1)
201ho 6-9 Baekjegobun-ro 39-gil, Songpa-gu, Seoul, 05616, Korea (South)
Tel.: (82) 234469242
Medical Equipment Distr
N.A.I.C.S.: 423450

Venus Concept UK Limited (1)
4th Floor No 1 Farriers Yard 77-85 Fulham Palace Road, London, W6 8JA, United Kingdom
Tel.: (44) 2087482221
Medical Equipment Distr
N.A.I.C.S.: 423450

VENUS JSC
ul Boris Arsov 3B, Sofia, 1700, Bulgaria
Tel.: (359) 2 987 19 49
Web Site: http://www.venus.eu.com
VNS—(BUL)
Sales Range: Less than $1 Million
Real Estate Manangement Services
N.A.I.C.S.: 531390
Ioannis Petros Bonakis (Chm)

VENUS MEDTECH (HANGZHOU) INC.
Jiangling Science Park Road, Hangzhou Binjiang 88 M Round The Second Building On The Third Floor, Hangzhou, 310000, China
Tel.: (86) 571 8777 2183
Web Site: http://www.venusmedtech.com
Year Founded: 2009
Medical Device Mfr
N.A.I.C.S.: 339112

Subsidiaries:

InterValve Inc. (1)
2445 Xenium Ln N, Plymouth, MN 55441
Tel.: (952) 303-3539
Web Site: http://www.intervalveinc.com
Medical Device Mfr
N.A.I.C.S.: 339112
Mark Ungs (Pres & CEO)

VENUS METALS CORPORATION
Unit 2 8 Alvan Street, Perth, 6008, WA, Australia
Tel.: (61) 893217541
Web Site: https://www.venusmetals.com.au
VMC—(ASX)
Rev.: $22,387
Assets: $17,405,101
Liabilities: $283,150
Net Worth: $17,121,950
Earnings: $19,675,690
Fiscal Year-end: 06/30/24
Mineral Exploration Services
N.A.I.C.S.: 213115
Matthew Vernon Hogan (Mng Dir)

VENUS PIPES & TUBES LIMITED
Survey No 233/2 And 234/1, Bhuj Bhachau Highway Village Dhaneti, Kutch, 370020, Gujarat, India
Tel.: (91) 7048898899
Web Site: https://www.venuspipes.com
Year Founded: 2015
543528—(BOM)
Rev.: $53,108,738

Assets: $33,837,258
Liabilities: $16,292,367
Net Worth: $17,544,891
Earnings: $4,322,682
Fiscal Year-end: 03/31/22
Pipe & Cable Product Mfr
N.A.I.C.S.: 331210

VENUS REMEDIES LIMITED
51-52 Industrial Area Phase-1
Panchkula, Chandigarh, 134113,
Haryana, India
Tel.: (91) 1722933090
Web Site:
https://www.venusremedies.com
526953—(BOM)
Rev.: $77,498,325
Assets: $75,873,975
Liabilities: $21,235,250
Net Worth: $54,638,725
Earnings: $8,430,977
Emp.: 837
Fiscal Year-end: 03/31/21
Pharmaceuticals Product Mfr
N.A.I.C.S.: 325412
Pawan Chaudhary *(Chm & Co-Mng Dir)*

Subsidiaries:

Salehiya Trading Company (1)
PO Box 911, Riyadh, 11421, Saudi Arabia
Tel.: (966) 114646955
Web Site: https://www.salehiya.com
Medical Equipment Distr
N.A.I.C.S.: 423450

Venus Pharma GmbH (1)
AM Bahnhof 1-3, 59368, Werne, Germany
Tel.: (49) 2389925910
Web Site:
https://www.venuspharmagmbh.de
Pharmaceutical Firm Mfr
N.A.I.C.S.: 325412
Pawan Chaudary *(Chm & Mng Dir)*

VENUSTECH GROUP INC.
Venustech Plaza 21 Zhongguancun
Software Park, No 8 Dongbeiwang
West Road Haidian District, Beijing,
100193, China
Tel.: (86) 1082779088
Web Site:
https://www.venusense.com
Year Founded: 1996
002439—(SSE)
Rev.: $622,942,052
Assets: $1,404,292,776
Liabilities: $363,914,919
Net Worth: $1,040,377,857
Earnings: $87,898,108
Emp.: 3,100
Fiscal Year-end: 12/31/22
Network Security Management Services
N.A.I.C.S.: 561621
Wei Bing *(Chm)*

VENZEE TECHNOLOGIES INC.
422 Richards St Suite 170, Vancouver, V6B 2Z4, BC, Canada BC
Web Site: https://www.venzee.com
Year Founded: 1996
VENZ—(TSXV)
Assets: $20,513
Liabilities: $1,129,826
Net Worth: ($1,109,313)
Earnings: ($493,380)
Fiscal Year-end: 03/31/24
Gold Mining, Exploration & Development Services
N.A.I.C.S.: 212220
Nick Wong *(Dir)*

VEOLIA ENVIRONNEMENT S.A.
21 rue La Boetie, 75008, Paris, France
Tel.: (33) 185577000 FR
Web Site: https://www.veolia.com
Year Founded: 1853
VEOEF—(OTCIQ)
Rev.: $46,282,430,391
Assets: $79,110,835,312
Liabilities: $63,066,263,760
Net Worth: $16,044,571,552
Earnings: $1,076,624,218
Emp.: 213,684
Fiscal Year-end: 12/31/22
Waste Recycling Services
N.A.I.C.S.: 562211
Antoine Frerot *(Chm)*

Subsidiaries:

Altvater Ternopil LLC (1)
3 Brodivska Griga Str, Ternopil, 46020, Ukraine
Tel.: (380) 352235591
Waste Management Services
N.A.I.C.S.: 562998

Amendis S.A. (1)
23 Rue Carnot, Tangiers, Morocco
Tel.: (212) 539 32 80 00
Environmental Consulting Services
N.A.I.C.S.: 541620

Apa Nova Bucuresti Srl (1)
Str Dinu Vintila no 11 sector 2 Euro Tower Building, Ground floor entrance from Lacul Tei Blvd, Bucharest, 10146, Romania
Tel.: (40) 21 207 7777
Web Site: https://www.apanovabucuresti.ro
Water Supply Services
N.A.I.C.S.: 221310
Lavinia Saniuta *(Gen Dir)*

Aquiris SA (1)
Avenue De Vilvorde 450, 1130, Brussels, Belgium
Tel.: (32) 2 243 9660
Web Site: https://www.aquiris.be
Water Line Construction Services
N.A.I.C.S.: 237110

Biocycling GmbH (1)
Hammerbrookstrasse 69, 20097, Hamburg, Germany
Tel.: (49) 404210370
Waste Management Services
N.A.I.C.S.: 562998

Biomasseanlage Essenheim GmbH (1)
Am Kleinbirkenfeld 1, Essenheim, 55270, Bingen, Germany
Tel.: (49) 6132790470
Waste Management Services
N.A.I.C.S.: 562998

Braunschweiger Netz GmbH (1)
Taubenstrasse 7, 38106, Braunschweig, Germany
Tel.: (49) 531 3830
Web Site: https://www.bs-netz.de
Emp.: 400
Natural Gas Distr
N.A.I.C.S.: 486210

Braunschweiger Versorgungs - AG & Co.KG (1)
Taubenstrasse 7, Braunschweig, 38106, Germany
Tel.: (49) 53 13830
Web Site: http://www.bs-energy.de
Sales Range: $550-599.9 Million
Emp.: 100
Electric Power Generation & Distribution Services
N.A.I.C.S.: 221118
Mukesh Bansal *(Gen Mgr)*

Bs Energie (1)
Taubenstrasse 7, 38106, Braunschweig, Germany
Tel.: (49) 531 3830
Web Site: https://www.bs-energy.de
Electric Utility Services
N.A.I.C.S.: 221122
Lars Nebert *(Head-IT)*

Compagnie Fermiere de Services Publics SCA (1)
6 Rue Nathalie Sarraute, Nantes, 44200, Loire-Atlantique, France
Tel.: (33) 251846000
Waste Treatment Services
N.A.I.C.S.: 221310

Compagnie Mediterraneenne d'Exploitation des Services d'Eau - CMESE (1)
12 Boulevard Rene Cassin, 06200, Nice, France
Tel.: (33) 4 92 29 80 00
Water Supply Services
N.A.I.C.S.: 221310

Dalkia International S.A. (1)
37 avenue du Marechal de Lattre de Tassigny, BP 38, Saint-Andre-lez-Lille, 59350, France
Tel.: (33) 3 20 63 42 42
Heating & Air Conditioning Equipment Repair & Maintenance Services
N.A.I.C.S.: 811412

EOLFI SA (1)
12 Rond-Point des Champs-Elysees Marcel-Dassault, Paris, 75008, France
Tel.: (33) 140079500
Web Site: http://www.eolfi.veolia.com
Sales Range: $125-149.9 Million
Emp.: 130
Eletric Power Generation Services
N.A.I.C.S.: 221118

Subsidiary (Non-US):

EOLFI POLSKA Sp. z o.o. (2)
Warsaw Tower Ul Sienna 39, 00-121, Warsaw, Poland
Tel.: (48) 22 595 14 70
Sales Range: $75-99.9 Million
Emp.: 1
Electric Power Distribution Services
N.A.I.C.S.: 221122

EOLFI WIND HELLAS S.A. (2)
Paradissou 10 Maroussi, 11528, Athens, Greece
Tel.: (30) 210 3608000
Sales Range: $50-74.9 Million
Emp.: 12
Eletric Power Generation Services
N.A.I.C.S.: 221118

Subsidiary (US):

RIDGELINE ENERGY, LLC (2)
1300 N Northlake Way 2nd Fl, Seattle, WA 98103
Tel.: (425) 455-9014
Web Site: http://www.ridgelineenergy.com
Sales Range: $50-74.9 Million
Emp.: 30
Electric Power Generation Services
N.A.I.C.S.: 221118
Dennis Meany *(Pres)*

Eurologistik-Umweltservice GmbH (1)
Spremberger Strasse 80, 01968, Senftenberg, Germany
Tel.: (49) 35 733 7720
Web Site: https://www.wer-entsorgt.com
Emp.: 160
Logistics Container Services
N.A.I.C.S.: 561790
Mario Klemann *(Mng Dir)*

Gasversorgung Gorlitz GmbH (1)
Demianiplatz 23, 02826, Gorlitz, Germany
Tel.: (49) 35 813 3535
Web Site: https://www.gvg-netz.de
Gas Distr
N.A.I.C.S.: 424720

Hvt Handel Vertrieb Transport GmbH (1)
Nordstrasse 15, 04420, Markranstadt, Germany
Tel.: (49) 34 205 7380
Web Site: https://www.hvt-logistik.de
Logistics & Disposal Services
N.A.I.C.S.: 562112

Introtec Schwarza GmbH (1)
Fritz-Bolland-Strasse 6, 07407, Rudolstadt, Germany
Tel.: (49) 3672314327
Waste Management Services
N.A.I.C.S.: 562998

Job & Mehr GmbH (1)
Heinrich-Rau-Strasse 4, 16816, Neuruppin, Germany
Tel.: (49) 339 140 0255

Web Site: http://www.jobundmehr.de
Placement Services
N.A.I.C.S.: 561311

KJ Engineering Sdn. Bhd (1)
25 Jalan SS18/6, 47500, Subang Jaya, Selangor Darul Ehsan, Malaysia
Tel.: (60) 3 56 33 78 21
Web Site: http://www.kjeng.com.my
Emp.: 120
Air Conditioning Equipment Installation Services
N.A.I.C.S.: 238220
Hon Wong Cho *(CEO)*

Kanalbetriebe Fritz Withofs GmbH (1)
Carl-Bosch-Strasse 4, 65203, Wiesbaden, Germany
Tel.: (49) 611210120
Waste Management Services
N.A.I.C.S.: 562998

Kom-Dia GmbH (1)
Taubenstrasse 7, 38106, Braunschweig, Germany
Tel.: (49) 5319 667 0819
Web Site: https://www.kom-dia.de
Wireless Telecommunication Services
N.A.I.C.S.: 517112
Daniel Hunnerkopf *(Project Mgr)*

Multipet GmbH (1)
Parkstrasse 17, 06406, Bernburg, Germany
Tel.: (49) 347164040
Waste Management Services
N.A.I.C.S.: 562998
Herbert Snell *(Mng Dir)*

Multiport GmbH (1)
Ernst-Grube-Strasse 1, 06406, Bernburg, Germany
Tel.: (49) 347164040
Waste Management Services
N.A.I.C.S.: 562998
Herbert Snell *(Mng Dir)*

OTUS (1)
26 Avenue Des Champs Pierreux, Nanterre, 92000, Hauts De Seine, France
Tel.: (33) 155696900
Waste Material Recycling Services
N.A.I.C.S.: 562998
Heather Adams *(VP-Ops & People)*

Okotec Energiemanagement GmbH (1)
EUREF-Campus Haus 13 Torgauer Strasse 12-15, 10829, Berlin, Germany
Tel.: (49) 30 536 3970
Web Site: https://www.oekotec.de
Emp.: 60
Consulting Management Services
N.A.I.C.S.: 541618
Christoph Zschocke *(Mng Dir)*

Onyx Est S.A. (1)
Hardt Rte De Haspelschiedt Zi, 57230, Bitche, Moselle, France
Tel.: (33) 472015000
Web Site: http://www.veolia.com
Waste Treatment Services
N.A.I.C.S.: 562219

Onyx Ta-Ho Environmental Services Co. Ltd. (1)
7F No 16-5 DeHui Street, Taipei, 10461, Taiwan (100%)
Tel.: (886) 225860177
Web Site: https://www.tahoho.com.tw
Waste Management Services
N.A.I.C.S.: 562998

Ostthuringer Wasser Und Abwasser GmbH (1)
Kantstrasse 3, 07548, Gera, Germany
Tel.: (49) 3658562280
Waste Management Services
N.A.I.C.S.: 562998

Paul Grandjouan SACO (1)
Avenue Lotz Cosse, 44200, Nantes, Loire Atlantique, France
Tel.: (33) 2 51 72 72 00
Sales Range: $25-49.9 Million
Emp.: 10
Waste Material Recycling Services
N.A.I.C.S.: 562998

Prazske Vodovody A Kanalizace a.s. (1)

VEOLIA ENVIRONNEMENT S.A.

Veolia Environnement S.A.—(Continued)
Ke Kablu 971/1, Hostivar, 102 00, Prague, Czech Republic
Tel.: (420) 60 127 4274
Web Site: https://www.pvk.cz
Sales Range: $1-4.9 Billion
Emp.: 140
Waste Treatment Services
N.A.I.C.S.: 221310
Philippe Guitard *(Chm)*

Proactiva Medio Ambiente S.A. (1)
C/Cardenal Marcelo Spinola 8 - 3a Plta, 28016, Madrid, Spain
Tel.: (34) 913876100
Web Site: http://www.proactiva.es
Wastewater Services
N.A.I.C.S.: 562998

Subsidiary (Non-US):

Proactiva Medio Ambiente Argentina (2)
C/Tucuman 1321 Piso 3, 1050, Buenos Aires, Argentina
Tel.: (54) 11 43716858
Web Site: http://www.proactiva.es
Sales Range: $250-299.9 Million
Emp.: 1,766
Waste Management
N.A.I.C.S.: 562998

Proactiva Medio Ambiente Brasil (2)
Condominio Edif Millenium Off Park Av Chedid Jafet 222, Bloco C cj 12, Vila Olimpia, CEP 04551 065, Sao Paulo, Brazil
Tel.: (55) 11 3046 9007
Web Site: http://www.proactiva.es
Sales Range: $150-199.9 Million
Emp.: 834
Wastewater Services
N.A.I.C.S.: 562998

Proactiva Medio Ambiente Chile (2)
Avenida Apoquindo 4775 Ofic 701, Las Condes, Santiago, 7580097, Chile
Tel.: (56) 23361200
Web Site: http://www.proactiva.es
Sales Range: $300-349.9 Million
Emp.: 600
Wastewater Services
N.A.I.C.S.: 562998
Elier Gonzalez *(Gen Mgr)*

Proactiva Medio Ambiente Colombia (2)
Calle 98 B 9-03 Ofic 804, Edificio Torre Sancho, Bogota, Colombia
Tel.: (57) 1 634 6815
Web Site: http://www.proactiva.es
Sales Range: $300-349.9 Million
Emp.: 2,131
Wastewater Services
N.A.I.C.S.: 562998

Proactiva Medio Ambiente Mexico (2)
C/ Tomas Alva Edison 176 3er piso, Colonia San Rafael, Mexico, 06470, Districto Federal, Mexico
Tel.: (52) 55 5722 7700
Web Site: http://www.proactiva.es
Sales Range: $300-349.9 Million
Emp.: 2,363
Wastewater Services
N.A.I.C.S.: 562998

Proactiva Medio Ambiente Peru (2)
Avenida del Pinar 180 Oficina 1201 Surco, Lima, Peru
Tel.: (51) 1 2069700
Web Site: http://www.proactiva.es
Wastewater Services
N.A.I.C.S.: 562998

Proactiva Medio Ambiente Venezuela (2)
Av Francisco de Miranda Edif Parque Cristal Torre Este, piso 15 of 15-10 Los Palos Grandes, Caracas, Venezuela
Tel.: (58) 212 283 5990
Web Site: http://www.proactiva.es
Sales Range: $300-349.9 Million
Emp.: 1,111
Wastewater & Environmental Services
N.A.I.C.S.: 562998

Recypet Ag (1)
Langfeldstrasse 80, 8500, Frauenfeld, Switzerland
Tel.: (41) 52 730 1415
Web Site: https://www.recypet.ch
Environmental Recycling Services
N.A.I.C.S.: 562119

Redal Sa (1)
19 Avenue Ibn Sina Agdal, Rabat, Morocco
Tel.: (212) 537238299
Web Site: http://www.redal.ma
Electrical & Electronic Mfr
N.A.I.C.S.: 336320

Routiere de l'Est Parisien (1)
26 Avenue Des Champs Pierreux, Nanterre, 92000, Hauts De Seine, France
Tel.: (33) 139331500
Waste Material Recycling Services
N.A.I.C.S.: 562998

SOCIETE DES EAUX DE MELUN S.C.A. (1)
198 rue Foch Zone Industrielle, Vaux-le-Penil, 77000, France
Tel.: (33) 164102277
Water Supply Services
N.A.I.C.S.: 221310

Sade-Compagnie Generale de Travaux d'Hydraulique SA (1)
28 Rue de La Baume, 75008, Paris, France
Tel.: (33) 1 53 75 99 11
Web Site: http://www.sade-cgth.fr
Rev.: $1,757,461,914
Emp.: 9,052
Civil Engineering Construction Services
N.A.I.C.S.: 237990
Donald Peck *(Gen Mgr)*

Severoceske Vodovody A Kanalizace a.s (1)
Pritkovska 1689, 415 50, Teplice, Czech Republic
Tel.: (420) 84 011 1111
Web Site: https://www.scvk.cz
Emp.: 358
Water Supply & Treatment Services
N.A.I.C.S.: 221320

Sharqiyah Desalination Co. SAOC (1)
Al Mahmiyut Building Shatti Al Qurum, PO Box 685, 114, Jibroo, Oman
Tel.: (968) 24693890
Sales Range: $50-74.9 Million
Emp.: 35
Sewage Treatment Services
N.A.I.C.S.: 221320

Societe Francaise de Distribution d'Eau SCA (1)
7 Rue Tronson Du Coudray, Paris, 75008, France
Tel.: (33) 144902300
Water Supply Services
N.A.I.C.S.: 221310

Societe d'Assainissement Rationnel et de Pompage (1)
52 Av des Champs Pierreux, 92000, Nanterre, France
Tel.: (33) 1 71 07 86 06
Waste Treatment & Recycling Services
N.A.I.C.S.: 562219

Societe des Eaux de Marseille S.A. (1)
25 Rue Edouard Delanglade, BP 80029, Marseille, 13254, France
Tel.: (33) 4 91 57 60 60
Web Site: http://www.eauxdemarseille.com
Sales Range: $1-4.9 Billion
Emp.: 1,938
Waste Treatment Services
Loic Fauchon *(Pres)*

Sofiyska Voda AD (1)
Business Park Sofia Mladost 4 Building 2A, Sofia, 1766, Bulgaria
Tel.: (359) 2812 24 88
Web Site: http://www.sofiyskavoda.bg
Emp.: 1,140
Water & Sewage Utility Services
N.A.I.C.S.: 221310
Iteva Mariana *(Gen Mgr)*

Stadtentwasserung Braunschweig GmbH (1)
Taubenstrasse 7, 38106, Braunschweig, Germany
Tel.: (49) 5313 834 5000
Web Site: https://www.stadtentwaesserung-braunschweig.de
Sewage Disposal Services
N.A.I.C.S.: 221320

Stadtreinigung Dresden GmbH (1)
Pfotenhauerstrasse 46, 01307, Dresden, Germany
Tel.: (49) 351 445 5118
Web Site: https://www.srdresden.de
Emp.: 380
Waste Management Services
N.A.I.C.S.: 562998

Stadtwerke Gorlitz Aktiengesellschaft (1)
Demianiplatz 23, 02826, Gorlitz, Germany
Tel.: (49) 35 813 3535
Web Site: https://www.stadtwerke-goerlitz.de
Electric Utility Services
N.A.I.C.S.: 221122

Stadtwerke Pulheim Dienste GmbH (1)
Christinastrasse 39, 50259, Pulheim, Germany
Tel.: (49) 22389570211
Web Site: http://www.stadtwerke-pulheim.de
Natural Gas Distribution Services
N.A.I.C.S.: 221210

Stadtwerke Weisswasser GmbH (1)
Tel.: (49) 3 576 2660
Web Site: https://www.stadtwerke-weisswasser.de
Natural Gas Distr
N.A.I.C.S.: 486210

Suez SA (1)
Tour CB21 - 16 place de l'Iris La Defense, 92040, Paris, Cedex, France
Tel.: (33) 158812000
Web Site: http://www.suez-environnement.com
Rev.: $21,136,782,160
Assets: $43,705,937,808
Liabilities: $33,819,342,752
Net Worth: $9,886,595,056
Earnings: $91,381,056
Emp.: 88,775
Fiscal Year-end: 12/31/2020
Holding Company; Water Supply, Recycling & Waste Management Services
N.A.I.C.S.: 551112
Jean-Marc Boursier *(COO & Sr Exec VP-Grp)*

Subsidiary (Non-US):

EnviroServ Holdings Limited (2)
Brickfield Road, Germiston, 008 2008, South Africa (51%)
Tel.: (27) 114565660
Web Site: http://www.enviroserv.co.za
Sales Range: $100-124.9 Million
Holding Company; Waste Management Services
N.A.I.C.S.: 551112

Subsidiary (Domestic):

SUEZ Environnement SAS (2)
Tour CB21 - 16 place de l'Iris, La Defense, 92040, Paris, Cedex, France (100%)
Tel.: (33) 1 5881 2000
Web Site: http://www.suez-environnement.com
Water Supply, Recycling & Waste Management Services
N.A.I.C.S.: 562998
Marie-Ange Debon *(Sr VP-Intl)*

Subsidiary (Domestic):

Degremont S.A. (3)
183 Ave Du 18 Juin 1940, Rueil-Malmaison, 92508, France
Tel.: (33) 146256000
Web Site: http://www.degremont.com
Sales Range: $500-549.9 Million
Emp.: 800
Wastewater Treatment
N.A.I.C.S.: 221320
Isabelle Censi *(Dir-Comm)*

Subsidiary (Non-US):

Degremont (4)

INTERNATIONAL PUBLIC

Talcahuano 718 Piso 6, Buenos Aires, 1013, Argentina
Tel.: (54) 1153712200
Web Site: http://www.degremont.com
Sales Range: $50-74.9 Million
Emp.: 30
Water & Waste Water Treatment Svcs
N.A.I.C.S.: 221310

Degremont SA (4)
Parc Industriel des Hauts-Sarts, Rue de Hermee 225, 4040, Herstal, Belgium
Tel.: (32) 42405050
Web Site: http://www.degremont.com
Sales Range: $75-99.9 Million
Emp.: 55
Water & Waste Water Treatment Systems
N.A.I.C.S.: 221310

Degremont SpA (4)
via Benigno Crespi 57, 20159, Milan, Italy
Tel.: (39) 02693311
Web Site: http://www.degremont.com
Water & Waste Water Treatment Sys
N.A.I.C.S.: 221310

Degremont Technologies AG (4)
Stettbachstrasse 1, 8600, Dubendorf, Switzerland
Tel.: (41) 448018511
Web Site: http://www.degremont-technologies.com
Sales Range: $25-49.9 Million
Emp.: 80
Mfr of Ozone & UV Disinfection Systems
N.A.I.C.S.: 333310

Subsidiary (Domestic):

Ozonia International Holding S.A (5)
Stettbachstrasse 1, 8600, Dubendorf, Switzerland
Tel.: (41) 44 801 85 11
Web Site: http://www.ozonia.com
Sales Range: $250-299.9 Million
Emp.: 700
Holding Company; Ozone & Ultraviolet Treatment System Mfr
N.A.I.C.S.: 551112

Subsidiary (Non-US):

Ozonia Korea Co., Ltd (6)
342 1 Yatap-dong, Seongnam, Gyeonggi-do, Korea (South)
Tel.: (82) 317019036
Web Site: http://www.ozoniakorea.com
Sales Range: $1-9.9 Million
Emp.: 40
Mfr of Ozone & UV Disinfection Sys
N.A.I.C.S.: 333310
Jae Yong Lee *(CEO)*

Subsidiary (US):

Ozonia North America, LLC (6)
600 Willow Tree Rd, Leonia, NJ 07605
Tel.: (201) 676-2525
Web Site: http://www.ozonia.com
Sales Range: $25-49.9 Million
Emp.: 45
Mfr of Ozone & UV Disinfection Sys
N.A.I.C.S.: 333248

Subsidiary (Non-US):

Ozonia OOO (6)
st B Pecherskaya 26 office 807, 603155, Nizhniy Novgorod, Russia
Tel.: (7) 8314341628
Web Site: http://www.ozonia.ru
Mfr of Ozone & UV Disinfection Sys
N.A.I.C.S.: 333310

Triogen Ltd (6)
Triogen House, Craigton, Glasgow, G52 1BD, United Kingdom
Tel.: (44) 1418104861
Web Site: http://www.triogen.co.uk
Sales Range: $25-49.9 Million
Emp.: 20
Mfr of Ozone & UV Disinfection Sys
N.A.I.C.S.: 333310

Subsidiary (Domestic):

Fairtec SAS (4)
38 avenue Jean Jaures, 78440, Gargenville, France
Tel.: (33) 130981294
Web Site: http://www.fairtec.fr

AND PRIVATE COMPANIES

VEOLIA ENVIRONNEMENT S.A.

Waste Management Engineering Services
N.A.I.C.S.: 562998

Subsidiary (Non-US):

Lydec (3)
48 Boulevard Mohamed Diouri, PO Box 16048, 20110, Casablanca, Morocco **(51%)**
Tel.: (212) 522549054
Web Site: http://www.client.lydec.ma
Water & Power Supply Company
N.A.I.C.S.: 221310

Subsidiary (Domestic):

Lyonnaise des Eaux France (3)
18 Sq Edouard VII, 75316, Paris, Cedex, France
Tel.: (33) 158184000
Web Site: http://www.lyonnaise-des-eaux.fr
Water Supply Company
N.A.I.C.S.: 221310

Subsidiary (Domestic):

Aquasource SAS (4)
20 Ave Didier Daurat, PO Box 64050, 31700, Toulouse, France
Tel.: (33) 561363036
Web Site: http://www.aquasource.fr
Sales Range: $10-24.9 Million
Emp.: 35
Water Filtration Sys Mfr
N.A.I.C.S.: 221310
Marc Messerli (COO)

Eau ET Force (4)
300 Rue Paul Vaillant Couturier, 92000, Nanterre, France
Tel.: (33) 46975252
Sales Range: $75-99.9 Million
Emp.: 25
Water Utility
N.A.I.C.S.: 221310

Eaux de Marseille (4)
50 rue de la Republique, 13003, Marseilles, Cedex 6, France
Tel.: (33) 969394050
Web Site: http://www.eauxdemarseille.fr
Sales Range: $450-499.9 Million
Emp.: 800
Water Supply Company
N.A.I.C.S.: 221310

La Societe Stephanoise des Eaux (4)
28 Rue Eugene Beaune, 42043, Saint Etienne, Cedex, France
Tel.: (33) 810368368
Web Site: http://www.stephanoise-eaux.fr
Water Supply Company
N.A.I.C.S.: 221310

Novergie (4)
132 Rue Des Trois Fontanot, 92758, Nanterre, Cedex, France
Tel.: (33) 142916643
Web Site: http://www.novergie.fr
Waste Treatment & Processing Svcs
N.A.I.C.S.: 562998

Teris (4)
54 Rue Pierre Curie ZI Des Gatines, 78370, Plaisir, Cedex, France
Tel.: (33) 130793080
Web Site: http://www.teris.fr
Sales Range: $75-99.9 Million
Emp.: 300
Waste Management & Treatment Services
N.A.I.C.S.: 562998

Subsidiary (Domestic):

Nantaise des Eaux Services SAS (3)
26 rue de la Rainiere, PO Box 53987, 44339, Nantes, Cedex 3, France
Tel.: (33) 240188400
Web Site: http://www.ndes.fr
Sales Range: $10-24.9 Million
Waste Water Disposal Services
N.A.I.C.S.: 221320

Ondeo Industrial Solutions (3)
23 Rue Du Professeur Pauchet, 92420, Vaucresson, France
Tel.: (33) 147958800
Sales Range: $125-149.9 Million
Emp.: 200
Provider of Solutions & Svcs to the Water Industry
N.A.I.C.S.: 221310

Subsidiary (Non-US):

Ondeo Industrial Solutions Limited (4)
Boness Road, PO Box 21, Grangemouth, SK3 9XD, United Kingdom
Tel.: (44) 1324475278
Web Site: http://www.ondeo-is.co.uk
Sales Range: $50-74.9 Million
Emp.: 100
Supplier of Industrial Water Supply Solutions
N.A.I.C.S.: 221310
John Boulton (Mng Dir)

Ondeo Industrial Solutions Srl (4)
Via Benigno Crespi 57, 20159, Milan, Italy
Tel.: (39) 02693311
Supplier of Industrial Water Supply Solutions
N.A.I.C.S.: 221310

Subsidiary (Non-US):

SITA Belgium S.A. (3)
Leopold III 2 Avenue des Olympiades, 1140, Brussels, Belgium
Tel.: (32) 27450510
Web Site: http://www.sita.be
Water Services
N.A.I.C.S.: 221310

SITA Deutschland GmbH (3)
Industriestrasse 161, Cologne, 50999, Germany
Tel.: (49) 22363770
Web Site: http://www.sita-deutschland.de
Sales Range: $25-49.9 Million
Emp.: 150
Waste Management Services
N.A.I.C.S.: 562998
Oliver Gross (CEO)

Subsidiary (Domestic):

SITA France (3)
Tour CB 21 16 place de l Iris, La Defense, 92040, Paris, Cedex, France
Tel.: (33) 158812000
Web Site: http://www.sita.fr
Sales Range: $100-124.9 Million
Emp.: 400
Development & Sales of Compactor Trucks & Multi-Purpose Street Cleaning Vehicles; Landfill Management; Gas Recovery; Smokestack Emmission Control
N.A.I.C.S.: 336120

Subsidiary (Domestic):

Lorval (4)
Zi De Borny 5 Rue Des Drapiers, 57070, Metz, Moselle, France
Tel.: (33) 387759000
Web Site: http://www.setr.fr
Rev.: $10,100,000
Emp.: 42
Recyclable Material Distr
N.A.I.C.S.: 423930
Patrice Leveel (Pres)

Subsidiary (Non-US):

SITA Polska (3)
ul Zawodzie 5, 02-981, Warsaw, Poland
Tel.: (48) 224924300
Web Site: http://www.nowastrona.sitapolska.pl
Waste Management & Treatment Services
N.A.I.C.S.: 562998

SITA Sverige AB (3)
Blidogatan 24, 211 24, Malmo, Sweden
Tel.: (46) 406934306
Web Site: http://www.sita.se
Sales Range: $25-49.9 Million
Emp.: 55
Waste Management & Treatment Services
N.A.I.C.S.: 562998
Mats Lundsgard (Reg Mgr)

Subsidiary (Non-US):

SITA Finland Oy AB (4)
Viikintie 31-35, 00560, Helsinki, Finland
Tel.: (358) 105400
Web Site: http://www.remeo.fi

Sales Range: $10-24.9 Million
Emp.: 30
Waste Management & Treatment Services
N.A.I.C.S.: 562998

Subsidiary (Non-US):

SITA UK (3)
SITA House Grenfell Rd, Maidenhead, SL6 1ES, United Kingdom
Tel.: (44) 1628513100
Web Site: http://www.sita.co.uk
Sales Range: $25-49.9 Million
Emp.: 170
Waste Management Services
N.A.I.C.S.: 562998
David Jones (Mng Dir)

SITA Waste Services Limited (3)
2801 Island Place Tower, 510 Kings Road, North Point, China (Hong Kong)
Tel.: (852) 25630661
Web Site: http://www.swiresita.com
Sales Range: $250-299.9 Million
Emp.: 1,800
Waste Management Services
N.A.I.C.S.: 562998

Branch (Non-US):

SITA Waste Services Ltd. (4)
Ren-Wu Plant 100 Ren-An Second Lane, Wu-Lin Village Ren-Wu, Kaohsiung, 814, Taiwan
Tel.: (886) 73743855
Web Site: http://www.sita.hk
Emp.: 70
Waste Management Services
N.A.I.C.S.: 562998

Subsidiary (Non-US):

SUEZ Environnement Spain, S.L. (3)
19 Ibarrekolanda, 48015, Bilbao, Spain
Tel.: (34) 94 400 5000
Web Site: http://www.ondeo-is.es
Supplier of Industrial Water Supply Solutions
N.A.I.C.S.: 221310

Subsidiary (Domestic):

Ondeo Degremont SA (4)
Camino De Ibarrekolanda 19, 48015, Bilbao, Spain
Tel.: (34) 944763800
Web Site: http://www.degremont.es
Sales Range: $450-499.9 Million
Emp.: 500
Water & Waste Water Treatment Svcs
N.A.I.C.S.: 221310

Sociedad General de Aguas de Barcelona, S.A. (4)
Av Diagonal 211 Torre Agbar, 08018, Barcelona, Spain **(75%)**
Tel.: (34) 933422000
Web Site: http://www.agbar.es
Sales Range: $1-4.9 Billion
Emp.: 16,511
Water Supply, Waste Treatment & Construction Services
N.A.I.C.S.: 221310
Jean-Louis Chaussade (Vice Chm)

Subsidiary (Non-US):

Agbar UK Ltd. (5)
Bridgwater Road, Bristol, BS99 7AU, United Kingdom **(100%)**
Tel.: (44) 1179633755
Sales Range: $150-199.9 Million
Emp.: 450
Holding Company
N.A.I.C.S.: 551112

Inversiones Aguas Metropolitanas S.A. (5)
Avda Presidente Balmaceda N 1398 piso 14, Santiago, Chile **(56.6%)**
Tel.: (56) 225692301
Web Site: https://www.iam.cl
Rev.: $727,416,254
Assets: $3,060,689,094
Liabilities: $1,746,245,959
Net Worth: $1,314,443,135
Earnings: $149,645,192
Emp.: 2,137
Fiscal Year-end: 12/31/2023

Holding Company; Water Supply Investment Services
N.A.I.C.S.: 551112
Alberto Muchnik Mlynarz (VP)

Subsidiary (Domestic):

Aguas Andinas SA (6)
Ave Presidente Balmaceda 1398, Santiago, Chile
Tel.: (56) 26881000
Web Site: http://www.aguasandinas.cl
Sales Range: $1-4.9 Billion
Emp.: 1,200
Water Supply & Waste Water Treatment Company
N.A.I.C.S.: 221310
Jesus Garcia (Gen Mgr)

Subsidiary (Non-US):

SUEZ Nederland Holding B.V. (3)
Meester E N van Kleffenstraat 10, 6842 CV, Arnhem, Netherlands
Tel.: (31) 648878839
Web Site: http://www.suez.nl
Sales Range: $25-49.9 Million
Emp.: 150
Holding Company; Waste Management & Treatment Services
N.A.I.C.S.: 551112

Subsidiary (US):

SUEZ North America Inc. (3)
461 From Rd Ste 400, Paramus, NJ 07652
Tel.: (201) 767-9300
Web Site: http://www.suez-na.com
Emp.: 2,800
Holding Company; Regional Managing Office; Water & Waste Recycling Services
N.A.I.C.S.: 551112
Gary Albertson (Sr VP-Bus Dev)

Subsidiary (Non-US):

Anderson Water Systems Limited (4)
1295 Cormorant Rd, Suite 200, Ancaster, L9G 4V5,, ON, Canada
Tel.: (905) 627-9233
Web Site: http://www.awsl.com
Sales Range: $50-74.9 Million
Emp.: 75
Design, Installation & Mfr of Industrial Water Sys
N.A.I.C.S.: 221310
Mart Klepp (VP-Engrg)

Subsidiary (Domestic):

SUEZ Treatment Solutions Inc. (4)
8007 Discovery Dr, Richmond, VA 23229
Tel.: (804) 756-7600
Web Site: http://www.infilcodegremont.com
Sales Range: $50-74.9 Million
Emp.: 173
Waste & Water Treatment Engineering Services
N.A.I.C.S.: 333310
Ky Dangtran (Mgr-Tech)

SUEZ Water Inc. (4)
461 From Rd, Paramus, NJ 07652
Tel.: (201) 767-9300
Web Site: http://www.mysuezwater.com
Sales Range: $800-899.9 Million
Emp.: 2,600
Water Treatment & Supply Services
N.A.I.C.S.: 221310
David Stanton (Pres)

Subsidiary (Domestic):

SUEZ Water Idaho Inc. (5)
8248 W Victory Rd, Boise, ID 83709
Tel.: (208) 362-7304
Web Site: http://www.mysuezwater.com
Sales Range: $25-49.9 Million
Emp.: 68
Water Supply
N.A.I.C.S.: 221310
Cathy Cooper (Dir-Engrg)

SUEZ Water New Jersey Inc. (5)
461 From Rd, Paramus, NJ 07652
Tel.: (201) 767-9300
Web Site: http://www.mysuezwater.com
Emp.: 200
Water Supply
N.A.I.C.S.: 221310

VEOLIA ENVIRONNEMENT S.A.

Veolia Environnement S.A.—(Continued)

Subsidiary (Domestic):

SUEZ Water Toms River Inc. (6)
15 Adafre Ave, Toms River, NJ 08754-0668
Tel.: (732) 349-0227
Web Site: http://www.unitedwater.com
Rev.: $13,808,726
Emp.: 49
Water Supply & Treatment Svcs
N.A.I.C.S.: 221310
Curt Nemeth (Mgr-Ops)

Subsidiary (Domestic):

SUEZ Water New York Inc. (5)
162 Old Mill Rd, West Nyack, NY 10994-0223
Tel.: (845) 623-1500
Web Site: http://www.mysuezwater.com
Sales Range: $100-124.9 Million
Emp.: 103
Water Supply & Treatment Svcs
N.A.I.C.S.: 221310

Subsidiary (Domestic):

SUEZ Water Westchester Inc. (6)
2525 Palmer Ave, New Rochelle, NY 10801-0469
Tel.: (914) 632-6900
Web Site: http://www.mysuezwater.com
Sales Range: $50-74.9 Million
Emp.: 48
Water Supply & Treatment Services
N.A.I.C.S.: 221310

Subsidiary (Domestic):

SUEZ Water Pennsylvania Inc. (5)
8189 Adams Dr, Hummelstown, PA 17036
Tel.: (717) 561-1103
Web Site: http://www.mysuezwater.com
Sales Range: $75-99.9 Million
Emp.: 60
Water Supply & Treatment Svcs
N.A.I.C.S.: 221310
Xavier Boulat (CFO & Exec VP)

Subsidiary (Domestic):

SUEZ Water Rhode Island Inc. (5)
10 High St Ste K, Wakefield, RI 02879
Tel.: (401) 789-0271
Web Site: http://www.mysuezwater.com
Sales Range: Less than $1 Million
Emp.: 10
Water Supply & Treatment Svcs
N.A.I.C.S.: 221310

Subsidiary (Domestic):

SUEZ Water Technologies & Solutions (4)
4636 Somerton Rd, Trevose, PA 19053
Tel.: (215) 355-3300
Web Site: http://www.suezwatertechnologies.com
Sales Range: $350-399.9 Million
Water Treatment, Wastewater Treatment & Water Processing Systems & Services
N.A.I.C.S.: 221310
Samir Patel (Mgr-Middle Market Program)

Affiliate (Non-US):

Sino French Water Development Co. Ltd. (3)
718 Avenida do Conselheiro Borja, Macau, China (Macau)
Tel.: (853) 220440
Web Site: http://www.sinofrench.com
Water Services
N.A.I.C.S.: 221310

Subsidiary (Domestic):

Macao Water (4)
718 Avenida do Conselheiro Borja, Macau, China (Macau) (85%)
Tel.: (853) 28220088
Web Site: http://www.macaowater.com
Sales Range: $125-149.9 Million
Emp.: 250
Water Supply & Waste Water Treatment Svcs
N.A.I.C.S.: 221310
Francois Fevrier (Mng Dir)

Subsidiary (Non-US):

SUEZ NWS R&R (Hong kong) Limited (2)
Room 701 7/F Lee Garden Two 28 Yun Ping Road, Causeway Bay, China (Hong Kong)
Tel.: (852) 28240212
Waste Management Services
N.A.I.C.S.: 562998
Terry Liu (Project Mgr)

SUEZ Polska sp. z o.o. (2)
Zawodzie 5, 02-981, Warsaw, Poland
Tel.: (48) 222742360
Web Site: http://www.suez.pl
Waste Management Services
N.A.I.C.S.: 562998
Stephane Heddesheimer (CEO)

SUEZ Recycling AB (2)
Transportgatan 9, 262 71, Angelholm, Sweden
Tel.: (46) 431444000
Web Site: http://www.suez.se
Waste Management Services
N.A.I.C.S.: 562998

SUEZ Recycling and Recovery Holdings UK Ltd. (2)
Suez House Grenfell Road, Maidenhead, SL6 1ES, Berkshire, United Kingdom
Tel.: (44) 8000931103
Web Site: http://www.suez.co.uk
Emp.: 150
Waste Management Services
N.A.I.C.S.: 562998
John Scanlon (CEO)

Transdev Auckland Ltd (1)
Level 7 Citibank Centre 23 Customs Street East, Auckland, 1143, New Zealand
Tel.: (64) 9969 7777
Web Site: http://www.transdev.co.nz
Sales Range: $75-99.9 Million
Emp.: 550
Passenger Rail Services
N.A.I.C.S.: 485999
Terry Scott (Mng Dir)

UAB Vilnius Energija (1)
Jocioniu G 13, Vilnius, 02300, Lithuania
Tel.: (370) 52667199
Web Site: http://www.vilniaus-energija.lt
Eletric Power Generation Services
N.A.I.C.S.: 221118

VWS MEMSEP s.r.o. (1)
Sokolovska 100/94, Karlin, 186 00, Prague, Czech Republic
Tel.: (420) 251561468
Web Site: https://www.memsep.cz
Sales Range: $50-74.9 Million
Emp.: 45
Waste Treatment Services
N.A.I.C.S.: 221310
Ladislav Cabejsek (Dir-Comml)

Veolia Apa Servicii SRL (1)
Str Profesorilor Nr 2 Sector 4, 40156, Bucharest, Romania
Tel.: (40) 213123556
Sales Range: $75-99.9 Million
Emp.: 6
Waste Treatment Services
N.A.I.C.S.: 221310

Veolia Eau - Compagnie Generale des Eaux S.C.A. (1)
52 Rue d'Anjou, 75008, Paris, France
Tel.: (33) 1 49 24 49 24
Web Site: http://www.veoliaeau.com
Waste Treatment Services
N.A.I.C.S.: 221310

Veolia Energia Polska S.A. (1)
ul Pulawska 2, 02-566, Warsaw, Poland
Tel.: (48) 22 568 8100
Web Site: https://www.veolia.pl
Heat & Electricity Supply Services
N.A.I.C.S.: 238220
Norbert Skibinski (Dir-Dev)

Veolia Energia Slovensko A.S. (1)
Einsteinova 21, 851 01, Bratislava, Slovakia
Tel.: (421) 26 820 7233
Web Site: https://www.vesr.sk
Heat & Electricity Supply Services
N.A.I.C.S.: 238220
Jozef Lovas (Project Mgr)

Veolia Energia Warszawa S.A. (1)
ul Batorego 2, 02-591, Warsaw, Poland
Tel.: (48) 22 658 5858
Web Site: http://www.energiadlawarszawy.pl

Heat & Electricity Supply Services
N.A.I.C.S.: 238220
Jakub Patalas (Dir-Technical)

Veolia Energie (1)
Quartier Valmy Espace 21, 92981, Paris, Cedex, France (100%)
Tel.: (33) 171007100
Web Site: http://www.veolia-energie.com
Sales Range: $5-14.9 Billion
Emp.: 48,000
Facilities, Environmental & Energy Management Services
N.A.I.C.S.: 561210

Division (Domestic):

Dalkia (2)
37 Ave Du Marechal De Lattre De Tassigny, PO Box 38, 59350, Saint-Andre-lez-Lille, France (100%)
Tel.: (33) 320634242
Web Site: http://www.dalkia.com
Sales Range: $5-14.9 Billion
Emp.: 40,100
Facilities, Environmental & Energy Management Services
N.A.I.C.S.: 561210
Olivier Barbaroux (Pres)

Subsidiary (Non-US):

AS Erakute (3)
Punane 36, 13619, Tallinn, Estonia (97%)
Tel.: (372) 6107212
Sales Range: $25-49.9 Million
Emp.: 18
Facilities Management & Air Conditioning Services
N.A.I.C.S.: 561210
Priit Nomm (Gen Mgr)

DALKIA ENERGY & SERVICES LTD.
Aba Even 1 Street, 46725, Herzliya Pituach, Israel
Tel.: (972) 9 952 00 66
Web Site: http://www.dalkia.co.il
Sales Range: $250-299.9 Million
Emp.: 40
Eletric Power Generation Services
N.A.I.C.S.: 221118
Ronen Shtarkman (Head-Quality)

DALKIA MEXICO SA de CV (3)
Lago Victoria No 80 Piso 7 Col Granada, Seccion Miguel Hidalgo, 11520, Mexico, DF, Mexico
Tel.: (52) 55 52 46 00 00
Web Site: http://www.dalkia.com.mx
Electric Power Distribution Services
N.A.I.C.S.: 221122

Dalkia (China) Energy Management Co., Ltd. (3)
23/F Office Building 1 8 North Dongsanhuan Road, Chaoyang District, Beijing, 100004, China
Tel.: (86) 10 5953 2000
Emp.: 300
Electric Power Distribution Services
N.A.I.C.S.: 221122
Ma Lijia (Project Mgr)

Dalkia - Hanbul Energy Management Co., Ltd. (3)
1A-1008 U-Space 670 Sampyeong-dong, Budang-gu, Seongnam, 463-400, Gyeonggi-do, Korea (South)
Tel.: (82) 2 511 0845
Web Site: http://www.hemco.co.kr
Sales Range: $150-199.9 Million
Emp.: 800
Energy Consulting Services
N.A.I.C.S.: 541690
Jh Kim (Gen Mgr-HR)

Dalkia - Prometheus Rt (3)
Budafoki Ut 91-93, 1117, Budapest, Hungary
Tel.: (36) 1 265 16 17
Web Site: http://www.prometheus.hu
Environmental Consulting Services
N.A.I.C.S.: 541620

Subsidiary (Domestic):

Dalkia - Saint-Andre (3)
37 Avenue Mar de Lattre de Tassigny, 59350, Saint-Andre-lez-Lille, France

Tel.: (33) 3 20 63 42 42
Web Site: http://www.dalkia.com
Environmental Consulting Services
N.A.I.C.S.: 541620
Antoine Frerot (Chm)

Subsidiary (Non-US):

Dalkia AB (3)
Halsingegatan 47, PO Box 6613, 11384, Stockholm, Sweden
Tel.: (46) 0855050000
Web Site: http://www.dalkia.com
Sales Range: $150-199.9 Million
Emp.: 600
Provider of Facilities Management Services
N.A.I.C.S.: 561210
Philippe Charles (Chm & CEO)

Subsidiary (Domestic):

Dalkia Facilities Management AB (4)
Halsingegatan 47, PO Box 6613, Stockholm, 11384, Sweden
Tel.: (46) 855050000
Web Site: http://www.dalkia.se
Building & Energy Services
N.A.I.C.S.: 541610
Tomas Falkaner (Dir-Fin)

Dalkia Industripartner AB (4)
Halsingegatan 47, PO Box 6613, Stockholm, 113 84, Sweden
Tel.: (46) 855050000
Web Site: http://www.dalkia.com
Sales Range: $250-299.9 Million
Industrial Maintenance Services
N.A.I.C.S.: 811310
Mikael Seansson (Mng Dir)

Subsidiary (Non-US):

Dalkia Argentina S.A. (3)
Tronador 4890 14 Fl, C1072AAP, Buenos Aires, Argentina
Tel.: (54) 1140180100
Web Site: http://www.veolia.com.ar
Sales Range: $300-349.9 Million
Emp.: 50
Electric Power Generation & Distribution Services
N.A.I.C.S.: 221118
Gabriel Orue (Mgr-Ops)

Dalkia Asia Pacific (3)
3 Temasek Ave, Centennial Tower 30 03, 39190, Singapore, Singapore
Tel.: (65) 68389250
Web Site: http://www.dalkia.com
Provider of Energy Management Services
N.A.I.C.S.: 221122

Dalkia Brasil S/A (3)
Rua Alexandre Dumas 2200 - 4 Andar Chacara Santo Antonio, 04717 910, Sao Paulo, Brazil
Tel.: (55) 11 4083 0001
Web Site: http://www.dalkia.com.br
Electric Power Generation & Distribution Services
N.A.I.C.S.: 221118

Joint Venture (Non-US):

United Water International (4)
Level 1 180 Greenhill Road, Parkside, 5063, Australia (50%)
Tel.: (61) 883012700
Web Site: http://www.uwi.com.au
Sales Range: $50-74.9 Million
Emp.: 500
Water Utility Company
N.A.I.C.S.: 221310
Alan Hesketh (Mng Dir)

Subsidiary (Non-US):

Dalkia Brezno, a.s. (3)
Clementisova 5, 977 01, Brezno, Slovakia
Tel.: (421) 48 6713 999
Web Site: http://www.dalkia.sk
Electric Power Distribution Services
N.A.I.C.S.: 221122

Dalkia Canada Inc. (3)
The Exchange Tower 130 King Street West Suite 1800, PO Box 427, Toronto, M5X 1E3, ON, Canada
Tel.: (416) 860-6232
Web Site: http://www.dalkia.ca
Electric Power Distribution Services

AND PRIVATE COMPANIES
VEOLIA ENVIRONNEMENT S.A.

N.A.I.C.S.: 221122
Servanne Fowlds (Mgr)

Subsidiary (Domestic):

Dalkia Centre Mediterranee S.C.A. (3)
Le Laser 184 Cours Lafayette, 69441, Lyon, France
Tel.: (33) 4 72 35 66 68
Sales Range: $1-4.9 Billion
Emp.: 200
Eletric Power Generation Services
N.A.I.C.S.: 221118

Subsidiary (Non-US):

Dalkia Ceska Republika, a.s (3)
28 Rijna 3337-7, 70974, Ostrava, Czech Republic (100%)
Tel.: (420) 596609111
Web Site: http://www.dalkia.cz
Sales Range: $1-4.9 Billion
Emp.: 1,783
Provider of Energy Management Services
N.A.I.C.S.: 221122
Zdenek Duba (Chm & CEO)

Subsidiary (Domestic):

Dalkia Commodities CZ, s.r.o. (4)
28 Rijna 3337/7, 709 74, Ostrava, Moravska Ostrava, Czech Republic
Tel.: (420) 596 609 609
Web Site: http://www.dalkiacommodities.cz
Rev.: $152,221,000
Emp.: 1
Electric Power Distribution Services
N.A.I.C.S.: 221122
Pavel Lunacek (Mng Dir)

Dalkia Kolin, a.s. (4)
Tovarni 21, 280 63, Kolin, Czech Republic
Tel.: (420) 321 752 211
Web Site: http://www.dalkia.cz
Eletric Power Generation Services
N.A.I.C.S.: 221118
Rostislav Krempasky (Vice Chm & CEO)

Dalkia Marianske Lazne, s.r.o. (4)
Nadrazni Namesti 294, 353 01, Marianske Lazne, Czech Republic
Tel.: (420) 354 627 079
Rev.: $8,398,400
Emp.: 26
Eletric Power Generation Services
N.A.I.C.S.: 221118
Pavel Kolar (Mng Dir)

Subsidiary (Non-US):

Dalkia Chile S.A. (3)
Avinada del Valle N 945 Oficina 1603-Edificio Pacio Mayor, Ciudad Empresarial, Huechuraba, Santiago, Chile
Tel.: (56) 2 580 99 00
Web Site: http://www.dalkia.cl
Emp.: 6
Electric Power Generation Services
N.A.I.C.S.: 221118
Francisco Munoz (Dir Gen)

Dalkia Croatia (3)
Radnicka Cesta 22, 10000, Zagreb, Croatia
Tel.: (385) 1 6168 727
Web Site: http://www.veolia.com
Environmental Consulting Services
N.A.I.C.S.: 541620

Dalkia Energia Zrt. (3)
Budafoki ut 91-93, H-1117, Budapest, Hungary (100%)
Tel.: (36) 12650286
Web Site: http://www.dalkia.hu
Energy Management Services
N.A.I.C.S.: 221122

Dalkia Energia y Servicios S.A de C.V. (3)
Paseo De Las Palmas 275 Torre Optima II Officina 102, Lomas de Chapultepec, 11000, Mexico, Mexico (100%)
Tel.: (52) 5255208475
Web Site: http://www.dalkia.com.mx
Provider of Facilities & Energy Management Services
N.A.I.C.S.: 541690

Dalkia Enerji San ve Tic A.S. (3)
Meydan Street Spring Giz Plaza 1st Floor No 8, Istanbul, 34398, Turkiye
Tel.: (90) 212 346 15 56
Web Site: http://www.dalkia.com
Sales Range: $75-99.9 Million
Emp.: 3
Eletric Power Generation Services
N.A.I.C.S.: 221118

Dalkia Espana S.L. (3)
Cl Juan Ignacio Luca De Tgna 4, 28027, Madrid, Spain
Tel.: (34) 915153600
Web Site: http://www.dalkia.es
Emp.: 300
Environmental Consulting Services
N.A.I.C.S.: 541620

Subsidiary (Domestic):

Dalkia Energia y Servicios SA (4)
Juan Ignacio Luca de Tena 4, 28027, Madrid, Spain (100%)
Tel.: (34) 915153600
Web Site: http://www.veolia.com
Sales Range: $75-99.9 Million
Emp.: 100
Energy Management Services
N.A.I.C.S.: 221122

Subsidiary (Domestic):

Agefred SA (5)
Escultor Canet 35-37, 08028, Barcelona, Spain
Tel.: (34) 93 260 9400
Web Site: https://www.agefred.es
Sales Range: $50-74.9 Million
Provider of Energy Management Services
N.A.I.C.S.: 541690

Ageval SA (5)
Avinguda Ausias March 28, Valencia, 46006, Spain (100%)
Tel.: (34) 963355781
Web Site: http://www.ageval.es
Sales Range: $25-49.9 Million
Air Conditioning Equipment Installation & Design
N.A.I.C.S.: 333415

Ageval Servicio SA (5)
Edificio Gumbau Center, Jose M Guinot, Jalan 5, 12003, Castellon de la Plana, Spain
Tel.: (34) 964260502
Web Site: http://www.ageval.es
Facilities Management & Energy Services
N.A.I.C.S.: 561210

Ageval Servicio SA (5)
C Auso I Monzo 16 Piso 7 Despicho 1, 3006, Alicante, Spain (100%)
Tel.: (34) 965246144
Web Site: http://www.ageval.es
Facilities Management & Energy Services
N.A.I.C.S.: 561210

Giroa SA (5)
Edif. Beyza, Planta 2, Of 201, Camino de Portuexte, 53A, 20009, San Sebastian, Spain
Tel.: (34) 943323780
Energy & Environmental Management Services
N.A.I.C.S.: 541690

Subsidiary (Domestic):

Dalkia Est S.C.A. (3)
Dalkia Est 6 rue de Trezelots, BP 7, Pulnoy, 54425, France
Tel.: (33) 3 83 18 11 11
Electric Power Distribution Services
N.A.I.C.S.: 221122

Subsidiary (Non-US):

Dalkia GmbH (3)
Carl Ulrich 4, 63263, Neu-Isenburg, Germany (100%)
Tel.: (49) 61027430
Web Site: http://www.dalkia.de
Sales Range: $75-99.9 Million
Emp.: 60
Provider of Facilities & Energy Management Services
N.A.I.C.S.: 221122

Subsidiary (Domestic):

Dalkia Ile-de-France (3)
2 Allee des Moulineaux, Issy-les-Moulineaux, 92138, France
Tel.: (33) 1 46 62 70 00
Web Site: http://www.dalkia.com
Electric Power Distribution Services
N.A.I.C.S.: 221122

Subsidiary (Non-US):

Dalkia Latvia, Ltd. (3)
Valnu Street 5, Riga, 1050, Latvia
Tel.: (371) 67 22 36 79
Sales Range: $75-99.9 Million
Emp.: 2
Electric Power Distribution Services
N.A.I.C.S.: 221122
Eriks Timpars (CFO)

Dalkia Lodz SA (3)
Ul J Andrzejewskiej 5, 92550, Lodz, Poland
Tel.: (48) 42 675 51 16
Web Site: http://www.dalkia.pl
Electric Power Generation & Distribution Services
N.A.I.C.S.: 221118
Jaroslaw Gornik (Dir-Social Affairs & Admin)

Dalkia Ltd (3)
145 Lakeview Dr Airside Business Park, Swordsville, Dublin, Ireland (100%)
Tel.: (353) 18701200
Web Site: http://www.dalkia.ie
Sales Range: $75-99.9 Million
Emp.: 450
Facilities Management & Energy Management Services
N.A.I.C.S.: 561210

Dalkia Lucenec a.s. (3)
Partizanska 1/1990, 984 01, Lucenec, Slovakia
Tel.: (421) 47 45 130 10
Electric Power Distribution Services
N.A.I.C.S.: 221122

Joint Venture (Non-US):

Dalkia NV-SA (3)
Quai Fernand Demets 52, 1070, Brussels, Belgium (50%)
Tel.: (32) 25251002
Web Site: http://www.dalkia.com
Sales Range: $1-4.9 Billion
Emp.: 1,500
Provider of Energy Management Services
N.A.I.C.S.: 221122

Subsidiary (Domestic):

Dalkia Nord S.C.A. (3)
37 Av du Marechal de Lattre de Tassigny, Saint-Andre-lez-Lille, 59350, France
Tel.: (33) 3 20 63 42 42
Electric Power Distribution Services
N.A.I.C.S.: 221122

Subsidiary (Non-US):

Dalkia Podunajske Biskupice s.r.o. (3)
Einsteinova 25 - Digital Park II, 851 01, Bratislava, Slovakia
Tel.: (421) 2 6345 1003
Web Site: http://www.dalkia.sk
Electric Power Distribution Services
N.A.I.C.S.: 221122

Dalkia Polska SA (3)
Ul Mysia 5, 00-496, Warsaw, Poland
Tel.: (48) 22 433 17 00
Web Site: http://www.dalkia.pl
Electric Power Generation & Distribution Services
N.A.I.C.S.: 221118
Pascal Bonne (CEO)

Subsidiary (Domestic):

Dalkia Energy & Technical Services Sp. z o.o. (4)
Solidarnosci 46, 60-321, Poznan, Poland
Tel.: (48) 61829921
Sales Range: $250-299.9 Million
Emp.: 33
Eletric Power Generation Services
N.A.I.C.S.: 221118

Dalkia Powerline Sp. z o.o. (4)
Ul Morcinka 17, 43-417, Kaczyce, Poland
Tel.: (48) 32 469 40 32
Web Site: http://www.dalkiapowerline.pl
Eletric Power Generation Services

N.A.I.C.S.: 221118
Laurent Tupinier (Chm)

Stoleczne Przedsiebiorstwo Energetyki Cieplnej S.A. (4)
Ul Stefana Batorego 2, 02-591, Warsaw, Poland
Tel.: (48) 22 576 10 00
Electric Power Distribution Services
N.A.I.C.S.: 221122

Subsidiary (Non-US):

Dalkia Poprad a.s. (3)
Siroka 2, 058 94, Poprad, Slovakia
Tel.: (421) 52 7880 908
Electric Power Distribution Services
N.A.I.C.S.: 221122

Dalkia Portugal (3)
Estrada De Paco De Arcos 42, Oeiras, 2770-129, Portugal (100%)
Tel.: (351) 214404700
Web Site: http://www.dalkia.com
Sales Range: $50-74.9 Million
Emp.: 50
Provider of Energy Management Services
N.A.I.C.S.: 221122
Jose Melodandaera (Gen Mgr)

Dalkia SGPS SA (3)
Estrada De Paco De Arcos 42, Oeiras, Paco d'Arcos, 2770-129, Portugal
Tel.: (351) 214404700
Web Site: http://www.dalkia.pt
Environmental Consulting Services
N.A.I.C.S.: 541620

Dalkia Saudi Arabia L.L.C. (3)
PO Box 65394, Riyadh, 11556, Saudi Arabia
Tel.: (966) 1 291 69 78
Web Site: http://www.dalkia-me.com
Sales Range: $25-49.9 Million
Emp.: 100
Facilities Management & Services
N.A.I.C.S.: 237990
Alexandre Mussallam (CEO)

Dalkia Senec a.s. (3)
Sokolska 6, 903 01, Senec, Slovakia
Tel.: (421) 2 4592 7096
Web Site: http://www.dalkia.sk
Emp.: 14
Electric Power Distribution Services
N.A.I.C.S.: 221122

Dalkia Services Sp. z o.o. (3)
Ul Mysia 5, 00-496, Warsaw, Poland
Tel.: (48) 22 433 17 00
Web Site: http://www.dalkiaservices.pl
Emp.: 20
Electric Power Distribution Services
N.A.I.C.S.: 221122
Agata Mazurek-Bak (Gen Mgr)

Dalkia SrL (3)
Via Sempione 230, Pero, 20016, Milan, Italy
Tel.: (39) 022381921
Web Site: http://www.dalkia.com
Provider of Energy Management Services
N.A.I.C.S.: 221122

Dalkia Varna EAD (3)
Janosh Huniadi Blvd 5, PO Box 26, Varna, Bulgaria
Tel.: (359) 800 14448
Web Site: http://www.dalkia.bg
Electric Power Generation & Distribution Services
N.A.I.C.S.: 221118

Dalkia Vrable a.s. (3)
Sidlisko Zitava 1399/16, 952 01, Vrable, Slovakia
Tel.: (421) 37 7832 994
Electric Power Distribution Services
N.A.I.C.S.: 221122

Dalkia do Brasil Ltda (3)
Edificio E Tower Rua Funchal 418 14 Flr, Vila Olimpia, 04551 060, Sao Paulo, SP, Brazil
Tel.: (55) 1140830001
Web Site: http://www.dalkia.com
Energy Management Services
N.A.I.C.S.: 221122

Dalkia plc (3)
210 Pentonville Road, London, N19JY, United Kingdom (100%)

VEOLIA ENVIRONNEMENT S.A.

Veolia Environnement S.A.—(Continued)
Tel.: (44) 1784496200
Web Site: http://www.veolia.co.uk
Sales Range: $10-24.9 Million
Emp.: 50
Provider of Energy & Facilities Management Services
N.A.I.C.S.: 561210
Estelle Brachoianoff *(Chm & CEO)*

Subsidiary (Non-US):

Dalkia plc (4)
Innovation House DCU Innovation Campus
Old Finglas Road, 56-60 London Rd, Dublin, Ireland **(100%)**
Tel.: (353) 1784496200
Web Site: http://www.dalkia.co.uk
Sales Range: $10-24.9 Million
Emp.: 50
Decontamination Services to the Healthcare Industry
N.A.I.C.S.: 541620

Subsidiary (Non-US):

Dalkia term S.A. (3)
ul Ostrobramska 75 C, 04-175, Warsaw, Poland
Tel.: (48) 22 611 76 20
Web Site: http://www.dalkiaterm.pl
Sales Range: $75-99.9 Million
Emp.: 85
Energy Management Services
N.A.I.C.S.: 221122
Jean-Pierre Corbin *(Pres & Gen Dir)*

Affiliate (Non-US):

Esener S.A. (3)
Av Vitacura 2909, Oficina 204, Vitacura, Santiago, Chile
Tel.: (56) 2 335 6824
Web Site: http://www.esener.cl
Provider of Facilities Management & Energy Management Services. Joint Venture of Dalkia (50%) & Compania General de Electricidad (50%) of Chile.
N.A.I.C.S.: 221122

Hanbul Energy Management Co. Ltd. (3)
1A-1008 U-Space 670 Sampyeong-Dong, Bundang-gu, Seongnam, 463-400, Korea (South) **(50%)**
Tel.: (82) 25110845
Web Site: http://www.hemco.co.kr
Sales Range: $10-24.9 Million
Emp.: 650
Provider of Energy Management Services
N.A.I.C.S.: 221122
William Chang *(CEO)*

Subsidiary (Non-US):

Sadmitec S.A. (3)
Bernardo De Irigoyen 722 1st Fl, C 1072 AAP, Buenos Aires, Argentina **(100%)**
Tel.: (54) 1140180100
Web Site: http://www.veolia.com.ar
Sales Range: $250-299.9 Million
Emp.: 500
Provider of Energy Management Services
N.A.I.C.S.: 221122
Gestapo Calvi *(Gen Dir)*

Siram SPA (3)
Via Anna Maria Mozzoni 12, 20152, Milan, MI, Italy
Tel.: (39) 02412981
Web Site: https://www.siram.veolia.it
Electric Power Generation & Distribution Services
N.A.I.C.S.: 221118
Frederik Anhwm *(Gen Mgr)*

Tallinna Kute (3)
Punane 36, 13619, Tallinn, Estonia **(100%)**
Tel.: (372) 6107100
Web Site: http://www.soojus.ee
Sales Range: $75-99.9 Million
Emp.: 270
Energy Management Services
N.A.I.C.S.: 541690
Kristjan Rahu *(Gen Mgr)*

Valorec Services AG (3)
Post Sach, CH 4019, Basel, Switzerland **(100%)**
Tel.: (41) 614688888
Web Site: http://www.valorec.com
Sales Range: $75-99.9 Million
Emp.: 300
Facilities Management & Energy Management Services
N.A.I.C.S.: 561210

Veolia Energia Vychodne Slovensko, s.r.o. (3)
Moldavska 8/A, 040 11, Kosice, Slovakia **(100%)**
Tel.: (421) 55 6427 886
Web Site: http://www.veoliaenergia.sk
Electric Power Distribution Services
N.A.I.C.S.: 221122

Veolia Energy Romania (3)
Barbu Vacarescu 241A Sector 2, 021532, Bucharest, Romania
Tel.: (40) 213228637
Web Site: http://www.veolia.ro
Drinking Water Supply, Energy & Sanitation Services
N.A.I.C.S.: 221310
Maria Leonte *(Dir-HR)*

Veolia Industriediensten B.V. (3)
Tel.: (31) 20 446 9000
Web Site: https://www.veolia.nl
Energy Management Services
N.A.I.C.S.: 221122
Ronald Hopman *(Dir-Bus Dev)*

Vilniaus Energija (3)
Jocioniu g13, LT-02300, Vilnius, Lithuania
Tel.: (370) 52667455
Web Site: http://www.dalkia.lt
Energy Production & Maintenance Services
N.A.I.C.S.: 541690

Subsidiary (US):

Veolia Energy North America, LLC (2)
53 State St 14 Flr, Boston, MA 02110 **(100%)**
Tel.: (617) 849-6678
Web Site: http://www.veolianorthamerica.com
Sales Range: $400-449.9 Million
Emp.: 600
Heating, Cooling & Renewable Energy Services
N.A.I.C.S.: 221330
Jason Salgo *(CFO & Exec VP-Fin)*

Subsidiary (Domestic):

Enovity, Inc. (3)
100 Montgomery St Ste 600, San Francisco, CA 94104
Tel.: (415) 974-0390
Web Site: https://www.enovity.com
Emp.: 200
Consulting & Engineering Services
N.A.I.C.S.: 541310
Michael Juniphant *(Mgr-Bus Dev)*

Joint Venture (Domestic):

Medical Area Total Energy Plant, LLC (3)
474 Brookline Ave, Boston, MA 02215
Tel.: (617) 598-2700
Web Site: https://www.matep.com
Cogeneration Power Facility Provides Heating, Chilled Water Services & Electricity to Hospitals
N.A.I.C.S.: 221118
Richard E. Kessel *(Pres & CEO)*

Subsidiary (Domestic):

Veolia Energy Baltimore Corporation (3)
1400 Ridgely St, Baltimore, MD 21230-2028
Tel.: (410) 649-2200
Web Site: http://www.veoliaenergyna.com
Rev.: $30,000,000
Emp.: 85
Heating & Cooling Supplier
N.A.I.C.S.: 221330
Pamela Clark *(Project Mgr)*

Veolia Energy Boston, Inc. (3)
53 State St 14th Fl, Boston, MA 02109
Tel.: (617) 482-8080
Web Site: http://www.veoliaenergyna.com
Rev.: $42,452,401
Emp.: 95
Heating & Cooling Supplier
N.A.I.C.S.: 221330
Cristine Gooch *(Mgr)*

Veolia Energy Kansas City, Inc. (3)
115 Grand Blvd, Kansas City, MO 64106
Tel.: (816) 889-4900
Web Site: http://www.veoliaenergyna.com
Sales Range: $50-74.9 Million
Emp.: 44
Heating & Cooling Supplier
N.A.I.C.S.: 221330

Veolia Energy Missouri, Inc. (3)
1 Ashley St, Saint Louis, MO 63102
Tel.: (314) 621-3550
Web Site: http://www.veoliaenergyna.com
Heating & Cooling Supplier
N.A.I.C.S.: 221330

Veolia Energy Philadelphia Corporation (3)
2600 Christian St, Philadelphia, PA 19146-2316
Tel.: (215) 875-6900
Web Site: http://www.veoliaenergyna.com
Sales Range: $75-99.9 Million
Emp.: 90
Heating & Cooling Supplier
N.A.I.C.S.: 221330
Michael Smedley *(VP-Mid Atlantic)*

Veolia Energy Trenton, L.P. (3)
320 S Warren Str, Trenton, NJ 08608
Tel.: (609) 396-7651
Web Site: http://www.veoliaenergyna.com
Rev.: $1,000,000
Emp.: 5
Heating & Cooling Supplier
N.A.I.C.S.: 221330

Veolia Energie Cr A.S. (1)
28 rijna 3337/7, Moravska, 702 00, Ostrava, Czech Republic
Tel.: (420) 59 660 9111
Web Site: https://www.vecr.cz
Heat & Electricity Supply Services
N.A.I.C.S.: 238220
Maxime Marsault *(CFO)*

Veolia Energie Praha, A.S. (1)
Enterprise Office Centrum Pikrtova 1737/1a, 140 00, Prague, Czech Republic
Tel.: (420) 22 151 1925
Web Site: https://www.vecr.cz
Emp.: 83
Electric Energy Equipment Mfr & Distr
N.A.I.C.S.: 335999
Alena Janotkova *(Project Mgr-Industry)*

Veolia Environmental Services Asia Pte Ltd (1)
5 Loyang Way 1 WMX Technologies Building, Singapore, 508706, Singapore
Tel.: (65) 6549 1815
Waste Management & Cleaning Services
N.A.I.C.S.: 562998

Veolia Environnement Suisse S.A. (1)
Reusseggstrasse 17, 1030, Emmenbrucke, Switzerland
Tel.: (41) 584043700
Web Site: http://www.veolia-es.ch
Emp.: 60
Waste Management Services
N.A.I.C.S.: 562998
Markus Eichenberger *(Gen Mgr)*

Veolia Espana S.L.U. (1)
C/Torrelaguna 60, 28043, Madrid, Spain
Tel.: (34) 915153600
Web Site: http://www.veolia.es
Electric Energy Equipment Mfr & Distr
N.A.I.C.S.: 335999

Veolia Gebaudeservice Deutschland GmbH (1)
Heinrich-Rau-Strasse 4, 16816, Neuruppin, Germany
Tel.: (49) 339184020
Waste Management Services
N.A.I.C.S.: 562998

Veolia Industrie Deutschland GmbH (1)
Am Torhaus 52, 66113, Saarbrucken, Germany
Tel.: (49) 681948160
Waste Management Services
N.A.I.C.S.: 562998

INTERNATIONAL PUBLIC

Veolia Industriepark Deutschland GmbH (1)
Boos-Fremery-Strasse 62, 52525, Heinsberg, Germany
Tel.: (49) 2452150
Waste Management Services
N.A.I.C.S.: 562998

Veolia Klarschlammverwertung Deutschland GmbH (1)
Nordstr 15, 04420, Markranstadt, Germany
Tel.: (49) 342057380
Waste Management Services
N.A.I.C.S.: 562998

Veolia Nederland Bv (1)
Tupoleviaan 69, 1119 PA, Schiphol-Rijk, Netherlands
Tel.: (31) 20 446 9000
Web Site: https://www.veolia.nl
Electrical Contracting Services
N.A.I.C.S.: 238210
Fred Degenaars *(Reg Mgr)*

Veolia Nordic Ab (1)
Norra Stationsgatan 67, 113 64, Stockholm, Sweden
Tel.: (46) 77 154 5000
Web Site: https://www.veolia.se
Industrial Remediation Services
N.A.I.C.S.: 562910
Jenny Regner *(CIO)*

Veolia North America Regeneration Services LLC (1)
125 S 84th St Ste 200, Milwaukee, WI 53214
Tel.: (414) 778-7000
Sulfuric Acid & Hydrofluoric Acid Regeneration Services
N.A.I.C.S.: 424690

Veolia North America, LLC (1)
53 State St 14th Fl, Boston, MA 02109
Tel.: (617) 849-6600
Web Site: https://www.veolianorthamerica.com
Industrial Cleaning & Maintenance; Energy Efficient Solutions & Regulated Waste Management Services
N.A.I.C.S.: 541620
John Gibson *(COO-Municipal & Comml Bus & Exec VP)*

Subsidiary (Domestic):

Kurion, Inc. (2)
2040 Main St Ste 800, Irvine, CA 92614-8257
Tel.: (949) 398-6350
Web Site: http://www.kurion.com
Nuclear & Hazardous Waste Management Solutions
N.A.I.C.S.: 562112
Gaetan Bonhomme *(CTO)*

US Industrial Technologies, Inc. (2)
13075 New Burgh Rd, Livonia, MI 48150-5009
Tel.: (734) 462-4100
Web Site: http://www.usitcorp.com
Specialized Freight Trucking
N.A.I.C.S.: 484230
Charlie Page *(Project Mgr)*

Veolia Nuclear Solutions. Inc. (1)
1150 W 120th Ave Ste 400, Westminster, CO 80234
Tel.: (720) 417-7055
Web Site: https://www.nuclearsolutions.veolia.com
Radiological Laboratory Services
N.A.I.C.S.: 541380

Veolia Nv-Sa (1)
Quai Fernand Demets 52, 1070, Brussels, Belgium
Tel.: (32) 2 525 1011
Web Site: https://www.veolia.be
Waste Management Services
N.A.I.C.S.: 562998
Peter De Vylder *(Comml Dir)*

Joint Venture (Non-US):

QCP B.V. (2)
Polymeerstraat 1, 6161 RE, Geleen, Netherlands **(50%)**
Tel.: (31) 886000500
Web Site: http://www.qcpolymers.com

AND PRIVATE COMPANIES — VEOLIA ENVIRONNEMENT S.A.

Polyethylene & Polypropylene Compound Mfr
N.A.I.C.S.: 325211
Raf Bemelmans *(Co-Founder)*

Veolia Pet Germany GmbH (1)
Hammerbrookstrasse 69, 20097, Hamburg, Germany
Tel.: (49) 4078101672
Waste Management Services
N.A.I.C.S.: 562998

Veolia Pet Svenska Ab (1)
Hanholmsvagen 67, 602 38, Norrkoping, Sweden
Tel.: (46) 1 119 0486
Web Site: https://www.cleanaway.se
Environmental Recycling Services
N.A.I.C.S.: 562119

Veolia Proprete (1)
169 Ave Georges Clemenceau, F-92735, Nanterre, Cedex, France **(100%)**
Tel.: (33) 146693000
Web Site: http://www.veolia-proprete.com
Sales Range: $5-14.9 Billion
Emp.: 80,700
Waste Collection, Treatment & Recycling Services
N.A.I.C.S.: 562998

Subsidiary (Non-US):

AS Veolia Keskkonnateenused (2)
Artelli 15, Tallinn, 10621, Estonia
Tel.: (372) 6400 888
Web Site: http://www.veolia.ee
Sales Range: $25-49.9 Million
Emp.: 250
Waste Management Services
N.A.I.C.S.: 562998

CGEA Israel Ltd (2)
10 Dubnov Street, Tel Aviv, 64732, Israel **(100%)**
Tel.: (972) 36088777
Web Site: http://www.onyx-environnement.com
Waste Management Services
N.A.I.C.S.: 562998

Subsidiary (Domestic):

ECOGRAS SAS (2)
17 Rue De Gardinoux, 93300, Aubervilliers, France **(100%)**
Tel.: (33) 143520280
Web Site: http://www.ecogras.com
Rev.: $549,491
Emp.: 40
Treatment & Recycling of Cooking Oils
N.A.I.C.S.: 425120

GRS Valtech (2)
2/4 Avenue Des Canuts, Lyon, 69140, France **(100%)**
Tel.: (33) 472018181
Web Site: http://www.grsvaltech.fr
Sales Range: $25-49.9 Million
Emp.: 270
Waste Management Services; Treatment of Contaminated Land
N.A.I.C.S.: 562998
Philidert Pearregoel *(Pres)*

Grandjouan Saco SA (2)
Lodzcosse Ave, PO Box 30305, 44203, Nantes, Cedex, France **(100%)**
Tel.: (33) 251727200
Web Site: http://www.onyx-environment.com
Sales Range: $75-99.9 Million
Emp.: 400
Waste Management
N.A.I.C.S.: 562998
Franck Arlen *(Pres)*

Subsidiary (Non-US):

IPODEC Ciste Mesto a.s (2)
Bestakova 457, 182 00, Prague, 8, Czech Republic
Tel.: (420) 49 364 7931
Web Site: http://www.ipodec.cz
Waste Management Services
N.A.I.C.S.: 562998

Subsidiary (Domestic):

Plastic Recycling SA (2)
1 allee Pierre Burelle, 92593, Levallois-Perret, Cedex, France
Tel.: (33) 40876400
Web Site: http://www.plasticomnium.com
Plastics Product Mfr
N.A.I.C.S.: 326199

Subsidiary (Non-US):

PureChem Veolia ES Pte. Ltd. (2)
7 Tuas Avenue 10, Singapore, 639131, Singapore **(100%)**
Tel.: (65) 68616668
Rev.: $5,815,300
Emp.: 250
Waste Management Services. Joint Venture of Pure Chemicals Industries & CGEA Asia Holdings Pte Ltd.
N.A.I.C.S.: 562998

Division (Domestic):

PureChem Veolia Environmental Services (3)
7 Tuas Avenue 10, Singapore, 639131, Singapore **(100%)**
Tel.: (65) 62641788
Web Site: http://www.purechemveolia-es.sg
Sales Range: $10-24.9 Million
Emp.: 45
Waste Management Services
N.A.I.C.S.: 562998

Subsidiary (Domestic):

Renosol (2)
Energy Park IV, 162 166 Blvd De Verdun, 92413, Courbevoie, Cedex, France **(100%)**
Tel.: (33) 141163060
Web Site: http://www.renosol-onyx.com
Industrial Cleaning Services
N.A.I.C.S.: 562998

Subsidiary (Non-US):

CONNECT Multiservices Kft (3)
Rokolya Utca 25, 1131, Budapest, Hungary
Tel.: (36) 12390290
Web Site: http://www.connectms.hu
Industrial Cleaning Services
N.A.I.C.S.: 562998

Subsidiary (Non-US):

Residuos Industriales Multiquim, S.A. de C.V (2)
Av Lazaro Cardenas 2400 Pte Edificio Losoles B-21, Garza Garcia, 66260, Nuevo Leon, Mexico
Tel.: (52) 81 81 52 21 00
Web Site: http://www.rimsa.com.mx
Waste Management Services
N.A.I.C.S.: 562998

Plant (Domestic):

Residuos Industriales Multiquim, S.A. de C.V - Chihuahua TRANSFER STATION FACILITY (3)
Federal Highway 45 No 16001 Col Rancheria Juarez, Chihuahua, 31060, Mexico
Tel.: (52) 614 435 1650
Waste Management Services
N.A.I.C.S.: 562998

Residuos Industriales Multiquim, S.A. de C.V - Ciudad Juarez TRANSFER STATION FACILITY (3)
Rio Chuviscar Manzana 9-E Km 29 Col Valle Dorado 5 Seccion Samalayuca, Samalayuca Mpio de, Ciudad Juarez, 32730, Chihuahua, Mexico
Tel.: (52) 656 633 2854
Sales Range: $25-49.9 Million
Emp.: 16
Waste Management Services
N.A.I.C.S.: 562998
Gucedo Saocaedo *(Mgr)*

Residuos Industriales Multiquim, S.A. de C.V - Coatzacoalcos (3)
Av Independencia No 500 Desp 205 Col Maria de la Piedad, Coatzacoalcos, 96410, Veracruz, Mexico
Tel.: (52) 921 214 0846
Waste Management Services
N.A.I.C.S.: 562998

Residuos Industriales Multiquim, S.A. de C.V - Guadalajara TREATMENT AND FINAL DISPOSAL FACILITY (3)
Circunvalacion Agustin Yanez No 2551 Local 21, Col Arcos Vallarta, Guadalajara, 44130, Jalisco, Mexico
Tel.: (52) 33 3615 5871
Web Site: http://www.rimsa.com.mx
Emp.: 3
Waste Management Services
N.A.I.C.S.: 562998

Residuos Industriales Multiquim, S.A. de C.V - HEAT TREATMENT PLANT (3)
R/a Anacleto Canabal S/N R/a Anacleto Canabal 3a Seccion, Villahermosa, 86280, Tabasco, Mexico
Tel.: (52) 993 337 9232
Waste Management Services
N.A.I.C.S.: 562998

Residuos Industriales Multiquim, S.A. de C.V - Hermosillo TRANSFER STATION FACILITY (3)
Edward W Villa 319 Col Olivares, Hermosillo, 83180, Sonora, Mexico
Tel.: (52) 662 260 7018
Waste Management Services
N.A.I.C.S.: 562998

Residuos Industriales Multiquim, S.A. de C.V - Mexicali TRANSFER STATION FACILITY (3)
Km 12 5 Carretera A San Luis Rio Colorado, Mexicali, 21600, Baja California, Mexico
Tel.: (52) 686 561 0727
Web Site: http://www.rimsa.com.mx
Sales Range: $25-49.9 Million
Emp.: 25
Waste Management Services
N.A.I.C.S.: 562998
Cesar Tamayo *(Gen Mgr)*

Residuos Industriales Multiquim, S.A. de C.V - Silao TRANSFER STATION FACILITY (3)
Carretera Silao-Romita km 2 5, 36100, Silao, Guanajuato, Mexico
Tel.: (52) 472 722 5035
Web Site: http://www.rimsa.com.mx
Emp.: 2
Waste Management Services
N.A.I.C.S.: 562998
Fernando Hernandez *(Mgr)*

Residuos Industriales Multiquim, S.A. de C.V - TREATMENT AND FINAL DISPOSAL FACILITY (3)
Carretera Monterrey-Monclova Km 86 Puerto San Bernabe, Mina, Nuevo Leon, Mexico
Tel.: (52) 81 8152 2174
Web Site: http://www.rimsa.com.mx
Waste Treatment Services
N.A.I.C.S.: 562219
Juan Carlos Rivera *(Gen Mgr)*

Residuos Industriales Multiquim, S.A. de C.V - Tijuana TRANSFER STATION FACILITY (3)
Km 14 5 Carretera Escenica La Joya, Tijuana-Ensenada, Tijuana, 22710, Baja California, Mexico
Tel.: (52) 664 630 0310
Web Site: http://www.rimsa.com.mx
Waste Management Services
N.A.I.C.S.: 562998

Subsidiary (Non-US):

SARPI Dorog Kft. (2)
Becsi ut 131, 2510, Dorog, Hungary
Tel.: (36) 33512700
Web Site: https://www.sarpi.hu
Sales Range: $25-49.9 Million
Emp.: 80
Waste Management Services
N.A.I.C.S.: 562998

Subsidiary (Domestic):

Sarp Industries-Limay (2)
451 Route du Hazay, Zone Portuaire, 78520, Limay, France **(100%)**
Tel.: (33) 134972500
Web Site: http://www.sarpindustries.fr
Sales Range: $75-99.9 Million
Emp.: 350
Hazardous Waste Management Services
N.A.I.C.S.: 562211
Jean-Francois Nogrette *(Gen Mgr)*

Subsidiary (Non-US):

VES Israel (2)
Aba Even 1 street, 46725, Herzliya Pituach, Israel
Tel.: (972) 9 952 00 00
Web Site: http://www.veolia-es.co.il
Waste Management Services
N.A.I.C.S.: 562998

Veolia Environmental Services (2)
8600 Rue Jarry Est, Anjou, Montreal, H1J 1X7, QC, Canada
Tel.: (514) 352-2000
Web Site: http://www.veolia.com
Sales Range: $10-24.9 Million
Emp.: 30
Waste Management & Plumbing Services
N.A.I.C.S.: 562998

Veolia Environmental Services (China) Co., Ltd. (2)
Unit 02A Floor 23rd Tower 1 8 North Dongsanhuan Road, Chaoyang District, Beijing, 100004, China
Tel.: (86) 10 59532000
Web Site: http://www.veolia-es.cn
Waste Management Services
N.A.I.C.S.: 562998
Zhou Xiaohua *(Gen Mgr)*

Veolia Environmental Services (HK) Hong-Kong Co., Ltd (2)
Room 4109-19 Sun Hung Kai Center 30 Harbour Road, Wanchai, China (Hong Kong)
Tel.: (852) 2827 1383
Environmental Consulting Services
N.A.I.C.S.: 541620

Veolia Environmental Services (Ireland) Limited (2)
Ballymount Cross, Tallaght, Dublin, D 24, Ireland
Tel.: (353) 141 36500
Web Site: http://www.veolia.ie
Sales Range: $25-49.9 Million
Emp.: 200
Waste Management & Recycling Services
N.A.I.C.S.: 562998

Veolia Environmental Services (UK) plc (2)
210 Pentonville Road, London, N1 9JY, United Kingdom **(100%)**
Tel.: (44) 2078125000
Web Site: http://www.veoliaenvironmentalservice.com
Rev.: $2,163,777,024
Emp.: 12,500
Waste Collection, Treatment & Recycling Services
N.A.I.C.S.: 562998
Gavin Graveson *(Exec VP)*

Veolia Environmental Services Australia (2)
Level 4 65 Pirrama Road, Pyrmont, 2009, NSW, Australia **(100%)**
Tel.: (61) 28 571 0000
Web Site: http://www.veoliaes.com.au
Sales Range: $500-549.9 Million
Emp.: 2,500
Waste & Facilities Management Services
N.A.I.C.S.: 562998
Doug Dean *(Mng Dir)*

Division (Domestic):

Veolia Environmental Services (3)
166 Boundary Rd, PO Box 933, Rocklea, 4106, Australia **(100%)**
Tel.: (61) 732750111
Web Site: http://www.veolia.com.au
Sales Range: $25-49.9 Million
Emp.: 100
Waste Management
N.A.I.C.S.: 562998
Lev Osman *(Gen Mgr)*

Veolia Environmental Services (3)
500 Churchill Road, Kilburn, 5084, SA, Australia
Tel.: (61) 132955
Web Site: http://www.veoliaes.com.au
Sales Range: $75-99.9 Million
Emp.: 300
Waste Management

VEOLIA ENVIRONNEMENT S.A.

Veolia Environnement S.A.—(Continued)
N.A.I.C.S.: 562998
Laurie Kozlovic (Gen Mgr)

Veolia Environmental Services (3)
13 Beaton Road, PO Box 331, Berrimah, 0828, NT, Australia (100%)
Tel.: (61) 132955
Web Site: http://www.veoliaes.com.au
Sales Range: $10-24.9 Million
Emp.: 40
Waste Management
N.A.I.C.S.: 562998

Veolia Environmental Services (3)
75 Mornington Rd, PO Box 431, Mornington, 7018, TAS, Australia (100%)
Tel.: (61) 362440000
Web Site: http://www.veoliaes.com.au
Rev.: $2,635,485
Emp.: 200
Waste Management
N.A.I.C.S.: 562998

Veolia Environmental Services (3)
Level 1 85 Buckhurst St South, Melbourne, 3205, VIC, Australia
Tel.: (61) 396262222
Web Site: http://www.veoliaes.com.au
Sales Range: $10-24.9 Million
Emp.: 50
Waste Management Services
N.A.I.C.S.: 562998
Simon Torr (Gen Mgr)

Veolia Industrial Services WA (3)
4-6 Rivers Street, Bibra Lake, 6163, WA, Australia (100%)
Tel.: (61) 894189300
Web Site: http://www.veoliaes.com.au
Sales Range: $10-24.9 Million
Emp.: 50
Waste Management Services
N.A.I.C.S.: 562998

Subsidiary (Non-US):

Veolia Environmental Services Belgium N.V. (2)
Mechelsesteenweg 642, 1800, Vilvoorde, Belgium
Tel.: (32) 78155555
Web Site: http://www.veolia-es.be
Waste Management Services
N.A.I.C.S.: 562998

Subsidiary (Domestic):

Veolia Environmental Services France (2)
169 Avenue Georges-Clemenceau, 92735, Nanterre, France
Tel.: (33) 1 46 69 30 00
Web Site: http://www.veolia-proprete.fr
Emp.: 70
Environmental Consulting Services
N.A.I.C.S.: 541620
Pascal Decary (Exec VP-HR)

Subsidiary (Non-US):

Veolia ES Canada Industrial Services Inc. (3)
141 Properity Way, Chatham, N7M 5J3, ON, Canada
Tel.: (519) 352-7773
Waste Management Services
N.A.I.C.S.: 562998

Veolia Proprete Senegal (3)
Route de Pikine, BP 18961, Pikine, Senegal
Tel.: (221) 33 85 32 431
Waste Management Services
N.A.I.C.S.: 562998

Subsidiary (Non-US):

Veolia Environmental Services Lietuva UAB (2)
E Simkunaites Str 10 3 Floor, 4130, Vilnius, Lithuania
Tel.: (370) 5 2635550
Web Site: http://www.veolia-es.lt
Waste Management Services
N.A.I.C.S.: 562998

Subsidiary (US):

Veolia Environmental Services North America Corp. (2)

700 E Butterfield Rd Ste 201, Lombard, IL 60148-5671 (100%)
Tel.: (630) 218-1500
Web Site: http://www.veoliaes.com
Sales Range: $10-24.9 Million
Emp.: 45
Waste Collection, Treatment & Recycling Services
N.A.I.C.S.: 541690
Terri Anne Powers (Dir-IR-North America)

Subsidiary (Domestic):

Veolia ES Industrial Services, Inc. (3)
2525 S Blvd Ste 410, League City, TX 77573
Tel.: (713) 307-2160
Industrial Wastes Treatment Services
N.A.I.C.S.: 562211

Veolia ES Technical Solutions LLC (3)
700 E Butterfield Rd, Lombard, IL 60148-5671
Tel.: (630) 218-1647
Web Site: http://www.veolianorthamerica.com
Environmental Services
N.A.I.C.S.: 541620
Robert Capotonna (Pres)

Veolia Industrial Services, Inc. (3)
3018 N Hwy 146, Baytown, TX 77520
Tel.: (713) 307-2150
Provider of Waste Management Services
N.A.I.C.S.: 238990
Tim Wood (Mgr-Sls)

Division (Non-US):

Veolia Industrial Services (4)
2800 de Letchemin, Levis, G6W 7X6, QC, Canada
Tel.: (418) 835-3750
Web Site: http://www.veoliaesse.com
Sales Range: $10-24.9 Million
Emp.: 80
Waste Management Services
N.A.I.C.S.: 562998

Subsidiary (Non-US):

Veolia Environmental Services Qatar L.L.C. (2)
Musaffah MW4 Street 16, PO Box 9755, Abu Dhabi, 9755, United Arab Emirates
Tel.: (971) 2 55 11 557
Web Site: http://www.veolia.com
Sales Range: $75-99.9 Million
Emp.: 35
Waste Management Services
N.A.I.C.S.: 562998
Alberto Vazquez (Gen Mgr)

Veolia Environmental Services Singapore (2)
23 Pandang Avenue, Singapore, 609389, Singapore
Tel.: (65) 6861 6668
Web Site: http://www.veolia.com.sg
Sales Range: $125-149.9 Million
Emp.: 1,000
Waste Management Services
N.A.I.C.S.: 562998
John Edward Dalton (Gen Mgr)

Veolia Environmental Services Ukraine (2)
25/2 V Zhitomirska Str, 01025, Kiev, Ukraine
Tel.: (380) 44 594 0072
Web Site: http://www.veolia-es.com.ua
Waste Management Services
N.A.I.C.S.: 562998
Oleksandr Korolyuk (Mng Dir)

Subsidiary (Domestic):

Veolia Proprete (2)
163 Avenue Georges, Clemenceau, 69008, Bordeaux, France (100%)
Tel.: (33) 171750000
Web Site: http://www.veoliaproprete.com
Sales Range: $125-149.9 Million
Emp.: 700
Waste Management Services
N.A.I.C.S.: 562998

Subsidiary (Non-US):

Veolia Umweltservice GmbH (2)
Hammerbrookstr 69, 20097, Hamburg, Germany (100%)
Tel.: (49) 4 078 1010
Web Site: http://www.veolia-umweltservice.de
Sales Range: $10-24.9 Million
Emp.: 15
Waste Management
N.A.I.C.S.: 562998
Holger Schmitz (Gen Mgr)

Subsidiary (Domestic):

Onyx Rohr- und Kanal-Service GmbH & Co. KG (3)
Vahrenwalder Strasse 217, 30165, Hannover, Germany (100%)
Tel.: (49) 51 196 6900
Web Site: https://onyx-rks.de
Sewerage Systems
N.A.I.C.S.: 221320

Veolia Umweltservice GmbH (3)
Hammerbrookstr 69, 20097, Hamburg, Germany (100%)
Tel.: (49) 4 078 1010
Web Site: https://www.veolia.de
Industrial Waste Management Services
N.A.I.C.S.: 562998

Veolia Umweltservice Industrie Reinigung GmbH & Co. KG (3)
Kruppstrasse 9, 41540, Dormagen, Germany (100%)
Tel.: (49) 21332640
Web Site: http://www.veolia-umweltservice.de
Waste Management & Industrial Cleaning Services
N.A.I.C.S.: 562998

Subsidiary (Non-US):

Veolia Uslugi dla Srodowiska S.A. (2)
Ul 17 Stycznia 45B, 02-146, Warsaw, Poland
Tel.: (48) 22 331 91 62
Web Site: http://www.veolia-es.pl
Emp.: 15
Waste Treatment & Disposal Services
N.A.I.C.S.: 562211
Yves Basset (Mng Dir)

Veolia Recycling & Recovery Holdings ANZ Pty. Ltd. (1)
Level 4 65 Pirrama Road, Pyrmont, 2009, NSW, Australia
Tel.: (61) 285710000
Energy Management Services
N.A.I.C.S.: 541690

Veolia Term Sa (1)
ul Pulawska 2, 02-566, Warsaw, Poland
Tel.: (48) 22 568 8200
Web Site: http://www.veoliaterm.pl
Electric Power Distribution Services
N.A.I.C.S.: 221122

Veolia Transport Israel (1)
Aba Even 1 Street, Herzliya Pituach, 46725, Israel
Tel.: (972) 9 952 00 00
Web Site: http://www.veolia-transport.co.il
Rural Bus Transportation Services
N.A.I.C.S.: 485210

Veolia Umweltservice & Consulting GmbH (1)
Hammerbrookstrasse 69, 20097, Hamburg, Germany
Tel.: (49) 4078101444
Waste Management Services
N.A.I.C.S.: 562998
Guido Adomssent (Mng Dir)

Veolia Umweltservice Dual GmbH (1)
Henrik-Ibsen-Str 20 A, 18106, Rostock, Germany
Tel.: (49) 38187715320
Waste Management Services
N.A.I.C.S.: 562998

Veolia Umweltservice Nord GmbH (1)
Werner-Siemens-Strasse 20, 22113, Hamburg, Germany
Tel.: (49) 40733270
Waste Management Services
N.A.I.C.S.: 562998
Jan-Peter Ungelenk (Acct Mgr)

Veolia Umweltservice Ost GmbH & Co. Kg (1)
Rosenstrasse 99, 01159, Dresden, Germany
Tel.: (49) 35149730
Waste Management Services
N.A.I.C.S.: 562998

Subsidiary (Domestic):

GUD GERAER Umweltdienste GmbH & Co. Kg (2)
Am Fuhrpark 1, 07548, Gera, Germany (100%)
Tel.: (49) 36584000
Waste Management Services
N.A.I.C.S.: 562998

Veolia Umweltservice PET Recycling GmbH (1)
Hammerbrookstrasse 69, 20097, Hamburg, Germany
Tel.: (49) 4078101672
Web Site: https://www.recypet.ch
Waste Treatment Services
N.A.I.C.S.: 221310

Veolia Umweltservice Ressourcenmanagement GmbH (1)
Hammerbrookstrasse 69, 20097, Hamburg, Germany
Tel.: (49) 4078101573
Waste Management Services
N.A.I.C.S.: 562998

Veolia Umweltservice Sud GmbH & Co. Kg. (1)
Bergwerkstrasse 1, 91247, Pegnitz, Germany
Tel.: (49) 92419880
Waste Management Services
N.A.I.C.S.: 562998

Veolia Umweltservice Wertstoffmanagement GmbH (1)
Hammerbrookstrasse 69, 20097, Hamburg, Germany
Tel.: (49) 40781010
Waste Management Services
N.A.I.C.S.: 562998

Veolia Umweltservice West GmbH (1)
Werrestrasse 65, 32049, Herford, Germany
Tel.: (49) 522113310
Waste Management Services
N.A.I.C.S.: 562998
Markus Binding (Mng Dir)

Veolia Viz Zrt. (1)
Huvosvolgyi ut 18, Budapest, 1021, Hungary
Tel.: (36) 1 486 3710
Web Site: http://www.veoliaviz.hu
Sales Range: $1-4.9 Billion
Emp.: 1,800
Water Supply & Treatment Services
N.A.I.C.S.: 221320
Gyorgy Palko (Country-Dir)

Veolia Voda SA (1)
52 Rue D Anjou, 75008, Paris, France
Tel.: (33) 1 49 24 49 24
Web Site: http://www.Veolia.com
Emp.: 10
Waste Treatment Services
N.A.I.C.S.: 221310
David Park (Chm)

Veolia Wasser Deutschland GmbH (1)
Walter-Kohn-Strasse 1a, 04356, Leipzig, Germany
Tel.: (49) 341241760
Waste Management Services
N.A.I.C.S.: 562998
Christophe Sardet (Mgr-Technical)

Veolia Wasser Storkow GmbH (1)
Furstenwalder Strasse 66, Storkow Mark, 15526, Brandenburg, Germany
Tel.: (49) 33678404990
Waste Management Services
N.A.I.C.S.: 562998

AND PRIVATE COMPANIES

VEOLIA ENVIRONNEMENT S.A.

Veolia Wasser Wagenfeld GmbH (1)
Zu den Auenwiese, Wagenfeld, 49419, Diepholz, Germany
Tel.: (49) 54445600
Waste Management Services
N.A.I.C.S.: 562998

Veolia Water - Gabon (1)
Avenue Felix Eboue, BP 2187, Libreville, Gabon
Tel.: (241) 76 12 82
Water & Electric Power Distribution Services
N.A.I.C.S.: 221310

Veolia Water Brasil (1)
Rua Jundiai 50 - 5 Andar - Jardim Paulista, 04001-140, Sao Paulo, Brazil
Tel.: (55) 11 3846 3170
Web Site: http://www.veoliawaterst.com.br
Water Supply Services
N.A.I.C.S.: 221310

Veolia Water SA (1)
38 Avenue Klebert, 75799, Paris, Cedex 2-16, France **(100%)**
Tel.: (33) 1 49 24 49 24
Sales Range: $5-14.9 Billion
Emp.: 77,841
Water Supply & Related Services
N.A.I.C.S.: 221310
Jacques-Louis David *(Gen Dir)*

Subsidiary (Non-US):

Aquaflow Ltd (2)
Kirkkokatu 7 B, PO Box 116, 57100, Savonlinna, Finland **(100%)**
Tel.: (358) 20 744 1600
Web Site: https://www.aquaflow.fi
Water Supply Services
N.A.I.C.S.: 221310

Elga Berkefeld GmbH (2)
Lueckenweg 5, PO Box 3202, 29227, Celle, Germany **(100%)**
Tel.: (49) 51418030
Web Site: http://www.berkefeld.com
Sales Range: $25-49.9 Million
Emp.: 230
Mfr of Water Conditioning & Purification Equipment & Related Products
N.A.I.C.S.: 333301
Christian Ausseoder *(Gen Mgr)*

Kruger A/S (2)
Gladsaxevej 363, 2860, Soborg, Denmark **(100%)**
Tel.: (45) 3 969 0222
Web Site: https://www.kruger.dk
Emp.: 450
Water Supply & Sewerage Services
N.A.I.C.S.: 221310
Niels Matsen *(CFO)*

Division (Domestic):

Kruger Aquacare (3)
Fabriksparken 50, 2600, Glostrup, Denmark **(100%)**
Tel.: (45) 43451676
Web Site: https://www.kruger.dk
Sales Range: $75-99.9 Million
Emp.: 57
Supplier of Water Treatment Services & Equipment
N.A.I.C.S.: 221310

Subsidiary (Non-US):

Kruger Akvapur AB (2)
Vretemvadem 13, 17154, Stockholm, Sweden **(100%)**
Tel.: (46) 858766300
Web Site: http://www.kruger.se
Sales Range: $75-99.9 Million
Emp.: 100
Water Supply & Sewerage Services
N.A.I.C.S.: 221310
Par Lindstrom *(Gen Mgr)*

Kruger Oy (2)
Halsuantie 14, PO Box 00390, 420, Helsinki, Finland **(100%)**
Tel.: (358) 947709041
Web Site: http://www.kruger.dk
Sales Range: $75-99.9 Million
Emp.: 2
Water Supply & Sewerage Services
N.A.I.C.S.: 221310
Seppo Wallinmaa *(Dir)*

Subsidiary (Domestic):

Sade CGTH (2)
23-25 BC of Doctor Lannelongue, 75014, Paris, France **(98.4%)**
Tel.: (33) 153759911
Web Site: https://www.sade-cgth.fr
Sales Range: $900-999.9 Million
Emp.: 250
Hydraulic Projects Construction
N.A.I.C.S.: 327310
Patrick Leleu *(Mng Dir)*

Subsidiary (Non-US):

Veolia Agua S.A. (2)
Pol Ind Santa Ana C/ del Electrodo 52, 28522, Rivas-Vaciamadrid, Spain
Tel.: (34) 91 660 40 00
Waste Treatment Services
N.A.I.C.S.: 221310

Veolia Deutschland GmbH (2)
Unter den Linden 21, 10117, Berlin, Germany **(100%)**
Tel.: (49) 302 062 9560
Web Site: https://www.veolia.de
Sales Range: $800-899.9 Million
Emp.: 5
Water Supply Services
N.A.I.C.S.: 221310
Michel Cunnac *(Member-Mgmt Bd)*

Veolia Wasser GmbH (2)
Unter Den Linden 21, Berlin, 10117, Germany
Tel.: (49) 3020629560
Web Site: http://www.veoliawasser.de
Water Supply Services
N.A.I.C.S.: 221310

Veolia Water AB (2)
Kaserngatan 1, 761 30, Norrtalje, Sweden **(100%)**
Tel.: (46) 176208590
Sales Range: $50-74.9 Million
Emp.: 20
Water Supply Services
N.A.I.C.S.: 221310
Jacob Illeris *(Gen Mgr)*

Veolia Water Armenia (2)
Yerevan Djur 66a Rue Abovyan, Yerevan, 0025, Armenia
Tel.: (374) 10 56 13 26
Web Site: http://www.veoliadjur.am
Rev.: $22,962,000
Emp.: 1,450
Water Supply Services
N.A.I.C.S.: 221310

Veolia Water Asia Pacific Ltd (2)
21/F AIG Tower 1 Connaught Road, Central, China (Hong Kong)
Tel.: (852) 2167 8206
Web Site: http://www.veolia.com
Waste Treatment Services
N.A.I.C.S.: 221310

Veolia Water Australia (2)
Bay Ctr Level 4, 65 Pirrama Rd, Pyrmont, 2009, NSW, Australia **(100%)**
Tel.: (61) 285720300
Web Site: http://www.veoliawater.com.au
Sales Range: $400-449.9 Million
Emp.: 800
Water Supply Services
N.A.I.C.S.: 221310

Veolia Water Czech Republic (2)
Pariszka 11, 110 00, Prague, Czech Republic **(100%)**
Tel.: (420) 222321648
Sales Range: $400-449.9 Million
Emp.: 600
Water Supply Services
N.A.I.C.S.: 221310
Philippe Gitar *(Gen Mgr)*

Subsidiary (Domestic):

Veolia Water France (2)
52 Rue d'Anjou, 75008, Paris, France
Tel.: (33) 1 49 24 49 24
Water Supply Services
N.A.I.C.S.: 221310

Subsidiary (Non-US):

Veolia Water India Pvt Ltd (2)
B-1 Marble Arch 9 Prithviraj Road, New Delhi, 110 011, India
Tel.: (91) 11 2465 1465
Sales Range: $75-99.9 Million
Emp.: 80
Waste Treatment Services
N.A.I.C.S.: 221310
Patrick Rousseau *(Mng Dir)*

Veolia Water Ireland (2)
Dublin Road, Celbridge, Kildare, Ireland
Tel.: (353) 16303333
Web Site: http://www.elgaprocesswater.com
Sales Range: $50-74.9 Million
Emp.: 30
Water Supply Services
N.A.I.C.S.: 221310

Veolia Water Israel (2)
Aba Even 1 Street, 46725, Herzliya Pituach, Israel
Tel.: (972) 9 952 00 00
Web Site: http://www.veoliawater.com
Water Desalination Services
N.A.I.C.S.: 237110

Veolia Water Japan K.K. (2)
Yokoso Rainbow Tower 11F 3-20-20 Kaigan, Minato-Ku, Tokyo, 1080-022, Japan
Tel.: (81) 3 5441 7010
Web Site: http://www.veoliawater.jp
Waste Water Treatment Services
N.A.I.C.S.: 221320
Jersale Christian *(Pres)*

Veolia Water Malaysia Holding Sdn Bhd (2)
Unit 20-1 and 20-2 Level 20 Mercu 3 No 3 Jalan Bangsar KL Eco City, 59200, Kuala Lumpur, Malaysia
Tel.: (60) 322641818
Emp.: 30
Waste Water Treatment Services
N.A.I.C.S.: 221320
Mohammed Akhir *(Mng Dir)*

Subsidiary (Domestic):

Veolia Water Solutions & Technologies (2)
Immeuble l'Aquarene 1 place Montgolfier, 94410, Saint Maurice, France
Tel.: (33) 14 511 5555
Web Site: http://www.veoliawaterst.com
Sales Range: $1-4.9 Billion
Emp.: 8,900
Waste Treatment Services
N.A.I.C.S.: 221310
Jean-Michel Herrewyn *(CEO)*

Subsidiary (Non-US):

ATS Aritim Teknolojileri Sanayi Tic AS (3)
DES Sanayi Sitesi 118 Sk C31 Blok No 1 Y Dudullu-Umraniye, Istanbul, 34758, Turkiye
Tel.: (90) 216 499 60 90
Web Site: http://www.ats.com.tr
Waste Water Treatment Services
N.A.I.C.S.: 221320

AnoxKaldnes AB (3)
Klosterangsvagen 11A, 226 47, Lund, Sweden
Tel.: (46) 4 618 2150
Web Site: https://www.anoxkaldnes.com
Sales Range: $50-74.9 Million
Emp.: 47
Industrial Waste Water Treatment Services
N.A.I.C.S.: 221320
Marie Fremner *(CFO)*

COVSPOL, a.s. (3)
Magnetova 12 budova PPC, 831 04, Bratislava, Slovakia
Tel.: (421) 24 342 5070
Web Site: https://www.covspol.sk
Sales Range: $75-99.9 Million
Emp.: 6
Waste Treatment Services
N.A.I.C.S.: 221310
Pavol Fitko *(Chm)*

Hydrotech AB (3)
Mejselgatan 6, 235 32, Vellinge, Sweden
Tel.: (46) 40429530
Web Site: https://www.hydrotech.se
Sales Range: $50-74.9 Million
Emp.: 45
Waste Water Treatment Services
N.A.I.C.S.: 221320

Rikard Olsson *(VP)*

Kruger Kaldnes AS (3)
Nordre Fokserod 9, 3217, Sandefjord, Norway
Tel.: (47) 91608000
Web Site: https://www.krugerkaldnes.no
Emp.: 75
Waste Treatment Services
N.A.I.C.S.: 221310

Subsidiary (Domestic):

MSE (3)
L'Aquarene 1 Place Montgolfier, 94417, Saint Maurice, France
Tel.: (33) 1 45 11 55 55
Web Site: http://www.mse-eau.com
Waste Water Treatment Services
N.A.I.C.S.: 221320

OTV France S.N.C. (3)
L Aquarene 1 Place Montgolfier, 94417, Saint Maurice, Cedex, France
Tel.: (33) 14 511 5555
Web Site: http://www.otv.fr
Emp.: 60
Waste Water Treatment Services
N.A.I.C.S.: 221320

Subsidiary (Non-US):

OTV TURKEY ARITMA iNS.SAN.VE TiC.A.S (3)
Ataturk Cad Sitki Bey Plaza N 82 Kat 11, Kozyatagi - Kadikoy, 34736, Istanbul, Turkiye
Tel.: (90) 216 468 33 00
Web Site: http://www.otvturkey.com.tr
Waste Treatment Services
N.A.I.C.S.: 221310

Subsidiary (Domestic):

Opalium (3)
178 Avenue du Marechal de Lattre de Tassigny, Fontenay-sous-Bois, 94120, France
Tel.: (33) 1 45 14 12 12
Web Site: http://www.opalium.com
Sales Range: $75-99.9 Million
Emp.: 17
Waste Treatment Services
N.A.I.C.S.: 221310

Subsidiary (Non-US):

PT Veolia Water Technologies Indonesia (3)
Ventura Building 6th floor suite 605 JI R A Kartini 26, Cilandak, Jakarta, 12430, Indonesia
Tel.: (62) 21 750 4707
Web Site: http://www.veoliawaterst-sea.com
Waste Water Treatment Services
N.A.I.C.S.: 221320
Michel Otten *(Dir-Technical)*

SIBA S.p.a (3)
Via Lampedusa 13, 20141, Milan, Italy
Tel.: (39) 02 42991
Web Site: http://www.sibaspa.it
Waste Water Treatment Services
N.A.I.C.S.: 221320

Subsidiary (Domestic):

Sidem (3)
1 rue Giovanni Battista Pirelli, 94410, Saint-Maurice-de-Beynost, France
Tel.: (33) 14 995 7676
Web Site: https://www.sidem-desalination.com
Sales Range: $125-149.9 Million
Emp.: 250
Waste Treatment Services
N.A.I.C.S.: 221310
Vincent Baujat *(Dir-Publication)*

Subsidiary (Domestic):

Entropie SAS (4)
Immeuble le Vermont 28 boulevard de Pesaro, 92000, Nanterre, France **(100%)**
Tel.: (33) 155676000
Web Site: https://www.entropie.com
Emp.: 50
Thermal Engineering & Water Treatment Svcs
N.A.I.C.S.: 541330

VEOLIA ENVIRONNEMENT S.A.

Veolia Environnement S.A.—(Continued)

Subsidiary (Domestic):

Entropie SAS (5)
20-22 rue de Clichy, 75009, Paris, France
Tel.: (33) 156353500
Web Site: http://www.entropie.com
Water Treatment Facility Design & Engineering Services
N.A.I.C.S.: 221310

Subsidiary (Non-US):

Sidem Saudi Ltd. (4)
PO Box 31761, Al Khobar, Saudi Arabia
Tel.: (966) 38894068
Water Desalination Plant Construction Services
N.A.I.C.S.: 237110

Subsidiary (Non-US):

Sidem Libya (3)
Gargaresh KM 7 5 Near Shuruk Supermarket, PO Box 6440, Tripoli, Libya
Tel.: (218) 21 483 7451
Web Site: http://www.sidem-desalination.com
Water Line Construction Services
N.A.I.C.S.: 237110

VA-Ingenjorerna AB (3)
Vretenvagen 9, 171 54, Solna, Sweden
Tel.: (46) 8 473 0000
Web Site: https://www.vaing.se
Waste Water Treatment Services
N.A.I.C.S.: 221320

VWS Emirates LLC (3)
Office 1401-A 48 Burj Gate Tower Sheikh Zayed Road, Dubai, United Arab Emirates
Tel.: (971) 4 341 6940
Web Site: http://www.veoliawaterst.com
Sales Range: $50-74.9 Million
Emp.: 50
Water Treatment Facility Design & Engineering Services
N.A.I.C.S.: 221310
Emmanuel Gayan (Gen Mgr)

VWS Industrial Services (Malaysia) SDN BHD (3)
41 Jalan Bertam 5 Taman Daya, 81100, Johor Bahru, Malaysia
Tel.: (60) 7 352 17 98
Industrial Waste Water Treatment Services
N.A.I.C.S.: 221310

VWS MPP Systems B.V. (3)
Celsiusstraat 34, 6716 BZ, Ede, Netherlands
Tel.: (31) 318 66 4010
Web Site: http://www.vwsmppsystems.com
Sales Range: $25-49.9 Million
Emp.: 25
Water Treatment System Mfr & Distr
N.A.I.C.S.: 333310
Erik Middelhoek (Mng Dir)

VWS Netherlands (3)
Celsiusstraat 34, 6716 BZ, Ede, Netherlands
Tel.: (31) 318691500
Web Site: http://www.veoliawaterst.nl
Sales Range: $50-74.9 Million
Emp.: 80
Waste Water Treatment Services
N.A.I.C.S.: 924110
Mark Dyson (Mng Dir)

Subsidiary (Domestic):

VWS Oil & Gas (3)
Immeuble Parc 2 - ZAC De La Croix De Berny, 10 Place Du General De Gaulle, 92160, Antony, France
Tel.: (33) 1 40 83 65 00
Web Site: http://www.vwsoilandgas.com
Waste Water Treatment Services
N.A.I.C.S.: 221320

Subsidiary (Non-US):

VWS Romania Industrial SRL (3)
Dimitrie Pompei Blvd 9 Iride Business Park Building 40, 8th Floor Sector 2, 20331, Bucharest, Romania
Tel.: (40) 21 243 07 91
Emp.: 10
Waste Water Treatment Services
Jens Beckman (Gen Mgr)

VWS Serbia (3)
Kralja Milana 21/2, Belgrade, 11000, Serbia
Tel.: (381) 11 32 40 763
Sales Range: $75-99.9 Million
Emp.: 16
Industrial Waste Water Treatment Services
N.A.I.C.S.: 221320

VWS Westgarth Ltd. (3)
149 Newlands Rd, Carthcart, Glasgow, G44 4EX, Scotland, United Kingdom
Tel.: (44) 1416331336
Web Site: http://www.vwswestgarth.com
Sales Range: $50-74.9 Million
Emp.: 150
Water Treatment & Desalination Plant Design & Construction Services
N.A.I.C.S.: 237110

VWS-Hungary Inc. (3)
Budafoki Street 187-189, 1094, Budapest, Hungary
Tel.: (36) 13232210
Web Site: http://www.veoliawaterst.hu
Emp.: 30
Industrial Waste Water Treatment Services
N.A.I.C.S.: 221320
Tomosi Karole (CEO)

Subsidiary (Domestic):

Veolia Water STI (3)
Immeuble l'Aquarene 1 place Montgolfier, 94410, Saint-Maurice-de-Beynost, France
Tel.: (33) 14 511 5555
Web Site: http://www.veoliawaterst.com
Water Supply Services
N.A.I.C.S.: 221310
Jean-Michel Herrewyn (Chm & CEO)

Subsidiary (Non-US):

Veolia Water Solutions & Technologies (Beijing) Co., Ltd. (3)
Room708 7/F South Tower China Overseas Plaza No8 Guanghuadongli, Chaoyang Qu, Beijing, 100020, China
Tel.: (86) 105 798 8000
Web Site: http://www.veolia.com
Waste Treatment Services
N.A.I.C.S.: 221310

Veolia Water Solutions & Technologies (New Zealand) Limited (3)
61-63 O'Shannessey Street, Parnell, Auckland, 2110, New Zealand
Tel.: (64) 9 354 4174
Web Site: http://www.veoliawaterst.co.nz
Emp.: 1
Waste Water Treatment Services
N.A.I.C.S.: 221310
Peter Pritchard (Office Mgr)

Veolia Water Solutions & Technologies (Philippines), Inc. (3)
16 Philcrest Compound Km 23 West Service Road Cupang, Muntinlupa, 1771, Philippines
Tel.: (63) 2809 4011
Sales Range: $50-74.9 Million
Emp.: 60
Waste Water Treatment Services
N.A.I.C.S.: 221320
Jean-Philippe Filhol (Mgr)

Veolia Water Solutions & Technologies (SEA) Pte Ltd (3)
No 5 Loyang Way 1, 508706, Singapore, Singapore
Tel.: (65) 6546 1110
Web Site: http://www.veoliawaterst-sea.com
Emp.: 8
Waste Water Treatment Services
N.A.I.C.S.: 221320

Veolia Water Solutions & Technologies (Shanghai) Co., Ltd. (3)
28F New Bund Center No 555 West Haiyang Road, Pudong Xinqu, Shanghai, 200126, China
Tel.: (86) 216 193 8088
Web Site: http://www.veoliawaterst.com
Sales Range: $125-149.9 Million
Emp.: 15
Waste Water Treatment Services
N.A.I.C.S.: 221320

Veolia Water Solutions & Technologies (Thailand) Ltd. (3)
7th A Fl Q House Ploenjit Bldg 598 Ploenjit Rd Lumpini, Pathumwan, Bangkok, 10330, Thailand
Tel.: (66) 2 650 8384
Web Site: http://www.veoliawaterst-sea.com
Waste Treatment Services
N.A.I.C.S.: 221310

Veolia Water Solutions & Technologies Argentina (3)
Herrera 2121, C1295ACO, Buenos Aires, Argentina
Tel.: (54) 11 4302 7181
Web Site: http://www.veoliawaterst.com.ar
Waste Treatment Services
N.A.I.C.S.: 221310

Veolia Water Solutions & Technologies Brazil LTDA (3)
Rua Jundiai 50 - 2 Andar - Jardim Paulista, Sao Paulo, 04001-140, Brazil
Tel.: (55) 1138888800
Web Site: http://www.veoliawaterst.com.br
Emp.: 40
Waste Treatment Services
N.A.I.C.S.: 221310
Ruddi Souza (Gen Mgr)

Veolia Water Solutions & Technologies Chile Limitada (3)
Av Santa Maria 2880 Oficina 301, 7520422, Santiago, Chile
Tel.: (56) 2 889 9900
Web Site: http://www.veoliawaterst.cl
Sales Range: $50-74.9 Million
Emp.: 33
Waste Treatment Services
N.A.I.C.S.: 221310
Ebert Aguilera (Mgr-Sls)

Veolia Water Solutions & Technologies China (3)
19th Floor - Pidemco Tower 318 Fuzhou Road, Shanghai, 200001, China
Tel.: (86) 21 6391 3288
Web Site: http://www.veoliawaterst.com.cn
Sales Range: $125-149.9 Million
Emp.: 200
Waste Treatment Services
N.A.I.C.S.: 221310

Veolia Water Solutions & Technologies Egypt (3)
Unit 8 3rd Floor Building 3 Downtown Complex Road 90 Fifth Settelment, 11835, Cairo, Egypt
Tel.: (20) 2 231 46 101
Web Site: http://www.veoliawaterst.com
Sales Range: $125-149.9 Million
Emp.: 150
Waste Treatment Services
N.A.I.C.S.: 221310

Veolia Water Solutions & Technologies Iberica (3)
C/Electrodo 52 Poligono Ind Santa Ana, Rivas-Vaciamadrid, 28529, Madrid, Spain
Tel.: (34) 916604000
Web Site: http://www.veoliawaterst.es
Sales Range: $250-299.9 Million
Emp.: 30
Waste Treatment Services
N.A.I.C.S.: 221310
Jose Angel Legaz (CEO)

Veolia Water Solutions & Technologies Italia S.r.l. (3)
Via Pra di Risi 3, 33080, Zoppola, PN, Italy
Tel.: (39) 043 451 6311
Web Site: http://www.veoliawaterst.it
Waste Treatment Services
N.A.I.C.S.: 221310

Veolia Water Solutions & Technologies Japan K.K. (3)
Yokoso Rainbow Tower 11F 3-20-20 Kaigan, Minato-Ku, Tokyo, 108-0022, Japan
Tel.: (81) 3 5441 7070
Web Site: http://veoliawatertechnologies.com
Waste Water Treatment Services
N.A.I.C.S.: 221320

Veolia Water Solutions & Technologies Lebanon (3)
Corniche Al-Nahr 8th Victoria Tower, PO Box 55653, Beirut, Lebanon
Tel.: (961) 1 429 303
Web Site: http://www.veoliawaterst.com
Emp.: 40
Waste Treatment Services
N.A.I.C.S.: 221310
Johnny Obeid (Gen Mgr)

Veolia Water Solutions & Technologies Ltd (3)
Aqua House 2620 Kings Court, Birmingham Business Park, Birmingham, B377YE, West Midlands, United Kingdom
Tel.: (44) 203 567 7400
Web Site: http://www.veoliawaterst.co.uk
Sales Range: $75-99.9 Million
Emp.: 6
Waste Treatment Services
N.A.I.C.S.: 221310
Bob Hook (Gen Mgr)

Veolia Water Solutions & Technologies Magyarorszag Zrt. (3)
Szabadsag ut 301, 2040, Budaors, Hungary
Tel.: (36) 2 351 3960
Web Site: https://www.veolia.hu
Sales Range: $75-99.9 Million
Emp.: 2
Waste Water Treatment Services
N.A.I.C.S.: 221310
Tomosi Karoly (Gen Mgr)

Veolia Water Solutions & Technologies Nordic Region (3)
Gladsaxevej 363, 2860, Soborg, Denmark
Tel.: (45) 39 69 02 22
Web Site: http://www.kruger.dk
Sales Range: $250-299.9 Million
Emp.: 50
Waste Water Treatment Services
N.A.I.C.S.: 221320
Ole Roesdahl (Gen Mgr)

Veolia Water Solutions & Technologies Pty Limited (3)
Level 3 One Innovation Rd, Pyrmont, 2113, NSW, Australia
Tel.: (61) 2 8572 0400
Web Site: http://www.veoliawaterst.com.au
Sales Range: $125-149.9 Million
Emp.: 20
Waste Water Treatment Services
N.A.I.C.S.: 221310
Christian Dube (Mgr-Client Mining)

Veolia Water Solutions & Technologies Romania SRL (3)
5 Fabrica de Glucoza Street Novo Park Business Centre F Building, 8th Floor Sector 2, Bucharest, 20335, Romania
Tel.: (40) 21 243 07 91
Web Site: http://www.vws.ro
Waste Treatment Services
N.A.I.C.S.: 221310
Cristian Cojocaru (Dir-Indus Dept)

Veolia Water Solutions & Technologies Saudi Arabia (3)
Veolia Buildings Prince Musaed Bin Abdul Aziz Street, Central, Riyadh, 11442, Saudi Arabia
Tel.: (966) 1 478 7001
Web Site: http://www.veolia.com
Sales Range: $125-149.9 Million
Emp.: 25
Waste Treatment Services
N.A.I.C.S.: 221310
Majd Al-Mallouhi (Mgr-Sls)

Veolia Water Solutions & Technologies South Africa (Pty) Ltd. (3)
S04 Modderfontein House Moddercrest Office Park High Street, Modderfontein, 1609, South Africa
Tel.: (27) 11 663 3600
Web Site: http://www.veoliawaterst.co.za
Sales Range: $75-99.9 Million
Emp.: 100
Waste Treatment Services
N.A.I.C.S.: 221310
Gunter Rencken (Mng Dir)

Subsidiary (Domestic):

Malutsa (Pty) Ltd (4)
Malutsa House 1 Maent St, Wellington Industrial Park, Wellington, 7655, Western Cape, South Africa
Tel.: (27) 21 864 2620
Web Site: https://www.malutsa.co.za

AND PRIVATE COMPANIES

Sales Range: $10-24.9 Million
Emp.: 150
Waste Water Treatment Plant Construction Services
N.A.I.C.S.: 237110
Bernard B. Cannon *(Co-Founder & Mng Dir)*

Membratek (Pty) Ltd (4)
5 De Vreugde Crescent Daljosaphat, 7646, Paarl, Western Cape, South Africa
Tel.: (27) 218711877
Sales Range: $25-49.9 Million
Emp.: 25
Industrial Machinery Mfr
N.A.I.C.S.: 333248
Bernard Bidwell Cannon *(Gen Mgr)*

VWS Envig (Pty) Ltd.-Membratek Division (4)
5 De Vreugde Crescent, PO Box 7240, Noor Der, Paarl, 7623, South Africa
Tel.: (27) 218711877
Web Site: http://www.vwsenvig.com
Sales Range: $25-49.9 Million
Water Purification Process Engrng Svcs
N.A.I.C.S.: 541330
Gunter Rencken *(Mng Dir)*

Subsidiary (Non-US):

VWS Envig Botswana Pty Ltd (4)
Unit 5 Plot No 50629 Mabeleapudi Road, Block 3 Industrial, Gaborone, Botswana
Tel.: (267) 3953888
Web Site: http://www.vwsenvig.co.za
Sales Range: $50-74.9 Million
Emp.: 14
Water Purification Systems Mfr
N.A.I.C.S.: 221310
Peter Healy *(Mng Dir)*

Subsidiary (Non-US):

Veolia Water Solutions & Technologies South Korea (3)
East 16F Signature Towers 100 Cheonggyecheon-no, Jung-gu, Seoul, 04500, Korea (South)
Tel.: (82) 26 323 2800
Web Site: http://www.veoliawaterst.co.kr
Sales Range: $75-99.9 Million
Emp.: 10
Waste Treatment Services
N.A.I.C.S.: 221310

Veolia Water Solutions & Technologies Taiwan Corporation (3)
4F N 14 Lane 609 Section 5 Chung-Shing Road, Sanchung, Taipei, Taiwan
Tel.: (886) 2 2278 1006
Web Site: http://www.veoliawaterst.com
Waste Treatment Services
N.A.I.C.S.: 221310

Veolia Water Solutions & Technologies Turkey (3)
Izci Sokak N 6/8, Gaziosmanpasa, 06700, Ankara, Turkiye
Tel.: (90) 312 447 10 72
Waste Water Treatment Services
N.A.I.C.S.: 221320

Veolia Water Solutions & Technologies Venezuela (3)
Avenida Venezuela Torre Oxal Piso 3 Oficina 3B El Rosal, Caracas, Venezuela
Tel.: (58) 212 9525016
Web Site: http://www.veoliawaterst.com.ve
Sales Range: $75-99.9 Million
Emp.: 16
Waste Treatment Services
N.A.I.C.S.: 221310
Bruzual Claudio *(CEO)*

Veolia Water Solutions Technologies (SEA) Pte Ltd (3)
5 Loyang Way 1, Singapore, 508706, Singapore
Tel.: (65) 6 546 1110
Web Site: http://www.veoliawaterst-sea.com
Emp.: 85
Waste Treatment Services
N.A.I.C.S.: 221310
Jean-Philippe Filhol *(Mng Dir)*

Veolia Water Solutions Technologies Deutschland Holding GmbH (3)
Luckenweg 5, 29227, Celle, Germany
Tel.: (49) 5141 803 0

Emp.: 43
Waste Water Treatment Services
N.A.I.C.S.: 221320
Christian Ausfelder *(Gen Mgr)*

Veolia Water Systems (Gulf) FZC (3)
B2-12 SAIF Zone, PO Box 8206, Sharjah, United Arab Emirates
Tel.: (971) 6 5570703
Web Site: http://www.veoliawatertechnologies.com
Sales Range: $75-99.9 Million
Emp.: 7
Waste Treatment Services
N.A.I.C.S.: 221310
Tariq Afana *(Mgr-Chemical)*

Veolia Water Systems South Asia Sdn (3)
Taman Subang Indah, Petaling Jaya, Selangor, Malaysia
Tel.: (60) 3 5631 5719
Sales Range: $75-99.9 Million
Emp.: 25
Waste Water Treatment Services
N.A.I.C.S.: 221310

Subsidiary (US):

Veolia Water Technologies, Inc. (3)
23563 W Main St IL Route 126, Plainfield, IL 60544
Tel.: (815) 609-2000
Web Site: http://www.veoliawatertech.com
Water Supply & Sewerage Services
N.A.I.C.S.: 221310
Laurent Auguste *(Pres & CEO-Americas)*

Subsidiary (Domestic):

ELGA LabWater LLC (4)
5 Earl Ct Ste 100, Woodridge, IL 60517
Tel.: (630) 343-5251
Web Site: https://www.elgalabwater.com
Waste Water Treatment Services
N.A.I.C.S.: 221320
Steve Bryant *(Mgr)*

Subsidiary (Non-US):

John Meunier Inc. (4)
4105 Sartelon, Saint Laurent, H4S 2B3, QC, Canada
Tel.: (514) 334-7230
Web Site: http://www.johnmeunier.com
Emp.: 200
Water & Waste Treatment Services
N.A.I.C.S.: 333310
Alain Gadbois *(VP-Tech)*

Veolia Water Canada Inc. (4)
150 Pony Drive 2, Newmarket, L3Y-7B6, ON, Canada
Tel.: (905) 868-9683
Waste Treatment Services
N.A.I.C.S.: 221310

Subsidiary (Domestic):

Veolia Water North America Operating Services, LLC (4)
101 W Washington Ste 1400 E, Indianapolis, IN 46204
Tel.: (317) 917-3700
Waste Water Treatment Services
N.A.I.C.S.: 221320
Jonathan Carpenter *(Dir-Sls-Central Reg)*

Subsidiary (Non-US):

Veolia Water Solutions & Technologies Canada Inc. (4)
2000 Argentia Road Plaza IV Suite 430, Mississauga, L5N 1W1, ON, Canada
Tel.: (905) 286-4846
Web Site: http://www.veoliawaterst.ca
Waste Treatment Services
N.A.I.C.S.: 221310

Subsidiary (Domestic):

Veolia Water Solutions & Technologies Puerto Rico (4)
Road 156 Km 58 2 ST 13 Valle Tolima, Caguas, PR 00726
Tel.: (787) 747-9439
Waste Water Treatment Services
N.A.I.C.S.: 221320

Whittier Filtration, Inc. (4)

315 N Puente St Unit A, Brea, CA 92821
Tel.: (714) 986-5300
Emp.: 45
Filtration System Sales & Installation Services
N.A.I.C.S.: 423830
Kenneth Severing *(Dir-Bus Dev)*

Subsidiary (Non-US):

Veolia Water Solutions & Technologies (2)
ZI West-Grijpen 2073 5 Esperantolaan, 5 Esperantolaan, 3300, Tienen, Belgium (100%)
Tel.: (32) 1 678 1620
Web Site: http://www.veoliawaterst.com
Sales Range: $50-74.9 Million
Emp.: 20
Water Supply & Sewerage Services
N.A.I.C.S.: 221310
Kris Lumbert *(Dir)*

Veolia Water Systems (2)
Dublin Road, Celbridge, Co Kildare, Ireland (100%)
Tel.: (353) 16303333
Web Site: http://www.elgaprocesswater.ie
Sales Range: $50-74.9 Million
Emp.: 40
Water Supply & Sewerage Services
N.A.I.C.S.: 221310

Veolia Water Systems Ltd (2)
Marlow International Pkwy, Marlow, SL7 1YL, Buckinghamshire, United Kingdom (100%)
Tel.: (44) 1494887700
Web Site: http://www.veoliawater.co.uk
Sales Range: $75-99.9 Million
Emp.: 100
Waste Treatment Services
N.A.I.C.S.: 221310

Subsidiary (Domestic):

Veolia Water Industrial Outsourcing Limited (3)
Blackwell House 3 Valleys Way, Bushey, WD232LG, Herts, United Kingdom (100%)
Tel.: (44) 01923814217
Web Site: http://www.vwio.com
Sales Range: $50-74.9 Million
Emp.: 50
Water Treatment & Waste Processing Services
N.A.I.C.S.: 221310

Subsidiary (Non-US):

Veolia Water Systems Sp. z o.o. (2)
Baohcka 48, 30148, Krakow, Poland (100%)
Tel.: (48) 124233866
Web Site: http://www.veoliawaterst.pl
Sales Range: $75-99.9 Million
Emp.: 70
Water Supply & Sewerage Services
N.A.I.C.S.: 221310

Veolia Water Systems Switzerland (2)
Sempacherstrasse 57, CH-4053, Basel, Switzerland
Tel.: (41) 613616561
Web Site: http://www.veoliawatersystems.com
Waste Treatment Services
N.A.I.C.S.: 221310

Veolia Water Technologies Benelux (2)
Celsiusstraat 34, 6726 BZ, Ede, Netherlands (100%)
Tel.: (31) 318691500
Web Site: http://www.veoliawaterst.nl
Sales Range: $75-99.9 Million
Emp.: 75
Water Treatment & Supply Services
N.A.I.C.S.: 221310
W. Buids *(Mng Dir)*

Veolia Water UK PLC (2)
Kings Place 90 York Way 5th Floor, London, N1 9AG, United Kingdom
Tel.: (44) 20 7843 8500
Web Site: http://www.veoliawater.co.uk
Water Supply & Wastewater Management Services
N.A.I.C.S.: 221310

Veolia Woda Sp. z o.o. (2)
Al Jana Pawla II 61-10, 01031, Warsaw, Poland (100%)
Tel.: (48) 226367863
Web Site: http://www.veoliawoda.pl
Sales Range: $100-124.9 Million
Emp.: 146
Water Supply Services
N.A.I.C.S.: 221310
Piotr Gepert *(Mng Dir)*

Veolia Water Technologies Sa (1)
28 Boulevard de Pesaro, 92000, Nanterre, France
Tel.: (33) 156353500
Sewage Treatment Services
N.A.I.C.S.: 221320

Wastebox Deutschland GmbH (1)
Banksstrasse 4, 20097, Hamburg, Germany
Tel.: (49) 401 823 3420
Web Site: https://www.wastebox.biz
Sewage Treatment Services
N.A.I.C.S.: 221320

VEON LTD.

Claude Debussylaan 88, 1082 MD, Amsterdam, Netherlands
Tel.: (31) 207977200 BM
Web Site: https://www.veon.com
VEON—(NASDAQ)
Rev.: $3,755,000,000
Assets: $15,083,000,000
Liabilities: $14,316,000,000
Net Worth: $767,000,000
Earnings: ($9,000,000)
Emp.: 44,159
Fiscal Year-end: 12/31/22
Holding Company; Mobile Telecommunications Services
N.A.I.C.S.: 551112
Gennady G. Gazin *(Chm)*

Subsidiaries:

Global Telecom Holding S.A.E. (1)
Nile City Towers - North Tower 2005, Cornish El Nile Ramlet Beaulac, Cairo, 11221, Egypt (100%)
Tel.: (20) 31708918453
Web Site: https://www.gtelecom.com
Rev.: $3,014,700,000
Assets: $5,333,200,000
Liabilities: $5,244,400,000
Net Worth: $88,800,000
Earnings: ($41,800,000)
Emp.: 14,839
Fiscal Year-end: 12/31/2017
Telecommunication Servicesb
N.A.I.C.S.: 517112
Gerbrand Nijman *(CEO)*

Joint Venture (Non-US):

Orascom Telecom Algerie SpA (2)
Rue Mouloud Feraoun, Lot 8A Dar El-Beida, Algiers, Algeria (49%)
Tel.: (213) 770857777
Web Site: http://www.djezzy.com
Emp.: 4,000
Cellular & Wireless Telecommunications
N.A.I.C.S.: 517112
Waleed El-Sonbaty *(CIO)*

Subsidiary (Non-US):

Orascom Telecom Bangladesh Ltd. (2)
Tigers' Den House No 4 SW, Bir Uttam mir Shawkat Sharak, Bir Uttam Mir Shawkat Sharak Gulshan 1, Dhaka, 1212, Bangladesh
Tel.: (880) 1911304121
Web Site: https://www.banglalink.net
Sales Range: $200-249.9 Million
Emp.: 670
Mobile Communications
N.A.I.C.S.: 517112

Subsidiary (Domestic):

Orascom Telecom Media & Technology Holding SAE (2)
Nile City Building 2005C Cournich El-Nil Ramlet, Ramlet Boulaq, Cairo, Egypt
Tel.: (20) 225747000
Mobile Telecommunications Services

VEON LTD.

VEON Ltd.—(Continued)
N.A.I.C.S.: 517112

Golden Telecom LLC (1)
Kyivstar Gegtiarevska 5th St, Kiev, 03113, Ukraine
Tel.: (380) 444900090
Web Site: http://www.kyivstar.ua
Wireless Telecommunication Services
N.A.I.C.S.: 517112

Italiaonline S.p.A. (1)
Via del Bosco Rinnovato 8, 20057, Assago, MI, Italy
Tel.: (39) 0800011411
Web Site: https://www.italiaonline.it
Rev.: $373,605,278
Assets: $734,293,736
Liabilities: $376,845,635
Net Worth: $357,448,100
Earnings: ($9,989,862)
Emp.: 1,664
Fiscal Year-end: 12/31/2018
Web Hosting & Directory Publishing Services
N.A.I.C.S.: 513140
Onsi Naguib Sawiris *(Chm)*

Subsidiary (Domestic):

Consodata S.p.A. (2)
Via Ugo Foscolo 4, 20121, Milan, MI, Italy
Tel.: (39) 0800802064
Web Site: https://www.consodata.it
Sales Range: $10-24.9 Million
Emp.: 125
Direct Mail Advertising
N.A.I.C.S.: 541860
Francesca Genova *(CFO)*

PRONTOSEAT srl (2)
Corso Svizzera 185 at Piero della Francesca, 10149, Turin, Italy
Tel.: (39) 0117173111
Web Site: http://www.prontoseat.it
Digital Printing Services
N.A.I.C.S.: 323111

Kyivstar GSM JSC (1)
Degtyarivska 53, 3113, Kiev, Ukraine
Tel.: (380) 674660466
Web Site: https://www.kyivstar.ua
Mobile Telecommunications Services
N.A.I.C.S.: 517112

LLC Sky Mobile (1)
121 Chui Ave, Bishkek, 720011, Kyrgyzstan
Tel.: (996) 775588000
Wireless Telecommunications Services
N.A.I.C.S.: 517112

VimpleCom Lao Co., Ltd (1)
Lane Xang Business Center 14 Lane Xang Avenue Unit 4 Ban Hatsadi, PO Box 4693, Chanthabury District, Vientiane, Lao People's Democratic Republic
Tel.: (856) 20 77 800 700
Web Site: http://www.beeline.la
Emp.: 300
Mobile Telecommunications Services
N.A.I.C.S.: 517112

Wind Telecomunicazioni S.p.A. (1)
Casella Postale 14155, 20152, Milan, Italy
Tel.: (39) 0683114600
Web Site: http://www.wind.it
Sales Range: $5-14.9 Billion
Fixed Line, Mobile & Data Telecommunications Services
N.A.I.C.S.: 517112

Subsidiary (Non-US):

Wind Hellas Telecommunications S.A. (2)
66 Kifissias Avenue, Maroussi, 151 25, Athens, Greece
Tel.: (30) 2106158000
Web Site: http://www.wind.com
Mobile Telecommunications Services
N.A.I.C.S.: 517112
Nikolaos Kostaras *(CIO)*

VERA SYNTHETIC LIMITED

Office No Upper Level UI 27 Pattani Plaza Devubaug Dairy Road, Nilam Baug, Bhavnagar, 364002, Gujarat, India
Tel.: (91) 9879108404
Web Site: https://www.sujlonropes.com
Year Founded: 2000
VERA—(NSE)
Rev.: $4,900,833
Assets: $2,780,457
Liabilities: $486,673
Net Worth: $2,293,783
Earnings: $218,152
Fiscal Year-end: 03/31/23
Fishing Net Mfr &
N.A.I.C.S.: 314999
Sunil Makwana *(Chm & Mng Dir)*

VERALLIA SA

Tour Carpe Diem 31 Place des Corolles Esplanad, 92400, Courbevoie, France
Tel.: (33) 171131000
Web Site: https://www.verallia.com
VRLA—(VIE)
Rev.: $4,309,305,663
Assets: $4,923,611,878
Liabilities: $3,865,548,074
Net Worth: $1,058,063,804
Earnings: $524,671,597
Emp.: 10,495
Fiscal Year-end: 12/31/23
Packaging Product Mfr & Distr
N.A.I.C.S.: 326113
Michel Giannuzzi *(Chm & CEO)*

Subsidiaries:

Allied Glass Containers Ltd. (1)
South Accommodation Road, Leeds, LS10 1NQ, United Kingdom
Tel.: (44) 1132451568
Web Site: http://www.allied-glass.com
Glass Container Mfr
N.A.I.C.S.: 327213
Jonathan Culley *(Dir-Sls)*

VERANDA LEARNING SOLUTIONS LTD.

34 Thirumalai Pillai Road, T Nagar, Chennai, 600 017, Tamil Nadu, India
Tel.: (91) 4442967777
Web Site: https://www.verandalearning.com
Year Founded: 2018
VERANDA—(NSE)
Rev.: $347,297
Assets: $1,572,425
Liabilities: $1,564,304
Net Worth: $8,122
Earnings: ($1,129,715)
Fiscal Year-end: 03/31/21
Educational Support Services
N.A.I.C.S.: 611710
Kalpathi S. Suresh *(Chm)*

Subsidiaries:

Veranda IAS Learning Solutions Private Limited (1)
5th Floor GR Complex 810 Anna Salai, Nandanam, Chennai, 600 035, India
Tel.: (91) 8925521735
Web Site: https://verandaias.com
Education Technology Services
N.A.I.C.S.: 611710

Veranda Race Learning Solutions Private Limited (1)
5th Floor GR Complex 810 Anna Salai, Nandanam, Chennai, 600 035, India
Tel.: (91) 7397303030
Education Technology Services
N.A.I.C.S.: 611710

VERANDA RESORT PUBLIC COMPANY LIMITED

555 Rasa Building Unit 2701-2704 27th Floor Phaholyothin Road, Chatuchak, Bangkok, 10900, Thailand
Tel.: (66) 6625133003   TH
Web Site: https://www.verandaresort.com
Year Founded: 1991
VRANDA—(THA)
Rev.: $40,940,801
Assets: $140,223,148
Liabilities: $88,030,688
Net Worth: $52,192,459
Earnings: ($4,109,315)
Emp.: 905
Fiscal Year-end: 12/31/23
Resort Operator
N.A.I.C.S.: 721110
Verawat Ongvasith *(Vice Chm, CEO & VP-Bus & Property Dev Dept)*

Subsidiaries:

Huahin Pool Suite Co., Ltd. (1)
555 Rasa Tower Unit 2701-2704 Floor 27 Paholyothin Road, Chatuchak, Bangkok, 10900, Thailand
Tel.: (66) 25133300
Hotel Operator
N.A.I.C.S.: 721110

Oak Tree Co., Ltd. (1)
No 2 North Sathorn Silom, Bangrak, Bangkok, 10500, Thailand
Tel.: (66) 25133300
Hotel Operator
N.A.I.C.S.: 721110

Oak Tree Realty Co., Ltd. (1)
555 Rasa Tower Unit 2701-2704 Floor 27 Paholyothin Road, Chatuchak, Bangkok, 10900, Thailand
Tel.: (66) 25133300
Commercial Building Rental & Leasing Services
N.A.I.C.S.: 531120

The ISA Resort Co., Ltd. (1)
438/1 Moo 1 T Maret, Koh Samui, Surat Thani, 84310, Thailand
Tel.: (66) 77332888
Web Site: http://www.rockyresort.com
Hotel Operator
N.A.I.C.S.: 721110

Veranda Beach Pattaya Co., Ltd. (1)
211 Moo 1 Na Jomtien Soi 4, Pattaya, 20250, Chonburi, Thailand
Tel.: (66) 38111899
Resort Operator
N.A.I.C.S.: 721110

Veranda Cuisine Co., Ltd. (1)
555 Rasa Tower Unit 2701-2704 Floor 27 Paholyothin Road, Chatuchak, Bangkok, 10900, Thailand
Tel.: (66) 25133300
Food & Beverage Distr
N.A.I.C.S.: 445131

VERBAND DER VEREINE CREDITREFORM E.V.

Hellersbergstrasse 12, Neuss, 41460, Germany
Tel.: (49) 21311090
Web Site: http://www.creditreform.de
Sales Range: $500-549.9 Million
Emp.: 3,900
Credit Monitoring Services; Directory Publisher
N.A.I.C.S.: 561450
Michael Aumuller *(VP)*

VERBIO SE

Ritterstrabe 23, 04109, Leipzig, Germany
Tel.: (49) 3413085300
Web Site: https://www.verbio.de
VBK—(DEU)
Rev.: $1,779,762,563
Assets: $1,478,915,139
Liabilities: $485,271,714
Net Worth: $993,643,426
Earnings: $21,425,463
Emp.: 1,369
Fiscal Year-end: 06/30/24
Biofuel Producer & Provider
N.A.I.C.S.: 324110
Alexander von Witzleben *(Chm-Supervisory Bd)*

Subsidiaries:

VERBIO Agrar GmbH (1)
Thura Mark 20, 06780, Zorbig, Germany
Tel.: (49) 34956303700
Bio-fuel Mfr
N.A.I.C.S.: 324199

VERBIO Bitterfeld GmbH (1)
Chemiepark Bitterfeld-Wolfen Areal B OT Greppin, Westliche Stickstoffstrasse 3, 06749, Bitterfeld-Wolfen, Germany
Tel.: (49) 34947200600
Sales Range: $100-124.9 Million
Emp.: 55
Biodiesel Mfr & Power Generation Services
N.A.I.C.S.: 221118

VERBIO Bitterfeld GmbH (1)
Chemiepark Bitterfeld-Wolfen Areal B OT Greppin, Westliche Stickstoffstrasse 3, 06749, Bitterfeld-Wolfen, Germany
Tel.: (49) 34947200600
Biodiesel & Glycerine Mfr
N.A.I.C.S.: 325199

VERBIO Diesel Schwedt GmbH & Co. KG (1)
Passower Chaussee 111, 16303, Schwedt an der Oder, Brandenburg, Germany
Tel.: (49) 33322699100
Sales Range: $25-49.9 Million
Emp.: 50
Biodiesel Mfr
N.A.I.C.S.: 324110
Harald Senst *(Mng Dir)*

VERBIO Ethanol Schwedt GmbH & Co. KG (1)
Passower Chaussee 111, Schwedt an der Oder, 16303, Brandenburg, Germany
Tel.: (49) 33322699557
Web Site: http://www.verbio.de
Sales Range: $50-74.9 Million
Emp.: 120
Bioethanol Mfr
N.A.I.C.S.: 325193
Klaus-Dieter Bettien *(Gen Mgr)*

VERBIO Ethanol Zorbig GmbH & Co. KG (1)
Thura Mark 18, 06780, Zorbig, Germany
Tel.: (49) 34956303600
Web Site: http://www.verbio.de
Sales Range: $25-49.9 Million
Emp.: 90
Bioethanol Mfr
N.A.I.C.S.: 325193
Claus Sauter *(Gen Mgr)*

VERBIO Logistik GmbH (1)
Passower Chaussee 111, 16303, Schwedt an der Oder, Germany
Tel.: (49) 33322699400
Bio-fuel Mfr
N.A.I.C.S.: 324199

VERBIO North America Corporation (1)
17199 N Laurel Park Dr Ste 320, Livonia, MI 48152
Web Site: https://www.verbio-north-america.com
Bio-fuel Mfr
N.A.I.C.S.: 324199
Alicia Webber *(CFO)*

VERBIO Pinnow GmbH (1)
Industrie-und Gewerbegebiet 43 a, 16278, Pinnow, Germany
Tel.: (49) 33322699500
Bio-fuel Mfr
N.A.I.C.S.: 324199

VERBIO Polska Spolka z o.o. (1)
UI Mieszka I 82-83, 71-011, Szczecin, Poland
Tel.: (48) 914830300
Web Site: https://www.verbio.pl
Bio-fuel Mfr
N.A.I.C.S.: 324199

VERBIO Schwedt GmbH (1)
Passower Chaussee 111, 16303, Schwedt an der Oder, Germany
Tel.: (49) 33322699500
Biodiesel & Glycerine Mfr
N.A.I.C.S.: 325199

VERBIO Zorbig GmbH (1)

Thura Mark 18, 06780, Zorbig, Germany
Tel.: (49) 34956303600
Bioethanol & Biome Thane Mfr
N.A.I.C.S.: 325199

VERBIT SOFTWARE LIMITED
Alon Tower II 14th Floor 94 Yigal Alon Street, Tel Aviv, Israel
Tel.: (972) 39678803
Web Site: http://verbit.ai
Emp.: 170
Information Technology & Services
N.A.I.C.S.: 541512
Tom Livne *(Founder & CEO)*

Subsidiaries:

Vitac Corporation (1)
101 Hillpointe Dr, Canonsburg, PA 15317
Tel.: (724) 514-4000
Web Site: http://www.vitac.com
Closed Captioning & Subtitling Services
N.A.I.C.S.: 561492
Doug Karlovits *(Chief Bus Dev Officer)*

Division (Domestic):

Caption Colorado, L.L.C. (2)
8300 E Maplewood Ave Ste 300, Greenwood Village, CO 80111
Tel.: (720) 489-5662
Closed Captioning & Encoding Services
N.A.I.C.S.: 512191
Tad Polumbus *(Pres & CEO)*

VERBREC LIMITED
Level 14 200 Mary Street, PO Box 3291, Brisbane, 4000, QLD, Australia
Tel.: (61) 730587000   AU
Web Site: https://verbrec.com
VBC—(ASX)
Rev.: $62,333,734
Assets: $31,846,955
Liabilities: $19,049,813
Net Worth: $12,797,142
Earnings: $3,174,412
Emp.: 450
Fiscal Year-end: 06/30/24
Mining & Beverage Mfr
N.A.I.C.S.: 722515
Dominic Wood *(Gen Mgr-Asset Mgmt)*

Subsidiaries:

Competency Training Pty Ltd (1)
70 Sylvan Rd, Toowong, 4066, QLD, Australia
Tel.: (61) 732178066
Web Site: https://competencytraining.com
Sales Range: $10-24.9 Million
Emp.: 10
Electrical Training Courses
N.A.I.C.S.: 611513
Jayne Rayner *(Mgr-Customer Engagement)*

LogiCamms (Central) Pty Ltd (1)
431 King William St, Adelaide, 5000, SA, Australia
Tel.: (61) 884445111
Web Site: http://www.logicamms.com.au
Sales Range: $25-49.9 Million
Emp.: 90
Electronic Services
N.A.I.C.S.: 541330
Tony Petruzzelli *(Mgr-Bus Dev)*

LogiCamms Consultants (1)
PO Box 200, West Perth, 6872, WA, Australia
Tel.: (61) 893658888
Web Site: http://www.logicamms.com.au
Sales Range: $25-49.9 Million
Emp.: 70
Management Consulting Services
N.A.I.C.S.: 541618

Process Essentials Pty Ltd (1)
PO Box 510, Spring Hill, 4004, QLD, Australia
Tel.: (61) 732577770
Web Site: http://www.processessentials.com.au
Engineering Design Services
N.A.I.C.S.: 541330

VERBUND AG
Am Hof 6a, 1010, Vienna, Austria
Tel.: (43) 503130
Web Site: https://www.verbund.com
Year Founded: 1947
OEWA—(MUN)
Rev.: $11,534,889,565
Assets: $21,509,260,188
Liabilities: $10,504,647,694
Net Worth: $11,004,612,494
Earnings: $2,501,523,962
Emp.: 3,804
Fiscal Year-end: 12/31/23
Electricity Distribution Services
N.A.I.C.S.: 238210
Michael Strugl *(Chm-Exec Bd)*

Subsidiaries:

ASGM Austrian Strategic Gas Storage Management GmbH (1)
Florisdorfer Hauptstrasse 1, A-1210, Vienna, Austria
Tel.: (43) 127560
Web Site: https://www.asgm.at
Emp.: 30
Gas Storage & Transportation Services
N.A.I.C.S.: 211130

HalloSonne GmbH (1)
An den Kohlenrutschen 10, 1020, Vienna, Austria
Tel.: (43) 12532173
Web Site: https://www.hallosonne.com
Emp.: 60
Solar Panel Product Mfr & Distr
N.A.I.C.S.: 335313

SMATRICS GmbH & Co. KG (1)
Europaplatz 2 Stiege 4 4 OG, 1150, Vienna, Austria
Tel.: (43) 15322400
Web Site: https://www.smatrics.com
Emp.: 120
E-Mobility Project Management Services
N.A.I.C.S.: 541618

VERBUND Energy4 Business Germany GmbH (1)
Luise-Ullrich-Str 20, 80636, Munich, Germany
Tel.: (49) 898905621900
Energy Product Distr
N.A.I.C.S.: 424690

VERBUND Green Power Deutschland GmbH (1)
Energie-Allee 1, 55286, Worrstadt, Germany
Tel.: (49) 15172404401
Photovoltaic & Wind Power Plant Operator
N.A.I.C.S.: 423410

VERBUND Green Power Deutschland Photovoltaik GmbH (1)
Brandenburg Airport Center Willy Brandt Platz 2, 12529, Schonefeld, Germany
Tel.: (49) 15172404401
Photovoltaic & Wind Power Plant Operator
N.A.I.C.S.: 423410

VERBUND Green Power Iberia, S.L.U. (1)
Paseo de la Castellana 163 Planta 7A, 28046, Madrid, Spain
Tel.: (34) 913578174
Hydroelectric Power Mfr & Distr
N.A.I.C.S.: 333611

VERBUND Tourismus GmbH (1)
Europaplatz 2, 1150, Vienna, Austria   (99.9%)
Tel.: (43) 503 132 3201
Web Site: https://www.verbund.com
Tourism Information Services
N.A.I.C.S.: 561591

VUM Verfahren Umwelt Management GmbH (1)
Lakeside B06 b, Worthersee, A-9020, Klagenfurt, Austria
Tel.: (43) 5032032521
Web Site: https://www.vum.co.at
Environmental Management Services
N.A.I.C.S.: 541620

Verbund Sales GmbH (1)
Am Hof 6a, 1010, Vienna, Austria

Tel.: (43) 5031351800
Electrical Energy Distr
N.A.I.C.S.: 221122

Verbund-Austrian Hydro Power AG (1)
Am Hof 6 A, PO Box 88, Vienna, Austria   (80.33%)
Tel.: (43) 1531130
Web Site: http://www.verbund.com
Sales Range: $25-49.9 Million
Emp.: 60
Heavy & Civil Engineering Construction
N.A.I.C.S.: 237990

Subsidiary (Domestic):

Verbund Management Service GmbH (2)
Am Hof 6 A, Vienna, 1010, Austria   (100%)
Tel.: (43) 5031350030
Web Site: http://www.verbund.com
Electricity Generation, Transmission & Sales
N.A.I.C.S.: 221122

Verbund-Austrian Power Sales GmbH (2)
Europa Platz 2, Vienna, 1150, Austria   (100%)
Tel.: (43) 503130
Web Site: http://www.verbund.com
Electrical Contractor
N.A.I.C.S.: 238210

Verbund-Finanzierungsservice GmbH (2)
Am Hof 6 A, 1010, Vienna, Austria   (100%)
Tel.: (43) 1531130
Web Site: http://www.verbund.com
Business Finance Services
N.A.I.C.S.: 561499

Verbund-Austrian Power Trading Slovakia, S.r.o. (1)
Zamocka 30, 81101, Bratislava, Slovakia   (100%)
Tel.: (421) 259200298
Electric Power Distribution
N.A.I.C.S.: 221122

Verbund-Umwelttechnik GmbH (1)
Lakeside B06 b, 9020, Klagenfurt, Austria   (100%)
Tel.: (43) 503 133 2357
Web Site: https://www.verbund.com
Engineeering Services
N.A.I.C.S.: 541330

VERDANE CAPITAL ADVISORS AS
Hieronymus Heyerdahlsgate 1, 0160, Oslo, Norway
Tel.: (47) 24137000
Web Site: http://www.verdane.com
Year Founded: 1985
Financial Investment Activities
N.A.I.C.S.: 523999
Bjarne K. Lie *(Mng Partner)*

Subsidiaries:

Akerstroms Bjorbo AB (1)
Bjorbovagen 143, 785 45, Bjorbo, Sweden
Tel.: (46) 241 250 00
Web Site: http://www.akerstroms.com
Application Software Development Services
N.A.I.C.S.: 541511
Hakan Holmstrom *(Pres & Mng Dir)*

Design Tanks LLC (1)
612 W Blackhawk St, Sioux Falls, SD 57104
Tel.: (605) 965-1600
Web Site: http://www.designtanks.com
Sales Range: $1-9.9 Million
Emp.: 45
Fiberglass-Reinforced Plastics Mfr
N.A.I.C.S.: 326199

Re-Match Holding A/S (1)
HI-Park 415, 7400, Herning, Denmark
Tel.: (45) 77346734
Web Site: https://www.re-match.com
Rev.: $3,960,744
Assets: $51,711,373
Liabilities: $50,206,489
Net Worth: $1,504,885

Earnings: ($12,677,938)
Emp.: 55
Fiscal Year-end: 12/31/2022
Holding Company
N.A.I.C.S.: 551112

Subsidiary (Domestic):

Re-Match A/S (2)
HI-Park 415, 7400, Herning, Denmark
Tel.: (45) 77346734
Synthetic Turf Recycling Services
N.A.I.C.S.: 562920

Subsidiary (Non-US):

Re-Match Netherlands B.V. (2)
Panovenweg 12, 4004 JE, Tiel, Netherlands
Tel.: (31) 640567690
Synthetic Turf Recycling Services
N.A.I.C.S.: 562920

Silva Sweden AB (1)
Mariehällsvägen 37 C Bromma, Stockholm, 168 65, Sweden
Tel.: (46) 86234300
Web Site: https://silvasweden.com
Holding Company: Pedometers, Headlamps, Outdoor Instruments, Binoculars, Professional instruments & Orienteering Equipment
N.A.I.C.S.: 551112
Richard Jägrud *(CEO)*

Subsidiary (Domestic):

Primus AB (2)
Hemvarnsgatan 15, 6041, 171 54, Solna, Sweden
Tel.: (46) 856484230
Clothing Retailer
N.A.I.C.S.: 458110

Subsidiary (Non-US):

Primus Eesti OU (3)
Ravila 53, 51014, Tartu, Estonia
Tel.: (372) 7424903
Clothing Retailer
N.A.I.C.S.: 458110

Upplevelseakuten AB (1)
Tullhus 1 Skeppsbron 21, 111 30, Stockholm, Sweden
Tel.: (46) 86601610
Web Site: http://www.upplevelsepresent.se
Travel Tour Operator
N.A.I.C.S.: 561520
Steffen Gausemel Backe *(CEO)*

VERDANT EARTH TECHNOLOGIES LIMITED
Level 33 52 Martin Place, Sydney, 2000, NSW, Australia
Tel.: (61) 29 227 8911   AU
Web Site: https://www.verdantearth.tech
Year Founded: 2018
VDNT—(NASDAQ)
Rev.: $100,000
Assets: $11,738,375
Liabilities: $8,574,244
Net Worth: $3,164,131
Earnings: ($14,597,176)
Emp.: 15
Fiscal Year-end: 06/30/21
Holding Company
N.A.I.C.S.: 551112
Richard Poole *(Exec Dir, CEO & Mng Dir)*

VERDE AGRITECH PLC
Salatin House 19 Cedar Road Sutton, Surrey, SM2 5DA, BC, Canada
Tel.: (416) 866-2966   UK
Web Site: http://www.verdepotash.com
Year Founded: 2006
NPK—(OTCIQ)
Rev.: $7,171,161
Assets: $22,476,469
Liabilities: $5,939,070
Net Worth: $16,537,399
Earnings: $430,254
Emp.: 69

VERDE AGRITECH PLC

Verde AgriTech Plc—(Continued)
Fiscal Year-end: 12/31/20
Potash Exploration Services
N.A.I.C.S.: 212390
Cristiano Veloso *(Founder, Chm & CEO)*

Subsidiaries:

Verde Fertilizantes Ltda (1)
Av Antonio Abrahao Caram 430 sl 301, Sao Jose, 31275-000, Belo Horizonte, Brazil
Tel.: (55) 31 3245 0205
Thermopotash Mfr
N.A.I.C.S.: 325314

VERDE RESOURCES, INC.
Block B-5 20/F Great Smart Tower
230 Wanchai Rd, Wanchai, China (Hong Kong)
Tel.: (852) 21521223   NV
Year Founded: 2010
VRDR—(OTCIQ)
Rev.: $26,559
Assets: $33,059,154
Liabilities: $17,289,229
Net Worth: $15,769,925
Earnings: ($774,849)
Emp.: 1
Fiscal Year-end: 06/30/21
Gold Mining Services
N.A.I.C.S.: 212220
Balakrishnan B. S. Muthu *(CFO, Treas & Gen Mgr)*

VERDEMAR INVESTMENT CORPORATION SA
BMW Plaza Building 10th Floor Calle 50 & Via Porras, Panama, Panama
Tel.: (507) 3075077
VERDE085PREFA—(PAN)
Sales Range: Less than $1 Million
Residential Building Construction Services
N.A.I.C.S.: 236220
Alberto Vallarino Clement *(Pres)*

VERDER INTERNATIONAL B.V.
Utrechtseweg 4A, 3451 GG, Vleuten, Netherlands
Tel.: (31) 306779211
Web Site: http://www.verder.com
Sales Range: $250-299.9 Million
Emp.: 850
Holding Company; Technical Equipment Mfr & Distr
N.A.I.C.S.: 551112
Andries Verder *(CEO)*

Subsidiaries:

Carbolite Gero GmbH & Co. KG (1)
Hesselbachstr 15, 75242, Neuhausen, Germany
Tel.: (49) 723495220
Web Site: http://www.carbolite-gero.com
Industrial Machinery Mfr
N.A.I.C.S.: 332510
Sebastian Becht *(Mgr-Sls)*

Endecotts Inc. (1)
616 E Devonhurst Ln, Ponte Vedra Beach, FL 32081
Tel.: (904) 814-8418
Measuring Equipment Mfr
N.A.I.C.S.: 334513

Glen Creston Ltd. (1)
9 Lombard Road, London, SW19 3TZ, United Kingdom
Tel.: (44) 208 545 9140
Web Site: http://www.glencreston.com
Industrial Machinery Mfr & Distr
N.A.I.C.S.: 333131

KNF Flodos AG (1)
Wassermatte 2, 6210, Sursee, Switzerland
Tel.: (41) 41 925 00 25
Web Site: http://www.knf-flodos.ch
Laboratory Vacuum Pump Mfr
N.A.I.C.S.: 339113

KNF Italia s.r.l. (1)
Via Flumendosa 10, 20132, Milan, Italy
Tel.: (39) 02 27203860
Web Site: http://www.knf.it
Laboratory Vacuum Pump Whslr
N.A.I.C.S.: 423450
Andrea Andretta *(Mng Dir)*

KNF Japan Co., Ltd. (1)
Across Shinkawa Bldg Annex 3F 1-16-14 Shinkawa, Chuo-ku, Tokyo, 104-0033, Japan
Tel.: (81) 3 3551 7931
Web Site: http://www.knf.co.jp
Laboratory Vacuum Pump Whslr
N.A.I.C.S.: 423450

KNF Korea Ltd. (1)
Woosan Bldg Rm 202 336-4 Hwikyungdong, Dongdaemun-Ku, 130-090, Seoul, Korea (South)
Tel.: (82) 2 959 0255
Web Site: http://www.knfkorea.com
Laboratory Vacuum Pump Whslr
N.A.I.C.S.: 423450

KNF Micro AG (1)
Zelglimatte 1b, 6260, Reiden, Switzerland
Tel.: (41) 62 787 88 88
Web Site: http://www.knf-micro.ch
Laboratory Vacuum Pump Mfr
N.A.I.C.S.: 339113
Christian Kissling *(Gen Mgr)*

KNF Neuberger (UK) Ltd (1)
Avenue Two Station Lane Industrial Estate, Witney, OX28 4FA, Oxfordshire, United Kingdom
Tel.: (44) 1993 778373
Web Site: http://www.knf.co.uk
Laboratory Vacuum Pump Whslr
N.A.I.C.S.: 423450
Simon Barwick *(Mng Dir)*

KNF Neuberger AB (1)
Mejerivagen 4, 117 43, Stockholm, Sweden
Tel.: (46) 8 744 51 13
Web Site: http://www.knf.se
Laboratory Vacuum Pump Whslr
N.A.I.C.S.: 423450
Mikael Belbo *(Mgr-Sls)*

KNF Neuberger AG (1)
Stockenstrasse 6, 8362, Baltersvil, Switzerland
Tel.: (41) 71 973 99 30
Web Site: http://www.knf.ch
Emp.: 25
Laboratory Vacuum Pump Whslr
N.A.I.C.S.: 423450
Thomas Muggli *(Mng Dir)*

KNF Neuberger GmbH (1)
Alter Weg 3, 79112, Freiburg, Germany
Tel.: (49) 7664 5909 0
Web Site: http://www.knf.de
Laboratory Vacuum Pump Mfr & Whslr
N.A.I.C.S.: 339113
Gunter Emig *(CEO & Mng Dir)*

KNF Neuberger SAS (1)
4 Boulevard d Alsace, 68128, Village-Neuf, France
Tel.: (33) 3 89 70 35 00
Web Site: http://www.knf.fr
Laboratory Vacuum Pump Mfr
N.A.I.C.S.: 339113

KNF Neuberger, Inc. (1)
2 Black Forest Rd, Trenton, NJ 08691-1810
Tel.: (609) 890-8600
Web Site: http://www.knfusa.com
Laboratory Vacuum Pump Mfr & Whslr
N.A.I.C.S.: 339113
Dave Vanderbeck *(Mgr-Bus Dev)*

KNF Pumps + Systems India Pvt. Ltd. (1)
Ganga Estate Near Rajiv Gandhi Infotech Park Phase 1, Hinjewadi, Pune, 411 057, Maharashtra, India
Tel.: (91) 20 640 13 923
Web Site: http://www.knfpumps.in
Emp.: 11
Laboratory Vacuum Pump Whslr
N.A.I.C.S.: 423450
Sanjay Gupta *(Bus Mgr)*

KNF Taiwan Ltd. (1)
9F-2 No 24 Lane 123 Section 6 Ming Chuan East Road, Taipei, Taiwan
Tel.: (886) 2 2794 1011

Web Site: http://www.knftwn.com.tw
Laboratory Vacuum Pump Whslr
N.A.I.C.S.: 423450
Bryan Lin *(Gen Mgr)*

KNF-Verder N.V. (1)
Kontichsesteenweg 17, 2630, Aartselaar, Belgium
Tel.: (32) 3 8719624
Web Site: http://www.knf.be
Emp.: 3
Laboratory Vacuum Pump Whslr
N.A.I.C.S.: 423450
Patrik Roelants *(Engr-Sls)*

Subsidiary (Non-US):

KNF Technology (Shanghai) Co., Ltd (2)
Building No 36 Lane 1000 Zhang Heng Road Zhang Jiang, Pudong District, Shanghai, 201203, China
Tel.: (86) 21 51099695
Web Site: http://www.knf.com.cn
Emp.: 36
Laboratory Vacuum Pump Whslr
N.A.I.C.S.: 423450
Michael Chen *(Gen Mgr)*

Microtrac Inc. (1)
215 Keystone Dr, Montgomeryville, PA 18936
Tel.: (215) 619-9920
Web Site: http://www.microtrac.com
Particle Size Analyzers Mfr
N.A.I.C.S.: 334516

ProMinent GmbH (1)
Im Schuhmachergewann 5-11, 69123, Heidelberg, Germany
Tel.: (49) 6221 842 0
Web Site: http://www.prominent.com
Measuring System Mfr & Whslr
N.A.I.C.S.: 334513
Andreas Dulger *(Chm-Mgmt Bd)*

Subsidiary (Non-US):

Heidelberg ProMinent Fluid Controls India Pvt. Ltd. (2)
2/2 MES Road, Yeshwanthpur, Bengaluru, 560 022, India
Tel.: (91) 23370730
Web Site: http://www.prominentindia.com
Measuring Equipment Mfr & Whslr
N.A.I.C.S.: 334513
P. Prasanna Kumar Rao *(Mng Dir)*

ProMinent Algeria (2)
Au WTCA 13 rue Semani Mohamed, Hydra, Algeria
Tel.: (213) 216 943 83
Measuring Equipment Whslr
N.A.I.C.S.: 423830

ProMinent Argentina S.A. (2)
Avenida de Mayo 204, Villa Adelina, B1607DCP, Buenos Aires, Argentina
Tel.: (54) 11 47654521
Web Site: http://www.prominent-argentina.com
Measuring Equipment Whslr
N.A.I.C.S.: 423830

ProMinent Belgium S.A. (2)
Z I Saintes Avenue Landas 11, 1480, Tubize, Belgium
Tel.: (32) 2 391 42 80
Web Site: http://www.prominent.be
Measuring Equipment Whslr
N.A.I.C.S.: 423830
Dominique Berger *(Gen Mgr)*

ProMinent Brasil Ltda. (2)
Rua Alfredo Dumont Villares 115, 09672-070, Sao Bernardo do Campo, Brazil
Tel.: (55) 11 41 76 0722
Web Site: http://www.prominent.com.br
Measuring Equipment Whslr
N.A.I.C.S.: 423830

ProMinent Chile S.A. (2)
Lotta No 2250 Providencia, Santiago, Chile
Tel.: (56) 2 33 54 799
Web Site: http://www.prominent.cl
Measuring Equipment Whslr
N.A.I.C.S.: 423830

ProMinent Colombia S.A.S (2)
Cra 13 No 93 Of 411, 110221, Bogota, Colombia

INTERNATIONAL PUBLIC

Tel.: (57) 16513 756
Measuring Equipment Whslr
N.A.I.C.S.: 423830
Jorge Yanez *(Gen Mgr)*

Subsidiary (Domestic):

ProMinent Deutschland GmbH (2)
Maassstrasse 32/1, 69123, Heidelberg, Germany
Tel.: (49) 6221 842 1800
Measuring Equipment Mfr
N.A.I.C.S.: 334513
Ralf Kiermaier *(Mng Dir)*

Subsidiary (Non-US):

ProMinent Doserteknik AB (2)
Sodra Hildedalsgatan 10, 417 05, Gothenburg, Sweden
Tel.: (46) 31 656600
Web Site: http://www.prominent.se
Measuring Equipment Whslr
N.A.I.C.S.: 423830
Stefan Strom *(Gen Mgr)*

ProMinent Dosiertechnik AG (2)
Trockenloostrasse 85, 8105, Regensdorf, Switzerland
Tel.: (41) 44 870 61 11
Web Site: http://www.prominent.ch
Measuring Equipment Whslr
N.A.I.C.S.: 423830
Ralph Maron *(Reg Sls Mgr)*

ProMinent Dosiertechnik CS s.r.o. (2)
Sobieskeho 1, 770 10, Olomouc, Czech Republic
Tel.: (420) 585 757 011
Web Site: http://www.prominent.cz
Emp.: 10
Measuring Equipment Whslr
N.A.I.C.S.: 423830

ProMinent Dosiertechnik Vietnam Co., Ltd (2)
4th Floor Viconship Building 6-8 Doan Van Bo Street District 4, Ho Chi Minh City, Vietnam
Tel.: (84) 8 39431394
Web Site: http://www.prominent.vn
Emp.: 18
Measuring Equipment Whslr
N.A.I.C.S.: 423830
Bao Lam *(Gen Mgr)*

ProMinent Dosiruyushaya Technika LLC (2)
Ul Lyusinovskaya 36 build 2, 115093, Moscow, Russia
Tel.: (7) 495 640 73 95
Web Site: http://www.prominent.ru
Measuring Equipment Whslr
N.A.I.C.S.: 423830

ProMinent Dozaj Teknikleri Ltd. (2)
Serifali Bayraktar Dergah Sokak No 3 Kat 1, Umraniye, 34775, Istanbul, Turkiye
Tel.: (90) 216 415 9980
Measuring Equipment Whslr
N.A.I.C.S.: 423830

ProMinent Dozotechnika Sp.z.o.o. (2)
ul Jagiellonska 2 B, Mirkow, 55-095, Wroclaw, Poland
Tel.: (48) 71 398 06 00
Web Site: http://www.prominent.pl
Measuring Equipment Whslr
N.A.I.C.S.: 423830
Jacek Buchwald *(Mgr-Food & Beverage Indus)*

ProMinent Finland OY (2)
Orapihlajatie 39, 00320, Helsinki, Finland
Tel.: (358) 9 47 77 890
Web Site: http://www.prominent.fi
Measuring Equipment Whslr
N.A.I.C.S.: 423830

ProMinent Fluid Controls (Dalian) Co., Ltd (2)
No 14 Road Liaohexisan Dalian Economic & Technical Development Zone, 116600, Dalian, China
Tel.: (86) 411 8731 5738
Measuring Equipment Whslr
N.A.I.C.S.: 423830
RuiJin Yang *(Mgr-IT)*

AND PRIVATE COMPANIES — VERDER INTERNATIONAL B.V.

ProMinent Fluid Controls (FE) Pte. Ltd. (2)
158 Kallang Way 02-06 Performance Building, Singapore, 349245, Singapore
Tel.: (65) 6747 4935
Emp.: 10
Measuring Equipment Whslr
N.A.I.C.S.: 423830
Allen Mak *(Mng Dir)*

ProMinent Fluid Controls (M) Sdn. Bhd. (2)
7 Jalan Bandar Bukit Puchong, BP 4/9, 47120, Puchong, Selangor, Malaysia
Tel.: (60) 3 8068 2578
Web Site: http://www.pfc-prominent.com.my
Measuring Equipment Whslr
N.A.I.C.S.: 423830
Allen Mak *(Mng Dir)*

ProMinent Fluid Controls (Taiwan) Ltd. (2)
8F2 No 288-9 Hsinya Road, Kaohsiung, Taiwan
Tel.: (886) 7 813 5122
Web Site: http://www.prominent.com.tw
Measuring Equipment Whslr
N.A.I.C.S.: 423830

ProMinent Fluid Controls (Thailand) Co. Ltd. (2)
2991/7 Visuthanee Office Park Ladprao Road, Klongchan Bangkapi, Bangkok, 10240, Thailand
Tel.: (66) 2376000812
Web Site: http://www.prominent.com.mx
Measuring Equipment Whslr
N.A.I.C.S.: 423830

ProMinent Fluid Controls (UK) Ltd. (2)
Resolution Road, Ashby de la Zouch, LE65 1DW, Leicestershire, United Kingdom
Tel.: (44) 1530 560555
Measuring Equipment Whslr
N.A.I.C.S.: 423830
Stephen Ellix *(Mng Dir)*

ProMinent Fluid Controls BG Ltd. (2)
260 Botevgradsko Shosse Boulevard 3rd Floor, 1839, Sofia, Bulgaria
Tel.: (359) 2 945 53 03
Web Site: http://www.prominent.bg
Measuring Equipment Whslr
N.A.I.C.S.: 423830

Subsidiary (US):

ProMinent Fluid Controls Inc. (2)
136 Industry Dr, Pittsburgh, PA 15275
Tel.: (412) 787-2484
Web Site: http://www.prominent.us
Emp.: 2,100
Measuring Equipment Mfr & Whslr
N.A.I.C.S.: 334513
Tarrah Myers *(Mgr-HR)*

Subsidiary (Non-US):

ProMinent Fluid Controls Ltd. (2)
490 Southgate Drive, Guelph, N1G 4P5, ON, Canada
Tel.: (519) 836-5692
Web Site: http://www.prominent.ca
Measuring Equipment Whslr
N.A.I.C.S.: 423830
Michael McNulty *(Member-Exec Bd & Mgr-Technical)*

ProMinent Fluid Controls Pty Ltd. (2)
Corner Hurricane road and Dakota Crescent Airport park Ext 4, Lambton, Germiston, South Africa
Tel.: (27) 11 323 5000
Web Site: http://www.prominent.co.za
Measuring Equipment Whslr
N.A.I.C.S.: 423830
Jock Bartolo *(Mng Dir)*

ProMinent Fluid Controls de Mexico S.A. de C.V. (2)
Anillo Vial Fray Junipero Serra 16950 No Int, 3-1 Fraccionamiento San Pedrito El Alto, 76148, Santiago de Queretaro, Mexico
Tel.: (52) 442 2189920
Web Site: http://www.prominent.com.mx
Measuring Equipment Whslr
N.A.I.C.S.: 423830

ProMinent France S.A.S
8 rue des Freres Lumiere, BP 39, 67038, Strasbourg, Cedex, Eckbolsheim, France
Tel.: (33) 388 10 15 10
Web Site: http://www.prominent.fr
Measuring Equipment Whslr
N.A.I.C.S.: 423830

ProMinent Hellas Ltd. (2)
43 Dilou & Parnithos Str, Metamorfosi, 14452, Athens, Greece
Tel.: (30) 210 513 46 21
Measuring Equipment Whslr
N.A.I.C.S.: 423830

ProMinent Iberia, SA (2)
Edificio Ramazzotti Av do Forte N 6 - 6A, 2790-072, Carnaxide, Portugal
Tel.: (351) 219267040
Web Site: http://www.prominent.pt
Measuring Equipment Whslr
N.A.I.C.S.: 423830

ProMinent Italiana S.r.l. (2)
via A Durer 29, 39100, Bolzano, Italy
Tel.: (39) 04 71 92 00 00
Web Site: http://www.prominent.it
Measuring Equipment Whslr
N.A.I.C.S.: 423830

ProMinent Japan Ltd. (2)
19-2 Taitou-1, Taitou-ku, Tokyo, 110-0016, Japan
Tel.: (81) 3 5812 7831
Measuring Equipment Whslr
N.A.I.C.S.: 423830

ProMinent Korea Co., Ltd. (2)
707-2 Gongse-dong, Giheung-gu, Yongin, 446-902, Gyeonggi, Korea (South)
Tel.: (82) 31 895 2000
Web Site: http://www.prominent.co.kr
Measuring Equipment Whslr
N.A.I.C.S.: 423830
Moonjae Lee *(Mng Dir)*

ProMinent Magyarorsz g Kft. (2)
Ives u 2, 9027, Gyor, Hungary
Tel.: (36) 96 511 400
Web Site: http://www.prominent.hu
Measuring Equipment Mfr
N.A.I.C.S.: 334513

ProMinent Norge AS (2)
Cellulosen 9, 3048, Drammen, Norway
Tel.: (47) 32 21 31 30
Web Site: http://www.prominent.no
Measuring Equipment Whslr
N.A.I.C.S.: 423830
Robert Meinseth *(Mgr-Sls)*

ProMinent Scotland Ltd. (2)
91 Bothwell Road, Hamilton, ML3 0DW, United Kingdom
Tel.: (44) 1698 424353
Measuring Equipment Whslr
N.A.I.C.S.: 423830

ProMinent Slovensko, s.r.o. (2)
Rolnicka 21, Vajnory, 83107, Bratislava, Slovakia
Tel.: (421) 2 482 00 111
Web Site: http://www.prominent.sk
Industrial Measuring Equipment Whslr
N.A.I.C.S.: 423830
Frantisek Grejtak *(Mng Dir)*

ProMinent Systems spol. s.r.o. (2)
Fugnerova 567, 336 01, Blovice, Czech Republic
Tel.: (420) 378 227 100
Web Site: http://www.prominentsystems.cz
Emp.: 250
Water Treatment Equipment Mfr
N.A.I.C.S.: 333310
Stefan Maile *(Mng Dir)*

ProMinent Verder srl (2)
Calea Dumbravii nr 65, 550324, Sibiu, Romania
Tel.: (40) 269 234 408
Web Site: http://www.prominent.ro
Emp.: 10
Measuring Equipment Whslr
N.A.I.C.S.: 423830
Mircea Liviu Trufasiu *(Gen Mgr)*

RETSCH France (1)
PO Box 80040, 95610, Eragny-sur-Oise, France
Tel.: (33) 1 34642953
Web Site: http://www.retsch.fr

Industrial Machinery & Equipment Whslr
N.A.I.C.S.: 423830

RETSCH Korea & Co. Ltd. (1)
9 Dongwonbuk-ro, Bundang-gu, Seongnam, 13547, Gyeonggi-do, Korea (South)
Tel.: (82) 31 7065725
Web Site: http://www.retsch.co.kr
Emp.: 5
Industrial Machinery & Equipment Whslr
N.A.I.C.S.: 423830
Gerald Lee *(Pres)*

RETSCH Norge AS (1)
Tross, 6963, Dale, Norway
Tel.: (47) 577 39000
Web Site: http://www.retsch.no
Industrial Machinery & Equipment Whslr
N.A.I.C.S.: 423830

Retsch GmbH (1)
Retsch-Allee 1-5, 42781, Haan, Germany
Tel.: (49) 21042333100
Molding Machine Mfr
N.A.I.C.S.: 333517

Retsch Osterreich Verder Ges.m.b.H. (1)
Eitnergasse 21, 1230, Vienna, Austria
Tel.: (43) 186510740
Industrial Machinery Distr
N.A.I.C.S.: 423830

Sauermann Industrie S.A. (1)
Parc d'activite de l'Oree de Chevry Route de Ferolles, 77173, Paris, Seine Et Marne, France
Tel.: (33) 160620606
Web Site: http://www.sauermannpumps.fr
Pumps & Pumping Equipment Mfr
N.A.I.C.S.: 333914

VERDER BULGARIA EOOD (1)
Bd Bulgaria no 110 et 2 ap 15-16, 1618, Sofia, Bulgaria
Tel.: (359) 878407370
Industrial Machinery Distr
N.A.I.C.S.: 423830

VERDER SCIENTIFIC GmbH & Co. KG (1)
Retsch-Allee 1-5, 42781, Haan, Germany
Tel.: (49) 2104 2333 500
Web Site: http://www.verder-scientific.com
Emp.: 800
Industrial Furnace Mfr & Distr
N.A.I.C.S.: 333994

Subsidiary (Non-US):

Carbolite Limited (2)
Parsons Lane Hope, Hope Valley, S33 6RB, United Kingdom
Tel.: (44) 1433 620011
Web Site: http://www.carbolite.com
Industrial Furnace & Oven Mfr
N.A.I.C.S.: 333994
John Bailey *(Mng Dir)*

Subsidiary (Non-US):

Carbolite GmbH (3)
Hesselbachstrasse 15, 75242, Neuhausen, Germany
Tel.: (49) 7234 95 22 40
Web Site: http://www.carbolite.de
Industrial Furnace & Oven Distr
N.A.I.C.S.: 423830

Subsidiary (Non-US):

Verder Scientific Co. Ltd. (2)
5-8-8 Shinjuku, Shinjuku-ku, Tokyo, 160-0022, Japan
Tel.: (81) 3 5367 2651
Web Site: http://www.verder-scientific.co.jp
Industrial Furnace Distr
N.A.I.C.S.: 423830

Verder Scientific LLC (2)
ul Bumazhnaya d 17, 190020, Saint Petersburg, Russia
Tel.: (7) 8127771107
Web Site: http://www.verder-scientific.ru
Emp.: 800
Industrial Furnace Distr
N.A.I.C.S.: 423830
Gimogrog Serjey *(Gen Mgr)*

Verder Scientific srl (2)
Largo delle Industrie 10, Torre Boldone,

24020, Bergamo, Italy
Tel.: (39) 035 3690369
Web Site: http://www.verder-scientific.it
Emp.: 5
Industrial Furnace Distr
N.A.I.C.S.: 423830
Pablo Gardani *(Mng Dir)*

Subsidiary (US):

Verder Scientific, Inc. (2)
11 Penns Trl, Newtown, PA 18940
Tel.: (267) 757-0351
Emp.: 100
Industrial Machinery Distr
N.A.I.C.S.: 423830
Georg Schick *(Pres)*

Van Wijk & Boerma Verder (1)
Leningradweg 5, Groningen, 9723 TP, Netherlands
Tel.: (31) 505495900
Web Site: http://www.wijkboerma.nl
Sales Range: $25-49.9 Million
Emp.: 44
Industrial Pump Mfr
N.A.I.C.S.: 333914
Verner Bosman *(Mng Dir)*

Verder - Polska Sp. z o.o. (1)
ul Ligonia 8/1, 40-036, Katowice, Poland
Tel.: (48) 32 781 50 32
Web Site: http://www.verder.pl
Industrial Pump Distr
N.A.I.C.S.: 423830

Verder A/S (1)
H J Holstvej 26, 2610, Rodovre, Denmark
Tel.: (45) 3636 4600
Web Site: http://www.verder.dk
Emp.: 2
Industrial Machinery Distr
N.A.I.C.S.: 423830
Werner Bosman *(Gen Mgr)*

Verder AG (1)
Auf dem Wolf 19, 4052, Basel, Switzerland
Tel.: (41) 61 331 33 13
Web Site: http://www.verder.ch
Industrial Machinery Distr
N.A.I.C.S.: 423830

Verder B.V. (1)
Leningradweg 5, Groningen, 9723 TP, Netherlands
Tel.: (31) 505495900
Web Site: http://www.verderliquids.com
Industrial Pump Distr
N.A.I.C.S.: 423830

Verder GmbH (1)
Eitnergasse 21, 1230, Vienna, Austria
Tel.: (43) 1 865 10 74
Web Site: http://www.verder.at
Emp.: 10
Industrial Pump Distr
N.A.I.C.S.: 423830

Verder Hungary Kft (1)
Budafoki ut 187-189, 1117, Budapest, Hungary
Tel.: (36) 1 365 1140
Web Site: http://www.verder.hu
Industrial Pump Distr
N.A.I.C.S.: 423830

Verder Inc. (1)
110 Gateway Dr, Macon, GA 31210
Tel.: (855) 441-2400
Web Site: http://www.verder-us.com
Industrial Pump Distr
N.A.I.C.S.: 423830
Kerry Ayres *(Reg Mgr-Sls)*

Verder India Pumps PVT. LTD (1)
Plot No-3b 3part 11 D-1 Block MIDC Block, Chinchwad, Pune, 411 019, India
Tel.: (91) 2027468485
Web Site: http://www.verder.co.in
Pipe Fitting Distr
N.A.I.C.S.: 423830
Gulshan Mehendiratta *(Mgr-Sls-North)*

Verder N.V. (1)
Kontichsesteenweg 17, 2630, Aartselaar, Belgium
Tel.: (32) 8081738
Web Site: http://www.verder.be
Pipe Fitting Mfr
N.A.I.C.S.: 331511

VERDER INTERNATIONAL B.V.

Verder International B.V.—(Continued)

Verder Pumps South-Africa (1)
197 Flaming Rock Avenue Northlands Business Park Newmarket Street, Northriding, Randburg, South Africa
Tel.: (27) 10 040 3356
Web Site: http://www.verder.co.za
Industrial Pump Distr
N.A.I.C.S.: 423830
Laetitia Moller (Mgr-Mktg)

Verder Retsch Shanghai Trading Co., Ltd. (1)
Building 8 Fuhai Business Park No 299 Bisheng Road, Zhangjiang Hiteck Park, Shanghai, 201204, China
Tel.: (86) 21 33932950
Web Site: http://www.retsch.cn
Industrial Machinery & Equipment Whslr
N.A.I.C.S.: 423830

Verder Romania S.R.L. (1)
Drumul Balta Doamnei 57-61 Sector 3, 032624, Bucharest, Romania
Tel.: (40) 21 335 45 92
Web Site: http://www.verder.ro
Industrial Pump Distr
N.A.I.C.S.: 423830

Verder S.R.O.
Vodnanska 651/6, Kyje, 198 00, Prague, Czech Republic
Tel.: (420) 225 379 993
Web Site: http://www.verder.cz
Industrial Pump Distr
N.A.I.C.S.: 423830

Verder Sarl (1)
2 Av du Gros Chene, 95610, Eragny-sur-Oise, France
Tel.: (33) 73138822
Web Site: http://www.verder.fr
Pipe Fitting Mfr
N.A.I.C.S.: 331511
Simon Rundstrom (Mgr-Bus)

Verder Scientific Private Limited (1)
Plot No- 5A/10-11 1st Floor, ID Nacharam Road 1 Uppal Mandal, Hyderabad, 500 076, India
Tel.: (91) 4029806688
Industrial Machinery Distr
N.A.I.C.S.: 423830

Verder Shanghai Instruments and Equipment Co., Ltd. (1)
Rm 1013-1015 Jinao International Office Building, No 17 Madian East Road Haidian District, Beijing, 100088, China
Tel.: (86) 2133932950
Industrial Machinery Distr
N.A.I.C.S.: 423830

Verder Slovakia sro (1)
Raciancka 66, 831 02, Bratislava, Slovakia
Tel.: (421) 905 615 530
Web Site: http://www.verderliquids.com
Industrial Pump Distr
N.A.I.C.S.: 423830

Verder UK Ltd (1)
Unit 3 California Drive, Castleford, WF10 5QH, United Kingdom
Tel.: (44) 1924 669038
Web Site: http://www.verder.co.uk
Industrial Pump Distr
N.A.I.C.S.: 423830
Kenneth McCartney (Mng Dir)

Verdermix BV (1)
Utrechtseweg 4a, Vleuten, 3451 GG, Netherlands
Tel.: (31) 306779231
Pipe Fitting Mfr
N.A.I.C.S.: 331511

VERDITEK PLC

29 Farm Street, London, W1J 5RL, United Kingdom
Tel.: (44) 2071291110 UK
Web Site: http://www.verditek.com
Year Founded: 2016
VDTK—(AIM)
Rev.: $146,134
Assets: $3,692,224
Liabilities: $1,152,320
Net Worth: $2,539,904
Earnings: ($1,322,527)
Emp.: 11
Fiscal Year-end: 12/31/21
Power Generation Services
N.A.I.C.S.: 221114
Lord David Willetts (Chm)

VERDO A/S

Agerskellet 7, 8920, Randers, Denmark
Tel.: (45) 8911 4811 DK
Web Site: http://www.verdo.dk
Sales Range: $250-299.9 Million
Emp.: 400
Holding Company; Water, Heat & Electricity Distr
N.A.I.C.S.: 551112
Kenneth R. H. Jeppesen (CFO & Member-Exec Bd)

Subsidiaries:

Carbon Partners AS (1)
Ostre Strandgt 5, 4610, Kristiansand, Norway
Tel.: (47) 38145940
Web Site: http://www.carbonpartners.no
Coal & Coke Product Distr
N.A.I.C.S.: 423520

Subsidiary (US):

Carbon Partners Inc. (2)
8880 Cedar Springs Ln, Knoxville, TN 37923
Tel.: (865) 769-9094
Coal & Coke Product Distr
N.A.I.C.S.: 423520

GF Energy B.V. (1)
Groothandelsgebouw - Unit C7 097 Weena 723, 3013 AM, Rotterdam, Netherlands
Tel.: (31) 102400201
Web Site: http://www.gfverdo.eu
Wood Product Mfr & Distr
N.A.I.C.S.: 321113
Roeland Reesinck (Mng Dir)

Verdo Energy A/S (1)
Kulholmsvej 22, Randers, 8930, NO, Denmark
Tel.: (45) 8911 4727
Emp.: 15
Biomass Fuel Products & Coal Distr
N.A.I.C.S.: 424990
Thomas W. Bornerup (Mng Dir)

Verdo Hillerod El-net A/S (1)
Askvang 4, DK-3400, Hillerod, Denmark
Tel.: (45) 8911 4811
Web Site: http://www.verdohillerodelnet.dk
Electric Power Distr
N.A.I.C.S.: 221122

Verdo Produktion A/S (1)
Kulholmsvej 12, Randers, 8900, NO, Denmark
Tel.: (45) 8911 4811
Web Site: http://www.verdo.dk
Biofuel Power Plant Operator
N.A.I.C.S.: 221118

Verdo Randers El-net A/S (1)
Agerskellet 7, DK-8920, Randers, NV, Denmark
Tel.: (45) 8911 4811
Web Site: http://www.verdo.dk
Electric Power Distr
N.A.I.C.S.: 221122
Jesper S. Sahl (Mng Dir)

Verdo Renewables Ltd. (1)
45 Macadam Way West Portway Industrial Estate, Andover, SP10 3XW, Hampshire, United Kingdom
Tel.: (44) 1264 342 000
Web Site: http://www.verdorenewables.co.uk
Wood Products Mfr
N.A.I.C.S.: 321113

Verdo Vand A/S (1)
Agerskellet 7, Randers, 8920, NV, Denmark
Tel.: (45) 8911 4811
Web Site: http://www.verdo.dk
Emp.: 100
Water Distr
N.A.I.C.S.: 221310

Jesper S. Sahl (Mng Dir)

Verdo Varme A/S (1)
Agerskellet 7, 8920, Randers, Denmark
Tel.: (45) 8911 4811
Web Site: http://www.verdo.dk
Heating Services
N.A.I.C.S.: 221330
Karsten Randrup (Dir-Ops)

VEREINIGTE FILZFABRIKEN AG

Giengener Weg 66, Hermaringen, 89568, Giengen an der Brenz, Germany
Tel.: (49) 73221440
Web Site: https://www.vfg.de
VFF—(STU)
Sales Range: Less than $1 Million
Net Mfr
N.A.I.C.S.: 326199

VEREN INC.

Suite 2000 585-8th Avenue SW, Calgary, T2P 1G1, AB, Canada
Tel.: (403) 693-0020 AB
Web Site: https://vrn.com
Year Founded: 1994
VRN—(NYSE)
Rev.: $2,799,310,752
Assets: $7,421,020,992
Liabilities: $2,341,364,040
Net Worth: $5,079,656,952
Earnings: $1,160,434,152
Emp.: 768
Fiscal Year-end: 12/31/22
Petroleum & Natural Gas Exploration, Development & Extraction
N.A.I.C.S.: 211120
Kenneth R. Lamont (CFO)

Subsidiaries:

Crescent Point Energy U.S. Corp. (1)
555 17 St Ste 1800, Denver, CO 80202
Tel.: (720) 880-3610
Web Site: http://www.crescentpointenergy.com
Emp.: 75
Petroleum & Natural Gas Exploration, Development & Extraction
N.A.I.C.S.: 211120
Anthony Baldwin (Pres)

VEREYA-TOUR AD

Bulgaria Blvd Tsar Simeon Veliki 100, 6000, Stara Zagora, 6000, Bulgaria
Tel.: (359) 42919373
Web Site: https://www.hotel-vereya.com
VERY—(BUL)
Sales Range: Less than $1 Million
Hotel & Restaurant Operator
N.A.I.C.S.: 721110

VERGNET S.A.

12 rue des Chataigniers, 45140, Ormes, France
Tel.: (33) 238523560
Web Site: https://www.vergnet.fr
ALVER—(EUR)
Sales Range: $10-24.9 Million
Emp.: 166
Wind Turbine & Water Supply Machinery Mfr
N.A.I.C.S.: 333611
Jerome Douat (Chm-Mgmt Bd & CEO)

Subsidiaries:

Vergnet Hydro SAS (1)
6 Rue Lavoisier, 45140, Ingre, France
Tel.: (33) 238227510
Web Site: http://www.vergnet-hydro.com
Sales Range: $25-49.9 Million
Emp.: 20
Wind Turbine Mfr
N.A.I.C.S.: 333611
Marc Vergnet (Founder)

INTERNATIONAL PUBLIC

VERIDIS ENVIRONMENT LTD

Aba Even 1 Street, 46725, Herzliya Pituach, Israel
Tel.: (972) 99520000
Web Site: http://www.veridis.co.il
VRDS—(TAE)
Sales Range: $300-349.9 Million
Waste Management Services
N.A.I.C.S.: 562998

Subsidiaries:

Infinya Ltd. (1)
Maizer Street Industrial Area, PO Box 142, Hadera, 3810101, Israel
Tel.: (972) 46349349
Web Site: http://www.hadera-paper.co.il
Rev.: $466,411,868
Assets: $662,407,776
Liabilities: $371,125,481
Net Worth: $291,282,295
Earnings: $6,566,382
Emp.: 1,756
Fiscal Year-end: 12/31/2019
Household & Sanitary Paper Products Mfr
N.A.I.C.S.: 322120
Ishay Davidi (Chm)

Subsidiary (Domestic):

Amnir Recycling Industries Ltd. (2)
Industrial Zone, PO Box 142, Hadera, 38191, Israel (100%)
Tel.: (972) 46349582
Web Site: http://www.aipm.co.il
Paper & Cardboard Waste Collection & Recycling Services
N.A.I.C.S.: 562920
Uzi Carmi (Gen Mgr)

Carmel Container Systems Ltd. (2)
2 Chalamish St Caesarea Industrial Park, 38900, Caesarea, Israel (89.3%)
Tel.: (972) 46239350
Sales Range: $100-124.9 Million
Corrugated Packaging & Related Products Mfr
N.A.I.C.S.: 322211
Robert K. Kraft (Chm)

Subsidiary (Domestic):

Frenkel-CD Ltd. (3)
Caesarea Industrial Park Garnit 4, PO Box 3054, Caesarea, 32000, Israel
Tel.: (972) 46179179
Web Site: http://www.frenkel-cd.co.il
Sales Range: $75-99.9 Million
Emp.: 200
Paperboard Packaging Products Designer & Mfr
N.A.I.C.S.: 322211
Guy Frenkel (Mng Dir)

Tri-Wall Ltd (3)
Northern Industrial Zone, PO Box 13283, 42113, Netanya, Israel
Tel.: (972) 98822215
Web Site: http://www.tri-wall.co.il
Corrugated & Solid Fiber Box Mfr
N.A.I.C.S.: 322211

VERIMARK HOLDINGS LIMITED

Cnr Witkoppen and Riverbend rd, Randburg, South Africa
Tel.: (27) 11699 8000
Web Site: http://www.verimark.co.za
Rev.: $41,037,151
Assets: $18,281,428
Liabilities: $4,750,402
Net Worth: $13,531,026
Earnings: $2,721,407
Emp.: 334
Fiscal Year-end: 02/28/18
Fitness Products Distr
N.A.I.C.S.: 423910
Michael J. van Straaten (CEO)

Subsidiaries:

Verimark (Pty) Ltd. (1)
Cnr Witkoppen and Riverbend rd Entrance Through Garage, Randburg, South Africa
Tel.: (27) 116998000
Household Appliance & Educational Toy Distr

N.A.I.C.S.: 423620

VERIMATRIX SA
Impasse des carres de Arc Rond-point du Canet, 13590, Meyreuil, France
Tel.: (33) 442905905　　　　FR
Web Site: https://www.verimatrix.com
VMX—(OTCIQ)
Rev.: $94,893,000
Assets: $260,606,000
Liabilities: $113,194,000
Net Worth: $147,412,000
Earnings: ($10,407,000)
Fiscal Year-end: 12/31/20
Security Software & Technologies Developer
N.A.I.C.S.: 541511
Amedeo D'Angelo *(Chm)*

Subsidiaries:

SypherMedia International, Inc.　(1)
5455 Garden Grove Blvd #300, Westminster, CA 92683
Tel.: (310) 977-4700
Circuit Camouflage IP Protection, Content Protection & Security Related Services
N.A.I.C.S.: 518210

Verimatrix GmbH　(1)
Fraunhoferstr 7, 85737, Ismaning, Germany
Tel.: (49) 8955265100
Cyber Security Services
N.A.I.C.S.: 561612

Verimatrix, Inc.　(1)
6059 Cornerstone Ct W, San Diego, CA 92121
Tel.: (858) 677-7800
Web Site: http://www.verimatrix.com
Security System Services
N.A.I.C.S.: 561621

VERIS GOLD CORP.
688 West Hastings Street Suite 900, Vancouver, V6B 1P1, BC, Canada
Tel.: (604) 891-8425　　　　BC
Web Site: http://www.ey.com
Year Founded: 1988
Sales Range: $150-199.9 Million
Emp.: 404
Gold Ore Exploration, Mining & Development
N.A.I.C.S.: 212220
Graham C. Dickson *(COO)*

Subsidiaries:

Castle Exploration Inc.　(1)
1600 Stout St Ste 1370, Denver, CO 80202　　　　(100%)
Tel.: (303) 260-7772
Web Site: http://www.yukon-nevadagold.com
Gold Ole Mine Exploration
N.A.I.C.S.: 213114

VERIS LIMITED
Tel.: (61) 862413333　　　　AU
Web Site: https://www.veris.com.au
VRS—(ASX)
Rev.: $61,827,382
Assets: $41,678,995
Liabilities: $26,297,604
Net Worth: $15,381,391
Earnings: ($3,131,701)
Emp.: 450
Fiscal Year-end: 06/30/24
Consulting Services
N.A.I.C.S.: 541611
Adam Lamond *(Exec Dir)*

Subsidiaries:

Whelans (WA) Pty Ltd.　(1)
Level 10 3 Hasler Road, PO Box 9, Osborne Park, 6017, WA, Australia
Tel.: (61) 862413333
Web Site: http://www.whelans.com.au
Emp.: 80
Geographic Mapping Services
N.A.I.C.S.: 541360
Michael Shirley *(CEO)*

VERISANTE TECHNOLOGY, INC.
170-422 Richards Street, Vancouver, V6B 2Z4, BC, Canada
Tel.: (604) 716-5133　　　　BC
Web Site: https://www.verisante.com
VRSEF—(OTCIQ)
Medical Device Mfr
N.A.I.C.S.: 339112
Thomas A. Braun *(Pres & CEO)*

VERISILICON HOLDINGS CO., LTD.
Room 20F 560 Songtao Road Zhangiang Center Hi-Tech Park, Pudong New Area, Shanghai, 201203, China
Tel.: (86) 2151311118　　　　Ky
Web Site: http://www.verisilicon.com
Year Founded: 2001
Sales Range: $125-149.9 Million
Semiconductor Components Mfr
N.A.I.C.S.: 334413
Wayne Wei-Ming Dai *(Founder, Chm, Pres & CEO)*

Subsidiaries:

VeriSilicon Europe　(1)
Les Algorithmes Bat Aristote A, 2000 Route des Lucioles, 06901, Sophia-Antipolis, France
Tel.: (33) 497100138
Semiconductor Components Mfr
N.A.I.C.S.: 334413

VeriSilicon K.K.　(1)
The Imperial Tower 8th floor Uchisaiwaicho, Chiyoda-ku, Tokyo, 100-0011, Japan
Tel.: (81) 3 3507 3005
Semiconductor Distr
N.A.I.C.S.: 423690

VeriSilicon Microelectronics (Beijing) Co., Ltd.　(1)
A106 Information Center Zhongguancun Software Park 8 Dongbeiwang, West Road Haidian District, Beijing, 100193, China
Tel.: (86) 10 8282 6693
Semiconductor Distr
N.A.I.C.S.: 423690

VeriSilicon Microelectronics (Chengdu) Co., Ltd.　(1)
23F Building 10 Zone C Tianfu Software Park No 219 of 2nd Tianhua Road, Gaoxin District, Chengdu, 610040, China
Tel.: (86) 28 6890 2800
Semiconductor Distr
N.A.I.C.S.: 423690

VeriSilicon Microelectronics (Shanghai) Co., Ltd.　(1)
20F No 560 Songtao Road Zhangjiang Hi-Tech Park, Pudong New Area, Shanghai, 201203, China
Tel.: (86) 2151311118
Web Site: http://www.verisilicon.com
Sales Range: $100-124.9 Million
Emp.: 355
Semiconductor Components Mfr
N.A.I.C.S.: 334413
Jinsong Zhang *(VP-Engrg)*

VeriSilicon Taiwan, Inc.　(1)
5F No306 Sec1 Neihu Rd Rd, Wall Sttreet Building, Taipei, 114, Taiwan
Tel.: (886) 226562606
Semiconductor Components Mfr
N.A.I.C.S.: 334413

VeriSilicon, Inc.　(1)
4699 Old Ironsides Dr Ste 350, Santa Clara, CA 95054
Tel.: (408) 844-8560
Web Site: http://www.verisilicon.com
Sales Range: $25-49.9 Million
Emp.: 40
Semiconductor Components Mfr
N.A.I.C.S.: 334413
Bill Wang *(Gen Mgr)*

VERITAS PENSIONSFOR-SAKRING
PO Box 133, Olavintie 2, 20101, Turku, Finland
Tel.: (358) 01055010
Web Site: http://www.veritas.fi
Statutory Employment Pension Insurance Solutions Provider
N.A.I.C.S.: 524298
Carl Pettersson *(CEO)*

VERITAS PHARMA, INC.
Suite 101-2386 East Mall, Vancouver, V6T 1Z3, BC, Canada
Tel.: (416) 918-6785
Web Site: http://www.veritaspharmainc.com
Pharmaceuticals Product Mfr
N.A.I.C.S.: 325412
Peter McFadden *(CEO & CFO)*

VERITE CO., LTD.
3-33-8 Tsuruya-cho, Kanagawa-ku, Yokohama, 221-8705, Japan
Tel.: (81) 454158800　　　　JP
Web Site: https://www.verite.jp
Year Founded: 1948
9904—(TKS)
Sales Range: Less than $1 Million
Emp.: 407
Jewelry Store Operator
N.A.I.C.S.: 458310
Apran Jaweri *(Exec Dir)*

VERITY CORPORATION
Office E 7/F 45 Pottinger Street, Central, China (Hong Kong)
Tel.: (852) 6 358 5597　　　　Ky
Year Founded: 2019
Assets: $99,667
Liabilities: $86,002
Net Worth: $13,665
Earnings: ($2,827)
Fiscal Year-end: 12/31/20
Investment Services
N.A.I.C.S.: 523999
Bing Lin *(CEO & Chm)*

VERIUM AG
Farberstrasse 6, CH-8008, Zurich, Switzerland
Tel.: (41) 44 269 60 90
Web Site: http://www.verium.ch
Year Founded: 2011
Privater Equity Firm
N.A.I.C.S.: 523999
Marc Erni *(Mng Partner & Head-Private Equity)*

Subsidiaries:

Toradex AG　(1)
Altsagenstrasse 5, Horw, 6048, Lucerne, Switzerland
Tel.: (41) 41 500 48 00
Modular Computing Platforms for Industrial Applications
N.A.I.C.S.: 541519
Stephan Dubach *(CEO)*

Subsidiary (US):

Toradex, Inc.　(2)
219 1st Ave S Ste 410, Seattle, WA 98104-2551
Tel.: (206) 452-2031
Web Site: http://www.toradex.com
Computer & Computer Peripheral Equipment & Software Merchant Whslr
N.A.I.C.S.: 423430
Daniel Lang *(VP)*

VERKKOKAUPPA.COM OYJ
Tyynenmerenkatu 11, 00220, Helsinki, Finland
Tel.: (358) 103095555
Web Site: https://www.verkkokauppa.com
Year Founded: 1992
VERK—(HEL)
Rev.: $581,264,839
Assets: $185,829,916
Liabilities: $157,263,112
Net Worth: $28,566,803
Earnings: $1,802,288
Emp.: 640
Fiscal Year-end: 12/31/22
Online Retailer
N.A.I.C.S.: 449210
Panu Porkka *(CEO)*

VERLAG DAS BESTE GMBH
Vordernbergstrasse 6, 70191, Stuttgart, Germany
Tel.: (49) 71166020
Web Site: http://www.readersdigest-verlag.com
Magazine Publisher
N.A.I.C.S.: 513120

VERLAGSGRUPPE GEORG VON HOLTZBRINCK GMBH
Gruneisenstrasse 26, Stuttgart, 105369, Germany
Tel.: (49) 71121500　　　　De
Web Site: http://www.holtzbrinck.com
Year Founded: 1948
Sales Range: $1-4.9 Billion
Emp.: 15,473
Holding Company; Books, Magazines, Newspapers & Electronic Media Publisher
N.A.I.C.S.: 551112
Stefan von Holtzbrinck *(Co-CEO & Partner)*

Subsidiaries:

Georg von Holtzbrinck GmbH & Co. KG　(1)
Gaensheidestrasse 26, Stuttgart, 70184, Germany　　　　(100%)
Tel.: (49) 71121500
Web Site: http://www.holtzbrinck.com
Sales Range: $50-74.9 Million
Emp.: 100
Book, Magazine, Newspaper & Internet Publisher
N.A.I.C.S.: 513130
Johann Butting *(Member-Exec Bd)*

Subsidiary (Domestic):

Argon Verlag GmbH　(2)
Neue Grunstr 17, Hof 1 Aufgang 5, 10179, Berlin, Germany　　　　(100%)
Tel.: (49) 3025762060
Web Site: http://www.argon-verlag.de
Sales Range: $25-49.9 Million
Emp.: 10
Book Publishing
N.A.I.C.S.: 513130
Christian Doettinger *(Gen Mgr)*

HGV Hanseatische Gesellschaft fur Verlagsservice mbH　(2)
Weidestrasse 122 A, 22083, Hamburg, Germany
Tel.: (49) 40 84 00 08
Web Site: http://www.hgv-online.de
Book Publishers
N.A.I.C.S.: 513130

Holtzbrinck Digital GmbH　(2)
Landsberger Str 187, 80687, Munich, Germany
Tel.: (49) 89 452285 100
Web Site: http://www.holtzbrinck-digital.com
Book Publishers
N.A.I.C.S.: 513130
Carolin Ruhl *(Mgr-Investment)*

Subsidiary (Domestic):

devbliss GmbH　(3)
Saarbrucker Strasse 38 A, 10405, Berlin, Germany
Tel.: (49) 30 652 157056
Web Site: http://www.devbliss.com
Software Development Services
N.A.I.C.S.: 541511
Karsten Zimmer *(Mng Dir)*

searchmetrics GmbH　(3)
Greifswalder Strasse 212, 10405, Berlin, Germany
Tel.: (49) 3032295350

VERLAGSGRUPPE GEORG VON HOLTZBRINCK GMBH

Verlagsgruppe Georg von Holtzbrinck GmbH—(Continued)

Web Site: http://www.searchmetrics.com
Software Development Services
N.A.I.C.S.: 541511
Marcus Tober *(Founder & Chief Innovation Officer-Market Innovation Lab)*

Subsidiary (US):

Holtzbrinck Publishers, LLC (2)
175 5th Ave, New York, NY 10010
Tel.: (212) 674-5151
Web Site: http://www.macmillan.com
Book Publishers
N.A.I.C.S.: 513130

Subsidiary (Domestic):

Bedford, Freeman & Worth Publishing Group LLC (3)
41 Madison Ave Fl 35, New York, NY 10010-2202
Tel.: (212) 576-9400
Web Site: http://www.bfwpub.com
Rev.: $570,000
Emp.: 192
Book Publishing
N.A.I.C.S.: 513130
John Sterling *(Pres)*

Subsidiary (Domestic):

W.H. Freeman & Co. (4)
41 Madison Ave, New York, NY 10010-2202 (100%)
Tel.: (212) 576-9400
Web Site: http://www.whfreeman.com
Sales Range: $25-49.9 Million
Emp.: 100
Book Publishers
N.A.I.C.S.: 513130
John Britch *(Mgr-Mktg)*

WP Holding Corp. (4)
1 Newyork Plz, New York, NY 10004 (100%)
Tel.: (212) 576-9400
Sales Range: $125-149.9 Million
Emp.: 100
Books Publishing Services
N.A.I.C.S.: 513130
John Britch *(Dir-Mktg)*

Subsidiary (Domestic):

Farrar, Straus & Giroux, Inc. (3)
18 W 18th St, New York, NY 10011 (100%)
Tel.: (212) 741-6900
Web Site: http://www.fsgbooks.com
Sales Range: $50-74.9 Million
Emp.: 120
Publisher of Books
N.A.I.C.S.: 513130
Jonathan Galassi *(Pres & Publr)*

Division (Domestic):

North Point Press (4)
18 W 18th St, New York, NY 10011 (100%)
Tel.: (212) 741-6900
Web Site: http://www.fsgbooks.com
Sales Range: $25-49.9 Million
Emp.: 75
Book Publishing
N.A.I.C.S.: 513130

Subsidiary (Domestic):

Henry Holt & Co. Publishing (3)
175 5th Ave, New York, NY 10010 (100%)
Tel.: (646) 307-5095
Web Site: http://www.henryholt.com
Rev.: $17,500,000
Emp.: 80
Publishing of Trade & Professional Books
N.A.I.C.S.: 513120
Dan Farley *(Pres)*

Macmillan Audio (3)
175 5th Ave, New York, NY 10010
Tel.: (646) 307-5041
Web Site: http://us.macmillan.com
Sales Range: $25-49.9 Million
Emp.: 30
Audio/Video Literature Recording
N.A.I.C.S.: 512110
Mary Beth *(Pres)*

Subsidiary (Domestic):

J.B. Metzler'sche Verlagsbuchhandlung und C. E. Poeschel Verlag GmbH (2)
Werastrasse 21 23, 70182, Stuttgart, Germany (100%)
Tel.: (49) 71121940
Web Site: http://www.metzlerverlag.de
Sales Range: $25-49.9 Million
Emp.: 15
Trade & Professional Books
N.A.I.C.S.: 513130
Olker Dadelstein *(Mng Dir)*

LR Medienverlag GmbH (3)
Strabe Der Jurgend 54, PSF 100279, Cottbus, 03002, Germany (55%)
Tel.: (49) 3554810
Web Site: http://www.ir-online.de
Sales Range: $100-124.9 Million
Book Publishing
N.A.I.C.S.: 513130
Andreas Heinkel *(Gen Mgr)*

Subsidiary (Non-US):

MacMillan Ltd. (2)
4 Crinan St, London, N1 9XW, United Kingdom (100%)
Tel.: (44) 2078433600
Web Site: http://www.macmillan.com
Sales Range: $125-149.9 Million
Publishing Company
N.A.I.C.S.: 513130
Stefan von Holtzbrinck *(Chm)*

Subsidiary (Non-US):

Editorial Macmillan de Venezuela S.A. (3)
Calle Chama Quinta Susana, Urb Colinas de Bello Monte, Caracas, 1050, Venezuela
Tel.: (58) 212 751 91 70
Book Publishers
N.A.I.C.S.: 513130
Emilio Martin *(Gen Mgr)*

MacMillan Botswana Publishing Co. (3)
Plot 131 Unit 9 Nkwe Square, PO Box 1155, Gaborone, Botswana (100%)
Tel.: (267) 3911770
Web Site: http://www.macmillan.co.za
Sales Range: $25-49.9 Million
Emp.: 12
Book Publishing
N.A.I.C.S.: 513130
Felicity Leburusianga *(CEO)*

Subsidiary (Domestic):

MacMillan Childrens Books Limited (3)
20 Newwharf Rd, London, N19RR, United Kingdom (100%)
Tel.: (44) 2070146000
Web Site: http://www.macmillan.co.uk
Sales Range: $50-74.9 Million
Emp.: 250
Publisher of Children's Books
N.A.I.C.S.: 513130
Allison Verost *(VP-Publicity)*

MacMillan Distribution Ltd. (3)
Brunel Rd, Houndmills, Basingstoke, RG21 6XS, United Kingdom (100%)
Tel.: (44) 256329242
Web Site: http://www.macmillandistribution.co.uk
Sales Range: $125-149.9 Million
Emp.: 400
Book Distributor
N.A.I.C.S.: 459210

Subsidiary (Non-US):

MacMillan Nigeria Publishers Ltd. (3)
4 Industrial Avenue Ilupeju Industrial Estate, PO Box 164, Yaba, Lagos, Nigeria (100%)
Tel.: (234) 17745892
Web Site: http://www.macmillan-africa.com
Publisher of Books, Textbooks Paperback Books
N.A.I.C.S.: 513130

MacMillan Publishers (China) Ltd. (3)
811 8th Floor Exchange Tower 33 Wang Chiu Road, Hungto Rd Kwun Tong, Kowloon, China (Hong Kong) (100%)
Tel.: (852) 28117122
Web Site: http://www.macmillaneducation.com
Sales Range: $25-49.9 Million
Emp.: 100
Publisher of Secondary Textbooks
N.A.I.C.S.: 513130

MacMillan Publishers Australia Pty. Ltd. (3)
Level 1 15-19 Clairemont St, Yarra, 3141, VIC, Australia (100%)
Tel.: (61) 398251000
Web Site: http://www.macmillan.com.au
Sales Range: $25-49.9 Million
Emp.: 100
Book Publishers
N.A.I.C.S.: 513130
Sue Knox *(Mgr-Sls-WA)*

Subsidiary (Domestic):

MacMillan Publishing Ltd. (3)
Macmillan Campus 4 Crinan Street, London, N1 9XW, United Kingdom (100%)
Tel.: (44) 2078334000
Web Site: http://www.macmillaneducation.com
Sales Range: $25-49.9 Million
Emp.: 100
Publisher of Educational Texts
N.A.I.C.S.: 513130

Subsidiary (Non-US):

Springer Science+Business Media Deutschland GmbH (4)
Heidelberger Platz 3, 14197, Berlin, Germany (100%)
Tel.: (49) 30 827 870
Web Site: http://www.springer.com
Scientific & Business Book & Journal Publisher
N.A.I.C.S.: 921140

Subsidiary (Domestic):

Springer-Verlag GmbH (5)
Tiergartenstrasse 17, 69121, Heidelberg, Germany
Tel.: (49) 6221 487 0
Web Site: http://www.springer.com
Scientific & Business Book & Journal Publisher
N.A.I.C.S.: 513130
Martin P. Mos *(Mng Dir)*

Subsidiary (Domestic):

Springer Fachmedien Munchen GmbH
Aschauer Strasse 30, 81549, Munich, Germany
Tel.: (49) 89 203043 2299
Web Site: http://www.springerfachmedien-muenchen.de
Business-to-Business, Transport & Logistics Book & Journal Publisher
N.A.I.C.S.: 513130
Peter Lehnert *(Mng Dir)*

Springer Fachmedien Wiesbaden GmbH (6)
Abraham-Lincoln-Strasse 46, 65189, Wiesbaden, Germany
Tel.: (49) 611 78 78 0
Web Site: http://www.springer.com
Business-to-Business, Technology & Transportation Book Publisher
N.A.I.C.S.: 513130

Subsidiary (US):

Springer Science+Business Media, LLC (6)
233 Spring St, New York, NY 10013
Tel.: (212) 460-1500
Web Site: http://www.springer.com
Scientific & Business Book & Journal Publisher
N.A.I.C.S.: 513130
Annette Triner *(Mgr-Journals Production)*

Subsidiary (Non-US):

MacMillan Swaziland National Publishing Co. (3)
Plot 230/231 1st Ave Matsapa Industrial Estate, Manzini, Eswatini (100%)
Tel.: (268) 5184533
Web Site: http://www.macmillan.co.za
Sales Range: $25-49.9 Million
Emp.: 25
Book Publishing
N.A.I.C.S.: 513130

MacMillan do Brasil (3)
Rua Jose Felix De Oliveira 383, Granja Viana, 06708 645, Cotia, SP, Brazil (100%)
Tel.: (55) 146132277
Web Site: http://www.macmillan.com.br
Book Publishing
N.A.I.C.S.: 513130

Macmillan Aidan Ltd (3)
Millenium Business Park-Warehouse No A9, PO Box 75773, Dar es Salaam, Tanzania
Tel.: (255) 22 240 1466
Book Publishers
N.A.I.C.S.: 513130
Leila Abdallah *(Gen Mgr)*

Macmillan Boleswa (Pty) Limited (3)
PO Box 7545, Maseru, 100, Lesotho
Tel.: (266) 22 317340
Book Publishers
N.A.I.C.S.: 513130

Macmillan Educacao Mozambique Limitada (3)
PO Box 2976, Maputo, Mozambique
Tel.: (258) 821 416220
Book Publishers
N.A.I.C.S.: 513130

Macmillan Education Australia Pty Limited (3)
Level 1 15 Claremont Street, South Yarra, 3141, VIC, Australia
Tel.: (61) 3 9394 3213
Book Publishers
N.A.I.C.S.: 513130

Macmillan Education Limited (3)
PO Box 840971, Jebel Amman, 11184, Amman, Jordan
Tel.: (962) 6 553 4166
Book Publishers
N.A.I.C.S.: 513130
Susan Winslow *(Mng Dir-Higher Education)*

Macmillan Education Nambia Publishers (Pty) Limited (3)
PO Box 22830, Windhoek, Namibia
Tel.: (264) 461 232165
Book Publishers
N.A.I.C.S.: 513130

Macmillan Heinemann ELT (3)
Zumrutevler Mali Hanimeli Cad 5 3, Maltepe, Istanbul, 34852, Türkiye (100%)
Tel.: (90) 2164410010
Web Site: http://www.macmillaneducation.com
Book Publishing
N.A.I.C.S.: 513130

Macmillan Iberia SA (3)
Edificio Eurocentro Calle del Capitan Haya 1 planta 14, 28020, Madrid, Spain
Tel.: (34) 915 24 94 20
Web Site: http://www.macmillan.es
Emp.: 300
Book Publishers
N.A.I.C.S.: 513130

Macmillan Information Consulting Services (Shanghai) Co., Ltd (3)
Unit 10-11 42F The Center 989 Changle Road, Xuhui District, Shanghai, 200031, China
Tel.: (86) 21 2422 5000
Book Publishers
N.A.I.C.S.: 513130

Macmillan Korea Publishers Ltd (3)
Suite 1832 Gwanghwamun Officia 163 Sinmunro 1-ga, Jongno-gu, Seoul, 100-999, Korea (South)
Tel.: (82) 2 723 8422 3
Web Site: http://www.macmillanenglish.com
Book Publishers
N.A.I.C.S.: 513130
Young Kwang *(Mgr-Sls & Mktg)*

Macmillan Language House Ltd. (3)
3rd Floor Chiyoda Building 2-37 Ichigaya-tamachi Shinjuku-ku, Shinjuku-ku, Tokyo, 162-0843, Japan

AND PRIVATE COMPANIES

Tel.: (81) 3 5227 3584
Web Site: http://www.mlh.co.jp
Book Publishers
N.A.I.C.S.: 513130
Haruo Ono (Mng Dir)

Macmillan Malawi Ltd (3)
Kenyatta Drive near BP Filling Station, Private Bag 140, Chitawira, Blantyre, Malawi
Tel.: (265) 1875773
Book Publishers
N.A.I.C.S.: 513130

Subsidiary (US):

Macmillan New Ventures, LLC (3)
33 Irving Pl 9th Fl, New York, NY 10003
Tel.: (510) 999-6283
Web Site:
 http://www.macmillannewventures.com
Software Development Services
N.A.I.C.S.: 541511
Troy Williams (Pres)

Subsidiary (Non-US):

Macmillan Polska SP Zoo (3)
Al Jerozolimskie 146A, 02-305, Warsaw, Poland
Tel.: (48) 22 32 11 900
Web Site: http://www.macmillan.pl
Book Publishers
N.A.I.C.S.: 513130
Tomasz Dukeat (Mgr-IT)

Macmillan Production (Asia) Limited (3)
Suite 811 8F Exchange Tower 33 Wang Chiu Road, Kowloon Bay, Hong Kong, China (Hong Kong)
Tel.: (852) 2811 8781
Web Site:
 http://www.macmillanproductionasia.com
Book Publishers
N.A.I.C.S.: 513130
Andrew Lam (Gen Mgr)

Macmillan Publishers (Zambia) Ltd (3)
Plot No 9212 Lumumba Road South End Opposite Duly Motors & Afe, Private Bag RX 348X, Lusaka, Zambia
Tel.: (260) 1 286 702
Book Publishers
N.A.I.C.S.: 513130

Macmillan Publishers Egypt Ltd (3)
3 Mohammed Tawfik Diab, Al Manteqah as Sadesah, Cairo, Egypt
Tel.: (20) 2 2272 1490
Book Publishers
N.A.I.C.S.: 513130

Macmillan Publishers India Limited (3)
3A 5th Floor DLF Corporate Park Phase 3 MG Road, Gurgaon, 122 002, India
Tel.: (91) 124 3079600
Web Site: http://www.macmillaneducation.in
Book Publishers
N.A.I.C.S.: 513130
Rajesh Pasari (Dir-Fin & Ops)

Macmillan Publishers New Zealand Limited (3)
6 Ride Way, Albany, 0745, New Zealand (100%)
Tel.: (64) 94140350
Web Site: http://www.macmillan.co.nz
Sales Range: $25-49.9 Million
Emp.: 30
Publisher of Textiary Textbooks, General Books, School Books
N.A.I.C.S.: 513130

Macmillan Publishers S.A de CV (3)
Insurgentes Sur 1886 Col Florida, 01030, Mexico, Mexico
Tel.: (52) 55 5482 2200
Web Site: http://www.macmillan.com.mx
Book Publishers
N.A.I.C.S.: 513130

Macmillan Publishers SA (3)
Av Blanco Encalada 104, Boulogne, B1609EEO, San Isidro, Buenos Aires, Argentina
Tel.: (54) 11 4708 8000
Web Site: http://www.macmillan.com.ar
Emp.: 100

Book Publishers
N.A.I.C.S.: 513130
Marita Messuti (Gen Mgr)

Macmillan Publishers SAS (3)
Calle 119 13-45 Officina 403, Bogota, Colombia
Tel.: (57) 2130200
Web Site: http://www.macmillan.com.co
Book Publishers
N.A.I.C.S.: 513130

Macmillan Taiwan Ltd (3)
11F-2 83 Yenpeing South Road, Taipei, Taiwan
Tel.: (886) 2 2388 3208
Web Site: http://www.macmillan.com.tw
Book Publishers
N.A.I.C.S.: 513130
Sandra Lu (Gen Mgr)

Subsidiary (Domestic):

Nature America, Inc. (3)
The Macmillan Building 4 Crinan Street, London, N1 9XW, United Kingdom (100%)
Tel.: (44) 2078334000
Web Site: http://www.nature.com
Book Publishing
N.A.I.C.S.: 513130
Alice Henchley (Head-Journals Press)

Pan MacMillan Ltd. (3)
20 Newwharf Rd, London, N19RR, United Kingdom (100%)
Tel.: (44) 2070146000
Web Site: http://www.panmacmillan.co.uk
Sales Range: $50-74.9 Million
Emp.: 150
Publisher of Hardback Books
N.A.I.C.S.: 513130
Antony Forbes Watson (Mng Dir)

Subsidiary (Non-US):

Pan Macmillan Australia Pty Ltd (4)
Level 25 1 Market Street, Sydney, 2000, NSW, Australia
Tel.: (61) 2 9285 9100
Web Site: http://www.panmacmillan.com.au
Book Publishers
N.A.I.C.S.: 513130

Pan Macmillan SA (Pty) Ltd (4)
2nd Floor Melrose Piazza 34 Whiteley Road, Melrose North, Johannesburg, 2076, South Africa
Tel.: (27) 11 731 3440
Web Site: http://www.panmacmillan.co.za
Book Publishers
N.A.I.C.S.: 513130
Laura Hammond (Mgr-Mktg)

Subsidiary (US):

St. Martins Press, Inc. (3)
175 5th Ave, New York, NY 10010-7703 (100%)
Tel.: (212) 674-5151
Web Site: http://www.macmillan.com
Book Publishers
N.A.I.C.S.: 513130
John Sargent (Pres & CEO)

Subsidiary (Domestic):

Manus Presse GmbH (2)
Rotebuhl st 87, 70178, Stuttgart, Germany (42%)
Tel.: (49) 71171863360
Web Site: http://www.manuspresse.de
Sales Range: $25-49.9 Million
Emp.: 70
TV & Broadcasting-Music & Art
N.A.I.C.S.: 516120

Mediengruppe Main-Post GmbH (2)
Berner Str 2, 97084, Wurzburg, Germany (100%)
Tel.: (49) 93160010
Web Site: http://www.mediengruppe-mainpost.de
Sales Range: $25-49.9 Million
Emp.: 100
Newspaper Publishing Services
N.A.I.C.S.: 513110

Subsidiary (Non-US):

Moran (EA) Publishers Ltd (2)
JUDDA Complex Prof Wangari Maathai Road, PO Box 30797-00100, Nairobi, Kenya
Tel.: (254) 20 2013580
Web Site: http://moranpublishers.com
Book Publishers
N.A.I.C.S.: 513130
David Muita (CEO)

Moran Publishers Uganda Ltd (2)
Plot 4010 Freedom City Mall Basement Entebbe Road, Nakasero, Kampala, Uganda
Tel.: (256) 41 4 236111
Web Site: http://www.moranpublisher.co.ug
Book Publishers
N.A.I.C.S.: 513130
Betty Mukasa (Gen Mgr)

Prognos AG (2)
Henric Petri-Strasse 9, CH-4010, Basel, Switzerland (100%)
Tel.: (41) 613273200
Web Site: http://www.prognos.com
Sales Range: $25-49.9 Million
Emp.: 30
Business & Science Publications
N.A.I.C.S.: 513140
Christian Bollhoff (Mng Partner & CEO)

Subsidiary (Non-US):

Prognos AG (3)
Goethe Strasse 85, 10623, Berlin, Germany (100%)
Tel.: (49) 30520059210
Web Site: http://www.prognos.com
Book Publishing
N.A.I.C.S.: 513130

Subsidiary (Domestic):

Rowohlt Verlag GmbH (2)
Hamburger Strasse 17, Reinbek, 21465, Hamburg, Germany (100%)
Tel.: (49) 4072720
Web Site: http://www.rowohlt.de
Sales Range: $50-74.9 Million
Emp.: 140
Trade & Professional Books
N.A.I.C.S.: 513130
Peter Kraus Vom Cleff (Mng Dir)

S Fischer Verlag GmbH (2)
Hedderichstrasse 114, 60596, Frankfurt am Main, Germany (100%)
Tel.: (49) 6960620
Web Site: http://www.fischerverlag.de
Sales Range: $50-74.9 Million
Trade & Professional Books
N.A.I.C.S.: 513130
Monika Schoeller (Editor)

Subsidiary (Domestic):

Scherz Verlag AG (3)
Hedderichstr 114, 60620, Frankfurt, Germany (100%)
Tel.: (49) 6960620
Web Site: http://www.fischerverlage.de
Book Publishers
N.A.I.C.S.: 513130

Wolfgang Krueger Verlag GmbH (3)
Hedderichstrasse 114, 60596, Frankfurt am Main, Germany (100%)
Tel.: (49) 6960620
Web Site: http://www.fischerverlage.de
Sales Range: $50-74.9 Million
Trade & Professional Books
N.A.I.C.S.: 513130
Monika Schoeller (Publr)

Subsidiary (US):

Sapling Learning, Inc. (2)
211 E 7th St 4th Fl, Austin, TX 78701
Tel.: (512) 323-6565
Web Site: http://www.saplinglearning.com
Software Development Services
N.A.I.C.S.: 541511
Alex von Rosenberg (VP-Sls & Mktg)

Scientific American, Inc. (2)
75 Varick St, New York, NY 10013 (100%)
Tel.: (212) 451-8200
Web Site: http://www.sciam.com
Sales Range: $50-74.9 Million
Emp.: 100
Magazine Publisher
N.A.I.C.S.: 513120
Christian Dorbrandt (Mng Dir-Consumer Mktg)

VERLAGSGRUPPE GEORG VON HOLTZBRINCK GMBH

Division (Domestic):

Scientific American Magazine (3)
One New York Plz Ste 4500, New York, NY 10004-1562 (100%)
Tel.: (212) 754-0550
Web Site: http://www.sciam.com
Sales Range: $25-49.9 Million
Emp.: 100
Magazine Publisher
N.A.I.C.S.: 513120

Subsidiary (Domestic):

Spectra-Lehrmittel-Verlag GmbH (2)
Booholder St 259, Essen, 45141, Germany (100%)
Tel.: (49) 201478480
Web Site: http://www.spectra-verlag.de
Sales Range: $25-49.9 Million
Emp.: 10
Educational Book Publishing
N.A.I.C.S.: 513130

Spotlight-Verlag GmbH (2)
Fraunhoferstrasse 22, 82152, Planegg, Germany (100%)
Tel.: (49) 89856810
Web Site: http://www.spotlight-verlag.de
Sales Range: $25-49.9 Million
Emp.: 80
Miscellaneous Publishing
N.A.I.C.S.: 513140
Wolfgang Stock (Mng Dir)

Urban & Fischer Verlag GmbH & Co. KG (2)
Hackerpruecke 6, 80335, Munich, Germany (100%)
Tel.: (49) 8953830
Web Site: http://www.elsevier.com
Sales Range: $25-49.9 Million
Emp.: 100
N.A.I.C.S.: 513130
Olas Lodprok (Mng Dir)

Subsidiary (Non-US):

Verlag E. DORNER GmbH (2)
Hainburger Strasse 33, 1030, Vienna, Austria (100%)
Tel.: (43) 153356360
Web Site: http://www.dorner-verlag.at
Book Publishing
N.A.I.C.S.: 513130

Subsidiary (Domestic):

Verlag Kiepenheuer & Witsch GmbH & Co. KG (2)
Bahnhofsvorplatz 1, Cologne, 50667, Germany (100%)
Tel.: (49) 221376850
Web Site: http://www.kiwi-koln.de
Sales Range: $25-49.9 Million
Emp.: 30
N.A.I.C.S.: 513130

Verlag Moritz Diesterweg GmbH & Co. (2)
Waldschmid 39, 60316, Frankfurt am Main, Germany (100%)
Tel.: (49) 69420810
Web Site: http://www.diesterweg.de
Sales Range: $25-49.9 Million
Emp.: 60
Book Publishing
N.A.I.C.S.: 513130

Verlag der Tagesspiegel GmbH (2)
Potsdamer Strasse 77 87, PO Box 10876, 10785, Berlin, Germany (100%)
Tel.: (49) 30260090
Web Site: http://www.tagesspiegel.de
Sales Range: $50-74.9 Million
Newspaper Publishing
N.A.I.C.S.: 513110
Lorenz Maroldt (Editor-in-Chief)

Verlagsgruppe Droemer Knaur GmbH (2)
Hiblestrasse 54, Munich, 80636, Germany (100%)
Tel.: (49) 8992710
Web Site: http://www.droemer-knaur.de
Sales Range: $50-74.9 Million
Trade & Professional Books
N.A.I.C.S.: 513130
Christina Korch (Mng Dir)

VERLAGSGRUPPE GEORG VON HOLTZBRINCK GMBH

Verlagsgruppe Georg von Holtzbrinck GmbH—(Continued)

Verlagsgruppe Handelsblatt GmbH (2)
Kasernenstrasse 67, 40213, Dusseldorf, Germany (100%)
Tel.: (49) 2118870
Web Site: http://www.vhb.com
Emp.: 1,000
Business & Science Publications
N.A.I.C.S.: 513140
Laurence Mehl (Mng Dir)

Subsidiary (Domestic):

Handelsblatt-Dow Jones GmbH (3)
Gruneburgweg 149, 60323, Frankfurt am Main, Germany
Tel.: (49) 69 172681
Business & Science Publications
N.A.I.C.S.: 513140

Subsidiary (Domestic):

Volksfreund-Druckerei Nikolaus Koch GmbH & Co. KG (2)
Nikolaus Koch Platz 1 3 Hannf Martin Schleyer St 8, 54294, Trier, Germany (100%)
Tel.: (49) 65171990
Web Site: http://www.volksfreund.de
Sales Range: $100-124.9 Million
Internet Shop
N.A.I.C.S.: 517810
Inga Scholz (Mng Dir)

Zeitverlag Gerd Bucerius GmbH (2)
Buceriusstrasse Eingang Speersort 1, 20095, Hamburg, Germany (100%)
Tel.: (49) 4032800
Web Site: http://www.zeit.de
Sales Range: $100-124.9 Million
Weekly Newspaper
N.A.I.C.S.: 513110
Rainer Esser (Mng Dir)

gutefrage.net GmbH (2)
Erika-Mann-Strasse 23, Munich, 80636, Germany
Tel.: (49) 89 515 146 100
Web Site: http://www.gutefrage.net
Emp.: 70
Internet Publishing Services
N.A.I.C.S.: 513199
Florian Geuppert (CEO)

tutoria GmbH (2)
Muhldorfstrasse 1, 81671, Munich, Germany
Tel.: (49) 89 1222 494 0
Web Site: http://www.tutoria.de
Educational Support Services
N.A.I.C.S.: 611691
Jennifer Sehnert (Sr Mgr-Acct & Sls)

Subsidiary (Non-US):

tutoria.at GmbH (3)
Am Heumarkt 7, 1030, Vienna, Austria
Tel.: (43) 1 2530 222 47
Web Site: http://www.tutoria.at
Educational Support Services
N.A.I.C.S.: 611691

VERLINVEST S.A.
Place Eugene Flagey 18, 1050, Brussels, Belgium
Tel.: (32) 26269870
Web Site: http://www.verlinvest.be
Year Founded: 1995
Investment Holding Company
N.A.I.C.S.: 551112
Frederic de Mevius (Founder, Chm & Mng Dir)

Subsidiaries:

Harris Interactive AG (1)
Beim Strohhause 31, 20097, Hamburg, Germany
Tel.: (49) 406696250
Web Site: http://www.harris-interactive.de
Marketing Research & Consulting Services
N.A.I.C.S.: 541910
Ali Mirza (Exec Dir)

Harris Interactive SAS (1)
39 rue Crozatier, 75012, Paris, France
Tel.: (33) 144876030
Web Site: http://www.harrisinteractive.fr
Sales Range: $25-49.9 Million
Marketing Research & Consulting Services
N.A.I.C.S.: 541910
Nathalie Perrio-combeaux (Mng Dir)

Harris Interactive UK Limited (1)
Harris Interactive Vantage W 6th Fl Great W Rd, Brentford, TW8 9AG, United Kingdom (100%)
Tel.: (44) 2082635200
Web Site: http://www.harrisinteractive.com
Sales Range: $25-49.9 Million
Surveys & Polls
N.A.I.C.S.: 541910
Lee Langford (Dir-Telecom, Media, Tech & Entertainment)

ToLuna plc (1)
8 Walpole Ct, Ealing Green, London, W1J 7TL, United Kingdom
Tel.: (44) 2030585000
Web Site: http://www.toluna-group.com
Sales Range: $50-74.9 Million
Emp.: 479
Market Research Technology & Services
N.A.I.C.S.: 541910
Frederic-Charles Petit (CEO)

Subsidiary (Non-US):

Toluna (Israel) Ltd (2)
Matam Ctr Bldg 1, POB 15075, 34495, Haifa, Israel
Tel.: (972) 48501584
Web Site: http://www.toluna.com
Sales Range: $25-49.9 Million
Emp.: 20
Market Research Technology & Services
N.A.I.C.S.: 541910

Toluna Australia Pty Ltd. (2)
Level 4 Suite 402 83 Kippax Street, Surrey Hills, Sydney, 2010, New South Wales, Australia
Tel.: (61) 286654902
Sales Range: $25-49.9 Million
Emp.: 7
Online Data Collection Services
N.A.I.C.S.: 518210
Neil Hayes (Dir-Australia & New Zealand)

Toluna Germany GmbH (2)
Wilhelm-Leuschner-Strasse 41, 60329, Frankfurt am Main, Germany
Tel.: (49) 69870019900
Web Site: http://www.toluna-group.com
Sales Range: $25-49.9 Million
Online Data Collection Services
N.A.I.C.S.: 541513
Thomas Rodenhaus (Mng Dir)

Toluna Nederland BV (2)
Damrak 37-I, 1012 LK, Amsterdam, Netherlands
Tel.: (31) 208466743
Web Site: http://www.toluna-group.com
Online Data Collection Services
N.A.I.C.S.: 518210
F C Petit (CEO)

Toluna SAS (2)
1 bis rue Collange, 92300, Levallois-Perret, Hauts-De-Seine, France
Tel.: (33) 140897100
Web Site: http://www.toluna-group.com
Sales Range: $25-49.9 Million
Online Data Collection Services
N.A.I.C.S.: 541513

Subsidiary (US):

Toluna USA Inc (2)
16200 Dallas Pkwy Ste 140, Dallas, TX 75248
Tel.: (972) 732-7323
Web Site: http://www.toluna.com
Online Data Collection Services
N.A.I.C.S.: 541513
Mark Simon (Mng Dir)

Subsidiary (Non-US):

MetrixLab BV (3)
Wilhelminakade 312, 3072 AR, Rotterdam, Netherlands
Tel.: (31) 102030700
Web Site: http://www.metrixlab.com
Emp.: 120
Online Consumer Research Services; Supplier of Digital & Cross Media Campaign Tracking, Advertising Pre-Testing & Website Usability Testing
N.A.I.C.S.: 541910
Thomas Marteijn (Dir-E-Business Performance Res Grp)

Valtech Limited (1)
46 Colebrooke Row, London, N1 8AF, United Kingdom
Tel.: (44) 20 7014 0800
Web Site: http://www.valtech.com
Digital Agency
N.A.I.C.S.: 541511
Sebastian Lombardo (Chm & CEO)

Subsidiary (Non-US):

Valtech A/S (2)
Kanonbadsvej 2, 1437, Copenhagen, Denmark
Tel.: (45) 32 88 20 00
Web Site: http://www.valtech.dk
Software Development, Outsourcing & Organizational Transformation Services; Digital Marketing
N.A.I.C.S.: 513210

Valtech AB (2)
Hantverkargatan 5, 112 21, Stockholm, Sweden
Tel.: (46) 8 56 22 33 00
Web Site: http://www.valtech.se
Software Development, Outsourcing & Organizational Transformation Services; Digital Marketing
N.A.I.C.S.: 513210

Valtech GmbH (2)
Bahnstrasse 16, 40212, Dusseldorf, Germany
Tel.: (49) 211 179237 0
Web Site: http://www.valtech.de
Software Development, Outsourcing & Organizational Transformation Services; Digital Marketing
N.A.I.C.S.: 513210

Valtech India Systems Private Ltd. (2)
Maas Unique 30/A 1st Main Road, Industrial Suburb 3rd Phase, JP Nagar, Bengaluru, 560078, India
Tel.: (91) 80 2607 9999
Web Site: http://www.valtech.co.in
Software Development, Outsourcing & Organizational Transformation Services; Digital Marketing
N.A.I.C.S.: 513210

Valtech Paris (2)
148 rue de Courcelles, 75017, Paris, France
Tel.: (33) 1 76 21 15 00
Web Site: http://www.valtech.com
Software Development, Outsourcing & Organizational Transformation Services; Digital Marketing
N.A.I.C.S.: 334610

Subsidiary (US):

Valtech Solutions, Inc. (2)
7200 Bishop Rd Ste 280, Dallas, TX 75024
Tel.: (469) 930-4554
Web Site: http://www.valtech.com
Computer System Design Services
N.A.I.C.S.: 541512

VERMEG GROUP N.V
Strawinskylaan 411 WTC Tower A 4th Floor, 1077 XX, Amsterdam, Netherlands
Tel.: (31) 858080016 NI
Web Site: http://www.vermeg.com
Year Founded: 1993
Emp.: 1,100
Financial Software Publisher
N.A.I.C.S.: 513210
Badreddine Ouali (Founder & Exec Chm)

Subsidiaries:

Vermeg Management Limited (1)
3rd Floor 17 Bevis Marks, London, EC3A 7LN, United Kingdom
Tel.: (44) 20 7593 6700

INTERNATIONAL PUBLIC

Web Site: http://www.vermeg.com
Trading, Valuation & Risk Management Solution Providers
N.A.I.C.S.: 523160
Paul Thomas (Gen Mgr)

Subsidiary (Domestic):

Vermeg Compliance Limited (2)
3rd Floor 17 Belvis Marks, London, EC3A 7LN, United Kingdom
Tel.: (44) 2070893700
Management Software Development Services
N.A.I.C.S.: 541511

Subsidiary (Non-US):

Vermeg International (Hong Kong) Limited (2)
Unit 901 9th Floor Harcourt House 39 Gloucester Road, Wanchai, China (Hong Kong)
Tel.: (852) 2689 9100
Web Site: http://www.vermeg.com
Application Software Development Services
N.A.I.C.S.: 541511

Subsidiary (US):

Vermeg International (USA) Inc. (2)
205 Lexington Avenue 14th Floor, New York, NY 10016
Tel.: (212) 682-4930
Web Site: http://www.vermeg.com
Software Development & Information Services
N.A.I.C.S.: 541511

Subsidiary (Non-US):

Vermeg International Singapore Pte. Limited (2)
112 Robinson Road #11-03, Singapore, 068902, Singapore
Tel.: (65) 6720 1012
Web Site: http://www.vermeg.com
Application Software Development Services
N.A.I.C.S.: 541511

VERMILION ENERGY INC.
3500 520 - 3rd Avenue SW, Calgary, T2P 0R3, AB, Canada
Tel.: (403) 269-4884 AB
Web Site:
https://www.vermilionenergy.com
VET—(NYSE)
Rev.: $2,671,651,261
Assets: $5,468,964,852
Liabilities: $2,808,385,200
Net Worth: $2,660,579,652
Earnings: $1,027,182,141
Emp.: 740
Fiscal Year-end: 12/31/22
Oil & Natural Gas Exploration & Production Services
N.A.I.C.S.: 211120
Lorenzo Donadeo (Chm)

Subsidiaries:

Aventura Energy, Inc. (1)
2800 400 4th Ave SW, Calgary, T2P 0J4, AB, Canada (100%)
Tel.: (403) 233-7443
Sales Range: $50-74.9 Million
Emp.: 5
Multinational Oil & Gas Exploration & Production Company
N.A.I.C.S.: 213112

Leucrotta Exploration Inc. (1)
639 5th Avenue Southwest Suite 700, Calgary, T2P 0M9, AB, Canada
Tel.: (403) 705-4525
Web Site: http://www.leucrotta.ca
Rev.: $18,144,985
Assets: $163,016,200
Liabilities: $19,573,428
Net Worth: $143,442,772
Earnings: ($86,719,649)
Emp.: 14
Fiscal Year-end: 12/31/2020
Oil & Natural Gas Exploration
N.A.I.C.S.: 211120
Nolan Chicoine (CFO & VP-Fin)

AND PRIVATE COMPANIES

Vermilion Energy Germany GmbH & Co. KG (1)
Baumschulenallee 16, 30625, Hannover, Germany
Tel.: (49) 5115441450
Web Site: https://en.vermilionenergy.de
Eletric Power Generation Services
N.A.I.C.S.: 221118
Sven Tummers *(Mng Dir)*

Vermilion Energy Hungary Kft. (1)
Oktober huszonharmadika utca 8-10, 1117, Budapest, Hungary
Tel.: (36) 18823570
Eletric Power Generation Services
N.A.I.C.S.: 221118
Gerard Schut *(VP)*

Vermilion Energy Netherlands BV (1)
Zuidwalweg 2, 8861 NV, Harlingen, Netherlands
Tel.: (31) 517493333
Web Site: https://en.vermilionenergy.nl
Eletric Power Generation Services
N.A.I.C.S.: 221118

Vermilion Exploration & Production Ireland Limited (1)
Embassy House Herbert Park Lane Ballsbridge, Dublin, 304 H6Y0, Ireland
Web Site: http://www.vermilionenergy.ie
Oil & Gas Exploration Services
N.A.I.C.S.: 213112
Darcy Kerwin *(Mng Dir-Ireland Bus Unit)*

Vermilion Oil & Gas Australia Pty Ltd. (1)
Level 5 30 The Esplanade, Perth, 6000, WA, Australia
Tel.: (61) 892150300
Eletric Power Generation Services
N.A.I.C.S.: 221118

Vermilion REP SAS (1)
(100%)
Tel.: (33) 558829500
Sales Range: $75-99.9 Million
Oil & Gas Distribution Services
N.A.I.C.S.: 211120

VERMODA S.P.A.
Vicolo Teatro Filarmonico 1, Verona, 37121, Italy
Tel.: (39) 0458063611
Web Site: http://www.dismero.it
Sales Range: $10-24.9 Million
Emp.: 25
Spotswear
N.A.I.C.S.: 315250
A. D'Auria *(Pres)*

VERMOGENSVERWALTUNG ERBEN DR. KARL GOLDSCHMIDT GMBH
Moltkestrasse 29, 45138, Essen, Germany
Tel.: (49) 201 43759 740
Web Site: http://www.vvgoldschmidt.de
Year Founded: 1936
Emp.: 920
Financial Holding Company
N.A.I.C.S.: 551112
Florian Von Gropper *(CEO)*

Subsidiaries:

Goldschmidt Thermit GmbH (1)
Hugo-Licht-Strasse 3, 04109, Leipzig, Germany
Tel.: (49) 341 355918 0
Web Site: http://www.goldschmidt-thermit.com
Products & Services for Railway Track Systems
N.A.I.C.S.: 488210
Hans-Juergen Mundinger *(CEO)*

Subsidiary (US):

Orgo-Thermit, Inc. (2)
3500 Colonial Dr N, Manchester Township, NJ 08759
Tel.: (732) 657-5781
Web Site: http://www.orgothermit.com

Sales Range: $1-9.9 Million
Emp.: 67
Rail Welding Equipment Mfr
N.A.I.C.S.: 333992
David M. Randolph *(Pres & CEO)*

PortaCo, Inc. (2)
1805 2nd Ave N, Moorhead, MN 56560
Tel.: (218) 236-0223
Web Site: http://www.portaco.com
Sales Range: $1-9.9 Million
Emp.: 20
Mfr of Hydraulic Tools & Other Equipment for Service & Maintenance of Rail Systems
N.A.I.C.S.: 333991
Craig Cook *(Sls Mgr-North America)*

Subsidiary (Non-US):

SRS Sjolanders AB (2)
Klovervagen 17, 283 50, Osby, Sweden
Tel.: (46) 479 175 00
Web Site: http://www.srsroadrail.se
Road-Rail Vehicles Distr
N.A.I.C.S.: 488210
Hakan Mattisson *(Mng Dir)*

VERNON BUILDING SOCIETY
19 St Petersgate, Stockport, SK1 1HF, United Kingdom
Tel.: (44) 161 4296262
Web Site: http://www.thevernon.co.uk
Year Founded: 1924
Rev.: $10,530,836
Assets: $405,868,062
Liabilities: $375,870,458
Net Worth: $29,997,604
Earnings: $590,220
Emp.: 56
Fiscal Year-end: 12/31/19
Mortgage Lending & Other Financial Services
N.A.I.C.S.: 522310

VERNON D'EON LOBSTER PLUGS LTD.
West Pubnico, PO Box 70, Yarmouth, B0W 2M0, NS, Canada
Tel.: (902) 762-2217
Web Site: http://www.vernondeon.com
Year Founded: 1975
Rev.: $13,041,743
Emp.: 60
Seafood Mfr
N.A.I.C.S.: 311710
Lloyd d'Eon *(Gen Mgr)*

VERNON KIA
6365 Highway 97, Vernon, V1B 3R4, BC, Canada
Tel.: (250) 545-7281
Web Site: http://www.vernonkia.ca
Year Founded: 1975
Sales Range: $10-24.9 Million
Emp.: 18
Car Dealer
N.A.I.C.S.: 441110

VEROD CAPITAL MANAGEMENT LIMITED
Heritage Place 6th Floor 21 Lugard Avenue, Ikoyi, Lagos, Nigeria
Tel.: (234) 14628646
Web Site: http://www.verod.com
Year Founded: 2008
Privater Equity Firm
N.A.I.C.S.: 523999
Danladi Verheijen *(Co-Founder & Mng Partner)*

VERONA PHARMA PLC
3 More London Riverside, London, SE1 2RE, United Kingdom
Tel.: (44) 2032834200   UK
Web Site: https://www.veronapharma.com
Year Founded: 2006
VRNA—(NASDAQ)
Assets: $308,124,000

Liabilities: $58,841,000
Net Worth: $249,283,000
Earnings: ($54,369,000)
Emp.: 79
Fiscal Year-end: 12/31/23
Biotechnology Research & Development Services
N.A.I.C.S.: 541715
Claire Poll *(Gen Counsel)*

VERONICA PRODUCTION LTD.
302 Pig Point Complex Dr Yagnik Road, Opp Swami Vivekanand Statue, Rajkot, 360 001, Gujarat, India
Tel.: (91) 281 2362500
Year Founded: 1990
Sales Range: Less than $1 Million
Investment Services
N.A.I.C.S.: 523999
Hitesh Kurjibhai Rupareliya *(CEO & Mng Dir)*

VEROPAM S.A.
16-18 rue Leon Jouhaux ZI Fosse a la Barbiere, 93600, Aulnay-sous-Bois, France
Tel.: (33) 1 55 81 27 27
Web Site: http://www.veropam.com
Sales Range: $25-49.9 Million
Household Goods Distr
N.A.I.C.S.: 423620
Rene Bensoussan *(Chm)*

Subsidiaries:

Verotrade SARL (1)
18 Rue Leon Jouhaux, 93600, Aulnay-sous-Bois, France
Tel.: (33) 1 55 81 27 27
Web Site: http://www.verotrade-groupe.com
Leather Goods Mfr
N.A.I.C.S.: 316990

Subsidiary (Domestic):

Lamarthe S.A. (2)
19 avenue de lOpera, 75001, Paris, France
Tel.: (33) 1 42 96 54 80
Web Site: http://www.lamarthe.com
Leather Band Mfr
N.A.I.C.S.: 316990

VEROTOOL TECHNIK GMBH
Robert Zapp Strasse 6-8, 40880, Ratingen, Germany
Tel.: (49) 2102700760
Web Site: http://www.verotool.de
Year Founded: 1980
Rev.: $10,207,560
Emp.: 21
Wear Parts Distr
N.A.I.C.S.: 423710
Kai Rosenbrock *(Mng Dir)*

VERSABANK
140 Fullarton Street Suite 2002, London, N6A 5P2, ON, Canada
Tel.: (519) 645-1919   Ca
Web Site: https://www.versabank.com
Year Founded: 2002
VBNK—(NASDAQ)
Rev.: $82,532,510
Assets: $3,577,187,991
Liabilities: $3,282,049,229
Net Worth: $295,138,762
Earnings: $29,386,491
Emp.: 199
Fiscal Year-end: 10/31/24
Commericial Banking
N.A.I.C.S.: 522110
R. Shawn Clarke *(CFO)*

Subsidiaries:

Arctic Financial Ltd. (1)
Ste 250 441 5th Ave SW, Calgary, T2P 2V1, AB, Canada   (100%)
Tel.: (867) 669-0091

VERSATILE CREATIVE BERHAD

Sales Range: $50-74.9 Million
Emp.: 3
Financial Services
N.A.I.C.S.: 523999

DRT Cyber Inc. (1)
1140 Connecticut Ave NW Ste 510, Washington, DC 20036
Tel.: (202) 410-6102
Web Site: https://drtcyber.com
Cyber Security Services
N.A.I.C.S.: 922190
David R. Taylor *(Pres)*

Versabanq Innovations Inc. (1)
Ste 1202 140 Fullarton St, London, N6A 5P2, ON, Canada
Tel.: (519) 488-1280
Sales Range: $25-49.9 Million
Emp.: 45
Financial Software Developer
N.A.I.C.S.: 513210
David R. Taylor *(CEO)*

VERSALINK HOLDINGS LIMITED
Lot 6119 Jalan Haji Salleh Batu 5 1/2 Off Jalan Meru, 41050, Klang, Selangor Darul Ehsan, Malaysia
Tel.: (60) 333926888
Web Site: https://www.versalink.com
Year Founded: 1991
40N—(SES)
Rev.: $8,211,580
Assets: $7,393,775
Liabilities: $2,859,817
Net Worth: $4,533,957
Earnings: ($1,540,270)
Emp.: 300
Fiscal Year-end: 02/29/24
Holding Company; Office Furniture
N.A.I.C.S.: 551112
Matthew Kian Siong Law *(CEO)*

VERSARIEN PLC
Units 1A-D Monmouth Road, Longhope Business Park, Gloucester, GL17 0QZ, Gloucestershire, United Kingdom
Tel.: (44) 1242269122   UK
Web Site: https://www.versarien.com
Year Founded: 2013
VRS—(AIM)
Rev.: $8,916,147
Assets: $34,274,284
Liabilities: $11,880,050
Net Worth: $22,394,234
Earnings: ($10,954,085)
Emp.: 93
Fiscal Year-end: 03/31/21
Holding Company; Semiconductor & Other Electronics Component Heat Transfer Material Developer & Mfr
N.A.I.C.S.: 551112
Neill Ricketts *(CEO)*

Subsidiaries:

Total Carbide Limited (1)
H3 Westcott Venture Park, Aylesbury, HP18 0XB, Buckinghamshire, United Kingdom
Tel.: (44) 1844275171
Tungsten Carbide Component Mfr
N.A.I.C.S.: 332999
Andy Hunt *(Dir-Sls)*

Versarien Technologies Limited (1)
2 Chosen View Road, Forest Vale Industial Estate, Cheltenham, GL51 9LT, Gloucestershire, United Kingdom
Tel.: (44) 1242269122
Web Site: http://www.versarien.com
Semiconductor & Other Electronics Component Heat Transfer Material Developer & Mfr
N.A.I.C.S.: 339999

VERSATILE CREATIVE BERHAD
No 808 Jalan 17/24, Ara Damansara, 46400, Petaling Jaya, Selangor Darul Ehsan, Malaysia

VERSATILE CREATIVE BERHAD

Versatile Creative Berhad—(Continued)
Tel.: (60) 380843751 MY
Web Site: https://www.vc-b.com
Year Founded: 2003
VERSATL—(KLS)
Rev.: $10,366,232
Assets: $20,116,866
Liabilities: $3,903,931
Net Worth: $16,212,935
Earnings: $1,319,679
Emp.: 200
Fiscal Year-end: 03/31/21
Paper & Boxboard Packaging Products Mfr
N.A.I.C.S.: 322130
Chee How Khat *(Exec Dir)*

Subsidiaries:

Fairpoint Plastic Industries Sdn. Bhd. (1)
5 Jalan Teras 4 Taman Industri Selesa Jaya, 43300, Balakong, 43300, Selangor Darul Ehsan, Malaysia
Tel.: (60) 3 8961 3013
Web Site: http://www.vc-b.com
Sales Range: $25-49.9 Million
Emp.: 100
Injection Molded Plastic Products Mfr
N.A.I.C.S.: 326199
Mark Teo *(Mng Dir)*

Imagescan Creative Sdn. Bhd. (1)
Lot 30745 Jalan Pandan Indah, Pandan Indah Ampang, 55100, Kuala Lumpur, Selangor, Malaysia
Tel.: (60) 342921288
Web Site: http://www.imagescancreative.com
Sales Range: $25-49.9 Million
Emp.: 60
Color Separation Services
N.A.I.C.S.: 323120
Kennet Ngew *(Mng Dir)*

Versatile Creative Plastic Sdn Bhd (1)
Lot 3233 2-20, Jalan Perindustrian Mahkota Utama Taman Perindustrian Mahkota, 43700, Beranang, Selangor, Malaysia
Tel.: (60) 175523138
Printing & Packaging Solutions Services
N.A.I.C.S.: 561910

Versatile Paper Boxes Sdn. Bhd. (1)
Lot 30745 Jalan Pandan Indah, Pandan Indah, 55100, Kuala Lumpur, Federal Territory, Malaysia
Tel.: (60) 342921288
Web Site: https://www.vc-b.com
Sales Range: $50-74.9 Million
Paper & Cardboard Packaging Products Mfr
N.A.I.C.S.: 322212
Richard Kin Seng Chook *(Mgr-Mktg)*

VERSES AI INC.
205-810 Quayside Drive, New Westminster, V3M 6B9, BC, Canada
Tel.: (604) 283-9679 BC
Web Site: https://www.verses.ai
Year Founded: 2021
VRSSF—(OTCQX)
Rev.: $1,605,104
Assets: $8,640,747
Liabilities: $7,799,374
Net Worth: $841,373
Earnings: ($19,458,438)
Fiscal Year-end: 03/31/23
Software Development Services
N.A.I.C.S.: 541511
Dan Mapes *(Pres)*

VERSION 1 SOFTWARE LTD.
Millennium House Millennium Walkway, Dublin, D01 F5P8, Ireland
Tel.: (353) 1 8657800
Web Site: http://www.version1.com
Year Founded: 1996
Emp.: 1,000
IT Services
N.A.I.C.S.: 541511
Justin Keatinge *(Co-Founder)*

VERSOBANK AS
Hallivanamehe 4, 11317, Tallinn, Estonia
Tel.: (372) 6 802 500 EE
Web Site: http://www.versobank.com
Year Founded: 1999
Rev.: $9,498,221
Assets: $214,302,084
Liabilities: $194,241,250
Net Worth: $20,060,834
Earnings: $1,364,988
Fiscal Year-end: 12/31/16
Commercial Banking Services
N.A.I.C.S.: 522110
Mart Veskimaegi *(Member-Mgmt Bd)*

VERSPEETEN CARTAGE LTD.
274129 Wallace Line, Ingersoll, N5C 3J7, ON, Canada
Tel.: (519) 425-7881
Web Site: http://www.verspeeten.com
Year Founded: 1953
Rev.: $90,976,202
Emp.: 440
Automobile Mfr
N.A.I.C.S.: 336110
George Randall *(Mgr-Ops)*

VERSUS SYSTEMS INC.
1558 Hastings Street, Vancouver, V6G 3J4, BC, Canada
Tel.: (604) 639-4457 BC
Web Site: https://www.versussystems.com
Year Founded: 1988
VS—(NASDAQ)
Rev.: $4,172
Assets: $659,837
Liabilities: $359,415
Net Worth: $300,423
Earnings: ($617,116)
Fiscal Year-end: 12/31/15
Holding Company; Business-to-Business Software
N.A.I.C.S.: 551112
Matthew Pierce *(Founder & CEO)*

VERT COMPANHIA SECURITIZADORA S.A.
Rua Cardeal Arcoverde 2365 7A Andar Pinheiros, Sao Paulo, 05407-003, Brazil
Tel.: (55) 1133851800
Web Site: http://www.vert-capital.com
Emp.: 100
Financial Investment Services
N.A.I.C.S.: 523940
Fernanda Mello *(Partner)*

VERTEC LTD.
32-36 Ellis Street, Frankton, Hamilton, 3204, New Zealand
Tel.: (64) 7 847 0024
Web Site: http://www.vertec.co.nz
Year Founded: 1919
Sales Range: $25-49.9 Million
Emp.: 20
Plastic Bins Retailer
N.A.I.C.S.: 455219
Jason Whitley *(Mng Dir)*

VERTEC SCIENTIFIC SA (PTY) LTD.
8 Charmaine Avenue Presidents Ridge, Randburg, 2194, South Africa
Tel.: (27) 11 789 7177
Web Site: http://www.vertecsa.co.za
Year Founded: 2006
Sales Range: $25-49.9 Million
Emp.: 23
Medical Device Mfr
N.A.I.C.S.: 334510
Cindy McCabe *(Dir)*

VERTEX MINERALS LIMITED
Unit 38 460 Stirling Highway, Peppermint Grove, Perth, 6011, WA, Australia
Tel.: (61) 863837828 AU
Web Site: https://www.vertexminerals.com
Year Founded: 2021
VTX—(ASX)
Assets: $5,065,815
Liabilities: $201,686
Net Worth: $4,864,129
Earnings: ($632,405)
Fiscal Year-end: 06/30/23
Mineral Exploration Services
N.A.I.C.S.: 212390
Alex Neuling *(Sec)*

VERTEX RESOURCE GROUP LTD.
161 2055 Premier Way, Sherwood Park, T8H 0G2, AB, Canada
Tel.: (780) 464-3295 AB
Web Site: https://www.vertex.ca
Year Founded: 2014
VTX—(TSXV)
Rev.: $192,734,563
Assets: $184,829,967
Liabilities: $134,307,153
Net Worth: $50,522,814
Earnings: $1,856,085
Emp.: 1,050
Fiscal Year-end: 12/31/23
Environmental & Industrial Support Services
N.A.I.C.S.: 561499
Paul Blenkhorn *(VP-Consulting Svcs)*

Subsidiaries:

Cordy Oilfield Services Inc. (1)
5366 55 Street SE, Calgary, T2C 3G9, AB, Canada
Tel.: (403) 262-7667
Web Site: http://www.cordy.ca
Rev.: $14,531,633
Assets: $13,736,837
Liabilities: $15,039,333
Net Worth: ($1,302,496)
Earnings: $52,413
Emp.: 344
Fiscal Year-end: 12/31/2020
Oilfield & Construction Services
N.A.I.C.S.: 213112

Subsidiary (Domestic):

Battle River Oilfield Construction Ltd. (2)
1301 3rd St Ne, Manning, T0H 2M0, AB, Canada
Tel.: (780) 836-3498
Web Site: http://www.battleriveroilfield.com
Emp.: 15
Oil & Gas Pipeline Construction Services
N.A.I.C.S.: 237120
Keith Hutchison *(Mgr-Ops & PR)*

Cordy Environmental Inc. (2)
5366 55th St SE, Calgary, T2C 3G9, AB, Canada
Tel.: (403) 262-7667
Web Site: https://www.cordy.ca
Emp.: 30
Septic Sludge Disposal Services
N.A.I.C.S.: 562212

Coverall Pipeline Construction Ltd. (2)
1101 Main Avenue East, Box 769, Sundre, T0M 1X0, AB, Canada
Tel.: (403) 638-2666
Web Site: http://www.coverallpipeline.com
Oil & Gas Pipeline Construction Services
N.A.I.C.S.: 237120

Hartwell Oilfield Ltd. (2)
5366 55 Street SE Calgary, PO Box 479, Stettler, T2C 3G9, AB, Canada
Tel.: (403) 358-4278
Web Site: http://www.cordy.ca
Emp.: 25
Oil Drilling & Trucking Services
N.A.I.C.S.: 213111

Lamont Bit Services Ltd. (2)
6-1304 44 Avenue NE, Calgary, T2E 6L6, AB, Canada
Tel.: (403) 291-3711
Web Site: http://www.lamontbits.com
Drill Bit & Down Hole Tool Mfr & Distr
N.A.I.C.S.: 333132

New West Pipelines Ltd. (2)
14801-89 Street, Grande Prairie, T8X 0J2, AB, Canada
Tel.: (780) 513-2223
Web Site: http://www.newwestpipelines.com
Sales Range: $50-74.9 Million
Emp.: 200
Oil & Gas Pipeline Construction Services
N.A.I.C.S.: 237120

Nohels Group Inc. (2)
200 Industrial Road 1, PO Box 1227, Sparwood, V0B 2G0, BC, Canada
Tel.: (250) 425-2519
Web Site: http://www.nohels.com
Mining Equipment Distr
N.A.I.C.S.: 423810
Michael Sharp *(Gen Mgr)*

Subsidiary (Domestic):

Elkford Industries Ltd. (3)
200 Industrial Rd Unit 1, Sparwood, V0B 2G0, BC, Canada
Tel.: (250) 425-2519
Oil & Gas Pipeline Construction Services
N.A.I.C.S.: 237120

Fernie Contractors Ltd. (3)
200 Industrial Rd Unit 1, Sparwood, V0B 2G0, BC, Canada
Tel.: (250) 425-2519
Oil & Gas Pipeline Construction Services
N.A.I.C.S.: 237120

Hi-Hevi Rigging Ltd. (3)
200 Industrial Rd Unit 1, Sparwood, V0B 2G0, BC, Canada
Tel.: (250) 425-2519
Heavy Machinery Transportation Services
N.A.I.C.S.: 484220

Subsidiary (Domestic):

RB2 Energy Services Inc. (2)
5366 55 St SE, Calgary, T2C 3G9, AB, Canada
Tel.: (403) 203-2344
Oil & Gas Pipeline Construction Services
N.A.I.C.S.: 237120

Sphere Drilling Supplies Ltd. (2)
3112 - 80th Avenue S E, Calgary, T2C 1J3, AB, Canada
Tel.: (403) 720-9333
Web Site: http://www.sphere-drilling.com
Sales Range: $25-49.9 Million
Emp.: 30
Drilling Machines Mfr
N.A.I.C.S.: 333131

Tawow Resources Inc. (2)
115 239 Midpark Way SE, PO Box 415, Calgary, T2X 1M2, AB, Canada
Tel.: (403) 238-5190
Web Site: http://www.tawowresources.com
Seismic Line Clearing Services
N.A.I.C.S.: 541360
Mark Tatem *(VP-Ops)*

Vertex Logistics USA Inc. (1)

VERTEX SECURITIES LIMITED
403 Regent Chambers, Nariman Point, Mumbai, 400 021, India
Tel.: (91) 2266306090
Web Site: https://www.vertexbroking.com
531950—(BOM)
Rev.: $1,004,964
Assets: $5,883,244
Liabilities: $4,794,089
Net Worth: $1,089,155
Earnings: ($65,847)
Emp.: 68
Fiscal Year-end: 03/31/23
Securities Brokerage Services
N.A.I.C.S.: 523150
Pranali Kadam *(Officer-Nodal)*

VERTICAL EXPLORATION INC.

789 West Pender Street Suite 1240, Vancouver, V6C 1H2, BC, Canada
Tel.: (604) 683-3995
Web Site: https://www.vertxinc.com
Year Founded: 2006
CVVRF—(OTCIQ)
Assets: $4,147,996
Liabilities: $451,069
Net Worth: $3,696,927
Earnings: ($416,204)
Fiscal Year-end: 02/28/23
Metal Mining Services
N.A.I.C.S.: 212290
Peter P. Swistak *(Pres & CEO)*

VERTICAL INDUSTRIES LIMITED
Flat No 106 1st Floor Nirmal Towers Dwarakapuri Colony, Hyderabad, 500082, India
Tel.: (91) 40 64523706
Web Site:
http://www.verticalindustries.in
Year Founded: 1990
Rev.: $8,387
Assets: $87,945
Liabilities: $56,925
Net Worth: $31,019
Earnings: ($3,509)
Fiscal Year-end: 03/31/18
Stone Mining Services
N.A.I.C.S.: 212311
P. Janardhan Reddy *(Chm & Mng Dir)*

VERTICAL INTERNATIONAL HOLDINGS LIMITED
Unit 2212 22/F Global Gateway Tower 63 Wing Hong Street, Cheung Sha Wan Kowloon, Hong Kong, China (Hong Kong)
Tel.: (852) 36902560
Web Site:
http://www.verticaltech.com.cn
Year Founded: 2006
8375—(HKG)
Rev.: $11,012,303
Assets: $17,042,033
Liabilities: $4,148,978
Net Worth: $12,893,055
Earnings: ($2,364,615)
Emp.: 137
Fiscal Year-end: 12/31/22
Capacitor Mfr & Distr
N.A.I.C.S.: 334416
Henry Ho Yin Boon *(Chm, CEO & Compliance Officer)*

Subsidiaries:

Vertical International Holdings Limited - Dongguan Factory (1)
Room 201 building 1 76 Baiye Road, Liaobu, Dongguan, 523416, Guangdong, China
Tel.: (86) 76982879898
Electronic Equipment Whslr
N.A.I.C.S.: 423690

VERTICAL PEAK HOLDINGS INC
77 King Street West Suite 2905, PO Box 121, Toronto, M5K 1H1, ON, Canada
Web Site: http://www.highfusion.com
FUZN—(CNSX)
Rev.: $4,935,689
Assets: $9,973,431
Liabilities: $15,179,034
Net Worth: ($5,205,603)
Earnings: $7,601,465
Fiscal Year-end: 07/31/22
Marijuana-Infused Edible Products & Oil Extracts
N.A.I.C.S.: 311999
David Andrew Posner *(Co-Chm)*

VERTICALSCOPE HOLDINGS INC.
111 Peter St Suite 600, Toronto, M5V 2H1, ON, Canada
Tel.: (416) 341-8950
Web Site:
https://www.verticalscope.com
Year Founded: 1999
FORA—(TSX)
Rev.: $80,488,146
Assets: $177,555,834
Liabilities: $96,060,250
Net Worth: $81,495,584
Earnings: ($24,772,051)
Emp.: 245
Fiscal Year-end: 12/31/22
Holding Company
N.A.I.C.S.: 551112
Brandon Seibel *(CTO)*

Subsidiaries:

Second Media Inc. (1)
30800 Telegraph Rd Ste 1921, Bingham Farms, MI 48025
Tel.: (416) 341-8950
Web Site: https://www.secondmedia.com
Digital Marketing Services
N.A.I.C.S.: 541613

VERTICE TRESCIENTOS SESENTA GRADOS, S.A.
Agastia Street 80, Madrid, 28043, Spain
Tel.: (34) 91 794 06 00
Web Site: http://www.vertice360.com
VER—(MAD)
Sales Range: Less than $1 Million
Motion Picture Production Services
N.A.I.C.S.: 512110

VERTOZ ADVERTISING LIMITED
602 Avior Nirmal Galaxy Lbs Marg, Mulund West, Mumbai, 400080, India
Tel.: (91) 2261426030
Web Site: https://www.vertoz.com
Year Founded: 2012
VERTOZ—(NSE)
Rev.: $10,042,791
Assets: $15,610,155
Liabilities: $3,325,928
Net Worth: $12,284,228
Earnings: $1,323,278
Emp.: 127
Fiscal Year-end: 03/31/23
Advertising Agencies Services
N.A.I.C.S.: 541810
Ashish Shah *(Founder & CEO)*

Subsidiaries:

AdMozart Inc. (1)
1250 Broadway 36th Fl Ste 3600, New York, NY 10001
Tel.: (646) 893-0583
Web Site: https://www.admozart.com
Advertising Services
N.A.I.C.S.: 541810

AdZurite Inc. (1)
1250 Broadway Ste 3600, New York, NY 10001
Tel.: (646) 808-0439
Advertising Services
N.A.I.C.S.: 541810

AdZurite Solutions Private Limited (1)
602 Avior Nirmal Galaxy LBS Marg Mulund West, Mumbai, 400080, India
Tel.: (91) 2261426050
Web Site: https://www.adzurite.com
Advertising Services
N.A.I.C.S.: 541810

Vertoz Ltd. (1)
Kimberley House 31 Burnt Oak Broadway, Edgware, London, HA8 5LD, United Kingdom
Tel.: (44) 2033184422
Advertising Services
N.A.I.C.S.: 541810

VERTU MOTORS PLC
Vertu House Fifth Avenue Business Park, Team Valley, Gateshead, NE11 0XA, Tyne & Wear, United Kingdom
Tel.: (44) 1914912121
Web Site:
https://www.vertumotors.com
Year Founded: 2006
VTU—(LSE)
Rev.: $4,835,513,430
Assets: $1,665,185,115
Liabilities: $1,253,992,905
Net Worth: $411,192,210
Earnings: $30,750,885
Fiscal Year-end: 02/28/23
Management Services
N.A.I.C.S.: 561110
Karen Anderson *(CFO)*

Subsidiaries:

Bristol Street Group Limited (1)
Vertu House Kingsway N Team Vly, Gateshead, NE11 0JH, Tyne & Wear, United Kingdom
Tel.: (44) 8452669900
Web Site: http://www.bristolstreet.co.uk
Used & New Motor Vehicle Sales
N.A.I.C.S.: 423110

Typocar Ltd (1)
Haughton Rd, Darlington, DL1 2BP, County Durham, United Kingdom
Tel.: (44) 1325354145
Sales Range: $250-299.9 Million
Emp.: 1,000
Used & New Motor Vehicle Sales
N.A.I.C.S.: 423110

Vertu Motors (VMC) Limited (1)
Virtue House 5th Ave Business Park, Gateshead, NE11 0XA, Tyne and Wear, United Kingdom
Tel.: (44) 1914912121
Sales Range: $150-199.9 Million
Emp.: 300
Motor Vehicle Retailers
N.A.I.C.S.: 423110
Robert Forrester *(CEO)*

Wiper Blades Limited (1)
Units 5-8 Saxon Shore Business Park Castle Road Eurolink Industrial, Sittingbourne, Kent, United Kingdom
Tel.: (44) 3300128486
Web Site: https://www.wiperblades.co.uk
Automobile Parts Mfr
N.A.I.C.S.: 423120

VERTUA LTD.
Suite 301/44 Miller St, PO BOX 630, North Sydney, 2060, NSW, Australia
Tel.: (61) 86246135
Web Site: https://www.vertua.com.au
VER—(NSXA)
Rev.: $4,729,848
Assets: $11,609,124
Liabilities: $3,934,669
Net Worth: $7,674,455
Earnings: ($118,135)
Fiscal Year-end: 03/31/19
Financial Investment Services
N.A.I.C.S.: 523999
Christopher Bregenhoj *(Chm)*

VERUSA HOLDING A.S.
Eski Buyukdere Cad Ayazaga Yolu Iz Plaza Giz No 9 Kat 14 D 51-52, Maslak, 34398, Istanbul, Turkiye
Tel.: (90) 2122907490
Web Site: http://www.verusa.com.tr
VERUS—(IST)
Rev.: $11,058,690
Assets: $73,114,569
Liabilities: $13,293,559
Net Worth: $59,821,010
Earnings: $15,218,091
Emp.: 102
Fiscal Year-end: 12/31/22
Venture Capital
N.A.I.C.S.: 523999
Mustafa Unal *(Chm)*

Subsidiaries:

Aciselsan Acipayam Seluloz Sanayi Ve Ticaret A.S. (1)
Aciselsan Str No 25, Asagi District Acipayam, 20800, Denizli, Turkiye
Tel.: (90) 2585181122
Web Site: http://www.aciselsan.com.tr
Chemicals Mfr
N.A.I.C.S.: 325199

Aciselsan Acipayam Seluloz Sanayi ve Ticaret (1)
Aciselsan Caddesi No 1 Acipayam, Denizli, 30800, Turkiye (76.8%)
Tel.: (90) 258 518 11 22
Web Site: http://www.aciselsan.com.tr
Chemicals Mfr
N.A.I.C.S.: 325998

Aldem Celik Endustri San. Ve Tic. A.S. (1)
Esentepe Mah Milangaz Caddesi No 56, Kartal, Istanbul, Turkiye
Tel.: (90) 2163531556
Web Site: https://www.aldem.com.tr
Stainless Steel & Aluminium Product Mfr
N.A.I.C.S.: 332999
Ergin Akdik *(Chm)*

Ata Elektrik Enerjisi Toptan Satis A.S. (1)
Maslak Mahallesi Eski Buyukdere Caddesi No 9 iz Plaza Giz Kat 15 D 53, Sariyer, 34398, Istanbul, Turkiye
Tel.: (90) 2126309191
Web Site: https://www.ataelektrik.com.tr
Electric Power Distribution Services
N.A.I.C.S.: 221122

Epias Enerji Piyasalari Isletme A.S. (1)
Maslak Mahallesi Tasyoncasi Sokak No 1/F F2 Blok, Sariyer, 34485, Istanbul, Turkiye
Tel.: (90) 2122641570
Web Site: https://www.epias.com.tr
Electric Power Distribution Services
N.A.I.C.S.: 221122
Abdullah Tancan *(Chm)*

Golive Yazilim Hizmetleri A.S. (1)
Kozyatagi Mahallesi Sehit ilknur Keles Sokak No 8 Kat 8 Tema Plaza, Kozyatagi Kadikoy, Istanbul, Turkiye
Tel.: (90) 2163255111
Web Site: https://golive.com.tr
Software Development Services
N.A.I.C.S.: 541511

Mavi Hospital Saglik Hizmetleri A.S. (1)
Kethuda 374 Sk No 2, Akhisar, 45200, Manisa, Turkiye
Tel.: (90) 2364040404
Web Site: https://mavihospital.com
Hospital Services
N.A.I.C.S.: 622110

Pamel Yenilenebilir Elektrik Uretim A.S. (1)
Maslak Mah Saat Sk Spine Tower Sitesi No 5/93, Sariyer, Istanbul, Turkiye
Tel.: (90) 2122907470
Web Site: https://www.pamel.com.tr
Hydroelectric Power Generation Services
N.A.I.C.S.: 221111

Standard Boksit Isletmeleri A.S. (1)
Eski Buyukdere Caddesi Ayazaga Yolu iz Plaza Giz No 9/49 Kat 14, 34393, Maslak, Istanbul, Turkiye
Tel.: (90) 2122120090
Web Site: https://www.standardboksit.com.tr
Aluminium Ore Mfr
N.A.I.C.S.: 331524
Mustafa Unal *(Chm)*

VERUSATURK GIRISIM SERMAYESI YATIRIM ORTAKLIGI A.S.
Maslak Mah Saat Sk Spine Tower Sitesi No 5/94 Sariyer, Maslak Sariyer, 34398, Istanbul, Turkiye
Tel.: (90) 2122907491
Web Site:
https://www.verusaturk.com.tr
Year Founded: 2012

VERUSATURK GIRISIM SERMAYESI YATIRIM ORTAKLIGI A.S.

Verusaturk Girisim Sermayesi Yatirim Ortakligi A.S.—(Continued)

VERTU—(IST)
Sales Range: Less than $1 Million
Asset Management Services
N.A.I.C.S.: 531390
Mustafa Unal *(Chm)*

Subsidiaries:

Pamukova Elektrik Uretim A.S. **(1)**
Maslak Mah Saat Sk Spine Tower Sitesi No 5/93, Sariyer, Istanbul, Turkiye
Tel.: (90) 2122907490
Web Site:
  https://www.pamukovaelektrik.com.tr
Electricity Generation Services
N.A.I.C.S.: 221118

Subsidiary (Domestic):

Tortum Elektrik Uretim A.S. **(2)**
Eski Buyukdere Cad Ayazaga yolu Iz Plaza Giz Binasi No 9 Kat 14 D 51, Maslak, Istanbul, Turkiye
Tel.: (90) 2122907490
Web Site: http://www.tortumelektrik.com.tr
Hydroelectric Power Generation Services
N.A.I.C.S.: 221111

VERVE GROUP SE
St Christopher Street 168, Valletta, VLT 1467, Malta
Tel.: (356) 1703769571
Web Site: http://mgi.group
M8G—(OMX)
Rev.: $350,144,615
Assets: $1,127,410,965
Liabilities: $780,179,150
Net Worth: $347,231,815
Earnings: ($22,021,368)
Emp.: 767
Fiscal Year-end: 12/31/22
Privater Equity Firm
N.A.I.C.S.: 523940
Remco Westermann *(Chm & CEO)*

Subsidiaries:

Adspree media GmbH **(1)**
Behringstrasse 16 b, 22765, Hamburg, Germany
Tel.: (49) 404118850
Web Site: https://www.adspreemedia.com
Online Gambling Services
N.A.I.C.S.: 513210

Dataseat Ltd. **(1)**
1st Floor 33 Hyde Park Square, London, W22NW, United Kingdom
Tel.: (44) 8458385284
Web Site: https://dataseat.com
Software Development Services
N.A.I.C.S.: 541511

Freenet Digital GmbH **(1)**
Karl-Liebknecht-Strasse 32, 10178, Berlin, Germany
Tel.: (49) 3032500110
Web Site: http://www.freenetdigital.com
Telecommunication Servicesb
N.A.I.C.S.: 517810
Thomas Kothuis *(CEO)*

Just Digital GmbH **(1)**
Schlesische Strasse 27c, 10997, Berlin, Germany
Tel.: (49) 30340600666
Web Site: https://www.justdigital.studio
Online Gambling Services
N.A.I.C.S.: 513210

Smaato Pte. Ltd. **(1)**
16 Raffles Quay 32-03 Hong Leong Building, Singapore, 048581, Singapore
Tel.: (65) 63366815
Software Development Services
N.A.I.C.S.: 541511

gamigo AG **(1)**
Behringstrasse 16b, D-22765, Hamburg, Germany **(99.9%)**
Tel.: (49) 404118850
Web Site: http://corporate.gamigo.com
Rev.: $65,977,672
Assets: $139,521,118
Liabilities: $105,708,065
Net Worth: $33,813,053
Earnings: $2,143,412
Emp.: 377
Fiscal Year-end: 12/31/2019
Online Games Publisher & Developer
N.A.I.C.S.: 513210
Jens Knauber *(CEO)*

Subsidiary (US):

KingsIsle Entertainment, Inc. **(2)**
PO Box 82543, Austin, TX 78708
Tel.: (972) 265-1900
Web Site: http://www.kingsisle.com
Online Games Developer & Mfr
N.A.I.C.S.: 541519
Josef Hall *(VP & Dir-Creative)*

WildTangent, Inc. **(2)**
800 Bellevue Way NE Ste 500, Bellevue, WA 98004
Tel.: (425) 497-4500
Web Site: http://company.wildtangent.com
Video Game Software Developer
N.A.I.C.S.: 513210
Tom Grina *(CFO)*

gamigo US Inc. **(1)**
2700 La Frontera Blvd, Round Rock, TX 78681
Tel.: (650) 273-9618
Web Site: https://www.trionworlds.com
Online Gambling Services
N.A.I.C.S.: 513210

VERY GOOD TOUR CO., LTD.
11F Yeonho Bldg No 135 Seosomun-Ro, Jung-Gu, Seoul, 6645, Korea (South)
Tel.: (82) 221884137
Web Site:
  http://www.verygoodtour.com
Year Founded: 2007
094850—(KRS)
Rev.: $10,459,434
Assets: $84,402,830
Liabilities: $25,338,903
Net Worth: $59,063,927
Earnings: ($9,377,844)
Emp.: 243
Fiscal Year-end: 12/31/22
Bicycle Whslr
N.A.I.C.S.: 423910
Lee Jong-Woo *(Pres)*

VERZATEC, S.A.B. DE C.V.
Calzada del Valle 110 Ote 2nd Floor Col del Valle San Pedro, 66220, Garza Garcia, Nuevo Leon, Mexico
Tel.: (52) 81 8151 8300
Web Site: http://www.verzatec.com
Sales Range: $500-549.9 Million
Holding Company Production & Distribution of Building Material
N.A.I.C.S.: 551112
Fernando de Jesus Canales Clariond *(Chm & Pres)*

Subsidiaries:

Stabilit S.A. de C.V. **(1)**
Humberto Lobo No 9317, Complejo Industrial Mitras, Garza Garcia, 66000, NL, Mexico
Tel.: (52) 8181518300
Web Site: http://www.stabilit.com
Sales Range: $200-249.9 Million
Emp.: 520
Fiber Glass Construction Product Mfr
N.A.I.C.S.: 326199

Subsidiary (US):

Stabilit America, Inc. **(2)**
285 Industrial Dr, Moscow, TN 38057
Tel.: (901) 877-3010
Web Site: http://www.glasteel.com
Sales Range: $25-49.9 Million
Emp.: 100
Fiberglass Construction & Transportation Products Mfr
N.A.I.C.S.: 326199
Don Parrish *(Mgr-Tech Svcs)*

Division (Domestic):

Stabilit America, Inc.-Glasteel Div. **(3)**
285 Industrial Dr, Moscow, TN 38057-3452
Tel.: (901) 877-3010
Web Site: http://www.glasteel.com
Sales Range: $25-49.9 Million
Emp.: 100
Fiberglass Construction & Transportation Products Mfr
N.A.I.C.S.: 326199

Stabilit America, Inc.-Resolite Div. **(3)**
285 Industrial Ave, Moscow, TN 38057
Tel.: (724) 877-3010
Web Site: http://www.resolite.com
Sales Range: $25-49.9 Million
Emp.: 5
Fiberglass Construction Panel Mfr
N.A.I.C.S.: 326199
Joe Hepp *(Mgr-Eastern Area)*

VES S.A.
Str Mihai Viteazu Nr 102, 545400, Sighisoara, Mures, Romania
Tel.: (40) 365808884
Web Site: https://raport.ves.ro
VESY—(BUC)
Rev.: $4,938,455
Assets: $10,146,879
Liabilities: $15,428,819
Net Worth: ($5,281,940)
Earnings: ($1,852,534)
Emp.: 351
Fiscal Year-end: 12/31/20
Cookware Mfr
N.A.I.C.S.: 335220

VESCO FOODS PTY. LTD.
14 Neil Street, Osborne Park, 6017, WA, Australia
Tel.: (61) 892736100
Web Site:
  http://www.vescofoods.com.au
Year Founded: 1974
Food Products Distr
N.A.I.C.S.: 424490
Bernie Pummell *(CEO & Mng Dir)*

VESELIN MASLESA A.D. BANJA LUKA
Aleja Sv Save 16, 78000, Banja Luka, Bosnia & Herzegovina
Tel.: (387) 51 303 307
Web Site: http://www.maslesa-folklor.org
Year Founded: 1948
Emp.: 19
Training Cultural & Artistic Activities
N.A.I.C.S.: 611610
Predrag Donjak *(Chm-Mgmt Bd)*

VESON HOLDINGS LIMITED
Suite 5505 55/F Central Plaza 18 Harbour Road, Wanchai, China (Hong Kong)
Tel.: (852) 28057888
Web Site: http://www.scudcn.com
Year Founded: 1997
1399—(HKG)
Sales Range: $350-399.9 Million
Rechargeable Battery Packs Mfr & Sales
N.A.I.C.S.: 335910
Jin Fang *(Chm)*

Subsidiaries:

Scud Battery Co., Ltd. **(1)**
SCUD Industial Zone Mawei Economic and Technological Development Zone, Fuzhou, 350015, Fujian, China
Tel.: (86) 59187308850
Web Site:
  http://www.scud.gmc.globalmarket.com
Emp.: 1,000
Batteries Mfr & Sales
N.A.I.C.S.: 335910

INTERNATIONAL PUBLIC

VESPA CAPITAL LLP
Amadeus House, 27b Floral Street, London, WC2E 9DP, United Kingdom
Tel.: (44) 20 7812 7145
Web Site:
  http://www.vespacapital.com
Year Founded: 2007
Emp.: 9
Private Investment Firm
N.A.I.C.S.: 523999
Tom Chaloner *(Partner)*

Subsidiaries:

Vespa Capital France **(1)**
41 avenue George V, 75008, Paris, France
Tel.: (33) 179972430
Investment Management Service
N.A.I.C.S.: 523940

Vespa Capital SA **(1)**
12F rue Guillaume Kroll, 1882, Luxembourg, Luxembourg
Tel.: (352) 27125053
Investment Management Service
N.A.I.C.S.: 523940

VESPA INC.
8th Floor JM Building 15 Teheran-ro 83-gil, Gangnam-Gu, Seoul, Korea (South)
Tel.: (82) 269540889
Web Site: https://www.vespainc.com
Year Founded: 2013
299910—(KRS)
Rev.: $4,202,222
Assets: $1,129,946
Liabilities: $8,326,006
Net Worth: ($7,196,060)
Earnings: ($3,605,515)
Emp.: 352
Fiscal Year-end: 12/31/22
Software Development Services
N.A.I.C.S.: 541511
Jin Kim *(CEO)*

VESSEL CO., LTD.
281 Industrial-ro 155beon-gil, Kwonseon-gu, Suwon, Gyeonggi-do, Korea (South)
Tel.: (82) 316833953
Web Site: https://www.vessel21.com
Year Founded: 2004
177350—(KRS)
Rev.: $33,846,246
Assets: $64,916,415
Liabilities: $41,363,784
Net Worth: $23,552,630
Earnings: ($10,780,768)
Emp.: 105
Fiscal Year-end: 12/31/22
Flat Panel Display & Semiconductor Equipment Mfr
N.A.I.C.S.: 334419
Hyun-Ki Kwon *(CEO)*

Subsidiaries:

SKCS Co., Ltd. **(1)**
Sansu-ro 554beon-gil Chowol-eup, Gwangju, 12729, Gyeonggi-do, Korea (South)
Tel.: (82) 317618445
Web Site: https://www.skcs.co.kr
Film Mfr & Distr
N.A.I.C.S.: 325992
Kyungjin Cho *(CEO)*

Plant (Domestic):

SKCS Co., Ltd. - 2nd Factory **(2)**
29 Daepyeonggyo-gil Gwangdeok-myeon Dongnam-gu, Cheonan, 330-992, Chungcheongnam-do, Korea (South)
Tel.: (82) 415578445
Emp.: 30
Optical Film Product Mfr
N.A.I.C.S.: 333310

VESTAS WIND SYSTEMS A/S
Hedeager 42, 8200, Aarhus, N, Denmark

VESTAS WIND SYSTEMS A/S

Tel.: (45) 97300000   DK
Web Site: https://www.vestas.com
Year Founded: 1898
VWS—(CSE)
Rev.: $19,144,576,880
Assets: $24,211,066,880
Liabilities: $18,363,416,240
Net Worth: $5,847,650,640
Earnings: $216,170,240
Emp.: 29,427
Fiscal Year-end: 12/31/21
Holding Company; Wind Turbine Power Systems Components Mfr, Whslr, Installation, Maintenance & Repair Services
N.A.I.C.S.: 551112
Juan Araluce *(Chief Sls Officer-Sls)*

Subsidiaries:

Vestas Americas A/S   (1)
1417 NW Everett, Portland, OR 97209   **(100%)**
Tel.: (503) 327-2000
Web Site: https://www.vestas.com
Sales Range: $150-199.9 Million
Emp.: 430
Holding Company; Regional Managing Office; Wind Turbine Power Systems Whslr & Support Services
N.A.I.C.S.: 551112
David Hardy *(VP-Sls)*

Subsidiary (Domestic):

Vestas-American Wind Technology, Inc.   (2)
1417 NW Everett St, Portland, OR 97209   **(100%)**
Tel.: (503) 327-2000
Web Site: https://us.vestas.com
Rev.: $31,800,000
Emp.: 200
Wind Turbine Power Systems Whslr & Support Services
N.A.I.C.S.: 423830
Steen Moller *(CFO)*

Subsidiary (Non-US):

Vestas-Canadian Wind Technology Inc.   (2)
65 Queen Street West Suite 2000, Box 56, Toronto, M5H 2M5, ON, Canada   **(100%)**
Tel.: (614) 837-6114
Web Site: http://www.vestas.com
Wind Turbine Power Systems Whslr & Support Services
N.A.I.C.S.: 423830

Vestas Argentina S.A.   (1)
Tel.: (54) 1122064800
Wind Turbine Distr
N.A.I.C.S.: 423830

Vestas Asia Pacific A/S   (1)
The Metropolis Tower 1 05-02/03 9 North Buona Vista Drive, Singapore, 138588, Singapore   **(100%)**
Tel.: (65) 63036500
Holding Company; Regional Managing Office; Wind Turbine Power Systems Whslr & Support Services
N.A.I.C.S.: 551112

Subsidiary (Domestic):

Vestas Asia Pacific Wind Technology Pte. Ltd.   (2)
#26-03 PSA Building 460 Alexandra Roady, Singapore, 119963, Singapore   **(100%)**
Tel.: (65) 63036500
Sales Range: $25-49.9 Million
Emp.: 100
Wind Turbine Power Systems Whslr & Support Services
N.A.I.C.S.: 423830

Subsidiary (Non-US):

Vestas Korea Wind Technology Ltd.   (2)
5F KDB Life tower Dongia-dong 372 Hangang-daero, Yongsan-gu, Seoul, 04373, Korea (South)   **(100%)**
Tel.: (82) 220218290
Sales Range: $25-49.9 Million
Emp.: 4

Wind Turbine Power Systems Whslr & Support Services
N.A.I.C.S.: 423830

Vestas New Zealand Wind Technology Ltd.   (2)
23 Valor Drive, PO Box 4251, Palmerston North, 4414, New Zealand   **(100%)**
Tel.: (64) 63566841
Wind Turbine Power Systems Whslr & Support Services
N.A.I.C.S.: 423830
Anthony Winstar *(Mng Dir)*

Vestas Taiwan Ltd.   (2)
Taipei Nan Shan Plaza 6F-1 No 100 Songren Rd, Xinyi Dist, Taipei, 11073, Taiwan   **(100%)**
Tel.: (886) 227201898
Emp.: 12
Wind Turbine Power Systems Whslr & Support Services
N.A.I.C.S.: 423830
Danny Nelson *(COO)*

Vestas Wind Technology (Beijing) Co., Ltd.   (2)
22nd Floor Ping An International Financial Center 1-3 Xinyuan S Road, Chaoyang District, Beijing, 100027, China   **(100%)**
Tel.: (86) 1059232000
Wind Turbine Power Systems Whslr & Support Services
N.A.I.C.S.: 423830

Vestas Wind Technology Japan Co., Ltd.   (2)
8f Metro City Kamiyacho 5-1-5 Toranomon, Minato-ku, Tokyo, 105-0001, Japan   **(100%)**
Tel.: (81) 3 4588 8600
Web Site: http://www.vestas.com
Wind Turbine Power Systems Whslr & Support Services
N.A.I.C.S.: 423830

Vestas-Australian Wind Technology Pty. Ltd.   (2)
Level 4 312 Saint Kilda Road, Melbourne, 3004, VIC, Australia   **(100%)**
Tel.: (61) 386987300
Web Site: http://www.vestas.com
Sales Range: $25-49.9 Million
Emp.: 115
Wind Turbine Power Systems Whslr & Support Services
N.A.I.C.S.: 423830

Vestas Central Europe A/S   (1)
Otto-Hahn Strasse 2-4, 25813, Husum, Germany   **(100%)**
Tel.: (49) 48419710
Web Site: https://www.vestas.com
Sales Range: $300-349.9 Million
Emp.: 600
Holding Company; Regional Managing Office; Wind Turbine Power Systems Whslr & Support Services
N.A.I.C.S.: 551112

Subsidiary (Non-US):

Vestas Benelux B.V.   (2)
Delta 85, 6800 AE, Arnhem, Netherlands   **(100%)**
Tel.: (31) 264971500
Sales Range: $75-99.9 Million
Emp.: 180
Wind Turbine Power Systems Whslr & Support Services
N.A.I.C.S.: 423830

Subsidiary (Domestic):

Vestas Deutschland GmbH   (2)
Otto-Hahn Str 2-4, 25813, Husum, Germany   **(100%)**
Tel.: (49) 48419710
Sales Range: $250-299.9 Million
Wind Turbine Power Systems Whslr & Support Services
N.A.I.C.S.: 423830

Subsidiary (Domestic):

Vestas Services GmbH   (3)
Otto-Hahn-Strasse 2-4, 25813, Husum, Germany   **(100%)**
Tel.: (49) 48419710

Sales Range: $150-199.9 Million
Emp.: 800
Wind Turbine Power Systems Support Services
N.A.I.C.S.: 541990

Subsidiary (Non-US):

Vestas Osterreich GmbH   (2)
Vorgartenstrasse 206 B-C, A-1020, Vienna, Austria   **(100%)**
Tel.: (43) 17013800
Sales Range: $75-99.9 Million
Emp.: 114
Wind Turbine Power Systems Whslr & Support Services
N.A.I.C.S.: 423830

Vestas Manufacturing A/S   (1)
Hedeager 42, 8200, Arhus, Denmark   **(100%)**
Tel.: (45) 97300000
Holding Company; Wind Turbine Power Systems Components Mfr
N.A.I.C.S.: 551112

Subsidiary (Domestic):

Vestas Blades A/S   (2)
Smed Hansensvej 19, 6940, Lem, Denmark   **(100%)**
Tel.: (45) 97300000
Web Site: http://www.vestas.com
Wind Power Turbine Propeller Mfr
N.A.I.C.S.: 332999

Subsidiary (US):

Vestas Blades America, Inc.   (3)
11140 Eastman Dr, Windsor, CO 80550-3397   **(100%)**
Tel.: (970) 674-6100
Wind Power Turbine Propeller Mfr
N.A.I.C.S.: 332999

Subsidiary (Non-US):

Vestas Blades Deutschland GmbH   (3)
John-Schehr-Str 7, 01979, Lauchhammer, Germany   **(100%)**
Tel.: (49) 357446540
Web Site: https://www.vestas.com
Wind Power Turbine Propeller Mfr
N.A.I.C.S.: 332999

Vestas Blades Italia S.r.l.   (3)
Via Ludovico Ariosto 12, 74100, Taranto, Italy   **(100%)**
Tel.: (39) 0994606111
Wind Power Turbine Propeller Mfr
N.A.I.C.S.: 332999

Vestas Blades Spain S.L.U.   (3)
Avda de los Vientos num 2, 13250, Daimiel, Spain   **(100%)**
Tel.: (34) 926 2628 00
Wind Power Turbine Propeller Mfr
N.A.I.C.S.: 332999
Dieter Uberegger *(Gen Mgr)*

Subsidiary (Domestic):

Vestas Control Systems A/S   (2)
Frankrigsvej 15, 8450, Hammel, Denmark   **(100%)**
Tel.: (45) 9 730 0000
Web Site: http://www.vestas.com
Wind Power Turbine Control Systems Mfr
N.A.I.C.S.: 335314

Subsidiary (Non-US):

Vestas Control Systems Spain S.L.U.   (3)
Poligono Industrial Los Canos, 42110, Olvega, Spain   **(100%)**
Tel.: (34) 976192500
Web Site: https://www.vestas.com
Wind Power Turbine Control Systems Mfr
N.A.I.C.S.: 335314

Subsidiary (Domestic):

Vestas Nacelles A/S   (2)
Smed Sorensens Vej 5, 6950, Ringkobing, Denmark   **(100%)**
Tel.: (45) 97300000
Web Site: http://www.vestas.com
Wind Power Turbine Nacelle Mfr
N.A.I.C.S.: 332999

Subsidiary (US):

Vestas Nacelles America, Inc.   (3)
1500 E Crown Prince Blvd Bldg N, Brighton, CO 80603   **(100%)**
Tel.: (303) 655-5400
Wind Power Turbine Nacelle Mfr
N.A.I.C.S.: 332999

Subsidiary (US):

Vestas Towers America, Inc.   (2)
100 Towers Rd, Pueblo, CO 81004   **(100%)**
Tel.: (719) 288-2200
Web Site: http://www.vestas.com
Wind Turbine Towers Mfr
N.A.I.C.S.: 331210

Vestas Mediterranean A/S   (1)
Serrano Galvache Street 56 Madrono Building, 28033, Madrid, Spain   **(100%)**
Tel.: (34) 913628200
Sales Range: $75-99.9 Million
Emp.: 300
Holding Company; Regional Managing Office; Wind Turbine Power Systems Whslr & Support Services
N.A.I.C.S.: 551112
Marco Graziano *(Pres)*

Subsidiary (Non-US):

Vestas Chile Turbinas Eolica Limitade   (2)
Los Militares 4611 7th Floor, Las Condes, 7550653, Chile   **(100%)**
Tel.: (56) 28225900
Web Site: http://www.vestas.com
Sales Range: $25-49.9 Million
Wind Turbine Power Systems Whslr & Support Services
N.A.I.C.S.: 423830

Subsidiary (Domestic):

Vestas Eolica S.A.U.   (2)
Serrano Galvache 56, Madrid, 28033, Spain   **(100%)**
Tel.: (34) 915670051
Wind Turbine Power Systems Whslr & Support Services
N.A.I.C.S.: 423830
Nicolas Wolff *(Gen Mgr)*

Subsidiary (Non-US):

Vestas France SAS   (2)
770 Avenue Alfred Sauvy Batiment Latitude Parc de l'Aeroport, 34470, Perols, France   **(100%)**
Tel.: (33) 467202202
Wind Turbine Power Systems Whslr & Support Services
N.A.I.C.S.: 423830

Vestas Hellas Wind Technology S.A.   (2)
74-76 Vorioy Ipirou Str & Konitsis, GR 15125, Maroussi, Greece   **(100%)**
Tel.: (30) 2130164700
Wind Turbine Power Systems Whslr & Support Services
N.A.I.C.S.: 423830

Vestas Italia S.r.l.   (2)
Via Ludovico Ariosto 12, Zona Industriale, 74123, Taranto, Italy   **(100%)**
Tel.: (39) 0994606111
Sales Range: $50-74.9 Million
Emp.: 100
Wind Turbine Power Systems Whslr & Support Services
N.A.I.C.S.: 423830

Vestas MED (Cyprus) Ltd.   (2)
1 Iras Street 1st Floor, Nicosia, 1060, Cyprus   **(100%)**
Tel.: (357) 22763340
Wind Turbine Power Systems Whslr & Support Services
N.A.I.C.S.: 423830

Vestas Ruzgar Enerjisi Sistemleri Sanayi ve Ticaret Ltd. Sirketi   (2)
Degirmen Sok Nida Kule No 18 Kat 14 Kozyatagi Mah, 34742, Istanbul, Turkiye   **(100%)**
Tel.: (90) 2166653000
Web Site: https://www.tureb.com.tr

VESTAS WIND SYSTEMS A/S

Vestas Wind Systems A/S—(Continued)
Emp.: 50
Wind Turbine Power Systems Whslr & Support Services
N.A.I.C.S.: 423830
Olcayto Yigit *(Gen Mgr-Sls)*

Vestas do Brasil Ltda. (2)
Avenida das Nacoes Unidas 12901 Centro Empresarial Nacoes Unida, 12 901 -Torre Norte -20 Andar, 04578 000, Sao Paulo, Brazil (100%)
Tel.: (55) 11 2755 8000
Web Site: http://www.vestas.com
Emp.: 70
Wind Turbine Power Systems Whslr & Support Services
N.A.I.C.S.: 423830

Vestas Northern Europe A/S (1)
Hedeager 42, 8200, Arhus, Denmark (100%)
Tel.: (45) 9730 0000
Holding Company; Regional Managing Office; Wind Turbine Power Systems Whslr & Support Services
N.A.I.C.S.: 551112

Subsidiary (Non-US):

Vestas Northern Europe AB (2)
Grophusgatan 5, 21586, Malmo, Sweden (100%)
Tel.: (46) 40376700
Sales Range: $125-149.9 Million
Emp.: 150
Wind Turbine Power Systems Whslr & Support Services
N.A.I.C.S.: 423830

Vestas Norway AS (2)
Advocatfirma Da Ruselokkveien 26, Oslo, 0251, Norway (100%)
Tel.: (47) 40720812
Wind Turbine Power Systems Whslr & Support Services
N.A.I.C.S.: 423830

Vestas Poland Sp. z o.o. (2)
Al Niepodleglosci 44, 70-404, Szczecin, Poland (100%)
Tel.: (48) 913071002
Web Site: https://www.vestas.pl
Sales Range: $25-49.9 Million
Emp.: 200
Wind Turbine Power Systems Whslr & Support Services
N.A.I.C.S.: 423830

Vestas-Celtic Wind Technology Ltd. (2)
302 Bridgewater Place Birchwood Park, Warrington, WA3 6XG, United Kingdom (100%)
Tel.: (44) 1925857 100
Web Site: http://www.vestas.com
Sales Range: $25-49.9 Million
Wind Turbine Power Systems Whslr & Support Services
N.A.I.C.S.: 423830

Vestas Spare Parts & Repair A/S (1)
Alstervej 8, 8940, Randers, Denmark (100%)
Tel.: (45) 97 30 00 00
Web Site: http://www.vestas.com
Sales Range: $150-199.9 Million
Emp.: 800
Wind Turbine Repair & Maintenance Services & Parts Whslr
N.A.I.C.S.: 811310

Subsidiary (Non-US):

Vestas Spare Parts & Repair Spain, S.L. (2)
Calle Arroyo de Valdebebas 4, Madrid, 28050, Spain (100%)
Tel.: (34) 915 6700 51
Web Site: http://www.vestas.com
Sales Range: $75-99.9 Million
Emp.: 300
Wind Turbine Repair & Maintenance Services & Parts Whslr
N.A.I.C.S.: 811310

Vestas Technology (UK) Limited (1)
West Medina Mills Stag Lane, Newport, PO30 5TR, Isle of Wight, United Kingdom (100%)
Tel.: (44) 1983288000
Sales Range: $50-74.9 Million
Wind Turbine Power Systems Research & Development Services
N.A.I.C.S.: 541715

Vestas Technology R&D Chennai Pte. Ltd. (1)
Block A 8th Floor TECCI Park No 285 Rajiv Gandhi Salai, Sholinganallur 600-119, Chennai, India (100%)
Tel.: (91) 4466889000
Emp.: 1,000
Wind Turbine Power Systems Research & Development Services
N.A.I.C.S.: 541715

Vestas Technology R&D Singapore Pte. Ltd. (1)
20 Pasir Panjang Road Tower 20 West 14-25 Mapletree Business City, Singapore, 117439, Singapore (100%)
Tel.: (65) 6303 6500
Wind Turbine Power Systems Research & Development Services
N.A.I.C.S.: 541715

VESTASIA LIMITED
2010 Excellence Mansion 98 Fuhua 1st Road, Futian, Shenzhen, 518048, China
Tel.: (86) 755 6168 0933 HK
Sales Range: $1-9.9 Million
Investment Banking Services
N.A.I.C.S.: 523150
Tingting Wu *(Chm & Pres)*

VESTATE GROUP HOLDINGS LIMITED
Unit E 22nd Floor Tower A Billion Centre, 1 Wang Kwong Road Kowloon Bay, Kowloon, China (Hong Kong)
Tel.: (852) 31908000 Ky
Web Site: http://www.walkershop.com.hk
Year Founded: 1993
Rev.: $14,090,464
Assets: $67,559,374
Liabilities: $96,709,341
Net Worth: ($29,149,967)
Earnings: ($32,865,618)
Emp.: 261
Fiscal Year-end: 03/31/19
Investment Holding Company; Footwear Whslr
N.A.I.C.S.: 424340
Jiaying Cai *(Exec Dir)*

Subsidiaries:

Walker Shop Footwear Limited (1)
7/F Hopesea Industrial Centre 26 Lam Hing Street, Kowloon Bay, Kowloon, China (Hong Kong)
Tel.: (852) 31908000
Web Site: http://www.walkershop.com
Footwear Whslr
N.A.I.C.S.: 424340

VESTEL BEYAZ ESYA SANAYI VE TICARET AS
Levent 199 Buyukdere Cad No 199, Sisli, 34394, Istanbul, Turkiye
Tel.: (90) 2124562200
VESBE—(IST)
Rev.: $1,171,036,030
Assets: $837,577,764
Liabilities: $534,023,086
Net Worth: $303,554,678
Earnings: $95,470,180
Emp.: 7,821
Fiscal Year-end: 12/31/19
Air Conditioner Mfr
N.A.I.C.S.: 333415
Ergun Guler *(Chm)*

VESTEL ELEKTRONIK SANAYI VE TICARET A.S.
Levent 199 Buyukdere Cad No 199, Sisli, 34394, Istanbul, Turkiye
Tel.: (90) 2124562200
Web Site: https://vestelyatirimciiliskileri.com
Year Founded: 1983
Sales Range: $1-4.9 Billion
Emp.: 13,779
Television Mfr & Whslr
N.A.I.C.S.: 334310
Enis Turan Erdogan *(CEO)*

VESTFROST A/S
Falkavea 12, DK-6705, Esbjerg, Denmark
Tel.: (45) 79142222
Web Site: http://www.vestfrostsolution.com
Year Founded: 1963
Sales Range: $150-199.9 Million
Emp.: 400
Refrigerator Equipment Mfr
N.A.I.C.S.: 335220
Jens Damgaard *(COO)*

VESTIGO CAPITAL ADVISORS LLP
23 Berkeley Square, London, W1J 6HE, United Kingdom
Tel.: (44) 203 859 8047
Web Site: http://www.vestigocapital.com
Investment Services
N.A.I.C.S.: 523999

Subsidiaries:

ACCENTRO Real Estate AG (1)
KantstraSSe 44/45, 10625, Berlin, Germany (87.84%)
Tel.: (49) 308871810
Web Site: https://www.accentro.ag
Rev.: $176,168,226
Assets: $935,196,006
Liabilities: $685,726,530
Net Worth: $249,469,476
Earnings: ($15,705,126)
Emp.: 118
Fiscal Year-end: 12/31/2022
Real Estate Investment Services
N.A.I.C.S.: 531390
Axel Harloff *(Chm-Supervisory Bd)*

VESTNER AUFZUGE GMBH
Humboldstrasse 10, D-85609, Dornach, Germany
Tel.: (49) 89320880 De
Web Site: http://www.vestner.de
Year Founded: 1930
Elevators & Moving Stairway Construction Services
N.A.I.C.S.: 238190
Paul Vestner *(Mng Dir)*

Subsidiaries:

Vestner Fujitec Deutschland GmbH (1)
Wallenroter Str 7, 13435, Berlin, Germany
Tel.: (49) 302699480
Industrial Machinery & Equipment Whslr
N.A.I.C.S.: 423830

VESTUM AB
Kungsgatan 26, 111 35, Stockholm, Sweden
Tel.: (46) 812134432
Web Site: https://www.vestum.se
Year Founded: 1999
VESTUM—(OMX)
Rev.: $549,766,723
Assets: $792,992,833
Liabilities: $409,036,284
Net Worth: $383,956,549
Earnings: $9,842,613
Emp.: 1,787
Fiscal Year-end: 12/31/23
Clothing Distr
N.A.I.C.S.: 458110
Joseph Janus *(CEO & Officer-IR)*

VESUVIUS INDIA LIMITED

INTERNATIONAL PUBLIC

P-104 Taratala Road, Kolkata, 700 088, India
Tel.: (91) 3361090500
Web Site: https://vesuviusindia.in
Year Founded: 1991
VESUVIUS—(NSE)
Rev.: $163,712,008
Assets: $159,563,575
Liabilities: $39,931,659
Net Worth: $119,631,917
Earnings: $14,002,758
Emp.: 485
Fiscal Year-end: 12/31/22
Refractory Products Mfr
N.A.I.C.S.: 327120
Biswadip Gupta *(Chm)*

Subsidiaries:

Vesuvius India Limited - Mehsana Factory (1)
212/B G I D C Estate, Mehsana, 384 002, Gujarat, India
Tel.: (91) 2762252948
Refractory Products Mfr
N.A.I.C.S.: 327120

Vesuvius India Limited - Visakhapatnam Factory 1 (1)
Plot No 13 14 & 15 Block E IDA Autonagar, Visakhapatnam, 530 012, India
Tel.: (91) 8913011300
Refractory Products Mfr
N.A.I.C.S.: 327120
Purushottam Bedare *(Head-Cement Bus)*

Vesuvius India Limited - Visakhapatnam Factory 2 (1)
Survey No 90 & 98 Part Block G Industrial Park Autonagar, Fakirtakya Village, Visakhapatnam, 530 012, India
Tel.: (91) 8913983715
Refractory Products Mfr
N.A.I.C.S.: 327120

VESUVIUS PLC
165 Fleet Street, London, EC4A 2AE, United Kingdom
Tel.: (44) 2078220000 UK
Web Site: https://www.vesuvius.com
VSVS—(OTCIQ)
Rev.: $1,979,963,076
Assets: $2,783,190,228
Liabilities: $1,247,880,452
Net Worth: $1,535,309,776
Earnings: $62,183,576
Emp.: 10,354
Fiscal Year-end: 12/31/20
Holding Company; Advanced Refractories & Molten Metal Flow Engineering Services
N.A.I.C.S.: 551112
Mark Collis *(CFO)*

Subsidiaries:

Advent Process Engineering Inc. (1)
333 Prince Charles Drive, PO Box 220, Welland, L3B 5P4, ON, Canada
Tel.: (905) 732-4441
Steel Mfr & Distr
N.A.I.C.S.: 331513

Avemis SAS (1)
2 Hotel d entreprises ZI Grange Eglise or ZI Colombier, 69590, Saint-Symphorien-d'Ozon, France
Tel.: (33) 472818852
Steel Mfr & Distr
N.A.I.C.S.: 331513

CCPI Inc. (1)
838 Cherry St, Blanchester, OH 45107
Tel.: (937) 783-2476
Refractory Materials & Molten Metal Products Provider
N.A.I.C.S.: 331524

Foseco (Thailand) Limited (1)
22nd Floor Ocean Tower 1 170/69 Rachadapisek Road, Klongtoey, Bangkok, 10110, Thailand
Tel.: (66) 22613164
Chemical Material Mfr & Distr
N.A.I.C.S.: 325199

AND PRIVATE COMPANIES — VESUVIUS PLC

Foseco Espanola SA (1)
Igorreko Industrialdea E-7, 48140, Igorre, Bizkaia, Spain
Tel.: (34) 946315393
Steel Mfr & Distr
N.A.I.C.S.: 331513

Foseco Foundry (China) Limited (1)
806-807 Innov Tower Block A No 1801 Hongmei Road, Xuhui District, Shanghai, 200233, China
Tel.: (86) 2133678188
Steel Mfr & Distr
N.A.I.C.S.: 331513

Foseco Golden Gate Company Limited (1)
No 6 Kung Yeh 2nd Road, Ping Tung Industrial District, Ping-tung, 90049, Taiwan
Tel.: (886) 87228108
Metal Product Distr
N.A.I.C.S.: 423510

Foseco Industrial e Comercial Ltda. (1)
Via Raposo Tavares km 15, 05577-100, Sao Paulo, Brazil
Tel.: (55) 1137199788
Steel Mfr & Distr
N.A.I.C.S.: 331513

Foseco International Holding (Thailand) Limited (1)
22 nd Floor Ocean Tower 1 170/69 Rachadapisek Road, Klongtoey, Bangkok, 10110, Thailand
Tel.: (66) 2261316467
Steel Mfr & Distr
N.A.I.C.S.: 331513

Foseco International Limited (1)
Vesuvius Emirates FZE Warehouse No 1J-09/3 Hamriyah Free Zone, PO Box 49261, Sharjah, United Arab Emirates
Tel.: (971) 65262370
Steel Mfr & Distr
N.A.I.C.S.: 331513

Foseco Japan Ltd. (1)
Orix Kobe Sannomiya Bldg 6-1-10 Gokodori, Chuo-ku, Kobe, 651-0087, Japan
Tel.: (81) 782522231
Steel Mfr & Distr
N.A.I.C.S.: 331513

Foseco Korea Limited (1)
74 Jeongju-ro, Wonmi-gu, Bucheon, 14523, Gyeonggi, Korea (South)
Tel.: (82) 326753211
Steel Mfr & Distr
N.A.I.C.S.: 331513

Foseco Nederland BV (1)
Binnenhavenstraat 20, PO Box 8, Hengelo, 7550 AA, Netherlands
Tel.: (31) 742492100
Foundry Consumable Distr.
N.A.I.C.S.: 423830

Foseco Philippines Inc. (1)
Unit 401 4th Floor 8 Antonio Center, Prime Street Madrigal Business Park 2 Alabang, Muntinlupa, 1770, Philippines
Tel.: (63) 28347716
Steel Mfr & Distr
N.A.I.C.S.: 331513

Foseco Portugal Produtos Para Fundicao Lda. (1)
Apartado 5101, 4456-901, Perafita, Portugal
Tel.: (351) 1229999530
Steel Mfr & Distr
N.A.I.C.S.: 331513

Foseco Pty. Limited (1)
1/25 Manton Street, Morningside, Brisbane, 4170, QLD, Australia
Tel.: (61) 738992733
Steel Mfr & Distr
N.A.I.C.S.: 331513

Foseco SAS (1)
7 Mail Barthelemy Thimmonier, 77185, Lognes, France
Tel.: (33) 164735562
Steel Mfr & Distr
N.A.I.C.S.: 331513

Foseco Vietnam Limited (1)
R 717 1 7F Me Linh Point Tower No 2 Ngo Duc Ke, Ben Nghe Ward Dist 1, Ho Chi Minh City, Vietnam
Tel.: (84) 38237850
Steel Mfr & Distr
N.A.I.C.S.: 331513

Mastercodi Industrial Ltda. (1)
Rodovia Presidente Dutra Km 298 Polo Industrial Resende City, Rio de Janeiro, Brazil
Tel.: (55) 2421080200
Steel Mfr & Distr
N.A.I.C.S.: 331513

P.T. Foseco Indonesia (1)
Jalan Rawagelam 2/No 5 Kawasan Industri, Pulogadung, Jakarta Timur, 13930, Indonesia
Tel.: (62) 214605555
Steel Mfr & Distr
N.A.I.C.S.: 331513

Process Metrix, LLC (1)
6622 Owens Dr, Pleasanton, CA 94588
Tel.: (925) 460-0385
Web Site: http://www.processmetrix.com
Sales Range: $1-9.9 Million
Emp.: 15
Mfg Instrumentation For Reactor Controls
N.A.I.C.S.: 334519

SIDERMES Inc. (1)
175 Calixa-Lavallee, Vercheres, J0L 2R0, QC, Canada
Tel.: (450) 583-3917
Steel Mfr & Distr
N.A.I.C.S.: 331513

SIDERMES S.p.A. (1)
via Mantova 10, 20835, Muggio, Monza and Brianza, Italy
Tel.: (39) 03 927 1111
Web Site: https://www.sidermes.com
Steel Mfr & Distr
N.A.I.C.S.: 331513

SIR Feuerfestprodukte GmbH (1)
Siegener Strasse 152, 57223, Kreuztal, Germany
Tel.: (49) 27327970
Steel Mfr & Distr
N.A.I.C.S.: 331513

Universal Refractories Inc. (1)
915 Clyde St, Wampum, PA 16157
Tel.: (724) 535-4374
Web Site: http://www.unreco.com
Castable Refractories: Clay
N.A.I.C.S.: 327120
Walter Sylvester (Pres)

VSV Advanced Ceramics (Anshan) Co., Ltd. (1)
Xiao Tai Zi Village, Ning Yuan Town Qian Shan District, Anshan, Liaoning, China
Tel.: (86) 4128921408
Steel Mfr & Distr
N.A.I.C.S.: 331513

Vesuvius (V.E.A.R.) S.A. (1)
Urquiza 919 1st Floor Rosario, S2000ANC, Santa Fe, Argentina
Tel.: (54) 3414495008
Steel Mfr & Distr
N.A.I.C.S.: 331513

Vesuvius Advanced Ceramics (China) Co., Ltd. (1)
Xing Ming Street China-Singapore Suzhou Industrial Park, Suzhou, 215021, JiangSu, China
Tel.: (86) 51267412088
Steel Mfr & Distr
N.A.I.C.S.: 331513

Vesuvius Advanced Ceramics (Suzhou) Co. Ltd (1)
No 221 Xingming Street Suzhou Industrial Park, Suzhou, 215021, China
Tel.: (86) 512 6741 2088
Aluminium Carbon Ceramic Mfr
N.A.I.C.S.: 327120

Vesuvius Australia Pty. Ltd. (1)
40-46 Gloucester, Boulevarde, Port Kembla, 2505, NSW, Australia
Tel.: (61) 24 267 9000
Web Site: http://www.vesuviusaustralia.com.au
Steel Mfr & Distr
N.A.I.C.S.: 331513

Vesuvius Belgium N.V. (1)
Zandvoordestraat 366, 8400, Oostende, Belgium
Tel.: (32) 59508810
Steel Mfr & Distr
N.A.I.C.S.: 331513

Vesuvius CSD Sp z.o.o. (1)
Ul Jasnogorska 11, 31-358, Krakow, Poland
Tel.: (48) 122999601
Steel Mfr & Distr
N.A.I.C.S.: 331513

Vesuvius Canada, Inc. (1)
2111 Industrial Drive, Regina, S4P 3Y3, SK, Canada (100%)
Tel.: (306) 545-5677
Web Site: http://www.vesuvius.com
Sales Range: $25-49.9 Million
Emp.: 80
Non-Clay Refractories Mfr
N.A.I.C.S.: 327120

Vesuvius China Holdings Co. Limited (1)
Unit 01 82/F International Commerce Centre 1 Austin Road West, Kowloon, China (Hong Kong)
Tel.: (852) 36697888
Steel Mfr & Distr
N.A.I.C.S.: 331513

Vesuvius Colombia SAS (1)
Carrera 7 numero 71-21 Torre B piso 15 Oficin, 1531, Bogota, Colombia
Tel.: (57) 13251154
Steel Mfr & Distr
N.A.I.C.S.: 331513

Vesuvius Corporation SA (1)
Salita Delle Ginestre 10, 6900, Lugano, Switzerland
Tel.: (41) 91 972 45 71
Emp.: 10
Engineeering Services
N.A.I.C.S.: 541330
Ombretta Bardelli (Office Mgr)

Vesuvius Emirates FZE (1)
Warehouse IJ-09/3 Hamariyah Free Zone Phase 1, Sharjah, United Arab Emirates
Tel.: (971) 65262370
Steel Mfr & Distr
N.A.I.C.S.: 331513

Vesuvius Foundry Products (Suzhou) Co., Ltd. (1)
12 Wei Wen Road Suzhou Industrial Park, Suzhou, 215122, Jiangsu, China
Tel.: (86) 51262991113
Steel Mfr & Distr
N.A.I.C.S.: 331513

Vesuvius Foundry Technologies (Jiangsu) Co., Ltd. (1)
Changchun Road Changshu Economic and Technological Zone, Changshu, 215537, Jiangsu, China
Tel.: (86) 51282367313
Steel Mfr & Distr
N.A.I.C.S.: 331513

Vesuvius Gmbh (1)
Gelsenkirchener Strasse 10, 46325, Borken, Germany
Tel.: (49) 28 61 830
Web Site: http://www.vesuvius.de
Steel Products Mfr
N.A.I.C.S.: 331513

Vesuvius Group S.A./N.V. (1)
Rue De Douvrain 17, PO Box 1, 7011, Ghlin, Belgium (100%)
Tel.: (32) 6 540 0810
Web Site: http://www.vesuvius.com
Sales Range: $125-149.9 Million
Refractory Material Mfr
N.A.I.C.S.: 327120

Vesuvius Iberica Refractarios S.A. (1)
Calle Guinicio Parcelas R-56/57, Miranda de Ebro, Burgos, Spain
Tel.: (34) 947314595
Steel Mfr & Distr
N.A.I.C.S.: 331513

Vesuvius Istanbul Refrakter Sanayi ve Ticaret AS (1)
GOSB 1700 sk No 1704, 41420, Kocaeli, Turkiye
Tel.: (90) 2626770999
Steel Mfr & Distr
N.A.I.C.S.: 331513

Vesuvius Italia SPA (1)
Piazza Borgo Pila 40 Torre A - 10 Piano, 16129, Genoa, Italy
Tel.: (39) 01056021
Steel Mfr & Distr
N.A.I.C.S.: 331513

Vesuvius Japan Inc. (1)
Daini-Naruse Akihabara Bldg 3F 27-10 1-chome Taito, Taito-ku, Tokyo, 110-0016, Japan
Tel.: (81) 358177065
Steel Mfr & Distr
N.A.I.C.S.: 331513

Vesuvius LLC (1)
Myasishcheva str 1 office 502 Zhoukovsky, 140180, Moscow, Russia
Tel.: (7) 4956420967
Steel Mfr & Distr
N.A.I.C.S.: 331513

Vesuvius Malaysia Sdn. Bhd. (1)
Lot PT 11693 Jalan Pelabuhan Utara Kawasan Industri, Bandar Sultan Suleiman, 42000, Port Klang, Selangor, Malaysia
Tel.: (60) 331760508
Steel Mfr & Distr
N.A.I.C.S.: 331513

Vesuvius Mexico S.A. de C.V. (1)
Av Ruiz Cortines 140 Col Jardines de San Rafael, Guadalupe, 67119, Nuevo Leon, Mexico
Tel.: (52) 8183194500
Steel Mfr & Distr
N.A.I.C.S.: 331513

Vesuvius Mid-East Limited (1)
New Cairo Bldg N 56 Rd 15 app 103, Maadi, Cairo, Egypt
Tel.: (20) 23595502
Steel Mfr & Distr
N.A.I.C.S.: 331513

Vesuvius Moravia, s.r.l (1)
Konska 740, Trinec, 739 61, Frydek-Mistek, Czech Republic
Tel.: (420) 558307511
Steel Mfr & Distr
N.A.I.C.S.: 331513

Vesuvius Poland Spolka z.o.o (1)
Ul Tyniecka 12, 32-050, Skawina, Poland
Tel.: (48) 122775100
Steel Mfr & Distr
N.A.I.C.S.: 331513

Vesuvius Ras Al Khaimah FZ-LLC (1)
PO Box 86408, Ras al Khaimah, United Arab Emirates
Tel.: (971) 72067999
Steel Mfr & Distr
N.A.I.C.S.: 331513

Vesuvius Refractarios de Chile SA (1)
San Martin 870 Oficina 308 Torre B, Concepcion, Chile
Tel.: (56) 412178710
Steel Mfr & Distr
N.A.I.C.S.: 331513

Vesuvius Refratarios Ltda. (1)
Av Brazil 49 550 Campo Grande, 23065-480, Rio de Janeiro, Brazil
Tel.: (55) 2124140606
Steel Mfr & Distr
N.A.I.C.S.: 331513

Vesuvius Scandinavia AB (1)
Forradsgatan 4, 662 34, Amal, Sweden
Tel.: (46) 532607730
Steel Mfr & Distr
N.A.I.C.S.: 331513

Vesuvius South Africa (Pty) Ltd. (1)
Pebble Lane, PO Box X2, Olifantsfontein, 1665, South Africa
Tel.: (27) 112061800
Steel Mfr & Distr
N.A.I.C.S.: 331513

Vesuvius UK Limited (1)

VESUVIUS PLC

Vesuvius plc—(Continued)

1 Midland Way Central Park, Barlborough Links, Chesterfield, S43 4XA, Derbyshire, United Kingdom **(100%)**
Tel.: (44) 1246 571 700
Web Site: http://www.vesuvius.com
Emp.: 100
Refractory Material Mfr
N.A.I.C.S.: 327120

Vesuvius USA Corp. **(1)**
1404 Newton Dr, Champaign, IL 61822-1069 **(100%)**
Tel.: (217) 351-5000
Web Site: http://www.vesuvius.com
Rev.: $80,000,000
Emp.: 300
Specialty Ceramic Product & Industrial Process Equipment Mfr
N.A.I.C.S.: 327120

Subsidiary (Domestic):

Foseco Metallurgical Inc. **(2)**
20200 Sheldon Rd, Cleveland, OH 44142-1315
Tel.: (440) 826-4548
Sales Range: $100-124.9 Million
Metallurgical Chemicals Mfr & Supplier
N.A.I.C.S.: 325998

Vesuvius Zyarock Ceramics (Suzhou) Co., Ltd. **(1)**
58 Kua Chun Road Kuatang China-Singapore Suzhou Industrial Park, Suzhou, 215021, Jiangsu, China
Tel.: (86) 51262748972
Steel Mfr & Distr
N.A.I.C.S.: 331513

Yingkou Bayuquan Refractories Co., Ltd. **(1)**
Qing Long Shan Street Yingkou Industrial Park, Bayuquan, Yingkou, 115007, Liaoning, China
Tel.: (86) 4176233888
Steel Mfr & Distr
N.A.I.C.S.: 331513

VETEKS AD

Vardarska 50 str, 1400, Veles, North Macedonia
Tel.: (389) 43234455
Web Site: https://veteks.mk
Year Founded: 1973
VTKS—(MAC)
Rev.: $6,295,267
Assets: $5,822,018
Liabilities: $2,060,637
Net Worth: $3,761,381
Earnings: $143,579
Fiscal Year-end: 12/31/21
Cotton Thread Mfr
N.A.I.C.S.: 313110

VETERANPOOLEN AB

Verkstadsgatan 7, 43442, Kungsbacka, Sweden
Tel.: (46) 30070724
Web Site: https://www.veteranpoolen.se
Household & Staffing Services
N.A.I.C.S.: 814110
Mats Claesson (CEO)

VETERINARSKA STANICA A.D.

Gavrila Principa 1, 78250, Laktasi, Bosnia & Herzegovina
Tel.: (387) 51 832 031
Web Site:
http://www.veterinarskabn.com
VSLA—(BANJ)
Sales Range: Less than $1 Million
Emp.: 12
Veterinary Services
N.A.I.C.S.: 541940
Aleksandar Nalesnik (Chm-Mgmt Bd)

VETERINARSKA STANICA A.D.

Modran bb, 76330, Ugljevik, Bosnia & Herzegovina
Tel.: (387) 55 776 237
VSUG—(BANJ)
Sales Range: Less than $1 Million
Emp.: 7
Veterinary Services
N.A.I.C.S.: 541940
Dragan Jelusic (Chm-Mgmt Bd)

VETERINARSKA STANICA A.D., BANJA LUKA

Knjaza Milosa 23, 78000, Banja Luka, Bosnia & Herzegovina
Tel.: (387) 51303043 BA
Year Founded: 1948
VSBL—(BANJ)
Sales Range: Less than $1 Million
Emp.: 20
Veterinary Services
N.A.I.C.S.: 541940
Mladinko Lulic (Member-Mgmt Bd)

VETERINARSKA STANICA A.D., BIJELJINA

Racanska 56, 76300, Bijeljina, Bosnia & Herzegovina
Tel.: (387) 55209826 BA
Year Founded: 1947
VSBN—(BANJ)
Sales Range: Less than $1 Million
Emp.: 22
Veterinary Services
N.A.I.C.S.: 541940

VETERINARSKA STANICA A.D., DOBOJ

Krnjinskih Srpskih Brigada, 74101, Doboj, Bosnia & Herzegovina
Tel.: (387) 53242059 BA
Web Site:
http://www.veterinarskabn.com
Year Founded: 1947
VSDB—(BANJ)
Sales Range: Less than $1 Million
Emp.: 18
Veterinary Services
N.A.I.C.S.: 541940
Branko Stevanovic (Chm-Mgmt Bd)

VETERINARSKA STANICA A.D., KIKINDA

Svetozar Miletica no 24, Kikinda, Serbia
Tel.: (381) 23439582 RS
Web Site: https://vskikinda.rs
Year Founded: 1989
VTSK—(BEL)
Sales Range: $1-9.9 Million
Emp.: 18
Veterinary Medical Services
N.A.I.C.S.: 541940
Tomic Tomic (CEO)

VETERINARSKA STANICA A.D., NEVESINJE

Nemanjica bb, 88280, Nevesinje, Bosnia & Herzegovina
Tel.: (387) 59601190 BA
VSNE—(BANJ)
Sales Range: Less than $1 Million
Emp.: 5
Veterinary Services
N.A.I.C.S.: 541940

VETERINARSKA STANICA A.D., VLASENICA

Ustanicka 22, 75440, Vlasenica, Bosnia & Herzegovina
Tel.: (387) 56733209 BA
Year Founded: 2002
VSVL—(BANJ)
Sales Range: Less than $1 Million
Emp.: 6
Veterinary Services
N.A.I.C.S.: 541940

VETERINARSKA STANICA A.D., ZVORNIK

Brace Jugovica 41, 75400, Zvornik, Bosnia & Herzegovina
Tel.: (387) 56210400 BA
Year Founded: 1937
VSZV—(BANJ)
Sales Range: Less than $1 Million
Veterinary Services
N.A.I.C.S.: 541940
Rada Jokic (Chm-Mgmt Bd)

VETERINARSKA STANICA KOCELJEVA A.D.

Mice Stanojlovica 8, Koceljeva, Serbia
Tel.: (381) 64 2259 431
Year Founded: 1967
VSKC—(BEL)
Sales Range: Less than $1 Million
Veterinary Medical Services
N.A.I.C.S.: 541940
Vladimir Panic (Gen Mgr)

VETERINARSKA STANICA KRAGUJEVAC A.D.

19 oktobra 3, Kragujevac, Serbia
Tel.: (381) 34 335 640
Year Founded: 1974
Sales Range: Less than $1 Million
Veterinary Medical Services
N.A.I.C.S.: 541940

VETERINARSKA STANICA MIONICA A.D.

Ribnicka 5, Mionica, Serbia
Tel.: (381) 14 3421 146
Year Founded: 1989
Sales Range: Less than $1 Million
Veterinary Medical Services
N.A.I.C.S.: 541940
Slobodan Visic (Mgr)

VETERINARSKA STANICA SABAC A.D.

Vojvode Putnika 52, 15000, Sabac, Serbia
Tel.: (381) 648520770
Web Site: https://www.vssabac.rs
Year Founded: 1992
VSSA—(BEL)
Rev.: $2,340,445
Assets: $1,034,414
Liabilities: $118,793
Net Worth: $915,621
Earnings: $22,735
Fiscal Year-end: 12/31/23
Veterinary Medical Services
N.A.I.C.S.: 541940
Davor Sasic (Exec Dir)

VETERINARSKA STANICA TOPOLA A.D.

Bulevar Vozda Karadorda 181, Topola, Serbia
Tel.: (381) 34811210
Year Founded: 1993
VSTP—(BEL)
Sales Range: Less than $1 Million
Veterinary Medical Services
N.A.I.C.S.: 541940
Milenkovic Dragoljub (Exec Dir)

VETERINARSKA STANICA ZRENJANIN AD

Koce Kolarova 38, Zrenjanin, Serbia
Tel.: (381) 23 525 772
Web Site:
http://www.vetstanicazr.com
Year Founded: 1993
Sales Range: Less than $1 Million
Veterinary Medical Services
N.A.I.C.S.: 541940

VETERINARSKI CENTAR KRALJEVO A.D.

Zicki put 1, Kraljevo, 36 000, Serbia
Tel.: (381) 36 515 00 60
Web Site:
http://www.veterinarskicentar.co.rs
Year Founded: 1993
VTKV—(BEL)
Sales Range: Less than $1 Million
Emp.: 60
Veterinary Medical Services
N.A.I.C.S.: 541940
Ljiljana Belopavlovic (Exec Dir)

VETERINARY MEDICINE INSTITUTE ZEMUN INC., BELGRADE

Batajnicki drum br 4, PO Box 41, Zemun, 11 080, Belgrade, Serbia
Tel.: (381) 11 377 95 50
Web Site:
http://www.vetzavodzemun.com
Biological Research Services
N.A.I.C.S.: 325414
Dragan Djuric (Chm-Mgmt Bd)

VETO SWITCHGEARS & CABLES LIMITED

506 5th Floor Plot No B-9 Land Mark Building New Link Road, Andheri West, Mumbai, 400058, India
Tel.: (91) 1416667775 In
Web Site:
https://www.vetoswitchgears.com
Year Founded: 1967
VETO—(NSE)
Rev.: $24,941,275
Assets: $37,369,889
Liabilities: $10,847,214
Net Worth: $26,522,674
Earnings: $2,025,056
Emp.: 403
Fiscal Year-end: 03/31/21
Electrical Cable Mfr & Distr
N.A.I.C.S.: 332618
Narain Das Gurnani (CFO)

Subsidiaries:

Vankon Modular Private Limited **(1)**
4 5 Meghdoot Signature Waliv Phata Sativali Road, Behind IPOL Vasai-East, Mumbai, 401208, India
Tel.: (91) 9004688642
Web Site: https://www.vankonmodular.com
Electrical Product Mfr & Distr
N.A.I.C.S.: 335311

Veto Overseas Private F.Z.E. **(1)**
Ice-Ci-520B Ajman Free Zone, Ajman, United Arab Emirates
Tel.: (971) 551239577
Wire & Cable Distr
N.A.I.C.S.: 423610
Ashish Goklani (Mgr)

VETOQUINOL S.A.

34 rue du Chene Sainte Anne, Magny-Vernois, 70204, Lure, Cedex, France
Tel.: (33) 384625555
Web Site:
https://www.vetoquinol.com
VETO—(EUR)
Rev.: $584,248,813
Assets: $764,137,322
Liabilities: $182,273,982
Net Worth: $581,863,340
Earnings: $61,337,896
Emp.: 2,483
Fiscal Year-end: 12/31/23
Veterinary Pharmaceutical Mfr
N.A.I.C.S.: 325412
Etienne Frechin (Chm)

Subsidiaries:

Ascor Chimici s.r.l. **(1)**
Via Piana, 47032, Bertinoro, Italy
Tel.: (39) 053462411
Web Site: http://www.vetoquinol.it

Veterinary Pharmaceutical Mfr
N.A.I.C.S.: 325412
Roberto Dall'Ara *(Mng Dir)*

Bioniche Animal Health A/Asia Pty. Ltd. (1)
46 Seaton St, Armidale, 2350, NSW, Australia
Tel.: (61) 267720677
Web Site: http://www.bionicheanimalhealth.com
Sales Range: $25-49.9 Million
Emp.: 9
Veterinary Pharmaceutical Mfr
N.A.I.C.S.: 325412
Andrew Grant *(Country Mgr)*

Bioniche Animal Health USA, Inc. (1)
1551 Jennings Mill Rd Ste 3200A, Bogart, GA 30622 **(100%)**
Tel.: (706) 549-4503
Web Site: http://www.bionicheanimalhealth.com
Sales Range: $25-49.9 Million
Emp.: 20
Veterinary Pharmaceutical Mfr
N.A.I.C.S.: 325412
Heather Meadows *(Mgr)*

Semyung Vetoquinol (1)
45 Emunbite, Koyang, 10477, Korea (South)
Tel.: (82) 319678853
Web Site: http://www.vetoquinol.korea.com
Sales Range: $25-49.9 Million
Emp.: 12
Veterinary Pharmaceutical Mfr
N.A.I.C.S.: 325412
Kyung Woo Roh *(Country Mgr)*

Vetoquinol AG (1)
Freiburgstrasse 255, 3018, Bern, Switzerland
Tel.: (41) 318185656
Web Site: https://www.vetoquinol.ch
Sales Range: $25-49.9 Million
Emp.: 9
Veterinary Pharmaceutical Mfr
N.A.I.C.S.: 325412

Vetoquinol Australia Pty Ltd (1)
Unit 302 2 6-12 Boronia Road Da Vinci Business Park Airport, Brisbane, 4008, QLD, Australia
Tel.: (61) 1800032355
Web Site: http://www.vetoquinol.com.au
Pharmaceutical Product Whslr
N.A.I.C.S.: 424210

Vetoquinol B.V. (1)
Tel.: (31) 104980079
Web Site: http://www.vetoquinol.nl
Sales Range: $25-49.9 Million
Emp.: 5
Veterinary Pharmaceutical Mfr
N.A.I.C.S.: 325412

Vetoquinol Biowet Poland Sp. z.o.o. (1)
Kosynierow Gdynskich 13/14, 66-400, Gorzow Wielkopolski, Poland
Tel.: (48) 957285500
Web Site: https://www.vetoquinol.pl
Veterinary Drug Mfr & Distr
N.A.I.C.S.: 325412

Vetoquinol Biowet Sp.z o.o. (1)
Ul Kosynierow Gdynskich 13/14, 66-400, Gorzow Wielkopolski, Poland
Tel.: (48) 957285500
Web Site: http://www.vetoquinol.pl
Sales Range: $125-149.9 Million
Emp.: 312
Veterinary Pharmaceutical Mfr
N.A.I.C.S.: 325412
Cyryl Przybyl *(Mng Dir-Proxy)*

Vetoquinol E.V.S.A. (1)
Ctra Fuencarral 24 Edificio Europa I Portal 3 2 5, Alcobendas, 28108, Madrid, Spain
Tel.: (34) 914903792
Web Site: http://www.vetoquinol.es
Veterinary Pharmaceutical Mfr
N.A.I.C.S.: 325412

Vetoquinol Especialidades Veterinarias S.A. (1)
Ctra Fuencarral 24 Edificio Europa I Portal 3 2 5, Puerta 5, 28108, Alcobendas, Spain

Tel.: (34) 914903792
Web Site: http://www.vetoquinol.es
Veterinary Drug Mfr & Distr
N.A.I.C.S.: 325412

Vetoquinol GmbH (1)
Reichenbachstrasse 1, 85737, Ismaning, Germany
Tel.: (49) 8999979740
Web Site: https://www.vetoquinol.de
Sales Range: $25-49.9 Million
Emp.: 40
Veterinary Pharmaceutical Mfr
N.A.I.C.S.: 325412
Wolfgang Haag *(Mng Dir)*

Vetoquinol India Animal Health Private Ltd. (1)
5th and 6th Floor Hamilton Building B-Wing Hiranandani Business Park, Hiranandani Estate Ghodbunder Road, Thane, 400 607, Maharashtra, India
Tel.: (91) 2261322600
Web Site: https://www.vetoquinol.in
Pharmaceutical Product Whslr
N.A.I.C.S.: 424210
Gautam Chatterjee *(Mng Dir)*

Vetoquinol Italia S.R.L. (1)
Via Luigi Galvani 18, 47122, Forli, Italy
Tel.: (39) 0543462411
Web Site: https://www.vetoquinol.it
Emp.: 40
Veterinary Drug Mfr & Distr
N.A.I.C.S.: 325412

Vetoquinol N.V. (1)
Galileilaan 11/401, 2845, Niel, Belgium
Tel.: (32) 38774434
Web Site: https://www.vetoquinol.be
Sales Range: $25-49.9 Million
Emp.: 20
Veterinary Pharmaceutical Mfr
N.A.I.C.S.: 325412

Vetoquinol North America, Inc. (1)
2000 Chemin Georges, Lavaltrie, J5T 3S5, QC, Canada
Tel.: (450) 586-2252
Web Site: http://www.vetoquinol.ca
Sales Range: $25-49.9 Million
Emp.: 50
Veterinary Pharmaceutical Mfr
N.A.I.C.S.: 325412

Vetoquinol Osterreich GmbH (1)
Gusshausstrasse 14/5, 1040, Vienna, Austria
Tel.: (43) 14163910
Web Site: https://www.vetoquinol.at
Sales Range: $25-49.9 Million
Emp.: 10
Veterinary Pharmaceutical Mfr
N.A.I.C.S.: 325412

Vetoquinol Saude Animal Ltda (1)
Av Fausto Dallape 90, Terra Preta Mairipora, Sao Paulo, 07662-670, Brazil
Tel.: (55) 1135681111
Web Site: http://www.vetoquinol.com.br
Pharmaceutical Product Whslr
N.A.I.C.S.: 424210

Vetoquinol Scandinavia AB (1)
Tel.: (46) 4267603
Web Site: http://www.vetoquinol-scandinavia.com
Pharmaceutical Product Whslr
N.A.I.C.S.: 424210

Vetoquinol Trading (Shanghai) Co., Ltd. (1)
Room 1607 Building C Oriental International Building, 85 Loushanguan Road Changning District, Shanghai, 200336, China
Tel.: (86) 2152570660
Web Site: https://www.vetoquinol.cn
Pharmaceutical Product Whslr
N.A.I.C.S.: 424210

Vetoquinol UK Ltd. (1)
Steadings Barn Pury Hill Business Park Nr Alderton, Towcester, NN12 7LS, Northamptonshire, United Kingdom
Tel.: (44) 1280814500
Web Site: https://www.vetoquinol.co.uk
Sales Range: $25-49.9 Million
Emp.: 35
Veterinary Pharmaceutical Mfr
N.A.I.C.S.: 325412

Caitrina Oakes *(Mng Dir)*

Vetoquinol USA, Inc. (1)
4250 N Sylvania Ave, Fort Worth, TX 76137
Tel.: (817) 529-7500
Web Site: http://www.vetoquinolusa.com
Sales Range: $25-49.9 Million
Emp.: 40
Animal Health Product Mfr & Marketer
N.A.I.C.S.: 325412

Vetoquinol Unipessoal LDA. (1)
Rua Amilcar Cabral n 7 3 Piso Sala 5 Agualva, 2735-534, Agualva-Cacem, Portugal
Tel.: (351) 214340300
Web Site: https://www.vetoquinol.pt
Sales Range: $25-49.9 Million
Emp.: 11
Veterinary Pharmaceutical Mfr
N.A.I.C.S.: 325412

Vetoquinol de Mexico S.A de C.V (1)
Blvd Manuel Avila Camacho No 118 Piso 22 Desp 2202, Colonia Lomas de Chapultepec, 11000, Mexico, Mexico
Tel.: (52) 5552627540
Web Site: http://www.vetoquinolmx.com
Sales Range: $25-49.9 Million
Emp.: 21
Veterinary Pharmaceutical Mfr
N.A.I.C.S.: 325412

Vetoquinol s.r.o. (1)
Walterovo namesti 329/3, 158 00, Prague, 5, Czech Republic
Tel.: (420) 325513822
Web Site: https://www.vetoquinol.cz
Emp.: 20
Veterinary Pharmaceutical Mfr
N.A.I.C.S.: 325412
Christian Hartel *(Mng Dir)*

Vetoquinol-Zenoaq K.K. (1)
Saikon 1-13-26, Koriyama, 963-8862, Fukushima, Japan
Tel.: (81) 676860668
Pharmaceuticals Product Mfr
N.A.I.C.S.: 325412
Antonio Ferreira *(Country Mgr)*

VETROPACK HOLDING AG
Schuetzenmattstrasse 48, CH-8180, Bulach, Switzerland
Tel.: (41) 448633131
Web Site: https://www.vetropack.com
VETN—(SWX)
Rev.: $1,068,219,639
Assets: $1,502,020,449
Liabilities: $609,816,974
Net Worth: $892,203,474
Earnings: $75,231,757
Emp.: 3,602
Fiscal Year-end: 12/31/23
Glass Container Manufacturing
N.A.I.C.S.: 327213
David Zak *(CFO)*

Subsidiaries:

JSC Vetropack Gostomel (1)
2 Rekunova Sq, Kyiv region, Gostomel, 08290, Ukraine
Tel.: (380) 443924100
Web Site: http://www.vetropack.ua
Sales Range: $50-74.9 Million
Glass Packaging Mfr
N.A.I.C.S.: 327213

Muller + Krempel AG (1)
Schutzenmattstrasse 46, 8180, Bulach, Switzerland
Tel.: (41) 448633520
Web Site: https://www.mk-ag.ch
Sales Range: $10-24.9 Million
Glass & Plastic Container & Packaging Mfr
N.A.I.C.S.: 327213
Mark Isler *(Mgr)*

Vetro-Recycling AG (1)
Schutzenmattstrasse 48, CH 8180, Bulach, Switzerland
Tel.: (41) 448633636
Web Site: http://www.vetrorecycling.ch
Sales Range: $75-99.9 Million
Emp.: 120
Glass Recycling Services

N.A.I.C.S.: 423930

Vetroconsult AG (1)
Schutzenmattstrasse 48, CH 8180, Bulach, Switzerland
Tel.: (41) 448633232
Web Site: http://www.vetroconsult.ch
Sales Range: $25-49.9 Million
Emp.: 32
Consulting Services
N.A.I.C.S.: 541690

Vetropack AG (1)
Schutzenmattstrasse 48, 8180, Bulach, Switzerland
Tel.: (41) 448633434
Web Site: http://www.vetropack.ch
Sales Range: $75-99.9 Million
Emp.: 202
Glass Packaging Mfr
N.A.I.C.S.: 327213

Vetropack Austria GmbH (1)
Manker Strasse 49, 3380, Pochlarn, Austria
Tel.: (43) 27577541
Web Site: http://www.vetropack.at
Sales Range: $200-249.9 Million
Glass Packaging Mfr
N.A.I.C.S.: 327213

Vetropack Italia S.r.l. (1)
Via San Cristoforo 51, 20090, Trezzano sul Naviglio, MI, Italy
Tel.: (39) 02458771
Web Site: http://www.vetropack.it
Emp.: 301
Glass Packaging Mfr & Distr
N.A.I.C.S.: 327213

Vetropack Moravia Glass a.s. (1)
Havlickova 180/18, 697 01, Kyjov, Czech Republic
Tel.: (420) 518733111
Web Site: http://www.vetropack.cz
Sales Range: $100-124.9 Million
Glass Packaging Mfr
N.A.I.C.S.: 327213

Vetropack Nemsova s.r.o. (1)
Zeleznicna 207/9, 914 41, Nemsova, Slovakia
Tel.: (421) 326557111
Web Site: http://www.vetropack.sk
Sales Range: $50-74.9 Million
Emp.: 408
Glass Packaging Mfr
N.A.I.C.S.: 327213

Vetropack Straza d.d. (1)
Hum na Sutli 203, HR 49231, Hum na Sutli, 49231, Croatia
Tel.: (385) 49326326
Web Site: http://www.vetropack.hr
Sales Range: $100-124.9 Million
Glass Packaging Mfr
N.A.I.C.S.: 327213
Dragutin Spiljak *(Chm-Supervisory Bd)*

Vetroreal AG (1)
Schutzenmattstrasse 48, 8180, Bulach, ZH, Switzerland
Tel.: (41) 448633333
Web Site: http://www.vetroreal.ch
Real Estate Services
N.A.I.C.S.: 531390
Fabian Rittener *(Mng Dir)*

VETRYA S.P.A.
Via Dell Innovazione 1, 05018, Orvieto, Italy
Tel.: (39) 07634801
Web Site: http://www.vetrya.com
VTY—(ITA)
Sales Range: $50-74.9 Million
Media Advertising Services
N.A.I.C.S.: 541840
Luca Tomassini *(Co-Founder, Pres & CEO)*

VEXILLA VIET NAM GROUP JOINT STOCK COMPANY
G Floor The Manor 2 Building 91 Nguyen Huu Canh Ward 22, Binh Thanh District, Ho Chi Minh City, Vietnam
Tel.: (84) 835790106
Web Site: http://www.solavina.vn

Vexilla Viet Nam Group Joint Stock Company—(Continued)
Year Founded: 2005
SVN—(HNX)
Rev.: $3,306,259
Assets: $9,735,931
Liabilities: $498,520
Net Worth: $9,237,411
Earnings: $29,540
Emp.: 6
Fiscal Year-end: 12/31/23
Civil Construction Services
N.A.I.C.S.: 236210
Cuong Viet Pham *(Chm-Mgmt Bd)*

VEXT SCIENCE, INC.
Suite 2250 - 1055 West Georgia Street, Vancouver, V6E 4N7, BC, Canada
Tel.: (416) 283-0178
Web Site:
 https://www.vextscience.com
VEXT—(CNSX)
Rev.: $22,322,568
Assets: $38,780,494
Liabilities: $13,107,296
Net Worth: $25,673,198
Earnings: $2,793,324
Fiscal Year-end: 12/31/19
Cannabis Product Mfr
N.A.I.C.S.: 325412
Stephan Bankösz *(CFO)*
Subsidiaries:

Herbal Wellness Center, LLC (1)
4126 W Indian School Rd, Phoenix, AZ 85019
Tel.: (602) 635-3502
Wellness Centre Services
N.A.I.C.S.: 812199

Pure Touch Botanicals, LLC (1)
4152 N 39th Ave, Phoenix, AZ 85019
Tel.: (602) 288-7228
Web Site:
 http://www.puretouchbotanicals.com
Emp.: 140
Botanical Product Whslr
N.A.I.C.S.: 424210

Vapen, LLC (1)
4223 N 40th Ave, Phoenix, AZ 85019
Tel.: (602) 288-7228
Web Site: https://vapenbrands.com
Botanical Product Whslr
N.A.I.C.S.: 424210

VF ALTERNATIVE AD
St G S Rakovski No 193 entry A fl 1 apartment 2, 1000, Sofia, Bulgaria
Tel.: (359) 24486020
Web Site:
 https://www.vfalternative.com
VFAL—(BUL)
Sales Range: Less than $1 Million
Financial Investment Services
N.A.I.C.S.: 523940

VF CAPITAL GMBH
Hanauer Landstrasse 220, 60314, Frankfurt am Main, Germany
Tel.: (49) 69 4059 1303   De
Web Site: http://www.vfcapital.de
Private Equity Services
N.A.I.C.S.: 523999
Peter Vey *(Mng Dir)*

VFS THREAD DYEING LTD.
House 257 3rd Flr Rd-3 Baridhara DOHS, Dhaka, 1206, Bangladesh
Tel.: (880) 28419542
Web Site: https://www.vfsthread.com
VFSTDL—(CHT)
Rev.: $5,025,412
Assets: $23,741,102
Liabilities: $4,418,521
Net Worth: $19,322,581
Earnings: $674,504
Emp.: 168
Fiscal Year-end: 06/30/23
Sewing Thread Mfr
N.A.I.C.S.: 313110
Sarwat Khaled *(Chm)*

VGD
Belehradska 18, 140 00, Prague, Czech Republic
Tel.: (420) 241015111
Web Site: http://www.vgd.cz
Sales Range: $25-49.9 Million
Emp.: 150
Audit, Taxes, Accounting, Payroll & Business Consulting Services
N.A.I.C.S.: 541219
Josef Zizala *(Co-Founder & Mng Partner-Prague)*

VGI PARTNERS GLOBAL INVESTMENTS LIMITED
Level 47 Gateway 1 Macquarie Place, Sydney, 2000, NSW, Australia
Tel.: (61) 292909600   AU
Web Site:
 http://www.vgipartnersglobal.com
Year Founded: 2017
VG1—(ASX)
Rev.: $90,333,497
Assets: $573,964,401
Liabilities: $144,529,366
Net Worth: $429,435,035
Earnings: $42,832,672
Fiscal Year-end: 06/30/24
Open-End Investment Funds
N.A.I.C.S.: 525910
Robert M. P. Luciano *(Chm & Portfolio Mgr)*
Subsidiaries:

Regal Asian Investments Limited (1)
39 Phillip Street, Sydney, 2000, NSW, Australia
Tel.: (61) 292378923
Investment Management Service
N.A.I.C.S.: 522320

VGN DEVELOPERS PVT. LTD.
No 15 Wallace Garden 2nd Street, Nungambakkam, Chennai, 600 006, India
Tel.: (91) 4443439900
Web Site: http://www.vgn.in
Year Founded: 1942
Real Estate Services
N.A.I.C.S.: 531390
V. N. Devadoss *(Chm)*

VGP N.V.
Cerveny dvur Jenisovice 59, 468 33, Jablonec nad Nisou, Jenisovice, Czech Republic
Tel.: (420) 483346060   BE
Web Site: https://www.vgpparks.eu
VGP—(EUR)
Rev.: $125,534,827
Assets: $4,868,864,114
Liabilities: $2,424,425,434
Net Worth: $2,444,438,680
Earnings: $96,359,422
Emp.: 368
Fiscal Year-end: 12/31/23
Logistics Complexes & Semi-Industrial Parks Mfr, Construction & Leasing Services
N.A.I.C.S.: 236210
Dirk Stoop *(CFO)*
Subsidiaries:

VGP Denmark ApS (1)
Vesterballevej 5, Fredericia, Denmark
Tel.: (45) 31663668
Real Estate Development & Management Services
N.A.I.C.S.: 531390

VGP Estonia OU (1)
Vaike Karja 3 Sauna, Tallinn, 10140, Estonia
Tel.: (372) 6306460
Logistics Management Consulting Services
N.A.I.C.S.: 541614

VGP Industrialni Stavby s.r.o. (1)
Jenisovice 59, 468 33, Jablonec, Czech Republic
Tel.: (420) 483346060
Web Site: http://www.vgp.cz
Industrial Building Construction Services
N.A.I.C.S.: 236220

VGP Latvia S.I.A. (1)
Mukusalas 29, Riga, 1004, Latvia
Tel.: (371) 29136661
Web Site: http://www.vgpparks.eu
Logistics Management Consulting Services
N.A.I.C.S.: 541614
Andrejs Konstantins *(Mgr)*

VGP Latvija, SIA (1)
Krisjana Valdemara iela 21-18, Riga, Latvia
Tel.: (371) 26599412
Industrial Park Design & Construction Services
N.A.I.C.S.: 236210

VH GLOBAL SUSTAINABLE ENERGY OPPORTUNITIES PLC
6th Floor 125 London Wall, London, EC2Y 5AS, United Kingdom
Tel.: (44) 2071291141   UK
Web Site: https://www.vh-gseo.com
Year Founded: 2020
GSEO—(LSE)
Rev.: $41,598,081
Assets: $577,712,699
Liabilities: $619,793
Net Worth: $577,092,906
Earnings: $35,602,121
Emp.: 23
Fiscal Year-end: 12/31/22
Asset Management Services
N.A.I.C.S.: 523999
Subsidiaries:

Coleambally East Solar Farm Pty. Ltd. (1)
Neoen Australia Level 21 570 George St, Sydney, 2000, NSW, Australia
Tel.: (61) 1800966215
Web Site:
 https://coleamballysolarfarm.com.au
Emp.: 3
Solar Electric Power Services
N.A.I.C.S.: 221114

VHCL INDUSTRIES LIMITED
Survey No 285 Gala No II Main Khanvel Kherdi Road, Village Kherdi Silvassa Dadra, Silvassa, 396230, Dadra & Nagar Havel, India
Tel.: (91) 2267911073   In
Year Founded: 1991
Welding Equipment Distr
N.A.I.C.S.: 423830
Pankaj H. Valia *(Mng Dir)*

VHM LIMITED
Tel.: (61) 407421185   AU
Web Site: https://www.vhmltd.com.au
Year Founded: 2014
VHM—(ASX)
Exploration & Mining Services
N.A.I.C.S.: 213115
Michael Sheridan *(CFO)*

VHQ MEDIA HOLDINGS LTD.
Room A5 2F No 31 Lane 258 Ruiguang Road, Neihu District, Taipei, 114, Taiwan
Tel.: (886) 22 657 7886
Year Founded: 1987
4803—(TPE)
Rev.: $38,319,597
Assets: $131,592,496
Liabilities: $100,771,660
Net Worth: $30,820,836
Earnings: ($46,759,575)
Emp.: 600
Fiscal Year-end: 12/31/20
Video Production Services
N.A.I.C.S.: 512110
Kuo-Hua Liu *(Chm & CEO)*
Subsidiaries:

Vhq Digital Media Beijing Co Ltd. (1)
Room A402 4th Floor Block A Shang 8 Cultural Development Park No 2, Chenjialin jia Balizhuang Village Gaobeidian Township Chaoyang, Beijing, 100025, China
Tel.: (86) 1087215891
Television Content & Visual Mfr
N.A.I.C.S.: 334220

VI NA TA BA TRADING & INVESTMENT JOINT STOCK COMPANY
No 24 Alley 1 Lane 46 Pham Ngoc Thach Street Phuong Liet, Ward Dong Da District, Hanoi, Vietnam
Tel.: (84) 82528745
VTJ—(HNX)
Assets: $10,185,000
Liabilities: $894,400
Net Worth: $9,290,600
Earnings: $108,400
Fiscal Year-end: 12/31/22
Tobacco Product Mfr
N.A.I.C.S.: 312230
Le Chi Long *(Chm)*

VIA HOLDINGS INC.
2nd floor Waseda Matsuura Building 519 Waseda Tsurumakicho, Shinjuku-ku, Tokyo, 162-0041, Japan
Tel.: (81) 351556801
Web Site: https://www.via-hd.co.jp
Year Founded: 1948
7918—(TKS)
Rev.: $112,244,410
Assets: $48,338,930
Liabilities: $39,706,270
Net Worth: $8,632,660
Earnings: $1,427,760
Emp.: 618
Fiscal Year-end: 03/31/24
Restaurant Business Services
N.A.I.C.S.: 722511
Koichi Saeki *(Sr Mng Exec Officer)*

VIA RAIL CANADA INC.
3 Place Ville Marie Suite 500, Montreal, H3B 2C9, QC, Canada
Tel.: (514) 871-6000   Ca
Web Site: http://www.viarail.ca
Year Founded: 1977
Sales Range: $250-299.9 Million
Emp.: 2,899
Passenger Rail Services
N.A.I.C.S.: 485999
Yves Desjardins-Siciliano *(Pres & CEO)*

VIA TECHNOLOGIES, INC.
8F No 533 Zhongzheng Rd, Xindian Dist, Taipei, 231, Taiwan
Tel.: (886) 222185452   TW
Web Site: https://viatech.com
Year Founded: 1994
2388—(TAI)
Rev.: $413,325,698
Assets: $767,415,714
Liabilities: $286,592,651
Net Worth: $480,823,063
Earnings: $16,103,600
Emp.: 110
Fiscal Year-end: 12/31/23
System Logic Chip Sets & Associated Computer Peripherals Designer & Mfr
N.A.I.C.S.: 334413
Subsidiaries:

Amertek Limited (1)
Industrial Zone, St Hamatehet 26, 20101, Karmiel, Israel
Tel.: (972) 49980948

Web Site: http://www.amertek.co.il
Electronic Parts & Equipment Whslr
N.A.I.C.S.: 423690

Centaur Technology, Inc. (1)
9111 Jollyville Rd Ste 206, Austin, TX 78759-7470
Tel.: (512) 418-5700
Web Site: http://www.centtech.com
Research & Development in the Physical Engineering & Life Sciences
N.A.I.C.S.: 541715

Chander Electronics Corp. (1)
8th Floor 6-3 Pau chian Road, Hsin Tien, Taiwan
Tel.: (886) 289126200
Web Site: http://www.Chander.com.tw
Sales Range: $75-99.9 Million
Emp.: 102
Electronic Parts & Equipment Merchant Whslr
N.A.I.C.S.: 423690

First International Company, Inc. (1)
Room 703 7th Floor, Free Trade Ctr Kwun Tong, Kowloon, China (Hong Kong)
Tel.: (852) 23430295
Web Site: http://www.firstint.com.cn
Non-Durable Goods Whslr
N.A.I.C.S.: 424990

VIA Communication, Inc. (1)
666 Dundee Rd Ste 701, Northbrook, IL 60062-2734
Tel.: (847) 498-0080
Web Site: http://www.viacreative.com
Commercial Equipment Whslr
N.A.I.C.S.: 423440

VIA Labs, Inc. (1)
7F No 529-1 Zhongzheng Rd, Xindian Dist, New Taipei City, 231615, Taiwan
Tel.: (886) 222181838
Web Site: https://www.via-labs.com
Universal Serial Bus Distr
N.A.I.C.S.: 423690

VIA Networking Technologies, Inc. (1)
5th Floor 527 Chung Cheng Rd, Hsin Tien, Taiwan
Tel.: (886) 222182078
Web Site: http://www.via.com.tw
Electronic Components Mfr
N.A.I.C.S.: 334419

VIA Next Technologies (Shanghai) Co., Ltd. (1)
Building B 2537 Jinke Rd Zhangjiang Hi-Tech Park, Pudong New Area, Shanghai, China
Tel.: (86) 2138764688
Electronic Component Mfr & Distr
N.A.I.C.S.: 334419

VIA Optical Solution, Inc. (1)
10th Floor 527 Chung Cheng Rd, Hsin Tien, 231, Taiwan
Tel.: (886) 222185452
Web Site: http://www.via.com.tw
Electronic Parts & Equipment Whslr
N.A.I.C.S.: 423690

VIA Technologies (China) Ltd. (1)
VIA China Core Building Building 7 No 1 Zhongguancun East Road, Haidian Dist, Beijing, 100084, China
Tel.: (86) 4008185166
Web Site: https://www.viatech.com.cn
Marketing Research
N.A.I.C.S.: 541910

VIA Technologies (HK) Inc. Ltd. (1)
Unit B 16 Floor V Ga Bldg 532 Castle Peak Road, Kowloon, China (Hong Kong)
Tel.: (852) 29593770
Computer Peripheral Equipment Distr
N.A.I.C.S.: 423430

VIA Technologies (Shanghai) Co., Ltd. (1)
2537 Jinke Rd Zhangjiang Hi-Tech Park, Pudong New Area, Shanghai, 201203, China
Tel.: (86) 21 38764688
Web Site: http://www.via.com.tw
Computer Peripheral Equipment Distr
N.A.I.C.S.: 423430

VIA Technologies (Shenzhen) Co., Ltd. (1)
9966 VIA Technologies Building Shennan Ave, Nanshan Dist, Shenzhen, 518057, China
Tel.: (86) 75566821000
Web Site: http://www.via.com.tw
Computer Peripheral Equipment Distr
N.A.I.C.S.: 423430

VIA Technologies GmbH (1)
Mottmannstr 12, Troisdorf, Germany
Tel.: (49) 2241397780
Computer Equipment & Software Whslr
N.A.I.C.S.: 423430

VIA Technologies Japan K.K. (1)
3-15-7 Hulic Ebisu bldg 6F Higashi, Shibuya-ku, Tokyo, 150-0011, Japan
Tel.: (81) 354661637
Web Site: http://www.viatech.co.jp
Sales Range: $25-49.9 Million
Emp.: 5
Semiconductor & Related Device Mfr
N.A.I.C.S.: 334413

VIA Technologies, Korea (1)
2F Sangjin Bldg 417 Dogok-Dong, Gangnam-Gu, Seoul, 135 854, Korea (South)
Tel.: (82) 2 571 2986
Web Site: http://kr.viatech.com
Emp.: 6
Computer Peripheral Equipment Distr
N.A.I.C.S.: 423430

VIA Telecom Co., Ltd. (1)
6th Floor 531 Chung Cheng Road, Hsin Tien, Taiwan
Tel.: (886) 222185452
Web Site: http://www.via-telecom.com
Sales Range: $150-199.9 Million
Emp.: 300
Electronic Parts & Equipment Whslr
N.A.I.C.S.: 423690

Subsidiary (US):

VIA Telecom Inc. (2)
3390 Carmel Mountain Rd Ste 100, San Diego, CA 92121
Tel.: (858) 350-5560
Semiconductor Equipment Mfr
N.A.I.C.S.: 334413
Frank Jungman *(Dir-Tech Mktg)*

Vate Technology Co., Ltd. (1)
No 9 Li-Hsin Rd V, Science-Based Industrial Park, Hsin-chu, Taiwan **(66.28%)**
Tel.: (886) 35770345
Web Site: https://www.vate.com.tw
Bare Printed Circuit Board Mfr
N.A.I.C.S.: 334412

Via-Cyrix, Inc. (1)
20333 State Hwy 249, Houston, TX 77070-2617
Tel.: (281) 374-0090
Sales Range: $25-49.9 Million
Emp.: 57
Semiconductor & Related Device Mfr
N.A.I.C.S.: 334413

Wondermedia Technologies, Inc. (1)
10F 529-1 Chung-Cheng Road Hsin-Tien, Taipei, 231, Taiwan
Tel.: (886) 2 2218 2250
Web Site: http://www.wondermedia.com.tw
Computer Peripheral & Integrated Circuit Distr
N.A.I.C.S.: 423430

Xander International Corp. (1)
3rd Floor No 24 Ln 123, Min Chuan E Rd Sec 6, Taipei, Taiwan
Tel.: (886) 289126000
Web Site: http://www.xander.com.tw
Computer Equipment Mfr
N.A.I.C.S.: 334118

VIAAN INDUSTRIES LIMITED
Saisha Bungalow No 10/87 Mhada SVP Nagar, Janki Devi School Road Versova Andheri West, Mumbai, 400053, India
Tel.: (91) 2226316866
Web Site: https://www.v-ind.com
Year Founded: 1982
537524—(BOM)
Rev.: $516,346
Assets: $1,580,140
Liabilities: $1,915,850
Net Worth: ($335,710)
Earnings: ($227,141)
Emp.: 7
Fiscal Year-end: 03/31/21
Glass Product Mfr & Whslr
N.A.I.C.S.: 327215
Ripu Sudan Kundra *(Chm, CEO & Mng Dir)*

VIAFIN SERVICE OYJ
Varkkitie 13, 61300, Kurikka, Finland
Tel.: (358) 103274000
Web Site: https://www.viafinservice.fi
VIAFIN—(HEL)
Emp.: 592
Pipeline Installation Services
N.A.I.C.S.: 237120
Mika Riekkola *(CEO)*

VIAGOGO AG
Rue Du Commerce 4, Geneva, 1204, Switzerland
Tel.: (41) 225083203
Web Site: http://www.viagogo.com
Year Founded: 2006
Live Sport, Music & Entrainment Ticket Retailer
N.A.I.C.S.: 561599
Eric Baker *(Founder & CEO)*

Subsidiaries:

StubHub, Inc. (1)
199 Fremont St, San Francisco, CA 94105
Tel.: (415) 222-8400
Web Site: http://www.stubhub.com
Online Ticket Buying & Selling Marketplace
N.A.I.C.S.: 518210
Jeff Poirier *(Gen Mgr-Music)*

VIAGOLD RARE EARTH RESOURCES HOLDINGS LIMITED
7th Floor 53 Bailian Road Jida, Zhuhai, 519000, Guangdong, China
Tel.: (86) 7563320271   BM
Web Site: http://www.viagold.ws
VIA—(ASX)
Rev.: $26,082,464
Assets: $42,434,659
Liabilities: $36,327,454
Net Worth: $6,107,205
Earnings: $299,752
Fiscal Year-end: 03/31/22
Investment Management Service
N.A.I.C.S.: 523940
Longguang Shi *(Chm)*

VIAJES MARSANS S.A.
Serrano St 41 7th Fl, Madrid, 28001, Spain
Tel.: (34) 913433000
Web Site: http://www.marsans.es
Travel Arrangement Services
N.A.I.C.S.: 561599
Gonzalo Pascual Arias *(Chm)*

Subsidiaries:

Air Comet Group (1)
Edificio Air Plus, C Bahia De Pollensa 21 23, 28042, Madrid, Spain
Tel.: (34) 912036300
Sales Range: $75-99.9 Million
Emp.: 300
Travel Service Company
N.A.I.C.S.: 561510

VIALIFE SA
7 impasse Marie Blanche, 75018, Paris, France
Tel.: (33) 172871676
Web Site: https://www.viapresse.com
ALVIA—(EUR)
Sales Range: $1-9.9 Million
Online Subscription Management Services
N.A.I.C.S.: 516210

Vincent Mareine *(Chm & CEO)*

VIANET GROUP PLC
One Surtees Way Surtees Business Park, Stockton-on-Tees, TS18 3HR, United Kingdom
Tel.: (44) 1642358800
Web Site: http://www.vianetplc.com
VNET—(AIM)
Rev.: $17,528,007
Assets: $40,701,237
Liabilities: $8,455,416
Net Worth: $32,245,821
Earnings: $199,930
Emp.: 143
Fiscal Year-end: 03/31/23
Pub, Restaurant & Arcade Management & Monitoring Systems
N.A.I.C.S.: 561499
Mark Hardwick Foster *(CFO)*

Subsidiaries:

Coin Metrics Limited (1)
One Surtees Way, Surtees Business Park, Stockton-on-Tees, TS18 3HR, Cleveland, United Kingdom
Tel.: (44) 1642867967
Web Site: https://www.brulines.com
Sales Range: $25-49.9 Million
Monitoring Services
N.A.I.C.S.: 561621
Jeff Anspach *(Mng Dir)*

Machine Insite Limited (1)
One Surtees Way, Surtees Business Park, Stockton-on-Tees, TS18 3HR, Cleveland, United Kingdom
Tel.: (44) 1642358800
Sales Range: $25-49.9 Million
Machine Management Services
N.A.I.C.S.: 333998

Vianet Limited (1)
Buchan House Carnegie Campus S, Queensferry Rd, Dunfermline, KY11 8PL, Fife, United Kingdom
Tel.: (44) 1383748000
Web Site: http://www.vianet.co.uk
Sales Range: $25-49.9 Million
Emp.: 20
Data Processing Services
N.A.I.C.S.: 518210
Steven Alton *(Mng Dir-Smart Zones)*

VIAPLAY GROUP AB
Ringvagen 52, 118 67, Stockholm, Sweden
Tel.: (46) 856202500   SE
Web Site: https://www.nentgroup.com
Year Founded: 2018
VPLAY.B—(OMX)
Rev.: $1,843,171,155
Assets: $1,957,333,208
Liabilities: $2,065,538,979
Net Worth: ($108,205,772)
Earnings: ($967,597,848)
Emp.: 1,313
Fiscal Year-end: 12/31/23
Media Advertising Services
N.A.I.C.S.: 541840
David Chance *(Chm)*

VIARO INVESTMENT LTD.
111 Buckingham Palace Road, London, SW1W 0SR, United Kingdom
Tel.: (44) 20 7390 0240
Web Site: http://www.viaro.co.uk
Investment Management
N.A.I.C.S.: 523940
Francesco Mazzagatti *(CEO)*

Subsidiaries:

Viaro Energy Limited (1)
111 Buckingham Palace Road, London, SW1W 0SR, United Kingdom
Tel.: (44) 20 7390 0240
Oil & Gas Distr
N.A.I.C.S.: 333132
Francesco Mazzagatti *(CEO)*

VIARO INVESTMENT LTD.

Viaro Investment Ltd.—(Continued)

Subsidiary (Domestic):

RockRose Energy Plc (2)
Halton House 5th Floor 20 23 Holborn, London, EC1N 2JD, United Kingdom
Tel.: (44) 203 826 4800
Web Site: http://www.rockroseenergy.com
Rev.: $250,987,000
Assets: $1,479,279,000
Liabilities: $1,325,332,000
Net Worth: $153,947,000
Earnings: $84,091,000
Emp.: 161
Fiscal Year-end: 12/31/2019
Oil & Gas Exploration
N.A.I.C.S.: 213111
Peter Mann (Mng Dir)

VIATRON TECHNOLOGIES, INC.
139 Saneop-ro 155 beon-gil
Gwonseon-gu, Suwon, Gyeonggi-do, Korea (South)
Tel.: (82) 7040163200
Web Site: http://www.viatrontech.com
Year Founded: 2002
141000—(KRS)
Rev.: $54,437,859
Assets: $149,912,548
Liabilities: $19,967,756
Net Worth: $129,944,792
Earnings: $12,362,183
Emp.: 126
Fiscal Year-end: 12/31/22
Semiconductor Mfr
N.A.I.C.S.: 334413
Hyoung-June Kim (Founder & CEO)

VIAU FORD (1990) INC.
600 Notre Dame Ville, Saint-Remi, J0L 2L0, QC, Canada
Tel.: (450) 454-7501
Web Site: http://www.viauford.com
Rev.: $15,158,740
Emp.: 45
New & Used Car Dealers
N.A.I.C.S.: 441110
Pascal Ste-Marie (Co-Owner)

VIAVID BROADCASTING, INC.
3955 Graveley Street, Burnaby, V5C 3T4, BC, Canada
Tel.: (604) 669-0047
Video Broadcasting Services
N.A.I.C.S.: 516120
Brian Kathler (Pres)

VIB VERMOGEN AG
Tilly-Park 1, 86633, Neuburg an der Donau, Germany
Tel.: (49) 843190770
Web Site: https://www.vib-ag.de
VIH1—(DEU)
Rev.: $101,213,037
Assets: $1,712,075,329
Liabilities: $908,326,139
Net Worth: $803,749,191
Earnings: $57,822,145
Emp.: 33
Fiscal Year-end: 12/31/22
Real Estate Services
N.A.I.C.S.: 531390
Jurgen Wittmann (Deputy Chm-Supervisory Bd)

Subsidiaries:

BBI Burgerliches Brauhaus Immobilien AG (1)
Tilly-Park 1, 86633, Neuburg an der Donau, Germany (94.88%)
Tel.: (49) 84319077151
Web Site: https://www.bbi-immobilien-ag.de
Real Estate Services
N.A.I.C.S.: 531390

Gewerbe park Gunzburg GmbH (1)
Luitpoldstrabe 70, Neuburg an der Donau, 86633, Germany

Tel.: (49) 8431 504951
Real Estate Development Services
N.A.I.C.S.: 531390

Interpark Immobilien GmbH (1)
Luitpoldstrabe C 70 Bayern, Neuburg an der Donau, 86633, Germany
Tel.: (49) 8431504952
Real Estate Manangement Services
N.A.I.C.S.: 531390

Merkur GmbH (1)
Martin-Kollar-Str 1, 81829, Munich, Germany
Tel.: (49) 896895080
Web Site: https://www.merkur-gmbh.de
Emp.: 20
Investment Management Service
N.A.I.C.S.: 523940

VSI GmbH (1)
Zschockestrasse 1, 67657, Kaiserslautern, Germany
Tel.: (49) 6313106980
Web Site: https://www.vsi-gmbh.de
Real Estate Services
N.A.I.C.S.: 531390

WHD Immobilien GmbH (1)
Luitpoldstrabe C 70 Bayern, Neuburg an der Donau, 86633, Germany
Tel.: (49) 8431504951
Web Site: http://www.vin-ag.de
Sales Range: $50-74.9 Million
Emp.: 35
Real Estate Manangement Services
N.A.I.C.S.: 531390
Ludwig Schlosser (CEO)

VIBE GROWTH CORPORATION
250-997 Seymour Street, Vancouver, V6B 3M1, BC, Canada
Tel.: (403) 453-3298 ON
Web Site: https://www.vibebycalifornia.com
Year Founded: 2011
VIBEF—(OTCQB)
Rev.: $14,149,174
Assets: $16,278,895
Liabilities: $15,200,142
Net Worth: $1,078,753
Earnings: ($11,132,006)
Emp.: 110
Fiscal Year-end: 12/31/23
Cannabis Grower & Products Retailer
N.A.I.C.S.: 111419
Mark Waldron (CEO)

VIBHAVADI MEDICAL CENTER PUBLIC COMPANY LIMITED
51/3 Ngamwongwan Rd, Jatujak, Bangkok, 10900, Thailand
Tel.: (66) 29412800
Web Site: http://www.vibhavadi.com
Sales Range: $10-24.9 Million
Emp.: 750
Hospital Operations
N.A.I.C.S.: 622110
Suriya Phalakornkul (Vice Chm)

VIBRA FINISH, LIMITED
5329 Maingate Dr, Mississauga, L4W 1G6, ON, Canada
Tel.: (905) 625-9955
Web Site: https://www.vibra.com
Year Founded: 1971
Rev.: $13,911,192
Emp.: 120
Machine Part Mfr
N.A.I.C.S.: 333242

VIBRANT GLOBAL CAPITAL LIMITED
Vibrant Global Group 202-Tower A Peninsula Business Park, Senapati Bapat Marg Lower Parel, Mumbai, 400 013, Maharashtra, India
Tel.: (91) 2241731000
Web Site: https://www.vibrantglobalgroup.com

Year Founded: 1995
538732—(BOM)
Rev.: $23,657,215
Assets: $21,145,303
Liabilities: $8,010,359
Net Worth: $13,134,944
Earnings: ($937,246)
Emp.: 4
Fiscal Year-end: 03/31/23
Financial Services
N.A.I.C.S.: 525990
Jalpesh Darji (Officer-Compliance & Sec)

Subsidiaries:

Vibrant Global Salt Private Limited (1)
1st Floor Laxmi Complex New Market Sambhar Lake, Jaipur, 303604, Rajasthan, India
Tel.: (91) 9166824005
Web Site: https://www.vibrantglobalsalt.in
Emp.: 60
Salt Product Mfr
N.A.I.C.S.: 311942

VIBRANT GROUP LIMITED SG
Web Site: http://www.vibrant.com.sg
Year Founded: 1981
BIP—(SES)
Rev.: $102,944,794
Assets: $354,236,383
Liabilities: $186,419,414
Net Worth: $167,816,969
Earnings: $1,276,769
Emp.: 366
Fiscal Year-end: 04/30/24
Freight Logistics Systems, Real Estate & Financial Services
N.A.I.C.S.: 541614
Henry Tiong Hock Chua (Chief Corp Dev Officer & Exec Dir)

Subsidiaries:

Crystal Freight Services Distripark Pte. Ltd. (1)
146 Gul Circle, Singapore, 629604, Singapore
Tel.: (65) 62626988
Freight Forwarding Services
N.A.I.C.S.: 488510

Crystal Freight Services Pte. Ltd. (1)
51 Penjuru Road 03-00 Freight Links Express Logisticentre, Singapore, 609143, Singapore
Tel.: (65) 6 267 5622
Web Site: https://www.crystalfreight.com.sg
Freight Transportation Services
N.A.I.C.S.: 488510
Vincent Yong (VP)

Fervent Industrial Development (Suzhou) Co., Ltd. (1)
55 Sunshine Avenue, Changshu, 215500, Jiangsu, China
Tel.: (86) 5128 065 6666
Web Site: http://www.fervent-industrial.com
Real Estate Investment Services
N.A.I.C.S.: 531390

Freight Links E-logistics Technopark Pte. Ltd. (1)
30 Tuas Avenue 10, Singapore, 639150, Singapore
Tel.: (65) 66653773
Logistic Services
N.A.I.C.S.: 541614

Freight Links Express (M) Sdn. Bhd. (1)
C-2-7 Blok C One Lebuh Batu Nilam 2, Bandar Bukit Tingi, 41200, Klang, Selangor, Malaysia
Tel.: (60) 333244040
Freight Forwarding Services
N.A.I.C.S.: 488510

Freight Links Express (Pg) Sdn. Bhd. (1)
Level 11 Unit 11 B Wisma Boon Siew No 1 Penang Road, 10000, Penang, Malaysia
Tel.: (60) 42634390

INTERNATIONAL PUBLIC

Freight Forwarding Services
N.A.I.C.S.: 488510

Freight Links Express Archivers Pte. Ltd. (1)
30 Tuas Avenue 10, Singapore, 639150, Singapore
Tel.: (65) 62626966
Logistic Services
N.A.I.C.S.: 541614

Freight Links Express Logisticpark Pte. Ltd. (1)
33/35 Penjuru Lane, Singapore, 609200, Singapore
Tel.: (65) 62626988
Logistic Services
N.A.I.C.S.: 541614

Freight Links Express Pte. Ltd. (1)
51 Penjuru Road 03-00 Freight Links Express Logisticentre, Singapore, 609143, Singapore
Tel.: (65) 65662866
Shipping Services
N.A.I.C.S.: 561431
Alex Ng Boon Chuan (Exec VP)

Freight Links Logistics Pte. Ltd. (1)
51 Penjuru Road 03-00 Freight Links Express Logisticentre, Singapore, 609143, Singapore
Tel.: (65) 62626988
Warehousing Management Services
N.A.I.C.S.: 531130

Freight Links M&S (H.K.) Ltd. (1)
Suite 1116 11/F Tower 3 China Hong Kong City 33 Canton Road, Tsimshatsui, Kowloon, China (Hong Kong)
Tel.: (852) 28269113
Freight Transportation Services
N.A.I.C.S.: 488510

Freight Links Properties Pte. Ltd. (1)
47 Changi South Avenue 2, Singapore, 486148, Singapore
Tel.: (65) 62626988
Logistic Services
N.A.I.C.S.: 541614

Hub & Port Services Pte. Ltd. (1)
51 Penjuru Road 04-00 Freight Links Express Logisticentre, Singapore, 609143, Singapore
Tel.: (65) 69708651
International Freight Forwarding & Logistics Services
N.A.I.C.S.: 541614

LTH Logistics (Singapore) Pte. Ltd. (1)
146 Gul Circle, Singapore, 629604, Singapore
Tel.: (65) 62689595
Logistic Services
N.A.I.C.S.: 541614
Justin Tay (Bus Mgr)

Lee Thong Hung Trading & Transport Sdn. Bhd. (1)
Lot PT 131622 Lot Asal 14856 Jalan Udang Gantung 1, Klang Selatan KS10 Telok Gong, 42000, Klang, Selangor, Malaysia
Tel.: (60) 331341878
Freight Transportation Services
N.A.I.C.S.: 488510

Sinolink Financial Leasing Co., Ltd. (1)
Rm 217 No 568 Hong Xu Road, Minhang District, Shanghai, 201130, China
Tel.: (86) 2158309077
Financial Lending Services
N.A.I.C.S.: 523999

VIBROPOWER CORPORATION LIMITED
11 Tuas Avenue 16, Singapore, 638929, Singapore
Tel.: (65) 62682322 SG
Web Site: https://www.vibropower.com
Year Founded: 1995
BJD—(SES)
Rev.: $9,280,846
Assets: $23,336,123
Liabilities: $8,734,248

AND PRIVATE COMPANIES

VICAT S.A.

Net Worth: $14,601,875
Earnings: $112,491
Fiscal Year-end: 12/31/20
Stationary Generators Mfr
N.A.I.C.S.: 334515
Benedict Onn Meng Chen *(Co-Founder, Chm, CEO & Mng Dir)*

Subsidiaries:

GMTM Holdings Pte. Ltd. (1)
11 Tuas Avenue 16, Singapore, 638929, Singapore
Tel.: (65) 68978009
Sales Range: $50-74.9 Million
Emp.: 50
Investment Management Service
N.A.I.C.S.: 523940

Subsidiary (Non-US):

VibroPower (UK) Limited (2)
Ste 05 Manorcrown Buiseness Ctr, Meadow Drove, Bourne, PE10 0BP, Lincolnshire, United Kingdom
Tel.: (44) 1778425067
Web Site: http://www.vibropower.com
Sales Range: $25-49.9 Million
Emp.: 2
Power Generator Mfr
N.A.I.C.S.: 335312
Keith Wall *(Mgr-Sls)*

Shanghai VibroPower Generators Equipment Co. Ltd (1)
Room 2315 No 660 Shangcheng Road, Pu-dong, Shanghai, China
Tel.: (86) 2158949328
Power Generator Mfr
N.A.I.C.S.: 335312

Shanxi Weineng Coal Mine Gas Development Co., Ltd. (1)
No 189 East Street, Pingding, Yangquan, Shanxi, China
Tel.: (86) 3535681550
Generator Installation Services
N.A.I.C.S.: 238210

VibroPower Generators (India) Private Limited (1)
304 Atlanta Estate Dr Ambedkar Chowk, Goregaon East, Mumbai, 400063, India
Tel.: (91) 2229277402
Generator Installation Services
N.A.I.C.S.: 238210

VibroPower Generators Sdn. Bhd. (1)
No 27-A First Floor Jalan Sungai Besi Indah 1/19, Taman Sungei Besi Indah, 43300, Seri Kembangan, Selangor, Malaysia
Tel.: (60) 389429328
Generator Installation Services
N.A.I.C.S.: 238210

VibroPower Pte. Ltd. (1)
11 Tuas Avenue 16, Singapore, 638929, Singapore
Tel.: (65) 62682322
Sales Range: $25-49.9 Million
Emp.: 20
Industrial Generators Mfr
N.A.I.C.S.: 334513

VIBROS ORGANICS LIMITED

B-159 Sector 63, Noida, 201 307, India
Tel.: (91) 120 4341000
Web Site: http://www.vibrosorganics.com
Year Founded: 1987
Chemical Product Whslr
N.A.I.C.S.: 424690
Naveen Kohli *(Chm & Mng Dir)*

VIBROSYSTM INC.

2727 Jacques Cartier East Blvd, Longueuil, J4N 1L7, QC, Canada
Tel.: (450) 646-2157
Web Site: http://www.vibrosystm.com
Year Founded: 1986
Rev: $13,741,360
Emp.: 50
Measuring & Monitoring Industrial Systems Distr
N.A.I.C.S.: 334519
Marius Cloutier *(Pres)*

VICAT S.A.

4 Rue Aristide Berges Les Trois Vallons, 38080, L'Isle-d'Abeau, Cedex, France
Tel.: (33) 474275900
Web Site: https://www.vicat.com
Year Founded: 1853
VCT—(EUR)
Rev: $4,346,169,556
Assets: $7,025,437,687
Liabilities: $3,694,087,648
Net Worth: $3,331,350,039
Earnings: $326,005,078
Emp.: 9,993
Fiscal Year-end: 12/31/23
Cement, Ready-Mixed Concrete & Aggregates Mfr
N.A.I.C.S.: 327310
Jean-Pierre Souchet *(CFO)*

Subsidiaries:

ALPES INFORMATIQUE (1)
Les Trois Vallons 4 Rue Aristide Berges, 38080, L'Isle-d'Abeau, France
Tel.: (33) 474275900
Web Site: http://www.alpesinformatique.com
Cement Mfr
N.A.I.C.S.: 327310

Altola AG (1)
Gosgerstrasse 154, 4600, Olten, Switzerland
Tel.: (41) 622872372
Web Site: https://www.altola.ch
Waste Management Services
N.A.I.C.S.: 562998

Atelier du Granier S.A.R.L (1)
436 route Barraux, 38530, Chapareillan, France
Tel.: (33) 476452003
Web Site: http://www.vicat.fr
Metal Products Mfr
N.A.I.C.S.: 332999

BETON AG INTERLAKEN (1)
Oberabernick Strasse 65, Interlaken, 3800, Switzerland
Tel.: (41) 338232765
Sales Range: $50-74.9 Million
Emp.: 4
Concrete Product Distr
N.A.I.C.S.: 423320

BETON CONTROLE COTE D (1)
217 Route De Grenoble, 06200, Nice, France
Tel.: (33) 474275900
Cement Whslr
N.A.I.C.S.: 423320

BETON VICAT (1)
Route de Paris, 31150, Fenouillet, France
Tel.: (33) 56 170 2202
Web Site: https://www.beton-vicat.fr
Cement Mfr
N.A.I.C.S.: 327310

BETONPUMPEN OBERLAND AG (1)
Tel.: (41) 336578021
Concrete Products Mfr
N.A.I.C.S.: 327390
Christoph Kunzi *(Mng Dir)*

BHARATHI CEMENT CORPORATION PRIVATE LTD (1)
Reliance Majestic Building 8-2-626 Road No 10, Banjara Hills, Hyderabad, 500 034, India
Tel.: (91) 4030006999
Web Site: https://www.bharathicement.com
Sales Range: $50-74.9 Million
Emp.: 160
Cement Mfr
N.A.I.C.S.: 327310
Y. S. Bharathi Reddy *(Chm)*

Bastas Baskent Cimento (1)
Samsun Yolu 35 km, Elmada, Ankara, TR 06780, Turkiye
Tel.: (90) 3128640100
Web Site: http://www.bastas.com.tr
Sales Range: $50-74.9 Million
Emp.: 200
Cement Mfr
N.A.I.C.S.: 327310

Subsidiary (Domestic):

Bastas Hazir Beton Sanayi ve Ticaret A.S. (2)
Ugur Mumcu Neighborhood Fatih Sultan Mehmet Bul No 316, Batikent, 06370, Ankara, Turkiye (100%)
Tel.: (90) 3122527007
Web Site: https://www.bastasbeton.com.tr
Concrete Products Mfr
N.A.I.C.S.: 327331
H. Burak Akin *(Chm)*

Beton AG Basel (1)
Grenzstr 199, 4057, Basel, Switzerland
Tel.: (41) 61 633 30 30
Web Site: http://www.vigier-beton-mittelland.ch
Concrete Cement Mfr
N.A.I.C.S.: 327390

Beton Travaux (1)
Tour Manhattan 6 Pl De L Iris, Courbevoie, 92400, France
Tel.: (33) 158868686
Web Site: http://www.vicat.com
Cement Making Machinery Whslr
N.A.I.C.S.: 423830

Subsidiary (Domestic):

BETON GRANULATS IDF (2)
52 Rue Jacquard, 77400, Lagny-sur-Marne, France
Tel.: (33) 164121960
Concrete Products Mfr
N.A.I.C.S.: 327390

BETON RHONE ALPES (2)
Les Trois Vallons 4 Rue Aristide Berges, L'Isle-d'Abeau, 38080, France
Tel.: (33) 474275900
Building Materials Distr
N.A.I.C.S.: 423390

BETONS GRANULATS DU CENTRE (2)
Chemin Des Martailles, 63430, Les Martres-d'Artiere, France
Tel.: (33) 473837040
Concrete Products Mfr
N.A.I.C.S.: 327390

SATMA (2)
4 Rue Aristide Berges, BP 34, 38081, L'Isle-d'Abeau, France
Tel.: (33) 474275930
Cement Mfr
N.A.I.C.S.: 327310

Builders Concrete Inc. (1)
17125 E Kings Canyon Rd, Sanger, CA 93657
Tel.: (559) 225-3664
Concrete Product Distr
N.A.I.C.S.: 423320

CEWAG (1)
Murtenstrasse 25, 3186, Dudingen, Switzerland
Tel.: (41) 26 492 94 50
Web Site: http://www.cewag.ch
Concrete Products Mfr
N.A.I.C.S.: 327390

CONDENSIL (1)
265 Rue Des Epinettes Zone Des Landiers Nord, 73000, Chambery, France
Tel.: (33) 479627403
Web Site: http://www.condensil.com
Cement Mfr
N.A.I.C.S.: 327310
Alain Picot *(Gen Mgr)*

COVIT SA (1)
Les Lavannes 7, Saint-Blaise, 2072, Switzerland
Tel.: (41) 327531856
Cement Mfr
N.A.I.C.S.: 327310

Cementi Centro Sud SpA (1)
Torre A Piazza Borgo Pila 40/57 F-G, 16129, Genoa, GE, Italy
Tel.: (39) 0105469711
Sales Range: $25-49.9 Million
Emp.: 6
Cement Mfr
N.A.I.C.S.: 327310
Pretro Cala *(Gen Mgr)*

Ciments et Materiaux du Mali (1)
Niarela Street 449 Achkabad Door 127, 2895, Bamako, Mali
Tel.: (223) 44900492
Web Site: https://www.cmmali.com
Cement Mfr
N.A.I.C.S.: 327310

DELTA POMPAGE SARL (1)
1327 Avenue De La Houille Blanche, 73000, Chambery, France
Tel.: (33) 479620818
Web Site: http://www.vicat.fr
Cement Mfr
N.A.I.C.S.: 327310

EMME KIES + BETON AG (1)
Pfaffenboden, Grunenmatt, 3452, Lutzelfluh, Switzerland
Tel.: (41) 344311880
Cement Mfr
N.A.I.C.S.: 327310

ETS ANTOINE FOURNIER (1)
4 Rue Aristide Berges, 38080, L'Isle-d'Abeau, France
Tel.: (33) 471667207
Cement Mfr
N.A.I.C.S.: 327310

FBF FRISCHBETON AG (1)
Bahnhofstrasse, Frutigen, 3714, Switzerland
Tel.: (41) 336713305
Cement Mfr
N.A.I.C.S.: 327310

FRISCHBETON AG (1)
Rutiweg 13, Zuchwil, 4528, Switzerland
Tel.: (41) 326816060
Cement Mfr
N.A.I.C.S.: 327310

Frischbeton Thun AG (1)
Tel.: (41) 332251406
Web Site: https://frischbetonthun.ch
Sales Range: $25-49.9 Million
Emp.: 8
Cement Concrete Mfr
N.A.I.C.S.: 327390
Daniel Haldimann *(Gen Mgr)*

GECAMINES (1)
Yaye Fatou Dieng Building Street 1 PE 43 Point-E, BP 2247, Dakar, Senegal
Tel.: (221) 338325780
Web Site: https://www.gecamines.sn
Emp.: 200
Cement Mfr
N.A.I.C.S.: 327310
Philippe Gaesoul *(Gen Mgr)*

GRANDY AG (1)
Berlinweg 7, 4513, Langendorf, Switzerland
Tel.: (41) 326223263
Cement Mfr
N.A.I.C.S.: 327310

GRANULATS RHONE-ALPES S.A.S. (1)
4 Rue Aristide Berges, 38080, L'Isle-d'Abeau, France
Tel.: (33) 4 74 27 59 00
Web Site: http://www.vicat.fr
Emp.: 450
Cement Mfr
N.A.I.C.S.: 327310

JAMBYL CEMENT LLP (1)
Avenue Dostyk 38, 050010, Almaty, Kazakhstan
Tel.: (7) 7272440229
Cement Mfr
N.A.I.C.S.: 327310

KIESWERK AEBISHOLZ AG (1)
Tel.: (41) 623885163
Sales Range: $25-49.9 Million
Emp.: 1
Cement Mfr
N.A.I.C.S.: 327310
Felix Hofer *(Mgr-Sls)*

KIRKPATRICK CONCRETE, INC (1)
305 6th St S, Oneonta, AL 35121-1828

VICAT S.A.

Vicat S.A.—(Continued)
Tel.: (205) 625-3071
Concrete Products Mfr & Distr
N.A.I.C.S.: 327320
Bo Canning *(Mgr-QA & QC)*

Konya Cimento (1)
Horozluhan Mah Cihan Sk No 15, selcuklu,
42300, Konya, Turkiye
Tel.: (90) 3323450355
Web Site: https://www.konyacimento.com.tr
Cement Mfr
N.A.I.C.S.: 327310

**Konya Hazir Beton Sanayi Ve Ticaret
A.S.** (1)
Horozluhan Mah Cihan Sok No 15, Sel-
cuklu, Konya, Turkiye
Tel.: (90) 3323460369
Web Site:
 https://www.konyahazirbeton.com.tr
Concrete Products Mfr
N.A.I.C.S.: 327390

**MBW Materialbewirtschaftung Mitholz
AG** (1)
Mitholz, 3717, Blausee-Mitholz, Switzerland
Tel.: (41) 336578029
Cement Mfr
N.A.I.C.S.: 327310

**MICHEL & CO AG SAND-UND
KIESWERKE** (1)
Lutschinenstrasse, 3806, Bonigen, Switzer-
land
Tel.: (41) 338222839
Concrete Products Mfr
N.A.I.C.S.: 327390

**National Cement Company of
Alabama** (1)
2000 Southbridge Pkwy Ste 600, Birming-
ham, AL 35209
Tel.: (205) 423-2600
Sales Range: $125-149.9 Million
Emp.: 300
Cement Mfr
N.A.I.C.S.: 327310
Stephen Snipes *(VP-Sls)*

Division (Domestic):

National Cement Co. (2)
80 National Cement Dr, Ragland, AL 35131
Tel.: (205) 472-2191
Sales Range: $50-74.9 Million
Emp.: 150
Cement Mfr
N.A.I.C.S.: 327310
Jean Claude Brochetone *(Plant Mgr)*

**National Cement Company of
California** (1)
15821 Ventura Blvd Ste 475, Encino, CA
91436-4778
Tel.: (818) 728-5200
Cement Mfr
N.A.I.C.S.: 327310
Donald Unmacht *(Pres)*

National Ready Mixed Inc. (1)
15821 Ventura Blvd Ste 475, Los Angeles,
CA 91436-4778
Tel.: (818) 728-5200
Web Site: http://www.nrmcc.com
Cement Concrete Mfr
N.A.I.C.S.: 327390
Chris Heilmann *(VP-Sls)*

PAPETERIES DE VIZILLE (1)
1176 Avenue Aristide Briand, Vizille, 38220,
Grenoble, France
Tel.: (33) 476685400
Web Site: http://www.vizille-vicat.com
Paper Products Mfr
N.A.I.C.S.: 322299

RUDIGOZ (1)
Les Communaux Route De St Maurice De
Gourclans, 01800, Perouges, France
Tel.: (33) 4 74 46 08 30
Web Site: http://www.rudigoz.fr
Cement Mfr
N.A.I.C.S.: 327310

**SHB STEINBRUCH + HARTSCHOT-
TERWERK BLAUSEE-MITHOLZ
AG** (1)
Butschi 253, Postfach 93, 3717, Blausee-

Mitholz, Switzerland
Tel.: (41) 336728060
Web Site: https://www.shb-naturstein.ch
Construction Materials Mfr
N.A.I.C.S.: 327331

SIGMA BETON (1)
4 Rue Aristide Berges, 38080, L'Isle-
d'Abeau, France
Tel.: (33) 474275880
Web Site: http://www.sigmbeton.fr
Sales Range: $25-49.9 Million
Emp.: 10
Concrete Products Mfr
N.A.I.C.S.: 327390

**SOCIETE AZUREENNE DE
GRANULATS** (1)
217 Route De Grenoble, 06200, Nice,
France
Tel.: (33) 493832654
Cement Mfr
N.A.I.C.S.: 327310

SOCOCIM Industries (1)
Km 33 old road to Thies, BP 29, Rufisque,
Dakar, Senegal
Tel.: (221) 338398888
Web Site: https://www.sococim.com
Cement Mfr
N.A.I.C.S.: 327310

Sinai Cement Company (1)
Sama Administrative Tower Ring Road,
Katameya, 11411, Cairo, Egypt
Tel.: (20) 227262344
Web Site: https://sinaicement.net
Cement Mfr & Distr
N.A.I.C.S.: 327310

Sonneville AG (1)
Industriezone 2, Muntschemier, 3225, Bern,
Switzerland
Tel.: (41) 589092850
Web Site: https://www.sonneville.ch
Building Materials Mfr
N.A.I.C.S.: 327331
Peter Laborenz *(Pres)*

Steinbruch AG Vorberg Bozingen (1)
Werkstrasse 3, Safnern, 2553, Bern, Swit-
zerland
Tel.: (41) 32 356 00 16
Web Site: http://www.steinbruchag.ch
Sales Range: $50-74.9 Million
Emp.: 6
Stone Blocks Mfr & Supplier
N.A.I.C.S.: 327390
Christian Schlappi *(Mgr-Sls)*

**TAMTAS Yapi Malzemeleri Sanayi Ve
Ticaret AS** (1)
Samsun Yolu 35 KM, Elmadag, Ankara,
Turkiye
Tel.: (90) 3128640427
Web Site: https://www.tamtas.com.tr
Sales Range: $25-49.9 Million
Emp.: 85
Cement Mfr
N.A.I.C.S.: 327310

**UNITED READY MIXED CONCRETE
COMPANY, INC** (1)
4988 Firestone Blvd, South Gate, CA 90280
Tel.: (323) 564-1866
Cement Mfr
N.A.I.C.S.: 327310

VIBETON SAFNERN AG (1)
Werkstrasse 3, Safnern, 2553, Bern, Swit-
zerland
Tel.: (41) 323560234
Web Site: http://www.vigier-beton.ch
Emp.: 100
Concrete Products Mfr
N.A.I.C.S.: 327390
Erich Walti *(Office Mgr)*

**VICAT INTERNATIONAL
TRADING** (1)
4 Quai Papacino, 06300, Nice, France
Tel.: (33) 492001880
Cement Mfr
N.A.I.C.S.: 327310

VIGIER CEMENT AG (1)
Zone Industrielle Rondchatel, 2603, Pery,
Switzerland
Tel.: (41) 324850300
Web Site: https://www.vigier-ciment.ch

Sales Range: $50-74.9 Million
Emp.: 165
Cement Mfr
N.A.I.C.S.: 327310
Daniel Sthapp *(Mgr)*

VIGIER MANAGEMENT AG (1)
Schachenweg 24, 3250, Lyss, Switzerland
Tel.: (41) 323871033
Web Site: http://www.vigier.ch
Management Consulting Services
N.A.I.C.S.: 541618
Lukas Epple *(Office Mgr)*

**VIKING READY MIXED COMPANY,
INC** (1)
3664 W Ashlan Ave, Fresno, CA 93722-
4439
Tel.: (559) 225-3667
Emp.: 20
Readymix Concrete Mfr
N.A.I.C.S.: 327320
Charlie Wensley *(Branch Mgr)*

VIRO AG (1)
Wylihof 1, 4542, Luterbach, Switzerland
Tel.: (41) 32 681 31 00
Web Site: http://www.vigier.ch
Sales Range: $25-49.9 Million
Emp.: 8
Cement Mfr
N.A.I.C.S.: 327310
Walter Schicker *(Gen Mgr)*

VITRANS SA (1)
Tel.: (41) 324850342
Sales Range: $50-74.9 Million
Emp.: 165
Cement Mfr
N.A.I.C.S.: 327310

Vicat l'Isle d'Abeau (1)
4 Rue Aristide Berges Les Trois Vallons,
L'Isle d'Abeau, 38080, Grenoble, Cedex,
France
Tel.: (33) 47 427 5900
Web Site: https://www.vicat.fr
Sales Range: $125-149.9 Million
Emp.: 460
Ready-Mixed Concrete & Aggregates Pro-
ducer & Cement Mfr
N.A.I.C.S.: 327310
Merceron Vicat *(Pres)*

Vigier Beton Romandie SA (1)
Aergerstrasse 18, 1734, Tentlingen, Fri-
bourg, Switzerland (100%)
Tel.: (41) 264181288
Web Site: https://www.vigier-beton-
romandie.ch
Cement Mfr
N.A.I.C.S.: 327310
Gerald Rebetez *(Bus Dir)*

Vigier Holding AG (1)
Wylihof 1, 4542, Luterbach, Switzerland
Tel.: (41) 326813100
Web Site: https://www.vigier.ch
Sales Range: $450-499.9 Million
Emp.: 750
Cement Mfr
N.A.I.C.S.: 327310
Markus Oberle *(Gen Mgr)*

Subsidiary (Domestic):

CREABETON MATERIAUX SA (2)
Busswilstrasse 44, 3250, Lyss, Switzerland
Tel.: (41) 58 458 8080
Web Site: https://www.creabeton-
materiaux.ch
Emp.: 375
Concrete Products Mfr
N.A.I.C.S.: 327331
Adrian Forrer *(Gen Mgr)*

KIESTAG STEINIGAND AG (2)
Steinigand, Wimmis, 3752, Bern, Switzer-
land
Tel.: (41) 336578020
Cement Mfr
N.A.I.C.S.: 327310

Vigier Rail AG (1)
Industriezone 3, Muntschemier, 3225, Bern,
Switzerland
Tel.: (41) 589092800
Web Site: https://www.vigier-rail.ch
Cement Concrete Mfr
N.A.I.C.S.: 327390

Jose Manuel Barrios Fragoso *(Gen Mgr-
Technical & Innovation)*

WYSS KIESWERK AG (1)
Werkstrasse 101, 4534, Flumenthal, Swit-
zerland
Tel.: (41) 326816118
Cement Mfr
N.A.I.C.S.: 327310

VICEM GYPSUM & CEMENT
JOINT STOCK COMPANY

No 24 Ha Noi street, Hue, Thua
Thien Hue, Vietnam
Tel.: (84) 543825432
Web Site:
 https://www.thachcaoximang.com.vn
Year Founded: 1978
TXM—(HNX)
Rev.: $11,097,100
Assets: $13,538,800
Liabilities: $2,451,600
Net Worth: $11,087,200
Earnings: ($466,700)
Fiscal Year-end: 12/31/23
Construction Material Mfr & Whslr
N.A.I.C.S.: 327420

VICEM PACKAGING BIM SON
JOINT STOCK COMPANY

Lam Son Ward, Bim Son, Thanh
Hoa, Vietnam
Tel.: (84) 373825632
Web Site: http://www.baobibimson.vn
Year Founded: 1985
BPC—(HNX)
Rev.: $22,762,000
Assets: $18,704,400
Liabilities: $9,318,000
Net Worth: $9,386,400
Earnings: $112,800
Fiscal Year-end: 12/31/23
Packaging Products Mfr
N.A.I.C.S.: 322120

VICEM PACKAGING BUT SON
JOINT STOCK COMPANY

Km No 2 Van Cao Road, Nam Dinh,
Vietnam
Tel.: (84) 3503845183
Web Site:
 http://www.baobibutson.com.vn
Year Founded: 2003
BBS—(HNX)
Rev.: $44,842,100
Assets: $34,351,200
Liabilities: $23,447,100
Net Worth: $10,904,100
Earnings: $781,300
Fiscal Year-end: 12/31/22
Cement Sack Mfr
N.A.I.C.S.: 322220

VICEROY HOMES LIMITED

414 Croft St E, Port Hope, L1A 4H1,
ON, Canada
Tel.: (905) 800-0712 ON
Web Site: https://viceroycanada.com
Year Founded: 1955
Real Estate Services
N.A.I.C.S.: 531390

Subsidiaries:

Viceroy Homes Inc. (1)
15405 53rd Ave S, Tukwila, WA 98188
Tel.: (253) 922-1999
Sales Range: $25-49.9 Million
Prefabricated Wood Building Mfr
N.A.I.C.S.: 321992

VICEROY HOTELS LTD

8-2-120/112/88 & 89 3rd Floor, Opp
KBR Park Road No 2, Hyderabad,
500 034, Telangana, India
Tel.: (91) 4040204383
Web Site:
 https://www.viceroyhotels.in

AND PRIVATE COMPANIES — VICTOR HASSELBLAD AB

VICEROY—(NSE)
Rev.: $17,330,995
Assets: $58,598,450
Liabilities: $112,906,529
Net Worth: ($54,308,079)
Earnings: ($2,300,877)
Emp.: 463
Fiscal Year-end: 03/31/20
Hotel & Restaurant Operator
N.A.I.C.S.: 721110
Sreedhar Singh M. *(CEO, Compliance Officer & Sec)*

Subsidiaries:

Crustum Products Pvt. Ltd. (1)
108 109 & 113 First Fl Bhuvana Towers S D Rd, Secunderabad, 500003, Andhra Pradesh, India
Tel.: (91) 4044552727
Web Site: http://www.breadtalk.com
Sales Range: $25-49.9 Million
Emp.: 25
Bakery Products Mfr
N.A.I.C.S.: 311821

VICHITBHAN PALMOIL PUBLIC COMPANY LIMITED
2044 Chavananand Building Phetburi Extension Road Bangkabi, Huai Kwang, Bangkok, 10310, Thailand
Tel.: (66) 23144101   TH
Web Site:
 https://www.vcbpalmoil.com
Year Founded: 1987
VPO—(THA)
Rev.: $36,975,249
Assets: $32,748,150
Liabilities: $14,916,863
Net Worth: $17,831,287
Earnings: ($977,461)
Emp.: 352
Fiscal Year-end: 12/31/20
Crude Palm Oil Mfr & Distr
N.A.I.C.S.: 324199
Bandhoon Supakavanich *(Chm, Pres & Chm-Audit Committee)*

Subsidiaries:

Ragtai Center Co., Ltd. (1)

VICINITY LIMITED
Level 4 Chadstone Tower One 1341 Dandenong Road, PO Box 104, Chadstone, Melbourne, 3148, VIC, Australia
Tel.: (61) 370014000   AU
Web Site: https://www.vicinity.com.au
CNRAF—(OTCIQ)
Rev.: $905,943,056
Assets: $11,916,246,594
Liabilities: $3,576,191,825
Net Worth: $8,340,054,769
Earnings: $931,074,088
Emp.: 1,266
Fiscal Year-end: 06/30/22
Investment Holding Company; Shopping Center Real Estate Investment Trust
N.A.I.C.S.: 551112
Carolyn Reynolds *(Gen Counsel)*

Subsidiaries:

Vicinity Centres RE Ltd. (1)
Level 28 35 Collins Street, Melbourne, 3000, VIC, Australia
Tel.: (61) 392366300
Web Site: http://www.vicinity.com.au
Shopping Center Real Estate Investment Trust
N.A.I.C.S.: 525990
Carolyn Reynolds *(Gen Counsel)*

Subsidiary (Domestic):

Vicinity Centres PM Pty Ltd (2)
Level 4 Chadstone Tower One 1341 Dandenong Road, PO Box 104, Chadstone, 3148, VIC, Australia   (100%)
Tel.: (61) 370014000

Web Site: https://www.vicinity.com.au
Retail Properties Management & Development
N.A.I.C.S.: 531312

Unit (Domestic):

Chatswood Chase, Sydney (3)
345 Victoria Ave, Chatswood, 2067, NSW, Australia
Tel.: (61) 294225300
Web Site:
 https://www.chatswoodchasesydney.com
Shopping Plaza Property Manager & Unit Lessor
N.A.I.C.S.: 531120

VICINITY MOTOR CORP.
3168 262nd Street, Aldergrove, V4W 2Z6, BC, Canada
Tel.: (604) 607-4000   BC
Web Site:
 http://www.grandewest.com
Year Founded: 2008
VEV—(NASDAQ)
Rev.: $18,475,000
Assets: $55,032,000
Liabilities: $18,200,000
Net Worth: $36,832,000
Earnings: ($17,948,000)
Emp.: 57
Fiscal Year-end: 12/31/22
Bus Mfr
N.A.I.C.S.: 336999
William R. Trainer *(Pres & CEO)*

VICKERS-WARNICK
870 Arvin Ave, Stoney Creek, L8E 5P2, ON, Canada
Tel.: (905) 662-7737
Web Site: http://www.vickers-warnick.com
Rev.: $12,241,849
Emp.: 45
Safety, Guarding, Sensing & Motion Control Machinery Distr
N.A.I.C.S.: 333248

VICO INTERNATIONAL HOLDINGS LIMITED
Unit D 11/F Billion Plaza II No 10 Cheung Yue Street, Cheung Sha Wan, Kowloon, China (Hong Kong)
Tel.: (852) 27280263   Ky
Web Site:
 http://www.vicointernational.hk
Year Founded: 1997
1621—(HKG)
Rev.: $129,672,218
Assets: $33,254,040
Liabilities: $7,360,065
Net Worth: $25,893,975
Earnings: $1,121,490
Emp.: 31
Fiscal Year-end: 03/31/23
Diesel & Lubricant Oil Whslr
N.A.I.C.S.: 424720
Pui Sing Hui *(Founder & Chm)*

VICON HOLDINGS LIMITED
Office D 16/F MG Tower 133 Hoi Bun Road, Kowloon,
China (Hong Kong)   Ky
Web Site: https://www.vicon.com.hk
Year Founded: 2016
3878—(HKG)
Rev.: $53,298,273
Assets: $43,315,271
Liabilities: $10,314,389
Net Worth: $33,000,882
Earnings: $305,571
Emp.: 22
Fiscal Year-end: 03/31/23
Holding Company
N.A.I.C.S.: 551112
Kwok Chun Chow *(Chm)*

VICORE PHARMA HOLDING AB
Kronhusgatan 11, 411 05, Gothenburg, Sweden
Tel.: (46) 317880560
Web Site:
 https://www.vicorepharma.com
Year Founded: 2000
VICO—(OMX)
Rev.: $224,320
Assets: $31,658,378
Liabilities: $4,582,315
Net Worth: $27,076,063
Earnings: ($27,014,152)
Emp.: 23
Fiscal Year-end: 12/31/22
Biotechnology Research & Development Services
N.A.I.C.S.: 541714
Carl-Johan Dalsgaard *(CEO)*

Subsidiaries:

Vicore Pharma AB (1)
Kornhamnstorg 53, 111 27, Stockholm, Sweden
Tel.: (46) 317880560
Pharmaceuticals Product Mfr
N.A.I.C.S.: 325412

VICPLAS INTERNATIONAL LTD
35 Joo Koon Circle, Singapore, 629110, Singapore
Tel.: (65) 62623888
Web Site: https://www.vicplas.com
569—(SES)
Rev.: $95,751,019
Assets: $88,196,369
Liabilities: $29,983,698
Net Worth: $58,212,671
Earnings: $3,140,422
Fiscal Year-end: 07/31/23
Pipes Mfr
N.A.I.C.S.: 339992
Ying Hui Gan *(CFO)*

Subsidiaries:

Arrow Medical Limited (1)
Hatton Gardens Industrial Estate, Kington, HR5 3RB, Herefordshire, United Kingdom
Tel.: (44) 1544231760
Web Site: https://www.arrowmedical.co.uk
Medical Equipment Mfr
N.A.I.C.S.: 334510

Forefront (Xiamen) Medical Devices Co., Ltd. (1)
Xiamen Export Processing Zone Hai Cang Hai Jing Dong Road No 28, Xiamen, China
Tel.: (86) 5923675888
Medical Devices
N.A.I.C.S.: 621610

Forefront Medical Technology (Pte) Ltd (1)
35 Joo Koon Circle, Singapore, 629110, Singapore
Tel.: (65) 63493888
Web Site: https://forefrontmedical.com
Sales Range: $100-124.9 Million
Emp.: 300
Medical Device Mfr
N.A.I.C.S.: 334510

Rimplas Industries Sdn Bhd (1)
Lot 62981 jalan gajus Jalan Taman Tampoi, 81200, Johor Bahru, Johor, Malaysia
Tel.: (60) 72358028
Web Site: http://www.vicplas.com
Sales Range: $25-49.9 Million
Emp.: 72
Pipe Fittings Mfr & Distr
N.A.I.C.S.: 331511
Chong Suinkee *(Mgr)*

VicPlas Holdings Pte Ltd (1)
35 Joo Koon Circle, Singapore, 629110, Singapore
Tel.: (65) 62623888
Web Site: https://www.vicplas.com.sg
Sales Range: $50-74.9 Million
Emp.: 100
Pipe Fittings Mfr & Distr

N.A.I.C.S.: 326122
XentiQ (Pte.) Ltd. (1)
35 Joo Koon Circle Vicplas Building 6th Floor, Singapore, 629110, Singapore
Tel.: (65) 68610889
Web Site: https://www.xentiq.sg
Complex Prototype Mfr
N.A.I.C.S.: 336414

VICTEK CO., LTD.
25 Songdogwahak-ro 55 beon-gil, Yeonsu-gu, Incheon, 21984, Gyeonggi-do, Korea (South)
Tel.: (82) 328137301
Web Site: https://www.victek.co.kr
Year Founded: 1996
065450—(KRS)
Rev.: $57,045,542
Assets: $73,794,625
Liabilities: $26,974,187
Net Worth: $46,820,438
Earnings: ($177,683)
Emp.: 205
Fiscal Year-end: 12/31/22
Power Supply Device Mfr
N.A.I.C.S.: 335999
Lim Man Kyu *(CEO)*

VICTOR CHANDLER INTERNATIONAL LTD.
Chandler House Suite 1a 1st Fl Leanse Place 50 Town Range, Gibraltar, Gibraltar
Tel.: (350) 200 45522   GI
Web Site: http://www.betvictor.com
Year Founded: 1946
Sales Range: $200-249.9 Million
Emp.: 600
Sports Betting Services & Online Gaming Platform Operator
N.A.I.C.S.: 713290
Michael Tabor *(Owner)*

VICTOR GROUP HOLDINGS LIMITED
Level 26 1 Bligh Street, Sydney, 2000, NSW, Australia
Tel.: (61) 282268786
Web Site: https://www.sinovictor.com
VIG—(ASX)
Rev.: $5,674,624
Assets: $9,161,397
Liabilities: $4,759,180
Net Worth: $4,402,217
Earnings: ($2,357,941)
Fiscal Year-end: 06/30/24
Marketing Consulting Services
N.A.I.C.S.: 541613
Zhang Bin *(Deputy Chm & CEO)*

VICTOR HASSELBLAD AB
Utvecklingsgatan 2, 417 56, Gothenburg, Sweden
Tel.: (46) 31102460
Web Site: http://www.hasselblad.com
Year Founded: 1941
Sales Range: $75-99.9 Million
Emp.: 180
Camera Mfr
N.A.I.C.S.: 333310
Paul Bram *(CEO)*

Subsidiaries:

Hasselblad (UK) Ltd. (1)
385 Centenial Avenue, Elstree, WD6 3TJ, Herts, United Kingdom
Tel.: (44) 2087313250
Web Site: http://www.hasselblad.co.uk
Sales Range: $25-49.9 Million
Emp.: 20
Marketing & Sales
N.A.I.C.S.: 541613
Ian Rawcliffe *(CEO)*

Hasselblad A/S (1)
Hejrevej 30, Copenhagen, DK-2400, Denmark
Tel.: (45) 70260800
Web Site: http://www.hasselbled.com

VICTOR HASSELBLAD AB

Victor Hasselblad AB—(Continued)
Sales Range: $25-49.9 Million
Camera Mfr
N.A.I.C.S.: 333310

Hasselblad Bron Inc. (1)
1080A Garden State Rd, Union, NJ 07083
Tel.: (908) 754-5800
Web Site: http://www.hasselbladbron.com
Photographic Equipment Distr
N.A.I.C.S.: 423410
Greg Hollmann *(Reg Mgr-Sls-NYC Metro)*

Hasselblad France S.A. (1)
5 Passage Piver, 75011, Paris,
France **(100%)**
Tel.: (33) 155289310
Web Site: http://www.hasselblad.fr
Sales Range: $25-49.9 Million
Emp.: 5
Marketing & Sales Consulting
N.A.I.C.S.: 541613
Franck Bernard *(Mgr-Sls)*

Hasselblad Japan KK (1)
1-10-32 Jingumae, Shibuya-ku, Tokyo, 150-0001, Japan
Tel.: (81) 3 6434 9567
Web Site: http://www.hasselblad.jp
Photographic Equipment Mfr & Distr
N.A.I.C.S.: 333310

Hasselblad USA, Inc. (1)
1080A Garden State Rd, Union, NJ 07004-2330
Tel.: (973) 227-7320
Web Site: http://www.hasselbladusa.com
Sales Range: $25-49.9 Million
Emp.: 35
Importer & Distributor of Cameras
N.A.I.C.S.: 423410

Hasselblad Vertriebsgesellschaft GmbH (1)
An Der Strusbek 32, 22926, Ahrensburg,
Germany **(100%)**
Tel.: (49) 410249101
Web Site: http://www.hasselblad.de
Sales Range: $1-9.9 Million
Emp.: 11
Marketing Sales
N.A.I.C.S.: 541613
Renate Duwe *(Controller)*

VICTOR INNOVATEX INC.
2805 90th St, Saint-Georges, G6A 1K1, QC, Canada
Tel.: (418) 227-9897
Web Site: http://www.victorgroup.com
Year Founded: 1947
Sales Range: $25-49.9 Million
Emp.: 150
Fabric & Apparel Mfr
N.A.I.C.S.: 313210
Alain Duval *(Pres & CEO)*

Subsidiaries:

Victor Innovative Textiles (1)
941 Grinnell St 81 Commerce Dr, Fall River, MA 02720-5215
Tel.: (508) 678-1951
Web Site: http://www.victorgroup.com
Sales Range: $150-199.9 Million
Upholstery & Fabric Mfr
N.A.I.C.S.: 313210

VICTOR INTERNATIONAL A/S
Lyngbyvej 70, 2100, Copenhagen, Denmark
Tel.: (45) 39181870
Web Site: http://www.hmj-group.dk
Year Founded: 1996
Real Estate Property Management & Leasing Services
N.A.I.C.S.: 531110
Anders Hillerup *(Chm)*

VICTORIA CAPITAL PARTNERS LP
Bouchard 547 13th Fl, Buenos Aires, Argentina
Tel.: (54) 11 4312 3505
Web Site: http://www.victoriacp.com

Privater Equity Firm
N.A.I.C.S.: 523999
Carlos Garcia *(Mng Partner)*

VICTORIA GOLD CORP.
80 Richmond Street West Suite 204, Toronto, M5H 2A4, ON, Canada
Tel.: (416) 866-8800
Web Site:
  https://vgcx2023.s0.adnetcms.com
VGCX—(OTCIQ)
Rev.: $139,830,850
Assets: $607,644,295
Liabilities: $316,583,517
Net Worth: $291,060,778
Earnings: $11,649,643
Emp.: 399
Fiscal Year-end: 12/31/20
Gold Exploration & Mining Services
N.A.I.C.S.: 212220
Terence Sean Harvey *(Chm)*

Subsidiaries:

Golden Predator Mining Corp. (1)
Suite 250 200 Burrard Street, Vancouver, V6C 3L6, BC, Canada
Tel.: (604) 757-7180
Web Site: http://www.goldenpredator.com
Assets: $9,794,622
Liabilities: $2,346,885
Net Worth: $7,447,737
Earnings: ($7,067,375)
Fiscal Year-end: 12/31/2019
Gold Ore Exploration & Mining Development Services
N.A.I.C.S.: 213114

Subsidiary (Domestic):

Yukon Mint Corporation. (2)
250-200 Burrard Street, Vancouver, V6C 3L6, BC, Canada
Tel.: (604) 260-0289
Web Site: http://www.yukonmint.com
Gold & Silver Mining Services
N.A.I.C.S.: 212220

VICTORIA GROUP A.D.
Bulevar Mihajla Pupina 115b, 11070, Novi Beograd, Serbia
Tel.: (381) 113532700   RS
Web Site: http://www.victoriagroup.rs
Year Founded: 2001
Emp.: 1,500
Holding Company; Agricultural Products Processor & Distr
N.A.I.C.S.: 551112
Thomas Boitani FitzGerald *(Chief Strategy Officer & Member-Exec Bd)*

Subsidiaries:

Fertil d.o.o. (1)
Industrijska zona 35, 21400, Backa
Palanka, Serbia **(100%)**
Tel.: (381) 21 7551 801
Web Site: http://www.fertil.rs
Mineral Fertilizer Mfr
N.A.I.C.S.: 325314
Igor Rados *(Gen Mgr)*

Luka Backa Palanka d.o.o. (1)
II Zeleznicko nasalje 2A, 21400, Backa
Palanka, Serbia **(100%)**
Tel.: (381) 21 60 40 064
Web Site: http://www.lukabp.rs
Emp.: 33
Transport & Nautical Port Services; Construction Material Mfr & Distr
N.A.I.C.S.: 488310
Milivoje Kujundzic *(Gen Mgr & Dir)*

Riboteks d.o.o. (1)
Industrijska zona BB, 15320, Ljubovija,
Serbia **(100%)**
Tel.: (381) 31 856 850
Web Site: http://www.riboteks.rs
Emp.: 14
Rainbow Trout & Trout Juvenile Farming & Distr
N.A.I.C.S.: 112511
Bora Krstic *(Gen Mgr)*

SP Laboratorija a.d. (1)

Industrijska 3, 21220, Becej,
Serbia **(100%)**
Tel.: (381) 21 6811 603
Web Site: http://www.splaboratorija.rs
Emp.: 378
Laboratory Testing Services
N.A.I.C.S.: 541380
Aleksandra Bauer *(CEO)*

Victoria Logistic d.o.o. (1)
Hajduk Veljkova 11, 21000, Novi Sad,
Serbia **(100%)**
Tel.: (381) 21 4886 508
Web Site: http://www.victorialogistic.rs
Emp.: 252
Integrated Logistics Services
N.A.I.C.S.: 484121
Mladen Jovanovic *(Gen Mgr)*

Victoria Phosphate d.o.o. (1)
Bulevar Mihajla Pupina 115b, 11070, Novi
Beograd, Serbia **(100%)**
Tel.: (381) 11 3532 700
Web Site: http://www.victoriagroup.rs
Mine & Phosphate Flotation Facility Designer & Developer
N.A.I.C.S.: 236210

Victoria Starch d.o.o. (1)
Petra Drapsina 1, 23000, Zrenjanin,
Serbia **(100%)**
Tel.: (381) 23 3155 050
Web Site: http://www.victoriagroup.rs
Emp.: 25
Starch Mfr
N.A.I.C.S.: 311221

Victoriaoil a.d. (1)
Branka Erica br 2, 22240, Sid,
Serbia **(100%)**
Tel.: (381) 22725419
Web Site: http://www.victoriaoil.rs
Emp.: 305
Cooking Oils, Biodiesel & Other Related Products Mfr & Whslr
N.A.I.C.S.: 311225
Srdan Popov *(Dir-Ops)*

VICTORIA MILLS LTD.
Victoria House Pandurang Budhkar Marg Lower Parel, Mumbai, 400013, India
Tel.: (91) 2224971192
Web Site: https://www.victoriamills.in
503349—(BOM)
Rev.: $3,123,542
Assets: $7,921,000
Liabilities: $1,474,852
Net Worth: $6,446,148
Earnings: $280,523
Emp.: 6
Fiscal Year-end: 03/31/23
Textile Fabric Mfr
Aditya Harshavadan Mangaldas
(Chm & Mng Dir)

VICTORIA NISSAN LTD
3361 Oak Street, Victoria, V8X 1R2, BC, Canada
Tel.: (250) 475-2227
Web Site:
  https://www.campusnissan.com
Rev.: $25,758,891
Emp.: 55
New & Used Car Dealers
N.A.I.C.S.: 441110
Rick Roorda *(Mgr-Sls)*

VICTORIA OIL & GAS PLC
Hatfield House 52-54 Stamford Street, London, SE1 9LX, United Kingdom
Tel.: (44) 207 921 8820   UK
Web Site:
  www.victoriaoilandgas.com
VOG—(LSE)
Sales Range: $25-49.9 Million
Oil & Gas Exploration
N.A.I.C.S.: 213112
Kevin Foo *(Chm)*

INTERNATIONAL PUBLIC

Subsidiaries:

Gaz du Cameroun Sarl (1)
Rue Vasnitex Bonapriso, BP 12874,
Douala, Cameroon
Tel.: (237) 233428209
Web Site: http://www.gazducameroun.com
Natural Gas Distribution Services
N.A.I.C.S.: 221210
Eric Friend *(Mng Dir)*

VICTORIA PLC
Worcester Six Business Park, Worcester, WR4 0AE, Worcestershire, United Kingdom
Tel.: (44) 2079338780
Web Site: https://www.victoriaplc.com
VCP—(AIM)
Rev.: $899,217,956
Assets: $1,838,895,968
Liabilities: $1,556,218,664
Net Worth: $282,677,304
Earnings: $3,801,616
Emp.: 3,475
Fiscal Year-end: 04/03/21
Textile Mfr
N.A.I.C.S.: 313110
Geoffrey Wilding *(Chm)*

Subsidiaries:

Abingdon Flooring Limited (1)
Wharfedale Business Park Edward Street, Bradford, BD4 9RT, United Kingdom
Tel.: (44) 127 465 5694
Web Site:
  https://www.abingdonflooring.co.uk
Emp.: 300
Textile Products Mfr
N.A.I.C.S.: 313310
Steve Byrne *(Mng Dir)*

Carpet Line Direct Limited (1)
Park View Road East Brenda Rd, Hartlepool, TS25 1HT, United Kingdom
Tel.: (44) 142 989 2500
Web Site: https://www.carpetlinedirect.co.uk
Floor Covering Product Whslr
N.A.I.C.S.: 449121
Nick Finlay *(Comml Dir)*

Ceramiche Serra S.p.A. (1)
Via Estense Nr 10589, Torremaina Di, 41053, Maranello, Italy
Tel.: (39) 053 695 9100
Web Site: https://www.ceramicheserra.com
Ceramic Mfr
N.A.I.C.S.: 327110

Colin Campbell & Sons Ltd (1)
55-8385 Fraser St, Vancouver, V5X 3X8, BC, Canada
Tel.: (604) 734-2758
Web Site: http://www.colin-campbell.ca
Sales Range: $25-49.9 Million
Emp.: 14
Carpets & Rugs Mfr
N.A.I.C.S.: 314110
Chris Dragan *(VP-Fin & Gen Mgr)*

Distinctive Flooring Limited (1)
Worcester Road, Kidderminster, DY10 1JR, United Kingdom
Tel.: (44) 156 274 9300
Web Site:
  https://www.victoriadesignfloors.co.uk
Floor Covering & Carpet Distr
N.A.I.C.S.: 449121

Gaskell Mackay Carpets Limited (1)
ParkView Road East, Hartlepool, TS25 1HT, United Kingdom
Tel.: (44) 142 989 2525
Web Site: https://www.gaskell.co.uk
Floor Covering Mfr & Distr
N.A.I.C.S.: 321918

Interfloor Ltd. (1)
Broadway, Haslingden, Rossendale, BB4 4LS, Lancashire, United Kingdom
Tel.: (44) 1706213131
Web Site: https://www.interfloor.com
Sales Range: $1-4.9 Billion
Emp.: 6,000
Carpeting, Flooring Adhesives & Underlays Mfr
N.A.I.C.S.: 314110
John Cooper *(CEO & Mng Dir)*

International Wholesale Tile, LLC (1)
3500 SW 42nd Ave, Palm City, FL 34990-5613
Tel.: (772) 223-5151
Web Site:
http://www.internationalwholesaletile.com
Construction Material Merchant Whslr
N.A.I.C.S.: 423390
Grey Perna (Dir-Builder Programs)

Keradom S.r.l. (1)
Via Botticelli 10, 42048, Rubiera, Italy
Tel.: (39) 052 299 9377
Web Site: https://www.keradom.it
Ceramic & Concrete Mfr
N.A.I.C.S.: 327999
Mauro Cavazzoli (Chm & Gen Mgr)

Millennium Weavers N.V. (1)
Industrie Park Klein Frankrijkstraat 38, 9600, Ronse, Belgium
Tel.: (32) 5 550 9054
Web Site:
https://www.millenniumweavers.be
Carpet Distr
N.A.I.C.S.: 423220
Jan Van Damme (Mng Dir)

The Victoria Carpet Company Pty Limited (1)
7-29 Gladstone Road, Dandenong, 3175, VIC, Australia
Tel.: (61) 397945855
Web Site: http://www.victoriacarpets.com.au
Sales Range: $25-49.9 Million
Emp.: 200
Carpet Mfr & Whslr
N.A.I.C.S.: 314110
Phil Smith (Mng Dir)

Victoria Carpets Limited (1)
Worcester Road, Kidderminster, DY10 1JR, Worcestershire, United Kingdom
Tel.: (44) 1562749300
Web Site: http://www.victoriacarpets.com
Sales Range: $25-49.9 Million
Emp.: 250
Carpet Mfr & Whslr
N.A.I.C.S.: 314110

View Logistics Limited (1)
View Logistics ParkView Road East, Hartlepool, TS25 1HT, United Kingdom
Tel.: (44) 142 989 2550
Web Site: https://www.viewlogistics.co.uk
Logistic Services
N.A.I.C.S.: 541614

VICTORIA RACING CLUB LIMITED
448 Epsom Rd, Flemington, 3031, VIC, Australia
Tel.: (61) 392584666 AU
Web Site: http://www.vrc.net.au
Year Founded: 1864
Sales Range: $100-124.9 Million
Emp.: 250
Horse Racing Management & Services
N.A.I.C.S.: 711219
Julian Sullivan (Gen Mgr-Membership Svcs)

VICTORIA STAR MOTORS INC.
125 Centennial RD, Kitchener, N2B 3E9, ON, Canada
Tel.: (519) 579-4460
Web Site:
http://www.victoriastar.mercedes-benz.ca
Rev.: $15,633,200
Emp.: 35
New & Used Car Dealers
N.A.I.C.S.: 441110
Justin Nesbitt (Gen Mgr)

VICTORIAN PLUMBING GROUP PLC
22 Grimrod Place, Skelmersdale, WN8 9UU, United Kingdom
Tel.: (44) 2037271000 UK
Web Site:
https://www.victorianplumbing.com
Year Founded: 2021

VIC—(AIM)
Rev.: $359,883,868
Assets: $124,968,442
Liabilities: $63,367,836
Net Worth: $61,600,606
Earnings: $14,895,228
Emp.: 612
Fiscal Year-end: 09/30/23
Ecommerce Retailer
N.A.I.C.S.: 459999

VICTORIAS MILLING COMPANY, INC.
VMC Compound J J Ossorio St Barangay XVI, Negros Occidental, Victorias, 6119, Philippines
Tel.: (63) 344887900 PH
Web Site:
https://www.victoriasmilling.com
Year Founded: 1919
VMC—(PHI)
Rev.: $208,683,386
Assets: $240,986,513
Liabilities: $42,052,188
Net Worth: $198,934,325
Earnings: $27,947,403
Emp.: 649
Fiscal Year-end: 08/31/23
Sugar Mill & Refinery
N.A.I.C.S.: 311314
Eduardo V. Concepcion (CEO)

Subsidiaries:

Victorias Foods Corporation (1)
Vicmico Compound Victorias, Victorias, Negros Occidental, Philippines
Tel.: (63) 343993513
Sales Range: $25-49.9 Million
Emp.: 30
Food Processing Services
N.A.I.C.S.: 311991
Taime Unsol (Mgr)

VICTORINOX AG
Schmiedgasse 57 Ibach, 6438, Schwyz, Switzerland
Tel.: (41) 418181211
Web Site: http://www.victorinox.com
Year Founded: 1884
Sales Range: $125-149.9 Million
Emp.: 950
Pocket Knife & Cutlery Mfr & Distr
N.A.I.C.S.: 332215
Gloria Dix (Head-Global Travel Retail & Fragrances Sls)

Subsidiaries:

Victorinox Swiss Army, Inc. (1)
7 Victoria Dr, Monroe, CT 06468
Tel.: (203) 929-6391
Web Site: http://www.swissarmy.com
Sales Range: $75-99.9 Million
Emp.: 150
Cutlery & Pocket Knives Watch Apparel Luggage & Travel Accessory Marketer & Distr
N.A.I.C.S.: 423710
Carl Elsener (CEO)

VICTORY BATTERY METALS CORP.
Suite 1780 355 Burrard St, Vancouver, V6C 2G8, BC, Canada
Tel.: (236) 317-2822 Ca
Web Site:
https://www.victorybatterymetal.com
Year Founded: 1984
VR—(CNSX)
Rev.: $1,074
Assets: $1,893,640
Liabilities: $473,010
Net Worth: $1,420,630
Earnings: ($2,024,401)
Emp.: 10
Fiscal Year-end: 02/29/24
Minerals Exploration
N.A.I.C.S.: 213114

Subsidiaries:

Victory Resources Corporation
U.S.A. (1)
701 W Deer Valley Rd Ste 2, Phoenix, AZ 85027
Tel.: (623) 251-4443
Mineral Exploration Services
N.A.I.C.S.: 213115

VICTORY CAPITAL JOINT STOCK COMPANY
12 Tan Trao Phuong Tan Phu Quan 7, Ho Chi Minh City, Vietnam
Tel.: (84) 854161020
Web Site:
http://www.petroland.com.vn
PTL—(HOSE)
Rev.: $827,955
Assets: $26,568,520
Liabilities: $6,515,533
Net Worth: $20,052,988
Earnings: $98,303
Emp.: 22
Fiscal Year-end: 12/31/23
Real Estate Investment Services
N.A.I.C.S.: 531390

VICTORY CITY INTERNATIONAL HOLDINGS LIMITED
Flat D 3rd Floor Winfield Industrial Building 3 Kin Kwan Street, Tuen Mun, New Territories, China (Hong Kong)
Tel.: (852) 24623807 BM
Web Site:
http://www.victorycity.com.hk
Year Founded: 1983
0539—(HKG)
Rev.: $586,097,782
Assets: $1,593,699,720
Liabilities: $746,448,614
Net Worth: $847,251,106
Earnings: $21,571,853
Emp.: 3,610
Fiscal Year-end: 03/31/20
Holding Company; Knitted Fabric Mfr
N.A.I.C.S.: 551112
Wing Shuen Sy (Mgr-Sls)

Subsidiaries:

Best Linkage (Macao Commercial Offshore) Limited (1)
10 F Flat L Ed Macau Plz Ave Infante D Henrique, Macau, China (Macau)
Tel.: (853) 28259793
Quality Inspection Services
N.A.I.C.S.: 541350

Top Star Limited (1)
19 Fl 37-39 Wing Hong St, Kowloon, China (Hong Kong)
Tel.: (852) 24846688
Web Site: http://www.teelocker.com
Sales Range: $50-74.9 Million
Emp.: 70
Property Holding Services
N.A.I.C.S.: 531311

V-Apparel International Limited (1)
Unit D 3 F Winfield Indus Bldg 3 Kin Kwan St, Tuen Mun, 852, New Territories, China (Hong Kong)
Tel.: (852) 24623807
Garments Whslr
N.A.I.C.S.: 424350

Victory City Company Limited (1)
No 1 Indus Rd E Luokeng, Xinhui Dist, Jiangmen, 529157, Guangdong, China
Tel.: (86) 7506462168
Knitted Fabric Mfr
N.A.I.C.S.: 313240

VICTORY GIANT TECHNOLOGY HUIZHOU CO., LTD.
Xingcheng Technology Park Danshui Street, Huiyang District, Huizhou, Guangdong, China
Tel.: (86) 7523723668
Web Site: https://www.shpcb.com

300476—(CHIN)
Rev.: $1,107,075,060
Assets: $2,008,249,308
Liabilities: $1,034,314,164
Net Worth: $973,935,144
Earnings: $111,007,260
Emp.: 9,000
Fiscal Year-end: 12/31/22
Circuit Board Mfr & Distr
N.A.I.C.S.: 334412

VICTORY GROUP LIMITED
Room 1609 New East Ocean Centre 9 Science Museum Road Tsimshatsui East, Kowloon, China (Hong Kong)
Tel.: (852) 27213823 BM
Web Site: http://www.victoryg.com
Sales Range: $1-9.9 Million
Automotive Products Whslr
N.A.I.C.S.: 423120
Wai Kei Leung (Sec)

VICTORY METALS, INC.
PO Box 48264, Bentall Centre, Vancouver, V7X 1A1, BC, Canada
Tel.: (604) 618-4919
Web Site: http://www.victorymetals.ca
VMX—(TSXV)
Rev.: $43,041
Assets: $7,194,441
Liabilities: $95,576
Net Worth: $7,098,864
Earnings: ($1,950,719)
Fiscal Year-end: 03/31/20
Copper & Cobalt Mining Services
N.A.I.C.S.: 212290
Collin Kettell (Co-Founder & CEO)

VICTORY MINES LIMITED
Ground Floor BGC Centre 28 The Esplanade, Perth, 6000, WA, Australia
Tel.: (61) 863162200
Web Site:
http://www.victorymines.com
Year Founded: 2011
JAV—(ASX)
Rev.: $4,446
Assets: $4,417,154
Liabilities: $180,563
Net Worth: $4,236,591
Earnings: ($2,532,393)
Fiscal Year-end: 06/30/24
Metal Ore Mining
N.A.I.C.S.: 212290
Dane Etheridge (Sec)

VICTORY MOUNTAIN VENTURES LTD.
Suite 430-609 Granville Street, Vancouver, V7Y IG5, BC, Canada
Tel.: (604) 683-5445 BC
Web Site: http://victorymv.com
Year Founded: 1996
Sales Range: Less than $1 Million
Mineral Exploration Services
N.A.I.C.S.: 212290
Douglas McFaul (CFO)

VICTORY NEW MATERIALS LIMITED COMPANY
Qingyang Lianyu Industrial Area, Jinjiang, Fujian, China
Tel.: (86) 59582889862
Web Site: http://www.vnm.com.tw
1340—(TAI)
Rev.: $165,569,991
Assets: $876,130,179
Liabilities: $38,008,648
Net Worth: $838,121,531
Earnings: ($62,724,164)
Emp.: 930
Fiscal Year-end: 12/31/19
Shoe Mfr
N.A.I.C.S.: 316210

VICTORY NEW MATERIALS LIMITED COMPANY

Victory New Materials Limited Company—(Continued)

Subsidiaries:

Chandra Shoes Industry Co., Ltd. (1)
Jinjiang Lianyu Industrial Zone Airport Diagonally Opposite, Jinjiang, 362200, China
Tel.: (86) 59585661222
Web Site:
http://www.chengchangshoes.com
Footwear Mfr
N.A.I.C.S.: 316210

VICTORY NICKEL INC.
Victory Building 80 Richmond Street West 18th Floor, Toronto, M5H 2A4, ON, Canada
Tel.: (416) 363-8527   ON
Web Site: http://www.victorynickel.ca
Year Founded: 2007
NI—(CNSX)
Rev.: $450,000
Assets: $16,995,000
Liabilities: $25,607,000
Net Worth: ($8,612,000)
Earnings: ($6,144,000)
Emp.: 41
Fiscal Year-end: 12/31/20
Nickel Mining & Exploration Services
N.A.I.C.S.: 212230
Cynthia P. Thomas *(Chm)*

VICTORY PRODUCTION & COMPANY
70 Gukjegeumyung-ro
Yeongdeungpo-gu, Seoul, 150733, Korea (South)
Tel.: (82) 27862245
Television Production
N.A.I.C.S.: 512110

VICTORY SECURITIES (HOLDINGS) COMPANY LTD.
Room 1101-03 11/F Yardley Commercial Building 3 Connaught Road West, Hong Kong, China (Hong Kong)
Tel.: (852) 25252437   Ky
Web Site:
http://www.victorysec.com.hk
Year Founded: 1993
8540—(HKG)
Rev.: $9,831,165
Assets: $46,591,135
Liabilities: $22,498,247
Net Worth: $24,092,888
Earnings: ($3,091,111)
Emp.: 57
Fiscal Year-end: 12/31/22
Securities Trading Services
N.A.I.C.S.: 523150
Kuen Kou *(CEO)*

VICTORY SQUARE TECHNOLOGIES, INC.
800 - 1500 West Georgia, Vancouver, V6G 2Z6, BC, Canada
Tel.: (604) 283-9166
Web Site:
https://www.victorysquare.com
VSQTF—(OTCQX)
Rev.: $4,379,919
Assets: $17,859,218
Liabilities: $8,074,304
Net Worth: $9,784,913
Earnings: $21,118,688)
Fiscal Year-end: 12/31/22
Asset Management Services
N.A.I.C.S.: 523940
Shafin Diamond Tejani *(CEO)*

VICTORY SUPERMARKET CHAIN LTD.
Shidlovsky St 3, Yavne, 70800, Israel
Tel.: (972) 88674994
Web Site: https://www.victory.co.il

Year Founded: 2007
VCTR—(TAE)
Rev.: $627,736,565
Assets: $524,378,559
Liabilities: $424,655,659
Net Worth: $99,722,900
Earnings: $10,005,152
Emp.: 579
Fiscal Year-end: 12/31/22
Supermarket Operator
N.A.I.C.S.: 445110
Eyal Ravid *(CEO)*

VICTREX PLC
Victrex Technology Centre Hillhouse International, Thornton, FY5 4QD, Lancashire, United Kingdom
Tel.: (44) 1253897700   UK
Web Site: https://www.victrexplc.com
Year Founded: 1978
VCT—(LSE)
Rev.: $361,153,520
Assets: $746,067,140
Liabilities: $93,003,820
Net Worth: $653,063,320
Earnings: $73,588,424
Emp.: 978
Fiscal Year-end: 09/30/20
Polymer & Thermoplastic Mfr
N.A.I.C.S.: 326199
Martin Court *(Chief Comml Officer)*

Subsidiaries:

Invibio Limited (1)
Hillhouse International, Thornton Cleveleys, Thornton, FY5 4QD, Lancashire, United Kingdom
Tel.: (44) 1253898000
Sales Range: $25-49.9 Million
Emp.: 30
Polymer Mfr & Sls
N.A.I.C.S.: 325211

Victrex Europa GmbH (1)
Langgasse 16, 65719, Hofheim, Germany
Tel.: (49) 619296490
Sales Range: $25-49.9 Million
Emp.: 30
Polymer Mfr & Sls
N.A.I.C.S.: 325211

Victrex High-Performance Materials (Shanghai) Co., Ltd. (1)
Part B Building G No 1688 Zhuanxing Road, Xinzhuang Industry Park, Shanghai, 201108, China
Tel.: (86) 2161136900
Sales Range: $25-49.9 Million
Emp.: 20
Polymer Mfr & Sales
N.A.I.C.S.: 325211

Victrex USA, Inc (1)
300 Conshohocken State Rd Ste 120, West Conshohocken, PA 19428
Tel.: (484) 342-6001
Emp.: 50
Polymer Mfr & Sales
N.A.I.C.S.: 325211

Subsidiary (Domestic):

Kleiss Gears, Inc. (2)
390 Industrial Ave, Grantsburg, WI 54840
Tel.: (715) 598-4492
Web Site: http://www.kleissgears.com
Sales Range: $1-9.9 Million
Plastic Gear Mfr
N.A.I.C.S.: 326199

VICUNHA TEXTIL S.A.
Rod Doutor Mendel Steinbruch - Km 09/bloco 1, 61939-210, Fortaleza, CE, Brazil
Tel.: (55) 8540081000
Web Site: http://www.vicunha.com.br
Sales Range: $550-599.9 Million
Textile Products Mfr
N.A.I.C.S.: 313210
Jose Mauricio D'isep Costa *(Dir-IR)*

VICUS GROUP AG

Thomaskirchhof 20, 04109, Leipzig, Germany
Tel.: (49) 3412308647
Web Site: http://www.vicus.ag
Commercial Real Estate
N.A.I.C.S.: 531390
Michael Klemmer *(CEO & Partner)*

VIDACHIM AD
Yuzhna promishlena zona, 3700, Vidin, Bulgaria
Tel.: (359) 94600230
Web Site: http://www.vidachim.com
VIDA—(BUL)
Sales Range: Less than $1 Million
Tiles Mfr
N.A.I.C.S.: 326211

VIDAVO SA
10th km Thessalonikis-N Moudanion Balkan Center Building D, 57001, Thessaloniki, Greece
Tel.: (30) 2310474762
Web Site: https://www.vidavo.eu
Year Founded: 2002
VIDAVO—(ATH)
Emp.: 21
Software Development Services
N.A.I.C.S.: 541511
Markella Psimarnou *(CEO)*

VIDEE S.P.A.
Via Roggiuzzole 3, 33170, Pordenone, Italy
Tel.: (39) 0434361016   IT
Web Site: http://www.videe.it
Year Founded: 1988
Motion Picture & Video Production
N.A.I.C.S.: 512110
Bruno Mercuri *(Co-Founder)*

VIDELIO SA
13/15 rue Louis Kerautret Botmel, 35000, Rennes, France
Tel.: (33) 223355757
Web Site: http://www.videlio.com
VDLO—(EUR)
Sales Range: $200-249.9 Million
Audio & Visual Equipment
N.A.I.C.S.: 334310
Guillaume Durieux *(Co-CEO, Member-Exec Bd & VP)*

Subsidiaries:

Auvi One (1)
27 41 Blvd Louise Michel, 92622, Gennevilliers, France
Tel.: (33) 146884200
Web Site: http://www.auvione.eu
Sales Range: $250-299.9 Million
Emp.: 600
Sound Equipment Distr
N.A.I.C.S.: 423690

Cap Cine (1)
3 Rue Villaret de Joyeuse, 75017, Paris, France
Tel.: (33) 140555999
Web Site: http://www.videlio-capcine.fr
Emp.: 17
Audio Equipment Maintenance Services
N.A.I.C.S.: 334310
David Fontaine *(Mng Dir)*

HMS Corporate (1)
25 Rue Louis Brguet BP 11752, 44600, Saint Nazaire, France
Tel.: (33) 251105020
Web Site: http://www.hmsgroup.com
Sales Range: $25-49.9 Million
Emp.: 10
Multimedia System Integration Services
N.A.I.C.S.: 541512

Preview GM System SAS (1)
191-193 Route de Saint Leu, Epinay-sur-Seine, 93800, Paris, Epinay, France
Tel.: (33) 148137171
Web Site: http://www.preview-gm.com

Sales Range: $25-49.9 Million
Emp.: 45
Television Broadcasting Services
N.A.I.C.S.: 516120
Herminio Gaspar *(Dir-Tech)*

Wartsila FUNA International GmbH (1)
Stedinger Str 11, 26723, Emden, Germany   (100%)
Tel.: (49) 49219670
Web Site: http://www.funa.com
Emp.: 200
Engineeering Services
N.A.I.C.S.: 541330

VIDENDUM PLC
Bridge House Heron Square, Richmond, TW9 1EN, United Kingdom
Tel.: (44) 2083324600
Web Site:
https://www.vitecgroup.com
VTC—(LSE)
Rev.: $394,417,660
Assets: $454,293,112
Liabilities: $256,880,624
Net Worth: $197,412,488
Earnings: ($7,195,916)
Emp.: 1,569
Fiscal Year-end: 12/31/20
Supplier of Equipment & Services to the Broadcasting Industry
N.A.I.C.S.: 334220
Martin Green *(Fin Dir)*

Subsidiaries:

Anton/Bauer Inc. (1)
14 Progress Dr, Shelton, CT 06484
Tel.: (203) 929-1100
Web Site: http://www.antonbauer.com
Sales Range: $25-49.9 Million
Emp.: 100
Video Equipments & Accessories Retailer
N.A.I.C.S.: 449210

Autoscript Limited (1)
Bridge House Heron Square, Richmond, TW9 1EN, United Kingdom
Tel.: (44) 845 671 5502
Web Site: https://www.autocue.com
Television Broadcasting Services
N.A.I.C.S.: 516120

Camera Corps Ltd. (1)
Unit 2 111 Chertsey Road, Byfleet, KT14 7AX, Surrey, United Kingdom
Tel.: (44) 193 233 6052
Web Site: https://www.cameracorps.co.uk
Camera Equipment Whslr
N.A.I.C.S.: 423410
Phil Beckett *(VP)*

Gitzo SA (1)
Parc Tertiaire Silic 44 Rue de la Couture, BP 70411, 94150, Rungis, France
Tel.: (33) 178120212
Web Site: http://www.gitzo.fr
Emp.: 16
Camera Mfr
N.A.I.C.S.: 333310
Francesco Bernardi *(Pres)*

Haigh-Farr, Inc. (1)
43 Harvey Rd, Bedford, NH 03110
Tel.: (603) 644-6170
Web Site: http://www.haigh-farr.com
Sales Range: $1-9.9 Million
Emp.: 14
Mfg Radio/Tv Communication Equipment Engineering Services Noncommercial Research Organization
N.A.I.C.S.: 334220

Litepanels Inc. (1)
10932 Burbank Blvd, North Hollywood, CA 91601
Tel.: (818) 752-7009
Web Site: http://www.litepanels.com
Lighting Panels Mfr
N.A.I.C.S.: 335132

Manfrotto Bag Limited (1)
8 Hrtum street, 91450, Jerusalem, Israel
Tel.: (972) 2 5388844
Bags & Leather Apparels Mfr
N.A.I.C.S.: 316990

AND PRIVATE COMPANIES

Manfrotto Distribution Inc. (1)
565 E Crescent Ave, Ramsey, NJ 07446
Tel.: (201) 818-0060
Web Site: http://www.manfrottodistribution.us
Sales Range: $50-74.9 Million
Emp.: 65
Video Equipments & Accessories Distr
N.A.I.C.S.: 423690

Reco Srl (1)
Via Adriano Olivetti 9, Osnago, LC, Italy
Tel.: (39) 039 990 7632
Web Site: https://www.recosrl.it
Automotive Wheel Services
N.A.I.C.S.: 811111

Rycote Microphone Windshields Ltd. (1)
Libbys Drive Slad Road, Stroud, GL5 1RN, Gloucestershire, United Kingdom
Tel.: (44) 145 375 9338
Camera Equipment Mfr & Distr
N.A.I.C.S.: 333310

SmallHD, LLC (1)
301 Gregson Dr, Cary, NC 27511-3600
Tel.: (919) 439-2166
Web Site: https://www.smallhd.com
Sales Range: $1-9.9 Million
Audio & Video Equipment Mfr
N.A.I.C.S.: 334310

Syrp Limited (1)
415 Great South Road, Ellerslie, Auckland, 1051, New Zealand
Tel.: (64) 9 360 9570
Web Site: https://syrp.co
Photographic Equipment Mfr & Distr
N.A.I.C.S.: 333310

Syrp, Inc. (1)
120 E Main St, Ramsey, NJ 07446
Tel.: (201) 818-9500
Web Site: https://syrp.co
Photographic Equipment Mfr & Distr
N.A.I.C.S.: 333310

Teradek, LLC (1)
8 Mason, Irvine, CA 92618
Tel.: (949) 743-5780
Web Site: https://teradek.com
Photographic Equipment Mfr & Distr
N.A.I.C.S.: 333310

The Camera Store Limited (1)
Unit 2 Heathlands Close, Twickenham, TW1 4BP, United Kingdom
Tel.: (44) 208 891 8900
Web Site: https://thecamerastore.co.uk
Photographic Equipment Mfr & Distr
N.A.I.C.S.: 333310

Vitec Imaging Distribution Australia Pty Ltd (1)
2 Baldwin Road, Altona North, Melbourne, 3025, VIC, Australia
Tel.: (61) 130 012 3325
Photographic Equipment Mfr & Distr
N.A.I.C.S.: 333310

Vitec Imaging Distribution GmbH (1)
Ferdinand Porsche Str 19, 51149, Cologne, Germany
Tel.: (49) 22 039 3960
Photographic Equipment Mfr & Distr
N.A.I.C.S.: 333310

Vitec Imaging Distribution HK Limited (1)
Unit 901-902 9th Floor Metroplaza Tower 2 No 223 Hing Fong Road, Kwai Fong, China (Hong Kong)
Tel.: (852) 2 327 6728
Photographic Equipment Mfr & Distr
N.A.I.C.S.: 333310

Vitec Imaging Distribution KK (1)
Shibakoen 3-Chome Bldg 1F 3-1-38 Shibakoen, Minato-ku, Tokyo, 105-0011, Japan
Tel.: (81) 33 405 6521
Photographic Equipment Mfr & Distr
N.A.I.C.S.: 333310

Vitec Imaging Distribution Shanghai Limited (1)
Rm 2704-05 No 2299 West Yanan Road, Shanghai, China
Tel.: (86) 216 236 0808
Photographic Equipment Mfr & Distr

N.A.I.C.S.: 333310

Vitec Imaging Solutions SpA (1)
Via Valsugana 100 Cassola, 36022, Vicenza, Italy
Tel.: (39) 0424555855
Web Site: https://videndummediasolutions.com
Photographic Paper Mfr
N.A.I.C.S.: 325992

Subsidiary (US):

Savage Universal Corporation (2)
550 E Elliot Rd, Chandler, AZ 85225
Tel.: (480) 632-1320
Web Site: https://www.savageuniversal.com
Board & Paper Products Mfr
N.A.I.C.S.: 325992
Henry Coy-Burt *(Plant Mgr)*

Vitec Imaging Solutions UK Limited (1)
Resolution Road, Ashby de la Zouch, LE65 1DW, Leicestershire, United Kingdom
Tel.: (44) 153 056 6090
Photographic Equipment Mfr & Distr
N.A.I.C.S.: 333310

Vitec Production Solutions GmbH (1)
Parkring 29, 85748, Garching, Germany
Tel.: (49) 893 215 8200
Photographic Equipment Mfr & Distr
N.A.I.C.S.: 333310

Vitec Production Solutions KK (1)
Shibakoen 3-chome Bldg 1F 3-1-38 Shibakoen, Minato-ku, Tokyo, 105-0011, Japan
Tel.: (81) 35 457 1381
Photographic Equipment Mfr & Distr
N.A.I.C.S.: 333310

Vitec Production Solutions Limited (1)
William Vinten Building Easlea Road Moreton Hall Estate, Bury Saint Edmunds, IP32 7BY, Suffolk, United Kingdom
Tel.: (44) 128 477 6700
Photographic Equipment Mfr & Distr
N.A.I.C.S.: 333310

Vitec Production Solutions Pte. Limited (1)
6 New Industrial Road 02-02 Hoe Huat Industrial Building, Singapore, 536199, Singapore
Tel.: (65) 6 297 5776
Photographic Equipment Mfr & Distr
N.A.I.C.S.: 333310

Vitec Productions Solutions Limitada (1)
Parque Industrial de Cartago Edificio Numero 68, Cartago, Costa Rica
Tel.: (506) 2 573 1600
Photographic Equipment Mfr & Distr
N.A.I.C.S.: 333310

Vitec Videocom Ltd (1)
Western Way, Bury Saint Edmunds, IP33 3TB, Suffolk, United Kingdom
Tel.: (44) 1284752121
Web Site: http://www.vitecvideocom.com
Sales Range: $75-99.9 Million
Emp.: 250
Camera Equipment
N.A.I.C.S.: 333310

Wooden Camera, Inc. (1)
1826 W Commerce St, Dallas, TX 75208
Web Site: https://www.woodencamera.com
Camera Equipment Whslr
N.A.I.C.S.: 423410

VIDENTE CO., LTD.

12F 84 Gasan digital 1-ro, Geumcheon-gu, Seoul, 08590, Korea (South)
Tel.: (82) 7086686611
Web Site: https://vidente.co.kr
Year Founded: 2002
121800—(KRS)
Rev.: $12,517,911
Assets: $591,577,679
Liabilities: $140,467,189
Net Worth: $451,110,491
Earnings: ($143,607,104)

Emp.: 60
Fiscal Year-end: 12/31/22
Broadcasting Equipment Mfr
N.A.I.C.S.: 334220
Lim Geun *(CEO)*

VIDEOCON INDUSTRIES LIMITED

14 Kms Stone Aurangabad-Paithan Road Chittegaon Taluka Paithan, Aurangabad, 431 105, Maharashtra, India
Tel.: (91) 2431251501
Web Site: https://videoconindustriesltd.com
Year Founded: 1986
Electronic Products Mfr & Distr
N.A.I.C.S.: 334419
Venugopal N. Dhoot *(Chm, CEO & Mng Dir)*

VIDEOTON HOLDING ZRT.

Berenyi ut 72-100, H-8000, Szekesfehervar, Hungary
Tel.: (36) 22533000
Web Site: http://www.videoton.hu
Year Founded: 1938
Rev.: $658,385,851
Assets: $573,867,778
Liabilities: $121,753,419
Net Worth: $452,114,359
Earnings: $71,658,722
Emp.: 9,700
Fiscal Year-end: 12/31/18
Plastic Injection Moulding, Painting, Printing, Machining & Hot Stamping
N.A.I.C.S.: 333511
Peter Lakatos *(Co-CEO)*

Subsidiaries:

KVJ Muvek ZRt. (1)
2 KVJ Muvek Street, Nagyvenyim, 2421, Hungary
Tel.: (36) 25 259 450
Web Site: http://www.kvjmuvek.hu
Emp.: 125
Machine Parts Whslr
N.A.I.C.S.: 332710

Pannonfacility Property Management Kft. (1)
Huvosvolgyi ut 54, 1021, Budapest, Hungary
Tel.: (36) 1 392 1220
Web Site: http://www.pannonfacility.hu
Facility Management Services
N.A.I.C.S.: 561210
Gyula Badacsonyi *(Mng Dir)*

VT Informatika Kft (1)
Berenyi ut 72-100, Szekesfehervar, 8000, Hungary
Tel.: (36) 22533700
Web Site: http://www.inform.videoton.hu
Sales Range: $10-24.9 Million
Emp.: 360
Computer, Peripherals & Software Whslr
N.A.I.C.S.: 423430
Agota Nagy *(Project Mgr)*

VT Mechatronics Kft. (1)
Juharfa 24, Industrial Park, 9027, Gyor, Hungary
Tel.: (36) 96 510 400
Web Site: http://www.vtmechatronics.hu
Semiconductor Machinery Mfr
N.A.I.C.S.: 333242
Zsolt Andrasko *(Co-Mng Dir)*

VT Metal Kft (1)
Berenyi 72, PO Box 342, 8001, Szekesfehervar, Hungary
Tel.: (36) 22533640
Sales Range: $10-24.9 Million
Emp.: 380
Electrical Industrial Apparatus Mfr
N.A.I.C.S.: 335999

VT Plastic Kft. (1)
Berenui ut 72-100, 8000, Szekesfehervar, Hungary
Tel.: (36) 22 533 750
Web Site: http://www.plastic.videoton.hu

Emp.: 340
Plastic Injection Molding
N.A.I.C.S.: 326199

VT Rendszertechnika Kft (1)
Berenyi ut 72-100, 8000, Szekesfehervar, Hungary
Tel.: (36) 22533790
Web Site: http://www.vtsys.videoton.hu
Sales Range: $25-49.9 Million
Emp.: 25
Electrical Equipment & Supply Mfr
N.A.I.C.S.: 335999
Lajos Szucs *(Plant Mgr)*

VT Soft Kft (1)
Pacsirtamezo ut 41, 1036, Budapest, Hungary
Tel.: (36) 14360540
Web Site: http://www.vtsoft.es
Sales Range: $25-49.9 Million
Emp.: 90
Computer Related Services
N.A.I.C.S.: 541511
Edit Ferik *(Mng Dir)*

VTBH-DZU BULGARIA (1)
10 Nikola Petkov Bldv, 6000, Stara Zagora, Bulgaria
Tel.: (359) 42 697 115
Web Site: http://www.dzu-bg.com
Emp.: 800
Semiconductor Machinery Mfr
N.A.I.C.S.: 333242

VTCD Kft. (1)
Aszalvolgyi ut 7, Szekesfehervar, 8000, Hungary
Tel.: (36) 22 533 571
Web Site: http://www.vtcd.hu
CD & Dvds Mfr
N.A.I.C.S.: 334419
Tamas Herczeg *(Mng Dir)*

VTES Kft. - Torokszentmiklos Plant (1)
Dozsa Gyorgy ut 13, 5200, Torokszentmiklos, Hungary
Tel.: (36) 56 390 313
Semiconductor Machinery Mfr
N.A.I.C.S.: 333242

Ventifilt ZRt. (1)
Furdo ut 2-4, PQ Box 26, 4080, Hajdunanas, Hungary
Tel.: (36) 52 381 166
Web Site: http://www.ventifilt.hu
Emp.: 150
Fabricated Steel Mfr
N.A.I.C.S.: 332312

Videoton Autoelektronika Kft (1)
Berenyi ut 72-100, 8000, Szekesfehervar, Hungary
Tel.: (36) 22533500
Sales Range: $300-349.9 Million
Emp.: 1,300
General Auto Repair
N.A.I.C.S.: 811111

Videoton Electronic Assembly Services Kft. (1)
Berenyi ut 72-100, 8000, Szekesfehervar, Hungary
Tel.: (36) 22 533 800
Web Site: http://www.videoton.hu
Sales Range: $200-249.9 Million
Emp.: 610
PCB Assemblies, Electromechanical Subassemblies & Box Build & Final Product Integration
N.A.I.C.S.: 334418
Klambauer Csaba *(Mng Dir)*

Videoton Elektro-Plast Kft. (1)
3 Izzo Str, Kaposvar, 7400, Hungary
Tel.: (36) 82 502 100
Web Site: http://www.vtep.videoton.hu
CD & Dvds Mfr
N.A.I.C.S.: 334310
Balazs Fabian *(Mng Dir)*

Videoton Mechlabor Fejleszto es Gyarto Kft (1)
Huvosvolgyi ut 54, 1021, Budapest, Hungary
Tel.: (36) 13225685
Communication Equipment Mfr
N.A.I.C.S.: 334290

Videoton Precision Kft. (1)

VIDEOTON HOLDING ZRT.

Videoton Holding Zrt.—(Continued)
Berenyi Ut 72-100, 8000, Szekesfehervar, Hungary
Tel.: (36) 22 533 760
Web Site: http://www.preciz.videoton.hu
Machine Parts Whslr
N.A.I.C.S.: 332710
David Herbay *(Deputy Gen Mgr)*

VIDHI SPECIALTY FOOD INGREDIENTS LIMITED
E/27 Commerce Centre 78 Tardeo Road, Mumbai, 400 034, India
Tel.: (91) 2261406666
Web Site:
 https://www.vidhifoodcolours.com
Year Founded: 1994
531717—(BOM)
Rev.: $36,582,300
Assets: $30,792,202
Liabilities: $8,770,930
Net Worth: $22,021,272
Earnings: $4,990,317
Emp.: 67
Fiscal Year-end: 03/31/21
Synthetic Food Colors Trader & Mfr
N.A.I.C.S.: 311999
Bipin M. Manek *(Chm & Co-Mng Dir)*

VIDLI RESTAURANTS LTD.
D-09 Eastern Business District LBS Road Bhandup West, Mumbai, 400078, India
Tel.: (91) 9960092683
Web Site:
 https://www.kamatsindia.com
539659—(BOM)
Rev.: $3,126,383
Assets: $2,674,480
Liabilities: $1,080,067
Net Worth: $1,594,413
Earnings: $182,891
Emp.: 87
Fiscal Year-end: 03/31/23
Restaurant Operators
N.A.I.C.S.: 722511
Vidhi V. Kamat *(Mng Dir)*

VIDRALA S.A.
Barrio Munegazo 22, 01400, Llodio, Spain
Tel.: (34) 946719700
Web Site: https://www.vidrala.com
VID—(MAD)
Rev.: $1,131,991,443
Assets: $1,632,600,219
Liabilities: $822,539,410
Net Worth: $810,060,810
Earnings: $160,447,942
Emp.: 3,766
Fiscal Year-end: 12/31/19
Glass Bottle Mfr
N.A.I.C.S.: 327213
Carlos Delclaux Zulueta *(Chm)*

Subsidiaries:

AIALA VIDRIO, S.A.U. (1)
Barrio Munegazo 22, Llodio, 1400, Alava, Spain
Tel.: (34) 946 719 700
Emp.: 400
Glass Container Mfr
N.A.I.C.S.: 327213
Ricardo Silva *(Gen Mgr)*

CASTELLAR VIDRIO, S.A. (1)
Bergueda 67, Castellar Del Valles, Barcelona, 8211, Spain
Tel.: (34) 937 366 520
Emp.: 300
Glass Container Mfr & Distr
N.A.I.C.S.: 327213
Julio Rubio *(Mng Dir)*

CRISNOVA VIDRIO, S.A. (1)
Calle Carlos Delclaux s/n Poligono Los Villares, Caudete, 2660, Albacete, Spain
Tel.: (34) 965 823 800
Web Site: http://www.vidrala.com
Glass Container Mfr

GALLO VIDRO, S.A. (1)
Rua Vieira de Leiria 1, Marinha Grande, 2430-300, Portugal
Tel.: (351) 244555000
Sales Range: $150-199.9 Million
Emp.: 300
Glass Container Mfr & Whslr
N.A.I.C.S.: 327213
Luis Morna *(Mgr-Production)*

MD VERRE, S.A. (1)
Rue Des Ayettes 2, Ghlin, 7011, Belgium
Tel.: (32) 65 39 52 80
Glass Container Mfr & Distr
N.A.I.C.S.: 327213

OMEGA IMMOBILIERE ET FINANCIERE,S.A. (1)
Rue Des Ayettes 2, Mons, 7011, Hainaut, Belgium
Tel.: (32) 65761000
Real Estate Manangement Services
N.A.I.C.S.: 531390

VIDRARU SA
Str Traian 10, Arges, Romania
Tel.: (40) 248 721900
Sales Range: $1-9.9 Million
Emp.: 7
Real Estate Manangement Services
N.A.I.C.S.: 531390

VIDULLANKA PLC
Level 4 Access Towers No 278 Union Place, 2, Colombo, 2, Sri Lanka
Tel.: (94) 114760000
Web Site: https://www.vidullanka.com
Year Founded: 1997
VLL—(COL)
Rev.: $12,770,665
Assets: $43,353,344
Liabilities: $20,420,401
Net Worth: $22,932,942
Earnings: $3,405,380
Emp.: 240
Fiscal Year-end: 03/31/23
Electrical Energy Transmission Services
N.A.I.C.S.: 221121
S. Ranjan Mather *(Co-Founder)*

VIDWRX INC.
401-220 Cambie Street, Vancouver, V6B 2M9, BC, Canada
Tel.: (604) 683-5510
Year Founded: 2006
Sales Range: Less than $1 Million
Video Content Production Software & Services
N.A.I.C.S.: 513210
George Alexander Fleming *(Founder & CEO)*

VIEGA GMBH & CO. KG
Viega Platz 1, 57439, Attendorn, Germany
Tel.: (49) 2722610
Web Site: http://www.viega.de
Sales Range: $75-99.9 Million
Emp.: 500
Plumbing & Heating Technology Products
N.A.I.C.S.: 332913
Katharina Schulte *(Dir-PR)*

Subsidiaries:

Viega North America (1)
301 N Main St, Wichita, KS 67202
Tel.: (316) 425-7400
Web Site: http://www.stadlerviega.com
Heating System Mfr
N.A.I.C.S.: 333414
Dave Garlow *(Pres & CEO)*

Subsidiary (Domestic):

Viega (2)
2211 Viega Ave, McPherson, KS 67460
Tel.: (620) 241-6369
Web Site: http://www.viega.net

Sales Range: $50-74.9 Million
Emp.: 220
Mfr of Plastic Pipes & Fittings
N.A.I.C.S.: 326122
Nathan Spearman *(CFO)*

VIEL & COMPAGNIE SA
9 place Vendome, 75001, Paris, France
Tel.: (33) 156437020
Web Site: http://www.viel.com
Year Founded: 1920
VIL—(EUR)
Rev.: $1,055,145,638
Assets: $2,850,734,125
Liabilities: $2,226,668,073
Net Worth: $624,066,052
Earnings: $113,473,534
Emp.: 2,477
Fiscal Year-end: 12/31/22
Investment Banking, Securities Dealing & Financial Investment Activities
N.A.I.C.S.: 523150
Patrick Combes *(Chm & CEO)*

Subsidiaries:

Compagnie Financiere Tradition S.A. (1)
11 Rue Langallerie, Case postale 7559, 1002, Lausanne, Switzerland **(67.56%)**
Tel.: (41) 213435252
Web Site: https://www.traditiongroup.com
Rev.: $1,069,833,703
Assets: $1,194,318,182
Liabilities: $703,723,947
Net Worth: $490,594,235
Earnings: $108,002,217
Emp.: 390,167
Fiscal Year-end: 12/31/2022
Holding Company & Securites Broker
N.A.I.C.S.: 551112
Patrick Combes *(Chm, CEO & Member-Exec Bd)*

Subsidiary (Non-US):

ABC Clearing Ltd (2)
The Octagon 27 Middlborough, CO11RA, Colchester, United Kingdom **(100%)**
Tel.: (44) 1206771100
Insurance Agencies & Brokerages
N.A.I.C.S.: 524210

Subsidiary (US):

FXDirectDealer LLC (2)
7 World Trade Ctr 32nd Fl 250 Greenwich St, New York, NY 10007
Tel.: (212) 791-3950
Web Site: http://www.fxdd.com
Sales Range: $25-49.9 Million
Emp.: 170
Develops & Markets Online Foreign Exchange Trading Systems to Financial Institutions & Advisors
N.A.I.C.S.: 541512

Subsidiary (Non-US):

Finacor & Associes S.A. (2)
Ave Fonsny 38 Boite 4, Brussels, 1060, Belgium **(100%)**
Tel.: (32) 22190832
Web Site: http://www.finacor.be
Sales Range: $10-24.9 Million
Emp.: 15
Business Service Centers
N.A.I.C.S.: 561439

Finacor Deutschland GmbH (2)
Hochstrasse 43, 60313, Frankfurt am Main, Germany **(100%)**
Tel.: (49) 69205000
Web Site: http://www.finacor.de
Investment Banking & Securities Brokering Services
N.A.I.C.S.: 523150

Finacor Deutschland GmbH (2)
Landsberger Strasse 404, 81241, Munich, Germany
Tel.: (49) 89293556
Web Site: http://www.finacor.de
Sales Range: $50-74.9 Million
Emp.: 18
Investment Advice
N.A.I.C.S.: 523940

INTERNATIONAL PUBLIC

Finance 2000 S.A. (2)
253 Boulevard Pereire, 75017, Paris, France
Tel.: (33) 156437020
Web Site: http://www.viel.com
Sales Range: $50-74.9 Million
Emp.: 250
Holding Company
N.A.I.C.S.: 551112

Subsidiary (Domestic):

Finarbit SA (2)
Kohlrainstrasse 10, Kusnacht, 8700, Switzerland
Tel.: (41) 449138100
Web Site: http://www.finarbit.ch
Sales Range: $50-74.9 Million
Emp.: 15
Securities & Commodity Exchanges
N.A.I.C.S.: 523210

Subsidiary (Non-US):

Gaitame.com Co., Ltd. (2)
4th floor Palazzo Astec 2-8-1, Minato, Tokyo, 105-0021, Japan **(41.82%)**
Tel.: (81) 357333065
Web Site: http://www.gaitame.com
Insurance Agencies & Brokerages
N.A.I.C.S.: 524210

Subsidiary (US):

Govdesk LLC (2)
999 N Sepulveda Blvd Ste 550, El Segundo, CA 90245-2723 **(35%)**
Tel.: (310) 937-2261
Investment Advice
N.A.I.C.S.: 523940
Ania James *(Dir-Ops & Compliance)*

MTS Markets International, Inc. (2)
28 Liberty St 58th Fl, New York, NY 10005
Tel.: (212) 314-1100
Web Site: http://www.mtsmarkets.com
Electronic Bond Trading Platform Operator
N.A.I.C.S.: 523150

Subsidiary (Non-US):

Meitan Tradition Co. Ltd (2)
5-29-17 Toyo Koto-ku, Tokyo, Japan **(55.34%)**
Tel.: (81) 356343065
Web Site: http://www.Meitan-tradition.jp
Sales Range: $50-74.9 Million
Emp.: 130
Holding Company
N.A.I.C.S.: 551111

S.P. Angel & Co. Ltd (2)
35 Berkeley Square, W1J 5BF, London, United Kingdom - England **(100%)**
Tel.: (44) 2076479650
Web Site: http://www.spangel.co.uk
Sales Range: $50-74.9 Million
Emp.: 20
Financial Investment
N.A.I.C.S.: 523999

Subsidiary (US):

StreamingEdge.com Inc. (2)
75 Park Pl Fl 4, New York, NY 10007-2190
Tel.: (212) 791-6026
Web Site: http://www.streamingedge.com
Sales Range: $10-24.9 Million
Emp.: 50
Computer Programming Services
N.A.I.C.S.: 541511
Yann L. Huillier *(CEO)*

Subsidiary (Non-US):

TFS Currencies Pte Ltd. (2)
3 Shenton Way NR 23-02, Shenton House, 068805, Singapore, Singapore **(100%)**
Tel.: (65) 6226 5616
Web Site: http://www.traditionasia.com
Commodity Contracts Brokerage
N.A.I.C.S.: 523160

TFS Currency Options Ltd (2)
109-117 Middlesex Street, East India House, E17JF, London, United Kingdom **(100%)**
Tel.: (44) 2072569594
Web Site: http://www.tfsbrokerage.com
Securities Brokerage
N.A.I.C.S.: 523150

AND PRIVATE COMPANIES — VIENNA INSURANCE GROUP AG WIENER VERSICHERUNG GRUPPE

TFS Dubai Ltd (2)
Currency House Level 2 Unit 3 Difc, PO Box 506530, Dubai, United Arab Emirates
Tel.: (971) 43641400
Web Site: http://www.tradition.com
Sales Range: $50-74.9 Million
Emp.: 18
Commodity Contracts Brokerage
N.A.I.C.S.: 523160

TFS Energy (S) Pte Ltd (2)
63 Market St Bldg #07-01, 048942, Singapore, Singapore (100%)
Tel.: (65) 62265616
Sales Range: $50-74.9 Million
Emp.: 20
Commodity Contracts Brokerage
N.A.I.C.S.: 523160

Subsidiary (US):

TFS Energy Futures LLC (2)
32 Olbslit 34 Fl, New York, NY 10005 (100%)
Tel.: (212) 943-6916
Web Site: http://www.tfsbrokerage.com
Sales Range: $50-74.9 Million
Emp.: 70
Securities Brokerage
N.A.I.C.S.: 523150

TFS Energy, LLC (2)
9 West Broad Street 9th Floor, Stamford, CT 06902
Tel.: (203) 351-9520
Securities Brokerage
N.A.I.C.S.: 523150

Subsidiary (Non-US):

The Recruitment Company Pty Ltd (2)
L 7 275-281 George St, Sydney, 2000, NSW, Australia (89.9%)
Tel.: (61) 283466700
Web Site: http://www.therecruitmentco.com
Emp.: 55
Employment Placement Agencies
N.A.I.C.S.: 561311
Dennis Trattitt (Mng Dir)

Tradition (Asia) Ltd. (2)
25th Floor Entertainment Building 30 Queens Road Central, Hong Kong, China (Hong Kong) (100%)
Tel.: (852) 34133600
Web Site: http://www.tradition.com
Sales Range: $75-99.9 Million
Emp.: 150
Securities Brokerage
N.A.I.C.S.: 523150

Tradition (Beaufort House) Ltd (2)
Beaufort House 15 St Botolph St, London, EC3A 7QX, United Kingdom (100%)
Tel.: (44) 2071981500
Web Site: http://www.tradition.com
Sales Range: $300-349.9 Million
Emp.: 700
Activities Related to Credit Intermediation
N.A.I.C.S.: 522390

Subsidiary (US):

Tradition (Global Clearing) Inc. (2)
255 Greenwich St 4th Fl, New York, NY 10007 (100%)
Tel.: (212) 791-4500
Web Site: http://www.tradition-na.com
Sales Range: $150-199.9 Million
Emp.: 400
Securities Brokerage
N.A.I.C.S.: 523150
Mike Liebowitz (CEO)

Tradition (Government Securities) Inc. (2)
255 Greenwich St, New York, NY 10007 (100%)
Tel.: (212) 791-4500
Web Site: http://www.tradition-na.com
Sales Range: $150-199.9 Million
Emp.: 500
Securities Brokerage
N.A.I.C.S.: 523150
Mike Liebowitz (CEO)

Subsidiary (Non-US):

Tradition (London Clearing) Ltd (2)
15 St Botolph Street Beaufort House, London, EC3A 7QX, United Kingdom (100%)
Tel.: (44) 2074223500
Web Site: http://www.traditiongroup.com
Sales Range: $300-349.9 Million
Emp.: 1,000
Financial Investment Services

Subsidiary (US):

Tradition (North America) Inc. (2)
32 Old Slip 28 Fl, New York, NY 10005
Tel.: (212) 791-4500
Web Site: http://www.tradition-na.com
Sales Range: $150-199.9 Million
Emp.: 400
Real Estate Agents & Brokers Offices
N.A.I.C.S.: 531210
John Nocera (Mgr-IT)

Subsidiary (Non-US):

Tradition (UK) Ltd (2)
15 St Botolph St, London, EC3A 7QX, United Kingdom (100%)
Tel.: (44) 2074223500
Web Site: http://www.tradition.co.uk
Sales Range: $300-349.9 Million
Emp.: 1,000
Insurance Related Activities
N.A.I.C.S.: 524298

Tradition Argentina SA (2)
Av Corrientes 456 4 Piso Oficinia 46, C1043AAR, Buenos Aires, Argentina (100%)
Tel.: (54) 1143940559
Web Site: http://www.tradition-acvn.com
Computer Peripheral Equipment Mfr
N.A.I.C.S.: 334118

Subsidiary (US):

Tradition Asiel Securities Inc. (2)
255 Greenwich St 4th Fl, New York, NY 10007 (100%)
Tel.: (212) 791-4500
Web Site: http://www.tradition-na.com
Sales Range: $150-199.9 Million
Emp.: 400
Insurance Agencies & Brokerages
N.A.I.C.S.: 524210
Tony Aragona (COO)

Subsidiary (Non-US):

Tradition Bond Brokers Ltd (2)
Beauford House, London, EC3A 7QX, United Kingdom (100%)
Tel.: (44) 2074223500
Web Site: http://www.tradition.co.uk
Sales Range: $300-349.9 Million
Emp.: 700
Insurance Related Activities
N.A.I.C.S.: 524298

Tradition Chile Agentes de Valores Limitada (2)
Apoquindo 3650 Of 801, Las Condes, Santiago, Chile (100%)
Tel.: (56) 222107200
Web Site: http://www.tradition.cl
Sales Range: $25-49.9 Million
Emp.: 30
Depository Credit Intermediation
N.A.I.C.S.: 522180

Tradition Financial Services GmbH (2)
Hochstrasse 43, 60313, Frankfurt, Germany
Tel.: (49) 69283622
Web Site: http://www.traditiongroup.com
Emp.: 20
Business Service Centers
N.A.I.C.S.: 561439
Helmut Gaussmann (CEO)

Subsidiary (US):

Tradition Financial Services Inc. (2)
17 State St 41, New York, NY 10004-1501 (100%)
Tel.: (212) 943-8100
Sales Range: $50-74.9 Million
Emp.: 75
Securities Brokerage
N.A.I.C.S.: 523150

Subsidiary (Non-US):

Tradition Financial Services Japan Ltd (2)
2nd Floor PALAZZO ASTEC 2-8-1, Higashi Shinbashi Minato-Ku, Tokyo, 105-0021, Japan (100%)
Tel.: (81) 343603940
Sales Range: $25-49.9 Million
Emp.: 10
Business Service Centers
N.A.I.C.S.: 561439

Tradition Financial Services Ltd (2)
Beaufort House 15 St Botolph Street, London, EC3A 7QX, United Kingdom (100%)
Tel.: (44) 2071981500
Emp.: 500
Financial Investment
N.A.I.C.S.: 523999
Michael Leibowitz (CEO)

Joint Venture (Domestic):

TFS-ICAP Limited (3)
Beaufort House 15 St Botolph Street, London, EC3A 7QX, United Kingdom
Tel.: (44) 207 422 3500
Web Site: http://www.tradition.com
Sales Range: $350-399.9 Million
Emp.: 700
Securities Brokerage
N.A.I.C.S.: 523150

Subsidiary (US):

TFS-ICAP Holdings LLC (4)
3232 OldSlip 34th Fl, New York, NY 10005-1501
Tel.: (212) 943-6916
Web Site: http://www.tfsbrokerage.com
Sales Range: $50-74.9 Million
Emp.: 15
Holding Company
N.A.I.C.S.: 551112
David Pinchin (Mng Dir)

Subsidiary (Domestic):

TFS-ICAP LLC (5)
32 Oozslip 34th Fl, New York, NY 10005
Tel.: (212) 943-6916
Web Site: http://www.tfsbrokerage.com
Sales Range: $25-49.9 Million
Securities Brokerage
N.A.I.C.S.: 523150
David Pinchin (Mng Dir)

Subsidiary (Non-US):

Tradition Italia SIM S.p.A (2)
Via Nino Bonnet 6/A, 20154, Milan, Italy (100%)
Tel.: (39) 0230315020
Web Site: http://www.tradition.com
Sales Range: $25-49.9 Million
Emp.: 9
Real Estate Agents & Brokers Offices
N.A.I.C.S.: 531210

Tradition Luxembourg S.A. (2)
9 Rue Gabriel Lippmann, 5365, Munsbach, Luxembourg
Tel.: (352) 465601
Web Site: http://www.tradition.co.uk
Sales Range: $50-74.9 Million
Emp.: 15
Securities Brokerage
N.A.I.C.S.: 523150

Tradition Securities And Futures S.A. (2)
9 Place Vendome, 75001, Paris, France
Tel.: (33) 156437020
Web Site: http://www.tradition-paris.com
Sales Range: $75-99.9 Million
Emp.: 300
Business Service Centers
N.A.I.C.S.: 561439

Tradition Services S.A. de C.V. (2)
Paseo De Los Laureles 458 Oficina 305, Colonia Bosques De Las Lomas Cuajimalpa, 50120, Mexico, Mexico (100%)
Tel.: (52) 5553508100
Web Site: http://www.tradition.com
Sales Range: $25-49.9 Million
Emp.: 40
Investment Advice
N.A.I.C.S.: 523940

Tradition Singapore (Pte) Ltd (2)
63 Market Street No 07-01, Singapore, 48942, Singapore (100%)
Tel.: (65) 62262323

Web Site: http://www.traditionasia.com
Sales Range: $75-99.9 Million
Emp.: 120
Securities Brokerage
N.A.I.C.S.: 523150

VIEL Tradition S.A. (2)
9 Palce Vendome, 75001, Paris, France
Tel.: (33) 156437020
Web Site: http://www.viel.com
Sales Range: $75-99.9 Million
Emp.: 200
Open-End Investment Funds
N.A.I.C.S.: 525910

VIEN LIEN JOINT STOCK COMPANY

A3 4A 12 The Goldview Apartment 346 Ben Van Don, District 4, Ho Chi Minh City, Vietnam
Tel.: (84) 83 620 0538
Web Site: http://www.vienlien.com.vn
UNI—(HNX)
Rev.: $33,121
Assets: $10,467,086
Liabilities: $3,938,512
Net Worth: $6,528,574
Earnings: $701
Fiscal Year-end: 12/31/21
Telecommunication Equipment Distr
N.A.I.C.S.: 423690
Pham Dinh Dung (Gen Dir)

VIENNA INSURANCE GROUP AG WIENER VERSICHERUNG GRUPPE

Schottenring 30, PO Box 80, A-1011, Vienna, Austria
Tel.: (43) 5039022000 AT
Web Site: https://group.vig
Year Founded: 1824
VIG—(VIE)
Rev.: $13,554,113,965
Assets: $53,177,219,944
Liabilities: $48,391,785,021
Net Worth: $4,785,434,923
Earnings: $502,850,205
Emp.: 28,832
Fiscal Year-end: 12/31/22
Investment Management Service
N.A.I.C.S.: 551112
Gunter Geyer (Chm-Supervisory Bd)

Subsidiaries:

AUTODROM SOSNOVA u Ceske Lipy a.s (1)
Sosnova 200, 470 02, Ceska Lipa, Czech Republic
Tel.: (420) 725999560
Web Site: https://www.autodrom-sosnova.cz
Traffic Safety Services
N.A.I.C.S.: 541370

Agras Vienna Insurance Group S.A. (1)
Alexandru Philippide St 9B Sector 2, RO-020 666, Bucharest, Romania
Tel.: (40) 213137993
Insurance Services
N.A.I.C.S.: 524298

Alpenlandische Gemeinnutzige Wohnbau GmbH (1)
Viktor-Dankl-Strasse 6, A - 6020, Innsbruck, Austria
Tel.: (43) 512571411
Web Site: https://www.alpenlaendische.at
Housing Cooperative Services
N.A.I.C.S.: 624229

Arealis Liegenschaftsmanagement GmbH (1)
Aspernbruckengasse 2, 1020, Vienna, Austria
Tel.: (43) 1217180
Web Site: https://www.arealis.at
Property Insurance Services
N.A.I.C.S.: 524126

Asigurarea Romaneasca - ASIROM Vienna Insurance Group S.A. (1)
Carol I Boulevard 31-33, Bucharest, Romania

VIENNA INSURANCE GROUP AG WIENER VERSICHERUNG GRUPPE

Vienna Insurance Group AG Wiener Versicherung Gruppe—(Continued)
Tel.: (40) 219599
Web Site: http://www.asirom.ro
Fire Insurance Services
N.A.I.C.S.: 524113
Grigoras Eren *(Mgr-Unit)*

BCR Asigurari de Viata Vienna Insurance Group S.A. (1)
Rabat Street no 21, sector 1, Bucharest, 11835, Romania
Tel.: (40) 212069040
Web Site: http://www.bcrasigviata.ro
Fire Insurance Services
N.A.I.C.S.: 524113
Franz Fuchs *(Pres)*

BTA Baltic Insurance Company AAS (1)
Sporta Iela 11, Riga, 1013, Latvia
Tel.: (371) 26121212
Web Site: http://www.bta.lv
Emp.: 1,000
Fire Insurance Services
N.A.I.C.S.: 524113
Wolfgang Stockmeyer *(Co-Chm)*

Benefia Ubezpieczenia Spolka z ograniczona odpowiedzialnoscia (1)
Aleje Jerozolimskie 162A, 02-342, Warsaw, Poland
Tel.: (48) 22 544 1470
Web Site: https://www.benefia.pl
Insurance Claims Services
N.A.I.C.S.: 524298

Bulstrad Life Vienna Insurance Group Joint Stock Company (1)
6 Sveta Sofia Str, Sofia, 1301, Bulgaria
Tel.: (359) 2 401 4000
Web Site: https://www.bulstradlife.bg
Fire Insurance Services
N.A.I.C.S.: 524113
Donka Terzieva *(Dir-HR)*

Bulstrad Vienna Insurance Group (1)
Pl Positano 5, 1000, Sofia, Bulgaria
Tel.: (359) 2 985 6610
Web Site: https://www.bulstrad.bg
Sales Range: $150-199.9 Million
Emp.: 250
Life Insurance, Direct Property & Casualty Insurance Carriers
N.A.I.C.S.: 524113
Ivan Ivanov *(Deputy CEO & Member-Mgmt Bd)*

CAPITOL, akciova spolocnos (1)
Rajska 15 / A, 811 08, Bratislava, Slovakia
Tel.: (421) 90 730 6257
Web Site: http://www.capitol.sk
Vehicle Insurance Services
N.A.I.C.S.: 524128

Camelot Informatik und Consulting Gesellschaft m.b.H. (1)
Schottenring 30, 1010, Vienna, Austria
Tel.: (43) 5010075840
Web Site: http://www.camelot.gmbh
Emp.: 50
Product Liability Insurance Services
N.A.I.C.S.: 524128

Ceska podnikatelska pojistovna, a.s. (1)
Pobrezni 665/23 8 karlin, 186 00, Prague, Czech Republic
Tel.: (420) 957444555
Web Site: https://www.cpp.cz
Insurance Services
N.A.I.C.S.: 524298
Jaroslav Besperat *(Chm)*

Compensa Dystrybucja Sp. z o.o. (1)
Al Jerozolimskie 162, 02-342, Warsaw, Poland
Tel.: (48) 22 501 6100
Web Site: https://www.compensadystrybucja.pl
Product Liability Insurance Services
N.A.I.C.S.: 524128

Compensa Towarzystwo Ubezpieczen S.A. (1)
Aleje Jerozolimskie 162A, 02-342, Warsaw, Poland
Tel.: (48) 22 501 6000
Web Site: http://www.compensa.pl
Insurance Services
N.A.I.C.S.: 524298

Subsidiary (Domestic):

Benefia TU Majatkowych S.A. (2)
Aleje Jerozolimskie 162A, 02-342, Warsaw, Poland
Tel.: (48) 225441470
Web Site: http://www.benefia.pl
Emp.: 60
Insurance Services
N.A.I.C.S.: 524298

Benefia TU na Zycie S.A. (2)
Aleje Jerozolimskie 162A, 02-342, Warsaw, Poland
Tel.: (48) 225441470
Web Site: http://www.benefia.pl
Sales Range: $50-74.9 Million
Emp.: 60
Insurance Services
N.A.I.C.S.: 524298

Royal Polska TU na Zycie S.A. (2)
Ul Rydygiera 21, PL-01-793, Warsaw, Poland
Tel.: (48) 225251111
Web Site: http://www.royalpolska.com
Sales Range: $50-74.9 Million
Emp.: 10
Insurance Services
N.A.I.C.S.: 524298

TU InterRisk S.A. (2)
ul Stanislawa Noakowskiego 22, 00-668, Warsaw, Poland
Tel.: (48) 22 575 2525
Web Site: https://interrisk.pl
Sales Range: $75-99.9 Million
Emp.: 120
Insurance Services
N.A.I.C.S.: 524298

TU Polski Zwiazek Mororowy S.A. (2)
ul Kazimierzowska 66, 02-518, Warsaw, Poland
Tel.: (48) 225420100
Web Site: http://www.pzmtu.pl
Insurance Services
N.A.I.C.S.: 524298

TU na Zycie Compensa S.A. (2)
Aleje Jerozolimskie 162, 02-342, Warsaw, Poland
Tel.: (48) 225016100
Web Site: http://www.compensa.pl
Insurance Services
N.A.I.C.S.: 524298

Compensa Vienna Insurance Group, ADB (1)
Ukmerges st 280, 06115, Vilnius, Lithuania
Tel.: (370) 5 250 6600
Web Site: https://www.compensa.lt
Fire Insurance Services
N.A.I.C.S.: 524113
Nicolas Mucherl *(CFO)*

DV Asset Management EAD (1)
13 B Tintyava Street entrance A 2nd floor, Iztok Residential Complex, Sofia, 1113, Bulgaria
Tel.: (359) 2 935 0633
Web Site: https://www.dvam.bg
Asset Management Services
N.A.I.C.S.: 523940
Krasimir Petkov *(Exec Dir)*

Donau Versicherungs AG (1)
Schottenring 15, 1010, Vienna, Austria
Tel.: (43) 503 307 0000
Web Site: https://www.donauversicherung.at
Insurance Services
N.A.I.C.S.: 524298

EBS Wohnungsgesellschaft mbH (1)
Ziegeleistrasse 37, 4020, Linz, Austria
Tel.: (43) 73 265 2411
Web Site: https://www.ebs-linz.at
Property Development Services
N.A.I.C.S.: 531390

EGW Wohnbau gemeinnutzige Ges.m.b.H. (1)
Emil Kralik Gasse 3, 1050, Vienna, Austria
Tel.: (43) 154515670
Property Management Services

N.A.I.C.S.: 531311

EUROPEUM Business Center s.r.o. (1)
Suche Myto 7045/1, 811 03, Bratislava, Slovakia
Tel.: (421) 254430644
Web Site: https://www.europeum-bratislava.sk
Office Space Rental Services
N.A.I.C.S.: 531120

Erste Biztositasi Alkusz Kft. (1)
Baross u 1, 1082, Budapest, Hungary
Tel.: (36) 614841700
Web Site: https://www.erstealkusz.hu
Insurance Claims Services
N.A.I.C.S.: 524298

Erste Vienna Insurance Group Biztosito Zrt (1)
Baross u, H-1138, Budapest, Hungary
Tel.: (36) 14841700
Web Site: http://www.esb.hu
Insurance Services
N.A.I.C.S.: 524298

Erste gemeinnutzige Wohnungsgesellschaft Heimstatte Gesellschaft m.b.H. (1)
Emil-Kralik-Gasse 3, 1050, Vienna, Austria
Tel.: (43) 154515670
Web Site: http://www.egw.at
Property Rental Services
N.A.I.C.S.: 531120

Erste osiguranje Vienna Insurance Group d.d. (1)
Miramarska 23, HH-10000, Zagreb, Croatia
Tel.: (385) 6237 2700
Web Site: http://www.erste-osiguranje.hr
Insurance Services
N.A.I.C.S.: 524298

European Insurance & Reinsurance Brokers Ltd. (1)
8 -11 Crescent, London, EC3N 2LY, United Kingdom
Tel.: (44) 207 480 1117
Web Site: https://www.eirbltd.co.uk
Reinsurance Services
N.A.I.C.S.: 524130

GEO Hospitals LLC (1)
Spring Street 18, Vake district, Tbilisi, Georgia
Tel.: (995) 32 250 5222
Web Site: https://www.gh.ge
Health Care Srvices
N.A.I.C.S.: 621610
Sophie Gasitashvili *(Gen Dir)*

Gemeinnutzige Industrie-Wohnungsaktiengesellschaft (1)
Welser Strasse 41, 4060, Leonding, Austria
Tel.: (43) 508888
Web Site: https://www.giwog.at
Property Rental Services
N.A.I.C.S.: 531120

Gemeinnutzige Murz-Ybbs Siedlungsanlagen-GmbH (1)
Am Sagacker 2a, 8605, Kapfenberg, Austria
Tel.: (43) 50 888 2100
Web Site: https://www.gemysag.at
Property Rental Services
N.A.I.C.S.: 531120

Global Assistance Polska Sp.z.o.o. (1)
Al Jerozolimskie 162 A, 02-342, Warsaw, Poland
Tel.: (48) 22 602 4000
Web Site: https://www.global-assistance.pl
Insurance Claims Services
N.A.I.C.S.: 524298
Michal Makarczyk *(Pres)*

Global Assistance Services S.r.o. (1)
Building G Nakupni 1127, Jesenice, 252 42, Jesenice, Czech Republic
Tel.: (420) 77 387 2067
Web Site: https://gservices.cz
Online Application Development Services
N.A.I.C.S.: 541511

Global Assistance Slovakia S.r.o. (1)
Stefanovicova 4, 811 04, Bratislava, Slovakia

INTERNATIONAL PUBLIC

Tel.: (421) 26 353 2236
Web Site: https://www.globalassistance.sk
Customer Center Services
N.A.I.C.S.: 561422

Global Services Bulgaria JSC (1)
23 Sitnyakovo Blvd, 1138, Sofia, Bulgaria
Tel.: (359) 2 401 5600
Web Site: https://www.globalservices.bg
Customer Center Services
N.A.I.C.S.: 561422
Nedyalko Chandarov *(Chm)*

Horizont Personal- Team- Und Organisationsentwicklung GmbH (1)
Obere Donaustrasse 63/1/1, 1020, Vienna, Austria
Tel.: (43) 503 307 2280
Web Site: https://www.horizont.co.at
Educational Support Services
N.A.I.C.S.: 611710

IRAO Ltd. (1)
A Kazbegi Str 46, GE-0162, Tbilisi, Georgia
Tel.: (995) 32 949 111
Insurance Services
N.A.I.C.S.: 524298

Insurance Company Nova Ins EAD (1)
Positano Square 5, Triaditsa District, 1000, Sofia, Bulgaria
Tel.: (359) 29333046
Web Site: http://www.novains.bg
Property Insurance Services
N.A.I.C.S.: 524126

Insurance Company Vienna Osiguranje d.d. (1)
Fra Andela Zvizdovica 1/A9, 71000, Sarajevo, Bosnia & Herzegovina
Tel.: (387) 3 394 3640
Web Site: https://www.viennaosiguranje.ba
Fire Insurance Services
N.A.I.C.S.: 524113

Insurance Macedonia ad Skopje Vienna Insurance Group (1)
Street 11 October No 25, 1000, Skopje, North Macedonia (92.9%)
Tel.: (389) 2 311 5188
Web Site: https://www.insumak.mk
Emp.: 196
General Insurance Services
N.A.I.C.S.: 524210

InterRisk Towarzystwo Ubezpieczen S.A. (1)
ul Stanislawa Noakowskiego 22, 00-668, Warsaw, Poland
Tel.: (48) 225752525
Web Site: https://interrisk.pl
Insurance Services
N.A.I.C.S.: 524210

InterRisk Versicherungs AG (1)
Carl-Bosch-Str 5, 65203, Wiesbaden, Germany
Tel.: (49) 6 112 7870
Web Site: https://www.interrisk.de
Sales Range: $100-124.9 Million
Emp.: 110
Insurance Services
N.A.I.C.S.: 524298

Subsidiary (Domestic):

InterRisk Lebensversicherungs AG (2)
Carl-Bosch-Str 5, 65203, Wiesbaden, Germany
Tel.: (49) 6 112 7870
Web Site: https://www.interrisk.de
Sales Range: $75-99.9 Million
Emp.: 105
Fire Insurance Services
N.A.I.C.S.: 524113

Interalbanian Sh.a (1)
Rr. Sulejman Delvina Zayed Business Center, Tirana, Albania
Tel.: (355) 4 2229578
Web Site: http://www.interalbanian.com
Insurance Services
N.A.I.C.S.: 524298

International Insurance Company IRAO Ltd. (1)
Bochorishvili St 88/15, Tbilisi, 0160, Georgia
Tel.: (995) 32 294 9949

AND PRIVATE COMPANIES — VIENNA INSURANCE GROUP AG WIENER VERSICHERUNG GRUPPE

Web Site: https://www.irao.ge
Insurance Services
N.A.I.C.S.: 524298

JSC GPI Insurance Company Holding (1)
67 Kostava Street, 0171, Tbilisi, Georgia
Tel.: (995) 32 250 5111
Web Site: https://www.gpih.ge
Insurance Services
N.A.I.C.S.: 524298

Jahorina Auto D.o.o. (1)
Kninska 1a, Banja Luka, Bosnia & Herzegovina
Tel.: (387) 51931100
Property Insurance Services
N.A.I.C.S.: 524126
Zeljko Vasilic *(Gen Mgr)*

Jahorina Insurance Plc (1)
Svetosavska 24, 71420, Pale, Bosnia & Herzegovina
Tel.: (387) 57 201 320
Web Site:
  http://www.jahorinaosiguranje.com
Emp.: 216
Insurance Services
N.A.I.C.S.: 524113

Joint Stock Insurance Company WINNER-Vienna Insurance Group (1)
Boris Trajkovski Boulevard no 62, 1000, Skopje, North Macedonia
Tel.: (389) 2 323 1631
Web Site: https://www.winner.mk
Property Insurance Services
N.A.I.C.S.: 524126
Blagoj Petkovski *(Officer-Compliance)*

Subsidiary (Domestic):

Osiguruvane Makedonija AD (2)
St 11 Oktomvri nr 25, 1000, Skopje, North Macedonia
Tel.: (389) 23115188
Web Site: https://www.insumak.mk
Sales Range: Less than $1 Million
Insurance Services
N.A.I.C.S.: 524298
Christoph Rath *(Chm-Supervisory Bd)*

KAPITOL, a.s. (1)
Vlnena 526/3, 602 00, Brno, Czech Republic
Tel.: (420) 910880088
Web Site: https://www.kapitol.cz
Car Financial Services
N.A.I.C.S.: 541611

Kapitol pojistovaci a financni poradenstvi, a.s. (1)
Vlnena 526/3, 602 00, Brno, Czech Republic
Tel.: (420) 910880088
Web Site: http://www.kapitol.cz
Property Insurance Services
N.A.I.C.S.: 524126

Komunalna Poisfovna, A.S. (1)
Stefanikova 17, 811 05, Bratislava, Slovakia
Tel.: (421) 248210544
Fire Insurance Services
N.A.I.C.S.: 524113

Komunalna poist'ovna, a.s. (1)
Stefanikova 17, 811 05, Bratislava, Slovakia
Tel.: (421) 263532236
Web Site: http://www.kpas.sk
Insurance Services
N.A.I.C.S.: 524298

Kooperativa Poisfovna, A.S. (1)
Stefanovicova 4, 816 23, Bratislava, Slovakia
Tel.: (421) 2572999684
Fire Insurance Services
N.A.I.C.S.: 524113

Kooperativa pojistovna, a.s. (1)
Pobrezni 665/21, 186 00, Prague, Czech Republic
Tel.: (420) 95 642 1111
Web Site: https://www.koop.cz
Insurance Services
N.A.I.C.S.: 524298

Kupala Belarusian-austrian Closed Joint Stock Insurance Company (1)
St Nemiga 40 entrance 2 Office 702, Minsk, Belarus
Tel.: (375) 17 200 8027
Web Site: https://www.kupala.by
Property Insurance Services
N.A.I.C.S.: 524126

Omniasig Vienna Insurance Group S.A. (1)
Aleea Alexandru Nr 51 sector 1, Bucharest, Romania
Tel.: (40) 214057420
Web Site: http://www.omniasig.ro
Insurance Services
N.A.I.C.S.: 524298
Mihai Tecau *(Chm-Mgmt Bd)*

Subsidiary (Domestic):

Omniasig Asigaurari de Viata S.A. (2)
Str Pechea Nr 13 Sector 1, RO-013-982, Bucharest, Romania
Tel.: (40) 214089100
Sales Range: $150-199.9 Million
Insurance Services
N.A.I.C.S.: 524298

Osiguranje Helios d.d. (1)
Poljicka 5, 10002, Zagreb, Croatia
Tel.: (385) 16116766
Web Site: http://www.wiener.hr
Insurance Services
N.A.I.C.S.: 524298

Osterreichisches Verkehrsburo Aktiengesellschaft (1)
Lassallestrasse 3, 1020, Vienna, Austria
Tel.: (43) 1588000
Investment Management Service
N.A.I.C.S.: 523940
Wolfgang Baier *(Mgr)*

PJSC Insurance Company (1)
Street Ivan Fedorov 32 Letter A, 03038, Kiev, Ukraine
Tel.: (380) 442370255
Web Site: http://ukringroup.ua
Insurance Services
N.A.I.C.S.: 524298

PJSC Jupiter Life Insurance (1)
Vul Zolotoustivska 10-12A, UA-01135, Kiev, Ukraine
Tel.: (380) 44 490 0155
Web Site: http://www.jupiter.kiev.ua
Insurance Services
N.A.I.C.S.: 524298

PJSC UIC Kniazha (1)
Hlybochytska 44, Kiev, 04050, Ukraine
Tel.: (380) 44 207 7272
Web Site: http://www.kniazha.ua
Insurance Services
N.A.I.C.S.: 524298

Palais Hansen Immobilienentwicklung GmbH (1)
Absberggasse 47, 1100, Vienna, Austria
Tel.: (43) 6646268862
Web Site: http://www.palaishansen.com
Restaurant Operators
N.A.I.C.S.: 722511

Pension Assurance Company Doverie AD (1)
13B Tintyava Street, Sofia Municipality Izgrev district, 1113, Sofia, Bulgaria
Tel.: (359) 70013400
Web Site: https://www.poc-doverie.bg
Emp.: 100
Pension Fund Management Services
N.A.I.C.S.: 525110

Pension Insurance Company Doverie AD (1)
13 B Tintyava Str, 1113, Sofia, Bulgaria
Tel.: (359) 24646173
Web Site: http://www.old.poc-doverie.bg
Pension Insurance Services
N.A.I.C.S.: 524292
Daniela Petkova *(Chm)*

Poistovna Slovenskej sporitel'ne a.s. (1)
Tomasikova 48, SK-832 68, Bratislava, Slovakia
Tel.: (421) 248629300
Web Site: http://www.pslsp.sk
Insurance Services

N.A.I.C.S.: 524298

Pojistovna Ceske sporitelny, a.s. (1)
Nam Republiky 115, CZ-530 02, Pardubice, Czech Republic
Tel.: (420) 466 051 522
Web Site: http://www.pojistovnacs.cz
Insurance Services
N.A.I.C.S.: 524298

Polisa - Zycie Ubezpieczenia Sp.z.o.o. (1)
Aleje Jerozolimskie 162A, 02-342, Warsaw, Poland
Tel.: (48) 22 501 6889
Web Site: https://www.polisa-zycie.pl
Fire Insurance Services
N.A.I.C.S.: 524113

Projektbau GesmbH (1)
Lindengasse 55, 1070, Vienna, Austria
Tel.: (43) 152336160
Web Site: https://www.projektbau.at
Construction Services
N.A.I.C.S.: 541990

Ray Sigorta A.S. (1)
Haydar Aliyev Cad No 28, Tarabya Sanyer, 34457, Istanbul, Turkiye
Tel.: (90) 212 363 2500
Web Site: https://www.raysigorta.com.tr
Emp.: 300
Insurance Services
N.A.I.C.S.: 524298

Risk Consult Sicherheits- und Risiko-Managementberatung Gesellschaft m.b.h. (1)
Schottenring 35/4, 1010, Vienna, Austria
Tel.: (43) 1 532 1308
Web Site: https://www.riskconsult.at
Insurance Claims Services
N.A.I.C.S.: 524298

S - budovy, a.s. (1)
Opletalova 1626/36, 110 00, Prague, Czech Republic
Tel.: (420) 602642164
Web Site: https://www.s-budovy.cz
Real Estate Manangement Services
N.A.I.C.S.: 531210

S.C. Societatea Training In Asigurari S.r.l. (1)
Str Rabat nr 21 et3 Sector 1, Bucharest, Romania
Tel.: (40) 753059405
Web Site: http://www.e-sta.ro
Vocational Training Services
N.A.I.C.S.: 624310

SBA ZASO Kupala (1)
St Nemiga 40 entrance 2 Office 702, 220004, Minsk, Belarus
Tel.: (375) 17 200 8027
Web Site: https://www.kupala.by
Emp.: 65
Insurance Services
N.A.I.C.S.: 524298

SC Asigurarea Romaneasca Asirom S.A. (1)
Ion Ghica Street Nr 7 Et 1 Sector3, RO-020 912, Bucharest, Romania
Tel.: (40) 213128745
Web Site: http://www.asirom.com.ro
Insurance Services
N.A.I.C.S.: 524298

Schwarzatal Gemeinnutzige Wohnungs-und Siedlungsanlagen-GmbH (1)
Stella-Klein-Low-Weg 13 4 OG, 1020, Vienna, Austria
Tel.: (43) 508887
Web Site: https://www.schwarzatal.at
Property Rental Services
N.A.I.C.S.: 531120

Sigma Sh.a (1)
Rruga Komuna e Parisit, Pall Lura POB 1714, Tirana, Albania
Tel.: (355) 42 258 254
Web Site: http://www.sigma-al.com
Insurance Services
N.A.I.C.S.: 524298

Slovexperta, s.r.o. (1)
MRStefanika 32, 010 01, Zilina, Slovakia
Tel.: (421) 41 507 1921

Web Site: https://www.slovexperta.sk
Insurance Claims Services
N.A.I.C.S.: 524298
Ivan Veverka *(Mgr-HR)*

Sozialbau Gemeinnutzige Wohnungsaktiengesellschaft (1)
Lindengasse 55, 1072, Vienna, Austria
Tel.: (43) 152 1950
Web Site: https://www.sozialbau.at
Property Rental Services
N.A.I.C.S.: 531120

Sparkassen Versicherung AG (1)
Wipplingerstrasse 36-38, 1010, Vienna, Austria
Tel.: (43) 50100 75400
Web Site: http://www.s-versicherung.at
Insurance Services
N.A.I.C.S.: 524298

Spoldzielnia Uslugowa Vig Ekspert W Warszawie (1)
Al Jerozolimskie 162, 02-342, Warsaw, Poland
Tel.: (48) 22 501 6565
Web Site: https://www.vigekspert.pl
Insurance Claims Services
N.A.I.C.S.: 524298

TBI Info EOOD (1)
3 Balsha Str Building 8, 1408, Sofia, Bulgaria
Tel.: (359) 888313005
Web Site: https://www.tbiinfo.eu
Mobile Application Services
N.A.I.C.S.: 513210
Evgeniya Simeonova *(Head-Oracle)*

TBIH Financial Services Group N.V. (1)
Claude Debussylaan 30 Vinoly Bldg 13th Fl, Amsterdam, 1082 MD, Netherlands
Tel.: (31) 203050010
Web Site: http://www.kardan.nl
Sales Range: $50-74.9 Million
Emp.: 50
Holding Company; Insurance & Pension Services & Financial Services
N.A.I.C.S.: 551112

Twinformatics GmbH (1)
Obere Donaustrasse 63, 1020, Vienna, Austria
Tel.: (43) 503 902 0400
Web Site: https://www.twinformatics.at
Product Liability Insurance Services
N.A.I.C.S.: 524128

Union Vienna Insurance Group Biztosito Zrt. (1)
Bem J u 8, 1027, Budapest, Hungary
Tel.: (36) 61 486 4343
Web Site: https://union.hu
Sales Range: $100-124.9 Million
Emp.: 250
Insurance Services
N.A.I.C.S.: 524298
Judit Havasi *(Chm-Supervisory Bd)*

VBV - Betriebliche Altersvorsorge AG (1)
Obere Donaustrasse 49 - 53, 1020, Vienna, Austria
Tel.: (43) 124 0100
Web Site: https://www.vbv.at
Pension Insurance Services
N.A.I.C.S.: 524292

VIG Asset Management, a.s. (1)
Templova 747/5, Stare Mesto, 110 00, Prague, Czech Republic
Tel.: (420) 956420391
Web Site: http://www.vigam.cz
Asset Management Services
N.A.I.C.S.: 523940

VIG RE zajist'ovna, a.s. (1)
Templova 747/5, 110 01, Prague, Czech Republic
Tel.: (420) 95 644 5505
Web Site: https://www.vig-re.com
Reinsurance Services
N.A.I.C.S.: 524130
Patrick Chevrel *(Head-Western & Southern Europe)*

VIG Services Bulgaria EOOD (1)
4 Inzhiner Georgi Belov Str, District Gorublyane, Sofia, 1138, Bulgaria

VIENNA INSURANCE GROUP AG WIENER VERSICHERUNG GRUPPE

Vienna Insurance Group AG Wiener Versicherung Gruppe—(Continued)
Tel.: (359) 2 892 7255
Web Site: https://www.vig-sb.bg
Insurance Claims Services
N.A.I.C.S.: 524298
Ivo Gruev *(Mgr)*

Vienna International Underwriters GmbH (1)
Schottenring 30, 1010, Vienna, Austria
Tel.: (43) 503 902 6111
Web Site: https://www.viunderwriters.com
Insurance Claims Services
N.A.I.C.S.: 524298

Vienna Life Towarzystwo Ubezpieczen na Zycie S.A. (1)
Al Jerozolimskie 162A, 02-342, Warsaw, Poland
Tel.: (48) 22 460 2222
Web Site: https://www.viennalife.pl
Product Liability Insurance Services
N.A.I.C.S.: 524128

Vienna-Life Lebensversicherung AG (1)
Industriestrasse 2, Bendern, 9487, Gamprin, Liechtenstein
Tel.: (423) 235 0660
Web Site: https://www.vienna-life.li
Emp.: 10
Fire Insurance Services
N.A.I.C.S.: 524113
Hannes Fahrnberger *(CEO)*

Wiener Stadtische Donau Leasing GmbH (1)
Am Belvedere 1, 1100, Vienna, Austria
Tel.: (43) 501 007 4700
Web Site: https://www.wsd-leasing.at
Emp.: 170
Vehicle Leasing Services
N.A.I.C.S.: 532112

Wiener Stadtische Versicherung AG (1)
Shottenring 30, A-1010, Vienna, Austria
Tel.: (43) 5035020000
Web Site: http://www.wienerstaedtische.at
Insurance Services
N.A.I.C.S.: 524298

Wiener Stadtische osiguranje a.d.o. (1)
Tresnjinog cveta br 1, 11070, Belgrade, Serbia
Tel.: (381) 11 220 9800
Web Site: https://www.wiener.co.rs
Insurance Services
N.A.I.C.S.: 524298

Wiener Towarzystwo Ubezpieczen Spolka Akcyjna (1)
Ul Woloska 22 A, 02-675, Warsaw, Poland
Tel.: (48) 224696969
Web Site: https://www.wiener.pl
Property Insurance Services
N.A.I.C.S.: 524126

Wiener Verein Bestattungs- Und Versicherungsservicegesellschaft M.b.h. (1)
Esslinggasse 15, 1010, Vienna, Austria
Tel.: (43) 50350360
Web Site: https://www.wienerverein.at
Fire Insurance Services
N.A.I.C.S.: 524113

Wiener osiguranje Vienna Insurance Group d.d. (1)
Slovenska Ulica 24, 10000, Zagreb, Croatia
Tel.: (385) 72100200
Web Site: https://www.wiener.hr
Insurance Services
N.A.I.C.S.: 524298
Peter Hofinger *(Chm/Deputy Chm-Supervisory Bd)*

arithmetica Consulting GmbH (1)
Schottenring 13-15 2nd floor, 1010, Vienna, Austria
Tel.: (43) 13 105 9010
Web Site: https://www.arithmetica.at
Financial Consulting Services
N.A.I.C.S.: 541611
Philip Gruber *(Mgr-Product)*

twinfaktor GmbH (1)
Obere Donaustrasse 63, 1020, Vienna, Austria
Tel.: (43) 5039026000
Web Site: http://www.twinfaktor.at
Application Development Services
N.A.I.C.S.: 541511

VIERPOOL B.V.
Industrieweg 2, Maarssen, 3606 AS, Netherlands
Tel.: (31) 346594511
Web Site: http://www.vierpool.nl
Year Founded: 1975
Sales Range: $25-49.9 Million
Emp.: 26
Industrial Equipment Distr
N.A.I.C.S.: 423830
Coos Smiesing *(Mgr-Tech Support)*

VIERTEL MOTOREN GMBH
Sigmundstrasse 154, Nuremberg, 90431, Germany
Tel.: (49) 911326430
Web Site: http://www.viertel-motoren.de
Rev.: $20,090,000
Emp.: 80
Automotive Parts Repair & Service
N.A.I.C.S.: 811198
Christian Viertel *(Member-Mgmt Bd)*

VIESSMANN WERKE GMBH & CO. KG
Viessmannstrasse 1 Eder, 35108, Allendorf, Germany
Tel.: (49) 6452 70 0 De
Web Site: http://www.viessmann.com
Year Founded: 1917
Heating & Cooling Products Mfr
N.A.I.C.S.: 333415
Maximilian Viessmann *(Owner-Climate Solutions & CEO)*

Subsidiaries:

BIOFerms GmbH (1)
Bayernwerk 8, 92421, Schwandorf, Germany
Tel.: (49) 9431 751 0
Generator Distr
N.A.I.C.S.: 423730

Etanomics Service GmbH (1)
Kurhessenstrasse 2, 64546, Morfelden-Walldorf, Germany
Tel.: (49) 61053200890
Web Site: http://www.etanomics.com
Generator Distr
N.A.I.C.S.: 423730

HKB Ketelbouw BV (1)
Ankerkade 6 Gebaude 5916, 5928 PL, Venlo, Netherlands
Tel.: (31) 773872424
Web Site: http://www.hkb-kesselbau.de
Generator Distr
N.A.I.C.S.: 423730

Schmack Biogas GmbH (1)
Bayernwerk 8, 92421, Schwandorf, Germany
Tel.: (49) 9431 751 0
Web Site: http://www.schmack-biogas.com
Natural Gas Exploration Service
N.A.I.C.S.: 211130
Tino Weber *(Mng Dir)*

Subsidiary (Domestic):

Schmack Biogas Komponenten GmbH (2)
Oberaign 9, 84558, Kirchweidach, Germany
Tel.: (49) 862398730
Generator Distr
N.A.I.C.S.: 423730

Schmack Biogas Service GmbH (2)
Bayernwerk 8, 92421, Schwandorf, Germany
Tel.: (49) 94317510
Web Site: http://www.schmack-biogas.com
Natural Gas Exploration Service
N.A.I.C.S.: 211130
Tino Weber *(Mng Dir)*

Subsidiary (Non-US):

Schmack Biogas UK Ltd (2)
Hortonwood 30, Telford, TF1 7YP, Shropshire, United Kingdom
Tel.: (44) 8708073058
Web Site: http://www.schmack-biogas.co.uk
Generator Distr
N.A.I.C.S.: 423730
Tino Weber *(Mng Dir)*

Subsidiary (Domestic):

Schmack Carbotech GmbH (2)
Natorpstrasse 27, 45139, Essen, Germany
Tel.: (49) 20150709300
Web Site: http://www.carbotech.info
Generator Distr
N.A.I.C.S.: 423730
Alfons Schulte-Schulze Berndt *(Mng Dir)*

Viessmann (Schweiz) AG (1)
Hardlistrasse 11, 8957, Spreitenbach, Switzerland
Tel.: (41) 564186711
Web Site: http://www.viessmann.ch
Generator Distr
N.A.I.C.S.: 423730

Viessmann A/S (1)
Guldalderen 2, 2640, Hedehusene, Denmark
Tel.: (45) 46559500
Web Site: http://www.viessmann.dk
Generator Distr
N.A.I.C.S.: 423730

Viessmann China Ltd. (1)
Unit 16 17th Floor Millennium City 2 378 Kwun Tong Road, Kwun Tong, Kowloon, China (Hong Kong)
Tel.: (852) 25440807
Web Site: http://www.viessmann.hk
Generator Distr
N.A.I.C.S.: 423730

Viessmann Eis-Energiespeicher GmbH (1)
Rheinlandstrasse 10, 71636, Ludwigsburg, Germany
Tel.: (49) 714199170010
Web Site: http://www.eis-energiespeicher.de
Generator Distr
N.A.I.C.S.: 423730

Viessmann France SAS (1)
Avenue Andre Gouy BP33, Faulquemont, 57380, France
Tel.: (33) 33387291700
Generator Distr
N.A.I.C.S.: 423730

Viessmann Futestechnika Kft (1)
Sussen u 3, H2045, Torokbalint, Hungary
Tel.: (36) 23334334
Web Site: http://www.viessmann.hu
Generator Distr
N.A.I.C.S.: 423730

Viessmann Gesellschaft m.b.H. (1)
Viessmannstrasse 1, Steinhaus, 4641, Wels, Austria
Tel.: (43) 724262381110
Web Site: http://www.viessmann.at
Generator Distr
N.A.I.C.S.: 423730

Viessmann Heating Technology Beijing Co., Ltd. (1)
Beijing Tianzhu Airport Industrial Zone B No 26 Yumin Street, Shunyi, Beijing, 101318, China
Tel.: (86) 1080490888
Web Site: http://www.viessmann.hk
Generator Distr
N.A.I.C.S.: 423730
Natalie Lemke *(Dir-Mktg)*

Viessmann Holzheiztechnik GmbH (1)
Flotzbachstrasse 33, 6922, Wolfurt, Austria
Tel.: (43) 557467700
Generator Distr
N.A.I.C.S.: 423730
Christian Kirchhoff *(Product Mgr)*

Viessmann Isi Teknikleri Ticaret A.S. (1)
Serifali Mah Soylesi Sok No 39, Umraniye, 34775, Istanbul, Turkiye

INTERNATIONAL PUBLIC

Tel.: (90) 2165284600
Web Site: http://www.viessmann.com.tr
Generator Distr
N.A.I.C.S.: 423730

Viessmann Kraft-Warme-Kopplung GmbH (1)
Emmy-Noether-Strasse 3, 86899, Landsberg am Lech, Germany
Tel.: (49) 819192790
Generator Distr
N.A.I.C.S.: 423730

Viessmann Kuhlsysteme GmbH (1)
Schleizer Strasse 100, Hof, 95030, Germany
Tel.: (49) 92818140
Generator Distr
N.A.I.C.S.: 423730

Viessmann Limited (1)
Hortonwood 30, Telford, TF1 7YP, United Kingdom
Tel.: (44) 1952675000
Web Site: http://www.viessmann.co.uk
Generator Distr
N.A.I.C.S.: 423730

Viessmann Manufacturing Company (U.S.) Inc. (1)
45 Access Rd, Warwick, RI 02886
Tel.: (401) 732-0667
Web Site: http://www.viessmann-us.com
Generator Distr
N.A.I.C.S.: 423730
Michael Luz *(Pres & CEO)*

Subsidiary (Non-US):

Viessmann Manufacturing Company Inc. (2)
750 McMurray Road, Waterloo, N2V 2G5, ON, Canada
Tel.: (519) 885-6300
Web Site: https://www.viessmann.ca
Generator Distr
N.A.I.C.S.: 423730

Viessmann Middle East FZE (1)
Dubai Silicon Oasis Building E-Wing Office No 603-605, PO Box 341330, Dubai, United Arab Emirates
Tel.: (971) 43724240
Web Site: http://www.viessmann.ae
Generator Distr
N.A.I.C.S.: 423730
Philipp Ampferl *(Mng Dir)*

Viessmann S.L. (1)
Area Empresarial Andalucia C Sierra Nevada 13, Pinto, 28320, Madrid, Spain
Tel.: (34) 916497400
Web Site: http://www.viessmann.es
Generator Distr
N.A.I.C.S.: 423730

Viessmann S.r.l. (1)
Via Brennero 56 Balconi di, Pescantina, 37026, Verona, Italy
Tel.: (39) 0456768999
Web Site: http://www.viessmann.it
Generator Distr
N.A.I.C.S.: 423730

Viessmann SIA (1)
Kadaka tee 36, 10621, Tallinn, Estonia
Tel.: (372) 6997195
Web Site: https://www.viessmann.ee
Generator Distr
N.A.I.C.S.: 423730

Viessmann SIA (1)
Araisu iela 37, 1039, Riga, Latvia
Tel.: (371) 67545292
Web Site: http://www.viessmann.lv
Generator Distr
N.A.I.C.S.: 423730

Viessmann SRL (1)
DN 1 KM 174 941 Nr 2, Ghimbav, 507075, Brasov, Romania
Tel.: (40) 268407800
Web Site: http://www.viessmann.ro
Generator Distr
N.A.I.C.S.: 423730

Viessmann Sp. z o.o. (1)
ul Karkonoska 65, 53-015, Wroclaw, Poland
Tel.: (48) 713607100
Web Site: http://www.viessmann.pl
Generator Distr

AND PRIVATE COMPANIES

N.A.I.C.S.: 423730

Viessmann UAB (1)
Gelezinio Vilko g 6a, 3150, Vilnius, Lithuania
Tel.: (370) 52364333
Web Site: http://www.viessmann.lt
Generator Distr
N.A.I.C.S.: 423730

Viessmann d.o.o. (1)
Tabanovacka 3, 11000, Belgrade, Serbia
Tel.: (381) 113097887
Web Site: http://www.viessmann.rs
Generator Distr
N.A.I.C.S.: 423730

Viessmann d.o.o. (1)
C XIV divizije 116 a, 2000, Maribor, Slovenia
Tel.: (386) 24805550
Web Site: http://www.viessmann.si
Generator Distr
N.A.I.C.S.: 423730

Viessmann d.o.o. (1)
Dr L Naletilica 29, 10020, Zagreb, Croatia
Tel.: (385) 16593650
Web Site: http://www.viessmann.hr
Generator Distr
N.A.I.C.S.: 423730

Viessmann, s.r.o. (1)
Ivanska cesta 30/A, 821 04, Bratislava, Slovakia
Tel.: (421) 232230100
Web Site: http://www.viessmann.sk
Generator Distr
N.A.I.C.S.: 423730

Viessmann, spol. s r.o. (1)
Chrastany 189, 252 19, Rudna, Czech Republic
Tel.: (420) 257090900
Web Site: http://www.viessmann.cz
Generator Distr
N.A.I.C.S.: 423730

Viessmann-Belgium BVBA (1)
Hermesstraat 14, Nossegem, 1930, Zaventem, Belgium
Tel.: (32) 27120666
Web Site: http://www.viessmann.be
Generator Distr
N.A.I.C.S.: 423730

Viessmann-Luxembourg (1)
35 rue J F Kennedy, 7327, Steinsel, Luxembourg
Tel.: (352) 2633621
Web Site: http://www.viessmann.lu
Generator Distr
N.A.I.C.S.: 423730

Viessmann-Nederland B.V. (1)
Lisbaan 8, 2908 LN, Capelle aan den IJssel, Netherlands
Tel.: (31) 104584444
Web Site: http://www.viessmann.nl
Generator Distr
N.A.I.C.S.: 423730
Alex Dinther van *(Acct Mgr)*

VIET HUNG MANGEMENT CORPORATION
89 Hoang Quoc Viet Street, Phu Thuan Ward District 7, Ho Chi Minh City, Vietnam
Tel.: (84) 2837760871
Construction Design Services
N.A.I.C.S.: 541310

VIET NAM POWER INVESTMENT AND DEVELOPMENT JSC
03B the C9 Group Commander of the Infantry, Kim Giang Ward, Thanh Xuan District, Hanoi, Vietnam
Tel.: (84) 435626614
Web Site: http://www.v-power.vn
Emp.: 80
Electric Power Generation & Distr
N.A.I.C.S.: 221118
Anh V. Nguyen *(Chm-Mgmt Bd)*

VIET NAM RUBBER GROUP LTD.
No 177 Hai Ba Trung, Ward 6 District 3, Ho Chi Minh City, Vietnam
Tel.: (84) 2839325235
GVR—(HNX)
Rubber Products Mfr
N.A.I.C.S.: 326291
Seongyoung Lee *(CEO & Gen Dir)*

VIET NHAT SEAFOOD CORPORATION
No 586 Cong Hoa, Ward 13 Tan Binh District, Ho Chi Minh City, Vietnam
Tel.: (84) 2862974559
Web Site: https://www.vietnhat.com
Year Founded: 2002
Emp.: 1,000
Seafood Mfr & Whslr
N.A.I.C.S.: 311710

Subsidiaries:

Phu Nhat Canning Company Limited (1)
Ben Luc District, Luong Hoa, Long An, Vietnam
Tel.: (84) 72 3637179
Web Site: http://www.phunhat.com
Sales Range: $100-124.9 Million
Emp.: 400
Fish & Seafood Canning Services
N.A.I.C.S.: 311710

VIET THANG CORPORATION
127 Le Van Chi, Linh Trung Ward Thu Duc District, Ho Chi Minh City, Vietnam
Tel.: (84) 2838969337
Web Site: https://www.vietthang.com.vn
Year Founded: 1960
Rev.: $22,143,112
Assets: $65,266,210
Liabilities: $41,785,352
Net Worth: $23,480,858
Earnings: $636,210
Fiscal Year-end: 12/31/19
Textile Products Mfr
N.A.I.C.S.: 313310
Nguyen Duc Khiem *(Chm)*

VIET THANH GARMENT TRADING J.S.C.
Lot B3-B4 Giao Long Industrial Park, Chau Thanh District, Chau Thanh, 930000, Ben Tre, Vietnam
Tel.: (84) 2753637333 VN
Web Site: http://www.vietthanhgarment.com
Year Founded: 2014
Emp.: 2,300
Fashion & Medical Wear Mfr
N.A.I.C.S.: 315250

VIET TIEN SON REAL ESTATE HOLDING CO
Viet Tien Son Office Building KDC East of Yet Kieu Street, Cong Hoa Ward Chi Linh Town, Hai Duong, Vietnam
Tel.: (84) 22062965831
Web Site: http://www.viettienson.com
AAV—(HNX)
Rev.: $3,012,214
Assets: $37,825,761
Liabilities: $5,693,922
Net Worth: $32,131,839
Earnings: ($713,914)
Fiscal Year-end: 12/31/23
Real Estate Manangement Services
N.A.I.C.S.: 531390

VIETFRACHT TRANSPORT AND CHARTERING CORP.
No 74 Nguyen Du, Hai Ba Trung Dist, Hanoi, Vietnam
Tel.: (84) 438228915 VN
Web Site: https://vietfracht.vn
Year Founded: 1963
VFR—(HNX)
Rev.: $11,186,900
Assets: $34,235,300
Liabilities: $12,971,500
Net Worth: $21,263,800
Earnings: $3,242,700
Fiscal Year-end: 12/31/22
Marine Shipping Agency
N.A.I.C.S.: 488510
Tran Binh Phu *(CEO & Gen Dir)*

VIETNAM AIRLINES CORPORATION
200 Nguyen Son Str, Long Bien Dist, Hanoi, Vietnam
Tel.: (84) 38730314 VN
Web Site: http://www.vietnamairlines.com
Year Founded: 1956
Sales Range: $1-4.9 Billion
Emp.: 9,500
Airline Services
N.A.I.C.S.: 481111
Ngoc Minh Pham *(Chm)*

Subsidiaries:

General Aviation Import Export JSC (1)
414 Nguyen Van Cu Street, Long Bien District, Hanoi, Vietnam
Tel.: (84) 2438770266
Web Site: https://www.airimex.vn
Rev.: $7,658,270
Assets: $4,796,479
Liabilities: $3,341,022
Net Worth: $1,455,457
Earnings: $77,260
Fiscal Year-end: 12/31/2021
Aircrafts & Aircraft Parts Importer & Exporter
N.A.I.C.S.: 423860

Viet Nam Air Services Company (1)
114 Bach Dang Rd Ward 2, Tan Binh, Ho Chi Minh City, Vietnam
Tel.: (84) 8 38488507
Web Site: http://www.vasco.com.vn
Travel Services
N.A.I.C.S.: 561599

Vietnam Airlines Caterers Ltd. (1)
Tan Son Nhat Int'l Airport, Tan Binh, Ho Chi Minh City, Vietnam
Tel.: (84) 8 38 448 367
Web Site: http://www.vnaircaterers.com
Flight Catering Services
N.A.I.C.S.: 722310
Bert Dinkel *(Deputy Gen Mgr)*

Vietnam National Aviation Insurance Company (1)
16th Fl Viettower Building No 1A Thai Ha Street, Dong Da, Hanoi, Vietnam
Tel.: (84) 4 62765555
Web Site: http://www.vna-insurance.com
General Insurance Services
N.A.I.C.S.: 524298

VIETNAM BANK FOR INDUSTRY & TRADE SECURITIES JSC
1st to 4th Floor Building N02T2 Diplomatic Corps Area, Bac Tu Liem District, Hanoi, Vietnam
Tel.: (84) 2439741771 VN
Web Site: https://www.cts.vn
Year Founded: 2000
CTS—(HOSE)
Rev.: $47,142,317
Assets: $348,430,584
Liabilities: $264,467,662
Net Worth: $83,962,922
Earnings: $7,720,921
Emp.: 245
Fiscal Year-end: 12/31/23
Securities Brokerage Services
N.A.I.C.S.: 523150
Ong Tran Phuc Vinh *(Member-Mgmt Bd)*

VIETNAM CONSTRUCTION STOCK CORPORATION
Vinaconex Tower 34 Lang Ha, Dong Da, Hanoi, Vietnam
Tel.: (84) 2462849234
Web Site: https://www.vinaconex.com.vn
VCG—(HOSE)
Rev.: $523,395,654
Assets: $1,264,608,044
Liabilities: $842,676,825
Net Worth: $421,931,219
Earnings: $16,333,246
Emp.: 5,586
Fiscal Year-end: 12/31/23
Heavy Engineering & Construction Services
N.A.I.C.S.: 237990
Nguyen Xuan Dong *(Gen Dir)*

Subsidiaries:

An Khanh New city development Joint Venture Company Limited (1)
An Khanh Commune, Hoai Duc District, Hanoi, Vietnam
Tel.: (84) 43 755 6541
Sales Range: $25-49.9 Million
Emp.: 64
Construction Engineering Services
N.A.I.C.S.: 237990
Kwak Won Kap *(Gen Dir)*

BGI Group JSC (1)
3rd floor of Vinaconex 7 building No 61 K2 street Cau Dien ward, Nam Tu Liem District, Hanoi, Vietnam
Tel.: (84) 422173159
Web Site: http://www.vinaconex7.net
Rev.: $4,982,542
Assets: $30,552,185
Liabilities: $10,036,687
Net Worth: $20,515,499
Earnings: $419,646
Emp.: 630
Fiscal Year-end: 12/31/2021
Civil Construction Engineering Services
N.A.I.C.S.: 237990
Hoang Trong Duc *(Chm-Mgmt Bd)*

BV Life Joint Stock Company (1)
5th floor 25T1 Building Tran Duy Hung str Trung Hoa, Cau Giay dist, Hanoi, Vietnam
Tel.: (84) 42511300
Web Site: http://www.vinaconexmec.vn
Rev.: $1,159,087
Assets: $3,664,045
Liabilities: $821,349
Net Worth: $2,842,696
Earnings: $38,844
Emp.: 70
Fiscal Year-end: 12/31/2021
Employment & Training Services
N.A.I.C.S.: 561311
Nguyen Van Hiep *(Member-Mgmt Bd & Gen Dir)*

Construction JSC No 1 (1)
D9 - Khuat Duy Tien - Thanh Xuan Bac Ward, Thanh Xuan, Hanoi, Vietnam (55.14%)
Tel.: (84) 438543416
Web Site: http://www.vinaconex1.com.vn
Rev.: $9,174,746
Assets: $29,233,625
Liabilities: $19,023,482
Net Worth: $10,210,143
Earnings: $107,985
Emp.: 564
Fiscal Year-end: 12/31/2023
Civil Construction Engineering Services
N.A.I.C.S.: 237990
Hoang Van Trinh *(Member-Mgmt Bd & Gen Dir)*

Construction JSC No 12 (1)
57 Vu Trong Phung Thanh Xuan Trung Ward, Thanh Xuan District, Hanoi, Vietnam
Tel.: (84) 422143724
Web Site: https://www.vinaconex12.com.vn
Rev.: $19,672,484
Assets: $52,256,720
Liabilities: $48,636,834
Net Worth: $3,619,885
Earnings: $246,149
Emp.: 1,000
Fiscal Year-end: 12/31/2019
Civil Engineering Services

VIETNAM CONSTRUCTION STOCK CORPORATION

Vietnam Construction Stock Corporation—Continued
N.A.I.C.S.: 237990
Nguyen Huu Toi *(Chm-Mgmt Bd)*

Construction JSC No. 3 (1)
Floor 11 Geleximco building 36 Hoang Cau O Cho Dua ward, Dong Da district, Hanoi, Vietnam
Tel.: (84) 437560333
Web Site: http://www.vinaconex3.vn
Rev.: $33,220,466
Assets: $138,792,047
Liabilities: $83,574,200
Net Worth: $55,217,847
Earnings: $5,808,046
Fiscal Year-end: 12/31/2023
Civil Construction Engineering Services
N.A.I.C.S.: 237990

Construction JSC No.9 (1)
4th anf 5th floor Vinaconex 8 building Lot HH2-2 Pham Hung street, Me Tri Ward Nam Tu Liem District, Hanoi, Vietnam
Tel.: (84) 435540606
Web Site: http://www.vinaconex-9.vn
Rev.: $39,402,500
Assets: $118,595,300
Liabilities: $117,453,400
Net Worth: $1,141,900
Earnings: $185,300
Emp.: 1,851
Fiscal Year-end: 12/31/2022
Civil Construction Engineering Services
N.A.I.C.S.: 237990
Pham Thai Duong *(Gen Dir & Member-Mgmt Bd)*

Northern Electricity Development & Investment Joint-Stock Company No 2 (1)
No 100 Hoang Lien, Coc Leu ward, Lao Cai, Vietnam
Tel.: (84) 20822757
Construction Services
N.A.I.C.S.: 236220

VIMECO JOINT-STOCK COMPANY (1)
Lot E9 Pham Hung Trung Hoa, Cau Giay district, Hanoi, Vietnam
Tel.: (84) 2437848204
Web Site: https://www.vimeco.com.vn
Rev.: $30,635,979
Assets: $40,665,888
Liabilities: $26,701,414
Net Worth: $13,964,474
Earnings: $146,725
Emp.: 1,000
Fiscal Year-end: 12/31/2021
Industrial Park Construction Services
N.A.I.C.S.: 236210

VIWACO Joint-Stock Company (1)
1st Floor House 17 T7 Trung Hoa-Nhan Chinh Urban Area, Nhan Chinh Ward Thanh Xuan District, Hanoi, Vietnam
Tel.: (84) 2462511520
Web Site: http://www.viwaco.vn
Construction Services
N.A.I.C.S.: 236220

Vicostone Joint stock Company (1)
Hoa Lac Hi-tech Park Thach Hoa Commune, Thach That District, Hanoi, Vietnam
Tel.: (84) 2432477286
Web Site: https://www.vicostone.com
Rev.: $566,026,500
Assets: $658,990,500
Liabilities: $172,116,700
Net Worth: $486,873,800
Earnings: $114,870,200
Emp.: 800
Fiscal Year-end: 12/31/2022
Construction Materials Production & Sales
N.A.I.C.S.: 423990

Vietnam Infrastructure Development and Financial Investment Corporation (1)
4th 5th Floor VIT Tower 519 Kim ma, Hanoi, Vietnam
Tel.: (84) 4 37711668
Financial Management Services
N.A.I.C.S.: 523999

Vietnam Manpower Supply and Commercial Joint-stock company (1)
Sport and Green Park Complex, Kien Hung Ward Hadong, Hanoi, Vietnam
Tel.: (84) 433555688
Web Site: http://www.vinamex.com
Sales Range: $25-49.9 Million
Emp.: 4
Employment Consulting Services
N.A.I.C.S.: 541612
Nguyen Trung Hieu *(Mng Dir)*

Vina2 Investment and Construction JSC (1)
2-4 Floor B Building Kim Van Kim Lu Dai Kim ward, Hoang Mai District, Hanoi, Vietnam
Tel.: (84) 2437534256
Web Site: http://www.vinaconex2jsc.vn
Rev.: $44,831,739
Assets: $114,276,687
Liabilities: $77,547,876
Net Worth: $36,728,811
Earnings: $631,926
Fiscal Year-end: 12/31/2023
Construction Engineering Services
N.A.I.C.S.: 236220
Quynh Trong Do *(Chm-Mgmt Bd)*

Vinaconex 15 JSC (1)
53 Ngo Quyen street May Chai ward, Ngo Quyen district, Haiphong, Vietnam
Tel.: (84) 31 3768612
Web Site: http://www.vinaconex15.com.vn
Sales Range: Less than $1 Million
Emp.: 220
Civil Engineering Services
N.A.I.C.S.: 237990
Yen D. Le *(Chm-Mgmt Bd)*

Vinaconex 21 Joint Stock Company (1)
3rd floor Vinacnonex 21 building Ba La Phu La ward, Ha Dong District, Hanoi, Vietnam
Tel.: (84) 463256588
Web Site: https://www.vinaconex21.vn
Rev.: $6,122,000
Assets: $31,711,400
Liabilities: $19,526,700
Net Worth: $12,184,700
Earnings: $92,900
Emp.: 1,400
Fiscal Year-end: 12/31/2022
Construction & Real Estate Services
N.A.I.C.S.: 236220
Nguyen Viet *(Chm)*

Vinaconex 25 JSC (1)
No 89A Phan Dang Luu Street Hoa Cuong Nam Ward, Hai Chau District, Da Nang, Vietnam
Tel.: (84) 2363621632
Web Site: https://www.vinaconex25.com.vn
Rev.: $119,780,700
Assets: $128,190,600
Liabilities: $101,002,500
Net Worth: $27,188,100
Earnings: $818,700
Fiscal Year-end: 12/31/2023
Construction Engineering Services
N.A.I.C.S.: 236220

Vinaconex 39 Joint Stock Company (1)
Floor 1 Building CT2A Co Nhue New Urban Area, Co Nhue 1 Ward Bac Tu Liem, Hanoi, Vietnam
Tel.: (84) 2437875938
Web Site: http://pvv.com.vn
Sales Range: $1-9.9 Million
Heavy Engineering & Construction Services
N.A.I.C.S.: 237990

Vinaconex Construction Consultant Joint-Stock Company (1)
4th & 5th Floor D9 Building, Thanh Xuan Bac Ward Thanh Xuan District, Hanoi, Vietnam
Tel.: (84) 45541758
Construction Services
N.A.I.C.S.: 236220

Vinaconex Dung Quat Joint-Stock Company (1)
Van Tuong New Urban Area Binh Tri Commune, Binh Son District, Quang Ngai, Vietnam
Tel.: (84) 553616025
Construction Services
N.A.I.C.S.: 236220

Vinaconex Housing & Urban Development Investment Joint-Stock Company (1)
1st Floor 17T7 Building Trung Hoa-Nhan Chinh Urban Area, Nhan Chinh Ward, Hanoi, Vietnam
Tel.: (84) 42815204
Construction Services
N.A.I.C.S.: 236220

Vinaconex Infrastructure Development and Construction Investment Joint Stock Company (1)
Office 7 Trung Hoa Nhan Chinh, New Urban Area Thanh Xuan District, Hanoi, Vietnam
Tel.: (84) 42510058
Web Site: http://www.vinaconex34.com.vn
Sales Range: $100-124.9 Million
Emp.: 350
Construction & Engineering Services
N.A.I.C.S.: 237990

Vinaconex Investment and Tourism Development Joint Stock Company (1)
Floor 12 Vinaconex Building No 34 Lang Ha Street, Dong Da, Hanoi, Vietnam
Tel.: (84) 2462511666
Web Site: http://www.vitc.com.vn
Sales Range: Less than $1 Million
Emp.: 180
Recreation & Tourism Real Estate Development & Investment Services
N.A.I.C.S.: 531390
Duong Van Mau *(Chm)*

Vinaconex Sai Gon Joint-stock company (1)
Vinaconex Building 1st Storey 47 Dien Bien Phu St, Da Kao Precinct 1st District, Ho Chi Minh City, Vietnam
Tel.: (84) 89104913
Web Site: http://www.vinaconexsaigon.com.vn
Construction Materials Mfr
N.A.I.C.S.: 327120

Vinaconex Service and Construction Joint-stock company (1)
89A Phan Dang Luu Street, Hai Chau District, Da Nang, Vietnam
Tel.: (84) 5113640660
Web Site: http://www.vinaconex.com.vn
Construction Engineering Services
N.A.I.C.S.: 541330

Vinaconex Trading Joint-stock company (1)
34 Lang Ha str, Dong Da dist, Hanoi, Vietnam
Tel.: (84) 462849234
Web Site: http://www.vinaconex.com.vn
Construction Engineering Services
N.A.I.C.S.: 541330

Vinaconex Transportation JSC (1)
2 Floor VIMECO Building Plot E9 Pham Hung Road, Trung Hoa Ward Cau Giay District, Hanoi, Vietnam
Tel.: (84) 47833602
Web Site: http://www.vinaconextrans.com
Marine Transportation Services
N.A.I.C.S.: 483111

Visicons Construction And Investment Joint Stock Company (1)
Floor 5 - T2 29 Building - Hoang Dao Thuy Street, Trung Hoa Ward Cau Giay district, Hanoi, Vietnam
Tel.: (84) 2462513155
Web Site: https://visicons.vn
Sales Range: $25-49.9 Million
Real Estate Investment & Construction Services
N.A.I.C.S.: 531390
Hoa Cuong Hoang *(Gen Dir & Deputy Gen Dir)*

Xuan Mai Investment and Construction Corporation (1)
4th floor Xuan Mai Tower To Hieu street, Ha Cau Ward Ha Dong, Hanoi, Vietnam
Tel.: (84) 2473038866
Web Site: http://www.xmcc.com.vn
Rev.: $61,147,402
Assets: $106,176,742
Liabilities: $86,767,928
Net Worth: $19,408,814
Earnings: ($1,301,321)
Emp.: 2,000

INTERNATIONAL PUBLIC

Fiscal Year-end: 12/31/2012
Building Materials Mfr & Distr
N.A.I.C.S.: 444180

VIETNAM CONTAINER SHIPPING CORPORATION
5-6-7 th Floor TD TOWER Building No 01 Lot 3A New Urban Area, Nga Nam Cat Bi Air Port Le Hong Phong Str Dong khe Wd Ngo Quyen Dist, Haiphong, Vietnam
Tel.: (84) 2253836705
Web Site: https://www.viconship.com
Year Founded: 1985
Cargo Handling Services
N.A.I.C.S.: 488320
Nguyen Due Dung *(Chm)*

Subsidiaries:

Central Container Joint Stock Company (1)
So 75 Quang Trung, Hai Chau District, Da Nang, Vietnam
Tel.: (84) 2363822922
Web Site: http://www.viconshipdanang.com
Container Shipping ervices
N.A.I.C.S.: 488510

VIETNAM CORPORATION
No 36 Hoang Hoa Tham Street Bo Son Quarter, Vo Cuong Ward, Bac Ninh, Vietnam
Tel.: (84) 2413823679   VN
Display Equipment Mfr
N.A.I.C.S.: 337215

VIETNAM DAIRY PRODUCTS JOINT STOCK COMPANY
No 10 Tan Trao Street Tan Phu Ward District 7, Ho Chi Minh City, Vietnam
Tel.: (84) 2854155555   VN
Web Site: https://www.vinamilk.com.vn
Year Founded: 1976
VNM—(HOSE)
Rev.: $6,036,891,600
Assets: $5,267,337,100
Liabilities: $1,764,762,700
Net Worth: $3,502,574,400
Earnings: $887,381,200
Emp.: 5,000
Fiscal Year-end: 12/31/23
Milk & Dairy Products Mfr & Sales
N.A.I.C.S.: 311511
Mai Kieu Lien *(CEO)*

Subsidiaries:

Angkor Dairy Products Co., Ltd. (1)
Lot P2-096 and P2-097 Phnom Penh Special Economic Zone, National Highway 4 Sangkat Phleung Chhes Totes Khan Po-SenChey, Phnom Penh, Cambodia
Tel.: (855) 246839999
Milk Production Services
N.A.I.C.S.: 112120

Driftwood Dairy (1)
10724 E Lowr Azusa Rd, El Monte, CA 91734
Tel.: (626) 444-9591
Web Site: http://www.driftwooddairy.net
Holding Company; Milk & Dairy Products Mfr
N.A.I.C.S.: 551112

Driftwood Dairy Holding Corporation (1)
10724 E Lower Azusa Rd, El Monte, CA 91734
Web Site: https://www.driftwooddairy.com
Dairy Products Distr
N.A.I.C.S.: 424430

Lao-Jagro Development XiengKhouang Co., Ltd. (1)
Poungvene Village, Paek District, Phonsavan, Xiangkhouang, Lao People's Democratic Republic
Tel.: (856) 21563053
Dairy Farm Raising Services
N.A.I.C.S.: 112111

AND PRIVATE COMPANIES

Thong Nhat Thanh Hoa Dairy Cow Limited Company (1)
Quarter 1 NT Thong Nhat Town, Yen Dinh District, Thong Nhat, Thanh Hoa, Vietnam
Tel.: (84) 2373514020
Milk Production Services
N.A.I.C.S.: 112120

Vibev Food & Beverage Joint Venture Company Limited (1)
10 Tan Trao, Tan Phu Ward District 7, Ho Chi Minh City, Vietnam
Tel.: (84) 27454165166
Food & Beverage Mfr
N.A.I.C.S.: 311999

Vietnam Dairy Cow One Member Limited Company (1)
No 10 Tan Trao, Tan Phu Ward District 7, Ho Chi Minh City, Vietnam
Tel.: (84) 2854155555
Dairy Farm Raising Services
N.A.I.C.S.: 112111

Vietnam Dairy Products Joint Stock Company - Beverage Factory (1)
Lot NA7 Street My Phuoc II Industrial Park, Ben Cat, Binh Duongv, Vietnam
Tel.: (84) 650 355 68 39
Beverages Mfr
N.A.I.C.S.: 312140

Vietnam Dairy Products Joint Stock Company - Binh Dinh Milk Factory (1)
1 Hoang Van Thu Street, Quy Nhon, Binh Dinh, Vietnam
Tel.: (84) 56 62 53 555
Fluid Milk Mfr
N.A.I.C.S.: 311511

Vietnam Dairy Products Joint Stock Company - Can Tho Dairy Factory (1)
Block 46 Tra Noc I Industrial Park, Tra Noc Ward Binh Thuy District, Can Tho, Vietnam
Tel.: (84) 2926258555
Milk Production Services
N.A.I.C.S.: 112120

Vietnam Dairy Products Joint Stock Company - Da Nang Dairy Factory (1)
Block Q The 7 Street Hoa Khanh Industrial Park, Hoa Khanh Bac Ward Lien Chieu District, Da Nang, Vietnam
Tel.: (84) 2366259777
Milk Production Services
N.A.I.C.S.: 112120

Vietnam Dairy Products Joint Stock Company - Dielac Dairy Factory (1)
No 10 Tan Trao Street, Tan Phu Ward, Ho Chi Minh City, Dong Nai, Vietnam
Tel.: (84) 2854155555
Web Site: http://www.vinamilk.com.vn
Dairy Product Mfr & Whslr
N.A.I.C.S.: 424430

Vietnam Dairy Products Joint Stock Company - Lam Son Dairy Factory (1)
Le Mon Industrial Park, Thanh Hoa, Vietnam
Tel.: (84) 2373912540
Milk Production Services
N.A.I.C.S.: 112120

Vietnam Dairy Products Joint Stock Company - Nghe An Dairy Factory (1)
Sao Nam Street, Nghi Thu Ward, Cua Lo, Nghe An, Vietnam
Tel.: (84) 2386259555
Milk Production Services
N.A.I.C.S.: 112120

Vietnam Dairy Products Joint Stock Company - Sai Gon Milk Factory (1)
Lot 1-18 G1 Area-Tan Thoi Hiep Industrial Park 80 Village Road, Hiep Thanh Ward District 12, Ho Chi Minh City, Vietnam
Tel.: (84) 8 62 528 555
Fluid Milk Mfr
N.A.I.C.S.: 311511

Vietnam Dairy Products Joint Stock Company - Thong Nhat Milk Factory (1)
12 Dang Van Bi Truong Tho Ward, Thu Duc, Ho Chi Minh City, Vietnam
Tel.: (84) 8 62 529 555
Fluid Milk Mfr
N.A.I.C.S.: 311511

Vietnam Dairy Products Joint Stock Company - Tien Son Dairy Factory (1)
Tien Son Industrial Park, Hoan Son Ward Tien Du District, Dai Dong, Bac Ninh, Vietnam
Tel.: (84) 2223739568
Milk Production Services
N.A.I.C.S.: 112120

Vietnam Dairy Products Joint Stock Company - Truong Tho Dairy Factory (1)
No 32 Dang Van Bi Street, Truong Tho Ward Thu Duc District, Ho Chi Minh City, Vietnam
Tel.: (84) 2862527555
Milk Production Services
N.A.I.C.S.: 112120

Vietnam Dairy Products Joint Stock Company - Vietnam Beverages Factory (1)
Block A NA7 Street My Phuoc II Industrial Park, My Phuoc Town, Ben Cat, Binh Duong, Vietnam
Tel.: (84) 2743556839
Milk Production Services
N.A.I.C.S.: 112120

Vietnam Dairy Products Joint Stock Company - Vietnam Dairy Factory (1)
Block A-4-CN A-5-CN A-6-CN A-7-CN My Phuoc II Industrial Park, Ben Cat, Binh Duong, Vietnam
Tel.: (84) 2743559988
Milk Production Services
N.A.I.C.S.: 112120

Vietnam Dairy Products Joint Stock Company - Vietnam Powdered Milk Factory (1)
No 9 Tu Do Avenue VSIP1 Industrial Park, Thuan An, Binh Duong, Vietnam
Tel.: (84) 2743799628
Milk Production Services
N.A.I.C.S.: 112120

Vietnam Diary Cow One Member Co., Ltd. (1)
10 Tan Trao Street, Tan Phu Ward District 7, Ho Chi Minh City, Vietnam
Tel.: (84) 2854155555
Dairy Farm Development Services
N.A.I.C.S.: 112120

Vietnam Livestock Corporation (1)
Lot EI-2 EI-3 & EI-4, Giao Long Industrial Park Phase II An Phuoc Commune, Chau Thanh, Ben Tre, Vietnam
Tel.: (84) 2753656999
Animal Food Mfr & Distr
N.A.I.C.S.: 311119

Vietnam Sugar Joint Stock Company (1)
Thuy Xuong Hamlet, Suoi Hiep Village Dien Khanh District, Nha Trang, Khanh Hoa, Vietnam
Tel.: (84) 2583745453
Sugar Products Mfr
N.A.I.C.S.: 311314

Vinamilk EuropeSpostka Z Ogranic-zona Odpowiedzialnoscia (1)
ul Gwiazdzista 7a/4, 01-651, Warsaw, Poland
Tel.: (48) 221185976
Web Site: http://www.vinamilk.pl
Dairy Raw Material Distr
N.A.I.C.S.: 424430
Pawet Redzisz *(Mng Dir)*

VIETNAM ELECTRICITY CONSTRUCTION JOINT STOCK CORPORATION
344 Phan Chu Trinh Street, Hai Chau District, Da Nang, Vietnam
Tel.: (84) 511562361
Web Site: https://www.vneco.vn
Year Founded: 1998
VNE—(HOSE)
Rev.: $43,576,869
Assets: $154,679,714
Liabilities: $113,208,371
Net Worth: $41,471,343
Earnings: ($1,175,848)
Fiscal Year-end: 12/31/23
Power Transmission Services
N.A.I.C.S.: 221121
Ngon Dang Trong *(Chm)*

Subsidiaries:

VNECO 1 Electricity Construction JSC (1)
489 Nguyen Luong Bang Str, Da Nang, Vietnam
Tel.: (84) 2363772001
Web Site: https://www.vneco1.com.vn
Rev.: $419,600
Assets: $3,147,500
Liabilities: $136,200
Net Worth: $3,011,300
Earnings: ($494,200)
Fiscal Year-end: 12/31/2022
Electric Power System Construction Services
N.A.I.C.S.: 237130

VNECO 3 Electricity Construction JSC (1)
Block 3 Trung Do ward, Vinh, Nghe An, Vietnam
Tel.: (84) 383855619
Web Site: https://www.vneco3.com.vn
Rev.: $5,070,937
Assets: $3,903,221
Liabilities: $3,143,709
Net Worth: $759,513
Earnings: $51,121
Fiscal Year-end: 12/31/2021
Electric Power System Construction Services
N.A.I.C.S.: 237130
Huy Huu Minh Pham *(Chm-Mgmt Bd)*

VNECO 9 Investment & Construction JSC (1)
44 Nguyen Thi Minh Khai Street Loc Tho Ward, Nha Trang, Khanh Hoa, Vietnam
Tel.: (84) 58525404
Web Site: http://www.vneco9.com
Rev.: $95,914
Assets: $782,347
Liabilities: $397,333
Net Worth: $385,014
Earnings: ($510,921)
Emp.: 4
Fiscal Year-end: 12/31/2023
Electric Power System Construction Services
N.A.I.C.S.: 237130
Nguyen Van Duy *(Chm)*

VNECO4 Electricity Construction JSC (1)
No 197 Nguyen Truong To Street, Dong Vinh Ward, Vinh, Nghe An, Vietnam
Tel.: (84) 383531065
Web Site: https://www.vneco4.com.vn
Rev.: $3,785,538
Assets: $3,311,038
Liabilities: $2,922,275
Net Worth: $388,763
Earnings: ($161,463)
Emp.: 72
Fiscal Year-end: 12/31/2023
Electric Power System Construction Services
N.A.I.C.S.: 237130

Vietnam Electricity Construction 2 JSC (1)
No 13 Mai Hac De Street, Vinh, Nghe An, Vietnam
Tel.: (84) 383842195
Web Site: http://www.vneco2.com.vn
Rev.: $8,110,700
Assets: $6,612,000
Liabilities: $5,934,500
Net Worth: $677,500
Earnings: ($1,662,600)
Fiscal Year-end: 12/31/2022
Electric Power System Construction Services
N.A.I.C.S.: 237130

VIETNAM ENTERPRISE INVESTMENT & DEVELOPMENT JOINT STOCK COMPANY
5th floor Thang Long Star Building - No 36 Hoang Cau street O Cho Dua, Dong Da, Hanoi, Vietnam
Tel.: (84) 439336999
Web Site: https://www.vndi.vn
FID—(HNX)
Rev.: $3,464,220
Assets: $12,695,904
Liabilities: $1,678,529
Net Worth: $11,017,374
Earnings: ($1,125,996)
Emp.: 6
Fiscal Year-end: 12/31/23
Hotel & Restaurant Operator
N.A.I.C.S.: 721110

VIETNAM ENTERPRISE INVESTMENTS LTD.
1501 Me Linh Point 2 Ngo Duc Ke, District 1, Ho Chi Minh City, Vietnam
Tel.: (84) 2838239355
Web Site: https://www.veil-dragoncapital.com
Year Founded: 1995
VEIL—(LSE)
Rev.: $199,840,121
Assets: $1,754,720,861
Liabilities: $11,463,153
Net Worth: $1,743,257,708
Earnings: $160,948,589
Fiscal Year-end: 12/31/23
Investment Services
N.A.I.C.S.: 525910
Dien Vu Huu *(Portfolio Mgr)*

VIETNAM EXPORT IMPORT COMMERCIAL JOINT STOCK BANK
8th Floor - Vincom Center 72 Le Thanh Ton, District 1, Ho Chi Minh City, Vietnam
Tel.: (84) 18001199
Web Site: http://www.eximbank.com.vn
Year Founded: 1989
EIB—(HOSE)
Rev.: $189,400,685
Assets: $8,298,373,602
Liabilities: $7,373,639,643
Net Worth: $924,733,959
Earnings: $89,202,079
Emp.: 6,232
Fiscal Year-end: 12/31/23
Banking Services
N.A.I.C.S.: 522110
Tan Loc Tran *(Deputy CEO)*

VIETNAM FUMIGATION JOINT STOCK COMPANY
29 Ton Duc Thang St District 1, Ho Chi Minh City, Vietnam
Web Site: http://www.vfc.com.vn
Year Founded: 1960
VFG—(HOSE)
Rev.: $134,411,704
Assets: $121,359,050
Liabilities: $70,039,176
Net Worth: $51,319,874
Earnings: $12,177,772
Fiscal Year-end: 12/31/23
Fumigating Services
N.A.I.C.S.: 561990
Truong Cong Cu *(Gen Dir)*

Subsidiaries:

VFC Cambo Ltd. (1)
33 Street 371, Sangkat Boeng Tompon Khan Mean Chey, Phnom Penh, Cambodia
Tel.: (855) 974747714
Agrochemical Product Mfr
N.A.I.C.S.: 325320

VIETNAM GERMANY STEEL

VIETNAM GERMANY STEEL

VIETNAM GERMANY STEEL—(CONTINUED)
PIPE JOINT STOCK COMPANY
Binh Xuyen Industrial Zone Dao Duc Commune, Binh Xuyen, Vinh Phuc, Vietnam
Tel.: (84) 2113887863
Web Site: https://www.vgpipe.com.vn
Year Founded: 2002
VGS—(HNX)
Rev.: $848,323,700
Assets: $216,490,400
Liabilities: $123,830,600
Net Worth: $92,659,800
Earnings: $10,011,000
Fiscal Year-end: 12/31/22
Steel Pole Mfr
N.A.I.C.S.: 331210

VIETNAM HOLDING LTD
De Catapan House Grange Road, Saint Peter Port, GY1 2QG, Guernsey
Tel.: (44) 9494544
Web Site:
 http://www.vietnamholding.com
Year Founded: 2006
VNH—(LSE)
Rev.: $103,980,000
Assets: $200,420,000
Liabilities: $4,340,000
Net Worth: $196,080,000
Earnings: $100,150,000
Fiscal Year-end: 06/30/21
Investment Services
N.A.I.C.S.: 523999
Hiroshi Funaki *(Chm)*

Subsidiaries:

VietNam Holding Asset Management Ltd. (1)
Gartenstrasse 19, 8002, Zurich, Switzerland
Tel.: (41) 43 500 2810
Web Site: http://www.vnham.com
Emp.: 5
Asset Management Services
N.A.I.C.S.: 523999
Gyentsen Zatul *(Mgr-IR)*

VIETNAM INDUSTRIAL & COMMERCIAL SECURITIES JOINT STOCK COMPANY
3th Villa 02 Bis Nguyen Thi Minh Khai Str, District 1, Ho Chi Minh City, Vietnam
Tel.: (84) 2839110788
Web Site: http://vics.vn
VIG—(HNX)
Rev.: $1,705,227
Assets: $14,329,484
Liabilities: $485,748
Net Worth: $13,843,736
Earnings: $1,279,796
Emp.: 38
Fiscal Year-end: 12/31/23
Securities Brokerage Services
N.A.I.C.S.: 523150
Nguyen Phuc Long *(Co-Chm & CEO)*

VIETNAM INDUSTRIAL INVESTMENTS LIMITED
Unit 5A 1 Station Street, Subiaco, 6008, WA, Australia
Tel.: (61) 8 9388 0155
Web Site: http://www.vii.net.au
Rev.: $299,358,500
Assets: $143,479,038
Liabilities: $99,203,401
Net Worth: $44,275,637
Earnings: $2,645,861
Emp.: 663
Fiscal Year-end: 12/31/17
Investment Services
N.A.I.C.S.: 523940
Lam Van Hung *(Chm-Acting & CEO)*

Subsidiaries:

Austnam Joint Stock Corporation (1)
Austnam Building-109 Truong Chinh, Hanoi, Vietnam
Tel.: (84) 43 869 1579
Web Site: http://www.austnam.com.vn
Steel Building Product Mfr & Distr
N.A.I.C.S.: 327390

VIETNAM INVESTMENT PRODUCTION & TRADING JSC
Level 11 Building Vinaconex 9 Lot HH2-2 Tri Ha Urban Area, Pham Hung Q Nam Tu Liem, Hanoi, Vietnam
Tel.: (84) 4 3768 9658
Web Site: http://www.vitravico.com
Year Founded: 2008
Mining & Construction Machinery Mfr
N.A.I.C.S.: 333131
Tuan Minh Nguyen *(Mgr)*

VIETNAM JOINT STOCK COMMERCIAL BANK FOR INDUSTRY AND TRADE
108 Tran Hung Dao Hoan Kiem, Hanoi, Vietnam
Tel.: (84) 2439418868
Web Site: https://www.vietinbank.vn
Year Founded: 1988
VTG—(HOSE)
Rev.: $4,779,195,500
Assets: $180,842,976,400
Liabilities: $170,026,210,700
Net Worth: $10,816,765,700
Earnings: $1,677,507,400
Emp.: 24,105
Fiscal Year-end: 12/31/22
Banking Services
N.A.I.C.S.: 522110
Le Duc Tho *(Chm)*

Subsidiaries:

VietinBank Debt Management & Asset Exploitation Company Ltd. (1)
76 Nguyen Van Cu Street, Nguyen Cu Trinh Ward District I, Ho Chi Minh City, Vietnam
Tel.: (84) 839202020
Web Site: https://www.vietinbankamc.vn
Asset Management Services
N.A.I.C.S.: 531390

VietinBank Fund Management Company Ltd. (1)
6th Floor 34 Cua Nam Street, Hoan Kiem District, Hanoi, Vietnam
Tel.: (84) 439388855
Fund Management Services
N.A.I.C.S.: 523940

VietinBank Gold & Jewellery Trading Company Ltd. (1)
11st Floor 34 Cua Nam Building Cua Nam Street, Hoan Kiem District, Hanoi, Vietnam
Tel.: (84) 439421051
Gold Whslr
N.A.I.C.S.: 423520

VietinBank Insurance Company Ltd. (1)
10th 11th Floor 126 Doi Can Street, Ba Dinh District, Hanoi, Vietnam
Tel.: (84) 439425650
General Insurance Services
N.A.I.C.S.: 524113

VietinBank Lao Limited (1)
No 029 Khounboulom Vatchan, Chanthabouly District, Vientiane, Lao People's Democratic Republic
Tel.: (856) 21263997
Web Site: http://www.vietinbank.com.la
Financial Banking Services
N.A.I.C.S.: 523150

VietinBank Leasing Company Ltd. (1)
16 Phan Dinh Phung street, Ba Dinh District, Hanoi, Vietnam
Tel.: (84) 438233045
Web Site: http://www.lc.vietinbank.vn
Financial Banking Services
N.A.I.C.S.: 523150

VietinBank Securities Joint Stock Company (1)
306 Ba Trieu Street, Hai Ba Trung District, Hanoi, Vietnam
Tel.: (84) 462780012
Securities Brokerage Services
N.A.I.C.S.: 523150

VIETNAM LPG TRADING JOINT STOCK COMPANY
11th Floor-Vietnam Petroleum Institute Building-167 Trung Kinh, Cau Giay, Hanoi, Vietnam
Tel.: (84) 439445555
Web Site: https://pvgaslpg.com.vn
Year Founded: 1990
PVG—(HNX)
Rev.: $438,173,500
Assets: $179,972,200
Liabilities: $131,636,800
Net Worth: $48,335,400
Earnings: $108,600
Fiscal Year-end: 12/31/23
Gas Transportation Services
N.A.I.C.S.: 486210
Tran Trong Huu *(Chm-Mgmt Bd)*

VIETNAM MACHINERY INSTALLATION CORPORATION JSC
124 Minh Khai Street, Hai Ba Trung District, Hanoi, Vietnam
Tel.: (84) 2438633067
Web Site: https://www.lilama.com.vn
Year Founded: 1960
LLM—(HNX)
Rev.: $209,256,036
Assets: $262,449,191
Liabilities: $223,577,733
Net Worth: $38,871,458
Earnings: ($803,318)
Emp.: 20,000
Fiscal Year-end: 12/31/23
Heavy Construction & Civil Engineering Services
N.A.I.C.S.: 237990
Duc Kien Bui *(Chm-Mgmt Bd)*

Subsidiaries:

CTCI Vietnam Company Limited (1)
6 Floor Charmvit Tower 117 Tran Duy Hung Road, Cau Giay District, Hanoi, Vietnam (33%)
Tel.: (84) 2438335513
Web Site: https://www.vietnam.ctci.com
Sales Range: $50-74.9 Million
Emp.: 200
Engineering & Construction Services
N.A.I.C.S.: 541330

LILAMA 10 JSC (1)
LILAMA10 Tower To Huu Street Trung Van Nam Tu Liem, Hanoi, Vietnam
Tel.: (84) 4 38649 584
Web Site: http://www.lilama10.com
Emp.: 2,780
Steel Products Mfr
N.A.I.C.S.: 331221
Do van Nhuan *(Mgr-Technical)*

LILAMA 18 JSC (1)
9 - 19 Ho Tung Mau Q1, Ho Chi Minh City, Vietnam
Tel.: (84) 8 38 298 490
Web Site: http://www.lilama18.com
Industrial Machinery Mfr
N.A.I.C.S.: 333998
Tran Manh Hung *(Sr Project Mgr)*

LILAMA 45-1 JSC (1)
138 - 140 Dien Bien Phu Phuong Da Kao Quan 1, Ho Chi Minh City, Vietnam
Tel.: (84) 8 3829 7527
Web Site: http://www.lilama45-1.com.vn
Emp.: 2,000
Steel Products Mfr
N.A.I.C.S.: 331221

LILAMA 45-3 Joint Stock Company (1)
Lot 4K-Ton Duc Thang Street, Le Hong Phong Ward, Quang Ngai, Vietnam

INTERNATIONAL PUBLIC

Tel.: (84) 553710321
Web Site: http://www.lilama45-3.com
Sales Range: $10-24.9 Million
Industrial Building Construction Services
N.A.I.C.S.: 236210
Hoang Viet *(Chm & Gen Dir)*

LILAMA 45-4 Joint Stock Company (1)
Hanoi Highway Binh Da Ward, Bien Hoa, Dong Nai, Vietnam
Tel.: (84) 613813188
Web Site: http://www.lilama454.com.vn
Sales Range: $10-24.9 Million
Industrial Machinery & Piping System Installation Services
N.A.I.C.S.: 238290
Hoang Van Du *(Chm)*

LILAMA 5 Joint Stock Company (1)
179 Tran Phu street, Ba Dinh, Binh Soon, Thanh Hoa, Vietnam
Tel.: (84) 37 3824421
Web Site: http://www.lilama5.com.vn
Sales Range: $10-24.9 Million
Prefabricated Metal Building & Component Mfr
N.A.I.C.S.: 332311
Doan Hanh Nguyen *(Chm-Mgmt Bd)*

LILAMA 69-1 Joint Stock Company (1)
No 17 Ly Thai To Street, Bac Ninh, Vietnam
Tel.: (84) 2413 821212
Web Site: http://www.lilama69-1.com.vn
Sales Range: $25-49.9 Million
Power Plant Boiler Installation Services
N.A.I.C.S.: 238290
Bui Quang Vinh *(Chm)*

LILAMA 69-3 JSC (1)
515 Dien Bien Phu, Hai Duong, Vietnam
Tel.: (84) 3203 852 584
Web Site: http://www.lilama69-3.vn
Industrial Machinery Mfr
N.A.I.C.S.: 333998
Sanghp Thesang *(Sr Engr-Matls Dept)*

LILAMA 7 Joint Stock Company (1)
332 2/9 st, Hai Chau district, Da Nang, Vietnam
Tel.: (84) 5113642666
Web Site: http://www.lilama7.com.vn
Sales Range: $1-9.9 Million
Emp.: 550
Construction & Engineering Services
N.A.I.C.S.: 237990
Nguyen Van Kien *(Chm)*

LILAMA Erection Mechanical Joint Stock Company (1)
72E Hoang Dieu, Thanh Binh, Ninh Binh, Vietnam
Tel.: (84) 30871125
Web Site: http://www.lilamaemc.vn
Sales Range: $1-9.9 Million
Emp.: 800
Structural Metal Products, Boilers, Pressure Tanks, Steel Pipes, Girders & Construction Cranes
N.A.I.C.S.: 332312
Le Huu Dieu *(Chm)*

VIETNAM MANUFACTURING AND EXPORT PROCESSING (HOLDINGS) LIMITED
40th Floor Sunlight Tower No 248 Queen s Road East, Wanchai, China (Hong Kong)
Tel.: (852) 35972788
Web Site: http://www.vmeph.com
0422—(HKG)
Rev.: $132,899,372
Assets: $127,020,051
Liabilities: $76,137,305
Net Worth: $50,882,746
Earnings: ($200,346)
Emp.: 1,155
Fiscal Year-end: 12/31/22
Scooter & Motorbike Mfr
N.A.I.C.S.: 336991
Wu Hsiung Liu *(Chm)*

VIETNAM MECHANIZATION ELECTRIFICATION AND CON-

AND PRIVATE COMPANIES

STRUCTION JOINT STOCK COMPANY
102 Truong Chinh, Dong Da, Hanoi, Vietnam
Tel.: (84) 42138536
Web Site: https://www.mecojsc.vn
Year Founded: 1969
MCG—(HOSE)
Rev.: $1,585,623
Assets: $54,370,816
Liabilities: $44,529,619
Net Worth: $9,841,197
Earnings: ($42,560)
Fiscal Year-end: 12/31/23
Engineeering Services
N.A.I.C.S.: 541330
Ngoc Binh Nguyen *(Chm)*

VIETNAM NATIONAL PETROLEUM CORPORATION
No 1 Kham Thien Street, Hanoi, Vietnam
Tel.: (84) 48512603
Web Site:
   http://www.petrolimex.com.vn
Year Founded: 1956
Petroleum & Petrochemical Mfr & Whslr
N.A.I.C.S.: 325110
Ngoc Bao Bui *(Chm-Mgmt Bd)*

Subsidiaries:

Hai Phong Petrolimex Transportation & Services JSC **(1)**
No 61 Ngo Quyen, Ngo Quyen District, Haiphong, Vietnam
Tel.: (84) 3837441
Web Site:
   https://ptshaiphong.petrolimex.com
Rev.: $39,381,700
Assets: $25,793,900
Liabilities: $16,253,000
Net Worth: $9,540,900
Earnings: $42,000
Fiscal Year-end: 12/31/2023
Petroleum Product Whslr
N.A.I.C.S.: 424720
Kien Manh Dao *(Member-Mgmt Bd)*

PETROLIMEX CANTHO CO., LTD **(1)**
No 21 Cach Mang Thang 8 Rd, Can Tho, Vietnam
Tel.: (84) 71 823913
Web Site:
   http://www.taynambo.petrolimex.com.vn
Petroleum Product Distr
N.A.I.C.S.: 424720

PETROLIMEX DA NANG TRANSPORTATION AND SERVICE JSC **(1)**
430 Ong Ich Khiem, Da Nang, Vietnam
Tel.: (84) 511 827 834
Web Site:
   http://www.petajicodanang.vn
Petroleum Product Distr
N.A.I.C.S.: 424720

PETROLIMEX GIA LAI CO., LTD **(1)**
No 1 Nguyen Du, Pleiku, Gia Lai, Vietnam
Tel.: (84) 59 823922
Web Site: http://www.bactaynguyen.com.vn
Petroleum Product Distr
N.A.I.C.S.: 424720

PETROLIMEX HAGIANG CO., LTD **(1)**
Group 17 - P Nguyen Trai, Ha Giang, Vietnam
Tel.: (84) 19 867121
Web Site:
   http://www.hagiang.petrolimex.com.vn
Petroleum Product Distr

PETROLIMEX HATAY CO., LTD. **(1)**
151 Tran Phu st Ha Dong, Hanoi, Vietnam
Tel.: (84) 4 33824821
Web Site:
   http://www.hasonbinh.petrolimex.com.vn
Petroleum Product Distr

PETROLIMEX KHANHHOA CO., LTD **(1)**
No 10B Nguyen Thien Thuat st, Nha Trang, Khanh Hoa, Vietnam
Tel.: (84) 58 3523650
Web Site:
   http://www.phukhanh.petrolimex.com.vn
Petroleum Product Distr
N.A.I.C.S.: 424720

PETROLIMEX LAOCAI CO., LTD. **(1)**
495 - Hoang Lien Rd, Kim Tan Dist, Lao Cai, Vietnam
Tel.: (84) 20 841180
Web Site:
   http://www.laocai.petrolimex.com.vn
Petroleum Product Distr
N.A.I.C.S.: 424720

PETROLIMEX PHUTHO CO., LTD. **(1)**
2470 Hung Vuong Highway P Van Co, Viet Tri, Phu Tho, Vietnam
Tel.: (84) 210 952341
Web Site:
   http://www.phutho.petrolimex.com.vn
Petroleum Product Distr
N.A.I.C.S.: 424720

PETROLIMEX QUANG BINH CO., LTD **(1)**
118 Huu Nghi st, Hanoi, Quang Binh, Vietnam
Tel.: (84) 52 3822 384
Web Site:
   http://www.quangbinh.petrolimex.com.vn
Petroleum Product Distr
N.A.I.C.S.: 424720

PETROLIMEX QUANG TRI CO., LTD. **(1)**
So 1 Kham Thien Dong Da, Hanoi, Quang Tri, Vietnam
Tel.: (84) 2438512603
Web Site:
   http://www.quangtri.petrolimex.com.vn
Petroleum Product Distr
N.A.I.C.S.: 424720

PETROLIMEX QUANGNINH CO., LTD. **(1)**
No 1 Bai Chay st, Ha Long, Quang Ninh, Vietnam
Tel.: (84) 33 3846360
Web Site: http://www.b12.petrolimex.com.vn
Emp.: 150
Petroleum Product Distr
N.A.I.C.S.: 424720

PETROLIMEX VINH LONG CO., LTD. **(1)**
114A Le Thai To P 2, Vinh Long, Vietnam
Tel.: (84) 70 3829539
Web Site:
   http://www.vinhlong.petrolimex.com.vn
Petroleum Product Distr
N.A.I.C.S.: 424720

Petroleum Logistic Service and Investment Joint stock company **(1)**
So 1 Kham thien, Dong da, Hanoi, Vietnam
Tel.: (84) 4 3513 0135
Web Site:
   http://www.pland.petrolimex.com.vn
Petroleum Product Distr
N.A.I.C.S.: 424720

Petrolimex (Lao) LTD **(1)**
534 150 bets hospital Rd Ban Phontongsavath, Chanthaboury district, Vientiane, Lao People's Democratic Republic
Tel.: (856) 2156 3069
Web Site: http://www.lao.petrolimex.com.vn
Petroleum Product Distr
N.A.I.C.S.: 424720
Nguyen Tien Dung *(Mgr-IT Dept)*

Petrolimex Angiang **(1)**
145/1 Tran Hung Doo - P My Phuoc, Long Xuyen, An Giang, Vietnam
Tel.: (84) 76 943563
Web Site:
   http://www.angiang.petrolimex.com.vn
Petroleum Product Distr

Petrolimex Bariavungtau Co., Ltd.

VIETNAM NATIONAL PETROLEUM CORPORATION

So 12 Hoang Hoa Tham Phuong 2, Vung Tau, Tinh Ba Ria-Vung Tau, Vietnam
Tel.: (84) 64 3832043
Web Site:
   http://www.bariavungtau.petrolimex.com.vn
Petroleum Product Distr
N.A.I.C.S.: 424720

Petrolimex Ben Tre Co., Ltd. **(1)**
So 199B Nguyen Dinh Chieu, Phuong 8, Ben Tre, Vietnam
Tel.: (84) 75 3822345
Web Site:
   http://www.bentre.petrolimex.com.vn
Petroleum Product Distr
N.A.I.C.S.: 424720

Petrolimex Camau Co., Ltd **(1)**
989 Ly Thuong Kiet - P 6, Ca Mau, Vietnam
Tel.: (84) 780 560872
Web Site:
   http://www.camau.petrolimex.com.vn
Petroleum Product Distr
N.A.I.C.S.: 424720

Petrolimex Caobang Co., Ltd **(1)**
P Song Bang, Hanoi, Vietnam
Tel.: (84) 26 852402
Web Site:
   http://www.caobang.petrolimex.com.vn
Petroleum Product Distr
N.A.I.C.S.: 424720

Petrolimex Daklak **(1)**
No 6 Nguyen Tat Thanh, Buon Ma Thuot, Daklak, Vietnam
Tel.: (84) 500 856948
Web Site: http://www.namtaynguyen.com.vn
Petroleum Product Distr
N.A.I.C.S.: 424720

Petrolimex Dongnai **(1)**
No 40 National Rd, Bien Hoa, Dong Nai, Vietnam
Tel.: (84) 61 819374
Web Site:
   http://www.dongnai.petrolimex.com.vn
Petroleum Product Distr
N.A.I.C.S.: 424720

Petrolimex Dongthap **(1)**
So 34 Ly Thuong Kiet Phuong 1, Cao Lanh, Dong Thap, Vietnam
Tel.: (84) 67 3859407
Web Site:
   http://www.dongthap.petrolimex.com.vn
Petroleum Product Distr
N.A.I.C.S.: 424720

Petrolimex Equipment Joint Stock Company **(1)**
84/9 Ngoc khanh, Ba dinh, Hanoi, Vietnam
Tel.: (84) 4 3834 3654
Web Site:
   http://www.peco.petrolimex.com.vn
Petroleum Product Distr
N.A.I.C.S.: 424720

Petrolimex HABAC **(1)**
So 38 Chau Xuyen Le Loi, Hanoi, Bac Giang, Vietnam
Tel.: (84) 240 3854307
Web Site:
   http://www.habac.petrolimex.com.vn
Petroleum Product Distr

Petrolimex Hanoi Transportation & Trading JSC **(1)**
No 1 Kham Thien St Kham Thien Ward, Dong Da District, Hanoi, Vietnam
Tel.: (84) 436559177
Web Site: https://www.petajicohanoi.com
Rev.: $120,125,600
Assets: $23,173,300
Liabilities: $7,910,600
Net Worth: $15,262,700
Earnings: $3,173,000
Fiscal Year-end: 12/31/2023
Petroleum Product Whslr
N.A.I.C.S.: 424720
Bui Van Thanh *(Chm-Mgmt Bd)*

Petrolimex Hanoi co., Ltd **(1)**
26 Duc Giang Long Bien, Hanoi, Vietnam
Tel.: (84) 4 38271400
Web Site: http://www.kv1.petrolimex.com.vn
Petroleum Product Distr
N.A.I.C.S.: 424720

Petrolimex Hue Co., Ltd **(1)**

No 40 Hung Vuong, Hue, Vietnam
Tel.: (84) 54 822204
Web Site:
   http://www.thuathienhue.petrolimex.com
Petroleum Product Distr
N.A.I.C.S.: 424720

Petrolimex Insurance Corporation **(1)**
21st 22nd Floor - MIPEC Tower 229 Tay Son Road, Dong Da District, Hanoi, Vietnam
Tel.: (84) 437760867
Web Site: https://www.pjico.com.vn
Rev.: $132,917,710
Assets: $306,887,264
Liabilities: $230,064,838
Net Worth: $76,822,426
Earnings: $9,438,343
Emp.: 1,572
Fiscal Year-end: 12/31/2023
Insurance Services
N.A.I.C.S.: 524298
Thai Huong Dinh *(Chm)*

Petrolimex Lamdong **(1)**
So 132 Nguyen Van Troi Phuong 2, Da Lat, Lam Dong, Vietnam
Tel.: (84) 63 3822803
Web Site:
   http://www.lamdong.petrolimex.com.vn
Petroleum Product Distr
N.A.I.C.S.: 424720

Petrolimex Longan **(1)**
151 Quoc lo 1A Phuong 2, Tan An, Tinh Long An, Vietnam
Tel.: (84) 72 3826158
Web Site:
   http://www.longan.petrolimex.com.vn
Petroleum Product Distr
N.A.I.C.S.: 424720

Petrolimex NamDinh Co., Ltd **(1)**
So 143 Tran Nhan Tong, Nam Dinh, Vietnam
Tel.: (84) 350 3849 444
Web Site:
   http://www.hanamninh.petrolimex.com.vn
Petroleum Product Distr
N.A.I.C.S.: 424720

Petrolimex Nghean **(1)**
No 4 Nguyen Sy Sach rd, Vinh, Nghe An, Vietnam
Tel.: (84) 38 844701
Web Site:
   http://www.nghean.petrolimex.com.vn
Petroleum Product Distr
N.A.I.C.S.: 424720

Petrolimex Petrochemical Corporation **(1)**
No 1 Kham Thien St Kham Thien Ward, Dong Da district, Hanoi, Vietnam
Tel.: (84) 2438512603
Web Site: https://www.petrolimex.com.vn
Rev.: $860,098,300
Assets: $462,125,700
Liabilities: $339,261,200
Net Worth: $122,864,500
Earnings: $11,695,700
Fiscal Year-end: 12/31/2022
Real Estate Development Services
N.A.I.C.S.: 531390
Ngo Duc Giang *(Chief Acctg Officer)*

Petrolimex Saigon Co., Ltd. **(1)**
No 15 Le Duan st, District 1, Ho Chi Minh City, Vietnam
Tel.: (84) 8 38292081
Web Site: http://www.kv2.petrolimex.com.vn
Petroleum Product Distr
N.A.I.C.S.: 424720

Petrolimex Singapore Pte. Ltd. **(1)**
200 Cantonment road 02-02 Southpoint, Singapore, 089763, Singapore
Tel.: (65) 67358139
Web Site:
   http://www.singapore.petrolimex.com.vn
Petroleum Product Distr
N.A.I.C.S.: 424720

Petrolimex Songbe **(1)**
So 8 duong Cach Mang Thang Tam Phuong Phu Tho, Hanoi, Tinh Binh Duong, Vietnam
Tel.: (84) 650 3822351

VIETNAM NATIONAL PETROLEUM CORPORATION

Vietnam National Petroleum Corporation—(Continued)
Web Site:
http://www.songbe.petrolimex.com.vn
Petroleum Product Distr
N.A.I.C.S.: 424720

Petrolimex Tay Ninh Co., Ltd (1)
13D2 CM Thang 8 Rd - No 3 street - P. 3,
Tay Ninh, Vietnam
Tel.: (84) 66 824083
Web Site:
http://www.tayninh.petrolimex.com.vn
Petroleum Product Distr
N.A.I.C.S.: 424720

Petrolimex ThaiBinh Co., Ltd (1)
No 38 Trung Trac P Le Hong Phong, Thai Binh, Vietnam
Tel.: (84) 36 833920
Web Site:
http://www.thaibinh.petrolimex.com.vn
Petroleum Product Distr
N.A.I.C.S.: 424720

Petrolimex Thainguyen (1)
Luong Son, Thai Nguyen, Vietnam
Tel.: (84) 280 845 044
Web Site:
http://www.bacthai.petrolimex.com.vn
Petroleum Product Distr
N.A.I.C.S.: 424720

Petrolimex Thanhhoa (1)
305 Ba Trieu Rd - P Ham Rong, Hanoi, Vietnam
Tel.: (84) 37 961785
Web Site:
http://www.thanhhoa.petrolimex.com.vn
Petroleum Product Distr
N.A.I.C.S.: 424720

Petrolimex Thua Thien Hue Transportation and Service Joint Stock Company (1)
40 Hung vuong, Phu Hoi District, Hue, Thua Thien Hue, Vietnam
Tel.: (84) 543822204
Web Site:
https://thuathienhue.petrolimex.com.vn
Petroleum Product Distr
N.A.I.C.S.: 424720

Petrolimex Tiengiang Co., Ltd (1)
50th National Road, Tan My Chanh town, My Tho, Tien Giang, Vietnam
Tel.: (84) 73 872980
Web Site:
http://www.tiengiang.petrolimex.com.vn
Petroleum Product Distr
N.A.I.C.S.: 424720

Petrolimex Travinh (1)
So 24 Nguyen Thi Minh Khai phuong 2 TP, Tra Vinh, Tinh Tra Vinh, Vietnam
Tel.: (84) 743863321
Web Site: http://www.travinh.petrolimex.com.vn
Petroleum Product Distr
N.A.I.C.S.: 424720

Petrolimex Tuyen Quang (1)
P Minh xuan, Hanoi, Vietnam
Tel.: (84) 27 822443
Web Site:
http://www.tuyenquang.petrolimex.com.vn
Petroleum Product Distr
N.A.I.C.S.: 424720

Petrolimex Yenbai (1)
P Yen ninh, Yen Bai, Vietnam
Tel.: (84) 29 862836
Web Site:
http://www.yenbai.petrolimex.com.vn
Petroleum Product Distr
N.A.I.C.S.: 424720

Quang Ngai Petrolimex Company (1)
Dinh Tien Hoang Rd, Quang Ngai, Vietnam
Tel.: (84) 55 822544
Web Site:
http://www.quangngai.petrolimex.com.vn
Petroleum Product Distr
N.A.I.C.S.: 424720

Vietnam Petroleum Transport Joint Stock Company (1)
Hang Hai Lien Minh building No 802 Le Hong Phong, Hai An District, Haiphong, Vietnam
Tel.: 313838680
Web Site: https://vipco.petrolimex.com.vn
Rev.: $22,644,097
Assets: $58,808,633
Liabilities: $6,290,581
Net Worth: $52,518,052
Earnings: $3,581,846
Emp.: 486
Fiscal Year-end: 12/31/2023
Marine Transportation
N.A.I.C.S.: 483111
Thinh Dao Nguyen (Chm)

Vietnam Tanker Joint Stock Company (1)
236/106/1A Dien Bien Phu Street, Ward 17 Binh Thanh District, Ho Chi Minh City, Vietnam (51.92%)
Tel.: (84) 2835146024
Rev.: $44,356,826
Assets: $67,726,620
Liabilities: $20,582,861
Net Worth: $47,143,759
Earnings: $3,114,679
Fiscal Year-end: 12/31/2023
Petroleum & Petroleum Products Transportation
N.A.I.C.S.: 483111
Nguyen Quang Cuong (Gen Dir)

VIETNAM NATIONAL REINSURANCE CORPORATION
141 Le Duan, Hoan Kiem District, Hanoi, Vietnam
Tel.: (84) 439422354
Web Site: https://www.vinare.com.vn
Year Founded: 1994
VNR—(HNX)
Rev.: $151,430,800
Assets: $712,647,900
Liabilities: $366,914,800
Net Worth: $345,733,100
Earnings: $38,015,700
Emp.: 100
Fiscal Year-end: 12/31/22
Reinsurance Services
N.A.I.C.S.: 524130
Tuan Anh Nguyen (Chm-Mgmt Bd)

VIETNAM OCEAN SHIPPING JOINT STOCK COMPANY
215 Lach Tray Street, Dang Giang Ward Ngo Quyen District, Haiphong, Vietnam
Tel.: (84) 2253731090
Web Site: https://www.vosco.vn
Year Founded: 1970
VOS—(HOSE)
Rev.: $131,323,888
Assets: $111,864,015
Liabilities: $42,971,765
Net Worth: $68,892,250
Earnings: $6,401,285
Fiscal Year-end: 12/31/23
Cargo Handling Services
N.A.I.C.S.: 488320
Cao Minh Tuan (Chm & CEO)

Subsidiaries:

VOSCO Agency and Logistics One Member Limited Company (1)
215 Lach Tray Str Dang Giang Ward, Ngo Quyen Dist, Haiphong, Vietnam
Tel.: (84) 31 3731 441
Sales Range: $25-49.9 Million
Emp.: 30
Logistics Consulting Servies
N.A.I.C.S.: 541614

VOSCO MARITIME SERVICES ONE MEMBER LIMITED COMPANY (1)
No 9 Ham Nghi Str, Nguyen Thai Binh Ward Dist 1, Ho Chi Minh City, Vietnam
Tel.: (84) 8 38298460
Marine Transportation Services
N.A.I.C.S.: 483111

VOSCO TRADING AND SERVICE JOINT STOCK COMPANY (1)
15 Cu Chinh Lan Minh Khai Ward, Hong Bang District, Haiphong, Vietnam
Tel.: (84) 31 3842160
Sales Range: $25-49.9 Million
Emp.: 33
Powder Coating Distr
N.A.I.C.S.: 423840

VIETNAM OIL AND GAS GROUP
18 Lang Ha St, Hanoi, Vietnam
Tel.: (84) 438252526
Web Site: http://www.pvn.vn
Year Founded: 1975
Sales Range: $5-14.9 Billion
Emp.: 17,000
Oil & Gas Exploration, Production, Refinery, Petrochemicals, Storage, Transportation & Service
N.A.I.C.S.: 211120
Tran Sy Thanh (Chm)

Subsidiaries:

Binh Son Refining and Petrochemical Company Limited (1)
208 Hung Vuong Street, Quang Ngai, Vietnam
Tel.: (84) 55 3825 825
Web Site: http://www.bsr.com.vn
Petroleum Product Mfr & Distr
N.A.I.C.S.: 324191
Nguyen Hoai Giang (Chm)

PetroVietnam - Nghe An Construction Joint Stock Corporation (1)
45 Tran Phu Street, Vinh, Nghe An, Vietnam
Tel.: (84) 383588888
Web Site: http://www.pvnc.vn
Construction Services
N.A.I.C.S.: 236220
Trieu Hai Phan (Chm)

PetroVietnam Construction joint stock corporation (1)
14th floor Vietnam Petroleum Institute building 167 Trung Kinh street, Yen Hoa Ward Cau Giay District, Hanoi, Vietnam
Tel.: (84) 437689291
Web Site: https://petrocons.vn
Rev.: $62,611,635
Assets: $319,386,807
Liabilities: $269,845,805
Net Worth: $49,541,002
Earnings: ($6,699,794)
Emp.: 6,000
Fiscal Year-end: 12/31/2020
Petroleum Refinery Services
N.A.I.C.S.: 324110
Bui Ngoc Thang (Chm)

Subsidiary (Domestic):

Petroleum Equipment Assembly & Metal Structure Joint Stock Company (2)
02 Nguyen Huu Canh Street, Ward Thang Nhat, Vung Tau, Vietnam
Tel.: (84) 543848229
Web Site: https://www.pvc-ms.vn
Rev.: $16,991,828
Assets: $33,812,016
Liabilities: $28,925,820
Net Worth: $4,886,196
Earnings: ($6,551,047)
Emp.: 763
Fiscal Year-end: 12/31/2023
Engineeering Services
N.A.I.C.S.: 541330

Petroleum Pipeline & Tank Construction Joint Stock Company (2)
6th Floor Petroland Tower 12 Tan Trao Street, Tan Phu ward District 7, Ho Chi Minh City, Vietnam
Tel.: (84) 2854160800
Web Site: http://www.pvc-pt.vn
Heavy Construction Services
N.A.I.C.S.: 237990
Ho Sy Hoang (Chm)

PetroVietnam Drilling and Well Service Corporation (1)
4th Floor Sailing Tower 111A Pasteur Street Ben Nghe Ward District 1, Ho Chi Minh City, Vietnam
Tel.: (84) 839142012
Web Site: https://www.pvdrilling.com.vn
Rev.: $543,160,500

INTERNATIONAL PUBLIC

Assets: $2,070,404,700
Liabilities: $662,553,800
Net Worth: $1,407,850,900
Earnings: ($10,294,900)
Emp.: 1,971
Fiscal Year-end: 12/31/2022
Drilling Services
N.A.I.C.S.: 213111
Tien Dung Pham (Chm)

PetroVietnam Fertilizer and Chemicals Corporation - JSC (1)
43 Mac Dinh Chi, Da Kao Ward District 1, Ho Chi Minh City, Vietnam
Tel.: (84) 838256258
Web Site: https://www.dpm.vn
Rev.: $1,356,918,600
Assets: $1,330,926,000
Liabilities: $176,406,000
Net Worth: $1,154,520,000
Earnings: $51,946,700
Emp.: 1,500
Fiscal Year-end: 12/31/2023
Fertilizer Mfr
N.A.I.C.S.: 325314
Kien Cao (Chm-Mgmt Bd)

Subsidiary (Domestic):

North Petro Vietnam Fertilizer & Chemicals Joint Stock Company (2)
4th Floor Vietnam Petroleum Institute Building No 167 Trung Kinh, Yen Hoa Ward Cau Giay District, Hanoi, Vietnam
Tel.: (84) 435378256
Rev.: $214,635,700
Assets: $18,493,100
Liabilities: $4,061,700
Net Worth: $14,431,400
Earnings: $632,800
Fiscal Year-end: 12/31/2023
Food Catering Services
N.A.I.C.S.: 722320
Bui Tuan Anh (Mgr)

PetroVietnam Premier Recreation Joint Stock Company (1)
143 85 Ha Dinh Thanh Xuan Trung ward, Thanh Xuan distr, Hanoi, Vietnam
Tel.: (84) 914919699
Web Site: http://www.pvr.vn
Rev.: $284,840
Assets: $39,909,680
Liabilities: $21,078,080
Net Worth: $18,831,600
Earnings: $68,800
Fiscal Year-end: 12/31/2021
Golf Courses, Hotels, Resorts, Amusement Parks & Restaurants Developer & Operator
N.A.I.C.S.: 713990

PetroVietnam Technical Services Corporation (1)
5th Floor PetroVietnam Tower 1-5 Le Duan Street, District 1, Ho Chi Minh City, Vietnam
Tel.: (84) 2839102828
Web Site: https://www.ptsc.vn
Rev.: $1,637,897,396
Assets: $2,582,777,164
Liabilities: $1,287,917,684
Net Worth: $1,294,859,480
Earnings: $94,445,194
Emp.: 6,935
Fiscal Year-end: 12/31/2022
Shipbuilding & Marine Services
N.A.I.C.S.: 336611
Phan Thanh Tung (Chm)

PetroVietnam Transportation Corporation (1)
2nd Floor PVFCCo Tower 43 Mac Dinh Chi Da Kao Ward District 1, Ho Chi Minh City, Vietnam
Tel.: (84) 2839111301
Web Site: https://www.pvtrans.com
Rev.: $393,706,335
Assets: $720,586,064
Liabilities: $348,533,790
Net Worth: $372,052,274
Earnings: $50,325,841
Emp.: 868
Fiscal Year-end: 12/31/2023
Oil & Gas Transportation Services
N.A.I.C.S.: 213112
Viet Anh Pham (Chm)

Subsidiary (Domestic):

Viet Nam Gas and Chemicals Transportation Corporation (2)

10th Floor Tower 1 of the Office Trade Service Hotel project The Nexus, 3A-3B Ton Duc Thang Street Ben Nghe Ward District 1, Ho Chi Minh City, Vietnam
Tel.: (84) 2862582331
Web Site: https://www.pct.com.vn
Rev.: $40,943,700
Assets: $123,853,200
Liabilities: $66,276,200
Net Worth: $57,577,000
Earnings: $3,772,400
Fiscal Year-end: 12/31/2023
Car & Taxi Rental Services
N.A.I.C.S.: 485310
Nguyen Thi Hong Thuy *(Chm)*

Petrovietnam Camau Fertilizer Company Limited (1)
Lot D Ward 1 Industrial Park, Ngo Quyen Street Ward 1 Dist, Ca Mau, Vietnam
Tel.: (84) 7803819000
Web Site: http://www.pvcfc.com.vn
Petroleum Product Distr
N.A.I.C.S.: 457210

Petrovietnam Chemical and Services Corporation (1)
Floor 6 VPI Tower No 167 Trung Kinh Street, Yen Hoa Commune Cau Giay District, Hanoi, Vietnam
Tel.: (84) 2438562861
Web Site: http://pvdmc.com.vn
Rev.: $132,743,351
Assets: $101,848,089
Liabilities: $58,599,543
Net Worth: $43,248,546
Earnings: $843,900
Fiscal Year-end: 12/31/2023
Petrochemical Mfr
N.A.I.C.S.: 325110
Truong Dai Nghia *(Chm)*

Petrovietnam Exploration Production Corporation (1)
26th Floor Charm Vi Tower, 117 Tran Duy Hung St Cau Giay, Hanoi, Vietnam
Tel.: (84) 4 3 772 6001
Web Site: http://www.pvep.com.vn
Oil & Gas Exploration Services
N.A.I.C.S.: 211120
Cao Huu Binh *(VP)*

Petrovietnam Gas Joint Stock Corporation (1)
673 Nguyen Huu Tho Street, Phuoc Kien Commune, Ho Chi Minh City, Vietnam
Tel.: (84) 8 3781 6777
Web Site: http://www.pvgas.com.vn
Natural Gas Distr
N.A.I.C.S.: 486910
Bui Ngoc Quang *(VP)*

Petrovietnam General Services Joint Stock Company (1)
Floor 6 PetroVietNam Tower No 1-5 Le Duan St Ben Nghe Ward, District 1, Ho Chi Minh City, Vietnam
Tel.: (84) 2839177777
Web Site: https://www.petrosetco.com.vn
Rev.: $709,372,989
Assets: $390,554,411
Liabilities: $300,480,499
Net Worth: $90,073,912
Earnings: $5,726,676
Fiscal Year-end: 12/31/2023
Oil & Gas Extraction Services
N.A.I.C.S.: 213112
Vu Tien Duong *(Gen Dir & Member-Mgmt Bd)*

Petrovietnam Low Pressure Gas Distribution Joint Stock Company (1)
Floor 7 PV Gas Tower building 673 Nguyen Huu Tho street, Phuoc Kien Nha Be, Ho Chi Minh City, Vietnam
Tel.: (84) 2837840386
Web Site: https://www.pvgasd.com.vn
Oil & Gas Distribution Services
N.A.I.C.S.: 221210
Tran Trung Chinh *(Chm)*

Petrovietnam Oil Corporation (1)
14th-17th Floor Petro Vietnam Tower, 1-5 Le Duan Ben Nghe Ward, Ho Chi Minh City, Vietnam
Tel.: (84) 8 39106990
Web Site: http://www.pvoil.com.vn
Petroleum Product Mfr
N.A.I.C.S.: 211120

Doan Van Nhuom *(Pres & CEO)*

Subsidiary (Domestic):

Thai Binh PetroVietnam Oil JSC (2)
No 545 Tran Lam, Tran Lam ward, Thai Binh, Thai Binh, Vietnam
Tel.: (84) 2273833522
Oil & Gas Exploration Services
N.A.I.C.S.: 213112
Nguyen Thi Mai *(Head-Admin Dept)*

Petrovietnam Petrochemicals and Fibre Joint Stock Company (1)
Plot CN 5 5A Dinhvu Industrial Zone, Dong Hai 2 Ward Hai An Distric, Haiphong, Vietnam
Tel.: (84) 31 3 614 615
Web Site: http://www.pvtex-dv.vn
Textile Fiber Product Mfr
N.A.I.C.S.: 325220

Petrovietnam Phuoc An Port Investment and Operation Joint Stock Company (1)
Nhon Trach 3 Industrial Park, Tin Nghia Building, Nhon Trach, Vietnam
Tel.: (84) 613 569534
Web Site: http://www.pap.vn
Petroleum Product Distr
N.A.I.C.S.: 457210
Dao Minh Tung *(Member-Mgmt Bd)*

Petrovietnam Power Corporation (1)
VPI Building 173 Trung Kinh, Cau Giay, Hanoi, Vietnam
Tel.: (84) 4 22210 288
Web Site: http://www.pv-power.vn
Electric Power Generation Services
N.A.I.C.S.: 221111

Public Joint Stock Commercial Bank (1)
22 Ngo Quyen, Quan Hoan Kiem, Hanoi, Vietnam
Tel.: (84) 4 3942 6800
Web Site: http://www.pvfc.com.vn
Commercial Banking Services
N.A.I.C.S.: 522110

Saigon Petroleum Construction and Investment Joint Stock Company (1)
11Bis Nguyen Gia Thieu, Ward 6, District 3, Ho Chi Minh City, Vietnam
Tel.: (84) 839301980
Construction Services
N.A.I.C.S.: 236220

VIETNAM POSTS & TELECOMMUNICATIONS CORPORATION
57 Huynh Thuc Khang Str Lang Ha Ward, Dong Da District, Hanoi, 10000, Vietnam
Tel.: (84) 435775104 VN
Web Site: http://www.vnpt.vn
Year Founded: 1995
Sales Range: $1-4.9 Billion
Emp.: 86,000
National Telecommunications & Postal Services
N.A.I.C.S.: 491110
Kiet Ly *(Deputy Gen Dir)*

Subsidiaries:

P&T MATERIAL SUPPLY JSC (1)
270 Ly Thuong Kiet Street, Ward 14 District 10, Ho Chi Minh City, Vietnam
Tel.: (84) 838640021
Web Site: http://www.potmasco.com.vn
Wireless Communication Equipment Mfr
N.A.I.C.S.: 334220

Quangnam Post-Telecoms Construction and Services Corporation (1)
Phan Boi Chau Street, Thanh Tan Ward, Tam Ky, Quang Nam, Vietnam
Tel.: (84) 5103811811
Web Site: http://www.qtc.com.vn
Emp.: 110
Post, Telecommunications, Electrical & Broadcasting Structures Construction Services
N.A.I.C.S.: 237130

VASC SOFTWARE AND MEDIA COMPANY (1)
97 Nguyen Chi Thanh, Dong Da, Hanoi, Vietnam
Tel.: (84) 4 3772 2728
Web Site: http://www.vasc.com.vn
Emp.: 400
Information Technology Support Services
N.A.I.C.S.: 541512
Nguyen Van Thang *(Branch Mgr)*

VIETNAM DATA COMMUNICATION COMPANY (1)
Internet Lot IIA international village of Thang Long Dich Vong, Cau Giay, Hanoi, Vietnam
Tel.: (84) 4 37930569
Web Site: http://www.vdc.com.vn
Wireless Telecommunication Services
N.A.I.C.S.: 517112
Hung Tran Viet *(Deputy Dir-Technical)*

VIETNAM MOBILE TELECOM SERVICES COMPANY (1)
Lot VP1 Yen Hoa Cau Giay, Hanoi, Vietnam
Tel.: (84) 43 78 31 733
Web Site: http://www.mobifone.com.vn
Wireless Telecommunication Services
N.A.I.C.S.: 517112

VIETNAM TELECOM SERVICES COMPANY (1)
216 Tran Duy Hung Street, Cau Giay, Hanoi, Vietnam
Tel.: (84) 4 835 8816
Web Site: http://www.vinaphone.com.vn
Wireless Telecommunication Services
N.A.I.C.S.: 517112
Ngo Hy *(Dir-Value Added Svc Center)*

Vietnam Telecom International (1)
142 Dien Bien Phu St District #1, Ho Chi Minh City, Vietnam
Tel.: (84) 838810217
Web Site: http://vti.com.vn
Rev.: $7,929,851
Emp.: 1,400
International Telecommunications Services
N.A.I.C.S.: 517810

Vietnam Telecom National (1)
57A Huynh Thuc Khang St, Dong Da, Hanoi, Vietnam
Tel.: (84) 47734185
Web Site: http://www.vtn.com.vn
Telecommunications Networking in Vietnam
N.A.I.C.S.: 517810

VIETNAM PROSPERITY JOINT-STOCK COMMERCIAL BANK
89 Lang Ha St, Dong Da Dist, Hanoi, Vietnam
Tel.: (84) 2439288869
Web Site: https://www.vpbank.com
VPB—(HOSE)
Rev.: $3,566,057,356
Assets: $34,803,823,870
Liabilities: $28,852,728,285
Net Worth: $5,951,095,584
Earnings: $361,596,859
Emp.: 24,973
Fiscal Year-end: 12/31/23
Bank Holding Company
N.A.I.C.S.: 551111
Duc Vinh Nguyen *(CEO)*

VIETNAM RAILWAY CORPORATION
118 Le Duan, Hanoi, Vietnam
Tel.: (84) 2439425972
Web Site: http://www.vr.com.vn
Sales Range: $550-599.9 Million
Emp.: 4,500
Railway Transportation Services
N.A.I.C.S.: 485112

Subsidiaries:

Construction Joint Stock Company No. 6 (1)
Block 4 Dong Anh, Hanoi, Vietnam
Tel.: (84) 4 38835681
Web Site: http://www.ctcpct6.com.vn
Rev.: $3,776,477
Assets: $6,774,822
Liabilities: $5,030,002
Net Worth: $1,744,820

Earnings: ($389,556)
Fiscal Year-end: 12/31/2018
Heavy Construction Including Railways, Highways, Streets, Bridges & Ports
N.A.I.C.S.: 237990
Lai Van Quan *(Chm)*

VIETNAM SEA TRANSPORT AND CHARTERING JOINT STOCK COMPANY
428 Nguyen Tat Thanh St Dist 4, Ho Chi Minh City, Vietnam
Tel.: (84) 8 39404271
Web Site:
http://www.vitranschart.com.vn
Year Founded: 1975
Sales Range: $75-99.9 Million
Emp.: 1,170
Cargo Handling Services
N.A.I.C.S.: 488320
Hong Vu Huynh *(Chm)*

VIETNAM STEEL CORPORATION
91 Lang Ha Street, Dong Da District, Hanoi, Vietnam
Tel.: (84) 438561767 VN
Web Site: http://www.vnsteel.vn
Year Founded: 1995
Sales Range: $1-9.9 Million
Emp.: 20,500
Mining & Processing of Iron Ore, Coal & Other Raw Materials; Production & Sale of Iron, Steel, Steel Products & Refractory Materials; Design & Construction of Steel Production Facilities
N.A.I.C.S.: 212210
Nghiem Xuan Da *(CEO)*

VIETNAM SUN CORPORATION
648 Nguyen Trai St Ward 11, Dist 5, Ho Chi Minh City, Vietnam
Tel.: (84) 838277178
Web Site:
http://www.vinasuncorp.com
Year Founded: 2003
VNS—(HOSE)
Rev.: $50,214,560
Assets: $68,105,536
Liabilities: $19,987,068
Net Worth: $48,118,469
Earnings: $6,211,271
Fiscal Year-end: 12/31/23
Taxi Service
N.A.I.C.S.: 485310
Dang Thi Lan Phuong *(Gen Mgr)*

VIETNAM TECHNOLOGICAL & COMMERCIAL JOINT STOCK BANK
Techcombank Tower 191 Ba Trieu, Hai Ba Trung District, Hanoi, Vietnam
Tel.: (84) 2439446699
Web Site: https://techcombank.com
Year Founded: 1993
VND—(HOSE)
Rev.: $2,769,112,000
Assets: $84,948,201,200
Liabilities: $71,786,594,700
Net Worth: $13,161,606,500
Earnings: $1,800,380,200
Fiscal Year-end: 12/31/23
Commercial Banking Services
N.A.I.C.S.: 522110
Ho Hung Anh *(Chm)*

VIETNAM URBAN DEVELOPMENT INVESTMENT CORPORATION
151 ter Nguyen Dinh Chieu Ward 6, District 3, Ho Chi Minh City, Vietnam
Tel.: (84) 2838438883
Web Site: http://www.idico.com.vn
IDC—(HNX)
Rev.: $748,539,000

VIETNAM URBAN DEVELOPMENT INVESTMENT CORPORATION

Vietnam Urban Development Investment Corporation—(Continued)

Assets: $1,701,341,100
Liabilities: $1,088,548,800
Net Worth: $612,792,300
Earnings: $176,750,700
Emp.: 5,000
Fiscal Year-end: 12/31/22
Industrial Building Construction Services
N.A.I.C.S.: 236210
Hoang Van Hien *(Chm-Supervisory Bd)*

Subsidiaries:

IDICO Urban and Industrial Zone Development Co., Ltd. (1)
Ton Duc Thang Street 1 Industrial Park, Phuoc Thien Commune, Nhon Trach, Dong Nai, Vietnam
Tel.: (84) 613560475
Web Site: https://www.idico.vn
Emp.: 350
Industrial Building Construction Services
N.A.I.C.S.: 236210

Idico Construcuion Company Limited (1)
No 48 Zone 3, An Hoa Commune, Bien Hoa, Dong Nai, Vietnam
Tel.: (84) 2513831215
Construction Services
N.A.I.C.S.: 236220

Idico Infrastructure Development Investment JSC (1)
Km 1906 700 National Highway 1A KP5, Binh Hung Hoa B Ward Binh Tan District, Ho Chi Minh City, Vietnam
Tel.: (84) 837503042
Web Site: https://www.idico-idi.com.vn
Electric Power Distribution Services
N.A.I.C.S.: 221122

Idico Investment Construction Oil & Natural Gas JSC (1)
326 Nguyen An Ninh, Ward 7, Vung Tau, Ba Ria - Vung Tau, Vietnam
Tel.: (84) 643838423
Web Site: https://idicoconac.vn
Construction Services
N.A.I.C.S.: 236220

Idico Investment Consultancy JSC (1)
No 100 Nguyen Gia Tri, Ward 25 Binh Thanh District, Ho Chi Minh City, Vietnam
Tel.: (84) 2838995588
Web Site: https://idico-incon.com.vn
Construction Services
N.A.I.C.S.: 236220

Idico Long An Investment Construction JSC (1)
No 88 National Highway 1 Rogue Bypass, Ward 6, Tan An, Long An, Vietnam
Tel.: (84) 2723826497
Web Site: https://idico-linco.com.vn
Construction Management Services
N.A.I.C.S.: 236220

Idico Machinery Erection Construction Investment JSC (1)
Km 23 National Highway 51 Hamlet 1, Long An Commune Long Thanh District, Long Thanh, Long Nai, Vietnam
Tel.: (84) 2513569439
Web Site: https://www.lamaidico.com.vn
Structural Steel Mfr & Distr
N.A.I.C.S.: 332312

Idico Material Development & Construction Invesment JSC (1)
Road No 3, Nhon Trach 1 Industrial Park Phuoc Thien Commune, Nhon Trach, Dong Nai, Vietnam
Tel.: (84) 2513560724
Web Site: https://idico-mci.com.vn
Construction Services
N.A.I.C.S.: 236220

Idico No.10 Investment Construction JSC (1)
43A - 3/2 Street, Xuan Khanh Ward - Ninh Kieu District, Can Tho, Bac Thai, Vietnam
Tel.: (84) 2923830191

Web Site: https://inco10.com
Construction Services
N.A.I.C.S.: 236220

Idico Urban & House Development Investment JSC (1)
Nhon Trach 1 Industrial Zone, Hiep Phuoc Commune Nhon Trach District, Nhon Trach, Dong Nai, Vietnam
Tel.: (84) 613560614
Web Site: https://www.idico-udico.com.vn
Electric Power Distribution Services
N.A.I.C.S.: 221122

Urban & Industrial Development Investment Idico - Que Vo JSC (1)
13th Floor Sudico Building Me Tri Street, My Dinh 1 Ward Nam Tu Liem District, Hanoi, Vietnam
Tel.: (84) 437877937
Web Site: https://www.idicoquevo.com.vn
Construction Services
N.A.I.C.S.: 236220

VIETNAMNET INVESTMENT JOINT STOCK COMPANY

4th Floor Kinh Do Building 292 Tay Son, Trung Liet Ward, Dong Da District, Hanoi, Vietnam
Tel.: (84) 4 5148460
Web Site: http://www.vinaic.com.vn
Newspaper Holding Company
N.A.I.C.S.: 551112
Quang Chinh Tran *(Gen Dir)*

VIETTRONICS TAN BINH JOINT STOCK COMPANY

248A No Trang Long St, Binh Thanh District, Ho Chi Minh City, Vietnam
Tel.: (84) 835163885
Web Site: http://www.vtb.com.vn
Year Founded: 2004
VTB—(HOSE)
Rev: $4,653,993
Assets: $9,503,274
Liabilities: $1,822,358
Net Worth: $7,680,916
Earnings: $445,125
Emp.: 260
Fiscal Year-end: 12/31/23
Electrical Products Mfr
N.A.I.C.S.: 335999

VIEWBIX INC.

14 Aryeh Shenkar Street, Hertzeliy, 4809174, Israel
Tel.: (972) 2124007198
Web Site: http://www.virtual-crypto.com
Year Founded: 1989
VBIX—(OTCIQ)
Rev: $96,000
Assets: $225,000
Liabilities: $2,303,000
Net Worth: ($2,078,000)
Earnings: ($443,000)
Emp.: 2
Fiscal Year-end: 12/31/20
Investment Services
N.A.I.C.S.: 523999
Shahar Marom *(CFO)*

VIEWORKS CO., LTD.

41-3 Burim-ro 170beon-gil Dongan-gu, Anyang, 14055, Gyeonggi-do, Korea (South)
Tel.: (82) 7070116161
Web Site: http://www.vieworks.com
Year Founded: 1999
100120—(KRS)
Rev: $182,491,399
Assets: $221,209,910
Liabilities: $60,662,335
Net Worth: $160,547,576
Earnings: $20,294,343
Emp.: 492
Fiscal Year-end: 12/31/22
Digital Medical Imaging Processing Systems Mfr

N.A.I.C.S.: 339112
Jang Hwan *(CFO)*

Subsidiaries:

Japan Vieworks Co., Ltd. (1)
4th floor west wing Time 24 Building 2-4-32 Aomi, Koto-ku, Tokyo, 135-0064, Japan
Tel.: (81) 355796516
Web Site: https://vieworks.co.jp
Optical Instrument Distr
N.A.I.C.S.: 423410

Vieworks America, Ltd. (1)
970 Woodlands Pkwy, Vernon Hills, IL 60061
Tel.: (847) 613-4338
Web Site: https://www.vieworks.us
Medical Imaging Equipment Distr
N.A.I.C.S.: 423450
Peter Lee *(Pres)*

Vieworks EU GmbH (1)
Talbotstr 25, 52068, Aachen, Nordrhein-Westfalen, Germany
Tel.: (49) 24191615268
Medical Imaging Equipment Distr
N.A.I.C.S.: 423450

VIEWTRAN GROUP, INC.

15fl Tower C Skyworth Building, High-Tech Industrial Park Nanshan, Shenzhen, 518057, China
Tel.: (86) 75526988211 MD
Web Site: http://www.viewtran.com
Year Founded: 1995
Sales Range: $75-99.9 Million
Supply Chain Financial Services & Enterprise Solutions for Technology Industry
N.A.I.C.S.: 561499
Xianhang Wang *(CEO)*

Subsidiaries:

Comtech Communication Technology (Shenzhen) Co., Ltd. (1)
Comtech Tower Floor 11 No 55 Gaoxin South 9th Road, Nanshan District, Shenzhen, China
Tel.: (86) 1051726678
Web Site: http://en.comtech.com.cn
Sales Range: $100-124.9 Million
Emp.: 300
Electronic Components Mfr
N.A.I.C.S.: 334416
Jeffrey Kang *(Founder & CEO)*

VIG VODOVOD I GREJANJE A.D.

Sentandrejski put 165, Novi Sad, Serbia
Tel.: (381) 21 6413 722
Year Founded: 1989
Sales Range: Less than $1 Million
Emp.: 3
Construction Engineering Services
N.A.I.C.S.: 541330

VIGENCELL INC.

9F 11F The Reason Valley 66 Gasan-ro 9-gil, Geumcheon-gu, Seoul, 08513, Korea (South)
Tel.: (82) 27850201
Web Site: https://www.vigencell.com
Year Founded: 2013
308080—(KRS)
Research & Experimental Development Services
N.A.I.C.S.: 541715
Tai-Gyu Kim *(CEO)*

VIGLACERA HA LONG J.S.C.

No 1 Thang Long Avenue, Hanoi, Quang Ninh, Vietnam
Tel.: (84) 2435536664
Web Site: https://viglacerahalong.vn
HLY—(HNX)
Rev: $2,044,548
Assets: $1,915,824
Liabilities: $1,371,144
Net Worth: $544,679

Earnings: $5,432
Fiscal Year-end: 12/31/19
Clay Brick & Flooring Tile Mfr
N.A.I.C.S.: 327120

VIGLACERA TUSON JSC

Tran Phu Road Dinh Bang Ward, Tu Son Town, Bac Ninh, Vietnam
Tel.: (84) 2413831642
Web Site: http://www.vtsc.vn
VTS—(HNX)
Rev: $1,232,009
Assets: $2,097,390
Liabilities: $346,452
Net Worth: $1,750,938
Earnings: ($166,007)
Fiscal Year-end: 12/31/19
Clay Building Material Mfr
N.A.I.C.S.: 327120

VIGLEN LTD.

VHQ 7 Handley Page Way, Old Parkbury Lane, Saint Albans, AL2 2DQ, Herts, United Kingdom
Tel.: (44) 1727201800
Web Site: http://www.viglen.co.uk
Year Founded: 1975
Rev: $150,020,000
Emp.: 200
Information Technology Services
N.A.I.C.S.: 541513
Bordaa Tkachuk *(Chm)*

VIGMED HOLDING AB

Garnisonsgatan 10, SE 254 66, Helsingborg, Sweden
Tel.: (46) 4 228 0090
Web Site: http://www.vigmed.com
Year Founded: 2010
VIG—(OMX)
Medical Device Mfr
N.A.I.C.S.: 339112
Fredrik Thorne *(Dir-R&D)*

VIGO FINANCE A.S.

U Pruhonu 1589/13a, 170 00, Prague, 7, Czech Republic
Tel.: (420) 220361111 CZ
Web Site: http://www.vigogroup.cz
Holding Company
N.A.I.C.S.: 551112
Pavel Rehak *(CEO)*

Subsidiaries:

VIGO Investments a.s. (1)
U Pruhonu 1589/13a, 170 00, Prague, 7, Czech Republic
Tel.: (420) 220361111
Web Site: http://www.vigoinvestments.com
Equity Investment Firm
N.A.I.C.S.: 523999
Pavel Rehak *(CEO & Partner)*

VIGO PHOTONICS S.A.

129/133 Poznanska St, 05-850, Ozarow Mazowiecki, Poland
Tel.: (48) 227335410
Web Site: https://vigophotonics.com
VGO—(WAR)
Rev: $19,155,234
Assets: $81,877,540
Liabilities: $31,526,931
Net Worth: $50,350,610
Earnings: ($757,622)
Emp.: 220
Fiscal Year-end: 12/31/23
High Operating Temperature Cadmium Mercury Telluride (HgCdTe) Detectors Mfr
N.A.I.C.S.: 334519
Przemyslaw Danowski *(Chm-Supervisory Bd)*

VIGOR KOBO CO., LTD.

6F No 87-1 Sec 1 Chengtai Rd, Wugu District, Taipei, 248, Taiwan
Tel.: (886) 222919122

2733—(TAI)
Food Products Distr
N.A.I.C.S.: 445298
Kuang-I Tung *(VP)*

VIJAY SHANTHI BUILDERS LIMITED
Old Door No 8 New Door No 21 First Avenue Indira Nagar, Adyar, Chennai, 600020, India
Tel.: (91) 4440004600
Web Site:
http://www.vijayshanthibuilders.com
Rev.: $3,869,721
Assets: $32,302,413
Liabilities: $15,614,267
Net Worth: $16,688,146
Earnings: ($1,527,970)
Emp.: 36
Fiscal Year-end: 03/31/19
Property Development Services
N.A.I.C.S.: 531311
Chandan Kumar *(Mng Dir)*

VIJAY SOLVEX LIMITED
Bhagwati Sadan Swami Dayanand Marg, Alwar, 301001, Rajasthan, India
Tel.: (91) 1442332922
Web Site:
https://www.vijaysolvex.com
531069—(BOM)
Rev.: $292,100,450
Assets: $48,444,566
Liabilities: $10,135,148
Net Worth: $38,309,418
Earnings: $2,038,847
Emp.: 127
Fiscal Year-end: 03/31/23
Edible Oil Mfr & Distr
N.A.I.C.S.: 311225
Vijay Data *(Mng Dir)*

VIJAY TEXTILES LTD.
Surya Towers Ground Floor 104 Sardar Patel Road, Secunderabad, 500 003, Telangana, India
Tel.: (91) 4027844086
Web Site: https://www.vijaytextiles.in
Year Founded: 1990
530151—(BOM)
Rev.: $3,149,128
Assets: $42,293,843
Liabilities: $34,086,530
Net Worth: $8,207,314
Earnings: ($782,351)
Emp.: 109
Fiscal Year-end: 03/31/23
Home Furnishing Products Mfr
N.A.I.C.S.: 314120
Susheel Kumar Gupta *(CFO)*

VIJAYA DIAGNOSTIC CENTRE PVT. LTD.
3-6-16 & 17 Street No 19, Himayatnagar, Hyderabad, 500029, India
Tel.: (91) 40 2342 0422   In
Web Site:
http://www.vijayadiagnostic.com
Year Founded: 1981
Medical Diagnostic Imaging Centers
Owner & Operator
N.A.I.C.S.: 621512
Surender Reddy *(Founder)*

Subsidiaries:

Medinova Diagnostic Services
Limited   (1)
7 1 58 A FF 8 Flat No 8, Amrutha Business Complex Ameerpet, Hyderabad, 500 016, India   (62.14%)
Tel.: (91) 4042604250
Web Site: https://www.medinovaindia.com
Rev.: $1,758,065
Assets: $596,833
Liabilities: $1,621,251
Net Worth: ($1,024,419)
Earnings: $259,992
Emp.: 77
Fiscal Year-end: 03/31/2021
Medical Diagnostic Services
N.A.I.C.S.: 621512
Sura Surendranath Reddy *(Chm)*

Unit (Domestic):

Medinova Diagnostic Services Limited - Bansdroni Unit   (2)
1 H L Sarkar Road Opp Ravindra Sarobar Stadium, Kolkata, 700 070, India
Tel.: (91) 9830341212
Medical Diagnostic Services
N.A.I.C.S.: 621512

VIJAYA LAGHUBITTA BITTIYA SANSTHA LTD.
Kavrepalanchowk, Dhulikhel, Nepal
Tel.: (977) 11490671
Web Site: https://vlbs.com.np
VLBS—(NEP)
Commercial Banking Services
N.A.I.C.S.: 522110

VIJI FINANCE LIMITED
11/2 Jaora Compound Ushaganj, Indore, 452001, MP, India
Tel.: (91) 7314246092
Web Site: https://www.vijifinance.com
Year Founded: 1994
537820—(NSE)
Rev.: $128,917
Assets: $2,149,079
Liabilities: $625,184
Net Worth: $1,523,895
Earnings: $60,957
Emp.: 4
Fiscal Year-end: 03/31/21
Non Banking Financial Services
N.A.I.C.S.: 523999
Vijay Kothari *(Mng Dir)*

VIK A.D.
Nevesinjska Bb, Vrsac, Serbia
Tel.: (381) 13801391
Year Founded: 2000
VIKD—(BEL)
Sales Range: Less than $1 Million
Emp.: 7
Consumer Electronic Product Whslr
N.A.I.C.S.: 423620

VIKALP SECURITIES LIMITED
25/38 Karachi Khana, Kanpur, 208 001, Uttar Pradesh, India
Tel.: (91) 5122372665
Web Site: https://vikalpsecurities.com
Year Founded: 1986
531334—(BOM)
Rev.: $28,324
Assets: $592,742
Liabilities: $5,196
Net Worth: $587,547
Earnings: ($935)
Emp.: 5
Fiscal Year-end: 03/31/21
Security Brokerage Services
N.A.I.C.S.: 523150
Shubhani Gupta *(Compliance Officer & Sec)*

VIKAS ECOTECH LIMITED
34/1 Vikas House East Punjabi Bagh, New Delhi, 110026, India
Tel.: (91) 1143144444
Web Site:
https://www.vikasecotech.com
VECO.RE1—(NSE)
Rev.: $16,480,356
Assets: $44,459,959
Liabilities: $26,900,190
Net Worth: $17,559,769
Earnings: $1,958,786
Emp.: 40
Fiscal Year-end: 03/31/21
Petrochemical Product Distr
N.A.I.C.S.: 424720

Vikas Garg *(Mng Dir)*

VIKAS LIFECARE LTD.
House No G-1 34/1 East Punjabi Bagh, New Delhi, 110026, India
Tel.: (91) 1140450110
Web Site:
https://www.vikaslifecarelimited.com
Year Founded: 1995
VIKASLIFE—(NSE)
Rev.: $10,375,341
Assets: $20,331,842
Liabilities: $11,231,444
Net Worth: $9,100,398
Earnings: ($477,991)
Emp.: 21
Fiscal Year-end: 03/31/21
Chemicals Mfr
N.A.I.C.S.: 325998
Vivek Garg *(Mng Dir)*

VIKAS PROPPANT & GRANITE LIMITED
F88/89 RIICO Industrial Area, Sri Ganganagar, 335002, Rajasthan, India
Tel.: (91) 1542494319
Web Site:
https://www.vikasproppantltd.in
Year Founded: 1994
531518—(BOM)
Rev.: $3,221,195
Assets: $53,083,881
Liabilities: $27,470,448
Net Worth: $25,613,433
Earnings: ($1,554,326)
Fiscal Year-end: 03/31/21
Proppant Product Mfr
N.A.I.C.S.: 327999

VIKAS WSP LIMITED
B-86-87 Udyog Vihar RIICO Industrial Area, Sri Ganganagar, 335 001, India
Tel.: (91) 1542494512
Web Site: https://www.vikaswspltd.in
Year Founded: 1988
VIKASWSP—(NSE)
Rev.: $2,769,582
Assets: $179,612,182
Liabilities: $74,996,991
Net Worth: $104,615,191
Earnings: ($19,606,858)
Emp.: 700
Fiscal Year-end: 03/31/22
Guar Gum Powder Mfr & Whslr
N.A.I.C.S.: 325194
Kamini Jindal *(Exec Dir)*

VIKING FUND MANAGERS LTD.
Metic House Ripley Dr, Normanton, WF6 1QT, West Yorkshire, United Kingdom
Tel.: (44) 1924227237
Web Site:
http://www.vikingfundmanagers.com
Year Founded: 2004
Fund Management Services
N.A.I.C.S.: 523940
Andrew Burton *(Mng Dir)*

VIKING GOLD EXPLORATION INC.
Suite 2B - 2900 John Street, Markham, L3R 5G3, ON, Canada
Tel.: (905) 752-2008
Web Site: https://www.vikinggold.ca
Year Founded: 1936
Sales Range: $1-9.9 Million
Mineral Exploration Services
N.A.I.C.S.: 212290
Dominic Verdejo *(CEO)*

VIKING KAGIT VE SELULOZ AS
Yali Mah Hurriyet Cad No 474,
Aliaga, 35800, Izmir, Turkiye
Tel.: (90) 2326160600
Web Site: https://www.viking.com.tr
Year Founded: 1969
VKING—(IST)
Sales Range: Less than $1 Million
Sanitary Paper Product Mfr
N.A.I.C.S.: 322291
Idil Yigitbasi *(Chm)*

VIKING LINE ABP
Norragatan 4, PO Box 166, AX 22101, Mariehamn, Aland, Finland
Tel.: (358) 1827000
Web Site: https://www.vikingline.fi
Year Founded: 1959
VIK1V—(HEL)
Rev.: $533,887,330
Assets: $679,365,422
Liabilities: $365,853,659
Net Worth: $313,511,763
Earnings: $24,821,930
Emp.: 2,428
Fiscal Year-end: 12/31/22
Cargo Carrier & Passenger Services
N.A.I.C.S.: 488320
Jan Hanses *(Pres & CEO)*

Subsidiaries:

OU Viking Line Eesti   (1)
Hobujaama 4, EE-10111, Tallinn, Estonia
Tel.: (372) 6663966
Web Site: https://www.vikingline.ee
Passenger & Cargo Marine Transportation
N.A.I.C.S.: 483114

Viking Line Bus Ab   (1)
Storagatan 3, Mariehamn, 21100, Aland, Finland
Tel.: (358) 18 263 11
Web Site: http://www.vikinglinebus.ax
Emp.: 20
Passenger & Cargo Marine Transportation
N.A.I.C.S.: 483212
Jim Haggblom *(Mng Dir)*

Viking Line Finnlandverkehr
GmbH   (1)
Grosse Altefahre 20-22, DE-23552, Lubeck, Germany
Tel.: (49) 451 384630
Web Site: http://www.vikingline.de
Passenger & Cargo Marine Transportation
N.A.I.C.S.: 483114
Ralf Buchfink *(Mgr-Sls)*

Viking Line Skandinavien AB   (1)
Box 4154, SE-116 04, Nacka, Sweden
Tel.: (46) 84524100
Passenger & Cargo Marine Transportation
N.A.I.C.S.: 483114

Viking Rederi AB   (1)
Box 4154, SE-13104, Nacka, Sweden
Tel.: (46) 8 452 4100
Passenger & Cargo Marine Transportation
N.A.I.C.S.: 483114

VIKING MINES LIMITED
15-17 Old Aberdeen Place, West Perth, 6005, WA, Australia
Tel.: (61) 862450870
Web Site:
https://www.vikingmines.com
Year Founded: 2007
VKA—(ASX)
Rev.: $98,733
Assets: $5,864,180
Liabilities: $1,068,613
Net Worth: $4,795,567
Earnings: $1,847,044
Fiscal Year-end: 06/30/24
Gold & Coal Exploration Services
N.A.I.C.S.: 212220
Raymond Whitten *(Chm)*

VIKING VENTURE MANAGEMENT AS
Nedre Bakklandet 77, 7014, Trondheim, Norway

VIKING VENTURE MANAGEMENT AS

Viking Venture Management AS—(Continued)
Tel.: (47) 73 60 01 90
Web Site:
http://www.vikingventure.com
Venture Capital Investment Firm
N.A.I.C.S.: 523999
Erik Hagen *(Mng Partner)*

VIKOS S.A.
Perivleptos, 45 500, Ioannina, Greece
Tel.: (30) 26510 61951
Web Site: http://www.vikoswater.gr
Year Founded: 1990
Sales Range: $75-99.9 Million
Emp.: 201
Bottled & Canned Water Mfr
N.A.I.C.S.: 312112
Konstantinos Sepetas *(Mgr-Super Market Sls & Comm)*

Subsidiaries:

I.Q.BRANDS AE (1)
Ag Fanouriou & Ag Sotira Str, Acharnes, Athens, 13671, Greece
Tel.: (30) 2102445555
Soft Drink Distr
N.A.I.C.S.: 424490

VIKRAM THERMO (INDIA) LTD.
A 704-714 The Capital Science City Road, Ahmedabad, 380 060, Gujarat, India
Tel.: (91) 7948481010
Web Site:
https://www.vikramthermo.com
530477—(BOM)
Rev.: $13,535,316
Assets: $15,251,616
Liabilities: $4,499,658
Net Worth: $10,751,957
Earnings: $2,027,792
Emp.: 138
Fiscal Year-end: 03/31/23
Pharmaceutical Products Mfr & Distr
N.A.I.C.S.: 325412
Chimanbhai Khodidas Patel *(Chm)*

VIKSIT ENGINEERING LTD.
Room No 1-2 Kapadia Chambers 5 1 Bharuch Street, Masjid Bunder E, Mumbai, 400009, India
Tel.: (91) 73166150223
Web Site: https://www.viksit.in
Year Founded: 1983
506196—(BOM)
Assets: $256,639
Liabilities: $263,210
Net Worth: ($6,570)
Earnings: ($671,686)
Emp.: 2
Fiscal Year-end: 03/31/23
Iron & Steel Product Mfr
N.A.I.C.S.: 331110
Raghunandan Khandelwal *(Mng Dir)*

VIL RESINS LIMITED
The Valley, Bolton, BL2 2DT, United Kingdom
Tel.: (44) 1204388800
Web Site: http://www.vilresins.co.uk
Surface Coating Resins Mfr
N.A.I.C.S.: 325211
Jamie Maugham *(Dir-Sls)*

VILKYSKIU PIENINE AB
P Lukosaicio st 14, Vilkyskiai, 99254, Taurage, Lithuania
Tel.: (370) 44155330
Web Site: https://vilvigroup.eu
Year Founded: 1934
Dairy Products Mfr
N.A.I.C.S.: 311514
Lina Braske *(Project Mgr-Mktg)*

VILLA KUNALAI PUBLIC COMPANY LIMITED
819 Moo 7 Pimonrat, Bangbuatong, Nonthaburi, 11110, Thailand
Tel.: (66) 2834493840
Web Site: http://www.kunalai.co.th
Year Founded: 2007
KUN—(THA)
Rev.: $21,522,072
Assets: $83,886,921
Liabilities: $61,203,592
Net Worth: $22,683,328
Earnings: $1,479,449
Fiscal Year-end: 12/31/23
Real Estate Development Services
N.A.I.C.S.: 531390
Tawatchai Sudtikitpisan *(Chm)*

VILLA SISTEMI MEDICALI S.P.A.
Via delle Azalee 3, 20090, Buccinasco, MI, Italy
Tel.: (39) 02488591   IT
Web Site: http://www.villasm.com
Year Founded: 1958
Sales Range: $25-49.9 Million
Emp.: 130
Medical Imaging & Diagnostic Systems Mfr
N.A.I.C.S.: 339112
Walt Schneider *(Gen Mgr)*

Subsidiaries:

Owandy SAS (1)
2 rue des Vieilles Vignes, Croissy-Beaubourg, 77183, France
Tel.: (33) 164111818
Web Site: http://www.owandy.com
Emp.: 35
Dental Equipment & Instrument Mfr
N.A.I.C.S.: 334510
Eric Fauvarque *(Gen Mgr)*

Subsidiary (Non-US):

Owandy Iberia SL (2)
C General Margallo 25, 28020, Madrid, Spain
Tel.: (34) 912 534 332
Web Site: http://www.owandy.es
Dental Equipment & Instrument Mfr
N.A.I.C.S.: 339114

Owandy Radiologie Italia Srl (2)
Via del Guado 57, Desio, 20033, Monza, Italy
Tel.: (39) 0362621106
Dental Equipment & Instruments Mfr
N.A.I.C.S.: 339114

Villa Radiology Systems (1)
91 Willenbrock Rd B-1, Oxford, CT 06478
Tel.: (203) 262-8836
Web Site: http://www.villaus.com
Radiology System Mfr
N.A.I.C.S.: 334510

VILLAGE CHRYSLER DODGE JEEP LTD.
201 Bayly Street West, Ajax, L1S 3K3, ON, Canada
Tel.: (905) 683-5358
Web Site:
http://www.villagechryslerjeep.ca
Rev.: $17,436,510
Emp.: 49
New & Used Car Dealers
N.A.I.C.S.: 441110
Frank Smith *(Bus Mgr)*

VILLAGE FARMS INTERNATIONAL INC.
4700-80th Street, Delta, V4K 3N3, BC, Canada
Tel.: (604) 940-6012   Ca
Web Site:
https://www.villagefarms.com
VFF—(NASDAQ)
Rev.: $293,572,000
Assets: $465,285,000
Liabilities: $161,455,000
Net Worth: $303,830,000
Earnings: ($101,146,000)
Emp.: 1,800
Fiscal Year-end: 12/31/22
Tomatoes, Peppers & Cucumbers
N.A.I.C.S.: 311411
Michael A. DeGiglio *(Founder, Pres & CEO)*

Subsidiaries:

Pure Sunfarms Corp. (1)
4431 80 Street, Delta, V4K 3N3, BC, Canada
Web Site: https://puresunfarms.com
Aromatic Cannabis Mfr
N.A.I.C.S.: 325199

Village Farms, LP (1)
7 Christopher Way, Eatontown, NJ 07724-3325
Tel.: (732) 676-3000
Web Site: http://www.villagefarms.com
Sales Range: $25-49.9 Million
Emp.: 20
Producer & Marketer of Hydroponic Produce
N.A.I.C.S.: 325320

Division (Domestic):

Village Farms of Marfa (2)
State Hwy 17 N, Marfa, TX 79843
Tel.: (432) 729-5000
Web Site: http://www.villagefarms.com
Fruit & Vegetable Packing, Canning & Industrial Fabrication
N.A.I.C.S.: 424480

Village Farms of Texas (2)
State Hwy 17 N, Fort Davis, TX 79843
Tel.: (432) 426-2301
Web Site: http://www.villagefarms.com
Sales Range: $25-49.9 Million
Emp.: 250
Providing Fruit & Vegetable Packing, Canning & Industrial Fabrication Services
N.A.I.C.S.: 111219

Village Farms, Inc. Distribution Center (2)
195 International Parkway, Heathrow, FL 32746
Tel.: (407) 936-1190
Web Site: http://www.villagefarms.com
Fruit & Vegetable Packing, Canning & Industrial Fabrication
N.A.I.C.S.: 311421

VILLAGE FORD LINCOLN SALES LTD.
1708 Main Street North, Moose Jaw, S6J 1L4, SK, Canada
Tel.: (306) 693-3673
Web Site:
http://www.villagefordlincoln.com
Year Founded: 1982
Rev.: $13,409,397
Emp.: 28
New & Used Car Dealers
N.A.I.C.S.: 441110
Jordan Zimmerman *(Owner)*

VILLAGE NISSAN
25 South Unionville Ave, Markham, L3R 6B8, ON, Canada
Tel.: (289) 806-1041
Web Site:
http://www.villagenissan.com
New & Used Car Dealers
N.A.I.C.S.: 441110
Matthew Tan *(Mgr-Parts)*

VILLAGE ROADSHOW LIMITED
Level 1 500 Chapel St, South Yarra, 3141, VIC, Australia
Tel.: (61) 392811000   AU
Web Site:
http://www.villageroadshow.com.au
Year Founded: 1954
VRL—(ASX)
Rev.: $732,420,000
Assets: $1,442,413,000
Liabilities: $1,194,576,000

INTERNATIONAL PUBLIC

Net Worth: $247,837,000
Earnings: ($124,549,000)
Fiscal Year-end: 06/30/20
Cinema Exhibition, Film Distribution & Production Services; Radio Stations & Theme Parks
N.A.I.C.S.: 512120
Graham W. Burke *(CEO)*

Subsidiaries:

Opia Limited (1)
184 Shepherds Bush Road, London, W6 7NL, United Kingdom
Tel.: (44) 333 888 4020
Web Site: https://www.opia.com
Marketing Services
N.A.I.C.S.: 541613

Roadshow Films Pty. Limited (1)
Level 1 1 Garden Street, South Yarra, 3141, VIC, Australia
Tel.: (61) 39 281 1000
Entertainment Services
N.A.I.C.S.: 711190

Village Roadshow Entertainment Group (BVI) Ltd. (1)
100 N Crescent Dr Ste 323, Beverly Hills, CA 90210   (47%)
Tel.: (310) 385-4300
Web Site: http://www.vreg.com
Motion Picture & Music Production Services
N.A.I.C.S.: 512110

Village Roadshow Theme Parks Pty Ltd (1)
Movie World Pacific Motorway, Oxenford, 4210, QLD, Australia
Tel.: (61) 75 573 3999
Entertainment Services
N.A.I.C.S.: 711190

VILLAGE VANGUARD CO., LTD.
1-901 Kamiyashiro Meito-ku, Nagoya, 465-0025, Aichi, Japan
Tel.: (81) 527691150
Web Site: http://www.village-v.co.jp
Year Founded: 1998
2769—(TKS)
Rev.: $163,921,390
Assets: $151,454,930
Liabilities: $110,327,510
Net Worth: $41,127,420
Earnings: ($7,561,840)
Emp.: 404
Fiscal Year-end: 05/31/24
Book & Disc Distr
N.A.I.C.S.: 459210
Keiichi Kikuchi *(Chm)*

VILLAR INTERNATIONAL LTD.
Hashel st 3, PO Box 3146, Caesarea Industrial Park, Caesarea, 3088900, Israel
Tel.: (972) 46272770
Web Site: https://www.villar.co.il
Year Founded: 1975
VILR—(TAE)
Rev.: $86,268,544
Assets: $1,229,388,018
Liabilities: $340,530,731
Net Worth: $888,857,287
Earnings: $69,262,604
Emp.: 100
Fiscal Year-end: 12/31/23
Commercial & Institutional Building Construction
N.A.I.C.S.: 236220
Shlomo Tisser *(CEO)*

Subsidiaries:

Archivit S.R.L. (1)
Dn - Cb nr 261, Judetul Ilfov, Popesti-Leordeni, Romania
Tel.: (40) 214670534
Web Site: https://www.archivit.ro
Archive Management & Archive Storing Services
N.A.I.C.S.: 541611

AND PRIVATE COMPANIES

VILLARS HOLDING SA
Route Jo-Siffert 4, 1762, Givisiez, Switzerland
Tel.: (41) 264262660
Web Site:
https://www.villarsholding.ch
VILN—(SWX)
Sales Range: Less than $1 Million
Holding Company
N.A.I.C.S.: 551112
Andreas Giesbrecht *(Chm)*

VILLE-MARIE SUZUKI
3010 Hochelaga Street, Montreal, H1W 1G1, QC, Canada
Tel.: (514) 598-8666
Web Site:
http://www.villemariesuzuki.ca
Sales Range: $25-49.9 Million
Emp.: 53
Automobile Sales
N.A.I.C.S.: 441110

VILLENEUVE CONSTRUCTION CO. LTD.
1533 Hwy 11 West, PO Box 1720, Hearst, P0L 1N0, ON, Canada
Tel.: (705) 372-1838
Web Site: http://www.villeneuve.on.ca
Year Founded: 1976
Sales Range: $10-24.9 Million
Emp.: 100
Construction Services
N.A.I.C.S.: 237310
Ghislain Lacroix *(Pres)*

Subsidiaries:

Villeneuve Construction - Cochrane (1)
109 Highway 11 West, PO Box 2306, Cochrane, P0L 1C0, ON, Canada
Tel.: (705) 272-4201
Web Site: http://www.villeneuve.on.ca
Emp.: 70
Construction Services
N.A.I.C.S.: 237310

Villeneuve Construction Co. Ltd. - Ready-mix Cement Operations Facility (1)
65 Gurney Road, Kapuskasing, P5N 2X7, ON, Canada
Tel.: (705) 335-5600
Cement Mfr
N.A.I.C.S.: 327310

VILLEROY & BOCH AG
Saaruferstrasse 1-3, 66693, Mettlach, Germany
Tel.: (49) 6864811227 De
Web Site: https://www.villeroy-boch.com
Year Founded: 1748
VIB3—(DUS)
Rev.: $995,580,353
Assets: $1,210,062,294
Liabilities: $785,734,666
Net Worth: $424,327,628
Earnings: $67,004,909
Emp.: 6,477
Fiscal Year-end: 12/31/23
Bathroom Fixture, Tile & Tableware Products Mfr & Whslr
N.A.I.C.S.: 327110
Alexander von Boch-Galhau *(Chm-Supervisory Bd)*

Subsidiaries:

Gastehaus Schlob Saareck Betreibergesellschaft mbH (1)
Im Saareckpark, 66693, Mettlach, Germany
Tel.: (49) 6864811711
Web Site: http://www.schloss-saareck.de
Hotel Operator
N.A.I.C.S.: 721110

Sales Design Vertriebsgesellschaft mbH (1)
Rieffstrasse 46, 66663, Merzig, Germany
Tel.: (49) 6864813020
Web Site:
https://www.salesdesigntableware.com
Home Interior Services
N.A.I.C.S.: 541410
Jens-Peter Schlingmann *(CEO)*

Sanipa Badmobel Treuchtlingen GmbH (1)
Markt Berolzheimer Str 6, Treuchtlingen, 91757, Weissenburg, Germany
Tel.: (49) 9142978978
Web Site: http://www.sanipa.de
Sanitary Products Mfr
N.A.I.C.S.: 322291

Vilbomex S.A. de C.V. (1)
Blvd Isidro Lopez Zertuche 3745, 25280, Saltillo, Coahuila, Mexico
Tel.: (52) 8444119000
Web Site: http://www.vilbomex.com
Toilet Seat Cover Distr
N.A.I.C.S.: 423220

Villeroy & Boch (Schweiz) AG (1)
Bahnhofstrasse 6, 5600, Lenzburg, Switzerland
Tel.: (41) 80068648110
Home Furnishings Products Whslr
N.A.I.C.S.: 423220

Villeroy & Boch Asia Pacific Pte. Ltd. (1)
491B River Valley RD 04-01A Valley Point, Singapore, 248373, Singapore
Tel.: (65) 65003560
Web Site: https://www.villeroy-boch.com.sg
Home Furnishings Products Whslr
N.A.I.C.S.: 423220

Villeroy & Boch Australia Pty. Ltd. (1)
Suite 225 117 Old Pittwater Road, Brookvale, 2100, NSW, Australia
Tel.: (61) 1800252770
Web Site: https://www.villeroy-boch.com.au
Home Furnishings Products Whslr
N.A.I.C.S.: 423220

Villeroy & Boch Danmark A/S (1)
Hvidsvaermervej 165G, 2610, Rodovre, Denmark
Tel.: (45) 36708055
Web Site: https://www.villeroy-boch.dk
Home Furnishings Products Whslr
N.A.I.C.S.: 423220

Villeroy & Boch Gustavsberg AB (1)
Odelbergs Vag 11, PO Box 400, 134 40, Gustavsberg, Sweden
Tel.: (46) 857039100
Web Site: https://www.gustavsberg.com
Bathroom Tile & Tableware Product Mfr
N.A.I.C.S.: 332913

Villeroy & Boch Gustavsberg Oy (1)
Laippatie 14 B, 00880, Helsinki, Finland
Tel.: (358) 932918811
Bathroom Tile & Tableware Product Mfr
N.A.I.C.S.: 327110
Kalle Viljakainen *(Comml Dir)*

Villeroy & Boch Magyarorszag Kft. (1)
Erzsebeti Ut 7, 6800, Hodmezovasarhely, Hungary
Tel.: (36) 62530565
Home Furnishings Products Whslr
N.A.I.C.S.: 423220
Csaba Kis *(Mgr-Production)*

Villeroy & Boch OOO (1)
2nd Khutorskaya 38A bldg 8 7th floor, 127287, Moscow, Russia
Tel.: (7) 4956096560
Web Site: https://www.villeroy-boch.ru
Home Furnishings Products Whslr
N.A.I.C.S.: 423220

Villeroy & Boch Polska Sp. z o.o. (1)
Aleja Wyscigowa 6 premises no, 02-681, Warsaw, Poland
Tel.: (48) 496864810
Web Site: https://www.villeroy-boch.pl
Home Furnishings Products Whslr
N.A.I.C.S.: 423220
Jacek Kotula *(Reg Sls Mgr)*

Villeroy & Boch Tableware B.V. (1)
Dwazziewegen 13, 9301 ZR, Roden, Netherlands
Tel.: (31) 6864810
Web Site: http://www.villeroy-boch.nl
Home Furnishings Products Whslr
N.A.I.C.S.: 423220
Frank Goring *(CEO)*

Villeroy & Boch Tableware Ltd. (1)
38 Berczy Street Rear Unit, Aurora, L4G 1W9, ON, Canada (100%)
Tel.: (905) 713-0077
Web Site: http://www.villeroy-boch.ca
Sales Range: $25-49.9 Million
Emp.: 5
Tableware Whslr
N.A.I.C.S.: 423220

Villeroy & Boch Tableware Oy (1)
Laippatie 14, 00880, Helsinki, Finland
Tel.: (358) 932918811
Home Furnishings Products Whslr
N.A.I.C.S.: 423220

Villeroy & Boch Trading (Shanghai) Co. Ltd. (1)
10F Jin Hong Qiao Business Building No 8 Lane 555 Gu Bei Road, Chang Ning District, Shanghai, 200051, China
Tel.: (86) 4008201748
Web Site: http://www.villeroy-boch.cn
Ceramic Mfr
N.A.I.C.S.: 327110

Villeroy & Boch USA, Inc. (1)
3 S Middlesex Ave, Monroe Township, NJ 08831-3726 (100%)
Tel.: (609) 395-1647
Web Site: http://www.villeroy-boch.com
Sales Range: $50-74.9 Million
Emp.: 65
Bathroom Fixture, Tile & Tableware Products Mfr & Whslr
N.A.I.C.S.: 327110

Villeroy & Boch Wellness N.V. (1)
Divisie Badkamer en Wellness Populierstraat 1 B8800 Roeselare, PO Box 40361, 3504 AD, Utrecht, Netherlands
Tel.: (31) 302473453
Home Furnishings Products Whslr
N.A.I.C.S.: 423220

VILNIAUS BALDAI AB
Volunteer ave 178B, 03154, Vilnius, Lithuania
Tel.: (370) 52525700
Web Site:
https://www.vilniausbaldai.lt
VBL1L—(VSE)
Rev.: $108,134,392
Assets: $91,055,174
Liabilities: $62,596,608
Net Worth: $28,458,566
Earnings: $1,569,343
Emp.: 700
Fiscal Year-end: 08/31/22
Furniture Product Distr
N.A.I.C.S.: 449110
Vytautas Bucas *(Chm)*

VILTORIA INVEST SA
48 avenue Victor Hugo, 75116, Paris, France
Tel.: (33) 153839560
Web Site: http://www.viktoria-invest-group.com
Sales Range: $10-24.9 Million
Holding Company
N.A.I.C.S.: 551112
Pierre Nollet *(CEO)*

VIMAL OIL & FOODS LTD.
Nr Palavasna Rly Over Bridge Highway, Mehsana, 384002, Gujarat, India
Tel.: (91) 2762 225700
Web Site: http://www.vimaloil.com
Rev.: $73,408,314
Assets: $5,946,083
Liabilities: $111,965,465
Net Worth: ($106,019,398)
Earnings: ($30,082,568)
Emp.: 91
Fiscal Year-end: 03/31/18
Edible Oil Mfr
N.A.I.C.S.: 311225
Jayeshbhai Chandubhai Patel *(Chm & Mng Dir)*

VIMEDIMEX MEDI - PHARMA JOINT STOCK COMPANY
Floor 8 Vimedimex Group Building No 46-48 Ba Trieu Steet, Hang Bai Ward Hoan Kiem District, Hanoi, Vietnam
Tel.: (84) 839254264
Web Site:
http://www.vietpharm.com.vn
Year Founded: 1984
VMD—(HOSE)
Rev.: $146,011,976
Assets: $76,458,878
Liabilities: $58,990,902
Net Worth: $17,467,976
Earnings: $1,284,987
Emp.: 47
Fiscal Year-end: 12/31/23
Medical Equipment Whslr
N.A.I.C.S.: 423450
Thi Nguyen Loan *(Chm)*

VIMETCO N.V.
Strawinskylaan 403 World Trade Center A Tower 4th floor, 1077 XX, Amsterdam, Netherlands
Tel.: (31) 208813139
Web Site: http://www.vimetco.com
Sales Range: $1-4.9 Billion
Aluminum Production, Refining & Smelting Services; Aluminum Products Mfr
N.A.I.C.S.: 331524
Vitali Machitski *(Chm)*

Subsidiaries:

Alro S.A. (1)
Rivergate Center No 64 Splaiul Unirii, District 4, 040036, Bucharest, Romania
Tel.: (40) 214083500
Web Site: https://www.alro.ro
Rev.: $613,515,259
Assets: $628,776,729
Liabilities: $412,924,287
Net Worth: $215,852,442
Earnings: ($98,689,531)
Emp.: 2,704
Fiscal Year-end: 12/31/2023
Aluminum Mfr
N.A.I.C.S.: 331313
Marian Nastase *(Chm)*

Global Aluminium Ltd. (1)
Via Augusta 106 Entresuelo 3, 08006, Barcelona, Spain
Tel.: (34) 934153079
Web Site: http://www.global-aluminium.com
Sales Range: $25-49.9 Million
Emp.: 10
Aluminum Mfr
N.A.I.C.S.: 331313

Vimetco Management GmbH (1)
Thurgauerstrasse 54, 8050, Zurich, Switzerland
Tel.: (41) 43 299 69 11
Web Site: http://www.vimetco.com
Sales Range: $25-49.9 Million
Emp.: 6
Aluminum Mfr
N.A.I.C.S.: 331313

Vimetco Trading S.r.l. (1)
Rivergate Ctr No 64 Splaiul Unirii, 040036, Bucharest, Romania
Tel.: (40) 750067713
Web Site: http://www.alro.ro
Aluminum Mfr
N.A.I.C.S.: 331313
William Berger *(CEO)*

VIMI FASTENERS S.P.A.
Via Labriola 19, Novellara, 42017, Reggio Emilia, Italy
Tel.: (39) 0522655611
Web Site:
https://www.vimifasteners.com

VIMI FASTENERS S.P.A.

Vimi Fasteners S.p.A.—(Continued)

Year Founded: 1967
VIM—(ITA)
Rev.: $67,719,395
Assets: $84,481,731
Liabilities: $49,875,262
Net Worth: $34,606,469
Earnings: $2,161,386
Emp.: 273
Fiscal Year-end: 12/31/23
Industrial Fastener Mfr & Distr
N.A.I.C.S.: 332722
Fabio Storchi (Pres)

Subsidiaries:

M.F. Inox Srl (1)
Via Meucci 12, Albese con Cassano, 22032, Como, Italy
Tel.: (39) 031428124
Web Site: https://www.mfinox.com
Machined Nickel Alloy Mfr
N.A.I.C.S.: 331110

Vimi Fasteners Inc. (1)
3540 Toringdon Way, Charlotte, NC 28277
Tel.: (704) 887-5291
Mechanical Fastener Mfr & Distr
N.A.I.C.S.: 332722

VIMIAN GROUP AB

Riddargatan 19, 114 57, Stockholm, Sweden
Web Site: https://www.vimian.com
Year Founded: 2020
VIMIAN—(OMX)
Rev.: $358,007,770
Assets: $1,050,813,728
Liabilities: $482,379,668
Net Worth: $568,434,060
Earnings: $11,314,483
Emp.: 1,100
Fiscal Year-end: 12/31/23
Veterinary Services
N.A.I.C.S.: 541940
Carl-Johan Ehn (Gen Counsel)

Subsidiaries:

AdVetis Medical S.A.S. (1)
Immeuble Le Melies 261 Rue De Paris, 93100, Montreuil, France
Tel.: (33) 155861040
Web Site: https://advetis-medical.com
Orthopaedics Surgery Equipment Mfr & Distr
N.A.I.C.S.: 339113

Arstakliniken AB (1)
Lindetorpsvagen 17, 12163, Johanneshov, Sweden
Tel.: (46) 8191233
Web Site: https://arstakliniken.se
Veterinary Clinics Operator
N.A.I.C.S.: 541940

Avedore Dyreklinik ApS (1)
Kettevej 25, 2650, Hvidovre, Denmark
Tel.: (45) 36786844
Web Site: https://avedoredyreklinik.dk
Veterinary Clinics Operator
N.A.I.C.S.: 541940

Bova Specials UK Ltd. (1)
7-9 Gorst Rd Park Royal, London, NW10 6LA, United Kingdom
Tel.: (44) 2030343100
Web Site: https://bova.co.uk
Pharmaceutical Product Mfr & Distr
N.A.I.C.S.: 325412

Brondby Dyreklinik ApS (1)
Kirkebjerg Parkvej 32, 2605, Brondby, Denmark
Tel.: (45) 43633808
Web Site: https://broendbydyreklinik.dk
Veterinary Clinics Operator
N.A.I.C.S.: 541940

Brunder Dyrehospital ApS (1)
Nordens Alle 55, 9700, Bronderslev, Denmark
Tel.: (45) 98800600
Web Site: https://brunderdyrehospital.dk
Veterinary Clinics Operator
N.A.I.C.S.: 541940

Check Points B.V. (1)
Binnenhaven 5, 6709 PD, Wageningen, Netherlands
Tel.: (31) 317453908
Web Site: https://www.checkandtrace.com
Deoxyribonucleic Acid Testing Services
N.A.I.C.S.: 621511

Check Points Health B.V. (1)
Binnenhaven 5, 6709 PD, Wageningen, Netherlands
Tel.: (31) 317453908
Web Site: https://check-pointshealth.com
Deoxyribonucleic Acid Testing Services
N.A.I.C.S.: 621511

Freelance Surgical Ltd. (1)
Unit 2 Havyatt Business Park Havyatt Road Wrington, Somerset, BS40 5PA, United Kingdom
Tel.: (44) 1934864280
Web Site: https://www.freelance-surgical.co.uk
Emp.: 17
Veterinary Surgical Equipment Distr
N.A.I.C.S.: 423490

Gentofte Dyreklinik ApS (1)
Bernstorffsvej 131, 2900, Hellerup, Denmark
Tel.: (45) 39620200
Web Site: https://dyrlaege.dk
Veterinary Clinics Operator
N.A.I.C.S.: 541940

Heiland GmbH (1)
Hegestrasse 40, D-20251, Hamburg, Germany
Tel.: (49) 4040119221
Web Site: https://www.home.heiland.com
Veterinary Pharmacy Services
N.A.I.C.S.: 541940

Hojbjerg Dyreklinik ApS (1)
Oddervej 70, 8270, Hojbjerg, Denmark
Tel.: (45) 86273344
Web Site: https://www.hoejbjergdyreklinik.dk
Veterinary Clinics Operator
N.A.I.C.S.: 541940

Independent Vets of Australia (IVA) Pty. Ltd. (1)
PO Box 2141, Smithfield, 2164, NSW, Australia
Tel.: (61) 1300838583
Web Site: https://independentvetsofaustralia.com.au
Veterinary Clinics Operator
N.A.I.C.S.: 541940

Indical Bioscience GmbH (1)
Deutscher Platz 5b, 04103, Leipzig, Germany
Tel.: (49) 3411245426
Web Site: https://www.indical.com
Veterinary Laboratory Services
N.A.I.C.S.: 541940

Kahu Veterinary Equipment Limited (1)
PO Box 76205, Manukau, Auckland, 2241, New Zealand
Tel.: (64) 800524883
Web Site: https://www.kahuvet.co.nz
Orthopaedics Surgery Equipment Mfr & Distr
N.A.I.C.S.: 339113

Knight Benedikt Australia Pty. Ltd. (1)
2/33 Prime Drive, Seven Hills, 2147, NSW, Australia
Tel.: (61) 1800960300
Web Site: https://www.knightbenedikt.com.au
Veterinary Equipment Mfr & Distr
N.A.I.C.S.: 325412

Kyon AG (1)
Hardturmstrasse 103, 8005, Zurich, Switzerland
Tel.: (41) 432041313
Web Site: https://www.kyon.ch
Orthopaedic Implant Mfr & Distr
N.A.I.C.S.: 339113

Laboratoire de Dermo-Cosmetique Animale S.A.S. (1)
3 Rue Pierre-Gilles De Gennes Espace D Entreprises-ZA Le Causse, 81100, Castres, France
Tel.: (33) 563711819
Web Site: https://www.dermoscent.com
Pet Healthcare Services
N.A.I.C.S.: 541940

Movora LLC (1)
310 Commerce Lake Dr Ste 107, Saint Augustine, FL 32095
Tel.: (904) 436-6540
Web Site: https://movora.com
Veterinary Clinics Operator
N.A.I.C.S.: 541940

Nextmune B.V. (1)
Vijzelweg 11, 8243 PM, Lelystad, Netherlands
Tel.: (31) 320783100
Web Site: https://nextmune.com
Pet Pharmacy Services
N.A.I.C.S.: 541940

Nextmune Italy S.r.l. (1)
Via GB Benzoni 50, 26020, Palazzo Pignano, Italy
Tel.: (39) 0373982024
Web Site: https://www.nextmuneitaly.it
Pet Healthcare Services
N.A.I.C.S.: 541940

Nextmune S.L. (1)
Valentin Beato 24, 28037, Madrid, Spain
Tel.: (34) 914134472
Pet Healthcare Services
N.A.I.C.S.: 541940

Nextmune Scandinavia AB (1)
Snickarvagen 7, S-673 32, Charlottenberg, Sweden
Tel.: (46) 57120230
Pet Healthcare Services
N.A.I.C.S.: 541940

Nextmune US LLC (1)
2801 S 35th St, Phoenix, AZ 85034
Veterinary Clinics Operator
N.A.I.C.S.: 541940

Practical CPD Limited (1)
PO Box 76205, Manukau, Auckland, 2241, New Zealand
Tel.: (64) 800524883
Web Site: https://www.practicalcpd.co.nz
Veterinary Clinics Operator
N.A.I.C.S.: 541940

Rodkaersbro Dyreklinik ApS (1)
Handvaerkervej 10, 8840, Rodkaersbro, Denmark
Tel.: (45) 86658611
Web Site: https://roedkaersbrodyreklinik.dk
Veterinary Clinics Operator
N.A.I.C.S.: 541940

Skovshoved Dyreklinik ApS (1)
Strandvejen 325, 2920, Charlottenlund, Denmark
Tel.: (45) 39646462
Web Site: https://skovshoved-dyreklinik.dk
Veterinary Clinics Operator
N.A.I.C.S.: 541940

Smadjursveterinaren A6 AB (1)
Smadjursveterinaren A6 Kompanigatan 8, 55550, Jonkoping, Sweden
Tel.: (46) 36363700
Web Site: https://www.smadjursveterinaren.com
Veterinary Clinics Operator
N.A.I.C.S.: 541940

VOI Europe, S.A.R.L. (1)
Bureaux 2D 21 Rue des Genets, 94310, Orly, France
Tel.: (33) 669485353
Veterinary Orthopaedics Services
N.A.I.C.S.: 541940

Vertical Vet LLC (1)
10402 Bailey Rd Ste 507, Cornelius, NC 28031
Web Site: https://verticalvet.com
Emp.: 1,300
Veterinary Clinics Operator
N.A.I.C.S.: 541940

VetFamily ApS (1)
Kroyer Kielbergs Vej 3 4 th, 8660, Skanderborg, Denmark
Tel.: (45) 86784488
Web Site: https://vetfamily.dk
Emp.: 180
Veterinary Clinics Operator
N.A.I.C.S.: 541940

VetFamily B.V. (1)
Johan Huizingalaan 400, 1066 JS, Amsterdam, Netherlands
Tel.: (31) 611813533
Web Site: https://vetfamily.nl
Veterinary Clinics Operator
N.A.I.C.S.: 541940

VetFamily Brazil Ltda. (1)
Av Nicolas Boer N 399, Sao Paulo, 1140-060, Brazil
Tel.: (55) 1151080992
Web Site: https://vetfamilybrasil.com.br
Veterinary Clinics Operator
N.A.I.C.S.: 541940

VetFamily GmbH (1)
Hohenzollernstrasse 93, 47799, Krefeld, Germany
Tel.: (49) 2152552844
Web Site: https://vetfamily.de
Veterinary Clinics Operator
N.A.I.C.S.: 541940

VetFamily Limited (1)
G/F Veristrong Industrial Centre 34-36 Au Pui Wan Street, Shatin, Fotan, China (Hong Kong)
Tel.: (852) 36116344
Web Site: https://familyvethk.com
Veterinary Clinics Operator
N.A.I.C.S.: 541940

VetFamily Partners S.L.U. (1)
C/ Sant Cugat 56, Barcelona, 08302, Mataro, Spain
Tel.: (34) 609885691
Web Site: https://vetfamily.es
Veterinary Clinics Operator
N.A.I.C.S.: 541940

Veterinary Orthopedic Implants, LLC (1)
310 Commerce Lk Dr Ste 107, Saint Augustine, FL 32095
Tel.: (904) 436-6540
Web Site: https://vetimplants.com
Veterinary Orthopaedics Services
N.A.I.C.S.: 541940

VIMICRO INTERNATIONAL CORPORATION

16/F Shining Tower No 35 Xueyuan Road, Haidian District, Beijing, 100083, China
Tel.: (86) 10 68948888
Web Site: http://www.vimicro.com
Year Founded: 1999
Sales Range: $100-124.9 Million
Video Surveillance Products Designer, Developer & Marketer
N.A.I.C.S.: 334413
Zhonghan Deng (Founder, Chm & CEO)

Subsidiaries:

Viewtel Corporation (1)
1758 N Shoreline Blvd, Mountain View, CA 94043-1318
Tel.: (650) 966-1882
Web Site: http://www.vimicro.com
Computer System Design Services
N.A.I.C.S.: 541512

Vimicro Electronics International Limited (1)
Unit 905 9th Fl Metro Loft 38 Kwai Hei St New Territo, Kwai Chung, China (Hong Kong)
Tel.: (852) 27822086
Web Site: http://www.vimicro.com
Sales Range: $50-74.9 Million
Emp.: 100
Other Electronic Parts & Equipment Whslr
N.A.I.C.S.: 423690

VIMPEX HANDELSGESELLSCHAFT MBH

Kaerntner Ring 4, PO Box 148, 1010, Vienna, Austria
Tel.: (43) 1501510

AND PRIVATE COMPANIES

VINACOMIN - COC SAU COAL

Web Site: http://www.vimpex.at
Year Founded: 1974
Sales Range: $25-49.9 Million
Emp.: 100
Paper Products Mfr
N.A.I.C.S.: 322120
Nabil R. Kuzbari *(Pres & CEO)*

Subsidiaries:

Consolidated Paper Co. (1)
3rd Industrial Area Plot 91, 6th Of October City Giza, Cairo, Egypt **(100%)**
Tel.: (20) 28335341
Web Site: http://www.paperisbetter.com
Sales Range: $50-74.9 Million
Paper Distribution
N.A.I.C.S.: 322211

Gimpex-Gulf Import Export L.L.C. (1)
Al Quoz Industrial Area 4 St 26 Bldg No 88, Dubai, 53366, Alquoz, United Arab Emirates **(100%)**
Tel.: (971) 43474588
Web Site: http://www.gimpexgulf.com
Sales Range: $25-49.9 Million
Emp.: 18
Paper Distribution
N.A.I.C.S.: 322211

Limpex-Kuzbari & Anan Enterprises S.A.L. (1)
Center Verdun 2000, PO Box 136122, Verdun, Beirut, Lebanon
Tel.: (961) 1792200
Web Site: http://www.kuzbarigroup.com
Sales Range: $25-49.9 Million
Emp.: 30
Paper Distribution
N.A.I.C.S.: 322211

Misrimpex for Paper Trading L.L.C. (1)
Kasr El Nil 4 Behler Passage, PO Box 2531, Cairo, Egypt **(100%)**
Tel.: (20) 2 3933325
Web Site: http://www.kuzbarigroup.com
Sales Range: $25-49.9 Million
Emp.: 15
Paper Distribution
N.A.I.C.S.: 322299

SIMPEX-Dammam (1)
Dammam Sea Port Rd Near Al Zahid Troctor Near Al Manquor Warehouse, PO Box 2033, Dammam, 31451, Al Khaldiah, Saudi Arabia
Tel.: (966) 38573791
Web Site: http://www.simpex.com.sa
Paper Distribution
N.A.I.C.S.: 322211

SIMPEX-Jeddah (1)
Al Badawey Al Moulasam St 34 Bldg, Al Bawady District, 21451, Jeddah, Saudi Arabia
Tel.: (966) 26913960
Web Site: http://www.simpex.com.sa
Paper Distribution
N.A.I.C.S.: 322211

SIMPEX-Riyadh (1)
Al Kharj Rd, 11421, Riyadh, Saudi Arabia
Tel.: (966) 14951624
Web Site: http://www.simpex.com.sa
Sales Range: $25-49.9 Million
Emp.: 15
Paper Distribution
N.A.I.C.S.: 322211

VIMPEX North America (1)
7075 Drumcashel Ct, Mississauga, L5N 7L3, ON, Canada **(100%)**
Tel.: (905) 286-1040
Web Site: http://www.vimpexna.com
Sales Range: $25-49.9 Million
Emp.: 1
Paper Distribution
N.A.I.C.S.: 322211

Vimpex (Austria) CO., LTD (1)
World Trade Center B-1606 Haiyu Bei Road 45, Changshu, Jiangsu, China
Tel.: (86) 512 520 90 580
Tape Distr
N.A.I.C.S.: 424120

Vimpex Brasil Representacoes Ltda (1)
Rua Miranda Montenegro 141, 05412-020, Sao Paulo, Brazil
Tel.: (55) 11 3872 9324
Tape Distr
N.A.I.C.S.: 424120

Vimpex Germany Gmbh (1)
Neuer Wall 26-28, 20354, Hamburg, Germany
Tel.: (49) 40 3070 9180
Tape Distr
N.A.I.C.S.: 424120

Vimpex North Africa s.a.r.l. (1)
Cite 445 Lgts bt 23 No 02 Sidi Menif, Zeralda, Algiers, Algeria
Tel.: (213) 21 330 895
Tape Distr
N.A.I.C.S.: 424120

VIMTA LABS LIMITED
142 IDA Phase II Cherlapally, Hyderabad, 500 051, Andhra Pradesh, India
Tel.: (91) 4027264141
Web Site: https://www.vimta.com
Year Founded: 1984
VIMTALABS—(NSE)
Rev.: $28,870,842
Assets: $37,449,731
Liabilities: $10,916,588
Net Worth: $26,533,143
Earnings: $2,921,783
Emp.: 1,096
Fiscal Year-end: 03/31/21
Research & Testing Services
N.A.I.C.S.: 541380
V. Harriman *(Exec Dir-Ops)*

Subsidiaries:

Emtac Laboratories Private Limited (1)
Plot No 11/6 Road No 9 Ida, Nacharam, Hyderabad, 500 076, India
Tel.: (91) 7095499900
Web Site: https://emtac.in
Laboratory & Certification Services
N.A.I.C.S.: 541380

VINA CONCHA Y TORO S.A.
Casilla 213 Nueva Tajamar 481Torre Norte Piso 15, Santiago, Chile
Tel.: (56) 2 476 5000   CL
Web Site: http://www.conchaytoro.com
Year Founded: 1883
Rev.: $884,345,623
Assets: $1,650,482,074
Liabilities: $826,581,403
Net Worth: $823,900,671
Earnings: $70,720,010
Emp.: 2,321
Fiscal Year-end: 12/31/18
Wine Mfr & Distr
N.A.I.C.S.: 312130
Alfonso Larrain Santa Maria *(Chm)*

Subsidiaries:

Concha y Toro Norway AS (1)
Karenslyst Alle 10, 0278, Oslo, Norway
Tel.: (47) 23 08 38 70
Web Site: http://www.vctnorway.com
Sales Range: $50-74.9 Million
Emp.: 3
Alcoholic Beverage Distr
N.A.I.C.S.: 424820
Anne Eliasson *(Country Mgr)*

Concha y Toro Sweden AB (1)
Dobelnsgatan 21, 111 40, Stockholm, Sweden
Tel.: (46) 850566760
Web Site: http://www.cytsweden.se
Sales Range: $50-74.9 Million
Emp.: 8
Alcoholic Beverage Distr
N.A.I.C.S.: 424820

Subsidiary (Non-US):

Concha y Toro Finland OY. (2)
Pietarinkuja 3, 140, Helsinki, Finland
Tel.: (358) 9 278 4265

Web Site: http://www.cytfinland.fi
Sales Range: $25-49.9 Million
Emp.: 4
Alcoholic Beverage Distr
N.A.I.C.S.: 424820
Jaakko Siimeslahti *(Country Mgr)*

Concha y Toro UK Limited (1)
6 Ashurst Court London Road, Wheatley, Oxford, OX33 1ER, United Kingdom
Tel.: (44) 1865 873 713
Web Site: http://www.cyt-uk.com
Wine Mfr & Distr
N.A.I.C.S.: 312130
Simon Doyle *(Gen Mgr)*

Fetzer Vineyards (1)
12901 Old River Rd, Hopland, CA 95449
Tel.: (707) 744-7600
Web Site: http://www.fetzer.com
Sales Range: $125-149.9 Million
Emp.: 300
Wine Producer
N.A.I.C.S.: 312130
Scott Ferleman *(Mgr-Customer Svc)*

Inversiones Concha y Toro S.A. (1)
Avda Santa Rosa 0837 Paradero 43, 755 0099, Puente Alto, Santiago, Chile
Tel.: (56) 24765500
Web Site: http://www.conchaytoro.com
Wine Mfr
N.A.I.C.S.: 312130

Holding (Domestic):

Comercial Peumo Ltda. (2)
Ave Santa Rosa 0837 Paradero 43, Puente Alto, Santiago, Chile
Tel.: (56) 24765500
Wine Whslr & Retailer
N.A.I.C.S.: 312130

Sociedad Exportadora y Comercial Vina Maipo Ltda. (2)
Nueva Tajamar 481 Torre Norte Oficina 505, Las Condes, Santiago, Chile
Tel.: (56) 24761259
Web Site: http://www.vinamaipo.com
Sales Range: $25-49.9 Million
Emp.: 20
Wine Mfr & Distr
N.A.I.C.S.: 312130

VCT Internacional S.A. (2)
Nueva Tajamar 48 Torre Norte piso 15, Las Condes, Santiago, 7550099, Chile
Tel.: (56) 24765200
Investment & Management Services
N.A.I.C.S.: 523999
Alfonso Larrain Santa Maria *(Chm)*

Subsidiary (Non-US):

Trivento Bodegas y Vinedos S.A. (3)
Canal Pescara 9347, Russell CP5517, Maipu, Mendoza, Argentina **(100%)**
Tel.: (54) 2614990270
Web Site: http://www.trivento.com
Sales Range: $75-99.9 Million
Emp.: 400
Wine Mfr & Distr
N.A.I.C.S.: 312130

Subsidiary (Domestic):

Vina Cono Sur S.A. (2)
Ave Nueva Tajamar 481 Fl 21 Torre Sur Oficina 1602, Santiago, Chile **(50%)**
Tel.: (56) 24765090
Web Site: http://www.conosur.com
Sales Range: $10-24.9 Million
Emp.: 30
Wine Mfr & Distr
N.A.I.C.S.: 312130

Transportes Viconto Ltda. (1)
Nueva Tajamar 481 Torre Sur Piso 15, Las Condes, Santiago, Chile
Tel.: (56) 24765200
Freight & Transport Services
N.A.I.C.S.: 488510

Vina Almaviva S.A. (1)
Avda Santa Rosa 821 Paradero 45 Casilla 274, Puente Alto, Santiago, Chile **(50%)**
Tel.: (56) 28529300
Web Site: http://www.almavivawinery.com
Sales Range: $25-49.9 Million
Emp.: 50
Wine Mfr & Distr

N.A.I.C.S.: 312130

Vina Canepa S.A. (1)
Av Nueva Tajamar 481 Torre Sur Oficina 1001, Las Condes, Santiago, Chile
Tel.: (56) 2 4765602
Web Site: http://www.canepawines.cl
Beverage Product Distr
N.A.I.C.S.: 424820

Vina Maycas del Limari Ltda. (1)
Avda Nueva Tajamar 481, Torre Norte Piso 5, Santiago, Chile
Tel.: (56) 24765200
Web Site: http://www.maycasdellimari.com
Sales Range: $25-49.9 Million
Emp.: 50
Wineries
N.A.I.C.S.: 312130

Vina Palo Alto Ltda. (1)
Nueva Tajamar 481 Torre Norte Piso 15, Las Condes, Santiago, Chile
Tel.: (56) 24765109
Web Site: http://www.conchaytolo.com
Sales Range: $350-399.9 Million
Emp.: 2,000
Wine Packaging & Distr
N.A.I.C.S.: 561910

VINA TECH CO., LTD.
15 Unam-ro, Deokjin-gu, Jeonju, 54853, Jeollabuk-Do, Korea (South)
Tel.: (82) 637153020
Web Site: https://vinatech.com
Year Founded: 1999
126340—(KRS)
Sales Range: $10-24.9 Million
Emp.: 60
Supercapacitors & Single Cell Capacitors Mfr
N.A.I.C.S.: 334419
Do-Kyung Sung *(CEO)*

VINACAPITAL VIETNAM OPPORTUNITY FUND, LTD.
17th Floor Sun Wah Tower 115 Nguyen Hue, District 1, Ho Chi Minh City, Vietnam
Tel.: (84) 838219930
Web Site: https://vinacapital.com
VCVOF—(OTCIQ)
Rev.: $53,126,000
Assets: $1,157,219,000
Liabilities: $33,352,000
Net Worth: $1,123,867,000
Earnings: ($15,019,000)
Emp.: 200
Fiscal Year-end: 06/30/23
Investment Services
N.A.I.C.S.: 523999
Don Di Lam *(CEO)*

Subsidiaries:

Thai Hoa International Hospital JSC (1)
No 01 Bis - Le Thi Rieng, Ward 1, Cao Lanh, Dong Thap, Vietnam
Tel.: (84) 673878878
Web Site: http://www.thaihoahospital.com
Hospital Operator
N.A.I.C.S.: 622110

VINACOMIN - CAO SON COAL JOINT STOCK COMPANY
Cam Son ward, Cam Pha, Quang Ninh, Vietnam
Tel.: (84) 33 862210
Web Site: http://www.thancaoson.com.vn
Year Founded: 1974
Rev.: $188,086,398
Assets: $91,730,753
Liabilities: $78,155,514
Net Worth: $13,575,240
Earnings: $2,822,620
Fiscal Year-end: 12/31/18
Coal Mining Services
N.A.I.C.S.: 212115

VINACOMIN - COC SAU COAL

VINACOMIN - COC SAU COAL

**VINACOMIN - COC SAU COAL —(CONTINUED)
JOINT STOCK COMPANY**
Cam Phu Ward, Cam Pha, Quang Ninh, Vietnam
Tel.: (84) 203862062
Web Site: https://www.cocsau.com
TC6—(HNX)
Rev.: $323,700,100
Assets: $142,007,200
Liabilities: $108,811,900
Net Worth: $33,195,300
Earnings: $157,400
Fiscal Year-end: 12/31/22
Coal & Other Minerals Extraction & Processing Services
N.A.I.C.S.: 213113
Nguyen Van Kiem *(Chm-Mgmt Bd)*

VINACOMIN - DEO NAI COAL JOINT STOCK COMPANY
Cam Tay Ward, Cam Pha, Quang Ninh, Vietnam
Tel.: (84) 33864251
Web Site: http://www.deonai.com.vn
Year Founded: 1960
TDN—(HNX)
Rev.: $398,050,100
Assets: $126,061,900
Liabilities: $83,685,400
Net Worth: $42,376,500
Earnings: $10,274,500
Fiscal Year-end: 12/31/23
Exploiting Coal & Construction Mining Services
N.A.I.C.S.: 532412
Tot Trong Nguyen *(Chm-Mgmt Bd)*

VINACOMIN - HA TU COAL JOINT STOCK COMPANY
Group 6 Area 3 Ha Tu Ward, Ha Long, Quang Ninh, Vietnam
Tel.: (84) 2033835169
Web Site: https://www.hatucoal.vn
THT—(HNX)
Rev.: $434,421,300
Assets: $161,187,100
Liabilities: $120,861,000
Net Worth: $40,326,100
Earnings: $7,135,500
Fiscal Year-end: 12/31/23
Coal Mining, Processing & Consumption Services
N.A.I.C.S.: 213113

VINACOMIN - MONG DUONG COAL JOINT STOCK COMPANY
Mong Duong, Cam Pha, Quang Ninh, Vietnam
Tel.: (84) 333868271
Web Site: http://www.mongduongcoal.vn
MDC—(HNX)
Rev.: $280,152,300
Assets: $144,532,000
Liabilities: $113,060,500
Net Worth: $31,471,500
Earnings: $8,963,600
Fiscal Year-end: 12/31/22
Coal & Minerals Exploration Services
N.A.I.C.S.: 213113

VINACOMIN - VANG DANH COAL JOINT STOCK COMPANY
969 Bach Dang Street, Quang Trung Ward Uong Bi, Quang Ninh, Vietnam
Tel.: (84) 203853125
Web Site: https://www.vangdanhcoal.com.vn
Year Founded: 2007
TVD—(HNX)
Rev.: $269,300,092
Assets: $87,575,214
Liabilities: $58,426,791
Net Worth: $29,148,423
Earnings: $5,693,263
Emp.: 5,680
Fiscal Year-end: 12/31/23
Oil & Gas Exploration Services
N.A.I.C.S.: 213112

VINACOMIN-COAL IMPORT EXPORT JOINT STOCK COMPANY
No 47 Quang Trung Tran Hung Dao, Hoan Kiem, Hanoi, Vietnam
Tel.: (84) 439424634
CLM—(HNX)
Rev.: $1,322,726,400
Assets: $95,577,600
Liabilities: $44,652,300
Net Worth: $50,925,300
Earnings: $33,883,400
Fiscal Year-end: 12/31/22
Mining Services
N.A.I.C.S.: 213114

VINACONTROL GROUP CORPORATION
54 Tran Nhan Tong, Hai Ba Trung District, Hanoi, Vietnam
Tel.: (84) 2439433840
Web Site: https://www.vinacontrol.com.vn
Year Founded: 1957
VNC—(HNX)
Rev.: $70,895,300
Assets: $42,059,600
Liabilities: $12,495,900
Net Worth: $29,563,700
Earnings: $3,652,500
Emp.: 780
Fiscal Year-end: 12/31/23
Commodity Inspection Services
N.A.I.C.S.: 541990
Subsidiaries:
Vinacontrol Property Valuation Joint Stock Company (1)
54 Tran Nhan Tong, Nguyen Du Ward Hai Ba Trung Dist, Hanoi, Vietnam
Tel.: (84) 2438226024
Quality Inspection Services
N.A.I.C.S.: 541350

VINAFCO JOINT STOCK CORPORATION
838 Bach Dang Street Thanh Luong Ward, Hai Ba Trung District, Hanoi, Vietnam
Tel.: (84) 4 37684464
Web Site: http://www.vinafco.com.vn
Year Founded: 1987
Sales Range: $25-49.9 Million
Emp.: 500
Transportation & Logistics Services
N.A.I.C.S.: 541614
Thi Minh Thuan Nguyen *(Dir-Fin)*

VINAFREIGHT JOINT STOCK COMPANY
Floor No 1 Block C WASECO Office Building 10 Pho Quang str, Tan Binh Dist, Ho Chi Minh City, Vietnam
Tel.: (84) 2838446409
Web Site: https://www.vinafreight.com
Year Founded: 1997
Sales Range: $75-99.9 Million
Airfreight & Logistics Services
N.A.I.C.S.: 481112

VINALCOOL SA
Calea Moinesti 24, Bacau, Romania
Tel.: (40) 234 519 375
Sales Range: Less than $1 Million
Emp.: 9
Wine Mfr
N.A.I.C.S.: 312130

VINAM JSC
1st Floor Lot BT5 - Block 36 New Urban Area Phap Van - Tu Hiep, Hoang Liet Ward Hoang Mai District, Hanoi, Vietnam
Tel.: (84) 2436343085
Web Site: https://www.vinamgroup.com.vn
Year Founded: 2007
CVN—(HNX)
Rev.: $10,792,900
Assets: $40,114,600
Liabilities: $867,900
Net Worth: $39,246,700
Earnings: $699,100
Fiscal Year-end: 12/31/22
Civil Construction Services
N.A.I.C.S.: 237990
Takishita Akira *(Chm-Mgmt Bd)*

VINAR SYSTEMS PVT. LTD.
9C Lord Sinha Road, Kolkata, 700071, India
Tel.: (91) 33 2282 3661
Web Site: http://www.vinar.co.in
Year Founded: 1972
Conveyor Systems Mfr, Whslr & Installation Svcs
N.A.I.C.S.: 333922
Vinod Kumar Lohia *(Exec Dir)*
Subsidiaries:
Wevin Private Limited (1)
143-E Bommasandra Industrial Area I & II Phase, Bengaluru, 560099, India
Tel.: (91) 8110 304 730
Web Site: http://www.wevin.co.in
Custom-Designed Material Handling & Conveyor Systems Mfr, Whslr & Installation Services
N.A.I.C.S.: 333922
R. A. Srinivas *(Pres)*

VINARIJA CITLUK D.D.
Kralja Tomislava 28, 88260, Citluk, Bosnia & Herzegovina
Tel.: (387) 36 642 232
Web Site: http://www.hercegovinavino.com
Emp.: 69
Wine Mfr
N.A.I.C.S.: 312130

VINATEX
Sentienel Place Building 41A Ly Thai to Street, Hanoi, Vietnam
Tel.: (84) 438257700
Web Site: http://www.vinatex.com.vn
Year Founded: 1995
Sales Range: $5-14.9 Billion
Emp.: 100,000
Production & Export of Yarn, Woven & Knitted Fabrics & Clothing
N.A.I.C.S.: 313210
Tran Quang Nghi *(Chm-Mgmt Bd)*
Subsidiaries:
Viet Tien Garment Company (1)
07 Le Minh Xuan, Tan Binh District, Ho Chi Minh City, Vietnam
Tel.: (84) 838640800
Web Site: http://www.viettien.com.vn
Sales Range: $1-4.9 Billion
Emp.: 12,000
Clothing Distr
N.A.I.C.S.: 458110
Bui Van Tien *(Gen Dir)*

Vinatex Trading Joint-stock Company (1)
96 Ly Tu Trong Str, Ben Thanh Ward District 1, Ho Chi Minh City, Vietnam
Tel.: (84) 8 38293649
Web Site: http://www.vinatexhcmc.com.vn
Textile Products Distr
N.A.I.C.S.: 424310

VINATI ORGANICS LTD

INTERNATIONAL PUBLIC

Parinee Crescenzo 11th Floor 1102 A-Wing G Block Behind MCA, Bandra-Kurla Complex Bandra East, Mumbai, 400051, Maharashtra, India
Tel.: (91) 2261240444
Web Site: https://www.vinatiorganics.com
VINATIORGA—(NSE)
Rev.: $133,783,978
Assets: $236,666,444
Liabilities: $25,991,033
Net Worth: $210,675,410
Earnings: $36,762,303
Emp.: 953
Fiscal Year-end: 03/31/21
Organic Chemical Mfr
N.A.I.C.S.: 424690
Vinati Saraf Mutreja *(CEO & Mng Dir)*
Subsidiaries:
Veeral Organics Pvt. Ltd. (1)
Parinee Crescenzo 1102 11th Floor A Wing Plot No C38 & C39, G Block Bandra-Kurla Complex Bandra East, Mumbai, 400 051, India
Tel.: (91) 2261240444
Chemical Mfr & Distr
N.A.I.C.S.: 325611

VINATRANS INTERNATIONAL FREIGHT FORWARDERS
406 Nguyen Tat Thanh Ward 18 Dist 4, Ho Chi Minh City, Vietnam
Tel.: (84) 839414919
Web Site: http://www.vinatrans.com
Sales Range: $100-124.9 Million
Emp.: 300
Freight Transportation & Forwarding Services
N.A.I.C.S.: 488510
Bui Ngoc Loan *(Mng Dir)*

VINAY CEMENTS LTD
21/3 Darga Road Block A 3rd Floor, Kolkata, 700017, India
Tel.: (91) 3340222121
Web Site: http://www.vinaycements.com
Year Founded: 1987
Sales Range: $10-24.9 Million
Cement Mfr
N.A.I.C.S.: 327310
Binod Kumar Bawri *(Mng Dir)*

VINAYAK POLYCON INTERNATIONAL LIMITED
312 Navjeevan Complex 29 Station Road, Jaipur, 302 006, Rajasthan, India
Tel.: (91) 1412377007
Web Site: https://www.vinayakpolycon.com
534639—(BOM)
Rev.: $2,622,469
Assets: $1,432,336
Liabilities: $893,963
Net Worth: $538,373
Earnings: $14,028
Emp.: 45
Fiscal Year-end: 03/31/23
Speciality Packaging Product Mfr
N.A.I.C.S.: 326199
Vikram Baid *(CFO)*

VINCENT MEDICAL HOLDINGS LIMITED
Flat B2 7/F Phase 2 Hang Fung Industrial Building 2G Hok Yuen Street, Hung Hom, Kowloon, China (Hong Kong)
Tel.: (852) 23655688
Web Site: http://www.vincentmedical.com
Year Founded: 1997
1612—(HKG)
Rev.: $80,228,355
Assets: $92,654,123

AND PRIVATE COMPANIES

Liabilities: $29,080,965
Net Worth: $63,573,158
Earnings: ($2,344,725)
Emp.: 1,226
Fiscal Year-end: 12/31/22
Medical Product Mfr & Distr
N.A.I.C.S.: 334510
Man Shing Choi *(Founder & Chm)*

Subsidiaries:

Inspired Medical Japan Co., Ltd. (1)
3-31-1 Yushima Nakagawa Building 302,
Bunkyo-ku, Tokyo, 113-0034, Japan
Tel.: (81) 358178471
Web Site: https://www.inspired-medical.co.jp
Medical Device Mfr & Distr
N.A.I.C.S.: 339112

Rehab-Robotics Company
Limited (1)
Unit 307 3/F 12W Building Phase 3 No 12
Science Park West Avenue, Hong Kong
Science Park, Sha Tin, China (Hong Kong)
Tel.: (852) 24164832
Web Site: http://www.rehab-robotics.com
Rev.: $534,894
Mobility Device Mfr
N.A.I.C.S.: 334510
Michael Kam Fai Tsui *(CEO)*

Vincent Medical Holdings Limited -
Dongguan Factory (1)
11 Shabu Street, Qiaolong District Tangxia
Town, Dongguan, 523730, Guangdong,
China
Tel.: (86) 76987723899
Medical Device Mfr
N.A.I.C.S.: 334510

VINCENZO ZUCCHI S.P.A.

Via Legnano 24, Rescaldina, 20027,
Milan, Italy
Tel.: (39) 0331448211   IT
Web Site:
  https://www.gruppozucchi.it
ZUC—(ITA)
Sales Range: $350-399.9 Million
Emp.: 3,000
Household Linen Mfr
N.A.I.C.S.: 314120
Michel Lhoste *(CEO)*

Subsidiaries:

Bassetti S.p.A. (1)
Via Legnano 24, 20027, Rescaldina, 20027,
Milan, Italy   **(100%)**
Tel.: (39) 0331448111
Web Site: http://www.zucchigroup.it
Sales Range: $750-799.9 Million
Emp.: 300
Natural & Synthetic Fiber Textiles Production & Distribution
N.A.I.C.S.: 314999

Subsidiary (Non-US):

Baseuropa S.A. (2)
1219 Luxembourg, 17 Rue Beaumont,
L-2233, Luxembourg, Luxembourg
Tel.: (352) 453370
Holding Company
N.A.I.C.S.: 551112

Subsidiary (Domestic):

Basitalia Leasing S.p.A. (2)
Via Alfieri 1, 31015, Conegliano, TV, Italy
Tel.: (39) 04383601
Leasing Company
N.A.I.C.S.: 531120

Subsidiary (Non-US):

Bassetti Deutschland GmbH (2)
Fraunhoferstrasse 5, Martinsried, 82152,
Munich, Germany   **(100%)**
Tel.: (49) 898956200
Web Site: http://www.bassetti.com
Sales Range: $25-49.9 Million
Emp.: 20
Distribution of Household Linen
N.A.I.C.S.: 423220
Alberto Gallo *(Gen Mgr)*

Bassetti Espanola S.A. (2)
Poligono Industrial la Borda, Calle Barcelonas Nave 4, Caldes de Montbui, 08140,
Barcelona, Spain
Tel.: (34) 938654946
Web Site: http://www.Bassetti.com
Distribution of Household Linen
N.A.I.C.S.: 423220

Bassetti Schweiz A.G. (2)
Via A Giacometti 1, Buochs, 6374, Lugano,
Switzerland
Tel.: (41) 416200444
Web Site: http://www.bassetti.com
Sales Range: $25-49.9 Million
Emp.: 1
Distribution of Household Linen
N.A.I.C.S.: 423220
Retardo Rankoni *(Country Mgr)*

Descamps Ltd. (2)
197 Sloane St, London, SW1X 9QX, United
Kingdom
Tel.: (44) 2072356957
Distribution of Household Linen
N.A.I.C.S.: 423220

Descamps S.A.S. (2)
71 Avenue Franklin D Roosevelt, 75009,
Paris, France   **(100%)**
Tel.: (33) 153322730
Web Site: http://www.descamps.com
Sales Range: $10-24.9 Million
Emp.: 30
Household Linen Mfr & Distr
N.A.I.C.S.: 314120

Subsidiary (Domestic):

Mascioni S.p.A. (2)
Via Mascioni 4, Cuvio, 21030, Varese, Italy
Tel.: (39) 0332650600
Web Site: http://www.mascioni.it
Sales Range: $75-99.9 Million
Emp.: 446
Treatment & Finishing of Textiles
N.A.I.C.S.: 313310

Subsidiary (US):

Mascioni USA Ltd. (2)
20 W 22nd St Ste 1410, New York, NY
10010-5840
Tel.: (212) 674-5145
Web Site: http://www.mascioni.com
Sales Range: $25-49.9 Million
Emp.: 9
Distr of Household Linen
N.A.I.C.S.: 313240

VINCI PARTNERS INVESTIMENTOS LTDA.

Av Ataulfo de Paiva 153 5 andar Leblon, 22440 032, Rio de Janeiro, Brazil
Tel.: (55) 21 2159 6000
Web Site:
  http://www.vincipartners.com
Privater Equity Firm
N.A.I.C.S.: 523999

VINCI PARTNERS INVESTMENTS LTD.

Av Bartolomeu Mitre 336, Leblon, Rio
de Janeiro, 22431-002, Brazil
Tel.: (55) 2121596000   Ky
Web Site: https://vincipartners.com
Year Founded: 2020
VINP—(NASDAQ)
Rev.: $90,621,199
Assets: $458,613,820
Liabilities: $183,257,553
Net Worth: $275,356,267
Earnings: ($43,764,882)
Emp.: 275
Fiscal Year-end: 12/31/23
Holding Company
N.A.I.C.S.: 551112
Alessandro Monteiro Morgado Horta
(CEO)

Subsidiaries:

Vinci Partners USA LLC (1)
780 3rd Ave 25th Fl, New York, NY 10017
Tel.: (646) 559-8000
Real Estate Manangement Services
N.A.I.C.S.: 531390

VINCI S.A.

1973 bd de La Defense, CS 10268,
92757, Nanterre, Cedex, France
Tel.: (33) 157986100   FR
Web Site: https://www.vinci.com
Year Founded: 1899
DG—(OTCIQ)
Rev.: $75,133,822,577
Assets: $127,949,492,769
Liabilities: $93,371,465,573
Net Worth: $34,578,027,196
Earnings: $5,074,465,789
Emp.: 279,266
Fiscal Year-end: 12/31/23
Construction Engineering Services
N.A.I.C.S.: 551112
Christian Labeyrie *(CFO & Exec VP)*

Subsidiaries:

ADVITAM SA (1)
280 Avenue Napoleon Bonaparte, BP 102,
78143, Rueil-Malmaison, France
Tel.: (33) 1 46 01 85 00
Web Site: http://www.advitam-group.com
Infrastructure Management Software Development Services
N.A.I.C.S.: 541511

Subsidiary (Non-US):

Advitam Belgium (2)
Harensesteenweg 299, 1800, Vilvoorde,
Flemish Brabant, Belgium
Tel.: (32) 2 257 43 23
Web Site: http://www.vinci.com
Emp.: 100
Infrastructure Management Software Development Services
N.A.I.C.S.: 541511

Subsidiary (US):

Advitam Inc. (2)
44880 Falcon Pl Ste 198, Sterling, VA
20166-9544
Tel.: (703) 674-0485
Sales Range: $25-49.9 Million
Emp.: 10
Software Development Services
N.A.I.C.S.: 541511

Subsidiary (Non-US):

Advitam Solutions Inc (2)
8200 Boulevard Decarie - Bureau 200,
Montreal, H4P 2P5, QC, Canada
Tel.: (514) 739-3291
Software Consulting Services
N.A.I.C.S.: 541512

Advitam Switzerland (2)
Z I Le Grand Pre, Case Postale 111, 1510,
Moudon, Switzerland
Tel.: (41) 21 905 0 905
Software Consulting Services
N.A.I.C.S.: 541512

Advitam Taiwan - Paa International
Eng. Corp (2)
20F-3 241 Wen Hsin Road Sec 3, Taichung, Taiwan
Tel.: (886) 4 229 355 56
Web Site: http://www.advitam-group.com
Software Development Services
N.A.I.C.S.: 541511

AEROLAC (1)
7 rue Ernest Flammarion ZAC du Petit Le
Roy Chevilly-Larue, 94659, Rungis, France
Tel.: (33) 1 49 61 71 00
Web Site: http://www.aerolac.fr
Environmental Remediation Services
N.A.I.C.S.: 562910

AMA - Asphaltmischwerke Anklam
GmbH (1)
Dorfstr 1 Woserow, Anklam, Germany
Tel.: (49) 3971210285
Construction & Engineering Services
N.A.I.C.S.: 236220

ARBONIS (1)
RN 79 - Lieu dit Chevannes, 71220,
Verosvres, France
Tel.: (33) 671276917
Web Site: http://www.arbonis.com
Construction Engineering Services
N.A.I.C.S.: 541330

AVT Beijing Co., Ltd. (1)
Room 90110 Building 9 Beijing Friendship
Hotel No 1, Zhongguancun South Street
Haidian District, Beijing, 100080, China
Tel.: (86) 1068419737
Web Site: http://www.a-vt.cn
Automated Material Handling Equipment
Mfr
N.A.I.C.S.: 333998

AVT Europe NV (1)
Postbaan 65, 2910, Essen, Belgium
Tel.: (32) 35463900
Web Site: http://www.a-vt.be
Emp.: 100
Heavy Load Transport Services
N.A.I.C.S.: 484121

AXIANS Audiovisual Belgium NV (1)
Industrieweg 39, 8800, Roeselare, Belgium
Tel.: (32) 51357210
Web Site: https://www.audiovisual.axians.be
Audio Visual Installation Services
N.A.I.C.S.: 238210
Frederik Degryse *(Mgr-Projects-Aftersales)*

Actemium (Shenyang) Industrial Engineering Co., Ltd. (1)
Road Huahai N 36 Shenyang Zone Developpement Zhuang Bei Building Room,
Economique et Technologique Fu Wu Ye
Building 7th Floor, Shenyang, 110141,
China
Tel.: (86) 473196800
Construction & Engineering Services
N.A.I.C.S.: 236220

Actemium ASAS, S.L. (1)
C/ La Granja 3, Almussafes, 46440, Valencia, Spain
Tel.: (34) 936002800
Web Site: http://www.actemiumasas.com
Construction Services
N.A.I.C.S.: 236220

Actemium BEA GmbH (1)
An der Heide, 03130, Spremberg, Germany
Tel.: (49) 35643777856
Web Site: http://www.actemium.de
Technical & Electronic Consulting Services
N.A.I.C.S.: 541690

Actemium BEA Polska Sp. z o.o. (1)
ul Ukrainian 4 D, 54-401, Wroclaw, Poland
Tel.: (48) 717804005
Electrical Engineering Services
N.A.I.C.S.: 541330

Actemium Cegelec Automation Control System (Beijing) Limited (1)
Unit 706-07 Tower B Chengjian Plaza No
18 Beitaipingzhuang Road, Haidian District,
Beijing, 100088, China
Tel.: (86) 1082255858
Industrial Automation Products Mfr
N.A.I.C.S.: 333998

Actemium Cegelec Services
GmbH (1)
Oulustrasse 12, 51375, Leverkusen, Germany
Tel.: (49) 214510555
Industrial Automation Products Mfr
N.A.I.C.S.: 333998

Actemium Controlmatic GmbH (1)
Colmarer Strasse 11, 60528, Frankfurt am
Main, Germany
Tel.: (49) 6950050
Industrial Automation Products Mfr
N.A.I.C.S.: 333998

Actemium Energy Projects
GmbH (1)
Torgauer Strasse 12-15, 10829, Berlin, Germany
Tel.: (49) 16090191856
Industrial Automation Products Mfr
N.A.I.C.S.: 335314

Actemium Fordertechnik Rheinland
GmbH (1)
Rudi-Conin-Strasse 4, 50829, Cologne,
Germany
Tel.: (49) 2215491300
Industrial Automation Products Mfr
N.A.I.C.S.: 333998
Bernd Loose *(Mng Dir)*

VINCI S.A.

VINCI S.A.—(Continued)

Actemium H&F GmbH (1)
Zeppelinstrasse 1, Kavelstorf, 18196, Rostock, Germany
Tel.: (49) 382086990
Industrial Automation Products Mfr
N.A.I.C.S.: 333998
Axel Postler *(Mng Dir)*

Actemium Kappelhoff GmbH (1)
Gabelsberger Str 2, 46238, Bottrop, Germany
Tel.: (49) 2041400100
Industrial Automation Products Mfr
N.A.I.C.S.: 333998

Actemium Langer GmbH (1)
Schollinger Feld 44, 58300, Wetter, Germany
Tel.: (49) 233563040
Industrial Automation Products Mfr
N.A.I.C.S.: 333998

Actemium Leitec AG (1)
Brunnmattstrasse 40, 3000, Bern, Switzerland
Tel.: (41) 313805757
Industrial Automation Products Mfr
N.A.I.C.S.: 333998
Christian Moser *(Mgr-BU)*

Actemium Mechatronic GmbH (1)
Max-Stromeyer-Strasse 168, 78467, Konstanz, Germany
Tel.: (49) 753189240
Industrial Automation Products Mfr
N.A.I.C.S.: 333998
Alexander Breiner *(Mgr-Bus Unit)*

Actemium Schweiz AG (1)
Wien-Strasse 2, 4002, Basel, Switzerland
Tel.: (41) 613166700
Web Site: http://www.actemium.ch
Industrial Equipment Whsr
N.A.I.C.S.: 423830
Andreas Mathiuet *(Mgr-BU Automation & MES)*

Activskeen SAS (1)
280 Avenue Napoleon Bonaparte, 92500, Rueil-Malmaison, France
Tel.: (33) 147764262
Web Site: http://www.activskeen.com
Construction Services
N.A.I.C.S.: 236220

Agregats Ste Clotilde Inc. (1)
1597 Rang 1, Sainte-Clotilde-de-Chateauguay, Chateauguay, J0L 1W0, QC, Canada
Tel.: (450) 641-8000
Construction & Engineering Services
N.A.I.C.S.: 236220

Ammann + Schmid AG (1)
Freiestrasse 39, 8610, Uster, Switzerland
Tel.: (41) 433992599
Web Site: http://www.ammann-schmid.ch
Heating Equipment Whslr
N.A.I.C.S.: 423720

Ancelin SAS (1)
13 Zone d'Activite de l'Anjouinière, Vivonne, 86370, Port-la-Nouvelle, France
Tel.: (33) 549629290
Construction Services
N.A.I.C.S.: 236220

Anyway Solution SAS (1)
40 rue de l'Est, Billancourt, 92100, Boulogne, France
Tel.: (33) 141860078
Web Site: http://www.anywaysolution.fr
Software Development Services
N.A.I.C.S.: 541511

Appex SAS (1)
42 Rue Galilee, 75016, Paris, France
Tel.: (33) 149249361
Web Site: http://www.appex.fr
Application Development Services
N.A.I.C.S.: 541511
Dominique Sanjivy *(Co-Founder & CTO)*

Arcour SA (1)
1 Cours Ferdinand de Lesseps, 92851, Rueil-Malmaison, Cedex, France
Tel.: (33) 1 41 14 71 34
Web Site: http://www.vinci.com
Road Construction & Maintenance Services
N.A.I.C.S.: 237310

Aridos Especiales Spa (1)
Costanera Rivera Norte 1 6800 Areneras sector, Hualpen, Chile
Tel.: (56) 942392154
Web Site: http://www.aridoslz.cl
Aggregate Product Mfr
N.A.I.C.S.: 327999

Arko Technology a.s. (1)
Videnska 108, Brno, Czech Republic
Tel.: (420) 547423211
Web Site: http://www.arko-brno.cz
Waste Treatment Services
N.A.I.C.S.: 221310

Atem Polska Sp. z o.o. (1)
Luzycka 2 Street, 81-537, Gdynia, Poland
Tel.: (48) 586622912
Web Site: http://www.axians.pl
Telecommunication Servicesb
N.A.I.C.S.: 517810
Artur Juszkiewicz *(Project Mgr)*

Atexia SAS (1)
17 rue Gustave Eiffel, La Possession, 97419, Selles-Saint-Denis, France
Tel.: (33) 262223535
Construction & Engineering Services
N.A.I.C.S.: 236220

Atlante Srl (1)
Via Alessandria 1, Canegrate, 20010, Milan, Italy
Tel.: (39) 0331414567
Web Site: http://www.atlanteingegneria.it
Building Materials Mfr
N.A.I.C.S.: 327120

Autochim SA (1)
9 Avenue des froides Bouillies, 91420, Morangis, France
Tel.: (33) 169796161
Web Site: https://www.autochim.com
Turnkey Package Mfr & Distr
N.A.I.C.S.: 321992
Arnaud Crosnier *(Mgr-Bus Unit)*

Autoroutes Trafic SAS (1)
3 rue Edmond Valentin, 75007, Paris, France
Tel.: (33) 149553354
Web Site: http://www.autoroutes-trafic.fr
Traffic Information Services
N.A.I.C.S.: 519290

Auvergne Productique Ingenierie SAS (1)
Zone d'Activite Les Vignettes, Chamalieres, 63400, Le Puy-Notre-Dame, France
Tel.: (33) 473196800
Industrial Equipment Services
N.A.I.C.S.: 811310

Axians AB (1)
Rasundavagen 4, 169 67, Solna, Sweden
Tel.: (46) 86725000
Web Site: https://www.axians.se
Information Technology Services
N.A.I.C.S.: 541511
Patrik Dzoic *(Head-Windows Server-Server Applications)*

Axians Business Solutions BV (1)
Eemsgolaan 15, 9727 DW, Groningen, Netherlands
Tel.: (31) 885975500
Information Technology Services
N.A.I.C.S.: 541511

Axians Ewaste GmbH (1)
Horvelsinger Weg 17, 89081, Ulm, Germany
Tel.: (49) 7311551115
Web Site: https://www.axians-ewaste.com
Software Development Services
N.A.I.C.S.: 541511
Bernhard Hagemann *(Mng Dir)*

Axians Gns AG (1)
Franz-Burckhardt-Strasse 11, 8404, Winterthur, Switzerland
Tel.: (41) 523687979
Telecommunication Servicesb
N.A.I.C.S.: 517810

Axians ICT AB (1)
Teknikringen 6, 583 30, Linkoping, Sweden
Tel.: (46) 706569801
Construction & Engineering Services
N.A.I.C.S.: 236220

Axians ICT Austria GmbH (1)
Hafenstrasse 2a, 4020, Linz, Austria
Tel.: (43) 517150
Web Site: https://www.axians.at
Information Technology Services
N.A.I.C.S.: 541511
Elisabeth Haeusler *(Acct Mgr)*

Axians ICT BV (1)
Hogeweg 41, 5301 LJ, Zaltbommel, Netherlands
Tel.: (31) 418570700
Construction & Engineering Services
N.A.I.C.S.: 236220

Axians IKVS AG (1)
Riedstrasse 1, 6343, Rotkreuz, Switzerland
Tel.: (41) 417250960
Web Site: http://www.axians-ikvs.ch
Information Technology Services
N.A.I.C.S.: 541511

Axians IKVS GmbH (1)
Lindenstrasse 21, 25421, Pinneberg, Germany
Tel.: (49) 41013690840
Web Site: http://www.axians-ikvs.de
Information Technology Services
N.A.I.C.S.: 541511

Axians Industrial Applications & Services GmbH (1)
Hoervelsinger Weg 17, PO Box 2826, 89081, Ulm, Germany
Tel.: (49) 73115510
Web Site: https://www.axians-ias.com
Information Technology Services
N.A.I.C.S.: 541511
Marc Graner *(Co-CEO)*

Axians IoT Nordic AB (1)
Teknikringen 6, 583 30, Linkoping, Sweden
Tel.: (46) 706569886
Construction & Engineering Services
N.A.I.C.S.: 236220

Axians It Security GmbH (1)
Arndtstrasse 25, 22085, Hamburg, Germany
Tel.: (49) 402716610
Information Technology Services
N.A.I.C.S.: 541511
Volker Scholz *(Mgr-SOC)*

Axians It&T AG (1)
Riedstrasse 1, 6343, Rotkreuz, Switzerland
Tel.: (41) 417250900
Information Technology Services
N.A.I.C.S.: 541511
Clinton Chin *(Mgr-Intl Bus)*

Axians Lynx GmbH (1)
Johannskirchplatz 6, 33615, Bielefeld, Germany
Tel.: (49) 52152470
Web Site: http://www.lynx.de
Information Technology Services
N.A.I.C.S.: 541511

Axians Micatel AG (1)
Pulverstrasse 8, 3063, Ittigen, Switzerland
Tel.: (41) 319259125
Information Technology Services
N.A.I.C.S.: 541511

Axians Neo Solutions & Technology GmbH (1)
Gunther-Wagner-Allee 7, 30177, Hannover, Germany
Tel.: (49) 5111235490
Information Technology Services
N.A.I.C.S.: 541511
Michael Scharff *(Mgr-Sls & SAP Alliance)*

Axians Networks & Solutions GmbH (1)
Von-der-Wetter-Str 15, 51149, Cologne, Germany
Tel.: (49) 220310250
Telecommunication Servicesb
N.A.I.C.S.: 517810
Judith Woocker *(Mgr-Pur)*

Axians Networks Limited (1)
Viables 3 Jays Close, Basingstoke, RG22 4BS, United Kingdom
Tel.: (44) 1256312350
Web Site: http://www.axians.co.uk
Information Technology Services

INTERNATIONAL PUBLIC

N.A.I.C.S.: 541511
Mandy Jeffery Atkins *(Mgr-Human Resources)*

Axians Networks Poland Sp. Z O.O (1)
Zupnicza 17 Street, 03-821, Warsaw, Poland
Tel.: (48) 225189500
Web Site: http://www.axians.pl
Telecommunication Services
N.A.I.C.S.: 517810
Remigiusz Kodrzycki *(Mgr-Bus Unit)*

Axians Performance Solutions BV (1)
Hogeweg 41, 5301 LJ, Zaltbommel, Netherlands
Tel.: (31) 889889000
Information Technology Services
N.A.I.C.S.: 541511

Axians Redtoo Inc. (1)
26 Columbia Tpke, Florham Park, NJ 07932
Tel.: (973) 531-2900
Web Site: http://www.axiansredtoo.us
Information Technology Services
N.A.I.C.S.: 541511
Jim Coleman *(Mgr-Bus Unit)*

Axians Redtoo S.R.O (1)
Na Strzi 2097/63, 140 00, Prague, Czech Republic
Tel.: (420) 226231000
Web Site: http://www.axians.cz
Information Technology Services
N.A.I.C.S.: 541511
Ales Hamouz *(Mgr-Svc)*

Axians Saiv S.p.A. (1)
Via Zamenhof 843, 36100, Vicenza, VI, Italy
Tel.: (39) 0444587500
Information Technology Services
N.A.I.C.S.: 541511
Enrico Cera *(Engr-Pe Sls Sys)*

Axians Sirecom Srl (1)
Corso Peschiera 203, 10141, Turin, TO, Italy
Tel.: (39) 0113828938
Information Technology Services
N.A.I.C.S.: 541511
Francesco Vuozzo *(Mgr-Procurement & Logistics)*

Axians Sirecom US Inc. (1)
1 Selleck St, Norwalk, CT 35100
Tel.: (203) 855-2858
Construction Services
N.A.I.C.S.: 236220
Alexia Belen Minca *(Ops Mgr)*

Axians Tecninfo Angola S.A. (1)
Centro de Logistica de Arm C01 Gleba GU03-Zona CCB1, Talatona, Luanda, Luanda Sul, Angola
Tel.: (244) 927620104
Energy Transition Services
N.A.I.C.S.: 221118

Axians Telematics BV (1)
Rivium Boulevard 41, 2909 LK, Capelle aan den IJssel, Netherlands
Tel.: (31) 889889000
Information Technology Services
N.A.I.C.S.: 541511

BARRIQUAND S.A.S (1)
Route de Choisy-au-Bac, BP 10439, 60204, Compiegne, Cedex, France
Tel.: (33) 344384858
Web Site: https://www.barriquand.fr
Construction Engineering Services
N.A.I.C.S.: 541330

BEA Elektrotechnik und Automation Technische Dienste Lausitz GmbH - Dusseldorf Business Unit (1)
Technisches Buro Dusseldorf Am Trippelsberg 45, 40589, Dusseldorf, Germany
Tel.: (49) 211 7108263
Web Site: http://www.bea-tdl.de
Sales Range: $75-99.9 Million
Emp.: 350
Electrical Engineering Services
N.A.I.C.S.: 541330

BEA Elektrotechnik und Automation Technische Dienste Lausitz GmbH - Eisenhuttenstadt facility (1)

AND PRIVATE COMPANIES

Werkstr 20a, Eisenhuttenstadt, 15890, Germany
Tel.: (49) 3364 28018 10
Web Site: http://www.bea-tdl.de
Electrical Engineering Services
N.A.I.C.S.: 541330

BEA Elektrotechnik und Automation Technische Dienste Lausitz GmbH - Nochten/Reichwalde opencast mining Facility (1)
Auf Dem Vattenfallgelande Schacht 1, Muhlrose, 02959, Trebendorf, Germany
Tel.: (49) 35773 8 4427
Web Site: http://www.bea-tdl.de
Sales Range: $25-49.9 Million
Emp.: 30
Electrical Engineering Services
N.A.I.C.S.: 541330

BEA Elektrotechnik und Automation Technische Dienste Lausitz GmbH - Spremberg Mining Engineering Business Unit (1)
OT Schwarze Pumpe An der Heide, 03130, Spremberg, Germany
Tel.: (49) 3564 377 7841
Web Site: http://www.bea-tdl.de
Sales Range: $75-99.9 Million
Emp.: 300
Mining Engineering Services
N.A.I.C.S.: 541330

BEA Elektrotechnik und Automation Technische Dienste Lausitz GmbH - Spremberg Power Engineering Business Unit (1)
OT Schwarze Pumpe An der Heide, 03130, Spremberg, Germany
Tel.: (49) 3564 377 7838
Eletric Power Generation Services
N.A.I.C.S.: 221118
Holger Strecker *(Mgr)*

BEA Elektrotechnik und Automation Technische Dienste Lausitz GmbH - Thyssen Krupp Nirosta Krefeld facility (1)
Oberschlesienstrasse-Tor 2, 47807, Krefeld, Germany
Tel.: (49) 2151 833928
Eletric Power Generation Services
N.A.I.C.S.: 221118

BEA Elektrotechnik und Automation Technische Dienste Lausitz GmbH - West Facilities (1)
Am Posenberg, 41517, Grevenbroich, Germany
Tel.: (49) 2181 495551
Web Site: http://www.sanofi.com.ar
Sales Range: $25-49.9 Million
Emp.: 20
Electrical Engineering Services
N.A.I.C.S.: 541330

BEA Elektrotechnik und Automation Technische Dienste Lausitz GmbH - Zeitz Facility (1)
Hauptstrasse 30 Bau 37, Elsteraue Ot Alttroglitz, 06729, Elsteraue, Germany
Tel.: (49) 3441 8290 800
Web Site: http://www.bea-tdl.de
Electrical Engineering Services
N.A.I.C.S.: 541330

BTM Baustoff-Technik + Mischwerke GmbH (1)
Gasselstr 29, Bielefeld, Germany
Tel.: (49) 520991070
Construction & Engineering Services
N.A.I.C.S.: 236220

Bachy Soletanche Australia Pty. Ltd. (1)
Level 5 13-15 Lyonpark Road, Macquarie Park, 2113, NSW, Australia
Tel.: (61) 298142990
Web Site: http://www.soletanche-bachy.com.au
Engineering Services
N.A.I.C.S.: 541330

Bateg SA (1)
1 rue du Petit-Clamart L'Emeraude, 78347, Velizy-Villacoublay, France
Tel.: (33) 1 41 28 23 00
Web Site: http://www.bateg.fr

Construction Engineering Services
N.A.I.C.S.: 237990

Batifoix SAS (1)
10 route des Maitres de Forges, Saint-Mathieu, 87440, Rochechouart, France
Tel.: (33) 555003102
Construction Services
N.A.I.C.S.: 236220

Bessac Andina SA (1)
Calle 125 19-24 Floor 4, Distrito Capital, Bogota, Colombia
Tel.: (57) 16922355
Web Site: http://www.bessac-andina.com
Construction Maintenance & Rehabilitation Services
N.A.I.C.S.: 237310

Biarritz Ocean SAS (1)
Plateau Atalaye, 64200, Biarritz, France
Tel.: (33) 559227540
Web Site: http://www.biarritzocean.com
Amusement & Recreation Industry Services
N.A.I.C.S.: 713990

Bitumix S.A. (1)
Bishop Arturo Espinoza Campos 3172, Macul, Santiago, Chile
Tel.: (56) 226803000
Web Site: http://www.bitumix.cl
Road & Infrastructure Construction Services
N.A.I.C.S.: 237310

Boiron SAS (1)
8 Chemin Feignes Galand lieu dit Fallieres, Saint-Nabord, 88200, Saint-Die-des-Vosges, France
Tel.: (33) 329620177
Web Site: http://www.sas-boiron.com
Construction Services
N.A.I.C.S.: 236220

Booth & Associates LLC (1)
5811 Glenwood Ave Ste 109, Raleigh, NC 27612
Tel.: (919) 851-8770
Web Site: http://www.booth-assoc.com
Engineering Consulting Services
N.A.I.C.S.: 541330
Michael L. Clements *(Exec VP)*

Botte Fondations (1)
Petit Leroy ZAC 5 rue Ernest Flammarion - Chevilly Larue, 94659, Chevilly-Larue, Cedex, France
Tel.: (33) 49614800
Web Site: http://www.botte-fondations.fr
Construction Engineering Services
N.A.I.C.S.: 541330

Bourgeois SAS (1)
10-12 Rue Stalingrad, 69120, Vaulx-en-Velin, France
Tel.: (33) 4 78 79 06 12
Web Site: http://www.bourgeois-entreprise.fr
Historical Monument Construction Services
N.A.I.C.S.: 236220

Bud-Inz Sp.z. o o. (1)
Lodzka 4/8, 95-100, Zgierz, Poland
Tel.: (48) 427162033
Construction Services
N.A.I.C.S.: 236220

C2C SAS (1)
ZAC Les Portes de l Oise rue Henri Becquerel-Bet B6, 60230, Chambly, France
Tel.: (33) 139372222
Web Site: http://www.c2c-reseaux.fr
Construction Services
N.A.I.C.S.: 236220

CAILLAUD LAMELLE (1)
13 rue Bompas Zone Industrielle du Bompas, 49120, Chemille, France
Tel.: (33) 2 41 30 73 90
Web Site: http://www.arbonis.com
Custom Designed Interior Services
N.A.I.C.S.: 541410

CAMPENON BERNARD CONSTRUCTION (1)
1 rue du Petit-Clamart L'Emeraude, 78457, Velizy-Villacoublay, France
Tel.: (33) 41282300
Web Site: http://www.cbconstruction.fr
Construction Engineering Services
N.A.I.C.S.: 541330

CAP Securite SAS (1)

27 rue Honore Petetin, 69700, Givors, France
Tel.: (33) 437201605
Web Site: http://www.capsecurite.com
Construction Services
N.A.I.C.S.: 236220

CEE Allier SAS (1)
18 rue Blaise Sallard, Yzeure, 03400, Saint Vallier, France
Tel.: (33) 470444108
Web Site: http://www.cee-allier.fr
Construction Services
N.A.I.C.S.: 236220

CEF Nord SAS (1)
Rue de la Grande Pree Zl n 1, 60880, Le Meux, France
Tel.: (33) 344917917
Web Site: http://www.cefnord.com
Construction Services
N.A.I.C.S.: 236220

CG3N SA (1)
ZA Le Cafe Cochon, Virandeville Normandy, 50690, Caen, Cedex, France
Tel.: (33) 233015144
Construction Services
N.A.I.C.S.: 236220

COCA Sud-Est (1)
Quartier Mauboule Z I de la Motte, BP 509, 26005, Valence, France
Tel.: (33) 4 75 86 14 30
Web Site: http://www.cocasudest.fr
Pipeline Construction Engineering Services
N.A.I.C.S.: 237120

Cannes Maria Amenagement SAS (1)
Cristal Palace 369 371, Promenade des Anglais, 06200, Nice, France
Tel.: (33) 493380450
Web Site: http://www.cannesmaria.com
Commercial Services
N.A.I.C.S.: 561499

Caraibes Qualite Service SAS (1)
1 200 KM route du Vert Pre Chemin Bois Quarre, Lamentin, France
Tel.: (33) 596512081
Construction Services
N.A.I.C.S.: 236220

Cardem SAS (1)
7 rue de L'uranium, Bischheim, France
Tel.: (33) 388817281
Web Site: http://www.cardem.fr
Explosive Demolition & Deconstruction Services
N.A.I.C.S.: 238910

Cargonet Software SAS (1)
Immeuble Le Mathis 200 Avenue de Colmar, 67100, Strasbourg, France
Tel.: (33) 388797950
Express & Parcel Software Development Services
N.A.I.C.S.: 541511

Carmacks Maintenance Services Ltd. (1)
13930-52 Street NE, Calgary, T3N 1B7, AB, Canada
Tel.: (403) 543-0305
Road Construction Services
N.A.I.C.S.: 237310

Carpi Brasil Ltda. (1)
Viaduto Nove de Julho 160 cj 15, Sao Paulo, 01050-060, Brazil
Tel.: (55) 1132572346
Construction Bridge Product Distr
N.A.I.C.S.: 423390

Carpi Tech BV (1)
PO Box 103, Berkel en Rodenrijs, Netherlands
Tel.: (31) 105110559
Concrete Material Distr
N.A.I.C.S.: 423320

Carpi Tech Bulgaria o.o.d. (1)
126 Tsar Boris III Blvd- Fl 5, Sofia, Bulgaria
Tel.: (359) 29555999
Bridge Product Distr
N.A.I.C.S.: 423840

Carpi Tech CZ A.S (1)
Pristavni 39, Prague, Czech Republic
Tel.: (420) 283872241

Concrete Material Distr
N.A.I.C.S.: 423320

Carpi Tech Italia Srl (1)
SS 32 Ticinese, Pombia, Novara, NO, Italy
Tel.: (39) 0321958044
Concrete Material Mfr
N.A.I.C.S.: 327390

Carpi Tech SA (1)
Via Passeggiata 1, Balerna, Switzerland
Tel.: (41) 916954000
Web Site: http://www.carpitech.com
Waterproofing Contracting Services
N.A.I.C.S.: 238390

Carpi USA Inc. (1)
4370 Starkey Rd Ste 4D, Roanoke, VA 24018
Tel.: (540) 776-7727
Construction Engineering Services
N.A.I.C.S.: 541330

Carrieres Rauscher SAS (1)
3 rue de la Gare, BP 2, Adamswiller, 67320, Saverne, France
Tel.: (33) 627503135
Web Site: http://www.carrieres-rauscher.eu
Stand Stone Extraction Services
N.A.I.C.S.: 212319

Carrieres de Chateaupanne SAS (1)
Chateaupanne, Montjean-sur-Loire, 49570, Angers, France
Tel.: (33) 241721460
Construction Services
N.A.I.C.S.: 236220

Cegelec Bourgogne SAS (1)
6 rue Champeau, CS 10034, 21801, Quetigny, Cedex, France
Tel.: (33) 380368500
Web Site: http://www.cegelec-bourgogne.com
Electrical & Electronic Product Mfr
N.A.I.C.S.: 336320

Cegelec Building Services SA (1)
Avenue du Port 86C, Box 201, 1000, Brussels, Belgium
Tel.: (32) 24222611
Construction & Engineering Services
N.A.I.C.S.: 236220

Cegelec Cameroun SA (1)
Autoroute de l Aviation lieudit Bonaloka, BP 4507, Douala, Cameroon
Tel.: (237) 233421964
Construction Services
N.A.I.C.S.: 236220
Pius Ateba *(Engr-Instrument & Control)*

Cegelec Cem SAS (1)
Inovallee Montbonnot 110 rue Blaise Pascal, CS 10070, 38334, Saint Ismier, Cedex, France
Tel.: (33) 456457000
Web Site: http://www.cegelec-cem.com
Emp.: 240
Turnkey Package Mfr
N.A.I.C.S.: 321992
Mayeul Mollaret *(Mgr-Project Control)*

Cegelec Control System & Services SA (1)
Avenue Jean Mermoz 22, 6041, Gosselies, Belgium
Tel.: (32) 71257680
Web Site: http://www.cegelec-css.com
Switchgear & Switchboard Mfr
N.A.I.C.S.: 335313
Vincenzo Mistretta *(Bus Mgr)*

Cegelec Dauphine SAS (1)
4 rue de l Octant Parc Sud Galaxie, CS 60237, 38433, Echirolles, Cedex, France
Tel.: (33) 476604343
Construction Services
N.A.I.C.S.: 236220

Cegelec Defense SAS (1)
1 Rond-point du General Eisenhower, CS 40605, 31106, Toulouse, Cedex, France
Tel.: (33) 562870000
Web Site: https://www.cegelec-defense.com
Construction Services
N.A.I.C.S.: 236220

Cegelec Defense et Naval Sud-Est SAS (1)

VINCI S.A.

VINCI S.A.—(Continued)
ZAE de Malbousquet, 83200, Toulon, France
Tel.: (33) 494227000
Construction Services
N.A.I.C.S.: 236220

Cegelec Elmo SAS (1)
7 rue Edmond Michelet ZA La Fontaine du Vaisseau, 93360, Neuilly-Plaisance, France
Tel.: (33) 172881500
Construction Services
N.A.I.C.S.: 236220

Cegelec Enterprise S.A. (1)
10 Avenue du Stade de France, 93200, Saint Denis, Cedex, France
Tel.: (33) 155514000
Web Site: http://www.cegelec.com
Sales Range: $1-4.9 Billion
Emp.: 25,000
Electrical Contracting Services
N.A.I.C.S.: 238210

Subsidiary (Non-US):

Cegelec B.V. (2)
Laan van Europa 450, Dordrecht, NL-3317 DB, Netherlands
Tel.: (31) 787508200
Web Site: http://www.cegelec.com
Emp.: 450
Business Technology Services
N.A.I.C.S.: 541990

Subsidiary (Non-US):

Cegelec S.A.-Luxembourg (3)
1 Rue Goethe, L 8287, Luxembourg, Luxembourg
Tel.: (352) 43 888 1
Web Site: http://www.cegelec.nl
Electrical Contractor Services
N.A.I.C.S.: 238210

Subsidiary (Non-US):

Cegelec Brasil Ltda (2)
Av Engenheiro Eusebio Stevaux No 1444, Jurubatuba, 04696-000, Sao Paulo, SP, Brazil
Tel.: (55) 11 0177 70045
Web Site: http://www.cegelec.com.br
Sales Range: $50-74.9 Million
Emp.: 2,500
Engineering, Implementation & Operation & Facilities Management
N.A.I.C.S.: 541330

Subsidiary (Domestic):

Cegelec Centre Est S.A. (2)
Z I 1 Chemin du Pilon St-Maurice-de-Beynost, BP 350, 01703, Miribel, France
Tel.: (33) 4 78 55 70 00
Sales Range: $100-124.9 Million
Emp.: 300
Construction & Maintenance Services
N.A.I.C.S.: 237990

Subsidiary (Non-US):

Cegelec Deutschland GmbH (2)
Colmarer Strasse 11, 60528, Frankfurt am Main, Germany
Tel.: (49) 6950050
Web Site: http://www.cegelec.de
Infrastructure, HVAC, Plumbing, Data & Electrical Services
N.A.I.C.S.: 238210

Subsidiary (Non-US):

Cegelec Austria GmbH (3)
Lichtblaustrasse 17, 1220, Vienna, Austria
Tel.: (43) 1277440
Web Site: http://www.cegelec.at
Sales Range: $25-49.9 Million
Emp.: 100
Infrastructure, HVAC, Plumbing, Data & Electrical Services
N.A.I.C.S.: 238210

Division (Domestic):

Cegelec Deutschland GmbH-East (3)
Colditzstrasse 34-36, D-12099, Berlin, Germany
Tel.: (49) 3070025350

Web Site: http://www.cegelec.com
Sales Range: $100-124.9 Million
Emp.: 500
Electrical Work
N.A.I.C.S.: 238210

Division (Domestic):

Cegelec Contracting GmbH (4)
Industriestrasse 70, 04435, Leipzig, Schkeuditz, Germany
Tel.: (49) 34 204 7067 0
Web Site: http://www.cegelec.de
Electrical Contractor
N.A.I.C.S.: 238210

Division (Domestic):

Cegelec Deutschland GmbH-North (3)
Industrieweg 21, 30179, Hannover, Germany
Tel.: (49) 511 47310 100
Web Site: http://www.cegelec.com
Sales Range: $25-49.9 Million
Emp.: 30
Infrastructure, HVAC, Plumbing, Data & Electrical Services
N.A.I.C.S.: 238210

Subsidiary (Domestic):

Cegelec Anlagen-und Automatisierungstechnik GmbH & Co. KG (4)
Industrieweg 21, 30179, Hannover, Germany
Tel.: (49) 51147310100
Web Site: http://www.cegelec.com
Sales Range: $25-49.9 Million
Emp.: 100
Infrastructure, HVAC, Plumbing, Data & Electrical Services
N.A.I.C.S.: 238210

Division (Domestic):

Cegelec Enterprises S.A.-France-Mid East (3)
ZI 1 Chemin du Pilon, BP 350, St-Maurice-de-Beynost, F-01703, Lyon, Cedex, France
Tel.: (33) 478557100
Sales Range: $400-449.9 Million
Emp.: 2,200
Transport Infrastructure Services
N.A.I.C.S.: 488490

Cegelec Enterprises S.A.-France-North & East (2)
1 bis Rue du Molinel, BP 169, 59444, Wasquehal, France
Tel.: (33) 320813900
Web Site: http://www.cegelec.com
Sales Range: $100-124.9 Million
Emp.: 350
Electronic Services
N.A.I.C.S.: 238210

Cegelec Enterprises S.A.-France-South East (2)
Route de Salon, BP 9, F-13755, Les Pennes-Mirabeau, Cedex, France
Tel.: (33) 442023179
Web Site: http://www.cegelec.com
Sales Range: $350-399.9 Million
Emp.: 1,300
Electrical Work
N.A.I.C.S.: 238210

Division (Domestic):

Cegelec Enterprise S.A.-Non Destructive Testing Division (3)
ZI du Bois des Bordes, F-91229, Bretigny-sur-Orge, France
Tel.: (33) 169886762
Web Site: http://www.ndt.cegelec.com
Sales Range: $10-24.9 Million
Emp.: 50
Testing Laboratory
N.A.I.C.S.: 541380

Division (Non-US):

Cegelec Non Destructive Systems (4)
Guttenstetter Strasse 14A, 90449, Nuremberg, Germany
Tel.: (49) 91199430
Web Site: http://www.ndt.cegelec.com

Sales Range: $10-24.9 Million
Emp.: 37
Testing Laboratory
N.A.I.C.S.: 541380

Division (Domestic):

Cegelec Enterprises S.A.-France-South West (2)
11 impasse des Arenes, F-31082, Toulouse, Cedex, France
Tel.: (33) 561316000
Web Site: http://www.cegelec.com
Sales Range: $400-449.9 Million
Emp.: 2,000
Industrial, Mechanical & Building Maintenance
N.A.I.C.S.: 238210

Cegelec Enterprises S.A.-France-West (2)
La Belle Etoile 5 rue Vega, BP 80622, 44476, Carquefou, Cedex, France
Tel.: (33) 228092222
Sales Range: $50-74.9 Million
Emp.: 150
Electrical, Telecommunication & Infrastructure Services
N.A.I.C.S.: 517810

Cegelec Enterprises S.A.-Paris (2)
51 rue des Trois-Fontanot, F-92002, Nanterre, Cedex, France
Tel.: (33) 00146952000
Web Site: http://www.cegelec.com
Sales Range: $300-349.9 Million
Emp.: 1,600
Electrical Work
N.A.I.C.S.: 238210

Subsidiary (Non-US):

Cegelec Instalacoes e Sistemas de Automacao, Lda. (2)
National Road 115 Km 78 67, Sao Juliao do Tojal, Loures, 2664-502, Portugal
Tel.: (351) 218450000
Web Site: https://www.actemium.pt
Sales Range: $10-24.9 Million
Emp.: 45
Techniological Systems Services
N.A.I.C.S.: 541990
Jose Sacramento *(Gen Mgr)*

Subsidiary (Domestic):

Cegelec Nord-Est SA (2)
1bis Rue du Molinel, BP 169, 59444, Wasquehal, France
Tel.: (33) 3 20 81 39 00
Construction & Maintenance Services
N.A.I.C.S.: 237990

Subsidiary (Non-US):

Cegelec Nouvelle Caledonie S.A. (2)
Numbo 250 Route de la Baie des Dames, BP J2, Noumea, 98849, New Caledonia
Tel.: (687) 27 56 46
Construction Engineering Services
N.A.I.C.S.: 237990

Subsidiary (Domestic):

Cegelec Paris S.A. (2)
51 Rue des Trois-Fontanot, BP 202, 92002, Nanterre, France
Tel.: (33) 1 46 95 20 00
Web Site: http://www.cegelec.com
Rev.: $290,705,800
Emp.: 1,600
Air Conditioning Equipment Installation Services
N.A.I.C.S.: 238220

Subsidiary (Non-US):

Cegelec Polynesie (2)
ZI de Fare Ute, BP 5020, 98716, Pirae, Tahiti, French Polynesia
Tel.: (689) 414141
Web Site: http://cegelecpolynesie.intahiti.com
Sales Range: $50-74.9 Million
Emp.: 200
Electrical Contractor Services
N.A.I.C.S.: 238210
Frederic Dock *(Mng Dir)*

Cegelec Pte Ltd (2)

INTERNATIONAL PUBLIC

103 Defu Lane 10, 02-02 BTH Building, Singapore, 539223, Singapore
Tel.: (65) 64169555
Web Site: http://www.cegelec.com
Sales Range: $75-99.9 Million
Emp.: 7
Infrastructure & Water Fields Services
N.A.I.C.S.: 221310

Cegelec S.A.-Cameroon (2)
100 rue Vasnitex, BP 4507, Douala, Cameroon
Tel.: (237) 33421964
Web Site: http://www.cegelec.com
Sales Range: $125-149.9 Million
Emp.: 360
Telecommunications, Maintenance & Service Industry
N.A.I.C.S.: 517810

Cegelec SA/NV (2)
Boulevard de la Woluwe 60, B-1200, Brussels, Belgium
Tel.: (32) 27759020
Web Site: http://www.ceglec.be
Sales Range: $400-449.9 Million
Emp.: 1,800
Infrastructure, HVAC, Plumbing, Data & Electrical Services
N.A.I.C.S.: 238210

Subsidiary (Domestic):

Cegelec B.U. Ensysta (2)
Interleuvenlaan 27A, 3001, Heverlee, Belgium
Tel.: (32) 16 24 02 11
Web Site: http://www.ensysta.be
Rev.: $36,998,920
Emp.: 250
Industrial Equipment Installation Services
N.A.I.C.S.: 238290

Subsidiary (Non-US):

Cegelec S.A.-Casablanca (3)
129 boulevard du Fouarat, 20351, Casablanca, Morocco
Tel.: (212) 522639301
Web Site: http://www.maroc.cegelec.com
Sales Range: $400-449.9 Million
Emp.: 1,700
Electrical Contractor Services
N.A.I.C.S.: 238210
Michel Bouskila *(Dir-Sls & Dev)*

Cegelec Sp. z.o.o. (3)
ul Solec 38, 00 394, Warsaw, Poland
Tel.: (48) 224582471
Web Site: http://www.cegelec.pl
Sales Range: $25-49.9 Million
Emp.: 100
Electrical Contractor Services
N.A.I.C.S.: 238210

Cegelec SpA (3)
Campagne Sammar Lot n485, Birkhadem, 16000, Algiers, Algeria
Tel.: (213) 21 54 02 51
Web Site: http://www.cegelec.com
Oil & Gas Infrastructure Services
N.A.I.C.S.: 213112

ZAO Cegelec (3)
Pokrovski Bulv 4/17 Bldg 3, 101000m, Moscow, Russia
Tel.: (7) 4959175239
Web Site: http://www.cegelec.com
Electrical Contractor Services
N.A.I.C.S.: 238210

Subsidiary (Non-US):

Cegelec SDN BHD (2)
Damansara 1 No 9 Jalan 16/11, Unit 901 Block B Pusat Perdagangan Phileo, Damansara, 46350, Petaling Jaya, Selangor Darul Ehsan, Malaysia
Tel.: (60) 7493 1822
Electrical Contractor Services
N.A.I.C.S.: 238210

Subsidiary (Domestic):

Cegelec Sud-Est SA (2)
Route de Salon, BP 9, 13755, Les Pennes-Mirabeau, France
Tel.: (33) 4 42 02 31 79
Electrical Installation Services
N.A.I.C.S.: 238210

AND PRIVATE COMPANIES
VINCI S.A.

Cegelec Telecoms Sud-Ouest (2)
11 Impasse des Arenes, 31 100, Toulouse, France
Tel.: (33) 5 61 31 60 00
Web Site: http://www.cegelec.com
Rev.: $396,417,000
Emp.: 2,000
Electrical Engineering & Technology Services
N.A.I.C.S.: 541330

Subsidiary (Non-US):

Cegelec a.s. (2)
Chodovska 228/ 3, 141 00, Prague, Czech Republic
Tel.: (420) 271003422
Web Site: http://www.cegelec.cz
Sales Range: $75-99.9 Million
Emp.: 110
Electrical Equipment Installation, Repair, Inspection, Testing & Mfr
N.A.I.C.S.: 238210

Cegelec, S.A.-Madrid (2)
Avda de Castilla 2 Parque Empresarial, San Fernando Edificio Japon I, Escalera B 2 Piso, 28830, Madrid, Spain
Tel.: (34) 916786200
Web Site: http://www.cegelec.es
Sales Range: $150-199.9 Million
Emp.: 700
Electrical Contractor Services
N.A.I.C.S.: 238210

Subsidiary (Domestic):

Cirma Enterprise S.A. (2)
12 avenue du Chemin de la Vie, 33440, Ambares, France
Tel.: (33) 557771477
Web Site: http://www.aerospace-technology.net
Electrical Pre-wired Subset Mfr
N.A.I.C.S.: 335999

Joint Venture (Non-US):

Comsip Al A'ali W.L.L. (2)
PO Box 26949, Adliya, Bahrain
Tel.: (973) 17773006
Web Site: http://www.comsip.com.bh
Sales Range: $125-149.9 Million
Emp.: 400
Electrical Work & Instrumentation Mfr
N.A.I.C.S.: 238210

Subsidiary (Non-US):

Comsip Al A'ali W.L.L. (3)
PO Box 23342, Doha, Qatar
Tel.: (974) 444 0232
Electrical Work
N.A.I.C.S.: 238210

Subsidiary (Non-US):

PT Indokomas Buana Perkasa (2)
Kawasan Industri Pulogadung, Jalan Rawagelam IV/9, Jakarta, 13 930, Indonesia
Tel.: (62) 21 461 02 01
Web Site: http://www.cegelec.co.id
Sales Range: $50-74.9 Million
Emp.: 200
Electrical Contract Work
N.A.I.C.S.: 238210

Prime Atlantic Cegelec Nigeria Ltd (2)
Plot 71 Molade Okoya Thomas Street, Victoria Island, Lagos, Nigeria
Tel.: (234) 1 870 46 66
Sales Range: $50-74.9 Million
Emp.: 150
Electrical Contractor Services
N.A.I.C.S.: 238210

Cegelec Fire Solutions BV (1)
Calandstraat 1, 3316 EA, Dordrecht, Netherlands
Tel.: (31) 888319696
Web Site: http://www.cegelec.nl
Electrical Installation Services
N.A.I.C.S.: 238210
Erik Bergman *(Mgr-Bus Unit)*

Cegelec Franche-Comte SAS (1)
685 rue Armand Japy ZA Technoland, 25460, Etupes, France
Tel.: (33) 381993640
Construction Services

Cegelec GSS (1)
10 avenue du Stade de France, 93200, Saint Denis, France
Tel.: (33) 1 58 69 40 00
Web Site: http://www.vinci-energies.com
Emp.: 600
Construction & Maintenance Services
N.A.I.C.S.: 237990

Subsidiary (Non-US):

Cegelec Abu Dhabi (2)
Al Ain Ahlia Insurance Building 2nd Floor, PO Box 47055, Hamdan Street, Abu Dhabi, United Arab Emirates
Tel.: (971) 2 403 0600
Construction & Maintenance Services
N.A.I.C.S.: 237990

Subsidiary (Domestic):

Cegelec SAS (2)
10 Avenue Du Stade de France, 93200, Saint Denis, France
Tel.: (33) 1 58 69 40 00
Web Site: http://www.cegelec.com
Emp.: 70
Electrical Engineering Services
N.A.I.C.S.: 541330

JETEC INGENIERIE SA (2)
Immeuble Les Eureka 13 Rue Ernest Renan, Nanterre, 92500, France
Tel.: (33) 141293939
Sales Range: $25-49.9 Million
Emp.: 100
Civil Engineering Construction Services
N.A.I.C.S.: 237990
Frederik Tirand *(Gen Mgr)*

Cegelec Guyane SAS (1)
Carrefour de Larrivot Route de Matoury, BP 90420, 97329, Cayenne, Cedex, French Guiana
Tel.: (594) 350950
Construction & Engineering Services
N.A.I.C.S.: 236220

Cegelec Haute-Normandie SAS (1)
3 Xhemin des plans D'eau, 76430, Oudalle, France
Tel.: (33) 235134231
Construction Services
N.A.I.C.S.: 236220

Cegelec Industrie Sud-Est SAS (1)
Route de Salon-Chemin de la Pourranque, BP 9, 13755, Les Pennes-Mirabeau, France
Tel.: (33) 442023000
Construction Services
N.A.I.C.S.: 236220

Cegelec Industry NV/SA (1)
Baarbeek 8, 2070, Zwijndrecht, Belgium
Tel.: (32) 38005208
Construction & Engineering Services
N.A.I.C.S.: 236220

Cegelec Infra Bretagne SAS (1)
117 avenue Gros Malhon, CS 54230, 35042, Rennes, France
Tel.: (33) 299844927
Construction Services
N.A.I.C.S.: 236220

Cegelec Loire Auvergne SAS (1)
6 rue de la Transcevenole ZI de Corsac, 43700, Brives-Charensac, France
Tel.: (33) 477911440
Electrical & Electronic Product Mfr
N.A.I.C.S.: 336320

Cegelec Lorraine Alsace SAS (1)
5 rue du Mouzon, BP 21020, 54521, Laxou, Cedex, France
Tel.: (33) 383975757
Construction Services
N.A.I.C.S.: 236220

Cegelec Missenard SAS (1)
67 Avenue de Fontainebleau, 94270, Le Kremlin-Bicetre, France
Tel.: (33) 145153030
Construction & Engineering Services
N.A.I.C.S.: 236220

Cegelec Mobility SAS (1)
22 Avenue Lionel Terray, 69330, Jonage, France
Tel.: (33) 478558740

Web Site: https://www.mobility-way.com
Mobility Equipment Mfr
N.A.I.C.S.: 335313
Delphine Franc *(Comm Mgr)*

Cegelec Network & Security Systems Company
Al Mizan Tower 2nd Floor Olaya St, PO Box 63 388, 11512, Riyadh, Saudi Arabia
Tel.: (966) 138328355
Web Site: http://www.cegelec-nss.com
Telecommunication Servicesb
N.A.I.C.S.: 517810

Cegelec Nord Industrie SAS (1)
24 route de Fort Mardyck, Saint-Pol-sur-Mer, 59430, Dunkerque, Cedex, France
Tel.: (33) 328267373
Construction Services
N.A.I.C.S.: 236220

Cegelec Nord Tertiaire SAS (1)
31 rue Pasteur, CS 60169, 59444, Wasquehal, Cedex, France
Tel.: (33) 320813900
Construction Services
N.A.I.C.S.: 236220
Eric Ammeux *(Bus Mgr)*

Cegelec Nucleaire Sud-Est SAS (1)
Route de Salon La Gavotte, 13170, Les Pennes-Mirabeau, France
Tel.: (33) 442023000
Construction Services
N.A.I.C.S.: 236220

Cegelec Pays de Savoie SASU (1)
147 allee des Blacheres, 73024, Chambery, Cedex, France
Tel.: (33) 479691607
Construction Services
N.A.I.C.S.: 236220

Cegelec Picardie Industrie SAS (1)
39 rue de Poulainville, 80080, Amiens, France
Tel.: (33) 322224710
Construction Services
N.A.I.C.S.: 236220

Cegelec Portes de Bretagne SA (1)
117 Avenue Gros Malhon, 35042, Rennes, Cedex, France
Tel.: (33) 299844949
Construction Services
N.A.I.C.S.: 236220

Cegelec RDC Sarl (1)
Avenue Poids Lourds 32 Bis, Gombe, Kinshasa, Congo, Democratic Republic of
Tel.: (243) 999333943
Construction Services
N.A.I.C.S.: 236220
Manuel Parres-Albert *(Project Mgr)*

Cegelec Reseaux Auvergne Drome Ardeche SAS (1)
5 rue Robert Estienne, Zone industrielle Gerzat Sud, 63360, Gerzat, France
Tel.: (33) 473162401
Construction Services
N.A.I.C.S.: 236220

Cegelec Sdem SARL (1)
Cours Bourbon, BP 87, Martin Eglise, 76203, Dieppe, France
Tel.: (33) 235068920
Construction Services
N.A.I.C.S.: 236220

Cegelec Space SA (1)
Place Newton Immeuble Vercors, 97310, Kourou, French Guiana
Tel.: (594) 320524
Construction Services
N.A.I.C.S.: 236220

Cegelec Tertiaire IDF SA (1)
85 avenue Victor Hugo, CS 20040, 92563, Rueil-Malmaison, Cedex, France
Tel.: (33) 146952000
Web Site: http://www.cegelec-tertiaireidf.com
Construction Services
N.A.I.C.S.: 236220

Cegelec Toulouse SA (1)
4 rue du Professeur Pierre Vellas Europarc-Batiment Jupiter B10, CS 77604, 31076, Toulouse, Cedex, France
Tel.: (33) 561316000

Construction Services
N.A.I.C.S.: 236220

Cegelec Troyes SA (1)
4 Rue Amand Poron ZI des Ecrevolles, 10000, Troyes, France
Tel.: (33) 325704888
Web Site: http://www.cegelec-troyes.com
Construction Services
N.A.I.C.S.: 236220

Cegelec, S.A. (1)
Avda de Castilla 2 Parque Empresarial S Fernando-Edif Italia 1 Piso, 28830, San Fernando de Henares, Spain
Tel.: (34) 916786200
Construction & Engineering Services
N.A.I.C.S.: 236220

Ceriel S.A. (1)
Vatine Technological Activity Park 7 rue Andrei Sakharov, 76130, Mont-Saint-Aignau, France
Tel.: (33) 235608909
Web Site: http://www.ceriel.fr
Construction Services
N.A.I.C.S.: 236220

Chain Electric Company Inc. (1)
1308 W Pine St, Hattiesburg, MS 39401
Tel.: (601) 545-3800
Web Site: http://www.chainelectric.com
Industrial Engineering Services
N.A.I.C.S.: 541330
Bobby Chain *(Founder)*

Charantelec SAS (1)
Zone Emploi-Les voutes, BP 10020, 16730, Fleac, France
Tel.: (33) 545253000
Construction Services
N.A.I.C.S.: 236220

Chatel SA (1)
466 route des Contamines, BP 66, Ayze, 74130, Haute-Marne, France
Tel.: (33) 450972270
Construction Services
N.A.I.C.S.: 236220

Chatenet SAS (1)
9 Avenue des Mondaults Parc d'Activites des Mondaults, 33270, Floirac, France
Tel.: (33) 557773180
Web Site: http://www.chatenet-sas.fr
Construction Services
N.A.I.C.S.: 236220

Chb Elektro Und Fernmeldebau GmbH (1)
Kreuzacker 2a, 94469, Deggendorf, Germany
Tel.: (49) 9931895950
Web Site: http://www.chb.eu
Eletric Power Generation Services
N.A.I.C.S.: 221118

Citeos Saumur SAS (1)
14 Avenue du Pin, 49071, Beaucouze, Cedex, France
Tel.: (33) 241723636
Web Site: http://www.citeos-saumur.com
Construction Services
N.A.I.C.S.: 236220

City & You SAS (1)
59 rue Yves Kemen, 92130, Boulogne-Billancourt, France
Tel.: (33) 184604442
Web Site: http://www.cityandyou.com
Real Estate Services
N.A.I.C.S.: 531390

City Electric SARL (1)
71 rue de Merl, 2146, Luxembourg, Luxembourg
Tel.: (352) 252472
Web Site: http://www.city-electric.lu
Electrical Installation Services
N.A.I.C.S.: 238210

Clede SAS (1)
12 rue Johannes Kepler Zone Europa, 64000, Pau, France
Tel.: (33) 559133055
Web Site: http://www.clede.fr
Construction Services
N.A.I.C.S.: 236220

Clos Saint Fiacre SAS (1)
560 Rue St Fiacre, Mareau aux Pres,

VINCI S.A. — INTERNATIONAL PUBLIC

VINCI S.A.—(Continued)
45370, Orleans, France
Tel.: (33) 238456155
Web Site: http://www.clossaintfiacre.fr
Window Mfr
N.A.I.C.S.: 312130

Cochery Ile-de-France SAS (1)
8 quai Lucien Lefranc, 93300, Aubervilliers, France
Tel.: (33) 143520105
Construction Services
N.A.I.C.S.: 236220

Cofex Littoral S.N.C. (1)
3 rue Gaspard Monge, PO Box 20050, 33603, Pessac, Cedex, France
Tel.: (33) 56862626
Web Site: http://www.cofex-littoral.fr
Construction Engineering Services
N.A.I.C.S.: 541330

Cogit SA (1)
11 lotissement Calimbe, BP 824, 97338, Cayenne, Cedex, French Guiana
Tel.: (594) 351200
Construction Services
N.A.I.C.S.: 236220

Comantec NV (1)
Hogenakkerhoekstraat 10, 9150, Kruibeke, Belgium
Tel.: (32) 7350660
Web Site: http://www.comantec.be
Building Technical Installation Services
N.A.I.C.S.: 238290

Comari SAS (1)
Parc d'Activite des Lats-Allee Pres Rouets, Messimy, 69510, Lyon, France
Tel.: (33) 478456545
Web Site: http://www.comari.fr
Construction Services
N.A.I.C.S.: 236220

Compagnie Generale de Batiment et de Construction SAS (1)
9C Avenue Pierre et Marie Curie, 59260, Lezennes, France
Tel.: (33) 972300930
Web Site: http://www.cgc-constructions.com
Construction Services
N.A.I.C.S.: 236220

Compart SAS (1)
ZI Synerpole Avenue du Moulinas, 30340, Salindres, France
Tel.: (33) 466540540
Web Site: http://www.compart.fr
Construction Services
N.A.I.C.S.: 236220

Comsip SAS (1)
266 Avenue du President Wilson, 93210, La Plaine Saint-Denis, France
Tel.: (33) 158925012
Web Site: https://www.comsip.fr
Construction Services
N.A.I.C.S.: 236220
Yannick Seigneur *(Mgr-Bus Unit)*

Concept Ingenieurs BV (1)
Baron van Nagellstraat 144-146, Barneveld, Netherlands
Tel.: (31) 342231260
Web Site: http://www.conceptingenieurs.nl
Civil Engineering Services
N.A.I.C.S.: 541330

Concreative LLC (1)
Nad Al Hammar, PO Box 212573, Dubai, United Arab Emirates
Tel.: (971) 42322939
Web Site: https://www.concreative.me
Concrete Additive Mfr
N.A.I.C.S.: 325520
Mirjana Loncarevic *(Coord-Communications)*

Concreet Betonherstel BV (1)
Tweelingenlaan 51, Apeldoorn, Netherlands
Tel.: (31) 557630850
Web Site: http://www.concreetbetonherstel.nl
Concrete Repair Services
N.A.I.C.S.: 238110

Concrete Sarl (1)
2-4 rue Jean Baptiste Huet, 78350, Jouy-en-Josas, France
Tel.: (33) 30676680
Web Site: http://www.concretepathology.com
Emp.: 92
Engineering Consulting Services
N.A.I.C.S.: 541330

Conductor AS (1)
Sverresgate 8, 1706, Sarpsborg, Norway
Tel.: (47) 98487200
Construction & Engineering Services
N.A.I.C.S.: 236220

Conetec Australia Pty. Ltd. (1)
6 Chapman Place, Eagle Farm, 4009, QLD, Australia
Tel.: (61) 407208389
Construction Services
N.A.I.C.S.: 236220

Conetec Inc. (1)
3452 Bacor Rd, Houston, TX 77084
Tel.: (281) 944-9013
Construction Engineering Services
N.A.I.C.S.: 541330

Conetec Investigations Ltd. (1)
201 - 8327 Eastlake Drive, Burnaby, V5A 4W2, BC, Canada
Tel.: (604) 273-4311
Web Site: https://www.conetec.com
Oil & Gas Field Machinery Mfr
N.A.I.C.S.: 333132

Conetec Peru S.A.C (1)
Av Villa Marina 216 Av Defensores del Morro, Chorrillos, Lima, Peru
Tel.: (51) 17192404
Civil Engineering Services
N.A.I.C.S.: 541330

Conetec Spa (1)
Los Conquistadores 1700 piso 16, Providencia, Santiago, Chile
Tel.: (56) 993510696
Civil Engineering Services
N.A.I.C.S.: 541330

Conflex BV (1)
Tweelingenlaan 51, Apeldoorn, Netherlands
Tel.: (31) 557630850
Web Site: http://www.conflexx.nl
Concrete Renovation Services
N.A.I.C.S.: 238110

Consortium Stade de France S.A. (1)
Zone D Activite Du Cornillon Nord, 93216, Saint Denis, France
Tel.: (33) 1 55 93 00 00
Stadium Rental Services
N.A.I.C.S.: 531120
Philip Roaur *(Gen Mgr)*

Coraso SAS (1)
48 Avenue Gustave Eiffel ZAC de Canejan, 33600, Pessac, France
Tel.: (33) 557896434
Construction Services
N.A.I.C.S.: 236220

Coteb Entreprises SAS (1)
15 rue des Longues Raies, 25220, Thise, France
Tel.: (33) 381881855
Web Site: http://www.coteb-entreprises.fr
Electrical Installation Services
N.A.I.C.S.: 238210

Cougar Automation Limited (1)
Wellington Gate Silverthorne Way, Waterlooville, PO7 7XY, Hampshire, United Kingdom
Tel.: (44) 2392269960
Web Site: http://www.cougar-automation.com
Information Technology Development Services
N.A.I.C.S.: 541511
Callum Kimmett *(Project Mgr)*

Crapie SAS (1)
2 rue Yves Toudic, 69363, Venissieux, Cedex, France
Tel.: (33) 472056655
Construction & Engineering Services
N.A.I.C.S.: 236220

Ctm Chili SA (1)
Prat 827 Of 702, Valparaiso, Chile
Tel.: (56) 322213014
Web Site: http://www.ctmchile.cl
Waste Management Services
N.A.I.C.S.: 562998
Cristian Alvarez *(Gen Mgr)*

DEGW France SAS (1)
43 rue bobillot, 75013, Paris, France
Tel.: (33) 145893839
Web Site: http://www.degwfrance.com
Construction Services
N.A.I.C.S.: 236220

DELAIR CFD (1)
ZAC Du Petit Leroy 7 Rue Ernest Flammarion Chevilly Larue, 94659, Rungis, France
Tel.: (33) 1 49 61 71 73
Web Site: http://www.delaircfd.fr
Building Demolition Services
N.A.I.C.S.: 238910

DEV GmbH (1)
Muhlweg 2, 82054, Sauerlach, Germany
Tel.: (49) 81048899432
Web Site: http://www.devgmbh.com
Mechanical & Electronic Component Mfr
N.A.I.C.S.: 334419

DUCLOUX SA (1)
Route de Chatillon, 45390, Puisieux-et-Clanlieu, France
Tel.: (33) 2 38 33 65 01
Timber Frame Mfr
N.A.I.C.S.: 321999

DUMEZ LAGORSSE (1)
P A T La Pardieu 11 Rue Patrick Depailler, 63063, Clermont-Ferrand, France
Tel.: (33) 4 73 28 77 77
Web Site: http://www.dumezlagorsse.fr
Construction Engineering Services
N.A.I.C.S.: 541330

Darlavoix SAS (1)
ZA Bourdelas 4 rue de la Chataigne, Saint-Yrieix-la-Perche, 87500, Hautevelle, France
Tel.: (33) 555083200
Construction Services
N.A.I.C.S.: 236220

Dauphinoise de Materiaux Enrobes SAS (1)
Rue du Vernay, Nivolas-Vermelle, 38300, La Tour-du-Pin, France
Tel.: (33) 474276888
Construction & Engineering Services
N.A.I.C.S.: 236220

De Bosman Bedrijven B.V. (1)
Heliumweg 38, 3812 RE, Amersfoort, Netherlands
Tel.: (31) 334699199
Web Site: http://www.bosmanbedrijven.nl
Construction Services
N.A.I.C.S.: 236220

Dechanoz SAS (1)
100 Route de Loyettes, Saint-Romain-de-Jalionas, 38460, Saint-Romain, France
Tel.: (33) 478327045
Construction Services
N.A.I.C.S.: 236220

Degreane Horizon SAS (1)
730 Rue de l'Initiative, 83390, Cuers, France
Tel.: (33) 498163163
Web Site: https://www.degreane-horizon.com
Measuring System Mfr
N.A.I.C.S.: 335313
Jean-Luc Vigouroux *(Mgr-Bus Unit)*

Delaire-SDEL SAS (1)
ZA Le Grand Mouton Route de Sauze-Vaussais, Chef-Boutonne, 79110, Port-la-Nouvelle, France
Tel.: (33) 549074750
Web Site: http://www.sas-delaire.fr
Construction Services
N.A.I.C.S.: 236220

Delporte SAS (1)
29 Avenue de la Marne Parc des 3 Chenes, 59290, Wasquehal, France
Tel.: (33) 320266868
Construction Contracting Services
N.A.I.C.S.: 236220

Demarais SAS (1)
4 rue Paul Riquet, BP 409, Zone Industrielle Nord, 82004, Montauban, Cedex, France
Tel.: (33) 563630501
Construction Contracting Services
N.A.I.C.S.: 236220

Deton, Inc. (1)
3033 S Parker Rd Ste 1100, Aurora, CO 80014
Tel.: (303) 806-8160
Web Site: http://www.slatonbros.com
Construction Engineering Services
N.A.I.C.S.: 541330
Mike McKenzie *(Pres)*

Dodin Guadeloupe SAS (1)
Impasse E Dessout, Zone Industrielle Jarry Baie Mahault, 97122, Les Ulis, Cedex, France
Tel.: (33) 590380239
Construction Services
N.A.I.C.S.: 236220

Dodin Quebec Inc. (1)
3500 De Maisonneuve West Suite 940, Montreal, H3Z 3C1, QC, Canada
Tel.: (514) 889-4706
Construction Services
N.A.I.C.S.: 236220

Domaine de Bellevue SAS (1)
19 rue de l'eglise, Neufmoutiers en Brie, 77610, Provins, France
Tel.: (33) 164071105
Web Site: http://www.domaine-de-bellevue.net
Restaurant Operators
N.A.I.C.S.: 722511

Dordogne Enrobes SAS (1)
ZA La Rampisolle sud Route d'Atur, Coulounieix-Chamiers, 24660, Perigueux, France
Tel.: (33) 553055530
Construction & Engineering Services
N.A.I.C.S.: 236220

Dormann + Winkels GmbH (1)
Industriestr 8, Kerken, 47647, Kleve, Germany
Tel.: (49) 283392400
Web Site: http://www.dormann-winkels.de
Electrical Engineering System Mfr
N.A.I.C.S.: 335999

Drw - Delitzscher Anlagenbau GmbH (1)
Flurstrasse 16, 04509, Delitzsch, Germany
Tel.: (49) 3420235390
Plumbing Installation Services
N.A.I.C.S.: 236220

Dumez Gtm SAS (1)
RT 1 Auteuil, BP 2086, 98846, Noumea, Cedex, New Caledonia
Tel.: (687) 687414040
Web Site: http://www.dumez.nc
Construction Services
N.A.I.C.S.: 236220

Dumez Ile-De-France (1)
11 Avenue Dubonnet, 92407, Courbevoie, France
Tel.: (33) 1 49 97 27 00
Web Site: http://www.dumez-idf.fr
Construction Engineering Services
N.A.I.C.S.: 541330

Dura Soletanche Bachy Mozambique, Lda. (1)
279 rua Dar Es Salaam, Maputo, Mozambique
Tel.: (258) 823800089
Construction Contracting Services
N.A.I.C.S.: 236220

Duval Electricite SAS (1)
Rue Gustave Eiffel, 76235, Bois-Guillaume, Cedex, France
Tel.: (33) 235614444
Web Site: http://www.duval-electricite.fr
Electric Power Distribution Services
N.A.I.C.S.: 221122

EF2I SAS (1)
1 Chemin de la Marniere, Marolles-en-Hurepoix, 91630, Palaiseau, France
Tel.: (33) 169141480
Construction Contracting Services
N.A.I.C.S.: 236220

AND PRIVATE COMPANIES　　　　　　　　　　　　　　　　　　　　　　　　　　　　　VINCI S.A.

EJL Alsace SAS (1)
ZI du Ried - Schweighouse sur Moder, BP 80307, 67507, Haguenau, Cedex, France
Tel.: (33) 388727200
Construction Services
N.A.I.C.S.: 236220

EJL Lorraine SAS (1)
voie Romaine, BP 40620, 57146, Woippy, Cedex, France
Tel.: (33) 387511314
Construction Services
N.A.I.C.S.: 236220

ETF Luxembourg SA (1)
2 Eucosider Street, 4701, Petange, Luxembourg
Tel.: (352) 5046021
Urban Transport Construction Services
N.A.I.C.S.: 237310

ETF Polska Sp. z o.o. (1)
Ul Hydro 3, 32-500, Chrzanow, Poland
Tel.: (48) 713351001
Construction & Engineering Services
N.A.I.C.S.: 236220

ETF SAS (1)
133 Bd National, 92500, Rueil-Malmaison, France
Tel.: (33) 171139000
Web Site: https://www.etf.fr
Railway Transport Services
N.A.I.C.S.: 488210
Fabrice Guegan (CEO)

ETF Services SAS (1)
10 Avenue de Entreprise Campus St Christophe-Galilee 2, 95863, Cergy, France
Tel.: (33) 130174729
Railway Transport Services
N.A.I.C.S.: 488210

EUROVIA SK, a.s. - Michalovce Plant (1)
Stanicna 11, 071 65, Michalovce, Slovakia
Tel.: (421) 563812627
Web Site: http://www.eurovia.sk
Sales Range: $25-49.9 Million
Emp.: 70
Road Construction Engineering Services
N.A.I.C.S.: 237310

EVT NV (1)
Postbaan 65, 2910, Essen, Belgium
Tel.: (32) 36673572
Web Site: http://www.e-vt.be
Electricity Industrial Services
N.A.I.C.S.: 238210

Eger Martinique SAS (1)
Lot n 9 ZAC de Manhity, 97232, Lamentin, Martinique
Tel.: (596) 596515494
Construction Contracting Services
N.A.I.C.S.: 236220

Egev SAS (1)
Chemin de Farnier Zone, Industrielle de Chassende, 43000, Le Puy, France
Tel.: (33) 471090663
Construction Contracting Services
N.A.I.C.S.: 236220

Eitech AB (1)
Mariehemsvagen 6, 903 04, Umea, Sweden
Tel.: (46) 90154600
Web Site: http://www.eitech.se
Engineeering Services
N.A.I.C.S.: 541330

Eitech Electro AB (1)
Reningsverksgatan 8, Vastra Frolunda, 421 47, Gothenburg, Sweden
Tel.: (46) 31672700
Engineeering Services
N.A.I.C.S.: 541330

Elajo Engineering AB (1)
Forradsgatan 6, Box 904, Oskarshamn, Sweden
Tel.: (46) 491767600
Web Site: http://www.elajo.se
Construction Materials Mfr
N.A.I.C.S.: 327999
Alf Josefsson (Pres & CEO)

Elec Ouest SAS (1)
7 rue de la bise Zone d'activite des Alleux, Taden, 22100, Saint-Brieuc, France
Tel.: (33) 296859650
Web Site: http://www.elec-ouest.fr
Electrical Wiring Installation Services
N.A.I.C.S.: 238210

Electricite Millot SAS (1)
182 rue de la Voivre ZI de la Croisette, 88800, Vittel, France
Tel.: (33) 329050101
Construction Contracting Services
N.A.I.C.S.: 236220

Electrix Limited (1)
2 George Bourke Dr, Mt Wellington, Auckland, 1060, New Zealand
Tel.: (64) 92701700
Web Site: http://www.electrix.co.nz
Sales Range: $25-49.9 Million
Emp.: 100
Electrical Contracting Services
N.A.I.C.S.: 238210

Electrolor SAS (1)
Route de Saulnes, BP 3, Hussigny-Godbrange, 54590, Nancy, France
Tel.: (33) 382444034
Construction Contracting Services
N.A.I.C.S.: 236220

Electromontage SAS (1)
Avenue du Midi Zone d'Activite Agen Sud, Agen, 47901, Port-la-Nouvelle, Cedex, France
Tel.: (33) 553985656
Construction Contracting Services
N.A.I.C.S.: 236220

Elgie SAS (1)
60 Chemin du Moulin Carron, 69570, Dardilly, France
Tel.: (33) 472191100
Construction Contracting Services
N.A.I.C.S.: 236220

Elphi Vm SRL (1)
Via Gallarate 205, 20151, Milan, MI, Italy
Tel.: (39) 0235949851
Web Site: http://www.actemium.it
Electrical Engineering Services
N.A.I.C.S.: 541330

Emi Tertiaire SAS (1)
7 rue des Vieilles Vignes - Bat B - 3rd Floor, 77183, Croissy-Beaubourg, France
Tel.: (33) 169677010
Web Site: http://www.emi-tertiaire.fr
Electrical Wiring Installation Services
N.A.I.C.S.: 238210

Emulithe SAS (1)
Voie de Seine, BP 05, 94290, Villeneuve-le-Roi, France
Tel.: (33) 149614700
Construction Services
N.A.I.C.S.: 236220

Energilec SAS (1)
10/14 avenue Louis Armand, CS 90015, 95124, Ermont, Cedex, France
Tel.: (33) 139473636
Construction Contracting Services
N.A.I.C.S.: 236220

Enfrasys SAS (1)
482 rue des Mercieres, 69140, Rillieux-la-Pape, France
Tel.: (33) 437850404
Web Site: http://www.enfrasys.fr
Information Technology Services
N.A.I.C.S.: 541511

Enrobes de L'Ondaine SAS (1)
Zone d'Activite de Monterrand, Le Chambon-Feugerolles, 42500, Saint-Etienne, France
Tel.: (33) 477561733
Construction Services
N.A.I.C.S.: 236220

Entrepose Asia Sdn. Bhd. (1)
Plaza See Hoy Chan Suite 1801-A 18th Floor, 50200, Kuala Lumpur, Malaysia
Tel.: (60) 320319613
Construction Services
N.A.I.C.S.: 236220

Entrepose Contracting S.A. (1)
165 Boulevard de Valmy, 92700, Colombes, France
Tel.: (33) 157609300
Web Site: http://www.entrepose.fr
Sales Range: $1-4.9 Billion
Emp.: 1,050
Oil & Gas Engineering Services
N.A.I.C.S.: 213112

Subsidiary (US):

ABO Supply S.A. (2)
8860 Fallbrook Dr, Houston, TX 77064
Tel.: (713) 482-2060
Web Site: http://www.abosupply.com
Sales Range: $25-49.9 Million
Emp.: 25
Industrial Equipment Supplier
N.A.I.C.S.: 423830
Gregory Chevrier (Gen Mgr)

Subsidiary (Domestic):

CMP Dunkerque S.A. (2)
Avenue de la Gironde Z I de Petite-Synthe, 59640, Dunkerque, France
Tel.: (33) 3 28 29 65 00
Web Site: http://www.cmpdk.com
Emp.: 90
Drilling Support Services
N.A.I.C.S.: 237990

CMPEA S.A.R.L (2)
Route De Sedan Wadelincourt, 8209, Sedan, Cedex, France
Tel.: (33) 3 24 29 44 33
Web Site: http://www.cmpea.fr
Sales Range: $50-74.9 Million
Emp.: 10
Drilling Services
N.A.I.C.S.: 213112

Challenger SOS S.A. (2)
21/23 Rue du Petit Albi, 95892, Cergy-Pontoise, France
Tel.: (33) 1 75 72 98 56
Web Site: http://www.challenger-sos.com
Sales Range: $50-74.9 Million
Emp.: 14
Oil & Gas Exploration Services
N.A.I.C.S.: 213112

Cofor S.A. (2)
41 Route de La Ferte Alais, Maisse, 91720, France
Tel.: (33) 1 64 99 09 12
Web Site: http://www.cofor.com
Emp.: 122
Offshore Drilling Services
N.A.I.C.S.: 213111

Subsidiary (Non-US):

Entrepose Algerie EURL (2)
Immeuble Zephir Center 11 Chemin Doudou Mokhtar, Ben Aknoun, 16035, Algiers, Algeria
Tel.: (213) 21 91 37.12
Natural Gas Transportation Services
N.A.I.C.S.: 486210

Subsidiary (Domestic):

Entrepose Projets S.A.S. (2)
Immeuble Hampton 165 Boulevard de Valmy, 92707, Colombes, France
Tel.: (33) 1 57 60 93 00
Construction Engineering Services
N.A.I.C.S.: 541330

Entrepose Services S.A.S. (2)
21/23 Rue Du Petit Albi, 95800, Cergy, France
Tel.: (33) 1 34 48 97 30
Web Site: http://www.numrs.com
Sales Range: $25-49.9 Million
Emp.: 60
Natural Gas Transportation Services
N.A.I.C.S.: 486210
Jean-Michel Naud (Gen Mgr)

Geocean S.A. (2)
Quartier du Bregadan ZA Technoparc, CS 60001, 13711, Cassis, Cedex, France
Tel.: (33) 4 42 18 02 18
Web Site: http://www.geocean.fr
Offshore Drilling Services
N.A.I.C.S.: 213111

Horizontal Drilling International (HDI) S.A. (2)
165 Boulevard de Valmy, 92700, Colombes, France
Tel.: (33) 1 57 60 93 21
Web Site: http://www.hdi.fr
Sales Range: $25-49.9 Million
Emp.: 20
Horizontal Drilling Pipe Installation Services
N.A.I.C.S.: 237990

Nymphea Environnement S.A. (2)
Quartier du Bregadan Z A Technoparc - CS 60001, 13711, Cassis, France
Tel.: (33) 4 42 18 02 18
Web Site: http://www.nymphea.fr
Sales Range: $25-49.9 Million
Emp.: 7
Marine Engineering Services
N.A.I.C.S.: 541330
Bruno Maerten (Chm)

Spiecapag S.A. (2)
165 Boulevard de Valmy, 92700, Colombes, France
Tel.: (33) 1 57 60 95 15
Web Site: http://www.spiecapag.fr
Sales Range: $25-49.9 Million
Emp.: 10
Oil & Gas Pipeline Construction Services
N.A.I.C.S.: 237120

Subsidiary (Non-US):

Spiecapag UK Ltd (2)
46 West Bar, Banbury, OX16 9RZ, Oxfordshire, United Kingdom
Tel.: (44) 1295 220 330
Web Site: http://www.spiecapag.co.uk
Natural Gas Transportation Services
N.A.I.C.S.: 486210

Entrepose Group SAS (1)
165 Boulevard de Valmy, 92707, Colombes, Cedex, France
Tel.: (33) 157609300
Web Site: http://www.entrepose.com
Oil & Energy Construction Services
N.A.I.C.S.: 237120
Stephane Tourneur (Dir-Comm)

Subsidiary (Non-US):

Asia Pacific Solutions Pte. Ltd. (2)
10 Ubi Crescent UBI Techpark 03-82, Singapore, 408564, Singapore
Tel.: (65) 68418403
Construction Services
N.A.I.C.S.: 236220

Delattre Bezons Nigeria Limited (2)
7th and 8th Floors CBC Towers 11 Olubunmi Owa Street, Off Admiralty Way Lekki Phase 1, Lagos, Nigeria
Tel.: (234) 9055511419
Oil & Gas Construction Services
N.A.I.C.S.: 237120

Entrepose Chile Spa (2)
Calle Monsenor Sotero Sanz 5 Piso, Providencia, Santiago, Chile
Tel.: (56) 225849000
Construction Services
N.A.I.C.S.: 236220

Subsidiary (Domestic):

Entrepose Industries SAS (2)
Avenue of the Gironde, Petite-Synthe Industrial Zone, 59640, Dunkirk, France
Tel.: (33) 328296500
Oil & Energy Construction Services
N.A.I.C.S.: 237120

Subsidiary (Non-US):

Entrepose de Mexico S.A. de C.V. (2)
Av Paseo de la Reforma 300 piso 3 Col Juarez, 06600, Mexico, Mexico
Tel.: (52) 5556691563
Construction Services
N.A.I.C.S.: 236220

Geocean Peru S.A.C. (2)
SAC Edifio LIT ONE Avenida Jose Pardo Oficina 401, Miraflores, Lima, Peru
Tel.: (51) 6429059
Construction Services
N.A.I.C.S.: 236220

Subsidiary (Domestic):

Geogreen SAS (2)
2 rue des Martinets, CS 70030, 92569, Rueil-Malmaison, Cedex, France
Tel.: (33) 147087300

VINCI S.A.

VINCI S.A.—(Continued)
Construction Services
N.A.I.C.S.: 236220

Subsidiary (Non-US):

Geostock Asia Pte Ltd. (2)
03-27 Nordic European Centre, 3 International Business Park, Singapore, 609927, Singapore
Tel.: (65) 68960659
Construction Services
N.A.I.C.S.: 236220

Subsidiary (US):

Geostock Sandia Inc. (2)
8860 Fallbrook Dr, Houston, TX 77064
Tel.: (346) 314-4347
Construction Services
N.A.I.C.S.: 236220

Subsidiary (Non-US):

Pt Istana Karang Laut (2)
Cibis NINE 7th Floor Jl TB Simatupang No 2 Cilandak Timur, Jakarta Selatan, 12560, Indonesia
Tel.: (62) 2180682820
Construction Services
N.A.I.C.S.: 236220

Ugs GmbH (2)
Berliner Chaussee 2, Mittenwalde, 15749, Brandenburg, Germany
Tel.: (49) 33764820
Web Site: https://www.ugsnet.de
Engineeering Services
N.A.I.C.S.: 541330
Robert Scheler *(Mng Dir)*

Entreprise Bodin SAS (1)
ZI Bd Pascal, BP 439, 85304, Challans, Cedex, France
Tel.: (33) 251930822
Web Site: http://www.bodin-tp.com
Construction Services
N.A.I.C.S.: 236220

Entreprise Gabarre SAS (1)
ZA Lieu-dit Aigueros, Castelnau-Durban, 09420, Ariege, France
Tel.: (33) 561660222
Web Site: http://www.gabarre-sas.webnode.fr
Telecom Network Services
N.A.I.C.S.: 517810

Entreprise d'Electricite de Picardie SAS (1)
Avenue Robert Schuman, BP 70417, Zone Industrielle, 80104, Abbeville, Cedex, France
Tel.: (33) 322201400
Construction Contracting Services
N.A.I.C.S.: 236220

Entreprise de Travaux Electriques Valette & Cie SAS (1)
Avenue d'Anduze, BP 70047, 30101, Ales, France
Tel.: (33) 466522530
Web Site: http://www.valette-ete.fr
Electrical Installation Services
N.A.I.C.S.: 238210

Entsorgung GmbH (1)
Nissanstrasse 17, Luckau, Brandenburg, Germany
Tel.: (49) 354450380
Web Site: http://www.entsorgungs-gmbh.de
Waste Disposal Services
N.A.I.C.S.: 562998

Eperly SAS (1)
chemin de la Belle Cordiere, 69647, Caluire-et-Cuire, Cedex, France
Tel.: (33) 472274300
Construction & Engineering Services
N.A.I.C.S.: 236220

Ertex Solar Technik GmbH (1)
Peter-Mitterhofer-Strasse 4, Amstetten, Austria
Tel.: (43) 747228260629
Web Site: http://www.ertex-solar.at
Solar Module Mfr
N.A.I.C.S.: 334413
Daniel Gutlederer *(Project Mgr)*

Esi SAS (1)
218 chaussee Jules Cesar Le Victor N7, 95250, Beauchamp, France
Tel.: (33) 134117143
Construction Contracting Services
N.A.I.C.S.: 236220

Especialidades Asfalticas Bitumix CVV S.A. (1)
Old Road to Bulnes N 3320 Palomares Concepcion Sector Fundo Las Ulloa, Palomares, 4030000, Concepcion, Chile
Tel.: (56) 412186830
Road & Infrastructure Construction Services
N.A.I.C.S.: 237310

Essener Teerschotter GmbH (1)
Am Stadthafen 23, 45356, Essen, Germany
Tel.: (49) 201835560
Urban Development Construction Services
N.A.I.C.S.: 236220

Est Maintenance Service SAS (1)
4 rue de la Fontaine Chaudron, BP 90652, 57146, Woippy, France
Tel.: (33) 3387346271
Construction Contracting Services
N.A.I.C.S.: 236220

Etablissements Jean Graniou SAS (1)
Industrial and Tertiary Systems ZI Farmers' Lane Sector, 06700, Saint-Laurent-du-Var, France
Tel.: (33) 497221010
Web Site: http://www.jeangraniou.fr
Electrical Installation Services
N.A.I.C.S.: 238210

Etavis Barboni+Collaud SA (1)
Karrweg 4, 1700, Fribourg, Switzerland
Tel.: (41) 263471300
Web Site: http://www.etavis.ch
Electrical Engineering Services
N.A.I.C.S.: 541330

Etavis Eglin SA (1)
Old Pointe 24, 1920, Martigny, Switzerland
Tel.: (41) 277217475
Electrical Engineering Services
N.A.I.C.S.: 541330

Etavis EISA SA (1)
Chemin St-Hubert 18, 1950, Sion, Switzerland
Tel.: (41) 273276210
Electrical Engineering Services
N.A.I.C.S.: 541330

Etavis Elcom AG (1)
Kanalstrasse 3, 9496, Balzers, Liechtenstein
Tel.: (423) 3800101
Web Site: http://www.etavis.li
Electrical Engineering Services
N.A.I.C.S.: 541330

Eurobud Asfalty Sp z o.o. (1)
Ul Sosnowiecka 11, 41-400, Mysłowice, Poland
Tel.: (48) 323183528
Construction Services
N.A.I.C.S.: 236220

Euroliner SAS (1)
30 Rue du General de Rascas, Boulay-Moselle, 57220, Boulay, France
Tel.: (33) 387794838
Urban Development Construction Services
N.A.I.C.S.: 236220

Euromark GmbH (1)
Heideloh Hasenwinkel 3, Industrial Area Grosszoberitz, Zorbig, Germany
Tel.: (49) 34956249600
Web Site: http://www.euromark-berlack.com
Thermoplastic Material Mfr
N.A.I.C.S.: 325211

Eurovia Alpes SAS (1)
Espace Comboire 4 rue du Drac, BP 308, Echirolles, Cedex, France
Tel.: (33) 476750209
Construction Services
N.A.I.C.S.: 236220
Daniel Do Nascimento *(Head-Agency)*

Eurovia Alsace-Lorraine SAS (1)
13 Route Industrielle de la Hardt, CS 49114, 67129, Molsheim, France
Tel.: (33) 388479919
Construction Services
N.A.I.C.S.: 236220
Pierre Munch *(Head-Agency)*

Eurovia Atlantique SAS (1)
3 Rue de la Metallurgie, BP 20215, 44472, Carquefou, France
Tel.: (33) 240301375
Construction Services
N.A.I.C.S.: 236220

Eurovia Bazalty SA (1)
Ul Stawowa 18, Luban, Zgorzelec, Poland
Tel.: (48) 757223045
Construction & Engineering Services
N.A.I.C.S.: 236220

Eurovia Bourgogne FC SAS (1)
7 rue Colbert, BP 33, 21601, Longvic, France
Tel.: (33) 380682460
Construction Services
N.A.I.C.S.: 236220

Eurovia British Columbia Inc. (1)
18964 96 Avenue, Surrey, V4N 3R2, BC, Canada
Tel.: (604) 455-3300
Web Site: https://www.euroviabc.com
Road Construction Services
N.A.I.C.S.: 237310
Francois-Xavier Laumonier *(Pres & CEO)*

Eurovia Champagne Ardennes SAS (1)
Parc Industriel Pompelle, BP 107, 51684, Reims, France
Tel.: (33) 326877220
Construction Services
N.A.I.C.S.: 236220

Eurovia Concrete Technologies GmbH (1)
Franz-Ehrlich-Strasse 5, 12489, Berlin, Germany
Tel.: (49) 3054684822
Construction & Engineering Services
N.A.I.C.S.: 236220

Eurovia Dala SAS (1)
20 rue des Littes, 42650, Saint-Jean-Bonnefonds, France
Tel.: (33) 477481600
Construction Services
N.A.I.C.S.: 236220

Eurovia Gestein GmbH (1)
Franz-Ehrlich-Strasse 5, 12489, Berlin, Germany
Tel.: (49) 357925760
Urban Development Construction Services
N.A.I.C.S.: 236220

Eurovia Gironde SAS (1)
20 rue Thierry Sabine Domaine de Bellevue, BP 60140, 33706, Merignac, France
Tel.: (33) 557290460
Construction Services
N.A.I.C.S.: 236220

Eurovia Grands Travaux SAS (1)
Parc d'Entreprises Brive Ouest Rue Jean Dallet, CS 60222, 19108, Brive-la-Gaillarde, France
Tel.: (33) 555187210
Construction Services
N.A.I.C.S.: 236220

Eurovia Haute Normandie SAS (1)
Chemin des Prairies, Arques-la-Bataille, 76880, Arques, France
Tel.: (33) 235048484
Construction Services
N.A.I.C.S.: 236220

Eurovia Infra GmbH (1)
Franz-Ehrlich-Strasse 5, 12489, Berlin, Germany
Tel.: (49) 3054684822
Urban Development Construction Services
N.A.I.C.S.: 236220

Eurovia Kamenolomy a.s. (1)
Londynska 637/79a Liberec XI, Ruzodol I, Liberec, Czech Republic
Tel.: (420) 48525191
Web Site: http://www.euroviakamenolomy.cz
Crushed & Mined Aggregate Processing Services
N.A.I.C.S.: 212312

Eurovia Kruszywa Sp. z o.o. (1)

INTERNATIONAL PUBLIC

Ul Szwedzka 5, Bielany Wrocławskie, Kobierzyce, Poland
Tel.: (48) 713800300
Construction & Engineering Services
N.A.I.C.S.: 236220

Eurovia Languedoc-Roussillon SAS (1)
82 rue JB Calvignac, CS 70013, 34671, Baillargues, France
Tel.: (33) 467912626
Construction Services
N.A.I.C.S.: 236220

Eurovia Lyon SAS (1)
La Tour de Millery, CS 96939, 69390, Vernaison, France
Tel.: (33) 472308060
Construction Services
N.A.I.C.S.: 236220

Eurovia Management Espana SA (1)
Calle Gobelas 25-27, Madrid, Spain
Tel.: (34) 917082954
Web Site: http://www.eurovia-es.com
Road Maintenance & Construction Services
N.A.I.C.S.: 237310

Eurovia Picardie SAS (1)
474 rue du General de Gaulle ZA de la Blanche Tache, Camon, 80450, Amiens, France
Tel.: (33) 322702770
Construction Services
N.A.I.C.S.: 236220

Eurovia Quebec Grands Projets Inc. (1)
4085 St-Elzear East, Laval, H7E 4P2, QC, Canada
Tel.: (450) 431-7887
Road Construction Services
N.A.I.C.S.: 237310

Eurovia SA (1)
18 Place de L'Europe, 92565, Rueil-Malmaison, Cedex, France (100%)
Tel.: (33) 147163800
Web Site: http://www.eurovia.com
Highway Construction Services & Materials
N.A.I.C.S.: 237310

Subsidiary (Non-US):

BA Blacktop Ltd. (2)
201-111 Forester Street, North Vancouver, V7H 0A6, BC, Canada
Tel.: (604) 985-0611
Web Site: https://www.bablacktop.com
Emp.: 40
Road Construction & Maintenance Services
N.A.I.C.S.: 237310
Martin Logan-Hill *(COO & Sr VP)*

Subsidiary (Domestic):

Coquitlam Ridge Constructors Ltd. (3)
18964 96 Avenue, Surrey, V4N 3R2, BC, Canada
Tel.: (604) 455-3330
Web Site: http://www.coquitlamridge.com
Bridge Construction Engineering Services
N.A.I.C.S.: 237310

Martens Asphalt Ltd. (3)
44550 South Sumas Road, Chilliwack, V2R 5M3, BC, Canada
Tel.: (604) 858-2145
Web Site: http://www.bablacktop.com
Road Construction & Maintenance Services
N.A.I.C.S.: 237310

Safety Grid Pavements Ltd. (3)
201 - 111 Forester Street, North Vancouver, V7H 0A6, BC, Canada
Tel.: (604) 985-0617
Web Site: http://www.bablacktop.com
Sales Range: $25-49.9 Million
Emp.: 8
Road Construction & Maintenance Services
N.A.I.C.S.: 237310

Subsidiary (Non-US):

Bitumix (Chile) Ltda. (2)
Obispo Arturo Espinoza Campos 3172 Macul, 7810857, Santiago, Chile
Tel.: (56) 226803060
Web Site: http://www.bitumix.cl

AND PRIVATE COMPANIES — VINCI S.A.

Road Construction & Maintenance Services
N.A.I.C.S.: 237310

Carmacks Enterprises Ltd (2)
701 - 25 Avenue, Nisku, T9E 0C1, AB, Canada
Tel.: (780) 955-5545
Web Site: http://carmacksent.com
Sales Range: $100-124.9 Million
Emp.: 300
Road Construction & Maintenance Services
N.A.I.C.S.: 237310

Subsidiary (Domestic):

Carriere de Luche (2)
La Menardiere, Luche Thouarsais, 79330, Sainte-Gemme-la-Plaine, France
Tel.: (33) 5 49 96 66 90
Web Site: http://www.eurovia.fr
Construction Engineering Services
N.A.I.C.S.: 541330

Carrieres Kleber Moreau SA (2)
La Motte-La Meilleraie Tillay, BP 257, 85702, Pouzauges, Cedex, France
Tel.: (33) 2 51 65 89 49
Web Site: http://www.kmoreau.fr
Crushed Stone Mining Services
N.A.I.C.S.: 212319

Subsidiary (Non-US):

Carrieres Unies de Porphyre SA (2)
Chaussee Gabrielle Richet 193b, Lessines, 7860, Belgium
Tel.: (32) 68 26 87 60
Web Site: http://www.cup.be
Emp.: 20
Road Construction Services
N.A.I.C.S.: 237310
Patrick Pawlicki (Office Mgr)

Construction DJL Inc. (2)
1550 Rue Ampere Bureau 200, Boucherville, J4B 7L4, QC, Canada
Tel.: (450) 641-8000
Web Site: http://www.djl.ca
Sales Range: $25-49.9 Million
Emp.: 50
Highway Construction & Maintenance Services
N.A.I.C.S.: 237310
Patrick Sulliot (Pres)

Subsidiary (Domestic):

Pavage Rolland Fortier Inc. (3)
825 Rue Fernand-Dufour, Quebec, G1M 3B2, QC, Canada
Tel.: (418) 681-0164
Web Site: http://www.pavagefortier.com
Road Construction & Maintenance Services
N.A.I.C.S.: 237310

Subsidiary (Non-US):

Constructora de Pavimentos Asfalticos Bitumix Limitada (2)
Bishop Arturo Espinoza Campos 3172, Macul, Santiago, Chile
Tel.: (56) 2 680 3000
Web Site: http://www.bitumix.cl
Sales Range: $150-199.9 Million
Emp.: 600
Highway Construction Services & Materials
N.A.I.C.S.: 237310

Subsidiary (Domestic):

Productos Bituminosos SA (3)
Bishop Arturo Espinoza Campos 3172, Macul, Santiago, Chile
Tel.: (56) 226803000
Web Site: http://www.bitumix.cl
Highway Surfacing Materials Mfr
N.A.I.C.S.: 237310

Subsidiary (Domestic):

ETF-Eurovia Travaux Ferroviaires S.A. (2)
267 Chaussee Jules Cesar, BP 62, 95250, Beauchamp, France
Tel.: (33) 1 30 40 59 00
Web Site: http://www.eurovia-travaux-ferroviaires.com
Sales Range: $350-399.9 Million
Emp.: 2,000
Railroad Construction & Maintenance Services
N.A.I.C.S.: 237990

Subsidiary (Domestic):

Europeenne De Travaux Ferroviaires S.A. (3)
2 Rue De Saint-Petersbourg, Paris, 75008, France
Tel.: (33) 1 53 04 95 19
Railroad Construction & Maintenance Services
N.A.I.C.S.: 237990

Subsidiary (Domestic):

EUROVIA BETON S.A.S. (2)
6 Avenue du 14 Juillet 1789, 91410, Dourdan, France
Tel.: (33) 1 60 81 52 00
Civil Engineering Construction Services
N.A.I.C.S.: 237990

EUROVIA BOURGOGNE S.N.C. (2)
64 Rue Guynemer, BP 167, Auxerre, 89003, France
Tel.: (33) 3 86 94 26 80
Web Site: http://www.eurovia.fr
Emp.: 100
Road Construction Engineering Services
N.A.I.C.S.: 237310
Sylvain Bouland (Gen Mgr)

EUROVIA BRETAGNE SAS (2)
5 Rue Manoir De Servigne, Rennes, 35000, Ille Et Vilaine, France
Tel.: (33) 2 99 14 04 24
Sales Range: $25-49.9 Million
Emp.: 12
Construction & Maintenance Services
N.A.I.C.S.: 237310
Le Blay Tanguy (Gen Mgr)

EUROVIA CENTRE LOIRE S.A.S. (2)
2 Rue Joseph Cugnot, 37300, Joue-les-Tours, Indre Et Loire, France
Tel.: (33) 2 47 53 80 40
Construction & Maintenance Services
N.A.I.C.S.: 237310

Subsidiary (Non-US):

EUROVIA CS, a.s. (2)
U Michelskeho lesa 1581/2, 140 00, Prague, Czech Republic (92%)
Tel.: (420) 224951111
Web Site: http://www.eurovia.cz
Sales Range: $800-899.9 Million
Emp.: 3,000
Highway Construction & Maintenance Services
N.A.I.C.S.: 237310

Subsidiary (Domestic):

EUROVIA Jakubcovice, sro. (3)
Vitkov 40, Jakubcovice nad Odrou, Ostrava, Moravian-Silesia, Czech Republic
Tel.: (420) 556748511
Highway Construction & Maintenance Services
N.A.I.C.S.: 237310

Subsidiary (Non-US):

EUROVIA Kamenolomy, as (3)
sro Osloboditeov 66, 040 17, Kosice, Slovakia
Tel.: (421) 413812996
Web Site: http://www.eurovia-kamenolomy.sk
Highway Construction & Maintenance Services
N.A.I.C.S.: 237310

Subsidiary (Domestic):

EUROVIA Silba, a.s. (3)
Lobezska 1191/74, 326 00, Plzen, Czech Republic
Tel.: (420) 377457384
Web Site: https://www.euroviasilba.cz
Road Construction Engineering Services
N.A.I.C.S.: 237310
Jan Muzika (CEO)

EUROVIA Stone CZ, s.r.o. (3)
K Hajum 946, Stodulky, 155 00, Prague, Czech Republic
Tel.: (420) 224 951 111
Road Construction Engineering Services
N.A.I.C.S.: 237310
Josef Stary (CEO)

Jihoceska obalovna, spol. s r.o. (3)
Plana 76, PO Box 76, 370 01, Ceske Budejovice, Czech Republic
Tel.: (420) 387203450
Road Construction Engineering Services
N.A.I.C.S.: 237310

Vychodoceska obalovna, s.r.o. (3)
Kutnohorska 227, Placice, 500 04, Hradec Kralove, Czech Republic
Tel.: (420) 495 454 010
Construction Engineering Services
N.A.I.C.S.: 541330

Subsidiary (Non-US):

EUROVIA GmbH (2)
Rheinbabenstrasse 75, 46240, Bottrop, Germany
Tel.: (49) 2041792301
Web Site: http://www.eurovia.de
Sales Range: $25-49.9 Million
Highway Construction Services & Materials
N.A.I.C.S.: 237310

Subsidiary (Domestic):

EUROVIA Beton GmbH (3)
Caputher Chaussee 1A, 14552, Michendorf, Germany (100%)
Tel.: (49) 3320576201
Web Site: http://www.eurovia.com.de
Sales Range: $50-74.9 Million
Emp.: 175
Highway Construction Services & Materials
N.A.I.C.S.: 237310

EUROVIA Industrie GmbH (3)
Rheinbabenstr 75, 46240, Bottrop, Germany (100%)
Tel.: (49) 2041792301
Web Site: http://www.eurovia.de
Sales Range: $25-49.9 Million
Emp.: 85
Highway Construction Services & Materials
N.A.I.C.S.: 237310

EUROVIA SERVICES GmbH (3)
Rheinbabenstr 75, 46240, Bottrop, Germany (100%)
Tel.: (49) 20419930
Web Site: http://www.eurovia.de
Sales Range: $25-49.9 Million
Emp.: 100
Highway Construction Services & Materials
N.A.I.C.S.: 237310

EUROVIA Teerbau GmbH (3)
Rheinbabenstr 75, 46240, Bottrop, Germany (100%)
Tel.: (49) 20419930
Web Site: http://www.eurovia.de
Sales Range: $50-74.9 Million
Emp.: 200
Highway Construction Services & Materials
N.A.I.C.S.: 237310

EUROVIA Verkehrsbau Union GmbH (3)
Frank Zappa Strasse 5, Berlin, 12489, Germany (100%)
Tel.: (49) 30546840
Web Site: http://www.eurovia.de
Highway Construction Services & Materials
N.A.I.C.S.: 237310

Branch (Domestic):

EUROVIA Verkehrsbau Union GmbH-Leipzig (4)
Gewerbestrasse 10 Markranstadt OT Frankenheim, 4420, Leipzig, Germany (100%)
Tel.: (49) 341520140
Web Site: http://www.eurovia.de
Sales Range: $25-49.9 Million
Emp.: 120
Highway Construction Services & Materials
N.A.I.C.S.: 237310

EUROVIA Verkehrsbau Union GmbH-Magdeburg (4)
Am Zweigkanal 16, 39126, Magdeburg, Germany (100%)
Tel.: (49) 39150700
Web Site: http://www.eurovia.de
Sales Range: $10-24.9 Million
Emp.: 50
Highway Construction Services & Materials
N.A.I.C.S.: 237310

EUROVIA Verkehrsbau Union GmbH-Neubrandenburg (4)
Warliner Str 5, 17034, Neubrandenburg, Germany (100%)
Tel.: (49) 39545070
Web Site: http://www.eurovia.de
Sales Range: $10-24.9 Million
Emp.: 50
Highway Construction Services & Materials
N.A.I.C.S.: 237310

Subsidiary (Non-US):

Elbekies GmbH (2)
Boragker Strasse 14, 04931, Muhlberg, Germany
Tel.: (49) 35342840
Web Site: http://www.eurovia.de
Sales Range: $10-24.9 Million
Construction Engineering Services
N.A.I.C.S.: 541330

Subsidiary (Domestic):

Euro Concept Etancheite (2)
20 Rue Du Marechal Juin, BP 50094, 95210, Saint Gratien, Cedex, France
Tel.: (33) 1 34 28 07 08
Web Site: http://www.euro-concept-etancheite.fr
Sales Range: $25-49.9 Million
Emp.: 22
Construction & Maintenance Services
N.A.I.C.S.: 237310

Eurovia Aquitaine SAS (2)
26 boulevard Jean Moulin, Coulounieix Chamiers, 24660, Bordeaux, France
Tel.: (33) 5 53 45 61 61
Road Construction & Maintenance Services
N.A.I.C.S.: 237310
Philippe Sauvageot (Head-Agency)

Eurovia Basse-Normandie S.A.S. (2)
Zone Portuaire, Blainville-sur-Orne, 14550, Calvados, France
Tel.: (33) 2 31 78 71 18
Emp.: 100
Construction Engineering Services
N.A.I.C.S.: 541330

Subsidiary (Non-US):

Eurovia Belgium SA (2)
Allee Hof Ter Vleest 1, Anderlecht, 1070, Brussels, Belgium
Tel.: (32) 2 370 64 50
Web Site: http://www.eurovia.com
Road Construction Engineering Services
N.A.I.C.S.: 237310

Subsidiary (Domestic):

Eurovia Champagne Ardenne (2)
Route de Paris, BP 50039, 51302, Vitry-le-Francois, Cedex, France
Tel.: (33) 3 26 74 13 55
Web Site: http://www.eurovia.fr
Road Construction Engineering Services
N.A.I.C.S.: 237310

Eurovia Etancheite (2)
175 Av des Freres Lumiere, BP 47, 69726, Genay, Cedex, France
Tel.: (33) 4 78 32 16 46
Web Site: http://www.eurovia-etancheite.fr
Pipeline Construction Engineering Services
N.A.I.C.S.: 237120

Eurovia Ile-de-France S.A.S. (2)
32 Rue Jean Rostand, Combs-la-Ville, 77380, Seine-et-Marne, France
Tel.: (33) 1 60 34 50 50
Road Construction & Maintenance Services
N.A.I.C.S.: 237310

Subsidiary (Non-US):

Eurovia Infrastructure Limited (2)
Albion House 38 Springfield Road, Horsham, RH12 2RW, West Sussex, United Kingdom
Tel.: (44) 14 03 21 58 00
Web Site: http://www.ringway.co.uk
Sales Range: $25-49.9 Million
Emp.: 200
Construction & Maintenance Services
N.A.I.C.S.: 237990

VINCI S.A.

VINCI S.A.—(Continued)

Eurovia Lietuva UAB (2)
Liepkalnio g 85, 02120, Vilnius, Lithuania
Tel.: (370) 5 2152050
Web Site: http://www.eurovia.lt
Road Construction & Maintenance Services
N.A.I.C.S.: 237310

Subsidiary (Domestic):

Eurovia Lorraine S.A.R.L. (2)
Zi La Chenois, BP 50202, 54154, Briey, France
Tel.: (33) 3 82 46 51 80
Web Site: http://www.eurovia.fr
Road Construction Engineering Services
N.A.I.C.S.: 237310

Eurovia Management SNC (2)
18 Place de l'Europe, Rueil-Malmaison, 92565, France
Tel.: (33) 1 47 16 49 75
Web Site: http://www.eurovia.com
Sales Range: $50-74.9 Million
Emp.: 200
Highway & Street Construction Services
N.A.I.C.S.: 237310

Eurovia Midi-Pyrenees SAS (2)
308 Avenue Des Etats-Unis, 31200, Toulouse, France
Tel.: (33) 5 62 72 72 73
Road Construction & Maintenance Services
N.A.I.C.S.: 237310

Eurovia Pas-de-Calais (2)
ZAC Marcel Doret - 720 rue Louis Breguet, BP 397, 62106, Calais, France
Tel.: (33) 321978458
Web Site: http://www.eurovia.fr
Construction & Maintenance of Road & Rail Transport Infrastructures
N.A.I.C.S.: 237310
Gerald Dereumetz (Head-Agency)

Eurovia Poitou Charentes Limousin Poitiers (2)
ZI de la Demi Lune, BP 1004, 86060, Poitiers, France
Tel.: (33) 549376010
Web Site: http://www.eurovia.fr
Road Construction & Maintenance Services
N.A.I.C.S.: 237310

Subsidiary (US):

Hubbard Construction Company (2)
1936 Lee Rd, Winter Park, FL 32789
Tel.: (407) 645-5500
Web Site: http://www.hubbard.com
Sales Range: $100-124.9 Million
Emp.: 750
Construction Services
N.A.I.C.S.: 237310
Fred O'Dea (CFO)

Subsidiary (Domestic):

Blythe Construction, Inc. (3)
2911 N Graham St, Charlotte, NC 28206
Tel.: (704) 375-8474
Web Site: http://www.blytheconstruction.com
Emp.: 100
Civil Engineering Construction Services
N.A.I.C.S.: 237990
Chuck Gallant (Mgr-Bus Dev)

Division (Domestic):

BCI Materials, Inc. (4)
1131 Atando Ave, Charlotte, NC 28206
Tel.: (704) 334-5014
Web Site: http://www.bcimaterials.com
Construction Engineering Services
N.A.I.C.S.: 541330

Plant (Domestic):

Blythe Construction, Inc. - Charlotte Plant (4)
11333 Reames Rd, Charlotte, NC 28213
Tel.: (704) 596-2319
Web Site: http://www.blytheconstruction.com
Readymix Concrete Mfr
N.A.I.C.S.: 327320

Blythe Construction, Inc. - Concord Plant (4)
7450 Poplar Tent Rd, Concord, NC 28207
Tel.: (704) 788-9733
Web Site: http://www.blytheconstruction.com
Readymix Concrete Mfr
N.A.I.C.S.: 327320

Blythe Construction, Inc. - Matthews Plant (4)
1021 Sam Newell Rd, Matthews, NC 28105
Tel.: (704) 841-4444
Web Site: http://blytheconstruction.com
Sales Range: $25-49.9 Million
Civil Engineering Construction Services
N.A.I.C.S.: 237990

Blythe Construction, Inc. - Pineville Plant (4)
12610 Nations Ford Rd, Pineville, NC 28134
Tel.: (704) 564-5596
Web Site: http://www.blytheconstruction.com
Sales Range: $25-49.9 Million
Civil Engineering Construction Services
N.A.I.C.S.: 237990

Division (Domestic):

Hubbard Construction Co. - Atlantic Coast Asphalt Division (3)
11231 Philips Industrial Blvd Ste 200, Jacksonville, FL 32256
Tel.: (804) 786-1020
Web Site: http://www.hubbard.com
Sales Range: $10-24.9 Million
Emp.: 20
Road Construction Services
N.A.I.C.S.: 324121

Hubbard Construction Co. - East Coast Paving Division (3)
2269 Indian Rd Bldg 3, West Palm Beach, FL 33409-3200
Tel.: (561) 683-8459
Web Site: http://www.hubbard.com
Sales Range: $50-74.9 Million
Asphalt Paving
N.A.I.C.S.: 237310

Hubbard Construction Co. - Orlando Paving Division (3)
1936 Lee Rd, Winter Park, FL 32789
Tel.: (407) 645-5500
Web Site: http://www.hubbard.com
Sales Range: $50-74.9 Million
Emp.: 950
Asphalt Paving
N.A.I.C.S.: 237310
Tom Craft (Sr VP)

Subsidiary (Domestic):

Roadway Management, Inc. (3)
1936 Lee Rd 3rd Fl, Winter Park, FL 32789
Tel.: (407) 566-4200
Web Site: http://www.hubbard.com
Road Construction Engineering Services
N.A.I.C.S.: 237310

Tampa Pavement Constructors, Inc. (3)
918 E Busch Blvd, Tampa, FL 33612-8542
Tel.: (813) 990-8949
Sales Range: $25-49.9 Million
Emp.: 40
Asphalt Paving Services
N.A.I.C.S.: 237310
Kristy Hernandez (Dir-Mktg)

Plant (Domestic):

Tampa Pavement Constructors, Inc. - TPC Asphalt Plant (4)
5430 N 56th St, Tampa, FL 33610
Tel.: (813) 627-9500
Web Site: http://www.vinci.com
Asphalt Mfr
N.A.I.C.S.: 212390

Subsidiary (Domestic):

INTERDESCO (2)
134 avenue de la Gare, 121220, Gevrey-Chambertin, France
Tel.: (33) 380340075
Web Site: http://www.interdesco.com
Sales Range: $25-49.9 Million
Emp.: 35
Construction & Maintenance Services
N.A.I.C.S.: 237310

Subsidiary (Non-US):

NAPC Ltd. (2)
Apex Plaza 6th Floor No 3 Nungambakkam High Road, Nungambakkam, Chennai, 600034, India
Tel.: (91) 4449261212
Web Site: http://www.napcindia.com
Road Construction & Maintenance Services
N.A.I.C.S.: 237310

Probisa Tecnologia y Construccion SA (2)
Calle Gobelas 25-27 3rd Floor, 28023, Madrid, Spain (100%)
Tel.: (34) 917082954
Web Site: http://www.probisa.com
Sales Range: $25-49.9 Million
Emp.: 100
Highway Construction & Maintenance Services
N.A.I.C.S.: 237310

Subsidiary (Domestic):

Ovisa Pavimentos y Obras SA (3)
San Martin De Guillar, PO Box 400, Otero De Rey, 27154, Lugo, Spain (100%)
Tel.: (34) 982200920
Web Site: http://www.probisa.com
Highway & General Construction Services
N.A.I.C.S.: 237310

Serie Productos SA (3)
Poligono Industrial Las Arenas, Chiloeches, Guadalajara, 19160, Spain (99%)
Tel.: (34) 916914411
Web Site: http://www.serie.net
Sales Range: $1-9.9 Million
Emp.: 50
Industrial Chemicals Mfr
N.A.I.C.S.: 325998

Subsidiary (Non-US):

Ringway Group Ltd (2)
Albion House Springfield Road, Horsham, RH12 2RW, West Sussex, United Kingdom (100%)
Tel.: (44) 1403215800
Web Site: http://www.ringway.co.uk
Sales Range: $25-49.9 Million
Emp.: 70
Highway Construction & Maintenance Services
N.A.I.C.S.: 237310

Subsidiary (Domestic):

Euromark Roadmarking (3)
Euromark House Astoria Court, Tom Dando Close, Normanton, WF6 1TP, United Kingdom (100%)
Tel.: (44) 1924227250
Web Site: http://www.ringway.co.uk
Sales Range: $25-49.9 Million
Mfr & Installation of Highway Marking Products
N.A.I.C.S.: 237310

Eurosigns (UK) Ltd. (3)
Winterstoke Rd, Weston-super-Mare, BS24 9BQ, Somerset, United Kingdom (100%)
Tel.: (44) 1934421400
Web Site: http://www.eurosignsgb.co.uk
Sales Range: $25-49.9 Million
Mfr & Installation of Highway Signs
N.A.I.C.S.: 339950

LCR Highways Ltd (3)
Haddington Ln, Aubourn, Lincoln, LN5 9FE, Lincs, United Kingdom (100%)
Tel.: (44) 1522502100
Web Site: http://www.ringway.co.uk
Sales Range: $25-49.9 Million
Civil Engineering Services
N.A.I.C.S.: 237310

Ringway Infrastructure Services Ltd. (3)
Western Ext Dagenham Dock, Chequers Ln, Dagenham, RN9 6QD, United Kingdom (100%)
Tel.: (44) 2085932245
Web Site: http://www.ringway.co.uk
Sales Range: $10-24.9 Million
Emp.: 70
Highway Surfacing Materials Mfr
N.A.I.C.S.: 324121

Subsidiary (Domestic):

Sept Resine (2)
7 Route Principale du Port CE 481, 92638, Gennevilliers, Cedex, France
Tel.: (33) 1 41 47 37 77
Web Site: http://www.sept-resine.com
Sales Range: $25-49.9 Million
Emp.: 75
Plastic Material & Resin Mfr
N.A.I.C.S.: 325211

Subsidiary (Non-US):

Signature Hellas A.E. (2)
B Deligianni 28 Street Metamorfosi Attikis, 14454, Athens, Greece
Tel.: (30) 210 28 19 570
Web Site: http://www.signaturehellas.gr
Emp.: 2
Road Construction & Maintenance Services
N.A.I.C.S.: 237310
Chronis Papadopoulos (Gen Mgr)

Subsidiary (Domestic):

Signature SAS (2)
103/105 rue des Trois Fontanots, 92022, Nanterre, Cedex, France
Tel.: (33) 1 41 20 31 00
Web Site: http://www.groupe-signature.com
Road Construction Engineering Services
N.A.I.C.S.: 237310

Societe de Travaux et de Routes Francilienne (STRF) Sarl (2)
57 rue de la Liberation, 91590, Boissy-le-Cutte, France
Tel.: (33) 169232626
Sales Range: $25-49.9 Million
Emp.: 154
Road Construction
N.A.I.C.S.: 237310

VALENTIN Environnement & travaux publics S.A.S. (2)
Chemin de Villeneuve, BP 96, 94140, Alfortville, France
Tel.: (33) 141790101
Web Site: https://www.valentintp.com
Civil Engineering Construction Services
N.A.I.C.S.: 237990
Didier Masseron (Dir-Operations)

Subsidiary (Non-US):

Viarom Construct SRL (2)
Str Intrarea Glucozei nr 37-39 Tronson1, Bucharest, 023828, Romania
Tel.: (40) 21 242 06 87
Web Site: http://www.viarom.ro
Sales Range: $75-99.9 Million
Construction Engineering Services
N.A.I.C.S.: 541330
Marius Badina (Gen Mgr)

Subsidiary (US):

Virginia Paving Company (2)
14500 Avion Pkwy Ste 310, Chantilly, VA 20151
Tel.: (703) 230-0850
Web Site: http://www.virginiapaving.com
Asphalt Paving Mixture Mfr & Contract Paving Services
N.A.I.C.S.: 237310
Alan M. Cahill (Pres & CEO)

Eurovia Str SAS (1)
Rue Armand Carrel, CS 30026, 59944, Dunkerque, France
Tel.: (33) 328249140
Construction Services
N.A.I.C.S.: 236220

Extract-Ecoterre SA (1)
87 Rue Paul Bert, 94290, Villeneuve-le-Roi, France
Tel.: (33) 49619000
Web Site: http://www.extract-ecoterres.fr
Waste Water Treatment Services
N.A.I.C.S.: 221310

FABRE CONSTRUCTION (1)
6 Rue Jacquart, 15000, Aurillac, France
Tel.: (33) 4 71 64 00 36
Web Site: http://www.fabre-construction.fr
Construction Engineering Services
N.A.I.C.S.: 541330

Faceo FM SAS (1)
3 Boulevard Jean Moulin Parc Omega Batiment 2, 78990, Elancourt, France
Tel.: (33) 130972200
Construction Contracting Services

AND PRIVATE COMPANIES

VINCI S.A.

N.A.I.C.S.: 236220

Fic USA Inc. (1)
800 W Airport Fway Ste 401, Irving, TX 75062
Tel.: (972) 721-9964
Web Site: http://www.fic-usa.com
Agricultural Product Whslr
N.A.I.C.S.: 424910

Flan Terrassement SAS (1)
73 rue des Pechers, Plaisir, France
Tel.: (33) 130141818
Construction Services
N.A.I.C.S.: 236220

Fondatrav SAS (1)
RN 20, Grisolles, 82170, Montauban, France
Tel.: (33) 563643046
Construction Services
N.A.I.C.S.: 236220

Foreva Solution Pty Ltd. (1)
Unit 11 9-11 Butterfield St, Blacktown, 2148, NSW, Australia
Tel.: (61) 294917177
Web Site: http://www.foreva.com.au
Concrete Repair Services
N.A.I.C.S.: 238110

Foundation Alliance Pte. Ltd. (1)
28 Senang Crescent 03-07 Bizhub28, Singapore, 416601, Singapore
Tel.: (65) 64404066
Web Site: http://www.foundation-alliance.com
Construction Foundation Services
N.A.I.C.S.: 238110
Tan Hock Seng (Gen Mgr)

Fournie Grospaud Reseaux SAS (1)
Le Pestre, Bourg-Saint-Bernard, 31570, Toulouse, France
Tel.: (33) 561837854
Construction Contracting Services
N.A.I.C.S.: 236220

Fournie Grospaud Toulouse SAS (1)
14 Avenue Mercure, CS 20144, Quint Fonsegrives, 31133, Balma, Cedex, France
Tel.: (33) 562884400
Web Site: http://www.fgtlse.fr
Electrical Installation Services
N.A.I.C.S.: 238210

Fradin Bretton SAS (1)
4 rue Jean Mermoz Zone de la Ferriere, BP 22, 79330, Bressuire, France
Tel.: (33) 549740330
Web Site: http://www.fradin-bretton.fr
Electrical Installation Services
N.A.I.C.S.: 238210

Freycan Major Projects Ltd. (1)
5448 Timberlea Boulevard Unit 1, Mississauga, L4W 2T7, ON, Canada
Tel.: (416) 900-6057
Construction Contracting Services
N.A.I.C.S.: 236220

Freyssima (Maroc) Sarl (1)
22 rue Annarjisse Hay Ryad Secteur 16, Rabat, Morocco
Tel.: (212) 537564435
Construction Contracting Services
N.A.I.C.S.: 236220

Freyssinet Adria Specialni Inzeniring d.o.o. (1)
Znidarciceva ulica 37, Sempeter pri Gorici, Slovenia
Tel.: (386) 58500731
Web Site: http://en.freyssinet-adria.si
Construction Materials Mfr
N.A.I.C.S.: 327999

Freyssinet Bulgaria EOOD (1)
49 A Boulevard Bulgaria Etage 4 / Office 40, Sofia, Bulgaria
Tel.: (359) 29588431
Civil Engineering Services
N.A.I.C.S.: 541330

Freyssinet Canada Ltee (1)
5448 Timberlea Boulevard Unit 1, Mississauga, L4W 2T7, ON, Canada
Tel.: (416) 900-6057
Web Site: http://www.freyssinet.com
Construction Engineering Services
N.A.I.C.S.: 541330

Freyssinet Chile Spa (1)
Monsignor Sotero Sanz 161 Office 304, Providencia, Santiago, Chile
Tel.: (56) 232236700
Web Site: http://www.freyssinet.cl
Civil Engineering Services
N.A.I.C.S.: 541330

Freyssinet East Africa (Kenya) Ltd. (1)
CIC Plaza Mara Road Upper Hill, Nairobi, Kenya
Tel.: (254) 731555968
Civil Engineering Services
N.A.I.C.S.: 541330

Freyssinet International & Cie SAS (1)
280 Avenue Napoleon Bonaparte, CS 60002, Rueil-Malmaison, Paris, France
Tel.: (33) 147764262
Construction Contracting Services
N.A.I.C.S.: 236220

Freyssinet Luxembourg SA (1)
3 rue Geespelt, Livange, Luxembourg
Tel.: (352) 28102511
Civil Engineering Services
N.A.I.C.S.: 541330

Freyssinet Macau Ltd. (1)
Alameda Dr Carlos D'Assumpcao 181 Edf Centro Commercial do Grupo, Brilhantismo 10 Andar C, Macau, China (Macau)
Tel.: (853) 28723945
Civil Engineering Services
N.A.I.C.S.: 541330

Freyssinet Menard Northern Emirates LLC (1)
PO Box 36211, Sharjah, United Arab Emirates
Tel.: (971) 65598850
Construction Contracting Services
N.A.I.C.S.: 236220

Freyssinet Menard Saudi Arabia Ltd. (1)
King Abdul Aziz Rd, PO Box 1088, Al Somaymaniah District, Riyadh, Saudi Arabia
Tel.: (966) 112885606
Civil Engineering Services
N.A.I.C.S.: 541330

Freyssinet Middle East LLC (1)
PO Box 28752, Abu Dhabi, United Arab Emirates
Tel.: (971) 25591162
Construction Contracting Services
N.A.I.C.S.: 236220

Freyssinet Myanmar Co., Ltd. (1)
Times City-Office Tower n2-16th Floor-Units 11 and 12 CCI France, Between Hanthawaddy and Kyuntaw Road Kamayut Township Nil, Yangon, Myanmar
Tel.: (95) 1523700
Construction Services
N.A.I.C.S.: 236220

Freyssinet New Zealand Limited (1)
Unit A 6 Polaris Place, East Tamaki, 2013, Auckland, New Zealand
Tel.: (64) 99507744
Construction Bridge Product Distr
N.A.I.C.S.: 423390
Niraj Ranjit (Project Mgr)

Freyssinet Products Company Asia Pte. Ltd. (1)
10 UBI Crescent 03-82 Ubi Techparkl, Singapore, 408564, Singapore
Tel.: (65) 67445177
Construction Contracting Services
N.A.I.C.S.: 236220

Freyssinet Suisse SA (1)
ZI du Grand Pre 3d, Case postale 111, Moudon, Switzerland
Tel.: (41) 219050905
Web Site: http://www.freyssinet.ch
Civil Engineering Services
N.A.I.C.S.: 541330

Freyssinet Terra Armada Portugal Ltda. (1)
Rua Padre Americo N 8b Escritorio 2-Terracos S Paulo, Lisbon, Portugal
Tel.: (351) 217161675
Civil Engineering Services

N.A.I.C.S.: 541330

Freyssinet Tierra Armada Colombia SAS (1)
Calle 119 Nr 13-51 Office 301, Bogota, Colombia
Tel.: (57) 17442757
Web Site: http://www.freyssinet.co
Construction Materials Mfr
N.A.I.C.S.: 327999

Freyssinet Tierra Armada Peru S.A.C. (1)
El Nuevo Trigal Business Center-Calle Los Antares 320 Torre B Of 301, Santiago de Surco, Lima, Peru
Tel.: (51) 17480700
Web Site: http://www.tierra-armada.pe
Civil Engineering Services
N.A.I.C.S.: 541330

Freyssinet Tierra Armada de Panama SA (1)
Av Ricardo J Alfaro PH Plaza Aventura 4th Floor Office 415J, El Dorado, Panama, Panama
Tel.: (507) 2363185
Construction Materials Mfr
N.A.I.C.S.: 327999

Freyssinet de Mexico S.A. de C.V. (1)
Gauss 9-102 Col Anzures, Mexico, Mexico
Tel.: (52) 5552507000
Web Site: http://www.freyssinet.com
Civil Engineering Services
N.A.I.C.S.: 541330

Frimeca SAS (1)
12 Avenue de la Pointe, 33610, Canejan, France
Tel.: (33) 556072299
Web Site: http://www.frimeca.com
Refrigeration Maintenance Services
N.A.I.C.S.: 811412

Froid 14 SAS (1)
Rue de l'Industrie, 14500, Vire, France
Tel.: (33) 231681842
Web Site: http://www.froid14.com
Refrigeration Maintenance Services
N.A.I.C.S.: 811412

G+H Bautec Unterstutzungskasse GmbH (1)
August- Borsig- Strasse 6, 68199, Mannheim, Germany
Tel.: (49) 62185097440
Electrical Engineering Services
N.A.I.C.S.: 541330

G+H Industrie Service GmbH (1)
Burgermeister-Grunzweig-Strasse 1, 67059, Ludwigshafen, Germany
Tel.: (49) 6216718350
Electrical Engineering Services
N.A.I.C.S.: 541330

G+H Insulation India Pvt. Ltd. (1)
Citipoint 'A' Wing 502 - 5TH Floor Andheri - Kurla Rd J B Nagar, Andheri East, Mumbai, 400059, Maharashtra, India
Tel.: (91) 2240744700
Web Site: http://www.gnhind.com
Electrical Engineering Services
N.A.I.C.S.: 541330
Vikas Pasricha (Mng Dir)

G+H Kuhllager- und Industriebau GmbH (1)
Sigmund-Schuckert-Strasse 3, 68199, Mannheim, Germany
Tel.: (49) 62185097561
Web Site: http://www.guh-kuehllagerbau.de
Cold Storage & Warehouse Services
N.A.I.C.S.: 493120

G+H Metalltechnik GmbH (1)
Auf den Holln 47, 44894, Bochum, Germany
Tel.: (49) 2 34 2 68 1 65
Web Site: http://www.guh-metalltechnik.de
Processed Sheet Metal Mfr
N.A.I.C.S.: 332322
Rainer Bolz (Mng Dir)

G+H Montage Bulgaria GmbH (1)
Petra Strasse 6-8, 1504, Sofia, Bulgaria
Tel.: (359) 35924006901
Electrical Engineering Services

N.A.I.C.S.: 541330

G+H Montage N.V. (1)
Antwerpsebaan 26 Haven 712, 2040, Antwerp, Belgium
Tel.: (32) 35686017
Web Site: http://www.ghmontage.be
Sales Range: $25-49.9 Million
Emp.: 60
Fire Insulation & Protection Services
N.A.I.C.S.: 238310
Ivo Belmans (Gen Mgr)

G+H Reinraumtechnik GmbH (1)
August- Borsig- Strasse 6, 68199, Mannheim, Germany
Tel.: (49) 621850970
Electrical Engineering Services
N.A.I.C.S.: 541330

GFA Gesellschaft Fur Anlagenbau mbH (1)
Zum Wartturm 3, 63571, Gelnhausen, Germany
Tel.: (49) 60514860
Plumbing Installation Services
N.A.I.C.S.: 238220
Petra Gaida (Sls Mgr)

GRANIOU Itelcom (1)
41 Rue Du Puits Rozan, BP 40605, Saint-Jean-Bonnefonds, 42653, France
Tel.: (33) 4 77 50 97 50
Web Site: http://www.graniou.com
Telecommunication Servicesb
N.A.I.C.S.: 517810

GRANIOU Mobilcom (1)
3 Allee Fourneyron, BP 330, La Talaudiere, 42350, France
Tel.: (33) 4 77 48 13 20
Telecommunication Servicesb
N.A.I.C.S.: 517810

GRANIOU Services Centre East (1)
Parc d'activite des Echets Rue des Monts d'Or ZAC des Folliouses Sud, Les Echets, 01700, Miribel, France
Tel.: (33) 4 37 26 22 20
Telecommunication Servicesb
N.A.I.C.S.: 517810

GT Azur SAS (1)
463 Route de Saint-Hubert, 72470, Champagney, France
Tel.: (33) 243829900
Web Site: https://www.gtazur.com
Turnkey Product Mfr
N.A.I.C.S.: 321992
Guillaume Desautel (Mng Dir)

GT Forlux SAS (1)
860 boulevard Charles Cros ZAC Object'ifs Sud, 14123, Ifs, France
Tel.: (33) 231340034
Construction Contracting Services
N.A.I.C.S.: 236220

GT Morbihan SAS (1)
Parc d'activites de la Niel Bretagne, 56920, Noyal-Pontivy, France
Tel.: (33) 297383206
Web Site: http://www.gt-morbihan.com
Electric Power Distribution Services
N.A.I.C.S.: 221122

GT Vendee SAS (1)
11 Rue de Longrais Parc d'Activite Polaris, BP 53, Chantonnay, 85111, La Roche-sur-Yon, Cedex, France
Tel.: (33) 251944657
Web Site: http://www.gt-vendee.fr
Telecom Network Services
N.A.I.C.S.: 517810

GTIE Armorique SAS (1)
9 rue Alfred Kastler ZI de Kergaradec, BP 30214, 29804, Brest, Cedex, France
Tel.: (33) 298412400
Web Site: http://www.gtie-armorique.com
Telecom Network Services
N.A.I.C.S.: 517810

GTIE Lorraine SAS (1)
7 rue des Intendants Joba, BP 62128, 57053, Metz, Cedex, France
Tel.: (33) 387311313
Engineeering Services
N.A.I.C.S.: 541330

GTIE Rennes SAS (1)

VINCI S.A. — INTERNATIONAL PUBLIC

VINCI S.A.—(Continued)
ZA La Massue 13 rue Edouard Branly, BP 37417, 35174, Bruz, France
Tel.: (33) 299830500
Web Site: http://www.gtie-rennes.com
Electrical Engineering Services
N.A.I.C.S.: 541330

GTIE Telecoms SAS (1)
8 route La Cardon Parc Gutenberg, 91120, Palaiseau, France
Tel.: (33) 164532030
Web Site: http://www.gtietelecoms.com
Broadband Connectivity Services
N.A.I.C.S.: 517111

GTIE Tertiaire SAS (1)
Zone d'activites des Pouards 5-7 allees des Vignes, 91160, Champlan, France
Tel.: (33) 169747030
Web Site: http://www.gtie-tertiaire.com
Electrical Installation Services
N.A.I.C.S.: 238210

GTM Normandie Centre (1)
335 rue du Rouvray, 76650, Petit-Couronne, France
Tel.: (33) 232114679
Web Site: http://www.gtm-normandie.fr
Civil Engineering Construction Services
N.A.I.C.S.: 237990

GTM Sud-Ouest TPGC (1)
90 Route de Seysses, BP 78103, 31081, Toulouse, France
Tel.: (33) 5 61 19 22 51
Web Site: http://www.gtm-sudouest-tp-gci.fr
Construction Engineering Services
N.A.I.C.S.: 541330

Gaude SAS (1)
ZI Rue des Gillieres, 26100, Romans-sur-Isere, France
Tel.: (33) 475700229
Construction Contracting Services
N.A.I.C.S.: 236220

Gauriau Entreprise SAS (1)
ZAC de l'Ecuyere Square de l'Epiau, BP 10324, 49303, Cholet, Cedex, France
Tel.: (33) 241468980
Web Site: http://www.gauriau-entreprise.fr
Electrical Installation Services
N.A.I.C.S.: 238210

Geofundaciones S.A.S. (1)
Calle 125 19 - 24 - Of 401, Soacha, Colombia
Tel.: (57) 16842100
Web Site: http://www.geofundaciones.com
Construction Excavation Services
N.A.I.C.S.: 238910

Geomat Antilles SAS (1)
Rue Ferdinand Forest ZI Jarry, BP 2292, Jarry, Guadeloupe
Tel.: (590) 590268330
Web Site: http://www.geomat-antilles.com
Concrete Material Mfr
N.A.I.C.S.: 327390

Getelec Guadeloupe SAS (1)
ZI des Peres Blancs, Baillif, 97123, Vieux-Thann, France
Tel.: (33) 992882
Web Site: http://www.getelec-guadeloupe.fr
Telecom Network Services
N.A.I.C.S.: 517810

Getelec Guyane SAS (1)
4 rue des Lucioles ZI Collery 4, 97337, Cayenne, French Guiana
Tel.: (594) 305352
Web Site: http://www.getelec-guyane.fr
Electrical Network Installation Services
N.A.I.C.S.: 238210

Getelec Martinique SAS (1)
Getelec Collectivites Place d'Armes, BP 408, 97292, Le Lamentin, Cedex 2, Martinique
Tel.: (596) 596669310
Web Site: http://www.getelec-martinique.fr
Communication Network Services
N.A.I.C.S.: 517210

Getelec SAS (1)
375 Avenue Morane Saulnier, CS 34030, 78535, Buc, Cedex, France
Tel.: (33) 139204242
Web Site: http://www.getelec.com
Mold Product Mfr
N.A.I.C.S.: 326112

Getelec TP SASU (1)
Rue Charles Lindbergh, BP 1, Baillif, France
Tel.: (33) 590992878
Construction Services
N.A.I.C.S.: 236220

Giffard Genie Civil SAS (1)
ZI Les Herbages, 76170, Lillebonne, France
Tel.: (33) 235383296
Road Construction Services
N.A.I.C.S.: 237310

Giorgi SAS (1)
177 rue jean Monnet, 84300, Cavaillon, France
Tel.: (33) 490711154
Construction Contracting Services
N.A.I.C.S.: 236220

Givrauval Enrobes SAS (1)
RD 966, Givrauval, Han-sur-Meuse, France
Tel.: (33) 329780576
Construction Services
N.A.I.C.S.: 236220

Gk Sprinkler Sp.Z.O.O (1)
ul Bydgoska 18, 59-220, Legnica, Poland
Tel.: (48) 768626804
Plumbing Installation Services
N.A.I.C.S.: 238220
Mariusz Wydurski (Project Mgr)

Global Procurement Solutions Shangai Ltd. (1)
Modern Plaza Block 1 Room 3006 369 Xianxia Road, Changning District, Shanghai, 200336, China
Tel.: (86) 2151097870
Construction Services
N.A.I.C.S.: 236220

Gottschalk Feuerschutzanlagen GmbH (1)
Am Kortenhoop 47, 32425, Minden, Germany
Tel.: (49) 57194510
Plumbing Installation Services
N.A.I.C.S.: 238220

Goulard Enrobes SAS (1)
92 rue Gambetta, BP 7, Avon, France
Tel.: (33) 160745650
Construction Services
N.A.I.C.S.: 236220

Graniou Azur SAS (1)
280 rue du 8 Mai 1945, BP 72, 78368, Montesson, Cedex, France
Tel.: (33) 130867000
Web Site: http://www.axians.fr
Information Technology Services
N.A.I.C.S.: 541511
Olivier Genelot (Brand Dir)

Granulats Negoce Transports SAS (1)
ZAL du Champ du Clerc Rue de Rouen, Aix-Noulette, Hauts-de-France, France
Tel.: (33) 321458150
Construction Services
N.A.I.C.S.: 236220

Granulats Recycles de Normandie SAS (1)
Rue du manoir Queval, 76140, Le Petit-Quevilly, France
Tel.: (33) 235037362
Construction Services
N.A.I.C.S.: 236220

Granulats de Basse Normandie SAS (1)
La Jaunaie, Bourguenolles, Saint-Lo, France
Tel.: (33) 233512584
Construction Services
N.A.I.C.S.: 236220

Graves de Mer SAS (1)
ZI Zone Bleue, 76370, Rouxmesnil-Bouteilles, France
Tel.: (33) 235849799
Construction Services
N.A.I.C.S.: 236220

Green SA
9 rue de Tessy, Gourfaleur, 50750, Saint-Lo, France
Tel.: (33) 233773434
Construction Contracting Services
N.A.I.C.S.: 236220

Greenaffair SAS (1)
Immeuble Le Cinco - 5 Place de Marivel, 92310, Sevres, France
Tel.: (33) 146038010
Web Site: http://www.greenaffair.com
Environmental Services
N.A.I.C.S.: 562910

Grizaco NV (1)
Scheepvaartkaai 4, Hasselt, Belgium
Tel.: (32) 11260444
Construction Services
N.A.I.C.S.: 236220

Groupement d'Entreprises Routieres de L'Est SAS (1)
1 rue Dominique d'Hausen, BP 20309, 57203, Sarreguemines, France
Tel.: (33) 387273930
Construction Services
N.A.I.C.S.: 236220

Guilbaud SAS (1)
106 avenue de la Gare, 29900, Concarneau, France
Tel.: (33) 298970098
Web Site: http://www.sas-guilbaud.fr
Building Renovation Services
N.A.I.C.S.: 236118

HEB Construction Ltd. (1)
105 Wiri Station Road, Auckland, New Zealand
Tel.: (64) 92959000
Web Site: https://www.heb.co.nz
Construction Services
N.A.I.C.S.: 237990
Mark Evans (CEO)

Haefeli SAS (1)
Rue des Berniers Zone d'Activite Saline, BP 63, 70202, Lure, Cedex, France
Tel.: (33) 384890280
Construction Contracting Services
N.A.I.C.S.: 236220

Handling Systems SAS (1)
4 rue de l'Artisanat, 68500, Guebwiller, France
Tel.: (33) 389285960
Construction Contracting Services
N.A.I.C.S.: 236220

Horlemann Automation & IT GmbH (1)
Horlemannplatz 1, 47589, Uedem, Germany
Tel.: (49) 2825890
Renewable Energy Services
N.A.I.C.S.: 221114

Horlemann Elektrobau GmbH (1)
Horlemannplatz 1, 47589, Uedem, Germany
Tel.: (49) 2825890
Electric Equipment Mfr
N.A.I.C.S.: 335999

Horlemann Rohrleitungs- und Anlagenbau GmbH (1)
Horlemannplatz 1, 47589, Uedem, Germany
Tel.: (49) 2825890
Construction Services
N.A.I.C.S.: 236220

Hydrocar Industrie NV (1)
Rue Maurice Brosius 47, Flawinne, Namur, Belgium
Tel.: (32) 81711409
Construction Services
N.A.I.C.S.: 236220

Hydroplus Inc. (1)
401 Harbor Place Dr Ste 1321, Tampa, FL 33602
Tel.: (813) 252-9975
Web Site: http://www.hydroplus.com
Sales Range: $25-49.9 Million
Emp.: 8
Bridge Construction Engineering Services
N.A.I.C.S.: 237310

I.F.C.E.N. SAS (1)
85 avenue Archimede, 13857, Aix-en-Provence, France
Tel.: (33) 475542010
Web Site: http://www.ifcen.com

Construction Services
N.A.I.C.S.: 236220

ICM SAS (1)
9 Allee Romain Rolland, 76410, Saint-Aubin les Elbeut, France
Tel.: (33) 235819458
Web Site: http://www.icm-automation.com
Industrial Equipment Mfr
N.A.I.C.S.: 333248

INAC Process AB (1)
Ostra Storgatan 67, 553 21, Jonkoping, Sweden
Tel.: (46) 36345150
Engineeering Services
N.A.I.C.S.: 541330
Magnus Falkman (CEO)

INP Canada Inc. (1)
2275 Upper Middle Rd E Suite 101, Oakville, L6H 0C3, ON, Canada
Tel.: (289) 291-5264
Construction Services
N.A.I.C.S.: 236220

ISDEL Energy SAS (1)
1 Rue Paul Rieupeyroux, CS 10135, Saint-Priest, 69800, Lyon, Cedex, France
Tel.: (33) 426205560
Construction Services
N.A.I.C.S.: 236220

ITC-2, S.A (1)
Pablo Iglesias 98-100, L Hospitalet Llobrega, 08908, Barcelona, Spain
Tel.: (34) 934 314 666
Web Site: http://www.itc2.com
Energy Consulting Services
N.A.I.C.S.: 541690

Icorda NV (1)
Verlenbroodstraat 122, 9820, Merelbeke, Belgium
Tel.: (32) 92276676
Web Site: https://www.icorda.be
Computer Support Services
N.A.I.C.S.: 541519
Ivan Eeckhout (CFO)

Ifat SAS (1)
Macon-Loche Company Space 59 rue Pouilly Vinzelles, 71000, Macon, France
Tel.: (33) 385356360
Web Site: http://www.ifat.fr
NDT Training Services
N.A.I.C.S.: 541380

Imhoff SAS (1)
64 Boulevard Kelsch, BP 49, 88400, Gerardmer, France
Tel.: (33) 329601010
Web Site: http://www.imhoff.fr
Engineeering Services
N.A.I.C.S.: 541330

Imoptel SAS (1)
102 avenue Jean Jaures, 94200, Ivry-sur-Seine, France
Tel.: (33) 155535235
Construction Contracting Services
N.A.I.C.S.: 236220

In-Situ Sarl (1)
5 rue Geespelt, 3378, Luxembourg, Luxembourg
Tel.: (352) 42499245
Construction Services
N.A.I.C.S.: 236220

Industrielle de Chauffage Entreprises SAS (1)
Immeuble Le Volta 17-19 Rue Jeanne Braconnier, Meudon La Foret, 92360, Meudon, Cedex, France
Tel.: (33) 146012810
Web Site: http://www.ic-entreprises.fr
Engineeering Services
N.A.I.C.S.: 541330

Infrastructures Urbaines Et Routiers SAS (1)
1 rue du docteur Charcot, 91420, Morangis, France
Tel.: (33) 169101610
Construction Services
N.A.I.C.S.: 236220

Infratek Norge AS (1)
Innspurten 15, 0663, Oslo, Norway
Tel.: (47) 23128800

AND PRIVATE COMPANIES

Web Site: http://www.omexom.no
Renewable & Environment Services
N.A.I.C.S.: 221112

Infratel Services SAS (1)
53 Boulevard Ornano, 93200, La Plaine
Saint-Denis, Cedex, France
Tel.: (33) 175343260
Construction Contracting Services
N.A.I.C.S.: 236220

Ing3E GmbH (1)
Baumschulenweg 2, 70736, Fellbach, Germany
Tel.: (49) 711510994450
Web Site: http://www.ing3e.de
Construction Services
N.A.I.C.S.: 236220

Ingenieurgesellschaft Fur Energie Und Kraftwerkstechnik mbH (1)
Inselstrasse 24, 03046, Cottbus, Germany
Tel.: (49) 355756670
Web Site: http://www.iek-engineering.de
Engineering Consultancy Services
N.A.I.C.S.: 541330

Inspa Industrieservice Fur Pumpenantriebe GmbH (1)
Wenderter Str 12 a, 31157, Sarstedt, Germany
Tel.: (49) 5066808247
Web Site: http://www.inspa-pumpenservice.de
Industrial Equipment Mfr
N.A.I.C.S.: 333248

Installatietechniek Belgie NV (1)
Baarbeek 8, 2070, Zwijndrecht, Belgium
Tel.: (32) 38005100
Web Site: http://www.itb.be
Computer Support Services
N.A.I.C.S.: 541519

Insulex GmbH (1)
Beisinger Weg 1a, 45657, Recklinghausen, Germany
Tel.: (49) 2361908460
Construction Services
N.A.I.C.S.: 236220

Ipsicom SAS (1)
Carrefour de l'Artois ZAL, Fresnes-les-Montauban, 62490, Calais, France
Tel.: (33) 321605820
Construction Contracting Services
N.A.I.C.S.: 236220

Is Ingenierie SAS (1)
Business Hotel Le Drakkar Parc Eco-Normandie, 76430, Saint-Romain-de-Colbosc, France
Tel.: (33) 279189920
Web Site: http://www.is-ingenierie.com
Engineeering Services
N.A.I.C.S.: 541330

Izen International NV (1)
Hoeksken 56, Lille, 2275, Antwerp, Belgium
Tel.: (32) 14558319
Web Site: http://www.izen.be
Solar Electric Power Generation Services
N.A.I.C.S.: 221114

Izen Renewable Energy BV (1)
Bijsterhuizen 24-13, 6604 LK, Wijchen, Netherlands
Tel.: (31) 247440340
Solar Electric Power Generation Services
N.A.I.C.S.: 221114

J&P Richardson Industries Pty. Ltd. (1)
114 Campbell Avenue, Wacol, 4076, QLD, Australia
Tel.: (61) 732712911
Web Site: https://www.jpr.com.au
Electrical Engineering Services
N.A.I.C.S.: 541330
Gavan Jackson *(Chm)*

Jean Lefebvre Pacifique SA (1)
24 rue Fernand Forest ZI Ducos, Noumea, New Caledonia
Tel.: (687) 242820
Web Site: http://www.jlp.nc
Construction Services
N.A.I.C.S.: 236220
Andrew Devanand *(Project Mgr)*

Jean Lefevre UK Ltd. (1)
Station House 191-195 Windmill Lane, Cheshunt, EN8 9AW, Herts, United Kingdom
Tel.: (44) 1992784200
Web Site: https://www.jluk.co.uk
Pavement Engineering Services
N.A.I.C.S.: 541330
Jonathan Core *(Dir-Technical)*

Jomos Brandschutz AG (1)
Sagmattstrasse 5, Balsthal, 4710, Thal, Switzerland
Tel.: (41) 623861717
Web Site: https://www.jomos.ch
Construction Services
N.A.I.C.S.: 236220
Andreas Hamm *(Controller)*

Jomos Eurosprinkler AG (1)
Sagmattstrasse 5, Balsthal, 4710, Thal, Switzerland
Tel.: (41) 623861830
Web Site: https://www.eurosprinkler.eu
Construction Services
N.A.I.C.S.: 236220
Thoma Markus *(Mng Dir)*

KASTT, spol. s r.o. (1)
Jizni 870, 500 03, Hradec Kralove, Czech Republic
Tel.: (420) 495404010
Web Site: https://www.kastt.cz
Air Conditioning Product Mfr
N.A.I.C.S.: 333415
Jan Horak *(Fin Mgr)*

KUHNE & VOGEL GmbH (1)
Zunftstrasse 6, 91154, Roth, Germany
Tel.: (49) 917196560
Web Site: http://www.kuehneundvogel-pa.de
Construction Services
N.A.I.C.S.: 236220
Reinhold Kuhne *(Mng Dir)*

Kellal Maintenance SA (1)
Parc Lyon Sud 4 rue de L Arsenal, Venissieux, 69631, Lyon, Cedex, France
Tel.: (33) 472210380
Construction Services
N.A.I.C.S.: 236220

Klim'Top Controls SAS (1)
Le Peckel, Hardifort, 59670, Lille, France
Tel.: (33) 328500981
Web Site: http://www.klimtop.eu
Air Conditioning & Refrigeration Equipment Mfr
N.A.I.C.S.: 333415

Koning & Hartman BV (1)
Energieweg 1, 2627 AP, Delft, Netherlands
Tel.: (31) 152609906
Web Site: http://www.koningenhartman.nl
Emp.: 400
Telecommunication Servicesb
N.A.I.C.S.: 517810

Korlam NV (1)
Breulstraat 111, Moorslede, 8890, Belgium
Tel.: (32) 51 78 88 88
Web Site: http://www.korlam.be
Emp.: 50
Wood Products Mfr
N.A.I.C.S.: 321999

L'Essor SAS (1)
21 rue du Docteur Roux, 95117, Sannois, France
Tel.: (33) 130258181
Construction Services
N.A.I.C.S.: 236220

L'Ete SAS (1)
158 route de Petit Palais, 84800, L'Isle-sur-la-Sorgue, France
Tel.: (33) 490209222
Web Site: http://www.ete-electricite.fr
Public Work Services
N.A.I.C.S.: 237310
Rose Marolho *(Sec)*

La Reine Blanche SAS (1)
2 Bis Passage Ruelle, 75018, Paris, France
Tel.: (33) 142054731
Web Site: http://www.reineblanche.com
Theater Operator
N.A.I.C.S.: 512131

Lafitte TP SAS (1)
Parc d'activites Atlantisud 1268 rue Bel-harra, 40230, Saint-Geours-de-Maremne, France
Tel.: (33) 558574160
Construction Services
N.A.I.C.S.: 236220

Lagrange TWM GmbH (1)
In Allweiden 5, 55606, Kirn, Germany
Tel.: (49) 67529010
Web Site: https://www.lagrange-twm.de
Construction Services
N.A.I.C.S.: 236220

Lamcol NV (1)
Z I Aux Mineres 12, 6900, Marche-en-Famenne, Belgium
Tel.: (32) 84 31 52 74
Web Site: http://www.lamcol.be
Wood Products Mfr
N.A.I.C.S.: 321999

Le Domaine du Plessis SAS (1)
4 Rue du Moulin, Le Plessis Luzarches, 95270, Ile-de-France, France
Tel.: (33) 130290829
Web Site: http://www.domaine-du-plessis.com
Residential Services
N.A.I.C.S.: 623990
Nicolas Gendrot *(Dir-Publication)*

Le Mans Stadium S.A.S. (1)
Chemin aux Boeufs, 72055, Le Mans, France
Tel.: (33) 243166060
Web Site: http://www.mmarena.com
Sports Services
N.A.I.C.S.: 611620

Le Puy Enrobes SAS (1)
Route de Chadron, Solignac-sur-Loire, 43370, Saint Gervais-d'Auvergne, France
Tel.: (33) 471039857
Construction Services
N.A.I.C.S.: 236220

Les Calcaires Regionaux SAS (1)
Quartier La Salle, Bouc-Bel-Air, Gardanne, France
Tel.: (33) 442221070
Web Site: http://www.calcairesregionaux.com
Construction Services
N.A.I.C.S.: 236220

Les Paveurs de Montrouge SAS (1)
25 rue de Verdun, 94816, Villejuif, France
Tel.: (33) 143901170
Construction Services
N.A.I.C.S.: 236220

Les Sablieres de la Meurthe SAS (1)
Route de Contournement, BP 25, Rosieres-aux-Salines, 54110, Rosieres-pres-Troyes, France
Tel.: (33) 383468352
Construction Services
N.A.I.C.S.: 236220

Les Specialistes de L'Energie SA (1)
Km 6 5 Bld du Centenaire de la Commune de Dakar Ex Route de Rufisque, BP 968, Dakar, Senegal
Tel.: (221) 338652222
Web Site: http://www.lse-energies.com
Construction Services
N.A.I.C.S.: 236220

Lesens Actea SAS (1)
Zone Industrielle Les Buttes, 37420, Avoine, France
Tel.: (33) 247981717
Construction Services
N.A.I.C.S.: 236220

Lesens Centre Val de Loire SAS (1)
2 rue Paul Henri Spaak 1er etage, BP 27424, 37074, Tours, France
Tel.: (33) 247310690
Construction Contracting Services
N.A.I.C.S.: 236220

Lesens Electricite SAS (1)
917 rue de Cocherel, BP 1713, 27017, Evreux, Cedex, France
Tel.: (33) 232629440
Construction Contracting Services
N.A.I.C.S.: 236220

Lexy Enrobes SAS (1)
ZA Les Quemenes RD 172, Lexy, 54720, Saint Michel-sur-Meurthe, France
Tel.: (33) 382242949
Construction Services
N.A.I.C.S.: 236220

Liants Routiers de Garonne SAS (1)
365 Impasse d'Umberti ZI Umberti, 82710, Bressols, France
Tel.: (33) 563021471
Construction Services
N.A.I.C.S.: 236220

Liants de L'Ouest SAS (1)
4 rue Belouga Parc d'Activite du Chaffault, Bouguenais, France
Tel.: (33) 240752180
Construction Services
N.A.I.C.S.: 236220

Liants de Picardie SAS (1)
Boulevard Henri-Barbusse, BP 10064, 60777, Thourotte, France
Tel.: (33) 344904055
Construction Services
N.A.I.C.S.: 236220

Lille Digital Solutions SAS (1)
165 Avenue de Bretagne, 59000, Lille, France
Tel.: (33) 680894551
Engineeering Services
N.A.I.C.S.: 541330

Lille Process Solutions SAS (1)
rue des Marlieres ZA Les Marlieres, Avelin, 59710, Lille, France
Tel.: (33) 320622540
Engineeering Services
N.A.I.C.S.: 541330

Lojas Francas de Portugal SA (1)
Lisbon Airport Rua C Edificio 69 Piso 1, 1700-008, Lisbon, Portugal
Tel.: (351) 218525300
Web Site: http://www.lfp.pt
Grocery Product Distr
N.A.I.C.S.: 445110
Nuno Martins *(Dir-Sls & Ops)*

Lucitea Atlantique SAS (1)
2 rue du Clos bessere Zone des Six Croix, 44480, Donges, France
Tel.: (33) 240454242
Web Site: http://www.lucitea-atlantique.fr
Telecom Network Services
N.A.I.C.S.: 517810

Lucitea Ouest SAS (1)
6 rue des Landelles, CS 67764, 35577, Cesson Sevigne, Cedex, France
Tel.: (33) 299329956
Construction Contracting Services
N.A.I.C.S.: 236220

Luhring GmbH (1)
Gollerner Weg 16, Romstedt, Uelzen, Germany
Tel.: (49) 582143400
Web Site: http://www.zweiwegebagger-luehring.de
Rail Road Excavator Mfr
N.A.I.C.S.: 333120

MAKS GmbH (1)
Molkereistr 61, 47589, Uedem, Germany
Tel.: (49) 282589500
Web Site: http://www.maksmacht.de
Oil & Gas Distribution Services
N.A.I.C.S.: 221210

MERLE S.A.S. (1)
Rue de la Roche Buffeyre Z A la Bourzede, BP 44, 43300, Langeac, France
Tel.: (33) 4 71 77 69 20
Web Site: http://www.merle-btp.fr
Construction & Maintenance Services
N.A.I.C.S.: 237990

Maintel Sud-Est SAS (1)
200 rue du Beaujolais ZA des Folliouses Les Echets, 01700, Miribel, France
Tel.: (33) 437401740
Construction Contracting Services
N.A.I.C.S.: 236220

Makadamlabor Schwaben GmbH (1)
Leonberger Str 208/1, 71063, Sindelfingen, Germany
Tel.: (49) 7031988058810

VINCI S.A.

VINCI S.A.—(Continued)
Web Site: http://www.makadamlabor-schwaben.de
Construction Services
N.A.I.C.S.: 236220

Makadamwerk Schwaben GmbH & Co. KG (1)
Siemensweg 5, Bonlanden, Filderstadt, Germany
Tel.: (49) 711503190
Web Site: http://www.makadamwerk-schwaben.de
Asphalt Mix Mfr
N.A.I.C.S.: 324121

Manche Est SAS (1)
ZI Zone Bleue, 76370, Rouxmesnil-Bouteilles, France
Tel.: (33) 232144200
Construction Services
N.A.I.C.S.: 236220

Manei Lift SAS (1)
10-12 Boulevard Louise Michel, 92230, Gennevilliers, France
Tel.: (33) 146526810
Web Site: http://www.manei-lift.fr
Car Lift Repair & Maintenance Services
N.A.I.C.S.: 811310

Marcouly SAS (1)
Fon-Gourdou, BP 27, 46700, Pont-l'Eveque, France
Tel.: (33) 565213371
Construction Services
N.A.I.C.S.: 236220

Masselin Communication SAS (1)
6 rue Alfred Nobel, BP 11, 14123, Ifs, France
Tel.: (33) 231353070
Construction Contracting Services
N.A.I.C.S.: 236220

Mastran SNC (1)
Rue Etienne Godefroy, 13200, Arles, France
Tel.: (33) 4 90 96 16 96
Web Site: http://www.mastran.com
Monument Construction Services
N.A.I.C.S.: 236220

Materiaux Baie de Seine SAS (1)
Secteur 1387 Route des Gabions, 76700, Gonfreville-l'Orcher, France
Tel.: (33) 235266149
Construction Services
N.A.I.C.S.: 236220

Materiaux Routiers du Littoral SAS (1)
ZI du Renoir Rue Marcel Paul, 60340, Saint Leu d'Esserent, France
Tel.: (33) 344568292
Construction Services
N.A.I.C.S.: 236220

McRae American Corp. (1)
1624 Market St Ste 202, Denver, CO 80202
Tel.: (303) 376-6168
Web Site: http://www.mcraeamerican.com
Engineering Services
N.A.I.C.S.: 541330
Andrew Bentley (Pres)

McRae Integration Ltd. (1)
34 Meridian Rd, Toronto, M9W 4Z7, ON, Canada
Tel.: (416) 252-8833
Web Site: http://www.mcraeintegration.com
Emp.: 70
Engineering Services
N.A.I.C.S.: 541330
Andrew Bentley (Gen Mgr)

Me Engineering GmbH (1)
Am Alten Putt 14, 45772, Marl, Germany
Tel.: (49) 236596880
Web Site: http://www.me-marl.de
Engineering Consultancy Services
N.A.I.C.S.: 541330

Mejoramiento de Suelos Menard Mexico S.A. de C.V. (1)
Paseo de la Reforma 300 13th Floor, 06600, Ciudad Juarez, Mexico
Tel.: (52) 5580189657
Web Site: http://www.menard.com.mx
Construction Services

N.A.I.C.S.: 236220

Meldrum Limited (1)
Unit 14 Currock Trade Centre Currock Road, Carlisle, CA2 5AD, Cumbria, United Kingdom
Tel.: (44) 1228515233
Construction Services
N.A.I.C.S.: 236220

Menard Canada Inc. (1)
5005 boul Lapiniere 6070, Brossard, J4Z 0N5, QC, Canada
Tel.: (450) 449-2633
Web Site: https://www.menardcanada.ca
Construction Services
N.A.I.C.S.: 236220

Menard Geosystems Singapore Pte. Ltd. (1)
07-04 The Adelphi 1 Coleman Street, Singapore, 179803, Singapore
Tel.: (65) 62913039
Construction Services
N.A.I.C.S.: 236220

Menard Middle East Contracting LLC (1)
PO Box 28752, Abu Dhabi, United Arab Emirates
Tel.: (971) 25591162
Construction Services
N.A.I.C.S.: 236220

Mentor IMC (Australia) Pty. Ltd. (1)
Level 27 480 Queen Street, Brisbane, 4000, QLD, Australia
Tel.: (61) 731122958
Construction Services
N.A.I.C.S.: 236220

Mentor IMC (Singapore) Pte. Ltd. (1)
Duo Tower 3 Fraser Street 10-26, Singapore, 189352, Singapore
Tel.: (65) 31589971
Construction Services
N.A.I.C.S.: 236220

Mentor IMC (USA) Inc. (1)
3 Riverway Ste 725, Houston, TX 77056
Tel.: (713) 425-6307
Construction Services
N.A.I.C.S.: 236220
Geoff Hawley (VP-Americas)

Mentor IMC Group Ltd. (1)
City Reach 3rd Floor 5 Greenwich View Place Millharbour, London, E14 9NN, United Kingdom
Tel.: (44) 2075361140
Construction Services
N.A.I.C.S.: 236220

Mesea SAS (1)
Route de Mansle, Villognon, 16230, Confolens, France
Tel.: (33) 972123200
Web Site: http://www.mesea.fr
Construction Services
N.A.I.C.S.: 236220
Luca Fontana (Mgr-Export)

Methec BV (1)
Mercurion 24B, 6903 PZ, Zevenaar, Netherlands
Tel.: (31) 316585100
Industrial Instrument Mfr
N.A.I.C.S.: 334513

Midi Atlantique Fondations SAS (1)
Chemin de Casselevre, 31790, Haute-Goulaine, France
Tel.: (33) 561358455
Web Site: http://www.mafondations.fr
Paving Contractor Services
N.A.I.C.S.: 238990

Minpro Sp. z o.o. (1)
Krokusow 13 B, Pyskowice, Gliwice, Poland
Tel.: (48) 515368833
Mineral Processing Equipment Mfr
N.A.I.C.S.: 333131

Mobility Way Inc. (1)
3100 111 5th Avenue SW, Calgary, T2P 5L3, AB, Canada
Tel.: (403) 440-1917
Mobility Equipment Mfr
N.A.I.C.S.: 335313
Xavier Soulhol (Mgr-Bus Unit)

Mondelange Industries SAS (1)
La Petite Durrwiese Lieu Dit Notwos Port De Richemont, 57300, Rupt-sur-Moselle, France
Tel.: (33) 964074404
Construction Services
N.A.I.C.S.: 236220

Monnier SARL SAS (1)
Chemin de l'Echasserie La Jarriais, Saint-Martin-du-Limet, 53800, Mayenne, France
Tel.: (33) 243064304
Web Site: http://www.monnier-menuiserie.com
Building Renovation Services
N.A.I.C.S.: 236118

Montmelian Enrobes SAS (1)
ZA La Perouse, La Chavanne, Tours-en-Savoie, France
Tel.: (33) 479840330
Construction Services
N.A.I.C.S.: 236220

Moter SAS (1)
20 Rue Marcel Issartier, 33700, Merignac, France
Tel.: (33) 556133700
Construction Services
N.A.I.C.S.: 236220

Mpv - Materialprufungs Und Vertriebs GmbH (1)
Industriestrasse 1, Wandlitz OT Schonerlinde, 01458, Brandenburg, Germany
Tel.: (49) 3094009141
Construction Services
N.A.I.C.S.: 236220

Mud Bay Drilling Ltd. (1)
19545 Telegraph Trail, Surrey, V4N 4G9, BC, Canada
Tel.: (604) 888-2206
Web Site: https://www.mudbaydrilling.com
Engineering Services
N.A.I.C.S.: 541330

Navarra Terrassements Speciaux SAS (1)
61 avenue Jules Quentin, 92730, Nanterre, Cedex, France
Tel.: (33) 146957850
Construction Services
N.A.I.C.S.: 236220

Netlink BV (1)
Ptolemaeuslaan 40, 3528 BP, Utrecht, Netherlands
Tel.: (31) 302485200
Industrial Instrument Mfr
N.A.I.C.S.: 334513

Nickel Kraftwerk Service GmbH (1)
Colmarer Str 11, 60528, Frankfurt am Main, Germany
Tel.: (49) 2204845200
Web Site: http://www.nickel-kraftwerke.de
Construction Services
N.A.I.C.S.: 236220

Nofrayane SA (1)
Parc d'Activite de Matoury, BP 1166, 97345, Cayenne, Cedex, French Guiana
Tel.: (594) 298536
Construction Services
N.A.I.C.S.: 236220

Nord Audio Electronique SAS (1)
446 rue des Bourreliers, Hallennes-lez-Haubourdin, 59320, Lille, France
Tel.: (33) 320811367
Construction Contracting Services
N.A.I.C.S.: 236220

Nord Picardie Maintenance Service SAS (1)
287 rue Charles de Gaulle ZAC de la Blanche Tache, Camon, 80450, Ariege, France
Tel.: (33) 360601045
Construction Contracting Services
N.A.I.C.S.: 236220

Normandie Enrobes SAS (1)
Les Herbages ZI de Port Jerome, 76170, Lillebonne, France
Tel.: (33) 235383220
Construction Services
N.A.I.C.S.: 236220

Normandie Portuaire Services SAS (1)

INTERNATIONAL PUBLIC

Avenue du Cantipou Zone d'Activite du Campdolent, BP 07, 76700, Harfleur, France
Tel.: (33) 235511551
Construction Contracting Services
N.A.I.C.S.: 236220

North West Projects Limited (1)
Rutherford Point Eaton Avenue Matrix Park, Chorley, PR7 7NA, United Kingdom
Tel.: (44) 1257231604
Web Site: https://www.northwestprojects.co.uk
Electric Equipment Mfr
N.A.I.C.S.: 335313
Aidan McManus (Bus Mgr)

Nouveau Solutions Limited (1)
Alba House, Mulberry Business Park, Wokingham, RG41 2GY, Berkshire, United Kingdom
Tel.: (44) 1189699290
Web Site: http://www.nouveau.co.uk
Information Technology Development Services
N.A.I.C.S.: 541511
Ian Brown (Sls Mgr)

Novintel SAS (1)
22 ter rue Passavent, CS 67245, 35772, Vern-sur-Seiche, Cedex, France
Tel.: (33) 299227380
Construction Contracting Services
N.A.I.C.S.: 236220

Nucadvisor SAS (1)
168 boulevard de Verdun, 92400, Courbevoie, France
Tel.: (33) 147764262
Construction Services
N.A.I.C.S.: 236220

Nuvia AS (1)
Modrinova 1094, 674 01, Trebic, Czech Republic
Tel.: (420) 568409811
Web Site: http://www.nuvia.cz
Industrial Equipment Whsr
N.A.I.C.S.: 423830
Ales Dokulil (Comml Dir)

Nuvia Canada Inc. (1)
100 Simcoe St 303, Toronto, M5H 3G2, ON, Canada
Tel.: (647) 800-1319
Web Site: https://www.nuvia-canada.com
Oil & Energy Construction Services
N.A.I.C.S.: 237120
Arkell Farr (CEO)

Nuvia Dynamics Inc. (1)
5448 Timberlea Boulevard Unit No 1, Mississauga, L4W 2T7, ON, Canada
Tel.: (905) 760-9512
Web Site: https://www.nuvia.com
Construction Services
N.A.I.C.S.: 236220

Nuvia Instruments GmbH (1)
Ostdamm 139, 48249, Dulmen, Germany
Tel.: (49) 259494240
Web Site: http://www.nuvia-instruments.de
Engineering Services
N.A.I.C.S.: 541330

Nuvia Prevention SAS (1)
8 allee des Entrepreneurs ZA les Tomples, BP 106, 26700, Pierrelatte, France
Tel.: (33) 475965112
Engineering Services
N.A.I.C.S.: 541330

Nuvia Process SAS (1)
La Fosse Yvon, 50449, Beaumont-Hague, France
Tel.: (33) 233015680
Engineering Services
N.A.I.C.S.: 541330

Nuvia Protection SAS (1)
1306 route d'Argent, BP 19, Zone Industrielle, 38510, Morestel, France
Tel.: (33) 474800168
Engineering Services
N.A.I.C.S.: 541330

Nuvia Slovensko Sro. (1)
Piestanska 8188/35885, 917 01, Trnava, Slovakia
Tel.: (421) 335505885
Construction Services

AND PRIVATE COMPANIES — VINCI S.A.

N.A.I.C.S.: 236220

Nuvia Structure SAS (1)
76/78 rue d'Alsace, 69100, Villeurbanne, France
Tel.: (33) 472144490
Engineeering Services
N.A.I.C.S.: 541330

Nuvia Support SAS (1)
Zone Industrielle Drahy, Cruas, 07350, Saint Gervais-d'Auvergne, France
Tel.: (33) 475014002
Engineeering Services
N.A.I.C.S.: 541330

Nuvia Trading (Shenzhen) Co., Ltd. (1)
Room 1207 - Tiley Central Plaza 199 Haide Third Road, Nanshan District, Shenzhen, 518054, China
Tel.: (86) 75586331712
Construction Services
N.A.I.C.S.: 236220

OFM Communications GmbH & Co. KG (1)
Kulmbacher Strasse 72, 96224, Burgkunstadt, Germany
Tel.: (49) 957275660
Web Site: http://www.ofm.de
Semiconductor Product Mfr
N.A.I.C.S.: 334413

Obalovna Letkov a.s. (1)
Letkov 171, Plzen, Czech Republic
Tel.: (420) 377456030
Construction & Engineering Services
N.A.I.C.S.: 236220

Ohm Asphalt GmbH (1)
Pyramidenring 12, 12681, Berlin, Germany
Tel.: (49) 3094009152
Urban Development Construction Services
N.A.I.C.S.: 236220

Omexom Austria GmbH (1)
Hafenstrasse 2a, 4020, Linz, Austria
Tel.: (43) 7327756900
Web Site: http://www.omexom.at
Renewable Energy Services
N.A.I.C.S.: 221114

Omexom Magyarorszag Kft. (1)
Topark u 1/a, 2045, Torokbalint, Hungary
Tel.: (36) 23501100
Web Site: http://www.omexom.hu
Telecommunication Network Services
N.A.I.C.S.: 517810

Omexom Mobile Assets GmbH (1)
Horlemannplatz 1, 47589, Uedem, Germany
Tel.: (49) 2825890
Construction Contracting Services
N.A.I.C.S.: 236220
Norbert Pichel (CEO)

Omexom Mobile Power GmbH (1)
Horlemannplatz 1, 47589, Uedem, Germany
Tel.: (49) 282589444
Energy Utility Services
N.A.I.C.S.: 221122

Omexom Schaltanlagenbau GmbH (1)
Wehrstedter Strasse 48, 38820, Halberstadt, Germany
Tel.: (49) 394169830
Energy Utility Services
N.A.I.C.S.: 221122

Omexom Service GmbH (1)
Paradiesstrasse 208 a, 12526, Berlin, Germany
Tel.: (49) 3067983161
Web Site: http://www.omexom.de
Energy Utility Services
N.A.I.C.S.: 221122

Omexom Slovensko S.R.O. (1)
Dlha 923/88B, 010 09, Zilina, Slovakia
Tel.: (421) 413219905
Web Site: http://www.omexom.sk
Electrical Equipment Distr
N.A.I.C.S.: 423690

Omexom UK Limited (1)
Unit 5B 21 Old Channel Rd, Belfast, BT3 9DE, United Kingdom
Tel.: (44) 2890958110
Web Site: http://www.omexom.co.uk

Electricity Supply Services
N.A.I.C.S.: 221122
Simon Innis (Mng Dir)

Omexom Umspannwerke GmbH (1)
Paradiesstrasse 208 a, 12526, Berlin, Germany
Tel.: (49) 3067983138
Energy Utility Services
N.A.I.C.S.: 221122

Omexom eMobility GmbH (1)
Holzhauserstrasse 177, 13509, Berlin, Germany
Tel.: (49) 30270193561
Engineeering Services
N.A.I.C.S.: 541330

Oscar Savreux SAS (1)
Lieudit MAYOCQ, BP 10010, 80550, Le Crotoy, France
Tel.: (33) 322273100
Construction Services
N.A.I.C.S.: 236220

Osnova Solsif LLC (1)
St Kovpak 17, 30150, Kiev, Ukraine
Tel.: (380) 443001771
Web Site: http://www.osnova-group.com.ua
Construction Services
N.A.I.C.S.: 236220

Ovelia SAS (1)
139 rue Vendome, 69006, Lyon, France
Tel.: (33) 173600605
Web Site: http://www.ovelia.fr
Residence Services
N.A.I.C.S.: 721110

PETIT (1)
112 Boulevard de Verdun, 92415, Courbevoie, France
Tel.: (33) 1 49 97 32 00
Web Site: http://www.petit-construction.fr
Civil Engineering Construction Services
N.A.I.C.S.: 237990

PITANCE (1)
133-135 Rue Bataille, 69371, Lyon, France
Tel.: (33) 4 72 78 10 40
Web Site: http://www.entreprise-pitance.fr
Construction Engineering Services
N.A.I.C.S.: 541330

PPP Betrieb Schulen Eupen SA (1)
Werthplatz 4 8, 4700, Eupen, Belgium
Tel.: (32) 87305660
Construction Services
N.A.I.C.S.: 236220
Michael Kneppel (Mng Dir)

PT Freyssinet Total Technology (1)
Metropolitan Tower 9th Floor Jalan RA Kartini Kav 14, Cilandak, 12430, Jakarta Selatan, Jakarta, Indonesia
Tel.: (62) 2127826097
Web Site: http://www.freyssinet.co.id
Civil Engineering Services
N.A.I.C.S.: 541330
Vincent Bernier (Mng Dir)

Paumier SAS (1)
Parc d'Activites des Hautes, Falaises, 76400, Fecamp, France
Tel.: (33) 235102350
Construction Contracting Services
N.A.I.C.S.: 236220

Paves Cossutta (1)
22 rue de la Prairie, 02810, Gandelu, France
Tel.: (33) 3 23 71 42 20
Web Site: http://www.paves-cossutta.com
Sales Range: $25-49.9 Million
Emp.: 20
Crushed Stone Road Construction Services
N.A.I.C.S.: 237310

Perazio Engineering SAS (1)
137 rue Mayoussard Parc technologique Centr'Alp, 38430, Moirans, France
Tel.: (33) 476355169
Engineeering Services
N.A.I.C.S.: 541330

Pitagora Informations management GmbH (1)
Olympiastrasse 17, 6020, Innsbruck, Austria
Tel.: (43) 512586765
Web Site: https://www.pitagora.at
Information Technology Services

N.A.I.C.S.: 541511

Plant Solutions Noord-Oost BV (1)
Prinsentuin 1, 9641 PR, Veendam, Netherlands
Tel.: (31) 888318500
Construction Services
N.A.I.C.S.: 236220

Plemet Enrobes SAS (1)
Lieu-dit Fahelleau, 22210, Plemet, France
Tel.: (33) 296257494
Construction Services
N.A.I.C.S.: 236220

Plusine Systems BV (1)
Gooiland 70 SHE Building, 1948 RD, Beverwijk, Netherlands
Tel.: (31) 251261300
Construction Services
N.A.I.C.S.: 236220

Portway SA (1)
Aeroporto de Lisboa Rua C edif 124 piso 1, 1700-008, Lisbon, Portugal
Tel.: (351) 218413727
Web Site: https://www.portway.pt
Logistic Services
N.A.I.C.S.: 488510
Cesar Augusto (Head-Marketing-Sales)

Powell Engineering UK Limited (1)
Belton Road Sandtoft, Doncaster, DN8 5SX, United Kingdom
Tel.: (44) 1724712904
Construction Services
N.A.I.C.S.: 236220

Powertest Ltd. (1)
Delta House Bridge Rd, Haywards Heath, RH16 1UA, United Kingdom
Tel.: (44) 3006001001
Web Site: http://www.powertest.co.uk
Electrical & Electronic Product Mfr
N.A.I.C.S.: 335999
Tony Raikes (Mng Dir)

Prefa Pro A.S. (1)
Kralovicka 267, Zapy, Prague, Czech Republic
Tel.: (420) 326377821
Web Site: http://www.prefa-pro.cz
Transportation Construction Services
N.A.I.C.S.: 237310

Presqu'Ile Environnement SAS (1)
29 Rue de la Pierre, BP 15230, 44350, Guerande, France
Tel.: (33) 240620661
Urban Development Construction Services
N.A.I.C.S.: 236220

PrimeLine Utility Services LLC (1)
600 University St Ste 2520, Seattle, WA 98101
Tel.: (206) 693-3708
Web Site: http://www.primelineus.com
Construction Services
N.A.I.C.S.: 236220

Provelec Sud SAS (1)
410 Avenue de l'Europe, 83140, Six-Fours-les-Plages, France
Tel.: (33) 494105620
Web Site: http://www.provelec-sud.fr
Electric Power Distribution Services
N.A.I.C.S.: 221122

Qivy SAS (1)
12 Boulevard Louise Michel, 92238, Gennevilliers, France
Tel.: (33) 147916666
Construction Contracting Services
N.A.I.C.S.: 236220

Qivy Tertiaire SAS (1)
Immeuble Seine Avenue 2-8 rue Sarah Bernhardt, 92600, Asnieres-sur-Seine, France
Tel.: (33) 624205635
Web Site: http://www.qivy-tertiaire.fr
Building Renovation Services
N.A.I.C.S.: 236118

Qsi Group SAS (1)
13 Colmans Nook Billingham, Belasis Hall Technology Park Stockton on Tees, Billingham, TS23 4EG, United Kingdom
Tel.: (44) 1642564326
Construction Services
N.A.I.C.S.: 236220

Quadix SAS (1)
304 route Nationale 6 Batiment Avalon 1, 69760, Limonest, France
Tel.: (33) 478339990
Construction Contracting Services
N.A.I.C.S.: 236220

R3EI SAS (1)
15 rue des longues raies, 25220, Thise, France
Tel.: (33) 381474615
Construction Contracting Services
N.A.I.C.S.: 236220

ROHA Software Support GmbH (1)
Aegidiusplatz 15b, 53604, Bad Honnef, Germany
Tel.: (49) 22249600080
Information Technology Services
N.A.I.C.S.: 541511

ROHA Software Support GmbH (1)
Ameisgasse 49-51, 1140, Vienna, Austria
Tel.: (43) 14196700
Web Site: http://www.roha.at
Information Technology Services
N.A.I.C.S.: 541511

Radar Automation NV (1)
Leon Bekaertlaan 24, 9880, Aalter, Belgium
Tel.: (32) 92808383
Web Site: http://www.radaraut.com
Information Technology Development Services
N.A.I.C.S.: 541511

Radar Automation SARL (1)
Atlanparc Batiment K 1 Rue Marie Curie, Plescop, 56890, Vannes, France
Tel.: (33) 297683768
Web Site: http://www.radaraut.com
Information Technology Development Services
N.A.I.C.S.: 541511

Radio VINCI Autoroutes SA (1)
12 rue Louis Bleriot, 92506, Rueil-Malmaison, Cedex, France
Tel.: (33) 155947000
Financial Services
N.A.I.C.S.: 541611

Rault Granit SAS (1)
La Morinais, Louvigne-du-Desert, Fougeres, France
Tel.: (33) 299980166
Web Site: http://www.raultgranit.com
Granite Product Mfr
N.A.I.C.S.: 327991

Rb Technics NV (1)
Harensesteenweg 299, 1800, Vilvoorde, Belgium
Tel.: (32) 22520740
Construction Services
N.A.I.C.S.: 236220

Reinforced Earth Cny Ltd. (1)
7015 Macleaod Trail SW Suite 618, Calgary, T2H 2K6, AB, Canada
Tel.: (403) 452-4654
Construction Services
N.A.I.C.S.: 236220

Reinforced Earth Malaysia Sdn Bhd (1)
Block B Unit 902 Kelana Business Centre No35 Jalan SS7/2 SS7, 47301, Petaling Jaya, Selangor, Malaysia
Tel.: (60) 122231037
Web Site: http://www.reinforcedearth.com.my
Sales Range: $25-49.9 Million
Emp.: 20
Reinforced Wall Construction Services
N.A.I.C.S.: 237990

Reinforced Earth Sea (Singapore) Pte. Ltd. (1)
10 Bukit Batok Crescent 12-04 The Spire, Singapore, 658079, Singapore
Tel.: (65) 63166401
Construction Services
N.A.I.C.S.: 236220

Remea SAS (1)
Sebastien DESVIGNES 22-24 rue Lavoisier, 92000, Nanterre, France
Tel.: (33) 147765590
Engineeering Services
N.A.I.C.S.: 541330

VINCI S.A.

VINCI S.A.—Continued

Reseaux Lumiere d'Alsace SAS (1)
11 rue du burlat, 68260, Kingersheim, France
Tel.: (33) 389556070
Construction Contracting Services
N.A.I.C.S.: 236220

Reso Detect SAS (1)
ZI la Chenois, BP 50202, 54154, Briey, France
Tel.: (33) 382465180
Construction Services
N.A.I.C.S.: 236220

Reso Logistique SAS (1)
Parc d'activites des Chanteraines 10 rue du Commandant d'Estienne, d'Orves, 92390, Villeneuve-la-Garenne, France
Tel.: (33) 156042230
Web Site: http://www.e-reso.fr
Lifting Equipment Installation Services
N.A.I.C.S.: 238290

Ringway Hounslow Highways Limited (1)
Jubilee House Depot Road Airport, Hounslow, TW3 1SN, United Kingdom
Tel.: (44) 2085385678
Construction & Engineering Services
N.A.I.C.S.: 236220

Ringway Island Roads Limited (1)
St Christopher House 42 Daish Way, Newport, PO30 5XJ, Isle of Wight, United Kingdom
Tel.: (44) 1983822440
Web Site: https://www.islandroads.com
Emp.: 200
Road Construction Services
N.A.I.C.S.: 237310
Laura Haytack (Officer-Communications)

Robert Carrieres et Industries SAS (1)
346 rue de la Republique, Verfeuil, Nimes, France
Tel.: (33) 466729043
Construction & Engineering Services
N.A.I.C.S.: 236220

Rodio - Kronsa .S.A. (1)
C/Velazquez 50 7 planta, Madrid, Spain
Tel.: (34) 917817169
Web Site: http://www.rodiokronsa.es
Construction Services
N.A.I.C.S.: 236220

Rodio Swissboring Costa Rica S.A. (1)
De la Escuela San Francis 10 metros Este Contigua Bazar Pekis, San Jose, Costa Rica
Tel.: (506) 2972205
Construction Services
N.A.I.C.S.: 236220

Rodio Swissboring El Salvador S.A.C.V. (1)
Km 20 Crta al Puerto La Libertad y, Desvio a San Jose Villanueva Zaragoza, La Libertad, El Salvador
Tel.: (503) 3140340
Construction Services
N.A.I.C.S.: 236220

Rodio Swissboring Guatemala S.A. (1)
12 Calle 1-24 Zone 10, Casa Veranda Building 1er level Office 101, Guatemala, Guatemala
Tel.: (502) 22016600
Construction Services
N.A.I.C.S.: 236220

Rodio Swissboring Honduras S.A. (1)
Colonia San Carlos, Avenida Republica de Colombia 201, Tegucigalpa, Honduras
Tel.: (504) 22216922
Construction Services
N.A.I.C.S.: 236220

Rodio Swissboring Nicaragua S.A. (1)
ENTEL Monsenor Lezcano 1C al Sur 1/2 Arriba Of 2107, Managua, Nicaragua
Tel.: (505) 2662036
Construction Services

Rodio Swissboring Panama Sociedad Anonima (1)
Calle Gregorio Miro y Ricardo Miro Local n 39, Urbanizacion Industrial La Esperanza-Corregimiento Victoriano Lorenzo, San Miguelito, 0823-04574, Panama
Tel.: (507) 2301086
Construction Services
N.A.I.C.S.: 236220

Roger Bullivant Ltd. (1)
RB Walton Park Hearthcote Road, Swadlincote, DE11 9DU, Derbyshire, United Kingdom
Tel.: (44) 1332977300
Web Site: http://www.roger-bullivant.co.uk
Construction Services
N.A.I.C.S.: 236220

Roiret Energies SAS (1)
196 all Alexandre Borodine, 69800, Saint Priest, France
Tel.: (33) 472737373
Web Site: http://www.roiret-energies.com
Electrical Wiring Installation Services
N.A.I.C.S.: 238210

Roiret Transport SAS (1)
482 rue des Mercieres, 69140, Rillieux-la-Pape, France
Tel.: (33) 472880620
Web Site: http://www.roiret-transport.fr
Highway Construction Services
N.A.I.C.S.: 237310

Rol Normandie SAS (1)
Zone Industrielle du Mesnil, BP 119, Granville, 50401, Mesnil, Cedex, France
Tel.: (33) 233910940
Construction & Engineering Services
N.A.I.C.S.: 236220

Roussey SAS (1)
Rue Louis Freycinet, CS 20006, Saint-Andre-Les Vergers, 10120, Troyes, France
Tel.: (33) 325799019
Urban Development Construction Services
N.A.I.C.S.: 236220

Routiere des Pyrenees SAS (1)
ZI de Bastillac Sud, BP 922, 65009, Tarbes, France
Tel.: (33) 562445070
Urban Development Construction Services
N.A.I.C.S.: 236220

SATOB CONSTRUCTION BOIS (1)
ZA Peguilhan, 31350, Peguilhan, France
Tel.: (33) 61887851
Web Site: http://www.arbonis.com
Wooden Building Construction Services
N.A.I.C.S.: 238130

SBR SAS (1)
97 rue Saint-Antoine, 93100, Montreuil, France
Tel.: (33) 148545720
Urban Development Construction Services
N.A.I.C.S.: 236220

SCI Domaine de Saint Jean (1)
16 rue du Vieux Bourg, Saint-Jean-des-Mauvrets, Les Ponts-de-Ce, France
Tel.: (33) 241919201
Web Site: http://www.domainedesaintjean.com
Construction Services
N.A.I.C.S.: 236220

SCIE Puy de Dome SAS (1)
La Vaure, Courpiere, 63120, Le Puy, France
Tel.: (33) 473517480
Web Site: http://www.scie-pdd.com
Urban Equipment Mfr
N.A.I.C.S.: 336510

SDEL Atlantis SAS (1)
3 BD Flandres 1940, Dunkirk, 56100, Lorient, France
Tel.: (33) 297353140
Web Site: http://www.sdel-atlantis.fr
Construction Services
N.A.I.C.S.: 236220

SDEL Controle Commande SAS (1)
Aeropole D2A rue Nungesser et Coli, 44860, Saint-Aignan-Grandlieu, France
Tel.: (33) 240845000

Web Site: https://www.sdelcc.com
Emp.: 230
Electric Equipment Mfr
N.A.I.C.S.: 335313
Nicolas Girard (Bus Mgr)

SDEL Infi SAS (1)
71 75 Avenue du President Kennedy, Viry-Chatillon, 91170, Paris, France
Tel.: (33) 169843282
Construction Services
N.A.I.C.S.: 236220

SDEL Massif Central SAS (1)
17 rue Denis Papin, BP 135, 19361, Malemort-sur-Correze, France
Tel.: (33) 555921740
Construction Services
N.A.I.C.S.: 236220

SDEL Nantes SAS (1)
ZI de la Violette Chemin du, BP 501, Bocage, 49243, Avrille, France
Tel.: (33) 241345959
Web Site: http://www.sdel-grand-ouest.fr
Electric Utility Mfr
N.A.I.C.S.: 336510

SDEL Reseaux Aquitaine SAS (1)
15 route de Pitoys ZA de Maignon, 64600, Anglet, France
Tel.: (33) 559571313
Construction Services
N.A.I.C.S.: 236220

SDEL Reseaux Exterieurs SAS (1)
Parc d'Activites Chalaronne Centre, BP 34, 01400, Chatillon-sur-Chalaronne, France
Tel.: (33) 474555380
Construction Services
N.A.I.C.S.: 236220

SDEL Savoie Leman SAS (1)
51 Rue Adrastee, 74650, Chavanod, France
Tel.: (33) 450337620
Web Site: https://www.sdel-savoie-leman.fr
Electric Equipment Mfr
N.A.I.C.S.: 335313
Raffaella Ernesto (Project Mgr)

SDEL Tertiaire SAS (1)
Linea building 1 rue du General Leclerc, 92800, Puteaux, France
Tel.: (33) 158475880
Web Site: http://www.sdel-tertiaire.fr
Electrical Equipment Maintenance Services
N.A.I.C.S.: 811310

SEC TP SAS (1)
RD 150, Saint Hilaire de Villefranche, 17770, Saint-Jeannet, France
Tel.: (33) 546953002
Urban Development Construction Services
N.A.I.C.S.: 236220

SEIT Hydr'Eau SAS (1)
8 rue Lavoisier Ingre, BP 24626, 45146, Saint-Jean-de-la-Ruelle, Cedex, France
Tel.: (33) 238718100
Web Site: http://www.seithydreau.fr
Water Treatment & Pumping Services
N.A.I.C.S.: 221310

SER Puy de Dome SAS (1)
ZAC du Chancet, 63530, Volvic, France
Tel.: (33) 473387983
Public & Road Work Construction Services
N.A.I.C.S.: 237310

SER Semine SAS (1)
174 rue du Sorgia ZI de la Croisee, Chene En Semine, 74270, Saint-Julien-en-Genevois, France
Tel.: (33) 450650315
Public & Road Work Construction Services
N.A.I.C.S.: 237310

SER Travaux Publics et Routiers SAS (1)
7 Rue de l'Expansion ZI n 3, Frontenex, 73460, Tours-en-Savoie, France
Tel.: (33) 479314323
Public & Road Work Construction Services
N.A.I.C.S.: 237310

SICRA (1)
2 rue du Cottage Tolbiac ZAC du Petit Leroy, 94659, Chevilly-Larue, France
Tel.: (33) 1 72 46 40 00
Construction Engineering Services

INTERNATIONAL PUBLIC

N.A.I.C.S.: 541330

SKE International GmbH (1)
Am Sagewerk 10, 63773, Goldbach, Germany
Tel.: (49) 602132990
Building Renovation Services
N.A.I.C.S.: 236118
John Huhtala (Dir-Bus Area Government Svcs)

SKE Italie Srl (1)
Via Zamenhof 829, 31600, Vicenza, Italy
Tel.: (39) 0444912553
Construction Services
N.A.I.C.S.: 236220
John Huhtala (Mng Dir)

SKE Schul-Facility-Management GmbH (1)
Paul-Ehrlich-Str 11, 63225, Langen, Germany
Tel.: (49) 610383320100
Waste Water Management Services
N.A.I.C.S.: 562998

SKE Support Services GmbH (1)
Am Sagewerk 10, 63773, Goldbach, Germany
Tel.: (49) 602132990
Web Site: http://www.schreinerei-ske.de
Fire Protection Equipment Installation Services
N.A.I.C.S.: 922160

SKE Technical Services GmbH (1)
Am Sagewerk 10, 63773, Goldbach, Germany
Tel.: (49) 602132990
Building Renovation Services
N.A.I.C.S.: 236118
Ralf Hofer (Mng Dir)

SNEH Materiaux SAS (1)
Les carrieres rouges, Muneville-le-Bingard, Saint-Sauveur, France
Tel.: (33) 233451750
Construction & Engineering Services
N.A.I.C.S.: 236220

SOGAM (1)
ZAC Petit Leroy 4 rue du Cottage Tolbiac, Chevilly-Larue, 94550, Chevilly, France
Tel.: (33) 1 72 46 46 00
Web Site: http://www.sogam-immobilier.fr
Construction Engineering Services
N.A.I.C.S.: 541330

SRC (1)
34 Avenue de l'Europe Batiment Energy IV, Velizy-Villacoublay, 78147, France
Tel.: (33) 1 30 67 66 70
Web Site: http://www.src-batiment.fr
Emp.: 100
Civil Engineering Construction Services
N.A.I.C.S.: 237990

STINGL Gmbh (1)
Dachauer Str 511, Munich, 80993, Germany
Tel.: (49) 89 316020
Web Site: http://www.stingl-online.de
Heating & Air Conditioning Equipment Installation Services
N.A.I.C.S.: 238220

STS Traffic Solutions GmbH (1)
Franz-Ehrlich-Str 5, Berlin, Germany
Tel.: (49) 30889288740
Web Site: http://www.sts-trafficsolutions.com
Traffic Engineering Consulting Services
N.A.I.C.S.: 541330

Safeway Construction Enterprises LLC (1)
54-60 44th St, Maspeth, NY 11378
Tel.: (718) 349-6645
Web Site: http://www.safewayce.com
Construction Engineering Services
N.A.I.C.S.: 541330

Saga Tertiaire SAS (1)
41 rue Victor Hugo, 92270, Bois-Colombes, France
Tel.: (33) 141325151
Web Site: http://www.saga-tertiaire.fr
Plumbing Installation Services
N.A.I.C.S.: 238220

Saint Maixent Enrobes SAS (1)
Le Pre Donia, Saivres, 79400, Saint-Maixent-sur-Vie, France

AND PRIVATE COMPANIES — VINCI S.A.

Tel.: (33) 549057385
Construction Services
N.A.I.C.S.: 236220

Saldus Celinieks, SIA (1)
Brivibas Street 11a, Saldus, Riga, LV-3801, Latvia
Tel.: (371) 63807060
Web Site: http://www.sc.lv
Road Construction Services
N.A.I.C.S.: 237310
Uldis Datavs *(Mng Dir)*

Salendre Reseaux SAS (1)
3 rue Clement Ader, Zone Industrielle de Musinens, 01200, Bellegarde-sur-Valserine, France
Tel.: (33) 450560194
Construction Contracting Services
N.A.I.C.S.: 236220

Santerne Alsace SAS (1)
8 rue de la Redoute ZI, BP 20002, Niederhausbergen, 67014, Strasbourg, France
Tel.: (33) 388180777
Web Site: http://www.santerne-alsace.fr
Building Renovation Services
N.A.I.C.S.: 236118

Santerne Aquitaine SAS (1)
Avenue de Terrefort, CS 60062, Zone Industrielle Tertiaire, 33523, Bruges, Cedex, France
Tel.: (33) 556282504
Construction Contracting Services
N.A.I.C.S.: 236220

Santerne Bretagne SAS (1)
1 rue Jean Pierre Bertel, BP 76227, Montfort-sur-Meu, 35162, Rennes, Cedex, France
Tel.: (33) 299090145
Construction Contracting Services
N.A.I.C.S.: 236220

Santerne Camargue SAS (1)
Zone Aeropole, Garons, 30128, Nimes, France
Tel.: (33) 466706030
Construction Contracting Services
N.A.I.C.S.: 236220

Santerne Centre Est Energies SAS (1)
231 Allee de l'industrie, BP 70412, 42354, La Talaudiere, France
Tel.: (33) 477593642
Construction Contracting Services
N.A.I.C.S.: 236220

Santerne Energies Est SAS (1)
40 Avenue de l'Europe Parc du Grand Troyes, 10300, Sainte-Savine, France
Tel.: (33) 325791956
Construction Contracting Services
N.A.I.C.S.: 236220

Santerne Est Telecoms SAS (1)
101 rue de Thionville ZA Jacques Velers, 57300, Ars-sur-Moselle, France
Tel.: (33) 387377586
Construction Contracting Services
N.A.I.C.S.: 236220

Santerne Ile-de-France SAS (1)
12-16 rue Sarah Bernhardt Immeuble Front Office Aile C-5e etage, 92600, Asnieres-sur-Seine, Cedex, France
Tel.: (33) 146522464
Construction Contracting Services
N.A.I.C.S.: 236220

Santerne Marseille SAS (1)
1 Avenue Paul Heroult, 13015, Marseille, France
Tel.: (33) 491095630
Construction Contracting Services
N.A.I.C.S.: 236220

Santerne Mayenne SAS (1)
558 Boulevard Francois Mitterand, BP 80060, 53102, Mayenne, Cedex, France
Tel.: (33) 243042664
Construction Contracting Services
N.A.I.C.S.: 236220

Santerne Mediterranee SAS (1)
579 Avenue du Docteur Fleming, 30900, Nimes, France
Tel.: (33) 466626800
Construction Contracting Services
N.A.I.C.S.: 236220

Santerne Nord Picardie Infra SAS (1)
93 route de Bethune, CS 90127, Sainte-Catherine-les-Arras, 62054, Calais, Cedex, France
Tel.: (33) 321609369
Construction Contracting Services
N.A.I.C.S.: 236220

Santerne Nord Tertiaire SAS (1)
7 Rue Angele Richard, 62217, Beaurains, France
Tel.: (33) 321600660
Construction Contracting Services
N.A.I.C.S.: 236220

Santerne Toulouse SAS (1)
35 Chemin des Tournesols Zone, Industrielle Ribaute Quint-Fonsegrives, 31130, Toulouse, France
Tel.: (33) 561248400
Construction Contracting Services
N.A.I.C.S.: 236220

Sarlec SAS (1)
Route de Bretteville sur Ay, BP 102, Montgardon La Haye-du-Puits, 50250, Maiche, France
Tel.: (33) 233766700
Construction Contracting Services
N.A.I.C.S.: 236220

Sarrasola SAS (1)
Rue de la Gare, Gresy-sur-Isere, 73460, Tours-en-Savoie, France
Tel.: (33) 479379416
Web Site: http://www.sarrasola.com
Construction Services
N.A.I.C.S.: 236220

Sassi BTP SAS (1)
35 Avenue de l'Arcalod, BP 105, 74152, Rumilly, France
Tel.: (33) 450018790
Urban Development Construction Services
N.A.I.C.S.: 236220

Schoro Electricite SAS (1)
5 rue de l Industrie, BP 09, 67116, Reichstett, France
Tel.: (33) 388182440
Web Site: http://www.schoro.fr
Electric Equipment Mfr
N.A.I.C.S.: 335313

Schuh Bodentechnik GmbH (1)
August-Borsig-Strasse 6, 68199, Mannheim, Germany
Tel.: (49) 62185097488
Web Site: http://www.schuh-bodentechnik.de
Flooring Contracting Services
N.A.I.C.S.: 238330

Schuh Brandschutz Und Sanierung GmbH (1)
Bredowstr 10, 22113, Hamburg, Germany
Tel.: (49) 4073343141
Fire Protection Equipment Installation Services
N.A.I.C.S.: 922160

Schweighouse Enrobes SAS (1)
ZI du Ried, BP 80307, Schweighouse-sur-Moder, 67507, Haguenau, France
Tel.: (33) 388727200
Urban Development Construction Services
N.A.I.C.S.: 236220

Scorel SAS (1)
Chemin de Saint Mathurin, Ouarville, Chartres, France
Tel.: (33) 237221860
Construction & Engineering Services
N.A.I.C.S.: 236220

Scorvalia SAS (1)
Rue Rene Descartes ZA de Penhoat, Plabennec, 29860, Brest, France
Tel.: (33) 298379878
Construction & Engineering Services
N.A.I.C.S.: 236220

Scorvalis SAS (1)
Vignoc, CS 60006, 35190, Tinteniac, France
Tel.: (33) 299696666
Construction & Engineering Services
N.A.I.C.S.: 236220

Se Contracting NV (1)
Verlorenbroodstraat 122 Sluispark, 9820, Merelbeke, Belgium
Tel.: (32) 93856711
Web Site: http://www.se-contracting.be
Construction Services
N.A.I.C.S.: 236220
Ritchy Vandesteene *(Mgr-Bus Unit)*

Seves SAS (1)
3 ZA la Tuilerie, Dracy-le-Fort, 71640, Bourgogne, France
Tel.: (33) 820821281
Web Site: http://www.seves.fr
Electrical Equipment Maintenance Services
N.A.I.C.S.: 811310

Sge-C Congo SA (1)
120-121 Boulevard Lyautey, BP 212, Brazzaville, Congo, Republic of
Tel.: (242) 56210175
Construction Services
N.A.I.C.S.: 236220

Sif Groutbor S.A. (1)
Av du Tir Federal 14, 1024, Ecublens, Switzerland
Tel.: (41) 216347822
Web Site: http://www.sif-groutbor.ch
Construction Services
N.A.I.C.S.: 236220

Signature Vertical Et Mobility Solutions SAS (1)
3 rue de la Flottiere ZAC de la Liodiere, 37300, Joue-les-Tours, France
Tel.: (33) 247266666
Signage & Road Equipment Mfr
N.A.I.C.S.: 333120

Signeos GmbH (1)
Romeracker 16, Linkenheim-Hochstetten, Karlsruhe, Germany
Tel.: (49) 7247949590
Web Site: http://www.signeos.de
Road & Highway Construction Services
N.A.I.C.S.: 237310

Silesia Asfalty Sp z o.o. (1)
ul Nad Bytomka 1, 44-100, Gliwice, Poland
Tel.: (48) 323318342
Web Site: http://www.silesiaasfalty.pl
Asphalt Mixture Mfr
N.A.I.C.S.: 324121

Sistem Infraestructuras Y Operaciones Epc SA (1)
Calle La Red Tres n42 P I La Red, 41500, Sevilla, Spain
Tel.: (34) 952179339
Construction Services
N.A.I.C.S.: 236220

Sistem Melesur Energia SAU (1)
C/Angostura de la Capellania 1, Alhaurin de la Torre, 29130, Malaga, Spain
Tel.: (34) 952179339
Web Site: http://www.sistemastecnico.com
Construction Services
N.A.I.C.S.: 236220

Sixense Canada Inc. (1)
5448 Timberlea Boulevard Unit 1, Mississauga, L4W 2T7, ON, Canada
Tel.: (647) 361-4266
Construction Services
N.A.I.C.S.: 236220

Sixense Digital SAS (1)
280 Avenue Napoleon Bonaparte, CS 60002, 92506, Rueil-Malmaison, Cedex, France
Tel.: (33) 147764262
Computer Software Development Services
N.A.I.C.S.: 513210

Sixense Iberia Limitada (1)
Av Dos Combatentes 52 Apto 112- Abrunheira, 2710-034, Sintra, Portugal
Tel.: (351) 219158210
Construction Services
N.A.I.C.S.: 236220

Sixense Iberia S.A. (1)
C/Velazquez 50 7 Planta, 28001, Madrid, Spain
Tel.: (34) 915624610
Construction Services
N.A.I.C.S.: 236220

Sixense Limited (1)
London Bridge Office 2nd Floor 7 Holyrood Street, London, SE1 2EL, United Kingdom
Tel.: (44) 1622609920
Construction Services
N.A.I.C.S.: 236220

Sixense Limited (1)
23/F Po Shau Centre 115 How Ming Street, Kwun Tong, Kowloon, China (Hong Kong)
Tel.: (852) 24397899
Construction Services
N.A.I.C.S.: 236220

Sixense Maping SAS (1)
280 Av Napoleon Bonaparte, 95200, Rueil-Malmaison, France
Tel.: (33) 147768181
Computer Software Development Services
N.A.I.C.S.: 513210

Sixense Maroc Sarl (1)
28 Avenue Mehdi Ben Barka, Souissi, 10170, Rabat, Morocco
Tel.: (212) 661372687
Construction Services
N.A.I.C.S.: 236220
Yassine Mounad *(Ops Mgr)*

Sixense Numerical Engineering Et Consulting Services SAS (1)
196 rue Houdan, 92330, Sceaux, France
Tel.: (33) 141138660
Engineeering Services
N.A.I.C.S.: 541330

Sixense Oceania Pty. Ltd. (1)
92 Thistlethwaite St, South Melbourne, 3205, VIC, Australia
Tel.: (61) 395100582
Construction & Engineering Services
N.A.I.C.S.: 236220

Sixense Soldata SAS (1)
21 rue du Port Parc de l'Ile, 92022, Nanterre, France
Tel.: (33) 141448500
Computer Software Development Services
N.A.I.C.S.: 513210

Skubb - Sand + Kies Union GmbH (1)
Franz-Ehrlich-Str 5, Berlin, Germany
Tel.: (49) 3054684513
Web Site: http://www.sand-kies-union.de
Construction Aggregate Product Mfr
N.A.I.C.S.: 327320

Smart Building Energies SA (1)
41, avenue de l'Harmonie, CS 10663, 59656, Villeneuve d'Ascq, France
Tel.: (33) 320164170
Web Site: http://www.smart-building-energies.com
Computerized System Maintenance Services
N.A.I.C.S.: 811210

Smart Grid Energy SAS (1)
7 rue de la Palinette ZA Les Deux Pins Porte A, Capbreton, 40130, Saint-Vincent-de-Tyrosse, France
Tel.: (33) 531600131
Web Site: http://www.smartgridenergy.fr
Energy Equipment Mfr
N.A.I.C.S.: 335999

Smv SAS (1)
84 Rue du Faubourg de Neaufles, 27140, Gisors, France
Tel.: (33) 232278500
Web Site: http://www.smv-sas.fr
Steel Tank Mfr
N.A.I.C.S.: 332420

Sobea Gabon SA (1)
Boulevard Remi Issembe, BP 3936, Libreville, Gabon
Tel.: (241) 728876
Construction Services
N.A.I.C.S.: 236220

Societe Bourbonnaise Industrielle d'Enrobes (1)
Rue Henri Cornu ZA de Cambaie, Saint-Paul, Reunion
Tel.: (262) 262424530
Construction Services
N.A.I.C.S.: 236220

Societe Bourbonnaise Industrielle de Prefabrication et de Beton (1)

VINCI S.A.

VINCI S.A.—(Continued)
Rue Sully Prudhomme ZIC N 3, BP 92013, 97824, Le Port, Cedex, Reunion
Tel.: (262) 262424545
Construction Services
N.A.I.C.S.: 236220

Société Bourbonnaise de Maintenance Industrielle (1)
2 Bd de la Marine ZI Sud II, BP 2013, 97824, Le Port, Cedex, Reunion
Tel.: (262) 262424510
Web Site: http://www.sbmi.fr
Construction Services
N.A.I.C.S.: 236220

Societe Bourbonnaise de TP & de Construction (1)
28 rue Jules Verne Z I C N 2, B P 92013, 97824, Le Port, Cedex, Reunion
Tel.: (262) 262424500
Web Site: http://www.sbtpc.re
Construction Services
N.A.I.C.S.: 236220

Societe Caledonienne de Batiment (1)
40 rue Auer, BP 1603, Zone Industrielle de Ducos, Noumea, New Caledonia
Tel.: (687) 244260
Construction Services
N.A.I.C.S.: 236220
Ludovic David *(Mgr-Methods Svcs)*

Société Champardennaise d'Entrepises Electriques (1)
7 rue Paul Maino Ecoparc Reims Sud, CS 50003, 51689, Reims, France
Tel.: (33) 326793030
Web Site: http://www.sceereims.fr
Construction Services
N.A.I.C.S.: 236220

Societe Champenoise d'Enrobes (1)
Route de Chalons, Sommesous, 51320, Chalons-en-Champagne, France
Tel.: (33) 326674822
Urban Development Construction Services
N.A.I.C.S.: 236220

Societe Corse Travaux (1)
RN 200, Aleria, 20270, Haute-Marne, France
Tel.: (33) 495565160
Urban Development Construction Services
N.A.I.C.S.: 236220

Societe EMCC (1)
7 Rue Ernest Flammarion ZAC Du Petit Le Roy Chevilly-Larue, 94659, Rungis, France
Tel.: (33) 1 49 61 71 00
Web Site: http://www.entreprise-emcc.fr
Sales Range: $900-999.9 Million
Emp.: 3,000
Construction & Maintenance Services
N.A.I.C.S.: 237990

Societe Lorraine d'Enrobes (1)
Anciennes carrieres de Solvay, 54320, Maxeville, France
Tel.: (33) 383987558
Urban Development Construction Services
N.A.I.C.S.: 236220

Societe Lorraine d'Exploitation de Terrils (1)
Roman Way, CS 20734, 57147, Woippy, Cedex, France
Tel.: (33) 387533440
Web Site: http://www.solodet.fr
Coal Shale Mining Services
N.A.I.C.S.: 212115

Societe Mahoraise des Eaux (1)
ZI Kaweni, BP 22, Mamoudzou, Saint-Lo, France
Tel.: (33) 269611142
Web Site: http://www.mahoraisedeseaux.com
Construction Services
N.A.I.C.S.: 236220

Societe Monegasque Jean Lefebvre (1)
Stade Louis II-19 Avenue des Castelans, 98000, Monaco, Monaco
Tel.: (377) 97984332
Urban Development Construction Services
N.A.I.C.S.: 236220

Societe Nicoise d'Enrobage (1)
217 route de Grenoble, Nice, France
Tel.: (33) 493832557
Construction & Engineering Services
N.A.I.C.S.: 236220

Societe Perino & Bordone (1)
126 Chemin de l'Ile du Pont, BP 95, Voreppe, 38342, Moirans, Cedex, France
Tel.: (33) 476504530
Construction & Engineering Services
N.A.I.C.S.: 236220

Societe Reunionnaise de Renovation (1)
11 rue Paul Verlaine Z I C N 2, Le Port, Reunion
Tel.: (262) 262424860
Web Site: http://www.s2r.re
Construction Services
N.A.I.C.S.: 236220

Societe Routiere du Midi (1)
Rue de Belle Aureille, Gap, France
Tel.: (33) 492516031
Web Site: http://www.routiere-du-midi.fr
Public & Road Work Construction Services
N.A.I.C.S.: 237310

Societe Signature Ocean Indien (1)
3 rue Patrice Lumumba ZA Ravine in Marquet, La Possession, 97419, Reunion
Tel.: (262) 262330626
Construction & Engineering Services
N.A.I.C.S.: 236220

Societe Yvelinoise de Materiaux et d'Enrobes SAS (1)
R Louis Lormand, 78320, La Verriere, France
Tel.: (33) 130138514
Web Site: http://yvelinoisedematriauxetden.com
Public & Road Work Construction Services
N.A.I.C.S.: 237310

Societe d'Applications Routieres (1)
103/105 rue des Trois Fontanot, CS 30096, Nanterre, Cedex, France
Tel.: (33) 141203100
Web Site: http://www.sar.fr
Urban Painting Mfr
N.A.I.C.S.: 325510

Societe d'Exploitation de L'Aeroport du Pays d'Ancenis (1)
60 Place Helene Boucher Aeroport d'Ancenis, 44150, Ancenis, France
Tel.: (33) 240961390
Construction & Engineering Services
N.A.I.C.S.: 236220

Societe de Materiaux Agglomeres Grenoblois (1)
126 Chemin de l'Ile du Pont, Voreppe, France
Tel.: (33) 476505490
Web Site: http://www.smag-granulats.fr
Aggregate Product Mfr & Distr
N.A.I.C.S.: 327320

Societe de construction de canalisations et de lignes electriques (1)
Avenue du Bourbonnais, CS 30011, 23230, Gouzon, France
Tel.: (33) 555622204
Web Site: http://www.socalec.fr
Electrical Equipment Maintenance Services
N.A.I.C.S.: 811310

Societe des Carbonates Piketti (1)
17 rue Georges Villette, Ecuelles, 77250, Seine-et-Marne, France
Tel.: (33) 160701241
Construction & Engineering Services
N.A.I.C.S.: 236220

Societe des Carrieres de Chailloue (1)
Les Bruyeres-Chailloue, 61500, Alencon, France
Tel.: (33) 233812650
Urban Development Construction Services
N.A.I.C.S.: 236220

Societe des Carrieres de Dompierre (1)
Lieudit La Custodelle, PO Box n 8, Dompierre sur Helpe, 59440, Hauts-de-Seine, France
Tel.: (33) 327572660
Urban Development Construction Services
N.A.I.C.S.: 236220

Societe des Carrieres du Boischaut (1)
Segondet, Chateaumeillant, 18370, Saint-Amand-Montrond, France
Tel.: (33) 248620323
Urban Development Construction Services
N.A.I.C.S.: 236220

Societe des Enrobes de Moulins Et des Environs (1)
14 rue Blaise Sallard, Yzeure, 03400, Lyon, France
Tel.: (33) 470449740
Construction Services
N.A.I.C.S.: 236220

Societe des Enrobes du Clermontois (1)
Les Graves, Varennes-sur-Morge, 63720, Le Puy, France
Tel.: (33) 477283634
Construction Services
N.A.I.C.S.: 236220

Societe des Enrobes du Plateau (1)
Rang De Bemont, Flangebouche, 25390, Pontarlier, France
Tel.: (33) 381432751
Web Site: http://www.societe-enrobes-plateau.fr
Bituminous Mix Product Mfr
N.A.I.C.S.: 324121

Societe des Etablissements Rescanieres (1)
Lieu-dit Les Breilhs, Roumengoux, 09500, Pamiers, France
Tel.: (33) 561681225
Urban Development Construction Services
N.A.I.C.S.: 236220

Societe des Materiaux Caennais (1)
ZI Caen Canal Zone Portuaire, 14550, Blainville-sur-Orne, France
Tel.: (33) 231358200
Urban Development Construction Services
N.A.I.C.S.: 236220

Societe des Transports Savreux (1)
14 rue du petit Versailles, BP 70041, Hauts-de-Seine, France
Tel.: (33) 322273434
Construction & Engineering Services
N.A.I.C.S.: 236220

Societe des Travaux Publics de L'Ouest (1)
Rue de l'Avenir, La Milesse, Le Mans, France
Tel.: (33) 243253000
Web Site: http://www.travaux-publics-ouest-milesse.fr
Public & Road Work Construction Services
N.A.I.C.S.: 237310

Societe'd exploitation des parcs de la Defense (1)
1 Place de la Pyramide, 92911, Puteaux, France
Tel.: (33) 800 19 28 35
Car Parking Services
N.A.I.C.S.: 812930

Sodilor SAS (1)
18 rue Rene Francois Jolly, South Industrial Park-ZI Neuwald, Sarreguemines, France
Tel.: (33) 387982588
Web Site: http://www.sodilor.fr
Road Safety Equipment Mfr
N.A.I.C.S.: 334290

Sodim Caraibes SAS (1)
Quartier Mangot Vulcin Immeuble Bois Quarre, Lamentin, France
Tel.: (33) 596669646
Construction Services
N.A.I.C.S.: 236220

Sofalic SAS (1)
77 Avenue du Progres, Chassieu, France
Tel.: (33) 472476834
Construction & Engineering Services
N.A.I.C.S.: 236220

Sofraden Industrie SAS (1)
70 rue de la Montat, Saint-Etienne, 42000, Lyon, France
Tel.: (33) 477410204
Web Site: https://www.sofraden.com
Industrial Mixer Mfr
N.A.I.C.S.: 333241
Stephane Carlu *(Supvr-Construction Site)*

Sogea Guyane SAS (1)
Rue de l Industrie ZAE Degrad des Cannes, Remire-Montjoly, Cayenne, French Guiana
Tel.: (594) 287296
Construction Services
N.A.I.C.S.: 236220
Sebastien Gautier *(Project Mgr)*

Sogea Martinique SAS (1)
206 Avenue Maurice-Bishop, CS 40485, 97241, Fort-de-France, Martinique
Tel.: (596) 731900
Construction Services
N.A.I.C.S.: 236220

Sogea Mayotte SAS (1)
Zone Industrielle de Kaweni, BP 147, Mamoudzou, Grande-Synthe, France
Tel.: (33) 269618211
Construction Services
N.A.I.C.S.: 236220
Franck Isnard *(Sr Mgr-Acctg)*

Sogea Reunion SAS (1)
1 Boulevard du Chaudron, BP 60021, Sainte-Clotilde, 97491, Saint-Denis, Cedex, Reunion
Tel.: (262) 483900
Web Site: http://www.sogea.re
Construction Services
N.A.I.C.S.: 236220

Sogea Satom Benin SA (1)
Rue de l hotel Aledjo Accor Quartier Akpakpa, BP 2190, Cotonou, Benin
Tel.: (229) 21330094
Construction Services
N.A.I.C.S.: 236220

Sogea Satom Senegal SA (1)
Route de Rufisque-Km 6 5-Boulevard du Centenaire, BP 968, de la Commune de Dakar, Dakar, Senegal
Tel.: (221) 338652222
Construction Services
N.A.I.C.S.: 236220

Soil Engineering Geoservices Ltd. (1)
Dewsbury Road Parkside Lane, Leeds, LS11 5SX, United Kingdom
Tel.: (44) 1132711111
Construction Services
N.A.I.C.S.: 236220

Soletanche Bachy Canada Ltd. (1)
3 Studebaker Place Unit 2, Hamilton, L8L 0C8, ON, Canada
Tel.: (905) 528-7924
Web Site: https://www.sb-canada.com
Construction Services
N.A.I.C.S.: 236220
Steven England *(VP-Berminghammer)*

Soletanche Bachy Cimas S.A. (1)
Calle 125 No.19 - 24 Oficina 401, Bogota, Colombia
Tel.: (57) 16922355
Web Site: http://www.soletanche-bachy.com.co
Engineeering Services
N.A.I.C.S.: 541330

Soletanche Bachy Fondations Speciales SAS (1)
18 rue des Pyrenees, 94150, Rungis, France
Tel.: (33) 156704200
Web Site: http://www.sbfs.fr
Engineeering Services
N.A.I.C.S.: 541330

Soletanche Bachy LLC (1)
Villa 464 18th November Street North A21BA, PO Box 1098, 121, Muscat, Oman
Tel.: (968) 24590851
Construction Services
N.A.I.C.S.: 236220

Soletanche Bachy Paraguay Srl (1)
Fortin Toledo 490 esquina Boqueron Barrio Mercedes, Asuncion, 1404, Paraguay

AND PRIVATE COMPANIES

VINCI S.A.

Tel.: (595) 981976962
Construction Services
N.A.I.C.S.: 236220

Soletanche Bachy Peru S.A. (1)
Ca Los Antares 320 Torreo B Oficina 806, Lima, 15038, Peru
Tel.: (51) 5001770
Web Site: http://www.web.soletanche-bachy.pe
Construction Services
N.A.I.C.S.: 236220
Eric Mendes *(Mgr-Construction)*

Soletanche Bachy Qatar WLL (1)
Office 20 3rd Floor Unit 301 Ibn Seena St Muntazah, Doha, Qatar
Tel.: (974) 44310581
Construction Services
N.A.I.C.S.: 236220

Soletanche Bachy Uruguay S.A. (1)
Juncal 1385 Piso 7, Montevideo, Uruguay
Tel.: (598) 29009192
Construction Services
N.A.I.C.S.: 236220

Soletanche Ceska Republika S.R.O. (1)
K Trebonicum 100/34, 155 00, Prague, Czech Republic
Tel.: (420) 271745212
Web Site: https://www.soletanche.cz
Construction Services
N.A.I.C.S.: 236220
Tomas Hreus *(Production Mgr)*

Soletanche Freyssinet Jordan Ltd. (1)
Zahran Street Between 7th and 8th Circle, Al Husseini Building No 33 9th floor - Office 910, Amman, Jordan
Tel.: (962) 65833449
Construction Services
N.A.I.C.S.: 236220

Solution Fondation Afrique de L'Ouest SA (1)
2A Imm BB Marcory Zone 4C Intersection of P Langevin St, BP 656, Rue P et M Curie St 01, Abidjan, Cote d'Ivoire
Tel.: (225) 21245912
Web Site: http://www.sfao-fondations.com
Construction Services
N.A.I.C.S.: 236220

Sonil (1)
51 Chemin Du Moulin Carron, 69570, Dardilly, France
Tel.: (33) 4 37 46 15 39
Web Site: http://www.sonil.fr
Construction Engineering Services
N.A.I.C.S.: 541330

Sopelec Reseaux SAS (1)
Route de Bonnay Zone Industrielle, Corbie, 80800, Picardie, France
Tel.: (33) 322483244
Construction Services
N.A.I.C.S.: 236220

Soretub SAS (1)
Boulevard de la Marine, BP 107, Le Port, Reunion
Tel.: (262) 439215
Construction Services
N.A.I.C.S.: 236220

Sotecnica Acores Limitada (1)
Estrada Nacional 11 Km 78 67, 2664-502, Sao Juliao do Tojal, Portugal
Tel.: (351) 219737000
Web Site: http://www.sotecnica.pt
Electrical & Electronic Product Mfr
N.A.I.C.S.: 335999

Sotmoz Limitada (1)
Av Da Namaacha 415 EN n 4 Parcela 730 Talhao 4/5, Matola, Mozambique
Tel.: (258) 21723028
Eletric Power Generation Services
N.A.I.C.S.: 221118

South West Highways Ltd. (1)
Rockbeare Hill, Rockbeare, Exeter, EX5 2HB, United Kingdom
Tel.: (44) 1404821500
Web Site: http://www.swhgroup.co.uk
Highway & Bridge Construction Services
N.A.I.C.S.: 237310
Steve Guilbert *(Mktg Mgr)*

Southern Pipeline Contractors Proprietary Limited (1)
6 Main Reef Road Dunswart 1508, Boksburg, Gauteng, South Africa
Tel.: (27) 119148500123
Web Site: http://www.spc.co.za
Construction Equipment Distr
N.A.I.C.S.: 423810

Spanbo NV (1)
Breulstraat 111a, 8890, Moorslede, Belgium
Tel.: (32) 51 78 00 33
Web Site: http://www.spanbo.be
Sales Range: $25-49.9 Million
Wood Products Mfr
N.A.I.C.S.: 321999

Spoting SA (1)
35 Principala Str, Strejnicu Prahova, 107592, Ploiesti, Romania
Tel.: (40) 344802496
Construction Contracting Services
N.A.I.C.S.: 236220

Stizo Nuclear SA (1)
Str Valea Cismelei nr 3, 905200, Cernavoda, Romania
Tel.: (40) 241238663
Construction Contracting Services
N.A.I.C.S.: 236220
Cezar Dragoi *(Mng Dir)*

Student Factory SAS (1)
59 rue Yves Kermen, 92100, Boulogne-Billancourt, France
Tel.: (33) 171250820
Web Site: http://www.student-factory.com
Residence Services
N.A.I.C.S.: 721110
Eric Lapierre *(Mng Dir)*

Sylvestre Energies SAS (1)
Zone d'Activites Piquet Ouest, Etrelles, 35370, Fougeres, France
Tel.: (33) 299962156
Web Site: http://www.s-energies.fr
Electric Equipment Mfr
N.A.I.C.S.: 335313

Synerail SAS (1)
143 Avenue de Verdun, 92130, Issy-les-Moulineaux, France
Tel.: (33) 185321985
Web Site: https://www.synerail.com
Telecommunication Servicesb
N.A.I.C.S.: 517810
Marc Milosevic *(Chm)*

Sysoco SAS (1)
36 rue Vaucanson, 69150, Decines-Charpieu, France
Tel.: (33) 472145310
Construction Services
N.A.I.C.S.: 236220

Systelcom SAS (1)
67 Montee de Saint Menet Parc de la Buzine Batiment D Bat D, 13011, Marseille, France
Tel.: (33) 491272780
Construction Services
N.A.I.C.S.: 236220

THG - BauGesellschaft mbH (1)
Huttenstrasse 55, Dahlem Baasem, Berlin, Germany
Tel.: (49) 655792000
Web Site: http://www.thg-baugesellschaft.de
Construction & Engineering Services
N.A.I.C.S.: 541330

TKP Krachan GmbH (1)
Eseiterstrasse 11, Illingen, Germany
Tel.: (49) 682540080
Web Site: http://www.tkp-krachan.de
Industrial Construction Services
N.A.I.C.S.: 236210

TREV-2 GRUPP AS (1)
Parnu Mnt 463, Tallinn, Estonia
Tel.: (372) 6776500
Web Site: http://www.trev2.ee
Emp.: 370
Road & Bridge Construction Services
N.A.I.C.S.: 237310
Margit Asperk *(Mgr-Quality)*

TS Traffic Systems GmbH (1)
Hamborner Str 20, Duisburg, Germany
Tel.: (49) 20348459800
Web Site: http://www.ts-trafficsystems.com

Traffic Safety Construction Services
N.A.I.C.S.: 237310

Talce SIA (1)
Stendes Street 3, Talsi, LV-3201, Latvia
Tel.: (371) 63291311
Road Construction Services
N.A.I.C.S.: 237310

Tebecon BV (1)
Argon 10, 4751 XC, Oud Gastel, Netherlands
Tel.: (31) 165316180
Web Site: http://www.tebecon.nl
Construction Services
N.A.I.C.S.: 236220

Technic Automation SAS (1)
214 Route de la Touffiere, Saint-Martin-Bellevue, 74370, Annecy, France
Tel.: (33) 450608079
Web Site: http://www.technic-automation.fr
Emp.: 35
Electric Equipment Mfr
N.A.I.C.S.: 335313

Tecuni, S.A. (1)
Parque Empresarial Abra Industrial s/n, Ortuella, 48530, Spain
Tel.: (34) 944 970 036
Energy Consulting Services
N.A.I.C.S.: 541690

Telematic Solutions S.r.l. (1)
Via Gallarate 205, 20151, Milan, MI, Italy
Tel.: (39) 0230468151
Web Site: https://www.telematicsolutions.it
Aerospace Equipment Maintenance Services
N.A.I.C.S.: 811310
Luigi Passariello *(Mng Dir)*

Tema SAS (1)
7526 Route du Developpement, BP 212, 59820, Gravelines, France
Tel.: (33) 328652322
Construction Services
N.A.I.C.S.: 236220

Terre Armee K K (1)
3-109 6 -Chome Tamagawa Gakuen, Machida, Tokyo, Japan
Tel.: (81) 427221134
Construction Services
N.A.I.C.S.: 236220

Terre D'Azur SAS (1)
1904 Route de Pegomas, 06370, Mouans-Sartoux, France
Tel.: (33) 620600358
Web Site: https://www.terredazur.org
Medical Consulting Services
N.A.I.C.S.: 541611
Jeanne Meslier de Rocan *(Pres)*

Terryn Hout nv (1)
Nieuwstraat 8, Moorslede, 8890, Belgium
Tel.: (32) 51 78 03 56
Web Site: http://www.terrynhout.be
Sales Range: $25-49.9 Million
Emp.: 15
Wood Products Mfr
N.A.I.C.S.: 321999
Geert Terryn *(Gen Mgr)*

Tg Concept SAS (1)
109 rue du 1er Mars 1943 Actimart Batiment E, 69100, Villeurbanne, France
Tel.: (33) 437916740
Web Site: https://www.tgconcept.com
Aerospace Equipment Maintenance Services
N.A.I.C.S.: 811310
Pascal Teboul *(Mgr-Bus Unit)*

Tg Concept Suisse SA (1)
31 Route de l'aeroport, Case postale 813, 1215, Geneva, Switzerland
Tel.: (41) 227993041
Engineeering Services
N.A.I.C.S.: 541330

Thales (1)
Dari 33 2nd Floor Building 2, 50197, Zaragoza, Spain
Tel.: (34) 976 304 101
Web Site: http://www.thales.es
Energy Consulting Services
N.A.I.C.S.: 541690

Thermo Refrigeration SAS (1)
Zone Industrielle du Puits, Luceau, 72500, Chateau-du-Loir, France
Tel.: (33) 243381010
Web Site: https://www.thermorefrigeration.com
Refrigerator Equipment Mfr
N.A.I.C.S.: 333415
Xavier Farrugia *(Mgr-Bus Unit)*

Tierra Armada C.A. (1)
Av Principal de Los Ruices con 3ra Transversal, Edificio Lanex Piso 1 Ofic 1-B Los Ruices, Caracas, 1071, Venezuela
Tel.: (58) 2122388285
Construction Services
N.A.I.C.S.: 236220

Toll Collect GmbH (1)
Linkstrasse 4, 10785, Berlin, Germany
Tel.: (49) 3025291303
Web Site: https://www.toll-collect.de
Emp.: 650
Toll Highway Operator
N.A.I.C.S.: 488490
Gerhard Schulz *(CEO & Member-Exec Bd)*

Tout L'Temps Presse SAS (1)
28 rue Louis Guerin, 69100, Villeurbanne, France
Tel.: (33) 437286926
Construction Services
N.A.I.C.S.: 236220
Roland Vicaire *(CTO)*

Tpi s.r.o. (1)
Kralovska ulica 8/824, 927 01, Sala, Slovakia
Tel.: (421) 225988983
Fire Protection Equipment Installation Services
N.A.I.C.S.: 922160

Trabit S.A.U. (1)
Ctra de la Poveda a Velilla de San Antonio Km 2 800, Madrid, Spain
Tel.: (34) 916553505
Web Site: http://www.trabit.es
Bituminous Mixture Mfr
N.A.I.C.S.: 324121

Tranzcom NV (1)
Biestebroekkaai 300, 1070, Anderlecht, Belgium
Tel.: (32) 25296211
Web Site: http://www.tranzcom.com
Information Technology Development Services
N.A.I.C.S.: 541511

Travaux Publics Goulard SAS (1)
92 rue Gambetta, CS 80598, 77215, Avon, France
Tel.: (33) 160745650
Urban Development Construction Services
N.A.I.C.S.: 236220

Travesset SAS (1)
242 Avenue du Progres, Teyran, 34820, Montpellier, France
Tel.: (33) 467872110
Web Site: http://www.travesset-beziers.fr
Indoor Electricity Repairing Services
N.A.I.C.S.: 811198

Trellis s.r.o. (1)
Rybarska 5, 911 01, Trencin, Slovakia
Tel.: (421) 3265251613
Web Site: http://www.trellis.sk
Electrical Wiring Installation Services
N.A.I.C.S.: 238210

Trmc SAS (1)
629 Route des Carrieres, Saint Martin Belle Roche, 71118, Macon, France
Tel.: (33) 385239400
Urban Development Construction Services
N.A.I.C.S.: 236220

Truck Etape Bezier SAS (1)
Rue de Vienne, Vendres, 34350, Beziers, France
Tel.: (33) 467620620
Web Site: http://www.trucketape-beziers.com
Vehicle Parking Services
N.A.I.C.S.: 812930

Tunzini Antilles SAS (1)
1 2 km route du Vert Pre Chemin Bois Carre, 97284, Lamentin, Martinique
Tel.: (596) 596512321

VINCI S.A.

VINCI S.A.—(Continued)

Web Site: http://www.tunzini-antilles.fr
Engineering Services
N.A.I.C.S.: 541330

Tunzini Bordeaux SAS (1)
1 Alley of Megevie, 33170, Gradignan, France
Tel.: (33) 556077600
Web Site: http://www.tunzini-toulouse.fr
Electrical Equipment Maintenance Services
N.A.I.C.S.: 811310

Tunzini Guadeloupe SAS (1)
10 lot Vince Arnouville, Petit-Bourg, 97170, Basse Terre, Guadeloupe
Tel.: (590) 590384880
Construction Services
N.A.I.C.S.: 236220

Tunzini Limoges SAS (1)
45 Rue Philippe Lebon, 87280, Limoges, France
Tel.: (33) 555377825
Web Site: http://www.tunzini-grand-ouest.fr
Electrical Equipment Maintenance Services
N.A.I.C.S.: 811310

Tunzini Maintenance Nucleaire SAS (1)
259-261 Avenue Jean Jaures, CS 10218, Le Sunway Building, 69362, Lyon, Cedex, France
Tel.: (33) 472218340
Web Site: http://www.tunzinimn.fr
Nuclear Power Plant Maintenance Services
N.A.I.C.S.: 221113

Tunzini Nucleaire SAS (1)
60 route de Sartrouville Parc Des Grillons VI, 78230, Le Pecq, France
Tel.: (33) 130093475
Construction Services
N.A.I.C.S.: 236220
Romain Descourvieres *(Engr-Bid)*

Tunzini Protection Inc.endie SAS (1)
13 Allee Rosa Luxembourg Immeuble Le Regent, CS 50063, 95610, Eragny-sur-Oise, France
Tel.: (33) 130270990
Construction Services
N.A.I.C.S.: 236220

UNIASFALT s. r. o. (1)
Selpice 136, 919 09, Trnava, Slovakia
Tel.: (421) 902986327
Web Site: http://www.eurovia.sk
Road Construction & Maintenance Services
N.A.I.C.S.: 237310

Urbain Pro Valenton SAS (1)
10 rue de Penthievre, 75008, Paris, France
Tel.: (33) 662691472
Web Site: http://www.urbain-pro.com
Real Estate Property Services
N.A.I.C.S.: 531390

Uxello Grand Ouest SAS (1)
4 rue Charles Coude ZA La Porte de Ker Lann, CS 57214, 35174, Bruz, Cedex, France
Tel.: (33) 299834472
Construction Services
N.A.I.C.S.: 236220

Uxello Sud Ouest SAS (1)
19 Boulevard de l Industrie ZI du Pahin, 31170, Tournefeuille, France
Tel.: (33) 534552270
Construction Services
N.A.I.C.S.: 236220

VIA Structure GmbH (1)
Franz-Ehrlich-Strasse 5, Berlin, Germany
Tel.: (49) 3054684802
Construction & Engineering Services
N.A.I.C.S.: 236220

VIALAB s.r.o (1)
Narodni 138/10, Prague, Czech Republic
Tel.: (420) 224952222
Construction & Engineering Services
N.A.I.C.S.: 236220

VINCI Airports Japan KK (1)
1-2-3 Toranomon 5th Floor Toranomon Seiwa Bldg, Minato-ku, Tokyo, 105-0001, Japan
Tel.: (81) 345001397
Logistic Services

N.A.I.C.S.: 488510
Leo A. Chalon *(Mgr-Fin & Project)*

VINCI Airports SAS (1)
12/14 rue Louis Bleriot, PO Box 30071, Cedex, 92506, Rueil-Malmaison, Cedex, France **(100%)**
Tel.: (33) 147164640
Web Site: http://www.vinci-airports.com
Sales Range: $1-4.9 Billion
Emp.: 13,200
Airport Operation Services
N.A.I.C.S.: 488119
Nicholas Notebaert *(Pres)*

Subsidiary (Non-US):

Gatwick Airport Ltd. (2)
5th Floor Destinations Place Gatwick Airport, Gatwick, RH6 0NP, West Sussex, United Kingdom **(50.01%)**
Tel.: (44) 8448920322
Web Site: http://www.gatwickairport.com
Rev.: $1,028,921,416
Assets: $4,150,203,008
Liabilities: $3,810,993,962
Net Worth: $339,209,046
Earnings: $72,207,238
Emp.: 3,037
Fiscal Year-end: 03/31/2019
Airport Operator
N.A.I.C.S.: 488119
Stewart Wingate *(CEO)*

Subsidiary (Domestic):

SEACFA - Clermont-Ferrand airport (2)
Clermont-Ferrand Auvergne Airport, Clermont, France
Tel.: (33) 4 73 62 71 02
Airport Management Services
N.A.I.C.S.: 488119

SEAGI - Grenoble airport (2)
de St Geoirs, 38590, Saint Etienne, France
Tel.: (33) 4 76 65 48 48
Web Site: http://www.grenoble-airport.com
Emp.: 50
Airport Management Services
N.A.I.C.S.: 488119

SEAQC - Societe d'exploitation de l'aeroport de Quimper (2)
Quimper Cornouaille Airport, Pluguffan, 29700, France
Tel.: (33) 2 98 94 30 30
Web Site: http://www.quimper.aeroport.fr
Sales Range: $25-49.9 Million
Emp.: 36
Airport Management Services
N.A.I.C.S.: 488119

Societe Concessionnaire des Aeroports du Grand Ouest (2)
Aeroport Nantes Atlantique, 44346, Bouguenais, France
Tel.: (33) 8 92 56 88 00
Airport Management Services
N.A.I.C.S.: 488119

VINCI Concessions SA (1)
2 Rizariou Str, 152 33, Halandri, Greece
Tel.: (30) 2106858196
Construction & Engineering Services
N.A.I.C.S.: 236220

VINCI Concessions SAS (1)
1 Cours Ferdinand De Lesseps, 92851, Rueil-Malmaison, France **(100%)**
Tel.: (33) 147163500
Web Site: http://www.vinci-concessions.com
Sales Range: $1-4.9 Billion
Emp.: 1,000
Transport Infrastructure & Airport Engineering Services; Stadium & Parking Lot Builder & Operator
N.A.I.C.S.: 488119

Subsidiary (Domestic):

Autoroutes du Sud de la France (2)
9 place de l'europe, 92851, Rueil-Malmaison, France
Tel.: (33) 147164500
Web Site: http://www.asf.fr
Sales Range: $400-449.9 Million
Toll Road Builder & Operator
N.A.I.C.S.: 237310
Pierre Coppey *(Chm)*

Subsidiary (Domestic):

ESCOTA (3)
432 avenue de Cannes, BP 41, 06211, Mandelieu-la-Napoule, France
Tel.: (33) 4 93 48 50 00
Road Construction & Maintenance Services
N.A.I.C.S.: 237310

Subsidiary (Domestic):

Cofiroute SA (2)
6 10 Rue Troyon, 92316, Sevres, France
Tel.: (33) 141147018
Web Site: http://www.cofiroute.fr
Toll Road Builder & Operator
N.A.I.C.S.: 237310
Jerome Lejeune *(Dir-Ops)*

Subsidiary (US):

Cofiroute Corporation (3)
200 Spectrum Ctr Dr 1650, Irvine, CA 92618
Tel.: (949) 754-0198
Web Site: http://www.cofirouteusa.com
Sales Range: $25-49.9 Million
Emp.: 80
Toll Highway Operator
N.A.I.C.S.: 488490
Jan Mittermeier *(COO)*

Subsidiary (Non-US):

Cofiroute Uk Ltd (3)
Severn Crossings - Toll Administration Building Access road - Aust, BS35 4BE, Bristol, United Kingdom - England
Tel.: (44) 1454 632 457
Web Site: http://www.cofiroute.co.uk
Sales Range: $25-49.9 Million
Emp.: 6
Toll Highway Operator
N.A.I.C.S.: 488490

Subsidiary (Non-US):

GEFYRA LITOURGIA S.A. (2)
Antirion Aetoloakarnania, Antirrio, 30020, Greece
Tel.: (30) 26 34 03 9000
Construction & Maintenance Services
N.A.I.C.S.: 237310

Gefyra S.A. (2)
2 Rizariou St, 15233, Halandri, Athens, Greece
Tel.: (30) 2106858196
Web Site: http://www.gefyra.gr
Sales Range: $25-49.9 Million
Emp.: 100
Specialty Trade Contractors
N.A.I.C.S.: 238990

Granvia Operation s.r.o. (2)
SSUR Selenec, PO Box 19A, 949 01, Nitra, Slovakia
Tel.: (421) 91 7472 684
Highway Construction Engineering Services
N.A.I.C.S.: 237310

Societe Concessionnaire de la Aeroport (SCA) (2)
Phnom Penh International Airport National Road No 4, PO Box 1256, Kakab Commune Posenchey District, Phnom Penh, Cambodia **(70%)**
Tel.: (855) 23890520
Web Site: http://www.vinci-construction.com
Airport Construction & Operation
N.A.I.C.S.: 488119

VINCI Concessions Canada Inc. (2)
8200 Boulevard Decarie Bureau 200, Montreal, H4P 2P5, QC, Canada
Tel.: (514) 733-8616
Construction Engineering Services
N.A.I.C.S.: 541330

VINCI Concessions Deutschland GmbH (2)
Franz-Ehrlich-Strasse 5, 12489, Berlin, Germany
Tel.: (49) 30206033300
Web Site: http://www.vinci.com
Construction & Maintenance Services
N.A.I.C.S.: 237990

VINCI Concessions India Pvt. Ltd. (2)
Unit No 824 8th Floor DLF Tower-B Plot No

INTERNATIONAL PUBLIC

11, NH Commercial Centre Jasola, 110025, New Delhi, India
Tel.: (91) 11 40567660
Construction & Maintenance Services
N.A.I.C.S.: 237990

VINCI Concessions UK Limited (1)
1 Eversholt Street, London, NW1 2DN, United Kingdom
Tel.: (44) 2075540777
Construction & Engineering Services
N.A.I.C.S.: 236220
Henry Snow *(CFO)*

VINCI Construction Dom Tom SAS (1)
9 Place de l Europe, 92851, Rueil-Malmaison, Cedex, France
Tel.: (33) 147168008
Web Site: http://www.vinci-construction-domtom.com
Construction Services
N.A.I.C.S.: 236220
Philippe Goulley *(Pres)*

VINCI Construction SAS (1)
1 Cours Ferdinand De Lesseps, 92851, Rueil-Malmaison, Cedex, France **(100%)**
Tel.: (33) 147163500
Web Site: http://www.vinci-construction.com
Sales Range: $400-449.9 Million
Emp.: 2,500
Construction Services
N.A.I.C.S.: 236220
Hugues Fourmentraux *(Chm)*

Subsidiary (Domestic):

ADIM Est (2)
ZA Lesmenils, BP 69, 54703, Pont-a-Mousson, France
Tel.: (33) 3 83 80 83 34
Web Site: http://www.adim-est.fr
Property Development Services
N.A.I.C.S.: 531390

Subsidiary (Non-US):

APS Alkon a.s. (2)
Osloboditelov 66, 040 17, Kosice, Slovakia
Tel.: (421) 55 381 27 57
Web Site: http://www.apsalkon.sk
Civil Engineering Construction Services
N.A.I.C.S.: 237990

Subsidiary (Domestic):

Chanzy Pardoux (2)
19 route d'Eschau, 67411, Illkirch-Graffenstaden, France
Tel.: (33) 3 90 40 33 80
Historical Monument Maintenance Services
N.A.I.C.S.: 811198

Subsidiary (Non-US):

Cimentaciones Mexicanas S.A. DE C.V. (2)
Paseo de la Reforma 300-13, Col Juarez, 06600, Mexico, Mexico
Tel.: (52) 55 52 07 30 68
Web Site: http://www.cimesa.net
Civil Engineering Construction Services
N.A.I.C.S.: 237990

Subsidiary (Domestic):

DODIN CAMPENON BERNARD SAS (2)
20 Chemin de la Flambere, BP 83128, 31026, Toulouse, Cedex, France
Tel.: (33) 5 62 74 80 40
Web Site: http://www.dodincampenonbernard.fr
Construction Engineering Services
N.A.I.C.S.: 541330

Subsidiary (Non-US):

Dumez-GTM Caledonie (2)
route Territoriale 1 - Auteuil, BP 2086, Commune de Dumbea, 98846, Noumea, New Caledonia
Tel.: (687) 41 40 40
Construction Engineering Services
N.A.I.C.S.: 541330

Freyssinet International & Cie (2)
24 Rue Pasquier Brounde Bir Mourad Rais Les Sources, 16300, Algiers, Algeria
Tel.: (213) 21542800

AND PRIVATE COMPANIES VINCI S.A.

Web Site: http://www.vinci.com
Construction Engineering Services
N.A.I.C.S.: 541330

Subsidiary (Domestic):

GTM Batiment (2)
61 avenue Jules Quentin, 92730, Nanterre, Cedex, France **(100%)**
Tel.: (33) 146957000
Web Site: http://www.gtm-batiment.fr
Sales Range: $25-49.9 Million
Construction Services
N.A.I.C.S.: 236220

GTM Terrassement (2)
61 Ave Jules Quentin, 92000, Nanterre, Cedex, France **(100%)**
Tel.: (33) 146957850
Web Site: http://www.vinci-construction-terrassement.fr
Sales Range: $25-49.9 Million
Emp.: 50
Transport Infrastructure Construction Services
N.A.I.C.S.: 237310
Florence Ahnine *(Sec)*

Subsidiary (Non-US):

Hidepito Zrt. (2)
Karikas Frigyes u 20, 1138, Budapest, Hungary
Tel.: (36) 14652200
Web Site: http://www.hidepito.hu
Sales Range: $125-149.9 Million
Engineering & Construction Services
N.A.I.C.S.: 541330
Laszslo Sal *(CEO)*

Novkol A.D. (2)
Surcinski Put 1k, 11077, Belgrade, Serbia
Tel.: (381) 11 7129 180
Web Site: http://www.novkol.co.rs
Sales Range: $50-74.9 Million
Emp.: 120
Construction Engineering Services
N.A.I.C.S.: 237990

Prumstav a.s. (2)
Vyskocilova 1566, 140 00, Prague, Czech Republic
Tel.: (420) 244096111
Web Site: https://www.prumstav.cz
Construction Engineering Services
N.A.I.C.S.: 237990

SADUC - Saudi Arabian Dumez Co. Ltd (2)
PO Box 6645, 11452, Riyadh, Saudi Arabia
Tel.: (966) 14191395
Web Site: http://www.vinci-construction.com
Construction Services
N.A.I.C.S.: 236220

SMP CZ a.s. (2)
Vyskocilova 1566, 14000, Prague, Czech Republic
Tel.: (420) 222185111
Web Site: http://www.smp.cz
Construction Engineering Services
N.A.I.C.S.: 541330

Seymour Whyte Ltd. (2)
12 Electronics Street, PO Box 4436, Eight Mile Plains, 4113, QLD, Australia
Tel.: (61) 733404800
Web Site: https://www.seymourwhyte.com.au
Holding Company; Civil Engineering & Building Construction
N.A.I.C.S.: 551112
Steve Davies-Evans *(Mgr-Natl Precontracts-Seymour Whyte Constructions)*

Subsidiary (Domestic):

Seymour Whyte Constructions Pty Ltd (3)
Brisbane Technology Park 12 Electronics St, PO Box 4436, Eight Mile Plains, 4113, QLD, Australia
Tel.: (61) 733404800
Web Site: http://www.seymourwhyte.com.au
Civil Engineering & Construction
N.A.I.C.S.: 237990
Will Macdonald *(Mgr-Ops)*

Subsidiary (Domestic):

Sogea Est (2)
415 Avenue de Boufflers, 54520, Laxou, France
Tel.: (33) 383672500
Web Site: http://www.sogea-est.fr
Construction Engineering Services
N.A.I.C.S.: 541330

Sogea-Satom SA (2)
9 Place de l Europe, 92500, Rueil-Malmaison, France
Tel.: (33) 147163500
Web Site: http://www.sogea-satom.com
Construction Engineering Services
N.A.I.C.S.: 541330

Subsidiary (Non-US):

Sogea Maroc (3)
Quartier Industriel De Ain Atiq, PO Box 81, Oued Ykem, 12000, Temara, Morocco
Tel.: (212) 537 61 52 00
Web Site: http://sogea-maroc.com
Emp.: 2,100
Construction Engineering Services
N.A.I.C.S.: 541330

Sogea Satom Cameroun (3)
Nouvelle Route Bastos, BP 5680 Yaounde, Douala, Cameroon
Tel.: (237) 22 20 18 89
Construction Engineering Services
N.A.I.C.S.: 541330

Sogea Satom Kenya Ltd (3)
2nd Avenue Parklands, PO Box 39367, 00623, Nairobi, Kenya
Tel.: (254) 20 37 44 288
Construction Engineering Services
N.A.I.C.S.: 541330

Sogea-Satom Gabon (3)
Boulevard Remi Issembe Zone Industrielle d Oloumi, BP 781, Libreville, Gabon
Tel.: (241) 72 88 76
Construction Engineering Services
N.A.I.C.S.: 541330

Sogea-Satom Guinee Equatoriale (3)
Carretera del Puerto, Bata, Equatorial Guinea
Tel.: (240) 333 08 10 12
Construction Engineering Services
N.A.I.C.S.: 541330

Sogea-Satom Tanzanie (3)
Plot no 49/1 Block Mikocheni Service Industrial Area, PO Box 32 093, 255, Dar es Salaam, Tanzania
Tel.: (255) 22 27 72 290
Web Site: http://www.vinci-construction.com
Construction Engineering Services
N.A.I.C.S.: 541330

Sogea-Satom Togo (3)
Rue de la Mission Baptiste, BP 35, Lome, Togo
Tel.: (228) 261 55 82
Construction Engineering Services
N.A.I.C.S.: 541330

Subsidiary (Domestic):

Soletanche Freyssinet S.A. (2)
280 Avenue Napoleon Bonaparte, 92500, Rueil-Malmaison, France
Tel.: (33) 147764262
Web Site: https://www.soletanchefreyssinet.com
Emp.: 22,100
Civil Engineering Construction Services
N.A.I.C.S.: 237990
Manuel Peltier *(Chm)*

Subsidiary (Non-US):

AB Skandinavisk Spaendbetong (3)
Roersjoegatan 26, 211 37, Malmo, Sweden
Tel.: (46) 40 9814 00
Web Site: http://www.vinci-construction.com
Construction Engineering Services
N.A.I.C.S.: 541330

ALGA S.p.A. (3)
Via Dei Missaglia 97/A2, 20142, Milan, Italy
Tel.: (39) 02 48569 1
Web Site: http://www.alga.it
Construction Engineering Services
N.A.I.C.S.: 541330

Subsidiary (US):

Advanced Foundations Systems Inc. (3)
7108 S Alton Way Bldg D, Centennial, CO 80112-2106
Tel.: (303) 926-0411
Web Site: http://www.nicholsonconstruction.com
Emp.: 6
Construction Engineering Services
N.A.I.C.S.: 541330

Subsidiary (Non-US):

BVT DYNIV GmbH (3)
Hittfelder Kirchweg 2, 21220, Seevetal, Germany
Tel.: (49) 4105 6648 0
Web Site: http://www.dyniv.com
Construction Engineering Services
N.A.I.C.S.: 541330
John Luke Shomini *(Gen Mgr)*

Bachy Belgique (3)
Rue del Abreuvoir 1B, 1170, Brussels, Belgium
Tel.: (32) 2 733 20 12
Construction Engineering Services
N.A.I.C.S.: 541330
Daniel Viargues *(Dir)*

Bachy Fundaciones SA (3)
Av Ricardo J Alfaro, Panama, Panama
Tel.: (507) 230 10 86
Construction Engineering Services
N.A.I.C.S.: 541330

Bachy Soletanche Group Ltd (3)
305-8 Harcourt House 39 Gloucester Road, Wanchai, China (Hong Kong)
Tel.: (852) 2369 2869
Web Site: http://www.bachy-soletanche.com.hk
Emp.: 500
Construction Engineering Services
N.A.I.C.S.: 541330

Subsidiary (Non-US):

BSG Construction Malaysia SDN BHD (4)
C1-3-1 Solaris Dutamas 1 Jalan Dutamas 1, Kuala Lumpur, 50480, Malaysia
Tel.: (60) 3 6205 3693
Web Site: http://www.bachy-soletanche.com.hk
Emp.: 100
Construction Engineering Services
N.A.I.C.S.: 541330

Subsidiary (Non-US):

Bachy Soletanche Singapore PTE LTD (3)
1 Coleman Street 06-09 The Adelphi, Singapore, 179803, Singapore
Tel.: (65) 6538 1715
Web Site: http://www.bachy-soletanche.com.sg
Construction Engineering Services
N.A.I.C.S.: 541330

Bachy Soletanche Vietnam Co., Ltd. (3)
126 Nguyen Thi Minh Khai, District 3, Ho Chi Minh City, Vietnam
Tel.: (84) 8 3930 57 82
Web Site: http://www.bachy-soletanche.vn
Construction Engineering Services
N.A.I.C.S.: 541330

Bewehrte Erde GmbH (3)
An der Strusbek 60-62, 22926, Ahrensburg, Germany
Tel.: (49) 4102 457 220
Web Site: http://www.bewehrte-erde.de
Engineeering Services
N.A.I.C.S.: 541330

Subsidiary (US):

DGI Menard Inc. (3)
150 E Main St, Carnegie, PA 15106
Tel.: (412) 257-2750
Web Site: http://www.menardusa.com
Emp.: 100
Ground Engineering Services
N.A.I.C.S.: 541330
Brandon Buschmeier *(VP)*

Subsidiary (Domestic):

Epios (3)
Port Fluvial - 1ere Avenue, 59211, Santes, France
Tel.: (33) 3 20 18 08 10
Construction Engineering Services
N.A.I.C.S.: 541330

Subsidiary (Non-US):

Europile Palteknik AB (3)
Asperedsgatan 9, Gunnilse, 42457, Sweden
Tel.: (46) 31 330 32 30
Web Site: http://www.aarsleff.se
Emp.: 50
Construction Engineering Services
N.A.I.C.S.: 541330

F.K.K. Kyokuto Kogen Concrete Shinko Co. Ltd (3)
Gotanda TG Building 5th Floor 7-9-2 Nishi-Gotanda, Shinagawa-ku, Tokyo, 141-0031, Japan
Tel.: (81) 3 5719 2391
Web Site: http://www.fkk-j.co.jp
Civil Engineering Construction Services
N.A.I.C.S.: 237990

Fontec SA (3)
Avenue Delleur 15, 1170, Brussels, Belgium
Tel.: (32) 2 663 62 00
Construction Engineering Services
N.A.I.C.S.: 541330

Freyrom SA (3)
199a Soseaua Industriilor, Chiajna, 077040, Romania
Tel.: (40) 213 104567
Web Site: http://www.freyrom.ro
Sales Range: $25-49.9 Million
Construction Engineering Services
N.A.I.C.S.: 541330

Freyssinet - Terra Armada S.A. (3)
Rua Padre Americo N 8b Escritorio 2 - Terracos S Paulo, 1600-548, Lisbon, Portugal
Tel.: (351) 21 716 16 75
Web Site: http://www.terre-armee.com
Construction Engineering Services
N.A.I.C.S.: 541330

Freyssinet - Tierra Armada CA (3)
Av Principal de los Ruices con 3era Transversal Edif Lanex Piso 1, Ofic 1-B Los Ruices Municipio Sucre, Caracas, Venezuela
Tel.: (58) 212 238 82 85
Web Site: http://www.tierra-armada.com.ve
Construction Engineering Services
N.A.I.C.S.: 541330

Freyssinet - Tierra Armada S.A. (3)
Cerrito 1136 1 Piso Frente, C1010AAX, Buenos Aires, Argentina
Tel.: (54) 11 4372 7291
Web Site: http://www.vinci.com
Sales Range: $10-24.9 Million
Emp.: 50
Construction Engineering Services
N.A.I.C.S.: 541330

Freyssinet Arabian Sea LLC (3)
PO Box 1320, 112, Ruwi, Oman
Tel.: (968) 2 448 7152
Web Site: http://www.vinci.com
Construction Engineering Services
N.A.I.C.S.: 541330

Freyssinet Australia (3)
Level 3 13-15 Lyonpark Road, Macquarie Park, 2113, NSW, Australia
Tel.: (61) 2 9491 7177
Web Site: http://www.freyssinet.com.au
Construction Engineering Services
N.A.I.C.S.: 541330

Freyssinet Belgium N.V. (3)
Harensesteenweg 299, 1800, Vilvoorde, Belgium
Tel.: (32) 22520740
Web Site: http://www.en.freyssinet.be
Sales Range: $25-49.9 Million
Emp.: 40
Civil Engineering Construction Services
N.A.I.C.S.: 237990
Herman Wanzeele *(Gen Mgr)*

Subsidiary (Domestic):

Freyssinet France (3)
1 Bis Rue Du Petit Clamart Batiment, BP 135, 78148, Velizy-Villacoublay, France
Tel.: (33) 1 46 01 84 84

VINCI S.A.

VINCI S.A.—(Continued)
Web Site: http://www.freyssinet.fr
Sales Range: $150-199.9 Million
Emp.: 600
Construction & Maintenance Services
N.A.I.C.S.: 541330

Subsidiary (Non-US):

Freyssinet Gulf LLC (3)
Al Saraya Building Block A 1st floor, PO Box 36211, Dubai, 36211, United Arab Emirates
Tel.: (971) 4 2094 900
Emp.: 100
Site Preparation Services
N.A.I.C.S.: 238910
Khalil Doghri *(Gen Mgr)*

Freyssinet Hong Kong Ltd (3)
833 Cheung Sha Wan Road Room 705-706 7/F Tower 1, Cheung Sha Wan Plaza, Kowloon, China (Hong Kong)
Tel.: (852) 2794 0322
Web Site: http://www.vinci.com
Emp.: 60
Construction Engineering Services
N.A.I.C.S.: 541330

Subsidiary (US):

Freyssinet Inc. (3)
44880 Falcon Pl Ste 100, Sterling, VA 20166
Tel.: (703) 378-2500
Web Site: http://www.freyssinetusa.com
Emp.: 30
Construction Engineering Services
N.A.I.C.S.: 541330

Subsidiary (Non-US):

Freyssinet International & Cie (3)
13 Rue Mohamed Ibn Ishak Avenue Ahmed Balafrej Souissi, 10170, Rabat, Morocco
Tel.: (212) 537564435
Construction Engineering Services
N.A.I.C.S.: 541330

Freyssinet Ireland (3)
Unit J5 M7 Business Park Naas Co, Kildare, Ireland
Tel.: (353) 45 884896
Web Site: http://www.freyssinetireland.ie
Sales Range: $25-49.9 Million
Emp.: 3
Construction Engineering Services
N.A.I.C.S.: 541330

Freyssinet Jordan LLC (3)
Swefieh - Wakalat Street - Al-Fadi Building 2nd Floor Office No 2, PO Box 144618, 11814, Amman, Jordan
Tel.: (962) 6 583 3449
Construction Engineering Services
N.A.I.C.S.: 541330

Freyssinet Korea Co. Ltd (3)
5th Floor Dae Yong Building 216-18 Nonhyeon-dong, Gangnam-gu, 100011, Seoul, Korea (South)
Tel.: (82) 2 2056 0500
Web Site: http://www.freyssinet.co.kr
Sales Range: $25-49.9 Million
Emp.: 80
Construction Engineering Services
N.A.I.C.S.: 541330
Jiyeong Kim *(Mng Dir)*

Freyssinet Kuwait (3)
PO Box 23755, 13098, Kuwait, Kuwait
Tel.: (965) 222 50790
Civil Engineering Services
N.A.I.C.S.: 237990

Freyssinet Ltd (3)
Innovation House Euston Way, Telford, TF3 4LT, Shropshire, United Kingdom
Tel.: (44) 1952 201901
Web Site: http://www.freyssinet.co.uk
Construction Engineering Services
N.A.I.C.S.: 541330

Subsidiary (Domestic):

Corrosion Control Services Ltd. (4)
Innovation House Euston Way Town Centre, Telford, TF3 4LT, United Kingdom
Tel.: (44) 195 223 0900
Web Site: http://www.corrosioncontrolservices.co.uk
Civil Engineering Construction Services
N.A.I.C.S.: 237990

Subsidiary (US):

Refco Employee Services LLC (4)
7108 S Alton Way Bldg D, Centennial, CO 80112-2106
Tel.: (303) 806-8160
Web Site: http://www.slatonbros.com
Construction Engineering Services
N.A.I.C.S.: 541330

Subsidiary (Non-US):

Reinforced Earth (Pty) Ltd (4)
2nd Floor 1 Park Road Richmond, Johannesburg, 2006, South Africa
Tel.: (27) 11 726 6180
Web Site: http://www.recosa.co.za
Emp.: 17
Construction Engineering Services
N.A.I.C.S.: 541330

Subsidiary (Domestic):

Reinforced Earth Company Ltd (4)
Innovation House, Town Centre, Telford, TF3 4LT, Shropshire, United Kingdom
Tel.: (44) 1952204357
Web Site: http://www.reinforcedearth.co.uk
Civil Engineering Construction Services
N.A.I.C.S.: 237990

Subsidiary (Non-US):

Reinforced Earth India Pvt. Ltd (4)
Unit No 902 to 906 9th Floor DLF Tower-B Plot No 11 NH, Commercial Centre Jasola, 110025, New Delhi, India
Tel.: (91) 11 40567660
Web Site: http://www.recoindia.com
Construction Engineering Services
N.A.I.C.S.: 541330

Reinforced Earth Insaat Proje Ve Ticaret A.S. (4)
Alemdag Merkez Mah Resadiye Cad No 69/D, Cekmekoy, 34794, Istanbul, Turkiye
Tel.: (90) 216 484 41 75
Web Site: http://www.reinforcedearth.com.tr
Civil Engineering Construction Services
N.A.I.C.S.: 237990

Reinforced Earth Pacific Ltd (4)
833 Cheung Sha Wan Road Room 705-706 7/F Tower 1, Cheung Sha Wan Plaza, Kowloon, China (Hong Kong)
Tel.: (852) 2782 3163
Web Site: http://www.vinci.com
Construction Engineering Services
N.A.I.C.S.: 541330

Reinforced Earth Pty Ltd (4)
Level 4 20 George Street, PO Box 1521, Hornsby, 2077, NSW, Australia
Tel.: (61) 2 9910 99 10
Web Site: http://www.reco.com.au
Construction Engineering Services
N.A.I.C.S.: 541330

Reinforced Earth Pvt. Ltd (4)
Razia Sharif Plaza 92 blue area Fazal-ul Haq Road First floor, 44000, Islamabad, Pakistan
Tel.: (92) 512150201
Web Site: http://www.vinci.com
Construction Engineering Services
N.A.I.C.S.: 541330

Reinforced Earth Thailand (4)
15th Floor Sethiwan Tower 139 Pan Road Silom, 10500, Bangkok, Thailand
Tel.: (66) 2266 6088
Construction Engineering Services
N.A.I.C.S.: 541330

Subsidiary (US):

Slaton Bros. Inc. (4)
3033 S Parker Rd Ste 1100, Aurora, CO 80014
Tel.: (303) 806-8160
Web Site: http://www.slatonbros.com
Reinforced Wall Construction Services
N.A.I.C.S.: 237990
Mike McKenzie *(Pres)*

Subsidiary (Non-US):

Freyssinet Menard India Pvt Ltd (3)
Unit No 902 to 906 9th Floor DLF Tower-B Plot No 11, NH Commercial Centre Jasola, 110025, New Delhi, India
Tel.: (91) 11 40538600
Web Site: http://www.freyssinetindia.com
Sales Range: $25-49.9 Million
Emp.: 14
Construction Engineering Services
N.A.I.C.S.: 541330

Freyssinet Menard Qatar WLL (3)
Ibn Seena Street Muntazah Stanlli Offices Office 20 3rd Floor Flat 301, PO Box 47671, Doha, 47671, Qatar
Tel.: (974) 44 31 05 81
Web Site: http://www.menard-vibro.ae
Sales Range: $25-49.9 Million
Site Preparation Services
N.A.I.C.S.: 238910

Freyssinet Nederland B.V. (3)
Argon 10, 4751 XC, Oud Gastel, Netherlands
Tel.: (31) 165518948
Web Site: http://www.freyssinet.nl
Construction Engineering Services
N.A.I.C.S.: 541330

Freyssinet OOO (3)
Shchipok 11 Building 1, 115054, Moscow, Russia
Tel.: (7) 4956621566
Web Site: http://www.freyssinet.ru
Sales Range: $25-49.9 Million
Construction Engineering Services
N.A.I.C.S.: 541330

Freyssinet PSC (M) Sdn Bhd (3)
No 9 Jalan 2/137 B - Resource Industrial Centre Off 5th Mile, Jalan Klang Lama, 58000, Kuala Lumpur, Malaysia
Tel.: (60) 3 7982 8599
Sales Range: $10-24.9 Million
Emp.: 40
Construction Engineering Services
N.A.I.C.S.: 541330

Freyssinet Polska Sp. z.o.o. (3)
ul Gluszycka 5, 02-215, Warsaw, Poland
Tel.: (48) 22 203 17 00
Web Site: http://www.freyssinet.pl
Sales Range: $25-49.9 Million
Emp.: 110
Construction Engineering Services
N.A.I.C.S.: 541330

Freyssinet Posten (Pty) Ltd (3)
30 Industry road, PO Box 496, Clayville Industrial Township, 1665, Olifantsfontein, Gauteng, South Africa
Tel.: (27) 113162174
Web Site: http://www.freyssinet.co.za
Sales Range: $10-24.9 Million
Emp.: 35
Construction Engineering Services
N.A.I.C.S.: 541330

Subsidiary (Domestic):

Freyssinet Products Company (3)
Zone d'Activite du Monay - Saint Eusebe, BP 18, 71210, Montchanin, France
Tel.: (33) 385736903
Web Site: http://www.vinci.com
Sales Range: $25-49.9 Million
Emp.: 150
Construction Engineering Services
N.A.I.C.S.: 541330

Subsidiary (Non-US):

Freyssinet S.A. (3)
Uruguay 772 Piso 10 - Officina 102, 1015, Buenos Aires, Argentina
Tel.: (54) 11 4372 7291
Web Site: http://www.vinci.com
Construction Engineering Services
N.A.I.C.S.: 541330

Freyssinet SA (3)
Calle de Melchor Fernandez Almagro 23, 28029, Madrid, Spain
Tel.: (34) 913239549
Web Site: http://www.freyssinet.es
Civil Engineering & Construction Services
N.A.I.C.S.: 237990

INTERNATIONAL PUBLIC

Freyssinet Taiwan Engineering. Co, Ltd (3)
3 F N 101-1 Lane 397 Ming Shui Road 3 F N 101, 104, Taipei, Taiwan
Tel.: (886) 2 85098101
Construction Engineering Services
N.A.I.C.S.: 541330

Freyssinet Thailand Ltd. (3)
19th Floor Sethiwan Tower 139 Pan Road Silom, Bangkok, 10500, Thailand
Tel.: (66) 2266608890
Web Site: https://www.freyssinet.co.th
N.A.I.C.S.: 541330
Borvornbhun Vonganan *(Mng Dir)*

Freyssinet Tierra Armada Chile S.A. (3)
Avda Los Cerrillos 980 Casilla 122, Cerrillos, 727-0534, Santiago, Chile
Tel.: (56) 2 584 90 00
Web Site: http://www.tierra-armada.cl
Roadway Construction Engineering Services
N.A.I.C.S.: 237310

Freyssinet Tunisie (3)
5 Rue De La Banque, 1000, Tunis, Tunisia
Tel.: (216) 98 352 599
Sales Range: $25-49.9 Million
Emp.: 4
Construction Engineering Services
N.A.I.C.S.: 541330
Habib Doghri *(Gen Mgr)*

Freyssinet Vietnam (3)
Green Star Bldg Unit 9 A 70 Pham Ngoc Thach Dist 3, Ho Chi Minh City, Vietnam
Tel.: (84) 8 38 20 57 32
Sales Range: $25-49.9 Million
Emp.: 20
Construction Engineering Services
N.A.I.C.S.: 541330
Alliaume Benoit *(Area Mgr)*

Freyssinet de Mexico - Tierra Armada S.A. (3)
Gauss 9-109 Col Anzures, 11590, Mexico, Mexico
Tel.: (52) 55 5250 7000
Construction Engineering Services
N.A.I.C.S.: 541330

GFWA Pty Ltd (3)
113 Radium Street, Welshpool, 6106, WA, Australia
Tel.: (61) 892511050
Web Site: http://www.gfwa.com.au
Sales Range: $10-24.9 Million
Emp.: 50
Geotechnical Engineering Services
N.A.I.C.S.: 541330

HBM Ltd. (3)
Vaci ut 80, 1133, Budapest, Hungary
Tel.: (36) 15775000
Web Site: https://www.hbm.hu
Sales Range: $10-24.9 Million
Emp.: 50
Construction Engineering Services
N.A.I.C.S.: 541330
Istvan Stoetzer *(Dir-Procurement)*

Hebetec Engineering A.G. (3)
Sagi 1, Postfach 33, 3324, Hindelbank, Switzerland
Tel.: (41) 344117171
Web Site: https://www.hebetec.com
Sales Range: $25-49.9 Million
Emp.: 50
Construction Engineering Services
N.A.I.C.S.: 541330
Joss Beat *(Mgr-Megasteel Dept)*

MENARD (Madrid) (3)
Calle Velazquez 50 7 floor, 28001, Madrid, Spain
Tel.: (34) 913 239524
Web Site: http://www.menard.es
Emp.: 10
Construction Engineering Services
N.A.I.C.S.: 541330

MENARD VIBRO (3)
Al Saraya Avenue Building Al Garhoud Blk A Rm 202 2nd Flr, PO Box 36750, Dubai, United Arab Emirates
Tel.: (971) 4 2925 700
Web Site: http://www.menard-vibro.ae

AND PRIVATE COMPANIES — VINCI S.A.

Construction Engineering Services
N.A.I.C.S.: 541330

March Construction Ltd (3)
1220 Main North Road Belfast,
Christchurch, 8083, New Zealand
Tel.: (64) 3 323 8085
Web Site:
    http://www.marchconstruction.co.nz
Construction Engineering Services
N.A.I.C.S.: 541330
Guy March *(Gen Mgr)*

Subsidiary (Domestic):

Menard (3)
2 Rue Gutenberg Zone Industrielle de la
Butte, BP 28, 91260, Nozay, France
Tel.: (33) 169013738
Web Site: http://www.menard-web.com
Emp.: 150
Construction Engineering Services
N.A.I.C.S.: 541330

Subsidiary (Non-US):

Menard Bachy Pty Ltd (3)
13-15 Lyonpark road, Macquarie Park, Sydney, 2113, NSW, Australia
Tel.: (61) 2 9491 7100
Web Site: http://www.menardbachy.com.au
Construction Engineering Services
N.A.I.C.S.: 541330

Menard Freyssinet Egypt (3)
3/4 Anwer el Mofty St - Off Abbas Alakkad
St-Queen Plaza, Flat 27-2nd Floor - Nasr
City, Cairo, Egypt
Tel.: (20) 2 22 61 18 42
Web Site: http://www.vinci.com
Construction Engineering Services
N.A.I.C.S.: 541330

Menard Geosystems Sdn Bhd (3)
No 2-1 2-2 Jalan USJ10/1E, 47620, Subang Jaya, Selangor, Malaysia
Tel.: (60) 3 56 32 15 81
Web Site: http://www.menard-asia.com
Sales Range: $10-24.9 Million
Emp.: 50
Construction Engineering Services
N.A.I.C.S.: 541330

Menard Polska Sp. z o.o. (3)
Ul Powazkowska 44c, 01-797, Warsaw,
Poland
Tel.: (48) 225600300
Web Site: https://www.menard.pl
Sales Range: $25-49.9 Million
Emp.: 100
Construction Engineering Services
N.A.I.C.S.: 541330
Norbert Kurek *(Deputy CEO & Dir-Centre Branch)*

Menard Thailand (3)
6th Floor Sethiwan Tower 139 Pan Road
Silom, Bangrak, 10500, Bangkok, Thailand
Tel.: (66) 2 266 6088
Construction Engineering Services
N.A.I.C.S.: 541330

Menard Vietnam (3)
Green Star Building 2nd Floor Unit 7-A 70
Pham Ngoc Thach Street, District 3, Ho Chi
Minh City, Vietnam
Tel.: (84) 8 38 20 57 61
Sales Range: $25-49.9 Million
Emp.: 9
Construction Engineering Services
N.A.I.C.S.: 541330
Matthias Teichert *(Country Mgr)*

Subsidiary (Domestic):

Nuvia France (3)
85 Avenue Archimede, 13857, Aix-en-Provence, France
Tel.: (33) 4 42 61 27 00
Web Site: http://www.nuvia.fr
Sales Range: $25-49.9 Million
Emp.: 120
Nuclear Waste Management Services
N.A.I.C.S.: 562998

Subsidiary (Domestic):

MECATISS (4)
Zone Industrielle - 1306 route d'Argent, BP
19, Morestel, 38510, France
Tel.: (33) 4 74 80 01 68

Web Site: http://www.mecatiss.com
Sales Range: $10-24.9 Million
Emp.: 98
Disaster Protection Services
N.A.I.C.S.: 812990

Millennium (4)
Parc Valmy 36 avenue Francois Giroud,
21000, Dijon, France
Tel.: (33) 1 64 86 55 10
Web Site: http://www.millennium.fr
Civil Engineering Construction Services
N.A.I.C.S.: 237990

Salvarem (4)
ZA la Fosse Yvon, BP 907, 50449, Beaumont, France
Tel.: (33) 1 69 33 20 50
Web Site: http://www.salvarem.com
Engineeering Services
N.A.I.C.S.: 541330

VRACO SA (4)
1306 Route d'Argent Zone Industrielle, BP
54, Morestel, 38630, France
Tel.: (33) 4 74 80 89 22
Web Site: http://www.nuvia.fr
Emp.: 20
Fire Sprinkler System Installation Services
N.A.I.C.S.: 238220

Subsidiary (Non-US):

Nuvia India Pvt Ltd. (3)
Plot No E-11 B-1 Extension Mohan Cooperative Industrial Estate, Mathura Road,
New Delhi, 110044, India
Tel.: (91) 11 4938 4300
Web Site: http://www.nuvia-india.com
Emp.: 1,500
Nuclear Energy Consulting Services
N.A.I.C.S.: 541690

Nuvia Limited (3)
Chadwick House Birchwood Park, Risley,
Warrington, WA3 6AE, Cheshire, United
Kingdom
Tel.: (44) 1925866300
Web Site: http://www.nuvia.co.uk
Emp.: 500
Nuclear Plant Construction & Maintenance
Services
N.A.I.C.S.: 237990
Keith Collett *(CEO)*

Nuvia Nordic AB (3)
Fleminggatan 2, 602 24, Norrkoping, Sweden
Tel.: (46) 11133413
Web Site: http://www.nuvia-nordic.com
Sales Range: $25-49.9 Million
Nuclear Energy Consulting Services
N.A.I.C.S.: 541690

PSC Freyssinet (S) Pte Ltd (3)
28 Sin Ming Lane 07-140 Midview City, Singapore, 573972, Singapore
Tel.: (65) 6899 0323
Web Site: http://www.freyssinet.com.sg
Sales Range: $25-49.9 Million
Emp.: 150
Construction Engineering Services
N.A.I.C.S.: 541330

PT Inti Fajar Pratama Menard (3)
Bumi Daya Plaza 10th Floor Jl Imam Bonjoi
61, 10310, Jakarta, Indonesia
Tel.: (62) 21 39899351
Web Site: http://www.menard-asia.com
Sales Range: $25-49.9 Million
Emp.: 5
Construction Engineering Services
N.A.I.C.S.: 541330

Pannon Freyssinet Ltd (3)
Budafoki ut 111 Buda Plaza, 1117, Budapest, Hungary
Tel.: (36) 1 209 15 10
Sales Range: $25-49.9 Million
Emp.: 5
Construction Engineering Services
N.A.I.C.S.: 541330
Orsika Pletka *(Gen Mgr)*

Subsidiary (US):

Refco Holdings Inc. (3)
7108 S Alton Way Bldg D, Centennial, CO
80112-2106
Tel.: (303) 806-8160

Sales Range: $75-99.9 Million
Emp.: 80
Investment Management Service
N.A.I.C.S.: 523999

Subsidiary (Domestic):

Sigmatec Ingenierie (3)
Le Mesnil Forget, 91620, Nozay, France
Tel.: (33) 1 69 01 37 38
Web Site: http://www.memard.com
Construction Engineering Services
N.A.I.C.S.: 541330

Subsidiary (Non-US):

SolData Asia Ltd. (3)
Unit 4 16 Floor Prosperity Center 77-81
Container Port Road, Hong Kong, China
(Hong Kong)
Tel.: (852) 2615 9639
Web Site: http://www.soldataasia.com
Sales Range: $25-49.9 Million
Emp.: 80
Environmental Monitoring Services
N.A.I.C.S.: 561621

Soletanche Do Brazil (3)
Largo do Machado-54 GR 803, Laranjeiras,
22221 020, Rio de Janeiro, Brazil
Tel.: (55) 21 2 556 14 41
Construction Engineering Services
N.A.I.C.S.: 541330

Subsidiary (US):

Soletanche Inc. (3)
7205 Corporate Ctr Dr Ste 503, Miami, FL
33126
Tel.: (305) 715-2080
Construction Engineering Services
N.A.I.C.S.: 541330

Subsidiary (Non-US):

Soletanche Polska Sp. z o.o. (3)
Ul Powazkowska 44c - IRYDION, 01-797,
Warsaw, Poland
Tel.: (48) 226397411
Web Site: http://www.soletanche.pl
Civil Engineering Construction Services
N.A.I.C.S.: 237990

Soletanche Sam - Monaco (3)
13 Avenue des Castelans, 98000, Monaco,
Monaco
Tel.: (377) 92 05 64 64
Construction Engineering Services
N.A.I.C.S.: 541330

Soletanche Stroy Russie (3)
7 Bolchoi Strotchenovsky Pereulok Bur 508,
115054, Moscow, Russia
Tel.: (7) 495 959 27 78
Web Site: http://www.vinci.com
Sales Range: $25-49.9 Million
Emp.: 2
Construction Engineering Services
N.A.I.C.S.: 541330

Solsif Maroc S.A. (3)
28 Av Mehdi Ben Barka Souissi, 10170,
Rabat, Morocco
Tel.: (212) 537 63 45 44
Web Site: http://www.solsif-maroc.com
Sales Range: $25-49.9 Million
Emp.: 70
Bore Hole Drilling Services
N.A.I.C.S.: 238910

Terra Armada Ltda (3)
Rua Dos Invalidos 212 Sala 101, Rio de
Janeiro, 20231-048, Brazil
Tel.: (55) 21 2233 7353
Web Site: http://www.terraarmada.com.br
Civil Engineering Construction Services
N.A.I.C.S.: 237990

Subsidiary (Domestic):

Terre Armee Internationale SAS (3)
1 Bis rue du Petit Clamart - Batiment D, BP
135, 78148, Velizy-Villacoublay, France
Tel.: (33) 1 46 01 84 84
Web Site: http://www.terre-armee.com
Highway & Bridge Construction Services
N.A.I.C.S.: 237310

Subsidiary (Domestic):

**Maintenance & Travaux
Speciaux** (4)

3 rue des Tournesols, Sance, 71000, Macon, France
Tel.: (33) 3 85 39 43 13
Web Site: http://www.mts-fr.com
Construction Engineering Services
N.A.I.C.S.: 541330

Subsidiary (Non-US):

Terra Armada Ltda (4)
Rua Padre Americo N 8b Escritorio 2 - Terracos S Paulo, 1600-548, Lisbon, Portugal
Tel.: (351) 21 716 16 75
Sales Range: $25-49.9 Million
Emp.: 55
Civil Engineering Construction Services
N.A.I.C.S.: 237990
Francois Bignon *(Gen Mgr)*

Terra Armata S.r.l. (4)
Via Petritoli 19, 00138, Rome, Italy
Tel.: (39) 06 45 49 51 00
Web Site: http://www.fretai.com
Sales Range: $25-49.9 Million
Emp.: 10
Civil Engineering Construction Services
N.A.I.C.S.: 237990

Terre Armee B.V. (4)
Kievitsven 108, Postbus 318, 5249 JK,
Rosmalen, Netherlands
Tel.: (31) 886606303
Web Site: http://www.terrearmee.nl
Sales Range: $25-49.9 Million
Emp.: 4
Civil Engineering Construction Services
N.A.I.C.S.: 237990

Subsidiary (Non-US):

Terre Armee Maroc (3)
13 rue Mohamed Ibn Ishak Avenue Ahmed
Balafrej Souissi, 10000, Rabat, Morocco
Tel.: (212) 537564435
Web Site: http://www.terre-armee.com
Bridge Construction Engineering Services
N.A.I.C.S.: 237310

Tierra Armada S.A. (3)
C / Melchor Fernandez Almagro 23, 28029,
Madrid, Spain
Tel.: (34) 91 323 95 00
Web Site: http://www.tierra-armada.com
Construction Engineering Services
N.A.I.C.S.: 541330

Subsidiary (Domestic):

Soletanche S.A. (2)
280 avenue Napoleon Bonaparte, Rueil-Malmaison, 92504, France
Tel.: (33) 147764262
Web Site: http://www.soletanche-bachy.com
Holding Company; Geotechnical & Civil Engineering Contractors
N.A.I.C.S.: 551112

Subsidiary (Domestic):

Balineau S.A. (3)
3 avenue Paul Langevin Enora park, PO
Box 30039, 33615, Pessac, France
Tel.: (33) 557891678
Web Site: http://www.balineau.com
Sales Range: $25-49.9 Million
Emp.: 48
Marine & River Works & Special Foundations
N.A.I.C.S.: 488320

Subsidiary (Non-US):

Balineau SA (Antilles) (4)
12 rue Nobel - ZI de Jarry, PO Box 2183,
97195, Jarry, Guadeloupe
Tel.: (590) 32 59 10
Web Site: http://www.balineau.com
Marine & River Works & Special Foundations
N.A.I.C.S.: 488320

Subsidiary (Domestic):

Soletanche Bachy (3)
280 avenue napoleon bonaparte, 92500,
Rueil-Malmaison, France
Tel.: (33) 147764262
Web Site: http://www.soletanche-bachy.com
Sales Range: $1-4.9 Billion
Emp.: 200

VINCI S.A.

VINCI S.A.—(Continued)
Geotechnical & Civil Engineering Contractors
N.A.I.C.S.: 238990

Subsidiary (Non-US):

Bachy Soletanche Limited (4)
Henderson House Langley Place Higgins Lane, Burscough, L40 8JS, Lancashire, United Kingdom
Tel.: (44) 1704895686
Web Site: http://www.bacsol.co.uk
Emp.: 75
Underground Engineering & Construction Services
N.A.I.C.S.: 238190

Subsidiary (Non-US):

Mc Donnell Piling & Foundations (5)
Ballyrichard, Carrigtwohill, T45 EF44, Cork, Ireland
Tel.: (353) 21 461 3131
Web Site: http://www.mcdonnellpiling.ie
Geotechnical Engineering Services
N.A.I.C.S.: 541330

Subsidiary (Domestic):

Simplex Westpile Limited (5)
Unit 5 Lidstone Court Uxbridge Road, George Green, Buckingham, SL3 6AG, United Kingdom **(100%)**
Tel.: (44) 1753215350
Web Site: http://www.simplexwestpile.co.uk
Sales Range: $75-99.9 Million
Emp.: 15
Geotechnical Contractors; Piling Services
N.A.I.C.S.: 238910

Subsidiary (Domestic):

CSM Bessac (4)
ZI de la pointe Chemin de Casselevre, 31790, Saint Just-Saint Rambert, France
Tel.: (33) 561376363
Web Site: http://www.bessac.com
Sales Range: $50-74.9 Million
Emp.: 120
Tunneling Equipment Designer, Contractor & Mfr
N.A.I.C.S.: 238190

Subsidiary (Non-US):

Dura Soletanche Bachy Pty Ltd. (4)
104 Aeroton Road Aeroton Extension 2, PO Box 38041, Booysens, 2016, Johannesburg, Gauteng, South Africa
Tel.: (27) 114944058
Web Site: http://www.durasb.co.za
Sales Range: $10-24.9 Million
Emp.: 100
Construction Engineering Services
N.A.I.C.S.: 541330

Subsidiary (Domestic):

Inertec (4)
133 Boulezaug nationale Aueilnmal maison, 92500, Nanterre, France
Tel.: (33) 147765570
Web Site: http://www.inertec.fr
Sales Range: $800-899.9 Million
Treatment of Dangerous Industrial Wastes & Rehabilitation of Polluted Sites Through Stabilization
N.A.I.C.S.: 562213

MCCF (4)
18 rue des pyrenees SILIC 519, Wissous, 94623, Rungis, Cedex, France
Tel.: (33) 156702760
Web Site: http://www.mccf.fr
Rehabilitation Construction
N.A.I.C.S.: 237990

Subsidiary (US):

Nicholson Construction Company (4)
2400 Ansys Ste 303, Canonsburg, PA 15317
Tel.: (412) 221-4500
Web Site: http://www.nicholsonconstruction.com
Sales Range: $25-49.9 Million
Emp.: 150
Contracting & Construction Services
N.A.I.C.S.: 237990
John Wise *(Sr VP)*

Subsidiary (Domestic):

Sol Data-Nanterre (4)
Ile Park - 21 Rue Du Port, 92022, Nanterre, France
Tel.: (33) 141448500
Web Site: http://www.soldatagroup.com
Sales Range: $25-49.9 Million
Emp.: 25
Ground Environment Monitoring Services
N.A.I.C.S.: 327992

Sol Environment (4)
280 Avenue Napoleon Bonaparte, Rueil-Malmaison, 92500, France
Tel.: (33) 147764262
Web Site: http://www.solenvironment.com
Sales Range: $50-74.9 Million
Emp.: 5
Water Supply & Irrigation System Environmental Services
N.A.I.C.S.: 221310
Pierre-Yves Klein *(Dir-Publication)*

Sol-Expert International (4)
58 rue Pereire, 925004, Rueil-Malmaison, Cedex, France
Tel.: (33) 47765402
Web Site: http://www.solexpert.com
Geotechnical Studies & Design of Underground Structures
N.A.I.C.S.: 541990

Soldata Geophysic (4)
N 3209 Rn 1085, Nivolas-Vermelle, 38300, Isere, France
Tel.: (33) 474920795
Web Site: http://www.soldata-geophysic.com
Sales Range: $25-49.9 Million
Emp.: 18
Risk Analysis, Geotechnical & Environmental Solutions
N.A.I.C.S.: 541620
Pierre Frappin *(Gen Mgr)*

Subsidiary (Non-US):

Soletanche Bachy Argentina sa (4)
Avenida Ricardo Balbin 3432, C1430AAS, Buenos Aires, Argentina
Tel.: (54) 11 45 44 71 00
Web Site: http://www.soletanche-bachy.com.ar
Construction Engineering Services
N.A.I.C.S.: 541330

Soletanche Bachy C.A. (4)
Urb San Luis Av Principal Torre Mayupan Piso 2 Ofic 2-4, Caracas, Venezuela
Tel.: (58) 212 988 90 95
Web Site: http://www.vinci.com
Construction Engineering Services
N.A.I.C.S.: 541330

Soletanche Bachy Chile S.A. (4)
Av Los Cerrillos 980, Cerrillos, Santiago, Chile
Tel.: (56) 2 584 9000
Construction Engineering Services
N.A.I.C.S.: 541330

Soletanche Bachy Ecuador (4)
Rue Robles 603 c/o SODERE - Ofc 709, PO Box 17030515, Quito, Ecuador
Tel.: (593) 2 255 26 58
Construction Engineering Services
N.A.I.C.S.: 541330
Jean Rossi *(Chm)*

Subsidiary (Domestic):

Soletanche Bachy Pieux (4)
18 rue des Pyrenees, SILIC 582, 94663, Rungis, Wissous, France
Tel.: (33) 156704200
Web Site: http://www.sbpieux.fr
Sales Range: $25-49.9 Million
Emp.: 40
Piling & Retaining Structures Construction & Civil Engineering
N.A.I.C.S.: 237990

Subsidiary (Non-US):

Soletanche Bachy Romania SA (4)
Street Traian no 234 6th floor, 2nd district, 24046, Bucharest, Romania
Tel.: (40) 31 102 37 01
Web Site: http://www.sbr.ro
Sales Range: $10-24.9 Million
Emp.: 50
Construction Engineering Services
N.A.I.C.S.: 541330
Sata Laurent *(Mgr-Tech)*

Solhydro spol sro (4)
Panonska Cesta 17, PO Box 169, 850 00, Bratislava, Slovakia
Tel.: (421) 263810980
Web Site: http://www.solhydro.sk
Sales Range: $10-24.9 Million
Emp.: 40
Civil Engineering Construction Services
N.A.I.C.S.: 237990

Subsidiary (Domestic):

Sotem (4)
112-118 rue Hartmann, Evry, 94200, Sur Seine, France
Tel.: (33) 146704424
Web Site: http://www.sotem.net
Sales Range: $25-49.9 Million
Emp.: 70
Maintenance Service For Paris Underground
N.A.I.C.S.: 485112
Chales Paruig *(Mng Dir)*

TEC Systems (4)
14 rue Emile Zola, 86530, Naintre, Cedex, France
Tel.: (33) 549937600
Web Site: http://www.tec-sas.com
Sales Range: $150-199.9 Million
Emp.: 50
Plant & Equipment Design, Maintenance, Mfr & Repairs, Sales & Service
N.A.I.C.S.: 811310

The Vibroflotation Group (4)
2 rue Gutenberg, Zone industrielle de la Butte, 91620, Nozay, France
Tel.: (33) 69013738
Web Site: http://www.vibroflotation.com
Soil Improvement Design & Construction
N.A.I.C.S.: 115112

Subsidiary (Non-US):

Vibro Foundations Ltd. UAE (5)
Room 106 European Business Center, PO Box 282067, Dubai Investment Park, Dubai, United Arab Emirates
Tel.: (971) 4 813 5600
Vibration Ground Foundation Services
N.A.I.C.S.: 237990

Vibro Services Gmbh (5)
Schwarzbacherstrasse 19, Guteborn Ruhland, D-01945, Lauchhammer, Germany
Tel.: (49) 35752 5000
Vibratory Ground Improvement Project Services
N.A.I.C.S.: 237990

Subsidiary (Non-US):

Stavby Mostov Slovakia a.s. (2)
Partizanska cesta 91, Banska Bystrica, 97401, Slovakia
Tel.: (421) 48 414 26 22
Web Site: http://www.stavbymostov.sk
Construction Engineering Services
N.A.I.C.S.: 237310

Subsidiary (Domestic):

VINCI Construction France SAS (2)
61 Avenue Jules Quentin, 92730, Nanterre, France
Tel.: (33) 146957000
Web Site: http://www.vinci-construction.fr
Construction Services
N.A.I.C.S.: 236220
Aurelie Bourdet *(Mgr-Recruitment)*

Subsidiary (Domestic):

ADIM Cote d'Azur SAS (3)
Pal Saint Isidore, CS 43072, 06202, Nice, Cedex, France
Tel.: (33) 492295820
Real Estate Development Services
N.A.I.C.S.: 531390

ADIM Lyon SAS (3)
55 Avenue Paul Kruger, Villeurbanne, France

INTERNATIONAL PUBLIC

Tel.: (33) 472156668
Real Estate Development Services
N.A.I.C.S.: 531390

ADIM Nord-Picardie SAS (3)
106 quai de Boulogne, CS 60164, 59053, Roubaix, Cedex, France
Tel.: (33) 320997817
Real Estate Development Services
N.A.I.C.S.: 531390

ADIM Normandie Centre SAS (3)
10 Boulevard Ferdinand de Lesseps, Rouen, France
Tel.: (33) 227089099
Real Estate Development Services
N.A.I.C.S.: 531390

ADIM Nouvelle Aquitaine SAS (3)
52 Quai de Paludate, CS 61991, 33088, Bordeaux, Cedex, France
Tel.: (33) 556186319
Real Estate Development Services
N.A.I.C.S.: 531390

ADIM Occitanie SAS (3)
60 Boulevard de Thibaud, BP 90325, 31103, Toulouse, Cedex, France
Tel.: (33) 562111001
Real Estate Development Services
N.A.I.C.S.: 531390

ADIM Ouest SAS (3)
1 Allee de la Gallinule-Ilot Jallais-Building B3, BP 51815, Nantes, France
Tel.: (33) 251112808
Real Estate Development Services
N.A.I.C.S.: 531390

ADIM Paris Ile-de-France SAS (3)
83-35 rue Henri Barbusse, 92735, Nanterre, Cedex, France
Tel.: (33) 175334933
Real Estate Development Services
N.A.I.C.S.: 531390

ADIM Provence SAS (3)
22 rue Joseph Clerissy, CS 70180, 13426, Marseille, Cedex, France
Tel.: (33) 491875650
Real Estate Development Services
N.A.I.C.S.: 531390

ADIM SAS (3)
61 Avenue Jules Quentin, Nanterre, France
Tel.: (33) 146957000
Web Site: http://www.adim.fr
Real Estate Development Services
N.A.I.C.S.: 531390

Bourdarios SAS (3)
60 boulevard de Thibaud, BP 48484, 31084, Toulouse, Cedex, France
Tel.: (33) 562111000
Construction & Engineering Services
N.A.I.C.S.: 236220

Campenon Bernard Dauphine Ardeche SAS (3)
16 chemin de Malacher, CS 10133, 38244, Meylan, Cedex, France
Tel.: (33) 476616585
Construction & Engineering Services
N.A.I.C.S.: 236220

Campenon Bernard Regions SAS (3)
16 chemin de Malacher Building B, CS 80318, 38246, Meylan, Cedex, France
Tel.: (33) 476616420
Construction & Engineering Services
N.A.I.C.S.: 236220

Campenon Bernard TP Cote d'Azur SAS (3)
ZI de Carros-Espace, BP 166, Carros, France
Tel.: (33) 492084502
Civil Engineering Services
N.A.I.C.S.: 541330

Chantiers Modernes Construction SAS (3)
61 avenue Jules Quentin, Nanterre, France
Tel.: (33) 146957000
Web Site: http://www.chantiers-modernes.fr
Civil Engineering Services
N.A.I.C.S.: 541330

Chantiers Modernes Sud-Ouest SAS (3)

AND PRIVATE COMPANIES VINCI S.A.

3 rue Gaspard Monge, BP 10076, 33603, Pessac, Cedex, France
Tel.: (33) 556464520
Construction & Engineering Services
N.A.I.C.S.: 236220

Citinea SAS (3)
61-63 Avenue Paul Kruger, Villeurbanne, France
Tel.: (33) 472682550
Web Site: http://www.citinea.fr
Industrial Building Construction Services
N.A.I.C.S.: 236210

Cofex GTM Travaux Speciaux SAS (3)
24 rue Champ Dolin, CS 20236, Saint-Priest, Lyon, France
Tel.: (33) 472670390
Web Site: http://www.cofex-gtm.fr
Industrial Building Construction Services
N.A.I.C.S.: 236210

Cofex Mediterranee SAS (3)
3 rond-point de l Aeropole Zone Aeropole, Garons, Nimes, France
Tel.: (33) 466742173
Construction Services
N.A.I.C.S.: 236220

GTM Batiment Aquitaine SAS (3)
52 quai de Paludate, CS 41989, Bordeaux, France
Tel.: (33) 556346300
Construction Services
N.A.I.C.S.: 236220

GTM Ouest SAS (3)
1 Impasse Charles Trenet, CS 80086, Saint-Herblain, 44814, Le Havre, Cedex, France
Tel.: (33) 240858919
Web Site: http://www.gtm-ouest.fr
Construction Services
N.A.I.C.S.: 236220
Christophe Legros *(Project Dir)*

GTM Travaux Speciaux SAS (3)
Z A de l Etoile I 4 rue Pegase, Trange, Saint-Georges-sur-Loire, France
Tel.: (33) 243470460
Construction Services
N.A.I.C.S.: 236220

Gauthier SAS (3)
90 route de Seysses, CS 5063, Toulouse, France
Tel.: (33) 561727575
Construction Services
N.A.I.C.S.: 236220

Neom SAS (3)
ZA plateau ouest, Saint-Valery-en-Caux, Seine-et-Marne, France
Tel.: (33) 235575820
Construction Services
N.A.I.C.S.: 236220

Pateu et Robert SAS (3)
7 Rue Albert Thomas, Besancon, France
Tel.: (33) 381485485
Web Site: http://www.pateu-et-robert.com
Construction Services
N.A.I.C.S.: 236220

Sogea Idf SAS (3)
9 Allee de la Briarde, Emerainville, 77436, Marne-la-Vallee, Cedex, France
Tel.: (33) 160377600
Web Site: https://www.sogea-idf.fr
Construction Services
N.A.I.C.S.: 236220
Isabelle Perriot-Lopez *(Pres)*

Sogea Nord Hydraulique SAS (3)
106 quai de Boulogne, CS 60164, Roubaix, France
Tel.: (33) 320997878
Construction Services
N.A.I.C.S.: 236220

Sogea Nord Ouest Tp SAS (3)
Direction regionale 101 rue Stalingrad, 76142, Le Petit-Quevilly, Cedex, France
Tel.: (33) 232114617
Construction Services
N.A.I.C.S.: 236220

Sogea Provence SAS (3)
29 Avenue De Rome, CS 80177, Zone Industrielle Les Estroublans, Vitrolles, France
Tel.: (33) 442130200
Construction Services
N.A.I.C.S.: 236220

Sogea Rhone Alpes SAS (3)
34 rue Antoine Primat, CS 40250, 69603, Villeurbanne, Cedex, France
Tel.: (33) 472136300
Construction Services
N.A.I.C.S.: 236220

Sogea Sud Hydraulique SAS (3)
541 rue Georges Melies Batiment M'Otion, CS 40717, 34961, Montpellier, Cedex, France
Tel.: (33) 467697200
Construction Services
N.A.I.C.S.: 236220

Sogea Sud Ouest Hydraulique SAS (3)
3 rue Gaspard Monge, BP 70160, Parc Industriel de Pessac-Canejan, 33606, Pessac, Cedex, France
Tel.: (33) 556466800
Construction Services
N.A.I.C.S.: 236220

Solumat Ile-de-France SAS (3)
15 route de Cheptainville, Corbeil-Essonnes, France
Tel.: (33) 169263901
Construction Services
N.A.I.C.S.: 236220

Solumat SAS (3)
15 route de Cheptainville, Marolles-en-Hurepoix, 91630, Corbeil-Essonnes, Cedex, France
Tel.: (33) 164568818
Construction Services
N.A.I.C.S.: 236220

Structures Ile-de-France SAS (3)
61 Avenue Jules Quentin, 92730, Nanterre, Cedex, France
Tel.: (33) 141914310
Construction Services
N.A.I.C.S.: 236220

Travaux du Midi Var SAS (3)
300 rue Philemon Laugier, Hyeres, 83418, Toulon, Cedex, France
Tel.: (33) 494005800
Construction Services
N.A.I.C.S.: 236220

Triverio SAS (3)
2 Avenue du Dr Emile Roux, B P 3190, 06204, Nice, Cedex, France
Tel.: (33) 493181670
Web Site: http://www.triverio.fr
Construction Services
N.A.I.C.S.: 236220

Subsidiary (Non-US):

VCS SA (3)
GVA Center-Tour B Route de l'aeroport 31, Geneva, Switzerland
Tel.: (41) 764468990
Web Site: http://www.vcs-sa.ch
Construction Services
N.A.I.C.S.: 236220

Subsidiary (Domestic):

VINCI Construction Maritime Et Fluvial SAS (3)
7 rue Ernest Flammarion Z A C du Petit Le Roy, Chevilly-Larue, 94659, Rungis, Cedex, France
Tel.: (33) 149617100
Web Site: http://www.vinci-construction-maritime-fluvial.fr
Construction Services
N.A.I.C.S.: 236220

Subsidiary (Non-US):

VINCI Construction Monaco SARL (3)
7 rue du Gabian Le Gildo Pastor Center, Monaco, Monaco
Tel.: (377) 92053228
Construction Services
N.A.I.C.S.: 236220

Subsidiary (Domestic):

VINCI Construction Grands Projets (2)
5 Cours Ferdinand De Lesseps, Cedex, 92851, Rueil-Malmaison, Cedex, France
Tel.: (33) 147164700
Web Site: http://www.vinci-construction.com
Sales Range: $500-549.9 Million
Emp.: 2,000
Holding Company
N.A.I.C.S.: 551112

Subsidiary (Non-US):

Campenon Saigon Builders Ltd (3)
37 Ton Duc Thang Street Saigon Trade Center Floor 21st Suite 2109-2111, District 1, Ho Chi Minh City, Vietnam
Tel.: (84) 8 3 824 2242
Web Site: http://www.vinci-construction-projects.com
Construction Engineering Services
N.A.I.C.S.: 541330

Subsidiary (Domestic):

Hydroplus SA (3)
5 Cours Ferdinand De Lesseps, 92851, Rueil-Malmaison, Cedex, France
Tel.: (33) 1 47 16 39 84
Web Site: http://www.hydroplus.com
Emp.: 5
Fusegate System Construction Engineering Services
N.A.I.C.S.: 237990

Branch (Non-US):

Janin Atlas, Inc. (3)
8200 boulevard Decarie bureau 200, Montreal, H4P 2P5, QC, Canada (100%)
Tel.: (514) 739-3291
Web Site: http://www.janin.ca
Sales Range: $25-49.9 Million
Emp.: 2
Heavy Construction Services
N.A.I.C.S.: 236220

Subsidiary (Non-US):

Sainrapt Contracting Co L.L.C. (3)
902 Al Omran Twr 1st Floor 013, PO Box 661, Abu Dhabi, United Arab Emirates
Tel.: (971) 2 676 4007
Sales Range: $25-49.9 Million
Emp.: 10
Construction Engineering Services
N.A.I.C.S.: 237990
Mathew Abraham *(Gen Mgr)*

Saudi Arabian Dumez Co. Ltd (3)
PO Box 6645, 11452, Riyadh, Saudi Arabia
Tel.: (966) 1 419 1395
Construction Engineering Services
N.A.I.C.S.: 541330

Subsidiary (US):

Tunnel Detroit Mod Dro-2 (3)
20600 Eureka Rd Vinci/Frontier-Kemper JV Ste 604, Taylor, MI 48180
Tel.: (734) 250-7246
Construction Engineering Services
N.A.I.C.S.: 541330

Subsidiary (Non-US):

VINCI Construction Grands Projets (Abu Dhabi) (3)
12 - Al Omran Tower Tourist Club Area, PO Box 661, Abu Dhabi, 661, United Arab Emirates
Tel.: (971) 267 644 01
Sales Range: $50-74.9 Million
Emp.: 12
Construction Engineering Services
N.A.I.C.S.: 237990
Mathew Abraham *(Mgr-Admin & Fin)*

VINCI Construction Grands Projets (Algerie) (3)
17 rue du Bois de Boulogne El Mouradia, 16000, Algiers, Algeria
Tel.: (213) 2148 3102
Construction Engineering Services
N.A.I.C.S.: 541330

VINCI Construction Grands Projets (Beijing) (3)
Unit 610 Air China Plaza No 36 Xiaoyun Road, Chaoyang District, Beijing, 100027, China
Tel.: (86) 10 65 90 01 84
Web Site: http://www.vinci-construction-projets.com
Sales Range: $25-49.9 Million
Construction Engineering Services
N.A.I.C.S.: 237990

Branch (Non-US):

VINCI Construction Grands Projets (British Isles) (3)
Great West House GW1 Great West Road, 551 London Rd, Brentford, TW8 9DF, United Kingdom (100%)
Tel.: (44) 2085871880
Web Site: http://www.vinci-construction-projets.com
Sales Range: $25-49.9 Million
Emp.: 68
Construction Services
N.A.I.C.S.: 236220

Subsidiary (Non-US):

VINCI Construction Grands Projets (Pakistan) (3)
Razia Sharif Plaza 92 Blue Area Fazal-e-Haq Road First Floor, Islamabad, Pakistan
Tel.: (92) 51 227 3501
Construction Engineering Services
N.A.I.C.S.: 237990

VINCI Construction Grands Projets (Vietnam) (3)
No 8 Trang Thi Str - R 302-305 Hoan Kiem, Hanoi, Vietnam
Tel.: (84) 439 44 71 63
Web Site: http://www.vinci-construction-projects.com
Construction Engineering Services
N.A.I.C.S.: 237990

VINCI Construction Grands Projets Sdn. Bhd. (3)
Suite 12-02 12 Floor Menara OBYU No 4 Jalan PJU 8 8A, Damansara Perdana, 47820, Petaling Jaya, Malaysia
Tel.: (60) 376629000
Web Site: http://www.vinci-construction-projets.com
Sales Range: $25-49.9 Million
Emp.: 20
Construction Engineering Services
N.A.I.C.S.: 541330

Branch (Non-US):

VINCI Construction Grands Projets-Hong Kong (3)
3rd Floor Chung Nam Building 1 Lockhart Road, Wanchai, China (Hong Kong) (100%)
Tel.: (852) 26120548
Web Site: http://www.vinci-construction-projets.com
Sales Range: $25-49.9 Million
Emp.: 10
Construction Services
N.A.I.C.S.: 236220

VINCI Construction Grands Projets-Moscow (3)
Blagoveschenskiy lane 3 Bldg 1 floor 6, 123001, Moscow, Russia
Tel.: (7) 495 981 35 44
Web Site: http://www.vinci-construction.com
Construction Services
N.A.I.C.S.: 236220

VINCI Construction Grands Projets-Prague (3)
Pobrezni Ul 3/620, Budova IBC, 18600, Prague, Czech Republic
Tel.: (420) 221718226
Web Site: http://www.vinci-construction-projets.com
Construction Services
N.A.I.C.S.: 236220

Subsidiary (Non-US):

VINCI Construction Hellas S.A. (3)
Hatziapostolou & Antigonis, 10442, Athens, Greece
Tel.: (30) 2105158100
Web Site: http://www.vinci-construction-projets.com
Construction Engineering Services
N.A.I.C.S.: 541330

VINCI S.A.

VINCI S.A.—(Continued)

Subsidiary (Domestic):

Water Management International (3)
5 Cours Ferdinand de Lesseps, 92500, Rueil-Malmaison, France
Tel.: (33) 1 47 16 32 05
Web Site: http://www.wmi-water.com
Waste Treatment Services
N.A.I.C.S.: 221310

Subsidiary (Domestic):

VINCI Environnement SAS (2)
89 Boulevard Franklin Roosevelt, 92500, Rueil-Malmaison, France
Tel.: (33) 1 71 04 20 00
Web Site: http://www.vinci-environnement.com
Emp.: 170
Waste Treatment Services
N.A.I.C.S.: 221310
Hugues Seutin *(Mgr-Mechanical Biological Treatment)*

Subsidiary (Non-US):

VINCI Environnement Polska Sp. z o.o. (3)
ul Aleje Jerozolimskie 162a, 02-342, Warsaw, Poland
Tel.: (48) 22 567 60 00
Waste Treatment Services
N.A.I.C.S.: 221310

Subsidiary (Non-US):

VINCI plc (2)
Astral House Imperial Way, Watford, WD24 4WW, Hertfordshire, United Kingdom (100%)
Tel.: (44) 1923233433
Web Site: http://www.vinci.plc.uk
Emp.: 400
Construction Services
N.A.I.C.S.: 236220

Subsidiary (Domestic):

Conren Ltd (3)
Unit 1 The Bridge Business Centre Ash Road South, Wrexham Industrial Estate, Wrexham, LL13 9UG, United Kingdom
Tel.: (44) 1978 661 991
Web Site: http://www.conren.com
Emp.: 8
Interior Design Services
N.A.I.C.S.: 238320

VINCI Education Ltd. (3)
Astral House Imperial Way, Watford, WD24 4WW, United Kingdom
Tel.: (44) 1923233433
Construction Engineering Services
N.A.I.C.S.: 541330

VINCI Investments Ltd (3)
Floor 10 33 Cavendish Square, London, W1G 0PW, United Kingdom
Tel.: (44) 2072481655
Web Site: http://www.vinci.com
Investment Management Service
N.A.I.C.S.: 523999

Vinci Construction UK Limited (3)
Astral House Imperial Way, Watford, WD24 4WW, Hertfordshire, United Kingdom
Tel.: (44) 1923233433
Web Site: https://www.vinciconstruction.co.uk
Sales Range: $1-4.9 Billion
Emp.: 400
Corporate Construction, Facilities Management & Engineering Services
N.A.I.C.S.: 236220
Chris Hamer *(Mng Dir-Building Div)*

Subsidiary (Domestic):

Norwest Holst Soil Engineering Ltd. (4)
Parkside Lane Dewsbury Road, Leeds, LS11 5SX, Yorkshire, United Kingdom (100%)
Tel.: (44) 32711111
Web Site: http://www.soil-engineering.co.uk
Sales Range: $150-199.9 Million
Emp.: 260
Geotechnical Contractors & Soil Engineering Services
N.A.I.C.S.: 115112

VINCI Construction Terrassement (1)
61 Avenue Jules Quentin, 92730, Nanterre, France
Tel.: (33) 146957850
Web Site: http://www.vinci-construction-terrassement.com
Sales Range: $25-49.9 Million
Emp.: 100
Site Preparation Services
N.A.I.C.S.: 238910

Subsidiary (Domestic):

NAVARRA TS (2)
18 Avenue Gustave Eiffel, 33600, Pessac, France
Tel.: (33) 5 57 26 69 20
Web Site: http://www.navarrats.fr
Sales Range: $25-49.9 Million
Emp.: 20
Site Preparation Services
N.A.I.C.S.: 238910

VINCI Construction Terrassement Deutschland GmbH (1)
Ernst-Augustin-Strasse 2, 12489, Berlin, Germany
Tel.: (49) 3054684600
Engineering Services
N.A.I.C.S.: 541330

VINCI Deutschland GmbH (1)
Industriestr 19a, 67063, Ludwigshafen, Germany
Tel.: (49) 62196365311
Web Site: http://www.vinci-deutschland.de
Emp.: 40
Construction Engineering Services
N.A.I.C.S.: 541330
Rainer Beisel *(Mng Dir)*

VINCI Energies (1)
280 rue du 8 mai 1945, PO Box 72, 78368, Montesson, Cedex, France
Tel.: (33) 130867000
Web Site: http://www.vinci-energies.com
Sales Range: $75-99.9 Million
Emp.: 120
Holding Company; Energy & Information Technology Services
N.A.I.C.S.: 551112
Herve Adam *(Deputy Mng Dir & Gen Mgr)*

Subsidiary (Non-US):

ACTEMIUM Lisbon (2)
Estrada nacional 115 km 78 67, 2664-502, Sao Juliao do Tojal, Portugal
Tel.: (351) 218454000
Web Site: http://www.vinci.com
Emp.: 50
Industrial Consulting Services
N.A.I.C.S.: 541330

AXIANS Netlink B.V. (2)
Marconibaan 6-8, 3439 MS, Nieuwegein, Netherlands
Tel.: (31) 30 248 5200
Web Site: http://www.axians.nl
Sales Range: $10-24.9 Million
Human Resource Management Services
N.A.I.C.S.: 541612

Subsidiary (Domestic):

Actemium (2)
280 Rue du 8 Mai 1945, BP 72, 78368, Montesson, France
Tel.: (33) 130867007
Web Site: http://www.actemium.com
Emp.: 20
Industrial Consulting Services
N.A.I.C.S.: 541690

Subsidiary (Non-US):

Actemium Belgium SA (3)
Leon Bekaertlaan 24, 9880, Aalter, Belgium
Tel.: (32) 9 325 75 50
Web Site: http://www.actemium.be
Sales Range: $25-49.9 Million
Industrial Consulting Services
N.A.I.C.S.: 541690

Actemium UK (3)
2050 The Crescent Birmingham Business Park, Birmingham, B37 7YE, United Kingdom
Tel.: (44) 1217171831
Web Site: http://www.actemium.co.uk
Sales Range: $10-24.9 Million
Electrical Engineering Services
N.A.I.C.S.: 541330

Subsidiary (Domestic):

Actemium - Nancy ARS (2)
32 Avenue Des Erables Parc d Activites Nancy Porte Sud, Heillecourt, 54180, France
Tel.: (33) 3 83 57 18 19
Web Site: http://www.actemium.com
Sales Range: $25-49.9 Million
Emp.: 30
Industrial Consulting Services
N.A.I.C.S.: 541330

Subsidiary (Non-US):

Actemium BEA Balkan (2)
65 Shipchenski prohod Blvd Office 203, 1574, Sofia, Bulgaria
Tel.: (359) 2 971 71 23
Web Site: http://www.actemium.de
Electric Power Distribution Services
N.A.I.C.S.: 221122

Actemium Controlmatic AG (2)
Muttenzerstrasse 127, 4133, Pratteln, Switzerland
Tel.: (41) 61 319 99 46
Web Site: http://www.actemium.de
Electrical Engineering Services
N.A.I.C.S.: 541330

Actemium Controlmatic Enns (2)
Landstrasse 2d, Enns, 4470, Austria
Tel.: (43) 7223 89040
Industrial Consulting Services
N.A.I.C.S.: 541690

Actemium Kasachstan TOO (2)
Ul Zheltoksan 118 office 320, 050000, Almaty, Kazakhstan
Tel.: (7) 7272509532
Web Site: http://www.actemium.de
Sales Range: $75-99.9 Million
Electric Power Distribution Services
N.A.I.C.S.: 221122

Axians Network Services (2)
Beesley House Quinn Close, Coventry, CV3 4LH, West Midlands, United Kingdom
Tel.: (44) 2476 516070
Web Site: http://www.axians.co.uk
Sales Range: $25-49.9 Million
Network Support Services
N.A.I.C.S.: 541512

Axians SA (2)
c/ Valle de la Fuenfria 3, 28034, Madrid, Spain
Tel.: (34) 914560008
Web Site: https://www.axians.es
Information Technology Consulting Services
N.A.I.C.S.: 541690
Jose Manuel Sanchez Miron *(Pres)*

BEA-Polska Elektroniczka i Automatyzacja Sp. z o.o. (2)
Ul Grabiszynska 241 C, 53-234, Wroclaw, Poland
Tel.: (48) 71 7804005
Web Site: http://www.bea-tdl.de
Sales Range: $25-49.9 Million
Emp.: 8
Electrical Engineering Services
N.A.I.C.S.: 541330

Bauunternehmung Ehrenfels GmbH (2)
Wurzburger Strasse 9-11, 97753, Karlstadt, Germany
Tel.: (49) 9353 7909 0
Web Site: http://www.ehrenfels-online.de
Sales Range: $25-49.9 Million
Emp.: 100
Construction Engineering Services
N.A.I.C.S.: 541330

Calanbau Brandschutz Austria GmbH (2)
Lindengasse 20, 4040, Linz, Austria
Tel.: (43) 732 712175 0
Web Site: http://www.calanbau.at
Sales Range: $25-49.9 Million
Emp.: 9
Fire Protection Services

INTERNATIONAL PUBLIC

N.A.I.C.S.: 922160

Cegelec Angola (2)
Rua Francisco das Necessidades Castelo Brance N 45, Coqueiros, Luanda, Angola
Tel.: (244) 222 330 866
Web Site: http://www.cegelec.com
Sales Range: $75-99.9 Million
Crude Petroleum & Natural Gas Extraction Services
N.A.I.C.S.: 211120

Subsidiary (Domestic):

Cegelec Clermont-Ferrand (2)
5 Rue Robert Estienne, 63360, Gerzat, France
Tel.: (33) 4 73 16 24 00
Energy Consulting Services
N.A.I.C.S.: 541690

Cegelec Infrastructures & Mobility (2)
10 Avenue Du Stade de France, Saint Denis, 93210, France
Tel.: (33) 1 58 69 40 00
Energy Consulting Services
N.A.I.C.S.: 541690
Jean Michel Lang *(Mng Dir)*

Subsidiary (Non-US):

Cegelec Maroc S.A. (2)
62 Boulevard Oqba Bnou Nasia, 20670, Casablanca, Morocco
Tel.: (212) 522 63 93 93
Web Site: http://www.cegelec.ma
Construction Engineering Services
N.A.I.C.S.: 541330
Ahmed Rahmani *(Gen Mgr)*

Cegelec Qatar W.L.L. (2)
Jafco Building 1st Floor - Behind Muntazah Park C Ring Road 4th Floor, Doha, 23342, Qatar
Tel.: (974) 44 31 09 09
Web Site: http://www.cegelec.com
Emp.: 100
Construction Engineering Services
N.A.I.C.S.: 541330

Subsidiary (Domestic):

Citeos (2)
8 Rue Vega, 74650, Chavanod, France
Tel.: (33) 5 61 58 90 00
Web Site: http://www.citeos.com
Lighting & Illumination Equipment Mfr
N.A.I.C.S.: 335139

Subsidiary (Non-US):

Controlmatic Gesellschaft fur Automation und Elektrotechnik mbH (2)
Colmarer Strasse 11, 60528, Frankfurt am Main, Germany (100%)
Tel.: (49) 6950050
Web Site: http://www.controlmatic.de
Sales Range: $25-49.9 Million
Emp.: 18
Analyzers, Breakers, Control Panels, Controllers, Environmental Protection Equipment, Panelboards & Process Control Systems Mfr
N.A.I.C.S.: 335313

Subsidiary (Domestic):

Kappelhoff Industrietechnik GmbH (3)
Gabelsberger Strasse 2, 46238, Bottrop, Germany
Tel.: (49) 2041 400 10 0
Industrial Consulting Services
N.A.I.C.S.: 541690

Subsidiary (Non-US):

Dechow Dienstleistungs GmbH (2)
Bramfelder Strasse 110b, 22305, Hamburg, Germany
Tel.: (49) 406119110
Web Site: http://www.dechow-dl-gmbh.de
Air Conditioning Equipment Installation Services
N.A.I.C.S.: 238220

EBEHAKO GmbH (2)
Am Fuchsgraben 38, 08056, Zwickau, Germany
Tel.: (49) 375 87650

AND PRIVATE COMPANIES VINCI S.A.

Web Site: http://www.ebehako.de
Electric Power Transmission & Distribution Services
N.A.I.C.S.: 221121

ETAVIS AG (2)
Technoparkstrasse 1, 8021, Zurich, Switzerland
Tel.: (41) 44 446 66 00
Web Site: http://www.etavis.ch
Emp.: 80
Telecommunication Servicesb
N.A.I.C.S.: 517810

Subsidiary (Domestic):

ETAVIS Arnold AG (3)
Waldeggstrasse 47, 3097, Liebefeld, Switzerland
Tel.: (41) 31 309 66 66
Web Site: http://www.etavis.ch
Sales Range: $25-49.9 Million
Electrical Equipment Installation Services
N.A.I.C.S.: 238210

ETAVIS Beutler AG (3)
Ruegsaustrasse 5, 3400, Burgdorf, Switzerland
Tel.: (41) 344214444
Web Site: http://www.etavis.ch
Telecommunication Servicesb
N.A.I.C.S.: 517810

ETAVIS Broger AG (3)
Kreuzlingerstrasse 59, Mullheim, 8555, Switzerland
Tel.: (41) 52 762 74 44
Web Site: http://www.etavis.ch
Sales Range: $25-49.9 Million
Emp.: 70
Telecommunication Servicesb
N.A.I.C.S.: 517810
Ulrich Stiess *(Mng Dir)*

ETAVIS Elettro-Impianti SA (3)
Walter Cubisino Via Boschina 5, Pregassona, 6963, Lugano, Switzerland
Tel.: (41) 919733111
Web Site: https://www.etavis.ch
Emp.: 50
Telecommunication Equipment Installation Services
N.A.I.C.S.: 238210

ETAVIS Engineering AG (3)
Wien-Strasse 2, 4002, Basel, Switzerland
Tel.: (41) 61 316 68 00
Web Site: http://www.etavis.ch
Sales Range: $75-99.9 Million
Emp.: 300
Electrical Engineering Services
N.A.I.C.S.: 541330

ETAVIS GNS AG (3)
Im Halbiacker 7, Postfach 3280, 8404, Winterthur, Switzerland
Tel.: (41) 52 368 79 79
Web Site: http://www.etavisgns.ch
Information Technology Consulting Services
N.A.I.C.S.: 541512

ETAVIS Grossenbacher AG (3)
Oststrasse 25, Postfach 14, 9006, Saint Gallen, Switzerland
Tel.: (41) 71 243 66 44
Web Site: http://www.etavis.ch
Telecommunication Servicesb
N.A.I.C.S.: 517810

ETAVIS Jag Jakob AG (3)
Simon Stalder Mohnweg 5, 2504, Biel, Switzerland
Tel.: (41) 32 366 22 11
Web Site: http://www.etavis.ch
Sales Range: $50-74.9 Million
Emp.: 60
Electric Power Distribution Services
N.A.I.C.S.: 221122

ETAVIS Kriegel+Co. AG (3)
St Jakobs-Strasse 40, 4132, Muttenz, Switzerland
Tel.: (41) 61 465 65 65
Web Site: http://www.etavis.ch
Electrical Equipment Installation Services
N.A.I.C.S.: 238210

ETAVIS Kriegel+Schaffner AG (3)
Wien-Strasse 2, 4002, Basel, Switzerland
Tel.: (41) 61 316 60 60
Web Site: http://www.etavis.ch
Sales Range: $200-249.9 Million
Electrical Equipment Installation Services
N.A.I.C.S.: 238210

ETAVIS Micatel AG (3)
Pulverstrasse 8 Stufenbau, 3063, Bern, Switzerland
Tel.: (41) 31 925 91 11
Web Site: http://www.etavis.ch
Sales Range: $25-49.9 Million
Emp.: 60
Mobile Communications Services
N.A.I.C.S.: 517112
Herman Huber *(Gen Mgr)*

ETAVIS Services AG (3)
Wien-Strasse 1, 4142, Munchenstein, Switzerland
Tel.: (41) 844825825
Web Site: http://www.etavis.ch
Sales Range: $25-49.9 Million
Electrical Equipment Installation Services
N.A.I.C.S.: 238210

ETAVIS TSA SA (3)
Avenue de Sevelin 46, 1004, Lausanne, Switzerland
Tel.: (41) 21 614 44 44
Sales Range: $50-74.9 Million
Emp.: 116
Telecommunication Servicesb
N.A.I.C.S.: 517810

Subsidiary (Non-US):

Electrix Pty Limited (2)
Unit 1 8 Weddel Court, Laverton, 3026, VIC, Australia
Tel.: (61) 386982200
Web Site: http://www.electrix.com.au
Sales Range: $100-124.9 Million
Emp.: 500
Electrical Contracting Services
N.A.I.C.S.: 238210

Elphi S.r.l. (2)
Via Monte Santo 6, 20025, Legnano, Milan, Italy
Tel.: (39) 0331 545 175
Web Site: http://www.elphi.it
Electrical Equipment Installation Services
N.A.I.C.S.: 238210

Emil Lundgren AB (2)
Hildedalsgatan 2, PO Box 8019, 402 77, Gothenburg, Sweden
Tel.: (46) 31 659000
Web Site: http://www.emillundgren.se
Emp.: 50
Electrical Contractor
N.A.I.C.S.: 238210

Subsidiary (Domestic):

Entreprise Demouselle (2)
140 rue Chateau d Eau, 80100, Abbeville, France
Tel.: (33) 3 22 20 20 40
Electrical Engineering Services
N.A.I.C.S.: 541330

Entreprise d'Electricite et d'Equipement (2)
5 Rue Arnavielle CS 42001, 30907, Nimes, France
Tel.: (33) 4 66 63 75 00
Web Site: http://www.eee.fr
Emp.: 200
Electric Power Generation & Distribution Services
N.A.I.C.S.: 221118

Fournie Grospaud Synerys (2)
14 Rue Paule Raymondis, BP 2370, ZAC Gabardie, 31022, Toulouse, Cedex, France
Tel.: (33) 5 34 30 46 00
Web Site: http://www.fgsynerys.fr
Sales Range: $25-49.9 Million
Emp.: 113
Industrial Control Equipment Mfr
N.A.I.C.S.: 335314

GASQUET ENTREPRISE (2)
14 Avenue Marechal de Lattre de Tassigny, 71700, Tournus, France
Tel.: (33) 3 85 32 25 25
Web Site: http://www.gasquet.fr
Electric Power Distribution Services
N.A.I.C.S.: 221122

Subsidiary (Non-US):

GFA Ceska Rep. s.r.o. (2)
Radlicka 740/113d, 158 00, Prague, Czech Republic
Tel.: (420) 225 988 983
Web Site: http://www.vinci.com
Sales Range: $25-49.9 Million
Emp.: 1
Fire Sprinkler System Installation Services
N.A.I.C.S.: 238220

Subsidiary (Domestic):

GTIE Air & Defense (2)
Z A Courtaboeuf 1 6 Ave de la Baltique, 91140, Villebon-sur-Yvette, France
Tel.: (33) 1 69 93 80 69
Web Site: http://www.gtie-airdefense.fr
Emp.: 64
Defence Security Software Development Services
N.A.I.C.S.: 541511
Digard Henri *(Mng Dir)*

Garczynski Traploir (2)
24 Rue Thomas Edison, 72088, Le Mans, France
Tel.: (33) 2 43 77 77 77
Web Site: http://www.g-t.fr
Emp.: 70
Energy Consulting Services
N.A.I.C.S.: 541690

Subsidiary (Non-US):

Graniou ATEM Sp.z o.o. (2)
Ul Luzycka 2, 81-537, Gdynia, Poland
Tel.: (48) 58 662 29 12
Web Site: http://www.graniouatem.com.pl
Sales Range: $100-124.9 Million
Telecommunication Servicesb
N.A.I.C.S.: 517810
Iwar Przyklang *(Pres & CEO)*

Subsidiary (Domestic):

IDF Thermic SA (2)
3 Rue De Verdun Eurocampus, 78590, Noisy-le-Roi, France
Tel.: (33) 1 30 80 08 70
Air Conditioning Equipment Installation Services
N.A.I.C.S.: 238210

L'Entreprise Electrique (2)
18 rue de la Gantiere, CS 90324, 63009, Clermont-Ferrand, Cedex, France
Tel.: (33) 473263590
Web Site: https://www.lentreprise-electrique.fr
Electrical Engineering Services
N.A.I.C.S.: 541330
Patrick Meunier *(Pres)*

Subsidiary (Non-US):

LAGRANGE Energie - und Gebaudetechnik Gmbh (2)
In Allweiden 5, 55606, Kirn, Germany
Tel.: (49) 67 52 9 01 0
Web Site: http://lagrange-twm.de
Plumbing & Air Conditioning System Installation Services
N.A.I.C.S.: 238220

Subsidiary (Domestic):

Lefort Francheteau S.A.S. (2)
1 Avenue du President Georges Pompidou, 92508, Rueil-Malmaison, Cedex, France **(100%)**
Tel.: (33) 1 47 32 92 77
Web Site: http://www.lefort-francheteau.fr
Heating & Air Conditioning Equipment Installation Services
N.A.I.C.S.: 238220
Olivier Lemesle *(Dir)*

Mangin Egly Entreprises SAS (2)
Rue de la Fontaine Ludot, BP 80200, 51306, Vitry-le-Francois, France
Tel.: (33) 3 26 74 15 55
Web Site: http://www.mangin-egly.net
Emp.: 100
Energy Consulting Services
N.A.I.C.S.: 541690

Masselin Energie S.A.S (2)
14 bis rue Alfred Nobel, 14123, Ifs, France
Tel.: (33) 231350909
Sales Range: $25-49.9 Million
Emp.: 55
Energy Consulting Services
N.A.I.C.S.: 541690
Sajuais Fajuais *(Gen Mgr)*

Mercier (2)
12 rue del Industrie, BP 37, 41401, Montrichard, France
Tel.: (33) 2 54 71 26 26
Electrical Engineering Services
N.A.I.C.S.: 541330

Subsidiary (Non-US):

PT. JETEC INDONESIA - ACTEMIUM INDONESIA (2)
1st Floor Jl Mampang Prapatan Raya No 1, Mampang Prapatan, Jakarta, 12790, Indonesia
Tel.: (62) 21 7990088
Web Site: http://www.actemium.co.id
Sales Range: $25-49.9 Million
Engineeering Services
N.A.I.C.S.: 541330
Olivier Vifflantzeff *(Dir-Development)*

Subsidiary (Domestic):

Phibor Entreprises (2)
Paro icade-paris-orly-rungis 71 rue de Montlhery, 94523, Rungis, France
Tel.: (33) 1 56 70 57 00
Web Site: http://www.phiborentreprises.fr
Electrical Engineering Services
N.A.I.C.S.: 541330

Subsidiary (Non-US):

ProCS, s.r.o. (2)
Kralovska Ulica 8/824, 927. 01, Sala, Slovakia
Tel.: (421) 31 773 11 11
Web Site: http://www.actemium.sk
Sales Range: $25-49.9 Million
Industrial Process Control System Mfr
N.A.I.C.S.: 334513

Probisa S.A. (2)
Cerro Sombrero N 1010, Maipu, Santiago, Chile
Tel.: (56) 2 538 59 90
Sales Range: $25-49.9 Million
Emp.: 60
Road Construction Engineering Services
N.A.I.C.S.: 237310

Unit (Domestic):

Protec-Feu S.A. (2)
16 Rue Ambroise Croizat, BP 70106, F-95103, Argenteuil, France
Tel.: (33) 139963996
Web Site: http://www.protec-feu.com
Sales Range: $25-49.9 Million
Emp.: 230
Fire Protection & Sprinkler Systems Mfr
N.A.I.C.S.: 922160

Subsidiary (Domestic):

SAGA ENTREPRISE (2)
12 Boulevard Louise Michel Batiment B, 92238, Gennevilliers, France
Tel.: (33) 1 47 91 66 66
Web Site: http://www.saga-entreprise.fr
Plumbing & Air Conditioning System Installation Services
N.A.I.C.S.: 238220

Subsidiary (Non-US):

SKE Construction GMBH (2)
Siegmund-Schuckert-Strasse 3, 68199, Mannheim, Germany
Tel.: (49) 621 850 970
Web Site: http://www.vinci.com
Construction Engineering Services
N.A.I.C.S.: 541330

SKE Group Romania SRL (2)
18 Mircea Eliade Blvd, 12015, Bucharest, Romania
Tel.: (40) 318 055280
Web Site: http://www.ske.eu
Emp.: 5
Facilities Support Services
N.A.I.C.S.: 561210

Subsidiary (US):

SKE International, Inc. (2)
2 Jockey Hollow Rd, Warwick, NY 10990
Tel.: (845) 986-9762

VINCI S.A.

VINCI S.A.—(Continued)
Web Site: http://www.skeii.com
Sales Range: $10-24.9 Million
Emp.: 10
Facility Management Services
N.A.I.C.S.: 561210

Subsidiary (Domestic):

Santerne Centre Est (2)
3 Allee Fourneyron ZI Molina la Chazotte,
42350, La Talaudiere, France
Tel.: (33) 4 77 48 13 20
Telecommunication Servicesb
N.A.I.C.S.: 517810

Subsidiary (Non-US):

Sotecnica S.A. (2)
Estrada Nacional 115 Km 78 67, S Juliao
do Tojal, Lisbon, 2664-502, Portugal
Tel.: (351) 219737000
Web Site: http://www.sotecnica.pt
Energy Consulting Services
N.A.I.C.S.: 541690

Spark Iberica S.A. (2)
Miguel Hernandez 31-33, L'Hospitalet de
Llobregat, 8908, Barcelona, Spain **(100%)**
Tel.: (34) 934314666
Web Site: http://www.sparkiberica.com
Sales Range: $1-9.9 Million
Emp.: 100
Electrical Engineering Services
N.A.I.C.S.: 238210

TPI Ceska republika s.r.o. (2)
Radlicka 740 / 113d, Jinonice, 158 00,
Prague, Czech Republic
Tel.: (420) 225 988 983
Web Site: http://www.tpicr.cz
Emp.: 20
Fire Sprinkler System Installation Services
N.A.I.C.S.: 238220

Subsidiary (Domestic):

TUNZINI (2)
1 rue du 1er Mai 10003, Nanterre, 92000,
France
Tel.: (33) 1 74 54 45 00
Web Site: http://www.tunzini.fr
Heating & Air Conditioning Equipment Installation Services
N.A.I.C.S.: 238220

Tunzini Toulouse S.A.S. (2)
21 Chemin de la Menude - ZI d en Jacca,
31770, Colomiers, France
Tel.: (33) 5 61 16 81 80
Construction Engineering Services
N.A.I.C.S.: 541330

Subsidiary (Non-US):

VINCI Energies Benelux SA (2)
Boulevard de la Woluwe 60, 1020, Brussels, Belgium
Tel.: (32) 2 775 90 20
Energy Consulting Services
N.A.I.C.S.: 541690

VINCI Energies Deutschland GmbH (2)
Colmarer Strasse 11, 60528, Frankfurt am Main, Germany
Tel.: (49) 69 5005 0
Web Site: http://www.vinci-energies.de
Energy Consulting Services
N.A.I.C.S.: 541690
Stefan Falk *(Mng Dir)*

Subsidiary (Domestic):

Axians (NK Networks & Services GmbH) (3)
Von-der-Wettern-Str 15, 51149, Cologne, Germany
Tel.: (49) 2203 1025 0
Web Site: http://www.axians.de
Sales Range: $50-74.9 Million
Emp.: 150
Telecommunication Servicesb
N.A.I.C.S.: 517810

CALANBAU GFA Feuerschutz GmbH (3)
Wenderter Str 12, 31157, Sarstedt, Germany
Tel.: (49) 5066 808 230
Emp.: 50
Fire Protection Services
N.A.I.C.S.: 922160
Stefan Falk *(CEO)*

Calanbau Brandschutzanlagen GmbH (3)
Gerhart-Hauptmann-Str 20, 64347, Griesheim, Germany
Tel.: (49) 6950051586
Web Site: http://www.fire-protection-solutions.com
Sales Range: $25-49.9 Million
Emp.: 40
Fire Protection Services
N.A.I.C.S.: 922160

Felix Schuh Dammtechnik GmbH (3)
Ottheinrich Strasse 3, 86609, Donauworth, Germany
Tel.: (49) 906 21015
Web Site: http://www.felix-schuh.de
Emp.: 10
Heating & Air Conditioning Services
N.A.I.C.S.: 238220

G+H Fassadentechnik GmbH (3)
Auf den Holln 47, 44894, Bochum, Germany
Tel.: (49) 2 34 5 87 20
Web Site: http://www.guh-fassadentechnik.de
Sales Range: $25-49.9 Million
Emp.: 40
Industrial Building Construction Services
N.A.I.C.S.: 236210
Frank Schmidt *(Mgr-Unit)*

G+H Isolierung GmbH (3)
Industriestrasse 19 A, 67063, Ludwigshafen, Germany
Tel.: (49) 621502125
Web Site: http://www.guh-group.com
Fire Insulation & Protection Services
N.A.I.C.S.: 238310

G+H Schallschutz GmbH (3)
Industriestrasse 19 A, 67063, Ludwigshafen, Germany
Tel.: (49) 621502125
Web Site: http://www.guh-group.com
Sound Proof Insulation System Installation Services
N.A.I.C.S.: 238310

GA Holding GmbH (3)
Im Breitspiel 7, 69126, Heidelberg, Germany
Tel.: (49) 6221 9410
Web Site: http://www.ga-gruppe.de
Sales Range: $1-4.9 Billion
Emp.: 300
Holding Company
N.A.I.C.S.: 551112

Subsidiary (Domestic):

Frankenluk Energieanlagenbau GmbH (4)
Podeldorfer Strasse 86, Bamberg, 96052, Germany
Tel.: (49) 9511820
Web Site: http://www.frankenluk.de
Sales Range: $50-74.9 Million
Construction & Operation of Power Plants
N.A.I.C.S.: 237130
Otto Trautner *(Gen Mgr)*

GA Energieanlagenbau Nord GmbH (4)
Eisvögelstrasse 33, 39110, Magdeburg, Germany
Tel.: (49) 391 24351 0
Web Site: http://www.ga-ean.de
Sales Range: $75-99.9 Million
Emp.: 50
Electric Power Line Construction Services
N.A.I.C.S.: 237130

GA Energieanlagenbau Sud GmbH (4)
Schmidener Weg 3, 70736, Fellbach, Germany
Tel.: (49) 711 9573 9
Web Site: http://www.ga-eas.de
Emp.: 70
Power Line Construction Engineering Services
N.A.I.C.S.: 237130

GA Hochspannung Leitungsbau GmbH (4)
Schulstrasse 124, 29664, Walsrode, Germany
Tel.: (49) 5161 6004 0
High Voltage Cable System Installation Services
N.A.I.C.S.: 238210

GA Netztechnik GmbH (4)
Rotestrasse 24, 74321, Bietigheim-Bissingen, Germany
Tel.: (49) 7142 969 0
Web Site: http://www.ga-netztechnik.de
Telecommunication Network Installation
N.A.I.C.S.: 238210
Emil Hoellig *(Gen Mgr)*

Joint Venture (US):

INP North America, Inc. (3)
11390 Old Roswell Rd Ste 126, Alpharetta, GA 30009-0000 **(55%)**
Tel.: (678) 527-1400
Web Site: http://www.inp-e.com
Engineeering Services
N.A.I.C.S.: 541330
Andreas Droge *(Mng Dir)*

Subsidiary (Domestic):

Isolierungen Leipzig GmbH (3)
Hohmannstr 7c, 04129, Leipzig, Germany
Tel.: (49) 3415660300
Web Site: http://www.guh-group.com
Thermal Insulation & Protection Services
N.A.I.C.S.: 238310

Nohl Brandschutz GmbH (3)
Werner-von-Siemens-Str 2, 64319, Pfungstadt, Germany
Tel.: (49) 6157 1580 0
Fire Insulation & Protection Services
N.A.I.C.S.: 238310
Olaf Walter *(Gen Mgr)*

Subsidiary (Non-US):

Omexon AS (3)
Innspurten 15, 0663, Oslo, Norway **(100%)**
Tel.: (47) 23128800
Web Site: https://www.omexom.no
Energy, Communication & Railway Infrastucture Construction, Maintenance & Contingency Support Services
N.A.I.C.S.: 541330
Svein Lerberg *(Mgr-HR)*

Subsidiary (Non-US):

VINCI Energies International East GmbH (2)
Neubaugasse 1/5, 1070, Vienna, Austria
Tel.: (43) 17150574
Web Site: http://www.vinci.com
Sales Range: $25-49.9 Million
Emp.: 6
Electrical Equipment Installation Services
N.A.I.C.S.: 238210

Subsidiary (Non-US):

Nickel Klima Kft. (3)
Szolo street 9 2 floor 201, 1034, Budapest, Hungary
Tel.: (36) 12258361
Web Site: http://www.nickelklima.hu
Sales Range: $25-49.9 Million
Building Cleaning & Maintenance Services
N.A.I.C.S.: 561720
Andras Birtok *(Mng Dir)*

Subsidiary (Non-US):

VINCI Energies Netherlands BV (2)
Mountbattenweg 19, 5466 AX, Veghel, Netherlands
Tel.: (31) 888318000
Web Site: http://www.vinci-energies.nl
Sales Range: $25-49.9 Million
Energy Consulting Services
N.A.I.C.S.: 541690

Subsidiary (Domestic):

G+H Akoestiek B.V. (3)
Bruissingel 220, 5232 AD, 's-Hertogenbosch, Netherlands
Tel.: (31) 416 347054
Web Site: http://www.ghakoestiek.com

INTERNATIONAL PUBLIC

Industrial Sound & Noise Control Services
N.A.I.C.S.: 238310

Van der Linden & Veldhuis Isolatie B.V. (3)
Edisonstraat 5, 3133 KG, Vlaardingen, Netherlands
Tel.: (31) 10 445 66 00
Web Site: http://www.lindveld.nl
Construction Engineering Services
N.A.I.C.S.: 541330
B. Verschoor *(Branch Mgr)*

Vanderlinden (3)
Eisenhowerweg 39, 5466 AB, Veghel, Netherlands
Tel.: (31) 888318444
Web Site: http://www.vanderlindenbs.nl
Building Inspection Services
N.A.I.C.S.: 541350

Subsidiary (Non-US):

VINCI Energies Poland (2)
Ul Luzycka 2, 81-537, Gdynia, Poland
Tel.: (48) 58 66 22 912
Web Site: http://www.vinci-energies.pl
Industrial Consulting Services
N.A.I.C.S.: 541690

Subsidiary (Domestic):

TPI Ochrona Przeciwpozarowa Sp. z o. o. (3)
Al Jerozolimskie 200 building ERA 200, 02-486, Warsaw, Poland
Tel.: (48) 22 578 12 60
Web Site: http://www.tpi-op.pl
Fire Sprinkler System Installation Services
N.A.I.C.S.: 238220

Subsidiary (Non-US):

VINCI Energies Romania S.A. (2)
17 Pictor Arthur Verona Strada, 010312, Bucharest, Romania
Tel.: (40) 213021230
Web Site: http://www.vinci-energies.ro
Electrical Installation Services
N.A.I.C.S.: 238210

Subsidiary (Domestic):

STIZO Industrial Services S.R.L. (3)
Str Andrei Muresanu Nr 52, 100379, Ploiesti, Prahova, Romania
Tel.: (40) 244 407 500
Web Site: http://www.stizo-is.ro
Sales Range: $100-124.9 Million
Emp.: 400
Heating & Air Conditioning Equipment Installation Services
N.A.I.C.S.: 238220

TIAB SA (3)
17 Pictor Verona Street, District 1, 10312, Bucharest, Romania
Tel.: (40) 21 302 12 30
Web Site: http://www.tiab.ro
Sales Range: $200-249.9 Million
Emp.: 600
Heating & Plumbing Equipment Installation Services
N.A.I.C.S.: 238220

Subsidiary (Non-US):

VINCI Energies Schweiz AG (2)
Pfingstweidstrasse 106, 8021, Zurich, Switzerland
Tel.: (41) 44 947 77 00
Web Site: http://www.vinci-energies.ch
Sales Range: $10-24.9 Million
Energy Consulting Services
N.A.I.C.S.: 541690

VINCI Energies United Kingdom Plc (2)
2050 The Crescent Birmingham Business Park, Birmingham, B37 7YE, United Kingdom
Tel.: (44) 121 717 1820
Web Site: http://www.vinci-energies.co.uk
Process Control Instruments Mfr.
N.A.I.C.S.: 334513
Rochdi Rochdiziyat *(CEO)*

Subsidiary (Domestic):

Axians (3)
Quinn Close, Coventry, CV3 4LH, West

AND PRIVATE COMPANIES

VINCI S.A.

Midlands, United Kingdom
Tel.: (44) 2476 516070
Web Site: http://www.axians.co.uk
Emp.: 10,000
Human Resource Consulting Services
N.A.I.C.S.: 541612

Subsidiary (Non-US):

Axians Belgium (4)
Bourgetlaan 44, 1130, Brussels, Belgium
Tel.: (32) 27759045
Web Site: http://www.axians.be
Business Support Services
N.A.I.C.S.: 561499

Subsidiary (Domestic):

MESL Group Ltd. (3)
Cordwallis House Cordwallis Street, Maidenhead, SL6 7BG, Berks, United Kingdom
Tel.: (44) 1628 771 717
Web Site: http://www.meslgroup.co.uk
Sales Range: $25-49.9 Million
Emp.: 20
Mechanical & Electrical Building Services
N.A.I.C.S.: 541330

Subsidiary (Non-US):

Omexom (3)
23-27 Rue Delariviere Lefoullon, BP 2101, 92800, Puteaux, cedex, France
Tel.: (33) 183756819
Web Site: http://www.omexom.fr
Electric Power Generation & Distribution Services
N.A.I.C.S.: 221118

Subsidiary (Domestic):

Twyver Switchgear Limited (3)
Unit 9 Chancel Cl, Gloucester, GL4 3SN, United Kingdom
Tel.: (44) 1452 525096
Web Site: http://www.twyverswitchgear.co.uk
Emp.: 25
Electric Equipment Mfr
N.A.I.C.S.: 335999

Subsidiary (Domestic):

VINCI Facilities (2)
64 Avenue de Colmar, Rueil-Malmaison, 92500, France
Tel.: (33) 1 56 84 52 02
Web Site: http://www.vinci-facilities.com
Emp.: 20
Facility Management Services
N.A.I.C.S.: 561210

Subsidiary (Non-US):

G+H Innenausbau GmbH (3)
August-Borsig-Strasse 6, 68199, Mannheim, Germany
Tel.: (49) 6 21 8 50 97 400
Web Site: http://www.guh-innenausbau.de
Interior Design Services
N.A.I.C.S.: 541410

Subsidiary (Domestic):

VINCI Facilities - France Nord (3)
157 rue de la Miniere, 78530, Buc, France
Tel.: (33) 130972200
Sales Range: $550-599.9 Million
Emp.: 6,000
Facility & Property Management Services
N.A.I.C.S.: 561210

Subsidiary (Non-US):

VINCI Facilities Belgium NV/SA (3)
Havenlaan 86 C Bus 201, 1000, Brussels, Belgium
Tel.: (32) 24222611
Web Site: http://www.vinci-facilities.be
Facilities Management Services
N.A.I.C.S.: 561210

VINCI Facilities Deutschland GmbH (3)
August-Borsig-Strasse 2, 68199, Mannheim, Germany
Tel.: (49) 62185097100
Web Site: http://www.vinci-facilities.de
Sales Range: $350-399.9 Million
Emp.: 2,000
Construction Management Services
N.A.I.C.S.: 237990
Rainer Beisel (Gen Mgr)

VINCI Facilities GmbH (3)
Lise-Meitner-Str 4, 70736, Stuttgart, Germany
Tel.: (49) 711 93347 0
Web Site: http://www.vinci-facilities.de
Sales Range: $10-24.9 Million
Emp.: 40
Facilities Management Services
N.A.I.C.S.: 561210

VINCI Facilities UK Ltd. (3)
Astral House Imperial Way, Watford, WD24 4WW, Hertfordshire, United Kingdom
Tel.: (44) 1923 478400
Web Site: http://www.vincifacilities.com
Sales Range: $450-499.9 Million
Emp.: 2,200
Facilities Support Services
N.A.I.C.S.: 561210
Tony Raikes (Mng Dir)

Subsidiary (Non-US):

VM Impianti Elettrici S.r.l. (2)
Via Jucker 51/53, 20025, Legnano, Milan, Italy
Tel.: (39) 0331 464 633
Energy Consulting Services
N.A.I.C.S.: 541690

VINCI Energies Belgium NV (1)
Bourgetlaan 44, 1130, Brussels, Belgium
Tel.: (32) 27759045
Web Site: https://www.vinci-energies.be
Emp.: 2,800
Information Technology Development Services
N.A.I.C.S.: 541511
Marc Lemaire (Mng Dir)

VINCI Energies Chile SPA (1)
Avda Los Cerrillos 980 Casilla 122 Cerrillos, 7270534, Santiago, Chile
Tel.: (56) 25849000
Construction Services
N.A.I.C.S.: 236220

VINCI Energies Do Brazil Ltda. (1)
Avenida Nilo Pecanha n 50 Sala 2709, Centro, Rio de Janeiro, 200020-906, Brazil
Tel.: (55) 2135904101
Web Site: https://www.vinci-energies.com.br
Construction Services
N.A.I.C.S.: 236220
Alexandre Lopez (Mgr-Bus Ops)

VINCI Energies Espana S.A. (1)
Paseo de la Castellana 41, 28046, Madrid, Spain
Tel.: (34) 911271001
Web Site: http://www.vinci-energies.es
Construction Services
N.A.I.C.S.: 236220

VINCI Energies Italia Srl (1)
Via Gallarate 205, Milan, Italy
Tel.: (39) 0235949851
Web Site: http://www.vinci-energies.it
Construction Services
N.A.I.C.S.: 236220

VINCI Energies New Zealand Limited (1)
2 George Bourke Drive, PO Box 1688, Mt Wellington, Auckland, New Zealand
Tel.: (64) 92701700
Construction Services
N.A.I.C.S.: 236220

VINCI Energies Nordic AB (1)
Hildedalsgatan 2, 417 05, Gothenburg, Sweden
Tel.: (46) 31659000
Web Site: http://www.vinci-energies.se
Construction Services
N.A.I.C.S.: 236220

VINCI Energies Portugal Ltda. (1)
Edificio Atlantis Avenida D Joao II n 44 - 5 piso, 1990-095, Lisbon, Portugal
Tel.: (351) 214258000
Web Site: http://www.vinci-energies.pt
Information Technology Development Services
N.A.I.C.S.: 541511

VINCI Energies Srl (1)
Strada Pictor Arthur Verona nr 17, Bucharest, Romania
Tel.: (40) 213021230
Web Site: http://www.vinci-energies.ro
Construction Services
N.A.I.C.S.: 236220

VINCI Energies Srl (1)
Ringhofferova 115/1 Trebonice, Prague, Czech Republic
Tel.: (420) 257181911
Web Site: http://www.vinci-energies.cz
Construction Services
N.A.I.C.S.: 236220

VINCI Energies Sro (1)
Kralovska 8, 927 01, Sala, Slovakia
Tel.: (421) 317731111
Web Site: http://www.vinci-energies.sk
Construction Services
N.A.I.C.S.: 236220

VINCI Environnement Central Europe Sp. Z.O.O. (1)
Al Krakowska 271, 02-133, Warsaw, Poland
Tel.: (48) 223953912
Construction Services
N.A.I.C.S.: 236220
Katarzyna Tomiczek-Bura (Project Mgr)

VINCI Facilities Italia S.r.l. (1)
Via Gallarate 205, 20151, Milan, Italy
Tel.: (39) 0292148382
Construction Services
N.A.I.C.S.: 236220

VINCI Facilities Management GmbH (1)
August-Borsig-Strasse 6, 68199, Mannheim, Germany
Tel.: (49) 62185097100
Web Site: http://www.vinci-facilities.de
Construction Services
N.A.I.C.S.: 236220
Rainer Beisel (Gen Mgr)

VINCI Facilities Osterreich GmbH (1)
Schlossplatz 1, 2331, Vosendorf, Austria
Tel.: (43) 711933470
Construction Services
N.A.I.C.S.: 236220

VINCI Facilities Polska Sp z o.o. (1)
Ul Domaniewska 32, 02-672, Warsaw, Poland
Tel.: (48) 225676056
Web Site: https://www.vinci-facilities.pl
Construction Services
N.A.I.C.S.: 236220
Tomasz Ruczaj (Mng Dir)

VINCI Facilities S.R.O. (1)
Doudlebska 1699/5, 140 00, Prague, Czech Republic
Tel.: (420) 241409015
Construction Services
N.A.I.C.S.: 236220
Frantisek Malek (Mng Dir)

VINCI Facilities Schweiz AG (1)
Schaffhauserstrasse 611, 8052, Zurich, Switzerland
Tel.: (41) 443068060
Construction Services
N.A.I.C.S.: 236220

VINCI Facilities Solutions GmbH (1)
August-Borsig-Strasse 6, 68199, Mannheim, Germany
Tel.: (49) 62185097300
Web Site: http://www.solutions.vinci-facilities.de
Construction Services
N.A.I.C.S.: 236220

VINCI Highways SAS (1)
12-14 rue Louis Bleriot, CS 20070, 92506, Rueil-Malmaison, Cedex, France
Tel.: (33) 147163500
Facility Management Services
N.A.I.C.S.: 327910

Subsidiary (Non-US):

Northern Highway Operation LLC (2)
17 Chistoprudny Boulevard Building 1 3rd Floor, 101000, Moscow, Russia
Tel.: (7) 4957084204
Construction Services
N.A.I.C.S.: 236220

VINCI Concessions Colombia SAS (2)
Carrera 11 A 93 A 46 Oficina 102, Bogota, Colombia
Tel.: (57) 16171223
Construction Services
N.A.I.C.S.: 236220
Bernardo Serafim (Mng Dir & Head-Latam Bus Dev)

Subsidiary (US):

VINCI Concessions USA Inc. (2)
1221 Brickell Av ste 2040, Miami, FL 33131
Tel.: (786) 580-5947
Construction Services
N.A.I.C.S.: 236220
Cedric Antunes-Karrer (Fin Mgr)

Subsidiary (Non-US):

Via Solutions Sudwest GmbH (2)
Boschstrasse 2, 77815, Buhl, Germany
Tel.: (49) 7223281430
Web Site: https://www.via-suedwest.de
Construction Services
N.A.I.C.S.: 236220
Cyril Jansem (CFO-Proxy)

VINCI Immobilier Conseil SAS (1)
59 rue Yves Kermen, CS 20206, 92106, Boulogne-Billancourt, Cedex, France
Tel.: (33) 155388000
Construction Services
N.A.I.C.S.: 236220

VINCI Immobilier Gestion (1)
Gamma Tours 193 197 rue de Bercy, 75582, Paris, Cedex, France
Tel.: (33) 140046068
Web Site: http://www.vinci-immobilier-gestion.com
Sales Range: $25-49.9 Million
Property Management Services
N.A.I.C.S.: 531390
Olivier de la Roussiere (Pres)

VINCI Immobilier Mediterrannee SAS (1)
345 Avenue WA Mozart Le Sextius, 13100, Aix-en-Provence, France
Tel.: (33) 442646442
Construction Services
N.A.I.C.S.: 236220

VINCI Immobilier Monaco Sarl (1)
27 Boulevard d'Italie Margaret, 98000, Monaco, Monaco
Tel.: (377) 99907282
Real Estate Services
N.A.I.C.S.: 531390

VINCI Immobilier Nord Est SAS (1)
213 Boulevard de Turin, Euralille, 59777, Lille, France
Tel.: (33) 320883945
Construction Services
N.A.I.C.S.: 236220

VINCI Immobilier Property Management SAS (1)
9 rue Yves Kermen, CS 30107, 92650, Boulogne-Billancourt, Cedex, France
Tel.: (33) 155384500
Web Site: http://www.vinci-immobilier-pm.com
Real Estate Services
N.A.I.C.S.: 531390
Sherry-Ann Booth (Mgr-Property)

VINCI Immobilier Residences Gerees SAS (1)
139 rue Vendome, 69477, Lyon, Cedex, France
Tel.: (33) 437240909
Web Site: http://www.vinci-immobilier-rg.com
Residence Services
N.A.I.C.S.: 721110

VINCI Immobilier Rhone Alpes Auvergne SAS (1)
19 Quai Perrache Immeuble Quai 19, CS 50145, 69286, Lyon, Cedex, France
Tel.: (33) 472600791
Real Estate Services
N.A.I.C.S.: 531390

VINCI Immobilier SAS (1)
59 rue Yves Kermen, BP 126, 92100,

VINCI S.A.

VINCI S.A.—(Continued)
Boulogne-Billancourt, France
Tel.: (33) 339788309
Web Site: http://www.vinci-immobilier.com
Real Estate Development Services
N.A.I.C.S.: 531390

VINCI SAS (1)
1 Cours Ferdinand de Lesseps, 92851, Rueil-Malmaison, Cedex, France
Tel.: (33) 147163500
Web Site: http://www.vinci.com
Emp.: 4,000
Construction Services
N.A.I.C.S.: 236220
Pierre Duprat (Dir-Comm)

VINCI UK Developments Limited (1)
Stanbridge Road, Leighton Buzzard, LU7 4QH, Bedfordshire, United Kingdom
Tel.: (44) 3335669000
Web Site: http://www.technology-centre.co.uk
Construction Services
N.A.I.C.S.: 236220
Graham Lambert (Mng Dir)

Val de Loire Granulats SAS (1)
Le Bout de la Vallee Poiriou, Averdon, 41330, Blois, France
Tel.: (33) 254331458
Urban Development Construction Services
N.A.I.C.S.: 236220

Val de Loire Maintenance Service SAS (1)
103 Avenue du Danemark, CS 17539, 37075, Tours, France
Tel.: (33) 247885050
Construction Services
N.A.I.C.S.: 236220

Valentin SAS (1)
13 rue Edouard Vaillant, Feuquieres-en-Vimeu, France
Tel.: (33) 322603400
Web Site: http://www.valentin.fr
Sanitary Equipment Mfr
N.A.I.C.S.: 333415
Arnaud Valentin (CEO)

Valff Enrobes SAS (1)
4 rue de l'Industrie, BP 70339, Fegersheim, 67640, Strasbourg, Cedex, France
Tel.: (33) 388087144
Construction & Engineering Services
N.A.I.C.S.: 236220

Vandipaint NV (1)
Kalkhoevestraat 1, Waregem, Belgium
Tel.: (32) 493431285
Web Site: http://www.vandipaint-nv.business.site
Road Safety Equipment Mfr
N.A.I.C.S.: 334290

Vars Brno A.S. (1)
Kroftova 80c, 616 00, Brno, Czech Republic
Tel.: (420) 515514111
Web Site: https://www.vars.cz
Information Technology Services
N.A.I.C.S.: 541511
Ondrej Pokorny (Dir-ITS)

Vcd Business Intelligence B.V. (1)
Eemsgolaan 15, 9727 DW, Groningen, Netherlands
Tel.: (31) 885975500
Construction Services
N.A.I.C.S.: 236220

Vcd Business Solutions B.V. (1)
Eemsgolaan 17, 9727 DW, Groningen, Netherlands
Tel.: (31) 885975500
Construction Services
N.A.I.C.S.: 236220

Vdz SRO (1)
3 Kvetna 524, Vizovice, Czech Republic
Tel.: (420) 603215565
Web Site: http://www.vdz.cz
Disc & Wheel Mfr & Distr
N.A.I.C.S.: 336340

Verkerk Groep BV (1)
Molenvliet 1 en 1B, 3335 LH, Zwijndrecht, Netherlands
Tel.: (31) 786107100
Web Site: http://www.verkerk.com
Electrical & Electronic Product Mfr

N.A.I.C.S.: 335999
Pieter Visser (Mgr-Bus Unit)

Vermot SAS (1)
16 Rue Pasteur, Gilley, Pontarlier, France
Tel.: (33) 381685555
Web Site: http://www.vermot.fr
Public & Road Work Construction Services
N.A.I.C.S.: 237310

Ves SA (1)
9 rue Jules Cesar Zac des Beaux Soleils, 95520, Osny, France
Tel.: (33) 139474475
Construction Services
N.A.I.C.S.: 236220

Via Imc GmbH (1)
Franz-Ehrlich-Str 5, 12489, Berlin, Germany
Tel.: (49) 3054684801
Web Site: http://www.via-imc.com
Infrastructure Construction Services
N.A.I.C.S.: 236220
Dirk Ebersbach (Mng Dir)

Viafrance Normandie SAS (1)
La Fringale business park Voie de Ouvrage, 27100, Val-de-Reuil, France
Tel.: (33) 232402722
Urban Development Construction Services
N.A.I.C.S.: 236220

Vibro Menard Limited (1)
Block 6 Greenhill Industrial Estate, Coatbridge, ML5 2AG, United Kingdom
Tel.: (44) 1698863418
Web Site: http://www.vibromenard.co.uk
Construction Services
N.A.I.C.S.: 236220
Marc Evans (Mgr-Bus Unit)

Vigiprom SARL (1)
Mahaj Ryad Immeuble H, BP 2015, Hay Ryad, Rabat, Morocco
Tel.: (212) 537564884
Construction Services
N.A.I.C.S.: 236220

Voiries et Pavages du Nord SAS (1)
4 Avenue de l'Europe, Armentieres, France
Tel.: (33) 320354196
Web Site: http://www.pavage-nord.fr
Paving Construction Services
N.A.I.C.S.: 238990

Vonthron Entreprises SAS (1)
5 rue de l Industrie, 67116, Reichstett, France
Tel.: (33) 388324421
Construction Services
N.A.I.C.S.: 236220

W Genest Partner Ingenieurgesellschaft mbH (1)
Parkstrasse 70, 67061, Ludwigshafen, Germany
Tel.: (49) 621586150
Web Site: http://www.genest.de
Engineering Consultancy Services
N.A.I.C.S.: 541330

Wah Loon (M) Sdn. Bhd. (1)
No 65 Jalan Hujan Overseas Union Garden, 58200, Kuala Lumpur, Malaysia
Tel.: (60) 377836886
Electrical Engineering Services
N.A.I.C.S.: 541330
Jatin Varma (Mgr-IT)

Wah Loon Engineering Pte. Ltd. (1)
10 Tagore Drive Wah Loon Building, Singapore, 787625, Singapore
Tel.: (65) 67473773
Web Site: https://www.wahloon.com
Electrical Engineering Services
N.A.I.C.S.: 541330
Rajendran Sekar (Mgr-Construction)

Warbud Beton Sp. z o.o. (1)
Ul Gniewkowska 44, Warsaw, Poland
Tel.: (48) 225676360
Construction Services
N.A.I.C.S.: 236220

Warbud Sp. z o.o. (1)
ul Domaniewska 32, 02-672, Warsaw, Poland
Tel.: (48) 225676000
Web Site: https://www.warbud.pl
Emp.: 1,100
Construction Services

N.A.I.C.S.: 236220
Robert Bednarczyk (Mgr-BIM-Research & Development)

Watelet TP SAS (1)
7 route Principale du Port, 92230, Gennevilliers, France
Tel.: (33) 140850037
Urban Development Construction Services
N.A.I.C.S.: 236220

Water Management International Colombia Ltda. (1)
Carrera 11 86-60 Of 501, Bogota, Colombia
Tel.: (57) 314813934
Engineering Services
N.A.I.C.S.: 541330

Wrede & Niedecken GmbH (1)
Im Horst 13, 67133, Maxdorf, Germany
Tel.: (49) 623797640
Construction Services
N.A.I.C.S.: 236220

Xeria S.A. (1)
204 Impasse Augustin Fresnel Zone Industrielle Jarry, 97122, La Baie Mahault, Guadeloupe
Tel.: (590) 590383505
Construction Services
N.A.I.C.S.: 236220

Z Makina AS (1)
Site Building Cooperative 29 Sokak No 9 Koseler Mah, SS Istanbul Mermerciler Small Industry Dilovasi, 41455, Kocaeli, Turkiye
Tel.: (90) 2627281122
Web Site: http://www.zmakina.com.tr
Construction Services
N.A.I.C.S.: 236220
Omer Mumin Eryasar (Mgr-Research & Development)

Zetas Zemin Technology AS (1)
Alemdag Merkez Mah Resadiye Cad No 69/A, Cekmekoy, 34794, Istanbul, Turkiye
Tel.: (90) 2164300600
Web Site: http://www.zetas.com.tr
Construction Services
N.A.I.C.S.: 236220

societe Charpente Bois Et Couverture Industrialises (1)
Lot 107 PAE Degrad des Cannes Guyana, Remire-Montjoly, Cayenne, French Guiana
Tel.: (594) 354788
Web Site: http://www.cbci.fr
Construction Services
N.A.I.C.S.: 236220

societe Jean Lefebvre Polynesie (1)
Route des Plaines PK 11 2 Mountain Side Tahiti Tamanu, BP 380 622, Punaauia, Papeete, French Polynesia
Tel.: (689) 40420946
Construction & Engineering Services
N.A.I.C.S.: 236220

VINCITAG INVESTMENT MANAGEMENT AG

Promenadeplatz 12, 80333, Munich, Germany
Tel.: (49) 89 211128 200   De
Web Site: http://www.vincitag.de
Year Founded: 2006
Privater Equity Firm
N.A.I.C.S.: 523999
Hubert Bock (Co-Founder & Member-Mgmt Bd)

Subsidiaries:

Tectareal Property Management GmbH (1)
Alfredstrasse 236, D 45133, Essen, Germany
Tel.: (49) 201 824 5000
Web Site: http://www.tectareal.de
Sales Range: $150-199.9 Million
Emp.: 450
Real Estate Manangement Services
N.A.I.C.S.: 531390
Ralf Lehmann (Mng Dir)

VINDHYA TELELINKS LTD

Udyog Vihar, P O Chorhata, Chorhata, Rewa, 486006, Madhya Pradesh, India
Tel.: (91) 7662400400
Web Site: https://www.vtlrewa.com
VINDHYATEL—(NSE)
Rev.: $349,370,170
Assets: $727,587,495
Liabilities: $318,561,381
Net Worth: $409,026,114
Earnings: $22,218,284
Emp.: 592
Fiscal Year-end: 03/31/23
Jelly Filled Telecommunication Cables Supplier
N.A.I.C.S.: 238210
Harsh Vardhan Lodha (Chm)

VINEET LABORATORIES LIMITED

5-5-160 Malleswari Nilayam Opp Vishnu Theatre, Chintalakunta L B Nagar, Hyderabad, 500074, Telangana, India
Tel.: (91) 4024128833
Web Site: https://www.vineetlabs.co.in
Year Founded: 2007
543298—(BOM)
Rev.: $33,287,557
Assets: $14,843,218
Liabilities: $11,210,272
Net Worth: $3,632,946
Earnings: $243,009
Emp.: 87
Fiscal Year-end: 03/31/21
Pharmaceutical Product Mfr & Distr
N.A.I.C.S.: 325412
K. Murali Mohan (Dir-Ops)

VINERGY CAPITAL INC.

1000 409 Granville Street, Vancouver, V6C 1T2, BC, Canada
Tel.: (604) 602-0001
Year Founded: 2001
MBAIF—(OTCQB)
Rev.: $27,656
Assets: $4,661,761
Liabilities: $196,612
Net Worth: $4,465,149
Earnings: ($5,405,049)
Fiscal Year-end: 02/29/24
Investment Management Service
N.A.I.C.S.: 523940
Arif Merali (CEO)

VINEXPO S.A.S.

2 Cours du XXX Juillet, 33074, Bordeaux, Cedex, France
Tel.: (33) 556560022   FR
Web Site: http://www.vinexpo.com
Year Founded: 1981
Sales Range: $10-24.9 Million
Emp.: 20
Wine & Spirits Exhibition Organizer
N.A.I.C.S.: 561920
V. Christophe O. B. J. Navarre (Chm)

Subsidiaries:

Vinexpo Overseas S.A.S. (1)
2 Cours du XXX Juillet, 33074, Bordeaux, Cedex, France
Tel.: (33) 556560022
Web Site: http://www.vinexpo.com
Holding Company; Wine & Spirits Exhibition Organizer
N.A.I.C.S.: 551112

VINGROUP JOINT STOCK COMPANY

No 7 Bang Lang 1 Street, Viet Hung Ward Long Bien District, Hanoi, Vietnam
Tel.: (84) 2439749999   VN
Web Site: https://vingroup.net
Year Founded: 1993
VIC—(HOSE)
Rev.: $10,180,952,900

AND PRIVATE COMPANIES

Assets: $57,740,724,000
Liabilities: $44,175,179,100
Net Worth: $13,565,544,900
Earnings: $878,186,100
Emp.: 54,400
Fiscal Year-end: 12/31/22
Real Estate Manangement Services
N.A.I.C.S.: 531390
Nhat Vuong Pham *(Chm)*

Subsidiaries:

Bao Lai Investment JSC (1)
2a Floor 27a2 Building Green Star Urban Area 234 Pham Van Dong, Bac Tu Liem District, 123116, Hanoi, Vietnam
Tel.: (84) 975758866
Web Site: https://www.baolaimarble.net
Emp.: 200
White Marble Mfr & Distr
N.A.I.C.S.: 327991

Sai Dong Urban Development & Investment JSC (1)
No 7 Bang Lang 1 Street, Viet Hung Ward Long Bien District, Hanoi, Vietnam
Tel.: (84) 439749261
Web Site: https://saidongjsc.com
Real Estate & Civilian Construction Services
N.A.I.C.S.: 531320

VinBigData JSC (1)
Floor 9 Century Tower Times City 458 Minh Khai, Vinh Tuy Ward Hai Ba Trung District, Hanoi, Vietnam
Tel.: (84) 659892676
Web Site: https://vinbigdata.com
Artificial Intelligence & Data Science Research Services
N.A.I.C.S.: 518210

VinES Energy Solutions JSC (1)
Dinh Vu Cat Hai Economic Zone Cat Hai Island, Cat Hai Town Cat Hai District, Haiphong, Vietnam
Tel.: (84) 2471012888
Web Site: https://vines.net.vn
Emp.: 1,300
Batteries & Accumulators Mfr
N.A.I.C.S.: 332420

VinFast Auto Ltd. (1)
Dinh Vu-Cat Hai Economic Zone, Cat Hai Islands Cat Hai Town Cat Hai District, Haiphong, Vietnam
Tel.: (84) 2253969999
Web Site: www.vinfastauto.us
Rev.: $637,085,209
Assets: $4,836,177,578
Liabilities: $6,397,239,018
Net Worth: ($1,561,061,440)
Earnings: ($2,122,066,396)
Fiscal Year-end: 12/31/2022
Automobile Mfr
N.A.I.C.S.: 336320
David Thomas Mansfield *(CFO)*

VinHMS Software Production & Trading JSC (1)
188 Vo Thi Sau Street, Ward 7 District 3, Ho Chi Minh City, Vietnam
Tel.: (84) 2871099708
Web Site: https://vinhms.com
Software Programming Services
N.A.I.C.S.: 541511

Vinbus Ecology Transport Services LLC (1)
Hai Au 03 Street Vinhomes Ocean Park, Da Ton Commune Gia Lam District, Hanoi, Vietnam
Tel.: (84) 1900866663
Web Site: https://vinbus.vn
Transportation Services
N.A.I.C.S.: 926120

Vinmec International Hospital Joint Stock Company (1)
458 Minh Khai Street, Hai Ba Trung Dist, Hanoi, Vietnam
Tel.: (84) 439743556
Web Site: http://www.vinmec.com
Sales Range: $50-74.9 Million
Emp.: 500
Health Care Srvices
N.A.I.C.S.: 621999
Tan Poh Lan *(CEO)*

Vinpearl Landmark 81 JSC (1)
Hon Tre Island, Vinh Nguyen Ward, Nha Trang, Khanh Hoa, Vietnam
Tel.: (84) 1900232389
Web Site: https://vinpearl.com
Providing Food Services
N.A.I.C.S.: 722310

World Academy LLC (1)
138 Spit Brook Rd, Nashua, NH 03062
Tel.: (603) 888-1982
Web Site: https://worldacademynh.com
Providing Education Services
N.A.I.C.S.: 611710

VINH HOAN CORPORATION

National Road 30 Ward 11, Cao Lanh, Dong Thap, Vietnam
Tel.: (84) 2773891166
Web Site: https://www.vinhhoan.com
Year Founded: 1997
VHC—(HOSE)
Rev.: $415,121,675
Assets: $492,033,038
Liabilities: $138,081,540
Net Worth: $353,951,498
Earnings: $40,118,782
Emp.: 10,000
Fiscal Year-end: 12/31/23
Seafood Product Mfr
N.A.I.C.S.: 311710
Truong Thi Le Khanh *(Founder & Chm)*

Subsidiaries:

SA GIANG IMPORT EXPORT CORPORATION (1)
Lot CII-3 Road No 5 Industrial Park C, Sa Dec, Dong Thap, Vietnam **(76.72%)**
Tel.: (84) 2773763155
Web Site: https://sagiang.com.vn
Rev.: $15,343,305
Assets: $9,051,826
Liabilities: $2,993,925
Net Worth: $6,057,902
Earnings: $1,269,947
Fiscal Year-end: 12/31/2021
Meat Product Processing Services
N.A.I.C.S.: 311613
Nguyen Van Kiem *(Gen Dir)*

Plant (Domestic):

SA GIANG IMPORT EXPORT CORPORATION - SaGiang Food Factory (2)
281 Nguyen Hue St, Ward 1, Sa Dec, Dong Thap, Vietnam
Tel.: (84) 67 3864987
Meat Product Processing Services
N.A.I.C.S.: 311613

SA GIANG IMPORT EXPORT CORPORATION - Sagiang Shrimp Chips Factory 2 (2)
Lot III-2 & Lot III-3 Sector A1 SaDec Industrial Zone, Sa Dec, Dong Thap, Vietnam
Tel.: (84) 67 3762754
Meat Product Processing Services
N.A.I.C.S.: 311613

Vinh Technology Pte. Ltd. (1)
No 1 Scotts Road 24-10 Shaw Centre, Singapore, Singapore
Tel.: (65) 2838364849
Clinical Research Services
N.A.I.C.S.: 541715

VINH PHUC INFRASTRUCTURE DEVELOPMENT JOINT STOCK COMPANY

Khai Quang Industrial Park, Khai Quang Ward, Vinh Yen, Vin Phuc, Vietnam
Tel.: (84) 2113720945
Web Site: https://www.vpid.vn
Year Founded: 2003
IDV—(HNX)
Rev.: $18,434,500
Assets: $181,589,000
Liabilities: $102,143,800
Net Worth: $79,445,200
Earnings: $15,783,900
Fiscal Year-end: 12/31/23
Construction Services
N.A.I.C.S.: 236220

VINH PLASTIC & BAGS JSC

18 Phong Dinh Cang road, Ben Thuy ward, Vinh, Nghe An, Vietnam
Tel.: (84) 383855524
VBC—(HNX)
Rev.: $36,031,213
Assets: $15,992,398
Liabilities: $9,490,791
Net Worth: $6,501,607
Earnings: $1,156,443
Fiscal Year-end: 12/31/23
Plastics Bag Mfr
N.A.I.C.S.: 326111

VINH SON - SONG HINH HYDRO POWER JOINT STOCK COMPANY

21 Nguyen Hue Street, Quy Nhon, Binh Dinh, Vietnam
Tel.: (84) 563892792
Web Site:
https://www.vshpc.evn.com.vn
Year Founded: 1991
VSH—(HOSE)
Rev.: $105,968,130
Assets: $392,767,799
Liabilities: $203,459,361
Net Worth: $189,308,438
Earnings: $40,952,388
Fiscal Year-end: 12/31/23
Eletric Power Generation Services
N.A.I.C.S.: 221111
Vo Thanh Trung *(Chm)*

VINK + CO GMBH HANDELSGESELLSCHAFT UND CO KG

Eichenhohe 24, Kakenstorf, 21255, Harburg, Germany
Tel.: (49) 4186 888 00
Web Site: http://www.vink-co.de
Year Founded: 1980
Raw Materials, Spare Parts & Machinery Distr
N.A.I.C.S.: 424690
A.A. Vink *(Mng Dir)*

Subsidiaries:

Scomi Anticor S.A.S (1)
Z A du Mardaric, BP 19, 04310, Peyruis, France
Tel.: (33) 4 92 68 69 70
Web Site: http://www.anticor-chimie.com
Emp.: 8
Oil & Gas Field Drilling Services
N.A.I.C.S.: 213111
Pascal Jroshe *(Mng Dir)*

VINNY OVERSEAS LTD.

B/H Nissan Services Mutton Gali Road Near BMP Textile Mills Pvt Ltd, Narolgam, Ahmedabad, 382405, Gujarat, India
Tel.: (91) 7925731800
Web Site:
https://www.vinnyoverseas.in
Year Founded: 1992
VINNY—(NSE)
Rev.: $18,701,692
Assets: $11,533,807
Liabilities: $7,434,122
Net Worth: $4,099,684
Earnings: $53,592
Emp.: 205
Fiscal Year-end: 03/31/21
Textile Products Mfr
N.A.I.C.S.: 314999

VINO KALEM A.D.

Velika Drenova, 37245, Krusevac, Serbia
Tel.: (381) 37725455
Web Site: https://www.vino-kalem.com
Year Founded: 1997
VINK—(BEL)
Rev.: $2,831,315
Assets: $4,345,231
Liabilities: $2,864,136
Net Worth: $1,481,095
Earnings: $171,797
Emp.: 19
Fiscal Year-end: 12/31/23
Seedling Growing Services
N.A.I.C.S.: 111421
Zoran Miladinovic *(Exec Dir)*

VINO ZUPA INC

Krusevacka 36, 37230, Aleksandrovac, Serbia
Tel.: (381) 37552409
Web Site: https://www.vinozupa.com
Year Founded: 1956
VINZ—(BEL)
Rev.: $13,951,607
Assets: $21,797,428
Liabilities: $92,135,243
Net Worth: ($70,337,815)
Earnings: ($2,491,492)
Emp.: 398
Fiscal Year-end: 12/31/23
Beverage Producer
N.A.I.C.S.: 311421
Rade Jevtovic *(Gen Mgr)*

VINPAC INTERNATIONAL PTY. LIMITED

Stockwell Rd, Angaston, 5353, South Australia, Australia
Tel.: (61) 885610600
Web Site: http://www.vinpac.com.au
Sales Range: $1-4.9 Billion
Emp.: 10,300
Wine & Distilled Beverages
N.A.I.C.S.: 424810
David Hutton *(Gen Mgr)*

VINPAI SA

6 PA de la Fouee, Saint-Dolay, 56130, Rennes, France
Tel.: (33) 223100400
Web Site: https://www.vinpai-finance.com
Year Founded: 2011
ALVIN—(EUR)
Cosmetics Products Mfr
N.A.I.C.S.: 325620
Cyrille Damany *(Pres)*

VINSYS IT SERVICES INDIA LIMITED

Shivaji Niketan Tejas Society Behind Kothrud Bus Stand, Near Mantri Park Kothrud, Pune, 411038, India
Tel.: (91) 2067444700
Web Site: https://www.vinsys.com
Year Founded: 1999
VINSYS—(NSE)
Rev.: $11,712,840
Assets: $8,841,050
Liabilities: $5,863,272
Net Worth: $2,977,777
Earnings: $1,825,678
Emp.: 206
Fiscal Year-end: 03/31/23
Education Services
N.A.I.C.S.: 611310
Saneeka Nikhil Dhamankar *(CFO)*

Subsidiaries:

Vikvins Consultants Private Limited (1)
Shivaji Niketan Tejas Society Behind Dhondiba Sutar Bus Stand, Near Mantri Park Kothrud, Pune, 411038, Maharashtra, India
Tel.: (91) 7030934511
Web Site: https://www.vikvins.com
Human Resource Consulting Services

VINSYS IT SERVICES INDIA LIMITED

Vinsys IT Services India Limited—(Continued)
N.A.I.C.S.: 541612

Vinsys Corporation (1)
132 W 31st St 1st Fl, New York, NY 10001
Information Technology Services
N.A.I.C.S.: 541519

VINTAGE COFFEE & BEVERAGES LTD.
202 Oxford Plaza 9-1-129/1, SD Road, Secunderabad, 500003, Telangana, India
Tel.: (91) 9154080891
Web Site: https://vcbl.coffee
538920—(BOM)
Rev.: $28,994
Assets: $473,316
Liabilities: $29,042
Net Worth: $444,274
Earnings: $13,202
Fiscal Year-end: 03/31/21
Commercial Trading Services
N.A.I.C.S.: 425120
Kranthi Kumar (CFO)

Subsidiaries:

Delecto Foods Private Limited (1)
No 9-1-129 Oxford Plaza 202 1 SD Road, Secunderabad, 500003, Telangana, India
Tel.: (91) 4040266650
Web Site: https://delectofoods.in
Instant Coffee Product Mfr & Distr
N.A.I.C.S.: 311920

Vintage Coffee Private Limited (1)
202 Oxford Plaza No 9-1-129/1 S D Road, Secunderabad, 500003, Telangana, India
Tel.: (91) 4040266650
Web Site: https://www.vintagecoffee.in
Instant Coffee Product Mfr & Distr
N.A.I.C.S.: 311920

VINTAGE ENERGY LIMITED
58 King William Rd, Goodwood, 5034, SA, Australia
Tel.: (61) 874777680 AU
Web Site: https://www.vintageenergy.com.au
Year Founded: 2015
VEN—(ASX)
Rev.: $5,015,937
Assets: $35,405,913
Liabilities: $15,600,760
Net Worth: $19,805,153
Earnings: ($15,514,432)
Fiscal Year-end: 06/30/24
Asset Management Services
N.A.I.C.S.: 531390
Neil Gibbins (Mng Dir)

VINTAGE SECURITIES LTD.
58/3 B R B Basu Road, Kolkata, 700001, India
Tel.: (91) 3340132115
Web Site: https://www.vintage-securities.com
531051—(BOM)
Rev.: $8,857
Assets: $1,295,003
Liabilities: $145,591
Net Worth: $1,149,412
Earnings: $55
Emp.: 1
Fiscal Year-end: 03/31/21
Securities Brokerage Services
N.A.I.C.S.: 523150
Laxmi Kant Parwa (CFO)

VINTANA PLC
Unit 22 Cochran Close Crownhill Industrial Estate, Milton Keynes, MK8 0AJ, United Kingdom
Tel.: (44) 203 376 9420 UK
Web Site: http://www.cellcast.tv
Rev.: $14,301,953
Assets: $3,194,735
Liabilities: $1,378,713
Net Worth: $1,816,022

Earnings: ($317,769)
Emp.: 22
Fiscal Year-end: 12/31/18
Participatory Television Programming & Interactive Telephony Technology
N.A.I.C.S.: 517810
Craig Gardiner (CEO)

Subsidiaries:

Cellcast Middle East (1)
2nd Fl New Starco Bldg Omar Daouk St, Minet El Hosn, Beirut, 1107-2210, Lebanon
Tel.: (961) 1377520
Web Site: http://www.cellcastme.com
Mobile Marketing Services
N.A.I.C.S.: 561422

VINTCOM TECHNOLOGY PUBLIC COMPANY LIMITED
159/21 Serm-Mit Tower Unit 1401 14th Floor Sukhumvit 21 Road, North-Klongtoey Sub-District Wattana District, Bangkok, 10110, Thailand
Tel.: (66) 26617979 TH
Web Site: https://www.vintcom.co.th
Year Founded: 1992
VCOM—(THA)
Rev.: $61,067,137
Assets: $42,597,990
Liabilities: $24,106,697
Net Worth: $18,491,293
Earnings: $3,319,756
Emp.: 285
Fiscal Year-end: 12/31/23
Information Technology Services
N.A.I.C.S.: 541512
Songsri Srirungroungjit (Mng Dir & Exec Dir)

Subsidiaries:

I-Secure Company Limited (1)
55 Pradiphat 17 Alley Pradiphat Rd, Phaya Thai Sub-district Phaya Thai District, Bangkok, 10400, Thailand
Tel.: (66) 261570057
Web Site: http://www.i-secure.co.th
Network Security Monitoring Services
N.A.I.C.S.: 561621

vServePlus Company Limited (1)
88/1 Phatthana Chonnabot 3 Road, Kwaeng Khlong Song Ton Nun Khet Lat Krabang, Bangkok, 10520, Thailand
Tel.: (66) 26669600
Web Site: http://www.vserveplus.co.th
Information Technology Management Services
N.A.I.C.S.: 541511

VINTE VIVIENDAS INTEGRALES, S.A.B. DE C.V.
Av Via Real Mz 16 Lt 1 Local 1 Fracc Real del Sol, 55770, Mexico, Mexico
Tel.: (52) 5550107360
Web Site: https://www.vinte.com
Year Founded: 2001
VINTE—(MEX)
Rev.: $284,024,063
Assets: $690,405,314
Liabilities: $404,688,639
Net Worth: $285,716,675
Earnings: $25,825,715
Emp.: 2,155
Fiscal Year-end: 12/31/23
Residential Real Estate Development Services
N.A.I.C.S.: 531210
Sergio Leal Aguirre (Co-Founder, Chm & Pres)

VINTRON INFORMATICS LIMITED
D-88 Second Floor Okhla Industrial Area Phase -I, New Delhi, 110020, India
Tel.: (91) 114374000
Web Site: https://www.vintroninformatic.com
Year Founded: 1991

517393—(BOM)
Rev.: $1,702,769
Assets: $1,505,104
Liabilities: $2,836,074
Net Worth: ($1,330,971)
Earnings: ($425,129)
Emp.: 83
Fiscal Year-end: 03/31/21
Electronic Security & Surveillance Product Mfr
N.A.I.C.S.: 334290
Raj Kumar Gupta (Chm)

VINURI SI BAUTURI SA
Str Leliceni 49/B, Harghita, Miercurea Ciuc, Romania
Tel.: (40) 744 857491
Sales Range: Less than $1 Million
Alcoholic Beverages Whslr
N.A.I.C.S.: 424820
Zsido Vilmos (Gen Mgr)

VINVEST CAPITAL HOLDINGS BERHAD
No 4 Jalan Seri Utara 1 Seri Utara Batu 7 Jalan Ipoh, 68100, Kuala Lumpur, Malaysia
Tel.: (60) 362590111 MY
Web Site: https://www.vinvest.com.my
Year Founded: 2012
VINVEST—(KLS)
Rev.: $18,274,637
Assets: $126,031,377
Liabilities: $27,777,881
Net Worth: $98,253,496
Earnings: ($24,524,791)
Fiscal Year-end: 12/31/23
Telecommunication Engineering Services
N.A.I.C.S.: 541330
Anne Soo Ching Kung (Co-Sec)

Subsidiaries:

Instacom Engineering Sdn. Bhd. (1)
No 21 & 22 3rd Floor Stutong Commercial Centre Jalan Stutong, 93350, Kuching, Sarawak, Malaysia
Tel.: (60) 82366116
Web Site: http://www.instacom.com.my
Telecommunication Engineering Services
N.A.I.C.S.: 541330
Anne Soo Ching Kung (CEO)

Neata Aluminium (Malaysia) Sdn. Bhd. (1)
Lot 5308 KM28 Jalan, 43500, Semenyih, Selangor, Malaysia
Tel.: (60) 387239817
Web Site: https://neataaluminium.com
Aluminium Window & Door Mfr & Distr
N.A.I.C.S.: 332321
Albert Chia Kok Seng (Founder & CEO)

VINYAS INNOVATIVE TECHNOLOGIES LIMITED
KIADB Plot No 19 Survey No 26 & 273P 3rd Phase Koorgalli Industrial, Mysore, 570018, Karnataka, India
Tel.: (91) 8212404444
Web Site: https://www.vinyasit.com
Year Founded: 2001
VINYAS—(NSE)
Electric Equipment Mfr
N.A.I.C.S.: 335999
Narendra Narayanan (Founder)

VINYL CHEMICALS (INDIA) LTD.
Regent Chambers 7th Floor Jamnalal Bajaj Marg 208 Nariman Point, Mumbai, 400021, Maharashtra, India
Tel.: (91) 2222822708
Web Site: https://vinylchemicals.com
Year Founded: 1986
VINYLINDIA—(NSE)
Rev.: $55,353,444
Assets: $36,711,683

INTERNATIONAL PUBLIC

Liabilities: $27,418,010
Net Worth: $9,293,672
Earnings: $1,549,461
Emp.: 13
Fiscal Year-end: 03/31/21
Chemical Products Distr
N.A.I.C.S.: 424690
M. B. Parekh (Chm & Mng Dir)

VINYL WINDOW DESIGNS LTD.
300 Chrislea Road, Woodbridge, L4L 8A8, ON, Canada
Tel.: (905) 850-3222
Web Site: http://www.vinylwindowdesigns.com
Year Founded: 1986
Rev.: $39,479,963
Emp.: 250
Vinyl Windows Fabricators, Mfr & Distr
N.A.I.C.S.: 444180
Phil Spatafora (Pres)

VINYOFLEX LIMITED
307 Silver Chambers Tagore Road, Rajkot, 360 002, India
Tel.: (91) 2812460692
Web Site: https://www.vinyoflex.com
Year Founded: 1993
530401—(BOM)
Rev.: $6,728,460
Assets: $4,234,501
Liabilities: $3,716,666
Net Worth: $517,835
Earnings: $415,685
Fiscal Year-end: 03/31/23
Plastic Sheet & Film Mfr & Distr
N.A.I.C.S.: 326113
Mansukhlal Premjibhai Patel (Founder, Chm, CEO & Mng Dir)

VINZAVOD AD-ASENOVGRAD
75 Bulgaria Blvd, 4230, Asenovgrad, Bulgaria
Tel.: (359) 33169151
Web Site: https://www.mavrud.com
VINA—(BUL)
Sales Range: Less than $1 Million
Wine Mfr
N.A.I.C.S.: 312130
Rosen Chatalbashev (Chm & CEO)

VIOHALCO S.A.
30 Marnix Avenue, 1000, Brussels, Belgium
Tel.: (32) 22240911
Web Site: https://www.viohalco.com
Year Founded: 1937
Metal Products Mfr
N.A.I.C.S.: 331110
Evangelos Moustakas (CEO)

VIOHALCO SA/NV
30 Avenue Marnix, 1000, Brussels, Belgium
Tel.: (32) 22240911 BE
Web Site: http://www.viohalco.com
Year Founded: 2013
VIO—(ATH)
Rev.: $7,539,105,331
Assets: $6,507,873,948
Liabilities: $4,397,044,032
Net Worth: $2,110,829,916
Earnings: $326,342,543
Emp.: 10,762
Fiscal Year-end: 12/31/22
Holding Company; Metals Production, Processing & Trade
N.A.I.C.S.: 551112
Nikolaos M. Stassinopoulos (Chm)

Subsidiaries:

AEIFOROS SA (1)
12th km Old National Road Thessaloniki-

VIOHALCO SA/NV

Veria, PO Box 59, 57008, Thessaloniki, Greece
Tel.: (30) 2310790151
Web Site: https://www.aeiforos.gr
Steel Products Mfr
N.A.I.C.S.: 331110

Plant (Domestic):

AEIFOROS SA - Almyros Plant (2)
Tsiggeli, 37100, Almyros, Greece
Tel.: (30) 2422777302
Steel Products Mfr
N.A.I.C.S.: 331110

AKRO SA (1)
2-4 Messogeion Ave, 11527, Athens, Greece
Tel.: (30) 210 747 4577
Steel Products Mfr
N.A.I.C.S.: 331110

ALURAME S.r.l (1)
Via Antonio Stradivari 10, Palazzo Taurus, 20131, Milan, Monza e Brianza, Italy
Tel.: (39) 0297178130
Sales Range: $25-49.9 Million
Emp.: 3
Aluminum Extrusion Product Mfr
N.A.I.C.S.: 331313

ANAMET SA (1)
NATO Avenue, Aspropirgos, 19300, Athens, Greece
Tel.: (30) 2105596010
Web Site: https://www.anamet.gr
Metal Recycling Services
N.A.I.C.S.: 562920

ATTIKI SA (1)
Protomagias 9, 14568, Peristeri, Attiki, Greece
Tel.: (30) 210 5751896 8
Steel Products Mfr
N.A.I.C.S.: 331110

AWM S.p.A. (1)
SS 13 Pontebbana Km 146, Magnano in Riviera, 33010, Udine, Italy
Tel.: (39) 0432780311
Web Site: https://www.awm.it
Automatic Machine Mfr
N.A.I.C.S.: 334512

Aeiforos Bulgaria S.A. (1)
Vladaysko Vastanie Str 1, 2304, Pernik, Bulgaria
Tel.: (359) 76681603
Web Site: https://www.aeiforos.bg
Non Ferrous Metal Mfr
N.A.I.C.S.: 331529

Base Metal Ticaret ve Sanayi A.S. (1)
Barbaros Mahallesi Mustafa Pehlivan Sokak No 21/1 Uskudar, 34662, Istanbul, Turkiye
Tel.: (90) 216688764044
Web Site: https://www.base-metal.com.tr
Aluminium Product Mfr & Distr
N.A.I.C.S.: 331511

Bridgnorth Aluminium Limited (1)
Stourbridge Road, Bridgnorth, WV15 6AU, Shropshire, United Kingdom (75%)
Tel.: (44) 1746788111
Web Site: https://www.bridgnorthaluminium.co.uk
Sales Range: $250-299.9 Million
Emp.: 300
Lithographic Aluminum Strip Mfr
N.A.I.C.S.: 331318

CONSULTANT & CONSTRUCTION SOLUTIONS SA (1)
11-21 Sifnaion Agioplaston, 151 24, Maroussi, Greece
Tel.: (30) 2106199583
Web Site: http://www.enf.gr
Emp.: 5
Construction Materials Distr
N.A.I.C.S.: 423610
Shabtay Shalit (Gen Mgr)

Cablel Wires S.A. (1)
62nd km Athens-Lamia National Road, Viotia, 320 11, Oinofita, Greece
Tel.: (30) 2262048976
Web Site: https://www.cablelwires.com
Cable & Wire Mfr
N.A.I.C.S.: 332618

Corinth Pipeworks S.A. (1)
33 Amarousiou-Halandriou Str, 151 25, Maroussi, Attiki, Greece (78.55%)
Tel.: (30) 2106787680
Web Site: http://www.cpw.gr
Sales Range: $300-349.9 Million
Steel Pole Mfr
N.A.I.C.S.: 237120
Apostolos Papavasileiou (CEO)

Subsidiary (US):

CPW America Co. (2)
750 Town and Country Blvd Ste 675, Houston, TX 77024
Tel.: (281) 752-7300
Web Site: https://www.cpwamerica.com
Steel Product Distr
N.A.I.C.S.: 423510

Plant (Domestic):

Corinth Pipeworks S.A. - Thisvi Plant (2)
VI PE Thisvis, 32010, Domvrena, Greece
Tel.: (30) 2264022777
Steel Products Mfr
N.A.I.C.S.: 331110

DIA.VI.PE.THI.V SA (1)
33 Amarousiou Halandriou Str, Maroussi, 15125, Athens, Greece
Tel.: (30) 210 6787680
Web Site: http://www.diavipethiv.gr
Administrative Management Services
N.A.I.C.S.: 561110

DOMOPLEX LTD (1)
Ayios Athanasios Industrial Area, PO Box 54185, Limassol, CY-3721, Cyprus
Tel.: (357) 77771110
Web Site: https://www.domoplex.com.cy
Silo Mfr
N.A.I.C.S.: 332618

ERLIKON SA (1)
Panteleimon Nea Santa, PO Box 71, 61100, Kilkis, Greece
Tel.: (30) 2310 790250
Web Site: http://www.erlikon.gr
Silo Mfr
N.A.I.C.S.: 332618
Dimitrios Theocharidis (Deputy Gen Mgr & Mgr-Tech)

ETIL SA (1)
13th klm Thessaloniki - Veroia, PO Box 1002, Sindos, 57022, Thessaloniki, Greece
Tel.: (30) 2310722742
Web Site: https://etil.gr
Industrial Equipment Mfr
N.A.I.C.S.: 334513

Elkeme S.A. (1)
61st Km Athens-Lamia Nat Road, 320 11, Oinofita, Viotia, Greece
Tel.: (30) 2262604400
Web Site: https://www.elkeme.gr
Metal Testing Laboratory Services
N.A.I.C.S.: 541380

Elval Colour Iberica S.L.U. (1)
Pl El Canyet Nave 7B, El Papiol, 08754, Barcelona, Spain
Tel.: (34) 930095149
Building Materials Distr
N.A.I.C.S.: 423390

ElvalHalcor S.A. (1)
62nd km Athens - Lamia National Road, 32011, Athens, Greece (52.67%)
Tel.: (30) 2262048111
Web Site: https://www.elvalhalcor.com
Rev: $2,422,305,880
Assets: $1,915,325,538
Liabilities: $1,079,823,544
Net Worth: $835,501,994
Earnings: $73,549,128
Emp.: 577
Fiscal Year-end: 12/31/2018
Copper & Aluminum Sheet Mfr
N.A.I.C.S.: 331410
Periklis Sapountzis (Gen Mgr-Copper Segment)

Subsidiary (Domestic):

FITCO SA (2)
59th Km Nat Road Athens-Lamia, 32011, Oinofita, Greece
Tel.: (30) 2262053181

Web Site: https://www.fitco.gr
Copper Product Mfr
N.A.I.C.S.: 331523
Andreas D. Gontzes (CEO)

Hellenic Cables S.A. (2)
33 Amarousiou Halandriou Str, 151 25, Amaroussion, Greece (100%)
Tel.: (30) 2106787416
Web Site: https://www.cablel.com
Rev.: $1,026,400,986
Assets: $1,225,395,029
Liabilities: $1,001,640,995
Net Worth: $223,754,034
Earnings: $53,003,839
Emp.: 1,828
Fiscal Year-end: 12/31/2023
Submarine, High Voltage & Low Voltage Cable & Copper Rods Designer & Mfr
N.A.I.C.S.: 335921
Ioannis Batsolas (Chm & Exec Member)

Subsidiary (Non-US):

Genecos S.A. (3)
1 Rue Francois Jacob, 92500, Rueil-Malmaison, France
Tel.: (33) 145270754
Sales Range: $50-74.9 Million
Emp.: 9
Transportation Equipment & Supplies Whslr
N.A.I.C.S.: 423860

Icme Ecab SA (3)
42 Drumul intre Tarlale Str 3rd sector, 032982, Bucharest, Romania (99%)
Tel.: (40) 212090200
Web Site: http://www.cablel.ro
Sales Range: $200-249.9 Million
Emp.: 600
Cable & Other Program Distr
N.A.I.C.S.: 517111
Eusebiu Muthi (Exec Dir)

Metal Agencies Limited (3)
Suite 4 Cobb House 2-4 Oyster Lane, Byfleet, KT14 7DU, Surrey, United Kingdom (33%)
Tel.: (44) 1932331111
Web Site: https://www.metalagencies.com
Sales Range: $25-49.9 Million
Emp.: 10
Secondary Smelting Refining & Alloying Nonferrous Metal
N.A.I.C.S.: 331492
Nicolas Gauld (Mng Dir)

Metal Globe d.o.o. (3)
Bulevar Mihajla Pupina 10a Objekat G; Ulaz IV YBC Kompleks-Blok 12, 11070, Belgrade, Serbia (30%)
Tel.: (381) 11 3015876
Sales Range: $25-49.9 Million
Emp.: 15
Metal Service Centers & Metal Merchant Whslr
N.A.I.C.S.: 423510

Subsidiary (Non-US):

SOFIA MED AD (2)
4 Dimitar Peshev str, 1528, Sofia, Bulgaria
Tel.: (359) 29606209
Web Site: https://www.sofiamed.bg
Metal Products Mfr
N.A.I.C.S.: 331420

Epirus Metalworks S.A. (1)
Kefalovrysso Pogoniou, 44006, Ioannina, Greece
Tel.: (30) 2657041911
Web Site: https://www.epirusmetalworks.com
Coin Mfr & Distr
N.A.I.C.S.: 339910

Etem Bulgaria SA (1)
119 A Iliyantsi blvd, PO Box 115, 1220, Sofia, Bulgaria
Tel.: (359) 29219111
Web Site: https://etem.com
Holding Company
N.A.I.C.S.: 551112

Etem Systems Srl (1)
RO-077090 Ilfov com Domnesti Bretea Autostrada km 11 272, Bucuresti, Pitesti, Romania (51%)
Tel.: (40) 213518115
Copper Product Mfr
N.A.I.C.S.: 331420

Inos Balcan doo (1)
Mirka Obradovica bb, 14000, Valjevo, Serbia
Tel.: (381) 14221560
Web Site: https://www.inosbalkan.com
Non Ferrous Metal Mfr
N.A.I.C.S.: 331529

Inos Balkan Doo (1)
Mirka Obradovica bb, 14000, Valjevo, Serbia
Tel.: (381) 14221560
Web Site: https://www.inosbalkan.com
Waste Recycling Services
N.A.I.C.S.: 562920

International Trade S.A. (1)
4 Rue du Trone, 1000, Brussels, Belgium
Tel.: (32) 22352610
Web Site: https://www.internationaltrade.com
Aluminum Roll Product Mfr
N.A.I.C.S.: 331491
Jean Charles Faulx (Mng Dir)

KIFISSOS MALL SA (1)
Chimarras 16, Maroussi, Greece
Tel.: (30) 21 0686 1298
Steel Products Mfr
N.A.I.C.S.: 331110
Nikolas Liananttonakis (Gen Mgr)

Noval S.A. (1)
16 Himaras Street, 151 25, Maroussi, Greece
Tel.: (30) 2106861111
Holding Company
N.A.I.C.S.: 551112

Novometal doo (1)
Blvd Kuzman Josifovski Pitu 28/24 MK, 1000, Skopje, North Macedonia
Tel.: (389) 25204125
Holding Company
N.A.I.C.S.: 551112

Prosal Tubes S.A. (1)
1 Vladaisko Vastanie Street, 2304, Pernik, Bulgaria
Tel.: (359) 76681358
Holding Company
N.A.I.C.S.: 551112

Reynolds Cuivre S.A. (1)
1 rue Francois Jacob, CS 60099, 92508, Rueil-Malmaison, Cedex, France
Tel.: (33) 155472460
Web Site: https://www.reynolds-cuivre.fr
Copper Product Distr
N.A.I.C.S.: 423510

SANITAS SA (1)
26 Amaroussiou-Halandriou, Maroussi, Greece
Tel.: (30) 210 6197110
Steel Products Mfr
N.A.I.C.S.: 331110

STOMANA INDUSTRY SA (1)
1 Vladaisko Vastanie str, 2304, Pernik, Bulgaria
Tel.: (359) 76681023
Web Site: https://www.stomana.bg
Steel Products Mfr
N.A.I.C.S.: 331110

SYMETAL SA (1)
25th km Athens - Korinthos Nat Road, Mandra Attica, 19600, Athens, Greece
Tel.: (30) 2105556833
Web Site: https://www.symetal.gr
Aluminum Sheet Mfr
N.A.I.C.S.: 331315

Plant (Domestic):

SYMETAL SA - Oinofyta Plant (2)
Agios Thomas, Viotia, 32011, Oinofita, Greece
Tel.: (30) 2262053111
Aluminum Sheet Mfr
N.A.I.C.S.: 331315

Sidenor Steel Industry S.A. (1)
33 Amaroussiou-Chalandriou Street Maroussi, 15125, Athens, Greece
Tel.: (30) 2106787111
Web Site: https://www.sidenor.gr
Steel Products Mfr
N.A.I.C.S.: 331511

VIOHALCO SA/NV

Viohalco SA/NV—(Continued)

Siderom Steel Srl (1)
42 Drumul intre Tarlale 3rdSector, 032982,
Bucharest, Romania
Tel.: (40) 212090138
Holding Company
N.A.I.C.S.: 551112

Sidma S.A. (1)
188 Megaridos Avenue, Attikis, 19300, Aspropyrgos, Greece
Tel.: (30) 2103498200
Web Site: https://www.sidma.gr
Steel Products Mfr
N.A.I.C.S.: 331511

Steelmet Romania S.A (1)
Str Drumul intre Tarlale nr 42 Sector 3, PO Box 70, 032982, Bucharest, Romania
Tel.: (40) 212090570
Web Site: https://www.steelmet.ro
Sales Range: $25-49.9 Million
Emp.: 25
Stainless Steel Products Mfr
N.A.I.C.S.: 331110

Steelmet S.A (1)
119 A Ilienci Boulevard, PO Box 105, 1220, Sofia, Bulgaria
Tel.: (359) 2 92 19 111
Web Site: http://www.steelmet.bg
Stainless Steel Products Mfr
N.A.I.C.S.: 331513
George Mentzelopoulos (Pres)

TEPRO METAL AG (1)
Ursulastrasse 33-41, 50354, Hurth, Germany
Tel.: (49) 2233 39 62 0
Web Site: http://www.tepro-metall.com
Steel Products Mfr
N.A.I.C.S.: 331110

Thermolith S.A. (1)
Kalyves, Polygyros, 631 00, Greece
Tel.: (30) 2106861820
Web Site: http://www.thermolith.gr
Olivine Mining Services
N.A.I.C.S.: 212323

VITRUVIT SA (1)
14th km Thessaloniki - Edessa National Road, Ionia, 57011, Thessaloniki, Greece
Tel.: (30) 2310790209
Web Site: http://www.vitruvit.gr
Floor Tile Distr
N.A.I.C.S.: 423320

Viexal S.A. (1)
16 Himaras Str, 15125, Maroussi, Greece
Tel.: (30) 2106861423
Web Site: https://www.viexalsa.gr
Transport Services
N.A.I.C.S.: 561510

Viomal S.A. (1)
Vatontas - Nea Artaki, 346 00, Nea Artaki, Greece
Tel.: (30) 222104523640
Web Site: https://www.viomal.com
Roller Shutter Mfr
N.A.I.C.S.: 321918

VIOL CO., LTD.
C-808 809 Bundang Technopark C
744 Pangyo-Ro, Bundang-Gu,
Seongnam, 13510, Gyeonggi-do, Korea (South)
Tel.: (82) 3180177893
Web Site: https://violmedical.com
Year Founded: 2019
335890—(KRS)
Rev.: $23,860,070
Assets: $34,160,392
Liabilities: $4,295,946
Net Worth: $29,864,446
Earnings: $8,799,587
Emp.: 68
Fiscal Year-end: 12/31/22
Medical & Dental Instrument Mfr & Distr
N.A.I.C.S.: 339112
Sang-Jin Lee (Pres & CEO)

VIOLETA D.O.O.
Stjepana Radica 21, Grude, 88340, Bosnia & Herzegovina
Tel.: (387) 39660400
Web Site: http://www.violeta.com
Year Founded: 1990
Sales Range: $125-149.9 Million
Sanitary Paper Products Mfr; Foodstuffs & Hygienic Products Distr
N.A.I.C.S.: 322291
Petar Corluka (Pres)

Subsidiaries:

Prodex d.o.o. (1)
Stjepana Radica bb, 88340, Grude, Bosnia & Herzegovina
Tel.: (387) 39662830
Web Site: http://www.prodex.ba
Foodstuffs & Hygienic Paper Products Distr & Retailer
N.A.I.C.S.: 424410

VIOMI TECHNOLOGY CO., LTD
Wansheng Square Rm 1302 Tower C
Xingang East Road, Haizhu District,
Guangzhou, 510220, Guangdong,
China
Tel.: (86) 2089309496
Web Site: http://www.viomi.com
Year Founded: 2014
VIOT—(NASDAQ)
Rev.: $495,286,717
Assets: $442,117,178
Liabilities: $223,155,115
Net Worth: $218,962,063
Earnings: ($42,211,653)
Emp.: 916
Fiscal Year-end: 12/31/22
Holding Company
N.A.I.C.S.: 551112
Xiaoping Chen (Founder, Chm & CEO)

VION HOLDING N.V.
Noord Brabantlaan 303-307, 5657
GB, Eindhoven, Netherlands
Tel.: (31) 889953700
Web Site:
  http://www.vionfoodgroup.com
Sales Range: $5-14.9 Billion
Emp.: 21,000
Holding Company; Meat Processing Services
N.A.I.C.S.: 551112
Theo P. Koekkoek (Chm-Supervisory Bd)

Subsidiaries:

VION B.V. (1)
Boseind 10, Boxtel, 5281 RM, Netherlands
Tel.: (31) 411 658 555
Web Site: http://www.vionfood.nl
Meats Processor
N.A.I.C.S.: 311612
Uwe C. Tillmann (Chm-Exec Bd)

Subsidiary (Domestic):

Rousselot B.V. (2)
Kanaaldijk Noord 20, Son, 5691 NM, Netherlands
Tel.: (31) 499364100
Web Site: http://www.rousselot.com
Emp.: 25
Mfr of Gelatins & Collagens for Food, Pharmaceutical & Photographic Industries
N.A.I.C.S.: 325998
Sandor Noordermeer (VP-Global Sls & Mktg)

Subsidiary (US):

Rousselot Inc. (3)
227 Washington St, Peabody, MA 01960-5423
Tel.: (978) 573-5700
Web Site: http://www.rousselot.com
Sales Range: $25-49.9 Million
Gelatin Mfr
N.A.I.C.S.: 325998

Subsidiary (Non-US):

Rousselot S.A.S. (3)
4 rue de l'Abreuvoir, 92400, Courbevoie, France
Tel.: (33) 1 46 67 87 00
Web Site: http://www.rousselot.com
Emp.: 10
Sales of Gelatins & Collagens for Food, Pharmaceutical & Photographic Industries
N.A.I.C.S.: 424690
Jos Vervoort (Gen Mgr-EMEA)

Subsidiary (Non-US):

VION Food Group Limited (2)
7 Bain Sq, Kirkton Campus, Livingston, EH54 7DQ, United Kingdom
Tel.: (44) 1506400400
Web Site: http://www.vionfood.co.uk
Sales Range: $25-49.9 Million
Emp.: 40
Food Merchant Whslr
N.A.I.C.S.: 424470

Subsidiary (Domestic):

VION Food Nederland B.V. (2)
Boseind 15, 5281 RM, Boxtel, Netherlands
Tel.: (31) 889953555
Web Site: http://www.vionfoodgroup.com
Pork & Beef, Convenience Food Products & Vegetarian Consumer Products Mfr
N.A.I.C.S.: 311612

VION Brazil (1)
Av Brasil 2285 sl 02, 88330-053, Balneario Camboriu, Santa Catarina, Brazil
Tel.: (55) 47 3246 1680
Meat Product Distr
N.A.I.C.S.: 424470

VION Bulgaria Ltd. (1)
18 Daskal Manol Str entr 1 fl 1 ap 1, 1606, Sofia, Bulgaria
Tel.: (359) 2862 73 52
Emp.: 3
Meat Product Distr
N.A.I.C.S.: 424470
Aneta Nakova (Mng Dir)

VION Denmark ApS (1)
Laegardvej 91, 7500, Holstebro, Denmark
Tel.: (45) 961 18 020
Meat Product Distr
N.A.I.C.S.: 424470

VION Food Hellas Ltd. (1)
Kapodistriou 5, Metamorphosis, 14452, Athens, Greece
Tel.: (30) 2102 8123 23
Meat Product Distr
N.A.I.C.S.: 424470

VION Food International B.V. (1)
Boseind 10, 5281 RM, Boxtel, Netherlands
Tel.: (31) 411 658 555
Web Site: http://www.viofood.com
Veal Product Mfr
N.A.I.C.S.: 311612

VION Food International China (1)
No 18 North Cao Xi road, 200030, Shanghai, China
Tel.: (86) 21 642 77 337
Meat Product Distr
N.A.I.C.S.: 424470

VION Food International Pacific Ltd. (1)
31/F Tower One Times Square 1 Matheson Street, Causeway Bay, China (Hong Kong)
Tel.: (852) 2107 3628
Web Site: http://www.vionfood.com
Emp.: 5
Meat Product Distr
N.A.I.C.S.: 424470
Patrick Ballering (Reg Dir-Sls)

VION Food International Singapore PTE Ltd. (1)
16 Collyer Quay Level 20, Singapore, 049318, Singapore
Tel.: (65) 68189667
Meat Product Distr
N.A.I.C.S.: 424470

VION Food Portugal (1)
Av da Liberdade 262 2 Esq, 1250-149, Lisbon, Portugal
Tel.: (351) 21 35 53 295

INTERNATIONAL PUBLIC

Meat Product Distr
N.A.I.C.S.: 424470

VION France (1)
1 Rue Alfred de Vigny, 78112, Fourqueux, France
Tel.: (33) 139 21 85 20
Meat Product Distr
N.A.I.C.S.: 424470

VION GmbH (1)
Franz-Rennefeld-Weg 5, 40472, Dusseldorf, Germany
Tel.: (49) 211 44033 341
Web Site: http://www.vionfood.de
Meat Product Distr
N.A.I.C.S.: 424470

VION Hungary Kft. (1)
Mester u 30-32 VIII em, 1095, Budapest, Hungary
Tel.: (36) 1 766 38 01
Meat Product Distr
N.A.I.C.S.: 424470

VION International Ljubljana d.o.o. (1)
Dimiceva 13, 1000, Ljubljana, Slovenia
Tel.: (386) 1 5898 385
Meat Product Distr
N.A.I.C.S.: 424470

VION International Ukraine (1)
vul Budindustriji 5 k 314, 01013, Kiev, Ukraine
Tel.: (380) 44 285 65 11
Meat Product Distr
N.A.I.C.S.: 424470

VION Poland Sp.z.o.o. (1)
Lewartowskiego 6, 00-190, Warsaw, Poland
Tel.: (48) 22 206 99 10
Meat Product Distr
N.A.I.C.S.: 424470

VION Praha s.r.o. (1)
Drnovska 336/10, 161 00, Prague, Czech Republic
Tel.: (420) 220 40 5520
Meat Product Distr
N.A.I.C.S.: 424470

VION Romania Srl (1)
Str Pictor Theodor Aman nr 94C, 600164, Bacau, Romania
Tel.: (40) 334 405 089
Meat Product Distr
N.A.I.C.S.: 424470

VION SA (1)
Via Motta 12, 6830, Chiasso, Switzerland
Tel.: (41) 91 69663 23
Meat Product Distr
N.A.I.C.S.: 424470

VION Spain S.L. (1)
C/ Balmes 211 4 2, 8006, Barcelona, Spain
Tel.: (34) 93 36 88 487
Meat Product Distr
N.A.I.C.S.: 424470
Axel Reese Vion (Mng Dir)

VION Sweden AB (1)
Arenavagen 47 9 tr, Johanneshov, 121 77, Stockholm, Sweden
Tel.: (46) 87 2234 90
Meat Product Distr
N.A.I.C.S.: 424470

VIOR INC.
995 Wellington Street Suite 240,
Montreal, H3C 1V3, QC, Canada
Tel.: (613) 898-5052
Web Site: https://www.vior.ca
Year Founded: 1984
VIO—(TSXV)
Sales Range: Less than $1 Million
Gold Mining Services
N.A.I.C.S.: 212220
Claude St-Jacques (Founder & Chm)

VIOSOLAR INC.
Kolokotroni 2A Paleo Faliro, 17563,
Athens, Greece
Tel.: (30) 7083574891
Solar Energy Electric Production Services
N.A.I.C.S.: 221118

AND PRIVATE COMPANIES

Bill Kanatas *(VP)*

VIP CLOTHING LIMITED
C-6 Street No 22 MIDC Andheri East, Mumbai, 400 093, India
Tel.: (91) 2228257624
Web Site: https://www.vipclothing.in
Year Founded: 1991
VIPCLOTHNG—(NSE)
Rev: $19,808,662
Assets: $36,874,752
Liabilities: $18,440,126
Net Worth: $18,434,625
Earnings: ($142,711)
Emp.: 1,123
Fiscal Year-end: 03/31/21
Underwear Mfr & Sales
N.A.I.C.S.: 315120
Kapil J. Pathare *(Exec Dir)*

Subsidiaries:

Maxwell Industries Ltd - Stitching Units 2 (1)
SF 125 126 127 Appachimarmadam, Thingalur, Erode, 638055, Tamil Nadu, India
Tel.: (91) 4294 233971
Hosiery Knitting Services
N.A.I.C.S.: 424350

VIP GLOVES LIMITED
Level 26 360 Collins Street, Melbourne, 3000, VIC, Australia
Tel.: (61) 398677199   AU
Web Site: https://www.vipglove.com.my
Year Founded: 1992
VIP—(ASX)
Rev: $1,163,647
Assets: $4,936,410
Liabilities: $5,098,276
Net Worth: ($161,866)
Earnings: ($8,978,712)
Fiscal Year-end: 06/30/23
Investment Management Service
N.A.I.C.S.: 523940
Wee Min Chen *(Exec Dir)*

Subsidiaries:

VIP Glove Sdn. Bhd. (1)
No 17 Jalan Perusahaan 1 Kawasan Perusahaan, 43700, Beranang, Selangor Darul Ehsan, Malaysia
Tel.: (60) 387668191
Rubber & Nitrile Glove Mfr
N.A.I.C.S.: 326299

VIP INDUSTRIES LTD
5th Floor DGP House 88c Old Prabhadevi Road, Mumbai, 400025, India
Tel.: (91) 2266539000
Web Site: https://www.vipindustries.co.in
VIPIND—(NSE)
Rev: $251,711,528
Assets: $169,691,266
Liabilities: $92,754,631
Net Worth: $76,936,634
Earnings: $18,265,092
Emp.: 1,304
Fiscal Year-end: 03/31/23
Travel Products Mfr
N.A.I.C.S.: 316990
Dilip G. Piramal *(Chm)*

VIPO A.S.
Gen Svobodu 1069 4, 95801, Partizanske, Slovakia
Tel.: (421) 387493153
Web Site: https://www.vipo.sk
1VIP01AE—(BRA)
Sales Range: Less than $1 Million
Machinery Products Mfr
N.A.I.C.S.: 333998
Peter Duchovic *(Vice Chm-Mgmt Bd & Mng Dir)*

VIPOM JSC
9Tzar Ivan Asen II St, 3700, Vidin, 3700, Bulgaria
Tel.: (359) 94609025
Web Site: https://www.vipom.com
VPOM—(BUL)
Sales Range: Less than $1 Million
Pumps & Pumping Equipment Mfr
N.A.I.C.S.: 333914

VIPPY INDUSTRIES LTD
28 Industrial Area A B Road, Dewas, 455001, MP, India
Tel.: (91) 7272 258546
Web Site: http://www.vippysoya.com
Year Founded: 1973
Rev: $170,054,693
Assets: $69,190,569
Liabilities: $37,100,041
Net Worth: $32,090,528
Earnings: $5,573,119
Fiscal Year-end: 03/31/18
Soybean Mfr & Distr
N.A.I.C.S.: 111110
Rahul Mutha *(Co-Mng Dir)*

VIPPY SPINPRO LTD.
414 City Center 570 MG Road, Indore, 452001, MP, India
Tel.: (91) 7312546710
Web Site: https://www.vippyspinpro.com
Year Founded: 1992
514302—(BOM)
Rev: $18,877,190
Assets: $13,784,869
Liabilities: $5,233,967
Net Worth: $8,550,902
Earnings: $1,284,671
Emp.: 89
Fiscal Year-end: 03/31/23
Cotton Yarn Mfr & Distr
N.A.I.C.S.: 313110
Piyush Mutha *(Chm & Mng Dir)*

Subsidiaries:

VIPPY SPINPRO LTD. - Dewas Works (1)
14-A Industrial Area A-B Road, Dewas, 455001, MP, India
Tel.: (91) 7272 258251
Emp.: 500
Cotton Yarn Mfr
N.A.I.C.S.: 313110
Ashwini Kamadal *(Gen Mgr)*

VIPR INDUSTRIES, INC.
480 Barton Street, Hamilton, L8L 2Y8, ON, Canada
Tel.: (905) 521-8360
Web Site: http://www.viprtech.com
Sales Range: Less than $1 Million
Mobile Advertising
N.A.I.C.S.: 541890

VIPSHOP HOLDINGS LIMITED
No 128 Dingxin Road, Haizhu District, Guangzhou, 510335, China
Tel.: (86) 4006789888   Ky
Web Site: https://www.vip.com
Year Founded: 2008
VIPS—(NYSE)
Rev: $15,625,833,518
Assets: $10,013,651,141
Liabilities: $4,674,739,145
Net Worth: $5,338,911,996
Earnings: $1,135,536,525
Emp.: 14,638
Fiscal Year-end: 12/31/23
Online Retailer
N.A.I.C.S.: 449210
Arthur Xiaobo Hong *(Co-Founder, Vice Chm & COO)*

VIPUL LIMITED
Vipul Tech Square Golf Course Road Sec 43, Gurgaon, 122 009, Haryana, India
Tel.: (91) 1244065500
Web Site: https://www.vipulgroup.in
Year Founded: 2001
VIPULLTD—(NSE)
Rev: $10,170,361
Assets: $172,867,166
Liabilities: $158,746,802
Net Worth: $14,120,364
Earnings: ($14,068,473)
Emp.: 73
Fiscal Year-end: 03/31/23
Residential Construction
N.A.I.C.S.: 236115
Punit Beriwala *(Mng Dir)*

Subsidiaries:

Vipul Organics Limited (1)
102 Andheri Industrial Estate, Off Veera Desai Road Andheri W, Mumbai, 400 053, India
Tel.: (91) 2266139999
Web Site: https://www.vipulorganics.com
Rev: $16,065,859
Assets: $14,853,810
Liabilities: $8,497,956
Net Worth: $6,355,854
Earnings: $224,447
Emp.: 125
Fiscal Year-end: 03/31/2023
Dye Chemicals Mfr
N.A.I.C.S.: 325130
Vipul P. Shah *(Mng Dir)*

VIQ SOLUTIONS INC.
5915 Airport Road Suite 700, Mississauga, L4V 1T1, ON, Canada
Tel.: (905) 948-8266   ON
Web Site: https://www.viqsolutions.com
Year Founded: 1984
VQS—(NASDAQ)
Rev: $41,024,024
Assets: $29,675,195
Liabilities: $23,500,097
Net Worth: $6,175,098
Earnings: ($14,331,196)
Emp.: 334
Fiscal Year-end: 12/31/23
Computer-Based Digital Audio Capture & Management Software Mfr & Marketer
N.A.I.C.S.: 334610
Larry D. Taylor *(Exec Chm)*

Subsidiaries:

Hometech, Inc. (1)
5915 Airport Road Suite 700, Mississauga, L4V1T1, ON, Canada
Tel.: (905) 948-8266
Web Site: http://www.hometechinc.net
Document Preparation Services
N.A.I.C.S.: 561410

Net Transcripts, Inc. (1)
3707 N 7th St Ste 320, Phoenix, AZ 85014
Tel.: (480) 948-9241
Web Site: http://www.nettranscripts.com
Business Products & Services
N.A.I.C.S.: 518210

The Transcription Agency (VIQ) Company (1)
24-28 High Street, Hythe, CT21 5AT, Kent, United Kingdom
Tel.: (44) 1303230038
Web Site: https://thetranscriptionagency.com
Transcription Services
N.A.I.C.S.: 561410

Transcription Express, Inc. (1)
925 N McQueen Rd Ste 106, Gilbert, AZ 85233-2284
Tel.: (480) 497-1569
Court Reporting & Stenotype Services
N.A.I.C.S.: 561492

VIQ Australia (1)
Level 9 620 Bourke St, Perth, 3000, WA, Australia
Tel.: (61) 300502819
Web Site: http://www.viqsolutions.com

VIRAT LEASING LTD.

Sales Range: $50-74.9 Million
Emp.: 100
Holding Company
N.A.I.C.S.: 551112

Subsidiary (Domestic):

Spark & Cannon Pty Limited (2)
Level 9 620 Bourke St, Perth, 3000, WA, Australia
Tel.: (61) 300502819
Web Site: http://www.sparkandcannon.com.au
Sales Range: $25-49.9 Million
Emp.: 10
Digital Court Reporting Products & Services
N.A.I.C.S.: 561492

Viq Solutions, Inc (1)
20 E Thomas Rd Ste 2200, Phoenix, AZ 85012
Tel.: (813) 639-7534
Web Site: http://www.viqsolutions.com
Computer-Based Digital Audio Capture & Management Software Distr & Sales
N.A.I.C.S.: 423430

Wordzxpressed, Inc. (1)
3340 Peachtree Rd Ste 1800, Atlanta, GA 30326
Tel.: (404) 872-6079
Web Site: http://www.wordzx.com
Translation & Interpretation Services
N.A.I.C.S.: 541930

VIQUEL S.A.
14 Rue De Mantes, 92700, Colombes, Hauts De Seine, France
Tel.: (33) 146130283   FR
Web Site: http://www.viquel.fr
Year Founded: 1949
Rev: $31,200,000
Emp.: 202
Backpacks, Binders & Other Plastic School Supplies
N.A.I.C.S.: 326199
Christine Lombard *(Mgr-Manpower)*

VIRAT CRANE INDUSTRIES LIMITED
D No 25-18-54 Opp Main Road Sampath Nagar, Guntur, 522004, Andhra Pradesh, India
Tel.: (91) 8632223311
Web Site: https://viratcraneindustries.com
Year Founded: 1992
519457—(BOM)
Rev: $11,615,580
Assets: $8,722,748
Liabilities: $1,616,924
Net Worth: $7,105,824
Earnings: $827,873
Emp.: 77
Fiscal Year-end: 03/31/21
Tobacco Product Mfr & Whslr
N.A.I.C.S.: 312230
Puvvada Venkata Srihari *(CFO)*

VIRAT INDUSTRIES LTD.
A 1/2 GIDC Industrial Estate Kabilpore, Navsari, Gujarat, 396424, India
Tel.: (91) 2637265011
Web Site: https://www.viratindustries.com
Year Founded: 1995
530521—(BOM)
Rev: $4,606,319
Assets: $3,671,842
Liabilities: $674,804
Net Worth: $2,997,039
Earnings: $194,341
Emp.: 148
Fiscal Year-end: 03/31/23
Socks Mfr
N.A.I.C.S.: 315990
Adi Fredoon Madan *(Mng Dir)*

VIRAT LEASING LTD.
Jajodia Tower 3 Bentinck Street 4th

VIRAT LEASING LTD.

Virat Leasing Ltd.—(Continued)
Floor Room No D-8, Kolkata, West Bengal, India
Tel.: (91) 3322485664
Web Site: https://www.vll.co.in
Financial Management Services
N.A.I.C.S.: 522110
Rajeev Kothari *(Mng Dir)*

VIRAX BIOLABS GROUP LIMITED

BioCity Glasgow BoNess Road, Newhouse, ML1 5UH, Lanarkshire, United Kingdom
Tel.: (44) 2077887414   Ky
Web Site: https://viraxbiolabs.com
Year Founded: 2021
VRAX—(NASDAQ)
Rev.: $8,561
Assets: $9,812,416
Liabilities: $908,401
Net Worth: $8,904,015
Earnings: ($5,457,494)
Emp.: 11
Fiscal Year-end: 03/31/23
Holding Company
N.A.I.C.S.: 551112
Tomasz George *(Chief Scientific Officer)*

VIRBAC S.A.

13e rue LID - BP 27, 06511, Carros, Cedex, France
Tel.: (33) 492087100
Web Site:
    https://corporate.virbac.com
Year Founded: 1968
VIRP—(EUR)
Rev.: $1,376,422,343
Assets: $1,606,943,371
Liabilities: $602,509,107
Net Worth: $1,004,434,264
Earnings: $133,665,968
Emp.: 5,500
Fiscal Year-end: 12/31/23
Pet Health, Grooming, Dental & Parasiticide Products Mfr & Distr
N.A.I.C.S.: 325412
Marie-Helene Dick-Madelpuech *(Chm)*

Subsidiaries:

Bio Solutions International Co. Ltd.   (1)
134-4 Moo 5 Bangkradi Industrial Park, Tiwanon Rd Bangkradee Muang, 12000, Bangkok, Pathumtani, Thailand   **(100%)**
Tel.: (66) 25012045
Web Site: http://www.biohero.com
Sales Range: $25-49.9 Million
Emp.: 40
Biological Product Mfr
N.A.I.C.S.: 325414

Bio Veto Test SAS   (1)
285 Avenue de Rome, 83500, La Seyne-sur-Mer, France   **(100%)**
Tel.: (33) 494105894
Web Site: http://www.bvt.fr
Sales Range: $25-49.9 Million
Emp.: 19
Drugs & Druggists Sundries Whslr
N.A.I.C.S.: 424210

Francodex SAS   (1)
10 rue de l'Ormeau de Pied, 17100, Saintes, France   **(99.6%)**
Tel.: (33) 546979023
Web Site: http://www.francodex.com
Sales Range: $50-74.9 Million
Emp.: 10
Drugs & Druggists Sundries Whslr
N.A.I.C.S.: 424210
Mighau Aenp *(Mng Dir)*

Laboratorios Virbac Costa Rica SA   (1)
Av 24 El Prado Curridabat De McDonalds de Plaza del Sol, 700m sur y 75m este casa No 22 frente a la Embajada de El Salvador, San Jose, Costa Rica   **(100%)**

Tel.: (506) 87023797
Web Site: https://www.cr.virbac.com
Drugs & Druggists Sundries Whslr
N.A.I.C.S.: 424210

Laboratorios Virbac Mexico S.A. de C.V.   (1)
Av Inglaterra No 5070, Technology Park Zapopan, 45010, Guadalajara, Jalisco, Mexico   **(100%)**
Tel.: (52) 3350002500
Web Site: http://www.mx.virbac.com
Biological Product Mfr
N.A.I.C.S.: 325414

PP Manufacturing Corporation   (1)
175 Crossing Blvd, Framingham, MA 01702-4472
Tel.: (508) 766-2700
Veterinary Pharmaceutical Product Mfr
N.A.I.C.S.: 325412

Virbac (Australia) Pty Ltd.   (1)
361 Horsley Road, Milperra, 2214, NSW, Australia   **(100%)**
Tel.: (61) 297729772
Web Site: https://www.au.virbac.com
Emp.: 200
Medicinal & Botanical Mfr
N.A.I.C.S.: 325411

Virbac (Switzerland) AG   (1)
Cherstrasse 4, 8152, Glattbrugg, Switzerland   **(99.9%)**
Tel.: (41) 448091122
Web Site: https://www.ch.virbac.com
Sales Range: $25-49.9 Million
Emp.: 25
Drugs & Druggists Sundries Whslr
N.A.I.C.S.: 424210

Virbac Animal Health India Pvt. Ltd.   (1)
Western Edge 1 604 6th Fl Western Express Hwy, Opp Magathane Depo Borivali East, Mumbai, 400066, Maharashtra, India   **(100%)**
Tel.: (91) 2240081333
Web Site: https://in.virbac.com
Sales Range: $25-49.9 Million
Emp.: 40
Dental Equipment & Supplies Mfr
N.A.I.C.S.: 339114
Sathish Pasrija *(Mng Dir)*

Virbac Belgium SA   (1)
Esperantolaan 4, 3001, Leuven, Belgium   **(99.99%)**
Tel.: (32) 16387260
Web Site: https://www.be.virbac.com
Sales Range: $50-74.9 Million
Emp.: 13
Drugs & Druggists Sundries Whslr
N.A.I.C.S.: 424210

Virbac Chile SpA   (1)
Av Salomon Sack 255, Cerrillos, 9201310, Santiago, Chile
Tel.: (56) 225837700
Web Site: https://cl.virbac.com
Emp.: 350
Pharmaceuticals Product Mfr
N.A.I.C.S.: 325412

Virbac Colombia Ltda   (1)
CRA 54 n 76-20, Barrio Gaitan, Bogota, Colombia   **(100%)**
Tel.: (57) 12252100
Web Site: https://co.virbac.com
Animal Pharmaceutical Preparation Mfr
N.A.I.C.S.: 325412

Virbac Corporation   (1)
1301 Solana Blvd Ste 2400 Bldg 2, Westlake, TX 76262   **(60%)**
Tel.: (817) 831-5030
Web Site: https://www.us.virbac.com
Sales Range: $150-199.9 Million
Emp.: 269
Mfr & Distr of Health, Grooming, Dental & Parasiticide Products for Pets
N.A.I.C.S.: 325412
Michael Albo *(VP-Comm & Customer Svc)*

Virbac Danmark A/S   (1)
Profilvej 1, 6000, Kolding, Denmark
Tel.: (45) 75521244
Web Site: https://www.dk.virbac.com
Sales Range: $50-74.9 Million
Emp.: 1
Veterinary Pharmaceutical Products Distr

N.A.I.C.S.: 424210

Virbac Espana SA   (1)
Angel Guimera 179 181, Esplugues de Llobregat, 08950, Barcelona, Spain   **(100%)**
Tel.: (34) 934707940
Web Site: https://www.es.virbac.com
Sales Range: $25-49.9 Million
Emp.: 50
Pharmaceutical Preparation Mfr
N.A.I.C.S.: 325412

Virbac France SAS   (1)
13e Rue LID, BP 27, 06517, Carros, Cedex, France
Tel.: (33) 492087590
Web Site: https://fr.virbac.com
Drugs & Druggists Sundries Whslr
N.A.I.C.S.: 424210

Virbac Hellas SA   (1)
13th Km National Road Athens Lamia, 144 52, Metamorfosis, Greece   **(100%)**
Tel.: (30) 2106219520
Web Site: https://www.gr.virbac.com
Sales Range: $50-74.9 Million
Emp.: 16
Drugs & Druggists Sundries Whslr
N.A.I.C.S.: 424210

Virbac Japan Co. Ltd.   (1)
New Awajimachi Building, 6th Floor 1-3-14 Awajimachi Chuo, Osaka, 541-0047, Japan   **(100%)**
Tel.: (81) 662034817
Web Site: https://www.jp.virbac.com
Sales Range: $25-49.9 Million
Emp.: 30
Drugs & Druggists Sundries Whslr
N.A.I.C.S.: 424210

Virbac Korea Co. Ltd.   (1)
8F Jinnex Lake View B/D 65-2, Bangi dong Songpa pu, 138 828, Seoul, 138-828, Korea (South)   **(100%)**
Tel.: (82) 215889794
Web Site: https://www.kr.virbac.com
Sales Range: $25-49.9 Million
Emp.: 20
Dental Equipment & Supplies Mfr
N.A.I.C.S.: 339114

Virbac Ltd.   (1)
Woolpit Business Park Windmill Avenue, Bury Saint Edmunds, IP30 9UP, Suffolk, United Kingdom   **(99.95%)**
Tel.: (44) 1359243243
Web Site: https://www.uk.virbac.com
Sales Range: $25-49.9 Million
Emp.: 60
Drugs & Druggists Sundries Whslr
N.A.I.C.S.: 424210

Virbac Mexico SA de CV   (1)
Av Inglaterra No 5070 Guadalajara Technology Park, 45010, Zapopan, Jalisco, Mexico
Tel.: (52) 13350002500
Web Site: https://www.mx.virbac.com
Emp.: 250
Pharmaceuticals Product Mfr
N.A.I.C.S.: 325412
Pilar Sandoval *(Product Mgr)*

Virbac Nederland B.V.   (1)
Hermesweg 15, 3771 ND, Barneveld, Netherlands   **(75.28%)**
Tel.: (31) 342427127
Web Site: https://www.virbac.nl
Sales Range: $25-49.9 Million
Emp.: 30
Drugs & Druggists Sundries Whslr
N.A.I.C.S.: 424210

Virbac New Zealand Ltd.   (1)
26-30 Maui Street, Pukete, 3200, Hamilton, 3200, New Zealand
Tel.: (64) 78496782
Web Site: https://www.nz.virbac.com
Sales Range: $25-49.9 Million
Emp.: 25
Medical Dental & Hospital Equipment & Supplies Whslr
N.A.I.C.S.: 423450

Virbac Nutrition SAS   (1)
Zone Industrielle, 252 rue Philippe Lamour, 30600, Vauvert, France   **(100%)**
Tel.: (33) 466888436
Web Site: http://www.virbac.fr
Sales Range: $25-49.9 Million
Emp.: 50
Dog & Cat Food Mfr

INTERNATIONAL PUBLIC

N.A.I.C.S.: 311111

Virbac Osterreich GmbH   (1)
Hildebrandgasse 27, 1180, Vienna, Austria   **(100%)**
Tel.: (43) 121834260
Web Site: https://www.at.virbac.com
Sales Range: $25-49.9 Million
Emp.: 11
Drugs & Druggists Sundries Whslr
N.A.I.C.S.: 424210

Virbac Pharma Handelsgesellshaft mbH   (1)
23843 Bad Oldesloe, Schleswig, Germany   **(100%)**
Tel.: (49) 45318050
Testing Laboratories
N.A.I.C.S.: 541380

Virbac Philippines Inc.   (1)
Unit D 19th Floor Menarco Tower 32nd Street Corner 9th Avenue, Bonifacio Global City, Taguig, 1634, Philippines
Tel.: (63) 28433735
Web Site: https://www.ph.virbac.com
Sales Range: $25-49.9 Million
Emp.: 19
Testing Laboratories
N.A.I.C.S.: 541380

Virbac RSA (Pty) Ltd.   (1)
38 Landmarks Avenue Samrand Business Park, Centurion, 0157, South Africa   **(100%)**
Tel.: (27) 126576000
Web Site: https://www.za.virbac.com
Sales Range: $25-49.9 Million
Emp.: 130
Animal Production
N.A.I.C.S.: 112990

Virbac SP zoo   (1)
Ul Pulawska 314, 02-819, Warsaw, Poland
Tel.: (48) 228554046
Web Site: https://www.pl.virbac.com
Pharmaceuticals Product Mfr
N.A.I.C.S.: 325412

Virbac Srl   (1)
Via Ettore Bugatti 15, 20142, Milan, Italy   **(99.99%)**
Tel.: (39) 024092471
Web Site: https://www.it.virbac.com
Emp.: 80
Drugs & Druggists Sundries Whslr
N.A.I.C.S.: 424210

Virbac Taiwan Co. Ltd.   (1)
8th Floor No 13 Lane 35 Jihu Road, Neihu District, 114, Taipei, Taiwan   **(100%)**
Tel.: (886) 227987667
Web Site: https://tw.virbac.com
Sales Range: $25-49.9 Million
Emp.: 16
Medical Dental & Hospital Equipment & Supplies Whslr
N.A.I.C.S.: 423450

Virbac Thailand Co. Ltd.   (1)
Centralplaza Chaengwattana Office Tower 12th Floor Unit 1203 99/9, Chaengwattana Road Tumbon Bangtalad-Amphur Pakkred, Nonthaburi, 11120, Thailand   **(100%)**
Tel.: (66) 21938288
Web Site: https://www.th.virbac.com
Pet Products Mfr & Distr
N.A.I.C.S.: 459910

Virbac Tierarzneimittel GmbH   (1)
Rogen 20, 23843, Bad Oldesloe, Germany   **(100%)**
Tel.: (49) 4531805111
Web Site: https://de.virbac.com
Sales Range: $25-49.9 Million
Emp.: 80
Drugs & Druggists Sundries Whslr
N.A.I.C.S.: 424210
Alexandra Molzahn *(Mng Dir)*

Virbac Uruguay SA   (1)
Av Millan 4175, 12900, Montevideo, Uruguay
Tel.: (598) 23075757
Web Site: https://www.uy.virbac.com
Pharmaceuticals Product Mfr
N.A.I.C.S.: 325412
Pablo Macchi *(Comml Dir)*

Virbac Vietnam Co. Ltd.   (1)
6th Floor Minh Long Tower 17 Ba Huyen

AND PRIVATE COMPANIES

Thanh Quan Street, Ward 6 District 3, Ho Chi Minh City, Vietnam
Tel.: (84) 839333170
Web Site: https://www.vn.virbac.com
Pharmaceuticals Product Mfr
N.A.I.C.S.: 325412
Stephane Pham *(Mgr-Site)*

Virbac Vietnam JV Company (1)
12A 14 Me Linh Street, Ward 19 Binh Thanh District, Ho Chi Minh City, Vietnam
Tel.: (84) 8 3840 4629
Animal Health Pharmaceuticals
N.A.I.C.S.: 325412

Virbac de Portugal Laboratorios Lda (1)
Rua do Centro Empresarial Edificio 13 Piso 1, Escritorio 3 Quinta da Beloura, 2710-693, Sintra, Portugal **(100%)**
Tel.: (351) 219245020
Web Site: https://pt.virbac.com
Sales Range: $25-49.9 Million
Emp.: 13
Drugs & Druggists Sundries Whslr
N.A.I.C.S.: 424210

Virbac do Brasil Industria e Comercio Ltda. (1)
Av Queiroz Filho 1560 - Torre Canario - 1 Andar - Vila Hamburguesa, Sao Paulo, 05319-000, Brazil **(100%)**
Tel.: (55) 1155255000
Web Site: https://www.br.virbac.com
Veterinary Pharmaceutical Product Mfr
N.A.I.C.S.: 325412

Zirdac Sarl (1)
BP 27 06511 Carros Cedex, Carros, France **(100%)**
Tel.: (33) 492087300
Web Site: http://www.zirdac.com
Drugs & Druggists Sundries Whslr
N.A.I.C.S.: 424210

VIRGIN AUSTRALIA HOLDINGS LIMITED
56 Edmondstone Road, Bowen Hills, 4006, QLD, Australia
Tel.: (61) 732953000 **AU**
Web Site: http://www.virginaustralia.com
VAH—(ASX)
Rev.: $4,097,733,262
Assets: $4,548,567,604
Liabilities: $4,113,344,746
Net Worth: $435,222,858
Earnings: ($221,795,588)
Emp.: 10,620
Fiscal Year-end: 06/30/19
Holding Company; Commercial Airlines Owner & Operator
N.A.I.C.S.: 551112
Sharyn Page *(Sec)*

Subsidiaries:

Tiger Airways Australia Pty. Ltd. (1)
Building 166 1-5 Grants Road, Melbourne, 3000, VIC, Australia
Tel.: (61) 732952104
Web Site: http://www.tigerair.com.au
Emp.: 1,100
Airline Services
N.A.I.C.S.: 485999
Merren McArthur *(CEO)*

Virgin Australia Airlines Pty. Ltd. (1)
56 Edmondstone Rd, Bowen Hills, 4006, QLD, Australia
Tel.: (61) 732953000
Web Site: http://www.virginaustralia.com.au
Sales Range: $1-4.9 Billion
Emp.: 4,500
Commercial Airline Operator
N.A.I.C.S.: 481111
C. Jayne Hrdlicka *(CEO & Mng Dir)*

VIRGIN MANAGEMENT LIMITED
The Battleship Building 179 Harrow Road, London, W2 6NB, United Kingdom
Tel.: (44) 9892015729 **UK**
Web Site: http://www.virgin.com

Year Founded: 1986
Holding Company
N.A.I.C.S.: 551112
Josh Bayliss *(CEO)*

Subsidiaries:

Esporta Group Limited (1)
Trinity Court Molly Millars Lane, Wokingham, RG41 2PY, Berks, United Kingdom
Tel.: (44) 1189123500
Web Site: http://www.esporta.com
Holding Company; Health Club Owner & Operator
N.A.I.C.S.: 551112

Subsidiary (Domestic):

Esporta Limited (2)
Trinity Court Molly Millars Lane, Wokingham, RG41 2PY, Berks, United Kingdom **(100%)**
Tel.: (44) 1189123500
Web Site: http://www.esporta.com
Health Club Operator
N.A.I.C.S.: 713940

Vanson Developments Ltd. (1)
The School House 50 Brook Green, London, W6 7RR, United Kingdom **(100%)**
Tel.: (44) 2073132000
Web Site: http://www.virgin.com
Sales Range: $100-124.9 Million
Emp.: 100
Property Development
N.A.I.C.S.: 531210

Virgin Active Australia Pty Limited (1)
L 13 2 Bulletin Pl, Sydney, 2000, NSW, Australia
Tel.: (61) 299758600
Health & Fitness Center Operator
N.A.I.C.S.: 713940

Virgin Active Italia S.p.A. (1)
Via Archimede 2, Corsico, 20094, Milan, Italy
Tel.: (39) 02631161
Web Site: http://www.virginactive.it
Health & Fitness Center Operator
N.A.I.C.S.: 713940

Virgin Active Singapore Pte. Ltd. (1)
Level 6 Tower 2 One Raffles Place, Singapore, 048616, Singapore
Tel.: (65) 69087878
Web Site: http://www.virginactive.com.sg
Health & Fitness Center Operator
N.A.I.C.S.: 713940

Virgin Active South Africa (Proprietary) Limited (1)
Cnr Main Road & Campground Road, Claremont, Cape Town, 7708, South Africa
Tel.: (27) 860200911
Web Site: http://www.virginactive.co.za
Health & Fitness Center Operator
N.A.I.C.S.: 713940

Virgin Balloon Flights Ltd (1)
Jesson House Stafford Court, Telford, TF3 3BD, Shropshire, United Kingdom **(100%)**
Tel.: (44) 1952212750
Web Site: http://www.virginballoonflights.co.uk
Sales Range: $25-49.9 Million
Emp.: 100
Supplier of Balloon Flights
N.A.I.C.S.: 334511

Virgin Care Limited (1)
6600 Daresbury Business Park, Daresbury, WA4 4GE, United Kingdom
Tel.: (44) 3303327890
Web Site: http://www.virgincare.co.uk
Health & Fitness Center Operator
N.A.I.C.S.: 713940

Virgin Connect, ZAO (1)
Head office Victory plaza 5 Viktorenko-st bl 1, Aeroport metro station, Moscow, 125167, Russia
Tel.: (7) 4994055050
Web Site: http://www.virginconnect.ru
Telecommunication Services
N.A.I.C.S.: 517121

Virgin Enterprises Ltd (1)
120 Campden Hill Road, London, W87AR, United Kingdom
Tel.: (44) 2073132000
Internet Service Provider
N.A.I.C.S.: 517112

Virgin Health Bank Limited (1)
27 Old Gloucester Street, London, WC1N 3AX, United Kingdom
Tel.: (44) 8456209665
Web Site: http://www.virginhealthbank.com
Blood Bank Operator
N.A.I.C.S.: 621991

Virgin Limited Edition (1)
The Metro Building 1 Butterwick, London, W6 9ER, United Kingdom
Tel.: (44) 2086000486
Web Site: http://www.virginlimitededition.com
Hotel Operations
N.A.I.C.S.: 721110
Jon Brown *(Mng Dir)*

Virgin Mobile (Australia) Pty Ltd (1)
Tattersalls Arcade 211-225 Queen Street, Brisbane, 4000, QLD, Australia
Tel.: (61) 732295522
Web Site: http://www.virginmobile.com.au
Mobile Phone Whslr
N.A.I.C.S.: 449210

Virgin Mobile South Africa (PTY) Ltd (1)
Upper Level Cedar Square Corner Cedar Lane and Willow Avenue, Sandton, South Africa
Tel.: (27) 11 676 5000
Web Site: http://www.virginmobile.co.za
Surgical & Emergency Center Operator
N.A.I.C.S.: 621493

Virgin Money (Australia) Pty Limited (1)
Level 8 126 Philip Street, Sydney, 2000, NSW, Australia
Tel.: (61) 282498000
Web Site: http://www.virginmoney.com.au
Financial Services
N.A.I.C.S.: 522320

Virgin Money Giving Limited (1)
28 St Andrews Square, Edinburgh, EH1 2AF, United Kingdom
Tel.: (44) 3456011045
Web Site: http://www.uk.virginmoneygiving.com
Financial Services
N.A.I.C.S.: 541611

Virgin Travel Group Ltd (1)
120 Campden Hill Road, London, W8 7AR, United Kingdom
Tel.: (44) 20 7229 1282
Web Site: http://www.virgin.com
Sales Range: $50-74.9 Million
Emp.: 55
Holding Company
N.A.I.C.S.: 551112

Subsidiary (Domestic):

Virgin Atlantic Ltd. (2)
120 Campden Hill Road, London, W8 7AR, United Kingdom **(51%)**
Tel.: (44) 2072291282
Web Site: http://www.virgin-atlantic.com
Holding Company
N.A.I.C.S.: 551112
Anna Kowles *(Head-PR)*

Subsidiary (Domestic):

Virgin Atlantic Airways Ltd. (3)
The Office Manor Royal, Manor Royal, Crawley, RH10 9NU, West Sussex, United Kingdom
Tel.: (44) 1293562345
Web Site: http://www.virgin-atlantic.com
Sales Range: $1-4.9 Billion
Emp.: 8,000
Passenger & Cargo Air Transportation Services
N.A.I.C.S.: 481111
Richard Branson *(Founder)*

Division (Domestic):

Virgin Atlantic Cargo (4)
The Office Manor Royal, Crawley, RH10 9NU, United Kingdom

Tel.: (44) 844 209 7742
Freight Air Transportation Services
N.A.I.C.S.: 481112
Neil Vernon *(VP-Sls-Intl)*

Subsidiary (Domestic):

Virgin Holidays (2)
The Galleria Station Rd, Crawley, RH10 1WW, W Sussex, United Kingdom **(100%)**
Tel.: (44) 8702200088
Web Site: http://www.virginholidays.co.uk
Sales Range: $75-99.9 Million
Emp.: 400
Tour Operator
N.A.I.C.S.: 561510
Joe Thompson *(Mng Dir)*

Subsidiary (US):

Virgin Vacations (2)
19021 120th Ave NE Ste 102, Bothell, WA 98011
Web Site: http://www.virgin.com
Provider of Vacations Services
N.A.I.C.S.: 561520

VIRGIN MONEY UK PLC
20 Merrion Way, Leeds, LS2 8NZ, Yorks, United Kingdom
Tel.: (44) 8004561247 **UK**
Web Site: https://www.virginmoneyukplc.com
Year Founded: 2015
VUK—(ASX)
Rev.: $4,834,637,718
Assets: $115,862,156,021
Liabilities: $108,784,397,879
Net Worth: $7,077,758,142
Earnings: $310,527,645
Emp.: 7,166
Fiscal Year-end: 09/30/23
Holding Company; Banking Services
N.A.I.C.S.: 551111
Chris S. Rhodes *(CEO & Exec Dir)*

Subsidiaries:

CYB Investments Ltd. (1)
20 Merrion Way, Leeds, LS2 8NZ, Yorks, United Kingdom
Tel.: (44) 8000665998
Holding Company; Financial Services
N.A.I.C.S.: 551112
James Peirson *(Sec)*

Subsidiary (Domestic):

Clydesdale Bank PLC (2)
30 St Vincent Place, Glasgow, G1 2HL, United Kingdom **(100%)**
Tel.: (44) 1412487070
Web Site: http://www.cbonline.co.uk
Holding Company; Banking Services
N.A.I.C.S.: 522110
Ian Smith *(CFO)*

Subsidiary (Domestic):

Yorkshire Bank PLC (3)
4 Victoria Place Manor Rd, Leeds, LS11 5AE, United Kingdom
Tel.: (44) 1132001277
Web Site: http://www.ybonline.co.uk
Sales Range: $150-199.9 Million
Emp.: 500
Full Banking Services
N.A.I.C.S.: 522299

Subsidiary (Domestic):

Yorkshire Bank Home Loans Limited (4)
20 Merrion Way, Leeds, LS2 8NZ, United Kingdom
Tel.: (44) 113 247 2000
Financial Services
N.A.I.C.S.: 522310

Virgin Money Holdings (UK) Limited (1)
Jubilee House Gosforth Newcastle upon, Newcastle, NE3 4PL, United Kingdom
Tel.: (44) 1603215909
Web Site: http://www.virginmoney.com
Rev.: $1,292,456,960
Assets: $55,459,355,136
Liabilities: $52,997,346,048

VIRGIN MONEY UK PLC

Virgin Money UK PLC—(Continued)
Net Worth: $2,462,009,088
Earnings: $259,165,952
Emp.: 2,413
Fiscal Year-end: 12/31/2017
Holding Company; Financial, Banking & Insurance Services
N.A.I.C.S.: 551112
Chris S. Rhodes *(CEO & Exec Dir)*

Subsidiary (Domestic):

Virgin Money plc (2)
Jubilee House, Gosforth, Newcastle upon Tyne, NE3 4PL, United Kingdom
Tel.: (44) 1912857191
Web Site: http://www.virginmoney.com
Sales Range: $750-799.9 Million
Emp.: 1,934
Commercial Banking Services
N.A.I.C.S.: 522110
Glen Richard Moreno *(Chm)*

VIRGIN WINES UK PLC
St James Mill Whitefriars, Norwich, NR3 1TN, United Kingdom
Tel.: (44) 3432241001   UK
Web Site:
https://www.virginwinesplc.co.uk
Year Founded: 2000
VINO—(AIM)
Rev.: $74,473,618
Assets: $50,005,049
Liabilities: $22,458,975
Net Worth: $27,546,074
Earnings: ($749,811)
Emp.: 200
Fiscal Year-end: 06/30/23
Beverage Product Mfr & Distr
N.A.I.C.S.: 312111
John Risman *(Chm)*

Subsidiaries:

Virgin Wine Online Limited (1)
St James Mill Whitefriars, Norwich, NR3 1TN, United Kingdom
Tel.: (44) 3432241001
Web Site: https://www.virginwines.co.uk
Alcoholic Drink Retailer
N.A.I.C.S.: 424820

VIRGINIA HILLS OIL CORP.
1500 202 6 Av SW, Calgary, T2P 2R9, AB, Canada
Tel.: (403) 817-2550   AB
Year Founded: 2015
Oil & Gas Exploration
N.A.I.C.S.: 211120
Colin B. Witwer *(Pres & CEO)*

VIRIDIS TECHNOLOGIES INC.
250 Shields Ct #5, Markham, L3R 9W7, ON, Canada
Tel.: (905) 918-2836
Web Site: http://www.viridistech.com
Vehicle Dispensing Systems Mfr
N.A.I.C.S.: 336390
Ian Patterson *(Pres)*

VIRINCHI LTD.
8-2-672/5 and 6 4th Floor Ilyas Mohammed Khan Estate, Road No 1 Banjara Hills, Hyderabad, 500 034, Telangana, India
Tel.: (91) 4048199999
Web Site: https://www.virinchi.com
Year Founded: 1990
VIRINCHI—(NSE)
Rev.: $37,836,317
Assets: $94,315,053
Liabilities: $45,500,581
Net Worth: $48,814,472
Earnings: $1,540,555
Emp.: 537
Fiscal Year-end: 03/31/23
Information Technology Products Solution & Services
N.A.I.C.S.: 541511
Satyajeet Prasad *(CEO)*

Subsidiaries:

Asclepius Consulting & Technologies Pvt Ltd. (1)
4th Floor 8-2-672/5 and 6 Road No 1 Banjara Hills, Hyderabad, 500 034, Telangana, India
Tel.: (91) 4048199999
Web Site:
https://www.asclepiusconsulting.com
Management Consulting Services
N.A.I.C.S.: 541611

KSoft Systems Inc. (1)
Tel.: (732) 696-2555
Web Site: https://ksoftglobal.com
Computer Related Services
N.A.I.C.S.: 541519

Virinchi Health Care Pvt. Ltd. (1)
8-2-672/5 and 6 Road No 1, Banjara Hills, Hyderabad, 500034, India
Tel.: (91) 4046999999
Web Site: https://virinchihospitals.com
Hospital Services
N.A.I.C.S.: 622110
Satyajeet Prasad *(Head-Strategy)*

VIRNECT CO., LTD.
10-15 Hangang-daero 7-gil Benect Experience Center, Yongsan-gu, Seoul, 04379, Korea (South)
Tel.: (82) 7077332025
Web Site: https://www.virnect.com
Year Founded: 2016
438700—(KRS)
Emp.: 150
Software Development Services
N.A.I.C.S.: 541511
Dong Lak Park *(Dir)*

VIRO TVORNICA SECERA D.D.
Ul grada Vukovara 269G, 10000, Zagreb, Croatia
Tel.: (385) 1 2369 777
Web Site: http://www.secerana.hr
VIRO-R-A—(ZAG)
Sales Range: Less than $1 Million
Sugar Mfr
N.A.I.C.S.: 311314
Marinko Zadro *(Chm-Supervisory Bd)*

VIRO-IMMUN LABOR-DIAGNOSTIKA GMBH
In der Au 29, Oberursel, 61440, Hesse, Germany
Tel.: (49) 6171 6281 00
Web Site: http://www.viro-immun.de
Emp.: 27
Pharmaceutical Preparation Mfr
N.A.I.C.S.: 325412
Massoud Hodawand-Khani *(Gen Mgr)*

VIROTEC GLOBAL SOLUTIONS PTY. LTD.
Level 1 Building D 19 Harbour Village Parade, Coomera Waters, Coomera, 4209, QLD, Australia
Tel.: (61) 755733353   AU
Web Site: http://www.virotec.com
Sales Range: $10-24.9 Million
Emp.: 10
Waste Treatment & Soil Conservation Technologies Developer & Services
N.A.I.C.S.: 562998
Daniel Blair *(Gen Mgr)*

Subsidiaries:

VIROTEC ITALIA srl (1)
Via Nomentana 133, 00161, Rome, Italy
Tel.: (39) 06 4423 6608
Web Site: http://www.virotecitalia.it
Hazardous Waste Treatment & Disposal Services
N.A.I.C.S.: 562211
Vittorio Bello *(Mng Dir)*

VIRSCEND EDUCATION CO. LTD.
No 23 Xin Lu, Pidu District, Chengdu, China
Tel.: (86) 288 610 8106   Ky
Web Site:
http://www.virscendeducation.com
Year Founded: 2000
Rev.: $213,652,879
Assets: $905,815,988
Liabilities: $511,709,000
Net Worth: $394,106,988
Earnings: $58,392,671
Emp.: 4,853
Fiscal Year-end: 12/31/19
Educational Support Services
N.A.I.C.S.: 611710
Xiaoying Wang *(Chm)*

VIRTUAL GLOBAL EDUCATION LIMITED
103 Palco House 2162/T-10 Main Patel Road, New Delhi, 110008, India
Tel.: (91) 1125702148
Web Site:
http://www.virtualeducation.in
Year Founded: 1993
534741—(BOM)
Rev.: $160,005
Assets: $9,758,240
Liabilities: $2,161,113
Net Worth: $7,597,127
Earnings: $73,045
Emp.: 20
Fiscal Year-end: 03/31/23
Educational Support Services
N.A.I.C.S.: 923110
Neeraj Kaushik *(CFO)*

VIRTUAL UNIVERSE CORPORATION
4245 97th Street Suite 200, Edmonton, T6E 5Y7, AB, Canada
Tel.: (780) 469-7477   AB
Sales Range: Less than $1 Million
Information Technology Services
N.A.I.C.S.: 541511
Lorn Becker *(Owner, Pres & CEO)*

VIRTUAL1 LTD.
3rd Floor 8 Angel Court, London, EC2R 7HP, United Kingdom
Tel.: (44) 844 884 0800
Web Site: http://www.virtual1.com
Year Founded: 2007
Sales Range: $10-24.9 Million
Emp.: 37
Computer Network Management Services
N.A.I.C.S.: 541512
Tom OHagan *(Founder & Mng Dir)*

VIRTUALSOFT SYSTEMS LTD.
59 Okhla Industrial Estate Phase 3, New Delhi, 110020, Phase 1, India
Tel.: (91) 1142701491
Web Site: https://virtsoft.com
Year Founded: 1998
531126—(BOM)
Rev.: $430,726
Assets: $2,634,393
Liabilities: $5,253,372
Net Worth: ($2,618,979)
Earnings: ($497,746)
Fiscal Year-end: 03/31/23
Software Services
N.A.I.C.S.: 449210
Gokul Tandan *(Mng Dir)*

Subsidiaries:

Roam1 Telecom Ltd. (1)
59 Okhla Industrial Estate Phase 3, New Delhi, 110020, India
Tel.: (91) 9999585236
Web Site: https://www.roam1.com
Telecommunication Servicesb
N.A.I.C.S.: 517111

VIRTUALWARE 2007, S.A.

INTERNATIONAL PUBLIC

C/ Usausuaga 7, 48970, Basauri, Vizcaya, Spain
Tel.: (34) 946452130
Web Site:
https://www.virtualwareco.com
Year Founded: 2004
MLVIR—(EUR)
Rev.: $4,912,592
Assets: $8,475,477
Liabilities: $6,793,687
Net Worth: $1,681,790
Earnings: $20,717
Emp.: 45
Fiscal Year-end: 12/31/23
Information Technology Services
N.A.I.C.S.: 541512
Asier Extremo *(COO)*

VIRTUOSO OPTOELECTRONICS LIMITED
7 MIDC Area Trimbak Road Satpur, Nashik, 422007, Maharashtra, India
Tel.: (91) 2532309016
Web Site: https://www.voepl.com
Year Founded: 2015
543597—(BOM)
Rev.: $40,533,793
Assets: $33,151,202
Liabilities: $21,922,822
Net Worth: $11,228,380
Earnings: $931,251
Emp.: 134
Fiscal Year-end: 03/31/23
Electronic Components Mfr
N.A.I.C.S.: 334419

VIRTUS HEALTH LIMITED
Level 3 154 Pacific Highway, Greenwich, 2065, NSW, Australia
Tel.: (61) 294251722
Web Site:
https://www.virtushealth.com.au
Year Founded: 2008
VRT—(ASX)
Rev.: $248,706,806
Assets: $463,784,001
Liabilities: $233,457,327
Net Worth: $230,326,674
Earnings: $33,560,654
Emp.: 1,100
Fiscal Year-end: 06/30/21
Reproductive Health Services
N.A.I.C.S.: 621498
Kate Munnings *(Mng Dir & CEO)*

Subsidiaries:

Aagaard Fertilitetsklinik Aps (1)
Hedeager 35, 8200, Aarhus, Denmark
Tel.: (45) 86126121
Web Site: https://www.aagaardklinik.dk
Hospital & Health Care Services
N.A.I.C.S.: 621999
Aboubakar Cisse *(Dir-Medical)*

Hobart Specialist Day Hospital Pty Limited (1)
2 Melville Street, Hobart, 7000, TAS, Australia
Tel.: (61) 362127750
Web Site: https://www.hsdh.com.au
Hospital Services
N.A.I.C.S.: 622110

IVF Australia Pty Ltd (1)
Level 1 / 33 York Street, Sydney, 2000, NSW, Australia
Tel.: (61) 28 346 6800
Web Site: https://www.ivf.com.au
Health Care Srvices
N.A.I.C.S.: 621999

Subsidiary (Domestic):

City East Specialist Day Hospital Pty Ltd (2)
225 Maroubra Road, Maroubra, 2035, NSW, Australia
Tel.: (61) 2 8372 3260
Web Site: http://www.cesdh.com.au
Health Care Srvices
N.A.I.C.S.: 621999

AND PRIVATE COMPANIES

Carly Harridge *(Mgr-Practice)*

Melbourne IVF Holdings Pty Ltd (1)
344 Victoria Pde, Melbourne, 3002, VIC, Australia
Tel.: (61) 394734444
Holding Company
N.A.I.C.S.: 551112

North Shore Specialist Day Hospital Pty Ltd (1)
Level 1 176 Pacific Highway, Greenwich, 2065, NSW, Australia
Tel.: (61) 29 425 1678
Web Site: https://www.nssdh.com.au
Emp.: 50
Health Care Srvices
N.A.I.C.S.: 621999

Queensland Fertility Group Pty. Ltd. (1)
55 Little Edward Street Boundary Court, Spring Hill, 4000, QLD, Australia
Tel.: (61) 73 015 3000
Web Site: https://www.qfg.com.au
Emp.: 50
Health Care Srvices
N.A.I.C.S.: 621999
David Molloy *(Dir-Medical)*

Subsidiary (Domestic):

Mackay Specialist Day Hospital Pty Limited (2)
85 Willetts Road, MacKay, 4740, QLD, Australia
Tel.: (61) 74 977 5100
Web Site: https://www.msdh.com.au
Health Care Srvices
N.A.I.C.S.: 621999
Pam Barratt *(Dir-Nursing)*

Spring Hill Specialist Day Hospital Pty Limited (2)
Level 1 & 4 St Andrew's Place 33 North Street, Spring Hill, 4000, QLD, Australia
Tel.: (61) 73 307 3243
Web Site: https://www.shsdh.com.au
Emp.: 30
Health Care Srvices
N.A.I.C.S.: 621999

Sims Clinic Limited (1)
Clonskeagh Road, Clonskeagh, Dublin, D14 A312, Ireland (100%)
Tel.: (353) 1 208 0710
Web Site: https://www.sims.ie
Health Care Srvices
N.A.I.C.S.: 621999
Graham Coull *(Dir-Laboratory)*

Skejby Cryobank Aps (1)
Hedeager 35, 8200, Aarhus, Denmark
Tel.: (45) 86126140
Web Site: https://www.skejbycryobank.dk
Fertility Clinic Services
N.A.I.C.S.: 621410
Jens Michael Hertz *(Dir-Medical)*

Virtus Fertility Centre Singapore Pte Limited (1)
9 Scotts Road Units 9-01 to 05 Scotts Medical Center Pacific Plaza, Singapore, 228210, Singapore
Tel.: (65) 64604555
Web Site: https://www.virtusfertilitycentre.com.sg
Fertility Clinic Services
N.A.I.C.S.: 621410
Roland Chieng *(Dir-Medical)*

VIRTUS HOLDING APS
Skovstien 20 Haldum, 8382, Hinnerup, Denmark
Tel.: (45) 60204450   DK
Year Founded: 2011
Holding Company
N.A.I.C.S.: 551112
Simon Guldager *(Founder)*

Subsidiaries:

Nobly A/S (1)
Klamsagervej 21B, 8230, Abyhoj, Denmark
Tel.: (45) 70707470
Web Site: https://nobly.eu
Information Technology Consulting Services
N.A.I.C.S.: 519290
Jesper Frank *(CEO)*

Subsidiary (Non-US):

CSAM Kibi Finland Oy (2)
Teknobulevardi 3-5, 01530, Vantaa, Finland
Tel.: (358) 400451724
Business Support Services
N.A.I.C.S.: 561499

VIRU SA
Carretera Panamericana Norte Km 521, Viru, La Libertad, Peru
Tel.: (51) 44484040   Pe
Web Site: https://www.viru.com.pe
Year Founded: 1994
Fresh, Frozen & Canned Products Mfr & Distr
N.A.I.C.S.: 311999
Yoselyn Malamud *(CEO)*

Subsidiaries:

Superior Foods International, LLC (1)
275 Westgate Dr, Watsonville, CA 95076-2470
Tel.: (831) 728-3691
Web Site: http://www.superiorfoods.com
Sales Range: $1-9.9 Million
Emp.: 20
Fruit & Vegetable Distr
N.A.I.C.S.: 424480
R. Neil Happee *(Pres & CEO)*

VIRY S.A.S.
5 Zone Industriele de la Plaine, 88214, Eloyes, CEDEX, Remiremont, France
Tel.: (33) 329644545
Web Site: http://www.viry.fayat.com
Emp.: 100
Commercial Structure Architectural Design, Engineering & Construction Services
N.A.I.C.S.: 236220
Frederic Baudson *(Mgr-Comml)*

VIRYA RESOURCES LTD.
B-1 TSR Towers 6-3-1090 Rajbhavan Road, Somajiguda, Hyderabad, 500 082, India
Tel.: (91) 4023310330
Web Site: http://www.gtpltd.co.in
Year Founded: 1987
512479—(BOM)
Rev.: $113,902
Assets: $775,877
Liabilities: $79,048
Net Worth: $696,829
Earnings: $58,438
Fiscal Year-end: 03/31/23
Civil Construction Services
N.A.I.C.S.: 237990
Dinesh Vemula *(Compliance Officer & Sec)*

VIS CONTAINERS MANUFACTURING CO., LTD.
G Genimatas Ave Magoula, 190 18, Athens, Greece
Tel.: (30) 2106161300
Web Site: https://www.vis.gr
Year Founded: 1936
VIS—(ATH)
Rev.: $1,943,281,561
Assets: $3,434,442,832
Liabilities: $3,306,370,760
Net Worth: $128,072,072
Earnings: ($285,971,442)
Emp.: 46
Fiscal Year-end: 12/31/21
Cardboard & Paper Packaging Container Mfr
N.A.I.C.S.: 322219
Filippou I. Dimitrios *(Pres)*

Subsidiaries:

Hellenic Quality Foods S.A. (1)
G Genimatas Ave, 19018, Magoula, Greece
Tel.: (30) 2106161500
Web Site: http://www.hqf.gr
Sales Range: $25-49.9 Million
Food Products Mfr
N.A.I.C.S.: 311999

IOFIL S.A. (1)
G Gennimatas Ave Mazoula, Athens, 19018, Greece
Tel.: (30) 2106161000
Web Site: http://www.vis.gr
Food Products & Package Mfr
N.A.I.C.S.: 311999
Christos Zablakos *(Mgr)*

VIS D.D.
Setaliste Apolonija Zanelle 5, 21480, Dalmatia, Croatia
Tel.: (385) 21711164
Web Site: https://www.vis-hoteli.hr
Year Founded: 1972
VIS—(ZAG)
Sales Range: Less than $1 Million
Hotel Operator
N.A.I.C.S.: 721110

VISA STEEL LIMITED
Visa House 8/10 Alipore Road, Kolkata, 700027, West Bengal, India
Tel.: (91) 3330119000
Web Site: https://www.visasteel.com
Year Founded: 1994
VISASTEEL—(NSE)
Rev.: $134,835,929
Assets: $252,880,310
Liabilities: $573,154,082
Net Worth: ($320,273,772)
Earnings: ($163,427,901)
Emp.: 386
Fiscal Year-end: 03/31/21
Iron & Steel Mfr
N.A.I.C.S.: 331110
Vishal Agarwal *(Vice Chm, Deputy CEO & Mng Dir)*

Subsidiaries:

Kalinganagar Special Steel Private Limited (1)
VISA House 11 Ekamra Kanan Nayapalli, Bhubaneswar, 751015, Odisha, India
Tel.: (91) 674255247984
Stainless Steel Mfr
N.A.I.C.S.: 331110

VISACO MINERAL AND INVESTMENT JOINT STOCK COMPANY
No 5 Than Canh Phuc Hoa Cuong Bac Ward, Hai Chau District, Da Nang, Vietnam
Tel.: (84) 511 3674 588
Web Site: http://visacodn.com.vn
Construction Stone Production & Distr
N.A.I.C.S.: 327991

VISAGAR FINANCIAL SERVICES LIMITED
Dev Plaza 907/908 Swami Vivekananda Rd Navpada T E Colony, Vile Parle West Andheri, Mumbai, 400 058, India
Tel.: (91) 4065550120
Web Site: https://vfsl.visagar.com
Year Founded: 1994
531025—(BOM)
Rev.: $6,210,719
Assets: $9,303,147
Liabilities: $1,885,954
Net Worth: $7,417,193
Earnings: $153,312
Fiscal Year-end: 03/31/23
Financial Advisory Services
N.A.I.C.S.: 523940
Tilokchand M. Kothari *(Founder & Chm)*

VISAGAR POLYTEX LTD.
907/908 Dev Plaza SV Road, Andheri W, Mumbai, 400058, India
Tel.: (91) 2267424815
Web Site: https://www.visagar.com
Year Founded: 1983
VIVIDHA—(NSE)
Rev.: $698,208
Assets: $4,802,950
Liabilities: $2,044,827
Net Worth: $2,758,123
Earnings: $5,714
Fiscal Year-end: 03/31/21
Textile Product Mfr & Whslr
N.A.I.C.S.: 314999
Tilokchand Manaklal Kothari *(Chm & Mng Dir)*

VISAKA INDUSTRIES LIMITED
1-8-303/69/3 Visaka Tower S P Road, Secunderabad, 500 003, Telangana, India
Tel.: (91) 4027813833
Web Site: https://www.visaka.co
Year Founded: 1981
509055—(BOM)
Rev.: $157,674,576
Assets: $129,524,905
Liabilities: $43,950,570
Net Worth: $85,574,334
Earnings: $15,102,729
Emp.: 1,900
Fiscal Year-end: 03/31/21
Building Product Mfr
N.A.I.C.S.: 339999
G. Vivekanand *(Vice Chm)*

Subsidiaries:

Atum Life Private Limited (1)
Visaka Towers Ground Floor S P Road, Secunderabad, 500 003, India
Tel.: (91) 7780118532
Web Site: https://atumlife.com
Shopping Centre Services
N.A.I.C.S.: 531120

VISANG EDUCATION, INC.
48 Digital-Ro 33 Gil 20F Daerung Post-Tower 7th, Guro-Gu, 152-847, Seoul, 152-847, Korea (South)
Tel.: (82) 269705629
Web Site: https://global.visang.com
Year Founded: 1997
100220—(KRS)
Rev.: $194,072,966
Assets: $237,176,409
Liabilities: $85,916,275
Net Worth: $151,260,134
Earnings: ($783,610)
Emp.: 995
Fiscal Year-end: 12/31/22
Textbook Publishing Services
N.A.I.C.S.: 513130

VISASQ, INC.
9F-10F 4-7-7 Aobadai, Meguroku, Tokyo, 153-0042, Japan
Tel.: (81) 5031886626
Web Site: https://www.visasq.co.jp
Year Founded: 2012
4490—(TKS)
Rev.: $63,576,030
Assets: $51,707,370
Liabilities: $49,566,190
Net Worth: $2,141,180
Earnings: ($89,582,150)
Fiscal Year-end: 02/29/24
Management Consulting Services
N.A.I.C.S.: 541613
Eiko Hashiba *(Founder & CEO)*

VISCO TECHNOLOGIES CORPORATION
20th Floor New Pier Takeshiba North Tower 1111 Kaigan, Minato-ku, Tokyo, 105-0022, Japan
Tel.: (81) 364024500
Web Site: https://www.visco-tech.com

VISCO TECHNOLOGIES CORPORATION

ViSCO Technologies Corporation—(Continued)
Year Founded: 2003
6698—(TKS)
Rev: $21,171,830
Assets: $29,989,570
Liabilities: $8,169,960
Net Worth: $21,819,610
Earnings: ($1,110,480)
Emp.: 166
Fiscal Year-end: 03/31/24
Electronic Component Mfr & Distr
N.A.I.C.S.: 334413
Hideyuki Adachi (Pres & CEO)

Subsidiaries:

ViSCO Technologies (Shanghai) Co. Ltd. (1)
RoomRoom 300-A No 7 Bldg Pujiang Hi-Tech Plaza 2388, Chenhang Road Minhang District, Shanghai, 201114, China
Tel.: (86) 2150368755
Machine Vision Equipment Mfr & Distr
N.A.I.C.S.: 333310
Hideyuki Adachi (CEO)

ViSCO Technologies (Shenzhen) Co. Ltd. (1)
1618/F Xusheng Bldg No 4004 Baoan Road, Baoan District, Shenzhen, 518102, Guangdong, China
Tel.: (86) 75526514977
Machine Vision Equipment Mfr & Distr
N.A.I.C.S.: 333310

ViSCO Technologies (Thailand) Co., Ltd. (1)
54 BB Bldg 13th Floor Room 131 Sukhumvit 21 Road Asoke, Klongtoey-Nua Wattana, Bangkok, 10110, Thailand
Tel.: (66) 26643236
Machine Vision Equipment Distr
N.A.I.C.S.: 423460
Masaru Kuroda (VP)

ViSCO Technologies USA, Inc. (1)
855 E Golf Rd Ste 1125, Arlington Heights, IL 60005
Tel.: (773) 332-3775
Machine Vision Equipment Distr
N.A.I.C.S.: 423460

ViSCO Technologies Vietnam Company Limited (1)
18th Floor Office Bldg - Corporation 789 No 147 Hoang Quoc Viet, Nghia Do Ward Cau Giay District, 11307, Hanoi, Vietnam
Tel.: (84) 987020421
Machine Vision System Maintenance Services
N.A.I.C.S.: 561621

VISCO TRADE ASSOCIATES LIMITED

P-45 Goragacha Road New Alipore, Kolkata, 700053, West Bengal, India
Tel.: (91) 7872041394
Web Site:
https://www.viscotradeassociates.in
Year Founded: 1983
540097—(BOM)
Rev: $267,758
Assets: $949,631
Liabilities: $1,515
Net Worth: $948,115
Earnings: $62,845
Emp.: 2
Fiscal Year-end: 03/31/21
Investment Management Service
N.A.I.C.S.: 523150
Vinay Kumar Goenka (Chm & Mng Dir)

VISCOFAN SA

Poligono Industrial Berroa C/Berroa 15-4 planta, 31192, Pamplona, Navarra, Spain
Tel.: (34) 948198444
Web Site: https://www.viscofan.com
Year Founded: 1975
VIS—(MAD)
Rev: $1,353,115,134
Assets: $1,553,713,434
Liabilities: $496,453,251
Net Worth: $1,057,260,183
Earnings: $155,604,371
Emp.: 5,346
Fiscal Year-end: 12/31/23
Meat Processing Cellulose, Collagen & Plastic Casings Mfr
N.A.I.C.S.: 311613
Jose Domingo de Ampuero y Osma (Chm)

Subsidiaries:

Gamex CB s.r.o. (1)
Prumyslova 2, 37001, Ceske Budejovice, Czech Republic
Tel.: (420) 389109509
Web Site: http://www.viscofan.cz
Sales Range: $200-249.9 Million
Emp.: 800
Sausage Casings Mfr
N.A.I.C.S.: 326121
Jose Antonio Canales (CEO)

Koteks Viscofan d.o.o. (1)
Tel.: (381) 214899600
Web Site: http://www.koteks-viscofan.com
Sales Range: $125-149.9 Million
Emp.: 530
Collagen Casings Mfr
N.A.I.C.S.: 326121

Naturin Viscofan GmbH (1)
Badeniastrasse 13, Weinheim, 69469, Baden-Wurttemberg, Germany
Tel.: (49) 6201860
Web Site: http://www.naturin.de
Sales Range: $125-149.9 Million
Emp.: 400
Meat Casings Mfr
N.A.I.C.S.: 326121

Supralon Produktions und Vertriebs GmbH (1)
Industriestrasse 3, Alfhausen, 49594, Osnabruck, Germany
Tel.: (49) 546496060
Cellulose & Plastic Mfr
N.A.I.C.S.: 326121

Vector Europe NV (1)
Ekkelgaarden 2, 3500, Hasselt, Belgium
Tel.: (32) 11235309
Web Site: http://www.vectorcasings.eu
Plastic Packaging Film Mfr
N.A.I.C.S.: 326112
Andrew Lancaster (Mng Dir)

Viscofan CZ s.r.o. (1)
Prumyslova 377/2, 370 01, Ceske Budejovice, Czech Republic
Tel.: (420) 389109509
Web Site: http://www.viscofan.cz
Artificial Meat Casings Mfr
N.A.I.C.S.: 326121

Viscofan Canada Inc. (1)
290 Benjamin Hudon Ville, Saint Laurent, H4N 1J4, QC, Canada
Tel.: (514) 333-1700
Sales Range: $25-49.9 Million
Emp.: 25
Sausage Casings Distr
N.A.I.C.S.: 331529
David Flomen (Pres)

Viscofan Centroamerica Comercial, S.A. (1)
700M Oeste Y 200M Norte De La Entrada Principal, a Jardines del recuerdo Lagunilla, Heredia, Costa Rica
Tel.: (506) 22613433
Cellulose & Plastic Mfr
N.A.I.C.S.: 325211

Viscofan Collagen USA Inc. (1)
141 Southside Ave, Bridgewater, NJ 08807
Tel.: (908) 218-4400
Collagen Products Mfr & Distr
N.A.I.C.S.: 311999
Mydiam Soto (Dir-Qualtiy)

Viscofan Globus Australia PTY Ltd. (1)
I Hartzell Place, Bankstown, 2200, NSW, Australia
Tel.: (61) 287001700
Cellulose & Plastic Mfr
N.A.I.C.S.: 325211

Viscofan Globus New Zealand Ltd. (1)
2/120 Hutt Park Road, Gracefield, Lower Hutt, 5010, New Zealand
Tel.: (64) 45683929
Cellulose & Plastic Mfr
N.A.I.C.S.: 325211

Viscofan Technology (Suzhou) Co. Ltd. (1)
Zhao Feng World Trade Building 20th F Unit G Jiangsu Road, Channing, Shanghai, 200050, China
Tel.: (86) 2152400535
Web Site: http://www.viscofan.com
Sales Range: $25-49.9 Million
Emp.: 30
Casings Mfr & Distr
N.A.I.C.S.: 326121

Viscofan U.K. (1)
Unit 5-Plant Industrial State Maidstone Road Platt, Sevenoaks, TN15 8JL, Kent, United Kingdom
Tel.: (44) 1732884333
Emp.: 12
Sausage Casings Mfr
N.A.I.C.S.: 311999

Viscofan USA Inc. (1)
50 County Ct, Montgomery, AL 36105
Tel.: (334) 280-1000
Rev: $15,400,000
Emp.: 35
Food Casings Mfr
N.A.I.C.S.: 326121

Viscofan Uruguay, S.A. (1)
Ruta 8 Km 29500 Cno Sastre S/N Pando, 91001, Canelones, Uruguay
Tel.: (598) 22883048
Cellulose & Plastic Mfr
N.A.I.C.S.: 325211

Viscofan de Mexico S.R.L. de C.V. (1)
Av Del Siglo N 150, Parque Industrial Millennium Zona Industrial Del Potosi, 78395, San Luis Potosi, SLP, Mexico
Tel.: (52) 4448345900
Cellulose & Plastic Mfr
N.A.I.C.S.: 325211

Viscofan de Mexico Servicios S.R.L. de C.V. (1)
Av Del Siglo n 150 Parque Industrial Millennium, Zona Industrial del Potosi, 78395, San Luis Potosi, Mexico (99.99%)
Tel.: (52) 444 8345900
Web Site: http://www.viscofan.com
Artificial Sausage Casings Mfr & Distr
N.A.I.C.S.: 326121

Viscofan do Brasil soc. com. e ind. Ltda. (1)
Tel.: (55) 1151807400
Sausage Casings Mfr
N.A.I.C.S.: 326121

VISCOM AG

Carl-Buderus Str 9 - 15, 30455, Hannover, Germany
Tel.: (49) 511949960
Web Site: https://www.viscom.com
Year Founded: 1984
V6C—(DEU)
Rev: $131,117,679
Assets: $139,098,659
Liabilities: $72,733,994
Net Worth: $66,364,664
Earnings: $3,355,765
Emp.: 600
Fiscal Year-end: 12/31/23
Automated Optical Inspection System Mfr
N.A.I.C.S.: 333310
Volker Pape (Deputy Chm-Supervisory Bd)

Subsidiaries:

VICN Automated Inspection Technology (Huizhou) Co., Ltd. (1)
2nd Hechang Road No 25 Zhongkai High-tech Zone, Huizhou, 516006, China

INTERNATIONAL PUBLIC

Tel.: (86) 7522607785
Automatic Optical Machine Mfr
N.A.I.C.S.: 333248

Viscom France S.A.R.L. (1)
Zone du Vert Galant 6 rue Saint Simon, Saint-Ouen, 95310, France
Tel.: (33) 134641616
Web Site: https://www.viscom.fr
Sales Range: $25-49.9 Million
Emp.: 6
Automated Optical Inspection System Mfr
N.A.I.C.S.: 333310
Christian Morlier (Gen Mgr)

Viscom Inc. (1)
1775 Breckinridge Pkwy Ste 500, Duluth, GA 30096
Tel.: (678) 966-9835
Web Site: http://www.viscom.com
Sales Range: $25-49.9 Million
Emp.: 22
Automated Optical Inspection System Mfr
N.A.I.C.S.: 333310

Viscom Inc. (1)
Av Vallarta 6503 Concentro Local F-27, Zapopan, 45010, Jalisco, Mexico
Tel.: (52) 3331101567
Electrical & Electronic Product Mfr
N.A.I.C.S.: 334419

Viscom Machine Vision (India) Private Limited (1)
No 2 Katha No 279/283, Hulimangala Village Jigani Hobli Anekal Taluk, Bengaluru, 560105, India
Tel.: (91) 9481202030
Automated Optical X-Ray Inspection System Mfr & Distr
N.A.I.C.S.: 339112

Viscom Machine Vision Pte. Ltd. (1)
150 Kampong Ampat / 01-02 KA Centre, KA Center, Singapore, 368324, Singapore
Tel.: (65) 62859891
Automated Optical Inspection System Mfr
N.A.I.C.S.: 333310

Viscom Machine Vision Trading Co. Ltd. (1)
2nd floor Block D No 1010 Kaixuan Road, Shanghai, 200052, China
Tel.: (86) 2161619368
Sales Range: $25-49.9 Million
Emp.: 60
Optical Inspection Systems Mfr
N.A.I.C.S.: 333310

Viscom Tunisie S.A.R.L. (1)
Rahma Building App B5 Block B 2nd Floor Lac Houran Street, Berges du Lac, 1053, Tunis, Tunisia
Tel.: (216) 71960584
Electrical & Electronic Product Mfr
N.A.I.C.S.: 334419
Christian Morlier (Gen Mgr)

Viscom VXS S. DE R.L. DE C.V. (1)
Av Vallarta 6503 Concentro Local F-27, 45010, Zapopan, Mexico
Tel.: (52) 3331101567
Automated Optical X-Ray Inspection System Mfr & Distr
N.A.I.C.S.: 339112

VISCOUNT MINING CORP.

409-221 W Esplanade, North Vancouver, V7M 3J3, BC, Canada
Tel.: (604) 960-0535
Web Site:
https://www.viscountmining.com
Year Founded: 2011
VML—(OTCIQ)
Rev: $5,276
Assets: $6,074,744
Liabilities: $62,303
Net Worth: $6,012,441
Earnings: ($1,356,108)
Fiscal Year-end: 08/31/21
Silver & Gold Exploration Services
N.A.I.C.S.: 212220
William L. Macdonald (Sec)

VISDYNAMICS HOLDINGS BERHAD

AND PRIVATE COMPANIES

Lot 3844 Jalan TU 52 Kawasan Per-industrian Tasik Utama Ayer Kero, 75450, Melaka, Malaysia
Tel.: (60) 62323023 MY
Web Site: http://www.vis-dynamics.com
VIS—(KLS)
Rev.: $5,800,798
Assets: $16,198,098
Liabilities: $1,338,530
Net Worth: $14,859,569
Earnings: $617,306
Emp.: 110
Fiscal Year-end: 10/31/23
Management Services
N.A.I.C.S.: 551114

Subsidiaries:

VisDynamics Research Sdn. Bhd. (1)
Lot 3844 Jalan TU 52, Kawasan Perindustrian Tasik Utama Ayer Keroh, 75450, Melaka, Malaysia
Tel.: (60) 62323023
Web Site: https://www.vis-dynamics.com
Automated Testing Equipment Mfr
N.A.I.C.S.: 334519

VISEO S.A.S.
27 Qual Alphonse le Gallo, 92100, Boulogne-Billancourt, France
Tel.: (33) 156567100
Web Site: http://www.viseo.com
Year Founded: 1999
Sales Range: $25-49.9 Million
Emp.: 2,000
IT Consulting & Outsourcing Services
N.A.I.C.S.: 541690
Nicolas Commare (Mgr-Solution)

Subsidiaries:

Viseo USA Inc. (1)
116 Village Blvd Ste 200, Princeton, NJ 08540
Tel.: (609) 945-7419
IT Consulting & Outsourcing Services
N.A.I.C.S.: 541690

VISGENEER, INC.
No 335 Sec 6 Zhonghua Rd, Xiangshan Dist, Hsinchu, 30094, Taiwan
Tel.: (886) 35181918
Web Site: https://www.visgeneer.com
Year Founded: 2005
4197—(TAI)
Biomedical Product Mfr
N.A.I.C.S.: 339112
Keng-Shuo Tai (Chm & Pres)

VISHAL BEARINGS LIMITED
Survey No 22/1 Plot No 1 2 3 Shapar Village Road, Rajkot, 360 024, Gujarat, India
Tel.: (91) 2827252273
Web Site: https://www.vishalbearings.com
Year Founded: 1991
539398—(BOM)
Rev.: $13,855,081
Assets: $11,180,816
Liabilities: $7,181,788
Net Worth: $3,999,029
Earnings: $960,962
Emp.: 47
Fiscal Year-end: 03/31/23
Mechanical Parts Mfr & Distr
N.A.I.C.S.: 332991
Dilipkumar G. Changela (Chm & Mng Dir)

VISHAL FABRICS LIMITED
Ranipur Narol Road, Ahmedabad, 382405, India
Tel.: (91) 792 535 3977 In
Web Site: http://www.vishalfabricsltd.com
Year Founded: 1972

538598—(NSE)
Rev.: $132,312,180
Assets: $109,002,075
Liabilities: $72,875,985
Net Worth: $36,126,090
Earnings: $2,470,650
Emp.: 2,101
Fiscal Year-end: 03/31/21
Fabric Dyeing, Printing & Processing
N.A.I.C.S.: 313310
Brijmohan D. Chiripal (Chm, CEO & Mng Dir)

VISHNU CHEMICALS LTD.
Plot No C-23 Road No 8 Film Nagar Jubilee Hills, Hyderabad, 500 033, Telangana, India
Tel.: (91) 4023396817
Web Site: https://www.vishnuchemicals.com
Year Founded: 1990
VISHNU—(NSE)
Rev.: $93,025,282
Assets: $105,496,523
Liabilities: $78,723,236
Net Worth: $26,773,287
Earnings: $4,708,513
Emp.: 424
Fiscal Year-end: 03/31/21
Chemicals Mfr
N.A.I.C.S.: 325998
C. H. Krishna Murthy (Chm & Co-Mng Dir)

VISHNU PRAKASH R PUNGLIA LIMITED
B-31/32 Second Floor Industrial Estate New Power House Road, Jodhpur, 342003, Rajasthan, India
Tel.: (91) 9587024457
Web Site: https://www.vprp.co.in
Year Founded: 1986
543974—(BOM)
Rev.: $142,450,022
Assets: $100,378,733
Liabilities: $62,134,682
Net Worth: $38,244,051
Earnings: $11,022,189
Emp.: 800
Fiscal Year-end: 03/31/23
Construction Engineering Services
N.A.I.C.S.: 541330
Neha Matnani (Officer)

VISHNUSURYA PROJECTS & INFRA LIMITED
No 76 Second Floor Temple Towers North Mada Street, Mylapore, Chennai, 600004, India
Tel.: (91) 4424950019
Web Site: https://www.vishnusurya.com
Year Founded: 1996
VISHNUINFR—(NSE)
Rev.: $16,122,097
Assets: $14,671,599
Liabilities: $7,457,303
Net Worth: $7,214,297
Earnings: $2,009,617
Fiscal Year-end: 03/31/23
Construction Engineering Services
N.A.I.C.S.: 541330

VISHVAS PROJECTS LIMITED
606 Kailash Building 26 Kasturba Gandhi Marg, Connaught Place, New Delhi, 110001, India
Tel.: (91) 1123318698 In
Web Site: http://www.vishvasprojects.com
Year Founded: 1983
511276—(BOM)
Rev.: $89,730
Assets: $700,002
Liabilities: $632,668
Net Worth: $67,334

Earnings: $3,978
Emp.: 3
Fiscal Year-end: 03/31/19
Infrastructure Development Services
N.A.I.C.S.: 236220

VISHVPRABHA VENTURES LIMITED
Ground Floor Avighna Heights Survey No 45-4B Behind Sarvoday Park, Nandivali Road Dombivili East, Thane, 421201, Maharashtra, India
Tel.: (91) 2223027900
Web Site: https://www.vishvprabhaventure.com
Year Founded: 1985
512064—(BOM)
Rev.: $225,886
Assets: $1,462,334
Liabilities: $964,606
Net Worth: $497,728
Earnings: ($8,369)
Emp.: 11
Fiscal Year-end: 03/31/23
Trading & Investment Services
N.A.I.C.S.: 523150
Komal Bhagat (Sec)

VISHWARAJ SUGAR INDUSTRIES LIMITED
Bellad Bagewadi, Taluka Hukkeri, Belgaum, 591305, Karnataka, India
Tel.: (91) 8333251251
Web Site: https://www.vsil.co.in
Year Founded: 1995
VISHWARAJ—(BOM)
Rev.: $58,296,133
Assets: $97,191,399
Liabilities: $66,341,675
Net Worth: $30,849,723
Earnings: $1,131,981
Fiscal Year-end: 03/31/21
Sugar Mfr
N.A.I.C.S.: 311314
Umesh Katti (Chm)

VISIATIV SA
26 rue Benoit Bennier Green offices, 69260, Charbonnieres-les-Bains, France
Tel.: (33) 478872929
Web Site: https://www.visiativ.com
Year Founded: 1987
ALVIV—(EUR)
Sales Range: $200-249.9 Million
Emp.: 1,000
Software Publisher
N.A.I.C.S.: 513210
Christian Donzel (Co-Founder)

VISIBLE GOLD MINES INC.
147 Quebec Avenue, Rouyn-Noranda, J9X 6M8, QC, Canada
Tel.: (819) 762-0107 Ca
Web Site: https://www.visiblegoldmines.com
Year Founded: 2007
3V41—(DEU)
Rev.: $1,543
Assets: $594,523
Liabilities: $190,539
Net Worth: $403,984
Earnings: ($668,438)
Fiscal Year-end: 07/31/23
Gold Mining Services
N.A.I.C.S.: 212220
Martin Dallaire (Pres & CEO)

VISIOMED SAS
112 Avenue Kleber, 75116, Paris, France
Tel.: (33) 1 40 67 06 50
Web Site: http://www.visiomed-group.com
Year Founded: 2007
VMGBW—(EUR)

Sales Range: $10-24.9 Million
Emp.: 60
Medical Equipment Mfr
N.A.I.C.S.: 339112

Subsidiaries:

Visiomed SAS - Export Division (1)
8 Ave Kleber, Paris, 75116, France
Tel.: (33) 1 40 67 06 50
Web Site: http://www.en.visiomed-lab.com
Emp.: 30
Medical Device Mfr
N.A.I.C.S.: 334510
Eric Sebban (CEO)

VISION CAPITAL, LLP
55 St James's Street, London, SW1A 1LA, United Kingdom
Tel.: (44) 2073896410
Web Site: http://www.visioncapital.com
Year Founded: 1997
Sales Range: $1-4.9 Billion
Emp.: 30
Privater Equity Firm
N.A.I.C.S.: 551112
Julian Mash (Founder & CEO)

Subsidiaries:

ABL-TECHNIC Entlackung GmbH (1)
Beim Hammerschmied 4-6, 88299, Leutkirch, Germany
Tel.: (49) 756182680
Web Site: http://www.abl-technic.de
Sales Range: $10-24.9 Million
Waste Management Services
N.A.I.C.S.: 562998
Stefan Jost (CEO)

Subsidiary (Non-US):

ABL-TECHNIC Bogensberger Ges.m.b.H, (2)
Eisenstrasse 7, 4502, Sankt Marien, Austria
Tel.: (43) 7229785990
Web Site: http://www.abl.at
Paint Stripping Services
N.A.I.C.S.: 238320

Bormioli Rocco S.p.A. (1)
Viale Martiri della Liberta 1, 43036, Fidenza, PR, Italy
Tel.: (39) 0524 5111
Web Site: http://www.bormiolirocco.com
Plastic Packaging Mfr
N.A.I.C.S.: 326112
Riccardo Garre (Chm)

DeltaRail Group Limited (1)
Hudson House 2 Hudson Way Pride Park, Derby, DE24 8HS, United Kingdom (100%)
Tel.: (44) 1332 221000
Web Site: http://www.resonate.tech
Consultancy & Software Solutions for the Management & Maintenance of UK Rail Networks & Signalling Infrastructures
N.A.I.C.S.: 541614
Anna Matthews (CEO)

Branch (Domestic):

DeltaRail Group Limited (2)
One Eversholt Street 8th Floor, London, NW1 2DN, Derby, United Kingdom (100%)
Tel.: (44) 1332 221000
Web Site: http://www.resonate.tech
Rail Management & Operations
N.A.I.C.S.: 488210

Subsidiary (Non-US):

European Rail Software Applications (ERSA) (2)
1 Rue des Cicognes, 6700, Strasbourg, France (100%)
Tel.: (33) 3 88 07 1550
Web Site: http://ersa.clearsy.com
Software Engineering, Operational & Traffic Simulators Relating to Railway Services & Operations
N.A.I.C.S.: 488210

Grain D'Or (1)
Units 11-16 Townsend Inu Est, Waxlow Rd,

VISION CAPITAL, LLP

Vision Capital, LLP—(Continued)
London, NW10 7NU, United
Kingdom (100%)
Tel.: (44) 2089616955
Web Site: http://www.fletchersbakeries.co.uk
Sales Range: $25-49.9 Million
Emp.: 250
Croissants & Muffins Mfr
N.A.I.C.S.: 311812
Jas Randhawa (Gen Mgr)

Kara Foods (1)
Park 17 Moss Lane, Whitefield, Manchester, M45 8FJ, Greater Manchester,
United Kingdom (100%)
Tel.: (44) 1617667471
Web Site: http://www.karafs.co.uk
Sales Range: $50-74.9 Million
Fresh & Frozen Specialty Breads Mfr
N.A.I.C.S.: 311812
Jeff Dean (Gen Mgr)

Kinectrics Inc (1)
800 Kipling Ave Unit 2, Toronto, M8Z 5G5,
ON, Canada
Tel.: (416) 207-6000
Web Site: https://www.kinectrics.com
Sales Range: $25-49.9 Million
Engineering Services to the Power Industry
N.A.I.C.S.: 541330
David Harris (Pres & CEO)

Park Cake Bakeries Ltd. (1)
Ashton Road, Oldham, OL8 2ND, Lancs,
United Kingdom (100%)
Tel.: (44) 1616331181
Web Site: http://www.parkcakes.com
Sales Range: $200-249.9 Million
Cakes Mfr
N.A.I.C.S.: 311812
Anne Allen (Mng Dir)

Division (Domestic):

Park Cake Bakeries (2)
Bella Street, off Saint Helens Road, Bolton,
BL3 4DU, United Kingdom (100%)
Tel.: (44) 0120461226
Sales Range: $100-124.9 Million
Cakes Mfr
N.A.I.C.S.: 311812

Pork Farms Limited (1)
Queens Drive, PO Box 10523, Nottingham,
NG2 9QX, Nottingham, United
Kingdom (100%)
Tel.: (44) 1159866541
Web Site: http://www.pork-farms.co.uk
Sales Range: $125-149.9 Million
Emp.: 500
Hot & Cold Pies Mfr
N.A.I.C.S.: 311812

Division (Domestic):

Pork Farms - Riverside (2)
Crossgate Drive, Nottingham, NG2 1LW,
United Kingdom (100%)
Tel.: (44) 1159866462
Web Site: http://www.riverside-bakery.co.uk
Sales Range: $100-124.9 Million
Hot Pies, Quiches, Flans & Recipe Dishes
Mfr
N.A.I.C.S.: 311812
Deborah Bolton (Gen Mgr)

Pork Farms Limited -
Palethorpes (2)
Maer Lane, Market Drayton, TF9 3AL,
United Kingdom
Tel.: (44) 1630652271
Web Site: http://www.pork-farms.co.uk
Pies, Pastries, Sausage Rolls & Quiches
Mfr
N.A.I.C.S.: 311812

Vitopel Do Brasil Ltda. (1)
Rua Olimpiadas 66-13 Andar, Sao Paulo,
04551-000, Brazil
Tel.: (55) 11 3883 7701
Web Site: http://www.vitopel.com
Polypropylene Resin Mfr
N.A.I.C.S.: 325211

VISION CINEMAS LIMITED
No 14 1st Floor 5th Main 6th Cross
Jayamahal Extension, Bengaluru, 560
046, Karnataka, India
Tel.: (91) 8023338227
Web Site:
   https://www.visioncinemas.in
526441—(BOM)
Assets: $1,603,577
Liabilities: $444,316
Net Worth: $1,159,262
Earnings: ($49,964)
Emp.: 3
Fiscal Year-end: 03/31/21
Theater Operator
N.A.I.C.S.: 512131
Bindiganavale Rangvasanth (Mng Dir)

VISION CRITICAL INC.
200 Granville Street Mezzanine Floor,
Vancouver, V6C 1S4, BC, Canada
Tel.: (604) 647-1980
Web Site:
   http://www.visioncritical.com
Year Founded: 2000
Sales Range: $100-124.9 Million
Emp.: 260
Online Customer Panel & Market Research Services
N.A.I.C.S.: 541910
Mark Bergen (Exec VP-Sls)

Subsidiaries:

Vision Critical (Hong Kong)
Limited (1)
Unit 1104 11th Fl Office Plus Whan Chai
303 Hennessy Rd Whan Chai, Admiralty,
Hong Kong, China (Hong Kong)
Tel.: (852) 3489 7009
Market Research Services
N.A.I.C.S.: 541910

Vision Critical Communications (US)
Inc. (1)
1 Sansome St Ste 2910, San Francisco, CA
94104
Tel.: (415) 489-7100
Market Research Services
N.A.I.C.S.: 541910

Vision Critical Communications PTY
Limited (1)
Level 7, 309 George St, Sydney, 2000,
NSW, Australia
Tel.: (61) 2 9256 2000
Market Research Services
N.A.I.C.S.: 541910

Vision Critical Communications
SAS (1)
61 rue Monceau, Paris, 75008, France
Tel.: (33) 1 45 61 78 00
Web Site: http://www.visioncritical.fr
Market Research Services
N.A.I.C.S.: 541910

Vision Critical GMBH (1)
Hildeboldplatz 15-17, 50672, Cologne, Germany
Tel.: (49) 221 13080799 0
Web Site: http://www.visioncritical.de
Information Technology Consulting Services
N.A.I.C.S.: 541512
Alexander Trimborn (Mgr-Bus Dev)

Vision Critical Pte. Ltd. (1)
8 Marina Boulevard 05-02 Marina Bay Financial Centre, Singapore, 018981, Singapore
Tel.: (65) 6595 6666
Market Research Services
N.A.I.C.S.: 541910

Vision Critical Research Solutions
(UK) Ltd (1)
17 Hatfields 2nd Floor, London, SE1 8DS,
United Kingdom
Tel.: (44) 207 633 2900
Market Research Services
N.A.I.C.S.: 541910
Mike Steven (Mng Dir)

VISION DEAL HK ACQUISITION CORP.
5/F Manulife Place 348 Kwun Tong
Road, Kowloon,
China (Hong Kong)
Web Site: https://www.visiondeal.hk
Year Founded: 2022
7827—(HKG)
Investment Management Service
N.A.I.C.S.: 523999
Feng Lin (CEO)

VISION EXTRUSIONS LTD.
201 Zenway Blvd, Woodbridge, L4H
3H9, ON, Canada
Tel.: (905) 265-9970
Web Site:
   http://www.visionproducts.ca
Sales Range: $350-399.9 Million
Emp.: 1,000
Vinyl, Aluminum & Steel Building
Products Mfr
N.A.I.C.S.: 331318
Vic De Zen (Founder)

Subsidiaries:

Vision Hollow Metal Limited (1)
400 Zenway Blvd Unit 1, Woodbridge, L4H
0S7, ON, Canada
Tel.: (905) 851-1211
Web Site: https://visionhollowmetal.com
Steel Door & Frame Mfr
N.A.I.C.S.: 332321
Nick Siragusa (Pres)

Vision Outdoor Products Limited (1)
400 Zenway Blvd, Woodbridge, L4H 0S7,
ON, Canada
Tel.: (905) 850-9971
Web Site:
   http://www.visionoutdoorproducts.com
Steel Product Mfr & Distr
N.A.I.C.S.: 332323

VISION GROUP S.P.A.
Via Ripamonti 44, 20141, Milan, Italy
Tel.: (39) 02.92885300
Web Site: https://vision-group.it
Year Founded: 1989
Emp.: 120
Optical Products Mfr & Distr
N.A.I.C.S.: 333310

Subsidiaries:

GrandVision B.V. (1)
The Base Evert van de Beekstraat 1-80
Tower C 6th floor, 1118 CL, Schiphol, Netherlands
Tel.: (31) 88 887 01 00
Web Site: http://www.grandvision.com
Rev.: $4,275,489,929
Assets: $5,101,513,264
Liabilities: $3,683,485,619
Net Worth: $1,418,027,645
Earnings: ($54,929,349)
Emp.: 33,542
Fiscal Year-end: 12/31/2020
Optical Product Retailer
N.A.I.C.S.: 456130

VISION HEALTHCARE N.V.
Grote Markt 41, 8500, Kortrijk, Belgium
Tel.: (32) 56 22 15 47
Web Site:
   http://www.visionhealthcare.eu
Diversified Healthcare Holding Company
N.A.I.C.S.: 551112
Yvan Vindevogel (Founder & CEO)

Subsidiaries:

NaturaMed Pharma AS (1)
PO Box 1513, 3007, Drammen, Norway
Tel.: (47) 32216000
Web Site: http://www.naturamed-pharma.no
Dietary Supplements Mfr
N.A.I.C.S.: 325411
Bjorn Andre Lie (Mgr-IT)

VISION INTERNATIONAL HOLDINGS LTD.
3F China United Plaza 1002-1008 Tai

INTERNATIONAL PUBLIC

Nan West, Cheung Sha Wan, Kowloon, China (Hong Kong)
Tel.: (852) 36115480
Web Site: http://www.vision-holdings.com.hk
Year Founded: 2010
8107—(HKG)
Rev.: $20,447,813
Assets: $14,069,115
Liabilities: $7,215,353
Net Worth: $6,853,763
Earnings: $624,495
Emp.: 6
Fiscal Year-end: 12/31/22
Logistics & Supply Chain Management Services
N.A.I.C.S.: 541614
Yun Sin Ko (Chm)

VISION INTERNATIONAL PEOPLE GROUP PUBLIC LIMITED
Vision Tower 67 Limassol Avenue,
Aglantzia, 2121, Nicosia, Cyprus
Tel.: (357) 2 246 0606
Web Site: http://www.vipgpl.com
Year Founded: 1997
Sales Range: $75-99.9 Million
Emp.: 283
Food & Drug Retailer
N.A.I.C.S.: 424210
Nina Melnikova (CFO)

VISION INVESTMENTS LIMITED
Level-2 Vivrass Plaza, Laucala Beach
Estate, Fiji
Tel.: (679) 8925989
Web Site: https://www.vil.com.fj
Year Founded: 1971
Retail Company Distr Consumer
Electronics & Furniture
N.A.I.C.S.: 459999

VISION LITHIUM INC.
1019 Boulecard Des Pins, Val d'Or,
J9P 4T2, QC, Canada
Tel.: (819) 874-6200
Web Site:
   https://www.visionlithium.com
Year Founded: 1997
VLI—(TSXV)
Assets: $15,102,119
Liabilities: $389,500
Net Worth: $14,712,619
Earnings: ($1,550,355)
Fiscal Year-end: 08/31/23
Mineral Exploration Services
N.A.I.C.S.: 213114
Yves J. Rougerie (Pres & CEO)

VISION MARINE TECHNOLOGIES INC.
730 Boulevard du Cure-Boivin,
Boisbriand, J7G 2A7, QC, Canada
Tel.: (450) 951-7009
Web Site:
   https://www.visionmarinetech.com
Year Founded: 2012
VMAR—(NASDAQ)
Rev.: $4,216,020
Assets: $17,938,698
Liabilities: $9,311,628
Net Worth: $8,627,070
Earnings: ($15,574,381)
Emp.: 38
Fiscal Year-end: 08/31/23
Boat Mfr
N.A.I.C.S.: 336612
Alexandre Mongeon (Co-Founder & CEO)

VISION SIGMA LTD.
11 Galgalei Haplada Street, Herzliya
Pituach, 46722, Israel
Tel.: (972) 99709993

VISN—(TAE)
Rev.: $5,006,769
Assets: $93,741,123
Liabilities: $60,606,436
Net Worth: $33,134,687
Earnings: ($85,371)
Fiscal Year-end: 12/31/23
Other Activities Related to Real Estate
N.A.I.C.S.: 531390
Ophir Perelson *(CEO)*

VISION TRANSPORTATION INC.
7385 East Danbro Cres, Mississauga, L5N 6P8, ON, Canada
Tel.: (905) 858-7333
Web Site: http://www.visiontrans.com
Rev.: $16,550,000
Emp.: 24
Freight Transportation & Shipping Service
N.A.I.C.S.: 484122
Yves Bigras *(Gen Mgr)*

VISION TRAVEL SOLUTIONS
251 Consumers Road, Suite 700, Toronto, M2J 4R3, ON, Canada
Tel.: (416) 487-5385
Web Site: https://www.visiontravel.ca
Travel Agency
N.A.I.C.S.: 561510

Subsidiaries:

New Wave Travel (1)
1075 Bay Street, Toronto, M5S 2B1, ON, Canada
Tel.: (416) 928-3113
Web Site: http://www.newwavetravel.net
Travel & Tour Agency
N.A.I.C.S.: 561510

VISION VALUES HOLDINGS LIMITED
Units 902 9/F Shui Hing Centre 13 Sheung Yuet Road, Kowloon, China (Hong Kong)
Tel.: (852) 25006888 Ky
Web Site: http://www.visionvalues.com.hk
0862—(HKG)
Rev.: $7,109,378
Assets: $64,069,396
Liabilities: $20,868,577
Net Worth: $43,200,819
Earnings: ($9,147,262)
Emp.: 36
Fiscal Year-end: 06/30/21
Telecom Services
N.A.I.C.S.: 517810
Simon Lin Shing Lo *(Chm)*

Subsidiaries:

Vision Values Aviation Services Limited (1)
17/F 118 Connaught Road West, Hong Kong, China (Hong Kong)
Tel.: (852) 3 701 2300
Web Site: https://vision-vas.com
Air Transportation Support Services
N.A.I.C.S.: 488190

VISION, INC
8F Shinjuku East Side Square 27-30 Shinjuku 6-chome, Shinjuku-ku, Tokyo, 160-0022, Japan
Tel.: (81) 353250344
Web Site: https://www.vision-net.co.jp
Year Founded: 1995
9416—(TKS)
Rev.: $225,511,630
Assets: $151,484,940
Liabilities: $47,921,310
Net Worth: $103,563,630
Earnings: $21,447,250
Emp.: 688
Fiscal Year-end: 12/31/23
Telecommunication Related Services
N.A.I.C.S.: 517810
Kenichi Sano *(Founder, Pres & CEO)*

Subsidiaries:

Adval Co., Ltd. (1)
5th Floor KDX Higashi-Shinjuku Building 2-4-10 Kabukicho, Shinjuku-ku, Tokyo, 160-0021, Japan
Tel.: (81) 367096123
Web Site: https://www.adval.jp
Catering Services
N.A.I.C.S.: 722320

Alphatechno Co., Ltd. (1)
Shinjuku Island Tower 5f 6-5-1 Nishi-Shinjuku, Shinjuku-ku, Tokyo, 163-1305, Japan
Tel.: (81) 120159575
Web Site: http://www.alphatechno.jp
Office Equipment Distr
N.A.I.C.S.: 423420

BOS Inc. (1)
4th floor KDX Higashi-Shinjuku Building 2-4-10 Kabukicho, Shinjuku-ku, Tokyo, 160-0022, Japan
Tel.: (81) 120992478
Web Site: https://b-os.co.jp
Office Equipment Distr
N.A.I.C.S.: 423420

Best Link Inc. (1)
Tel.: (81) 120962303
Web Site: https://bestlink-net.co.jp
Wifi Communication Services
N.A.I.C.S.: 517112

Members Net Inc. (1)
8th floor Shinjuku East Side Square 6-27-30 Shinjuku, Shinjuku-ku, Tokyo, 160-0022, Japan
Tel.: (81) 352919606
Web Site: https://www.membersnet.co.jp
Office Equipment Distr
N.A.I.C.S.: 423420

Vision Mobile Korea Inc. (1)
16 Eulji-ro 702 7th floor Eulji-ro 1-ga, Jung-gu, Seoul, 4533, Korea (South)
Tel.: (82) 1 644 8435
Web Site: https://www.globalwifi.co.kr
Wifi Communication Services
N.A.I.C.S.: 517112

Vision Mobile USA Corp. (1)
18726 S Western Ave Ste 120, Gardena, CA 90248
Tel.: (424) 219-9224
Web Site: http://visionglobalwifi.com
Wifi Communication Services
N.A.I.C.S.: 517112

Vision Vietnam One Member Limited Liability Company (1)
Tel.: (84) 2839107939
Web Site: http://vision-vietnam.com
Internet Providing Services
N.A.I.C.S.: 517112

ZORSE Co., Ltd. (1)
2nd floor JR Sendai East Gate Building 1-1-1 Kotsugaoka, Miyagino-ku, Sendai, 983-0852, Miyagi, Japan
Tel.: (81) 227420550
Web Site: https://zorse.jp
Software Development Services
N.A.I.C.S.: 541519

VISIONARY EDUCATION TECHNOLOGY HOLDINGS GROUP INC.
105 Moatfield Dr Unit 1003, Toronto, M3B 0A2, ON, Canada
Tel.: (905) 739-0593 Ca
Web Site: https://www.visiongroupca.com
Year Founded: 2013
GV—(NASDAQ)
Rev.: $9,380,985
Assets: $87,859,701
Liabilities: $70,113,767
Net Worth: $17,745,934
Earnings: $967,249
Emp.: 67
Fiscal Year-end: 03/31/24

Holding Company
N.A.I.C.S.: 551112
Simon Tang *(Board of Directors & Vice Chm)*

VISIONARY GOLD CORP.
Suite 407 325 Howe Street, Vancouver, V6C 1Z7, BC, Canada
Tel.: (303) 809-4668 BC
Web Site: https://visionarymetalscorp.com
Year Founded: 2000
339—(DEU)
Assets: $3,279,087
Liabilities: $430,311
Net Worth: $2,848,776
Earnings: ($492,641)
Fiscal Year-end: 06/30/24
Mineral Exploration Services
N.A.I.C.S.: 212290
Robert Doyle *(CFO)*

VISIONARY HOLDINGS CO., LTD.
1-9-11 Nihonbashi Horidomecho, Chuo-Ku, Tokyo, 103-0012, Japan
Tel.: (81) 364536644
Web Site: http://www.visionaryholdings.co.jp
Year Founded: 2017
9263—(TKS)
Rev.: $178,401,057
Assets: $110,829,204
Liabilities: $85,358,441
Net Worth: $25,470,763
Earnings: ($2,946,812)
Fiscal Year-end: 04/30/23
Holding Company
N.A.I.C.S.: 551112
Naohiko Hoshizaki *(Pres)*

VISIONFLEX GROUP LIMITED
Unit 1/8 Prosperity Parade, Warriewood, 2102, NSW, Australia
Tel.: (61) 300266517 AU
Web Site: https://www.vfx-group.com
Year Founded: 2009
VFX—(ASX)
Rev.: $3,898,503
Assets: $3,200,459
Liabilities: $6,180,275
Net Worth: ($2,979,816)
Earnings: ($5,226,901)
Fiscal Year-end: 06/30/22
Holding Company; Online Healthcare Search & Appointment Booking Service
N.A.I.C.S.: 551112
Joshua Mundey *(CEO)*

Subsidiaries:

GObookings Systems Pty. Limited (1)
Level 4 17-21 Bellevue Street, Surry Hills, 2010, NSW, Australia
Tel.: (61) 130 067 3885
Web Site: https://www.gobookings.com.au
Healtcare Services
N.A.I.C.S.: 621610

Visionflex Pty. Ltd. (1)
Unit 1 8 Prosperity Parade, Warriewood, 2102, NSW, Australia
Tel.: (61) 289144000
Web Site: https://www.visionflex.com
Medical Device Mfr & Distr
N.A.I.C.S.: 339113

VISIONOX TECHNOLOGY INC.
21/F Building A Poly Zhonghui Plaza 157 Linhe West Road, Tianhe District, Guangzhou, Guangdong, China
Tel.: (86) 2066883333
Web Site: http://www.blackcow.cn
Year Founded: 1998
002387—(SSE)
Rev.: $1,049,727,641
Assets: $5,619,244,841

Liabilities: $3,485,236,627
Net Worth: $2,134,008,213
Earnings: ($290,581,598)
Emp.: 1,600
Fiscal Year-end: 12/31/22
Soybean Milk Powder Mfr
N.A.I.C.S.: 311224

VISIONSTATE CORP.
8634 53rd Avenue, Edmonton, T6E 5G2, AB, Canada
Tel.: (780) 425-9460
Web Site: https://www.visionstate.com
Year Founded: 2000
1VS1—(DEU)
Rev.: $218,412
Assets: $291,948
Liabilities: $484,237
Net Worth: ($192,290)
Earnings: ($1,304,600)
Fiscal Year-end: 09/30/23
Software Publisher
N.A.I.C.S.: 513210
John A. Putters *(Founder, Pres & CEO)*

VISIT WALES
Welsh Assembly Government, Brunel House 2 Fitzalan Rd, Cardiff, CF24 0UY, Wales, United Kingdom
Tel.: (44) 8450103300
Web Site: http://www.visitwales.co.uk
Sales Range: $50-74.9 Million
Emp.: 180
Tourism Promotion in Wales
N.A.I.C.S.: 923130
Jonathan Jones *(Dir-Mktg)*

VISITBRITAIN
Blacks Rd Thames Tower, London, W6 9EL, United Kingdom
Tel.: (44) 2088469000
Web Site: http://www.visitbritain.org
Sales Range: $100-124.9 Million
Emp.: 484
Tourism Services
N.A.I.C.S.: 561499
Christopher Rodrigues *(Chm)*

Subsidiaries:

British Travel Centre AB (1)
Box 3102, 103 62, Stockholm, Sweden
Tel.: (46) 8 4401700
Travel Agency Services
N.A.I.C.S.: 561510

VISPAK D.D.
Ozrakovici bb, 71 300, Visoko, Bosnia & Herzegovina
Tel.: (387) 32738334
VSPKR—(SARE)
Rev.: $25,748,003
Assets: $42,357,813
Liabilities: $13,066,466
Net Worth: $29,291,347
Earnings: $3,726,411
Emp.: 150
Fiscal Year-end: 12/31/21
Food Products Distr
N.A.I.C.S.: 311999

VISSEM ELECTRONICS CO., LTD.
53-11 Eondong-ro, Giheung-gu, Yongin, 16914, Gyeonggi-do, Korea (South)
Tel.: (82) 312883420
Web Site: https://www.vissem.com
072950—(KRS)
Rev.: $71,337,735
Assets: $64,058,436
Liabilities: $11,827,988
Net Worth: $52,230,448
Earnings: $1,684,099
Emp.: 111
Fiscal Year-end: 12/31/22

VISSEM ELECTRONICS CO., LTD.

Vissem Electronics Co., Ltd.—(Continued)
Electronic LED Display Mfr
N.A.I.C.S.: 334419

VISTA ALEGRE ATLANTIS SGPS S.A.
Lugar da Vista Alegre, 3830-292, Ilhavo, Portugal
Tel.: (351) 213232600
Web Site: https://vistaalegre.in
Year Founded: 1824
VAF—(EUR)
Rev.: $152,814,181
Assets: $254,160,756
Liabilities: $173,578,426
Net Worth: $80,582,330
Earnings: $5,965,389
Emp.: 2,504
Fiscal Year-end: 12/31/22
Ceramic & Crystal Product Mfr
N.A.I.C.S.: 327212

Subsidiaries:

Vista Alegre Espana S.A. (1)
Calle Jose Ortega & Gasset n 76, Madrid, 28006, Spain
Tel.: (34) 914026722
Web Site: http://www.vistaalegreatlantis.com
Sales Range: $50-74.9 Million
Porcelain, Crystal & Glassware Mfr
N.A.I.C.S.: 327212
Paulo Jose Lopes Varela *(Chm & CEO)*

Vista Alegre Usa Corp (1)
41 Madison Ave 9th Fl, New York, NY 10010
Tel.: (917) 831-4377
Web Site: http://www.myvistaalegre.com
Online Retailer
N.A.I.C.S.: 425120
Daniel L. Da Silva *(Pres)*

VISTA ENERGY, S.A.B. DE C.V.
Calle Volcan 150 Floor 5 Colonia Lomas de Chapultepec, Alcaldia Miguel Hidalgo, Mexico, 11000, Mexico
Tel.: (52) 5541669000   MX
Web Site: http://www.vistaoilandgas.com
Year Founded: 2017
VIST—(NYSE)
Rev.: $1,143,820,000
Assets: $2,037,979,000
Liabilities: $1,193,919,000
Net Worth: $844,060,000
Earnings: $269,535,000
Emp.: 465
Fiscal Year-end: 12/31/22
Oil & Gas Production & Exploration
N.A.I.C.S.: 211130
Miguel M. Galuccio *(Founder, Chm & CEO)*

VISTA GLOBAL HOLDING LTD.
Gate Village Building 11 DIFC Unit 106 Level 1, 507213, Dubai, United Arab Emirates
Tel.: (971) 4 875 2300
Web Site: http://www.vistaglobal.com
Year Founded: 2018
Holding Company; Aviation Services
N.A.I.C.S.: 551112
Thomas Flohr *(Founder & Chm)*

VISTA GROUP INTERNATIONAL LIMITED
Shed 12 City Works Depot 90 Wellesley St West, Auckland, 1010, New Zealand
Tel.: (64) 99844570
Web Site: https://vistagroup.co.nz
Year Founded: 2014
VGL—(ASX)
Rev.: $90,363,349
Assets: $139,273,301
Liabilities: $52,511,848
Net Worth: $86,761,453
Earnings: ($8,593,997)
Emp.: 716
Fiscal Year-end: 12/31/23
Software Solutions
N.A.I.C.S.: 513210
Murray Holdaway *(Founder & Chief Product Officer)*

Subsidiaries:

Ticketsoft LLC (1)
5400 LBJ Fwy Ste 1360, Dallas, TX 75240-1029
Tel.: (972) 982-8620
Web Site: http://www.ticketsoft.com
Cinema Management Software Solutions
N.A.I.C.S.: 513210
Philip Wood *(Founder & Pres)*

VISTA LAND & LIFESCAPES, INC.
Tel.: (63) 232263552
Web Site: https://www.vistaland.com.ph
VLL—(PHI)
Rev.: $616,344,994
Assets: $6,530,921,854
Liabilities: $4,190,361,734
Net Worth: $2,340,560,121
Earnings: $144,918,723
Emp.: 1,638
Fiscal Year-end: 12/31/21
Real Estate Services
N.A.I.C.S.: 531120
Manuel Paolo A. Villar *(Vice Chm, Pres & CEO)*

Subsidiaries:

Brittany Corporation (1)
The HQ 3/F Vista Hub at SOMO Daang Hari Road, Bacoor, Cavite, 1770, Philippines
Tel.: (63) 917 883 8103
Web Site: https://www.brittany.com.ph
Real Estate Property Development Services
N.A.I.C.S.: 531312

Crown Asia Properties, Inc. (1)
Lgf Building B Evia Lifestyle Center Daang Hari Road Almanza Dos, Daang-Hari, Las Pinas, 1750, Philippines
Tel.: (63) 2 882 7696
Web Site: http://www.crownasia.com.ph
Home Building & Construction Service
N.A.I.C.S.: 236116

Mella Hotel, Inc. (1)
Global South C5 Extension, Las Pinas, 6490, Metro Manila, Philippines
Tel.: (63) 28828181
Web Site: http://thebrittanyhotels.com
Hotel Operator
N.A.I.C.S.: 721110

Vista Residences, Inc. (1)
3F Worldwide Corporate Center Shaw Blvd, Mandaluyong, 1554, Philippines
Tel.: (63) 999 886 4262
Web Site: https://www.vistaresidences.com.ph
Sales Range: $25-49.9 Million
Emp.: 15
Condominium Development Services
N.A.I.C.S.: 236116

VISTA PROJECTS LIMITED
330-4000 4th St SE, Calgary, T2G 2W3, AB, Canada
Tel.: (403) 255-3455
Web Site: https://www.vistaprojects.com
Year Founded: 1985
Emp.: 350
Engineering & Procurement Services
N.A.I.C.S.: 541618
Alex Campbell *(Founder, Chm & Principal)*

VISTAJET HOLDING S.A.
Sterneckstrasse 35, Salzburg, 5020, Austria
Tel.: (43) 6626402000
Web Site: http://www.vistajet.com
Business Aviation Services
N.A.I.C.S.: 481211
Thomas Flohr *(Founder & Chm)*

Subsidiaries:

VistaJet (1)
Farnborough Airport, Farnborough, GU14 6XA, Hampshire, United Kingdom
Tel.: (44) 1252526630
Web Site: http://www.vistajet.com
Sales Range: $25-49.9 Million
Emp.: 25
Passenger & Charter Air Transportation Services
N.A.I.C.S.: 481111
Nick van der Meer *(COO)*

VistaJet US, Inc. (1)
120 Wooster St, New York, NY 10012
Tel.: (800) 793-5985
Emp.: 20
Air Charter Services
N.A.I.C.S.: 481211
Thomas Flohr *(Founder & Chm)*

VISTAL GDYNIA S.A.
ul Hutnicza 40, 81-061, Gdynia, Poland
Tel.: (48) 587833704
Web Site: http://www.vistal.pl
Year Founded: 1991
VTL—(WAR)
Rev.: $16,717,221
Assets: $19,928,185
Liabilities: $128,902,047
Net Worth: ($108,973,863)
Earnings: ($108,163,880)
Fiscal Year-end: 12/31/22
Construction Services
N.A.I.C.S.: 238120
Ryszard Matyka *(CEO)*

VISTAMALLS, INC.
Vista Mall Las Pinas CV Starr Avenue, Philamlife Village Pamplona Dos, Las Pinas, 1740, Philippines
Tel.: (63) 285715948   PH
Web Site: https://www.vistamalls.com.ph
Year Founded: 1969
STR—(PHI)
Rev.: $237,258,307
Assets: $1,792,429,036
Liabilities: $982,195,000
Net Worth: $810,234,036
Earnings: $154,103,462
Fiscal Year-end: 12/31/23
Real Estate Investment Services
N.A.I.C.S.: 531190
Manuel Paolo A. Villar *(Pres)*

VISTAR AMAR LIMITED
Plot-A4 APMC-MAFCO Yard Sector-18, Vashi, Navi Mumbai, 400703, India
Tel.: (91) 2227880820
Web Site: https://www.vistaramar.com
Year Founded: 1983
538565—(BOM)
Rev.: $7,695,282
Assets: $2,099,430
Liabilities: $533,769
Net Worth: $1,565,662
Earnings: $379,486
Fiscal Year-end: 03/31/23
Financial Banking Services
N.A.I.C.S.: 522110
Ramesh Babulal Panjri *(Mng Dir)*

VISTAR HOLDINGS LIMITED
Unit 2 13/F Tak King Industrial Building 27 Lee Chung Street, Chai Wan, China (Hong Kong)
Tel.: (852) 2 889 7022   Ky
Web Site: http://www.vistarholdings.com
Year Founded: 1972
8535—(HKG)
Rev.: $39,359,279

INTERNATIONAL PUBLIC

Assets: $30,767,921
Liabilities: $12,276,445
Net Worth: $18,491,476
Earnings: $3,677,349
Emp.: 132
Fiscal Year-end: 03/31/23
Building Maintenance Services
N.A.I.C.S.: 237110
Ken Ching Keung Poon *(Chm & CEO)*

Subsidiaries:

Guardian Engineering Limited (1)
Suite C 2/F 8 Hankow Road, Tsim Sha Tsui, Kowloon, China (Hong Kong)
Tel.: (852) 28897995
Web Site: http://www.guardianhk.com
Engineeering Services
N.A.I.C.S.: 541330

Guardian Fire Engineers & Consultants Limited (1)
Unit 2 13/F 27 Lee Chung Street, Tak King Industrial Building, Chai Wan, China (Hong Kong)
Tel.: (852) 28897022
Web Site: https://www.guardianhk.com
Engineeering Services
N.A.I.C.S.: 541330

VISTAREIT, INC.
Lower Ground Floor Building B Evia Lifestyle Center, Daang Hari Almanza Dos Metro Manila, Las Pinas, Philippines
Tel.: (63) 232263552
Web Site: https://www.vistareit.com.ph
VREIT—(PHI)
Rev.: $47,395,887
Assets: $523,530,119
Liabilities: $26,961,110
Net Worth: $496,569,009
Earnings: $45,485,904
Emp.: 33
Fiscal Year-end: 12/31/23
Real Estate Investment Trust Services
N.A.I.C.S.: 531190

VISTAVU SOLUTIONS INC.
3310 605 5th Ave SW, Calgary, T2P 3H5, AB, Canada
Tel.: (403) 263-2727
Web Site: https://vistavusolutions.com
Year Founded: 1996
Information Technology Consulting Services
N.A.I.C.S.: 541511
Jory Lamb *(Founder & CEO)*

Subsidiaries:

VistaVu Solutions Ltd. (1)
15995 N Barkers Landing Ste 111, Houston, TX 77079
Web Site: http://www.vistavusolutions.com
Sales Range: $1-9.9 Million
Emp.: 38
Information Technology Consulting Services
N.A.I.C.S.: 541511
Roy Garcia *(VP-SIs)*

Subsidiary (Domestic):

Achieve IT Solutions, Inc. (2)
640 Belle Terre Rd Bldg B, Port Jefferson, NY 11777
Tel.: (631) 543-3200
Web Site: http://www.achieveits.com
Sales Range: $1-9.9 Million
Emp.: 23
Information Technology Services
N.A.I.C.S.: 541511
Timothy Singleton *(CEO)*

VISTIN PHARMA ASA
Ostensjoveien 27, NO-0661, Oslo, Norway
Tel.: (47) 35984200   NO
Web Site: https://www.vistin.com

AND PRIVATE COMPANIES

VISY INDUSTRIES HOLDINGS PTY. LTD.

VISTN—(OSL)
Rev.: $28,159,339
Assets: $37,614,354
Liabilities: $12,372,991
Net Worth: $25,241,363
Earnings: ($435,618)
Emp.: 77
Fiscal Year-end: 12/31/22
Holding Company; Biopharmaceutical Mfr
N.A.I.C.S.: 551112
Kjell-Erik Nordby *(CEO)*

Subsidiaries:

Vistin Pharma AS (1)
Ostensjoveien 27, NO 0661, Oslo, Norway **(100%)**
Tel.: (47) 35984200
Web Site: https://www.vistin.com
Emp.: 150
Biopharmaceutical Mfr
N.A.I.C.S.: 325412
Kjell-Erik Nordby *(CEO)*

VISTRY GROUP PLC
11 Tower View Kings Hill, West Malling, ME19 4UY, Kent, United Kingdom
Tel.: (44) 1732280400
Web Site:
 http://www.vistrygroup.co.uk
VTY—(LSE)
Rev.: $3,445,382,479
Assets: $7,593,688,463
Liabilities: $3,491,603,131
Net Worth: $4,102,085,332
Earnings: $257,946,226
Emp.: 5,213
Fiscal Year-end: 12/31/22
Real Estate & Housing Development Services
N.A.I.C.S.: 531390
Earl Sibley *(COO & Exec Dir)*

Subsidiaries:

Bovis Homes Limited (1)
11 Tower View Kings Hill, West Malling, ME19 4UY, Kent, United Kingdom
Tel.: (44) 1474618222
Web Site: https://www.bovishomes.co.uk
Sales Range: $25-49.9 Million
Emp.: 100
Building Construction Services
N.A.I.C.S.: 236116

Brunel Street Works Energy Services Limited (1)
Broadway Chambers 2 Broadway, Stratford, London, E15 4QS, United Kingdom
Tel.: (44) 1243791880
Web Site: https://brunelstreetworks.co.uk
Steam Heat Distribution Services
N.A.I.C.S.: 221330

Countryside Partnerships PLC (1)
The Drive, Brentwood, CM13 3AT, Essex, United Kingdom
Tel.: (44) 1277260000
Web Site:
 http://www.countrysideproperties.com
Sales Range: $125-149.9 Million
Emp.: 850
House Building Services
N.A.I.C.S.: 236117
Tim Lawlor *(CFO)*

Subsidiary (Domestic):

Countryside Properties (Northern) Limited (2)
Ibis Court Centre Park, Warrington, WA1 1RL, Cheshire, United Kingdom
Tel.: (44) 1925428900
Real Estate Manangement Services
N.A.I.C.S.: 531210

Millgate Developments Limited (2)
Millgate House Ruscombe Lane, Ruscombe, Twyford, RG10 9JT, Berkshire, United Kingdom
Tel.: (44) 1189343344
Web Site: http://www.millgatehomes.co.uk
Residential Building Construction Services
N.A.I.C.S.: 236117

Paul Beaney *(Mng Dir)*

Drew Smith Homes Limited (1)
7-9 Mill Court The Sawmills, Durley, Southampton, SO32 2EJ, Hampshire, United Kingdom
Tel.: (44) 1489861400
Web Site:
 https://www.drewsmithhomes.co.uk
Property Management Services
N.A.I.C.S.: 531311

Linden Homes Eastern Limited (1)
Eastwood House Glebe Road, Chelmsford, CM1 1RS, Essex, United Kingdom
Tel.: (44) 1245343000
Property Managing Services
N.A.I.C.S.: 531311

Linden Homes South-East Limited (1)
Linden House Guards Avenue, Caterham, CR3 5XL, Surrey, United Kingdom
Tel.: (44) 1883334400
Property Management Services
N.A.I.C.S.: 531311

Linden Homes Southern Limited (1)
Central 40 Lime Tree Way Chineham Park, Basingstoke, Reading, RG24 8GU, United Kingdom
Tel.: (44) 1483705100
Property Management Services
N.A.I.C.S.: 531311

Linden Homes Western Limited (1)
Linden House The Jacobs Building Berkeley Place, Clifton, Bristol, BS8 1EH, United Kingdom
Tel.: (44) 1179304949
Property Management Services
N.A.I.C.S.: 531311

Stamford Homes Limited (1)
Ashurst Southgate Park, Bakewell Road Orton Southgate, Peterborough, PE26YS, United Kingdom
Tel.: (44) 01733396600
Web Site: http://www.stamford-homes.co.uk
Sales Range: $25-49.9 Million
Emp.: 50
New Multifamily Housing Construction
N.A.I.C.S.: 236116
Christopher Bond *(Mng Dir)*

Vistry (Jersey) Limited (1)
4th Floor St Pauls Gate 2224 New Street, Saint Helier, Jersey
Tel.: (44) 1534504700
Web Site: https://www.vistra.com
Financial Investment Services
N.A.I.C.S.: 523999

Vistry Partnerships Yorkshire Limited (1)
Thunderhead Ridge, Glasshoughton, Castleford, WF10 4UA, West Yorkshire, United Kingdom
Tel.: (44) 1977555550
Property Management Services
N.A.I.C.S.: 531311

Vistry Ventures Limited (1)
2 Broadway Stratford, London, E15 4QS, United Kingdom
Tel.: (44) 2082215000
Web Site: https://www.vistryventures.co.uk
Apartment Rental Services
N.A.I.C.S.: 531110

VISUAL CHINA GROUP CO., LTD.
South Gate 1st Floor Building 12301, Xitaihu Science and Technology Industrial Park Wujin District, Changzhou, 213149, Jiangsu, China
Tel.: (86) 1057950209
Web Site: https://www.vcg.com
000681—(SSE)
Rev.: $97,933,521
Assets: $546,927,105
Liabilities: $73,054,318
Net Worth: $473,872,787
Earnings: $13,925,434
Fiscal Year-end: 12/31/22
Computer System Design Services
N.A.I.C.S.: 541512

VISUAL COMMUNICATIONS GROUP LTD
1 Europa Park, Croft Way, Witham, CM8 2FN, Essex, United Kingdom
Tel.: (44) 1376533055
Web Site:
 http://www.vcgcorporate.com
Sales Range: $25-49.9 Million
Emp.: 280
Packaging Design & Brand Management Services
N.A.I.C.S.: 541430
Dave Amber *(CEO)*

Subsidiaries:

VCG Colourlink Ltd. (1)
1 Europa Park, Croft Way, Witham, CM8 2FB, Essex, United Kingdom
Tel.: (44) 1376533099
Web Site: http://www.vcg-colourlink.com
Sales Range: $25-49.9 Million
Emp.: 35
Large Format Graphic Printing Services
N.A.I.C.S.: 541430
Phil Holt *(Dir-Production)*

VCG Connect Limited (1)
Studio B 2 3 Roach Bank Rd, Pilsworth, Bury, BL9 8RQ, United Kingdom
Tel.: (44) 1617969696
Web Site: http://www.vcg-connect.com
Sales Range: $1-9.9 Million
Emp.: 40
Flexographic Reproduction, Pre-Press & Digital Printing Services
N.A.I.C.S.: 323111
Jim McCormack *(Mng Dir)*

VCG Kestrel Limited (1)
1 Europa Park, Croft Way, Witham, CM8 2FN, Essex, United Kingdom
Tel.: (44) 1376533055
Web Site: http://www.vcg-kestrel.com
Sales Range: $25-49.9 Million
Emp.: 200
Packaging Design & Brand Management Services
N.A.I.C.S.: 541430
Keith Parker *(Dir-Ops)*

VISUAL DEFENCE, INC.
9225 Leslie Street Suite 7, Richmond Hill, L4B 3H6, ON, Canada
Tel.: (905) 731-1254
Web Site:
 http://www.visualdefence.com
Sales Range: $25-49.9 Million
Emp.: 50
Commercial Safety & Security Products & Services
N.A.I.C.S.: 561621
Barry Tal *(Chm & CEO)*

VISUAL INTERNATIONAL HOLDINGS LIMITED
23 Kleinplaas Hohenhort Street, Stellenberg Western Cape, Cape Town, South Africa
Tel.: (27) 219198954 ZA
Web Site:
 https://www.visualinternational.co.za
Year Founded: 2006
VIS—(JSE)
Rev.: $58,901
Assets: $1,069,417
Liabilities: $2,110,204
Net Worth: ($1,040,787)
Earnings: ($271,521)
Emp.: 3
Fiscal Year-end: 02/28/23
Property Holding & Development Company
N.A.I.C.S.: 531311
Charles K. Robertson *(CEO)*

VISUAL PHOTONICS EPITAXY CO., LTD.
No 16 Gongye 1st Road Pingzhen Industrial Zone, Pingzhen District, Taoyuan, 324, Taiwan
Tel.: (886) 34192969
Web Site: https://www.vpec.com.tw
Year Founded: 1996
2455—(TAI)
Rev.: $88,103,074
Assets: $149,700,769
Liabilities: $49,326,628
Net Worth: $100,374,142
Earnings: $14,723,568
Emp.: 170
Fiscal Year-end: 12/31/23
Microelectronic Components Mfr
N.A.I.C.S.: 334419
Mao-Chang Chen *(Bd of Dirs & Chm)*

VISUALMED CLINICAL SOLUTIONS CORP.
1035 Laurier Street West, Montreal, H3V 2L3, QC, Canada
Tel.: (514) 274-1115
VMCS—(OTCIQ)
Assets: $10,897,030
Liabilities: $3,022,115
Net Worth: $7,874,915
Earnings: ($507,768)
Fiscal Year-end: 06/30/21
Software Development Services
N.A.I.C.S.: 541511
Gerard Dab *(Chm, Chief Compliance Officer & Sec)*

VISY INDUSTRIES HOLDINGS PTY. LTD.
Level 11 2 Southbank Boulevard, Southbank, 3006, VIC, Australia
Tel.: (61) 392474777 AU
Web Site: http://www.visy.com.au
Year Founded: 1948
Sales Range: $1-4.9 Billion
Emp.: 8,000
Packaging Products Mfr
N.A.I.C.S.: 322220
Chris Daly *(CEO)*

Subsidiaries:

Amalpak Ltd. (1)
Speybank St, PO Box 868, Lae, 411, Morobe, Papua New Guinea **(100%)**
Tel.: (675) 4725900
Web Site:
 http://www.nationwidepngpages.com
Sales Range: $50-74.9 Million
Emp.: 110
Mfr of Corrugated Cartons & Boxes from Recycled Paper
N.A.I.C.S.: 322211

Centre Line Die Formes (1)
262-266 Edwardes St, Reservoir, 3073, VIC, Australia **(100%)**
Tel.: (61) 392474042
Sales Range: $25-49.9 Million
Emp.: 27
Mfr of Dies
N.A.I.C.S.: 333514

Fine Art Graphics (1)
262 266 Edwardes St, Reservoir, 3073, VIC, Australia **(100%)**
Tel.: (61) 392474244
Web Site: http://www.visy.com.au
Sales Range: $25-49.9 Million
Emp.: 30
Provider of Designer Graphics for Packaging
N.A.I.C.S.: 541430

Fine Art Graphics (1)
Unit 10 10 Lyn Parade, Hoxton Park, 2170, VIC, Australia **(100%)**
Tel.: (61) 296081200
Web Site: http://www.visy.com.au
Sales Range: $25-49.9 Million
Emp.: 20
Provider of Designer Graphics for Packaging
N.A.I.C.S.: 541430

Fine Art Graphics (1)
38 Cobalt St, Carole Park, 4300, QL, Australia **(100%)**
Tel.: (61) 732481401
Web Site: http://www.visy.com

VISY INDUSTRIES HOLDINGS PTY. LTD.

Visy Industries Holdings Pty. Ltd.—(Continued)
Sales Range: $25-49.9 Million
Emp.: 6
Provider of Graphics Design for Packaging
N.A.I.C.S.: 541430

Fine Art Graphics (1)
24-26 White Rd, Gepps Cross, 5094, SA,
Australia **(100%)**
Tel.: (61) 883001600
Web Site: http://www.visy.com.au
Sales Range: $25-49.9 Million
Emp.: 10
Provider of Graphics Design for Packaging
N.A.I.C.S.: 541430

Fine Art Graphics (1)
49 Peel Rd, O'Connor, 6163, WA,
Australia **(100%)**
Tel.: (61) 893111980
Sales Range: $25-49.9 Million
Emp.: 10
Provider of Graphics Design for Packaging
N.A.I.C.S.: 541430

Market Express (1)
1 Dunn Ave 20 Redley Ave, Leeton, 2705,
NSW, Australia **(100%)**
Tel.: (61) 269532357
Web Site: http://www.marketx.com
Sales Range: $25-49.9 Million
Emp.: 2
Mfr of Corrugated Cartons & Boxes from
Recycled Paper
N.A.I.C.S.: 322211
Ralph Aerano *(Gen Mgr)*

Pratt Industries (USA), Inc. (1)
1800-B Sarasota Pkwy, Conyers, GA 30013
Tel.: (770) 918-5678
Web Site: https://www.prattindustries.com
Sales Range: $1-4.9 Billion
Emp.: 11,500
Corrugated & Solid Fiber Box Manufacturing
N.A.I.C.S.: 322211
Anthony Pratt *(Chm)*

Subsidiary (Domestic):

Minnesota Corrugated Box, Inc. (2)
2200 Yh Hanson Ave, Albert Lea, MN 56007
Web Site: http://www.mcbox.com
Corrugated & Solid Fiber Box Mfr
N.A.I.C.S.: 322211
Timothy Krebsbach *(Pres)*

Pratt Industries-Corrugating Division (2)
700 E 37th St N, Wichita, KS 67219-3510
Tel.: (316) 838-0851
Web Site: http://www.prattindustries.com
Sales Range: $150-199.9 Million
Emp.: 1,400
Corrugated Box Mfr & Retailer
N.A.I.C.S.: 322211
Ron McComas *(Gen Mgr)*

Subsidiary (Domestic):

Lewisburg Container Co. (3)
275 W Clay St, Lewisburg, OH 45338
Tel.: (937) 962-2681
Web Site: http://www.lewisburgcontainer.com
Sales Range: $25-49.9 Million
Emp.: 270
Wooden Crates & Corrugated Products Mfr
N.A.I.C.S.: 321920
David McKenny *(Mgr-Reg)*

Division (Domestic):

Pratt Industries-Corrugating Division (2)
2000 Beverly Ave SW, Grand Rapids, MI 49519
Tel.: (616) 452-2111
Web Site: http://www.prattindustries.com
Sales Range: $25-49.9 Million
Emp.: 100
Packaging Mfr
N.A.I.C.S.: 322211
Craig Stucky *(Gen Mgr)*

Plant (Domestic):

Pratt Industries-Humboldt (2)
221 Hwy 45, Humboldt, TN 38343
Tel.: (731) 784-2009
Web Site: http://www.prattindustries.com
Sales Range: $25-49.9 Million
Emp.: 100
Mfr of Corrugated Cartons & Boxes from Recycled Paper
N.A.I.C.S.: 322211
Jay Baldwin *(Gen Mgr)*

Pratt Industries-Statesville (2)
185 Deer Ridge Dr, Statesville, NC 28625-3190
Tel.: (704) 878-6615
Web Site: http://www.prattindustries.com
Sales Range: $50-74.9 Million
Emp.: 250
Corrugated Paper Mfr
N.A.I.C.S.: 322211
Jim Register *(Gen Mgr)*

The Packaging Company (1)
6 Modal Street, Canningvale, Kewdale, 6105, WA, Australia **(100%)**
Tel.: (61) 8 9256 5613
Web Site: http://www.visy.com.au
Sales Range: $25-49.9 Million
Emp.: 35
Mfr of Cardboard Cartons & Paper
N.A.I.C.S.: 322211

Visy Board Pty. Ltd. (1)
118 Hammond Rd, Dandenong, 3175, VIC, Australia **(100%)**
Tel.: (61) 392383333
Web Site: http://www.visyboard.com.au
Sales Range: $75-99.9 Million
Emp.: 100
Mfr of Corrugated Cartons & Boxes from Recycled Paper
N.A.I.C.S.: 322211
Damien Cooke *(Mgr-Sls)*

Visy Board Pty. Ltd. (1)
13 Reo Crescent, PO Box 74, Somerton Business Ctr, Campbellfield, 3061, VIC, Australia **(100%)**
Tel.: (61) 392474450
Sales Range: $125-149.9 Million
Emp.: 400
Mfr of Corrugated Cartons & Boxes from Recycled Paper
N.A.I.C.S.: 322211

Visy Board Pty. Ltd. (1)
86 Drummond Rd, Shepparton, 3630, VIC, Australia **(100%)**
Tel.: (61) 358219122
Web Site: http://www.visy.com
Sales Range: $25-49.9 Million
Emp.: 10
Distr of Corrugated Cartons & Boxes from Recycled Paper
N.A.I.C.S.: 322211

Visy Board Pty. Ltd. (1)
Benetook Ave, Mildura, 3500, VIC, Australia **(100%)**
Tel.: (61) 350230044
Web Site: http://www.visy.com
Sales Range: $25-49.9 Million
Emp.: 3
Mfr of Corrugated Cartons & Boxes from Recycled Paper
N.A.I.C.S.: 322211
Cosi Costa *(Gen Mgr)*

Visy Board Pty. Ltd. (1)
41-51 Scrivener St, Warwick Farm, 2170, NSW, Australia **(100%)**
Tel.: (61) 298281000
Sales Range: $50-74.9 Million
Emp.: 150
Mfr of Corrugated Cartons & Boxes from Recycled Paper
N.A.I.C.S.: 322211
Gerard Schouten *(Gen Mgr)*

Visy Board Pty. Ltd. (1)
11 Blumer Avenue, Griffith, 2680, NSW, Australia **(100%)**
Tel.: (61) 269626882
Web Site: http://www.visy.com.au
Mfr of Corrugated Cartons & Boxes from Recycled Paper
N.A.I.C.S.: 322211

Visy Board Pty. Ltd. (1)
24-26 White Rd, Gepps Cross, 5094, SA, Australia **(100%)**
Tel.: (61) 883001600
Web Site: http://www.visy.com.au
Sales Range: $125-149.9 Million
Emp.: 300
Corrugated Cartons & Boxe from Recycled Paper Mfr
N.A.I.C.S.: 322211

Visy Board Pty. Ltd. (1)
McKay Rd, Berri, 5343, SA, Australia **(100%)**
Tel.: (61) 85801200
Web Site: http://www.visy.com.au
Sales Range: $25-49.9 Million
Emp.: 10
Mfr of Corrugated Cartons & Boxes from Recycled Paper
N.A.I.C.S.: 322211

Visy Board Pty. Ltd. (1)
38 Cobalt St, Carole Park, 4300, QLD, Australia **(100%)**
Tel.: (61) 732481444
Web Site: http://www.visy.com.au
Sales Range: $25-49.9 Million
Emp.: 50
Mfr of Corrugated Cartons & Boxes from Recycled Paper
N.A.I.C.S.: 322211

Visy Board Pty. Ltd. (1)
Keocey Tier Rd, Latrobe, 7310, TAS, Australia **(100%)**
Tel.: (61) 364273010
Web Site: http://www.visy.com.au
Sales Range: $25-49.9 Million
Emp.: 4
Mfr of Corrugated Cartons & Boxes from Recycled Paper
N.A.I.C.S.: 322211

Visy Board Pty. Ltd. (1)
49 Peel Rd, O'Connor, 6163, WA, Australia **(100%)**
Tel.: (61) 893111999
Sales Range: $50-74.9 Million
Emp.: 115
Mfr of Fibre Packaging from Recycled Paper
N.A.I.C.S.: 322211
Paul Zanderzilt *(Gen Mgr)*

Visy Board Pty. Ltd. (1)
158 160 McCredie Rd, Herdiat Pl 2164, Smithfield, 2164, NSW, Australia **(100%)**
Tel.: (61) 297943000
Web Site: http://www.visy.com.au
Sales Range: $50-74.9 Million
Emp.: 200
Mfr of Corrugated Cartons & Boxes from Recycled Paper
N.A.I.C.S.: 322211
Brad Hinds *(Gen Mgr)*

Visy Board-New Zealand (1)
235 Roscommon Road, Wiri, 2104, Auckland, New Zealand **(100%)**
Tel.: (64) 92796400
Web Site: http://www.visy.com.au
Sales Range: $50-74.9 Million
Emp.: 200
Corrugated Carton & Box from Recycled Paper Mfr
N.A.I.C.S.: 322211
Andrew Gleason *(Gen Mgr)*

Visy Paper 3&6 (1)
6 Herbert Place, 6 Herbert Place, Smithfield, 2164, NSW, Australia **(100%)**
Tel.: (61) 297943120
Web Site: http://www.visy.com.au
Sales Range: $1-4.9 Billion
Emp.: 5,000
N.A.I.C.S.: 322211

Visy Paper 8 (1)
168 Paringa Rd, Gibsons Island, Brisbane, 4172, QLD, Australia **(100%)**
Tel.: (61) 732592444
Web Site: http://www.visypaper8.com.au
Sales Range: $25-49.9 Million
Emp.: 30
N.A.I.C.S.: 322211

Visy Paper Coatings (1)
13 Reo Crescent, Campbellfield, 3061, VIC, Australia **(100%)**
Tel.: (61) 392474500
Web Site: http://www.visy.com.au
Sales Range: $1-4.9 Billion
Emp.: 6,000
N.A.I.C.S.: 322211

INTERNATIONAL PUBLIC

Visy Recycling (1)
708 Princes Hwy, Springvale, 3171, VIC, Australia **(100%)**
Tel.: (61) 383269251
Web Site: http://www.visy.com.au
Sales Range: $25-49.9 Million
Emp.: 100
Mfr of Recycled Plastic Products
N.A.I.C.S.: 326199

Visy Recycling (1)
708 Princes Highway, Springvale, 3172, VIC, Australia **(100%)**
Tel.: (61) 1300 368 479
Web Site: http://www.visy.com.au
Sales Range: $25-49.9 Million
Emp.: 40
Recycling of Wastepaper & Waste Management Services
N.A.I.C.S.: 562998

Visy Recycling (1)
6 Herber Pl, Smithfield, 2164, NSW, Australia **(100%)**
Tel.: (61) 297943188
Web Site: http://www.visy.com.au
Sales Range: $25-49.9 Million
Emp.: 50
Recycler of Paper & Cardboard
N.A.I.C.S.: 322211

Visy Recycling (1)
168 Paringa Rd, Gibson Island, Brisbane, 4172, QLD, Australia **(100%)**
Tel.: (61) 732592466
Web Site: http://www.visy.com
Sales Range: $50-74.9 Million
Emp.: 150
Provider of Recycling Services
N.A.I.C.S.: 325998

Visy Recycling Europe Limited (1)
80 Caroline Street, Birmingham, B3 1UP, West Midlands, United Kingdom
Tel.: (44) 1212331449
Packaging Services
N.A.I.C.S.: 561910
Renny Craib *(Sr Mgr-Trading)*

Visy Specialities (1)
Level 11 2 Southbank Blvd, Southbank, 3006, VIC, Australia
Tel.: (61) 13 84 79
Boxes & Paper Mfr
N.A.I.C.S.: 322212

Visy Specialties (1)
262 266 Edwardes St, Reservoir, 3073, VIC, Australia
Tel.: (61) 1300 138 781
Corrugated Box Mfr
N.A.I.C.S.: 322211
Martin Laason *(Gen Mgr)*

Visy Technical Centre (1)
13 Reo Crescent, Campbellfield, 3061, VIC, Australia
Tel.: (61) 392474443
Provider of Automation & Packaging Systems
N.A.I.C.S.: 326199

Visy Trading Germany GmbH (1)
Hanse-Viertel Poststrasse 33 im 06, Hamburg, 20354, Germany
Tel.: (49) 35085448
Packaging Services
N.A.I.C.S.: 561910
Tristan Peil *(Mgr-Sls-Europe)*

Visy Trading Singapore Pte Ltd (1)
11-01 Suntec Tower Three 8 Temasek Blvd, Singapore, 038988, Singapore
Tel.: (65) 66814600
Packaging Services
N.A.I.C.S.: 561910
Jonathan Glickfeld *(Gen Mgr)*

Visyflex Preprint (1)
13 Reo Crescent, Private Bag 61, Somerton Business Ctr, Campbellfield, 3061, VIC, Australia **(100%)**
Tel.: (61) 392474550
Web Site: http://www.visyindustries.com.au
Sales Range: $25-49.9 Million
Emp.: 50
Provider of Printing Services
N.A.I.C.S.: 323120
Mark Ostenried *(Mgr)*

VITA 34 AG

Deutscher Platz 5A, D-04103,
Leipzig, Germany
Tel.: (49) 341487920
Web Site: https://www.vita34.de
Year Founded: 1997
V3V—(MUN)
Rev.: $85,064,222
Assets: $174,808,853
Liabilities: $148,801,676
Net Worth: $26,007,177
Earnings: ($2,053,198)
Emp.: 761
Fiscal Year-end: 12/31/23
Umbilical Cord Blood Bank
N.A.I.C.S.: 541715
Frank Kohler (Chm-Supervisory Bd)

Subsidiaries:

Bebecord Stemlife International
S.A. (1)
Rua Julio Dinis n 196, 4050-318, Porto, Portugal
Tel.: (351) 220109090
Web Site: https://www.bebecord.pt
Stem Cell Banking Services
N.A.I.C.S.: 621999

Celvitae Biomedica S.L. (1)
Santiago de Compostela 88, 28035, Madrid, Spain
Tel.: (34) 900901907
Web Site: https://www.celvitae.es
Biotechnology Research & Development Services
N.A.I.C.S.: 541714

Centre Marcel-la Mas, S. L. (1)
C/ Avenir 41 - Entlo 2, 08021, Barcelona, Spain
Tel.: (34) 900109051
Web Site: https://www.marcelamas.com
Health Care Srvices
N.A.I.C.S.: 621999

Cilmes Sunu Banka, SIA (1)
Terbatas street 4 - 1, Riga, LV-1050, Latvia
Tel.: (371) 26583773
Web Site: https://www.nabassaite.lv
Stem Cell Treatment Services
N.A.I.C.S.: 621111

Cryoprofil S.A. (1)
Ul Dzialkowa 85, Warsaw, Poland
Tel.: (48) 728833273
Web Site: https://www.cryoprofil.pl
Medical Device Mfr & Distr
N.A.I.C.S.: 339112

FamiCord Suisse S.A. (1)
Sumpfstrasse 26, 6302, Zug, Switzerland
Tel.: (41) 5880599
Web Site: https://www.famicord.ch
Biotechnology Research & Development Services
N.A.I.C.S.: 541714

Kamieniniu Lasteliu Bankas UAB
Imunolita (1)
Linkmenu g 28, LT-08217, Vilnius, Lithuania
Tel.: (370) 52729048
Web Site: http://www.klb.lt
Healthcare Services
N.A.I.C.S.: 621610
Irmantas Katilius (Head-IT Governance)

Krio Intezet Zrt. (1)
Kelemen Laszlo utca 12, 1026, Budapest, Hungary
Tel.: (36) 14140130
Web Site: https://krio.hu
Stem Cell Banking Services
N.A.I.C.S.: 621999

Polksi Bank Komorek Macierzystych
Sp. Z.o.o. (1)
al Jana Pawla II 29, 00-867, Warsaw, Poland
Tel.: (48) 224364050
Stem Cell Banking Services
N.A.I.C.S.: 621999

Secuvita S.L. (1)
Av Arroyo del Santo 6, 28042, Madrid, Spain
Tel.: (34) 917431400
Web Site: https://www.secuvita.es
Healtcare Services

N.A.I.C.S.: 621610
Irene Lopez Perez-Cejuela (Dir-Sls & Mktg)

Seracell Pharma GmbH (1)
Schillingallee 68, 18057, Rostock, Germany
Tel.: (49) 38144076102
Web Site: http://www.seracell-rostock.de
Pharmaceutical Drug Product Mfr
N.A.I.C.S.: 325412

Sevibe Cells S.L. (1)
Parc Tecnologic del Valles Avda Parc
Tecnologic n 3, 08290, Barcelona, Spain
Tel.: (34) 972183274
Web Site: https://www.sevibe.es
Stem Cell Banking Services
N.A.I.C.S.: 621999

Smart Cells International Ltd. (1)
Unit 7 Chancerygate Industrial Centre, Horton Cl, West Drayton, UB7 8EW, United Kingdom
Tel.: (44) 1895424430
Web Site: https://www.smartcells.com
Stem Cell Banking Services
N.A.I.C.S.: 621999

Vita 34 Gesellschaft fur Zelltransplantate mbH (1)
Hartackerstrasse 28, 1190, Vienna, Austria
Tel.: (43) 15339443
Web Site: https://www.vita34.at
Emp.: 100
Healthcare Services
N.A.I.C.S.: 621610
Gernot Erlach (Mng Dir)

Vita 34 Slovakia s.r.o. (1)
Prievozska 4D, 821 09, Bratislava, Slovakia
Tel.: (421) 341487920
Web Site: https://www.vita34.sk
Healtcare Services
N.A.I.C.S.: 621610
Falk Neukirch (Mng Dir)

Yasam Bankasi Saglik Hizmetleri ic
ve Dis Ticaret Anonim Sirketi (1)
Tepe Prime A Blok No 70, Cankaya, Turkiye
Tel.: (90) 8503028020
Web Site: https://www.kordonkanibankasi.com
Cord Blood & Cord Tissue Storage Services
N.A.I.C.S.: 621999

edicto GmbH (1)
Eschersheimer Landstrasse 42, 60322, Frankfurt am Main, Germany
Tel.: (49) 6990550550
Web Site: http://www.edicto.de
Public Relation Consulting & Communication Services
N.A.I.C.S.: 541820

VITA GROUP LIMITED

Vita Place 77 Hudson Road, Albion, 4010, QLD, Australia
Tel.: (61) 73 624 6666
Web Site: http://www.vitagroup.com.au
VTG—(ASX)
Rev.: $485,405,883
Assets: $208,589,098
Liabilities: $100,481,221
Net Worth: $108,107,877
Earnings: $20,179,912
Emp.: 1,700
Fiscal Year-end: 06/30/21
Mobile Communications Equipment Retailer
N.A.I.C.S.: 811210
Maxine J. Horne (CEO)

Subsidiaries:

Gould Holdings Pty. Ltd. (1)
9 Toorak Rd, South Yarra, Melbourne, 3141, VIC, Australia
Tel.: (61) 388661888
Sales Range: $50-74.9 Million
Emp.: 7
Diagnostic Devices Whslr
N.A.I.C.S.: 423450
Gary Gould (Gen Mgr)

One Zero Communications Pty.
Ltd. (1)
77 Hudson Rd Vita Pl, Albion, Brisbane, 4010, Queensland, Australia

Tel.: (61) 732531010
Web Site: http://onezero.net.au
Sales Range: $50-74.9 Million
Emp.: 150
Cellular Phone Services
N.A.I.C.S.: 517112
Maxine Horne (CEO)

VITA LIFE SCIENCES LIMITED

Unit 1/ 102 Bath Road, Kirrawee, 2232, NSW, Australia
Tel.: (61) 295452633
Web Site: https://www.vitalifesciences.com
VLS—(ASX)
Rev.: $50,514,951
Assets: $40,737,688
Liabilities: $11,222,669
Net Worth: $29,515,019
Earnings: $6,183,502
Emp.: 400
Fiscal Year-end: 12/31/23
Vitamins & Supplements Sales
N.A.I.C.S.: 325412
Chin L. Khoo (CFO & Sec)

Subsidiaries:

Vita Corporation Pte Limited (1)
Block 26 Kallang Pl 05 04 07, Kallang Basin Indus Estate, Singapore, 339157, Singapore
Tel.: (65) 62782778
Web Site: http://www.vitahealth.com.sg
Sales Range: $25-49.9 Million
Emp.: 30
Medical Systems & Supplements Retailer
N.A.I.C.S.: 456199

Vita Healthcare Asia Pacific Sdn
Bhd. (1)
81G Jalan SS21 60 Damansara Utama, 47400, Petaling Jaya, Selangor, Malaysia
Tel.: (60) 377258881
Web Site: http://www.vitahealth.com.my
Pharmaceuticals Product Mfr
N.A.I.C.S.: 325412

Subsidiary (Non-US):

Herbs of Gold Pty Limited (2)
Unit 1/102 Bath Rd, PO Box 3143, Kirrawee, 2232, NSW, Australia
Tel.: (61) 800852222
Web Site: https://herbsofgold.com.au
Sales Range: $25-49.9 Million
Emp.: 12
Herbal Medicine Products Mfr
N.A.I.C.S.: 325412

Subsidiary (Domestic):

Swiss Bio Pharma Sdn Bhd. (2)
81G Jalan SS21 60 Damansara Utama, 47400, Petaling Jaya, Selangor, Malaysia
Tel.: (60) 377293873
Web Site: http://www.vitahealth.com.my
Medical Systems & Supplements Whslr
N.A.I.C.S.: 423450

Subsidiary (Domestic):

Vitaron Jaya Sdn Bhd. (3)
81G Jalan SS21 60 Damansara Utama, 47400, Petaling Jaya, Selangor, Malaysia
Tel.: (60) 377258881
Web Site: http://vitaron.com.my
Sales Range: $25-49.9 Million
Emp.: 30
Medical Systems & Supplements Sales
N.A.I.C.S.: 423450

Subsidiary (Non-US):

VitaHealth Asia Pacific (S) Pte
Limited (2)
Block 26 Kallang Place 05-04/07, Kallang Basin Industrial Estate, Singapore, 339157, Singapore
Tel.: (65) 62782778
Sales Range: $25-49.9 Million
Emp.: 40
Medical Systems & Supplements Retailer
N.A.I.C.S.: 456199

VitaHealth Laboratories Australia Pty
Limited (2)
Unit 1 102 Bath Rd, PO Box 3143, Kir-

rawee, 2232, NSW, Australia
Tel.: (61) 295452633
Sales Range: $25-49.9 Million
Emp.: 12
Food Supplement Distr
N.A.I.C.S.: 456191

VITA MI HOLDINGS S.A.

103 James Bourchier Blvd 1st Floor, 1407, Sofia, Bulgaria
Tel.: (359) 2 962 14 88
Web Site: http://www.vitami.bg
Year Founded: 2008
VM5—(BUL)
Sales Range: Less than $1 Million
Information Services
N.A.I.C.S.: 519290

VITA SOCIETA EDITORIALE SPA

Via Marco d'Agrate 43, 20139, Milan, Italy
Tel.: (39) 02 552 2981
Web Site: http://www.vita.it
Sales Range: $1-9.9 Million
Magazine & Internet Publisher
N.A.I.C.S.: 513120
Riccardo Bonacina (Chm)

VITA ZAHNFABRIK H. RAUTER GMBH & CO. KG

Spitalgasse 3, Bad Sackingen, 79703, Germany
Tel.: (49) 77615620
Web Site: http://www.vita-zahnfabrik.com
Year Founded: 1924
Rev.: $233,960,034
Emp.: 800
Dental Equipment Mfr
N.A.I.C.S.: 339114
Robert Rauter (Mng Dir)

Subsidiaries:

VITA Italia Srl (1)
Via Riccardo Lombardi 19/18, 20153, Milan, Italy
Tel.: (39) 029039261
Dental Equipment Distr
N.A.I.C.S.: 423450

VITA Zahnfabrik Iberica, S.L. (1)
Avda Diagonal 429 3, 8036, Barcelona, Spain
Tel.: (34) 937678836
Dental Equipment Distr
N.A.I.C.S.: 423450
Jorge Gomez Rosas (Area Mgr-Sls)

VITAFOAM NIGERIA PLC.

140 Oba Akran Avenue, Ikeja, Lagos, Nigeria
Tel.: (234) 8174589640   NG
Web Site: https://www.vitafoamng.com
Year Founded: 1962
VITAFOAM—(NIGE)
Rev.: $59,953,127
Assets: $56,190,512
Liabilities: $36,495,883
Net Worth: $19,694,629
Earnings: $4,949,045
Fiscal Year-end: 09/30/23
Foam Furnishings Mfr
N.A.I.C.S.: 326140
Bamidele Osuolale Makanjuola (Chm)

Subsidiaries:

Vitablom Nigeria Limited (1)
25/27 Oke Aro road, Iju Ishaga, Lagos, Ogun, Nigeria
Tel.: (234) 8038186062
Web Site: https://vitablomng.com
Timber Product Mfr
N.A.I.C.S.: 314120

Vitapur Nigeria Limited (1)
326/328 Agege Motor Road, Ilupeju, Lagos, Nigeria
Tel.: (234) 8174589722

VITAFOAM NIGERIA PLC.

Vitafoam Nigeria Plc.—(Continued)
Web Site: https://www.vitapurinsulation.com
Insulation Product Mfr
N.A.I.C.S.: 327993

VITAFOSS INTERNATIONAL GROUP CO., LTD.
13F No 216 Jian 8th Rd, Zhonghe Dist, New Taipei City, 23444, Taiwan
Tel.: (886) 229295373
Web Site: http://www.kayeetv.com
Year Founded: 2012
2939—(TAI)
Rev.: $13,202,230
Assets: $30,390,169
Liabilities: $2,281,337
Net Worth: $28,108,832
Earnings: ($2,616,305)
Fiscal Year-end: 12/31/23
Home Product Equipment Distr
N.A.I.C.S.: 423990
Tsai Mo-Tsan (Chm)

VITAL A.D.
Marsala Tita 1, Vrbas, 21460, Serbia
Tel.: (381) 217955000
Web Site: http://www.vital.rs
Year Founded: 1855
VITL—(BEL)
Sales Range: Less than $1 Million
Food & Beverage Product Mfr
N.A.I.C.S.: 311999
Rajko Cavorovic (CEO)

VITAL ENERGY INC.
Suite 620 634 6th Avenue SW, Calgary, T2P 0S4, AB, Canada
Tel.: (403) 699-9668   AB
Web Site:
    https://www.vitalenergyoil.com
VTLE—(NYSE)
Rev.: $10,892,774
Assets: $22,458,608
Liabilities: $13,714,643
Net Worth: $8,743,964
Earnings: ($4,058,668)
Fiscal Year-end: 12/31/23
Oil & Gas Exploration
N.A.I.C.S.: 211120
Hai Zhou (Chm)

VITAL INNOVATIONS HOLDINGS LIMITED
4F No 55 Jiangchuang 2nd Road Zhongguancun Science Park, OPTO-Mechatronics Industrial Park Tongzhou District, Beijing, 101111, China
Tel.: (86) 1058929600   Ky
Web Site: http://www.vitalinno.com
6133—(HKG)
Rev.: $153,344,880
Assets: $87,105,704
Liabilities: $13,522,766
Net Worth: $73,582,938
Earnings: ($2,465,003)
Emp.: 29
Fiscal Year-end: 12/31/22
Smartphone Mfr & Distr
N.A.I.C.S.: 334220
Xiuli Rong (Chm)

VITAL KSK HOLDINGS, INC.
9F Kyodo Building 1-9-12 Muromachi, Chuou-ku, Tokyo, 103-0022, Japan
Tel.: (81) 332753301
Web Site: https://www.vitalksk.co.jp
Year Founded: 2009
3151—(TKS)
Rev.: $3,883,249,410
Assets: $2,097,075,380
Liabilities: $1,396,811,980
Net Worth: $700,263,400
Earnings: $38,622,230
Emp.: 3,705
Fiscal Year-end: 03/31/24

Investment Management Service
N.A.I.C.S.: 523940
Ken Suzuki (Chm)
Subsidiaries:
KSK Co., LTD.   (1)
5-7 Doshomachi 1-chome, Chuo-ku, Osaka, 541-0045, Japan
Tel.: (81) 6 6229 1231
Web Site: http://www.web-ksk.co.jp
Emp.: 1,402
Pharmaceuticals Product Mfr
N.A.I.C.S.: 325412
Soichiro Okamoto (Pres & CEO)

Subsidiary (Domestic):
Tanpopo Co., LTD.   (2)
2-3 Senjukawaracho, Adachi-Ku, Tokyo, 120-0037, Japan
Tel.: (81) 338822405
Pharmaceutical Products Distr
N.A.I.C.S.: 424210

VITAL-NET, Inc.   (1)
1-1 Otemachi, Aoba-ku, Sendai, 980-8570, Miyagi, Japan
Tel.: (81) 22 266 4511
Web Site: http://www.vitalnet.co.jp
Emp.: 1,375
Pharmaceuticals Product Mfr
N.A.I.C.S.: 325412
Ken Suzuki (Chm)

Subsidiary (Domestic):
Vital Agency Co., Ltd.   (2)
2-6-18 Omachi, Aoba-ku, Sendai, 980-0804, Miyagi, Japan
Tel.: (81) 222668091
Real Estate Management Services
N.A.I.C.S.: 531390

Vital Express Co., Ltd.   (2)
10 Kashima Shimoyoden, Natori, 981-1298, Miyagi, Japan
Tel.: (81) 191321871
Food Transportation Services
N.A.I.C.S.: 488490

VITAL LIMITED
Level 4 5 Tower B 49 Tory Street Te Aro, Wellington, 6011, New Zealand
Tel.: (64) 48021470
Web Site: https://www.vital.co.nz
Year Founded: 1994
VTL—(NZX)
Rev.: $15,763,158
Assets: $40,539,474
Liabilities: $27,690,191
Net Worth: $12,849,282
Earnings: ($109,450)
Emp.: 73
Fiscal Year-end: 06/30/23
Fibre Optics & Wireless Telecommunication Services
N.A.I.C.S.: 517111
Roger Sowry (Chm)

Subsidiaries:
Araneo Limited   (1)
Ground Floor 20 Kent Terrace, Wellington, 6011, New Zealand
Tel.: (64) 49787350
Web Site: http://www.araneo.net.nz
Sales Range: $25-49.9 Million
Emp.: 10
Wireless Broadband Network Connection Provider
N.A.I.C.S.: 517112
Nick Louranos (Gen Mgr)

CityLink Limited   (1)
Level 5 53 Boulcott Street, Wellington, 6011, New Zealand
Tel.: (64) 49170200
Web Site: http://www.citylink.co.nz
Sales Range: $25-49.9 Million
Emp.: 35
Broadband Network Connection Providers
N.A.I.C.S.: 517111
Ronald Martinez (Mgr-Channel)

VITAL METALS LTD
Kyle House Level 10 27 Macquarie Place, Sydney, 2000, NSW, Australia
Tel.: (61) 280290676
Web Site: https://vitalmetals.com
VML—(ASX)
Rev.: $1,772,631
Assets: $40,410,130
Liabilities: $1,627,444
Net Worth: $38,782,686
Earnings: ($3,357,058)
Fiscal Year-end: 06/30/24
Mineral Exploration Services
N.A.I.C.S.: 213115
Sebastian Andre (Sec)

VITALHUB CORP.
480 University Ave Suite 1001, Toronto, M5G 1V2, ON, Canada
Tel.: (416) 699-0123   ON
Web Site: https://www.vitalhub.com
Year Founded: 2015
VHIBF—(OTCQX)
Rev.: $39,874,204
Assets: $89,696,141
Liabilities: $27,847,099
Net Worth: $61,849,041
Earnings: $3,435,407
Emp.: 223
Fiscal Year-end: 12/31/23
Financial Investment Services
N.A.I.C.S.: 523999
Dan Matlow (Pres & CEO)

Subsidiaries:
Community Data Solutions Pty. Ltd.   (1)
214 Greenhill Rd, Eastwood, 5063, SA, Australia
Tel.: (61) 1800503981
Web Site: https://communityds.com.au
Software Development Services
N.A.I.C.S.: 541511

Coyote Software Corporation   (1)
3425 Harvester Road Suite 216, Burlington, L7N 3N1, ON, Canada
Tel.: (905) 639-8533
Web Site: https://www.coyotecorp.com
Software Development Services
N.A.I.C.S.: 541511

Hicom Technology Limited   (1)
Red House Cemetery Pales, Brookwood, GU24 0BL, Surrey, United Kingdom
Tel.: (44) 1483794945
Web Site: https://www.hicom.co.uk
Software Development Services
N.A.I.C.S.: 541511

Intouch with Health Limited   (1)
Red House Cemetery Pales, Brookwood, GU24 0BL, Surrey, United Kingdom
Tel.: (44) 1285657516
Web Site:
    https://www.intouchwithhealth.co.uk
Information Technology Services
N.A.I.C.S.: 541519

The Oak Group, Inc.   (1)
622 Cooper St, Camden, NJ 08102
Tel.: (856) 377-0060
Web Site: http://www.oakgroup.net
Engineeering Services
N.A.I.C.S.: 541330

VITALITY PRODUCTS INC.
304 837 W Hastings St, Vancouver, V6C 3N6, BC, Canada
Tel.: (604) 591-1322
Web Site: https://www.vitality.ca
Year Founded: 1946
VPI—(TSXV)
Rev.: $594,448
Assets: $600,425
Liabilities: $1,615,352
Net Worth: ($1,014,927)
Earnings: ($203,156)
Fiscal Year-end: 01/31/24
Health Care Products Mfr & Distr
N.A.I.C.S.: 456199
W. Douglas Grant (CFO & VP)

VITALL S.R.L.
Calea Combinatului 482A, 137180, Crevedia, Romania
Tel.: (40) 756 111 923   RO
Web Site: http://www.fermele-crevedia.ro
Year Founded: 2007
Poultry Production, Processing, Packaging & Distr
N.A.I.C.S.: 112390
Madalin Enescu (Owner & Gen Mgr)

VITAMINKA
Lece Koteski 23, 7500, Prilep, North Macedonia
Tel.: (389) 48407407
Web Site:
    https://www.vitaminka.com.mk
Year Founded: 1956
VITA—(MAC)
Rev.: $58,866,130
Assets: $57,390,955
Liabilities: $37,868,399
Net Worth: $19,522,556
Earnings: $1,500,910
Fiscal Year-end: 12/31/21
Food Products Mfr
N.A.I.C.S.: 311999

VITAMINS DIRECT (UK) LIMITED
Witan Gate West 500-600, York, MK9 1SH, United Kingdom
Tel.: (44) 800 634 9985
Web Site:
    http://www.goodvitamincompany.com
Emp.: 200
Vitamin & Nutritional Supplement Retailer
N.A.I.C.S.: 456191
Dan Conway (Mgr-Digital Mktg)

Subsidiaries:
Regina Health Ltd   (1)
York House Wetherby Road, PO Box 621, York, YO26 0EX, United Kingdom   (100%)
Tel.: (44) 20 8649 8500
Web Site: http://www.reginahealthcare.com
Natural Health Supplements & Herbal Extracts Mfr
N.A.I.C.S.: 424210

Vitamins Direct Holdings, LLC   (1)
2540 Metrocentre Blvd Ste 5, West Palm Beach, FL 33407
Tel.: (561) 615-4701
Sales Range: $10-24.9 Million
Emp.: 50
Mfr, Sale & Marketing of Nutritional Supplements
N.A.I.C.S.: 456191
William E. Hudson (CFO & Sec)

VITAN AGRO INDUSTRIES LIMITED
No 14 1st Floor Jagannathan Road, Nungambakkam, Chennai, 600 034, India
Tel.: (91) 44 42134344
Web Site:
    http://www.vitanagroindustriesltd.com
Sales Range: Less than $1 Million
Agricultural Product Whslr
N.A.I.C.S.: 424510

VITANIA LTD.
Raoul Wallenberg 4, Tel Aviv, Israel
Tel.: (972) 36441930
Web Site: https://vitania.co.il
Year Founded: 1995
VTNA—(TAE)
Rev.: $55,572,039
Assets: $752,284,834
Liabilities: $445,502,134
Net Worth: $306,782,700
Earnings: $22,186,490
Fiscal Year-end: 12/31/23
Other Activities Related to Real Estate

N.A.I.C.S.: 531390
Ofer Ziv (CEO)

VITAR INSULATION HOLDINGS LIMITED
Room 304-306 3/F Block B New Trade Plaza 6 On Ping Street, Siu Lek Yuen Shatin, Hong Kong, New Territories, China (Hong Kong)
Tel.: (852) 24113108   HK
Web Site: http://www.vitar.com.hk
Year Founded: 1978
Insulating Materials Mfr
N.A.I.C.S.: 326291

VITARICH CORPORATION
Marilao-San Jose Road Sta Rosa 1 Marilao, Bulacan, 3019, Philippines
Tel.: (63) 288433033   PH
Web Site: https://www.vitarich.com
Year Founded: 1950
VITA—(PHI)
Rev.: $201,849,054
Assets: $86,014,181
Liabilities: $52,378,526
Net Worth: $33,635,655
Earnings: $1,860,386
Emp.: 592
Fiscal Year-end: 12/31/21
Animal Feed Mfr & Distr
N.A.I.C.S.: 327910
Ricardo Manuel M. Sarmiento (Pres & CEO)

VITASCANNING AG
Daimlerstrasse 11, 75334, Straubenhardt, Germany
Tel.: (49) 52029779678
Web Site: http://www.vitascanning.de
Medical Digital Scanning Analysis Systems Mfr
N.A.I.C.S.: 541512
Basilius Halle (Mng Dir)

VITASOY INTERNATIONAL HOLDINGS LTD.
1 Kin Wong Street, Tuen Mun, New Territories, China (Hong Kong)
Tel.: (852) 24660333   HK
Web Site: https://www.vitasoy.com
Year Founded: 1940
0345—(HKG)
Rev.: $838,526,711
Assets: $877,982,338
Liabilities: $417,639,949
Net Worth: $460,342,389
Earnings: ($20,814,921)
Fiscal Year-end: 03/31/22
Holding Company; Soy Products Mfr
N.A.I.C.S.: 551112
Paggie Ah-Hing Tong (Sec)

Subsidiaries:

Hong Kong Gourmet Limited (1)
6 Ho Tin Street, Tuen Mun, New Territories, China (Hong Kong)   (100%)
Tel.: (852) 24603165
Web Site: http://www.hkgourmet.com.hk
Soy Food Mfr
N.A.I.C.S.: 311999

Shenzhen Vitasoy (Guang Ming) Foods & Beverage Company Limited (1)
No 513 Guangming Road, Guangming District, Shenzhen, Guangdong, China
Tel.: (86) 75527402888
Beverage Product Mfr & Distr
N.A.I.C.S.: 312111

Vitaland Services Limited (1)
6 Ho Tin Street, Tuen Mun, New Territories, China (Hong Kong)   (100%)
Tel.: (852) 24603165
Web Site: https://www.vitaland.com.hk
Sales Range: $10-24.9 Million
Emp.: 100
Restaurant
N.A.I.C.S.: 722511

Vitasoy (Dongguan) Company Limited (1)
No 3 Sizhong Road, Hengjiangxia Village Changping Town, Dongguan, Guangdong, China
Tel.: (86) 76989992888
Beverage Product Mfr & Distr
N.A.I.C.S.: 312111

Vitasoy (Foshan) Company Limited (1)
No 12 Jinda Road Xiaotang, Shishan Town Nanhai District, Foshan, Guangdong, China
Tel.: (86) 75781030808
Beverage Product Mfr & Distr
N.A.I.C.S.: 312111

Vitasoy (Shanghai) Company Limited (1)
No 118 Rongping Road, Songjiang District, Shanghai, China
Tel.: (86) 215 778 0083
Beverage Product Mfr & Distr
N.A.I.C.S.: 312111

Vitasoy (Wuhan) Company Limited (1)
No 36 Yubo Road, Yangluo Economic Development Zone Xinzhou District, Wuhan, Hubei, China
Tel.: (86) 2789002000
Beverage Product Mfr & Distr
N.A.I.C.S.: 312111

Vitasoy Australia Products Pty. Ltd. (1)
737 Bourke Street Docklands, PO Box 6089, Melbourne, 3008, VIC, Australia   (51%)
Tel.: (61) 800001029
Web Site: http://www.vitasoy.com.au
Sales Range: $25-49.9 Million
Emp.: 200
Soy Milk Mfr & Whslr
N.A.I.C.S.: 311224

Vitasoy Company Limited (1)
Room 918 No 37 Jinlong Road Nansha Street, Nansha District, Guangzhou, Guangdong, China
Tel.: (86) 2028607968
Beverage Product Mfr & Distr
N.A.I.C.S.: 312111

Vitasoy International Singapore Pte. Ltd. (1)
18 Senoko South Road, Singapore, 758089, Singapore
Tel.: (65) 67592855
Web Site: https://www.unicurd.com.sg
Soya Related Product Mfr & Distr
N.A.I.C.S.: 311224

VITEC MULTIMEDIA S.A.
99 Rue Pierre Semard, 92320, Chatillon, France
Tel.: (33) 146730606
Web Site: http://www.vitec.com
Year Founded: 1988
Emp.: 85
Digital Video Equipment Mfr
N.A.I.C.S.: 334310
Philippe Wetzel (Pres & CEO)

Subsidiaries:

Optibase Technologies Ltd. (1)
7 Shenkar St, PO Box 2170, Herzliyya, 46120, Israel   (100%)
Tel.: (972) 99709200
Web Site: http://www.optibase.com
Sales Range: $25-49.9 Million
Emp.: 50
Video Encoding, Decoding & Streaming Solutions
N.A.I.C.S.: 334310
Yaron Comarov (Mng Dir)

VITEC Multimedia, Inc. (1)
2200 Century Pkwy NE Ste 900, Atlanta, GA 30345-3150
Tel.: (404) 320-0110
Web Site: http://www.stradis.com
Sales Range: $25-49.9 Million
Emp.: 5
Digital Video Decoders Mfr
N.A.I.C.S.: 334310

Subsidiary (Domestic):

Focus (2)
931 Benecia Ave, Sunnyvale, CA 94085
Tel.: (650) 230-2400
Web Site: http://www.vitec.com
Sales Range: $25-49.9 Million
Wireless Technology, Video Conversion & Digital Media Services
N.A.I.C.S.: 334118
Kevin McDonald (VP-Mktg)

Subsidiary (Non-US):

VITEC GmbH (3)
   (100%)
Tel.: (49) 430783580
Web Site: https://www.vitec.com
Sales Range: $25-49.9 Million
Emp.: 25
Video Production, Media Management & Digital Signage Products Mfr
N.A.I.C.S.: 334310
Norman Schlomka (Mng Dir)

VITEC SOFTWARE GROUP AB
Tvistevagen 47 A, 907 29, Umea, Sweden
Tel.: (46) 90154900   SE
Web Site: https://www.vitecsoftware.com
Year Founded: 1985
VIT.B—(OMX)
Rev.: $180,031,010
Assets: $269,403,092
Liabilities: $166,446,924
Net Worth: $102,956,168
Earnings: $19,619,477
Emp.: 862
Fiscal Year-end: 12/31/20
Business Support Software Publisher
N.A.I.C.S.: 513210
Lars Stenlund (CEO)

Subsidiaries:

Vitec Acute Oy (1)
Tulli Business Park Akerlundinkatu 11 D 2, 33100, Tampere, Finland
Tel.: (358) 33 395 0900
Software Development Services
N.A.I.C.S.: 541511

Vitec Agrando AB (1)
Prastgardsgrand 2, Alvsjo, Stockholm, Sweden
Tel.: (46) 85 052 1900
Web Site: https://agrando.se
Software Development Services
N.A.I.C.S.: 541511

Vitec Agrando AS (1)
Langgata 97, 4306, Sandnes, Norway
Tel.: (47) 51700900
Web Site: https://www.agrando.no
Software Development Services
N.A.I.C.S.: 541511

Vitec Aloc A/S (1)
Edisonsvej 4, 5000, Odense, Denmark
Tel.: (45) 63136100
Web Site: https://www.vitecsoftware.com
Insurance Services
N.A.I.C.S.: 524210
Mikkel Rahbek Brunse (CEO)

Vitec Aloc AS (1)
Biskop Gunnerus gate 14A, NO-0185, Oslo, Norway
Tel.: (47) 23335100
Insurance Services
N.A.I.C.S.: 524210

Vitec Appva AB (1)
Masthamnsgatan 3, 413 27, Gothenburg, Sweden
Tel.: (46) 31850083
Web Site: https://www.appva.com
Software Development Services
N.A.I.C.S.: 541511

Vitec Autodata AS (1)
Biskop Gunnerus Gate 14 A Posthuset 14 etasje, 0185, Oslo, Norway
Tel.: (47) 23172030
Software Development Services
N.A.I.C.S.: 541511

Vitec Capitex AB (1)
Svensknabbev 25, Box 751, 393 51, Kalmar, Sweden
Tel.: (46) 480447400
Business Software Development Services
N.A.I.C.S.: 541511
Patrik Fransson (CEO)

Vitec Cito A/S (1)
Rypevang 1, 3450, Allerod, Denmark
Tel.: (45) 48143300
Web Site: https://www.vitec-cito.com
Software Development Services
N.A.I.C.S.: 541511

Vitec Energy AB (1)
Redegatan 1 B, Vastra Frolunda, 426 77, Gothenburg, Sweden
Tel.: (46) 317331860
Software Development Services
N.A.I.C.S.: 541511
Jerker Vallbo (CEO)

Vitec Fastighetssystem AB (1)
Sollentunav 63, Box 2113, 191 02, Sollentuna, Sweden
Tel.: (46) 90 15 49 00
Software Development Services
N.A.I.C.S.: 541511
Johan Kull (Mng Dir)

Vitec Fixit Systemer AS (1)
Bradbanken 1, 5003, Bergen, Norway
Tel.: (47) 55707060
Web Site: https://fixit.no
Software Development Services
N.A.I.C.S.: 541511

Vitec Futursoft Oy (1)
Klovinpellontie 1-3 Tower 2, 02180, Espoo, Finland
Tel.: (358) 20 728 8730
Web Site: https://www.vitecsoftware.com
Software Development Services
N.A.I.C.S.: 541511

Vitec HK Data AS (1)
Storgata 118, 2390, Moelv, Norway
Tel.: (47) 6 235 1680
Web Site: https://www.hk-data.no
Software Development Services
N.A.I.C.S.: 541511

Vitec IT-Makeriet AS (1)
Hammersborg Torg 3, 0179, Oslo, Norway
Tel.: (47) 22 99 20 50
Information Technology Consulting Services
N.A.I.C.S.: 541512

Vitec Infoeasy AS (1)
Bradbanken 1, 5003, Bergen, Norway
Tel.: (47) 55547100
Software Development Services
N.A.I.C.S.: 541511

Vitec Katrina Oy (1)
Kalliokatu 10, 26100, Rauma, Finland
Tel.: (358) 60094595
Web Site: https://www.vitec-katrina.com
Software Development Services
N.A.I.C.S.: 541511

Vitec LJ System AB (1)
Hedvig Mollers Gata 12, 223 55, Lund, Sweden
Tel.: (46) 20558000
Web Site: https://www.ljsystem.se
Software Development Services
N.A.I.C.S.: 541511

Vitec MV AB (1)
Davidshallsgatan 14, 211 45, Malmo, Sweden
Tel.: (46) 4 093 9150
Web Site: https://www.vitec-mv.com
Software Development Services
N.A.I.C.S.: 541511

Vitec MV AS (1)
Edisonsvej 4, 5000, Odense, Denmark
Tel.: (45) 65918022
Software Development Services
N.A.I.C.S.: 541511

Vitec Maklarsystem AB (1)
Redegatan 1 B, 426 77, Vastra Frolunda, Sweden
Tel.: (46) 31 3606100
Software Consulting Services
N.A.I.C.S.: 541512

Vitec Smart Visitor System AB (1)

VITEC SOFTWARE GROUP AB

Vitec Software Group AB—(Continued)
Vastra vagen 52, 803 24, Gavle, Sweden
Tel.: (46) 26656900
Software Development Services
N.A.I.C.S.: 541511

Vitec Visiolink ApS (1)
Bjornholms Alle 20, 8260, Viby, Denmark
Tel.: (45) 70233544
Web Site: https://www.visiolink.com
Newspaper Publishers
N.A.I.C.S.: 513110
Trine Norgaard Nielsen *(Mgr)*

Vitec WIMS AS (1)
Biskop Gunnerus gate 14 A, 0185, Oslo, Norway
Tel.: (47) 48241000
Web Site: https://wims.no
Software Development Services
N.A.I.C.S.: 541511

VITECO COMMUNICATION TECHNOLOGY JOINT STOCK COMPANY
No 35 Alley 61 Lac Trung Vinh Tuy Ward, Hai Ba Trung District, Hanoi, Vietnam
Tel.: (84) 438622727
Web Site: http://www.viteco.vn
VIE—(HNX)
Rev.: $707,692
Assets: $2,140,587
Liabilities: $248,807
Net Worth: $1,891,780
Earnings: $12,813
Emp.: 22
Fiscal Year-end: 12/31/23
Telecommunication Servicesb
N.A.I.C.S.: 517810
Tuan Anh Vo *(Chm-Mgmt Bd)*

VITESSE AGRO LIMITED
4th Floor Agrawal Complex Near CG Road, Ahmedabad, 380009, Gujarat, India
Tel.: (91) 7940093436 In
Web Site: http://www.vitesseagro.in
Year Founded: 1980
540823—(BOM)
Rev.: $2,729,981
Assets: $2,829,746
Liabilities: $1,804,905
Net Worth: $1,024,841
Earnings: $204,321
Fiscal Year-end: 03/31/21
Agricultural Product Whslr
N.A.I.C.S.: 424510
Roop Kishore Gola *(Exec Dir)*

VITINKA A.D. KOZLUK
Drinska dva no 30, Kozluk, 75413, Zvornik, Bosnia & Herzegovina
Tel.: (387) 56310114
Web Site: https://vitinka.com
Year Founded: 1880
Sales Range: $10-24.9 Million
Emp.: 180
Bottled Water Mfr
N.A.I.C.S.: 312112

VITKOVICE HOLDING, A.S.
Ruska 2887 101, 706 02, Ostrava, Vitkovice, Czech Republic
Tel.: (420) 595956000
Web Site: http://www.vitkovice.com
Year Founded: 1828
Sales Range: $100-124.9 Million
Emp.: 8,000
Steel Mfr & Engineering Supplies
N.A.I.C.S.: 331513
Jan Svetlik *(Chm)*

Subsidiaries:

CIDEGAS S.A. (1)
Av San Martin 6445, 1419, Buenos Aires, Argentina
Tel.: (54) 11 4571 7111
Web Site: http://www.cidegas.com.ar

Pressure Gas Cylinder Mfr
N.A.I.C.S.: 332420

LAHVARNA BROD d.o.o. (1)
Vladimira Filakovca 3, 35 000, Slavonski Brod, Croatia
Tel.: (385) 35 491 572
Industrial Supplies Whslr
N.A.I.C.S.: 423840

VITKOVICE IT SOLUTIONS a.s. (1)
Cihelni 1575/14, 706 02, Ostrava, Czech Republic
Tel.: (420) 596 663 111
Web Site: http://itsolutions.vitkovice.cz
Information Technology Support Services
N.A.I.C.S.: 541512
Vladimir Mekota *(CEO)*

VITKOVICE MECHANIKA a.s. (1)
Ruska 2929 / 101a, Vitkovice, 703 00, Ostrava, Czech Republic
Tel.: (420) 59 595 6970
Web Site: http://www.vitkovice-mechanika.cz
Mechanical Engineering Services
N.A.I.C.S.: 541330
Jan Svetlik *(Chm)*

VITKOVICE RECYCLING a.s. (1)
Ruska 2927, Vitkovice, 706 02, Ostrava, Czech Republic
Tel.: (420) 595 953 393
Web Site: http://www.vitkovice-recycling.cz
Metal Scrap Recycling Services
N.A.I.C.S.: 562920

VITKOVICE SLOVAKIA a.s. (1)
Zamocnicka 13, 811 03, Bratislava, Slovakia
Tel.: (421) 556 834 181
Web Site: http://www.slovakia.vitkovice.cz
Emp.: 13
Industrial Supplies Whslr
N.A.I.C.S.: 423840
Vladimir Bindzar *(Exec Dir)*

Vitkovice - Power Engineering A.S. (1)
Ruska 1142-30, 70600, Ostrava, Czech Republic
Tel.: (420) 595954315
Web Site: http://envi.vitkovice.cz
Special Needs Transportation
N.A.I.C.S.: 485991

Vitkovice Doprava A.S. (1)
Ruska 94-29, 70602, Ostrava, Czech Republic
Tel.: (420) 595956125
Web Site: http://www.vitkovice.cz
Freight Transportation Arrangement
N.A.I.C.S.: 488510
Jan Svetlik *(CEO)*

Vitkovice Gear Works A.S. (1)
Ruska 83/24, Vitkovice, 703 00, Ostrava, Czech Republic
Tel.: (420) 595956392
Web Site: http://www.gearworks.cz
Speed Changer Industrial High-Speed Drive & Gear Mfr
N.A.I.C.S.: 333612

Vitkovice Heavy Machinery A.S. (1)
Ruska ul 2887-101, 706 02, Ostrava, Czech Republic
Tel.: (420) 595956491
Web Site: http://www.vitkovicemachinery.com
Heavy & Civil Engineering Construction
N.A.I.C.S.: 237990

Vitkovice Its A.S. (1)
Ruska 1162-60, 70602, Ostrava, Czech Republic
Tel.: (420) 595955053
Inland Water Freight Transportation
N.A.I.C.S.: 483211

Vitkovice Testing Center S.r.o. (1)
Ruska 2887-101, 70602, Ostrava, Czech Republic
Tel.: (420) 595954620
Web Site: http://www.labatest.cz
Business Support Services
N.A.I.C.S.: 561499

VITOL HOLDING B.V.
KP van der Mandelelaan 130, 3062

MB, Rotterdam, Netherlands
Tel.: (31) 104987200 NI
Web Site: http://www.vitol.com
Year Founded: 1966
Holding Company; Oil, Gas & Coal Production
N.A.I.C.S.: 551112
Ian Taylor *(Chm)*

Subsidiaries:

Anchor Insurance Group, Inc. (1)
25 Church Street, PO Box HM 824, Hamilton, Bermuda
Tel.: (441) 295 9911
General Insurance Services
N.A.I.C.S.: 524210
Jide Fasanmi *(Gen Mgr-Mktg)*

Arawak Energy Corporation (1)
294 Heywood House, The Valley, Anguilla, Anguilla
Tel.: (264) 498 2645
Web Site: http://www.arawakenergy.com
Sales Range: $125-149.9 Million
Petroleum Drilling & Exploration
N.A.I.C.S.: 324110

Subsidiary (Non-US):

Altius Energy Corporation (2)
1122 Fourth St SW, Suite 920, Calgary, T2R 1M1, AB, Canada
Tel.: (403) 503-0820
Energy Production
N.A.I.C.S.: 211120

Affiliate (Non-US):

RF Energy Investments Ltd. (2)
Arch Makariou III, 58 Iris Tower 8th Fl, 1075, Nicosia, Cyprus (50%)
Tel.: (357) 22258500
Holding Company
N.A.I.C.S.: 551112

Arawak Energy International Ltd. (1)
Level 5 Precinct Building 2 Dubai International Financial Centre, PO Box No 506514, Dubai, United Arab Emirates
Tel.: (971) 4 453 1410
Oil & Gas Exploration Services
N.A.I.C.S.: 211120

Drax Generation Enterprise Limited
13 Queen's Road, Aberdeen, AB15 4YL, United Kingdom
Tel.: (44) 800 092 9290
Electricity Generation
N.A.I.C.S.: 221118

Fujairah Refinery Company Ltd. (1)
PO Box No 1592, Fujairah, United Arab Emirates
Tel.: (971) 9 228 1188
Oil & Gas Exploration Services
N.A.I.C.S.: 211120
Jose Coothur *(Mgr-Fin)*

JSC Ventspils nafta (1)
Elizabetes 1, Riga, LV-1010, Latvia
Tel.: (371) 67715910
Web Site: http://www.vnafta.lv
Investment Management Service
N.A.I.C.S.: 523999

Subsidiary (Domestic):

Ventspils nafta terminals (2)
Talsu iela 75, Ventspils, 3602, Latvia
Tel.: (371) 636 64090
Web Site: http://www1.vnt.lv
Emp.: 210
Oil & Gas Transhipment & Terminal Services
N.A.I.C.S.: 424710
Lars Pantzlaff *(Mng Dir)*

Petrol Ofisi A.S. (1)
Eski Buyukdere Caddesi No 33 Maslak, 34398, Istanbul, Turkiye
Tel.: (90) 2123291500
Web Site: http://www.petrolofisi.com.tr
Fuel & Lubricant Distr & Retailer
N.A.I.C.S.: 457120

Subsidiary (Domestic):

Erk Petrol Yatirimleri A.S. (2)
No 33 Sariye Eski Buyukdere Caddesi,

INTERNATIONAL PUBLIC

Maslak, Istanbul, Turkiye
Tel.: (90) 212 329 15 00
Web Site: http://www.erkpetrol.com.tr
Oil & Gas Exploration Services
N.A.I.C.S.: 213112
Yigit Suphi Meral *(Chm)*

Petrol Ofisi Akdeniz Rafinerisi Sanayi ve Ticaret A.S. (2)
Bilinmiyor, Maslak, Istanbul, 34600, Turkiye
Tel.: (90) 2123291518
Oil & Gas Exploration Services
N.A.I.C.S.: 213112

VPI Immingham LLP (1)
Rosper Road, South Killingholme, Immingham, DN40 3DZ, North Lincolnshire, United Kingdom
Tel.: (44) 1469 565 800
Web Site: http://www.vpi-i.com
Heat & Power Plant
N.A.I.C.S.: 221118

Varo Energy Germany GmbH (1)
Am Sandtorkai 77, 20457, Hamburg, Germany
Tel.: (49) 40 361 5760
Oil & Gas Exploration Services
N.A.I.C.S.: 211120

Vitol Argentina S.A. (1)
Juan Diaz de Solis 1860 2nd floor Office 2, Vicente Lopez, B1638BIH, Buenos Aires, Argentina
Tel.: (54) 11 4849 6800
Web Site: http://www.vitol.com.ar
Petroleum Product Whslr
N.A.I.C.S.: 424720
Fernando Aroca *(Gen Mgr)*

Vitol Asia Pte Ltd. (1)
260 Orchard Road The Heeren 15-02, Singapore, 238855, Singapore
Tel.: (65) 6737 9922
Oil & Gas Exploration Services
N.A.I.C.S.: 211120
Patrick Loh *(Mgr-Trading)*

Vitol Aviation UK Ltd. (1)
Belgrave House 76 Buckingham Palace Road, London, SW1W 9TQ, United Kingdom
Tel.: (44) 20 7973 4200
Fuel Distr
N.A.I.C.S.: 424720

Vitol Bahrain E.C. (1)
Bahrain World Trade Center 27th Floor West Tower Flat 271 Building 1B, Isa Al Kabeer Avenue, 316, Manama, Bahrain
Tel.: (973) 17218855
Web Site: http://www.vitol.com
Oil & Gas Exploration Services
N.A.I.C.S.: 211120
Daho Abidat *(Mgr-Fin)*

Vitol CDI Ltd (1)
Boulevard de la Republique Immeuble Tropique 3 Plateau 01, BP 7777, Abidjan, Cote d'Ivoire
Tel.: (225) 2022 9494
N.A.I.C.S.: 211120
Martin Shallcross *(Mgr-Ops)*

Vitol Capital Mangement Ltd. (1)
Magnolia Towers 2nd Floor 15 Parliament Street, Hamilton, Bermuda
Tel.: (441) 295 1408
Web Site: http://www.vitol.com
Oil & Gas Exploration Services
N.A.I.C.S.: 211120

Vitol Colombia S.A. (1)
Calle 71 5-97 of 505, Bogota, Colombia
Tel.: (57) 1 749 51 16
Oil & Gas Exploration Services
N.A.I.C.S.: 211120

Vitol Dubai Ltd. (1)
Level 5 Precinct Building 2 Dubai International Financial Centre, PO Box 506514, Dubai, United Arab Emirates
Tel.: (971) 4 278 2500
Web Site: http://www.vitol.com
Oil Marketing
N.A.I.C.S.: 213112

Vitol Energy Mexico S.A. DE C.V (1)
Calle Sierra Candela No 111 Suite 118, Lomas de Chapultepec, 11000, Mexico
Tel.: (52) 55 5202 6761

AND PRIVATE COMPANIES

Oil & Gas Exploration Services
N.A.I.C.S.: 211120
Luis Roca *(Mgr)*

Vitol Inc. (1)
2925 Richmond Ave 11th Fl, Houston, TX 77098
Tel.: (713) 230-1000
Web Site: http://www.vitol.com
Oil & Gas Exploration Services
N.A.I.C.S.: 211120

Subsidiary (Domestic):

Vitol Aviation Company (2)
300 Continental Blvd Ste555, El Segundo, CA 90245
Tel.: (310) 416-9180
Fuel Distr
N.A.I.C.S.: 424720
Christine Cohen *(Mgr-Ops & Acctg)*

Division (Domestic):

Vitol Inc. - Crude Oil Marketing Division (2)
6501 S CR 1110, Midland, TX 79706
Tel.: (405) 228-8100
Oil & Gas Exploration Services
N.A.I.C.S.: 211120

Vitol S.A. (1)
Boulevard du Pont d'Arve 28, 1205, Geneva, Switzerland
Tel.: (41) 22 322 1111
Petroleum Wholesale Trade Agency
N.A.I.C.S.: 425120

Subsidiary (Domestic):

Anchor Insurance S.A. (2)
Route des Acacias 54, 1227, Geneva, Switzerland
Tel.: (41) 223000435
Insurance Brokers
N.A.I.C.S.: 524210

Joint Venture (Domestic):

Varo Energy Holding S.A. (2)
c/o Vitol Boulevard du Pont d'Arve 28, CH-1205, Geneva, Switzerland (75%)
Tel.: (41) 22 322 1111
Web Site: http://www.varoenergy.com
Holding Company; Petroleum Refining & Marketing Services
N.A.I.C.S.: 551112

Subsidiary (Domestic):

Varo Energy Marketing AG (3)
Industriestrasse 24, Postfach 4713, Zug, 6304, Switzerland
Tel.: (41) 747 23 00
Web Site: http://www.varoenergy.com
Sales Range: $50-74.9 Million
Petroleum Wholesale Trade Distr
N.A.I.C.S.: 425120
Flitch Andras *(Mgr)*

Varo Refining Cressier S.A. (3)
Zone Industrielle Les Hugues, Case Postale 72, CH-2088, Cressier, Switzerland
Tel.: (41) 32 758 6111
Web Site: http://www.varoenergy.com
Sales Range: $50-74.9 Million
Petroleum Refiner
N.A.I.C.S.: 324110
Jilles Vollin *(Dir-Ops)*

Subsidiary (Domestic):

Vitol Central Asia S.A. (2)
Boulevard du Pont d'Arve 28, Geneva, CH-1205, Switzerland
Tel.: (41) 22 322 1111
Petroleum Wholesale Trade Agency
N.A.I.C.S.: 425120

Vitol Refining S.A. (2)
Boulevard du Pont d'Arve 28, CH-1205, Geneva, Switzerland
Tel.: (41) 22 322 1111
Refined Petroleum Wholesale Trade Agency
N.A.I.C.S.: 425120

Vitol Tank Terminals International B.V. (1)
KP van der Mandelelaan 130, PO Box 1546, Rotterdam, 3062 MB, Netherlands

Tel.: (31) 104987200
Web Site: http://www.vtti.com
Holding Company; Storage Terminals Operator
N.A.I.C.S.: 493190
Rob Nijst *(CEO)*

Subsidiary (Non-US):

Antwerp Terminal & Processing Company N.V. (2)
Beliweg 22 Haven 279, B-2030, Antwerp, Belgium
Tel.: (32) 3 303 1600
Oil Bulk Terminal & Refinery
N.A.I.C.S.: 424710
Pascal Demaeijer *(Gen Mgr)*

Vitol Trading Malaysia Labuan Ltd. (1)
Units 5 1 & 5 2 5th Floor Block B PTP Jalan Pelabuhan Tanjung Pelepas, 81560, Gelang Patah, Johor, Malaysia
Tel.: (60) 7 5049 488
Petroleum Product Whslr
N.A.I.C.S.: 424720

Vitol Upstream Ghana Ltd. (1)
H/No 219 North Airport Road Airport West Residential Area, PO Box KIA 30414, Accra, Ghana
Tel.: (233) 302 781 124
Oil & Gas Exploration Services
N.A.I.C.S.: 211120
Akua Ansa-Koram *(CFO)*

Vitol do Brasil Ltda. (1)
Rua do Passeio 70 - 9th Floor Cj 02 - Centro, 154 - 5th Floor, 20021-290, Rio de Janeiro, Brazil
Tel.: (55) 213235 8200
Web Site: http://www.vitol.com
Oil & Gas Exploration Services
N.A.I.C.S.: 211120

Vivo Energy PLC (1)
5th Floor - The Peak 5 Wilton Road, London, SW1V 1AN, United Kingdom
Tel.: (44) 2030343760
Web Site: http://www.vivoenergy.com
Rev.: $6,918,000,000
Assets: $3,268,000,000
Liabilities: $2,456,000,000
Net Worth: $812,000,000
Earnings: $90,000,000
Emp.: 2,698
Fiscal Year-end: 12/31/2020
Petroleum Product Distr
N.A.I.C.S.: 424720
Christian Chammas *(CEO)*

Subsidiary (Non-US):

Societe Malgache des Petroles Vivo Energy S.A. (2)
Batiment B4 Golden Business Center Lot II i I A bis, BP 12029 -101, Morarano Alarobia, Antananarivo, Madagascar
Tel.: (261) 202222728
Fuel Distr
N.A.I.C.S.: 457210
Tahina Ramaromandray *(Mgr-Comml)*

Societe Vivo Energy Tunisie S.A. (2)
24 26 Place du 14 janvier 2011, Tunis, 1001, Tunisia
Tel.: (216) 71120600
Fuel Distr
N.A.I.C.S.: 457210
Rchidi Zied *(Mgr-Territory)*

Vivo Energy Africa Services Sarl (2)
Casablanca Nearshore Park Shore 14 - 2eme Etage 1100 Bd Al Qods, Quartier Sidi Maarouf, 20270, Casablanca, Morocco
Tel.: (212) 522437500
Gasoline Station Operator
N.A.I.C.S.: 457120

Vivo Energy Botswana Pty Ltd. (2)
The Fields Precinct Plot 54349 CBD Office Block B 1st Floor, Corner of Molepolole & Western Commercial Rd Central Business District, Gaborone, Botswana
Tel.: (267) 3953025
Gas Distr
N.A.I.C.S.: 457110
Bokamoso Ethusang *(Country Mgr)*

Vivo Energy Burkina S.A. (2)
Rond Point des Nations Unies 01, BP 569,

Ouagadougou, Burkina Faso
Tel.: (226) 25327600
Gas Distr
N.A.I.C.S.: 457110

Vivo Energy Cabo Verde S.A. (2)
Caixa Postal 4, Sao Vicente, Cape Verde
Tel.: (238) 2307600
Fuel Distr
N.A.I.C.S.: 457210
Moussa Konate *(Mng Dir)*

Vivo Energy Gabon S.A. (2)
234 Boulevard Bessieux, Libreville, Gabon
Tel.: (241) 740101
Fuel & Lubricant Distr
N.A.I.C.S.: 457210
Caroline Manfoumbi *(Bus Mgr-HR Support)*

Vivo Energy Ghana Ltd. (2)
PO Box 1097, Accra, Ghana
Tel.: (233) 302664636
Oil & Natural Gas Distr
N.A.I.C.S.: 457210
Jean Michel Arlandis *(Fin Mgr)*

Vivo Energy Kenya Ltd. (2)
Vienna Court East Wing State House Crescent Road, PO Box 43561, Off State House Avenue, 00100, Nairobi, Kenya
Tel.: (254) 703075555
Emp.: 237
Fuel Distr
N.A.I.C.S.: 457210
Reda Badawi *(Mgr-Retail)*

Vivo Energy Mali S.A. (2)
Route de Koulikoro Immeuble N 3293, BP 199, Bamako, Mali
Tel.: (223) 20219504
Fuel Distr
N.A.I.C.S.: 457210
Aly Oumar Ba *(Mgr-Mining)*

Vivo Energy Maroc S.A. (2)
Immeuble le Zenith II Lotissement Attaoufik Route de Nouasseur, Sidi Maarouf, Casablanca, Morocco
Tel.: (212) 522972727
Gas Distr
N.A.I.C.S.: 457210
Jamal Maarouf *(Mgr-Tax)*

Vivo Energy Mocambique Lda (2)
Rua dos Desportistas n 480 Edificio Maputo Business Tower MBT 11, Maputo, Mozambique
Tel.: (258) 20607220
Fuel Distr
N.A.I.C.S.: 457210
Hermenegildo Penicela *(Controller-Fin)*

Vivo Energy Reunion S.A. (2)
1 Rue Sully Prud homme Z I N02 97420 Port, 97823, Le Port, Cedex, Reunion
Tel.: (262) 262427676
Fuel Distr
N.A.I.C.S.: 457210

Vivo Energy Rwanda Ltd. (2)
M and M Plaza 6th Floor KG 8 AV, PO Box 1342, Kigali, Rwanda
Tel.: (250) 788175100
Fuel Distr
N.A.I.C.S.: 457210

Vivo Energy Senegal S.A. (2)
Route Des Hydrocarbures Quartier Bel Air, BP 144, Dakar RP, 18524, Dakar, Senegal
Tel.: (221) 338493737
Fuel Distr
N.A.I.C.S.: 457210
Kader Maiga *(Mng Dir)*

Vivo Energy Tanzania Limited (2)
Mandela Road Kurasini, PO Box 78470, Dar es Salaam, Tanzania
Tel.: (255) 411200121
Petroleum Product Whslr
N.A.I.C.S.: 424720

Vivo Energy Uganda Ltd. (2)
7th Street Industrial Area Plot 9 11, PO Box 7082, Kampala, Uganda
Tel.: (256) 312210010
Gas Distr
N.A.I.C.S.: 457210

Vivo Energy Zambia Marketing Ltd. (2)
Plot 3132 Buyantanshi Road, PO Box

VITRO, S.A.B. DE C.V.

36521, Lusaka, Zambia
Tel.: (260) 21366660
Fuel & Lubricant Distr
N.A.I.C.S.: 457210
Jean-Blaise Ollomo *(Mng Dir)*

Vivo Energy de Guinee S.A. (2)
Aeroport de Gbessia, BP 312, Conakry, Guinea
Tel.: (224) 631407861
Fuel & Lubricant Distr
N.A.I.C.S.: 457210
Abou Sow *(Mng Dir)*

VITOROG A.D.
Gavrila Principa 1, 70270, Sipovo, Bosnia & Herzegovina
Tel.: (387) 50360420
VTRG—(BANJ)
Sales Range: Less than $1 Million
Grocery Store Operator
N.A.I.C.S.: 445110
Milenko Smanja *(Chm-Mgmt Bd)*

VITRA AG
Klunenfeldstrasse 22, 4127, Birsfelden, Switzerland
Tel.: (41) 61 377 00 00
Web Site: http://www.vitra.com
Year Founded: 1950
Emp.: 1,200
Furniture Mfr
N.A.I.C.S.: 337126
Eckart Maise *(Chief Design Officer)*

Subsidiaries:

Artek Oy AB (1)
Mannerheimintie 12 B 4th Floor, 00100, Helsinki, Finland (100%)
Tel.: (358) 106173410
Web Site: http://www.artek.fi
Sales Range: $25-49.9 Million
Emp.: 75
Furniture Mfr
N.A.I.C.S.: 337126
Marianne Goebl *(Mng Dir)*

VITREOUS GLASS INC.
212 East Lake Boulevard NE, Airdrie, T4A 2G2, AB, Canada
Tel.: (403) 948-7811
Web Site:
https://www.vitreousglass.ca
Year Founded: 1992
VCIGF—(OTCIQ)
Rev.: $7,139,455
Assets: $3,787,720
Liabilities: $815,945
Net Worth: $2,971,776
Earnings: $1,772,698
Fiscal Year-end: 09/30/24
Waste Glass Distr
N.A.I.C.S.: 423930
Barbara Hale *(Chief Compliance & Anti-Money Laundering Officer)*

VITRO, S.A.B. DE C.V.
Ricardo Margain Zozaya No 400
Valle Del Campestre, 66265, Garza Garcia, Nuevo Leon, Mexico
Tel.: (52) 8188631200   MX
Web Site: https://www.vitro.com
Year Founded: 1909
VITRO—(MEX)
Rev.: $2,180,000,000
Assets: $2,794,000,000
Liabilities: $1,364,000,000
Net Worth: $1,430,000,000
Earnings: $64,000,000
Emp.: 15,035
Fiscal Year-end: 12/31/19
Holding Company; Glass, Plastic, Aluminum Containers, Automotive & Architectural Glass, Glassware, Household Appliances & Chemical Products Mfr
N.A.I.C.S.: 551112
Adrian G. Sada Gonzalez *(Chm)*

VITRO, S.A.B. DE C.V.

Vitro, S.A.B. de C.V.—(Continued)

Subsidiaries:

Cristales Automotrices, S.A. de C.V. (1)
Cuauhtemoc 429 Esq Viaducto Miguel Aleman, Col Piedad Narvarte, 03020, Mexico, DF, Mexico
Tel.: (52) 8188631513
Web Site: http://www.vitro.com
Sales Range: $25-49.9 Million
Emp.: 100
Flat Glass Mfr & Distr for Automotive Industry
N.A.I.C.S.: 327211
Jose Antonio Julian *(Gen Mgr)*

Fabricacion de Maquinas S.A. de C.V. (1)
Keramos 225 Colonia Del Prado 6441, 6441, Monterrey, Nuevo Leon, Mexico
Tel.: (52) 8134840786
Web Site: https://fama.com.mx
Glass Products Mfr
N.A.I.C.S.: 327211

Pittsburgh Glass Works, LLC (1)
30 Isabella St Ste 500, Pittsburgh, PA 15212
Tel.: (412) 995-6500
Web Site: https://www.pgwglass.com
Emp.: 4,500
Automotive Glass Products Mfr, Distr & Services
N.A.I.C.S.: 327215

Subsidiary (Non-US):

Pittsburgh Glass Works (Germany) GmbH (2)
Tel.: (49) 7243531960
Glass Product Distr
N.A.I.C.S.: 423220

Pittsburgh Glass Works Poland Sp. z o.o. (1)
Tel.: (48) 223799441
Glass Product Distr
N.A.I.C.S.: 423220

Vidriera Guadalajuara S.A. de C.V. (1)
Calle Libra 225, Fracc Juan Manuel, 45120, Zapopan, Vallarta, Mexico
Tel.: (52) 33 3770 1100
Web Site: http://www.vitro.com
Mfr of Glass Containers
N.A.I.C.S.: 327213

Vidriera Guatemalteca, S.A. (1)
Av Petapa 48-01 Zona 12, Guatemala, 01901, Guatemala
Tel.: (502) 477 5406
Web Site: http://glassonline.it
Mfr of Glass Containers
N.A.I.C.S.: 327213

Vidriera Monterrey, S.A. de C.V. (1)
Magallanes 517 Oriente, Col Trevino, 64570, Monterrey, NL, Mexico (100%)
Tel.: (52) 8188631000
Sales Range: $450-499.9 Million
Emp.: 1,500
Mfr of Glass Containers
N.A.I.C.S.: 327213

Vidrio Lux S.A. (1)
Carretera Santa Cruz Km 3, Casilla, 2954, Cochabamba, Bolivia
Tel.: (591) 4 565 9193
Glass Container Mfr
N.A.I.C.S.: 327213

Vitro Autoglass LLC (1)
400 Guys Run Rd, Cheswick, PA 15024
Web Site: https://vitroautoglass.com
Automotive Glass Mfr
N.A.I.C.S.: 327215

Vitro Automotive S.A. de C.V. (1)
Ave Central 101, 55320, Mexico, Mexico (100%)
Tel.: (52) 5552276100
Web Site: http://www.vitro.com
Sales Range: $200-249.9 Million
Emp.: 1,000
Mfr of Flat Glass
N.A.I.C.S.: 327211

Vitro Chemicals, Fibers & Mining LLC (1)
216 W Village Blvd Ste 102, Laredo, TX 78041
Tel.: (956) 704-1151
Web Site: https://www.vcfm.mx
Chemical Product Mfr & Distr
N.A.I.C.S.: 325180

Vitro Envases, S.A. de C.V. (1)
Mexico-Toluca Highway Km 57 5, El Cocecillo Industrial Zone, 50200, Toluca, Mexico
Tel.: (52) 5550896900
Web Site: https://vitroenvases.com
Glass Products Mfr
N.A.I.C.S.: 327215

Vitro Flex, S.A. de C.V. (1)
Carretera A Garcia, 66000, Garza Garcia, NL, Mexico
Tel.: (52) 8183293700
Sales Range: $200-249.9 Million
Emp.: 800
Safety Glass Mfr & Marketer for Automotive Industry
N.A.I.C.S.: 327211

Vitro Meadville Flat Glass LLC (1)
5123 Victory Blvd, Cochranton, PA 16314
Tel.: (814) 336-4411
Glass Products Mfr
N.A.I.C.S.: 327211

Vitro, Sociedad Anonima (1)
Avenida Ricardo Margain Zozaya 400, Col Valle Del Campestre San Pe, Garza Garcia, 66250, NL, Mexico (100%)
Tel.: (52) 8188631500
Web Site: http://www.vitro.com
Rev.: $25,000,000
Emp.: 150
Capital Goods; Forming Machines for Glass Production, Molds & Ancillary Equipment
N.A.I.C.S.: 333517
Adrian Sada *(Gen Mgr)*

Vitrocar, S.A. de C.V. (1)
Madero 2950 Poniente Colonia Mitras Centro, 64460, Monterrey, Nuevo Leon, Mexico
Tel.: (52) 8001118487
Web Site: https://vitrocar.com.mx
Automotive Glass Mfr
N.A.I.C.S.: 327211

Vitrocrisa, S. de R.L. de C.V. (1)
Roble 660 Col Valle del Campestre, 66265, Garza Garcia, NL, Mexico (100%)
Tel.: (52) 88631600
Web Site: http://www.vitro.com
Sales Range: $50-74.9 Million
Emp.: 200
Mfr of Glassware
N.A.I.C.S.: 327212

VITROLIFE AB

Gustaf Werners Gata 2, SE-421 32, Gothenburg, Sweden
Tel.: (46) 317218000
Web Site: http://www.vitrolife.com
Year Founded: 1994
VITR—(OMX)
Rev.: $302,902,582
Assets: $1,924,845,692
Liabilities: $356,945,498
Net Worth: $1,567,900,194
Earnings: $36,902,788
Emp.: 1,034
Fiscal Year-end: 12/31/22
Stem Cell Cultivation & Transplantation
N.A.I.C.S.: 621491
Fredrik Mattsson *(Sr VP-New Bus & Strategic Dev)*

Subsidiaries:

A.T.S. Srl (1)
Via Pistrucci 26, 20137, Milan, Italy
Tel.: (39) 02 541 22100
Medical Equipment Distr
N.A.I.C.S.: 423450

HertArt Aps (1)
Korskildelund 6 DK, 2670, Greve, Denmark
Tel.: (45) 317218000
Reproductive Health Services
N.A.I.C.S.: 621410

Vitrolife (Beijing) Technical Service Co. Ltd. (1)
A-2006 Focus Square No 6 Futong East Avenue, Chaoyang District, Beijing, 100102, China
Tel.: (86) 1064036613
Biotechnology Lab Product Distr
N.A.I.C.S.: 423490

Vitrolife A/S (1)
Jens Juuls Vej 16, 8260, Viby, Denmark
Tel.: (45) 72217900
Biotechnology Lab Product Distr
N.A.I.C.S.: 423490

Vitrolife BV (1)
Zwaluwstraat 113, 1840, Londerzeel, Belgium
Tel.: (32) 25882468
Biotechnology Lab Product Distr
N.A.I.C.S.: 423490

Vitrolife K.K. (1)
MG Meguro Ekimae 313 2-15-19 Kamiosaki Shinagawa-ku, Minato-ku, Tokyo, 141-0021, Japan
Tel.: (81) 33560 3874
Sales Range: $50-74.9 Million
Emp.: 5
Diagnostic Medical Products Distr
N.A.I.C.S.: 423450
Masaki Inoue *(Mgr-Sls)*

Vitrolife Sweden AB (1)
Gustaf Werners Gata 2, 421 32, Frolunda, Sweden
Tel.: (46) 31 721 80 00
Diagnostic Medical Equipment Mfr
N.A.I.C.S.: 334510
Thomas Axelsson *(Gen Mgr)*

Vitrolife Sweden Instruments AB (1)
Billdalsvagen 2, Billdal, 427 36, Sweden
Tel.: (46) 31 68 77 77
Diagnostic Medical Equipment Mfr & Distr
N.A.I.C.S.: 334510

VITROX CORPORATION BERHAD

746 Persiaran Cassia Selatan 3 Batu Kawan Industrial Park, Bandar Cassia, 14110, Penang, Malaysia
Tel.: (60) 45459988
Web Site: https://www.vitrox.com
VITROX—(KLS)
Rev.: $158,782,857
Assets: $240,878,730
Liabilities: $55,994,497
Net Worth: $184,884,233
Earnings: $42,395,767
Emp.: 826
Fiscal Year-end: 12/31/22
Optical Inspection Equipment Mfr
N.A.I.C.S.: 333310
Ean Hoon Ooi *(Co-Sec)*

Subsidiaries:

Bergen Associates Pvt. Ltd. (1)
305-306 Magnum House-1 Commercial Complex Karampura, New Delhi, India
Tel.: (91) 1125920283
Optical Instrument Mfr
N.A.I.C.S.: 333310

Devon-Tech Technology Co., Ltd. (1)
No 49 Yanku St, Taoyuan Dist, Taoyuan, 330, Taiwan
Tel.: (886) 33576700
Optical Instrument Mfr
N.A.I.C.S.: 333310

Electronic Assembly Products, Ltd. (1)
2950 Production Ct, Dayton, OH 45414
Tel.: (937) 414-6652
Web Site: http://www.eapltd.com
Electronics Mfr
N.A.I.C.S.: 334419

Evotest Inc. (1)
3222 Arden Rd, Hayward, CA 94545
Tel.: (408) 876-6265
Web Site: https://www.evotest.com
Electronics Mfr
N.A.I.C.S.: 334419

INTERNATIONAL PUBLIC

HILPERT Electronics GmbH (1)
Ringstrasse 17, 82223, Eichenau, Germany
Tel.: (49) 814 136 3510
Web Site: https://www.hilpert-electronics.de
Electronics Mfr
N.A.I.C.S.: 334419

MK Technology Trading Limited (1)
1106b block a Qianhai Times Square, Baoan Central District, Shenzhen, China
Tel.: (86) 7552 334 4826
Web Site: https://www.mk-t.com.cn
Consulting Services
N.A.I.C.S.: 541618

MTSC Solution Sdn Bhd (1)
963 Jalan Perusahaan Kawasan Perindustrian Prai Pulau, 13600, Prai, Penang, Malaysia
Tel.: (60) 4 398 3984
Web Site: https://www.mtsc-solution.com
Industrial Equipment Whsr
N.A.I.C.S.: 423830
Tun Chyuan Lim *(Gen Mgr)*

MicroVision Technologies SRL (1)
24 Calea Urseni, Giroc, Timis, Romania
Tel.: (40) 72 916 1419
Web Site: https://www.mvtech.ro
Electronics Mfr
N.A.I.C.S.: 334419

Ming Cheng Integration Technology Co., Ltd. (1)
13F-1 No 46 Zhongshen Rd, North Dist, Hsinchu, 30046, Taiwan
Tel.: (886) 35721398
Optical Instrument Mfr
N.A.I.C.S.: 333310

SISPROD-Sistemas de Producao Electronica, Lda. (1)
Estrada Exterior da Circunvalacao 12252 2 30, Senhora da Hora, 4460-282, Porto, Portugal
Tel.: (351) 22 243 1941
Web Site: http://www.eng.sisprod.com
Equipment Whslr
N.A.I.C.S.: 423490
Ricardo Lopes *(Dir-Comml)*

SMTo Engineering, S.A. de C.V. (1)
Independencia 1018-Edificio 1 Interior 103 Parques del Bosque, San Pedro, 45609, Tlaquepaque, Jalisco, Mexico
Tel.: (52) 331 921 5061
Web Site: https://www.smto.mx
Electronics Mfr
N.A.I.C.S.: 334419
Edie Haro *(Gen Mgr)*

Shanghai Kingtest Electronic Technology Co., Ltd. (1)
Block2A-203 205 OET Park No 69 Weixing Road SIP, Suzhou, China
Tel.: (86) 18626154950
Optical Instrument Mfr
N.A.I.C.S.: 333310

Suzhou Link Ways Tech Co., Ltd. (1)
16F Block B Jin Shi Wang Hu Building No 18 Jia Rui alley SIP, Suzhou, China
Tel.: (86) 51280689962
Optical Instrument Mfr
N.A.I.C.S.: 333310

Tecnolab S.r.l. (1)
Via Legnano 13, 20821, Meda, MB, Italy
Tel.: (39) 036 234 7416
Web Site: https://www.tecnolab-srl.it
Electronics Mfr
N.A.I.C.S.: 334419

ViE Technologies Sdn. Bhd. (1)
746 Persiaran Cassia Selatan 3, Batu Kawan Industrial Park Bandar Cassia, 14110, Penang, Malaysia
Tel.: (60) 45459988
Web Site: https://www.vie.com.my
Sales Range: $50-74.9 Million
Emp.: 200
Electronic Communication Circuit Boards Mfr
N.A.I.C.S.: 334412

ViTrox Technologies (Suzhou) Co., Ltd. (1)
Room 102 -103 Building D No 93 Wei He Road, Wei Ting Town Suzhou Industrial

Park, Suzhou, 215122, Jiangsu, China
Tel.: (86) 51262519891
Optical Instrument Mfr
N.A.I.C.S.: 333310

ViTrox Technologies Sdn. Bhd. (1)
No 85-A Lintang Bayan Lepas 11 Bayan
Lepas Industrial Park Phase 4, Bayan
Lepas, 11900, Penang, Malaysia
Tel.: (60) 46466227
Web Site: http://www.vitrox.com
Sales Range: $50-74.9 Million
Emp.: 200
Automated Vision Inspection Systems Mfr
N.A.I.C.S.: 333310

iNETest (Vietnam) Co. Ltd. (1)
108/105 Tran Van Quang Street, Ward 10
Tan Binh District, Ho Chi Minh City, Vietnam
Tel.: (84) 836016797
Optical Instrument Mfr
N.A.I.C.S.: 333310

VITRU LIMITED
Rodovia Jose Carlos Daux 5500
Torre Jurere A 2nd floor, Saco
Grande State of Santa Catarina, Florianopolis, 88032-005, Brazil
Tel.: (55) 1130472699   Ky
Web Site: https://www.vitru.com.br
Year Founded: 2020
VTRU—(NASDAQ)
Rev.: $253,259,769
Assets: $1,087,957,938
Liabilities: $669,931,653
Net Worth: $418,026,285
Earnings: $17,940,770
Emp.: 10,177
Fiscal Year-end: 12/31/22
Online Education Services
N.A.I.C.S.: 611710
Edson Gustavo Georgette Peli *(Chm)*

Subsidiaries:

UNIASSELVI - Sociedade Educacional Leonardo da Vinci S/S Ltda. (1)
Rua Doutor Pedrinho anexo ao Shopping Vitoria Regia 79 Rio Morto, Indaial, SC, Brazil
Tel.: (55) 8007299009
Web Site: https://portal.uniasselvi.com.br
Educational Support Services
N.A.I.C.S.: 611710

VITRUM INDUSTRIES LTD.
9739 201 St, Langley, V1M 3E7, BC, Canada
Tel.: (604) 882-3513
Web Site: http://www.vitrum.ca
Year Founded: 1997
Rev.: $30,430,733
Emp.: 300
Glass Fabricator Mfr
N.A.I.C.S.: 327215
Bruce Robinson *(Mgr-Sls)*

Subsidiaries:

Vitrum Glass Ltd. (1)
291230 Wagon Wheel Rd, Rocky View County, Calgary, T4A 0E2, AB, Canada
Tel.: (403) 984-6573
Glass Mfr
N.A.I.C.S.: 327212

VITRUVIAN PARTNERS LLP
105 Wigmore Street, London, W1U 1QY, United Kingdom
Tel.: (44) 2075182800   UK
Web Site:
  http://www.vitruvianpartners.com
Year Founded: 2006
Emp.: 100
Privater Equity Firm
N.A.I.C.S.: 523999
Ian Riley *(Co-Founder)*

Subsidiaries:

Independent Media Distribution Plc (1)
Allan House, 10 John Princes St, London,
W1G 0JW, United Kingdom
Tel.: (44) 2074686868
Web Site: http://www.groupimd.com
Sales Range: $10-24.9 Million
Media Logistics Services
N.A.I.C.S.: 541519
Philip McDanell *(Dir-Fin)*

Subsidiary (Non-US):

IMD Adsat Limited (2)
62 Lower Mount St, Dublin, Ireland
Tel.: (353) 16629557
Web Site: http://www.imdadsat.com
Media Distribution Services
N.A.I.C.S.: 541870
Colette Harrop *(Office Mgr)*

Inenco Group Limited (1)
Ribble House Ballam Road, Lytham Saint Anne's, FY8 4TS, Lancashire, United Kingdom
Tel.: (44) 8451463626
Web Site: https://www.inenco.com
Sales Range: $25-49.9 Million
Energy Management & Procurement Services
N.A.I.C.S.: 221122
Richard Harrison *(CEO)*

Division (Domestic):

Inenco Direct (2)
The Corn Exchange, Drury Lane, Liverpool, L2 0PH, United Kingdom
Tel.: (44) 8451442244
Web Site: http://www.inencodirect.com
Electricity & Gas Brokering Services
N.A.I.C.S.: 221122
Michael Abbott *(Mng Dir)*

JacTravel Limited (1)
2nd Floor 3 Shortlands, Hammersmith, London, W6 8DA, United Kingdom
Tel.: (44) 20 8563 7878
Web Site: http://www.news.jactravel.com
Sales Range: $150-199.9 Million
Emp.: 220
Travel Services
N.A.I.C.S.: 561599

Subsidiary (Domestic):

TotalStay Limited (2)
8 Holmes Road, Kentish Town, London, NW5 3AB, United Kingdom
Tel.: (44) 208 8294275
Web Site: http://www.totalstaygroup.com
Sales Range: $1-9.9 Million
Emp.: 70
Travel Arrangement & Reservation Services
N.A.I.C.S.: 561599
Peter Clements *(CEO)*

KCAS, LLC (1)
12400 Shawnee Mission Pkwy, Shawnee, KS 66216
Tel.: (913) 248-3000
Web Site: http://www.kcasbio.com
Bioanalytical Services
N.A.I.C.S.: 541714
John Bucksath *(CEO)*

Meriplex Communications Ltd. (1)
11947 North Fwy, Houston, TX 77060
Tel.: (281) 404-2300
Web Site: http://www.meriplex.com
Rev.: $2,210,000
Emp.: 10
Computer System Design Services
N.A.I.C.S.: 541512
Arthur Henley *(Mgr)*

Subsidiary (Domestic):

Optimum Networking, Inc. (2)
14 Inverness Dr E, Englewood, CO 80112
Tel.: (303) 790-0975
Web Site:
  http://www.optimumnetworking.com
Sales Range: $1-9.9 Million
Emp.: 15
Custom Computer Programming Services
N.A.I.C.S.: 541511
Joseph Turnbough *(CEO)*

Reliable IT, LLC (2)
40 Shattuck Rd Ste 305, Andover, MA 01810
Tel.: (844) 420-3470
Web Site: http://www.reliableitmsp.com
Network Design, Integration, Wireless Technology & Storage Solutions
N.A.I.C.S.: 334112
David Cerce *(Sr Acct Exec)*

Systems Solution Inc. (2)
376 Crooked Ln, King of Prussia, PA 19406
Tel.: (610) 272-4884
Web Site: http://www.ssi-net.com
Rev.: $4,000,000
Emp.: 30
Other Accounting Services
N.A.I.C.S.: 541219
Scott Urosky *(CTO)*

OAG Aviation Worldwide Limited (1)
1 Capability Green, Luton, LU1 3LU, Beds, United Kingdom
Tel.: (44) 1582 695 050
Web Site: http://www.oag.com
Emp.: 200
Holding Company; Air Travel Information & Data Services
N.A.I.C.S.: 551112
Phil Callow *(CEO)*

Subsidiary (Domestic):

OAG Aviation Group Limited (2)
1 Capability Green, Luton, LU1 3LU, Beds, United Kingdom
Tel.: (44) 1582 695050
Web Site: http://www.oag.com
Air Travel Information & Data Services
N.A.I.C.S.: 488190
Stephen Bray *(Mng Dir)*

Subsidiary (US):

OAG Aviation Worldwide LLC (2)
801 Warrenville Rd Ste 555, Lisle, IL 60532
Tel.: (800) 342-5624
Web Site: http://www.oag.com
Travel & Transportation Guides Publisher; Air Travel Information & Data Services
N.A.I.C.S.: 513199

Subsidiary (Domestic):

FlightView, Inc. (3)
55 Chapel St Ste 103, Boston, MA 02458   (100%)
Tel.: (617) 787-4200
Web Site: http://www.flightview.com
Flight Information Services
N.A.I.C.S.: 519290

Phlexglobal Ltd. (1)
Mandeville House 62 The Broadway, Amersham, HP7 0HJ, Bucks, United Kingdom
Tel.: (44) 1494 720420
Web Site: http://www.phlexglobal.com
Emp.: 300
Pharmaceutical Trial Management Services
N.A.I.C.S.: 561110
Peter McNaney *(CTO)*

Subsidiary (US):

Phlexglobal, Inc (2)
400 Chesterfield Pkwy Ste120, Malvern, PA 19355
Tel.: (484) 324-7921
Web Site: http://www.phlexglobal.com
Pharmaceutical Trial Management Services
N.A.I.C.S.: 541511
Leigh Carter *(Mgr-eTMF Ops)*

Tinopolis plc (1)
Tinopolis Centre, Llanelli, SA15 3YE, Carmarthenshire, United Kingdom
Tel.: (44) 2072586800
Web Site: http://www.tinopolis.com
Sales Range: $125-149.9 Million
Emp.: 500
Television & New Media Services
N.A.I.C.S.: 516120
Ron Jones *(Chm)*

Subsidiary (Domestic):

Fiction Factory Ltd. (2)
10 Mount Stewart Square, Cardiff Bay, Cardiff, CF10 5EE, United Kingdom
Tel.: (44) 2920300320
Web Site: http://www.fictionfactoryfilms.com
Sales Range: $25-49.9 Million
Emp.: 5
Motion Picture & Video Production
N.A.I.C.S.: 512110
Ed Thomas *(Mng Dir)*

Mentorn International (2)
Elsinore House, 77 Fulham Palace Road, London, W6 8JA, United Kingdom
Tel.: (44) 2072586800
Web Site:
  http://www.mentorninternational.com
Sales Range: $25-49.9 Million
Emp.: 30
Television Production Company
N.A.I.C.S.: 516120

Subsidiary (Domestic):

Folio London Ltd. (3)
Elsinore House, 77 Fulham Palace Road, London, W68JA, United Kingdom
Tel.: (44) 2072586700
Web Site: http://www.folio.tv
Sales Range: $25-49.9 Million
Television Broadcasting
N.A.I.C.S.: 516120

Subsidiary (Domestic):

Sunset+Vine International Ltd. (2)
77 Fulham Palace Road, London, W6 8JA, United Kingdom
Tel.: (44) 2074787300
Web Site: http://www.sunsetvine.co.uk
Sales Range: $25-49.9 Million
Television Broadcasting
N.A.I.C.S.: 516120
Jeff Foulser *(Chm)*

Video Arts Ltd. (2)
77 Fulham Palace Rd Thomas Smith, W68JA, London, United Kingdom
Tel.: (44) 2074004800
Web Site: http://www.videoarts.com
Sales Range: $25-49.9 Million
Emp.: 15
Interactive, Training & Educational Video Production
N.A.I.C.S.: 512110
Martin Addison *(CEO)*

Travel Counsellors Ltd. (1)
Venus No 1 Old Park Ln, Manchester, M41 7HA, United Kingdom
Tel.: (44) 0161 4645000
Web Site: http://www.travelcounsellors.co.uk
Travel Agency Services
N.A.I.C.S.: 561510
Steve Byrne *(CEO)*

Universal Utilities Limited (1)
Universal House Longley House, Manchester, M22 4SY, United Kingdom
Tel.: (44) 161 946 4440
Web Site: http://www.universalutilities.co.uk
Emp.: 300
Telecommunications Consulting Services
N.A.I.C.S.: 541618
John Drinkwater *(Mgr-Mgmt Info)*

VITRUVIO REAL ESTATE SOCIMI SA
Calle Sagasta 15, 28004, Madrid, Spain
Tel.: (34) 915637159
Web Site:
  http://www.vitruviosocimi.com
YVIT—(MAD)
Sales Range: Less than $1 Million
Real Estate Manangement Services
N.A.I.C.S.: 531390
Joaquin Lopez-Chicheri Morales *(Chm & CEO)*

VITTORIA ASSICURAZIONI S.P.A.
Via Ignazio Gardella 2, 20149, Milan, Italy
Tel.: (39) 0248 2191
Web Site:
  http://www.vittoriaassicurazioni.com
Year Founded: 1921
Rev.: $1,375,350,873
Assets: $4,417,669,673
Liabilities: $169,660,404
Net Worth: $4,248,009,269
Earnings: $93,966,322
Emp.: 540
Fiscal Year-end: 12/31/17
Insurance Services

Vittoria Assicurazioni S.p.A.—(Continued)
N.A.I.C.S.: 524298
Andrea Acutis *(Chm)*

Subsidiaries:

Gestimmobili S.r.l. (1)
Via Caldera 21, Milan, 20149, Italy **(80%)**
Tel.: (39) 0248202263
Sales Range: $50-74.9 Million
Emp.: 4
Real Estate Agency
N.A.I.C.S.: 531210

Interimmobili Srl (1)
Piazza Ungheria 6, 198, Rome, Italy **(80%)**
Tel.: (39) 068842347
Web Site: http://www.interimmobili.it
Real Estate Property Lessors
N.A.I.C.S.: 531190

Plurico S.r.l. (1)
Via Enrico Fermi 58, Verona, Veneto, Italy
Tel.: (39) 0458620338
Web Site: http://ww.plurico.it
Insurance Management Services
N.A.I.C.S.: 524114

Vittoria Immobiliare S.p.A. (1)
Piazza Ungheria 6, Rome, Italy **(87.24%)**
Tel.: (39) 068842347
Web Site: http://www.interimmobili.com
New Housing Operative Builders
N.A.I.C.S.: 236117
Andrea Acutis *(Chm)*

VITTORIA FOOD & BEVERAGE PTY. LIMITED
118 Wetherill St, Silverwater, 2128, NSW, Australia
Tel.: (61) 297480299
Web Site: http://www.vittoriafandb.com
Year Founded: 1958
Emp.: 200
Food & Beverage Distr
N.A.I.C.S.: 424490

VITURA HEALTH LIMITED
Suite 8 Level 3 299 Toorak Road, PO Box 6168, South Yarra, 3141, VIC, Australia
Tel.: (61) 1300799491 AU
Web Site: https://www.vitura.com.au
Year Founded: 2018
VIT—(ASX)
Rev.: $76,510,160
Assets: $30,577,235
Liabilities: $7,820,595
Net Worth: $22,756,639
Earnings: $8,965,455
Emp.: 122
Fiscal Year-end: 06/30/23
Pharmaceutical Product Mfr & Distr
N.A.I.C.S.: 325412
Rodney D. Cocks *(CEO & Exec Dir)*

Subsidiaries:

Cannadoc Health Pty. Ltd. (1)
Level 3 175 Pitt Street, Sydney, 2000, NSW, Australia
Tel.: (61) 1300944033
Web Site: https://cannadoc.com.au
Natural & Plant-Based Medicine Distr
N.A.I.C.S.: 424210

NRT Australia Pty. Ltd. (1)
Sydney Metro City and Southwest, PO Box K659, Haymarket, 1240, NSW, Australia
Tel.: (61) 1800171386
Web Site: https://nrt.com.au
Automated Railway Services
N.A.I.C.S.: 237990

VITZROCELL CO., LTD.
256-41 Dugok-li Sinam-myun, Yesan, Chungcheongnam-do, Korea (South)
Tel.: (82) 413300236
Web Site: http://www.vitzrocell.com
Year Founded: 1987

082920—(KRS)
Rev.: $108,132,381
Assets: $181,918,226
Liabilities: $39,483,143
Net Worth: $142,435,083
Earnings: $17,726,814
Emp.: 389
Fiscal Year-end: 12/31/22
Battery Mfr
N.A.I.C.S.: 335910
Chang Bum-Su *(Dir)*

VITZROSYS CO.
701 7th floor 24 Gasan Digital 2-ro, Geumcheon-gu, Seoul, 3780, Korea (South)
Tel.: (82) 24602000
Web Site: https://www.vitzrosys.com
Year Founded: 1989
054220—(KRS)
Rev.: $15,453,995
Assets: $19,729,249
Liabilities: $6,778,652
Net Worth: $12,950,597
Earnings: $4,897,106
Emp.: 40
Fiscal Year-end: 03/31/22
Monitoring & Control Equipment Mfr
N.A.I.C.S.: 334419
Hyungjin Kim *(Vice Chm & Co-CEO)*

VITZROTECH CO., LTD.
VITZRO B/D 5F 7 Neungdong-ro 25-gil, Gwanjin-gu, Seoul, Gyeonggi-do, Korea (South)
Tel.: (82) 24602021
Web Site: https://www.vitzrotech.com
Year Founded: 1955
042370—(KRS)
Rev.: $297,898,375
Assets: $418,947,956
Liabilities: $127,899,026
Net Worth: $291,048,930
Earnings: $11,556,609
Emp.: 103
Fiscal Year-end: 12/31/21
Power Generating Equipment Mfr
N.A.I.C.S.: 335313

VIVA BIOTECH HOLDINGS
334 Aidisheng Road Zhangjiang Hi-Tech Park, Shanghai, 201203, China
Tel.: (86) 2160893288 Ky
Web Site: http://www.vivabiotech.com
Year Founded: 2008
1873—(HKG)
Rev.: $334,100,192
Assets: $1,112,088,042
Liabilities: $605,986,196
Net Worth: $506,101,846
Earnings: ($70,792,488)
Emp.: 2,601
Fiscal Year-end: 12/31/22
Holding Company
N.A.I.C.S.: 551112
Chen Cheney Mao *(Chm & CEO)*

Subsidiaries:

Ningbo Nuobai Pharmaceutical Co., Ltd. (1)
21 Jiangxia St, Ningbo, 315000, Zhejiang, China
Tel.: (86) 5748 726 0118
Web Site: https://www.nbpharm.com
Pharmaceuticals Product Mfr
N.A.I.C.S.: 325412

VIVA ENERGY GROUP LIMITED
Level 16 720 Bourke Street, Docklands, 3008, VIC, Australia
Tel.: (61) 388234444 AU
Web Site: https://www.vivaenergy.com.au
VEA—(ASX)
Rev.: $17,435,678,425
Assets: $5,921,823,042

Liabilities: $4,610,875,660
Net Worth: $1,310,947,382
Earnings: $2,477,668
Emp.: 700
Fiscal Year-end: 12/31/23
Energy, Oil, Gas & Lubricants Distr
N.A.I.C.S.: 213112
Scott Wyatt *(CEO)*

Subsidiaries:

LyondellBasell Australia Pty Ltd (1)
Level 4 650 Chapel St, South Yarra, 3141, VIC, Australia
Tel.: (61) 398299455
Web Site: http://www.lyondellbasell.com
Sales Range: $25-49.9 Million
Emp.: 40
Polypropylene & Advanced Polyolefins Products Mfr & Sales
N.A.I.C.S.: 325998

Joint Venture (Domestic):

PolyPacific Pty. Ltd. (2)
114-126 Dandenong Valley Highway, Dandenong, 3175, VIC, Australia
Tel.: (61) 397936000
Web Site: http://www.polypacific.com.au
Sales Range: $25-49.9 Million
Polypropylene Compounds Mfr & Marketer; Owned 50% by Basell Australia (Holdings) Pty Ltd & 50% by Mirlex Pty Ltd
N.A.I.C.S.: 325998

VIVA GOLD CORP.
302 - 8047 199 Street, Langley, V2Y 0E2, BC, Canada
Tel.: (303) 519-5149 BC
Web Site: https://www.vivagoldcorp.com
Year Founded: 2009
VAUCF—(OTCQB)
Rev.: $19
Assets: $2,718,707
Liabilities: $906,767
Net Worth: $1,811,940
Earnings: ($2,918,623)
Emp.: 4
Fiscal Year-end: 10/31/22
Investment Services
N.A.I.C.S.: 523999
Christopher Engle Herald *(Chm)*

VIVA GOODS COMPANY LIMITED
Room 3602-06 China Merchants Tower Shun Tak Centre 200 Connaught Road, Central, China (Hong Kong)
Tel.: (852) 37961111 Ky
Web Site: http://www.vivachina.hk
0933—(HKG)
Rev.: $879,799,725
Assets: $2,227,671,203
Liabilities: $825,397,133
Net Worth: $1,402,274,070
Earnings: $111,308,903
Emp.: 5,800
Fiscal Year-end: 12/31/22
Holding Company
N.A.I.C.S.: 551112
Ning Li *(Chm & CEO)*

Subsidiaries:

Bossini International Holdings Limited (1)
2/F PopOffice 9 Tong Yin Street, Tseung Kwan O, Kowloon, China (Hong Kong) **(73.43%)**
Tel.: (852) 23711688
Web Site: http://www.bossini.com
Rev.: $75,473,292
Assets: $66,268,763
Liabilities: $50,752,082
Net Worth: $15,516,681
Earnings: ($17,058,121)
Emp.: 1,000
Fiscal Year-end: 06/30/2022
Apparel Store Operator
N.A.I.C.S.: 458110

Edmund Tak Cheong Mak *(Co-CEO & Exec Dir)*

VIVA LEISURE LIMITED
Unit 5-8 Level 1 141 Flemington Road, PO Box 1, Mitchell, Mitchell Park, 2911, ACT, Australia
Tel.: (61) 261638011 AU
Web Site: https://vivaleisure.group
Year Founded: 2004
VVA—(ASX)
Rev.: $92,053,351
Assets: $292,766,465
Liabilities: $234,071,978
Net Worth: $58,694,487
Earnings: $2,219,166
Emp.: 1,700
Fiscal Year-end: 06/30/23
Fitness Club Operator
N.A.I.C.S.: 713940
Harry Konstantinou *(CEO & Mng Dir)*

Subsidiaries:

HIIT Republic Australia Pty. Limited (1)
4 Lonsdale Street, Braddon, 2612, ACT, Australia
Tel.: (61) 482088028
Web Site: https://www.hiitrepublic.com.au
Fitness Club Operator
N.A.I.C.S.: 713940

Plus Fitness (NZ) Limited (1)
9/43 Masefield Drive, Rolleston, 7614, New Zealand
Tel.: (64) 39259914
Web Site: https://www.plusfitness.co.nz
Fitness Training Services
N.A.I.C.S.: 713940

Plus Fitness Pty. Limited (1)
PO Box 76, Camden Park, 2570, NSW, Australia
Tel.: (61) 246482099
Web Site: https://www.plusfitness.com.au
Gymnasium Operator
N.A.I.C.S.: 713940

VIVA WINE GROUP AB
Blasieholmsgatan 4A, 111 48, Stockholm, Sweden
Tel.: (46) 8218388
Web Site: https://www.vivagroup.se
Year Founded: 1982
VIVA—(OMX)
Rev.: $358,479,000
Assets: $358,479,000
Liabilities: $187,272,000
Net Worth: $171,207,000
Earnings: $25,520,400
Emp.: 333
Fiscal Year-end: 12/31/22
Alcoholic Beverage Distr
N.A.I.C.S.: 424820
Anders Moberg *(Chm)*

Subsidiaries:

Giertz Vinimport AB (1)
Blasieholmsgatan 4A, 111 48, Stockholm, Sweden
Tel.: (46) 851806700
Web Site: https://www.giertz.se
Wine Mfr & Distr
N.A.I.C.S.: 312130

Iconic Wines AB (1)
Blasieholmsgatan 4A, 111 48, Stockholm, Sweden
Tel.: (46) 851806743
Web Site: https://www.iconicwines.se
Wine Mfr & Distr
N.A.I.C.S.: 312130

Norwegian Beverage Group AS (1)
Strandveien 50 Block A2, Lysaker, 1366, Oslo, Norway
Tel.: (47) 21059130
Web Site: https://www.nbgroup.no
Wine Mfr & Distr
N.A.I.C.S.: 312130

The Wine Team Global AB (1)

AND PRIVATE COMPANIES
VIVENDI SE

Blasieholmsgatan 4A, 111 48, Stockholm, Sweden
Tel.: (46) 84060177
Web Site: https://www.wineteam.se
Wine Mfr & Distr
N.A.I.C.S.: 312130

Tryffelsvinet AB (1)
Blasieholmsgatan 4A, 111 48, Stockholm, Sweden
Tel.: (46) 84408588
Web Site: https://tryffelsvinet.se
Wine Mfr & Distr
N.A.I.C.S.: 312130

Vicampo.de GmbH (1)
Taunusstrasse 57, 55118, Mainz, Germany
Tel.: (49) 6131302930
Web Site: https://www.vicampo.de
Wine Mfr & Distr
N.A.I.C.S.: 312130

Vinklubben i Norden AB (1)
Vegagatan 14 c/o Convendum, 113 29, Stockholm, Sweden
Tel.: (46) 703030029
Web Site: https://www.vinklubben.se
Wine Mfr & Distr
N.A.I.C.S.: 312130

Viva Wine & Spirits AB (1)
Blasieholmsgatan 4A, 111 48, Stockholm, Sweden
Tel.: (46) 87788900
Web Site: https://vivawines.se
Wine Mfr & Distr
N.A.I.C.S.: 312130

Wine in Black GmbH (1)
Taunusstrasse 57, D-55118, Mainz, Germany
Tel.: (49) 61319504996
Web Site: https://www.wine-in-black.de
Wine Mfr & Distr
N.A.I.C.S.: 312130

VIVA WORLD TRADE, INC.
Paseo de la Marina 249 Local 1 Marina Vallarta, Mexico, 48335, Jalisco, Mexico
Tel.: (52) 3222090837
Year Founded: 2003
VVWT—(OTCIQ)
Sales Range: Less than $1 Million
Alcoholic Beverage Distr
N.A.I.C.S.: 424820

VIVA! GROUP
Barbaros Bulvari 34100 Balmumcu, Istanbul, Turkiye
Tel.: (90) 2122670022
Web Site: http://www.groupviva.com
Sales Range: $25-49.9 Million
Emp.: 10
Holding Company
N.A.I.C.S.: 551112
Ozean Eruigcn *(Mng Dir)*

Subsidiaries:

BOREAL s.r.l. (1)
Via Staglloni Linora, Paestum Capaccio, 84063, Salerno, Italy
Tel.: (39) 0828 721726
Dairy Products Distr
N.A.I.C.S.: 424430

Viva! Prag (1)
V Celnici 10, 117 21, Prague, Czech Republic
Tel.: (420) 221033401
Casino & Hotel
N.A.I.C.S.: 721120

VIVAA TRADECOM LIMITED
17 Pirana Piplaj Road, Saijpur Gopalpur Piplej, Ahmedabad, 382405, Gujarat, India
Tel.: (91) 7573036727　　　　In
Web Site: https://www.vivaatrade.com
Year Founded: 1995
544002—(BOM)
Emp.: 4
Apparel Product Retailer

VIVAIT INVESTMENT COMPANY LTD.
Borodino Plaza Business Center 13 Rusakovskaya Str Office 10-03, 107140, Moscow, Russia
Tel.: (7) 4952807801
Web Site: http://www.vivait-ic.ru
Year Founded: 1995
Sales Range: Less than $1 Million
Investment Brokerage Services
N.A.I.C.S.: 523150
Alexander Sobolenko *(CEO)*

VIVANCO GRUPPE AG
Ewige Weide 15, 22926, Ahrensburg, Germany
Tel.: (49) 4102 231 0
Web Site: http://www.vivanco.de
Emp.: 180
Electronics Distr
N.A.I.C.S.: 423690
Philipp Oliver Gerding *(CEO)*

VIVANT CORPORATION
9th Floor Oakridge IT Center 3 Oakridge Business Park, A S Fortuna St Banilad Mandaue City, Cebu, 6014, Philippines
Tel.: (63) 322342256
Web Site: https://www.vivant.com.ph
Year Founded: 1990
VVT—(PHI)
Rev.: $149,422,361
Assets: $539,596,184
Liabilities: $185,022,478
Net Worth: $354,573,706
Earnings: $43,223,755
Emp.: 689
Fiscal Year-end: 12/31/23
Eletric Power Generation Services
N.A.I.C.S.: 221118
Ramontito E. Garcia *(Chm & CEO)*

VIVANTA INDUSTRIES LIMITED
402-403 Sarthik - II Nr Kiran Motors Opp RajPath Club S G Road, Ahmedabad, 380054, Gujarat, India
Tel.: (91) 7926870953
Web Site: https://vivantaindustries.com
541735—(BOM)
Rev.: $74,422
Assets: $3,242,662
Liabilities: $1,310,051
Net Worth: $1,932,610
Earnings: ($23,905)
Emp.: 8
Fiscal Year-end: 03/31/21
Construction Services
N.A.I.C.S.: 236220

VIVANZA BIOSCIENCES LTD.
403 Sarthik II S G Road, Ahmedabad, 380054, India
Tel.: (91) 7926870952
Web Site: https://www.vivanzabiosciences.com
Year Founded: 1982
530057—(BOM)
Rev.: $2,192,003
Assets: $2,694,886
Liabilities: $2,204,388
Net Worth: $490,498
Earnings: $71,734
Emp.: 5
Fiscal Year-end: 03/31/23
Pharmaceuticals Product Mfr
N.A.I.C.S.: 325412
Bhaskar Bhattacharya *(Mng Dir)*

VIVARA PARTICIPACOES S.A.
105 Arquiteto Olavo Redig De Campos Street 15 Floor Brooklin Paulista, Sao Paulo, 04709-000, Brazil
Tel.: (55) 1138962736
Web Site: http://www.vivara.com.br
Year Founded: 1962
VIVA3—(BRAZ)
Rev.: $390,943,074
Assets: $579,465,860
Liabilities: $233,794,165
Net Worth: $345,671,695
Earnings: $66,006,068
Fiscal Year-end: 12/31/23
Jewelry Product Retailer
N.A.I.C.S.: 423940
Otavio Chacon Do Amaral Lyra *(CFO & Dir-IR)*

VIVARTE S.A.
28 avenue de Flandre, Paris, 75019, France
Tel.: (33) 1 44 72 30 01
Web Site: http://www.vivarte.com
Year Founded: 1896
Footwear Distr
N.A.I.C.S.: 424340

VIVAT DIRECT LIMITED
157 Edgware Road, Canary Wharf, London, W2 2HR, United Kingdom
Tel.: (44) 207 715 8000　　　UK
Web Site: http://www.readersdigest.co.uk
Sales Range: $75-99.9 Million
Emp.: 300
Magazine Publisher
N.A.I.C.S.: 513120
Gill Hudson *(Editor-in-Chief)*

VIVATICKET
Via A Canova 16/20, 40138, Bologna, Italy
Tel.: (39) 051 588 1511
Web Site: http://www.bestunion.it
Rev.: $60,707,745
Assets: $58,182,089
Liabilities: $43,057,035
Net Worth: $15,125,054
Earnings: $2,549,191
Emp.: 650
Fiscal Year-end: 12/31/16
Event Support Services Including Electronic Ticket Sale, Access Control Software, Hardware & Security Services
N.A.I.C.S.: 711310
Luca Montebugnoli *(Chm)*

Subsidiaries:

AMIT Srl (1)
Viale Manzoni 53, Rome, 00185, Italy
Tel.: (39) 06 48 07 81
Web Site: http://www.amitsrl.it
Music & Entertainment Event Organizers
N.A.I.C.S.: 711310

Charta Srl (1)
Via S Martino 1/a, 48020, Sant'Agata sul Santerno, Ravenna, Italy
Tel.: (39) 0545 915000
Web Site: http://www.charta.it
Ticketing & Entrance Control Services
N.A.I.C.S.: 561599

Omniticket Network Ltd. (1)
15 Borough Road Berkeley Court, Newcastle-under-Lyme, ST5 1TT, Staffordshire, United Kingdom
Tel.: (44) 1782 714300
Web Site: http://www.omniticket.com
Sales Range: $50-74.9 Million
Emp.: 10
Event Organizing Services
N.A.I.C.S.: 711310
John Gibson *(Gen Mgr)*

Omniticket Network Pte Ltd (1)
54B Pagoda Street, Singapore, 059213, Singapore
Tel.: (65) 6635 1180

Sales Range: $50-74.9 Million
Emp.: 5
Event Organizing Services
N.A.I.C.S.: 711310
C. K. Tay *(Gen Mgr)*

Team 2015 Srl (1)
Via Giovanni Masera 10, 20129, Milan, Italy
Tel.: (39) 02 86915332
Web Site: http://www.team2015.it
Educational Event Organizing Services
N.A.I.C.S.: 611710

VIVENDI SE
42 avenue Friedland, 75008, Paris, France
Tel.: (33) 171711000　　　FR
Web Site: https://www.vivendi.com
Year Founded: 1987
VVU—(DEU)
Rev.: $11,342,542,629
Assets: $41,281,027,412
Liabilities: $22,678,609,972
Net Worth: $18,602,417,440
Earnings: $437,081,804
Emp.: 72,958
Fiscal Year-end: 12/31/23
Advertising Media Services
N.A.I.C.S.: 551112
Simon Gillham *(Member-Mgmt Bd & Sr Exec VP-Comm)*

Subsidiaries:

BETC Digital SAS (1)
1 Rue de l'Ancien Canal, 93500, Pantin, France
Tel.: (33) 156418100
Web Site: http://www.betcdesign.fr
Marketing & Advertising Services
N.A.I.C.S.: 541890

Canal+ Group (1)
1 Place du Spectacle, 92863, Issy-les-Moulineaux, Cedex, France
Tel.: (33) 171353535
Web Site: http://www.canalplusgroupe.com
Sales Range: $150-199.9 Million
Emp.: 300
Video, Music & Television Programming Production & Distribution Services
N.A.I.C.S.: 512120
Jean-Christophe Thiery *(Chm-Supervisory Bd)*

Subsidiary (Non-US):

Canal+ Cyfrowy Sp. z oo (2)
al gen W Sikorskiego 9, 02 758, Warsaw, Poland
Tel.: (48) 223282701
Pay Television Services
N.A.I.C.S.: 516120

Subsidiary (Domestic):

Canal+ France (2)
1 Place du Spectacle, 92130, Issy-les-Moulineaux, France　　　(80%)
Tel.: (33) 32329211734
Web Site: http://www.canalplus.com
Sales Range: $750-799.9 Million
Cable Television Broadcasting Services
N.A.I.C.S.: 516120

Subsidiary (Non-US):

Canal Digital (3)
Stationsparken 26 2, 2600, Glostrup, Denmark　　　(100%)
Tel.: (45) 70131919
Web Site: http://www.canaldigital.dk
Sales Range: $25-49.9 Million
Emp.: 60
Pay Television Services
N.A.I.C.S.: 812990

Canal Satelite Digital S.L (3)
Avenida Artesanos 6, 28760, Tres Cantos, Madrid, Spain　　　(100%)
Tel.: (34) 917367000
Web Site: http://www.plus.es
Sales Range: $50-74.9 Million
Emp.: 200
Pay Television Services
N.A.I.C.S.: 516120

Canal+ Belgium (3)

VIVENDI SE

Vivendi SE—(Continued)
Chaussee de Louvain, 656, 1030, Brussels, Belgium
Tel.: (32) 27304050
Web Site: http://www.canalplus.be
Sales Range: $50-74.9 Million
Emp.: 200
Provider of Pay Television Services
N.A.I.C.S.: 516120

Subsidiary (Domestic):

Canal+ Distribution S.A.S. (3)
1 Place du Spectacle, Issy-les-Moulineaux, 92863, France
Tel.: (33) 1 71 35 35 35
Television Broadcasting Services
N.A.I.C.S.: 516120
Guy Lafarge (CEO)

Subsidiary (Non-US):

Canal+ Finland (3)
Kutomotie 18 B, 00380, Helsinki, Finland
Tel.: (358) 941332300
Web Site: http://www.canalplus.fi
N.A.I.C.S.: 812990

Canal+ Flanders (3)
Tollaan 97, 1932, Saint-Stevens-Woluwe, Belgium
Tel.: (32) 2 174 1818
N.A.I.C.S.: 812990

Canal+ Norway (3)
Brynsveien 13, PO Box 80, 611, Oslo, Norway (100%)
Tel.: (47) 22939333
Web Site: http://www.canalplus.no
Sales Range: $25-49.9 Million
Emp.: 10
N.A.I.C.S.: 812990

Subsidiary (Domestic):

Canal+ Overseas S.A.S. (3)
48 Quai du Point du Jour, 92659, Boulogne-Billancourt, France
Tel.: (33) 141861515
Web Site:
 http://www.canalplus-overseas.com
Rev.: $607,839,400
Television Broadcasting Services
N.A.I.C.S.: 516120
Jacques-Aymar de Roquefeuil (Sr VP-Mktg & Ops)

Subsidiary (Non-US):

Canal+ Caledonie (4)
30 bis rue de la Somme Immeuble City Bay, BP 1797, 98845, Nouméa, New Caledonia
Tel.: (687) 26 53 20
Web Site: http://www.canalplus-caledonie.com
Television Broadcasting Services
N.A.I.C.S.: 516120

Canal+ Cameroun (4)
Immeuble Hibiscus 38 Vallee des Ministres Bonanjo, BP 72, Douala, Cameroon
Tel.: (237) 77 11 45 01
Web Site: http://www.canalplus-afrique.com
Television Broadcasting Services
N.A.I.C.S.: 516120

Canal+ Madagascar (4)
Immeuble KUBE D 3eme Etage Galaxy Andraharo, BP 3021, Antananarivo, Madagascar
Tel.: (261) 20 22 39 473
Web Site: http://www.canalplus-madagascar.com
Television Broadcasting Services
N.A.I.C.S.: 516120

Subsidiary (Domestic):

Canal+ Overseas Productions (4)
Espace Lumiere - Batiment E 48 Quai du Point du Jour, 92659, Boulogne-Billancourt, France
Tel.: (33) 1 41 86 15 15
Web Site: http://www.canalplus-overseas.com
Television Broadcasting Services
N.A.I.C.S.: 516120

Subsidiary (Non-US):

Canal+ Senegal (4)
31 Avenue Albert Sarraut, BP 1390, Dakar, Senegal
Tel.: (221) 33 889 50 50
Web Site: http://www.canalplus-overseas.com
Television Broadcasting Services
N.A.I.C.S.: 516120

Subsidiary (Domestic):

Canal+ SA (3)
1 place du spectacle, 92130, Issy-Moulineaux, Cedex 9, France (100%)
Tel.: (33) 892393910
Web Site: http://www.canalplus.com
Pay Television Services
N.A.I.C.S.: 516120
Marc-Andre Feffer (Gen Counsel)

Subsidiary (Non-US):

Canal+ Sweden (3)
Tegeluddsvagen 3, 11584, Stockholm, Sweden (100%)
Tel.: (46) 84592800
Web Site: http://www.canalplus.se
Sales Range: $25-49.9 Million
Emp.: 60
N.A.I.C.S.: 812990

Subsidiary (Domestic):

MultiThematiques (3)
48 Quai du Point du Jour, 92659, Boulogne-Billancourt, Cedex, France (64%)
Tel.: (33) 171101112
Sales Range: $100-124.9 Million
Emp.: 300
Broadcaster of Thematic Television Channels
N.A.I.C.S.: 516120

Unit (Domestic):

Canal Jimmy (4)
513 Blvd Da La Levtublique, 92100, Paris, Boulogme, France (100%)
Tel.: (33) 71353535
Web Site: http://www.canaljimmy.fr
Sales Range: $25-49.9 Million
Emp.: 150
Provider of Pay Television Services
N.A.I.C.S.: 516120

Cine-Cinema Cable (4)
5 Blvd Da La Levtublique, 92130, Boulogne, France (100%)
Tel.: (33) 171353535
Web Site: http://www.cinecinema.fr
Sales Range: $75-99.9 Million
Emp.: 300
Pay Television Services
N.A.I.C.S.: 516210

Subsidiary (Domestic):

Canal+ Regie (2)
5-13 bd de la Republique, 92 100, Boulogne-Billancourt, France
Tel.: (33) 1 71 35 35 35
Web Site: http://www.canalplusregie.fr
Television Broadcasting Services
N.A.I.C.S.: 516120

Subsidiary (Non-US):

Cyfra+ (2)
Ul Gen W Sikorskiego 9, 02758, Warsaw, Poland
Tel.: (48) 22 3282 701
Web Site: http://www.cyfraplus.pl
Television Broadcasting Services
N.A.I.C.S.: 516120

Subsidiary (Domestic):

Groupe Canal+ S.A. (2)
50 rue Camille Desmoulins, 92863, Issy-les-Moulineaux, France

I Television (2)
6 Allee De La 2 Eme DB, 75015, Paris, France (100%)
Tel.: (33) 153915000
Web Site: http://www.itele.fr
Sales Range: $25-49.9 Million
Emp.: 100
Provider of Pay Television Services
N.A.I.C.S.: 517111
Tierre Fraidenraich (CEO)

Joint Venture (Domestic):

Mezzo S.A. (2)
28 rue Francois 1er, 75008, Paris, France (50%)
Tel.: (33) 1 56 36 51 00
Web Site: http://www.mezzo.tv
Sales Range: $25-49.9 Million
Emp.: 11
Television Broadcasting Services
N.A.I.C.S.: 516120
Christophe Winckel (Mng Dir)

Subsidiary (Domestic):

STUDIOCANAL SA (2)
1 Place du Spectacle, 92130, Issy-les-Moulineaux, France
Tel.: (33) 71359535
Web Site: http://www.studiocanal.com
Sales Range: $150-199.9 Million
Production & Distribution of Films; Acquisition of Film Broadcast Rights
N.A.I.C.S.: 512120
Kalle Friz (CEO-Germany)

Subsidiary (Non-US):

N'Wave Studios S.A. (3)
282 Rue Des Allies, Brussels, 1190, Belgium
Tel.: (32) 2 347 63 19
Web Site: http://www.nwave.com
Emp.: 100
Video Production & Distribution Services
N.A.I.C.S.: 512110

Tandem Communications GmbH (3)
Sonnenstrasse 14, Munich, 80331, Germany
Tel.: (49) 89 96 22 83 00
Web Site: http://www.tandemcom.de
Television Broadcasting Services
N.A.I.C.S.: 516120
Rola Bauer (Founder)

Subsidiary (Domestic):

i)Tele (2)
6 Allee de la 2e DB, 75015, Paris, France
Tel.: (33) 1 53 91 50 00
Web Site: http://www.itele.fr
Television Broadcasting Services
N.A.I.C.S.: 516120

Dailymotion S.A. (1)
140 boulevard Malesherbes, 75017, Paris, France (90%)
Tel.: (33) 1 7735 1100
Web Site: http://www.dailymotion.com
Online Video Sharing Services
N.A.I.C.S.: 518210
Maxime Saada (CEO & Dir-Publ)

Gameloft Corporation (1)
14 rue Auber, 75009, Paris, France (95.77%)
Tel.: (33) 153162040
Web Site: http://www.gameloft.com
Sales Range: $250-299.9 Million
Game Software Publisher
N.A.I.C.S.: 513210
Baudouin Corman (COO)

Subsidiary (Non-US):

Gameloft Co., Ltd. (2)
230 Pangyoeok-Ro, Bundang-Gu, Seongnam, 135-280, Kyunggi-Do, Korea (South) (100%)
Tel.: (82) 7048480336
Web Site: http://www.gameloft.com
Software Games Publisher
N.A.I.C.S.: 513210
Misun Kim (Officer-PR)

Gameloft KK (2)
4F Shimomoto Bldg 1-46-3 Hatsudai, Shibuya-ku, Tokyo, 151-0061, Japan (100%)
Tel.: (81) 353584620
Web Site: http://www.gameloft.com
Gaming Software Publisher
N.A.I.C.S.: 513210
Kentaro Matsushita (Dir-Mktg)

Subsidiary (US):

Gameloft, Inc. (2)
156 5th Ave, New York, NY 10010 (100%)
Tel.: (212) 993-3000

INTERNATIONAL PUBLIC

Web Site: http://www.gameloft.com
Game Software Publisher
N.A.I.C.S.: 513210

Gameloft Iberica S.A. (1)
C/ Napoles 249 Planta 6, 08013, Barcelona, Spain
Tel.: (34) 933687107
Game Development Services
N.A.I.C.S.: 513210

Gameloft Software Beijing Ltd. (1)
B-5 Zhongguo Dianzi Dasha, Beijing, China
Tel.: (86) 1082607783
Game Development Services
N.A.I.C.S.: 513210

Groupe Telindus France SA (1)
12 avenue de l Oceanie ZA Courtaboeuf 3, Les Ulis, 91940, Essonne, France
Tel.: (33) 169183232
Web Site: http://www.telindus.fr
Sales Range: $300-349.9 Million
Emp.: 790
Information Technology Consulting Services
N.A.I.C.S.: 541512
Rhenry Juin (Mng Dir)

Havas S.A. (1)
29 30 quai de Dion Bouton, FR-92817, Puteaux, Cedex, France (59.2%)
Tel.: (33) 1 58 47 80 00
Web Site: http://www.havas.com
Advertising, Communications & Media Buying Services
N.A.I.C.S.: 541810

Subsidiary (Domestic):

FullSIX Group (2)
1-13 Rue de l Ancien Canal, 93500, Pantin, Cedex, France
Tel.: (33) 156413500
Web Site: http://www.fullsix.fr
Emp.: 600
Marketing Services
N.A.I.C.S.: 541613

HAVAS 10 (2)
29 Quai De Dion Bouton, 92800, Puteaux, France
Tel.: (33) 158478000
Marketing Research Service
N.A.I.C.S.: 541910

HAVAS EDITION (2)
29/30 quai de Dion Bouton, 92800, Puteaux, France
Tel.: (33) 146931680
Web Site: https://www.havasedition.com
Online Marketing Services
N.A.I.C.S.: 541613

HAVAS EVENTS (2)
29-30 Quai de Dion Bouton, 92800, Puteaux, France
Tel.: (33) 158478000
Web Site: http://www.havasevents.com
Emp.: 100
Event Organizing Services
N.A.I.C.S.: 711310

HAVAS FINANCES SERVICES SNC (2)
29/30 Quai de Dion Bouton, 92800, Puteaux, France
Tel.: (33) 158478000
Emp.: 11
Financial Services
N.A.I.C.S.: 523999

HAVAS IT (2)
29/30 Quai de Dion Bouton, 92800, Puteaux, France
Tel.: (33) 158478810
Information Technology Consulting Services
N.A.I.C.S.: 541512

Subsidiary (Non-US):

HAVAS MANAGEMENT ESPANA, S.L. (2)
Avenida General Peron 38, Madrid, 28020, Spain
Tel.: (34) 914569000
Business Management Consulting Services
N.A.I.C.S.: 541611

Subsidiary (Domestic):

HERCULES (2)

AND PRIVATE COMPANIES — VIVENDI SE

2bis rue Godefroy, 92800, Puteaux, France
Tel.: (33) 158479594
Web Site: https://www.hrcls.fr
Advertising Agencies
N.A.I.C.S.: 541810

Group (Domestic):

Havas Creative Group (2)
29-30 Quai de Dion Bouton, 92800, Puteaux, France
Tel.: (33) 146933333
Web Site: http://havascreative.com
Advertising Services
N.A.I.C.S.: 541810

Subsidiary (US):

Arnold Worldwide (3)
10 Summer St, Boston, MA 02199-7603
Tel.: (617) 587-8000
Web Site: http://www.arn.com
Advertising & Brand Development Services
N.A.I.C.S.: 541810
Sean McBride *(Chief Creative Officer)*

Subsidiary (Non-US):

Arnold KLP Ltd. (4)
Havas House Hermitage Court Hermitage Lane, Maidstone, ME16 9NT, Kent, United Kingdom
Tel.: (44) 20 7079 2200
Web Site: http://www.arn.com
Advertising Services
N.A.I.C.S.: 541810

Branch (Domestic):

ArnoldNYC (4)
200 Hudson St, New York, NY 10013
Tel.: (212) 463-1000
Web Site: http://arn.com
Advertising Services
N.A.I.C.S.: 541810
Laura Voigt *(Sr VP)*

Subsidiary (Non-US):

W&Cie (4)
1 cours de I ile Seguin, 92650, Boulogne-Billancourt, France
Tel.: (33) 1 72 27 00 00
Web Site: http://www.wcie.fr
Advertising Agency Services
N.A.I.C.S.: 541810

Subsidiary (Domestic):

Buzzman SAS (3)
126 Rue La Fayette, 75010, Paris, France (51%)
Tel.: (33) 158603610
Web Site: http://www.buzzman.fr
Advertising, Social Media & Viral Mktg
N.A.I.C.S.: 541810

Subsidiary (US):

Havas Worldwide, LLC (3)
200 Hudson St, New York, NY 10013-4504
Tel.: (212) 886-4100
Web Site: https://www.havas.com
Holding Company; Advertising Agencies
N.A.I.C.S.: 551112
Steve Netzney *(CEO)*

Affiliate (US):

ASL Marketing, LLC (4)
500 Bi County Blvd Ste 460, Farmingdale, NY 11735
Tel.: (516) 248-6100
Web Site: https://www.aslmarketing.com
Advertising Services
N.A.I.C.S.: 541860
Steven Stolls *(Exec VP)*

Subsidiary (Domestic):

H/Advisors Abernathy (4)
277 Park Ave 39th Fl, New York, NY 10172
Tel.: (212) 371-5999
Web Site: http://www.abmac.com
Public Relations Agency
N.A.I.C.S.: 541820
Carina C. Davidson *(Pres)*

Branch (Domestic):

The Abernathy MacGregor Group, Inc. - Los Angeles (5)
707 Wilshire Blvd Ste 3950, Los Angeles, CA 90017-3110
Tel.: (213) 630-6550
Web Site: http://www.abernathymacgregor.com
Public Relations & Communications
N.A.I.C.S.: 541820
Amy Shih-Hua Feng *(Executives)*

Subsidiary (Domestic):

Havas Discovery, LLC (4)
36 E Grand Ave Ste 3 & 4, Chicago, IL 60610
Tel.: (312) 640-6800
Web Site: http://www.havasheliana.com
Advertising Services
N.A.I.C.S.: 541810

Branch (Domestic):

Havas Discovery, LLC - Baltimore (5)
700 E Pratt Street Ste 1050, Baltimore, MD 21202-6174
Tel.: (410) 230-3700
Web Site: http://www.havasheliana.com
Advertising Services
N.A.I.C.S.: 541810

Havas Discovery, LLC - Richmond (5)
4860 Cox Road Ste 120, Glen Allen, VA 23060
Tel.: (804) 968-7400
Web Site: http://www.havasheliana.com
Advertising Services
N.A.I.C.S.: 541810

Subsidiary (Domestic):

Havas Edge LLC (4)
2386 Faraday Ave Ste 200, Carlsbad, CA 92008
Tel.: (760) 929-0041
Web Site: http://www.havasedge.com
Advertising Services
N.A.I.C.S.: 541810
Steve Netzley *(CEO-Edge Performance Network)*

Subsidiary (Domestic):

Havas Edge Boston LLC (5)
10 Summer St, Boston, MA 02110
Tel.: (617) 585-3000
Web Site: http://www.havasedge.com
Advertising Agencies
N.A.I.C.S.: 541810

Subsidiary (Domestic):

Havas Formula, LLC (4)
1215 Cushman Ave, San Diego, CA 92110
Tel.: (619) 234-0345
Web Site: http://havasformula.com
Public Relations & Communications Agency
N.A.I.C.S.: 541820
Ditas Mauricio *(Exec VP-Consumer-West)*

Branch (Domestic):

Havas Formula - El Segundo (5)
810 Parkview Dr N, El Segundo, CA 90245
Tel.: (310) 578-7050
Web Site: http://www.havasformula.com
Public Relations & Communications Agency
N.A.I.C.S.: 541820

Havas Formula - New York (5)
200 Hudson St, New York, NY 10013
Tel.: (212) 886-4100
Web Site: http://www.havasformula.com
Public Relations & Communications Agency
N.A.I.C.S.: 541820

Subsidiary (Domestic):

Havas Health, Inc. (4)
200 Madison Ave Fl 7, New York, NY 10016-3907
Tel.: (212) 532-1000
Web Site: http://www.havashealthandyou.com
Advertising Services
N.A.I.C.S.: 541810

Subsidiary (Domestic):

Symbiotix, LLC (5)
4040 Finn Way Ste 340, Lexington, KY 40517
Tel.: (859) 236-7942
Web Site: http://www.symbiotix.com
Management Consulting Services for Healthcare Industry
N.A.I.C.S.: 541611
Jo Ann Rice *(Co-Founder)*

Subsidiary (Domestic):

Havas Impact, LLC (4)
36 E Grand Ave, Chicago, IL 60611-3506
Tel.: (312) 799-7000
Web Site: http://www.annexexp.com
Advertising Services
N.A.I.C.S.: 541810
Ralph Hollingsworth *(Exec Creative Dir)*

Unit (Domestic):

Havas Impact, LLC - Operations & Training Center
2885 Pacific Dr Ste A, Norcross, GA 30071-1807
Tel.: (770) 263-0500
Web Site: http://www.annexexp.com
Advertising Services
N.A.I.C.S.: 541810
Brent Lamkin *(COO)*

Group (Domestic):

Havas Life (4)
11 E 35th St, New York, NY 10016
Tel.: (212) 532-1000
Web Site: http://havaslifenewyork.com
Advetising Agency
N.A.I.C.S.: 541810
Elizabeth Nabors Elizabeth Nabors *(Asst Project Mgr)*

Unit (Non-US):

Havas Brussels (5)
Rue des Boiteux 9 1000, 1180, Brussels, Belgium
Tel.: (32) 2 348 38 00
Web Site: http://www.be.havas.com
Health Care Advertising
N.A.I.C.S.: 541810
David Grunewald *(CEO)*

Havas Japan (5)
Tokyo Tatemono Aoyama Building 4th Floor 3-3-5 Kitaaoyama, Minato-ku, Tokyo, 107-0061, Japan
Tel.: (81) 3 6438 1350
Web Site: http://www.havas.com
Healthcare Advertising Services
N.A.I.C.S.: 541810

Havas Lemz BV (5)
Stadhouderskade 1, 1054 ES, Amstelveen, Netherlands
Tel.: (31) 204 565 000
Web Site: http://www.havaslemz.com
Advertising Services
N.A.I.C.S.: 541810

Havas Life - Lisbon (5)
Avenida da Liberdade 252, 1250-149, Lisbon, Portugal
Tel.: (351) 21 891 0600
Web Site: http://www.havas.pt
Advertising Services
N.A.I.C.S.: 541810
Carlos Guedes *(Mng Dir)*

Havas Life - Munich (5)
Lessingstr 11, Munich, 80336, Germany
Tel.: (49) 89 49067 0
Web Site: http://www.de.havas.com
Advertising Services
N.A.I.C.S.: 541810
Kris Vilhelmsson *(CEO)*

Havas Life - Paris (5)
29/30 quai de Dion Bouton, Puteaux, 92817, France
Tel.: (33) 616 124 115
Web Site: http://www.havashealthandyou.fr
Advertising Services
N.A.I.C.S.: 541810
Loris Repellin *(CEO)*

Havas Life AB (5)
Jakobsgatan 7, 10462, Stockholm, Sweden
Tel.: (46) 8 410 663 00
Web Site: http://www.bizkithavas.se
Advertising & Brand Strategy Services
N.A.I.C.S.: 541810

Havas Life Italy S.r.l. (5)
Via San Vito 7, 20123, Milan, Italy
Tel.: (39) 0220526328
Web Site: http://www.havaslife.it
Advertising Services
N.A.I.C.S.: 541810

Havas Life Medicom (5)
Ferry Works Summer Road, Thames Ditton, KT7 0QJ, Surrey, United Kingdom
Tel.: (44) 2084818100
Web Site: http://www.havaslifemedicom.com
Medical Communication Services
N.A.I.C.S.: 517810
Gaynor Hayburn *(Grp Mng Dir)*

Unit (Domestic):

Havas Life Metro - Chicago (5)
36 E Grand Ave, Chicago, IL 60611
Tel.: (312) 640-6800
Web Site: http://www.havaslifechicago.com
Advertising Services
N.A.I.C.S.: 541810

Havas Life Metro - New York (5)
200 Madison Ave, New York, NY 10016
Tel.: (212) 532-1000
Web Site: http://www.havashealthandyou.com
Advetising Agency
N.A.I.C.S.: 541810

Unit (Non-US):

Havas Life PR - Paris (5)
29/30 quai de Dion Bouton, 92817, Puteaux, France
Tel.: (33) 6 14 45 05 22
Web Site: http://havaspr.com
Public Relations Services
N.A.I.C.S.: 541820

Havas Life S.A. (5)
Calle Eloy Gonzalo 10 - Planta 2, 28010, Madrid, Spain
Tel.: (34) 913302323
Web Site: http://www.havasvillage.es
Advertising Services
N.A.I.C.S.: 541810

Havas Life Toronto (5)
Suite 300 473 Adelaide Street West, Toronto, M5V 1T1, ON, Canada
Tel.: (416) 933-4791
Web Site: http://havashealthandyou.com
Healthcare Advertising Services
N.A.I.C.S.: 541810

Havas Village Bogota (5)
Carrera 7 No 71-21 Torre A Piso 12, Edificio Avenida Chile, Bogota, 110221, Colombia
Tel.: (57) 13173010
Web Site: http://www.havasgroup.com.co
Advertising Services
N.A.I.C.S.: 541810

Group (Domestic):

Havas PR North America, Inc. (4)
200 Madison Ave, New York, NY 10016
Tel.: (212) 367-6800
Web Site: http://www.havaspr.com
Public Relations Agencies
N.A.I.C.S.: 541820
James Wright *(CEO)*

Group (Non-US):

Havas Worldwide Asia Pacific (4)
80 Robinson Road 20-01, Singapore, 048624, Singapore
Tel.: (65) 63176600
Web Site: http://www.havas.com
Regional Managing Office; Advertising Agency
N.A.I.C.S.: 551114

Subsidiary (Domestic):

Havas Singapore Pte. Ltd (5)
80 Robinson Road 20-02, Singapore, 068898, Singapore
Tel.: (65) 63176600
Web Site: https://sg.havas.com
Advertising Agency Services
N.A.I.C.S.: 541810

VIVENDI SE

Vivendi SE—(Continued)

Subsidiary (Non-US):

Havas Worldwide (Creative) India Pvt. Ltd. (5)
Valencia Bldg 4th Floor Raj Kamal Marg, Off Dr SS Rao Road Parel, Mumbai, 400012, India
Tel.: (91) 22 6177 6177
Web Site: http://www.in.havas.com
Advetising Agency
N.A.I.C.S.: 541810
Ravinder Siwach *(Exec Dir & Natl Creative Dir)*

Subsidiary (Domestic):

Havas Creative Bangalore (6)
#124 Surya Chambers 6th Floor Old Airport Road, Murugesh Pallya, Bengaluru, 560017, India
Tel.: (91) 22 6177 6177
Web Site: http://www.in.havas.com
Advertising Services
N.A.I.C.S.: 541810

Havas Creative Gurgaon (6)
6th Floor Tower C Building No 8 DLF Cyber City Phase III, Gurgaon, 122002, India
Tel.: (91) 124 468 4400
Web Site: http://www.havasworldwide.co.in
Advertising Services
N.A.I.C.S.: 541810
Nima D. T. Namchu *(Chief Creative Officer)*

Havas Creative Mumbai (6)
24th Floor Commerz II International Business Park Oberoi Garden City, Off Western Express Highway Goregaon East, Mumbai, 400063, India
Tel.: (91) 22 6177 6177
Web Site: http://www.in.havas.com
Advertising Services
N.A.I.C.S.: 541810

Subsidiary (Non-US):

Havas Worldwide Japan K.K. (5)
Tokyo Tatemono Aoyama Building 4th Floor 3-3-5 Kitaaoyama, Minato-ku, Tokyo, 107-0061, Japan
Tel.: (81) 364381350
Web Site: http://www.jp.havas.com
Advertising Agency Services
N.A.I.C.S.: 541810

Havas Worldwide Korea Co., Ltd. (5)
4F ILSHIN Bldg 98 Hannam-daero, Yongsan-gu, Seoul, 04418, Korea (South)
Tel.: (82) 2 757 3303
Web Site: http://www.havas.com
Advertising Services
N.A.I.C.S.: 541810

Porda Havas International Finance Communications Group Holdings Co., Ltd. (5)
Unit 2301 23/F The Centrium, 60 Wyndham Street, Central, China (Hong Kong)
Tel.: (852) 31506788
Web Site: http://www.pordahavas.com
Public Relations Services
N.A.I.C.S.: 541820
James Chang *(Founder)*

Subsidiary (Domestic):

Havas Worldwide Chicago, Inc. (4)
36 E Grand Ave, Chicago, IL 60611-3506
Tel.: (312) 337-4200
Web Site: http://www.chi.havas.com
Advetising Agency
N.A.I.C.S.: 541810

Havas Worldwide Dallas, LLC (4)
2800 N Dallas Pkwy Ste 300, Plano, TX 75093
Tel.: (972) 473-5600
Web Site: http://www.havas.com
Advertising Services
N.A.I.C.S.: 541810

Group (Non-US):

Havas Worldwide Europe & Africa (4)
29-30 quai de Dion Boulton, 92800, Puteaux, Cedex, France
Tel.: (33) 158479048
Web Site: http://www.havasparis.com
Regional Managing Office; Advertising Agencies
N.A.I.C.S.: 551114

Subsidiary (Domestic):

BETC (5)
1 Rue de l'Ancien Canal, 93500, Paris, Cedex, France
Tel.: (33) 1 56 41 35 00
Web Site: http://betc.com
Sales Range: $10-24.9 Million
Advertising Services
N.A.I.C.S.: 541810
Remi Babinet *(Co-Founder)*

Subsidiary (Non-US):

Conran Design Group Ltd. (5)
3 Pancras Square Kings Cross, London, N1C 4AG, United Kingdom
Tel.: (44) 2031968607
Web Site: http://conrandesigngroup.com
Advertising Services
N.A.I.C.S.: 541810
Thom Newton *(CEO)*

Difusion y Audiencias (5)
Av Diagonal 575 Edificio L'Illa, Escalera 2 P11, 08029, Barcelona, Spain
Tel.: (34) 932064980
Web Site: http://www.difusionyaudiencias.com
Advertising Agency Services
N.A.I.C.S.: 541810

Difusion y Audiencias (5)
Calle Eloy Gonzalo 10, 28020, Madrid, Spain
Tel.: (34) 91 330 23 23
Web Site: http://www.difusionyaudiencias.com
Advertising Agency Services
N.A.I.C.S.: 541810

Granath Havas Worldwide (5)
Peter Myndes Backe 8, PO Box 17089, 104 62, Stockholm, Sweden
Tel.: (46) 852246000
Web Site: http://www.granathreklam.se
Advertising Services
N.A.I.C.S.: 541810
David Granath *(CEO)*

H4B London Limited (5)
Havas House Hermitage Court, Hermitage Lane, Maidstone, ME16 9NT, Kent, United Kingdom
Tel.: (44) 2073793991
Web Site: http://havashealthandyou.com
Advertising Services
N.A.I.C.S.: 541810

Havas AG (5)
Morgartenstrasse 6, 8004, Zurich, Switzerland
Tel.: (41) 444666777
Web Site: http://www.swiss.havas.com
Advertising Agency
N.A.I.C.S.: 541810
Patrick Beeli *(Creative Dir)*

Havas Danmark A/S (5)
Langebrogade 6E 4, 1411, Copenhagen, K, Denmark
Tel.: (45) 77334400
Web Site: http://dk.havas.com
Advetising Agency
N.A.I.C.S.: 541810
Johnny Twile *(CEO)*

Havas Design + Portugal Lda. (5)
Avenida da Liberdade n 252, Parque das Nacoes, Lisbon, 1250-149, Portugal
Tel.: (351) 218910600
Web Site: http://www.havas.pt
Advertising Services
N.A.I.C.S.: 541810

Havas Dusseldorf GmbH (5)
Toulouser Allee 25, 40211, Dusseldorf, Germany
Tel.: (49) 211 9916 0
Web Site: http://de.havas.com
Public Relations Agency
N.A.I.C.S.: 541820

Havas EHS Discovery Ltd. (5)
Phoenix Way, Cirencester, GL7 1RY, Glos, United Kingdom
Tel.: (44) 1285 644744
Web Site: http://www.havashelia.co.uk
Advertising Services
N.A.I.C.S.: 541810

Havas Engage Pazarlama ve Iletisim Hizmetleri A.S. (5)
Olive Plaza Maslak Ahi Evran Cd No 11 Floor 2, Istanbul, 34485, Türkiye
Tel.: (90) 2123280604
Web Site: http://www.engageistanbul.com
Advertising Services
N.A.I.C.S.: 541810

Havas GmbH (5)
Toulouser Allee 25, 40211, Dusseldorf, Germany
Tel.: (49) 21199160
Web Site: http://de.havas.com
Emp.: 150
Advertising Agency
N.A.I.C.S.: 541810
Eric Schoeffler *(Chief Creative Officer)*

Havas Hamburg GmbH (5)
Lippmannstrasse 59, 22769, Hamburg, Germany
Tel.: (49) 40 43175 0
Web Site: http://de.havas.com
Public Relations Agency
N.A.I.C.S.: 541820

Havas Helia Limited (5)
Havas House Hermitage Court, Hermitage Lane, Maidstone, ME16 9NT, Kent, United Kingdom
Tel.: (44) 1622757241
Web Site: http://www.havashelia.co.uk
Advertising Services
N.A.I.C.S.: 541810

Branch (Domestic):

Havas EHS Limited - Cirencester (6)
Phoenix Way, Cirencester, GL7 1RY, United Kingdom
Tel.: (44) 1285 644 744
Web Site: http://www.havashelia.co.uk
Advertising Services
N.A.I.C.S.: 541810

Subsidiary (Non-US):

Havas Holding Deutschland GmbH (5)
Toulouser Allee 25, 40211, Dusseldorf, Germany
Tel.: (49) 2119916617
Web Site: http://www.de.havas.com
Advertising Services
N.A.I.C.S.: 541810

Havas PR - Tallinn (5)
Tartu mnt 13, Harju maakond, 10145, Tallinn, Estonia
Tel.: (372) 669 1000
Web Site: http://havas.ee
Advetising Agency
N.A.I.C.S.: 541810

Havas PR Milan Srl (5)
Via San Vito 7, 20123, Milan, Italy
Tel.: (39) 02 854 5701
Web Site: http://www.havaspr.it
Public Relations Agency
N.A.I.C.S.: 541820
Caterina Tonini *(CEO)*

Havas PR Prague s.r.o. (5)
Expo 58 Letenske Sady 1500, 17000, Prague, 7, Czech Republic
Tel.: (420) 2 20 39 76 00
Public Relations Agency
N.A.I.C.S.: 541820

Havas PR Warsaw Sp. z o.o. (5)
ul Jozefa Piusa Dziekonskiego 1, 00-728, Warsaw, Poland
Tel.: (48) 22 444 0 888
Web Site: http://pl.havas.com
Public Relations Agency
N.A.I.C.S.: 541820
Dorota Mazur *(CEO-Creative grp)*

Havas People Limited (5)
Havas House Hermitage Court, Hermitage Lane, Maidstone, ME16 9NT, Kent, United Kingdom
Tel.: (44) 207 022 4000
Web Site: http://www.havaspeople.com
Business-To-Business, Graphic Design, Print, Recruitment

N.A.I.C.S.: 541810

Branch (Domestic):

Havas People Limited - Birmingham (6)
Ground Floor 39 Dominion Court Station Road, Birmingham, B91 3RT, United Kingdom
Tel.: (44) 121 711 3433
Advetising Agency
N.A.I.C.S.: 541810

Havas People Limited - Cardiff (6)
2 Fitzalan Road, Cardiff, CF24 0EB, United Kingdom
Tel.: (44) 7885 812858
Web Site: http://www.havaspeople.com
Advetising Agency
N.A.I.C.S.: 541810

Subsidiary (Non-US):

Havas Warsaw Sp. z o.o. (5)
ul Jozefa Piusa Dziekonskiego 1, 00 728, Warsaw, Poland
Tel.: (48) 224440888
Web Site: http://pl.havas.com
Advertising Agency
N.A.I.C.S.: 541810
Dorota Mazur *(CEO-Creative Grp)*

Havas Wien GmbH (5)
Sandwirtgasse 16, A-1060, Vienna, Austria
Tel.: (43) 1 5011 80
Web Site: http://www.havas.wien
Advetising Agency
N.A.I.C.S.: 541810

Havas Worldwide AG - Geneva (5)
Rue Pecolat 1, 1201, Geneva, Switzerland
Tel.: (41) 227189494
Web Site: https://swiss.havas.com
Advertising Agency
N.A.I.C.S.: 541810
Camille Delesalle *(Co-Mng Dir & Ops Dir)*

Havas Worldwide Amsterdam B.V. (5)
Stadhouderskade 1, 1054 ES, Amsterdam, Netherlands
Tel.: (31) 20 456 5000
Web Site: http://www.havas.com
Advertising Agency
N.A.I.C.S.: 541810

Havas Worldwide Brussels SA (5)
Rue des Boiteux 9, Brussels, 1000, Belgium
Tel.: (32) 2 348 38 00
Web Site: http://be.havas.com
Advertising Agency
N.A.I.C.S.: 541810
David Grunewald *(CEO)*

Havas Worldwide Bucharest (5)
141 Calea Victoriei, Bucharest, 010071, Romania
Tel.: (40) 21 318 1447
Web Site: http://havas.ro
Advertising Agency
N.A.I.C.S.: 541810
Adrian Dura *(Mng Dir)*

Havas Worldwide Budapest Kommunikacios Zrt. (5)
Aliz u 1 A/7, Budapest, H-1117, Hungary
Tel.: (36) 1436 7270
Web Site: http://global.admin-na.havasww.com
Advertising & Marketing Services
N.A.I.C.S.: 541810

Havas Worldwide Helsinki Oy (5)
Koydenpunojankatu 2a D, 00180, Helsinki, Finland
Tel.: (358) 9 42 500 200
Web Site: http://havas.fi
Advertising Agency
N.A.I.C.S.: 541810
Niko Suomalainen *(Country Mgr)*

Havas Worldwide Istanbul Iletisim Hizmetleri A.S. (5)
Olive Plaza Maslak Mah Ahi Evran Cad No 11 Kat 1A, Maslak, Istanbul, 34398, Türkiye
Tel.: (90) 2123280638
Web Site: http://www.havasworldwide.com.tr
Advetising Agency
N.A.I.C.S.: 541810

AND PRIVATE COMPANIES — VIVENDI SE

Havas Worldwide Johannesburg (Pty) Ltd. (5)
13 Baker Street The Conservatory Rosebank, Johannesburg, 2196, South Africa
Tel.: (27) 11 549 3600
Web Site: http://za.havas.com
Advetising Agency
N.A.I.C.S.: 541810
Lynn Madeley (CEO)

Havas Worldwide Kiev (5)
41 Vozdvyzhenska Street, Kiev, 04071, Ukraine
Tel.: (380) 444518430
Web Site: http://global.admin-na.havasww.com
Advetising Agency
N.A.I.C.S.: 541810

Havas Worldwide London Limited (5)
The HKX Building 3 Pancras Square, London, N1C 4AG, United Kingdom
Tel.: (44) 20 3793 3800
Web Site: http://global.admin-na.havasww.com
Advetising Agency
N.A.I.C.S.: 541810

Havas Worldwide Milan S.r.l. (5)
Via San Vito 7, Milan, 20123, Italy
Tel.: (39) 02 802021
Web Site: http://it.havas.com
Advertising & Marketing Services
N.A.I.C.S.: 541810
Paolo Biondolillo (VP)

Havas Worldwide Moscow (5)
Kosmodamianskaya emb 52/1 Entrance A, Building 6, 115054, Moscow, Russia
Tel.: (7) 4952303014
Web Site: http://ru.havas.com
Sales Range: $10-24.9 Million
Emp.: 196
Advetising Agency
N.A.I.C.S.: 541810

Havas Worldwide Munchen GmbH (5)
Lessingstr 11, 80336, Munich, Germany
Tel.: (49) 89490670
Web Site: http://de.havas.com
Advetising Agency
N.A.I.C.S.: 541810
Kris Vilhelmsson (CEO)

Havas Worldwide Netherlands B.V. (5)
Stadhouderskade 1, 1018 GW, Amsterdam, Netherlands
Tel.: (31) 20 456 5000
Web Site: http://global.admin-na.havasww.com
Advetising Agency
N.A.I.C.S.: 541810

Havas Worldwide Portugal Lda. (5)
Avenida da Liberdade n 252, Parque das Nacoes, 1250-149, Lisbon, Portugal
Tel.: (351) 21 891 0600
Web Site: http://pt.havas.com
Advetising Agency
N.A.I.C.S.: 541810
Joao Paulo Ferreira (VP)

Havas Worldwide Prague A.S (5)
Forum Karlin Pernerova 51, 186 00, Prague, 8, Czech Republic
Tel.: (420) 724 639 103
Web Site: http://www.havas.cz
Advertising Agencies, Consumer Marketing, Internet/Web Design
N.A.I.C.S.: 541810

Havas Worldwide Sofia (5)
3 Hristo Stambolski fl 2, Sofia, 1463, Bulgaria
Tel.: (359) 2 4009400
Web Site: http://havas.bg
Advetising Agency
N.A.I.C.S.: 541810

Havas Worldwide Spain S.A. (5)
Eloy Gonzalo 10, Madrid, 28010, Spain
Tel.: (34) 91 330 2323
Advetising Agency
N.A.I.C.S.: 541810

Unit (Domestic):

ASCI DIRECT, S.A. (6)
C / Maria de Molina 54 Floor 1, Madrid, 28006, Spain
Tel.: (34) 913697430
Web Site: http://www.ascidirect.es
Direct Mail Advertising Services
N.A.I.C.S.: 541860
Jose Luis Carrera Anaya (CEO & Partner)

Subsidiary (Non-US):

Havas Worldwide Ukraine (5)
Vozdvizhenska St 41, Kiev, 04071, Ukraine
Tel.: (380) 444518400
Web Site: http://havasvillage.com.ua
Advertising Agency
N.A.I.C.S.: 541810

Marketing House Sp. zo.o (5)
Al Gen W Sikorskiego 9 A lok 11, 02-758, Warsaw, Poland
Tel.: (48) 603776377
Web Site: http://marketinghouse.pl
Advertising Agency
N.A.I.C.S.: 541810

Group (Non-US):

Havas Worldwide Latin America (4)
Av Magalhaes de Castro 4800 15 andar - Torre Continental, Sao Paulo, 05676-120, Brazil
Tel.: (55) 1121261000
Regional Managing Office; Advertising Agencies
N.A.I.C.S.: 551114

Subsidiary (Non-US):

AS Servicios de Publicidad S.A. (5)
Jose Contreras 62, Zona Universitaria, Santo Domingo, Dominican Republic
Tel.: (809) 535 3264
Web Site: http://global.admin-na.havasww.com
Advetising Agency
N.A.I.C.S.: 541810

Havas Guatemala (5)
18 Calle 24-69 Zona 10 Empresarial Zona Pradera Torre 4 Nivel 8, Oficina 805, 1001, Guatemala, Guatemala
Tel.: (502) 22245700
Web Site: https://www.havasgt.com
Advertising Services
N.A.I.C.S.: 541810

Havas Medellin (5)
Cra 43E No 9-10, Medellin, Colombia
Tel.: (57) 42687644
Advertising Services
N.A.I.C.S.: 541810

Havas Worldwide Buenos Aires S.A. (5)
Humberto Primo 133 9th Floor, Buenos Aires, CP 1103, Argentina
Tel.: (54) 1152886000
Advertising Services
N.A.I.C.S.: 541810

Havas Worldwide Colombia S.A.S. (5)
Carrera 7 No 71-21 Torre A Piso 12 Edificio Avenida Chile, Bogota, Colombia
Tel.: (57) 1 519 0792
Web Site: http://global.admin-na.havasww.com
Advertising Agency
N.A.I.C.S.: 541810

Havas Worldwide Gurisa (5)
Misiones 1574 Piso 3, Montevideo, 11000, Uruguay
Tel.: (598) 2915 9500
Web Site: http://gurisa.com.uy
Advertising Services
N.A.I.C.S.: 541810
Claudio Invernizzi (Founder)

Havas Worldwide Mexico S.A. de C.V. (5)
Corporativo Punta Santa Fe Prolongacion Paseo de la Reform, 1015 Torre A Piso 6 Col Desarrollo Santa Fe, Mexico, CP, Mexico
Tel.: (52) 55 9177 6000
Advetising Agency
N.A.I.C.S.: 541810

Subsidiary (US):

Havas Worldwide Puerto Rico, Inc. (5)
Metro Office Park 6 Calle 1 Ste 103, Guaynabo, PR 00968
Tel.: (787) 999-0600
Web Site: http://havas.com.pr
Advetising Agency
N.A.I.C.S.: 541810
Ananela Bonuccelli (Mng Dir)

Subsidiary (Non-US):

Havas Worldwide Santiago S.A. (5)
Admiral Pastene 333 Primer Piso Local 2, 7500506, Santiago, Chile
Tel.: (56) 22714 8100
Web Site: https://cl.havas.com
Advertising Agencies
N.A.I.C.S.: 541810
Esteban Calvo (CEO)

Havas Worldwide Vale SA de CV (5)
Lago Zurich No 219 piso 1401 de la Torre Carso II, Col. Ampliacion Granada Delegacion Miguel Hidalgo, CP 11529, Mexico, Mexico
Tel.: (52) 55 91 38 1000
Web Site: https://valenetwork.mx
Advetising Agency
N.A.I.C.S.: 541810

Quimica Publicidad (5)
Calle 50 Edificio Frontenac Piso 4, Panama, Panama
Tel.: (507) 269 8773
Web Site: http://www.q360.com.pa
Advetising Agency
N.A.I.C.S.: 541810

Group (Non-US):

Havas Worldwide Middle East (4)
Knowledge Village Al Sufouh 2 Street, PO Box 7602, Dubai, 21448, United Arab Emirates
Tel.: (971) 44556000
Web Site: https://me.havas.com
Regional Managing Office; Advertising Agencies
N.A.I.C.S.: 551114
Sandy Zavzavadjian (Dir-Art)

Subsidiary (Non-US):

Havas Worldwide Arabia (5)
Home Offices Building 37 Oruba Street, Riyadh, 11472, Saudi Arabia
Tel.: (966) 11250 5703
Advetising Agency
N.A.I.C.S.: 541810
Rami Husseini (Mng Dir)

Klem Euro RSCG (5)
25 Bd Mohamed Abdouh, Quartier Palmiers, Casablanca, 20100, Morocco
Tel.: (212) 22 25 4617
Advertising & Marketing Services
N.A.I.C.S.: 541810

Subsidiary (Domestic):

Havas Worldwide New York, Inc. (4)
200 Hudson St, New York, NY 10013
Tel.: (212) 886-2000
Web Site: http://www.nyc.havas.com
Advertising Services
N.A.I.C.S.: 541810

Subsidiary (Domestic):

Love The 88 LLC (5)
1918 Juniper Dr, Saginaw, MI 48603
Tel.: (989) 792-5675
Web Site: http://www.lovethe88.com
Advertising Services
N.A.I.C.S.: 541890
Steve H. Bock (Founder & CEO)

Subsidiary (Domestic):

Havas Worldwide San Francisco, LLC (4)
345 California St Ste 1800, San Francisco, CA 94104
Tel.: (415) 345-7700
Web Site: http://sf.havas.com
Advertising Services
N.A.I.C.S.: 541810
Monette Hagopian (Pres)

Unit (Domestic):

Havas Worldwide Tonic (4)
205 Hudson St, New York, NY 10013
Tel.: (212) 886-4100
Web Site: http://tonic.havas.com
Advertising Agency
N.A.I.C.S.: 541810
Phil Silvestri (Mng Partner & Chief Creative Officer)

Subsidiary (Non-US):

Havas Worldwide Toronto Inc. (4)
473 Adelaide St W Unit 300, Toronto, M5V 1T1, ON, Canada
Tel.: (416) 920-6864
Web Site: http://www.havas.com
Co-op Advertising, Direct Marketing, Event Marketing
N.A.I.C.S.: 541810

Subsidiary (Domestic):

Havas Life Toronto, Inc. (5)
Suite 200 590 King Street West Toronto, Toronto, M5V 1M3, ON, Canada
Tel.: (416) 933-4791
Web Site: http://www.havashealthandyou.com
Advertising Agencies
N.A.I.C.S.: 541810

Subsidiary (Non-US):

One Green Bean Pty. Ltd. (4)
121 Harrington Street, The Rock, 2000, NSW, Australia
Tel.: (61) 280201800
Web Site: http://onegreenbean.com
Public Relations Agency
N.A.I.C.S.: 541820
Kat Thomas (Co-Founder & Exec Creative Dir-Global)

Subsidiary (Non-US):

One Green Bean London Limited (5)
The HKX Building 3 Pancras Square, London, N1C 4AG, United Kingdom
Tel.: (44) 2031969673
Web Site: http://onegreenbean.com
Public Relations Agency
N.A.I.C.S.: 541820
Anthony Freedman (Co-Founder & CEO-Global)

Subsidiary (Non-US):

Vale Bates S.A. de C.V. (4)
C Lago Zurich 219 Amp Granada, Miguel Hidalgo, Mexico, 11529, Mexico
Tel.: (52) 5591381000
Web Site: http://valenetwork.mx
Advertising Agencies
N.A.I.C.S.: 541810

Group (Domestic):

Havas Media France Group (2)
2 bis rue Godefroy, 92800, Puteaux, France
Tel.: (33) 1 46 93 32 13
Web Site: http://www.havasmedia.com
Advertising Services
N.A.I.C.S.: 541810
Alfonso Rodes Vila (CEO-Global)

Subsidiary (Non-US):

Arena Media Limited (3)
The HKX Building 3 Pancras Square, London, N1C 4AG, United Kingdom
Tel.: (44) 20 3793 3800
Web Site: http://www.arenamedia.com
Media Buying Services
N.A.I.C.S.: 541810

Subsidiary (Domestic):

EUROMEDIA (3)
35 Avenue Georges Sand, Saint-Denis, 93210, Paris, France
Tel.: (33) 183726600
Web Site: http://www.euromediagroup.com
Television Broadcasting Services
N.A.I.C.S.: 516120

Subsidiary (Non-US):

HAVAS MEDIA, S.L. (3)
Av Diagonal 575 Edificio L Illa Esc. 2 P11, 08029, Barcelona, Spain
Tel.: (34) 93 306 8900
Web Site: http://www.havasmedia.com
Media Agencies

VIVENDI SE

Vivendi SE—(Continued)
N.A.I.C.S.: 541840

HAVAS Media AG (3)
Morgartenstrasse 6, 8004, Zurich, Switzerland
Tel.: (41) 442441200
Web Site: http://www.havasmedia.ch
Advertising Agencies
N.A.I.C.S.: 541810

Havas Ireland Limited (3)
48-50 Cuffe Street, Dublin, D02 V9P0, Ireland
Tel.: (353) 16766272
Advertising Services
N.A.I.C.S.: 541810

Havas Media Argentina (3)
Serrano 669, C1414DEM, Buenos Aires, Argentina
Tel.: (54) 11 5777 7400
Web Site: https://www.havasgroup.com
Media Buying Services
N.A.I.C.S.: 541830

Havas Media Belgium S.A. (3)
Rue des Boiteux 9, 1000, Brussels, Belgium
Tel.: (32) 23491560
Advertising Agencies
N.A.I.C.S.: 541810

Havas Media Colombia SAS (3)
Carrera 7 No 71-21 Torre A Piso 12, Edificio Avenida Chile, Bogota, 110231, Colombia
Tel.: (57) 1 317 3010
Advertising Agencies
N.A.I.C.S.: 541810

Havas Media Czech Republic, s.r.o. (3)
Mikuleckeho 1311/8, 147 00, Prague, Czech Republic
Tel.: (420) 241004500
Advetising Agency
N.A.I.C.S.: 541810

Havas Media Ecuador (3)
Av Francisco de Orellana y Justino Cornejo, Kennedy Norte Edificio WTC Torre A Piso 7 Oficina 701, Guayaquil, Ecuador
Tel.: (593) 4 600 33 70
Advetising Agency
N.A.I.C.S.: 541810

Subsidiary (Domestic):

Havas Media France (3)
2 bis rue Godefroy, 92800, Puteaux, France
Tel.: (33) 1 46 93 33 33
Web Site: http://www.havasmedia.com
Advertising Agencies
N.A.I.C.S.: 541810

Subsidiary (Non-US):

Havas Media Hungary Kft. (3)
Kapas u 6-12 A/5, 1027, Budapest, Hungary
Tel.: (36) 1 799 1800
Web Site: http://hu.havas.com
Advetising Agency
N.A.I.C.S.: 541810

Havas Media Ireland (3)
48-50 Cuffe Street, Dublin, D02 EK81, Ireland
Tel.: (353) 316766272
Web Site: http://www.havasmedia.com
Media Buying Services
N.A.I.C.S.: 541830

Havas Media Latvia (3)
Kr Barona 36-9, LV 1011, Riga, Latvia
Tel.: (371) 67 280125
Advetising Agency
N.A.I.C.S.: 541810

Havas Media Limited (3)
Sutton Yard 65 Goswell Rd, London, EC1V 7EN, United Kingdom
Tel.: (44) 203 330 7000
Web Site: http://www.havasmedia.com
Advetising Agency
N.A.I.C.S.: 541870

Havas Media Madrid (3)
Eloy Gonzalo 10, 28010, Madrid, Spain
Tel.: (34) 914569090
Web Site: http://havasmediagroup.com
Advertising Agencies
N.A.I.C.S.: 541810

Mike Wilson (CEO-ANZ)

Havas Media Madrid (3)
Eloy Gonzalo 10, 28010, Madrid, Spain
Tel.: (34) 914569090
Web Site: http://havasmedia.com
Advetising Agency
N.A.I.C.S.: 541810

Havas Media Mexico (3)
Paseo de la Reforma 296 Piso 44 Col Juarez Cuauhtemoc, 06600, Mexico, Mexico
Tel.: (52) 5591776000
Media Planning & Buying Agencies
N.A.I.C.S.: 541830

Havas Media Mumbai (3)
24th Floor Commerz II International Business Park Oberoi Garden City, Off Western Express Highway Goregaon East, Mumbai, 400 063, India
Tel.: (91) 2261776177
Advertising Agencies
N.A.I.C.S.: 541810

Havas Media Nederland B.V. (3)
Stadhouderskade 1, Amsterdam, 1054, Netherlands
Tel.: (31) 205450500
Web Site: http://www.havas.com
Media Agencies
N.A.I.C.S.: 541840

Havas Media Nicaragua (3)
2 Av Suroeste, Managua, 12066, Nicaragua
Tel.: (505) 22 680 607
Advertising Agencies
N.A.I.C.S.: 541810

Subsidiary (US):

Havas Media North America (3)
200 Hudson St, New York, NY 10013
Tel.: (646) 587-5000
Web Site: http://www.havasmedia.com
Advertising Agencies
N.A.I.C.S.: 541830

Branch (Domestic):

Havas Media Boston (4)
10 Summer St, Boston, MA 02110
Tel.: (617) 425-4100
Web Site: http://www.havasmedia.com
Advertising Agencies
N.A.I.C.S.: 541810

Havas Media Chicago (4)
36 E Grand Ave 5th Fl, Chicago, IL 60611
Tel.: (312) 640-4700
Web Site: http://www.havasmedia.com
Media Buying Services
N.A.I.C.S.: 541830

Havas Media International (4)
5201 Blue Lagoon Dr Ste 790, Miami, FL 33126
Tel.: (305) 377-1907
Web Site: http://havasmediagroup.com
Media Buying Services
N.A.I.C.S.: 541810

Havas Media New York (4)
200 Hudson St, New York, NY 10013
Tel.: (646) 587-5000
Web Site: http://www.havasmedia.com
Advertising Services
N.A.I.C.S.: 541810

Havas Media San Francisco (4)
345 California Stt Ste1800, San Francisco, CA 94104
Tel.: (415) 345-7700
Web Site: http://www.havasmedia.com
Media Buying Services
N.A.I.C.S.: 541830

Branch (Non-US):

Media Planning Canada, Inc. (4)
Suite 300 473 Adelaide Street West, Toronto, M5V 1T1, ON, Canada
Tel.: (416) 920-6864
Web Site: http://www.havasmedia.com
Advertising Agencies
N.A.I.C.S.: 541810

Subsidiary (Domestic):

OpenX Technologies, Inc (4)
888 E Walnut St 2nd Fl, Pasadena, CA 91101
Tel.: (207) 299-7497
Web Site: http://www.openx.com
Sales Range: $150-199.9 Million
Emp.: 264
Digital & Mobile Advertising Services
N.A.I.C.S.: 541890
Jason Fairchild (Founder & Chief Revenue Officer)

Subsidiary (Domestic):

JumpTime, Inc. (5)
3221 Hutchison Ave Ste H, Los Angeles, CA 90034
Tel.: (310) 815-8225
Web Site: http://www.jumptime.com
Online Analytics Publisher
N.A.I.C.S.: 513210

Subsidiary (Non-US):

Havas Media Panama (3)
Calle 64 Este San Francisco, Panama, Panama
Tel.: (507) 226 60 77
Advertising Agencies
N.A.I.C.S.: 541810

Havas Media Portugal Holding SGPS, S.A. (3)
Av da Liberdade 252, Lisbon, 1250-149, Portugal
Tel.: (351) 21 791 3300
Web Site: http://www.havasmedia.com
Advertising Agency
N.A.I.C.S.: 541810
Fernanda Marantes (CEO)

Havas Media Regiones, S.A. de C.V. (3)
Av Gomez Morin 305 oficina 602 Col Valle del Campestre, 66265, Leon, Mexico
Tel.: (52) 8180476650
Advertising Agencies
N.A.I.C.S.: 541810

Havas Media Romania SL (3)
Crystal Tower Floor 8 Iancu de Hunedoara 48, 011745, Bucharest, Romania
Tel.: (40) 21 318 1447
Emp.: 30
Advertising Agencies
N.A.I.C.S.: 541810

Havas Media Russia (3)
Kosmodamianskaya emb 52/1 Entrance A, 115054, Moscow, Russia
Tel.: (7) 4959337570
Emp.: 400
Advertising Agencies
N.A.I.C.S.: 541810

Havas Media S.r.l. (3)
Via San Vito 7, 20123, Milan, Italy
Tel.: (39) 02674431
Media Buying Services
N.A.I.C.S.: 541830

Havas Media Services S.A. de C.V. (3)
Prolongacion Paseo de la Reforma 1015 Torre A Piso 17 Col, Desarollo Santa Fe, Mexico, 01376, Mexico
Tel.: (52) 5591776000
Web Site: https://havasmediagroup.com
Advertising Agencies
N.A.I.C.S.: 541810

Havas Media Singapore (3)
80 Robinson Road 20-02, Singapore, 068898, Singapore
Tel.: (65) 6645 4700
Advertising Agencies
N.A.I.C.S.: 541810

Havas Media Slovakia (3)
Panonska cesta 7, 851 04, Bratislava, Slovakia
Tel.: (421) 910797577
Web Site: https://www.havasgroup.com
Advertising Agencies
N.A.I.C.S.: 541810

Havas Media Sp. z.o.o (3)
Dziekonskiego 1, Warsaw, 00-728, Poland
Tel.: (48) 228436660
Advertising Agencies
N.A.I.C.S.: 541810

INTERNATIONAL PUBLIC

Havas Media Ukraine (3)
4 Harmatna str 2nd floor, 4050, Kiev, Ukraine
Tel.: (380) 444946536
Advertising Agencies
N.A.I.C.S.: 541810

Subsidiary (Domestic):

Havas Sports Entertainment (3)
2 bis rue Godefroy, 92800, Puteaux, France
Tel.: (33) 146 93 32 13
Web Site: http://www.havasmedia.com
Sports Marketing Services
N.A.I.C.S.: 541613

Subsidiary (Non-US):

Havas Sports & Entertainment SA (4)
4th Floor Conservatory 13 Baker Street, Rosebank, 2196, South Africa
Tel.: (27) 11 549 3600
Web Site: http://www.havasmedia.com
Sports Marketing Services
N.A.I.C.S.: 541840

Havas Sports Argentina S.A. (4)
Serrano 669, C1414DEM, Buenos Aires, Argentina
Tel.: (54) 11 4010 7400
Web Site: http://www.havasmedia.com
Sports Marketing Services
N.A.I.C.S.: 541810

Havas Sports Limited (4)
The HKX Building 3 Pancras Square, London, 20 3793 3800, United Kingdom
Tel.: (44) 20 3793 3800
Sports Marketing Services
N.A.I.C.S.: 541613

Havas Sports, S.A. (4)
Av. Diagonal 575 Edificio L IIla Esc 2, P2, 08029, Barcelona, Spain
Tel.: (34) 93 306 89 00
Web Site: http://havasmedia.com
Sports Marketing Services
N.A.I.C.S.: 541820

Subsidiary (Non-US):

RESEARCH & DEVELOPMENT MARKETING LAB SL (3)
Calle Eloy Gonzalo 10, 28010, Madrid, Spain
Tel.: (34) 914569090
Marketing Consulting Services
N.A.I.C.S.: 541613

Subsidiary (Domestic):

Havas RH (2)
110 Avenue Barthelemy Buyer, CP 703, 69256, Lyon, France
Tel.: (33) 472575005
Web Site: http://www.havas.com
Advertising Agencies
N.A.I.C.S.: 541810

Subsidiary (Non-US):

Havas Riverorchid (2)
25A Street 566, Khan Toul Kork, Phnom Penh, 12151, Cambodia
Tel.: (855) 23885671
Web Site: https://www.havas.com
Advertising Agency
N.A.I.C.S.: 541810
Santiphong Pimolsaengsuriya (Founder & CEO)

Havas Shared Services Limited (2)
Hermitage Court Hermitage Lane, Maidstone, ME16 9NT, United Kingdom
Tel.: (44) 1622757241
Web Site: http://www.havas.com
Advertising Services
N.A.I.C.S.: 541810

Subsidiary (US):

Republica Havas, LLC (2)
2153 Coral Way, Miami, FL 33145
Tel.: (786) 347-4700
Web Site: http://republicahavas.com
Advertising Agency
N.A.I.C.S.: 541810
Jorge A. Plasencia (Co-founder, Chm & CEO)

AND PRIVATE COMPANIES

VIVENDI SE

Subsidiary (Non-US):

VISION INTERNATIONAL ROADSHOW COMPANY LIMITED (2)
Unit 2301 23/F The Centrium 60 Wyndham Street Central, Hong Kong, China (Hong Kong)
Tel.: (852) 3150 6788
Web Site: http://www.pordahavas.com
Public Relations Agencies
N.A.I.C.S.: 541820
Justin Chen (VP)

Interforum SAS (1)
3 Allee de la Seine, 94200, Ivry-sur-Seine, France
Tel.: (33) 149591010
Web Site: http://www.interforum.fr
Emp.: 1,200
Book Editing & Publishing Services
N.A.I.C.S.: 513130
Eric Levy (Chm & Dir-Publication)

L'Action Municipale (1)
17 Rue Du Zes, F 75108, Paris, Cedex, France **(49.98%)**
Tel.: (33) 140133030
Web Site: http://www.proutenonigeur.fr
Sales Range: $200-249.9 Million
Emp.: 602
Newsletters
N.A.I.C.S.: 513110

Lagardere SA (1)
4 rue de Presbourg, 75016, Paris, France **(60%)**
Tel.: (33) 140691600
Web Site: https://www.lagardere.com
Rev.: $5,502,515,200
Assets: $10,436,355,280
Liabilities: $9,420,600,800
Net Worth: $1,015,754,480
Earnings: ($845,029,120)
Emp.: 27,535
Fiscal Year-end: 12/31/2020
Investment Holding Company; Book & Magazine Publishing, Media Distribution, Audiovisual Content Production & Broadcasting, Sports & Entertainment Management, Marketing & Promotion Services
N.A.I.C.S.: 551112
Thierry Funck-Brentano (Co-Mng Partner & Chief HR, Comm & Sustainable Dev Officer)

Subsidiary (Non-US):

AMP (Agence et Messagerie de Presse) (2)
Lenniksebaan 451, 1070, Brussels, Belgium **(92.3%)**
Tel.: (32) 25251411
Web Site: http://ampnet.be
Sales Range: $200-249.9 Million
Emp.: 900
Distribution of Books, Papers & Periodicals
N.A.I.C.S.: 459210

Aito Media Oy (2)
Hameentie 157 4 Krs, 00560, Helsinki, Finland
Tel.: (358) 503804160
Web Site: http://www.aitomedia.fi
Media Production Services
N.A.I.C.S.: 512110
Ilkka Hynninen (Co-Founder & Co-CEO)

Algaida Editores SA (2)
Avda San Francisco Javier 22 Edif Hermes pl 4th mod 6, 41018, Seville, Spain
Tel.: (34) 954652311
Web Site: http://www.algaida.es
Books Publishing Services
N.A.I.C.S.: 513130

Subsidiary (Domestic):

Audiolib SA (2)
21 rue du Montparnasse, 75006, Paris, Cedex, France
Tel.: (33) 140093000
Web Site: http://www.audiolib.fr
Audio Book Publishing Services
N.A.I.C.S.: 513130

Subsidiary (Non-US):

Boomerang TV SA (2)
Maria Tubau 4 4 floor, 28050, Madrid, Spain
Tel.: (34) 916624756
Web Site: http://www.grupoboomerangtv.com
Film Production Services
N.A.I.C.S.: 541810
Christophe Thoral (CEO)

CZ Press, spol. s r.o. (2)
Strakonicka 3212/4a, 150 00, Prague, Czech Republic
Tel.: (420) 272 114 760
Web Site: http://www.czpress.cz
Foreign Newspaper & Magazine Distr
N.A.I.C.S.: 424920

Subsidiary (US):

Coffee Digital LLC (2)
177 Mott St, New York, NY 10012
Tel.: (212) 204-1211
Web Site: http://www.coffeeww.com
Marketing & Advertising Services
N.A.I.C.S.: 541810
Brian Fridell (VP)

Subsidiary (Non-US):

Commercial Grupo Anaya SA (2)
Juan Ignacio Luca de Tena 15, 28027, Madrid, Spain
Tel.: (34) 913938600
Web Site: http://www.cga.es
Books Publishing Services
N.A.I.C.S.: 513130
Alexander Gomez-Collins (Mng Dir-Mktg & CRM)

Subsidiary (Domestic):

Diffulivre SA (2)
Rue des Jordils 40 Case Postale 189 St-Sulpice, 1025, Paris, France
Tel.: (33) 41216950212
Web Site: http://www.diffulivre.ch
Books Publishing Services
N.A.I.C.S.: 513130

Subsidiary (Non-US):

Difusora Larousse Mexico SA de CV (2)
Renacimiento 180 Col San Juan Tlihuaca, Del Azcapotzalco Distrito Federal, 02400, Mexico, Mexico
Tel.: (52) 5511021300
Web Site: http://www.larousse.mx
Editorial Material Mfr
N.A.I.C.S.: 323111

Digital Property Guides Ltd. (2)
26 28 Hammersmith Grove, London, W6 7BA, United Kingdom
Tel.: (44) 2078980549
Web Site: http://www.propertyguides.com
Real Estate Services
N.A.I.C.S.: 531390
Kim Brown (Founder)

Ediciones Xerais de Galicia SA (2)
Doutor Maranon 12, 36211, Vigo, Spain
Tel.: (34) 986214888
Web Site: http://www.xerais.gal
Books Publishing Services
N.A.I.C.S.: 513130

Edif (2)
Viale Sarca, 235, 20126, Milan, Italy
Tel.: (39) 0266191
Web Site: http://www.elle.it
Publisher
N.A.I.C.S.: 513110

Subsidiary (Domestic):

Edifinance Participations SAS (2)
42 rue Washington Monceau, 75016, Paris, France
Tel.: (33) 140692077
Web Site: http://www.lagardere.com
Book Publishers
N.A.I.C.S.: 513130

Editions Jean-Claude Lattes SNC (2)
17 rue Jacob, 75006, Paris, France
Tel.: (33) 144417400
Web Site: http://www.editions-jclattes.fr
Books Publishing Services
N.A.I.C.S.: 513130
Veronique Cardi (Pres)

Editions Stock SAS (2)
21 rue Du Montparnasse, 75278, Paris, Cedex 06, France
Tel.: (33) 14 954 3655
Web Site: https://www.editions-stock.fr
Books Publishing Services
N.A.I.C.S.: 513130

Subsidiary (Non-US):

Editora Salvat do Brasil Ltda. (2)
Rua Purpurina 155 - 9 andar - cj 94 - Vila Madalena, Sao Paulo, 05435-030, Brazil
Tel.: (55) 1130225615
Web Site: http://br.salvat.com
Electronic Equipment Whslr
N.A.I.C.S.: 423690

Subsidiary (Domestic):

Elle International SA (2)
105 bis avenue Maurice Thorez, 94200, Ivry-sur-Seine, France
Tel.: (33) 175435020
Web Site: http://www.ellearoundtheworld.com
Magazine Publishing Services
N.A.I.C.S.: 513120

Fondation Jean-Luc Lagardere (2)
42 Washington Street Immeuble Monceau, 75781, Paris, France **(100%)**
Tel.: (33) 140691874
Web Site: http://www.fondation-jean-luc-lagardere.org
Sales Range: $25-49.9 Million
Emp.: 100
Charitable Grant Foundation
N.A.I.C.S.: 813211
Arnaud Lagardere (Pres)

Subsidiary (Non-US):

Galore Park Publishing Ltd. (2)
Carmelite House 50 Victoria Embankment, London, EC4Y 0DH, United Kingdom
Tel.: (44) 2031226405
Web Site: http://www.galorepark.co.uk
Books Publishing Services
N.A.I.C.S.: 513130
Diane Davis (Mgr-Customer Svc)

Subsidiary (Domestic):

Gigamic Sarl (2)
ZAL les Garennes, Wimereux, 62930, Boulogne-sur-Mer, France
Tel.: (33) 321333737
Web Site: http://en.gigamic.com
Emp.: 25
Game Distributing & Publishing Services
N.A.I.C.S.: 513199
Joseph Foussat (Project Mgr-Publ)

Subsidiary (Non-US):

HMH International, Inc. (2)
4200 Boulevard St Lauren Suite 1203, Montreal, H2W 2R2, QC, Canada
Tel.: (514) 590-4234
Learning Services
N.A.I.C.S.: 611420

Hachette Collections Japan K.K. (2)
1-2 Kagurazaka, Shinjuku, Tokyo, 162-0825, Japan
Tel.: (81) 570001070
Web Site: http://www.hachette-collections.jp
Books Publishing Services
N.A.I.C.S.: 513130
Ken Sato (Dir-Editorial)

Hachette Partworks Ltd. (2)
Unit 4 Pullman Business Park Pullman Way, Ringwood, BH24 1HD, Hampshire, United Kingdom
Tel.: (44) 3448927207
Web Site: http://hachettepartworks.com
Novel Publishing Services
N.A.I.C.S.: 513130
Helen Nally (Dir-Editorial & Publ)

Hachette Polska Sp. z o.o. (2)
ul Widok 8, 00-023, Warsaw, Poland
Tel.: (48) 224875333
Web Site: http://kolekcja-hachette.pl
Books Publishing Services
N.A.I.C.S.: 513130
Tomasz Gawlowski (Sls Dir)

Hodder & Stoughton Educational Ltd. (2)
Carmelite House 50 Victoria Embankment, London, EC4Y 0DZ, United Kingdom
Tel.: (44) 1235827720
Web Site: http://www.hodder.co.uk
Books Publishing Services
N.A.I.C.S.: 513130
Matthew Henry Hodder (Co-Founder)

Subsidiary (Domestic):

Image & Compagnie SA (2)
7 Rue du Dome, 92100, Boulogne-Billancourt, France
Tel.: (33) 144779512
Web Site: http://www.imageetcompagnie.fr
Motion Picture Production Services
N.A.I.C.S.: 512199
Christophe Thoral (Pres)

Subsidiary (Non-US):

International Duty Free SA (2)
132A Vliegveld, 1820, Steenokkerzeel, Belgium
Tel.: (32) 27151020
Web Site: http://www.idf-dutyfree.com
Cosmetics Mfr
N.A.I.C.S.: 325620
Isabelle Depoorter (Ops Mgr)

Jessica Kingsley (Publishers) Ltd. (2)
Carmelite House 50 Victoria Embankment, London, EC4Y 0DZ, United Kingdom
Tel.: (44) 2031226000
Web Site: http://uk.jkp.com
Books Publishing Services
N.A.I.C.S.: 513130
Sanphy Thomas (Mng Dir)

Johnnic Communication (2)
4 Biermann Ave, Rosebank, 1746, South Africa **(100%)**
Tel.: (27) 0112803000
Web Site: http://www.johnnic.com
Sales Range: $750-799.9 Million
Emp.: 3,005
Magazine Publisher
N.A.I.C.S.: 513120
Prakash Desai (CEO)

Subsidiary (Domestic):

Kwyk SAS (2)
61 rue de Maubeuge, 75009, Paris, France
Tel.: (33) 142588451
Web Site: http://www.kwyk.fr
Software Publishing Services
N.A.I.C.S.: 513130
Damien Fafchamps (CTO)

Subsidiary (Non-US):

LS Deutschland GmbH (2)
Daimlerring 34, Rodinghausen, 32289, Bad Oeynhausen, Germany
Tel.: (49) 522387900
Web Site: http://ce.ls-deutschland.de
Electronic Products Mfr
N.A.I.C.S.: 336320

LS Tr Italia Srl (2)
Via Di Pianvallico 12 D, Scarperia e San Piero, 50038, Florence, Italy
Tel.: (39) 0558430620
Web Site: http://www.larsitalia.it
Oil & Cooling Feeder Mfr
N.A.I.C.S.: 324191

LS Tr North America Inc. (2)
370 King Street West Suite 703, Toronto, M5V 1J9, ON, Canada
Tel.: (416) 863-6400
Web Site: http://www.paradieslagardere.com
Travel Retail Services
N.A.I.C.S.: 561510

LS Travel Retail Bulgaria Ltd. (2)
5 Oborishte Str Floor 5, 1504, Sofia, Bulgaria
Tel.: (359) 29502445
Travel Retail Services
N.A.I.C.S.: 561510
Mladen Yordanov (CEO)

LS Travel Retail Malaysia Sdn. Bhd. (2)
L1OF 46 and 47 Level 1 Gateway Klia 2, 64000, Sepang, Selangor, Malaysia

VIVENDI SE

Vivendi SE—(Continued)
Tel.: (60) 387878295
Travel Retail Services
N.A.I.C.S.: 561510
Ann Pang *(CEO)*

Subsidiary (Domestic):

La Diff Sarl (2)
Batiment Hachette Livre 58 Rue Jean Bleuzen, Vanves, 92170, Paris, France
Tel.: (33) 141318591
Web Site: http://www.ladiff.fr
Media Services
N.A.I.C.S.: 541840

Lagardere Global Advertising SA (2)
2 Rue de Cevennes, 75015, Paris, France
Tel.: (33) 187154040
Advertising Services
N.A.I.C.S.: 541810
Constance Benque *(CEO & VP)*

Lagardere Media SAS (2)
4 Rue de Presbourg, F-75016, Paris, France **(100%)**
Tel.: (33) 141346000
Web Site: http://www.lagardere.com
Sales Range: $550-599.9 Million
Emp.: 2,000
Media Holding Company
N.A.I.C.S.: 551112

Group (Domestic):

Hachette Livre SA (3)
58 Rue Jean Bleuzen, CS 70007, Vanves, 92178, Paris, Cedex, France **(100%)**
Tel.: (33) 143923000
Web Site: http://www.hachette.com
Book Publishers
N.A.I.C.S.: 513130
Fabrice Bakhouche *(COO)*

Subsidiary (Non-US):

ALLIANCE DISTRIBUTION SERVICES PTY LTD (4)
9 Pioneer Ave, Tuggerah, Sydney, 2259, Australia
Tel.: (61) 2 4390 1300
Sales Range: $25-49.9 Million
Emp.: 100
Books Publishing Services
N.A.I.C.S.: 513130
Phill Knight *(Gen Mgr)*

Subsidiary (Domestic):

ARMAND COLIN SAS (4)
21 Rue du Montparnasse, 75283, Paris, France
Tel.: (33) 820 065 095
Web Site: http://www.armand-colin.com
Book Publishers
N.A.I.C.S.: 513130

Subsidiary (Non-US):

Alianza Editorial, S.A. (4)
C/ Juan Ignacio Luca de Tena 15, 28027, Madrid, Spain
Tel.: (34) 91 393 88 88
Web Site: http://www.alianzaeditorial.es
Book Publishers
N.A.I.C.S.: 513130

COMERCIAL GRUPO ANAYA SA (4)
C/ Juan Ignacio Luca de Tena 15, Madrid, 28027, Spain
Tel.: (34) 913 938 800
Web Site: http://www.anaya.es
Book Publishers
N.A.I.C.S.: 513130
Jose Manuele Gomez *(Pres)*

Subsidiary (Domestic):

Calmann Levy S.A. (4)
31 rue de Fleurus, 75006, Paris, France
Tel.: (33) 1 49 54 36 00
Book Publishers
N.A.I.C.S.: 513130

Centre de Traitement des Retours (CTR) (4)
137 Route de Corbeil, F-91160, Longjumeau, France **(99.99%)**
Warehousing

N.A.I.C.S.: 493110

DUNOD EDITEUR SA (4)
11 rue Paul Bert, CS 30024, 92247, Malakoff, Cedex, France
Tel.: (33) 141236600
Web Site: http://www.dunod.com
Sales Range: $25-49.9 Million
Emp.: 50
Books Publishing Services
N.A.I.C.S.: 513130

Subsidiary (Non-US):

Diffulivre SA (4)
Rue des Jordils 41, PO Box 189, 1025, Saint Sulpice, Switzerland
Tel.: (41) 216950212
Web Site: http://www.diffulivre.ch
Sales Range: $25-49.9 Million
Emp.: 50
Book Publishers
N.A.I.C.S.: 513130

Dilibel SA (4)
Avenue de l'Energie 30, 4432, Alleur, Belgium
Tel.: (32) 4 246 38 63
Web Site: http://www.dilibel.be
Duty Free Product Distr
N.A.I.C.S.: 445320

Subsidiary (Domestic):

EDDL (4)
5 Rue Du Pont De Lodi, 75006, Paris, France
Tel.: (33) 1 53 73 00 40
Web Site: http://www.eddllivres.com
Sales Range: $25-49.9 Million
Emp.: 7
Book Retailer
N.A.I.C.S.: 459210
Veronique Torres *(Pres & Dir Gen)*

EDITIONS GRASSET ET FASQUELLE S.A. (4)
61 rue des Saints-Peres, 75006, Paris, France
Tel.: (33) 1 44 39 22 00
Web Site: http://www.grasset.fr
Books Publishing Services
N.A.I.C.S.: 513130

Subsidiary (Non-US):

EDITORIAL BARCANOVA SA (4)
Rosa Sensat 9-11 4a planta, 08005, Barcelona, Spain
Tel.: (34) 932 172 054
Web Site: http://www.barcanova.cat
Book Publishers
N.A.I.C.S.: 513130

Edelsa Grupo Didascalia S.A. (4)
c/ Juan Ignacio Luca de Tena 15, 28027, Madrid, Spain
Tel.: (34) 914 165 511
Web Site: http://www.edelsa.es
Emp.: 22
Book Publishers
N.A.I.C.S.: 513130
Laurent Bereau *(Sls Mgr-Export Dept)*

Subsidiary (Domestic):

Editions Hatier (4)
8 Rue d'Assas, 75278, Paris, Cedex 06, France **(100%)**
Tel.: (33) 149544850
Web Site: http://www.editions-hatier.fr
Sales Range: $25-49.9 Million
Emp.: 100
Book Publishers
N.A.I.C.S.: 513130

Editions Larousse SAS (4)
21 Rue de Montparnasse, Paris, 75006, France
Tel.: (33) 1 44 394 4 00
Web Site: http://www.editions-larousse.fr
Books Publishing Services
N.A.I.C.S.: 513130

Editions des Deux Terres SAS (4)
5 Rue de Savoie, 75006, Paris, France
Tel.: (33) 1 43 54 16 90
Web Site: http://www.les-deux-terres.com
Sales Range: $25-49.9 Million
Emp.: 3
Books Publishing Services

N.A.I.C.S.: 513130
Nachalie Jouven *(Pres)*

Fernand Hazan Editeur S A (4)
58 Rue Jean Bleuzen, CS 70007, 92178, Vanves, Cedex, France
Tel.: (33) 143923000
Web Site: http://www.editions-hazan.fr
Books Publishing Services
N.A.I.C.S.: 513130

Subsidiary (Non-US):

GRUPO ANAYA SA (4)
C/ Juan Ignacio Luca de Tena 15, 28027, Madrid, Spain
Tel.: (34) 913 938 800
Web Site: http://grupoanaya.es
Book Publishers
N.A.I.C.S.: 513130

GRUPO EDITORIAL BRUNO S.L. (4)
C/ Juan Ignacio Luca de Tena 15, 28027, Madrid, Spain
Tel.: (34) 917 244 800
Web Site: http://www.editorial-bruno.es
Emp.: 1,000
Book Publishers
N.A.I.C.S.: 513130

HDS Retail Asia Pacific (4)
Level 5/50 Holt St, Surry Hills, 2010, NSW, Australia
Tel.: (61) 292818655
Web Site: http://www.osaspac.com
Sales Range: $25-49.9 Million
Emp.: 70
Marketing Media Products & Convenience Services
N.A.I.C.S.: 459210

HDS Retail North America (4)
370 King St W 6th Fl, Toronto, M5V 1J9, ON, Canada **(100%)**
Tel.: (416) 863-6400
Web Site: http://www.lftrna.com
Sales Range: $25-49.9 Million
Emp.: 100
Retail Convenience Store & Gift Shops Operator
N.A.I.C.S.: 459420
Gerry Savaria *(Pres & CEO)*

Subsidiary (US):

Delstar Companies Inc. (5)
5060 N 40th St Ste 200, Phoenix, AZ 85018
Tel.: (602) 956-9600
Rev.: $26,000,000
Emp.: 20
Convenience Store & Gift Shop Operator
N.A.I.C.S.: 459420

Subsidiary (Domestic):

HL 93 (4)
43 Quai De Grenelle, 75015, Paris, France
Tel.: (33) 8 99 23 97 13
Financial Management Services
N.A.I.C.S.: 523999

HL FINANCES SARL (4)
3 rue Waldeck Rousseau, 24000, Perigueux, France
Tel.: (33) 5 53 05 98 98
Financial Management Services
N.A.I.C.S.: 523999

Subsidiary (Non-US):

Hachette Australia Pty. Ltd. (4)
Level 17 207 Kent St, Sydney, 2000, NSW, Australia **(100%)**
Tel.: (61) 282480800
Web Site: http://www.hachette.com.au
Sales Range: $25-49.9 Million
Emp.: 60
Booksellers & Distributors
N.A.I.C.S.: 459210
Michael Swarbrick *(Head-IT)*

Hachette Book Group Canada Ltd. (4)
2 Bloor St W, Toronto, M4W 3E2, ON, Canada
Tel.: (416) 415-8000
Books Publishing Services
N.A.I.C.S.: 513130

INTERNATIONAL PUBLIC

Hachette Book Publishing India Pvt Ltd
4th/5th Floors Corporate Centre Plot no 94 Sector 44, Gurgaon, 122003, Haryana, India
Tel.: (91) 1244195000
Web Site: http://www.hachetteindia.com
Sales Range: $25-49.9 Million
Emp.: 40
Books Publishing Services
N.A.I.C.S.: 513130
Thomas Abraham *(Mng Dir)*

Hachette Canada (4)
9001 boul de l'Acadie bureau 1002, Montreal, H4N 3H5, QC, Canada **(100%)**
Tel.: (514) 382-3034
Web Site: http://www.hachette.qc.ca
Sales Range: $25-49.9 Million
Emp.: 40
Distr of Books
N.A.I.C.S.: 513130

Subsidiary (Domestic):

Hachette Collections S.N.C. (4)
58 rue Jean Bleuzen, CS 70007, 92178, Vanves, Cedex, France
Tel.: (33) 160396514
Web Site: http://www.hachette-collections.com
Book Publishers
N.A.I.C.S.: 513130

Subsidiary (Non-US):

Hachette Distribution Services Polska (4)
AL Jerozilinskie 176, Warsaw, 2486, Poland **(51%)**
Tel.: (48) 225723200
Web Site: http://www.hds.pl
Sales Range: $25-49.9 Million
Emp.: 100
Press Distributor
N.A.I.C.S.: 459210
Dorota Karnkowska *(Mgr-Comm)*

Subsidiary (Domestic):

Hachette Education S.A.-N.V. (4)
58 rue Jean Bleuzen, CS 70007, 92178, Vanves, Cedex, France
Tel.: (33) 143923000
Web Site: http://www.hachette-education.com
Book Retailer
N.A.I.C.S.: 459210

Subsidiary (Non-US):

Hachette Fascicoli srl (4)
Via Melchiorre Gioia 61, 20124, Milan, Italy
Tel.: (39) 0262689100
Web Site: http://www.hachette-fascicoli.it
Book Publishers
N.A.I.C.S.: 513130

Hachette Filipacchi 2000 (4)
Na Zatorce 3 1, CZ 160 00, Bubenec, Prague, Czech Republic **(51%)**
Tel.: (420) 233023100
Sales Range: $50-74.9 Million
Emp.: 200
Magazine Publisher
N.A.I.C.S.: 513120

Hachette Filipacchi Global Advertising Italie (4)
Imbonati 18, 20121, Milan, Italy **(100%)**
Tel.: (39) 0262694441
Web Site: http://www.hearst.it
Sales Range: $25-49.9 Million
Emp.: 10
Advertising Services
N.A.I.C.S.: 541810

Hachette Filipacchi Presse Z.A.O. (4)
Oulitsa Miasnitskaia 35, 101959, Moscow, Russia **(100%)**
Tel.: (7) 952041653
Sales Range: $25-49.9 Million
Emp.: 35
Magazine Publisher
N.A.I.C.S.: 513120

Hachette Filipacchi S.A. (4)
Calle Santa Engracia 23, E 28010, Madrid, Spain **(66.19%)**

AND PRIVATE COMPANIES — VIVENDI SE

Tel.: (34) 917287060
Sales Range: $100-124.9 Million
Emp.: 450
Publisher
N.A.I.C.S.: 513130

Hachette Filipacchi UK Ltd. (4)
64 North Row, London, W1K 7LL, United Kingdom (100%)
Tel.: (44) 2071507000
Web Site: http://www.hachettefilipacchiuk.co.uk
Sales Range: $25-49.9 Million
Emp.: 20
Newspaper Publishing
N.A.I.C.S.: 513110

Subsidiary (Domestic):

Hachette Industrie et Services (4)
ZA De Coignieres Maurepas 1 Ave Gutenberg, 78316, Maurepas, Cedex, France (100%)
Tel.: (33) 130662119
Web Site: http://www.hachette.com
Sales Range: $450-499.9 Million
Wholesale Distrbution of Books
N.A.I.C.S.: 459210

Subsidiary (Non-US):

Hachette Latino America S.A. de C.V. (4)
Presidente Masaryk 101 4 To Piso, Colonia Chapultepec Morales, 11570, Mexico, Mexico (100%)
Tel.: (52) 5552034813
Web Site: http://www.hachettemex.com.mx
Sales Range: $25-49.9 Million
Emp.: 20
Book Publishing
N.A.I.C.S.: 513130

Subsidiary (Domestic):

Hachette Livre (4)
58 Rue Jeam Bleuzen Vanves, 92178, Paris, Cedex 15, France (100%)
Tel.: (33) 1 43 92 30 00
Web Site: http://www.hachette.com
Sales Range: $25-49.9 Million
Emp.: 500
Online Publisher
N.A.I.C.S.: 513120
Arnaud Nourry (Chm & CEO)

Subsidiary (Non-US):

Hachette Livre Espana SA (4)
Calle Juan Ignacio Luca De Tena 15, Madrid, 28027, Spain
Tel.: (34) 913938800
Books Publishing Services
N.A.I.C.S.: 513130

Subsidiary (US):

Hachette Livre USA, Inc. (4)
1290 Ave of the Americas, New York, NY 10104
Tel.: (212) 364-1100
Book Publishers
N.A.I.C.S.: 513130

Subsidiary (Domestic):

Hachette Book Group, Inc. (5)
1290 Avenue of the Americas, New York, NY 10104
Tel.: (212) 364-1100
Web Site: http://www.hachettebookgroup.com
Book Publishers
N.A.I.C.S.: 513130
Megan Tingley (Publr-Little, Brown Books for Young Readers & Exec VP)

Unit (Domestic):

Basic Books (6)
1290 Avenue of the Americas, New York, NY 10104
Tel.: (212) 364-1100
Web Site: http://www.basicbooks.com
Non-Fiction Book Publisher
N.A.I.C.S.: 513130
Tim Bartlett (Sr Exec Editor)

Hyperion Books (6)
77 W 66th St, New York, NY 10023
Tel.: (212) 456-0113

Web Site: http://www.hachettebookgroup.com
Sales Range: $100-124.9 Million
Publisher of Fiction & Non-Fiction Books
N.A.I.C.S.: 513130

Little, Brown & Company (6)
237 Park Ave, New York, NY 10017
Tel.: (212) 364-1100
Web Site: http://www.hachettebookgroup.com
Sales Range: $75-99.9 Million
Book Publishers
N.A.I.C.S.: 513130
Megan Tingley (Publr-Little, Brown Books for Young Readers & Sr VP)

PublicAffairs, LLC (6)
1290 Avenue of the Americas Fl 5, New York, NY 10104
Tel.: (212) 364-1100
Web Site: http://www.publicaffairsbooks.com
Book Publishers
N.A.I.C.S.: 513130
Peter Osnos (Founder)

Unit (Domestic):

Running Press (6)
2300 Chestnut St, Philadelphia, PA 19103
Tel.: (215) 567-5080
Web Site: http://www.runningpress.com
Book Publishers
N.A.I.C.S.: 513130
Karen Noble (Dir-Inventory Plng)

Westview Press (6)
2465 Central Ave, Boulder, CO 80301-2867
Tel.: (303) 444-3541
Web Site: http://www.westviewpress.com
Non-Fiction Book Publisher
N.A.I.C.S.: 513130

Subsidiary (Domestic):

Workman Publishing Company (6)
225 Barick St 9 Th Fl, New York, NY 10014
Tel.: (212) 254-5900
Web Site: http://www.workman.com
Book Publishers
N.A.I.C.S.: 513130
Barbie Altorfer (Dir-Calendar Art)

Subsidiary (Domestic):

Hachette Digital Inc. (5)
1271 Avenue of the Americas, New York, NY 10020
Tel.: (212) 364-1100
Book Retailer
N.A.I.C.S.: 459210
Christine Foltzer (Asst Dir-Art)

Subsidiary (Non-US):

Hachette New Zealand Ltd (4)
Level 2 23 O'Connell Street, Auckland, 1010, New Zealand
Tel.: (64) 93791480
Web Site: http://www.hachette.co.nz
Emp.: 110
Books Publishing Services
N.A.I.C.S.: 513130
Melanee Winder (Mng Dir)

Hachette UK Holding Limited (4)
338 Euston Rd, London, NW1 3BH, United Kingdom
Tel.: (44) 2078736000
Investment Management Service
N.A.I.C.S.: 523999

Subsidiary (Domestic):

Hachette UK Ltd (5)
Carmelite House 50 Victoria Embankment, London, EC4Y 0DZ, United Kingdom (100%)
Tel.: (44) 2031226000
Web Site: http://www.hachette.co.uk
Sales Range: $200-249.9 Million
Emp.: 650
Book Retailer & Distr
N.A.I.C.S.: 459210
Pierre de Cacqueray (Grp Dir-Fin)

Subsidiary (Domestic):

Bookpoint Ltd (6)
130 Park Drive Milton Park, Abingdon,

OX14 4SE, Oxfordshire, United Kingdom (100%)
Tel.: (44) 1235400400
Web Site: http://bookpoint.wp.hachette.co.uk
Sales Range: $25-49.9 Million
Emp.: 250
Book Distributor
N.A.I.C.S.: 459210

Hodder Wayland (6)
338 Euston Rd, London, NW1 3BH, United Kingdom (100%)
Tel.: (44) 2078736000
Web Site: http://www.hodderheadline.co.uk
Sales Range: $150-199.9 Million
Children Book Publisher
N.A.I.C.S.: 323117

LITTLE HAMPTON BOOK SERVICE LTD (6)
Faraday Close Durrington, Worthing, BN13 3RB, West Sussex, United Kingdom
Tel.: (44) 1903 828500
Web Site: http://www.lbsltd.co.uk
Sales Range: $25-49.9 Million
Emp.: 250
Book Publisher & Distr
N.A.I.C.S.: 513130
Matt Wright (CEO-Distr)

Subsidiary (Non-US):

Headline Publishing Group Ltd (4)
Carmelite House 50 Victoria Embankment, London, EC4Y 0DZ, United Kingdom
Tel.: (44) 2031227222
Web Site: http://www.headline.co.uk
Books Publishing Services
N.A.I.C.S.: 513130

Subsidiary (Domestic):

Headline Book Publishing Limited (5)
338 Euston Road, London, NW1 3BH, United Kingdom
Tel.: (44) 20 7873 6000
Book Publishers
N.A.I.C.S.: 513130

Subsidiary (Non-US):

Hearst Magazines Netherlands (4)
Moermanskkade 500, 1013 BC, Amsterdam, Netherlands
Tel.: (31) 205353600
Web Site: http://www.hearst.nl
Sales Range: $50-74.9 Million
Emp.: 150
Magazine Publisher & Other Media Services
N.A.I.C.S.: 513120

Hodder & Stoughton Ltd (4)
Carmelite House 50 Victoria Embankment, London, EC4Y 0DZ, United Kingdom
Tel.: (44) 2031226777
Web Site: http://www.hodder.co.uk
Books Publishing Services
N.A.I.C.S.: 513130

Hodder Education Ltd (4)
338 Euston Road, London, NW1 3BH, United Kingdom
Tel.: (44) 20 7873 6000
Web Site: http://www.hoddereducation.co.uk
Books Publishing Services
N.A.I.C.S.: 513130
Ian Cafferky (Dir-Comml)

Hodder Headline Ltd (4)
338 Euston Road, London, NW1 3BH, United Kingdom
Tel.: (44) 207 873 60 11
Books Publishing Services
N.A.I.C.S.: 513130

Subsidiary (Non-US):

Hodder Headline Ireland (5)
8 Castlecourt, Castleknock, Dublin, Ireland
Tel.: (353) 18246288
Web Site: http://www.hachettebooksireland.ie
Emp.: 3
Booksellers & Distributors
N.A.I.C.S.: 459210

Subsidiary (Domestic):

LES EDITIONS FOUCHER S N C (4)

8 rue d'Assas, 75006, Paris, France
Tel.: (33) 149544954
Web Site: http://www.editions-foucher.fr
Books Publishing Services
N.A.I.C.S.: 513130

LIBRAIRIE GENERALE FRANCAISE (4)
31 rue de Fleurus, 75278, Paris, France
Tel.: (33) 149543700
Web Site: http://www.librairiegeneralefrancaise.com
Emp.: 80
Book Publishers
N.A.I.C.S.: 513130

Subsidiary (Non-US):

Lagardere Travel Retail (4)
Strada George Constantinescu nr 2-4 Globalworth Campus, Cladirea C etaj 4 Sector 2, 020335, Bucharest, Romania (100%)
Tel.: (40) 314078250
Web Site: http://www.lagardere-tr.ro
Press Distribution & Travel Retail Services
N.A.I.C.S.: 459999
Dag Inge Rasmussen (Chm & CEO)

Subsidiary (Domestic):

Larousse (4)
21 rue du Montparnasse, 75006, Paris, France
Tel.: (33) 144394400
Web Site: http://www.larousse.fr
Dictionaries, Encyclopedias, Reference Books & Textbooks Publisher
N.A.I.C.S.: 513130

Subsidiary (Non-US):

Ediciones Larousse Argentina SA (5)
Acunia De Figueroa 352, C1180AAF, Buenos Aires, Argentina
Tel.: (54) 1148677000
Web Site: http://www.larousse.com.ar
Sales Range: $10-24.9 Million
Emp.: 35
Book Publishers
N.A.I.C.S.: 513130

Ediciones Larousse S.A. de C.V. (5)
Renacimiento 180 Col San Juan Tlihuaca Del Azcapotzalco, Ciudad De Mexico, 02400, Mexico, Distrito Federal, Mexico
Tel.: (52) 5511021300
Web Site: http://www.larousse.mx
Sales Range: $75-99.9 Million
Emp.: 300
Book Publishers
N.A.I.C.S.: 513130

Subsidiary (Non-US):

Larousse Editorial S.L. (4)
Mallorca 45 3a Planta, 08029, Barcelona, Spain
Tel.: (34) 93 241 35 05
Web Site: http://www.larousse.es
Book Publishers
N.A.I.C.S.: 513130

Subsidiary (Domestic):

Le Livre Paris SNC (4)
58 Rue Jean Bleuzen, F 92178, Vanves, France (100%)
Tel.: (33) 141236500
Sales Range: $25-49.9 Million
Emp.: 20
Publisher
N.A.I.C.S.: 513130

Les Editions Albert Rene S.A.R.L. (4)
Immeuble Louis Hachette 58 rue Jean Bleuzen, Vanves, 70007, Paris, France
Tel.: (33) 143923980
Web Site: http://www.asterix.com
Sales Range: $25-49.9 Million
Emp.: 15
Books Publishing Services
N.A.I.C.S.: 513130
Baptiste Cazaux (Head-Licensing & Dir-Licences)

Les Editions Didier S.N.C. (4)
3 Rue de l Odeon, 75006, Paris, France
Tel.: (33) 1 44 41 31 31

VIVENDI SE

Vivendi SE—(Continued)
Web Site: http://www.editionsdidier.com
Books Publishing Services
N.A.I.C.S.: 513130

Les Editions Hatier S.A (4)
8 Rue d'Assas, 75006, Paris, France
Tel.: (33) 149544850
Web Site: http://www.editions-hatier.fr
Books Publishing Services
N.A.I.C.S.: 513130

Librairie Artheme Fayard S.A. (4)
13 rue du Montparnasse, 75006, Paris, France
Tel.: (33) 145498200
Web Site: http://www.fayard.fr
Books Publishing Services
N.A.I.C.S.: 513130
Sophie de Closets *(Chm, CEO & Dir-Publication)*

MY BOOX (4)
58 Rue Jean Bleuzen, 92178, Vanves, France
Tel.: (33) 141236000
Web Site: http://www.myboox.fr
Newspaper & Book Publishing Services
N.A.I.C.S.: 513110
David Pavia *(Gen Mgr)*

Subsidiary (Non-US):

Octopus Publishing Group Ltd. (4)
Carmelite House 50 Victoria Embankment, London, EC4Y 0DZ, United Kingdom
Tel.: (44) 2031226400
Web Site: http://www.octopusbooks.co.uk
Sales Range: $50-74.9 Million
Emp.: 250
Trade Books & Illustrated Reference Books
N.A.I.C.S.: 513130

Subsidiary (Domestic):

Conran Octopus Limited (5)
Endeavour House 189 Shaftesbury Ave, London, WC2H 8JY, United Kingdom **(100%)**
Tel.: (44) 1903 828 503
Web Site: http://www.octopusbooks.co.uk
Rev.: $37,435,000
Emp.: 90
Book Publishing
N.A.I.C.S.: 513130

Hamlyn Publishing (5)
2 4 Heron Quays, London, E14 4JP, United Kingdom **(100%)**
Tel.: (44) 2075318400
Web Site: http://www.hamlyn.co.uk
Sales Range: $25-49.9 Million
Emp.: 60
Illustrated Book Publishing
N.A.I.C.S.: 513130

Millers Publications Ltd. (5)
2 4 Heron Quays, London, E14 4JP, United Kingdom **(100%)**
Tel.: (44) 2075318400
Web Site: http://www.millers.uk.com
Sales Range: $25-49.9 Million
Emp.: 15
Publishing
N.A.I.C.S.: 513130

Philip's (5)
Endeavour House, 189 Shaftesbury Ave, London, WC2H 8JY, United Kingdom **(100%)**
Tel.: (44) 207 632 5400
Web Site: http://www.octopusbooks.co.uk
Sales Range: $10-24.9 Million
Emp.: 40
Maps, Atlases & Reference Books Publishing Services
N.A.I.C.S.: 513130
Kevin Hawkins *(Dir-Trade Sls)*

Subsidiary (Domestic):

SAMAS SA (4)
58 Rue Jean Bleuzen, 92170, Vanves, France
Tel.: (33) 825 88 69 27
Books Publishing Services
N.A.I.C.S.: 513130

Subsidiary (Non-US):

Salvat Editores, S.A. (4)
45 Calle Mallorca, E 08029, Barcelona, Barcelona, Spain **(100%)**
Tel.: (34) 934955700
Web Site: http://www.salvat.com
Sales Range: $25-49.9 Million
Emp.: 40
Book Publishers
N.A.I.C.S.: 513130

Subsidiary (Domestic):

Telemarketing (TMS) (4)
58 Rue Jean Bleuzen, F 92178, Vanves, France **(100%)**
Tel.: (33) 160396508
Advertising Services
N.A.I.C.S.: 541870

Subsidiary (Non-US):

The Orion Publishing Group Limited (4)
Carmelite House 50 Victoria Embankment, London, EC4Y 0DZ, United Kingdom **(100%)**
Tel.: (44) 2031226444
Web Site: http://www.orionbooks.co.uk
Sales Range: $50-74.9 Million
Emp.: 150
Book Publishers
N.A.I.C.S.: 513130

The Watts Publishing Group Ltd. (4)
338 Euston Rd, London, NW1 3BH, United Kingdom **(100%)**
Tel.: (44) 2078736000
Web Site: http://www.hachette.co.uk
Sales Range: $25-49.9 Million
Emp.: 60
Book Publishers
N.A.I.C.S.: 513130

Group (Domestic):

Lagardere Active SAS (3)
149-151 rue Anatole, 92300, Levallois-Perret, France **(100%)**
Tel.: (33) 141346000
Web Site: http://www.lagardere.com
Emp.: 2,000
Holding Company; Magazine Publisher, Radio Network Operator, Television Broadcasting, Audiovisual Production & Advertising Sales Brokerage Services
N.A.I.C.S.: 551112

Subsidiary (Domestic):

Add-On Factory (4)
9 place Marie-Jeanne Bassot, 92300, Levallois-Perret, France
Tel.: (33) 1 41 34 81 90
Web Site: http://www.addonfactory.fr
Audio & Video Production Services
N.A.I.C.S.: 512240
Jean-Pierre Dupasquier *(Pres)*

EDI POLOGNE S.A. (4)
28 rue Francois 1er, 75008, Paris, France
Tel.: (33) 1 47 23 27 02
Radio Station Broadcasting Services
N.A.I.C.S.: 516110

Affiliate (Non-US):

EMAP Magazines Ltd. (4)
Telephone House 69-77 Paul Street, London, EC2A 4NQ, United Kingdom **(33.39%)**
Tel.: (44) 30332600
Web Site: http://www.emap.com
Sales Range: $200-249.9 Million
Emp.: 350
Magazine Publisher
N.A.I.C.S.: 513120
Natasha Christie-Miller *(CEO)*

Subsidiary (Domestic):

EUROPE 1 IMMOBILIER (4)
26 Bis Rue Francois 1er, 75008, Paris, France
Tel.: (33) 820 31 9000
Web Site: http://www.europe1.fr
Radio Station Broadcasting Services
N.A.I.C.S.: 516110
Denis Olivennes *(Pres & CEO)*

EUROPE 2 ENTREPRISES (4)
28 Rue Francois 1er, 75008, Paris, France
Tel.: (33) 1 47 23 11 00
Radio Station Broadcasting Services
N.A.I.C.S.: 516110

Subsidiary (Non-US):

Editora Abril (4)
62 Rua Cerro Cora 2175 1st floor Part A Vila Romana, Sao Paulo, 05061-450, SP, Brazil
Tel.: (55) 1142002006
Web Site: http://www.assine.abril.com.br
Magazine Publisher
N.A.I.C.S.: 513120

Elle Verlag GmbH (4)
Arabellastrasse 23, 81925, Munich, Germany **(33.39%)**
Tel.: (49) 8992503355
Web Site: http://www.elle.de
Sales Range: $50-74.9 Million
Emp.: 200
Publisher
N.A.I.C.S.: 513120
Sabine Nedelchev *(Editor-in-Chief)*

Subsidiary (Domestic):

Europe 1 Telecompagnie (4)
26 Bis Rue Francois 1er, 75008, Paris, France **(99.08%)**
Tel.: (33) 00144319000
Web Site: http://www.europe1.fr
Sales Range: $25-49.9 Million
Emp.: 50
Radio Broadcasting
N.A.I.C.S.: 516110
Alexandre Bompard *(Mng Dir)*

Subsidiary (Domestic):

Europe Audiovisuel (5)
25 Rue Francois 1 Er, F 75008, Paris, France **(45.06%)**
Tel.: (33) 147231382
Sales Range: $25-49.9 Million
Audio Visual Production
N.A.I.C.S.: 512240

Subsidiary (Domestic):

Groupe Interdeco (4)
23 Rue Baudin, PO Box 311, F 92534, Levallois-Perret, France **(100%)**
Tel.: (33) 141348000
Web Site: http://www.interdeco.fr
Sales Range: $75-99.9 Million
Emp.: 500
Media Planning Agency
N.A.I.C.S.: 541810

Subsidiary (Non-US):

Interdeco Espagne (5)
Calle Santa Engracia 23, E 28010, Madrid, Spain **(100%)**
Tel.: (34) 917287000
Web Site: http://www.interdeco.es
Publisher
N.A.I.C.S.: 513110
Francisco Abad *(Dir Gen)*

Subsidiary (US):

Hachette Filipacchi Holdings, Inc. (4)
1271 Ave of the Americas, New York, NY 10020 **(66.77%)**
Tel.: (212) 767-6000
Web Site: http://www.hfmus.com
Sales Range: $200-249.9 Million
Emp.: 800
Publisher of Magazines
N.A.I.C.S.: 513120

Unit (Domestic):

ELLE.com (5)
1633 Brdwy 44th Fl, New York, NY 10019
Tel.: (212) 767-5800
Web Site: http://www.elle.com
Online Women's Magazine
N.A.I.C.S.: 513120

Subsidiary (Domestic):

Hachette Filipacchi Global USA (5)
1633 Broadway 45th Fl, New York, NY 10019-6708
Tel.: (212) 767-6364
Web Site: http://www.hfmus.com

INTERNATIONAL PUBLIC

Sales Range: $100-124.9 Million
Emp.: 500
Publishing
N.A.I.C.S.: 513120

Subsidiary (Non-US):

Hearst Fujingaho Co., Ltd. (4)
Minami-Aoyama Tokyu Bldg 3F 3-8-38, Minato, Tokyo, 107 0062, Japan
Tel.: (81) 492741400
Web Site: http://www.hearst.co.jp
Book & Magazine Publisher
N.A.I.C.S.: 513130
Nicolas Floquet *(CEO)*

LAGARDERE ACTIVE ENTREPRISES JAPAN (4)
Tokyu Building 5F 3-8-38 Minami Aoyama, Minato-Ku, Tokyo, 107-0062, Japan
Tel.: (81) 363845400
Web Site: http://www.lagardere-active.co.jp
Emp.: 10
Magazine Publisher
N.A.I.C.S.: 513120
Laurent Patouillet *(Mng Dir & VP)*

Subsidiary (Domestic):

LAGARDERE MEDIA CONSULTING (4)
28 Rue Francois 1er, 75008, Paris, France
Tel.: (33) 1 41 34 67 16
Production Management Consulting Services
N.A.I.C.S.: 541618

LAGARDERE NEWS (4)
121 Avenue de Malakoff, 75216, Paris, France
Tel.: (33) 1 40 69 16 00
Newspaper Publishers
N.A.I.C.S.: 513110

LAGARDERE THEMATIQUES (4)
32 Rue Francois 1er, 75008, Paris, France
Tel.: (33) 147231063
Video Production Services
N.A.I.C.S.: 512110

Subsidiary (Non-US):

LEGION UK Ltd. (4)
Wilberforce House Station Road, London, NW4 4QE, United Kingdom
Tel.: (44) 20 7793 0200
Video Production Services
N.A.I.C.S.: 512110

Subsidiary (Domestic):

Lagardere Active Digital SAS (4)
149-151 rue Anatole France, 92300, Levallois-Perret, France
Tel.: (33) 1 4134 6000
Online Magazine Publisher
N.A.I.C.S.: 513120
Thomas Kouck *(Publr)*

Subsidiary (Domestic):

Groupe Psychologies SA (5)
17 Rue de Surene, 75019, Paris, France
Tel.: (33) 140179844
Web Site: https://www.psychologies.com
Online Health Magazine Publisher
N.A.I.C.S.: 513120

Subsidiary (Domestic):

Lagardere Active Finances (SAS) (4)
149 Rue Anatole France, 92300, Levallois-Perret, France
Tel.: (33) 1 41 34 61 46
Financial Management Services
N.A.I.C.S.: 523999

Lagardere Active Radio International S.A. (4)
28 Rue Francois 1er, 75008, Paris, France
Tel.: (33) 1 47 23 27 12
Radio Station Broadcasting Services
N.A.I.C.S.: 516110

Lagardere Active TV (4)
28 Rue Francois 1ER, 75 008, Paris, France
Tel.: (33) 1 4134 6000
Web Site: http://www.lagardere-tvdistribution.com

AND PRIVATE COMPANIES — VIVENDI SE

Television Programming Distr
N.A.I.C.S.: 512120
Jean-Rene Aucouturier *(Sr VP-Sls & New Bus)*

Lagardere Entertainment SAS (4)
7 rue du Dome, 92773, Boulogne-Billancourt, France
Tel.: (33) 1 4074 7888
Web Site: http://www.lagardere-entertainment.com
Television Program Production & Distribution Services
N.A.I.C.S.: 512110
Christophe Thoral *(Pres & Dir-Publ)*

Subsidiary (Domestic):

909 PRODUCTION (5)
7 rue du dome, 92100, Boulogne-Billancourt, France
Tel.: (33) 140742650
Web Site: http://www.909productions.tv
Sales Range: $25-49.9 Million
Emp.: 30
Video Production Services
N.A.I.C.S.: 512110

ANGO PRODUCTION (5)
7/15 Rue Du Dome, 92100, Boulogne-Billancourt, France
Tel.: (33) 140746262
Web Site: http://www.angoproductions.com
Sales Range: $25-49.9 Million
Emp.: 4
Video Production Services
N.A.I.C.S.: 512110
Ivan Sadik *(Mng Dir)*

AUBES PRODUCTIONS (5)
7 Rue Du Dome, 92100, Boulogne-Billancourt, France
Tel.: (33) 1 40 74 76 00
Emp.: 9
Video Production Services
N.A.I.C.S.: 512110
Antoine Perset *(Pres)*

Angel Productions SASU (5)
7-15 gome, Boulogne-Billancourt, 92100, France
Tel.: (33) 1 40 74 76 16
Web Site: http://www.lagardere.com
Video Production Services
N.A.I.C.S.: 512110

Atlantique Productions SA (5)
7 Rue du Dome, 92100, Boulogne-Billancourt, France
Tel.: (33) 1 40 74 78 88
Web Site: http://www.atlantique-productions.fr
Video Production Services
N.A.I.C.S.: 512110
Olivier Bibas *(Dir-Publ)*

CARSON PROD (5)
27 Rue Marbeuf, 75008, Paris, France
Tel.: (33) 1 40 73 82 50
Web Site: http://www.carson-prod.com
Television Broadcasting Services
N.A.I.C.S.: 516120

DEMD Productions S.A.S (5)
7/15 rue du Dome, 92100, Boulogne-Billancourt, France
Tel.: (33) 140747800
Web Site: http://www.demd-productions.com
Sales Range: $25-49.9 Million
Emp.: 12
Video Production Services
N.A.I.C.S.: 512110
Sebastien Pavard *(Gen Mgr)*

EDITIONS MUSICALES FRANCOIS 1er (5)
7 Rue du dome, 92100, Boulogne-Billancourt, France
Tel.: (33) 140747888
Web Site: http://www.editionsfrancois1er.com
Sales Range: $25-49.9 Million
Emp.: 10
Video Production Services
N.A.I.C.S.: 512110

Electron Libre Productions Sarl (5)
24-26 Quai Alphonse Le Gallo, 92100, Boulogne-Billancourt, France
Tel.: (33) 1 40 74 77 54

Sales Range: $25-49.9 Million
Emp.: 20
Video Production Services
N.A.I.C.S.: 512120
Michael Kazan *(Co-Mng Dir)*

GMT Productions S.A.S. (5)
64 Rue du Chateau, 92660, Boulogne-Billancourt, France
Tel.: (33) 1 41 22 30 00
Web Site: http://www.gmtproductions.fr
Sales Range: $25-49.9 Million
Emp.: 20
Video Production Services
N.A.I.C.S.: 512110

Leo Vision S.A.S. (5)
7/15 Rue du Dome, 92100, Boulogne-Billancourt, France
Tel.: (33) 1 40 74 77 00
Video Production Services
N.A.I.C.S.: 512110
Takis Candilis *(Pres)*

MAXIMAL PRODUCTIONS (5)
7 Rue du Dome, 92100, Boulogne-Billancourt, France
Tel.: (33) 140747888
Web Site: http://www.maximal-productions.com
Emp.: 200
Video Production Services
N.A.I.C.S.: 512110

Reservoir Prod SASU (5)
101 Boulevard Murat, 75016, Paris, France
Tel.: (33) 1 5384 3000
Web Site: http://www.reservoir-prod.fr
Sales Range: $10-24.9 Million
Emp.: 40
Television Program Production Services
N.A.I.C.S.: 512110

Subsidiary (Domestic):

MAXIMAL NEWS TELEVISION (4)
25 Rue Francois 1er, 75008, Paris, France
Tel.: (33) 147231680
Television Broadcasting Services
N.A.I.C.S.: 516120

Subsidiary (Non-US):

MONTREUX PUBLICATIONS S.A. (4)
Chemin Des Terrasses 12, BP 1, 1820, Montreux, Switzerland
Tel.: (41) 21962 80 60
Sales Range: $25-49.9 Million
Emp.: 10
Newspaper & Magazine Publishing Services
N.A.I.C.S.: 513110

Subsidiary (Domestic):

NEXTDATA S.R.L. (4)
149 rue Anatole France, 92300, Levallois-Perret, France
Tel.: (33) 1 74 31 37 89
Web Site: http://www.mynextdata.com
Social Media Advertising Services
N.A.I.C.S.: 541890

NEXTIDEA SAS (4)
16 rue du Dome, 92100, Boulogne-Billancourt, France
Tel.: (33) 1 74 31 36 36
Web Site: http://www.next-idea.fr
Digital Marketing Consulting Services
N.A.I.C.S.: 541613

NEXTPREMIUM SAS (4)
16 rue du Dome, 92100, Boulogne-Billancourt, France
Tel.: (33) 1 74 31 36 30
Web Site: http://www.nextpremium.fr
Advertising Agency Services
N.A.I.C.S.: 541810

Subsidiary (Non-US):

Ogaan Publications Pvt. Ltd. (4)
501 Nirman Kendra Off Dr E Moses Rd Famous Studio Lane Mahalaxmi, Mumbai, 400 011, Maharashtra, India **(100%)**
Tel.: (91) 22 24972884
Web Site: http://www.ellenow.com
Sales Range: $25-49.9 Million
Emp.: 60
Magazine, Book Publishing & English Publications

N.A.I.C.S.: 513120
Sonia Bajaj *(Gen Mgr-Mktg)*

Subsidiary (Domestic):

PERFORMANCES S.A. (4)
28 Rue Francois 1er, Paris, 75008, France
Tel.: (33) 142322000
Sales Range: $25-49.9 Million
Emp.: 100
Radio Station Broadcasting Services
N.A.I.C.S.: 516110

PROMOTION ET SPECTACLES D'EUROPE 1 (4)
26 B Rue Francois 1er, 75008, Paris, France
Tel.: (33) 147235678
Web Site: http://www.deurope1.com
Emp.: 300
Newspaper Publishers
N.A.I.C.S.: 513110
Denis Olivennes *(Pres)*

PUBLICATIONS GROUPE LOISIRS (4)
149 Rue Anatole France, 92534, Levallois-Perret, France
Tel.: (33) 1 41 34 62 33
Newspaper Publishing Services
N.A.I.C.S.: 513110

Subsidiary (Non-US):

Post International Media Co., Ltd, (4)
7/F Bangkok Post Building 136 Sunthornkosa Road, Klong Toey, Bangkok, 10110, Thailand **(32.72%)**
Tel.: (66) 26164666
Web Site: http://www.ellethailand.com
Magazine Publisher & Distr
N.A.I.C.S.: 513120

Subsidiary (Domestic):

RFM Entreprises S.A.S. (4)
28 rue Francois 1er, 75008, Paris, France
Tel.: (33) 1 42 32 20 00
Radio Broadcasting Services
N.A.I.C.S.: 516110

RFM RESEAU NORD S.A.S. (4)
10 boulevard des talards, 35400, Saint-Malo, France
Tel.: (33) 299403232
Radio Station Broadcasting Services
N.A.I.C.S.: 516110

RFM RESEAU SUD (4)
67 avenue de la republique, 46130, Biarrs-sur-Cere, France
Tel.: (33) 565386666
Radio Station Broadcasting Services
N.A.I.C.S.: 516110

Regie 1 S.C.S. (4)
31 Rue Du Colisee, 75008, Paris, France
Tel.: (33) 1 47 23 15 50
Advertising Agency Services
N.A.I.C.S.: 541810

SOCIETE DE PRESSE FEMININE (4)
149 Rue Anatole, 92300, Levallois-Perret, France
Tel.: (33) 141346000
Magazine Publisher
N.A.I.C.S.: 513120

Selma S.A (4)
11 Mail Camille Du Gast, 92600, Asnieres-sur-Seine, France
Tel.: (33) 140862679
Magazine Publishing Services
N.A.I.C.S.: 513120

Subsidiary (Non-US):

Studio Zet Sp. z o.o. (4)
Zurawia 8, 00-503, Warsaw, Poland
Tel.: (48) 225833180
Web Site: http://www.studiozet.pl
Sales Range: $25-49.9 Million
Emp.: 5
Video Production Services
N.A.I.C.S.: 512110
Justyna Wojtkowska *(Mng Dir)*

Subsidiary (Domestic):

VIRGIN RADIO RESEAU NORD (4)

14 rue francois robin, 56100, Lorient, France
Tel.: (33) 297839383
Radio Station Broadcasting Services
N.A.I.C.S.: 516110

Group (Domestic):

Lagardere Travel Retail SAS (3)
52 avenue Hoche, 75008, Paris, France **(100%)**
Tel.: (33) 142990700
Web Site: http://www.lagardere-tr.com
Sales Range: $1-4.9 Billion
Emp.: 22,000
Travel Retail Services
N.A.I.C.S.: 561599
Dag Inge Rasmussen *(Chm & CEO)*

Subsidiary (Non-US):

AELIA RETAIL ESPANA SA (4)
Avenida de Valdelaparra 29, 28108, Alcobendas, Madrid, Spain
Tel.: (34) 91 657 69 00
Books Publishing Services
N.A.I.C.S.: 513130

Subsidiary (Domestic):

Aelia (4)
22 rue Chaptal, CS 50117, 22000, Saint-Brieuc, Cedex, France
Tel.: (33) 296682600
Web Site: http://www.aelia.com
Convenience Store & Gift Shop Operator
N.A.I.C.S.: 459420
Bruno Bouchacourt *(Exec VP-Intl Ops)*

Subsidiary (Non-US):

Aelia Czech Republic S.R.O. (4)
Aviaticka 1048/12, Prague, 160 00, Czech Republic
Tel.: (420) 73 4357706
Airport Duty Free Retailer
N.A.I.C.S.: 459999

Aelia Uk Ltd (4)
Navigation House Airport Way London Luton Airport, Luton, LU2 9LY, Bedfordshire, United Kingdom
Tel.: (44) 1582 744 300
Cosmetic Product Retailer
N.A.I.C.S.: 456120
Philip Manning *(Mng Dir)*

Airport Fashion sa (4)
38 Avenue Vibert, 1227, Carouge, Switzerland
Tel.: (41) 219637200
Cosmetic Product Distr
N.A.I.C.S.: 456120

Alvadis NV (4)
Lenniksebaan 451, 1070, Anderlecht, Belgium
Tel.: (32) 255641 58
Web Site: http://www.alvadis.be
Prepaid Phone Card Distr
N.A.I.C.S.: 424130

BUVIHIR KFT (4)
Prielle Kornelia utca 4, 1117, Budapest, Hungary
Tel.: (36) 12079301
Newspaper Publishers
N.A.I.C.S.: 513110

Distrisud Sa (4)
Rue Ateliers Smulders 27, Grace-Hollogne, 4460, Belgium
Tel.: (32) 43402110
Duty Free Product Retailer
N.A.I.C.S.: 445320

Dynapresse Marketing SA (4)
38 Avenue Vibert, 1227, Carouge, Geneva, Switzerland
Tel.: (41) 22 308 08 08
Web Site: http://www.dynapresse.ch
Sales Range: $25-49.9 Million
Emp.: 20
Newspaper & Magazine Publishing Services
N.A.I.C.S.: 513110

EURO-EXCELLENCE INC. (4)
1625 Boulevard Dagenais West, Laval, H7L 5A3, QC, Canada
Tel.: (450) 632-9440
Web Site: http://www.euro-excellence.ca

VIVENDI SE

Vivendi SE—(Continued)
Confectionary Product Mfr
N.A.I.C.S.: 311999

Subsidiary (Domestic):

Eurodis S.A.S. (4)
36 Avenue De La Marne, 92600, Asnieres-sur-Seine, France
Tel.: (33) 147937571
Books Publishing Services
N.A.I.C.S.: 513130

Subsidiary (Non-US):

FERS
Bahnhofsplatz 1, Wiesbaden, 65189, Hessen, Germany
Tel.: (49) 6119730735
Books Publishing Services
N.A.I.C.S.: 513130

HDS INMEDIO ROMANIA (4)
Iride Business Park B-dul Dimitrie Pompeiu nr 9-9A cladirea 10, 020335, Bucharest, Romania
Tel.: (40) 314078250
Web Site: http://www.lsromania.ro
Magazine & Book Distr
N.A.I.C.S.: 424920
Stefan Picard *(Gen Mgr)*

HDS Polska Sp. z o.o. (4)
Aleje Jerozolimskie 176, 02-486, Warsaw, Poland
Tel.: (48) 225723200
Web Site: http://www.hds.pl
Book Store Operating Services
N.A.I.C.S.: 459210

HDS RETAIL CZ A.S. (4)
Lighthouse - Jankovcova 1569/2c, 170 00, Prague, Czech Republic
Tel.: (420) 234 379 300
Web Site: http://www.hds.cz
Commercial Books Retailer
N.A.I.C.S.: 459210
Richard Kalhous *(Gen Mgr)*

HUNGAROPRESS KFT (4)
Tablas u 32, 1097, Budapest, Hungary
Tel.: (36) 13484040
Web Site: http://www.hungaropress.hu
Sales Range: $25-49.9 Million
Magazine Publisher
N.A.I.C.S.: 424920

Hds Deutschland Gmbh (4)
Bahnhofsplatz 1, Wiesbaden, 65189, Hessen, Germany
Tel.: (49) 611973070
Web Site: http://www.lf-travelretail.de
Book Distr
N.A.I.C.S.: 424920
Thomas Wiesel *(Gen Mgr)*

Hirker ZRt (4)
Tablas Utca 39, 1097, Budapest, Hungary
Tel.: (36) 13477300
Newspaper Publishers
N.A.I.C.S.: 513110

Interpress Slovakia, spol. s.r.o. (4)
Vyhonska 13, Bratislava, 83106, Slovakia
Tel.: (421) 244871501
Web Site: http://www.interpress.sk
Newspaper & Magazine Publisher
N.A.I.C.S.: 513110

LAGARDERE SERVICES CHINA CO LIMITED (4)
7E07 Building A 492 Anhua Rd, 200050, Shanghai, China
Tel.: (86) 216268 2839
Duty Free Product Retailer
N.A.I.C.S.: 445260

LMPI (Les Messageries de Presse Internationale) (4)
8155 Rue Larrey, Anjou, H1J 2L5, QC, Canada (100%)
Tel.: (514) 355-5610
Web Site: http://www.lmpi.com
Sales Range: $50-74.9 Million
Magazine Publisher
N.A.I.C.S.: 513120

LS travel retail Deutschland GmbH (4)
Bahnhofsplatz 1, 65189, Wiesbaden, Germany
Tel.: (49) 611973070
Web Site: http://www.lagardere-tr.de
Travel Retail Outlets Owner & Operator
N.A.I.C.S.: 445320

Lagardere Services Bulgaria LTD (4)
Fridtjof Nansen No 9 7th Floor, 1142, Sofia, Bulgaria
Tel.: (359) 893 30 30 76
Web Site: http://www.lagardere-services.bg
Sales Range: $25-49.9 Million
Duty Free Product Retailer
N.A.I.C.S.: 445320

Lagardere Services Hong Kong Limited (4)
Shop 102A 1/F Regal Airport Hotel 9 Cheong Tat Road Hong Kong, International Airport, Hong Kong, China (Hong Kong)
Tel.: (852) 2116 8868
Sales Range: $25-49.9 Million
Travel Arrangement Services
N.A.I.C.S.: 561599

Lagardere Services Singapore Pte Ltd (4)
51 Bras Basah Road 07-03 Manulife Centre, Singapore, 189554, Singapore
Tel.: (65) 6593 1700
Books Publishing Services
N.A.I.C.S.: 513130
Lee Charn Cheng *(Gen Mgr)*

Lapker Zrt. (4)
Tablas utca 32, 1097, Budapest, Hungary (80.01%)
Tel.: (36) 13477300
Web Site: http://www.lapker.hu
Sales Range: $25-49.9 Million
Press Distribution & Retail
N.A.I.C.S.: 513110

NewsLink Pty Ltd (4)
Domestic Terminal Airport Dr, Brisbane, 4000, QLD, Australia
Tel.: (61) 7 3860 5789
Newspaper & Magazine Distr
N.A.I.C.S.: 424920
Garry Forsyth *(Area Mgr)*

PRESSE IMPORT SA (4)
Route Andre Piller 39, 1720, Corminboeuf, Switzerland
Tel.: (41) 26 467 51 11
Newspaper & Magazine Distr
N.A.I.C.S.: 424920

Subsidiary (US):

Paradies Lagardere (4)
2849 Paces Ferry Rd Overlook 1 Ste 400, Atlanta, GA 30339
Tel.: (404) 344-7905
Web Site: http://www.paradieslagardere.com
Emp.: 10,000
Airport Dining & Travel Essentials Retail & Services
N.A.I.C.S.: 722513
Gregg Paradies *(Pres & CEO)*

Subsidiary (Domestic):

Hojeij Branded Foods LLC (5)
1750 The Exchange SE, Atlanta, GA 30339
Tel.: (800) 426-5971
Airport Restaurant Operator
N.A.I.C.S.: 722511
Boutros Khalil *(Sr VP-Ops)*

Subsidiary (Domestic):

Taste, Inc. (6)
1161 Mission Ste 1st Fl, San Francisco, CA 94103
Tel.: (416) 986-2818
Wine Retailer
N.A.I.C.S.: 445320
Ellen Bozzo *(CFO)*

Subsidiary (US):

Paradies Lagardere (4)
2849 Paces Ferry Rd Overlook 1 Ste 400, Atlanta, GA 30339
Tel.: (404) 344-7905
Web Site: http://www.paradieslagardere.com
Emp.: 300
Airport Retail Store & Restaurants Operator
N.A.I.C.S.: 455219

Gerard Savaria *(Chief Dev Officer)*

Subsidiary (Non-US):

Payot Naville Distribution SA (4)
Avenue Vibert 38, Case postale 1536, Carouge, 1227, Switzerland
Tel.: (41) 22 308 04 44
Web Site: http://www.lagardere.com
Investment Management Service
N.A.I.C.S.: 523999
Jean-Marie Lebac *(CEO)*

Subsidiary (Domestic):

Naville S.A. (5)
38 Avenue Vibert, CP 1756, Carouge, 1227, Switzerland
Tel.: (41) 22 308 04 44
Web Site: http://www.naville.ch
Emp.: 30
Newspaper Distr
N.A.I.C.S.: 424920
Jean-Yves Leroux *(CEO)*

Unit (Domestic):

Naville S.A. - Naville Detail Unit (6)
38 Avenue Vibert, CP 1756, 1227, Carouge, Switzerland
Tel.: (41) 22 308 05 27
Web Site: http://www.naville.ch
Book Distr
N.A.I.C.S.: 424920

Naville S.A. - Naville Livre Unit (6)
Avenue Vibert 38, 1227, Carouge, Switzerland
Tel.: (41) 22 308 04 44
Web Site: http://www.naville.ch
Book Distr
N.A.I.C.S.: 424920

Naville S.A. - Naville Presse Unit (6)
38 Avenue Vibert, 1227, Carouge, Switzerland
Tel.: (41) 22 308 05 02
Sales Range: $150-199.9 Million
Magazine Distr
N.A.I.C.S.: 424920
Alain Meynier *(Gen Mgr)*

Naville S.A. - Naville Service Unit (6)
38 Avenue Vibert, CP 1756, Carouge, 1227, Switzerland
Tel.: (41) 22 308 04 83
Sales Range: $100-124.9 Million
Emp.: 4
Book Distr
N.A.I.C.S.: 424920

Subsidiary (Non-US):

Press Point International (4)
1st Derbenevsky side street offices 306-307, 5 Business Center, Derbenevskaya Plaza, R-125438, Moscow, Russia
Tel.: (7) 495 984 7287
Periodical & Foreign Magazine Publisher
N.A.I.C.S.: 513120

Press Shop ALG SA (4)
9 Alfons Gossetlaan, 1702, Groot-Bijgaarden, Belgium
Tel.: (32) 2 422 28 11
Web Site: http://www.press-shop.be
Sales Range: $25-49.9 Million
Duty Free Product Retailer
N.A.I.C.S.: 445320

Subsidiary (Domestic):

Relay France (4)
126 Rue Jules Guesde, PO Box 304, 92301, Levallois-Perret, France (100%)
Tel.: (33) 0140872600
Web Site: http://www.relay.fr
News Dealer
N.A.I.C.S.: 459210

Subsidiary (Non-US):

SGEL (Sociedad General Espanola de Libreria) (4)
Avda Valdelaparra 29, 28108, Alcobendas, Madrid, Spain (100%)
Tel.: (34) 916576902
Web Site: http://www.sgel.es

INTERNATIONAL PUBLIC

Sales Range: $100-124.9 Million
Newspapers
N.A.I.C.S.: 513110

THE PURELY GROUP PTY LTD (4)
Level 5 50 Holt Street, Surry Hills, 2010, NSW, Australia
Tel.: (61) 2 8218 1100
Web Site: http://www.purelyaustralian.com
Airport Duty Free Retailer
N.A.I.C.S.: 459999

Topcodi S.L. (4)
Avda Valdeparra 29, 28100, Alcobendas, Spain
Tel.: (34) 916576900
Books Publishing Services
N.A.I.C.S.: 513130

Zendis SL (4)
Avda Valdelaparra 29 Pol Ind Alcobendas, 28108, Alcobendas, Spain
Tel.: (34) 91 657 69 00
Web Site: http://www.zendis.es
Marketing Consulting Services
N.A.I.C.S.: 541613

Group (Domestic):

Lagardere Unlimited SAS (3)
16-18 Rue du Dome, Boulogne-Billancourt, 92100, France
Tel.: (33) 1 74 31 72 00
Web Site: http://www.lagardere-unlimited.com
Emp.: 250
Sports Academy Operator
N.A.I.C.S.: 711211

Subsidiary (US):

Blackwave Sports Investment Company LLC (4)
140 Broadway 46th Fl, New York, NY 10005
Tel.: (800) 420-7614
Financial Investment Services
N.A.I.C.S.: 523999

Subsidiary (Non-US):

EVENTERPRISE Gmbh (4)
Ernst-Merck-Str 12-14, Hamburg, 20099, Germany
Tel.: (49) 4028409990
Web Site: http://www.eventerprise-gmbh.de
Sales Range: $50-74.9 Million
Emp.: 5
Sports Event Management Services
N.A.I.C.S.: 711211
Michael Harms *(Dir-Tech)*

IEC HOLDING AB (4)
Artillerigatan 42, 114 45, Stockholm, Sweden
Tel.: (46) 86660402
Emp.: 46
Investment Management Service
N.A.I.C.S.: 523999
Martin Hakansson *(CEO)*

ISPR GmbH (4)
Nagelsweg 33-35, Hamburg, 20097, Germany
Tel.: (49) 40376770
Television Broadcasting Services
N.A.I.C.S.: 516120

Subsidiary (Domestic):

LAGARDERE FINANCE (4)
42 rue Washington, Paris, 75408, France
Tel.: (33) 1 40 69 16 00
Book Publishers
N.A.I.C.S.: 513130

LAGARDERE UNLIMITED LIVE ENTERTAINMENT (4)
16-18 rue du Dome, 92100, Boulogne-Billancourt, France
Tel.: (33) 1 74 31 70 50
Web Site: http://www.lagardere.com
Television Broadcasting Services
N.A.I.C.S.: 516120
Luthna Plocus *(Head-Comm & External Rels)*

LAGARDERE UNLIMITED STADIUM SOLUTIONS SAS (4)
16 rue du Dome, Boulogne-Billancourt, 92100, France

AND PRIVATE COMPANIES — VIVENDI SE

Tel.: (33) 1 74 31 72 00
Web Site: http://www.lu-stadiumsolutions.com
Stadium Marketing Consulting Services
N.A.I.C.S.: 541613

Subsidiary (Non-US):

LAGARDERE UNLIMITED TALENTS UK LIMITED (4)
Royalty House 32 Sackville Street, London, W1S 3EA, United Kingdom
Tel.: (44) 2074345760
Sports Club Operator
N.A.I.C.S.: 711211

Subsidiary (Domestic):

Lagardere Paris Racing Ressources SASP
Chemin de La Croix Catelan, 75016, Paris, France
Tel.: (33) 1 45 27 55 85
Web Site:
  http://www.lagardereparisracing.com
Sales Range: $75-99.9 Million
Emp.: 150
Sports Event Operator
N.A.I.C.S.: 711310

Subsidiary (Non-US):

PR EVENT I BASTAD AB (4)
Box 53210, 400 16, Gothenburg, Sweden
Tel.: (46) 31940250
Sport Event Organizer
N.A.I.C.S.: 711310

SPORTFIVE Asia Sdn Bhd (4)
Suite 11 03A Level 11 Menara Citibank 165 Jalan Ampang, 50450, Kuala Lumpur, Malaysia
Tel.: (60) 3 21 61 71 66
Sport Event Organizer
N.A.I.C.S.: 711310

SPORTFIVE EOOD (4)
11 Uzundjovska Street, Sofia, 1000, Bulgaria
Tel.: (359) 2 9810182
Web Site: http://www.sportfive.com
Sales Range: $50-74.9 Million
Emp.: 3
Sport Event Organizer
N.A.I.C.S.: 711310
Dragomir Draganov *(Mng Dir)*

SPORTFIVE GmbH & Co. KG (4)
Barcastrasse 5, 22087, Hamburg, Germany
Tel.: (49) 40 376 770
Web Site: http://sportfive.com
Sport Event Organizer
N.A.I.C.S.: 711310

Subsidiary (Domestic):

SPORTFIVE INTERMEDIATE GmbH (5)
Barcastrasse 5, Hamburg, Germany
Tel.: (49) 40 376 770
Television Broadcasting Services
N.A.I.C.S.: 516120

Subsidiary (Non-US):

SPORTFIVE INTERNATIONAL SA (4)
Place des Alpes 2-4, Geneva, 1201, Switzerland
Tel.: (41) 22 5963 700
Web Site: http://www.sportfive.com
Emp.: 30
Sport Event Organizer
N.A.I.C.S.: 711310
Laurence Amand Jules *(COO)*

Subsidiary (Non-US):

SPORTFIVE MEDIA SOLUTIONS SAS (5)
16-18 rue du Dome, 92100, Boulogne-Billancourt, France
Tel.: (33) 1 74 31 70 50
Television Broadcasting Services
N.A.I.C.S.: 516120

Subsidiary (Non-US):

SPORTFIVE SINGAPORE PTE LTD (4)
8 Shenton Way 30-03, Singapore, 068811, Singapore
Tel.: (65) 6578 5500
Web Site: http://www.sportfive.com
Sales Range: $50-74.9 Million
Emp.: 13
Sport Event Organizer
N.A.I.C.S.: 711310
Braden Clarke *(Mng Dir)*

SPORTFIVE UK Ltd (4)
4th Floor Cardinal Place 80 Victoria Street, London, SW1E 5JL, United Kingdom
Tel.: (44) 2030393740
Web Site: http://www.sportfive.co.uk
Sales Range: $50-74.9 Million
Emp.: 7
Sports Event Organizing Services
N.A.I.C.S.: 711310

SPORTFIVE VERWALTUNGS GmbH (4)
Barcastrasse 5, 22087, Hamburg, Germany
Tel.: (49) 40376770
Emp.: 300
Sports Event Operator
N.A.I.C.S.: 711310

Subsidiary (US):

SPORTS MEDIA ADVISORS LLC (4)
191 Elm St, New Canaan, CT 06840
Tel.: (203) 594-7598
Web Site:
  http://www.sportsmediaadvisors.com
Investment Advisory Services
N.A.I.C.S.: 523940
Douglas Perlman *(Founder & CEO)*

Subsidiary (Non-US):

Sportfive Italy SA (4)
Corso Einaudi 22, 10129, Turin, Italy
Tel.: (39) 0 11 4500750
Web Site: http://www.sportfive.com
Sports Marketing Agency Services
N.A.I.C.S.: 711410
Walter Crippa *(Mng Dir)*

THE SPORTS PROMOTERS GmbH (4)
Barcastrasse 5, 22087, Hamburg, Germany
Tel.: (49) 40 376 77 327
Web Site: http://www.the-sports-promoters.com
Sales Range: $50-74.9 Million
Emp.: 7
Sports Event Management Services
N.A.I.C.S.: 711310
Mark Schober *(Sr Mgr-Events)*

UPSOLUT EVENT GmbH (4)
Friesenweg 7, 22763, Hamburg, 22763, Germany
Tel.: (49) 40 88 18 00 10
Web Site: http://www.lagardere-unlimited.de
Emp.: 40
Sports Event Operator
N.A.I.C.S.: 711310
Frank Bertling *(Mng Dir & VP-Natl Events)*

UPSOLUT MERCHANDISING Gmbh & Co KG (4)
Friesenweg 7, 22763, Hamburg, Germany
Tel.: (49) 40 8818000
Sporting Goods Mfr & Distr
N.A.I.C.S.: 339920

UPSOLUT SPORT AG (4)
Friesenweg 7, 22763, Hamburg, 22763, Germany
Tel.: (49) 4088180010
Web Site: http://www.upsolut.de
Sales Range: $25-49.9 Million
Emp.: 40
Sports Event Management Services
N.A.I.C.S.: 711310
Olivier Guiguet *(Chm)*

UpSolut Verwaltungs GmbH (4)
Friesenweg 7, 22763, Hamburg, Germany
Tel.: (49) 408818000
Sales Range: $50-74.9 Million
Emp.: 60
Sports Event Management Services
N.A.I.C.S.: 711310

WORLD SPORT GROUP BEIJING LTD (4)
10/F East Tower Beijing World Financial Center No 1 Dong San Huan Zhon, Zhong Rd Chaoyang District, Beijing, 100020, China
Tel.: (86) 10 8587 6080
Web Site: http://www.worldsportgroup.com
Sports Event Management Services
N.A.I.C.S.: 711310

WORLD SPORT GROUP INDIA LTD (4)
602 Sapphire Plot 82 S V Road, Khar West, Mumbai, 400052, India
Tel.: (91) 22 2646 4672
Web Site: http://www.worldsportgroup.com
Sales Range: $50-74.9 Million
Emp.: 14
Sports Event Management Services
N.A.I.C.S.: 711310

WORLD SPORT GROUP LTD (4)
Suite 2505 25/F Great Eagle Centre 23 Harbour Road, Wanchai, China (Hong Kong)
Tel.: (852) 2891 2000
Web Site: http://www.worldsportgroup.com
Sales Range: $50-74.9 Million
Emp.: 20
Sports Event Management Services
N.A.I.C.S.: 711310

WORLD SPORT GROUP PTE LTD (4)
8 Shenton Way 30-01, Singapore, 068811, Singapore
Tel.: (65) 6826 2688
Web Site:
  http://www.worldsportgroup.com.sg
Sales Range: $75-99.9 Million
Emp.: 150
Sport Event Organizer
N.A.I.C.S.: 711310
Seamus O'Brien *(Founder, Chm & CEO)*

WORLD SPORT GROUP PTY LTD (4)
61 Victoria Street, McMahons Point, Sydney, 2060, NSW, Australia
Tel.: (61) 2 9929 9011
Sports Event Management Services
N.A.I.C.S.: 711310

Subsidiary (US):

Lagardere North America (2)
1271 Ave of the Americas, New York, NY 10020 **(100%)**
Tel.: (212) 767-6000
Web Site: http://www.hfmus.com
Sales Range: $150-199.9 Million
Emp.: 800
Publisher
N.A.I.C.S.: 513120

Subsidiary (Domestic):

Lagardere Participations (2)
4 Rue de Presbourg, 75116, Paris, France
Tel.: (33) 140691600
Web Site: http://www.lagardere.fr
Holding Company
N.A.I.C.S.: 551112

Lagardere Ressources S.A.S. (2)
Immeuble Octant 4-10 avenue Andre Malraux, 92689, Levallois-Perret, France
Tel.: (33) 1 40 69 16 00
Web Site: http://www.lagardere.com
Sales Range: $200-249.9 Million
Emp.: 600
Book Publishers
N.A.I.C.S.: 513130

Lagardere Sports & Entertainment S.A.S (2)
16 - 18 rue du Dome, 92100, Boulogne-Billancourt, France
Tel.: (33) 174317200
Sports & Entertainment Services
N.A.I.C.S.: 711410

Lagardere Studios Distribution, SA (2)
7 Rue du Dome, 92100, Boulogne-Billancourt, France
Tel.: (33) 140747676
Web Site: http://www.lagardere-studiosdistribution.com
Film Production & Distribution Services
N.A.I.C.S.: 512110

Emmanuelle Bouilhaguet *(Mng Dir)*

Lagardere Studios SAS (2)
7 Rue du Dome, 92100, Boulogne-Billancourt, France
Tel.: (33) 140747888
Web Site: http://www.lagardere-studios.com
Film Production Services
N.A.I.C.S.: 512110
Christophe Thoral *(Pres & CEO)*

Subsidiary (Non-US):

Lagardere Travel Retail AS (2)
Voctarova 2497/18, 180 00, Prague, Czech Republic
Tel.: (420) 228224111
Web Site: http://www.lagardere-tr.cz
Travel Retail Services
N.A.I.C.S.: 561510
Richard Prochazka *(CEO)*

Lagardere Travel Retail Austria GmbH (2)
Office Park 1 B05 01, 1300, Vienna, Austria
Tel.: (43) 1700765228
Travel Retail Services
N.A.I.C.S.: 561510
Ursula Furnhammer *(CEO)*

Lagardere Travel Retail Ehf (2)
Sundagardar 2 Sundaboginn, 104, Reykjavik, Iceland
Tel.: (354) 5686588
Web Site: http://www.lagardere-tr.is
Travel Retail Services
N.A.I.C.S.: 561510
Sigurour Skagfjord *(CEO)*

Subsidiary (Domestic):

Lagardere Travel Retail France SNC (2)
55 rue Deguingand, 92689, Levallois-Perret, Cedex, France
Tel.: (33) 140872600
Travel Retail Services
N.A.I.C.S.: 561510
Virginie Amiot *(Dir-Non Food Category)*

Subsidiary (Non-US):

Lagardere Travel Retail Hong Kong Ltd. (2)
102A Regal Airport Hotel 9 Cheong Tat Road, Hong Kong International Airport Chep Lap Kok, Hong Kong, China (Hong Kong)
Tel.: (852) 21179000
Travel Retail Services
N.A.I.C.S.: 561510
Wilson Ng *(Mgr-Wine Buying)*

Lagardere Travel Retail Italia Srl (2)
Via Fratelli Bandiera 7, Gaggio di Marcon, 30020, Venice, Italy
Tel.: (39) 0414561111
Web Site: http://www.lagardere-tr.it
Travel Retail Services
N.A.I.C.S.: 561510
Alberto Signor *(CIO & CTO)*

Lagardere Travel Retail Luxembourg SARL (2)
4 rue de Treves, Findel, 2632, Sandweiler, Luxembourg
Tel.: (352) 24647500
Travel Retail Services
N.A.I.C.S.: 561510
Vincent Romet *(CEO)*

Lagardere Travel Retail Netherlands Holding BV (2)
Singaporestraat 2, 1175 RA, Lijnden, Netherlands
Tel.: (31) 204109700
Web Site: http://www.lagardere-tr.nl
Travel Retail Services
N.A.I.C.S.: 561510
Michael Hendriks *(CFO)*

Lagardere Travel Retail Singapore Pte. Ltd. (2)
10 Eunos Road 8 09-03 SingPost Centre, Singapore, 408600, Singapore
Tel.: (65) 65931700
Travel Retail Services
N.A.I.C.S.: 561510
Shernice Jong *(Sr Acct Exec)*

VIVENDI SE

Vivendi SE—(Continued)

Lagardere Travel Retail Sp Zoo (2)
Al Jerozolimskie 174, 02-486, Warsaw, Poland
Tel.: (48) 225723200
Web Site: http://www.lagardere-tr.pl
Travel Retail Services
N.A.I.C.S.: 561510
Marzena Copiuk *(Mgr-Comml Processes Dev)*

Lagardere Travel Retail UK Ltd. (2)
346 Kensington High Street, London, W14 8NS, United Kingdom
Tel.: (44) 1908991430
Web Site: http://www.lagardere-tr.uk
Travel Retail Services
N.A.I.C.S.: 561510
Marion Engelhard *(Mng Dir)*

Lagardere UK Ltd. (2)
Royalty House 32 Sackville Street, London, W1S3EA, United Kingdom
Tel.: (44) 2074345760
Magazine Publisher
N.A.I.C.S.: 513120

Subsidiary (Domestic):

LeGuide.com S.A. (2)
12 rue Godot de Mauroy, 75009, Paris, France
Tel.: (33) 175 44 56 00
Web Site: http://www.leguidegroup.com
Sales Range: $25-49.9 Million
Emp.: 150
Shopping Guides & Online Shopping Directories Publisher
N.A.I.C.S.: 513140
Francois Michel *(CEO-dooyoo GmbH & Exec VP)*

Subsidiary (Non-US):

Dooyoo GmbH (3)
Paul-Lincke-Ufer 7, 10999, Berlin, Germany
Tel.: (49) 30 29395 0
Web Site: http://www.dooyoo.de
Online Shopping Services
N.A.I.C.S.: 425120

Subsidiary (Domestic):

Les Editions Musicales Francois 1er SNC (2)
7 Rue du Dome, 92100, Boulogne-Billancourt, France
Tel.: (33) 140747888
Web Site: http://www.editionsfrancois1er.com
Music Publishing Services
N.A.I.C.S.: 512230

Subsidiary (Non-US):

Librairie Papeterie Nationale S.A. (2)
El Farah II Lot n 3, Quartier Industriel, Mohammedia, Morocco
Tel.: (212) 523319630
Web Site: http://www.lpn.ma
Books Publishing Services
N.A.I.C.S.: 513130

Little, Brown Book Group Ltd. (2)
Carmelite House 50 Victoria Embankment, London, EC4Y 0DZ, United Kingdom
Tel.: (44) 2031227000
Web Site: http://www.littlebrown.co.uk
Books Publishing Services
N.A.I.C.S.: 513130
Charles Little *(Co-Founder)*

London Property Guide Ltd. (2)
95 High Street Harrow Weald, Harrow, HA3 5DL, Middlesex, United Kingdom
Tel.: (44) 2088646115
Web Site: http://www.london-properties.co.uk
Real Estate Services
N.A.I.C.S.: 531390

Subsidiary (Domestic):

MNC SA (2)
93 rue Vieille du Temple, 75003, Paris, France
Tel.: (33) 144594159
Mobile Software Mfr & Distr
N.A.I.C.S.: 334610

Subsidiary (Non-US):

Media Transcontinental (2)
1100 Rene-Levesque West Blvd 24th floor, Montreal, H3B 4X9, QC, Canada **(100%)**
Tel.: (514) 392-9000
Web Site: http://tctranscontinental.com
Sales Range: $100-124.9 Million
Emp.: 275
Book Publishing
N.A.I.C.S.: 513130

Subsidiary (Domestic):

Merlin Productions, SAS (2)
7 Rue du Dome, 92100, Boulogne-Billancourt, France
Tel.: (33) 140747840
Web Site: http://www.merlinprod.com
Film Production Services
N.A.I.C.S.: 512110

Subsidiary (Non-US):

Neon Play Ltd. (2)
The Old Museum, Cirencester, Gloucester, GL7 1UP, United Kingdom
Tel.: (44) 1285650600
Web Site: http://www.neonplay.com
Application Development Services
N.A.I.C.S.: 541511
Oli Christie *(Founder)*

Nova Veranda 2010 SL (2)
Rosello 34 4t 3a, 08029, Barcelona, Spain
Tel.: (34) 935539933
Web Site: http://www.veranda.tv
Film Production Services
N.A.I.C.S.: 512110

OLF SA (2)
Z I 3 Corminboeuf, PO Box 1152, 1701, Fribourg, Switzerland
Tel.: (41) 26467 51 11
Web Site: http://www.olf.ch
Emp.: 144
Book Distr
N.A.I.C.S.: 424920

Onside Sports GmbH (2)
Rodingsmarkt 9, 20459, Hamburg, Germany
Tel.: (49) 40334600021
Web Site: http://onside.net
Sports Services
N.A.I.C.S.: 713940

Subsidiary (Domestic):

Pika Edition SAS (2)
Louis Hachette Building - 58 rue Jean Bleuzen, CS 70007, Vanves, 92178, Paris, Cedex, France
Tel.: (33) 141102390
Web Site: http://www.pika.fr
Books Publishing Services
N.A.I.C.S.: 513130
Cathy Fernez *(Mktg Mgr)*

Subsidiary (Non-US):

Quercus Editions Ltd. (2)
Carmelite House 50 Victoria Embankment, London, EC4Y 0DZ, United Kingdom
Tel.: (44) 2031227200
Web Site: http://www.quercusbooks.co.uk
Books Publishing Services
N.A.I.C.S.: 513130

RADIO SALU - Euro-Radio Saar GmbH (2)
Richard-Wagner-Str 58-60, 66111, Saarbrucken, Germany
Tel.: (49) 6813909
Web Site: http://www.salue.de
Radio Station Operator
N.A.I.C.S.: 516110

Subsidiary (Domestic):

Rageot Editeur, S.N.C. (2)
8 rue d'Assas, 75006, Paris, France
Tel.: (33) 149544717
Web Site: http://www.rageot.fr
Novel Publishing Services
N.A.I.C.S.: 513130

Subsidiary (Non-US):

Rising Stars UK Ltd. (2)
Carmelite House 50 Victoria Embankment, London, EC4Y 0DZ, United Kingdom
Tel.: (44) 2031226000
Web Site: http://www.risingstars-uk.com
Books Publishing Services
N.A.I.C.S.: 513130
Alexandra Taylor *(Mktg Mgr)*

Subsidiary (US):

Rooftop2 Productions Inc. (2)
488 Madison Ave 16th Fl, New York, NY 10022
Tel.: (212) 767-5700
Web Site: http://rooftop2.com
Sports & Entertainment Services
N.A.I.C.S.: 711310
Marc Tarozzi *(Exec VP)*

Subsidiary (Domestic):

SCI Assas Raspail (2)
131 BD Raspail, 75006, Paris, France
Tel.: (33) 170939769
Web Site: http://www.assasraspail.fr
Real Estate Services
N.A.I.C.S.: 531210
Bouyer Pierrick *(Mgr)*

Subsidiary (Non-US):

Salvat do Brasil Ltda (2)
Rua Purpurina 155 9 andar cj 94 Vila Madalena, Sao Paulo, 05435-030, Brazil
Tel.: (55) 1135129460
Web Site: http://br.salvat.com
Books Publishing Services
N.A.I.C.S.: 513130

Shanghai Translation Publishing House (2)
193 Fujian Rd C, Shanghai, 200001, China **(100%)**
Tel.: (86) 2153954508
Web Site: http://www.yiwen.com.cn
Sales Range: $50-74.9 Million
Emp.: 150
Magazine Publisher
N.A.I.C.S.: 513120

Short Books Ltd. (2)
Unit 316 ScreenWorks 22 Highbury Grove, London, N5 2EF, United Kingdom
Tel.: (44) 2078339429
Web Site: http://shortbooks.co.uk
Books Publishing Services
N.A.I.C.S.: 513130
Rebecca Nicolson *(Co-Founder)*

Skyhigh TV BV (2)
Melkpad 29, 1217 KA, Hilversum, Netherlands
Tel.: (31) 356263000
Web Site: http://www.skyhightv.nl
Film Production Services
N.A.I.C.S.: 512110

Subsidiary (Domestic):

Sopredis SA (2)
5 rue Musau, 67100, Strasbourg, France
Tel.: (33) 3 88 34 29 44
Hazardous Waste Collection Services
N.A.I.C.S.: 562112

Subsidiary (Non-US):

Summersdale Publishers Ltd. (2)
46 West Street, Chichester, PO19 1RP, West Sussex, United Kingdom
Tel.: (44) 1243771107
Web Site: http://www.summersdale.com
Books Publishing Services
N.A.I.C.S.: 513130
Kenneth McKay *(Production Mgr)*

The Romanian Publishing Group S.R.L. (2)
Mircea Eliade nr 18 et 10, Bucharest, Sector 1, Romania
Tel.: (40) 212302877
Magazine Publisher
N.A.I.C.S.: 513120

M7 Group SA (1)
2 rue Albert Borschette, 1246, Luxembourg, Luxembourg
Tel.: (352) 26096100
Web Site: http://www.m7group.eu
Broadcasting Media Services
N.A.I.C.S.: 516120
Hans Troelstra *(CEO)*

INTERNATIONAL PUBLIC

See Group Ltd (1)
2nd Floor Norfolk House 47 Upper Parliament Street, Nottingham, NG1 2AB, United Kingdom
Tel.: (44) 870 264 3333
Web Site: http://www.seetickets.com
Event Ticket Reservation Services
N.A.I.C.S.: 711219

See Tickets Inc. (1)
6380 Wilshire Blvd Ste 900, Los Angeles, CA 90048
Tel.: (323) 908-0607
Web Site: http://www.seetickets.us
Event Planning Services
N.A.I.C.S.: 561920
Raymond Mesa *(Assoc Dir-Client Svc)*

T-Mobile Polska S.A. (1)
ul Marynarska 12, 02-674, Warsaw, Poland
Tel.: (48) 602900000
Web Site: https://www.t-mobile.pl
Sales Range: $400-449.9 Million
Emp.: 2,000
Teleinformatics & Unified Communications
N.A.I.C.S.: 517810

Univers Poche SA (1)
12 Avenue d'italie, 75627, Paris, Cedex, France
Tel.: (33) 144160500
Web Site: http://www.universpoche.com
Book Editing & Publishing Services
N.A.I.C.S.: 513130
Marie-Christine Conchon *(CEO)*

Vivendi Mobile Entertainment S.A. (1)
103/105 Rue Anatole France, 92300, Levallois-Perret, France
Tel.: (33) 153005300
Sales Range: $25-49.9 Million
Emp.: 40
Online Gaming Software Publisher
N.A.I.C.S.: 513210

Wengo SAS (1)
12 Rue de Penthievre, 75008, Paris, France
Tel.: (33) 175757575
Web Site: http://www.wengo.fr
Telecommunication Services
N.A.I.C.S.: 517810

VIVER INCORPORADORA E CONSTRUTORA S.A.

Avenida Brigadeiro Faria Lima 1656 - 1 andar, Vila Olimpia, Sao Paulo, 01452-002, Brazil
Tel.: (55) 1130463288 BR
Web Site: https://www.viver.com.br
Year Founded: 1992
VIVR3—(BRAZ)
Rev.: $12,430,239
Assets: $56,758,726
Liabilities: $55,812,551
Net Worth: $946,175
Earnings: ($13,004,594)
Emp.: 127
Fiscal Year-end: 12/31/23
Real Estate Development Services
N.A.I.C.S.: 531390
Michael Barry Lenard *(Chm)*

VIVESCIA

2 rue Clement Ader, 51100, Reims, France
Tel.: (33) 326786200 FR
Web Site: http://www.vivescia.com
Year Founded: 2012
Sales Range: $5-14.9 Billion
Emp.: 8,000
Holding Company; Grain Farming, Processing & Products Mfr
N.A.I.C.S.: 551112
Pascal Prot *(Pres)*

Subsidiaries:

Agro-Industrie Recherches et Developpements S.A. (1)
Route de Bazancourt, 51110, Pomacle, France **(53.2%)**
Tel.: (33) 3 26 05 42 80
Web Site: http://www.a-r-d.fr

AND PRIVATE COMPANIES

Sales Range: $25-49.9 Million
Emp.: 87
Agricultural Research & Development Services
N.A.I.C.S.: 541715
Yvon Le Henaff *(Gen Mgr)*

Subsidiary (Domestic):

WheatOleo (2)
Route de Bazancourt, 51110, Pomacle, France
Tel.: (33) 3 26 88 84 10
Web Site: http://www.wheatoleo.com
Chemical Products Mfr
N.A.I.C.S.: 325320
Cedric Ernenwein *(Mgr-R&D)*

Champ'energie SA (1)
Chemin du moulin de Vrilly, 51100, Reims, France
Tel.: (33) 26 78 64 28
Web Site: http://www.champ-energie.com
Fuel Oil Distr
N.A.I.C.S.: 424720

Chamtor SA (1)
Les Sohettes CS 30004, 51110, Bazancourt, Cedex, France
Tel.: (33) 3 26 89 59 50
Wheat-Based Products Mfr
N.A.I.C.S.: 311999
Marie Jo Attou *(Mgr-HR)*

Copam SAS (1)
Z I Rue de la Noue Hermandre, 51520, Saint-Martin-sur-le-Pre, France
Tel.: (33) 3 26 69 24 11
Web Site: http://www.copam-nutritionanimale.fr
Animal Food Distr
N.A.I.C.S.: 456191

Kalizea S.A.S. (1)
2 Rue Clement Ader, 51100, Reims, France
Tel.: (33) 3 26 78 63 00
Web Site: http://www.vivescia.fr
Sales Range: $25-49.9 Million
Emp.: 36
Corn Product Mfr
N.A.I.C.S.: 311999
Vincent Jacquot *(Mng Dir)*

Subsidiary (Non-US):

KALIZEA POLSKA Sp.zo.o. (2)
ul Polna 8a, 55-011, Siechnice, Poland
Tel.: (48) 71 792 80 23
Corn Product Mfr
N.A.I.C.S.: 311999
Lukasz Golubiewski *(Mgr-Logistics)*

Malteurop Groupe S.A. (1)
3 rue Chantal Delpla Droulers, 51100, Reims, France
Tel.: (33) 3 2678 6100
Web Site: http://www.malteurop.com
Holding Company; Barley-Malt-Beer Value Chain Control & Mfr
N.A.I.C.S.: 551112

Subsidiary (Non-US):

Intermalta, S.A. (2)
Paraje la Cerrada s/n, 31570, San Adrian, Spain
Tel.: (34) 948 672 000
Beer Mfr
N.A.I.C.S.: 312120

Malteurop (Baoding) Malting Co., Ltd (2)
Jiangcheng Road, Baoding, Hebei, China
Tel.: (86) 312 7031388
Web Site: http://www.malteuropchina.com
Emp.: 90
Malt Product Mfr
N.A.I.C.S.: 311213
Yang Zhenglong *(Gen Mgr)*

Malteurop Australia Pty Ltd (2)
32 Crowle Street, PO Box 235, North Geelong, 3215, VIC, Australia
Tel.: (61) 3 5277 1950
Web Site: http://www.malteurop.com
Emp.: 24
Malt Product Mfr
N.A.I.C.S.: 311213
Jack King *(Mgr-Grains)*

Malteurop Canada Ltd (2)
3001 Dugald Road, Winnipeg, R2C 5H4, MB, Canada
Tel.: (204) 943-0741
Malt Product Mfr
N.A.I.C.S.: 311213

Malteurop Deutschland GmbH (2)
Gennacher Strasse 1, Langerringen, 86853, Germany
Tel.: (49) 8232 96270
Web Site: http://www.malteurop.com
Emp.: 20
Malt Product Mfr
N.A.I.C.S.: 311213
Weitt Karl *(Pres)*

Subsidiary (US):

Malteurop North America Inc. (2)
3830 W Grant St, Milwaukee, WI 53215 **(100%)**
Tel.: (414) 671-1166
Web Site: http://www.malteurop.com
Sales Range: $125-149.9 Million
Emp.: 160
Malt Mfr
N.A.I.C.S.: 311213

Subsidiary (Non-US):

Malteurop Polska Spolka z o.o. (2)
ul Promowa 1, 80 702, Gdansk, Poland
Tel.: (48) 58 300 90 40
Emp.: 20
Malt Product Mfr
N.A.I.C.S.: 311213
Jolanta Jeziorowska *(Mgr-Fin)*

Minjard S.A.S. (1)
211 Rte de Champagnard, 69220, Saint-Jean-d'Ardieres, France
Tel.: (33) 4 74 07 72 60
Wine Distr
N.A.I.C.S.: 424820

Monfer Cereali Srl (1)
Via Arturo Felici 15, 12100, Cuneo, Italy
Tel.: (39) 0171344299
Web Site: http://www.monfercereali.it
Cereal Distr
N.A.I.C.S.: 424490

Subsidiary (Non-US):

Monfer France S.A. (2)
17 Rue Juliette Recamier, 69006, Lyon, France
Tel.: (33) 4 78 24 04 11
Cereal Distr
N.A.I.C.S.: 424490

NutriXo S.A.S. (1)
99 rue Mirabeau, 94200, Ivry-sur-Seine, France
Tel.: (33) 1 49 59 75 00
Web Site: http://www.nutrixo.com
Wheat Milling; Frozen Bakery Product Mfr
N.A.I.C.S.: 311211
Hubert Francois *(CEO)*

Subsidiary (Domestic):

Delifrance S.A. (2)
99 Rue Mirabeau, 94200, Ivry-sur-Seine, France **(100%)**
Tel.: (33) 149597500
Web Site: http://www.delifrance.com
Rev.: $40,200,000
Emp.: 383
Holding Company
N.A.I.C.S.: 551112

Grands Moulins de Paris S.A. (2)
44 Route Principle Duport, 92238, Gennevilliers, France
Tel.: (33) 141852020
Web Site: http://www.grandsmoulinsdeparis.com
Sales Range: $300-349.9 Million
Emp.: 2,245
Flour Milling Services
N.A.I.C.S.: 311211
Hubert Francois *(Pres & Gen Dir)*

Subsidiary (Domestic):

Grande Semoulerie de L'Ouest a Gond-Pontouvre (3)
44 Rue De Bourlion, 16160, Gond-Pontouvre, France **(74.3%)**
Tel.: (33) 545685922

Sales Range: $10-24.9 Million
Emp.: 25
Grain Milling
N.A.I.C.S.: 311211

Omnisolis SAS (1)
172 avenue du General Leclerc Sainte Savine, 10300, Troyes, France
Tel.: (33) 3 25 49 90 10
Web Site: http://www.omnisolis.com
Engineeering Services
N.A.I.C.S.: 541330

SeVeal S.A. (1)
12 boulevard du Val de Vesle, Reims, 51100, France **(69.34%)**
Tel.: (33) 3 26 36 77 77
Agriculture Product Distr
N.A.I.C.S.: 424910

Vauthier Sepac Sarl (1)
Avenue de Langres, BP 22, Montigny, 52140, France
Tel.: (33) 3 25 87 52 39
Fertilizer Distr
N.A.I.C.S.: 424910

VIVID GAMES SA
Oginskiego 2, 85092, Bydgoszcz, Poland
Tel.: (48) 523215728
Web Site:
https://www.vividgames.com
Year Founded: 2006
VVD—(WAR)
Rev.: $6,321,880
Assets: $3,533,354
Liabilities: $2,312,764
Net Worth: $1,220,589
Earnings: ($640,546)
Emp.: 70
Fiscal Year-end: 12/31/23
Mobile Game Development Services
N.A.I.C.S.: 541511
Remigiusz Koscielny *(Co-Founder & Chm)*

VIVID GLOBAL INDUSTRIES LIMITED
D-21/1 MIDC, Tarapur Via Boisar, Thane, 401 506, Maharastra, India
Tel.: (91) 9819329896
Web Site:
https://www.vividglobalinds.com
Year Founded: 1994
524576—(BOM)
Rev.: $4,392,122
Assets: $3,338,407
Liabilities: $1,574,014
Net Worth: $1,764,392
Earnings: ($22,559)
Emp.: 46
Fiscal Year-end: 03/31/23
Dye & Dye Intermediate Mfr
N.A.I.C.S.: 325130
Sumish Sudhir Mody *(Mng Dir)*

VIVID MERCANTILE LIMITED
Basement Medicare Centre B/h M J Library, Opp Stock-Exchange Ellisbridge, Ahmedabad, 380006, Gujarat, India
Tel.: (91) 9033033338
Web Site:
https://www.veeraminfra.com
Year Founded: 1994
542046—(BOM)
Rev.: $1,126,347
Assets: $4,016,894
Liabilities: $474,766
Net Worth: $3,542,129
Earnings: $519,977
Fiscal Year-end: 03/31/23
Printing Services
N.A.I.C.S.: 323111
Satishkumar Ramanlal Gajjar *(Mng Dir & CFO)*

VIVID TECHNOLOGY LIMITED
Level 2 53 Victoria Harbour Promenade, Docklands, 3008, VIC, Australia
Tel.: (61) 3 8625 0500
Web Site:
http://www.vividtechnology.com.au
Year Founded: 2006
Geothermal Exploration & Development Services
N.A.I.C.S.: 211120
Samuel R. Marks *(Mng Dir)*

VIVIDTHREE HOLDINGS LTD.
1093 Lower Delta Road 05-10, Singapore, 169204, Singapore
Tel.: (65) 62700818 SG
Web Site:
https://www.vividthreeholdings.com
Year Founded: 2006
OMK—(SES)
Rev.: $2,160,712
Assets: $15,087,983
Liabilities: $5,198,938
Net Worth: $9,889,046
Earnings: ($2,533,186)
Emp.: 40
Fiscal Year-end: 03/31/23
Motion Picture & Film Production Services
N.A.I.C.S.: 512110
Hong Wei Chien *(Co-Founder)*

VIVIEN CORP.
52 Seobinggoro 51-Gil, Yongsan-Gu, Seoul, Korea (South)
Tel.: (82) 237801114
Web Site: https://www.vivien.co.kr
002070—(KRS)
Rev.: $163,411,004
Assets: $154,213,926
Liabilities: $80,136,655
Net Worth: $74,077,270
Earnings: ($6,266,103)
Emp.: 206
Fiscal Year-end: 12/31/22
Innerwear Mfr
N.A.I.C.S.: 315250
Gyu Hwa Lee *(CEO)*

VIVIENNE WESTWOOD LTD.
9-15 Elcho Street, London, SW11 4AU, United Kingdom
Tel.: (44) 2079244747
Web Site:
http://www.viviennewestwood.com
Sales Range: $10-24.9 Million
Emp.: 90
Clothing & Accessories Designer & Retailer
N.A.I.C.S.: 315990
Carlo D'Amario *(Mng Dir)*

VIVIMED LABS LIMITED
North End Road No 2 Banjara Hills, Hyderabad, 500 034, Telangana, India
Tel.: (91) 4066086608 In
Web Site:
https://www.vivimedlabs.com
Year Founded: 1988
532660—(BOM)
Rev.: $22,548,768
Assets: $118,499,371
Liabilities: $113,772,675
Net Worth: $4,726,695
Earnings: ($39,390,085)
Emp.: 607
Fiscal Year-end: 03/31/23
Holding Company; Dyes, Cosmetics & Personal Care Products Mfr
N.A.I.C.S.: 551112
V. Manohar Rao *(Exec Dir)*

Subsidiaries:

Union Quimico Farmaceutica SA (1)
C/ Mallorca 262 3rd floor, 08008, Barcelona, Spain **(100%)**
Tel.: (34) 934674810

VIVIMED LABS LIMITED

Vivimed Labs Limited—(Continued)
Web Site: http://www.uquifa.com
Emp.: 1,000
Pharmaceutical Chemicals Mfr
N.A.I.C.S.: 325412
Mark Ian Robbins (CEO)

Subsidiary (Non-US):

Uquifa Mexico S.A. de C.V. (2)
Calle 37 Este No 126 CP, Civac, CP 62578,
Jiutepec, Morelos, Mexico (100%)
Tel.: (52) 7773 295000
Pharmaceutical Chemicals Mfr
N.A.I.C.S.: 325412

Vivimed Labs Europe Ltd (1)
Leeds Rd, PO Box B3, Huddersfield, HD1
6BU, West Yorkshire, United Kingdom
Tel.: (44) 1484320500
Sales Range: $25-49.9 Million
Emp.: 30
Dye Mfr
N.A.I.C.S.: 325130

VIVIONE BIOSCIENCES INC.

Suite 1900 520 3rd Avenue Southwest, Calgary, T2P 0R3, AB, Canada
Tel.: (214) 886-5733   AB
Web Site:
https://www.vivionebiosciences.com
Year Founded: 2011
VBI—(TSXV)
Sales Range: Less than $1 Million
Medical Technology Services
N.A.I.C.S.: 541715
Kevin Kuykendall (CEO)

Subsidiaries:

Vivione Biosciences, LLC (1)
34-161 Hoadley Rd Pine Bluff Arsenal, Pine Bluff, AR 71602
Medical Technology Services
N.A.I.C.S.: 541715
Peggy Cook (Acting Chief Science Officer)

VIVO BIOTECH LIMITED

3rd Floor Ilyas Mohammed Khan Estate 8-2-672/ 5 and 6, Road No 1
Banjara hills, Hyderabad, 500 034,
Telangana, India
Tel.: (91) 7326962555
Web Site: https://www.vivobio.com
Year Founded: 1987
511509—(BOM)
Rev: $5,454,263
Assets: $16,442,295
Liabilities: $9,919,795
Net Worth: $6,522,500
Earnings: $302,903
Emp.: 150
Fiscal Year-end: 03/31/24
Pharmaceutical Preparation Mfr
N.A.I.C.S.: 325412
Kalyan Kumar Korisapati (COO)

VIVO COLLABORATION SOLUTIONS LIMITED

315 3rd Floor HB Twin Tower Netaji Subhash Place Pitam Pura, Delhi, 110034, India
Tel.: (91) 7838651690
Web Site: https://www.vivo.ooo
Year Founded: 2012
VIVO—(NSE)
Rev: $962,928
Assets: $1,827,456
Liabilities: $116,552
Net Worth: $1,710,905
Earnings: $41,796
Fiscal Year-end: 03/31/23
Software Development Services
N.A.I.C.S.: 541511

VIVONIO FURNITURE GMBH

Leopoldstrasse 16, 80802, Munich, Germany
Tel.: (49) 89 1211 225 0   De
Web Site: http://www.vivonio.com

Sales Range: $250-299.9 Million
Emp.: 800
Holding Company; Home & Office Furniture Mfr & Distr
N.A.I.C.S.: 551112
Erik Kolb (COO)

Subsidiaries:

MAJA-WERK Manfred Jarosch GmbH & Co. KG (1)
Industriestrasse 14, 95359, Kasendorf, Germany
Tel.: (49) 9228 79 0
Web Site: http://www.maja-moebel.de
Emp.: 450
Home & Office Furniture Mfr & Distr
N.A.I.C.S.: 337122

Martin Staud GmbH (1)
Martin-Staud-Strasse 1, 88348, Saulgau, Germany
Tel.: (49) 7581 209 0
Web Site: http://www.staudmoebel.de
Emp.: 140
Home Furniture Mfr & Distr
N.A.I.C.S.: 337122

S.C.I.A.E. (1)
44 avenue Paul Girard, 10500, Dienville, France
Tel.: (33) 3 2592 3700
Web Site: http://www.sciae.com
Emp.: 250
Home Furniture Mfr & Distr
N.A.I.C.S.: 337122

VIVOPOWER INTERNATIONAL PLC

The Scalpel 18th Floor 52 Lime Street, London, EC3M 7AF, United Kingdom
Tel.: (44) 7941166696   UK
Web Site: https://www.vivopower.com
Year Founded: 2016
VVPR—(NASDAQ)
Rev: $15,060,000
Assets: $61,416,000
Liabilities: $57,670,000
Net Worth: $3,746,000
Earnings: ($24,355,000)
Emp.: 108
Fiscal Year-end: 06/30/23
Holding Company
N.A.I.C.S.: 551112
Kevin Chin (Founder, Chm & CEO)

Subsidiaries:

Kenshaw Electrical Pty Limited (1)
11/ 457 Victoria Street, Wetherill Park, 2164, NSW, Australia
Tel.: (61) 0249031500
Web Site: https://kenshaw.com.au
Appliances, Electrical & Electronics Mfr
N.A.I.C.S.: 335999

VIVORYON THERAPEUTICS N.V.

Weinbergweg 15, 6120, Halle, Germany
Tel.: (49) 3455559900
Web Site: https://www.vivoryon.com
Year Founded: 1997
VVY—(EUR)
Rev: $801,413
Assets: $34,031,350
Liabilities: $5,019,318
Net Worth: $29,012,032
Earnings: ($31,286,014)
Emp.: 11
Fiscal Year-end: 12/31/23
Pharmaceutical Mfr, Researcher & Developer
N.A.I.C.S.: 325412
Dinnies Johannes Von Der Osten (Vice Chm-Supervisory Bd)

VIVOTEK INC.

6F No 192 Lien-Cheng Rd, Chung-Ho, New Taipei City, 23553, Taiwan
Tel.: (886) 282455282

Web Site: https://www.vivotek.com
Year Founded: 2000
3454—(TAI)
Rev: $299,631,206
Assets: $209,269,556
Liabilities: $91,212,528
Net Worth: $118,057,028
Earnings: $16,707,511
Emp.: 355
Fiscal Year-end: 12/31/23
Network Video Surveillance Camera Mfr
N.A.I.C.S.: 334310
Zhenqi Liao (Gen Mgr)

Subsidiaries:

VATICS Inc. (1)
9F No 21 Qiaohe Rd, Zhonghe Dist, New Taipei City, 235, Taiwan
Tel.: (886) 28 245 1282
Web Site: https://www.vatics.com
Multimedia Embedded Surveillance Equipment Mfr
N.A.I.C.S.: 334310

VIVOTEK USA Inc (1)
2050 Ringwood Ave, San Jose, CA 95131
Tel.: (408) 773-8686
Web Site: http://www.vivotek.com
Video Surveillance Equipment Whslr
N.A.I.C.S.: 423690
David Liu (Pres)

VIZAG PROFILES LIMITED

Duvvada Station Road, Kurmanapalem, Visakhapatnam, Andhra Pradesh, India
Tel.: (91) 891 587573
Web Site:
http://www.vizagprofiles.com
Emp.: 500
Steel Mfr & Distr
N.A.I.C.S.: 331513
B. Suresh Kumar (Mng Dir)

VIZAG SEAPORT PRIVATE LIMITED

Administrative Block S4 Gallery Port Area, Visakhapatnam, 530 035, Andhra Pradesh, India
Tel.: (91) 8912556400
Web Site:
http://www.vizagseaport.com
Sales Range: $50-74.9 Million
Emp.: 85
Coal Import & Distr
N.A.I.C.S.: 423520
Rehan Khan (Asst Mgr-Engrg)

VIZIONE HOLDINGS BERHAD

Level 22 PJX-HM Shah Tower No 16A Persiaran Barat, 46050, Petaling Jaya, Selangor DE, Malaysia
Tel.: (60) 386053355
Web Site:
https://www.vizione.com.my
VIZIONE—(KLS)
Rev: $82,916,121
Assets: $174,469,024
Liabilities: $54,679,609
Net Worth: $119,789,415
Earnings: ($20,016,395)
Fiscal Year-end: 05/31/23
Electronic Products Mfr
N.A.I.C.S.: 334511
Aun Hooi Ng (Mng Dir)

Subsidiaries:

Vizione Development Sdn. Bhd. (1)
Level 22 PJX-HM Shah Tower No 16 A Persiaran Barat, 46050, Petaling Jaya, Selangor, Malaysia
Tel.: (60) 386053355
Construction Services
N.A.I.C.S.: 236220
Aun Hooi (Mng Dir)

Wira Syukur (M) Sdn. Bhd. (1)
No 15-B Jalan SS15/4B, 47500, Subang Jaya, Selangor, Malaysia

INTERNATIONAL PUBLIC

Tel.: (60) 356214727
Web Site: http://www.wirasyukur.my
Construction Services
N.A.I.C.S.: 236220
Yeuw Lung Chan (Project Mgr)

VIZOR ENTERIJERI A.D.

Zeleznicka 23, Temerin, Serbia
Tel.: (381) 21 845 848
Web Site: http://www.vizor.co.rs
Year Founded: 2003
Sales Range: Less than $1 Million
Emp.: 1
Furniture Product Mfr
N.A.I.C.S.: 337121

VIZSLA COPPER CORP.

595 Burrard Street - Suite 1723, Vancouver, V7X 1J1, BC, Canada
Tel.: (604) 364-2215   BC
Web Site: https://vizslacopper.com
Year Founded: 2017
VCU—(TSX)
Minerals Exploration
N.A.I.C.S.: 212290
Craig Parry (Exec Chm)

Subsidiaries:

Consolidated Woodjam Copper Corp. (1)
Suite 110-325 Howe Street, Vancouver, V6C 1Z7, BC, Canada
Tel.: (604) 681-7913
Web Site: https://www.woodjamcopper.com
Rev: $38
Assets: $6,694,550
Liabilities: $190,625
Net Worth: $6,503,924
Earnings: ($336,429)
Fiscal Year-end: 02/28/2022
Copper & Gold Mining
N.A.I.C.S.: 212230

RG Copper Corp. (1)

Universal Copper Ltd. (1)
830-1100 Melville St, Vancouver, V6E 4A6, BC, Canada
Tel.: (604) 341-6870
Web Site: https://www.universalcopper.com
Assets: $4,544,435
Liabilities: $311,654
Net Worth: $4,232,781
Earnings: ($878,325)
Fiscal Year-end: 12/31/2022
Oilfield Equipment & Services
N.A.I.C.S.: 333132
Alexander Helmel (CFO & CFO)

VIZSLA SILVER CORP.

Suite 700 1090 West Georgia Street, Vancouver, V6E 3V7, BC, Canada
Tel.: (604) 364-2215
Web Site: https://vizslasilvercorp.com
Year Founded: 2017
VZLA—(NYSEAMEX)
Rev: $715,966
Assets: $177,997,970
Liabilities: $4,816,065
Net Worth: $173,181,905
Earnings: ($10,139,429)
Emp.: 139
Fiscal Year-end: 04/30/23
Natural Resource Management Services
N.A.I.C.S.: 813312
Michael A. Konnert (Pres & CEO)

VJETRENICA D.D.

Hrvatskih Branitelja 1, 72 250, Vitez, Bosnia & Herzegovina
Tel.: (387) 30708118
VJTRR—(SARE)
Rev: $29,282
Assets: $466,564
Liabilities: $1,801
Net Worth: $464,763
Earnings: $20,196
Emp.: 1
Fiscal Year-end: 12/31/21
Consumer Goods Distr

AND PRIVATE COMPANIES — VKR HOLDING A/S

N.A.I.C.S.: 423620

VJTF EDUSERVICES LIMITED
Pawan Baug Road off S V Road Adjacent to Techniplex, Near Feast India Hotel Malad West, Mumbai, 400 064, India
Tel.: (91) 2261056800
Web Site: http://www.vjtf.com
Year Founded: 1984
509026—(BOM)
Rev.: $2,633,763
Assets: $20,153,300
Liabilities: $15,558,408
Net Worth: $4,594,892
Earnings: $40,897
Emp.: 139
Fiscal Year-end: 03/31/23
Educational Support Services
N.A.I.C.S.: 611710
Vinay Jain *(CEO & Mng Dir)*

VK COMPANY
Leningradsky prospekt 39 bld 79, 125167, Moscow, Russia
Tel.: (7) 4953631368
Web Site: http://www.dst-global.com
Year Founded: 2005
Sales Range: $25-49.9 Million
Emp.: 60
Internet-Related Investment Services
N.A.I.C.S.: 523999
Yuri Milner *(CEO & Founding Partner)*

Subsidiaries:

ICQ Inc. (1)
Kiriat Atidim Bldg #7, Tel Aviv, Israel
Tel.: (972) 37665555
Web Site: http://www.icq.com
Sales Range: $25-49.9 Million
Communication Tools, Content & Services to Online Communities
N.A.I.C.S.: 513210

VK COMPANY LTD.
28 Oktovriou 365 Vashiotis Seafront office 402, Neapoli, Limassol, 3107, Cyprus VG
Web Site: https://www.corp.mail.ru
Year Founded: 1998
61HE—(LSE)
Rev.: $1,316,961,900
Assets: $4,861,525,050
Liabilities: $2,597,056,410
Net Worth: $2,264,468,640
Earnings: ($52,667,700)
Emp.: 10,000
Fiscal Year-end: 12/31/22
Information Technology Services
N.A.I.C.S.: 541512

Subsidiaries:

Skillbox LLC (1)
St Timura Frunze House 11 Building 2 Floor 1 Room 1 Room 75, Moscow, Russia
Tel.: (7) 4994449036
Web Site: https://skillbox.ru
Real Estate Services
N.A.I.C.S.: 531320

Skillfactory LLC (1)
6 Leninsky Avenue Building 20 Floor 3 Room 21 Ext Ter, Yakimanka Municipal District, Moscow, 119049, Russia
Tel.: (7) 4952910912
Web Site: https://skillfactory.ru
Education Technology Services
N.A.I.C.S.: 611710

VKC HOLDINGS JSC
854 National Highway 1K Chau Thoi Quarter, Binh An, Di An, Binh Duong, Vietnam
Tel.: (84) 2743751501
Web Site: https://vkcholdings.vn
VKC—(HNX)
Rev.: $35,365,354
Assets: $27,263,003
Liabilities: $17,509,924
Net Worth: $9,753,078
Earnings: $92,890
Emp.: 110
Fiscal Year-end: 12/31/21
Cables, Tubes & Pipe Fittings Mfr
N.A.I.C.S.: 335921

VKJ INFRADEVELOPERS LIMITED
M-161/B Ground Floor Kalka Bhawan Commercial Centre, Gautam Nagar Road Yusuf Sarai, New Delhi, 110049, India
Tel.: (91) 1168888329
Web Site: http://www.vkjinfra.com
Rev.: $497,009
Assets: $5,668,589
Liabilities: $1,610,151
Net Worth: $4,058,438
Earnings: $68,970
Emp.: 3
Fiscal Year-end: 03/31/18
Land & Site Development Services
N.A.I.C.S.: 237210
Ameer Ahmad *(CFO & Compliance Officer)*

VKR HOLDING A/S
Breeltevej 18, 2970, Horsholm, Denmark
Tel.: (45) 39691144
Web Site: http://www.vkr-holding.com
Rev.: $3,270,886,290
Assets: $3,569,656,920
Liabilities: $686,887,620
Net Worth: $2,882,769,300
Earnings: $460,973,250
Emp.: 16,000
Fiscal Year-end: 12/31/19
Limited Holding & Investment Company
N.A.I.C.S.: 551112
Mads Kann-Rasmussen *(CEO)*

Subsidiaries:

A/S Gelsted Bygningsindustri (1)
Hylkedamvej 75, 5591, Gelsted, Denmark
Tel.: (45) 63 46 52 00
Roof Window Mfr
N.A.I.C.S.: 321911

A/S Ostbirk Bygningsindustri (1)
Ryvej 21, Ostbirk, 8752, Vejle, Denmark
Tel.: (45) 76 69 33 33
Roof Window Mfr
N.A.I.C.S.: 321911

ARCON Solar A/S (1)
Skorping Nord 3, 9520, Skorping, Denmark
Tel.: (45) 9839 1477
Web Site: http://www.arcon.dk
Solar Panel Mfr & Distr
N.A.I.C.S.: 334413

Altaterra Kft. (1)
1 Malom Koz, 9431, Fertod, Hungary
Tel.: (36) 99884009
Web Site: http://www.altaterra.eu
Emp.: 130
Roof Window Mfr & Whslr
N.A.I.C.S.: 332321

Subsidiary (Non-US):

Altaterra Polska Sp. z o.o. (2)
ul Taneczna 18, 02-829, Warsaw, Poland
Tel.: (48) 222922378
Web Site: http://www.roofliteplus.com
Roof Window Distr
N.A.I.C.S.: 423310

RoofLITE France S.A.R.L (2)
15 avenue Allees Marines, 64100, Bayonne, France
Tel.: (33) 5 59 59 43 55
Roof Window Distr
N.A.I.C.S.: 423310

BKR CR, s.r.o. (1)
Tovarni 724/2, 682 01, Vyskov, Czech Republic
Tel.: (420) 517543500
Emp.: 300
Roof Window Distr
N.A.I.C.S.: 423310
Eva Necasova *(Mgr)*

BT Components A/S (1)
Brudelysvej 23, Bagsvaerd, 2880, Denmark
Tel.: (45) 44373000
Roof Window Mfr
N.A.I.C.S.: 321911

DEUTSCHE-CAP GmbH (1)
Ferdinandstrase 3, 20095, Hamburg, Germany
Tel.: (49) 40 334010
Roof Window Distr
N.A.I.C.S.: 423310

DOVISTA A/S (1)
Bygholm Sopark 21D, 8700, Horsens, Denmark
Tel.: (45) 9674 6700
Web Site: http://dovista.dk
Window & Door Mfr & Distr
N.A.I.C.S.: 321911
Allan Lindhard Jorgensen *(Pres & CEO)*

Subsidiary (Non-US):

DOVISTA Polska Sp. z o.o. (2)
woj pomorskie, 83-115, Wedkowy, Poland
Tel.: (48) 58 530 77 00
Roof Window Distr
N.A.I.C.S.: 423310

DOVISTA UK Ltd. (2)
The Forum Ground Floor Lancaster Way, Ermine Business Park, Huntingdon, PE29 6XU, Cambridgeshire, United Kingdom
Tel.: (44) 1480759511
Web Site: https://rationel.co.uk
Window Distr
N.A.I.C.S.: 423220

Dakvenster.com B.V. (1)
Agriport 139, 1775 TA, Middenmeer, Netherlands
Tel.: (31) 227801970
Web Site: https://www.dakvenster.nl
Window Distr
N.A.I.C.S.: 423220

Fenster-webshop.de GmbH (1)
Gartenstrasse 49, 58511, Ludenscheid, Germany
Tel.: (49) 23516639600
Web Site: https://www.fenster-webshop.de
Window Mfr
N.A.I.C.S.: 321911

Gasdal Bygningsindustri A/S (1)
Baekgaardsvej 38, Skjern, 6900, Denmark
Tel.: (45) 99806666
Roof Window Mfr
N.A.I.C.S.: 321911

Lian Trevarefabrikk AS (1)
Industriveien 10, 7200, Kyrksaeterora, Norway
Tel.: (47) 72 45 02 22
Web Site: http://www.lian.no
Roof Window Distr
N.A.I.C.S.: 423310

Lian Vinduer AS (1)
Industriveien 10, Kyrksaeterora, Norway
Tel.: (47) 72450222
Web Site: https://www.lian.no
Window Mfr & Distr
N.A.I.C.S.: 321911

Mockfjards Fonsterentreprenad AB (1)
Ritargatan 6, Borlange, 781 70, Sweden
Tel.: (46) 24125500
Roof Window Distr
N.A.I.C.S.: 423310

Monodraught Limited (1)
Halifax House, Cressex Business Park, High Wycombe, HP12 3SE, Bucks, United Kingdom
Tel.: (44) 1494 897700
Web Site: http://www.monodraught.com
Ventilation System Mfr
N.A.I.C.S.: 333413
Andrew McCubbin *(Mng Dir)*

Natre Vinduer AS (1)
Engenvegen 1, Hunndalen, 2827, Gjovik, Norway
Tel.: (47) 61 18 80 10
Web Site: http://www.natre.no
Roof Window Distr
N.A.I.C.S.: 423310

O.H. Industri A/S (1)
Smedevej 17, 7430, Ikast, Denmark
Tel.: (45) 9725 1200
Web Site: http://www.oh-industri.com
Wood Panel Mfr
N.A.I.C.S.: 321911

Partizanske Building Components-SK s.r.o. (1)
Malobielicka 1/215, 958 04, Partizanske, Slovakia
Tel.: (421) 38 53 43 000
Roof Window Distr
N.A.I.C.S.: 423310

Rationel Vinduer A/S (1)
Dalgas Alle 7, 7400, Herning, Denmark
Tel.: (45) 7221 1100
Web Site: http://www.rationel.dk
Window & Door Mfr
N.A.I.C.S.: 321911

Subsidiary (Non-US):

Rationel Vinduer Ltd. (2)
Grande Central Rockbrook Blackthorn Drive, Sandyford, Dublin, Ireland
Tel.: (353) 12971005
Web Site: http://www.rationel.ie
Window & Door Mfr
N.A.I.C.S.: 321911

Rationel Windows (UK) Ltd. (1)
7 Avonbury Business Park, Howes Lane, Bicester, OX26 2UA, United Kingdom
Tel.: (44) 1869 248 181
Web Site: http://www.rationel.co.uk
Window & Door Mfr & Distr
N.A.I.C.S.: 321911

Skaerbaek Bygningsindustri A/S (1)
Industrivej 11, Skaerbaek, 6780, Tonder, Denmark
Tel.: (45) 73 95 18 88
Roof Window Mfr
N.A.I.C.S.: 321911

Snidex AB (1)
Skolgatan 1, 937 32, Burtrask, Sweden
Tel.: (46) 914 438 00
Web Site: http://www.snidex.se
Roof Window Mfr
N.A.I.C.S.: 321911

Svenska Fonster AB (1)
Snickarvagen 12, 828 30, Edsbyn, Sweden
Tel.: (46) 271 29 100
Web Site: http://www.svenskafonster.se
Window & Door Mfr
N.A.I.C.S.: 321911

The New West Port Corporation Limited (1)
Solway Industrial Estate, Maryport, CA15 8NF, Cumbria, United Kingdom
Tel.: (44) 190 081 4225
Web Site: http://www.west-port.co.uk
Emp.: 150
Roof Window Distr
N.A.I.C.S.: 423310

Thyregod Bygningsindustri A/S (1)
Nordre Ringvej 7, Give, 7323, Denmark
Tel.: (45) 75 73 47 88
Roof Window Mfr
N.A.I.C.S.: 321911

VELFAC A/S (1)
Bygholm Sopark 23, 8700, Horsens, Denmark
Tel.: (45) 70 110 200
Web Site: http://www.velfac.dk
Window & Door Mfr & Distr
N.A.I.C.S.: 321911

Subsidiary (Non-US):

VELFAC AB (2)
Ranhammarsvagen 20E, 16867, Bromma, Sweden
Tel.: (46) 8 756 28 00
Web Site: http://www.velfac.se
Window & Door Mfr
N.A.I.C.S.: 332321

VELFAC GmbH (2)

VKR HOLDING A/S

VKR Holding A/S—(Continued)

Lily-Braun-Strasse 19, 23843, Bad Oldesloe, Germany
Tel.: (49) 4531 1748
Window & Door Distr
N.A.I.C.S.: 423310

VELFAC Ireland Ltd. (2)
Grand Central RockbrookBlackthorn Drive
Sandyford, Dublin, Ireland
Tel.: (353) 12971027
Web Site: http://www.velfac.ie
Window & Door Mfr
N.A.I.C.S.: 321911

VELFAC Ltd. (2)
The Old Livery, Hildersham, Cambridge, CB21 6DR, United Kingdom
Tel.: (44) 1223 897100
Web Site: http://velfac.co.uk
Window & Door Mfr
N.A.I.C.S.: 321911

VELUX A/S (1)
Adalsvej 99, 2970, Horsholm, Denmark   (100%)
Tel.: (45) 4516 4000
Web Site: http://www.velux.dk
Holding Company; Roof Window & Modular Skylight Mfr & Whslr
N.A.I.C.S.: 551112
Lars Petersson (Pres & CEO)

Subsidiary (Non-US):

VELUX (CHINA) CO., Ltd. (2)
No 21 Baihe Road, Economic & Technical Development Zone, Langfang, 065001, Hebei, China
Tel.: (86) 4007076001
Web Site: http://www.velux.com.cn
Roof Window Distr
N.A.I.C.S.: 423310

Subsidiary (US):

VELUX America Inc. (2)
104 Ben Casey Dr, Fort Mill, SC 29708
Web Site: http://www.veluxusa.com
Roof Window Distr
N.A.I.C.S.: 423310

Subsidiary (Domestic):

Wasco Products, Inc. (3)
85 Spencer Dr Unit A, Wells, ME 04090
Tel.: (800) 888-3589
Web Site: http://www.wascoskylights.com
Skylights, Roof Windows, Heat & Smoke Vents, Patio Doors Mfr
N.A.I.C.S.: 327211
Jeff Frank (CEO)

Subsidiary (Non-US):

VELUX Argentina S.A. (2)
Colectora Panamericana Ramal Pilar KM 40, Complex 1 B10 Del Viso, B1669IEA, Buenos Aires, Argentina
Tel.: (54) 3484639944
Web Site: http://www.velux.com.ar
Roof Window Distr
N.A.I.C.S.: 423310

VELUX Australia Pty. Ltd. (2)
78 Henderson Road, Alexandria, 2015, NSW, Australia
Tel.: (61) 1300859856
Web Site: http://www.velux.com.au
Roof Window Distr
N.A.I.C.S.: 423310
David Nicolas Carneiro (Mgr-Territory)

VELUX Belgium S.A. (2)
Blvd de l'Europe 121, 1301, Wavre, Belgium
Tel.: (32) 10 420 909
Web Site: http://www.velux.be
Roof Window Distr
N.A.I.C.S.: 423310

VELUX Bosna i Hercegovina d.o.o. (2)
Dzemala Bijedica 295, Ilidxa, 71210, Ilidza, Bosnia & Herzegovina
Tel.: (387) 3362649
Web Site: http://www.velux.ba
Roof Window Distr
N.A.I.C.S.: 423310

VELUX Bulgaria EOOD (2)
Pelister Street 6, 1618, Sofia, Bulgaria
Tel.: (359) 29559930
Web Site: http://www.velux.bg
Roof Window Distr
N.A.I.C.S.: 423310

VELUX Canada Inc. (2)
2740 Sherwood Heights Drive, Oakville, L6J 7V5, ON, Canada
Tel.: (905) 829-0280
Web Site: http://www.velux.ca
Roof Window Distr
N.A.I.C.S.: 423310

VELUX Chile Limitada (2)
San Patricio 4099 oficina 201, Vitacura, Santiago, Chile
Tel.: (56) 2 2953 6789
Web Site: http://www.velux.cl
Roof Window Distr
N.A.I.C.S.: 423310

VELUX Company Ltd. (2)
Woodside Way, Glenrothes, KY7 4ND, Fife, United Kingdom
Tel.: (44) 1592 778225
Web Site: http://www.velux.co.uk
Roof Window Distr
N.A.I.C.S.: 423310

Subsidiary (Domestic):

Fife Joinery Manufacturing Limited (3)
Telford Road, Glenrothes, KY7 4NX, Fife, United Kingdom
Tel.: (44) 1592 773181
Roof Window Mfr
N.A.I.C.S.: 332321

Subsidiary (Domestic):

VELUX Danmark A/S (2)
Breeltevej 18, 2970, Horsholm, Denmark
Tel.: (45) 4516 4516
Web Site: http://www.velux.dk
Roof Window & Modular Skylight Mfr & Whslr
N.A.I.C.S.: 332321

Subsidiary (Non-US):

VELUX Deutschland GmbH (2)
Gazellenkamp 168, 22527, Hamburg, Germany
Tel.: (49) 40547070
Web Site: http://www.velux.de
Roof Window Distr
N.A.I.C.S.: 423310

VELUX Eesti OU (2)
Ulemiste tee 3, 11415, Tallinn, Estonia
Tel.: (372) 621 77 90
Web Site: http://www.velux.ee
Emp.: 10
Roof Window Distr
N.A.I.C.S.: 423310

VELUX France S.A.S. (2)
1 rue Paul Cezanne, 91420, Morangis, France
Tel.: (33) 153732222
Web Site: http://www.velux.fr
Emp.: 100
Roof Window Distr
N.A.I.C.S.: 423310

VELUX Hrvatska d.o.o. (2)
Avenija Veceslava Holjevca 40, 10010, Zagreb, Croatia
Tel.: (385) 1 5555 444
Web Site: http://www.velux.hr
Roof Window Distr
N.A.I.C.S.: 423310

VELUX Italia S.p.A. (2)
152 Via Stra, Colognola Ai Colli, Verona, 37030, Italy
Tel.: (39) 045 617 3666
Web Site: http://www.velux.it
Roof Window Distr
N.A.I.C.S.: 423310

VELUX Latvia SIA (2)
Liepajas Street 34, 1002, Riga, Latvia
Tel.: (371) 80008802
Web Site: http://www.velux.lv
Roof Window Distr
N.A.I.C.S.: 423310

VELUX Lietuva, UAB (2)
S Zukausko st 49 8th floor, 09131, Vilnius, Lithuania
Tel.: (370) 852709101
Web Site: http://www.velux.lt
Roof Window Distr
N.A.I.C.S.: 423310

VELUX Nederland B.V. (2)
Molensteijn 2, 3454 PT, De Meern, Netherlands
Tel.: (31) 306629610
Web Site: http://www.velux.nl
Emp.: 70
Roof Window Distr
N.A.I.C.S.: 423310
Mitchell Samberg (Mng Dir)

VELUX New Zealand Ltd. (2)
62B Princes Street, Onehunga, Auckland, 1061, New Zealand
Tel.: (64) 800 650 445
Web Site: http://www.velux.co.nz
Roof Window Distr
N.A.I.C.S.: 423310
David Williamson (Area Mgr)

VELUX Norge AS (2)
Gjerdrumsvei 10 d, PO Box 4224, Nydalen, 0401, Oslo, Norway
Tel.: (47) 22540600
Web Site: http://www.velux.no
Roof Window Distr
N.A.I.C.S.: 423310

VELUX Osterreich GmbH (2)
Veluxstrasse 1, 2120, Wolkersdorf im Weinviertel, Austria
Tel.: (43) 22453235
Web Site: http://www.velux.at
Roof Window Distr
N.A.I.C.S.: 423310

VELUX Polska Sp. z o.o. (2)
ul Krakowiakow 34, 02-255, Warsaw, Poland
Tel.: (48) 22 33 77 000
Web Site: http://www.velux.pl
Roof Window Distr
N.A.I.C.S.: 423310

VELUX Portugal, Lda. (2)
Travessa das Pedras Negras 1 - 2nd, 1100-404, Lisbon, Portugal
Tel.: (351) 21 880 00 60
Web Site: http://www.velux.pt
Roof Window Distr
N.A.I.C.S.: 423310

VELUX Schweiz AG (2)
Bahnhofstrasse 40, 4663, Aarburg, Switzerland
Tel.: (41) 62 289 44 45
Web Site: http://www.velux.ch
Roof Window Distr
N.A.I.C.S.: 423310

VELUX Slovenija d.o.o. (2)
Ljubljanska 51 a, 1236, Trzin, Slovenia
Tel.: (386) 1 724 68 68
Web Site: http://www.velux.si
Roof Window Distr
N.A.I.C.S.: 423310

VELUX Slovensko spol. s.r.o. (2)
Galvaniho 17/A, 821 04, Bratislava, Slovakia
Tel.: (421) 233000543
Web Site: http://www.velux.sk
Roof Window Distr
N.A.I.C.S.: 423310

VELUX Spain, S.A. (2)
C/ Anabel Segura 16, Alcobendas, 28108, Madrid, Spain
Tel.: (34) 915097100
Web Site: http://www.velux.es
Roof Window Distr
N.A.I.C.S.: 423310

VELUX Srbija d.o.o. (2)
Bulevar oslobodenja 301, 11040, Belgrade, Serbia
Tel.: (381) 11 20 57 500
Web Site: http://www.velux.rs
Roof Window Distr
N.A.I.C.S.: 423310

VELUX Suomi Oy (2)
Lammittajankatu 6, 00880, Helsinki, Finland
Tel.: (358) 207 290 800
Web Site: http://www.velux.fi

INTERNATIONAL PUBLIC

Roof Window Distr
N.A.I.C.S.: 423310

VELUX Svenska AB (2)
Karbingatan 22, 254 67, Helsingborg, Sweden
Tel.: (46) 42 20 83 80
Web Site: http://www.velux.se
Roof Window Distr
N.A.I.C.S.: 423310

VELUX-Japan Ltd. (2)
1-23-14 Benny leaf building, Sendagaya Shibuya-ku, Tokyo, 151-0051, Japan
Tel.: (81) 3 3478 8141
Web Site: http://www.velux.co.jp
Roof Window Distr
N.A.I.C.S.: 423310

VELUX Commercial Bramo AS (1)
Gjellebekkstubben 29, Lierskogen, Norway
Tel.: (47) 32240560
Web Site: https://commercial.velux.no
Window Mfr
N.A.I.C.S.: 321911

VELUX Commercial Domex A/S (1)
Neptunvej 6, Kongerslev, Aalborg, Denmark
Tel.: (45) 96771300
Web Site: https://commercial.velux.dk
Ventilation Services
N.A.I.C.S.: 561790

VKR France S.A.S. (1)
Avenue du Vimeu Vert, 80210, Feuquieresen-Vimeu, France
Tel.: (33) 3 22 30 33 85
Emp.: 300
Roof Window Distr
N.A.I.C.S.: 423310
Grasset Renaud (Gen Mgr)

Velserv A/S (1)
Aadalsvej 99, Horsholm, 2970, Denmark
Tel.: (45) 45 16 40 00
Roof Window Distr
N.A.I.C.S.: 423310

Velsol France S.A.S. (1)
19 Chemin de Saint-Romain, 74930, Reignier-Esery, France
Tel.: (33) 4 50 95 76 77
Roof Window Distr
N.A.I.C.S.: 423310

Velterm A/S (1)
Oskovvej 2, Braedstrup, Arhus, 8740, Denmark
Tel.: (45) 75753900
Emp.: 100
Roof Window Mfr
N.A.I.C.S.: 321911
Tobin Jacobson (Mgr)

WERU GmbH (1)
Zumhofer Strasse 25, Gleink, 73635, Ridersberg, Germany
Tel.: (49) 71833030
Web Site: https://www.weru.com
Window Mfr & Distr
N.A.I.C.S.: 321911

WindowMaster A/S (1)
Skelstedet 13, 2950, Vedbaek, Denmark
Tel.: (45) 4567 0300
Web Site: http://www.windowmaster.dk
Emp.: 120
Ventilation System Distr
N.A.I.C.S.: 423730
Erik Boyter (CEO)

Subsidiary (Non-US):

WindowMaster Control Systems Limited (2)
Lamport Close Kettering Parkway, Kettering, NN15 6XY, Northants, United Kingdom
Tel.: (44) 1536614070
Web Site: http://www.windowmaster.com
Ventilation System Distr
N.A.I.C.S.: 423730
Lars Fournais (Chm)

WindowMaster GmbH (1)
Griegstrasse 75 house 26a, 22763, Hamburg, Germany
Tel.: (49) 4087409560
Web Site: http://www.windowmaster.de
Ventilation System Distr
N.A.I.C.S.: 423730

AND PRIVATE COMPANIES

VLAAMSE PARTICIPATI-EMAATSCHAPPIJ NV
Karel Oomsstraat 37, 2018, Antwerpen, Belgium
Tel.: (32) 032902100 BE
Web Site: https://www.vlaanderen.be
RAPH—(OTC)
Emp.: 100
Financial Services
N.A.I.C.S.: 523999

VLAAMSE RADIO EN TELEVISIEOMROEP NV
August Reyerslaan 52, 1043, Brussels, Belgium
Tel.: (32) 27413111
Web Site: http://www.vrt.be
Sales Range: $450-499.9 Million
Emp.: 2,800
Radio & Television Broadcasting Services
N.A.I.C.S.: 516110
Hilde Cobbaut (Sec)

Subsidiaries:

Vlaamse Audiovisuele Regie n.v. (1)
Tollan 107b bus 3, B-1932, Saint-Stevens-Woluwe, Belgium
Tel.: (32) 27163411
Web Site: http://www.var.be
Sales Range: $10-24.9 Million
Emp.: 39
TV & Radio Support Services
N.A.I.C.S.: 561499
Anny Wuyts (Gen Mgr)

VLADI PRIVATE ISLANDS GMBH
Ballindamm 26, Hamburg, 20095, Germany
Tel.: (49) 40338989
Web Site: http://www.vladi-private-islands.de
Year Founded: 1975
Rev.: $27,588,000
Emp.: 50
Real Estate Services
N.A.I.C.S.: 531210

Subsidiaries:

Vladi Private Islands (Canada) Limited (1)
Suite 602 Summit Place 1601 Lower Water Street, Halifax, B3J 3P6, NS, Canada
Tel.: (902) 423-3202
Property Management Services
N.A.I.C.S.: 531311
Farhad Vladi (Pres)

Vladi Private Islands Pacific Limited (1)
Old Bank Arcade, PO Box 5373, Wellington, New Zealand
Tel.: (64) 49220600
Property Management Services
N.A.I.C.S.: 531311
Farhad Vladi (Pres)

VLADIMIR CHEMICAL PLANT PJSC
81 Bolshaya Nizhegorodskaya St, 600000, Vladimir, 600000, Russia
Tel.: (7) 4922495150
Web Site: https://vhz31.ru
Year Founded: 1941
VLHZ—(MOEX)
Sales Range: Less than $1 Million
Plastic Material Mfr & Distr
N.A.I.C.S.: 325211

VLS CAPITAL LTD.
C-489 Defence Colony, New Delhi, 110024, India
Tel.: (91) 11 51553081 In
Investment Holding Company
N.A.I.C.S.: 551112

Subsidiaries:

South Asian Enterprises Limited (1)
2nd Floor 13 Sant Nagar East Of Kailash, New Delhi, 110065, India (59.61%)
Tel.: (91) 1146656666
Web Site: https://www.sael.co.in
Rev.: $144,238
Assets: $995,377
Liabilities: $26,720
Net Worth: $968,657
Earnings: ($15,111)
Emp.: 18
Fiscal Year-end: 03/31/2021
Electric Equipment Mfr
N.A.I.C.S.: 335999
T. B. Gupta (Vice Chm & Mng Dir)

VLS FINANCE LTD.
Ground Floor 90 OKHLA INDUSTRIAL ESTATE PHASE III, New Delhi, 110020, India
Tel.: (91) 1146656666
Web Site: https://www.vlsfinance.com
Year Founded: 1986
511333—(BOM)
Rev.: $9,838,895
Assets: $367,224,171
Liabilities: $67,410,719
Net Worth: $299,813,452
Earnings: $6,710,725
Emp.: 34
Fiscal Year-end: 03/31/23
Privater Equity Firm
N.A.I.C.S.: 523999
Ajit Kumar (Chm)

Subsidiaries:

VLS Asset Management Limited (1)
Off 2nd Floor 13 Sant Nagar East of Kailash, New Delhi, 110065, India
Tel.: (91) 1146656666
Asset Management Services
N.A.I.C.S.: 523150

VLS Securities Ltd. (1)
Tel.: (91) 1146656666
Web Site: https://www.vlssecurities.com
Sales Range: $25-49.9 Million
Emp.: 3
Financial Consulting & Advisory Services
N.A.I.C.S.: 541611
Ramesh C. Pandey (Officer-Compliance)

VMOTO LIMITED
Level 48 152-158 St Georges Terrace, Perth, 6000, WA, Australia
Tel.: (61) 892263865
Web Site: https://www.vmoto.com
VMT—(ASX)
Rev.: $47,168,449
Assets: $65,606,566
Liabilities: $11,456,985
Net Worth: $54,149,581
Earnings: $4,943,805
Fiscal Year-end: 12/31/23
Investment Services; Sports & Leisure Products
N.A.I.C.S.: 523999
Charles Yi Ting Chen (Mng Dir)

Subsidiaries:

Vmoto Motor Cycles Australia (1)
Level 12 351 Adelaide, Perth, 6000, WA, Australia
Tel.: (61) 892282336
Web Site: http://www.vmoto.com.au
Motorcycle Mfr
N.A.I.C.S.: 336991

West Surfing Products (1)
Unit 1-3 53 Bushland Ridge, Bibra Lake, 6163, WA, Australia
Tel.: (61) 438238483
Web Site: https://www.westsurfing.com
Surfing Apparel
N.A.I.C.S.: 424590

VMS INDUSTRIES LTD.
808/C Pinnacle Business Park Corporate Road, Prahladnagar, Ahmedabad, 380015, Gujarat, India
Tel.: (91) 7940320484
Web Site: https://www.vmsil.in
Year Founded: 1991
533427—(BOM)
Rev.: $17,476,518
Assets: $10,498,052
Liabilities: $3,581,476
Net Worth: $6,916,576
Earnings: $299,442
Emp.: 22
Fiscal Year-end: 03/31/23
Ship Recycling, Offshore Support & Financial Services
N.A.I.C.S.: 336611
Sangeeta Jain (Exec Dir)

VMS REHAB SYSTEMS INC.
Suite 200 440 Laurier Avenue West, Ottawa, K1R 7X6, ON, Canada
Tel.: (613) 731-5935
Web Site: http://www.vmsrehabsystems.com
VRSYF—(OTCIQ)
Sales Range: Less than $1 Million
Medical Products & Pharmaceuticals Mfr
N.A.I.C.S.: 339112
Michael S. Wexler (Chm & CEO)

VMT GMBH
Stegwiesenstrasse 24, 76646, Bruchsal, Germany
Tel.: (49) 725196990
Web Site: http://www.vmt-gmbh.de
Year Founded: 1994
Rev.: $17,857,542
Emp.: 100
Tunnelling Products Whslr
N.A.I.C.S.: 423830
Michael Gunther (Gen Mgr)

Subsidiaries:

LLC Innovative Measuring Technologies Moscow (1)
ul Retschnikow 19, 115407, Moscow, Russia
Tel.: (7) 4956320108
Measuring Equipment Distr
N.A.I.C.S.: 423830
Denis Postnikov (Head-Sls)

VMT (Shanghai) Technical Measurement Co., Ltd. (1)
Room 1101 A Building 1 No 1158 Zhangdong Road, Shanghai, 201203, China
Tel.: (86) 2150750276
Web Site: http://www.vmt-china.com
Measuring Equipment Distr
N.A.I.C.S.: 423830

VMT (USA) Technical Measurement Solutions, Inc.
1613 132nd Ave E Ste 200, Sumner, WA 98390
Tel.: (253) 447-2399
Measuring Equipment Distr
N.A.I.C.S.: 423830
Mathias Knoll (Reg Mgr-Sls)

VMT Tunnel Guidance Pty Ltd (1)
Unit 14 28-36 Sabre Drive, Port Melbourne, 3207, VIC, Australia
Tel.: (61) 1300553905
Tunnel Equipment Distr
N.A.I.C.S.: 423860
Matthew Jarvis (Reg Mgr-Sls)

VNE S.P.A.
via Biagioni 371 -Querceta, Seravezza, 55047, Lucca, Italy
Tel.: (39) 0584742530
Web Site: https://www.vne.it
Year Founded: 1977
VNE—(EUR)
Emp.: 85
Computer Product Mfr
N.A.I.C.S.: 334118

VNSTEEL HOCHIMINH CITY METAL CORPORATION
No 56 Thu Khoa Huan Street, District 1, Ho Chi Minh City, Vietnam
Tel.: (84) 2838291539
Web Site: https://vnsteel.vn
Year Founded: 1975
HMC—(HOSE)
Rev.: $128,524,183
Assets: $52,731,221
Liabilities: $36,099,234
Net Worth: $16,631,987
Earnings: $871,339
Emp.: 4,416
Fiscal Year-end: 12/31/23
Metal Products Mfr
N.A.I.C.S.: 213114

VNV GLOBAL LTD.
Master Samuelsgatan 1, SE 111 44, Stockholm, Sweden
Tel.: (46) 854501550 SE
Web Site: https://www.vostoknewventures.com
Year Founded: 1996
VNV—(OMX)
Rev.: $493,000
Assets: $781,554,000
Liabilities: $168,120,000
Net Worth: $613,434,000
Earnings: ($781,998,000)
Emp.: 12
Fiscal Year-end: 12/31/22
Investment Services
N.A.I.C.S.: 523999
Per Brilioth (Mng Dir)

Subsidiaries:

Vostok Nafta Sverige AB (1)
Hovslagargatan 5 3rd Fl, Stockholm, 111 48, Sweden
Tel.: (46) 854501550
Web Site: http://www.vostoknafta.com
Sales Range: $25-49.9 Million
Investment Management Service
N.A.I.C.S.: 541618
Per Brilioth (Mng Dir)

VOCAR A.D.
Kneza Milosa 3, Svilajnac, Serbia
Tel.: (381) 35 322 838
Web Site: http://www.vocar.co.rs
Year Founded: 1948
VRBG—(BEL)
Sales Range: $1-9.9 Million
Emp.: 12
Fruit & Vegetable Preserving Services
N.A.I.C.S.: 311421
Ilic Zeljko (Exec Dir)

VOCENTO, S.A.
Josefa Valcarcel 40 Bis, 28027, Madrid, Spain
Tel.: (34) 917438104
Web Site: https://www.vocento.com
VOC—(BAR)
Rev.: $372,142,240
Assets: $464,138,787
Liabilities: $174,753,939
Net Worth: $289,384,848
Earnings: $13,906,756
Emp.: 2,922
Fiscal Year-end: 12/31/22
Newspaper & Magazine Publisher; Radio & TV Station Owner & Operator; Internet Publisher & Information Services
N.A.I.C.S.: 513120
Gonzalo Soto Aguirre (VP)

Subsidiaries:

Agencia Colpisa, S.L.U. (1)
Josefa Valcarcel 40bis Madrid 2 Planta, 28027, Madrid, Spain
Tel.: (34) 91 339 9627
Web Site: https://www.colpisa.com
Private Information Agency Services
N.A.I.C.S.: 519290

VOCENTO, S.A.

Vocento, S.A.—(Continued)

BIBAO EDITORIAL PRODUC-CIONES, S.L. (1)
Poligono industrial Torrelarragoiti P6 B1, 48170, Zamudio, Bizkaia, Spain
Tel.: (34) 944523400
Web Site: http://www.bepsa.es
Newspaper & Magazine Publisher
N.A.I.C.S.: 513110

Beralan S.L. (1)
Igarategi Industrialdea N 58, 20130, Urnieta, Gipuzkoa, Spain
Tel.: (34) 94 330 0432
Web Site: https://www.beralan.com
Logistic Services
N.A.I.C.S.: 541614

Comeco Grafico S.L.U. (1)
Calle Meridiano 19, Torrejon de Ardoz, 28850, Madrid, Spain
Tel.: (34) 91 179 1596
Web Site: https://www.comecografico.com
Offset Printing Paper Mfr
N.A.I.C.S.: 323111

Comeco Impresion S.L. (1)
Poligono Industrial Torrelarragoiti P6 B1, Zamudio, 48170, Vizcaya, Spain
Tel.: (34) 944523400
Web Site: http://www.beafa.af
Emp.: 61
Newspaper & Magazine Publisher
N.A.I.C.S.: 513110
Luis garcia *(Gen Mgr)*

Comercial Multimedia Vocento, S.A.U. (1)
Calle Josefa Valcarcel 40 BIS, 28027, Madrid, Spain
Tel.: (34) 91 327 8300
Web Site: https://www.cmvocento.com
Media Services
N.A.I.C.S.: 541810
Carmen Castillo *(Mgr)*

Diario El Correo. S.A.U. (1)
C/Gran Via 45 3 Planta, 48011, Bilbao, Spain
Tel.: (34) 94 487 0100
Web Site: https://www.elcorreo.com
Online Newspaper Services
N.A.I.C.S.: 513110

Ediciones Digitales Hoy, S.L.U. (1)
Avenida del Diario Hoy s/n, 06008, Badajoz, Spain
Tel.: (34) 92 491 0418
Web Site: https://www.hoy.es
Online Newspaper Services
N.A.I.C.S.: 513110

El Comercio, S.A. (1)
Calle Diario El Comercio number 1, Asturias, 33207, Gijon, Spain
Tel.: (34) 985179800
Web Site: http://www.elcomercio.es
Sales Range: $25-49.9 Million
Newspaper & Magazine Publisher
N.A.I.C.S.: 513110

El Correo Digital, S.L. (1)
Pintor Losada 7, 48004, Madrid, Spain
Tel.: (34) 944870100
Web Site: http://www.elcorreo.com
Newspaper & Magazine Publisher
N.A.I.C.S.: 513110

El Norte de Castilla S.A. (1)
Vazquez de Menchaca 10 Pol Ind De Argales, 47008, Valladolid, Spain
Tel.: (34) 983 412 100
Web Site: http://www.elnortedecastilla.es
Newspaper & Magazine Publisher
N.A.I.C.S.: 513110

Factor Moka, S.L.U. (1)
Juan Ignacio Luca de Tena 7, 28027, Madrid, Spain
Tel.: (34) 91 339 9823
Web Site: https://www.factormoka.es
Marketing & Advertising Services
N.A.I.C.S.: 541810

Grupo Europroducciones, S.A. (1)
c/ Virgilio 5 Edificio Overon Ciudad de la Imagen, Pozuelo de Alarcon, 28223, Madrid, 28223, Spain
Tel.: (34) 91 512 98 00
Web Site: http://www.europroducciones.com

Audiovisual Communication Services
N.A.I.C.S.: 512240
Carlo Boserman *(Gen Dir)*

Habitatsoft S.L.U. (1)
C/Anselm Clave 69-73 4, Granollers, 08402, Barcelona, Spain
Tel.: (34) 91 266 5214
Web Site: https://www.habitatsoft.com
Software Development Services
N.A.I.C.S.: 541511

Hill Valley, S.L. (1)
C / Enrique Jardiel Poncela 4 2, 28016, Madrid, Spain
Tel.: (34) 913834025
Web Site: http://www.hillvalley.es
Sales Range: $25-49.9 Million
Television Program Production Services
N.A.I.C.S.: 512191

Infoempleo, S.L. (1)
Paseo de la Castellana 70 1 planta, 28046, Madrid, Spain
Tel.: (34) 917823840
Web Site: http://www.infoempleo.com
Sales Range: $25-49.9 Million
Emp.: 80
Newspaper & Magazine Publisher
N.A.I.C.S.: 513110

La Verdad Multimedia, SA (1)
Camino Viejo de Monteagudo s/n, 30160, Murcia, Spain
Tel.: (34) 96 897 5820
Web Site: https://www.laverdad.es
Online Newspaper Services
N.A.I.C.S.: 513110

MateoMateo Comunicaciones, S.L.U. (1)
C/Padilla 78 Local izd, 28006, Madrid, Spain
Tel.: (34) 90 210 0219
Web Site: https://www.mateoandco.es
Marketing Consultancy Services
N.A.I.C.S.: 541613
Patricia Mateo *(CEO, Founder & Mng Dir)*

Nueva Rioja, SA (1)
Calle Vara De Rey Numero 74 Bajo, Logrono, Spain
Tel.: (34) 94 189 9208
Web Site: https://www.larioja.com
Online Newspaper Services
N.A.I.C.S.: 513110

PUNTO RADIO (1)
Juan Ignacio Luca de Tena 7, 28027, Madrid, Spain
Tel.: (34) 913399535
Web Site: http://www.puntoradio.com
Radio Broadcasting Services
N.A.I.C.S.: 516110

Produccions De Gastronomia, S.L.U. (1)
Calle Tuset 27 7 1, 08006, Barcelona, Spain
Tel.: (34) 93 241 2755
Web Site: https://www.grupgsr.com
Event Planning Services
N.A.I.C.S.: 561920
Roser Torras *(Mng Dir)*

Rotomadrid SL (1)
C/Meridiano 19, Torrejon de Ardoz, 28850, Madrid, Spain
Tel.: (34) 91 676 7504
Web Site: https://www.rotomadrid.com
Offset Printing Paper Mfr
N.A.I.C.S.: 323111

Sector MD, S.L. (1)
Pl Torrelarragoiti Parcela G6, 48170, Zamudio, Spain
Tel.: (34) 944456047
Web Site: http://www.sectormd.com
Newspaper & Magazine Publisher
N.A.I.C.S.: 513110

Taller de Editores, S.A. (1)
c/ Juan Ignacio Luca de Tena 6, 28027, Madrid, Spain
Tel.: (34) 91 327 83 00
Web Site: http://www.tallerdeeditores.com
Magazine Publisher
N.A.I.C.S.: 513199

Tango Comunicacion Estrategica, S.L. (1)

C/Balbina Valverde 15, 28002, Madrid, Spain
Tel.: (34) 91 825 4880
Web Site: https://www.agenciatango.es
Marketing & Advertising Services
N.A.I.C.S.: 541810

Tripictures, S.A. (1)
Enrique Jardiel Poncela 4, 28016, Madrid, Spain
Tel.: (34) 914009920
Web Site: http://www.tripictures.com
Sales Range: $25-49.9 Million
Emp.: 20
Motion Picture Production Services
N.A.I.C.S.: 512110

VERALIA S.A. (1)
Calle Juan Ignacio Luca de Tena 7, 28027, Madrid, Spain
Tel.: (34) 915123149
Television Program Production Services
N.A.I.C.S.: 512191

VODA VRNJCI A.D.

Kneza Milosa 162, 36210, Vrnjaacka Banja, Serbia
Tel.: (381) 36612500
Web Site: https://www.vodavrnjci.rs
Year Founded: 2002
VDAV—(BEL)
Rev.: $10,202,374
Assets: $15,683,230
Liabilities: $2,163,980
Net Worth: $13,519,250
Earnings: $98,639
Emp.: 145
Fiscal Year-end: 12/31/23
Mineral & Bottled Water Mfr
N.A.I.C.S.: 312112
Radovan Simovic *(Dir)*

VODAFONE GROUP PLC

Vodafone House The Connection, Newbury, RG14 2FN, Berkshire, United Kingdom
Tel.: (44) 163533251   UK
Web Site: https://www.vodafone.com
Year Founded: 1985
VOD—(NASDAQ)
Rev.: $39,625,512,555
Assets: $155,784,588,536
Liabilities: $89,954,672,834
Net Worth: $65,829,915,701
Earnings: $1,624,217,567
Emp.: 96,282
Fiscal Year-end: 03/31/24
Mobile Telecommunications Services
N.A.I.C.S.: 551112
Rosemary Martin *(Gen Counsel & Sec)*

Subsidiaries:

360Connect S.A. (1)
Simmachidon Pireos 163 and Echelidon, 11854, Athens, Greece
Tel.: (30) 213 003 0800
Web Site: https://www.360connect.gr
Emp.: 500
Contact Center Services
N.A.I.C.S.: 561422

Cable & Wireless Worldwide plc (1)
Waterside House Longshot Lane, Bracknell, RG12 1XL, Berks, United Kingdom
Tel.: (44) 333 200 7000
Sales Range: $1-4.9 Billion
Emp.: 6,510
Telecommunication Servicesb
N.A.I.C.S.: 517111

Subsidiary (Domestic):

Cable & Wireless UK Holdings Limited (2)
Liberty House 76 Hammersmith Road, Hammersmith, London, W14 8UD, United Kingdom
Tel.: (44) 1908845000
Sales Range: $50-74.9 Million
Emp.: 100
Holding Company; Telecommunications Services

N.A.I.C.S.: 551112

THUS Group plc (2)
1-2 Berkeley Square 99 Berkeley Street, Glasgow, G3 7HR, United Kingdom
Tel.: (44) 1415671234
Web Site: https://www.vodafone.com
Sales Range: $1-4.9 Billion
Emp.: 1,705
Business Telecommunications & Internet Services
N.A.I.C.S.: 517810

Grandcentrix GmbH (1)
Holzmarkt 1, 50676, Cologne, Germany
Tel.: (49) 221 677 8600
Web Site: https://www.grandcentrix.net
Emp.: 200
Software Development Services
N.A.I.C.S.: 541511
Matthias Kromer *(CEO)*

Kabel Deutschland Holding AG (1)
Betastrasse 6-8, 85774, Unterfohring, Germany **(93.9%)**
Tel.: (49) 8996010187
Web Site: http://www.kabeldeutschland.com
Cable Television Services
N.A.I.C.S.: 516210
Irena Gruhne *(Deputy Chm-Supervisory Bd)*

Mezzanine Ware Proprietary Limited (1)
14 Quantum road Techno Park, Stellenbosch, 7600, Western Cape, South Africa
Tel.: (27) 21 880 2033
Web Site: https://www.mezzanineware.com
Software Development Services
N.A.I.C.S.: 541511
Peter Breitenbach *(Head-Strategy)*

Navtrak Limited (1)
20-22 Wenlock Road, London, N1 7GU, United Kingdom
Tel.: (44) 796 332 1037
Web Site: https://www.navtrack.co.uk
Computer Software Services
N.A.I.C.S.: 541511

TKS Telepost Kabel-Service Kaiserslautern GmbH (1)
Altes Forsthaus 2, 67661, Kaiserslautern, Germany
Tel.: (49) 631 352 2499
Web Site: https://www.tkscable.com
Telecommunication Servicesb
N.A.I.C.S.: 517810
Patrick Abram *(Mng Dir)*

TPG Telecom Limited (1)
Level 1 177 Pacific Highway, Saint Leonards, 2060, NSW, Australia
Tel.: (61) 299644646
Web Site: http://www.vodafone.com.au
Rev.: $3,768,816,838
Assets: $13,396,907,567
Liabilities: $5,483,958,858
Net Worth: $7,912,948,709
Earnings: $33,376,473
Emp.: 6,000
Fiscal Year-end: 12/31/2023
Mobile Telecommunications Services
N.A.I.C.S.: 517112

Subsidiary (Domestic):

TPG Corporation Limited (2)
65 Waterloo Road, North Ryde, Sydney, 2113, NSW, Australia
Tel.: (61) 298500800
Web Site: http://www.tpg.com.au
Rev.: $1,947,478,648
Assets: $4,207,075,247
Liabilities: $2,034,034,989
Net Worth: $2,173,040,258
Earnings: $310,635,020
Emp.: 5,056
Fiscal Year-end: 07/31/2018
Telecommunications & Multi Media Services
N.A.I.C.S.: 517121

Subsidiary (Domestic):

TPG Holdings Limited (3)
Level 24 200 Barangaroo Ave, Sydney, 2000, NSW, Australia
Tel.: (61) 290073023
Web Site: https://www.tpg.com.au
Sales Range: $125-149.9 Million
Holding Company; Internet, Internet-Based Telecommunications & Information Technology Networking Services

AND PRIVATE COMPANIES
VODAFONE GROUP PLC

N.A.I.C.S.: 551112

Subsidiary (Domestic):

AAPT Limited (4)
680 George Street Level 23, Sydney, 2000, NSW, Australia
Tel.: (61) 2 8277 5405
Web Site: http://www.aapt.com.au
Sales Range: $350-399.9 Million
Emp.: 1,000
Telecommunication Servicesb
N.A.I.C.S.: 517111

Chariot Limited (4)
Level 1 5 Leigh Street, Adelaide, 5000, SA, Australia
Tel.: (61) 1300147425
Web Site: https://www.chariot.net.au
Sales Range: $10-24.9 Million
Internet Services
N.A.I.C.S.: 517810

Subsidiary (Non-US):

Kooee Pty Ltd (4)
Tel.: (61) 249265007
Telecommunication Servicesb
N.A.I.C.S.: 517810

Subsidiary (Non-US):

Kooee Communications Pty Ltd (5)
Tel.: (61) 249265007
Web Site: http://www.kooee.com.au
Emp.: 50
Telecommunication Servicesb
N.A.I.C.S.: 517810

Subsidiary (Domestic):

PIPE Transmission Pty Ltd (4)
L 17 Pipe Networks House 127 Creek St, Brisbane, 4000, QLD, Australia
Tel.: (61) 732339800
Web Site: http://www.pipenetworks.com
Emp.: 80
Telecommunication Servicesb
N.A.I.C.S.: 517810

SPT Telecommunications Pty Ltd (4)
11-17 Mosbri Crescent, Newcastle, 2300, NSW, Australia
Tel.: (61) 249265007
Sales Range: $25-49.9 Million
Emp.: 20
Telecommunication Servicesb
N.A.I.C.S.: 517810
Mik Watts (Gen Mgr)

Soul Communications Pty. Limited (4)
Level 14 201 Kent Street, GPO Box N800, Grosvenor Place, Sydney, 2000, NSW, Australia
Tel.: (61) 282206000
Web Site: http://www.soulaustralia.com.au
Sales Range: $350-399.9 Million
Emp.: 100
Mobile, Wired, Internet & Broadband Telecommunications Reseller
N.A.I.C.S.: 517121

Soul Pattinson Telecommunications Pty Ltd (4)
L 14 201 Kent St, Sydney, 2000, NSW, Australia
Tel.: (61) 282206000
Telecommunication Servicesb
N.A.I.C.S.: 517810

TPG Internet Pty. Ltd. (4)
65 Waterloo Rd, Macquarie Park, North Ryde, 2113, NSW, Australia
Tel.: (61) 298500800
Web Site: http://www.tpg.com.au
Emp.: 150
Internet & Internet-Based Telecommunications Services
N.A.I.C.S.: 517810

TPG Network Pty Ltd (4)
65 Waterloo Rd, North Ryde, 2113, NSW, Australia
Tel.: (61) 298500800
Network Systems Integration Services
N.A.I.C.S.: 541512

TPG Research Pty Ltd (4)
53 Dundas Ct, Phillip, Canberra, 2606, ACT, Australia
Tel.: (61) 262851711
Software Development Services
N.A.I.C.S.: 541511

iiNet Limited (4)
65 Waterloo Road, Macquarie Park, 2113, NSW, Australia
Tel.: (61) 8 9214 2222
Web Site: http://www.iinet.net.au
Internet Services
N.A.I.C.S.: 517810
Michael M. Malone (Founder)

Subsidiary (Domestic):

Westnet Ltd (5)
Locked Bag 16, Cloisters Square, Perth, 6850, WA, Australia
Tel.: (61) 131960
Web Site: https://www.westnet.com.au
Internet Broadband Services
N.A.I.C.S.: 517810

Talkmobile Limited (1)
Vodafone House The Connection, Newbury, RG14 2FN, Berkshire, United Kingdom
Tel.: (44) 333 304 8064
Web Site: https://www.talkmobile.co.uk
Mobile Network Services
N.A.I.C.S.: 517121

UPC Ceska Republica S.r.o (1)
Zavisova 502/5 Nusle, 140 00, Prague, Czech Republic
Tel.: (420) 241 005 100
Web Site: http://www.upc.cz
Cable Television, Internet & VoIP Services
N.A.I.C.S.: 516210

UPC Magyarorszag Kft (1)
Kinizsi Utca 30 36, Budapest, 1092, Hungary
Tel.: (36) 14562600
Cable Programming Services
N.A.I.C.S.: 516210

UPC Romania Srl (1)
Strada Nordului nr 62 D Sector 1, 014104, Bucharest, Romania
Tel.: (40) 311018100
Web Site: http://www.upc.ro
Cable & Other Subscription Programming
N.A.I.C.S.: 516210

Urbana Teleunion Rostock GmbH & Co. KG (1)
Nobelstrasse 55, 18059, Rostock, Germany
Tel.: (49) 38 140 5880
Web Site: https://www.infocity-rostock.de
Cable Television Services
N.A.I.C.S.: 516210

VM, S.A. (1)
Vodacom building at Rua dos Desportistas, 00649, Maputo, Mozambique
Tel.: (258) 840900000
Web Site: http://www.vm.co.mz
Telecommunication Servicesb
N.A.I.C.S.: 517112

VND S.p.A. (1)
Via Per Carpi 26/B, 42015, Correggio, RE, Italy
Tel.: (39) 052 273 3232
Web Site: https://www.vnd.it
Telecommunication Servicesb
N.A.I.C.S.: 517810

Vantage Towers Single Member Societe Anonyme (1)
2 Adrianeiou and Papada Str, 11525, Athens, Greece
Tel.: (30) 216 202 5900
Telecommunication Tower Services
N.A.I.C.S.: 237130
Athanasios Exarchos (Mng Dir)

Vantage Towers Zartkoruen Mukodo Reszvenytarsasag (1)
Lechner Odon Fasor 6, 1096, Budapest, Hungary
Tel.: (36) 70 458 4353
Telecommunication Tower Services
N.A.I.C.S.: 237130
Gergo Budai (Mng Dir)

Vodacom Group Limited (1)
082 Vodacom Boulevard, Midrand, 1685, South Africa (60.5%)
Tel.: (27) 116535000
Web Site: http://www.vodacom.com
Rev.: $6,219,482,300
Assets: $11,915,759,850
Liabilities: $6,831,044,720
Net Worth: $5,084,715,130
Earnings: $945,213,090
Emp.: 7,946
Fiscal Year-end: 03/31/2023
Holding Company; Mobile Telecommunications Services
N.A.I.C.S.: 551112
Mohamed Shameel Aziz-Joosub (Grp CEO)

Subsidiary (Domestic):

Vodacom Pty. Ltd. (2)
Vodacom Corporate Park 082 Vodacom Boulevard, Vodavalley, Midrand, 1685, South Africa
Tel.: (27) 116535000
Web Site: http://www.vodacom.com
Cellular Communications Network Operator
N.A.I.C.S.: 517112

Subsidiary (Domestic):

Vodacom International Holdings (Proprietary) Limited (3)
Vodacom Corporate Park 082 Vodacom Boulevard, Voda Valley, Midrand, 1685, South Africa
Tel.: (27) 0116535000
Web Site: http://www.vodacom.com
Sales Range: $50-74.9 Million
Emp.: 100
Holding Company
N.A.I.C.S.: 551112

Subsidiary (Non-US):

Vodacom DRCongo s.p.r.l (4)
292 Avenue de la Justice, Commune of Gombe, Kinshasa, Congo, Democratic Republic of
Tel.: (243) 813131000
Web Site: https://www.vodacom.cd
Emp.: 45
Cellular Communications Network Operator
N.A.I.C.S.: 517112

Vodacom Lesotho (Pty) Ltd (4)
Vodacom Park 585 Mabile Road, PO Box 7387, 100, Maseru, Lesotho
Tel.: (266) 52212398
Web Site: https://www.vodacom.co.ls
Sales Range: $25-49.9 Million
Cellular Communications Network Operator
N.A.I.C.S.: 517112

Vodacom Mozambique (4)
Rua dos Desportistas no 649, Av 25 de Setembro, Maputo, Mozambique
Tel.: (258) 840900000
Web Site: http://www.vm.co.mz
Cellular Communications Network Operator
N.A.I.C.S.: 517112

Subsidiary (Domestic):

Vodacom Service Provider Company (Proprietary) Limited (3)
82 Vodacom Boulevard, Vodavalley, Midrand, 1685, South Africa
Tel.: (27) 116535000
Web Site: http://www.vodacom.com
Sales Range: $900-999.9 Million
Emp.: 5,000
Business Telecommunication & Internet Services
N.A.I.C.S.: 517112

Subsidiary (Non-US):

Vodacom Tanzania Public Limited Company (2)
15th Floor Vodacom Tower Ursino Estate Plot 23 Old Bagamoyo Road, PO Box 2369, Dar es Salaam, Tanzania (75%)
Tel.: (255) 754700000
Web Site: https://vodacom.co.tz
Rev.: $418,988,130
Assets: $884,054,630
Liabilities: $541,092,220
Net Worth: $342,962,410
Earnings: ($12,945,580)
Emp.: 569
Fiscal Year-end: 03/31/2021
Communication Service
N.A.I.C.S.: 517121
Sitholizwe Mdlalose (Mng Dir)

Subsidiary (Domestic):

Vodacom Tanzania Limited (3)
15th Floor Vodacom Tower Ursino Estate Plot 23 Old Bagamoyo Road, PO Box 2369, Dar es Salaam, Tanzania
Tel.: (255) 754700000
Web Site: https://www.vodacom.co.tz
Cellular Communications Network Operator
N.A.I.C.S.: 517112

Vodacom Life Assurance Company (RF) Limited (1)
Vodacom Corporate Park 082 Vodacom Boulevard, Midrand, 1685, South Africa
Tel.: (27) 821 7800
Software Development Services
N.A.I.C.S.: 541511

Vodacom Payment Services (Proprietary) Limited (1)
Vodacom Corporate Park 082 Vodacom Boulevard, Midrand, 1685, South Africa
Tel.: (27) 821952
Software Development Services
N.A.I.C.S.: 541511

Vodafone Albania Sh.A (1)
Tirana-Durres highway Rr 'Pavaresia' No 61, PO Box 268/1, Kashar, Tirana, Albania
Tel.: (355) 699000140
Web Site: https://www.vodafone.al
Sales Range: $25-49.9 Million
Emp.: 10
Cellular Communications Network Operator
N.A.I.C.S.: 517112

Vodafone Automotive UK Limited (1)
Shuttleworth House 21 Bridgewater Close Network 65 Business Park, Hapton, Burnley, BB11 5TE, United Kingdom
Tel.: (44) 333 222 0799
Telecommunication Servicesb
N.A.I.C.S.: 517810

Vodafone Czech Republic a.s. (1)
namesti Junkovych 2, 155 00, Prague, 5, Czech Republic (100%)
Tel.: (420) 271171111
Web Site: https://www.vodafone.cz
Sales Range: $400-449.9 Million
Emp.: 2,119
Telecommunication Servicesb
N.A.I.C.S.: 517112
Petr Dvorak (CEO)

Vodafone Egypt Telecommunications S.A.E (1)
7A Corniche El-Nile, Dallah Tower, Maadi, 11431, Egypt
Tel.: (20) 25292769
Web Site: http://www.vodafone.com.eg
Sales Range: $400-449.9 Million
Emp.: 1,900
Cellular Communications Network Operator
N.A.I.C.S.: 517112
Osama Said (Dir-Tech)

Vodafone GmbH (1)
Ferdinand -Braun- Platz 1, 40549, Dusseldorf, Germany (100%)
Tel.: (49) 8001721212
Web Site: https://www.vodafone.de
Sales Range: $100-124.9 Million
Emp.: 700
Cellular Telecommunications Network Operator
N.A.I.C.S.: 517112
Anna Dimitrova (Mng Dir & Mgr-Fin & Strategy)

Subsidiary (Non-US):

Arcor AG & Co. KG (2) (100%)
Tel.: (49) 6921690
Web Site: http://www.arcor.de
Fixed-line Telecommunications Network Operator
N.A.I.C.S.: 517112

Subsidiary (Non-US):

Arcor Online GmbH (3)
Tel.: (49) 6963152175
Web Site: http://www.arcor.de
Internet Service Provider
N.A.I.C.S.: 517810

Vodafone Group Services Limited (1)

VODAFONE GROUP PLC

Vodafone Group Plc—(Continued)

Vodafone House The Connection, Newbury, RG14 2FN, United Kingdom
Tel.: (44) 163533251
Wireless Telecommunication Services
N.A.I.C.S.: 517112

Vodafone Innovus S.A.
12 5km National Rd Athens-Lamia, Metamorfosi, 14452, Athens, Greece
Tel.: (30) 210 427 6667
Web Site: https://www.vodafoneinnovus.com
Software Development Services
N.A.I.C.S.: 541511

Vodafone Institut Fur Gesellschaft Und Kommunikation GmbH (1)
Ferdinand-Braun-Platz 1, 40549, Dusseldorf, Germany
Tel.: (49) 302 061 7628
Web Site: https://www.vodafone-institut.de
Education Institute Services
N.A.I.C.S.: 611710
Thomas Holtmanns *(CFO)*

Vodafone Investments Luxembourg S.a r.l. (1)
15 rue Edward Steichen, 2540, Luxembourg, Luxembourg
Tel.: (352) 26127230
Investment Management Service
N.A.I.C.S.: 523999

Vodafone Ireland Ltd (1)
Mountainview, Leopardstown, Dublin, 18, Ireland **(100%)**
Tel.: (353) 12038232
Web Site: https://n.vodafone.ie
Cellular Communications Network Operator
N.A.I.C.S.: 517112

Vodafone Italia S.p.A. (1)
via Jervis 13, postale 190, 10015, Ivrea, TO, Italy **(100%)**
Tel.: (39) 03492000190
Web Site: https://privati.vodafone.it
Cellular Communications Network Operator
N.A.I.C.S.: 517112
Aldo Bisio *(CEO)*

Vodafone Limited (1)
Vodafone House, The Connection, Newbury, RG14 2FN, Berkshire, United Kingdom **(100%)**
Tel.: (44) 163533251
Web Site: https://www.vodafone.co.uk
Cellular Communications Network Operator
N.A.I.C.S.: 517112

Vodafone Magyarorszag Mobile Tavkozlesi Zartkoruen Mukodo Reszvenytarsasag (1)
Lechner Odon fasor 6, Budapest, 1096, Hungary
Tel.: (36) 12883288
Web Site: http://www.vodafone.hu
Mobile Telecommunications Services
N.A.I.C.S.: 517112

Vodafone Magyarorszag Tavkozlesi Zartkoruen Mukodo Reszvenytarsasag (1)
Lechner Odon Avenue 6, 1096, Budapest, Hungary
Tel.: (36) 70 700 1270
Web Site: https://www.vodafone.hu
Telecommunication Services b
N.A.I.C.S.: 517810

Vodafone Netherlands (1)
Avenue Ceramique 300, 6221 KX, Maastricht, Netherlands
Tel.: (31) 654500100
Web Site: https://www.vodafone.nl
Sales Range: $1-4.9 Billion
Emp.: 3,500
Holding Company
N.A.I.C.S.: 551112

Subsidiary (Domestic):

BelCompany BV (2)
Wageningselaan 2, 3903, Veenendaal, Netherlands **(100%)**
Tel.: (31) 318569898
Web Site: http://www.belcompany.nl
Sales Range: $125-149.9 Million
Emp.: 1,000
Mobile Communications Retailer & Supplier
N.A.I.C.S.: 517112

Subsidiary (Non-US):

Vodafone Hungary Mobile Telecommunications Limited (2)
Lechnerodon 6, H 1096, Budapest, Hungary **(87%)**
Tel.: (36) 12883288
Web Site: http://www.vodafone.hu
Sales Range: $150-199.9 Million
Emp.: 850
Telecommunication Services b
N.A.I.C.S.: 517112
Ahmed Elsayed *(Dir-Tech)*

Vodafone Portugal Comunicacoes Pessoais S.A. (1)
Av D Joao II no 36 - 8 Piso, Parque das Nacoe, 1998-017, Lisbon, Portugal **(50.9%)**
Tel.: (351) 213785480
Web Site: http://www.vodafone.pt
Sales Range: $200-249.9 Million
Emp.: 880
Telecommunication Services b
N.A.I.C.S.: 517112

Vodafone Qatar Q.S.C. (1)
Zone 3 Street 981 Building number 2 4th floor, PO Box 27727, Doha, Qatar
Tel.: (974) 44096666
Web Site: https://www.vodafone.qa
Rev.: $853,097,222
Assets: $1,998,663,388
Liabilities: $644,900,593
Net Worth: $1,353,762,794
Earnings: $148,099,274
Emp.: 299
Fiscal Year-end: 12/31/2023
Telecommunication Services b
N.A.I.C.S.: 517111
Abdulla Nasser Al-Misnad *(Chm)*

Vodafone Roaming Services S.a r.l. (1)
15 rue Edward Steichen, 2540, Luxembourg, Luxembourg
Tel.: (352) 261272
Web Site: http://www.roaming.vodafone.com
Wireless Telecommunication Services
N.A.I.C.S.: 517112

Vodafone Romania S.A. (1)
Globalworth Tower strada Barbu Vacarescu no 201 floor 4 sector 2, 020276, Bucharest, Romania
Tel.: (40) 372022222
Web Site: https://www.vodafone.ro
Mobile Telecommunications Services
N.A.I.C.S.: 517112
Murielle Lorillou *(CEO)*

Vodafone Stiftung Deutschland Gemeinnutzige GmbH (1)
Ferdinand-Braun-Platz 1, 40549, Dusseldorf, Germany
Tel.: (49) 302 061 7624
Web Site: https://www.vodafone-stiftung.de
Educational Support Services
N.A.I.C.S.: 611710

Vodafone Telekomunikasyon A.S. (1)
Vodafone Plaza Buyukdere Cd No 251, Maslak, Istanbul, 34398, Turkiye
Tel.: (90) 2123670000
Web Site: http://www.vodafone.com.tr
Sales Range: $400-449.9 Million
Emp.: 2,000
Wireless Telecommunication Services
N.A.I.C.S.: 517810

Vodafone US Inc. (1)
154 W 14th St 8th Fl, New York, NY 10011
Telecommunication Services b
N.A.I.C.S.: 517810
Chuck Pol *(Pres-Americas)*

Vodafone-Panafon Hellenic Telecommunications Company S.A. (1)
1-3 Tzavella Str, 152 31, Halandri, Greece **(55%)**
Tel.: (30) 2106702000
Web Site: http://www.vodafone.gr
Sales Range: $25-49.9 Million
Emp.: 45
Cellular Communications Network Operator
N.A.I.C.S.: 517112

Subsidiary (Domestic):

Cyta Hellas Telecommunications S.A (2)
128 Alexandras Avenue, Athens, 114 71, Greece
Tel.: (30) 210 62 66 100
Web Site: http://www.cyta.gr
Wireless Telecommunication Services
N.A.I.C.S.: 517112

hellas online S.A. (2)
2 Adrianiou Street, 115 25, Athens, Greece
Tel.: (30) 2130004195
Web Site: http://statheri.vodafone.gr
Telecommunications & Internet Services
N.A.I.C.S.: 517810

VODAFONE IDEA LIMITED
Suman Tower Plot No 18 Sector 11, Gandhinagar, 382 011, Gujarat, India
Tel.: (91) 7966714000 In
Web Site: https://www.myvi.in
532822—(BOM)
Rev.: $5,094,238,954
Assets: $24,847,754,931
Liabilities: $33,763,179,665
Net Worth: $(8,915,424,735)
Earnings: $3,513,110,725
Emp.: 9,226
Fiscal Year-end: 03/31/23
Telecommunication Services b
N.A.I.C.S.: 517810
Akshaya Moondra *(CFO)*

Subsidiaries:

Aditya Birla Telecom Limited (1)
Aditya Birla Ctr 1st Fl, S K Ahire Marg Worli, 400 030, Mumbai, India
Tel.: (91) 2266525000
Web Site: http://www.morestore.com
Sales Range: $100-124.9 Million
Emp.: 400
Wireless Telecommunication Services
N.A.I.C.S.: 517112

YOU Broadband India Limited (1)
10th Floor Birla Centurion Century Mills Compound, Pandurang Budhkar Marg Worli, Mumbai, 400 030, Maharashtra, India
Tel.: (91) 9594004000
Web Site: http://www.youbroadband.in
Emp.: 2,000
Broadband & Cable Services
N.A.I.C.S.: 517112

VODATEL NETWORKS HOLDINGS LIMITED
No 74 da Rua da Felicidade Edificio Vodatel, Taipa, China (Macau)
Tel.: (853) 28721182
Web Site: http://www.vodatelsys.com
8033—(HKG)
Rev.: $67,601,103
Assets: $55,925,240
Liabilities: $29,065,481
Net Worth: $26,859,759
Earnings: $690,264
Emp.: 150
Fiscal Year-end: 12/31/23
Network Solution & Telecommunication Services
N.A.I.C.S.: 517810
Jose Manuel Dos Santos *(Founder & Chm)*

Subsidiaries:

Mega Datatech Limited (1)
74 da Rua da Felicidade 1/F Edificio Vodatel, Taipa, China (Macau)
Tel.: (853) 28722131
Web Site: https://www.megadatatech.com
Emp.: 59
System Integration Services
N.A.I.C.S.: 541512

Tidestone Software (Shanghai) Corporation Limited (1)
Room 2303 Area A No 418 Guiping Road, Xuhui District, Shanghai, 200032, China
Tel.: (86) 2164226951
Web Site: http://www.tidestonesoft.com

INTERNATIONAL PUBLIC

Software Development Services
N.A.I.C.S.: 513210

Vodatel Networks (H.K.) Limited (1)
Room 713B 7th Floor Block B Sea View Estate 2-8 Watson Road, North Point, China (Hong Kong)
Tel.: (852) 25878868
System Infrastructure & Telecommunication Services
N.A.I.C.S.: 517810
Edwin Lin *(Mgr-Bus Dev)*

VODOPRIVREDA A.D.
Vuka Karadzica 17, Smederevska Palanka, Serbia
Tel.: (381) 26 321 782
Web Site: http://www.vodoprivreda.rs
Year Founded: 1956
VDSP—(BEL)
Sales Range: $1-9.9 Million
Waste Management Services
N.A.I.C.S.: 237110
Njegos Dokovic *(Exec Dir)*

VODOPRIVREDA A.D.
Svetosavska 33, Pozarevac, Serbia
Tel.: (381) 12 523 022
Year Founded: 1989
Sales Range: $1-9.9 Million
Emp.: 60
Hydraulic Structure Construction Services
N.A.I.C.S.: 236210
Nenad Milancovic *(Gen Mgr)*

VODOPRIVREDA TREBISNJICA A.D.
Republike Srpske 33, 89000, Trebinje, Bosnia & Herzegovina
Tel.: (387) 59 220 155
Sales Range: Less than $1 Million
Water Project Construction Services
N.A.I.C.S.: 237110

VODOPRIVREDA ZAGREB DD
Petrovaradinska 110, 10000, Zagreb, Croatia
Tel.: (385) 15631200
Web Site: https://www.vzg.hr
Year Founded: 1964
Waste Management Services
N.A.I.C.S.: 221310
Robert Laginja *(Pres)*

VODOPRIVREDNO DRUSTVO DUNAV AD
Trg Bratstva i jedinstva 21, 21400, Backa Palanka, Serbia
Tel.: (381) 21 7550 500
Web Site: http://www.vddunav.rs
Year Founded: 1989
VPDU—(BEL)
Sales Range: $10-24.9 Million
Emp.: 111
Flood Control Construction Services
N.A.I.C.S.: 237990
Novica Komad *(Head-Legal Services)*

VODOPRIVREDNO PREDUZECE A.D.
Cara Lazara Street No 109, 35230, Cuprija, Serbia
Tel.: (381) 35 8871 508
Web Site: http://www.vpcuprija.com
Year Founded: 2002
Sales Range: $1-9.9 Million
Emp.: 160
Waterpower Engineering Services
N.A.I.C.S.: 541330

VODOVOD I KANALIZACIJA A.D.
ulica Hajduk Stanka 20, 76300, Bijeljina, Bosnia & Herzegovina
Tel.: (387) 55226460
Web Site: https://bnvodovod.com

Year Founded: 1991
VIKM—(BANJ)
Sales Range: Less than $1 Million
Emp.: 35
Water Treatment & Supply Services
N.A.I.C.S.: 221310
Mitrovic Sladana *(Exec Dir-Economic & Legal Sector)*

VOESTALPINE AG
voestalpine-Strasse 1, 4020, Linz, Austria
Tel.: (43) 5030415
Web Site:
 https://www.voestalpine.com
Year Founded: 1938
VOE—(VIE)
Rev.: $19,668,789,122
Assets: $18,446,794,733
Liabilities: $10,061,946,903
Net Worth: $8,384,847,831
Earnings: $1,272,069,933
Emp.: 51,202
Fiscal Year-end: 03/31/23
Steel Products Mfr
N.A.I.C.S.: 331110
Robert Ottel *(CFO & Member-Exec Bd)*

Subsidiaries:

ACEROS BOEHLER UDDEHOLM S.A. (1)
Mozart 40 Centro Industrial Garin, B1619ADU, Buenos Aires, Argentina
Tel.: (54) 332 745 3200
Web Site: https://www.acerosboehler.com.ar
Metal Heat Treatment Services
N.A.I.C.S.: 332811

ACOS BOHLER-UDDEHOLM DO BRASIL LTDA. (1)
Estrada Yae Massumoto 353, 09842-160, Sao Bernardo do Campo, Sao Paulo, Brazil
Tel.: (55) 11 4393 45 60
Sales Range: $25-49.9 Million
Emp.: 50
Steel Mfrs
N.A.I.C.S.: 331110

ASSAB Celik ve Isil Islem A.S. (1)
Dudullu OSB 2 Cadde No 26, Umraniye, 34776, Istanbul, Turkiye
Tel.: (90) 216 420 19 26
Web Site: http://www.assab.com.tr
Sales Range: $50-74.9 Million
Emp.: 137
Metal Sales & Heat Treatment Services
N.A.I.C.S.: 332811
Aziz Hatman *(Dir-Sls & Mktg)*

ASSAB Steels (China) Ltd. (1)
Room 1701-1708 Grand Central Plaza Tower 2 138 Shatin Rural, Committee Road, Sha Tin, New Territories, China (Hong Kong)
Tel.: (852) 2487 1991
Web Site: http://www.busmi.com
Steel Products Mfr
N.A.I.C.S.: 331110

ASSAB Steels (HK) Ltd. (1)
Room 1702-1703 Tower 2 Grand Central Plaza 138, Shatin Rural Committee Road, Sha Tin, NT, China (Hong Kong)
Tel.: (852) 24871991
Web Site: https://www.assab.com
Strip Steel Mfr
N.A.I.C.S.: 331110
Dominic Ma *(Pres)*

ASSAB Steels (Korea) Co., Ltd. (1)
6 Namdongseo-ro 83beon-gil, Namdong-gu, Incheon, 21698, Korea (South)
Tel.: (82) 328214300
Web Site: https://www.assab.com
Sales Range: $25-49.9 Million
Emp.: 30
Steel Products Whslr
N.A.I.C.S.: 423510
Yang Il-Suk *(Mng Dir)*

ASSAB Steels (Malaysia) Sdn Bhd (1)
Lot PT 3812 Jalan 4D Seksyen U6, Kampung Baru Subang, 40150, Shah Alam, Selangor, Malaysia
Tel.: (60) 378481368
Web Site: https://www.assab.com
Sales Range: $50-74.9 Million
Emp.: 50
Steel Products Whslr
N.A.I.C.S.: 423510
Terry Hong *(Mng Dir)*

ASSAB Steels (Taiwan) Ltd. (1)
112 Wu Kung 1st Road, Wu Ku District New Taipei CityNew Taipei Industrial Park, Taipei, 248-87, Taiwan
Tel.: (886) 222992849
Web Site: https://www.assab.com
Sales Range: $50-74.9 Million
Emp.: 70
Steel Whslr
N.A.I.C.S.: 423510
Harvard Chen *(Mng Dir)*

ASSAB Steels (Thailand) Ltd. (1)
9/8 Moo 4 Soi Land Thai Thepharak Road, Bang Phli Yai Subdistrict, Bang Phli, 10540, Samut Prakan, Thailand
Tel.: (66) 23855937
Web Site: https://www.assab.com
Sales Range: $50-74.9 Million
Emp.: 80
Steel Products Whslr
N.A.I.C.S.: 423510
Chavalit Meesamanyont *(Mng Dir)*

ASSAB Steels Singapore (Pte) Ltd. (1)
18 Penjuru Close, Singapore, 608616, Singapore
Tel.: (65) 68622200
Web Site: https://www.assab.com
Sales Range: $25-49.9 Million
Emp.: 49
Tool Steel Distr
N.A.I.C.S.: 423510
Anthony Yim *(Mng Dir)*

ASSAB Tooling (Dong Guan) Co., Ltd. (1)
3 Gongye North 1 Road Dongguan Songshan Lake, High-tech Industrial Development Zone, Dongguan, 523808, China
Tel.: (86) 76922897888
Web Site: https://www.assab-china.com
Steel Product Distr
N.A.I.C.S.: 423510
David Liang *(Mng Dir)*

ASSAB Tooling (Qing Dao) Co., Ltd. (1)
8 Yi Sheng Bai Road, Jimo Environmental Protection Industrial Zone, Qingdao, 266200, China
Tel.: (86) 53287529999
Web Site: https://www.assab-china.com
Steel Distr
N.A.I.C.S.: 423510

ASSAB Tooling (Xiamen) Co., Ltd. (1)
Eastern G/F No 35 Huli Road, Xiamen, 361006, China
Tel.: (86) 5925624565
Web Site: https://www.assab-xiamen.com
Steel Mfrs
N.A.I.C.S.: 331110

ASSAB Tooling Technology (Chongqing) Co., Ltd. (1)
Plant C, Automotive Industrial Park, Northern New District, Chongqing, 401120, China
Tel.: (86) 2367455698
Web Site: https://www.assab-chongqing.com
Steel Mfrs
N.A.I.C.S.: 331110

ASSAB Tooling Technology (Ningbo) Co., Ltd. (1)
No 218 Longjiaoshan Road Vehicle Part Industrial Park, Ningbo Economic and Technology Development Zone, Ningbo, 315806, China
Tel.: (86) 57486807188
Web Site: https://www.assab-china.com
Metal Heat Treatment Services
N.A.I.C.S.: 332811
David Liang *(Mng Dir)*

ASSAB Tooling Technology (Shanghai) Co., Ltd. (1)
No 4088 Humin Road, Xin Zhuang Industrial Zone, Shanghai, 201108, China
Tel.: (86) 2124169688
Web Site: https://www.assab-china.com
Steel Product Distr
N.A.I.C.S.: 423510

Aceros Boehler del Ecuador S.A. (1)
Km 7 5 Via Daule, Guayaquil, Guayas, Ecuador
Tel.: (593) 4 2262922
Welding Equipment Mfr
N.A.I.C.S.: 333992

Aceros Bohler Uddeholm, S.A. de C.V. (1)
Calle 8 No 2 Letra C, Naucalpan, 53370, Mexico
Tel.: (52) 5591720242
Web Site: http://www.bu-mexico.com
Steel Products Mfr
N.A.I.C.S.: 331221

Advanced Tooling Tek (Shanghai) Co., Ltd. (1)
No 255 Xinxiao Rd, Xinqiao Town Songjiang Dist, Shanghai, 201612, China
Tel.: (86) 2133738146
Web Site: https://www.att-metal.com
Steel Product Mfr & Distr
N.A.I.C.S.: 331110
Zeno Zheng *(Mng Dir)*

Assab Japan KK (1)
Bancho M Building 2-8 Roku-Bancho, Chiyoda-ku, Tokyo, 102-0085, Japan
Tel.: (81) 352263771
Web Site: https://www.assab.com
Tool Steel Mfr & Distr
N.A.I.C.S.: 331110

Assab Steels Vietnam Company Limited (1)
TS 10/8 Road Tien Son IP, Tien Du, Hanoi, Bac Ninh, Vietnam
Tel.: (84) 2223734458
Tool Steel Mfr & Distr
N.A.I.C.S.: 331110

Assab Tooling (Beijing) Co., Ltd. (1)
No 10A Rong Jing Dong Jie, Beijing Business Development Area, Beijing, 100176, China
Tel.: (86) 1087530088
Web Site: https://www.assab-beijing.com
Tool Steel Mfr & Distr
N.A.I.C.S.: 331110

BOHLER Bleche GmbH (1)
Bohler-Gasse 1, 8680, Murzzuschlag, Austria
Tel.: (43) 38525 552 6201
Web Site: http://www.bohler-bleche.at
Metal Sheet Mfr
N.A.I.C.S.: 332322

BOHLER Edelstahl GmbH (1)
Mariazellerstrasse 25, 8605, Kapfenberg, Austria
Tel.: (43) 3862 20 6599
Web Site: http://www.bohler-uddeholm.co.za
Emp.: 2,000
Steel Products Mfr
N.A.I.C.S.: 331110
Johann Weigend *(Mgr-Fin)*

Subsidiary (Domestic):

BU Beteiligungs-und Vermogensverwaltung GmbH (2)
Modecenterstrasse 14/A/3, 1030, Vienna, Austria
Tel.: (43) 5 03 04 15
Steel Products Mfr
N.A.I.C.S.: 331110

BOHLER Edelstahl GmbH & Co KG (1)
Mariazeller-Strase 25, PO Box 96, 8605, Kapfenberg, Austria
Tel.: (43) 5 030 4200
Web Site: https://www.bohler-edelstahl.com
Sales Range: $900-999,9 Million
Emp.: 1,995
Steel Products Mfr
N.A.I.C.S.: 331110

Subsidiary (Domestic):

HOTEL BOHLERSTERN Gesellschaft m.b.H. (2)
Friedrich Bohler-Strasse 13, 8605, Kapfenberg, Austria
Tel.: (43) 50304 203 6375
Web Site: http://www.boehlerstern.at
Emp.: 40
Home Management Services
N.A.I.C.S.: 721110
Robert Hammer *(Gen Mgr)*

BOHLER UDDEHOLM AFRICA (PTY) LTD (1)
1 Isando Road, Isando, 1600, Johannesburg, South Africa
Tel.: (27) 11 571 2300
Web Site: http://www.bohler-uddeholm.co.za
Emp.: 141
Welding Equipment Mfr
N.A.I.C.S.: 333992
Gus Schroeder *(Mgr-Heat Treatment Div)*

BOHLER UDDEHOLM POLSKA Sp. z o.o. (1)
Kolejowa 291, Lomianki, 05-092, Poland
Tel.: (48) 22 42 92 200
Web Site: http://www.bohler-uddeholm.pl
Sales Range: $25-49.9 Million
Emp.: 40
Welding Electrode Mfr
N.A.I.C.S.: 333992
Fabisiewicz Thomas *(Mgr-Sls)*

BOHLER UDDEHOLM ROMANIA S.R.L. (1)
Atomistilor Street 96-102, Magurele, 77125, Ilfov, Romania
Tel.: (40) 21 405 58 40
Web Site: http://www.bohler.ro
Sales Range: $25-49,9 Million
Emp.: 17
Metal Heat Treatment Services
N.A.I.C.S.: 332811
Marius Micut *(Gen Mgr)*

BOHLER Warmebehandlung GmbH (1)
Nordwestbahnstrasse 12-14, Vienna, 1200, Austria
Tel.: (43) 1 3748775 0
Web Site: http://www.bohler.at
Emp.: 16
Metal Heat Treatment Services
N.A.I.C.S.: 332811
Werner Hahn *(Gen Mgr)*

BOHLER-UDDEHOLM (UK) LIMITED (1)
European Business Park Taylors Lane, Oldbury, B69 2BN, West Midlands, United Kingdom
Tel.: (44) 121 552 5681
Web Site: http://www.bohler-uddeholm.co.uk
Sales Range: $50-74.9 Million
Emp.: 100
Special Steel Whslr
N.A.I.C.S.: 423510
Caroline Moore *(Mgr-Extrusion)*

Subsidiary (Domestic):

Schoeller-Bleckmann (UK) Limited (2)
European Business Park Taylors Lane, Warley, Oldbury, B69 2BN, West Midlands, United Kingdom
Tel.: (44) 1215521535
Web Site: https://www.schoeller-bleckmann.co.uk
Stainless Tubular Product Whslr
N.A.I.C.S.: 423510
Tom Gowins *(Gen Mgr)*

BOHLER-UDDEHOLM UKRAINE LLC (1)
Suchkova Street 117, Novomoskovsk, 51200, Ukraine
Tel.: (380) 56 789 19 60
Web Site: http://www.bohler.com.ua
Steel Mfrs
N.A.I.C.S.: 331110

BOHLER-UDDEHOLM ZAGREB d.o.o. (1)
Slavonska Avenija 22d, Zagreb, 10000, Croatia
Tel.: (385) 12459300
Web Site: http://www.bohler-uddeholm.hr
Emp.: 7
Steel Products Mfr
N.A.I.C.S.: 331110

VOESTALPINE AG — INTERNATIONAL PUBLIC

voestalpine AG—(Continued)
Zoran Popovic *(Gen Mgr)*

BOHLER-YBBSTAL Profil GmbH (1)
Waidhofnerstrasse 8, 3333, Bohlerwerk, Austria
Tel.: (43) 7448 7007 0
Web Site: http://www.bohler-profil.com
Rev.: $27,088,495
Emp.: 128
Warm & Cold Rolling Steel Mfr
N.A.I.C.S.: 331221
Jorg Wagner *(VP-Sls, Mktg & Engrg)*

Bohlasia Steels Sdn. Bhd. (1)
No 18 Jalan Utarid U5/15 Seksyen U5, 40150, Shah Alam, Selangor, Malaysia
Tel.: (60) 378421448
Web Site: https://www.bohler-bohlasia.com.my
Sales Range: $25-49.9 Million
Emp.: 11
Steel Product Distr
N.A.I.C.S.: 423510
Tay Peng Kee *(Gen Mgr)*

Bohler High Performance Metals Private Limited (1)
A 409 Skylark Plot No 63 Sector 11 CBD Belapur, Navi Mumbai, 400 614, India
Tel.: (91) 22 27577441
Web Site: http://www.bohler.in
Sales Range: $25-49.9 Million
Emp.: 40
Steel Products Mfr
N.A.I.C.S.: 331110
Alok Jhamb *(Mng Dir)*

Bohler Schmiedetechnik GmbH & Co KG (1)
Mariazellerstrasse 25, Kapfenberg, 8605, Austria
Tel.: (43) 3862 20 7418
Web Site: http://www.bohler-forging.com
Rev.: $211,554,539
Emp.: 600
Aircraft Part Mfr
N.A.I.C.S.: 336413
Thomas Kornfeld *(Co-Mng Dir)*

Bohler Special Steels (Shanghai) Co., Ltd. (1)
No 335 Zhoujiabang Road, Dongjing Songjiang District, Shanghai, 201619, China
Tel.: (86) 2157077666
Web Site: https://www.bohler.com.cn
Tool Steel Mfr & Distr
N.A.I.C.S.: 331110

Bohler Uddeholm CZ s.r.o (1)
Ul silnice 949, 161 00, Prague, Czech Republic
Tel.: (420) 233 029 800
Web Site: http://www.bohler-uddeholm.co.za
Sales Range: $25-49.9 Million
Emp.: 40
Stainless Steel Whslr
N.A.I.C.S.: 423510

Bohler Welding Holding GmbH (1)
Peter-Muller-Strasse 14-14a, 40468, Dusseldorf, Germany
Tel.: (49) 211 580 660 0
Web Site: http://www.bohlerweldinggroup.com
Welding Consumables Mfr
N.A.I.C.S.: 333992
Thomas Binder-Krieglstein *(Mgr-Intl Mktg & Promo)*

Subsidiary (Non-US):

BOHLER WELDING GROUP ITALIA s.p.a. (2)
Via Palizzi 90, 20157, Milan, Italy
Tel.: (39) 02 39 017 239
Web Site: http://www.voestalpine.com
Emp.: 34
Welding Equipment Mfr
N.A.I.C.S.: 333992

Bohler Lastechniek Groep Nederland B.V. (2)
Haarlemmerstraatweg 89, Halfweg, 1165 MK, Netherlands
Tel.: (31) 204486622
Web Site: http://www.voestalpine.com
Emp.: 20
Welding Equipment Sales & Maintenance Services

N.A.I.C.S.: 423830
Rene Elfering *(Mng Dir)*

Subsidiary (Domestic):

Bohler Schweisstechnik Deutschland GmbH (2)
Unionstr 1, Hamm, 59067, Germany
Tel.: (49) 2381 271 02
Web Site: http://www.boehlerschweisstechnik.de
Welding Equipment Mfr & Whslr
N.A.I.C.S.: 333992

Subsidiary (Non-US):

Bohler Soldaduras S.A. de C.V. (2)
Avenida Henry Ford 16 Fracc Industrial San Nicolas, 54030, Tlalnepantla, Mexico
Tel.: (52) 55 5321 3070
Web Site: http://www.bsmex.com.mx
Steel Mfrs
N.A.I.C.S.: 331110

Bohler Tecnica de Soldagem Ltda. (2)
371 Arnaldo Magniccaro St, Sao Paulo, 04691-060, Brazil
Tel.: (55) 11 5694 8377
Web Site: http://www.btwbr.com.br
Welding Consumables Mfr
N.A.I.C.S.: 333992

Bohler Welding Group Canada Ltd. (2)
1745 Meyerfide Dr Unit 1-3, Mississauga, L5T 1c6, ON, Canada
Tel.: (905) 564-0589
Web Site: http://www.bwgca.com
Welding Equipment Mfr
N.A.I.C.S.: 333992
Paul Brooks *(Mgr-Natl Sls)*

Bohler Welding Group Central Eastern Europe GmbH (2)
Modecenterstrasse 14/A/3, 1030, Vienna, Austria
Tel.: (43) 1 7961681 0
Web Site: http://www.bwg-cee.com
Welding Equipment Mfr
N.A.I.C.S.: 333992
Martin Anzenberger *(Mng Dir)*

Subsidiary (Non-US):

BOHLER WELDING GROUP SRL (3)
Soseaua Brailei Nr 2, Buzau, 120118, Romania
Tel.: (40) 2387 10810
Web Site: http://www.boehler-welding.com
Sales Range: $50-74.9 Million
Emp.: 9
Welding Equipment Whslr
N.A.I.C.S.: 423830

Subsidiary (Non-US):

Bohler Welding Group Greece S.A. (2)
Spyrou Nousi 5 & Karkabitsa, Axarnai, Athens, 13672, Greece
Tel.: (30) 210 2818006
Web Site: http://www.voestalpine.com
Emp.: 5
Welding Equipment Distr
N.A.I.C.S.: 423830

Bohler Welding Group India Private Limited (2)
B 206 Universal Business Park Chandivili Farm Road Off Saki Vihar Road, Saki Naka, Mumbai, 400 072, India
Tel.: (91) 22 4228 4400
Web Site: http://www.bohlerweldinggroupindia.com
Alloy Metal Mfr
N.A.I.C.S.: 331529
Abby Joseph *(Mng Dir)*

Bohler Welding Group Middle East FZE (2)
Office 414 4th Floor JAFZA -16 Jebel Ali Free Zone, PO Box 262840, Dubai, 262840, United Arab Emirates
Tel.: (971) 4 8870 704
Web Site: http://www.bwgme.com
Emp.: 28
Welding Equipment Whslr
N.A.I.C.S.: 423830

Anders Andersson *(Mng Dir)*

Bohler Welding Group Schweiz AG (2)
Hertistrasse 15, 8304, Wallisellen, Switzerland
Tel.: (41) 44 832 88 55
Web Site: http://www.bohlerweldinggroup.ch
Welding Equipment Distr
N.A.I.C.S.: 423830

Bohler Welding Group UK Limited (2)
European Business Park Taylors Lane, Oldbury, B69 2BN, West Midlands, United Kingdom
Tel.: (44) 121 569 77 00
Web Site: http://www.bohlerweldinggroup.co.uk
Emp.: 25
Welding Equipment Mfr
N.A.I.C.S.: 333992
Deryk Webster *(Mng Dir)*

Bohler Welding Trading (Shanghai) Co., Ltd. (2)
Room 501-505 Metro Plaza 555 Lou Shan Guan Road, Shanghai, 200051, China
Tel.: (86) 21 6228 8080
Web Site: http://www.bw-group-china.com
Emp.: 40
Alloy Mfr
N.A.I.C.S.: 331110

Subsidiary (Domestic):

FONTARGEN Gesellschaft mit beschrankter Haftung (2)
Siemensstrasse 4, Postfach 12 80, Eisenberg, 67304, Germany
Tel.: (49) 63 51 401 0
Web Site: http://www.fontargen.com
Brazing Metal Treating Services
N.A.I.C.S.: 332811
Birgit Breuer-Kabuth *(Mng Dir)*

Subsidiary (Non-US):

Grupo Bohler Soldadura Espana S.A. (2)
Calle Schumann 15 Poligono Ind Can Jardi, 08191, Rubi, 08191, Barcelona, Spain
Tel.: (34) 93 5 88 69 07
Web Site: http://www.voestalpine.com
Emp.: 16
Specialty Steel Mfr
N.A.I.C.S.: 331110

PT Bohler Welding Group South East Asia (2)
Jl Indusri Selatan 2 Blok JJ No 7-10 Kawasan Industri, Jababeka Cikarang, Bekasi, 17530, Indonesia
Tel.: (62) 21 893 7572
Web Site: http://www.voestalpine.com
Emp.: 115
Welding Equipment Whslr
N.A.I.C.S.: 423830
Dinoharyadi Haryadi *(Gen Mgr)*

Soudokay S.A. (2)
4 rue de l'Yser, Seneffe, 7180, Belgium
Tel.: (32) 64 52 00 00
Web Site: http://www.soudokay.be
Welding Equipment Mfr & Whslr
N.A.I.C.S.: 333992
Marc Niset *(Co-Mng Dir)*

voestalpine Bohler Welding (China) Co., Ltd. (2)
121 Xingpu Road, Suzhou Industrial Park, Suzhou, CN-215126, China
Tel.: (86) 51267631288
Emp.: 200
Welding Equipment Whslr
N.A.I.C.S.: 333992
Steve Beswick *(Mng Dir)*

voestalpine Bohler Welding Austria GmbH (2)
Tel.: (43) 38623010
Welding Equipment Mfr
N.A.I.C.S.: 333992
Bernhard Riegler *(Co-Mng Dir)*

voestalpine Bohler Welding Russia LLC (2)
Mozhayskoye highway building 166, Moscow, Russia
Tel.: (7) 4957395828

Emp.: 17
Welding Equipment Whslr
N.A.I.C.S.: 423830
Vadim Sharyshev *(Mng Dir)*

Bohler-Uddeholm B.V. (1)
Isolatorweg 30 - 32, 1014 AS, Amsterdam, Netherlands
Tel.: (31) 205817101
Web Site: http://www.bohler-uddeholm.com
Sales Range: $50-74.9 Million
Emp.: 25
Metal Ore Mining Services
N.A.I.C.S.: 212290

Bohler-Uddeholm KK (1)
Bancho M Bldg 2-8 Rokubancho, Chiyoda-ku, Tokyo, 102-0085, Japan
Tel.: (81) 3 5226 3771
Web Site: http://www.bohler-uddeholm.jp
Sales Range: $25-49.9 Million
Emp.: 25
Steel Distr
N.A.I.C.S.: 423510
Yasunori Manabe *(Mng Dir)*

Bohler-Uddeholm Ltd. (1)
2595 Meadowvale Blvd, Mississauga, L5N 7Y3, ON, Canada
Tel.: (905) 812-9440
Web Site: http://www.bucanada.ca
Sales Range: $25-49.9 Million
Emp.: 40
Steel Mfr & Whslr
N.A.I.C.S.: 331110
Paul Cavanagh *(Pres)*

Plant (Domestic):

Bohler-Uddeholm Ltd. - Thermal Processing Facility (2)
2645 Meadowvale Blvd, Mississauga, L5N 7Y4, ON, Canada
Tel.: (905) 812-9440
Web Site: http://www.voestalpine.com
Sales Range: $25-49.9 Million
Emp.: 30
Metal Heat Treatment Services
N.A.I.C.S.: 332811

Bohler-Uddeholm SLOVAKIA, s.r.o. (1)
Ceskoslovenskej Armady 5622/5, 03601, Martin, Slovakia
Tel.: (421) 43 421 2001
Web Site: http://www.bohler-uddeholm.sk
Steel Products Mfr
N.A.I.C.S.: 331110

Buderus Edelstahl GmbH (1)
Dillfeld 40, D-35576, Wetzlar, Germany
Tel.: (49) 64413740
Web Site: https://www.buderus-steel.com
Steel Mfrs
N.A.I.C.S.: 331110
Martin Dietze *(Mng Dir)*

Subsidiary (Non-US):

Deville Rectification S.A.S. (2)
Z I Desforanges, BP 3, F - 43330, Pont-Salomon, France
Tel.: (33) 471662971
Web Site: https://www.deville-rectif.com
Emp.: 216
Stainless Steel Mfr
N.A.I.C.S.: 331110
Philippe Escofier *(Mgr-Publ)*

Edelstahlwerke Buderus Nederland B.V (2)
Bovendijk 132, Rotterdam, 3045, South Holland, Netherlands
Tel.: (31) 104220533
Emp.: 6
Steel Forging Services
N.A.I.C.S.: 332111
Van Hoff *(Gen Mgr)*

Contec GmbH (1)
Oberahrer Strasse 9, Sainerholz, 56244, Otzingen, Germany
Tel.: (49) 26 66 95 20 0
Web Site: http://www.contec-group.com
Railway Safety Equipment Mfr
N.A.I.C.S.: 336999

Control and Display Systems Limited (1)
Unit 1 Fulcrum 4 Solent Way, Fareham,

AND PRIVATE COMPANIES — VOESTALPINE AG

PO15 7FT, Hampshire, United Kingdom
Tel.: (44) 1489 571 771
Web Site: http://www.cdsrail.com
Sales Range: $25-49.9 Million
Emp.: 20
Railway Software Development Services
N.A.I.C.S.: 541512

DIN ACCIAI S.p.A. (1)
Viale Risorgimento 30, Senago, 20030, Milan, Italy
Tel.: (39) 0299481461
Web Site: http://www.dinacciai.it
Sales Range: $25-49.9 Million
Emp.: 15
Stainless Steel Mfr
N.A.I.C.S.: 331110
Giorgio Grussu *(Mgr-Admin)*

Densam Industrial Co. Ltd. (1)
2FL No 3-7 Fen Liao Road, Lin Ko Hsiang, Taipei, Taiwan
Tel.: (886) 22 299 2849
Steel Product Mfr & Distr
N.A.I.C.S.: 331110

ENPAR Sonderwerkstoffe GmbH (1)
Betriebsweg 10, 51645, Gummersbach, Germany
Tel.: (49) 2 261 7980
Web Site: https://www.enpar.de
Emp.: 50
Metal Processing Services
N.A.I.C.S.: 423510
Axel Veller *(Dir-Sls)*

Eschmann Textures International GmbH (1)
Dieringhauser Strasse 159, 51645, Gummersbach, Germany
Tel.: (49) 22 619 8990
Web Site: https://www.eschmanntextures.de
Sales Range: $50-74.9 Million
Emp.: 250
Electroplating & Polishing Services
N.A.I.C.S.: 332813
Peter Wolf *(Mgr-Engrg)*

Subsidiary (Non-US):

Eschmann Textura Internacional - Transformacao de Ferramentas, Unipessoal, Lda (2)
Rua 23 de Outubro 2a, 2445-583, Moita, Portugal
Tel.: (351) 244545360
Web Site: https://www.eschmanntextures.com
Sales Range: $25-49.9 Million
Emp.: 30
Metal Texturing Services
N.A.I.C.S.: 423510
Antonio Pedrosa *(Mgr)*

GMV Eschmann International SAS (2)
Tel.: (33) 384411143
Sales Range: $25-49.9 Million
Emp.: 11
Electroplating Services
N.A.I.C.S.: 332813
Thomas Porstner *(Mgr-Factory)*

Grabados Eschmann International S.L. (2)
C/Miguel Hernandez 35-37, 08908, L'Hospitalet de Llobregat, Barcelona, Spain
Tel.: (34) 93 2 63 47 90
Metal Stamping Services
N.A.I.C.S.: 332119
Cesar Faraudo *(Mgr-Factory)*

Gravutex Eschmann International Limited (2)
Peakdale Road, Brookfield Industrial Estate, Glossop, SK13 6LQ, Derbyshire, United Kingdom
Tel.: (44) 1457867627
Web Site: https://eschmanntextures.de
Sales Range: $25-49.9 Million
Emp.: 15
Engineeering Services
N.A.I.C.S.: 541330
Nigel Brooke *(Mng Dir)*

Eschmann Vermogensverwaltung GmbH (1)
Hermannsburgstr 37, Gummersbach, 51643, Nordrhein-Westfalen, Germany
Tel.: (49) 22617060
Investment Management Service
N.A.I.C.S.: 523999

Global Rollforming Corporation (1)
1070 Brooks Industrial Rd, Shelbyville, KY 40065
Tel.: (502) 633-4435
Web Site: https://www.rfcorp.com
Roll Forming Services
N.A.I.C.S.: 332114

Intersteel Stahlhandel GmbH (1)
Hansaallee 321, 40549, Dusseldorf, Germany
Tel.: (49) 211 522 2969
Web Site: http://www.intersteel.de
Steel Product Mfr & Distr
N.A.I.C.S.: 331110
Herbert Belada *(Mng Dir)*

Jiaxing NYC Industrial Co., Ltd. (1)
2501 Renmin Avenue Luoxing Street, Weitang Town, Jiashan, 314100, Zhejiang, China
Tel.: (86) 57384062599
Web Site: https://www.nyc-ind.com
Stamping Mold Mfr & Distr
N.A.I.C.S.: 333511

Jing Ying Industrial Co. Ltd. (1)
No 32 Tianhe Rd, Yuhang Economic-Technological Development Area, Hangzhou, Zhejiang, China
Tel.: (86) 57186239527
Web Site: https://www.cnlamp.com
Light Emitting Diode Mfr
N.A.I.C.S.: 334413

Liegenschaftsverwaltungs GmbH (1)
Kerpelystrasse 199, Leoben, Austria
Tel.: (43) 5030 426 4439
Steel Product Mfr & Distr
N.A.I.C.S.: 331110

Nedcon B.V. (1)
Nijverheidsweg 26, 7005 BJ, Doetinchem, Netherlands
Tel.: (31) 314334455
Warehousing & Storage Services
N.A.I.C.S.: 493110

OOO voestalpine High Performance Metals RUS (1)
P1 Orekhovskaya 80, Nizhniy Novgorod, Russia
Tel.: (7) 8312990202
Steel Product Mfr & Distr
N.A.I.C.S.: 331110

PT ASSAB Steels Indonesia (1)
PT ASSAB Steels Indonesia Jl Rawa Gelam III No 5 Kawasan Industri, Pulo Gadung, Jakarta, 13930, Indonesia
Tel.: (62) 216909308
Web Site: https://www.assab.com
Sales Range: $50-74.9 Million
Emp.: 100
Tool Steel Distr
N.A.I.C.S.: 423510

RFC-Sharon LLC (1)
250 Martin Luther King Blvd, Farrell, PA 16121
Tel.: (724) 982-0400
Steel Products Mfr
N.A.I.C.S.: 331110

Roll Forming Corporation (1)
1070 Industrial Rd, Shelbyville, KY 40065
Tel.: (502) 633-4435
Web Site: http://www.rfcorp.com
Sales Range: $25-49.9 Million
Emp.: 65
Provider of Metal Rolling Services
N.A.I.C.S.: 332322
Patty Sweasy *(Mgr-Safety)*

Subsidiary (Domestic):

Roll Forming Corporation - Pennsylvania (2)
250 Martin Luther King Blvd, Farrell, PA 16121
Tel.: (724) 982-0400
Web Site: http://www.rfcorp.com
Rolled Steel Products Mfr
N.A.I.C.S.: 331221

SST Signal & System Technik GmbH (1)
Bahnweg 1, 56427, Siershahn, Germany
Tel.: (49) 2623 6086 0
Web Site: http://www.sst.ag
Sales Range: $25-49.9 Million
Emp.: 100
Diagnostic System Repair & Maintenance Services
N.A.I.C.S.: 811210
Helmut Liebminger *(Mng Dir)*

STAMPTEC-Holding GmbH (1)
Daimlerstr 29, 72581, Dettingen an der Erms, Baden-Wurttemberg, Germany
Tel.: (49) 7123 97870
Sales Range: $200-249.9 Million
Emp.: 500
Investment Management Service
N.A.I.C.S.: 523999

Subsidiary (Domestic):

voestalpine Stamptec Birkenfeld GmbH (2)
Walter-Hugel-Strasse 1, 55765, Birkenfeld, Germany
Tel.: (49) 67 82 99 59 0
Web Site: http://www.voestalpine.com
Sales Range: $200-249.9 Million
Automotive Parts Mfr & Whslr
N.A.I.C.S.: 336390

Subsidiary (Non-US):

voestalpine Stamptec Romania S.R.L. (3)
Building C 1st Fl 1a Campul Linistii Str, Arad, 310349, Romania
Tel.: (40) 257202500
Web Site: http://www.voestalpine.com
Emp.: 200
Iron & Steel Product Mfr
N.A.I.C.S.: 331110
Adrian Kis *(Gen Mgr)*

Subsidiary (Domestic):

voestalpine Stamptec GmbH (2)
Daimlerstrasse 29, Dettingen an der Erms, 72581, Germany
Tel.: (49) 7123 9787 0
Web Site: http://www.voestalpine.com
Sales Range: $350-399.9 Million
Automotive Stamping Part Mfr
N.A.I.C.S.: 336370

Sacma Acciai Speciali S.p.A. (1)
Via Arrigo Olivetti 13/9, 10148, Turin, Italy
Tel.: (39) 011 29 189 1
Web Site: http://www.sacma-acciai.it
Metal Products Mfr & Whslr
N.A.I.C.S.: 423510

TSF-A GmbH (1)
Kirchdorfer Platz 1, 2752, Wollersdorf-Steinabruckl, Austria
Tel.: (43) 5 771 5401
Web Site: https://www.tsf-a.eu
Concrete Turnout Sleeper Mfr & Distr
N.A.I.C.S.: 327390

Uddeholm Eiendom AS (1)
Jernkroken 18, 0976, Oslo, Norway
Tel.: (47) 22918000
Real Estate Manungement Services
N.A.I.C.S.: 531390

Uddeholm Holding AB (1)
Hagfors Jarnvark, Hagfors, 683 85, Sweden
Tel.: (46) 56317000
Web Site: http://www.uddeholm.se
Emp.: 800
Investment Management Service
N.A.I.C.S.: 523940
Par Emanuelsson *(Mng Dir)*

Subsidiary (Non-US):

Uddeholms AB (2)
Tel.: (46) 56317000
Sales Range: $1-4.9 Billion
Emp.: 3,000
Steel Products Whslr
N.A.I.C.S.: 423510
Maria Norberg *(Mgr-Quality)*

Subsidiary (Domestic):

Uddeholm Svenska Aktiebolag (3)
Aminogatan 25B, Box 98, 431 53, Molndal, Sweden
Tel.: (46) 31679870
Web Site: http://www.uddeholm.se
Emp.: 16
Steel Forging Product Mfr
N.A.I.C.S.: 332111
Per-Anders Bardhs *(CEO)*

Vaps GmbH (1)
Kollberg 9, 30916, Isernhagen, Germany
Tel.: (49) 513693620
Web Site: https://www.vaps.de
Information Technology Services
N.A.I.C.S.: 541511

Voestalpine Bahnsysteme GmbH And Co Kg (1)
Kerpelystrasse 199, 8700, Leoben, Austria
Tel.: (43) 3842 202 4197
Railroad Switching Services
N.A.I.C.S.: 488210

Subsidiary (Domestic):

voestalpine VAE GmbH (2)
Alpinestrasse 1, 8740, Zeltweg, Austria
Tel.: (43) 50304280
Web Site: http://www.voestalpine.com
Turnout Systems Mfr
N.A.I.C.S.: 333924
Dieter Fritz *(CEO-Internationalisation, Sls & Mktg)*

Subsidiary (Domestic):

voestalpine HYTRONICS GmbH (3)
Alpinestrasse 1, 8740, Zeltweg, Austria
Tel.: (43) 50304 28 0
Web Site: http://www.voestalpine.com
Railway Track Monitoring & Diagnostic System Mfr
N.A.I.C.S.: 334290
Josef WINTER *(CEO)*

Subsidiary (Domestic):

Advanced Railway Systems GmbH (4)
Alpinestrasse 1, 8740, Zeltweg, Styria, Austria
Tel.: (43) 3577 750 0
Railway Infrastructure Research & Development Services
N.A.I.C.S.: 488210

Subsidiary (Domestic):

voestalpine Weichensysteme GmbH (3)
Alpinestrasse 1, 8740, Zeltweg, Austria
Tel.: (43) 50304 28 0
Web Site: http://www.voestalpine.com
Emp.: 800
Turnout System Mfr
N.A.I.C.S.: 488210

Voestalpine Klockner Bahntechnik Gmbh (1)
Am Silberpalais 1, Duisburg, 47057, Germany
Tel.: (49) 2037137640
Emp.: 35
Railway Track Engineering & Maintenance Services
N.A.I.C.S.: 237990
Michaela Konrad *(Co-Mng Dir)*

Voestalpine Rotec Gmbh (1)
Eisenhammerstrasse 15, 8670, Krieglach, Austria
Tel.: (43) 5 030 4240
Web Site: https://www.voestalpine.com
Sales Range: $200-249.9 Million
Emp.: 300
Steel Pipes & Tubes Mfr
N.A.I.C.S.: 331210
Klaus Pammer *(CEO)*

Subsidiary (Non-US):

voestalpine Elmsteel Group Limited (2)
2 Jacknell Road, Dodwells Bridge Industrial Estate, Hinckley, LE10 3BS, Leicestershire, United Kingdom
Tel.: (44) 1455 620 300
Web Site: http://www.voestalpine
Emp.: 60
Precision Cut Tube Mfr
N.A.I.C.S.: 333517

VOESTALPINE AG

INTERNATIONAL PUBLIC

voestalpine AG—(Continued)

voestalpine Additive Manufacturing Center GmbH (1)
Hansaallee 321, 40549, Dusseldorf, Germany
Tel.: (49) 2115222310
Additive Mfr
N.A.I.C.S.: 325998
Johannes Bruckwilder (Mgr-Business Development)

voestalpine Additive Manufacturing Centre Ltd. (1)
2595 Meadowvale Boulevard, Mississauga, L5N 7Y3, ON, Canada
Additive Mfr
N.A.I.C.S.: 325998

voestalpine Automotive Components (Tianjin) Co., Ltd. (1)
No 4 Factory No 8 of Quanming Road, Wuqing, Tianjin, 301700, China
Tel.: (86) 1234567
Automotive Components Mfr
N.A.I.C.S.: 336390
David Qian (CEO)

voestalpine Automotive Components Aguascalientes S. de R.L. de C.V. (1)
Carretera Panamericana Sur Km 112, 20340, Aguascalientes, Mexico
Tel.: (52) 4494784300
Emp.: 75
Automotive Components Mfr
N.A.I.C.S.: 336390
Jesus Barba (Mng Dir)

voestalpine Automotive Components Birkenfeld GmbH & Co. KG (1)
Walter-Huegel Strasse 1, 55765, Birkenfeld, Germany
Tel.: (49) 67 829 9590
Emp.: 400
Automotive Components Mfr
N.A.I.C.S.: 336390
Arno Theussen (Plant Mgr)

voestalpine Automotive Components Bohmenkirch GmbH & Co. KG (1)
Buchenstrasse 3, 89558, Bohmenkirch, Germany
Tel.: (49) 73 329 6220
Emp.: 150
Automotive Components Mfr
N.A.I.C.S.: 336390
Berthold Wirtz (Plant Mgr)

voestalpine Automotive Components Bunschoten B.V. (1)
Amersfoortseweg 9, 3751 LJ, Bunschoten, Netherlands
Tel.: (31) 332989511
Emp.: 1,050
Automotive Components Mfr
N.A.I.C.S.: 336390
Norman Willich (CEO, Mng Dir & Chm)

voestalpine Automotive Components Cartersville LLC (1)
21 voestalpine Dr NE, White, GA 30184
Tel.: (678) 535-5333
Automotive Components Mfr
N.A.I.C.S.: 336390

voestalpine Automotive Components Dettingen GmbH & Co. KG (1)
Daimlerstrasse 29, 72581, Dettingen an der Erms, Germany
Tel.: (49) 71 239 7870
Emp.: 700
Automotive Components Mfr
N.A.I.C.S.: 336390
Philippe Bandel (Plant Mgr-Commercial)

voestalpine Automotive Components Fontaine SA (1)
ZA Aeroparc De Fontaine, 90150, Fontaine, France
Tel.: (33) 384584877
Emp.: 250
Automotive Components Mfr
N.A.I.C.S.: 336390
Michael Nikodemus (Mgr)

voestalpine Automotive Components Linz GmbH (1)
Stahlstrasse 47, 4020, Linz, Austria
Tel.: (43) 50304159642
Emp.: 300
Automotive Components Mfr
N.A.I.C.S.: 336390

voestalpine Automotive Components Nagold GmbH & Co. KG (1)
Graf-Zeppelin-Str 29, 72202, Nagold, Germany
Tel.: (49) 74 528 4810
Emp.: 150
Automotive Components Mfr
N.A.I.C.S.: 336390
Christian Schneider (Plant Mgr)

voestalpine Automotive Components Schmolln GmbH (1)
Zum Wasserturm 79/1, 04626, Schmolln, Germany
Tel.: (49) 344915630
Emp.: 800
Automotive Components Mfr
N.A.I.C.S.: 336390
Lutz Klose (Plant Mgr)

voestalpine Automotive Components Schwabisch Gmund GmbH & Co. KG (1)
Voestalpine Strasse 1, 73529, Schwabisch Gmund, Germany
Tel.: (49) 7 171 9720
Emp.: 700
Automotive Components Mfr
N.A.I.C.S.: 336390

voestalpine Automotive Components Shenyang Co., Ltd. (1)
No 16 Yingkeso Road Three, Sujiatun District, Shenyang, 110101, China
Tel.: (86) 3355167566
Emp.: 170
Automotive Components Mfr
N.A.I.C.S.: 336390
David Qian (CEO)

voestalpine BWG GmbH & Co. KG (1)
Alte Wetzlarer Strasse 55, 35510, Butzbach, Germany
Tel.: (49) 6033 892 0
Web Site: http://www.voestalpine.com
Railway Track Construction & Installation Services
N.A.I.C.S.: 237990

Subsidiary (Domestic):

LASA Schienentechnik GmbH (2)
Mittelwendung 17 a, 28844, Weyhe, Germany
Tel.: (49) 42 038 1520
Web Site: https://www.lasatest.jimdo.com
Emp.: 40
Engineeering Services
N.A.I.C.S.: 541330

WBG Weichenwerk Brandenburg GmbH (2)
97 Uferstrasse Kirchmoeser, Brandenburg, 14774, Germany
Tel.: (49) 338 181 01 01
Metal Products Mfr
N.A.I.C.S.: 332999

Subsidiary (Non-US):

voestalpine BWG ltd. (2)
Room 807 Tower 7 Central Park No 6 Chaowai Street, Chaoyang District, Beijing, 100020, China
Tel.: (86) 106 533 6071
Web Site: http://www.voestalpine.com
Emp.: 6
Railroad Transit System Mfr
N.A.I.C.S.: 336510
Marco Graf (Gen Mgr)

voestalpine Bahnsysteme GmbH (1)
Kerpelystrasse 199, Leoben, 8700, Styria, Austria
Tel.: (43) 503 0426
Steel Products Mfr
N.A.I.C.S.: 331110

voestalpine Bahnsysteme Vermogensverwaltungs GmbH (1)
Kerpelystrasse 199, Leoben, 8700, Austria
Tel.: (43) 5030426
Steel Products Mfr
N.A.I.C.S.: 331110

Subsidiary (Domestic):

Voestalpine Stahl Donawitz Immobilien Gmbh (2)
Kerpelystr 199, Leoben, 8700, Austria
Tel.: (43) 384220 10
Rail Equipment Mfr & Whslr
N.A.I.C.S.: 333924

voestalpine Bohler Aerospace GmbH & Co. KG (1)
Mariazellen Strasse 25, 8605, Kapfenberg, Austria
Tel.: (43) 50304330
Web Site: https://www.voestalpine.com
Steel Product Mfr & Distr
N.A.I.C.S.: 331110
Thomas Kornfeld (Mng Dir-Commercial)

voestalpine Bohler Bleche GmbH & Co. KG (1)
Bohler-Gasse 1, A-8680, Murzzuschlag, Austria
Tel.: (43) 50304400
Web Site: https://www.bohler-bleche.com
Rolled Sheet & Plate Mfr
N.A.I.C.S.: 331221

voestalpine Bohler Edelstahl GmbH & Co. KG (1)
Mariazellen-Strasse 25, A-8605, Kapfenberg, Austria
Tel.: (43) 50304200
Web Site: https://www.bohler-edelstahl.com
Tool Steel Mfr & Distr
N.A.I.C.S.: 331110
Michael Rotpart (Mng Dir-Sales-Logistics)

voestalpine Bohler Weldcare AB (1)
Stenaldersgatan 7, 213 76, Malmo, Sweden
Tel.: (46) 40288301
Welding Equipment Distr
N.A.I.C.S.: 423830
Andre Fasth (Mng Dir)

voestalpine Bohler Welding France SAS (1)
164 Avenue Joseph Kessel-Bat 9, 78960, Voisins-le-Bretonneux, France
Tel.: (33) 130054949
Welding Equipment Distr
N.A.I.C.S.: 423830
Aziz Tabei (Mng Dir)

voestalpine Bohler Welding Germany GmbH (1)
Hafenstrasse 21, 59067, Hamm, Germany
Tel.: (49) 238127101
Welding Equipment Distr
N.A.I.C.S.: 423830
Thorge Peters (Mng Dir)

voestalpine Bohler Welding Germany Vertriebs-GmbH (1)
Hafenstrasse 21, 59067, Hamm, Germany
Tel.: (49) 238127102
Welding Equipment Distr
N.A.I.C.S.: 423830
Birgit Breuer-Kabuth (Mng Dir)

voestalpine Bohler Welding Group GmbH (1)
Peter-Muller-Strasse 14-14a, 40468, Dusseldorf, Germany
Tel.: (49) 2115806600
Welding Equipment Distr
N.A.I.C.S.: 423830
Stefan Glanz (CEO)

voestalpine Bohler Welding Hellas S.A. (1)
Spyrou Nousi 5 and Karkabitsa, Axamai, 136 72, Athens, Greece
Tel.: (30) 2102818006
Welding Equipment Distr
N.A.I.C.S.: 423830
Petros Megalis (Sls Mgr)

voestalpine Bohler Welding India Private Limited (1)
A-140 Metropolitan First Floor Road No 23 West, Wagle Industrial Estate, Thane, 400 604, Maharashtra, India
Tel.: (91) 2242284400
Welding Equipment Distr
N.A.I.C.S.: 423830
Abby K. Joseph (Mng Dir)

voestalpine Bohler Welding India Technology Private Limited (1)
Office No 201D IInd Floor D-21 Corporate Park Sector-21 Near Dwarka, Sector-8 Metro Station Dwarka, New Delhi, 110 075, India
Tel.: (91) 1141602108
Welding Equipment Distr
N.A.I.C.S.: 423830
Josef Kunik (Mng Dir)

voestalpine Bohler Welding Italia S.r.l. (1)
Via Filippo Palizzi 90, 20157, Milan, Italy
Tel.: (39) 02390171
Welding Equipment Distr
N.A.I.C.S.: 423830
Ivo Bonello (Mng Dir)

voestalpine Bohler Welding Middle East FZE (1)
Showroom No S3 A2 SR 04 Jebel Ali Free South Zone 3, PO Box 262840, Dubai, United Arab Emirates
Tel.: (971) 48870704
Welding Equipment Distr
N.A.I.C.S.: 423830
Herbert Abbott (Mng Dir)

voestalpine Bohler Welding Nederland B.V. (1)
Haarlemmerstraatweg 89, 1165 MK, Halfweg, Netherlands
Tel.: (31) 204486622
Welding Equipment Distr
N.A.I.C.S.: 423830
Rene Elfering (Mng Dir)

voestalpine Bohler Welding Romania SRL (1)
Sos Brailei Nr 2 Cladire Statie, Buzau, Romania
Tel.: (40) 238710810
Web Site: https://distribuitor-bohler-welding-romania.business.site
Welding Equipment Distr
N.A.I.C.S.: 423830

voestalpine Bohler Welding Schweiz AG (1)
Hertistrasse 15, 8304, Wallisellen, Switzerland
Tel.: (41) 448328855
Welding Equipment Distr
N.A.I.C.S.: 423830
Martin Kalberer (Mng Dir)

voestalpine Bohler Welding Selco S.r.l. (1)
Via Palladio 19 Onara di Tombolo, Onara, 35019, Padova, Italy
Tel.: (39) 0499413111
Welding Equipment Distr
N.A.I.C.S.: 423830
Mirco Frasson (Mng Dir)

voestalpine Bohler Welding Soldas do Brasil Ltda. (1)
Rua Arnaldo Magniccaro 371, Sao Paulo, 04691-060, Brazil
Tel.: (55) 1156948377
Welding Equipment Distr
N.A.I.C.S.: 423830
Newton De Andrade e Silva (Mng Dir)

voestalpine Bohler Welding Spain, S.A. (1)
Calle Schumann 15, Pol Ind Can Jardi, 8191, Rubi, Spain
Tel.: (34) 935886907
Welding Equipment Distr
N.A.I.C.S.: 423830
Mario Vinas (Mng Dir)

voestalpine Bohler Welding Trading (Shanghai) Co., Ltd. (1)
Room 514 Sanlian Building, Shanghai, 200062, China
Tel.: (86) 2162288080
Welding Equipment Distr
N.A.I.C.S.: 423830
Neil Smith (Mng Dir)

voestalpine Bohler Welding UK Limited (1)
European Business Park Taylors Lane Great Britain, Oldbury, B69 2BN, West Midlands, United Kingdom
Tel.: (44) 1215697700
Welding Equipment Distr
N.A.I.C.S.: 423830

AND PRIVATE COMPANIES

VOESTALPINE AG

Rene Elfering *(Mng Dir)*

voestalpine Bohler Welding UTP Maintenance GmbH (1)
Elsasser Strasse 10, Bad Krozingen, 79189, Freiburg, Germany
Tel.: (49) 76 334 0901
Welding Equipment Distr
N.A.I.C.S.: 423830
Arnaud Desamory *(Mng Dir)*

voestalpine Camtec Corp. (1)
1907 Albion Road, Toronto, M9W 5S8, ON, Canada
Tel.: (416) 617-6760
Steel Product Mfr & Distr
N.A.I.C.S.: 331110

voestalpine Camtec GmbH (1)
Voestalpine-Strasse 3, 4020, Linz, Austria
Tel.: (43) 50304150
Gate Valve Mfr & Distr
N.A.I.C.S.: 332911
Andreas Bretschneider *(CTO)*

voestalpine Czech Republic s.r.o. (1) **(100%)**
Karlovo Namesti 31, 120 00, Prague, Czech Republic
Tel.: (420) 224908105
Web Site: http://www.voestalpine.com
Sales Range: $50-74.9 Million
Emp.: 8
Coal Product Mfr
N.A.I.C.S.: 324199

voestalpine Deutschland GmbH (1) **(100%)**
Wilhelm-Wagenfeld-Strasse 26, 80807, Munich, Germany
Tel.: (49) 895 783 5270
Web Site: http://www.voestalpine.com
Sales Range: $25-49.9 Million
Emp.: 36
Wholesale Steel
N.A.I.C.S.: 423510
Thomas Gierlinger *(Mng Dir)*

voestalpine Edelstahl Deutschland GmbH (1)
Hansaallee 321, Dusseldorf, Germany
Tel.: (49) 2115220
Steel Product Mfr & Distr
N.A.I.C.S.: 331110

voestalpine Edelstahl GmbH (1)
Donau City Strasse 7, 1220, Vienna, Austria
Tel.: (43) 50304100
Web Site: http://www.voestalpine.com
Holding Company; Specialty Metals Mfr
N.A.I.C.S.: 551112
Franz Rotter *(Chm-Mgmt Bd)*

Subsidiary (Non-US):

Aceros Boehler S.A. (2) **(100%)**
Mozart 40, Buenos Aires, 1619, Argentina
Tel.: (54) 3327453200
Web Site: http://www.acerosboehler.com.ar
Wholesale Steel
N.A.I.C.S.: 423510

Aceros Boehler del Peru S.A. (2) **(100%)**
Calle Luis Castro Ronceros 777, Lima, Peru
Tel.: (51) 16193250
Web Site: http://www.bohlerperu.com
Sales Range: $50-74.9 Million
Emp.: 100
Sheet Metal Mfr & Machinery & Equipment Retailer
N.A.I.C.S.: 423510
Rosa Zambrano *(Mgr-Ops)*

Avesta Welding AB (2)
Kopperdalen, PO Box 501, SE 774 27, Avesta, Sweden
Tel.: (46) 22685700
Web Site: http://www.avestawelding.com
Sales Range: $25-49.9 Million
Emp.: 100
Stainless Steel Welding Consumables
N.A.I.C.S.: 423830
Jan Engseldt *(Mng Dir)*

Subsidiary (US):

Avesta Welding LLC (3)
3176 Abbott Rd, Orchard Park, NY 14127-1069
Tel.: (716) 827-4400
Web Site: http://www.avestawelding.com
Sales Range: $50-74.9 Million
Emp.: 10
Welding Products
N.A.I.C.S.: 324199

Subsidiary (Non-US):

BOHLER-UDDEHOLM France S.A.S (2)
12 rue Mercier Zone Industrielle de Mitry-Compans, 77297, Mitry-Mory, France
Tel.: (33) 1 60 93 80 50
Web Site: http://www.bohler-uddeholm.fr
Steel Mfrs
N.A.I.C.S.: 331110

Subsidiary (Domestic):

BOHLERSTAHL Vertriebsgesellschaft m.b.H. (2)
Nordwestbahnstrasse 12-14, 1200, Vienna, Austria
Tel.: (43) 1 33 137 0
Web Site: http://www.bohler.at
Stainless Steel Products Distr
N.A.I.C.S.: 423510

Subsidiary (Non-US):

Bohler BV (2) **(100%)**
Isolatorweg 30 32, 1014 AS, Amsterdam, Netherlands
Tel.: (31) 205817400
Web Site: http://www.bohler.nl
Sales Range: $25-49.9 Million
Emp.: 25
Steel Mfrs
N.A.I.C.S.: 332111

Subsidiary (Domestic):

Bohler International GmbH (2)
Modecenterstrasse 14/BC/2, 1030, Vienna, Austria
Tel.: (43) 1331430
Web Site: http://www.bohler-international.com
Steel Products Mfr
N.A.I.C.S.: 331110

Subsidiary (Non-US):

Bohler Kereskedalmi KFT (2) **(100%)**
Anyos Utca 25, PO Box 110, HU 2330, Dunaharaszti, Hungary
Tel.: (36) 24492692
Web Site: http://www.bohlerkft.hu
Sales Range: $1-9.9 Million
Emp.: 60
Steel Mfrs
N.A.I.C.S.: 332111

Subsidiary (Domestic):

Bohler Schmiedetechnik GmbH (2)
Mariazellerstrasse 25, Kapfenberg, 8605, Austria
Tel.: (43) 3862 20 7418
Web Site: http://www.bohler-forging.com
Emp.: 750
Aerospace Application Parts Mfr
N.A.I.C.S.: 334511
Gerhard Lichtenegger *(CEO)*

Bohler Schweisstechnik Austria GmbH (2) **(100%)**
Bohler Welding Strasse 1, PO Box 9, A 8605, Kapfenberg, Austria
Tel.: (43) 3862301
Web Site: http://www.bohler-welding.com
Sales Range: $1-9.9 Million
Emp.: 240
High-Precision Forgings, Rolling Mill
N.A.I.C.S.: 331221
Roland Haselsteiner *(Officer-Sls-DACH)*

Subsidiary (Non-US):

Bohler Welding Group Nordic AB (3)
Modellvaegen 2, Box 501, 774 27, Avesta, Sweden
Tel.: (46) 226 857 50
Web Site: http://www.bwgnordicsales.com
Welding Equipment Mfr
N.A.I.C.S.: 333992
Johnny Runvik *(Country Mgr)*

Groupe Bohler Soudage France S.A.S. (3)
164 Ave Joseph Kessel, 78960, Voisins-le-Bretonneux, France
Tel.: (33) 1 300 54 949
Web Site: http://www.voestalpine.com
Sales Range: $25-49.9 Million
Emp.: 22
Welding Equipment Mfr
N.A.I.C.S.: 333992
Aziz Tabei *(Mng Dir-Sls)*

Subsidiary (Non-US):

Bohler Thyssen Welding S.A. (2) **(100%)**
Spyrou Nousi 5 & Karkabitsa Axarnai, Athens, 13672, Greece
Tel.: (30) 2102818006
Web Site: http://www.voestalpine.com
Sales Range: $25-49.9 Million
Emp.: 5
Steel Production Services
N.A.I.C.S.: 332111
Stelios Oikonomou *(Mgr-Fin)*

Bohler-Uddeholm (Australia) Pty Ltd. (2) **(100%)**
PO Box 2397, Parramatta, 1750, NSW, Australia
Tel.: (61) 296813100
Web Site: http://www.buau.com.au
Sales Range: $25-49.9 Million
Emp.: 1,000
Engineering, Stainless & Tool Steel Suppliers
N.A.I.C.S.: 331513

Bohler-Uddeholm Colombia S.A. (2)
Calle 20A 43A 50 Int 2, BOG 6208, Bogota, Colombia
Tel.: (57) 3647300
Web Site: http://www.bohlercolombia.com
Steel Mfrs
N.A.I.C.S.: 332111

Subsidiary (US):

Bohler-Uddeholm Corporation (2) **(100%)**
2505 Millennium Dr, Elgin, IL 60124
Tel.: (847) 577-2220
Web Site: http://www.bucorp.com
Sales Range: $50-74.9 Million
Emp.: 175
Tool Die, Cold Rolled Precision Strip Steel
N.A.I.C.S.: 423510
Eric Henn *(Pres)*

Subsidiary (Domestic):

Bohler Welding Group USA Inc. (3)
10401 Greenbough Dr, Stafford, TX 77477
Tel.: (281) 499-1212
Web Site: http://www.bwgus.com
Sales Range: $25-49.9 Million
Emp.: 20
Welding Product Mfr & Distr
N.A.I.C.S.: 333992
Monica Isenhart *(Mgr-Ops)*

Bohler-Uddeholm Specialty Metals, LLC (3)
2306 Eastover Dr, South Boston, VA 24595
Tel.: (434) 575-7994
Web Site: http://www.busmi.com
High Speed Steels, Tool Steels & Specialty Metals Mfr
N.A.I.C.S.: 331221

EDRO Engineering, Inc. (3)
20500 Carrey Rd, Walnut, CA 91789
Tel.: (909) 594-5751
Custom Mold Base Mfr
N.A.I.C.S.: 331221

EDRO Specialty Steels, Inc. (3)
310 Wayne Ave, Ellwood City, PA 16117
Tel.: (724) 758-4475
Web Site: https://www.edro.com
Emp.: 35
Specialty Steel Distr
N.A.I.C.S.: 331221
Jon Surma *(Mgr-Production)*

Subsidiary (Non-US):

Edro Specialty Steels GmbH (4)
Industriestr 5c, D-77767, Appenweier, Germany
Tel.: (49) 7805915790
Web Site: https://de.edro.com
Sales Range: $25-49.9 Million
Emp.: 12
Mold Steel Mfr & Whslr
N.A.I.C.S.: 333511
Joachim Friedmann *(Mng Dir)*

Subsidiary (Non-US):

Bohler-Uddeholm Iberica S.A. (2) **(100%)**
Giufre 690 692, Badalona, 08918, Barcelona, Spain
Tel.: (34) 934609900
Web Site: http://www.bohler-uddeholm.es
Sales Range: $25-49.9 Million
Emp.: 40
Steel Mfrs
N.A.I.C.S.: 332111
Peter Urbanic *(Gen Mgr)*

Bohler-Uddeholm Limited (2) **(100%)**
2595 Meadowvale Blvd, Mississauga, L5N 7Y3, ON, Canada
Tel.: (905) 812-9440
Web Site: https://www.voestalpine.com
Sales Range: $25-49.9 Million
Emp.: 60
Steel Products Sales
N.A.I.C.S.: 423510
Martin Beaton *(Pres)*

Subsidiary (Domestic):

Sturdell Industries Inc. (3)
2595 Meadowvale Blvd, Mississauga, L5N 7Y3, ON, Canada
Tel.: (416) 675-2020
Web Site: https://www.sturdell.com
Sales Range: $10-24.9 Million
Molded Steel Machining Services
N.A.I.C.S.: 332710
Nick Laird *(Founder & Pres)*

Subsidiary (US):

Sturdell Industries, Inc. (4)
1529 Lyell Ave, Rochester, NY 14606
Tel.: (585) 464-0800
Web Site: https://www.sturdell.com
Sales Range: $25-49.9 Million
Emp.: 25
Molded Steel Machining Services
N.A.I.C.S.: 332710
Ed Toscano *(Gen Mgr)*

Subsidiary (Domestic):

Bohler-Uddeholm Precision Strip GmbH & Co KG (2) **(100%)**
Waidhofner Strasse 3, 3333, Bohlerwerk, Austria
Tel.: (43) 74426000
Web Site: http://www.voestalpine.com
Sales Range: $75-99.9 Million
Emp.: 600
Machine Tools & Strip Steel Mfr
N.A.I.C.S.: 332216
Lander Ahorner *(Mng Dir)*

Subsidiary (US):

BOHLER-UDDEHOLM Precision Strip LLC (3)
3052 Interstate Pkwy, Brunswick, OH 44212
Tel.: (330) 220-2242
Web Site: http://www.bohlerrule.com
Strip Steel Mfr
N.A.I.C.S.: 331110
Udo Koehler *(Pres)*

Subsidiary (Non-US):

Bohler Uddeholm Precision Steel AB (3)
Uddeholmsvagen 20, Box 503, 684 28, Munkfors, Vaermland, Sweden
Tel.: (46) 563 16000
Rolled Strip Steel Mfr
N.A.I.C.S.: 331221

Bohler Uddeholm Precision Strip Trading (Suzhou) Co., Ltd (3)
121 Xingpu Road Suzhou Industrial Park, 215126, Suzhou, China
Tel.: (86) 512 67631286
Steel Products Whslr
N.A.I.C.S.: 423510

Bohler Uddeholm Service Center AB (3)
Uddeholmsvagen 20, Munkfors, 684 92, Sweden
Tel.: (46) 563 160 00
Rolled Strip Steel Mfr

VOESTALPINE AG

INTERNATIONAL PUBLIC

voestalpine AG—(Continued)
N.A.I.C.S.: 331221

Bohler-Uddeholm Precision Strip AB (3)
Drottninggatan 40, Karlstad, 652 25, Sweden
Tel.: (46) 56316000
Web Site: http://www.uddeholm-strip.com
Emp.: 250
Steel Products Whslr
N.A.I.C.S.: 423510
Chris Millward (Mgr-R&D)

Bohler-Uddeholm Saw Steel AB (3)
Uddeholmsvagen 20, Box 503, 684 28, Munkfors, Vaermland, Sweden
Tel.: (46) 563 16000
Steel Strip Mfr & Distr
N.A.I.C.S.: 331110
Jguram Johson (CEO)

Compania de Industria y Comercio, S.A. de C.V. (3)
Cincinnati 149 Colonia La Aurora, 44460, Guadalajara, Jalisco, Mexico
Tel.: (52) 333 617 5900
Web Site: https://www.cicsacv.com
Paper Product Whslr
N.A.I.C.S.: 424110

Subsidiary (US):

Martin Miller North America, Inc. (3)
3052 Interstate Pkwy, Brunswick, OH 44212
Tel.: (330) 273-8606
Die Cutting Equipment Whslr
N.A.I.C.S.: 423830
Udo Koehler (Gen Mgr)

Subsidiary (Non-US):

Servitroquel - Notting, S.A. Unipersonal (3)
Poligono Industrial El Congost Sector J Cami Ral 1, Cami de Can Pla Nave G-H, 08170, Montornes del Valles, Barcelona, Spain
Tel.: (34) 93 860 45 69
Web Site: http://www.servitroquel-notting.com
Metal Strip Mfr & Whslr
N.A.I.C.S.: 333519

Subsidiary (Non-US):

Bohler-Uddeholm Schweiz AS (2)
Hertistrasse 15, 8304, Wallisellen, Switzerland (100%)
Tel.: (41) 448328811
Web Site: http://www.edelstahl-schweiz.ch
Stainless Steel Mfr
N.A.I.C.S.: 332111
Carsten Harms (Mng Dir)

Bohler-Uddenholm Deutschland GmbH (2)
Hansaallee 321, D-40549, Dusseldorf, Germany (100%)
Tel.: (49) 2115222226
Web Site: http://www.bohler-uddeholm.de
Sales Range: $125-149.9 Million
Emp.: 300
Wholesale Steel
N.A.I.C.S.: 423510

Subsidiary (Domestic):

BOHLER GRUNDSTUCKS BETEILIGUNGS GMBH (3)
Hansaallee 321, Dusseldorf, 40549, Nordrhein-Westfalen, Germany
Tel.: (49) 211 522 2534
Steel Products Mfr
N.A.I.C.S.: 331110

Bohler Grundstucks GmbH & Co. KG (3)
Hansaallee 321, 40549, Dusseldorf, 40549, Germany
Tel.: (49) 211 5222534
Web Site: http://www.bohler.de
Sales Range: $50-74.9 Million
Emp.: 250
Steel Products Whslr
N.A.I.C.S.: 423510
Markus Oberndorfer (CFO)

Eschmann Beteiligungsgesellschaft mbH (3)
Dieringhauser Str 161-183, 51645, Gummersbach, Germany
Tel.: (49) 2261 7060
Steel Mfrs
N.A.I.C.S.: 331110

EschmannStahl GmbH & Co. KG (3)
Otto-Hahn-Strasse 3, 51580, Reichshof, Germany
Tel.: (49) 22 659 9400
Web Site: https://www.eschmannstahl.de
Steel Products Mfr
N.A.I.C.S.: 331110
Markus Krepschik (Mng Dir)

Plant (Domestic):

EschmannStahl GmbH & Co. KG - Reichshof-Wehnrath Plant (4)
Otto-Hahn-Strasse 3, 51580, Reichshof, Germany
Tel.: (49) 22 659 9400
Web Site: https://www.eschmannstahl.de
Emp.: 150
Steel Products Mfr
N.A.I.C.S.: 331110
Markus Krepschik (Mng Dir)

Subsidiary (Non-US):

Oy Uddeholm AB (2)
PO Box 57, 01741, Vantaa, Finland (100%)
Tel.: (358) 10 841 4900
Web Site: https://www.uddeholm.com
Sales Range: $25-49.9 Million
Emp.: 30
Steel Mfrs
N.A.I.C.S.: 332111

Uddeholm A/S (2)
Kokmose 8, 6000, Kolding, Denmark
Tel.: (45) 75517066
Web Site: https://www.uddeholm.com
Sales Range: $25-49.9 Million
Emp.: 15
Steel Mfrs
N.A.I.C.S.: 332111

Uddeholm A/S (2)
PO Box 85, N-0902, Oslo, Norway
Tel.: (47) 22918000
Steel Mfrs
N.A.I.C.S.: 332111

Uddeholm KK (2)
3-14-16 Nishi Shinbashi Tokyo Building Atago East 10th Floor Minato Ku, Tokyo, 1050003, Japan (100%)
Tel.: (81) 354734641
Sales Range: $25-49.9 Million
Emp.: 20
Steel Mfrs
N.A.I.C.S.: 332111

Uddeholm N.V. (2)
Europark Oost 7, 9100, Saint-Niklaas, East Flanders, Belgium (100%)
Tel.: (32) 37805620
Web Site: http://www.uddeholm.be
Sales Range: $25-49.9 Million
Emp.: 15
Steel Mfrs
N.A.I.C.S.: 332111

Uddeholm Tooling AB (2)
PO Box 703, 683 85, Hagfors, Sweden (100%)
Tel.: (46) 56317000
Web Site: http://www.uddeholm.com
Sales Range: $150-199.9 Million
Emp.: 800
Mfr of Tool Steel, Stainless Steel Bar, Castings & Road Grader Blades
N.A.I.C.S.: 331110
Par Emanuelsson (Mgr-Sls & Mktg)

Villares Metals S.A. (2)
Rua Alfredo Dumont Villares 155 Jardim Santa Carolina, Sumare, CEP 13178902, SP, Brazil
Tel.: (55) 1933038000
Web Site: https://www.villaresmetals.com.br
Sales Range: $400-449.9 Million
Emp.: 1,500
Long Steel & Specialty Steel Products Mfr & Whslr
N.A.I.C.S.: 332111

Subsidiary (Non-US):

Villares Metals International B.V. (3)
Delftse Poort Unit 17 10-17 11 Weena 505, 3013 AL, Rotterdam, Netherlands (100%)
Tel.: (31) 615951451
Web Site: https://www.villaresmetalsnational.com
Long Steel Products Sales
N.A.I.C.S.: 423510
Pascal Jannink (Mgr-Logistics)

voestalpine Edelstahl Warmebehandlung GmbH (1)
Hansaallee 321, 40549, Dusseldorf, Germany
Tel.: (49) 211970760
Steel Product Mfr & Distr
N.A.I.C.S.: 331110

voestalpine Eifeler Coating GmbH (1)
Duderstadter Strasse 14, 40595, Dusseldorf, Germany
Tel.: (49) 211970760
Physical Vapour Deposition Coating Mfr
N.A.I.C.S.: 325510
Heinrich Scherngell (Chm)

voestalpine Eifeler Coatings, Inc. (1)
3800 Commerce Dr, Saint Charles, IL 60174
Tel.: (630) 587-1220
Metal Coating Product Mfr
N.A.I.C.S.: 332812
Jim Clay (Bus Mgr)

voestalpine Europlatinen GmbH & Co. (1)
Stahlstrasse 47, 4020, Linz, Austria (100%)
Tel.: (43) 73265858341
Sales Range: $150-199.9 Million
Emp.: 300
N.A.I.C.S.: 324199
Yosef Halwachs (Mng Dir-Technical)

voestalpine Finanzierungs GmbH (1)
voestalpine-Strasse 1, 4020, Linz, Austria
Tel.: (43) 732 65 85
Financial Management Services
N.A.I.C.S.: 523999

voestalpine Finanzierungs Holding GmbH (1)
Voestalpine-Str 1, 4020, Linz, Austria
Tel.: (43) 50304150
Web Site: http://www.voestalpine.com
Emp.: 300
Steel Mfrs
N.A.I.C.S.: 331110

Subsidiary (Non-US):

Voestalpine Dienstleistungs- Und Finanzierungs Gmbh (2)
Elsenheimerstrasse 59, 80687, Munich, Germany
Tel.: (49) 8957966460
Railway Infrastructure Services
N.A.I.C.S.: 488210

voestalpine France SAS (1)
6 rue de Dublin, 67300, Schiltigheim, France (100%)
Tel.: (33) 38 821 2377
Web Site: https://www.voestalpine.com
Sales Range: $25-49.9 Million
Emp.: 12
Wholesale Steel
N.A.I.C.S.: 423510
Sebastien Caspar (Mng Dir)

voestalpine HPM Denmark A/S (1)
Kokmose 8, 6000, Kolding, Denmark
Tel.: (45) 75517066
Steel Product Mfr & Distr
N.A.I.C.S.: 331110

voestalpine HPM Zagreb d.o.o. (1)
Slavonska Avenija 22d, 10 000, Zagreb, Croatia
Tel.: (385) 1 245 9300
Steel Product Mfr & Distr
N.A.I.C.S.: 331110

voestalpine High Performance Metal Anonim Sirketi (1)
TOSB 4 Cadde No 7, Sekerpinar Cayirova, 41420, Kocaeli, Turkiye
Tel.: (90) 2626588887
Steel Product Mfr & Distr
N.A.I.C.S.: 331110

voestalpine High Performance Metals (Australia) Pty. Ltd. (1)
17 Distribution Drive, Orchard Hills, Saint Marys, 2748, NSW, Australia
Tel.: (61) 24 744 9496
Steel Product Mfr & Distr
N.A.I.C.S.: 331110

voestalpine High Performance Metals Africa (Pty) Ltd. (1)
1 Isando Rd, Klopperpark, Kempton Park, 1600, South Africa
Tel.: (27) 11 571 2300
Steel Product Mfr & Distr
N.A.I.C.S.: 331110

voestalpine High Performance Metals Argentina S.A. (1)
Calle Mozart Nro 40 40, Centro Industrial Garin, AR-1619, Buenos Aires, Argentina
Tel.: (54) 1177004100
Steel Product Mfr & Distr
N.A.I.C.S.: 331110

voestalpine High Performance Metals CZ s.r.o. (1)
Prumyslova 591/1, 682 01, Vyskov, Czech Republic
Tel.: (420) 233029810
Steel Product Mfr & Distr
N.A.I.C.S.: 331110

voestalpine High Performance Metals Colombia S.A. (1)
Calle 20A No 43A-50 Int 2, AA 6208, Bogota, Colombia
Tel.: (57) 13647300
Steel Product Mfr & Distr
N.A.I.C.S.: 331110

voestalpine High Performance Metals Corporation (1)
2505 Millennium Dr, Elgin, IL 60124
Tel.: (630) 883-3000
Steel Product Mfr & Distr
N.A.I.C.S.: 331110
Marco Siscaro (CFO & COO)

voestalpine High Performance Metals Deutschland GmbH (1)
Hansaallee 321 321, D-40549, Dusseldorf, Germany
Tel.: (49) 2115220
Steel Product Mfr & Distr
N.A.I.C.S.: 331110

voestalpine High Performance Metals Finland Oy Ab (1)
Ritakuja 1, 01741, Vantaa, Finland
Tel.: (358) 108414900
Steel Product Mfr & Distr
N.A.I.C.S.: 331110
Andreas Johansson (Mng Dir)

voestalpine High Performance Metals France S.A.S. (1)
ZI Mitry-Compans-12 Rue Mercier, Mitry-Compans, F-77290, Mitry-Mory, Cedex, France
Tel.: (33) 160938050
Steel Product Mfr & Distr
N.A.I.C.S.: 331110

voestalpine High Performance Metals GmbH (1)
Donau-City-Strasse 7, AT-1220, Vienna, Austria
Tel.: (43) 50304100
Steel Product Mfr & Distr
N.A.I.C.S.: 331110
Franz Rotter (Chm)

voestalpine High Performance Metals Hungary Kft. (1)
Jedlik Anyos Ut 25 25, H-2330, Dunaharaszti, Hungary
Tel.: (36) 24526526
Steel Product Mfr & Distr
N.A.I.C.S.: 331110

voestalpine High Performance Metals Iberica, S.A.U. (1)
Andorra 59-61 Pol Ind Can Calderon, Can Calderon Industrial Park, 08840, Viladecans, Barcelona, Spain
Tel.: (34) 934609901
Steel Product Mfr & Distr
N.A.I.C.S.: 331110

AND PRIVATE COMPANIES — VOESTALPINE AG

voestalpine High Performance Metals India Private Limited (1)
409 A Skylark Plot No 63 Sector 11, CBD Belapur, Navi Mumbai, 400 614, Maharashtra, India
Tel.: (91) 2227577441
Steel Product Mfr & Distr
N.A.I.C.S.: 331110

voestalpine High Performance Metals International GmbH (1)
DC Tower Donau-City-Strasse 7, AT-1220, Vienna, Austria
Tel.: (43) 503043023100
Steel Product Mfr & Distr
N.A.I.C.S.: 331110
Martin Fuhrmann *(Mng Dir-Finance-Administration)*

voestalpine High Performance Metals Italia S.p.A. (1)
Via Palizzi 90, 20157, Milan, Italy
Tel.: (39) 02357971
Steel Product Mfr & Distr
N.A.I.C.S.: 331110

voestalpine High Performance Metals Ltd. (1)
2595 Meadowvale Boulevard, Mississauga, L5N 7Y3, ON, Canada
Steel Product Mfr & Distr
N.A.I.C.S.: 331110
Martin Beaton *(Pres)*

voestalpine High Performance Metals Norway AS (1)
PO Box 85, Kalbakken, 0902, Oslo, Norway
Tel.: (47) 22918000
Steel Product Mfr & Distr
N.A.I.C.S.: 331110

voestalpine High Performance Metals Pacific Pte. Ltd. (1)
8 Cross Street 27-04/05/06, Singapore, 048424, Singapore
Tel.: (65) 65345600
Steel Product Mfr & Distr
N.A.I.C.S.: 331110
Thomas G. Habeler *(Pres)*

voestalpine High Performance Metals Polska Sp. z o. o. (1)
Ul Kolejowa 291, Dziekanow Polski, 05-092, Lomianki, Poland
Tel.: (48) 224292200
Steel Product Mfr & Distr
N.A.I.C.S.: 331110

voestalpine High Performance Metals Romania S.R.L. (1)
Atomistilor Street 96-102, Ilfov District, Magurele, Romania
Tel.: (40) 214055840
Web Site: https://www.bohler.ro
Steel Product Mfr & Distr
N.A.I.C.S.: 331110

voestalpine High Performance Metals S.A. de C.V. (1)
Cerrada de la Noria No 200 Int A-14, Parque Industrial Queretaro, 76220, Queretaro, Mexico
Tel.: (52) 4426895900
Steel Product Mfr & Distr
N.A.I.C.S.: 331110
Axel Franco *(Pres)*

voestalpine High Performance Metals Schweiz AG (1)
Hertistrasse 15, 8304, Wallisellen, Switzerland
Tel.: (41) 448328811
Steel Product Mfr & Distr
N.A.I.C.S.: 331110
Carsten Harms *(CEO)*

voestalpine High Performance Metals Slovakia, s.r.o. (1)
5622 Ceskoslovenskej Armady 5, 036 01, Martin, Slovakia
Tel.: (421) 434212021
Web Site: https://www.bohler.sk
Tool Steel Mfr & Distr
N.A.I.C.S.: 331110

voestalpine High Performance Metals Sweden AB (1)
Aminogatan 25B, 431 53, Molndal, Sweden
Tel.: (46) 31679850

Steel Product Mfr & Distr
N.A.I.C.S.: 331110
Andreas Johansson *(Mng Dir)*

voestalpine High Performance Metals UK Limited (1)
Taylors Lane, Oldbury, B69 2BN, West Midlands, United Kingdom
Tel.: (44) 1215525681
Steel Product Mfr & Distr
N.A.I.C.S.: 331110
Mark Williams *(Country Mgr & Mng Dir)*

voestalpine High Performance Metals del Ecuador S.A. (1)
De las Avellanas E1-112 y Panamericana Norte Km 5 1/2, Quito, Ecuador
Tel.: (593) 22473080
Steel Product Mfr & Distr
N.A.I.C.S.: 331110

voestalpine High Performance Metals del Peru S.A. (1)
Luis Castro Ronceros Street 777, 15081, Lima, Peru
Tel.: (51) 16193232
Steel Product Mfr & Distr
N.A.I.C.S.: 331110

voestalpine Iberia S.L. (1)
Paseo Juan de Borbon 99 planta 2, Barcelona, Spain
Tel.: (34) 93 626 5571
Steel Product Mfr & Distr
N.A.I.C.S.: 331110
Dorian Valan *(Mng Dir)*

voestalpine Insurance Services GmbH (1)
Stahlstrasse 14, 4020, Linz, Austria
Tel.: (43) 5030 415 3474
Web Site: https://www.voestalpine.com
Emp.: 17
General Insurance Services
N.A.I.C.S.: 524298
Jurgen Reisinger *(Gen Mgr)*

voestalpine Krems GmbH (1)
Schmidhuttenstrasse 5, Donau, 3500, Krems, Austria **(100%)**
Tel.: (43) 50304140
Web Site: https://www.voestalpine.com
Sales Range: $150-199.9 Million
Emp.: 1,000
Mfr of Steel Tubes, Towers & Shelves
N.A.I.C.S.: 331210
Dirk Mahnke *(Mng Dir)*

Subsidiary (Non-US):

Metsec plc (2)
Broadwell Rd, Oldbury, B69 4HF, W Midlands, United Kingdom **(100%)**
Tel.: (44) 216016000
Web Site: http://www.metsec.com
Sales Range: $100-124.9 Million
Emp.: 450
Steel Works, Blast Furnaces, Including Coke Ovens & Rolling Mills
N.A.I.C.S.: 324199

Subsidiary (Domestic):

Metal Sections Limited (3)
Broadwell Road, Oldbury, B69 4HF, West Midlands, United Kingdom
Tel.: (44) 121 601 6000
Web Site: http://www.metsec.com
Sales Range: $100-124.9 Million
Emp.: 320
Steel Mfrs
N.A.I.C.S.: 331221
Neil Richardson *(Mng Dir)*

Subsidiary (Non-US):

Sadef N.V. (2)
Bruggesteenweg 60, B 8830, Hooglede, Belgium **(100%)**
Tel.: (32) 51261211
Web Site: http://www.sadef.com
Sales Range: $150-199.9 Million
Emp.: 550
Steel Works, Blast Furnaces, Including Coke Ovens & Rolling Mills
N.A.I.C.S.: 331110

Subsidiary (Non-US):

SADEF FRANCE S.A.R.L. (3)
2 Boulevard Albert 1, 94130, Nogent-sur-Marne, France
Tel.: (33) 14 324 6011
Web Site: http://www.sadef.be
Emp.: 11
Steel Tube Distr
N.A.I.C.S.: 423510
Olivier Zaniol *(Mng Dir)*

Subsidiary (Domestic):

voestalpine Krems Finaltechnik GmbH (2)
Schmidhuttenstrasse 5, 3500, Krems, Austria **(100%)**
Tel.: (43) 5030414686
Web Site: https://www.voestalpine.com
Emp.: 200
Steel Works, Blast Furnaces, Including Coke Ovens & Rolling Mills
N.A.I.C.S.: 331110
Karl Heinz Harrer *(Mgr-HR)*

Subsidiary (Non-US):

voestalpine Profilform S.R.O. (2)
Tovarni 4, CZ-682 23, Vyskov, Czech Republic **(100%)**
Tel.: (420) 517333701
Web Site: https://www.voestalpine.com
Sales Range: $25-49.9 Million
Emp.: 60
Steel Works, Blast Furnaces, Including Coke Ovens & Rolling Mills
N.A.I.C.S.: 324199
Marek Hladik *(Mng Dir)*

voestalpine Metal Forming GmbH (1)
Schmidhuttenstrasse 5, Donau, A-3500, Krems, Austria
Tel.: (43) 5030414681
Web Site: https://www.voestalpine.com
Emp.: 10
Metal Product Whslr
N.A.I.C.S.: 423510

voestalpine Metal Forming US Holding LLC (1)
1070 Brooks Industrial Rd, Shelbyville, KY 40065
Tel.: (502) 633-4435
Steel Products Mfr
N.A.I.C.S.: 331110

voestalpine Metsec plc (1)
Broadwell Road, Oldbury, B69 4HF, West Midlands, United Kingdom
Tel.: (44) 1216016000
Web Site: https://www.metsec.com
Roll Forming Product Mfr
N.A.I.C.S.: 332114

voestalpine Nederland B.V. (1)
Willem Witsenplein 4, BK Den Haag, 2596 BK, Hague, Netherlands **(100%)**
Tel.: (31) 70 314 1666
Web Site: http://www.voestalpine.com
Sales Range: $25-49.9 Million
Emp.: 8
Steel Works, Blast Furnaces, Including Coke Ovens & Rolling Mills
N.A.I.C.S.: 331110
Christian Schallauer *(Mng Dir)*

voestalpine Nortrak Inc. (1)
1740 Pacific Ave, Cheyenne, WY 82007-1004
Tel.: (307) 778-8700
Web Site: http://www.voestalpine.com
Railroad Transit System Mfr
N.A.I.C.S.: 336510
Brian Abbott *(COO)*

Subsidiary (Non-US):

Nortrak-Damy, Cambios de Via, S.A.P.I. de C.V. (2)
Av De Los Pinos 7-A Col Zapopan, Guadalajara, CP 45120, Zapopan, Jalisco, Mexico
Tel.: (52) 3338132525
Rail Track Material Mfr & Whslr
N.A.I.C.S.: 333924

Plant (Domestic):

voestalpine Nortrak Inc. - Birmingham Plant (2)
3930 Valley East Industrial Dr, Birmingham, AL 35217

Tel.: (205) 854-2884
Web Site: http://www.voestalpine.com
Railroad Transit System Mfr
N.A.I.C.S.: 336510

voestalpine Nortrak Inc. - Chicago Heights Plant (2)
2705 S State St, Chicago Heights, IL 60411-4894
Tel.: (708) 757-6568
Web Site: http://www.voestalpine.com
Emp.: 150
Railroad Transit System Mfr
N.A.I.C.S.: 336510

voestalpine Nortrak Inc. - Decatur Plant (2)
690 E Kenwood Ave, Decatur, IL 62526
Tel.: (217) 876-9160
Web Site: http://www.voestalpine.com
Railroad Transit System Mfr
N.A.I.C.S.: 336510
Sean Betty *(Gen Mgr)*

voestalpine Nortrak Inc. - Newton Plant (2)
405 W 1st St, Newton, KS 67114
Tel.: (316) 284-0088
Web Site: http://www.voestalpine.com
Railroad Transit System Mfr
N.A.I.C.S.: 336510

voestalpine Nortrak Inc. - Pueblo Plant (2)
2300 S Freeway, Pueblo, CO 81004
Tel.: (719) 564-0244
Web Site: http://www.voestalpine.com
Railroad Transit System Mfr
N.A.I.C.S.: 336510

voestalpine Nortrak Inc. - Seattle Plant (2)
5950 6th Ave S Ste 200, Seattle, WA 98108-3317
Tel.: (206) 622-0125
Web Site: http://www.voestalpine.com
Railroad Transit System Mfr
N.A.I.C.S.: 336510

Subsidiary (Non-US):

voestalpine Nortrak Ltd. (2)
5500 Parkwood Way, Richmond, V6V 2M4, BC, Canada
Tel.: (604) 273-3030
Web Site: https://www.voestalpine.com
Railroad Track Parts Mfr & Distr
N.A.I.C.S.: 336510
Andreas Mitterboeck *(Engr-Design)*

voestalpine Personal Services GmbH (1)
Stahlstrasse 30, PO Box 3, 4031, Linz, Austria
Tel.: (43) 5030 415 2500
Human Resource Consultancy Services
N.A.I.C.S.: 541612

voestalpine Polynorm BV (1)
Amersfoortseweg 9, Postbus 503, 3751 LJ, Bunschoten, Netherlands
Tel.: (31) 332989511
Sales Range: $200-249.9 Million
Emp.: 650
N.A.I.C.S.: 332111

Subsidiary (Non-US):

Polynorm Gmbh (2)
Steinbrink 3, 42555, Velbert, Germany
Tel.: (49) 2052 88702
Plumbing & Heating Equipment Whslr
N.A.I.C.S.: 423720

Subsidiary (Domestic):

Entwicklungsgesellschaft Gugling Verwaltungs GmbH (3)
Alemannenstr 65, 73529, Schwabisch Gmund, Germany
Tel.: (49) 7171 9720
Administrative Management Consulting Services
N.A.I.C.S.: 541611

Polynorm Immobilien GmbH & Co. KG (3)
Polynormstr 1, 73529, Schwabisch Gmund, Baden-Wurttemberg, Germany
Tel.: (49) 7171 9720

VOESTALPINE AG

voestalpine AG—(Continued)

Real Estate Manangement Services
N.A.I.C.S.: 531390

Subsidiary (Domestic):

Polynorm Immobilien Beteiligungs-GmbH (4)
Polynormstrasse 1, 73529, Schwabisch Gmund, Baden-Wurttemberg, Germany
Tel.: (49) 7171 9720
Investment Management Service
N.A.I.C.S.: 523999

Subsidiary (Non-US):

voestalpine Polynorm GmbH & Co. KG (2)
Polynormstrasse 1, D 73529, Schwabisch Gmund, Germany
Tel.: (49) 71719720
Web Site: http://www.polynorm.com
Sales Range: $75-99.9 Million
Emp.: 350
Iron & Steel Forgings
N.A.I.C.S.: 332111
Benno Trrxleo (Mgr)

Subsidiary (Domestic):

voestalpine Polynorm Beteiligungsgesellschaft m.b.H. (3)
Polynormstr 1, 73529, Schwabisch Gmund, Baden-Wurttemberg, Germany
Tel.: (49) 7171 972 0
Steel Products Mfr
N.A.I.C.S.: 331110

voestalpine Precision Strip AB (1)
PO Box 503, SE-684 28, Munkfors, Sweden
Tel.: (46) 56316000
Cold Rolled Strip Steel Product Mfr
N.A.I.C.S.: 331221

voestalpine Precision Strip Trading (Suzhou) Co., Ltd. (1)
Building 8B Modern Industrial Square No 333 Xingpu Road, Suzhou Industrial Park, Suzhou, 215127, China
Tel.: (86) 51267631668
Cold Rolled Strip Steel Product Mfr
N.A.I.C.S.: 331221

voestalpine Precision Strip WI, Inc. (1)
7888 102nd St, Pleasant Prairie, WI 53158
Tel.: (262) 947-5800
Web Site: https://www.voestalpine.com
Rolled Strip Steel Mfr
N.A.I.C.S.: 331221
Udo Koehler (Mng Dir)

voestalpine Precision Strip, S.A.U. (1)
P I El Congost Sector J Cami Ral 1, 08170, Montornes del Valles, Spain
Tel.: (34) 938604569
Cold Rolled Strip Steel Mfr
N.A.I.C.S.: 331221

voestalpine Profilform (China) Co., Ltd. (1)
No 1 Ruifu Lane, Suzhou Industrial Park, Suzhou, 215126, Jiangsu, China
Tel.: (86) 51267631650
Web Site: https://www.voestalpine-profilform.com
Roll Forming Steel Product Mfr
N.A.I.C.S.: 332114
Vincent Gu (Sls Dir)

voestalpine Profilform GmbH (1)
voestalpine-Strasse 1, Linz, 4020, Austria
Tel.: (43) 732 6585 0
Cold Rolled Tube Mfr
N.A.I.C.S.: 331210

Subsidiary (Non-US):

Nedcon Groep N.V. (2)
Nijverheidsweg 26, Doetinchem, 7005 BJ, Gelderland, Netherlands
Tel.: (31) 314334455
Sales Range: $25-49.9 Million
Emp.: 150
Storage Scaffolding System Mfr
N.A.I.C.S.: 332323
M. Nijhout (Gen Mgr)

Subsidiary (Non-US):

Nedcon Bohemia s.r.o. (3)
Holandska 34, 53301, Pardubice, Czech Republic
Tel.: (420) 46 700 2111
Web Site: https://www.nedcon.com
Emp.: 15
Rack Mfr & Whslr
N.A.I.C.S.: 332312
Barton Milan (Mgr)

Nedcon France SASU (3)
Immeuble Saphir 5 Rue du Parc, Oberhausbergen, 67205, France
Tel.: (33) 3 88 560 555
Sales Range: $25-49.9 Million
Emp.: 4
Storage Scaffolding System Mfr
N.A.I.C.S.: 332323
Laureng Ferrer (Gen Mgr)

Nedcon Lagertechnik GmbH (3)
Dinxperloer Strasse 18-20, 46399, Bocholt, Germany
Tel.: (49) 2 871 4789
Web Site: https://www.nedcon.com
Sales Range: $25-49.9 Million
Emp.: 10
Storage Scaffolding System Mfr
N.A.I.C.S.: 332323
Michiel Nijhout (Mng Dir)

Subsidiary (Domestic):

Nedcon Magazijninrichting B.V. (3)
Nijverheidsweg 26, 7005 BJ, Doetinchem, Netherlands
Tel.: (31) 314 334455
Web Site: http://www.nedcon.com
Sales Range: $50-74.9 Million
Emp.: 150
Storage Scaffolding System Mfr
N.A.I.C.S.: 332323

Subsidiary (US):

Nedcon USA Inc. (3)
10053 Simonson Rd Ste 1, Harrison, OH 45030
Tel.: (513) 367-2656
Sales Range: $25-49.9 Million
Emp.: 10
Rack Mfr
N.A.I.C.S.: 332313
Dan Middendorf (Acct Mgr & Mgr-Sls)

Subsidiary (Non-US):

Societe Automatique de Profilage (2)
Route De Paris, Gisors, 27140, France
Tel.: (33) 2 32 55 24 96
Structured Steel Products Mfr
N.A.I.C.S.: 331110

Societe Profilafroid (2)
2 rue de Beauvais, 60930, Bailleul-Sur-Therain, France
Tel.: (33) 34 407 5111
Web Site: http://www.profilafroid.com
Emp.: 130
Steel Shapes Whslr
N.A.I.C.S.: 423390
Christophe Mallick (Gen Mgr)

Voest-Alpine Krems U.K. Plc (2)
Broadwell Road, Oldbury, B69 4BL, United Kingdom
Tel.: (44) 1216016000
Web Site: https://www.metacc.com
Computer Software Development Services
N.A.I.C.S.: 541511

voestalpine Meincol S.A. (2)
Rua Abel Postali 539, Caxias do Sul, 95112-255, RS, Brazil
Tel.: (55) 5432209000
Web Site: https://www.voestalpine.com
Emp.: 240
Iron & Steel Forging Services
N.A.I.C.S.: 332111
Manfred Wuble (Mng Dir)

Subsidiary (Domestic):

voestalpine Profilform Beteiligung GmbH (2)
Schmidhuttenstrasse 5, 3500, Krems, Austria
Tel.: (43) 2732 885 0

Web Site: http://www.voestalpine.com
Steel Products Mfr
N.A.I.C.S.: 331110
Helmut Punz (CFO)

Subsidiary (Non-US):

ZAO voestalpine Arkada Profil (3)
Mashinostroitelnaya Bldg 5, Yarzevo Region, Smolensk, 215805, Russia
Tel.: (7) 4812 65 25 89
Web Site: http://www.arkada.ru
Sales Range: $125-149.9 Million
Emp.: 300
Construction Steel Product Mfr & Whslr
N.A.I.C.S.: 331110

voestalpine Prazisionsprofil Gmbh (3)
Franz-Tilgner-Str 10, 50354, Hurth, Germany
Tel.: (49) 22 336 1160
Web Site: https://www.voestalpine.com
Steel Mfrs
N.A.I.C.S.: 331110
Wolfgang Hochgatterer (CEO)

Subsidiary (Domestic):

voestalpine Strassensicherheit GmbH (2)
Schmidhuttenstrasse 5, Postfach 42, Lerchenfeld, 3500, Krems, Austria
Tel.: (43) 5030414670
Web Site: http://www.voestalpine.com
Sales Range: $25-49.9 Million
Emp.: 70
Road Restraint System Mfr
N.A.I.C.S.: 332312

voestalpine ROTEC Iberica S.A. (1)
ZudibiArte s/n Carretera Okondo-Llodlo, E-01409, Okondo, Alava, Spain
Tel.: (34) 945898497
Web Site: https://www.voestalpine.com
Sales Range: $25-49.9 Million
Emp.: 30
Cutting & Machine Tool Mfr
N.A.I.C.S.: 333515

voestalpine Rail Center Duisburg GmbH (1)
Lintorfer Waldweg 501A, PO Box 290272, 47262, Duisburg, Germany
Tel.: (49) 203998180
Web Site: http://www.voestalpine.com
Sales Range: $25-49.9 Million
Emp.: 60
Welding Equipment Repair & Maintenance Services
N.A.I.C.S.: 811310
Stefan Glanz (Co-Mng Dir)

voestalpine Rail Technology GmbH (1)
Kerpelystrasse 199, Donawitz, AT-8700, Leoben, Austria
Tel.: (43) 5030426
Emp.: 7,000
Rail Track Equipment Mfr & Distr
N.A.I.C.S.: 336510
Gunter Neureiter (CEO & Mng Dir)

voestalpine Railpro B.V. (1)
Nieuwe Crailoseweg 8, Hilversum, 1222 AB, Netherlands
Tel.: (31) 35 688 96 00
Sales Range: $50-74.9 Million
Emp.: 100
Rail Infrastructure Product Whslr
N.A.I.C.S.: 423990
Chris van Dranen (CEO)

Subsidiary (Domestic):

Rene Prinsen Spoorwegmaterialen B.V. (2)
Stationsweg Oost 259, 3931 ER, Woudenberg, Netherlands
Tel.: (31) 33 2865758
Web Site: http://www.reneprinsen.nl
Sales Range: $25-49.9 Million
Emp.: 25
Locomotive Parts Whslr
N.A.I.C.S.: 423860
Leanne Beckers (Gen Mgr)

voestalpine Railway Systems Australia Pty. Ltd. (1)
Suite 702, 3 Spring Street, Sydney, 2000, NSW, Australia
Tel.: (61) 74 952 4044
Rail Track Equipment Mfr & Distr
N.A.I.C.S.: 336510
Glenn Kyte (Sls Mgr)

voestalpine Railway Systems Beijing Co. Ltd. (1)
Room 807 Tower 7 Central Park No 6 Chaowai Street, Chaoyang District, Beijing, 100020, China
Tel.: (86) 1065336071
Rail Track Equipment Mfr & Distr
N.A.I.C.S.: 336510
Marco Graf (CEO & Mng Dir)

voestalpine Railway Systems Bulgaria OOD (1)
4 Ilyantsi Blvd, 1220, Sofia, Bulgaria
Tel.: (359) 28904800
Rail Track Equipment Mfr & Distr
N.A.I.C.S.: 336510
Zlatin Krumov (CEO & Mng Dir)

voestalpine Railway Systems Jez, S.L. (1)
Arantzar s/n, Laudio, 01400, Llodio, Alava, Spain
Tel.: (34) 946721200
Web Site: https://www.jez.es
Rail Track Equipment Mfr & Distr
N.A.I.C.S.: 336510

voestalpine Railway Systems Latvia SIA (1)
Granita street 17A, Rumbula Ropazu, Riga, LV-1057, Latvia
Tel.: (371) 67135988
Rail Track Equipment Mfr & Distr
N.A.I.C.S.: 336510
Andrius Daniulaitis (CEO & Mng Dir)

voestalpine Railway Systems MFA SASU (1)
65 Route d'Eiheraxar, 64120, Arberats-Sillegue, France
Tel.: (33) 559381875
Web Site: https://www.mfarberats.fr
Rail Track Equipment Mfr & Distr
N.A.I.C.S.: 336510

voestalpine Railway Systems Polska Sp. z o.o. (1)
ul Rzemieslnicza 7, 81-855, Sopot, Poland
Tel.: (48) 585557748
Web Site: https://www.vaepolska.pl
Rail Track Equipment Mfr & Distr
N.A.I.C.S.: 336510
Mariusz Bulawa (Pres)

voestalpine Railway Systems Romania SA (1)
Sos Brailei nr 2, 120118, Buzau, Romania
Tel.: (40) 238721627
Rail Track Equipment Mfr & Distr
N.A.I.C.S.: 336510
Marius Adascalitei (CEO & Mng Dir)

voestalpine Railway Systems Saudi Arabia Limited (1)
2nd Industrial City New Kharj Road Exit 13, Sarab Al-Modon Industrial Complex 6747, Riyadh, 12836, Saudi Arabia
Tel.: (966) 115119799
Rail Track Equipment Mfr & Distr
N.A.I.C.S.: 336510
Mouammar El Sayed (CEO)

voestalpine Rohstoffhandel GmbH (1)
Zinnergasse 6A, Vienna, A 1110, Austria (95%)
Tel.: (43) 0176715460
Web Site: http://www.rohstoffhandel.com
Sales Range: $25-49.9 Million
Emp.: 100
Scrap Iron
N.A.I.C.S.: 331110
Manfred Foedinger (Gen Mgr)

voestalpine Rotec AB (1)
Gjutaregatan 12, 302 60, Halmstad, Sweden
Tel.: (46) 35165000
Web Site: http://www.voestalpine.com
Sales Range: $25-49.9 Million
Emp.: 25
Fabricated Metal Product Mfr & Whslr
N.A.I.C.S.: 332999

AND PRIVATE COMPANIES — VOESTALPINE AG

Joakim Ohlsson *(Mng Dir)*

voestalpine Rotec France S.A. (1)
Zi 7 Rue Henri Francois, 77330, Ozoir-la-Ferriere, France
Tel.: (33) 1 64 40 76 00
Metal Stamping Die Mfr
N.A.I.C.S.: 332119

voestalpine Rotec GmbH & Co. KG (1)
In den Bruchwiesen 11-13, 76855, Annweiler am Trifels, Germany
Tel.: (49) 63 469 6420
Web Site: https://www.voestalpine.com
Sales Range: $50-74.9 Million
Emp.: 190
Tubular Component Mfr & Whslr
N.A.I.C.S.: 332999
Roland Braeuer *(Mng Dir)*

voestalpine Rotec Incorporated (1)
3709 US 52 S, Lafayette, IN 47905
Tel.: (765) 471-2808
Web Site: https://www.voestalpine.com
Sales Range: $50-74.9 Million
Emp.: 100
Metal Product Whslr
N.A.I.C.S.: 423510

voestalpine Rotec Limited (1)
Jacknell Road, Dodwells Bridge Industrial Estate, Hinckley, LE10 3BS, Leicestershire, United Kingdom
Tel.: (44) 1455620300
Web Site: https://www.voestalpine.com
Sales Range: $25-49.9 Million
Emp.: 100
Precision Tube Product Mfr & Whslr
N.A.I.C.S.: 332721

voestalpine Rotec North America Corp. (1)
4041 North Service Road Unit 1, Burlington, L7L 4X6, ON, Canada
Tel.: (905) 336-0014
Tubular Component Distr
N.A.I.C.S.: 423510

voestalpine Rotec Sp. z.o.o (1)
Komorniki ul Polna 7, 55-300, Sroda Slaska, Poland
Tel.: (48) 71 396 0400
Web Site: https://www.voestalpine.com
Sales Range: $50-74.9 Million
Emp.: 220
Precision Steel Tube Mfr & Distr
N.A.I.C.S.: 331210
Monica Myleskar *(Mgr-Quality)*

voestalpine S.A.P. (1)
2 Rue De Beauvais, 60930, Bailleul-Sur-Therain, France
Tel.: (33) 344075111
Rolled Steel Products Mfr
N.A.I.C.S.: 331221

voestalpine STAHL Sp.z.o.o. (1)
Ul Zwierzyniecka 29, 31 105, Krakow, Poland **(100%)**
Tel.: (48) 322063137
Web Site: http://www.voest.com
Wholesale Steel
N.A.I.C.S.: 423510

voestalpine STAHL d.o.o. (1)
Petrinjska Ulica 61, HR 10000, Zagreb, Croatia **(100%)**
Tel.: (385) 14880350
Web Site: http://www.voest.com
Sales Range: $25-49.9 Million
Emp.: 100
Steel Works, Blast Furnaces, Including Coke Ovens & Rolling Mills
N.A.I.C.S.: 324199

voestalpine Sadef NV (1)
Bruggesteenweg 200, Gits, 8830, Hooglede, Belgium
Tel.: (32) 51261211
Cold Roll Forming Product Mfr
N.A.I.C.S.: 332114
Peter Verbrugge *(Mng Dir)*

voestalpine Scandinavia AB (1)
Stenaldersgatan 7, 213 76, Malmo, Sweden **(100%)**
Tel.: (46) 4065 333 7099
Web Site: http://www.voestalpine.com
Sales Range: $50-74.9 Million
Emp.: 6
Wholesale Steel

N.A.I.C.S.: 423510
Johannes Laub *(Mng Dir & Gen Mgr)*

voestalpine Schienen GmbH & Co. KG (1)
Kerpelystrasse 199, 8700, Leoben, Bonawitz, Austria **(100%)**
Tel.: (43) 5030426398
Web Site: http://www.voestalpine.com
Sales Range: $100-124.9 Million
Emp.: 800
Steel Works, Blast Furnaces, Including Coke Ovens & Rolling Mills
N.A.I.C.S.: 331110
Frederick Kubler *(Chief Sls Officer)*

Subsidiary (Domestic):

VAE Aktiengesellschaft (2)
Rotenturmstrasse 5 9, A 1010, Vienna, Austria **(100%)**
Tel.: (43) 01531180
Web Site: http://www.vae-ag.com
Sales Range: $25-49.9 Million
Emp.: 50
Mfr of Switching Equipment
N.A.I.C.S.: 335313

Subsidiary (US):

VAE Nortrak North America (3)
3422 1st Ave S, Seattle, WA 98134
Tel.: (206) 622-0125
Web Site: http://www.nortrak.com
Structural & Rail Mill Products Mfr
N.A.I.C.S.: 331110

Subsidiary (Domestic):

voestalpine Austria Draht GmbH (2)
Bahnhof St 2, 8600, Bruck an der Mur, Austria **(100%)**
Tel.: (43) 38628930
Web Site: http://www.voestalpine.com
Emp.: 700
Mfr of Wire & Wire Products
N.A.I.C.S.: 332618

voestalpine Stahl Donawitz Gmbh (2)
Kerpelystrasse 199, 8700, Leoben, Austria **(100%)**
Tel.: (43) 50304250
Web Site: https://www.voestalpine.com
Mfr of Wire Rod & Rail
N.A.I.C.S.: 331491
Paul Felsberger *(Mng Dir-Human Resources-Security-Administration)*

voestalpine Tubulars GmbH & Co. KG (2)
Alpinestrasse 17, 8652, Kindberg, Austria **(50%)**
Tel.: (43) 5 030 4230
Web Site: https://www.voestalpine.com
Mfr of Steel Tubes
N.A.I.C.S.: 331210
Ted Christiansen *(CEO & Mng Dir)*

voestalpine Schienentechnik Beteiligungs GmbH (1)
Kerpelystrasse 199, 8700, Leoben, Steiermark, Austria
Tel.: (43) 5 03 04 26
Investment Management Service
N.A.I.C.S.: 523999

voestalpine Schweiz GmbH (1)
Hertistrasse 15, 8304, Wallisellen, Switzerland **(100%)**
Tel.: (41) 44 318 6533
Web Site: https://www.voestalpine.com
Sales Range: $50-74.9 Million
Emp.: 4
Wholesale Steel
N.A.I.C.S.: 423510
Sebastien Caspar *(Mng Dir)*

voestalpine Signaling Austria GmbH (1)
Alpinestrasse 1, 8740, Zeltweg, Austria
Tel.: (43) 50304280
Rail Track Equipment Mfr & Distr
N.A.I.C.S.: 336510
Heinz Schatz *(CEO & Mng Dir)*

voestalpine Signaling China Co. Ltd. (1)
121 Xingpu Rd, Suzhou Industrial Park, Suzhou, CN 215126, China

Tel.: (86) 51267631290
Rail Track Equipment Mfr & Distr
N.A.I.C.S.: 336510
Marco Graf *(CEO & Mng Dir)*

voestalpine Signaling Poland Sp. z o.o. (1)
Ul Jana z Kolna 26C, 81-859, Sopot, Poland
Tel.: (48) 585557748
Web Site: https://www.tens.pl
Rail Track Equipment Mfr & Distr
N.A.I.C.S.: 336510
Mariusz Bulawa *(CEO & Mng Dir)*

voestalpine Signaling Sainerholz GmbH (1)
Oberahrer Str 9, Sainerholz, 56244, Otzingen, Germany
Tel.: (49) 26669520100
Rail Track Equipment Mfr & Distr
N.A.I.C.S.: 336510
Holger Putz *(CEO & Mng Dir)*

voestalpine Signaling Siershahn GmbH (1)
Bahnweg 1, 56427, Siershahn, Germany
Tel.: (49) 262360860
Rail Track Equipment Mfr & Distr
N.A.I.C.S.: 336510
Helmut Leibminger *(CEO & Mng Dir)*

voestalpine Signaling UK Ltd. (1)
Unit 1 Fulcrum 4 Solent Way, Fareham, Whiteley, PO15 7FT, Hampshire, United Kingdom
Tel.: (44) 1489571771
Rail Track Equipment Mfr & Distr
N.A.I.C.S.: 336510
John Smith *(CEO & Mng Dir)*

voestalpine Signaling USA LLC (1)
815 14th St SW Bldg D Ste 250, Loveland, CO 80537
Tel.: (970) 461-1140
Emp.: 15
Rail Track Equipment Mfr & Distr
N.A.I.C.S.: 336510
James Bilodeou *(CEO, Mng Dir & CTO)*

voestalpine Specialty Metals (Shanghai) Co. Ltd. (1)
Room 412 building 5 No 1999 Shenkun Road, Minghang District, Shanghai, China
Tel.: (86) 13601998642
Steel Product Mfr & Distr
N.A.I.C.S.: 331110

voestalpine Stahl Aps (1)
Dag Hammarskjolds Alle 29, DK 2100, Copenhagen, Denmark **(100%)**
Tel.: (45) 35431844
Web Site: http://www.voest.com
Sales Range: $25-49.9 Million
Emp.: 12
Steel Works, Blast Furnaces, Including Coke Ovens & Rolling Mills
N.A.I.C.S.: 331110

voestalpine Stahl Donawitz GmbH & Co KG (1)
Kerpelystrasse 199, 8700, Leoben, Austria
Tel.: (43) 50304250
Web Site: https://www.voestalpine.com
Steel Products Mfr
N.A.I.C.S.: 331110
Axel Sormann *(Head-Metallurgical Dept)*

voestalpine Stahl GmbH (1)
voestalpine-Strasse 3, 4020, Linz, Austria **(100%)**
Tel.: (43) 50304150
Web Site: https://www.voestalpine.com
Sales Range: $1-4.9 Billion
Emp.: 6,000
Producer of Steel Cold & Hot Rolled Plate & Sheet
N.A.I.C.S.: 331221
Peter Ackerlaner *(Dir-Fin)*

Subsidiary (Domestic):

Caseli GmbH (2)
voestalpine-Strasse 3b, 4020, Linz, Austria
Tel.: (43) 73265854500
Web Site: https://www.caseli.at
Emp.: 320
Catering Services
N.A.I.C.S.: 722320
Horst Stister *(Gen Mgr)*

Kontext Druckerei Gmbh (2)
Spaunstrasse 3a, 4020, Linz, Austria
Tel.: (43) 73 265 0600
Web Site: https://www.kontextdruck.at
Office Stationery Products Mfr & Whslr
N.A.I.C.S.: 424120

Logistik Service GmbH (2)
Lunzerstrasse 41, 4031, Linz, Austria **(100%)**
Tel.: (43) 7326 598 2000
Web Site: https://www.logserv.at
Emp.: 900
Logistics & Freight Transportation Arrangement
N.A.I.C.S.: 541614

Subsidiary (Domestic):

Cargo Service GmbH (3)
Lunzer Strabe 41, Linz, 4031, Austria
Tel.: (43) 73265850
Logistics Consulting Servies
N.A.I.C.S.: 541614

Subsidiary (Domestic):

Scholz Rohstoffhandel GmbH (2)
Zinnergasse 6a, 1110, Vienna, Austria
Tel.: (43) 80 020 7800
Web Site: https://www.diealtmetallprofis.at
Emp.: 100
Steel Scrap Metal Trading, Recycling & Processing
N.A.I.C.S.: 423930
Manfred Foedinger *(Mng Dir)*

Werksgartnerei Gesellschaft M.B.H. (2)
Strattnerstr 33, 4030, Linz, Upper Austria, Austria
Tel.: (43) 732 658 54 14 7
Vegetable & Edible Roots Whslr
N.A.I.C.S.: 424590

vivo Mitarbeiter-Service GmbH (2)
Stahlstrasse 33, 4031, Linz, Austria
Tel.: (43) 7326 585 4430
Web Site: https://www.vivo-service.at
Investment Management Service
N.A.I.C.S.: 523940

voestalpine Anarbeitung GmbH (2)
Voestalpine-Strasse 3, 4020, Linz, Austria
Tel.: (43) 50304150
Web Site: http://www.voestalpine.com
Steel Processing
N.A.I.C.S.: 331110
Hans-Joerg Kirchweger *(Mng Dir-Logistics, Quality, Tech, IT, Customer Svc & Production)*

voestalpine Eurostahl GmbH (2)
voestalpine-Strasse 3, 4020, Linz, Austria **(100%)**
Tel.: (43) 50304150
Web Site: https://www.voestalpine.com
Sales Range: $25-49.9 Million
Emp.: 33
Steel Products Sales
N.A.I.C.S.: 423510
Wolf-Dieter Hohl *(Member-Mgmt Bd)*

Subsidiary (Non-US):

voestalpine Belgium NV/SA (3)
Jozef Van Elewijckstraat 59, 1853, Strombeek-Bever, Belgium
Tel.: (32) 2 777 1325
Web Site: http://www.voestalpine.com
Steel Product Mfr & Distr
N.A.I.C.S.: 331110

voestalpine CR, s.r.o. (3)
Karlovo namesti 31, 120 00, Prague, Czech Republic
Tel.: (420) 22 490 8105
Web Site: https://www.voestalpine.com
Sales Range: $50-74.9 Million
Emp.: 8
Steel Products Whslr
N.A.I.C.S.: 423510
Reinhard Schlick *(Mng Dir)*

voestalpine Danmark ApS. (3)
Frederiksborggade 3 / 2 sal, 1360, Copenhagen, Denmark
Tel.: (45) 35 431 844
Web Site: http://www.voestalpine.com

VOESTALPINE AG — INTERNATIONAL PUBLIC

voestalpine AG—(Continued)
Sales Range: $50-74.9 Million
Emp.: 3
Metal Product Whslr
N.A.I.C.S.: 423510

voestalpine Hungaria Kft. (3)
Gombocz Zoltan utca 14, 1118, Budapest, Hungary
Tel.: (36) 1 489 5500
Web Site: http://www.voestalpine.com
Sales Range: $50-74.9 Million
Emp.: 6
Steel Product Distr
N.A.I.C.S.: 423510
Daniela Schlattl *(Mng Dir)*

voestalpine Italia S.r.l. (3)
Via F Turati 29, 20121, Milan, Italy
Tel.: (39) 0229 0811
Web Site: http://www.voestalpine.com
Steel Product Distr
N.A.I.C.S.: 423510
Sabine Kollerer *(Engr-Resident)*

voestalpine Polska Sp.z o.o. (3)
ul Oswiecimska 403, 43-100, Tychy, Poland
Tel.: (48) 32 327 9150
Web Site: https://www.voestalpine.com
Sales Range: $25-49.9 Million
Emp.: 5
Metal Product Whslr
N.A.I.C.S.: 423510

voestalpine Romania S.R.L (3)
Strada Finlanda No 2 Ap 1 District 1, 011776, Bucharest, Romania
Tel.: (40) 21 22 4 1003
Web Site: http://www.voestalpine.com
Sales Range: $25-49.9 Million
Emp.: 5
Engineeering Services
N.A.I.C.S.: 541330
Claudia Robineau *(Mng Dir)*

voestalpine Slovakia s.r.o. (3)
A Zarnova 1, 917 02, Trnava, Slovakia
Tel.: (421) 33 534 1325
Web Site: http://www.voestalpine.com
Sales Range: $50-74.9 Million
Emp.: 5
Steel Product Distr
N.A.I.C.S.: 423510
Daniela Schlattl *(Mng Dir)*

voestalpine d.o.o. (3)
Zaharova 3, 10000, Zagreb, Croatia
Tel.: (385) 1 618 5881
Web Site: http://www.voestalpine.com
Sales Range: $50-74.9 Million
Emp.: 2
Steel Products Whslr
N.A.I.C.S.: 423510

voestalpine d.o.o. (3)
Jarska cesta 10b, 1000, Ljubljana, Slovenia
Tel.: (386) 1 523 3730
Web Site: https://www.voestalpine.com
Flat Rolled Product Mfr
N.A.I.C.S.: 331110
Igor Rup *(Mng Dir)*

Subsidiary (Domestic):

voestalpine Giesserei Linz GmbH (2)
Voestalpine-Strasse 3, 4020, Linz, Austria (100%)
Tel.: (43) 50304150
Web Site: https://www.voest-foundry.com
Sales Range: $75-99.9 Million
Emp.: 250
Steel Works, Blast Furnaces, Including Coke Ovens & Rolling Mills
N.A.I.C.S.: 324199
Friedrich Oberreiter *(Member-Mgmt Bd)*

Subsidiary (Domestic):

voestalpine Giesserei Traisen GmbH (3)
Mariazeller Str 75, 3160, Traisen, Austria (100%)
Tel.: (43) 50304130
Web Site: https://www.voestalpine.com
Sales Range: $100-124.9 Million
Steel Foundry
N.A.I.C.S.: 331513
Karl Neulinger *(Mng Dir)*

Subsidiary (Domestic):

voestalpine Grobblech GmbH (2)
Voestalpine-Strasse 3, 4020, Linz, Austria (100%)
Tel.: (43) 503 0415
Web Site: https://www.voestalpine.com
Sales Range: $200-249.9 Million
Emp.: 600
Structural Steel Plates Producer & Supplier
N.A.I.C.S.: 331221
Walter Buttinger *(Mng Dir-Comml)*

voestalpine Rohstoffbeschaffungs-GmbH (2)
Stahlstrasse 21, 4020, Linz, Austria (100%)
Tel.: (43) 50304170
Sales Range: $25-49.9 Million
Emp.: 17
Steel Works, Blast Furnaces, Including Coke Ovens & Rolling Mills
N.A.I.C.S.: 324199

voestalpine Stahl Service Center GmbH (2)
Industriezeile 28, 4020, Linz, Austria (100%)
Tel.: (43) 732749880
Web Site: http://www.voestalpine.com
Sales Range: $125-149.9 Million
Emp.: 400
Steel Works, Blast Furnaces, Including Coke Ovens & Rolling Mills
N.A.I.C.S.: 332111
Marcel Egger *(Head-Mktg)*

Subsidiary (Non-US):

voestalpine Steel Service Center Polska Sp. z o.o. (3)
ul Oswiecimska 403, 43-100, Tychy, Poland (100%)
Tel.: (48) 323279101
Sales Range: $25-49.9 Million
Emp.: 14
Steel Works, Blast Furnaces, Including Coke Ovens & Rolling Mills
N.A.I.C.S.: 332111
Gernot Schwarzhuber *(Mng Dir)*

Subsidiary (Domestic):

voestalpine Stahlwelt GmbH (2)
voestalpine-Strasse 4, 4020, Linz, Austria
Tel.: (43) 5030 415 8900
Web Site: https://www.voestalpine.com
Emp.: 7,000
Business Consulting Services
N.A.I.C.S.: 561499

voestalpine Standortservice GmbH (2)
voestalpine-Strasse 3, 4020, Linz, Upper Austria, Austria
Tel.: (43) 5030415
Facility Management Services
N.A.I.C.S.: 561210

voestalpine Stahl N.V./S.A. (1)
Gozef Van Elewiyck Straat 59, 1853, Strombeek-Bever, Belgium (100%)
Tel.: (32) 27700852
Web Site: http://www.voest.com
Sales Range: $50-74.9 Million
Emp.: 7
Wholesale Steel
N.A.I.C.S.: 423510
Christian Schallauer *(Mng Dir)*

voestalpine Stahl S.p.A. (1)
Via F Turati 29, I 20121, Milan, Italy (100%)
Tel.: (39) 0229081201
Web Site: http://www.voestalpine.com
Sales Range: $25-49.9 Million
Emp.: 16
Wholesale Steel
N.A.I.C.S.: 423510

voestalpine Stahl d.o.o. (1)
Proleterske Solidarnosti 18 3, 11070, Belgrade, Serbia, Serbia (100%)
Tel.: (381) 3118754
Web Site: http://www.voestalpine.com
Sales Range: $25-49.9 Million
Emp.: 3
Steel Works, Blast Furnaces, Including Coke Ovens & Rolling Mills
N.A.I.C.S.: 324199

voestalpine Stahl d.o.o. (1)
Poljanska Cesta 22C, SI 1000, Ljubljana, Slovenia
Tel.: (386) 14392660
Web Site: http://www.voestalpine.com
Sales Range: $25-49.9 Million
Emp.: 4
Steel Works, Blast Furnaces, Including Coke Ovens & Rolling Mills
N.A.I.C.S.: 324199
Igor Rup *(Mng Dir)*

voestalpine Stamptec Bohmenkirch GmbH & Co. KG (1)
Buchenstrasse 3, 89558, Bohmenkirch, Germany
Tel.: (49) 7332 9622 0
Web Site: http://www.voestalpine.com
Sales Range: $50-74.9 Million
Emp.: 160
Metal Seal Mfr
N.A.I.C.S.: 332999
Matthias Martin *(Mgr)*

Subsidiary (Domestic):

voestalpine Stamptec Beteiligungs GmbH (2)
Buchenstr 3, 89558, Bohmenkirch, Baden-Wurttemberg, Germany
Tel.: (49) 7332 96220
Sales Range: $75-99.9 Million
Emp.: 200
General Insurance Services
N.A.I.C.S.: 524298

voestalpine Stamptec France S.A. (1)
ZA Aeroparc, 90150, Fontaine, France
Tel.: 3 8458 4877
Automobile Parts Mfr
N.A.I.C.S.: 336390
Harald Traxler *(Exec Dir)*

voestalpine Stamptec Holding GmbH (1)
voestalpine-Str 1, 4020, Linz, Austria
Tel.: (43) 50 30415
Investment Management Service
N.A.I.C.S.: 523999

Subsidiary (Non-US):

voestalpine Stamptec Nagold GmbH & Co. KG (2)
Graf-Zeppelin-Strasse 29, Nagold, D-72202, Germany
Tel.: (49) 74 52 84 81 0
Web Site: http://www.voestalpine.com
Sales Range: $25-49.9 Million
Emp.: 150
High-Precision Stamping Parts & Components Mfr
N.A.I.C.S.: 336370
Harald Traxler *(Exec Dir)*

voestalpine Stamptec Pfaffenhofen GmbH & Co. KG (2)
Brackenheimer Strasse 44, 74397, Pfaffenhofen, Germany
Tel.: (49) 70 46 96 24 0
Web Site: http://www.voestalpine.com
Sales Range: $25-49.9 Million
Emp.: 40
Precision Stamping Parts Mfr
N.A.I.C.S.: 332721

voestalpine Steel & Service Center GmbH (1)
Voestalpine-Strasse 3, 4020, Linz, Austria
Tel.: (43) 50304150
Web Site: https://www.voestalpine.com
Steel Product Mfr & Distr
N.A.I.C.S.: 331110
Marcel Egger *(Head-Marketing)*

voestalpine Steel Middle East FZE (1)
Westwing 2nd Floor Suite 212 Dubai Airport Freezone, Dubai, United Arab Emirates
Tel.: (971) 4 299 4790
Steel Works, Blast Furnaces, Including Coke Ovens & Rolling Mills
N.A.I.C.S.: 324199

voestalpine Steel Service Center Romania SRL (1)
Tel.: (40) 346083053
Steel Product Mfr & Distr
N.A.I.C.S.: 331110
Dan Mihai Nidelea *(Mng Dir)*

voestalpine Steel Trading (Shenyang) Co., Ltd. (1)
No 16 Yingkeso Road Three, Sujiatun District, Shenyang, 110101, China
Tel.: (86) 3355167566
Steel Product Mfr & Distr
N.A.I.C.S.: 331110

voestalpine Steel US LLC (1)
11490 Westheimer Rd Ste 750, Houston, TX 77077
Tel.: (832) 390-3370
Steel Product Mfr & Distr
N.A.I.C.S.: 331110

voestalpine TENS Sp. z o.o. (1)
ul Jana z Kolna 26C, 81-859, Sopot, Poland
Tel.: (48) 58 555 77 22
Web Site: http://www.tens.pl
Sales Range: $25-49.9 Million
Emp.: 50
Railroad Transit System Mfr
N.A.I.C.S.: 336510
Mariusz Bulawa *(Gen Mgr)*

voestalpine Texas Holding LLC (1)
2800 Kay Bailey Hutchison Rd, Portland, TX 78374
Tel.: (361) 704-9000
Steel Product Mfr & Distr
N.A.I.C.S.: 331110

voestalpine Turkey Celik Limited (1)
Fatih Sultan Mehmet MahallesiPoligon Caddesi, Buyaka 2 Sitesi No 8C-Blok Daire 67 Tepeustu-Umraniye, 34771, Istanbul, Turkiye
Tel.: (90) 216 290 7520
Steel Product Mfr & Distr
N.A.I.C.S.: 331110
Kemal Bozyigit *(Mng Dir)*

voestalpine Turnout Technology Germany GmbH (1)
Alte Wetzlarer Strasse 55, 35510, Butzbach, Germany
Tel.: (49) 60338920
Steel Product Mfr & Distr
N.A.I.C.S.: 331110
Mario Roznak *(CFO)*

voestalpine Turnout Technology Netherlands B.V. (1)
Nieuwe Crailosweg 8, PO Box 205, 1222ab, Hilversum, Netherlands
Tel.: (31) 357000100
Emp.: 70
Rail Track Equipment Mfr & Distr
N.A.I.C.S.: 336510
Chris Dranen *(CEO & Mng Dir)*

voestalpine Turnout Technology UK Limited (1)
2 Sir Harry Lauder Road, Edinburgh, EH15 1DJ, United Kingdom
Tel.: (44) 1313227210
Rail Track Equipment Mfr & Distr
N.A.I.C.S.: 336510
Ian Fillingham *(CEO & Mng Dir)*

voestalpine U.K. Ltd. (1)
Voest-Alpine House, Hammersmith, London, W6 0QT, United Kingdom (100%)
Tel.: (44) 208 600 5800
Web Site: https://www.voestalpine.com
Sales Range: $50-74.9 Million
Emp.: 5
Wholesale Steel
N.A.I.C.S.: 423510
Peter Heinzl *(Sls Dir-Automotive Industry)*

voestalpine U.S.A. Corp. (1)
11490 Westheimer Rd Ste 750, Houston, TX 77077 (100%)
Tel.: (832) 390-3370
Web Site: http://www.voestalpine.com
Sales Range: $1-9.9 Million
Emp.: 3
Steel Works Blast Furnaces Including Coke Ovens & Rolling Mills
N.A.I.C.S.: 423510
Kai Bauer *(Mng Dir)*

voestalpine VAE APCAROM (1)
2 Brailei Street, 120118, Buzau, Romania
Tel.: (40) 238721627

AND PRIVATE COMPANIES

Web Site: http://www.voestalpine.com
Sales Range: $25-49.9 Million
Emp.: 219
Bolt Mfr
N.A.I.C.S.: 332722
Marius Adascalitei (CEO & Mng Dir)

voestalpine VAE Africa (Pty) Ltd. (1)
23 Anvil Road, Isando, 1600, Gauteng, South Africa
Tel.: (27) 119283700
Railroad Equipment Mfr & Whslr
N.A.I.C.S.: 336510
Gavin Holiday (Mgr-Logistic)

Subsidiary (Domestic):

voestalpine VAE SA (Pty) Ltd. (2)
23 Anvil Road, Isando, 1600, South Africa
Tel.: (27) 11 928 3700
Web Site: https://www.voestalpine.com
Railway Turnout System Mfr
N.A.I.C.S.: 332312
D. Marite (CEO)

voestalpine VAE Italia S.r.l. (1)
Via Alessandria 91, Rome, 00198, Italy
Tel.: (39) 0684241106
Industrial Machinery Whslr
N.A.I.C.S.: 423830

voestalpine VAE Legetecha UAB (1)
Draugystes str 8, Valciunai, 13220, Vilnius, Lithuania
Tel.: (370) 5 2493 261
Web Site: http://www.voestalpine.com
Sales Range: $25-49.9 Million
Emp.: 67
Railroad Equipment Mfr & Whslr
N.A.I.C.S.: 333924
Romas Smaliukas (Dir-Tech)

voestalpine VAE Polska Sp. z o.o. (1)
Kijowska 1, 03-738, Warsaw, Poland
Tel.: (48) 22 518 01 95
Web Site: http://www.voestalpine.com
Railway Turnout System Mfr
N.A.I.C.S.: 488210

voestalpine VAE Railway Systems Pty.Ltd. (1)
33 McLennan Street, Ooralea, MacKay, 4740, QLD, Australia
Tel.: (61) 263300400
Web Site: http://www.voestalpine.com
Emp.: 50
Railroad Transit System Mfr
N.A.I.C.S.: 336510
Glenn Kyte (Mgr-Sls)

voestalpine VAE UK Ltd. (1)
2 Sir Harry Lauder Road, Edinburgh, EH15 1DJ, United Kingdom
Tel.: (44) 1313227210
Web Site: http://www.voestalpine.com
Emp.: 40
Railroad Switch Mfr
N.A.I.C.S.: 488210
Ian Fillingham (CEO)

voestalpine Vae Vkn India Private Limited (1)
24/5 Sri Ram Road Civil Lines, New Delhi, 110 054, India
Tel.: (91) 1123965651
Rail Track Equipment Mfr & Distr
N.A.I.C.S.: 336510
Naresh Aggarwal (Mng Dir & Chm)

voestalpine WBN B.V. (1)
Nieuwe Crailoseweg 8, 1222 AB, Hilversum, Netherlands
Tel.: (31) 35 700 01 00
Web Site: http://www.voestalpine.com
Sales Range: $25-49.9 Million
Emp.: 100
Railway Transportation Services
N.A.I.C.S.: 488210
Daniel Poll Jonker (Product Mgr)

voestalpine Wire Germany GmbH (1)
Grenzstrasse 45, Finsterwalde, 03238, Brandenburg, Germany
Tel.: (49) 35317860
Iron Wire Mfr & Distr
N.A.I.C.S.: 331222

voestalpine Wire Italy s.r.l. (1)
Via Foscarini 44, 31040, Nervesa della Battaglia, Italy
Tel.: (39) 04227244
Iron Wire Mfr & Distr
N.A.I.C.S.: 331222

voestalpine Wire Rod Austria GmbH (1)
Drahtstrasse 1, 8792, Sankt Peter-Freienstein, Austria
Tel.: (43) 50304220
Web Site: https://www.voestalpine.com
Iron Wire Mfr & Distr
N.A.I.C.S.: 331222

voestalpine d.o.o. (1)
Vladimira Popovica 48/apt 371, Belgrade, 11070, Serbia
Tel.: (381) 11 311 8754
Web Site: http://www.voestalpine.com
Steel Products Mfr
N.A.I.C.S.: 331513
Igor Rup (Mng Dir)

voestalpine group-IT AB (1)
Hagfors Jarnverk, Hagfors, 68385, Sweden
Tel.: (46) 56317300
Information Technology Consulting Services
N.A.I.C.S.: 541512

voestalpine group-IT GmbH (1)
voestalpine-Strasse 3, 4020, Linz, Germany
Tel.: (49) 50304158411
Web Site: https://www.voestalpine.com
Information Technology Consulting Services
N.A.I.C.S.: 541512

voestalpine group-IT GmbH (1)
voestalpine-Strasse 3, Postfach 3, 4020, Linz, Austria
Tel.: (43) 50304150
Web Site: https://www.voestalpine.com
Emp.: 400
Information Technology Consulting Services
N.A.I.C.S.: 541512
Guenter Kirsch (Mng Dir)

Subsidiary (Non-US):

voestalpine group-IT Tecnologia da Informacao Ltda (2)
Rua Alfredo Dumont Villares 155, Sumare, 13177-900, Sao Paulo, Brazil
Tel.: (55) 1938648092
Information Technology Data Processing Services
N.A.I.C.S.: 518210

VOGIATZOGLOU SYSTEMS S.A.
12km National Av Athens-Lamia, 144-51, Metamorfosis, Attiki, Greece
Tel.: (30) 2102888600
Web Site: https://www.voyatzoglou.gr
Year Founded: 1992
VOSYS—(ATH)
Sales Range: Less than $1 Million
Emp.: 167
Hardware Distr
N.A.I.C.S.: 423710
Dimitris Skalaios (VP)

VOGO S.A.
Immeuble les Centuries II 101 Place Pierre Duhem, 34000, Montpellier, France
Tel.: (33) 467500398
Web Site: https://www.vogo-group.com
ALVGO—(EUR)
Sales Range: $1-9.9 Million
Digital Marketing Services
N.A.I.C.S.: 541840
Christophe Carniel (Founder, Chm, Pres & CEO)

VOHKUS LTD.
Centurion House Barnes Wallis Road Segensworth, Southampton, PO15 5TT, United Kingdom
Tel.: (44) 845 647 0400
Web Site: http://www.vohkus.com
Year Founded: 2001
Sales Range: $50-74.9 Million
Emp.: 83
Computer Hardware Whslr
N.A.I.C.S.: 423430
Ritchie Sharma (CEO)

VOHRINGER HOME TECHNOLOGY CO., LTD.
No 7001 Linhai Highway, Fengxian District, Shanghai, 201414, China
Tel.: (86) 2167192899
Web Site: http://www.vohringer.com
Year Founded: 1995
603226—(SHG)
Rev.: $73,931,214
Assets: $198,449,349
Liabilities: $46,871,094
Net Worth: $151,578,255
Earnings: $1,364,955
Fiscal Year-end: 12/31/22
Wood Flooring Product Mfr & Distr
N.A.I.C.S.: 337122
Jurgen Vohringer (Chm)

VOICESERVE INC.
Grosvenor House 1 High Street, Edgware, HA8 7TA, Mddx, United Kingdom
Tel.: (44) 208 136 9000 DE
Web Site: http://www.voipswitch.com
Sales Range: $1-9.9 Million
VoIP Software Products
N.A.I.C.S.: 513210
Michael Bibelman (CEO)

VOITH GMBH & CO. KGAA
Sankt Poltener Strasse 43, Heidenheim, 89522, Germany
Tel.: (49) 7321370 De
Web Site: http://www.voith.com
Year Founded: 1867
Rev.: $4,789,070,091
Assets: $5,325,646,531
Liabilities: $3,931,353,639
Net Worth: $1,394,292,892
Earnings: $79,186,420
Emp.: 19,410
Fiscal Year-end: 09/30/19
Operational Management Holding Company; Industrial Paper, Energy & Mobility Equipment & Systems Mfr & Maintenance Services
N.A.I.C.S.: 332911
Roland Munch (Member-Mgmt Bd)

Subsidiaries:

BTG Eclepens SA (1)
Z I Village, 1312, Eclepens, Switzerland (100%)
Tel.: (41) 218660066
Web Site: http://www.btg.com
Sales Range: $50-74.9 Million
Emp.: 107
Controlling Device Mfr
N.A.I.C.S.: 334519

ELIN Motoren GmbH (1)
Elin-Motoren-Strasse 1, Preding, 8160, Weiz, Austria
Tel.: (43) 3172906060
Web Site: http://www.elinmotoren.at
Generator Mfr
N.A.I.C.S.: 335312
Wolfgang Landler (CEO)

Toscotec S.P.A (1)
Viale Europa 317/F, Marlia, 55012, Lucca, Italy
Tel.: (39) 058340871
Web Site: http://www.toscotec.com
Paper & Board Machine Mfr
N.A.I.C.S.: 333248

Voith Hydro Holding GmbH & Co. KG (1)
Alexanderstrasse 11, 89522, Heidenheim, Germany (65%)
Tel.: (49) 7321376121
Web Site: http://www.voithhydro.com
Sales Range: $750-799.9 Million
Emp.: 440
Holding Company; Hydropower Equipment Mfr & Maintenance Services
N.A.I.C.S.: 551112

Subsidiary (Non-US):

VG Power AB (2)
Master Ahls gata 8, 72212, Vasteras, Sweden
Tel.: (46) 21382560
Web Site: http://www.vgpower.com
Sales Range: $10-24.9 Million
Emp.: 84
Electric Power Generation
N.A.I.C.S.: 221118
Magnus Wenna (Dir-Mktg & Sls)

Voith Hydro AB (2)
Kopparlundsvagen 7, 721 30, Vasteras, Sweden
Tel.: (46) 21382560
Hydropower Equipment Whslr
N.A.I.C.S.: 423720
Kirsten Lange (Member-Mgmt Bd)

Voith Hydro AS (2)
Ostre Aker vei 90, 613, Oslo, Norway
Tel.: (47) 92076000
Electric Power Generation Services
N.A.I.C.S.: 221111
Jurgen Sehnbruch (Member-Mgmt Bd)

Voith Hydro Inc. (2)
160 - 9955 rue de Chateauneuf, Brossard, J4Z 3V5, QC, Canada
Tel.: (450) 766-2100
Electric Power Generation Services
N.A.I.C.S.: 221111

Subsidiary (US):

Voith Hydro Inc. (2)
760 E Berlin Rd, York, PA 17408-8701
Tel.: (717) 792-7000
Web Site: http://www.york.voithhydro.com
Sales Range: $100-124.9 Million
Emp.: 400
Water Turbines & Digital Governors Mfr
N.A.I.C.S.: 333611

Subsidiary (Non-US):

Voith Hydro Ltda. (2)
Rua Friedrich von Voith 825 Predio 70, 02995-000, Sao Paulo, Brazil
Tel.: (55) 551139445100
Engine Mfr
N.A.I.C.S.: 336310
Kai Schlichtermann (Mgr-Comm)

Voith Hydro Ltda. (2)
Carrera 43 A 1 85, Antioquia, Medellin, Colombia
Tel.: (57) 43128993
Engine Mfr
N.A.I.C.S.: 336310
Daniel Rubinstein (Country Mgr)

Voith Hydro Private Limited (2)
A-20 21 Sector 59, 201 301, Noida, India
Tel.: (91) 1203074242
Mechanical Equipment Mfr
N.A.I.C.S.: 333613
Rashi Govil (Deputy Mgr)

Voith Hydro S.r.l. (2)
Via Paisiello 104, Cinisello Balsamo, Italy
Tel.: (39) 02618671
Mechanical Equipment Mfr
N.A.I.C.S.: 333613

Voith Hydro S.r.l. (2)
Sectorul 2 B-dul Profesor Dimitriea Pompei nr 8 etaj 10, 20337, Bucharest, Romania
Tel.: (40) 312236100
Mechanical Equipment Mfr
N.A.I.C.S.: 333613

Voith Hydro Sarpsborg AS (2)
Kortbolgen 11, Gamle, 1630, Fredrikstad, Norway
Tel.: (47) 69384600
Mechanical Equipment Mfr
N.A.I.C.S.: 333613
Katrine Lund Gronli (Accountant)

Voith Hydro Shanghai Ltd. (2)
No 555 Jiangchuan Rd, Shanghai, China
Tel.: (86) 2124089999
Mechanical Equipment Mfr
N.A.I.C.S.: 333613
Martin Andrae (Pres)

VOITH GMBH & CO. KGAA — INTERNATIONAL PUBLIC

Voith GmbH & Co. KGaA—(Continued)

Voith Hydro da Amazonia Ltda. (2)
Av Cupiuba 594, 69075 060, Manaus, Brazil
Tel.: (55) 9236178198
Electric Power Generation Services
N.A.I.C.S.: 221111
Kai Schlichtermann (Mgr-Comm)

Voith Hydro s.r.o. (2)
Bozkovske namesti 17 21, Plzen, Czech Republic
Tel.: (420) 371417200
Mechanical Equipment Mfr
N.A.I.C.S.: 333613

Voith Siemens Hydro Power Generation S.L. (2)
P Larramendi 8, 20400, Tolosa, Spain (100%)
Tel.: (34) 943673799
Web Site: http://www.voithsiemens.com
Sales Range: $25-49.9 Million
Emp.: 157
Mfr of Paper Machines & Water Turbines
N.A.I.C.S.: 333243

Voith Siemens Hydro Power Generation S.p.A. (2)
Via Fosse Ardeatine 7 9, 20092, Cinisello Balsamo, Milan, Italy (100%)
Tel.: (39) 02618671
Web Site: http://www.voithshydro.com
Sales Range: $25-49.9 Million
Emp.: 100
Mfr of Water Turbines
N.A.I.C.S.: 333243
Roberto Breder (Gen Mgr)

Voith IT Solutions Inc. (1)
3040 Black Creek Rd, Wilson, NC 27893
Tel.: (252) 265-4300
Information Technology Consulting Services
N.A.I.C.S.: 541512

Voith Meri Environmental Solutions, Inc. (1)
2620 E Glendale Ave, Appleton, WI 54911
Tel.: (920) 734-8485
Waste Water Treatment Services
N.A.I.C.S.: 221320

Voith Middle East FZE (1)
263461 Technopark, Jebel Ali, Dubai, United Arab Emirates
Tel.: (971) 48104000
Mechanical Equipment Mfr
N.A.I.C.S.: 333613
Babak Bahmandeji (Chief Admin Officer & Gen Mgr)

Voith Paper Holding GmbH & Co. KG (1)
St Poltener Strasse 43, 89522, Heidenheim, Germany (100%)
Tel.: (49) 73217254
Web Site: http://www.voithpaper.com
Sales Range: $1-4.9 Billion
Emp.: 9,977
Paper Manufacturing Technology Components & Systems Mfr
N.A.I.C.S.: 333243

Subsidiary (US):

Syn Strand Inc. (2)
215 Deming Way, Summerville, SC 29483 (100%)
Tel.: (843) 871-1444
Web Site: http://www.voith.com
Sales Range: $25-49.9 Million
Emp.: 65
Mfr of Monofilament Yarns
N.A.I.C.S.: 326199
Brian Good (Mgr-Ops)

Subsidiary (Non-US):

VOITH PAPER MEXICO S DE RL DE CV
Alabama No 34, Napoles, 3810, Colonia, Mexico
Tel.: (52) 5553406998
Paper Mfr
N.A.I.C.S.: 322120
Mario Gonzalez (Engr-Sls & Support)

VOITH Paper (Thailand) Co., Ltd. (2)
179 Bangkok City Tower 27 Fl South Sathorn Road Thungmahamek, Sathorn, Bangkok, Thailand
Tel.: (66) 22871882
Paper Mfr
N.A.I.C.S.: 322120

Unit (Non-US):

Voith Canada Inc.-Fabrics Division (2)
925 Tupper Street, Hawkesbury, K6A 3T5, ON, Canada (100%)
Tel.: (613) 632-4163
Web Site: http://www.voith.com
Sales Range: $25-49.9 Million
Emp.: 60
Press Fabrics
N.A.I.C.S.: 313230

Voith Fabrics Benelux (2)
Tolveg 13, 9655PD, Oud-Annerveen, Netherlands
Tel.: (31) 598491971
Paper Mfr
N.A.I.C.S.: 313210
Andreas Endters (Member-Mgmt Bd)

Subsidiary (Non-US):

Voith Fabrics de Mexico, S.A. de C.V. (2)
Resurreccion Oriente 44, Apartado Postal F-34, Puebla, 72310, Mexico (100%)
Web Site: http://www.voithmexico.com
Press & Dryer Fabrics
N.A.I.C.S.: 313230

Voith Paper (China) Co., Ltd. (2)
No 76-2 Tiexi Road, 111004, Liaoyang, Liaoning, China
Tel.: (86) 419 330 6000
Paper Mfr
N.A.I.C.S.: 322120
Ming Ming Liu (Pres)

Voith Paper AS (2)
Dolasletta 7, 3408, Tranby, Norway
Tel.: (47) 32 85 38 00
Paper Mfr
N.A.I.C.S.: 322120

Voith Paper Argentina S.A. (2)
Rosario 2302, Carapachay, B 1606 DLD, Buenos Aires, Argentina
Tel.: (54) 11 47 62 00 40
Paper Mfr
N.A.I.C.S.: 322120

Voith Paper B.V. (2)
Radeweg 14, 8171MD, Vaassen, Netherlands
Tel.: (31) 578579700
Paper Mfr
N.A.I.C.S.: 322120

Subsidiary (Domestic):

Voith Paper Fabric & Roll Systems GmbH & Co. KG (2)
Veldener Strasse 71-75, 52349, Duren, Germany
Tel.: (49) 242149020
Paper Mfr
N.A.I.C.S.: 313210

Subsidiary (US):

Voith Paper Fabric & Roll Systems, Inc. (2)
1831 Veterans Memorial Hwy, Austell, GA 30168-7936
Tel.: (770) 948-8086
Web Site: http://www.voithaustell.com
Emp.: 50
Paper Idustry Machinery Mfr
N.A.I.C.S.: 333243

Voith Paper Fabrics (2)
2200 N Roemer Rd, Appleton, WI 54911-8687 (100%)
Tel.: (920) 731-7724
Web Site: http://www.voith.com
Sales Range: $25-49.9 Million
Emp.: 250
Mechanical Fabrics, Textiles & Textile Fibers Mfr
N.A.I.C.S.: 313210

Voith Paper Fabrics (2)
2500 Scapa Rd, Waycross, GA 31503 (100%)
Tel.: (912) 490-4000
Web Site: http://www.voith.com
Sales Range: $25-49.9 Million
Emp.: 130
Dryer Fabrics Mfr
N.A.I.C.S.: 313210

Subsidiary (Non-US):

Voith Paper Fabrics Asia Pacific Sdn. Bhd. (2)
Jalan Kuala Kangsar, Ipoh, 31200, Negeri Perak, Malaysia
Tel.: (60) 52913100
Industrial Machinery Distr
N.A.I.C.S.: 423830
Ong Boon Chuan (Mgr-Ops)

Voith Paper Fabrics B.V. (2)
Goorsestraat 17, 7482 CB, Haaksbergen, Netherlands (100%)
Tel.: (31) 535739300
Web Site: http://voith.com
Sales Range: $10-24.9 Million
Emp.: 50
Dryer Fabrics
N.A.I.C.S.: 314999

Subsidiary (Domestic):

Voith Paper Fabrics Duren GmbH (2)
Veldener Strasse 71-75, Duren, 52349, Germany (100%)
Tel.: (49) 242149020
Web Site: http://www.voithfabrics.de
Sales Range: $25-49.9 Million
Emp.: 150
Paper Machinery Mfr
N.A.I.C.S.: 333243

Subsidiary (Non-US):

Voith Paper Fabrics GmbH (2)
Voithstrasse 1, 4890, Frankenmarkt, Austria
Tel.: (43) 7684 8521 0
Paper Mfr
N.A.I.C.S.: 322120
Hans Peter Sollinger (Mng Dir)

Voith Paper Fabrics Gusum AB (2)
Dalangsvagen 2, S-61040, Gusum, Sweden (100%)
Tel.: (46) 12353000
Web Site: http://www.voithfabrics.com
Sales Range: $25-49.9 Million
Emp.: 90
Forming Fabrics
N.A.I.C.S.: 313210

Voith Paper Fabrics Hogsjo AB (2)
Bruksvagen 6, 640 10, Hogsjo, Sweden
Tel.: (46) 151 47 100
Paper Mfr
N.A.I.C.S.: 322120
Tony Einarsson (CEO)

Voith Paper Fabrics India Ltd. (2)
113/114 A Sector-24, Faridabad, 121 005, Haryana, India
Tel.: (91) 1294292200
Web Site: http://www.voithpaperfabricsindia.com
Mfr of Paper Machine Clothing (PMC), Fibre-Cement Sheet Making Felts & Hi-Tech Textile Processing Felts
N.A.I.C.S.: 313210
Krishna Kumar R. (Mng Dir)

Voith Paper Fabrics Stubbins (2)
Stubbins Vale Mill, Bury, BL0 0NT, Lancashire, United Kingdom
Tel.: (44) 1706822951
Textile Products Mfr
N.A.I.C.S.: 313310

Voith Paper Fabrics, S.A. (2)
Carrer Tapioles 19, Guissona, Spain
Tel.: (34) 97 355 01 46
Paper Mfr
N.A.I.C.S.: 322120

Voith Paper GmbH (2)
Maretgasse 45, 2632, Wimpassing, Austria (100%)
Tel.: (43) 2630369000
Web Site: http://voith.com

Sales Range: $200-249.9 Million
Emp.: 900
Mfr of Paper Machines, Water Turbines; Motive Power Engineering
N.A.I.C.S.: 333243
Andreas Endters (Chm-Mgmt Bd)

Subsidiary (Domestic):

Voith Paper GmbH & Co. KG (2)
Veldenerstrasse 52, Duren, 52349, Germany (100%)
Tel.: (49) 24214990
Web Site: http://www.voithpaper.com
Sales Range: $25-49.9 Million
Emp.: 100
Mfr of Paper Machines
N.A.I.C.S.: 333243

Subsidiary (US):

Voith Paper Inc. (2)
2200 N Roemer Rd, Appleton, WI 54911-8687 (100%)
Tel.: (920) 731-7724
Web Site: http://www.us.voithpaper.com
Sales Range: $25-49.9 Million
Emp.: 163
Paper Machines
N.A.I.C.S.: 333243

Subsidiary (Non-US):

Voith Paper Kagit Sanayi Limited Sirketi (2)
Baris Mah Belediye Cad No 30 Ginza Lavinya A Blok Kat3 Ofis No 27, Beylikduz, Istanbul, Turkiye
Tel.: (90) 2128711275
Paper Mfr
N.A.I.C.S.: 322120

Voith Paper Ltd. (2)
Apex Works, Middleton, Manchester, M24 1GQ, United Kingdom
Tel.: (44) 161 643 9273
Emp.: 40
Engineeering Services
N.A.I.C.S.: 541330
Robert O'Shaughnessy (Mng Dir)

Voith Paper Maquinas e Equipamentos Ltda. (2)
PO Box 33, Mucuri, Sao Paulo, 45930 000, BA, Brazil (100%)
Tel.: (55) 733605 4800
Web Site: http://www.voith.com
Sales Range: $700-749.9 Million
Emp.: 4,000
Mfr of Paper Machines, Water Turbines; Motive Engineering
N.A.I.C.S.: 333243

Voith Paper Oy (2)
Ayritie 8 E, 01510, Vantaa, Finland
Tel.: (358) 9 276 615 0
Paper Mfr
N.A.I.C.S.: 322120

Voith Paper Rolls GmbH & Co KG (2)
Kernstrasse 1, Laakirchen, 4664, Oberweis, Austria
Tel.: (43) 7613 5770
Paper Mfr
N.A.I.C.S.: 322120

Voith Paper Rolls Guangzhou Co., Ltd. (2)
No 20 Guangsheng Road, Nansha, Guangzhou, 511458, China
Tel.: (86) 2039098900
Paper Mfr
N.A.I.C.S.: 322120

Voith Paper S.A. (2)
Poligono Apatta Baratzondo 1, Tolosa, 20400, Guipuzcoa, Spain
Tel.: (34) 943 67 37 99
Paper Mfr
N.A.I.C.S.: 322120

Voith Paper S.r.L. (2)
Via Daniele Manin 16/18, 36015, Vicenza, Italy
Tel.: (39) 0445690500
Paper Mfr
N.A.I.C.S.: 322120
Fabio Bargiacchi (Mgr-Sls)

AND PRIVATE COMPANIES

Voith Paper Technology (India) Private Limited (2)
ECOSPACE Block-3A 6th Floor IIF/11 New Town, 700 156, Kolkata, India
Tel.: (91) 33 2300 5500
Emp.: 70
Paper Product Distr
N.A.I.C.S.: 424130
Arindam Chakraborty *(Deputy Mgr)*

Voith Paper Technology Russia GmbH (2)
Renaissance Premium building Reshetnikov str 14 A, Saint Petersburg, Russia
Tel.: (7) 8123249797
Web Site: http://www.voithpaper.com
Sales Range: $25-49.9 Million
Emp.: 30
Paper Machinery Mfr
N.A.I.C.S.: 333243

Voith Paper Walztechnik AG (2)
Hardstrasse 319, 8005, Zurich, Switzerland
Tel.: (41) 442782829
Paper Mfr
N.A.I.C.S.: 322120

Voith Turbo GmbH & Co. KG (1)
St Poltener Strasse 43, 89522, Heidenheim, Germany (100%)
Tel.: (49) 7321370
Web Site: http://www.voithturbo.com
Sales Range: $1-4.9 Billion
Emp.: 4,000
Mechanical Drive Components & Systems Engineering & Mfr
N.A.I.C.S.: 333613
Cornelius Weitzmann *(Member-Mgmt Bd)*

Subsidiary (Non-US):

PT Voith Turbo (2)
Jl T B Simatupang Kav 22-26 Talavera Office Park 28th FL, 12430, Jakarta, Indonesia
Tel.: (62) 2175999848
Oil Exploration Services
N.A.I.C.S.: 213112
Carsten J. Reinhardt *(Pres & CEO)*

VOITH TURBO s.r.o. (2)
Holzova 2887/10b, 62 800, Brno, Czech Republic
Tel.: (420) 548 226 070
Mechanical Equipment Mfr
N.A.I.C.S.: 333613

Voith Safeset AB (2)
Ronningevagen 8, 82434, Hudiksvall, Sweden (100%)
Tel.: (46) 650540150
Web Site: http://voith.com
Sales Range: $25-49.9 Million
Emp.: 75
Paper Machinery Mfr
N.A.I.C.S.: 333243

Voith Turbo (Pty) Ltd (2)
Hughes Business Park 16 Saligna Street, 1459, Boksburg, Gauteng, South Africa
Tel.: (27) 114184000
Mechanical Equipment Mfr
N.A.I.C.S.: 333613

Voith Turbo A/S (2)
Egegaardsvej 5, 4621, Gadstrup, Denmark
Tel.: (45) 46 14 15 50
Energy Consulting Services
N.A.I.C.S.: 541690

Voith Turbo AS (2)
Lahaugmoveien 30A, 2013, Skjetten, Norway
Tel.: (47) 63847020
Web Site: http://www.voithturbo.no
Emp.: 20
Mechanical Equipment Distr
N.A.I.C.S.: 423840

Voith Turbo B.V. (2)
Koppelstraat 3, 7391 AK, Twello, Netherlands
Tel.: (31) 571 2796 00
Emp.: 24
Mechanical Equipment Distr
N.A.I.C.S.: 423840
Gerard Klein Nulent *(Mng Dir)*

Subsidiary (Domestic):

Voith Turbo BHS Getriebe GmbH (2)
Hans-Bockler-Strasse 7, 87527, Sonthofen, Germany
Tel.: (49) 8321802824
Mechanical Equipment Mfr
N.A.I.C.S.: 333613
Thomas Bein Sr. *(Mgr-Matl Mgmt)*

Subsidiary (Non-US):

Voith Turbo Colombia S.A.S. (2)
Calle 17 No 69-26 Centro Empresarial Montevideo, 110931, Bogota, Colombia
Tel.: (57) 14117664
Mechanical Equipment Mfr
N.A.I.C.S.: 333613

Branch (Domestic):

Voith Turbo GmbH & Co. KG (2)
Voithstrasse 1, 74564, Crailsheim, Germany (100%)
Tel.: (49) 7951320
Web Site: http://www.voithturbo.com
Sales Range: $350-399.9 Million
Emp.: 1,100
Industrial-Use Mechanical, Hydrodynamic, Electric & Electronic Power Transmission Systems Mfr
N.A.I.C.S.: 333248

Subsidiary (Non-US):

Voith Turbo Guc Aktarma Teknigi Ltd. Sti. (2)
Armada Is Merkezi Eskisehir Yolu No 6 A-Blok Kat 13, Sogutozu, 6520, Ankara, Turkiye
Tel.: (90) 3124950044
Mechanical Equipment Mfr
N.A.I.C.S.: 333613

Subsidiary (Domestic):

Voith Turbo H + L Hydraulic GmbH & Co. KG (2)
Schuckertstr 15, 71277, Ruteshiem, Germany
Tel.: (49) 7152 992 3
Mechanical Equipment Mfr
N.A.I.C.S.: 333613

Subsidiary (US):

Voith Turbo Inc. (2)
11221 Cutten Rd Bldg 6, Houston, TX 77066
Tel.: (281) 453-5500
Electric Power Transmission & Control Services
N.A.I.C.S.: 221121

Subsidiary (Non-US):

Voith Turbo Kft. (2)
Felveg ut 4, 2051, Biatorbagy, Hungary
Tel.: (36) 23 312 431
Mechanical Equipment Mfr
N.A.I.C.S.: 333613

Voith Turbo Limited (2)
908 Guardforce Centre 3 Hok Yuen Street East, HungHom, Kowloon, China (Hong Kong)
Tel.: (852) 2774 4083
Emp.: 15
Mechanical Equipment Mfr
N.A.I.C.S.: 333613
Hu Jinting *(Mgr-Acctg)*

Voith Turbo Limited (2)
6 Beddington Farm Road, Croydon, CR0 4XB, United Kingdom
Tel.: (44) 2086670333
Web Site: http://www.uk.voithturbo.com
Emp.: 155
Mechanical Equipment Mfr
N.A.I.C.S.: 333613

Subsidiary (Domestic):

Voith Turbo Lokomotivtechnik, eine Zweigniederlassung der Voith Turbo GmbH & Co. KG (2)
Uferstrasse 80, 24106, Kiel, Germany
Tel.: (49) 431 259 59 0
Mechanical Equipment Mfr
N.A.I.C.S.: 333613

Subsidiary (Non-US):

Voith Turbo Ltd. (2)
Degtyarivska Str 25 of 23 Building 1, 04119, Kiev, Ukraine
Tel.: (380) 44 489 4621
Mechanical Equipment Mfr
N.A.I.C.S.: 333613

Voith Turbo NZ Pty Limited (2)
Suite 31060 Cook street, 1010, Auckland, New Zealand
Tel.: (64) 93589078
Mechanical Equipment Mfr
N.A.I.C.S.: 333613

Voith Turbo OOO (2)
Michail Mil Str 33, 420127, Kazan, Russia
Tel.: (7) 8435620126
Mechanical Equipment Mfr
N.A.I.C.S.: 333613
Lilia Bilalowa *(CEO)*

Voith Turbo Power Transmission (Shanghai) Co., Ltd. (2)
No 36-A Workshop No 73 Gangyuan Road, 30008, Taiyuan, Shanxi, China
Tel.: (86) 351 756 2567
Mechanical Equipment Mfr
N.A.I.C.S.: 333613

Voith Turbo Private Ltd. (2)
PO Industrial Estate Nacharam, Hyderabad, 500 076, AP, India (100%)
Tel.: (91) 4027173561
Web Site: http://www.voithindia.com
Sales Range: $25-49.9 Million
Emp.: 200
Mfr of Paper Machines
N.A.I.C.S.: 333243

Voith Turbo Pte. Ltd. (2)
10 Jalan Lam Huat Voith Building, Singapore, 737923, Singapore
Tel.: (65) 6861 5100
Mechanical Equipment Mfr
N.A.I.C.S.: 333613

Voith Turbo Pty. Ltd. (2)
Building 2 1-47 Percival Road, Smithfield, 2164, NSW, Australia
Tel.: (61) 2 9609 9400
Mechanical Equipment Mfr
N.A.I.C.S.: 333613
David Banks *(Mgr-Application Engrg)*

Voith Turbo S.A. (2)
Largo da Lagoa 15J R / C Dto, 2795-116, Linda-a-Velha, Portugal
Tel.: (351) 214 155 950
Mechanical Equipment Mfr
N.A.I.C.S.: 333613

Voith Turbo S.A. (2)
Av Eduardo Frei Montalva 6115, Conchali, 8550189, Santiago, Chile
Tel.: (56) 2 944 6900
Mechanical Equipment Mfr
N.A.I.C.S.: 333613

Voith Turbo S.A. (2)
Avenida de Suiza 3 - P A L, 28821, Coslada, Spain
Tel.: (34) 916707800
Mechanical Equipment Mfr
N.A.I.C.S.: 333613

Voith Turbo S.A./N.V. (2)
Square Louisa 36, 1150, Brussels, Belgium
Tel.: (32) 2 76 26 100
Emp.: 8
Mechanical Equipment Mfr
N.A.I.C.S.: 333613
Bart Vanhaverbeke *(Gen Mgr)*

Voith Turbo S.A.C. (2)
Av Argentina 2415, Lima, Peru
Tel.: (51) 16523014
Mechanical Equipment Mfr
N.A.I.C.S.: 333613

Voith Turbo S.R.L. (2)
Via G Lambrakis 2, 42122, Reggio Emilia, Italy
Tel.: (39) 0522 356711
Web Site: http://voith.com
Electric Power Transmission & Control Services
N.A.I.C.S.: 221121

Voith Turbo SAS (2)
21-27 Bd du Champy Richardets, 93166, Noisy-le-grand, France
Tel.: (33) 1 48 15 69 00

VOJVODINA SPORT A.D.

Emp.: 70
Mechanical Equipment Mfr
N.A.I.C.S.: 333613
Thierry Constantin *(Mng Dir)*

Subsidiary (Domestic):

Voith Turbo SMI Technologies GmbH & Co. KG (2)
Alexanderstrasse 2, 89522, Heidenheim, Germany
Tel.: (49) 7321370
Mechanical Equipment Mfr
N.A.I.C.S.: 333613

Subsidiary (Non-US):

Voith Turbo Safeset AB (2)
Ronningevagen 8, 82434, Hudiksvall, Sweden
Tel.: (46) 650540150
Emp.: 70
Mechanical Equipment Mfr
N.A.I.C.S.: 333613
Bernd Hartkorn *(Gen Mgr)*

Subsidiary (Domestic):

Voith Turbo Scharfenberg GmbH & Co. KG (2)
Gottfried-Linke-Strasse 205, 38239, Salzgitter, Germany
Tel.: (49) 53412102
Mechanical Equipment Mfr
N.A.I.C.S.: 333613

Subsidiary (Non-US):

Voith Turbo Vertriebs GmbH & Co KG (2)
Lohnergasse 3a, 1210, Wiener Neudorf, Austria
Tel.: (43) 27428060
Mechanical Equipment Distr
N.A.I.C.S.: 423840

Voith Turbo d.o.o. (2)
Grebenscica 11, 10000, Zagreb, Croatia
Tel.: (385) 995544344
Mechanical Equipment Mfr
N.A.I.C.S.: 333613

Voith Turbo sp. z o.o. (2)
Majkow Duzy 74, 97-371, Lodz, Poland
Tel.: (48) 44 646 88 48
Geotechnical Engineering Services
N.A.I.C.S.: 541330

VOJVODINA A.D.
Svetog Save 1, Srbobran, Serbia
Tel.: (381) 21730172
Year Founded: 1954
VJSR—(BEL)
Sales Range: Less than $1 Million
Emp.: 1
Retail Store Operator
N.A.I.C.S.: 445110
Zoran Tomovic *(Exec Dir)*

VOJVODINA A.D.
Temerinski put 6, Novi Sad, Serbia
Tel.: (381) 21 6411 300
Year Founded: 1966
Sales Range: $1-9.9 Million
Emp.: 31
Building Construction Services
N.A.I.C.S.: 236115
Zoran Drakulic *(Exec Dir)*

VOJVODINA A.D.
Trg slobode 2, 21101, Novi Sad, Serbia
Tel.: (381) 216622122
Web Site:
 https://www.hotelvojvodina.rs
Year Founded: 1854
VJDN—(BEL)
Sales Range: $1-9.9 Million
Emp.: 55
Home Management Services
N.A.I.C.S.: 721110
Dragoljub Vasic *(Dir)*

VOJVODINA SPORT A.D.

VOJVODINA SPORT A.D.

Vojvodina sport a.d.—(Continued)
Nikolajevska 2, Novi Sad, Serbia
Tel.: (381) 21 527 866
Year Founded: 2003
VOSP—(BEL)
Sales Range: $1-9.9 Million
Emp.: 49
Retail Store Operator
N.A.I.C.S.: 459999
Vojvodic Dragisa (Exec Dir)

VOJVODINA TEHNOPROMET A.D.
Trg Cire Milekica 18, Sremska Mitrovica, Serbia
Tel.: (381) 22 621 165
Sales Range: Less than $1 Million
Hardware Product Retailer
N.A.I.C.S.: 444140
Slavica Donlic (Exec Dir)

VOJVODINAPUT A.D.
Dure Dakovica 10, 24000, Subotica, Serbia
Tel.: (381) 24 554 900
Web Site: http://www.vojput.com
Year Founded: 1998
Sales Range: $10-24.9 Million
Emp.: 250
Road Construction Services
N.A.I.C.S.: 237310

VOJVODINASPED A.D.
Industrijska bb, 21000, Novi Sad, Serbia
Tel.: (381) 21 443 965
Web Site: http://www.vojvodinasped.co.rs
Year Founded: 1945
VJSP—(BEL)
Sales Range: Less than $1 Million
Emp.: 18
Transportation Support Services
N.A.I.C.S.: 488999
Svetlana Berisavljevic (Gen Mgr)

VOK BEVERAGES PTY. LTD.
162 Cross Keys Rd, Salisbury, 5106, SA, Australia
Tel.: (61) 881821890
Web Site: http://www.vok.com.au
Sales Range: $25-49.9 Million
Emp.: 40
Beverage Mfr & Distr
N.A.I.C.S.: 312140
Angelo Kotses (Mng Dir)

VOLAC INTERNATIONAL LIMITED
Orwell, Royston, SG8 5QX, Hertfordshire, United Kingdom
Tel.: (44) 1223 208021
Web Site: http://www.volac.com
Year Founded: 1970
Sales Range: $150-199.9 Million
Emp.: 241
Nutrition Product Whslr
N.A.I.C.S.: 456191
Paul Frampton (CFO)

Subsidiaries:

Ecosyl Products Ltd (1)
Roseberry Court Ellerbeck Way, Stokesley, TS9 5QT, United Kingdom
Tel.: (44) 1642 718800
Feed Additive Mfr & Distr
N.A.I.C.S.: 325998

Volac Agro-Best spol. s r.o. (1)
Bestovice 115, 565 01, Chocen, Czech Republic
Tel.: (420) 465471763
Web Site: http://www.agrobest.cz
Dairy Products Mfr
N.A.I.C.S.: 112120

Volac Ireland Ltd (1)
Volac House Church Street, Killeshandra, Cavan, Ireland
Tel.: (353) 494334755
Web Site: http://www.volac.ie
Dairy Products Mfr
N.A.I.C.S.: 112120
Una Hickey (Sls Mgr-Natl)

Volac Socoor S.r.l. (1)
Via Mauro Macchi 65, 20124, Milan, Italy
Tel.: (39) 026701043
Web Site: http://www.volac.it
Dairy Products Mfr
N.A.I.C.S.: 112120

VOLANT TEXTILE MILLS LIMITED
Shreeniwas House Ground Floor H Somani Marg, Mumbai, 400 001, India
Tel.: (91) 22 4002 3270
Web Site: http://www.volant-textile.com
Year Founded: 1932
Sales Range: $1-9.9 Million
Textile Products Mfr
N.A.I.C.S.: 314999

VOLATI AB
Engelbrektsplan 1, 114 34, Stockholm, Sweden
Tel.: (46) 8216840   SE
Web Site: https://www.volati.se
Year Founded: 2003
VOLO—(OMX)
Rev.: $725,973,381
Assets: $626,223,459
Liabilities: $426,161,642
Net Worth: $200,061,817
Earnings: $40,555,602
Emp.: 1,892
Fiscal Year-end: 12/31/22
Industrial Investment Holding Company
N.A.I.C.S.: 551112
Patrik Wahlen (Co-Founder & Chm)

Subsidiaries:

Akademibokhandelsgruppen AB (1)
Lindhagensgatan 74, 11218, Stockholm, Sweden   (100%)
Tel.: (46) 10 744 1000
Web Site: https://www.akademibokhandeln.se
Book Stores
N.A.I.C.S.: 459210
Anita Jansson (Head-HR)

Beneli AB (1)
Porfyrgatan 5, 254 68, Helsingborg, Sweden
Tel.: (46) 42256000
Web Site: https://beneli.com
Electronic Products Mfr
N.A.I.C.S.: 334419

Besikta Bilprovning i Sverige AB (1)
Kallvattengatan 7, 212 23, Malmo, Sweden
Tel.: (46) 774400800
Web Site: https://www.besikta.se
Car Testing & Inspection Services
N.A.I.C.S.: 811198

Bokhandelsgruppen i Sverige AB (1)
Lindhagensgatan 74 8 tr, PO Box 2100, 103 13, Stockholm, Sweden
Tel.: (46) 107441000
Web Site: http://www.bokhandelsgruppen.se
Book Distr
N.A.I.C.S.: 459210

Bokus AB (1)
Lindhagensgatan 74, 112 18, Stockholm, Sweden
Tel.: (46) 107419800
Web Site: http://www.bokus.com
Book Distr
N.A.I.C.S.: 459210
Maria Edsman (CEO)

Corroventa Avfuktning AB (1)
Mekanikervagen 3, Bankeryd, 564 35, Jonkoping, Sweden   (100%)
Tel.: (46) 3 637 1200
Web Site: https://www.corroventa.se
Sales Range: $25-49.9 Million
Emp.: 44
Drying System Mfr
N.A.I.C.S.: 333414
Per Ekdahl (CEO)

Corroventa Avfuktning Norge AS (1)
Tvetenveien 152, 0671, Oslo, Norway
Tel.: (47) 9 748 4015
Web Site: https://www.corroventa.no
Water Damage Equipment Mfr & Distr
N.A.I.C.S.: 811310
Peter Nilsen (Mgr-Sls)

Corroventa Deshumidification S.A. (1)
Courtaboeuf-Batiment Epicea-E8 10 Avenue du Quebec, 91140, Villebon-sur-Yvette, France
Tel.: (33) 96 710 1991
Web Site: https://www.corroventa.fr
Water Damage Equipment Mfr & Distr
N.A.I.C.S.: 811310

Corroventa Entfeuchtnung GmbH (1)
Wagner-Schonkirch-Gasse Nr 9, 1230, Vienna, Austria
Tel.: (43) 16150090
Water Damage Equipment Mfr & Distr
N.A.I.C.S.: 811310
Christian Baumgartner (Country Mgr)

Corroventa Entfeuchtnung GmbH (1)
Siemensring 86, 47877, Willich, Germany
Tel.: (49) 2154884090
Web Site: http://www.corroventa.de
Water Damage Equipment Mfr & Distr
N.A.I.C.S.: 811310
Richard Zinken (Sls Mgr-Area)

Corroventa Entfeuchtnung GmbH (1)
Siemensring 86, 47877, Willich, Germany
Tel.: (49) 2154884090
Web Site: http://www.corroventa.de
Water Damage Equipment Mfr & Distr
N.A.I.C.S.: 811310
Richard Zinken (Sls Mgr-Area)

Corroventa Entfeuchtnung GmbH (1)
Wagner-Schonkirch-Gasse Nr 9, 1230, Vienna, Austria
Tel.: (43) 16150090
Water Damage Equipment Mfr & Distr
N.A.I.C.S.: 811310
Christian Baumgartner (Country Mgr)

Corroventa Ltd. (1)
Unit 47 Melford Court Hardwick Grange, Warrington, WA1 4RZ, United Kingdom
Tel.: (44) 161 244 9523
Web Site: https://www.corroventa.com
Water Damage Equipment Mfr & Distr
N.A.I.C.S.: 811310
Neale Vickery (Mgr-Natl)

Corroventa Osuszanie Sp.z.o.o. (1)
ul Rozwojowa 19, 41-103, Siemianowice, Poland
Tel.: (48) 66 217 6670
Web Site: https://www.corroventa.pl
Water Damage Equipment Mfr & Distr
N.A.I.C.S.: 811310
Rafal Mirocha (Country Mgr)

Duschprodukter Sweden AB (1)
Solbrackegatan 41A, 442 45, Kungalv, Sweden
Tel.: (46) 313300010
Web Site: https://dpsgroup.se
Bathroom Product Distr
N.A.I.C.S.: 423220

Duschy Marketing OU (1)
Kadaka tee 3A, Tallinn, Estonia
Tel.: (372) 6550108
Web Site: https://www.duschy.ee
Bathroom Product Distr
N.A.I.C.S.: 423220

Ettikettoprintcom AB (1)
Kantyxegatan 1B, 213 76, Malmo, Sweden
Tel.: (46) 40552700
Web Site: http://www.ettikettoprintcom.com
Self-Adhesive Label Machine Mfr
N.A.I.C.S.: 333993
Rikard Ahlin (CEO)

INTERNATIONAL PUBLIC

Ettikettoprintcom Atvidaberg AB (1)
Spargatan 11, 597 53, Atvidaberg, Sweden
Tel.: (46) 12085300
Self-Adhesive Label Machine Mfr
N.A.I.C.S.: 333993
Bjorn Gustafsson (Mgr-Production)

Habo Danmark A/S (1)
Trigevej 20 Soften, 8382, Hinnerup, Denmark
Tel.: (45) 86741323
Functional Fitting Mfr
N.A.I.C.S.: 332919
Henrik Kragh (Mgr-Sls)

Habo Finland Oy (1)
Sinimentie 10 B, 02630, Espoo, Finland
Tel.: (358) 207415550
Functional Fitting Mfr
N.A.I.C.S.: 332919
Henrik Lindroth (CEO)

Habo Gruppen AB (1)
Sodergatan 2, 566 32, Habo, Sweden
Tel.: (46) 364 8400
Web Site: https://habo.com
Functional Fitting Mfr
N.A.I.C.S.: 332919
Fredrick Sylva (CEO)

Habo Norge AS (1)
Brottemsveien 103, 7093, Tiller, Norway
Tel.: (47) 73956600
Functional Fitting Mfr
N.A.I.C.S.: 332919

Heco Nordiska AB (1)
Rocknevagen 16, 335 73, Hillerstorp, Sweden
Tel.: (46) 370375100
Web Site: https://www.heco.se
Building Materials Distr
N.A.I.C.S.: 423710

Jigraf AB (1)
Pilakersgatan 32, 261 41, Landskrona, Sweden
Tel.: (46) 41858115
Web Site: https://jigraf.se
Label Mfr & Distr
N.A.I.C.S.: 333993

Kellfri AB (1)
Munkatorpsgatan 6, 532 40, Skara, Sweden
Tel.: (46) 5 112 4250
Web Site: https://www.kellfri.se
Farm Product Distr
N.A.I.C.S.: 424590
Carl-Axel Svensson (CEO)

Kellfri ApS (1)
Trigevej 20, Soften, 8382, Hinnerup, Denmark
Tel.: (45) 7 690 2100
Web Site: https://www.kellfri.dk
Farm Product Distr
N.A.I.C.S.: 424590
Carsten Vesthammer (Sls Mgr-Area)

Lantbutiken Sverige AB (1)
Munkatorpsgatan 6, 532 37, Skara, Sweden
Tel.: (46) 511442200
Web Site: http://www.lantbutiken.se
Farm Product Distr
N.A.I.C.S.: 424590

Miljocenter i Malmo AB (1)
Kvalitetsvagen 1, 232 61, Arlov, Sweden
Tel.: (46) 40 668 0850
Web Site: https://www.miljocenter.com
Garden Equipments Distr
N.A.I.C.S.: 444230
Veronica Kajrup (CEO & Dir-Mktg)

NaturaMed Pharma AB (1)
Box 2093, 663 12, Hammaro, Sweden
Tel.: (46) 5 452 2540
Web Site: https://www.naturamed-pharma.se
Dietary Supplements Mfr
N.A.I.C.S.: 325411

Nordskiffer AB (1)
Verkstadsgatan 2b, 263 39, Hoganas, Sweden
Tel.: (46) 4 233 1398
Web Site: https://www.nordskiffer.com
Roofing Slate Distr
N.A.I.C.S.: 423330

OOO Tornum (1)

Rokosovskogo Str 62 of 5-02, 400050, Volgograd, Russia
Tel.: (7) 844299803
Grain Handling Equipment Mfr
N.A.I.C.S.: 333922
Mikhail Makeyev *(Gen Mgr)*

Olmed Ortopediska AB (1)
Jungfrudansen 21-23, 171 51, Solna, Sweden
Tel.: (46) 86192800
Web Site: http://www.olmed.se
Sales Range: $10-24.9 Million
Emp.: 150
Orthopedic Aid Mfr
N.A.I.C.S.: 339112

Oy Kellfri AB (1)
Pieleslehdontie 2, Leppavesi, 41310, Jyvaskyla, Finland
Tel.: (358) 20 722 9130
Web Site: https://www.kellfri.fi
Farm Product Distr
N.A.I.C.S.: 424590

Pharmapolar AS (1)
Pb 1555, 3007, Drammen, Norway
Tel.: (47) 3 100 4750
Web Site: https://www.ppinfo.no
Dietary Supplements Mfr
N.A.I.C.S.: 325411

Ragnar Sandberg & Soner AB (1)
Farborgvei 4, Fagersta, 737 30, Sweden (100%)
Tel.: (46) 22319090
Web Site: http://www.sandberg-soner.com
Component Mfr
N.A.I.C.S.: 332999

Salix Business Partner AB (1)
28 Bjurogatan, Skane Lan, 211 24, Malmo, Sweden
Tel.: (46) 40386000
Web Site:
https://www.salixbusinesspartner.se
Warehouse Logistics Services
N.A.I.C.S.: 493110

Subsidiary (Non-US):

Timberman Denmark A/S (2)
Havnevej 11, 9560, Hadsund, Denmark
Tel.: (45) 99525252
Web Site: https://www.timberman.dk
Wood Products Mfr
N.A.I.C.S.: 321999

Silokonsult Processteknik Sweden AB (1)
Skaragatan 13, 535 30, Kvanum, Sweden
Tel.: (46) 5 111 0365
Web Site: https://www.silokonsult.se
Grain Handling Equipment Distr
N.A.I.C.S.: 423830

Stenentreprenader i Hessleholm AB (1)
Helsingborgsvagen 8, 281 49, Hassleholm, Sweden
Tel.: (46) 45145770
Web Site: https://www.stenentreprenader.se
Construction Materials Distr
N.A.I.C.S.: 423390

Stenteknik i Karlstad AB (1)
Arstidsvagen 1, 665 33, Kil, Sweden
Tel.: (46) 5 541 0060
Web Site: https://www.sten-teknik.se
Dietary Supplements Mfr
N.A.I.C.S.: 325411

Swekip Sweden AB (1)
Kronoskogsvagen 8, 903 61, Umea, Sweden
Tel.: (46) 90777100
Web Site: https://www.swekip.com
Construction Equipment Distr
N.A.I.C.S.: 423810

T-Emballage Forpackning AB (1)
Nydalavagen 14, 574 35, Vetlanda, Sweden
Tel.: (46) 38359900
Web Site: https://www.t-emballage.se
Packaging Product Distr
N.A.I.C.S.: 424130

T-Emballage Thureson Aktiebolag (1)
Nydalavagen 14, 574 35, Vetlanda, Sweden
Tel.: (46) 38359900

Web Site: http://www.t-emballage.se
Sawmill Product Mfr & Distr
N.A.I.C.S.: 333243

TECCA AB (1)
Nydalavagen 14, 574 35, Vetlanda, Sweden
Tel.: (46) 38359900
Web Site: https://www.teccaworld.com
Construction Materials Distr
N.A.I.C.S.: 423390

Thomee Gruppen AB (1)
Bjurogatan 28, PO Box 50304, SE-202 13, Malmo, Sweden
Tel.: (46) 40386000
Web Site: https://www.thomee.se
Building Materials Distr
N.A.I.C.S.: 444180
Roger Andersson *(CEO)*

Tornum AB (1)
Skaragatan 13, SE-535 30, Kvanum, Sweden (100%)
Tel.: (46) 51229100
Web Site: https://www.tornum.com
Sales Range: $25-49.9 Million
Emp.: 65
Grain Equipment Supplier
N.A.I.C.S.: 333111

Tornum Asia Co., Ltd. (1)
48/72 Premium Place 8 Soi Sukonthasawat 38 Kwang Lad Prao, Khet Lad Prao, Bangkok, 10230, Thailand
Tel.: (66) 215027978
Grain Handling Equipment Mfr
N.A.I.C.S.: 333922
Narongsak Tabyam *(Area Mgr)*

Tornum Kft. (1)
Csapo utca 40, 4029, Debrecen, Hungary
Tel.: (36) 308241024
Grain Handling Equipment Mfr
N.A.I.C.S.: 333922
Balogh Laszlo *(Gen Mgr)*

Tornum LLC (1)
Nazarivska str 11 office 39, 01032, Kiev, Ukraine
Tel.: (380) 674431602
Grain Handling Equipment Mfr
N.A.I.C.S.: 333922
Oleksandr Kholod *(Gen Mgr)*

Tornum Polska Sp. z.o.o. (1)
Ul Skleczkowska 16, 99 300, Kutno, Poland
Tel.: (48) 242546520
Grain Handling Equipment Mfr
N.A.I.C.S.: 333922
Slawomir Kaca *(Gen Mgr)*

Tornum S.R.L. (1)
Str Alexandru Constantinescu Nr 38 Parter Apt 1 Sector 1, 011474, Bucharest, Romania
Tel.: (40) 314251542
Grain Handling Equipment Mfr
N.A.I.C.S.: 333922
Viorel Vecerdea *(Gen Mgr)*

Vaggmaterial Sverige AB (1)
Energigatan 11, 434 37, Kungsbacka, Sweden
Tel.: (46) 300563888
Web Site: https://www.vaggmaterial.se
Construction Engineering Services
N.A.I.C.S.: 541330

Ventotech AB (1)
Mekanikervagen 3, 564 35, Bankeryd, Sweden
Tel.: (46) 317804151
Web Site: https://www.corroventa.se
Water Damage Equipment Mfr & Distr
N.A.I.C.S.: 811310
Karl Jansson *(Mgr-Sls)*

Vinninga Cementvarufabrik AB (1)
Konvaljevagen 4, Box 3041, Vinninga, 531 03, Lidkoping, Sweden
Tel.: (46) 5 105 0500
Web Site: https://www.vinningacement.se
Emp.: 50
Lightweight Clinker Block Mfr
N.A.I.C.S.: 327331

VOLATUS CAPITAL CORP.
3043 - 595 Burrard Street, Vancouver, V7X 1J1, BC, Canada
Tel.: (778) 819-2710

Web Site:
https://volatuscapitalcorp.com
VC—(CNSX)
Rev.: $2,611
Assets: $139,653
Liabilities: $992,202
Net Worth: ($852,549)
Earnings: ($8,194,842)
Fiscal Year-end: 01/31/24
Mineral Exploration Services
N.A.I.C.S.: 213115
Fred Tejada *(CEO)*

VOLCAN HOLDINGS, INC.
Level 34, 50 Bridge Street, Sydney, 2000, NSW, Australia
Tel.: (61) 282160777 NV
Year Founded: 2006
VOHO—(OTCIQ)
Sales Range: Less than $1 Million
Bauxite Exploration & Mining Services
N.A.I.C.S.: 212290
Pnina Feldman *(Chm & Pres)*

VOLCANIC GOLD MINES INC.
200 Burrard Street Suite 650, Vancouver, V6C 3L6, BC, Canada
Tel.: (604) 801-5432 BC
Web Site: https://www.volgold.com
Year Founded: 2007
CKC2—(BER)
Rev.: $69,958
Assets: $4,391,482
Liabilities: $196,089
Net Worth: $4,195,393
Earnings: ($1,962,513)
Fiscal Year-end: 12/31/22
Mineral Exploration Services
N.A.I.C.S.: 213114
Simon Ridgway *(Founder)*

VOLCANO SPRING INTERNATIONAL HOLDINGS LIMITED
Bldg 33585 Sanlu Rd Pujiang Hi-tech Industrial Zone, Caohejing Hi-Tech Park, Shanghai, 201114, China
Tel.: (86) 2151692010 Ky
Web Site:
http://www.mijiholdings.com
1715—(HKG)
Rev.: $12,381,314
Assets: $27,210,082
Liabilities: $15,991,279
Net Worth: $11,218,802
Earnings: ($6,114,420)
Emp.: 173
Fiscal Year-end: 12/31/22
Kitchen Appliance Mfr & Distr
N.A.I.C.S.: 332215
Can Yue Maeck *(Founder, Chm & CEO)*

VOLEX PLC
Unit C1 Antura Bond Close, Richmond, Basingstoke, RG24 8PZ, United Kingdom
Tel.: (44) 1256442570 UK
Web Site: https://www.volex.com
Year Founded: 1919
VLX—(LSE)
Rev.: $614,600,000
Assets: $503,300,000
Liabilities: $294,800,000
Net Worth: $208,500,000
Earnings: $30,400,000
Emp.: 7,800
Fiscal Year-end: 04/03/22
Electrical & Electronic Cable Equipment Mfr
N.A.I.C.S.: 335999
Jon Boaden *(CFO)*

Subsidiaries:

De-Ka Elektroteknik Sanayi ve Ticaret Anonim Sirketi (1)

Akse Mah Fevzi Cakmak Cad No 140, Cayirova, 41420, Kocaeli, Turkiye
Tel.: (90) 262 743 6060
Web Site: https://www.de-ka.com
Plug Mfr
N.A.I.C.S.: 334417

G.T.K. (U.K.) Ltd. (1)
Antura Unit C2 Bond Close, Hampshire, Basingstoke, RG24 8PZ, United Kingdom
Tel.: (44) 125 647 2000
Web Site: https://www.gtk.co.uk
Electronics Solution Product Mfr
N.A.I.C.S.: 334419

GTK Electronics GmbH (1)
Romberg 25b, 51381, Leverkusen, Germany
Tel.: (49) 899 611 8390
Electronics Solution Product Mfr
N.A.I.C.S.: 334419

MC Electronics LLC (1)
9571 Pan American Dr, El Paso, TX 79927
Tel.: (831) 637-1651
Web Site: https://www.mcelectronics.com
Electronic Products Mfr
N.A.I.C.S.: 334417

PT Volex Indonesia (1)
Jalan Ir Sutami Kawasan Industri Sekupang, Batam, 29422, Riau Islands, Indonesia
Tel.: (62) 778321821
Web Site: http://www.volex.com
Cable Assemblies Mfr
N.A.I.C.S.: 333248

Silcotec Europe (SK) s.r.o. (1)
Druzstevna 14, 945 05, Komarno, Slovakia
Tel.: (421) 35 790 1911
Electronic Cable Mfr
N.A.I.C.S.: 335921

Silcotec Europe Ltd. (1)
Carraroe Industrial Estate, Carraroe, Galway, Ireland
Tel.: (353) 9 159 5108
Electro Mechanical Product Mfr
N.A.I.C.S.: 334418

Volex (Asia) Pte Ltd (1)
35 Tampines Street 92, Singapore, 528880, Singapore
Tel.: (65) 67887833
Sales Range: $50-74.9 Million
Emp.: 70
Electrical & Fibre Optic Cable Assemblies Distr
N.A.I.C.S.: 423610
Kenny Quah *(Dir-Sls)*

Subsidiary (Non-US):

Volex Cable Assembly (Vietnam) Pte Ltd (2)
Plot D-5B Thanglong Industrial Park, Dong Anh District, Hanoi, Vietnam
Tel.: (84) 4 3881 1493
Sales Range: $125-149.9 Million
Electrical & Fibre Optic Cable Assemblies Distr
N.A.I.C.S.: 423610

Volex (Taiwan) Co, Ltd (1)
11F-2 No 6 Sec 2 Dasing W Road Taoyuan Hsien 330, Taoyuan, Taiwan
Tel.: (886) 33012590
Electrical & Fibre Optic Cable Assemblies Distr
N.A.I.C.S.: 423610

Volex (Thailand) Co. Ltd. (1)
99/349 Moo 2 Chaengwattana Road Tungsong-hong, Laksi, Bangkok, 10210, Thailand
Tel.: (66) 25761861
Web Site: http://www.volex.com
Sales Range: $50-74.9 Million
Emp.: 3
Electrical & Fibre Optic Cable Assemblies Distr
N.A.I.C.S.: 423610

Volex Cable Assemblies (Phils) Inc. (1)
Unit 1 Lot 10 Phase 4 East Science Ave corner Trade Ave, Binan, 4024, Laguna, Philippines
Tel.: (63) 495411195
Web Site: http://www.volex.com

VOLEX PLC

Volex plc—(Continued)
Sales Range: $50-74.9 Million
Emp.: 2
Electrical & Fibre Optic Cable Assemblies Distr
N.A.I.C.S.: 423610

Volex Cable Assemblies Sdn Bhd (1)
Lot 3 Jalan Keluli 15/16, Shah Alam, 40000, Selangor, Malaysia
Tel.: (60) 355123233
Web Site: http://www.volex.com
Electrical & Fibre Optic Cable Assemblies Distr
N.A.I.C.S.: 423610

Volex Cable Assembly (Shenzhen) Co. Ltd. (1)
1173 Shenhui Road Henggang, Volex Building Baoan, Shenzhen, 518115, Guangdong, China
Tel.: (86) 75528687020
Web Site: http://www.volex.com
Sales Range: $550-599.9 Million
Emp.: 2,000
Electrical & Fibre Optic Cable Assemblies Distr
N.A.I.C.S.: 423610

Volex Cable Assembly (Zhongshan) Co., Ltd. (1)
No 2 Xin Da Bei Rd Zhongshan Torch Hi-Tech Industry Dev Zone, Zhongshan, 528437, Guangdong, China
Tel.: (86) 76085314358
Electrical & Fibre Optic Cable Assemblies Distr
N.A.I.C.S.: 423610

Volex Cables (HK) Ltd. (1)
Flat D 15th Fl Kee Shing Ctr 74-76 Kimberley Rd, Tsim Tsa Tsui, Kowloon, China (Hong Kong)
Tel.: (852) 26936961
Sales Range: $25-49.9 Million
Emp.: 4
Powercords Mfr
N.A.I.C.S.: 335929
Marvin Hsiao (Mgr)

Volex Europe Ltd (1)
Breaffy Road, Castlebar, Mayo, Ireland
Tel.: (353) 949023444
Web Site: http://www.volex.com
Sales Range: $50-74.9 Million
Emp.: 9
Electrical & Fibre Optic Cable Assemblies Distr
N.A.I.C.S.: 423610

Volex Interconnect (India) Pvt Ltd (1)
22/1-A First Street Kazura Gardens, Neelankarai, Chennai, 600041, Tamil Nadu, India
Tel.: (91) 4424493338
Sales Range: $100-124.9 Million
Emp.: 500
Electrical & Fibre Optic Cable Assemblies Mfr
N.A.I.C.S.: 335929

Volex Interconnect Systems (Suzhou) Co., Ltd. (1)
Weiting North Industrial Zone Weixin Road Suzhou Industrial Park, Suzhou, 215122, Jiangsu, China
Tel.: (86) 51262586673
Electrical & Fibre Optic Cable Assemblies Distr
N.A.I.C.S.: 423610

Volex Japan Co., Ltd. (1)
801 Sakai Suji Yamachu Building 1-22-23 Shimanouchi, Chuo-ku, Osaka, 542-0082, Japan
Tel.: (81) 6 6281 8873
Web Site: http://www.volex.com
Electrical & Fibre Optic Cable Assemblies Distr
N.A.I.C.S.: 423610

Volex Poland Sp. z.o.o. (1)
Ul Podluzna 11-13, 85 790, Bydgoszcz, Poland
Tel.: (48) 523274600
Wires & Cables Mfr
N.A.I.C.S.: 335929

Jan Makufak (Gen Mgr)

Volex do Brasil Ltda. (1)
Rua Waldomiro Anselmo 139 Jardim Marcondes, 12305-090, Jacarei, Sao Paulo, Brazil
Tel.: (55) 1221283000
Web Site: http://www.volex.com
Electrical & Fibre Optic Cable Assemblies Distr
N.A.I.C.S.: 423510

VOLGA GAS PLC
6th Floor 65 Gresham Street, London, EC2V 7QH, United Kingdom
Tel.: (44) 20 8622 4451
Web Site: http://www.volgagas.com
Rev: $45,875,000
Assets: $67,722,000
Liabilities: $10,096,000
Net Worth: $57,626,000
Earnings: $8,404,000
Emp.: 220
Fiscal Year-end: 12/31/18
Oil & Gas Exploration
N.A.I.C.S.: 213112
Mikhail Ivanov (Co-CEO)

Subsidiaries:

LLC Gaznefteservice (1)
15 1st Krasnogvardeyyskiy Proyezd, 123100, Moscow, Russia
Tel.: (7) 4993989761
Web Site: http://www.gaznefteservis.com
Crude Oil & Gas Mfr
N.A.I.C.S.: 324110
Ivanov David Valentinovich (Mng Dir)

VOLGA-DNEPR GROUP
Mezhdunarodnoye Shosse Skypoint Business Park 28B Bld, 141411, Moscow, Russia
Tel.: (7) 4957556850
Web Site: http://www.volga-dnepr.com
Year Founded: 1990
Sales Range: $1-4.9 Billion
Emp.: 1,600
Air Cargo Charter & Scheduled Services
N.A.I.C.S.: 481112
Alexey Isaikin (Pres)

Subsidiaries:

Volga-Dnepr Airlines LLC (1)
14 Karbysheva Str, Ulyanovsk, 432072, Russia
Tel.: (7) 8422 590059
Freight Forwarding Services
N.A.I.C.S.: 481212
Konstantin Vekshin (Exec VP-Charter Cargo Ops-London)

Volga-Dnepr China (1)
2006 Air China Building 36 Xiaoyun road, Chaoyang, Beijing, 100027, China
Tel.: (86) 10 8447 5502
Logistics Consulting Services
N.A.I.C.S.: 541614

Volga-Dnepr Japan (1)
Onarimon Yusen Building 9F 3-23-5 Nihi-Shimbashi, Minato-ku, Tokyo, 105-0003, Japan
Tel.: (81) 3 3578 3320
Logistics Consulting Services
N.A.I.C.S.: 541614

Volga-Dnepr Technics (1)
8 Aviatsionnaya str, Khimki, 141400, Russia
Tel.: (7) 495 737 73 39
Web Site: http://www.vd-technics.com
Airport Support Services
N.A.I.C.S.: 488190
Alexey Zimin (Dir-Bus Dev)

Subsidiary (Non-US):

Volga-Dnepr Technics (FZC) (2)
Sharjah Airport International Free Zone, PO Box 8353, Sharjah, United Arab Emirates
Tel.: (971) 6 557 01 27
Airport Support Services
N.A.I.C.S.: 488190

Volga-Dnepr Technics GmbH (2)
Towerstr 1, 04435, Schkeuditz, Germany
Tel.: (49) 34204 70 44 210
Airport Support Services
N.A.I.C.S.: 488190

Volga-Dnepr UK Ltd. (1)
Endeavour House Coopers End Road London-Stansted Airport, Stansted, CM24 1AL, Essex, United Kingdom
Tel.: (44) 1279 661166
Web Site: http://www.volga-dnepr.com
Logistics Consulting Services
N.A.I.C.S.: 541614
Tony Bauckham (Comml Dir-Charter Sls Ops-Global)

Volga-Dnepr Unique Air Cargo Inc. (1)
Town Ctr Plz 9400 Grogans Mill Rd Ste 220, The Woodlands, TX 77380
Tel.: (832) 585-8611
Emp.: 25
Logistics Consulting Services
N.A.I.C.S.: 541614
Alexey Isaykin (Pres & CEO)

VOLIA
27 Raduzhnaya St, Kiev, Ukraine
Tel.: (380) 445022220
Web Site: http://www.volia.com
Sales Range: $650-699.9 Million
Emp.: 3,000
Telecommunication Servicesb
N.A.I.C.S.: 517810
Alina Sigda (Head-Pub Rel)

VOLKSBANK VORARLBERG E GEN
Ringstrasse 27, 6830, Rankweil, Austria
Tel.: (43) 508828000
Web Site: http://www.volksbank-vorarlberg.at
VVPS—(VIE)
Sales Range: Less than $1 Million
Commercial Banking Services
N.A.I.C.S.: 522110
Gerhard Hamel (Chm-Mgmt Bd)

VOLKSVERMOGEN NV
Ravensteinstraat 2 bus 5, 9000, Gent, Belgium
Tel.: (32) 92660610
Web Site: http://www.volksvermogen.be
Year Founded: 1930
Rev.: $3,752,465
Assets: $61,225,715
Liabilities: $2,425,845
Net Worth: $58,799,870
Earnings: $2,582,898
Fiscal Year-end: 12/31/19
Investment Management Service
N.A.I.C.S.: 523940
Johan De Schamphelaere (Chm)

VOLLMER WERKE MASCHINENFABRIK GMBH
Ehinger Strasse 34, Biberach an der Riss, 88400, Germany
Tel.: (49) 73515710
Web Site: http://www.vollmer.com
Year Founded: 1909
Rev.: $100,000,000
Emp.: 600
Machines & Systems for Processing Tools & Saw Blades for Woodworking & Metalworking Industries Mfr
N.A.I.C.S.: 333517
Marten Kaeser (Mgr-Sls)

Subsidiaries:

T.A. Vollmer Espana S.L. (1)
C Miquel Servet 5 Pol Ind Sesrovires, Sant Esteves Sesrovires, 08635, Barcelona, Spain
Tel.: (34) 937714570
Web Site: http://www.vollmer-es.com

INTERNATIONAL PUBLIC

Sales Range: $50-74.9 Million
Emp.: 10
Machines & Systems for Processing Tools & Sawblades for Woodworking & Metalworking Industries Mfr
N.A.I.C.S.: 333517

VOLLMER AUSTRIA GmbH (1)
Aredstrasse 29, 2544, Leobersdorf, Austria
Tel.: (43) 2256 63058 0
Saw Blade & Handtool Distr
N.A.I.C.S.: 423830

VOLLMER FRANCE S.A.R.L (1)
23 Boulevard de Preval Z I, 22100, Dinan, France
Tel.: (33) 296 390904
Saw Blade & Handtool Distr
N.A.I.C.S.: 423830

VOLLMER Polska sp.z o.o (1)
Ul Nalkowskiej 11, 41-922, Radzionkow, Poland
Tel.: (48) 32 733 08 69
Web Site: http://www.vollmer-pl.com
Emp.: 8
Saw Blade & Handtool Distr
N.A.I.C.S.: 423830
Marcin Kurcon (CEO)

VOLLMER Scandinavia AB (1)
Vastra Esplanaden 9A, 35231, Vaxjo, Sweden
Tel.: (46) 76 1302040
Saw Blade & Handtool Distr
N.A.I.C.S.: 423830

Vollmer Do Brasil Industria de Maquinas Ltda. (1)
Rua Pe Estanislau, Trzebiatowski 69, Alto Boquerao, 81750 390, Curitiba, Brazil
Tel.: (55) 41 3286 2321
Web Site: http://www.vollmer-es.com
Machines & Systems for Processing Sawblades & Tools for Woodworking & Metalworking Industries Mfr
N.A.I.C.S.: 333515

Vollmer Italia Srl (1)
Via Meucci, Caldiero, 37042, Verona, Italy
Tel.: (39) 0457651260
Web Site: http://www.vollmer-group.com
Sales Range: $25-49.9 Million
Emp.: 10
Sharpening Tool & Machine for Woodworking & Metalworking Industry Mfr
N.A.I.C.S.: 333515

Vollmer Japan Corp. (1)
1 1199 Mihashi, Saitama Prefecture, Saitama, 338001, Japan
Tel.: (81) 486406363
Sales Range: $25-49.9 Million
Emp.: 12
Machines for Sharpening Wood & Metal Cutting Tools Mfr
N.A.I.C.S.: 333515
Daichi Hatakeyama (CEO)

Vollmer Taicang Co. Ltd. (1)
299 Liuzhou Road, 12 chaoyimg, Taicang, 215400, Jiangsu, China
Tel.: (86) 51253572870
Web Site: http://www.vollmer.de
Sales Range: $25-49.9 Million
Emp.: 40
Machines for Sharpening Wood & Metal Cutting Tools Mfr
N.A.I.C.S.: 333515
Johnny Yang (Gen Mgr)

Vollmer Technique D'Affutage S.A.R.L. (1)
14 rue de Roussillion, BP 40, 91223, Bretigny-sur-Orge, Cedex, France
Tel.: (33) 1 60849760
Web Site: http://www.vollmer-fr.com
Sharpening Machines & Tools for Woodworking & Metalworking Industries Mfr
N.A.I.C.S.: 333517

Vollmer Technologies India Private Ltd. (1)
Special Plot No 9 3rd Main 10th Cross 1st Stage, Peenya Industrial Area, Bengaluru, 560 058, Karnataka, India
Tel.: (80) 2839 4477
Emp.: 3
Saw Blade & Handtool Distr
N.A.I.C.S.: 423830

AND PRIVATE COMPANIES

Ravindra Dattatri Shimoga *(Mng Dir)*

Vollmer UK Ltd (1)
Orchard Park Ind Estate, Town St Sandiacre, Nottingham, NG10 5BP, United Kingdom
Tel.: (44) 01159491040
Web Site: http://www.vollmergroup.com
Sales Range: $25-49.9 Million
Emp.: 12
Sharpening Machines for Woodworking & Metalworking Mfr
N.A.I.C.S.: 333515

Vollmer of America Corp. (1)
105 Broadway Ave, Carnegie, PA 15106
Tel.: (412) 278-0655
Web Site: http://www.vollmer-us.com
Sales Range: $25-49.9 Million
Emp.: 25
Machines for Sharpening Wood & Metal Cutting Tools Mfr
N.A.I.C.S.: 333515

VOLPARA HEALTH TECHNOLOGIES LIMITED
Level 14 Simpl House 40 Mercer Street, Wellington Central, Wellington, 6011, New Zealand
Tel.: (64) 4 499 6029
Web Site:
http://www.volparasolutions.com
Year Founded: 2009
VHT—(ASX)
Rev.: $18,775,247
Assets: $58,228,215
Liabilities: $16,606,024
Net Worth: $41,622,191
Earnings: ($11,821,079)
Emp.: 183
Fiscal Year-end: 03/31/22
Medical Imaging Software Development & Distribution Services
N.A.I.C.S.: 513210
Ralph Highnam *(Co-Founder & Grp CEO)*

Subsidiaries:

Volpara Health Limited (1)
Level 14 Simpl House 40 Mercer Street, Wellington, 6011, New Zealand
Tel.: (64) 44996029
Web Site: https://www.volparahealth.com
Diagnostic Imaging Services
N.A.I.C.S.: 621512
Paul Reid *(Chm)*

Volpara Health, Inc. (1)
19000 33rd Ave W Ste 130, Lynnwood, WA 98036-4753
Tel.: (425) 563-1700
Web Site: https://www.volparahealth.com
Custom Computer Programming Services
N.A.I.C.S.: 541511

VOLT CARBON TECHNOLOGIES INC.
70 Country Hills Landing NW Suite 117, 888 3rd Street Southwest, Calgary, T3K 2L2, AB, Canada
Tel.: (647) 546-7049 AB
Web Site: https://www.voltcarbontech.com
Year Founded: 2004
TORVF—(OTCQB)
Assets: $3,569,591
Liabilities: $2,094,781
Net Worth: $1,474,811
Earnings: ($1,999,439)
Emp.: 7
Fiscal Year-end: 10/31/22
Mineral Exploration Services
N.A.I.C.S.: 213114
William E. Pfaffenberger *(Chm, Pres & Interim CFO)*

Subsidiaries:

Solid UltraBattery Inc. (1)

VOLT RESOURCES LTD.
Level 25 108 St Georges Terrace, Perth, 6000, WA, Australia
Tel.: (61) 894867788
Web Site:
https://www.voltresources.com
VRC—(ASX)
Rev.: $52,503
Assets: $17,485,116
Liabilities: $4,373,033
Net Worth: $13,112,083
Earnings: ($2,746,013)
Fiscal Year-end: 06/30/24
Graphite Exploration Services
N.A.I.C.S.: 212390
Asimwe Kabunga *(Chm)*

VOLTA ALUMINIUM CO. LTD. (VALCO)
Heavy Industrial Area, PO Box 625, Tema, 23321, Ghana
Tel.: (233) 302208787
Web Site: http://www.valcotema.com
Year Founded: 1964
Sales Range: $75-99.9 Million
Emp.: 300
Primary Aluminum Mfr
N.A.I.C.S.: 331313
Emmanuel Lartey *(Deputy CEO-Docks, Engrg & Maintenance)*

VOLTA FINANCE LIMITED
BNP Paribas House St Julian s Avenue, Saint Peter Port, GY1 1WA, Guernsey
Tel.: (44) 1481750800 GY
Web Site:
https://www.voltafinance.com
Year Founded: 2006
VTAS—(LSE)
Rev.: $36,513,403
Assets: $274,671,033
Liabilities: $19,994,702
Net Worth: $254,676,331
Earnings: $29,110,701
Fiscal Year-end: 07/31/23
Financial Investment Services
N.A.I.C.S.: 523999
Paul Jonathan Meader *(Chm)*

VOLTA METALS LTD.
130 king St West Suite 3680, PO Box 99, Toronto, M5X 1B1, ON, Canada
Tel.: (416) 919-9060 ON
Web Site: https://voltametals.ca
Year Founded: 2014
D0W—(DEU)
Rev.: $4,589
Assets: $913,697
Liabilities: $84,217
Net Worth: $829,479
Earnings: ($2,127,107)
Fiscal Year-end: 12/31/23
Mineral Mining Services
N.A.I.C.S.: 213115
Darren Morgans *(CFO)*

VOLTABOX AG
Technologiepark 32, 33100, Paderborn, Germany
Tel.: (49) 52516939690 De
Web Site: https://www.voltabox.ag
Year Founded: 2014
VBX—(MUN)
Rev.: $11,734,138
Assets: $5,364,808
Liabilities: $7,009,574
Net Worth: ($1,644,766)
Earnings: ($3,565,500)
Emp.: 33
Fiscal Year-end: 12/31/23
Battery Mfr & Distr
N.A.I.C.S.: 335910
Jurgen Pampel *(Chm-Mgmt Bd & CEO)*

Subsidiaries:

Concurrent Design, Inc. (1)
11500 Metric Blvd Ste 190, Austin, TX 78758
Tel.: (512) 219-8501
Engineering Services
N.A.I.C.S.: 541330
Hillman Bailey *(Sr Engr-Project)*

GreenCluster GmbH (1)
Technologiepark 32, 33100, Paderborn, Germany
Tel.: (49) 5251693969200
Web Site: https://www.green-cluster.de
Emp.: 20
Solar Energy Equipment Distr
N.A.I.C.S.: 423720

VOLTAGE INC.
Ebisu Garden Place Tower 28 Fl 4-20-3 Ebisu, Shibuya-ku, Tokyo, Japan
Tel.: (81) 354758141
Web Site: https://www.voltage.co.jp
Year Founded: 1999
3639—(TKS)
Rev.: $21,496,320
Assets: $17,639,920
Liabilities: $4,111,420
Net Worth: $13,528,500
Earnings: $31,100
Emp.: 238
Fiscal Year-end: 06/30/24
Information Retrieval Services
N.A.I.C.S.: 519290
Yuzi Tsutani *(Founder, Chm & Pres)*

Subsidiaries:

Voltage Entertainment USA, Inc. (1)
135 Main St Ste 1850, San Francisco, CA 94105
Tel.: (415) 371-8141
Web Site: http://www.voltage-ent.com
Application Software Development Services
N.A.I.C.S.: 541511
Yuzi Tsutani *(CEO & Chief Creative Officer)*

VOLTAGE METALS CORP.
5000 Yonge St Suite 1901, Toronto, M2N 7E9, ON, Canada
Tel.: (416) 218-2018 BC
Web Site:
https://www.voltagemetals.com
Year Founded: 2019
VOLT—(CNSX)
Assets: $3,414,548
Liabilities: $334,261
Net Worth: $3,080,287
Earnings: ($322,132)
Fiscal Year-end: 12/31/21
Metal Exploration Services
N.A.I.C.S.: 213114
Bob Breese *(CEO)*

VOLTAIRE LEASING & FINANCE LIMITED
206 2nd Floor Lokhandwala Township Akurli Road, Mumbai, 400 101, India
Tel.: (91) 9136082848
Web Site: https://www.volfltd.com
Year Founded: 1984
509038—(BOM)
Rev.: $95,678
Assets: $2,447,455
Liabilities: $93,687
Net Worth: $2,353,768
Earnings: $23,068
Emp.: 9
Fiscal Year-end: 03/31/23
Securities Investment Services
N.A.I.C.S.: 523150
Alok Kumar Behera *(Mng Dir)*

VOLTALIA S.A.
84 bd de Sebastopol, 75003, Paris, France
Tel.: (33) 181703700
Web Site: https://www.voltalia.com
Year Founded: 2004
VLTSA—(EUR)
Rev.: $546,615,521
Assets: $4,214,725,688
Liabilities: $2,687,708,357

VOLTAMP TRANSFORMERS LIMITED

Net Worth: $1,527,017,331
Earnings: $27,713,876
Emp.: 1,180
Fiscal Year-end: 12/31/23
Power Generation Services
N.A.I.C.S.: 221111
Gustavo Fernandes *(Head-Intl Dev)*

Subsidiaries:

Bockingfold Solar Limited (1)
Suite C Old Dutch Barn Westend Office Suites, Stonehouse, United Kingdom
Tel.: (44) 8006990081
Web Site: https://bockingfold-solar.co.uk
Renewable Solar Electricity Mfr
N.A.I.C.S.: 334515

Helexia Solar I S.L. (1)
Calle de la Princesa 25 Edificio Hexagono 3o 3a, 28008, Madrid, Spain
Tel.: (34) 919542730
Web Site: https://www.helexia.es
Solar Energy Distr
N.A.I.C.S.: 423720

Triton Timber S.A.S. (1)
84 boulevard de Sebastopol, 75003, Paris, France
Tel.: (33) 181703700
Web Site: https://tritontimber.com
Wood Product Distr
N.A.I.C.S.: 423310

Voltalia Distribution S.A.S. (1)
1340 rue de Pinville, 34000, Montpellier, France
Tel.: (33) 442535380
Renewable Energy Distr
N.A.I.C.S.: 486210

Voltalia Greece S.A. (1)
Kifissias Avenue 340, Box 65189, Neo Psychiko, 15451, Athens, Greece
Tel.: (30) 2106729523
Web Site: http://www.voltalia.gr
Hydroelectric Power Generation Services
N.A.I.C.S.: 221111

Voltalia Japan KK (1)
E4414 Deux Tours 3-13-1 Harumi, Chuo-ku, Tokyo, Japan
Tel.: (81) 8079442887
Renewable Energy Distr
N.A.I.C.S.: 486210

VOLTAMP ENERGY SAOG
Road No 7 Rusayl Industrial Estate, PO Box 75, 124, Rusayl, Oman
Tel.: (968) 24441200
Web Site:
https://www.voltampoman.com
Year Founded: 1987
VOES—(MUS)
Rev.: $81,684,339
Assets: $117,514,630
Liabilities: $67,126,956
Net Worth: $50,387,674
Earnings: ($1,774,976)
Emp.: 558
Fiscal Year-end: 12/31/21
Electrical Equipment Distr
N.A.I.C.S.: 423610
Sayyid Aymen Hamad Al Busaidi *(Chm)*

VOLTAMP TRANSFORMERS LIMITED
Makarpura, Vadodara, 390 014, Gujarat, India
Tel.: (91) 2652642011 In
Web Site:
https://www.voltamptransformers.com
Year Founded: 1967
VOLTAMP—(BOM)
Rev.: $159,726,704
Assets: $144,858,932
Liabilities: $16,256,017
Net Worth: $128,602,915
Earnings: $18,132,373
Emp.: 328
Fiscal Year-end: 03/31/22
Transformer Mfr

VOLTAMP TRANSFORMERS LIMITED

Voltamp Transformers Limited—(Continued)
N.A.I.C.S.: 334416
Kunjalbhai L. Patel *(Vice Chm & Mng Dir)*

VOLTRANS SA
Str M Kogalniceanu 48, Alba, Sebes, Romania
Tel.: (40) 258 732586
Sales Range: Less than $1 Million
Emp.: 42
Food Transportation Services
N.A.I.C.S.: 484121

VOLTRONIC POWER TECHNOLOGY CORPORATION
No 406 151 Xinhu 1st Road, Neihu District, Taipei, Taiwan
Tel.: (886) 227918296
Web Site: https://www.voltronicpower.com
Year Founded: 2008
6409—(TAI)
Rev.: $619,733,879
Assets: $482,556,606
Liabilities: $209,238,227
Net Worth: $273,318,378
Earnings: $118,465,478
Emp.: 1,862
Fiscal Year-end: 12/31/23
Power Supply Product Mfr
N.A.I.C.S.: 335311
Alex Hsieh *(Chm & Gen Mgr)*

Subsidiaries:
Zhongshan Voltronic Power Electronic Limited (1)
No 8 Shichong Road, Zhongshan Torch Hi-Tech Industrial Development Zone, Zhongshan, Guangdong, China
Tel.: (86) 76088280039
Uninterruptible Power Supply Mfr & Distr
N.A.I.C.S.: 335999

VOLUME LIMITED
Buckhurst Ct London Rd, Wokingham, RG40 1PA, Berkshire, United Kingdom
Tel.: (44) 1189775800
Web Site: http://www.volume.co.uk
Year Founded: 1996
Emp.: 100
N.A.I.C.S.: 541810
Chris Sykes *(CEO)*

VOLUTION GROUP PLC
Fleming Way, Crawley, RH10 9YX, West Sussex, United Kingdom
Tel.: (44) 1293441662 UK
Web Site: https://www.volutiongroupplc.com
Year Founded: 2002
FAN—(LSE)
Rev.: $407,322,818
Assets: $547,199,170
Liabilities: $266,241,920
Net Worth: $280,957,250
Earnings: $46,418,484
Fiscal Year-end: 07/31/23
Construction & Ventilation Material Distr
N.A.I.C.S.: 423390
Ronnie George *(CEO)*

Subsidiaries:
Energy Technique Limited (1)
Fleming Way, Crawley, RH10 9YX, West Sussex, United Kingdom
Tel.: (44) 2087830033
Air Conditioning & Heating Solutions Distr
N.A.I.C.S.: 333413

Torin-Sifan Limited (1)
Greenbridge, Swindon, SN3 3JB, Wiltshire, United Kingdom
Tel.: (44) 1793524291

Sales Range: $50-74.9 Million
Emp.: 200
Fans, Blowers & Ventilation Equipment Mfr
N.A.I.C.S.: 333413

Vent-Axia Ltd. (1)
Fleming Way, Crawley, RH10 9YX, West Sussex, United Kingdom
Tel.: (44) 3448560590
Heating, Ventilation & Air Conditioning Equipment Mfr
N.A.I.C.S.: 333413

VOLVERE PLC
Shire House Tachbrook Road, Leamington Spa, CV31 3SF, United Kingdom
Tel.: (44) 2076349700 UK
Web Site: https://www.volvere.co.uk
VLE—(AIM)
Rev.: $54,678,356
Assets: $57,810,109
Liabilities: $10,057,253
Net Worth: $47,752,856
Earnings: $3,195,406
Fiscal Year-end: 12/31/23
Management Services
N.A.I.C.S.: 541611
Nicholas Lander *(Co-CFO & Co-COO)*

Subsidiaries:
Naughty Vegan Limited (1)
Shire House Tachbrook Road, Leamington Spa, Warwickshire, United Kingdom
Tel.: (44) 1926355446
Web Site: https://naughty-vegan.co.uk
Food Mfr
N.A.I.C.S.: 311999

Shire Foods Limited (1)
Tachbrook Road, Leamington Spa, Warwickshire, United Kingdom
Tel.: (44) 1926335700
Web Site: https://shirefoods.com
Food Mfr
N.A.I.C.S.: 311999

Volvere Central Services Limited (1)
York House 74-82 Queen Victoria St, London, EC4N 4SJ, United Kingdom
Tel.: (44) 2079797596
Investment Management Service
N.A.I.C.S.: 523999

VOLVIK, INC
333 Yeongdong-daero, Gangnam-gu, Seoul, 137-864, Korea (South)
Tel.: (82) 24245211
Web Site: https://www.volvik.co.kr
Year Founded: 1980
Golf Equipment Mfr
N.A.I.C.S.: 339920
Seung-seog Hong *(CEO)*

Subsidiaries:
Volvik, Inc - Eumseong Factory (1)
628 Daegeum-ro Daeso-myeon Taesaeng-ri, Eumseong, 369-824, Chungcheongbuk, Korea (South)
Tel.: (82) 438771916
Golf Equipment Mfr
N.A.I.C.S.: 339920

VOLYNGAZ, PJSC
12 Ivana Franka str c, Lutsk, 43000, Volyn, Ukraine
Tel.: (380) 332 72 01 50
Natural & Liquefied Gas Distr
N.A.I.C.S.: 221210

VON CAPITAL CORP.
4400-181 Bay Street, Toronto, M5J 2T3, ON, Canada
Tel.: (647) 362-9675 Ca
Year Founded: 2018
XPRCF—(OTCIQ)
Assets: $2,293,903
Liabilities: $98,052
Net Worth: $2,195,851
Earnings: ($1,342,317)

Fiscal Year-end: 06/30/24
Business Consulting Services
N.A.I.C.S.: 522299

Subsidiaries:
Xplore Resources Holdings Corp. (1)

VON DER HEYDEN GROUP FINANCE PLC
Level 8 14 East Sliema Road, Gzira, GZR 1639, Malta
Tel.: (356) 27792200
Web Site: http://www.vonderheydengroup.com
Year Founded: 2017
VH24A—(MAL)
Rev.: $2,556,607
Assets: $44,456,595
Liabilities: $43,833,795
Net Worth: $622,799
Earnings: $179,355
Emp.: 200
Fiscal Year-end: 12/31/23
Real Estate Investment Services
N.A.I.C.S.: 531390
Sven Von Der Heyden *(Chm)*

VON MANNSTEIN WERBE-AGENTUR GMBH
Hackhausen 15, 42697, Solingen, Germany
Tel.: (49) 212728102 De
Web Site: http://www.mannstein.de
Year Founded: 1968
Rev.: $80,000,000
Emp.: 28
Full Service
N.A.I.C.S.: 541810
Coordt von Mannstein *(Chm & CEO)*

VONESEALS TECHNOLOGY (SHANGHAI) INC.
Room 226 Building 1 No 778 Jinji Road, Pudong New Area, Shanghai, 201201, China
Tel.: (86) 2168184680
Web Site: https://www.voneseals.com
Year Founded: 2008
301161—(CHIN)
Rev.: $47,796,372
Assets: $145,033,200
Liabilities: $14,025,960
Net Worth: $131,007,240
Earnings: $6,486,480
Fiscal Year-end: 12/31/22
Seals Product Mfr & Distr
N.A.I.C.S.: 339991
Jing Dong *(Chm)*

VONEX LTD.
Level 6/303 Coronation Dr, Milton, 4064, QLD, Australia
Tel.: (61) 863888888
Web Site: https://www.vonex.com.au
Year Founded: 2009
VN8—(ASX)
Rev.: $14,722,740
Assets: $8,991,649
Liabilities: $4,719,420
Net Worth: $4,272,229
Earnings: ($3,053,105)
Fiscal Year-end: 06/30/21
Wireless Telecommunications Carriers (except Satellite)
N.A.I.C.S.: 517112
Angus Parker *(Founder & CTO)*

VONGROUP LTD
17A EGL Tower 83 Hung To Road Kwun Tong, Kowloon, China (Hong Kong)
Tel.: (852) 21163838
Web Site: http://www.thevongroup.com

0318—(HKG)
Rev.: $24,943,184
Assets: $76,304,826
Liabilities: $13,954,346
Net Worth: $62,350,480
Earnings: $3,109,579
Emp.: 55
Fiscal Year-end: 04/30/22
Financial Services
N.A.I.C.S.: 541611
Siping Xu *(Exec Dir)*

Subsidiaries:
Four Directions Ecommerce Limited (1)
Room 1602 16/F Yen Sheng Centre 64 Hoi Yuen Road, Kwun Tong, China (Hong Kong)
Tel.: (852) 21540068
Web Site: https://www.4d.com.hk
Software Development Services
N.A.I.C.S.: 541519

VONOVIA SE
Universitatsstrasse 133, 44803, Bochum, Germany
Tel.: (49) 2343140 De
Web Site: https://www.vonovia.com
Year Founded: 2001
VNA—(DEU)
Rev.: $5,260,630,261
Assets: $99,283,293,762
Liabilities: $66,966,652,277
Net Worth: $32,316,641,485
Earnings: ($7,291,387,870)
Emp.: 10,692
Fiscal Year-end: 12/31/23
Residential Property Management & Leasing Services
N.A.I.C.S.: 531190
Rolf Buch *(CEO & Member-Mgmt Bd)*

Subsidiaries:
BUWOG AG (1)
Hietzinger Kai 131, 1130, Vienna, Austria (100%)
Tel.: (43) 1878281000
Web Site: http://www.buwog.com
Holding Company; Residential Real Estate Development, Multifamily Housing Construction & Sales
N.A.I.C.S.: 551112
Daniel Riedl *(CEO & Chm-Mgmt Bd)*

Subsidiary (Domestic):

BUWOG- Bauen und Wohnen Gesellschaft mbH (2)
Hietzinger Kai 131, Vienna, 1130, Austria
Tel.: (43) 878281130
Web Site: https://www.buwog.at
Residential Real Estate Development, Multi-family Housing Construction & Sales
N.A.I.C.S.: 237210

Subsidiary (Domestic):

ESG Wohnungsgesellschaft mbH Villach (3)
Tiroler Strasse 17, A-9500, Villach, Austria (99.98%)
Tel.: (43) 4242572000
Real Estate Manangement Services
N.A.I.C.S.: 531390

BUWOG Bautrager GmbH (1)
Rankestrasse 21, 10789, Berlin, Germany
Tel.: (49) 303385391900
Web Site: https://www.buwog.de
Real Estate Services
N.A.I.C.S.: 531390
Alexander Happ *(Co-CEO)*

BUWOG Sud GmbH (1)
Tiroler Strasse 17, 9500, Villach, Austria
Tel.: (43) 1878281130
Construction Services
N.A.I.C.S.: 531390

BUWOG-Lindenstrasse Development GmbH (1)
Rankestrasse 21, 10789, Berlin, Germany
Tel.: (49) 303385391915
Web Site: https://www.uferkrone.de

INTERNATIONAL PUBLIC

Residential Building Rental Services
N.A.I.C.S.: 531110

DAIG 2. Objektgesellschaft mbH (1)
Kleiner Schlossplatz 13, Stuttgart, 70173, Germany
Tel.: (49) 7114975204
Real Estate Manangement Services
N.A.I.C.S.: 531210

Deutsche Wohn-Inkasso GmbH (1)
Eulerstr 50, 40477, Dusseldorf, Germany
Tel.: (49) 21197266200
Real Estate Manangement Services
N.A.I.C.S.: 531210

Eisenbahn-Siedlungsgesellschaft Stuttgart gGmbH (1)
Katharinenstrasse 20, Stuttgart, 70182, Germany
Tel.: (49) 71121770
Real Estate Manangement Services
N.A.I.C.S.: 531210

GAGFAH Facility Management GmbH (1)
Schederhofstr 6, Ruhr, 45145, Essen, Germany
Tel.: (49) 201872320
Real Estate Manangement Services
N.A.I.C.S.: 531210

Hembla AB (1)
Hamngatan 15, 111 47, Stockholm, Sweden (100%)
Tel.: (46) 812131725
Web Site: http://www.hemblagroup.se
Rev.: $103,592,370
Assets: $3,651,992,670
Liabilities: $2,255,331,630
Net Worth: $1,396,661,040
Earnings: $368,081,160
Emp.: 258
Fiscal Year-end: 12/21/2018
Property Investment & Development
N.A.I.C.S.: 531390
Tommy Jansson *(Head-Property Mgmt)*

Immo Service Dresden GmbH (1)
Ostra-Allee 9, 01067, Dresden, Sachsen, Germany
Tel.: (49) 35125880
Real Estate Manangement Services
N.A.I.C.S.: 531210

KWG Immobilien GmbH (1)
Am Erlanger Weg 4, 91052, Erlangen, Germany
Tel.: (49) 9131695690
Real Estate Services
N.A.I.C.S.: 531390

Kieler Stadtentwicklungs- und Sanierungsgesellschaft mbH (1)
Bergenring 2, 24109, Kiel, Germany
Tel.: (49) 43153380
Real Estate Manangement Services
N.A.I.C.S.: 531210

Marina Tower Holding GmbH (1)
Rathausstrasse 1, A-1010, Vienna, Austria
Tel.: (43) 1878280
Web Site: https://www.marinatower.at
Real Estate Development Services
N.A.I.C.S.: 531390

NILEG Commercial Asset GmbH & Co. KG (1)
Mailander Strasse 2, 30539, Hannover, Niedersachsen, Germany
Tel.: (49) 51181160
Real Estate Manangement Services
N.A.I.C.S.: 531210

NILEG Norddeutsche Immobiliengesellschaft mbH (1)
Walter-Gieseking-Strasse 6, 30159, Hannover, Germany
Tel.: (49) 5118116255
Real Estate Manangement Services
N.A.I.C.S.: 531210

Osnabrucker Wohnungsbaugesellschaft mit beschrankter Haftung (1)
Hasetorwall 17, 49076, Osnabruck, Niedersachsen, Germany
Tel.: (49) 54120199800
Real Estate Manangement Services
N.A.I.C.S.: 531210

Parkhaus Prohlis GmbH (1)
Bayrische Strasse 14-16, 01069, Dresden, Germany
Tel.: (49) 35146901133
Web Site: http://www.parkhaus-prohlis.de
Property Management Services
N.A.I.C.S.: 531311

Prima Wohnbauten Privatisierungs-Management GmbH (1)
Mollendorffstrasse 48, Lichtenberg, 10367, Berlin, Germany
Tel.: (49) 309710780
Real Estate Manangement Services
N.A.I.C.S.: 531210

RVG Rheinauhafen Verwaltungsgesellschaft mbH (1)
Im Zollhafen 2 4 1st Floor, 50678, Cologne, Germany
Tel.: (49) 2213489901
Web Site: http://www.rheinauhafen-koeln.de
Law firm
N.A.I.C.S.: 541199

SYNVIA energy GmbH (1)
Erzbergerstr 1, 39104, Magdeburg, Germany
Tel.: (49) 39150860800
Real Estate Investment Services
N.A.I.C.S.: 531210

Siege Siedlungsgesellschaft fur das Verkehrspersonal mbH Mainz (1)
Bahnhofstrasse 8a, 55116, Mainz, Rheinland-Pfalz, Germany
Tel.: (49) 613123910
Real Estate Manangement Services
N.A.I.C.S.: 531210

Victoria Park Boras AB (1)
Solvarvsgatan 89 A, 507 40, Boras, Sweden
Tel.: (46) 102093900
Apartment Rental Services
N.A.I.C.S.: 531110

Victoria Park Malmo Centrum AB (1)
Ramels vag 53, 213 69, Malmo, Sweden
Tel.: (46) 102093900
Apartment Rental Services
N.A.I.C.S.: 531110

Victoria Park Markaryd AB (1)
Kaplansgatan 5l, 285 33, Markaryd, Sweden
Tel.: (46) 102093900
Apartment Rental Services
N.A.I.C.S.: 531110

Victoria Park Nykoping AB (1)
Mariebergsvagen 53, 611 66, Nykoping, Sweden
Tel.: (46) 102093900
Apartment Rental Services
N.A.I.C.S.: 531110

Victoria Park Orebro AB (1)
Varbergagatan 161, 703 52, Orebro, Sweden
Tel.: (46) 102093900
Apartment Rental Services
N.A.I.C.S.: 531110

Victoria Park Vaxjo S AB (1)
Sommarvagen 7B, 352 37, Vaxjo, Sweden
Tel.: (46) 102093900
Apartment Rental Services
N.A.I.C.S.: 531110

Victoriahem AB (1)
Box 2, 201 20, Malmo, Sweden (100%)
Tel.: (46) 102102200
Web Site: http://www.victoriapark.se
Real Estate Development & Management
N.A.I.C.S.: 237210

Vonovia Eigentumsservice GmbH (1)
Virchowstrasse 99, 45886, Gelsenkirchen, Germany
Tel.: (49) 20994580200
Web Site: https://www.eigentum.vonovia.de
Real Estate Services
N.A.I.C.S.: 531390

Vonovia Immobilien Treuhand GmbH (1)
Virchowstrasse 99, 45886, Gelsenkirchen, Germany
Tel.: (49) 20994580171
Web Site: http://www.vonovia-immobilientreuhand.de
Residential Building Construction Services
N.A.I.C.S.: 236115
Stefan Ollig *(Mng Dir)*

WOHNBAU NORDWEST GmbH (1)
Tannenstrasse 4b, 01099, Dresden, Sachsen, Germany
Tel.: (49) 35181810
Real Estate Manangement Services
N.A.I.C.S.: 531210

conwert Immobilien Invest GmbH (1)
Alserbachstrasse 32, 1090, Vienna, Austria (100%)
Tel.: (43) 1521450
Web Site: http://www.conwert.at
Real Estate Investment Services
N.A.I.C.S.: 523999

Subsidiary (Non-US):

BOKRETA Management Kft. (2)
IX ker Viola u 13 15 Fsz 2, 1094, Budapest, Hungary
Tel.: (36) 14570757
Web Site: http://www.bokreta.hu
Real Estate Manangement Services
N.A.I.C.S.: 531390

Subsidiary (Domestic):

CENTUM Immobilien GmbH (2)
Albertg 35, 1080, Vienna, Austria
Tel.: (43) 1521450
Real Estate Manangement Services
N.A.I.C.S.: 531390

CONWERT SECURITISATION Holding GmbH (2)
Albertgasse 35, Vienna, 1080, Austria
Tel.: (43) 1521450
Real Estate Investment Services
N.A.I.C.S.: 523999

Con Tessa Immobilienverwertung GmbH (2)
Alserbath strasse 32, 1080, Vienna, Austria
Tel.: (43) 152145450
Residential Property Management Services
N.A.I.C.S.: 531311

Con Wert Handelsges.m.b.H. (2)
Albertgasse 35, 1080, Vienna, Austria
Tel.: (43) 1521450
Residential Property Management Services
N.A.I.C.S.: 531311

Con value one Immobilien GmbH (2)
Albertg 35, 1080, Vienna, Austria
Tel.: (43) 1521450
Real Estate Manangement Services
N.A.I.C.S.: 531390

G-Unternhmensbeteilligung GmbH (2)
Albertgasse 35, 1080, Vienna, Austria
Tel.: (43) 1521450
Real Estate Manangement Services
N.A.I.C.S.: 531390

GJ-Beteiligungs GmbH (2)
alserpathstrasse 32, Vienna, 1090, Austria
Tel.: (43) 1521450
Investment Management Service
N.A.I.C.S.: 523999

Subsidiary (Non-US):

KWG Kommunale Wohnen GmbH (2)
Leipziger Platz 9, 10117, Berlin, Germany
Tel.: (49) 306090240
Real Estate Development Services
N.A.I.C.S.: 531390

Subsidiary (Domestic):

RESAG Property Management GmbH (2)
Albertgasse 35, 1080, Vienna, Austria
Tel.: (43) 1262600
Real Estate Manangement Services
N.A.I.C.S.: 531390

Subsidiary (Non-US):

conwert Alfhild Invest GmbH (2)
Auf der Eierwiese 10, 82031, Grunwald, Bavaria, Germany
Tel.: (49) 896496000
Real Estate Manangement Services
N.A.I.C.S.: 531390

conwert Deutschland Beteiligungsholding GmbH (2)
Charlottenstreet 18, Berlin, 10117, Germany
Tel.: (49) 30240830000
Investment Management Service
N.A.I.C.S.: 523999

conwert Deutschland GmbH (2)
Bahnhofstrasse 7, 74072, Heilbronn, Baden-Wurttemberg, Germany
Tel.: (49) 713160900
Residential Real Estate Management Services
N.A.I.C.S.: 531311

Subsidiary (Domestic):

alt+kelber Immobilienverwaltung GmbH (3)
Bahnhofstrasse 7, 74072, Heilbronn, Baden-Wurttemberg, Germany
Tel.: (49) 713160900
Sales Range: $50-74.9 Million
Emp.: 25
Real Estate Manangement Services
N.A.I.C.S.: 531390

Subsidiary (Non-US):

conwert Deutschland Holding GmbH (2)
Bahnhofstreet 7, Heilbronn, 74072, Baden-Wurttemberg, Germany
Tel.: (49) 713160900
Residential Property Development Services
N.A.I.C.S.: 236115

conwert Grazer Damm Development GmbH (2)
Charlottenstreet 18, Berlin, 10117, Germany
Tel.: (49) 30240830000
Residential Property Development Services
N.A.I.C.S.: 236116

Subsidiary (Domestic):

conwert Management GmbH (2)
Albertgasse 35, Vienna, 1080, Austria
Tel.: (43) 1521450
Real Estate Manangement Services
N.A.I.C.S.: 531390

VONPENDE HOLDINGS PLC
Office 306 Vesper Floor Akamantis Building 10 Egypt Street, 1097, Nicosia, Cyprus
Tel.: (357) 22029398
Web Site: http://www.vonpende.com.cy
VOPE—(CYP)
Rev.: $87,026,737
Assets: $686,880,719
Liabilities: $738,829,189
Net Worth: ($51,948,470)
Earnings: $34,852,454
Fiscal Year-end: 12/31/19
Holding Company
N.A.I.C.S.: 551112
Stella Koukounis *(Exec Dir)*

VONTOBEL HOLDING AG
Gotthardstrasse 43, CH-8022, Zurich, Switzerland
Tel.: (41) 582835900
Web Site: https://www.vontobel.com
Year Founded: 1924
VONN—(SWX)
Rev.: $262,280,052
Assets: $2,377,620,765
Liabilities: $1,130,205,060
Net Worth: $1,247,415,705
Earnings: $190,707,948
Emp.: 2,109
Fiscal Year-end: 12/31/21
Bank Holding Company; Private Banking, Investment Banking & Asset Management Services
N.A.I.C.S.: 551111
Herbert J. Scheidt *(Chm)*

VONTOBEL HOLDING AG

Vontobel Holding AG—(Continued)

Subsidiaries:

Alternative Investment Management Ltd. (1)
23 The Dene, Wembley, HA9 7QS, Middlesex, United Kingdom
Tel.: (44) 7973 316883
Investment Management Service
N.A.I.C.S.: 523999

Bank Vontobel AG (1)
Gotthardstrasse 43, CH-8022, Zurich, Switzerland
Tel.: (41) 582837704
Sales Range: $700-749.9 Million
Banking Services
N.A.I.C.S.: 522110

Branch (Domestic):

Bank Vontobel AG - Lucerne (2)
Schweizerhofquai 3a, 6002, Lucerne, Switzerland
Tel.: (41) 582832711
Web Site: http://www.vontobel.com
Banking Services
N.A.I.C.S.: 522110

Banque Vontobel SA - Geneve (2)
rue du rhone 31, 1204, Geneva, Switzerland
Tel.: (41) 582832500
Web Site: http://www.vontobel.com
Sales Range: $25-49.9 Million
Emp.: 50
Banking Services
N.A.I.C.S.: 522110

Division (Domestic):

VT Finance AG (2)
c/o Bellevue Asset Management AG See Strasse 16, 8700, Zurich, Switzerland
Tel.: (41) 442677251
Web Site: http://www.bbmedtech.ch
Sales Range: $1-9.9 Million
Emp.: 100
Medical Technology Investment Services
N.A.I.C.S.: 523999

Vontobel Asset Management AG (2)
Gotthardstrasse 43, 8022, Zurich, Switzerland
Tel.: (41) 582837150
Sales Range: $300-349.9 Million
Emp.: 1,000
Asset Management Services
N.A.I.C.S.: 523999

Vontobel Fonds Services AG (2)
Gotthardstrasse 43, PO Box 2999, 8022, Zurich, Switzerland
Tel.: (41) 582837477
Sales Range: $350-399.9 Million
Emp.: 800
Fund Advisory Services
N.A.I.C.S.: 525910

Vontobel Securities AG (2)
Gotthardstrasse 43, 8022, Zurich, Switzerland
Tel.: (41) 582837111
Sales Range: $300-349.9 Million
Emp.: 1,000
Securities Brokerage Services
N.A.I.C.S.: 523150

Bank Vontobel Europe AG (1)
Alter Hof 5, D-80331, Munich, Germany
Tel.: (49) 894118900
Sales Range: $50-74.9 Million
Emp.: 80
Banking Services
N.A.I.C.S.: 522110
Andreas Heinrichs (Member-Mgmt Bd & Head-Brokerage)

Branch (Domestic):

Bank Vontobel Europe AG - Frankfurt (2)
bockenheimer landstrasse 24, 60323, Frankfurt am Main, Germany
Tel.: (49) 692972080
Web Site: http://www.vontobel.de
Sales Range: $25-49.9 Million
Emp.: 26
Banking Services
N.A.I.C.S.: 522110

Bank Vontobel Osterreich AG (1)
Karntner Strasse 51, A-1010, Vienna, Austria
Tel.: (43) 15137640
Web Site: http://www.vontobel.ch
Sales Range: $100-124.9 Million
Emp.: 200
Banking Services
N.A.I.C.S.: 522110

Harcourt Investment Consulting AG (1)
Gotthardstrasse 43, 8022, Zurich, Switzerland
Tel.: (41) 44 365 1000
Web Site: http://www.harcourt.ch
Sales Range: $50-74.9 Million
Emp.: 68
Investment Management Service
N.A.I.C.S.: 523999

TwentyFour Asset Management LLP (1)
8th Floor The Monument Building 11 Monument Street, London, EC3R 8AF, United Kingdom (100%)
Tel.: (44) 2070158900
Web Site: https://www.twentyfouram.com
Financial & Investment Services
N.A.I.C.S.: 523999
John Magrath (Partner & Head-Distr)

UBS Swiss Financial Advisers AG (1)
Loewenstrasse 49, 8098, Zurich, Switzerland
Tel.: (41) 44 237 88 00
Web Site: http://www.ubs.com
Financial Investment Services
N.A.I.C.S.: 523999

Vontobel (Hong Kong) Ltd. (1)
15 Queens Road Central 1901 Gloucester Tower The Landmark, Hong Kong, China (Hong Kong)
Tel.: (852) 36553990
Asset Management Services
N.A.I.C.S.: 523940

Vontobel Asia Pacific Ltd. (1)
3601 Two International Finance Centre 8 Finance Street, Central, China (Hong Kong)
Tel.: (852) 3655 3990
Sales Range: $50-74.9 Million
Emp.: 1
Investment Advisory Services
N.A.I.C.S.: 523940
Ulrich Behm (CEO-Asset Mgmt)

Vontobel Asset Management Asia Pacific Limited (1)
1901 Gloucester Tower The Landmark 15 Queen's Road, Central, China (Hong Kong)
Tel.: (852) 36553990
Financial & Investment Services
N.A.I.C.S.: 523999
Ulrich Behm (CEO)

Vontobel Asset Management Australia Pty. Ltd. (1)
Level 20 Tower 2 201 Sussex St, Sydney, 2000, NSW, Australia
Tel.: (61) 290061282
Financial & Investment Services
N.A.I.C.S.: 523999

Vontobel Asset Management S.A. (1)
Tel.: (352) 2634741
Financial & Investment Services
N.A.I.C.S.: 523999

Vontobel Asset Management SGR SpA (1)
Piazza Degli Affari 2, Milan, 20123, Italy
Tel.: (39) 0263673411
Web Site: http://www.vontobel.com
Sales Range: $50-74.9 Million
Emp.: 14
Asset Management Services
N.A.I.C.S.: 523999

Vontobel Asset Management, Inc. (1)
Tel.: (212) 804-9300
Sales Range: $50-74.9 Million
Emp.: 40
Asset Management & Private Banking Services
N.A.I.C.S.: 523999
Matthew Benkendorf (Chief Investment Officer-Quality Growth & Portfolio Mgr)

Vontobel Europe S.A. (1)
18 Rue Erasme, 1468, Luxembourg, Luxembourg
Tel.: (352) 2634741
Web Site: http://www.vontobel.com
Sales Range: $50-74.9 Million
Emp.: 15
Banking Services
N.A.I.C.S.: 522110

Subsidiary (Domestic):

Vontobel Fund Advisory S.A. (2)
1 Cote D'Eich, L-1450, Luxembourg, Luxembourg
Tel.: (352) 26341719
Fund Advisory Services
N.A.I.C.S.: 525910

Vontobel Financial Products GmbH (1)
Bockenheimer Landstrasse 24, 60323, Frankfurt am Main, Germany
Tel.: (49) 699203730
Web Site: http://www.vontobel-zertifikate.de
Financial Management Services
N.A.I.C.S.: 523999

Vontobel Financial Products Ltd. (1)
Building 4 Level 5 Unit 502, PO Box 506814, Gate District International Financial Centre, Dubai, United Arab Emirates
Tel.: (971) 47038500
Financial & Investment Services
N.A.I.C.S.: 523999

Vontobel Invest Ltd. (1)
Liberty House Office 913 Dubai International Financial Centre, PO Box 506814, Dubai, United Arab Emirates
Tel.: (971) 4 703 8500
Emp.: 1
Investment Management Service
N.A.I.C.S.: 523999
Remigio Luongo (Vice Chm-Singapore)

Vontobel Limited (1)
15 Queen s Road 1901 Gloucester Tower The Landmark, Central, China (Hong Kong)
Tel.: (852) 36553990
Financial & Investment Services
N.A.I.C.S.: 523999

Vontobel Management S.A. (1)
18 rue Erasme, 1468, Luxembourg, Luxembourg
Tel.: (352) 2634741
Web Site: http://www.vontobel.com
Sales Range: $50-74.9 Million
Emp.: 6
Portfolio Management Services
N.A.I.C.S.: 523940

Vontobel Pte. Ltd. (1)
8 Marina Boulevard Marina Bay Financial Centre Tower 1 Level 04-03, Singapore, 018981, Singapore
Tel.: (65) 69928400
Financial & Investment Services
N.A.I.C.S.: 523999

Vontobel Swiss Wealth Advisors AG (1)
Gotthardstrasse 43, 8022, Zurich, Switzerland
Tel.: (41) 44 287 81 11
Web Site: http://www.vontobeladvisors.com
Sales Range: $50-74.9 Million
Emp.: 20
Investment Advisory Services
N.A.I.C.S.: 523940
Patrice E. Humbel (CEO)

Vontobel Treuhand AG (1)
Pflugstrasse 10-12, 9490, Vaduz, Liechtenstein
Tel.: (423) 2365757
Web Site: http://www.kaiserpartner.com
Sales Range: $50-74.9 Million
Emp.: 200
Banking Services
N.A.I.C.S.: 522110
Kaiser Fritz (Gen Mgr)

Vontobel Wealth Management (Hong Kong) Ltd. (1)
1901 Gloucester Tower The Landmark 15 Queen S Road, Central, China (Hong Kong)
Tel.: (852) 36553900
Financial & Investment Services
N.A.I.C.S.: 523999

Vontobel Wealth Management Società di Intermediazione Mobiliare S.p.A. (1)
Corso G Matteotti 1, 20121, Milan, Italy
Tel.: (39) 02124128791
Asset Management Services
N.A.I.C.S.: 523940

VONTRON TECHNOLOGY CO., LTD

1518 Li Yang Avenue Guiyang National Hi-tech Industrial Park, Guiyang, 550017, Guizhou, China
Tel.: (86) 1083619831
Web Site: https://en.vontron.com
Year Founded: 1999
000920—(SSE)
Rev.: $205,172,150
Assets: $410,207,621
Liabilities: $146,138,682
Net Worth: $264,068,939
Earnings: $20,354,279
Emp.: 4,000
Fiscal Year-end: 12/31/22
Artificial Fiber Product Mfr
N.A.I.C.S.: 325220
Cai Zhiqi (Chm)

VOPAK

Westerlaan 10, 3016, Rotterdam, Netherlands
Tel.: (31) 104002911
Web Site: http://www.vopak.com
Rev.: $868,884,660
Assets: $2,231,818,680
Liabilities: $1,468,873,980
Net Worth: $762,944,700
Earnings: $133,752,360
Emp.: 3,433
Fiscal Year-end: 12/31/05
Logistics Consulting Servies
N.A.I.C.S.:

VOPELIUS CHEMIE AG

Heinrich-Stranka-Strasse 18, 90765, Furth, Germany
Tel.: (49) 911979710
Web Site: http://www.vopelius.com
Year Founded: 1982
Sales Range: $15-24.9 Billion
Emp.: 50
Chemicals Mfr
N.A.I.C.S.: 325998
Oliver Weiss (Member-Exec Bd)

Subsidiaries:

Soderec International S.A. (1)
Chemin Des Agriculteurs, 26700, Pierrelatte, France (100%)
Tel.: (33) 475969653
Web Site: http://www.soderecsluor.com
Sales Range: $1-9.9 Million
Emp.: 15
Mfr & Producer of Inorganic Chemicals
N.A.I.C.S.: 325998

VORDERE PLC

11-12 St James's Square, London, SW1Y 4LB, United Kingdom
Tel.: (44) 2038727310
Web Site: http://www.vordere.com
Asset Management Services
N.A.I.C.S.: 523940

VORNDRAN MANNHEIMS CAPITAL ADVISORS GMBH

Graf-Adolf-Strasse 18, 40212, Dusseldorf, Germany
Tel.: (49) 21186286910
Web Site: http://www.ventizz.de
Sales Range: $10-24.9 Million
Emp.: 20
Privater Equity Firm

AND PRIVATE COMPANIES

N.A.I.C.S.: 523999
Travis O. Morris (Pres)
Subsidiaries:

Medos Medizintechnik AG (1)
Obere Steinfurt 8-10, 52222, Stolberg, Germany
Tel.: (49) 240296640
Web Site: http://www.medos-ag.com
Sales Range: $100-124.9 Million
Medical Device Mfr
N.A.I.C.S.: 339112

VORONOI, INC.
S 18th F Songdogwahak-ro 32 IT Center, Yeonsu-gu, Incheon, Korea (South)
Tel.: (82) 328304855
Web Site: https://www.voronoi.io
Year Founded: 2015
310210—(KRS)
Biotechnology Research & Development Services
N.A.I.C.S.: 541714
Sunghwan Kim (CTO)

VORTEX AQUATIC STRUCTURES INTERNATIONAL INC.
328 Avro Street, Pointe-Claire, H9R 5W5, QC, Canada
Tel.: (146) 43868
Web Site: http://www.vortex-intl.com
Year Founded: 1995
Aquatic Playground Equipment Mfr
N.A.I.C.S.: 339920
Stephen Hamelin (Pres & CEO)

VORTEX ENERGY CORP.
1177 West Hastings St Suite 1930, Vancouver, V6E 2K3, BC, Canada
Tel.: (778) 819-0164
Web Site: https://www.vortexenergy.ae
Year Founded: 2014
VRTX—(CNSX)
Assets: $1,382,469
Liabilities: $96,233
Net Worth: $1,286,236
Earnings: ($281,726)
Fiscal Year-end: 06/30/22
Mineral Exploration Services
N.A.I.C.S.: 213115

VORTEX PRODUCTION SERVICES LTD.
7201 - 50 Avenue, PO Box 1480, Stettler, T0C 2L0, AB, Canada
Tel.: (403) 742-6900
Web Site: https://www.vortexservices.ca
Year Founded: 2003
Sales Range: $10-24.9 Million
Emp.: 50
Oilfield Equipment Repair Services
N.A.I.C.S.: 811310
Brian Prehn (CFO)

VORTIV LIMITED
Unit 8-9 88 Forrest Street, Cottesloe, 6011, WA, Australia
Tel.: (61) 864441798
Web Site: http://www.vortiv.com
VOR—(ASX)
Rev.: $3,660,856
Assets: $45,755,334
Liabilities: $34,984,235
Net Worth: $10,771,099
Earnings: ($1,166,141)
Emp.: 500
Fiscal Year-end: 03/31/22
Electronic Financial Payment Services
N.A.I.C.S.: 522320
Gary P. Foster (Founder)

Subsidiaries:

Transaction Solutions International Pty Ltd (1)
24 Colin St, 6005, West Perth, WA, Australia
Tel.: (61) 865000226
Software Development Services
N.A.I.C.S.: 541511

VORWERK & CO. KG
Muhlenweg 17-37, 42270, Wuppertal, Germany
Tel.: (49) 2025640
Web Site: http://www.vorwerk.de
Year Founded: 1883
Sales Range: $1-4.9 Billion
Emp.: 12,545
Floor Care Equipment Mfr
N.A.I.C.S.: 333998
Reiner Strecker (Member-Exec Bd & Co-Mng Partner)

Subsidiaries:

Brugman C.V. (1)
Heerlenstraat 3, 6845 AD, Arnhem, Netherlands (100%)
Tel.: (31) 263812112
Web Site: http://www.brugman.nl
Sales Range: $100-124.9 Million
Emp.: 500
Kitchen & Bathroom Furniture Mfr
N.A.I.C.S.: 337110

Brugman Keukens & Badkamers B.V. (1)
Hoofdweg 46, 2908 LC, Capelle aan den IJssel, Netherlands (100%)
Tel.: (31) 102587555
Web Site: http://www.brugman.nl
Sales Range: $25-49.9 Million
Emp.: 100
Kitchen & Bathroom Furniture Mfr
N.A.I.C.S.: 337110

Distribuidora Jafra de Cosmeticos Ltda. (1)
Alameda dos Maracatins 659, Moema, Sao Paulo, 04089-011, Brazil
Tel.: (55) 11 3595 0708
Web Site: http://www.jafra.com.br
Cosmetic Product Distr
N.A.I.C.S.: 456120
Lasarocarmo Gunaor (Pres)

Guy Degrenne S.A. (1)
rue Guy Degrenne, 14502, Vire, Cedex, France (46.43%)
Tel.: (33) 231664490
Web Site: http://www.degrenne.fr
Crystal & Porcelain Tableware & Stainless Steel Flatware & Holloware Mfr
N.A.I.C.S.: 327110

Hectas Gebaudedienste Ges.m.b.H & Co. KG (1)
Dr. Hans Lechner Strase 6, Wals-Siezenheim, A-5071, Salzburg, Austria (95%)
Tel.: (43) 6628781140
Web Site: http://www.hectas.at
Sales Range: $300-349.9 Million
Emp.: 1,700
Facilities Support Management
N.A.I.C.S.: 561210

Hectas Gebaudedienste Stiftung & Co. KG (1)
Konsumstr 45, 42285, Wuppertal, Germany (100%)
Tel.: (49) 20294794300
Web Site: http://www.hectas.de
Sales Range: $150-199.9 Million
Emp.: 1,000
Facilities Support Services
N.A.I.C.S.: 561210

Hectas Gebaudemanagement GmbH & Co. KG (1)
Am Diek 52, D 42277, Wuppertal, Germany (100%)
Tel.: (49) 2025640
Web Site: http://www.hectas.de
Sales Range: $150-199.9 Million
Emp.: 1,000
Facilities Support Services

N.A.I.C.S.: 561210

Hectas Groep C.V. (1)
Geograaf 30, Duiven, 921 EW, Netherlands (95%)
Tel.: (31) 263171717
Web Site: http://www.hectas.nl
Sales Range: $10-24.9 Million
Emp.: 40
Facilities Support
N.A.I.C.S.: 561210

Hectas Sicherheitsdienste GmbH (1)
Konsumstrasse 45, 42285, Wuppertal, Germany (100%)
Tel.: (49) 2029479990
Web Site: http://www.hectas.de
Sales Range: $1-9.9 Million
Emp.: 1,000
Security Services
N.A.I.C.S.: 561613

Hectas Technicke a bezpecnostni Sluzby s.r.o. (1)
Luzicka 9, CZ 63800, Brno, Czech Republic (85.5%)
Tel.: (420) 545223735
Sales Range: $125-149.9 Million
Emp.: 500
Electric Equipment Mfr
N.A.I.C.S.: 335210

Jafra Cosmetics Ag (1)
Riedstrasse 3/5, 6330, Cham, Switzerland
Tel.: (41) 41 748 54 54
Web Site: http://www.jafra.ch
Cosmetic Product Distr
N.A.I.C.S.: 456120

Jafra Cosmetics Gmbh & Co. KG (1)
Leonrodstr 52, 80636, Munich, Germany
Tel.: (49) 89 149 93 0
Web Site: http://www.jafra.de
Cosmetic Product Distr
N.A.I.C.S.: 456120

Jafra Cosmetics International LLC (1)
Suschevskaya Street 27 Bldg 1, 127055, Moscow, Russia
Tel.: (7) 495 780 01 62
Cosmetic Product Distr
N.A.I.C.S.: 456120

Jafra Cosmetics S.p.A. (1)
Casella Postale 3, 21043, Castiglione Olona, Italy
Tel.: (39) 0800 552251
Cosmetic Product Distr
N.A.I.C.S.: 456120

Jafra Manufacturing S.A. de C.V. (1)
La Estacada No 201, Queretaro, 76246, Mexico
Tel.: (52) 4421015000
Cosmetics Products Mfr
N.A.I.C.S.: 325620

Jafra Ruchi Cosmetics India Private Ltd (1)
Odeon Cinema D Block Ground Floor & Mezzanine Floor, Connaught Place, New Delhi, 110 001, India
Tel.: (91) 11 4644 8000
Web Site: http://www.jafra.net.in
Cosmetic Product Distr
N.A.I.C.S.: 456120
Harish Singla (Co-Mng Dir)

L.u.x Company Ltd. (1)
117B Nguyen Dinh Chin Ward 15, Phu Nhuan Dist, Ho Chi Minh City, Vietnam
Tel.: (84) 8 844 51 30
Household Electronic Appliance Distr
N.A.I.C.S.: 423620

Lux Appliance Philippines, Inc (1)
986 Standford Street, corner EDSA, Mandaluyong, 1550, Philippines
Tel.: (63) 2 4708914
Web Site: http://www.lux.phillipines.com
Emp.: 3
Household Electronic Appliance Mfr
N.A.I.C.S.: 335220
Olivia Susa (Gen Mgr)

Lux Asia Pacific Pte Ltd. (1)
390 Havelock Road King s Centre, Singapore, 169662, Singapore
Tel.: (65) 6412 0388

VORWERK & CO. KG

Web Site: http://www.luxasiapacific.com
Emp.: 10
Home Cleaning System & Water Purification System Mfr
N.A.I.C.S.: 335220
Hakan Palm (Pres)

Lux Royal (Thailand) Co., Ltd. (1)
523-525 Lux Building Sukhumvit 71 Rd, Phakanong-Nue Wattana, 10110, Bangkok, Thailand
Tel.: (66) 2 381 3355
Web Site: http://www.lux.co.th
Household Electronic Appliance Mfr
N.A.I.C.S.: 335220

Neato Robotics, Inc. (1)
8100 Jarvis Ave, Newark, CA 94560
Tel.: (510) 795-1351
Web Site: http://www.neatorobotics.com
Robot Vacuum Cleaner Mfr
N.A.I.C.S.: 333998
Holly Anderson (CFO)

PT Jafra Cosmetics Indonesia (1)
Gedung Menara Duta Ground Floor JI H R Rasuna Said Kav B-9, Jakarta, 12910, Indonesia
Tel.: (62) 21 2955 2200
Web Site: http://www.jafra.co.id
Cosmetic Product Distr
N.A.I.C.S.: 456120

PT. Luxindo Raya (1)
JI Agung Timur 9 Blok 0-1/29-30, Sunter Agung Podamoro, 14350, Jakarta, Indonesia
Tel.: (62) 21 651 1513
Web Site: http://www.lux.co.id
Household Electronic Appliance Mfr
N.A.I.C.S.: 335220

SKF Slovenija d.o.o. (1)
Ukmarjeva Ulica 6, Ljubljana, 1000, Slovenia (100%)
Tel.: (386) 16008880
Web Site: http://www.skf.si
Sales Range: $25-49.9 Million
Emp.: 11
Electrical Products Mfr
N.A.I.C.S.: 335210
Gregor Kmecl (Mgr)

The Pinehill Partnership Ltd (1)
Thorp Building Whitmore Lane, Sunningdale, SL5 0NS, Berkshire, United Kingdom
Tel.: (44) 1344 622 344
Household Electronic Appliance Distr
N.A.I.C.S.: 423620

VK Direct Limited (1)
Unit A DeClare Industrial Park, Ponty Gwindy Road, Caerphilly, CF83 3HY, United Kingdom (100%)
Tel.: (44) 1189738042
Web Site: http://www.vkdirect.co.uk
Sales Range: $25-49.9 Million
Emp.: 15
Distr of Household Appliances
N.A.I.C.S.: 449210

Vorwerk & Co. Interholding GmbH (1)
Muehlenweg 17-37, D 42270, Wuppertal, Germany (100%)
Tel.: (49) 2025641221
Web Site: http://www.vorwerk.com
Sales Range: $1-9.9 Million
Emp.: 100
Household Vacuum Cleaner Mfr
N.A.I.C.S.: 335210

Vorwerk & Co. Teppichwerke GmbH & Co. KG. (1)
Kuhlmann Strasse 11, Hameln, 31785, Germany (100%)
Tel.: (49) 51511030
Web Site: http://www.vorwerk-carpet.com
Sales Range: $75-99.9 Million
Emp.: 330
Carpets
N.A.I.C.S.: 314110
Christian Otte (Mng Dir)

Vorwerk & Co. Thermomix GmbH (1)
Muhlenweg 17 37, D 42270, Wuppertal, Germany (100%)
Tel.: (49) 2025640

VORWERK & CO. KG

Vorwerk & Co. KG—(Continued)
Web Site: http://www.vorwerk.com
Sales Range: $50-74.9 Million
Emp.: 120
Marketing of Thermomix Mixer
N.A.I.C.S.: 449210

Vorwerk Asia Mittelsten Scheid & Co (1)
1-8-8 Nakameguro, Meguro-ku, Tokyo, 153-0061, Japan **(100%)**
Tel.: (81) 357221771
Web Site: http://www.vorwerk.co.jp
Sales of Floor-Care Equipment
N.A.I.C.S.: 449210

Vorwerk Austria Ges.m.b.H. (1)
Schafferhofstrasse 15, 6971, Hard, Bregenz, Austria **(100%)**
Tel.: (43) 557468550
Web Site: http://www.vorwerk.at
Sales Range: $100-124.9 Million
Emp.: 500
Sales of Electrical Appliances
N.A.I.C.S.: 449210
Wolfgant Mulner (Mng Dir)

Vorwerk Contempora S.r.l. (1)
Via Grazzini, 15, I-20157, Milan, Italy **(99.5%)**
Web Site: http://www.contempora.it
Sales of Electrical Appliances
N.A.I.C.S.: 449210

Vorwerk Deutschland Stiftung & Co. KG (1)
Muhlenweg 17-37, 42270, Wuppertal, Germany **(100%)**
Tel.: (49) 2025643727
Web Site: http://www.vorwerk.com
Sales Range: $150-199.9 Million
Emp.: 900
Charitable Foundation
N.A.I.C.S.: 813211
Espen Hahn (Pres)

Vorwerk Elektrowerke GmbH & Co. KG (1)
Muhlenweg 17 37, D 42270, Wuppertal, Germany **(100%)**
Tel.: (49) 1805377277
Web Site: http://www.vorwerk.com
Sales Range: $100-124.9 Million
Emp.: 300
Household Appliances Mfr
N.A.I.C.S.: 335210
Heinrich Peterwarth (Gen Mgr)

Vorwerk Espana M.S.L.S.C. (1)
Arroyo Del Santo 527, Madrid, 28042, Spain **(100%)**
Tel.: (34) 917283600
Web Site: http://www.vorwerk.es
Sales Range: $25-49.9 Million
Emp.: 100
Sales of Electrical Appliances
N.A.I.C.S.: 449210
Ignacio Fernandez-Simal (Gen Mgr)

Vorwerk Folletto s.a.s. di Achim Schwanitz & Co. (1)
Via G Frua 26, I 20146, Milan, Italy **(97%)**
Tel.: (39) 02480451
Web Site: http://www.folletto.it
Sales Range: $25-49.9 Million
Emp.: 20
Sales of Electrical Appliances
N.A.I.C.S.: 449210

Vorwerk France s.c.s. (1)
539 Route de St Joseph, CS 20811, 44308, Nantes, France **(100%)**
Tel.: (33) 251854700
Web Site: http://www.vorwerk.fr
Sales Range: $25-49.9 Million
Emp.: 40
Prefabricated Housing
N.A.I.C.S.: 321992

Vorwerk Household Appliances Co., Ltd. (1)
9 Vorwerk Plaza 1768 Yishan Road, Shanghai, 201103, China
Tel.: (86) 2151197711
Web Site: http://www.vorwerk.com.cn
Electrical Household Appliance Whslr
N.A.I.C.S.: 449210

Vorwerk Household Appliances Manufacturing (Shanghai) Co., Ltd (1)
655 Xinqu Road, Qingpu District, 201700, Shanghai, China
Tel.: (86) 400 820 7711
Household Electronic Appliance Mfr
N.A.I.C.S.: 335220

Vorwerk International Strecker & Co (1)
Verenastrasse 39, 8832, Wollerau, Switzerland
Tel.: (41) 44 786 01 11
Household Electronic Appliance Mfr
N.A.I.C.S.: 335220

Vorwerk Lux (Far East) Ltd. (1)
2F No 2 Ruiguang Road 114, Taipei, 114, Taiwan
Tel.: (886) 2 2793 8008
Web Site: http://www.lux-taiwan.com.tw
Household Electronic Appliance Mfr
N.A.I.C.S.: 335220

Vorwerk Mexico S. de R.L. de C.V. (1)
Cracovia 33, Col San Angelo, 01000, Mexico, Mexico
Tel.: (52) 56165560
Web Site: http://www.vorwerk.com
Household Electronic Appliance Mfr
N.A.I.C.S.: 335220

Vorwerk Polska Sp.z.o.o. (1)
Ul Strzegomska 46 B, PL 56311, Wroclaw, Poland **(100%)**
Tel.: (48) 717807200
Web Site: http://www.vorwerk.pl
Emp.: 34
Electrical Household Appliance Whslr
N.A.I.C.S.: 449210

Vorwerk Portugal Electrodomesticos LDA (1)
Rua Quinta do Paizinho No 8 1st Fl Y, Carnaxide, 2790237, Portugal **(100%)**
Tel.: (351) 214417315
Sales Range: $25-49.9 Million
Emp.: 105
Household Electrical Appliance Whslr
N.A.I.C.S.: 449210
Christina Goncalves (Mgr-Fin)

Vorwerk Semco S.A. (1)
20 Rte De Montigny, PO Box 80021, F 28220, Cloyes, France **(100%)**
Tel.: (33) 237445750
Web Site: http://www.vorwerk.com
Sales Range: $50-74.9 Million
Emp.: 200
Electrical Household Appliance Whslr
N.A.I.C.S.: 449210

Vorwerk Teppichwerke Co France (1)
30 Avenue de l'Amiral Lemonnier, 78160, Marly-le-Roi, France **(100%)**
Tel.: (33) 1 39 17 29 16
Web Site: http://www.vorwerk-carpet.com
Textiles
N.A.I.C.S.: 314999

Vorwerk Tornado AG (1)
Sternenhofstrasse 15A, CH-4135, Reinach, Switzerland
Tel.: (41) 617169888
Web Site: http://www.vorwerk.ch
Electrical Household Appliance Whslr
N.A.I.C.S.: 449210

ZEDA Gesellschaft fur Datenverarbeitung und EDV-Beratung mbH & Co. (1)
Am Diek 52, 42277, Wuppertal, Germany **(100%)**
Tel.: (49) 21123979300
Web Site: http://www.zeda.de
Sales Range: $50-74.9 Million
Emp.: 200
Provider of Applications Software & EDP Advisory Services
N.A.I.C.S.: 518210

afk leasing polska S.A. (1)
Al Armii Ludowej 26, 00-609, Warsaw, Poland
Tel.: (48) 22 417 83 77
Web Site: http://www.akf-polska.pl

Financial Management Services
N.A.I.C.S.: 523999
Lukasz Olesinki (Reg Dir-Sls)

akf Bank GmbH & Co. (1)
Friedrichstrasse 51, Wuppertal, 42105, Germany **(89%)**
Tel.: (49) 20249290
Web Site: http://www.akf.de
Sales Range: $50-74.9 Million
Emp.: 100
Investment Loans for Small to Medium-Sized Industrial Concerns; Leasing
N.A.I.C.S.: 522299
Martin Muderbach (Mgr-Sls)

akf Leasing GmbH & Co. (1)
Friedrichstrasse 51, D 42105, Wuppertal, Germany **(100%)**
Tel.: (49) 20249290
Web Site: http://www.akf.de
Sales Range: $25-49.9 Million
Emp.: 100
Provider of Leasing Services
N.A.I.C.S.: 561330

akf equiprent S.A. (1)
Avenida De Europa 12 - Plt 3 C Pq Empresarial La Moraleja, Alcobendas, Madrid, 28108, Spain
Tel.: (34) 916572296
Household Electronic Appliance Distr
N.A.I.C.S.: 423620

akf servicelease Gmbh (1)
Am Diek 50, 42277, Wuppertal, Germany
Tel.: (49) 202 25727 4000
Web Site: http://www.akf-servicelease.de
Financial Management Services
N.A.I.C.S.: 523999

VOSS VEKSEL-OG LANDMANDSBANK ASA
Tel.: (47) 56523500
Web Site: https://www.vekselbanken.no
VVL—(OSL)
Sales Range: Less than $1 Million
Commercial Banking Services
N.A.I.C.S.: 522110
Stig Gunnar Rothe (CEO)

VOSSLOH AG
Vosslohstr 4, 58791, Werdohl, Germany
Tel.: (49) 2392520 De
Web Site: https://www.vossloh.com
Year Founded: 1872
VOS—(MUN)
Rev.: $1,340,429,341
Assets: $1,537,359,749
Liabilities: $863,557,501
Net Worth: $673,802,248
Earnings: $42,719,769
Emp.: 4,145
Fiscal Year-end: 12/31/23
Rail Infrastructure & Technology Services
N.A.I.C.S.: 488210
Oliver Schuster (Member-Exec Bd)

Subsidiaries:

ATO-Asia Turnouts Limited (1)
South Sathorn Road Thungmahamek Sathorn, Bangkok, 10120, Thailand
Tel.: (66) 27161419
Rail Transportation Services
N.A.I.C.S.: 488210
Yves Hubert (Deputy Gen Mgr)

Austrak Pty. Ltd. (1)
Level 9295 Ann Street, GPO Box 606, Brisbane, 4000, QLD, Australia
Tel.: (61) 733285400
Web Site: http://www.austrak.com
Concrete Products Mfr
N.A.I.C.S.: 327390
Murray Adams (Gen Mgr)

Cleveland Track Material, Inc. (1)
6917 Bessemer Ave, Cleveland, OH 44127
Tel.: (216) 881-8800
Web Site: http://www.clevelandtrack.com
Sales Range: $25-49.9 Million
Emp.: 300

Railway Trackwork & Switching Component Mfr
N.A.I.C.S.: 532411

Imateq Italia S.r.l. (1)
Strada Comunale Savonesa 12/16 Interporto di Rivalta, Offices Building 39 - Workshop Building 60, 15057, Tortona, Italy
Tel.: (39) 0131850167
Web Site: http://www.en.imateq.it
Maintenance Repair Services
N.A.I.C.S.: 811210
Dirk Schwarzer (CEO)

Imateq SAS (1)
Rue de la Pichotiere, PO Box 20258, 37700, Saint-Pierre-des-Corps, Cedex 2, France
Tel.: (33) 982990310
Web Site: http://www.imateq.fr
Maintenance Repair Services
N.A.I.C.S.: 811210

Jacquemard AVR SA (1)
389 rue de Freres Lumiere ZI de Molina la Chazotte, 42650, Saint-Jean-Bonnefonds, France
Tel.: (33) 477476868
Rail Transportation Services
N.A.I.C.S.: 488210

Outreau Technologies SAS (1)
Rue Pierre Curie, 62230, Outreau, France
Tel.: (33) 321995300
Rail Track Mfr
N.A.I.C.S.: 331110

Rocla Concrete Tie, Inc. (1)
1819 Denver West Dr Ste 450, Lakewood, CO 80401
Tel.: (303) 296-3500
Web Site: http://www.roclatie.com
Concrete Railroad Ties Mfr
N.A.I.C.S.: 327390

Plant (Domestic):

Rocla Concrete Tie, Inc. - Bear Plant (2)
268 E Scotland Dr, Bear, DE 19701
Tel.: (302) 212-0510
Web Site: http://www.roclatie.com
Concrete Railroad Ties Mfr
N.A.I.C.S.: 327390
Mark Gaworowski (Mgr-Ops)

Vossloh Beekay Castings Ltd. (1)
25-28 Light Industrial Area, Bhilai, 490026, Chhattisgarh, India
Tel.: (91) 7882285471
Rail Transportation Services
N.A.I.C.S.: 488210

Vossloh Cogifer Australia Pty. Ltd. (1)
361 Barker Street, PO Box 1248, Castlemaine, 3450, VIC, Australia
Tel.: (61) 344111555
Rail Transportation Services
N.A.I.C.S.: 488210

Vossloh Cogifer Italia S.r.L. (1)
Viale G Bovio 48 int 8, 47521, Cesena, FC, Italy
Tel.: (39) 0547698010
Rail Transportation Services
N.A.I.C.S.: 488210

Vossloh Cogifer Kloos BV (1)
Lekdijk 270, 2957 CL, Nieuw-Lekkerland, Netherlands
Tel.: (31) 184687580
Rail Switch & Cross Mfr
N.A.I.C.S.: 331110

Vossloh Cogifer Polska Sp.z o.o. (1)
UL Ludwikowo 2, 85-502, Bydgoszcz, Poland
Tel.: (48) 523225224
Rail Transportation Services
N.A.I.C.S.: 488210

Vossloh Cogifer SA (1)
54 Avenue Victor Hugo, BP 56606, 92566, Rueil-Malmaison, Cedex, France **(100%)**
Tel.: (33) 55477300
Web Site: http://www.cogifer.com
Rev.: $375,000,000
Emp.: 45
Railway Equipment Mfr
N.A.I.C.S.: 333120

AND PRIVATE COMPANIES

Subsidiary (Non-US):

KIHN SA (2)
17 rue de l Usine, 3754, Rumelange, Luxembourg
Tel.: (352) 56 47 71 1
Web Site: http://www.kihn.com
Sales Range: $25-49.9 Million
Rail Fastening Systems Mfr
N.A.I.C.S.: 332999

Vossloh Cogifer Kihn SA (2)
17 rue de l'Usine, 3754, Rumelange, Luxembourg
Tel.: (352) 5647711
Rail Transportation Services
N.A.I.C.S.: 488210

Subsidiary (Non-US):

Vossloh Laeis GmbH (3)
Schonbornstrasse 1, 54295, Trier, Germany
Tel.: (49) 6515580
Rail Transportation Services
N.A.I.C.S.: 488210

Subsidiary (Non-US):

Vossloh Nordic Switch Systems AB (2)
Forskeppsgatan 8, PO Box 1512, 27100, Ystad, Skane, Sweden
Tel.: (46) 101601100
Web Site: https://www.vossloh-nordic.com
Sales Range: $25-49.9 Million
Rail Fastening Systems Mfr
N.A.I.C.S.: 332999
Susanne Klyft (Dir-Environment, Health & Safety)

Subsidiary (Non-US):

Vossloh Cogifer Finland Oy (3)
Hitsaamontie 5, 46400, Kaipiainen, Turku Ja Pori, Finland
Tel.: (358) 207299939
Rail Fastening Systems Mfr
N.A.I.C.S.: 332999

Vossloh Cogifer Signalling India Private Limited (1)
3G 3G-1 4P and 4P-1 Heavy Industrial Area Hathkhoj, Bhilai, 490026, Chhattisgarh, India
Tel.: (91) 7882291073
Rail Transportation Services
N.A.I.C.S.: 488210

Vossloh Cogifer Southern Africa Proprietary Limited (1)
Central Park Building - Block C 16th Road N 400, PO Box 5965, 1685, Midrand, South Africa
Tel.: (27) 113125846
Rail Transportation Services
N.A.I.C.S.: 488210

Vossloh Cogifer Turnouts India Private Limited (1)
Plot No 145/A IDA Bollaram Jinnaram M, Medak, 502325, Andhra Pradesh, India
Tel.: (91) 8458204088
Rail Transportation Services
N.A.I.C.S.: 488210

Vossloh Cogifer UK Limited (1)
80A Scotter Road, Scunthorpe, DN15 8EF, Lincolnshire, United Kingdom
Tel.: (44) 1724862131
Rail Transportation Services
N.A.I.C.S.: 488210

Vossloh Cogifer do Brasil Metalurgica MBM SA (1)
Avenida Comendador Pereira Inacio 1683, 18030-005, Sorocaba, Sao Paul, Brazil
Tel.: (55) 1532194020
Rail Transportation Services
N.A.I.C.S.: 488210

Vossloh Drazni Technica s.r.o. (1)
Zeleny Pruh 99, 14050, Prague, Czech Republic
Tel.: (420) 241445159
Web Site: http://www.vossloh-rail-systems.de
Sales Range: $25-49.9 Million
Emp.: 2
Rail Fastenings Mfr
N.A.I.C.S.: 332999

Vossloh Fastening Systems GmbH (1)
Tel.: (49) 2392520
Web Site: http://www.vossloh-fastening-systems.de
Sales Range: $100-124.9 Million
Emp.: 500
Rail Fastening Systems Mfr
N.A.I.C.S.: 331110

Subsidiary (US):

Vossloh Fastening Systems America Corporation (2)
316 Cotton Belt Pkwy, Waco, TX 76657
Tel.: (312) 376-3200
Web Site: http://www.vossloh-usa.com
Rail Fastening Systems Mfr
N.A.I.C.S.: 331110
Cecilia Lopez (Office Mgr)

Subsidiary (Non-US):

Vossloh Fastening Systems China Co. Ltd. (1)
158 Yuanfeng Road, Yushan Town, Kunshan, 215300, Jiangsu, China
Tel.: (86) 51281638788
Rail Fastening Systems Mfr
N.A.I.C.S.: 331110

Vossloh Rail Technology Limitet Sirketi (2)
Barbaros Blv Morbasan Sokak Koza is Merkezi B-Blok Kat 1, 34349, Besiktas, Istanbul, Turkiye
Tel.: (90) 2122759203
Emp.: 4
Rail Fastening Systems Mfr
N.A.I.C.S.: 332999
Sane Barak (Gen Mgr)

Vossloh Sistemi s.r.l. (2)
Viale G Bovio 48 int 8, 47521, Cesena, Forli-Cesena, Italy
Tel.: (39) 0547698010
Sales Range: $25-49.9 Million
Emp.: 3
Rail Fastening Systems Mfr
N.A.I.C.S.: 332999

Vossloh Skamo Sp.z.o.o. (2)
ul Kolejowa 18a, 63-460, Nowe Skalmierzyce, Poland
Tel.: (48) 627621523
Web Site: http://www.vossloh-skamo.pl
Rail Fastening Systems Mfr
N.A.I.C.S.: 332999

Vossloh Tehnika Feroviara S.R.L. (2)
Str N Constantinescu No 10 Bl 16A Sc 2 Ap 12 Sector 1, 011713, Bucharest, Romania
Tel.: (40) 2123 04271
Web Site: http://www.vossloh.ro
Sales Range: $25-49.9 Million
Emp.: 2
Rail Fastening Systems Mfr
N.A.I.C.S.: 331110

Vossloh Rail Inspection GmbH (1)
Hugo-Aurig-Str 1c, 04319, Leipzig, Germany
Tel.: (49) 3419898960
Rail Transportation Services
N.A.I.C.S.: 488210

Vossloh Rail Services Finland Oy (1)
Hitsaamontie 5a, 46400, Kaipiainen, Finland
Tel.: (358) 400738317
Rail Transportation Services
N.A.I.C.S.: 488210

Vossloh Rail Services GmbH (1)
Hannoversche Strasse 10, 21079, Hamburg, Germany
Tel.: (49) 404309310
Rail Transportation Services
N.A.I.C.S.: 488210

Subsidiary (Domestic):

Vossloh Logistics GmbH (2)
Ellernstrasse 42, 30175, Hannover, Germany
Tel.: (49) 511380980
Rail Transportation Services
N.A.I.C.S.: 488210

Vossloh Rail Center GmbH (2)
Reller 28, 21079, Hamburg, Germany
Tel.: (49) 407691860
Rail Transportation Services
N.A.I.C.S.: 488210

Subsidiary (Domestic):

Alpha Rail Team GmbH & Co. KG (3)
Rudower Chaussee 9, 12489, Berlin, Germany
Tel.: (49) 30585847401
Rail Transportation Services
N.A.I.C.S.: 488210

Vossloh Mobile Rail Services GmbH (3)
Hugo-Aurig-Strasse 3, 04319, Leipzig, Germany
Tel.: (49) 34165240310
Rail Switch Mfr
N.A.I.C.S.: 331110

Vossloh Rail Services Scandinavia AB (1)
Kindstugatan 1, 111 31, Stockholm, Sweden
Tel.: (46) 195555830
Rail Transportation Services
N.A.I.C.S.: 488210

Vossloh Ray Hizmetleri Limited Sirketi (1)
Bati Bulvan ATB Macun Mahallesi 174 Cad ATB Is Merkezi E/Blok No 1/101, 06105, Ankara, Turkiye
Tel.: (90) 2122759203
Rail Transportation Services
N.A.I.C.S.: 488210

Vossloh Services France SAS (1)
21 Avenue de Colmar, 92565, Rueil-Malmaison, Cedex, France
Tel.: (33) 388094950
Rail Transportation Services
N.A.I.C.S.: 488210

Vossloh Signaling USA, Inc. (1)
12799 Loma Rica Dr, Grass Valley, CA 95945
Tel.: (530) 272-8194
Rail Transportation Services
N.A.I.C.S.: 488210
David Ruskauff (Sr VP-Ops)

Vossloh Tehnica Feroviara SRL (1)
Str N Constantinescu No 10 Bl 16A Sc 2 Ap 12 Sector 1, 011713, Bucharest, Romania
Tel.: (40) 212304271
Rail Transportation Services
N.A.I.C.S.: 488210

Vossloh Tie Technologies Canada ULC (1)
Monte Lake Rd Thompson-Nicola L, Vancouver, V0E 2N0, BC, Canada
Tel.: (250) 375-2186
Rail Transportation Services
N.A.I.C.S.: 488210

Vossloh Track Material, Inc. (1)
5662 Leesport Ave, Reading, PA 19605-9802
Tel.: (304) 722-1890
Web Site: http://www.vossloh-track-material.com
Sales Range: $50-74.9 Million
New & Used Railroad Supplies
N.A.I.C.S.: 336510

Vossloh Utenzilija d.d. (1)
Samoborska cesta 129, 10090, Zagreb, Croatia
Tel.: (385) 13496740
Web Site: http://www.utenzilija.hr
Sales Range: $25-49.9 Million
Emp.: 40
Rail Fastenings Mfr
N.A.I.C.S.: 331110

Vossloh Werdohl GmbH (1)
Vosslohstr 4, Werdohl, 58791, Nordrhein-Westfalen, Germany
Tel.: (49) 2392520
Web Site: http://www.vossloh.de
Emp.: 300
Rail Fastenings Mfr
N.A.I.C.S.: 331110

Vossloh-Werke GmbH (1)

Vosslohstr 4, 58791, Werdohl, Nordrhein-Westfalen, Germany
Tel.: (49) 2392520
Investment Management Service
N.A.I.C.S.: 523999
Dominik Simon Schuetz (Mng Dir)

VOTI DETECTION, INC.
790 Begin Street St Laurent, Saint Laurent, H4M 2N5, QC, Canada
Tel.: (514) 782-1566
Web Site: http://www.votidetection.com
Year Founded: 2008
VOTI—(TSXV)
Rev.: $14,874,198
Assets: $16,829,900
Liabilities: $12,004,827
Net Worth: $4,825,073
Earnings: ($5,268,977)
Fiscal Year-end: 10/31/20
Electric Equipment Mfr
N.A.I.C.S.: 334419
Michael Ickman (CFO)

Subsidiaries:

VOTI Security Scanning International DWC-LLC. (1)
Building A3 Office 120 DWC-Dubai World Central, PO Box 712060, Dubai, United Arab Emirates
Tel.: (971) 48842585
Detection & Scanning System Mfr
N.A.I.C.S.: 334517

VOTORANTIM S.A.
Rua Amauri 255 13th Floor, Sao Paulo, 01448 000, Brazil
Tel.: (55) 1137043300 BR
Web Site: http://www.votorantim.com.br
Year Founded: 1918
Rev.: $7,651,955,060
Assets: $20,975,720,340
Liabilities: $9,362,485,280
Net Worth: $11,613,235,060
Earnings: $1,219,331,500
Emp.: 8,838
Fiscal Year-end: 12/31/19
Holding Company; Industrial & Financial Products & Services
N.A.I.C.S.: 551112
Jose Roberto Ermirio de Moraes (Vice Chm)

Subsidiaries:

Acerbrag S.A. (1)
Optima Business Park Torre 2 - Piso 5 Alferez Hipolito Bouchard, Vicente Lopez, 4191, Munro, Buenos Aires, Argentina
Tel.: (54) 1140067100
Web Site: http://www.acerbrag.com
Iron & Steel Mill Ferroalloy Mfr
N.A.I.C.S.: 331110
Andres Jersonsky (Comml Dir)

Banco Votorantim SA (1)
Av das Nacoes Unidas 14 171 Torre A 18th floor - Vila Gertrude, 04794-000, Sao Paulo, SP, Brazil (100%)
Tel.: (55) 1151711000
Web Site: http://www.bancovotorantim.com.br
Rev.: $3,961,266,859
Assets: $28,228,933,569
Liabilities: $25,443,555,939
Net Worth: $2,785,377,630
Earnings: $189,806,831
Emp.: 3,937
Fiscal Year-end: 12/13/2017
Banking Services
N.A.I.C.S.: 522110
Jose Luiz Majolo (Vice Chm)

Subsidiary (Domestic):

BV Leasing - Arrendamento Mercantil S.A. (2)
Alameda Rio Negro 1105 - 3 Floor, 09520-070, Barueri, SP, Brazil
Tel.: (55) 11 5185 1705
Financial Lending Services

VOTORANTIM S.A.

Votorantim S.A.—(Continued)
N.A.I.C.S.: 522220
Gabriel Jose Gama Ferreira (CEO)

Cia. Agro Industrial Igarassu (1)
Rodovia PE 41 Km 6, Araripe Igarassu, 536 00, Recife, PE, Brazil
Tel.: (55) 8135437100
Agricultural Chemical Mfr
N.A.I.C.S.: 325998

Companhia Brasileira de Aluminio (1)
Avenida Luis Carlos Berrini 105 - 14th floor Cidade Moncoes, PO Box 4624, Sao Paulo, 04571-010, SP, Brazil (30.93%)
Tel.: (55) 1155086800
Web Site: http://www.aluminiocba.com.br
Sales Range: $1-4.9 Billion
Aluminum Production
N.A.I.C.S.: 331313

Companhia Niquel Tocantins (1)
Av Dr Jose Artur Nova 1309, Paulista, 0809-000, Brazil
Tel.: (55) 1169568600
Web Site: http://www.vmetais.com
Sales Range: $100-124.9 Million
Emp.: 280
Provider of Chemicals
N.A.I.C.S.: 325998

Companhia Nordestina de Papel (CONPEL) (1)
BR 101 Km 06 Municipio do Conde, Paraiba do Sul, Brazil (0.71%)
Tel.: (55) 2182301
Provider of Paper
N.A.I.C.S.: 322120

Industria e Comercio Metalurgica Atlas S.A.
Av Jose Cesar de Oliveira 111, Vila Hamburguesa, Sao Paulo, 05317-000, Brazil (100%)
Tel.: (55) 11 3838 3838
Web Site: http://www.metalurgicaatlas.com.br
Sales Range: $350-399.9 Million
Emp.: 1,600
Provider of Metals Services
N.A.I.C.S.: 332812

Nexa Recursos Minerias S.A. (1)
Av Engenheiro Luis Carlos Berrini 105, Sao Paulo, 04571-010, Brazil
Tel.: (55) 1134054499
Web Site: http://www.nexaresources.com
Mineral Mining Services
N.A.I.C.S.: 213114
Alexandre Abe (Mgr-Logistics)

Nexa Resources Peru S.A.A. (1)
Av Circunvalacion del Golf los Incas 170, Santiago de Surco, Lima, Peru (80.24%)
Tel.: (51) 17105500
Web Site: http://www.nexaresources.com
Rev.: $735,337,000
Assets: $1,221,303,000
Liabilities: $513,118,000
Net Worth: $708,185,000
Earnings: $46,443,000
Emp.: 1,510
Fiscal Year-end: 12/31/2023
Zinc, Copper, Lead, Silver & Gold Mining Services
N.A.I.C.S.: 212290
Claudia Patricia Toress Beltran (CFO)

Nitro Quimica S.A. (1)
Av Dr Jose Arthur Nova 951, Sao Paulo, 08090 000, Brazil (100%)
Tel.: (55) 11 6137 3100
Web Site: http://www.nitroquimica.com.br
Sales Range: $100-124.9 Million
Emp.: 400
Chemicals Mfr
N.A.I.C.S.: 325998

United Materials LLC (1)
3949 Forest Park Way Ste 400, North Tonawanda, NY 14120-3760
Tel.: (716) 683-1432
Web Site: http://www.umconcrete.com
Sales Range: $10-24.9 Million
Emp.: 57
Ready Mixed Concrete
N.A.I.C.S.: 327320
Richard Holmes (Owner)

Votocel Filmes Flexiveis Ltda. (1)
Rua Irma Ferraresi s/n, 18115-350, Votorantim, SP, Brazil (10.52%)
Tel.: (55) 152429900
Provider of Textiles
N.A.I.C.S.: 313210

Votorantim Cementos EAA Inversiones, S.L. (1)
C/ Brasil No 56, 36204, Vigo, Spain
Tel.: (34) 986269000
Cement Material Mfr
N.A.I.C.S.: 327310
Maria Jose Martin Aradilla (Comm Mgr)

Votorantim Cementos International S.A. (1)
35 Avenue JF Kennedy 1st Floor A2, 1855, Luxembourg, Luxembourg
Tel.: (352) 27300356
Web Site: http://www.votorantimcimentos.lu
Cement Material Mfr
N.A.I.C.S.: 327310
Antonio Pelicano (CFO)

Votorantim Cimentos S.A. (1)
Edificio Sky Corporate - R Gomes de Carvalho 1996, Vila Olimpia, Sao Paulo, 04547-006, Brazil
Tel.: (55) 114572 4000
Web Site: http://vcimentos.mzweb.com.br
Rev.: $3,225,226,888
Assets: $7,425,883,820
Liabilities: $4,386,986,630
Net Worth: $3,038,897,190
Earnings: $135,980,839
Emp.: 3,353
Fiscal Year-end: 12/31/2019
Construction Supplies Mfr
N.A.I.C.S.: 327310
Osvaldo Ayres Filho (CEO-Global)

Subsidiary (Non-US):

St. Marys Cement Inc. (2)
55 Industrial St, Toronto, M4G 3W9, ON, Canada (100%)
Tel.: (416) 696-4411
Web Site: https://www.stmaryscement.com
Sales Range: $600-649.9 Million
Emp.: 1,500
Cement & Concrete Mfr
N.A.I.C.S.: 327310

Votorantim Energia Ltda. (1)
Avenida Doutora Ruth Cardoso 8 501, Pinheiros, Sao Paulo, 05425-070, SP, Brazil
Tel.: (55) 1128742590
Web Site: http://www.venergia.com.br
Sales Range: $50-74.9 Million
Emp.: 45
Energy Generation & Distribution Services
N.A.I.C.S.: 221122

Votorantim Metais Ltda. (1)
Praca Ramos de Azevedo 254, Sao Paulo, 01037 912, Brazil
Tel.: (55) 1132229975
Zinc & Nickel Mining & Steel Production
N.A.I.C.S.: 212230

VOTUM S.A.

ul Wyscigowa 56 i, 53-012, Wroclaw, Poland
Tel.: (48) 800217417
Web Site: https://www.votum-sa.pl
Year Founded: 2005
VOT—(WAR)
Rev.: $98,358,740
Assets: $112,865,345
Liabilities: $47,187,500
Net Worth: $65,677,845
Earnings: $34,017,022
Fiscal Year-end: 12/31/23
Auto Accident Advisory Services
N.A.I.C.S.: 541199
Bartlomiej Krupa (Chm & CEO)

Subsidiaries:

VOTUM-RehaPlus S.A (1)
ul Golikowka 6, 30-723, Krakow, Poland
Tel.: (48) 12 264 80 35
Web Site: http://www.votumrehaplus.pl
Disabled Rehabilitation Services
N.A.I.C.S.: 622310

VOUSSE CORP S.A.

Cl/ Escolano 20, 46001, Valencia, Spain
Tel.: (34) 963393663
Web Site: http://vousse.com
VOU—(MAD)
Sales Range: $1-9.9 Million
Aesthetic Medical Treatments
N.A.I.C.S.: 812990
Antonio Caparros (Gen Dir)

VOW ASA

Lysaker Torg 12, 1366, Lysaker, Norway
Tel.: (47) 67200300
Web Site: https://vowasa.com
Year Founded: 2011
VOW—(OSL)
Rev.: $90,293,345
Assets: $150,908,343
Liabilities: $111,940,154
Net Worth: $38,968,189
Earnings: ($14,971,885)
Emp.: 249
Fiscal Year-end: 12/31/23
Waste & Wastewater Processing
N.A.I.C.S.: 562211
Narve Reiten (Chm)

Subsidiaries:

C. H. Evensen Industriovner AS (1)
Tomteveien 19, 1618, Fredrikstad, Norway
Tel.: (47) 69949100
Web Site: https://www.che.no
Emp.: 50
Industrial Furnace & Equipment Mfr
N.A.I.C.S.: 333994

Scanship AS (1)
Nedre Langgate 19, 3126, Tonsberg, Norway
Tel.: (47) 33016400
Web Site: https://www.scanship.no
Hazardous Water & Disposal Services
N.A.I.C.S.: 562211

Scanship Americas Inc. (1)
3711 SW 47th Ave Ste 201, Davie, FL 33314
Tel.: (954) 651-6205
Hazardous Water & Disposal Services
N.A.I.C.S.: 562211

Scanship Poland Sp z o.o (1)
Al Zwyciestwa 96/98, 81-451, Gdynia, Poland
Tel.: (48) 501190058
Hazardous Water & Disposal Services
N.A.I.C.S.: 562211

VOW EUROPE LTD.

Kaye House Sheffield Business Park, Europa Link, Sheffield, S9 1XU, United Kingdom
Tel.: (44) 1142566000
Web Site: http://www.voweurope.com
Year Founded: 1999
Sales Range: $400-449.9 Million
Emp.: 1,100
Office Supplies Distr
N.A.I.C.S.: 423420
Steve Blowers (Dir-Dealer Grp)

VOX ROYALTY CORP.

66 Wellington Street West Suite 5300 TD Bank Tower, Box 48, Toronto, M5K 1E6, ON, Canada
Tel.: (345) 815-3939 ON
Web Site: https://www.voxroyalty.com
Year Founded: 2014
VOXR—(NASDAQ)
Rev.: $8,508,105
Assets: $41,805,456
Liabilities: $6,391,008
Net Worth: $35,414,448
Earnings: $328,179
Emp.: 7
Fiscal Year-end: 12/31/22
Mining Services
N.A.I.C.S.: 212210

INTERNATIONAL PUBLIC

Adrian Cochrane (VP)

VOX VALOR CAPITAL LIMITED

Suite A-02-02 Empire Office Tower Jalan SS16/1, 47500, Subang Jaya, Selangor, Malaysia
Tel.: (60) 356133377 Ky
Web Site: http://www.vertucapital.co.uk
VOX—(LSE)
Rev.: $5,572,881
Assets: $12,590,131
Liabilities: $3,539,021
Net Worth: $9,051,110
Earnings: ($187,455)
Emp.: 30
Fiscal Year-end: 12/31/23
Investment Management Service
N.A.I.C.S.: 523940
Simon Retter (Fin Dir)

VOXEL S.A.

ul Wielicka 265, 30-663, Krakow, Poland
Tel.: (48) 123122396
Web Site: https://www.voxel.pl
Year Founded: 2005
VOX—(WAR)
Rev.: $10,776,992
Assets: $13,440,889
Liabilities: $5,935,610
Net Worth: $7,505,279
Earnings: $2,088,717
Fiscal Year-end: 12/31/23
Medical Diagnostic Services
N.A.I.C.S.: 621512
Jacek Liszka (Chm)

VOXELJET AG

Paul-Lenz Strasse 1a, 86316, Friedberg, Germany
Tel.: (49) 8217483100 De
Web Site: https://www.voxeljet.de
VJTTY—(NASDAQ)
Rev.: $36,787,572
Assets: $50,294,525
Liabilities: $35,452,993
Net Worth: $14,841,532
Earnings: ($12,527,821)
Emp.: 259
Fiscal Year-end: 12/31/23
High-Speed, Large-Format 3D Printers Mfr
N.A.I.C.S.: 333248
Peter G. Nietzer (Chm-Supervisory Bd)

Subsidiaries:

Voxeljet of America Inc. (1)
41430 Haggerty Cir, Canton, MI 48188
Tel.: (734) 808-0025
Emp.: 20
Printing Machinery Distr
N.A.I.C.S.: 423830

voxeljet China Co. Ltd. (1)
No 558 Fenhu Avenue, FOHO New And Hi-Tech Industrial Development Zone, Suzhou, 215211, Jiangsu, China
Tel.: (86) 51280673618
Engineeering Services
N.A.I.C.S.: 541330

voxeljet India Pvt. Ltd. (1)
20th Floor Oberoi Commerz II, International Business Park Oberoi Garden City Goregaon East, Mumbai, 400063, Maharashtra, India
Tel.: (91) 9702330088
Engineeering Services
N.A.I.C.S.: 541330

VOXTUR ANALYTICS CORP.

175 Bloor Street East South Tower, Toronto, M4W 3R8, ON, Canada
Tel.: (519) 963-2015
Web Site: https://www.voxtur.com
Year Founded: 2000

AND PRIVATE COMPANIES

VXTR—(TSXV)
Rev.: $36,969,920
Assets: $76,798,724
Liabilities: $42,955,001
Net Worth: $33,843,723
Earnings: ($50,875,455)
Emp.: 171
Fiscal Year-end: 12/31/23
Software Development Services
N.A.I.C.S.: 541511
Gary Yeoman *(CEO)*

Subsidiaries:

Blue Water Financial Technologies
Holding Company, LLC (1)
18258 Minnetonka Blvd Ste 201, Deephaven, MN 55391
Tel.: (612) 286-1383
Web Site: https://bluewater-fintech.com
Financial Support Services
N.A.I.C.S.: 541611

Municipal Tax Equity Consultants
Inc. (1)
543 Ridout St N, London, N6A 2P8, ON, Canada
Tel.: (905) 878-7978
Web Site: http://www.mte.ca
Financial Support Services
N.A.I.C.S.: 541611

Starcap Marketing, LLC (1)
5039 Beckwith Blvd Ste 109, San Antonio, TX 78249
Tel.: (210) 699-6666
Web Site: http://www.apexwin.com
Prepackaged Software
N.A.I.C.S.: 513210

iLOOKABOUT Inc. (1)
383 Richmond St, London, N6A 3C4, ON, Canada
Tel.: (519) 963-2015
Web Site: https://www.ilookabout.com
Sales Range: $25-49.9 Million
Emp.: 20
Data Management Software Development Services
N.A.I.C.S.: 541511
Gary Yeoman *(CEO)*

VOYAGEUR MINERAL EXPLORERS CORP.
141 Adelaide Street West Suite 301, Toronto, M5H 3L5, ON, Canada
Tel.: (416) 628-5901 MB
Web Site: https://voyageurexplorers.com
Year Founded: 1973
VOY—(CNSX)
Rev.: $46,730
Assets: $806,147
Liabilities: $27,977
Net Worth: $778,170
Earnings: ($200,157)
Emp.: 5
Fiscal Year-end: 11/30/23
Copper Mining Services
N.A.I.C.S.: 212230
Stephen L. Masson *(VP-Exploration)*

VOYAGEUR PHARMACEUTICALS LTD.
Dome tower 800 333 7 Ave Street, Calgary, T2P 2Z1, AB, Canada
Tel.: (587) 779-6166 AB
Web Site: https://www.voyageurpharma.ca
Year Founded: 2008
VM—(TSXV)
Assets: $1,633,816
Liabilities: $549,632
Net Worth: $1,084,184
Earnings: ($1,056,761)
Fiscal Year-end: 11/30/23
Investment Services
N.A.I.C.S.: 523999
Brent Willis *(Pres & CEO)*

VOYAGEURS DU MONDE SA
55 rue Sainte Anne, 75002, Paris, France
Tel.: (33) 0142861600
Web Site: https://www.vdm.com
Year Founded: 1979
ALVDM—(EUR)
Sales Range: $500-549.9 Million
Travel Agency Services
N.A.I.C.S.: 561510
Jean-Francois Rial *(CEO)*

VOZ MOBILE CLOUD LTD.
190 Middle Road #19-05 Fortune Centre, Singapore, 688979, Singapore
Tel.: (65) 67958729 WA
Software Publisher
N.A.I.C.S.: 513210

VP BANK AG
Aeulestrasse 6, 9490, Vaduz, Liechtenstein
Tel.: (423) 2356655 LI
Web Site: https://www.vpbank.com
Year Founded: 1956
Sales Range: $100-124.9 Million
Emp.: 766
Banking Services
N.A.I.C.S.: 522110
Markus Thomas Hilti *(Vice Chm)*

Subsidiaries:

IFOS Internationale Fonds Service
AG (1)
Aeulestrasse 6, Vaduz, 9490, Liechtenstein
Tel.: (423) 2356767
Web Site: http://www.ifos.li
Sales Range: $50-74.9 Million
Emp.: 30
Investment Fund Services
N.A.I.C.S.: 523940
Alexander Boss *(Pres)*

IGT Intergestions Trust Reg. (1)
Aeulestrasse 6, Postfach 1242, 9490, Vaduz, Liechtenstein
Tel.: (423) 2331151
Sales Range: $50-74.9 Million
Emp.: 8
Private Banking Services
N.A.I.C.S.: 523999

VP Bank (BVI) Ltd. (1)
3076 Sir Francis Drakes Highway, PO Box 3463, Tortola, Virgin Islands (British)
Tel.: (284) 4941100
Web Site: http://www.vpbank.vg
Sales Range: $50-74.9 Million
Emp.: 8
Banking
N.A.I.C.S.: 522110

VP Bank (Luxembourg) S.A. (1)
Avenue de la liberte 26, PO Box 923, 2019, Luxembourg, Luxembourg
Tel.: (352) 4047701
Web Site: http://www.vpbank.com
Sales Range: $50-74.9 Million
Emp.: 100
Banking
N.A.I.C.S.: 522110
Yves de Vos *(Mng Dir)*

VP Bank (Schweiz) AG (1)
Talstrasse 59, 8001, Zurich, Switzerland
Tel.: (41) 442262424
Web Site: http://www.vpbank.ch
Rev.: $307,373,471
Assets: $13,087,682,636
Liabilities: $12,069,413,655
Net Worth: $1,018,268,981
Earnings: $67,363,607
Emp.: 780
Fiscal Year-end: 12/31/2017
Banking Services
N.A.I.C.S.: 522110
Siegbert Nascher *(CFO & Deputy CEO)*

VP Bank Fondsleitung AG (1)
Aeulestrasse 6, Vaduz, 9490, Liechtenstein
Tel.: (423) 2356655
Web Site: http://www.ifos.li
Sales Range: $50-74.9 Million
Emp.: 15
Banking

N.A.I.C.S.: 522110
Alfred Moeckli *(CEO)*

VP EXPLOITATIE N.V.
Bergstraat 28, 5051 HC, Goirle, Netherlands
Tel.: (31) 13 530 8120 NI
Web Site: http://vpcapital.eu
Investment Services
N.A.I.C.S.: 523999
Guus van Puijenbroek *(Mng Dir)*

Subsidiaries:

Mediahuis NV (1)
Katwilgweg 2, 2050, Antwerp, Belgium
Tel.: (32) 3 210 02 10
Web Site: http://www.mediahuis.be
Newspaper & Magazine Publishing Services
N.A.I.C.S.: 513110
Gert Ysebaert *(CEO)*

Subsidiary (Non-US):

Independent News & Media PLC (2)
Independent House 27-32 Talbot Street, Dublin, 1, Ireland
Tel.: (353) 14663200
Web Site: http://www.inmplc.com
Rev.: $350,972,980
Assets: $245,321,728
Liabilities: $154,164,582
Net Worth: $91,157,146
Earnings: $14,973,250
Emp.: 845
Fiscal Year-end: 12/31/2017
International Newspaper & Magazine Publishing
N.A.I.C.S.: 513110
Ryan Preston *(CFO)*

Subsidiary (Non-US):

Abbey Communications (Netherlands) B.V. (3)
Locatellikade 1, Amsterdam, 1076 AZ, Netherlands
Tel.: (31) 205755600
Newspaper Publishing Services
N.A.I.C.S.: 513110

Subsidiary (Domestic):

Drogheda Independent Company Limited (3)
9 Shop St, Drogheda, Ireland
Tel.: (353) 419838658
Web Site: http://www.drogheda-independent.ie
Sales Range: $25-49.9 Million
Emp.: 30
Newspaper Publishers
N.A.I.C.S.: 513110

INM Securities (Ireland) Limited (3)
27-32 Talbot Street, Dublin, 1, Ireland
Tel.: (353) 1 466 3200
Web Site: http://www.inmplc.com
Emp.: 300
Newspaper Publishing Services
N.A.I.C.S.: 513110

Independent Colleges Limited (3)
60 - 63 Dawson Street, Dublin, Ireland
Tel.: (353) 1 6725058
Web Site: http://www.independentcolleges.ie
Education Development Services
N.A.I.C.S.: 611310
Padraig Hourigan *(Pres & CEO)*

Independent Communications Limited (3)
Independent House 27-32 Talbot Street, Dublin, 1, Ireland
Tel.: (353) 1 466 3200
Holding Company; Newspaper Publisher
N.A.I.C.S.: 551112
Robert Pitt *(CEO)*

Subsidiary (Domestic):

Independent Communications (Ireland) Limited (4)
3050 Lake Drive Citywest Digital Park, 24, Dublin, Ireland
Tel.: (353) 14112000
Sales Range: $25-49.9 Million
Emp.: 50
Newspaper Publishers

N.A.I.C.S.: 513110

Subsidiary (Domestic):

Independent Digital Limited (3)
2023 Bianconi Avenue, Dublin, Ireland
Tel.: (353) 1 466 3200
Web Site: http://www.independent.ie
Newspaper Publishing Services
N.A.I.C.S.: 513110

Independent Newspapers (Ireland) Limited (3)
27232 Talbot St, 27-32 Talbot St, Dublin, 1, Ireland
Tel.: (353) 17055333
Web Site: http://www.independent.ie
Sales Range: $100-124.9 Million
Emp.: 400
Newspaper Publishers
N.A.I.C.S.: 513110

Independent Newspapers Management Services Limited (3)
2023 Bianconi Ave Citywest Business Campus, Dublin, Ireland
Tel.: (353) 1 466 3200
Web Site: http://www.independent.ie
Business Management Consulting Services
N.A.I.C.S.: 541611

Joint Venture (Domestic):

Independent Star Limited (3)
Independent House, 27-32 Talbot Street, Dublin, 1, Ireland
Tel.: (353) 14901228
Web Site: http://www.thestar.ie
Sales Range: $25-49.9 Million
Emp.: 100
Newspaper Publishers
N.A.I.C.S.: 513110

Subsidiary (Domestic):

Internet Interaction Limited (3)
3050 Lake Drive Citywest Digital Park, Dublin, Ireland
Tel.: (353) 14112000
Sales Range: $25-49.9 Million
Emp.: 50
Newspaper Publishers
N.A.I.C.S.: 513110

Newspread Limited (3)
3050 Lake Drive Citywest Digital Pk Naas Rd, Dublin, 24, Ireland
Tel.: (353) 14537262
Web Site: http://www.newspread.ie
Sales Range: $25-49.9 Million
Emp.: 65
Whslr, Distr & Publisher of Newspapar & Magazines
N.A.I.C.S.: 513199

Sunday Newspapers Limited (3)
Independent House 27-32 Talbot Street, Dublin, 1, Ireland
Tel.: (353) 18849000
Web Site: http://www.sundayworld.com
Sales Range: $25-49.9 Million
Emp.: 70
Newspaper Publishers
N.A.I.C.S.: 513110

The Kerryman Limited (3)
9 - 10 Denny St, Tralee, Ireland
Tel.: (353) 667145560
Web Site: http://www.kerryman.ie
Sales Range: $25-49.9 Million
Emp.: 25
Newspaper Publishers
N.A.I.C.S.: 513199

Subsidiary (Non-US):

Mediahuis Nederland B.V. (2)
Basisweg 30, 1043 AP, Amsterdam, Netherlands
Tel.: (31) 888242222
Web Site: http://www.mediahuis.nl
Newspaper, Magazine, Internet & Mobile Applications Publisher; Radio Operations
N.A.I.C.S.: 513110
Koos Boot *(CFO)*

Subsidiary (Domestic):

Metro Holland B.V. (3)
Delfandlaan 4, NL 1062 EB, Amsterdam, Netherlands

VP Exploitatie N.V.—(Continued)

Tel.: (31) 20 5114000
Web Site: http://www.metronieuws.nl
Newspaper Publishing
N.A.I.C.S.: 513110
Marshal Den Hoed (Dir-Comm)

Telegraaf Media Nederland (3)
Basisweg 30, 1043 AP, Amsterdam, Netherlands
Tel.: (31) 205859111
Web Site: http://www.telegraaf.nl
Media Holding Group
N.A.I.C.S.: 551112

Subsidiary (Domestic):

Nobiles Media BV (4)
Basisweg 30, Amsterdam, 1043 AP, Netherlands
Tel.: (31) 206231800
Web Site: http://www.speurders.nl
Online Information for Students
N.A.I.C.S.: 519290

VP PLC

Central House Beckwith Knowle Otley Road, Harrogate, HG3 1UD, North Yorkshire, United Kingdom
Tel.: (44) 1423533400
Web Site: https://www.vpplc.com
Year Founded: 1954
VP—(LSE)
Rev.: $476,444,314
Assets: $630,616,135
Liabilities: $404,440,349
Net Worth: $226,175,786
Earnings: $34,669,380
Emp.: 2,833
Fiscal Year-end: 03/31/22
Equipment Rental Services
N.A.I.C.S.: 532210
Jeremy F. G. Pilkington (Chm)

Subsidiaries:

Balfour Beatty Rail Ltd (1)
Kingsgate 62 High Street, Redhill, RH1 1SH, Surrey, United Kingdom
Tel.: (44) 173 785 4400
Web Site: https://www.balfourbeatty.com
Railway Infrastructure Services
N.A.I.C.S.: 488210
Mark William Bullock (CEO)

Subsidiary (Non-US):

Balfour Beatty Rail GmbH (2)
Garmischer Str 35, 81373, Munich, Germany
Tel.: (49) 8941 417 0610
Web Site: https://www.bbrail.de
Railway Electrification & Power Supply System Whslr
N.A.I.C.S.: 423610

Brandon Hire Limited (1)
72-75 Feeder Road, St Philips, Bristol, BS2 0TQ, United Kingdom
Tel.: (44) 1179719119
Web Site: http://www.hirestation.co.uk
Equipment Rental Services
N.A.I.C.S.: 532490
Brian Sherlock (Mng Dir)

Hire Station Limited (1)
Unit 2 St George's Industrial Estate Goodwood Road, Boyatt Wood, Eastleigh, SO50 4NT, United Kingdom
Tel.: (44) 2380332277
Web Site: http://www.hirestation.co.uk
Sales Range: $50-74.9 Million
Emp.: 13
Construction, Mining & Forestry Machinery & Equipment Rental & Leasing
N.A.I.C.S.: 532412
John Singleton (Mng Dir)

TPA Portable Roadways (1)
Dukeries Mill Claylands Avenue, Worksop, S81 7DJ, United Kingdom
Tel.: (44) 8702402381
Web Site: http://www.vp-tpa.com
Sales Range: $50-74.9 Million
Emp.: 100
Construction, Mining & Forestry Machinery & Equipment Rental & Leasing
N.A.I.C.S.: 532412

Tech Rentals (Malaysia) Sdn. Bhd. (1)
29 Jalan Serendah 26/39 iParc 2 Seksyen 26, 40400, Shah Alam, Selangor, Malaysia
Tel.: (60) 35 614 2930
Web Site: https://www.techrentals.com.my
Electronic Test & Measurement Equipment Mfr
N.A.I.C.S.: 334515

Torrent Trackside Ltd. (1)
Network House Europa Way, Britannia Enterprise Park, Lichfield, WS14 9TZ, United Kingdom (100%)
Tel.: (44) 1543421900
Web Site: http://www.torrent.co.uk
Sales Range: $50-74.9 Million
Emp.: 100
Construction, Mining & Forestry Machinery & Equipment Rental & Leasing
N.A.I.C.S.: 532412
David McNair (Mng Dir)

Vidcom New Zealand Limited (1)
27 Exmouth Street, Eden Terrace, Auckland, 1021, New Zealand
Tel.: (64) 9 353 4170
Web Site: https://www.vidcom.com
Audio Visual Services
N.A.I.C.S.: 532289
Lloyd Tessendorf (Mgr)

Vp GmbH (1)
TPA Mobile Strassen Lurgiallee 6-8, 60439, Frankfurt, Germany
Tel.: (49) 6995 107 4110
Web Site: https://www.vp-tpa.com
Construction Machinery Rental Services
N.A.I.C.S.: 532412

VPC SPECIALTY LENDING INVESTMENTS PLC

29 Wellington Street, Leeds, LS1 4DU, United Kingdom
Tel.: (44) 8716640300 UK
Web Site: https://www.vpcspecialtylending.com
Year Founded: 2007
VSL—(LSE)
Rev.: $138,266,344
Assets: $594,380,933
Liabilities: $166,461,147
Net Worth: $427,919,786
Earnings: $98,621,191
Fiscal Year-end: 12/31/21
Investment Management Service
N.A.I.C.S.: 523940
Richard Levy (Co-Founder, CEO & Chief Investment Officer)

VPE INVESTMENT MANAGEMENT LIMITED

Empire Tower 30th Floor Presnenskaya Embankment 6 Building 2, Moscow, 123317, Russia
Tel.: (7) 6466295502
Web Site: http://www.vpe-capital.com
Investment Services
N.A.I.C.S.: 523999
Roland Nash (Partner)

VPE WERTPAPIERHANDELSBANK AG

Maximiliansplatz 17, 80333, Munich, Germany
Tel.: (49) 89296491
Web Site: http://www.vpeag.com
P0E—(DEU)
Sales Range: $10-24.9 Million
Emp.: 25
Banking Services
N.A.I.C.S.: 522110
Marco V. Pfetten (CEO)

VPK PACKAGING GROUP NV

Kareelstraat 108, 9300, Aalst, Belgium
Tel.: (32) 52261911
Web Site: http://www.vpkgroup.com

Year Founded: 1935
Emp.: 6,100
Packaging Products Mfr
N.A.I.C.S.: 322220
Pierre MacHaris (CEO)

Subsidiaries:

Aquila GmbH (1)
Zeissstrasse 20, 37327, Leinefelde, Germany
Tel.: (49) 36052598320
Web Site: http://www.aquila1.de
Packaging Products Mfr
N.A.I.C.S.: 322212

Aquila Sp. z o.o. (1)
ul Objazdowa 6a, 62-300, Wrzesnia, Poland
Tel.: (48) 616501900
Web Site: http://www.aquila.vpk.pl
Packaging Products Mfr
N.A.I.C.S.: 322212

Corex (1)
F Liederikstraat 23, 8530, Harelbeke, Belgium
Tel.: (32) 56 70 21 21
Web Site: http://www.corexgroup.com
Packaging Products Mfr
N.A.I.C.S.: 322212

Subsidiary (Non-US):

COREX Czech s.r.o (2)
Prumyslova 7, 682 23, Vyskov, Czech Republic
Tel.: (420) 517342010
Packaging Product Distr
N.A.I.C.S.: 423840

COREX Deutschland GmbH (2)
Werkstrasse 32, 46395, Bocholt, Germany
Tel.: (49) 28712345860
Packaging Product Distr
N.A.I.C.S.: 423840

COREX France sas (2)
32 rue de la Papinerie, Leers, 59115, Lille, France
Tel.: (33) 328339292
Packaging Product Distr
N.A.I.C.S.: 423840

COREX Nederland BV (2)
Nijverheidsstraat 9, 7641 AB, Wierden, Netherlands
Tel.: (31) 546575075
Packaging Product Distr
N.A.I.C.S.: 423840

COREX Polska Sp. z o.o (2)
ul Bydgoska 1, 86-100, Swiecie, Poland
Tel.: (48) 523310961
Packaging Product Distr
N.A.I.C.S.: 423840

COREX romania srl (2)
Iosif Vulcan 35, 415500, Salonta, Bihor, Romania
Tel.: (40) 359730158
Packaging Product Distr
N.A.I.C.S.: 423840

Corenso (UK) Ltd (2)
Units 4 5 & 6 Hindley Green Business Park Leigh Road, Wigan, WN2 4TN, United Kingdom
Tel.: (44) 1204 675150
Cardboard Mfr
N.A.I.C.S.: 322130
Maxine Morley (Mgr-Sls)

Corenso Edam B.V. (2)
Nijverheidstraat 12, 1135 GE, Edam, Netherlands
Tel.: (31) 299 744 140
Cardboard Mfr
N.A.I.C.S.: 322211
Jeffrey Hermes (Gen Mgr)

Corenso France S.A.S. (2)
48 Rue Victor Hugo, Moulin-Neuf, 24700, Dordogne, France
Tel.: (33) 557 56 40 00
Cardboard Mfr
N.A.I.C.S.: 322130
Stephanie Claustres (Mill Dir)

Corenso Tolosana S.A. (2)
Hirigunea 74, 20493, Tolosa, Gipuzkoa, Spain

Tel.: (34) 943 683125
Paper Products Mfr
N.A.I.C.S.: 322299

Corex Germany GmbH & Co. KG (2)
Niedieckstrasse 45, 47803, Krefeld, Germany
Tel.: (49) 2151 4792 750
Web Site: http://www.corexgroup.com
Cardboard Mfr
N.A.I.C.S.: 322130

Corex Turkey Ambalay Sanayi Ve Ticaret Anonim Serketi (2)
Nilufer Organize Sanayi Bolgesi Minarelicavus Mah Akasya Cad, Nilufer, Bursa, Turkiye
Tel.: (90) 2244111540
Packaging Product Distr
N.A.I.C.S.: 423840

Plant (Non-US):

RIGID CONTAINERS IRELAND PLANT (2)
Galvone Business Park Galvone, Limerick, Ireland
Tel.: (353) 61402500
Packaging Product Distr
N.A.I.C.S.: 423840
Graham Leech (Acct Mgr)

Ondulys Industrie (2)
ZI Nord rue Paul Cornu, 14100, Lisieux, France
Tel.: (33) 231623821
Web Site: http://www.ondulys.fr
Rev.: $20,400,000
Emp.: 103
Converted Paper Product Mfr
N.A.I.C.S.: 322130

Subsidiary (Domestic):

Ondulys Saint-Quentin SAS (2)
Z1 de Rouvroy-Morcourt, 02100, Saint-Quentin, France
Tel.: (33) 323061515
Web Site: http://www.ondulys.com
Sales Range: $50-74.9 Million
Packaging Mfr
N.A.I.C.S.: 326199

Rigid (1)
Stoke Albany Road, Desborough, Kettering, NN14 2SR, Northamptonshire, United Kingdom
Tel.: (44) 1536 760266
Web Site: http://www.rigid.co.uk
Packaging Products Mfr
N.A.I.C.S.: 322212
Julian Freeman (Dir-Grp Sls & Mktg)

SC VPK Packaging srl (1)
Str Iosif Vulcan 35, 415500, Salonta, Romania
Tel.: (40) 359730160
Paper Product Distr
N.A.I.C.S.: 424130

Sas Ondulys (1)
Pole d activite de la Vallee, PO Box 72078, 14102, Lisieux, Cedex, France
Tel.: (33) 231312838
Web Site: http://www.ondulys.fr
Packaging Products Mfr
N.A.I.C.S.: 322212

Smart Packaging Solutions nv (1)
Europastraat 28, Meer, 2321, Brussels, Belgium
Tel.: (32) 33150424
Web Site: http://www.smart-packaging-solutions.com
Packaging Products Mfr
N.A.I.C.S.: 322212
Johan De Neef (Mng Dir)

VPK Display NV (1)
Wijngaardveld 34C, 9300, Aalst, Belgium
Tel.: (32) 53760860
Web Site: http://www.vpkdisplay.be
Packaging Products Mfr
N.A.I.C.S.: 322212

VPK Packaging bv (1)
Snoekweg 1, 4941 SC, Raamsdonksveer, Netherlands
Tel.: (31) 162581500
Web Site: http://www.vpk.nl

AND PRIVATE COMPANIES

Paper Product Distr
N.A.I.C.S.: 424130

VPK Paper NV (1)
Oude Baan 120, Oudegem, 9200, Dendermonde, Belgium
Tel.: (32) 52261911
Web Site: http://www.oudegempapier.com
Packaging Products Mfr
N.A.I.C.S.: 322212

VPN TECHNOLOGIES, INC.
Suite 400 - 1681 Chestnut Street, Vancouver, V6J 4M6, BC, Canada
Tel.: (604) 283-1262
Web Site: https://www.vpntech.ca
Year Founded: 2010
SAAS—(CNSX)
Rev.: $8,385
Assets: $104,837
Liabilities: $143,875
Net Worth: ($39,039)
Earnings: ($707,505)
Fiscal Year-end: 06/30/19
Investment Services
N.A.I.C.S.: 523999

VPOWER GROUP INTERNATIONAL HOLDINGS LIMITED
Units 2701-05 27/F Office Tower 1 The Harbourfront, 18-22 Tak Fung Street Hung Hom, Kowloon, China (Hong Kong)
Tel.: (852) 26876517   Ky
Web Site: http://www.vpower.com
1608—(HKG)
Rev.: $428,568,938
Assets: $1,136,194,320
Liabilities: $735,837,053
Net Worth: $400,357,268
Earnings: ($35,790,525)
Emp.: 400
Fiscal Year-end: 12/31/22
Eletric Power Generation Services
N.A.I.C.S.: 221118
Yee Lam (Co-Founder & Chm)

Subsidiaries:

VPower Engineering (Shenzhen) Limited (1)
B7 Building the North of Yanchuan Industrial Zone Songgang Road, Baoan District, Shenzhen, 518105, China
Tel.: (86) 75527064703
Web Site: http://www.vpower.cn
Generator Mfr
N.A.I.C.S.: 335312
Tony Chan (Gen Mgr)

VR-GROUP PLC
Radiokatu 3, Helsinki, FI-00240, Finland
Tel.: (358) 294343
Web Site: https://www.vrgroup.fi
Emp.: 100
Rail Transport
N.A.I.C.S.: 488210
Topli Simola (CEO)

Subsidiaries:

Arriva Sverige AB (1)
Liljeholmsstranden 5 1 tr, 117 43, Stockholm, Sweden
Tel.: (46) 841074474
Web Site: http://www.arriva.se
Sales Range: $100-124.9 Million
Bus, Train & Coach Service Provider
N.A.I.C.S.: 485113

VR-IMMOBILIEN NORDDEUTSCHLAND
Am Ochsenmarkt 2, 21335, Luneburg, Germany
Tel.: (49) 4131285285
Web Site: http://www.vr-nord.de
Year Founded: 1995
Real Estate Brokerage Services
N.A.I.C.S.: 531210
Thomas Steffens (Chm-Mgmt Bd)

Subsidiaries:

Raiffeisen Immobilien GmbH, Rendsburg (1)
Konigstr 7, 24768, Rendsburg, Germany
Tel.: (49) 433124545
Web Site: http://www.raiffeisen-immobilien-rd.de
Real Estate Brokerage Services
N.A.I.C.S.: 531210

VR-LEASING AG
Hauptstrasse 131-137, 65760, Eschborn, Germany
Tel.: (49) 6196995401   De
Web Site: http://www.vr-smart-finanz.de
Holding Company; Machinery & Vehicle Information Technology & Commercial Real Estate Leasing Services
N.A.I.C.S.: 551112
Theophil Graband (Chm-Exec Bd)

Subsidiaries:

VB Leasing International Holding GmbH (1)
Kolingasse 12, Vienna, 1090, Austria (50%)
Tel.: (43) 5040047135
Web Site: http://www.vbleasing.com
Sales Range: $350-399.9 Million
Emp.: 35
Holding Company; Sales Financing Services
N.A.I.C.S.: 551112
Werner Zimmerman (Mng Dir & Member-Mgmt Bd)

Subsidiary (Non-US):

VB Leasing BH d.o.o. (2)
Fra Andela Zvizdovica 1, Sarajevo, 71000, Bosnia & Herzegovina
Tel.: (387) 33276280
Web Site: http://www.vbleasing.ba
Sales Range: $10-24.9 Million
Financial Services
N.A.I.C.S.: 522220
Sulejman Hadzic (Mng Dir)

VB Leasing SK, spol. s.r.o. (2)
Kosicka 49, SK 82108, Bratislava, Slovakia
Tel.: (421) 259987411
Web Site: http://www.vbleasing.sk
Sales Range: $25-49.9 Million
Emp.: 87
Financial Services
N.A.I.C.S.: 522220
Igor Krigler (Mng Dir)

VB Leasing d.o.o. (2)
Horvatova 82, HR 10 000, Zagreb, Croatia
Tel.: (385) 12484111
Web Site: http://www.vbleasing.hr
Sales Range: $10-24.9 Million
Financial Services
N.A.I.C.S.: 522220

VB Leasing d.o.o. (2)
Dunasjska 128a, 1000, Ljubljana, Slovenia
Tel.: (386) 15634400
Web Site: http://www.vbs-leasing.si
Sales Range: $10-24.9 Million
Emp.: 51
Financial Services
N.A.I.C.S.: 522220
Damijan Cigan (Mng Dir)

VB Leasing d.o.o. Beograd (2)
Dorda Stanojevica 12, Beograd Office Park 1 Flat, 11070, Belgrade, Serbia
Tel.: (381) 112016500
Web Site: http://www.vbleasing.co.rs
Sales Range: $1-9.9 Million
Emp.: 40
Financial Services
N.A.I.C.S.: 522220
Milena Jerenic (Mgr-Mktg)

VB Penzugyi Lizing Rt. & Kft. (2)
Vaci ut 37, H 1134, Budapest, Hungary
Tel.: (36) 1 45 26 700
Web Site: http://www.vbleasing.hu
Financial Services
N.A.I.C.S.: 522220

VRANKEN-POMMERY MONOPOLE SA
5 place du General Gouraud, BP 1049, FR-51689, Reims, Cedex 2, France
Tel.: (33) 326616263
Web Site: https://www.vrankenpommery.com
Year Founded: 1976
VRAP—(EUR)
Rev.: $373,545,645
Assets: $1,475,668,396
Liabilities: $1,012,349,045
Net Worth: $463,319,351
Earnings: $6,738,051
Emp.: 657
Fiscal Year-end: 12/31/23
Champagne & Wine Mfr & Distr
N.A.I.C.S.: 312130
Paul-Francois Vranken (Founder)

VRANLACT SA
Calea Munteniei nr 1, Vrancea, Focsani, Romania
Tel.: (40) 237 228 740
Web Site: http://www.vranlact.ro
Year Founded: 1970
Sales Range: $1-9.9 Million
Emp.: 74
Milk Production Services
N.A.I.C.S.: 112120

VRBAS G.P. A.D.
Karadordeva 1, 78250, Laktasi, Bosnia & Herzegovina
Tel.: (387) 51300528
VRBS-RA—(BANJ)
Rev.: $489,262
Assets: $588,762
Liabilities: $561,500
Net Worth: $27,262
Earnings: $9,342
Emp.: 7
Fiscal Year-end: 12/31/12
Building Construction Services
N.A.I.C.S.: 236220
Drago Sekimic (Chm)

VRC REAL ESTATE & INVESTMENT JOINT STOCK COMPANY
54 Vo Thi Sau Phuong 2, Vung Tau, Ba Ria-Vung Tau, Vietnam
Tel.: (84) 643854906
Web Site: http://www.xaylapdiaoc.com.vn
Year Founded: 1980
VRC—(HOSE)
Rev.: $161,174
Assets: $70,829,310
Liabilities: $18,925,344
Net Worth: $51,903,966
Earnings: $16,604
Emp.: 15
Fiscal Year-end: 12/31/23
Accommodation Services
N.A.I.C.S.: 721110

VREF SEVILLE REAL ESTATE HOLDCO SOCIMI, S.A.
Planta 4 Calle Fortuny 6, 28010, Madrid, Spain
Tel.: (34) 971213232
Web Site: https://www.vrefseville.com
Year Founded: 2020
MLVRF—(EUR)
Rev.: $8,043,719
Assets: $163,350,182
Liabilities: $179,605,408
Net Worth: ($16,255,226)
Earnings: ($12,851,531)
Fiscal Year-end: 12/31/23
Real Estate Investment Services
N.A.I.C.S.: 531190
Federico Bros Tejedor (Chm)

VRG CAPITAL CORP.
70 University Avenue Suite 1200, Toronto, M5J 2M4, ON, Canada
Tel.: (416) 581-8850
Web Site: http://www.vrgcapital.com
Year Founded: 1982
Privater Equity Firm
N.A.I.C.S.: 523999
Patrick J. Marshall (Mng Dir)

VRG SA
Pilotow Street 10, 31-462, Krakow, Poland
Tel.: (48) 126561832
Web Site: https://www.vrg.pl
Year Founded: 1948
VRG—(WAR)
Rev.: $330,713,922
Assets: $388,666,412
Liabilities: $135,210,620
Net Worth: $253,455,792
Earnings: $25,845,782
Emp.: 2,340
Fiscal Year-end: 12/31/23
Men's Clothing Retailer & Mfr
N.A.I.C.S.: 458110
Jerzy Mazgaj (Chm-Supervisory Bd)

Subsidiaries:

BYTOM S.A. (1)
Ul Prof Michala zyczkowsKiego 19, 31-864, Krakow, Poland
Tel.: (48) 32 787 93 00
Web Site: http://www.bytom.com.pl
Textile Product Mfr & Distr
N.A.I.C.S.: 314999
Michal Wojcik (Chm)

VRL LOGISTICS LIMITED
Giriraj Annexe Circuit House Road, Hubli, 580029, Karnataka, India
Tel.: (91) 8362237511
Web Site: https://www.vrlgroup.in
Year Founded: 1976
VRLLOG—(NSE)
Rev.: $242,394,966
Assets: $163,606,689
Liabilities: $82,097,065
Net Worth: $81,509,624
Earnings: $6,151,768
Emp.: 19,763
Fiscal Year-end: 03/31/21
Transportation & Logistics Services
N.A.I.C.S.: 488999
Vijay Sankeshvar (Chm & Mng Dir)

VROEGOP RUHE & CO. B.V.
Jan van Galenstraat 4, 1051 KL, Amsterdam, Netherlands
Tel.: (31) 20 606 18 18   Nl
Web Site: http://www.vroegop.nl
Food Sales
N.A.I.C.S.: 311999
Wim Zomer (COO)

VRUNDAVAN PLANTATION LIMITED
307 Sun Avenue One Nr Sun Prima Ambawadi Na, Ahmedabad, 380006, Gujarat, India
Tel.: (91) 7935201135
Web Site: https://www.vrundavanplantation.com
Year Founded: 1997
544011—(BOM)
Rev.: $2,214,012
Assets: $3,024,606
Liabilities: $258,156
Net Worth: $2,766,450
Earnings: $241,483
Fiscal Year-end: 03/31/23
Nursery Product Distr
N.A.I.C.S.: 444240

VRX SILICA LIMITED
Tel.: (61) 892263780

VRX SILICA LIMITED

VRX Silica Limited—(Continued)
Web Site:
https://www.vrxsilica.com.au
VRX—(ASX)
Rev.: $1,039,413
Assets: $16,000,400
Liabilities: $635,240
Net Worth: $15,365,160
Earnings: ($834,849)
Fiscal Year-end: 06/30/21
Metal Mining Services
N.A.I.C.S.: 212290
Bruce Maluish (Mng Dir)

VS ENERGY INTERNATIONAL UKRAINE LLC
4-A Hospitalna str, 01601, Kiev, Ukraine
Tel.: (380) 44 490 9815   UA
Web Site: http://www.vsei.com.ua
Year Founded: 2006
Investment Holding Company
N.A.I.C.S.: 551112

VS MEDIA HOLDINGS LIMITED
6/F KOHO 75 Hung To Road, Kwun Tong, China (Hong Kong)
Tel.: (852) 28891313   VG
Web Site: https://www.vs-media.com
Year Founded: 2013
VSME—(NASDAQ)
Rev.: $9,028,187
Assets: $7,592,325
Liabilities: $5,973,237
Net Worth: $1,619,088
Earnings: $3,525,200
Emp.: 41
Fiscal Year-end: 12/31/22
Holding Company
N.A.I.C.S.: 551112
Nga Fan Wong (Chm)

VSA CAPITAL GROUP PLC
New Liverpool House 15-17 Eldon Street, London, EC2M 7LD, United Kingdom
Tel.: (44) 2030055000
Web Site: http://www.vsacapital.com
VSA—(AQSE)
Sales Range: $1-9.9 Million
Emp.: 16
Marketing, Selling, Distributing & Supporting Software Products
N.A.I.C.S.: 513210
Andrew Monk (CEO)

VSF PROJECTS LIMITED
Plot No 8-2-269/19/S/D Lavakusa residency Rd No 2, Banjara Hills, Hyderabad, 500 034, Telangana, India
Tel.: (91) 4040102929
Web Site: https://www.vsfproject.com
Year Founded: 1992
519331—(BOM)
Rev.: $195,708
Assets: $8,059,697
Liabilities: $7,643,463
Net Worth: $416,234
Earnings: $1,727
Emp.: 6
Fiscal Year-end: 03/31/23
Civil Engineering Services
N.A.I.C.S.: 237990

VSG VANGE SOFTWARE GROUP AG
Seefeldstrasse 69, 8008, Zurich, Switzerland
Tel.: (41) 43 488 37 05
Web Site: http://www.vsg-group.com
Sales Range: $50-74.9 Million
Emp.: 360
Software Publisher
N.A.I.C.S.: 513210
Zhiping Jiang (Chm)

VSMPO - AVISMA CORPORATION
1 Parkovaya St Verkhnaya Salda, Sverdlovsk region, Yekaterinburg, 624760, Russia
Tel.: (7) 3434562366   RU
Web Site: https://www.vsmpo.ru
Year Founded: 1933
VSMO—(MOEX)
Rev.: $1,628,625,000
Assets: $5,517,022,000
Liabilities: $2,578,471,000
Net Worth: $2,938,551,000
Earnings: $321,017,000
Fiscal Year-end: 12/31/19
Titanium & Aluminum Products Mfr
N.A.I.C.S.: 332999
Evgeny Yu. Pologov (Dir-Procurement)

Subsidiaries:

Tirus International SA (1)
Avenue Gratta-Paille 1, 1018, Lausanne, Switzerland
Tel.: (41) 216415500
Web Site: http://www.tirus-international.ch
Titanium Metal Product Distr
N.A.I.C.S.: 212290
Alexandra Baumann (Mktg Mgr)

VSMPO Titan Ukraine (1)
26 Gagarina Str Solyonoye, Dnepropetrovsk, 52400, Ukraine
Tel.: (380) 566638800
Web Site: http://www.tw-vsmpoavisma.com
Titanium Metal Product Distr
N.A.I.C.S.: 212290

VSMPO-TIRUS GmbH (1)
Carl-Benz-Strasse 39-41, 60386, Frankfurt am Main, Germany
Tel.: (49) 6990547722
Web Site: http://www.vsmpo.de
Titanium Metal Products Mfr
N.A.I.C.S.: 331491
Catherine Peltier (Mng Dir)

VSMPO-Tirus (Beijing) Metallic Materials Ltd. (1)
No A5 Shuguangxili Rm 2006, Building A Phoenix Place Chaoyang District, Beijing, 100028, China
Tel.: (86) 1084554688
Titanium Metal Product Distr
N.A.I.C.S.: 212290

VSMPO-Tirus Limited (1)
Unit 12 The IO Centre Nash Road, Redditch, B98 7AS, Worcestershire, United Kingdom
Tel.: (44) 1527514111
Web Site: http://www.vsmpo-tirus.co.uk
Titanium Metal Product Distr
N.A.I.C.S.: 212290
Colin Whitehouse (Mng Dir)

VSMPO-Tirus US Inc. (1)
1745 Shea Ctr Dr Ste 330, Highlands Ranch, CO 80129
Tel.: (720) 746-1023
Web Site: http://www.vsmpo-tirus.com
Metal Product Distr
N.A.I.C.S.: 423510
Michael Metz (Pres)

VSOLAR GROUP BHD
13-3 13th Floor Menara Lien Hoe No 8 Persiaran, Tropicana Golf & Country Resort, 47410, Petaling Jaya, Selangor Darul Ehsan, Malaysia
Tel.: (60) 376226981   MY
Web Site: https://www.vsolar.com.my
Year Founded: 2003
VSOLAR—(KLS)
Rev.: $1,893,402
Assets: $21,279,993
Liabilities: $1,923,505
Net Worth: $19,356,488
Earnings: ($3,147,971)
Emp.: 24
Fiscal Year-end: 06/30/23
Software Solution Distr
N.A.I.C.S.: 423430

Kok Keong Leung (Exec Dir)

VST HEMOVET D.O.O.
Novosadskog sajma 18, 21000, Novi Sad, Serbia
Tel.: (381) 214774012
Web Site:
http://www.vsthemovet.com
Year Founded: 1993
Emp.: 42
Mfr of Pharmaceuticals for Animal Diseases & Crop Protection Agents
N.A.I.C.S.: 325412
Drago Jaric (Mng Dir)

Subsidiaries:

VST Hemovet d.o.o. - PESTICIDE Factory (1)
Industrijska zona bb, 21 470, Backi Petrovac, Serbia
Tel.: (381) 21780566
Pesticide Mfr
N.A.I.C.S.: 325320

VST INDUSTRIES LIMITED
1-7-1063/1065 Azamabad, PO Box 1804, Hyderabad, 500 020, Telangana, India
Tel.: (91) 4027688000
Web Site: https://www.vsthyd.com
Year Founded: 1930
VSTIND—(NSE)
Rev.: $206,753,097
Assets: $202,810,294
Liabilities: $74,439,866
Net Worth: $128,370,429
Earnings: $42,423,422
Emp.: 780
Fiscal Year-end: 03/31/21
Cigarette Mfr
N.A.I.C.S.: 312230
Devraj Lahiri (Mng Dir)

VSTECS BERHAD
Lot 3 Jalan Teknologi 3/5 Taman Sains Selangor, Kota Damansara, 47810, Petaling Jaya, Selangor, Malaysia
Tel.: (60) 362868222   MY
Web Site: https://www.vstecs.com.my
Year Founded: 1985
856—(HKG)
Rev.: $593,640,622
Assets: $179,045,495
Liabilities: $79,690,902
Net Worth: $99,354,594
Earnings: $14,676,970
Emp.: 410
Fiscal Year-end: 12/31/23
Information & Communication Product Distr
N.A.I.C.S.: 423690
Foo Sen Chin (Founder)

Subsidiaries:

Vstecs Astar Sdn. Bhd. (1)
Lot 3 Jalan Teknologi 3/5 taman sains selangor, Kota Damansara, 47810, Petaling Jaya, Selangor, Malaysia
Tel.: (60) 36 286 8222
Web Site: https://www.ecsm-online.com.my
Emp.: 130
Hardware Equipment Distr
N.A.I.C.S.: 423710
Angeline Chuah (Sr Mgr-Comml)

VSTECS HOLDINGS LIMITED
Unit 3312 33/F China Merchants Tower Shun Tak Centre, 200 Connaught Road, Central, China (Hong Kong)
Tel.: (852) 27861836
Web Site: http://www.vstecs.com
Year Founded: 1991
0856—(HKG)
Rev.: $9,023,683,411
Assets: $3,795,310,148
Liabilities: $2,914,855,779

Net Worth: $880,454,368
Earnings: $137,696,468
Emp.: 3,414
Fiscal Year-end: 12/31/20
Holding Company; IT Products Distr
N.A.I.C.S.: 551112
Jialin Li (Chm & CEO)

Subsidiaries:

ECS China Technology (Shanghai) Company Limited (1)
4F ACCP Building No 799 TianShan Road W, Shanghai, 200335, China
Tel.: (86) 2151525709
Computer Peripheral Equipment Distr
N.A.I.C.S.: 423430

ECS Holdings Limited (1)
8 Temasek Boulevard 34 02 Suntec Tower 3, Singapore, 038988, Singapore (52.5%)
Tel.: (65) 66596888
Web Site: http://www.ecs.com.sg
Sales Range: $1-4.9 Billion
Emp.: 1,708
Information Technology Infrastructure Solutions
N.A.I.C.S.: 517810
Narong Intanate (Chm-The Value Systems Co., Ltd.)

Subsidiary (Domestic):

ECS Computers Asia Pte Ltd (2)
19 Kallang Avenue 07 153, Singapore, 339410, Singapore
Tel.: (65) 62999433
Web Site: http://www.ecs.com.sg
Computer & Systems Distr
N.A.I.C.S.: 423430

Subsidiary (Non-US):

ECS Indo Pte Ltd. (2)
Ruko Mangga Dua Sq, JL Gunung Sahari Raya 1, 14420, Jakarta, Indonesia
Tel.: (62) 2162312893
Web Site: http://www.ecsindo.com
Sales Range: $50-74.9 Million
Emp.: 180
Holding Company
N.A.I.C.S.: 551112
Nana Juhana Osay (Exec Dir)

Subsidiary (Domestic):

PT ECS Indo Jaya (3)
Komplek Mangga Dua Square Blok F7-11 Jl Gunung Sahari Raya No 1, Jakarta, 14430, Utara, Indonesia
Tel.: (62) 2122620699
Web Site: https://vstecsindo.net
Sales Range: $25-49.9 Million
Emp.: 50
Information Technology Solutions & Products Distr
N.A.I.C.S.: 459999

Subsidiary (Non-US):

ECS Infocom (Phils) Pte Ltd. (2)
Topy II Bldg 3 Economia Street, Libis, Quezon City, 1110, Philippines
Tel.: (63) 26883333
Web Site: http://www.msi-ecs.com.ph
Sales Range: $25-49.9 Million
Emp.: 450
Information Technology Infrastructure Solutions
N.A.I.C.S.: 513199

Subsidiary (Domestic):

MSI-ECS Phils., Inc. (3)
MSI-ECS COMPLEX M Eusebio Avenue San Miguel, Metro Manila, Pasig, 1600, Philippines
Tel.: (63) 28309999
Web Site: http://www.msi-ecs.com.ph
Sales Range: $25-49.9 Million
Emp.: 50
Information Technology Infrastructure Solutions
N.A.I.C.S.: 513199

Subsidiary (Non-US):

ECS Kush Sdn Bhd (2)
Lot 3 Jalan Teknologi 3/5, Taman Sains Selangor, 47810, Petaling Jaya, Kota Daman-

AND PRIVATE COMPANIES

sara, Malaysia
Tel.: (60) 362868222
Web Site: http://www.ecsm.com.my
Sales Range: $100-124.9 Million
Emp.: 200
Holding Company
N.A.I.C.S.: 551112
Sen Chin Foo *(Mng Dir)*

Subsidiary (Domestic):

ECS Astar Sdn Bhd (3)
Glomac Business Center, No 10 Jalan SS 6
1, 47301, Petaling Jaya, Selangor, Malaysia
Tel.: (60) 378045808
Web Site: http://www.ecsm.com.my
Information Technology Products Distr
N.A.I.C.S.: 459999

ECS Ku Sdn Bhd (3)
Lot 3 Jalan Teknologi 3/5 Damansains Selangor, Taman Sains Selangor, 47810, Petaling Jaya, Kota Damansara, Malaysia
Tel.: (60) 362868222
Web Site: http://www.ecsm.com.my
Sales Range: $125-149.9 Million
Emp.: 300
Information Technology Products Distr
N.A.I.C.S.: 459999
M. Nirmala *(Head-Tech Admin)*

ECS Pericomp Sdn Bhd (3)
Lot 3 Jalan Teknologi 3/5 Taman Sains Selangor, Kota Demansara, Petaling Jaya, 47810, Malaysia
Tel.: (60) 362868222
Web Site: http://www.ecsm.com.my
Sales Range: $125-149.9 Million
Information Technology Products Distr
N.A.I.C.S.: 459999
Yew Hwa Chang *(Gen Mgr)*

Subsidiary (Non-US):

ECS Technology China Ltd. (2)
No 299 Daysunritz Hotel 5th/6th Zhongshan Road West, Guangzhou, 510665, China
Tel.: (86) 2085529888
Web Site: http://www.ecschina.com
Sales Range: $200-249.9 Million
Emp.: 1,000
Information Technology Products Distr
N.A.I.C.S.: 519290
Wei Hiam Ong *(Grp CEO)*

The Value Systems Co., Ltd. (2)
922/328-331 New Petchburi Road,
Bangkapi Huay-Kwang, Bangkok, 10320,
Thailand
Tel.: (66) 23082900
Web Site: http://www.value.co.th
Information Technology Products Distr
N.A.I.C.S.: 459999
Somsak Pejthaveeporndej *(Pres)*

ECS Technology (Guangzhou) Company Limited (1)
Jiadu International Mansion No 50 Jianzhong Road Tianhe Software Park,
Guangzhou, 510665, Guangdong, China
Tel.: (86) 2085529888
Computer Peripheral Equipment Distr
N.A.I.C.S.: 423430

ECS Technology (HK) Co., Limited (1)
Rm 2201-03 22 F World-Wide Hse 19 Des Voeux Rd C, Central, Hong Kong, China (Hong Kong)
Tel.: (852) 23700108
Computer Peripheral Equipment Distr
N.A.I.C.S.: 423430

ECS Technology Company Limited (1)
7F Wanliuyicheng Building No 11 Changchunqiao Road, Haidian District, Beijing, 100089, China
Tel.: (86) 1058815599
Web Site: https://www.ecschina.com
Emp.: 1,000
Computer Peripheral Equipment Mfr
N.A.I.C.S.: 334118
Lee Tavit *(Gen Mgr)*

Exeed Pte Ltd (1)
19 Kallang Avenue 06-153, Singapore,
339410, Singapore
Tel.: (65) 63934772
Web Site: https://www.exeed.com.sg

Information Technology Consulting & Services
N.A.I.C.S.: 541511

Pacific City (Asia Pacific) Pte Ltd. (1)
IMM Building 2 Jurong East Street 21 02-17, Singapore, 609601, Singapore
Tel.: (65) 65625596
Web Site: https://www.pacificcity.com.sg
Electronic Components Distr
N.A.I.C.S.: 423690

VST Computers HK Limited (1)
Unit 1901 19/F W Tower Shun Tak Centre, 168 Connaught Road, Central, China (Hong Kong)
Tel.: (852) 27861836
Information Technology Products Distr
N.A.I.C.S.: 459999

VST ECS (Thailand) Co., Ltd. (1)
275 Soi Lat Phrao 101 Wat Bung Thonglang, Khlong Chao Khun Sing Wang Thonglang, Bangkok, 10310, Thailand
Tel.: (66) 20329999
Web Site: https://www.vstecs.co.th
Information & Communication Technology Services
N.A.I.C.S.: 519290
Somsak Pejthaveeporndej *(CEO)*

VSTECS (Cambodia) Co., Ltd. (1)
KT Tower 8th Floor at Building No 23 Street 112 Sangkat Phsar Depo 3, Khan Tuol Kok, Phnom Penh, Cambodia
Tel.: (855) 92232168
Information & Communication Technology Services
N.A.I.C.S.: 519290

VSTECS (Myanmar) Co., Ltd. (1)
No 6 3rd Floor 14 Quarter Kyaung Street, Yankin Township, 11081, Yangon, Myanmar
Tel.: (95) 1553878
Information & Communication Technology Services
N.A.I.C.S.: 519290

VSTECS (Singapore) Pte. Ltd. (1)
19 Kallang Avenue 07-153, Singapore, 339410, Singapore
Tel.: (65) 62999433
Web Site: https://www.vstecssingapore.com
Information & Communication Technology Services
N.A.I.C.S.: 519290

VT CO., LTD.

139 Saneopdanji-gil, Paju, Gyeonggi-do, Korea (South)
Tel.: (82) 319434600
Web Site: https://www.gmp.com
Year Founded: 1985
018290—(KRS)
Rev.: $184,265,081
Assets: $169,274,630
Liabilities: $90,466,728
Net Worth: $78,807,903
Earnings: $8,551,653
Emp.: 283
Fiscal Year-end: 12/31/22
Laminating Product Services
N.A.I.C.S.: 326112
Y. P. Kim *(Chm & CEO)*

Subsidiaries:

GMP PROGRAPHICS Germany GmbH (1)
Robert-Bosch-Strasse 4, 56751, Polch, Germany
Tel.: (49) 265494900
Web Site: https://www.gmp-germany.de
Printing Machinery Equipment Mfr
N.A.I.C.S.: 333248

VT HOLDINGS CO., LTD.

3-10-32 Nishiki, Naka-ku, Nagoya, Aichi, Japan
Tel.: (81) 522039500
Web Site: https://www.vt-holdings.co.jp
Year Founded: 1983
7593—(TKS)
Rev.: $2,059,702,440

Assets: $1,803,756,630
Liabilities: $1,261,723,410
Net Worth: $542,033,220
Earnings: $44,267,170
Emp.: 4,890
Fiscal Year-end: 03/31/24
New & Used Car Dealer
N.A.I.C.S.: 441110
Kazuho Takahashi *(Pres & CEO)*

Subsidiaries:

Archish Gallery Co., Ltd. (1)
Sakae VT Building 3-10-32 Nishiki, Naka-ku, Nagoya, 460-0003, Japan
Tel.: (81) 522188702
Web Site: https://www.archish-g.com
Commercial Construction Services
N.A.I.C.S.: 236220

Honda Cars Tokai Co., Ltd. (1)
Hachikoten 2F 62-1 Takikawa-cho, Showa-ku, Nagoya, Aichi, Japan
Tel.: (81) 52 837 3004
Web Site: https://www.hondacars-tokai.com
Automobile Maintenance Services
N.A.I.C.S.: 811111

J-net Rental & Lease Co., Ltd. (1)
1-7-28 Nishiki J-SQUARE Marunouchi Building, Naka-ku, Nagoya, 460-0003, Aichi, Japan
Tel.: (81) 52 231 8231
Web Site: https://www.j-netrentacar.co.jp
New Car Distr
N.A.I.C.S.: 441110

Koyo Auto Co., Ltd. (1)
6-437-1 Chuomiwa, Kitami, 090-0837, Japan
Tel.: (81) 15 736 4334
Web Site: https://www.koyo-jidousha.com
New Car Distr
N.A.I.C.S.: 441110

MG Sogo Service Co., Ltd. (1)
2-27-13 Suehiro, Ichinomiya, 491-0918, Aichi, Japan
Tel.: (81) 586431200
Web Site: https://mg-sougou.jp
Real Estate Condominium Development Services
N.A.I.C.S.: 531311

Mikawa Nissan Auto Co., Ltd. (1)
79-3 Oyamadanaka Yokoyama-cho, Anjo, Aichi, Japan
Tel.: (81) 56 674 5023
Web Site: https://www.ni-mikawa.nissan-dealer.jp
Automobile Maintenance Services
N.A.I.C.S.: 811111

Nagano Nissan Auto Co., Ltd. (1)
45-1 Nakagosho Okada 2nd Floor Sanno Building, Nagano, 380-0936, Japan
Tel.: (81) 26 221 2332
Web Site: https://www.ni-nagano.nissan-dealer.jp
Automobile Maintenance Services
N.A.I.C.S.: 811111

Nissan Satio Nara Co., Ltd. (1)
124-1 Kamimitsuhashi-cho, Yamatokoriyama, 639-1102, Japan
Tel.: (81) 74 354 2831
Web Site: https://www.ns-nara.nissan-dealer.jp
Automobile Maintenance Services
N.A.I.C.S.: 811111

Nissan-Satio-Saitama Co., Ltd. (1)
6-1-12 Kamiochiai, Chuo-ku, Saitama, 338-0001, Japan
Tel.: (81) 488533226
Web Site: https://www.nissan-satio-saitama.co.jp
Emp.: 225
New & Used Car Dealer
N.A.I.C.S.: 441110
Shin Tomita *(Pres)*

Subsidiary (Non-US):

CCR MOTOR CO. LTD. (2)
1 Vernon Court Meteor Business Park Cheltenham Road East, Staverton, Gloucester, GL2 9QG, Gloucestershire, United Kingdom
Tel.: (44) 145 264 0034
Web Site: https://www.ccrmotorco.co.uk

VT5 ACQUISITION COMPANY AG

New & Used Car Dealer
N.A.I.C.S.: 441110
Tim Bagnall *(Officer-Acctg)*

Shizuoka Nissan Auto Co., Ltd. (1)
1-7-48 Kuniyoshida, Suruga-ku, Shizuoka, 422-8512, Japan
Tel.: (81) 54 261 2311
Web Site: https://www.ni-shizuoka.nissan-dealer.jp
New Car Distr
N.A.I.C.S.: 441110

Sizuoka Nissan Auto Sales Co., Ltd (1)
1-7-48 Kuniyoshida, Suruga Ward, Shizuoka, 422-8512, Japan
Tel.: (81) 542612311
Web Site: https://ni-shizuoka.nissan-dealer.jp
Emp.: 381
New & Used Car Dealer
N.A.I.C.S.: 441110

Takihouse Co., Ltd. (1)
2-26-1 Shukugawara, Tama-ku, Kawasaki, 214-0021, Kanagawa, Japan
Tel.: (81) 449310086
Web Site: https://www.taki-house.co.jp
Real Estate & Brokerage Services
N.A.I.C.S.: 531210

Trust Absolut Auto (Pty.) Ltd. (1)
275 Beyers Naude Drive, Blackheath Randburg, Johannesburg, 2195, South Africa
Tel.: (27) 114762333
Web Site: https://trustautogroup.co.za
Automotive Distr
N.A.I.C.S.: 441110

Trust Co., Ltd. (1)
3-10-32 Nishiki, Naka-ku, Nagoya, 460-0003, Aichi, Japan
Tel.: (81) 522199058
Web Site: https://www.trust-ltd.co.jp
Rev.: $271,604,900
Assets: $331,385,740
Liabilities: $231,733,380
Net Worth: $99,652,360
Earnings: $7,363,540
Emp.: 518
Fiscal Year-end: 03/31/2024
Online Vehicle Marketing Services
N.A.I.C.S.: 441120
Kazushige Ito *(Dir-Overseas Bus Dev)*

Wessex Garages Holdings Limited (1)
Pennywell Road, Avon, Bristol, BS5 0TT, United Kingdom
Tel.: (44) 117 332 2646
Web Site: https://www.wessexgarages.com
New Car Distr
N.A.I.C.S.: 441110

Wessex Garrages Holding Limited (1)
Pennywell Road, Avon, Bristol, BS5 0TT, United Kingdom
Tel.: (44) 3309125070
Car Parts Distr
N.A.I.C.S.: 423140

VT INDUSTRIAL TECHNOLOGY CO., LTD.

No 32 Jianhong Road, Xinwu District, Wuxi, 214145, Jiangsu, China
Tel.: (86) 51068561147
Web Site: https://www.vt-ind.com
Year Founded: 2008
300707—(CHIN)
Rev.: $115,376,630
Assets: $278,902,184
Liabilities: $112,012,357
Net Worth: $166,889,827
Earnings: $2,861,495
Emp.: 800
Fiscal Year-end: 12/31/23
Automotive Parts Mfr & Distr
N.A.I.C.S.: 336370
Xiliang Zhang *(Chm)*

VT5 ACQUISITION COMPANY AG

Churerstrasse 25, 8808, Pfaffikon, Switzerland

VT5 ACQUISITION COMPANY AG

VT5 Acquisition Company AG—(Continued)
Tel.: (41) 552108080
Web Site: https://www.vt5.ch
Year Founded: 2021
VT5—(SWX)
Investment Management Service
N.A.I.C.S.: 523999
Markus Laesser *(CEO)*

VTB BANK GEORGIA JSC
14 G Chanturia St, 0108, Tbilisi, Georgia
Tel.: (995) 322242424
Web Site: http://www.vtb.ge
UGB—(GEOR)
Rev. $46,848,331
Assets: $645,674,362
Liabilities: $552,080,382
Net Worth: $93,593,980
Earnings: $8,091,671
Emp.: 1,051
Fiscal Year-end: 12/31/20
Commercial Banking Services
N.A.I.C.S.: 522110
Archil Kontselidze *(Chm & CEO)*

VTB LIFE INSURANCE JSC
19/3 Prospect Mira, Moscow, 129090, Russia
Tel.: (7) 4952216234
Web Site: http://www.vtbinslife.ru
Sales Range: Less than $1 Million
Fire Insurance Services
N.A.I.C.S.: 524113

VTC PARTNERS GMBH
Theatinersrasse 8, 80333, Munich, Germany
Tel.: (49) 89649490
Web Site: http://www.vtc.de
Year Founded: 1992
Sales Range: $25-49.9 Million
Emp.: 5
Privater Equity Firm
N.A.I.C.S.: 523999
Jurgen Max Leuze *(Mng Partner)*

Subsidiaries:

Europoles GmbH & Co. KG (1)
Ingolstadter Strasse 51, 92318, Neumarkt, Germany
Tel.: (49) 9181 896 0
Web Site: http://www.europoles.com
Sales Range: $250-299.9 Million
Emp.: 1,150
Steel, Spun Concrete & Fiberglass-Reinforced Plastic Utility Poles Mfr & Distr
N.A.I.C.S.: 339999
Ralph Friedwagner *(Mng Dir & Member-Mgmt Bd)*

FRIWO AG (1)
Von-Liebig-Strasse 11, 48346, Ostbevern, Germany
Tel.: (49) 2532 81 0
Web Site: http://www.friwo.com
Sales Range: $125-149.9 Million
Emp.: 350
Holding Company; Electronics Power Supply Products, Chargers & Accessories Mfr & Distr
N.A.I.C.S.: 551112
Lothar Schwemm *(Member-Mgmt Bd)*

Subsidiary (Domestic):

FRIWO Geratebau GmbH (2)
Von-Liebig-Strasse 11, Ostbevern, 48346, Germany
Tel.: (49) 2532 81 0
Web Site: http://www.friwo.de
Electronics Power Supply Products, Chargers & Accessories Mfr & Distr
N.A.I.C.S.: 334419

Global Castings A/S (1)
Smed Hansens vej 27, 6940, Lem, Denmark
Tel.: (45) 7217 0110
Web Site: http://www.globalcastings.com

Sales Range: $250-299.9 Million
Emp.: 1,000
Metal Casting Mfr
N.A.I.C.S.: 332999
Kim Kronborg *(CEO)*

Subsidiary (Non-US):

Global Castings (Tianjin) Co., Ltd. (2)
No. 97 Xinhuan Nan Street Teda West Zone, 300462, Tianjin, China
Tel.: (86) 22 5880 2701
Web Site: http://www.globalcastings.com
Emp.: 260
Wind Power Turbine Die-Cast Parts Mfr
N.A.I.C.S.: 331523
Peter Pallishoj *(Gen Mgr)*

Global Castings (Xuzhou) Co., Ltd. (2)
No 79 Zhen Xing Da Dao, XEDZ, Xuzhou, 221004, Jiangsu, China (100%)
Tel.: (86) 516 87892762
Wind Power Turbine Die-Cast Parts Mfr
N.A.I.C.S.: 331523
Monica Chen *(Mgr-HSE & HR)*

Global Castings Guldsmedshyttan AB (2)
Elwiksvaeg 1, 711 78, Guldsmeds-hyttan, Sweden (100%)
Tel.: (46) 581 451 00
Sales Range: $25-49.9 Million
Wind Power Turbine Die-Cast Parts Mfr
N.A.I.C.S.: 331523
Torbjoern Rudqvist *(VP)*

Global Castings Magdeburg Gmbh (2)
Alt Salbke 6-10, 39122, Magdeburg, Germany (100%)
Tel.: (49) 391 400 4011
Wind Power Turbine Die-Cast Parts Mfr
N.A.I.C.S.: 331523

Global Castings Stade GmbH (2)
Johann-Rathje-Koser-Strasse 7, 21683, Stade, Germany
Tel.: (49) 4146 9299 305
Web Site: http://www.globalcasting.com
Emp.: 140
Metal Casting Mfr
N.A.I.C.S.: 332999
Marcel Weitze *(Engr-Process)*

PRONTOR GmbH (1)
Gauthierstrasse 56, Bad Wilbad, 75323, Germany
Tel.: (49) 7081 781 1
Web Site: http://www.prontor.de
Sales Range: $50-74.9 Million
Medical Technologies Mfr
N.A.I.C.S.: 339112
Hans-Joachim Hermann *(Mng Dir)*

S+S Separation & Sorting Technology GmbH (1)
Regener Strasse 130, Schonberg, 94513, Germany
Tel.: (49) 8554 308 0
Web Site: http://www.sesotec.com
Sales Range: $50-74.9 Million
Industrial Inspection, Separation & Sorting Equipment Developer, Mfr & Distr
N.A.I.C.S.: 333248
Michael Perl *(Head-Sorting Bus)*

Subsidiary (Non-US):

S+S Inspection Asia Pte Ltd (2)
11 Woodlands Close 01 03/04, Singapore, 737853, Singapore
Tel.: (65) 6562 8875
Web Site: http://www.sesotec.com.sg
Industrial Machinery Mfr
N.A.I.C.S.: 334519
Tan Tong Liang *(Gen Mgr)*

S+S Inspection India Pvt. Ltd. (2)
Shatrunjay Apartment Shop No 4 & 5 A Wing Opp PL Deshpande Garden, Sinhgad Road Opp PL Deshpande Garden, Pune, 411 030, India
Tel.: (91) 20 2674 1012
Web Site: http://www.sesotec.in
Industrial Machinery Mfr
N.A.I.C.S.: 334519

S+S Separation & Sorting Technology (Qingdao) Co., Ltd (2)

Add 1B Building 13 No 518 Xinzhuan Road, Songjiang District, Shanghai, 201612, China
Tel.: (86) 21 37005075
Web Site: http://www.sesotec.com.cn
Industrial Machinery Mfr
N.A.I.C.S.: 334519

Subsidiary (US):

Sesotec Inc. (2)
1234 Hardt Cir, Bartlett, IL 60103
Tel.: (224) 208-1900
Web Site: http://www.sesotec.us
Industrial Machinery Mfr
N.A.I.C.S.: 334519
Doug Pedersen *(Dir-Sls-Canada)*

Subsidiary (Non-US):

Sesotec Ltd. (2)
24 Park Gate Business Centre Chandlers Way, Swanwick, SO31 1FQ, Hampshire, United Kingdom
Tel.: (44) 1489 553 740
Web Site: http://www.sesotec.co.uk
Industrial Machinery Mfr
N.A.I.C.S.: 333248
Chris Perkins *(Dir-Sls-Food)*

Sesotec S.r.l. (2)
Via San Benigno 4, 20133, Milan, Italy
Tel.: (39) 02 7010 2377
Web Site: http://www.sesotec.it
Emp.: 4
Industrial Machinery Mfr
N.A.I.C.S.: 334519

Sesotec Sarl (2)
4 rue Artisanale, 67310, Wasselonne, France
Tel.: (33) 388 04 2230
Web Site: http://www.sesotec.fr
Industrial Machinery Mfr
N.A.I.C.S.: 334519

VTC TELECOMMUNICATIONS JSC
750 3rd floor Dien Bien Phu Ward 11, District 10, Ho Chi Minh City, Vietnam
Tel.: (84) 838331106
Web Site: https://www.vtctelecom.com.vn
VTC—(HNX)
Rev. $26,128,600
Assets: $26,112,000
Liabilities: $17,715,500
Net Worth: $8,396,500
Earnings: $52,100
Fiscal Year-end: 12/31/22
Telecommunication Equipment Mfr & Whslr
N.A.I.C.S.: 334220

VTECH HOLDINGS LTD.
23rd Floor Tai Ping Industrial Centre Block 1 57 Ting Kok Road, Tai Po, New Territories, China (Hong Kong)
Tel.: (852) 26801000
Web Site: https://www.vtech.com
Year Founded: 1976
VTKLF—(OTCIQ)
Rev. $2,241,700,000
Assets: $1,318,400,000
Liabilities: $683,700,000
Net Worth: $634,700,000
Earnings: $149,200,000
Emp.: 21,600
Fiscal Year-end: 03/31/23
Holding Company; Design, Manufacture & Distribution of Consumer Electronics Products
N.A.I.C.S.: 551112
Allan Chi Yun Wong *(Founder, Chm & CEO)*

Subsidiaries:

Perseus Investments Limited (1)
23/F Tai Ping Indl Ctr Ph 1 57 Ting Kok Rd, Tai Po, New Territories, China (Hong Kong)
Tel.: (852) 26801000
Web Site: http://www.vtech.com
Emp.: 600

INTERNATIONAL PUBLIC

Investment Management Service
N.A.I.C.S.: 523999
Wong Allan *(CEO)*

Snom Solutions GmbH (1)
Aroser Allee 66, 13407, Berlin, Germany
Tel.: (49) 30398330
Telecommunications Technology Solutions
N.A.I.C.S.: 517810

VTech (OEM), Inc. (1)
16641 Madrone Ave, Los Gatos, CA 95030
Tel.: (408) 252-8550
Emp.: 5
Electronic Contract Manufacturing Services
N.A.I.C.S.: 334419
Gary Ashford *(Gen Mgr)*

VTech (Qingyuan) Plastic & Electronics Co., Ltd. (1)
Zone 1 Qingyuan Hi-Tech Industrial Development Zone, Qingyuan, 511517, Guangdong, China
Tel.: (86) 763 348 5666
Web Site: http://www.vtech.com
Plastics Product Mfr
N.A.I.C.S.: 326199

VTech Communications (Malaysia) Sdn. Bhd. (1)
No 5 Tanjung Agas Industrial Area, 84000, Muar, Johor Darul Takzim, Malaysia
Tel.: (60) 6 951 2111
Consumer Electronics Product Mfr
N.A.I.C.S.: 334419

VTech Communications Ltd. (1)
23/F Tai Ping Industrial Centre Block 1 57 Ting Kok Road, Tai Po, NT, China (Hong Kong)
Tel.: (852) 26801000
Web Site: http://www.vtechcms.com
Sales Range: $125-149.9 Million
Emp.: 4,000
Electronics Manufacturing, Logistics & After-Sales Customer Service
N.A.I.C.S.: 334419

Subsidiary (Non-US):

VTech Communications Japan Ltd. (2)
Okumura Building 3-14 Kanda Ogawamachi, Chiyoda-ku, Tokyo, 101-0052, Japan
Tel.: (81) 332940740
Web Site: https://www.vtechcms.com
Telecommunications Products Sales & Marketing
N.A.I.C.S.: 423690
Katsumi Akasu *(Mng Dir)*

VTech Communications Ltd. (2)
9 Manor Courtyard Hughenden Avenue, High Wycombe, HP13 5RE, Buckinghamshire, United Kingdom
Tel.: (44) 1494522510
Web Site: http://www.vtech.com
Telecommunications Products Sales & Marketing
N.A.I.C.S.: 423690

Subsidiary (US):

VTech Communications, Inc. (2)
9590 SW Gemini Dr, Beaverton, OR 97008
Tel.: (503) 596-1200
Web Site: https://vt.vtp-media.com
Telecommunications Products Sales & Marketing
N.A.I.C.S.: 423690
M. Levenson *(Pres)*

VTech Electronics (Japan) Inc. (1)
2F Shin-Osaka Building 1-1-36, Nishiwaji Higashiyodogawa-ku, Osaka, 533 0031, Japan
Tel.: (81) 649505100
Sales Range: $50-74.9 Million
Emp.: 5
Electronic Learning Products & Telecommunications Products Sales & Marketing
N.A.I.C.S.: 423690
Iteya Keiao *(Mgr)*

VTech Electronics Europe B.V. (1)
Copernicusstraat 7, PO Box 10042, 6000 GA, Weert, Netherlands
Tel.: (31) 495459123
Web Site: https://www.vtechnl.com

Emp.: 40
Electronic Learning Products & Telecommunications Products Sales & Marketing
N.A.I.C.S.: 423690
Gilles Sautier *(Pres)*

VTech Electronics Europe GmbH (1)
Martinstrasse 5, 70794, Filderstadt, Germany
Tel.: (49) 7117097472
Web Site: http://www.vtech.de
Emp.: 25
Electronic Learning Products & Telecommunications Products Sales & Marketing
N.A.I.C.S.: 423690

VTech Electronics Europe Plc (1)
Napier Court Abingdon Science Park, Abingdon, OX14 3YT, Oxfordshire, United Kingdom
Tel.: (44) 3306780149
Web Site: http://www.vtech.co.uk
Sales Range: $25-49.9 Million
Emp.: 30
Electronic Learning Products & Telecommunications Products Sales & Marketing
N.A.I.C.S.: 423690

VTech Electronics Europe S.A.S. (1)
24 allee des sablieres, 78293, Croissy-sur-Seine, France
Tel.: (33) 130098800
Web Site: http://www.vtech-jouets.com
Sales Range: $25-49.9 Million
Emp.: 25
Electronic Learning Products & Telecommunications Products Sales & Marketing
N.A.I.C.S.: 423690

VTech Electronics Europe, S.L. (1)
Avenida de Aragon 336 Oficina 1 Poligono, Las Mercedes, 28022, Madrid, Spain
Tel.: (34) 913120770
Web Site: http://www.vtech.es
Sales Range: $25-49.9 Million
Emp.: 25
Electronic Learning Products & Telecommunications Products Sales & Marketing
N.A.I.C.S.: 423690
Gilles Sautier *(CEO)*

VTech Electronics Industrial (Shenzhen) Co., Ltd. (1)
VTech Research & Development Building Keji South 12th Road No 5, District B-1 7th Floor Nanshan District, Shenzhen, 518057, Guangdong, China
Tel.: (86) 400 188 8628
Web Site: http://www.vtechchina.com.cn
Electronic Toys Mfr & Distr
N.A.I.C.S.: 339930

VTech Electronics Limited (1)
Room B1 6/F Tai Ping Industrial Centre Block 1 57 Ting Kok Road, Tai Po, New Territories, China (Hong Kong)
Tel.: (852) 27763223
Web Site: http://www.vtech.com
Emp.: 700
Electronic Products Mfr
N.A.I.C.S.: 334419

VTech Electronics North America, LLC (1)
1156 W Shure Dr Ste 200, Arlington Heights, IL 60004
Tel.: (847) 400-3600
Web Site: https://www.vtechkids.com
Sales Range: $25-49.9 Million
Emp.: 50
Educational Electronic Toys Sales & Marketing
N.A.I.C.S.: 423920

Subsidiary (Domestic):

LeapFrog Enterprises, Inc. (2)
6401 Hollis St Ste 100, Emeryville, CA 94608-1463
Tel.: (800) 701-5327
Interactive Educational Toy Mfr
N.A.I.C.S.: 339930

VTech Technologies Canada Ltd. (1)
Suite 222 - 13888 Wireless Way, Richmond, V6V 0A3, BC, Canada
Tel.: (604) 273-5131
Web Site: http://phones.vtechcanada.com
Sales Range: $50-74.9 Million
Emp.: 90

Electronic Learning Products & Telecommunications Products Sales & Marketing
N.A.I.C.S.: 423690
Gordon Chow *(Pres)*

VTech Telecom, L.L.C. (1)
237 Lexington St Ste 201, Woburn, MA 01801
Tel.: (781) 935-2510
Web Site: http://www.vtechcms.com
Telecommunication Equipment Distr
N.A.I.C.S.: 423690

VTech Telecommunications (Australia) Pty Limited (1)
24 Gilby Road, Mount Waverley, 3149, VIC, Australia
Tel.: (61) 1300 369 193
Web Site: http://auphones.vtech.com
Telephone Whslr
N.A.I.C.S.: 423690

VTech Telecommunications Limited (1)
Unit 1805 Stelux House 698 Prince Edward Road East, San Po Kong, Kowloon, China (Hong Kong)
Tel.: (852) 26665558
Web Site: http://www.hkphones.vtech.com
Emp.: 700
Telecommunications Equipment Mfr
N.A.I.C.S.: 334290

VTESSE NETWORKS LIMITED
John Tate Road, Hertford, SG13 7DT, Hertfordshire, United Kingdom
Tel.: (44) 1992 532100
Web Site: http://www.vtesse.com
Sales Range: $25-49.9 Million
Emp.: 45
Data Network Design, Construction & Management Services
N.A.I.C.S.: 517810
Aidan Paul *(CEO)*

VTEX
Av Brigadeiro Faria Lima 4 440 10 andar, Sao Paulo, 04538-132, Brazil
Tel.: (44) 2036957895
Web Site: https://vtex.com
Year Founded: 2000
Emp.: 1,349
Fiscal Year-end: 12/31/22
Holding Company; Cloud Based E-Commerce Platform & Omnichannel Solutions
N.A.I.C.S.: 551111
Geraldo do Carmo Thomaz *(Co-CEO)*

Subsidiaries:

WebLinc LLC (1)
340 North 12th St 2, Philadelphia, PA 19107
Tel.: (215) 925-1800
Web Site: http://www.weblinc.com
Rev.: $4,778,000
Emp.: 20
Custom Computer Programming Services
N.A.I.C.S.: 541511
Frank Lordi *(CFO)*

VTEX
Aviation House 3rd Floor room 03-A109 125 Kingsway, London, WC2B 6NH, United Kingdom
Tel.: (44) 2080392178 Ky
Web Site: https://www.vtex.com
Year Founded: 2018
VTEX—(NYSE)
Rev.: $201,517,000
Assets: $341,145,000
Liabilities: $100,813,000
Net Worth: $240,332,000
Earnings: ($13,694,000)
Emp.: 1,277
Fiscal Year-end: 12/31/23
Online Shopping Services
N.A.I.C.S.: 513210
Andre Spolidoro Ferreira Gomes *(CFO)*

VTION WIRELESS TECHNOLOGY AG
Westhafenplatz 1 Westhafen Tower, 60327, Frankfurt am Main, Germany
Tel.: (49) 69710456245
Web Site: http://www.vtion.de
Sales Range: $50-74.9 Million
Emp.: 238
Holding Company; Wireless Data Card Mfr
N.A.I.C.S.: 551112
Chen Guoping *(Chm-Mgmt Bd & CEO)*

Subsidiaries:

Vtion Wireless Technology AG - Corporate Headquarters (1)
20th Floor New Garden City Plaza, No 171 Wu Yi Bei Lu, Fuzhou, Fujian, China
Tel.: (86) 59187118888
Corporate Office
N.A.I.C.S.: 551114

VTL (HOLDINGS) LTD
St Thomas Road, Huddersfield, HD1 3LG, West Yorkshire, United Kingdom
Tel.: (44) 1484478700
Web Site: http://www.vtl-group.com
Year Founded: 1919
Sales Range: $50-74.9 Million
Emp.: 240
Automotive Components Mfr
N.A.I.C.S.: 336390
Bruno Jouan *(Mng Dir)*

Subsidiaries:

TWL Precision Inc. (1)
9551 Palmetto C, Ladson, SC 29456
Tel.: (843) 821-4688
Rev.: $10,000,000
Emp.: 25
Automotive Components Mfr
N.A.I.C.S.: 336390

VTL Group (USA) Inc (1)
9551 Palmetto Commerce Pkwy Unit 200, Ladson, SC 29456
Tel.: (843) 821-4688
Precision Engineering Component Mfr & Distr
N.A.I.C.S.: 332721

VTL Precision (1)
St Thomas' Road, Huddersfield, HD1 3LG, West Yorkshire, United Kingdom
Tel.: (44) 1484 478700
Automotive Components Mfr
N.A.I.C.S.: 336390
Zoe Moricon *(Mgr-Pur)*

VTL Precision (Bradley) Limited (1)
12 Station Road Bradley, West Yorkshire, Huddersfield, HD2 1US, United Kingdom
Tel.: (44) 1484 467 401
Precision Engineering Component Mfr & Distr
N.A.I.C.S.: 332721

VTL Precision (Japan) (1)
2-32-12 Nishiterao, Yokohama, Kanagawa-ku, Japan
Tel.: (81) 903 807 5886
Precision Engineering Component Mfr & Distr
N.A.I.C.S.: 327910

VTM LIMITED
Thiagarajar Mills Premises, Kappalur, Madurai, 625 008, India
Tel.: (91) 4522482595
Web Site: https://www.vtmill.com
Year Founded: 1946
532893—(BOM)
Rev.: $25,718,626
Assets: $32,301,361
Liabilities: $2,901,277
Net Worth: $29,400,084
Earnings: $1,095,654
Emp.: 446
Fiscal Year-end: 03/31/23
Fabrics Mfr

N.A.I.C.S.: 313310
T. Kannan *(Chm & Mng Dir)*

VTQ VIDEOTRONIK GMBH
Grune Strasse 2, 06268, Querfurt, Germany
Tel.: (49) 34771510
Web Site: http://www.vtq.de
Year Founded: 1953
Rev.: $20,588,151
Emp.: 140
Electric Device Mfr
N.A.I.C.S.: 334419
Steffen Enke *(Mgr)*

VTRON GROUP CO., LTD.
No 233 Kezhu Road, Highh-tech Industrial Development Zone, Guangzhou, 510670, Guangdong, China
Tel.: (86) 2022328888
Web Site: http://www.vtron.com
Year Founded: 2007
002308—(SSE)
Rev.: $72,240,700
Assets: $328,354,252
Liabilities: $51,295,561
Net Worth: $277,058,691
Earnings: $5,886,467
Fiscal Year-end: 12/31/22
Computer & Video Display System Mfr
N.A.I.C.S.: 541519
Lu Yu *(Chm)*

Subsidiaries:

Vtron Technologies (Hong Kong) Limited (1)
Unit 1608-09 16/F Tower 1 193 Prince Edward Road West, Grand Century Place Mongkok, Kowloon, China (Hong Kong)
Tel.: (852) 22643688
Video Wall System Distr
N.A.I.C.S.: 423410

VUB BANKA
Mlynske nivy 1, 829 90, Bratislava, Slovakia
Tel.: (421) 248555970
Web Site: https://www.vub.sk
Commercial Banking Services
N.A.I.C.S.: 522110
Alexander Resch *(Chm & CEO)*

VUENOW INFRATECH LIMITED
Unit No 406 & 407 A Wing Atrium Near ACME Plaza Andheri Kurla Road, Andheri East JB Nagar, Mumbai, 400059, Maharashtra, India
Tel.: (91) 2222820663
Year Founded: 1993
531997—(BOM)
Sales Range: Less than $1 Million
Irrigation Equipment Mfr
N.A.I.C.S.: 333111
Ruchi Srivastava *(Exec Dir)*

VUKILE PROPERTY FUND LIMITED
11 9th Street Houghton Estate, Melrose Estate, Johannesburg, South Africa
Tel.: (27) 112881000 ZA
Web Site: https://www.vukile.co.za
VKE—(JSE)
Rev.: $212,137,850
Assets: $2,336,156,855
Liabilities: $1,070,934,396
Net Worth: $1,265,222,459
Earnings: $85,024,132
Emp.: 49
Fiscal Year-end: 03/31/24
Real Estate Investment Trust
N.A.I.C.S.: 525990
Laurence Rapp *(CEO)*

VULCABRAS AZALEIA S.A.

VULCABRAS AZALEIA S.A.

Vulcabras Azaleia S.A.—(Continued)
Av Antonio Frederico Ozanan 1440, 13219001, Jundiai, 13219001, SP, Brazil
Tel.: (55) 1145321000
Web Site: https://www.vulcabras.com
Year Founded: 1952
VULC3—(BRAZ)
Rev.: $503,687,622
Assets: $496,085,684
Liabilities: $139,407,050
Net Worth: $356,678,634
Earnings: $88,465,166
Emp.: 14,000
Fiscal Year-end: 12/31/23
Footwear Mfr
N.A.I.C.S.: 339920
Pedro Grendene Bartelle *(Chm)*
Subsidiaries:

Vulcabras Azaleia CE, Calcados e Artigos Esportivos S.A. **(1)**
Avenida Presidente Castelo Branco 6847, Distrito Industrial, Belo Horizonte, 62880-000, Ceara, Brazil
Tel.: (55) 8533361733
Sport Shoe Mfr
N.A.I.C.S.: 316210

Subsidiary (Domestic):

Vulcabras Azaleia SP, Comercio de Artigos Esportivos Ltda. **(2)**
Avenida Antonio Frederico Ozanan 1440 Bairro da, Grama, Jundiai, 13219-001, Sao Paulo, Brazil
Tel.: (55) 1145321000
Footwear Sport Apparel & Accessory Distr
N.A.I.C.S.: 423910

Vulcabras Azaleia RS, Calcados e Artigos Esportivos S.A. **(1)**
Rua Dr Legendre 34 Centro, Parobe, Rio Grande, 95630-000, Rio Grande do Sul, Brazil
Tel.: (55) 5135431000
Sport Shoe Mfr & Distr
N.A.I.C.S.: 316210

Subsidiary (Non-US):

Calzados Azaleia Peru S.A. **(2)**
Av Prolongacion Arica N 2248, Lima, Peru
Tel.: (51) 16193637
Web Site: https://www.azaleia.pe
Sport Shoe Mfr & Distr
N.A.I.C.S.: 316210

Subsidiary (Domestic):

Vulcabras Azaleia BA, Calcados e Artigos Esportivos S.A. **(2)**
Avenida Julio Jose Rodrigues 1996, Vila Izabel Itapetinga, Rio de Janeiro, 45700-000, Bahia, Brazil
Tel.: (55) 7732618000
Sport Shoe Mfr & Distr
N.A.I.C.S.: 316210

VULCAN ENERGY RESOURCES LIMITED
Level 2 267 St Georges Terrace, Perth, 6000, WA, Australia
Tel.: (61) 863316156
Web Site: https://www.v-er.eu
Year Founded: 2018
VUL—(ASX)
Rev.: $7,487,581
Assets: $327,721,603
Liabilities: $31,573,021
Net Worth: $296,148,582
Earnings: ($29,763,771)
Emp.: 371
Fiscal Year-end: 12/31/23
Support Activities for Metal Mining
N.A.I.C.S.: 213114
Gavin Rezos *(Chm)*

VULCAN INDUSTRIAL & MINING CORPORATION
6th Floor Quad Alpha Centrum 125 Pioneer Street, Metro Manila, Mandaluyong, 1550, Philippines
Tel.: (63) 286315139
Web Site: http://www.vulcanminingcorp.com
VUL—(PHI)
Rev.: $3
Assets: $2,727
Liabilities: $29,552
Net Worth: ($26,824)
Earnings: ($16,909)
Emp.: 41
Fiscal Year-end: 12/31/20
Concrete Products Mfr
N.A.I.C.S.: 327331

VULCAN MINERALS INC.
333 Duckworth Street, Saint John's, A1C 1G9, NL, Canada
Tel.: (709) 754-3186
Web Site: https://www.vulcanminerals.ca
Year Founded: 1995
VUL—(TSXV)
Mineral Exploration Services
N.A.I.C.S.: 213112
Jennifer Button *(CFO, Sec & Mgr-Bus)*
Subsidiaries:

Atlas Salt Inc. **(1)**
100 New Gower Street Suite 910, Saint John's, A1C 6K3, NL, Canada **(65%)**
Tel.: (709) 739-9545
Web Site: https://atlassalt.com
Rev.: $429,408
Assets: $16,895,092
Liabilities: $451,488
Net Worth: $16,443,604
Earnings: ($3,653,280)
Fiscal Year-end: 12/31/2023
Mineral Mining Services
N.A.I.C.S.: 212390
Patrick J. Laracy *(Founder, Chm, Pres & CEO)*

VULCAN S.A.
15 Dumitru Brumarescu Street 4th Sector, Berceni District, 041838, Bucharest, Romania
Tel.: (40) 213199480
Web Site: http://www.vulcan.ro
Sales Range: $25-49.9 Million
Emp.: 1,022
Power Plant Boiler Mfr
N.A.I.C.S.: 332410
Lucia Varga *(Head-HR Dept)*

VULTURUL SA
Str Republicii Nr 4, Comarnic, Prahova, Romania
Tel.: (40) 244 360 011
Sales Range: Less than $1 Million
Refractory Products Mfr
N.A.I.C.S.: 327120

VULTUS AB
Klostergatan 9, 222 22, Lund, Sweden
Tel.: (46) 465402760
Web Site: https://www.vultus.se
Year Founded: 2016
V06—(DEU)
Software Development Services
N.A.I.C.S.: 541511
Ophir Mubarik *(Founder)*

VUNANI LIMITED
Vunani House Vunani Office Park, 151 Katherine Street Sandown, Sandton, 2196, South Africa
Tel.: (27) 112639500   ZA
Web Site: http://www.vunanilimited.co.za
Year Founded: 1997
VUN—(JSE)
Rev.: $27,034,325
Assets: $73,320,260
Liabilities: $52,088,267
Net Worth: $21,231,993
Earnings: $1,318,749
Emp.: 386
Fiscal Year-end: 02/29/24
Financial Management Services
N.A.I.C.S.: 523999
Ethan Dube *(CEO)*
Subsidiaries:

Vunani Fund Managers (Pty) Ltd **(1)**
6th Floor Letterstedt House Newlands on Main, Newlands, Cape Town, 7700, Western Cape, South Africa
Tel.: (27) 216704900
Web Site: http://www.vunanifm.co.za
Sales Range: $25-49.9 Million
Fund Management Consulting Services
N.A.I.C.S.: 523940
Tony Bell *(Head-Multi-Asset)*

VUNAR AS
TG Masaryka 4979/1, 940 02, Nove Zamky, Slovakia
Tel.: (421) 356428046
Web Site: https://www.vunar.eu
1VNR01AE—(BRA)
Sales Range: Less than $1 Million
Renewable Energy Consulting Services
N.A.I.C.S.: 541690
Alexandra Suchonova *(Chm-Mgmt Bd)*

VUNO INC.
9F 479 Gangnam-Daero, Seocho-Gu, Seoul, Korea (South)
Tel.: (82) 25156646
Web Site: https://www.vuno.co
Year Founded: 2014
338220—(KRS)
Rev.: $2,068,050
Assets: $32,757,371
Liabilities: $11,973,094
Net Worth: $20,784,277
Earnings: ($17,991,273)
Emp.: 126
Fiscal Year-end: 12/31/21
Data Processing & Hosting Services
N.A.I.C.S.: 518210
Sangjin Lee *(Mng Dir)*

VURAL, INC.
Alexandra Rudnaya 23, 01001, Zilina, Slovakia
Tel.: (421) 417235638
Web Site: http://www.vural.sk
Year Founded: 1966
Sales Range: $1-9.9 Million
Emp.: 220
Machine Tools, Jigs, Fixtures, Assembly Tools, Inspection Equipment, Conveyor Equipment, Precision Injection Moulding, Pressed Steel Sheets, Formed Components Developer, Designer & Mfr
N.A.I.C.S.: 333515
Slavoj Mirek *(Chm)*

VUWA INVESTMENTS (PTY) LTD
Ground Floor Building 2 21 Impala Road Chislehurston, Sandton, 2196, South Africa
Tel.: (27) 117835356
Web Site: http://www.vuwa.co.za
Year Founded: 2006
Privater Equity Firm
N.A.I.C.S.: 523999
Lungisa Dyosi *(CEO)*
Subsidiaries:

Buildmax Limited **(1)**
Portion 10 Tweefontein Farm Wolmarans Street, PO Box 1067, Bapsfontein, Benoni, 1510, South Africa
Tel.: (27) 861 691 177
Web Site: http://www.buildmax.co.za
Sales Range: $50-74.9 Million
Coal Mining Contractor & Construction Materials Supplier
N.A.I.C.S.: 236210
Gillian Hope Miller *(COO)*

Subsidiary (Domestic):

Buildmax Aggregates and Quarries (Pty) Limited **(2)**
Unit 19 First Fl E Block Cambridge Ofc Highveld Park, Centurion, 0067, Gauteng, South Africa
Tel.: (27) 116220544
Building Materials Distr
N.A.I.C.S.: 444180

Buildmax Management Services (Pty) Limited **(2)**
Unit 19 1st Fl E Cambridge Ofc Park, Pretoria, 1400, Gauteng, South Africa
Tel.: (27) 126850440
Sales Range: $50-74.9 Million
Emp.: 7
Construction Materials Whslr
N.A.I.C.S.: 423320

Crushco (Pty) Limited **(2)**
Private Bag X02 1514, Rynsfield, Benoni, 1514, South Africa
Tel.: (27) 118285722
Sales Range: $50-74.9 Million
Emp.: 70
Sand & Gravel Quarrying Services
N.A.I.C.S.: 212321

Diesel Power Open Cast Mining (Pty) Limited **(2)**
126 Tenth Rd Kew, Sandton, Johannesburg, 2090, Gauteng, South Africa
Tel.: (27) 11 882 2665
Mining & Earthmoving Contract Services
N.A.I.C.S.: 213114

Vukuza Earth Works (Pty) Limited **(2)**
516 Pretoria Rd, Benoni, 1501, Gauteng, South Africa
Tel.: (27) 119689300
Contract Mining Services
N.A.I.C.S.: 213115

Wit Deep Sand and Stone (Pty) Limited **(2)**
320 Main Reef Rd Knights, Germiston, 1413, Gauteng, South Africa
Tel.: (27) 861 948 3337
Construction Materials Distr
N.A.I.C.S.: 444180
Gillian Miller *(Sec)*

VV TIKVES AD SKOPJE
st Dimche Belovski no 2, 1000, Skopje, North Macedonia
Tel.: (389) 23181700
Web Site: https://tikves.com.mk
TKVS—(MAC)
Rev.: $41,239,445
Assets: $69,400,693
Liabilities: $27,201,223
Net Worth: $42,199,470
Earnings: $2,693,690
Fiscal Year-end: 12/31/21
Wine Mfr
N.A.I.C.S.: 312130
Svetozar Janevski *(Chm-Mgmt Bd)*

VVC EXPLORATION CORPORATION
2369 Kingston Road, PO Box 28059, Terry Town, Scarborough, M1N 4E7, ON, Canada
Tel.: (416) 619-5304
Web Site: https://www.vvcresources.com
Year Founded: 1983
VVC—(TSXV)
Rev.: $17,764
Assets: $3,091,095
Liabilities: $6,192,424
Net Worth: ($3,101,329)
Earnings: ($6,575,225)
Fiscal Year-end: 01/31/22
Mineral Exploration Services

AND PRIVATE COMPANIES

N.A.I.C.S.: 213114
Michel J. Lafrance *(Treas & Sec)*

Subsidiaries:

VVC Exploracion de Mexico, S. de R.L. de C.V.
CV Boulevard Ortiz Mena No 2807 Interior 22 Quintas del Sol, 31214, Chihuahua, Mexico
Tel.: (52) 6144235416
Gold Mining Services
N.A.I.C.S.: 212220

VVF LIMITED
109 Sion East, Mumbai, 400022, India
Tel.: (91) 2240282000
Web Site: http://www.vvfltd.com
Year Founded: 1939
Sales Range: $400-449.9 Million
Emp.: 2,500
Oleochemicals & Personal Care Products Mfr
N.A.I.C.S.: 325998
Rustom Godrej Joshi *(Chm & Mng Dir)*

Subsidiaries:

Green Planet Industries LLC (1)
Plot No 597/663 Dubai Investments Park, PO Box 25869, Dubai, United Arab Emirates
Tel.: (971) 4 885 7501
Personal Care Product Distr
N.A.I.C.S.: 424210
Tondapu PullaRao *(Sr Mgr-Production)*

VVF FZE (1)
Jebel Ali Free Zone, PO Box 61337, Dubai, United Arab Emirates
Tel.: (971) 4 8832204
Personal Care Product Distr
N.A.I.C.S.: 424210

VVF Limited (1)
1705 Kansas Ave, Kansas City, KS 66105
Tel.: (913) 281-7444
Web Site: http://www.vvfltd.com
Oleochemicals & Personal Care Products Mfr
N.A.I.C.S.: 325998

VVF Singapore Pte. Limited (1)
133 Cecil Street 09 O1A Keck Seng Tower, Singapore, 069535, Singapore
Tel.: (65) 62248871
Web Site: http://www.vvf.ltd.com
Emp.: 5
Chemical Products Distr
N.A.I.C.S.: 424690
Hariharan Subramaniyan *(Mng Dir)*

VVF Spolka Z.O.O (1)
Ul Stalowa 9, 47-400, Raciborz, Poland
Tel.: (48) 3275 42100
Personal Care Product Distr
N.A.I.C.S.: 424210

Vita Biopharma Pvt. Limited (1)
Plot No 141 / 143 Survey No 195 / 4 195 / 6 Panchal Udyog Nagar, Bhimpore, Daman, 396210, India
Tel.: (91) 260 2221075
Personal Care Product Mfr
N.A.I.C.S.: 325620
Mahendra Mistry *(Mgr)*

VXL INSTRUMENTS LIMITED
252 5th Floor Building No 2 Solitaire Corporate Park, Chakala Andheri East, Mumbai, 400093, Maharashtra, India
Tel.: (91) 2228245210
Web Site: http://www.vxl.net
Year Founded: 1976
517399—(BOM)
Rev.: $1,062,792
Assets: $2,184,912
Liabilities: $1,395,943
Net Worth: $788,969
Earnings: ($309,729)
Emp.: 50
Fiscal Year-end: 03/31/21
Computer Peripheral Equipment Mfr
N.A.I.C.S.: 334118
Vittal Mangalore Shetty *(Exec Dir)*

Subsidiaries:

VXL Instruments Limited (1)
Carrington Business Park, Carrington, Manchester, M31 4DD, United Kingdom
Tel.: (44) 161 775 4755
Web Site: http://www.vxl.net
Emp.: 10
Computer Peripheral Equipment Distr
N.A.I.C.S.: 423430
Ian Cope *(Mgr-Mktg & PR)*

VXL Instruments, Inc (1)
403 Corporate Woods Dr, Magnolia, TX 77354
Tel.: (877) 242-7801
Computer Peripheral Equipment Distr
N.A.I.C.S.: 423430

VYAPAR INDUSTRIES LTD.
Abbas Manzil 145 S V Road, Khar W, Mumbai, 400052, India
Tel.: (91) 2266989111
Web Site: http://www.vyaparindustries.com
506142—(BOM)
Rev.: $172,664
Assets: $9,080,272
Liabilities: $421,981
Net Worth: $8,658,292
Earnings: $34,426
Emp.: 5
Fiscal Year-end: 03/31/19
Embroidery Thread & Yarn Mfr
N.A.I.C.S.: 313110
Hussain Abbas Rassai *(Chm)*

VYBORG SHIPYARD PJSC
2b Primorskoe Shosse, 188800, Vyborg, 188800, Russia
Tel.: (7) 8137826432
Web Site: https://www.vyborgshipyard.ru
Year Founded: 1948
VSYD—(MOEX)
Sales Range: Less than $1 Million
Ship Building & Construction Services
N.A.I.C.S.: 336611
Alexander S. Solovyev *(CEO)*

VYCHODOSLOVENSKA ENERGETIKA A.S.
Mlynska 31, 042 91, Kosice, Slovakia
Tel.: (421) 556193681   Sk
Web Site: http://www.vse.sk
Year Founded: 1929
Sales Range: $700-749.9 Million
Emp.: 1,596
Electricity Power & gas Distribution Services
N.A.I.C.S.: 221122
Thomas Jan Hejcman *(Chm & CEO)*

VYKSA STEEL WORKS JSC
Ul Bratiev Batashevikh 45, Vyksa, Nizhniy Novgorod, 607060, Russia
Tel.: (7) 88002501150
Web Site: http://www.omksteel.com
Sales Range: Less than $1 Million
Oil & Gas Pipeline Construction Services
N.A.I.C.S.: 237120
Anatoly Sedykh *(Chm)*

VYNCO INDUSTRIES (NZ) LIMITED
388-396 Tuam Street, Philipstown, Christchurch, 8011, New Zealand
Tel.: (64) 3 379 9283
Web Site: http://www.vynco.co.nz
Year Founded: 1990
Sales Range: $25-49.9 Million
Emp.: 12
Electrical Equipment & Component Whslr
N.A.I.C.S.: 423610
Simon Vale *(Gen Mgr)*

VYSARN LIMITED
Level 1 640 Murray Street, West Perth, 6005, VIC, Australia
Tel.: (61) 861449777   AU
Web Site: https://www.vysarn.com.au
Year Founded: 2007
VYS—(ASX)
Rev.: $20,202,306
Assets: $34,734,978
Liabilities: $15,761,843
Net Worth: $18,973,135
Earnings: $264,197
Emp.: 100
Fiscal Year-end: 06/30/21
Gold, Copper, Nickel, Zinc, Iron Ore & Tin Mining
N.A.I.C.S.: 212210
Peter Hutchinson *(Chm)*

Subsidiaries:

Pentium Hydro Pty. Ltd. (1)
11 Gavranich Way, Wangara, 6065, WA, Australia
Tel.: (61) 861449777
Web Site: https://www.pentiumhydro.com.au
Dewatering Drilling Services
N.A.I.C.S.: 238910
Sheldon Burt *(Mng Dir)*

Pentium Test Pumping Pty. Ltd. (1)
11 Gavranich Way, Wangara, 6065, WA, Australia
Tel.: (61) 861449777
Web Site: https://pentiumtestpumping.com.au
Tailored Test Pumping Services
N.A.I.C.S.: 237110

Pentium Water Pty. Ltd. (1)
Level 1 640 Murray Street, West Perth, 6005, WA, Australia
Tel.: (61) 861821790
Web Site: https://www.pentiumwater.com.au
Environmental Management Services
N.A.I.C.S.: 541620

VYTRUS BIOTECH SA
Sant Gaieta 121 2nd, Terrassa, 08221, Barcelona, Spain
Tel.: (34) 931278106
Web Site: https://www.vytrus.com
Year Founded: 2009
VYT—(BAR)
Rev.: $4,011,310
Assets: $9,998,825
Liabilities: $4,318,003
Net Worth: $5,680,821
Earnings: $584,954
Emp.: 37
Fiscal Year-end: 12/31/23
Biotechnology Research & Development Services
N.A.I.C.S.: 541714
Albert Jane *(Pres)*

VZ HOLDING AG
Gotthardstrasse 6, 8002, Zurich, Switzerland
Tel.: (41) 442072727
Web Site: https://www.vermoegenszentrum.ch
VZN—(SWX)
Rev.: $458,888,027
Assets: $6,591,920,177
Liabilities: $5,736,855,876
Net Worth: $855,064,302
Earnings: $167,759,424
Emp.: 1,247
Fiscal Year-end: 12/31/22
Financial Advisory Services
N.A.I.C.S.: 522291
Fred Kindle *(Chm)*

Subsidiaries:

HypothekenZentrum Ltd. (1)
Gotthardstrasse 6, 8002, Zurich, Switzerland

W INTERACTIVE MEDIA

Tel.: (41) 445636333
Web Site: https://www.hypothekenzentrum.ch
Finance Management Services
N.A.I.C.S.: 524298
Christoph Huber *(Officer-Risk)*

Lumin Wealth Limited (1)
5 Sandridge Park Porters Wood, Saint Albans, AL3 6PH, Hertfordshire, United Kingdom
Tel.: (44) 3300564446
Web Site: https://luminwealth.co.uk
Financial Services
N.A.I.C.S.: 522320

Lumin Wealth Management Limited (1)
5 Sandridge Park Porters Wood, Saint Albans, AL3 6PH, Hertfordshire, United Kingdom
Tel.: (44) 1727893333
Financial Services
N.A.I.C.S.: 522320

VZ Depository Bank Ltd. (1)
Innere Guterstrasse 2, 6300, Zug, Switzerland
Tel.: (41) 584118080
Real Estate Manangement Services
N.A.I.C.S.: 531312

VZ Legal & Tax Consulting Ltd. (1)
Gotthardstrasse 6, 8002, Zurich, Switzerland
Tel.: (41) 442072727
Fiduciary Services
N.A.I.C.S.: 525920

VZ Operations Ltd. (1)
Gotthardstrasse 6, 8002, Zurich, Switzerland
Tel.: (41) 1442072727
Investment Banking Services
N.A.I.C.S.: 523150

VZ Rechts- und Steuerberatung Ltd. (1)
Gotthardstrasse 6, 8002, Zurich, Switzerland
Tel.: (41) 442072727
Banking & Financial Services
N.A.I.C.S.: 522110

VZ VermogensZentrum Bank Ltd. (1)
Maximiliansplatz 12, 80333, Munich, Germany
Tel.: (49) 892881170
Banking Services
N.A.I.C.S.: 522110

VZ VermogensZentrum GmbH (1)
Maximiliansplatz 12, 80333, Munich, Germany
Tel.: (49) 892881170
Web Site: https://www.vermoegenszentrum.de
Real Estate Manangement Services
N.A.I.C.S.: 531312

VZ VermogensZentrum Ltd. (1)
Gotthardstrasse 6, 8002, Zurich, Switzerland
Tel.: (41) 442072727
Web Site: https://www.vermoegenszentrum.ch
Real Estate Manangement Services
N.A.I.C.S.: 531312

VZ VersicherungsPool Ltd. (1)
Gotthardstrasse 6, 8002, Zurich, Switzerland
Tel.: (41) 583442000
Vehicle Insurance Services
N.A.I.C.S.: 524126

VZ VersicherungsZentrum Ltd. (1)
Gotthardstrasse 6, 8002, Zurich, Switzerland
Tel.: (41) 442072020
Real Estate Manangement Services
N.A.I.C.S.: 531312

W INTERACTIVE MEDIA
Obregon Sur 1366-40, Zona Centro, 25000, Saltillo, Coahuila, Mexico
Tel.: (52) 8444894400
Web Site: http://www.grupow.com

W INTERACTIVE MEDIA

W Interactive Media—(Continued)

Sales Range: $50-74.9 Million
Emp.: 60
N.A.I.C.S.: 541810
Miguel Calderon *(Co-Founder)*

W RESOURCES PLC
27/28 Eastcastle Street, London,
W1W 8DH, United Kingdom
Tel.: (44) 2071937463   UK
Web Site:
  http://www.wresources.com
WRES—(AIM)
Rev.: $3,086,567
Assets: $101,280,670
Liabilities: $79,004,082
Net Worth: $22,276,589
Earnings: ($4,276,732)
Emp.: 72
Fiscal Year-end: 12/31/20
Tungsten Mining Services
N.A.I.C.S.: 212290
Michael G. Masterman *(Founder & Chm)*

W T K HOLDINGS BERHAD
Bangunan Hung Ann No 1 Jalan Bujang Suntong, 96000, Sibu, Malaysia
Tel.: (60) 84326155
Web Site: https://wtkholdings.com
WTK—(KLS)
Rev.: $100,112,804
Assets: $240,629,841
Liabilities: $74,563,175
Net Worth: $166,066,667
Earnings: ($539,683)
Emp.: 4,328
Fiscal Year-end: 12/31/22
Lumber Mfr
N.A.I.C.S.: 321215
Patrick Haw Yeong Wong *(Mng Dir)*

Subsidiaries:

Cairnfield Sdn. Bhd. (1)
Lot 146 Block 38 Kemena Industrial Estate, Bintulu, 97008, Sarawak, Malaysia
Tel.: (60) 86338158
Lumber Whslr
N.A.I.C.S.: 423310

Central Mercantile Corporation (S) Ltd. (1)
86/88 Tagore Lane, Singapore, 787528, Singapore
Tel.: (65) 6 459 5477
Web Site: https://www.cmcs.com.sg
Industrial Packaging Materials Mfr & Distr
N.A.I.C.S.: 322220

General Aluminium Works (M) Sdn. Bhd. (1)
76 KM Ipoh Penang Main Trunk Road, PO Box 165, 34008, Taiping, Perak Darul Ridzuan, Malaysia
Tel.: (60) 5 820 8500
Web Site: https://www.gaw.com.my
Sales Range: $150-199.9 Million
Emp.: 300
Packaging Products Mfr
N.A.I.C.S.: 322220

Gopoint Sdn. Bhd. (1)
Bangunan Hung Ann No 1 Jalan Bujang Suntong, Sibu, 96007, Sarawak, Malaysia
Tel.: (60) 84326155
Web Site: http://www.wtk.com
Emp.: 200
Lumber Product Whslr
N.A.I.C.S.: 423310
Annie Wong *(Mgr-Mktg)*

Kuching Plywood Bhd. (1)
No 5415 Jln Pending, 93450, Kuching, Sarawak, Malaysia
Tel.: (60) 82332718
Sales Range: $50-74.9 Million
Emp.: 100
Plywood Mfr & Whslr
N.A.I.C.S.: 321211

Limpah Mewah Sdn. Bhd. (1)
No 72 1st Floor, Jln Wharf, Kapit, 96800, Sarawak, Malaysia
Tel.: (60) 84796823
Lumber Product Whslr
N.A.I.C.S.: 423990

Linshanhao Plywood (Sarawak) Sdn. Bhd. (1)
No 699 Jln Bako Kaw Perindustrian Sejingkat, Kuching, 93050, Sarawak, Malaysia
Tel.: (60) 82439119
Sales Range: $250-299.9 Million
Emp.: 800
Plywood Mfr & Whslr
N.A.I.C.S.: 321211
Kiong Liew Chee *(Mgr-Fin)*

Loytape Industries Sdn. Bhd. (1)
Lot 1017 Lorong Perusahaan Satu, Kawasan Perusahaan Perai Seberang Perai, 13600, Perai, Penang, Malaysia
Tel.: (60) 4 390 7049
Web Site: https://www.loytape.com.my
Emp.: 170
Adhesive Tape Mfr
N.A.I.C.S.: 325520

Subsidiary (Domestic):

Samanda Trading Sdn. Bhd. (2)
No 31 Jalan 10/91 Taman Shamelin Perkasa Cheras, Kuala Lumpur, 56100, Federal Territory, Malaysia
Tel.: (60) 392008199
Web Site: http://www.loytape.com.my
Sales Range: $25-49.9 Million
Emp.: 12
Adhesive Tape Distr
N.A.I.C.S.: 424990

Sarawak Moulding Industries Berhad (1)
Lot No 1939 Block 11, Engkilo Land District, 96000, Sibu, Sarawak, Malaysia
Tel.: (60) 84315805
Web Site: http://www.smipark.com
Sales Range: $50-74.9 Million
Emp.: 80
Sawn Timber Mfr & Distr
N.A.I.C.S.: 321113
Wong Kieyik *(Mng Dir)*

Song Logging Company Sendirian Berhad (1)
No 1 Jalan Bujang Suntong, Jln Bujang Suntong, 96000, Sibu, Sarawak, Malaysia
Tel.: (60) 84326155
Web Site: https://www.wtk.com.my
Sales Range: $75-99.9 Million
Emp.: 400
Timber Logging Services
N.A.I.C.S.: 113110
Annie Wong Hii *(Mgr-Mktg)*

Sut Sawmill (3064) Sdn. Bhd. (1)
No 1 Jalan Bujang Suntong, PO Box 256, 96007, Sibu, Sarawak, Malaysia
Tel.: (60) 84326155
Web Site: https://www.wtkholdings.com
Sales Range: $25-49.9 Million
Emp.: 45
Lumber Product Whslr
N.A.I.C.S.: 423990

W&K GESELLSCHAFT FUR INDUSTRIETECHNIK MBH
Frankenstrasse 1, 97906, Faulbach, Germany
Tel.: (49) 939292800
Web Site: http://www.wk-industrietechnik.de
Year Founded: 1985
Rev.: $43,632,600
Emp.: 176
Mechanical Installation Equipment Mfr
N.A.I.C.S.: 333248
Martin Kratzer *(Co-Mng Dir)*

Subsidiaries:

OOO WK Industrial Service (1)
Krasnoarmeiskaya Street 101 A, Ramenskoje, Moscow, Russia
Tel.: (7) 4964617613
Web Site: http://www.wkrussia.org
Construction Engineering Services
N.A.I.C.S.: 541330

W&K Hispana Tecnica Industrial S.L. (1)
C/Barrio Alto Nr 14, Algatocin, Malaga, Spain
Tel.: (34) 952150032
Web Site: http://www.wkspain.com
Construction Engineering Services
N.A.I.C.S.: 541330

W&K Industrietechnik Sp. z o.o. (1)
ul Chocianowska 20 d, Lubin, Poland
Tel.: (48) 767442242
Web Site: http://www.wkpoland.com
Construction Engineering Services
N.A.I.C.S.: 541330

W&K Industrietechnik s.r.o. (1)
Stvrt SNP 153, Trencianske Teplice, Slovakia
Tel.: (421) 322858002
Web Site: http://www.wkslovakia.com
Construction Engineering Services
N.A.I.C.S.: 541330
Lubomir Michalik *(Mng Dir)*

WK Endustri Sanayi ve Ticaret Limited Sirketi (1)
Inonu Mah 20 Sokak No 5, Muradiye, Manisa, Turkiye
Tel.: (90) 5321002406
Web Site: http://www.wkturkey.com
Construction Engineering Services
N.A.I.C.S.: 541330

WK Industrial Services Corp. (1)
9365 Industrial Trce, Alpharetta, GA 30004-3383
Tel.: (678) 679-4840
Web Site: http://www.wkamerica.com
Construction Engineering Services
N.A.I.C.S.: 541330
Michael Spegt *(CEO)*

WK Industrial Technology Consulting (Shanghai) Co., Ltd. (1)
No 2 Lane 28 63 Yu Lv Road Malu Town, Jiading District, Shanghai, China
Tel.: (86) 2139901700
Web Site: http://www.wk-shanghai.com
Construction Engineering Services
N.A.I.C.S.: 541330

W&R BARNETT LTD.
Clarendon House 23 Clarendon Road, Belfast, BT1 3BG, United Kingdom
Tel.: (44) 28 9032 5465
Web Site: http://www.wrbarnett.com
Sales Range: $550-599.9 Million
Emp.: 312
Molasses, Grain & Animal Feed Distr
N.A.I.C.S.: 425120
William Barnett *(CEO)*

Subsidiaries:

United Molasses Group Limited (1)
48 Gracechurch Street, London, EC3V 0EJ, United Kingdom
Tel.: (44) 20 7220 4650
Web Site: http://www.umgroup.com
Sales Range: $350-399.9 Million
Trading & Marketing of Molasses, Vegetable Oils & Related Products; Storage of Bulk Liquids
N.A.I.C.S.: 425120
Chris Roberts *(CEO)*

Subsidiary (Domestic):

Advanced Liquid Feeds Limited (2)
Athel House 167 Regent Road, Liverpool, L20 8DD, United Kingdom
Tel.: (44) 151 955 4880
Web Site: http://www.umgroup.com
Supplier of Blended Feed Fats for Animal Feed Industry
N.A.I.C.S.: 311225
Ian Beck *(Gen Mgr)*

Subsidiary (Non-US):

France Melasses SA (2)
27-29 rue Chateaubriand, 75008, Paris, France (66%)
Tel.: (33) 1 42 99 00 60
Web Site: http://www.francemelasses.net
Molasses marketer & Distr

INTERNATIONAL PUBLIC

N.A.I.C.S.: 424490

Hansa Melasse Handelsgesellschaft mbH (2)
Kap-Horn-Strasse 5A, 28237, Bremen, Germany
Tel.: (49) 421 3363 649 30
Web Site: http://www.melasse.de
Emp.: 4
Sales & Marketing of Molasses
N.A.I.C.S.: 424490
Annette Meine *(Country Mgr)*

UM Italia Srl (2)
Via XX Settembre 6/b, 20061, Carugate, MI, Italy
Tel.: (39) 02 9215 0000
Web Site: http://www.umgroup.com
Trading & Marketing of Molasses, Vegetable Oils & Related Products
N.A.I.C.S.: 425120

UM Korea Ltd (2)
Room No 607 Raemian Seocho Univil 1445-4 Seocho Dong, Seocho-gu, Seoul, 137-918, Korea (South)
Tel.: (82) 2 586 5505
Web Site: http://www.umgroup.com
Emp.: 4
Trading & Marketing of Molasses, Vegetable Oils & Related Products
N.A.I.C.S.: 425120
M. J. Kim *(Mng Dir)*

Subsidiary (Domestic):

United Molasses (Ireland) Ltd (2)
Duncrue Street, Belfast, BT3 9AQ, United Kingdom (100%)
Tel.: (44) 28 90747011
Web Site: http://www.umi.co.uk
Sales Range: $550-599.9 Million
Molasses Trading & Marketing
N.A.I.C.S.: 425120

Subsidiary (Non-US):

United Molasses Espana SA (2)
Raimundo Fernandez Villaverde 28 Oficina 113, 28003, Madrid, Spain
Tel.: (34) 91 533 4818
Web Site: http://www.umgroup.com
Trading & Marketing of Molasses, Vegetable Oils & Related Products
N.A.I.C.S.: 425120

Subsidiary (Domestic):

United Molasses GB Limited (2)
48 Gracechurch Street, London, EC3V 0EJ, United Kingdom
Tel.: (44) 20 7220 4669
Web Site: http://www.umgroup.com
Molasses Trading & Marketing
N.A.I.C.S.: 425120

United Molasses Marketing Limited (2)
48 Gracechurch Street, London, EC3V 0EJ, United Kingdom
Tel.: (44) 20 7220 4650
Web Site: http://www.umgroup.com
Molasses & Related Liquids Marketer & Distr
N.A.I.C.S.: 424490

Subsidiary (Non-US):

United Molasses Marketing Philippines Inc. (2)
6F Don Jacinto Building 141 Salcedo St, Legaspi Village, Makati, 1229, Philippines
Tel.: (63) 2 813 1904
Web Site: http://www.umgroup.com
Molasses, Vegetable Oils & Related Products Trading & Marketing
N.A.I.C.S.: 425120
Jo Trebol *(Mgr)*

Division (Domestic):

United Molasses Storage (2)
Athel House 167 Regent Road, Liverpool, L20 8DD, United Kingdom
Tel.: (44) 151 933 1010
Web Site: http://www.umgroup.com
Molasses & Other Bulk Liquid Storage
N.A.I.C.S.: 493190
Phill Maginn *(Head-Sls & Mktg)*

AND PRIVATE COMPANIES

Subsidiary (Domestic):

United Molasses Trading Limited (2)
48 Gracechurch Street, London, EC3V 0EJ, United Kingdom
Tel.: (44) 20 7220 4650
Web Site: http://www.umgroup.com
Molasses Trading & Marketing
N.A.I.C.S.: 425120
Brian Potter *(Dir-Trading)*

W-SCOPE CORPORATION
10F SUMITOMO-SEIMEI Gotanda Building 5-1-11 Osaki, Shinagawa-ku, Tokyo, 141-0032, Japan
Tel.: (81) 354367155
Web Site: https://www.w-scope.co.jp
Year Founded: 2005
6619—(TKS)
Rev.: $340,624,870
Assets: $1,212,390,000
Liabilities: $334,669,270
Net Worth: $877,720,730
Earnings: $6,657,510
Emp.: 1,321
Fiscal Year-end: 01/31/24
Plastic Film & Sheet Mfr
N.A.I.C.S.: 322220
Won-Kun Choi *(Pres)*

Subsidiaries:

W-SCOPE KOREA CO., LTD. (1)
106 Gwahaksanop 4 Sa -ro Ochang-eup, Cheongwon-gu, Cheongju, 28122, Chungcheong, Korea (South)
Tel.: (82) 43 240 8800
Web Site: http://w-scope.co.kr
Sales Range: $75-99.9 Million
Emp.: 300
Plastic Film Mfr & Whslr
N.A.I.C.S.: 322220
Won-geun Choi *(CEO)*

W-Scope Chungju Plant Co., Ltd. (1)
195 Megapolis-ro Daesowon-myeon, Chungju, 27461, Chungcheongbuk, Korea (South)
Paper Mfr
N.A.I.C.S.: 322220
John Hyun-Nam Park *(Deputy Gen Mgr-Production Tech)*

W-Scope New Energy (Shenzhen) Co., Limited (1)
Unit A3303 Golden Central Tower No 3307 Jintian Rd, Futian District, Shenzhen, China
Tel.: (86) 75583325191
Paper Mfr
N.A.I.C.S.: 322220

W. G. MCKAY LIMITED
Suite 602 40 University Avenue, Toronto, M5J 1J9, ON, Canada
Tel.: (416) 593-1380
Web Site: http://www.wgmckay.com
Year Founded: 1950
Rev.: $100,000,000
Emp.: 55
Customs Brokerage Services
N.A.I.C.S.: 425120
Cheryl I. Clarke *(Mgr-Customs)*

W. H. BRADY & CO. LTD.
Brady House 12 / 14 Veer Nariman Road, Fort, Mumbai, 400 001, India
Tel.: (91) 2222048361
Web Site: https://www.whbrady.in
Year Founded: 1895
501391—(BOM)
Rev.: $9,121,468
Assets: $9,762,508
Liabilities: $3,205,228
Net Worth: $6,557,281
Earnings: $653,762
Fiscal Year-end: 03/31/23
Aviation Support Services
N.A.I.C.S.: 488119
Pavan G. Morarka *(Chm & Mng Dir)*

Subsidiaries:

Brady Services Pvt. Ltd. (1)
LB-17 New Delhi House 27 Barakhamba Road, New Delhi, India
Tel.: (91) 1125675658
Web Site: https://bradyservices.in
Property Facilities Management Services
N.A.I.C.S.: 921190

W. HAKING ENTERPRISES LTD.
10/F Haking Tung Shing Industrial Building 34 Lee Chung Street, Chai Wan, China (Hong Kong)
Tel.: (852) 25794622
Web Site: http://www.haking.com
Year Founded: 1956
Sales Range: $25-49.9 Million
Emp.: 1,200
Prismatic Binoculars & APS Film & 35mm Camera Mfr
N.A.I.C.S.: 333310
Tony Tai *(CEO)*

W. LUCY & CO. LTD.
Eagle Works Walton Well Road, Oxford, OX2 6EE, Oxon, United Kingdom
Tel.: (44) 1865 311411   UK
Web Site: http://www.lucygroup.com
Emp.: 400
Lighting Mfr
N.A.I.C.S.: 335139
Richard Dick *(Exec Chm)*

Subsidiaries:

Lucy Asia Pacific SDN BHD (1)
Unit No L17-05-06 Level 17 PJX-HM Shah Tower No 16 Persiaran Barat, 46050, Petaling Jaya, Selangor, Malaysia
Tel.: (60) 379317775
Industrial Automation Equipments Mfr
N.A.I.C.S.: 334513

Lucy Electric (Thailand) Ltd. (1)
388 Exchange Tower 37th Floor Unit 3702 Sukhumvit Road Khlong Toei, Bangkok, 10110, Thailand
Tel.: (66) 26634290
Industrial Automation Equipments Mfr
N.A.I.C.S.: 334513
Panita Mungkalawong *(Mgr-Contracts)*

Lucy Electric Beijing Company Ltd. (1)
Room 1122 Towera Gateway Square No 18 Xiaguangli North Road Third Ring, Chaoyang, Beijing, China
Tel.: (86) 1059231176
Industrial Automation Equipments Mfr
N.A.I.C.S.: 334513

Lucy Electric India (Private) Limited (1)
F-10 Midc, Ambad, Nasik, 422010, India
Tel.: (91) 2676304900
Industrial Automation Equipments Mfr
N.A.I.C.S.: 334513
Sagar Patil *(Asst Mgr)*

Lucy Electric South Africa Pty Ltd. (1)
Unit 12 & 13 Block C Honeydew Business Park 1503 Citrus Street, Honeydew, Johannesburg, 2170, South Africa
Tel.: (27) 110257490
Industrial Automation Equipments Mfr
N.A.I.C.S.: 334513

Lucy Middle East FZE (1)
PO Box 17335, Jebel Ali, United Arab Emirates
Tel.: (971) 48129999
Industrial Automation Equipments Mfr
N.A.I.C.S.: 334513
Bassam Hakim *(Area Mgr-Sls)*

Lucy Zodion Limited (1)
Station Road, London, HX6 3AF, United Kingdom
Tel.: (44) 1422317337
Street Light Mfr
N.A.I.C.S.: 335139
David Hall *(Mgr-Sls)*

Sandawana Castings Limited (1)
Bromag Industrial Estate Burford Road, Witney, Oxford, OX29 0SR, United Kingdom
Tel.: (44) 1993775862
Die Casting & Metal Product Mfr
N.A.I.C.S.: 331513
Derrick Lawrence *(Mgr-Quality & Technical)*

Truscanian Foundries Limited (1)
St Martins Industrial Estate Engine Street, Oldbury, B69 4NL, West Midlands, United Kingdom
Tel.: (44) 1215523011
Die Casting & Metal Product Mfr
N.A.I.C.S.: 331513
Richard Ankcorn *(Mgr-Quality)*

W. SCHILDMEYER GMBH & CO. KG
Sachsenweg 55, 32547, Bad Oeynhausen, Germany
Tel.: (49) 573176000
Web Site: http://www.w-schildmeyer.de
Year Founded: 1947
Rev.: $24,533,383
Emp.: 85
Furniture Mfr
N.A.I.C.S.: 337126
A. Diekmann *(Mgr-Pur)*

W. SCHRAML SOFTWAREHAUS GMBH
Einsteinstr 39a, 82152, Martinsried, Germany
Tel.: (49) 89 89 41 35 0
Web Site: http://www.schramlsoft.de
Sales Range: $25-49.9 Million
Emp.: 15
Custom Computer Programming Services
N.A.I.C.S.: 541511
Arno Ohrmund *(Mng Dir)*

W.A.G PAYMENT SOLUTIONS PLC
1 Albemarle Street W1-Part 3rd Floor East, London, W1S 4HA, United Kingdom
Tel.: (44) 420233555111   UK
Web Site: https://www.investors.eurowag.com
Year Founded: 1995
WPS—(LSE)
Rev.: $2,908,781,836
Assets: $1,124,343,178
Liabilities: $735,527,839
Net Worth: $388,815,339
Earnings: $21,734,935
Emp.: 1,223
Fiscal Year-end: 12/31/22
Information Technology Services
N.A.I.C.S.: 541512
Emma Copland *(Chief HR Officer)*

Subsidiaries:

Aldobec Technologies, s.r.o. (1)
Twin City C Mlynske Nivy 16, 821 09, Bratislava, Slovakia
Tel.: (421) 918885588
Web Site: https://www.dispecer.sk
Information Technology Consulting Services
N.A.I.C.S.: 541512

E-Toll Services Hungary, Kft. (1)
East Gate Business Park D2 Epulet Akacos 0221/12 hrsz, 2151, Fot, Hungary
Tel.: (36) 202858202
Web Site: https://www.etsh.eu
Road Management Operator
N.A.I.C.S.: 926120

Eurowag d.o.o. (1)
Maksima Gorkog No 8 1st floor, 26000, Pancevo, Serbia
Tel.: (381) 62558948
Payment Solutions Services
N.A.I.C.S.: 522320

JITPay GmbH (1)
Willy-Brandt-Platz 16- 20, 38102, Braunschweig, Germany
Tel.: (49) 53138763010
Web Site: https://www.jitpay.eu
Payment Solutions Services
N.A.I.C.S.: 522320

KomTeS Chrudim s.r.o. (1)
Malecka 273, 537 05, Chrudim, Czech Republic
Tel.: (420) 469622535
Web Site: http://www.komtes.cz
Motor Vehicle Parts Mfr
N.A.I.C.S.: 336211

KomTeS SK s.r.o. (1)
Dopravna 7, 921 01, Piestany, Slovakia
Tel.: (421) 911779935
Web Site: https://www.sledovanie-vozidiel.sk
Emp.: 40
Software Development Services
N.A.I.C.S.: 541511

Liserteco LDA (1)
Rua das Industrias 236 - 1 Sl 104, 4785-625, Trofa, Portugal
Tel.: (351) 220968803
Web Site: https://www.liserteco.com
Software Development Services
N.A.I.C.S.: 541511

Princip a.s. (1)
Hvezdova 1689/2a, 140 00, Prague, Czech Republic
Tel.: (420) 233555111
Web Site: https://www.webdispecink.cz
Software Development Services
N.A.I.C.S.: 541511

Sygic, a.s. (1)
Twin City C Mlynske Nivy 16, 821 09, Bratislava, Slovakia
Tel.: (421) 232115350
Web Site: https://www.sygic.com
Information Center Services
N.A.I.C.S.: 519290

W.A.G. Payment Solutions BG EOOD (1)
18 Todor Aleksandrov blvd, 1303, Sofia, Bulgaria
Tel.: (359) 24928700
Payment Solutions Services
N.A.I.C.S.: 522320

W.A.G. Payment Solutions DE GmbH (1)
Torgauer Strasse 231-233, 04347, Leipzig, Germany
Tel.: (49) 34194679577
Payment Solutions Services
N.A.I.C.S.: 522320

W.A.G. Payment Solutions LT, UAB (1)
Lvovo g 25-702, LT-09320, Vilnius, Lithuania
Tel.: (370) 52596828
Payment Solutions Services
N.A.I.C.S.: 522320

W.A.G. payment solutions RO, s.r.l. (1)
River Plaza Splaiul Uniril 76 Corp B Et 8 Sector 4, 040037, Bucharest, Romania
Tel.: (40) 372400900
Commercial Road Transportation Services
N.A.I.C.S.: 532411

W.A.G. payment solutions, a.s. (1)
Na Vitezne plani 1719/4, 140 00, Prague, Czech Republic
Tel.: (420) 233555111
Web Site: https://www.eurowag.com
Emp.: 1,500
Commercial Road Transportation Services
N.A.I.C.S.: 532411

WebEye CZ s.r.o. (1)
Turanka 1222/115 building N, Slatina, 627 00, Brno, Czech Republic
Tel.: (420) 775550388
Software Development Services
N.A.I.C.S.: 541511

WebEye Deutschland GmbH (1)
Schatzbogen 33, 81829, Munich, Germany
Tel.: (49) 8945160990
Freight Forwarding & Transportation Services
N.A.I.C.S.: 561910

WebEye International s.r.l. (1)

W.A.G PAYMENT SOLUTIONS PLC

W.A.G Payment Solutions Plc—(Continued)
Oradea Trade Center- str Nufarului nr 28E et 5, 410583, Oradea, Romania
Tel.: (40) 359228058
Software Development Services
N.A.I.C.S.: 541511

WebEye Magyarorszag Kereskedelmi es Szolgaltato, Kft. (1)
East Gate Business Park building D2 Akacos 0221/12 hrsz, 2151, Fot, Hungary
Tel.: (36) 203403010
Software Development Services
N.A.I.C.S.: 541511

WebEye Slovakia s.r.o (1)
Sliacska 1E, 831 02, Bratislava, Slovakia
Tel.: (421) 948428950
Software Development Services
N.A.I.C.S.: 541511

Webeye Bulgaria Ltd. (1)
41 Nedelcho Bonchev str, 1592, Sofia, Bulgaria
Tel.: (359) 24341115
Software Development Services
N.A.I.C.S.: 541511

Webeye Hrvatska D.O.O. (1)
Buzinski prilaz 10, 10 000, Zagreb, Croatia
Tel.: (385) 12946578
Software Development Services
N.A.I.C.S.: 541511

Webeye International d.o.o (1)
Kidriceva Ulica 13 D, 1236, Trzin, Slovenia
Tel.: (386) 30703331
Web Site: https://www.webeye.eu
Emp.: 300
Software Development Services
N.A.I.C.S.: 541511

Webeye Polska sp. z.o.o. (1)
Krakow ul Wielicka 250 Biznes Park Wielicka, 30-663, Krakow, Poland
Tel.: (48) 122784243
Software Development Services
N.A.I.C.S.: 541511

W.C. WOOD COMPANY LIMITED
5 Arthur Street South, Guelph, N1H 6L9, ON, Canada
Tel.: (519) 823-9663
Year Founded: 1930
Rev.: $75,381,272
Emp.: 500
Freezers & Other Electronic Appliances Mfr
N.A.I.C.S.: 335220
John Fred Wood (Pres & CEO)

W.H. SMITH PLC
The Pavilions Bridgwater Road, Bristol, BS99 6ZZ, Wiltshire, United Kingdom
Tel.: (44) 3714950100   UK
Web Site:
   https://www.whsmithplc.co.uk
Year Founded: 1792
SMWH—(LSE)
Rev.: $2,226,547,400
Assets: $2,048,970,000
Liabilities: $1,626,758,000
Net Worth: $422,212,000
Earnings: $109,278,400
Fiscal Year-end: 08/31/23
Books, Magazines & Audio & Video Recordings Whslr & Retailers; Stationery Retailers & Distr
N.A.I.C.S.: 459210
Ian Houghton (Sec & Dir-Legal)

Subsidiaries:

InMotion Entertainment Group, LLC (1)
3755 W Sunset Rd, Las Vegas, NV 89118
Tel.: (904) 332-0450
Web Site: https://www.inmotionstores.com
Sales Range: $1-9.9 Million
Entertainment & Electronics Retailer
N.A.I.C.S.: 449210
Brian Manternach (Dir-Construction)

MRG Los Angeles, LLC (1)
3108 Glendale Blvd 167, Los Angeles, CA 90039
Tel.: (949) 500-0436
Management Consulting Services
N.A.I.C.S.: 541611

MRG Sacramento, LLC (1)
PO Box 561, Wilton, CA 95693
Tel.: (916) 261-7547
Management Consulting Services
N.A.I.C.S.: 541611

W.H. Smith Ltd. (1)
Greenbridge Road, Swindon, SN3 3LD, Wiltshire, United Kingdom (100%)
Tel.: (44) 1793616161
Web Site: https://www.whsmithplc.co.uk
Sales Range: $25-49.9 Million
Emp.: 100
Retailers of Books, Magazines & Audio & Video Recordings; Stationery Retailers & Distributors
N.A.I.C.S.: 459210

WH Smith Australia Pty Limited (1)
Level 4 80 William Street, Woolloomooloo, Sydney, 2011, NSW, Australia
Tel.: (61) 29 098 2800
Web Site: https://www.whsmith.com.au
Emp.: 500
Book Distr
N.A.I.C.S.: 459210
Tamara Larkin (Fin Dir)

W.J. TOWELL & CO. LLC
Ghala, PO Box 1040, Ruwi, Muscat, 112, Oman
Tel.: (968) 24526000
Web Site: http://www.wjtowell.com
Sales Range: $1-4.9 Billion
Emp.: 10,000
Holding Company
N.A.I.C.S.: 551112
Hussain Jawad (Chm & Mng Dir)

Subsidiaries:

Al Argan Towell Investment Co. (1)
ARGAN Business Park Free Trade Zone Shuwaikh Block F25 - F41, Kuwait, Kuwait
Tel.: (965) 22263222
Web Site: http://www.alargan.com
Investment Management Service
N.A.I.C.S.: 523940

Matrah Cold Stores LLC (1)
PO Box 1811, 130, Muscat, Oman
Tel.: (968) 24526333
Web Site: http://www.mcsoman.com
Automobile Component Distr
N.A.I.C.S.: 441330
Dominic C. R. Myers (CEO)

Mazoon Printing, Publishing & Advertising (L.L.C) (1)
PO Box 178, 114, Muscat, Oman
Tel.: (968) 24817004
Web Site: http://www.mazoonprinting.com
Printing Services
N.A.I.C.S.: 323111
Graeme Selby (Gen Mgr)

TR Oman LLC (1)
PO Box 1597, 114, Ruwi, Oman
Tel.: (968) 24642101
Automobile Component Distr
N.A.I.C.S.: 441330

Towel Auto Centre LLC (1)
PO Box 1101, Ruwi, 112, Oman
Tel.: (968) 2481 4567
Motor Vehicles, Parts & Accessories Import & Distribution
N.A.I.C.S.: 423110

Towell Construction & Maintenance Co. LLC (1)
Rm 11 1st Floor Sohar House Central Area, PO Box 1040, Madinat Al Sultan Qaboos, Ruwi, 112, Oman
Tel.: (968) 24603503
Construction & Construction Materials
N.A.I.C.S.: 236220

Towell Furniture Co LLC (1)
Towell Group Building Exhibition Road, Al Azaiba, 112, Muscat, Oman
Tel.: (968) 24526000

Automobile Component Distr
N.A.I.C.S.: 441330

Towell Mattress & Furniture Industry (1)
Warehouse Industrial Area 15, PO Box 28958, Sharjah, United Arab Emirates
Tel.: (971) 65345484
Web Site: http://www.towellmattress.ae
Emp.: 250
Automobile Component Distr
N.A.I.C.S.: 441330
David Nixon (Gen Mgr)

Towell Tools & Engineering Co. LLC (1)
PO Box 308, Wadi Kabir, Ruwi, 117, Oman
Tel.: (968) 24815277
Web Site: http://www.towell.com
Sales Range: $25-49.9 Million
Emp.: 23
Tools, Engineering, Safety & Hardware Products & Services
N.A.I.C.S.: 541330

W.O. STINSON & SON LTD.
4728 Bank Street, Gloucester, K1T 3W7, ON, Canada
Tel.: (613) 822-7400
Web Site: http://www.wostinson.com
Rev.: $51,517,781
Emp.: 175
Oil & Propane Furnace Distr
N.A.I.C.S.: 457210
Eric Stinson (Co-Owner)

W.S. INDUSTRIES (INDIA) LIMITED
108 Mount Poonamallee Road, Porur, Chennai, 600 116, Tamil Nadu, India
Tel.: (91) 8925802400
Web Site: https://www.wsindustries.in
Year Founded: 1961
504220—(BOM)
Assets: $9,912,630
Liabilities: $22,665,689
Net Worth: ($12,753,058)
Earnings: ($1,143,597)
Fiscal Year-end: 03/31/21
Electro Porcelain Insulator Mfr
N.A.I.C.S.: 327110
B. Swaminathan (CFO & Sec)

Subsidiaries:

W.S. Industries (India) Limited - Vizag Plant (1)
APSEZ Duppituru Village, Achutapuram Mandal, Visakhapatnam, 531 011, India
Tel.: (91) 8924 660124
Electro Porcelain Insulator Mfr
N.A.I.C.S.: 335932

W.SOHNGEN GMBH
Platter Strasse 84, Taunusstein, 65232, Germany
Tel.: (49) 612887355
Web Site: http://www.soehngen.com
Rev.: $26,001,690
Emp.: 135
Medical Equipment Mfr
N.A.I.C.S.: 339112
Sabine Wust (Mng Dir)

W5 SOLUTIONS AB
Jakobsdalsvagen 19, PO Box 1156, Strand, 131 52, Nacka, Sweden
Tel.: (46) 86500888
Web Site:
   https://www.w5solutions.com
Year Founded: 1940
EY7—(DEU)
Information Technology Services
N.A.I.C.S.: 541512
Anders Lundstrom (Chm)

Subsidiaries:

W5 Omnifinity AB (1)
Framtidsvagen 14, SE-352 22, Vaxjo, Sweden
Tel.: (46) 47655950

INTERNATIONAL PUBLIC

Web Site: https://www.omnifinity.se
Hardware Technology Services
N.A.I.C.S.: 541715

WA KAOLIN LIMITED
Tel.: (61) 84396300   AU
Web Site:
   https://www.wakaolin.com.au
Year Founded: 1998
WAK—(ASX)
Rev.: $898,566
Assets: $24,989,352
Liabilities: $20,802,032
Net Worth: $4,187,320
Earnings: ($5,785,707)
Fiscal Year-end: 06/30/22
Mineral Exploration Services
N.A.I.C.S.: 212390
Andrew Sorensen (CEO)

WA, INC.
7F 1-20-18 Ebisu, Shibuya-ku, Tokyo, 150-0013, Japan
Tel.: (81) 354233601   JP
Year Founded: 2002
7683—(TKS)
Rev.: $150,733,400
Assets: $87,752,930
Liabilities: $17,292,510
Net Worth: $70,460,420
Earnings: $8,245,670
Fiscal Year-end: 01/31/24
Womens Footwear Design, Mfr & Sales
N.A.I.C.S.: 316210
Xiao Junwei (Founder & Pres)

Subsidiaries:

HIMIKO Co., Ltd. (1)
6-17-10 Jingumae arajuku R-Building, Shibuya-ku, Tokyo, 150-0001, Japan
Tel.: (81) 354853711
Web Site: http://www.himiko.co.jp
Emp.: 166
Footwear Products Whslr
N.A.I.C.S.: 424340
Yasunori Sasaki (Pres & Dir)

WA1 RESOURCES LTD.
Lvl 2 55 Carrington Street, Nedlands, 6009, WA, Australia
Tel.: (61) 864787866   AU
Web Site: https://www.wa1.com.au
Year Founded: 2021
WA1—(ASX)
Rev.: $21
Assets: $3,594,550
Liabilities: $100,900
Net Worth: $3,493,649
Earnings: ($477,022)
Fiscal Year-end: 06/30/22
Exploration & Mining Services
N.A.I.C.S.: 213115
Paul Savich (Mng Dir)

WAA SOLAR LTD.
Madhav House Nr Panchratna Building, Subhanpura, Vadodara, 390023, India
Tel.: (91) 2652290722
Web Site: https://www.waasolar.org
541445—(BOM)
Rev.: $5,958,276
Assets: $35,789,353
Liabilities: $13,090,786
Net Worth: $22,698,567
Earnings: $1,180,121
Emp.: 14
Fiscal Year-end: 03/31/23
Solar Power Energy Services
N.A.I.C.S.: 221114
Amit Ashok Khurana (Chm & Mng Dir)

WAAGNER-BIRO AG
Leonard Bernstein Strasse 10, 1220, Vienna, Austria

AND PRIVATE COMPANIES

Tel.: (43) 1288440
Web Site: http://www.waagner-biro.at
Year Founded: 1854
Sales Range: $250-299.9 Million
Emp.: 1,300
Engineering & Construction Services
N.A.I.C.S.: 237990
Kurt Berger *(Vice Chm-Supervisory Bd)*

Subsidiaries:

OOO Waagner-Biro St. Petersburg
Stage Systems (1)
Petrowka-Street 15/13, 127051, Moscow, Russia
Tel.: (7) 495 775 70 82
Construction Engineering Services
N.A.I.C.S.: 237990

P. T. Waagner-Biro, Indonesia (1)
Talavera Suite 11th Floor Jl Let Jen TB Simatupang Kav 22-26, Jakarta, 12430, Indonesia
Tel.: (62) 21 7592 4355
Construction Engineering Services
N.A.I.C.S.: 237990
Zdenek Fukar *(Dir-Technical)*

Waagner Biro Gulf L.L.C. (1)
Tameem House 13th floor Tecom, PO Box 8542, Dubai, United Arab Emirates
Tel.: (971) 4 440 38 70
Construction Engineering Services
N.A.I.C.S.: 237990
Nikolas Tsimas *(COO)*

Waagner Biro Philippines, Inc. (1)
2/F Keystone Building 220 Sen Gil Puyat Avenue, Makati, 1200, Manila, Philippines
Tel.: (63) 2 893 03 51
Construction Engineering Services
N.A.I.C.S.: 237990

Waagner-Biro Bin Butti Engineering L.L.C. (1)
Hamdan Street, PO Box 73564, Abu Dhabi, United Arab Emirates
Tel.: (971) 2 674 16 36
Construction Engineering Services
N.A.I.C.S.: 237990

Waagner-Biro Stahlbau AG (1)
Leonard Bernstein Strasse 10, 1220, Vienna, Austria (100%)
Tel.: (43) 1288440
Web Site: http://www.bb.waagner-biro.at
Emp.: 300
Bridge Engineering Services
N.A.I.C.S.: 237310
Herbert W. Liaunig *(Chm-Supervisory Bd)*

Subsidiary (Non-US):

Waagner Biro Limited (2)
22 Fish Street Hill, London, EC3R 6DB, United Kingdom
Tel.: (44) 207 337 2240
Construction Engineering Services
N.A.I.C.S.: 237990

Waagner-Biro Emirates Contracting L.L.C. (2)
8th floor Office no 083 United Arab Bank Building Khalifa Street, PO Box 127687, Abu Dhabi, United Arab Emirates
Tel.: (971) 2 6260416
Construction Engineering Services
N.A.I.C.S.: 237990
Jason Wilson *(Gen Mgr)*

WAAGNER-BIRO AUSTRIA STAGE SYSTEMS AG
Stadlauer Strasse 54, A-1220, Vienna, Austria
Tel.: (43) 288440
Web Site: http://www.bt.waagner-biro.at
Sales Range: $25-49.9 Million
Emp.: 105
Stage & Stand Mfr
N.A.I.C.S.: 339999

Subsidiaries:

Waagner-Biro Bavaria Stage Systems GmbH (1)
Am Schonbuhl 12, Weiherhammer, 92729, Neustadt, Germany
Tel.: (49) 9605 92 22 0
Construction Engineering Services
N.A.I.C.S.: 237990

Waagner-Biro Luxembourg Stage Systems S.A. (1)
1 rue de l ecole, PO Box 10, 4813, Rodange, Luxembourg
Tel.: (352) 50 35 21
Web Site: http://www.waagner-biro.lu
Construction Engineering Services
N.A.I.C.S.: 237990

Waagner-Biro Spain Stage Systems S.A. (1)
c/Santisima Trinidad 30, 28010, Madrid, Spain
Tel.: (34) 91 447 57 29
Construction Engineering Services
N.A.I.C.S.: 237990

WAAREE ENERGIES LTD.
602 Western Edge I Off Western Express Highway Borivali, Mumbai, 400066, India
Tel.: (91) 2266444444
Web Site: http://www.waaree.com
Year Founded: 1989
Solar Power Generating Products Mfr
N.A.I.C.S.: 221114
Hitesh Doshi *(Chm & Mng Dir)*

Subsidiaries:

Waaree Renewable Technologies Limited (1)
504 Western Edge-I, Opp Western Express Highway Borivali E, Mumbai, 400066, India (51.89%)
Tel.: (91) 2266444444
Web Site: https://www.waareertl.com
Rev.: $2,104,731
Assets: $27,702,064
Liabilities: $20,299,371
Net Worth: $7,402,693
Earnings: ($323,035)
Emp.: 19
Fiscal Year-end: 03/31/2021
Renewable Energy; Power Generation & Consultancy Services
N.A.I.C.S.: 221114
Ruchi Sethi *(Sec & Officer-Compliance)*

WAAREE TECHNOLOGIES LIMITED
602 Western Edge I Western Express Highway, Borivali East, Mumbai, 400066, India
Tel.: (91) 2266444444
Web Site: https://waareetech.com
539337—(BOM)
Rev.: $6,172
Assets: $524,796
Liabilities: $25,929
Net Worth: $498,866
Earnings: ($19,189)
Fiscal Year-end: 03/31/21
Adhesive Tape Mfr
N.A.I.C.S.: 322220
Rushabh Pankaj Doshi *(CFO)*

WABASH MFG. INC.
9312 110A Street, Westlock, T7P 2M4, AB, Canada
Tel.: (780) 349-4282
Web Site: https://www.wabash.ca
Year Founded: 1981
Heavy Tank, Trailers & Supporting Product Mfr
N.A.I.C.S.: 336992
Ernie Hunt *(Owner)*

WABERER'S INTERNATIONAL NYRT
Nagykorosi ut 351, 1239, Budapest, 1239, Hungary
Tel.: (36) 14216666
Web Site: https://www.waberers.com
Year Founded: 1948
3WB—(DEU)

Transport Services
N.A.I.C.S.: 485999
Robert Ziegler *(CEO)*

Subsidiaries:

Waberer's - Szemerey Logisztika Kft. (1)
Európa u 6, 1239, Budapest, Hungary
Tel.: (36) 14218505
Web Site: http://www.waberers-szemerey.hu
Transportation Logistics Services
N.A.I.C.S.: 488510

Waberer's Romania S.A. (1)
Str Harghita Nr 101 Jud Harghita, Miercurea Ciuc, 530152, Romania
Tel.: (40) 752035811
Transportation Logistics Services
N.A.I.C.S.: 488510

WABI IRON & STEEL CORP.
330 Broadwood Avenue, PO Box 1510, New Liskeard, P0J 1P0, ON, Canada
Tel.: (705) 647-4383
Web Site: https://www.wabicorp.com
Year Founded: 1907
Sales Range: $10-24.9 Million
Emp.: 50
Metal Castings & Custom Engineered Fabrication Products Mfr
N.A.I.C.S.: 332312
Stan Gorzalczynski *(Pres)*

WAC HOLDINGS LTD.
Floor 9 9 Wing Hong Street, Cheung Sha Wan, Kowloon, China (Hong Kong)
Tel.: (852) 2 866 3011
Web Site: http://www.wcce.hk
8619—(HKG)
Rev.: $9,972,347
Assets: $11,412,795
Liabilities: $2,371,813
Net Worth: $9,040,982
Earnings: $814,509
Emp.: 102
Fiscal Year-end: 03/31/21
Engineering Consulting Services
N.A.I.C.S.: 541330
Yin Nin Chan *(Chm & Compliance Officer)*

WACHTEL GMBH & CO
Hans-Sachs-Strasse 2-6, 40721, Hilden, Germany
Tel.: (49) 210349040
Web Site: http://www.wachtel.de
Year Founded: 1923
Rev.: $27,588,000
Emp.: 93
Baking Ovens Mfr
N.A.I.C.S.: 333241
Stefan Kutska *(Head-Sls Cooling Equipment-Poland)*

WACKENHUT PAKISTAN (PRIVATE) LIMITED
11th Floor Kavish Crown Plaza Main Shahrah-e-Faisal, Karachi, Pakistan
Tel.: (92) 21 111 447 000
Web Site: http://www.g4s.com.pk
Sales Range: $100-124.9 Million
Emp.: 1,000
Security Services
N.A.I.C.S.: 561612
Ikram Sehgal *(Chm)*

WACKER CHEMIE AG
Hanns-Seidel-Platz 4, 81737, Munich, Germany
Tel.: (49) 8962790
Web Site: http://www.wacker.com
Year Founded: 1914
WCH—(DEU)
Rev.: $6,909,345,996
Assets: $9,555,795,381
Liabilities: $4,613,101,662

WACKER CHEMIE AG

Net Worth: $4,942,693,719
Earnings: $353,226,851
Emp.: 16,378
Fiscal Year-end: 12/31/23
Chemical Products Mfr
N.A.I.C.S.: 325998
Peter-Alexander Wacker *(Chm-Supervisory Bd)*

Subsidiaries:

ADL BIOPHARMA S.L.U. (1)
Avenida Antibioticos 59-61, 24009, Leon, Spain
Tel.: (34) 987895800
Web Site: http://www.adlbiopharma.com
Pharmaceutical Company
N.A.I.C.S.: 325412
Ignacio Urbelz *(Chm & CEO)*

Subsidiary (Domestic):

ADL Bionatur Solutions, S.A. (2)
Av Desarrollo Tecnologico 11, 11591, Jerez de la Frontera, Spain
Tel.: (34) 856818424
Web Site: http://www.adlbionatur.com
Biological Products Mfr & Researcher
N.A.I.C.S.: 325414
Victor Infante *(Exec VP)*

Alzwerke GmbH (1)
Auenstrasse 1, 84489, Burghausen, Germany
Tel.: (49) 8677 83 0
Electrical Energy Distr
N.A.I.C.S.: 221122

BBiW - Berufsbildungswerk Burghausen (1)
Johannes-Hess-Strasse 5, 84489, Burghausen, Germany
Tel.: (49) 8677 83 2004
Emp.: 5
Chemical Products Mfr
N.A.I.C.S.: 325998

DRAWIN Vertriebs-GmbH (1)
Rudolf-Diesel-Strasse 15, 85521, Ottobrunn, Germany
Tel.: (49) 89 60869 0
Chemical Products Mfr
N.A.I.C.S.: 325998

LLC Wacker Chemie Rus (1)
Varshavskoe Shosse 37A, 117105, Moscow, Russia
Tel.: (7) 4956044111
Chemical Products Mfr
N.A.I.C.S.: 325998

OOO WACKER CHEMIE RUS (1)
Varshavskoe Shosse 35, 117105, Moscow, Russia
Tel.: (7) 4957756810
Sales Range: $25-49.9 Million
Emp.: 23
Specialty Chemicals Mfr
N.A.I.C.S.: 325998

PT. Wacker Chemicals Indonesia (1)
Unit H3/28B Kabupaten, Tangerang, 400 063, Banten, Indonesia
Tel.: (62) 2242365505
Chemical Products Mfr
N.A.I.C.S.: 325998

WACKER CHEMICALS MIDDLE EAST (1)
Dubai Silicon Oasis, PO Box 341071, Dubai, United Arab Emirates
Tel.: (971) 47099999
Sales Range: $25-49.9 Million
Emp.: 3
Chemical & Semiconductor Silicon Mfr
N.A.I.C.S.: 325199

WACKER CHEMIE INDIA PVT. LTD. (1)
Off I B Patel Road, Goregaon E, Mumbai, 400 063, India
Tel.: (91) 224 236 5500
Web Site: http://www.wacker.com
Chemical & Semiconductor Silicone Mfr
N.A.I.C.S.: 325199

Wacker Asahikasei Silicone Co., Ltd. (1)
2-9 Kanda Nishikicho, Chiyoda-ku, Tokyo, 101-0054, Japan

WACKER CHEMIE AG

Tel.: (81) 3 5283 8850
Chemical Products Mfr
N.A.I.C.S.: 325998

Wacker Biotech GmbH (1)
Hans-Knoll-Strasse 3, 07745, Jena, Germany
Tel.: (49) 3641 5348 0
Chemical Products Mfr
N.A.I.C.S.: 325998

Wacker Biotech US Inc. (1)
10390 Pacific Ctr Ct, San Diego, CA 92121
Tel.: (858) 875-4700
Carbon Bio-Based Product Mfr & Distr
N.A.I.C.S.: 325199

Wacker Chemical Corporation (1)
3301 Sutton Rd, Adrian, MI 49221-9397
Tel.: (517) 264-8500
Web Site: https://www.wacker.com
Sales Range: $250-299.9 Million
Emp.: 16,000
Mfr of Silicone Basic Products
N.A.I.C.S.: 325199

Subsidiary (Domestic):

Wacker Polysilicon North America, L.L.C (2)
553 Wacker Blvd, Charleston, TN 37310-0446
Tel.: (423) 780-7950
Emp.: 650
Chemical Products Mfr
N.A.I.C.S.: 325998

Wacker Chemicals (China) Co., Ltd. (1)
Bldg 3 1535 Hongmei Road, Caohejing Hi-Tech Park, Shanghai, 200233, China
Tel.: (86) 21 6130 2000
Chemical Products Mfr
N.A.I.C.S.: 325998

Subsidiary (Domestic):

Wacker Chemicals (Nanjing) Co. Ltd. (2)
Nanjing Chemical Industry Park 169 Xiaoyinghe South Road, Nanjing, 210047, Jiangsu, China
Tel.: (86) 2566626400
Emp.: 170
Chemical Products Mfr
N.A.I.C.S.: 325998

Wacker Chemicals (Zhangjiagang) Co. Ltd. (2)
78 Changjiang Road Jiangsu Yangtze River International Chemical, Industry Park, Zhangjiagang, 215634, Jiangsu, China
Tel.: (86) 51281642000
Emp.: 420
Chemical Products Mfr
N.A.I.C.S.: 325998

Wacker Chemicals (South Asia) Pte. Ltd. (1)
61 Science Park Road 06-09/12, Singapore, 117525, Singapore
Tel.: (65) 6542 6638
Chemical Products Mfr
N.A.I.C.S.: 325998

Representative Office (Non-US):

Wacker Chemicals (South Asia) Pte. Ltd. (2)
Menara Citicon 13th Floor Suite F, Jl. Letjen S Parman Kav 72, Jakarta, 11410, Indonesia
Tel.: (62) 21 2953 2988
Chemical Products Mfr
N.A.I.C.S.: 325998

Wacker Chemicals (South Asia) Pte. Ltd. (2)
Level 16 1 Sentral, Jalan Stesen Sentral KL Sentral, Wilayah Persekutua, Kuala Lumpur, 50470, Malaysia
Tel.: (60) 32092 9500
Chemical Products Mfr
N.A.I.C.S.: 325998

Wacker Chemicals (South Asia) Pte. Ltd. (2)
Unit 3 9th Floor 11th Corporate Center, 11th Avenue corner Triangle Drive, Taguig, 1634, Philippines
Tel.: (63) 2 8830900
Chemical Products Mfr
N.A.I.C.S.: 325998

Wacker Chemicals (South Asia) Pte. Ltd. (2)
Office 163116th floor Daeha Business Centre, 360 Kim Ma Str Ba Dinh, Hanoi, Vietnam
Tel.: (84) 4 32673 522
Chemical Products Mfr
N.A.I.C.S.: 325998

Wacker Chemicals Australia Pty. Ltd. (1)
1/35 Dunlop Road, Mulgrave, 3170, Vic, Australia
Tel.: (61) 3 9541 8900
Chemical Products Mfr
N.A.I.C.S.: 325998

Wacker Chemicals East Asia Ltd. (1)
2-9 kanda Nishikicho, Chiyoda-ku, Tokyo, 101-0054, Japan
Tel.: (81) 3 6684 8655
Chemical Products Mfr
N.A.I.C.S.: 325998

Wacker Chemicals Fumed Silica (Zhangjiagang) Co. Ltd. (1)
Yangtze River International Chemical Industry Park, Zhangjiagang, Jiangsu, China
Tel.: (86) 51281642000
Chemical Products Mfr
N.A.I.C.S.: 325998

Wacker Chemicals Hong Kong Ltd. (1)
Room 606 6F No 136, Jen-Ai Road Sec 3, Taipei, 106, Taiwan
Tel.: (886) 2 8173 3533
Chemical Products Mfr
N.A.I.C.S.: 325998

Wacker Chemicals Korea Inc. (1)
S-3F 231 Pangyoyeok-ro, Bundang-gu Seongnam-si, Seoul, Korea (South)
Tel.: (82) 31 697 7200
Chemical Products Mfr
N.A.I.C.S.: 325998

Wacker Chemicals Ltd. (1)
Arlington Square Downshire Way, Bracknell, RG12 1WA, United Kingdom
Tel.: (44) 1344 887 676
Chemical Products Mfr
N.A.I.C.S.: 325998

Wacker Chemicals Malaysia Sdn. Bhd. (1)
Nr 2A Jalan Stesen Sentral 2, 50470, Kuala Lumpur, Sentral, Malaysia
Tel.: (60) 327318600
Carbon Bio-Based Product Mfr & Distr
N.A.I.C.S.: 325199

Wacker Chemicals Norway AS (1)
Hollaveien 482, 7200, Kyrksaeterora, Norway
Tel.: (47) 72 4506 0
Chemical Products Mfr
N.A.I.C.S.: 325998

Wacker Chemie AG - Nunchritz (1)
Friedrich-von-Heyden-Platz 1, 01612, Nunchritz, Germany
Tel.: (49) 352 6570
Web Site: https://www.wacker.com
Emp.: 1,500
Mfr of Silicone Chemicals & Products
N.A.I.C.S.: 325998

Wacker Chemie Italia S.r.l. (1)
Via XXV Aprile 2, 20097 San Donato Milanese, Milan, Italy
Tel.: (39) 02 51752 1
Chemical Products Mfr
N.A.I.C.S.: 325998

Wacker Chimie S.A.S. (1)
Ilot Saint-Joseph Bureaux Convergence Baliment C, 11 bis quai Perrache, 69002, Lyon, France
Tel.: (33) 478 176 010
Chemical Products Mfr
N.A.I.C.S.: 325998

Wacker Colombia S.A.S. (1)
Centro Empresarial Buro 26 oficina 405, Avenida El Dorado 102-20, 110911, Bogota, Colombia
Tel.: (57) 1 4324 195
Chemical Products Mfr
N.A.I.C.S.: 325998

Wacker Dymatic Silicones (Shunde) Co., Ltd. (1)
Bldg 3 1535 Hongmei Road, Caohejing Hi-tech Park, Shanghai, 200233, China
Tel.: (86) 21 6130 2000
Chemical Products Mfr
N.A.I.C.S.: 325998

Wacker Kimya Tic. Ltd. Sti. (1)
Tevfik Fikret Cad No 32/4, Atasehir, 34750, Istanbul, Turkiye
Tel.: (90) 2165697050
Chemical Products Mfr
N.A.I.C.S.: 325998

Wacker Metroark Chemicals Pvt. Ltd. (1)
House No 30 Road 08, Dhaka, 1230, Bangladesh
Tel.: (880) 19 111 133 06
Chemical Products Mfr
N.A.I.C.S.: 325998

Wacker Mexicana, S.A. de C.V. (1)
Av Insurgentes Sur No 2453 - Of 10-01 Col Tizapan, 01090, Mexico, Mexico (100%)
Tel.: (52) 559 136 5240
Web Site: https://www.wacker.com
Mfr of Silicone Products
N.A.I.C.S.: 325211

Wacker Polymers GmbH & Co. KG. (1)
Johannes Hess Strasse 24, 84489, Burghausen, Germany
Tel.: (49) 8677832252
Sales Range: $25-49.9 Million
Emp.: 75
Dispersions for Adhesives
N.A.I.C.S.: 325520
Peter Summo (Pres-Polymers)

Wacker Quimica Iberica, S.A. (1)
Calle Corcega 303, 08008, Barcelona, Spain
Tel.: (34) 93 2920700
Chemical Products Mfr
N.A.I.C.S.: 325998

Wacker Quimica do Brasil Ltda. (1)
Rua Municipal 325, 06612-060 Jandira, Seo Paulo, Brazil
Tel.: (55) 11 4789 8300
Chemical Products Mfr
N.A.I.C.S.: 325998

Wacker Sterbekasse VVaG (1)
Hanns-Seidel-Platz 4, 81737, Munich, Germany
Tel.: (49) 89 6279 1790
Chemical Products Mfr
N.A.I.C.S.: 325998

Wacker-Chemia Polska Sp. z o.o. (1)
Al Jana Pawla II 27, 00-867, Warsaw, Poland
Tel.: (48) 22 530 9420
Web Site: https://www.wacker.com
Emp.: 10
Chemical Products Mfr
N.A.I.C.S.: 325998

Wacker-Chemie Benelux B.V. (1)
Heiligeweg 166, 1561 DM, Krommenie, Netherlands
Tel.: (31) 75 647 6000
Chemical Products Mfr
N.A.I.C.S.: 325998

Wacker-Chemie Hungary Kft. (1)
Fehervari ut 50-52, 1117, Budapest, Hungary
Tel.: (36) 1 801 9550
Emp.: 13
Chemical Products Mfr
N.A.I.C.S.: 325998

Wacker-Chemie Versicherungsvermittlung GmbH (1)
Hanns-Seidel-Platz 4, 81737, Munich, Germany
Tel.: (49) 89 6279 1191
Chemical Products Mfr
N.A.I.C.S.: 325998

Wacker-Chemie, s.r.o. (1)
halaBP6 Podnikatelska 1186/45, 301 00, Plzen, Czech Republic
Tel.: (420) 378 010 103
Chemical Products Mfr
N.A.I.C.S.: 325998

Wacker-Kemi AB (1)
Frosundaviks Alle 1, 169 70, Solna, Sweden
Tel.: (46) 8 5220 5220
Chemical Products Mfr
N.A.I.C.S.: 325998

WACKER NEUSON SE

Preussenstrasse 41, 80809, Munich, Germany
Tel.: (49) 8935402427
Web Site: https://www.wackerneuson.de
WKRCF—(OTCIQ)
Rev.: $2,930,664,463
Assets: $2,919,625,763
Liabilities: $1,264,151,924
Net Worth: $1,655,473,839
Earnings: $205,209,433
Emp.: 6,579
Fiscal Year-end: 12/31/23
Light Equipment & Compact Construction Machine Mfr
N.A.I.C.S.: 333120
Karl Tragl (Chm-Exec Bd)

Subsidiaries:

Kramer-Werke GmbH (1)
Wacker Neuson Strasse 1, 88630, Pfullendorf, Germany
Tel.: (49) 755292880
Web Site: https://www.kramer-online.com
Sales Range: $50-74.9 Million
Emp.: 450
Compact Construction Machine Mfr
N.A.I.C.S.: 333120

Wacker Neuson (Pty) Ltd. (1)
1031 Katrol Avenue Robertville Ext 10, PO Box 2163, Florida, 1710, Gauteng, South Africa
Tel.: (27) 116720847
Web Site: http://www.wackerneuson.co.za
Sales Range: $25-49.9 Million
Emp.: 33
Construction Equipment Distr
N.A.I.C.S.: 423810
Eugene Brown (Mng Dir)

Wacker Neuson AB (1)
Skattebergavagen 13, Sodra Sandby, 247 34, Lund, Sweden
Tel.: (46) 4657870
Construction Equipment Distr
N.A.I.C.S.: 423810

Wacker Neuson AG (1)
Geissbuelstrasse 5 Volketswil, 8604, Zurich, Switzerland
Tel.: (41) 448353939
Web Site: http://www.wackerneuson.ch
Sales Range: $25-49.9 Million
Emp.: 33
Construction Equipment Whslr
N.A.I.C.S.: 423810
Benjamin Wasinger (Mng Dir-Switzerland)

Wacker Neuson AS (1)
Tyriveien 7, 1481, Hagan, Norway
Tel.: (47) 67 05 13 10
Construction Equipment Distr
N.A.I.C.S.: 423810

Wacker Neuson B.V. (1)
Cobolweg 1, 3821 BJ, Amersfoort, Utrecht, Netherlands
Tel.: (31) 885057510
Construction Equipment Distr
N.A.I.C.S.: 423810

Wacker Neuson Beteiligungs GmbH (1)
Haidfeldstrasse 37, 4060, Leonding, Austria
Tel.: (43) 732905900
Sales Range: $125-149.9 Million
Emp.: 350
Compact Construction Machines Mfr & Distr

AND PRIVATE COMPANIES

N.A.I.C.S.: 333120

Wacker Neuson Corporation (1)
N92 W15000 Anthony Ave, Menomonee Falls, WI 53051-1504
Tel.: (262) 255-0500
Web Site: http://www.wackerneuson.com
Light Equipment & Compact Construction Machine Mfr
N.A.I.C.S.: 333120

Wacker Neuson Equipment Private Ltd.
12E Sadaramangala Industrial Estate, Krishnarajapuram Hobli, Bengaluru, 560048, Karnataka, India
Tel.: (91) 8028412156
Sales Range: $25-49.9 Million
Emp.: 16
Construction Equipment Distr
N.A.I.C.S.: 423810

Wacker Neuson GmbH (1)
Urzhumskaya Ulitsa 4, 129343, Moscow, 129343, Russia
Tel.: (7) 4959001046
Emp.: 30
Construction Equipment Distr
N.A.I.C.S.: 423810
Vladimir Terentyev (Mng Dir)

Wacker Neuson GmbH (1)
Schemmerlstrasse 82, 1110, Vienna, Austria
Tel.: (43) 17671515
Web Site: http://www.wackerneuson.at
Sales Range: $25-49.9 Million
Emp.: 50
Construction Machinery Mfr
N.A.I.C.S.: 333120
Benjamin Wasinger (Mng Dir-Switzerland)

Wacker Neuson Kft (1)
Torbagy u 17, Torokbalint, 2045, Pest, Hungary
Tel.: (36) 23331214
Web Site: http://www.wackerneuson.hu
Sales Range: $25-49.9 Million
Emp.: 19
Construction Equipment Distr
N.A.I.C.S.: 423810

Wacker Neuson Limited (1)
Unit 6 G/F Yuen Long Trading Centre 33 Wang Yip Street W, Yuen Long, Hong Kong, New Territories, China (Hong Kong)
Tel.: (852) 24092359
Web Site: http://www.wackerneuson.hk
Sales Range: $25-49.9 Million
Emp.: 30
Construction Equipment Distr
N.A.I.C.S.: 423810

Subsidiary (Non-US):

Wacker Neuson Machinery Trading (Shenzhen) Ltd. Co. (2)
Ground Floor 12 Dong Wei Ming Ying Gong Ye Yuen Zong Jiang Jie Dao, Bao An, Shenzhen, Guangdong, China
Tel.: (86) 75527146867
Construction Equipment Distr
N.A.I.C.S.: 423810

Wacker Neuson Limited (1)
888/4 Moo 2 Bangplee Tumru Road, T Prekkasamai, Samut Prakan, 10280, Thailand
Tel.: (66) 21822045
Sales Range: $50-74.9 Million
Emp.: 7
Construction Equipment Distr
N.A.I.C.S.: 423810
Waisan Nualyai (Mng Dir)

Wacker Neuson Linz GmbH (1)
Flughafenstrasse 7, 4063, Horsching, Austria
Tel.: (43) 722468363
Web Site: http://www.wackerneuson.com
Light Equipment & Compact Construction Machine Mfr
N.A.I.C.S.: 333120

Wacker Neuson Ltd. (1)
WN Place, Stafford, ST18 0WL, Staffordshire, United Kingdom
Tel.: (44) 1785785700
Sales Range: $25-49.9 Million
Emp.: 25
Construction Equipment Distr

Wacker Neuson Ltd. (1)
3600 Ridgeway Drive Unit 6, Mississauga, L5L 0B4, ON, Canada
Tel.: (905) 795-1661
Web Site: http://www.wackerneuson.com
Sales Range: $25-49.9 Million
Emp.: 24
Construction Machinery Mfr
N.A.I.C.S.: 333120

Wacker Neuson Makine Ltd. Sti. (1)
TEM Yanyol Katip Celebi cad No 15, Orhanli Tuzla, 34956, Istanbul, Turkiye
Tel.: (90) 2165740474
Web Site: http://www.wackerneuson.com.tr
Sales Range: $25-49.9 Million
Emp.: 23
Construction Machinery Distr
N.A.I.C.S.: 423810

Wacker Neuson Manila, Inc. (1)
First Cavite Industrial Estate FCIE, Dasmarinas, 4126, Cavite, Philippines
Tel.: (63) 464020205
Web Site: http://www.corporate.wackerneuson.com
Emp.: 68
Construction Machinery & Vehicles Mfr
N.A.I.C.S.: 333120
Ronald Hess (Pres)

Wacker Neuson Maquinas Ltda. (1)
Rodovia Dom Pedro I km 104 140, Itatiba, Jundiai, 13251-705, Sao Paulo, Brazil
Tel.: (55) 1131830222
Web Site: http://www.wackerneuson.com.br
Sales Range: $25-49.9 Million
Emp.: 20
Construction Equipment Distr
N.A.I.C.S.: 423810

Wacker Neuson Pty Ltd (1)
913 Princes Hwy, Springvale, 3171, VIC, Australia
Tel.: (61) 395474033
Construction Equipment Distr
N.A.I.C.S.: 423810

Wacker Neuson S.A. (1)
Poligono Industrial Las Monjas Calle Primavera 11, 28850, Torrejon de Ardoz, Spain
Tel.: (34) 916757525
Web Site: http://www.wackerneuson.es
Sales Range: $25-49.9 Million
Emp.: 20
Construction Equipment Distr
N.A.I.C.S.: 423810

Wacker Neuson S.A. de C.V. (1)
San Pedro Barrientos, Colonia San Pedro Barrientos, 54010, Tlalnepantla, Mexico
Tel.: (52) 5519402300
Web Site: http://www.wackerneuson.mx
Emp.: 23
Construction Equipment Distr
N.A.I.C.S.: 423810

Wacker Neuson S.A.S. (1)
335 Rue Gloriette, 77170, Brie-Comte-Robert, Seine-et-Marne, France
Tel.: (33) 160623000
Construction Equipment Distr
N.A.I.C.S.: 423810

Wacker Neuson s.r.o. (1)
Michalkovicka 2051/120, Slezska, 710 00, Ostrava, Czech Republic
Tel.: (420) 725703683
Web Site: https://www.wackerneuson.cz
Construction Machinery Mfr & Distr
N.A.I.C.S.: 333120

Wacker Neuson srl con socio unico (1)
Via 2 Agosto 1980 - 3, 40016, San Giorgio di Piano, Bologna, Italy
Tel.: (39) 0516651566
Industrial Machinery Sales & Maintenance Services
N.A.I.C.S.: 423830

Weidemann GmbH (1)
Elfringhauser Weg 24, 34497, Korbach, Germany
Tel.: (49) 56315016940
Web Site: https://www.weidemann.de
Sales Range: $50-74.9 Million
Emp.: 250
Construction Machinery Mfr

N.A.I.C.S.: 333120

Subsidiary (Domestic):

Weidemann Maschinenfabrik Gotha GmbH (2)
Gleichenstr 20, 99867, Gotha, Germany
Tel.: (49) 3621 45 95
Construction Machinery Mfr
N.A.I.C.S.: 333120

WACO INTERNATIONAL LTD.
No 2 Harrowdene Office Park, 128 Western Services Road, Woodmead, 2148, South Africa
Tel.: (27) 11 461 1400 ZA
Web Site:
http://www.wacointernational.co.za
Sales Range: $750-799.9 Million
Emp.: 4,000
Holding Company; Scaffolding & Modular Building Mfr & Contractor Services
N.A.I.C.S.: 551112
Stephen J. M. Goodburn (CEO)

Subsidiaries:

Waco Africa Pty. Ltd. (1)
181 Barbara Road Cnr Barbara & Tunney Roads, Elandsfontein, Gauteng, South Africa
Tel.: (27) 118424000
Web Site: http://www.wacoafrica.co.za
Holding Company; Formwork, Shoring & Scaffolding Products
N.A.I.C.S.: 551112

WACOAL HOLDINGS CORP.
29 Nakajima-cho Kisshoin, Minami-ku, Kyoto, 601-8530, Japan
Tel.: (81) 756943111 JP
Web Site:
https://www.wacoalholdings.jp
Year Founded: 1949
WA5—(DEU)
Rev.: $1,352,204,640
Assets: $2,048,175,030
Liabilities: $517,509,090
Net Worth: $1,530,665,940
Earnings: ($12,733,920)
Emp.: 19,147
Fiscal Year-end: 03/31/23
Holding Company; Intimate Apparel, Lingerie, Bathing Suits & Sportswear Mfr & Distr
N.A.I.C.S.: 551112
Yoshikata Tsukamoto (Chm)

Subsidiaries:

Ai Co., Ltd. (1)
Wacoal Asakusabashi Bldg 8F 1-23-6 Yanagibashi, Taito-ku, Tokyo, 111-8540, Japan
Tel.: (81) 358296221
Swimwear Mfr & Distr
N.A.I.C.S.: 315250

Dalian Wacoal Co., Ltd. (1)
6 Fu An Street Economic & Technical Development Zone, Dalian, 116600, Liaoning, China (100%)
Tel.: (86) 411 8733 7722
Women Apparel Mfr
N.A.I.C.S.: 315250

Eveden Canada Ltd. (1)
181 Bay street Suite 4400, Toronto, M5J 2T3, ON, Canada
Tel.: (617) 361-7559
Apparel Retailer
N.A.I.C.S.: 424310

Eveden Israel Limited (1)
11Kehilat Saloniki St, Tel Aviv, Israel
Tel.: (972) 37283210
Apparel Retailer
N.A.I.C.S.: 424310

Eveden Ltd. (1)
The Corsetry Factory, Northampton, NN14 2PG, United Kingdom
Tel.: (44) 1536760282
Web Site: http://www.eveden.com

Sales Range: $100-124.9 Million
Emp.: 465
Women's & Children's Underwear Mfr
N.A.I.C.S.: 315120
Geff Embley (CEO)

Subsidiary (Non-US):

Eveden Australia Pty Ltd (2)
3/169 Pascoe Vale Road, Moonee Ponds, Melbourne, 3039, VIC, Australia
Tel.: (61) 3 9326 0318
Lingerie & Swimwear Mfr
N.A.I.C.S.: 315250

Fukuoka Wacoal Sewing Corp. (1)
778-1 Tanushimarumachiimae, Kurume, 839-1223, Fukuoka, Japan
Tel.: (81) 943720385
Lingerie & Swimwear Mfr
N.A.I.C.S.: 315250

G Tech Material Co., Ltd. (1)
241 243 245 247 Soi Charoenrat 7 Bangklo, Bangkholaem, Bangkok, 10120, Thailand
Tel.: (66) 22915725
Raw Material Mfr & Distr
N.A.I.C.S.: 339113

Guangdong Wacoal Inc. (1)
Huahai Industrial District Xinhua Town, Huadu Qu, Guangzhou, China (100%)
Tel.: (86) 20 8686 1170
Women Apparel Mfr
N.A.I.C.S.: 315250

Hokuriku Wacoal Sewing Corp. (1)
254 characters 31-1 Shimohyo, Sakai-cho, Sakai, 919-0527, Fukui, Japan
Tel.: (81) 77 672 3883
Web Site: https://www.hokuriku.wacoal.co.jp
Emp.: 204
Women's Clothing Mfr
N.A.I.C.S.: 315250

Indonesia Wacoal Co., Ltd. (1)
Jl Tarikolot Rt 01/Rk 001 No 59, Citeureup, Bogor, 16810, Indonesia (42%)
Tel.: (62) 21 560 0715
Web Site: http://www.wacoal.co.id
Sales Range: $500-549.9 Million
Emp.: 1,500
Womens Intimate Apparel
N.A.I.C.S.: 315210
Suryadi Sasmita (Pres)

Intimates Online, Inc. (1)
48 W 38th St 10th Fl, New York, NY 10018
Apparel Retailer
N.A.I.C.S.: 424310

Kyushu Wacoal Manufacturing Corp. (1)
1572 Saigo Shin, Mizuho-cho, Unzen, 857-1206, Nagasaki, Japan (100%)
Tel.: (81) 95 777 2171
Web Site: https://www.kyushu.wacoal.co.jp
Emp.: 512
Women's Clothing Mfr
N.A.I.C.S.: 315250

Plant (Domestic):

Kyushu Wacoal Manufacturing Corp. - Fukuoka Factory (2)
778-1 Imae Tanushimaru-cho, Kurume, 839-1223, Fukuoka, Japan
Tel.: (81) 9437 2 0385
Lingerie & Swimwear Mfr
N.A.I.C.S.: 315250

Kyushu Wacoal Manufacturing Corp. - Kumamoto Factory (2)
2883 Noboritate Ohyano-machi, Kami-Amakusa, 869-3601, Kumamoto, Japan
Tel.: (81) 964 56 0393
Web Site: http://www.kyusyu.wacoal.co.jp
Lingerie & Swimwear Mfr
N.A.I.C.S.: 315250

Lecien (Cambodia) Co., Ltd. (1)
PLOT P1 021 022 Phnom Penh Special Economic Zone National Road No 4, Khan Posenchey, Phnom Penh, Cambodia
Tel.: (855) 23729453
Apparel Mfr & Distr
N.A.I.C.S.: 315990

Lecien (Vietnam) Co., Ltd. (1)
Tan Thuan Export Processing Zone, Tan

WACOAL HOLDINGS CORP.

Wacoal Holdings Corp.—(Continued)
Thuan Dong ward District 7, Ho Chi Minh City, Vietnam
Tel.: (84) 2837701971
Ladies Innerwear Mfr
N.A.I.C.S.: 315990

Lecien Corporation (1)
6F 7F Wacoal Osaka Bldg 1-7-51 Nishimi-yahara, Yodogawa-ku, Osaka, 532-0004, Japan (100%)
Tel.: (81) 66 350 8450
Web Site: https://www.lecien.co.jp
Emp.: 17
Womens' Wear Fabrics, Clothes, Lingerie, Accessories, Lace Fabrics, Handicraft Materials & Cotton Fabrics Mfr & Whslr
N.A.I.C.S.: 313210
Naofumi Nomura (Chm)

Lecien Nagasaki Corporation (1)
1588 Nakagumi-go, Kawatana-cho Higashisonogi-gun, Nagasaki, Japan
Tel.: (81) 956824651
Swimwear Accessory Mfr
N.A.I.C.S.: 315990

Linge Noel Co., Ltd. (1)
6 Wacoal Shin-Kyoto Building 6 Nishikujo, Kitanouchi-cho Minami-ku, Kyoto, 601-8506, Japan
Tel.: (81) 75 556 0112
Web Site: https://www.lingenoel.co.jp
Emp.: 150
Swimwear Accessory Distr
N.A.I.C.S.: 423910

Nanasai Co., Ltd. (1)
Wacoal Osaka Building 1-7-51 Nishinomi-yabara, Yodogawa-ku, Osaka, 532-0004, Japan
Tel.: (81) 66 395 9245
Web Site: https://www.nanasai.co.jp
Sales Range: $125-149.9 Million
Emp.: 258
Mfr of Display Fixtures, Moldings & Mannequins; Store Planning & Design; Construction & Planning for Special Events & Exhibitions
N.A.I.C.S.: 541850

Niigata Wacoal Sewing Corp. (1)
263 Hataya, Niigata, 959 0423, Niigata, Japan (100%)
Tel.: (81) 256 88 3000
Women's Clothing Mfr
N.A.I.C.S.: 315250

Peach John Co., Ltd. (1)
3-1-2 Kita-Aoyama Aoyama St Sion Building, Minato-ku, Tokyo, 150 0001, Japan (100%)
Tel.: (81) 12 006 6107
Web Site: https://www.peachjohn.co.jp
Emp.: 480
Womens' Apparel Mail-Order Services
N.A.I.C.S.: 424310

Peach John Hong Kong Company Limited (1)
Shop No 45-46 3/F Sogo 555 Hennessy Road, Causeway Bay, China (Hong Kong)
Tel.: (852) 25776012
Web Site: https://www.peachjohn.com.hk
Apparel Retailer
N.A.I.C.S.: 424310

Peach John Shanghai Co.,Ltd. (1)
2306 Jiangnan Bldg NO 600 Luban Road, Huangpu District, Shanghai, 200023, China
Tel.: (86) 2153026973
Apparel Retailer
N.A.I.C.S.: 424310

Shanghai Lecien Co., Ltd. (1)
Room No 2407 Jiangnan Building 600 Lu Ban Road, Shanghai, 200023, China
Tel.: (86) 2162957923
Cloth Embroidery Distr
N.A.I.C.S.: 424310

ShinYoung Wacoal Inc. (1)
345-54 Gasan-Dong, Geumcheon-Gu, Seoul, 153-023, Korea (South) (25%)
Tel.: (82) 28185114
Web Site: https://www.shinyoungwacoal.co.kr
Rev.: $154,507,506
Assets: $326,592,020
Liabilities: $48,385,208
Net Worth: $278,206,812

Earnings: $18,026,370
Emp.: 394
Fiscal Year-end: 12/31/2022
Intimate Apparel, Lingerie, Bathing Suits & Sportswear Mfr
N.A.I.C.S.: 315210
Ho Seong Lee (CEO)

Taiwan Wacoal Co., Ltd. (1)
15 Ching Kuo Road, Taoyuan, Taiwan (50%)
Tel.: (886) 3 326 9369
Web Site: https://www.wacoalholdings.jp
Womens Intimate Apparel
N.A.I.C.S.: 315210

Thai Wacoal Public Co., Ltd. (1)
132 Soi Charoen Rat 7, Bang Khlo Bang Kho Laem, Bangkok, 10120, Thailand (34%)
Tel.: (66) 22 893 1009
Web Site: https://www.wacoal.co.th
Sales Range: $500-549.9 Million
Emp.: 2,500
Women's Intimate Apparel
N.A.I.C.S.: 315210
Boondee Amnuayskul (CEO, Mng Dir & Member-Exec Bd)

Torica Inc. (1)
3-2-10 Higashi-Oota, Ibaraki, 567-0012, Osaka, Japan
Tel.: (81) 726 26 7341
Bras, Panties & Knit Wear Mfr
N.A.I.C.S.: 315250

Unenana Cool Corp. (1)
Wacoal New Kyoto Bldg 5F 6 Kitanouchi-cho Nishikujo, Minami-ku, Kyoto, 601-8506, Japan (100%)
Tel.: (81) 75 556 0110
Web Site: http://www.une-nana-cool.com
Womens' & Mens' Clothing Mfr & Retailer
N.A.I.C.S.: 315250

Vietnam Wacoal Corp. (1)
No 110 Amata Street, Amata Industrial Park Long Binh Ward, Bien Hoa, Dong Nai, Vietnam
Tel.: (84) 283 517 1232
Web Site: https://wacoal.com.vn
Emp.: 2,150
Womens' Intimate Apparel Distr
N.A.I.C.S.: 424350

WACOAL CANADA INC. (1)
1000 de la Gauchetiere Street West Suite 2400, Montreal, H3B 4W5, QC, Canada
Tel.: (514) 448-2173
Lingerie Mfr

Wacoal (Shanghai) Human Science R&D Co., Ltd. (1)
5th Floor Jiangnan Zaochuan Bldg 600 Lu Ban Road, Lu Wan District, Shanghai, 200023, China
Tel.: (86) 21 6390 7448
Research & Development for Womens' Apparel
N.A.I.C.S.: 541715

Wacoal America, Inc. (1)
136 Madison Ave, New York, NY 10016 (100%)
Tel.: (212) 532-6100
Web Site: http://www.wacoal-america.com
Sales Range: $150-199.9 Million
Emp.: 1,000
Intimate Apparel, Lingerie, Bathing Suits & Sportswear Mfr
N.A.I.C.S.: 315210

Wacoal Art Center Co., Ltd. (1)
5-6-23 Minami-Aoyama, Minato-ku, Tokyo, 107-0062, Japan
Tel.: (81) 33 498 1171
Web Site: https://www.spiral.co.jp
Sales Range: $50-74.9 Million
Emp.: 120
Shopping Center Leasing Services
N.A.I.C.S.: 531120

Wacoal Career Service Corp. (1)
29 Nakajima-cho Kisshoin, Minami-ku, Kyoto, 601-8530, Japan
Tel.: (81) 12 085 6169
Web Site: https://www.e-wacs.co.jp
Swimwear Accessory Distr
N.A.I.C.S.: 423910

Wacoal China Co., Ltd. (1)
No 16 Tongji North Road, Beijing Economic and Technological Development Zone, Beijing, 100176, China (100%)
Tel.: (86) 400 184 0048
Web Site: https://www.wacoal.com.cn
Womens' Intimate Apparel Mfr & Distr
N.A.I.C.S.: 315250

Wacoal Corp. (1)
29 Nakajima-cho Kisshoin, Minami-ku, Kyoto, 601-8530, Japan (100%)
Tel.: (81) 75 682 5111
Web Site: https://www.wacoal.jp
Sales Range: $25-49.9 Million
Emp.: 4,822
Research & Development & Business Development Services
N.A.I.C.S.: 561499

Wacoal Distribution Corp. (1)
1-1 Chishiro-cho, Moriyama, 524 0034, Shiga, Japan (100%)
Tel.: (81) 77 514 1250
Womens' Clothing Distr
N.A.I.C.S.: 424350

Wacoal Dominicana Corp. (1)
Las Americas Industrial Free Zone KM22 Autopista Las Americas, Santo Domingo, Dominican Republic (100%)
Tel.: (809) 549 1090
Womens' Intimate Apparel Distr
N.A.I.C.S.: 424350

Wacoal EMEA Ltd. (1)
The Corsetry Factory Rothwell Road, Desborough, NN14 2PG, Northants, United Kingdom
Tel.: (44) 153 676 0282
Web Site: https://www.wacoal-europe.com
Emp.: 465
Swimwear Accessory Mfr
N.A.I.C.S.: 315990
Laura Simon (CMO)

Wacoal Europe SAS (1)
4 Allee Du Moulin Berger, Ecully, 69130, Lyon, France
Tel.: (33) 43 759 8030
Web Site: https://www.wacoal-europe.com
Lingerie & Swimwear Mfr
N.A.I.C.S.: 315250
Geoff Embley (CEO)

Wacoal Hong Kong Co., Ltd. (1)
8th Floor EGL Tower 83 Hung To Road, Kwun Tong, Kowloon, China (Hong Kong) (80%)
Tel.: (852) 2 811 3202
Web Site: https://en.wacoal.com.hk
Sales Range: $25-49.9 Million
Emp.: 40
Womens' Intimate Apparel
N.A.I.C.S.: 315210

Wacoal I Next Corp. (1)
29 Nakajima-cho Kisshoin, Minami-ku, Kyoto, 601-8530, Japan
Tel.: (81) 756821114
Swimwear Accessory Distr
N.A.I.C.S.: 423910

Wacoal India Private Limited (1)
403 Ackruti Star MIDC Central Rd MIDC Andheri East, Mumbai, 400093, Maharashtra, India
Tel.: (91) 8956969418
Web Site: https://www.wacoalindia.com
Ladies Innerwear Distr
N.A.I.C.S.: 424310

Wacoal International Corp. (1)
1 Wacoal Plz, Lyndhurst, NJ 07071
Tel.: (201) 933-8400
Web Site: https://www.wacoalholdings.jp
Lingerie & Swimwear Mfr
N.A.I.C.S.: 315250

Wacoal International Hong Kong Co., Ltd. (1)
8th Floor EGL Tower 83 Hung To Road, Kwun Tong, Kowloon, China (Hong Kong) (100%)
Tel.: (852) 2561 9191
Emp.: 2
Holding Company
N.A.I.C.S.: 551112

Subsidiary (Non-US):

Philippine Wacoal Corp. (2)

INTERNATIONAL PUBLIC

3F 6788 Ayala Avenue Oledan Square, Makati, 1226, Metro Manila, Philippines (67%)
Tel.: (63) 8 892 5706
Web Site: https://www.wacoal.ph
Sales Range: $25-49.9 Million
Womens' Intimate Apparel Distr
N.A.I.C.S.: 424350
Christian Pelisoc (Pres)

Wacoal Lanka(Private) Limited (1)
Wepz Wathupitiwela, Nittambuwa, Sri Lanka
Tel.: (94) 334671166
Ladies Innerwear Mfr
N.A.I.C.S.: 315990

Wacoal Malaysia Sdn. Bhd. (1)
5th Floor Plaza Hamodal Lot 15 Jalan 13/2 Section 13, Petaling Jaya, 46200, Selangor, Malaysia (50%)
Tel.: (60) 3 7960 8308
Womens' Intimate Apparel Distr
N.A.I.C.S.: 424350

Wacoal Manufacturing Japan Corp. (1)
1572 Saigoshin Mizuho-cho, Unzen, 859-1206, Japan
Tel.: (81) 957772171
Nightwear Apparel Mfr & Distr
N.A.I.C.S.: 315990

Wacoal Minette Co., Ltd. (1)
27-1-20 Minami Ichijo Nishi, Chuo-ku, Sapporo, 064-0801, Japan
Tel.: (81) 11 642 7111
Web Site: http://www.minette.co.jp
Swimwear Accessory Distr
N.A.I.C.S.: 423910

Wacoal Netherlands B.V. (1)
Poppenbouwing 29, 4191NZ, Geldermalsen, Netherlands
Tel.: (31) 345799600
Women Apparel Mfr & Distr
N.A.I.C.S.: 315990

Wacoal Service Co., Ltd. (1)
29 Nakajima-cho Kisshoin, Minami-ku, Kyoto, 601-8530, Japan
Tel.: (81) 75 682 1043
Web Site: https://www.wacoalholdings.jp
Business Support Services
N.A.I.C.S.: 561499

Wacoal Singapore Pte. Ltd. (1)
215 Henderson Road 01-08 Henderson Industrial Park, Singapore, 159554, Singapore (100%)
Tel.: (65) 6 270 2887
Web Site: https://www.wacoal.com.sg
Sales Range: $25-49.9 Million
Emp.: 18
Womens' Intimate Apparel Distr
N.A.I.C.S.: 424350
Kota Hashimoto (Gen Mgr)

Wacoal Sports Science Corp. (1)
136 Madison Ave, New York, NY 10016 (100%)
Tel.: (212) 743-9849
Web Site: http://www.cw-x.com
Sportswear & Athletic Apparel Marketer & Distr
N.A.I.C.S.: 424350
Marielle Mori (Coord-Production & Ops)

Zhe Jiang Jiaxing Lecien Co., Ltd. (1)
733 Heping Street, Jiaxing, Zhejiang, China
Tel.: (86) 57382200061
Yarn-Dyed Threads Product Mfr & Distr
N.A.I.C.S.: 313110

WACOM CO., LTD.

2-510-1 Toyonodai, Kazo, 349-1148, Saitama, Japan
Tel.: (81) 480781211
Web Site: https://www.wacom.com
Year Founded: 1983
11W—(DEU)
Rev.: $785,234,950
Assets: $526,288,200
Liabilities: $288,539,720
Net Worth: $237,748,480
Earnings: $30,154,820
Emp.: 1,076
Fiscal Year-end: 03/31/24

Computer Peripherals Mfr
N.A.I.C.S.: 334118
Yoichi Machida (CFO & CFO)

Subsidiaries:

Wacom Australia Pty. Ltd. (1)
Ground floor Building 1 3 Richardson Place,
North Ryde, 2113, NSW, Australia
Tel.: (61) 294226700
Web Site: http://www.wacom.com
Sales Range: $25-49.9 Million
Emp.: 10
Computer Peripheral Equipment Mfr
N.A.I.C.S.: 334118

Wacom Europe GmbH (1)
Zollhof 11-15, 40221, Dusseldorf, Germany
Tel.: (49) 211385480
Web Site: http://www.wacom.eu
Sales Range: $25-49.9 Million
Emp.: 160
Computer Peripherals Mfr
N.A.I.C.S.: 334118
Stefan Kirmse (Sr VP-Corp Brand & PR)

Wacom Korea Co., Ltd. (1)
Rm 1211 12F 1601 Sangam-dong KGIT
Sangam Center, Mapo-gu, Seoul, 03925,
Korea (South)
Tel.: (82) 25573894
Web Site: http://www.wacom.com
Sales Range: $25-49.9 Million
Emp.: 17
Computer Peripheral Equipment Mfr
N.A.I.C.S.: 334118

Wacom Taiwan Information Co.,
Ltd. (1)
9F-1 No 237 Songjiang Rd, Zhongshan
Dist, Taipei, 104, Taiwan
Tel.: (886) 225161718
Web Site: http://www.wacom.com.tw
Sales Range: $25-49.9 Million
Emp.: 7
Computer Peripheral Equipment Mfr
N.A.I.C.S.: 334118

WACUL, INC.
3-26-8 Kanda Ogawamachi 3-chome
Building 2F, Chiyoda-Ku, Tokyo, 101-
0052, Japan
Tel.: (81) 352445535
Web Site: https://www.wacul.co.jp
Year Founded: 2010
4173—(TKS)
Digital Marketing Services
N.A.I.C.S.: 541870
Ryohei Obuchi (Chm, Pres, CEO &
Dir-Rep)

WADAKOHSAN CORPORATION
4-2-13 Sakaemachidori, Chuo-ku,
Kobe, 650-0023, Hyogo, Japan
Tel.: (81) 783611100
Web Site:
https://www.wadakohsan.co.jp
Year Founded: 1979
89310—(TKS)
Rev.: $355,941,633
Assets: $781,814,426
Liabilities: $577,433,265
Net Worth: $204,381,161
Earnings: $16,700,361
Fiscal Year-end: 02/28/19
Real Estate Development Services
N.A.I.C.S.: 531110

WADEX SA
ul Klimasa 45, 50-515, Wroclaw, Poland
Tel.: (48) 71 3367080
Web Site: http://www.wadex.pl
Year Founded: 1990
Stainless Steel Products Mfr
N.A.I.C.S.: 331210
Zbigniew Krzysztof Piechocinski
(Chm-Mgmt Bd & CEO)

WAFA INSURANCE, INC.
305 Akaria-2 Olaya Street, PO Box
341413, Riyadh, 11333, Saudi Arabia
Tel.: (966) 12150983
Web Site:
http://www.wafainsurance.com
Year Founded: 2007
8110—(SAU)
Rev.: $2,592,246
Assets: $22,324,705
Liabilities: $51,085,118
Net Worth: ($28,760,414)
Earnings: ($9,213,172)
Emp.: 219
Fiscal Year-end: 12/31/19
General Insurance Services
N.A.I.C.S.: 524210
Abdulrahman Abdullah Al Sahli (CEO)

WAFA KUNSTSTOFFTECHNIK GMBH
Schafweidstrasse 37, 86179, Augsburg, Germany
Tel.: (49) 8218030
Web Site: http://www.demmel.de
Year Founded: 1998
Sales Range: $75-99.9 Million
Emp.: 500
Plastic Injection Molding Components Mfr
N.A.I.C.S.: 326199
Wolfgang K. Muller (Mng Dir)

WAFANGDIAN BEARING CO., LTD.
No 1 Gongji Street 1st Section, Wafangdian, 116300, Liaoning, China
Tel.: (86) 41162198008
Web Site: http://www.zwz-
bearing.com
Year Founded: 1997
200706—(SSE)
Rev.: $329,705,616
Assets: $466,798,775
Liabilities: $400,768,234
Net Worth: $66,030,541
Earnings: ($19,641,609)
Emp.: 8,400
Fiscal Year-end: 12/31/22
Industrial Bearings, C.V.Joint & Precision Ball Screws Mfr
N.A.I.C.S.: 332991
Zhang Xinghai (Chm)

WAFFER TECHNOLOGY, CORP.
5F Building A No 209 Sec 1 Nangang
Rd, Nangang Dist, Taoyuan, 115,
Taiwan
Tel.: (886) 34502688
Web Site: https://www.waffer.com.tw
6235—(TAI)
Rev.: $188,828,928
Assets: $270,956,234
Liabilities: $141,417,438
Net Worth: $129,538,796
Earnings: $26,245,429
Fiscal Year-end: 12/31/23
Metal Products Mfr
N.A.I.C.S.: 332999
Luo Xujuan (Deputy Gen Mgr)

Subsidiaries:

Waffer Technology (Maanshan)
Limited (1)
1430 Huxinan Road Economic & Technological Development Zone, Ma'anshan, Anhui, China
Tel.: (86) 5555215168
Aluminium Product Mfr & Distr
N.A.I.C.S.: 331313

WAFRAH FOR INDUSTRY & DEVELOPMENT CO.
PO Box 131, Riyadh, 11383, Saudi Arabia
Tel.: (966) 114035888
Web Site: https://www.wafrah.com
Year Founded: 1989
2100—(SAU)
Rev.: $36,008,055
Assets: $82,924,015
Liabilities: $23,809,848
Net Worth: $59,114,168
Earnings: $5,063,900
Emp.: 312
Fiscal Year-end: 12/31/22
Food Product Mfr & Whslr
N.A.I.C.S.: 311999
Zenan Salim Ali AlYami (CEO)

WAGA ENERGY SA
5 Avenue Raymond Chanas, 38320,
Eybens, France
Tel.: (33) 772771185
Web Site: https://www.waga-
energy.com
Year Founded: 2015
WAGA—(EUR)
Rev.: $37,573,684
Assets: $214,796,335
Liabilities: $106,756,816
Net Worth: $108,039,519
Earnings: ($17,046,032)
Emp.: 165
Fiscal Year-end: 12/31/23
Natural Gas Distribution Services
N.A.I.C.S.: 221210
Nicolas Paget (CTO)

WAGE INDUSTRI AB
Industrigatan 12, Toreboda, 545 31,
Vastra Gotaland, Sweden
Tel.: (46) 506 121 30
Rev.: $3,427,500
Valves & Pumps
N.A.I.C.S.: 332911

WAGNER & CO SOLAR TECHNOLOGY GMBH
Zimmermannstrasse 12, 35091, Hessen, Germany
Tel.: (49) 642180070
Solar Installation Distr
N.A.I.C.S.: 221118

Subsidiaries:

Wagner & Co Solar France
SARL (1)
Rue des Fontaines ZIC des Fontaines,
71290, Paris, France
Tel.: (33) 85274020
Solar Power Distribution Services
N.A.I.C.S.: 238220

Wagner & Co Solar-Italia S.r.l. (1)
via del Commercio 2, 26026, Pizzighettone,
Italy
Tel.: (39) 0372744972
Web Site: http://www.it.wagner-solar.com
Emp.: 150
Solar Power Distribution Services
N.A.I.C.S.: 238220

Wagner Solar GmbH (1)
Sonnenallee 2, 35274, Kirchhain, Germany
Tel.: (49) 642180070
Web Site: http://www.wagner-solar.com
Solar Power Distribution Services
N.A.I.C.S.: 238220

Wagner Solar S.L. (1)
C/Petroleo 24-26, Madrid, 28918, Leganes,
Spain
Tel.: (34) 914880080
Web Site: http://www.es.wagner-solar.com
Solar Power Distribution Services
N.A.I.C.S.: 238220

Wagner Solar UK Ltd (1)
Unit 3 Keynor Farm, Sidlesham, Chichester,
PO20 7LL, West Sussex, United Kingdom
Tel.: (44) 1243649035
Web Site: http://uk.wagner-solar.com
Solar Power Distribution Services
N.A.I.C.S.: 238220
Carsten Pump (Mng Dir)

WAGNER KABLO SANAYI VE TICARET A.S.
Liman Sb Mahallesi Serbest Bolge
Free Zone Pk8, 07070, Antalya, Turkiye
Tel.: (90) 242 310 53 00
Web Site: http://www.wagner.com.tr
Year Founded: 1992
Sales Range: $25-49.9 Million
Emp.: 250
Wiring Harness Mfr
N.A.I.C.S.: 335999
Ahmet Unsal (Chm)

WAGNERS HOLDING COMPANY LIMITED
Drayton North, PO Box 151, Toowoomba, 4350, QLD, Australia
Tel.: (61) 746377777   AU
Web Site:
https://www.wagner.com.au
Year Founded: 2017
WGN—(ASX)
Rev.: $321,612,965
Assets: $275,850,739
Liabilities: $185,996,974
Net Worth: $89,853,765
Earnings: $6,865,703
Emp.: 990
Fiscal Year-end: 06/30/24
Construction Material Mfr & Distr
N.A.I.C.S.: 327120
Denis Wagner (Co-Founder)

Subsidiaries:

Wagners CFT LLC (1)
19077 S US Hwy 377, Cresson, TX 76035
Tel.: (817) 470-7821
Web Site: https://www.wagnerscft.com
Fiber Material Mfr
N.A.I.C.S.: 335991

Wagners Global Services (Malaysia)
Sdn Bhd (1)
Plaza Mont Kiara Suite A-6-10 Block A
Plaza Mont Kiara No 2, Jalan Kiara Mont
Kiara, 50480, Kuala Lumpur, Malaysia
Tel.: (60) 362011872
Concrete Products Mfr
N.A.I.C.S.: 333120

WAGO KONTAKTTECHNIK GMBH & CO. KG
Hansastr 27, 32423, Minden, Germany
Tel.: (49) 5718870   De
Web Site: http://www.wago.com
Year Founded: 1951
Sales Range: $500-549.9 Million
Emp.: 4,700
Terminals Connector & Electronic
Module Mfr
N.A.I.C.S.: 335931
Axel Borner (CFO)

Subsidiaries:

OOO Wago (1)
Dmitrovskoe shosse 157 bldg 12/5, 127411,
Moscow, Russia
Tel.: (7) 4956633305
Web Site: http://www.wago.ru
Electronic Equipment Distr
N.A.I.C.S.: 423690
Natalia Klimova (Sr Mgr-Logistics)

WAGO & Controls (India) Ltd. (1)
C-27 Sector-58 Phas III, Noida, 201 301,
Gautam Budh Nagar, India
Tel.: (91) 1202580409
Web Site: http://www.wago.com
Sales Range: $125-149.9 Million
Emp.: 250
Electronic Components Mfr
N.A.I.C.S.: 334419

WAGO BeLux nv (1)
Excelsiorlaan 11, 1930, Zaventem, Belgium
Tel.: (32) 27179090
Web Site: http://www.wago.be
Electronic Equipment Distr
N.A.I.C.S.: 423690
Niki Claes (Mgr-Technical Dept)

WAGO Co. of Japan Ltd. (1)
Kotoku Kameido 1-5-7 Kinshitho Prime

WAGO KONTAKTTECHNIK GMBH & CO. KG

WAGO Kontakttechnik GmbH & Co. KG—(Continued)
Tower, Kameido, Tokyo, 136-0071, Japan
Tel.: (81) 3 5627-2050
Web Site: http://www.wago.co.jp
Sales Range: $25-49.9 Million
Emp.: 100
Terminal Blocks & Connectors Mfr
N.A.I.C.S.: 449210
A. Kusa (CEO)

WAGO Contact SA (1)
Rte de I Indstured 19, 1564, Domdidier, Switzerland
Tel.: (41) 266767586
Web Site: http://www.wago.ch
Sales Range: $75-99.9 Million
Emp.: 400
Electronic Components Mfr
N.A.I.C.S.: 335931
Carole Demierre (Mgr-HR)

WAGO Contact SA (1)
Paris Nord 2, PO Box 55065, 83 Rue Des Chardonnerets, F 95947, Charles de Gaulle, France
Tel.: (33) 148172590
Web Site: http://www.wago.fr
Sales Range: $75-99.9 Million
Emp.: 120
Electronic Components Mfr
N.A.I.C.S.: 335931

WAGO Contact, Ltd (1)
5F No 168 Jiankang Rd, Zhonghe, Taipei, Taiwan
Tel.: (886) 222250123
Electronic Equipment Distr
N.A.I.C.S.: 423690

WAGO Corporation (1)
N120 W19129 Freistadt Rd, Germantown, WI 53022
Tel.: (262) 255-6222
Web Site: http://www.wago.us
Sales Range: $75-99.9 Million
Emp.: 140
Electronic Terminal Blocks Mfr
N.A.I.C.S.: 423610
Greg Rinn (VP-Ops)

WAGO Denmark A/S (1)
Lejrvej 17, 3500, Vaerlose, Denmark
Tel.: (45) 44357777
Web Site: http://www.wago.dk
Trucking Except Local
N.A.I.C.S.: 484121
Carsten Bovin (Gen Mgr)

WAGO ELECTRONIC (TIANJIN) Co. LTD (1)
No 5 Quan Hui Road Wuqing Development Area, Tianjin, 301700, China
Tel.: (86) 2259677688
Web Site: http://www.wago.com.cn
Electronic Equipment Distr
N.A.I.C.S.: 423690
Dongchao Wang (Project Mgr)

WAGO ELWAG sp. z o. o. (1)
ul Piekna 58 a, 50-506, Wroclaw, Poland
Tel.: (48) 713602970
Web Site: http://www.wago.pl
Electronic Equipment Distr
N.A.I.C.S.: 423690
Marcin Surma (Mgr-Market)

WAGO Electronic Pte Ltd. (1)
10 Upper Aljunied Link 04-04 Johnson Controls Building, Singapore, 367904, Singapore
Tel.: (65) 62866776
Electronic Equipment Distr
N.A.I.C.S.: 423690

WAGO Elektro spol. sr. o. (1)
Rozvodova 1116/36, Modrany, 143 00, Prague, Czech Republic
Tel.: (420) 261090143
Web Site: http://www.wago.cz
Electronic Equipment Distr
N.A.I.C.S.: 423690

WAGO Elektronik Sanayi ve Ticaret Ltd. Sti. (1)
Yukari Dudullu Mahallesi Bayraktar Bulvari Cad Hattat Sok No 10, Umraniye, 34775, Istanbul, Turkiye
Tel.: (90) 2164721133
Web Site: http://www.wago.com.tr

Electronic Equipment Distr
N.A.I.C.S.: 423690

WAGO Eletroeletronicos Ltda (1)
Rua Americo Simoes 1470 Sau Roque da Chave, Itupeva, 13295-000, Sao Paulo, Brazil
Tel.: (55) 1145910199
Web Site: http://www.wago.com.br
Electronic Equipment Distr
N.A.I.C.S.: 423690

WAGO Elettronica SRL (1)
Via Parini 1, 40033, Casalecchio di Reno, Bologna, Italy
Tel.: (39) 0516132112
Web Site: http://www.wago.it
Electronic Equipment Distr
N.A.I.C.S.: 423690
Alberto Ferracini (Mgr-Sls)

WAGO Finland Oy (1)
Vellamonkatu 30 B, 00550, Helsinki, Finland
Tel.: (358) 97744060
Web Site: http://www.wago.fi
Electronic Equipment Distr
N.A.I.C.S.: 423690

WAGO Hungaria KFT (1)
Ipari Park Gyar u 2, 2040, Budapest, Hungary
Tel.: (36) 23502170
Web Site: http://www.wago.hu
Electronic Equipment Distr
N.A.I.C.S.: 423690

WAGO Kontakttechnik Ges.m.b.H. (1)
Europaring F15 602 Campus 21, 2345, Brunn am Gebirge, Austria
Tel.: (43) 16150780
Electronic Equipment Distr
N.A.I.C.S.: 423690

WAGO Korea Co., Ltd. (1)
Room 205 AnyangMegaValley 268 Haguiro, Dohgan-gu, Anyang, 14056, Gyeonggi-do, Korea (South)
Tel.: (82) 314219500
Web Site: http://www.wago.co.kr
Electronic Equipment Distr
N.A.I.C.S.: 423690
Hae-Yong Kim (Dir-Sls)

WAGO Limited (1)
Triton Park Swift Valley Industrial Estate, Rugby, CV21 1SG, Warwickshire, United Kingdom
Tel.: (44) 1788568008
Web Site: http://www.wago.com
Sales Range: $10-24.9 Million
Emp.: 80
Electronic Components Mfr
N.A.I.C.S.: 335931
Tony Hoyle (Mng Dir)

WAGO Middle East (FZC) (1)
Q4- 282 Sharjah Airport International Free Zone, PO Box 120665, Sharjah, United Arab Emirates
Tel.: (971) 65579920
Web Site: http://www.wago.ae
Electronic Equipment Distr
N.A.I.C.S.: 423690
Imad Albreem (Mgr-Sls)

WAGO Nederland B.V. (1)
Laan van de Ram 19, 7324 BW, Apeldoorn, Netherlands
Tel.: (31) 553683500
Electronic Equipment Distr
N.A.I.C.S.: 423690
Herman Bouwman (Gen Mgr)

WAGO Norge AS (1)
Jerikoveien 20, 1067, Oslo, Norway
Tel.: (47) 22309450
Web Site: http://www.wago.no
Electronic Equipment Distr
N.A.I.C.S.: 423690
Stian Karlsen (Mgr-Sls-O&G)

WAGO Pty. Ltd. (1)
2-4 Overseas Drive, Noble Park, 3174, VIC, Australia
Tel.: (61) 387916300
Web Site: http://www.wago.com.au
Electronic Equipment Distr
N.A.I.C.S.: 423690

WAGO SA de CV (1)

Av Del Marques 38 Bodega 3 P I Bernardo Quintana, El Marques, 76246, Queretaro, Mexico
Tel.: (52) 4422215946
Electronic Equipment Distr
N.A.I.C.S.: 423690
Daniel Hernandez (Gen Mgr)

WAGO Sverige AB (1)
Adolfsbergsv 31, PO Box 11127, 161 11, Bromma, Sweden
Tel.: (46) 858410680
Web Site: http://www.wago.se
Electronic Equipment Distr
N.A.I.C.S.: 423690
Urban Wase (Gen Mgr)

WAGOKORO CO., LTD.
3-20-12 Sendagaya, Shibuya-Ku, Tokyo, 151-0051, Japan
Tel.: (81) 357850556
Web Site: https://www.wagokoro.co.jp
9271—(TKS)
Rev: $9,429,700
Assets: $7,260,160
Liabilities: $6,253,380
Net Worth: $1,006,780
Earnings: ($92,170)
Fiscal Year-end: 12/31/23
Apparel Accessory Retailer
N.A.I.C.S.: 458110
Tomohiro Mori (Founder, Chm & Pres)

WAGRAM EQUITY PARTNERS BV
Balsemkruidstraat 5, 2215 VD, Voorhout, Netherlands
Tel.: (31) 252224107
Web Site: http://www.wagram.nl
Year Founded: 1996
Holding Company
N.A.I.C.S.: 551112
Arthur Hopmans (Partner)

Subsidiaries:

FrieslandCampina Creamy Creation B.V. (1)
Hoogeindsestraat 31, 5447 PE, Rijkevoort, Netherlands
Tel.: (31) 485 378 900
Web Site: http://www.creamy-creation.com
Beverages Mfr
N.A.I.C.S.: 311514
Maurice Smeets (Dir-Sls-Alcoholic Beverages)

Subsidiary (US):

FrieslandCampina Creamy Creation LLC (2)
24 Masse Pl, Batavia, NY 14020
Tel.: (585) 344-3303
Beverage Whslr
N.A.I.C.S.: 424810
Rutger van den Noort (VP)

WAH FU EDUCATION GROUP LIMITED
L207b Hesheng Fortune Plaza No 13 Deshengmenwai Street, Xicheng District, Beijing, 100088, China
Tel.: (86) 1059942599 VG
Web Site: http://www.edu-edu.com
Year Founded: 2012
WAFU—(NASDAQ)
Rev: $7,223,220
Assets: $16,156,423
Liabilities: $3,997,187
Net Worth: $12,159,236
Earnings: ($376,860)
Emp.: 122
Fiscal Year-end: 03/31/24
Learning Support Services
N.A.I.C.S.: 611691
Yang Yu (Chm)

WAH HA REALTY COMPANY LIMITED

INTERNATIONAL PUBLIC

Room 2500 Dominion Centre 43-59 Queens Road East, Wanchai, China (Hong Kong)
Tel.: (852) 2 527 1821
Web Site: http://www.wahha.com
0278—(HKG)
Rev: $1,184,509
Assets: $171,878,667
Liabilities: $9,418,302
Net Worth: $162,460,365
Earnings: $395,353
Emp.: 20
Fiscal Year-end: 03/31/21
Property Management Services
N.A.I.C.S.: 531312
Raymond Wing Man Chu (Sec)

Subsidiaries:

Galy Property Management Limited (1)
Ground Fl Best-O-Best Comml Ctr 32-36 Ferry St, Yau Ma Tei, Kowloon, China (Hong Kong)
Tel.: (852) 27712810
Property Management Services
N.A.I.C.S.: 531311

Wah Ha Construction Company Limited (1)
Rm 2500 25 F Dominion Ctr 43-59 Queens Rd E, Wanchai, China (Hong Kong)
Tel.: (852) 25271821
Emp.: 50
Commercial Building Construction Services
N.A.I.C.S.: 236220

WAH HONG INDUSTRIAL CORP.
11F -6 No 235 Chung Cheng 4th Road, Kaohsiung, Taiwan
Tel.: (886) 79717777
Web Site: https://www.wahhong.com
8240—(TPE)
Year Founded: 1973
Rev: $287,124,160
Assets: $266,856,955
Liabilities: $134,501,767
Net Worth: $132,355,189
Earnings: $8,885,064
Emp.: 1,386
Fiscal Year-end: 12/31/22
Lighting Equipment Mfr
N.A.I.C.S.: 335139
Ray C. Chang (Chm)

Subsidiaries:

Ningbo Changhong Optoelectronics Ltd. (1)
No 436 Sungari River Road, Beilun, Ningbo, China
Tel.: (86) 57456806555
Industrial Material Mfr & Distr
N.A.I.C.S.: 333511

P.T. Wah Hong Indonesia (1)
Jl Pinang Blok F16 12D Delta Silicon 3, Kabupaten Bekasi, Lippo Cikarang, Jawa Barat, Indonesia
Tel.: (62) 2129288462
Moulded Plastic Product Mfr & Distr
N.A.I.C.S.: 326199

Qingdao Changhong Optoelectronics Ltd. (1)
11F-6 No 235 Chung, Cheng West of Zhanqian Avenue Jiulong Sub- district Office, Jiaozhou, China
Tel.: (86) 53288056111
Optical Component Mfr & Distr
N.A.I.C.S.: 334413

SIP Chang Hong Optoelectronics Ltd. (1)
No 73 Tinghe Road Suzhou Industrial Park, Weiting Town, Jiangsu, China
Tel.: (86) 51262715615
Industrial Material Mfr & Distr
N.A.I.C.S.: 333511

Sun Hong Optronics Ltd. (1)
No11 Sheng Hua Road Zhongkai Hi-tech Zone, Huizhou, China
Tel.: (86) 7525855988

AND PRIVATE COMPANIES

Industrial Material Mfr & Distr
N.A.I.C.S.: 333511

Wah Ma Technology Sdn. Bhd. (1)
Lot 2969 Mukim 16 Kawasan Perusahaan Acku Sungai Lokan, SPU Butterworth, 13400, Penang, Malaysia
Tel.: (60) 43243812815
Web Site: https://www.wahma.com.my
Industrial Electrical & Electronic Product Mfr
N.A.I.C.S.: 334513

Xiamen Guang Hong Electronics Co., Ltd. (1)
No 160 Jihe Road, Tongan District, Xiamen, China
Tel.: (86) 5927230988
Industrial Material Mfr & Distr
N.A.I.C.S.: 333511

WAH KWONG MARITIME TRANSPORT HOLDINGS LIMITED

Unit 2103 21st Floor Shanghai Industrial Invest B, Hennessy Road, Wanchai, China (Hong Kong)
Tel.: (852) 28635333
Web Site: http://www.wkmt.com.hk
Bulk Carriers & Tankers
N.A.I.C.S.: 488390
George Chao *(Chm)*

WAH LEE INDUSTRIAL CORP.

10F No 235 Chung Cheng 4th Rd, Kaohsiung, 801, Taiwan
Tel.: (886) 72164311
Web Site: https://www.wahlee.com
Year Founded: 1968
3010—(TAI)
Rev.: $2,183,930,393
Assets: $1,641,038,265
Liabilities: $973,141,531
Net Worth: $667,896,734
Earnings: $75,743,972
Emp.: 1,097
Fiscal Year-end: 12/31/23
Printed Circuit Board Mfr
N.A.I.C.S.: 334412
Ray-Ching Chang *(Bd of Dirs & Chm)*

Subsidiaries:

Hightech Polymer Sdn. Bhd. (1)
Lot 2969 Mukim 16 Kawasan Perusahaan ACKU, Seberang Perai Utara, 13400, Butterworth, Malaysia
Tel.: (60) 43243800
Industrial Material Distr
N.A.I.C.S.: 424690

Hua Gang International Trading Co., Ltd. (1)
23 25FL Diwang Plaza Changqing Rd, Chang AnTown, Dongguan, 523845, China
Tel.: (86) 76985416451
Industrial Material Distr
N.A.I.C.S.: 424690

Kingstone Energy Technology Corporation (1)
10F No 15 Minquan Rd, East Dist, Hsinchu, 30043, Taiwan
Tel.: (886) 37551357
Web Site: https://kingstone-group.com
Solar Product Mfr & Distr
N.A.I.C.S.: 334519

P.T. Wah Tech Indonesia (1)
Jl Cakung Industri I No 12 Kawasan Industri Cakung, Jakarta Utara, 14140, Indonesia
Tel.: (62) 2158352380
Industrial Material Distr
N.A.I.C.S.: 424610

P.T. Wahlee Indonesia (1)
Jl Cakung Industri I No 12 Kawasan Industri Cakung, Jakarta Utara, 14140, Indonesia
Tel.: (62) 2122580083
Bare Printed Circuit Board Mfr
N.A.I.C.S.: 334412

Raycong Industrial (H.K.) Ltd. (1)
Units 1008-1011 10th Floor Tower II Metro Plaza HingFong Road, Kwai Chung, China (Hong Kong)
Tel.: (852) 24181089

Web Site: http://www.raycong.com
Emp.: 200
Plastic Material Whslr
N.A.I.C.S.: 424610

Sakuragawa Solar Ltd. (1)
Yodoyabashisogo Kaikei 4-3-7 Kita Bld Koraibashi, Chuo-ku, Osaka, 541-0043, Japan
Tel.: (81) 662082018
Bare Printed Circuit Board Mfr
N.A.I.C.S.: 334412

Shanghai Yikang Chemicals and Industries Co., Ltd. (1)
Block 01-02 20th Floor Zhaofeng Plaza No 1027 Changning Road, Shanghai, China
Tel.: (86) 2152419090
Web Site: https://www.shanghaiyk.com
Chemical Products Distr
N.A.I.C.S.: 424690

W.L. (Wei Lee) Pte. Ltd. (1)
60 Paya Lebar Road 07-17 Paya Lebar Square, Singapore, 409051, Singapore
Tel.: (65) 67739120
Bare Printed Circuit Board Mfr
N.A.I.C.S.: 334412

Wah Lee Japan Corp. (1)
825-7 Kamonomiya, Odawara, 250-0874, Kanagawa, Japan
Tel.: (81) 50138111115
Bare Printed Circuit Board Mfr
N.A.I.C.S.: 334412

Wah Lee Korea Inc. (1)
No 401-39 Giantcube Ansan Center 50-3 Gangdeok 2nd Rd, Danwon Gu, Ansan, Korea (South)
Tel.: (82) 1092045386
Bare Printed Circuit Board Mfr
N.A.I.C.S.: 334412

Wah Lee Philippines Inc. (1)
IBP Tower Unit 1 21st Floor Dona Julia Vargas Jade Drive, Ortigas Center, Pasig, 1605, Philippines
Tel.: (63) 271188514
Industrial Material Distr
N.A.I.C.S.: 424610

Wah Lee Philippines International Corp. (1)
1321 E Rodriguez Sr Ave, Barangay Kristong Hari Cubao, Quezon City, 1112, Philippines
Tel.: (63) 27247553
Industrial Material Distr
N.A.I.C.S.: 424690

Wah Lee Tech (Singapore) A Pte. Ltd. (1)
60 Paya Lebar Road 07-17 Paya Lebar Square, Singapore, 409051, Singapore
Tel.: (65) 67739120
Semiconductor Material & Equipment Distr
N.A.I.C.S.: 423690

Wah Lee Tech(Singapore) Pte. Ltd (1)
Paya Lebar Road 60 Unit No 07-01 Paya Lebar Square, Singapore, 409051, Singapore
Tel.: (65) 6773 9120
Sales Range: $25-49.9 Million
Emp.: 20
Semiconductor Devices Mfr
N.A.I.C.S.: 334417

Wah Lee Vietnam Co., Ltd. (1)
27th Floor Worc Q2 office building 21 Vo Truong Toan, Thao Dien Ward Thu Duc City, Ho Chi Minh City, Vietnam
Tel.: (84) 2836363685
Bare Printed Circuit Board Mfr
N.A.I.C.S.: 334412

Wah Tech Industrial Co., Ltd. (1)
141/21-22 Skulthai Surawongse Tower 18th FL Surawongse Rd, Suriyawongse, Bangrak, 10500, Bangkok, Thailand
Tel.: (66) 22379842
Web Site: https://www.wahtech.co.th
Plastic Fabrication Mfr
N.A.I.C.S.: 326199

WAH NOBEL CHEMICALS LIMITED

GT Road, Wah Cantt, Pakistan

Tel.: (92) 514545243
Web Site: https://wahnobel.com
WAHN—(PSX)
Rev.: $15,769,430
Assets: $9,281,594
Liabilities: $2,787,666
Net Worth: $6,493,928
Earnings: $1,616,108
Emp.: 180
Fiscal Year-end: 06/30/23
Formaldehyde & Resins Mfr
N.A.I.C.S.: 325199
Tanveer Elahi *(CFO & Sec)*

Subsidiaries:

Wah Nobel Acetates Ltd. (1)
GT Road, Wah Cantt, Pakistan
Tel.: (92) 515568760
Web Site: https://wahnobel.com
Chemical Products Mfr
N.A.I.C.S.: 325998
Brig R Shiraz Ullah Choudhry *(CEO)*

WAH SEONG CORPORATION BERHAD

Suite 19 01 Level 19 The Gardens North Tower Mid Valley City, Lingkaran Syed Putra, 59200, Kuala Lumpur, Malaysia
Tel.: (60) 326856800
Web Site: https://wascoenergy.com
Year Founded: 1999
WASCO—(KLS)
Rev.: $567,193,735
Assets: $641,412,716
Liabilities: $462,834,135
Net Worth: $178,578,582
Earnings: $32,678,059
Emp.: 5,352
Fiscal Year-end: 12/31/23
Pipe Coating & Pipe Mfr
N.A.I.C.S.: 237120
P. R. Singaram *(CFO-Oil & Gas Div)*

Subsidiaries:

Ashburn Offshore Oil & Gas Equipment & Engineering (Tianjin) Co. Ltd. (1)
16A Minhe Road Jianfu Industrial Park Xiqing Economic Development Area, Tianjin, 300385, China
Tel.: (86) 2288298140
Oil & Gas Equipment Mfr & Distr
N.A.I.C.S.: 333132

Jutasama Sdn. Bhd. (1)
PT 15926 Jalan Bandar Lama Kawasan Perusahaan Segenting, Telok Panglima Garang, 42500, Kuala Langat, Selangor Darul Ehsan, Malaysia
Tel.: (60) 33 122 5088
Web Site: https://jutasama.com.my
Sales Range: $50-74.9 Million
Emp.: 250
Pressure Vessels Mfr
N.A.I.C.S.: 333248

Subsidiary (Domestic):

PMT Industries Sdn. Bhd. (2)
Lot 1929 Jalan Bukit Kemuning Seksyen 32, Seksyen 32, 40460, Shah Alam, Selangor Darul Ehsan, Malaysia
Tel.: (60) 35 525 7555
Web Site: https://www.pmt-grp.com
Sales Range: $25-49.9 Million
Emp.: 100
Palm Oil Manufacturing Equipments & Spares Distr
N.A.I.C.S.: 423830

Kanssen (Yadong) Pipe Coating Service Co., Ltd. (1)
Room 968 Towercrest Plaza No 3 Mai-Zi-Dian-Xi Road, Chaoyang District, Beijing, 100016, China
Tel.: (86) 1084580258
Web Site: http://www.kanssen.com
Pipe Coating Services
N.A.I.C.S.: 332812

Mackenzie Industries Sdn. Bhd. (1)
Lot 1930 Batu 7 Jalan Bukit Kemuning

Seksyen 32, 40460, Shah Alam, Selangor, Malaysia
Tel.: (60) 51230018
Web Site: http://www.mackenzieind.com
Oil & Gas Equipment Mfr & Distr
N.A.I.C.S.: 333132

PPSC Industries Sdn. Bhd. (1)
Lot 2 Kawasan Lembaga Pelabuhan Kuantan Kilometer 25, PO Box 240, Jalan Kuantan Kemaman, 25720, Kuantan, Pahang, Malaysia
Tel.: (60) 95838456
Sales Range: $100-124.9 Million
Emp.: 350
Pipe Coating Services
N.A.I.C.S.: 332812
Jonathan Brown *(VP)*

PT PMT Industri (1)
Jl Haji Misbah dalam Komplek Multatuli Indah Block A No 15, Medan, 2015, Indonesia
Tel.: (62) 614529833
Food Products Distr
N.A.I.C.S.: 424490

Petro-Pipe Industries (M) Sdn. Bhd. (1)
2431 Lorong Perusahaan 10, Prai Industrial Estate, 13600, Prai, Penang, Malaysia
Tel.: (60) 43907960
Web Site: http://www.ppimalaysia.com
Sales Range: $50-74.9 Million
Emp.: 181
Steel Pole Mfr
N.A.I.C.S.: 327332

STH Sri Bulatan Sdn. Bhd. (1)
7 Jln 1 57B Off Jln Segambut Atas, Kuala Lumpur, 51200, Federal Territory, Malaysia
Tel.: (60) 362576454
Web Site: http://www.wascoenergy.com
Building Materials Distr
N.A.I.C.S.: 444180

Spirolite (Myanmar) Company Limited (1)
No 4(A) Kun Aut Thar Min Thar Street, Dagon Seikkan Township, Yangon, Myanmar
Tel.: (95) 9972679696
Web Site: http://www.spirolite.my
Pipe & Tank Mfr
N.A.I.C.S.: 332999

Syn Tai Hung (Cambodia) Co. Ltd. (1)
Vtrust Building 10 Unit-2F Street 109 Sangkat Mettapheap Khan 7 Makara, Phnom Penh, 12252, Cambodia
Tel.: (855) 23998646
Leading Building Material Distr
N.A.I.C.S.: 444180
Ing Veasna *(Mng Dir)*

Syn Tai Hung Corporation Sdn. Bhd. (1)
59 3 The Boulevard Mid Valley City, Lingkaran Syed Putra, 59200, Kuala Lumpur, Malaysia
Tel.: (60) 322879218
Web Site: http://www.syntaihung.com
Emp.: 100
Investment Management Service
N.A.I.C.S.: 523999

Syn Tai Hung Trading Sdn. Bhd. (1)
Lot 59-6 6th Floor The Boulevard Mid Valley City, Lingkaran Syed Putra, 59200, Kuala Lumpur, Federal Territory, Malaysia
Tel.: (60) 322879218
Sales Range: $25-49.9 Million
Emp.: 100
Building Materials Distr
N.A.I.C.S.: 444180

Subsidiary (Domestic):

Spirolite (M) Sdn. Bhd. (2)
59-3 The Boulevard Mid Valley City Lingkaran Syed Putra, 59200, Kuala Lumpur, Malaysia **(100%)**
Tel.: (60) 322019433
Web Site: http://www.spirolite.my
Emp.: 13
Plastics & Rubber Industry Machinery Mfr
N.A.I.C.S.: 333248

Turn Key Pipeline Services B.V. (1)
Wijnkamp 3, 7471 CA, Goor, Netherlands

WAH SEONG CORPORATION BERHAD

Wah Seong Corporation Berhad—(Continued)
Tel.: (31) 547357010
Web Site: http://www.tk-ps.com
Oil Pipe Mill & Gas Contractor Services
N.A.I.C.S.: 237120

WDG Resources Sdn. Bhd. (1)
Lot 1929 Jalan Bukit Kemuning Seksyen 32, 40460, Shah Alam, Selangor, Malaysia
Tel.: (60) 51225522
Web Site: http://wdg-resources.com.my
Power Generation & Construction Equipment Industry Mfr
N.A.I.C.S.: 333120
Danny C. S. Ang *(Co-Founder)*

WEGL Offshore Investments Pte. Ltd. (1)
9 Raffles Place 15-02 Republic Plaza, Singapore, Singapore
Tel.: (65) 62651010
Marine Logistics Services
N.A.I.C.S.: 488320

Wasco (Australia) Pty. Ltd. (1)
60 Commercial Drive, Shailer Park, Logan, 4128, QLD, Australia
Tel.: (61) 73 255 6550
Web Site: https://www.wascoenergy.com.au
Investment & Management Services
N.A.I.C.S.: 523940

Wasco Energy Ltd. (1)
Suite 19 01 Level 19 The Gardens North Tower Mid Valley City Lingkaran, Syed Putra, Kuala Lumpur, 59200, Federal Territory, Malaysia
Tel.: (60) 326856800
Web Site: http://www.wascoenergy.com
Sales Range: $25-49.9 Million
Emp.: 100
Industrial Engineering Services
N.A.I.C.S.: 541330

Subsidiary (Non-US):

Mackenzie Hydrocarbons (Australia) Pty. Ltd. (2)
60 Commercial Drive, Shailer Park, Logan, 4128, QLD, Australia
Tel.: (61) 73 255 6550
Web Site: https://www.mackenziehydrocarbons.com
Sales Range: $25-49.9 Million
Emp.: 15
Industrial Engineering Services
N.A.I.C.S.: 541330

P.T. Megaron Semesta (2)
Jl Brigjend Katamso Km 5 Tanjung Uncang Propinsi Kepulauan Riau, Batam, 29424, Indonesia
Tel.: (62) 778 396 212
Web Site: http://www.wascoenergy.com
Construction Engineering Services
N.A.I.C.S.: 541330

PMT Phoenix Industries Sdn. Bhd. (2)
Kawasan Industri Jababeka 3 Block A8-A, Bekasi, 17500, Jawa Barat, Indonesia
Tel.: (62) 2189842393
Web Site: http://www.pmt-grp.com
Centrifugal Fan Mfr
N.A.I.C.S.: 333413

Subsidiary (Domestic):

PPI Industries Sdn. Bhd. (2)
Lot 4 Jalan P/2A, Kawasan Perindustrian Bangi, 43650, Bandar Baru Bangi, Selangor, Malaysia
Tel.: (60) 38 925 0306
Web Site: https://www.ppimalaysia.com
Sales Range: $25-49.9 Million
Steel Pole Mfr
N.A.I.C.S.: 332919

Subsidiary (Non-US):

WS Engineering Technologies Pte. Ltd (2)
5 Pandan Road, Singapore, 609299, Singapore
Tel.: (65) 62668878
Web Site: http://www.wascoenergy.com
Industrial Engineering Services
N.A.I.C.S.: 541330

Wah Seong China Limited (2)
Suite 1108 Sino Life Tower No 707 Zhangyang Road, Shanghai, 200120, China
Tel.: (86) 2158361700
Web Site: http://www.wahseongchina.com
Sales Range: $25-49.9 Million
Emp.: 10
Oil & Gas Equipments Distr
N.A.I.C.S.: 423440
Ton Qian *(CEO)*

Wasco Energy (2)
5 Pandan Road, Singapore, 609299, Singapore
Tel.: (65) 68980388
Web Site: http://www.wascoenergy.com
Sales Range: $50-74.9 Million
Emp.: 100
Gas Compression & Custom Fabrication Services
N.A.I.C.S.: 213112

Plant (Domestic):

Wasco Energy Ltd. - Kuantan Plant (2)
Sub Lot 2 Kawasan Perindustrian Miel Gebeng Km 25, PO Box 240, Jalan Kuantan Kemaman, Kuantan, 25720, Pahang Darul Makmur, Malaysia
Tel.: (60) 95838456
Web Site: http://www.wascoenergy.com
Sales Range: $75-99.9 Million
Pipe Coating Services
N.A.I.C.S.: 332812

Division (Domestic):

Wasco Energy Ltd. - Pipecoating Division (2)
Suite 19 01 Level 19 The Gardens North Tower Mid Valley City, Lingkaran Syed Putra, 59200, Kuala Lumpur, Federal Territory, Malaysia
Tel.: (60) 326856800
Web Site: http://www.wascoenergy.com
Emp.: 70
Pipe Coating Services
N.A.I.C.S.: 332812

Plant (Domestic):

Wasco Energy Ltd. - Kota Kinabalu Plant (2)
Kota Kinabalu Industrial Park Lot 13 General Industrial Zone, KKIP Mile 15 Jalan Telipok, 88450, Kota Kinabalu, Sabah, Malaysia
Tel.: (60) 88493737
Web Site: http://www.wascoenergy.com
Sales Range: $25-49.9 Million
Emp.: 5
Pipe Coating Services
N.A.I.C.S.: 332812

Subsidiary (Domestic):

Wasco Oilfield Services Sdn Bhd (2)
No 59-3 No 59-10 The BlvdMid Valley City, Lingkaran Syed Putra, 59200, Kuala Lumpur, Malaysia
Tel.: (60) 322878996
Brine Filtration Services
N.A.I.C.S.: 221310

Wasco Engineering Group Limited (1)
Oilfields Supply Center Building 5, PO Box 42245, Dubai, United Arab Emirates
Tel.: (971) 48839600
Web Site: http://www.wascoenergy.com
Emp.: 30
Industrial Engineering Services
N.A.I.C.S.: 541330
Shinu Thomas *(VP)*

Wasco Engineering International Ltd. (1)
Oilfield Supply Center Bldg 5 Jebel Ali FreeZone, Dubai, United Arab Emirates
Tel.: (971) 4 883 9600
Web Site: https://www.gsidubai.ae
Oilfield Distr
N.A.I.C.S.: 424720
Shinu Varghese *(VP)*

WAH SUN HANDBAGS INTERNATIONAL HOLDINGS LIMITED
Room 9 6 F Wah Yiu Industrial Centre 30-32 Au Pui Wan Street Fo Tan, Sha Tin, New Territories, China (Hong Kong)
Tel.: (852) 26011032 Ky
Web Site: https://www.wahsun.com.hk
Year Founded: 1989
2683—(HKG)
Rev.: $56,931,045
Assets: $48,753,068
Liabilities: $17,572,050
Net Worth: $31,181,018
Earnings: $765,893
Emp.: 3,477
Fiscal Year-end: 03/31/23
Bag Product Mfr & Distr
N.A.I.C.S.: 339910
Man Hing Ma *(Chm & Exec Dir)*

Subsidiaries:

Dongguan Quickmind Handbag Factory Co., Ltd. (1)
Feng Hua Road, Fu Shan Management Zone Liao Bu, Dongguan, China
Tel.: (86) 76983218668
Emp.: 100
Handbag Mfr
N.A.I.C.S.: 316990

Wah Sun HK Factory (Cambodia) Co., Ltd. (1)
Trach Village, Kahaeng Commune Samrang Tong District, Bavet, Kampong Speu, Cambodia
Tel.: (855) 256500232
Emp.: 5,300
Handbag Mfr
N.A.I.C.S.: 316990

WAH WO HOLDINGS GROUP LIMITED
Flat A & D 4/F Phase 1 36-40 Tai Lin Pai Road, Kwai Shing Industrial Building, Kwai Chung, New Territories, China (Hong Kong)
Tel.: (852) 21522880 Ky
Web Site: https://www.wahwoalum.com
Year Founded: 2002
9938—(HKG)
Rev.: $26,564,625
Assets: $35,903,108
Liabilities: $4,570,620
Net Worth: $31,332,488
Earnings: $363,630
Emp.: 85
Fiscal Year-end: 03/31/23
Holding Company
N.A.I.C.S.: 551112
Ka Keung Lee *(Sr Mgr-Quality Control)*

WAHA CAPITAL PJSC
Etihad Towers Tower 42 & 43 Ras Al Akhdar Area, Abu Dhabi, United Arab Emirates
Tel.: (971) 26677343
Web Site: https://www.wahacapital.com
Year Founded: 1997
WAHA—(ABU)
Rev.: $38,233,869
Assets: $3,686,600,046
Liabilities: $1,870,886,737
Net Worth: $1,815,713,309
Earnings: $223,292,676
Emp.: 66
Fiscal Year-end: 12/31/23
Financial Services
N.A.I.C.S.: 525990
Ahmed Ali Al Dhaheri *(Vice Chm)*

Subsidiaries:

Al Waha Maritime LLC (1)
Aseel Building Buteen Towers, Abu Dhabi, United Arab Emirates
Tel.: (971) 26677343

INTERNATIONAL PUBLIC

Sales Range: $25-49.9 Million
Emp.: 13
Marine Shipping Services
N.A.I.C.S.: 488320
Simon Cook *(Gen Mgr)*

Oasis International Leasing (USA), Inc. (1)
16275 NE 85th St, Redmond, WA 98052
Tel.: (425) 558-9055
Sales Range: $50-74.9 Million
Emp.: 1
Provider of Leasing Services
N.A.I.C.S.: 532490

WAHANA PRONATURAL TBK
Gedung Bumi Mandiri Tower II Lt 9 No 907, Jl Panglima Sudirman 66-68, Surabaya, 60271, Indonesia
Tel.: (62) 315352705
Web Site: https://www.wapo.co.id
WAPO—(INDO)
Rev.: $27,336,738
Assets: $8,567,886
Liabilities: $3,940,780
Net Worth: $4,627,106
Earnings: $14,194
Emp.: 8
Fiscal Year-end: 12/31/23
Dehydrated Food Mfr
N.A.I.C.S.: 311423
Iwan Setiawan *(Sec)*

WAI CAPITAL INVESTMENTS CORP.
800-500 5th Ave SW, Calgary, T2P 3L5, AB, Canada
Tel.: (403) 262-0242 BC
Web Site: http://www.razor-energy.com
Year Founded: 1987
Rev.: $76,655,621
Assets: $144,751,268
Liabilities: $150,987,974
Net Worth: ($6,236,706)
Earnings: ($22,630,443)
Fiscal Year-end: 12/31/19
Metal Exploration Services
N.A.I.C.S.: 213114

Subsidiaries:

Sky Alliance Resources Guinee S.A. (1)
Coleah Limbata Corniche Sud Conakry, BP 1387, Conakry, Papua New Guinea
Tel.: (675) 67 44 44 40
Iron Ore Mining Services
N.A.I.C.S.: 212210

WAI CHI HOLDINGS COMPANY LIMITED
6/F Liven House 63 King Yip Street Kwun Tong, Kowloon, China (Hong Kong)
Tel.: (852) 37602888 Ky
Web Site: https://www.waichiholdings.com
Year Founded: 1984
1305—(HKG)
Rev.: $282,584,880
Assets: $347,155,343
Liabilities: $241,789,215
Net Worth: $105,366,128
Earnings: $7,496,490
Emp.: 2,904
Fiscal Year-end: 12/31/22
Light Emitting Diode Product Mfr & Distr
N.A.I.C.S.: 334413
Chung Po Chen *(Chm, CEO & Exec Dir)*

Subsidiaries:

Huizhou Wai Chi Electronics Company Limited (1)
Hongda International Industry Manufacture Area Louyang Town, Boluo County, Huizhou, China
Tel.: (86) 7526959999

AND PRIVATE COMPANIES

Lighting Product Mfr & Distr
N.A.I.C.S.: 334413
Kwan Wai Yiu *(Asst Gen Mgr)*

Sanxia Wai Chi Opto Technology (Yichang) Limited (1)
No 8 Yanjiaba Yiling Industrial Park Yiling, Yichang, Hubei, China
Tel.: (86) 7177818111
Lighting Product Installation Services
N.A.I.C.S.: 238210

Wai Chi Opto Technology (Shenzhen) Limited (1)
1/F-4/F Block C 1/F-2/F Block D 1/F-3/F Block A, No 4 San Wei Industry Zone San Wei Village Xixiang Street Baoan, Shenzhen, China
Tel.: (86) 75527476888
Lighting Product Mfr & Distr
N.A.I.C.S.: 334413
Jian Hui Yong *(Head-Sls Dept & Deputy Gen Mgr)*

WAI CHUN BIO-TECHNOLOGY LIMITED
13/F Admiralty Centre 2 18 Harcourt Road, Admiralty, Hong Kong, China (Hong Kong)
Tel.: (852) 31029989
Web Site: http://www.0660.hk
0660—(HKG)
Rev.: $128,416,215
Assets: $31,868,880
Liabilities: $31,099,163
Net Worth: $769,718
Earnings: ($177,225)
Emp.: 156
Fiscal Year-end: 06/30/22
Athletic & Golf Shoes Mfr
N.A.I.C.S.: 316210
Ching Kui Lam *(Chm & CEO)*

WAI CHUN GROUP HOLDINGS LIMITED
13/F Admiralty Centre 2 18 Harcourt Road Admiralty, Hong Kong, China (Hong Kong)
Tel.: (852) 3 102 9989   BM
Web Site: http://www.1013.hk
1013—(HKG)
Rev.: $30,171,775
Assets: $17,862,827
Liabilities: $41,608,045
Net Worth: ($23,745,218)
Earnings: ($16,435,534)
Emp.: 17
Fiscal Year-end: 03/31/22
Holding Company; Network & System Integration Services
N.A.I.C.S.: 551112
Ching Kui Lam *(Chm & CEO)*

WAI HUNG GROUP HOLDINGS LTD
Unit 13 24 F Honour Industrial Centre 6 Sun Yip St, Chai Wan, China (Hong Kong)
Tel.: (852) 25605654
3321—(HKG)
Rev.: $63,399,691
Assets: $62,482,507
Liabilities: $24,136,955
Net Worth: $38,345,551
Earnings: $5,726,517
Emp.: 110
Fiscal Year-end: 12/31/20
Holding Company
N.A.I.C.S.: 551112
Hung Li Kam *(CEO)*

Subsidiaries:

Wai Hung Hong Engineering (Macau) Co., Ltd. (1)
Alameda Dr Carlos D Assumpcao No 258, Praca Kin Heng Long 16 Andar F-H, Macau, China (Macau)
Tel.: (853) 28722936
Fit-Out Construction Services
N.A.I.C.S.: 238130

Wai Hung Hong Engineering Company Limited (1)
Unit 13 24/F Honour Industrial Centre 6 Sun Yip Street, Chai Wan, China (Hong Kong)
Tel.: (852) 25605654
Residential & Commercial Property Maintenance Services
N.A.I.C.S.: 531210

WAI KEE HOLDINGS LIMITED
Unit 1103 11/F East Ocean Centre 98 Granville Road, Tsimshatsui, Kowloon, China (Hong Kong)
Tel.: (852) 22723800
Web Site: http://www.waikee.com
Year Founded: 1970
0610—(HKG)
Rev.: $1,610,340,683
Assets: $2,242,991,985
Liabilities: $855,834,953
Net Worth: $1,387,157,033
Earnings: $22,436,558
Emp.: 3,529
Fiscal Year-end: 12/31/22
Holding Company; Toll Roads & Expressways; Civil Engineering; Quarrying; Bio-Technology
N.A.I.C.S.: 551112
William Wei Pao Zen *(Chm)*

Subsidiaries:

Excel Asphalt Limited (1)
Unit 1103 11/F East Ocean Centre 98 Granville Road, Tsimshatsui, Kowloon, China (Hong Kong)
Tel.: (852) 22723800
Construction Services
N.A.I.C.S.: 236220

Excel Concrete Limited (1)
Unit 1103 11/F East Ocean Centre 98 Granville Road, Tsimshatsui, Kowloon, China (Hong Kong)
Tel.: (852) 22093200
Construction Services
N.A.I.C.S.: 236220

WK Securities Limited (1)
Room 1501 15th Floor Tai Tung Building 8 Fleming Road, Wanchai, China (Hong Kong)
Tel.: (852) 22723880
Web Site: https://portal.wksecuritiesltd.com
Corporate Finance & Brokerage Services
N.A.I.C.S.: 523999
Anthony Chan *(Exec Dir)*

Wuhan Nature's Favour Bioengineering Company Limited (1)
5 F Tianhui Bldg Huazhong Agricultural University, 430070, Wuhan, China
Tel.: (86) 2787287609
Web Site: https://naturesfavour.chemmade.com
Sales Range: $350-399.9 Million
Emp.: 1,280
Biotechnology Research & Development Services
N.A.I.C.S.: 541714

WAIDA MFG. CO., LTD.
Tel.: (81) 368113251
Web Site: https://www.waida.co.jp
Year Founded: 1946
6158—(TKS)
Rev.: $49,826,180
Assets: $80,298,280
Liabilities: $13,160,510
Net Worth: $67,137,770
Earnings: $4,805,470
Emp.: 165
Fiscal Year-end: 03/31/24
Machine Tools Mfr
N.A.I.C.S.: 333515
Mitsuo Waida *(Chm & CEO)*

Subsidiaries:

Japan EM Co., Ltd. (1)
300-1 Toyooka-cho, Kita-ku, Hamamatsu, 433-8103, Shizuoka, Japan
Tel.: (81) 53 523 6711

Web Site: http://www.japanem.co.jp
Electrical Equipment Distr
N.A.I.C.S.: 423610
Hisao Daizen *(Pres & CEO)*

WAIDA MFG. CO., LTD. - Gifu Plant (1)
191 Kinzoku-Danchi, Kakamigahara, 504-0957, Gifu, Japan
Tel.: (81) 583823218
Industrial Machinery Mfr
N.A.I.C.S.: 333310

WAJA KONSORTIUM BERHAD
Level 16 B01 A Menara 2 No 3 Jalan Bangsar KL Eco City, 59200, Kuala Lumpur, Malaysia
Tel.: (60) 322023399   MY
Web Site: http://www.connectcounty.com
Year Founded: 2003
WAJA—(KLS)
Rev.: $12,288,136
Assets: $11,312,746
Liabilities: $3,556,940
Net Worth: $7,755,806
Earnings: ($9,459,002)
Fiscal Year-end: 06/30/23
Investment Holding Services
N.A.I.C.S.: 551112
Chuang Juay Ang *(Deputy Chm)*

Subsidiaries:

Connect Security Solution Sdn. Bhd. (1)
Level 16 BO1-A Menara 2 No 3 Jalan Bangsar KL Eco City, 59200, Kuala Lumpur, Malaysia
Tel.: (60) 322023399
Connector & Related Product Mfr
N.A.I.C.S.: 334417

Rapid Conn (S) Pte. Ltd. (1)
4012 Ang Mo Kio Ave 10 03-07 Techplace 1, Singapore, 569628, Singapore
Tel.: (65) 68414517
Electronic Connectors Distr
N.A.I.C.S.: 423690
Corina Yong *(Gen Mgr)*

Rapid Conn (ShenZhen) Co., Ltd. (1)
12 Long Shang Road 6th Lane Luo Tian Social District Songgang Street, Baoan, Shenzhen, 518105, China
Tel.: (86) 755 2972 6660
Electronic Connector Mfr & Distr
N.A.I.C.S.: 334417
Clifford Lim *(Gen Mgr)*

Subsidiary (Domestic):

ShenZhen Rapid Power Co., Ltd. (2)
2 - 5 Floor B Building Tongfu Hanhaida Creative Zone 10th Jiangfu Road, Jiangshi Area Gong Ming Town Guang Ming District, Shenzhen, 518106, China
Tel.: (86) 75529726661
Electronic Cable Mfr & Distr
N.A.I.C.S.: 334419

ShenZhen Rapid Resin Co., Ltd. (2)
12 Long Shang Road 6th Lane SongGang Street, Luo Tian Social District, Shenzhen, 518105, China
Tel.: (86) 75529726660
Web Site: http://www.rapidconn.org
Emp.: 250
Thermoplastic Elastomer Mfr & Distr
N.A.I.C.S.: 325211
Steven Lim *(Dir)*

Rapid Conn Inc. (1)
25172 Arctic Ocean Dr Ste 106, Lake Forest, CA 92630
Tel.: (949) 951-1020
Web Site: http://www.rapidconn.org
Electronic Connector Mfr & Distr
N.A.I.C.S.: 334417

WAJAX CORPORATION
2250 Argentia Road, Mississauga, L5N 6A5, ON, Canada
Tel.: (905) 202-3300   Ca
Web Site: https://www.wajax.com

Year Founded: 2010
WJX—(TSX)
Rev.: $1,112,909,077
Assets: $767,721,769
Liabilities: $512,973,852
Net Worth: $254,747,917
Earnings: $24,761,509
Emp.: 2,461
Fiscal Year-end: 12/31/20
Heavy Equipment, Bearings, Seals & Power Transmission Products Distr
N.A.I.C.S.: 423840
A. Mark Foote *(Pres & CEO)*

Subsidiaries:

Detroit Diesel-Allison Canada East (1)
2997 Rue Watt, Quebec, G1X 3W1, QC, Canada   (100%)
Tel.: (418) 651-5371
Sales Range: $25-49.9 Million
Emp.: 90
Sales & Repair of Diesel Engines
N.A.I.C.S.: 811111
Mark Nadeau *(Gen Mgr-IT)*

Groupe Delom Inc. (1)
13065 Jean-Grou, Montreal, H1A 3N6, QC, Canada
Tel.: (514) 642-8220
Web Site: http://www.groupedelom.ca
Emp.: 400
Aluminum Roll Product Mfr
N.A.I.C.S.: 331491

Modern Machinery Inc (1)
22431 83rd Ave S, Kent, WA 98032-1989
Tel.: (253) 872-3500
Web Site: http://www.modernmachinery.com
Emp.: 40
Distr of Heavy Equipment
N.A.I.C.S.: 423810

NorthPoint Technical Services ULC (1)
4920 43rdStreet Southeast, Calgary, T2B 3N3, AB, Canada
Tel.: (403) 279-2211
Web Site: http://www.northpointts.com
Industrial Machinery Repair Services
N.A.I.C.S.: 811310
Paul Crawford *(CEO)*

Wajax Equipment (1)
11061 269th St, Acheson, T7X 6E1, AB, Canada   (100%)
Tel.: (780) 948-5444
Web Site: http://www.wajaxequipment.com
Sales Range: $50-74.9 Million
Emp.: 900
Mobile Equipment & Power Systems Distr
N.A.I.C.S.: 423810

Wajax Industrial Components (1)
2202 52nd Avenue, Lachine, H8T 2Y3, QC, Canada   (100%)
Tel.: (514) 636-3333
Web Site: http://www.wajaxindustrial.com
Sales Range: $75-99.9 Million
Emp.: 100
Industrial Equipment Distr
N.A.I.C.S.: 423830

Branch (Domestic):

Wajax Industrial Components (2)
19269 96th Avenue, Surrey, V4N 4C4, BC, Canada   (100%)
Tel.: (604) 513-0351
Web Site: http://www.wajax-industrial-components.ca
Sales Range: $25-49.9 Million
Emp.: 7
Industrial Equipment Distr
N.A.I.C.S.: 423830

Wajax Industrial Components (2)
1 Moyal Court, Concord, L4K 4R8, ON, Canada   (100%)
Tel.: (905) 879-2009
Web Site: http://www.wajax-industrial-components.ca
Sales Range: $25-49.9 Million
Emp.: 45
Industrial Equipment Distr
N.A.I.C.S.: 423830

Wajax Industrial Components (2)

WAJAX CORPORATION

Wajax Corporation—(Continued)
100 Wright Ave Unit 7, Dartmouth, B3B 1L2, NS, Canada
Tel.: (902) 468-4455
Web Site: http://www.wajax-industrial-components.ca
Sales Range: $25-49.9 Million
Emp.: 12
Industrial Equipment Distr
N.A.I.C.S.: 423830

Wajax Power Systems (1)
10025 51 Ave NW, Edmonton, T6E 0A8, AB, Canada (100%)
Tel.: (780) 437-8200
Web Site: http://www.wajaxpower.com
Sales Range: $50-74.9 Million
Emp.: 150
Heavy-Duty Diesel & Gaseous Fueled Engines, Transmissions & Power Generation Equipment Distr
N.A.I.C.S.: 423830

WAKACHIKU CONSTRUCTION CO., LTD.
2-23-18 Shimo-Meguro, Meguro-ku, Tokyo, 153-0064, Japan
Tel.: (81) 334920271
Web Site: https://www.wakachiku.co.jp
Year Founded: 1890
1888—(TKS)
Rev.: $627,401,370
Assets: $600,022,750
Liabilities: $286,814,510
Net Worth: $313,208,240
Earnings: $33,658,120
Emp.: 93
Fiscal Year-end: 03/31/24
Construction Engineering Services
N.A.I.C.S.: 541330
Katsuhiko Karasuda (Pres)

WAKAMOTO PHARMACEUTICAL CO., LTD.
2-2-2 Nihonbashi Honcho, Chuo-ku, Tokyo, 103-8330, Japan
Tel.: (81) 332790371
Web Site: https://www.wakamoto-pharm.co.jp
Year Founded: 1929
4512—(TKS)
Sales Range: Less than $1 Million
Emp.: 306
Pharmaceutical Product Mfr & Distr
N.A.I.C.S.: 325412
Noboru Yamazaki (Sr Exec Officer)

WAKEFIELD CANADA INC.
3620 Lakeshore Blvd W, Toronto, M8W 1P2, ON, Canada
Tel.: (416) 201-0844
Web Site: http://www.wakefieldcanada.ca
Sales Range: $50-74.9 Million
Emp.: 220
Motor Oil, Degreaser & Other Products Distr
N.A.I.C.S.: 424720
Dave Fifield (Pres)

Subsidiaries:

SuperClean Brands, LLC (1)
1380 Corporate Ctr Curve, Eagan, MN 55121
Tel.: (651) 365-7590
Web Site: http://www.superclean.com
Cleaning Product Distr
N.A.I.C.S.: 424690
Michael Lofgren (Dir-Sls & Mktg)

Wakefield Canada Inc. - Edmonton Warehouse Facility (1)
16727 - 116 Avenue, Edmonton, T5M 3V1, AB, Canada
Lubricating Oil Mfr
N.A.I.C.S.: 324191

Wakefield Canada Inc. - Laval Warehouse Facility (1)
2150 Avenue Francis-Hughes, Laval, H7S 1N7, QC, Canada
Lubricating Oil Mfr
N.A.I.C.S.: 324191

Wakefield Canada Inc. - Vancouver Warehouse Facility (1)
225 North Road, Coquitlam, V3K 3V7, BC, Canada
Tel.: (866) 240-1099
Lubricating Oil Mfr
N.A.I.C.S.: 324191

WAKENBY LIMITED
Suite 201 Level 2 60 York Street, Sydney, 2000, NSW, Australia
Tel.: (61) 2 8090 3517 AU
Year Founded: 2006
Holding Company; Legal & Other Business Support Services
N.A.I.C.S.: 551112
Aron William Harkham (Exec Dir)

WAKITA & CO., LTD.
1-3-20 Edobori, Nishi-ku, Osaka, 550-0002, Japan
Tel.: (81) 664491901
Web Site: https://www.wakita.co.jp
Year Founded: 1949
8125—(TKS)
Rev.: $628,556,860
Assets: $1,020,562,960
Liabilities: $305,557,730
Net Worth: $715,005,230
Earnings: $22,390,220
Emp.: 612
Fiscal Year-end: 02/29/24
Construction Equipment Leasing Services
N.A.I.C.S.: 532412
Teiji Wakita (Pres)

WAKOL GMBH
Bottenbacher Strasse 30, 66954, Pirmasens, Germany
Tel.: (49) 633180010
Web Site: http://www.wakol.de
Rev.: $14,276,790
Emp.: 150
Industrial Product Distr
N.A.I.C.S.: 423830
Christian Gross (CEO)

Subsidiaries:

Loba-Wakol, LLC (1)
Eagleton Downs Dr 521-C, Pineville, NC 28134
Tel.: (800) 230-6456
Web Site: http://www.loba-wakol.com
Adhesive Distr
N.A.I.C.S.: 424690
Karen Atilano (Office Mgr)

Wakol Adhesa AG (1)
Schutzengasse 28, 9410, Heiden, Switzerland
Tel.: (41) 319210755
Web Site: http://www.wakoladhesa.ch
Adhesive Distr
N.A.I.C.S.: 424690

Wakol Foreco srl (1)
Via Kennedy 75, Marcallo con Casone, 20010, Milan, Italy
Tel.: (39) 029761939
Web Site: http://www.wakolforeco.it
Adhesive Mfr
N.A.I.C.S.: 325520
Barbara Pastore (CEO)

Wakol GmbH (1)
Industriestrasse 5, 6841, Mader, Austria
Tel.: (43) 552364700
Web Site: http://www.wakol.at
Adhesive Distr
N.A.I.C.S.: 424690

WAKOU SHOKUHIN CO., LTD.
3-504-1 Zenibako, Otaru, 047-0261, Hokkaido, Japan
Tel.: (81) 134620505
Web Site: https://www.wakoushokuhin.co.jp
Year Founded: 1964
2813—(TKS)
Rev.: $101,899,760
Assets: $89,671,260
Liabilities: $39,395,600
Net Worth: $50,275,660
Earnings: $7,204,900
Fiscal Year-end: 03/31/24
Food Products Mfr
N.A.I.C.S.: 311999
Akihiro Kazuyama (Chm & Pres)

Subsidiaries:

Wakou USA Inc. (1)
13930 Borate St, Santa Fe Springs, CA 90670
Tel.: (562) 207-0000
Web Site: http://www.wakouusa.com
Spice Mfr
N.A.I.C.S.: 311941

WAKUNAGA PHARMACEUTICAL CO., LTD.
4-5-36 Miyahara, Yodogawa-ku, Osaka, 532-0003, Japan
Tel.: (81) 663503555
Web Site: http://www.wakunaga.co.jp
Year Founded: 1955
Rev.: $97,391,400
Emp.: 450
Pharmaceuticals Mfr
N.A.I.C.S.: 325412
Kanji Wakunaga (Pres)

Subsidiaries:

Wakunaga Agricultural Development Co., Ltd. (1)
1624 Shimokotachi, Koda-cho, Akitakata, 739-1195, Hiroshima, Japan
Tel.: (81) 826452441
Pharmaceuticals Product Mfr
N.A.I.C.S.: 325412

Wakunaga of America Co., Ltd. (1)
23501 Madero, Mission Viejo, CA 92691
Tel.: (949) 855-2776
Web Site: http://www.kyolic.com
Pharmaceutical Products, Nutritional & Herbal Supplements Mfr
N.A.I.C.S.: 325412
Teri Evans (Coord-Acctg)

WALAA COOPERATIVE INSURANCE CO
Adel Khashoggi Building Custodian of the Two Holy Mosques Road, PO Box 31616, Al Khobar, 31952, Saudi Arabia
Tel.: (966) 920001742
Web Site: https://www.walaa.com
8060—(SAU)
Rev.: $323,671,576
Assets: $541,335,527
Liabilities: $357,345,677
Net Worth: $183,989,851
Earnings: $11,302,995
Fiscal Year-end: 12/31/19
Insurance Advisory Services
N.A.I.C.S.: 524298
Suliman A. Al Kadi (Chm)

WALAA COOPERATIVE INSURANCE COMPANY
Adel khashoggi Building Custodian of Two Holy Mosques Road, PO Box 31616, Al Khobar, 34621, Saudi Arabia
Tel.: (966) 820001742
Web Site: https://www.walaa.com
Insurance Services
N.A.I.C.S.: 524298
Johnson Varughese (CEO)

Subsidiaries:

MetLife - AIG - ANB Cooperative Insurance Company (1)
Ibdaa Tower King Fahd Rd, PO Box 56437,

INTERNATIONAL PUBLIC

Olaya District, Riyadh, 11554, Saudi Arabia
Tel.: (966) 11 5109300
Web Site: http://www.metlifeaiganb.com
Sales Range: $25-49.9 Million
Emp.: 68
Insurance Management Services
N.A.I.C.S.: 524298
Saif Abbasi (CFO)

WALCHAND PEOPLEFIRST LIMITED
1st Floor Construction House
5-walchand Hirachand Marg, Ballard Estate, Mumbai, 400001, India
Tel.: (91) 2267818181
Web Site: https://www.walchandpeoplefirst.com
Year Founded: 1920
501370—(BOM)
Rev.: $2,653,301
Assets: $3,343,254
Liabilities: $681,749
Net Worth: $2,661,504
Earnings: $251,938
Emp.: 47
Fiscal Year-end: 03/31/22
Professional Training & Consulting Services
N.A.I.C.S.: 611430
Shruthi Patni (CFO & Head-Ops)

WALCHANDNAGAR INDUSTRIES LTD.
3 Walchand Terraces Tardeo Road, Mumbai, 400 034, Maharashtra, India
Tel.: (91) 2223612195
Web Site: https://www.walchand.com
507410—(BOM)
Rev.: $41,286,494
Assets: $99,290,210
Liabilities: $68,039,086
Net Worth: $31,251,124
Earnings: $2,347,581
Emp.: 1,365
Fiscal Year-end: 03/31/23
Iron Producer
N.A.I.C.S.: 332911
Chakor Lalchand Doshi (Chm)

Subsidiaries:

Walchandnagar Industries Ltd - Foundry (1)
Satara Rd, 415010, Satara, Maharashtra, India
Tel.: (91) 2163227201
Sales Range: $200-249.9 Million
Emp.: 800
Industrial Machinery Mfr & Supplier
N.A.I.C.S.: 333248

Walchandnagar Industries Ltd - Precision Instrument Division (1)
Instrumentation Division Attikolla, Hubli-Dharwad, 580 003, Karnataka, India
Tel.: (91) 8362242382
Web Site: http://www.walchand.com
Sales Range: $50-74.9 Million
Emp.: 220
Precision Instrument Mfr
N.A.I.C.S.: 332721

Walchandnagar Industries Ltd - Tiwac Division (1)
Attikolla, Hubli-Dharwad, 580003, Karanataka, India
Tel.: (91) 8362448565
Web Site: http://www.wiltiwac.com
Sales Range: $100-124.9 Million
Emp.: 250
Pressure & Temperature Gauge Mfr
N.A.I.C.S.: 334513

Walchandnagar Industries Ltd - Walchandnagar Industries Ltd. Oil and Gas Division (1)
215 Raikar Chambers, Govandi E, Mumbai, 400 088, Maharashtra, India
Tel.: (91) 2225502807
Web Site: http://www.walchand.com
Sales Range: $750-799.9 Million
Emp.: 1,500
Oil & Gas Field Exploration Services

WALCOM GROUP LIMITED
N.A.I.C.S.: 213112

WALCOM GROUP LIMITED
Part D Mingtai Bldg No 351 Guo Shou Jing Road ZJ Hi-tech Park, Shanghai, 201203, China
Tel.: (86) 215027 3720
Web Site: http://www.walcomgroup.com
Rev.: $4,429,698
Assets: $2,274,649
Liabilities: $1,514,003
Net Worth: $760,646
Earnings: ($1,211,120)
Fiscal Year-end: 12/31/18
Animal Feed Additive Products Mfr & Distr
N.A.I.C.S.: 311119
Francis Chi *(Founder, CEO & CFO-Interim)*

Subsidiaries:

Shanghai Walcom Bio-Chem Co., Ltd. (1)
Block 3 999 Ningqiaolu Jinqiao, Pudong, 201206, Shanghai, China
Tel.: (86) 21 50273720
Biological Product Mfr
N.A.I.C.S.: 325414

Walcom Bio-Chemicals Industrial Limited (1)
Ste 121 Tower 2 Silvercord 30 Canton Rd, Kowloon, China (Hong Kong)
Tel.: (852) 24940133
Web Site: http://www.walcom-biochem.com
Emp.: 2
Biological Product Mfr
N.A.I.C.S.: 325414

WALDEN GROUP
97 rue Mirabeau Ivry sur Seine, Paris, 94200, France
Tel.: (33) 443866309
Web Site: http://www.walden-group.com
Year Founded: 1951
Healthcare Transport Services
N.A.I.C.S.: 488510
Stephane Baudry *(CEO)*

Subsidiaries:

Movianto Deutschland GmbH (1)
In Der Vogelsbach 1, 66540, Neunkirchen, Germany
Tel.: (49) 682150160
Emp.: 500
Logistics Consulting Servies
N.A.I.C.S.: 541614
Thomas Creuzberger *(Mng Dir)*

WALKABOUT RESOURCES LTD
45 Ventnor Avenue, West Perth, 6005, WA, Australia
Tel.: (61) 894298874   AU
Web Site: https://www.wkt.com.au
Year Founded: 2006
WKT—(ASX)
Rev.: $16
Assets: $51,116,260
Liabilities: $24,462,710
Net Worth: $26,653,550
Earnings: ($5,695,476)
Fiscal Year-end: 06/30/24
Copper, Platinum & Coal Exploration
N.A.I.C.S.: 212230
Andrew Cunningham *(CEO)*

Subsidiaries:

Lindi Jumbo Ltd. (1)
Cape town Fish Market 3rd Floor Plot No 180 Block B, PO Box 33773, Msasani Village, Dar es Salaam, Tanzania
Tel.: (255) 22 260 2770
Web Site: https://lindijumbo.co.tz
Mineral Mining Services
N.A.I.C.S.: 212390

Linia Prava Uranium OJSC (1)
36 1 Sukhomlinov St, Bishkek, Chuy Province, Kyrgyzstan
Tel.: (996) 312 54 17 11
Uranium Mining Services
N.A.I.C.S.: 212290

WALKER CRIPS GROUP PLC
Old Change House 128 Queen Victoria Street, London, EC4V 4BJ, United Kingdom
Tel.: (44) 2031008000
Web Site: https://www.wcgplc.co.uk
WCW—(LSE)
Rev.: $39,255,782
Assets: $78,332,744
Liabilities: $52,048,805
Net Worth: $26,283,939
Earnings: $519,072
Emp.: 206
Fiscal Year-end: 03/31/23
Investment Management Service
N.A.I.C.S.: 523940
Rodney A. Fitzgerald *(Sec & Dir-Fin-Grp)*

Subsidiaries:

London York Fund Managers Limited (1)
Foss Islands House Foss Islands Rd, York, YO31 7UJ, North Yorkshire, United Kingdom
Tel.: (44) 1904544300
Web Site: http://www.londonyork.co.uk
Sales Range: $50-74.9 Million
Emp.: 35
Pension Fund Management Services
N.A.I.C.S.: 525110

Walker Crips Stockbrokers Limited (1)
103-105 Bunhill Row Finsbury Tower, London, EC1Y 8LZ, United Kingdom
Tel.: (44) 2031008000
Web Site: http://www.wcgplc.co.uk
Sales Range: $100-124.9 Million
Emp.: 50
Stock Brokerage Services
N.A.I.C.S.: 523150
Glenn Cooper *(Dir-Ops)*

Walker Crips Wealth Management Limited (1)
Finsbury Tower 103-105 Bunhill Row, London, EC1Y 8LZ, United Kingdom
Tel.: (44) 2031008600
Web Site: http://www.wcgplc.co.uk
Sales Range: $100-124.9 Million
Emp.: 100
Stockbroking & Investment Management Solutions
N.A.I.C.S.: 523150

WALKER INDUSTRIES HOLDINGS LTD.
2800 Thorold Townline Road, Niagara Falls, L2E 6S4, ON, Canada
Tel.: (905) 227-4142
Web Site: https://www.walkerind.com
Year Founded: 1987
Sales Range: $100-124.9 Million
Construction, Emulsions, Environmental Project Management, Waste Management, Renewable Energy Projects & Green Building Services
N.A.I.C.S.: 236220
Mike DePrez *(Gen Mgr-Sls)*

Subsidiaries:

All Treat Farms Limited (1)
7963 Wellington Rd 109, Arthur, N0G 1A0, ON, Canada
Tel.: (519) 848-3145
Web Site: http://www.alltreat.com
Farm Products Mfr
N.A.I.C.S.: 424910
Mark Kowalchuk *(Bus Mgr)*

Walker Aggregates Inc. (1)
2800 Thorold Townline Road, PO Box 100, Thorold, L2V 3Y8, ON, Canada
Tel.: (905) 680-3755
Web Site: https://walkeraggregates.com
Construction Materials Distr
N.A.I.C.S.: 423320
Donna Anger *(Office Mgr)*

Walker Emulsions (USA) Inc. (1)
700 Prosperity Dr, Orangeburg, SC 29115
Tel.: (803) 585-0149
Paint Distr
N.A.I.C.S.: 424950

Walker Emulsions Inc. (1)
4401 SE Johnson Creek Blvd, Portland, OR 97222-9218
Tel.: (503) 659-1708
Web Site: http://www.walkerind.com
Specialty Chemicals Mfr
N.A.I.C.S.: 325199

Walker Emulsions Limited (1)
4365 Corporate Drive, Burlington, L7L 5P7, ON, Canada
Tel.: (905) 336-1216
Web Site: http://www.walkerind.com
Chemical Products Mfr
N.A.I.C.S.: 325998

Walker Environmental Group Inc. (1)
160 Carnegie Street, Ingersoll, N5C 4A8, ON, Canada
Web Site: http://www.walkerea.com
Environmental Management Services
N.A.I.C.S.: 541620

Division (Domestic):

Walker Environmental - Grease Trap, UCO & Organic Recycling (2)
3700 Steeles Avenue West Unit 601, Woodbridge, L4L 8K8, ON, Canada
Tel.: (905) 264-7700
Web Site: http://www.walkerind.com
Non-Hazardous & Organic Wastes Collection, Transportation, Disposal & Recycling
N.A.I.C.S.: 562219

WALKER RIVER RESOURCES CORP.
Suite 820 1130 West Pender St, Vancouver, V6E 4A4, BC, Canada
Tel.: (819) 874-0030
Web Site: https://www.wrrgold.com
1WV0—(DEU)
Assets: $6,957,981
Liabilities: $378,523
Net Worth: $6,579,457
Earnings: ($1,372,239)
Fiscal Year-end: 11/30/22
Mining & Gold Exploration Services
N.A.I.C.S.: 212220
Christopher J. Hobbs *(CFO)*

WALKERS SHORTBREAD LTD.
Aberlour House, Aberlour, AB38 9LD, Banffshire, United Kingdom
Tel.: (44) 1340871555
Web Site: http://www.walkersshortbread.com
Year Founded: 1898
Sales Range: $125-149.9 Million
Emp.: 1,500
Packaged Desserts Mfr
N.A.I.C.S.: 311821
Joseph Walker *(Founder)*

Subsidiaries:

Walkers Shortbread, Inc. (1)
170 Commerce Dr, Hauppauge, NY 11788-3944
Tel.: (631) 273-0011
Web Site: http://www.uswalkersshortbread.com
Sales Range: $25-49.9 Million
Emp.: 24
Grocery & Related Products Whslr
N.A.I.C.S.: 424490
Steve Tawson *(Pres & CEO)*

WALL FINANCIAL CORPORATION
1010 Burrard Street, Vancouver, V6Z 2R9, BC, Canada
Tel.: (604) 893-7131   BC
Web Site: https://www.wallfinancialcorp.com
Year Founded: 1969
WFC—(TSX)
Rev.: $188,567,635
Assets: $683,762,337
Liabilities: $490,175,841
Net Worth: $193,586,495
Earnings: $17,789,704
Emp.: 332
Fiscal Year-end: 01/31/22
Residential Real Estate Rental Property & Hotel Owner
N.A.I.C.S.: 531390
Peter Wall *(Founder)*

Subsidiaries:

W.F.C. Properties Inc. (1)
696 Torbay Road, Saint John's, A1A 5J1, NL, Canada
Tel.: (709) 260-5577
Web Site: https://wfcpropertyservices.ca
Real Estate Property Services
N.A.I.C.S.: 531190

WALL STREET SECURITIES JOINT STOCK COMPANY
9th Floor ICON4 Building 243A De La Thanh, Dong Da District, Hanoi, Vietnam
Tel.: (84) 439367083
Web Site: https://www.wss.com.vn
Year Founded: 2007
WSS—(HNX)
Rev.: $1,751,412
Assets: $21,366,279
Liabilities: $153,058
Net Worth: $21,213,221
Earnings: $67,856
Fiscal Year-end: 12/31/23
Securities Brokerage Services
N.A.I.C.S.: 523150
Nguyen Dinh Tu *(Chm)*

WALLACE & CAREY INC.
5445 8 Street NE, Calgary, T2K 5R9, AB, Canada
Tel.: (403) 275-7360
Web Site: http://www.wacl.com
Year Founded: 1921
Rev.: $1,924,080
Emp.: 500
Logistic Services
N.A.I.C.S.: 541614
Frank Carey *(Chm & CEO)*

WALLACE BISHOP PTY LTD
55 Doggett St, Newstead, 4006, QLD, Australia
Tel.: (61) 732536400
Web Site: http://www.wallacebishop.com.au
Year Founded: 1917
Sales Range: $25-49.9 Million
Emp.: 350
Jewelry Designer, Mfr & Retailer
N.A.I.C.S.: 339910
J.E. Bishop *(Mng Dir)*

WALLBOX N.V.
Carrer del Foc 68, 8038, Barcelona, Spain
Tel.: (34) 930181668   NI
Web Site: https://www.wallbox.com
Year Founded: 2015
WBX—(NYSE)
Rev.: $177,093,784
Assets: $518,297,628
Liabilities: $310,540,832
Net Worth: $207,756,796
Earnings: ($77,133,472)
Emp.: 1,267
Fiscal Year-end: 12/31/22
Electric Vehicle Mfr & Distr
N.A.I.C.S.: 336320
Eduard Castaneda *(Chief Innovation Officer)*

WALLBRIDGE MINING COMPANY LIMITED

Wallbridge Mining Company Limited—(Continued)

WALLBRIDGE MINING COMPANY LIMITED
129 Fielding Road, Lively, P3Y 1L7, ON, Canada
Tel.: (705) 682-9297 ON
Web Site: https://www.wallbridgemining.com
WM—(TSX)
Rev.: $330,967
Assets: $273,868,896
Liabilities: $23,449,695
Net Worth: $250,419,202
Earnings: ($6,174,940)
Emp.: 74
Fiscal Year-end: 12/31/21
Nickel & Copper Mining & Exploration Services
N.A.I.C.S.: 212230
Alar Soever (Chm)

WALLENIUS WILHELMSEN ASA
Strandveien 20, PO Box 33, N-1324, Lysaker, Norway
Tel.: (47) 52465000 NO
Web Site: https://www.walleniuswilhelmsen.com
0N0B—(LSE)
Rev.: $5,045,000,000
Assets: $8,394,000,000
Liabilities: $4,886,000,000
Net Worth: $3,508,000,000
Earnings: $794,000,000
Emp.: 7,433
Fiscal Year-end: 12/31/22
Holding Company; Maritime Shipping & Logistics Services
N.A.I.C.S.: 551112
Lars Hakan Larsson (Chm)

Subsidiaries:

Armacup Maritime Services Ltd. (1)
Level 5 152 Quay Street, PO Box 106-001, Auckland, 1143, New Zealand
Tel.: (64) 93033314
Web Site: https://www.armacup.co.nz
Marine Cargo Handling Services
N.A.I.C.S.: 488320

Keen Transport, Inc. (1)
1951 Harrisburg Pike, Carlisle, PA 17015
Tel.: (717) 243-6622
Web Site: http://www.keentransport.com
Trucking Service
N.A.I.C.S.: 484230

Mid-Atlantic Terminal LLC (1)
2700 Broening Hwy Bldg 602A, Baltimore, MD 21222
Tel.: (443) 216-1660
Terminal Services
N.A.I.C.S.: 488310

Wallenius Wilhelmsen Logistics Americas LLC (1)
500 E Water St, Wilmington, CA 90744
Tel.: (310) 835-6000
Web Site: http://www.2wglobal.com
Rev.: $95,225,378
Emp.: 300
General Warehousing, Supply Chain Management, Inland Distribution & Storage Services
N.A.I.C.S.: 493110
Grace Valgellini (Suprv-Customer Svc)

Wallenius Wilhelmsen Logistics Americas LLC (1)
188 Broadway, Woodcliff Lake, NJ 07677
Tel.: (201) 307-1300
Web Site: http://www.2wglobal.com
Sales Range: $50-74.9 Million
Emp.: 150
Deep Sea Foreign Transportation Of Freight
N.A.I.C.S.: 483111
Gary Jones (VP-Atlantic)

Wallenius Wilhelmsen Logistics Zeebrugge NV (1)
Quay 530 Alfred Ronsestraat 101, 8380, Zeebrugge, Belgium
Tel.: (32) 50557940
Terminal Services
N.A.I.C.S.: 488310

WALLENSTAM AB
Tel.: (46) 31200000
Web Site: http://www.wallenstam.se
Year Founded: 1944
WALL.B—(OMX)
Rev.: $271,010,786
Assets: $6,635,396,305
Liabilities: $3,607,620,130
Net Worth: $3,027,776,175
Earnings: ($44,672,108)
Emp.: 264
Fiscal Year-end: 12/31/23
Real Estate Development Services
N.A.I.C.S.: 531390
Hans Wallenstam (CEO)

WALLENSTEIN FEED & SUPPLY LTD.
7307 Line 86 Highway, PO Box 22, Wallenstein, N0B 2S0, ON, Canada
Tel.: (519) 669-5143
Web Site: http://www.wfs.ca
Rev.: $14,606,752
Emp.: 120
Feeds Mfr
N.A.I.C.S.: 112112
Rick Martin (Gen Mgr)

WALLEO, INC.
5th St Dalong Bldg Ste 14 International Furniture Center, Inner Mongolia, Manzhouli, 021400, China
Tel.: (86) 852 8191 1379 NV
Year Founded: 2016
Emp.: 1
Furniture Fitting & Accessory Distr
N.A.I.C.S.: 423220
Xianfeng Wang (Pres, Treas & Sec)

WALLFORT FINANCIAL SERVICES LTD.
205A Hari Chambers 58/64 S B Singh Road, Fort, Mumbai, 400 001, India
Tel.: (91) 2266184016
Web Site: https://www.wallfort.com
Year Founded: 1994
532053—(BOM)
Rev.: $2,402,106
Assets: $15,218,507
Liabilities: $882,928
Net Worth: $14,335,580
Earnings: $604,887
Emp.: 57
Fiscal Year-end: 03/31/23
Securities Brokerage & Financial Advisory Services
N.A.I.C.S.: 523150
Deepak Moolchand Lahoti (CFO)

WALLIS ZRT.
Honved utca 20, Budapest, 1055, Hungary
Tel.: (36) 18999800 HU
Web Site: http://www.wallis.hu
Year Founded: 1994
Emp.: 35
Investment, Real Estate & Portfolio Management Services
N.A.I.C.S.: 523999
Zsolt Mullner (Gen Mgr)

WALLISER KANTONALBANK
Place des Cedres 8, 1951, Sion, Switzerland
Tel.: (41) 848765765
Web Site: https://www.bcvs.ch
WKBN—(SWX)
Sales Range: Less than $1 Million
Commercial Banking Services
N.A.I.C.S.: 522110
Oliver Schnyder (CEO)

WALLIX GROUP SA
250 Bis rue du Faubourg Saint Honore, FR-75008, Paris, France
Tel.: (33) 153421281
Web Site: https://www.wallix.com
ALLIX—(EUR)
Rev.: $27,173,538
Assets: $55,119,793
Liabilities: $36,229,225
Net Worth: $18,890,568
Earnings: ($6,477,444)
Emp.: 191
Fiscal Year-end: 12/31/22
IT Security Software Publisher
N.A.I.C.S.: 513210
Jean-Noel de Galzain (Founder & CEO)

WALLS & FUTURES REIT PLC
Octagon Point 5 Cheapside, London, EC2V 6AA, United Kingdom
Tel.: (44) 3337007171
Web Site: https://www.reit.wallsandfutures.com
Year Founded: 2008
Investment Management Service
N.A.I.C.S.: 525990
Joe Mctaggart (CEO)

WALLWIN ELECTRIC SERVICES LTD.
50 Innisfil Street, Barrie, L4N 4K5, ON, Canada
Tel.: (705) 726-1859
Web Site: http://www.wallwinelectric.com
Year Founded: 1951
Rev.: $12,465,558
Emp.: 105
Industrial & Commercial Electrical Contracting Services
N.A.I.C.S.: 238210
Craig Wallwin (Pres & CEO)

WALNUT CAPITAL LIMITED
Unit 3107 31/F West Tower Shun Tak Centre, 168-200 Connaught Road, Central, China (Hong Kong)
Tel.: (852) 31522700 Ky
Year Founded: 1998
905—(HKG)
Sales Range: Less than $1 Million
Emp.: 12
Investment Management Service
N.A.I.C.S.: 523940
Kin Keung Mung (Chm)

WALPAR NUTRITIONS LIMITED
2nd Floor L5 377 Plot No 5 Omkar Estate Opp Sabarmati Gas Station, Khatraj Road Khatraj Kalol, Gandhinagar, 382721, Gujarat, India
Tel.: (91) 2764662626
Web Site: https://www.walparnutritions.com
Year Founded: 2009
WALPAR—(NSE)
Rev.: $828,865
Assets: $2,479,888
Liabilities: $1,827,816
Net Worth: $652,072
Earnings: $20,501
Fiscal Year-end: 03/31/21
Pharmaceutical Product Mfr & Distr
N.A.I.C.S.: 325412

WALSER PRIVATBANK AG
Walserstrasse 61, 6991, Riezlern, Austria
Tel.: (43) 551720201 AT
Web Site: http://www.walserprivatbank.com
Year Founded: 1894
Sales Range: $100-124.9 Million
Emp.: 166

INTERNATIONAL PUBLIC

Investment Banking, Financial Advisory & Asset Management Services
N.A.I.C.S.: 523150
Erhard Tschmelitsch (Member-Mgmt Bd)

Subsidiaries:

Raiffeisen Bank (Liechtenstein) AG (1)
Austrasse 51, Vaduz, 9490, Liechtenstein
Tel.: (423) 2370707
Web Site: http://www.raiffeisen.li
Sales Range: $50-74.9 Million
Emp.: 40
Investment Advisory & Asset Management Services
N.A.I.C.S.: 523150

WALSH PUBLIC RELATIONS
Huband House, 16 Upper Mount Street, Dublin, 2, Ireland
Tel.: (353) 53 1 661 3515
Web Site: http://www.walshpr.ie
Year Founded: 1984
Sales Range: $10-24.9 Million
Emp.: 10
Advetising Agency
N.A.I.C.S.: 541810
Jim Walsh (Mng Dir)

WALSIN LIHWA CORPORATION
25F No1 Songzhi Rd, Taipei, 11047, Taiwan
Tel.: (886) 287262211
Web Site: https://www.walsin.com
WLSR1—(LUX)
Rev.: $6,208,169,621
Assets: $8,710,880,700
Liabilities: $3,660,051,466
Net Worth: $5,050,829,235
Earnings: $194,291,827
Emp.: 10,476
Fiscal Year-end: 12/31/23
Steel Products Mfr
N.A.I.C.S.: 331210
Patricia Chiao (Vice Chm)

Subsidiaries:

Borrego Solar System Inc. Ltd. (1)
5005 Texas St Ste 400, San Diego, CA 92108
Web Site: http://www.borregosolar.com
Solar Product Installation Services
N.A.I.C.S.: 238220
Mike Hall (CEO-Northwest)

Borrego Solar Systems, Inc. (1)
1810 Gillespie Way Ste 108, El Cajon, CA 92020-0919
Tel.: (888) 898-6273
Web Site: http://www.borregosolar.com
Sales Range: $50-74.9 Million
Solar Power System Installation Services
N.A.I.C.S.: 238990
Michael Hall (CEO)

Changshu Walsin Specialty Steel Co., Ltd. (1)
No 2 Haiyang Road, Haiyu Town, Changshu, 215519, Jiangsu, China
Tel.: (86) 51252102501
Stainless Steel Products Mfr
N.A.I.C.S.: 331110

Cogne Acciai Speciali S.p.A. (1)
Via Paravera 16, 11100, Aosta, Italy (70%)
Tel.: (39) 01653021
Web Site: https://www.cogne.com
Stainless Steel Mfr
N.A.I.C.S.: 331210

Dongguan Walsin Wire & Cable Ltd. (1)
No 680 Meijing West Road Xiniupo Management Zone, Dalang Town, Dongguan, 523799, Guangdong, China
Tel.: (86) 76983195252
Copper Wires Mfr
N.A.I.C.S.: 331420

Green Lake Exchange, LLC. (1)

AND PRIVATE COMPANIES

2500 Venture Oaks Way, Sacramento, CA 95833
Tel.: (415) 335-8866
Steel Cable Distr
N.A.I.C.S.: 423510

Jiangyin Walsin Specialty Alloy Materials Co., Ltd. (1)
No 677 Binjiang West Road, Jiangyin, 214443, Jiangsu, China
Tel.: (86) 51086402144
Stainless Steel Products Mfr
N.A.I.C.S.: 331110

Jiangyin Walsin Steel Cable Co., Ltd. (1)
No 679 Binjiang West Road, Jiangyin, 214443, Jiangsu, China
Tel.: (86) 5108 640 2144
Steel Wire & Cable Mfr
N.A.I.C.S.: 331222
Witty Liao *(Chm)*

Joint Success Enterprises Limited (1)
Rm 410 Block G 4/F Kwai Shing Industrial Building 42-46, Tai Lin Pai Road, Hong Kong, China (Hong Kong)
Tel.: (852) 24347372
Steel Cable Distr
N.A.I.C.S.: 423510

Min Maw Precision Industry Corp. (1)
No 12 Char-Juan Rd Kwei-San Hsiang, Taoyuan, Taiwan
Tel.: (886) 33296661
Steel Cable Mfr
N.A.I.C.S.: 331210

Nanjing Walsin Metal Co., Ltd. (1)
No 59 HengJing Road Nanjing Economical & Technical Development Zone, Jiangsu, 210046, China
Tel.: (86) 2585805588
Copper Wires Mfr
N.A.I.C.S.: 331420

P.T Walsin Lippo Industries (1)
Jl MH Thamrin Blok A1-1, Delta Silicon Industrial Park Lippo, Cikarang, 17550, Bekasi, Indonesia
Tel.: (62) 21 897 2391
Web Site: https://www.walsinlippo.co.id
Steel Wire & Cable Mfr
N.A.I.C.S.: 331222

Shanghai Baihe Walsin Lihwa Specialty Steel Products Co., Ltd. (1)
No 2402 Wusongjiang Bridge, Baihe Town Qingou District, Shanghai, 201709, China
Tel.: (86) 2159746686
Stainless Steel Products Mfr
N.A.I.C.S.: 331110

Shanghai Walsin Lihwa Power Wire & Cable Co., Ltd. (1)
No 1128 Liu Xiang Road, Na XiangJia Din District, Shanghai, 201802, China
Tel.: (86) 2169177599
Cable Mfr
N.A.I.C.S.: 335921

Walsin (Nanjing) Development Co., LTD. (1)
15F No 179 Yanshan Road, Jianye, Nanjing, 210019, Jiangsu, China
Tel.: (86) 2587767700
Real Estate Management Services
N.A.I.C.S.: 531210

Walsin China Investment Co., Ltd. (1)
28F Shanghai Mart Tower 2299 Yanan West Road, Shanghai, 200336, China
Tel.: (86) 2162360868
Holding Company
N.A.I.C.S.: 551112

Walsin Info-Electric Corp. (1)
No 256 Hsinshu Rd, Hsin Chuang Dist, New Taipei City, Taiwan
Tel.: (886) 222038020
Eletric Power Generation Services
N.A.I.C.S.: 221111

Walsin Lihwa Corporation - Hsinchuang Plant (1)
No 397 Xinshu Rd, Xinzhuang Dist, New Taipei City, 24262, Taiwan

Tel.: (886) 222029121
Cable Mfr
N.A.I.C.S.: 335921

Walsin Lihwa Corporation - Yangmei Plant (1)
No 566 Gaoshi Road, Yangmei Dist, Taoyuan, 32668, Taiwan
Tel.: (886) 34786171
Copper Wires Mfr
N.A.I.C.S.: 331420

Walsin Lihwa Corporation - Yenshui Plant (1)
No 3-10 Shijou Liau Chinshuei Li, Yenshui Dist, T'ainan, 73743, Taiwan
Tel.: (886) 66520911
Steel Products Mfr
N.A.I.C.S.: 331110

Walsin Precision Technology Sdn. Bhd. (1)
2115-1 Kawasan Perindustrian Air Keroh Fasa IV, Air Keroh, 75450, Melaka, Malaysia
Tel.: (60) 62331818
Stainless Steel Foil Mfr
N.A.I.C.S.: 332999

XiAn Walsin Metal Product Co., Ltd. - Baoji Plant (1)
No 90 Gaoxin Avenue, Weibin District, Baoji, 721006, Shaanxi, China
Tel.: (86) 9178662755
Stainless Steel Products Mfr
N.A.I.C.S.: 331110

XiAn Walsin United Technology Co., Ltd. (1)
No 15 Shanglinyuan 1st New Industrial Park Xi'an, Hi-tech Industries Development Zone, Xi'an, 710119, China
Tel.: (86) 2987607808
Steel Cable Mfr
N.A.I.C.S.: 331210

Yantai Walsin Stainless Steel Co., Ltd. (1)
No 2 Wuzhishan Road ETDZ, Yantai, 264006, Shantung, China
Tel.: (86) 5352166688
Stainless Steel Products Mfr
N.A.I.C.S.: 331110

WALSIN TECHNOLOGY CORPORATION
566-1 Ko-Shi Road, Yangmei, Taoyuan, 32668, Taiwan
Tel.: (886) 34758711
Web Site:
https://www.passivecomponent.com
Year Founded: 1992
2492—(TAI)
Rev.: $1,072,555,341
Assets: $3,088,499,442
Liabilities: $1,237,040,144
Net Worth: $1,851,459,298
Earnings: $86,919,844
Emp.: 8,774
Fiscal Year-end: 12/31/23
Ceramic Capacitor Mfr
N.A.I.C.S.: 334416
Richard Chang *(VP-MLCC SBU)*

Subsidiaries:

Dongguan Walsin Technology Electronics Co., Ltd (1)
Tel.: (86) 76983115168
Web Site:
http://www.passivecomponent.com
Electronic Components Mfr, Sales & Distr
N.A.I.C.S.: 334416

Fine Bright Technology Limited (1)
Room 2303 23 F The Centre Mark 287-299 Queens Road, Central, China (Hong Kong)
Tel.: (852) 28972177
Investment Management Service
N.A.I.C.S.: 523999

Inpaq Technology (Suzhou) Co., Ltd. (1)
No 5 Chunqiu Road Panyang Industrial Park, Huangdai Town Xiangcheng Zone, Suzhou, 215143, Jiangsu, China

Tel.: (86) 51265719988
Power Electronic Component Mfr & Distr
N.A.I.C.S.: 334419

Kamaya Electric (HK) Limited (1)
No 638 Mei Jing West Road, Xiniupo Administrative Zone Dalang Town, Dongguan, 523799, Guangdong, China
Tel.: (86) 76981069331
Electronic Component Mfr & Distr
N.A.I.C.S.: 334419

Kamaya Electric Co., Ltd. (1)
PSA Building 6-1-6 Chuo, Yamato, 242-0021, Kanagawa, Japan
Tel.: (81) 462048806
Electronic Components Mfr
N.A.I.C.S.: 334419
Ming-chan Zeng *(Chm & CEO)*

Subsidiary (Domestic):

Soshin Electric Co., Ltd. (2)
Hamamatsucho Building 14F 1-1-1 Shibaura, Minato-ku, Tokyo, 105-0023, Japan
Tel.: (81) 357304500
Web Site: https://www.soshin.co.jp
Rev.: $116,663,360
Assets: $152,663,280
Liabilities: $37,326,080
Net Worth: $115,337,200
Earnings: $11,228,800
Emp.: 767
Fiscal Year-end: 03/31/2022
Complex Circuits Components Mfr
N.A.I.C.S.: 334412
Takashi Kamioka *(Pres)*

Plant (Domestic):

Soshin Electric Co., Ltd. - Asama Plant (3)
No 800-38 Nagatoro, Saku, Nagano, Japan
Tel.: (81) 267674131
Electronic Components Mfr
N.A.I.C.S.: 334416

Subsidiary (Non-US):

Soshin Electronics (M) Sdn. Bhd. (3)
Lot 14 Batu Berendam FTZ PhaseIII Batu Berendam, 75350, Malacca, Malaysia
Tel.: (60) 62848501
Electronic Components Distr
N.A.I.C.S.: 423690

Soshin Electronics (SZ) Limited (3)
1408 Level 14A Taiping Financial Tower No 6001 Yitian Road, Futian District, Shenzhen, 518048, China
Tel.: (86) 75532900333
Electronic Components Distr
N.A.I.C.S.: 423690

Subsidiary (Domestic):

Soshin Powertech Co., Ltd (3)
No 2333-7 Hananoki Yamanokuchi-Town, Miyakonojo, Miyazaki, Japan
Tel.: (81) 986572141
Electronic Components Mfr
N.A.I.C.S.: 334416

Kamaya Electric(M) Sdn. Bhd. (1)
No 2 Jalan Klebang 1/5 Zone Perindustrian Bebas, Kinta Jalan Kuala Kangsar, 31200, Chemor, Perak, Malaysia
Tel.: (60) 52915522
Web Site: http://www.kamaya.co.jp
Sales Range: $200-249.9 Million
Emp.: 600
Electronic Components Mfr
N.A.I.C.S.: 334419

Kamaya Electronic Co., Ltd. (1)
PSA Bldg 3F 6-1-6 Chuou, Yamato, 242-0021, Kanagaw, Japan
Tel.: (81) 462048640
Web Site: https://www.kamaya.co.jp
Emp.: 146
Electronic Components Mfr & Sls
N.A.I.C.S.: 334419
YK Chen *(Pres)*

Kamaya, Inc. (1)
6407 Cross Creek Blvd, Fort Wayne, IN 46818
Tel.: (260) 489-1533
Web Site: https://www.kamaya.com

Sales Range: $50-74.9 Million
Emp.: 9
Electronic Components Distr
N.A.I.C.S.: 423690

Nitsuko Electronics Corporation (1)
2031-1 Ogawara Suzaka-shi, Nagano-ken, Suzaka, 382-0071, Nagono, Japan
Tel.: (81) 262451260
Web Site: https://www.nitsuko-ele.co.jp
Emp.: 104
Electronic Component Mfr & Distr
N.A.I.C.S.: 334419
Susumu Fujimoto *(Pres)*

Pan Overseas (Guangzhou) Electronic Co., Ltd. (1)
No 277 Hong Ming Road Eastern Section, Economic and Technology Development Zone, Guangzhou, China
Tel.: (86) 2082237476
Electronic Component Mfr & Distr
N.A.I.C.S.: 334419

Suzhou Walsin Technology Electronics Co., Ltd. (1)
No 369 Changyang Street Suzhou Industrial Park, Suzhou, 215126, Jiangsu, China
Tel.: (86) 51262836888
Web Site:
http://www.passivecomponent.com
Passive Components Sales
N.A.I.C.S.: 423690

Walsin Electronics (S) Pte. Ltd. (1)
Jurong East Street 21 04-33F IMM Building, Singapore, 609601, Singapore
Tel.: (65) 68963871
Web Site:
http://www.passivecomponent.com
Passive Components Mfr & Sales
N.A.I.C.S.: 334416

Walsin Technology Corporation - Dalang Plant (1)
Xinup Administrative Zone, Dalang Town, Dongguan, 523799, Guangdong, China
Tel.: (86) 76983115168
Electronic Components Mfr
N.A.I.C.S.: 334419

Walsin Technology Corporation - Kaohsiung plant (1)
1st West 13 Street K E P Z, Kaohsiung, Taiwan
Tel.: (886) 7 821 8171
Web Site:
http://www.passivecomponent.com
Electronic Components Mfr
N.A.I.C.S.: 334416

Walsin Technology Corporation - Suzhou Plant (1)
No 369 Changyan Street Suzhou Industrial Park, Suzhou, 215126, Jiangsu, China
Tel.: (86) 512 6283 6888
Passive Components Sales
N.A.I.C.S.: 423690

Walsin Technology Corporation - Yang-Mei Plant (1)
566-1 Ko-Shi Road, Yang-mei, Taoyuan, Taiwan
Tel.: (886) 34758711
Capacitor Mfr
N.A.I.C.S.: 334416

WALSTEAD INVESTMENTS LTD.
The Bentall Complex Colchester Road, Heybridge, Maldon, CM9 4NW, Essex, United Kingdom
Tel.: (44) 1621877777
Web Site:
http://www.wyndeham.co.uk
Year Founded: 2008
Investment Holding Company
N.A.I.C.S.: 551112
Mark Scanlon *(Chm)*

Subsidiaries:

Southernprint Ltd. (1)
17-21 Factory Road Upton Industrial Estate, Poole, BH16 5SN, Dorset, United Kingdom
Tel.: (44) 1202 628 300
Commercial Printing Services
N.A.I.C.S.: 323111

WALSTEAD INVESTMENTS LTD.

Walstead Investments Ltd.—(Continued)
Brian Nicol (Mgr-Works)

Wyndeham Press Group Limited (1)
Fleet House 8-12 New Bridge Street, London, EC4V 6AL, United Kingdom
Tel.: (44) 20 7822 1830
Sales Range: $125-149.9 Million
Emp.: 5
Printing Services
N.A.I.C.S.: 323111
Paul G. Utting (CEO)

Subsidiary (Domestic):

Rhapsody Limited (2)
109-123 Clifton Street, London, EC2A 4LD, United Kingdom
Tel.: (44) 2077291000
Web Site: http://www.rhapsodymedia.co.uk
Sales Range: $25-49.9 Million
Emp.: 200
Magazine Pre-Press & Online Production Services
N.A.I.C.S.: 323120
Peter Cannon (Dir-Sls)

Wyndeham Gait Limited (2)
Victoria Street, Grimsby, DN31 1PY, United Kingdom
Tel.: (44) 1472356158
Sales Range: $25-49.9 Million
Emp.: 50
Sheet-Fed Printing Services
N.A.I.C.S.: 323111
Michael Gait (Mng Dir)

Wyndeham Grange Limited (2)
Butts Road, Southwick, BN42 4EJ, W Sussex, United Kingdom
Tel.: (44) 1273592244
Sales Range: $25-49.9 Million
Emp.: 70
Sheet-Fed Magazine Printing Services
N.A.I.C.S.: 323111
Bob Day (Mng Dir)

Wyndeham Heron Limited (2)
The Bentall Complex Colchester Rd, Maldon, CM9 4NW, Essex, United Kingdom
Tel.: (44) 1621877777
Sales Range: $50-74.9 Million
Emp.: 200
Web Offset Printing Services
N.A.I.C.S.: 323111

Wyndeham Impact Limited (2)
Impact House Grafton Way, West Ham Indust Est, Basingstoke, RG22 6HY, United Kingdom
Tel.: (44) 1256479816
Sales Range: $25-49.9 Million
Emp.: 100
Web Offset Printing Services
N.A.I.C.S.: 323111

Wyndeham Peterborough Limited (2)
Storeys Bar Road, Peterborough, PE1 5YS, Cambs, United Kingdom (100%)
Tel.: (44) 1733 555 567
Sales Range: $100-124.9 Million
Emp.: 350
Commercial Printing
N.A.I.C.S.: 323111

Wyndeham Print Direct Limited (2)
Horsfield Way Castlehill Industrial Park, Bredbury, Stockport, SK6 2SU, United Kingdom
Tel.: (44) 1614067232
Sales Range: $25-49.9 Million
Emp.: 40
Continuous Direct Mail Stationery Producer
N.A.I.C.S.: 323111
Ian Mackintosh (Mng Dir)

Wyndeham Roche Limited (2)
Victoria Business Park, Roche, Saint Austell, PL26 8LX, United Kingdom (100%)
Tel.: (44) 1726 892 400
Sales Range: $50-74.9 Million
Emp.: 200
Commercial Printing
N.A.I.C.S.: 323111
Jon Roberts (Mng Dir)

WALTECH PLC
2nd Floor Trower House, Castle Street, Douglas, IM1 2EZ, Isle of Man
Tel.: (44) 2070258973
Year Founded: 2003
Sales Range: $10-24.9 Million
Emp.: 41
Investment Services; Online Payment Systems
N.A.I.C.S.: 523999
D.J.D. Vanrenen (Chm)

Subsidiaries:

Minerva Data Limited (1)
54 Pont Street, London, SW1X 0AE, United Kingdom
Tel.: (44) 207 590 2411
Web Site: http://www.minervadatalimited.com
Payment Collection Services
N.A.I.C.S.: 522320

WALTER CAPITAL PARTNERS INC.
1 Westmount Square Suite 1805, Westmount, H3Z 2P9, QC, Canada
Tel.: (514) 630-3034
Web Site: http://www.waltercapital.ca
Year Founded: 2015
Privater Equity Firm
N.A.I.C.S.: 523999
Eric Doyon (Mng Partner)

Subsidiaries:

Ergoresearch Inc. (1)
2101 Le Carrefour Suite 200, Laval, H7S 2J7, QC, Canada
Tel.: (450) 973-6700
Web Site: http://www.ergoresearch.com
Sales Range: $10-24.9 Million
Orthopaedic Product Mfr
N.A.I.C.S.: 339112

WALTER DE GRUYTER GMBH & CO. KG
Genthiner Strasse 13, 10785, Berlin, Germany
Tel.: (49) 30260050
Web Site: http://www.degruyter.com
Sales Range: $25-49.9 Million
Emp.: 220
Textbook & Other Educational Book Publisher
N.A.I.C.S.: 513130
Thorsten Feldmann (Officer-Data Security)

Subsidiaries:

Walter de Gruyter, Inc. (1)
121 High St 3rd Floor, Boston, MA 02110 (100%)
Tel.: (857) 284-7073
Web Site: http://www.degruyter.com
Book Publishers
N.A.I.C.S.: 513130

WALTER ESSER
Industriestrasse 4, D-26446, Friedberg, Germany
Tel.: (49) 446594820
Web Site: http://www.esser-gmbh.de
Year Founded: 1946
Rev.: $16,552,800
Emp.: 63
Plastic Injection Molding Mfr
N.A.I.C.S.: 333248
Klaus M. Junginger (Co-Mng Dir)

WALTER HUNGER KG HYDRAULICS
Rodenbacher Strasse 50, 97816, Lohr am Main, Germany
Tel.: (49) 93525010   De
Web Site: http://www.hunger-hydraulik.de
Year Founded: 1945
Sales Range: $25-49.9 Million
Emp.: 153
Seal & Bearing Element for Hydraulic & Pneumatic Mfr
N.A.I.C.S.: 339991
Ingrid Hunger (Pres)

Subsidiaries:

Hunger (Tianjin) Hydraulic Engineering Co., Limited (1)
358 Nanjing Rd Jinwan Mansion Rm 1504, Tianjin, 300 100, China (100%)
Tel.: (86) 22 272367 70
Web Site: http://www.hunger-group.com
Sales Range: $25-49.9 Million
Emp.: 7
Seals & Bearing Elements for Hydraulics & Pneumatics Mfr
N.A.I.C.S.: 333248

Hunger DFE GmbH Dichtungs- und Fuhrungselemente (1)
Alfred-Nobel-Strasse 26, 97080, Wurzburg, Germany (100%)
Tel.: (49) 931900970
Web Site: http://www.hunger-dichtungen.de
Sales Range: $25-49.9 Million
Emp.: 60
Hydraulic & Pneumatic Seals & Bearing Elements Mfr
N.A.I.C.S.: 339991

Hunger GmbH & Co. KG (1)
Chemnitzer Strasse 61a, DE-09669, Frankenberg, Germany (100%)
Tel.: (49) 3720660080
Web Site: http://www.hunger-group.com
Seals & Bearing Elements for Hydraulics & Pneumatics Mfr
N.A.I.C.S.: 238290

Hunger Hydraulic UK Ltd. (1)
Redwood House Templars Way Industrial Estate, Marlborough Rd, Wootton Bassett, SNA 7SR, Wiltshire, United Kingdom (100%)
Tel.: (44) 1793859615
Web Site: http://www.hunger-hydraulics.co.uk
Sales Range: $25-49.9 Million
Emp.: 3
Seals & Bearing Elements for Hydraulics & Pneumatics Mfr
N.A.I.C.S.: 332991

Hunger Hydraulics C.C., Limited (1)
63 Dixie Hwy, Rossford, OH 43460-0037 (100%)
Tel.: (419) 666-4510
Web Site: http://www.hunger-group.com
Sales Range: $25-49.9 Million
Emp.: 10
Repair & Distribution of Hydraulic Component & Cylinder Mfr
N.A.I.C.S.: 333995
Armin Hunger (Gen Mgr)

Hunger Maschinen GmbH (1)
Alfred-Nobel-Str 26, 97080, Wurzburg, Germany (100%)
Tel.: (49) 931900970
Web Site: http://www.hunger-maschinen-gmbh.de
Sales Range: $25-49.9 Million
Emp.: 40
Seals & Bearing Elements for Hydraulics & Pneumatics Mfr
N.A.I.C.S.: 332991
Ingrid Hunger (Mng Dir)

Hunger Schleifmittel GmbH (1)
Alfred Nobel Strasse 26, Wurzburg, 97080, Germany (100%)
Tel.: (49) 931900970
Web Site: http://www.hunger-group.com
Sales Range: $25-49.9 Million
Emp.: 60
Cutting Tools & Abrasive Agents (Honing Stones) Mfr
N.A.I.C.S.: 333515
Ingrid Hunger (Mng Dir)

W. Hunger Hydraulics India Pvt. Ltd (1)
New Plot No 1 Poly Park Sankrail, Howrah, Kolkata, 711 302, West Bengal, India (100%)
Tel.: (91) 3326616073
Web Site: http://www.hunger-group.com
Sales Range: $50-74.9 Million
Emp.: 2
Seals & Bearing Elements for Hydraulics & Pneumatics Mfr
N.A.I.C.S.: 339991

WALTER LILLY & CO LTD.
Knollys House 17 Addiscombe Road, Croydon, CR0 6SR, Surrey, United Kingdom
Tel.: (44) 2087306200
Web Site: https://www.walterlilly.co.uk
Year Founded: 1924
Sales Range: $25-49.9 Million
Emp.: 450
New Single-Family Housing Construction
N.A.I.C.S.: 236115

Subsidiaries:

YJL Ltd. (1)
616 Chiswick High Rd, London, W4 5RX, United Kingdom
Tel.: (44) 2089824200
Web Site: http://www.yjl.plc.uk
Engineering Services
N.A.I.C.S.: 333120

Subsidiary (Domestic):

Britannia Construction Limited (2)
Staverton Technology Park, Cheltenham, GL51 6TQ, United Kingdom (100%)
Tel.: (44) 452859880
Web Site: http://www.britanniaconstruction.co.uk
Sales Range: $25-49.9 Million
Emp.: 60
Engineering Services
N.A.I.C.S.: 237120
Andrew Mitchell (Head-Comml)

WALTER POTTHOFF GMBH
Friedrich-Ebert-Strasse 306-314, 58566, Kierspe, Germany
Tel.: (49) 2359 293 810   De
Web Site: http://www.w-potthoff.de
Year Founded: 1972
Plastics Product Mfr
N.A.I.C.S.: 326199
Norman Sack (CEO)

WALTER RAU LEBENSMITTELWERKE GMBH
Munsterstrasse 9 11 Hilter, Osnabruck, 49176, Germany
Tel.: (49) 54243660
Web Site: http://www.walter-rau.de
Year Founded: 1903
Rev.: $243,589,018
Emp.: 260
Margarine & Spreads Product Mfr
N.A.I.C.S.: 424490
Thomas Mussweiler (Mng Dir)

WALTER TOSTO S.P.A.
Via Erasmo Piaggio 62, Chieti, 66100, Italy
Tel.: (39) 0871 5801
Web Site: http://www.waltertosto.it
Hydrocarbon & Power Industries Equipment Mfr
N.A.I.C.S.: 423810

Subsidiaries:

Belleli Energy Critical Process Equipment S.r.l. (1)
G Taliercio st 1, 46100, Mantua, Italy
Tel.: (39) 03764901
Web Site: http://www.belleli.it
Power Industries Critical Process Equipment Design & Mfr
N.A.I.C.S.: 213112
Paolo Fedeli (CEO)

WALTHER-WERKE FERDINAND WALTHER GMBH
Ramsener Str 6, 67304, Eisenberg, Germany
Tel.: (49) 63514750
Web Site: http://www.walther-werke.de

AND PRIVATE COMPANIES

Year Founded: 1897
Rev.: $38,252,466
Emp.: 250
Electrical Component Mfr
N.A.I.C.S.: 335999
Kai Kalthoff (Mng Dir)

Subsidiaries:

F. Walther Electric Corp. (1)
12F/12G Worlds Fair Dr, Somerset, NJ 08873
Tel.: (732) 537-9201
Web Site: http://www.waltherelectric.com
Electronic Connectors Distr
N.A.I.C.S.: 423690
Ray Stark (Mng Dir, VP & Gen Mgr)

F. Walther Sarl. (1)
ZI de Dorignies - 100 rue E Branly, 59500, Douai, France
Tel.: (33) 327081717
Web Site: http://www.walther-fr.com
Electronic Connectors Distr
N.A.I.C.S.: 423690

WALTHER Electric GmbH (1)
Bayernstrasse 39, 5071, Wals-Siezenheim, Austria
Tel.: (43) 662854700
Electronic Connectors Distr
N.A.I.C.S.: 423690

WALTON ADVANCED ENGINEERING, INC.
18 N 1st Rd, Qianzhen Dist, Kaohsiung, Taiwan
Tel.: (886) 78111330
Web Site: http://www.walton.com.tw
8110—(TAI)
Rev.: $237,943,318
Assets: $565,890,296
Liabilities: $218,386,303
Net Worth: $347,503,993
Earnings: ($3,683,966)
Emp.: 1,904
Fiscal Year-end: 12/31/23
Semiconductor Assembly & Testing Services
N.A.I.C.S.: 334413
Chiao Yu Heng (Chm)

Subsidiaries:

Walton Advanced Engineering (Suzhou) Inc (1)
No 369 Changyang Street Suzhou Industrial Park, Suzhou, 215000, Jiangsu, China
Tel.: (86) 512 6283 3968
Electronic Components Mfr
N.A.I.C.S.: 334419

WALVAX BIOTECHNOLOGY CO., LTD.
No 395 Kexin Road High-tech Zone, Kunming, 650101, Yunnan, China
Tel.: (86) 87168312889
Web Site: https://www.walvax.com
Year Founded: 2001
300142—(CHIN)
Sales Range: $1-4.9 Billion
Emp.: 1,000
Biological & Pharmaceutical Products Mfr
N.A.I.C.S.: 325414
Yunchun Li (Chm)

WAM ACTIVE LIMITED
Level 26 Governor Phillip Tower 1
Farrer Place, Sydney, 2000, NSW, Australia
Tel.: (61) 292476755
Web Site: http://www.wilsonmanagement.com
Year Founded: 2007
WAA—(ASX)
Sales Range: $1-9.9 Million
Investment Fund
N.A.I.C.S.: 525910
Linda Vo (Sec & Mgr-Fin)

WAM CAPITAL LIMITED
Level 26 Governor Phillip Tower 1
Farrer Place, Sydney, 2000, NSW, Australia
Tel.: (61) 292476755 AU
Web Site: http://www.wilsonmanagement.com
WAM—(ASX)
Rev.: $27,133,838
Assets: $1,160,621,687
Liabilities: $31,340,334
Net Worth: $1,129,281,353
Earnings: $112,992,857
Fiscal Year-end: 06/30/23
Investment Management Service
N.A.I.C.S.: 523999
Geoffrey Wilson (Founder & Chm)

Subsidiaries:

Ozgrowth Limited (1)
Level 18 Alluvion, 58 Mounts Bay Road, Perth, 6000, WA, Australia
Tel.: (61) 89 321 7877
Web Site: http://www.ozgrowth.com.au
Sales Range: $1-9.9 Million
Investment Services
N.A.I.C.S.: 523999
Anthony Hewett (Sec)

Westoz Investment Company Limited (1)
Level 18 Alluvion 58 Mounts Bay Road, Perth, 6000, WA, Australia
Tel.: (61) 89 321 7877
Web Site: http://www.westozfunds.com.au
Sales Range: $1-9.9 Million
Investment Services
N.A.I.C.S.: 523999
Jay Hughes (Chm)

Wilson Asset Management (International) Pty Limited (1)
Level 11 139 Macquarie Street, Sydney, 2000, NSW, Australia
Tel.: (61) 2 9247 6755
Emp.: 7
Asset Management Services
N.A.I.C.S.: 523940
Nikhil Kumar (Mng Dir)

Subsidiary (Domestic):

WAM Alternative Asset Limited (2)
Level 26 Governor Phillip Tower 1 Farrer Place, Sydney, 2000, NSW, Australia
Tel.: (61) 292476755
Web Site: http://wilsonassetmanagement.com.au
Rev.: $5,906,930
Assets: $185,407,745
Liabilities: $31,551,156
Net Worth: $153,856,589
Earnings: $4,235,788
Fiscal Year-end: 06/30/2024
Investment Fund
N.A.I.C.S.: 525990
Michael Cottier (Chm)

amaysim Australia Limited (1)
Level 6 17-19 Bridge Street, Sydney, 2000, NSW, Australia (79.8%)
Tel.: (61) 282030100
Web Site: http://www.amaysim.com.au
Rev.: $355,873,411
Assets: $191,962,972
Liabilities: $117,505,913
Net Worth: $74,457,059
Earnings: ($10,302,015)
Emp.: 669
Fiscal Year-end: 06/30/2019
Telecommunication Servicesb
N.A.I.C.S.: 517810
Peter O'Connell (Founder, CEO & Mng Dir)

WAM GLOBAL LIMITED
Level 26 Governor Phillip Tower 1
Farrer Place, Sydney, 2000, NSW, Australia
Tel.: (61) 292476755
Web Site: http://www.wilsonmanagement.com
Year Founded: 1997
WGB—(ASX)
Rev.: $5,633,145
Assets: $580,929,848
Liabilities: $26,934,268
Net Worth: $553,995,579
Earnings: $49,370,543
Fiscal Year-end: 06/30/24
Asset Management Services
N.A.I.C.S.: 523940
Geoff Wilson Ao (Chm & Chief Investment Officer)

WAM LEADERS LIMITED
Level 26 Governor Phillip Tower 1
Farrer Place, Sydney, 2000, NSW, Australia
Tel.: (61) 292476755 AU
Web Site: http://www.wilsonmanagement.com
WLE—(ASX)
Rev.: $38,804,931
Assets: $1,162,434,290
Liabilities: $32,087,927
Net Worth: $1,130,346,363
Earnings: $14,918,064
Fiscal Year-end: 06/30/24
Portfolio Management Services
N.A.I.C.S.: 523940
Geoff Wilson (Chm)

Subsidiaries:

Absolute Equity Performance Fund Limited (1)
Level 12 Grosvenor Place 225 George Street, Sydney, 2000, NSW, Australia
Tel.: (61) 280162819
Rev.: $4,282,388
Assets: $263,612,726
Liabilities: $179,304,023
Net Worth: $84,308,703
Earnings: $1,103,501
Fiscal Year-end: 06/30/2021
Investment Management Service
N.A.I.C.S.: 525990

CENTURY AUSTRALIA INVESTMENTS LIMITED (1)
Level 12 680 George Street, Sydney, 2000, NSW, Australia
Tel.: (61) 2 8280 7100
Web Site: http://www.centuryaustralia.com.au
Telecommunication Servicesb
N.A.I.C.S.: 517111
Matthew McShane (Sec)

WAM MICROCAP LIMITED
Level 26 Governor Phillip Tower 1
Farrer Place, Sydney, 2000, NSW, Australia
Tel.: (61) 292476755 AU
Web Site: https://www.wilsonmanagement.com
Year Founded: 1997
WMI—(ASX)
Rev.: $5,172,931
Assets: $187,776,182
Liabilities: $7,938,989
Net Worth: $179,837,193
Earnings: $17,161,950
Fiscal Year-end: 06/30/23
Investment Management Service
N.A.I.C.S.: 523999
Geoff Wilson AO (Chm)

WAM RESEARCH LTD.
Tel.: (61) 292476755 AU
Year Founded: 2002
WAX—(ASX)
Rev.: $3,293,975
Assets: $156,008,006
Liabilities: $12,667,943
Net Worth: $143,340,064
Earnings: $21,682,235
Fiscal Year-end: 06/30/24
Asset Management Services
N.A.I.C.S.: 523940
Kate Thorley (CEO)

WAM STRATEGIC VALUE LIMITED
Level 26 Governor Phillip Tower 1
Farrer Place, Sydney, 2000, NSW, Australia
Tel.: (61) 292476755
Web Site: https://www.wilsonmanagement.com
Year Founded: 1997
WAR—(ASX)
Rev.: $6,829,632
Assets: $142,805,217
Liabilities: $440,559
Net Worth: $142,364,657
Earnings: $10,294,599
Emp.: 34
Fiscal Year-end: 06/30/23
Asset Management Services
N.A.I.C.S.: 523999

WAMEJA LIMITED
c/o Simpsons Solicitors Level 2 Pier 8/9, 23 Hickson Road, Millers Point, 2000, NSW, Australia
Tel.: (61) 2 8014 5050
Web Site: http://www.wameja.com
Rev.: $48,957
Assets: $28,911,384
Liabilities: $189,535
Net Worth: $28,721,849
Earnings: ($9,224,954)
Fiscal Year-end: 12/31/19
Mobile Payment Services
N.A.I.C.S.: 561499
Tom Rowe (Sec)

WAMET (DEMETRIADES) LTD.
79 Aglantjia Avenue, Aglantjia, 2107, Nicosia, Cyprus
Tel.: (357) 22336660 CY
Web Site: http://www.wamet.com.cy
Year Founded: 1976
Industrial Machinery Whslr
N.A.I.C.S.: 423830

WAMGROUP S.P.A.
Via Cavour 338, Ponte Motta, 41032, Cavezzo, Modena, Italy
Tel.: (39) 0535 618-111 IT
Web Site: http://www.wamgroup.com
Year Founded: 1969
Emp.: 2,100
Bulk Solids Handling & Processing Equipment Designer, Mfr & Distr
N.A.I.C.S.: 333998
Vainer Marchesini (Chm & CEO)

Subsidiaries:

Conquip Engineering Co. Ltd. (1)
Rm 29 7/F Thriving Industrial Centre 26-38 Sha Tsui Road, New Territories, Tsuen Wan, China (Hong Kong)
Tel.: (852) 2 413 0082
Web Site: https://www.conquip.com.hk
Professional Equipment Distribution Services
N.A.I.C.S.: 423490

Enviro-Care Co., Inc. (1)
5701 Industrial Ave, Loves Park, IL 61111
Tel.: (815) 636-8306
Web Site: http://www.enviro-care.com
Sales Range: $1-9.9 Million
Emp.: 15
Screening & Grit Management Equipment Mfr
N.A.I.C.S.: 333248
Charlene Low (Mgr-Mktg)

FLITECH S.r.l. (1)
Via M Biagi 21, 46025, Poggio Rusco, Mantua, Italy
Tel.: (39) 0386 52 29 11
Web Site: http://www.flitech.it
Steel Products Mfr
N.A.I.C.S.: 331110

HAS CZ a.s. (1)
Pribylova 28, Kuncice, 719 00, Ostrava, Czech Republic
Tel.: (420) 59 524 5019
Web Site: https://www.has.cz
Plastics Product Mfr

WAMGROUP S.P.A.

WAMGROUP S.p.A.—(Continued)
N.A.I.C.S.: 326199

Komponent Kft. (1)
Becsi Ut 98, 1034, Budapest, Hungary
Tel.: (36) 1 210 4138
Web Site: https://komponent.hu
Industrial Machinery Distr
N.A.I.C.S.: 423830

MAP Mischsysteme GmbH (1)
Gersdorfer Strasse 1-5, 68804, Altlussheim, Germany
Tel.: (49) 6205 394 9710
Web Site: https://www.mapgmbh.com
Industrial Machine Mfr & Whslr
N.A.I.C.S.: 333248
Werner Schmidt (Mng Dir)

OLI Benelux B.V. (1)
H-Geestmolenstraat 116, 9160, Lokeren, Belgium
Tel.: (32) 49 151 1414
Electric & Pneumatic Vibrator Mfr
N.A.I.C.S.: 333120
Carolin Knobl (Deputy Gen Mgr)

OLI Russia LLC (1)
Mazhorov Pereulok 14, 107023, Moscow, Russia
Tel.: (7) 4956415775
Web Site: http://www.olivibra.com
Electric & Pneumatic Vibrator Mfr
N.A.I.C.S.: 335312
Marco Ratti (Gen Mgr)

OLI S.p.A. (1)
Via Canalazzo 35, 41036, Medolla, Modena, Italy
Tel.: (39) 0535 41 06 11
Web Site: http://www.olivibra.com
Industrial Equipment Mfr
N.A.I.C.S.: 333998
Davide Saetti (Mgr-Sector)

Subsidiary (Non-US):

OLI Electrical Vibrators South Africa (2)
49 Loper Avenue, Kempton Park, Johannesburg, 1619, South Africa
Tel.: (27) 11 39 21 054
Web Site: http://www.olivibra.co.za
Emp.: 10
Industrial Equipment Distr
N.A.I.C.S.: 423830
Deborah Marchand (Mgr-Warehouse & Logistics)

OLI Makine San.Ve Tic. Ltd. (2)
Calca Mah 2 OSB 1 Cad No 4 Merkez, Kutahya, Türkiye
Tel.: (90) 274 333 0 654
Web Site: http://turkey.olivibra.com
Industrial Equipment Distr
N.A.I.C.S.: 423830
Kubilay Tas (Engr-Sls)

OLI VIBRA Ltd. (2)
HF 18 Hal Far Industrial Estate, Hal Far, Birzebbuga, 3000, Malta
Tel.: (356) 2165 3066
Web Site: http://www.olivibra.com
Industrial Equipment Distr
N.A.I.C.S.: 423830
Charles Spiteri (Gen Mgr)

OLI Vibra Nordic AB (2)
Arenavagen 41 12tr, Globen, 121 77, Stockholm, Sweden
Tel.: (46) 8 50 56 88 88
Web Site: http://www.olivibra.se
Industrial Equipment Distr
N.A.I.C.S.: 423830
Federico Rodriguez (Reg Mgr-Sls)

OLI Vibra UK Ltd. (2)
Unit 13 Alexandra Way Ashchurch Business Centre, Tewkesbury, GL20 8NB, Gloucestershire, United Kingdom
Tel.: (44) 1684 275 527
Web Site: http://www.olivibra.co.uk
Industrial Equipment Distr
N.A.I.C.S.: 423830
Colin Billington (Gen Mgr)

Subsidiary (US):

OLI Vibrator U.S.A. Inc. (2)
4070 Buford Hwy - Ste 5, Duluth, GA 30096
Tel.: (770) 622-1494
Web Site: http://www.olivibra.us
Emp.: 10
Industrial Equipment Mfr
N.A.I.C.S.: 333998
Alan Lewandowski (Engr-Application)

Subsidiary (Non-US):

OLI Vibrators PTY Ltd (2)
Factory 4 3 Gatwick Road, Bayswater, 3153, VIC, Australia
Tel.: (61) 3 8761 6911
Web Site: http://www.olivibrators.com.au
Emp.: 3
Industrial Equipment Distr
N.A.I.C.S.: 423830
Mark Thompson (Gen Mgr)

OLI Spain 2006, S.L.U. (1)
Pol Ind Station Plan Avda Plan of the Station 97 Nave C, Santa Margarida and the Monks, 08730, Barcelona, Spain
Tel.: (34) 93 898 3764
Web Site: https://www.olivibra.es
Electric & Pneumatic Vibrator Mfr
N.A.I.C.S.: 335312
Marc Asensi (Gen Mgr)

OLI Wolong Company (1)
No 1801 Renmin West Road, Shangyu, 312352, Zhejiang, China
Tel.: (86) 5758 217 6722
Industrial Machine Mfr & Whslr
N.A.I.C.S.: 333248

OLI do Brasil Equipamentos Industriais Ltda. (1)
Rua Lagoa Santa 70 Chacaras Reunidas, Sao Jose dos Campos, 12238-410, Brazil
Tel.: (55) 123 933 3738
Web Site: http://www.olivibra.com.br
Electric & Pneumatic Vibrator Mfr
N.A.I.C.S.: 335312

OOO WAM - Moscow (1)
Ryabinovaya street 38V, 121471, Moscow, Russia
Tel.: (7) 4956632239
Web Site: http://www.wammoscow.ru
Industrial Equipment Distr
N.A.I.C.S.: 423830
Alfredo Baioni (Gen Mgr)

OST S.r.l. (1)
Via Alessio Baldovinetti 85, 00142, Rome, Italy
Tel.: (39) 06 87 46 51 85
Web Site: http://www.ostsrl.com
Broadcasting Equipment Distr
N.A.I.C.S.: 423690

OU WAM Baltic (1)
Moigu Tehnopark Kuma tee 1, Rae vald, 75312, Harjumaa, Estonia
Tel.: (372) 68 35 185
Web Site: http://www.wamgroup.ee
Industrial Equipment Distr
N.A.I.C.S.: 423830

Oli Vibrators India Pvt. Ltd. (1)
84/85 7th Main Peenya Industrial Area, Bengaluru, 560058, Karnataka, India
Tel.: (91) 804 886 2142
Web Site: https://www.olivibrators.in
Electric & Pneumatic Vibrator Mfr
N.A.I.C.S.: 335312
Sundaram Subramaniam Iyer (Mng Dir)

PSC Group s.a.l. (1)
City Hospital Street Aoun Center, PO Box 90-2028, Bouchrieh Jdeidet El Metn, Beirut, Lebanon
Tel.: (961) 190 1199
Web Site: https://pscgroup-lb.com
Industrial Machinery Distr
N.A.I.C.S.: 423830

PT. WAMGROUP Indonesia Trading (1)
Bizpark I Commercial Estate Block A3 No 7 JL Raya Bekasi, Pulogadung, East Jakarta, 13920, Indonesia
Tel.: (62) 21 460 0811
Web Site: https://www.wamgroup.co.id
Industrial Machine Mfr & Whslr
N.A.I.C.S.: 333248

Pt. WAMGROUP Tr. Indonesia (1)
Bizpark I Commercial Estate Block A3 No 7 JL Raya Bekasi, Pulogadung KM 21, East Jakarta, 13920, Indonesia
Tel.: (62) 21 28 88 08 40
Web Site: http://www.wamgroup.co.id
Industrial Equipment Distr
N.A.I.C.S.: 423830

RONCUZZI S.r.l (1)
Via del Campo Sportivo 40, Mezzano, 48133, Ravenna, Italy
Tel.: (39) 0544 411011
Web Site: http://www.roncuzzi.com
Industrial Equipment Distr
N.A.I.C.S.: 423830

SAVECO Germany GmbH (1)
Dornierstrasse 10, 68804, Altlussheim, Germany
Tel.: (49) 62 053 9490
Web Site: https://www.saveco-water.de
Industrial Machine Mfr & Whslr
N.A.I.C.S.: 333248

SAVECO Iberica SL (1)
Avda Bellvei 5 Pol Ind Els Massets, 43719, Tarragona, Spain
Tel.: (34) 91 818 8107
Web Site: https://www.saveco-water.es
Industrial Machine Mfr & Whslr
N.A.I.C.S.: 333248

SAVECO North America Inc. (1)
1570 St Paul Ave, Gurnee, IL 60031
Tel.: (815) 636-8306
Industrial Machine Mfr & Whslr
N.A.I.C.S.: 333248

SAVECO S.A.S. (1)
Paris Nord II 13 rue de la Perdrix Les Fregates 6 Hall C, BP 52413, Roissy Charles de Gaulle, 95944, Tremblay-en-France, Cedex, France
Tel.: (33) 14 817 7110
Web Site: https://www.saveco-water.fr
Industrial Machine Mfr & Whslr
N.A.I.C.S.: 333248

SAVECO UK Ltd. (1)
Unit 3B Delta Drive Tewkesbury Business Park, Tewkesbury, GL20 8HB, United Kingdom
Tel.: (44) 168 429 9104
Web Site: https://www.saveco-water.co.uk
Industrial Machine Mfr & Whslr
N.A.I.C.S.: 333248
Jon Goddard (Mng Dir)

SAVECO s.r.l. (1)
Via Cavour 346, Ponte Motta di, 41032, Cavezzo, MO, Italy
Tel.: (39) 053 574 8111
Web Site: https://www.saveco-water.it
Industrial Machine Mfr & Whslr
N.A.I.C.S.: 333248

SAVI S.r.l. (1)
Via Roma 80, Roncoferraro, 46037, Mantua, Italy
Tel.: (39) 0376 663721
Web Site: http://www.savi.mn.it
Industrial Equipment Mfr
N.A.I.C.S.: 333998

SC WAM Romania S.r.l. (1)
Via Ciuperceasca 1000A, Urleta str Belu, Banesti, Prahova, Romania
Tel.: (40) 344 111 201
Web Site: http://www.wamgroup.ro
Industrial Equipment Mfr
N.A.I.C.S.: 423830

Saveco Middle East FZE (1)
Jafza 22 211, PO Box 26 36 22, Dubai, United Arab Emirates
Tel.: (971) 4 886 8664
Web Site: https://www.saveco-water.ae
Industrial Machine Mfr & Whslr
N.A.I.C.S.: 333248

TECTRA Ltd. (1)
Lavriou Ave 47, Kantza, 153 51, Pallini, Greece
Tel.: (30) 210 604 1400
Web Site: http://www.tectra.gr
Industrial Machinery Mfr
N.A.I.C.S.: 423830

TOREX S.p.A. (1)
Via Canaletto 139/a, 41030, San Prospero, Modena, Italy
Tel.: (39) 059 80 80 811
Web Site: http://www.torex.it

INTERNATIONAL PUBLIC

Industrial Equipment Mfr
N.A.I.C.S.: 333998

Unico Syndicate Pakistan Pvt. Ltd. (1)
1/11 Arkay Square 1St Floor Room No 11 - 1St Floor, Shahrah-E-Liaquat New Challi, Karachi, 74000, Pakistan
Tel.: (92) 213 242 3266
Web Site: https://www.unicosyndicate.com
Industrial Machinery Whslr
N.A.I.C.S.: 423830

VISAM S.r.l. (1)
Via Nuova Ponente 27/G, 41012, Carpi, Modena, Italy
Tel.: (39) 059 6258411
Web Site: http://www.visam.it
Industrial Equipment Mfr
N.A.I.C.S.: 423830

W.A.M. Equipment Trading (Pvt.) Ltd. (1)
420 R A De Mel Mawatha, Colombo, 00300, Sri Lanka
Tel.: (94) 71 115 1888
Web Site: https://www.wamgroup.lk
Industrial Machine Mfr & Whslr
N.A.I.C.S.: 423830

WAM (M.H.E.) Ltd. (1)
Unit D 29 Hannigan Drive St Johns, Auckland, 1702, New Zealand
Tel.: (64) 9 622 2803
Web Site: https://www.wamgroup.co.nz
Industrial Machine Mfr & Whslr
N.A.I.C.S.: 333248

WAM Adria D.o.o. (1)
Hum Breznicki 7/A, 42225, Breznicki Hum, Croatia
Tel.: (385) 42 40 23 00
Web Site: http://www.wamadria.com
Industrial Equipment Distr
N.A.I.C.S.: 423830

WAM Argentina S.A. (1)
Agustin Delgado 5478, San Lorenzo, X5020DQH, Cordoba, Argentina
Tel.: (54) 351 450 87 42
Web Site: http://www.wamgroup.com.ar
Industrial Equipment Distr
N.A.I.C.S.: 423830

WAM Australia PTY Ltd. (1)
5 Eastspur Court, PO Box 560, Kilsyth, 3137, VIC, Australia
Tel.: (61) 3 97 37 47 00
Web Site: http://www.wamaust.com.au
Industrial Equipment Distr
N.A.I.C.S.: 423830

Subsidiary (Non-US):

WAMGROUP (MHE) Ltd. (2)
Unit D 29 Hannigan Drive, St Johns, Auckland, 1702, New Zealand
Tel.: (64) 9 62 22 803
Web Site: http://www.wamgroup.co.nz
Industrial Equipment Distr
N.A.I.C.S.: 423830

WAM B.H.E.I. (Thailand) Co. Ltd. (1)
162/1 Soi Pattanakarn 78 Pattanakarn Road, Bangkok, 10 250, Thailand
Tel.: (66) 2 722 23 01 5
Web Site: http://www.wamgroup.co.th
Industrial Equipment Distr
N.A.I.C.S.: 423830

WAM B.H.M. (Bulk Handling Machinery) N.V. (1)
Heirweg 138 a, 9270, Laarne, Belgium
Tel.: (32) 9 365 30 10
Web Site: http://www.wamgroup.be
Emp.: 7
Industrial Equipment Distr
N.A.I.C.S.: 423830
Michel Paridaens (Pres)

WAM Bulk Handling Equipment Industry (Thailand) Co., Ltd. (1)
162/1 Soi Pattanakarn 78 Pattanakarn Road, Bangkok, 10250, Thailand
Tel.: (66) 27 222 3015
Web Site: https://www.wamgroup.co.th
Industrial Machine Mfr & Whslr
N.A.I.C.S.: 333248

WAM Bulk Handling Machinery (Shanghai) Co. Ltd. (1)
No 1111 Shi Wan 6th Road, Pu Dong New Area, Shanghai, 201202, China
Tel.: (86) 21 68 96 68 88
Web Site: http://www.wamgroup.com.cn
Industrial Equipment Mfr & Distr
N.A.I.C.S.: 333998
Stephan Wang (Reg Mgr-Sls)

WAM Bulk Solid Handling (M) Sdn Bhd (1)
No 5 Jalan Astaka U8/84A Seksyen U8 Bukit Jelutong Industrial Park, 40100, Shah Alam, Selangor, Malaysia
Tel.: (60) 37 734 0456
Web Site: https://www.wamgroup.my
Industrial Machine Mfr & Whslr
N.A.I.C.S.: 333248

WAM Bulk Solid Handling (MT) SDN BHD (1)
No 5 Jalan Astaka U8/84A Seksyen U8, Bukit Jelutong Industrial Park, 40100, Shah Alam, Selangor, Malaysia
Tel.: (60) 3 7734 0456
Web Site: http://www.wamgroup.my
Industrial Equipment Distr
N.A.I.C.S.: 423830
Yee Jy Ho (Sr Engr-Sls)

WAM Chile S.A. (1)
Calle Los Nogales Oriente 190-D, Lampa, 9380000, Santiago, Chile
Tel.: (56) 273 87 124
Web Site: http://www.wamgroup.cl
Emp.: 8
Industrial Equipment Distr
N.A.I.C.S.: 423830
Alfonso Almerge (Mgr)

WAM Egypt S.A.E. (1)
Building No 97 Extension of 3rd Industrial Zone Banks Area Street, 6th October Industrial Zone, Giza, Cairo, Egypt
Tel.: (20) 106 618 6766
Web Site: https://www.wamgroup.com.eg
Miscellaneous Product Mfr
N.A.I.C.S.: 339999

WAM Finland OY (1)
Valajantie 13 A, 48230, Kotka, Finland
Tel.: (358) 10 38 78 660
Web Site: http://www.wamgroup.fi
Industrial Equipment Distr
N.A.I.C.S.: 423830
Jani Tossavainen (Engr-Sls)

WAM France S.A. (1)
Paris Nord II 13 rue de la Perdrix Les Fregates 6 Hall C, PO Box 54438, Roissy Charles de Gaulle, 95944, Tremblay-en-France, Cedex, France
Tel.: (33) 1 58 02 00 30
Web Site: http://www.wamgroup.fr
Industrial Equipment Distr
N.A.I.C.S.: 423830

WAM GmbH (1)
Dornierstrasse 10, 68804, Altlussheim, Germany
Tel.: (49) 6205 39 49 0
Web Site: http://www.wamgroup.de
Industrial Equipment Distr
N.A.I.C.S.: 423830

Subsidiary (Domestic):

EMT Mischtechnik GmbH (2)
Gersdorfer Strasse 1-5, 68804, Altlussheim, Germany
Tel.: (49) 6205 39 49 710
Web Site: http://www.emtgmbh.de
Industrial Equipment Distr
N.A.I.C.S.: 423830

OLI Vibrationstechnick GmbH (2)
Parkstrasse 9, Taunus, 65618, Lohnberg, Germany
Tel.: (49) 6483 91 97 00
Web Site: http://www.oligmbh.de
Emp.: 10
Industrial Equipment Distr
N.A.I.C.S.: 423830
Angelbert Weil (Mgr)

WAM Group Egypt (1)
Zahraa El Maadi, Cairo, Egypt
Tel.: (20) 2 297 05 136
Web Site: http://www.wamgroup.com.eg
Industrial Equipment Distr
N.A.I.C.S.: 423830

WAM Helvetia GmbH (1)
Gauerhof Industriepark LC2, 6246, Bern, Switzerland
Tel.: (41) 62 823 68 58
Web Site: http://www.wamgroup.ch
Industrial Equipment Distr
N.A.I.C.S.: 423830

WAM Holland B.H.E. (Bulk Handling Equipment) B.V. (1)
Honderdland 500, 2676 LV, Maasdijk, Netherlands
Tel.: (31) 17 452 1988
Web Site: https://www.wamholland.nl
Miscellaneous Product Mfr
N.A.I.C.S.: 339999

WAM Holland Bulk Handling Equipment B.V. (1)
Honderdland 201, 2676 LV, Maasdijk, Netherlands
Tel.: (31) 174 52 19 88
Web Site: http://www.wamholland.nl
Emp.: 6
Industrial Equipment Distr
N.A.I.C.S.: 423830
Barry Nijman (Mgr-Sector Sls)

WAM Inc. (1)
1300 Triad Blvd, Saginaw, TX 76131
Tel.: (817) 232-2678
Web Site: http://www.waminc.com
Emp.: 30
Bulk Solid Handling Equipment Mfr
N.A.I.C.S.: 333248
Jim Rogers (Sls Mgr-Texas)

WAM India Pvt. Ltd. (1)
Bhimashankar Bhavan Plot No C/7 RSC - 2, Vasant Vihar, Thane, 400 610, Maharashtra, India
Tel.: (91) 22 41 12 31 00
Web Site: http://www.wamgroup.in
Industrial Equipment Distr
N.A.I.C.S.: 423830
Amit Popatwala (Mng Dir)

WAM Italia S.p.A (1)
Via Cavour 346, Ponte Motta Cavezzo, 41032, Modena, Italy
Tel.: (39) 0535 74 01 11
Web Site: http://www.wamgroup.it
Industrial Equipment Distr
N.A.I.C.S.: 423830

WAM Japan Co. Ltd. (1)
2414 Nakao, Midori-Ku, Saitama, 336-0932, Japan
Tel.: (81) 48 876 51 21
Web Site: http://www.wam.co.jp
Industrial Equipment Distr
N.A.I.C.S.: 423830

WAM Korea Co., Ltd (1)
Room 502 Moden Venture Town 1673 Shingil-7dong, Youngdengpo-gu, 150-856, Seoul, Korea (South)
Tel.: (82) 2 833 84 26
Web Site: http://www.wamgroup.co.kr
Industrial Equipment Distr
N.A.I.C.S.: 423830

WAM Maroc Sarl (1)
259 ZI Sud Ouest, Mohammedia, Casablanca, Morocco
Tel.: (212) 523 310 125
Web Site: http://www.wamgroup.ma
Industrial Equipment Distr
N.A.I.C.S.: 423830

WAM Middle East FZ CO (1)
PO Box 26 17 45, Jebel Ali, Dubai, United Arab Emirates
Tel.: (971) 4 88 60 210
Web Site: http://www.wamgroup.ae
Emp.: 13
Industrial Equipment Distr
N.A.I.C.S.: 423830
Marialessandra Carletti (Mng Dir)

WAM Polska SP. Z.o.o. (1)
Aleja Glowna 28, Kruszyn, 59-700, Boleslawiec, Poland
Tel.: (48) 75 73 21 341
Web Site: http://www.wamgroup.pl
Industrial Equipment Distr
N.A.I.C.S.: 423830

WAM Romania S.r.l. (1)
Sat Urleta str Ciuperceasca 1000A, Prahova, Banesti, Romania
Tel.: (40) 34 411 1201
Web Site: https://www.wamgroup.ro
Industrial Machine Mfr & Whslr
N.A.I.C.S.: 333248

WAM Scandinavia A/S (1)
Italiensvej 4, 8450, Hammel, Denmark
Tel.: (45) 87 622 000
Web Site: http://www.wamgroup.dk
Industrial Equipment Distr
N.A.I.C.S.: 423830
Mads Gandrup (Engr-Sls)

WAM Singapore BHM Pte. Ltd. (1)
10 Admiralty Street North Link Building 03-65, Singapore, 757695, Singapore
Tel.: (65) 6753 25 33
Web Site: http://www.wamgroup.com.sg
Industrial Equipment Distr
N.A.I.C.S.: 423830

WAM South Africa (Pty) Ltd. (1)
Unit 1 Dundas Park 23 Junction Rd Parow Industria, Cape Town, 7493, South Africa
Tel.: (27) 21 951 1840
Web Site: https://www.wamgroup.co.za
Industrial Machine Mfr & Whslr
N.A.I.C.S.: 333248

WAM Spain 2004, S.L. (1)
Avda Pla de la Estacio 97 nave A y B, Santa Margarida i Els Monjos, 08730, Barcelona, Spain
Tel.: (34) 93 8 98 33 27
Web Site: http://www.wamgroup.es
Industrial Equipment Distr
N.A.I.C.S.: 423830

Subsidiary (Domestic):

SPECO Hidrotechnologia S.L. (2)
Avda Monte Boyal 56 - Pol Ind Monte Boyal, Casarrubios del Monte, 45950, Toledo, Spain
Tel.: (34) 91 818 8107
Web Site: http://www.wamgroup.es
Industrial Equipment Distr
N.A.I.C.S.: 423830

WAM U.S.A Inc. (1)
75 Boulderbrook Cir, Lawrenceville, GA 30045
Tel.: (770) 339-6767
Web Site: http://www.waminc.com
Emp.: 25
Industrial Equipment Distr
N.A.I.C.S.: 423830
Naum Brodsky (CFO)

Subsidiary (Domestic):

EXPORT WAMGROUP LLC (2)
655 Andover St, Miami, FL 33161
Tel.: (305) 573-6766
Web Site: http://www.wamlatin.com
Emp.: 4
Industrial Equipment Distr
N.A.I.C.S.: 423830
Lorenzo Draghi (Mgr-Ops)

Subsidiary (Non-US):

LATINWAM Trading, S DE RL DE CV (2)
Calle La Brida 247 Int 22 Colonia Lopez Cotilla, Tlaquepaque, 45615, Jalisco, Mexico
Tel.: (52) 3336127789
Web Site: http://www.wam.com.mx
Industrial Equipment Distr
N.A.I.C.S.: 423830

Division (Domestic):

WAM U.S.A Inc. - Texas Division (2)
1300 Triad Blvd, Fort Worth, TX 76131
Tel.: (817) 232-2678
Industrial Equipment Mfr
N.A.I.C.S.: 333998

WAM Ukraine Ltd. (1)
ul Murmanskaya 7, 02660, Kiev, Ukraine
Tel.: (380) 44 50 24 829
Web Site: http://www.wamgroup.com.ua
Industrial Equipment Distr
N.A.I.C.S.: 423830

WAM do Brasil Equipamentos Industriais Ltda (1)
Rua Jaguarao 346 Chacaras Reunidas, 12238-410, Sao Jose dos Campos, Sao Paulo, Brazil
Tel.: (55) 12 39 33 50 00
Web Site: http://www.wamgroup.com.br
Industrial Equipment Mfr
N.A.I.C.S.: 333998

WAMGROUP Vietnam Ltd (1)
140/1 Ly Chinh Thang Street, Ward 7 District 3 3rd Floor, Ho Chi Minh City, Vietnam
Tel.: (84) 8 38 46 98 12
Web Site: http://www.wamgroup.com.vn
Emp.: 6
Industrial Equipment Distr
N.A.I.C.S.: 423830

WAN CHENG METAL PACKAGING COMPANY LIMITED
No 3 Huada Road Ronggui Street, Hi-tech Industrial Development Zone Shunde District, Foshan, Guangdong, China
Web Site: https://www.wanchengholdings.com
Year Founded: 1997
8291—(HKG)
Rev: $6,721,450
Assets: $15,735,905
Liabilities: $27,828,146
Net Worth: ($12,092,241)
Earnings: ($3,743,631)
Emp.: 92
Fiscal Year-end: 12/31/23
Metal Products Mfr
N.A.I.C.S.: 332999
Yun Wang (Officer)

WAN HAI LINES LTD.
10F No 136 Sung Chiang Rd, Taipei, 10417, Taiwan
Tel.: (886) 225677961
Web Site: http://www.wanhai.com.tw
Year Founded: 1965
2615—(TAI)
Rev: $3,133,540,944
Assets: $10,398,529,563
Liabilities: $3,946,224,463
Net Worth: $6,452,305,100
Earnings: ($180,820,905)
Emp.: 5,062
Fiscal Year-end: 12/31/23
Marine Transportation Services
N.A.I.C.S.: 488390
Po-Ting Chen (Chm)

Subsidiaries:

Wan Hai (Vietnam) Ltd. (1)
Mezz Floor & 9th Floor MB Sunny Tower 259 Tran Hung Dao St, Co Giang Ward 1st Dist, Ho Chi Minh City, Vietnam
Tel.: (84) 839203000
Freight Transportation Services
N.A.I.C.S.: 488510

Wan Hai Lines (India) Pvt. Ltd. (1)
A/102 and 103 The Qube Near to International Airport, Marol Village Andheri East, Mumbai, 400 059, India
Tel.: (91) 2249204500
Freight Transportation Services
N.A.I.C.S.: 488510

Wan Hai Lines (Korea) Ltd. (1)
15f 43 Dadong-gil, Jung-gu, Seoul, 100-180, Korea (South)
Tel.: (82) 237073000
Freight Transportation Services
N.A.I.C.S.: 488510

Wan Hai Lines (Phils.), Inc. (1)
10th Floor Rufino Pacific Tower VA Rufino Street 1223, 6784 Ayalal Avenue Corner, Makati, Philippines
Tel.: (63) 286595888
Freight Transportation Services
N.A.I.C.S.: 488510

Wan Hai Lines (Singapore) Pte Ltd. (1)
79 Anson Road 10-01, Singapore, 079906, Singapore
Tel.: (65) 62261588

WAN HAI LINES LTD.

Wan Hai Lines Ltd.—(Continued)
International Freight Transportation Services
N.A.I.C.S.: 483111

Subsidiary (Non-US):

Shenzhen Uniwin International Logistics Ltd. (2)
25/F Tianmian City Tower Middle Shennan Blvd, Shenzhen, 518026, China
Tel.: (86) 755 82816280
International Freight Transportation Services
N.A.I.C.S.: 483111

Wan Hai Lines (HK) Ltd. (2)
3rd Floor Singga Commercial Centre 148 Connaught Road West, Hong Kong, China (Hong Kong)
Tel.: (852) 28596100
Cargo Handling Services
N.A.I.C.S.: 488320

Wan Hai Lines (USA) Ltd. (1)
301 E Ocean Blvd Ste 1650, Long Beach, CA 90802
Tel.: (562) 901-9400
Freight Transportation Services
N.A.I.C.S.: 488510

Wan Hai Lines Peru S.A.C. (1)
Calle Bolognesi 180 Oficina 604, Miraflores, Lima, Peru
Tel.: (51) 12059960
Freight Transportation Services
N.A.I.C.S.: 488510

WanHai Lines Ecuador S.A. (1)
Avenue Joaquin Orrantia Agora 21 Building 7th Floor Office 707, Guayaquil, 090513, Ecuador
Tel.: (593) 43907200
Freight Transportation Services
N.A.I.C.S.: 488510

WAN KEI GROUP HOLDINGS LIMITED

Room 1802 18th Floor AXA Centre No 151 Gloucester Road, Wanchai, China (Hong Kong)
Tel.: (852) 3 793 3520 Ky
Web Site: http://www.wankei.com.hk
Year Founded: 2014
1718—(HKG)
Rev.: $33,949,711
Assets: $59,114,879
Liabilities: $36,967,315
Net Worth: $22,147,564
Earnings: ($1,645,344)
Emp.: 124
Fiscal Year-end: 03/31/22
Foundation Piling Services
N.A.I.C.S.: 238910
Hon Hung Fong (CEO)

WAN LEADER INTERNATIONAL LTD.

Office Tower Units 901-902 Hutchison Logistics Centre Terminal 4, Kwai Chung Container Port 18 Container Port Road South, Kwai Chung, New Territories, China (Hong Kong)
Tel.: (852) 37412025 Ky
Web Site: http://www.wanleader.com
8482—(HKG)
Rev.: $26,384,340
Assets: $10,632,225
Liabilities: $2,763,690
Net Worth: $7,868,535
Earnings: ($3,413,303)
Emp.: 33
Fiscal Year-end: 03/31/23
Freight Forwarding Services
N.A.I.C.S.: 488510
Thomas Hak Yu Loy (Chm & CEO)

WAN SHYH SHING CO., LTD.

13th Fl 139 Kien Kwo N Rd Section 2, Taipei, 104, Taiwan
Tel.: (886) 225058856
Web Site:
http://www.wanshyhshing.com
Year Founded: 1984

Sales Range: $25-49.9 Million
Emp.: 30
Leather Hides Wholesale Trade & Distribution Services
N.A.I.C.S.: 425120
Huang Chengsa (CEO)

Subsidiaries:

Ayers Music Co. (1)
13F 139 Kien Kwo N Rd Section 2, Taipei, 104, Taiwan
Tel.: (886) 225058856
Web Site: http://www.ayersguitar.com
Sales Range: $50-74.9 Million
Guitar Sales & Distr
N.A.I.C.S.: 459140
Cheng-Fa Huang (Owner & Pres)

WANBANGDE PHARMACEUTICAL HOLDING GROUP CO., LTD.

No 1688 Dongliang Road, Zhili Town, Huzhou, 317500, Zhejiang, China
Tel.: (86) 57686183899
Web Site:
http://www.dongliang.com.cn
Year Founded: 1984
002082—(SSE)
Sales Range: $1-4.9 Billion
Non-ferrous Metal Product Mfr; Aluminum Decorative Sheets & PS Aluminum Base Plates
N.A.I.C.S.: 331318
Shouming Zhao (Chm & Gen Mgr)

WANBURY LIMITED

BSEL Techpark B Wing 10th Floor Sector 30-A Opp Vashi Railway Station, Vashi, Navi Mumbai, 400703, Maharashtra, India
Tel.: (91) 2267942222
Web Site: https://www.wanbury.com
Year Founded: 1990
WANBURY—(NSE)
Rev.: $53,906,785
Assets: $39,472,579
Liabilities: $60,799,830
Net Worth: ($21,327,251)
Earnings: ($1,720,678)
Emp.: 1,156
Fiscal Year-end: 03/31/21
Pharmaceuticals Product Mfr
N.A.I.C.S.: 325412
K. Chandran (Vice Chm)

WANDA MOVIE CO., LTD.

11th Floor Building B Wanda Plaza, 93 Jianguo Road, Beijing, China
Tel.: (86) 4000806060
Web Site: http://www.wandafilm.com
002739—(SSE)
Rev.: $1,361,222,465
Assets: $3,749,638,272
Liabilities: $2,736,372,988
Net Worth: $1,013,265,284
Earnings: $269,989,621)
Fiscal Year-end: 12/31/22
Movie Theater Owner & Operator
N.A.I.C.S.: 512131

Subsidiaries:

Propaganda GEM Ltd. (1)
23 rue des Vollandes, 1207, Geneva, Switzerland
Tel.: (41) 22 339 90 80
Web Site: http://www.propagandagem.com
Advetising Agency
N.A.I.C.S.: 541810
Ruben Igielko-Herrlich (Owner)

WANDERER WERKE AG

Werner-von-Siemens-Strasse 1, Augsburg, 86159, Germany
Tel.: (49) 821 59030
Automotive Parts Mfr & Distr
N.A.I.C.S.: 336590
Gerhard Schmidt (Member-Mgmt Bd)

WANFENG AUTO HOLDING GROUP CO., LTD.

Wanfeng Science & Technology Garden, Xinchang, Shaoxing, 312500, Zhejiang, China
Tel.: (86) 575 8629 8888
Web Site: http://www.wfjt.com
Emp.: 7,000
Automobile Parts Mfr & Distr
N.A.I.C.S.: 336390
Ailian Chen (Chm & Pres)

Subsidiaries:

Diamond Aircraft Industries Inc. (1)
1560 Crumlin Sideroad, London, N5V 1S2, ON, Canada (60%)
Tel.: (519) 457-4000
Web Site: http://www.diamondaircraft.com
Aircraft Mfr
N.A.I.C.S.: 336411

Meridian Lightweight Technologies Holdings Inc. (1)
4000 Town Ctr Ste 1000, Southfield, MI 48075
Tel.: (248) 663-8100
Emp.: 1,500
Holding Company
N.A.I.C.S.: 551112
Joe Petrillo (Dir-Sls-North America)

Division (Domestic):

Magnesium Products of America (2)
2001 Industrial Dr, Eaton Rapids, MI 48827
Tel.: (517) 663-2700
Web Site: http://www.meridian-mag.com
Emp.: 40
Magnesium Products Mfr
N.A.I.C.S.: 331523
Debbie Hutchison (Dir-HR)

Meridian Business Development (2)
352 N Main St, Plymouth, MI 48170
Tel.: (734) 416-8600
Web Site: http://www.meridian-mag.com
Sales Range: $25-49.9 Million
Emp.: 15
Business Development & Sales Services
N.A.I.C.S.: 423510
Joe Petrillo (Sls Dir-North America)

Subsidiary (Non-US):

Meridian Lightweight Technologies Deutschland GmbH (2)
Leopoldstrasse 244, 80807, Munich, Germany
Tel.: (49) 89 208 039 268
Web Site: http://www.meridian-mag.com
Sales Range: $25-49.9 Million
Emp.: 4
Magnesium Die Casting Services
N.A.I.C.S.: 331523

Meridian Lightweight Technologies Inc. (2)
155 High St E, Strathroy, N7G 1H4, ON, Canada
Tel.: (519) 245-4040
Web Site: http://www.meridian-mag.com
Sales Range: $350-399.9 Million
Emp.: 1,350
Magnesium Die Casting Designer & Mfr
N.A.I.C.S.: 331523
Matt MacDonald (Plant Mgr)

Division (Domestic):

Meridian Technologies - Global Technology Center (3)
25 MacNab Ave, Strathroy, N7G 4H6, ON, Canada
Tel.: (519) 246-9600
Web Site: https://www.meridian-mag.com
Sales Range: $75-99.9 Million
Emp.: 500
Magnesium Die Casting Technology Services
N.A.I.C.S.: 331523

Subsidiary (Non-US):

Meridian Lightweight Technologies UK Limited (2)
Orchard Way Calladine Park, Sutton in Ash-

INTERNATIONAL PUBLIC

field, NG17 1JU, Nottinghamshire, United Kingdom
Tel.: (44) 1623444920
Web Site: http://www.meridian-mag.com
Sales Range: $25-49.9 Million
Emp.: 120
Casting of Light Metals
N.A.I.C.S.: 331523
David Turner (Mgr)

Meridian Technologies Mexico, S. de R.L. de C.V. (2)
Blvd Santa Maria 1955, Parque Industrial Santa Maria, Ramos Arizpe, Coahuila, Mexico
Tel.: (52) 844 866 99 00
Lightweight Magnesium Cast Metal Production
N.A.I.C.S.: 332999

Shanghai Meridian Magnesium Products Limited (2)
777 Taishun Road Anting Town, Jiading District, Shanghai, 201814, China (60%)
Tel.: (86) 2159502388
Web Site: http://www.meridian-mag.com
Sales Range: $50-74.9 Million
Emp.: 150
Magnesium Product Mfr & Services
N.A.I.C.S.: 331523

Weihai Wanfeng Aowei Auto Wheel Co., Ltd. (1)
No 218 Huoju Road High & New Zone, Weihai, 264209, Shandong, China
Tel.: (86) 6315621989
Automobile Parts Mfr & Distr
N.A.I.C.S.: 336390

Weihai Wanfeng Magnesium Science and Technology Development Co., Ltd (1)
Keji Road No 254 Hi-tech Development Zone, Weihai, 264209, china
Tel.: (86) 6315625586
Web Site: http://www.wfmg.cn
Automobile Parts Mfr & Distr
N.A.I.C.S.: 336390

Zhejiang Wanfeng Auto Wheel Co., Ltd. (1)
Industrial Park, Xinchang County, Xinchang, 312500, Zhejiang, China
Tel.: (86) 57586298392
Web Site: https://www.wfaw.com.cn
Rev.: $2,300,076,310
Assets: $2,553,447,499
Liabilities: $1,377,427,728
Net Worth: $1,176,019,772
Earnings: $113,587,756
Emp.: 12,000
Fiscal Year-end: 12/31/2022
Automotive Wheel Mfr
N.A.I.C.S.: 336390
Yinfeng Zhang (Deputy Gen Mgr)

Subsidiary (US):

The Paslin Company (2)
25303 Ryan Rd, Warren, MI 48091
Tel.: (586) 758-0200
Web Site: http://www.paslin.com
Designs, Assembles & Integrates Robotic Assembly Lines
N.A.I.C.S.: 333517

WANFRIED-DRUCK KALDEN GMBH

Vor dem Untertor, 37281, Wanfried, Hesse, Germany
Tel.: (49) 56559870
Web Site: http://www.wanfried-druck.de
Sales Range: $25-49.9 Million
Emp.: 180
Packaging & Label Printing Services
N.A.I.C.S.: 561910
Wolf-Arthur Kalden (Partner)

WANG & LEE GROUP, INC.

5/F Wing Tai Factory Building 3 Tai Yip Street, Kwun Tong, Kowloon, China (Hong Kong)
Tel.: (852) 28891313 VG
Web Site:
https://www.wangnlee.com.hk

AND PRIVATE COMPANIES

Year Founded: 1981
WLGS—(NASDAQ)
Rev.: $6,825,879
Assets: $11,790,806
Liabilities: $5,781,881
Net Worth: $6,008,925
Earnings: ($648,854)
Emp.: 25
Fiscal Year-end: 12/31/23
Construction Engineering Services
N.A.I.C.S.: 541330
Gary Yuk Ming Ma (CFO)

WANG ON GROUP LTD
Suite 3202 32/F Skyline Tower 39
Wang Kwong Road Kowloon Bay,
Kowloon, China (Hong Kong)
Tel.: (852) 2 312 8288
Web Site: http://www.wangon.com
1222—(HKG)
Rev.: $239,392,168
Assets: $2,586,880,534
Liabilities: $1,348,699,104
Net Worth: $1,238,181,430
Earnings: ($32,601,372)
Emp.: 2,145
Fiscal Year-end: 03/31/22
Property Development & Investment Services
N.A.I.C.S.: 531311
Yuk Yin Yau (Co-Founder & Deputy Chm)

Subsidiaries:

Allied Victory Investment Limited (1)
5F Wai Yuen Tong Medicine Building 9
Wang Kwong Rd, Kowloon, China (Hong Kong) **(100%)**
Tel.: (852) 2312 8288
Web Site: http://www.astudios.com.hk
Sales Range: $25-49.9 Million
Emp.: 30
Apartment Rental Services
N.A.I.C.S.: 531110
Liu Sheng (Mgr)

Denox Management Limited (1)
5 F Wai Yuen Tong Medicine Bldg 9 Wang
Kwong Rd, Kowloon Bay, Kowloon, China (Hong Kong)
Tel.: (852) 35266719
Real Estate Property Management Services
N.A.I.C.S.: 531210

Goodtech Management Limited (1)
Top Fl Ping Tin Comml Ctr On Tin St, Lam Tin, Kowloon, China (Hong Kong)
Tel.: (852) 29523882
Shopping Mall Management Services
N.A.I.C.S.: 561439

Lica Parking Company Limited (1)
5 F Wai Yuen Tong Medicine Bldg 9 Wang
Kwong Rd, Kowloon Bay, Kowloon, China (Hong Kong)
Tel.: (852) 23128338
Parking Lot Operation Services
N.A.I.C.S.: 812930

Wai Yuen Tong Medicine Holdings Limited (1)
Suite 3101 31/F Skyline Tower 39 Wang
Kwong Road, Kowloon Bay, Kowloon,
China (Hong Kong) **(58.08%)**
Tel.: (852) 2 312 8202
Web Site: http://www.wyth.net
Rev.: $179,464,191
Assets: $979,953,023
Liabilities: $469,113,416
Net Worth: $510,839,607
Earnings: ($11,327,411)
Emp.: 1,872
Fiscal Year-end: 03/31/2022
Pharmaceuticals Product Mfr
N.A.I.C.S.: 325412
Ching Ho Tang (Chm & Mng Dir)

Subsidiary (Domestic):

Luxembourg Medicine Company Limited (2)
Room 101 31st Floor Grand Sky Plaza 39
Wang Kwong Road, Kowloon Bay, Kowloon, China (Hong Kong)
Tel.: (852) 35266666

Web Site: http://www.lux-mp.com
Pharmaceuticals Products Mfr & Sales
N.A.I.C.S.: 325412

Wai Yuen Tong Medicine Company Limited (2)
Room 3101 31/F Grand Plaza 39 Wang
Kwong Road, Kowloon Bay, Kowloon, China (Hong Kong)
Tel.: (852) 27278911
Web Site: http://www.wyt.hk
Pharmaceuticals Product Mfr
N.A.I.C.S.: 325412

Wang On Majorluck Limited (1)
5 F Wai Yuen Tong Medicine Bldg 9 Wang
Kwong Rd, Kowloon Bay, Kowloon, China (Hong Kong)
Tel.: (852) 23128288
Chinese Wet Markets Management Services
N.A.I.C.S.: 445250

Wang On Shopping Centre Management Limited (1)
Podium Level Ping Tin Shopping Ctr, Lam Tin, Kowloon, China (Hong Kong)
Tel.: (852) 29523162
Shopping Mall Management Services
N.A.I.C.S.: 531120

WANG ON PROPERTIES LTD.
Suite 3201 32/F Skyline Tower 39
Wang Kwong Road, Kowloon Bay,
Kowloon, China (Hong Kong)
Tel.: (852) 23128288 BM
Web Site:
http://www.woproperties.com
Year Founded: 1987
1243—(HKG)
Rev.: $304,600,077
Assets: $1,122,099,100
Liabilities: $516,528,840
Net Worth: $605,570,260
Earnings: $60,593,854
Emp.: 126
Fiscal Year-end: 03/31/20
Residential & Commercial Property
Development Services
N.A.I.C.S.: 531210
Ho Hong Tang (CEO)

WANGFUJING GROUP CO., LTD.
No 253 Wangfujing Street,
Dongcheng District, Beijing, 100006, China
Tel.: (86) 1085291118
Web Site: https://www.wfj.com.cn
Year Founded: 1955
600859—(SHG)
Rev.: $1,516,304,865
Assets: $5,081,370,854
Liabilities: $2,281,344,647
Net Worth: $2,800,026,207
Earnings: $27,366,375
Fiscal Year-end: 12/31/22
Departmental Store Operator
N.A.I.C.S.: 455110
Bai Fan (Chm)

WANGLE TECHNOLOGIES LIMITED
Suite 9 330 Churchill Avenue, Subiaco, 6008, WA, Australia
Tel.: (61) 864891600
Year Founded: 2014
Rev.: $9,538
Assets: $386,962
Liabilities: $659,356
Net Worth: ($272,394)
Earnings: ($4,686,196)
Fiscal Year-end: 06/30/18
Investment Services
N.A.I.C.S.: 523999
Alistair McCall (Chief Data Officer)

Subsidiaries:

Premium Pipe Services Pty Ltd. (1)
Unit 6 110 Inspiration Dr, Wangara, 6065,

WA, Australia
Tel.: (61) 894561002
Sales Range: $25-49.9 Million
Emp.: 1
Pipe Repair & Rehabilitation Services
N.A.I.C.S.: 237120

WANGLI SECURITY & SURVEILLANCE PRODUCT CO., LTD.
No 9 Aigang Road Economic Development Zone, Yongkang Economic
Development Zone, Yongkang,
321300, Zhejiang, China
Tel.: (86) 57989291280
Web Site:
https://www.wanglianfang.com
Year Founded: 2005
605268—(SHG)
Rev.: $309,262,071
Assets: $529,119,064
Liabilities: $288,894,902
Net Worth: $240,224,161
Earnings: ($6,035,108)
Fiscal Year-end: 12/31/22
Door Product Mfr & Distr
N.A.I.C.S.: 321911
Yuebin Wang (Chm & Gen Mgr)

WANGNENG ENVIRONMENT CO., LTD.
No 899 Huanshan Road Longxi
Street, Wuxing District, Huzhou,
313000, Zhejiang, China
Tel.: (86) 5722208888 CN
Web Site:
https://www.wannaenergy.com
Year Founded: 1993
002034—(SSE)
Rev.: $439,965,441
Assets: $1,996,356,945
Liabilities: $1,097,039,793
Net Worth: $899,317,152
Earnings: $83,508,100
Fiscal Year-end: 12/31/23
Waste Management Services
N.A.I.C.S.: 562998
Yong Rui (Chm)

WANGSU SCIENCE & TECHNOLOGY CO., LTD.
5/F Building A Guangqi Culture Plaza
2899 Xitu Road, Xuhui, Shanghai,
200030, China
Tel.: (86) 2124261717
Web Site: https://www.wangsu.com
Year Founded: 2000
300017—(CHIN)
Rev.: $662,769,098
Assets: $1,544,938,930
Liabilities: $166,191,746
Net Worth: $1,378,747,184
Earnings: $86,354,515
Emp.: 2,300
Fiscal Year-end: 12/31/23
E Commerce Site Operator
N.A.I.C.S.: 335910
Jiang Wei (CFO & Deputy Gen Mgr)

WANGTON CAPITAL CORP.
1055 West Georgia Street Suite 115,
Vancouver, V6E 4N7, BC, Canada
Tel.: (604) 765-4794 AB
Year Founded: 2010
WTH—(TSXV)
Rev.: $4,359
Assets: $168,313
Liabilities: $24,402
Net Worth: $143,912
Earnings: ($38,050)
Fiscal Year-end: 12/31/23
Investment Services
N.A.I.C.S.: 523999
Tagdeer Gill (CFO)

WANGUO INTERNATIONAL

WANHUA CHEMICAL GROUP CO., LTD.

MINING GROUP LIMITED
Wanguo Mining Area Yifeng Xinzhuang Township, Yifeng County,
Shanghai, Jiangxi, China
Tel.: (86) 7952977888 Ky
Web Site: http://www.wgmine.com
Year Founded: 2011
3939—(HKG)
Rev.: $95,671,087
Assets: $286,130,005
Liabilities: $82,606,306
Net Worth: $203,523,700
Earnings: $23,828,407
Emp.: 774
Fiscal Year-end: 12/31/22
Copper & Iron Ore Mining Services
N.A.I.C.S.: 212230
Mingqing Gao (Chm & CEO)

WANHUA CHEMICAL GROUP CO., LTD.
No 3 Sanya Road YEDA, Yantai,
Shandong, China
Tel.: (86) 4009600309 CN
Year Founded: 1998
600309—(SHG)
Rev.: $24,280,147,278
Assets: $35,035,499,391
Liabilities: $21,957,545,290
Net Worth: $13,077,954,101
Earnings: $2,328,278,065
Emp.: 19,000
Fiscal Year-end: 12/31/23
Chemical Products Mfr
N.A.I.C.S.: 325998
Limin Li (CFO)

Subsidiaries:

Guangdong Wanhua Rongwei Polyurethanes Co., Ltd. (1)
No 508 Mingcheng Town Industrial Zone,
Gaoming District, Foshan, Guangdong, China
Tel.: (86) 757 88832828
Web Site: http://www.ytpu.com
Chemical Products Mfr & Distr
N.A.I.C.S.: 325998

Ningbo Daxie Development Zone
Wanhua Industry Park Thermal
Power Co., Ltd. (1)
Wanhua Industrial Park Ningbo Daxie Development Zone, 39 Huandao Road North,
Ningbo, 315812, Zhejiang, China
Tel.: (86) 57486716113
Chemical Products Mfr & Distr
N.A.I.C.S.: 325180

Ningbo Daxie Wanhua Port Co., Ltd. (1)
Wanhua Industrial Park Ningbo Daxie Development Zone, 39 Huandao Road North,
Ningbo, Zhejiang, China
Tel.: (86) 57486716577
Web Site: http://www.ytpu.com
Chemical Products Mfr
N.A.I.C.S.: 325998

Wanhua (Japan) Co., Ltd. (1)
3rd Floor 32 Shibakoen Building 3-4-30
Shibakoen, Minato-ku, Tokyo, 105-0011, Japan
Tel.: (81) 3 5777 6787
Web Site: http://www.ytpu.com
Chemical Products Distr
N.A.I.C.S.: 424690
Yoshiyuki Aoshima (Mng Dir)

Wanhua (Netherlands) B.V. (1)
Schiphol Boulevard 301, Luchthaven Schiphol, 1118 BJ, Schiphol, Netherlands
Tel.: (31) 202065130
Emp.: 7
Chemical Products Mfr & Distr
N.A.I.C.S.: 325510
Jihua Zou (Gen Mgr)

Wanhua Borsodchem Latin America
Comercio de Produtos Quimicos
Ltda (1)
E-Tower Rua Funchal 418 34th Floor Office
3414, Sao Paulo, 04551-060, Brazil
Tel.: (55) 112 321 0244

WANHUA CHEMICAL GROUP CO., LTD.

Wanhua Chemical Group Co., Ltd.—(Continued)
Chemical Innovative Product Distr
N.A.I.C.S.: 424690

Wanhua Borsodchem Rus LLC (1)
Lotte Business Centre Profsoyuznaya ul 65, Moscow, Russia
Tel.: (7) 4959809462
Chemical Innovative Product Distr
N.A.I.C.S.: 424690

Wanhua Chemical (America) Co., Ltd. (1)
3803 W Chester Pike Ste 240, Newtown Square, PA 19073
Tel.: (610) 331-4096
Chemical Innovative Product Distr
N.A.I.C.S.: 424690

Wanhua Chemical (Japan) Co., Ltd. (1)
5F Circles Shiodome 2-9-1, Higashishimbashi Minato-ku, Tokyo, 105-0021, Japan
Tel.: (81) 35 777 6787
Chemical Innovative Product Distr
N.A.I.C.S.: 424690

Wanhua Chemical (Singapore) Pte. Ltd. (1)
33-06 Singapore Land Tower 50 Raffles Place, Singapore, 048623, Singapore
Tel.: (65) 6 224 0614
Chemical Innovative Product Distr
N.A.I.C.S.: 424690

Wanhua International (India) Private Limited (1)
S22 Vatika Business Centre 7th Floor Supreme Business Park, Hiranandani Gardens Powai, Mumbai, India
Tel.: (91) 224 201 9131
Chemical Innovative Product Distr
N.A.I.C.S.: 424690

WANHWA ENTERPRISE CO., LTD.

No 52 Emei Street, Taipei, Taiwan
Tel.: (886) 23753211
Web Site: https://www.wanhwa.com.tw
Year Founded: 1958
2701—(TAI)
Rev.: $9,718,597
Assets: $312,662,534
Liabilities: $41,729,846
Net Worth: $270,932,689
Earnings: $7,761,535
Emp.: 21
Fiscal Year-end: 12/31/23
Property Leasing Services
N.A.I.C.S.: 531120
Cai Maochang (Chm)

WANJIA GROUP HOLDINGS LIMITED

Suite 1801 18/F Tower 1 The Gateway Harbour City, 25 Canton Road Tsim Sha Tsui, Kowloon, China (Hong Kong)
Tel.: (852) 2 366 3375
Web Site: http://www.wanjia-gp.com
0401—(HKG)
Rev.: $19,969,071
Assets: $24,740,686
Liabilities: $8,218,864
Net Worth: $16,521,822
Earnings: ($6,569,854)
Emp.: 184
Fiscal Year-end: 03/31/22
Pharmaceutical & Healthcare Products
N.A.I.C.S.: 456110
Jia Jun Wang (CEO)

WANKA ONLINE, INC.

F/L 4 Building 6 No 60 Anli Road, Chaoyang District, Beijing, 100101, China
Tel.: (86) 1064820535 Ky

Web Site: http://www.wankaonline.com
1762—(HKG)
Rev.: $323,042,850
Assets: $268,318,440
Liabilities: $75,573,950
Net Worth: $192,744,490
Earnings: ($18,049,543)
Emp.: 220
Fiscal Year-end: 12/31/22
Electronic Product Mfr & Distr
N.A.I.C.S.: 334220
Dinan Gao (Founder, Chm & CEO)

WANKAI NEW MATERIALS CO., LTD.

No 15 Wenlan Road, Jiaxing Jianshan District, Haining, 314415, ZheJiang, China
Tel.: (86) 57387801168
Web Site: https://wkaiglobal.com
Year Founded: 2008
301216—(SSE)
Rev.: $2,721,800,451
Assets: $1,626,485,688
Liabilities: $841,171,795
Net Worth: $785,313,894
Earnings: $134,349,939
Fiscal Year-end: 12/31/22
Packaging Materials Mfr
N.A.I.C.S.: 333993
Zhigang Shen (Chm)

WANMA TECHNOLOGY CO., LTD.

11F Tianji Building No 181 Tianmushan Road, Xihu District, Hangzhou, 311306, Zhejiang, China
Tel.: (86) 57161101902
Web Site: https://www.wanma-tech.cn
Year Founded: 1997
300698—(CHIN)
Rev.: $73,337,384
Assets: $126,120,597
Liabilities: $59,687,892
Net Worth: $66,432,705
Earnings: $9,078,937
Emp.: 500
Fiscal Year-end: 12/31/23
Communication Equipment Mfr & Distr
N.A.I.C.S.: 334220
Zhang Heyang (Chm)

WANMO

8/F Fuband Building No16 Dong Sanhuan Zhonglu, Chaoyang District, Beijing, 100022, China
Tel.: (86) 1051672255 CN
Web Site: http://www.madeforchina.com
Year Founded: 1997
Sales Range: $10-24.9 Million
Emp.: 30
Consumer Marketing, Direct Marketing, Electronic Media
N.A.I.C.S.: 541860
Micah Truman (Chm)

Subsidiaries:

Wanmo (1)
Rm. 1216, 12/F Shenshi Mansion No 511, Weihai Road Jing'an District, Shanghai, 200041, China
Tel.: (86) 21 6258 3355
Web Site: http://www.wanmo.com
Emp.: 10
N.A.I.C.S.: 541860
Astrid von Rudloff (CEO)

WANNITUBE

23 rue Royale, 69001, Lyon, France
Tel.: (33) 478615065
Web Site: http://www.wannitube.fr
Rev.: $23,800,000
Emp.: 67

Water Pipe Systems Construction Services
N.A.I.C.S.: 237110
Denis Janin (Dir-Publ)

WANSHIH ELECTRONICS CO., LTD.

Floor 3-5 No 72 Wugong 6th Road, New Taipei Industrial Park, New Taipei City, 24891, Taiwan
Tel.: (886) 222988066
Web Site: https://www.wanshih.com.tw
Year Founded: 1987
6134—(TPE)
Rev.: $45,203,827
Assets: $53,826,095
Liabilities: $26,900,447
Net Worth: $26,925,648
Earnings: ($2,252,384)
Emp.: 1,600
Fiscal Year-end: 12/31/22
Cable Mfr
N.A.I.C.S.: 335929
Ringo Chang (Chm)

Subsidiaries:

Dongguan Humen Wanshih Electronic Co., Ltd. (1)
Longyan Ind Area, Hu-men, Dongguan, Guangdong, China
Tel.: (86) 76985552215
Power Cords Mfr
N.A.I.C.S.: 335999
Lake Chang (Chm)

Draco Electronics, LLC (1)
4575 Cushing Pkwy, Fremont, CA 94538
Tel.: (510) 656-1650
Equipment Cables Mfr & Distr
N.A.I.C.S.: 335929

Suzhou Wanshih Electronic Element Co., Ltd. (1)
No 168 Wen Du Road, Wan Ting Town, Suzhou, Wuxian, China
Tel.: (86) 51266702220
Mobile Cable Mfr
N.A.I.C.S.: 334210
Lake Chang (Chm)

Suzhou Wanshih Optical Communication Co., Ltd. (1)
No 168 Wen Du Road, Wan Ting Town, Suzhou, Wuxian, China
Tel.: (86) 51266702733
Antenna Assembly Parts Mfr
N.A.I.C.S.: 334220
Lake Chang (Chm)

Wanshih Electronic (H.K) Co., Ltd. (1)
RM 214 2/F International Plaza 20 Sheung Yuet Rd, Kowloon Bay, Kowloon, China (Hong Kong)
Tel.: (852) 27543188
Power Cords Mfr
N.A.I.C.S.: 335999
Ringo Chang (Chm)

Wanshih Electronic Element Company Limited (1)
Workshop G6 Lot XN6II Dai An Expansion Industrial zone, Lai CachTown Cam Giang District, Hai Duong, Vietnam
Tel.: (84) 2203516867
Wireless Antenna Mfr & Distr
N.A.I.C.S.: 334220

WANT WANT CHINA HOLDINGS LTD.

1088 East Hong Song East Road, Shanghai, 201103, China
Tel.: (86) 216 115 1111 Ky
Web Site: http://www.want-want.com
0151—(HKG)
Rev.: $3,674,725,150
Assets: $4,574,541,269
Liabilities: $2,014,589,392
Net Worth: $2,559,951,877
Earnings: $641,814,156
Emp.: 41,265

INTERNATIONAL PUBLIC

Fiscal Year-end: 03/31/22
Snack Food Mfr
N.A.I.C.S.: 311919
Ching-Tsun Liao (Vice Chm)

Subsidiaries:

Beijing Be-Want Foods Ltd (1)
No 8 Area Xinggu Economic Development Zone, Pinggu District, Beijing, China (100%)
Tel.: (86) 1069966789
Food Mfr
N.A.I.C.S.: 311999

Beijing Big-Want Foods Ltd (1)
No 1088 Hong Song East Road, Shanghai, 201103, China (100%)
Tel.: (86) 10 21 6115 1111
Web Site: http://www.hot-kid.com.cn
Food Mfr
N.A.I.C.S.: 311999

First Family Enterprise Co., Ltd. (1)
3F 72 Hisn Ning N Road, Taipei, 10346, Taiwan
Tel.: (886) 2 25545300
Convenience Foods Mfr
N.A.I.C.S.: 311999

Guangzhou Big-Want Foods Ltd. (1)
No 3 Xinyuan Road Yonghe Economic Area, Guangzhou, 511356, Guangdong, China
Tel.: (86) 2022209888
Food & Beverages Mfr & Distr
N.A.I.C.S.: 311999

Huaian Want Want Foods Ltd. (1)
No 21 Wangwang Road, Qinghe New District, Huai'an, 223001, Jiangsu, China
Tel.: (86) 51783721389
Food Products Mfr & Distr
N.A.I.C.S.: 311999

I Lan Foods Industrial Co., Ltd. (1)
72 Hsi Ning N Road, Taipei, 10342, Taiwan
Tel.: (886) 225545300
Food Products Mfr & Distr
N.A.I.C.S.: 311999

Nanjing Want Want Foods Ltd (1)
No 112 Dongcun Rd, Development Zone Jiangning Dis, Nanjing, China (91%)
Tel.: (86) 2551180188
Food Mfr
N.A.I.C.S.: 311999

Union Insurance Co., Ltd. (1)
12Th Floor 219 Sec 4 Chung-Hsiao E Road, Daan District, Taipei, 10690, Taiwan
Tel.: (886) 27765567
Web Site: https://www.wwunion.com
Rev.: $416,497,090
Assets: $651,690,842
Liabilities: $452,186,385
Net Worth: $199,504,456
Earnings: $39,253,931
Emp.: 1,110
Fiscal Year-end: 12/31/2023
Insurance Services
N.A.I.C.S.: 524126
Ji-Xiong Hong (Chm)

Want Want Food Pte Ltd (1)
400 Orchard Road, 238805, Singapore, Singapore (100%)
Tel.: (65) 67349717
Web Site: http://www.wantwant.com
Sales Range: $50-74.9 Million
Emp.: 10
Holding Company
N.A.I.C.S.: 551112

Want Want Holdings Ltd. (1)
400 Orchard Road Orchard Towers 17-05, Singapore, 238875, Singapore
Tel.: (65) 6225 1588
Investment Management Service
N.A.I.C.S.: 523999

Wingate Overseas Holdings Ltd. (1)
C/O Caribbean Corporate Services Limited 3rd Floor Omar Hodge Building, Road Town, Virgin Islands (British)
Tel.: (284) 494 5108
Investment Management Service
N.A.I.C.S.: 523999

WANTED LAB INC.

AND PRIVATE COMPANIES

35th floor Lotte World Tower 300 Olympicro, Songpa-gu, Seoul, Korea (South)
Tel.: (82) 25397118
Web Site: https://www.wanted.co.kr
Year Founded: 2015
376980—(KRS)
Rev: $6,862,753
Assets: $43,638,626
Liabilities: $10,680,066
Net Worth: $32,958,560
Earnings: $7,212,934
Emp.: 186
Fiscal Year-end: 12/31/22
Recruitment Services
N.A.I.C.S.: 561311

WANTEDLY, INC.
MG Shirokanedai Building 4F 5-12-7 Shirokanedai, Minato-ku, Tokyo, 108-0071, Japan
Tel.: (81) 363692018
Web Site: https://wantedlyinc.com
3991—(TKS)
Rev: $29,370,840
Assets: $32,766,960
Liabilities: $7,855,860
Net Worth: $24,911,100
Earnings: $6,443,920
Fiscal Year-end: 08/31/24
Application Development Services
N.A.I.C.S.: 541511

WANXIANG DONEED CO., LTD.
No 18 Yushan Road, Nangang District, Harbin, 150090, Heilongjiang, China
Tel.: (86) 45182368448
Web Site: https://www.wxdoneed.com
Year Founded: 1995
600371—(SHG)
Rev: $32,990,027
Assets: $126,115,100
Liabilities: $37,873,925
Net Worth: $88,241,175
Earnings: $10,104,981
Fiscal Year-end: 12/31/22
Crop Seed Farming Services
N.A.I.C.S.: 111998

WANXIANG GROUP CORPORATION
Wanxiang Rd, Xiaoshan District, Hangzhou, 311215, Zhejiang, China
Tel.: (86) 57182832999 CN
Web Site: http://www.wanxiang.com.cn
Year Founded: 1969
Sales Range: $5-14.9 Billion
Emp.: 40,000
Holding Company; Automotive Components Mfr & Distr
N.A.I.C.S.: 551112
Guangqui Lu *(Pres)*

Subsidiaries:

Wanxiang America Corporation (1)
88 Airport Rd, Elgin, IL 60123
Tel.: (847) 622-8838
Web Site: http://www.wanxiang.com
Sales Range: $1-4.9 Billion
Emp.: 45
Furniture Merchant Whslr
N.A.I.C.S.: 423210
Gary E. Wetzel *(CFO & COO)*

Wanxiang Australia Pty, Ltd. (1)
PO Box 8046, Dunoon, 2480, NSW, Australia
Tel.: (61) 2 6689 5977
Automobile Component Distr
N.A.I.C.S.: 423120
Roger Tyrrell *(Mng Dir)*

Wanxiang Europe GmbH (1)
Henry-Ford-Strasse 1, 52351, Duren, Germany

Tel.: (49) 2421 277 2388
Automobile Parts Distr
N.A.I.C.S.: 423120

WANXIANG INTERNATIONAL LIMITED
No 4309 Hunan Road, Zhoupu Industrial District Pudong, Shanghai, China
Tel.: (86) 2168116892 SG
Web Site: http://www.wxintl.com
Sales Range: $75-99.9 Million
Natural & Synthetic Ingredient Mfr
N.A.I.C.S.: 325620
Jie Chen *(CFO)*

Subsidiaries:

Huaian Wanbang Aromatic Chemicals Industry Co., Ltd (1)
No 216 East Changjiang Road, Huaiyin District, Huai'an, Jiangsu, China
Tel.: (86) 51784801086
Perfume Mfr
N.A.I.C.S.: 325620

Shanghai Wanxiang Flavors & Fragrances Co., Ltd. (1)
No 4309 Hunan Road, Pudong, Shanghai, China
Tel.: (86) 2168116334
Perfume Mfr
N.A.I.C.S.: 325620

Wanxiang International (Europe) Limited (1)
88 Wood Street 10th - 15th Floor, London, EC2V 7RS, United Kingdom
Tel.: (44) 2085281098
Perfume Distr
N.A.I.C.S.: 456120

Wanxiang International (USA) Ltd (1)
140 E Ridgewood Ave Ste 415 S Tower, Paramus, NJ 07652
Tel.: (201) 940-7297
Perfume Distr
N.A.I.C.S.: 456120

Wanxiang International Flavors & Fragrances Pte Ltd (1)
81 Anson Road Suite 8-21, Singapore, 79908, Singapore
Tel.: (65) 65006311
Perfume Distr
N.A.I.C.S.: 456120

WANXIANG QIANCHAO CO., LTD.
Wanxiang Road, Xiaoshan District, Hangzhou, 311215, China
Tel.: (86) 57182832999
Web Site: https://www.wxqc.com.cn
Year Founded: 1969
000559—(SSE)
Rev: $1,967,699,724
Assets: $2,694,033,880
Liabilities: $1,441,757,533
Net Worth: $1,252,276,347
Earnings: $113,596,966
Fiscal Year-end: 12/31/22
Automobile Equipment Mfr
N.A.I.C.S.: 336110
Ni Pin *(Chm)*

WANZL METALLWARENFABRIK GMBH
Rudolf-Wanzl-Strasse 4, 89340, Leipheim, Germany
Tel.: (49) 8221 729 0
Web Site: http://www.wanzl.com
Year Founded: 1918
Shopping Cart, Basket & Display Product Mfr
N.A.I.C.S.: 332299
Ralph Boehlke *(Mng Dir-Expansion)*

Subsidiaries:

Expedit a/s (1)
Toftegaardsvej 4, DK-8370, Hadsten, Denmark (33.53%)
Tel.: (45) 87612200

Web Site: http://www.expedit.eu
Shopfittings Distr
N.A.I.C.S.: 424410

Subsidiary (Non-US):

Expedit AB (2)
Dammvagen 1, Fredriksdal, S-571 75, Jonkoping, Sweden
Tel.: (46) 104761700
Web Site: http://www.expedit.se
Shopfitting Specialists
N.A.I.C.S.: 337127

Expedit Finland Oy (2)
Puutarhatie 24a, FI-01300, Vantaa, Finland
Tel.: (358) 20 741 4640
Web Site: http://www.expedit.fi
Shopfitting Specialists
N.A.I.C.S.: 337127

Expedit Norge A/S (2)
Thoroyaveien 21, N 2026, Skjetten, Norway
Tel.: (47) 33 42 32 80
Web Site: http://www.expedit.no
Shopfittings Mfr
N.A.I.C.S.: 337127

The French Company LLC (1)
8289 Darrow Rd, Twinsburg, OH 44087
Tel.: (330) 963-4344
Web Site: http://www.frenchcompanyllc.com
Sales Range: $1-9.9 Million
Emp.: 100
Shopping Cart Repair & Maintenance Services
N.A.I.C.S.: 811310
Diane Nichols *(Mgr-HR)*

WANZL SK, s.r.o. (1)
Cukrovárska 427, 926 01, Sered, Slovakia
Tel.: (421) 317891381
Logistics Consulting Servies
N.A.I.C.S.: 541614

WANZL spol. s r.o. (1)
Okr Olomouc, 783 47, Olomouc, Czech Republic
Tel.: (420) 585751555
Automated Storage System Distr
N.A.I.C.S.: 423830

Wanzl (Schweiz) AG (1)
Industrie Hegi 2, 9425, Thal, Switzerland
Tel.: (41) 718869010
Automated Storage System Distr
N.A.I.C.S.: 423830
Adrian Eschbach *(Acct Mgr)*

Wanzl Australia Pty. Ltd. (1)
97 Highbury Road, Burwood, 3125, VIC, Australia
Tel.: (61) 98082299
Automated Storage System Mfr
N.A.I.C.S.: 337215

Wanzl Commercial Equipment (Shanghai) Co. Ltd. (1)
No 838 Shu Hai Rd, 201611, Shanghai, China
Tel.: (86) 2167601558
Automated Storage System Distr
N.A.I.C.S.: 423830

Wanzl Equipamiento Comercial, S.L. (1)
Poligono Industrial el pla, Molins de Rei, Barcelona, Spain
Tel.: (34) 936803650
Automated Storage System Distr
N.A.I.C.S.: 423830

Wanzl Gesellschaft m.b.H. (1)
Fachmarktstrasse 10, 2334, Voesendorf, Austria
Tel.: (43) 161625460
Automated Storage System Mfr
N.A.I.C.S.: 337215

Wanzl India Pvt Ltd (1)
C-306 Golden Petals, 411052, Pune, India
Tel.: (91) 9049986858
Automated Storage System Distr
N.A.I.C.S.: 423830

Wanzl Italia S.r.l. (1)
Via Del Ferro n 8/10, 25039, Travagliato, Italy
Tel.: (39) 0306863949
Logistics Consulting Servies
N.A.I.C.S.: 541614

Giuseppe Migliorati *(CEO)*

Wanzl Korea Ltd. (1)
302A Richtown Bldg 325 Giljuro, Wonmi-Gu, Bucheon, Gyeonggi, Korea (South)
Tel.: (82) 323281434
Automated Storage System Distr
N.A.I.C.S.: 423830

Wanzl Ltd. (1)
Europa House, Warwick, CV34 6SP, United Kingdom
Tel.: (44) 1926451951
Logistics Consulting Servies
N.A.I.C.S.: 541614
Avtar Mann *(Acct Mgr)*

Wanzl Magyarorszag KFT (1)
Kunigunda u 58, 1037, Budapest, Hungary
Tel.: (36) 13873793
Interior Design Services
N.A.I.C.S.: 541410

Wanzl Middle East FZE (1)
Gold Diamond Park, Dubai, United Arab Emirates
Tel.: (971) 43418555
Automated Storage System Distr
N.A.I.C.S.: 423830

Wanzl Nederland b.v. (1)
Karolusstraat 4, 4903 RJ, Oosterhout, Netherlands
Tel.: (31) 162422250
Automated Storage System Distr
N.A.I.C.S.: 423830

Wanzl SAS (1)
10 avenue Ledru Rolin, 75012, Paris, France
Tel.: (33) 144750202
Industrial Equipment Distr
N.A.I.C.S.: 423610

Wanzl Sp. z o.o. (1)
ul Mszczonowska 69, 05-830, Nadarzyn, Poland
Tel.: (48) 227395000
Logistics Consulting Servies
N.A.I.C.S.: 541614

Wanzl b.v.b.a. (1)
Ambachtenlaan 36, 3001, Heverlee, Belgium
Tel.: (32) 16402830
Automated Storage System Distr
N.A.I.C.S.: 423830

WAPPLE.NET LTD
The Meadows Brockhill Court Brockhill Lane, Redditch, B97 6RB, Worchestershire, United Kingdom
Tel.: (44) 1527 558 247
Web Site: http://www.wapple.net
Year Founded: 2004
Sales Range: $1-9.9 Million
Mobile Websites, Applications & Marketing
N.A.I.C.S.: 541519
Rich Holdsworth *(CEO)*

WAPS CO., LTD.
45 Centumdongro, Haeundae-gu, Busan, 48059, Korea (South)
Tel.: (82) 518966390
Web Site: https://waps.com
Year Founded: 2001
196700—(KRS)
Rev: $26,100,038
Assets: $47,203,232
Liabilities: $21,473,743
Net Worth: $25,729,490
Earnings: ($6,517,944)
Emp.: 90
Fiscal Year-end: 12/31/22
Plastics Product Mfr
N.A.I.C.S.: 326199
Jae-Choon Lee *(CEO)*

WARABA GOLD LIMITED
Suite 1080 789 West Pender Street, Vancouver, V6C 1H2, BC, Canada
Tel.: (312) 235-2605
Web Site: https://warabagold.com
WBGD—(CNSX)

WARABA GOLD LIMITED

Waraba Gold Limited—(Continued)
Assets: $558,391
Liabilities: $186,460
Net Worth: $371,931
Earnings: ($912,363)
Fiscal Year-end: 07/31/23
Mineral Exploration Services
N.A.I.C.S.: 213115
Carl Esprey *(CEO)*

WARABEYA NICHIYO HOLDINGS CO., LTD.

13-19 Tomihisa-cho, Shinjuku-ku, Tokyo, 162-8020, Japan
Tel.: (81) 353637010 JP
Web Site:
https://www.warabeya.co.jp
Year Founded: 1964
2918—(TKS)
Rev.: $1,467,693,810
Assets: $722,896,400
Liabilities: $337,845,590
Net Worth: $385,050,810
Earnings: $30,295,570
Emp.: 1,948
Fiscal Year-end: 02/29/24
Holding Company; Prepared Food Product Mfr & Whslr
N.A.I.C.S.: 551112
Hiroyuki Otomo *(Chm & Pres)*

Subsidiaries:

Bestrans Co., Ltd. (1)
30-83 Okinohama, Sakaide, 762-0052, Kanagawa, Japan
Tel.: (81) 877466610
Web Site: https://www.bestrans.co.jp
Food Processing Machinery Maintenance Services
N.A.I.C.S.: 811310

Nichiyo Co., Ltd. (1)
7F Ningyocyo Ouchi Building 1-6-9 Ningyo-cho Nihonbashi, Chuo-Ku, Tokyo, 103-0031, Japan
Tel.: (81) 356496658
Web Site: http://www.nichiyo-jp.com
Emp.: 30
Logistic Services
N.A.I.C.S.: 488510

Prosystas Co., Ltd. (1)
7-1-29 Nishinakajima Building 8F, Yodogawa-ku, Osaka, 532-0011, Japan
Tel.: (81) 663035503
Web Site: https://www.prosysta.co.jp
Emp.: 50
Electric Equipment Mfr
N.A.I.C.S.: 335999

Trust K Porter Co., Ltd. (1)
3-838-3 Kurashiki, Higashiyamato-shi, Tokyo, 207-0032, Japan
Tel.: (81) 425658811
Web Site: https://www.trust-k-p.co.jp
Foodstuff & Soft Drink Distr
N.A.I.C.S.: 424490

WARATAH RESOURCES LIMITED

Level 2 66 Hunter Street, Sydney, 2000, NSW, Australia
Tel.: (61) 2 8249 4436
Web Site:
http://www.waratahresources.com
Sales Range: Less than $1 Million
Emp.: 7
Iron & Gold Exploration & Mining Services
N.A.I.C.S.: 212220
Anne Adaley *(Sec)*

WARBA BANK (K.S.C.P.)

Al Hamra Tower 25 th Floor Abdulaziz Al Saqr Street, PO Box 13001, Safat, Kuwait, 1220, Kuwait
Tel.: (965) 22287000 KW
Web Site:
https://www.warbabank.com
Year Founded: 2010

WARBABANK—(KUW)
Rev.: $420,234,652
Assets: $13,653,212,649
Liabilities: $12,437,973,285
Net Worth: $1,215,239,364
Earnings: $62,686,470
Emp.: 671
Fiscal Year-end: 12/31/22
Commercial Banking Services
N.A.I.C.S.: 522110
Abdulwahab Abdullah Al Houti *(Chm)*

WARBA CAPITAL HOLDING COMPANY

Al Sharq Khalid Bin Al-Waleed St Al-Dhow Tower Floor 28, PO Box 2383, Safat, Kuwait, 13024, Kuwait
Tel.: (965) 22064610 KW
Web Site: https://warbacap.com
Year Founded: 2004
Rev.: $889,774
Assets: $55,388,316
Liabilities: $8,865,386
Net Worth: $46,522,930
Earnings: ($1,728,851)
Fiscal Year-end: 07/31/17
Holding Company
N.A.I.C.S.: 551112
Abdulteef M. Al-Dabbous *(Chm)*

WARBA INSURANCE AND REINSURANCE COMPANY K.S.C.P.

Derwazat Abdul Razak - Opposite to the Banking Complex - Warba Tower, PO Box 24282, Sharq - Ahmad Al Jaber Street, 13103, Kuwait, 13103, Kuwait
Tel.: (965) 1808181
Web Site: https://www.warba.insure
Year Founded: 1976
WINS—(KUW)
Rev.: $132,821,479
Assets: $321,873,525
Liabilities: $196,166,492
Net Worth: $125,707,033
Earnings: $10,113,189
Emp.: 214
Fiscal Year-end: 12/31/22
Insurance Services
N.A.I.C.S.: 524126
Mohammad Al-Jarrah Al-Sabah *(Vice Chm)*

Subsidiaries:

LIC (International) B.S.C. (1)
Ali Alwazzan Bldg 1st Fl al Khalifa Ave, PO Box 584, Manama, 584, Bahrain
Tel.: (973) 17210610
Web Site: http://www.licinternational.com
Insurance Services
N.A.I.C.S.: 524113
M. R. Kumar *(Chm)*

Wapmed TPA Services Company K.S.C.C. (1)
PO Box 26739, Safat, Kuwait, Kuwait
Tel.: (965) 1868700
Web Site: https://www.wapmed.net
Health Insurance Services
N.A.I.C.S.: 524114

WARBURTONS LIMITED

Hereford House Hereford Street, Bolton, BL1 8JB, United Kingdom
Tel.: (44) 1204 556600
Web Site:
http://www.warburtons.co.uk
Year Founded: 1876
Sales Range: $750-799.9 Million
Emp.: 4,659
Bakery Products Mfr
N.A.I.C.S.: 311821
Brett Warburton *(Exec Dir)*

WARDWIZARD HEALTHCARE LIMITED

11 Windward Business Park Opp Aadicura Hospital Jetalpura Road, Dadar W, Vadodara, 390 007, Gujarat, India
Tel.: (91) 6359158825
Web Site:
https://www.ayokimerchantile.com
512063—(BOM)
Rev.: $30,759
Assets: $15,884
Liabilities: $4,124
Net Worth: $11,759
Earnings: ($7,049)
Fiscal Year-end: 03/31/21
Commodity Trading Services
N.A.I.C.S.: 523160
Kalachand Mukherjee *(Mng Dir)*

WARDWIZARD INNOVATIONS & MOBILITY LIMITED

401 Floor-4 23/25 Dhun Building Janmabhoomi Marg, Horniman Circle Fort, Mumbai, 400001, Maharashtra, India
Tel.: (91) 9727755083
Web Site: https://wardwizard.in
Year Founded: 1982
538970—(BOM)
Rev.: $28,689,203
Assets: $26,761,705
Liabilities: $16,188,742
Net Worth: $10,572,963
Earnings: $1,061,267
Emp.: 178
Fiscal Year-end: 03/31/23
Real Estate Development Services
N.A.I.C.S.: 531210
Nitin Manohar Pradhan *(Mng Dir)*

WARDWIZARD SOLUTIONS INDIA PRIVATE LIMITED

C 222 Makarpura GIDC, Vadodara, 390010, Gujarat, India
Tel.: (91) 7574895544
Web Site: http://www.wardwizard.in
Electronic Vehicles Mfr
N.A.I.C.S.: 425120

WAREHOUSE REIT PLC

55 Wells Street, London, W1T 3PT, United Kingdom
Tel.: (44) 2030112160 UK
Web Site:
https://www.warehousereit.co.uk
Year Founded: 2017
WHR—(LSE)
Rev.: $64,415,679
Assets: $1,084,488,390
Liabilities: $408,407,777
Net Worth: $676,080,613
Earnings: $43,309,856
Fiscal Year-end: 03/31/24
Lessors of Other Real Estate Property
N.A.I.C.S.: 531190
Andrew Bird *(Mng Dir)*

WAREHOUSES DE PAUW COMM. VA

Blakebergen 15, 1861, Wolvertem, Belgium
Tel.: (32) 52338400
Web Site: http://www.wdp.be
Year Founded: 1977
WPH—(DEU)
Sales Range: Less than $1 Million
Emp.: 33
Warehousing & Distribution Services
N.A.I.C.S.: 493110
Mark Duyck *(Chm)*

Subsidiaries:

WDP Nederland N.V. (1)
Hoge Mosten 2, 4822 NH, Breda, Netherlands
Tel.: (31) 765236650
Real Estate Development Services

INTERNATIONAL PUBLIC

N.A.I.C.S.: 531390
Tony De Pauw *(Mng Dir)*

WAREHOUSES ESTATES BELGIUM SCA

29 Avenue Jean Mermoz, 6041, Gosselies, Belgium
Tel.: (32) 71259259
Web Site: https://www.w-e-b.be
WEB—(EUR)
Rev.: $24,919,253
Assets: $355,938,727
Liabilities: $171,031,368
Net Worth: $184,907,360
Earnings: $9,568,527
Emp.: 250
Fiscal Year-end: 12/31/23
Residential Real Estate Management Services
N.A.I.C.S.: 531311
Claude Desseille *(CEO)*

WARGAMING PUBLIC COMPANY LIMITED

105 Agion Omologiton Avenue, Nicosia, 1080, Cyprus
Tel.: (357) 22 86 4444
Web Site: http://www.wargaming.net
Year Founded: 1998
Emp.: 5,000
Videogame Software Developer, Publisher & Distr
N.A.I.C.S.: 513210
Victor Kislyi *(Founder & CEO)*

Subsidiaries:

BigWorld Pty Limited (1)
Level 2 1-3 Smail St, Ultimo, 2007, NSW, Australia
Tel.: (61) 2 8570 5400
Web Site: http://www.bigworldtech.com
Videogame Software Publisher & Distr
N.A.I.C.S.: 513210

Branch (Domestic):

BigWorld Pty. Ltd. - Development Studio (2)
Level 2 Suite 202 1-3 Smail St, Wentworth Park Road, Sydney, 2007, NSW, Australia
Tel.: (61) 2 8570 5400
Web Site: http://www.bigworldtech.com
Videogame Software Developer & Publisher
N.A.I.C.S.: 513210

Wargaming America Inc. (1)
1480 64th Street Ste 300, Emeryville, CA 94608-5401
Tel.: (510) 962-6747
Web Site:
http://www.wargamingamerica.com
Emp.: 120
Videogame Software Developer, Publisher & Distr
N.A.I.C.S.: 513210
Chris Cook *(Dir-Comm-North America)*

Branch (Domestic):

Wargaming Seattle (2)
5000 148th Ave NE Ste 200, Redmond, WA 98052-5135
Tel.: (425) 522-1600
Web Site: http://www.wargaming.com
Sales Range: $10-24.9 Million
Emp.: 50
Videogame Software Developer, Publisher & Distr
N.A.I.C.S.: 513210
Michelle Hippe *(Dir-Ops)*

WARIMPEX FINANZ- UND BETEILIGUNGS AG

Floridsdorfer Hauptstrasse 1, A-1210, Vienna, Austria
Tel.: (43) 13105500
Web Site: https://www.warimpex.com
Year Founded: 1959
WXF—(WAR)
Rev.: $48,711,418
Assets: $491,115,908
Liabilities: $307,337,578

AND PRIVATE COMPANIES

Net Worth: $183,778,329
Earnings: $46,259,443
Emp.: 80
Fiscal Year-end: 12/31/22
Real Estate Development & Investment Services
N.A.I.C.S.: 531390
Daniel Folian *(Deputy Chm-Mgmt Bd & CFO)*

Subsidiaries:

Art Nouveau Palace
Hotel-Prague (1)
Panska 12, 111 21, Prague, Czech Republic
Tel.: (420) 224093111
Web Site: http://www.palacehotel.cz
Sales Range: $10-24.9 Million
Emp.: 70
Hotel Services
N.A.I.C.S.: 721110
Martin Kotatko *(Gen Mgr)*

Balnex 1 a.s (1)
Novaloka 11, 36021, Karlovy Vary, Czech Republic
Tel.: (420) 353102111
Web Site: http://www.v-hotels.com
Hotel Properties Development Services
N.A.I.C.S.: 531312

Comtel Focus S.A. (1)
Calea Bucurestilor Nr 283, Otopeni, 75100, Ilfov, Romania
Tel.: (40) 212036500
Sales Range: $50-74.9 Million
Emp.: 70
Hotel Properties Development Services
N.A.I.C.S.: 531312
Romana Stefan *(Gen Mgr)*

Kopernik Development Sp.z.o.o. (1)
Prozna-9, 00121, Warsaw, Poland
Tel.: (48) 224887311
Real Estate Manangement Services
N.A.I.C.S.: 531390
Pirzy Krogulec *(Pres & Mgr)*

Le Palais Praha s.r.o. (1)
U Zvonarky 1, 12000, Prague, Czech Republic
Tel.: (420) 234634111
Web Site: http://www.lepalaishotel.eu
Sales Range: $10-24.9 Million
Emp.: 60
Hotel Services
N.A.I.C.S.: 721120

Prozna Properties Sp.z.o.o. (1)
Prozna 9, 00 107, Warsaw, Poland
Tel.: (48) 224887311
Web Site: http://www.warimpex.com
Sales Range: $50-74.9 Million
Emp.: 3
Property Management Services
N.A.I.C.S.: 531312
Christian Fojtl *(Gen Mgr)*

Recoop Tour a.s. (1)
Evropska 15, Prague, 16041, Czech Republic
Tel.: (420) 296559111
Web Site: http://www.vi-hotels.com
Hotel Properties Development Services
N.A.I.C.S.: 531312

Revital Property Development
Incorporated (1)
Hungaria krt 140-144, 1146, Budapest, Hungary
Tel.: (36) 14715174
Web Site: http://www.revital.hu
Property Management Services
N.A.I.C.S.: 531312

Subsidiary (Domestic):

Goldmark kft (2)
Lajos utca 26, H-1023, Budapest, Hungary
Tel.: (36) 1 428 6070
Sales Range: $50-74.9 Million
Emp.: 1
Property Management Services
N.A.I.C.S.: 531312

Warimpex Leasing GmbH (1)
Floridsdorfer Hauptstrasse 1, 1210, Vienna, Austria
Tel.: (43) 13105500
Web Site: http://www.warimpex.com
Emp.: 30
Financial Lending Services
N.A.I.C.S.: 522320

Subsidiary (Non-US):

Evropsky Investicni Holding a.s. (2)
Keplerova 6/218, 118 00, Prague, Czech Republic
Tel.: (420) 224302122
Web Site: http://www.hotelsavoyprague.com
Emp.: 30
Hotel Properties Development Services
N.A.I.C.S.: 531312
Natalie Filonova *(CEO)*

Golf Amber Baltic Sp.z.o.o. (2)
ul Baltycka 13, 72 514, Kolsva, Poland
Tel.: (48) 913265110
Web Site: http://www.abgc.pl
Sales Range: $25-49.9 Million
Emp.: 20
Golf Club Services
N.A.I.C.S.: 713910

Warimpex Polska Sp.z.o.o. (1)
Tel.: (48) 224887319
Web Site: http://www.warimpex.at.com
Sales Range: $50-74.9 Million
Emp.: 15
Real Estate Development & Investment Services
N.A.I.C.S.: 531390

WARISAN TC HOLDINGS BERHAD

No 15-3 Tingkat 3 Jalan Ipoh Kecil, 50350, Kuala Lumpur, Malaysia
Tel.: (60) 340479733   MY
Web Site:
    https://www.warisantc.com.my
Year Founded: 1997
5016—(KLS)
Rev.: $99,084,023
Assets: $157,990,206
Liabilities: $100,025,686
Net Worth: $57,964,519
Earnings: ($529,168)
Emp.: 968
Fiscal Year-end: 12/31/23
Holding Company
N.A.I.C.S.: 551112
Heng Chew Tan *(Pres)*

Subsidiaries:

Angka-Tan Motor Sdn Bhd (1)
No 117-119 Jalan SS15/5A, 47500, Subang Jaya, Selangor, Malaysia
Tel.: (60) 35 638 6888
Web Site:
    https://www.angkatanmotor.com.my
Car Retailer
N.A.I.C.S.: 441110
Choong Sok Yee *(Mgr-Fin)*

Jentrakel Sdn Bhd (1)
Lot 9 Jalan Delima 1/1, Subang Hi-Tech Industrial Park, 40000, Shah Alam, Selangor, Malaysia
Tel.: (60) 35 632 6281
Web Site: https://jrental.com.my
Power Generator & Air Compressor Distr
N.A.I.C.S.: 423830

Kereta Komersil Seladang (M) Sdn Bhd (1)
117-119 Jalan SS15/5A Darul Ehsan, 47500, Subang Jaya, Selangor, Malaysia
Tel.: (60) 356386888
Investment Holding Company Services
N.A.I.C.S.: 551112

MAT Tours & Travel (Cambodia) Pte. Ltd. (1)
The iCON Professional Building 89 - E1 1st Floor 216 Norodom Blvd, Tonle Bassac Chamkarmorn, Phnom Penh, Cambodia
Tel.: (855) 2 396 6589
Web Site:
    https://www.mayflowercambodia.com
Tour Operator
N.A.I.C.S.: 561520

MUV Marketplace Sdn Bhd (1)
Lot 3 Jalan 6/3 Kawasan Perindustrian Seri Kembangan, 43300, Seri Kembangan, Selangor, Malaysia
Tel.: (60) 38 947 6888
Web Site: https://www.muv-x.com
Car Retailer
N.A.I.C.S.: 441110

Mayflower Car Rental Sdn Bhd (1)
Mayflower Building 18 Jalan Segambut Pusat, 51200, Kuala Lumpur, Malaysia
Tel.: (60) 362531888
Investment Holding Company Services
N.A.I.C.S.: 551112

Mayflower Corporate Travel Services Sdn Bhd (1)
Office Suite 13-1 13/F Wisma UOA II 21 Jalan Pinang, 50450, Kuala Lumpur, Malaysia
Tel.: (60) 32 167 5700
Web Site: https://www.mayflower-gbt.com
Travel Management Services
N.A.I.C.S.: 561510
Khairi Rizal *(Mgr-Sls & Implementation)*

Mayflower Holidays Sdn Bhd (1)
Menara Mayflower No 1 Jalan Metro Pudu 1 Fraser Business Park, Off Jalan Yew, 55100, Kuala Lumpur, Malaysia
Tel.: (60) 39 232 1888
Web Site: https://www.mayflower.com.my
Transport Services
N.A.I.C.S.: 485999
Andy Soo *(Sr Geh Mgr)*

Subsidiary (Domestic):

Discovery Tours (Sabah) Sdn Bhd (2)
Lot G22 G/F Wisma Sabah Jalan Tun Fuad Stephen, 88000, Kota Kinabalu, Sabah, Malaysia
Tel.: (60) 8 825 7368
Web Site:
    https://www.discoverytours.com.my
Travel Management Services
N.A.I.C.S.: 561510

TCIM Sdn Bhd (1)
Lot 9 Jalan Delima 1/1 Taman Industri Teknologi Tinggi Subang, Darul Ehsan, 40000, Shah Alam, Selangor, Malaysia
Tel.: (60) 356364786
Investment Holding Company Services
N.A.I.C.S.: 551112

Tan Chong Apparels Manufacturer Sdn Bhd (1)
No 3 Jln Perusahaan Perkhidmatan Pengkalan Taman Pengkalan Maju, Simpang, Taiping, Perak, Malaysia
Tel.: (60) 58492094
Investment Holding Company Services
N.A.I.C.S.: 551112

WTC Automotif (M) Sdn Bhd. (1)
No 72 Ground Floor Jalan Sultan Azlan Shah, 51200, Kuala Lumpur, Malaysia
Tel.: (60) 340478998
Web Site: https://gacmotor.com.my
New Car Dealers
N.A.I.C.S.: 441110

Warisan Captive Incorporated (1)
No 63 1st Floor Jalan Merdeka, Labuan, 87007, Malaysia
Tel.: (60) 340479738
Tour Operator
N.A.I.C.S.: 561520

Warisan TC Automotive Manufacturers (M) Sdn Bhd (1)
249 Jalan Segambut, 51200, Kuala Lumpur, Malaysia
Tel.: (60) 340479733
Investment Holding Company Services
N.A.I.C.S.: 551112

WARKA BANK FOR INVESTMENT & FINANCE J.S.C.

Al-Kalanie sequare, Baghdad, Iraq
Tel.: (964) 1 8869880
Web Site: http://www.warka-bank.com
Year Founded: 1999
Commercial Banking Services
N.A.I.C.S.: 522110

Saad S. Al-Bunnia *(Chm & CEO)*

WARNE MARKETING & COMMUNICATIONS

65 Overlea Blvd Suite 112, Toronto, ON, Canada
Tel.: (416) 927-0881
Web Site: http://www.warne.com
Year Founded: 1979
Advetising Agency
N.A.I.C.S.: 541810
S.A. Warne *(Pres)*

WARNER MULTIMEDIA LIMITED

3rd floor P-27 Princep Street, Kolkata, 7000072, West Bengal, India
Tel.: (91) 33 2229 9198
Web Site:
    http://www.warnermultimedia.in
Year Founded: 1983
Rev.: $131,747
Assets: $914,961
Liabilities: $1,150,898
Net Worth: ($235,937)
Earnings: ($18,427)
Fiscal Year-end: 03/31/18
Pharmaceutical Preparation Mfr
N.A.I.C.S.: 325412
Jagdish Prasad Purohit *(Chm & Mng Dir)*

WARNING SAS

56 Boulevard du 11 Novembre 1918, Batiment Les Cedres, 69160, Tassin-la-Demi-Lune, France
Tel.: (33) 820301301
Web Site: http://www.warning.fr
Road Transportation of Freight & Logistics Services
N.A.I.C.S.: 541614

WAROM TECHNOLOGY INCORPORATED COMPANY

No 555 Baoqian Road, Jiading District, Shanghai, 201808, China
Tel.: (86) 2139977076   CN
Web Site:
    https://www.waromgroup.com
Year Founded: 1987
603855—(SHG)
Rev.: $427,226,838
Assets: $596,808,276
Liabilities: $339,328,365
Net Worth: $257,479,911
Earnings: $50,288,626
Emp.: 2,000
Fiscal Year-end: 12/31/22
Explosion Proof Product Mfr & Distr
N.A.I.C.S.: 335132
Hu Zhirong *(Chm & Pres)*

WARPAINT LONDON PLC

Units B&C Orbital Forty Six The Ridgeway Trading Estate, Iver, SL0 9HW, Buckinghamshire, United Kingdom
Tel.: (44) 1753639130   UK
Web Site:
    https://www.warpaintlondonplc.com
W7L—(AIM)
Rev.: $80,860,894
Assets: $64,822,015
Liabilities: $17,133,300
Net Worth: $47,688,715
Earnings: $7,889,422
Emp.: 122
Fiscal Year-end: 12/31/22
Cosmetic Product Mfr & Distr
N.A.I.C.S.: 339910
Samuel Bazini *(Co-CEO)*

Subsidiaries:

Badgequo Hong Kong Limited (1)
Room 1607 16/F No 93-103 Wing Lok Street, Sheung Wan, China (Hong Kong)

Warpaint London PLC—(Continued)

Tel.: (852) 51497902
Web Site: https://www.badgequo.com
Cosmetic & Personal Care Product Distr
N.A.I.C.S.: 456120

Retra Holdings Limited (1)
Number 8 Belton Road, Silsden, Keighley, BD20 0EE, West Yorkshire, United Kingdom
Tel.: (44) 153 565 0850
Web Site: https://www.retra-group.com
Cosmetic & Personal Care Product Distr
N.A.I.C.S.: 456120

WARREGO ENERGY LIMITED

Level 6 10 Bridge Street, Sydney, 2000, NSW, Australia
Tel.: (61) 2 9254 9000
Web Site: http://www.warregoenergy.com
WGO—(ASX)
Rev.: $378,053
Assets: $57,922,123
Liabilities: $9,231,626
Net Worth: $48,690,497
Earnings: ($4,892,957)
Emp.: 3
Fiscal Year-end: 06/30/21
Oil & Gas Exploration Services
N.A.I.C.S.: 211120
Ian Kirkham *(CFO & Co-Sec)*

Subsidiaries:

Warrego Energy UK Ltd. (1)
39 Albert Street, Aberdeen, AB25 1XU, United Kingdom
Tel.: (44) 1224974980
Oil & Natural Gas Services
N.A.I.C.S.: 213112

WARREN GIBSON LIMITED

206 Church Street S, PO Box 100, Alliston, L9R 1T9, ON, Canada
Tel.: (705) 435-4342
Web Site: https://www.warrengibson.com
Year Founded: 1946
Rev.: $81,902,143
Emp.: 700
Transportation Services
N.A.I.C.S.: 488999
Warren Gibson *(Founder)*

WARREN TEA LIMITED

Deohall Tea Estate, POHoogrijan Dist Tinsukia, Assam, 786 601, India
Tel.: (91) 3322360025
Web Site: https://www.warrentea.com
Year Founded: 1850
508494—(BOM)
Rev.: $14,742,819
Assets: $24,266,165
Liabilities: $10,053,716
Net Worth: $14,212,448
Earnings: $4,162,841
Emp.: 5,759
Fiscal Year-end: 03/31/21
Tea Producer
N.A.I.C.S.: 311920
Siddhartha Roy *(Compliance Officer, Pres-Legal & Sec)*

Subsidiaries:

James Warren Tea Limited (1)
PO Borahapjan, Tinsukia, 786 150, Assam, India
Tel.: (91) 3759 247922
Web Site: http://www.jameswarrentea.com
Rev.: $18,287,779
Assets: $19,888,924
Liabilities: $4,591,082
Net Worth: $15,297,842
Earnings: $3,953,040
Emp.: 6,900
Fiscal Year-end: 03/31/2021
Tea Mfr & Whslr
N.A.I.C.S.: 311920
Akhil Kumar Ruia *(CEO)*

WARRIEDAR RESOURCES LIMITED

Suite 1 245 Churchill Avenue, Subiaco, 6008, WA, Australia
Tel.: (61) 864655500 AU
Web Site: http://www.anovametals.com.au
WA8—(ASX)
Rev.: $207,852
Assets: $48,715,363
Liabilities: $13,135,396
Net Worth: $35,579,967
Earnings: ($14,257,959)
Fiscal Year-end: 06/30/24
Gold & Other Metal Mining Services
N.A.I.C.S.: 212220
Mingyan Wang *(Mng Dir)*

WARRIX SPORT PUBLIC COMPANY LIMITED

849/6-8 Stadium One Rama VI Road, Wang Mai Subdistrict Pathum Wan District, Bangkok, 10330, Thailand
Tel.: (66) 21171300
Web Site: https://www.warrix.co.th
WARRIX—(THA)
Rev.: $36,519,446
Assets: $52,537,372
Liabilities: $11,450,550
Net Worth: $41,086,822
Earnings: $3,718,473
Fiscal Year-end: 12/31/23
Sports Equipment Mfr
N.A.I.C.S.: 339920
Pasu Decharin *(Chm)*

WARSTEINER BRAUEREI HAUS CRAMER KG

Domring 4-10, Warstein, 59581, Germany
Tel.: (49) 2902880 De
Web Site: http://www.warsteiner-gruppe.de
Year Founded: 1753
Sales Range: $100-124.9 Million
Emp.: 2,200
Beer Brewer & Whslr
N.A.I.C.S.: 312120
Peter Himmelsbach *(CTO)*

Subsidiaries:

Dusseldorfer Privatbrauerei Frankenheim GmbH & Co. KG (1)
Wielandstrasse 12, 40211, Dusseldorf, Germany
Tel.: (49) 211 16902 0
Web Site: http://www.frankenheim.de
Beverage Distr
N.A.I.C.S.: 424820

Getranke Hornung GmbH (1)
Am Gut Baarking 6 Industriepark Bocholt, 46395, Bocholt, Germany
Tel.: (49) 28 71 25 55 0
Web Site: http://www.hornung-getraenke.de
Beverage Distr
N.A.I.C.S.: 424820

Getranke Krietemeyer GmbH (1)
Hafenstrasse 117, 59067, Hamm, Germany
Tel.: (49) 23 81 41 81 0
Web Site: http://www.getraenke-krietemeyer.de
Beverage Distr
N.A.I.C.S.: 424820

Herforder Brauerei GmbH & Co. KG (1)
Gebr-Uekermann-Str 1, 32120, Hiddenhausen, Germany
Tel.: (49) 52 21 965 0
Web Site: http://www.herforder.de
Emp.: 100
Beverage Distr
N.A.I.C.S.: 424820
Frank Rottmann *(Gen Mgr)*

Kamphenkel GmbH & Co. Vertriebs KG (1)
Wolframstrasse 95-96, 12105, Berlin, Germany

Tel.: (49) 30 757 55 3
Web Site: http://www.getraenke-kamphenkel.de
Beverage Distr
N.A.I.C.S.: 424820

Konig Ludwig GmbH & Co. KG Schlossbrauerei Kaltenberg (1)
Augsburger Strasse 41, 82256, Fuerstenfeldbruck, Germany
Tel.: (49) 8141 243 0
Web Site: http://www.koenig-ludwig-brauerei.com
Beverage Distr
N.A.I.C.S.: 424820

Paderborner Brauerei Haus Cramer GmbH & Co. KG (1)
Halberstadter Str 45, 33106, Paderborn, Germany
Tel.: (49) 5251 707 7291
Web Site: http://www.paderborner-brauerei.de
Emp.: 90
Beverage Distr
N.A.I.C.S.: 424820
Henning Behrens *(Gen Mgr)*

Sauerland Getranke GmbH & Co KG (1)
Alte Heeresstrasse 19, Altenburen, 59929, Brilon, Germany
Tel.: (49) 2961962840
Web Site: http://www.sauerland-getraenke.de
Beverage Distr
N.A.I.C.S.: 424820

Warsteiner International KG (1)
Domring 4-10, 59581, Warstein, Germany
Tel.: (49) 2902880
Web Site: http://www.warsteiner.com
Beer Whslr
N.A.I.C.S.: 424810
Peter Himmelsbach *(Member-Mgmt Bd)*

Subsidiary (US):

Warsteiner Importers Agency, Inc. (2)
9359 Allen Rd, West Chester, OH 45069 (100%)
Tel.: (513) 942-9872
Web Site: http://www.warsteiner-usa.com
Sales Range: $25-49.9 Million
Emp.: 35
Beer Importer & Distr
N.A.I.C.S.: 424810

WARSZAWSKA KOLEJ DOJAZDOWA SP. Z O.O.

ul Batorego 23, 05-825, Grodzisk Mazowiecki, Poland
Tel.: (48) 227555564
Web Site: http://www.wkd.com.pl
Sales Range: $25-49.9 Million
Emp.: 219
Commuter Railway Services
N.A.I.C.S.: 485112
Grzegorz Dymecki *(CEO)*

WARTECK INVEST AG

Munchensteinerstrasse 117, 4053, Basel, Switzerland
Tel.: (41) 616909220
Web Site: https://www.warteck-invest.ch
WARN—(SWX)
Sales Range: Less than $1 Million
Real Estate Development Services
N.A.I.C.S.: 531390
Daniel Petitjean *(CEO)*

WARTSILA CORPORATION

Hiililaiturinkuja 2, FI-00180, Helsinki, Finland
Tel.: (358) 107090000 FI
Web Site: https://www.wartsila.com
Year Founded: 1834
WRT1V—(OTCIQ)
Rev.: $5,549,439,000
Assets: $6,276,447,800
Liabilities: $4,217,204,600
Net Worth: $2,059,243,200

Earnings: $248,179,400
Emp.: 16,216
Fiscal Year-end: 12/31/23
Diesel & Gas Engines & Power Plants; Special Steels Mfr
N.A.I.C.S.: 333618
Kari Hietanen *(Member-Mgmt Bd & Exec VP-Corp Rels & Legal Affairs)*

Subsidiaries:

AGFA HEALTHCARE INDIA PRIVATE LTD. (1)
402 4th Floor NITCO BIZ PARK Plot No.C/19 Road No 16, Wagle Industrial Estate, Thane, 400 604, India
Tel.: (91) 22 40642900
Web Site: http://www.agfahealthcare.com
Healthcare Software Development Services
N.A.I.C.S.: 541511

Burriel Navarro S.L. (1)
Tel.: (34) 963675875
Web Site: http://www.burrielnavarro.es
Marine Support Services
N.A.I.C.S.: 488390

Cedervall Espana S.A. (1)
Polig Ind As Gandaras Parcela 206 Nave B-3, 36475, Porrino, Pontevedra, Spain
Tel.: (34) 986 34 40 48
Sales Range: $25-49.9 Million
Emp.: 80
Shaft Bearing Mfr
N.A.I.C.S.: 332991
Jesus Fernandez *(Mgr-Ops)*

Cedervall Zhangjiagang Marine Products Co. Ltd. (1)
Hexing St Jinfeng Town, Zhangjiagang, 215626, Jiangsu, China
Tel.: (86) 512 585 05 110
Web Site: http://www.cedervall.com
Sales Range: $25-49.9 Million
Emp.: 59
Marine Shaft Seal & Bearing System Mfr
N.A.I.C.S.: 332999

Defense Maritime Solutions, Inc. (1)
3617 Koppens Way, Chesapeake, VA 23323
Tel.: (757) 558-3625
Web Site: https://dmsamerica.com
Marine Engineering Services
N.A.I.C.S.: 541330

Eniram Oy (1)
Hiililaiturinkuja 2, 00180, Helsinki, Finland
Tel.: (358) 108433800
Engine Equipment Mfr
N.A.I.C.S.: 333618
Jeff N. Joseph *(Acct Mgr)*

Greensmith Energy Management Systems, Inc. (1)
485 Springpark Pl Ste 1500, Herndon, VA 20170
Tel.: (844) 814-4367
Web Site: http://www.greensmithenergy.com
Software Development Services
N.A.I.C.S.: 541511
Andrew Tang *(Sr VP-Bus Dev)*

Guidance Marine LLC (1)
1313 MacArthur Ave, Harvey, LA 70058
Tel.: (504) 733-2500
Engine Equipment Mfr
N.A.I.C.S.: 333618

Guidance Marine Ltd. (1)
5 Tiber Way Meridian Business Park, Leicester, LE19 1QP, United Kingdom
Tel.: (44) 1162292600
Web Site: http://www.guidance.eu.com
Marine Support Services
N.A.I.C.S.: 488390

Guidance Marine Pte. Ltd. (1)
16/18 Jalan Kilang Barat Cyber Centre Level 2, Singapore, 159358, Singapore
Tel.: (65) 67346365
Oil & Gas Equipment Services
N.A.I.C.S.: 213112

Lock-N-Stitch, Inc. (1)
1015 S Soderquist Rd, Turlock, CA 95380
Tel.: (209) 632-2345
Web Site: https://www.locknstitch.com
Cast Iron Parts Repair Services & Machine Tool Accessories Mfr

AND PRIVATE COMPANIES — WARTSILA CORPORATION

N.A.I.C.S.: 333515

PT. Wartsila Indonesia (1)
Tel.: (62) 2129667820
Sales Range: $50-74.9 Million
Emp.: 350
Marine Engine Repair & Maintenance Services
N.A.I.C.S.: 336611

Plant (Domestic):

PT. Wartsila Indonesia - Jawa Barat Power Plant (2)
Cikarang Industrial Estate Jl Jababeka XVI Kav W-28 Cikarang, Bekasi, 17530, Jawa Barat, Indonesia
Tel.: (62) 21 893 7654
Sales Range: $100-124.9 Million
Emp.: 20
Eletric Power Generation Services
N.A.I.C.S.: 221118
Bjorn Lindell (Mng Dir)

Quantiparts B.V. (1)
Tel.: (31) 889802600
Web Site: https://www.quantiparts.com
Marine Support Services
N.A.I.C.S.: 488390

Transas Marine GmbH (1)
Behringstrase 120, 22763, Hamburg, Germany
Tel.: (49) 4088253000
Engine Equipment Mfr
N.A.I.C.S.: 333618

Transas Navigator Ltd. (1)
54-4 Maly Pr V O St, Saint Petersburg, 199178, Russia
Tel.: (7) 8123253131
Engine Equipment Mfr
N.A.I.C.S.: 333618

Trident B.V (1)
Mr F J Haarmanweg 75, NL-4538 AN, Terneuzen, Netherlands
Tel.: (31) 115612872
Web Site: http://www.trident-diving.com
Marine Support Services
N.A.I.C.S.: 488390

Trident Italia Srl (1)
Via delle Cateratte 84 int 16/17, 57122, Livorno, Italy
Tel.: (39) 05861751922
Underwater Propulsion & Repair Services
N.A.I.C.S.: 336611

Trident Las Palmas S.L. (1)
C/ Nelson Mandela 11, Telde, 35214, Las Palmas, Spain
Tel.: (34) 828905839
Marine Support Services
N.A.I.C.S.: 488390

Wartsila (Malaysia) Sdn Bhd (1)
Menara AIA Central Level 35 Unit 35 1 No 30 Jalan Sultan, Ismail, 50250, Kuala Lumpur, Malaysia
Tel.: (60) 321485072
Emp.: 15
Engine Equipment Mfr
N.A.I.C.S.: 333618

Wartsila Argentina S.A. (1)
Carlos Pellegrini 1363 Piso 8, Chalet No 1, C1011AAA, Buenos Aires, Argentina (100%)
Tel.: (54) 9116 936 6920
Web Site: https://www.wartsila.com
Sales Range: $1-9.9 Million
Emp.: 10
Engine Equipment Mfr
N.A.I.C.S.: 333618

Wartsila Australia Pty. Ltd. (1)
48 Huntingwood Drive, Huntingwood, Sydney, 2148, NSW, Australia (100%)
Tel.: (61) 296728200
Web Site: https://www.wartsila.com
Sales Range: $25-49.9 Million
Emp.: 75
N.A.I.C.S.: 333618

Plant (Domestic):

Wartsila Australia Pty Ltd. - Henderson Power Plant (2)
19 Alacrity Place, Henderson, 6166, WA, Australia

Tel.: (61) 8 9410 1300
Sales Range: $50-74.9 Million
Emp.: 22
Eletric Power Generation Services
N.A.I.C.S.: 221118
Steve Jones (Gen Mgr)

Branch (Domestic):

Wartsila Australia Pty. Ltd., Bassendeen (2)
109 Broadway, Bassendean, 6054, WA, Australia (100%)
Tel.: (61) 893773337
Web Site: http://www.wartsila.com.au
Sales Range: $25-49.9 Million
Emp.: 12
N.A.I.C.S.: 333618

Wartsila Azerbaijan LLC (1)
Nobel Ave 108E, AZ1023, Baku, Azerbaijan (100%)
Tel.: (994) 123720680
Web Site: https://www.wartsila.com
Emp.: 32
Power & Marine Solutions
N.A.I.C.S.: 221118

Wartsila BLRT Estonia Ou (1)
Tel.: (372) 6102241
Web Site: https://www.wartsila.com
Sales Range: $25-49.9 Million
Emp.: 50
Marine Engine Repair & Maintenance Services
N.A.I.C.S.: 811210

Wartsila Bangladesh Ltd. (1)
(100%)
Tel.: (880) 258817866
Sales Range: $25-49.9 Million
Emp.: 38
N.A.I.C.S.: 333618

Wartsila Brasil Ltda. (1)
Rua Carlos Gomes 72, Barreto Niteroi, Rio de Janeiro, 24110-075, RJ, Brazil (100%)
Tel.: (55) 212 206 2500
Web Site: https://www.wartsila.com
Sales Range: $50-74.9 Million
Emp.: 200
Engines & Propulsion Packages for Ships
N.A.I.C.S.: 333618

Plant (Domestic):

Wartsila Brasil Ltda. - Infoglobo Power Plant (2)
Rodovia Washington Luiz 3 000 - Vila Sao Luiz, Rio de Janeiro, 25085-000, Brazil
Tel.: (55) 21 2534 9589
Web Site: http://www.wartsila.com
Emp.: 7
Eletric Power Generation Services
N.A.I.C.S.: 221118
Wagner Gama (Office Mgr)

Wartsila Brasil Ltda. - Petrolina Power Plant (2)
Perimetro Irrigado Senador Nilo Coelho S/No Lotes Agri FS 644/645, N2 - Zona Rural, Petrolina, 56304-000, Pernambuco, Brazil
Tel.: (55) 87 3867 6000
Web Site: http://www.wartsila.com
Eletric Power Generation Services
N.A.I.C.S.: 221118

Wartsila Canada, Inc. (1)
Unit 3 90 Cutler Avenue, Dartmouth, Halifax, B3B 0J6, NS, Canada (100%)
Tel.: (902) 468-1264
Sales Range: $25-49.9 Million
Emp.: 25
Repair Services of Diesel Engines
N.A.I.C.S.: 333618

Plant (Domestic):

Wartsila Canada Inc. - Vancouver Power Plant (2)
1771 Savage Road, Richmond, Vancouver, V6V 1R1, BC, Canada
Tel.: (604) 244-8181
Web Site: http://www.wartsila.com
Emp.: 70
Eletric Power Generation Services
N.A.I.C.S.: 221118
Mark Kennedy (Mgr-Bus Dev-Power Plants)

Wartsila Caribbean, Inc. (1)
Road 887 Km 0 6 Street A Lot 5 Industrial Park Julio N Matos, Carolina, PR 00986-7039
Tel.: (787) 701-2288
Engine Equipment Mfr
N.A.I.C.S.: 333618

Wartsila Central Africa Ltd. (1)
Wartsila Base Essengue, Douala, Cameroon
Tel.: (237) 33505400
Engine Equipment Mfr
N.A.I.C.S.: 333618

Wartsila Chile Ltda. (1)
Calle Limache N 3421 Oficinas 604-605, Edificio Reitz II, 2562126, Vina del Mar, Chile (100%)
Tel.: (56) 322204433
Sales Range: $25-49.9 Million
Emp.: 25
Power Plants & Energy Services
N.A.I.C.S.: 335311

Wartsila China Ltd (1)
Units 2809-2815 The Octagon No 6 Sha Tsui Road, Tsuen Wan, New Territories, China (Hong Kong) (100%)
Tel.: (852) 2 528 6605
Web Site: https://www.wartsila.cn
Sales Range: $25-49.9 Million
Emp.: 60
N.A.I.C.S.: 333618

Plant (Non-US):

Wartsila China Ltd. - Beijing Power Plant (2)
Room 2601 Full Tower No 9 DongSanHuan Middle Road, Chaoyang District, Beijing, 100020, China
Tel.: (86) 106 409 6211
Web Site: http://www.wartsila.com
Eletric Power Generation Services
N.A.I.C.S.: 221118

Subsidiary (Non-US):

Wartsila Services (Shanghai) Co., Ltd. (2)
3rd Floor Building 11 No 170 Jin Feng Road, Pudong New District, Shanghai, 201201, China (100%)
Tel.: (86) 215 858 5500
Web Site: https://www.wartsila.cn
Sales Range: $25-49.9 Million
Emp.: 20
Shipyard Services
N.A.I.C.S.: 336611

Wartsila-CME Zhenjiang Propeller Co. Ltd (2)
8 JingSan Road, Ding Mao New District, Zhenjiang, 212009, Jiangsu, China
Tel.: (86) 511 8451 1719
Marine Fixed Pitch Propeller Mfr
N.A.I.C.S.: 332999
Tamara de Gruyter (Gen Mgr)

Wartsila Colombia S.A. (1)
Carrera 19B 83-63 Piso 5 Torre Anato, 110221, Bogota, Colombia
Tel.: (57) 1 635 8168
Web Site: http://www.wartsila.com
Sales Range: $25-49.9 Million
Emp.: 25
Diesel & Gas Engines & Power Plants; Special Steels
N.A.I.C.S.: 333618

Plant (Domestic):

Wartsila Colombia S.A. - Caacolito Power Plant (2)
Km 3 Via Buenos Aires - Payande Planta Caracolito, Ibague, Colombia
Tel.: (57) 8 2 70 9170
Web Site: http://www.wartsila.com
Eletric Power Generation Services
N.A.I.C.S.: 221118

Wartsila Corp. - Services Business (1)
Kauppapuistkko 15 Fl 2, 65100, Vaasa, Finland
Tel.: (358) 107090000
Web Site: http://www.wartsila.fi
Sales Range: $400-449.9 Million
Emp.: 1,600
N.A.I.C.S.: 333618

Wartsila Cyprus Ltd (1)
Tel.: (357) 25313761
Emp.: 12
Marine Power Plant Construction Services
N.A.I.C.S.: 237130

Wartsila Danmark A/S (1)
(100%)
Tel.: (45) 99569956
Sales Range: $50-74.9 Million
Emp.: 150
N.A.I.C.S.: 333618

Branch (Domestic):

Wartsila Danmark A/S - Copenhagen (2)
H C Andersens Boulevard 11 3rd floor, 1553, Copenhagen, Denmark (100%)
Tel.: (45) 99569956
Web Site: https://www.wartsila.com
Emp.: 13
N.A.I.C.S.: 333618

Plant (Domestic):

Wartsila Danmark A/S - Hirtshals Power Plant (3)
Jens Munksvej 1, PO Box 67, 9850, Hirtshals, Denmark
Tel.: (45) 99 569 956
Sales Range: $25-49.9 Million
Emp.: 75
Marine Power Plant Construction Services
N.A.I.C.S.: 237130
Claus Bogel (Mng Dir)

Wartsila Deutschland GmbH (1)
(100%)
Tel.: (49) 40751900
Sales Range: $100-124.9 Million
Emp.: 270
N.A.I.C.S.: 333618

Plant (Domestic):

Wartsila Deutschland GmbH - Hamburg Power Plant (2)
Schlenzigstrasse 6, 21107, Hamburg, Germany
Tel.: (49) 40 75 190 0
Emp.: 28
Eletric Power Generation Services
N.A.I.C.S.: 221118
Thomas Becker (Mng Dir & Dir-Svc Unit DE & CH)

Wartsila Development & Financial Services OY (1)
John Stenbergin Ranta 2, PO Box 196, Helsinki, 531, Finland (100%)
Tel.: (358) 107090000
Web Site: http://www.wartsila.com
Sales Range: $100-124.9 Million
Emp.: 300
N.A.I.C.S.: 333618

Branch (Domestic):

Wartsila Development & Financial Services OY, Vaasa (2)
Jarvikatu 2-4, PO Box 244, Vaasa, 65101, Finland (100%)
Tel.: (358) 107090000
Web Site: http://www.wartsila.com
Sales Range: $25-49.9 Million
Emp.: 200
N.A.I.C.S.: 333618

Wartsila Doha WLL (1)
Erhama Bin Jaber Al Jalahma Shipyard Southern Breakwater, PO Box 2388, Ras Laffan Industrial City, Doha, Qatar
Tel.: (974) 16199110
Engine Equipment Mfr
N.A.I.C.S.: 333618

Wartsila Dynamic Positioning Inc. (1)
12131 Community Rd, Poway, CA 92064
Tel.: (858) 679-5500
Engine Equipment Mfr
N.A.I.C.S.: 333618

Wartsila Ecuador S.A. (1)
Tel.: (593) 23931560
Sales Range: $125-149.9 Million
Emp.: 11
Eletric Power Generation Services

WARTSILA CORPORATION

Wartsila Corporation—(Continued)
N.A.I.C.S.: 221118

Plant (Domestic):

Wartsila Ecuador S.A. - Quito Power Plant (2)
Los Floripondios N57-120 y, Leonardo Murialdo, Quito, Ecuador
Tel.: (593) 2 281 1215
Eletric Power Generation Services
N.A.I.C.S.: 221118
Remigio Penarreta *(Gen Mgr)*

Wartsila Enpa Dis Ticaret A.S. (1)
Aydintepe Mah D-100 Highway E-5 Cad No 14/E Bahar Business Center, Tuzla, 34947, Istanbul, Turkiye
Tel.: (90) 216 494 5050
Web Site: https://www.wartsila.com
Emp.: 100
Marine Engine & Power Plant Repair & Maintenance Services
N.A.I.C.S.: 811310

Plant (Domestic):

Wartsila Enpa Dis Ticaret A.S. - Istanbul Power Plant (2)
Aydintepe Mah E-5 Karayolu Uzeri No 14 Bahar Is Merkezi A Blok, Tuzla, 34947, Istanbul, Turkiye
Tel.: (90) 216 494 50 50
Eletric Power Generation Services
N.A.I.C.S.: 221118

Wartsila FUNA International Inc. (1)
2900 SW 42nd St, Fort Lauderdale, FL 33312 (100%)
Tel.: (305) 622-2878
Web Site: http://www.funa.com
Engineeering Services
N.A.I.C.S.: 541330

Wartsila Finland Oy (1)
Teollisuuskatu 1, Vaasa, Finland
Tel.: (358) 107090000
Web Site: https://www.wartsila.com
Emp.: 3,700
Engine Equipment Mfr
N.A.I.C.S.: 333618

Plant (Domestic):

Wartsila Finland Oy - Turku Power Plant (2)
Stalarminkatu 45, PO Box 50, 20810, Turku, Finland
Tel.: (358) 107090000
Web Site: https://www.wartsila.com
Sales Range: $100-124.9 Million
Emp.: 280
N.A.I.C.S.: 333618

Wartsila Finland Oy - Vaasa, Power Plants & Services (2)
Puotikuja 1, 65380, Vaasa, Finland
Tel.: (358) 107090000
Web Site: http://www.wartsila.com
Emp.: 1,600
N.A.I.C.S.: 333618

Wartsila Finland Oy - Vaasa, Ship Power & Services (2)
Tarhaajantie No 2, PO Box 196, 65101, Vaasa, Finland
Tel.: (358) 107090000
Web Site: http://www.wartsila.fi
Emp.: 900
N.A.I.C.S.: 333618

Wartsila France S.A.S. (1)
28 rue Carl Hack, CS 91210, 68054, Mulhouse, Cedex, France (100%)
Tel.: (33) 38 966 6868
Web Site: https://www.wartsila.com
Emp.: 400
N.A.I.C.S.: 333618

Subsidiary (Domestic):

Wartsila Automation Services France S.A.S. (2)
54 rue Demidoff, 76600, Le Havre, France
Tel.: (33) 235 24 09 05
Emp.: 300
Power Plant Equipment Installation Services
N.A.I.C.S.: 238210

Plant (Domestic):

Wartsila France S.A.S. - Mulhouse Power Plant (2)
100 Quai d Alger CS 91210, BP 1210, 68054, Mulhouse, France
Tel.: (33) 3 8966 6868
Sales Range: $25-49.9 Million
Emp.: 70
Power Generating Equipment Mfr
N.A.I.C.S.: 333611

Wartsila France S.A.S. - Paris Power Plant (2)
Les Collines de l Arche Imm Opera E 76 Route de la Demi-Lune, 92057, Paris, France
Tel.: (33) 1 4776 8920
Emp.: 2
Power Generating Equipment Mfr
N.A.I.C.S.: 333611
Damian Matewski *(Mng Dir)*

Wartsila Greece S.A. (1)
17 Posidonos Av and 1-3 Pindou Str, 183 44, Moschato, Greece (100%)
Tel.: (30) 2104135450
Web Site: https://www.wartsila.com
Emp.: 60
N.A.I.C.S.: 333618

Plant (Domestic):

Wartsila Greece S.A. - Piraeus Power Plant (2)
17 Posidonos Av and 1-3 Pindou Str, 183 44, Moschato, Greece
Tel.: (30) 2104135450
Web Site: https://www.wartsila.com
Eletric Power Generation Services
N.A.I.C.S.: 221118

Wartsila Guatemala S.A. (1)
Km 19 5 Carretera al Pacifico Parque Empresarial Naciones Unidas No 5, 01064, Guatemala, Guatemala
Tel.: (502) 2384 9600
Web Site: http://www.wartsila.com
Sales Range: $25-49.9 Million
Emp.: 40
Marine Engine & Power Plant Equipment Repair & Maintenance Services
N.A.I.C.S.: 811310

Wartsila Gulf FZE (1)
Tel.: (971) 48857222
Sales Range: $50-74.9 Million
Emp.: 20
Marine Engine & Power Plant Equipment Repair & Maintenance Services
N.A.I.C.S.: 811310

Wartsila Hungary Kft (1)
Gyar u 2, 2040, Budaors, Hungary
Tel.: (36) 23532127
Web Site: https://www.wartsila.com
Sales Range: $50-74.9 Million
Emp.: 80
Electric Power Distribution Services
N.A.I.C.S.: 221122

Subsidiary (Non-US):

Wartsila Hungary Kft - Varna Power Plant (2)
5 Dunav Street Floor 3, 9000, Varna, Bulgaria
Tel.: (359) 5 261 3725
Web Site: http://www.wartsila.com
Marine Engine Mfr
N.A.I.C.S.: 333618

Wartsila Iberica S.A. (1)
Poligono Industrial Landabaso s/n, ES-48370, Bermeo, Vizcaya, Spain
Tel.: (34) 946170100
Web Site: https://www.wartsila.com
Sales Range: $125-149.9 Million
Emp.: 283
Marine Engine & Propeller Mfr
N.A.I.C.S.: 333618

Plant (Domestic):

Wartsila Iberica S.A. - Bermeo Power Plant (2)
Poligono Industrial Landabaso s/n, 48370, Bermeo, Spain
Tel.: (34) 946 170 100
Sales Range: $25-49.9 Million
Emp.: 135
Engine & Propeller Mfr
N.A.I.C.S.: 336413
John Sabin *(Gen Mgr)*

Wartsila India Ltd. (1)
10th Floor Tower 1 Seawoods Grand Central Sector 40, Seawoods Railway Station Nerul Node, Navi Mumbai, 400 706, Maharashtra, India (100%)
Tel.: (91) 222 781 8300
Web Site: https://www.wartsila.com
Sales Range: $75-99.9 Million
Emp.: 6
Sustainable Power Systems
N.A.I.C.S.: 221122
Kari Hietanaen *(Chm)*

Plant (Domestic):

Wartsila India Ltd. - Chennai Power Plant (2)
Sheryas Vriddhi 132 Velachery Main Road, Guindy, Chennai, 600 032, India
Tel.: (91) 44 2230 1080
Eletric Power Generation Services
N.A.I.C.S.: 221118
James Rajan *(Dir-Svc)*

Wartsila India Ltd. - Navi Mumbai Power Plant (2)
Kesar Solitaire 21st Floor Plot No 5 Sector No 19 Palm Beach Road, Sanpada, 400 705, Navi Mumbai, India
Tel.: (91) 22 2781 8300
Web Site: http://www.wartsila.com
Eletric Power Generation Services
N.A.I.C.S.: 221118

Wartsila India Ltd. - Secunderabad Power Plant (2)
Door No 1-8-271 Flat No 109 1F Ashokabhopal Chambers Sardhar Patel Rd, Secunderabad, 500003, India
Tel.: (91) 4027715383
Sales Range: $50-74.9 Million
Emp.: 15
Eletric Power Generation Services
N.A.I.C.S.: 221118
Gollapudi Sreeram *(Gen Mgr)*

Wartsila Italia S.p.A. (1)
Bagnoli della Rosandra 334, San Dorligo della Valle, 34018, Trieste, Italy
Tel.: (39) 0403195000
Web Site: https://www.wartsila.com
Sales Range: $450-499.9 Million
Emp.: 1,300
Marine Engine Equipment Mfr & Distr
N.A.I.C.S.: 333618
Michele Cafagna *(VP-)*

Plant (Domestic):

Wartsila Italia S.p.A. Energy Solutions (2)
Via al Molo Giano, 16128, Genoa, Italy
Tel.: (39) 010 599 5800
Web Site: https://www.wartsila.com
Marine Engine Equipment Mfr
N.A.I.C.S.: 333618

Wartsila Japan Ltd. (1)
Shin-Kasumigaseki Building 3F 3-3-2 Kasumigaseki, Chiyoda-ku, Tokyo, 100-0013, Japan
Tel.: (81) 366317670
Web Site: https://www.wartsila.com
Sales Range: $100-124.9 Million
Emp.: 200
Products & Solutions for Marine & Energy Markets
N.A.I.C.S.: 333618

Plant (Domestic):

Wartsila Japan Company Ltd - Kobe Power Plant (2)
6-7-2 Minatojima, Cho-ku, Kobe, 650-0045, Japan
Tel.: (81) 78 304 7501
Web Site: https://www.wartsila.com
Emp.: 50
Eletric Power Generation Services
N.A.I.C.S.: 221118

Wartsila Japan Company Ltd - Tokyo Power Plant (2)
Yaesu mid Bldg 5th Floor 1-11-2 Kyobashi, Cho-ku, Tokyo, 104 0031, Japan
Tel.: (81) 3 3564 1732
Web Site: http://www.wartsila.com
Sales Range: $50-74.9 Million
Emp.: 50
Eletric Power Generation Services

INTERNATIONAL PUBLIC

N.A.I.C.S.: 221118

Wartsila Japan Company Ltd - Toyama Factory (2)
761-1 Mizuhashi Nakamura, Toyama, 939-3551, Japan
Tel.: (81) 76 403 6020
Web Site: https://www.wartsila.com
Emp.: 120
Eletric Power Generation Services
N.A.I.C.S.: 221118

Wartsila Korea Ltd. (1)
Tel.: (82) 513290500
Sales Range: $25-49.9 Million
Emp.: 236
Marine Engine Equipment Repair & Maintenance Services
N.A.I.C.S.: 811114
SuHae Yea *(Gen Mgr-HR)*

Wartsila LLC (1)
Dip Plot 597-572 Dubai Investment Park 2, Dubai, United Arab Emirates
Tel.: (971) 48857222
Marine Engineering Services
N.A.I.C.S.: 541330

Wartsila Lanka (Pvt) Ltd. (1)
Tel.: (94) 112980907
Sales Range: $25-49.9 Million
Emp.: 13
Marine Engine & Power Plant Equipment Repair & Maintenance Services
N.A.I.C.S.: 811310

Wartsila Marine and Power Services Nigeria Ltd. (1)
23 Oba Akinjobi Street Ikeja GRA, Lagos, Nigeria
Tel.: (234) 9078080936
Web Site: https://www.wartsila.com
Marine Engine & Power Plant Equipment Repair & Maintenance Services
N.A.I.C.S.: 811310

Wartsila Netherlands B.V. (1)
Tel.: (31) 889804000
Sales Range: $200-249.9 Million
Emp.: 900
Marine Propulsion Systems
N.A.I.C.S.: 336611

Plant (Domestic):

Wartsila Netherlands B.V. - Zwolle Power Plant (2)
Hanzelaan 95, 8017 JE, Zwolle, Netherlands
Tel.: (31) 384253253
Eletric Power Generation Services
N.A.I.C.S.: 221118

Wartsila New Zealand Ltd (1)
HMNZ Dockyard Queens Parade, Devonport, Auckland, 0624, New Zealand
Tel.: (64) 94453495
Power Plant Repair & Maintenance Services
N.A.I.C.S.: 811310

Wartsila North America, Inc. (1)
11710 N Gessner Rd Ste A, Houston, TX 77064
Tel.: (281) 233-6200
Web Site: https://www.wartsila.com
Marine Vessel Power Plants, Operation & Lifetime Care Services
N.A.I.C.S.: 336611
Ricardo Opperman *(Mng Dir)*

Subsidiary (Domestic):

Wartsila Defence Inc. (2)
3617 Koppens Way, Chesapeake, VA 23323
Tel.: (757) 558-3625
Web Site: http://www.wartsila.com
Sales Range: $25-49.9 Million
Emp.: 100
Marine Propeller Maintenance Services & Whslr
N.A.I.C.S.: 332999

Wartsila Defense, Inc. (2)
26264 Twelve Trees Ln, Poulsbo, WA 98370
Tel.: (360) 779-1444
Web Site: http://www.wartsila.com
Navy Ship Equipment Sales & Maintenance Services

AND PRIVATE COMPANIES — WARTSILA CORPORATION

N.A.I.C.S.: 488390

Wartsila Development & Financial Services Inc. (2)
900 Bestgate Rd Ste 400, Annapolis, MD 21401
Tel.: (410) 573-2100
Web Site: http://www.wartsila.com
Eletric Power Generation Services
N.A.I.C.S.: 221118

Plant (Domestic):

Wartsila North America, Inc. - Annapolis Power Plant (2)
900 Bestgate Rd Ste 400, Annapolis, MD 21401
Tel.: (410) 573-2100
Web Site: http://www.wartsila.com
Eletric Power Generation Services
N.A.I.C.S.: 221118

Wartsila Norway A/S (1)
Tel.: (47) 53422500
Sales Range: $550-599.9 Million
Emp.: 200
Industrial Machinery Distr
N.A.I.C.S.: 423830

Subsidiary (Domestic):

Wartsila Moss AS (2)
Vaerftsgata 9A, PO Box 1053, N-1510, Moss, Norway
Tel.: (47) 69279900
Web Site: https://www.wartsila.com
Sales Range: $25-49.9 Million
Marine Fluid Handling Systems Mfr
N.A.I.C.S.: 333996

Wartsila Norway Alesund ASA (2)
Maritime Service Tonningsgate 11, 6006, Alesund, Norway
Tel.: (47) 70 10 23 40
Sales Range: $25-49.9 Million
Emp.: 35
Marine Power Plant Construction Services
N.A.I.C.S.: 237130

Wartsila PNG Ltd (1)
Avara Annex Building Level 4 Section 7 Allotment 45 Brampton Street, NCD, 121, Port Moresby, Papua New Guinea
Tel.: (675) 3200171
Web Site: https://www.wartsila.com
Sales Range: $25-49.9 Million
Emp.: 2
Marine Engine & Power Plant Repair & Maintenance Services
N.A.I.C.S.: 811114

Wartsila Pakistan (Pvt.) Ltd. (1)
16 km Raiwind Road, Lahore, Pakistan
Tel.: (92) 4235905900
Web Site: https://www.wartsila.com
Sales Range: $100-124.9 Million
Emp.: 350
Power Plant Sales & Maintenance Services
N.A.I.C.S.: 811310

Plant (Domestic):

Wartsila Pakistan (Pvt.) Ltd. - Karachi Power Plant (2)
E-7 Block 4 Gulshan-e-Iqbal, Karachi, Pakistan
Tel.: (92) 213 497 0214
Web Site: http://www.wartsila.com
Sales Range: $50-74.9 Million
Emp.: 100
Eletric Power Generation Services
N.A.I.C.S.: 221118

Wartsila Panama S.A. (1)
Panama Pacifico Flex 2- Local 3-Brujas Ave Business International Park, Corregimiento de Veracruz, Arraijan, Panama
Tel.: (507) 304 7400
Web Site: http://www.wartsila.com
Sales Range: $25-49.9 Million
Emp.: 3
Marine Engine & Power Plant Equipment Repair & Maintenance Services
N.A.I.C.S.: 811114
Nadia Rey (Coord-HR)

Wartsila Peru S.A.C. (1)
Tel.: (51) 17307520
Web Site: https://www.wartsila.com
Sales Range: $75-99.9 Million
Emp.: 16
Eletric Power Generation Services
N.A.I.C.S.: 221118

Plant (Domestic):

Wartsila Peru S.A.C. - Lima Power Plant (2)
Av Ricardo Palma 341 Platino Business Center Floor 6 Office 604, Miraflores, Lima, 18, Peru
Tel.: (51) 1 241 7030
Web Site: https://www.wartsila.com
Eletric Power Generation Services
N.A.I.C.S.: 221118

Wartsila Philippines Inc. (1)
No 6 Diode St Light Industry and Science Park I Bo Diezmo, Cabuyao, 4025, Laguna, Philippines
Tel.: (63) 28437301
Web Site: https://www.wartsila.com
Emp.: 80
Eletric Power Generation Services
N.A.I.C.S.: 221118

Wartsila Polska Sp. z.o.o. (1)
ul Twarda 12, 80-871, Gdansk, Poland
Tel.: (48) 583478500
Web Site: https://www.wartsila.com
Sales Range: $50-74.9 Million
Emp.: 80
Marine Engine & Power Plant Equipment Distr
N.A.I.C.S.: 423830

Plant (Domestic):

Wartsila Polska Sp.z.o.o. - Warszawa Power Plant (2)
Ul Jakuba Kubickiego 13, 02-954, Warsaw, Poland
Tel.: (48) 22 550 6172
Web Site: http://www.wartsila.com
Marine Power Plant Construction Services
N.A.I.C.S.: 237130

Wartsila Portugal Lda. (1)
Tel.: (351) 253724400
Sales Range: $75-99.9 Million
Emp.: 2
Eletric Power Generation Services
N.A.I.C.S.: 221118

Wartsila Power Contracting Saudi Arabia Ltd. (1)
Office No 805B 8th Floor Tower B Bin Homran Comercial Cente, PO Box 6686, Prince Mohammed Bin Abdulaziz Street Ar Rawdah Dist, Jeddah, 23432, Saudi Arabia
Tel.: (966) 920001898
Engine Equipment Mfr
N.A.I.C.S.: 333618
Seppo Hautajoki (Mng Dir)

Wartsila Propulsion (Wuxi) Co. Ltd. (1)
No 53 Xi Qin Road, Wuxi National High and New Tech Development Area, Wuxi, 214028, Jiangsu, China
Tel.: (86) 51068860218
Marine Engine & Power Plant Repair & Maintenance Services
N.A.I.C.S.: 811114

Wartsila Puregas Solutions A/S (1)
Birkemose Alle 39, 6000, Kolding, Denmark
Tel.: (45) 701644312
Engine Equipment Mfr
N.A.I.C.S.: 333618

Wartsila Puregas Solutions AB (1)
Torsasgatan 3A, 392 39, Kalmar, Sweden
Tel.: (46) 480770000
Web Site: http://www.purac-puregas.com
Marine Support Services
N.A.I.C.S.: 488390

Wartsila Puregas Solutions GmbH (1)
Deichstrasse 1, 20359, Hamburg, Germany
Tel.: (49) 16090662951
Engine Equipment Mfr
N.A.I.C.S.: 333618

Wartsila Puregas Solutions Ltd. (1)
BIC Enterprise Park East, Sunderland, SR5 2TA, United Kingdom
Tel.: (44) 1915166662
Engine Equipment Mfr
N.A.I.C.S.: 333618

Wartsila Shanghai Services Ltd. (1)
3rd Floor Building 11 No 170 Jin Feng Road, Pudong New District, Shanghai, 201201, China
Tel.: (86) 215 858 5500
Web Site: http://www.wartsila.com
Sales Range: $25-49.9 Million
Emp.: 200
Marine Engine & Power Plant Repair & Maintenance Services
N.A.I.C.S.: 811114

Wartsila Ship Design (Shanghai) Co., Ltd. (1)
Building 13 No 170 Jinfeng Road, Pudong New District, Shanghai, 201201, China
Tel.: (86) 2158585500
Engine Equipment Mfr
N.A.I.C.S.: 333618

Wartsila Ship Design Germany GmbH (1)
Bernhard-Nocht-Str 113, 20359, Hamburg, Germany
Tel.: (49) 40 37 60 90
Ship Building Services
N.A.I.C.S.: 336611

Wartsila Ship Design Poland Sp. z.o.o. (1)
Ul Luzycka 2, 81-537, Gdynia, Poland
Tel.: (48) 58 718 6150
Web Site: https://www.wartsila.com
Sales Range: $25-49.9 Million
Emp.: 75
Ship Building Services
N.A.I.C.S.: 336611

Wartsila Ship Design Singapore Pte Ltd (1)
14 Benoi Crescent, Singapore, 629977, Singapore
Tel.: (65) 65621138
Sales Range: $25-49.9 Million
Emp.: 5
Ship Building Services
N.A.I.C.S.: 336611
Kelvin Koh (Gen Mgr-Fin & Bus Control)

Wartsila Ship Design, Conan Wu & Associates Pte Ltd (1)
55-02 Jalan Molek 3/1 Taman Molek, 81100, Johor Bahru, Malaysia
Tel.: (60) 7 355 5560
Web Site: http://www.wartsila.com
Sales Range: $25-49.9 Million
Emp.: 13
Ship Designing Services
N.A.I.C.S.: 541490

Wartsila Singapore Pte Ltd (1)
11 Pandan Crescent, Singapore, 128467, Singapore
Tel.: (65) 62659122
Web Site: https://www.wartsila.com
Emp.: 500
Shaft Seal & Bearing System Mfr
N.A.I.C.S.: 332991

Wartsila Singapore Pte Ltd. (1)
11 Pandan Crescent, Singapore, 128467, Singapore
Tel.: (65) 6 265 9122
Web Site: https://www.wartsila.com
Sales Range: $150-199.9 Million
Emp.: 500
Marine Engine & Power Plant Repair & Maintenance Services
N.A.I.C.S.: 811114
Mervin Ong (Gen Mgr-Ship Power)

Wartsila South Africa (Pty) Ltd. (1)
Tel.: (27) 215111230
Sales Range: $25-49.9 Million
Emp.: 150
Marine Engine Equipment Repair & Maintenance Services
N.A.I.C.S.: 811114

Plant (Domestic):

Wartsila South Africa (Pty) Ltd. - Cape Town Power Plant (2)
20 Dorsetshire Street, Paarden Eiland, Cape Town, 7405, South Africa
Tel.: (27) 21 511 1230

Sales Range: $50-74.9 Million
Emp.: 4
Eletric Power Generation Services
N.A.I.C.S.: 221118

Wartsila Sweden AB (1)
Karebogatan 8, PO Box 8006, 418 78, Gothenburg, Sweden
Tel.: (46) 317444600
Web Site: https://www.wartsila.com
Sales Range: $100-124.9 Million
Emp.: 352
Marine Equipment Mfr
N.A.I.C.S.: 336999

Plant (Domestic):

Wartsila Sweden AB - Gothenburg Power Plant (2)
Gotaverksgatan 10, Gothenburg, 40277, Sweden
Tel.: (46) 31 744 4600
Web Site: http://www.wartsila.com
Eletric Power Generation Services
N.A.I.C.S.: 221118
Bjorn Ullbro (CEO)

Wartsila Switzerland Ltd. (1)
Schlossmuhlestrasse 9, PO Box 414, 8500, Frauenfeld, Switzerland
Tel.: (41) 525500100
Web Site: https://www.wartsila.com
Sales Range: $200-249.9 Million
Emp.: 57
Marine Engine Mfr
N.A.I.C.S.: 333618

Wartsila Taiwan Ltd. (1)
4F No 68 Sec 2 Zhongshan N Road, Zhongshan District, Taipei, 10448, Taiwan
Tel.: (886) 225222239
Sales Range: $75-99.9 Million
Emp.: 20
Power Generation Services & Marine Engine Equipment Distr
N.A.I.C.S.: 221118

Wartsila Technology Oy Ab (1)
John Stenbergin Ranta 2, Helsinki, 530, Finland
Tel.: (358) 107090000
Web Site: http://www.wartsila.com
Sales Range: $100-124.9 Million
Emp.: 30
Shipping Equipment Mfr
N.A.I.C.S.: 336999
Bjoern Rosengren (CEO)

Wartsila UK Ltd. (1) (100%)
Tel.: (44) 1489550050
Sales Range: $50-74.9 Million
Emp.: 200
Marine Seals Mfr
N.A.I.C.S.: 339991

Subsidiary (Domestic):

Wartsila Hamworthy Limited (2)
Fleets Corner, Poole, BH17 0JT, Dorset, United Kingdom
Tel.: (44) 1202662600
Web Site: http://www.hamworthy.com
Sales Range: $200-249.9 Million
Emp.: 961
Holding Company
N.A.I.C.S.: 551112

Subsidiary (Non-US):

Hamworthy (Suzhou) Limited (3)
121 Dengwei Road, Suzhou, 215011, Jiangsu, China
Tel.: (86) 51268243108
Oil & Gas Field Engineering Services
N.A.I.C.S.: 213112

Hamworthy B.V. (3)
Aploniastraat 33 3084 CC, Rotterdam, 3084 CC, Zuid-Holland, Netherlands
Tel.: (31) 104624777
Marine Engineering Services
N.A.I.C.S.: 541330

Hamworthy Baltic Design Centre Limited (3)
15/8 Skwer Koaeciuszki, Gdynia, 81537, Pomeranian, Poland
Tel.: (48) 587186150
Web Site: http://www.wartsila.com

WARTSILA CORPORATION

Wartsila Corporation—(Continued)

Sales Range: $25-49.9 Million
Emp.: 52
Ship Designing & Consulting Services
N.A.I.C.S.: 541330

Hamworthy Greenship BV (3)
Bankastraat 77, Groningen, 9715 CJ, Netherlands
Tel.: (31) 505891334
Marine Engineering Services
N.A.I.C.S.: 541330

Subsidiary (US):

Hamworthy Inc. (3)
1011 Hwy 6 S Ste 208, Houston, TX 77077
Tel.: (281) 759-3280
Web Site: http://www.hamworthy.com
Oil & Gas Field Engineering Services
N.A.I.C.S.: 211120

Subsidiary (Non-US):

Hamworthy India Pvt Ltd (3)
117 Mittal Chambers Nariman Point, Mumbai, 400 021, Maharastra, India
Tel.: (91) 2230287711
Web Site: http://www.hamworthy.com
Sales Range: $25-49.9 Million
Emp.: 15
Marine Engineering Services
N.A.I.C.S.: 541330

Hamworthy Korea Limited (3)
8th Floor Yoosung Plaza Building 655-6 Woo-dong Haeundae-gu, 612 020, Busan, Korea (South)
Tel.: (82) 517413724
Web Site: http://www.hamworthy.com
Sales Range: $25-49.9 Million
Emp.: 15
Marine Engineering Services
N.A.I.C.S.: 541330

Hamworthy Middle East (FZC) (3)
SAIF Zone, PO Box 120691, Sharjah, United Arab Emirates
Tel.: (971) 65574806
Web Site: http://www.hamworthy.com
Sales Range: $25-49.9 Million
Emp.: 15
Marine Engineering Services
N.A.I.C.S.: 541330

Hamworthy Pte Limited (3)
15 Benoi Crescent, Jurong, Singapore
Tel.: (65) 62616066
Web Site: http://www.hamworthy.com
Marine Engineering Services
N.A.I.C.S.: 541330

Hamworthy Pump Systems AS (3)
Avenida Doutor Touron 1 - 1 Vilagarcia De Arousa, Pontevedra, 36600, Spain
Tel.: (34) 986 566 538
Marine Engineering Services
N.A.I.C.S.: 541330

Hamworthy Serck Como GmbH (3)
Pankower Str 16-18, 21502, Geesthacht, Germany
Tel.: (49) 41528050
Web Site: http://www.wartsila.com
Sales Range: $25-49.9 Million
Emp.: 35
Industrial Heat Exchangers Mfr
N.A.I.C.S.: 332410
Matthias Becker (Mng Dir)

Wartsila Oil & Gas Systems AS (3)
Sondraaveien 10, PO Box 144, N-1383, Asker, Norway
Tel.: (47) 81548500
Web Site: http://www.wartsila.com
Marine Transport Gas Handling Systems & Services
N.A.I.C.S.: 333242
Tore Lunde (Mng Dir-Wartsila Norway AS)

Subsidiary (Domestic):

Wartsila Water Systems Ltd. (3)
Merchants House Vanguard Road, Poole, BH15 1PH, Dorset, United Kingdom
Tel.: (44) 1202662600
Sales Range: $50-74.9 Million
Emp.: 130
Marine Vessel Water Treatment & Waste Separation Equipment Mfr
N.A.I.C.S.: 221320

Plant (Domestic):

Wartsila UK Ltd - Seals & Bearings Factory (2)
4 Marples Way, Havant, PO9 1NX, Hampshire, United Kingdom
Tel.: (44) 239 240 0121
Web Site: https://www.wartsila.com
Emp.: 150
Marine Engine Equipment Mfr
N.A.I.C.S.: 333618

Wartsila Valmarine AS (1)
Ing Rydbergsgt 99, N-3007, Drammen, Norway
Tel.: (47) 32218100
Engine Equipment Mfr
N.A.I.C.S.: 333618

Wartsila Valves Ltd. (1)
D Shed West 72-74 Humber Enterprise Park Skua Road, Kingston upon Hull, HU15 1EQ, East Yorkshire, United Kingdom
Tel.: (44) 482323163
Engine Equipment Mfr
N.A.I.C.S.: 333618
Rob Moulds (Mng Dir)

Wartsila Venezuela, C.A. (1)
Oficinas y Taller, Av 88-A entre calles 131 y 132, Valencia, Venezuela
Tel.: (58) 241 842 3808
Web Site: http://www.wartsila.com
Industrial Machinery Parts Mfr
N.A.I.C.S.: 333132

Plant (Domestic):

Wartsila Venezuela, C.A. - Valencia Power Plant (2)
Zona Industrial II Av Branger Centro Comercial e Industiral, Local No 13 Estado Carabobo, Valencia, 2010, Venezuela
Tel.: (58) 241 838 4659
Eletric Power Generation Services
N.A.I.C.S.: 221118
Luis Enriquez (Mgr)

Wartsila Voyage Limited (1)
13-18 City Quay 2, Dublin, D02 ED70, Ireland
Tel.: (353) 214710400
Engine Equipment Mfr
N.A.I.C.S.: 333618

Wartsila Voyage Middle East DMCEST (1)
Dubai Investment Park 2 Plot No 57-572, Dubai, United Arab Emirates
Tel.: (971) 48857222
Marine Engineering Services
N.A.I.C.S.: 541330

Wartsila Voyage Pacific Pte. Ltd. (1)
16/18 Jalan Kilang Barat Cyber Centre Level 2, Singapore, 159358, Singapore
Tel.: (65) 62710200
Engine Equipment Mfr
N.A.I.C.S.: 333618

Wartsila Voyage UK Limited (1)
Tel.: (44) 1489550050
Engine Equipment Mfr
N.A.I.C.S.: 333618

Wartsila West Africa S.A. (1)
Tel.: (221) 338654100
Sales Range: $25-49.9 Million
Emp.: 2
Marine Engine & Power Plant Equipment Repair & Maintenance Services
N.A.I.C.S.: 811310

Wartsila de Mexico SA (1)
Tel.: (52) 19381381500
Sales Range: $25-49.9 Million
Emp.: 2
Marine Engine & Power Plant Equipment Repair & Maintenance Services
N.A.I.C.S.: 811310

Wartsila-Enpa A.S. (1)
Aydintepe Mah D-100 Karayolu E-5 Cad No 14/E Bahar Is Merkezi, Tuzla, 34947, Istanbul, Turkiye
Tel.: (90) 2164945050
Web Site: https://www.wartsila.com
Eletric Power Generation Services
N.A.I.C.S.: 221118

Wartsla Argentina S.A. (1)
Carlos Pellegrini 1363 Piso 8, C1011AAA, Buenos Aires, Argentina
Tel.: (54) 1143168600
Engine Equipment Mfr
N.A.I.C.S.: 333618

Wartsla Colombia S.A. (1)
Carrera 19B 83-63 5 Tower Anato Apartment, 110221, Bogota, Colombia
Tel.: (57) 16358168
Engine Equipment Mfr
N.A.I.C.S.: 333618

Wartsla Eastern Africa S.A. (1)
ABC Towers-7A ABC Place Waiyaki Way, PO Box 66782, 00800, Nairobi, Kenya
Tel.: (254) 207602400
Engine Equipment Mfr
N.A.I.C.S.: 333618
Rashid Shamsi (Mng Dir)

Wartsla Ecuador S.A. (1)
La Mancha Business Center Highway E35 km 24 1/2 Tababela, Quito, Ecuador
Tel.: (593) 23931560
Engine Equipment Mfr
N.A.I.C.S.: 333618
Remigio Penarreta (Mng Dir)

Wartsla Energy Mauritanie SAU (1)
10 Rue Mamadou Konate, Nouakchott, Mauritania
Tel.: (222) 45250819
Engine Equipment Mfr
N.A.I.C.S.: 333618

Wartsla Guatemala S.A. (1)
10a Calle 12-50 Zona 14 Ofibodegas La Villa Bodega 18, 01014, Guatemala, Guatemala
Tel.: (502) 23849600
Engine Equipment Mfr
N.A.I.C.S.: 333618

WARTSILA VOSTOK, LLC

Business Centre Linkor 36 A Petrogradskaya Naberezhnaya, 197101, Saint Petersburg, Russia
Tel.: (7) 812 448 32 48
Year Founded: 2006
Sales Range: $75-99.9 Million
Emp.: 134
Power Plant Equipment Distr
N.A.I.C.S.: 423830
Dmitry Firsov (Gen Mgr)

Subsidiaries:

Wartsila Vostok, LLC - St. Petersburg Plant (1)
Business centre Linkor 36 A Petrogradskaya naberezhnaya, 197101, Saint Petersburg, Russia
Tel.: (7) 812 448 3248
Sales Range: $25-49.9 Million
Emp.: 158
Engine Equipment Mfr
N.A.I.C.S.: 333618
Dmitry Firsov (Gen Mgr)

WARWICK CAPITAL PARTNERS LLP

86 Duke of York Square, London, SW3 4LY, United Kingdom
Tel.: (44) 207 850 8080
Web Site: http://www.warwickcap.com
Year Founded: 2010
Privater Equity Firm
N.A.I.C.S.: 551111
Ian Burgess (Partner & Co-Chief Investment Officer)

Subsidiaries:

Porcher Industries SA (1)
75 D 1085, Badinieres, 38300, France **(100%)**
Tel.: (33) 4 74 43 10 10
Specialty Glass & Textile Mfr
N.A.I.C.S.: 313210
P. Vermorel (CFO)

Valmieras Stikla Skiedra AS (1)
Cempu 13, Valmiera, 4201, Latvia **(83.14%)**

INTERNATIONAL PUBLIC

Tel.: (371) 64202216
Web Site: http://www.valmiera-glass.com
Glass Fibre Product Mfr
N.A.I.C.S.: 327212
Stefan Jugel (Chm)

WASAYA AIRWAYS LP

300 Anemki Pl Ste B RR4, Thunder Bay, P7J 1H9, ON, Canada
Tel.: (807) 473-1200
Web Site: http://www.wasaya.com
Sales Range: $75-99.9 Million
Emp.: 429
Oil Transportation Services
N.A.I.C.S.: 481111
Adam Fiddler (Chm)

WASCOSA AG

Werftestrasse 4, 6005, Lucerne, Switzerland
Tel.: (41) 41 727 6767 CH
Web Site: http://www.wascosa.ch
Year Founded: 1964
Rail Freight Car Leasing & Management Services
N.A.I.C.S.: 532411
Philipp Muller (Chm)

Subsidiaries:

Wascosa GmbH (1)
Alter Steinweg 1, 20459, Hamburg, Germany
Tel.: (49) 40 3208 5830
Web Site: http://www.wascosa.com
Rail
N.A.I.C.S.: 532411

WASECO RESOURCES INC.

2 Queen St East Suite 1500, Toronto, M5C 3G5, ON, Canada
Tel.: (416) 364-3123
Web Site: https://www.wasecoresources.com
WSRUF—(OTCIQ)
Rev: $2,325
Assets: $5,598
Liabilities: $530,679
Net Worth: ($525,082)
Earnings: ($38,387)
Fiscal Year-end: 02/29/24
Mineral Exploration Services
N.A.I.C.S.: 213114
Richard Williams (Pres & CEO)

WASEDA ACADEMY CO., LTD.

2-53-7 Ikebukuro, Toshima-ku, Tokyo, 171-0014, Japan
Tel.: (81) 120973737
Web Site: https://www.waseda-ac.co.jp
Year Founded: 1974
4718—(TKS)
Rev: $217,250,870
Assets: $152,406,770
Liabilities: $58,128,340
Net Worth: $94,278,430
Earnings: $14,092,520
Emp.: 1,090
Fiscal Year-end: 03/31/24
Educational Support Services
N.A.I.C.S.: 611710
Yutaka Yamamoto (Pres)

WASGAU PRODUKTIONS & HANDELS AG

Blocksbergstrasse 183, 66955, Pirmasens, 66955, Germany
Tel.: (49) 63315580
Web Site: https://www.wasgau.de
Year Founded: 1925
MSH—(DEU)
Rev: $695,647,835
Assets: $396,167,904
Liabilities: $276,828,519
Net Worth: $119,339,386
Earnings: $4,735,602
Emp.: 3,702
Fiscal Year-end: 12/30/23

AND PRIVATE COMPANIES

Consumer Goods Mfr & Distr
N.A.I.C.S.: 337126
Christian Mielsch *(Chm-Supervisory Bd)*

Subsidiaries:

WASGAU Backerei GmbH (1)
Molkenbrunner Strasse 24, 66954, Pirmasens, Germany
Tel.: (49) 63315260
Food Product Retailer
N.A.I.C.S.: 445298

WASGAU Frischwaren GmbH (1)
Blocksbergstr 183, 66955, Pirmasens, Germany
Tel.: (49) 63315580
Food Product Retailer
N.A.I.C.S.: 445298

WASGAU Metzgerei GmbH (1)
Rheinstrasse 27, 66955, Pirmasens, Germany
Tel.: (49) 633171040
Food Product Retailer
N.A.I.C.S.: 445298

WASH HOUSE CO., LTD.
86-1 Shin-ei-cho, Miyazaki, 880-0831, Japan
Tel.: (81) 985240000   JP
Web Site: https://www.wash-house.jp
Year Founded: 2001
6537—(TKS)
Rev.: $13,570,260
Assets: $29,274,610
Liabilities: $16,767,850
Net Worth: $12,506,760
Earnings: ($233,970)
Emp.: 95
Fiscal Year-end: 12/31/23
Coin-Operated Laundry Services
N.A.I.C.S.: 812310

WASHINGTON H. SOUL PATTINSON & COMPANY LIMITED
Level 14 151 Clarence Street, Sydney, 2000, NSW, Australia
Tel.: (61) 292107070   AU
Web Site:
  https://www.soulpatts.com.au
Year Founded: 1903
SOL—(ASX)
Rev.: $1,261,613,817
Assets: $5,745,265,755
Liabilities: $1,796,643,528
Net Worth: $3,948,622,226
Earnings: $245,517,157
Emp.: 220
Fiscal Year-end: 07/31/21
Investment Holding Company
N.A.I.C.S.: 551112
Ian David Bloodworth *(Sec)*

Subsidiaries:

Ampcontrol Pty. Ltd. (1)
21 Old Punt Road, Tomago, 2322, NSW, Australia
Tel.: (61) 2 4961 9000
Web Site: http://www.ampcontrolgroup.com
Sales Range: $200-249.9 Million
Emp.: 900
Electrical & Electronic Products Mfr
N.A.I.C.S.: 335999
Peter Cockbain *(Founder)*

Subsidiary (Domestic):

ATF Mining Electrics Pty Ltd (2)
17 Old Punt Rd, Tomago, 2322, NSW, Australia
Tel.: (61) 249544199
Construction & Mining Equipment Mfr
N.A.I.C.S.: 333120

Subsidiary (Non-US):

Ampcontrol UK Ltd. (2)
66 Third Avenue Heatherhouse Industrial Estate Irvine, Irvine, KA12 8HN, United Kingdom

Tel.: (44) 1294273111
Flameproof Electrical Distribution & Motor Control Equipment Mfr
N.A.I.C.S.: 335999
Graham Muir *(Office Mgr)*

Subsidiary (Domestic):

Austech Instruments Pty Ltd (2)
Unit 2 71 Prince William Drive, Seven Hills, 2147, NSW, Australia
Tel.: (61) 296209600
Web Site: http://www.aus-tech.com.au
Gas Detection Equipment Mfr
N.A.I.C.S.: 334511

Burn Brite Lights Pty. Ltd. (2)
1/100 New Street, Ringwood, 3134, VIC, Australia
Tel.: (61) 388705500
Web Site: http://www.ampcontrolgroup.com
Lighting System Mfr & Distr
N.A.I.C.S.: 335132

Capacitor Technologies Pty. Ltd. (2)
Unit 13 40 Edina Road, PO Box 240, Ferntree Gully, Melbourne, 3156, VIC, Australia
Tel.: (61) 397585866
Web Site: http://www.captech.com.au
Sales Range: $25-49.9 Million
Emp.: 12
Mfr & Supplier of Components for Energy Saving Equipment
N.A.I.C.S.: 334416
Yury Brodsky *(Gen Mgr)*

Lithgow Cable Services Pty Ltd (2)
3 O Connor Street, Lithgow, 2790, NSW, Australia
Tel.: (61) 263522944
Cable Distr
N.A.I.C.S.: 423510

ResTech (2)
The University of Newcastle Level 9 Room A941 NIER Building, Callaghan, 2308, NSW, Australia
Tel.: (61) 240339155
Web Site: http://www.restech.net.au
Engineeering Services
N.A.I.C.S.: 541330

Exco Resources Limited (1)
Level 32/10 Eagle Street, Brisbane, 4000, QLD, Australia
Tel.: (61) 0738356200
Web Site: http://www.excoresources.com.au
Mineral Interests Exploration & Evaluation
N.A.I.C.S.: 213115
Paul Griffin *(Sr Project Mgr)*

Milton Corporation Limited (1)
Level 4 50 Pitt Street, Sydney, 2000, NSW, Australia
Tel.: (61) 280065357
Web Site: http://www.milton.com.au
Financial Investment Services
N.A.I.C.S.: 523150
D. Nishantha Seneviratne *(CFO)*

Subsidiary (Domestic):

Chatham Investment Co. Pty. Limited (2)
Level 4 50 Pitt St, Sydney, 2000, NSW, Australia (100%)
Tel.: (61) 292334166
Sales Range: $50-74.9 Million
Investment Management Service
N.A.I.C.S.: 523940

Pitt Capital Partners Limited (1)
Barrack Place L14 151 Clarence St, Sydney, 2000, NSW, Australia
Tel.: (61) 29 210 7000
Web Site: https://www.pcap.com.au
Financial Advisory Services
N.A.I.C.S.: 523940
David Scammell *(Mng Dir)*

Souls Private Equity Limited (1)
Level 2 160 Pitt St Mall, Sydney, 2000, NSW, Australia
Tel.: (61) 292107000
Sales Range: $25-49.9 Million
Emp.: 14
Private Equity Fund
N.A.I.C.S.: 523999
T. Barlow *(Gen Mgr)*

Subsidiary (Domestic):

Cromford Group Pty. Ltd. (2)

120-122 Ballandella Road, Pendle Hill, 2145, NSW, Australia
Tel.: (61) 298969400
Emp.: 45
Mfr & Distr of Polyethylene Pipe & Industrial Plastics
N.A.I.C.S.: 326122

WASHINGTON HOTEL CORPORATION
23-5 Uchiyama 3-chome, Chikusa-Ku, Nagoya, 464-0075, Japan
Tel.: (81) 527459030
Web Site:
  https://www.washingtonhotel.co.jp
Year Founded: 1961
4691—(TKS)
Rev.: $191,528,480
Assets: $258,301,120
Liabilities: $118,473,520
Net Worth: $139,827,600
Earnings: $3,949,440
Fiscal Year-end: 03/31/20
Hotel & Restaurant Operator
N.A.I.C.S.: 721110
Kazuo Uchida *(Pres)*

WASHTEC AG
Argonstrasse 7, 86153, Augsburg, Germany
Tel.: (49) 82155840
Web Site: https://www.washtec.de
Year Founded: 1885
WSU—(DEU)
Rev.: $540,311,249
Assets: $299,490,970
Liabilities: $204,823,078
Net Worth: $94,667,891
Earnings: $30,875,244
Emp.: 1,768
Fiscal Year-end: 12/31/23
Car Wash Machinery Mfr
N.A.I.C.S.: 333310
Gunter Blaschke *(Chm-Supervisory Bd)*

Subsidiaries:

AUWA-Chemie GmbH & Co. KG (1)
Argonstrasse 7, D-86153, Augsburg, Germany
Tel.: (49) 82155840
Web Site: https://www.auwa.de
Sales Range: $250-299.9 Million
Emp.: 600
Car Washing Equipments & Chemicals Whslr
N.A.I.C.S.: 423850
Ralf Koeppe *(Gen Mgr)*

Mark VII Equipment Inc. (1)
5981 Tennyson St, Arvada, CO 80003
Tel.: (303) 323-4910
Web Site: https://www.markvii.net
Sales Range: $50-74.9 Million
Emp.: 150
Car Washing Machinery Mfr
N.A.I.C.S.: 333310

WashTec Bilvask AS (1)
Slependveien 108, 1396, Billingstad, Norway
Tel.: (47) 2 291 8180
Web Site: https://www.washtec.no
Car Wash & Maintenance Services
N.A.I.C.S.: 811192

WashTec CZ, spol. S.r.o. (1)
U trati 1440/48, Strasnice, 100 00, Prague, Czech Republic
Tel.: (420) 27 402 1231
Web Site: https://www.washtec.cz
Sales Range: $25-49.9 Million
Emp.: 21
Car Wash Equipment Sales
N.A.I.C.S.: 423850

WashTec Cleaning Technology GmbH (1)
Argonstrasse 7, 86153, Augsburg, Germany
Tel.: (49) 82155840
Web Site: http://www.washtec.eu
Sales Range: $150-199.9 Million
Emp.: 500

Carwash Equipment Whslr & Cleaning Services
N.A.I.C.S.: 423850

Subsidiary (Non-US):

WashTec Benelux B.V. (2)
Radonstraat 9, 2718 SV, Zoetermeer, Netherlands
Tel.: (31) 793683701
Web Site: https://www.washtec.nl
Sales Range: $25-49.9 Million
Emp.: 20
Car Wash Equipment Sales
N.A.I.C.S.: 423850
Ron Stook *(Dir-Fin)*

WashTec Cleaning Technology GmbH (2)
Wehlistrasse 27b, 1200, Vienna, Austria
Tel.: (43) 13 343 0650
Web Site: https://www.washtec.at
Car Wash & Maintenance Services
N.A.I.C.S.: 811192
Matthias Bertoldi *(Mng Dir)*

Subsidiary (Non-US):

WashTec Polska Sp. z o.o. (3)
ul Sienna 73, 00-833, Warsaw, Poland
Tel.: (48) 78 240 2999
Web Site: https://www.washtec-polska.pl
Car Wash & Maintenance Services
N.A.I.C.S.: 811192
Agnieszka Turska *(Mng Dir)*

WashTec S.r.l. (3)
Via Achille Grandi 16/E, 15033, Casale Monferrato, Italy
Tel.: (39) 01 427 6364
Web Site: https://www.washtec.it
Emp.: 100
Car Wash & Maintenance Services
N.A.I.C.S.: 811192

Subsidiary (Non-US):

WashTec Denmark AS (2)
Guldalderen 10, 2640, Hedehusene, Denmark
Tel.: (45) 7 010 1533
Web Site: https://www.washtec.dk
Car Wash Systems Sales
N.A.I.C.S.: 423850

WashTec France SAS (2)
200 rue du Grand Bouland, 45760, Boigny-sur-Bionne, France
Tel.: (33) 238607060
Web Site: https://www.washtec.fr
Car Wash Equipment Sales
N.A.I.C.S.: 423850

WashTec Spain SA (2)
C/Isla Graciosa, 28703, San Sebastian de los Reyes, Madrid, Spain
Tel.: (34) 916636070
Web Site: https://www.washtec.es
Sales Range: $25-49.9 Million
Emp.: 16
Car Wash Equipment Sales
N.A.I.C.S.: 423850

WashTec UK Ltd. (2)
Unit 14a Chelmsford Rd, Oak Industrial Estate, Great Dunmow, CM6 1XN, Essex, United Kingdom
Tel.: (44) 1371878800
Web Site: https://www.washtec-uk.com
Sales Range: $25-49.9 Million
Emp.: 84
Car Wash Equipment Sales
N.A.I.C.S.: 423850

WashTec Financial Services GmbH (1)
Argonstrasse 7, 86153, Augsburg, Germany
Tel.: (49) 82155841611
Web Site: http://www.washtec.de
Financial Support Services
N.A.I.C.S.: 523940

WashTec Ireland Ltd. (1)
Unit 72A Western Parkway Business Park Ballymount Road, Dublin, 12, Leinster, Ireland
Tel.: (353) 1 429 4294
Web Site: http://www.washtec.eu
Emp.: 120
Car Wash Equipment Sales
N.A.I.C.S.: 423850

WASHTEC CAR CLEANING EQUIPMENT (SHANGHAI) CO. LTD.

WashTec Car Cleaning Equipment (Shanghai) Co. Ltd.—(Continued)

WASHTEC CAR CLEANING EQUIPMENT (SHANGHAI) CO. LTD.
Building 1 No 1688 Jiugong Road, Zhuxing Town Jinshan Industrial Zone, Shanghai, 201505, China
Tel.: (86) 213 728 6669
Web Site: https://www.washtec.cn
Year Founded: 2008
Sales Range: $25-49.9 Million
Emp.: 20
Car Wash Equipment Sales
N.A.I.C.S.: 423850

WASION HOLDINGS LIMITED
Unit 2605 26F West Tower Shun Tak Centre 168-200 Connaught Rd Central, Sheung Wan, Hong Kong, China (Hong Kong)
Tel.: (852) 28652228
Web Site: http://www.wasion.com
3393—(HKG)
Rev.: $822,160,498
Assets: $1,828,858,122
Liabilities: $968,420,092
Net Worth: $860,438,030
Earnings: $71,766,864
Emp.: 4,521
Fiscal Year-end: 12/31/22
Energy Metering & Managing Services
N.A.I.C.S.: 334515
Choi Wai Lung Edward *(CFO & Sec)*

Subsidiaries:

Gam Sheng Macao Commercial Offshore Limited (1)
Rm G&H 8F Centro Hotline 315-363 Alameda Dr Carlos, Macau, China (Macau)
Tel.: (853) 28751068
Sales Range: $50-74.9 Million
Emp.: 8
Electronic Components Trading Services
N.A.I.C.S.: 425120
Hong Hu Yong *(Mgr-Pur)*

Hunan Switchgear Co. Ltd. (1)
No 32 Lijiang Avenue, Lijiang Industrial Park, Changsha, Hunan, China
Tel.: (86) 7318 528 3708
Web Site: https://wshnkg.cn
Switchgear Mfr
N.A.I.C.S.: 335313

Smart Metering Solution (Changsha) Co., Ltd. (1)
468 Tongzipo Road, Hi-Tech Park, Changsha, 410205, China
Tel.: (86) 7318 829 5218
Web Site: https://en.smsc-cs.com
Data Management Software Services
N.A.I.C.S.: 518210

Wasion Energy Technology Co., Ltd. (1)
No 28 Baishi Road Jiuhua Economic & Technological Development Zone, Xiangtan, Hunan, China
Tel.: (86) 4008572588
Web Site: https://www.wasionelectric.com
Smart Power Distribution System Mfr & Distr
N.A.I.C.S.: 335311

Willfar Information Technology Co., Ltd. (1)
No 468 Tongzipo West Road, Wasion Industrial Park Yuelu District, Changsha, 410205, Hunan, China
Tel.: (86) 73188619798
Web Site: https://www.willfar.com
Rev.: $281,307,349
Assets: $550,118,481
Liabilities: $164,039,022
Net Worth: $386,079,459
Earnings: $56,182,618
Fiscal Year-end: 12/31/2022
Information Technology Services
N.A.I.C.S.: 541512
Zhe Ji *(Chm)*

WASKAHIGAN OIL & GAS CORP.
Suite 203 221-10th Avenue SE, Calgary, T2G 0V9, AB, Canada
Tel.: (403) 265-7544
Web Site: https://www.waskahiganoil.com
Year Founded: 2007
WOGC—(CNSX)
Rev.: $606,667
Assets: $2,192,954
Liabilities: $1,913,583
Net Worth: $279,371
Earnings: ($12,551)
Fiscal Year-end: 12/31/21
Oil & Gas Exploration Services
N.A.I.C.S.: 213112
Gregory J. Leia *(Co-Founder & Co-CEO)*

Subsidiaries:

Odaat Oil Corp. (1)
Suite 203 221 - 10th Avenue SE, Calgary, T2G 0V9, AB, Canada
Tel.: (403) 265-7544
Oil & Gas Exploration Services
N.A.I.C.S.: 213112

WASKO S.A.
Ul Berbeckiego 6, 44-100, Gliwice, Poland
Tel.: (48) 323325500
Web Site: https://www.wasko.pl
WAS—(WAR)
Rev.: $135,696,646
Assets: $121,948,424
Liabilities: $60,176,575
Net Worth: $61,771,849
Earnings: ($170,224)
Emp.: 1,400
Fiscal Year-end: 12/31/23
Information & Communication Technology Services
N.A.I.C.S.: 519290
Pawel Kuch *(Vice Chm-Mgmt Bd)*

Subsidiaries:

COIG SA (1)
ul Mikolowska 100, 40-065, Katowice, Poland
Tel.: (48) 327574224
Web Site: http://www.coig.pl
Information Technology Services
N.A.I.C.S.: 541511
Pawel Kuch *(Chm)*

FONON Sp. z o.o. (1)
ul Czackiego 7/9/11, 00-043, Warsaw, Poland
Tel.: (48) 225058101
Web Site: http://www.fonon.com.pl
Telecommunication Servicesb
N.A.I.C.S.: 517810
Wlodzimierz Sosnowski *(Chm)*

LogicSynergy Sp. z o.o. (1)
ul At Sikornik 27A, 30-216, Krakow, Poland
Tel.: (48) 124226249
Web Site: http://www.logicsynergy.pl
Computer Software Development Services
N.A.I.C.S.: 541511

WASSERMAN & PARTNERS ADVERTISING INC.
1020 Mainland St Ste 160, Vancouver, V6B 2T4, BC, Canada
Tel.: (604) 684-1111
Web Site: http://www.wasserman-partners.com
Year Founded: 1995
Sales Range: $10-24.9 Million
Emp.: 42
Brand Development, Broadcast, Interactive Agencies, Media Buying Services, Print, Production, Strategic Planning/Research
N.A.I.C.S.: 541810
Alvin Wasserman *(Pres & Writer)*

WASTBYGG GRUPPEN AB
Johan Willins Gata 6, 416 64, Gothenburg, Sweden
Tel.: (46) 0317332300
Web Site: https://wbgr.se
Year Founded: 1981
WBGR.B—(OMX)
Rev.: $495,463,308
Assets: $401,354,068
Liabilities: $284,511,689
Net Worth: $116,842,379
Earnings: ($36,631,128)
Emp.: 530
Fiscal Year-end: 12/31/23
Engineering & Construction Services
N.A.I.C.S.: 541330
Robin Sundin *(COO)*

WASTE CONNECTIONS, INC.
6220 Hwy 7 Suite 600, Woodbridge, L4H 4G3, ON, Canada
Tel.: (905) 532-7510
Web Site: https://www.wasteconnections.com
WCN—(NYSE)
Rev.: $8,021,951,000
Assets: $17,915,876,000
Liabilities: $10,218,095,000
Net Worth: $7,697,781,000
Earnings: $762,800,000
Emp.: 22,539
Fiscal Year-end: 12/31/23
Holding Company; Waste Management & Recycling Services
N.A.I.C.S.: 551112
Ronald J. Mittelstaedt *(Founder, Pres & CEO)*

Subsidiaries:

A.C.M.S., Inc. (1)
4770 Biscayne Blvd Ste 850, Miami, FL 33137
Tel.: (305) 438-3788
Web Site: https://www.acmsinc.com
Software Services
N.A.I.C.S.: 541511
Andrae Corrigan *(Pres & Founder)*

Alaska Waste-Ketchikan, LLC (1)
5010 N Tongass Hwy, Ketchikan, AK 99901
Tel.: (907) 225-5562
Waste Recycling Services
N.A.I.C.S.: 562119

Alaska Waste-Nome, LLC (1)
120 E 1st Ave, Nome, AK 99762
Tel.: (907) 443-5590
Waste Recycling Services
N.A.I.C.S.: 562119

Blue Compactor Services, LLC (1)
8984 215th St W, Lakeville, MN 55044
Tel.: (952) 469-9866
Web Site: https://www.bluecompactor.com
Waste Recycling Services
N.A.I.C.S.: 562119

Champ Landfill Company, LLC (1)
2305 Creve Coeur Mill Rd, Maryland Heights, MO 63043
Tel.: (314) 279-5777
Web Site: https://www.champlandfill.com
Waste Management Services
N.A.I.C.S.: 562998

Complexe Enviro Connexions Ltee (1)
3779 chemin des Quarante-Arpents, Terrebonne, J6V 9T6, QC, Canada
Tel.: (450) 474-2423
Web Site: https://www.complexenviroconnexion.com
Waste Collection & Disposal Services
N.A.I.C.S.: 562111
Patrick Pool *(CEO)*

Dick's Sanitation Service, Inc. (1)
8984 215th St W, Lakeville, MN 55044-8338
Tel.: (952) 469-2239
Web Site: https://www.dickssanitation.com
Waste Management Services
N.A.I.C.S.: 562998
MaryAnn Clemmer *(Founder)*

INTERNATIONAL PUBLIC

E.L. Harvey & Sons Inc. (1)
68 Hopkinton Rd, Westborough, MA 01581
Tel.: (508) 836-5088
Web Site: http://www.elharvey.com
Waste Management & Remediation Services
N.A.I.C.S.: 562998
James Harvey *(CEO)*

Eagle Disposal of PA Inc. (1)
1251 E Earl Rd, East Earl, PA 17519
Tel.: (717) 355-9560
Web Site: https://www.eagledisposalofpa.com
Waste Management Services
N.A.I.C.S.: 562998

Enviro Connexions, Inc. (1)
4799 Bernard Lefebvre, Laval, H7C 0A5, QC, Canada
Tel.: (450) 661-5080
Web Site: http://www.entreprisesanitairefa.com
Local Freight Trucking
N.A.I.C.S.: 484110

Hampton Roads Recovery Center, LLC (1)
1613 Centerville Tpke, Virginia Beach, VA 23464
Tel.: (757) 420-0128
Web Site: https://www.hrrecovery.com
Waste Management Services
N.A.I.C.S.: 562998

IESI-BFC Holdings, Inc. (1)
610 Applewood Crescent, Vaughan, L4K-0C3, ON, Canada
Tel.: (905) 532-7510
Investment Management Service
N.A.I.C.S.: 523999

Iowa Waste Services, LLC (1)
59722 290th St, Malvern, IA 51551
Tel.: (712) 624-8039
Web Site: https://www.iawaste.com
Waste Management Services
N.A.I.C.S.: 562998

Lone Star Disposal, LP (1)
10415 Tanner Rd, Houston, TX 77041-7439
Tel.: (713) 466-6767
Web Site: https://www.lonestar-disposal.com
Solid Waste Collection Services
N.A.I.C.S.: 562111

MTG Disposal, LLC (1)
19 Industrial Way, Seekonk, MA 02771
Tel.: (508) 336-8466
Web Site: https://www.megadisposal.com
Garbage Dump Services
N.A.I.C.S.: 562211

Ridge (Chatham) Holdings G.P. Inc. (1)
610 Applewood Crescent, Vaughan, L4K-0C3, ON, Canada
Tel.: (905) 532-7510
Investment Management Service
N.A.I.C.S.: 523999

Ridge Landfill Corporation Limited (1)
20262 Erieau Road, Blenheim, N0P 1A0, ON, Canada
Tel.: (519) 676-5000
Web Site: http://www.ridgelandfill.com
Waste Management Services
N.A.I.C.S.: 562998

Right Away Disposal, L.L.C. (1)
3755 S Royal Palm Rd, Apache Junction, AZ 85119
Tel.: (480) 983-9100
Web Site: https://www.rightawaydisposal.com
Waste Management Services
N.A.I.C.S.: 562998

Trojan Recycling Inc (1)
71 Forest St, Brockton, MA 02302
Tel.: (508) 588-2332
Web Site: http://www.trojanrecycling.com
Rev.: $1,100,000
Emp.: 10
Hazardous Waste Treatment & Disposal
N.A.I.C.S.: 562211
Francis F. Trojano *(Treas)*

Waste Connections US, Inc. (1)
3 Waterway Sq Pl, The Woodlands, TX 77380
Tel.: (832) 442-2200
Web Site: http://www.wasteconnections.com

AND PRIVATE COMPANIES

WASTE CONNECTIONS, INC.

Sales Range: $1-4.9 Billion
Holding Company; Regional Managing Office; Waste Management & Recycling Services
N.A.I.C.S.: 551112
Worthing F. Jackman (Pres)

Subsidiary (Domestic):

ACE SOLID WASTE, INC. (2)
6601 McKinley St NW, Ramsey, MN 55303
Tel.: (763) 427-3110
Web Site: https://www.acesolidwaste.com
Industrial Waste Collection & Recycling Services
N.A.I.C.S.: 562111

ADVANCED SYSTEMS PORTABLE RESTROOMS, INC. (2)
1300 SE Wilson Ave, Bend, OR 97702
Tel.: (541) 389-5646
Web Site: https://www.advancedportabletoilets.com
Waste Collection, Transfer, Disposal & Recycling Services
N.A.I.C.S.: 562111

ALASKA WASTE-INTERIOR, LLC (2)
3941 Easy St, Fairbanks, AK 99701
Tel.: (907) 452-2009
Solid Waste Collection & Recycling Services
N.A.I.C.S.: 562111

ALASKA WASTE-KENAI PENINSULA, LLC (2)
47323 Merrywood Ave, Soldotna, AK 99669
Tel.: (907) 283-9390
Waste Collection & Recycling Services
N.A.I.C.S.: 562111

ANDERSON COUNTY LANDFILL, INC. (2)
203 Landfill Rd, Belton, SC 29627
Tel.: (864) 338-1815
Web Site: http://www.andersoncountylandfill.com
Solid Waste Landfill Operator
N.A.I.C.S.: 562212

Alaska Waste-Juneau, LLC (2)
5211 Stark St, Juneau, AK 99801
Tel.: (907) 780-7800
Web Site: http://www.alaskawaste.net
Waste Collection & Disposal Services
N.A.I.C.S.: 562998

Alaska Waste-Sitka, LLC (2)
220 Smith St, Sitka, AK 99835
Tel.: (907) 747-5669
Waste Collection & Disposal Services
N.A.I.C.S.: 562998

BRENT RUN LANDFILL, INC. (2)
8335 Vienna Rd, Montrose, MI 48457
Tel.: (810) 639-3077
Web Site: http://www.brentrunlandfill.com
Solid Waste Landfill Operator
N.A.I.C.S.: 562212

BUTLER COUNTY LANDFILL, INC. (2)
3588 R Rd, David City, NE 68632
Tel.: (402) 367-4662
Web Site: https://www.wasteconnections.com
Solid Waste Landfill Operator
N.A.I.C.S.: 562212

CAMINO REAL ENVIRONMENTAL CENTER, INC. (2)
1000 Camino Real Blvd, Sunland Park, NM 88063
Tel.: (575) 589-9440
Web Site: https://www.wasteconnections.com
Solid Waste Disposal Services
N.A.I.C.S.: 562219

COLUMBIA RIVER DISPOSAL, INC. (2)
41 Frontage Rd, Carson, WA 98610
Tel.: (541) 386-2272
Industrial Waste Collection & Recycling Services
N.A.I.C.S.: 562111

COUNTY WASTE - ULSTER, LLC (2)
465 Ross Ruland Rd, South Cairo, NY 12482
Tel.: (518) 877-7007
Solid Waste Collection, Transfer, Disposal & Recycling Services
N.A.I.C.S.: 562111

COUNTY WASTE AND RECYCLING SERVICE, INC. (2)
1927 Route 9, Clifton Park, NY 12065
Tel.: (518) 877-7007
Web Site: https://www.county-waste.com
Solid Waste Collection, Transfer, Disposal & Recycling Services
N.A.I.C.S.: 562111

CRI HOLDINGS, LLC (2)
4507 W Carlsbad Hwy, Hobbs, NM 88241
Tel.: (575) 393-1089
Holding Company
N.A.I.C.S.: 551112

CURRY TRANSFER & RECYCLING, INC. (2)
17498 Carpenterville Rd, Brookings, OR 97415
Tel.: (541) 469-2425
Web Site: https://www.currytransferrecycling.com
Solid Waste Collection, Transfer, Disposal & Recycling Services
N.A.I.C.S.: 562111

CWR Holdings, LLC (2)
606 Post Rd E #512, Westport, CT 06880
Tel.: (800) 915-9160
Web Site: http://www.cleanwaterresources.com
Sewer Line & Utility Infrastructure Advisory Services
N.A.I.C.S.: 541690
John D. Redfern (Chm)

Carolina Waste & Recycling LLC (2)
4285 Pace St, North Charleston, SC 29405
Tel.: (843) 576-1100
Web Site: http://www.carolinawaste.com
Waste Collection & Disposal Services
N.A.I.C.S.: 562219

Cold Canyon Land Fill, Inc. (2)
2268 Carpenter Canyon Rd, San Luis Obispo, CA 93401
Tel.: (805) 549-8332
Web Site: https://www.wasteconnections.com
Solid Waste Landfill Operator
N.A.I.C.S.: 562212

D.M. DISPOSAL CO., INC. (2)
4822 70th Ave E, Fife, WA 98424
Tel.: (253) 414-0361
Web Site: https://www.dm-recycling.com
Solid Waste Collection, Transfer, Disposal & Recycling Services
N.A.I.C.S.: 562111

DENVER REGIONAL LANDFILL, INC. (2)
1830 Weld County Rd 6, Erie, CO 80516
Tel.: (303) 673-9431
Solid Waste Landfill Operator
N.A.I.C.S.: 562212

ECOSORT, L.L.C. (2)
3425 E 17th Ave, Eugene, OR 97403
Tel.: (541) 726-7552
Web Site: https://www.ecosort.com
Industrial Waste Collection & Recycling Services
N.A.I.C.S.: 562111

EL PASO DISPOSAL, LP (2)
5539 El Paso Dr, El Paso, TX 79905
Tel.: (915) 772-7495
Web Site: https://www.elpasodisposal.com
Solid Waste Disposal Services
N.A.I.C.S.: 562219

ENVIRONMENTAL TRUST COMPANY (2)
233 County Rd 166, Athens, TN 37303
Tel.: (423) 745-6396
Web Site: http://www.meadowbranchlandfill.com
Solid Waste Collection, Transfer, Disposal & Recycling Services
N.A.I.C.S.: 562111

Evergreen Disposal, Inc. (2)
55 W Vly Dr, Kalispell, MT 59901
Tel.: (406) 257-1739
Web Site: https://www.evergreengarbage.com
Solid Waste Collection, Transfer, Disposal & Recycling Services
N.A.I.C.S.: 562111

FINLEY-BUTTES LIMITED PARTNERSHIP (2)
73221 Bombing Range Rd, Boardman, OR 97818
Tel.: (541) 481-2233
Web Site: https://www.wasteconnections.com
Solid Waste Landfill Operator
N.A.I.C.S.: 562212

FINNEY COUNTY LANDFILL, INC. (2)
1250 S Raceway Rd, Garden City, KS 67846
Tel.: (620) 275-4421
Web Site: https://www.wasteconnections.com
Solid Waste Landfill Operator
N.A.I.C.S.: 562212

FORT ANN TRANSFER STATION, LLC (2)
10913 State Route 149, Fort Ann, NY 12827
Tel.: (518) 798-3444
Web Site: https://www.acecarting.com
Solid Waste Disposal Services
N.A.I.C.S.: 562219

GOD BLESS THE USA, INCORPORATED (2)
3405 Westwood Industrial Dr, Monroe, NC 28110
Tel.: (704) 708-5872
Web Site: http://www.godblesstheusainc.com
Industrial Waste Collection & Recycling Services
N.A.I.C.S.: 562111

GREEN WASTE SOLUTIONS OF ALASKA, LLC (2)
6301 Rosewood St, Anchorage, AK 99518
Tel.: (907) 563-3717
Industrial Waste Collection & Recycling Services
N.A.I.C.S.: 562111

Groot Industries Inc. (2)
2500 Landmeier Rd, Elk Grove Village, IL 60007
Tel.: (847) 734-6400
Web Site: https://www.groot.com
Solid Waste Management Services
N.A.I.C.S.: 562111

Subsidiary (Domestic):

Groot Recycling & Waste Services, Inc. (3)
2500 Landmeier Rd, Elk Grove Village, IL 60007
Tel.: (773) 242-1977
Web Site: http://www.groot.com
Waste Management Services
N.A.I.C.S.: 562111

Subsidiary (Domestic):

Groveland Transfer and Recycling, Inc. (2)
109 Sampey Rd, Groveland, FL 34736
Tel.: (352) 429-3009
Recyclable Materials Collection Services
N.A.I.C.S.: 562111

HARDIN SANITATION, INC. (2)
1840 NE 10th Ave, Payette, ID 83661
Tel.: (208) 642-2629
Web Site: https://www.hardinsanitation.com
Waste Collection & Recycling Services
N.A.I.C.S.: 562111

Harold LeMay Enterprises, Inc. (2)
4111 192nd St E, Tacoma, WA 98446
Tel.: (253) 875-5053
Web Site: https://www.lemaypiercecountyrefuse.com
Waste Collections, Transfer & Recycling Services
N.A.I.C.S.: 562111

ISLAND DISPOSAL, INC. (2)
19832 State Rt 20, Coupeville, WA 98239
Tel.: (360) 678-5701
Web Site: https://www.islanddisposalinc.com
Waste Collection, Transfer & Recycling Services
N.A.I.C.S.: 562111

LAKESHORE DISPOSAL, INC. (2)
200 Industrial Loop, McCall, ID 83638
Tel.: (208) 634-7176
Recycling & Garbage Collection Services
N.A.I.C.S.: 562111

MASON COUNTY GARBAGE CO., INC. (2)
81 E Wilbur Way, Shelton, WA 98584
Tel.: (360) 426-8729
Web Site: http://www.masoncountygarbage.com
Waste Collection, Transfer & Recycling Services
N.A.I.C.S.: 562111

MBO, LLC (2)
19141 Gro Racca Rd, Iowa, LA 70647
Tel.: (337) 588-4558
Waste Collection, Transfer & Recycling Services
N.A.I.C.S.: 562111

MILLENNIUM WASTE INCORPORATED (2)
3606 78th Ave W, Rock Island, IL 61201
Tel.: (309) 787-2303
Web Site: https://www.millenniumwasteinc.com
Waste Collection, Transfer & Recycling Services
N.A.I.C.S.: 562111

MURREY'S DISPOSAL COMPANY, INC. (2)
970 Carlsborg Rd, Sequim, WA 98382-8391
Tel.: (360) 452-7278
Web Site: http://www.murreysdisposal.com
Waste Collection, Transfer & Recycling Services
N.A.I.C.S.: 562111

Millennium Waste Incorporated (2)
3606 78th Ave W, Rock Island, IL 61201
Tel.: (309) 787-2303
Web Site: http://www.millenniumwasteinc.com
Solid Waste Landfill Services
N.A.I.C.S.: 562998

NOBLES COUNTY LANDFILL, INC. (2)
22341 Knauf Ave, Rushmore, MN 56168
Tel.: (507) 376-9218
Web Site: https://www.wasteconnections.com
Solid Waste Landfill Operator
N.A.I.C.S.: 562212

OSAGE LANDFILL, INC. (2)
83 Co Rd 2712, Bartlesville, OK 74003
Tel.: (918) 336-3159
Web Site: https://www.wasteconnections.com
Solid Waste Landfill Operator
N.A.I.C.S.: 562212

PIERCE COUNTY RECYCLING, COMPOSTING AND DISPOSAL, LLC (2)
17925 Meridian St E, Puyallup, WA 98375
Tel.: (253) 847-7555
Web Site: https://www.lriservices.com
Solid Waste Landfill Operator
N.A.I.C.S.: 562212

PSI ENVIRONMENTAL SERVICES, INC. (2)
6769 W Overland Dr, Idaho Falls, ID 83402
Tel.: (208) 529-8084
Web Site: https://www.psiidahofalls.com
Solid Waste Disposal Services
N.A.I.C.S.: 562219

PSI Environmental Systems, Inc. (2)
222 Gem St, Twin Falls, ID 83301
Tel.: (208) 733-4441
Web Site: https://www.psitwinfalls.com
Waste Collection, Transfer & Recycling Services
N.A.I.C.S.: 562111

R.A. BROWNRIGG INVESTMENTS, INC. (2)

WASTE CONNECTIONS, INC.

Waste Connections, Inc.—(Continued)
1300 SE Wilson Ave, Bend, OR 97702
Tel.: (541) 382-6660
Web Site: http://www.cascadedisposal.com
Waste Collection, Transfer & Recycling Services
N.A.I.C.S.: 562111

R360 Environmental Solutions, LLC (2)
3 Waterway Sq Pl, The Woodlands, TX 77380
Tel.: (832) 442-2900
Web Site:
https://www.r360environmentsolution.com
Oilfield Waste Management Services
N.A.I.C.S.: 562211

Subsidiary (Domestic):

Prairie Disposal LLC (3)
102C10 52 St NW, Tioga, ND 58852
Tel.: (701) 664-3383
Oilfield Waste Disposal Services
N.A.I.C.S.: 562211

R360 Permian Basin, LLC (3)
4507 W Carlsbad Hwy, Hobbs, NM 88241
Tel.: (575) 393-1079
Web Site:
http://www.r360environmentalsolution.com
Oilfield Waste Disposal Services
N.A.I.C.S.: 562211

Subsidiary (Domestic):

RED CARPET LANDFILL, INC. (2)
38558 S County Rd 270, Meno, OK 73760
Tel.: (815) 478-7274
Web Site:
https://www.wasteconnections.com
Solid Waste Landfill Operator
N.A.I.C.S.: 562212

Rock River Environmental Services, Inc. (2)
4002 S Main St, Rockford, IL 61102
Tel.: (815) 965-2489
Web Site: https://www.rockriverdisposal.com
Waste Collection & Disposal Services
N.A.I.C.S.: 562998
John Lichty (Pres & CEO)

Rrd Holding Company (2)
1050 Greenlee St, Marengo, IL 60152
Tel.: (815) 568-7274
Web Site: http://www.mdces.com
Waste Collection & Disposal Services
N.A.I.C.S.: 562998

SAN LUIS GARBAGE COMPANY (2)
4388 Old Santa Fe Rd, San Luis Obispo, CA 93401
Tel.: (805) 543-0875
Web Site: https://www.sanluisgarbage.com
Solid Waste Collection & Recycling Services
N.A.I.C.S.: 562111

SANIPAC, INC. (2)
1650 Glenwood Blvd, Eugene, OR 97440
Tel.: (541) 736-3600
Web Site: https://www.sanipac.com
Emp.: 130
Recycling & Garbage Collection Services
N.A.I.C.S.: 562111
Aaron Donley (Mgr-Sls)

SCOTT SOLID WASTE DISPOSAL COMPANY (2)
300 Roberta Ln, Oneida, TN 37841
Tel.: (423) 569-5702
Web Site: https://www.scottsolidwaste.com
Garbage Disposal Services
N.A.I.C.S.: 562212

SCOTT WASTE SERVICES, LLC (2)
1212 Eastland St, Bowling Green, KY 42102
Tel.: (270) 783-4016
Web Site: https://www.scottwaste.com
Waste Collection, Transfer & Recycling Services
N.A.I.C.S.: 562111

SHALE GAS SERVICES, LLC (2)
1155 Hwy 64 W, Beebe, AR 72012
Tel.: (501) 882-2044
Web Site:
https://www.shalegasservices.com
Industrial Waste Collection & Recycling Services
N.A.I.C.S.: 562111

Subsidiary (Domestic):

ARKANSAS RECLAMATION COMPANY, LLC (3)
1155 Hwy 64 W, Beebe, AR 72012
Tel.: (501) 882-2044
Industrial Waste Collection & Recycling Services
N.A.I.C.S.: 562111

EAGLE FORD RECLAMATION COMPANY, LLC (3)
119 N Hwy 281 A, Three Rivers, TX 78071
Tel.: (361) 786-3960
Industrial Waste Collection & Recycling Services
N.A.I.C.S.: 562111
Lee Rivera (Supvr-Production)

Subsidiary (Domestic):

SILVER SPRINGS ORGANICS L.L.C. (2)
13835 Military Rd SE, Rainier, WA 98576
Tel.: (360) 446-7645
Web Site:
https://www.silverspringsorganics.com
Composting Facility Services
N.A.I.C.S.: 562219
Georgia Frost (Office Mgr)

SKB Environmental, Inc. (2)
251 Starkey St, Saint Paul, MN 55107
Tel.: (651) 224-6329
Web Site: https://www.skbinc.com
Waste Processing, Recycling, Hauling & Environmentally Sound Waste Disposal Services
N.A.I.C.S.: 562212

SLD Landfill, Inc. (2)
30199 Zemel Rd, Punta Gorda, FL 33955
Tel.: (941) 833-9201
Web Site:
https://www.wasteconnections.com
Waste Collection & Disposal Services
N.A.I.C.S.: 562998

SOUTH COUNTY SANITARY SERVICE, INC. (2)
4388 Old Santa Fe Rd, San Luis Obispo, CA 93401
Tel.: (805) 489-4246
Web Site:
http://www.southcountysanitary.com
Solid Waste Collection, Transfer, Disposal & Recycling Services
N.A.I.C.S.: 562111

STUTZMAN REFUSE DISPOSAL, INC. (2)
315 W Blanchard Ave, South Hutchinson, KS 67505
Tel.: (620) 662-2559
Web Site: https://www.stutzmanrefuse.com
Solid Waste Collection, Transfer, Disposal & Recycling Services
N.A.I.C.S.: 562111

Sanford Recycling and Transfer, Inc. (2)
563 N White Cedar Rd, Sanford, FL 32771
Tel.: (407) 323-4480
Waste Collection, Transfer & Recycling Services
N.A.I.C.S.: 562111

Seneca Meadows, Inc. (2)
1786 Salcman Rd, Waterloo, NY 13165
Tel.: (315) 539-5624
Web Site: http://www.senecameadows.com
Emp.: 160
Waste Management Services
N.A.I.C.S.: 562998

Sun Country Materials, LLC (2)
11457 County Rd 672, Riverview, FL 33598
Tel.: (813) 642-9594
Solid Waste Landfill & Transfer Station Services
N.A.I.C.S.: 562212

TACOMA RECYCLING COMPANY, INC. (2)
2318 S Tacoma Way, Tacoma, WA 98446
Tel.: (253) 474-9559
Web Site: https://www.tacomarecycling.com
Industrial Waste Collection & Recycling Services
N.A.I.C.S.: 562111

Taft Recycling, Inc. (2)
375 W 7th St, Orlando, FL 32824
Tel.: (407) 851-0074
Web Site:
https://www.wasteconnections.com
Waste Management Services
N.A.I.C.S.: 562119
Wilson Esteves (Mgr-Div)

WASTE CONNECTIONS OF MISSOURI, INC. (2)
196 NW Industrial Ct, Bridgeton, MO 63044
Tel.: (636) 321-2100
Solid Waste Management Services
N.A.I.C.S.: 562998

WASTE CONNECTIONS OF NORTH CAROLINA, INC. (2)
5516 Rozzelles Ferry Rd, Charlotte, NC 28214
Tel.: (704) 398-4488
Web Site:
http://www.wasteconnectionscharlotte.com
Solid Waste Collection, Transfer, Disposal & Recycling Services
N.A.I.C.S.: 562111

WASTE CONNECTIONS OF OSCEOLA COUNTY, LLC (2)
1501 Omni Way, Saint Cloud, FL 32773
Tel.: (407) 891-3720
Web Site:
https://www.wasteconnections.com
Solid Waste Landfill Operator
N.A.I.C.S.: 562212

WASTE CONNECTIONS OF SOUTH CAROLINA, INC. (2)
1010 Rogers Bridge Rd, Duncan, SC 29334
Tel.: (864) 801-1436
Web Site:
http://www.wasteconnectionscarolina.com
Solid Waste Collection, Transfer, Disposal & Recycling Services
N.A.I.C.S.: 562111

WASTE CONNECTIONS OF WASHINGTON, INC. (2)
12115 NE 99th St Ste 1830, Vancouver, WA 98682
Tel.: (360) 892-5370
Web Site: https://www.wcnorthwest.com
Garbage Collection & Recycling Services
N.A.I.C.S.: 562111

WEST COAST RECYCLING AND TRANSFER, INC. (2)
1210 S Broadway, Coos Bay, OR 97420
Tel.: (541) 267-2848
Web Site: http://www.lessanitary.com
Garbage Collection & Recycling Services
N.A.I.C.S.: 562111

WEST VALLEY COLLECTION & RECYCLING, LLC (2)
1333 Oakland Rd, San Jose, CA 95112
Tel.: (408) 283-9250
Web Site:
https://www.westvalleyrecycles.com
Solid Waste Collection, Transfer, Disposal & Recycling Services
N.A.I.C.S.: 562111

Wasco County Landfill, Inc. (2)
2550 Steele Rd, The Dalles, OR 97058
Tel.: (541) 296-4082
Web Site:
https://www.wasteconnections.com
Solid Waste Collection, Transfer & Recycling Services
N.A.I.C.S.: 562111

Waste Connections Bayou, Inc. (2)
632 Meadow Lark Dr, Monroe, LA 71203
Tel.: (318) 343-4628
Solid Waste Collection Services
N.A.I.C.S.: 562111

Waste Connections of Colorado, Inc. (2)
7770 Palmer Park Blvd, Colorado Springs, CO 80951
Tel.: (719) 591-5000

INTERNATIONAL PUBLIC

Solid Waste Collection, Transfer, Disposal & Recycling Services
N.A.I.C.S.: 562111

Waste Connections of Iowa, Inc. (2)
4705 NE 22nd St, Des Moines, IA 50313
Tel.: (515) 265-7374
Web Site:
https://www.wasteconnections.com
Solid Waste Collection, Transfer, Disposal & Recycling Services
N.A.I.C.S.: 562111

Waste Connections of Kansas, Inc. (2)
2745 N Ohio, Wichita, KS 67219
Tel.: (316) 838-4920
Web Site:
http://www.wasteconnectionswichita.com
Solid Waste Collection, Transfer, Disposal & Recycling Services
N.A.I.C.S.: 562111

Waste Connections of Kentucky, Inc. (2)
3612 E Hwy 552, Lily, KY 40740
Tel.: (606) 864-7996
Web Site:
http://www.wasteconnectionsky.com
Solid Waste Collection, Transfer, Disposal & Recycling Services
N.A.I.C.S.: 562111

Waste Connections of Louisiana, Inc. (2)
632 Meadow Lark Dr, Monroe, LA 71203
Tel.: (318) 343-4628
Web Site:
https://www.wasteconnections.com
Solid Waste Collection & Recycling Services
N.A.I.C.S.: 562111

Waste Connections of Minnesota, Inc. (2)
27008 US Hwy 59, Worthington, MN 56187
Tel.: (507) 376-9218
Web Site: http://www.schaapsanitation.com
Solid Waste Collection Services
N.A.I.C.S.: 562111

Waste Connections of Mississippi, Inc. (2)
2941 County Rd 302, Walnut, MS 38683
Tel.: (662) 223-6800
Solid Waste Collection, Transfer, Disposal & Recycling Services
N.A.I.C.S.: 562111

Waste Connections of Montana, Inc. (2)
211 Humdinger Ln, Victor, MT 59875
Tel.: (406) 363-3630
Web Site:
https://www.bitterrootdisposal.com
Solid Waste Disposal Services
N.A.I.C.S.: 562219

Waste Connections of Nebraska, Inc. (2)
1200 Hamilton, Fremont, NE 68026
Tel.: (402) 721-7511
Web Site:
https://www.wasteconnections.com
Solid Waste Collection, Transfer, Disposal & Recycling Services
N.A.I.C.S.: 562111

Waste Connections of North Dakota, Inc. (2)
1108 8th St E, Williston, ND 58801
Tel.: (701) 572-9773
Web Site:
http://www.armstrongsanitation.com
Waste Collection & Disposal Services
N.A.I.C.S.: 562998

Waste Connections of Pennsylvania, Inc. (2)
3747 White Church Rd, Chambersburg, PA 17202
Tel.: (717) 709-1700
Web Site:
https://www.wasteconnections.com
Waste Collection & Disposal Services
N.A.I.C.S.: 562998

Waste Connections of Tennessee, Inc. (2)

2400 Chipman St, Knoxville, TN 37917
Tel.: (865) 522-8161
Web Site:
 http://www.wasteconnectionstn.com
Solid & Liquid Waste Management Services
N.A.I.C.S.: 562111

Waste Connections of Wyoming, Inc. (2)
3040 N 6 Mile Rd, Casper, WY 82604
Tel.: (815) 478-7274
Web Site: http://www.wasteconnections.com
Waste Collection, Recycling & Disposal Services
N.A.I.C.S.: 562111

Winnebago Landfill Company, LLC (2)
8403 Lindenwood Rd, Rockford, IL 61109
Tel.: (815) 874-4806
Web Site:
 https://www.wasteconnections.com
Solid Waste Landfill Services
N.A.I.C.S.: 562212

Waste Connections of Canada Inc. (1)
25 Fawcett Road, Coquitlam, V3K 6V2, BC, Canada
Tel.: (604) 525-2072
Web Site:
 http://www.wasteconnectionscanada.com
Waste Collection & Disposal Services
N.A.I.C.S.: 562111

Waste Masters Solutions, LLC (1)
19 Davidson Ln, New Castle, DE 19720
Tel.: (302) 824-0909
Web Site: https://wastemasters.com
Waste Management Services
N.A.I.C.S.: 562998
Steve Masterson *(Co-Founder)*

WASTE PLASTIC UPCYCLING A/S
Hojgardsvej 13A, 4540, Farevejle, Denmark
Tel.: (45) 24453484
Web Site: https://www.wpu-dk.com
Year Founded: 2020
WPU—(OSL)
Rev.: $38,487
Assets: $23,327,638
Liabilities: $19,728,375
Net Worth: $3,599,263
Earnings: ($4,564,688)
Emp.: 19
Fiscal Year-end: 12/31/23
Waste Recycling Services
N.A.I.C.S.: 562211
Niels Stielund *(Chm)*

WASU MEDIA HOLDING CO., LTD.
9th Floor Block B No 179 Changjiang Road, Wasu Digital TV Industrial Park Binjiang District, Hangzhou, 310056, Zhejiang, China
Tel.: (86) 57128327789
Web Site: http://www.wasu.com.cn
Year Founded: 1994
000156—(SSE)
Rev.: $1,317,801,785
Assets: $3,806,354,130
Liabilities: $1,708,626,231
Net Worth: $2,097,727,899
Earnings: $111,280,549
Fiscal Year-end: 12/31/22
Holding Company
N.A.I.C.S.: 551112
Bao Linqiang *(Chm)*

WATA CHEMICALS LTD.
17/B Monipuripara 3rd Floor Sangshad Avenue, Dhaka, 1215, Bangladesh
Tel.: (880) 58152001
Web Site:
 https://www.watachemicals.com
Year Founded: 1981
WATACHEM—(CHT)
Rev.: $6,609,823
Assets: $30,439,246
Liabilities: $20,084,448
Net Worth: $10,354,798
Earnings: $1,055,105
Fiscal Year-end: 06/30/21
Chemical Products Mfr
N.A.I.C.S.: 325199
Nazrul Islam *(CEO & Mng Dir)*

WATAHAN & CO., LTD.
Watahan Nohara Bldg 1-4 Yotsuya, Shinjuku-ku, Tokyo, Japan
Tel.: (81) 333412766
Web Site: https://watahan.co.jp
Year Founded: 1932
3199—(TKS)
Rev.: $846,555,920
Assets: $523,974,700
Liabilities: $373,339,410
Net Worth: $150,635,290
Earnings: $12,254,940
Emp.: 4,624
Fiscal Year-end: 03/31/24
Home Center & Construction Retailer & Distr
N.A.I.C.S.: 444110
Akio Kobayashi *(VP)*

Subsidiaries:

Watahan Fresh Market Co., Ltd. (1)
11 Sanogo-mae, Chiaki-cho, Ichinomiya, 491-0804, Aichi, Japan
Tel.: (81) 586760234
Web Site: http://www.watahan-freshmarket.co.jp
Emp.: 342
Food Store Operator
N.A.I.C.S.: 445110
Yoshihiko Makishima *(VP)*

Watahan Home-Aid Co., Ltd. (1)
205 Minami Nagaike, Nagano, 381-0024, Japan
Tel.: (81) 262433200
Web Site: http://www.watahan.jp
Emp.: 2,519
Supermarket Operator
N.A.I.C.S.: 445110
Toshiaki Maezawa *(VP)*

Watahan Solutions Co., Ltd. (1)
1023-1 Kitagata, Iida, 395-0193, Nagano, Japan
Tel.: (81) 265258181
Emp.: 593
Construction Engineering Services
N.A.I.C.S.: 541330

Watahan-Nohara Sekizenkai, A Social Welfare Corporation (1)
2100 Mikkaichiba, Iida, 395-8648, Nagano, Japan
Tel.: (81) 265282260
Web Site: https://www.wn-sekizenkai.or.jp
Nursing Home Operator
N.A.I.C.S.: 623110

Yume House Co., Ltd. (1)
288 Mika Seigo-cho, Kitakanbara-gun, Niigata, 957-0122, Japan
Tel.: (81) 254215511
Web Site: https://www.yume-h.com
Civil Engineering Services
N.A.I.C.S.: 236220

WATAMI CO., LTD.
1-1-3 Haneda, Ota-ku, Tokyo, 144-0043, Japan
Tel.: (81) 357372288   JP
Web Site: https://www.watami.co.jp
7522—(TKS)
Rev.: $544,016,220
Assets: $424,044,720
Liabilities: $277,527,460
Net Worth: $146,517,260
Earnings: $27,695,900
Emp.: 368
Fiscal Year-end: 03/31/24
Holding Company
N.A.I.C.S.: 551112
Kuniaki Shimizu *(Pres & COO)*

Subsidiaries:

Tohma Green Life Inc. (1)
4-johigashi 3-6-1 Toma-cho, Kamikawa-gun, Hokkaido, 078-1314, Japan
Tel.: (81) 166842044
Web Site: https://www.tohmagreenlife.co.jp
Farming Services
N.A.I.C.S.: 111419

Watami (China) Co., Ltd. (1)
Unit 901-902 9/F 9 Chong Yip Street, Kwun Tong, Kowloon, China (Hong Kong)
Tel.: (852) 23171028
Web Site: https://watami.com.hk
Sales Range: $50-74.9 Million
Emp.: 500
Restaurant Management Services
N.A.I.C.S.: 722511
Matthew Chung *(COO)*

Watami Farm Co., Ltd. (1)
1-1-3 Haneda, Ota-ku, Tokyo, 144 0043, Japan
Tel.: (81) 357372802
Web Site: http://www.watamifarm.co.jp
Sales Range: $10-24.9 Million
Emp.: 40
Farming Services
N.A.I.C.S.: 111419

WATANABE PIPE CO., LTD.
Hamarikyu Parkside Place 6th fl 5-6-10 Tsukiji, Chuo-ku, Tokyo, 104-0045, Japan
Tel.: (81) 335493111
Web Site: http://www.sedia-system.co.jp
Housing Construction Services
N.A.I.C.S.: 423390
Hajime Watanabe *(Pres & CEO)*

Subsidiaries:

Mikado Chemical M.F.G. Co. (1)
2298-1-4 Uruidochojahara, Ichihara, 290-0171, Chiba, Japan
Tel.: (81) 436741371
Web Site: http://www.mikadokakou.com
Plastics Product Mfr
N.A.I.C.S.: 326199
Akihide Sato *(CEO)*

WATANABE SATO CO., LTD.
1-18-4 Minamiazabu, Minato-Ku, Tokyo, 106-8567, Japan
Tel.: (81) 334537351
Web Site:
 https://www.watanabesato.co.jp
Year Founded: 1938
1807—(TKS)
Rev.: $253,824,000
Assets: $232,222,520
Liabilities: $92,487,120
Net Worth: $139,735,400
Earnings: $7,945,220
Emp.: 497
Fiscal Year-end: 03/31/24
Civil Engineering Services
N.A.I.C.S.: 237990

WATANIYA INSURANCE COMPANY
EA Juffali & Brothers HO Building Madina Road, PO Box 5832, Before Emirate of Makkah Region, Jeddah, 21432, Saudi Arabia
Tel.: (966) 126606200
Web Site:
 https://www.wataniya.com.sa
Year Founded: 2010
8300—(SAU)
Rev.: $148,719,371
Assets: $510,902,546
Liabilities: $409,460,339
Net Worth: $101,442,208
Earnings: ($4,891,081)
Emp.: 248
Fiscal Year-end: 12/31/22
Insurance Management Services
N.A.I.C.S.: 524298
Haitham Habib Albakree *(CEO)*

WATAWALA PLANTATIONS PLC
60 Dharmapala Mawatha, 03, Colombo, Sri Lanka
Tel.: (94) 114702400
Web Site:
 https://www.watawalaplantations.lk
WATA—(COL)
Rev.: $34,445,197
Assets: $47,303,817
Liabilities: $9,533,568
Net Worth: $37,770,250
Earnings: $18,395,491
Emp.: 1,653
Fiscal Year-end: 03/31/22
Tea Mfr
N.A.I.C.S.: 311920
Vish Govindasamy *(Mng Dir)*

WATCHDATA SYSTEM CO., LTD.
7F Qiming International Building 101 Lize Middle Park, Chaoyang District, Beijing, 100102, China
Tel.: (86) 10 6472 2288   CN
Web Site: http://www.watchdata.com
Year Founded: 1994
Sales Range: $50-74.9 Million
Emp.: 292
Electronic Transaction Applications Data Security & Encryption Technology Services
N.A.I.C.S.: 334610
Michael Yu *(Pres-Ops-Intl)*

Subsidiaries:

WATCHDATA TECHNOLOGIES PRIVATE LIMITED (1)
11 Collyer Quay 16-01 The Arcade, Singapore, 049317, Singapore
Tel.: (65) 6572 9300
Web Site: http://www.watchdata.com.sg
Sales Range: $25-49.9 Million
Emp.: 50
Data Security Technology
N.A.I.C.S.: 334610

Watchdata Technologies Co. Ltd. (1)
11F No 456 Sec 4 Hsinyi Road, Taipei, Taiwan
Tel.: (886) 2 5551 5582
Software Development Services
N.A.I.C.S.: 541511

Watchdata Technologies USA Inc. (1)
895 Dove St Ste 300, Newport Beach, CA 92660
Tel.: (949) 851-4660
Web Site:
Software Development Services
N.A.I.C.S.: 541511

WATCHES OF SWITZERLAND GROUP PLC
Tel.: (44) 8008495051   UK
Web Site:
 https://www.thewosgroupplc.com
Year Founded: 1924
WOSG—(LSE)
Rev.: $1,914,769,080
Assets: $1,532,758,500
Liabilities: $950,310,270
Net Worth: $582,448,230
Earnings: $151,165,980
Fiscal Year-end: 04/30/23
Jewelry, Watch, Precious Stone & Precious Metal Merchant Wholesalers
N.A.I.C.S.: 423940
Dennis Millard *(Chm)*

Subsidiaries:

Watches of Switzerland (Nevada) LLC (1)
3131 S Las Vegas Blvd, Las Vegas, NV 89109
Tel.: (702) 792-0183
Watch Distr
N.A.I.C.S.: 458310
David Barnash *(Ops Mgr)*

WATCHSTONE GROUP PLC

Watches of Switzerland Group PLC—(Continued)

WATCHSTONE GROUP PLC
Highfield Court Tollgate Chandler s Ford, Eastleigh, SO53 3TY, Hampshire, United Kingdom
Tel.: (44) 1329836720   UK
Web Site:
https://www.watchstonegroup.com
Year Founded: 2005
Rev.: $48,262,100
Assets: $88,700,691
Liabilities: $29,305,479
Net Worth: $59,395,212
Earnings: ($23,989,554)
Emp.: 694
Fiscal Year-end: 12/31/18
Holding Company; Business Consulting, Software & Technology Outsourcing Solutions
N.A.I.C.S.: 551112
Stefan Leon Borson (CEO-Grp)

Subsidiaries:

Crusader Assistance Group Holdings Limited   (1)
UK House 82 Heath Road, Twickenham, TW1 4BW, United Kingdom
Tel.: (44) 20 8744 4000
Web Site:
http://www.crusaderassistance.co.uk
Claims Management Services
N.A.I.C.S.: 524298
Mark O'Shaughnessy (Mng Dir)

Intelligent Claims Management Limited   (1)
Suite 304 - 306 Cotton Exchange Bixteth Street, Liverpool, L3 9LQ, Mersyside, United Kingdom
Tel.: (44) 844 873 3662
Web Site: http://www.intelligentclaims.com
Claims Management Services
N.A.I.C.S.: 524298
Jonny White (CEO)

Maine Finance Limited   (1)
Quindell Court 1 Barnes Wallis Road, Segensworth East, Fareham, PO15 5UA, Hampshire, United Kingdom
Tel.: (44) 1489 571119
Web Site: http://www.maine-finance.co.uk
Insurance Advisory Services
N.A.I.C.S.: 524298
David Pollard (Mgr-Ops)

Metaskil Group Limited   (1)
Riverside House 4 Meadows Business Park Camberley, Aldermaston, Surrey, GU17 9AB, United Kingdom
Tel.: (44) 8447793418
Web Site: http://www.metaskil.com
Insurance Software Development Services
N.A.I.C.S.: 541511

Mobile Doctors Group Limited   (1)
58 Mosley Street, Manchester, M2 3HZ, United Kingdom   (100%)
Tel.: (44) 3445671111
Web Site: http://mobiledoctors.co.uk
Sales Range: $25-49.9 Million
Emp.: 1,000
Holding Company; Medical Evidence Services
N.A.I.C.S.: 551112

Subsidiary (Domestic):

Mobile Doctors Solutions Limited   (2)
4 Bourne Court Southend Road, Woodford Green, Woodford, IG8 8HD, Essex, United Kingdom
Tel.: (44) 2085518360
Hospital & Medical Services
N.A.I.C.S.: 524114

Subsidiary (Domestic):

Mobile Doctors Limited   (3)
4 Bourne Court Southend Road, Woodford Green, Woodford, IG8 8HD, Essex, United Kingdom
Tel.: (44) 2085518360
Medical Evidence Report Providers
N.A.I.C.S.: 524114
Neil Ross (COO)

Subsidiary (Domestic):

MDL Medical Administration Limited   (4)
4 Bourne Court Southend Road, Woodford Green, Woodford, IG8 8HD, Essex, United Kingdom
Tel.: (44) 2087872092
Health Administration Services
N.A.I.C.S.: 923120

Quindell Limited   (1)
Quindell Court 1 Barnes Wallis Road Segensworth, Wickham, Fareham, PO15 5UA, Hampshire, United Kingdom
Tel.: (44) 1329836720
Web Site: http://www.quindell.com
Sales Range: $1-9.9 Million
Business Consulting, Software & Technology Outsourcing Solutions
N.A.I.C.S.: 561499

Subsidiary (Domestic):

Quindell Business Process Services Limited   (2)
Indemnity House Sir Frank Whittle Way, Blackpool, FY4 2FB, Lancashire, United Kingdom
Tel.: (44) 844 571 3333
Web Site: http://www.quindell.com
Emp.: 500
Motor Claims Management Services
N.A.I.C.S.: 524298
Nigel Allen (Mng Dir)

Quindell Enterprise Technology Solutions Limited   (2)
304 High Street, Aldershot, GU12 4LT, Hampshire, United Kingdom
Tel.: (44) 844 779 3083
Web Site: http://www.quindell.com
Claims Management Services
N.A.I.C.S.: 524298

Subsidiary (Non-US):

Quintica Group FZ LLC   (2)
Suite 202 Building 25, PO Box 505107, Dubai, United Arab Emirates
Tel.: (971) 4 426 7303
Web Site: http://www.quintica.com
Information Technology Consulting Services
N.A.I.C.S.: 541512

Quintica SA (Pty) Limited   (2)
Culross on Main Building 2 34 Culross Road, Cnr Harrison Avenue and Sloane Streets, Bryanston, 2021, South Africa
Tel.: (27) 11 026 5990
Web Site: http://www.quintica.com
Emp.: 40
Information Technology Consulting Services
N.A.I.C.S.: 541512

iSaaS Technology Limited   (1)
Unit 4 The Courtyard Calvin Street, Bolton, BL1 8PB, United Kingdom
Tel.: (44) 1133201117
Web Site: http://www.isaastechnology.com
Insurance Software Development Services
N.A.I.C.S.: 541511
Adam Tulk (CEO)

WATER MIST ENGINEERING AS
Lohnelia 70, 4640, Sogne, Norway
Tel.: (47) 38019070   NO
Web Site: http://www.wme.no
Year Founded: 2003
Sales Range: $10-24.9 Million
Emp.: 29
Fire Fighting & Fire Prevention Systems Mfr
N.A.I.C.S.: 333998
Pal Stampe (Mng Dir)

WATER OASIS GROUP LIMITED
18/F World Trade Center 280 Gloucester Road, Causeway Bay, China (Hong Kong)
Tel.: (852) 2 890 7428
Web Site:
http://www.wateroasis.com.hk

1161—(OTCIQ)
Rev.: $107,045,016
Assets: $175,182,700
Liabilities: $128,909,190
Net Worth: $46,273,510
Earnings: $21,931,501
Emp.: 968
Fiscal Year-end: 09/30/21
Skin Care Products Distr
N.A.I.C.S.: 424210
Alan Siu Kei Tam (CEO)

Subsidiaries:

Fancy Cheer Limited   (1)
Flat 1907 19/F Block B 18 Ka Yip Street, Ming Pao Industrial Centre, Chai Wan, China (Hong Kong)
Tel.: (852) 2 777 8134
Web Site: https://www.kikifg.com.hk
Restaurant Operators
N.A.I.C.S.: 722511

Oasis Beauty Company Limited   (1)
Century Sq 1-13 Rm 16012, Central, China (Hong Kong)
Tel.: (852) 29730288
Web Site: http://www.oasisbeauty.com.hk
Beauty Care Services
N.A.I.C.S.: 812112

Oasis Medical Clinic Company Limited   (1)
18th Floor World Trade Centre 280 Gloucester Road, Causeway Bay, China (Hong Kong)
Tel.: (852) 31827777
Web Site:
https://www.oasismedicalcentre.com
Medical Beauty Treatments, Consultation & Services
N.A.I.C.S.: 812112

Oasis Spa Company Limited   (1)
Central Entertainment Bldg 10 Fl, Hong Kong, China (Hong Kong)
Tel.: (852) 21101998
Web Site: http://www.oasisspa.com.hk
Emp.: 30
Spas & Beauty Care Services
N.A.I.C.S.: 713940
Doby Yau (Area Mgr)

Water Babe Company Limited   (1)
2F No 178 Sec 2 Minsheng E Rd, Jhongshan Dist, 104, Taipei, Taiwan
Tel.: (886) 225158085
Web Site: http://www.h2oplus.com.tw
Sales Range: $50-74.9 Million
Emp.: 100
Skin Care & Body Care Products Retailer
N.A.I.C.S.: 424210

Water Oasis Company Limited   (1)
18F World Trade Center 280 Gloucester Road, Causeway Bay, China (Hong Kong)
Tel.: (852) 28907428
Web Site: http://www.wateroasis.com.hk
Skin Care Products Retailer
N.A.I.C.S.: 424210

Water Oasis E.L. (HK) Company Limited   (1)
Shop No 2403 Level 2 Gateway Arcade Harbour City, Tsim Tsa Tsui, Kowloon, China (Hong Kong)
Tel.: (852) 21750688
Web Site: http://www.ernolaszlo-hk.com
Skin Care Products Retailer
N.A.I.C.S.: 424210

WATER WAYS TECHNOLOGIES INC.
77 King Street West Suite 3000, PO Box 95, TD Centre, Toronto, M5K 1G8, ON, Canada
Tel.: (519) 264-2708   ON
Web Site: https://www.water-ways-technologies.com
Year Founded: 2007
WWT—(DEU)
Rev.: $16,159,000
Assets: $12,085,000
Liabilities: $12,853,000
Net Worth: ($768,000)
Earnings: ($5,303,000)

INTERNATIONAL PUBLIC

Emp.: 16
Fiscal Year-end: 12/31/21
Investment Services
N.A.I.C.S.: 523999
Ohad Haber (Chm & CEO)

Subsidiaries:

Heartnut Grove WWT Inc.   (1)
21831 Cooks Rd, Mount Brydges, Strathroy, N0L 1W0, ON, Canada
Tel.: (519) 264-2708
Web Site: http://www.heartnutgrove.com
Agricultural Product Mfr
N.A.I.C.S.: 325320
Ruth Derks (Office Mgr)

Irri - Al Tal Ltd.   (1)
Kibbutz Ramat-David, POB 7, 3658700, Tel Aviv, Israel
Tel.: (972) 722201417
Web Site: http://www.irri-altal.com
Water Treatment Equipment Mfr
N.A.I.C.S.: 333310

WWT Georgia RC Group LLC   (1)
47 Cosmonauts Coast, Tbilisi, Georgia
Tel.: (995) 599035353
Irrigation Equipment Mfr & Distr
N.A.I.C.S.: 333111

WATER.IO LTD.
2 Bergman St Entrance A 2Nd Floor, Park Hamada, Rehovot, 7670503, Israel
Tel.: (972) 83730370
Web Site: https://www.impacx.io
Year Founded: 2015
WATR—(TAE)
Rev.: $5,205,000
Assets: $3,407,000
Liabilities: $2,402,000
Net Worth: $1,005,000
Earnings: ($2,516,000)
Fiscal Year-end: 06/30/23
Information Technology Services
N.A.I.C.S.: 541519
Nimrod Kaplan (Co-Founder & CTO)

WATERCO LIMITED
Unit 7 2-8 South Street, Rydalmere, 2116, NSW, Australia
Tel.: (61) 298988600   AU
Web Site:
https://www.waterco.com.au
WAT—(ASX)
Rev.: $163,492,800
Assets: $172,123,340
Liabilities: $85,419,972
Net Worth: $86,703,368
Earnings: $9,248,867
Emp.: 989
Fiscal Year-end: 06/30/24
PVC Pipes Fittings Mfr
N.A.I.C.S.: 326122
Gerard Doumit (CFO & Co-Sec)

Subsidiaries:

Global Leisure Products Sdn Bhd   (1)
Lot 832 Jalan Kusta Kawasan Perindustrian SB Jaya, 47000, Sungai Buloh, Selangor Darul Ehsan, Malaysia
Tel.: (60) 361456000
Web Site: http://www.wateco.com.my
Sales Range: $50-74.9 Million
Emp.: 200
Water Treatment Equipment Mfr & Sales
N.A.I.C.S.: 333310
Ong Toon Kiat (Gen Mgr)

PT Waterco Indonesia   (1)
Inkopal Plaza Kelapa Gading Blok B No 31-32, Kelapa Gading Barat, Jakarta Utara, 14240, Indonesia
Tel.: (62) 2145851481
Web Site: https://www.waterco.co.id
Sales Range: $25-49.9 Million
Emp.: 25
Water Treatment Equipment Mfr & Sales
N.A.I.C.S.: 333310

Solar-Mate Sdn. Bhd.   (1)

AND PRIVATE COMPANIES

No 1 Jalan Perunding U1/17 Seksyen U1
Hicom-Glenmarie Industrial Park, 40150,
Shah Alam, Selangor, Malaysia
Tel.: (60) 355691688
Web Site: http://www.solarmate.com.my
Solar Heaters Distr
N.A.I.C.S.: 423720

Swimart (NZ) Ltd (1)
1 Tony Street, Henderson, Auckland, 0610,
New Zealand
Tel.: (64) 98361121
Web Site: https://www.swimart.co.nz
Sales Range: $50-74.9 Million
Emp.: 5
Pool Equipment & Chemicals Sales
N.A.I.C.S.: 423910
Donovan Bali (Mgr)

Waterco (Europe) Ltd (1)
Radfield London Road Teyham, Sittingbourne, ME9 9PS, Kent, United Kingdom
Tel.: (44) 1795521733
Web Site: https://www.waterco.eu
Sales Range: $25-49.9 Million
Emp.: 13
Water Treatment Equipment Mfr & Whslr
N.A.I.C.S.: 333310

Waterco (Guangzhou) Ltd. (1)
No 132 Buling Road, GETDD Yonghe District, Guangzhou, 511356, China
Tel.: (86) 2032222180
Waste Treatment Services
N.A.I.C.S.: 221310

Waterco (NZ) Ltd (1)
7 Industry Road, Penrose, Auckland, 1061,
New Zealand
Tel.: (64) 95257570
Web Site: https://www.waterco.com.au
Sales Range: $25-49.9 Million
Emp.: 8
Water Treatment Equipment Mfr & Sales
N.A.I.C.S.: 333310
Michael Alexander (Mgr)

Waterco Engineering Sdn Bhd (1)
Lot 832 Jalan Kusta Kawasan Perindustrian
SB Jaya, 47000, Sungai Buloh, Selangor
Darul, Malaysia
Tel.: (60) 361456000
Web Site: http://www.waterco.com.my
Sales Range: $75-99.9 Million
Emp.: 250
Water Treatment Equipment Mfr & Sales
N.A.I.C.S.: 423830
Ong Poon Kiat (CEO)

Waterco International Pte Ltd (1)
37 Jalan Pemimpin 6-14 MAPEX, Singapore, 577177, Singapore
Tel.: (65) 63442378
Web Site: https://www.waterco.com.sg
Sales Range: $25-49.9 Million
Emp.: 3
Water Treatment Equipment Mfr & Sales
N.A.I.C.S.: 333310
Goh Soonsinn (Mng Dir)

Waterco USA Inc (1)
1812 Tobacco Rd, Augusta, GA 30906
Tel.: (706) 793-7291
Web Site: https://www.waterco.us
Sales Range: $25-49.9 Million
Emp.: 13
Electric Heat Pumps Mfr & Distr
N.A.I.C.S.: 333914
Tim Acevedo (Mgr-Sls)

Zane Solar Systems Australia Pty Ltd (1)
77 Nealdon Dr, Meadowbrook, Meadowbrook, 4131, QLD, Australia
Tel.: (61) 732999900
Solar Heating Equipment Mfr & Sales
N.A.I.C.S.: 333414

WATERDROP INC.
No 2 Lize Zhonger Road Block C
Wangjing Science and Technology
Park, Chaoyang District, Beijing,
China
Tel.: (86) 1053394997   Ky
Web Site: https://www.waterdrop-inc.com
Year Founded: 2018

WDH—(NYSE)
Rev.: $429,258,875
Assets: $907,343,786
Liabilities: $177,125,315
Net Worth: $730,218,471
Earnings: $93,108,322
Emp.: 2,719
Fiscal Year-end: 12/31/22
Holding Company
N.A.I.C.S.: 551112
Peng Shen (Co-Founder, Chm & CEO)

WATERFORD FINANCE & INVESTMENT LTD.
King House 9 Haymarket West End,
London, SW1Y 4BP, United Kingdom
Tel.: (44) 20 7839 8143
Web Site: http://www.waterfordgroup.co.uk
Year Founded: 1995
Privater Equity Firm
N.A.I.C.S.: 523999
Michael Kroupeev (Chm)

WATERFRONT PHILIPPINES, INCORPORATED
27th Floor Wynsum Corporate Tower,
22 Emerald Avenue Ortigas Center,
Pasig, 1605, Philippines
Tel.: (63) 27067888   PH
Web Site: https://www.waterfronthotels.com.ph
Year Founded: 1994
WPI—(PHI)
Rev.: $20,753,994
Assets: $353,612,712
Liabilities: $110,877,479
Net Worth: $242,735,233
Earnings: $11,040,674
Emp.: 383
Fiscal Year-end: 12/31/21
Holding Company; Casino Hotel &
Resort Owner & Operator
N.A.I.C.S.: 551112
Renato B. Magadia (Chm)

Subsidiaries:

Acesite (Phils.) Hotel Corporation (1)
7th Floor Manila Pavilion Hotel, United Nations Avenue, Ermita, Manila, 1000,
Philippines   **(69.32%)**
Tel.: (63) 25261212
Sales Range: $1-9.9 Million
Emp.: 450
Casino Hotel Owner & Operator
N.A.I.C.S.: 721120
Kenneth T. Gatchalian (Pres & CEO)

Citygym Inc (1)
320 Central Ave, Saint Petersburg, FL
33701-3823
Tel.: (727) 898-3302
Sales Range: $50-74.9 Million
Emp.: 3
Recreational Services
N.A.I.C.S.: 713940

Waterfront Cebu City Casino Hotel, Inc. (1)
1 Salinas Drive, Lahug, Cebu, 6000,
Philippines   **(100%)**
Tel.: (63) 322326888
Sales Range: $100-124.9 Million
Emp.: 546
Casino Hotel Operator
N.A.I.C.S.: 721120
Phillippe Frugere (Gen Mgr)

Waterfront Food Concepts, Inc. (1)
Salinas Drive, Lahug, Cebu, 6000, Philippines
Tel.: (63) 322326888
Restaurant Services
N.A.I.C.S.: 722511

Waterfront Insular Hotel Davao Inc (1)
Km 7 Lanang, 8000, Davao, Philippines
Tel.: (63) 822332881

Web Site: http://www.waterfronthotels.com.ph
Casino Operations Services
N.A.I.C.S.: 721110

WATERLAND PRIVATE EQUITY INVESTMENTS B.V.
Brediusweg 31, 1401 AB, Bussum,
Netherlands
Tel.: (31) 356941680   NI
Web Site: https://www.waterlandpe.com
Year Founded: 1999
Emp.: 190
Privater Equity Firm
N.A.I.C.S.: 523999
Rob Thielen (Founder & Principal)

Subsidiaries:

Ballast Phoenix Ltd (1)
1 Victoria Stables South Road, Bourne,
PE8 9JZ, Lincolnshire, United Kingdom
Tel.: (44) 1778423345
Web Site: http://www.ballastphoenix.co.uk
Primary & Secondary Building Materials
Supplier; Recycling & Industrial Residuals
N.A.I.C.S.: 423390
David York (Chm)

Bontexgeo NV (1)
Industriestraat 39, 9240, Zele, Belgium
Tel.: (32) 52457411
Web Site: http://www.bontecgeosynthetics.com
Sales Range: $100-124.9 Million
Emp.: 375
Broadwoven Fabric Mills
N.A.I.C.S.: 313210
Orwig Speltdoorn (Mng Dir)

Subsidiary (Non-US):

Low & Bonar Hungary Kft (2)
TVK Industrial Area, 3580, Tiszaujvaros,
Hungary
Tel.: (36) 49 540 190
Web Site: http://tipptex.hu
Sales Range: $25-49.9 Million
Emp.: 130
Nonwoven Textile Product Mfr
N.A.I.C.S.: 313230

RHM Klinik- und Altenheimbetriebe B.V. & Co. KG (1)
Weinstrasse 1, 67146, Deidesheim, Germany
Tel.: (49) 6326 7009 0
Web Site: http://www.rhm-kliniken.de
Healtcare Services
N.A.I.C.S.: 621491

United Petfood Producers NV (1)
Terdonkkaai 16, 9042, Gent, Belgium
Tel.: (32) 9 253 80 45
Web Site: http://www.unitedpetfood.eu
Animal Feed Mfr
N.A.I.C.S.: 311119

Waterland Private Equity GmbH (1)
Neuer Zollhof 1, 40221, Dusseldorf, Germany
Tel.: (49) 2116878400
Web Site: http://www.waterland.de
Sales Range: $50-74.9 Million
Privater Equity Firm
N.A.I.C.S.: 523999
Jorg Dreisow (Mng Partner)

Waterland Private Equity N.V. (1)
NV Jan Van Rijswijcklaan 162 - bus 4, Antwerp, 2020, Belgium
Tel.: (32) 32929660
Web Site: http://www.waterland.be
Privater Equity Firm
N.A.I.C.S.: 523999
Frank Vlayen (Mng Dir)

Waterland Private Equity Sp. z.o.o (1)
Plac Trzech Krzyży 18, 00-499, Warsaw,
Poland
Tel.: (48) 22 417 85 30
Healtcare Services
N.A.I.C.S.: 621491
Tomek Karpinski (Mgr-Investment)

WATEROUS ENERGY FUND

WATERLINKS INVESTMENTS LTD.
Unit 3 First Floor, Ashted Lock Dartmouth Middleway Aston Science
Park, Birmingham, B7 4AZ, United
Kingdom
Tel.: (44) 1213 593 335
Web Site: http://www.waterlinksinvestment.com
Investment Firm
N.A.I.C.S.: 523999
Sue Watson (Owner)

Subsidiaries:

Dartex Coatings Ltd. (1)
Acton Close, Long Eaton, Nottingham,
NG10 1FZ, United Kingdom
Tel.: (44) 1159837676
Web Site: http://www.dartexcoatings.com
Sales Range: $10-24.9 Million
Emp.: 60
Transfer Coating & Transfer Laminating
Services
N.A.I.C.S.: 332812
David Ritley (Mng Dir)

Subsidiary (US):

Dartex Coatings Inc. (2)
22 Steel St, Slatersville, RI 02876
Tel.: (401) 766-1500
Web Site: http://www.dartexusa.com
Transfer Coating & Transfer Laminating
Services
N.A.I.C.S.: 332812
Patricia Tilden (Gen Mgr)

WATERLOO IMPORTED CARS INC
141 Northfield Drive West, Waterloo,
N2L 5A6, ON, Canada
Tel.: (519) 884-3660
Web Site: http://www.waterloonissan.com
Year Founded: 1984
Rev.: $11,042,009
Emp.: 30
New Car Dealers
N.A.I.C.S.: 441110
Glen Yates (Owner)

WATEROUS ENERGY FUND
301 8th Avenue SW Suite 600, Calgary, T2P 1C5, AB, Canada
Tel.: (403) 930-6048
Web Site: https://www.waterous.com
Privater Equity Firm
N.A.I.C.S.: 523999
Adam Waterous (CEO & Mng Partner)

Subsidiaries:

Cona Resources Ltd. (1)
1900 421-7 Avenue SW, Calgary, T2P 4K9,
AB, Canada
Tel.: (403) 930-3000
Web Site: http://www.conaresources.com
Rev.: $293,212,034
Assets: $945,637,565
Liabilities: $472,830,333
Net Worth: $472,807,232
Earnings: $69,300,144
Fiscal Year-end: 12/31/2017
Oil & Gas Exploration
N.A.I.C.S.: 211120
Michael Makinson (CFO & VP-Fin)

Subsidiary (Domestic):

Pengrowth Energy Corp. (2)
Suite 1600 222 Third Avenue SW, Calgary,
T2P 0B4, AB, Canada
Tel.: (403) 233-0224
Web Site: http://www.pengrowth.com
Rev.: $423,945,198
Assets: $1,070,776,278
Liabilities: $870,115,257
Net Worth: $200,661,021
Earnings: ($445,532,787)
Emp.: 104
Fiscal Year-end: 12/31/2018
Petroleum & Natural Gas Properties Operator

WATEROUS ENERGY FUND

Waterous Energy Fund—(Continued)
N.A.I.C.S.: 211120
Christopher G. Webster (CFO)

Subsidiary (Domestic):

NAL Energy Corp. (3)
Ste 2100 222 3rd Avenue SW, Calgary, T2P 0B4, AB, Canada
Tel.: (403) 213-3764
Web Site: http://www.nalenergy.com
Sales Range: $200-249.9 Million
Emp.: 344
Oil & Gas Exploration & Extraction
N.A.I.C.S.: 211120

Strathcona Resources Ltd. (1)
421-7 Avenue SW Suite 1900, Calgary, T2P 4K9, AB, Canada (99.7%)
Tel.: (403) 930-3000
Web Site: https://www.strathconaresources.com
Oil & Natural Gas Exploration Services
N.A.I.C.S.: 211120

Subsidiary (Domestic):

Pipestone Energy Corp. (2)
3700 888 - 3rd Street SW, Calgary, T2P 5C5, AB, Canada
Tel.: (587) 392-8411
Web Site: https://www.pipestonecorp.com
Rev.: $47,843,570
Assets: $507,978,556
Liabilities: $224,782,363
Net Worth: $283,196,193
Earnings: ($10,701,881)
Emp.: 22
Fiscal Year-end: 07/31/2019
Oil & Natural Gas Exploration Services
N.A.I.C.S.: 213112
Craig Nieboer (CFO)

WATERTITE GUTTERING (PTY) LIMITED

7 Neutron Street Triangle Farm, Bellvile, Cape Town, 7530, South Africa
Tel.: (27) 219463205
Web Site: http://www.watertite.co.za
Year Founded: 1973
Sales Range: $25-49.9 Million
Emp.: 76
Aluminium Gutters Mfr & Installation Services
N.A.I.C.S.: 238170
Nelia Jansen (Mng Dir)

WATERTON GLOBAL RESOURCE MANAGEMENT INC.

Commerce Court West 199 Bay Street Suite 5050, Toronto, M5L 1E2, ON, Canada
Tel.: (415) 504-3505
Web Site: http://www.watertonresource.com
Mineral Resource Investment Holding Company
N.A.I.C.S.: 551112
James Hennessy (Chm)

WATES GROUP LIMITED

Leatherhead Wates House Station Approach, Leatherhead, KT22 7SW, Surrey, United Kingdom
Tel.: (44) 1372 861000
Web Site: http://www.wates.co.uk
Year Founded: 1897
Rev.: $2,030,404,018
Assets: $1,018,458,712
Liabilities: $273,497,455
Net Worth: $744,961,256
Earnings: $37,018,598
Emp.: 3,763
Fiscal Year-end: 12/31/19
Construction Services
N.A.I.C.S.: 236220
James Wates (Chm)

Subsidiaries:

Gambado Limited (1)
7 Station Court Townmead Road, Chelsea, London, SW6 2PY, United Kingdom
Tel.: (44) 207 384 1635
Web Site: https://www.gambado.com
Children Play Center Services
N.A.I.C.S.: 713990
Andrew Wates (Chm)

Needspace Limited (1)
Earlsfield Business Centre 9 Lydden Road, London, SW18 4LT, United Kingdom
Tel.: (44) 208 059 9538
Web Site: https://www.needspace.co.uk
Commercial Real Estate Services
N.A.I.C.S.: 531312
Edward Snowdon (Sls Mgr)

Wates Construction Ltd (1)
Suite 7225 Building 7200 IQ Cambridge Beach Drive Waterbeach, Cambridge, CB25 9TL, United Kingdom
Tel.: (44) 1223 815666
Web Site:
Construction Engineering Services
N.A.I.C.S.: 541330
Richard Scarrott (Bus Dir-East & West Midlands)

Wates Homes (Cambridge) Limited (1)
Blenheim House Cambridge Innovation Park Denny End Road, Waterbeach, Cambridge, CB25 9QE, United Kingdom
Tel.: (44) 122 362 7140
Web Site:
Construction Engineering Services
N.A.I.C.S.: 541330

WATFORD LEISURE LIMITED

Vicarage Road Stadium, Watford, WD18 0ER, Herts, United Kingdom
Tel.: (44) 1923 496000
Web Site: http://www.watfordfc.com
Sales Range: $10-24.9 Million
Emp.: 150
Investment Management Service
N.A.I.C.S.: 523940
Peter Wastall (Sec)

Subsidiaries:

The Watford Association Football Club Limited (1)
Vicarage Road Stadium Vicarage Road, Watford, WD18 0ER, Hertfordshire, United Kingdom
Tel.: (44) 1923496000
Web Site: http://www.watfordfc.com
Football Club Management Services
N.A.I.C.S.: 711211
Rob Smith (Dir-Community)

WATFORD ROOF TRUSS LTD.

330 Front Street, Watford, N0M 2S0, ON, Canada
Tel.: (519) 876-2612
Web Site: http://www.watfordtruss.on.ca
Year Founded: 1972
Sales Range: $25-49.9 Million
Emp.: 75
Truss Mfr
N.A.I.C.S.: 321215
Garry Lindsay (Mgr-Product & Shipping)

WATKIN JONES & SON LIMITED

Llandygai Industrial Estate, Bangor, LL57 4YH, Gwynedd, United Kingdom
Tel.: (44) 1248 362516
Web Site: http://www.watkinjones.com
Year Founded: 1791
Sales Range: $250-299.9 Million
Emp.: 245
Construction Engineering Services
N.A.I.C.S.: 541330
G. Watkin Jones (Chm)

WATKIN JONES PLC

Llys Y Bont Parc Menai, Bangor, LL57 4BN, Gwynedd, United Kingdom
Tel.: (44) 1248362516 UK
Web Site: https://www.watkinjonesplc.com
WJG—(AIM)
Rev.: $460,895,976
Assets: $438,116,112
Liabilities: $237,773,322
Net Worth: $200,342,790
Earnings: $15,205,446
Fiscal Year-end: 09/30/22
Construction Management Services
N.A.I.C.S.: 236220
Richard Simpson (CEO)

WATKIN MOTORS

4602 27th Street, Vernon, V1T 4Y6, BC, Canada
Tel.: (250) 545-0611
Web Site: https://www.watkinmotors.com
Rev.: $28,294,410
Emp.: 75
New & Used Car Dealers
N.A.I.C.S.: 441110
Brad Thomas (Mgr-Fin Svcs)

WATOS COREA CO., LTD.

31 Jeonjanonggongdanji 1-Gil Donghwa-myeon, Donghwa-myeon Jangseong-gun, Gwangju, 57241, Jeollanam-do, Korea (South)
Tel.: (82) 613923685
Web Site: https://www.watos.com
Year Founded: 1973
079000—(KRS)
Rev.: $14,964,993
Assets: $63,519,691
Liabilities: $3,768,161
Net Worth: $59,751,530
Earnings: $4,074,366
Emp.: 110
Fiscal Year-end: 12/31/22
Plastics Product Mfr
N.A.I.C.S.: 326191
Taeyang Song (CEO)

WATRIUM AS

Kanalen 5 Tjuvholmen, 0252, Oslo, Norway
Tel.: (47) 22010481
Web Site: https://watrium.no
Emp.: 100
Investment Services
N.A.I.C.S.: 523999

WATSON & COX CONSTRUCTION LTD

Brunel Close Park Farm Estate, Wellingborough, NN8 6QX, Northants, United Kingdom
Tel.: (44) 1933677777
Web Site: https://www.watsoncox.com
Rev.: $15,613,250
Emp.: 35
Construction Services
N.A.I.C.S.: 236220
William Gardiner (Mng Dir)

WATT INTERNATIONAL, INC.

590 King St West Suite 300, Toronto, M5V 1M3, ON, Canada
Tel.: (416) 364-9384 ON
Web Site: http://www.wattisretail.com
Year Founded: 1966
Sales Range: $10-24.9 Million
Emp.: 50
Brand Development & Integration
N.A.I.C.S.: 541810
Mike Grace (Partner-Fin & Ops)

WATT MANN CO., LTD.

27-13 Tsurugaminehoncho 1-chome, Asahi-ku, Yokohama, 241-0021, Kanagawa, Japan
Tel.: (81) 459591100
Web Site: https://www.wattmann.co.jp
Year Founded: 1967

INTERNATIONAL PUBLIC

9927—(TKS)
Rev.: $51,895,110
Assets: $32,673,230
Liabilities: $11,270,050
Net Worth: $21,403,180
Earnings: $3,033,990
Emp.: 565
Fiscal Year-end: 03/31/24
Retail Store Operator
N.A.I.C.S.: 459999
Kazusato Shimizu (Chm)

WATT'S S.A.

Avenida Presidente Jorge Alessandri N 10501, 8060052, San Bernardo, 8060052, Chile
Tel.: (56) 24414000
Web Site: https://www.watts.cl
Year Founded: 1930
WATTS—(SGO)
Sales Range: Less than $1 Million
Food Products Mfr
N.A.I.C.S.: 311511
Fernando Larrain Pena (Pres)

WATTA HOLDING BERHAD

12th Floor Menara Cosway Plaza Berjaya, Jalan Imbi, 55100, Kuala Lumpur, Malaysia
Tel.: (60) 321442929 MY
Web Site: https://www.watta.com.my
WATTA—(KLS)
Rev.: $2,362,371
Assets: $14,105,191
Liabilities: $2,594,170
Net Worth: $11,511,021
Earnings: ($182,409)
Emp.: 134
Fiscal Year-end: 12/31/22
Automobile Batteries Mfr
N.A.I.C.S.: 335910
Chong Keat Yeoh (Co-Sec)

Subsidiaries:

Mobile Technic Sdn. Bhd. (1)
W-10-21 10th Floor Melawangi Business Suite AMCORP Trade Centre 18, Jalan Persiaran Barat, 46050, Petaling Jaya, Selangor Darul Ehsan, Malaysia
Tel.: (60) 379572211
Web Site: https://www.mobiletechnic.com
Mobile Phone Services
N.A.I.C.S.: 811210

Syarikat Perniagaan Leko Sdn. Bhd. (1)
251 Kampung Chempaka Pengkalan Chepa, 16100, Kota Baharu, Kelantan, Malaysia
Tel.: (60) 97731668
Motor Vehicle Batteries Distr
N.A.I.C.S.: 423120

Watta Battery Industries Sdn. Bhd. (1)
Lot 8 Jalan Satu Kawasan Perusahaan, Cheras Jaya, 43200, Balakong, Selangor Darul Ehsan, Malaysia
Tel.: (60) 390751919
Sales Range: $25-49.9 Million
Emp.: 90
Automobile Batteries Mfr
N.A.I.C.S.: 335910
Stanley Cheong (Sr Mgr-Intl Mktg & Asst Mgr-Intl Mktg)

WATTANA KARNPAET PCL

70/7-8 Suppakijjanya Road, Muang District, Udon Thani, 41000, Thailand
Tel.: (66) 42219888
Web Site: https://wattanahospital.net
Year Founded: 1985
NEW—(THA)
Rev.: $14,082,563
Assets: $18,006,463
Liabilities: $3,922,939
Net Worth: $14,083,524
Earnings: $1,640,220
Emp.: 250

Fiscal Year-end: 12/31/23
Health Care Srvices
N.A.I.C.S.: 621610
Phiphat Tangsubkul (Chm & CEO)

WATTANAPAT HOSPITAL TRANG PCL LTD.
Wattanapat Hospital Trang 247/2 Pattalung Road, Amphur Muang, Trang, 92000, Thailand
Tel.: (66) 75205555
Web Site:
https://www.wattanapat.co.th
WPH—(THA)
Rev.: $42,882,128
Assets: $75,035,040
Liabilities: $43,963,691
Net Worth: $31,071,349
Earnings: $2,712,226
Fiscal Year-end: 12/31/23
Health Care Srvices
N.A.I.C.S.: 621619
Amara Leelawat (Vice Chm)

WATTELIER SAS
Rue Emile Combes, 60600, Erquery, Oise, France
Tel.: (33) 344501507
Web Site: http://www.wattellier.com
Rev.: $24,200,000
Emp.: 28
Camping Cars, Caravans, Mobile Homes Decking & Accessories
N.A.I.C.S.: 336214
Bernard Wattelier (Pres)

WATTLE HEALTH AUSTRALIA LIMITED
17/71 Victoria Crescent, Abbotsford, 3067, VIC, Australia
Tel.: (61) 3 8399 9419
Web Site:
http://www.wattlehealth.com.au
Year Founded: 2011
Rev.: $1,229,272
Assets: $50,235,458
Liabilities: $2,204,884
Net Worth: $48,030,574
Earnings: ($15,484,141)
Fiscal Year-end: 06/30/18
Dairy Product Mfr & Distr
N.A.I.C.S.: 311514
Lazarus Karasavvidis (Co-Founder)

Subsidiaries:
Little Innoscents Pty. Ltd. (1)
17/71 Victoria Crescent, Abbotsford, 3067, VIC, Australia
Tel.: (61) 1300554980
Web Site: http://www.littleinnoscents.com.au
Skin Care Product Mfr
N.A.I.C.S.: 325620

WATTLE HILL RHC FUNDS
Level 13 179 Elizabeth Street, Sydney, 2000, NSW, Australia
Tel.: (61) 2 8964 0820
Web Site:
http://www.wattlehillcap.com
Privater Equity Firm
N.A.I.C.S.: 523999
Albert Tse (Co-founder)

Subsidiaries:
Capilano Honey Limited (1)
399 Archerfield Road, PO Box 531, Richlands, 4077, QLD, Australia
Tel.: (61) 7 3712 8282
Web Site: http://www.capilanohoney.com
Rev.: $108,111,805
Assets: $81,370,495
Liabilities: $28,049,037
Net Worth: $53,321,458
Earnings: $7,667,381
Fiscal Year-end: 06/30/2018
Honey Producer
N.A.I.C.S.: 311999
Dirk Kemp (Gen Mgr-Fin)

WATTS CO., LTD.
1-4-70 Shiromi, Chuo-ku, Osaka, 540-0001, Japan
Tel.: (81) 647923280
Web Site: https://www.watts-jp.com
Year Founded: 1995
2735—(TKS)
Rev.: $381,018,540
Assets: $188,341,600
Liabilities: $110,485,860
Net Worth: $77,855,740
Earnings: $5,622,880
Emp.: 3,146
Fiscal Year-end: 08/31/24
Retail Services
N.A.I.C.S.: 459999

Subsidiaries:
Daisen Co., Ltd. (1)
2-25 Komamba-cho, Nakatsugawa, 508-0014, Gifu Prefecture, Japan
Tel.: (81) 573660555
Web Site: https://www.daisen-inc.co.jp
Molding Machine Mfr
N.A.I.C.S.: 327910

Subsidiary (Non-US):
DAISEN INTERNATIONAL TRADING (SHANGHAI) CO., LTD. (2)
No 9919 Songze Avenue, Qingpu District, Shanghai, 201700, China
Tel.: (86) 21 6921 2515
Plastics Product Mfr
N.A.I.C.S.: 326199

DAISEN SINGAPORE PTE. LTD. (2)
102F Pasir Panjang Road 08-10 Citilink Warehouse Complex, Singapore, 118530, Singapore
Tel.: (65) 62712164
Plastics Product Mfr
N.A.I.C.S.: 326199

Plant (Domestic):
Daisen Co., Ltd. - Kanto Plant (2)
564-1 Mukouyama Oaza, Ageo, 362-0045, Saitama, Japan
Tel.: (81) 48 781 3311
Plastics Product Mfr
N.A.I.C.S.: 326199

Daisen Co., Ltd. - Kyushu Plant (2)
80-66 Yotsuyamamachi, Omuta, 836-0067, Fukuoka, Japan
Tel.: (81) 944 43 1141
Web Site: http://www.daisen-inc.co.jp
Plastics Product Mfr
N.A.I.C.S.: 326199

WATTS INTERNATIONAL MARITIME COMPANY LIMITED
5/F Tower 17 2816 Yixian Road, Baoshan, Shanghai, China
Tel.: (86) 2156443129
Web Site:
http://www.wattsinternational.com
2258—(HKG)
Rev.: $291,415,644
Assets: $483,161,047
Liabilities: $380,435,141
Net Worth: $102,725,906
Earnings: $3,804,559
Emp.: 557
Fiscal Year-end: 12/31/22
Logistics & Supply Chain Services
N.A.I.C.S.: 541614
Wang Shizhong (Chm)

WAUTERS ET FILS
Rue De La Prairie, 91140, Villebon-sur-Yvette, Essonne, France
Tel.: (33) 169341561
Web Site: http://www.ch-wauters.com
Rev.: $18,700,000
Emp.: 43
N.A.I.C.S.: 323120
Jacques Wauters (Mng Dir, Mng Dir & Chm)

WAVE ELECTRONICS CO., LTD.
402 114-6 Central town-ro, Yeongtong-gu, Suwon, Gyeonggi-do, Korea (South)
Tel.: (82) 312690010
Web Site: https://www.wavetc.com
Year Founded: 1999
095270—(KRS)
Rev.: $45,388,628
Assets: $73,577,369
Liabilities: $20,892,541
Net Worth: $52,684,828
Earnings: ($6,793,452)
Emp.: 114
Fiscal Year-end: 12/31/22
Communication Equipment Mfr
N.A.I.C.S.: 334290
Cheon-Seok Park (CEO)

Subsidiaries:
Wave Electronics Co., Ltd. - OLED Factory (1)
14 Pyeongtaekhang-ro 268beon-gil, Poseung-eup, Pyeongtaek, Gyeonggi-do, Korea (South)
Tel.: (82) 316821601
Wireless Telecommunication Services
N.A.I.C.S.: 517111

WAVE EXPONENTIAL PUBLIC COMPANY LIMITED
2445/19 Tararom Business Tower 14th Floor New Petchaburi Rd, Bang Kapi Huai Khwang, Bangkok, 10310, Thailand
Tel.: (66) 26656705
Web Site: https://www.wave-groups.com
Year Founded: 1988
WAVE—(THA)
Rev.: $13,087,629
Assets: $47,525,961
Liabilities: $17,397,355
Net Worth: $30,128,606
Earnings: ($638,759)
Emp.: 375
Fiscal Year-end: 12/31/23
Television Production & Distribution Services
N.A.I.C.S.: 512110
Matthew Kichodhan (Chm, CEO & COO)

Subsidiaries:
Jeffer Restaurant Co., Ltd. (1)
3199 Maleenont Tower Floor 16 Rama 4 Rd, Khlong Tan Khlong Toei, Bangkok, 10110, Thailand
Tel.: (66) 61 415 6655
Web Site: https://www.jeffersteak.com
Catering Services
N.A.I.C.S.: 722310

Wall Street English (Thailand) Co., Ltd. (1)
3199 Maleenont Tower 15th Floor Rama IV Road, Klongton Klongtoey, Bangkok, 10110, Thailand
Tel.: (66) 1211
Web Site: https://www.wallstreetenglish.in.th
English Learning Services
N.A.I.C.S.: 611630

WAVE LIFE SCIENCES LTD.
7 Straits View No 12-00, Marina One East Tower, Singapore, 018936, Singapore
Tel.: (65) 62363388
Web Site:
https://www.wavelifesciences.com
Year Founded: 2012
WVE—(NASDAQ)
Rev.: $3,649,000
Assets: $146,386,000
Liabilities: $191,477,000
Net Worth: ($45,091,000)
Earnings: ($161,823,000)
Emp.: 250

Fiscal Year-end: 12/31/22
Holding Company; Biopharmaceutical Developer & Mfr
N.A.I.C.S.: 551112
Paul B. Bolno (Pres & CEO)

Subsidiaries:
Wave Life Sciences USA, Inc. (1)
733 Concord Ave, Cambridge, MA 02138
Tel.: (617) 949-2900
Biopharmaceutical Developer & Mfr
N.A.I.C.S.: 325412
Paul B. Bolno (Pres & CEO)

WAVEFRONT TECHNOLOGY SOLUTIONS INC.
5621 - 70 Street, Edmonton, T6B 3P6, AB, Canada
Tel.: (780) 486-2222
Web Site:
https://www.onthewavefront.com
WEE—(OTCIQ)
Rev.: $1,256,140
Assets: $1,893,501
Liabilities: $848,792
Net Worth: $1,044,709
Earnings: ($1,075,132)
Fiscal Year-end: 08/31/21
Mineral Exploration Services
N.A.I.C.S.: 213114
D. Bradley Paterson (CFO)

WAVELOCK HOLDINGS CO., LTD.
St Lukes Tower 13th Floor 8-1 Akashi-cho Chuo-ku, Tokyo, 104-0044, Japan
Tel.: (81) 368306000
Web Site: http://www.wavelock-holdings.com
7940—(TKS)
Rev.: $155,724,990
Assets: $188,120,600
Liabilities: $81,626,890
Net Worth: $106,493,710
Earnings: $3,014,160
Emp.: 587
Fiscal Year-end: 03/31/24
Business Management Services
N.A.I.C.S.: 561110
Jun Kinebuchi (Co-Pres & Co-CEO)

Subsidiaries:
Eizen Corporation Co., Ltd. (1)
1527-9 Kogure Fujimi-cho, Maebashi, 371-0103, Japan
Tel.: (81) 272888111
Web Site: https://é-eizen.jp
Construction Engineering Services
N.A.I.C.S.: 541330

Innovex Co., Ltd. (1)
8-1 Akashi-cho, Chuo-ku, Tokyo, 104-0044, Japan
Tel.: (81) 368307001
Web Site: https://www.innovex-w.co.jp
Synthetic Fiber Product Mfr
N.A.I.C.S.: 325220

Wavelock Advanced Technology Co., Ltd. (1)
St-Lukes Tower 13F 8-1 Akashi-cho, Chuo-ku, Tokyo, 104-0044, Japan
Tel.: (81) 368303500
Web Site: https://www.wavelock-at.co.jp
Decorative Metallic Film Mfr
N.A.I.C.S.: 326112
Kotaro Shimada (Pres & CEO)

Wavelock Advanced Technology GmbH. (1)
Regus Ko-Bogen 510 5th floor Konigsallee 2b, 40212, Dusseldorf, Germany
Tel.: (49) 21154057016
Decorative Metallic Film Mfr
N.A.I.C.S.: 326112

Wavelock Advanced Technology Inc. (1)
123 S Main St Ste 210, Royal Oak, MI 48067
Tel.: (248) 850-7907

WAVELOCK HOLDINGS CO., LTD.

Wavelock Holdings Co., Ltd.—(Continued)
Decorative Metallic Film Mfr
N.A.I.C.S.: 326112

Wavelock Interior Co., Ltd. (1)
St Luke No 8 No 1 Akashi-cho Tower 13F,
Chuo-ku, Tokyo, 104-0044, Japan
Tel.: (81) 368305000
Web Site: http://www.w-interior.com
Paperboard Product Mfr
N.A.I.C.S.: 322130

WAVERLEY PHARMA, INC.
4-1250 Waverley Street, Winnipeg,
R3T 6C6, MB, Canada
Tel.: (204) 928-7907
Web Site:
  https://www.waverleypharma.com
Year Founded: 2014
WAVE—(TSX)
Rev.: $1,075,717
Assets: $2,731,634
Liabilities: $1,133,563
Net Worth: $1,598,071
Earnings: ($552,104)
Fiscal Year-end: 12/31/20
Pharmaceuticals Product Mfr
N.A.I.C.S.: 325412
Larry Thiessen (Pres & CEO)

WAVES HOME APPLIANCES LIMITED
9-KM Multan Road, Lahore, Pakistan
Tel.: (92) 42111313233
Web Site: https://waves.net.pk
Year Founded: 1970
WAVESAPP—(PSX)
Rev.: $18,210,310
Assets: $62,231,046
Liabilities: $34,837,301
Net Worth: $27,393,745
Earnings: $416,292
Emp.: 777
Fiscal Year-end: 12/31/23
Textile Mill Operator
N.A.I.C.S.: 314999

WAVESTONE SA
Tour Franklin 100-101 Terrasse
Boieldieu, La Defense, 92042, Paris,
Cedex, France
Tel.: (33) 149032000   FR
Web Site:
  https://www.wavestone.com
Year Founded: 1990
WAVE—(EUR)
Rev.: $763,848,450
Assets: $1,065,204,150
Liabilities: $440,593,800
Net Worth: $624,610,350
Earnings: $63,844,700
Emp.: 5,894
Fiscal Year-end: 03/31/23
Holding Company; Corporate Consulting Services
N.A.I.C.S.: 551112
Pascal Imbert (Chm-Mgmt Bd & CEO)

Subsidiaries:

Wavestone Advisors SAS (1)
Tour Franklin 100-101 Terrasse Boieldieu,
La Defense, 92042, Paris, Cedex, France
Tel.: (33) 1 4903 2000
Business Management Consulting Services
N.A.I.C.S.: 541611

Subsidiary (Non-US):

Xceed Group Limited (2)
29-30 Cornhill, London, EC3V 3NF, United Kingdom
Tel.: (44) 20 3002 1760
Information Technology Consultancy Services
N.A.I.C.S.: 541512

Wavestone HK Limited (1)
21/F On Building 162 Queen's Road, Central, China (Hong Kong)

Tel.: (852) 34622414
Business Management Services
N.A.I.C.S.: 541611
Chadi Hantouche (Partner)

Wavestone Luxembourg SA (1)
12 rue du Chateau d'Eau, L-3364, Leudelange, Luxembourg
Tel.: (352) 2637741
Web Site: http://www.wavestone.lu
Business Management Consulting Services
N.A.I.C.S.: 541611
Eric Crabie (Partner)

Wavestone US, Inc. (1)
600 N 2nd St Ste 401, Harrisburg, PA 17101
Tel.: (610) 854-2700
Consulting Services
N.A.I.C.S.: 541618
Siva Saravanan (Chief Digital Officer & Mng Dir)

Subsidiary (Domestic):

Newvantage Partners, LLC (2)
400 Stuart St Ste 20E, Boston, MA 02116
Tel.: (781) 449-9235
Web Site: http://www.newvantage.com
Scientific & Technical Consulting Services
N.A.I.C.S.: 541690
Blaise Heltai (Partner)

WAWEL S.A.
ul Wladyslawa Warnenczyka 14, 30-520, Krakow, Poland
Tel.: (48) 122527100
Web Site: https://www.wawel.com.pl
WWL—(WAR)
Rev.: $146,998,442
Assets: $187,193,137
Liabilities: $26,497,764
Net Worth: $160,695,373
Earnings: $9,289,052
Emp.: 999
Fiscal Year-end: 12/31/22
Confectionery Mfr
N.A.I.C.S.: 311351
Wojciech Winkel (Member-Mgmt Bd)

WAWI-SCHOKOLADE AG
Landgrafenstrasse 29, 66953, Pirmasens, Germany
Tel.: (49) 633127460   De
Web Site: http://www.wawi.de
Sales Range: $150-199.9 Million
Emp.: 30
Holding Company; Chocolate & Ice Cream Mfr
N.A.I.C.S.: 551112
Walter Mueller (Chm & CEO)

Subsidiaries:

WAWI Chocolate (Aus) Pty. Ltd. (1)
13 Rocco Drive, Scoresby, 3179, VIC, Australia
Tel.: (61) 397642262
Web Site: http://www.wawi-schokolade.de
Chocolate Confectionery Mfr
N.A.I.C.S.: 311352

WAWI Chocolate (Xiamen) Co., Ltd. (1)
38 Xinjia Road Xinyang Industrial Zone, Haicang, Xiamen, 361026, China
Tel.: (86) 5926512200
Web Site: http://www.wawi-schokolade.de
Chocolate Confectionery Mfr
N.A.I.C.S.: 311352
Chen Chang Liu (Gen Mgr)

WAWI Prague, spol s.r.o. (1)
Na Dlouhem 85, 25101, Ricany, Jazlovice, Czech Republic
Tel.: (420) 774297220
Chocolate Confectionery Mfr
N.A.I.C.S.: 311352

WAWI-Euro GmbH (1)
Landgrafenstrasse 29, Pirmasens, 66953, Germany
Tel.: (49) 633127460
Web Site: http://www.wawi-schokolade.com

Sales Range: $25-49.9 Million
Emp.: 100
Chocolate Confectionery Mfr
N.A.I.C.S.: 311351
Alexandra Serret (Mng Dir)

WAWI-Susswaren Saisonspezialitaten GmbH (1)
Unterer Sommerwaldweg 18-20, 66953, Pirmasens, Germany
Tel.: (49) 6331 239990
Chocolate Distr
N.A.I.C.S.: 424450

WAX LYRICAL LTD.
London Road Lindal-In-Furness,
Cumbria, Ulverston, LA12 0LD,
United Kingdom
Tel.: (44) 1229461140
Web Site: http://www.wax-lyrical.com
Sales Range: $10-24.9 Million
Emp.: 150
Provider of Candles & Decorative Items
N.A.I.C.S.: 339999
Joanne Barber (Mng Dir)

WAY 2 VAT LTD.
3 Tozeret Haaretz St Y Building 3rd floor, Sydney, 2000, NSW, Australia
Tel.: (61) 97235080022
Web Site: https://www.way2vat.com
Year Founded: 2014
W2V—(ASX)
Rev.: $2,049,000
Assets: $4,146,000
Liabilities: $5,151,000
Net Worth: ($1,005,000)
Earnings: ($4,251,000)
Fiscal Year-end: 12/31/23
Software Development Services
N.A.I.C.S.: 541511
Smadar Noy (CFO)

WAY OF WILL INC.
110 Mack Ave Unit 1-A, Scarborough,
M1L 1N3, ON, Canada
Tel.: (647) 350-2038   ON
Web Site: https://www.wayofwill.com
Year Founded: 2016
WAY—(CNSX)
Skin Care Products Distr
N.A.I.C.S.: 424210
Willie Tsang (CEO & Founder)

WAYI INTERNATIONAL DIGITAL ENTERTAINMENT CO., LTD.
4th Floor No 39 Lane 141 Xingai Road, Nei Hu District, Taipei, 114, Taiwan
Tel.: (886) 255590070
Web Site: https://www.wayi.net
Year Founded: 1993
3086—(TPE)
Rev.: $4,604,509
Assets: $10,921,396
Liabilities: $1,111,809
Net Worth: $9,809,586
Earnings: $1,145,671
Fiscal Year-end: 12/31/22
Software Development Services
N.A.I.C.S.: 541511
Shi Shukai (Chm)

WAYNE PITMAN FORD LINCOLN
895 Woodlawn Road West, Guelph,
N1K 1B7, ON, Canada
Tel.: (519) 824-6400
Web Site:
  http://www.waynepitman.ca
Year Founded: 1976
Rev.: $39,038,283
Emp.: 77
New & Used Car Dealers
N.A.I.C.S.: 441110
Wayne Pitman (Chm)

INTERNATIONAL PUBLIC

WAYNE WATSON CONSTRUCTION LTD.
730 Third Avenue, Prince George,
V2L 3C5, BC, Canada
Tel.: (250) 562-8251
Web Site:
  http://www.waynewatson.ca
Year Founded: 1972
Rev.: $19,000,000
Emp.: 129
Construction Services
N.A.I.C.S.: 236220
Ken Watson (Pres)

WAYPOINT REIT LIMITED
Level 15 720 Bourke Street, Docklands, 3008, VIC, Australia
Tel.: (61) 388234444   AU
Web Site:
  https://www.waypointreit.com.au
Year Founded: 2016
WPR—(ASX)
Rev.: $111,299,910
Assets: $1,905,789,585
Liabilities: $657,514,095
Net Worth: $1,248,275,490
Earnings: ($53,878,965)
Fiscal Year-end: 12/31/23
Property Management & Leasing Services
N.A.I.C.S.: 531190
Tina Mitas (Gen Counsel & Sec)

WAYPORT (H.K) CO., LTD.
Suite 2008 20F Jardine House 1
Connaught, Central, China (Hong Kong)
Tel.: (852) 573 8322 5888
Web Site: http://www.yattool.co.kr
900130—(KRS)
Sales Range: $100-124.9 Million
Holding Company
N.A.I.C.S.: 551112
Yong Chen (CEO)

WAYS ELECTRON CO., LTD.
No 299 Yunque Road, Precision Machinery Industrial Park Kunshan Development Zone, Kunshan, 215300, Jiangsu, China
Tel.: (86) 51257158688
Web Site: https://www.ksways.com
Year Founded: 2003
605218—(SHG)
Rev.: $190,766,338
Assets: $212,535,526
Liabilities: $43,871,125
Net Worth: $168,664,401
Earnings: $13,498,632
Fiscal Year-end: 12/31/22
Electronic Product Mfr & Distr
N.A.I.C.S.: 334419

WAYS TECHNICAL CORP.
NO 1-1 Ln28 Kaoching Rd, Yangmei,
Taoyuan, 326, Taiwan
Tel.: (886) 34965000
Web Site: https://www.waystech.net
3508—(TPE)
Rev.: $37,741,050
Assets: $89,614,264
Liabilities: $63,812,776
Net Worth: $25,801,488
Earnings: ($6,558,828)
Fiscal Year-end: 12/31/22
Plastics Product Mfr
N.A.I.C.S.: 326199
Shih Wen Liao (Chm & Pres)

Subsidiaries:

Nanobit Tech. Co., Ltd. (1)
No 1-1 Ln 28 Gaoqing Rd, Yangmei Dist, Taoyuan, 32667, Taiwan
Tel.: (886) 34965000
Web Site: https://www.nanobit.com.tw
Transparent Conductive Film Mfr
N.A.I.C.S.: 326112

Vincent Huang (VP-Bus Dev-Global)

WAYSIS BV
H J E Wenckebachweg 80, 1114 AD, Amsterdam, Netherlands
Tel.: (31) 204620462
Web Site: http://www.waysis.com
Year Founded: 1927
Sales Range: $25-49.9 Million
Emp.: 130
Traffic Sign Technology & Services
N.A.I.C.S.: 339950
Paul Staartjes (Pres)

Subsidiaries:

Simac Business Applications bv (1)
Amperestraat 36, Ede, 6716 BN, Netherlands
Tel.: (31) 8 64 96 66
Web Site: http://www.simac.com
Business Application Software Consulting Services
N.A.I.C.S.: 541512
Andre Wielaard (Mng Dir)

Taxameter Centrale B.V. (1)
H J E Wenckebachweg 80, Duivendrecht, 1114 AD, Amsterdam, Netherlands
Tel.: (31) 204620462
Web Site: http://www.taxameter.nl
Emp.: 75
Parking Meter Whslr
N.A.I.C.S.: 423850
Randy Piet (Acct Mgr)

WAYSTREAM GROUP AB
Farogatan 33, Kista, 164 51, Sweden
Tel.: (46) 856269450
Web Site:
  https://www.waystream.com
Year Founded: 2001
WAYS—(OMX)
Rev.: $13,144,511
Assets: $11,911,920
Liabilities: $4,849,813
Net Worth: $7,062,107
Earnings: $1,925,689
Emp.: 23
Fiscal Year-end: 12/31/22
Information Technology Services
N.A.I.C.S.: 541512
Susanne Torrbacka (CEO)

Subsidiaries:

Shanghai Shuling Network Technology Co., Ltd. (1)
Room 302 West Yuanzhong Scientific Research Building No 1905, Hongmei Road Xuhui District, Shanghai, 200233, China
Tel.: (86) 54489787
Fibre Network Equipment Mfr & Distr
N.A.I.C.S.: 335921

Waystream AB (1)
Farogatan 33, 164 51, Kista, Sweden
Tel.: (46) 856269450
Broadband Network Services
N.A.I.C.S.: 517111

WAZIR ALI INDUSTRIES LTD.
F-33 Hub River Road SITE, Karachi, 75700, Pakistan
Tel.: (92) 21 2579683
Web Site: http://www.wazirali.com.pk
Sales Range: $1-9.9 Million
Palm, Cottonseed, Sunflower & Soybean Oil Processor
N.A.I.C.S.: 311224
Yawar Ali (Chm & CEO)

WAZOKU LIMITED
St Magnus House 3 Lower Thames Street, London, EC3R 6HD, United Kingdom
Tel.: (44) 20874 35724 UK
Web Site: http://www.wazoku.com
Year Founded: 2011
Software Management Services
N.A.I.C.S.: 513210
Simon Hill (CEO)

Subsidiaries:

InnoCentive, Inc. (1)
245 Winter St 2nd Fl, Waltham, MA 02451
Tel.: (978) 482-3300
Web Site: http://www.innocentive.com
Technical Consulting Services
N.A.I.C.S.: 541990
Richard Barletta (Sr VP-Fin & Admin)

WB BURGERS ASIA, INC.
3F K's Minamiaoyama 6-6-20 Minamiaoyama, Minato-ku, Tokyo, 107-0062, Japan
Tel.: (81) 9060024978 NV
Web Site: https://wb-burgers.asia
Year Founded: 2019
WBBA—(OTCEM)
Rev.: $581,798
Assets: $1,259,223
Liabilities: $413,056
Net Worth: $846,167
Earnings: ($3,921,665)
Emp.: 5
Fiscal Year-end: 07/31/23
Holding Company
N.A.I.C.S.: 551112
Koichi Ishizuka (Board of Directors, Pres, CEO, CFO, Treas & Sec)

WBF RESORT OKINAWA CO., LTD.
184-6 Senaga, Tomigusuku, Okinawa, 901-0233, Japan
Tel.: (81) 988401886
Web Site: http://www.wbfresort-okinawa.com
Restaurant Operators
N.A.I.C.S.: 722511
Yoshinari Kaneshiro (Pres)

WBPR PUBLIC RELATIONS & MARKETING MBH
Munchner Str 18, 85774, Unterfohring, Germany
Tel.: (49) 89 99 59 06 0 De
Web Site: http://www.wbpr.de
Year Founded: 1980
Emp.: 60
Public Relations Agency
N.A.I.C.S.: 541820
Dietrich von Gumppenberg (Mng Partner)

Subsidiaries:

wbpr Hungaria Kft. (1)
Jozsef Attila u 1, H-1051, Budapest, Hungary
Tel.: (36) 1 485 02 10
Web Site: http://www.wbpr.de
Emp.: 5
N.A.I.C.S.: 541820

wbpr Public Relations & Marketing mbH (1)
Parkstrasse 2, 14469, Potsdam, Germany
Tel.: (49) 3 31 2 01 66 0
Web Site: http://www.wbpr.de
Emp.: 13
N.A.I.C.S.: 541820

wbpr Public Relations & Marketing mbH (1)
Schumannstrasse 5, 10117, Berlin, Germany
Tel.: (49) 30 28 87 61 0
Web Site: http://www.wbpr.de
Sales Range: $10-24.9 Million
Emp.: 15
N.A.I.C.S.: 541820

WCE HOLDINGS BERHAD
Unit 30-01 Level 30 Tower A Vertical Business Suite, Avenue 3 Bangsar South No 8 Jalan Kerinchi, 59200, Kuala Lumpur, Malaysia
Tel.: (60) 327839191
Web Site: https://www.wcehb.com.my
WCEHB—(KLS)
Rev.: $130,099,682
Assets: $1,583,466,866
Liabilities: $1,394,015,227
Net Worth: $189,451,639
Earnings: ($33,355,555)
Emp.: 291
Fiscal Year-end: 03/31/24
Property Development Services
N.A.I.C.S.: 531311
Koon Beng Raw (Co-Sec)

Subsidiaries:

Angsana Mestika Sdn. Bhd. (1)
11 Jalan Teluk Bahang, 11050, Penang, Malaysia
Tel.: (60) 48170888
Hotel & Resort Services
N.A.I.C.S.: 721110

WCF LTD
Crawhall, Brampton, Carlisle, CA8 1TN, Cumbria, United Kingdom
Tel.: (44) 1697745050
Web Site: http://www.wcf.co.uk
Year Founded: 1911
Rev.: $192,500,000
Emp.: 250
Food Products Distr
N.A.I.C.S.: 484121
Jo L. Ritzema (Mng Dir)

Subsidiaries:

WCF Distribution (1)
Briars Lane, Ormskirk, L40 5TQ, Lancashire, United Kingdom
Tel.: (44) 1704893226
Food Product Whslr
N.A.I.C.S.: 424420
J L Ritzema (Mng Dir)

WCF Fuels North West (1)
Station Goods Yard Warton Road, Carnforth, LA5 9EU, Lancashire, United Kingdom
Tel.: (44) 1524733669
Web Site: http://www.wcfnw.co.uk
Fuel Distr
N.A.I.C.S.: 424720

WCF Horticulture (1)
Cromwellstore, Almondbank, Perth, PH1 3GT, United Kingdom
Tel.: (44) 1738582020
Web Site: http://www.wcfhorticulture.co.uk
Emp.: 200
Seed Whslr
N.A.I.C.S.: 424910
Patricia Somerville (Mgr-Sls)

WCF Pet & Equestrian (1)
Old Jam Works Station Road, Wigton, CA7 9AX, Cumbria, United Kingdom
Tel.: (44) 1697341005
Web Site:
  http://www.wcfpetandequestrian.co.uk
Animal Farming Services
N.A.I.C.S.: 112990

WCM GLOBAL GROWTH LIMITED
Level 6 10 Spring Street, Sydney, 2000, NSW, Australia
Tel.: (61) 1300052054 AU
Web Site:
  https://www.associateglobal.com
Year Founded: 2017
WQG—(ASX)
Rev.: $87,389,157
Assets: $415,763,001
Liabilities: $26,363,540
Net Worth: $389,394,461
Earnings: $56,504,806
Fiscal Year-end: 06/30/23
Investment Management Service
N.A.I.C.S.: 523999
Marty Switzer (Mng Dir)

WCM GLOBAL LONG SHORT LIMITED
Level 6 10 Spring Street, Sydney, 2000, NSW, Australia
Tel.: (61) 1300001750 AU
Web Site:
  http://www.contango.com.au
Year Founded: 2012
WLS—(ASX)
Rev.: $7,233,600
Assets: $74,642,230
Liabilities: $1,498,668
Net Worth: $73,143,562
Earnings: $2,921,482
Fiscal Year-end: 06/30/21
Investment Management Service
N.A.I.C.S.: 523940

Subsidiaries:

Switzer Asset Management Pty. Limited (1)
Level 6 10 Spring Street, Sydney, 2000, NSW, Australia
Tel.: (61) 1300052054
Web Site:
  http://www.switzerassetmanagement.com
Financial Services
N.A.I.C.S.: 523999
Peter Switzer (Chm)

WCON ELECTRONICS (GUANGDONG) CO., LTD.
No 7 Changxing Road, Humen Town, Dongguan, 523935, Guangdong, China
Tel.: (86) 76985358920
Web Site: https://www.wcon.cn
Year Founded: 2002
301328—(CHIN)
Rev.: $67,432,716
Assets: $281,615,724
Liabilities: $22,598,784
Net Worth: $259,016,940
Earnings: $15,748,668
Emp.: 800
Fiscal Year-end: 12/31/22
Electronic Component Mfr & Distr
N.A.I.C.S.: 334419

Subsidiaries:

Kunshan Wcon Electronics Co., Ltd. (1)
Qipu Road Beibu industrial Park, Qiandeng Town, Kunshan, China
Tel.: (86) 51257468408
Electronic Connector Mfr & Distr
N.A.I.C.S.: 334417

Wcon Electronics Europe S.R.L. (1)
Via dei Mille 8020861, Brugherio, Monza & Brianza, Italy
Tel.: (39) 0396774129
Electronic Connector Mfr & Distr
N.A.I.C.S.: 334417

WCT HOLDINGS BERHAD
B-30-01The Ascent Paradigm No 1 Jalan SS7/26A, Kelana Jaya, 47301, Petaling Jaya, Selangor Darul Ehsan, Malaysia
Tel.: (60) 378066688
Web Site: https://www.wct.com.my
WCT—(KLS)
Rev.: $445,474,709
Assets: $1,757,406,138
Liabilities: $930,631,534
Net Worth: $826,774,603
Earnings: $36,569,524
Emp.: 2,091
Fiscal Year-end: 12/31/22
Engineering & Construction Management Services
N.A.I.C.S.: 236220
Loke Yew Khor (Dir-Legal Affairs & Secretarial)

Subsidiaries:

Atlanta Villa Sdn. Bhd. (1)
No 63 Lorong Batu Nilam 1A Bandar Bukit Tinggi, 41200, Klang, Selangor, Malaysia
Tel.: (60) 33243255
Web Site: https://www.lamangreenville.com
Engineering & Construction Services
N.A.I.C.S.: 541330

WCT HOLDINGS BERHAD

WCT Holdings Berhad—(Continued)

Camellia Tropicana Sdn. Bhd. (1)
Lot 6 The Residency at Sutra Jalan Utama Sutera Harbour, 88100, Kota Kinabalu, Sabah, Malaysia
Tel.: (60) 88312333
Residential Property Development Services
N.A.I.C.S.: 531210
Kinsung Sik *(Mgr)*

Jelas Puri Sdn. Bhd. (1)
B-G-03 Jln Ss7/13b Amanseri Kelana Jaya, 47301, Petaling Jaya, Selangor, Malaysia
Tel.: (60) 378778080
Residential Property Development Services
N.A.I.C.S.: 531210

WCT Construction Sdn. Bhd. (1)
Lot 44 12 Jalan Majistret U1/26 Section U1 Hicom, Glenmarie Industrial Park, Shah Alam, 40150, Selangor, Malaysia
Tel.: (60) 378052266
Sales Range: $25-49.9 Million
Emp.: 150
Construction Engineering Services
N.A.I.C.S.: 541330
Ooi Bok Thian *(Sr Mgr-Contracts)*

Subsidiary (Domestic):

WCT Machinery Sdn. Bhd. (2)
3 Jalan Kenanga 4 Seksyen BB 11, Bukit Beruntung, Rawang, 48300, Selangor, Malaysia
Tel.: (60) 360283768
Industrial Machinery Repair & Maintenance Services
N.A.I.C.S.: 811310

WCT Engineering Vietnam Company Limited (1)
B2-17 Ha Huy Tap Nam Thien 2 Phu My Hung, District 7, Ho Chi Minh City, Vietnam
Tel.: (84) 854122474
Investment & Management Services
N.A.I.C.S.: 541611
Uyen Minh Nguyen Nu *(Office Mgr)*

WCT Land Sdn. Bhd. (1)
No 63 Lorong Batu Nilam 1A, Bandar Bukit Tinggi, 41200, Klang, Selangor Darul Ehsan, Malaysia
Tel.: (60) 33 324 3255
Web Site: http://www.wctland.com.my
Sales Range: $75-99.9 Million
Emp.: 160
Real Estate Consulting Service
N.A.I.C.S.: 531210

Subsidiary (Domestic):

Labur Bina Sdn. Bhd. (2)
No 63 Lorong Batu Nilam 1 A, Bandar Bukit Tingi, Kelang, 41200, Selangor, Malaysia
Tel.: (60) 333243258
Web Site: https://www.wct.com.my
Sales Range: $75-99.9 Million
Emp.: 130
Residential Property Development Services
N.A.I.C.S.: 531390

WCT OUG Development Sdn. Bhd. (1)
B-30-01 The Ascent Paradigm No 1 Jalan SS7/26A Paradigm, Kelana Jaya, Petaling Jaya, 47301, Selangor, Malaysia
Tel.: (60) 78878080
Web Site: https://www.waltzresidences.com
Investment & Management Services
N.A.I.C.S.: 523940

WDB COCO CO., LTD.

1-8-11 Harumi, Chuo-Ku, Tokyo, 104-6127, Japan
Tel.: (81) 351442250
Web Site: https://wdb-g.com
Year Founded: 1984
7079—(TKS)
Medicinal Product Mfr
N.A.I.C.S.: 339112
Haruhiko Taniguchi *(Pres)*

WDB HOLDINGS CO., LTD.

79 Toyozawa-cho, Himeji, 670-0964, Hyogo, Japan
Tel.: (81) 792870111
Web Site: https://www.wdbhd.co.jp
Year Founded: 1985
2475—(TKS)
Rev.: $325,853,170
Assets: $263,256,470
Liabilities: $57,354,970
Net Worth: $205,901,500
Earnings: $23,452,280
Emp.: 968
Fiscal Year-end: 03/31/24
Help Supply Services
N.A.I.C.S.: 561320
Toshimitsu Nakano *(Pres & CEO)*

Subsidiaries:

WDB Medical Data, Inc. (1)
707 State Rd Ste 222, Princeton, NJ 08540 **(100%)**
Tel.: (609) 212-2111
Web Site: http://www.wdb-md.com
Human Resources Services for Pharmaceutical & Medical Industries
N.A.I.C.S.: 541612
Nino Norifumi Ninokata *(Pres & CEO)*

Subsidiary (Domestic):

DZS Software Solutions, Inc. (2)
1661 Rte 22 W, Bound Brook, NJ 08805 **(100%)**
Tel.: (732) 764-6970
Web Site: https://dzs.com
Sales Range: $1-9.9 Million
Custom Computer Programming Services
N.A.I.C.S.: 541511
Doron Z. Steger *(Founder)*

WDI CORPORATION

Roi Bldg 8F and 9F 5-5-1 Roppongi, Minato-ku, Tokyo, 106-8522, Japan
Tel.: (81) 334043704
Web Site: https://www.wdi.co.jp
Year Founded: 1954
3068—(TKS)
Rev.: $185,681,760
Assets: $164,337,360
Liabilities: $113,527,040
Net Worth: $50,810,320
Earnings: $7,018,000
Fiscal Year-end: 03/31/22
Restaurant Services
N.A.I.C.S.: 722511
Yoji Shimizu *(Chm)*

Subsidiaries:

INAKAYA NEW YORK, L.L.C. (1)
231 W 40th St, New York, NY 10018
Tel.: (212) 354-2195
Web Site: http://www.inakayany.com
Restaurant Operators
N.A.I.C.S.: 722511
Chris Matsumoto *(Gen Mgr)*

WDI International, Inc. (1)
21171 S Western Ave Ste 250, Torrance, CA 90501
Tel.: (310) 533-3201
Web Site: http://www.wdiinternational.com
Restaurant Operators
N.A.I.C.S.: 721110
Jun Horiuchi *(Pres)*

WDS COMPONENT PARTS LTD.

Richardshaw Road Grangefield Industrial Estate, Leeds, LS28 6LE, West Yorks, United Kingdom
Tel.: (44) 1132909852 **UK**
Web Site: http://www.wdsltd.co.uk
Year Founded: 1952
Sales Range: $10-24.9 Million
Emp.: 35
Jig & Fixtures Mfr
N.A.I.C.S.: 333514
Chris Putman *(Mgr-Mktg)*

WDX S.A.

ul Tasmowa 7, 02-677, Warsaw, Poland
Tel.: (48) 22 417 0 299 **PL**
Web Site: http://www.wdx.pl
Year Founded: 1995
Warehouse Equipment Mfr & Distr
N.A.I.C.S.: 333922
Jacek Andrzejewski *(VP-Mgmt Bd)*

Subsidiaries:

Aporter Sp. z o.o. (1)
Szczawinska 54-58, 95-100, Zgierz, Lodz, Poland
Tel.: (48) 427164225
Web Site: http://www.aporter.pl
Sales Range: $25-49.9 Million
Emp.: 100
Warehouse Conveyors Mfr
N.A.I.C.S.: 333922

Heavy-Net Sp. z o o (1)
St Szczawinska 54/58, 95-100, Zgierz, Lodz, Poland
Tel.: (48) 427177764
Web Site: http://www.heavy-net.pl
Forklift Truck Distr
N.A.I.C.S.: 423830
Marek Skrzeczynski *(Pres)*

WE & WIN DEVELOPMENT CO., LTD.

36th Floor No 68 Section 5 Zhongxiao East Road, Xinyi District, Taipei, Taiwan
Tel.: (886) 27229898
Web Site: https://www.5v.com.tw
2537—(TAI)
Rev.: $17,850,485
Assets: $515,734,210
Liabilities: $382,464,030
Net Worth: $133,270,180
Earnings: ($1,966,513)
Fiscal Year-end: 12/31/23
Real Estate Projects & Computer Equipment Installation Services
N.A.I.C.S.: 531390
Su Yung Yi *(Chm)*

WE BUY ANY CAR LIMITED

Nixon Street, Rochdale, OL11 3JW, United Kingdom
Tel.: (44) 84 4854 7256
Web Site: http://www.webuyanycar.com
Year Founded: 2006
Sales Range: $450-499.9 Million
Emp.: 250
Used Automobile Purchasing & Distribution Services
N.A.I.C.S.: 423110
Darren McKee *(Co-Founder)*

WE COMPONENTS PTE. LTD.

10 Ubi Crescent 03 94/95/96 Ubi Techpark Lobby E, Singapore, 408564, Singapore
Tel.: (65) 63112900 **SG**
Plastic Moulding Product Mfr
N.A.I.C.S.: 326199
K. S. Tan *(Mgr-Product Mktg)*

Subsidiaries:

Kin Wai technology Ltd. (1)
Room 2202/22F Desay Building South No 1 Road, Hi-Tech Industrial Park Nanshan District, Shenzhen, 518005, China
Tel.: (86) 75583048857
Web Site: http://www.kinwaitech.com
Electronic Parts Mfr
N.A.I.C.S.: 334419

WE Components (Penang) Sdn. Bhd. (1)
62-1 Persiaran Bayan Indah Bayan Bay, SG Nibong, Penang, 11900, Malaysia
Tel.: (60) 46469888
Plastic Moulding Product Mfr
N.A.I.C.S.: 326199

WE Components (Shanghai) Co. Ltd. (1)
Room 106 B The Market Business Building Yang Gao North Road No 2001, Waigaoqiao Free Trade Zone, Shanghai, 200131, China

INTERNATIONAL PUBLIC

Tel.: (86) 75582995835
Electronic Component & Equipment Distr
N.A.I.C.S.: 423690

WE Components (Shenzhen) Co. Ltd. (1)
Room 1001A/10F Desay Building South No 1 Road, High-Tech Industrial Park Nanshan District, Shenzhen, 518057, China
Tel.: (86) 75582995835
Electronic Component & Equipment Distr
N.A.I.C.S.: 423690

WE Components Co., Ltd. (1)
19/1-2 FL 2nd A B Wangdek Bld 2 Viphavadee-Rangsit Rd, Jomphol Jatujak, Bangkok, 10900, Thailand
Tel.: (66) 2617426770
Plastic Moulding Product Mfr
N.A.I.C.S.: 326199

WE Components India Pvt Ltd (1)
No 20 Lakshmi 2nd Floor Shankarmutt Road, Shankarpuram Basavanagudi, Bengaluru, 560004, India
Tel.: (91) 8026677767
Electronic Component & Equipment Distr
N.A.I.C.S.: 423690
Sriram Krishna *(Country Dir)*

We Components (Hong Kong) Limited (1)
Rooms 1318-20 13/F Hollywood Plaza 610 Nathan Road Mongkok, Kowloon, China (Hong Kong)
Tel.: (852) 23109787
Plastic Moulding Product Mfr
N.A.I.C.S.: 326199

We Components (Shanghai) Co., Ltd. (1)
Room 2202/22F Desay Building South No 1 Road, High-Tech Industrial Park Nanshan District, Shenzhen, China
Tel.: (86) 75582995835
Plastic Moulding Product Mfr
N.A.I.C.S.: 326199

WE WIN LIMITED

C6 IT Park Badwai Road Badwai, Bhopal, 462047, India
Tel.: (91) 7554278897
Web Site: https://www.wewinlimited.com
Year Founded: 2007
WEWIN—(NSE)
Rev.: $4,982,089
Assets: $3,913,962
Liabilities: $1,343,896
Net Worth: $2,570,066
Earnings: $171,886
Emp.: 205
Fiscal Year-end: 03/12/21
Information Technology Services
N.A.I.C.S.: 541512
Sonika Gupta *(Chm)*

WE&WIN DIVERSIFICATION CO., LTD.

17th Floor No 185 Fuguo Road, Zuoying District, Kaohsiung, 813, Taiwan
Tel.: (886) 75575242
Web Site: https://kh.vvvvv.com.tw
Year Founded: 1998
4113—(TPE)
Rev.: $2,705,625
Assets: $439,046,712
Liabilities: $337,152,206
Net Worth: $101,894,506
Earnings: ($4,508,802)
Fiscal Year-end: 12/31/22
Medical Equipment Distr
N.A.I.C.S.: 423450
Yung-I Su *(Chm & Pres)*

WEALTH DEFENDER EQUITIES LIMITED

Level 19 56 Pitt Street, Sydney, 2000, NSW, Australia
Tel.: (61) 1800 645 202

AND PRIVATE COMPANIES

Web Site:
http://wealthdefenderequities.com
WDE—(ASX)
Investment Services
N.A.I.C.S.: 523999
Alan Schoenheimer *(Chm)*

WEALTH DRAGONS GROUP PLC
Scorpio Linford Wood Business Park, Linford Wood Buckinghamshire, Milton Keynes, MK14 6LY, Buckinghamshire, United Kingdom
Tel.: (44) 1908032432   UK
Web Site:
https://www.wealthdragons.co.uk
Year Founded: 2009
WDG—(VIE)
Sales Range: $1-9.9 Million
Educational Consulting Services
N.A.I.C.S.: 611710
Vincent Wong *(Co-Founder, Co-CEO & COO)*

WEALTH FIRST PORTFOLIO MANAGERS LIMITED
Capitol House 10 Paras-II Nr Prahladnagar Garden, Ahmedabad, 380 015, India
Tel.: (91) 7940240000
Web Site: https://www.wealth-firstonline.com
WEALTH—(NSE)
Rev.: $4,548,808
Assets: $9,786,504
Liabilities: $832,595
Net Worth: $8,953,909
Earnings: $2,682,730
Emp.: 56
Fiscal Year-end: 03/31/21
Financial Management Services
N.A.I.C.S.: 541611
Ashish Navnitlal Shah *(Founder & Mng Dir)*

WEALTH GLORY HOLDINGS LIMITED
12/F The Pemberton 22-26 Bonham Strand, Sheung Wan, Hong Kong, China (Hong Kong)
Tel.: (852) 2 548 1838   Ky
Web Site: http://www.wealthglory.com
8269—(HKG)
Rev.: $6,649,048
Assets: $9,868,518
Liabilities: $3,676,704
Net Worth: $6,191,814
Earnings: ($3,624,209)
Emp.: 8
Fiscal Year-end: 03/31/22
Merchandise Product Mfr & Distr
N.A.I.C.S.: 326111
Su Lin *(Exec Dir)*

WEALTH MANAGEMENT INC.
1-12-32 Akasaka, Minato-ku, Tokyo, 107-6033, Japan
Tel.: (81) 362292140
Web Site: https://www.wealth-mngt.com
Year Founded: 1999
3772—(TKS)
Rev.: $189,211,250
Assets: $365,070,300
Liabilities: $242,487,850
Net Worth: $122,582,450
Earnings: $12,056,640
Fiscal Year-end: 03/31/24
Financial Management Services
N.A.I.C.S.: 523999
Kazutoshi Senno *(Pres)*

Subsidiaries:

SANYO KOGYO CO., LTD. (1)
Higashiyama Building 3F 1-1-2 Higashiyama, Meguro-ku, Tokyo, 153-0043, Kanagawa, Japan
Tel.: (81) 364524350
Web Site: https://www.sanyokogyo.co.jp
Electric Machinery Distr
N.A.I.C.S.: 423830

WEALTH MINERALS LTD.
570 200 Burrard Street, Vancouver, V6C 3L6, BC, Canada
Tel.: (604) 331-0096   BC
Web Site:
https://www.wealthminerals.com
WMLLF—(OTCQB)
Assets: $43,345,930
Liabilities: $1,605,106
Net Worth: $41,740,824
Earnings: ($3,645,844)
Fiscal Year-end: 11/30/22
Rare Earth Minerals & Uranium Mining Services
N.A.I.C.S.: 212290
Hendrick Van Alphen *(CEO)*

WEALTHINK AI-INNOVATION CAPITAL LIMITED
Room 3910-13 39/F COSCO Tower Grand Millennium Plaza 183 Queen's Road, Central, China (Hong Kong)
Tel.: (852) 28429688   Ky
Web Site: https://www.1140.com.hk
Year Founded: 2002
1140—(HKG)
Rev.: $60,013,675
Assets: $1,452,605,851
Liabilities: $173,227,089
Net Worth: $1,279,378,762
Earnings: $18,707,810
Emp.: 33
Fiscal Year-end: 03/31/23
Investment Management Service
N.A.I.C.S.: 523999
Bing Mei *(CFO)*

WEALTHNAVI, INC.
2-22-3 Shibuya Shibuya East Exit Building 9F, Shibuya-Ku, Tokyo, 150-0002, Japan
Tel.: (81) 366329578
Web Site:
https://corp.wealthnavi.com
Year Founded: 2015
7342—(TKS)
Financial Management Consulting Services
N.A.I.C.S.: 541611
Kazuhisa Shibayama *(Founder, Chm, Pres, CEO & Dir-Rep)*

WEALTHY WAY GROUP LIMITED
Room 3402 34/F China Resources Building 26 Harbour Road, Wanchai, China (Hong Kong)
Tel.: (852) 35800808   Ky
Web Site: http://www.cwl.com
Year Founded: 2012
3848—(HKG)
Rev.: $13,982,155
Assets: $102,429,241
Liabilities: $24,593,306
Net Worth: $77,835,935
Earnings: $3,385,325
Emp.: 75
Fiscal Year-end: 12/31/22
Financial Planning Services
N.A.I.C.S.: 523940
Wai Ho Lo *(Founder, Chm & CEO)*

Subsidiaries:

Grand Partners Securities Limited (1)
Room 3402 34/F China Resources Building 26 Harbour Road, Wanchai, China (Hong Kong)
Tel.: (852) 37013200
Web Site:
https://www.gpsl.grandpartners.com.hk
Securities Brokerage Services
N.A.I.C.S.: 523150
Keung Kam Chuen *(Officer-Daily Ops, Mktg & Controlling)*

Wealthy Way (China) Finance Lease Limited (1)
Floor 18 Block D Caifugang Building Bao Yuan Road Xixiang Street, Bao'an District, Shenzhen, China
Tel.: (86) 75523093909
Financial Services
N.A.I.C.S.: 523940

WEARABLE DEVICES LTD.
Hatnufa 5 street, Yokneam, 2066717, Israel
Tel.: (972) 46185670   Il
Web Site:
https://www.wearabledevices.co.il
Year Founded: 2014
WLDS—(NASDAQ)
Rev.: $45,000
Assets: $11,224,000
Liabilities: $1,244,000
Net Worth: $9,980,000
Earnings: ($6,496,000)
Emp.: 28
Fiscal Year-end: 12/31/22
Electric Device Mfr
N.A.I.C.S.: 334419
Asher Dahan *(CEO & Co-Founder)*

WEARNES AUTOMOTIVE PTE. LTD.
45 Leng Kee Road, Singapore, 159103, Singapore
Tel.: (65) 6475 7132   SG
Web Site:
http://www.wearnesauto.com
Year Founded: 1906
New Car Dealerships Operator & Motor Vehicle Distr
N.A.I.C.S.: 423110
Cheong Yan *(Gen Mgr)*

Subsidiaries:

CT-WEARNES VIETNAM CO LTD (1)
Ground floor Interserco Trade Center 2 Ton That Thuyet, Hanoi, 0084, Vietnam
Tel.: (84) 4 3837 8888
Web Site: http://www.wearnesauto.com
Car Dealer
N.A.I.C.S.: 441110
Pham Dong *(Gen Mgr)*

WEARNES AUTOMOTIVE CHANGCHUN CO. LTD (1)
No 2088 Jingyue Street, Changchun, 130117, China
Tel.: (86) 431 8181 8111
Web Site: http://www.wearnesauto.com
Car Dealer
N.A.I.C.S.: 441110

Wearnes Automotive Sdn Bhd (1)
5 & 7 Jalan Dua Jalan Sungei Besi, 55200, Kuala Lumpur, Malaysia
Tel.: (60) 3 9236 2929
Web Site: http://www.wearnesauto.com
Motor Vehicles Sales & Servicing
N.A.I.C.S.: 441110
Basil Tan *(Country Mgr)*

Wearnes Automotive Services Pte. Ltd. (1)
249 Alexandra Rd, Singapore, 159935, Singapore
Tel.: (65) 64731488
Web Site: http://www.wearnesauto.com
Car Delarship; Auto Insurance Services
N.A.I.C.S.: 441110

Wearnes Motors (HK) Ltd (1)
GF OTB Building 160 Gloucester Road, Wanchai, China (Hong Kong)
Tel.: (852) 2927 3388
Web Site: http://www.wearnesauto.com
Automotive Distr
N.A.I.C.S.: 423110
Eric Tam *(Gen Mgr)*

WEATHERNEWS INC.

WEATHERHAVEN
8355 Riverbend Court, Burnaby, V3N 5E7, BC, Canada
Tel.: (604) 451-8900
Web Site:
http://www.weatherhaven.com
Year Founded: 1981
Rev.: $16,424,088
Emp.: 50
Portable Shelters Mfr
N.A.I.C.S.: 332311
Ray Castelli *(CEO)*

Subsidiaries:

Weatherhaven Australia Pty Ltd (1)
11 Bellevue Street, PO Box 1556, Nowra, 2541, NSW, Australia
Tel.: (61) 244220881
Web Site: http://www.weatherhaven.com.au
Prefabricated Metal Component Distr
N.A.I.C.S.: 423390

Weatherhaven Global Solutions Limited (1)
Oakley's Yard Gatehouse Road Rotherwas Industrial Estate, Hereford, HR2 6LR, United Kingdom
Tel.: (44) 1432373000
Web Site: http://www.weatherhaven.co.uk
Prefabricated Metal Component Distr
N.A.I.C.S.: 423390

Weatherhaven International Ltd. (1)
L'Horizon Gunsite Rd Brittons Hill, Saint Michael, 10000, Barbados
Tel.: (246) 2464373835
Prefabricated Metal Component Distr
N.A.I.C.S.: 423390

Weatherhaven Peru S.A. (1)
Cll Rivera Navarrete Ricardo 2507, Lince, Lima, Peru
Tel.: (51) 14227798
Prefabricated Metal Component Distr
N.A.I.C.S.: 423390
Alberto Moreno *(Mng Dir)*

Weatherhaven Resources Inc. (1)
8846 Wood Duck Way, Blaine, WA 98230
Tel.: (360) 746-8077
Prefabricated Metal Component Distr
N.A.I.C.S.: 423390

Weatherhaven do Brasil Ltda. (1)
Av Joao Paulo I 400 - Embu das Artes, Sao Paulo, Brazil
Tel.: (55) 11 4704 0696
Web Site: http://www.whdobrasil.com.br
Prefabricated Metal Component Distr
N.A.I.C.S.: 423390

WEATHERLY INTERNATIONAL PLC
Orion House Bessemer Road, Welwyn Garden City, AL7 1HH, United Kingdom
Tel.: (44) 1707 800774
Web Site:
http://www.weatherlyplc.com
Rev.: $75,082,000
Assets: $134,366,000
Liabilities: $144,460,000
Net Worth: ($10,094,000)
Earnings: ($40,069,000)
Emp.: 151
Fiscal Year-end: 06/30/17
Copper Ore Mining & Smelting
N.A.I.C.S.: 331410
Kevin Ellis *(CFO & Sec)*

Subsidiaries:

Weatherly Mining Namibia Limited (1)
PO Box 40798, Ausspannplatz, Windhoek, Namibia
Tel.: (264) 61385000
Web Site: http://www.weatherlyplc.com
Copper Mining Operations
N.A.I.C.S.: 212230
Craig Thomas *(Mng Dir)*

WEATHERNEWS INC.
Makuhari Techno Garden Nakase

WEATHERNEWS INC.

Weathernews Inc.—(Continued)
1-3, Mihama-ku, Chiba, 261-0023, Japan
Tel.: (81) 432745550
Web Site:
https://jp.weathernews.com
Year Founded: 1978
4825—(TKS)
Rev.: $147,019,620
Assets: $152,413,380
Liabilities: $21,614,700
Net Worth: $130,798,680
Earnings: $16,108,570
Emp.: 1,152
Fiscal Year-end: 05/31/24
Weather Forecasting Services
N.A.I.C.S.: 541990
Chihito Kusabiraki *(Pres & CEO)*

Subsidiaries:

Weathernews America Inc. **(1)**
350 David L Boren Blvd Ste 1000, Norman, OK 73072
Tel.: (405) 310-2800
Sales Range: $1-9.9 Million
Weather Broadcasting Services
N.A.I.C.S.: 541990

Weathernews Benelux B.V. **(1)**
Weteringpad 2, 3762 EN, Soest, Netherlands
Tel.: (31) 356039003
Emp.: 15
Weather Broadcasting Services
N.A.I.C.S.: 541990

Weathernews France SAS **(1)**
39-41 rue de la Chaussee d'Antin, 75009, Paris, France
Tel.: (33) 155078575
Web Site: https://en.weathernews.fr
Weather Risk Management & Weather Business Intelligence Solutions & Services
N.A.I.C.S.: 513210
Pascal Bouquet *(Sls Mgr)*

Weathernews Hong Kong Ltd. **(1)**
Unit B on the 6th Floor of China Insurance Building No 48 Cameron Road, Tsimshatsui, Kowloon, China (Hong Kong)
Tel.: (852) 25743232
Web Site: https://global.weathernews.com
Weather Broadcasting Services
N.A.I.C.S.: 541990

Weathernews Korea Inc. **(1)**
10F 76 Sangamsan-ro Sangam-dong YTN Newsquare, Mapo-gu, Seoul, 03926, Korea (South)
Tel.: (82) 234550500
Weather Broadcasting Services
N.A.I.C.S.: 541990

Weathernews Nepal Pvt. Ltd. **(1)**
Subidha Nagar Tinkune, PO Box 20419, Kathmandu, Nepal
Tel.: (977) 9851030640
Weather Broadcasting Services
N.A.I.C.S.: 541990

Weathernews Shanghai Ltd. **(1)**
Room A12/6F No 333 Oriental Viking building Xian Xia Road, Chang Ning District, Shanghai, 200336, China
Tel.: (86) 2162791105
Weather Broadcasting Services
N.A.I.C.S.: 541990

Weathernews Singapore Pte. Ltd. **(1)**
80 Anson Road 32-03 Fuji Xerox Towers, Singapore, Singapore
Tel.: (65) 62385538
Weather Broadcasting Services
N.A.I.C.S.: 541990

Weathernews Taiwan Ltd. **(1)**
14F-1 No 394 Sec 1 Keelung Rd, Xinyi Dist, Taipei, 11051, Taiwan
Tel.: (886) 227586361
Weather Broadcasting Services
N.A.I.C.S.: 541990

Weathernews U.K. Ltd **(1)**
210 Euston Road, London, NW1 2DA, United Kingdom
Tel.: (44) 7880527723

Web Site: https://www.weathernews.co.uk
Weather Broadcasting Services
N.A.I.C.S.: 541990

WEB ELEMENT SOLUTIONS LIMITED
301 Corporate Arena Aarey Piramal Cross Road West, Goregaon, Mumbai, 400062, India
Tel.: (91) 2267828282
Web Site:
http://www.webelementinc.com
780016—(BOM)
Rev.: $167,051
Assets: $869,122
Liabilities: $20,870
Net Worth: $848,253
Earnings: $3,355
Emp.: 13
Fiscal Year-end: 03/31/21
Information Technology Services
N.A.I.C.S.: 541511
Yadvender Kanwar *(Mng Dir)*

WEB MEDIA GROUP AD
20 Frederic Joliot Curie St, 1113, Sofia, Bulgaria
Tel.: (359) 7548300
Web Site: https://www.wmg.bg
WMG—(BUL)
Sales Range: Less than $1 Million
Media Advertising Services
N.A.I.C.S.: 541840

WEBAC HOLDING AG
Rosenheimer Strasse 12, 81669, Munich, 81669, Germany
Tel.: (49) 2251129128
Web Site: https://www.webac-ag.com
RKB—(DEU)
Rev.: $377,725
Assets: $3,680,121
Liabilities: $345,349
Net Worth: $3,334,772
Earnings: ($21,584)
Emp.: 1
Fiscal Year-end: 12/31/23
Holding Company
N.A.I.C.S.: 551112
John Gajland *(Chm-Supervisory Bd)*

WEBASTO SE
Kraillinger Strasse 5, Munich, 82131, Germany
Tel.: (49) 89857940   De
Web Site: http://www.webasto.com
Year Founded: 1901
Sales Range: $1-4.9 Billion
Emp.: 8,597
Mfr of Sun Roofs, Heaters & Air Conditioning Systems
N.A.I.C.S.: 336390
Holger Engelmann *(Chm-Mgmt Bd)*

Subsidiaries:

Hollandia Sunroofs de Mexico, S.A. de C.V. **(1)**
Av Cuauhtemoc 1146 Col Sta Cruz Atoyac, Benito Juarez DF, 03310, Mexico, Mexico **(100%)**
Tel.: (52) 5556010203
Web Site: http://www.hollandia.com.mx
Motor Vehicle Sunroof Mfr
N.A.I.C.S.: 336390

Vertriebsburo Webasto Product Benelux **(1)**
Constructieweg 47, 8263 BC, Kampen, Netherlands
Tel.: (31) 383371137
Automobile Parts Distr
N.A.I.C.S.: 423120

Webasto (Changchun) Ltd. **(1)**
No 1398 Fuao Road Automotive Industries Development Area, 130011, Changchun, China
Tel.: (86) 4314649768
Automobile Parts Distr
N.A.I.C.S.: 423120

Tony Chen *(Project Mgr)*

Webasto (Chongqing) Ltd. **(1)**
No 12 Lijie Road New North Zone, 401122, Chongqing, China
Tel.: (86) 2367880808
Automobile Parts Distr
N.A.I.C.S.: 423120
Derrick Yang *(Dir-Sls)*

Webasto (Shanghai) Ltd. **(1)**
No 33 Lane 466 Yindu Road, 201108, Shanghai, China
Tel.: (86) 2133577000
Automobile Parts Distr
N.A.I.C.S.: 423120
Michael Gorontzi *(Dir-Sls)*

Webasto AG - Global Comfort Solutions **(1)**
Friedrichshafenerstrasse 9, 82205, Gilching, Germany
Tel.: (49) 89 85794 0
Web Site: http://www.webasto.com
Motor Vehicle Heating, Cooling & Ventilation Systems Developer & Mfr
N.A.I.C.S.: 336390

Subsidiary (Non-US):

Webasto Product Australia Pty. Ltd. **(2)**
423-427 The Blvd, Kirrawee, 2232, NSW, Australia **(100%)**
Tel.: (61) 295404811
Web Site: http://www.webasto.com.au
Sales Range: $25-49.9 Million
Emp.: 20
Motor Vehicle Air Conditioning Systems Distr
N.A.I.C.S.: 423120
Christian Mahr *(Mng Dir)*

Subsidiary (US):

Webasto Product North America, Inc. **(2)**
15083 N Rd, Fenton, MI 48430
Tel.: (810) 593-6000
Web Site: http://www.webasto.us
Sales Range: $25-49.9 Million
Emp.: 60
Motor Vehicle Heating & Air Conditioning Systems Mfr
N.A.I.C.S.: 336390
Jeff Russel *(CEO)*

Webasto Donghee Auto Parts (Beijing) Co., Ltd **(1)**
NO 4 Xinggu Industrial Development Zone, Pinggu, 101200, Beijing, China
Tel.: (86) 1069958782
Automobile Parts Distr
N.A.I.C.S.: 423120

Webasto Donghee Co., Ltd. **(1)**
13-21 Sujan Ri Sinchang Myung, Chung-Nam, 336 884, Asan, Korea (South)
Tel.: (82) 415385200
Web Site: http://www.webasto.com
Motor Vehicle Sunroof Mfr
N.A.I.C.S.: 336390

Webasto Donghee Holdings Co., Ltd. **(1)**
6 Cheoyongsanup-Ro Onsan-Eup, Ulsan, Ulju, Korea (South) **(50%)**
Tel.: (82) 522594500
Automobile Parts Distr
N.A.I.C.S.: 423120

Webasto Donghee Slovakia s.r.o **(1)**
Snp 768/150, 1324, Strecno, Slovakia
Tel.: (421) 415079680
Automobile Parts Distr
N.A.I.C.S.: 423120

Webasto Fahrzeugtechnik GmbH **(1)**
Jochen Rindt Strasse 19, 1230, Vienna, Austria
Tel.: (43) 16043780
Automobile Parts Distr
N.A.I.C.S.: 423120

Webasto Guangzhou Co., Ltd. **(1)**
No 1 Tianyuan Road Yonghe Economic Zone Getdd, 511356, Guangzhou, China
Tel.: (86) 2032066383
Automobile Parts Distr
N.A.I.C.S.: 423120

INTERNATIONAL PUBLIC

Ralf Bohm *(Mgr-Quality-Bus)*

Webasto Japan Co. Ltd. **(1)**
5 10 Taguchi Research Complex, Higashi-ku, Hiroshima, 739-0038, Japan **(100%)**
Tel.: (81) 824253111
Web Site: http://www.webasto.co.jp
Sales Range: $100-124.9 Million
Emp.: 308
Motor Vehicle Sunroof & Convertible Systems Developer & Mfr
N.A.I.C.S.: 336390
Yuji Kobayashi *(Pres)*

Webasto Korea Inc. **(1)**
Indeogwon IT Valley Bldg B Suite 612 40 Imi-ro, 437-120, Uiwang, Gyeonggi, Korea (South)
Tel.: (82) 3180170241
Automobile Parts Distr
N.A.I.C.S.: 423120

Webasto Neubrandenburg GmbH **(1)**
Werner-Baier-Strasse 1, 17033, Neubrandenburg, Germany
Tel.: (49) 39555920
Automobile Body Parts Mfr
N.A.I.C.S.: 336370
Ingeborg Schumacher *(Plant Mgr-IT)*

Webasto Petemer SP. z.o.o. **(1)**
ul Warszawska 205/219, 05-092, Lomianki, Poland
Tel.: (48) 227327370
Automobile Parts Distr
N.A.I.C.S.: 423120
Jacek Pieterwas *(Pres & CEO)*

Webasto Romania SRL **(1)**
Platforma Industriala Werner Baier Nr 1 Zimandu Nou, 317425, Arad, Romania
Tel.: (40) 372827235
Automobile Parts Distr
N.A.I.C.S.: 423120
Ciprian Herte *(Mgr-IT)*

Webasto Romania Trading Srl **(1)**
Str Horia Closca si Crisan nr 61-63, 75100, Otopeni, Ilfov County, Romania
Tel.: (40) 213139678
Automobile Parts Distr
N.A.I.C.S.: 423120
Florin Tudor *(Mng Dir)*

Webasto Roof & Components Czech Republic s.r.o. **(1)**
Ceske mladeze 452 Liberec VIII-Dolni Hanychov, 460 08, Liberec, Czech Republic
Tel.: (420) 485229111
Automobile Parts Distr
N.A.I.C.S.: 423120

Webasto Roof Systems Brasil Ltda. **(1)**
R Dr Pedro de Toledo 7, Guararema, 08900-000, Sao Paulo, Brazil
Tel.: (55) 1146932305
Automobile Parts Distr
N.A.I.C.S.: 423120

Webasto Roof Systems Ltd. **(1)**
Unit 7 Kingsbury Business Park Kingsbury Road Minworth, Sutton Coldfield, B76 9DL, West Midlands, United Kingdom
Tel.: (44) 1213135600
Automobile Parts Distr
N.A.I.C.S.: 423120
Gregg Kempin *(Mgr-Quality)*

Webasto Roof Systems, Inc. **(1)**
1757 Northfield Dr, Rochester Hills, MI 48309 **(100%)**
Tel.: (248) 997-5100
Web Site: http://www.webasto.com
Sales Range: $200-249.9 Million
Emp.: 1,000
Structural Precast Concrete Products Mfr
N.A.I.C.S.: 327390

Webasto Roofsystems India Ltd. **(1)**
Sanaswadi Pune Nagar Highway Near Dawat Hotel Gat 838/1, 412 208, Pune, Maharashtra, India
Tel.: (91) 2137619900
Automobile Parts Distr
N.A.I.C.S.: 423120
Vikas Prasad *(VP)*

Webasto Rus OOO **(1)**

Altayskaya ulitsa 19-1a, 107065, Moscow, Russia
Tel.: (7) 4957770245
Automobile Parts Distr
N.A.I.C.S.: 423120
Roman Semenov *(Mgr-Bus Dev)*

Webasto S.p.A. (1)
Corso Asti 4-14, Venaria Reale, 10078, Turin, Italy
Tel.: (39) 0114244111
Emp.: 50
Automobile Parts Distr
N.A.I.C.S.: 423120
Giuseppe Barile *(Gen Mgr)*

Webasto Schierling GmbH (1)
Fruhaufstrasse 7, 84069, Regensburg, Germany
Tel.: (49) 9451200
Automobile Parts Mfr
N.A.I.C.S.: 336390

Webasto South Africa (Pty) Ltd. (1)
7 Venus Way Hillstar Industria, 7780, Cape Town, Wetton, South Africa
Tel.: (27) 217619971
Web Site: http://www.webasto.co.za
Emp.: 10
Motor Vehicle Air Conditioning System Mfr
N.A.I.C.S.: 336390
Jeremy Powell *(Mng Dir)*

Webasto Systemes Carrosserie S.A.S. (1)
Z I du Guittion, 85700, Les Chatelliers-Chateaumur, France
Tel.: (33) 251667158
Automobile Parts Distr
N.A.I.C.S.: 423120

Webasto Termo & Conforto Brasil LTDA (1)
Rua Santa Cruz 481 Barra Funda, Vinhedo, 13280-000, Sao Paulo, Brazil
Tel.: (55) 1933435900
Automobile Parts Distr
N.A.I.C.S.: 423120
Christian Fox *(Mng Dir)*

Webasto Thermo & Comfort (Beijing) Co. Ltd. (1)
A2103 Tower 2 Boya International Center 1 Lize Zhongyi Road, Chaoyang, 100102, Beijing, China
Tel.: (86) 1084782320
Automobile Parts Distr
N.A.I.C.S.: 423120
Chong Li *(Mgr-PR)*

Webasto Thermo & Comfort Australia Pty. Ltd. (1)
423-427 The Boulevarde, Kirrawee, 2232, NSW, Australia
Tel.: (61) 285364800
Automobile Parts Distr
N.A.I.C.S.: 423120
Anand Ganatra *(Dir-Fin)*

Webasto Thermo & Comfort Czech Republic s.r.o. (1)
Na Strzi 1373, 140 00, Prague, Czech Republic
Tel.: (420) 2410454507
Automobile Parts Distr
N.A.I.C.S.: 423120

Webasto Thermo & Comfort Denmark A/S (1)
Islevdalvej 180, 2610, Rodovre, Denmark
Tel.: (45) 44522000
Automobile Parts Distr
N.A.I.C.S.: 423120
Hasse Melms *(Area Mgr-Sls)*

Webasto Thermo & Comfort France S.A.S. (1)
Rue du Camp d'Aviation, 44320, Saint-Viaud, France
Tel.: (33) 240218550
Automobile Parts Distr
N.A.I.C.S.: 423120

Webasto Thermo & Comfort Hungaria S.R.L. (1)
Szent Lazlo ut 73, 1135, Budapest, Hungary
Tel.: (36) 13502338
Automobile Parts Distr
N.A.I.C.S.: 423120

Webasto Thermo & Comfort Iberica SLU (1)
C/Mar Tirreno 33, San Fernando de Henares, 28830, Madrid, Spain
Tel.: (34) 916268611
Automobile Parts Distr
N.A.I.C.S.: 423120

Webasto Thermo & Comfort Italy S.r.l. (1)
Via Nobili 2, Molinella, 40062, Bologna, Italy
Tel.: (39) 0516906111
Automobile Parts Distr
N.A.I.C.S.: 423120
maurizio pistis *(Project Mgr)*

Webasto Thermo & Comfort Japan Co., Ltd. (1)
3-19-5 Shin-Yokohama, Yokohama, 222-0033, Kanagawa, Japan
Tel.: (81) 454741761
Automobile Parts Distr
N.A.I.C.S.: 423120
Yutaka Usami *(Mgr-Technical Grp)*

Webasto Thermo & Comfort Schweiz AG (1)
Hagmattstrasse 4, 4123, Allschwil, Basel-Landschaft, Switzerland
Tel.: (41) 614869580
Automobile Parts Distr
N.A.I.C.S.: 423120

Webasto Thermo & Comfort Slovakia s.r.o. (1)
Galgovecka ulica 3, 040 11, Kosice, Slovakia
Tel.: (421) 557871000
Automobile Parts Distr
N.A.I.C.S.: 423120
Silvia Brndiarova *(Mgr-Sls)*

Webasto Thermo & Comfort UK Ltd. (1)
Webasto House White Rose Way Doncaster Carr, Doncaster, DN4 5JH, Yorkshire, United Kingdom
Tel.: (44) 1302322232
Emp.: 50
Automobile Parts Distr
N.A.I.C.S.: 423120
Jonathan Reader *(Project Mgr-Engrg)*

Webasto Thermo & Comfort Ukraina TzoW (1)
Chervonoprapornastr 135, 3083, Kiev, Ukraine
Tel.: (380) 445930840
Emp.: 10
Automobile Parts Distr
N.A.I.C.S.: 423120
Mariia Myroshnichenko *(Mgr-Mktg)*

Webasto Thermo & Comfort, avtomobilska tehnika d.o.o. (1)
Cesta v Gorice 34, 1000, Ljubljana, Slovenia
Tel.: (386) 12008712
Automobile Parts Distr
N.A.I.C.S.: 423120

Webasto Thermo Comfort Iklimlendirme Sistemleri Tic. Ltd. Sti. (1)
Manisa Organize Sanayi Bolgesi IV Kisim Ahmet Nazif Zorlu Bulvari No 8, 45000, Manisa, Turkiye
Tel.: (90) 236226900080
Automobile Parts Distr
N.A.I.C.S.: 423120

Webasto Utting GmbH (1)
Industriestrasse 12, 86919, Utting, Germany
Tel.: (49) 8806710
Automobile Parts Mfr
N.A.I.C.S.: 336390

Webasto Xiangyang Co., Ltd (1)
Jinfeng Road Hi-tech Industrial Development Zone, 441000, Xiangyang, Hubei, China
Tel.: (86) 266618517
Automobile Parts Distr
N.A.I.C.S.: 423120

Webasto-Edscha Cabrio GmbH (1)
Scharwaechter Strasse 5, 94491, Hengersberg, Germany
Tel.: (49) 9901 2002 0

Web Site: http://www.webasto.com
Sales Range: $450-499.9 Million
Emp.: 1,350
Motor Vehicle Convertible Roof Systems Mfr
N.A.I.C.S.: 336390
Axel Schulmeyer *(Chm-Mgmt Bd)*

Subsidiary (US):

Webasto-Edscha Cabrio USA Inc. (2)
14967 Pilot Dr, Plymouth, MI 48170 (100%)
Tel.: (734) 582-5900
Web Site: http://www.webasto.us
Sales Range: $25-49.9 Million
Emp.: 150
Motor Vehicle Convertible Roof Systems Mfr
N.A.I.C.S.: 336390
Mark Denny *(CEO)*

Subsidiary (Non-US):

Webasto-Edscha Cabrio Mexico, S.A. de C.V. (3)
Rio San Bernardo 408, 72730, Puebla, Mexico (100%)
Tel.: (52) 2222737500
Web Site: http://www.webasto.com
Sales Range: $50-74.9 Million
Emp.: 200
Motor Vehicle Convertible Roof Systems Mfr
N.A.I.C.S.: 336390
Carlos Gonzalez *(Gen Dir)*

Webasto-Edscha Cabrio Slovakia s.r.o. (1)
Taborska 66/1684, 93201, Velky Meder, Slovakia
Tel.: (421) 315901111
Automobile Parts Distr
N.A.I.C.S.: 423120
Ladislav Fekete *(Mgr-IT)*

WEBB'S FORD LTD
4802 50 Street, Vermilion, T9X 1M3, AB, Canada
Tel.: (780) 853-2841
Web Site: http://www.webbsford.com
Rev.: $13,911,192
Emp.: 50
New & Used Car Dealers
N.A.I.C.S.: 441110
Darcy Fadden *(Mgr-Sls)*

WEBCASH CORP.
20th floor KnK Digital Tower 220 Yeongsin-ro, Yeongdeungpo-gu, Seoul, 07228, Korea (South)
Tel.: (82) 27841690
Web Site: https://www.webcash.co.kr
Year Founded: 1999
053580—(KRS)
Rev.: $67,393,623
Assets: $98,876,278
Liabilities: $19,853,767
Net Worth: $79,022,511
Earnings: $8,846,581
Emp.: 267
Fiscal Year-end: 12/31/22
Electronic Finance Services
N.A.I.C.S.: 522320
Gangwon Province *(CEO)*

WEBCREW INC.
Sun Towers Center Bldg 4F 2-11-22 Sangenjaya, Setagaya-ku, Tokyo, 154-0024, Japan
Tel.: (81) 368593660 JP
Web Site: http://www.webcrew.co.jp
Year Founded: 1999
Emp.: 1,462
Website Operations Providing Insurance & Credit Related Information Services
N.A.I.C.S.: 519290
Yoshitaka Fujishima *(Pres & CEO)*

Subsidiaries:

Agasta Co., Ltd. (1)
2F Premier Dogenzaka Bldg 1-18-3 Dogenzaka, Shibuya-ku, Tokyo, 150-0043, Japan
Tel.: (81) 3 4330 9090
Web Site: http://www.agasta.co.jp
Emp.: 25
Used Car Sales & Online Retailer
N.A.I.C.S.: 441120
Michiyo Watanabe *(CEO)*

HOKENMINAOSHIHONPO Co., Ltd. (1)
6F Shibuya Infosutawa 20-1 Sakuragaokacho, Tokyo, 150-0031, Japan
Tel.: (81) 334613704
Insurance Services
N.A.I.C.S.: 524210

WEBER INDUSTRIES SAS
12 Rue de la Boisellerie, 67580, Mertzwiller, France
Tel.: (33) 3 88 90 31 07
Web Site: http://www.weber-industries.com
Year Founded: 1922
Sales Range: $100-124.9 Million
Emp.: 700
Furniture Mfr
N.A.I.C.S.: 337122

Subsidiaries:

We Bed SAS (1)
ZAC Porte de Masevaux, 68290, Masevaux, France
Tel.: (33) 3 89 38 60 46
Web Site: http://www.we-bed.com
Sales Range: $10-24.9 Million
Emp.: 35
Slatted Bed Frame Designer, Mfr & Distr
N.A.I.C.S.: 337126

WEBER INVESTISSEMENTS SAS
21 rue Weber, 75016, Paris, France
Tel.: (33) 153645260
Emp.: 4
Financial Investment
N.A.I.C.S.: 523999
Christian Gueugnier *(CEO)*

WEBER MOTORS LTD.
5611 104 Street, Edmonton, T6H 2K2, AB, Canada
Tel.: (780) 431-5100
Web Site: http://www.webermotorsltd.com
Rev.: $18,519,274
Emp.: 40
New & Used Car Dealers
N.A.I.C.S.: 441110
Gordie Gerbrandt *(Gen Mgr)*

WEBER SHANDWICK-FCC
Hambleden House 19-26 Lower Pembroke Street, Dublin, Ireland
Tel.: (353) 676 0168
Web Site: http://www.webershandwick.co.uk
Year Founded: 1989
Sales Range: $25-49.9 Million
Emp.: 13
Public Relations
N.A.I.C.S.: 541820
Siobhan Molloy *(Mng Dir)*

WEBER-HYDRAULIK GMBH
Heilbronner Strasse 30, 74363, Guglingen, Germany
Tel.: (49) 7135 71 0 De
Web Site: http://www.weber-hydraulik.com
Year Founded: 1939
Sales Range: $300-349.9 Million
Emp.: 2,060
Hydraulic Equipment & Components Mfr
N.A.I.C.S.: 333995

WEBER-HYDRAULIK GMBH

Weber-Hydraulik GmbH—(Continued)
Christine Grotz *(Mng Dir & Partner)*

Subsidiaries:

Log Aggregatebau GmbH (1)
Lippenstrasse 41, Unterahrain, 84051, Landshut, Germany
Tel.: (49) 870393110
Steering & Suspension System Mfr
N.A.I.C.S.: 336330

Log Hydraulik GmbH (1)
Siemensstrasse 17, Worth an der Isar, 84109, Landshut, Germany
Tel.: (49) 870393110
Steering & Suspension System Mfr
N.A.I.C.S.: 336330

Weber-Hydraulik GmbH (1)
Emil Weber Platz 1, Losenstein, 4460, Steyr, Austria
Tel.: (43) 725562370
Steering & Suspension System Mfr
N.A.I.C.S.: 336330

Weber-Hydraulik V.S.E (1)
Ravelijn 2, 3905 NV, Veenendaal, Netherlands
Tel.: (31) 318545744
Steering & Suspension System Mfr
N.A.I.C.S.: 336330

Weber-Hydraulik Valvetech GmbH (1)
Felix-Wankel-Strasse 4, 78467, Konstanz, Germany
Tel.: (49) 753197480
Steering & Suspension System Mfr
N.A.I.C.S.: 336330

Weber-Hydraulika Sp. Z O.O. (1)
Ul Wyzwolenia 52, 59-730, Wykroty, Poland
Tel.: (48) 757349708
Steering & Suspension System Mfr
N.A.I.C.S.: 336330

WEBER-INGENIEURE GMBH

Bauschlotter Strasse 62, 75177, Pforzheim, Germany
Tel.: (49) 72315830
Web Site: http://www.weber-ing.de
Year Founded: 1959
Rev.: $15,035,460
Emp.: 100
Waste Water Management Services
N.A.I.C.S.: 562998
Jan Weber *(Mng Dir)*

Subsidiaries:

AGWE Lda. (1)
Rua de Santa Catarina 781 2, 400-454, Porto, Portugal
Tel.: (351) 220998237
Web Site: http://www.agwe.eu
Waste Water Treatment Services
N.A.I.C.S.: 221320

Weber Romania S.R.L (1)
Str Romanitei No 15, 300523, Timisoara, Romania
Tel.: (40) 256455090
Web Site: http://www.weber.romania.ro
Engineering Services
N.A.I.C.S.: 541330

WEBINSTORE AG

Wegedornstr. 36, 12524, Berlin, Germany
Tel.: (49) 30 76 76 70 0
Web Site: http://www.webinstore.de
IT Hardware Repair & Other Services
N.A.I.C.S.: 811210
Jan Hoschel *(CEO)*

WEBIS HOLDINGS PLC

Viking House Nelson Street, Douglas, IM1 2AH, Isle of Man
Tel.: (44) 1624652594   IM
Web Site: https://www.webisholdingsplc.com
Year Founded: 1998
WEB—(AIM)
Rev.: $50,020,000
Assets: $6,326,000
Liabilities: $5,753,000
Net Worth: $573,000
Earnings: ($745,000)
Emp.: 50
Fiscal Year-end: 05/31/23
E-Commerce Leisure Betting Services
N.A.I.C.S.: 713290
Ed Comins *(Mng Dir)*

Subsidiaries:

betinternet.com (IOM) Limited (1)
Viking House Nelson St, Douglas, IM1 2AH, Isle of Man
Tel.: (44) 1624698141
Web Site: http://www.betinternet.com
Online Sport Betting Services
N.A.I.C.S.: 561422

WEBJET LIMITED

Level 2 509 St Kilda Road, Melbourne, 3004, VIC, Australia
Tel.: (61) 398289500   AU
Web Site: https://www.webjet.com.au
Year Founded: 1998
WEB—(ASX)
Rev.: $29,498,315
Assets: $904,104,200
Liabilities: $438,950,251
Net Worth: $465,153,949
Earnings: ($119,985,354)
Fiscal Year-end: 03/31/21
Travel Related Services
N.A.I.C.S.: 561510
John Guscic *(Mng Dir)*

Subsidiaries:

FitRuums Pte Ltd (1)
1 Maritime Square 11-05 HarbourFront Centre, Singapore, 099253, Singapore
Tel.: (65) 69142000
Hotel Booking Services
N.A.I.C.S.: 561599

Search Republic Limited (1)
Level 7 Spark City 167 Victoria Street West, Auckland, 1010, New Zealand
Tel.: (64) 99502633
Online Travel Booking Services
N.A.I.C.S.: 561599
Megan Hiew *(Mgr-Search Engine Optimization)*

SunHotels Ltd. (1)
8 Holmes Road, London, NW5 3AB, United Kingdom
Tel.: (44) 2030965221
Web Site: https://www.sunhotels.com
Hotel Booking Services
N.A.I.C.S.: 561599

Umrah Holidays International FZ LLC (1)
Shatha Tower 32nd Floor Suites 3210-3212, PO Box 502115, Dubai, United Arab Emirates
Tel.: (971) 44400600
Web Site: https://www.uhitravel.com
Religious Travel Services
N.A.I.C.S.: 561510

Webjet Marketing Pty Ltd (1)
509 St Kilda Road, Melbourne, 3004, VIC, Australia
Tel.: (61) 398209214
Travel Agencies
N.A.I.C.S.: 561510

Webjet Operations Pty Ltd (1)
L 9 492 St Kilda Rd, Melbourne, 3004, VIC, Australia
Tel.: (61) 398209214
Travel Agencies
N.A.I.C.S.: 561510

WEBORAMA SA

15 rue Clavel, 75019, Paris, France
Tel.: (33) 1 53 19 21 40
Web Site: http://www.weborama.com
Year Founded: 1998
Rev.: $36,904,384
Earnings: ($1,127,777)
Emp.: 275
Fiscal Year-end: 12/31/18
Online Advertising Services
N.A.I.C.S.: 541810

Subsidiaries:

Weborama Iberica SL (1)
C/ Manuel Tovar 25-4, 28034, Madrid, Spain
Tel.: (34) 91 523 33 30
Online Advertising Services
N.A.I.C.S.: 541810
Abelardo Ibanez *(Mng Dir)*

Weborama Italia srl (1)
Via Atto Vannucci 13, 20135, Milan, Italy
Tel.: (39) 02 36 60 11 00
Web Site: http://www.weboramaitalia.it
Online Advertising Services
N.A.I.C.S.: 541810
Vivian Ceresero *(Head-Client Svcs)*

Weborama Nederland B.V. (1)
Keizersgracht 256, Amsterdam, 1016 EV, Netherlands
Tel.: (31) 20 524 66 90
Web Site: http://www.weborama.nl
Emp.: 22
Online Advertising Services
N.A.I.C.S.: 541810
Nomkwazi Hooplot *(Mng Dir)*

Weborama Portugal (1)
Rua do Cardal de Sao Jose 61, 1150-089, Lisbon, Portugal
Tel.: (351) 218 239 647
Online Advertising Services
N.A.I.C.S.: 541810

Weborama Russia (1)
Kalanchevskaya St 16 Kalanchevskaya Plaza, 129090, Moscow, Russia
Tel.: (7) 495 784 7740
Online Advertising Services
N.A.I.C.S.: 541810
Angela Fedorchenko *(Mng Dir)*

Weborama UK Ltd. (1)
77 Oxford Street, London, W1D 2ES, United Kingdom
Tel.: (44) 207 025 8160
Online Advertising Services
N.A.I.C.S.: 541810

WEBSOL ENERGY SYSTEM LIMITED

Sector II Falta Special Economic Zone Falta, South 24 Pargana, Kolkata, 743504, West Bengal, India
Tel.: (91) 3174222932
Web Site: https://www.webelsolar.com
517498—(BOM)
Rev.: $2,425,910
Assets: $32,021,294
Liabilities: $9,087,453
Net Worth: $22,933,841
Earnings: ($2,839,866)
Emp.: 225
Fiscal Year-end: 03/31/23
Solar Photovoltaic Cells Mfr
N.A.I.C.S.: 334413
Sohan Lal Agarwal *(CEO & Mng Dir)*

WEBSOLUS CO., LTD.

1201 Byoksan 3 Cha Digital Valley Guro 3-dong, Guro-gu, Seoul, Korea (South)
Tel.: (82) 2 6917 0700
Web Site: http://www.websolus.co.kr
Year Founded: 2001
Emp.: 100
Water Resource Engineering & Water Supply Management Software
N.A.I.C.S.: 513210
Hongsik Kim *(Pres)*

WEBSOLUTE SPA

Strada Della Campanara 15, 61122, Pesaro, Italy
Tel.: (39) 0721411112
Web Site: https://www.websolute.com
WEB—(ITA)
Sales Range: Less than $1 Million
Digital Marketing Services
N.A.I.C.S.: 541613
Lamberto Mattioli *(Chm & CEO)*

WEBUY GLOBAL LTD.

35 Tampines Street 92, Singapore, 528880, Singapore
Tel.: (65) 88599762   Ky
Web Site: https://www.webuysg.com
Year Founded: 2022
WBUY—(NASDAQ)
Rev.: $61,686,170
Assets: $30,233,191
Liabilities: $24,577,464
Net Worth: $5,655,727
Earnings: ($5,162,454)
Emp.: 218
Fiscal Year-end: 12/31/23
Online Shopping Services
N.A.I.C.S.: 425120

WEBZEN, INC.

242 Pangyo-ro, Bundang-gu, Seongnam, 463-400, Gyeonggi-do, Korea (South)
Tel.: (82) 316276600   KR
Web Site: https://www.webzen.com
Year Founded: 2000
069080—(KRS)
Rev.: $185,721,564
Assets: $496,147,297
Liabilities: $55,613,402
Net Worth: $440,533,896
Earnings: $55,525,259
Emp.: 493
Fiscal Year-end: 12/31/22
Online Games Developer & Distr
N.A.I.C.S.: 513210
Kim Nanhui *(Dir-Div)*

Subsidiaries:

Webzen Taiwan Inc. (1)
7F-3 176 Cheng Yi Road, Chungho City, Taipei, 235, Taiwan   (100%)
Tel.: (886) 282272880
Web Site: http://company.webzen.com
Online Game Developer
N.A.I.C.S.: 513210

WECOMMERCE HOLDINGS LTD

250 Howe Street Suite 2000 20th Floor, Vancouver, V6C 3S7, BC, Canada
Tel.: (416) 863-4384   Ca
Web Site: https://www.wecommerce.co
Year Founded: 2019
TNYZF—(OTCIQ)
Holding Company
N.A.I.C.S.: 551112
Alex Persson *(CEO)*

WECON HOLDINGS LTD.

18/F Tung Hip Commercial Building Des Voeux Road, Central, 244-252, China (Hong Kong)
Tel.: (852) 25298308
Web Site: http://www.wecon.com.hk
1793—(HKG)
Rev.: $110,801,580
Assets: $57,977,183
Liabilities: $22,041,818
Net Worth: $35,935,365
Earnings: $758,243
Emp.: 226
Fiscal Year-end: 03/31/23
Construction Services
N.A.I.C.S.: 236220
Ka Yip Tsang *(Chm)*

Subsidiaries:

Wecon Limited (1)
18/F Tung Hip Commercial Building 244-252 Des Voeux Road, Central, China (Hong Kong)

AND PRIVATE COMPANIES — WEG S.A.

Tel.: (852) 25298308
Web Site: https://www.wecon.com.hk
Building Construction Services
N.A.I.C.S.: 236210

WECONNECT SA
3 Avenue Hoche, 75008, Paris, France
Tel.: (33) 156696180
Web Site: http://www.connect-we.fr
ALWEC—(EUR)
Sales Range: $250-299.9 Million
Computer Peripheral Equipment Mfr & Distr
N.A.I.C.S.: 334118
Moshey Gorsd (Chm & CEO)

WEDGE INDUSTRIAL CO., LTD.
8th Floor Building B Guangming Building No 23 Zhuchi Road, Shantou, 515041, Guangdong, China
Tel.: (86) 75583241679
Web Site: https://www.wedgeind.com
Year Founded: 1992
000534—(SSE)
Rev.: $111,455,557
Assets: $341,846,608
Liabilities: $167,725,252
Net Worth: $174,121,356
Earnings: $14,281,362
Fiscal Year-end: 12/31/22
Real Estate Development Services
N.A.I.C.S.: 531311
Tianxiao Bi (Gen Mgr, Deputy Gen Mgr & Dir)

WEDIA S.A.
Tel.: (33) 144648760 FR
Web Site: http://www.wedia-group.com
Year Founded: 2001
ALWED—(EUR)
Sales Range: $10-24.9 Million
Emp.: 50
Software Publisher
N.A.I.C.S.: 513210
Nicolas Boutet (Co-Founder, Chm & Pres)

WEDS CO., LTD.
1-6-8 WiRA Omori Bld 6F Omorikita, Ota-ku, Tokyo, 143-0016, Japan
Tel.: (81) 357538216
Web Site: https://www.weds.co.jp
Year Founded: 1965
7551—(TKS)
Rev.: $229,902,410
Assets: $164,985,600
Liabilities: $47,770,470
Net Worth: $117,215,130
Earnings: $9,954,660
Fiscal Year-end: 03/31/24
Automobile Parts Mfr
N.A.I.C.S.: 336390

Subsidiaries:

Autotechnik Tuning Pty. Ltd. (1)
Unit 11 / 10 Anderson St, Banksmeadow, 2019, NSW, Australia
Tel.: (61) 293166500
Web Site: https://www.autotechnik.com.au
Automotive Parts & Accessory Distr
N.A.I.C.S.: 811121

Bigeyes Auto Parts Co., Ltd. (1)
No 327 Huide St, Nantun District, Taichung, 408, Taiwan
Tel.: (886) 934257735
Automotive Parts & Accessory Distr
N.A.I.C.S.: 811121

Driven Asia-Pacific Pte. Ltd. (1)
42 Kallang Place, Singapore, 339170, Singapore
Tel.: (65) 67444484
Web Site: https://www.driven.com.sg
Vehicle Component Mfr & Distr
N.A.I.C.S.: 336992

Eleven (Langfang) Auto Accessories Co., Ltd. (1)
No 119 Furao Road Longhe Economic Development Zone Langfang, Anci District, Langfang, China
Tel.: (86) 3165176366
Automotive Parts & Accessory Distr
N.A.I.C.S.: 811121

Footwork International, Inc. (1)
22138 S Vermont Ave Unit-C, Torrance, CA 90502
Tel.: (310) 787-9720
Web Site: https://www.wedswheelsna.com
Automotive Parts & Accessory Distr
N.A.I.C.S.: 811121

Hanshin-Imports Sarl LLC (1)
Chemin Du Geffry 9, 1073, Savigny, Switzerland
Tel.: (41) 217845050
Web Site: https://hanshin-imports.ch
Automotive Wheel Mfr & Distr
N.A.I.C.S.: 336390

JP MATERIAL CHINA Shanghai Peak International Trade Co., Ltd. (1)
No 99 4205 Lane Jinsan Avenue, Jinshan District, Shanghai, China
Tel.: (86) 2157260855
Automotive Parts & Accessory Distr
N.A.I.C.S.: 811121

N Sports Co., Ltd. (1)
568 Soi Pradiphat5 Rama 6 Road Sansen-Nai, Phayathai, Bangkok, 10400, Thailand
Tel.: (66) 876667777
Web Site: https://www.nsports-online.com
Automotive Parts & Accessory Distr
N.A.I.C.S.: 811121

Prosport Auto Ltd. (1)
PO Box 298, Pukekohe, Auckland, NZ 2120, New Zealand
Tel.: (64) 92383560
Web Site: https://www.prosportauto.co.nz
Automotive Parts & Accessory Distr
N.A.I.C.S.: 811121

Tegiwa Imports Ltd. (1)
Tegiwa House Sutherland Road, Stoke-on-Trent, ST3 1HZ, United Kingdom
Tel.: (44) 1782334440
Web Site: https://www.tegiwaimports.com
Automotive Wheel Mfr & Distr
N.A.I.C.S.: 336390

WEE HUR HOLDINGS LTD.
39 Kim Keat Road Wee Hur Building, Singapore, 328814, Singapore
Tel.: (65) 62581002
Web Site: https://www.weehur.com.sg
E3B—(SES)
Rev.: $170,296,145
Assets: $737,540,710
Liabilities: $261,251,988
Net Worth: $476,288,722
Earnings: $121,364,841
Emp.: 208
Fiscal Year-end: 12/31/23
Property Development & Management Services
N.A.I.C.S.: 531311
Ching Chek Tan (Co-Sec)

Subsidiaries:

Wee Hur (Woodlands 12) Pte. Ltd. (1)
39 Woodlands Close, Singapore, 737856, Singapore
Tel.: (65) 81188882
Property Development Services
N.A.I.C.S.: 531210

Y Suites Australia Pty. Ltd. (1)
128 Waymouth Street, Adelaide, SA, Australia
Tel.: (61) 391210405
Web Site: https://www.ysuites.co
Student Accommodation Services
N.A.I.C.S.: 721310

WEEBIT NANO LIMITED
Level 7 330 Collins Street, Melbourne, 3000, VIC, Australia
Tel.: (61) 386899997 AU
Web Site: https://www.weebit-nano.com
Year Founded: 2015
WBT—(ASX)
Assets: $17,016,725
Liabilities: $799,122
Net Worth: $16,217,603
Earnings: ($8,626,717)
Fiscal Year-end: 06/30/21
Data Storage Technology
N.A.I.C.S.: 334112
Yoav Nissan-Cohen (Exec Dir)

Subsidiaries:

Weebit Nano Ltd. (1)
24 Hanagar St, Hod Hasharon, 4527713, Israel
Tel.: (972) 97797832
Memory Storage Device Mfr
N.A.I.C.S.: 334112

Weebit Nano SARL (1)
7 parvis Louis Neel, CS 20050, 38040, Grenoble, Cedex 9, France
Tel.: (33) 781542168
Memory Storage Device Mfr
N.A.I.C.S.: 334112

WEEKEND UNLIMITED
1055 Dunsmuir Street Suite 734, Vancouver, V7X 1B1, BC, Canada
Tel.: (236) 317-2812
Web Site: http://www.weekendunlimited.com
0OS2—(BER)
Health Care Products Mfr
N.A.I.C.S.: 325411

WEFORMA DAMPFUNGSTECHNIK GMBH
Werther Str 44, Stolberg, 52224, Germany
Tel.: (49) 240298920
Web Site: http://www.weforma.com
Year Founded: 1980
Rev.: $15,173,400
Emp.: 120
Hydraulic Components Mfr
N.A.I.C.S.: 332911
Armin Schmidt (Co-Mng Dir)

Subsidiaries:

Weforma Dampfungstechnik GmbH (1)
Fischauergasse 148/2, 2700, Wiener Neustadt, Austria
Tel.: (43) 2622882330
Automotive Spare Parts Distr
N.A.I.C.S.: 423120
Franz Geyer (Mgr-Sls)

Weforma Dampfungstechnik S.A.R.L. (1)
Parc d'Activites Le Moulin Basset 12 Chemin du Moulin Basset Bat 3, 93200, Saint Denis, France
Tel.: (33) 142350121
Automotive Spare Parts Distr
N.A.I.C.S.: 423120

Weforma Dampfungstechnik S.r.l. (1)
Via Roma 55, 35027, Noventa Padovana, Italy
Tel.: (39) 0498936194
Automotive Spare Parts Distr
N.A.I.C.S.: 423120
Pierguido Crestanello (Mgr-Sls)

WEG S.A.
Av Pref Waldemar Grubba 3300, Jaragua do Sul, 89256-900, SC, Brazil
Tel.: (55) 4732764000 BR
Web Site: https://www.weg.net
Year Founded: 1961
WEGE3—(BRAZ)
Rev.: $6,481,922,624
Assets: $6,281,038,987
Liabilities: $2,720,409,612
Net Worth: $3,560,629,375
Earnings: $1,170,129,624
Emp.: 40,793
Fiscal Year-end: 12/31/23
Automobile Parts Mfr & Distr
N.A.I.C.S.: 336110
Nildemar Secches (Vice Chm)

Subsidiaries:

Antriebstechnik Katt Hessen GmbH (1)
Bahnhofstrasse 66, 34576, Homberg (Ohm), Germany
Tel.: (49) 568199520
Web Site: http://www.akh-antriebstechnik.de
Electric Motor Mfr
N.A.I.C.S.: 335312

Autrial S.L. (1)
P I Fuente del Jarro Villa de Madrid 69, 46988, Paterna, Valencia, Spain
Tel.: (34) 961379296
Web Site: https://www.autrial.es
Electrical Panel Mfr
N.A.I.C.S.: 335313
Enrique Rubio Carpio (Pres)

Birmind Automacao e Servicos S.A. (1)
Av Rudolf Dafferner 400 Edificio Roma Sala 308, Sorocaba Boa Vista, Sao Paulo, 18085-005, Brazil
Tel.: (55) 1532285448
Web Site: https://www.birmind.com.br
Software Program Development Services
N.A.I.C.S.: 541714

Bluffton Motor Works (1)
410 E Spring St, Bluffton, IN 46714-6714
Web Site: http://www.blmworks.com
Engineeering Services
N.A.I.C.S.: 541330
David Shearer (Mgr-HR)

Electric Machinery Company LLC (1)
800 Central Ave NE, Minneapolis, MN 55413
Tel.: (612) 378-8000
Web Site: http://www.electricmachinery.com
Electric Equipment Mfr
N.A.I.C.S.: 335312
Kimberly Ripley Hunt (Project Mgr)

Hidraulica Indl. S.A. Ind. e Com (1)
Rua Luiz Specht 75 Centro, Joacaba, 89600-000, Santa Catarina, Brazil
Tel.: (55) 49 3551 9200
Web Site: http://www.hisa.com.br
Turbine Mfr
N.A.I.C.S.: 333611

Instrutech Ltda (1)
Rua Maratona 61 - Vila Alexandria, Sao Paulo, 04635-040, Brazil
Tel.: (55) 11 5031 5188
Web Site: http://www.instrutech.com.br
Electronic Sensor Mfr
N.A.I.C.S.: 334511

Mvisia Desenv. Inovadores S.A. (1)
Villa Lobos Office Park Avenida Queiroz Filho, 1700 - Torre C sala 704 Vila Hamburguesa, Sao Paulo, 05319-000, Brazil
Tel.: (55) 1143025902
Web Site: https://mvisia.com.br
Software Development Services
N.A.I.C.S.: 541511

Ppi Multitask Sistemas E Automacao S.A (1)
Rua Vila Madalena 300, Vila Madalena, Sao Paulo, Brazil
Tel.: (55) 1130973100
Web Site: http://www.ppi-multitask.com.br
Industrial Software Development Services
N.A.I.C.S.: 541511
C. Vinicius Buonamici (Dir-Sls & Svcs)

Siei Areg GmbH (1)
Gottlieb-Daimler-Strasse 17/3, 74385, Pleidelsheim, Germany
Tel.: (49) 7144897360
Web Site: http://www.sieiareg.de
Mechanical Power Transmission Equipment Mfr
N.A.I.C.S.: 333613

WEG S.A.

WEG S.A.—(Continued)

V2Com Participacoes S.A. (1)
Sao Gualter Avenue 1741, Alto de Pinheiros, Sao Paulo, 05455-002, Brazil
Tel.: (55) 1130313322
Web Site: http://www.v2com.com
Information Technology Services
N.A.I.C.S.: 541519

Voltran S.A. de C.V. (1)
Sur 2 11, Zona Industrial, 43804, Tizayuca, Hidalgo, Mexico
Tel.: (52) 5553509338
Web Site: http://www.voltran.com.mx
Electrical Engineering Services
N.A.I.C.S.: 541330

WEG Australia Pty Ltd (1)
14 Lakeview Drive, Scoresby, 3179, VIC, Australia
Tel.: (61) 397654600
Web Site: http://www.weg.net
Sales Range: $25-49.9 Million
Electric Motor Mfr
N.A.I.C.S.: 335312

WEG Benelux S.A (1)
Rue de l Industrie 30 D, 1400, Nivelles, Walloon Brabant, Belgium
Tel.: (32) 67888420
Web Site: http://www.weg.net
Sales Range: $25-49.9 Million
Electric Motor Mfr
N.A.I.C.S.: 335312

WEG Chile S.A (1)
Calle Salar de Llamara N 808 - 810 Lote A2-3 Proyecto Dona, Hortensia Nieto II Macro Lote B ENEA - Comuna Pudahuel, Santiago, 8320000, Chile
Tel.: (56) 227848900
Web Site: http://www.weg.net
Electric Motor Mfr
N.A.I.C.S.: 335312

WEG Colombia SAS (1)
Km 2 via Siberia - Tenjo Terminales Logisticos de Colombia, Manzana 2 Tenjo, Bogota, Colombia
Tel.: (57) 1 416 0166
Web Site: http://www.weg.net
Electric Equipment Mfr
N.A.I.C.S.: 335999

WEG Electric (India) Private Limited (1)
Eshwari Arcade No 250 14th Main 7th Sector, HSR layout, Bengaluru, 560 102, Karnataka, India
Tel.: (91) 8046437450
Web Site: http://www.weg.net
Sales Range: $25-49.9 Million
Electric Motor Mfr
N.A.I.C.S.: 335312

WEG Electric Corp. (1)
6655 Sugarloaf Pkwy, Duluth, GA 30097
Tel.: (678) 249-2000
Web Site: http://www.weg.net
Sales Range: $200-249.9 Million
Electric Motor Mfr
N.A.I.C.S.: 335312

Subsidiary (Domestic):

CG Power Systems USA Inc. (2)
1 Pauwels Dr, Washington, MO 63090 (100%)
Tel.: (636) 239-9300
Web Site: http://www.cgglobal.com
Power Distribution & Specialty Transformer Mfr
N.A.I.C.S.: 335311
Stephen Oakes (Mgr-Engrg)

WEG Electric Motors (Uk) Ltd (1)
28/29 Walkers Road Manorside Industrial Estate North Moons Moat, Redditch, B98 9HE, Worcestershire, United Kingdom
Tel.: (44) 1527596748
Web Site: http://www.weg.net
Electric Motor Mfr
N.A.I.C.S.: 335312

WEG Elektrik Sanayi Anonim Sirketi (1)
Koseler Mah Kobi Osb 39 Sok Idari Bina Blok No 7, Dilovasi, Kocaeli, Turkiye
Tel.: (90) 8502172529
Electric Motor Mfr
N.A.I.C.S.: 336320

WEG Equipamentos Eletricos S.A. (1)
Av Pref Waldemar Grubba 3000, Jaragua do Sul, 89256-900, Santa Catarina, Brazil
Tel.: (55) 47 3276 4000
Web Site: http://www.weg.net
Industrial Equipment Mfr
N.A.I.C.S.: 333248

WEG Euro Industria Electrica S.A. (1)
Rua Eng Frederico Ulrich Sector V Maia Apartado 6074, 4470-605, Porto, Portugal
Tel.: (351) 229477700
Web Site: http://www.weg.net
Sales Range: $50-74.9 Million
Electric Motor Mfr
N.A.I.C.S.: 335312

WEG Germany GmbH (1)
Industriegebiet Turnich 3 Geigerstrasse 7, 50169, Kerpen, Germany
Tel.: (49) 2237 9291 0
Web Site: http://www.weg.net
Sales Range: $25-49.9 Million
Electric Motor Mfr
N.A.I.C.S.: 335312

WEG Iberia Industrial S.L. (1)
C/ Tierra de Barros 5-7, 28823, Coslada, Spain
Tel.: (34) 916277416
Electrical & Electronic Product Mfr
N.A.I.C.S.: 334419

WEG Iberia S.A. (1)
Avenida de la Industria 25, 28823, Coslada, Madrid, Spain
Tel.: (34) 916553008
Electric Motor Mfr
N.A.I.C.S.: 335312

WEG Italia S.R.L (1)
Via Vigano de Vizzi 93/95, 20092, Cinisello Balsamo, Milan, Italy
Tel.: (39) 0261293535
Web Site: http://www.weg.net
Sales Range: $25-49.9 Million
Electric Motor Mfr
N.A.I.C.S.: 335312
Luciano Albertalli (Mng Dir)

WEG Mexico, S.A. de C.V. (1)
Carretera Jorobas Tula Km 3 5 Manzana 5 Lote 1, Fraccionamiento Parque Industrial Huehuetoca, 54680, Huehuetoca, Mexico
Tel.: (52) 55 5321 4275
Web Site: http://www.weg.net
Electric Motor Mfr
N.A.I.C.S.: 335312

WEG Middle East Fze (1)
JAFZA One Tower B Office No 1322, PO Box 262508, Jebel Ali Free Zone North, Dubai, 262508, United Arab Emirates
Tel.: (971) 48130800
Web Site: http://www.weg.net
Sales Range: $25-49.9 Million
Electric Motor Mfr
N.A.I.C.S.: 335312

WEG Nantong Electric Motor Manufacturing Co Ltd (1)
No 128 Xinkai Nan Road Nantong Economic and Technological, Development Area, Nantong, 226010, China
Tel.: (86) 51385989329
Electric Motor Mfr
N.A.I.C.S.: 335312

WEG Rus LLC (1)
1 Verkhny Pereulok 12 lit V Office 222, Saint Petersburg, 194292, Russia
Tel.: (7) 8126005505
Electric Motor Mfr
N.A.I.C.S.: 336320

WEG Scandinavia AB (1)
Verkstadgatan 9, PO Box 10196, 434 22, Kungsbacka, Sweden
Tel.: (46) 30073400
Electric Motor Mfr
N.A.I.C.S.: 335312

WEG Singapore Pte. Ltd. (1)
67B Joo Koon Circle, Singapore, 629082, Singapore
Tel.: (65) 68622220
Web Site: http://www.weg.net

Sales Range: $25-49.9 Million
Wind Turbine Mfr
N.A.I.C.S.: 333611

WEG Tintas Ltda (1)
Rodovia BR 280 Km 50 6 918 - Bloco A, Guaramirim, 89270-000, Santa Catarina, Brazil
Tel.: (55) 47 3276 4000
Web Site: http://www.weg.net
Paints & Varnishes Mfr
N.A.I.C.S.: 325510

Watt Drive Antriebstechnik GmbH (1)
Wollersdorfer Strasse 68, Markt Piesting, 2753, Wiener Neustadt, Austria
Tel.: (43) 26334040
Web Site: https://www.wattdrive.com
Electric Motor Mfr
N.A.I.C.S.: 335312
Hans Wustinger (Founder)

Watt Drive GmbH (1)
Heinrich-Hertz-Strasse 14, 59423, Unna, Germany
Tel.: (49) 2303986870
Electric Equipment Mfr
N.A.I.C.S.: 335999

Weg (Nantong) Electric Motor Co., Ltd. (1)
128 Xinkai South Road, Nantong Economic and Technological Development Area, Nantong, Jiangsu, China
Tel.: (86) 51385989333
Electrical & Electronic Component Mfr
N.A.I.C.S.: 335999
Peter Xu (Suprv-Product Engrg)

Weg (UK) Ltd. (1)
Broad Ground Road, Lakeside, Redditch, B98 8YP, Worcestershire, United Kingdom
Tel.: (44) 1527513800
Electrical Engineering Services
N.A.I.C.S.: 541330
Susan Harvey (Mgr-IT)

Weg Central Asia Llp (1)
Tole Bi St Building 101 Block B 9th Floor, 050012, Almaty, Kazakhstan
Tel.: (7) 7085330237
Electrical & Electronic Component Mfr
N.A.I.C.S.: 335999

Weg Electric Cis OOO (1)
6 Verkhniy Pereulok 12A, 194292, Saint Petersburg, Russia
Tel.: (7) 8123632172
Electrical Engineering Services
N.A.I.C.S.: 541330

Weg Electric Motors Japan Co., Ltd. (1)
Yokohama Sky Building 20F 2 -19-12, Takashima Nishi-ku, Yokohama, 220-0011, Kanagawa, Japan
Tel.: (81) 455503030
Electrical Engineering Services
N.A.I.C.S.: 541330

Weg Equipamientos Electricos S.A. (1)
Sgo Pampiglione 4849, Parque Industrial San Francisco 2400-San Francisco, Cordoba, Argentina
Tel.: (54) 3564421484
Electrical & Electronic Component Mfr
N.A.I.C.S.: 335999

Weg France SAS (1)
60 Avenue des Arrivaux, ZI de Chesnes La Noiree, 38070, Saint-Quentin-Fallavier, France
Tel.: (33) 474991135
Electrical Engineering Services
N.A.I.C.S.: 541330
Stephane Romanet (Acct Mgr)

Weg Holding GmbH (1)
Ghegastrasse 3, 1030, Vienna, Austria
Tel.: (43) 17962050
Electrical & Electronic Component Mfr
N.A.I.C.S.: 335999
Jailson Luis Satler (Mng Dir)

Weg Industrias Venezuela C.A. (1)
Valencia Offices 06-16 and 6-17 of the Type 2 Floor Level 5, Valencia, Carabobo, Venezuela
Tel.: (58) 2418210582

Electrical Engineering Services
N.A.I.C.S.: 541330

Weg Industries (India) Private Ltd. (1)
No 250 14th Main 7th Sector HSR layout Eshwari Arcade, Bengaluru, 560102, Karnataka, India
Tel.: (91) 8046437450
Electrical Engineering Services
N.A.I.C.S.: 541330

Weg International Trade GmbH (1)
Ghegastrasse 3, 1030, Vienna, Austria
Tel.: (43) 17962048
Electrical & Electronic Component Mfr
N.A.I.C.S.: 335999
Luis Gustavo Lopes Iensen (Mng Dir)

Weg Peru S.A. (1)
Av Iquitos 1159, La Victoria, Lima, Peru
Tel.: (51) 12097600
Electrical Engineering Services
N.A.I.C.S.: 541330
Erick Vargas (Sls Mgr)

Weg-Cestari Redutores E Motoredutores S.A. (1)
Monte Alto / Vista Alegre Highway KM -03, Monte Alto, 15910-000, Sao Paulo, Brazil
Tel.: (55) 1632441000
Web Site: https://www.wegcestari.com.br
Industrial Automation Products Mfr
N.A.I.C.S.: 333998
Walmir Fernandes Navarro (Mgr-R&D)

Wurttembergische Elektromotoren GmbH (1)
Olgastrasse 23, PO Box 101262, 72336, Balingen, Germany
Tel.: (49) 743390410
Web Site: http://www.weg-antriebe.de
Electrical Engineering Services
N.A.I.C.S.: 541330

Zest Weg Electric (Pty) Ltd. (1)
47 Galaxy Avenue Linbro Business Park, Private Bag X100 01, Sandton, Johannesburg, 2146, Gauteng, South Africa
Tel.: (27) 117236000
Electrical & Electronic Component Mfr
N.A.I.C.S.: 335999
Ruveer Persad (Mgr-Proposals)

WEGAMES CORPORATION

5F No 189 Yanping S Rd, Zhongzheng Dist, Taipei, 100, Taiwan
Tel.: (886) 277267770
Web Site: http://www.wegames.biz
Year Founded: 2013
6626—(TAI)
Software Development Services
N.A.I.C.S.: 541511
Hsu Su-Chi (Pres & Mng Dir)

WEGLOKOKS S.A.

Mickiewicza 29, 40 085, Katowice, Poland
Tel.: (48) 32 258 24 31 PL
Web Site:
  http://www.weglokoks.com.pl
Year Founded: 1951
Coal Mining, Processing & Export
N.A.I.C.S.: 212115
Jerzy Podsiadlo (Chm, Pres-Mgmt Bd & Dir Gen)

WEGMANS HOLDINGS BERHAD

Lot PTD 6967 Jalan Kempas 3 Kawasan Perindustrian Bakri, 84200, Muar, Johor, Malaysia
Tel.: (60) 69867897
Web Site:
  https://www.wegmans.com.my
0197—(KLS)
Rev: $30,937,247
Assets: $40,963,775
Liabilities: $14,980,814
Net Worth: $25,982,961
Earnings: $4,233,427
Fiscal Year-end: 12/31/22
Home Furniture Product Mfr & Distr
N.A.I.C.S.: 337122

AND PRIVATE COMPANIES

Keh Wee Kiet *(Mng Dir)*
Subsidiaries:

Wegmans Furniture Industries Sdn Bhd (1)
Lot PTD 6967 Jalan Kempas 3, Kawasan Perindustrian Bakri, 84200, Muar, Johor, Malaysia
Tel.: (60) 69867897
Web Site:
https://www.wegmansfurniture.com.my
Emp.: 535
Furniture Mfr & Whslr
N.A.I.C.S.: 333242
Wynce Keh *(Mktg Mgr)*

WEI CHIH STEEL INDUSTRIAL CO., LTD.
No 123 Nan Pu Village, Kuan Tien District, T'ainan, Taiwan
Tel.: (886) 65790213
Web Site:
https://www.weichih.com.tw
2028—(TAI)
Rev.: $342,855,313
Assets: $282,713,813
Liabilities: $136,879,029
Net Worth: $145,834,783
Earnings: $13,578,501
Emp.: 350
Fiscal Year-end: 12/31/23
Iron & Steel Mfr
N.A.I.C.S.: 331110
Su Hui Kuo *(Gen Mgr)*

WEI LONG GRAPE WINE CO., LTD.
No 567 Weilong Avenue, Longkou, 265701, China
Tel.: (86) 4001603779
Web Site: https://www.weilong.com
Year Founded: 2007
603779—(SHG)
Rev.: $70,036,968
Assets: $201,653,684
Liabilities: $102,295,875
Net Worth: $99,357,809
Earnings: $1,655,246
Fiscal Year-end: 12/31/22
Wine Mfr & Distr
N.A.I.C.S.: 312130
Zhu Qiuhong *(Chm)*

WEI YUAN HOLDINGS LIMITED
37 Kranji Link, Singapore, 728665, Singapore
Tel.: (65) 63623333   Ky
Web Site:
http://www.weiyuanholdings.com
Year Founded: 1991
1343—(HKG)
Rev.: $76,933,273
Assets: $82,797,092
Liabilities: $40,157,540
Net Worth: $42,639,552
Earnings: $1,019,465
Emp.: 633
Fiscal Year-end: 12/31/23
Holding Company
N.A.I.C.S.: 551112
Tian Soo Ng *(Chm)*
Subsidiaries:

Geecomms Pte. Ltd. (1)
37 Kranji Link, Singapore, 728643, Singapore
Tel.: (65) 63623333
Web Site: http://www.geecomms.com
Wiring Installation Services
N.A.I.C.S.: 238210

Road Builders Singapore Pte. Ltd. (1)
37 Kranji Link, Singapore, 728645, Singapore
Tel.: (65) 62696118
Web Site: https://www.roadbuilders.com.sg
Emp.: 100
Road Construction Services
N.A.I.C.S.: 237310

WEI-CHUAN FOOD CORPORATION
10F No 125 Songjiang Rd, Zhongshan Dist, Taipei, 104, Taiwan
Tel.: (886) 225065020
Web Site:
https://www.weichuan.com.tw
Year Founded: 1953
1201—(TAI)
Rev.: $702,323,594
Assets: $589,545,581
Liabilities: $351,081,284
Net Worth: $238,464,297
Earnings: $8,813,761
Emp.: 4,760
Fiscal Year-end: 12/31/23
Various Food Products & Sauces Mfr & Distr
N.A.I.C.S.: 311423
Lin Jian-Hong *(CEO-Wide Ops & Mgmt)*
Subsidiaries:

Great Eastern Company USA Inc. (1)
7439 Langtry St, Houston, TX 77040-6635
Tel.: (713) 690-6669
Web Site: http://www.weichuanusa.com
Sales Range: $25-49.9 Million
Emp.: 50
Groceries & Related Products
N.A.I.C.S.: 424490
Robert Huang *(Pres)*

King Can Industry Corporation (1)
No 561 Zhongzheng Rd, Wufeng Dist, Taichung, 413, Taiwan
Tel.: (886) 423397711
Web Site: https://www.kingcan.com.tw
Plastic Container Mfr
N.A.I.C.S.: 326112

Wei-Chuan USA (1)
6655 S Garfield Ave, Bell Gardens, CA 90201-1807
Tel.: (562) 372-2020
Web Site: http://www.weichuanusa.com
Sales Range: $150-199.9 Million
Emp.: 500
Mfr of Frozen Food & Packaged Goods
N.A.I.C.S.: 424420
Steve Lin *(Pres)*

WEICHAI HEAVY MACHINERY CO., LTD.
No 17 Fuhai Street Binhai, Economic and technological development zone, Weifang, 261108, Shandong, China
Tel.: (86) 4006183066
Web Site:
https://www.weichaihm.com
Year Founded: 1998
000880—(SSE)
Rev.: $485,014,018
Assets: $715,057,284
Liabilities: $459,010,576
Net Worth: $256,046,708
Earnings: $19,761,876
Fiscal Year-end: 12/31/22
Diesel Engine Mfr
N.A.I.C.S.: 324199

WEIDA (M) BHD.
Wisma Hock Peng Ground 2nd Floor 123 Green Heights, PO Box 2424, Jalan Lapangan Terbang, 93748, Kuching, Sarawak, Malaysia
Tel.: (60) 82456456
Web Site: http://www.weida.com.my
Rev.: $57,832,868
Assets: $141,326,467
Liabilities: $32,472,374
Net Worth: $108,854,092
Earnings: $5,463,530
Emp.: 1,000
Fiscal Year-end: 03/31/18
Water Tank Mfr
N.A.I.C.S.: 332420
Tin Ngee Wang *(Co-Sec)*
Subsidiaries:

Weida (M) Bhd. - NEGERI SEMBILAN Manufacturing Plant (1)
Lot 109 Jalan Permata Arab-Malaysian Industrial Park, 71800, Nilai, Negeri Sembilan, Malaysia
Tel.: (60) 67990990
Sales Range: $75-99.9 Million
Emp.: 140
Polyethylene Pipes & Storage Tanks Mfr
N.A.I.C.S.: 327332

Weida (M) Bhd. - PHILIPPINES Manufacturing Plant (1)
Lot 11 & 13 Block 3 Dasmarinas Technopark Governor's Drive, Dasmarinas, 4114, Cavite, Philippines
Tel.: (63) 25296193
Web Site: http://www.weida.com.my
Sales Range: $25-49.9 Million
Emp.: 50
Water Storage Tanks Mfr
N.A.I.C.S.: 332420

Weida (M) Bhd. - SARAWAK Manufacturing Plant (1)
Lot 472 Block 8 MTLD Sejingkat Industrial Park Jalan Bako, PO Box 1807, Petra Jaya, 93736, Kuching, Sarawak, Malaysia
Tel.: (60) 82435435
Web Site: http://www.weida.com.my
Sales Range: $50-74.9 Million
Emp.: 200
Sewage Treatment Tanks Mfr
N.A.I.C.S.: 332420

Weida Integrated Industries Sdn Bhd (1)
Lot 57 SEDCO Light Industrial Estate, Lok Kawi, Kota Kinabalu, 88801, Sabah, Malaysia
Tel.: (60) 88752996
Web Site: http://www.weida.com.my
Polyethylene Pipes & Storage Tanks Mfr
N.A.I.C.S.: 332420
Vincent Ho *(Mgr)*

Weida Integrated Industries Sdn. Bhd. (1)
Lot 472 Blok 8 Mtld Sejingkat Industrial Park Jalan, Bako Petra Jaya, Kuching, 93748, Sarawak, Malaysia
Tel.: (60) 82439745
Sales Range: $125-149.9 Million
Emp.: 300
High Density Polyethylene Mfr & Distr
N.A.I.C.S.: 325211
Choon Chin Lee *(Mng Dir)*

Weida Marketing Sdn. Bhd. (1)
No 21 & 23 Jln PJU 3/49 Sunway Damansara Technology Park, 47810, Petaling Jaya, Selangor, Malaysia
Tel.: (60) 3 7806 2002
Chemical Storage Tanks Mfr
N.A.I.C.S.: 332420

Weida Philippines Inc. (1)
3/F BT&T Ctr 20 E Rodriguez Jr Ave C-5, Brgy Bagumbayan Libis, Quezon City, 1110, Philippines
Tel.: (63) 27062002
Web Site: http://www.weida.com.ph
Sales Range: $25-49.9 Million
Emp.: 20
Polyethylene Pipes Mfr & Whslr
N.A.I.C.S.: 326122
Michael Sy *(Gen Mgr)*

Weida Water Sdn. Bhd. (1)
1st Floor Wisma Hock Peng Lrg Lapangan Terbang 2, 93250, Kuching, Sarawak, Malaysia
Tel.: (60) 82456456
Water Storage Tanks Distr
N.A.I.C.S.: 488390
Lee Choon Chin *(Mng Dir)*

Weidaline Sdn. Bhd. (1)
8th Floor Wawasan Plaza, 88000, Kota Kinabalu, Sabah, Malaysia
Tel.: (60) 88264555
Sales Range: $550-599.9 Million
Emp.: 1,004
High Density Polyethylene Pipes Distr
N.A.I.C.S.: 423320

Ku Fiew Fung *(Controller-Fin)*

WEIDAI LTD.
No 9 Baiyun Road, Jianggan District, Hangzhou, Zhejiang, China
Tel.: (86) 5715 697 9013   Ky
Web Site: http://www.weidai.com.cn
Year Founded: 2011
WEI—(NYSE)
Rev.: $108,390,713
Assets: $183,800,981
Liabilities: $117,107,749
Net Worth: $66,693,233
Earnings: ($174,761,438)
Emp.: 531
Fiscal Year-end: 12/31/21
Automobile Finance Services
N.A.I.C.S.: 522220
Hong Yao *(Founder, Chm & CEO)*

WEIDMULLER INTERFACE GMBH & CO. KG
Klingenbergstrasse 16, D-32758, Detmold, Germany
Tel.: (49) 5231 14 0   De
Web Site:
http://www.weidmueller.com
Year Founded: 1850
Electric Power Systems Mfr
N.A.I.C.S.: 335999
Christian Glasel *(Chm-Supervisory Bd)*
Subsidiaries:

Weidmuller Inc. (1)
821 Southlake Blvd, Richmond, VA 23236
Tel.: (804) 794-2877
Web Site: http://www.weidmuller.com
Electronic Parts & Equipment Mfr
N.A.I.C.S.: 334419
Terry Hodgson *(Pres & Exec VP-North America)*

Subsidiary (Non-US):

Weidmuller Ltd. (2)
10 Spy Court, Markham, L3R 5H6, ON, Canada
Tel.: (905) 475-1507
Web Site: https://www.weidmuller.ca
Electronic Parts Mfr
N.A.I.C.S.: 334419

Weidmuller SA de C.V. (2)
Blvd Hermanos Serdan 698 Col San Rafael Oriente, Puebla, CP 72029, Mexico
Tel.: (52) 2222686267
Web Site: http://www.weidmuller.mx
Electronic Components Distr
N.A.I.C.S.: 334220

Weidmuller Monitoring Systems GmbH (1)
Else-Sander-Strasse 8, 01099, Dresden, Germany
Tel.: (49) 35121391650
Web Site: http://www.bladecontrol.de
Mechanical Equipment Mfr
N.A.I.C.S.: 333613

WEIFANG TRICOL TRADING CO. LTD.
11/F Jiankang East Street No 6888, Weifang, 261205, Shandong, China
Tel.: (86) 536 6101095
Web Site: http://www.tricolgroup.com
Year Founded: 1992
Emp.: 1,800
Microfiber Mfr
N.A.I.C.S.: 313110
Hongwei Duan *(Pres)*
Subsidiaries:

Tricol Biomedical, Inc. (1)
720 SW Washington Street Ste 200, Portland, OR 97205-3504
Tel.: (503) 245-0459
Web Site: http://www.hemcon.com
Bandage & First Aid Product Mfr
N.A.I.C.S.: 339113
Brian H. Clare *(VP-Tech & Product Innovation)*

WEIFANG TRICOL TRADING CO. LTD.

Weifang Tricol Trading Co. Ltd.—(Continued)
Subsidiary (Non-US):

HemCon Medical Technologies Europe, Ltd. (2)
Paramount Court Corrig Rd Sandyford Industrial Estate, Dublin, Ireland
Tel.: (353) 5032450459
Web Site: http://www.tricolbiomedical.com
Bandage & First Aid Product Mfr
N.A.I.C.S.: 339113

WEIFANG YAXING CHEMICAL CO., LTD.
No 321 East Beigong Street, Kuiwen District, Weifang, 261031, Shandong, China
Tel.: (86) 5368662251
Web Site:
   https://www.chinayaxing.com
Year Founded: 1994
600319—(SHG)
Rev.: $118,870,123
Assets: $268,814,543
Liabilities: $179,274,247
Net Worth: $89,540,297
Earnings: $15,281,712
Fiscal Year-end: 12/31/22
Chemical Product Mfr & Distr
N.A.I.C.S.: 325998
Han Haibin (Chm)

WEIGANG ENVIRONMENTAL TECHNOLOGY HOLDING GROUP LIMITED
Room 3507 35F Youbang Square 183 Electric Road, North Point, China (Hong Kong)
Tel.: (852) 36110360   Ky
Web Site: http://www.gzweigang.com
1845—(HKG)
Rev.: $48,989,491
Assets: $104,455,073
Liabilities: $35,203,334
Net Worth: $69,251,738
Earnings: ($10,955,693)
Emp.: 362
Fiscal Year-end: 12/31/22
Hazardous Waste Treatment Services
N.A.I.C.S.: 562211
Zhuhua Cai (Chm & CEO)

WEIGHTMANS LLP
100 Old Hall Street, Liverpool, L3 9QJ, United Kingdom
Tel.: (44) 0345 073 990   UK
Web Site:
   http://www.weightmans.com
Year Founded: 1827
Sales Range: $125-149.9 Million
Emp.: 1,400
Law firm
N.A.I.C.S.: 541110
Chris Ball (Gen Partner)

WEIHAI CITY COMMERCIAL BANK CO., LTD.
9 Bao Quan Road, Weihai, 264200, Shandong, China
Tel.: (86) 6315236187   CN
Web Site: https://www.whccb.com
Year Founded: 1997
9677—(CHIN)
Rev.: $2,160,611,293
Assets: $54,258,532,621
Liabilities: $50,380,612,123
Net Worth: $3,877,920,497
Earnings: $293,016,310
Emp.: 774
Fiscal Year-end: 12/31/23
Bank Holding Company
N.A.I.C.S.: 551111
Xianguo Tan (Chm)

WEIHAI GUANGTAI AIRPORT EQUIPMENT CO., LTD.
No 16 Huanghe Street, Weihai, 264200, Shandong, China
Tel.: (86) 6313953326
Web Site:
   https://www.guangtai.com.cn
Year Founded: 1991
002111—(SSE)
Rev.: $329,363,841
Assets: $760,235,196
Liabilities: $329,610,214
Net Worth: $430,624,982
Earnings: $33,703,146
Emp.: 2,800
Fiscal Year-end: 12/31/22
Aircraft Equipment Mfr
N.A.I.C.S.: 336413
Guangtai Li (Founder & Chm)

WEIHAI GUANGWEI COMPOSITES CO., LTD.
No 130 Tianjin Road, High-tech Zone, Weihai, 264202, Shandong, China
Tel.: (86) 6315298586
Web Site: https://www.gwcfc.com
Year Founded: 1992
300699—(CHIN)
Rev.: $354,617,665
Assets: $994,061,030
Liabilities: $215,170,164
Net Worth: $778,890,866
Earnings: $122,985,797
Fiscal Year-end: 12/31/23
Fabricated Metal Products Mfr
N.A.I.C.S.: 332999
Lu Zhaojun (Chm)

WEIHAI HUADONG AUTOMATION CO., LTD.
No 698 Huanshan Road, Weihai, Shandong, China
Tel.: (86) 6315968012
Web Site:
   https://www.huadongcnc.com
Year Founded: 2002
002248—(SSE)
Rev.: $35,726,591
Assets: $78,727,952
Liabilities: $68,012,273
Net Worth: $10,715,679
Earnings: $1,637,303
Fiscal Year-end: 12/31/22
Machine Tools Mfr
N.A.I.C.S.: 333517
Lian Xiaoming (Chm)

WEIKENG INDUSTRIAL CO., LTD.
11F No 308 Sec 1 Neihu Rd, Neihu Dist, Taipei, 114, Taiwan
Tel.: (886) 226590202   TW
Web Site:
   https://www.weikeng.com.tw
Year Founded: 1977
3033—(TAI)
Rev.: $2,318,336,451
Assets: $1,263,818,259
Liabilities: $977,143,755
Net Worth: $286,674,504
Earnings: $25,728,996
Emp.: 756
Fiscal Year-end: 12/31/23
Electronic Components & Peripherals Distr
N.A.I.C.S.: 423430
Chiu-Chiang Hu (Chm & Chm)

Subsidiaries:

WEIKENG Technology Pte LTD (1)
No 10 Upper Aljunied Link 02-09, Singapore, 367904, Singapore
Tel.: (65) 62847278
Web Site: http://www.weikeng.com.tw
Sales Range: $25-49.9 Million
Emp.: 30
Electronic Components Distr
N.A.I.C.S.: 423430

Weikeng International Co., Ltd (1)
Unit A 17/F Ever Gain Centre 28 On Muk Street, Sha Tin, New Territories, China (Hong Kong)
Tel.: (852) 27999035
Sales Range: $25-49.9 Million
Emp.: 100
Electronic Components Mfr
N.A.I.C.S.: 334419

Subsidiary (Non-US):

WEIKENG INTERNATIONAL (Shanghai) CO., LTD (2)
8/F Tower A 1068 West Tianshan Road, Changning District, Shanghai, 200335, China
Tel.: (86) 2133538989
Electronic Components Distr
N.A.I.C.S.: 423690

WEILI HOLDINGS LTD.
New Industrial Park, Miersi Hongan, Huanggang, Hubei, China   Ky
Web Site:
   https://www.weiliholdings.com
Year Founded: 2011
2372—(HKG)
Rev.: $26,437,749
Assets: $50,556,048
Liabilities: $20,066,183
Net Worth: $30,489,865
Earnings: ($354,453)
Emp.: 99
Fiscal Year-end: 12/31/23
Holding Company
N.A.I.C.S.: 551112
Tsz Ngo Yu (Sec)

WEILONG DELICIOUS GLOBAL HOLDINGS LTD.
The Southwest Corner of the crossing of Dongfanghong Road, Zhongshan Road Zhaoling, Luohe, Henan, China
Tel.: (86) 4001999085   Ky
Web Site:
   https://www.weilongshipin.com
Year Founded: 2001
9985—(HKG)
Rev.: $709,702,579
Assets: $1,061,796,625
Liabilities: $215,401,463
Net Worth: $846,395,163
Earnings: $23,180,213
Emp.: 6,307
Fiscal Year-end: 12/31/22
Holding Company
N.A.I.C.S.: 551112
Yinong Sun (CEO)

WEIMOB, INC.
Weimob Building 258 Changjiang Road, Baoshan Di, Shanghai, 230061, China
Tel.: (86) 2166198866
2013—(HKG)
Rev.: $258,193,915
Assets: $1,119,088,526
Liabilities: $804,445,668
Net Worth: $314,642,858
Earnings: ($269,529,530)
Emp.: 6,278
Fiscal Year-end: 12/31/22
General Marketing Services
N.A.I.C.S.: 541613
Taoyong Sun (Founder, Chm & CEO)

WEINBERG CAPITAL PARTNERS SAS
1 rue Euler, 75008, Paris, France
Tel.: (33) 1 53 53 55 00   FR
Web Site:
   http://www.weinbergcapital.com
Year Founded: 2005
Private Equity & Real Estate Investment Firm
N.A.I.C.S.: 523999
Serge Weinberg (Co-Founder & Chm)

INTERNATIONAL PUBLIC

WEINERT INDUSTRIES AG
Mittlere-Motsch-Straße 26, 96515, Sonneberg, Germany
Tel.: (49) 3676481100
Web Site: https://weinert-industries.com
Year Founded: 2021
Appliances, Electrical & Electronics Mfg.
N.A.I.C.S.: 334512
Andreas Weinert (CTO)

Subsidiaries:

j-plasma GmbH (1)
Im Semmicht 1, 7751, Jena, Germany
Tel.: (49) 364153244
Fabricated Wire Products Distr
N.A.I.C.S.: 423610

WEINMANN GERATE FUR MEDIZIN GMBH & CO. KG
Kronsaalsweg 40, 22525, Hamburg, Germany
Tel.: (49) 40547020   De
Web Site: http://www.weinmann-medical.com
Sales Range: $75-99.9 Million
Medical Equipment Mfr & Distr
N.A.I.C.S.: 423450
Wilfried Schmidt (Mng Dir)

WEISS KOREA OPPORTUNITY FUND
One Bartholomew Lane, London, EC2N 2AX, United Kingdom
Tel.: (44) 2074963000
Web Site:
   https://www.weisskoreafund.com
Year Founded: 2013
WKOF—(AIM)
Assets: $151,266,177
Liabilities: $2,507,948
Net Worth: $148,758,230
Earnings: ($8,211,301)
Fiscal Year-end: 12/31/23
Management Investment Services
N.A.I.C.S.: 525910
Gillian Yvonne Morris (Chm)

WEISS REALTY LTD.
222 Glenforest Drive, Thornhill, L4J 8N3, ON, Canada
Tel.: (905) 886-0171
Web Site: http://www.weissrealty.com
Rev.: $18,617,812
Emp.: 300
Real Estate Services
N.A.I.C.S.: 531210
Michael Weiss (Branch Mgr)

WEITMANN & KONRAD GMBH & CO KG
Friedrich List Strasse 20-24, 70771, Leinfelden-Echterdingen, Germany
Tel.: (49) 71179880
Web Site: http://www.weko.net
Year Founded: 1953
Rev.: $21,533,387
Emp.: 140
Powdering & Moistening Machinery Mfr
N.A.I.C.S.: 333998
Carlheinz Weitmann (Co-Mng Dir)

Subsidiaries:

WEKO Italia SRL (1)
Via Palmanova 67, 20132, Milan, Italy
Tel.: (39) 0228901934
Web Site: http://www.wekoitalia.it
Industrial Machinery & Equipment Distr
N.A.I.C.S.: 423830

WEKO North America, Inc. (1)
896 West St John St, Spartanburg, SC 29301
Tel.: (864) 278-8449
Web Site: http://www.wekona.com
Industrial Machinery & Equipment Distr

N.A.I.C.S.: 423830
Herbert Skerjanz (VP)

WEKO UK Ltd (1)
2 Park Road, Kingston upon Thames, KT2 6AY, Surrey, United Kingdom
Tel.: (44) 2085498039
Web Site: http://www.weko.co.uk
Industrial Machinery & Equipment Distr
N.A.I.C.S.: 423830

Weko America Latina Equipamentos Industriais Ltda (1)
Rua Albany 140, 89130-000, Indaial, Santa Catarina, Brazil
Tel.: (55) 4733331320
Web Site: http://www.weko.net.br
Industrial Machinery & Equipment Distr
N.A.I.C.S.: 423830

WEIYE CONSTRUCTION GROUP CO LTD
Podium Building of Zhenye Jingzhou Building, west of Xinzhou Road & south of Lianhua Road Futian District, Shenzhen, China
Tel.: (86) 75583260088
Web Site: https://www.szweiye.com
Year Founded: 1994
300621—(CHIN)
Rev.: $2,075,019,336
Assets: $1,707,624,828
Liabilities: $1,578,605,652
Net Worth: $129,019,176
Earnings: $930,852
Fiscal Year-end: 12/31/22
Architecture Decorating Services
N.A.I.C.S.: 541410
Zhang Wei (Chm)

WEIYE HOLDINGS LIMITED
Floor 19 XaingHu International Building A Yang Qiao Road, Zhengzhou, Henan, China
Tel.: (86) 37158506982 SG
Web Site:
  https://www.weiyeholdings.com
Year Founded: 1999
1570—(HKG)
Rev.: $186,235,686
Assets: $791,964,529
Liabilities: $534,656,819
Net Worth: $257,307,710
Earnings: $6,557,522
Emp.: 294
Fiscal Year-end: 12/31/22
Air Conditioner Mfr
N.A.I.C.S.: 333415
Wei Zhang (Chm)

WEIZMANN LIMITED
Empire House 214 Dr D N Road Ent A K Nayak Marg, Fort, Mumbai, 400 001, India
Tel.: (91) 2222071501 In
Web Site:
  https://www.weizmann.co.in
Year Founded: 1985
523011—(BOM)
Rev.: $13,415,548
Assets: $16,068,002
Liabilities: $5,898,424
Net Worth: $10,169,578
Earnings: $707,971
Fiscal Year-end: 03/31/21
Textile Mfr & Distr
N.A.I.C.S.: 313310
Neelkamal V. Siraj (Vice Chm & Mng Dir)

Subsidiaries:

Karma Energy Limited (1)
Empire House 214 Dr D N Road Ent A K Nayak Marg Fort, Mumbai, 400 001, India
Tel.: (91) 2222071501
Web Site: https://www.karmaenergy.co
Rev.: $2,165,590
Assets: $6,650,453
Liabilities: $2,037,636
Net Worth: $4,612,817
Earnings: $706,229
Fiscal Year-end: 03/31/2023
Renewable Energy Including Wind Power & Hydro Power
N.A.I.C.S.: 221118
Dharmendra G. Siraj (Chm)

Subsidiary (Domestic):

Batot Hydro Power Limited (2)
Karyan Hardass Pura, Chamba, 176318, Himachal Pradesh, India (59%)
Tel.: (91) 1899 220698
Hydroelectric Power Generation Services
N.A.I.C.S.: 221111

Greenweiz Projects Limited (2)
214 Empire House Dr D N Road A K Nayak Marg Fort, Mumbai, 400001, Maharashtra, India
Tel.: (91) 22 22071501
Web Site: http://www.weizmann.co.in
Sales Range: $50-74.9 Million
Emp.: 50
Eletric Power Generation Services
N.A.I.C.S.: 221118

WEJO GROUP LIMITED
Canon's Court 22 Victoria Street, Hamilton, HM12, Bermuda
Tel.: (441) 8002343065 BM
Web Site: https://www.wejo.com
Year Founded: 2013
WEJO—(NASDAQ)
Rev.: $8,396,000
Assets: $31,133,000
Liabilities: $99,896,000
Net Worth: ($68,763,000)
Earnings: ($159,253,000)
Emp.: 251
Fiscal Year-end: 12/31/22
Holding Company; Transportation Software Development & Data Processing Services
N.A.I.C.S.: 551112
John T. Maxwell (CFO)

Subsidiaries:

Virtuoso Acquisition Corp. (1)
180 Post Rd E, Westport, CT 06880
Tel.: (203) 227-1978
Investment Holding Company
N.A.I.C.S.: 551112
Jeffrey D. Warshaw (CEO)

WEKA HOLDING GMBH & CO.KG
Postfach 13 31 Romerstrasse 4, D-86438, Kissing, Germany
Tel.: (49) 82 33 23 0
Web Site: http://www.weka-holding.de
Year Founded: 1973
Publishing Services
N.A.I.C.S.: 513199
Wolfgang Materna (Mng Dir)

Subsidiaries:

FORUM Media Group GmbH (1)
Mandichostrasse 18, 86504, Merching, Germany
Tel.: (49) 8233 381 341
Web Site: http://www.forum-media.com
Emp.: 1,200
Magazine Publisher
N.A.I.C.S.: 513120
Ronald Herkert (Chm)

Subsidiary (Domestic):

DoldeMedien Verlag GmbH (2)
Naststrasse 19B, 70327, Stuttgart, Germany
Tel.: (49) 711553490
Web Site: http://www.doldemedien.de
Magazine Publisher
N.A.I.C.S.: 513120
Roland Hradek (Exec Dir)

WELBE, INC.
7F GINZA Namiki-dori Bldg 2-3-6 Ginza, Chuo-Ku, Tokyo, 104-0061, Japan
Tel.: (81) 362689542
Web Site:
  https://corporate.welbe.co.jp
Year Founded: 2011
6556—(TKS)
Rev.: $103,217,840
Assets: $79,821,280
Liabilities: $47,025,440
Net Worth: $32,795,840
Earnings: ($13,261,600)
Emp.: 1,343
Fiscal Year-end: 03/31/23
Disability Welfare Services
N.A.I.C.S.: 923130
Makoto Ohta (Pres & CEO)

WELBY, INC.
4F Kanden Real Estate Yaesu Building 1-11-1 Kyobashi, Chuo-Ku, Tokyo, 104-0031, Japan
Tel.: (81) 362062937
Web Site: https://www.welby.jp
Year Founded: 2011
4438—(TKS)
Rev.: $4,076,750
Assets: $8,543,450
Liabilities: $623,920
Net Worth: $7,919,530
Earnings: ($3,580,450)
Fiscal Year-end: 12/31/23
Software Development Services
N.A.I.C.S.: 541511
Takeru Hiki (Founder, Chm, Pres & CEO)

WELCO LUMBER CORP.
Suite 204 - 1433 King George Blvd, Surrey, V4A 4Z5, BC, Canada
Tel.: (778) 292-5671
Web Site:
  http://www.welcolumber.com
Year Founded: 1983
Sales Range: $10-24.9 Million
Emp.: 20
Lumber Merchant Whslr
N.A.I.C.S.: 423310
Brad Johansen (Pres & CEO)

WELCRON CO., LTD.
12 Digital-ro 27-gil, Guro-dong Guro-gu, Seoul, 08381, Korea (South)
Tel.: (82) 221076600
Web Site: https://www.welcron.com
Year Founded: 1992
065950—(KRS)
Rev.: $341,859,652
Assets: $260,189,278
Liabilities: $161,307,011
Net Worth: $98,882,267
Earnings: $493,991
Emp.: 200
Fiscal Year-end: 12/31/22
Microfiber Textile Products Mfr & Sales
N.A.I.C.S.: 339999
Young-kyu Rhee (CEO)

Subsidiaries:

Welcron Co., Ltd. - Eumseong Factory (1)
383 CheongYong-ro Samseong-myeon, Eumseong, Chungcheongbuk-do, Korea (South)
Tel.: (82) 438798851
Textile Products Mfr
N.A.I.C.S.: 313230

Welcron Global Vina Co. Ltd. (1)
Long Thanh Industrial Zone, Ho Chi Minh City, Dong Nai, Vietnam
Tel.: (84) 613514198
Textile Product Mfr & Distr
N.A.I.C.S.: 313310

Welcron Healthcare Co., Ltd. - Bupyeong Factory (1)
90 Yeomgok-ro Seo-gu, Incheon, Korea (South)
Tel.: (82) 325744640
Sanitary Napkin Mfr
N.A.I.C.S.: 322291

Welcron Healthcare Corporation (1)
90 yeomgok-ro, Seo-gu, Incheon, Korea (South)
Tel.: (82) 325744640
Medicine Sanitary Pad Distr
N.A.I.C.S.: 423450

WELCRON HANTEC CO., LTD.
12 Digital-ro 27-gil, Guro-gu, Seoul, Korea (South)
Tel.: (82) 313508900
Web Site: https://www.hantec.co.kr
Year Founded: 1994
076080—(KRS)
Rev.: $250,609,835
Assets: $154,115,373
Liabilities: $104,463,742
Net Worth: $49,651,631
Earnings: $1,978,588
Emp.: 290
Fiscal Year-end: 12/31/22
Industrial Plant Construction Services
N.A.I.C.S.: 236210
Young-kyu Rhee (CEO)

WELCURE DRUGS & PHARMACEUTICALS LIMITED
33/36 Basement West Patel Nagar Near Ram Jass Ground, West Delhi, Delhi, 110008, India
Tel.: (91) 9717670337
Web Site: https://welcuredrugs.com
Year Founded: 1992
524661—(BOM)
Rev.: $28,433
Assets: $183,305
Liabilities: $1,634
Net Worth: $181,671
Earnings: $12,196
Fiscal Year-end: 03/31/23
Pharmaceutical Drug Mfr & Distr
N.A.I.C.S.: 424210
Sudhir Chandra (Mng Dir)

WELDE GES.M.B.H.
Donaufelderstrasse 216, 1220, Vienna, Austria
Tel.: (43) 1 203 28 50 AT
Web Site: http://www.welde.at
Year Founded: 1989
Plywood Mfr & Distr
N.A.I.C.S.: 423310
Ivan Stamenov (CEO & Member-Exec Bd)

Subsidiaries:

WELDE Bulgaria AD (1)
kv Velchevski, 5600, Troyan, Bulgaria (94.9%)
Tel.: (359) 670 6 22 78
Web Site: http://www.welde.bg
Plywood Mfr
N.A.I.C.S.: 321211

WELDERS SUPPLIES LIMITED.
150 McPhillips Street, Winnipeg, R3E 2J9, MB, Canada
Tel.: (204) 772-9476
Web Site: http://www.welders-supplies.com
Year Founded: 1946
Rev.: $11,302,844
Emp.: 40
Gas Welding & Related Metal Products Services
N.A.I.C.S.: 333992
Russell Sward (Mgr-Svc)

WELGENE BIOTECH CO., LTD.
12F No 3 Yuanyuan Street, Nangang District, Taipei, 115, Taiwan
Tel.: (886) 266160001
Web Site:
  https://www.welgene.com.tw

Welgene Biotech Co., Ltd.—(Continued)
6661—(TPE)
Rev.: $10,064,691
Assets: $13,623,269
Liabilities: $4,119,720
Net Worth: $9,503,549
Earnings: $298,346
Fiscal Year-end: 12/31/22
Medical Care Services
N.A.I.C.S.: 621512
Cheng Fu Chian (Chm & CEO)

WELICHEM BIOTECH INC.
316-4475 Wayburne Drive, Burnaby,
V5G 3L1, BC, Canada
Tel.: (604) 432-1703   BC
Web Site: http://www.welichem.com
Year Founded: 2004
Sales Range: Less than $1 Million
Biological Laboratories
N.A.I.C.S.: 621511
Liren Tang (Pres & CEO)

WELIFE TECHNOLOGY LIMITED
Unit 2 14/F Win Century Centre No
2A Mong Kok Road, Kowloon, China
(Hong Kong)
Tel.: (852) 28348016   Ky
Web Site: http://www.palace-rest.com.hk
Year Founded: 2006
1703—(HKG)
Rev.: $38,805,390
Assets: $32,614,245
Liabilities: $31,101,203
Net Worth: $1,513,043
Earnings: ($884,850)
Emp.: 224
Fiscal Year-end: 03/31/23
Holding Company
N.A.I.C.S.: 551112
Shou Ming Chan (Founder & Chm)

WELINVEST AG
Petersgraben 35, PO Box 439, Basel,
4051, Switzerland
Tel.: (41) 612683111   CH
Web Site: http://www.welinvest.ch
Year Founded: 1859
Real Estate Services
N.A.I.C.S.: 531390

Subsidiaries:

Basler Handels-Gesellschaft AG (1)
Petersgraben 35, PO Box 728, Basel, 4009,
Switzerland   **(100%)**
Tel.: (41) 612683111
Web Site: http://www.welinvest.ch
Sales Range: $25-49.9 Million
Provider of Business Services
N.A.I.C.S.: 561499
G Ammann (Pres)

Welinvest Immobilien AG (1)
Petersgraben 35, PO Box 728, CH 4003,
Basel, Switzerland
Tel.: (41) 612683111
Web Site: http://www.welinvest.ch
Real Estate Services
N.A.I.C.S.: 531390

WELKER SPINTECH GMBH
Lachener Strasse 57, 67433,
Neustadt, Germany
Tel.: (49) 6321187960   De
Web Site: http://www.welker-spintech.com
Year Founded: 1856
Sales Range: $25-49.9 Million
Emp.: 8
Textile Machines Mfr; Conditioning, Steaming, Vacuum Drying & Sterilizing Technologies Producer
N.A.I.C.S.: 333248
Claus Koch (Pres, CEO & Mng Dir)

WELL BIOTEC CO., LTD.
5F17 Yeongdong-daero 106-gil,
Gangnam-gu, Seoul, 06170, Korea
(South)
Tel.: (82) 269021300
Web Site: https://www.wellbiotec.com
Year Founded: 1975
010600—(KRS)
Rev.: $146,448,985
Assets: $46,179,392
Liabilities: $17,188,694
Net Worth: $28,990,698
Earnings: ($4,813,262)
Emp.: 37
Fiscal Year-end: 12/31/22
Biotechnology Business; Leather
Products Mfr
N.A.I.C.S.: 541714
Se-Hyun Gu (CEO)

Subsidiaries:

Lodestar Sea& Air Co., Ltd. (1)
9F Danam Bldg 10 Sowol-ro, Jung-gu,
Seoul, Korea (South)
Tel.: (82) 27550242
Web Site: https://www.lodestars.com
Supply Chain Management Services
N.A.I.C.S.: 541614

WELL GRADED ENGINEERING PUBLIC COMPANY LIMITED
50/1203 Moo 9, Bangpood Pakkred
District, Nonthaburi, 11120, Thailand
Tel.: (66) 29817992   TH
Web Site: https://www.well-graded.com
Year Founded: 2010
WGE—(THA)
Rev.: $52,568,605
Assets: $45,948,644
Liabilities: $37,261,868
Net Worth: $8,686,776
Earnings: ($6,465,600)
Fiscal Year-end: 12/31/23
Construction Services
N.A.I.C.S.: 237900
Kraingsak Buanoom (Mng Dir)

WELL HEALTH TECHNOLOGIES CORP.
Suite 200-322 Water Street, Vancouver, V6B 1B6, BC, Canada
Tel.: (604) 628-7266   BC
Web Site: http://www.well.company
Year Founded: 2010
W7V—(DEU)
Rev.: $586,013,896
Assets: $1,064,192,126
Liabilities: $425,250,359
Net Worth: $638,941,768
Earnings: $12,562,931
Emp.: 4,500
Fiscal Year-end: 12/31/23
Holding Company
N.A.I.C.S.: 551112
Brian Levinkind (Sr VP-Corp Dev)

Subsidiaries:

AwareMD, Inc. (1)
110 Sheppard Avenue East Suite 309,
North York, M2N 6Y8, ON, Canada
Tel.: (416) 977-8010
Web Site: https://www.awaremd.com
Healthcare Technology Solution Services
N.A.I.C.S.: 541511

Brooklin Medical Centre (1)
Suite 1A - 5959 Anderson Street, Brooklin,
L1M 2E9, ON, Canada
Tel.: (905) 655-3321
Medical & Health Care Services
N.A.I.C.S.: 621498

CRH Medical Corporation (1)
Suite 619 -999 Canada Place World Trade
Center, Vancouver, V6C 3E1, BC, Canada
Tel.: (604) 633-1440
Web Site: http://www.crhmedcorp.com
Rev.: $106,172,165
Assets: $191,784,730
Liabilities: $85,836,444
Net Worth: $105,948,286
Earnings: ($22,912,884)
Emp.: 52
Fiscal Year-end: 12/31/2020
Medicinal Product Mfr
N.A.I.C.S.: 339112
Richard Bear (CFO)

Subsidiary (US):

Arapahoe Gastroenterology Anasthesia Associates LLC (2)
13918 E Mississippi Ave 61331, Aurora, CO
80012
Tel.: (303) 722-8987
Freestanding Ambulatory Surgical & Emergency Centers
N.A.I.C.S.: 621493
Sharon Saba (Mgr-HR)

Circle Medical Technologies, Inc. (1)
333 1st St A, San Francisco, CA 94105
Web Site: https://www.circlemedical.com
Medical Software Development Services
N.A.I.C.S.: 541511

Cloud Practice Inc. (1)
302 - 31 Bastion Square, Victoria, V8W
1J1, BC, Canada
Tel.: (250) 900-7373
Web Site: http://www.junoemr.com
Software Development Services
N.A.I.C.S.: 541511

Destin Anesthesia, LLC (1)
PO Box 735771, Dallas, TX 75373-5771
Web Site:
https://www.destinanesthesiallc.com
Endoscopic Services
N.A.I.C.S.: 621111

Durham Nuclear Imaging Inc. (1)
1615 Dundas Street East Whitby Mall Main
Floor, Whitby, L1N 2L1, ON, Canada
Tel.: (905) 240-6500
Web Site:
https://www.durhamnuclearimaging.com
Diagnostic Imaging Services
N.A.I.C.S.: 621512

ExecHealth Inc. (1)
401-116 Albert Street, Ottawa, K1P 5G3,
ON, Canada
Tel.: (613) 216-3932
Web Site: https://exechealth.ca
Medical Care Services
N.A.I.C.S.: 621111

Greater Washington Anesthesia Associates, LLC (1)
PO Box 731002, Dallas, TX 75373-1002
Web Site:
https://www.washingtonanesthesia.com
Surgical Anaesthesia Services
N.A.I.C.S.: 621111

MedBASE Software Inc. (1)
1730 McPherson Court Unit 30, Pickering,
L1W 3E6, ON, Canada
Tel.: (416) 417-2743
Web Site: https://www.medbase.ca
Medical Billing Services
N.A.I.C.S.: 561110

New England Anesthesia Associates,
LLC (1)
PO Box 735881, Dallas, TX 75373
Web Site:
https://www.newenglandanesthesia.com
Surgical Anaesthesia Services
N.A.I.C.S.: 621111

Pinellas County Anesthesia Associates, LLC (1)
PO Box 730996, Dallas, TX 75373-0996
Web Site:
https://www.pinellascountyanesthesia.com
Surgical Anaesthesia Services
N.A.I.C.S.: 621111

Seekintoo Ltd. (1)
204 - 1109 17th Ave SW, Calgary, T2T
5R9, AB, Canada
Web Site: https://www.seekintoo.com
Cyber Security Services
N.A.I.C.S.: 541519

SleepWorks Medical Inc. (1)
103-15240 56 Ave, Surrey, V3S 5K7, BC,
Canada
Tel.: (604) 372-4000
Web Site:
https://www.sleepworksmedical.com
Sleeping Disorder Treatment Services
N.A.I.C.S.: 621498

Spring Medical Centre Ltd. (1)
4453 Lougheed Highway, Burnaby, V5C
3Z2, BC, Canada
Tel.: (604) 428-1363
Web Site:
https://www.springmedicalcentre.com
Sleeping Disorder Treatment Services
N.A.I.C.S.: 621498

WELL Health Brickyard Inc. (1)
Suite 150 - 17475 56 Ave, Surrey, V3S
2X6, BC, Canada
Tel.: (604) 576-7701
Medical Clinic Services
N.A.I.C.S.: 621399

WELL Health City View Inc. (1)
2480 Heather Street, Vancouver, V5Z 3H9,
BC, Canada
Tel.: (604) 879-3900
Medical Clinic Services
N.A.I.C.S.: 621399

WELL Health Clayton Heights
Inc. (1)
Suite 204 - 18730 Fraser Hwy, Surrey, V3S
7Y4, BC, Canada
Tel.: (604) 575-0501
Medical Clinic Services
N.A.I.C.S.: 621399

WELL Health Clover Care Inc. (1)
Suite 102 - 17770 56th Avenue, Surrey,
V3S 1C7, BC, Canada
Tel.: (604) 574-7883
Medical Clinic Services
N.A.I.C.S.: 621399

WELL Health Colebrook Inc. (1)
Suite 107-15240 56 Ave, Surrey, V3S 5K7,
BC, Canada
Tel.: (778) 574-1414
Medical Clinic Services
N.A.I.C.S.: 621399

WELL Health Coquitlam Inc. (1)
Suite 56 - 2991 Lougheed Highway, Coquitlam, V3B 6J6, BC, Canada
Tel.: (604) 945-7819
Medical Clinic Services
N.A.I.C.S.: 621399

WELL Health Fleetwood Inc. (1)
Suite 306 - 9014 152 Street, Surrey, V3R
4E7, BC, Canada
Tel.: (604) 581-3550
Medical Clinic Services
N.A.I.C.S.: 621399

WELL Health Hasting Sunrise
Inc. (1)
Suite 102 - 2280 E Hastings Street, Vancouver, V5L 1V4, BC, Canada
Tel.: (604) 253-3166
Medical Clinic Services
N.A.I.C.S.: 621399

WELL Health Kerrisdale Inc. (1)
2077 W 42nd Ave, Vancouver, V6M 2B4,
BC, Canada
Tel.: (604) 261-9494
Medical Clinic Services
N.A.I.C.S.: 621399

WELL Health Lonsdale Inc. (1)
Suite 110 - 1100 Lonsdale Ave, North Vancouver, V7M 2H3, BC, Canada
Tel.: (604) 904-8804
Medical Clinic Services
N.A.I.C.S.: 621399

WELL Health Oval Inc. (1)
Suite 1100 160 - 6111 River Road, Richmond, V7C 0A2, BC, Canada
Tel.: (604) 821-1112
Medical Clinic Services
N.A.I.C.S.: 621399

WELL Health Panorama Village
Inc. (1)
Suite 103 - 15157 Highway 10, Surrey, V3S
9A5, BC, Canada
Tel.: (604) 574-0481

Medical Clinic Services
N.A.I.C.S.: 621399

WELL Health Pemberton Marine Inc. (1)
1256 Marine Drive, North Vancouver, V7P 1T2, BC, Canada
Tel.: (604) 986-0677
Medical Clinic Services
N.A.I.C.S.: 621399

WELL Health Point Grey Inc. (1)
4448 West 10th Avenue, Vancouver, V6R 2H9, BC, Canada
Tel.: (778) 379-4448
Medical Clinic Services
N.A.I.C.S.: 621399

WELL Health Richmond Central Inc. (1)
Suite 150 - 7997 Westminster Highway, Richmond, V6X 1A4, BC, Canada
Tel.: (778) 297-4700
Medical Clinic Services
N.A.I.C.S.: 621399

WELL Health Scott Road Inc. (1)
7154 120 Street, Vancouver, V3W 3M8, BC, Canada
Tel.: (604) 590-5811
Medical Clinic Services
N.A.I.C.S.: 621399

WELL Health Triton Inc. (1)
Suite 102 - 12565 88 Ave, Surrey, V3W 3J7, BC, Canada
Tel.: (604) 594-9990
Medical Clinic Services
N.A.I.C.S.: 621399

WELL LEAD MEDICAL CO., LTD.
47 Guomao Avenue South, Panyu District, Guangzhou, 511434, China
Tel.: (86) 2084758878
Web Site: https://www.welllead.com
Year Founded: 2004
603309—(SHG)
Rev.: $191,414,705
Assets: $334,659,265
Liabilities: $90,396,751
Net Worth: $244,262,515
Earnings: $23,386,611
Fiscal Year-end: 12/31/22
Medical Catheter Mfr & Distr
N.A.I.C.S.: 339112
Xiang Bin (Chm)

Subsidiaries:

Jiangxi Langhe Medical Instrument Co., Ltd. (1)
4F Tower D No 346 Panyu Ave North, Guangzhou, 511400, China
Tel.: (86) 2031046252
Web Site: https://www.jxlhyl.com
Medical Product Mfr & Distr
N.A.I.C.S.: 325412

Well Lead Trading Co., Ltd. (1)
Pu Three Road 21 Get 55 56 Silver Billion Riverside Building 805, Shanghai, 200127, China
Tel.: (86) 2158397623
Medical Disposable Product Mfr
N.A.I.C.S.: 339113

Zhangjiagang Shagong Medical Device Co., Ltd. (1)
No 7 Yuefeng Road Zhangjiagang EconomicDevelopment Zone, Zhangjiagang, 215600, China
Tel.: (86) 51258185182
Dialysis Product Mfr
N.A.I.C.S.: 334510

Zhangjiagang Shagong Medical Technology Co., Ltd. (1)
No 7 Yuefeng Road Zhangjiagang Economic Development Zone, Zhangjiagang, 215600, Jiangsu, China
Tel.: (86) 51258185182
Clinical Care Package Product Mfr & Whslr
N.A.I.C.S.: 339113

WELL LINK GROUP HOLDINGS LTD.
Unit 13-15 11/F China Merchants Tower Shun Tak Centre, Connaught Road Central, 168-200, Hong Kong, China (Hong Kong)
Tel.: (852) 3150 7888
Web Site: http://www.welllinkgroup.com
Holding Company
N.A.I.C.S.: 551112
Chujia Xu (Chm)

Subsidiaries:

Banco Well Link, S.A. (1)
28/F No 323 Av Dr Mario Soares, Bank of China Building, Macau, China (Macau) (75%)
Tel.: (853) 2878 5222
Web Site: http://www.wlbank.com.mo
Commercial & Investment Banking
N.A.I.C.S.: 522110
Sheng Man Zhang (Chm)

WELL SA
112 avenue Kleber, 75116, Paris, France
Tel.: (33) 153058000
Web Site: http://www.wellinvestcorp.com
MLKRI—(EUR)
Sales Range: $1-9.9 Million
Business Consulting Services
N.A.I.C.S.: 541611

WELL SERVICES GROUP
Phileas Foggstraat 65, Emmen, Netherlands
Tel.: (31) 591668155
Web Site: http://www.wellservices-group.com
Oil & Energy Services
N.A.I.C.S.: 211120
Geert Prins (CEO)

Subsidiaries:

Central Industrial Services, Inc. (1)
State Rd 2 Km 57.2, Barceloneta, PR 00617
Tel.: (787) 846-5454
Web Site: http://www.centralindustrialpr.com
Insulation of Pipes & Boilers
N.A.I.C.S.: 238990
Enrique Perez (Pres)

WELL SHIN TECHNOLOGY CO., LTD.
No 196 Xinhu 3rd, Neihu District, Taipei, 114, Taiwan
Tel.: (886) 227911119
Web Site: https://www.wellshin.com.tw
Year Founded: 1986
3501—(TAI)
Rev.: $174,262,919
Assets: $269,870,358
Liabilities: $55,978,513
Net Worth: $213,891,846
Earnings: $16,596,716
Emp.: 1,139
Fiscal Year-end: 12/31/23
Power Cords Mfr
N.A.I.C.S.: 314994

Subsidiaries:

Conntek Integrated Solutions Inc (1)
4640 W Ironwood Dr, Franklin, WI 53132
Tel.: (414) 423-1701
Web Site: https://conntekisi.com
Sales Range: $25-49.9 Million
Emp.: 10
Electrical Products Mfr
N.A.I.C.S.: 335931
Drew Leu (COO)

Dongguan Well Shin Electronic Products Co., Ltd. (1)
Chang Long Control Dist Hwang Jiang Cheng, Dongguan, 523766, Guandong, China
Tel.: (86) 76983622694
Electrical Equipment & Component Mfr
N.A.I.C.S.: 335999

Well Shin Electronic (Kun Shan) Co., Ltd. (1)
No 389 Kun Kai Rd, Jin Xi Town, Kunshan, 215324, China
Tel.: (86) 51257229101
Electronic Parts Mfr & Distr
N.A.I.C.S.: 327110

Well Shin Technology Co., Ltd. - Kun Shan Plant (1)
No 389 Kun Kai Rd, Jin Xi Town, Kunshan, 215324, Jiangsu, China
Tel.: (86) 512 5722 9101
Web Site: http://www.wellshin.com.tw
Sales Range: $400-449.9 Million
Emp.: 1,500
Electrical Products Mfr
N.A.I.C.S.: 335999

Well Shin Technology Co., Ltd. - Taiwan Plant (1)
1 Sec 1 Yen Hai Road Mai Tsuo Chun, Fu Hsing Hsiang, Chang-Hua, Taiwan
Tel.: (886) 47703081
Power Cords Mfr
N.A.I.C.S.: 335999

WELLAND FORGE
139 Centre St, PO Box 216, Welland, L3B 5P4, ON, Canada
Tel.: (905) 732-7536
Web Site: http://www.imtforgegroup.com
Sales Range: $10-24.9 Million
Emp.: 100
Iron & Steel Forging Mfr
N.A.I.C.S.: 332111
Ken Hunter (Dir-Fin)

WELLARD LIMITED
Manning Buildings Suite 20 Level 1 135 High Street, Fremantle, 6160, WA, Australia
Tel.: (61) 894322800 AU
Web Site: https://www.wellard.com.au
Year Founded: 1950
WLD—(ASX)
Rev.: $34,943,000
Assets: $42,188,000
Liabilities: $5,125,000
Net Worth: $37,063,000
Earnings: ($815,000)
Fiscal Year-end: 06/30/24
Livestock Exporting
N.A.I.C.S.: 424520
John Klepec (Chm)

WELLCALL HOLDINGS BERHAD
Plot 48 Jalan Johan 2/5 Kawasan Perindustrian Pengkalan II Fasa II, 31550, Ipoh, Perak Darul Ridzuan, Malaysia
Tel.: (60) 53668805
Web Site: https://www.wellcallholdings.com
WELLCAL—(KLS)
Rev.: $45,959,486
Assets: $37,107,410
Liabilities: $7,475,569
Net Worth: $29,631,841
Earnings: $11,698,099
Emp.: 435
Fiscal Year-end: 09/30/23
Rubber Hose Mfr
N.A.I.C.S.: 326220
Sha Huang (Mng Dir)

Subsidiaries:

Wellcall Hose (M) Sdn. Bhd. (1)
Plot 48 Jalan Johan 2/5 Kawasan Perindustrian Pengkalan II Fasa II, Pusing Perak Darul Ridzuan, 31550, Perak, Malaysia
Tel.: (60) 53668805
Web Site: https://www.wellcall.com.my
Sales Range: $125-149.9 Million
Emp.: 450
Industrial Rubber Hose Mfr
N.A.I.C.S.: 326220

WELLCO HOLDINGS CORPORATION
370 Fukudome-machi, Hakusan, 924-0051, Ishikawa, Japan
Tel.: (81) 762779811
Web Site: https://www.wellco-corp.com
Year Founded: 1979
7831—(TKS)
Rev.: $62,505,440
Assets: $79,195,300
Liabilities: $48,722,480
Net Worth: $30,472,820
Earnings: $14,180
Emp.: 309
Fiscal Year-end: 10/31/23
Holding Company
N.A.I.C.S.: 551112
Yukiko Wakabayashi (Chm & Pres)

Subsidiaries:

We'll Corporation Co., Ltd - Direct Marketing Plant (1)
400 Miyanagashin-machi Hakusan, Ishikawa, 924-0018, Japan
Tel.: (81) 762774160
Commercial Printing Services
N.A.I.C.S.: 323111

We'll Corporation Co., Ltd - Kanto No.1 Plant (1)
1-48 Mitodai Tako-machi, Katori-gun, Chiba, 289-2247, Japan
Tel.: (81) 479793722
Commercial Printing Services
N.A.I.C.S.: 323111

We'll Corporation Co., Ltd - Kanto No.2 Plant (1)
2700-92 Koike-Mizuguchi Shibayama-machi, Sanbu-gun, Chiba, 289-1624, Japan
Tel.: (81) 479773220
Commercial Printing Services
N.A.I.C.S.: 323111

We'll Corporation Co., Ltd - Kyoto Plant (1)
28 Shimokoma Kanetsukida Seika-cho, Souraku-gun, Kyoto, 619-0245, Japan
Tel.: (81) 774983575
Commercial Printing Services
N.A.I.C.S.: 323111

WELLDONE CO., LTD.
No 181 Anmei Street, Neihu District, Taipei, 11484, Taiwan
Tel.: (886) 227965959
Web Site: https://www.welldone.com.tw
Year Founded: 1977
6170—(TPE)
Rev.: $77,190,820
Assets: $98,991,777
Liabilities: $54,963,574
Net Worth: $44,028,202
Earnings: $7,808,961
Emp.: 72
Fiscal Year-end: 12/31/22
Telecommunication Servicesb
N.A.I.C.S.: 517112
Tun-Jen Chen (Chm)

WELLE ENVIRONMENTAL GROUP CO., LTD.
No 156 Hanjiang West Road, Xinbei District, Changzhou, 213125, Jiangsu, China
Tel.: (86) 51985125884
Web Site: https://www.wellegroup.com
Year Founded: 2003
300190—(CHIN)
Rev.: $292,721,364
Assets: $1,390,764,492
Liabilities: $833,963,364
Net Worth: $556,801,128
Earnings: ($63,123,840)
Emp.: 2,000
Fiscal Year-end: 12/31/22

WELLE ENVIRONMENTAL GROUP CO., LTD.

WELLE Environmental Group Co., Ltd.—(Continued)
Industrial Waste Water Treatment & Environmental Consulting Services
N.A.I.C.S.: 562211
Yuezhong Li (Chm & Gen Mgr)

Subsidiaries:

Beijing Huiheng Environmental Engineering Co., Ltd. (1)
5th Floor Hengrun International Building No 32, North Third Ring West Road Haidian District, Beijing, 100086, China
Tel.: (86) 1064419809
Web Site: http://www.huiheng-china.com
Waste Water Treatment Services
N.A.I.C.S.: 221320

Changzhou Jinyuan Machinery Equipment Co., Ltd (1)
No 1 Anjia Anning Road Weicun Street, Xinbei District, Changzhou, China
Tel.: (86) 4008288590
Web Site: https://www.czjyjx.net
Emp.: 280
Industrial Machinery Mfr & Distr
N.A.I.C.S.: 333248

Hangzhou Energy & Environmental Engineering Co,. Ltd. (1)
15th Floor Building 1 Block B Zhonghao Wufutiandi, No 207 Fengqi East Road, Hangzhou, 310020, China
Tel.: (86) 5718 604 1861
Web Site: https://www.hzeeec.com
Biogas Plant Construction Services
N.A.I.C.S.: 236210
Cai Changda (Founder)

Nanjing Doule Refrigeration Equipment Co., Ltd. (1)
Lishui Economic Development Zone, South District, Nanjing, 211200, China
Tel.: (86) 2556236601
Web Site: https://www.doule-ref.com
Refrigerator Equipment Mfr
N.A.I.C.S.: 333415

WELLE (Suzhou) Energy Technology Co., Ltd. (1)
West of the North Section of Avenue, Zhangjiagang East District, Zhangjiagang, Jiangsu, China
Tel.: (86) 512563603688018
Waste Leachate Treatment Services
N.A.I.C.S.: 221320

WELLELL INC.

No 9 Min Sheng St, Tu-Cheng, Taipei, 23679, Taiwan
Tel.: (886) 222685568
Web Site: https://www.wellell.com
Year Founded: 1990
4106—(TAI)
Rev.: $86,566,660
Assets: $105,459,429
Liabilities: $28,907,910
Net Worth: $76,551,519
Earnings: $5,003,826
Fiscal Year-end: 12/31/23
Medicinal Product Mfr
N.A.I.C.S.: 339112

Subsidiaries:

Apex Medical (Kunshan) Co., Ltd. (1)
No 1368 ZiZhu Road, Kunshan, Jiangsu, China
Tel.: (86) 51286171660
Medical Equipment Distr
N.A.I.C.S.: 456199

Apex Medical (Kunshan) Corp. (1)
No 1368 ZiZhu Road, Kunshan, Jiangsu, China
Tel.: (86) 51286188866
Medical Equipment Distr
N.A.I.C.S.: 456199

Apex Medical France SASU (1)
Elcano 8 Bd de I Eperviere ZI de Beuzon, 49000, Ecouflant, France
Tel.: (33) 272792713
Medical Equipment Distr
N.A.I.C.S.: 456199

Apex Medical Limited (1)
Unit 21 Optima Park Thames Road, Crayford, DA1 4QX, Kent, United Kingdom
Tel.: (44) 1322520560
Emp.: 25
Medical Equipment Distr
N.A.I.C.S.: 456199
Haydn Pugh (Mgr)

Apex Medical S.L. (1)
Elcano 9 6a planta, 48008, Bilbao, Vizcaya, Spain
Tel.: (34) 944706408
Medical Equipment Distr
N.A.I.C.S.: 456199

Apex Medical Thailand Co., Ltd. (1)
65/100 Chamnanphenjati Business Center Bldg 11/F Rama 9 Road Huaykwang, Bangkok, 10320, Thailand
Tel.: (66) 9484848
Medical Equipment Distr
N.A.I.C.S.: 456199

Apex Medical USA Corp. (1)
927 Mariner St, Brea, CA 92821
Tel.: (714) 671-3818
Medical Equipment Distr
N.A.I.C.S.: 456199

Apex Medicalcorp India Pvt. Ltd. (1)
303 Third Floor Block 4A DLF Corporate Park Phase - ill, Gurgaon, Haryana, India
Tel.: (91) 1166544138
Web Site: http://apexmedicalcorp.in
Medical Equipment Distr
N.A.I.C.S.: 456199

WELLEX INDUSTRIES INC.

35th Floor One Corporate Center, Julia Vargas Ave corner Meralco Ave Ortigas Center, Pasig, 1605, Philippines
Tel.: (63) 27067888 PH
Web Site:
https://www.wellexindustries.com
Year Founded: 1956
WIN—(PHI)
Rev.: $464,911
Assets: $29,315,097
Liabilities: $7,580,789
Net Worth: $21,734,307
Earnings: $65,100
Emp.: 18
Fiscal Year-end: 12/31/23
Business Enterprises Development Operations
N.A.I.C.S.: 561499

WELLFIELD TECHNOLOGIES INC.

666 Burrard St 2500, Vancouver, V6C 2X8, BC, Canada
Tel.: (972) 547-4027 BC
Web Site: https://www.wellfield.io
Year Founded: 2021
WFLD—(TSXV)
Information Technology Services
N.A.I.C.S.: 541512
Neal Sample (Chm)

WELLFULLY LIMITED

Level 1 284 Oxford Street, Leederville, 6007, WA, Australia
Tel.: (61) 894433011
Web Site: http://www.wellfully.net
WFL—(ASX)
Rev.: $1,006,617
Assets: $2,327,035
Liabilities: $3,468,719
Net Worth: ($1,141,684)
Earnings: ($4,242,453)
Fiscal Year-end: 06/30/23
Drug Research & Development
N.A.I.C.S.: 325411
Jeffrey David Edwards (Mng Dir)

Subsidiaries:

Bodyguard Lifesciences Pty. Ltd. (1)
284 Oxford Street, Leederville, 6007, WA, Australia
Tel.: (61) 894433011

Web Site: http://www.bgls.com.au
Wearable Product Distr
N.A.I.C.S.: 423450
George Tsadilas (Product Mgr)

WELLHOPE FOODS CO., LTD.

No 169 Huishan Street, Shenbei New District, Shenyang, 110164, Liaoning, China
Tel.: (86) 2488082666
Web Site: https://en.wellhope-ag.com
Year Founded: 1995
603609—(SHG)
Rev.: $4,606,770,851
Assets: $2,161,221,482
Liabilities: $987,937,755
Net Worth: $1,173,283,727
Earnings: $72,099,949
Fiscal Year-end: 12/31/22
Animal Feed Mfr
N.A.I.C.S.: 311119
Weidong Jin (Co-Founder & Chm)

Subsidiaries:

Dalian Zhongjia Food Co., Ltd. (1)
Zhang Tun Village Sun St Office, Wafangdian City, Dalian, Liaoning, China
Tel.: (86) 41185365988
Web Site: http://www.en.dlzjfood.cn
Emp.: 650
Chicken Farming Mfr
N.A.I.C.S.: 311615

Shenyang Fame Bio-Tech Co., Ltd. (1)
No 67 Shenying Road, Hunnan District, Shenyang, 110179, China
Tel.: (86) 2431375277
Web Site: http://www.wellhope-bio.com
Veterinary Medicine Mfr
N.A.I.C.S.: 325412

WELLMASTER PIPE & SUPPLY INC.

1494 Bell Mill Road, Tillsonburg, N4G 4J1, ON, Canada
Tel.: (519) 688-0500 ON
Web Site: http://www.wellmaster.ca
Year Founded: 1987
Sales Range: $10-24.9 Million
Emp.: 20
Metal Material Handling Cart Rack Coupling Drive Shoe & Other Fabricated Metal Product Mfr
N.A.I.C.S.: 332999
Doug White (Pres-Fin)

WELLNEO SUGAR CO., LTD.

14-1 Nihonbashi-Koamicho, Chuo-ku, Tokyo, 103-8536, Japan
Tel.: (81) 336682422
Web Site: https://www.nissin-sugar.co.jp
2117—(TKS)
Rev.: $609,389,120
Assets: $634,017,980
Liabilities: $164,000,710
Net Worth: $470,017,270
Earnings: $36,513,640
Emp.: 376
Fiscal Year-end: 03/31/24
Holding Company; Sugar Mfr
N.A.I.C.S.: 551112
Yoichi Higuchi (Chm & CEO)

Subsidiaries:

Wellneo Sugar Co., Ltd. (1)
14-1 Nihonbashi-Koamicho, Chuo-ku, Tokyo, 103-0016, Japan
Tel.: (81) 336681103
Web Site: https://www.wellneo-sugar.co.jp
Business Management Services
N.A.I.C.S.: 561110

WELLNESS AND BEAUTY SOLUTIONS LIMITED

14/347 Bay Road, Cheltenham, 3192, VIC, Australia
Tel.: (61) 3 9532 2639

Web Site: http://www.wnbltd.com.au
Rev.: $6,984,381
Assets: $9,995,569
Liabilities: $5,450,658
Net Worth: $4,544,911
Earnings: ($9,424,554)
Fiscal Year-end: 06/30/19
Cosmetics & Related Services
N.A.I.C.S.: 456120
Christine Parkes (CEO & Mng Dir)

WELLNESS NONI LIMITED

Door Plot No 48 Thirumalai Nagar Annexe First Main Road Perungudi, Chennai, 600 096, Tamil Nadu, India
Tel.: (91) 4424960030
Web Site:
http://www.wellnessnoni.net
Year Founded: 1992
531211—(BOM)
Rev.: $257,735
Assets: $138,016
Liabilities: $28,013
Net Worth: $110,003
Earnings: ($314,293)
Emp.: 13
Fiscal Year-end: 03/31/22
Food Products Mfr
N.A.I.C.S.: 311999
S. Kala (Mng Dir)

WELLNET CORPORATION

1-7 Uchisaiwaicho 1-chome, Chiyoda-ku, Tokyo, 100-0011, Japan
Tel.: (81) 335800199 JP
Web Site: http://www.well-net.jp
Year Founded: 1983
2428—(TKS)
Electronic Transaction Settlement & Bill Payment Services
N.A.I.C.S.: 518210
Takashi Yanagimoto (Chm)

WELLSPIRE HOLDINGS BERHAD

Lot D/E Level 12 Tower 1 Etiqa Twins 11 Jalan Pinang, Wilayah Persekutuan KL, 50450, Kuala Lumpur, Malaysia
Tel.: (60) 397797066
Web Site:
https://www.wellspireholdings.com
Year Founded: 2021
WELLS—(KLS)
Rev.: $27,183,233
Assets: $15,524,172
Liabilities: $2,279,281
Net Worth: $13,244,890
Earnings: $969,467
Emp.: 100
Fiscal Year-end: 12/31/23
Holding Company
N.A.I.C.S.: 551112

WELLTEND TECHNOLOGY CORPORATION

6F No 59 Tung Hsing Rd, Xinyi Dist, Taipei, 110, Taiwan
Tel.: (886) 287682688
Web Site: http://www.welltend.com.tw
3021—(TAI)
Rev.: $97,996,595
Assets: $95,973,082
Liabilities: $45,779,716
Net Worth: $50,193,366
Earnings: $4,207,757
Emp.: 963
Fiscal Year-end: 12/31/23
Electronic Products Mfr
N.A.I.C.S.: 334419
Chang Yun Teng (Chm)

WELSPUN GROUP

Welspun House 7th Floor Kamala Mills Compound Senapati Bapat

Marg, Lower Parel, Mumbai, 400 013, India
Tel.: (91) 22 66136000
Web Site: http://www.welspun.com
Year Founded: 1985
Holding Company; Pipes, Plates & Coils & Home Textiles Mfr
N.A.I.C.S.: 551112
Balkrishan Goenka *(Chm)*

Subsidiaries:

Aym Syntex Limited (1)
9th Floor Trade World B Wing Kamala City, Senapati Bapat Marg Lower Parel, Mumbai, 400013, India
Tel.: (91) 2261637000
Web Site: https://www.aymsyntex.com
Rev.: $175,726,959
Assets: $110,348,444
Liabilities: $59,962,005
Net Worth: $50,386,440
Earnings: $858,702
Emp.: 1,131
Fiscal Year-end: 03/31/2023
Polyester Filament Yarn Mfr
N.A.I.C.S.: 313110
Kushboo Mandawewala *(Head-HR)*

Welspun Corp. Limited (1)
Welspun City Village Versamedi Taluka Anjar, District Kutch, Ahmedabad, 370 110, Gujarat, India
Tel.: (91) 2836662222
Web Site: https://www.welspuncorp.com
Rev.: $1,208,330,436
Assets: $1,839,141,538
Liabilities: $1,258,344,224
Net Worth: $580,797,314
Earnings: $23,879,863
Emp.: 2,105
Fiscal Year-end: 03/31/2023
Steel Pole Mfr
N.A.I.C.S.: 331210
Rajesh R. Mandawewala *(Grp Mng Dir)*

Subsidiary (Domestic):

Sintex BAPL Limited (2)
2011 2nd Floor Farena Corporate Park Hadapsar - Kharadi Bypass Road, Hadapsar, Pune, 411013, India
Tel.: (91) 2071055600
Web Site: https://www.sintexbapl.co.in
Raw Material & Equipment Distr
N.A.I.C.S.: 423490
Indru Advani *(Pres)*

Sintex Prefab and Infra Limited (2)
4th Floor BVM building Nr Seven Garnala B/H Railway Crossing, Kalol, 382721, India
Tel.: (91) 2764253000
Web Site: http://www.sintexinfraprojects.com
Plastics Product Mfr
N.A.I.C.S.: 326199
Manish Kaushik *(Gen Mgr)*

Plant (Domestic):

Welspun Corp Limited - Plant I (2)
Near Dahej Taluka Vagra, Village Jolva Vadadla, Bharuch, 392 130, Gujarat, India
Tel.: (91) 2641 256281
Steel Pole Mfr
N.A.I.C.S.: 331210

Welspun Corp Limited - Plant II (2)
Welspun City, Kutch, Anjar, 370 110, Gujarat, India
Tel.: (91) 2836 662222
Steel Pole Mfr
N.A.I.C.S.: 331210

Welspun Enterprises Limited (1)
C8 BKT House Trade World Kamala City, Senapati Bapat Marg Lower Parel, Mumbai, 400 013, India
Tel.: (91) 2266136000
Web Site: https://www.welspunenterprises.com
Rev.: $183,557,010
Assets: $476,697,585
Liabilities: $218,142,015
Net Worth: $258,555,570
Earnings: $12,754,560
Emp.: 1,006
Fiscal Year-end: 03/31/2022
Holding Company; Industrial Construction Services
N.A.I.C.S.: 551112

Balkrishan K. Goenka *(Chm)*

Subsidiary (Domestic):

Michigan Engineers Private Limited (2)
Shop No D-7 Commerce Center Co-Operative Society Limited No 78, Javji Dadaji Marg Tardeo Rd Janata Nagar Tardeo, Mumbai, 400 034, India (50.1%)
Tel.: (91) 2223514871
Dam & Tunnel Construction Services
N.A.I.C.S.: 237990
Rupen Patel *(Mng Dir)*

Welspun India Limited (1)
Welspun House 6th Floor Kamala Mills Compound Senapati Bapat Marg, Lower Parel, Mumbai, 400 013, India
Tel.: (91) 2266136000
Web Site: https://www.welspunindia.com
Rev.: $984,964,930
Assets: $1,037,117,679
Liabilities: $534,026,737
Net Worth: $503,090,942
Earnings: $24,280,319
Emp.: 1,350
Fiscal Year-end: 03/31/2023
Textile Products Mfr
N.A.I.C.S.: 314999
Rajesh R. Mandawewala *(Co-Mng Dir)*

Welspun Middle East Pipes Coating Company LLC (1)
2nd Ind City, PO Box 12943, Dammam, 31483, Saudi Arabia
Tel.: (966) 3 812 1999
Steel Pole Mfr
N.A.I.C.S.: 331210

Welspun Retail Limited (1)
Trade World B Wing 9th Floor Kamala Mills Compound S B Marg, Lower Parel, Mumbai, 400 013, India
Tel.: (91) 6613 6000
Furniture Distr
N.A.I.C.S.: 423220
Ajay Khemani *(Asst Mgr-Fin, Acct & Comml)*

Welspun Speciality Solutions Ltd. (1)
Welspun House 5th Floor Kamala Mills Compound, Senapati Bapat Marg Lower Parel West, Mumbai, 400013, Maharashtra, India
Tel.: (91) 2266136000
Web Site: https://www.welspunspecialty.com
Rev.: $24,898,965
Assets: $50,839,425
Liabilities: $49,812,945
Net Worth: $1,026,480
Earnings: ($4,201,470)
Emp.: 506
Fiscal Year-end: 03/31/2022
Steel Products Mfr
N.A.I.C.S.: 331210
Anuj Burakia *(CEO)*

Welspun Steel Limited - Kutch Plant (1)
Survey no 650 PO-Versamedi, District Kutch, Anjar, 370 110, Gujarat, India
Tel.: (91) 2836 279051
Steel Pole Mfr
N.A.I.C.S.: 331210

Welspun Tubular LLC (1)
9301 Frazier Pk, Little Rock, AR 72206
Tel.: (501) 301-8800
Steel Pipe Distr
N.A.I.C.S.: 423510
Dave Delie *(Pres)*

Welspun U.S.A. Inc. (1)
Ste No 1118-1120 295 Textile Bldg 5th Ave, New York, NY 10016
Tel.: (212) 620-2000
Web Site: http://www.welspun.com
Emp.: 30
Apparel Product Distr
N.A.I.C.S.: 424110
Nancy Golden *(Sr VP-Mktg)*

Welspun UK Limited (1)
Park Square Bird Hall Lane, Cheadle, SK8 0XF, Cheshire, United Kingdom
Tel.: (44) 161 367 5800
Steel Pipe Distr
N.A.I.C.S.: 423510

Joel Rosenblatt *(Mng Dir)*

WELSPUN INVESTMENTS & COMMERCIALS LIMITED
Welspun House 7th Floor Kamala Mills Compound, Senapati Bapat Marg Lower Parel W, Mumbai, 400 013, India
Tel.: (91) 2266136000
Web Site:
    https://www.welspuninvestment.com
Year Founded: 2008
WELINV—(NSE)
Rev.: $917,715
Assets: $23,400,576
Liabilities: $455,800
Net Worth: $22,944,775
Earnings: $657,251
Emp.: 2
Fiscal Year-end: 03/31/23
Investment Services
N.A.I.C.S.: 523150
Atul Desai *(Chm)*

WELTERMAN INTERNATIONAL LIMITED
Plot No 39 1 MIDC Industrial Area, Dhatav Tal Raigad, Roha, 402109, Maharashtra, India
Tel.: (91) 2653050843
Web Site:
    https://www.welterman.com
Year Founded: 1992
526431—(BOM)
Rev.: $101,253
Assets: $228,871
Liabilities: $1,678,496
Net Worth: ($1,449,625)
Earnings: ($35,945)
Fiscal Year-end: 03/31/23
Leather Soles Mfr
N.A.I.C.S.: 316210
Narendra M. Patel *(CFO)*

WELTREND SEMICONDUCTOR, INC.
2F No 24 Industry E 9th Rd Hsinchu Science Park, Hsin-chu, 300, Taiwan
Tel.: (886) 35780241
Web Site:
    https://www.weltrend.com.tw
Year Founded: 1989
2436—(TAI)
Rev.: $94,364,103
Assets: $191,371,947
Liabilities: $58,817,618
Net Worth: $132,554,330
Earnings: $6,772,164
Fiscal Year-end: 12/31/23
Integrated Circuits Mfr
N.A.I.C.S.: 334413
Sam Lin *(Chm & CEO)*

WELVIC AUSTRALIA PTY. LTD.
Gate 6 Tilburn Road, Deer Park, 3023, VIC, Australia
Tel.: (61) 3 9361 8700 AU
Web Site: http://www.welvic.com.au
Emp.: 30
Plastic Resin Mfr
N.A.I.C.S.: 325211
Michael Starcevic *(Mgr-Ops)*

Subsidiaries:

Boron Molecular Pty. Limited (1)
500 Princes Highway, Noble Park, 3174, VIC, Australia
Tel.: (61) 3 8558 8000
Web Site: http://www.boronmolecular.com
Emp.: 10
Biomolecular Compound Chemicals Mfr
N.A.I.C.S.: 325414
Ken Sullivan *(Dir-Sls & Mktg)*

WEMA BANK PLC.
54 Marina, Lagos, Nigeria
Tel.: (234) 8039003700 NG

Web Site:
    https://www.wemabank.com
Year Founded: 1945
WEMABANK—(NIGE)
Rev.: $79,968,491
Assets: $1,067,265,468
Liabilities: $1,006,167,383
Net Worth: $61,098,084
Earnings: $8,402,712
Emp.: 1,415
Fiscal Year-end: 12/31/22
Commercial Banking Services
N.A.I.C.S.: 522110
Ademola Adebise *(CEO & Mng Dir)*

WEMADE CO., LTD.
Tower 49 Daewangpangyoro 644beongil, Bundang-gu Seongnam-si, Seoul, 152-848, Gyeonggi-do, Korea (South)
Tel.: (82) 237092000
Web Site: https://www.wemade.com
112040—(KRS)
Rev.: $355,498,031
Assets: $1,096,680,516
Liabilities: $686,850,693
Net Worth: $409,829,823
Earnings: ($142,474,672)
Emp.: 130
Fiscal Year-end: 12/31/22
Online Game Developing Services
N.A.I.C.S.: 513210
Kwan Ho Park *(Chm)*

WEMADE MAX CO., LTD
Wemade Tower 4F 49 Daewangpangyo-ro 644beon-gil, Bundang-gu, Seongnam, Gyeonggi-do, Korea (South)
Tel.: (82) 24208854
Web Site:
    https://www.wemademax.com
Year Founded: 1997
101730—(KRS)
Rev.: $66,142,454
Assets: $94,163,661
Liabilities: $33,050,408
Net Worth: $61,113,253
Earnings: $19,376,786
Emp.: 23
Fiscal Year-end: 12/31/22
Game Developing Services
N.A.I.C.S.: 513210
Gilhyung Lee *(CEO)*

WEMADE PLAY CO., LTD.
9F 42 Hwangsaeul-ro 360beon-gil, Bundang-gu, Seongnam, Gyeonggi-do, Korea (South)
Tel.: (82) 3118339782
Web Site:
    https://corp.wemadeplay.com
Year Founded: 2009
123420—(KRS)
Rev.: $102,612,611
Assets: $309,971,555
Liabilities: $139,449,522
Net Worth: $170,522,033
Earnings: $408,488
Emp.: 253
Fiscal Year-end: 12/31/22
Game Software Development Services
N.A.I.C.S.: 513210

WEMBLEY SOCIEDADE ANONIMA
R Aimores 981, 30140071, Belo Horizonte, MG, Brazil
Tel.: (55) 31 247 1877
Year Founded: 1965
Textile Product Mfr & Distr
N.A.I.C.S.: 314999
Joao Batista Da Cunha Bomfim *(Dir-IR)*

WENCAN GROUP CO., LTD.

Wencan Group Co., Ltd.—(Continued)

WENCAN GROUP CO., LTD.
No 125 Heshun Avenue, Lishui Town
Nanhai District, Foshan, 528241,
Guangdong, China
Tel.: (86) 75785121488
Web Site: http://www.wencan.com
Year Founded: 1998
603348—(SHG)
Rev.: $734,232,190
Assets: $1,032,030,432
Liabilities: $604,286,921
Net Worth: $427,743,510
Earnings: $33,355,937
Emp.: 200
Fiscal Year-end: 12/31/22
Die Casting Parts Mfr & Distr
N.A.I.C.S.: 331523
Jiexiong Tang (Vice Chm)

Subsidiaries:

Guangdong Wencan Mould & Tooling
Co., Ltd. (1)
Heshun Da Road, Nanhai, Foshan, 528241,
Guangdong, China
Tel.: (86) 75785119488
Aluminium Alloy Die Casting Mfr & Distr
N.A.I.C.S.: 331523

Hongbang Die Casting (Nantong)
Co., Ltd. (1)
West Zhaoxia Tongzhou Economic Development Zone, Nantong, 226300, Jiangsu,
China
Tel.: (86) 51386559488
Aluminium Alloy Die Casting Mfr & Distr
N.A.I.C.S.: 331523

Tianjin Hongbang Die Casting Co.,
Ltd. (1)
Economic and Technological Development
Zone, Tianjin, China
Tel.: (86) 2259002488
Aluminium Alloy Die Casting Mfr & Distr
N.A.I.C.S.: 331523
Fan SongTao (Mgr-Die Casting)

WENDEL S.A.
4 rue PaulCezanne, 75008, Paris,
Cedex 09, France
Tel.: (33) 142853000 FR
Web Site:
https://www.wendelgroup.com
Year Founded: 1704
MF—(EUR)
Rev.: $9,389,596,374
Assets: $15,516,943,665
Liabilities: $10,513,490,179
Net Worth: $5,003,453,486
Earnings: $1,103,064,969
Emp.: 93,717
Fiscal Year-end: 12/31/22
Equity Investment Firm
N.A.I.C.S.: 523999
David Darmon (Deputy CEO &
Member-Exec Bd)

Subsidiaries:

Association of Certified Anti-Money
Laundering Specialists LLC (1)
500 W Monroe St Ste 28, Chicago, IL
60661
Tel.: (305) 373-0020
Web Site: http://www.acams.org
Financial Crime Educational Support Services
N.A.I.C.S.: 611710

Subsidiary (Non-US):

ACAMS (Australia) Pty. Ltd. (2)
Level 26 1 Bligh Street, Sydney, 2000,
NSW, Australia
Tel.: (61) 280170295
Anti-Financial Crime Training Services
N.A.I.C.S.: 813219

ACAMS (HK) Ltd. (2)
23/F One Island East 18 Westlands Road,
Quarry Bay, China (Hong Kong)
Tel.: (852) 37507684

Financial Crime Educational Support Services
N.A.I.C.S.: 611710

Subsidiary (Non-US):

ACAMS (Taiwan) Limited (3)
Level 57 Taipei 101 Tower No 7 Section 5
Xinyi Road, Xinyi District, Taipei, 110, Taiwan
Tel.: (886) 287292988
Financial Crime Educational Services
N.A.I.C.S.: 611710

ACAMS Consulting (Beijing) Co., (3)
8 Jianguomen North Street Room 1201-51
China Resources Building, Dong Cheng
District, Beijing, 100005, China
Tel.: (86) 1058111797
Web Site: http://www.acams.org.cn
Financial Crime Educational Services
N.A.I.C.S.: 611710

Subsidiary (Non-US):

ACAMS (Panama) S. de R.I. (2)
PH Destiny Avenida Balboa, Panama,
Panama
Tel.: (507) 63065899
Financial Crime Educational Services
N.A.I.C.S.: 611710

ACAMS (Singapore) Pte. Ltd. (2)
Level 25 North Tower One Raffles Quay,
Singapore, 048583, Singapore
Tel.: (65) 66225611
Financial Crime Educational Services
N.A.I.C.S.: 611710

ACAMS (UK) Ltd. (2)
Level 25 40 Bank Street, Canary Wharf,
London, E14 5NR, United Kingdom
Tel.: (44) 2037557400
Financial Crime Educational Services
N.A.I.C.S.: 611710

ACAMS France SAS (2)
23 rue Balzac, 75008, Paris, France
Tel.: (33) 153536815
Financial Crime Educational Services
N.A.I.C.S.: 611710

ACAMS Japan K.K. (2)
Level 26 Kyobashi Edogrand 2-2-1 Kyobashi, Chuo-ku, Tokyo, 104-0031, Japan
Tel.: (81) 368310622
Web Site: http://www.japan.acams.org
Financial Crime Educational Services
N.A.I.C.S.: 611710

ACAMS Mexico, S. de R.L. de
C.V. (2)
Virgilio St 9th, Polanco, 11550, Mexico,
Mexico
Tel.: (52) 15571117810
Education Management Services
N.A.I.C.S.: 611710

Crisis Prevention Institute, Inc. (1)
10850 W Park Pl Ste 250, Milwaukee, WI
53224
Web Site: http://www.crisisprevention.com
Emp.: 38,000
Professional Training & Coaching Services
N.A.I.C.S.: 611430
Algene Caraulia Sr. (Founder)

Cromology SAS (1)
71 Boulevard du General Leclerc, 92110,
Clichy, France (81%)
Tel.: (33) 1 41 27 62 00
Web Site: http://www.cromology.com
Sales Range: $1-4.9 Billion
Emp.: 4,000
Holding Company; Specialty Building Materials Mfr & Whslr
N.A.I.C.S.: 551112
Philippe Ronphe (Dir-HR)

Subsidiary (Domestic):

Materis Peintures S.A.S. (2)
71 Boulevard du General Leclerc, F-92583,
Clichy, Cedex, France
Tel.: (33) 141276200
Sales Range: $900-999.9 Million
Emp.: 4,190
Paint & Wall Coating Mfr & Whslr
N.A.I.C.S.: 325510
Olivier Legrain (Pres)

Subsidiary (Non-US):

Materis Paints Italia S.p.A. (3)
Via Nino Bixio 47/49, 20026, Nova Milanese, MI, Italy
Tel.: (39) 02354701
Paint & Wall Coatings Mfr
N.A.I.C.S.: 325510

Unit (Domestic):

Materis Paints Italia S.p.A. Divisione
Viero (4)
Via Provinciale 309, 21030, Cassano Valcuvia, Italy
Tel.: (39) 0332999311
Web Site: http://www.viero-coatings.it
Specialty Paint & Wall Coatings Mfr
N.A.I.C.S.: 325510

Oranje-Nassau Groep B.V. (1)
Rembrandt Tower 22nd Floor Amsteinplein 1,
1096 HA, Amsterdam, Netherlands (100%)
Tel.: (31) 205677102
Web Site: https://www.oranje-nassau.com
Sales Range: $400-449.9 Million
Emp.: 5
Equity Investment Firm
N.A.I.C.S.: 523999
Jean-Yves Hemery (Exec Dir)

Subsidiary (Domestic):

Oranje-Nassau Participaties B.V. (2)
Amstelplein 1, Amsterdam, 1096 HA,
Netherlands (100%)
Tel.: (31) 205677102
Web Site: http://www.oranje-nassau.com
Sales Range: $75-99.9 Million
Emp.: 4
Private Equity Investment & Management
Firm
N.A.I.C.S.: 523999

Stahl Holdings B.V. (1)
Sluisweg 10, 5145 PE, Waalwijk,
Netherlands (75.3%)
Tel.: (31) 416689111
Web Site: https://www.stahl.com
Sales Range: $800-899.9 Million
Emp.: 1,800
Holding Company; Leather Treatment
Chemical & Performance Coating Products
Mfr & Whslr
N.A.I.C.S.: 551112
Huub Van Beijeren (CEO)

Subsidiary (US):

Eagle Performance Products,
Inc. (2)
340 Beamer Road SW, Calhoun, GA 30701
Tel.: (706) 629-1044
Web Site:
http://www.eagleperformanceproduct.com
Emp.: 11
Flame Retardant Products Mfr
N.A.I.C.S.: 325998
John D. Friddle (Bus Mgr)

Subsidiary (Domestic):

Stahl B.V. (2)
Sluisweg 10, 5145 PE, Waalwijk, Netherlands
Tel.: (31) 416 689 111
Web Site: http://www.stahl.com
Leather Treatment Chemicals & Performance Coatings Mfr & Whslr
N.A.I.C.S.: 325998
Uwe Siebgens (Grp Dir-Performance Coatings & Polymers)

Tsebo Solutions Group Pty Ltd. (1)
Tsebo House 7 Arnold Road, Rosebank,
Johannesburg, South Africa
Tel.: (27) 114415300
Web Site: http://www.tsebo.com
Facility Services
N.A.I.C.S.: 561210
Chris Jardine (Co-CEO-Grp)

Wendel Japan KK (1)
Level 20 Marunouchi Trust Tower Main
1-8-3 Marunouchi, Chiyoda-Ku, Tokyo, 100-0005, Japan
Tel.: (81) 362693244
Web Site: http://www.wendelgroup.co.jp
Investment Management Service
N.A.I.C.S.: 523999

INTERNATIONAL PUBLIC

WENDELL INDUSTRIAL CO., LTD.
6F No 188 Baoqiao Rd, Xindian Dist,
New Taipei City, 23145, Taiwan
Tel.: (886) 229175770
Web Site:
https://www.wendell.com.tw
Year Founded: 1979
6761—(TPE)
Rev.: $60,126,599
Assets: $60,241,785
Liabilities: $28,498,359
Net Worth: $31,743,426
Earnings: $6,046,587
Fiscal Year-end: 12/31/22
Electronic Component Mfr & Distr
N.A.I.C.S.: 334419
Zhi-Hong Gao (Pres)

WENDELL MOTOR SALES LTD.
549 Fairway Road South, Kitchener,
N2C 1X4, ON, Canada
Tel.: (519) 893-1501
Web Site:
http://www.wendellmotor.com
Year Founded: 1956
Sales Range: $25-49.9 Million
New & Used Car Dealers
N.A.I.C.S.: 441110
Craig Hendry (Pres)

WENDT (INDIA) LIMITED
69-70 SIPCOT Industrial Complex,
Hosur, 635125, Tamilnadu, India
Tel.: (91) 4344276851
Web Site:
https://www.wendtindia.com
Year Founded: 1980
WENDT—(NSE)
Rev.: $19,189,975
Assets: $25,249,811
Liabilities: $5,678,113
Net Worth: $19,571,698
Earnings: $1,742,504
Emp.: 412
Fiscal Year-end: 03/31/21
Tool Mfr
N.A.I.C.S.: 333517
Shrinivas G. Shirgurkar (Chm)

Subsidiaries:

Wendt Grinding Technologies
Limited (1)
109/21 Moo 4 Eastern Seaboard Industrial
Estate Rayong Tambol, Amphur Pluakdaeng, Rayong, 21140, Thailand
Tel.: (66) 38955490
Sales Range: $25-49.9 Million
Emp.: 9
Grinding Wheel Mfr
N.A.I.C.S.: 327910
Praveen Jaduvanshi (Head-Ops)

Wendt Middle East FZE (1)
Warehouse No W3-8, PO Box 50732, Hamriyah Free Zone, Sharjah, 50732, United
Arab Emirates
Tel.: (971) 50 1153343
Web Site: http://www.wendtindia.com
Sales Range: $25-49.9 Million
Emp.: 5
Precision Turned Product Mfr
N.A.I.C.S.: 332721

WENFENG GREAT WORLD CHAIN DEVELOPMENT CORPORATION
No 59 Qingnian Middle Road, Nantong, 226007, Jiangsu, China
Tel.: (86) 51385505666
Web Site: http://www.wfdsj.com.cn
Year Founded: 1995
601010—(SHG)
Rev.: $335,923,511
Assets: $933,326,045
Liabilities: $322,706,002
Net Worth: $610,620,042

AND PRIVATE COMPANIES

Earnings: ($22,738,833)
Fiscal Year-end: 12/31/22
Departmental Store Operator
N.A.I.C.S.: 455110
Wang Yue *(Chm)*

WENG FINE ART AG
Rheinpromenade 8, 40789, Monheim am Rhein, Germany
Tel.: (49) 21736908700
Web Site:
   https://www.wengfineart.com
Year Founded: 1994
Commercial Industrial Machinery Mfr
N.A.I.C.S.: 333310
Jan Vermeulen *(Project Mgr)*

WENLING ZHEJIANG MEASURING & CUTTING TOOLS TRADING CENTRE COMPANY LIMITED
Qianyangxia Village, Wenqiao Town, Wenling, Zhejiang, China
Tel.: (86) 57686970099   CN
Web Site: https://www.cnglj.com
Year Founded: 2003
1379—(HKG)
Cutting Tool Product Mfr
N.A.I.C.S.: 333515
Haihong Pan *(Chm, CEO & Exec Dir)*

WENS FOODSTUFF GROUP CO., LTD.
No 9 Dongdi North Road, Xincheng Town Xinxing County, Yunfu, Guangdong, China
Tel.: (86) 7662292926
Web Site: https://www.wens.com.cn
300498—(CHIN)
Rev.: $12,665,386,865
Assets: $13,084,280,483
Liabilities: $8,035,227,617
Net Worth: $5,049,052,866
Earnings: ($899,983,949)
Emp.: 49,300
Fiscal Year-end: 12/31/23
Livestock Production Services
N.A.I.C.S.: 112990
Zhifen Wen *(Chm)*

WENTRONIC HOLDING GMBH
Pillmannstrasse 12, 38112, Braunschweig, Germany
Tel.: (49) 531 21058 0   De
Web Site: http://www.wentronic.com
Year Founded: 1992
Holding Company
N.A.I.C.S.: 551112
Dietmar Wendt *(Founder & Mng Dir)*

Subsidiaries:

Cellnet Group Limited   (1)
E1/5 Grevillea Place, Brisbane, 4008, QLD, Australia   **(100%)**
Tel.: (61) 1300255563
Web Site: http://www.cellnet.com.au
Rev.: $60,206,444
Assets: $36,016,293
Liabilities: $16,233,268
Net Worth: $19,783,026
Earnings: ($1,762,237)
Emp.: 70
Fiscal Year-end: 06/30/2022
Telecommunications, Audio Visual & Information Technology Products Distr
N.A.I.C.S.: 423620
Dave Clark *(CEO)*

Subsidiary (Non-US):

Cellnet Limited   (2)
10a Orbit Drive, Rosedale, Auckland, 0632, New Zealand
Tel.: (64) 800235538
Web Site: http://www.webcell.co.nz
Telecommunications, Audio Visual & Information Technology Products Distr
N.A.I.C.S.: 423620
Dave Clark *(Dir)*

Subsidiary (Domestic):

VME Systems Pty Ltd   (2)
2 Varman Court, Nunawading, 3131, Australia
Tel.: (61) 398452611
Mobile Accessories Whslr
N.A.I.C.S.: 423690

Wentronic Asia Pacific Ltd.   (1)
Unit 1207-08 12th Floor Prosperity Millenia Plaza, 663 Kings Road, Quarry Bay, China (Hong Kong)
Tel.: (852) 2525 1630
Electronic Equipment & Accessories Distr
N.A.I.C.S.: 423690
Brian Danos *(Gen Mgr & Head-Sls)*

Wentronic GmbH   (1)
Pillmannstrasse 12, 38112, Braunschweig, Germany
Tel.: (49) 531 210 58 0
Web Site: http://www.wentronic.de
Electronic Equipment & Accessories Distr
N.A.I.C.S.: 423690
Marco Winkler *(Sls Mgr-Export)*

Wentronic Italia S.r.l.   (1)
Via Provinciale Osovana 5, 33030, Buja, Udine, Italy
Tel.: (39) 0432 9694 50
Web Site: http://www.wentronic.it
Electronic Equipment & Accessories Distr
N.A.I.C.S.: 423690
Luca Ceschiutti *(Gen Mgr & Head-Sls)*

Wentronic UK Ltd.   (1)
PO Box 3206, Eastbourne, BN21 9QW, United Kingdom
Tel.: (44) 7961 008223
Electronic Equipment & Accessories Distr
N.A.I.C.S.: 423690
Tony Pulford *(Country Mgr)*

WENTWORTH RESOURCES LIMITED
2nd Floor Coco Plaza 254 Toure Drive, PO Box 203, Oyster Bay, Dar es Salaam, Tanzania
Tel.: (255) 222 601 139
Web Site:
   http://www.wentworthresources.com
Sales Range: $1-9.9 Million
Oil & Natural Gas Exploration
N.A.I.C.S.: 211120
Robert P. McBean *(Chm)*

Subsidiaries:

Wentworth Resources Limited   (1)
630 715 - 5th Avenue SW, Calgary, T2P 2X6, AB, Canada
Tel.: (403) 294-1530
Web Site:
   http://www.wentworthresources.com
Natural Gas Exploration Service
N.A.I.C.S.: 213112

WENTWORTH TECHNOLOGIES CO. LTD.
156 Adams Blvd, Brantford, ON, Canada
Tel.: (800) 233-0874
Web Site: http://www.wtbvc.com
Year Founded: 1990
Injection Molding & Plastics Mfr
N.A.I.C.S.: 333511
Ark Wolos *(VP & Gen Mgr-Wentworth Tech Tooling Group)*

Subsidiaries:

AMTECH GmbH   (1)
Vaasbuttel 16-22, D-24594, Hohenwestedt, Germany
Tel.: (49) 4871370
Sales Range: $25-49.9 Million
Injection Molding
N.A.I.C.S.: 333511

Accurate Mold USA Inc.   (1)
852 Scholz Dr, Vandalia, OH 45377
Tel.: (937) 898-8460
Injection Molding
N.A.I.C.S.: 333511

Amhil Europa Sp. z o.o.   (1)
Ul Okrezna 3, Kartoszyno, Krokowa, Poland
Tel.: 587746161
Web Site: http://www.wtbvc.com
Sales Range: $50-74.9 Million
Plastic Lids for Disposable Containers & Other Drink & Food Packaging Products Mfr
N.A.I.C.S.: 326160
Adam Laskowski *(VP & Gen Mgr)*

EN Tool & Supply Limited   (1)
367 Barton Street East, Stoney Creek, L8E 2L2, ON, Canada
Tel.: (905) 560-3292
Web Site: http://www.entool.on.ca
Machine Tool Distr
N.A.I.C.S.: 423830

Electra Form Industries   (1)
852 Scholz Dr, Vandalia, OH 45377
Tel.: (937) 898-8460
Web Site: http://www.electraform.com
Sales Range: $25-49.9 Million
PET Mfr
N.A.I.C.S.: 326199
Brian Karns *(VP & Gen Mgr)*

Kartpol Group Sp. z o.o.   (1)
ul Lukasiewicza 11 d, 05-200, Wolomin, Poland
Tel.: (48) 22 787 66 46
Web Site: http://www.kartpol.eu
Cartridge Mfr & Distr
N.A.I.C.S.: 339940

Stone Straw Limited   (1)
72 Plant Farm Blvd, Brantford, N3S 7W3, ON, Canada
Tel.: (519) 756-1974
Web Site: http://www.stonestraw.com
Emp.: 100
Straw Mfr & Distr
N.A.I.C.S.: 326199

Wentworth Mold Inc.   (1)
156 Adams Blvd, Brantford, N3S 7V7, ON, Canada
Tel.: (519) 754-5400
Web Site: https://wentworthmold.com
Blow Mold Mfr
N.A.I.C.S.: 333511

Wentworth Mold Limited   (1)
Lanes House 9 Millway Old Mill Lane Industrial Estate, Woodhouse, Mansfield, NG19 9BG, Notts, United Kingdom
Tel.: (44) 01623658416
Web Site: http://www.wentworthmold.com
Sales Range: $25-49.9 Million
Emp.: 3
Blow Mold Mfr
N.A.I.C.S.: 333511

Wentworth Tech Central Sp. z o.o.   (1)
Ul Srebrna 20, 85-461, Bydgoszcz, Poland
Tel.: (48) 525817770
Injection Molding
N.A.I.C.S.: 333511

Wentworth Tech Sp. z o.o.   (1)
Ul Srebrna 20, 85-641, Bydgoszcz, Poland
Tel.: (48) 525817770
Web Site: http://www.wtcentral.com.pl
Blow Mold Mfr
N.A.I.C.S.: 333511

WENYE GROUP HOLDINGS LIMITED
No 105 Sha Zui Industrial Area Fuqiang Road, Futian, Shenzhen, China
Tel.: (86) 75583288118   Ky
Web Site: http://www.szwyzs.com.cn
Year Founded: 1989
1802—(HKG)
Rev.: $191,138,821
Assets: $299,169,643
Liabilities: $203,290,212
Net Worth: $95,879,431
Earnings: $3,152,296
Emp.: 366
Fiscal Year-end: 12/31/20
Holding Company
N.A.I.C.S.: 551112
Shaozhou Fan *(Chm & CEO)*

WENZHOU HONGFENG ELECTRICAL ALLOY CO., LTD.
No 5600 Ou Jin Avenue, Marine Economic District, Wenzhou, 325026, Zhejiang, China
Tel.: (86) 57785515910
Web Site: https://www.wzhf.com
Year Founded: 1997
300283—(CHIN)
Rev.: $299,556,036
Assets: $346,202,532
Liabilities: $207,164,412
Net Worth: $139,038,120
Earnings: $4,258,332
Fiscal Year-end: 12/31/22
Electrical Component Mfr
N.A.I.C.S.: 335999
Chen Xiao *(Chm & Pres)*

Subsidiaries:

Hongfeng Composite Materials Corp.   (1)
2028 Garner Station Blvd, Raleigh, NC 27603
Tel.: (919) 803-4096
Plastic Materials Mfr
N.A.I.C.S.: 325211

Hongfeng Elektrowerkstoffe GmbH   (1)
Hollerithallee 17, 30419, Hannover, Germany
Tel.: (49) 51159031412
Plastic Materials Mfr
N.A.I.C.S.: 325211

Shanghai Hiwave Advanced Materials Technology Co., Ltd.   (1)
1F No 322 Lane 953 Jianchuan Road, Minhang District, Shanghai, China
Tel.: (86) 2154337983
Web Site: http://www.ihiwave.com
Biotechnology Research & Development Services
N.A.I.C.S.: 541714

Wenzhou Hongfeng Alloy Co. Ltd   (1)
No 1633 Binghai First Avenue, Economic and Technological Development Zone, Wenzhou, 325025, Zhejiang, China
Tel.: (86) 57786800988
Electrical Component Mfr
N.A.I.C.S.: 335999

Wenzhou Hongfeng Metal-matrix Engineered Composite Material Co., Ltd.   (1)
No 808 Binhai 2nd Avenue Road 9, Wenzhou Economic & Technological Development Zone, Hangzhou, 325000, China
Tel.: (86) 57786800999
Plastic Materials Mfr
N.A.I.C.S.: 325211

Wenzhou Hongfeng Special Material Co., Ltd.   (1)
No 5600 Oujin Avenue, Oujiangkou Industrial Cluster, Wenzhou, 325026, Zhejiang, China
Tel.: (86) 57785515910
Plastic Materials Mfr
N.A.I.C.S.: 325211

WENZHOU KANGNING HOSPITAL CO., LTD.
Shengjin Road, Lucheng District, Wenzhou, China
Tel.: (86) 4000002120   CN
Web Site: https://www.knhosp.cn
Year Founded: 1996
2120—(HKG)
Rev.: $208,480,387
Assets: $370,345,352
Liabilities: $184,188,624
Net Worth: $186,156,728
Earnings: ($1,540,025)
Emp.: 4,196
Fiscal Year-end: 12/31/22
Psychiatric Specialty Hospital Services
N.A.I.C.S.: 623220
Weili Guan *(Founder, Chm & Exec Dir)*

WENZHOU KANGNING HOSPITAL CO., LTD.

Wenzhou Kangning Hospital Co., Ltd.—(Continued)
Subsidiaries:
Wenzhou Yining Geriatric Hospital
Co., Ltd. (1)
Ouhai Lou Bridge Street in the Department
of Road 55, Wenzhou, China
Tel.: (86) 89896789
Geriatric Hospital Services
N.A.I.C.S.: 622110
Guan Weili *(Gen Mgr & Exec Dir)*

WENZHOU YIHUA CONNECTOR CO., LTD.
No 2 Huaxing Road Yihua Technology Park Wengyang street, Yueqing, 325606, Zhejiang, China
Tel.: (86) 13868769820
Web Site:
  https://www.chinaconnector.com
Year Founded: 1995
002897—(SSE)
Rev.: $703,512,543
Assets: $639,684,162
Liabilities: $409,691,103
Net Worth: $229,993,059
Earnings: $33,665,617
Fiscal Year-end: 12/31/22
Electronic Parts Mfr & Distr
N.A.I.C.S.: 334417
Cai Shengcai *(Chm)*

Subsidiaries:
Dongguan Yizhao Electronic Co.,
Ltd. (1)
Yihua Industrial Park, S358 Provincial Road Village Head Management Area Humen Town, Dongguan, China
Tel.: (86) 76986240111
Emp.: 900
Electronic Connector Mfr
N.A.I.C.S.: 334417

Dongguan Zhengde Connector Co.,
Ltd. (1)
Yihua Industrial Park, S358 Provincial Road Village Head Management Area Humen Town, Dongguan, China
Tel.: (86) 76985440658
Emp.: 400
Electronic Connector Mfr
N.A.I.C.S.: 334417

WENZHOU YUANFEI PET TOYS PRODUCTS CO., LTD.
No 1 Chongle Road Biaozhun Park, Shuitou Town Pingyang County, Nan'an, 325405, Zhejiang, China
Tel.: (86) 57763870169
Web Site: https://www.wzyuanfei.com
Year Founded: 2004
001222—(SSE)
Rev.: $133,899,620
Assets: $195,907,758
Liabilities: $19,764,642
Net Worth: $176,143,116
Earnings: $22,258,609
Fiscal Year-end: 12/31/22
Pet Product Mfr & Distr
N.A.I.C.S.: 311119
Mingyun Zhuang *(Chm)*

WEP SOLUTIONS LTD.
40/1 A Basappa Complex Lavelle Road, Bengaluru, 560001, India
Tel.: (91) 9019915738
Web Site: https://wepsol.in
Year Founded: 1988
532373—(BOM)
Rev.: $11,221,893
Assets: $9,262,850
Liabilities: $2,354,307
Net Worth: $6,908,543
Earnings: $700,330
Emp.: 109
Fiscal Year-end: 03/31/23
Information Technology Services
N.A.I.C.S.: 541519
Ram N. Agarwal *(Chm & Mng Dir)*

Subsidiaries:
WeP Digital Services Limited (1)
40/1A Basappa Complex Lavelle Road, Bengaluru, 560001, Karnataka, India
Tel.: (91) 7338335033
Web Site: http://www.wepdigital.com
Information Technology Services
N.A.I.C.S.: 541511

WEPA HYGIENEPRODUKTE GMBH & CO. KG
Ronkhauser Strasse 26, 59757, Arnsberg, Germany
Tel.: (49) 2932 307 0
Web Site: http://www.wepa.de
Emp.: 3,800
Hygienic Paper Product Mfr
N.A.I.C.S.: 322291
Martin Krengel *(Chm-Mgmt Bd)*

Subsidiaries:
Arjowiggins SAS (1)
32 avenue Pierre Grenier, 92517, Boulogne-Billancourt, Cedex, France
Tel.: (33) 1 5775 9212
Web Site: http://www.arjowiggins.com
Sales Range: $1-4.9 Billion
Specialty Paper Products Mfr & Whslr
N.A.I.C.S.: 322120
Pascal Lebard *(CEO)*

Subsidiary (Non-US):
Arjowiggins Fine Papers Limited (2)
Fine Papers House Lime Tree Way, Chineham, Basingstoke, RG24 8WZ, Hants, United Kingdom
Tel.: (44) 1256 728 771
Web Site: http://www.arjowiggins-castingpapers.com
Sales Range: $25-49.9 Million
Emp.: 100
Specialty Paper Mfr
N.A.I.C.S.: 322120

Arjowiggins Graphic Benelux (2)
't Hofveld 6F4, 1702, Groot-Bijgaarden, Belgium
Tel.: (32) 24810515
Web Site:
  http://www.arjowigginsgraphic.com
Sales Range: $25-49.9 Million
Emp.: 5
Specialty Paper Retailer
N.A.I.C.S.: 322220
Aemps Roger *(Mng Dir)*

Northwood & WEPA Ltd. (1)
3rd Floor Newspaper House 40 Churchgate, Bolton, BL1 1HL, United Kingdom
Tel.: (44) 1204 545 445
Web Site: http://www.northwoodwepa.com
Emp.: 230
Hygienic Paper Product Mfr & Distr
N.A.I.C.S.: 322291

WEPA Italia s.r.l. (1)
Localita Salanetti Fraz Lunata, 55012, Capannori, Lucca, Italy
Tel.: (39) 0583269640
Emp.: 325
Hygienic Paper Product Distr
N.A.I.C.S.: 424130
Massimo Serafini *(Mgr-Pur & B2B)*

WEPA Leuna GmbH (1)
An der B91 Alter Maienweg, 06237, Leuna, Germany
Tel.: (49) 3461431400
Emp.: 175
Hygienic Paper Product Mfr
N.A.I.C.S.: 322291

WEPA Papierfabrik Sachsen GmbH (1)
An der Zschopau 2, 09648, Kriebstein, Germany
Tel.: (49) 3432766660
Emp.: 180
Hygienic Paper Product Mfr
N.A.I.C.S.: 322291

WEPA Troyes SAS (1)
ZI de Torvilliers RN 60, BP 19, La Riviere de Corpes, 10440, Troyes, France (100%)
Tel.: (33) 3 2579 0606
Web Site: http://www.wepa.de

Emp.: 150
Tissue Paper & Converted Tissue Paper Products Mfr
N.A.I.C.S.: 322291
Alessandro Pasquini *(Mng Dir)*

WEQAYA TAKAFUL INSURANCE & REINSURANCE COMPANY
North Ring Road - Between Exits 6 & 7, PO Box 84770, Riyadh, 11681, Saudi Arabia
Tel.: (966) 11 450 1001
Web Site: http://www.weqaya.com.sa
Year Founded: 2009
8220—(SAU)
Sales Range: $75-99.9 Million
Insurance Management Services
N.A.I.C.S.: 524298

WERELDHAVE N.V.
WTC Schiphol Tower A 3rd Floor
Schiphol Boulevard 233, 1118 BH, Schiphol, Netherlands
Tel.: (31) 207027800
Web Site:
  http://www.wereldhave.com
Year Founded: 1930
WHA—(EUR)
Rev.: $175,551,479
Assets: $2,264,251,025
Liabilities: $1,052,031,081
Net Worth: $1,212,219,944
Earnings: $82,027,844
Emp.: 118
Fiscal Year-end: 12/31/22
Property Investment Services
N.A.I.C.S.: 525990
Adriaan Nuhn *(Chm-Supervisory Bd)*

Subsidiaries:
Espamad S.L. (1)
Calle Fernando El Santo 15, Madrid, 28010, Spain
Tel.: (34) 913103827
Property Management Services
N.A.I.C.S.: 531312

Wereldhave Belgium S.C.A. (1)
Medialaan 30/6, 1800, Vilvoorde, Belgium
Tel.: (32) 2 732 1900
Web Site:
  https://www.wereldhavebelgium.com
Sales Range: $50-74.9 Million
Emp.: 30
Real Estate Property Lessors
N.A.I.C.S.: 531190

Wereldhave Development B.V. (1)
Nassaulaan 23, NL-2514 JT, Hague, Netherlands
Tel.: (31) 703469325
Real Estate Manangement Services
N.A.I.C.S.: 531390

Wereldhave Finland Oy (1)
1B Itakatu, FIN-00930, Helsinki, Finland
Tel.: (358) 93436480
Web Site: http://www.wereldhave.com
Emp.: 15
Real Estate Property Lessors
N.A.I.C.S.: 531190

Wereldhave Management Holding B.V. (1)
Schiphol Boulevard 233 Schiphol Airport, Amsterdam, 1118 BH, Netherlands (100%)
Tel.: (31) 703469325
Web Site: http://www.wereldhave.nl
Sales Range: $50-74.9 Million
Emp.: 60
Holding Company
N.A.I.C.S.: 551112

Wereldhave Management Spain S.L. (1)
Calle Fernando El Santo 15, Madrid, 28010, Spain
Tel.: (34) 913103827
Sales Range: $50-74.9 Million
Emp.: 6
Real Estate Agency
N.A.I.C.S.: 531210
Michel Daned *(Office Mgr)*

INTERNATIONAL PUBLIC

Wereldhave Management USA, Inc. (1)
3 Manhattanville Rd 2nd Fl, Purchase, NY 10577
Tel.: (914) 694-5900
Web Site: http://www.wereldhave.nl
Sales Range: $50-74.9 Million
Emp.: 13
Real Estate Agency
N.A.I.C.S.: 531210

Wereldhave Nederland B.V. (1)
Schiphol Boulevard 233, Schiphol, 1118 BH, Netherlands (100%)
Tel.: (31) 703469325
Web Site: http://www.wereldhave.nl
Sales Range: $50-74.9 Million
Emp.: 60
Holding Company
N.A.I.C.S.: 551112

Wereldhave Property Management Co. Ltd. (1)
39 Sloane Street, SW1X9WR, London, United Kingdom
Tel.: (44) 2072352080
Web Site: http://www.wereldhave.nl
Sales Range: $50-74.9 Million
Emp.: 14
Nonresidential Buildings Lessors
N.A.I.C.S.: 531120

Wereldhave U.K. Holdings Ltd. (1)
39 Sloane St, London, SW1X 9WR, United Kingdom
Tel.: (44) 2072352080
Sales Range: $50-74.9 Million
Emp.: 13
Real Estate Manangement Services
N.A.I.C.S.: 531390

WERFEN LIFE GROUP, S.A.U.
Plaza de Europa 21-23, 08908, L'Hospitalet de Llobregat, Barcelona, Spain
Tel.: (34) 934010101
Web Site: http://www.werfenlife.com
Year Founded: 1985
Sales Range: $550-599.9 Million
Emp.: 4,350
Medical Devices & Diagnostics Products Mfr & Distr
N.A.I.C.S.: 339112
Jose M. Rubiralta *(Pres & CEO)*

Subsidiaries:
Biokit S.A. (1)
Can Male s/n, Llica d'Amunt, 08186, Barcelona, Spain
Tel.: (34) 93 860 90 00
Web Site: http://www.biokit.com
Medical Equipment Mfr
N.A.I.C.S.: 339112
Ricard Forns *(Dir-Mktg)*

Bolton Medical Espana S.L.U. (1)
C/ Newton 22-24, Sant Esteve Sesrovires, 08635, Barcelona, Spain
Tel.: (34) 93 817 63 23
Web Site: http://www.boltonmedical.com
Medical Equipment Mfr
N.A.I.C.S.: 339112
Francesc Pages Andreu *(Mgr-QA & RA)*

Bolton Medical S.p.A (1)
Viale Monza 338, 20128, Milan, Italy
Tel.: (39) 02 25712320
Web Site: http://www.boltonmedical.it
Medical Equipment Mfr
N.A.I.C.S.: 339112
Clodio Caiola *(Country Mgr)*

Comesa Budapest kft. (1)
Folyondar U 1, 1037, Budapest, Hungary
Tel.: (36) 1 439 2910
Web Site: http://www.comesa.hu
Medical Equipment Mfr
N.A.I.C.S.: 339112

Comesa Polska Sp. z o. o. (1)
Ul Wolinska 4, 03 699, Warsaw, Poland
Tel.: (48) 22 336 18 00
Web Site: http://www.comesa.pl
Medical Equipment Mfr
N.A.I.C.S.: 339112
Maria Dale *(Dir-Fin)*

AND PRIVATE COMPANIES

Comesa spol.s.r.o. (1)
Plananska 1, 108 00, Prague, Czech Republic
Tel.: (420) 246 090 911
Web Site: http://www.comesa.cz
Medical Equipment Mfr
N.A.I.C.S.: 339112

Hospitalares S.A. + Cormedica S.A. (1)
Rua do Proletariado 1, Quinta do Paizinho, 2790-138, Carnaxide, Portugal
Tel.: (351) 214 247 300
Web Site: http://www.medicinalia-cormedica.pt
Medical Equipment Mfr
N.A.I.C.S.: 339112

I.L. Diagnostics, S.A. de C.V. (1)
Lago Victoria No 80 Delegacion Miguel Hidalgo, Col Granada, 11520, Mexico, Mexico
Tel.: (52) 55 5262 1760
Web Site: http://www.ildiagnostics.com
Diagnostic Laboratory Services
N.A.I.C.S.: 621511

I.L. Japan Co. Ltd. (1)
Mita-Kanda Bldg 1-3-30 Mita, Minato-ku, Tokyo, 108-0073, Japan
Tel.: (81) 3 5419 1301
Web Site: http://www.il-japan.jp
Diagnostic Laboratory Services
N.A.I.C.S.: 621511
Cesar Roure *(Mgr-Fin)*

INOVA Diagnostics, Inc. (1)
9900 Old Grove Rd, San Diego, CA 92131-1638
Tel.: (858) 586-9900
Web Site: http://www.inovadx.com
Autoimmune Disease In-Vitro Diagnostic Products Developer & Mfr
N.A.I.C.S.: 325413

IZASA SCIENTIFIC, S.L.U. (1)
Plaza de Europa N 21-23 L'Hospitalet de Llobregat, 08908, Barcelona, Spain
Tel.: (34) 902 20 30 80
Web Site: http://www.izasa.es
Medical Equipment Distr
N.A.I.C.S.: 423450

Immucor, Inc. (1)
3130 Gateway Dr, Norcross, GA 30091-5625
Tel.: (770) 441-2051
Web Site: http://www.immucor.com
Rev.: $379,972,000
Assets: $1,707,633,000
Liabilities: $1,363,087,000
Net Worth: $344,546,000
Earnings: ($43,767,000)
Emp.: 1,125
Fiscal Year-end: 05/31/2016
Blood Testing Equipment Developer, Mfr & Sales
N.A.I.C.S.: 339112
Dominique Petitgenet *(CFO & COO)*

Subsidiary (Domestic):

Bioarray Solutions, Ltd. (2)
35 Technology Dr Ste 100, Warren, NJ 07059
Tel.: (908) 226-8200
Sales Range: $10-24.9 Million
Emp.: 50
Molecular Analysis System Mfr
N.A.I.C.S.: 334516
Jiacheng Yang *(Dir-Product Dev)*

Subsidiary (Non-US):

Dominion Biologicals Ltd. (2)
5 Isnor Drive, Dartmouth, B3B 1M1, NS, Canada (100%)
Tel.: (902) 468-3992
Web Site: https://www.immucor.com
Sales Range: $10-24.9 Million
Emp.: 40
Clinical Transfusion Laboratory Products Mfr
N.A.I.C.S.: 334516
Susan MacKenzie *(Mgr-Customer Svc)*

IBG Immucor Ltd. (2)
4 Riverside Business Centre Brighton Road, Shoreham-by-Sea, BN43 6RE, West Sussex, United Kingdom
Tel.: (44) 1273 440 130
Sales Range: $25-49.9 Million
Emp.: 13
Medical Equipment Distr
N.A.I.C.S.: 423450

Immucor (Portugal) Diagnosticos Medicos, Lda. (2)
Av. da Quinta Grande No 53 Piso 7 Fraccao A, Alfragide, 2614 521, Amadora, Portugal (100%)
Tel.: (351) 213010486
Web Site: http://www.immucor.com
Sales Range: $1-9.9 Million
Emp.: 8
Blood Testing Equipment
N.A.I.C.S.: 334516

Immucor Medizinische Diagnostik GmbH (2)
Adam-Opel-Strasse 26A, Rodermark, 63322, Germany (100%)
Tel.: (49) 607484200
Web Site: http://www.immucor.com
Sales Range: $10-24.9 Million
Emp.: 70
Blood Testing Products
N.A.I.C.S.: 334516
Helmut Butterweck *(Mng Dir)*

Instrumentation Lab. (Lietuva) B.I (1)
Savanoriu Pr 281A, Kaunas, 50128, Lithuania
Tel.: (370) 37 313157
Web Site: http://www.ill.lt
Emp.: 14
Diagnostic Laboratory Services
N.A.I.C.S.: 621511
Sarunas Saudargas *(Gen Mgr)*

Instrumentation Laboratory (1)
180 Hartwell Rd, Bedford, MA 01730
Tel.: (781) 861-0710
Web Site: http://www.instrumentationlaboratory.com
Sales Range: $400-449.9 Million
Emp.: 1,332
Medical Diagnostic Instrument Mfr
N.A.I.C.S.: 339112
Ramon E. Benet *(CEO)*

Subsidiary (Domestic):

Accriva Diagnostics, Inc. (2)
6260 Sequence Dr, San Diego, CA 92121
Tel.: (858) 263-2300
Web Site: http://www.instrumentationlaboratory.com
Holding Company; Medical Point-of-Care Diagnostic Device Developer, Mfr & Distr
N.A.I.C.S.: 551112

Instrumentation Laboratory (Canada) Ltd. (1)
155 East Beaver Creek Unit 24 Suite 882, Richmond Hill, L4B 2N1, ON, Canada
Tel.: (800) 552-2025
Diagnostic Laboratory Services
N.A.I.C.S.: 621511

Instrumentation Laboratory GmbH (1)
Klausnerring 4, 85551, Kirchheim, Germany
Tel.: (49) 89 90907
Web Site: http://www.il-ger.de
Diagnostic Laboratory Services
N.A.I.C.S.: 621511

Instrumentation Laboratory S.A. (1)
88-94 Rue Andre Joineau, 93310, Le Pre-Saint-Gervais, France
Tel.: (33) 182 30 86 00
Web Site: http://www.il-france.fr
Diagnostic Laboratory Services
N.A.I.C.S.: 621511

Instrumentation Laboratory, B.V. (1)
Brugsteen 6, Breda, 4815 PL, Netherlands
Tel.: (31) 76 5480100
Web Site: http://www.werfen.com
Diagnostic Laboratory Services
N.A.I.C.S.: 621511

Nicolai Medizintechnik GmbH (1)
Ostpassage 7, 30853, Langenhagen, Germany
Tel.: (49) 511 9 24 79 00
Web Site: http://www.nicolai-medizintechnik.de
Medical Equipment Distr
N.A.I.C.S.: 423450
Olaf Kreuzkam *(Mgr-Purchase & Logistics)*

Werfen Australia Pty Limited (1)
59-61 Dickson Avenue, Artarmon, 2064, NSW, Australia
Tel.: (61) 2 9098 0200
Emp.: 30
Diagnostic Laboratory Services
N.A.I.C.S.: 621511
Sharon Dearden *(Mgr-Mktg)*

Werfen Czech s.r.o (1)
Pocernicka 272/96, 108 00, Prague, Czech Republic
Tel.: (420) 246 090 931
Web Site: http://www.werfen.cz
Diagnostic Laboratory Services
N.A.I.C.S.: 621511

Werfen Hong Kong Limited (1)
31st Fl No 88 Hing Fat Street, Hong Kong, China (Hong Kong)
Tel.: (852) 2792 7773
Diagnostic Laboratory Services
N.A.I.C.S.: 621511

Werfen Hungary Kft. (1)
Montevideo U 2/c II lh, 1037, Budapest, Hungary
Tel.: (36) 1 882 7310
Web Site: http://www.hu.werfen.com
Emp.: 8
Diagnostic Laboratory Services
N.A.I.C.S.: 621511
Domotor Gergely *(Gen Mgr)*

Werfen Limited (1)
Kelvin Close Birchwood Science Park, Warrington, WA3 7PB, Cheshire, United Kingdom
Tel.: (44) 1925 810141
Web Site: http://uk.werfen.com
Emp.: 60
Diagnostic Laboratory Services
N.A.I.C.S.: 621511

Werfen Medical IL, Ltd. (1)
1F Nashil Bldg 604-1 Yeoksam-Dong, Gangnam-gu, 135-907, Seoul, Korea (South)
Tel.: (82) 2 571 9246
Web Site: http://www.werfenmedical.com
Diagnostic Laboratory Services
N.A.I.C.S.: 621511

Werfen Medical International Trading (Shanghai) Co., Ltd (1)
Room 610-611 Baohua International Square, 555 West Guangzhong Road, Shanghai, 200072, China
Tel.: (86) 21 66308671
Web Site: http://www.werfen.com
Emp.: 200
Diagnostic Laboratory Services
N.A.I.C.S.: 621511
Grace Tong *(Gen Mgr)*

Werfen MedicalDevice Trading (Beijing) Co., Ltd (1)
Room 201 Tower B18B Universal Business Park O 10 Jiuxianqiao Road, Chaoyang District, Beijing, 100015, China
Tel.: (86) 10 59756055
Diagnostic Laboratory Services
N.A.I.C.S.: 621511

Werfen/ Instrumentation Laboratory Pvt Ltd. (1)
Plot No E-4 Office No 271-274 Aggarwal Millenium Tower II, Netaji Subhash Place Pitampura, New Delhi, 110 034, India
Tel.: (91) 11 49029550
Web Site: http://www.il-india.com
Diagnostic Laboratory Services
N.A.I.C.S.: 621511
Anil Grover *(Dir-Sls & Mktg)*

WERK EN VAKMANSCHAP
Markt 41, PO Box 1532, 4701 PB, Roosendaal, Netherlands
Tel.: (31) 165524680
Web Site: http://www.werkenvakmanschap.nl
Sales Range: $10-24.9 Million
Emp.: 50
Employment Agency Services
N.A.I.C.S.: 561311

WESCAN ENERGY CORP.

Michael Dakx *(Mgr-Fin)*

WERKLUND CAPITAL CORPORATION
Suite 4500 Devon Tower 400 - 3rd Avenue SW, Calgary, T2P 4H2, AB, Canada
Tel.: (403) 231-6545
Web Site: http://www.werklund.com
Investment Holding Company
N.A.I.C.S.: 551112
David Werklund *(Founder & Chm)*

Subsidiaries:

RS Technologies Inc. (1)
3553 31 Street NW, Calgary, T2L 2K7, AB, Canada
Tel.: (403) 219-8001
Web Site: http://www.groupsrsi.com
Sales Range: $1-9.9 Million
Advanced Composite Material Products Developer & Mfr
N.A.I.C.S.: 325211
David P. Werklund *(Chm)*

Subsidiary (Domestic):

RS Advanced Structures Inc. (2)
22 Industrial Park Rd, Tilbury, N0P 2L0, ON, Canada
Tel.: (519) 682-1110
Wood Products Mfr
N.A.I.C.S.: 321999

Werklund Foundation (1)
Suite 4500 Devon Tower 400 - 3rd Avenue SW, Calgary, T2P 4H2, AB, Canada
Tel.: (403) 231-6545
Web Site: http://www.werklund.com
Emp.: 14
Charity Organization
N.A.I.C.S.: 813211
Deanna Werklund *(Co-Founder)*

WERNER WEITNER GMBH
Sollnau 14, 85072, Eichstaett, Germany
Tel.: (49) 842198160
Web Site: http://www.werner-weitner.com
Year Founded: 1968
Rev.: $24,597,944
Emp.: 181
Industrial Equipment Mfr
N.A.I.C.S.: 333248
Heinz Weitner *(Mng Dir)*

WERNER WILHELM GMBH
Im Erlenteich 65, Pirmasens, 66955, Germany
Tel.: (49) 6331241100
Web Site: http://www.werner-gmbh.com
Year Founded: 1948
Rev.: $16,276,920
Emp.: 25
Footwear Material Mfr
N.A.I.C.S.: 339999
Werner Wilhelm *(Co-Mng Dir)*

WESBRIDGE CONSTRUCTION LIMITED
1510 31 Street North, Lethbridge, T1H 5J8, AB, Canada
Tel.: (403) 328-8022
Web Site: http://www.wesbridgeconstruct.com
Year Founded: 1971
Construction Services
N.A.I.C.S.: 236220
Lyal Sakamoto *(Gen Mgr)*

WESCAN ENERGY CORP.
Tel.: (403) 265-9464 AB
Web Site: https://www.wescanenergycorp.com
Year Founded: 1999
GPIPF—(OTCIQ)
Rev.: $2,611,082
Assets: $5,252,302

WESCAN ENERGY CORP.

WesCan Energy Corp.—(Continued)
Liabilities: $4,061,062
Net Worth: $1,191,240
Earnings: ($101,146)
Fiscal Year-end: 03/31/23
Oil & Gas Exploration Services
N.A.I.C.S.: 211120
Gregory T. Busby *(Pres & CEO)*

WESCAN GOLDFIELDS INC.
602224 4th Avenue South, Saskatoon, S7K 5M5, SK, Canada
Tel.: (306) 244-5480   **AB**
Web Site:
   https://www.wescangoldfields.com
Year Founded: 2003
WGF—(TSXV)
Sales Range: Less than $1 Million
Gold Mining & Exploration Services
N.A.I.C.S.: 212220
Kenneth E. MacNeill *(Chm, Pres & CEO)*

WESCAST INDUSTRIES INC.
200 Water Street, Wingham, N0G 2W0, ON, Canada
Tel.: (519) 357-3450   **ON**
Web Site: https://www.wescast.com
Year Founded: 1901
Cast Iron Exhaust Manifolds Mfr & Supplier for Passenger Cars & Light Trucks
N.A.I.C.S.: 336390

Subsidiaries:

United Machining Inc.   (1)
6300 18 1/2 Mile Rd, Sterling Heights, MI 48314-3112   **(100%)**
Tel.: (586) 323-4300
Web Site: http://www.wescast.com
Sales Range: $50-74.9 Million
Emp.: 100
N.A.I.C.S.: 336340
Lou Sabel *(Plant Mgr)*

Wescast Hungary Autoipari Zrt.   (1)
Szent Borbala ut 16, Oroszlany, 2840, Hungary
Tel.: (36) 34 562 100
Sales Range: $200-249.9 Million
Emp.: 1,000
Exhaust Manifolds Mfr
N.A.I.C.S.: 336310

Wescast Industries (China) Co., Ltd.   (1)
E Beijing Rd 465 Material Building 18th Fl, Shanghai, 200336, China
Tel.: (86) 2162707980
Web Site: http://www.wescast.com
Emp.: 7
Exhaust Manifolds Mfr
N.A.I.C.S.: 336310
Scanny Cai *(Dir-Sls-Asia)*

Wescast Industries GmbH   (1)
Druselstalstr 5-9, 34131, Kassel, Hesse, Germany
Tel.: (49) 561937470
Web Site: http://www.wescast.com
Exhaust Manifolds Mfr
N.A.I.C.S.: 336310

Wescast Industries Inc. - Brantford Machining   (1)
150 Savannah Oaks Dr, Brantford, N3T 5V7, ON, Canada
Tel.: (519) 750-0000
Web Site: http://www.wescast.com
Sales Range: $50-74.9 Million
Emp.: 75
Lost-Wax Casting for Precious & Semi-Precious Metals
N.A.I.C.S.: 339910

Wescast Industries Inc. - Stratford Magalloy   (1)
130 Wright Blvd, Stratford, N4Z 1H3, ON, Canada
Tel.: (519) 273-2330
Web Site: http://www.wescast.com
Sales Range: $25-49.9 Million
Emp.: 80
Mfr of Stainless Steel Pump Components
N.A.I.C.S.: 336330

Wescast Industries Inc. - Strathroy Machining   (1)
28648 Ctr Rd, Strathroy, N7G 3H6, ON, Canada
Tel.: (519) 245-6402
Web Site: http://www.wescast.com
Sales Range: $50-74.9 Million
Emp.: 62
N.A.I.C.S.: 336340

Wescast Industries Inc. - Wingham Casting   (1)
200 Water Street, PO Box 450, Wingham, N0G 2W0, ON, Canada
Tel.: (519) 357-3450
Web Site: http://www.wescast.com
Sales Range: $150-199.9 Million
Emp.: 330
Industrial Castings
N.A.I.C.S.: 336340

Wescast Japan, K.K   (1)
Helios Kannai Building 7F 3-21-2 Montohama-cho, Naka-ku, Yokohama, 231-0004, Kanagawa, Japan
Tel.: (81) 452228328
Exhaust Manifolds Mfr
N.A.I.C.S.: 336310

WESCO HOLDINGS INC.
2-5-35 Shimada Honmachi, Kita-ku, Okayama, 700-0033, Japan
Tel.: (81) 862546111
Web Site: https://www.wescohd.co.jp
Year Founded: 2014
6091—(TKS)
Rev.: $97,809,500
Assets: $129,120,980
Liabilities: $28,500,040
Net Worth: $100,620,940
Earnings: $4,776,960
Emp.: 376
Fiscal Year-end: 07/31/24
Holding Company; Civil Engineering Consulting Services
N.A.I.C.S.: 551112
Toshinao Matsubara *(Pres & CEO)*

WESDOME GOLD MINES LTD.
220 Bay St Suite 1200, Toronto, M5J 2W4, ON, Canada
Tel.: (416) 360-3743   **ON**
Web Site: https://www.wesdome.com
Year Founded: 1980
WDO—(TSX)
Rev.: $205,666,888
Assets: $433,163,299
Liabilities: $124,025,800
Net Worth: $309,137,499
Earnings: $102,703,977
Emp.: 269
Fiscal Year-end: 12/31/21
Gold Ore Exploration, Mining & Production
N.A.I.C.S.: 212220
Lindsay Carpenter Dunlop *(VP-IR)*

WESFARMERS LIMITED
Level 14 Brookfield Place Tower 2 123 St Georges Terrace, Perth, 6000, WA, Australia
Tel.: (61) 893274211   **AU**
Web Site:
   https://www.wesfarmers.com.au
Year Founded: 1914
WES—(OTCIQ)
Rev.: $28,395,383,713
Assets: $17,308,469,714
Liabilities: $11,909,108,691
Net Worth: $5,399,361,022
Earnings: $1,607,224,359
Emp.: 3,689
Fiscal Year-end: 06/30/23
Investment Management Service
N.A.I.C.S.: 551112
Robert Scott *(Mng Dir)*

Subsidiaries:

Australian Gold Reagents Pty Ltd   (1)
           (75%)
Tel.: (61) 86 378 5777
Web Site: https://agrcyanide.com
Sales Range: $100-124.9 Million
Emp.: 110
Chemicals & Fertilizers Distr
N.A.I.C.S.: 212390

Australian Graphics Pty Ltd   (1)
38 Geddes Street, Mulgrave, 3170, VIC, Australia
Tel.: (61) 39 545 1400
Web Site: https://www.agsservice.com.au
Pre-Press Digital Finishing Equipment Distr
N.A.I.C.S.: 423830

Australian Pharmaceutical Industries Limited   (1)
Level 5 250 Camberwell Road, Camberwell, 3124, VIC, Australia
Tel.: (61) 388553000
Web Site: http://www.api.net.au
Rev.: $3,079,719,860
Assets: $1,182,208,950
Liabilities: $831,488,543
Net Worth: $350,720,408
Earnings: ($6,081,250)
Fiscal Year-end: 08/31/2020
Pharmaceutical Product Whslr
N.A.I.C.S.: 424210
Richard C. Vincent *(CEO & Mng Dir)*

Subsidiary (Domestic):

API (Canberra) Pty Limited   (2)
27 Hinksman St, Queanbeyan, 2620, ACT, Australia
Tel.: (61) 261249502
Pharmaceutical Products Distr
N.A.I.C.S.: 424210

Subsidiary (Non-US):

API Healthcare Holdings (NZ) Limited   (2)
14 Norman Spencer Drive, Auckland, 2241, Manukau, New Zealand
Tel.: (64) 92797979
Web Site: http://www.api.net.nz
Emp.: 250
Pharmaceutical Products Distr
N.A.I.C.S.: 424210
Martin Gyde *(Gen Mgr)*

Subsidiary (Domestic):

PAF (New Zealand) Ltd   (3)
9 Halladale Road, Papakowhai, 5024, New Zealand
Tel.: (64) 42370040
Pharmaceutical Products Distr
N.A.I.C.S.: 424210

Subsidiary (Domestic):

Making Life Easy - Mobility and Independent Living Superstores Pty Ltd   (2)
Locked Bag 3002, Hawthorn, 3122, VIC, Australia
Tel.: (61) 1300653279
Web Site: http://www.mle.com.au
Mobility Equipment Distr
N.A.I.C.S.: 423450

New Price Retail Pty Ltd   (2)
885 Mountain Hwy, Bayswater, 3153, VIC, Australia
Tel.: (61) 387203000
Pharmaceutical Products Distr
N.A.I.C.S.: 424210

Silk Laser Australia Limited   (2)
1/137 The Parade, Norwood, 5067, SA, Australia
Tel.: (61) 872256489
Web Site: https://www.silklaser.com.au
Rev.: $52,114,494
Assets: $120,439,460
Liabilities: $57,555,585
Net Worth: $62,883,876
Earnings: $4,616,939
Fiscal Year-end: 06/30/2023
Personal Care Services
N.A.I.C.S.: 611511
Martin Perelman *(Founder)*

INTERNATIONAL PUBLIC

Subsidiary (Domestic):

ASC MacArthur Square Pty Ltd.   (3)
Shop L91 Level 2 Macarthur Square Shopping Centre 200 Gilchrist Drive, Campbelltown, 2560, NSW, Australia
Tel.: (61) 246272722
Web Site:
   https://www.australianskinclinics.com.au
Skin Care Services
N.A.I.C.S.: 812112

ASC Warringah Mall Pty Ltd.   (3)
Westfield Warringah Mall 1243 Pittwater Road, Brookvale, 2100, NSW, Australia
Tel.: (61) 280393444
Web Site:
   https://australianskinclinics.com.au
Skin Care Services
N.A.I.C.S.: 812199

Subsidiary (Non-US):

Cosmetic Clinic Ltd.   (3)
246 Queen St CBD, Auckland, 1010, New Zealand
Tel.: (64) 92204366
Web Site:
   https://www.thecosmeticclinic.co.nz
Skin Care Services
N.A.I.C.S.: 812112

Subsidiary (Domestic):

SILK Laser Clinic Elizabeth Pty Ltd.   (3)
Shop 83A Elizabeth Shopping Centre 50 Elizabeth Way, Elizabeth, 5112, SA, Australia
Tel.: (61) 882522878
Skin Care Services
N.A.I.C.S.: 812112

SILK Laser Clinic Hobart Pty Ltd.   (3)
2/56 Elizabeth Street, Hobart, 7000, TAS, Australia
Tel.: (61) 362924001
Skin Care Services
N.A.I.C.S.: 812112

SILK Laser Clinic Hyde Park Pty Ltd.   (3)
177 King William Road, Hyde Park, 5061, SA, Australia
Tel.: (61) 882727828
Skin Care Services
N.A.I.C.S.: 812112

SILK Laser Clinic Norwood Pty Ltd.   (3)
3/185 The Parade, Norwood, SA, Australia
Tel.: (61) 883627686
Skin Care Services
N.A.I.C.S.: 812112

SILK Laser Clinic Rundle Mall Pty Ltd.   (3)
152 Rundle Mall, Adelaide, 5000, SA, Australia
Tel.: (61) 883593338
Skin Care Services
N.A.I.C.S.: 812112

SLC Belconnen Pty Ltd.   (3)
Shop 217 Westfield Belconnen Benjamin Way, Belconnen, 2617, ACT, Australia
Tel.: (61) 251103221
Skin Care Services
N.A.I.C.S.: 812199

SLC Bundaberg Pty Ltd.   (3)
Shop 63 16 Maryborough Street, Bundaberg, 4670, QLD, Australia
Tel.: (61) 741996157
Skin Care Services
N.A.I.C.S.: 812199

SLC Burleigh Pty Ltd.   (3)
Shop 053 Stockland Burleigh Heads 149 W Burleigh Rd, Burleigh Heads, 4220, QLD, Australia
Tel.: (61) 755077702
Skin Care Services
N.A.I.C.S.: 812199

SLC Burnside Pty Ltd.   (3)
Shop T66 Burnside Village 447 Portrush Rd, Glenside, 5065, SA, Australia
Tel.: (61) 883662378
Skin Care Services
N.A.I.C.S.: 812199

AND PRIVATE COMPANIES

WESFARMERS LIMITED

SLC Innaloo Pty Ltd. (3)
Shop 1034 Westfield Innaloo Shopping Centre Ellen Stirling Blvd, Innaloo, Perth, 6018, WA, Australia
Tel.: (61) 894682314
Skin Care Services
N.A.I.C.S.: 812199

SLC Joondalup Pty Ltd. (3)
Lakeside Joondalup Shopping City 420 Joondalup Drive, Joondalup, 6027, WA, Australia
Tel.: (61) 861462015
Skin Care Services
N.A.I.C.S.: 812199

SLC Mackay Pty Ltd. (3)
Caneland Central Shopping Centre Mangrove Road, MacKay, QLD, Australia
Tel.: (61) 749769203
Skin Care Services
N.A.I.C.S.: 812199

SLC Mandurah Pty Ltd. (3)
Shop 145 Mandurah Forum 330 Pinjarra Road, Mandurah, 6210, WA, Australia
Tel.: (61) 895394088
Skin Care Services
N.A.I.C.S.: 812199

SLC Midland Gate Pty Ltd. (3)
Shop T-144 Midland Gate Shopping Centre 274 Great Eastern Highway, Midland, 6056, WA, Australia
Tel.: (61) 894682310
Skin Care Services
N.A.I.C.S.: 812199

SLC Morayfield Pty Ltd. (3)
Tenancy 14 Morayfield Shopping Centre 171 Morayfield Rd, Morayfield, 4506, QLD, Australia
Tel.: (61) 721119878
Skin Care Services
N.A.I.C.S.: 812199

SLC Morley Pty Ltd. (3)
Tenancy SP064 Galleria Shopping Centre Cnr Collier & Walter Roads, Morley, 6062, WA, Australia
Tel.: (61) 864006672
Skin Care Services
N.A.I.C.S.: 812199

SLC Perth Pty Ltd. (3)
Shop H115 enex100 683-703 Hay Street, Perth, 6000, WA, Australia
Tel.: (61) 894682313
Skin Care Services
N.A.I.C.S.: 812199

SLC Rockhampton Pty Ltd. (3)
Stockland Rockhampton 120-331 Yaamba Road, Rockhampton, 4701, QLD, Australia
Tel.: (61) 749622500
Skin Care Services
N.A.I.C.S.: 812199

SLC Rockingham Pty Ltd. (3)
1 Council Ave, Rockingham, 6168, WA, Australia
Tel.: (61) 897213042
Skin Care Services
N.A.I.C.S.: 812199

SLC Strathpine Pty Ltd. (3)
Tenancy 73 Strathpine Centre 295 Gympie Rd, Strathpine, 4500, QLD, Australia
Tel.: (61) 731866397
Skin Care Services
N.A.I.C.S.: 812199

SLC Warwick Pty Ltd. (3)
Tenancy SP036 Warwick Grove Shopping Centre Beach Road, Warwick, 6024, WA, Australia
Tel.: (61) 864006671
Skin Care Services
N.A.I.C.S.: 812199

SLC Woden Pty Ltd. (3)
Westfield Woden Keltie Street, Phillip, 2606, ACT, Australia
Tel.: (61) 261886823
Skin Care Services
N.A.I.C.S.: 812199

BWP Management Limited (1)
Level 14 Brookfield Place Tower 2 123 St Georges Terrace, Perth, 6000, WA, Australia
Tel.: (61) 89 327 4356
Web Site: https://www.bwptrust.com.au
Real Estate Services
N.A.I.C.S.: 531210
Erich Fraunschiel *(Chm)*

Blacksmith Jacks Pty Ltd (1)
17 John Vella Drive, Paget, 4740, QLD, Australia
Tel.: (61) 74 944 3200
Web Site: https://www.blacksmithjacks.com.au
Gas Equipment Distr
N.A.I.C.S.: 449129

Bullivants Pty Limited (1)
Unit 1 41 Eastern Creek Drive, Eastern Creek, 2766, NSW, Australia
Tel.: (61) 288734715
Emp.: 35
Industrial Lifting Services
N.A.I.C.S.: 713920

Bunnings Joondalup Pty Ltd (1)
9 Sundew Rise, Joondalup, 6027, WA, Australia
Tel.: (61) 892333500
Home Improvement Product Distr
N.A.I.C.S.: 449129

CSBP Limited (1)
Kwinana Beach Road, Kwinana, 6167, WA, Australia
Tel.: (61) 86 378 5777
Web Site: https://www.csbp.com.au
Emp.: 700
Chemicals & Fertilizers Mfr & Distr
N.A.I.C.S.: 424690

Subsidiary (Domestic):

Australian Vinyls Corporation Pty Ltd (2)
3 Jesica Rd, Campbellfield, 3061, VIC, Australia
Tel.: (61) 383597300
Web Site: https://www.av.com.au
Emp.: 70
Vinyl Resins Mfr & Whslr
N.A.I.C.S.: 325211

Joint Venture (Domestic):

Queensland Nitrates Management Pty Ltd (2)
4 Three Chain Rd, Moura, 4718, QLD, Australia (50%)
Tel.: (61) 749975100
Chemicals & Fertilizers Mfr
N.A.I.C.S.: 325311

Queensland Nitrates Pty Ltd. (2)
4 Three Chain Rd, Moura, 4718, QLD, Australia (50%)
Tel.: (61) 749975100
Sales Range: $25-49.9 Million
Emp.: 88
Nitrogenous Fertilizer Mfr
N.A.I.C.S.: 325311
David Armstrong *(Gen Mgr)*

Catch.com.au Pty Ltd (1)
Level 14 Brookfield Place Tower 2 123 St Georges Terrace, Perth, 6000, WA, Australia
Tel.: (61) 130 022 2824
Web Site: https://www.catch.com.au
Online Product Distr
N.A.I.C.S.: 423690

Coregas NZ Limited (1)
141 Roscommon Road, PO Box 76351, Manukau, 2241, New Zealand
Tel.: (64) 9 278 0145
Web Site: https://www.coregas.co.nz
Core Gas Mfr & Distr
N.A.I.C.S.: 333912
Peter Neate *(Gen Mgr)*

Fitzinn Pty Ltd (1)
24 Albert St, Waterford, 4133, QLD, Australia
Tel.: (61) 732005301
Sales Range: $25-49.9 Million
Emp.: 25
Departmental Stores Operating Services
N.A.I.C.S.: 455110

GPML Pty Ltd (1)
Level 17 167 Macquarie Street, Sydney, 2000, NSW, Australia
Tel.: (61) 292215133
Web Site: http://www.gresham.com.au
Sales Range: $100-124.9 Million
Emp.: 120
Securities Brokerage Services
N.A.I.C.S.: 523150

Geeks2U Pty Limited (1)
PO Box 4793, North Rocks, 2151, NSW, Australia
Tel.: (61) 130 096 1087
Web Site: https://www.geeks2u.com.au
Computer Repair Services
N.A.I.C.S.: 811210

Greencap Holdings Limited (1)
Level 1 / 677 High Street East, Kew, 3102, VIC, Australia
Tel.: (61) 39 896 8600
Web Site: https://www.greencap.com.au
Emergency Management Services
N.A.I.C.S.: 624230
Dean Comrie *(Gen Mgr)*

Harris Technology (NZ) Pty Ltd (1)
45 Epping Road, North Ryde, 2113, NSW, Australia
Tel.: (61) 288795000
Computer Peripheral Equipment Distr
N.A.I.C.S.: 423430

HouseWorks Co Pty Ltd (1)
126-128 Pilbara St, Welshpool, 6106, WA, Australia
Tel.: (61) 893507300
Home Appliances Retailer
N.A.I.C.S.: 449210

J Blackwood & Son Pty Ltd (1)
Unit 2 115 Catherine Crescent, Lavington, Albury, 2640, NSW, Australia
Tel.: (61) 260494908
Consumer Goods Distr
N.A.I.C.S.: 424990

KAS Services India Private Limited (1)
Manyata Embassy Business Park Banyan Block L-1 5th Floor, Embassy Manyata Business Park SEZ Outer Ring Road, Bengaluru, 560045, Karnataka, India
Tel.: (91) 804 683 4000
Web Site: https://www.kasservices.co.in
Software Technology Services
N.A.I.C.S.: 541511
Vineet Mehta *(Head)*

Kidman Resources Limited (1)
NE Suite Level 30 140 Williams St, South Melbourne, 3000, VIC, Australia
Tel.: (61) 39 692 7222
Web Site: http://www.kidmanresources.com.au
Sales Range: $400-449.9 Million
Metal Mining Services
N.A.I.C.S.: 212290
Martin Donohue *(Mng Dir)*

Kleenheat Pty Ltd (1)
Myaree Business Centre, PO Box 4184, Myaree, 6960, WA, Australia
Tel.: (61) 89 312 9299
Web Site: https://www.kleenheat.com.au
Natural Gas Distribution Services
N.A.I.C.S.: 221210

Life's Tiles Pty. Ltd. (1)
37 Sherriffs Rd, Lonsdale, 5160, SA, Australia
Tel.: (61) 883814204
Web Site: https://www.lifestiles.com.au
Floor Tile Distr
N.A.I.C.S.: 423320

Liftco Pty Limited (1)
Unit 5/50 Montague Street North, Wollongong, 2500, NSW, Australia
Tel.: (61) 29 829 4411
Web Site: https://www.liftco.com.au
Conductor Bar Mfr
N.A.I.C.S.: 335931

Meredith Distribution Pty Ltd (1)
10 Overlord Pl, Acacia Ridge, 4110, QLD, Australia
Tel.: (61) 738794222
Web Site: http://www.meredithdist.com.au
Emp.: 12
Fastener Equipment Distr
N.A.I.C.S.: 423710
Phil Haughton *(Branch Mgr)*

Subsidiary (Domestic):

Meredith Distribution (NSW) Pty Ltd (2)
1600B Canterbury Rd, Punchbowl, 2196, NSW, Australia
Tel.: (61) 297078700
Construction Equipment Whslr
N.A.I.C.S.: 423810

Modwood Technologies Pty Ltd (1)
5 Jesica Road, Campbellfield, 3061, VIC, Australia
Tel.: (61) 393578866
Sales Range: $25-49.9 Million
Emp.: 20
Wood Products Mfr & Distr
N.A.I.C.S.: 321999

Neat N' Trim Uniforms Pty Ltd (1)
Level 1-187 Todd Road, Port Melbourne, 3207, VIC, Australia
Tel.: (61) 130 065 2554
Web Site: https://www.nnt.com.au
Cloth Whslr
N.A.I.C.S.: 424350

OAMPS Ltd (1)
289 Wellington Pde South, Melbourne, 3002, VIC, Australia
Tel.: (61) 394121555
Web Site: http://www.oamps.com.au
Sales Range: $100-124.9 Million
Emp.: 200
Insurance Brokerage Services
N.A.I.C.S.: 524210

Subsidiary (Domestic):

OAMPS Consulting Pty Ltd (2)
168 Greenhill Road, Parkside, Adelaide, 5063, SA, Australia
Tel.: (61) 881728000
Insurance Consulting Services
N.A.I.C.S.: 524298

OAMPS Corporate Risk Pty Ltd (2)
Level 4 289 Wellington Parade South East, Melbourne, 3002, VIC, Australia
Tel.: (61) 394121555
Insurance Management Services
N.A.I.C.S.: 524298

OAMPS Gault Armstrong Pty Ltd (2)
Level 9 60 Miller Street, North Sydney, 2060, NSW, Australia
Tel.: (61) 294241870
Web Site: http://www.oampsgaultarmstrong.com.au
Sales Range: $50-74.9 Million
Emp.: 20
Marine Insurance Services
N.A.I.C.S.: 524126
Simon Gosnell *(Gen Mgr)*

OAMPS Life Solutions Ltd (2)
289 Wellington Parade South, Melbourne, 3002, VIC, Australia
Tel.: (61) 394121136
Web Site: http://www.oamps.com.au
Insurance Management Services
N.A.I.C.S.: 524298

OHES Environmental Limited (1)
3 Forest Court, Oaklands Business Park, Wokingham, RG41 2FD, Berkshire, United Kingdom
Tel.: (44) 3336002424
Environmental Consulting Services
N.A.I.C.S.: 541620
Dan Jones *(Mng Dir)*

Officeworks Holdings Pty Ltd (1)
15-17 Loyalty Road, North Rocks, 2151, NSW, Australia
Tel.: (61) 130 063 3423
Web Site: https://www.officeworks.com.au
Stationery Product Whslr
N.A.I.C.S.: 424120

Officeworks NZ Limited (1)
485 Peake Road Bruntwood, Cambridge, 3493, New Zealand
Tel.: (64) 7 827 5497
Web Site: https://www.officeworks.co.nz
Software Services
N.A.I.C.S.: 541519

PTF Training Limited (1)
Estuary Road, Kings Lynn, Norfolk, PE30 2HH, United Kingdom

WESFARMERS LIMITED

Wesfarmers Limited—(Continued)
Tel.: (44) 1553769666
Web Site: http://www.ptftraining.co.uk
Sales Range: $25-49.9 Million
Emp.: 3
Training & Consultancy Services
N.A.I.C.S.: 541618
Ken Taylor *(Mgr-Trng)*

Protector Alsafe (1)
445 Victoria St, Wetherill Park, 2164, NSW, Australia
Tel.: (61) 132832
Web Site: http://www.protectoralsafe.com.au
Sales Range: $75-99.9 Million
Emp.: 175
Industrial Protective & Safety Products Distr
N.A.I.C.S.: 423840

SiSU Wellness Pty. Ltd. (1)
442 Auburn Road, Hawthorn, 3122, VIC, Australia
Tel.: (61) 398183998
Web Site: https://www.sisuhealthgroup.com
Wellness & Healthcare Services
N.A.I.C.S.: 621999

Sotico Pty Ltd (1)
2 Adams Dr, Welshpool, 6106, WA, Australia
Tel.: (61) 89 351 6222
Web Site: https://www.sotico.chinaexporter.com
Furniture Mfr
N.A.I.C.S.: 337121

The Workwear Group Holding Pty Ltd (1)
Level 1/187 Todd Road, Port Melbourne, 3207, VIC, Australia
Tel.: (61) 180 064 4517
Web Site: https://www.workwaregroup.com.au
Cloth Whslr
N.A.I.C.S.: 424250

Wesfarmers Bunnings Limited (1)
126 Pilbara Street Welshpool, Perth, 6084, WA, Australia
Tel.: (61) 893651555
Sales Range: $150-199.9 Million
Emp.: 350
Hardware Product Whslr
N.A.I.C.S.: 423710

Subsidiary (Domestic):

Bunnings Pty., Ltd. (2)
Botanicca 3 - Level 2 East Tower 570 Swan Street, Burnley, Melbourne, 3121, VIC, Australia
Tel.: (61) 38 831 9777
Web Site: https://www.bunnings.com.au
Emp.: 30,000
Home & Garden Improvement Products & Building Materials
N.A.I.C.S.: 459999

Subsidiary (Non-US):

Bunnings Limited (3)
Central Business Park Building 1 Level 3 660 Great South Road, Ellerslie, Auckland, 1051, New Zealand
Tel.: (64) 9 978 2200
Web Site: https://www.bunnings.co.nz
Sales Range: $50-74.9 Million
Emp.: 140
Home Improvement Products & Building Supplies
N.A.I.C.S.: 444180

Subsidiary (Domestic):

Bunnings Management Services Pty Ltd (3)
139 Boulder Rd, Kalgoorlie, 6430, WA, Australia
Tel.: (61) 890910700
Hardware Equipment Mfr
N.A.I.C.S.: 332510

Wesfarmers Chemicals, Energy & Fertilisers (1)
Building 161 Car Park 12 Murdoch University off Campus Drive, Murdoch, 6150, WA, Australia
Tel.: (61) 89 312 9222
Web Site: https://www.wescef.com.au
Sales Range: $300-349.9 Million
Emp.: 1,400
Energy, Chemicals & Fertilizer Production & Distribution
N.A.I.C.S.: 221122

Subsidiary (Domestic):

Coregas Pty Ltd (2)
66 Loftus Road, Yennora, 2161, NSW, Australia
Tel.: (61) 130 060 7577
Web Site: https://www.coregas.com.au
Sales Range: $25-49.9 Million
Emp.: 80
Oxygen, Nitrogen, Argon & Hydrogen Production
N.A.I.C.S.: 325120

Subsidiary (Domestic):

Lawvale Pty Ltd (3)
668 Somerville Road, Sunshine, 3020, VIC, Australia
Tel.: (61) 393133100
Web Site: http://www.migomag.com.au
Welding Equipment Distr
N.A.I.C.S.: 423830

Subsidiary (Domestic):

Curragh Queensland Mining Pty. Ltd. (2)
Blackwater-Cooroorah Road, Blackwater, 4717, QLD, Australia
Tel.: (61) 749869211
Web Site: http://www.curragh.com.au
Sales Range: $300-349.9 Million
Emp.: 600
Coal Mining
N.A.I.C.S.: 212115

Wesfarmers Energy (Gas Sales) Limited (2)
Campus Dr, Murdoch, 6150, WA, Australia
Tel.: (61) 893129222
Web Site: http://www.wes.com.au
Emp.: 30
Chemical Product Whslr
N.A.I.C.S.: 424690
Tom Oleary *(Mng Dir)*

Wesfarmers Kleenheat Gas Pty. Ltd. (2)
Building 161 Car Park 12 Murdoch University, Murdoch, 6150, WA, Australia
Tel.: (61) 893129299
Web Site: http://www.wescef.com.au
Sales Range: $100-124.9 Million
Emp.: 300
Liquefied Petroleum Gas Distr
N.A.I.C.S.: 457210

Subsidiary (Domestic):

Wesfarmers LNG Pty Ltd (3)
Building 161 Car Park 12 Murdoch University, Murdoch, 6150, WA, Australia
Tel.: (61) 893129382
Emp.: 5
Liquefied Natural Gas Distr
N.A.I.C.S.: 221210

Subsidiary (Domestic):

Wesfarmers LPG Pty. Ltd. (2)
Donaldson Road, Kwinana, 6167, WA, Australia
Tel.: (61) 894391222
Web Site: http://www.wesfarmerslpg.com.au
Sales Range: $50-74.9 Million
Emp.: 100
Mfr & Distr of Liquid Petroleum Gas
N.A.I.C.S.: 211120
Albert Romano *(Mgr-Production)*

Wesfarmers Curragh Pty Ltd (1)
GPO Box 51, Brisbane, 4000, QLD, Australia
Tel.: (61) 730317777
Emp.: 60
Coal Mining Services
N.A.I.C.S.: 213113
Swert Eutel *(Mng Dir)*

Subsidiary (Domestic):

Curragh Coal Sales Co. Pty. Ltd. (2)
Level 31 345 Queens St, PO Box 51, Brisbane, 4000, QLD, Australia
Tel.: (61) 730317777
Web Site: http://www.wesresources.com.au
Sales Range: $25-49.9 Million
Emp.: 60
Coal Sales
N.A.I.C.S.: 423520
Stewart Buteo *(Mng Dir)*

Wesfarmers Coal Resources Pty Ltd (2)
GPO Box 51, Brisbane, 4001, QLD, Australia
Tel.: (61) 730317777
Web Site: http://www.wesresources.com.au
Coal Mining Services
N.A.I.C.S.: 213113
Stewart Butel *(Mng Dir)*

Wesfarmers Industrial and Safety Pty Ltd (1)
Level 4 26 Talavera Road, Macquarie Park, Macquarie Park, 2113, NSW, Australia
Tel.: (61) 288734800
Sales Range: $75-99.9 Million
Emp.: 120
Industrial Safety Products Distr
N.A.I.C.S.: 423450
Olivier Chretien *(Mng Dir)*

Subsidiary (Non-US):

Wesfarmers Industrial & Safety NZ Limited (2)
401 Great South Road Penrose, 1061, Auckland, New Zealand
Tel.: (61) 95792880
Web Site: http://www.nzsafety.co.nz
Sales Range: $25-49.9 Million
Emp.: 70
Distr of Industrial, Engineering & Safety Supplies
N.A.I.C.S.: 541870

Subsidiary (Domestic):

Wesfarmers Industrial & Safety Holdings NZ Limited (3)
401 Great South Road, Penrose, Auckland, 1006, New Zealand
Tel.: (64) 95792880
Sales Range: $25-49.9 Million
Emp.: 40
Packaging Plastic Material Mfr
N.A.I.C.S.: 326113
Prashant Billimoria *(Mgr-Fin)*

Wesfarmers Insurance Investments Pty. Ltd. (1)
L 11 40 The Esplande, Perth, 6000, WA, Australia
Tel.: (61) 893274211
Holding Company; Insurance Products & Services
N.A.I.C.S.: 551112

Subsidiary (Domestic):

Hadrill Insurance Brokers Pty Ltd (2)
137 Harrington Street, Hobart, 7000, TAS, Australia
Tel.: (61) 362238333
Emp.: 15
Insurance Brokerage Services
N.A.I.C.S.: 524210
Sane Quentin *(Mgr)*

MIB Insurance Brokers Pty Ltd (2)
Level 2 8 Gardner Close, Milton, 4064, QLD, Australia
Tel.: (61) 732409600
Insurance Brokerage Services
N.A.I.C.S.: 524210

Subsidiary (Non-US):

Monument Insurance (NZ) Limited (2)
L 3 15-21 Dixon St, Wellington, New Zealand
Tel.: (64) 800177987
Insurance Brokerage Services
N.A.I.C.S.: 524210

Subsidiary (Domestic):

OMP Insurance Brokers Ltd. (2)
PO Box 852, Melbourne, 8002, VIC, Australia
Tel.: (61) 394121555
Insurance Brokerage Services
N.A.I.C.S.: 524210

INTERNATIONAL PUBLIC

Parks Insurance Pty Ltd (2)
6 Margaret Street, Wyong, 2259, NSW, Australia
Tel.: (61) 243511188
Insurance Brokerage Services
N.A.I.C.S.: 524210

Wesfarmers Resources Limited (1)
Level 31 Central Plaza 345 Queen Street, Brisbane, 4000, QLD, Australia
Tel.: (61) 730317777
Web Site: http://www.wesresources.com.au
Emp.: 70
Coal Mining Services
N.A.I.C.S.: 213112
Stewart Butel *(Mng Dir)*

Wesfarmers Retail Pty Ltd (1)
L 11 40 The Esplanade, Perth, 6000, WA, Australia
Tel.: (61) 893274211
Web Site: http://www.wesfarmers.com.au
Hardware Component Retailer
N.A.I.C.S.: 444140

Subsidiary (Domestic):

Kmart Australia Limited (2)
100 Burwood Rd, Burwood, 2134, NSW, Australia
Tel.: (61) 287463500
Emp.: 800
Department Stores Operation Services
N.A.I.C.S.: 455110
Ian Bailey *(Grp Mng Dir)*

Liquorland (Australia) Pty Ltd (2)
800 Toorak Road, Hawthorn East, 3123, VIC, Australia
Tel.: (61) 1300656644
Sales Range: $250-299.9 Million
Emp.: 1,000
Alcoholic Products Distr
N.A.I.C.S.: 424820

Target Australia Pty. Ltd. (2)
Cnr Brougham Moorabool Streets, Geelong, 3220, VIC, Australia
Tel.: (61) 352730300
Sales Range: $200-249.9 Million
Emp.: 900
All Other General Merchandise Retailers
N.A.I.C.S.: 455219

Wesfarmers Securities Management Pty Ltd (1)
L 11 40 The Esplanade, Perth, 6000, WA, Australia
Tel.: (61) 893274211
Securities Brokerage Services
N.A.I.C.S.: 523150

WESGAR INC.
1634 Kebet Way, Port Coquitlam, V3C 5W9, BC, Canada
Tel.: (604) 942-9558
Web Site: https://www.wesgar.com
Year Founded: 1965
Emp.: 210
Sheet Metal Components Mfr
N.A.I.C.S.: 332322
John Purdy *(Chm)*

WESIZWE PLATINUM LIMITED
Wesizwe House Devcon Park 9 Autumn Road, Rivonia, 2128, South Africa
Tel.: (27) 119944600   ZA
Web Site: https://www.wesizwe.co.za
WEZ—(JSE)
Rev.: $1,697,573
Assets: $1,323,736,074
Liabilities: $1,109,535,255
Net Worth: $214,200,819
Earnings: ($1,372,392)
Emp.: 746
Fiscal Year-end: 12/31/23
Platinum Mining Services
N.A.I.C.S.: 212290
Zhimin Li *(CEO)*

Subsidiaries:

Bakubung Minerals (Pty) Limited (1)
Private Bag X16, Northlands, 2116, South Africa

Tel.: (27) 119944600
Web Site: http://www.wesizwe.com
Stone Mining & Quarrying Services
N.A.I.C.S.: 212319

WEST AFRICAN RESOURCES LIMITED
Level 1 1 Alvan Street, Subiaco, 6008, WA, Australia
Tel.: (61) 894817344
Web Site:
http://www.westafricanresource.com
WAF—(OTCIQ)
Rev.: $396,575,601
Assets: $572,931,473
Liabilities: $90,068,462
Net Worth: $482,863,011
Earnings: $119,779,618
Emp.: 729
Fiscal Year-end: 12/31/22
Gold Mining Services
N.A.I.C.S.: 212220
Richard Hyde (Founder, Chm & CEO)

WEST BAY FOREST PRODUCTS LTD.
Unit 215 20780 Willoughby Town Centre Drive, Langley, V2Y 0M7, BC, Canada
Tel.: (604) 881-2850
Web Site:
http://www.westbaygroup.com
Year Founded: 1988
Sales Range: $10-24.9 Million
Emp.: 80
Western Red Cedar Products Mfr
N.A.I.C.S.: 321113
Chad Findlay (VP)

WEST BENGAL STATE ELECTRICITY TRANSMISSION COMPANY LIMITED
Vidyut Bhavan Bidhannagar Block - DJ Sector - II, Kolkata, 700 091, India
Tel.: (91) 3323582608
Web Site: http://www.wbsetcl.in
Year Founded: 2007
Electric Power Generation & Distribution Services
N.A.I.C.S.: 221118
Rajesh Pandey (Mng Dir)

WEST BROMWICH BUILDING SOCIETY
2 Providence Place, West Bromwich, B70 8AF, United Kingdom
Tel.: (44) 345 241 3784
Web Site: http://www.westbrom.co.uk
WBS—(LSE)
Rev.: $90,695,696
Assets: $7,832,007,820
Liabilities: $7,302,632,792
Net Worth: $529,375,028
Earnings: $6,924,372
Emp.: 675
Fiscal Year-end: 03/31/21
Investment Management Service
N.A.I.C.S.: 523999
Mark Nicholls (Chm)

Subsidiaries:

CL Mortgages Limited (1)
14 Funtley Court 19 Funtley Hill, Fareham, PO16 7UY, United Kingdom
Tel.: (44) 1329759759
Web Site: https://www.clmortgages.co.uk
Mortgage Adviser Services
N.A.I.C.S.: 522310

Insignia Finance Limited (1)
374 High Street, West Bromwich, B70 8LR, West Midlands, United Kingdom
Tel.: (44) 20 8736 0100
Consumer Lending Services
N.A.I.C.S.: 522291

West Bromwich Commercial Limited (1)
2 Providence Place, West Bromwich, B70 8AF, W Midlands, United Kingdom
Tel.: (44) 1215257070
Mortgage Lending Services
N.A.I.C.S.: 522310

West Bromwich Homes Limited (1)
374 High Street, West Bromwich, B70 8LR, W Midlands, United Kingdom
Tel.: (44) 1215257070
Residential Property Investment Services
N.A.I.C.S.: 531390

White Label Lending Limited (1)
2 Providence Place, West Bromwich, B70 8AF, West Midlands, United Kingdom
Tel.: (44) 8453387527
Emp.: 6
Consumer Lending Services
N.A.I.C.S.: 522291
Jonathan Westhoff (CEO)

WEST CHINA CEMENT LIMITED
No 336 4th Shenzhou Road Aerospace Industrial Base, Changan District, Xi'an, Shaanxi, China
Tel.: (86) 2989254988
Web Site:
https://www.westchinacement.com
2233—(HKG)
Rev.: $1,191,874,554
Assets: $4,245,591,121
Liabilities: $2,365,389,281
Net Worth: $1,880,201,840
Earnings: $188,713,746
Emp.: 7,736
Fiscal Year-end: 12/31/22
Cement Mfr
N.A.I.C.S.: 327310
Jimin Zhang (Founder & Chm)

Subsidiaries:

Shaanxi Yaobai Special Cement Co. Ltd (1)
Gaonian Village Hanjing Town, Pucheng County, Weinan, 715517, Shaanxi, China
Tel.: (86) 9137596255
Cement Mfr
N.A.I.C.S.: 327310

Subsidiary (Domestic):

Hanzhong Yaobai Cement Co. Ltd (2)
Xiecun Town Yangxian, Hanzhong, 723309, Shaanxi, China
Tel.: (86) 9168525118
Cement Mfr
N.A.I.C.S.: 327310

WEST COACH STATION JSC
395 Kinh Duong Vuong An Lac Ward, Binh Tan District, Ho Chi Minh City, Vietnam
Tel.: (84) 2838752953
Web Site: http://www.bxmt.com.vn
WCS—(HNX)
Rev.: $14,025,900
Assets: $28,420,500
Liabilities: $8,129,200
Net Worth: $20,291,300
Earnings: $6,648,200
Emp.: 160
Fiscal Year-end: 12/31/23
Bus Transportation & Parking Services
N.A.I.C.S.: 485210

WEST COAST CAPITAL LIMITED
Marathon House Olympic Business Park, Drybridge Road, Dundonald, KA2 9AE, Ayrshire, United Kingdom
Tel.: (44) 1563852251
Web Site:
http://www.westcoastcapital.co.uk
Year Founded: 2000
Sales Range: $25-49.9 Million
Emp.: 12
Privater Equity Firm
N.A.I.C.S.: 523999
Jim McMahon (Founder & Partner)

WEST COAST PAPER MILLS LTD.
31 Jawaharlal Nehru Road, Kolkata, 700016, West Benga, India
Tel.: (91) 3371500500
Web Site:
https://www.westcoastpaper.com
500444—(NSE)
Rev.: $468,999,326
Assets: $456,289,743
Liabilities: $178,507,848
Net Worth: $277,781,895
Earnings: $47,212,716
Emp.: 2,386
Fiscal Year-end: 03/31/22
Paper Mfr
N.A.I.C.S.: 327910
Kumar Bangur (Chm & Co-Mng Dir)

Subsidiaries:

Andhra Paper Limited (1)
8th Floor Krishe Sapphire Building 1-89/3/B40 to 42/KS/801, Hitec City Main Road Madhapur, Hyderabad, 500 081, Telangana, India (55%)
Tel.: (91) 4068101200
Web Site: https://andhrapaper.com
Rev.: $194,528,539
Assets: $204,465,561
Liabilities: $55,121,949
Net Worth: $149,343,613
Earnings: $19,073,418
Emp.: 1,811
Fiscal Year-end: 03/31/2022
Pulp & Paper Mfr
N.A.I.C.S.: 322120
Prabhakar Cherukumudi (Sec & Sr VP-Corp Affairs)

Unit (Domestic):

The A.P. Paper Mills Ltd - CP Unit (2)
Industrial Area Kadiam Mandalam, MR Palem East Godavari District, Rajahmundry, 533 126, Andhra Pradesh, India
Tel.: (91) 8836685355
Web Site: http://company.naukri.com
Pulp & Paper Mfr
N.A.I.C.S.: 322120

Sudarshan Telecom (1)
Plot No 386 387 KIADB Electronic City, Hebbal Industrial Area, Mysore, 570 016, Karnataka, India
Tel.: (91) 8212404060
Web Site:
http://www.sudarshantelecom.com
Sales Range: $50-74.9 Million
Emp.: 150
Optical Fiber Cable Mfr
N.A.I.C.S.: 335921
S.D. Kulkarni (Head-Tech)

West Coast Opticable Limited (1)
31 Chowringhee Road, Kolkata, 700016, West Bengal, India
Tel.: (91) 3371500500
Web Site:
https://www.westcoastopticable.com
Optical Fiber Cable Mfr
N.A.I.C.S.: 335921
Virendraa Bangur (Chm)

WEST COBAR METALS LIMITED
Tel.: (61) 894810389 AU
Web Site:
https://www.westcobarmetals.com
Year Founded: 2021
WC1—(ASX)
Rev.: $28,498
Assets: $8,853,325
Liabilities: $579,333
Net Worth: $8,273,992
Earnings: ($845,264)
Fiscal Year-end: 06/30/23
Metal Exploration Services
N.A.I.C.S.: 213114
Craig McNab (Sec)

WEST COUNTRY MOTORHOMES LTD
38A Turnpike Road Lower Weare, North Axbridge, Somerset, BS26 2JG, United Kingdom
Tel.: (44) 1278761200
Web Site:
http://www.westcountrymotors.com
Sales Range: $25-49.9 Million
Emp.: 52
Motorhome Dealers & Distr
N.A.I.C.S.: 441210
Steve Taylor (Mng Dir & Mgr-Sls-Brent Knoll)

WEST FRASER TIMBER CO., LTD.
885 West Georgia Street Suite 1500, Vancouver, V6C 3E8, BC, Canada
Tel.: (604) 895-2700 BC
Web Site:
https://www.westfraser.com
Year Founded: 1955
WFG—(NYSE)
Rev.: $6,454,000,000
Assets: $9,415,000,000
Liabilities: $2,192,000,000
Net Worth: $7,223,000,000
Earnings: ($167,000,000)
Emp.: 10,800
Fiscal Year-end: 12/31/23
Lumber & Wood Products Mfr, Exporter & Sales; Sawmill Operator
N.A.I.C.S.: 321113
Raymond W. Ferris (Pres & CEO)

Subsidiaries:

Blue Ridge Lumber Inc. (1)
595007 Hwy 658, PO Box 87, Blue Ridge, T0E 0B0, AB, Canada
Tel.: (780) 648-6200
Lumber Mfr
N.A.I.C.S.: 321212

Decker Lake Forest Products Ltd. (1)
10345 Lewis Road, PO Box 250, Burns Lake, V0J 1E0, BC, Canada (100%)
Tel.: (250) 698-7304
Sales Range: $25-49.9 Million
Emp.: 100
Sawmill Operator
N.A.I.C.S.: 321113

Manning Forest Products Ltd. (1)
PO Box 370, Manning, T0H 2M0, AB, Canada
Tel.: (780) 836-3111
Web Site: https://www.mdfp.ca
Lumber Mfr
N.A.I.C.S.: 321212

Norbord Inc. (1)
1 Toronto Street Suite 600, Toronto, M5C 2W4, ON, Canada
Tel.: (416) 365-0705
Web Site: http://www.norbord.com
Rev.: $2,407,000,000
Assets: $2,477,000,000
Liabilities: $1,357,000,000
Net Worth: $1,120,000,000
Earnings: $497,000,000
Emp.: 2,500
Fiscal Year-end: 12/31/2020
Building Materials; Mill Operators; Market Lumber & Pulp
N.A.I.C.S.: 321211
Peter C. Wijnbergen (Pres & CEO)

Subsidiary (Domestic):

Norbord Industries, Inc. (2)
One Toronto Street Suite 600, Toronto, M5C 2W4, ON, Canada (100%)
Tel.: (416) 365-0705
Web Site: http://www.norbord.com
Sales Range: $25-49.9 Million
Emp.: 90
Building Materials Including Panelboard, Oriented Strand Board, Medium Density Fibreboards & Particleboard
N.A.I.C.S.: 444180

WEST FRASER TIMBER CO., LTD.

West Fraser Timber Co., Ltd.—(Continued)

Plant (US):

Norbord Jefferson (3)
500 Norbord Blvd, Jefferson, TX 75657
Tel.: (903) 665-5800
Web Site: http://www.norbord.com
Sales Range: $50-74.9 Million
Producer of Oriented Strand Board
N.A.I.C.S.: 321219

Norbord Nacogdoches (3)
2301 SE Stallings Dr Loop224, Nacogdoches, TX 75961-6873
Tel.: (936) 568-8000
Web Site: http://www.norbord.com
Sales Range: $50-74.9 Million
Emp.: 12
Oriented Strandboard
N.A.I.C.S.: 321219

Sundre Forest Products Ltd. (1)
Hwy 584 West, Bag 1, Sundre, T0M 1X0, AB, Canada **(100%)**
Tel.: (403) 638-3772
Web Site: http://www.fraser.com
Sales Range: $125-149.9 Million
Emp.: 550
Sawmill Operator
N.A.I.C.S.: 321113

West Fraser Mills Ltd. (1)
1250 Brownmiller Road, Quesnel, V2J 6P5, BC, Canada
Tel.: (250) 992-9244
Timber & Wood Plywood Products Mfr
N.A.I.C.S.: 321211

West Fraser Newsprint Ltd. (1)
858 Beatty Street Suite 501, Vancouver, V6B 1C1, BC, Canada
Tel.: (604) 895-2700
Web Site: https://www.westfraser.com
Paper Products Mfr
N.A.I.C.S.: 322299

West Fraser Timber Co., Ltd. - 100 Mile Lumber Division (1)
910 Exeter Station Rd, PO Box 97, 100 Mile House, V0K 2E0, BC, Canada
Tel.: (250) 395-8200
Web Site: http://www.westfraser.com
Sales Range: $50-74.9 Million
Timber & Plywood Product Mfr
N.A.I.C.S.: 321211

West Fraser Timber Co., Ltd. - Alberta Plywood Division (1)
9919 - 65 Avenue, Edmonton, T6E 0L1, AB, Canada
Tel.: (780) 413-9800
Wood Panel & Plywood Product Mfr
N.A.I.C.S.: 321211

West Fraser Timber Co., Ltd. - Alberta Plywood Mill (1)
9923 - 65th Avenue, Edmonton, T6E 0L1, AB, Canada
Tel.: (780) 413-9800
Sales Range: $50-74.9 Million
Emp.: 20
Plywood & Timber Products Mfr
N.A.I.C.S.: 321211
Dan Lewis (Gen Mgr)

West Fraser Timber Co., Ltd. - Chasm Sawmills Division (1)
1020 Chasm Road, PO Box 190, 70 Mile House, V0K 2K0, BC, Canada
Tel.: (250) 459-2229
Web Site: http://www.westfraser.com
Sales Range: $50-74.9 Million
Emp.: 17
Timber & Plywood Product Mfr
N.A.I.C.S.: 321211

West Fraser Timber Co., Ltd. - Chetwynd Forest Industries Division (1)
3598 West Fraser Road, PO Box 330, Chetwynd, V0C 1J0, BC, Canada
Tel.: (250) 788-2686
Web Site: https://www.westfraser.com
Timber & Plywood Product Mfr
N.A.I.C.S.: 321211

West Fraser Timber Co., Ltd. - Fraser Lake Sawmills Division (1)
6626 Highway 16 East, PO Box 100, Fraser Lake, V0J 1S0, BC, Canada
Tel.: (250) 699-6235
Web Site: https://www.westfraser.com
Sales Range: $25-49.9 Million
Plywood & Timber Product Mfr
N.A.I.C.S.: 321211

West Fraser Timber Co., Ltd. - Hinton Pulp (1)
760 Switzer Drive, Hinton, T7V 1V7, AB, Canada **(100%)**
Tel.: (780) 865-2251
Web Site: https://www.westfraser.com
Sales Range: $200-249.9 Million
Emp.: 650
Pulp Mill Operators
N.A.I.C.S.: 322110

West Fraser Timber Co., Ltd. - Hinton Wood Products (1)
99 West River Road, Hinton, T7V 1Y7, AB, Canada **(100%)**
Tel.: (780) 865-8900
Web Site: https://www.westfraser.com
Sales Range: $50-74.9 Million
Emp.: 250
Sawmill Operator
N.A.I.C.S.: 321113

West Fraser Timber Co., Ltd. - Pacific Inland Resources Division (1)
2375 Tatlow Road, PO Box 3130, Smithers, V0J 2N0, BC, Canada
Tel.: (250) 847-2656
Sales Range: $50-74.9 Million
Emp.: 240
Wood & Plywood Timber Mfr
N.A.I.C.S.: 321999
Dean McDonald (Gen Mgr)

West Fraser Timber Co., Ltd. - Quesnel Plywood (1)
1000 Plywood Rd PO Box 2000, Quesnel, V2J 5W1, BC, Canada **(100%)**
Tel.: (250) 992-5511
Web Site: https://www.westfraser.com
Sales Range: $125-149.9 Million
Emp.: 350
Hardwood Veneer & Plywood Sales
N.A.I.C.S.: 321211

West Fraser Timber Co., Ltd. - Quesnel Sawmills (1)
1250 Brownmiller Road, Quesnel, V2J 6P5, BC, Canada
Tel.: (250) 992-9244
Web Site: https://www.westfraser.com
Sales Range: $450-499.9 Million
Timber & Plywood Product Mfr
N.A.I.C.S.: 321211

West Fraser Timber Co., Ltd. - Ranger Board Division (1)
PO Box 6, Blue Ridge, T0E 0B0, AB, Canada
Tel.: (780) 648-6333
Web Site: http://www.westfraser.com
Timber & Plywood Product Mfr
N.A.I.C.S.: 321211

West Fraser Timber Co., Ltd. - Sundre Forest Products Division (1)
Hwy 584 West Bag 1, Bag 1, Sundre, T0M 1X0, AB, Canada
Tel.: (403) 638-3772
Web Site: https://www.westfraser.com
Plywood & Timer Product Mfr
N.A.I.C.S.: 321211

West Fraser Timber Co., Ltd. - West Fraser LVL Division (1)
Secondary Hwy 752, PO Box 1737, Rocky Mountain House, T4T 1B3, AB, Canada
Tel.: (403) 845-4104
Web Site: https://www.westfraser.com
Timber & Plywood Products Mfr
N.A.I.C.S.: 321211

West Fraser Timber Co., Ltd. - West-Pine MDF Division (1)
300 Carradice Road, Quesnel, V2J 5Z7, BC, Canada
Tel.: (250) 991-7100
Web Site: https://www.westfraser.com
Plywood & Timber Products Mfr
N.A.I.C.S.: 321211

West Fraser Timber Co., Ltd. - Williams Lake Plywood (1)
4200 N McKenzie Ave, Williams Lake, V2G 2V5, BC, Canada **(100%)**
Tel.: (250) 392-7731
Sales Range: $125-149.9 Million
Emp.: 320
Plywood Mfr
N.A.I.C.S.: 321212
Dave Walgren (Gen Mgr)

West Fraser Timber Co., Ltd. - Williams Lake Timber (1)
PO Box 4360, Williams Lake, V2G 2V4, BC, Canada
Tel.: (250) 392-7784
Timber & Plywood Product Mfr
N.A.I.C.S.: 321211

West Fraser, Inc. (1)
1900 Exeter Rd Ste 105, Germantown, TN 38138
Tel.: (901) 620-4200
Wood & Timber Products Whslr
N.A.I.C.S.: 423310

Plant (Domestic):

West Fraser - Armour Division (2)
361 Federal Rd, Riegelwood, NC 28456-7117
Tel.: (910) 655-4106
Web Site: https://www.westfraser.com
Sales Range: $50-74.9 Million
Emp.: 200
Lumber Mill
N.A.I.C.S.: 321113

West Fraser - Henderson Division (2)
609 Industrial Dr, Henderson, TX 75653
Tel.: (903) 657-4575
Web Site: http://www.westfraser.com
Sales Range: Less than $1 Million
Emp.: 155
Lumber Mill
N.A.I.C.S.: 423310

West Fraser - Leola Division (2)
1400 Main St, Leola, AR 72084
Tel.: (870) 765-6200
Web Site: http://www.westfraser.com
Sales Range: $50-74.9 Million
Emp.: 120
Lumber Mill
N.A.I.C.S.: 321113

West Fraser - Maplesville Division (2)
7475 Alabama Hwy 22, Maplesville, AL 36750
Tel.: (334) 366-2971
Web Site: http://www.westfraser.com
Sales Range: $75-99.9 Million
Emp.: 150
Lumber Mill
N.A.I.C.S.: 423310

West Fraser - McDavid Division (2)
401 Champion Dr, McDavid, FL 32568
Tel.: (850) 418-6821
Web Site: https://www.westfraser.com
Sales Range: $50-74.9 Million
Emp.: 240
Lumber Mill
N.A.I.C.S.: 321113

West Fraser - New Boston Division (2)
Hwy 82 E, New Boston, TX 75570
Tel.: (903) 628-2506
Web Site: https://www.westfraser.com
Sales Range: $75-99.9 Million
Emp.: 150
Lumber Mill
N.A.I.C.S.: 321113
Roger Chitwood (Reg Mgr)

West Fraser - Newberry Division (2)
3287 College St, Newberry, SC 29108-1637
Tel.: (803) 276-4311
Web Site: https://www.westfraser.com
Sales Range: $50-74.9 Million
Emp.: 160
Lumber Mill
N.A.I.C.S.: 321113

West Fraser - Opelika Division (2)
2100 Industrial Blvd, Opelika, AL 36801
Tel.: (334) 749-6281
Web Site: http://www.westfraser.com

Sales Range: $25-49.9 Million
Emp.: 96
Lumber Mill
N.A.I.C.S.: 321113

West Fraser - Seaboard Division (2)
4400 NC Hwy 186E, Seaboard, NC 27876
Tel.: (252) 589-2011
Web Site: https://www.westfraser.com
Sales Range: $50-74.9 Million
Emp.: 175
Lumber Mill
N.A.I.C.S.: 321113

West Fraser - Whitehouse Division (2)
109 Halsema Rd S, Whitehouse, FL 32220-1657
Tel.: (904) 695-3800
Web Site: https://www.westfraser.com
Sales Range: $25-49.9 Million
Emp.: 106
Lumber Mill
N.A.I.C.S.: 321113

West Fraser Mills - Augusta Division (2)
2474 Doug Barnard Pkwy, Augusta, GA 30906
Tel.: (706) 793-8753
Web Site: http://www.westfraser.com
Sales Range: $50-74.9 Million
Timber & Plywood Products Mfr
N.A.I.C.S.: 321211

West Fraser Mills Ltd. - Huttig Sawmill Division (2)
502 Olin Ave, Huttig, AR 71747
Tel.: (870) 943-2211
Web Site: http://www.westfraser.com
Timber & Plywood Products Mfr
N.A.I.C.S.: 321999

West Fraser Mills Ltd. - Joyce Sawmill Division (2)
6481 Hwy 34 N, Joyce, LA 71440
Tel.: (318) 648-3300
Web Site: http://www.westfraser.com
Lumber & Plywood Products Mfr
N.A.I.C.S.: 321211

West Fraser, Inc. - Mansfield Lumber Mill (2)
700 S Hwy 71 E, Mansfield, AR 72944
Tel.: (479) 928-4446
Sales Range: $1-9.9 Million
Emp.: 85
Sawmills
N.A.I.C.S.: 321113

WEST HIGH YIELD (W.H.Y.) RESOURCES LTD.
PO Box 68121, Calgary, T3G 3N8, AB, Canada
Tel.: (403) 283-5555
Web Site:
https://www.whyresources.com
Year Founded: 2003
W0H—(DEU)
Assets: $1,399,919
Liabilities: $4,560,206
Net Worth: ($3,160,287)
Earnings: ($2,368,376)
Fiscal Year-end: 12/31/23
Mineral Exploration Services
N.A.I.C.S.: 213114
Shelina Hirji (CFO)

WEST HOLDINGS CORPORATION
West 1st Building 1-15-24 Kusunoki-cho, Nishi-ku, Hiroshima, 733-0002, Japan
Tel.: (81) 825033900
Web Site: http://www.west-gr.co.jp
Year Founded: 2006
1407—(TKS)
Rev: $313,425,800
Assets: $783,079,340
Liabilities: $575,337,560
Net Worth: $207,741,780
Earnings: $42,028,540
Emp.: 535
Fiscal Year-end: 08/31/24

AND PRIVATE COMPANIES

WEST JAPAN RAILWAY COMPANY

Holding Company
N.A.I.C.S.: 551111
Takashi Kikkawa *(Chm & CEO)*

Subsidiaries:

Stadtwerke Japan Co., Inc. (1)
32F Tokyo Opera City Tower 3-20-2 Nishi-shinjuku Shinjuku-ku, Tokyo, 163-1432, Japan
Tel.: (81) 353020308
Web Site: http://www.stadtwerke.jp
Lifestyle Support Services
N.A.I.C.S.: 561210
Kenji Araki *(Pres)*

West Energy Solution Inc. (1)
3-6-2 Nihonbashi Nihonbashi Front 4F, Chuo-ku, Tokyo, 103-0027, Japan
Tel.: (81) 362626635
Web Site: http://www.west-es.jp
Solar Power Generation Services
N.A.I.C.S.: 221114

WEST ISLE ENERGY INC.
#503 1078-6 Ave SW, Calgary, T2P 5N6, AB, Canada
Tel.: (403) 263-1977 AB
Sales Range: Less than $1 Million
Oil & Natural Gas Exploration Services
N.A.I.C.S.: 211120
Nitin S. Kasliwal *(Chm & Mng Dir)*

WEST JAPAN RAILWAY COMPANY
2-4-24 Shibata, Kita-ku, Osaka, 530-8341, Japan
Tel.: (81) 663758981 JP
Web Site: https://www.westjr.co.jp
Year Founded: 1987
9021—(TKS)
Rev.: $9,981,077,040
Assets: $35,839,435,280
Liabilities: $25,441,072,800
Net Worth: $10,398,362,480
Earnings: ($1,095,756,640)
Emp.: 46,779
Fiscal Year-end: 03/31/22
Railway, Bus & Ferry Services; Retail Stores; Hotel Development; Real Estate Development
N.A.I.C.S.: 485112
Kazuaki Hasegawa *(Pres & Exec Officer)*

Subsidiaries:

Chugoku JR Bus Company (1)
2-24 Kyobashicho, Minami-ku, Hiroshima, 732-0828, Japan
Tel.: (81) 570010666
Web Site: https://www.chugoku-jrbus.co.jp
Sales Range: $200-249.9 Million
Emp.: 459
Bus Transportation Services
N.A.I.C.S.: 488999

Chugoku SC Development Company (1)
1-2 Matsubara-cho, Minami-ku, Hiroshima, 732-0822, Japan
Tel.: (81) 825062556
Web Site: https://cskaihatu.co.jp
Emp.: 66
Shopping Center Development & Management Services
N.A.I.C.S.: 541611

JR WEST IT Solutions Company (1)
4-1-6 Miyahara Across Shin-Osaka, Yodogawa-ku, Suita, 532-0003, Japan
Tel.: (81) 677123448
Web Site: https://www.j-wits.co.jp
Sales Range: $100-124.9 Million
Emp.: 500
Information Technology Consulting Services
N.A.I.C.S.: 519290

JR West Financial Management Co., Ltd. (1)
9F St Annex Building 5-11-8 Nishinakajima, Yodogawa-ku, Osaka, 532-0011, Japan
Tel.: (81) 663070501
Web Site: https://www.jwfm.co.jp
Emp.: 410
Financial Support Services
N.A.I.C.S.: 523999

JR West Japan Communications Company (1)
1-6-20 Dojima Dojima Avanza 8F, Kita-ku, Osaka, 530-0003, Japan
Tel.: (81) 663445138
Web Site: https://www.jcomm.co.jp
Emp.: 369
Advertising Services
N.A.I.C.S.: 541890

JR West Japan LINEN Co., Ltd (1)
5-4-20 Nishinakajima Chuo Building 8f, Yodogawa-Ku, Osaka, 532-0011, Japan
Tel.: (81) 648052161
Linen Distr
N.A.I.C.S.: 812331

JR West Japan MARUNIX Co., Ltd (1)
Tel.: (81) 663968620
Web Site: http://jrwmarunix.com
Logistic Services
N.A.I.C.S.: 541614

JR West Maintec Co., Ltd. (1)
4-44 Miyahara, Yodogawa-ku, Osaka, Japan
Tel.: (81) 671758250
Web Site: https://j-maintec.co.jp
Emp.: 2,232
Hotel Cleaning & Maintenance Services
N.A.I.C.S.: 561720

JR West Miyajima Ferry Co., Ltd. (1)
Miyajimaguchi 1-11-5, Hatsukaichi, 739-0411, Hiroshima-ken, Japan
Tel.: (81) 829562045
Web Site: https://jr-miyajimaferry.co.jp
Sales Range: $25-49.9 Million
Emp.: 50
Ferry Transportation Services
N.A.I.C.S.: 483114

JR-West Japan Consultants Company (1)
9F Central Building 5-4-20 Nishinakajima, Yodogawa-ku, Osaka, 532-0011, Japan
Tel.: (81) 663036971
Web Site: https://www.jrnc.co.jp
Emp.: 437
Railway Consulting Services
N.A.I.C.S.: 541618

JR-West Japan Real Estate & Development Company (1)
3-11-22 Nishikujo, Konohana-Ku, Osaka, 554-0012, Japan
Tel.: (81) 664671536
Real Estate Lending Services
N.A.I.C.S.: 531190

Japan Railway Service Net Fukuoka Company (1)
1-32-1 Hakataeki-mae, Hakata-ku, Fukuoka, Japan
Tel.: (81) 924755833 **(100%)**
General Merchandise Retailer
N.A.I.C.S.: 459999

Japan Railway Service Net Yonago Company (1)
141 Mannomachi, Yonago, 683-0065, Japan
Tel.: (81) 859224675
General Merchandise Retailer
N.A.I.C.S.: 459999

KOBE SC DEVELOPMENT COMPANY (1)
1-2-1 Sumiyoshihonmachi, Higashinada-Ku, Kobe, 658-0051, Hyogo, Japan
Tel.: (81) 788434650
Web Site: http://www.kobe-sc.co.jp
Emp.: 94
Commercial Property Management Services
N.A.I.C.S.: 531312

Kanazawa Terminal Development Co., Ltd. (1)
1-1 Kinoshinbocho, Ishikawa, Kanazawa, 920-0858, Japan
Tel.: (81) 762603700
Web Site: https://www.100bangai.co.jp
Sales Range: $25-49.9 Million
Emp.: 40
Real Estate Lending Services
N.A.I.C.S.: 531190

Kyoto Eki-Kanko Department Store Company (1)
52 Kamitonodacho Higashikujo Kkd Bldg, Minami-Ku, Kyoto, 601-8002, Japan
Tel.: (81) 756811341
Web Site: http://www.thecube.co.jp
Sales Range: $50-74.9 Million
Emp.: 99
Commercial Property Management Services
N.A.I.C.S.: 531312

Kyoto Station Building Development Co., Ltd (1)
8th floor Shin-Kyoto Center Building 614 Higashi-Shiokoji-cho, Shiokoji-dori Karasuma Nishiiri Shimogyo-ku, Kyoto, 600-8216, Japan **(61.9%)**
Tel.: (81) 753614394
Web Site: https://www.kyoto-station-building.co.jp
Real Estate Lending Services
N.A.I.C.S.: 531190
Takao Fukuyama *(Exec Dir)*

Kyoto Station Center Co., Ltd. (1)
Sagaru Karasumadori Shiokoji 902 Higashi-ishiokojicho, Shimogyo-Ku, Kyoto, 600-0000, Japan
Tel.: (81) 753657513
Real Estate Lending Services
N.A.I.C.S.: 531190

Nara Hotel Co., Ltd. (1)
1096 Takabatake-cho, Nara, 630-8301, Japan
Tel.: (81) 742263300
Web Site: https://www.narahotel.co.jp
Hotel Operator
N.A.I.C.S.: 721110

Nippon Travel Agency Co., Ltd. (1)
Nihonbashi Dia Bldg 11F, 1-19-1 Nihonbashi, Chuo-ku, Tokyo, 103-8266, Japan **(79.8%)**
Tel.: (81) 368958344
Web Site: https://www.ntainbound.com
Sales Range: $1-4.9 Billion
Emp.: 5,061
Travel Agencies
N.A.I.C.S.: 561510

Subsidiary (Non-US):

P.T. Jabato International Tour & Travel (2)
Gedung Summitmas II Lantai 3 Jl Jendral Sudirman Kav 61-62, Jakarta, 12190, Indonesia
Tel.: (62) 215202091
Web Site: https://www.jabatowisata.com
Travel Agency
N.A.I.C.S.: 561510
Yasuyuki Masamoto *(Dir & Pres)*

Osaka Terminal Building Company (1)
2-Chome Shibata, Kita-ku, Osaka, 530-8341, Japan
Tel.: (81) 570004146
Web Site: https://osakastationcity.com
Emp.: 58
Real Estate Lending Services
N.A.I.C.S.: 531190

Railway Track and Structures Technology Co., Ltd. (1)
3-8-21 Futabanosato, Higashi-Ku, Hiroshima, 732-0057, Japan
Tel.: (81) 822619320
Construction Engineering Services
N.A.I.C.S.: 541330

Sagano Scenic Railway (1)
Sagatenryuji Kuradocho, Ukyo-ku, Kyoto, 616 8373, Japan **(100%)**
Tel.: (81) 758618511
Web Site: http://www.sagano-kanko.co.jp
Emp.: 100
Railway Services
N.A.I.C.S.: 485112
Tetsuro Nishida *(Pres)*

Sannomiya Terminal Building Co., Ltd. (1)
8-1-2 Kumoidori, Chuo-Ku, Kobe, 651-0096, Japan
Tel.: (81) 782910056
Web Site: http://www.sth-hotel.co.jp
Sales Range: $10-24.9 Million
Emp.: 50
Home Management Services
N.A.I.C.S.: 721110

Tennoji Station Building Co., Ltd (1)
10-48 Hiden-Incho Station Plz Tennoji 6f, Tennoji-Ku, Osaka, 543-0055, Japan
Tel.: (81) 667791551
Web Site: http://www.tennoji-sb.co.jp
Commercial Property Management Services
N.A.I.C.S.: 531312

Tennoji Terminal Building Co., Ltd. (1)
10-39 Hiden-Incho Tennoji Mio 12f, Tennoji-Ku, Osaka, 543-0055, Japan
Tel.: (81) 667701111
Web Site: http://www.tennoji-mio.co.jp
Commercial Property Management Services
N.A.I.C.S.: 531312

Toyama Terminal Building Company (1)
1-1-61 Sakuramachi, Toyama, 930-0003, Japan
Tel.: (81) 764454511
Web Site: http://www.marier-toyama.co.jp
Emp.: 30
Commercial Property Management Services
N.A.I.C.S.: 531312

Wakayama Station Building Co., Ltd. (1)
5-61 Misonocho, Wakayama, 640-8331, Japan
Tel.: (81) 734246311
Real Estate Lending Services
N.A.I.C.S.: 531190

Wakayama Terminal Building Co., Ltd. (1)
5-18 Tomoda-cho, Wakayama, 640-8342, Japan
Tel.: (81) 734253333
Web Site: http://www.granvia-wakayama.co.jp
Sales Range: $75-99.9 Million
Emp.: 130
Commercial Property Management Services
N.A.I.C.S.: 531312

West Japan Electric System Co., Ltd. (1)
4-24 Shibata 2-chome Kita-ku, Osaka, 530-8341, Japan **(51.5%)**
Tel.: (81) 663968701
Web Site: http://www.westjr.co.jp
Railway Electric Facility Maintenance Services
N.A.I.C.S.: 561210
Yoshio Ohkubo *(Exec Officer & Dir)*

West Japan Railway Daily Service Net Company (1)
1-2-12 Shioe, Amagasaki, 661-0976, Japan **(100%)**
Tel.: (81) 649609100
Web Site: http://www.westjr.co.jp
Emp.: 5,600
Retail Sales & Food Services
N.A.I.C.S.: 455219

West Japan Railway Fashion Goods Co., Ltd. (1)
4-20 Nishinakajima 5-Chome, Yodogawa-ku, Osaka, 532 0011, Japan **(100%)**
Tel.: (81) 663908601
Web Site: http://www.jst-inc.com
Sales Range: $50-74.9 Million
Emp.: 250
Fashion Retail Stores
N.A.I.C.S.: 458110

West Japan Railway Food Service Net Company (1)
5-4-20 Nishinakajima, Yodogawa-ku, Osaka, 532-0011, Japan
Tel.: (81) 668853573
Web Site: https://www.jwfsn.co.jp
Sales Range: $100-124.9 Million
Emp.: 2,200
Railway Catering Services
N.A.I.C.S.: 722320

West Japan Railway Fukuchiyama MAINTEC Co., LTD. (1)
209-6 Ohashi Amada, Fukuchiyama, 620-0000, Japan

WEST JAPAN RAILWAY COMPANY

West Japan Railway Company—(Continued)
Tel.: (81) 773220805
Railcar Cleaning Services
N.A.I.C.S.: 488210

West Japan Railway Fukuoka MAINTEC Co., LTD. (1)
3-2-8 Hakataekimae Sumitomoseimeihakata Bldg 13f, Hakata-Ku, Fukuoka, 812-0011, Japan
Tel.: (81) 924745321
Railcar Cleaning Services
N.A.I.C.S.: 488210

West Japan Railway Hiroshima MAINTEC Co., LTD.b (1)
16-1 Kamiosugacho, Higashi-Ku, Hiroshima, 732-0056, Japan
Tel.: (81) 822624252
Web Site: http://www.j-h-maintec.co.jp
Railcar Cleaning Services
N.A.I.C.S.: 488210

West Japan Railway Hotel Development Limited (1)
901 Higashi-shiokoji-cho Shiokoji-sagaru Karasuma-dori, Shimogyo-ku, Kyoto, 600-8216, Japan (100%)
Tel.: (81) 753448888
Web Site: http://www.granviakyoto.com
Sales Range: $50-74.9 Million
Emp.: 460
Hotel Development
N.A.I.C.S.: 721110
Kazunori Minato (Pres)

Subsidiary (Domestic):

Hotel Granvia Hiroshima Co., Ltd. (2)
1-5 Matsubaracho, Minami-ku, Hiroshima, 732-0822, Hiroshima Prefecture, Japan (93.8%)
Tel.: (81) 822621111
Web Site: https://www.hgh.co.jp
Emp.: 187
Home Management Services
N.A.I.C.S.: 721110

Hotel Granvia Okayama Co., Ltd. (2)
1-5 Ekimoto-machi, Kita-ku, Okayama, 700-8515, Japan
Tel.: (81) 862847000
Web Site: http://www.granvia-oka.co.jp
Sales Range: $50-74.9 Million
Emp.: 280
Home Management Services
N.A.I.C.S.: 721110
Tughiro Watanade (Pres)

West Japan Railway Isetan Limited (1)
901 Higashishiokoujimachi Karasuma-dori, Shiokoji, Shimogyo-ku, Kyoto, 600 8216, Japan (60%)
Tel.: (81) 753425600
Sales Range: $125-149.9 Million
Emp.: 438
Department Stores
N.A.I.C.S.: 455110

West Japan Railway Kanazawa MAINTEC Co., LTD. (1)
1-17-23 Nishinen, Kanazawa, 920-0024, Ishikawa Prefecture, Japan
Tel.: (81) 762216520
Web Site: https://www.westjr-k-maintec.co.jp
Emp.: 696
Railcar Cleaning Services
N.A.I.C.S.: 488210

West Japan Railway Maintec Co., Ltd. (1)
4-4-44 Miyahara, Yodogawa-ku, Osaka, 532-0003, Japan (100%)
Tel.: (81) 671758250
Web Site: https://j-maintec.co.jp
Emp.: 2,232
Railcar Related Cleaning Services
N.A.I.C.S.: 488210

West Japan Railway Technos Corporation (1)
10th floor Pierce Tower 3-19-3 Toyosaki, Kita-ku, Osaka, 531-0072, Japan
Tel.: (81) 672238760
Web Site: https://www.wjtechnos.co.jp

Emp.: 1,013
Railcar Facilities Maintenance & Services
N.A.I.C.S.: 488210
Mori Fumio (Mgr- Acctg)

West Japan Railway Techsia Co.,Ltd (1)
1-1-33 Shioe, Amagasaki, 661-0976, Hyogo, Japan
Tel.: (81) 649607910
Web Site: https://www.techsia.co.jp
Emp.: 590
Industrial Equipment Mfr & Maintenance Services
N.A.I.C.S.: 333248

West Japan Railway Yonago MAINTEC Co., LTD. (1)
141-81 Sanno-cho, Tottori, Yonago, 683-0065, Japan
Tel.: (81) 859332870
Web Site: http://www.yonago-maintec.co.jp
Sales Range: $100-124.9 Million
Emp.: 353
Railcar Cleaning Services
N.A.I.C.S.: 488210
Koji Ozaki (Dir)

WEST LAKE ENERGY CORP.
Suite 700 600 - 3 Ave SW, Calgary, T2P 0G5, AB, Canada
Tel.: (403) 215-2045
Web Site: https://www.westlakeenergy.ca
Oil & Natural Gas Company
N.A.I.C.S.: 213112
Bruce McDonald (CEO)

WEST LEISURE RESORTS LIMITED
Mall Office 2nd Floor Netivali Kalyan E, Metro Junction Mall of West Pioneer Properties I Pvt Ltd, Thane, 421306, Maharashtra, India
Tel.: (91) 2512352387
Web Site: https://www.westleisureresort.co.in
Year Founded: 2008
538382—(BOM)
Rev.: $45,897
Assets: $2,334,189
Liabilities: $12,026
Net Worth: $2,322,163
Earnings: $8,980
Fiscal Year-end: 03/31/23
Financial Management Services
N.A.I.C.S.: 523999
Vaibhav Dodia (Officer-Compliance & Sec)

WEST MINING CORP.
1100-1199 West Hastings Street, PO Box 49114, Vancouver, V6E 3T5, BC, Canada
Tel.: (778) 881-4631
Web Site: https://www.westminingcorp.ca
1HL0—(DEU)
Rev.: $763
Assets: $6,496,616
Liabilities: $205,040
Net Worth: $6,291,576
Earnings: ($853,222)
Fiscal Year-end: 10/31/23
Business Consulting Services
N.A.I.C.S.: 522299
Nicolas Houghton (Pres)

WEST MOUNTAIN ENVIRONMENTAL CORP.
137 LeMarchant Road, Saint John's, A1C 2H3, NL, Canada
Tel.: (709) 726-5198 AB
Web Site: http://www.westmountaincapital.com
Year Founded: 2005
Sales Range: $1-9.9 Million
Investment Holding Company
N.A.I.C.S.: 551112

WEST PIONEER PROPERTIES LIMITED
125 Old Broad Street, London, EC2N 1AR, United Kingdom
Tel.: (44) 2073987700 VG
Web Site: http://www.west-pioneer.com
Sales Range: $1-9.9 Million
Real Estate Manangement Services
N.A.I.C.S.: 531390
Amit Jatia (Chm)

WEST RED LAKE GOLD MINES LTD.
Suite 3123 595 Burrard Street, Vancouver, V7X 1J1, BC, Canada
Tel.: (604) 609-6132 BC
Web Site: https://westredlakegold.com
Year Founded: 1979
WRLG—(TSXV)
Rev.: $9,074
Assets: $1,580,073
Liabilities: $30,898
Net Worth: $1,549,175
Earnings: ($138,682)
Fiscal Year-end: 11/30/21
Mineral Exploration Services
N.A.I.C.S.: 212290
Shane Williams (Pres, CEO & Dir)

Subsidiaries:

Pure Gold Mining Inc. (1)
Suite 1900 - 1055 West Hastings Street, Vancouver, V6E 2E9, BC, Canada
Tel.: (604) 646-8000
Web Site: http://www.puregoldmining.ca
Rev.: $533,869
Assets: $194,373,985
Liabilities: $147,075,090
Net Worth: $47,298,895
Earnings: ($21,085,261)
Emp.: 245
Fiscal Year-end: 12/31/2020
Gold Exploration Services
N.A.I.C.S.: 212220
Graeme Currie (Chm)

West Red Lake Gold Mines (Ontario) Ltd (1)
82 Richmond Street East Suite 200, Toronto, M5C 1P1, ON, Canada
Tel.: (416) 203-9181
Web Site: http://www.westredlakegold.com
Rev.: $359,020
Assets: $74,010,994
Liabilities: $24,147,365
Net Worth: $49,863,629
Earnings: ($24,546,280)
Emp.: 82
Fiscal Year-end: 11/30/2023
Gold Mining Services
N.A.I.C.S.: 212220
Thomas W. Meredith (Chm)

WEST SHANGHAI AUTOMOBILE SERVICE CO., LTD.
22F West Shanghai Building No 1018 Moyu South Road, Anting Town Jiading, Shanghai, 201805, China
Tel.: (86) 2162952682
Web Site: https://www.wsasc.com.cn
Year Founded: 2002
605151—(SHG)
Rev.: $174,384,873
Assets: $279,078,528
Liabilities: $86,066,562
Net Worth: $193,011,966
Earnings: $16,224,020
Emp.: 2,000
Fiscal Year-end: 12/31/22
Logistic Services
N.A.I.C.S.: 541614
Yanyang Zhu (Chm & Pres)

WEST SIBERIAN COMMERCIAL BANK PJSC
8 March Street 1, Tyumen, 625000, Russia
Tel.: (7) 3452522000

INTERNATIONAL PUBLIC

Web Site: http://www.zapsibkombank.ru
Sales Range: Less than $1 Million
Mortgage Banking Services
N.A.I.C.S.: 522292
Aleksander Borisovich Surin (Chm-Mgmt Bd & Pres)

WEST VAULT MINING INC.
Suite 838 - 1100 Melville Street, Vancouver, V6E 4A6, BC, Canada
Tel.: (604) 685-8311 BC
Web Site: https://www.westvaultmining.com
Year Founded: 2007
05EA—(DEU)
Rev.: $185,590
Assets: $39,029,171
Liabilities: $8,340,444
Net Worth: $30,688,727
Earnings: ($1,270,922)
Fiscal Year-end: 12/31/23
Mineral Exploration Services
N.A.I.C.S.: 213114
Frank R. Hallam (CFO & Sec)

Subsidiaries:

WK Mining (USA) Inc. (1)
429 Court St, Elko, NV 89801
Tel.: (775) 738-3209
Sales Range: $50-74.9 Million
Emp.: 2
Gold Mining Services
N.A.I.C.S.: 212220

WEST WITS MINING LIMITED
Level 6 400 Collins Street, CARLTON, Melbourne, 3000, VIC, Australia
Tel.: (61) 386929049
Web Site: https://www.westwitsmining.com
WWI—(ASX)
Rev.: $59,763
Assets: $11,868,283
Liabilities: $1,967,576
Net Worth: $9,900,707
Earnings: ($416,041)
Emp.: 6
Fiscal Year-end: 06/30/21
Gold & Uranium Explorer
N.A.I.C.S.: 213114
Michael Quinert (Chm)

WEST YORK LEASING
1785 St Clair Avenue West, Toronto, M6N 1J6, ON, Canada
Tel.: (416) 656-1200
Web Site: http://www.westyorkmotors.com
Year Founded: 1990
New & Used Car Dealers
N.A.I.C.S.: 441110
Chris Seedhouse (Pres)

WESTAG AG
Hellweg 15, 33378, Rheda-Wiedenbruck, Germany
Tel.: (49) 5242170 De
Web Site: https://www.westag.de
Year Founded: 1901
WUG3—(DEU)
Rev.: $235,885,980
Assets: $149,463,998
Liabilities: $61,916,068
Net Worth: $87,547,930
Earnings: $3,002,526
Emp.: 997
Fiscal Year-end: 12/31/23
Wood & Plastic Products Mfr
N.A.I.C.S.: 321211
Michael Sindram (CEO & Member-Exec Bd)

WESTAR RESOURCES LIMITED
Level 1 19 Ord Street, West Perth, 6005, WA, Australia

Tel.: (61) 865566000   AU
Web Site: https://www.westar.net.au
Year Founded: 2019
WSR—(ASX)
Rev.: $257
Assets: $4,578,908
Liabilities: $190,995
Net Worth: $4,387,913
Earnings: ($1,790,371)
Fiscal Year-end: 06/30/22
Exploration & Mining Services
N.A.I.C.S.: 213115
Ben Donovan *(Sec)*

WESTBOND ENTERPRISES CORPORATION
7403 Progress Way Unit 101, Delta, V4G 1E7, BC, Canada
Tel.: (604) 940-3939   BC
Web Site: https://www.westbond.ca
Year Founded: 1989
WBE—(TSXV)
Rev.: $8,901,290
Assets: $11,157,500
Liabilities: $5,062,621
Net Worth: $6,094,879
Earnings: $542,292
Fiscal Year-end: 03/31/22
Paper Converter
N.A.I.C.S.: 322120
Gennaro Magistrale *(Pres & CEO)*

Subsidiaries:

WestBond Industries Inc.   (1)
7403 Progress Way Unit 101, Delta, V4G 1E7, BC, Canada
Tel.: (604) 940-3939
Web Site: https://www.westbond.ca
Medical Equipment Supplier
N.A.I.C.S.: 423450

WESTBORO AUTO IMPORTS LTD
225 Richmond Road, Ottawa, K1Z 6W7, ON, Canada
Tel.: (613) 728-5813
Year Founded: 1977
Rev.: $12,900,000
Emp.: 25
New Car Dealers & Services
N.A.I.C.S.: 441110
Tanya Koller *(Pres)*

WESTBORO FLOORING AND DECOR
195 Colonnade Road S, Ottawa, K2E 7K3, ON, Canada
Tel.: (613) 226-3830
Web Site:
  http://www.westboroflooring.com
Year Founded: 1962
Rev.: $16,922,014
Emp.: 60
Flooring & Decor Services
N.A.I.C.S.: 238330
Steven Kimmel *(Pres)*

WESTBRIDGE CAPITAL LTD.
110-318 Wellman Lane, Saskatoon, S7T 0JI, SK, Canada
Tel.: (780) 695-7777
Web Site:
  http://www.westbridgecapital.ca
Privater Equity Firm
N.A.I.C.S.: 523999
Michael Meekins *(Pres & CEO)*

Subsidiaries:

Reside Worldwide, Inc.   (1)
6525 240th St SE, Woodinville, WA 98072
Tel.: (425) 375-2773
Web Site: http://staywithreside.com
Hospitality Services
N.A.I.C.S.: 721199
Lee Curtis *(Founder, Partner & CEO)*

Subsidiary (Domestic):

ABODA, Inc.   (2)
6525 240th St SE Bldg B, Woodinville, WA 98072
Tel.: (425) 861-0500
Web Site: http://www.aboda.com
Housing Management Services
N.A.I.C.S.: 531110
Dave Caple *(Pres)*

WESTBRIDGE RENEWABLE ENERGY CORP.
Suite 615 800 West Pender Street, Vancouver, V6C 2V6, BC, Canada
Tel.: (604) 687-7767   BC
Web Site:
  https://www.westbridge.energy
Year Founded: 1956
WEB—(TSXV)
Sales Range: Less than $1 Million
Oil & Gas Exploration Services
N.A.I.C.S.: 211120
Francesco Paolo Cardi *(VP)*

Subsidiaries:

Sunnynook Solar Energy Inc.   (1)
203-304 Main Street SE, PO Box 406, Airdrie, T4B 3C3, AB, Canada
Tel.: (587) 997-4602
Web Site: https://www.sunnynooksolar.com
Solar & Energy Storage Services
N.A.I.C.S.: 926130

WESTBURY NATIONAL SHOW SYSTEMS LTD.
772 Warden Avenue, Toronto, M1L 4T7, ON, Canada
Tel.: (416) 752-1371
Web Site: http://www.westbury.com
Year Founded: 1989
Rev.: $12,821,717
Emp.: 100
Entertainment Technology Services
N.A.I.C.S.: 561920
Christopher Pegg *(Mgr-Lighting Dept)*

WESTBURY STREET HOLDINGS LIMITED
300 Thames Valley Park Drive, Reading, RG6 1PT, Berks, United Kingdom
Tel.: (44) 118 935 6705   UK
Web Site: http://www.wshlimited.com
Holding Company; Catering & Hospitality Services
N.A.I.C.S.: 551112

Subsidiaries:

Bartlett Mitchell Ltd.   (1)
80 High Street Egham, Egham, TW20 9HE, Surrey, United Kingdom
Tel.: (44) 1784 471411
Web Site: http://www.bartlettmitchell.co.uk
Emp.: 1,100
Catering Services
N.A.I.C.S.: 722320
Ian Mitchell *(Chm)*

WESTCAP MGT. LTD.
830 410 22nd Street East, Saskatoon, S7K 5T6, SK, Canada
Tel.: (306) 652-5557
Web Site: http://westcapmgt.ca
Venture Capital & Private Equity
N.A.I.C.S.: 523940
Grant J. Kook *(Founder, Pres & CEO)*

Subsidiaries:

Fort Garry Brewing Company Ltd.   (1)
130 Lowson Crescent, Winnipeg, R3P 2H8, MB, Canada
Tel.: (204) 487-3678
Web Site: https://www.fortgarry.com
Beer Distr & Brewer
N.A.I.C.S.: 312120

WESTCON GROUP AS
Jektevikvegen 45, Olensvag, 5582, Vindafjord, Norway
Tel.: (47) 53775000   NO
Web Site: http://www.westcon.no
Holding Company; Marine & Offshore Products & Services
N.A.I.C.S.: 551112
Helge Jorgensen *(Gen Mgr)*

Subsidiaries:

Westcon Design Poland Sp. z o.o.   (1)
ul Lukasinskiego 116, 71 215, Szczecin, Poland   (100%)
Tel.: (48) 918 149 555
Web Site: http://english.westcon.no
Maritime Design & Engineering Services
N.A.I.C.S.: 541490
Piotr Zelazek *(Mng Dir)*

Westcon Geo AS   (1)
Keiser Wilhelms gate 23, 6003, Alesund, Norway   (100%)
Tel.: (47) 5377 5000
Web Site: http://english.westcon.no
Emp.: 250
Seismic Vessel Rental Services
N.A.I.C.S.: 532411
Noralf Matre *(Mgr)*

Westcon Loftetekninkk AS   (1)
Grannesgata 25, 5523, Haugesund, Norway   (100%)
Tel.: (47) 5271 9300
Web Site: http://english.westcon.no
Crane & Lifting Solutions Rental & Sales
N.A.I.C.S.: 532490
Karl Johan Jentoft *(Mng Dir)*

Westcon Olvondo AS   (1)
Wichmannvegen 3, 5420, Rubbestadneset, Norway   (100%)
Tel.: (47) 5301 4440
Web Site: http://english.westcon.no
Machine Shops
N.A.I.C.S.: 332710
Frode Bukkoy *(Production Mgr)*

Westcon Power & Automation AS   (1)
Husoyvegen 31, 4262, Avaldsnes, Norway   (100%)
Tel.: (47) 4746 8000
Web Site: http://english.westcon.no
Electrical & Automation Products Mfr
N.A.I.C.S.: 335999
Gunvald Mortvedt *(Mng Dir)*

Westcon Yards AS   (1)
Jektevikvegen 45, Olensvag, 5582, Vindafjord, Norway   (100%)
Tel.: (47) 5377 5000
Web Site: http://english.westcon.no
Ship Building & Repairing Services
N.A.I.C.S.: 336611
Oystein Matre *(Mng Dir)*

Affiliate (Domestic):

Westcon Helgeland AS   (2)
Langsetvagen, 8700, Nesna, Norway   (50%)
Tel.: (47) 7506 6555
Web Site: http://english.westcon.no
Ship Building & Repair Services
N.A.I.C.S.: 336611
Arnt Skogsoy *(Gen Mgr)*

Subsidiary (Domestic):

Westcon Yards Floro AS   (2)
Ole Aaserudgate 7, 6900, Floro, Norway
Tel.: (47) 57746800
Web Site: http://english.westcon.no
Ship Building & Repairing Services
N.A.I.C.S.: 336611
Trygve Solaas *(Dir-Shipyard)*

WESTCORE ENERGY LTD.
Suite 602-224 4th Avenue South, Saskatoon, S7K 5M5, SK, Canada
Tel.: (306) 653-2692   AB
Web Site:
  https://www.westcoreenergy.ca
Year Founded: 2007
WTR—(TSXV)
Rev.: $25,740

Assets: $364,388
Liabilities: $3,696,636
Net Worth: ($3,332,248)
Earnings: ($2,175,750)
Fiscal Year-end: 12/31/19
Energy Sector Investment Services
N.A.I.C.S.: 523999
Jeff Sheppard *(CFO)*

WESTCORP PROPERTIES INC.
College Plaza 200-8215 112 St NW, Edmonton, T6G 2C8, AB, Canada
Tel.: (780) 431-3300
Web Site: https://www.westcorp.net
Year Founded: 1980
Rev.: $127,548,242
Emp.: 400
Real Estate Development Services
N.A.I.C.S.: 531390

WESTDALE PROPERTIES
35 Lesmill Road, Toronto, M3B 2T3, ON, Canada
Tel.: (416) 703-1877
Web Site:
  http://www.westdaleproperties.com
Real Estate Services
N.A.I.C.S.: 531190
Ryan Kimel *(Dir-Ops)*

Subsidiaries:

Shelborne South Beach Hotel   (1)
1801 Collins Ave, Miami Beach, FL 33139
Tel.: (305) 531-1271
Web Site: http://www.shelborne.com
Hotel
N.A.I.C.S.: 721110

WESTDEUTSCHE ALLGEMEINE VERLAGSGESELLSCHAFT
Friedrichstrasse 3638, 45128, Essen, Germany
Tel.: (49) 2018040
Web Site: http://www.waz-mediengruppe.de
Year Founded: 1948
Sales Range: $1-4.9 Billion
Emp.: 16,000
Newspaper Publishers
N.A.I.C.S.: 513110
Erich Schumann *(CEO)*

Subsidiaries:

Funke Medien NRW GmbH   (1)
Friedrich Strasse 34-38, Essen, 45128, Germany
Tel.: (49) 800 60 60 760
Web Site: http://www.derwesten.de
Magazine & Newspaper Whslr
N.A.I.C.S.: 513199
Michael Roemer *(Gen Mgr)*

MZV GmbH & Co. KG   (1)
Ohmstrasse 1, 85716, Unterschleissheim, Germany
Tel.: (49) 89 319 06 0
Web Site: http://www.mzv.de
Magazine & Newspaper Whslr
N.A.I.C.S.: 424920

MZV direkt GmbH & Co.KG   (1)
Sternstr 9-11, 40479, Dusseldorf, Germany
Tel.: (49) 211 6907890
Web Site: http://www.mzv-direkt.de
Sales Range: $25-49.9 Million
Emp.: 40
Magazine & Newspaper Whslr
N.A.I.C.S.: 424920

WAZ NewMedia GmbH & Co. KG   (1)
Friedrichstrasse 12, 45128, Essen, Germany
Tel.: (49) 201 8040
Web Site: http://www.derwesten.de
Multimedia Service Provider
N.A.I.C.S.: 516210
Volker Wentz *(Mng Dir)*

WAZ-Logistik NRW GmbH & Co. KG   (1)

WESTDEUTSCHE ALLGEMEINE VERLAGSGESELLSCHAFT

Westdeutsche Allgemeine
verlagsgesellschaft—(Continued)

Friedrichstr 34-38, 45128, Essen, Germany
Tel.: (49) 201 804 0
Web Site: http://www.waz-logistik.de
Magazine & Newspaper Whslr
N.A.I.C.S.: 513199

WESTDEUTSCHER RUND-FUNK WDR
Appellhofplatz 1, Cologne, 50667, Germany
Tel.: (49) 221 2200
Web Site: http://www1.wdr.de
Year Founded: 1955
Sales Range: $550-599.9 Million
Emp.: 4,576
Broadcasting Services
N.A.I.C.S.: 516120
Tom Buhrow *(Dir)*

Subsidiaries:

WDR Mediagroup GmbH (1)
Ludwig Strasse 11, Cologne, 50667, Germany
Tel.: (49) 22120350
Web Site: http://www.wdr-mediagroup.com
Sales Range: $100-124.9 Million
Emp.: 400
Broadcasting Services
N.A.I.C.S.: 516120
Michael R. Loeb *(Mng Dir)*

WESTECK WINDOWS
8104 Evans Rd, Chilliwack, V2R 5R8, BC, Canada
Tel.: (604) 792-6700
Web Site:
https://www.westeckwindows.com
Rev.: $10,994,435
Emp.: 110
Windows, Doors & Related Products Mfr
N.A.I.C.S.: 321911
Casey Kerkhoff *(CEO)*

WESTERKIRK CAPITAL INC.
95 Wellington Street Ste 140, Toronto, M5J 2N7, ON, Canada
Tel.: (416) 927-2232 Ca
Sales Range: $1-4.9 Billion
Emp.: 5,000
Equity Investment Firm
N.A.I.C.S.: 523999
James J. Lawson *(Pres & CEO)*

Subsidiaries:

Sleep Country Canada Income
Fund (1)
140 Wendell Ave Unit 2, Toronto, M9N 3R2, ON, Canada
Tel.: (416) 242-4774
Web Site: http://www.sleepcountry.ca
Sales Range: $350-399.9 Million
Emp.: 900
Holding Company; Owned by Birch Hill Equity Partners Management Inc. & Westerkirk Capital Inc.
N.A.I.C.S.: 551112
Christine A. Magee *(Pres)*

WESTERN & ORIENTAL TRAVEL LIMITED
Layden House 76-86 Turnmill Street, London, EC1M 5QU, United Kingdom
Tel.: (44) 20 3588 6035
Web Site:
http://www.westernoriental.com
Sales Range: $25-49.9 Million
Emp.: 150
Travel Services
N.A.I.C.S.: 561520
Matthew Rushbrooke *(Gen Mgr)*

WESTERN AUSTRALIA ENERGY RESOURCES LIMITED
53 / 188 Newcastle Street, Perth, 6000, WA, Australia

Tel.: (61) 861845683 AU
Web Site: https://www.waer.com.au
Year Founded: 2022
WER—(ASX)
Exploration & Mining Services
N.A.I.C.S.: 213115
Andrew Lambert *(Mng Dir)*

WESTERN COPPER AND GOLD CORPORATION
15th Floor 1040 West Georgia Street, Vancouver, V6E 4H1, BC, Canada
Tel.: (604) 684-9497 BC
Web Site:
https://www.westerncopper.com
Year Founded: 2006
WRN—(NYSEAMEX)
Rev.: $457,252
Assets: $89,479,177
Liabilities: $3,630,035
Net Worth: $85,849,142
Earnings: ($3,906,846)
Emp.: 14
Fiscal Year-end: 12/31/22
Copper & Gold Mining Services
N.A.I.C.S.: 212230
Paul West-Sells *(Pres & CEO)*

Subsidiaries:

Casino Mining Corp. (1)
301 - 303 Strickland Street, Whitehorse, YT, Canada
Tel.: (867) 668-5704
Web Site: https://casinomining.com
Mineral Exploration & Property Evaluation Services
N.A.I.C.S.: 213115

WESTERN DEVELOPMENT BANK LIMITED
New Road, Ghorahi, 22400, Nepal
Tel.: (977) 82560732
Year Founded: 2005
WDBL—(NEP)
Commercial Banking Services
N.A.I.C.S.: 522110

WESTERN DODGE CHRYSLER JEEP
1788 Main Street North, Moose Jaw, S6J 1L4, SK, Canada
Tel.: (306) 692-1808
Web Site:
http://www.westerndodge.ca
New & Used Car Dealers
N.A.I.C.S.: 441110
Kyle Knight *(Dealer Principal-Western Auto Grp)*

WESTERN ENERGY SERVICES CORP.
1700 215 - 9th Avenue SW, Calgary, T2P 1K3, AB, Canada
Tel.: (403) 984-5916 AB
Web Site: https://www.wesc.ca
Year Founded: 1996
WRG—(TSX)
Rev.: $81,109,920
Assets: $387,717,525
Liabilities: $213,681,347
Net Worth: $174,036,178
Earnings: ($32,308,946)
Emp.: 460
Fiscal Year-end: 12/31/20
Oilfield Services & Supplier
N.A.I.C.S.: 213112
Alex R. N. MacAusland *(Pres & CEO)*

Subsidiaries:

Aero Rentals Services Division (1)
27323-144 Township RD 394 Aspelund Industrial Park, South Blackfalds, Red Deer, T0M 0J0, AB, Canada
Tel.: (403) 340-0800
Web Site: https://www.aerorentals.ca
Emp.: 30
Equipment Rental Services
N.A.I.C.S.: 532490

Scott Sondergaard *(Gen Mgr)*

Eagle Well Servicing Division (1)
27323-144 Township Rd 394, Blackfalds, Red Deer, T0M 0J0, AB, Canada
Tel.: (403) 346-7789
Sales Range: $50-74.9 Million
Emp.: 25
Oil & Gas Field Drilling Services
N.A.I.C.S.: 213111

Horizon Drilling Inc. (1)
1700 215 - 9th Avenue SW, Calgary, T2P 1K3, AB, Canada
Tel.: (403) 984-5916
Web Site: http://www.horizondrilling.ca
Sales Range: $50-74.9 Million
Emp.: 28
Oil & Gas Wells Drilling Services
N.A.I.C.S.: 213111
Alex Macauseland *(Pres & COO)*

StimSol Canada Inc. (1)
1700 215 9th Ave SW, Calgary, T2P 1K3, AB, Canada
Tel.: (403) 984-5916
Web Site: http://www.wesc.ca
Oil & Gas Engineering Services
N.A.I.C.S.: 213112

WESTERN FOREST PRODUCTS INC.
800 - 1055 West Georgia Street, PO Box 11122, Royal Centre Building, Vancouver, V6E 3P3, BC, Canada
Tel.: (604) 648-4500
Web Site:
https://www.westernforest.com
Year Founded: 1955
WFSTF—(OTCIQ)
Rev.: $618,084,348
Assets: $598,800,300
Liabilities: $229,495,476
Net Worth: $369,304,824
Earnings: ($35,736,708)
Emp.: 2,210
Fiscal Year-end: 12/31/19
Timber Harvesting & Lumber Production, Sales & Marketing
N.A.I.C.S.: 423310
Michael T. Waites *(Chm)*

Subsidiaries:

Calvert Co. Inc. (1)
3559 Truman St, Washougal, WA 98671-8671
Tel.: (360) 693-0971
Web Site: http://www.calvertglulam.com
All Other Manufacturing
N.A.I.C.S.: 339999
Doug Calvert *(Pres)*

Columbia Vista Corporation (1)
18637 SE Evergreen Hwy, Vancouver, WA 98683
Tel.: (360) 892-0770
Web Site: http://www.columbiavistacorp.com
Rev.: $37,300,000
Emp.: 85
Sawmills
N.A.I.C.S.: 321113
Jerri Hasz *(Mgr-Acctg)*

WFP Forest Products Ltd. (1)
435 Trunk Rd Ste 300, Duncan, V9L 2P9, BC, Canada
Tel.: (250) 748-3711
Lumber Product Whslr
N.A.I.C.S.: 423310

WESTERN GMC BUICK, LTD.
18325 Stony Plain Road, Edmonton, T5S 1C6, AB, Canada
Tel.: (780) 486-3333
Web Site: http://www.westerngm.com
Year Founded: 1962
New & Used Car Dealers
N.A.I.C.S.: 441110
Alan Walker *(Mgr-New Vehicle Sls)*

WESTERN GOLD EXPLORATION LTD.

INTERNATIONAL PUBLIC

1600 421 - 7th Avenue SW, Calgary, T2P 4K9, AB, Canada
Tel.: (781) 372-6523
Web Site:
https://www.westerngoldexplore.com
Year Founded: 2018
WGLD—(TSXV)
Assets: $4,941,064
Liabilities: $47,700
Net Worth: $4,893,363
Earnings: ($3,313,708)
Fiscal Year-end: 12/31/20
Asset Management Services
N.A.I.C.S.: 523940

WESTERN INDUSTRIAL CONTRACTORS
4912 John Hart Hwy, Prince George, V2K 3A1, BC, Canada
Tel.: (250) 962-6011
Web Site: https://www.wicltd.com
Rev.: $22,165,280
Emp.: 40
Construction & Project Management Services
N.A.I.C.S.: 236220
Brian Savage *(VP & COO)*

WESTERN LOGISTICS
1555 Brigantine Dr, Coquitlam, V3K 7C2, BC, Canada
Tel.: (604) 525-7200
Web Site:
http://www.westernlogistics.com
Year Founded: 1990
Rev.: $29,260,000
Emp.: 100
Freight Transportation Services
N.A.I.C.S.: 488510
Bob Hartin *(Founder & Chm)*

WESTERN MAGNESIUM CORPORATION
580 Hornby Street - 9th Floor, Vancouver, V6C 3B6, BC, Canada
Tel.: (604) 423-2709 BC
Web Site:
https://www.westernmagnesium.com
Year Founded: 1966
MLYF—(OTCIQ)
Assets: $1,349,988
Liabilities: $1,592,973
Net Worth: ($242,985)
Earnings: ($5,050,097)
Emp.: 15
Fiscal Year-end: 10/31/19
Metal Exploration & Mining Services
N.A.I.C.S.: 212290
Edward C. Lee *(Chm)*

Subsidiaries:

Nevada Moray Inc (1)
9120 Double Diamond Pkwy Ste 3910, Reno, NV 89521
Tel.: (775) 841-7101
Gold Exploration Services
N.A.I.C.S.: 212220

WESTERN METAL MATERIALS CO., LTD.
No 15 Xijin Road West Section, Jingwei Industrial Park Economic Development Zone, Xi'an, 710201, Shaanxi, China
Tel.: (86) 2986968418
Web Site: http://www.c-wmm.com
Year Founded: 2000
002149—(SSE)
Rev.: $412,958,955
Assets: $897,901,370
Liabilities: $449,272,840
Net Worth: $448,628,530
Earnings: $25,959,918
Emp.: 1,423
Fiscal Year-end: 12/31/22
Metal Products Mfr

AND PRIVATE COMPANIES

N.A.I.C.S.: 331410
Yang Yanan *(Chm)*
Subsidiaries:

Western Titanium Technologles Co., Ltd. (1)
No 15 Xijin Road Jingwei Industry Park
Xian Etdz, Xi'an, 710201, Shaanxi, China
Tel.: (86) 2986968620
Web Site: http://www.c-wtt.com
Nonferrous Metal Smelting & Refining Mfr
N.A.I.C.S.: 331410

Xi'an Filter Metal Materials Co., Ltd. (1)
No 15 Xijin Road Jingwei Industrial Park,
Xian Economic and Technological Development Zone, Shaanxi, 710201, China
Tel.: (86) 2986968425
Web Site: http://www.xianfilter.com
Nonferrous Metal Smelting & Refining Mfr
N.A.I.C.S.: 331410

Xi'an Refra Tungsten & Molybdenum Co., Ltd. (1)
No 16 North Jinggao Road ingwei Industrial Park, Xi an Economic and Technological Development Zone, Shaanxi, 710201, China
Tel.: (86) 2986969919
Web Site: https://www.c-rmm.org
Mobile Network Services
N.A.I.C.S.: 517112

Xi'an Tianli Clad Metal Materials Co., Ltd. (1)
Xijin Road Jingwei Industrial Park, Xian Economic and Technologic Development Zone, Shaanxi, 710201, China
Tel.: (86) 2986968301
Web Site: http://www.c-tlc.com.cn
Nonferrous Metal Smelting & Refining Mfr
N.A.I.C.S.: 331410

Xi'an United Pressure Vessel Co., Ltd. (1)
No 19 Xijin Road Jingwei Industrial Park, Xi'an, 710201, Shaanxi, China
Tel.: (86) 2986968348
Web Site: http://www.unitedvessel.com
Nonferrous Metal Smelting & Refining Mfr
N.A.I.C.S.: 331410

WESTERN MINES GROUP LTD.
Level 3 33 Ord Street, West Perth, 6005, WA, Australia
Tel.: (61) 475116798 AU
Web Site:
https://www.westernmines.com.au
Year Founded: 2020
WMG—(ASX)
Rev.: $30,812
Assets: $5,813,313
Liabilities: $556,138
Net Worth: $5,257,175
Earnings: ($684,713)
Fiscal Year-end: 06/30/23
Other Nonmetallic Mineral Mining & Quarrying
N.A.I.C.S.: 212390
Caedmon Marriott *(Mng Dir)*

WESTERN MINING CO., LTD.
No 52 Wusi Street, Xining, 810000, Qinghai, China
Tel.: (86) 9716123888 CN
Web Site:
https://www.westmining.com
Year Founded: 2000
601168—(SHG)
Rev.: $5,582,652,740
Assets: $7,415,460,033
Liabilities: $4,528,969,736
Net Worth: $2,886,490,297
Earnings: $483,817,291
Emp.: 2,600
Fiscal Year-end: 12/31/22
Ferrous & Non-Ferrous Metals Mining
N.A.I.C.S.: 212290
Zhong Yongsheng *(Chm)*

Subsidiaries:

CICC Capital Management Co., Ltd. (1)
28th Floor China World Office 2 No 1 Jianguomenwai Avenue, Beijing, 100004, China
Tel.: (86) 4008209068
Financial Services
N.A.I.C.S.: 522320

Inter-Citic Minerals Inc. (1)
60 Columbia Way Suite 501, Markham, L3R 0C9, ON, Canada
Tel.: (905) 479-5072
Web Site: http://www.inter-citic.com
Sales Range: $50-74.9 Million
Emp.: 5
Gold Exploration Services
N.A.I.C.S.: 212220

WESTERN MINISTIL LIMITED
163 - 164 Mittal Tower A Wing 16th Floor Nariman Point, Mumbai, 400 021, India
Tel.: (91) 2222823653
Web Site:
httрр://www.westernministil.com
Year Founded: 1972
504998—(BOM)
Assets: $420
Liabilities: $521,084
Net Worth: ($520,664)
Earnings: ($21,078)
Fiscal Year-end: 03/31/23
Steel Material Mfr & Distr
N.A.I.C.S.: 331110

WESTERN PACIFIC TRUST COMPANY
Suite 920789 West Pender Street, Vancouver, V6C 1H2, BC, Canada
Tel.: (604) 683-0455 BC
Web Site:
https://www.westernpacifictrust.com
Year Founded: 1965
WP—(TSXV)
Rev.: $828,962
Assets: $1,195,408
Liabilities: $344,740
Net Worth: $850,668
Earnings: $59,985
Fiscal Year-end: 12/31/20
Financial Consulting Services
N.A.I.C.S.: 523940
Alison Alfer *(Pres & CEO)*

WESTERN PLASTICS
Ballybrit Industrial Estate Upper Ballybrit, Galway, Ireland
Tel.: (353) 91771588
Web Site:
http://www.westernplastics.ie
Year Founded: 1976
Sales Range: $10-24.9 Million
Emp.: 25
Packaging Supplies & Machinery Mfr & Distr
N.A.I.C.S.: 333993
Noel Cunningham *(Gen Mgr)*

Subsidiaries:

Western Plastics, California (1)
41995 Remington Ave, Temecula, CA 92590
Tel.: (951) 695-1983
Web Site: http://www.wplastics.com
Mfr of Packing Supplies
N.A.I.C.S.: 326113
Henry Lim *(Gen Mgr)*

Western Plastics, Canada (1)
5725 McLaughlin Road, Mississauga, L5R 3K5, ON, Canada
Tel.: (647) 560-7716
Web Site: https://wpinnova.com
Mfr of Packing Equipment
N.A.I.C.S.: 488991

Western Plastics, Dublin (1)
U7 Crosslands Bus Pk Ballymount Rd, Dublin, Ireland

Tel.: (353) 14566919
Web Site: http://www.westernplastics.ie
Mfr of Packaging Supplies
N.A.I.C.S.: 488991
Hugh Sitzgeralg *(Gen Mgr)*

Western Plastics, Georgia (1)
2399 Us 41 High SW, Calhoun, GA 30703
Tel.: (706) 625-5260
Web Site: http://www.westernplastics.com
Mfr of Packaging Supplies
N.A.I.C.S.: 326113
Kem Mcnese *(Plant Mgr)*

WESTERN POTASH CORP.
1400-1111 West Georgia Street, Vancouver, V6E 4M3, BC, Canada
Tel.: (604) 689-9378 BC
Web Site:
http://www.westernpotash.com
Potash Mining Services
N.A.I.C.S.: 212390
Patrick Power *(Founder)*

WESTERN REGION GOLD CO., LTD.
No 501 Ronghe South Road, Economic and Technological Development Zone, Urumqi, 830023, Xinjiang, China
Tel.: (86) 9913771795
601069—(SHG)
Rev.: $618,884,983
Assets: $870,616,750
Liabilities: $203,933,232
Net Worth: $666,683,517
Earnings: $24,737,483
Fiscal Year-end: 12/31/22
Gold Ore Mining Services
N.A.I.C.S.: 212220
Sun Jianhua *(Sec)*

WESTERN REGIONS TOURISM DEVELOPMENT CO., LTD.
No 229 Junggar Road Xinjiang Uygur Autonomous Region, Fukang, Changji, 831500, China
Tel.: (86) 9943225611
Web Site: http://www.xylygf.com
Year Founded: 2001
300859—(SSE)
Rev.: $14,359,705
Assets: $95,911,269
Liabilities: $9,809,959
Net Worth: $86,101,311
Earnings: ($1,305,874)
Fiscal Year-end: 12/31/22
Travel Agency Services
N.A.I.C.S.: 561510
Shengchun Zhu *(Chm)*

WESTERN RESOURCES CORPORATION
2200 - 1021 West Hastings Street, Vancouver, V6C 0B2, BC, Canada
Tel.: (306) 924-9378
Web Site:
https://www.westernresources.com
WRX—(TSX)
Potash Mining Services
N.A.I.C.S.: 212390

WESTERN RV COUNTRY LTD
61 E Lake Ramp NE, Airdrie, T4A 2K4, AB, Canada
Tel.: (403) 912-2634
Web Site:
https://www.westernrvcountry.com
Year Founded: 2000
Rev.: $24,900,000
Emp.: 55
Recreational Vehicle Dealers
N.A.I.C.S.: 441210

WESTERN SECURITIES CO., LTD.
Room 10000 Building 8 No 319

WESTERN URANIUM & VANADIUM CORP.

Dongxin Street, Xincheng District, Xi'an, 710004, Shaanxi, China
Tel.: (86) 2987406171
Web Site:
https://www.west95582.com
Year Founded: 2001
002673—(SSE)
Rev.: $745,303,558
Assets: $13,431,342,357
Liabilities: $9,618,211,484
Net Worth: $3,813,130,873
Earnings: $60,099,680
Emp.: 2,500
Fiscal Year-end: 12/31/22
Securities Brokerage
N.A.I.C.S.: 523150
Zhaohui Xu *(Chm & Sec)*

WESTERN STAR RESOURCES INC.
Unit 615 - 800 West Pender St, Vancouver, V6C 2V6, BC, Canada
Tel.: (236) 878-4938
Web Site:
https://www.westernstarresource.com
Year Founded: 2020
WSR—(CNSX)
Assets: $872,679
Liabilities: $164,500
Net Worth: $708,179
Earnings: $427,186
Fiscal Year-end: 12/31/22
Mineral Exploration Services
N.A.I.C.S.: 212390

WESTERN STAR TRUCKS NORTH LTD
15205 112 Avenue, Edmonton, T5M 2V7, AB, Canada
Tel.: (780) 453-3452
Web Site: http://www.wsnorth.com
Year Founded: 1987
Sales Range: $10-24.9 Million
Emp.: 110
Specialty Trucks Supplier
N.A.I.C.S.: 532120
Bruce Kozyra *(Mgr-Body Shop)*

WESTERN STERLING TRUCKS LTD.
18353 118 Ave, Edmonton, T5S 1M8, AB, Canada
Tel.: (780) 481-7400
Web Site:
http://www.westernsterling.com
Sales Range: $10-24.9 Million
Emp.: 45
Truck Dealers & Service
N.A.I.C.S.: 441227
Mitch Mason *(Pres & Gen Mgr)*

WESTERN SUPERCONDUCTING TECHNOLOGIES CO., LTD.
No 12 Mingguang Road, Xi'an, 710018, Shaanxi, China
Tel.: (86) 2986514505
Web Site: https://www.c-wst.com
Year Founded: 2003
688122—(SHG)
Rev.: $593,495,805
Assets: $1,587,343,446
Liabilities: $694,219,902
Net Worth: $893,123,544
Earnings: $151,630,933
Emp.: 800
Fiscal Year-end: 12/31/22
Magnetic Material Mfr
N.A.I.C.S.: 334610
Pingxiang Zhang *(Chm)*

WESTERN URANIUM & VANADIUM CORP.
330 Bay Street Suite 1400, Toronto, M5H 2S8, ON, Canada

WESTERN URANIUM & VANADIUM CORP.

Western Uranium & Vanadium Corp.—(Continued)
Tel.: (970) 864-2125 ON
Web Site: https://www.western-uranium.com
Year Founded: 2006
WSTRF—(OTCQX)
Rev.: $7,858,972
Assets: $33,202,798
Liabilities: $3,944,890
Net Worth: $29,257,908
Earnings: ($713,767)
Emp.: 10
Fiscal Year-end: 12/31/22
Uranium Ore Exploration, Development & Mining
N.A.I.C.S.: 213114
George E. L. Glasier (Pres & CEO)

WESTERNONE INC.
Suite 910 925 West Georgia Street, Vancouver, V6C 3L2, BC, Canada
Tel.: (604) 678-4042
Web Site: http://www.weq.ca
WEQ—(TSX)
Rev.: $63,416,530
Assets: $79,721,134
Liabilities: $67,704,574
Net Worth: $12,016,560
Earnings: ($1,271,358)
Emp.: 361
Fiscal Year-end: 12/31/17
Investment Services
N.A.I.C.S.: 523999
Andrew Greig (Mgr-IR)

Subsidiaries:

WEQ Deerfoot Rentals LP (1)
110 13 St S, Lethbridge, T1J 4N5, AB, Canada
Tel.: (403) 329-1998
Web Site: http://www.westernone.ca
Sales Range: $50-74.9 Million
Emp.: 12
Construction Equipment Rental Services
N.A.I.C.S.: 532412

WEQ Heat & Propane LP. (1)
1415 78 Ave NW, Edmonton, T6P 1L8, AB, Canada
Tel.: (780) 440-6466
Web Site: http://www.westernone.ca
Sales Range: $25-49.9 Million
Emp.: 26
Building Equipment Installation Services
N.A.I.C.S.: 238390

WEQ Production Equipment LP (1)
1156 Kingsway, Port Coquitlam, V3C 3Y9, BC, Canada
Tel.: (604) 945-5004
Web Site: http://www.westernone.ca
Emp.: 30
Construction Equipment Rental Sservices & Distr
N.A.I.C.S.: 532412

WESTERWOOD (WG) GLOBAL LTD.
Unit H1, Maynooth Business Campus, Maynooth, Kildare, W23 E4A8, Ireland
Tel.: (353) 16510121
Web Site: https://westerwoodglobal.com
Year Founded: 2000
Emp.: 295
Semiconductor Mfr
N.A.I.C.S.: 333242
Basil Holian (Owner)

Subsidiaries:

NSTAR Global Services Inc. (1)
104 State Ave Ste 103, Clayton, NC 27520
Tel.: (919) 553-8412
Web Site: http://www.nstarglobalservices.com
Technical Solutions, Resources & Employee Placement Services
N.A.I.C.S.: 561311
Randy Nelson (CEO)

WESTGATE ENERGY INC
Suite 420 2020 4 Street SW, Calgary, T2S 1W3, AB, Canada
Tel.: (403) 351-1779 AB
Year Founded: 1993
TCI—(CNSX)
Rev.: $434,707
Assets: $2,557,114
Liabilities: $84,434
Net Worth: $2,472,680
Earnings: ($682,530)
Fiscal Year-end: 03/31/19
Investment Services
N.A.I.C.S.: 523999

WESTGOLD RESOURCES LIMITED
Level 6/200 St Georges Terrace, Perth, 6000, WA, Australia
Tel.: (61) 894623400 AU
Web Site: https://www.westgold.com.au
WGX—(TSX)
Rev.: $478,417,391
Assets: $702,796,283
Liabilities: $240,853,012
Net Worth: $461,943,271
Earnings: $63,589,902
Emp.: 2,127
Fiscal Year-end: 06/30/24
Gold Ore Exploration & Mining Services
N.A.I.C.S.: 212220
Paul D. Hucker (Co-COO)

Subsidiaries:

Karora Resources Inc. (1)
141 Adelaide Street West Suite 1608, Toronto, M5H 3L5, ON, Canada
Tel.: (416) 363-0649
Web Site: https://www.karoraresources.com
Rev.: $97,978,269
Assets: $136,042,071
Liabilities: $65,424,194
Net Worth: $70,617,878
Earnings: ($5,312,296)
Emp.: 173
Fiscal Year-end: 12/31/2019
Mineral Exploration & Mining Services
N.A.I.C.S.: 212230
Timothy L. Hollaar (VP-Fin)

WESTHAVEN GOLD CORP.
1056 - 409 Granville St, Vancouver, V6C 1T2, BC, Canada
Tel.: (604) 681-5558 BC
Web Site: https://www.westhavengold.com
Year Founded: 1998
1W5—(DEU)
Rev.: $506,629
Assets: $24,877,625
Liabilities: $1,029,612
Net Worth: $23,848,013
Earnings: ($1,989,888)
Fiscal Year-end: 12/31/23
Investment Services
N.A.I.C.S.: 523999
D. Grenville Thomas (Chm)

WESTHOUSE MEDICAL SERVICES PLC
Unit D The Black Barn Whites Farm, Barleylands Road Noak Bridge, Basildon, SS15 4BG, Essex, United Kingdom
Tel.: (44) 1268 206 101
Web Site: http://www.westhousemedical.com
Medical Device Mfr; Ambulance Services
N.A.I.C.S.: 339112
Jack Kaye (Chm)

WESTINDIA AB
Sturnansgatan, PO Box 14237, 104 40, Stockholm, Sweden
Tel.: (46) 86709873
Sales Range: $125-149.9 Million
Emp.: 40
Holding Company
N.A.I.C.S.: 551112

Subsidiaries:

Landauer Ltd. (1)
24 Beaufort Ct, Admirals Way, London, E14 9XL, United Kingdom
Tel.: (44) 2075385383
Web Site: http://www.landauergroup.co.uk
Sales Range: $25-49.9 Million
Emp.: 21
Seafood
N.A.I.C.S.: 311710

Subsidiary (Domestic):

Sea Products International Ltd. (2)
Ocean House Wholesale Markets Precinct Pershore Street, Pershore Street, Birmingham, B5 6UU, United Kingdom (100%)
Tel.: (44) 1216225111
Web Site: http://www.seaproductsint.com
Sales Range: $25-49.9 Million
Emp.: 26
Importor & Distr of Frozen Seafood
N.A.I.C.S.: 424460
Tom Hansen (Dir-Sls)

WESTKAM GOLD CORP.
Suite 900 570 Granville Street, Vancouver, V6C 3P1, BC, Canada
Tel.: (250) 216-5674
Web Site: https://www.westkamgold.com
Year Founded: 1984
WKGFF—(OTCIQ)
Rev.: $9,151
Assets: $288,620
Liabilities: $648,100
Net Worth: ($359,480)
Earnings: ($53,327)
Fiscal Year-end: 10/31/22
Gold Exploration Services
N.A.I.C.S.: 212220
Pamela Lynch Saulnier (CFO)

WESTKEY GRAPHICS
8315 Riverbend Court, Burnaby, V3N 5E7, BC, Canada
Tel.: (604) 549-2350
Web Site: https://www.westkeygraphics.com
Rev.: $12,172,293
Emp.: 120
Printing & Related Products Mfr
N.A.I.C.S.: 333248
Alfie Karmal (Pres & CEO)

WESTLAND GUMMIWERKE GMBH & CO. KG
Westlandstrasse 6, 49324, Melle, Germany
Tel.: (49) 5422 702 0 De
Web Site: http://www.westland.eu
Year Founded: 1920
Sales Range: $50-74.9 Million
Emp.: 750
Rubber Products Mfr
N.A.I.C.S.: 326299

Subsidiaries:

Impreglon Oberflachentechnik GmbH (1)
Hohenhorststrasse 1, 21337, Luneburg, Germany
Tel.: (49) 413188210
Web Site: http://www.impreglon.de
Surface Coatings Mfr
N.A.I.C.S.: 325510
Carsten Gralla (Mgr-Grp)

Ligum spol. s.r.o. (1)
M Svabinskeho 4679/30a, 466 05, Jablonec, Czech Republic
Tel.: (420) 483 305710
Web Site: http://www.ligum.cz
Printing Rollers Mfr
N.A.I.C.S.: 326299
Jaroslav Pluhar (Gen Mgr)

INTERNATIONAL PUBLIC

WESTLAND HORTICULTURE LTD.
14 Granville Industrial Estate Granville Road, 90 Granville Road, Dungannon, BT70 1NJ, County Tyrone, United Kingdom
Tel.: (44) 28 8772 7500 UK
Web Site: http://www.gardenhealth.com
Year Founded: 1990
Emp.: 300
Gardening Product Mfr
N.A.I.C.S.: 333112

Subsidiaries:

Cranswick Pet & Aquatics Ltd. (1)
Pexton Road, Kelleythorpe Industrial Estate, Driffield, YO25 9DJ, East Yorkshire, United Kingdom
Tel.: (44) 1377200888
Sales Range: $50-74.9 Million
Pet Product Mfr
N.A.I.C.S.: 311119

Subsidiary (Domestic):

Tropical Marine Centre Ltd. (2)
Solesbridge Lane, Chorleywood, WD3 5SX, Hertfordshire, United Kingdom
Tel.: (44) 1923284151
Web Site: http://www.tmc-ltd.co.uk
Sales Range: $10-24.9 Million
Emp.: 70
Marine Fish Invertebrates Supplier; Filtration Equipment & Aquatic Products Mfr & Distr
N.A.I.C.S.: 112519
Paul West (Mng Dir)

WESTLAND INSURANCE GROUP LTD.
2121 160th St Suite 200, Surrey, V3Z 9N6, BC, Canada
Tel.: (604) 543-7788 Ca
Web Site: http://www.westlandinsurance.ca
Year Founded: 1980
Emp.: 1,600
Insurance Brokerage Services
N.A.I.C.S.: 524210
Jamie Lyons (Pres & CEO)

Subsidiaries:

Gillons Insurance Brokers Ltd. (1)
326 Church St, Fort Frances, P9A 1E1, ON, Canada
Tel.: (807) 274-7716
Web Site: http://www.gillons.on.ca
Rev.: $3,256,977
Emp.: 32
Insurance Brokerage Services
N.A.I.C.S.: 524210
Ted Fitzgerald (Sr VP-Insurance Ops)

WESTLEY GROUP LIMITED
Doulton Road, Cradley Heath, B64 5QN, West Midlands, United Kingdom
Tel.: (44) 1384410111 UK
Web Site: http://www.westleygroup.co.uk
Sales Range: $75-99.9 Million
Emp.: 200
Holding Company; Metal Foundries Owner & Operator & Metals Engineering Services
N.A.I.C.S.: 551112
James Salisbury (Mng Dir)

Subsidiaries:

Francis W Birkett & Sons Limited (1)
Hightown Road, PO Box 16, Cleckheaton, BD19 5JT, W Yorkshire, United Kingdom
Tel.: (44) 1274 873 366
Web Site: http://www.fwbirkett.com
Sales Range: $50-74.9 Million
Emp.: 100
Non-Ferrous Metal Alloying, Casting & Machining Services
N.A.I.C.S.: 331420
Stuart Higham (Head-Technical Dept)

AND PRIVATE COMPANIES

Trent Foundries Ltd. (1)
Chemical Lane, Stoke-on-Trent, ST6 4PB, United Kingdom
Tel.: (44) 1782 826831
Ferrous & Non Ferrous Metal Mfr
N.A.I.C.S.: 331110

Walter Frank & Sons Limited (1)
Hightown Road, PO Box 16, Cleckheaton, BD19 5JT, W Yorkshire, United Kingdom
Tel.: (44) 1274 873 366
Web Site: http://www.walterfrank.co.uk
Non-Ferrous Metal Casting Foundry Operator
N.A.I.C.S.: 331523
Andrew Mansell *(Gen Mgr)*

Westley Of Cardiff Limited (1)
Po Box 84, Port Talbot West Ayton, London, SA13 2ZU, United Kingdom
Tel.: (44) 1639875061
Ferrous & Non Ferrous Metal Mfr
N.A.I.C.S.: 331110

Westleys Limited (1)
Doulton Road, Cradley Heath, B64 5QN, W Midlands, United Kingdom
Tel.: (44) 1384 410 111
Web Site: http://www.westley.co.uk
Steel Castings Foundry & Machine Shop Operator
N.A.I.C.S.: 331512
Ian McWhirter *(Dir-Bus Dev)*

WESTLIFE DEVELOPMENT LIMITED
1001 Tower 3 10th Floor Indiabulls Finance Centre Senapati Bapat Marg, Elphinstone Road, Mumbai, 400 013, India
Tel.: (91) 2249135000
Web Site: https://www.westlife.co.in
Year Founded: 1982
505533—(BOM)
Rev.: $140,640,455
Assets: $235,275,495
Liabilities: $169,587,464
Net Worth: $65,688,032
Earnings: ($13,571,239)
Emp.: 7,889
Fiscal Year-end: 03/31/21
Restaurant Operators
N.A.I.C.S.: 722511
Banwari Lal Jatia *(Chm)*

Subsidiaries:

Hardcastle Restaurants Private Limited (1)
1001 Tower-3 10th Floor One International Center, Senapati Bapat Marg Prabhadevi, Mumbai, 400013, Maharashtra, India
Tel.: (91) 2249135000
Franchise Restaurant Operator
N.A.I.C.S.: 722513
Arvind R. P. *(Dir-Mktg & Comm)*

WESTMINSTER GROUP PLC
Westminster House Blacklocks Hill, Banbury, OX17 2BS, Oxfordshire, United Kingdom
Tel.: (44) 1295756300
Web Site: https://www.wg-plc.com
WSG—(AIM)
Rev.: $11,438,295
Assets: $9,605,640
Liabilities: $4,562,679
Net Worth: $5,042,961
Earnings: ($3,930,729)
Fiscal Year-end: 06/30/24
Fire Safety & Security Solutions
N.A.I.C.S.: 334290
Stuart Fowler *(COO)*

Subsidiaries:

Longmoor Services Limited (1)
Talbot Hall Heythrop Park Resort, Chipping Norton, OX7 5UE,, United Kingdom
Tel.: (44) 1295756380
Web Site: http://www.longmoor-security.com
Sales Range: $10-24.9 Million
Emp.: 40
Security Consulting & Training Services

N.A.I.C.S.: 561612
Michael Hanley *(Co-Founder)*

RMS Integrated Solutions Limited (1)
Westminster House Blacklocks Hill, Banbury, OX17 2BS, Oxfordshire, United Kingdom
Tel.: (44) 1295257770
Web Site: http://www.rms-is.com
Sales Range: $10-24.9 Million
Emp.: 30
Security System Sales & Services
N.A.I.C.S.: 561622

Westminster International Limited (1)
Westminster House Blacklocks Hill Banbury Lane, Banbury, OX17 2BS, Oxfordshire, United Kingdom
Tel.: (44) 1295756300
Web Site: http://www.wi-ltd.com
Sales Range: $25-49.9 Million
Emp.: 30
Security Consulting Services
N.A.I.C.S.: 541690

WESTMONT HOSPITALITY GROUP
5090 Explorer Drive Suite 500, Mississauga, L4W 4T9, ON, Canada
Tel.: (905) 629-3400
Web Site: https://www.whg.com
Year Founded: 1975
Rev.: $3,500,000,000
Emp.: 100
Hotel Management & Property Development
N.A.I.C.S.: 721110
Majid Mangalji *(Pres)*

Subsidiaries:

Hospitality Services S.A.R.L. (1)
46a avenue J F Kennedy, 1855, Luxembourg, Luxembourg
Tel.: (352) 26 200 12123
Home Management Services
N.A.I.C.S.: 721110

Westmont Development Inc. (1)
5847 San Felipe St Ste 4650, Houston, TX 77057-3277
Tel.: (713) 787-6222
Web Site: http://www.wht.com
Sales Range: $10-24.9 Million
Emp.: 50
Hotel Management & Property Development
N.A.I.C.S.: 721110

Westmont Services B.V. (1)
Boelelaan 2, 1083 HJ, Amsterdam, Netherlands
Tel.: (31) 20 517 2625
Home Management Services
N.A.I.C.S.: 721110

WESTMOUNT ENERGY LIMITED
Floor 4 Liberation House Castle Street, Saint Helier, JE1 4HH, Jersey
Tel.: (44) 1534823059
Web Site: https://www.westmountenergy.com
WMELF—(OTCQB)
Assets: $21,301,261
Liabilities: $53,676
Net Worth: $21,247,585
Earnings: ($1,379,741)
Fiscal Year-end: 06/30/21
Holding Company
N.A.I.C.S.: 551111
Gerard Walsh *(Chm)*

WESTMOUNT MINERALS CORP.
Suite 520-470 Granville St, Vancouver, V6C 1V5, BC, Canada
Tel.: (604) 683-1991
Web Site: https://www.westmountminerals.com
Year Founded: 2021
WMC—(CNSX)

Gold Exploration Services
N.A.I.C.S.: 212220
David Tafel *(CEO)*

WESTMOUNT STOREFRONT SYSTEMS LTD.
20 Riverview Pl, Kitchener, N2B 3X8, ON, Canada
Tel.: (519) 570-2850
Web Site: http://www.westmountstorefront.ca
Year Founded: 1993
Rev.: $12,540,000
Emp.: 45
Glass Design Mfr
N.A.I.C.S.: 327211
Timothy Mitchell *(Founder & Pres)*

WESTPAC BANKING CORPORATION
Level 18 275 Kent Street, Sydney, 2000, NSW, Australia
Tel.: (61) 497132032 AU
Web Site: https://www.westpac.com.au
Year Founded: 1817
WEBNF—(OTCIQ)
Rev.: $39,517,908,380
Assets: $744,679,882,960
Liabilities: $694,885,466,280
Net Worth: $49,794,416,680
Earnings: $4,830,719,100
Emp.: 36,146
Fiscal Year-end: 09/30/24
Banking & Financial Services
N.A.I.C.S.: 522110
David Stephen *(Chief Risk Officer)*

Subsidiaries:

BT Financial Group Pty Ltd (1)
GPO Box 2675, Sydney, 2001, NSW, Australia
Tel.: (61) 132135
Web Site: http://www.bt.com.au
Sales Range: $900-999.9 Million
Emp.: 1,300
Investment, Margin Lending, Superannuation & Retirement Income Streams Services
N.A.I.C.S.: 523999

Subsidiary (Domestic):

Asgard Wealth Solutions Ltd. (2)
Level 12 400 Kent Street, Sydney, 2000, NSW, Australia
Tel.: (61) 299471200
Web Site: http://www.asgardwealthsolutions.com.au
Open-End Investment Funds
N.A.I.C.S.: 525910

Branch (Domestic):

Asgard Wealth Solutions Ltd. - Melbourne (3)
Level 7 530 Collins Street, Melbourne, 3000, VIC, Australia
Tel.: (61) 399413355
Web Site: http://www.asgardwealthsolutions.com.au
Sales Range: $25-49.9 Million
Emp.: 28
Open-End Investment Funds
N.A.I.C.S.: 327910

Subsidiary (Domestic):

BT Finance Pty Limited (2)
L 15 275 Kent St, Sydney, 3000, NSW, Australia
Tel.: (61) 282532999
Fund Management Services
N.A.I.C.S.: 523940
Bradley Cooper *(CEO)*

Subsidiary (Non-US):

BT Funds Management (NZ) Limited (2)
Westpac on Takutai Square 16 Takutai Square, Auckland, 1141, New Zealand
Tel.: (64) 93673300
Web Site: https://www.btonline.co.nz
Financial Investment Management Services

WESTPAC BANKING CORPORATION

N.A.I.C.S.: 523999

BT Investment Management Limited (2)
Tel.: (61) 292202000
Private Equity & Investment Management Services
N.A.I.C.S.: 523999
Cameron Williamson *(CFO)*

Holding (Non-US):

J O Hambro Capital Management Limited (3)
Tel.: (44) 2077475678
Sales Range: $50-74.9 Million
Emp.: 90
Investment Services
N.A.I.C.S.: 523999
Markus Lewandowski *(COO)*

Capital Finance Australia Limited (1)
Level 3 20 Lexington Drive, Norwest Business Park, Bella Vista, 2153, NSW, Australia
Tel.: (61) 8884 8000
Web Site: http://www.capitalfinance.com.au
Sales Range: $150-199.9 Million
Emp.: 375
Banking Services
N.A.I.C.S.: 522320

Hastings Funds Management Limited (1)
Tel.: (61) 0386503600
Web Site: http://www.hfm.com.au
Sales Range: $50-74.9 Million
Emp.: 60
Investment Fund Management Services
N.A.I.C.S.: 523940

Subsidiary (Non-US):

Hastings Funds Management (UK) Limited (2)
Tel.: (44) 2073376720
Investment Fund Management Services
N.A.I.C.S.: 523999
Cameron Price *(COO)*

Hastings Investment Management Pty. Ltd. (2)
Tel.: (61) 386503600
Web Site: http://www.hastingsinfra.com
Sales Range: $50-74.9 Million
Emp.: 80
Investment Fund Management
N.A.I.C.S.: 523940

Joint Venture (Non-US):

Porterbrook Leasing Company Limited (2)
Ivatt House 7 The Point Pinnacle Way, Pride Park, Derby, DE24 8ZS, United Kingdom
Tel.: (44) 1332285050
Web Site: https://www.porterbrook.co.uk
Rolling Stock Leasing Services
N.A.I.C.S.: 532411

Magnitude Group Pty Limited (1)
GPO Box 3371, Sydney, 2001, NSW, Australia
Tel.: (61) 282545415
Web Site: http://www.magnitude.com.au
Financial Advisory Services
N.A.I.C.S.: 523940

Qvalent Pty Limited (1)
Level 1 Wallsend Plaza, PO Box 321, Wallsend, Newcastle, 2287, NSW, Australia
Tel.: (61) 249510000
Web Site: http://www.qvalent.com
Financial Software Development Services
N.A.I.C.S.: 541511

RAMS Financial Group Pty Limited (1)
Locked Bag 5001, Concord West, 2138, NSW, Australia
Tel.: (61) 296476967
Web Site: https://www.rams.com.au
Mortgage Loan Brokerage Services
N.A.I.C.S.: 522310

St. George Bank Limited (1)
4 16 Montgomery St, Kogarah, 2217, NSW, Australia
Web Site: http://www.stgeorge.com.au

WESTPAC BANKING CORPORATION

Westpac Banking Corporation—(Continued)
Sales Range: $5-14.9 Billion
Emp.: 8,420
Commercial Banking Services
N.A.I.C.S.: 522110

Division (Domestic):

Bank SA (2)
93 King William Street, Adelaide, 5000, SA, Australia
Web Site: http://www.banksa.com.au
Sales Range: $200-249.9 Million
Emp.: 100
Commericial Banking
N.A.I.C.S.: 522110
Ben Owen *(Gen Mgr-Retail Banking)*

Subsidiary (Domestic):

St. George Motor Finance Limited (2)
4-16 Montgomery St, Kogarah, 2217, NSW, Australia
Tel.: (61) 292361111
Web Site: http://www.stgeorge.com.au
Vehicle Financing Services
N.A.I.C.S.: 522310

Westpac Americas Inc (1)
1105 N Market St Ste 1300, Wilmington, DE 19801-1241
Tel.: (302) 655-0388
Packaging Material Distr
N.A.I.C.S.: 423840

Westpac Bank-PNG-Limited (1)
9th Floor Deloitte Tower Douglas Street, PO Box 706, Port Moresby, Papua New Guinea
Tel.: (675) 322 0511
Web Site: http://www.westpac.com.pg
Sales Range: $200-249.9 Million
Emp.: 400
Commercial Banking Services
N.A.I.C.S.: 522110

Westpac Banking Corporation (Jersey) Ltd. (1)
23 Camomile Court Camomile Street, Saint Helier, EC3A 7LL, Jersey (100%)
Tel.: (44) 2076217000
Web Site: http://www.westpac.com.au
Sales Range: $50-74.9 Million
Emp.: 100
Representative Office
N.A.I.C.S.: 522299

Westpac Banking Corporation - Hong Kong Office (1)
Room 3303 05 2 Exchange Square, 8 Connaught Place, Central, 852, China (Hong Kong)
Tel.: (852) 28429888
Web Site: http://www.westpac.com.au
Sales Range: $50-74.9 Million
Emp.: 35
Foreign Exchange & Bullion Trading
N.A.I.C.S.: 523991

Westpac Banking Corporation - London Office (1)
Camomile Court 23 Camomile St, London, EC3A 7LL, United Kingdom
Tel.: (44) 2076217000
Web Site: http://www.westpac.com
Sales Range: $100-124.9 Million
Emp.: 75
Banking Services
N.A.I.C.S.: 522299

Westpac Banking Corporation - New Zealand Office (1)
Level 15 188 Quay Street, Auckland, 10001, New Zealand
Tel.: (64) 9 367 3882
Web Site: http://www.westpac.co.nz
Sales Range: $1-4.9 Billion
Emp.: 3,500
Financial & Banking Services
N.A.I.C.S.: 522110

Unit (Domestic):

WestpacTrust Financial Services (2)
PO Box 27031, 6141, Wellington, New Zealand (100%)
Tel.: (64) 49180243
Web Site: http://www.westpac.co.nz

Sales Range: $50-74.9 Million
Emp.: 12
Provider of Financial Services
N.A.I.C.S.: 523940

Westpac Equity Holdings Pty Limited (1)
Westpac Pl L 20 275 Kent St, Sydney, 2000, NSW, Australia
Tel.: (61) 292263171
Financial Investment Services
N.A.I.C.S.: 523999

Westpac Financial Services Group Limited (1)
Level 36 60 Margaret St, Sydney, 2000, NSW, Australia
Tel.: (61) 292263311
Web Site: http://www.westpac.com.au
Provider of Investment Advice, Insurance & Fund Management
N.A.I.C.S.: 523940

Westpac Funds Management Limited (1)
283 to 285 Kent St, Sydney, 2000, NSW, Australia
Tel.: (61) 282542750
Web Site: http://www.westpacfunds.com.au
Asset Funds Management
N.A.I.C.S.: 523999
Sue Jackson *(Mgr-Women's Markets)*

Subsidiary (Domestic):

Westpac Essential Services Trust (2)
Level 6 275 Kent Street, Sydney, 2000, NSW, Australia
Tel.: (61) 292939270
Web Site: http://www.westpac.com.au
Investment Services
N.A.I.C.S.: 523999

Joint Venture (Domestic):

Airport Link Co. Pty Ltd. (3)
Mascot Station, PO Box 604, Cnr Church Ave & Bourke Road, Mascot, 2020, NSW, Australia
Web Site: http://www.airportlink.com.au
Sales Range: $25-49.9 Million
Emp.: 10
Operation & Management of Railway Stations
N.A.I.C.S.: 488210

Westpac Investment Vehicle Pty Limited (1)
L 20 Westpac Pl 275 Kent St, Sydney, 2000, NSW, Australia
Tel.: (61) 2 8253 3589
Automobile Financing Services
N.A.I.C.S.: 522220

Westpac Matching Gifts Limited (1)
Westpac Place Level 20 275 Kent Street, Sydney, 2000, NSW, Australia
Tel.: (61) 282530920
Business Support Services
N.A.I.C.S.: 561499

Westpac Securitisation Management Pty Limited (1)
L 20 275 Kent St, Sydney, 2000, NSW, Australia
Tel.: (61) 282533589
Financial Management Services
N.A.I.C.S.: 523999

Westpac Singapore Limited (1)
12 Marina View 27-01 Asia Square Tower 2, Singapore, 018961, Singapore
Tel.: (65) 65309898
Sales Range: $50-74.9 Million
Emp.: 100
Investment Banking Services
N.A.I.C.S.: 523150

Westpac-Australian Capital Territory (1)
53 Alinga St, Canberra, 2601, ACT, Australia
Tel.: (61) 262485855
Web Site: http://www.westpac.com
Sales Range: $50-74.9 Million
Emp.: 7
Banking
N.A.I.C.S.: 522110

Westpac-New South Wales (1)
341 George Street, Sydney, 2000, NSW, Australia
Tel.: (61) 294556817
Web Site: http://www.westpac.com.au
Banking
N.A.I.C.S.: 522110

Westpac-Northern Territory (1)
The Mall 24 Smith Street, Darwin, 800, NT, Australia (100%)
Tel.: (61) 292939270
Web Site: http://www.westpac.com.au
Sales Range: $50-74.9 Million
Emp.: 40
Banking
N.A.I.C.S.: 522110

Westpac-Queensland (1)
260 Queen St, Brisbane, 4000, QLD, Australia
Tel.: (61) 732272222
Web Site: http://www.westpac.com.au
Sales Range: $50-74.9 Million
Emp.: 40
Banking
N.A.I.C.S.: 522110

Westpac-South Australia (1)
275 Kent Street, Sydney, 2000, NSW, Australia (100%)
Tel.: (61) 132032
Web Site: http://www.westpac.com.au
Sales Range: $200-249.9 Million
Emp.: 300
Banking
N.A.I.C.S.: 522110

Westpac-Victoria (1)
360 Collins Street, Melbourne, 3000, VIC, Australia (100%)
Tel.: (61) 396083205
Web Site: http://www.westpac.com.au
Sales Range: $700-749.9 Million
Emp.: 2,000
Banking
N.A.I.C.S.: 522110

Westpac-Western Australia (1)
109 St Georges Ter, Perth, 6000, WA, Australia (100%)
Tel.: (61) 894262580
Web Site: http://www.westpac.com.au
Sales Range: $100-124.9 Million
Emp.: 200
Banking
N.A.I.C.S.: 522110

WESTPAY AB
Kanalvagen 14 2tr, 194 61, Upplands Vasby, Sweden
Tel.: (46) 850668450
Web Site: https://www.westpay.se
Year Founded: 1988
WPAY—(OMX)
Rev.: $6,595,671
Assets: $5,776,129
Liabilities: $5,225,397
Net Worth: $550,732
Earnings: ($821,415)
Emp.: 48
Fiscal Year-end: 12/31/22
Investment Banking Services
N.A.I.C.S.: 523150
Sten Karlsson *(CEO)*

WESTPOINT AUTOS (QLD) PTY. LTD.
440 Moggill Road, Indooroopilly, Brisbane, 4068, QLD, Australia
Tel.: (61) 738780440
Web Site:
http://www.westpointautos.com.au
Year Founded: 1988
Emp.: 200
Automotive Retailer
N.A.I.C.S.: 441110
Naz Maghsoodi *(Bus Mgr-Fin & Insurance)*

WESTPORT CHRYSLER DODGE LIMITED
3965 Portage Avenue Unit 90, Winnipeg, R3K 2H3, MB, Canada

INTERNATIONAL PUBLIC

Tel.: (204) 888-2343
Web Site:
http://www.winnipegdodge.ca
Rev.: $20,129,930
Emp.: 55
New & Used Car Dealers
N.A.I.C.S.: 441110
Ron Eisbrenner *(Pres)*

WESTPORT FUEL SYSTEMS INC.
1691 West 75th Ave, Vancouver, V6P 6P2, BC, Canada
Tel.: (604) 718-2000 **AB**
Web Site: https://www.wfsinc.com
Year Founded: 1995
WPRT—(NASDAQ)
Rev.: $305,698,000
Assets: $407,451,000
Liabilities: $203,485,000
Net Worth: $203,966,000
Earnings: ($32,695,000)
Emp.: 1,820
Fiscal Year-end: 12/31/22
Fuel Systems & Engines
N.A.I.C.S.: 336310
James D. Arthurs *(Exec VP)*

Subsidiaries:

BAF Technologies, Inc. (1)
2180 French Settlement Rd, Dallas, TX 75212
Tel.: (214) 231-1450
Web Site: http://www.westport.
Emp.: 30
Natural Gas Vehicle Conversion System Mfr
N.A.I.C.S.: 811114

Subsidiary (Domestic):

ServoTech Industries, Inc. (2)
510 Savage Rd, Belleville, MI 48111
Tel.: (734) 697-5555
Web Site: http://www.servotechco.com
Natural Gas Fueling Systems Design & Engineering Services
N.A.I.C.S.: 541330

Fuel Systems Solutions, Inc. (1)
780 3rd Ave 25th Fl, New York, NY 10017
Tel.: (646) 502-7170
Fuel Systems & Components Designer, Mfr & Distr
N.A.I.C.S.: 336310

Subsidiary (Non-US):

BRC S.r.l. (1)
Via La Morra 1, Cherasco, 12062, Cuneo, Italy
Tel.: (39) 017248681
Web Site: https://www.brc.it
Alternative Gaseous Fuel Engine Conversion Services
N.A.I.C.S.: 541330

GFI Control Systems, Inc. (2)
5 Goddard Crescent Unit 101, Cambridge, N3E 0C8, ON, Canada
Tel.: (519) 576-4270
Web Site: https://www.gficontrolsystems.eu
Alternative Fuel Systems Mfr
N.A.I.C.S.: 333618

Zavoli, S.r.l. (2)
Via Pitagora 400, 47521, Cesena, Forli Cesena, Italy
Tel.: (39) 0547646409
Web Site: http://www.zavoli.com
Alternative Fuel System Components Mfr
N.A.I.C.S.: 333618

Westport Fuel Systems Inc. (1)
2675 Temple Ave, Signal Hill, CA 90755 (100%)
Tel.: (562) 256-9922
Fuel System Components Mfr
N.A.I.C.S.: 336310

Westport Innovations (Australia) Pty Ltd (1)
21 Barry Street Unit 20, Bayswater, 3153, VIC, Australia
Tel.: (61) 397295009
Alternative Fuel Vehicle Engines & Fuel Systems Distr

Westport Power Inc. (1)
1750 West 75th Avenue Suite 101, Vancouver, V6P 6G2, BC, Canada
Tel.: (604) 718-2000
Web Site: http://www.westport.com
Emp.: 100
Fuel Systems & Engines
N.A.I.C.S.: 336310

Joint Venture (Domestic):

Cummins Westport Inc. (2)
1750 West 75th Ave Suite 101, Vancouver, V6P 6G2, BC, Canada
Tel.: (604) 718-8100
Web Site: http://www.cumminswestport.com
Sales Range: $25-49.9 Million
Emp.: 60
Alternative Fuel Engines Mfr
N.A.I.C.S.: 336310
Roe C. East (Gen Mgr-On-Highway Natural Gas Bus)

Subsidiary (Domestic):

Westport Light Duty Inc. (2)
1750 W 75th Ave Suite 101, Vancouver, V6P 6G2, BC, Canada (100%)
Tel.: (604) 718-2000
Web Site: http://www.westport.com
Emp.: 100
Natural Gas & LPG Engine & Fuel Systems Mfr
N.A.I.C.S.: 336310

Subsidiary (Non-US):

Emer S.p.A. (3)
Via Bormioli 19, Z IND S Eufemia, 25135, Brescia, Italy
Tel.: (39) 0302510391
Web Site: https://www.emer.it
Mfr of Natural Gas & Liquefied Petroleum Gas Valves & Components for Vehicles
N.A.I.C.S.: 336310

Subsidiary (Domestic):

Valtek SpA Unipersonale (4)
Via Salvo d'Acquisto 6, 42020, Albinea, 42020, Reggio Emilia, Italy
Emp.: 35
Development & Production of Liquefied Petroleum Gas & Compressed Natural Gas Injectors, Filters & Valves for Automotive Applications
N.A.I.C.S.: 336310

Subsidiary (Non-US):

OMVL S.p.A. (3)
Via Rivella 20, Pernumia, Padua, Italy
Tel.: (39) 0429 764111
Web Site: http://www.omvlgas.it
Designer, Mfr & Marketer of Alternative Fuel Systems for Vehicles
N.A.I.C.S.: 336310

Westport AB (3)
TLA Security Gate Volvo Torslanda, Pressvagen 2, 418 78, Gothenburg, Sweden (100%)
Tel.: (46) 317578500
Emp.: 29
Fuel Systems & Engines
N.A.I.C.S.: 336310
Anders Johanssons (CEO)

WESTPORTS HOLDINGS BERHAD
12th Floor Menara Symphony No 5 Jalan Prof Khoo Kay Kim Seksyen 13, PO Box 266, Pulau Indah, 42009, Port Klang, Malaysia
Tel.: (60) 331694000
Web Site: https://www.westportsholdings.com
WPRTS—(KLS)
Rev.: $437,886,138
Assets: $1,117,817,778
Liabilities: $424,832,804
Net Worth: $692,984,974
Earnings: $148,058,836
Emp.: 5,773
Fiscal Year-end: 12/31/22
Container, Cargo & Marine Services
N.A.I.C.S.: 488310
G. Gnanalingam (Chm)

WESTRIDGE CONSTRUCTION LTD.
2909 Saskatchewan Drive, Regina, S4T 1H4, SK, Canada
Tel.: (306) 352-2434
Web Site: http://www.westridge.ca
Year Founded: 1989
Rev.: $12,163,157
Emp.: 55
Building Construction Services
N.A.I.C.S.: 236220
Colin Olfert (CEO)

WESTRISE CO LTD
Bongeunsa-ro 214 8F, Gangnam-gu, Seoul, Korea (South)
Tel.: (82) 5566474
Web Site: https://www.westrise.co.kr
Year Founded: 1991
064090—(KRS)
Rev.: $22,524,524
Assets: $6,627,177
Liabilities: $3,784,117
Net Worth: $2,843,060
Earnings: ($11,500,997)
Emp.: 26
Fiscal Year-end: 12/31/22
Telecommunications Equipment Mfr
N.A.I.C.S.: 334220

WESTSHORE TERMINALS INVESTMENT CORPORATION
1 Roberts Bank, Delta, V4M 4G5, BC, Canada
Tel.: (604) 946-4491 Ca
Web Site: https://www.westshore.com
Year Founded: 2010
WTE—(TSX)
Rev.: $288,199,775
Assets: $978,945,192
Liabilities: $399,606,616
Net Worth: $579,338,576
Earnings: $99,283,848
Emp.: 465
Fiscal Year-end: 12/31/20
Financial Investment Services
N.A.I.C.S.: 523999
William W. Stinson (Chm, Pres & CEO)

WESTSIDE CORPORATION LIMITED
Level 17 300 Queen Street, Brisbane, 4000, QLD, Australia
Tel.: (61) 730200900 AU
Web Site: http://www.westsidecorporation.com
Year Founded: 2005
Gas Exploration & Development Services
N.A.I.C.S.: 213112
Simon Mewing (COO)

WESTSTAR GROUP
Menara Weststar Dataran Weststar Jalan Lingkaran, Ampang, 68000, Malaysia
Tel.: (60) 34102222
Web Site: http://www.weststar.com.my
Year Founded: 2003
Holding Company
N.A.I.C.S.: 551112
Azman Ibrahim (Founder & Mng Dir)

Subsidiaries:

Global Komited Sdn Bhd (1)
No 17 Jalan 31/62 Seksyen 31, Kota Kemuning, 40460, Shah Alam, Malaysia
Tel.: (60) 3 5121 1343
Defense Vehicle Mfr & Distr
N.A.I.C.S.: 336992
Mohd Nasser Israil (CEO)

Weststar Auto Sdn Bhd (1)
No 68 Jalan Ampang, 50450, Kuala Lumpur, Malaysia
Tel.: (60) 3 2031 5151
Automotive Repair & Maintenance Services
N.A.I.C.S.: 811111
Andrew Tan (Mgr-Sls)

Weststar Aviation Services Sdn. Bhd. (1)
No 70 Jalan Ampang, Kuala Lumpur, 50450, Malaysia (100%)
Tel.: (60) 3 2031 5818
Web Site: http://weststar.com.my
Emp.: 200
Oil & Gas Industry Offshore Helicopter Transportation Services
N.A.I.C.S.: 481211
Azman Ibrahim (Founder & Chm)

Weststar Construction & Property (1)
Level 4 Menara Weststar Dataran Weststar Jalan Lingkaran Tengah II, 68000, Ampang, Selangor, Malaysia
Tel.: (60) 3 4102 2333
Web Site: http://www.weststar.com.my
Building Construction Services
N.A.I.C.S.: 236220

Weststar Insurance Limited (1)
Level 5 Menara Weststar Dataran Weststar Jalan Lingkaran Tengah II, 68000, Ampang, Selangor, Malaysia
Tel.: (60) 3 4102 2222
Insurance Management Services
N.A.I.C.S.: 524298

Weststar Maxus Sdn. Bhd. (1)
No 70 Jalan Ampang, Kuala Lumpur, 50450, Malaysia
Tel.: (60) 3 2031 2525
Automobile Designer, Mfr & Distr
N.A.I.C.S.: 336110
Azman Ibrahim (Founder, Chm & Mng Dir)

Subsidiary (Domestic):

Weststar Maxus Distributors Sdn. Bhd. (2)
366 Jalan Tun Razak, Kuala Lumpur, 50400, Malaysia
Tel.: (60) 3 2143 3331
Web Site: http://www.maxus-distributors.com
Emp.: 19
Automotive Distr
N.A.I.C.S.: 423110
Azlan Ahmad (Gen Mgr)

WESTVIEW FORD SALES LTD.
4901 North Island Hwy, Courtenay, V9N 5Y2, BC, Canada
Tel.: (250) 334-3161
Web Site: https://www.westviewford.ca
Sales Range: $10-24.9 Million
Emp.: 35
Car Dealer
N.A.I.C.S.: 441110

WESTWARD ADVISORS LTD.
300-1090 Homer Street, Vancouver, V6B 2W9, BC, Canada
Tel.: (604) 687-1507
Web Site: https://www.westwardadvisors.com
Year Founded: 1997
Rev.: $20,291,010
Emp.: 8
Insurance for Tax & Estate Planning
N.A.I.C.S.: 524298
Rob Darnbrough (Pres-Insurance & Tax Plng Advisor)

Subsidiaries:

Westward Advisors Ltd. (1)
300 - 1090 Homer Street, Vancouver, V6B 2W9, BC, Canada
Tel.: (604) 687-1507
Web Site: https://www.westwardadvisors.com
Insurance for Estate Planning & Tax
N.A.I.C.S.: 541213
Mai Furuhashi (Sr Mgr-Insurance)

WESTWARD FORD SALES LTD.
2653 Saskatchewan Avenue W, Portage la Prairie, R1N 4A5, MB, Canada
Tel.: (204) 857-3912
Web Site: https://www.westwardford.com
Year Founded: 1988
Rev.: $18,867,054
Emp.: 40
New & Used Car Dealers
N.A.I.C.S.: 441110
Rhoda Martens (Mgr-Fin Svcs)

WESTWARD GOLD INC.
Royal Centre 1500 - 1055 W Georgia, Vancouver, V6E 4N7, BC, Canada
Tel.: (604) 828-7027
Web Site: https://westwardgold.com
IM50—(DEU)
Assets: $6,069,992
Liabilities: $163,693
Net Worth: $5,906,299
Earnings: ($1,073,881)
Fiscal Year-end: 03/31/23
Mineral Exploration Services
N.A.I.C.S.: 213115

WESTWING GROUP SE
Moosacher Strasse 88, 80809, Munich, Germany
Tel.: (49) 895505440
Web Site: https://www.westwing.com
Year Founded: 2011
WEW—(DEU)
Rev.: $473,118,682
Assets: $224,527,158
Liabilities: $141,736,908
Net Worth: $82,790,250
Earnings: ($13,687,988)
Emp.: 1,614
Fiscal Year-end: 12/31/23
Interior Design & Furnishing Services
N.A.I.C.S.: 541410
Stefan Smalla (Co-Founder, CEO & Member-Mgmt Bd)

Subsidiaries:

WW E-Services Iberia S.L. (1)
Av Diagonal 507 6 7 8, 08029, Barcelona, Spain
Tel.: (34) 912582937
Web Site: https://www.westwing.es
Home Furnishing Product Distr
N.A.I.C.S.: 449129

Westwing B.V. (1)
Singel 512-2, 1017 AX, Amsterdam, Netherlands
Tel.: (31) 858889079
Web Site: https://www.westwing.nl
Home Furnishing Product Distr
N.A.I.C.S.: 449129

WESTWOOD GLOBAL ENERGY GROUP
38 Albyn Place, Aberdeen, AB10 1YN, United Kingdom
Tel.: (44) 1224 502 640
Web Site: http://www.westwoodenergy.com
Consulting Services
N.A.I.C.S.: 541613
David Clark (CFO)

Subsidiaries:

Rigzone.com, Inc. (1)
14531 FM 529 Ste 225, Houston, TX 77095
Tel.: (281) 345-4040
Web Site: http://www.rigzone.com
Online Magazine Services
N.A.I.C.S.: 513120
Sandy Esslemont (Pres & CEO)

WESURE GLOBAL TECH LTD.

WESURE GLOBAL TECH LTD.

Wesure Global Tech Ltd.—(Continued)
Abba Hillel Silver 12, Ramat Gan, Israel
Tel.: (972) 6835
Web Site: https://www.we-sure.co.il
Year Founded: 2016
WESR—(TAE)
Rev.: $982,631,011
Assets: $4,875,256,451
Liabilities: $4,708,504,140
Net Worth: $166,752,311
Earnings: $15,443,293
Fiscal Year-end: 12/31/23
Computer System Design Services
N.A.I.C.S.: 541512

WETHAQ TAKAFUL INSURANCE COMPANY K.C.S.C.
Sharq - Khaled Bin Al Waleed St - City Tower, Kuwait, Kuwait
Tel.: (965) 1866662
Web Site: https://www.wethaq.com
WETHAQ—(KUW)
Rev.: $388,472
Assets: $13,734,740
Liabilities: $469,183
Net Worth: $13,265,556
Earnings: $269,778
Emp.: 65
Fiscal Year-end: 12/31/22
Insurance Services
N.A.I.C.S.: 524126
Abdullah Mashari Al-Homaidhi *(Vice Chm)*

WETOUCH TECHNOLOGY INC.
No 29 Third Main Avenue Shigao Town Renshou County, Meishan, Sichuan, 620500, China
Tel.: (86) 2837390666
Year Founded: 1992
WETH—(OTCQB)
Rev.: $37,923,112
Assets: $73,105,752
Liabilities: $4,271,565
Net Worth: $68,834,187
Earnings: $8,730,446
Emp.: 126
Fiscal Year-end: 12/31/22
Construction Services
N.A.I.C.S.: 236220
Zongyi Lian *(Pres & CEO)*

WETTON CLEANING SERVICES LIMITED
Wetton House 278 280 St Jamess Road, London, SE1 5JX, United Kingdom
Tel.: (44) 2072372007
Web Site: http://www.wettons.co.uk
Year Founded: 1949
Sales Range: $25-49.9 Million
Emp.: 3,000
Cleaning Service
N.A.I.C.S.: 561720
Nicola Holmes *(Mng Dir)*

WETZEL S.A.
Rua Dona Francisca 8300 Block H, Perini Business Park Distrito Industrial, Joinville, 89219-600, SC, Brazil
Tel.: (55) 34518510
Web Site: https://www.wetzel.com.br
Year Founded: 1932
MWET4—(BRAZ)
Rev.: $55,249,047
Assets: $61,770,634
Liabilities: $62,964,245
Net Worth: ($1,193,612)
Earnings: ($5,221,638)
Fiscal Year-end: 12/31/23
Electrical Products Mfr
N.A.I.C.S.: 335932
Andre Luis Wetzel Da Silva *(Chm)*

WEXFORD CREAMERY LIMITED
Glanbia Ireland 3008 Lake Drive City-west Business Campus, Dublin, Ireland
Tel.: (353) 1850202366
Web Site: http://www.wexfordcreamery.com
Year Founded: 1959
Sales Range: $50-74.9 Million
Emp.: 100
Cheese Mfr
N.A.I.C.S.: 311513
Frank Ronan *(Gen Mgr)*

WEYA SA
36 Ave Pierre Brosselette, 92240, Malakoff, France
Tel.: (33) 77700515
Web Site: https://www.weya.fr
MLWEY—(EUR)
Sales Range: Less than $1 Million
Wood Pellet Boilers Designer, Installer & Maintenance Services
N.A.I.C.S.: 332410

WEYERMANN MALZFABRIK
Brennerstrasse 17-19, Bamberg, 96052, Germany
Tel.: (49) 951932200
Web Site: http://www.weyermannmalt.com
Year Founded: 1879
Emp.: 140
Brewing & Distilling Supplier
N.A.I.C.S.: 424820
Sabine Weyermann *(Pres-Sls, Mktg & PR)*

WFB ECONOMIC DEVELOPMENT GMBH
Langenstrasse 2-4, Bremen, 28195, Germany
Tel.: (49) 421960010
Web Site: http://www.wfb-bremen.de
Rev.: $41,982,430
Emp.: 220
Investment Management Service
N.A.I.C.S.: 523940
Michael Gobel *(Dir-Comml Svcs Unit)*

WFM MOTORS PTY LTD.
60 O'Riordan Street, Alexandria, 2015, NSW, Australia
Tel.: (61) 2 9331 5000
Web Site: http://www.cityford.com.au
Car Dealership
N.A.I.C.S.: 423110
Nicholas George Polites *(Owner)*

Subsidiaries:

Barloworld Australia (Pty) Limited (1)
972 Nepean Highway, Moorabbin, 3189, Australia
Tel.: (61) 3 8506 6700
Web Site: http://www.barloworld.com.au
New Car Dealers
N.A.I.C.S.: 441110

WFV WERKZEUG- FORMEN- UND VORRICHTUNGSBAU GMBH & CO. KG.
Im Seefeld 10, Huttenfeld, 68623, Lampertheim, Hesse, Germany
Tel.: (49) 625683030
Web Site: http://www.wfv-germany.de
Year Founded: 1985
Sales Range: $25-49.9 Million
Emp.: 75
Alloy Wheel Moulds Mfr
N.A.I.C.S.: 331511
Hans-Peter Hofmann *(Mng Dir)*

WG TECH (JIANGXI) CO., LTD.
Woge Industrial Park Xicheng Avenue, High-tech Industrial Development Zone, Xinyu, 338004, Jiangxi, China
Tel.: (86) 76922893773
Web Site: http://www.wgtechjx.com
Year Founded: 2009
603773—(SHG)
Rev.: $196,374,826
Assets: $452,134,220
Liabilities: $240,941,886
Net Worth: $211,192,334
Earnings: ($46,085,977)
Emp.: 1,300
Fiscal Year-end: 12/31/22
Photoelectric Glass Product Mfr & Distr
N.A.I.C.S.: 334419
Wenjun Xu *(Pres)*

WG WEARNE LIMITED
1 Main Road, PO Box 192, Aureus, Randfontein, 1760, Gauteng, South Africa
Tel.: (27) 114594500
Web Site: http://www.wearne.co.za
Year Founded: 1910
WEA—(JSE)
Rev.: $18,733,419
Assets: $20,199,306
Liabilities: $20,608,067
Net Worth: ($408,761)
Earnings: ($1,458,245)
Emp.: 400
Fiscal Year-end: 02/28/19
Concrete & Building Materials Distr
N.A.I.C.S.: 444180
John Wearne *(CEO)*

WGI WESTMAN GROUP, INC.
2976 Day Street, Winnipeg, R2C 2Z2, MB, Canada
Tel.: (204) 777-5345
Web Site: http://www.westmangroup.com
Year Founded: 1976
Holding Company
N.A.I.C.S.: 551112

Subsidiaries:

Behlen Industries LP (1)
927 Douglas Street, Brandon, R7A 7B2, MB, Canada
Tel.: (204) 728-1188
Web Site: https://www.behlen.ca
Steel Building Systems Mfr
N.A.I.C.S.: 332111
Rosamalia Villamizar *(Dir-Mktg & Bus Dev)*

Canada Culvert Inc. (1)
201 10423-178 Street, Edmonton, T5S 1R5, AB, Canada
Tel.: (780) 487-3404
Web Site: http://www.canadaculvert.com
Mfr of Infrastructure Products for Drainage, Including Corrugated Steel Pipe & Water Control Products
N.A.I.C.S.: 331210
Scott McRae *(Mgr-Dev & Engrg)*

Convey-All Industries Inc. (1)
130 Canada Street, PO Box 2008, Winkler, R6W 0J3, MB, Canada
Tel.: (204) 325-4195
Web Site: https://www.convey-all.com
Conveyor System Mfr
N.A.I.C.S.: 333922

Meridian Manufacturing, Inc. (1)
3125 24 Avenue North, Lethbridge, T1H 5G2, AB, Canada
Tel.: (403) 320-7070
Web Site: https://www.meridianmfg.com
Oil & Gas Storage Tanks & Agricultural & Industrial Storage Equipment Mfr
N.A.I.C.S.: 423820
Paul Cunningham *(Pres)*

Plant (US):

Meridian Manufacturing, Inc. - Storm Lake (2)
2902 Expansion Blvd, Storm Lake, IA 50588-7317
Tel.: (712) 732-1780

INTERNATIONAL PUBLIC

Web Site: http://www.meridianmfg.com
Farm Machinery & Equipment Mfr
N.A.I.C.S.: 333111
Peter Trebuschnoj *(Dir-Ops)*

Westman Steel Industries (1)
2976 Day St, Springfield, Winnipeg, R2C 2Z2, MB, Canada
Tel.: (204) 222-7354
Web Site: https://westmansteel.com
Metal Roofing & Siding Products Mfr
N.A.I.C.S.: 332999
Jack Squair *(Gen Mgr-Langley)*

WH GROUP LIMITED
RM 7602B-7604A Level 76 International Commerce Centre, 1 Austin Road West, Kowloon, China (Hong Kong)
Tel.: (852) 28682828
Web Site: https://www.wh-group.com
0288—(HKG)
Rev.: $3,632,587,506
Assets: $2,655,488,480
Liabilities: $1,191,293,753
Net Worth: $1,464,194,728
Earnings: $119,073,992
Emp.: 101,000
Fiscal Year-end: 12/31/23
Frozen Food Product Distr
N.A.I.C.S.: 551112
Long Wan *(Chm & Exec Dir)*

Subsidiaries:

Henan Shuanghui Investment & Development Co., Ltd. (1)
No 288 Mudanjiang Road, Luohe, 462000, Henan, China
Tel.: (86) 3952622616
Web Site: https://www.shuanghui.net
Rev.: $8,807,372,098
Assets: $5,112,241,950
Liabilities: $1,997,823,401
Net Worth: $3,114,418,549
Earnings: $789,172,352
Emp.: 14,739
Fiscal Year-end: 12/31/2022
Chemical Products & Meat Packing & Consulting Services
N.A.I.C.S.: 424470
Wan Hongwei *(Chm)*

Rotary Vortex Limited (1)
1 Austin Road West, Kowloon, China (Hong Kong)
Tel.: (852) 28682828
Web Site: http://www.wh-group.com
Emp.: 35
Asset Management Services
N.A.I.C.S.: 531390

Smithfield Foods, Inc. (1)
200 Commerce St, Smithfield, VA 23430
Tel.: (757) 365-3000
Web Site: https://www.smithfieldfoods.com
Rev.: $14,438,400,000
Assets: $9,894,000,000
Liabilities: $5,073,000,000
Net Worth: $4,821,000,000
Earnings: $422,300,000
Emp.: 50,236
Fiscal Year-end: 01/03/2016
Meat Processing & Packing Services
N.A.I.C.S.: 311612
Joseph B. Sebring *(Pres-Packaged Meats Div)*

Subsidiary (Domestic):

AgProtein, Inc. (2)
1994 Cornwallis Rd, Rose Hill, NC 28458-8736
Tel.: (910) 289-4811
Emp.: 50
Agricultural Consulting Services
N.A.I.C.S.: 541690

Subsidiary (Non-US):

Agri Plus S.A. (2)
street Marcelinska 92, 60-324, Poznan, Poland
Tel.: (48) 616657960
Web Site: https://www.agriplus.pl
Sales Range: $125-149.9 Million
Crop Farming
N.A.I.C.S.: 111130

AND PRIVATE COMPANIES

WH GROUP LIMITED

Agri Plus Sp. z.o.o. (2)
ul Marcelinska 92, 60-324, Poznan, Poland
Tel.: (48) 61 665 7960
Web Site: https://www.agriplus.pl
Emp.: 1,000
Animal Feeding & Production Services
N.A.I.C.S.: 112990

Agroalim Distribution S.R.L. (2)
Bd Timisoara nr 26Z Sector 6 Cladirea Anchor Plaza Et 5, Bucharest, 061331, Romania
Tel.: (40) 212006300
Web Site: http://www.agroalim.ro
Food Products Distr
N.A.I.C.S.: 424480

Subsidiary (Domestic):

American Skin Food Group LLC (2)
140 Industrial Dr, Burgaw, NC 28425-5081
Tel.: (910) 259-2232
Web Site: https://asfg.com
Pork Meat Distr
N.A.I.C.S.: 424420

Subsidiary (Non-US):

Animex Foods Sp. z.o.o. S.K.A. (2)
Morliny 15, Morliny, 14-100, Ostroda, Poland
Tel.: (48) 896477112
Food Products Distr
N.A.I.C.S.: 424480

Animex Grupa Paszowa S.A. (2)
Wroclawska 61, Grodkow, 49-200, Poland
Tel.: (48) 774246300
Food Mfr
N.A.I.C.S.: 311991

Subsidiary (Domestic):

Best Solutions LLC (2)
22500 King Richard Ct, Beverly Hills, MI 48025
Tel.: (248) 792-6708
Electrical Contractor
N.A.I.C.S.: 238210

Circle Four LLC (2)
PO Box 100, Milford, UT 84751 (100%)
Tel.: (435) 387-2107
Sales Range: $150-199.9 Million
Livestock Producers
N.A.I.C.S.: 424520

Clougherty Packing, LLC (2)
3049 E Vernon Ave, Los Angeles, CA 90058-1800
Web Site: http://www.farmerjohn.com
Meat Processing & Packing Services
N.A.I.C.S.: 311611

Subsidiary (Domestic):

Saag's Products, LLC (3)
1799 Factor Ave, San Leandro, CA 94577-5617
Tel.: (510) 352-8000
Web Site: http://www.saags.com
Food Products Mfr
N.A.I.C.S.: 311999
Scott Shaffer *(Sls Mgr-Food Svc)*

Subsidiary (Domestic):

Duplin Marketing Company, LLC (2)
3319 NE Hwy 54, Guymon, OK 73942
Tel.: (580) 338-2711
Animal Boarding Services
N.A.I.C.S.: 812910
Greg Adams *(Mgr)*

John Morrell & Co. (2)
PO Box 405020, Cincinnati, OH 45240-5020 (100%)
Tel.: (513) 346-3540
Sales Range: $1-4.9 Billion
Emp.: 6,700
Processed Meats & Fresh Pork Distributor & Marketer
N.A.I.C.S.: 311611

Subsidiary (Domestic):

Armour-Eckrich Meats, LLC (3)
4225 Naperville Rd Ste 600, Lisle, IL 60532
Tel.: (630) 281-5000
Web Site: https://eckrich.sfdbrands.com

Sales Range: $25-49.9 Million
Emp.: 250
Meats Processor & Distr
N.A.I.C.S.: 424470

Subsidiary (Domestic):

Murphy-Brown LLC (2)
2822 Hwy 24 W, Warsaw, NC 28398 (100%)
Tel.: (910) 293-3434
Web Site: http://www.murphybrown.com
Sales Range: $1-4.9 Billion
Emp.: 4,860
Producers of Hogs & Turkeys
N.A.I.C.S.: 112210
Joan Lee *(Controller)*

Unit (Domestic):

Murphy-Brown LLC - Rose Hill (3)
4134 Hwy 117, Rose Hill, NC 28458-0759
Tel.: (910) 289-2111
Web Site: http://www.murphybrownllc.com
Sales Range: $800-899.9 Million
Emp.: 1,000
Swine Genetics Research & Development Laboratory
N.A.I.C.S.: 541715

Subsidiary (Domestic):

Murphy-Brown of Missouri LLC (3)
805 Pennsylvania Ave Ste 200, Princeton, MO 64673-9802
Tel.: (660) 748-4647
Food Products Distr
N.A.I.C.S.: 424480

Joint Venture (Non-US):

Norson Alimentos S de RL de CV (2)
Blvd Capomo No 2 local 2 entre Berrendo, PO Box 1223, Y Sierra Azul Colonia Nuevo, 83299, Hermosillo, Mexico (50%)
Tel.: (52) 6622595800
Web Site: http://www.norson.net
Sales Range: $100-124.9 Million
Emp.: 700
Pork Processing Services
N.A.I.C.S.: 311423
Jesus Huerta *(Pres)*

Subsidiary (Domestic):

North Side Foods Corp. (2)
2200 Rivers Edge Dr, Arnold, PA 15068-5800
Tel.: (724) 335-5800
Web Site: http://www.northsidefoods.com
Rev.: $97,000,000
Emp.: 350
Sausages & Other Prepared Meats
N.A.I.C.S.: 311612
Mark Wilhelm *(VP)*

Patrick Cudahy Inc. (2)
1 Sweet Apple Wood Ln, Cudahy, WI 53110
Tel.: (414) 744-2000
Web Site: https://patrickcudahy.sfdbrands.com
Sales Range: $400-449.9 Million
Emp.: 1,100
Bacon, Ham & Sausage Products Mfr
N.A.I.C.S.: 311612

Subsidiary (Non-US):

S.C. Comtim Group S.R.L. (2)
Str Dr Liviu Gabor Nr 1, 300004, Timisoara, Romania
Tel.: (40) 256492066
Sales Range: $200-249.9 Million
Emp.: 500
Meats Processor
N.A.I.C.S.: 311999

SF Holding Sp. z o.o. (2)
ul T Chalubinskiego 8, 00-613, Warsaw, Poland
Tel.: (48) 223345900
Web Site: https://sfholding.pl
Sales Range: $25-49.9 Million
Emp.: 60
Holding Company
N.A.I.C.S.: 551112

Subsidiary (Domestic):

Animex Fish Sp. z o.o. (3)

Felczaka 20 B, Szczecin, 71-417, Poland
Tel.: (48) 0914228063
Web Site: http://www.animexfish.pl
Sales Range: $50-74.9 Million
Emp.: 10
Fish Importer & Distr
N.A.I.C.S.: 424460

Animex Grupa Drobiarska sp z.o.o. (3)
Oddzial w Debica ul Sloneczna 53, 39-200, Debica, Poland
Tel.: (48) 146776707
Web Site: http://www.animex.debica.net.pl
Meat Packing & Distribution
N.A.I.C.S.: 311423

Animex SF Sp. z.o.o Pasze S.K.A. (3)
Ul Wroclawska 61, 49-200, Grodkow, Poland
Tel.: (48) 774042940
Web Site: http://www.contipasz.com.pl
Farm Supplies Distr
N.A.I.C.S.: 424910

Animex Sp. z o.o. (3)
ul Chalubinskiego 8, 00-613, Warsaw, Poland (85%)
Tel.: (48) 223345900
Web Site: http://www.animex.pl
Rev.: $410,000,000
Emp.: 17
Meat Packing & Distribution
N.A.I.C.S.: 424420

Animex-Pasze sp. z o.o. (3)
ul Namyslowskiego 3, 22-400, Zamosc, Poland
Tel.: (48) 8463920321
Meat Packing & Distribution
N.A.I.C.S.: 311999

Constar S.A. (3)
ul Krancowa 4, Starachowice, 27-200, Poland (100%)
Tel.: (48) 412766100
Web Site: http://www.constar.pl
Animal Slaughtering
N.A.I.C.S.: 311611

Grupa Animex S.A. (3)
Morliny 15 14-100 Ostroda, ul Valery Slawek 8A, 30-633, Krakow, Poland
Tel.: (48) 123784100
Web Site: http://www.animex.krakow.pl
Meat Packing & Distribution
N.A.I.C.S.: 311612

Zaklady Miesne Agryf S.A. (3)
Ul Pomorska 115b, 70-812, Szczecin, Poland
Tel.: (48) 914691738
Meat Packing & Distribution
N.A.I.C.S.: 311999

Zaklady Miesne Mazury w Elku Sp. Z o.o. (3)
Ul Suwalska 86, 19-300, Elk, Poland
Tel.: (48) 876102263
Web Site: http://www.zm-mazury.pl
Meat Packing & Distribution
N.A.I.C.S.: 311999

Subsidiary (Domestic):

SFFC, Inc. (2)
103 Baynard Bldg 3411 Silverside Rd, Wilmington, DE 19810
Tel.: (302) 477-1300
Emp.: 4
Investment Management Service
N.A.I.C.S.: 523940

Group (Domestic):

Smithfield Deli Group (2)
111 Commerce St, Smithfield, VA 23430
Tel.: (757) 357-1696
Emp.: 25
Deli Meats Sales Office
N.A.I.C.S.: 311999

Subsidiary (Non-US):

Smithfield Ferme S.R.L. (2)
4 Polona Street Building A, 300523, Timisoara, Romania
Tel.: (40) 256278800
Web Site: http://www.smithfieldferme.ro
Animal Feeding & Production Services

N.A.I.C.S.: 112990

Smithfield Foods Ltd. (2)
Norfolk Tower 48-52 Surrey Street, Norwich, NR1 3PA, United Kingdom
Tel.: (44) 1603252400
Web Site: https://www.smithfieldfoods.co.uk
Sales Range: $50-74.9 Million
Emp.: 50
Meat Processing Services
N.A.I.C.S.: 311612

Group (Domestic):

Smithfield Foodservice Group (2)
111 Commerce St, Smithfield, VA 23430
Tel.: (800) 444-5226
Rev.: $340,000,000
Emp.: 35
Foodservice Sales
N.A.I.C.S.: 311999

Subsidiary (Non-US):

Smithfield France S.A.S. (2)
Usine des Pins, Lampau Guimiliau, Landivisiau, 29400, France
Tel.: (33) 298686868
Sales Range: $250-299.9 Million
Emp.: 550
Food Mfr
N.A.I.C.S.: 311999

Smithfield France Services (2)
Usine des Pins, Lampaul Guimlliau, Landivisiau, 29400, France
Tel.: (33) 472148500
Web Site: http://www.groupeaoste.com
Sales Range: $350-399.9 Million
Food Mfr
N.A.I.C.S.: 311423

Group (Domestic):

Smithfield Global Products (2)
3500 E Barnard Ave, Cudahy, WI 53110
Tel.: (414) 744-1920
Sales Range: $25-49.9 Million
Ham Importer
N.A.I.C.S.: 311999
Dan Incaudo *(VP)*

Subsidiary (Domestic):

Smithfield International Investments, Inc. (2)
3411 Silverside Rd 103, Wilmington, DE 19810-4811
Tel.: (302) 477-1358
Food Mfr
N.A.I.C.S.: 311999

Smithfield Packing Transportation Co., Inc. (2)
201 Berry Hill Rd, Smithfield, VA 23430
Tel.: (757) 365-3556
Web Site: http://www.smithfield.com
Sales Range: $25-49.9 Million
Emp.: 50
Trucking Service
N.A.I.C.S.: 484121

Smithfield Transportation Co., Inc. (2)
201 Berry Hill Rd, Smithfield, VA 23430
Tel.: (757) 365-3556
Sales Range: $150-199.9 Million
Trucking Service
N.A.I.C.S.: 484121
Joseph W. Luter III *(Pres)*

Stefano Foods, Inc. (2)
4825 Hovis Rd, Charlotte, NC 28208 (80%)
Tel.: (704) 399-3935
Rev.: $18,000,000
Emp.: 75
Italian Food Mfr
N.A.I.C.S.: 311999
Giusto Piraino *(Co-Founder & Pres)*

The Smithfield Inn Corporation (2)
112 N Main St, Smithfield, VA 23430
Tel.: (757) 357-1752
Web Site: https://smithfieldinn.net
Sales Range: Less than $1 Million
Emp.: 30
Bed & Breakfast, Restaurant, Tavern & Inn
N.A.I.C.S.: 721191
Nicole Johnson *(Gen Mgr)*

WH GROUP LIMITED

WH Group Limited—(Continued)

The Smithfield Packing Co., Inc. (2)
111 Commerce St, Smithfield, VA 23430
Tel.: (757) 357-4321
Web Site: http://www.smithfield.com
Sales Range: $1-4.9 Billion
Emp.: 9,330
Meat Processing
N.A.I.C.S.: 311611

WH IRELAND GROUP PLC

24 Martin Lane, London, EC4R 0DR, United Kingdom
Tel.: (44) 2072201666
Web Site:
https://www.whirelandplc.com
WHI—(AIM)
Rev.: $40,132,845
Assets: $37,422,836
Liabilities: $16,938,915
Net Worth: $20,483,922
Earnings: $1,565,451
Emp.: 139
Fiscal Year-end: 03/31/21
Investment Services
N.A.I.C.S.: 523999
Katy Mitchell (Sec)

Subsidiaries:

DJ Carmichael Pty Limited (1)
14 Parmelia House 191 St Georges Terrace, Perth, 6000, WA, Australia (51%)
Tel.: (61) 892635200
Web Site: http://www.djcarmichael.com.au
Sales Range: $50-74.9 Million
Emp.: 60
Investment Services
N.A.I.C.S.: 523999
Belinda Roychowdhury (Mgr-Admin)

Fitel Nominees Limited (1)
11 Saint James Square, Manchester, M2 6WH, United Kingdom
Tel.: (44) 1618326644
Web Site: http://www.wh-ireland.co.uk
Emp.: 8
Investment Management Service
N.A.I.C.S.: 523999

WH Ireland Limited (1)
11 Saint James Square, Manchester, M2 6WH, United Kingdom
Tel.: (44) 1618322174
Sales Range: $100-124.9 Million
Emp.: 108
Investment Banking Services
N.A.I.C.S.: 523150
Robert Race (Head-Wealth Mgmt)

WH Ireland Trustee Limited (1)
11 Saint James Square, Manchester, M2 6WH, United Kingdom
Tel.: (44) 1618322174
Web Site: http://www.wh-ireland.co.uk
Emp.: 100
Investment Management Service
N.A.I.C.S.: 523999

WHA CORPORATION PUBLIC COMPANY LIMITED

777 WHA TOWER 23rd-25th Floor Moo 13 Debaratna Road, Bangna-Trad KM 7 Bang Kaeo Bang Phli, Samut Prakan, 10540, Thailand
Tel.: (66) 27533750 TH
Web Site: https://www.wha-group.com
Year Founded: 2003
WHA—(THA)
Rev.: $434,228,212
Assets: $2,633,844,118
Liabilities: $1,544,329,091
Net Worth: $1,089,515,027
Earnings: $147,407,337
Emp.: 146
Fiscal Year-end: 12/31/23
Warehousing Services
N.A.I.C.S.: 493110
Jareeporn Jarukornsakul (Chm)

Subsidiaries:

Hemaraj Land & Development Public Company Limited (1)
18th Floor UM Tower 9 Ramkhamhaeng Road, Suanluang, Bangkok, 10250, Thailand
Tel.: (66) 2 719 9555
Web Site: http://www.hemaraj.com
Sales Range: $200-249.9 Million
Emp.: 332
Industrial & Infrastructure Developer
N.A.I.C.S.: 236220
Jakrit Chaisanit (Co-COO)

Subsidiary (Domestic):

Eastern Industrial Estate Company Limited (2)
18th Floor UM Tower 9 Ramkhamhaeng Road, Suanluang, Bangkok, 10250, Thailand (99.99%)
Tel.: (66) 2719 9555
Web Site: http://www.hemaraj.com
Property Development Services
N.A.I.C.S.: 531311

H-Phoenix Property Company Limited (2)
18 Floor UM Tower 9 Ramkhamhaeng Road, Suanluang, Bangkok, 10250, Thailand
Tel.: (66) 27199555
Web Site: http://www.hemaraj.com
Office Building Rental & Leasing Services
N.A.I.C.S.: 531120

Hemaraj Water Company Limited (2)
18th Floor UM Tower 9 Ramkhamhaeng Road, Suanluang, Bangkok, 10250, Thailand
Tel.: (66) 27199555
Web Site: http://www.hemaraj.com
Water Resources Development & Management Services
N.A.I.C.S.: 561990

WHA Industrial Development Public Company Limited (1)
777 WHA TOWER 23rd-25th Floor Moo 13 Debaratna Road Bangna-Trad KM 7, Bang Kaeo Bang Phli, Samut Prakan, 10540, Thailand
Tel.: (66) 27199555
Web Site: https://www.wha-industrialestate.com
Real Estate Services
N.A.I.C.S.: 531390
Vivat Jiratikarnsakul (COO)

WHA PREMIUM GROWTH FREEHOLD & LEASEHOLD REAL ESTATE INVESTMENT TRUST

400/22 KASIKORN Bank Building 6th Floor Phaholyothin Road, Samsen Nai Sub-District Phayathai District, Bangkok, Thailand
Tel.: (66) 26733999
Web Site: https://www.whareit.com
Year Founded: 2014
WHART—(THA)
Rev.: $99,184,910
Assets: $1,614,322,827
Liabilities: $520,818,555
Net Worth: $1,093,504,272
Earnings: $76,338,913
Fiscal Year-end: 12/31/23
Real Estate Investment Trust Services
N.A.I.C.S.: 525990
Jareeporn Jarukornsakul (Chm)

WHA UTILITIES & POWER PCL

777 Wha Tower 22nd Floor Unit 2203-2205 Moo 13 Debaratna Road, Bangna-Trad KM 7 Bang Kaeo, Bang Phli, 10540, Samut Prakarn, Thailand
Tel.: (66) 27199559 TH
Web Site: https://www.wha-up.com
Year Founded: 2008
WHAUP—(THA)
Rev.: $81,201,764
Assets: $870,420,054
Liabilities: $474,380,679
Net Worth: $396,039,374
Earnings: $47,619,588
Emp.: 194
Fiscal Year-end: 12/31/23
Electric Power Distribution Services
N.A.I.C.S.: 221118
Prapon Chinudomsub (CFO)

WHA YU INDUSTRIAL CO., LTD.

No 326 Section 2 Gongdao 5th Road, Hsinchu, 30070, Taiwan
Tel.: (886) 35714225
Web Site: https://www.whayu.com
3419—(TAI)
Rev.: $45,831,844
Assets: $67,025,996
Liabilities: $23,551,325
Net Worth: $43,474,671
Earnings: $(4,112,103)
Emp.: 111
Fiscal Year-end: 12/31/23
Antenna Mfr
N.A.I.C.S.: 334220

Subsidiaries:

DONGGUAN AEON TECH CO., LTD. (1)
(100%)
Tel.: (86) 76985655858
Web Site: http://www.whayu.com
Antenna Mfr
N.A.I.C.S.: 334220

Hang Jian Technology Co., Ltd. (1)
No 326 Section 2 Gongdao 5th Road, East District, Hsinchu, Taiwan
Tel.: (886) 35734260
Web Site: http://www.hjuavs.com
Aircraft Parts Mfr & Distr
N.A.I.C.S.: 336413

WHANIN PHARAM CO LTD

8F11F Whanin Building 11 Beobwon-ro 6-gil, Songpa-gu, Seoul, 05855, Korea (South)
Tel.: (82) 24053000
Web Site: https://www.whanin.com
016580—(KRS)
Rev.: $152,582,941
Assets: $283,310,289
Liabilities: $27,187,416
Net Worth: $256,122,872
Earnings: $18,203,661
Emp.: 562
Fiscal Year-end: 12/31/22
Pharmaceuticals Product Mfr
N.A.I.C.S.: 325412
Wonbum Lee (Pres & CEO)

WHAT'S COOKING GROUP NV

Beke 1, 9950, Waarschoot, Belgium
Tel.: (32) 93701211
Web Site: https://whatscooking.group
Year Founded: 1948
TERB—(EUR)
Rev.: $843,281,891
Assets: $436,497,949
Liabilities: $306,373,840
Net Worth: $130,124,110
Earnings: $4,878,049
Emp.: 2,442
Fiscal Year-end: 12/31/22
Processed Meat & Fresh Ready Meal Mfr
N.A.I.C.S.: 311612
Dirk Goeminne (Chm)

Subsidiaries:

Berkhout Langeveld BV (1)
Bijsterhuizen 24-04, 6604 LL, Wijchen, Netherlands
Tel.: (31) 246489900
Web Site: http://www.langeveldsleegers.nl
Emp.: 150

INTERNATIONAL PUBLIC

Processed Meat Mfr
N.A.I.C.S.: 311612
Allan Blake (Gen Mgr)

Binet SA (1)
Rue De Hermee 2, 4040, Herstal, Belgium
Tel.: (32) 33500611
Sales Range: $25-49.9 Million
Emp.: 25
Processed Meat Mfr
N.A.I.C.S.: 311612

FreshMeals Deutschland GmbH (1)
Carl-Benz-Strasse 6, Schweitenkirchen, 85301, Pfaffenhofen, Germany
Tel.: (49) 8444 924 7733
Web Site: https://www.fresh-meals.de
Welding Machine Distr
N.A.I.C.S.: 445132

FreshMeals Iberica SL (1)
Attica Business Complex Building 6 floor 3a Workshop B1, 28224, Pozuelo de Alarcon, Spain
Tel.: (34) 913518580
Web Site: http://www.terbeke.com
Emp.: 8
Food Products Mfr & Distr
N.A.I.C.S.: 311999

FreshMeals NV (1)
Beke 1, Lievegem, 9950, Waarschoot, Belgium
Tel.: (32) 9 370 1211
Web Site: http://www.terbeke.com
Sales Range: $25-49.9 Million
Emp.: 25
Ready Meal Mfr
N.A.I.C.S.: 311999

FreshMeals Nederland BV (1)
Bijsterhuizen 2404, 6604 LL, Wijchen, Netherlands
Tel.: (31) 246489900
Food Products Mfr
N.A.I.C.S.: 311999

H.J. Berkhout Verssnijlijn BV (1)
Grotenoord 41, Hendrik-Ido-Ambacht, 3341 LT, Netherlands
Tel.: (31) 78 681 7311
Sales Range: $25-49.9 Million
Emp.: 150
Processed Meat Mfr
N.A.I.C.S.: 311612

KK Fine Foods Plc (1)
Estuary House 10th Ave, Zone 3 Deeside Industrial Park, Deeside, CH5 2UA, Flintshire, United Kingdom
Tel.: (44) 124 428 6200
Web Site: https://www.kkfinefoods.co.uk
Emp.: 500
Food Distr
N.A.I.C.S.: 445298
Leyla Edwards (Founder & CEO)

Pluma Fleischwarenvertrieb GmbH (1)
Ostwall 175, 47798, Krefeld, Germany
Tel.: (49) 3 350 0632
Web Site: https://www.pluma-fleischwaren.de
Meat Product Whslr
N.A.I.C.S.: 424470

Pluma NV (1)
Antoon van der Pluymstraat 1, 2160, Wommelgem, Belgium
Tel.: (32) 3 350 0606
Web Site: http://www.terbeke.com
Processed Meat Mfr
N.A.I.C.S.: 311612

Stefano Toselli SAS (1)
Zone Industrielle Espace Zuckermann Route de Percy, PO Box 56, Mezidon-Canon, 14270, Lisieux, France
Tel.: (33) 23 120 0596
Web Site: https://www.stefano-toselli.com
Frozen Pasta Mfr
N.A.I.C.S.: 311412

Ter Beke France SA (1)
Zone Espace Leaders 428 Allee De Marigny, 74540, Alby-sur-Cheran, France
Tel.: (33) 4 50 68 16 95
Sales Range: $25-49.9 Million
Emp.: 35
Ready Meal Mfr
N.A.I.C.S.: 311999

AND PRIVATE COMPANIES

Ter Beke Vleeswarenproduktie NV (1)
Beke 1, Waarschoot, 9950, Belgium
Tel.: (32) 9 370 12 11
Emp.: 270
Processed Meat Mfr
N.A.I.C.S.: 311612
Dirk Goeminne *(CEO)*

TerBeke-Pluma NV (1)
Antoon Van Der Pluymstraat 1, Wommelgem, 2160, Belgium
Tel.: (32) 3 350 06 06
Processed Meat Mfr
N.A.I.C.S.: 311612

Subsidiary (Non-US):

Langeveld/Sleegers BV (2)
Bijsterhuizen 24/04, 6604 LL, Wijchen, Netherlands
Tel.: (31) 24 648 9900
Web Site: http://www.langeveld-sleegers.nl
Emp.: 15
Processed Meat Mfr
N.A.I.C.S.: 311612

TerBeke-Pluma Nederland BV (1)
Bijsterhuizen 2404, 6604 LL, Wijchen, Netherlands
Tel.: (31) 246489900
Meat Product Distr
N.A.I.C.S.: 424470
Marc Hofman *(Mgr)*

WHAT'S NEXT PARTNERS
4 place de l Opera, 75002, Paris, France
Tel.: (33) 1 84 86 09 00
Web Site: http://www.wnp.fr
Advertising Services
N.A.I.C.S.: 541810
Tristan Beauchesne *(Sr Partner-WNP Consulting)*

WHEATON CHEVROLET
260 Albert Street North, Regina, S4R 3C1, SK, Canada
Tel.: (306) 543-1555
Web Site:
  http://www.wheatonchev.com
Year Founded: 1984
Rev.: $29,403,928
Emp.: 80
New & Used Car Dealers
N.A.I.C.S.: 441110

WHEATON GMC BUICK CADILLAC LTD
2102 Millar Ave, Saskatoon, S7K 6P4, SK, Canada
Tel.: (306) 244-8131
Web Site:
  http://www.wheatonsaskatoon.com
Sales Range: $25-49.9 Million
New & Used Car Dealers
N.A.I.C.S.: 441110
Shawn Robson *(Gen Mgr-Sls)*

WHEATON PRECIOUS METALS CORP.
Suite 3500 - 1021 West Hastings St, Vancouver, V6E 0C3, BC, Canada
Tel.: (604) 684-9648
Web Site:
  https://www.wheatonpm.com
WPM—(NYSE)
Rev.: $1,016,045,000
Assets: $7,031,185,000
Liabilities: $45,669,000
Net Worth: $6,985,516,000
Earnings: $537,644,000
Emp.: 42
Fiscal Year-end: 12/31/23
Mineral Mining Services
N.A.I.C.S.: 212220
Gary Brown *(CFO & Sr VP)*

Subsidiaries:

Silver Wheaton (Caymans) Ltd. (1)
94 Solaris Avenue Suite 300, PO Box 1791, Grand Cayman, Camana Bay, KY1-1109, Cayman Islands
Tel.: (345) 9453584
Silver Mining Services
N.A.I.C.S.: 212220

WHEATSHEAF GROUP LIMITED
The Quarry Hill Road, Eccleston, Chester, CH4 9HQ, United Kingdom
Tel.: (44) 1244670970
Web Site:
  http://www.wheatsheafgroup.com
Food & Agriculture Mfr
N.A.I.C.S.: 311999
Fiona Emmett *(Dir-Fin)*

WHEB CAPITAL PARTNERS LLP
23 Hanover Street, London, W1S 1JB, United Kingdom
Tel.: (44) 20 3219 3441 UK
Web Site: http://www.whebgroup.com
Equity Investment Firm
N.A.I.C.S.: 523999
George Latham *(Mng Partner-Listed Equity & Chief Investment Officer)*

Subsidiaries:

Wireless Energy Management Systems International Limited (1)
The Mission Wellington Street, Stockport, SK1 3AH, United Kingdom
Tel.: (44) 1614751777
Web Site: http://www.wems.co.uk
Emp.: 100
Application Software Development Services
N.A.I.C.S.: 541511
Paul Summers *(CEO)*

WHEELOCK & COMPANY LIMITED
23rd Floor Wheelock House 20 Pedder Street, Hong Kong, China (Hong Kong)
Tel.: (852) 21182118
Web Site:
  http://www.wheelockcompany.com
Year Founded: 1857
WHLKF—(OTCIQ)
Rev.: $6,230,324,790
Assets: $78,254,723,330
Liabilities: $27,698,037,000
Net Worth: $50,556,686,330
Earnings: $1,539,892,720
Emp.: 12,500
Fiscal Year-end: 12/31/19
Holding Company; Real Estate Development
N.A.I.C.S.: 551112
Paul Yiu Cheung Tsui *(CFO-Grp)*

Subsidiaries:

Harriman Property Management Limited (1)
20/F World Tech Centre 95 How Ming Street, Kwun Tong, Kowloon, China (Hong Kong)
Tel.: (852) 21182628
Web Site: http://www.harriman.com.hk
Real Estate Services
N.A.I.C.S.: 531390

The Star Ferry Company Limited (1)
Star Ferry Pier Kowloon Point, Tsim Sha Tsui, Tsim Tsa Tsui, Kowloon, China (Hong Kong)
Tel.: (852) 23677065
Web Site: http://www.starferry.com.hk
Ferry Transportation Services
N.A.I.C.S.: 483114

The Wharf (Holdings) Limited (1)
16th Floor Ocean Centre Harbour City, Kowloon, China (Hong Kong)
Tel.: (852) 21188118
Web Site: https://www.wharfholdings.com
Rev.: $2,421,818,089
Assets: $26,183,368,052
Liabilities: $7,242,961,391
Net Worth: $18,940,406,661
Earnings: $141,219,472
Emp.: 64,000
Fiscal Year-end: 12/31/2023
Real Estate Development Services
N.A.I.C.S.: 531390
Paul Yiu Cheung Tsui *(Vice Chm & CFO-Grp)*

Subsidiary (Domestic):

Wharf China Limited (2)
16th Fl Ocean Ctr Harbour City Canton Rd, Kowloon, China (Hong Kong)
Tel.: (852) 21188118
Web Site: http://www.wharfholding.com
Sales Range: $75-99.9 Million
Emp.: 300
Holding Company; Hotels & Real Estate
N.A.I.C.S.: 551112

Subsidiary (Domestic):

Modern Terminals Limited (3)
Berth One, Kwai Chung, China (Hong Kong)
Tel.: (852) 21153838
Web Site: http://www.modernterminals.com
Container Terminal Operator
N.A.I.C.S.: 424710

The Marco Polo Hotel (Hong Kong) Limited (3)
No 3 Canton Road Harbour City, Tsim Sha Tsui, Kowloon, China (Hong Kong)
Tel.: (852) 21130088
Web Site: http://www.marcopolohotels.com
Sales Range: $50-74.9 Million
Emp.: 500
Hotel
N.A.I.C.S.: 721110
Thomas Salg *(VP-Ops)*

The Prince Hotel Limited (3)
No 23 Canton Road Harbour City, Tsim Sha Tsui, Kowloon, China (Hong Kong)
Tel.: (852) 21131888
Web Site: http://www.marcopolohotels.com
Sales Range: $10-24.9 Million
Emp.: 100
Hotel
N.A.I.C.S.: 721110

Subsidiary (Domestic):

Wharf Communications Limited (2)
16th Floor Ocean Centre, Harbour City Canton Road, Kowloon, China (Hong Kong)
Tel.: (852) 21188118
Sales Range: $100-124.9 Million
Emp.: 200
Holding Company; Communications, Media & Entertainment Services
N.A.I.C.S.: 551112
Peter Kwong Ching Woo *(Chm)*

Subsidiary (Domestic):

COL Limited (3)
Unit 825-876 8th Floor KITEC 1 Trademart Drive, Kowloon Bay, China (Hong Kong)
Tel.: (852) 21183888
Web Site: http://www.col.com.hk
Sales Range: $25-49.9 Million
Computer Services
N.A.I.C.S.: 541519

Subsidiary (Non-US):

Wharf COL (Shanghai) Limited (4)
6/F Shanghai Times Square Office 93 Huai Hai Zhong Road, Shanghai, 200021, China
Tel.: (86) 2163910578
Web Site: http://www.wharfcol.com.cn
Sales Range: $10-24.9 Million
Emp.: 25
Computer Services
N.A.I.C.S.: 541519

Subsidiary (Domestic):

i-CABLE Communications Limited (3)
7th Floor Cable TV Building 9 Hoi Shing Road, Tsuen Wan, China (Hong Kong)
Tel.: (852) 21126868
Web Site: https://www.i-cablecomm.com
Rev.: $149,063,079
Assets: $241,249,902
Liabilities: $159,065,319
Net Worth: $82,184,583
Earnings: ($50,974,404)
Emp.: 1,433
Fiscal Year-end: 12/31/2019
Pay-TV Services Owner & Operator
N.A.I.C.S.: 516210
Raymond Wai Man Chan *(CTO)*

Subsidiary (Domestic):

Wharf Estates Development Limited (2)
16th Floor Ocean Centre, Harbour City Canton Road, Kowloon, China (Hong Kong)
Tel.: (852) 21188118
Web Site: http://www.wharfholdings.com
Emp.: 1,000
Holding Company; Real Estate Development Services
N.A.I.C.S.: 551112

Wharf Estates Limited (2)
16th Floor Ocean Centre, Harbour City Canton Road, Kowloon, China (Hong Kong) (100%)
Tel.: (852) 21188118
Web Site: http://www.wharfholdings.com
Holding Company; Real Estate Services
N.A.I.C.S.: 551112

Subsidiary (Domestic):

Harbour Centre Development Limited (3)
16th Floor Ocean Centre Harbour City Canton Road, Kowloon, China (Hong Kong)
Tel.: (852) 21188118
Web Site: https://www.harbourcentre.com.hk
Rev.: $145,222,500
Assets: $2,403,247,500
Liabilities: $448,162,500
Net Worth: $1,955,085,000
Earnings: ($28,942,500)
Emp.: 1,200
Fiscal Year-end: 12/31/2022
Holding Company; Property & Hotel Operator
N.A.I.C.S.: 551112
Stephen Tin-Hoi Ng *(Chm)*

Subsidiary (Domestic):

Wheelock Properties (China) Limited (2)
23F Wheelock House 20 Pedder St, Central, China (Hong Kong)
Tel.: (852) 21182118
Web Site:
  http://www.wheelockpropertieshk.com
Property Development Services
N.A.I.C.S.: 531210

Wharf Real Estate Investment Company Limited. (1)
16th Floor Ocean Centre, Harbour City, Kowloon, China (Hong Kong)
Tel.: (852) 21183118
Web Site: https://www.wharfreic.com
Rev.: $1,700,512,480
Assets: $31,352,256,317
Liabilities: $6,353,598,221
Net Worth: $24,998,658,096
Earnings: $593,505,182
Emp.: 2,900
Fiscal Year-end: 12/31/2023
Real Estate Development Services
N.A.I.C.S.: 531190
Stephen Tin Hoi Ng *(Chm & Mgr Dir)*

Wheelock Properties (Hong Kong) Limited (1)
5th Floor Wheelock House 20 Pedder Street, Central, China (Hong Kong) (100%)
Tel.: (852) 21182668
Web Site:
  http://www.wheelockpropertieshk.com
Property Development, Sales & Marketing & Asset Management
N.A.I.C.S.: 531312

Wheelock Properties Limited (1)
23rd Floor Wheelock House, 20 Pedder Street, Central, China (Hong Kong) (74%)
Tel.: (852) 21182118
Web Site:
  http://www.wheelockcompany.com
Sales Range: $100-124.9 Million
Emp.: 110
Holding Company; Real Estate Development Services

WHEELOCK & COMPANY LIMITED

Wheelock & Company Limited—(Continued)
N.A.I.C.S.: 551112
Subsidiary (Non-US):

Wheelock Properties (Singapore)
Limited (2)
501 Orchard Road 11-01 Wheelock Place,
Singapore, 238880, Singapore (56%)
Tel.: (65) 6738 8660
Web Site:
http://www.wheelockproperties.com.sg
Sales Range: $300-349.9 Million
Holding Company; Property & Real Estate
Development & Investment
N.A.I.C.S.: 551112
Stephen Tin-Hoi Ng *(Chm)*

Wheelock Travel Limited (1)
Unit No 1111 11th Floor Telecom Tower
Wharf T&T Square, 123 Hoi Bun Road,
Kwun Tong, China (Hong Kong)
Tel.: (852) 21183998
Sales Range: $25-49.9 Million
Emp.: 7
Travel Agencies
N.A.I.C.S.: 561510

WHERRELZ IT SOLUTIONS LTD.
3VJJ WFG Bail Bajar, Saki Naka,
Navi Mumbai, 400072, Maharashtra,
India
Tel.: (91) 9429794200
Web Site: https://www.wherrelz.in
543436—(BOM)
Rev.: $76,326
Assets: $168,355
Liabilities: $9,617
Net Worth: $158,738
Earnings: ($6,015)
Emp.: 8
Fiscal Year-end: 03/31/23
Information Technology Services
N.A.I.C.S.: 541519
Chaitanya Dhareshwar *(Founder & Mng Dir)*

WHISSELL CONTRACTING LTD.
200 2500-107 Avenue SE, Calgary,
T2Z 3R7, AB, Canada
Tel.: (403) 236-2200
Web Site: https://www.whissell.ca
Year Founded: 1970
Emp.: 425
General Contracting Services
N.A.I.C.S.: 237990
Jarrad Whissell *(Pres)*

WHITBREAD PLC
Whitbread Court Houghton Hall Business Park, Porz Avenue, Dunstable,
LU5 5XE, United Kingdom
Tel.: (44) 1582424200 UK
Web Site: http://www.whitbread.co.uk
Year Founded: 1742
WTBDY—(OTCIQ)
Rev.: $3,259,973,360
Assets: $12,346,969,040
Liabilities: $7,241,432,520
Net Worth: $5,105,536,520
Earnings: $346,213,840
Emp.: 40,000
Fiscal Year-end: 03/02/23
Holding Company; Hotels, Restaurants & Leisure Clubs
N.A.I.C.S.: 722511
Alison Brittain *(CEO)*

Subsidiaries:

Healthy Retail Limited (1)
100 Moorgate, London, EC2M 6AB, United Kingdom
Tel.: (44) 207 240 1555
Web Site: https://www.pure.co.uk
Food Mfr
N.A.I.C.S.: 311999

Premier Inn (Isle of Man) Limited (1)
Market Street, Douglas, IM1 1EU, Isle of Man
Tel.: (44) 3301359312
Hotel & Restaurant Operator
N.A.I.C.S.: 721110

Premier Inn (Jersey) Limited (1)
21-28 Charing Cross, Saint Helier, JE2 3RP, Jersey
Tel.: (44) 3332346555
Hotel & Restaurant Operator
N.A.I.C.S.: 721110

Premier Inn Essen City Hauptbahnhof GmbH (1)
Am Hauptbahnhof 3, 45127, Essen, Germany
Tel.: (49) 20156571892
Hotel & Restaurant Operator
N.A.I.C.S.: 721110

Premier Inn Frankfurt City Ostbahnhof GmbH (1)
Europa-Allee 22, 60327, Frankfurt am Main, Germany
Tel.: (49) 6966778738
Hotel & Restaurant Operator
N.A.I.C.S.: 721110

Premier Inn Glasgow Limited (1)
80 Ballater Street, Glasgow, G5 0TW, United Kingdom
Tel.: (44) 3337777295
Hotel & Restaurant Operator
N.A.I.C.S.: 721110

Premier Inn Hamburg Nordanalstrasse GmbH (1)
Nordkanalstrasse 20, 20097, Hamburg, Germany
Tel.: (49) 4080908514
Hotel & Restaurant Operator
N.A.I.C.S.: 721110

Premier Inn Holding GmbH (1)
Europa-Allee 22, 60327, Frankfurt am Main, Germany
Tel.: (49) 69244330431
Web Site: https://www.premierinn.com
Hotel & Restaurant Operator
N.A.I.C.S.: 721110

Premier Inn Manchester Airport Limited (1)
Runger Lane Wilmslow Road Manchester Airport, Manchester, M90 5DL, United Kingdom
Tel.: (44) 3333211299
Hotel & Restaurant Operator
N.A.I.C.S.: 721110

Premier Inn Manchester Trafford Limited (1)
18-20 Trafford Boulevard, Urmston, Manchester, M41 7JE, United Kingdom
Tel.: (44) 3333211316
Hotel & Restaurant Operator
N.A.I.C.S.: 721110

Premier Inn Munchen Frankfurter Ring GmbH (1)
Frankfurter Ring 182, 80807, Munich, Germany
Tel.: (49) 8924445050
Hotel & Restaurant Operator
N.A.I.C.S.: 721110

Premier Inn Munchen Messe GmbH (1)
Muenchener Str 33, Haar, 85540, Munich, Germany
Tel.: (49) 892 444 5159
Hotel & Restaurant Operator
N.A.I.C.S.: 721110

Premier Inn Nurnberg City Nordost GmbH (1)
Leipziger Platz 22, 90491, Nuremberg, Germany
Tel.: (49) 9118 819 9025
Hotel & Restaurant Operator
N.A.I.C.S.: 721110

Premier Inn Stuttgart Feuerbach GmbH (1)
Heilbronner Strasse 321, 70469, Stuttgart, Germany
Tel.: (49) 7112 070 1987
Hotel & Restaurant Operator
N.A.I.C.S.: 721110

Whitbread Group PLC (1)
Whitbread Court Houghton Hall Business Park, Porz Avenue, Dunstable, LU5 5XE, United Kingdom (100%)
Tel.: (44) 1582424200
Hotel & Restaurant Operator
N.A.I.C.S.: 561599

Subsidiary (Domestic):

Coffee Nation Limited (2)
3 Knaves Beech Loudwater, High Wycombe, HP10 9QR, Buckinghamshire, United Kingdom
Tel.: (44) 1628536130
Web Site: http://www.coffeenation.com
Coffee Mfr
N.A.I.C.S.: 311920
Scott Martin *(CEO)*

Premier Inn Limited (2)
Oakley House Oakley Road, Luton, LU4 9QH, United Kingdom
Tel.: (44) 333 003 8101
Web Site: https://www.premier-inn.net
Hotel Services
N.A.I.C.S.: 721110

Subsidiary (Domestic):

Premier Inn Hotels Limited (3)
Whitbread Court Houghton Hall Business Park, Porz Avenue, Dunstable, LU5 5XE, United Kingdom
Tel.: (44) 1582567890
Web Site: https://www.premierinn.com
Home Management Services
N.A.I.C.S.: 721110

Subsidiary (Domestic):

Whitbread Hotel Company Ltd (2)
Whitbread House Park St W, Luton, LU1 3VG, Herdfordshire, United Kingdom (100%)
Tel.: (44) 2076064455
Web Site: http://www.whitbread.co.uk
Hotel Operator
N.A.I.C.S.: 721110

Whitbread Properties Ltd. (2)
Whitbread Court Houghton Hall Business Park Porz Avenue, Dunstable, LU5 5XE, Beds, United Kingdom (100%)
Tel.: (44) 2076064455
Acquirer & Developer of Property
N.A.I.C.S.: 531210

Subsidiary (Non-US):

Whitbread Restaurants Holding GmbH (2)
Elisabethstrasse 22, 40217, Dusseldorf, Germany
Tel.: (49) 211386280
Web Site: http://www.maredo.de
Sales Range: $25-49.9 Million
Emp.: 80
Holding Company
N.A.I.C.S.: 551112
Uwe Buscher *(Mng Dir)*

Subsidiary (Non-US):

Maredo Restaurants GmbH (3)
Opernring 3-5, 1010, Vienna, Austria
Tel.: (43) 15867722
Web Site: http://www.maredo.com
Restaurant Group
N.A.I.C.S.: 722511

WHITE CLIFF MINERALS LIMITED
Level 8 99 St Georges Tce, Perth, 6000, WA, Australia
Tel.: (61) 894864036 AU
Web Site: https://www.wcminerals.com.au
Year Founded: 2007
WCN—(ASX)
Rev.: $172,290
Assets: $3,717,472
Liabilities: $207,265
Net Worth: $3,510,207
Earnings: ($9,018,615)
Fiscal Year-end: 06/30/24
Gold & Nickekl Exploration Services
N.A.I.C.S.: 212220

INTERNATIONAL PUBLIC

Nicholas Ong *(Sec)*
Subsidiaries:

Magnet Resource Company Pty. Ltd. (1)
Level 1 23 Ventnor Ave, West Perth, WA, Australia
Tel.: (61) 892261777
Web Site: https://www.magres.com.au
Gold Mining Exploration Services
N.A.I.C.S.: 541219

WHITE ENERGY COMPANY LIMITED
Lobby 1 Level 2 76 Skyring Terrace, Newstead, 4006, QLD, Australia
Tel.: (61) 732299035
Web Site:
https://www.whiteenergyco.com
WEC—(OTCIQ)
Rev.: $179,288
Assets: $13,068,903
Liabilities: $33,733,813
Net Worth: ($20,664,910)
Earnings: ($14,562,207)
Emp.: 55
Fiscal Year-end: 06/30/21
Coal Explorer
N.A.I.C.S.: 213113
David Franks *(Sec)*

Subsidiaries:

Binderless Coal Briquetting Company Pty Ltd (1)
Level 9 20 Hunter Street, N Sydney, Sydney, 2000, NSW, Australia
Tel.: (61) 299590000
Web Site: http://www.whiteenergyco.com
Emp.: 20
Coal Briquettes Mfr
N.A.I.C.S.: 324199

Mountainside Coal Company Inc. (1)
7692 S Hwy 25W, Williamsburg, KY 40769
Tel.: (606) 786-2121
Coal Mining Services
N.A.I.C.S.: 212114

WHITE FOX VENTURES, INC.
2-5-16-901 Shirogane, Minato-ku, Tokyo, 108-0072, Japan
Tel.: (81) 8046363573 NV
Year Founded: 2010
AWAW—(OTCIQ)
Sales Range: Less than $1 Million
Education Services
N.A.I.C.S.: 611710
Shinsuke Nakano *(Chm & CEO)*

WHITE GOLD CORP.
82 Richmond St E, Toronto, M5C 1P1, ON, Canada
Tel.: (647) 930-1880 BC
Web Site:
https://www.whitegoldcorp.ca
Year Founded: 1987
WGO—(NASDAQ)
Rev.: $113,458
Assets: $101,554,837
Liabilities: $10,765,244
Net Worth: $90,789,592
Earnings: $1,673,189
Fiscal Year-end: 12/31/23
Gold Exploration Services
N.A.I.C.S.: 212220
David D'Onofrio *(CEO)*

WHITE HORSE BERHAD
PLO 464 Jalan Gangsa Kawasan Perindustrian Pasir Gudang, 81700, Pasir Gudang, Johor Darul Takzim, Malaysia
Tel.: (60) 72535300
Web Site: https://whitehorse.my
WTHORSE—(KLS)
Rev.: $128,257,509
Assets: $230,254,740
Liabilities: $74,139,016

AND PRIVATE COMPANIES

Net Worth: $156,115,724
Earnings: ($15,573,490)
Emp.: 1,394
Fiscal Year-end: 12/31/19
Ceramic Tile Mfr
N.A.I.C.S.: 327120
Soon Mong Cheng *(Deputy Mng Dir)*

Subsidiaries:

White Horse Berhad - Plant 3 (1)
PLO 29 Tanjung Langsat Industrial Estate, 81700, Pasir Gudang, Johor, Malaysia
Tel.: (60) 72563888
Clay Building Material Mfr
N.A.I.C.S.: 327120

White Horse Ceramic Industries (Vietnam) Co., Ltd. (1)
Phuoc Lap Quater My Xuan Ward, Phu My, Ba Ria - Vung Tau, Vietnam
Tel.: (84) 2543932333
Web Site: https://www.whitehorse.vn
Ceramic Mfr
N.A.I.C.S.: 327110

White Horse Ceramic Industries Sdn. Bhd. (1)
PLO 464 Jalan Gangsa Zone 11, Kawasan Perindustrian Pasir Gudang, 81700, Pasir Gudang, Johor, Malaysia
Tel.: (60) 72535300
Ceramic Tiles Mfr & Distr
N.A.I.C.S.: 327120

Subsidiary (Non-US):

P.T. WH Ceramic Indonesia (2)
Komplek Pergudangan Jembatan 3 No D7 Block A-B, Pluit -Jakarta Utara, Jakarta, 14440, Indonesia
Tel.: (62) 2166604643
Web Site: http://www.whitehorse.com.tw
Ceramic Tiles Distr
N.A.I.C.S.: 423320

White Horse Ceramic (Phil) Inc. (2)
Tel.: (63) 22681928
Sales Range: $25-49.9 Million
Emp.: 20
Ceramic Tiles Distr
N.A.I.C.S.: 423320

White Horse Ceramic (S) Pte. Ltd. (2)
No 1 Sungei Kadut Way, Singapore, 728770, Singapore
Tel.: (65) 62690555
Web Site: https://www.whitehorse.com.sg
Sales Range: $25-49.9 Million
Emp.: 70
Ceramic Tiles Distr
N.A.I.C.S.: 423320

White Horse Ceramic (Thailand) Ltd. (2)
34/9 Moo 13 Bangpleeyai, Bang Phli, 10540, Samutprakarn, Thailand
Tel.: (66) 23163788
Sales Range: $25-49.9 Million
Emp.: 40
Ceramic Tiles Distr
N.A.I.C.S.: 444180

White Horse Marketing Sdn. Bhd. (1)
Plo 464 Jalan Gangsa Zone II, Pasir Gudang Industrial Estate, Pasir Gudang, 81700, Johor, Malaysia
Tel.: (60) 72518555
Web Site: https://www.whitehorse.com
Ceramic Tiles Distr
N.A.I.C.S.: 423320

WHITE IRON, INC.
533 1201 5th St SW Ste 1500 340, Calgary, T2R 0Y6, AB, Canada
Tel.: (403) 298-4700
Web Site: http://www.whiteiron.tv
Year Founded: 1990
Sales Range: $10-24.9 Million
Emp.: 35
Media Services for Television, Film & Internet Projects
N.A.I.C.S.: 512110

Subsidiaries:

White Iron Digital (1)
1500 340 12th Avenue SW, Calgary, T2R 1L5, AB, Canada
Tel.: (403) 298-4700
Digital Production
N.A.I.C.S.: 512110

White Iron Pictures, Inc. (1)
340 12th Avenue Suite 1500 Southwest, Calgary, T2R 1L5, AB, Canada
Tel.: (403) 298-4714
Movie Production Services
N.A.I.C.S.: 512110

White Iron Productions, Inc. (1)
1201 5th Street Southwest Suite 533, Calgary, T2R 0Y6, AB, Canada
Tel.: (403) 880-7663
Web Site: http://www.whiteiron.com
TV & Video Production Services
N.A.I.C.S.: 512110

White Iron Voicelink, Inc. (1)
1201 5th Street Southwest Suite 533, Calgary, T2R 0Y6, AB, Canada
Tel.: (403) 716-1249
Video Production Services
N.A.I.C.S.: 512110

WHITE MOUNTAIN TITANIUM CORPORATION
Augusto Leguia 100 Oficina 1401, Las Condes, Santiago, Chile
Tel.: (56) 26571800 NV
Web Site: http://www.wmtcorp.com
Year Founded: 1998
WMTM—(NYSE)
Emp.: 10
Mineral Exploration Services
N.A.I.C.S.: 327999
Brian Flower *(Exec VP)*

WHITE OAK TRANSPORT LIMITED
365 Lewis Rd North, Stoney Creek, L8E-5N4, ON, Canada
Tel.: (905) 643-9500
Web Site: http://www.whiteoaktransport.com
Year Founded: 1966
Rev.: $11,215,899
Emp.: 85
Truck Load & Logistic Transportation Services
N.A.I.C.S.: 484121
Steve Sharples *(Pres & CEO)*

WHITE ORGANIC AGRO LIMITED
312A Kailash Plaza Vallabh Baug Lane, Ghatkopar East, Mumbai, 400 077, Maharashtra, India
Tel.: (91) 2225011983 In
Web Site: https://www.whiteorganicagro.com
Year Founded: 1990
513713—(BOM)
Rev.: $194
Assets: $168
Liabilities: $76
Net Worth: $92
Earnings: $1
Emp.: 8
Fiscal Year-end: 03/31/21
Organic Agricultural Products Farming, Cultivation, Harvesting, Processing, Wholesale & Export
N.A.I.C.S.: 111219
Prashant Mahesh Rupani *(CFO)*

WHITE ORGANIC RETAIL LIMITED
B Unit No 2001 2002 20th Floor Lotus Corporate Park, Mumbai, 400063, Maharashtra, India
Tel.: (91) 2225011983
Web Site: https://whiteorganicretaillimited.com
Year Founded: 2011
542667—(BOM)
Rev.: $33,057,850
Assets: $35,258,714
Liabilities: $30,534,021
Net Worth: $4,724,693
Earnings: ($454,014)
Emp.: 2
Fiscal Year-end: 03/31/23
Organic Food Product Distr
N.A.I.C.S.: 424410
Darshak Rupani *(Mng Dir)*

WHITE ROCK CHRYSLER LTD
3050 King George Blvd, Surrey, V4P 1A2, BC, Canada
Tel.: (604) 531-9156
Web Site: http://www.haleysdodge.com
Year Founded: 1985
Rev.: $15,731,430
Emp.: 60
New Car Dealers
N.A.I.C.S.: 441110
Joseph Haley *(Pres)*

WHITE ROCK MINERALS LIMITED
12 Anderson Street West, Ballarat, 3350, VIC, Australia
Tel.: (61) 353314644
Web Site: http://www.whiterockminerals.com
WRM—(ASX)
Rev.: $59,573
Assets: $41,920,864
Liabilities: $6,871,694
Net Worth: $35,049,170
Earnings: ($7,434,381)
Fiscal Year-end: 06/30/21
Gold & Silver Mining Services
N.A.I.C.S.: 212220
Rohan Worland *(Mgr-Exploration)*

Subsidiaries:

White Rock Minerals (MTC) Pty. Ltd. (1)
24 Skipton St, Ballarat, 3350, VIC, Australia
Tel.: (61) 353314644
Web Site: http://www.whiterockminerals.com.au
Sales Range: $50-74.9 Million
Emp.: 4
Mineral Exploration Services
N.A.I.C.S.: 213115

WHITEBARK ENERGY LIMITED
Tel.: (61) 865556000 AU
Web Site: https://www.whitebarkenergy.com
WBE—(ASX)
Rev.: $3,598
Assets: $2,390,637
Liabilities: $4,261,475
Net Worth: ($1,870,838)
Earnings: ($4,162,050)
Fiscal Year-end: 06/30/24
Oil & Gas Exploration
N.A.I.C.S.: 213112
Mark Lindh *(Chm)*

WHITECAP MOTORS
804 Main Street SW, Slave Lake, T0G 2A0, AB, Canada
Tel.: (780) 849-2600
Web Site: http://www.whitecapmotors.ca
Year Founded: 1988
Rev.: $15,823,981
Emp.: 50
New & Used Car Dealers
N.A.I.C.S.: 441110
Neil Deas *(Mgr-Fixed Ops)*

WHITECAP RESOURCES INC.
3800 525 - 8th Avenue SW Eighth Avenue Place East Tower, Calgary, T2P 1G1, AB, Canada
Tel.: (403) 266-0767 AB
Web Site: https://www.wcap.ca
Year Founded: 2001
WCP—(TSX)
Rev.: $729,005,167
Assets: $2,645,209,415
Liabilities: $1,865,314,587
Net Worth: $779,894,828
Earnings: ($1,443,285,478)
Emp.: 278
Fiscal Year-end: 12/31/20
Oil Exploration Services
N.A.I.C.S.: 211120
Grant B. Fagerheim *(Pres & CEO)*

Subsidiaries:

TORC Oil & Gas Ltd. (1)
Suite 1800 Eighth Avenue Place 525 - 8th Avenue SW, Calgary, T2P 1G1, AB, Canada
Tel.: (403) 930-4120
Rev.: $444,843,960
Assets: $1,605,731,406
Liabilities: $517,274,691
Net Worth: $1,088,456,715
Earnings: ($28,413,361)
Emp.: 106
Fiscal Year-end: 12/31/2019
Natural Gas Exploration Service
N.A.I.C.S.: 211130

XTO Energy Canada ULC (1)
321 6 Ave SW Suite 400, Calgary, T2P 3H3, AB, Canada
Tel.: (587) 476-3513
Web Site: http://www.xtoenergy.com
Oil & Gas Operation Services
N.A.I.C.S.: 213112

WHITECROFT ESSENTIALS LTD.
Building 6 Vantage Point Business Village, Mitcheldean, GL15 4QG, Gloucestershire, United Kingdom
Tel.: (44) 01594 546464
Web Site: http://www.whitecroft.co.uk
Year Founded: 1910
Mfr of Clothing Fasteners & Stationery Sundries, Including Pins & Clips
N.A.I.C.S.: 339993
Laura Beddis *(Mng Dir)*

WHITEFIELD LIMITED
Level 19 68 Pitt St, Sydney, 2000, NSW, Australia
Tel.: (61) 282157900
Web Site: https://www.whitefield.com.au
Year Founded: 1923
WHF—(ASX)
Rev.: $16,093,763
Assets: $471,983,915
Liabilities: $69,645,087
Net Worth: $402,338,828
Earnings: $13,323,143
Fiscal Year-end: 03/31/24
Investment Services
N.A.I.C.S.: 523940
Angus J. Gluskie *(Chm, Chm, Mng Dir & Mng Dir)*

WHITEHAT INC.
5500 North Service Road Suite 101 Millennium Tower, Burlington, L7L 6W6, ON, Canada
Tel.: (905) 332-6677
Web Site: http://www.whitehatinc.com
Sales Range: $25-49.9 Million
Emp.: 10
Security Software Development Services
N.A.I.C.S.: 541511
Wayne McDowell *(COO)*

WHITEHAVEN COAL LIMITED
Level 28 259 George Street, Sydney, 2000, NSW, Australia

Whitehaven Coal Limited—(Continued)

Tel.: (61) 282221100 **AU**
Web Site:
https://www.whitehavencoal.com.au
Year Founded: 1999
WHITF—(OTCIQ)
Rev.: $3,954,318,967
Assets: $4,897,247,832
Liabilities: $1,467,290,865
Net Worth: $3,429,956,967
Earnings: $1,739,619,221
Emp.: 1,290
Fiscal Year-end: 06/30/23
Operation Of Coal Mines
N.A.I.C.S.: 213113
Michael J. Quillen *(Founder)*

Subsidiaries:

Namoi Mining Pty Ltd. (1)
Level 9 1 York St, Sydney, 2000, NSW, Australia
Tel.: (61) 730005690
Coal Mining Services
N.A.I.C.S.: 213113

Narrabri Coal Operations Pty Ltd. (1)
10 Kurrajong Creek Road, Narrabri, 2390, NSW, Australia
Tel.: (61) 267944755
Coal Mining Services
N.A.I.C.S.: 213113
Paul Flynn *(CEO & Mng Dir)*

Werris Creek Coal Pty Ltd. (1)
PO Box 125, Werris Creek, 2341, NSW, Australia
Tel.: (61) 267687071
Sales Range: $50-74.9 Million
Emp.: 86
Coal Mining Services
N.A.I.C.S.: 213113

WHITEHAWK LIMITED

Level 28 140 St Georges Terrace, Perth, 6000, WA, Australia
Tel.: (61) 863114636
Year Founded: 2015
WHK—(ASX)
Rev.: $1,800,081
Assets: $777,602
Liabilities: $1,583,593
Net Worth: ($805,991)
Earnings: ($2,844,279)
Fiscal Year-end: 12/31/23
Software Development Services
N.A.I.C.S.: 541511
Kevin Kye *(Sec)*

WHITEHELM CAPITAL PTY LTD

Level 1 39 Brisbane Ave, Canberra, 2600, Australia
Tel.: (61) 2 6273 1222
Web Site:
http://www.whitehelmcapital.com
Private Investment Firm
N.A.I.C.S.: 523999
Graham Matthews *(CEO)*

WHITEHORSE MOTORS

4178 4th Avenue, Whitehorse, Y1A 1J6, YT, Canada
Tel.: (867) 667-7866
Web Site:
http://www.whitehorsemotors.com
Rev.: $20,128,030
Emp.: 45
New & Used Car Dealers
N.A.I.C.S.: 441110
Tina Woodland *(Gen Mgr)*

WHITEMUD RESOURCES INC.

6713 Fairmount Drive SE, Calgary, T2H 0X6, AB, Canada
Tel.: (403) 281-2215 **AB**
Web Site:
https://www.whitemudresources.com
Year Founded: 2005
WMK—(TSXV)
Rev.: $458,079
Assets: $2,648,577
Liabilities: $3,135,008
Net Worth: ($486,431)
Earnings: ($1,669,369)
Emp.: 32
Fiscal Year-end: 12/31/21
Metakaolin Exploration & Production Services
N.A.I.C.S.: 212290
Stan Owerko *(CEO)*

WHITENI RCAJAL SOCIMI SA

Manuel Tovar 43, 28034, Madrid, Spain
Tel.: (34) 911594248
Web Site: https://www.whiteni.es
Year Founded: 2009
MLWRC—(EUR)
Rev.: $135,155
Assets: $10,118,394
Liabilities: $5,633,481
Net Worth: $4,484,913
Earnings: ($1,961,733)
Emp.: 3
Fiscal Year-end: 12/31/23
Real Estate Manangement Services
N.A.I.C.S.: 531390

WHITEOAK FORD LINCOLN SALES

3285 Mavis Rd, Mississauga, L5C1T7, ON, Canada
Tel.: (905) 270-8210
Web Site:
http://www.whiteoakfordlincoln.com
Year Founded: 1996
Rev.: $23,802,595
Emp.: 50
New & Used Car Dealers
N.A.I.C.S.: 441110
Ron Loveys *(Pres)*

WHITESMOKE, INC.

Kehilat Saloniki 11 2nd Floor, Tel Aviv, 6971069, Israel
Tel.: (972) 36376800 **DE**
Web Site:
http://www.whitesmoke.com
Year Founded: 2002
English Language Improvement Software
N.A.I.C.S.: 513210

WHITEWATER WEST INDUSTRIES LTD.

6700 McMillan Way, Richmond, V6W 1J7, BC, Canada
Tel.: (604) 273-1068
Web Site:
http://www.whitewaterwest.com
Year Founded: 1981
Rev.: $26,083,485
Emp.: 250
Aquatic Entertainment Construction Service
N.A.I.C.S.: 236220
Paul Chutter *(Pres)*

WHITTALLS WINE MERCHANTS 1 LTD.

European House, Darlaston Road, Walsall, WS2 9SQ, West Midlands, United Kingdom
Tel.: (44) 207 198 8740
Web Site: http://www.oddbins.com
Sales Range: $100-124.9 Million
Wine Retailer
N.A.I.C.S.: 445320
Simon Baile *(Mng Dir)*

WHITTAN STORAGE SYSTEMS LTD.

Whittan Group Halesfield 6, Telford, TF7 4LN, Shropshire, United Kingdom
Tel.: (44) 1952682251
Web Site: http://www.whittan-storage.com
Sales Range: $25-49.9 Million
Emp.: 1,000
Holding Company
N.A.I.C.S.: 551112
John Halliday *(Mng Dir-Link 51)*

Subsidiaries:

Link 51 (Storage Products) (1)
Link House, Halesfield 6, Telford, TF7 4LN, Shropshire, United Kingdom (100%)
Tel.: (44) 1384472500
Web Site: http://www.link51.co.uk
Emp.: 350
Mfr of Comml & Indus Pallet & Racking Sys
N.A.I.C.S.: 321920
Simon Jelley *(Mgr-HR)*

Link 51 Shelving and Storage (1)
Mill St, PO Box 16, Brierley Hill, Dudley, DY5 2TB, West Midlands, United Kingdom (99%)
Tel.: (44) 1384472500
Web Site: http://www.link51.co.uk
Sales Range: $25-49.9 Million
Emp.: 85
Mfr of Comml & Indus Pallet & Racking Sys
N.A.I.C.S.: 321920
Steve Pugh *(Gen Mgr)*

Link International (1)
Haldane House, Halesfield 1, Telford, TF7 4EH, Shropshire, United Kingdom (100%)
Tel.: (44) 1952683950
Web Site: http://www.linkint.co.uk
Sales Range: $25-49.9 Million
Emp.: 4
Mfr of Comml & Indus Shelving, Pallet & Racking Sys
N.A.I.C.S.: 337215
Chris O'Connor *(Gen Mgr)*

Link Lockers (1)
Link House Halesfield 6, Telford, TF7 4LN, Shropshire, United Kingdom (100%)
Tel.: (44) 1952682380
Web Site: http://www.linklockers.co.uk
Sales Range: $50-74.9 Million
Emp.: 110
Mfr of Sporting, Comml & Indus Locker Room Equipment & Storage Solutions
N.A.I.C.S.: 337215
John Holliday *(Mng Dir)*

Moresecure Ltd. (1)
Haldane House, Halesfield 1, Telford, TF7 4EH, Shropshire, United Kingdom (100%)
Tel.: (44) 1952 683900
Web Site: http://www.moresecure.co.uk
Sales Range: $10-24.9 Million
Emp.: 40
Mfr of Storage Products
N.A.I.C.S.: 493110
Chris O'Connor *(Mng Dir)*

N.C. Brown (Storage Equipment) Ltd. (1)
Hutchinson House Firwood Industrial Est, Bolton, BL2 3TR, Lankshire, United Kingdom (100%)
Tel.: (44) 204590200
Mfr of Lockers, Cabinets & Cupboards
N.A.I.C.S.: 337215

Permar Sistemas De Almacenaje S.A. (1)
Bidebarrieta 1A, Industrial Est, Iurreta, 48215, Vizcaya, Spain (100%)
Tel.: (34) 946210500
Web Site: http://www.permar.com
Sales Range: $25-49.9 Million
Emp.: 80
Mfr of Comml & Indus Storage & Racking Sys
N.A.I.C.S.: 337215
Carlos Juarros *(Mng Dir)*

Subsidiary (Domestic):

La Ferretera Vizcaina S.A (2)
Avenida Sue del Aeropuerto de Barajas No 28 Planta 5, 28042, Madrid, Spain (100%)
Tel.: (34) 916719145

Web Site: http://www.permar.com
Sales Range: $25-49.9 Million
Emp.: 10
Mfr of Commercial & Industrial Shelving & Racking Systems
N.A.I.C.S.: 337215

La Ferretera Vizcaina S.A (2)
Poeta Mas i Ros 88, 46022, Valencia, Spain
Tel.: (34) 963568390
Web Site: http://www.permar.com
Sales Range: $25-49.9 Million
Emp.: 3
Mfr of Comml & Indus Shelving & Racking Sys
N.A.I.C.S.: 337215
Alphonso Enchasusta *(Gen Mgr)*

Polypal (1)
Polypal House Monckton Road Industrial Estate, Wakefield, WF2 7AL, Westyorkshire, United Kingdom (100%)
Tel.: (44) 1924200015
Web Site: http://www.polypal.co.uk
Sales Range: $25-49.9 Million
Emp.: 53
Storage & Display Equipment Mfr
N.A.I.C.S.: 493110
Paul Davis *(Mng Dir)*

Polypal France SNC (1)
Zone Industrielle Des Radais, Rousseau, F 91350, Grigny, France (100%)
Tel.: (33) 169432626
Web Site: http://www.polypal.fr
Sales Range: $25-49.9 Million
Emp.: 27
Mfr of Comml & Indus Shelving & Racking Sys
N.A.I.C.S.: 337215
Batler Andrew *(Mgr)*

Polypal Germany GmbH (1)
Industriesplatz 426, Oberursel, 61440, Germany (100%)
Tel.: (49) 6172996690
Web Site: http://www.polypal.de
Sales Range: $1-9.9 Million
Emp.: 15
Mfr of Comml & Indus Shelving & Racking Sys
N.A.I.C.S.: 337215
Peter Van Wallenburg *(Mng Dir)*

Polypal Netherlands BV (1)
Bosstraat 107a, 6071 PX, Swalmen, Netherlands (100%)
Tel.: (31) 900 765 9725
Web Site: http://www.polypal.nl
Sales Range: $25-49.9 Million
Emp.: 14
Mfr of Comml & Indus Pallet & Racking Sys
N.A.I.C.S.: 321920

Polypal SA (1)
Avenue de Jupille 19, 4020, Herstal, Liege, Belgium (100%)
Tel.: (32) 42569100
Web Site: http://www.polypal.be
Sales Range: $25-49.9 Million
Emp.: 100
Mfr of Comml & Indus Shelving & Racking Sys
N.A.I.C.S.: 337215

WHITTARD OF CHELSEA PLC

Windrush House Windrush Park Road, Witney, 0X29 7DX, Oxon, United Kingdom
Tel.: (44) 1993 893 715 **UK**
Web Site: http://www.whittard.co.uk
Year Founded: 1886
Coffee & Tea Retail Shop Operator
N.A.I.C.S.: 445110
Sara Holton *(Mng Dir)*

WHITWORTH BROS LTD.

Victoria Mills, Wellingborough, NN8 2DT, Northants, United Kingdom
Tel.: (44) 1933 441000 **UK**
Web Site:
http://www.whitworthbros.ltd.uk
Year Founded: 1886
Sales Range: $50-74.9 Million
Emp.: 500

Flour Milling
N.A.I.C.S.: 311211
Roger Butler *(Mng Dir)*

WHOLE EASY INTERNET TECHNOLOGY CO., LTD.
Room 1701 Dong'an Building No 258 Chunxu Road Kunshan Development Zone, Kunshan, 215335, Jiangsu, China
Tel.: (86) 512 3686 0986
Web Site: http://www.wholeasy.com
Year Founded: 1993
002464—(SSE)
Sales Range: $50-74.9 Million
Business-to-Consumer Game Vertical E-Commerce Platforms Services
N.A.I.C.S.: 518210
Yuzhi Zheng *(Chm, CFO & Gen Mgr)*

Subsidiaries:

KEE Europe GmbH (1)
Richard-Klinger-Strasse 3 D, 65510, Idstein, Germany
Tel.: (49) 61269595030
Customer Management Services
N.A.I.C.S.: 541613

KEE TAIWAN CO., LTD. (1)
10F No 13 Sec 2 Beitou Rd Beitou Dist, Taipei, 11268, Taiwan
Tel.: (886) 277030999
Marketing Consulting Services
N.A.I.C.S.: 541613

Kee Interface Technology, Inc. (1)
580 W Central Ave Ste C, Brea, CA 92821
Tel.: (714) 695-9638
Customer Management Services
N.A.I.C.S.: 541613
Stanley Ho *(Project Mgr)*

WHOLE SHINE MEDICAL TECHNOLOGY CO., LTD.
No 98 Yingbin Road Chuanying District, Jilin, 100102, China
Tel.: (86) 1085660586
Web Site: http://www.royalholding.cn
Year Founded: 1986
002622—(SSE)
Rev.: $17,518,031
Assets: $205,384,133
Liabilities: $71,929,031
Net Worth: $133,455,103
Earnings: ($45,521,755)
Emp.: 536
Fiscal Year-end: 12/31/20
Magnet Switch Product Mfr
N.A.I.C.S.: 335313
Lu Lu *(Chm)*

WHOLESALE & RETAIL TRADE VENTURE JSC
481/3 Syinbay Ave, Almaty, 050030, Kazakhstan
Tel.: (7) 273560765
ORPT—(KAZ)
Rev.: $4,604,497
Assets: $22,631,049
Liabilities: $16,961,873
Net Worth: $5,669,176
Earnings: $784,240
Fiscal Year-end: 12/31/19
Consumer Goods Distr
N.A.I.C.S.: 423620
Zakarlyuk Anatoliy *(Pres)*

WHOLETECH SYSTEM HITECH LTD.
No 487 Gaofeng Rd, East District, Hsinchu, 300, Taiwan
Tel.: (886) 35228823
Web Site: https://www.wholetech.com
Year Founded: 1990
3402—(TPE)
Rev.: $149,380,108
Assets: $192,998,781
Liabilities: $137,225,026
Net Worth: $55,773,755
Earnings: $12,059,750
Fiscal Year-end: 12/31/22
Semiconductor Equipment Mfr
N.A.I.C.S.: 333242
Yung-Hung Wen *(Chm & CEO)*

WIA GOLD LIMITED
130 Hay Street, Subiaco, 6009, WA, Australia
Tel.: (61) 894208270   AU
Web Site: https://wiagold.com.au
WIA—(ASX)
Rev.: $50,444
Assets: $29,224,506
Liabilities: $781,553
Net Worth: $28,442,954
Earnings: ($2,414,297)
Fiscal Year-end: 06/30/24
Gold & Copper Mining Services
N.A.I.C.S.: 212220
Josef El-raghy *(Exec Chm)*

WIABLE CORP.
28 Beobwon-ro 11-gil, Songpa-Gu, Seoul, 05836, Korea (South)
Tel.: (82) 220773114
Web Site: http://www.krtnet.co.kr
Year Founded: 1996
065530—(KRS)
Rev.: $49,305,476
Assets: $96,257,578
Liabilities: $38,261,206
Net Worth: $57,996,372
Earnings: $1,867,822
Emp.: 152
Fiscal Year-end: 12/31/22
Wireless Communication Equipment Mfr
N.A.I.C.S.: 334220
Moon-Hwan Kim *(CEO)*

WICAKSANA OVERSEAS INTERNATIONAL TBK
Jl Ancol Barat VII Blok A5D No 2, Jakarta, 14430, Indonesia
Tel.: (62) 216927293
Web Site: https://www.wicaksana.co.id
Year Founded: 1973
WICO—(INDO)
Rev.: $92,415,851
Assets: $20,727,115
Liabilities: $20,356,854
Net Worth: $370,261
Earnings: ($7,209,858)
Emp.: 487
Fiscal Year-end: 12/31/23
Cigarette Product Distr
N.A.I.C.S.: 424940
Tay Lim Pin *(Chm)*

WICE LOGISTICS PUBLIC COMPANY LIMITED
88/8 Nonsee Road Chong-Nonsee, Yannawa, Bangkok, 10120, Thailand
Tel.: (66) 26816181
Web Site: http://www.wice.co.th
Year Founded: 1993
WICE—(THA)
Rev.: $111,852,033
Assets: $83,373,271
Liabilities: $28,094,996
Net Worth: $55,278,275
Earnings: $6,269,980
Emp.: 663
Fiscal Year-end: 12/31/23
Freight Forwarding & Logistics Consulting Services
N.A.I.C.S.: 488510
Ruth Banomyong *(Chm)*

Subsidiaries:

Euroasia Total Logistics Public Company Limited (1)
19 21 Motorway Road, Klong Songtonnoon Lat Krabang, Bangkok, 10520, Thailand
Tel.: (66) 21231727
Web Site: https://www.etl.co.th
Transportation Logistics Services
N.A.I.C.S.: 488510

Euroasia Transport Company Limited (1)
19 21 Motorway Road, Klongsongtonnoon Lat Krabang, Bangkok, 10520, Thailand
Tel.: (66) 232681689
Logistic Services
N.A.I.C.S.: 541614

Guangzhou WICE Logistics Co., Ltd. (1)
Unit A1-A2 28/F Tower B Huahai Building No 232, Jiangnan Da Dao Zhong Road Haizhu District, Guangzhou, 510245, China
Tel.: (86) 2089626267
Freight Transportation Services
N.A.I.C.S.: 488510
Andy Wong *(Mng Dir)*

WICE Logistics (Singapore) Pte. Ltd. (1)
1 Tai Seng Ave 04-05 Tai Seng Exchange Tower A, Box 698, Changi Airfreight Centre, Singapore, 536464, Singapore
Tel.: (65) 65424911
Web Site: https://www.wice.com.sg
Freight Transportation Services
N.A.I.C.S.: 488510

WICKAISSLA
6 Donnor Pl Mount Wellington, PO Box 92081, Auckland, 1020, New Zealand
Tel.: (64) 95711900
Web Site: http://www.wickaissla.co.nz
Sales Range: $25-49.9 Million
Emp.: 350
Commercial Printing of Business Forms & Related Products
N.A.I.C.S.: 323111

WICKEDER WESTFALENSTAHL GMBH
Hauptstrasse 6, Wickede, 58739, Germany
Tel.: (49) 237791701
Web Site: http://www.wickeder.de
Year Founded: 1913
Sales Range: $10-24.9 Million
Emp.: 500
Rolled Steel & Clad Metals Production
N.A.I.C.S.: 331221
Juergen Platt *(CEO)*

Subsidiaries:

Auerhammer Metallwerk GmbH (1)
Hammerplatz 1, 08280, Aue, Germany
Tel.: (49) 3771 272 0
Web Site: http://www.auerhammer.com
Die Casting & Metal Product Mfr
N.A.I.C.S.: 333514
Detlef Becker *(Gen Mgr)*

Engineered Materials Solutions Inc. (1)
39 Perry Ave, Attleboro, MA 02703
Tel.: (508) 342-2100
Web Site: http://www.emsclad.com
Sales Range: $50-74.9 Million
Emp.: 390
Clad Metal Products Mfr
N.A.I.C.S.: 332999

Subsidiary (Domestic):

Engineered Materials Solutions (2)
600 Vly Rd, Hamburg, PA 19526-8387
Tel.: (610) 562-3841
Web Site: http://www.emsclad.com
Clad Metal Products Mfr
N.A.I.C.S.: 332999

MICROMETAL GmbH (1)
Renkenrunsstrasse 24, Mullheim, 79379, Germany
Tel.: (49) 7631936880
Web Site: http://www.micrometal.de
Emp.: 60
Precision Metal Components Mfr
N.A.I.C.S.: 332999
Marzellinus Zipfel *(Mng Dir)*

WICKES GROUP PLC
Vision House 19 Colonial Way, Watford, WD24 4JL, United Kingdom   UK
Web Site: https://www.wickesplc.co.uk
Year Founded: 1854
WIX—(LSE)
Rev.: $2,083,964,428
Assets: $1,570,746,268
Liabilities: $1,352,424,892
Net Worth: $218,321,376
Earnings: $79,833,936
Emp.: 6,484
Fiscal Year-end: 01/31/22
Household Appliances, Electric Housewares & Consumer Electronics Merchant Wholesalers
N.A.I.C.S.: 423620
Christopher Rogers *(Chm)*

WICKLIFFE LTD.
6 Donnor Pl Mount Wellington, Auckland, 1060, New Zealand
Tel.: (64) 34775033
Web Site: http://www.wickliffe.co.nz
Year Founded: 1948
Sales Range: $50-74.9 Million
Emp.: 400
Printing Services
N.A.I.C.S.: 513199
Steve D'Souza *(Co-Owner)*

Subsidiaries:

Stocklink Distribution Ltd. (1)
7 Vestey Dr, Mt Wellington, Auckland, New Zealand
Tel.: (64) 92590820
Web Site: http://www.stocklink.co.nz
Sales Range: $25-49.9 Million
Emp.: 15
Courier Service
N.A.I.C.S.: 492110
Chris Loomans *(Mgr)*

WIDAD BUSINESS GROUP SDN. BHD.
Level 11 Widad Semantan, 3 Jalan Semantan Damansara Heights, 50490, Kuala Lumpur, Malaysia
Tel.: (60) 3 2094 0009   MY
Web Site: http://www.widadgroup.com
Year Founded: 2002
Diversified Commercial Services
N.A.I.C.S.: 561499
Feizal Feizal *(Chm)*

Subsidiaries:

Dataprep Holdings Berhad (1)
Suite 5 02 Level 5 Wisma Academy 4A Jalan 19/1, 46300, Petaling Jaya, Selangor Darul Ehsan, Malaysia
Tel.: (60) 378431600
Web Site: https://www.dp.com.my
Rev.: $5,952,804
Assets: $18,718,730
Liabilities: $4,552,381
Net Worth: $14,166,349
Earnings: ($3,922,751)
Emp.: 369
Fiscal Year-end: 12/31/2022
Holding Company; IT Services
N.A.I.C.S.: 551112
Mun Mooi Geng *(CFO & Co-Sec)*

Widad Group Berhad (1)
Level 11 Widad Semantan No 3 Jalan Semantan, Damansara Heights, 50490, Kuala Lumpur, Malaysia   (93.4%)
Tel.: (60) 320940009
Web Site: https://www.widadgroup.com
Rev.: $18,578,176
Assets: $183,206,246
Liabilities: $107,456,749
Net Worth: $75,749,498
Earnings: $14,982,268
Fiscal Year-end: 12/31/2021
Investment Holding Company; Industrial Labels, Nameplates & Laser/Die-Cut Products
N.A.I.C.S.: 551112

WIDAM FOOD COMPANY Q.S.C.

Widam Food Company Q.S.C.—(Continued)

WIDAM FOOD COMPANY Q.S.C.
Al Sadd Suhaim Bin Hamad Street Al Shomoukh Towers Fifth Floor, 22240, Doha, Qatar
Tel.: (974) 44243333
Web Site: https://www.widam.com.qa
Year Founded: 2003
WDAM—(QE)
Rev.: $145,011,994
Assets: $140,921,829
Liabilities: $99,053,339
Net Worth: $41,868,490
Earnings: ($9,206,025)
Emp.: 97
Fiscal Year-end: 12/31/23
Meat & Livestock Products Distr
N.A.I.C.S.: 424470
Mohammed Badr Al Sada *(Chm)*

WIDE LEISURE CO., LTD.
2413-1 Ogura, Fukuoka, 838-0141, Japan
Tel.: (81) 942 72 75 34   JP
Web Site:
  http://www.wideleisure.co.jp
Year Founded: 1970
Emp.: 219
Amusement & Gaming
N.A.I.C.S.: 713990
Yasuo Kiku Ike *(CEO)*

WIDE OPEN AGRICULTURE LIMITED
5 Marchesi Street, Kewdale, 6105, WA, Australia
Tel.: (61) 861617412   AU
Web Site:
  https://www.wideopenculture.com
WOA—(ASX)
Rev.: $2,149,086
Assets: $7,201,447
Liabilities: $2,358,301
Net Worth: $4,843,146
Earnings: ($6,362,542)
Fiscal Year-end: 06/30/24
Food & Agriculture Product Mfr & Distr
N.A.I.C.S.: 115112
Anthony Maslin *(Founder & Chm)*

WIDECH S.P.A.
Via Santa Maria Fulcorina 2, 20123, Milan, Italy
Tel.: (39) 03497130611
Web Site: https://www.widech.com
MLSMP—(EUR)
Sales Range: Less than $1 Million
Vehicle Detection Equipment Mfr
N.A.I.C.S.: 334519
Andrea Angelino *(Co-CEO)*

WIDEFORM PTY. LTD.
245-247 Berkeley Rd, PO Box 1183, Unanderra, 2526, NSW, Australia
Tel.: (61) 242240300
Web Site:
  http://www.wideform.com.au
Building Construction Services
N.A.I.C.S.: 236220
Sash Krstevski *(Mng Dir)*

WIDER PLANET INC.
28 Nonhyeon-ro 98-gil, Gangnam-Gu, Seoul, Korea (South)
Tel.: (82) 220383266
Web Site:
  https://www.widerplanet.com
Year Founded: 2010
321820—(KRS)
Rev.: $32,587,273
Assets: $57,124,301
Liabilities: $33,560,222
Net Worth: $23,564,079
Earnings: ($7,315,194)
Emp.: 87
Fiscal Year-end: 12/31/21
Software Development Services
N.A.I.C.S.: 541511
Edward Kyo-Sik Koo *(Co-Founder & CEO)*

WIDGIE NICKEL LIMITED
Level 4 220 St Georges Tce, Perth, 6000, WA, Australia
Tel.: (61) 863817250   AU
Web Site: https://winmetals.com.au
Year Founded: 2007
WIN—(ASX)
Rev.: $141,845
Assets: $30,617,254
Liabilities: $2,642,259
Net Worth: $27,974,995
Earnings: ($1,340,848)
Fiscal Year-end: 06/30/23
Mineral Exploration Services
N.A.I.C.S.: 212390
Andrew Parker *(Chm)*

WIDOS WILHELM DOMMER SOHNE GMBH
Einsteinstrasse 5, 71254, Ditzingen, Germany
Tel.: (49) 715299390
Web Site: http://www.widos.de
Year Founded: 1946
Emp.: 105
Industrial Equipment Mfr
N.A.I.C.S.: 333248
Juergen Dommer *(Mng Dir)*

Subsidiaries:

WIDOS AUS NZ Pty. Ltd.   (1)
Unit 4/1 Sawmill Circuit, Hume, 2620, ACT, Australia
Tel.: (61) 417094367
Industrial Machinery Distr
N.A.I.C.S.: 423830
Bernd Emmert *(Mng Dir)*

WIDOS Benelux B.V.   (1)
Houven van Oordtstraat 12, 8191 AV, Wapenveld, Netherlands
Tel.: (31) 384470747
Web Site: http://www.widos.nl
Industrial Machinery Distr
N.A.I.C.S.: 423830

WIDOS LLC   (1)
1375 Highlands Ridge Road, Smyrna, GA 30082
Tel.: (678) 766-1250
Web Site: http://www.widoswelding.com
Industrial Machinery Distr
N.A.I.C.S.: 423830
Jim Leary *(VP-Sls & Ops)*

WIDOS Technology (Asia Pacific) Pte. Ltd.   (1)
No 6 Tagore Drive 03-13 Tagore Building, Singapore, 787623, Singapore
Tel.: (65) 64582722
Web Site: http://www.widostechnology.com
Industrial Machinery Distr
N.A.I.C.S.: 423830

WIEGAND-GLAS GMBH
Otto-Wiegand-Strasse 9, 96361, Steinbach am Wald, Germany
Tel.: (49) 9263 80 0
Web Site: http://www.wiegand-glas.de
Sales Range: $250-299.9 Million
Emp.: 1,220
Glass Container Mfr
N.A.I.C.S.: 327213
Nikolaus Wiegand *(Mng Dir)*

Subsidiaries:

Thuringer Behalterglas GmbH   (1)
Suhler Str 60, 98553, Schleusingen, Germany
Tel.: (49) 36841270
Web Site: http://www.thueringer-behaelterglas.de
Glass Products Mfr
N.A.I.C.S.: 327213
Jens Lutzke *(Mgr-Food & Wine)*

WIELAND HOLDING GMBH
Brennerstrasse 10 14, D 96052, Bamberg, Germany
Tel.: (49) 95193240
Web Site: http://www.wieland-electric.com
Sales Range: $350-399.9 Million
Emp.: 1,200
Mfr of Electrical Components
N.A.I.C.S.: 551112

Subsidiaries:

STOCKO Contact GmbH & Co. KG   (1)
Simonshofchen 31, 42327, Wuppertal, Germany
Tel.: (49) 202 97 33 0
Web Site: http://www.stocko-contact.com
Emp.: 550
Electric Equipment Mfr
N.A.I.C.S.: 335999

Subsidiary (Non-US):

STOCKO CONTACT Eurl   (2)
7 Route d Eichhoffen, Andlau, Barr, 67145, France
Tel.: (33) 3 88585858
Web Site: http://www.stocko.com
Emp.: 200
Electric Equipment Mfr
N.A.I.C.S.: 335999
Zaegel Jean-Philippe *(Mng Dir)*

Plant (Domestic):

STOCKO Contact GmbH & Co. KG - Hellenthal Factory   (2)
Oleftalstr 26, 53940, Hellenthal, Germany
Tel.: (49) 2482 84 0
Web Site: http://www.stocko-contact.com
Electric Equipment Mfr
N.A.I.C.S.: 335999

Subsidiary (Non-US):

STOCKO do Brasil Ltda.   (2)
Eng Jorge Vukotich Rua Americo Brazilse 1490-CJ 123, 04715-002, Sao Paulo, Brazil
Tel.: (55) 11 5524 2041
Web Site: http://www.stockdobrasil.com.br
Electric Equipment Mfr
N.A.I.C.S.: 335999

Wieland Electric GmbH   (1)
Brennerstrasse 10-14, PO Box 2043, Bamberg, 96052, Germany   (100%)
Tel.: (49) 95193240
Web Site: http://www.wieland-electric.com
Sales Range: $200-249.9 Million
Emp.: 800
Sale & Marketing of Conductive Wiring Components
N.A.I.C.S.: 335999
Oliver Eitrich *(Gen Mgr)*

Subsidiary (Non-US):

Wieland Electric A/S   (2)
Valloraekken 26, 4600, Koge, Denmark
Tel.: (45) 70 26 66 35
Web Site: http://www.wieland-electric.dk
Emp.: 10
Electric Equipment Mfr
N.A.I.C.S.: 335999

Wieland Electric AG   (2)
Harzachstrasse 2b, 8404, Winterthur, Switzerland
Tel.: (41) 52 2352100
Electric Equipment Mfr
N.A.I.C.S.: 335999

Wieland Electric Co., Ltd.   (2)
Three One Building 1F 3-20-5 Shinyokohama, Kouhoku-ku, Yokohama, 222-0033, Japan
Tel.: (81) 45 473 5085
Electric Equipment Mfr
N.A.I.C.S.: 335999

Wieland Electric S.L.   (2)
Maria Auxiliadora 2 bajos, 08017, Barcelona, Spain
Tel.: (34) 93 252 38 20

INTERNATIONAL PUBLIC

Web Site: http://www.wieland-electric.com
Emp.: 13
Electric Equipment Mfr
N.A.I.C.S.: 335999

Wieland Electric S.r.l.   (2)
Via Edison 209, 20019, Settimo Milanese, Italy
Tel.: (39) 02 48916357
Web Site: http://www.wieland-electric.com
Emp.: 13
Electric Equipment Mfr
N.A.I.C.S.: 335999

Wieland Electric SARL   (2)
Le Cerame-Hall 6 47 avenue des Genottes, CS 48313, 95803, Cergy-Pontoise, Cedex, France
Tel.: (33) 1 30 32 07 07
Web Site: http://www.wieland-electric.com
Electric Equipment Mfr
N.A.I.C.S.: 335999

Wieland Electric Sp. z.o.o.   (2)
ul Sw Antoniego 8, 62-080, Swadzim, Poland
Tel.: (48) 61 22 25 400
Emp.: 20
Electric Equipment Mfr
N.A.I.C.S.: 335999

WIELAND-WERKE AG
Graf-Arco-Strasse 36, 89079, Ulm, Germany
Tel.: (49) 731 944 0   De
Web Site: http://www.wieland.de
Year Founded: 1820
Emp.: 7,000
Copper & Copper Alloy Products Mfr
N.A.I.C.S.: 331420
Werner T. Traa *(CMO & Member-Exec Bd)*

Subsidiaries:

ABM Kupral Kft.   (1)
Torokko utca 5-7, 1037, Budapest, Hungary
Tel.: (36) 1 436 7150
Web Site: http://www.abmkupral.hu
Sales Range: $25-49.9 Million
Emp.: 20
Copper & Copper Alloy Products Whslr
N.A.I.C.S.: 423510

B. Mason & Sons Ltd.   (1)
Wharf Street, Aston, Birmingham, B6 5SA, United Kingdom
Tel.: (44) 121 327 0181
Web Site: http://www.bmason.co.uk
Sales Range: $50-74.9 Million
Emp.: 150
Copper Alloy Products Mfr
N.A.I.C.S.: 331420
Rolf Herold *(Mng Dir)*

CIMSA Cintas Metalicas, S.A.   (1)
Poligono Industrial Can Bernades-Subira, Bergueda s / n comer C / Maresme, 08130, Barcelona, Spain
Tel.: (34) 935446575
Web Site: http://www.cimsaww.com
Sales Range: $25-49.9 Million
Emp.: 28
Copper & Copper Alloy Product Whslr
N.A.I.C.S.: 423510
Valerio Bauer *(Mng Dir)*

Global Brass and Copper Holdings, Inc.   (1)
475 N Martingale Rd Ste 1050, Schaumburg, IL 60173
Tel.: (847) 240-4700
Web Site: http://www.gbcholdings.com
Rev.: $1,765,400,000
Assets: $691,000,000
Liabilities: $503,200,000
Net Worth: $187,800,000
Earnings: $58,200,000
Emp.: 1,882
Fiscal Year-end: 12/31/2018
Holding Company; Copper & Brass Products Mfr
N.A.I.C.S.: 551112
John Wasz *(Pres & CEO)*

Subsidiary (Domestic):

Global Brass & Copper, Inc.   (2)

AND PRIVATE COMPANIES

WIELAND-WERKE AG

475 N Martingale Rd Ste 1050, Schaumburg, IL 60173
Tel.: (847) 240-4700
Web Site: http://www.gbcmetals.com
Copper Mfr & Distr
N.A.I.C.S.: 331529

Subsidiary (Domestic):

Bryan Metals, LLC (3)
1103 S Main St, Bryan, OH 43506-2440
Tel.: (419) 636-4571
Web Site: http://www.olinbrass.com
Sales Range: $50-74.9 Million
Emp.: 50
Copper Alloys Retailer & Mfr
N.A.I.C.S.: 331420

Chase Brass & Copper Company, Inc. (3)
14212 County Rd M50, Montpelier, OH 43543
Tel.: (419) 485-3193
Web Site: http://www.chasebrass.com
Rev.: $231,892,000
Emp.: 300
Engineered Materials Mfr
N.A.I.C.S.: 331420

Subsidiary (Non-US):

Olin Brass International Group (3)
2 Bukit Merah Central, #18-02, Singapore, 159835, Singapore
Tel.: (65) 6 631 9922
Web Site: http://www.olinbrass.com
Sales Range: $25-49.9 Million
Emp.: 8
Brass Products Supplier
N.A.I.C.S.: 331420

Olin Mexico S.A. de C.V. (3)
Avenida La Griega No 117 Parque Industrial Queretaro, Queretaro, 76620, Mexico
Tel.: (52) 4422294000
Web Site: http://www.olinbrass.com
Sales Range: $25-49.9 Million
Emp.: 20
Metal Supplier
N.A.I.C.S.: 331410
Joe Woo *(Dir-Mexico)*

Subsidiary (Domestic):

Wieland Metal Services LLC (3)
301 Metro Ctr Blvd Ste 204, Warwick, RI 02886
Tel.: (401) 736-2600
Web Site: http://www.wieland-metalservices.com
Metals & Related Materials & Equipment Purchaser, Mfr & Distr
N.A.I.C.S.: 423510
Greg Keown *(Pres)*

Subsidiary (Domestic):

A.J. Oster Caribe Inc. (4)
Centro Industrial Rio Canas Lote 29, Caguas, PR 00725
Tel.: (787) 747-7575
Web Site: http://www.olinbrass.com
Emp.: 21
Metals & Related Materials & Equipment Purchaser, Mfr & Distr
N.A.I.C.S.: 423510
Alfred Martinez *(Gen Mgr)*

A.J. Oster Foils, Inc. (4)
2081 McCrea St, Alliance, OH 44601-2704
Tel.: (330) 823-1700
Web Site: http://www.ajoster.com
Emp.: 60
Aluminium Foils & Brass Sheets Mfr
N.A.I.C.S.: 423510
Brian Vonderhaar *(VP-Midwest)*

Subsidiary (Non-US):

A.J. Oster Mexico S.A. de CV (4)
Avenida la Griega 117 Parque Industrial Queretaro, Santa Rosa Jauregui, 76220, Queretaro, Mexico
Tel.: (52) 442294000
Web Site: http://www.ajoster.com
Specialty Metal Products Mfr
N.A.I.C.S.: 331492
Georgina D. Sandoval *(Gen Mgr)*

Subsidiary (Domestic):

A.J. Oster West (4)
22833 La Palma Ave, Yorba Linda, CA 92887-4767
Tel.: (714) 692-1000
Web Site: http://www.ajoster.com
Emp.: 38
Rolled & Slit Metal Products
N.A.I.C.S.: 331420
Donna Van Diggelen *(Mgr-Ops)*

Branch (Domestic):

Wieland Metal Services LLC (4)
150 Lackawanna Ave, Parsippany, NJ 07054
Metal Product Whslr
N.A.I.C.S.: 423510

Unit (Domestic):

Wieland Metal Services LLC (4)
180 Alexandra Way, Carol Stream, IL 60188
Tel.: (630) 260-1040
Metal Product Whslr
N.A.I.C.S.: 423510

Branch (Domestic):

Wieland Metal Services LLC (4)
3735 Zip Industrial Blvd SE, Atlanta, GA 30354
Metal Product Whslr
N.A.I.C.S.: 423510

Wieland Metal Services LLC (4)
7100 Business Park Dr Ste 100, Houston, TX 77041
Metal Product Whslr
N.A.I.C.S.: 423510

Manner Metal A/S (1)
Hammerholmen 18, 2650, Hvidovre, Denmark
Tel.: (45) 36 771401
Web Site: http://www.mannermetal.dk
Sales Range: $50-74.9 Million
Emp.: 9
Copper & Copper Alloy Products Distr
N.A.I.C.S.: 423510

Marjan Inc. (1)
44 Railroad Hill St, Waterbury, CT 06708
Tel.: (203) 573-1742
Web Site: http://www.marjaninc.com
Rev.: $1,800,000
Emp.: 19
Metal Coating, Engraving, except Jewelry & Silverware & Allied Services to Manufacturers
N.A.I.C.S.: 332812
George Strobel *(Treas)*

Metalix Metallhandel AG (1)
Gurzelenstrasse 5, 4512, Bellach, Switzerland (100%)
Tel.: (41) 32 617 39 39
Web Site: http://www.almeta-metallhandel.ch
Emp.: 23
Steel & Metal Products Distr
N.A.I.C.S.: 423510
Ivan Di Stefano *(Mng Dir)*

Metallwerk Mollersdorf Handelsgesellschaft m.b.H. (1)
Lutzowgasse 12-14, 1140, Vienna, Austria
Tel.: (43) 1 910 86 0
Web Site: http://www.mmhg.at
Sales Range: $25-49.9 Million
Emp.: 20
Copper & Copper Alloy Products Whslr
N.A.I.C.S.: 423510
Johannes Pfeil *(Mng Dir)*

Nemco Metals International Ltd. (1)
Pennard Close, Brackmills, Northampton, NN4 7BE, United Kingdom
Tel.: (44) 1604 766 181
Web Site: http://www.nemcometals.com
Sales Range: $25-49.9 Million
Emp.: 37
Copper & Copper Alloy Products Whslr
N.A.I.C.S.: 423510
Fred Weyer *(Mng Dir)*

Randall Bearings, Inc. (1)
1046 Greenlawn Ave, Lima, OH 45802
Tel.: (419) 223-1075
Web Site: http://www.randallbearings.com
Rev.: $6,666,666
Emp.: 65

Mechanical Power Transmission Equipment Mfr
N.A.I.C.S.: 333613
Tim Toland *(Mgr-Plant)*

The Miller Company (1)
275 Pratt St, Meriden, CT 06450-8600
Tel.: (203) 235-4474
Web Site: http://www2.diehl.com
Strip & Coil Brass Phosphor Bronze Distr
N.A.I.C.S.: 331420

Wieland (Schweiz) AG (1)
Gewerbestrasse 5, 6330, Cham, Switzerland
Tel.: (41) 41 780 4655
Web Site: http://www.wieland.com
Copper & Copper Alloy Products Whslr
N.A.I.C.S.: 423510

Wieland (South Africa) (Pty.) Ltd. (1)
56 Plantation Road, PO Box 1048, Eastleigh Edenvale, Bedfordview, 2008, South Africa
Tel.: (27) 11 609 8325
Web Site: http://www.wielandsa.com
Sales Range: $25-49.9 Million
Emp.: 31
Copper & Copper Alloy Products Production & Sales
N.A.I.C.S.: 423510
Johnny van der Merwe *(Mng Dir)*

Wieland Anlagentechnik GmbH (1)
Turmstrasse 61, 89231, Neu-Ulm, Germany
Tel.: (49) 7319441800
Web Site: http://www.wieland-anlagentechnik.de
Industrial Machinery Mfr
N.A.I.C.S.: 333248
Daniel Krettenauer *(Mng Dir)*

Wieland Austria Ges.m.b.H. (1)
Fabrikstrasse 4, Amstetten, 3300, Austria
Tel.: (43) 74726060
Emp.: 800
Copper Material Mfr
N.A.I.C.S.: 331420

Wieland Benelux s.a.-n.v. (1)
Rue Forestiere 22 B6 Bosstraat, 1050, Brussels, Belgium
Tel.: (32) 26408040
Industrial Supplies Whslr
N.A.I.C.S.: 423840

Wieland Caro GmbH (1)
Wilhelm-Maisel-Strasse 20a, 90530, Wendelstein, Germany
Tel.: (49) 912940060
Web Site: http://www.wieland-caro.com
Emp.: 20
Metal Product Whslr
N.A.I.C.S.: 423510
Florian Hudelmaier *(Mng Dir)*

Wieland Cimsa, S.A. (1)
C/Bergueda esq Maresme Poligono Can Bernades-Subira, 08130, Santa Perpetua de Mogoda, Barcelona, Spain
Tel.: (34) 935446570
Web Site: http://www.wieland-cimsa.com
Emp.: 21
Copper Material Mfr
N.A.I.C.S.: 331420
Valerio Bauer *(Mng Dir)*

Wieland Delari Caro Srl (1)
Via Lodi 29 E/F, 24047, Treviglio, BG, Italy
Tel.: (39) 03633191
Web Site: http://www.wieland-delari.com
Emp.: 12
Metal Product Whslr
N.A.I.C.S.: 423510
Claudio Bergamaschi *(CEO)*

Wieland Diversified, LLC (1)
49 Main St, Monson, MA 01057
Tel.: (413) 267-5101
Rev.: $6,813,600
Emp.: 22
Metal Product Whslr
N.A.I.C.S.: 423510

Wieland Duro GmbH (1)
Albert-Einstein-Str 1, 70806, Kornwestheim, Germany
Tel.: (49) 715482550
Web Site: http://www.wieland-duro.com
Emp.: 40
Metal Product Whslr

N.A.I.C.S.: 423510
Christoph Altrichter *(Mng Dir)*

Wieland Espana, S.A. (1)
c/ Bergueda esq Maresme Poligono Can Bernades-Subira, Sta Perpetua de Mogoda, 08130, Barcelona, Spain
Tel.: (34) 93 544 6650
Web Site: http://www.wieland.com
Sales Range: $50-74.9 Million
Emp.: 4
Copper & Copper Alloy Products Whslr
N.A.I.C.S.: 423510
Valerio Bauer *(Mng Dir)*

Wieland Eucaro GmbH (1)
Senator-Helmken-Str 3, 28197, Bremen, Germany
Tel.: (49) 421520250
Web Site: http://www.wieland-eucaro.de
Emp.: 80
Copper Material Mfr
N.A.I.C.S.: 331420
Ronald Zurkuhle *(Mng Dir)*

Wieland Fudickar GmbH (1)
Verbandsstrasse 99, 58093, Hagen, Germany
Tel.: (49) 233496030
Web Site: http://www.wieland-fudickar.de
Emp.: 4
Metal Product Whslr
N.A.I.C.S.: 423510
Henning Winterstein *(Gen Mgr)*

Wieland Hungaria Kft. (1)
Torokko utca 5-7, 1037, Budapest, Hungary
Tel.: (36) 1 427 1320
Web Site: http://www.wieland.hu
Copper & Copper Alloy Products Whslr
N.A.I.C.S.: 423510
Gyorgy Csornay *(Mng Dir)*

Wieland Italia S.r.l. (1)
Via Giuseppe Frua 22, 20146, Milan, Italy
Tel.: (39) 0248 14961
Web Site: http://www.wieland.com
Sales Range: $50-74.9 Million
Emp.: 10
Copper & Copper Alloy Products Whslr
N.A.I.C.S.: 423510
Claudio Bergamaschi *(Mng Dir)*

Wieland Japan Co., Ltd. (1)
Daiwa Jisho Bldg 10th Floor 74-1 Yamashita-cho, Naka-ku, Yokohama, 231 0023, Kanagawa, Japan
Tel.: (81) 45 222 6950
Web Site: http://www.wieland.com
Sales Range: $50-74.9 Million
Emp.: 2
Copper & Copper Alloy Products Whslr
N.A.I.C.S.: 423510
Hiroki Takahashi *(Mng Dir)*

Wieland Metals India Pvt. Ltd. (1)
Plot No 18A&B Bommasandra Industrial Area, Hebbagodi Village Anekal Taluk, Bengaluru, 562158, India
Tel.: (91) 80 49 123 500
Web Site: http://www.wieland.com
Copper & Copper Alloy Products Mfr & Whslr
N.A.I.C.S.: 331420
Nagaraj Hegde *(Plant Mgr)*

Wieland Metals Rus OOO (1)
Vereyskaya Ulitsa 17 Room 34 indoor 1 1st, 121357, Moscow, Russia
Tel.: (7) 4955459075
Copper Product Mfr
N.A.I.C.S.: 331420

Wieland Metals Shanghai Ltd. (1)
399 Fu Te Zhong Road, Wai Gao Qiao Free Trade Zone, Shanghai, 200131, China
Tel.: (86) 21 5153 6800
Web Site: http://www.wieland.com.cn
Sales Range: $50-74.9 Million
Emp.: 90
Copper & Copper Alloy Products Whslr
N.A.I.C.S.: 423510
Annie Gao *(Gen Mgr)*

Wieland Metals Shenzhen Limited (1)
1st & 2nd Floor Building B HaoShengLong Industrial Park Dalang, Community, Dalang Street BaoAn District, Shenzhen, 518109, China

WIELAND-WERKE AG

Wieland-Werke AG—(Continued)
Tel.: (86) 755 6186 4928
Web Site: http://www.wieland.com.cn
Copper & Copper Alloy Products Whslr
N.A.I.C.S.: 423510
Dave Ng (Gen Mgr)

Wieland Metals Singapore (Pte.) Ltd. (1)
3 Pioneer Walk Wieland Building, Singapore, 627750, Singapore
Tel.: (65) 6861 9788
Web Site: http://www.wieland.com.sg
Sales Range: $50-74.9 Million
Emp.: 160
Copper & Copper Alloy Products Mfr & Whslr
N.A.I.C.S.: 331420

Wieland Metals, Inc. (1)
567 Northgate Pkwy, Wheeling, IL 60090-2682
Tel.: (847) 537-3990
Web Site: http://www.wielandmetals.com
Sales Range: $25-49.9 Million
Emp.: 120
Copper & Copper Alloy Products Mfr & Whslr
N.A.I.C.S.: 331420
Markus Schuler (Exec VP)

Subsidiary (Domestic):

Wieland Copper Products LLC (2)
3990 US 311 Hwy N, Pine Hall, NC 27042
Tel.: (336) 445-4500
Web Site: http://www.wielandcopper.com
Copper Tube Mfr
N.A.I.C.S.: 331420
Tom Baker (CEO)

Wieland Mexico SA (1)
Avenida Antea No 1088 Level 3, Colonia Jurica, 76100, Queretaro, Mexico
Tel.: (52) 4423885353
Copper Material Mfr
N.A.I.C.S.: 331420

Wieland Nemco Ltd. (1)
5 Pennard Close, Brackmills, Northampton, NN4 7BE, United Kingdom
Tel.: (44) 1604766181
Web Site: http://www.wieland-nemco.com
Emp.: 32
Copper Material Mfr
N.A.I.C.S.: 331420
David Handley (Mng Dir)

Wieland Polska Sp. z o. o. (1)
ul Jana Pawla II 80 ap C-14, 00 175, Warsaw, Poland
Tel.: (48) 22 63731 05
Web Site: http://www.wieland.pl
Sales Range: $50-74.9 Million
Emp.: 5
Copper & Copper Alloy Products Whslr
N.A.I.C.S.: 423510
Grzegorz Kwiatkowski (Mng Dir)

Wieland Portugal, Lda. (1)
Edificio Tower Plaza, Rotunda Eng Edgar Cardoso 23 Piso 5 F, 4400-676, Vila Nova de Gaia, Portugal
Tel.: (351) 227 539 268
Copper & Copper Alloy Products Whslr
N.A.I.C.S.: 423510
Samuel Figueiredo (Mng Dir)

Wieland Prometa GmbH (1)
Am Schuttenhof 5, 40472, Dusseldorf, Germany
Tel.: (49) 21196540
Web Site: http://www.wieland-prometa.de
Metal Product Whslr
N.A.I.C.S.: 423510
Henning Winterstein (Gen Mgr)

Wieland Recycling GmbH (1)
Daimlerstrasse 20, 89079, Ulm, Germany
Tel.: (49) 731946230
Web Site: http://www.wieland-recycling.com
Emp.: 48
Copper Material Mfr
N.A.I.C.S.: 331420
Thomas Weig (Mng Dir)

Wieland Roessler GmbH (1)
Josefsthaler Str 4, 87600, Kaufbeuren, Germany
Tel.: (49) 834197980

Web Site: http://www.wieland-roessler.de
Emp.: 19
Copper Material Mfr
N.A.I.C.S.: 331420
Holger Schanz (Mng Dir)

Wieland Rolled Products North America LLC
4801 Olympia Park Plz Ste 3500, Louisville, KY 40241
Tel.: (502) 873-3000
Web Site: http://www.wieland-rolledproductsna.com
Copper Product Mfr
N.A.I.C.S.: 331420
Dale R. Taylor (Pres)

Wieland SAS
PA Pariest 1 Rue Leon Jouhaux, 77435, Marne-la-Vallee, cedex 2, France
Tel.: (33) 1 60 95 15 00
Web Site: http://www.wieland.fr
Emp.: 45
Copper & Copper Alloy Products Distr
N.A.I.C.S.: 423510

Wieland SMH GmbH (1)
Industriestrasse 18, 78647, Trossingen, Germany
Tel.: (49) 74259470
Web Site: http://www.wieland-smh.de
Emp.: 24
Metal Product Whslr
N.A.I.C.S.: 423510
Ralf Pleier (Mng Dir)

Wieland Scandinavia A/S (1)
Hammerholmen 18, 2650, Hvidovre, Denmark
Tel.: (45) 45 808010
Web Site: http://www.wieland.com
Sales Range: $25-49.9 Million
Emp.: 15
Copper & Copper Alloy Products Distr
N.A.I.C.S.: 423510
Ernst Genckel (Mng Dir)

Wieland Scandinavia AB (1)
Hangpilsgatan 6, 426 77, Vastra Frolunda, Sweden
Tel.: (46) 31698303
Steel Tube Mfr
N.A.I.C.S.: 331210

Wieland Scandinavia Metall AB (1)
Energigatan 10 B, 434 37, Kungsbacka, Sweden
Tel.: (46) 708922345
Copper Product Mfr
N.A.I.C.S.: 331420

Wieland Scandinavia Oy (1)
Kristiinankatu 9 3 krs, 20100, Turku, Finland
Tel.: (358) 44 7474 074
Web Site: http://www.wieland.com
Copper & Copper Alloy Products Distr
N.A.I.C.S.: 423510

Wieland Slaskie Metale Sp. z o.o. (1)
ul Wypoczynkowa 34, 43-382, Bielsko-Biala, Poland
Tel.: (48) 333339083
Web Site: http://www.wieland-slaskie-metale.pl
Emp.: 11
Metal Product Whslr
N.A.I.C.S.: 423510
Grzegorz Kwiatkowski (Mng Dir)

Wieland Thermal Solutions (Shanghai) Co., Ltd. (1)
No 168 RenJie Road, Fengxian, Shanghai, 201402, China
Tel.: (86) 2157464000
Steel Tube Mfr
N.A.I.C.S.: 331210

Wieland Thermal Solutions Lda. (1)
Estrada Nacional 103 Zona Ind, PO Box 21, Palmeira de Faro, 4740-591, Esposende, Portugal
Tel.: (351) 253969390
Web Site: http://www.wieland-thermalsolutions.com
Steel Tube Mfr
N.A.I.C.S.: 331210

Wieland Ventures GmbH (1)
Graf-Arco-Strasse 36, 89079, Ulm, Germany

Tel.: (49) 7319440
Web Site: http://www.wieland-ventures.com
Metal Product Whslr
N.A.I.C.S.: 423510
Erwin Mayr (Mng Dir)

Wieland Wicoatec GmbH (1)
Graf-Arco-Strasse 36, 89079, Ulm, Germany
Tel.: (49) 7319441120
Web Site: http://www.wieland-wicoatec.com
Emp.: 30
Copper Material Mfr
N.A.I.C.S.: 331420
Andreas Torka (Mng Dir)

Wieland do Brasil Ltda. (1)
Praca Padre Mario Fontana 94 - 93C, Sao Paulo, 03127-030, SP, Brazil
Tel.: (55) 11 98712 0046
Web Site: http://www.wieland.de
Copper & Copper Alloy Products Sales & Marketing
N.A.I.C.S.: 423510

Wieland-Buntmetall s.r.o. (1)
Farni 866/11, 162 00, Prague, 6, Czech Republic
Tel.: (420) 242 486 833
Web Site: http://www.wieland.de
Sales Range: $50-74.9 Million
Emp.: 8
Copper & Copper Alloy Products Whslr
N.A.I.C.S.: 423510
Martin Ruml (Mng Dir)

Wieland-Kessler, LLC (1)
500 Green St, Woodbridge, NJ 07095
Web Site: http://www.wieland-kessler.com
Plumbing Product Whslr
N.A.I.C.S.: 423720
Tim Hagan (Pres)

Wieland-Werke (UK) Ltd. (1)
Pennard Close, Brackmills, Northampton, NN4 7BE, United Kingdom
Tel.: (44) 1604 667640
Web Site: http://www.wieland.com
Emp.: 5
Copper & Copper Alloy Products Whslr
N.A.I.C.S.: 423510
Fred Weyler (Mng Dir)

Wolverine Tube Inc. (1)
2100 Market St NE, Decatur, AL 35601
Tel.: (256) 353-1310
Web Site: http://www.wlv.com
Copper, Copper Alloy Tube, Fabricated Products, Metal Joining Products, Copper Alloy Rod & Bar Products Mfr
N.A.I.C.S.: 331420

buntmetall amstetten Ges.m.b.H. (1)
Fabrikstrasse 4, 3300, Amstetten, Austria
Tel.: (43) 7472 606
Web Site: http://www.buntmetall.at
Sales Range: $200-249.9 Million
Emp.: 631
Copper & Copper Alloy Products Mfr
N.A.I.C.S.: 331420
Alfred Hintringer (Mng Dir)

WIELTON S.A.
ul Rymarkiewicz 6, 98-300, Wielun, Poland
Tel.: (48) 438434510
Web Site: https://www.wieltongroup.com
WLT—(WAR)
Rev.: $819,416,411
Assets: $508,728,149
Liabilities: $349,351,879
Net Worth: $159,376,270
Earnings: $26,413,364
Emp.: 3,448
Fiscal Year-end: 12/31/23
Automotive Trailer Mfr
N.A.I.C.S.: 336110
Mariusz Golec (Member-Mgmt Bd & VP)

WIENER PRIVATBANK SE
Parkring 12, 1010, Vienna, Austria
Tel.: (43) 1534310
Web Site:
https://www.wienerprivatbank.com

INTERNATIONAL PUBLIC

WPB—(VIE)
Sales Range: $1-9.9 Million
Emp.: 123
Commercial Banking Services
N.A.I.C.S.: 522110
Helmut Hardt (Member-Mgmt Bd-Real Estate & Ops)

Subsidiaries:

Matejka & Partner Asset Management GmbH (1)
Parking ring 12 Stairs 3 Floor 3 Top 79, 1010, Vienna, Austria
Tel.: (43) 153377830
Web Site: http://www.mp-am.com
Asset Management Services
N.A.I.C.S.: 523940
Florian Rainer (Mgr-Asset)

WIENERBERGER AG
Wienerbergerplatz 1, 1100, Vienna, Austria
Tel.: (43) 1601920   AT
Web Site:
https://www.wienerberger.com
WIE—(VIE)
Rev.: $4,877,718,110
Assets: $6,023,024,888
Liabilities: $3,383,453,608
Net Worth: $2,639,571,280
Earnings: $383,296,857
Emp.: 17,624
Fiscal Year-end: 12/31/21
Bricks & Clay Tiles Mfr & Whslr
N.A.I.C.S.: 327120
Peter Michael Johnson (Chm-Supervisory Bd)

Subsidiaries:

Aberson B.V. (1)
Gouwe 1, 8032 CA, Zwolle, Netherlands
Tel.: (31) 881185700
Web Site: https://www.aberson.nl
Sales Range: $25-49.9 Million
Emp.: 2
Brick & Tile Distr
N.A.I.C.S.: 423320
Raymond Roelofzen (Controller)

Arriscraft International LP (1)
875 Speedsville Rd, PO Box 3190, Cambridge, N3H 4R6, ON, Canada
Tel.: (519) 653-3275
Web Site: http://www.arriscraft.com
Sales Range: $50-74.9 Million
Emp.: 25
Concrete Block & Brick Mfr
N.A.I.C.S.: 327331

Bramac Dachsysteme International GmbH (1)
Bramacstrasse 9, 3380, Pochlarn, Austria
Tel.: (43) 2 757 4010
Web Site: https://www.bramac.com
Sales Range: $150-199.9 Million
Roofing Tiles & Products Distr
N.A.I.C.S.: 423330
Alexander Koch (Co-CEO)

Subsidiary (Non-US):

Bramac Kft. (2)
Hazgyari ut 1, 8200, Veszprem, Hungary
Tel.: (36) 88590891
Web Site: https://www.bramac.hu
Roofing Tile & Product Distr
N.A.I.C.S.: 423330
Gabor Miheller (Mng Dir)

Bramac Pokrovni Sistemi d.o.o. (2)
Buzinski Prilaz 10, 10010, Zagreb, Croatia
Tel.: (385) 1 659 4200
Web Site: https://www.bramac.com
Sales Range: $25-49.9 Million
Emp.: 15
Roofing Tiles & Products Distr
N.A.I.C.S.: 423330

Bramac Stresni Sistemi d.o.o. (2)
Dobruska vas 45, 8275, Skocjan, Slovenia
Tel.: (386) 73846200
Web Site: http://www.bramac.si
Sales Range: $25-49.9 Million
Roofing Tiles & Product Distr
N.A.I.C.S.: 423330

AND PRIVATE COMPANIES — WIENERBERGER AG

Bramac Stresni Systemy spol. s r.o. (2)
Kolbenova 882/5a, 19000, Prague, Czech Republic
Tel.: (420) 266770111
Web Site: http://www.bramac.cz
Sales Range: $125-149.9 Million
Emp.: 350
Roofing Tiles & Products Distr
N.A.I.C.S.: 423330

Cihelna Kinsky, spol. s r. o. (1)
Halkova 1359, Kostelec nad Orlici, 517 41, Hradec Kralove, Czech Republic
Tel.: (420) 383823781
Building Materials Mfr
N.A.I.C.S.: 327120

Dryfix GmbH (1)
Hauptstrasse 2, Hennersdorf, Austria
Tel.: (43) 1605030
Hardware & Paint Whslr
N.A.I.C.S.: 444140

Egernsund Tegl A.m.b.a. (1)
Sundgade 3, 6320, Egernsund, Denmark
Tel.: (45) 74442540
Building Materials Distr
N.A.I.C.S.: 423390

General Shale Brick, Inc. (1)
3015 Bristol Hwy, Johnson City, TN 37601
Tel.: (423) 282-4661
Web Site: https://generalshale.com
Exterior Building Material Mfr
N.A.I.C.S.: 327120
Charles Smith (CEO)

Subsidiary (Domestic):

Columbus Brick Company (2)
114 Brickyard Rd, Columbus, MS 39701
Tel.: (662) 328-4931
Web Site: https://www.columbusbrick.com
Brick & Structural Clay Tile Mfr
N.A.I.C.S.: 327120

Subsidiary (Non-US):

General Shale Brick Inc. (2)
Tel.: (423) 282-4661
Sales Range: $25-49.9 Million
Emp.: 50
Masonry Product Supplier
N.A.I.C.S.: 423320

Subsidiary (Domestic):

Watsontown Brick Company (3)
86 Portmay Rd, Watsontown, PA 17777-0068
Tel.: (570) 538-2555
Web Site: https://watsontownbrick.com
Bricks Mfr
N.A.I.C.S.: 327331

Subsidiary (Domestic):

Meridian Brick LLC (2)
6455 Shiloh Rd, Alpharetta, GA 30005
Tel.: (704) 341-8750
Web Site: http://www.meridianbrick.com
Clay Brick & Tile Mfr
N.A.I.C.S.: 327120
Paul Samples (CEO)

Plant (Domestic):

Meridian Brick LLC - Athens (3)
200 Athens Brick Rd, Athens, TX 75751
Tel.: (903) 675-2256
Clay Brick Mfr
N.A.I.C.S.: 327120

Meridian Brick LLC - Columbia (3)
5100 Brick Yard Rd, Columbia, SC 29203
Tel.: (803) 786-1260
Clay Brick Mfr
N.A.I.C.S.: 327120

Inter Act GmbH (1)
Stadtring 17, 48527, Nordhorn, Germany
Tel.: (49) 59217276804
Industrial Automation & System Integration Services
N.A.I.C.S.: 541512

Isoterm AS (1)
Flyplassvegen 16, 2630, Ringebu, Norway
Tel.: (47) 99481400
Web Site: http://www.isoterm.no
Water & Drain Pipe Mfr
N.A.I.C.S.: 332913

Keramo Wienerberger Immo NV (1)
Tel.: (32) 11210232
Web Site: http://www.steinzeug-keramo.com
Sales Range: $75-99.9 Million
Emp.: 13
Real Estate Development Services
N.A.I.C.S.: 531390

MR Erwerbs GmbH & Co KG (1)
Kardinal Faulhaber Str, 80335, Munich, Germany
Tel.: (49) 89 288111 50
Brick & Tile Mfr
N.A.I.C.S.: 327120

Pipelife Belgium NV (1)
Brasschaatsteenweg 302, B-2920, Kalmthout, Belgium
Tel.: (32) 36201360
Web Site: https://www.pipelife.be
Plastic Pipe System Distr
N.A.I.C.S.: 424610

Pipelife Bulgaria EOOD (1)
Str Industrial 3, P k 65, Botevgrad, 2140, Sofia, Bulgaria
Tel.: (359) 893551765
Web Site: https://www.pipelife.bg
Plastic Pipe System Distr
N.A.I.C.S.: 424610

Pipelife Hafab AB (1)
Foretagsvagen 5, 955 23, Haparanda, Sweden
Tel.: (46) 306002200
Plastic Pipe System Distr
N.A.I.C.S.: 424610

Pipelife International GmbH (1)
Wienerbergerplatz 1, 1100, Vienna, Austria (100%)
Tel.: (43) 16 022 0300
Web Site: https://www.pipelife.com
Sales Range: $1-4.9 Billion
Emp.: 2,350
Holding Company; Plastic Pipe Systems Mfr
N.A.I.C.S.: 551112

Subsidiary (Domestic):

Pipelife Austria GmbH & Co. KG (2)
Wienerbergerplatz 1, 1100, Vienna, Austria
Tel.: (43) 22 366 7020
Web Site: https://www.pipelife.at
Emp.: 280
Chemical Products Mfr
N.A.I.C.S.: 325998
Frank Schneider (Mng Dir)

Subsidiary (Non-US):

Pipelife Czech s.r.o. (2)
Kucovaniny 1778, 765 02, Otrokovice, Czech Republic (100%)
Tel.: (420) 57 711 1213
Web Site: https://www.pipelife.cz
Sales Range: $10-24.9 Million
Emp.: 100
Plastic Piping Systems Mfr
N.A.I.C.S.: 326122

Pipelife Deutschland GmbH & Co.KG (2)
Steinfeld 40, 26160, Bad Zwischenahn, Germany
Tel.: (49) 4 403 6050
Web Site: https://www.pipelife.de
Sales Range: $50-74.9 Million
Emp.: 150
Chemical Manufacturing Services
N.A.I.C.S.: 325998

Pipelife Eesti AS (2)
Porguvalja Tee 4 Lehmja Rae Vald, 75306, Harjumaa, Estonia
Tel.: (372) 605 5160
Web Site: https://www.pipelife.ee
Emp.: 105
Producer & Retailer of Water & Sewerage Pipes & Systems
N.A.I.C.S.: 326122

Pipelife Finland Oy (2)
Kiviharjunlenkki 1 E, 90220, Oulu, Finland
Tel.: (358) 306002200
Web Site: https://www.pipelife.fi
Emp.: 275
Plastic Pipe Systems Mfr
N.A.I.C.S.: 326122
Kimmo Kedonpaa (Mng Dir)

Pipelife France S.A. (2)
6 rue de la Bergerie, 27600, Gaillon, France
Tel.: (33) 23 277 2424
Web Site: https://www.pipelife.fr
Sales Range: $50-74.9 Million
Emp.: 150
Industrial Chemicals Mfr
N.A.I.C.S.: 325998
Christian Gagne (Gen Mgr)

Pipelife Hellas S.A. (2)
5th km PEO, Thiva-Chalkida, 32200, Thebes, Greece
Tel.: (30) 226 202 1400
Web Site: https://www.pipelife.gr
Industrial Chemicals Mfr
N.A.I.C.S.: 325998

Pipelife Hungaria Muanyagipari Kft. (2)
Kishegyesi ut 263, 4031, Debrecen, Hungary
Tel.: (36) 5 251 0701
Web Site: https://www.pipelife.hu
Plastic Tank Mfr
N.A.I.C.S.: 326122

Subsidiary (US):

Pipelife Jet Stream Inc. (2)
1700 S Lincoln St, Siloam Springs, AR 72761
Tel.: (479) 524-5151
Web Site: https://jetstreampipes.com
Pipes Mfr
N.A.I.C.S.: 332996
Wayne Voorhees (VP-Mfg)

Subsidiary (Non-US):

Pipelife Nederland B.V. (2)
Flevolaan 7, PO Box 380, 1601 MA, Enkhuizen, Netherlands
Tel.: (31) 228355555
Web Site: https://www.pipelife.nl
Emp.: 230
Chemicals Mfr
N.A.I.C.S.: 325998

Pipelife Norge AS (2)
Hamnesvegen 97, PO Box 6650, 6650, Surnadal, Norway
Tel.: (47) 7 165 8800
Web Site: https://www.pipelife.no
Sales Range: $50-74.9 Million
Emp.: 200
Chemical Products Mfr
N.A.I.C.S.: 325998

Pipelife Polska Sp. z.o.o. (2)
Ul Torfowa 4, Kartoszyno, 84-110, Krokowa, Poland
Tel.: (48) 58 774 8888
Web Site: https://www.pipelife.pl
Emp.: 358
Chemical Manufacturing Services
N.A.I.C.S.: 325998

Pipelife Sverige AB (2)
Industrivagen 1, SE-524 41, Ljung, Sweden (100%)
Tel.: (46) 51322100
Web Site: https://www.pipelife.se
Sales Range: $50-74.9 Million
Emp.: 200
Plastic Piping Systems Mfr
N.A.I.C.S.: 326122

Pipelife UK Ltd. (2)
13 Saxon Way East, Corby, NN18 9EY, Northants, United Kingdom
Tel.: (44) 8452419490
Web Site: https://www.pipelife.co.uk
Sales Range: $25-49.9 Million
Emp.: 4
Pipes Mfr
N.A.I.C.S.: 332996

Pipelife Ireland Ltd. (1)
White's Cross, PO Box 29, Cork, T23 T992, Ireland
Tel.: (353) 21 488 4700
Web Site: https://www.pipelife.ie
Plastic Pipe System Distr
N.A.I.C.S.: 424610
Gerard Healy (Mng Dir)

Pipelife Latvia SIA (1)
K Ulmana Gatve 2, Riga, LV-1004, Latvia
Tel.: (371) 67807721
Web Site: https://www.pipelife.lv
Plastic Pipe System Distr
N.A.I.C.S.: 424610

Pipelife RUS LLC (1)
St Pervomayskaya 9/16, Kaluga region, 249192, Zhukovskiy, Russia
Tel.: (7) 4843255095
Web Site: http://www.pipelife.ru
Plastic Pipe System Distr
N.A.I.C.S.: 424610

Pipelife Romania S.R.L. (1)
Tel.: (40) 364401686
Web Site: https://www.pipelife.ro
Plastic Pipe System Distr
N.A.I.C.S.: 424610

Pipelife Serbia d.o.o. (1)
Tel.: (381) 114076008
Web Site: https://www.pipelife.rs
Plastic Pipe System Distr
N.A.I.C.S.: 424610

Pipelife Slovakia s r.o. (1)
Kuzmanyho 13, 921 01, Piestany, Slovakia
Tel.: (421) 337627173
Web Site: https://www.pipelife.sk
Plastic Pipe & Fitting System Mfr
N.A.I.C.S.: 326122

Pipelife Slovenija d.o.o. (1)
Ljubljanska 52, 1236, Trzin, Slovenia
Tel.: (386) 15302220
Web Site: https://www.pipelife.si
Plastic Pipe & Fitting System Mfr
N.A.I.C.S.: 326122

Pipelife-Hrvatska Cijevni Sustavi D.O.O. (1)
Prosinacka 7, Kerestinec, 10431, Sveta Nedelja, Croatia
Tel.: (385) 13377340
Web Site: https://www.pipelife.hr
Plastic Pipe System Distr
N.A.I.C.S.: 424610

Preflexibel NV (1)
Elisabethlaan 153, 9400, Ninove, Belgium
Tel.: (32) 54344664
Web Site: https://www.preflex.be
Flexible Pre Wired Conduit Mfr
N.A.I.C.S.: 335929

QPS AS (1)
Rinnleiret 70, 7609, Levanger, Norway
Tel.: (47) 70307170
Web Site: https://qps-norge.no
Plastic Pipe Mfr & Distr
N.A.I.C.S.: 326122

SEMMELROCK STEIN + DESIGN Dlazby s.r.o. (1)
Trnavska cesta 3728/95, 926 01, Sered, Slovakia
Tel.: (421) 17891201
Web Site: https://www.wienerberger.sk
Emp.: 10
Iron Product Mfr & Whslr
N.A.I.C.S.: 331511

Salzburger Ziegelwerk GmbH & Co KG (1)
Lukasedt 11, Weitworth, Nussdorf am Haunsberg, 5151, Austria
Tel.: (43) 6272 4394 0
Brick & Tile Mfr & Distr
N.A.I.C.S.: 327120

Sandtoft Roof Tiles Ltd. (1)
Belton Road Sandtoft, Doncaster, DN8 5SY, United Kingdom (74%)
Tel.: (44) 8449395900
Web Site: http://www.sandloft.com
Sales Range: $75-99.9 Million
Emp.: 417
Roof Tile Mfr & Distr
N.A.I.C.S.: 327120
Simon Oldridge (Mng Dir)

Semmelrock Baustoffindustrie GmbH (1)
Stadlweg 30 Sudring, Klagenfurt, 9020, Austria
Tel.: (43) 5038382
Web Site: http://www.semmelrock.com
Construction Machinery Mfr
N.A.I.C.S.: 333120
Josef Stockinger (Mng Dir)

WIENERBERGER AG

INTERNATIONAL PUBLIC

Wienerberger AG—(Continued)

Semmelrock Industriebeteiligungsverwaltung GmbH (1)
Wienerbergstrasse 11, 1100, Vienna, Austria
Tel.: (43) 1601920
Web Site: http://www.semmelrock.com
Sales Range: $50-74.9 Million
Emp.: 14
Investment Management Service
N.A.I.C.S.: 523999
Robert Holzer *(Gen Mgr)*

Semmelrock Stein & Design Burkolatko Kft. (1)
Bajcsy-Zsilinszky ut 108, 2364, Ocsa, Hungary
Tel.: (36) 29578112
Web Site: http://www.semmelrock.hu
Paving Stone Mfr
N.A.I.C.S.: 324121

Semmelrock Stein & Design Dlazby a.s. (1)
Ledcice 235, Ledcice, 277 08, Melnik, Czech Republic
Tel.: (420) 315636701
Web Site: http://www.semmelrock.cz
Paving Stone Mfr
N.A.I.C.S.: 324121
Daniel Vesely *(Dir-Comml)*

Semmelrock Stein & Design Kft. (1)
Bajcsy-Zsilinszky Ut 108, 2364, Ocsa, Hungary
Tel.: (36) 29 578 112
Web Site: http://www.semmelrock.hu
Sales Range: $25-49.9 Million
Emp.: 10
Brick & Tile Mfr
N.A.I.C.S.: 327120

Semmelrock Stein & Design Sp. z o.o. (1)
Tel.: (48) 225142100
Web Site: http://www.semmelrock.pl
Brick & Tile Mfr
N.A.I.C.S.: 327120

Semmelrock Stein & Design d.o.o. (1)
Tel.: (385) 47819200
Brick & Tile Mfr
N.A.I.C.S.: 327120

Semmelrock Stein + Design S.R.L. (1)
Tel.: (40) 372156151
Web Site: http://www.semmelrock.ro
Sales Range: $25-49.9 Million
Emp.: 10
Building Materials Mfr
N.A.I.C.S.: 327120

Semmelrock Stein und Design EOOD (1)
Sub-Balkan highway 6 E 871, Grigorevo village Elin Pelin municipality, 2108, Elin Pelin, Bulgaria
Tel.: (359) 70015477
Web Site: http://www.semmelrock.bg
Concrete Slab & Decorative Element Mfr
N.A.I.C.S.: 327390

Semmelrock Tlakovci d.o.o. (1)
Opekarniska 5, 2270, Ormoz, Slovenia
Tel.: (386) 47819200
Web Site: http://www.semmelrock.si
Paving Stone Mfr
N.A.I.C.S.: 324121

Soluforce B.V. (1)
Flevolaan 7, 1601 MA, Enkhuizen, Netherlands
Tel.: (31) 228355555
Web Site: https://www.soluforce.com
Flexible Composite Pipe Mfr & Distr
N.A.I.C.S.: 326122

Steinzentrale Nord Leeuwis GmbH (1)
Adlerstrasse 70, 25462, Rellingen, Germany
Tel.: (49) 410131036
Web Site: https://www.steinzentrale.de
Bricks & Roof Tile Whslr
N.A.I.C.S.: 327120

Steinzeug-Keramo GmbH (1)
Tel.: (49) 22345070
Web Site: https://www.steinzeug-keramo.com
Sales Range: $200-249.9 Million
Clay Pipe & Molded Component Mfr
N.A.I.C.S.: 327120
Marcin Dudek *(Mng Dir & CFO)*

Subsidiary (Non-US):

Steinzeug Keramo s r.o. (2)
Placheho 388/28, CZ - 370 46, Ceske Budejovice, Czech Republic
Tel.: (420) 387981303
Brick & Tile Mfr & Distr
N.A.I.C.S.: 327120

Steinzeug-Keramo N.V. (2)
Paalsteenstraat 36, 3500, Hasselt, Belgium
Tel.: (32) 11210232
Web Site: https://www.steinzeug-keramo.com
Emp.: 15
Clay Pipe & Fitting Mfr
N.A.I.C.S.: 327120
Marcin Dudek *(CFO)*

Talokaivo Oy (1)
Hakkilankaari 2A, 01380, Vantaa, Finland
Tel.: (358) 105433000
Web Site: https://www.talokaivo.fi
Emp.: 80
Plastics Product Mfr
N.A.I.C.S.: 326199

Tondach Beteiligungs GmbH (1)
Wienerbergstrasse 11, 1100, Vienna, Austria
Tel.: (43) 1601920
Investment Management Service
N.A.I.C.S.: 523999

Subsidiary (Domestic):

Tondach Gleinstatten AG (2)
Graschach 38, 8443, Gleinstatten, Austria **(82.19%)**
Tel.: (43) 3 457 2218
Web Site: http://www.tondach.com
Sales Range: $200-249.9 Million
Emp.: 1,830
Roofing Tiles & Bricks Mfr
N.A.I.C.S.: 327120

Subsidiary (Non-US):

Potisje Kanjiza d.d. (3)
Suboticki put 57, 24420, Kanjiza, Serbia
Tel.: (381) 24 873 303
Web Site: http://www.tondach.rs
Brick & Structural Tile Mfr
N.A.I.C.S.: 327120
Istvan Jenei *(Mng Dir)*

Tondach Bosna i Hercegovina d.o.o. (3)
Dzenetica Cikma 1, 71000, Sarajevo, Bosnia & Herzegovina
Tel.: (387) 33 262820
Web Site: http://www.tondach.ba
Brick & Structural Tile Sales
N.A.I.C.S.: 423330
Jasmin Hoso *(Mng Dir & Coord-South East Europe)*

Tondach Bulgaria EOOD (3)
Pimen Sografski Str 4 Business Building 2 Office 1, 1172, Sofia, Bulgaria
Tel.: (359) 2 988 36 20
Web Site: http://www.tondach.com
Brick & Structural Tile Mfr
N.A.I.C.S.: 327120

Tondach Ceska republika s.r.o. (3)
Bekitinska, PO Box 18, 75301, Hranice, Czech Republic
Tel.: (420) 581 673111
Web Site: http://www.tondach.cz
Brick & Structural Tile Mfr
N.A.I.C.S.: 327120

Tondach Hrvatska d.d. (3)
Matije Gupca 2, HR 49 221, Bedekovcina, Croatia
Tel.: (385) 49 200300
Web Site: http://www.tondach.hr
Brick & Structural Tile Mfr
N.A.I.C.S.: 327120

Tondach Magyarorszag Rt. (3)
Cserepgyari ut 1, H 9300, Csorna, Hungary
Tel.: (36) 96 592404
Web Site: http://www.tondach.hu
Brick & Structural Tile Mfr
N.A.I.C.S.: 327120
Felegyi Mihaly *(CTO)*

Tondach Makedonija d.o.o. (3)
Ul IGM Proleter br 1, 2310, Vinica, North Macedonia
Tel.: (389) 33 361332
Web Site: http://www.wienerberger.mk
Brick & Structural Tile Mfr
N.A.I.C.S.: 327120

Tondach Romania SRL (3)
Str Podului 127, RO 550263, Sibiu, Romania
Tel.: (40) 269235904
Web Site: http://www.tondach.ro
Brick & Structural Tile Mfr
N.A.I.C.S.: 327120

Tondach Slovenija d.o.o. (3)
Boreci 49, Krizevci pri Ljutomeru, 9242, Krizevci, Slovenia
Tel.: (386) 2 5888600
Web Site: http://www.tondach.si
Brick & Structural Tile Mfr
N.A.I.C.S.: 327120

Tondach Slovensko, s.r.o. (3)
Nadrazna 79/28, SK 97213, Nitrianske Pravno, Slovakia
Tel.: (421) 46 5189 912
Web Site: http://www.tondach.sk
Brick & Structural Tile Mfr
N.A.I.C.S.: 327120

Vargon d.o.o. (1)
Kukuljanovo 352, 51227, Kukuljanovo, Croatia
Tel.: (385) 51499201
Web Site: https://www.vargon.hr
Plastic Pipe & Fitting Mfr
N.A.I.C.S.: 326122

WIENERBERGER Industrija opeke d.j.l. (1)
Behdzeta Mutevelica 61, Sarajevo, 71000, Bosnia & Herzegovina
Tel.: (387) 33714522
Bricks Mfr
N.A.I.C.S.: 327120

WIENERBERGER PARTICIPATIONS SAS (1)
8 Rue Du Canal, 67204, Achenheim, France
Tel.: (33) 390646464
Brick & Clay Roof Tile Whslr
N.A.I.C.S.: 423320

WIENERBERGER S.R.L. (1)
Ploiesti Road No 42-44 Sector 1 Building A2 Floor 3, Baneasa Business and Technology Park, 013696, Bucharest, Romania
Tel.: (40) 372669980
Web Site: http://www.wienerberger.ro
Building Materials Whslr
N.A.I.C.S.: 423320

WIENERBERGER SAS (1)
8 Rue du Canal, Achenheim, France
Tel.: (33) 390646464
Web Site: https://www.wienerberger.fr
Brick & Clay Roof Tile Mfr & Whslr
N.A.I.C.S.: 327120

Wideco Sweden AB (1)
Vevgatan 10, 504 64, Boras, Sweden
Tel.: (46) 33101810
Web Site: https://wideco.se
Software Development Services
N.A.I.C.S.: 541511

Wienerberger A.S. (1)
Sonderskovvej 120 Northern Skob, DK 6800, Varde, Denmark
Tel.: (45) 75298211
Web Site: http://www.wienerberger.dk
Sales Range: $25-49.9 Million
Emp.: 80
Mfr of Brick
N.A.I.C.S.: 327331

Wienerberger AB (1)
Arlovsvagen 12, 211 24, Malmo, Sweden
Tel.: (46) 771424350
Web Site: https://www.wienerberger.se
Brick & Facade Tile Mfr
N.A.I.C.S.: 327120

Wienerberger AS (1)
Kordoni 1, Viru-Nigula vald, 43401, Aseri, Laane-Virumaa, Estonia
Tel.: (372) 334 2130
Web Site: https://www.wienerberger.ee
Construction Materials Mfr & Distr
N.A.I.C.S.: 327120

Wienerberger AS (1)
Brobekkveien 40, NO-0598, Oslo, Norway
Tel.: (47) 22072600
Web Site: https://www.wienerberger.no
Ceramic Building Material Mfr
N.A.I.C.S.: 327110

Wienerberger Anteilsverwaltung GmbH (1)
Wienerbergstr 11 Twin Towers, 1100, Vienna, Austria
Tel.: (43) 160192
Investment Management Service
N.A.I.C.S.: 523999

Wienerberger B.V. (1)
Hogeweg 95, 5301 LK, Zaltbommel, Netherlands
Tel.: (31) 881185111
Web Site: https://www.wienerberger.nl
Building Materials Mfr
N.A.I.C.S.: 327120

Subsidiary (Domestic):

Deko Solutions BV (2)
Van de Spiegelhof 5, 5121 HH, Rijen, Netherlands
Tel.: (31) 62 151 3008
Web Site: https://www.deko-solutions.nl
Packaging & Logistics Services
N.A.I.C.S.: 561910

Deko Steenzagerij BV (2)
Peppelenbos 16, 6662 WB, Elst, Netherlands
Tel.: (31) 481366466
Web Site: https://www.deko.nu
Saw Transformation Product Mfr
N.A.I.C.S.: 332216

Wienerberger Backa d.o.o. (1)
15 Kulski Put, Mali Idos, 24323, Serbia
Tel.: (381) 24730100
Sales Range: $25-49.9 Million
Emp.: 7
Bricks Mfr
N.A.I.C.S.: 327120

Wienerberger Bausysteme GmbH (1)
Wienerbergerplatz 1, 1100, Vienna, Austria
Tel.: (43) 1605030
Web Site: https://www.wienerberger-bausysteme.at
Building Materials Distr
N.A.I.C.S.: 423390

Wienerberger Brick Industry Private Limited (1)
88/4 Richmond Road, 560 025, Bengaluru, Karnataka, India
Tel.: (91) 80 41491 682
Web Site: http://www.wienerberger.in
Building Material Mfr & Distr
N.A.I.C.S.: 327120

Wienerberger Ceramika Budowlana Sp. z o.o. (1)
Tel.: (48) 225142100
Web Site: https://www.wienerberger.pl
Brick & Clay Roof Tile Mfr
N.A.I.C.S.: 327120

Wienerberger DOOEL Vinica (1)
IGM Proleter No 1, 2310, Vinica, North Macedonia
Tel.: (389) 33361332
Web Site: https://www.wienerberger.mk
Building Materials Distr
N.A.I.C.S.: 423320

Wienerberger EOOD (1)
Tel.: (359) 28066777
Web Site: https://www.wienerberger.bg
Emp.: 100
Building Materials Mfr
N.A.I.C.S.: 327120

Wienerberger Eurostroj, spol. s r.o. (1)
Placheho 388/28, 370 01, Ceske Budejov-

ice, Czech Republic
Tel.: (420) 383826111
Web Site: https://eurostroj.cz
Building Materials Mfr
N.A.I.C.S.: 327120
Vaclav Aulicky *(Head-Production)*

Wienerberger Finance Service B.V. (1)
Hogeweg 95, 5301LK, Zaltbommel, Netherlands
Tel.: (31) 881185111
Web Site: http://www.wienerberger.nl
Financial Management Services
N.A.I.C.S.: 523999

Wienerberger Finanz Service GmbH (1)
Wienerbergstr 11 Twin Towers, 1100, Vienna, Austria
Tel.: (43) 1601920
Web Site: http://www.wienerberger.com
Sales Range: $50-74.9 Million
Emp.: 4
Financial Management Services
N.A.I.C.S.: 523999

Wienerberger GmbH (1)
Oldenburger Allee 26, 30659, Hannover, Germany
Tel.: (49) 511610700
Web Site: https://www.wienerberger.de
Brick & Clay Roof Tile Mfr & Distr
N.A.I.C.S.: 327120

Subsidiary (Domestic):

ArGeTon GmbH (2)
Oldenburger Allee 26, 30659, Hannover, Germany
Tel.: (49) 511610700
Web Site: https://www.argeton.com
Ceramic Facade Panel Mfr
N.A.I.C.S.: 327910
Siegfried Gummels *(Sls Mgr-Export)*

Wienerberger Ilovac d.o.o. (1)
Donje Pokupje 2, 47000, Karlovac, Croatia
Tel.: (385) 4 769 4111
Web Site: https://www.wienerberger.hr
Building Materials Mfr
N.A.I.C.S.: 327120
Vladislav Matan *(Asst Mgr-Plant)*

Wienerberger Industriebeteiligungsverwaltung GmbH (1)
Wienerbergstr 11 Twin Towers, Vienna, 1100, Austria
Tel.: (43) 160192
Web Site: http://www.wienerberger.com
Investment Management Service
N.A.I.C.S.: 523999

Wienerberger Ltd. (1)
Wienerberger House Cheadle Royal Business Park Brooks Drive, Cheadle, SK8 3SA, Cheshire, United Kingdom
Tel.: (44) 161 491 8200
Web Site: https://www.wienerberger.co.uk
Sales Range: $25-49.9 Million
Emp.: 70
Clay Bricks & Roofing Tiles Mfr
N.A.I.C.S.: 327120

Wienerberger NV (1)
Chapel ter Bede 88, 8500, Kortrijk, Belgium
Tel.: (32) 56249638
Web Site: https://www.wienerberger.be
Emp.: 1,100
Building Materials Mfr
N.A.I.C.S.: 327120

Wienerberger OY AB (1)
Tel.: (358) 207489211
Web Site: https://www.wienerberger.fi
Emp.: 50
Brick & Tile Mfr
N.A.I.C.S.: 327120
Jari Berglund *(CEO)*

Wienerberger Opekarna Ormoz d.d. (1)
Opekarniska Cesta 5, Ormoz, 2270, Slovenia
Tel.: (386) 27410520
Web Site: http://www.wienerberger.com
Emp.: 5
Brick & Tile Mfr
N.A.I.C.S.: 327120

Wienerberger Osterreich GmbH (1)
Wienerbergerplatz 1, 1100, Vienna, Austria
Tel.: (43) 1605030
Web Site: https://www.wienerberger.at
Emp.: 500
Brick Masonry & Ceramic Roof System Mfr
N.A.I.C.S.: 327120

Wienerberger S.p.A. (1)
Via Railhiera 1, Mordano fraz, 40027, Bologna, BO, Italy
Tel.: (39) 054256811
Web Site: https://www.wienerberger.it
Bricks Mfr
N.A.I.C.S.: 327331

Wienerberger Sisteme de Caramizi S.R.L. (1)
Bucharest - Ploiesti Road Nr 42-44 Sector 1, Baneasa Business & Technology Park Building A1 Floor 1, 013696, Bucharest, Romania
Tel.: (40) 72 776 0849
Web Site: https://www.wienerberger.ro
Brick & Ceramic Block Mfr
N.A.I.C.S.: 327120

Wienerberger Slovenske Tehelne, spol. s r. o. (1)
Tehelna 1203/6, 953 01, Zlate Moravce, Slovakia
Tel.: (421) 26 593 5875
Web Site: https://www.wienerberger.sk
Brick Masonry & Ceramic Roof System Mfr
N.A.I.C.S.: 327120
Roman Toth *(Mgr-HR)*

Wienerberger TOV (1)
Street Extreme 1-b, 02222, Kiev, Ukraine
Tel.: (380) 44 594 50 46
Web Site: http://www.wienerberger.ua
Building Materials Mfr & Whslr
N.A.I.C.S.: 327120

Wienerberger Teglaipari zRt. (1)
Bartfai u 34, 1119, Budapest, Hungary
Tel.: (36) 1 464 7030
Construction Machinery Mfr
N.A.I.C.S.: 333120

Wienerberger West European Holding GmbH (1)
Wienerbergstr 11 Twin Towers, Vienna, 1100, Austria
Tel.: (43) 160192
Web Site: http://www.wienerberger.com
Sales Range: $100-124.9 Million
Emp.: 15
Investment Management Service
N.A.I.C.S.: 523999

Wienerberger ZZ Holding GmbH (1)
Wienerbergstr 11 Twin Towers, 1100, Vienna, Austria
Tel.: (43) 160192
Web Site: http://www.wienerberger.com
Emp.: 170
Investment Management Service
N.A.I.C.S.: 327910

Wienerberger d.o.o. (1)
Bulevar Mese Selimovica 81b, 71000, Sarajevo, Bosnia & Herzegovina
Tel.: (387) 33618419
Web Site: https://www.wienerberger.ba
Building Materials Distr
N.A.I.C.S.: 423390

Wienerberger euroform, spol. s r. o. (1)
Placheho 388/28, Ceske Budejovice, 370 46, Czech Republic
Tel.: (420) 844111123
Brick & Tile Mfr
N.A.I.C.S.: 327120

Wienerberger s.r.o. (1)
Placheho 388/28, 370 01, Ceske Budejovice, Czech Republic
Tel.: (420) 383826111
Web Site: https://www.wienerberger.cz
Building Materials Mfr
N.A.I.C.S.: 327120

Wienerberger zRt. (1)
Bartfai utca 34, 1119, Budapest, Hungary
Tel.: (36) 14647030
Web Site: https://www.wienerberger.hu
Building Materials Whslr
N.A.I.C.S.: 423320

ZZ Wancor AG (1)
Eichwatt 1, 8105, Regensdorf, Switzerland
Tel.: (41) 582190901
Web Site: http://www.zzwancor.ch
Emp.: 166
Building Materials Whslr
N.A.I.C.S.: 423320

WIESON TECHNOLOGIES CO., LTD.
15F No 237 Sec 1 Datong Rd, Xizhi Dist, New Taipei City, 22161, Taiwan
Tel.: (886) 226471896
Web Site: https://www.wieson.com
Year Founded: 1990
6272—(TAI)
Industrial Machinery Maintenance Services
N.A.I.C.S.: 811310
Chung-Pin Huang *(CEO)*

WIEST S.A.
Rua Erwino Menegotti 588 - Bairro Agua Verde, 89254-000, Jaragua do Sul, SC, Brazil
Tel.: (55) 47 3372 5100
Web Site: http://www.wiest.com.br
Year Founded: 1947
Automobile Parts Mfr
N.A.I.C.S.: 336390

WIETZES TOYOTA
7080 Dufferin Street, Vaughan, L4K 0A1, ON, Canada
Tel.: (905) 761-5133
Web Site: http://www.wietzestoyota.com
Year Founded: 1969
Rev.: $39,738,500
Emp.: 55
New & Used Car Dealers
N.A.I.C.S.: 441110
Kevin Wietzes *(Gen Mgr-Sls)*

WIFAG MASCHINENFABRIK AG
26 Route de la Glane, PO Box 1184, Fribourg, 1701, Switzerland
Tel.: (41) 264261888
Web Site: http://www.wifag.ch
Sales Range: $125-149.9 Million
Emp.: 550
Printing Machinery Mfr
N.A.I.C.S.: 333248
Peter Ruth *(CEO)*

WIHLBORGS FASTIGHETER AB
Dockplatsen 16, Box 97, 201 20, Malmo, Sweden
Tel.: (46) 406905700
Web Site: https://www.wihlborgs.se
Year Founded: 1924
WIHLY—(OTCIQ)
Rev.: $385,272,109
Assets: $5,695,395,892
Liabilities: $3,472,611,094
Net Worth: $2,222,784,798
Earnings: ($2,680,326)
Emp.: 226
Fiscal Year-end: 12/31/23
Real Estate Agents & Brokerage Services
N.A.I.C.S.: 531210
Anders Jarl *(Chm)*

Subsidiaries:

Exab Utvecklings AB (1)
Dockplatsen 16, PO Box 97, 20120, Malmo, Sweden
Tel.: (46) 406905700
Web Site: http://www.wihlborjs.se
Emp.: 120
Property Management Services
N.A.I.C.S.: 531311
Andars Jarl *(Mgr)*

Fastighets AB Oxigenium (1)
PO Box 97, Malmo, 20120, Skane, Sweden
Tel.: (46) 406905700
Sales Range: $50-74.9 Million
Emp.: 80
Property Management Services
N.A.I.C.S.: 531311

Hundlokan 10 i Malmo AB (1)
PO Box 97, 20120, Malmo, Skane, Sweden
Tel.: (46) 406905700
Real Estate Rental & Leasing Services
N.A.I.C.S.: 531390

Malmo Borshus AB (1)
Skeppsbron 2, 211 20, Malmo, Skane, Sweden
Tel.: (46) 406997000
Web Site: http://www.malmoborshus.se
Sales Range: $25-49.9 Million
Emp.: 4
Conference Management Services
N.A.I.C.S.: 541618

Medeon Fastigheter AB (1)
Per Albin Hanssons Veg 41, 211 20, Malmo, Skane, Sweden
Tel.: (46) 40321000
Real Estate Rental Services
N.A.I.C.S.: 531390

Wihlborgs A/S (1)
Milleparken 22B 3 Sal, 2740, Skovlunde, Denmark
Tel.: (45) 39616157
Web Site: https://www.wihlborgs.dk
Real Estate Services
N.A.I.C.S.: 531210

Wihlborgs Boplatsgatan 5 AB (1)
PO Box 97, 201 20, Malmo, Skane, Sweden
Tel.: (46) 406905700
Web Site: http://www.wihlborgs.se
Sales Range: $50-74.9 Million
Emp.: 120
Real Estate Rental & Leasing Services
N.A.I.C.S.: 531390

Wihlborgs Borgeby AB (1)
PO Box 97, 20120, Malmo, Skane, Sweden
Tel.: (46) 406905700
Sales Range: $25-49.9 Million
Emp.: 50
Real Estate Rental & Leasing Services
N.A.I.C.S.: 531390

Wihlborgs Fisken 18 AB (1)
PO Box 97, 20120, Malmo, Skane, Sweden
Tel.: (46) 406905700
Sales Range: $50-74.9 Million
Emp.: 90
Real Estate Rental & Leasing Services
N.A.I.C.S.: 531390

Wihlborgs Flintan 3 AB (1)
PO Box 97, 201 20, Malmo, Sweden
Tel.: (46) 406905700
Real Estate Rental & Leasing Services
N.A.I.C.S.: 531390

Wihlborgs Havskryssaren AB (1)
PO Box 97, 201 20, Malmo, Skane, Sweden
Tel.: (46) 406905700
Real Estate Rental & Leasing Services
N.A.I.C.S.: 531390

Wihlborgs Kirseberg AB (1)
PO Box 97, 201 20, Malmo, Skane, Sweden
Tel.: (46) 406905700
Real Estate Rental & Leasing Services
N.A.I.C.S.: 531390

Wihlborgs Kranen AB (1)
PO Box 97, 201 20, Malmo, Skane, Sweden
Tel.: (46) 406905700
Web Site: http://www.wihlborgs.se
Sales Range: $50-74.9 Million
Emp.: 80
Real Estate Rental & Leasing Services
N.A.I.C.S.: 531390

Wihlborgs Motorseglaren AB (1)
PO Box 97, 201 20, Malmo, Skane, Sweden
Tel.: (46) 406905700
Web Site: http://www.wihlborgs.com
Sales Range: $50-74.9 Million
Emp.: 80
Real Estate Rental & Leasing Services

WIHLBORGS FASTIGHETER AB

Wihlborgs Fastigheter AB—(Continued)
N.A.I.C.S.: 531390

Wihlborgs Polisett AB (1)
PO BOX 97 201, 201 20, Malmo, Skane, Sweden
Tel.: (46) 406905700
Web Site: http://www.wihlborgs.com
Residential Property Lessors
N.A.I.C.S.: 531110
Andrews Jarl *(Mng Dir)*

Wihlborgs Ritaren 1 AB (1)
PO Box 97, 201 20, Malmo, Skane, Sweden
Tel.: (46) 406905700
Web Site: http://www.wihlborgs.se
Residential Property Lessors
N.A.I.C.S.: 531110
Anders Grrl *(Pres)*

Wihlborgs Soderarm 11 AB (1)
PO Box 97, 201 20, Malmo, Skane, Sweden
Tel.: (46) 406905700
Sales Range: $25-49.9 Million
Emp.: 50
Residential Property Lessors
N.A.I.C.S.: 531110

Wihlborgs Sqvalpan AB (1)
PO Box 97, 21119, Malmo, Skane, Sweden
Tel.: (46) 406905700
Web Site: http://www.wihlborges.se
Emp.: 60
Residential Property Lessors
N.A.I.C.S.: 531110

Wihlborgs Vikingen 10 AB (1)
Garrison 25 A, 254 66, Helsingborg, Skane, Sweden
Tel.: (46) 424904600
Web Site: http://www.wihlborgs.se
Real Estate Rental & Leasing Services
N.A.I.C.S.: 531390

WIIT SPA
Via Dei Mercanti 12, 20121, Milan, Italy
Tel.: (39) 0236607500
Web Site: https://www.wiit.cloud
Year Founded: 1996
WIIT—(ITA)
Rev.: $128,217,287
Assets: $326,968,733
Liabilities: $283,533,248
Net Worth: $43,435,485
Earnings: $8,461,086
Emp.: 532
Fiscal Year-end: 12/31/22
Information Technology Support Services
N.A.I.C.S.: 541512
Alessandro Cozzi *(Founder & CEO)*

Subsidiaries:

Adelante S.r.l. (1)
Via Sandro Pertini 7 - Loc Antella, 50012, Bagno a Ripoli, Fl, Italy
Tel.: (39) 0555381062
Web Site: http://www.adelante.cloud
Information Technology Services
N.A.I.C.S.: 541511

Boreus GmbH (1)
Zur Schwedenschanze 2, 18435, Stralsund, Germany
Tel.: (49) 38313676416
Web Site: https://www.boreus.de
Software Development Services
N.A.I.C.S.: 541511

Codefit Sp. z o.o. (1)
Porcelanowa 19, 40-246, Katowice, Poland
Tel.: (48) 327056890
Web Site: https://codefit.pl
Software Development Services
N.A.I.C.S.: 541511

ICT Watcher Sh.p.k. (1)
Rr Brigade VIII no 16 Kati 5 Apt 29, 1019, Tirana, Albania
Tel.: (355) 555381062
Web Site: http://www.ictw.pro
Business Process Outsourcing Services
N.A.I.C.S.: 541611

Matika S.p.A. (1)
Viale Fusinato 8, 36100, Vicenza, VI, Italy
Tel.: (39) 0444324910
Web Site: http://www.matika.it
Information Technology Services
N.A.I.C.S.: 541519

Reventure GmbH (1)
Arndtstr 23, 12489, Berlin, Germany
Tel.: (49) 3022379391
Web Site: https://reventure.de
Information Technology Services
N.A.I.C.S.: 541511

myLoc managed IT AG (1)
Am Gatherhof 44, 40472, Dusseldorf, Germany
Tel.: (49) 211617080
Web Site: http://www.myloc.de
Emp.: 60
Web Hosting Services
N.A.I.C.S.: 518210

WIKA ALEXANDER-WIEGAND GMBH & CO. KG
Alexander Wiegand Strasse 30, Klingenberg, 63911, Germany
Tel.: (49) 93721320
Web Site: http://www.ewika.com
Sales Range: $1-4.9 Billion
Emp.: 7,300
Pressure & Temperature Controls Mfr
N.A.I.C.S.: 335314

Subsidiaries:

Instrumentos WIKA Colombia S.A.S.
Dorado Plaza Avenida Calle 26 No 85D-55 Local 126 y 126 A, Bogota, Colombia
Tel.: (57) 1 744 3455
Web Site: http://www.wika.co
Industrial Gas Distr
N.A.I.C.S.: 423840

Instrumentos WIKA Mexico S.A. de C.V. (1)
Calzada San Isidro No 97 P1-1, Col San Francisco Tetecala Deleg Azcapotzalco, Mexico, 02730, Mexico
Tel.: (52) 55 50205300
Web Site: http://www.wika.com.mx
Emp.: 30
Measuring Device Mfr
N.A.I.C.S.: 334513
Fritz Thompson *(Gen Mgr)*

Instrumentos WIKA, S.A.U. (1)
C/Josep Carner 11-17, 08205, Barcelona, Spain
Tel.: (34) 933 9386 30
Web Site: http://www.wika.es
Measuring Device Mfr & Distr
N.A.I.C.S.: 334513
Juan David Falcon Sagimon *(Mng Dir)*

TOV WIKA Prylad (1)
vul General Almazova 18/7 of 101, 01133, Kiev, Ukraine
Tel.: (380) 44 496 83 80
Web Site: http://www.wika.ua
Measuring Device Mfr & Distr
N.A.I.C.S.: 334513
Alexander Borko *(Gen Mgr)*

WIKA Argentina S.A. (1)
Gral Lavalle 3568, Villa Martelli, B1603AUH, Buenos Aires, Argentina
Tel.: (54) 11 4730 1800
Web Site: http://www.wika.com.ar
Measuring Device Mfr & Distr
N.A.I.C.S.: 334513
Pablo Gomez *(Mgr-Sls)*

WIKA Australia Pty. Ltd (1)
Unit K 10-16 South Street, Rydalmere, 2116, NSW, Australia
Tel.: (61) 2 8845 5222
Web Site: http://www.wika.com.au
Measuring Device Mfr & Distr
N.A.I.C.S.: 334513
Michael Whittingham *(Mng Dir)*

WIKA Azerbaijan LLC (1)
Caspian Business Center 9th floor 40 J Jabbarli str, 1065, Baku, Azerbaijan
Tel.: (994) 12 49704 61
Measuring Device Mfr & Distr

N.A.I.C.S.: 334513
Sabuhi Agayev *(Mgr-Sls)*

WIKA BELRUS (1)
Ul Zaharova Nr 50B Office 3H, 220088, Minsk, Belarus
Tel.: (375) 17 294 57 11
Web Site: http://www.wika.by
Emp.: 5
Measuring Device Mfr & Distr
N.A.I.C.S.: 334513
Alexander Martysiuk *(Gen Mgr)*

WIKA Benelux (1)
Industrial estate De Berk Newtonweg 12, 6101 WX, Echt, Netherlands
Tel.: (31) 475 535500
Web Site: http://www.wika.nl
Measuring Device Mfr & Distr
N.A.I.C.S.: 334513
Ivon Janssen *(Mgr-Fin & HR)*

WIKA Bulgaria EOOD (1)
205 Alexander Stamboliyski Blvd, Sofia, 1309, Bulgaria
Tel.: (359) 2 821 38 10
Web Site: http://www.wika.bg
Emp.: 3
Measuring Device Mfr & Distr
N.A.I.C.S.: 334513

WIKA Chile S.p.A. (1)
Coronel Pereira 72 Oficina 101, Las Condes, Santiago, Chile
Tel.: (56) 2 2365 1719
Web Site: http://www.wika.cl
Measuring Device Mfr & Distr
N.A.I.C.S.: 334513
Rafael Rodriguez *(Gen Mgr)*

WIKA Croatia d.o.o. (1)
Hrastovicka 19, Lucko, 10250, Zagreb, Croatia
Tel.: (385) 1 6531034
Web Site: http://www.wika.hr
Measuring Device Mfr
N.A.I.C.S.: 334513

WIKA DO BRASIL Industria e Comercio Ltda. (1)
Av Ursula Wiegand 03, Ipero, 18560-000, Sao Paulo, Brazil
Tel.: (55) 15 3459 9700
Web Site: http://www.wika.com.br
Emp.: 200
Measuring Device Mfr
N.A.I.C.S.: 334513
Alexander Wiegand *(Owner)*

WIKA Finland Oy (1)
Melkonkatu 24, 00210, Helsinki, Finland
Tel.: (358) 9 682 49 20
Web Site: http://www.wika.fi
Measuring Device Mfr & Distr
N.A.I.C.S.: 334513
Tapio Moisio *(Mng Dir)*

WIKA Instrument Corporation (1)
1000 Wiegand Blvd, Lawrenceville, GA 30043
Tel.: (770) 513-8200
Web Site: http://www.wika.com
Sales Range: $50-74.9 Million
Emp.: 400
Pressure & Temperature Controls Mfr
N.A.I.C.S.: 334513
Jeff Carrier *(Reg Mgr-Sls)*

WIKA Instrumentation (M) Sdn Bhd (1)
No 27 & 29 Jalan Puteri 5/20, Bandar Puteri, 47100, Puchong, Selangor, Malaysia
Tel.: (60) 3 8063 1080
Web Site: http://www.wika.com.my
Emp.: 39
Measuring Device Mfr & Distr
N.A.I.C.S.: 334513
Shawnn Liew *(Gen Mgr)*

WIKA Instrumentation (Suzhou) Co., Ltd. (1)
81 Ta Yuan Road, Suzhou, 215011, China
Tel.: (86) 512 6878 8000
Web Site: http://www.wika.com.cn
Emp.: 180
Measuring Device Mfr & Distr
N.A.I.C.S.: 334513
Steven Tang *(Bus Mgr-ETM)*

WIKA Instrumentation Corporation (Thailand) Co., Ltd. (1)

INTERNATIONAL PUBLIC

850/7 Ladkrabang Road Ladkrabang, Bangkok, 10520, Thailand
Tel.: (66) 2 326 6876 80
Web Site: http://www.wika.co.th
Measuring Device Mfr & Distr
N.A.I.C.S.: 334513

WIKA Instrumentation PTE. LTD. (1)
13 Kian Teck Crescent, Singapore, 628878, Singapore
Tel.: (65) 6844 5506
Web Site: http://www.wika.com.sg
Measuring Device Mfr & Distr
N.A.I.C.S.: 334513
Raymond Chai *(Product Mgr)*

WIKA Instrumentation Pars Kish (KFZ) Ltd. (1)
Apt 307 3rd Floor 8-12 Vanak Str, Vanak Sq, 1991945138, Tehran, Iran
Tel.: (98) 21 88 20 65 96 9
Web Site: http://www.wika.ir
Measuring Device Mfr & Distr
N.A.I.C.S.: 334513

WIKA Instrumentation Taiwan Ltd (1)
No 26 Alley 53 Lane 118 Sec Shuang-Lien 2 Min-Tsu Road Pinjen, Taoyuan, Taiwan
Tel.: (886) 3 420 6052
Web Site: http://www.wika.com.tw
Measuring Device Mfr & Distr
N.A.I.C.S.: 334513
C. C. Chen *(Gen Mgr)*

WIKA Instruments (Pty.) Ltd. (1)
No 1 Chilvers St, PO Box 75225, Gardenview, 2047, South Africa
Tel.: (27) 11 621 00 00
Web Site: http://www.wika.co.za
Emp.: 200
Measuring Device Mfr
N.A.I.C.S.: 334513

Subsidiary (Non-US):

WIKA Instruments Namibia (Pty) Ltd. (2)
PO Box 31263, Pionierspark, Windhoek, Namibia
Tel.: (264) 4 61238811
Web Site: http://www.wika.com.na
Measuring Device Mfr & Distr
N.A.I.C.S.: 334513

WIKA Instruments Canada Ltd. (1)
3103 Parsons Road, Edmonton, T6N 1C8, AB, Canada
Tel.: (780) 463-7035
Web Site: https://www.wika.ca
Emp.: 175
Measuring Device Mfr & Distr
N.A.I.C.S.: 334513
Wyan Shankaruk *(VP-Production Svcs)*

WIKA Instruments India Pvt. Ltd. (1)
Plot No 40 GAT No 94 100 High Cliff Industrial Estate, Village Kesnand Wagholi, Pune, 412 207, India
Tel.: (91) 20 66293 200
Web Site: http://www.wika.co.in
Emp.: 400
Measuring Device Mfr & Distr
N.A.I.C.S.: 334513
Anil Shinde *(Mgr-Sls)*

WIKA Instruments Istanbul Ltd. (1)
Bayraktar Bulvari No 17, Serifali Mah Umraniye, 34775, Istanbul, Turkiye
Tel.: (90) 216 4159066
Web Site: http://www.wika.com.tr
Measuring Device Mfr
N.A.I.C.S.: 334513
Osman Keceli *(Mng Dir)*

WIKA Instruments Limited (1)
4 Gatton Park Business Centre Wells Place, Merstham, Redhill, RH1 3LG, United Kingdom
Tel.: (44) 1737 644008
Web Site: http://www.wika.co.uk
Measuring Device Mfr & Distr
N.A.I.C.S.: 334513
Karen Florence *(Mgr-Fin)*

WIKA Instruments Philippines Inc. (1)
Unit 102 Skyway Twin Towers 351 Capt Henry Javier St, Pasig, 1600, Philippines
Tel.: (63) 2 234 1270
Web Site: http://www.wika.com.ph

AND PRIVATE COMPANIES — WILDERNESS HOLDINGS LIMITED

Measuring Device Mfr & Distr
N.A.I.C.S.: 334513

WIKA Instruments Romania S.R.L. (1)
Bucuresti Sector 5 Calea Rahovei Nr. 266-268 Corp 61 Etaj 1, Bucharest, 050912, Romania
Tel.: (40) 21 404 83 27
Web Site: http://www.wika.ro
Measuring Device Mfr & Distr
N.A.I.C.S.: 334513
Cristina Stanica (Mgr-Fin)

WIKA International Trading (Shanghai) Co., Ltd. (1)
Room 706 Unit 5 100, Suzhou, Shanghai, China
Tel.: (86) 21 5385 2572
Measuring Device Mfr & Distr
N.A.I.C.S.: 334513

WIKA Italia Srl & C. Sas (1)
Via Guglielmo Marconi 8, 20020, Arese, Milano, Italy
Tel.: (39) 02 938611
Web Site: http://www.wika.it
Measuring Device Mfr & Distr
N.A.I.C.S.: 334513
Enrico Della Grazia (Dir-Fin)

WIKA Japan K.K. (1)
MG Shibaura Bldg 6F 1-8-4 Shibaura, Minato-ku, Tokyo, 105-0023, Japan
Tel.: (81) 3 5439 6673
Web Site: http://www.wika.co.jp
Measuring Device Mfr & Distr
N.A.I.C.S.: 334513

WIKA Kazakhstan LLP (1)
Darkhan Microdistrict 13/1 Askarov Str, 050067, Almaty, Kazakhstan
Tel.: (7) 7272208008
Web Site: http://www.wika.kz
Measuring Device Mfr & Distr
N.A.I.C.S.: 334513

WIKA Kereskedelmi Kepviselete (1)
Dobi I u 1, 2870, Kisber, Hungary
Tel.: (36) 203848121
Measuring Device Mfr & Distr
N.A.I.C.S.: 334513

WIKA Korea Ltd. (1)
704 Daeryung Technotown II 33-33 Gasan Digital 1-Ro, Geumcheon-gu, Seoul, 153-771, Korea (South)
Tel.: (82) 2 869 0505
Web Site: http://www.wika.co.kr
Emp.: 70
Measuring Device Mfr & Distr
N.A.I.C.S.: 334513
Daesung Rhie (Gen Mgr)

WIKA Merna Tehnika d.o.o. (1)
Sime Solaje 15, 11060, Belgrade, Serbia
Tel.: (381) 11 2763 722
Web Site: http://www.wika.rs
Measuring Device Mfr & Distr
N.A.I.C.S.: 334513
Zoran Markovic (Head-Calibration Laboratory)

WIKA Messgeratevertrieb GmbH & Co KG (1)
Perfektastrasse 73, 1230, Vienna, Austria
Tel.: (43) 1 8691631
Web Site: http://www.wika.at
Measuring Device Mfr & Distr
N.A.I.C.S.: 334513

WIKA Middle East FZE (1)
Warehouse No RB08JB02 Jebel Ali Free Zone, PO Box 17492, Dubai, 17492, United Arab Emirates
Tel.: (971) 4 883 90 90
Web Site: http://www.wika.ae
Emp.: 60
Measuring Device Mfr & Distr
N.A.I.C.S.: 334513
Syed Shazad (Dir-Sls)

WIKA Near East Ltd. (1)
Villa No 6 Mohamed Fahmy Mohdar St, 1st District, Nasr, Cairo, Egypt
Tel.: (20) 2 240 13130
Web Site: http://www.wika.com.eg
Measuring Device Mfr & Distr
N.A.I.C.S.: 334513
Louay Hassan (Product Mgr-Calibration)

WIKA Polska (1)
ul Legska 29/35, 87-800, Wloclawek, Poland
Tel.: (48) 54 23 01 100
Web Site: http://www.wikapolska.pl
Emp.: 1,300
Measuring Device Mfr & Distr
N.A.I.C.S.: 334513
Israel Luna-Vazquez (Mgr-Process Engrg)

WIKA Process Solutions LP (1)
950 Hall Ct, Deer Park, TX 77536
Tel.: (713) 475-0022
Emp.: 90
Measuring Device Mfr
N.A.I.C.S.: 334513
Arek Dyrdol (VP-Ops)

WIKANA S.A.
U Cisowa 11, 20-703, Lublin, Poland
Tel.: (48) 814446480
Web Site: https://www.wikana.pl
Year Founded: 1994
WIK—(WAR)
Rev.: $19,910,061
Assets: $69,660,823
Liabilities: $43,198,679
Net Worth: $26,462,144
Earnings: $3,704,522
Fiscal Year-end: 12/31/23
Real Estate Services
N.A.I.C.S.: 531390
Piotr Kwasniewski (Chm-Mgmt Bd & Pres)

WIKORA GMBH
Friedrichstr 9, 89568, Heidenheim, Germany
Tel.: (49) 732296050
Web Site: http://www.wikora.de
Year Founded: 1950
Rev.: $12,115,000
Emp.: 67
Alternative Energy Sources Equipment & Systems Mfr
N.A.I.C.S.: 488390
Leonhard Joob (CEO)

WILCOMPUTE SYSTEMS GROUP, INC.
40 Executive Court, Toronto, M1S 4N4, ON, Canada
Tel.: (416) 299-2808
Web Site: https://wilcompute.com
Emp.: 100
Software Devolepment
N.A.I.C.S.: 513210

Subsidiaries:

GrowerIQ (1)
40 Executive Court, Toronto, M1S 4N4, ON, Canada
Tel.: (855) 892-7500
Web Site: https://groweriq.ca
Software Publr
N.A.I.C.S.: 513210

Subsidiary (Domestic):

Ample Organics Inc. (2)
629 Eastern Ave Building B, Toronto, M4M 1E3, ON, Canada
Web Site: https://www.ampleorganics.com
Software Development Services
N.A.I.C.S.: 541511
Tom Ritchie (Pres)

WILCON DEPOT, INC.
90 E Rodriguez Jr Ave Ugong Norte, Quezon City, 1110, Metro Manila, Philippines
Tel.: (63) 9209492716
Web Site: https://shop.wilcon.com.ph
Year Founded: 1977
WLCON—(PHI)
Rev.: $578,493,436
Assets: $672,615,355
Liabilities: $309,064,550
Net Worth: $363,550,804
Earnings: $53,278,788
Fiscal Year-end: 12/31/21

Household Goods Distr
N.A.I.C.S.: 423620
Bertram B. Lim (Chm)

WILD BUNCH AG
Michaelkirchstr 1718, 10179, Berlin, Germany
Tel.: (49) 3088091700
Web Site: https://www.wildbunch.eu
Year Founded: 1979
WBAG—(DEU)
Rev.: $92,017,776
Assets: $316,986,452
Liabilities: $198,526,541
Net Worth: $118,459,911
Earnings: ($13,362,170)
Emp.: 125
Fiscal Year-end: 12/31/19
Film Production Services
N.A.I.C.S.: 512120
Tarek Malak (Chm-Supervisory Bd)

Subsidiaries:

BIM Distribuzione s.r.l (1)
Via Lorenzo Magalotti 15, 00197, Rome, Italy
Tel.: (39) 063231057
Web Site: https://www.bimfilm.com
Film Production Services
N.A.I.C.S.: 512110
Giulio Bruno (Mktg Mgr)

Central Film Verleih GmbH (1)
Michaelkirchstr 17-18, 10179, Berlin, Germany
Tel.: (49) 3021492200
Web Site: https://www.centralfilm.de
Media Streaming Distribution Services
N.A.I.C.S.: 541511

Elle Driver SAS (1)
44 rue Blanche, 75009, Paris, France
Tel.: (33) 156434870
Web Site: https://www.elledriver.fr
Film Production Services
N.A.I.C.S.: 512110
Alexis Reybet-Degat (Mgr-Acquisitions)

Senator Film Produktion GmbH (1)
Knesebeckstrasse 59 - 61, 10719, Berlin, Germany
Tel.: (49) 3088091700
Web Site: http://www.senator.de
Film Production Services
N.A.I.C.S.: 512110

Vertigo Films S.L (1)
C/Carranza 25-7th Floor, 28004, Madrid, Spain
Tel.: (34) 915240819
Web Site: http://www.vertigofilms.es
Film Production Services
N.A.I.C.S.: 512110

Wild Bunch Germany Gmbh (1)
Holzstrasse 30, 80469, Munich, Germany
Tel.: (49) 89444556644
Web Site: http://www.wildbunch-germany.de
Film Production Services
N.A.I.C.S.: 512110

WILDBRAIN LTD.
25 York St Suite 1201, Toronto, M5J 2V5, ON, Canada
Tel.: (416) 363-8034
Web Site: https://www.wildbrain.com
WILD—(TSX)
Kids & Family Entertainment
N.A.I.C.S.: 713990
Ricardo Curtis (Gen Mgr-House of Cool)

Subsidiaries:

House of Cool International Inc. (1)
345 Adelaide St W 6th Floor, Toronto, M5V 1R5, ON, Canada
Tel.: (416) 591-6500
Web Site: http://www.houseofcool.com
Motion Picture Production Services
N.A.I.C.S.: 512110
Wes Lui (Co-Founder)

Wild Brain Entertainment, Inc. (1)
15000 Ventura Blvd, Sherman Oaks, CA 91403
Tel.: (818) 290-7080
Web Site: http://www.wildbrain.com
Sales Range: $10-24.9 Million
Emp.: 85
Animation Studio
N.A.I.C.S.: 512110

WILDCAT EXPLORATION LTD.
450-789 West Pender Street, Vancouver, V6C 1H2, BC, Canada
Tel.: (604) 428-5690   Ca
Web Site:
  http://www.wildcatexploration.com
Year Founded: 1998
Metal Mining Exploration Service
N.A.I.C.S.: 213114

WILDCAT PETROLEUM PLC
Belmont House Third Floor Suite ASCO-303 Belmont Road, Uxbridge, London, UB8 1HE, United Kingdom   UK
Web Site:
  https://www.wildcatpetroleum.co.uk
Year Founded: 2020
WCAT—(LSE)
Assets: $193,768
Liabilities: $57,470
Net Worth: $136,298
Earnings: ($330,721)
Emp.: 2
Fiscal Year-end: 06/30/23
Natural Gas Distribution
N.A.I.C.S.: 221210

WILDCAT RESOURCES LTD.
Suite 3 Ground Floor 16 Ord Street, West Perth, 6005, WA, Australia
Tel.: (61) 861691433   AU
Web Site:
  https://www.wildcatresources.com.au
WC8—(ASX)
Rev.: $7,562
Assets: $5,392,244
Liabilities: $219,135
Net Worth: $5,173,109
Earnings: ($707,972)
Fiscal Year-end: 06/30/21
Mineral Exploration Services
N.A.I.C.S.: 212290
Zane Lewis (Co-Sec)

WILDERNESS HOLDINGS LIMITED
373 Rivonia Boulevard, PO Box 5219, Rivonia, 2128, South Africa
Tel.: (27) 112575000   BW
Web Site: http://www.wilderness-group.com
Year Founded: 1983
Rev.: $120,721,952
Assets: $152,223,788
Liabilities: $93,113,359
Net Worth: $59,110,429
Earnings: $8,718,177
Emp.: 2,491
Fiscal Year-end: 02/28/18
Safari Touring Operations & Management Services
N.A.I.C.S.: 561520
Keith Vincent (CEO)

Subsidiaries:

African Experience Limited (1)
African Experience Limited, Dallas, TX 75205
Tel.: (214) 528-9760
Web Site: http://www.africanexperience.com
Ecotourism Services
N.A.I.C.S.: 561599
William Armstrong Taylor (Founder & Pres)

Wilderness Safaris Zimbabwe (Pvt) Limited (1)
366 Gibson Rd, Victoria Falls, Matabeleland North, Zimbabwe
Tel.: (263) 1343371
Web Site: http://www.wilderness.com

WILDERNESS HOLDINGS LIMITED

Wilderness Holdings Limited—(Continued)
Ecotourism Services
N.A.I.C.S.: 561520
Tracy Harding *(Mgr-HR)*

WILDFLOWER BRANDS INC.
400-1505 West 2nd, Vancouver, V6H 3Y4, BC, Canada
Tel.: (604) 559-0420   **BC**
Web Site: https://buywildflower.com
Year Founded: 1983
WLDFF—(OTCEM)
Rev.: $5,193,256
Assets: $43,828,119
Liabilities: $9,343,191
Net Worth: $34,484,927
Earnings: ($3,631,523)
Fiscal Year-end: 06/30/19
Marijuana Mfr
N.A.I.C.S.: 325412
Stephen Pearce *(CFO)*

WILDPACK BEVERAGE INC.
2900 - 550 Burrard St., Vancouver, V6C 0A3, BC, Canada
Tel.: (443) 619-3860
Web Site: https://wildpackbev.com
Year Founded: 2018
CANS—(TSX)
Assets: $381,153
Liabilities: $18,317
Net Worth: $362,836
Earnings: ($43,691)
Fiscal Year-end: 12/31/19
Food & Beverage Services
N.A.I.C.S.: 311999

WILDSKY RESOURCES INC.
507 - 700 West Pender St, Vancouver, V6C 1G8, BC, Canada
Tel.: (778) 889-4966
Web Site: https://www.wildskyresources.com
Year Founded: 2006
HWTHF—(OTCIQ)
Rev.: $95,493
Assets: $4,472,587
Liabilities: $91,584
Net Worth: $4,381,003
Earnings: ($2,021,269)
Fiscal Year-end: 11/30/23
Mineral Exploration Services
N.A.I.C.S.: 213114
Wilson Jin *(CEO & Pres)*

WILEE VEGETABLE OILS SDN. BHD.
03-09-01 1 Jalan Pengaturcara U1/51A Pusat Perniagaan UOA, 40150, Shah Alam, Malaysia
Tel.: (60) 126196552
Web Site: https://wileevegetableoils.com
Emp.: 100
Animal Nutritional Products Mfr
N.A.I.C.S.: 311119

WILH. WERHAHN KG
Konigstrasse 1, 41460, Neuss, Germany
Tel.: (49) 21319160   **De**
Web Site: http://www.werhahn.de
Year Founded: 1846
Sales Range: $1-4.9 Billion
Holding Company; Finance, Building Materials, Baking Products & Real Estate
N.A.I.C.S.: 551102
Anton Werhahn *(Chm-Mgmt Bd)*

Subsidiaries:

Basalt-Actien-Gesellschaft   (1)
Linzhausenstrasse 20, Linz, 53545, Germany
Tel.: (49) 26445630
Web Site: http://www.basalt.de

Sales Range: $800-899.9 Million
Emp.: 200
Mining Aggregates & Asphalt Construction Materials Production
N.A.I.C.S.: 324121
Peter Vos *(Gen Mgr)*

Rathscheck Schiefer und Dach-Systeme KG   (1)
St Barbara Strasse 3, 56727, Mayen, Germany
Tel.: (49) 26519550
Web Site: http://www.rathscheck.de
Sales Range: $25-49.9 Million
Emp.: 45
Slate Supply Distr
N.A.I.C.S.: 423840
Andreas Jaegeo *(Mng Dir)*

Stace Pty Ltd.   (1)
42 Zedora Turn, Henderson, 6166, WA, Australia
Tel.: (61) 892362999
Web Site: http://www.stace.com.au
Sales Range: $25-49.9 Million
Emp.: 20
Mechanical Engineering Services
N.A.I.C.S.: 541330
Michael Gartside *(Mng Dir)*

Werhahn Muhlen GmbH & Co. KG   (1)
Hansastrasse 6, Neuss, 41460, Germany
Tel.: (49) 213127950
Web Site: http://www.werhahn-muehlen.de
Sales Range: $300-349.9 Million
Emp.: 140
Industrial & Bakery Flours; Baking Convenience & Retail-brand Products
N.A.I.C.S.: 311211
Philipp Holthaus *(Controller)*

Subsidiary (Non-US):

Gb Plange Portugal S.A.   (2)
Apartado 2293, 1107 001, Lisbon, Portugal
Tel.: (351) 214258800
Yeast Mfr
N.A.I.C.S.: 311999

Gb Plange the Netherlands B.V.   (2)
Mijlweg 77, 3316BE, Dordrecht, Netherlands   (100%)
Tel.: (31) 786525610
Web Site: http://www.abmauri.com
Emp.: 60
Yeast & Bakery Products Distr
N.A.I.C.S.: 424490

Wilh. Werhahn KG ZN Haus & Grund   (1)
Konigstrasse 1, 41460, Neuss, Germany
Tel.: (49) 2131916139
Web Site: http://www.hausundgrund.de
Sales Range: $50-74.9 Million
Emp.: 10
Commercial & Real Estate Land Management
N.A.I.C.S.: 531390

Zwilling J.A. Henckels AG   (1)
Grunewalder Strasse 14-22, 42659, Solingen, Germany
Tel.: (49) 2128820
Web Site: http://www.zwilling.com
Sales Range: $200-249.9 Million
Emp.: 1,600
Cutting Utensils Mfr
N.A.I.C.S.: 332215
Claus Holst-Gydesen *(CEO)*

Subsidiary (Domestic):

United Salon Technologies GmbH   (2)
Ketzberger Strasse 34, 42653, Solingen, Germany
Tel.: (49) 212658625
Web Site: http://www.ust-germany.com
Sales Range: $25-49.9 Million
Emp.: 100
Hair Scissors Mfr
N.A.I.C.S.: 332215
Thomas Wenzel *(Mng Dir)*

abcfinance GmbH   (1)
Kamekestrasse 2-8, 50672, Cologne, Germany
Tel.: (49) 221579080
Web Site: http://www.abcfinance.de

Emp.: 496
Leasing & Rental Agreement Services
N.A.I.C.S.: 532310
Michael Mohr *(Mng Dir)*

WILH. WILHELMSEN HOLDING ASA
Strandveien 20, NO-1366, Lysaker, Norway
Tel.: (47) 67584000   **NO**
Web Site: http://www.wilhelmsen.com
Year Founded: 1861
0P0T—(LSE)
Rev.: $958,000,000
Assets: $3,628,000,000
Liabilities: $1,273,000,000
Net Worth: $2,355,000,000
Earnings: $282,000,000
Emp.: 15,899
Fiscal Year-end: 12/31/22
Holding Company; Maritime Shipping & Logistics Services
N.A.I.C.S.: 551112
Diderik Schnitler *(Chm)*

Subsidiaries:

Compagnie d'Affretement et de Transport (C.A.T.) SAS   (1)
49 Quai Alphonse le Gallo, 92100, Boulogne-Billancourt, France
Tel.: (33) 1 47 12 80 00
Web Site: http://www.groupecat.com
Automobile Trucking & Automotive Logistics Services
N.A.I.C.S.: 484230

Subsidiary (Non-US):

Sintax Logistica, S.A.   (2)
c/o Diputacion no 279 Atico 60, Barcelona, 08007, Spain
Tel.: (34) 93 496 25 00
Web Site: http://www.sintax.com
Logistics Consulting Servies
N.A.I.C.S.: 541614

NorSea Group AS   (1)
Risavika Havnering 14, 4056, Tananger, Norway
Tel.: (47) 40004321
Web Site: https://www.norseagroup.com
Holding Company; Support Activities for Oil & Gas Operations
N.A.I.C.S.: 551112
May Britt Lilletvedt *(CEO-)*

Subsidiary (Domestic):

NorSea AS   (2)
Risavika Havnering 14, 4056, Tananger, Norway
Tel.: (47) 4 000 4321
Web Site: https://www.norseagroup.com
Sales Range: $75-99.9 Million
Emp.: 200
Supply Base Logistic & Onshore & Offshore Industry Support Service
N.A.I.C.S.: 213112

Vestbase AS   (2)
Omagaten 110 C, N 6500, Kristiansund, Norway
Tel.: (47) 71572200
Web Site: http://www.vestbase.com
Sales Range: $50-74.9 Million
Emp.: 220
Logistics Supplier for Offshore Related Activities
N.A.I.C.S.: 211120
Alf Dahl *(Mng Dir)*

Treasure ASA   (1)
PO Box 33, NO-1324, Lysaker, Norway   (78.48%)
Tel.: (47) 67584000
Web Site: https://www.treasureasa.com
Rev.: $608,000
Assets: $547,101,000
Liabilities: $210,000
Net Worth: $546,891,000
Earnings: ($34,914,000)
Fiscal Year-end: 12/31/2022
Investment Management Service
N.A.I.C.S.: 523940
Morten Lertro *(CFO)*

INTERNATIONAL PUBLIC

Wilhelmsen Maritime Services AS   (1)
Tel.: (47) 67584000
Emp.: 600
Maritime & Offshore Environmental, Safety, HVAC-R & Power Services
N.A.I.C.S.: 541990

Subsidiary (Domestic):

Wilhelmsen Ships Service AS   (2)
Strandveien 20, Lysaker, NO-1366, Skien, Norway   (100%)
Tel.: (47) 67584000
Web Site: https://www.wilhelmsen.com
Sales Range: $800-899.9 Million
Ocean Transport & Warehousing Services
N.A.I.C.S.: 483111

Subsidiary (Domestic):

Barwil Agencies AS   (3)
Strandveien 20, PO Box 33, 1324, Lysaker, Norway   (100%)
Tel.: (47) 6758 4550
Web Site: http://www.yarwil.com
Sales Range: $50-74.9 Million
Emp.: 100
Holding Company; Ships Agency Services
N.A.I.C.S.: 551112

Affiliate (Non-US):

Binzagr Barwil Maritime Transport Co. Ltd.   (4)
6th Fl Al Higgi Trade Centre King Abdul Aziz St, PO Box 286, Yanbu, 14911, Saudi Arabia
Tel.: (966) 43223696
Web Site: http://www.wilhelmsen.com
Emp.: 70
Ships Agency Services
N.A.I.C.S.: 488390

Joint Venture (Non-US):

Denholm Barwil Ltd.   (4)
Liner House Test Road Eastern Docks, Southampton, SO14 3GE, United Kingdom   (40%)
Tel.: (44) 2380713140
Web Site: http://www.denholm-barwil.com
Sales Range: $25-49.9 Million
Ships Agency Services
N.A.I.C.S.: 488390
Gary Tranter *(Mng Dir)*

Subsidiary (Domestic):

Wilhelmsen Technical Solutions AS   (2)
Strandveien 20, 1366, Lysaker, Norway
Tel.: (47) 6758 4000
Emp.: 500
Maritime & Offshore Environmental, Safety, HVAC-R & Power Services
N.A.I.C.S.: 541990
Arnstein Stavnheim *(Mgr-Sls-Northern Europe Reg)*

Subsidiary (Non-US):

Wilhelmsen Technical Solutions AB   (3)
Karragardsvagen 6, Uddevalla, 451 63, Sweden   (100%)
Tel.: (46) 522668600
Web Site: http://www.wilhelmsen.com
Sales Range: $25-49.9 Million
Emp.: 100
Marine Systems Services
N.A.I.C.S.: 483111

Subsidiary (Non-US):

Wilhelmsen Technical Solutions A/S   (4)
Lille Tornbjerg Vej 30, DK-5220, Odense, S, Denmark   (100%)
Tel.: (45) 70263501
Web Site: http://www.wilhelmsen.com
Sales Range: $25-49.9 Million
Emp.: 35
Maritime Systems Services
N.A.I.C.S.: 483111

Subsidiary (Domestic):

Wilhelmsen Technical Solutions Sweden AB   (4)

AND PRIVATE COMPANIES
WILKO RETAIL LTD.

Lunnagardsgatan 4, 431 87, Molndal, Sweden **(100%)**
Tel.: (46) 3139 2200
Sales Range: $25-49.9 Million
Emp.: 99
Marine Ventiliation Mfr
N.A.I.C.S.: 333415

Subsidiary (Non-US):

Wilhelmsen Technical Solutions Pte. Ltd. (3)
31 International Business Park 05-10 Creative Resource, Singapore, 609921, Singapore **(100%)**
Tel.: (65) 6450 9191
Web Site: http://www.wilhelmsen.com
Emp.: 20
Maritime Systems Services
N.A.I.C.S.: 483111

Subsidiary (US):

Wilhelmsen Technical Solutions, Inc. (3)
2785 N Commerce Parkway, Miramar, FL 33025
Tel.: (954) 585-5800
Web Site: http://www.wilhelmsen.com
Emp.: 10
Maritime Systems Services
N.A.I.C.S.: 483111
Tom Eccles *(CEO)*

Joint Venture (Domestic):

Yarwil AS (3)
Stranveien 20, Lysaker, 3466, Norway **(50%)**
Tel.: (47) 6758 6900
Web Site: http://www.yarwil.com
Ship Exhaust Gas Emissions Control Services
N.A.I.C.S.: 541990
Kai Latun *(Mng Dir)*

Wilhelmsen Port Service (Gibraltar) Limited (1)
Unit 1 Candytuft House, PO Box 624, Terraces, GX11 1AA, Waterport, Gibraltar
Tel.: (350) 20003999
Maritime Logistics Services
N.A.I.C.S.: 541614

Wilhelmsen Port Service Canarias S.A. (1)
Av Juan XXIII 1 1 Gran Canaria, 35004, Las Palmas, Spain
Tel.: (34) 928464896
Maritime Logistics Services
N.A.I.C.S.: 541614

Wilhelmsen Port Services (Japan) Pte. Ltd. (1)
GotenYama Trust Tower 13th Floor 7-35 Kitashinagawa 4 Chome, Shinagawa-Ku, Tokyo, Japan
Tel.: (81) 363860181
Maritime Logistics Services
N.A.I.C.S.: 541614

Wilhelmsen Port Services Amsterdam B.V. (1)
Capriweg 28, 1044 AL, Amsterdam, Netherlands
Tel.: (31) 204488700
Maritime Logistics Services
N.A.I.C.S.: 541614

Wilhelmsen Port Services Antwerp N.V. (1)
Houtdok-Noordkaai 25a, 2030, Antwerp, Belgium
Tel.: (32) 32214422
Maritime Logistics Services
N.A.I.C.S.: 541614

Wilhelmsen Port Services Bulgaria Ltd. (1)
54 Osmi Primorski Polk Blvd Level 4 Office 18 Central Point Building, 9002, Varna, Bulgaria
Tel.: (359) 52724915
Maritime Logistics Services
N.A.I.C.S.: 541614

Wilhelmsen Port Services Germany GmbH (1)
Palmaille 45, 22767, Hamburg, Germany
Tel.: (49) 403178950

Maritime Logistics Services
N.A.I.C.S.: 541614

Wilhelmsen Port Services India Private Limited (1)
Mittal Towers Tower C 3rd Floor 210, Nariman Point, Mumbai, 400 021, India
Tel.: (91) 2266375500
Maritime Logistics Services
N.A.I.C.S.: 541614

Wilhelmsen Port Services Japan Co., Ltd. (1)
Gotenyama Trust Tower 13th Floor 4-7-35, Kita Shinagawa Shinagawa-ku, Tokyo, 140-0001, Japan
Tel.: (81) 363860178
Maritime Logistics Services
N.A.I.C.S.: 541614

Wilhelmsen Port Services Portugal S.A. (1)
Empreendimento Alcantara Rio Rua Fradesso Da Silveira 2 2nd FL A, 1300-260, Lisbon, Portugal
Tel.: (351) 213210900
Maritime Logistics Services
N.A.I.C.S.: 541614

Wilhelmsen Port Services Romania S.R.L. (1)
Mamaia Blvd 251 - 253, Constanta, Romania
Tel.: (40) 241673737
Maritime Logistics Services
N.A.I.C.S.: 541614

Wilhelmsen Port Services Rotterdam B.V. (1)
Havenstraat 21,, 3115, Schiedam, Netherlands
Tel.: (31) 102942222
Tank Storage & Logistics Services
N.A.I.C.S.: 484230

Subsidiary (Non-US):

Vopak Agency Germany GmbH (2)
Palmaille 45, 22767, Hamburg, Germany
Tel.: (49) 403178950
Oil & Chemical Transportation Services
N.A.I.C.S.: 488999

Wilhelmsen Port Services South Africa (Pty.) Ltd. (1)
2nd Floor D Berth Building Duncan Dock South Arm Road, Cape Town, 8001, South Africa
Tel.: (27) 215279360
Maritime Logistics Services
N.A.I.C.S.: 541614

Wilhelmsen Port Services Terneuzen B.V. (1)
Schuttershofweg 1, 4538 AA, Terneuzen, Netherlands
Tel.: (31) 115683260
Maritime Logistics Services
N.A.I.C.S.: 541614

Wilhelmsen Port Services, S.A. (1)
Tower 3815 Floor 4 Suite 401, Panama Pacifico International Business Park, Panama, Panama
Tel.: (507) 2637755
Maritime Logistics Services
N.A.I.C.S.: 541614

Wilhelmsen Ships Service Bulgaria Ltd. (1)
54 Osmi Primorski Polk Blvd Level 4 Office, 17-18 Central Point Building, 9002, Varna, Bulgaria
Tel.: (359) 52724915
Maritime Logistics Services
N.A.I.C.S.: 541614

WILHELM BILSTEIN GMBH&CO.KG
Kolnerstr 27-29, Vilkerath, 51491, Overath, Germany
Tel.: (49) 220660060
Web Site: http://www.bilstein.net
Sales Range: $10-24.9 Million
Emp.: 80
Cutting Knives Mfr
N.A.I.C.S.: 332215
Hans-Willi Bilstein *(Mng Dir)*

WILHELM FENNERS
Weserstrasse 15-17, 47506, Neunkirchen, Germany
Tel.: (49) 284596600
Web Site: http://www.fenners-bau.de
Year Founded: 1936
Rev.: $13,130,017
Emp.: 50
Construction & Engineering Services
N.A.I.C.S.: 237990
Ulrich Dopper *(Owner)*

WILHELM GEIGER GMBH & CO. KG
Wilhelm-Geiger-Strasse 1, 87561, Oberstdorf, Germany
Tel.: (49) 8322180
Web Site: http://www.w-geiger.de
Year Founded: 1923
Sales Range: $650-699.9 Million
Emp.: 1,800
Construction & Recycling Services
N.A.I.C.S.: 212319
Pius Geiger *(Mng Dir)*

Subsidiaries:

Geiger Bauwerksanierung GmbH & Co. KG (1)
Karl-Benz-Strasse 5, 70794, Filderstadt, Germany
Tel.: (49) 711 342539 10
Civil Engineering Services
N.A.I.C.S.: 236220

Geiger Beton GmbH & Co. KG (1)
Daimlerstrasse 39, 87437, Kempten, Germany
Tel.: (49) 831 575254 26
Building Materials Mfr
N.A.I.C.S.: 321992

Geiger Kanaltechnik GmbH & Co. KG (1)
Bahnhofstrasse 100, 73240, Wendlingen am Neckar, Germany
Tel.: (49) 7024 40999 0
Waste Disposal Services
N.A.I.C.S.: 562119

Geiger Umwelt GmbH (1)
Trattnerring 13, 2435, Ebergassing, Austria
Tel.: (43) 2230 21375
Waste Disposal Services
N.A.I.C.S.: 562119

SAM-Truck GmbH & Co. KG (1)
Bleicherstrasse 8, 87437, Kempten, Germany
Tel.: (49) 831 512889
Web Site: http://www.samtruck.de
Building Exterior Cleaning Services
N.A.I.C.S.: 561790

WILHELM MAASS GMBH
Zeche Ernestine 18, 45141, Essen, Germany
Tel.: (49) 201294930
Web Site: http://www.maassglobal.com
Stainless & Alloy Flanges Mfr
N.A.I.C.S.: 332919
Luisa Laskowski *(Mgr-Procurement)*

WILHELM SCHEIDT BAUUNTERNEHMUNG GMBH
Lilienhalstrasse 11, 32052, Herford, Germany
Tel.: (49) 522197490 De
Web Site: http://www.wilhelm-scheidt-herford.de
Year Founded: 1889
Civil Engineering & Concrete Construction Contracting Services
N.A.I.C.S.: 238110
Andreas Balzar *(Mng Dir)*

WILHELM SCHIMMEL PIANOFORTEFABRIK GMBH
Friedrich-Seele-Strasse 20, 38122, Braunschweig, Germany
Tel.: (49) 53180180

Web Site: http://www.schimmel-piano.de
Year Founded: 1885
Rev.: $30,287,500
Emp.: 182
Musical Instrument Mfr
N.A.I.C.S.: 339992
Hannes Schimmel-Vogel *(Pres)*

WILKENING + HAHNE GMBH + CO. KG
Fritz-Hahne-Strasse 8, 31848, Bad Munder am Deister, Germany
Tel.: (49) 5042 999 0 De
Web Site: http://www.wilkhahn.com
Sales Range: $100-124.9 Million
Emp.: 500
Office Furniture Mfr
N.A.I.C.S.: 337214
Jochen Hahne *(Pres)*

Subsidiaries:

Wilkhahn AG (1)
Postgasse 17, 3011, Bern, Switzerland
Tel.: (41) 31 310 13 13
Web Site: http://www.wilkhahn.ch
Office Furniture Distr
N.A.I.C.S.: 423210

Wilkhahn Asia Pacific (1)
A2 Alexandria Industrial Estate 46 62 Maddox Street, Alexandria, NSW, Australia
Tel.: (61) 2 9310 3355
Web Site: http://www.wilkhahn.com.au
Emp.: 30
Office Furniture Distr
N.A.I.C.S.: 423210
Constanze Scholpp *(Mgr-Mktg)*

Wilkhahn Handelsges.m.b.H. (1)
Wimbergergasse 12 Kundeneingang Kaiserstrasse 69, 1070, Vienna, Austria
Tel.: (43) 1 894 21 68 0
Office Furniture Distr
N.A.I.C.S.: 423210

Wilkhahn Japan Co., Ltd. (1)
Tokyotatemono Aoyama Building B1 3-3-5 Kitaaoyama, Minato-ku, Tokyo, 107-0061, Japan
Tel.: (81) 3 5414 8088
Web Site: http://www.wilkhahn.co.jp
Office Furniture Distr
N.A.I.C.S.: 423210
Yoshioka Ryota *(Product Mgr)*

Wilkhahn Ltd. (1)
Morelands 5-23E Old Street, London, EC1V 9HL, United Kingdom
Tel.: (44) 207 324 2900
Office Furniture Distr
N.A.I.C.S.: 423210
Fiona Gunn *(Mgr-A&D)*

Wilkhahn S.A. (1)
Apolonio Morales 6, 28036, Madrid, Spain
Tel.: (34) 91 515 85 80
Web Site: http://www.wilkhahn.es
Emp.: 5
Office Furniture Distr
N.A.I.C.S.: 423210
Andres Valle *(CEO)*

Wilkhahn, Inc. (1)
601 W 26th St Ste 820, New York, NY 10001
Tel.: (212) 229-9455
Web Site: http://www.wilkhahn.com
Emp.: 11
Office Furniture Distr
N.A.I.C.S.: 423210
Robert M. Craven *(VP-Sls)*

WILKO RETAIL LTD.
JK House Roebuck Way Manton Wood, Worksop, S80 3EG, Nottinghamshire, United Kingdom
Tel.: (44) 8000329329
Web Site: http://www.wilko.com
Year Founded: 1930
Furniture & Other General Merchandise Retailer
N.A.I.C.S.: 449110
Andrew Moore *(Exec Mng Dir)*

WILL GROUP, INC.

Wilko Retail Ltd.—(Continued)

WILL GROUP, INC.
27th floor Harmony Tower 1-32-2 Honcho, Nakano-ku, Tokyo, 164-0012, Japan
Tel.: (81) 368598880
Web Site: https://www.willgroup.co.jp
6089—(TKS)
Rev.: $913,680,470
Assets: $340,699,230
Liabilities: $224,905,250
Net Worth: $115,793,980
Earnings: $18,362,580
Emp.: 102
Fiscal Year-end: 03/31/24
Staffing Services
N.A.I.C.S.: 561320
Ryosuke Ikeda (Chm & Chm)

Subsidiaries:

Agensi Pekerjaan Asia Recruit (Johor) Sdn. Bhd. (1)
12-01 Jalan Molek 1/31 Taman Molek, Johor Bahru, Johor, Malaysia
Tel.: (60) 72892122
Human Resource Consulting Services
N.A.I.C.S.: 541612
Jane Ng (Mgr-Consulting)

Agensi Pekerjaan Asia Recruit (Melaka) Sdn. Bhd. (1)
No 32A 1st Floor Jalan PB1 Taman Padang Balang, 75350, Batu Berendam, Melaka, Malaysia
Tel.: (60) 63170020
Human Resource Consulting Services
N.A.I.C.S.: 541612

Agensi Pekerjaan Asia Recruit Sdn. Bhd. (1)
Unit No 7-03-A Level 3 Menara Jebsen and Jessen Tower 7, UOA Business Park Shah Alam No 1 Jalan Pengaturcara U1/51A Seksyen U1, 40150, Shah Alam, Selangor, Malaysia
Tel.: (60) 350311223
Web Site: http://www.asiarecruit.com.my
Human Resource Consulting Services
N.A.I.C.S.: 541612
Richard Koh (Mng Dir)

Borderlink, Inc. (1)
Across 8F 2-16-1 Shimomachi, Omiya-ku, Saitama, 330-0844, Japan **(51%)**
Tel.: (81) 486310230
Web Site: https://www.borderlink.co.jp
Language Interpretation Services
N.A.I.C.S.: 541930
Yusuke Nishigori (CEO)

DFP Recruitment Holdings Pty. Ltd. (1)
Level 16 31 Queen St, Melbourne, 3000, VIC, Australia
Tel.: (61) 38 632 9900
Web Site: https://www.dfp.com.au
Administrative Professional Support Services
N.A.I.C.S.: 561110
Robert Van Stokrom (CEO)

Dream Job Myanmar Ltd. (1)
Room No 14-A 14th Floor Dagon Center 2 Pyay Road, Sanchaung Township, Yangon, Myanmar
Tel.: (95) 9978980232
Web Site: http://www.dreamjobmyanmarjp.com
Human Resource Support Services
N.A.I.C.S.: 541612

Good Job Creations (Singapore) Pte. Ltd. (1)
238A Thomson Road 12-08/10 Novena Square Tower A, Singapore, 307684, Singapore
Tel.: (65) 62588051
Web Site: https://www.goodjobcreations.com.sg
Human Resource Consulting Services
N.A.I.C.S.: 541612

Net Jinzai Bank, INC. (1)
2-chome 23-1 ARK Hills Front Tower RoP 705 Akasaka Minato-ku, Tokyo, 107-0052, Japan
Tel.: (81) 368930650
Web Site: http://www.netjinzaibank.co.jp
Emp.: 20
Human Resource Consulting Services
N.A.I.C.S.: 541612
Yuichiro Shimizu (Pres)

Oriental Aviation International Pte. Ltd. (1)
111 North Bridge Road 22-04/05 Peninsula Plaza, Singapore, 179098, Singapore
Tel.: (65) 63377580
Web Site: https://www.orientalgroupsg.com
Temporary Staffing Services
N.A.I.C.S.: 561320

Quay Appointments Pty Ltd (1)
Level 43 25 Martin Place, Sydney, 2000, NSW, Australia
Tel.: (61) 28 257 0500
Web Site: https://www.quayappointments.com.au
Information Technology Services
N.A.I.C.S.: 541511
Philip Divilly (Mng Dir)

SAINT MEDIA, INC. (1)
3F Keio Shinjuku 3-chome Building 3-1-24 Shinjuku, Shinjuku-ku, Tokyo, 160-0022, Japan
Tel.: (81) 353126311
Web Site: https://willof.jp
Emp.: 3,811
Temporary Staffing Services
N.A.I.C.S.: 561320

Scientec Consulting Pte. Ltd. (1)
1 Maritime Square 10-33A/B HarbourFront Centre, Singapore, 099253, Singapore
Tel.: (65) 62253272
Web Site: http://www.scientecconsulting.com
Human Resource Consulting Services
N.A.I.C.S.: 541612
Karen Tok (Founder)

Something Fun, Inc. (1)
7th Floor Kudanminami 3-1-1 Kudanminami, Chiyoda-ku, Tokyo, 102-0074, Japan
Tel.: (81) 36 261 5375
Web Site: https://www.somethingfun.co.jp
Video Production Services
N.A.I.C.S.: 512110

Willof Challenge, Inc. (1)
8th Floor Higashi Shinjuku Building 3-4-1 Shinjuku, Shinjuku-ku, Tokyo, 160-0022, Japan
Tel.: (81) 36 893 8884
Web Site: https://willof-challenge.co.jp
Administrative Outsourcing Services
N.A.I.C.S.: 541611

Willof Construction, Inc. (1)
55F Shinjuku Mitsui Building 2-1-1 Nishi Shinjuku, Shinjuku-ku, Tokyo, 163-0455, Japan
Tel.: (81) 36 863 3711
Web Site: https://willof-construction.co.jp
Human Resouce Services
N.A.I.C.S.: 541612

Willof Work, Inc. (1)
3rd Floor Keio Shinjuku 3-chome Building 3-1-24 Shinjuku, Shinjuku-ku, Tokyo, 160-0022, Japan
Tel.: (81) 35 312 6311
Web Site: https://willof-work.co.jp
Staffing & Recruiting Services
N.A.I.C.S.: 561311

u&u Holdings Pty Ltd (1)
Level 12 259 Queen Street, Brisbane, 4000, QLD, Australia
Tel.: (61) 73 232 9100
Web Site: https://www.uandu.com
Staffing & Recruiting Services
N.A.I.C.S.: 561311
Chad Lawson (Gen Mgr)

WILL SEMICONDUCTOR CO., LTD.
Floor 7 Building 4 No 3000 Longdong Ave Pudong, Shanghai, 201203, China
Tel.: (86) 2150278110
Web Site: http://www.willsemi.com
Year Founded: 2007
603501—(SHG)
Rev.: $2,818,976,402
Assets: $4,940,698,773
Liabilities: $2,399,426,397
Net Worth: $2,541,272,376
Earnings: $139,004,943
Fiscal Year-end: 12/31/22
Semiconductor Devices Mfr
N.A.I.C.S.: 334413

WILL, CO., LTD.
Sakasegawa 1-14-39, Takarazuka, 665-0035, Hyogo, Japan
Tel.: (81) 797747272
Web Site: https://www.wills.co.jp
Year Founded: 1995
3241—(TKS)
Rev.: $81,903,680
Assets: $102,025,100
Liabilities: $70,488,780
Net Worth: $31,536,320
Earnings: $3,693,890
Fiscal Year-end: 12/31/23
Real Estate Brokerage Services
N.A.I.C.S.: 531390

WILLARD MEATS INTERNATIONAL INC.
2455 Cawthra Road Suite 77, Mississauga, L5A 3P1, ON, Canada
Tel.: (905) 566-9855
Web Site: http://www.willardmeats.com
Year Founded: 1989
Rev.: $41,509,595
Emp.: 15
Meat & Meat Products Distr
N.A.I.C.S.: 424470
Dale Willard (Pres)

WILLAS-ARRAY ELECTRONICS (HOLDINGS) LTD.
24/F Wyler Centre Phase 2 200 Tai Lin Pai Road, New Territories, Kwai Chung, China (Hong Kong)
Tel.: (852) 24183700 BM
Web Site: http://www.willas-array.com
Year Founded: 1981
0854—(HKG)
Rev.: $399,767,708
Assets: $257,268,098
Liabilities: $169,214,558
Net Worth: $88,053,540
Earnings: $344,505
Emp.: 377
Fiscal Year-end: 03/31/23
Holding Company; Electronic Components Distr
N.A.I.C.S.: 551112
Kar Chun Hon (Mng Dir)

Subsidiaries:

Array Electronics (China) Limited (1)
Xishanqiao Yuhuatai Zone, Nanjing, 210041, China
Tel.: (86) 255 280 1556
Web Site: https://www.array.sh
Electronic Components Mfr
N.A.I.C.S.: 334419

Willas-Array Electronics (Hong Kong) Limited (1)
24/F Wyler Centre Phase 2 200 Tai Lin Pai Road, Kwai Chung, 852, New Territories, China (Hong Kong)
Tel.: (852) 24183700
Electronic Components Distr
N.A.I.C.S.: 423690

Willas-Array Electronics (Shanghai) Limited (1)
33/F International Corporate City 3000 North Zhongshan Road, Shanghai, 200063, China
Tel.: (86) 2160650288
Electronic Components Distr
N.A.I.C.S.: 423690

Willas-Array Electronics (Shenzhen) Limited (1)
14/F Jinyun Century Building 6033 Shennan Main Road, Futian District, Shenzhen, 518031, China
Tel.: (86) 75588295600
Electronic Components Distr
N.A.I.C.S.: 423690

Willas-Array Electronics (Taiwan) Inc. (1)
2F No 77 Zhou Zi Street, Nei Hu District, Taipei, Taiwan
Tel.: (886) 226560515
Emp.: 13
Electronic Components Distr
N.A.I.C.S.: 423690
Chris Lam (Gen Mgr)

WILLERBY LANDSCAPES LTD.
Bridge Nurseries Four Elms, Edenbridge, TN8 6RN, Kent, United Kingdom
Tel.: (44) 1732 700646
Web Site: http://www.willerby-landscapes.co.uk
Year Founded: 1983
Landscaping
N.A.I.C.S.: 561730
John Melmoe (Dir-Contracts)

WILLI-FOOD INVESTMENTS LTD.
Nachal Harif Street Northern Industrial Area, Yavne, 81106022, Israel
Tel.: (972) 89321000
Web Site: https://www.willi-food.com
Year Founded: 1992
WLFD—(TAE)
Rev.: $150,093,104
Assets: $166,499,514
Liabilities: $12,321,315
Net Worth: $154,178,199
Earnings: $8,662,246
Emp.: 300
Fiscal Year-end: 12/31/23
Offices of Other Holding Companies
N.A.I.C.S.: 551112

Subsidiaries:

G. Willi-Food International Ltd. (1)
4 Nahal Harif St Northern Industrial Zone, Yavne, 81106, Israel **(70%)**
Tel.: (972) 89321000
Web Site: https://www.willi-food.com
Rev.: $149,783,000
Assets: $164,608,000
Liabilities: $12,351,000
Net Worth: $152,257,000
Earnings: $8,728,000
Emp.: 207
Fiscal Year-end: 12/31/2023
Food Products Importer & Distr
N.A.I.C.S.: 424410
Joseph Williger (Co-Chm)

Subsidiary (Domestic):

Gold Frost Ltd (2)
4 Nahal Harif Street, Yavne, Israel
Tel.: (972) 89321000
Web Site: http://goldfrost.co.il
Sales Range: $25-49.9 Million
Emp.: 4
Frozen Food Whslr
N.A.I.C.S.: 424420

WILLIAM COOK HOLDINGS LIMITED
Parkway Avenue, Sheffield, S9 4UL, United Kingdom
Tel.: (44) 1142731252
Web Site: http://www.william-cook.co.uk
Year Founded: 1852
Sales Range: $100-124.9 Million
Emp.: 701
Steel Casting Mfr
N.A.I.C.S.: 331513
Andrew Cook (Chm)

AND PRIVATE COMPANIES

Subsidiaries:

William Cook Cast Products Ltd Leeds Plant (1)
Cross Green, Leeds, LS9 ODX, United Kingdom
Tel.: (44) 1132496363
Steel Products Mfr
N.A.I.C.S.: 331513

William Cook Cast Products Ltd Precision plant (1)
Station Road, Sheffield, S20 3GD, United Kingdom
Tel.: (44) 1142510410
Steel Products Mfr
N.A.I.C.S.: 331513

WILLIAM E. BURROWES INC.
1570 de Montarville Blvd suite B, Boucherville, J4B 5Y3, QC, Canada
Tel.: (450) 655-6023
Web Site: http://www.burrowes.ca
Sales Range: $25-49.9 Million
Insurance Agencies
N.A.I.C.S.: 524210
John Burrowes (*Pres*)

WILLIAM GRANT & SONS LTD.
Strathclyde Business Park, Phoenix Crescent, Bellshill, ML4 3AN, Lanarkshire, United Kingdom
Tel.: (44) 1698 843 843   UK
Web Site: http://www.williamgrant.com
Year Founded: 1887
Distilled Spirit Distr & Mfr
N.A.I.C.S.: 312140
Gary Keogh (*Reg Dir-Mktg-EMEA*)

Subsidiaries:

Raynal & Cie SAS (1)
58 Ave Du Marshall Leclerc, 16103, Cognac, Charente, France (100%)
Tel.: (33) 545821616
Web Site: http://www.raynal-brandy.com
Sales Range: $25-49.9 Million
Emp.: 50
Production of Cognac & Spirits
N.A.I.C.S.: 312140

The Drambuie Liqueur Company Ltd. (1)
Springburn Bond Carlisle Street, Glasgow, G21 1EQ, United Kingdom
Tel.: (44) 131 526 3242
Web Site: http://www.drambuie.com
Distilled Spirits Mfr & Whslr
N.A.I.C.S.: 312140

Tuthilltown Spirits, LLC (1)
14 Grist Mill Ln, Gardiner, NY 12525
Tel.: (845) 419-2964
Web Site: http://www.tuthilltown.com
Distillery Services
N.A.I.C.S.: 312140
Ralph Erenzo (*Co-Founder*)

William Grant & Sons, Inc. (1)
130 Fieldcrest Ave, Edison, NJ 08837
Tel.: (732) 225-9000
Web Site: http://www.grantusa.com
Sales Range: $75-99.9 Million
Emp.: 140
Importer/Distributor of Fine Wines & Spirits
N.A.I.C.S.: 424820
Theodore C. Roman (*Sr VP-Sls*)

WILLIAM HILL PLC
1 Bedford Avenue, London, WC1B 3AU, United Kingdom
Tel.: (44) 2076123000   UK
Web Site: http://www.williamhillplc.com
Year Founded: 1934
WMH—(OTCIQ)
Rev.: $1,798,028,596
Assets: $2,902,669,588
Liabilities: $2,088,987,992
Net Worth: $813,681,596
Earnings: $69,243,720
Emp.: 11,615
Fiscal Year-end: 12/31/20

Bookmaking Services
N.A.I.C.S.: 713290
Joe Asher (*CEO-USA*)

Subsidiaries:

AWI Manufacturing, Inc. (1)
3902 230th St, Winsted, MN 55395
Tel.: (320) 485-2471
Web Site: https://www.awimfg.com
Metal Fabrication Mfr
N.A.I.C.S.: 332312
Gary Scherping (*Pres*)

American Wagering, Inc. (1)
6325 S Rainbow Dr, Las Vegas, NV 89118
Tel.: (702) 735-0101
Web Site: http://www.americanwagering.com
Sales Range: $100-124.9 Million
Emp.: 163
Holding Company; Sports Wagering Systems; Gambling Establishments & Operations
N.A.I.C.S.: 551112

Centrebet International Limited (1)
110 Bourke Rd, Alexandria, 2015, NSW, Australia
Tel.: (61) 292068933
Web Site: http://www.centrebet.com
Sales Range: $50-74.9 Million
Sports Product Mfr
N.A.I.C.S.: 423910

Subsidiary (Domestic):

Centrebet Pty Ltd (2)
110-116 Bourke Rd, Alexandria, 2015, NSW, Australia
Tel.: (61) 292068888
Sales Range: $25-49.9 Million
Emp.: 80
Online Sport Betting Services
N.A.I.C.S.: 713290

SportOdds Systems Pty Limited (2)
110-116 Bourke Rd, Alexandria, 2015, NSW, Australia
Tel.: (61) 292068888
Web Site: http://www.sportodds.com
Online Sport Betting Services
N.A.I.C.S.: 713290

Team Greyhounds (Brough Park) Limited (1)
Fossway, Newcastle upon Tyne, NE62XJ, Tyne and Wear, United Kingdom
Tel.: (44) 1912105300
Web Site: http://www.newcastledogs.com
Sales Range: $25-49.9 Million
Emp.: 40
Stadium Operating Services
N.A.I.C.S.: 711310

The Regal Sunderland Stadium Limited (1)
Newcastle Rd, Sunderland, SR5 1RP, United Kingdom
Tel.: (44) 1915686200
Web Site: http://www.sunderlanddogs.com
Sales Range: $50-74.9 Million
Emp.: 100
Stadium Operating Services
N.A.I.C.S.: 711310
Joe.O.Donald Donnell (*Mng Dir*)

William Hill Credit Limited (1)
Greenside House 50 Station Rd, Wood Green, London, United Kingdom
Tel.: (44) 8000856296
Entertainment Services
N.A.I.C.S.: 516210

William Hill Organization Limited (1)
Greenside House 50 Station Rd, Wood Green, London, N22 7TP, United Kingdom
Tel.: (44) 2089183600
Web Site: http://www.williamhill.co.uk
Sales Range: $50-74.9 Million
Emp.: 180
Entertainment Services
N.A.I.C.S.: 516210

Willstan Racing (Ireland) Limited (1)
57 Lr Georges St, Dun Laoghaire, Dublin, Ireland
Tel.: (353) 214271834
Gaming & Entertainment Services
N.A.I.C.S.: 516210

WILLIAM PRYM GMBH & CO. KG
Zweifaller Strasse 130, D 52224, Stolberg, Germany
Tel.: (49) 2402142567   De
Web Site: http://www.prym.com
Sales Range: $200-249.9 Million
Emp.: 3,900
Holding Company
N.A.I.C.S.: 551112
Klaus Hilgert (*Mng Dir*)

Subsidiaries:

Fiocchi Prym S.p.A. (1)
Via Col di Lana 3, Lecco, 23900, Italy
Tel.: (39) 0341297111
Web Site: http://www.fiocchi.com
Sales Range: $50-74.9 Million
Emp.: 200
Rivetable Fastenings Mfr
N.A.I.C.S.: 339993
Marco Coorti (*Gen Mgr*)

Gold-Zack Kurzwaren GmbH (1)
Zweifaller Str 130, 52224, Stolberg, Germany
Tel.: (49) 2402142567
Web Site: http://www.prym-consumer.com
Sales Range: $75-99.9 Million
Emp.: 250
Elastic Mfr
N.A.I.C.S.: 424350
Hede Ehlen (*Mng Dir*)

Gutermann & Prym Consumer Italia S.R.L. (1)
Via Cottolengo 19 D, 10072, Caselle Torinese, Italy
Tel.: (39) 0114248513
Apparel & Accessory Mfr
N.A.I.C.S.: 314999

Inovan Gmbh & Co KG (1)
Industrie St 44, Birkenfeld, D 75217, Germany (100%)
Tel.: (49) 72314930
Web Site: http://www.inovan.de
Sales Range: $125-149.9 Million
Emp.: 500
Contact Materials Mfr
N.A.I.C.S.: 332618
Armin Winter (*Mgr-Sls*)

PSA Maschinenbau GmbH (1)
Zweifaller Strasse 130, D 52224, Stolberg, Germany
Tel.: (49) 2402142277
Wire Product Mfr
N.A.I.C.S.: 332618

Prym Consumer Canada Inc. (1)
Beaulac 1854, Saint Laurent, H4R 2E7, QC, Canada (100%)
Tel.: (514) 336-5874
Web Site: http://www.prymconsumercanada.com
Sales Range: $50-74.9 Million
Emp.: 7
Sewing Notion & Quilting Notion Dist
N.A.I.C.S.: 424310

Prym Consumer Finland Oy (1)
Huhtimontie 6, 04200, Kerava, Finland
Tel.: (358) 9274871
Apparel & Accessory Mfr
N.A.I.C.S.: 314999
Matti Ikonen (*Mgr-IT*)

Prym Consumer GmbH & Co. KG (1)
Zweifaller Strasse 130, 52224, Stolberg, Germany (100%)
Tel.: (49) 2402142228
Web Site: http://www.prym.com
Sales Range: $50-74.9 Million
Emp.: 150
Sewing & Handicraft Article Distr
N.A.I.C.S.: 459130

Subsidiary (US):

Prym Consumer USA (2)
950 Brisack Rd, Spartanburg, SC 29303
Tel.: (864) 576-5050
Web Site: http://www.dritz.com
Sales Range: $50-74.9 Million
Emp.: 120

Sewing Notions, Straight Pins, Safety Pins, Snap Fasteners, Needles, Thimbles, Buttons, Special Wire Forms, Scissors & Shears, Elastics, Clothing Care Items Mfr & Distr
N.A.I.C.S.: 424310
Hans H. Koehl (*Chm*)

Prym Consumer Malaysia Sdn. Bhd. (1)
Tanjong Kling Free Trade Zone, Tanjong Kling, 76409, Melaka, Malaysia
Tel.: (60) 63511211
Web Site: http://www.prym-consumer.com.my
Emp.: 300
Clothing Fasteners Mfr
N.A.I.C.S.: 339993
Robert Ng (*Mng Dir*)

Prym Fashion Asia Pacific & Co. (1)
24 New Lee Wah Center No 88 Tokwawan Road, Kowloon, China (Hong Kong) (50%)
Tel.: (852) 23444499
Web Site: http://www.prym.com
Sales Range: $25-49.9 Million
Emp.: 100
Clothing Fasteners Mfr
N.A.I.C.S.: 339993
Frank Bruwer (*Mng Dir*)

Prym Fashion GmbH & Co. KG (1)
Zweifaller Strasse 130, 52224, Stolberg, Germany (100%)
Tel.: (49) 24021405
Web Site: http://www.prym.com
Sales Range: $100-124.9 Million
Emp.: 500
Mfr of Garment Fasteners
N.A.I.C.S.: 339993

Subsidiary (US):

Prym Fashion Americas, LLC (2)
470 7th Ave, New York, NY 10018
Tel.: (212) 760-9660
Web Site: http://www.sherplastics.net
Durable Goods Merchant Whslr
N.A.I.C.S.: 423990

Subsidiary (Domestic):

Sher Plastics, LLC (3)
470 7th Ave, New York, NY 10018
Tel.: (212) 760-9660
Web Site: http://www.sherplastics.com
Durable Goods Merchant Whslr
N.A.I.C.S.: 423990
Greg Adler (*Pres & COO*)

Subsidiary (US):

Prym Fashion Inc. (2)
950 Brisack Rd, Spartanburg, SC 29303-4709
Tel.: (864) 587-5220
Web Site: http://www.prym-fashion.com
Sales Range: $50-74.9 Million
Emp.: 125
Clothing Fasteners Mfr
N.A.I.C.S.: 339993

Subsidiary (Domestic):

Schaeffer GmbH (2)
Schutzen Strasse 23, D 42281, Wuppertal, Germany (100%)
Tel.: (49) 202518285
Web Site: http://www.prymfashion.de
Sales Range: $1-9.9 Million
Emp.: 500
Fastener Mfr
N.A.I.C.S.: 339993

Prym Inovan GmbH & Co. KG (1)
Zweifaller Strasse 130, 52224, Stolberg, Germany (100%)
Tel.: (49) 24021402
Web Site: http://www.inovan.de
Sales Range: $50-74.9 Million
Emp.: 180
Wire Connectors Mfr
N.A.I.C.S.: 332618

Prym Intimates Europe Ltd. (1)
Whitecroft, Lydney, GL15 4QG, Glos, United Kingdom (100%)
Tel.: (44) 1594 560 423
Web Site: http://www.prym-intimates.com

WILLIAM PRYM GMBH & CO. KG

William Prym GmbH & Co. KG—(Continued)
Sales Range: $25-49.9 Million
Emp.: 50
Clothing Fasteners Mfr
N.A.I.C.S.: 339993

Prym Moda GmbH (1)
Barmer Strasse 63-65, 42899, Remscheid,
Germany (100%)
Tel.: (49) 2191562670
Web Site: http://www.prym-moda.de
Sales Range: $25-49.9 Million
Emp.: 23
Clothing Accessories
N.A.I.C.S.: 315990

Prym Newey (HK) Ltd (1)
16/F Wah Ming Bldg 37 Wong Chuk Hang
Rd, Aberdeen, China (Hong Kong) (100%)
Tel.: (852) 25520125
Web Site: http://www.prymnewey.com.hk
Sales Range: $25-49.9 Million
Emp.: 40
Clothing Fasteners Mfr
N.A.I.C.S.: 339993

Rump & Prym GmbH & Co. KG (1)
Zweifaller Str 130, D-52224, Stolberg, Germany
Tel.: (49) 2402142567
Sales Range: $25-49.9 Million
Emp.: 100
Knitting Products Mfr
N.A.I.C.S.: 332618

William Prym de Mexico S.A. (1)
Via Jose Lopez Portillo No 8, Col Cecheria
Tultitlan, Mexico, 54940, Mexico (100%)
Tel.: (52) 55 5884 7519
Web Site: http://www.prym.com
Clothing Fasteners Mfr
N.A.I.C.S.: 339993

WILLIAMS & GOSLING LTD.
80-82 Harris Road, PO Box 79, Suva,
Fiji
Tel.: (679) 3312633
Web Site: http://www.wgfiji.com.fj
Year Founded: 1935
Sales Range: $75-99.9 Million
Emp.: 300
Freight Forwarding Services
N.A.I.C.S.: 483111
Dave Aidney (Mng Dir)

WILLIAMSON MAGOR & CO. LIMITED
Four Mangoe Lane Surendra Mohan
Ghosh Sarani, Kolkata, 700001, India
Tel.: (91) 3322435391
Web Site: https://www.wmtea.com
WILLAMAGOR—(NSE)
Rev.: $13,502,089
Assets: $90,421,859
Liabilities: $105,778,259
Net Worth: ($15,356,400)
Earnings: $6,896,198
Emp.: 2
Fiscal Year-end: 03/31/21
Holding Company
N.A.I.C.S.: 551112
Aditya Khaitan (Chm)

Subsidiaries:

Williamson Financial Services Limited (1)
Export Promotion Industrial Park Plot No 1,
Amingaon, Guwahati, 781031, Assam, India
Tel.: (91) 3322435391
Web Site: https://www.williamsonfinancial.in
Rev.: $5,561,913
Assets: $72,572,285
Liabilities: $100,025,871
Net Worth: ($27,453,586)
Earnings: ($27,587,141)
Fiscal Year-end: 03/31/2019
Investment Management Service
N.A.I.C.S.: 523999
S. R. Mundhra (CEO, CFO & Mgr)

WILLIAMSON TEA KENYA PLC
The Acacia Block 2nd Floor Karen
Office Park Langata Road, PO Box
42281, 00100, Nairobi, Kenya
Tel.: (254) 7396133524 KE
Web Site:
    https://www.williamsontea.com
Year Founded: 1869
WTK—(NAI)
Rev.: $32,436,316
Assets: $68,638,904
Liabilities: $16,871,168
Net Worth: $51,767,736
Earnings: $4,005,548
Fiscal Year-end: 03/31/24
Tea Mfr
N.A.I.C.S.: 311920
Alan L. Carmichael (Mng Dir & Exec Dir)

WILLING NEW ENERGY CO., LTD.
294 Anqian Road, Anshan, 114051,
Liaoning, China
Tel.: (86) 4125235088
Web Site: http://www.anheavy.com
002667—(SSE)
Rev.: $166,507,380
Assets: $366,170,220
Liabilities: $188,273,592
Net Worth: $177,896,628
Earnings: $11,567,556
Emp.: 530
Fiscal Year-end: 12/31/22
Mining Machinery Mfr
N.A.I.C.S.: 333131

WILLINGS CO., LTD.
73 Choburo 54beongil Mohyeoneup,
Cheoin-Gu, Yongin, 17037,
Gyeonggi-do, Korea (South)
Tel.: (82) 313263000
Web Site: https://www.willings.co.kr
Year Founded: 2003
313760—(KRS)
Rev.: $33,217,567
Assets: $53,549,106
Liabilities: $20,428,350
Net Worth: $33,120,755
Earnings: ($272,179)
Emp.: 100
Fiscal Year-end: 12/31/21
Electric Motor Mfr
N.A.I.C.S.: 335312
Kang-Soon Ahn (Pres & CEO)

WILLIS SUPPLY CO LIMITED
1149 Pioneer Rd, Burlington, L7M
1K5, ON, Canada
Tel.: (888) 994-5547
Web Site: http://www.4willis.com
Year Founded: 1967
Rev.: $10,868,119
Emp.: 30
Building Materials Distr & Mfr
N.A.I.C.S.: 444180
Dallas Gabriel (Pres)

WILLIS TOWERS WATSON PUBLIC LIMITED COMPANY
51 Lime Street, London, EC3M 7DQ,
United Kingdom
Tel.: (44) 2031246000 IE
Web Site:
    https://www.willistowerswatson.com
Year Founded: 1828
WTW—(NASDAQ)
Rev.: $9,483,000,000
Assets: $29,090,000,000
Liabilities: $19,497,000,000
Net Worth: $9,593,000,000
Earnings: $1,055,000,000
Emp.: 48,000
Fiscal Year-end: 12/31/23
Holding Company; Insurance Brokerage Services
N.A.I.C.S.: 551112
Matthew S. Furman (Gen Counsel)

Subsidiaries:

Acclaris Business Solutions Private Ltd (1)
Tower 2-b Ecospace Business Park New
Town Rajarhat, Kolkata, 700156, West Bengal, India
Tel.: (91) 3330202200
Insurance Brokerage Services
N.A.I.C.S.: 551112
Arpita Gangopadhyay (Assoc VP)

Acclaris Holdings, Inc. (1)
1511 N W Shore Blvd Ste 350, Tampa, FL 33607
Tel.: (813) 873-2020
Insurance Brokerage Services
N.A.I.C.S.: 551112

Acclaris, Inc. (1)
Tel.: (813) 873-2020
Web Site:
    http://www.willistowerswatson.com
Healthcare Reimbursement Administration Technology & Services
N.A.I.C.S.: 524292

Aqueous Management Limited (1)
69-71 Clarendon Road Watford, Hertford,
WD17 1DS, United Kingdom
Tel.: (44) 1923797021
Web Site: http://www.aqueousuw.com
Insurance Brokerage Services
N.A.I.C.S.: 551112
Danny French (CEO)

CKA Risk Solutions Pty Limited (1)
Level 4 / 88 William Street, Perth, 6000,
WA, Australia
Tel.: (61) 892147400
Web Site: http://www.ckarisksolutions.com
Insurance Agency Services
N.A.I.C.S.: 524210

Carsa Consultores, Agente de Seguros y de Fianzas, S.A. de C.V. (1)
Av De La Paz 2661 Col Arcos Vallarta Sur,
Guadalajara, Jalisco, Mexico
Tel.: (52) 3336300233
Insurance Brokerage Services
N.A.I.C.S.: 551112

Drustvo za posredovanje u osiguranju (1)
Bulevar Mihajla Pupina 115g, 11070, Belgrade, Serbia
Tel.: (381) 116558100
Insurance Agency Services
N.A.I.C.S.: 524210
Zoran Loncar (Acct Mgr)

ECA Sp z.o.o. (1)
Marynarska 11, Warsaw, Poland
Tel.: (48) 223188200
Insurance Brokerage Services
N.A.I.C.S.: 551112

Extend Health, Inc. (1)
10975 S Sterling View Dr, South Jordan,
UT 84095
Tel.: (650) 288-4800
Web Site: http://www.my.viabenefits.com
Holding Company; Health & Medical Insurance Services
N.A.I.C.S.: 551112

Subsidiary (Domestic):

Extend Insurance Services, LLC (2)
10975 S Sterling View Dr, South Jordan,
UT 84095
Tel.: (866) 322-2824
Web Site: http://my.viabenefits.com
Medicare Exchange Services to Retirees & Employers
N.A.I.C.S.: 524114

Branch (Domestic):

Extend Insurance Services - Illinois (3)
300 Knightsbridge Pkwy Ste 150, Lincolnshire, IL 60069
Tel.: (866) 322-2824
Web Site: http://my.viabenefits.com
Medicare Exchange Services to Retirees & Employers
N.A.I.C.S.: 524114

Gras Savoye Grand Sud Ouest SAS (1)

INTERNATIONAL PUBLIC

5 Avenue Manaud, PO Box 30015, Bruges,
33522, Belgium
Tel.: (32) 556009090
Insurance Brokerage Services
N.A.I.C.S.: 551112

Gras Savoye NSA (1)
Pole Pixel - 26 rue Emile decorps -
CS20037, 69625, Villeurbanne, CEDEX,
France
Tel.: (33) 472421242
Web Site: http://www.nsa-garanties.com
Insurance Agency Services
N.A.I.C.S.: 524210

Gras Savoye NSA - Garantia E Assistancia Automovel SA (1)
Rua Fernao Teles de Menezes 30 1 Andar,
2001-906, Santarem, Portugal
Tel.: (351) 243305730
Web Site: http://www.nsa.pt
Product Warranty Insurance Services
N.A.I.C.S.: 524128

InsClear AB (1)
Storgatan 22, 852 30, Sundsvall, Sweden
Tel.: (46) 60195200
Web Site: http://www.insclear.se
Product Warranty Insurance Services
N.A.I.C.S.: 524128
Eva Fundin (Product Mgr-Mktg & Sls)

Integra Capital Limited (1)
2020 Winston Park Drive Suite 200, Oakville, L6H 6X7, ON, Canada
Tel.: (905) 829-1131
Web Site: http://www.integra.com
Emp.: 25
Investment Management Service
N.A.I.C.S.: 523940
Graham S. Rennie (Pres)

Liazon Corporation (1)
199 Scott St, Buffalo, NY 14204
Web Site: http://www.liazon.com
Private Benefits Exchange, Group Benefits & Health Insurance Services
N.A.I.C.S.: 524210

Lime Street Insurance PCC Limited (1)
Development House St Anne Street, Floriana, Malta
Tel.: (356) 21322076
Insurance Brokerage Services
N.A.I.C.S.: 551112

MG, LLC (1)
2200 Fletcher Ave 4th Fl, Fort Lee, NJ 07024
Tel.: (201) 461-5665
Web Site: http://www.tranzact.net
Emp.: 1,300
Marketing Consulting Services
N.A.I.C.S.: 541613
Kevin S. Waldman (CFO)

Miller Insurance Services (Singapore) Pte. Limited (1)
10 Collyer Quay 07-04/05 Ocean Financial
Centre, Singapore, 049315, Singapore
Tel.: (65) 63495720
Web Site: https://www.miller-insurance.com
Insurance Agency Services
N.A.I.C.S.: 524210
Edward Soh (Head-Claims)

Navigera AB (1)
Lastmakargatan 22, PO Box 5908, 114 89,
Stockholm, Sweden
Tel.: (46) 86130500
Web Site: http://www.navigera.se
Financial Investment Fund Services
N.A.I.C.S.: 523940
Britt Ehrling (Pres & CEO)

PBW LLC (1)
2201 Double Creek Dr Ste 4004, Round Rock, TX 78664
Tel.: (512) 671-3434
Web Site: http://www.pbwllc.com
Insurance Brokerage Services
N.A.I.C.S.: 551112
Cindy Behling (CFO)

PMI Health Group Limited (1)
The Courtyard Hall Lane Wincham, Cheshire, Northwich, CW9 6DG, Cheshire, United Kingdom
Tel.: (44) 1606352035

AND PRIVATE COMPANIES — WILLIS TOWERS WATSON PUBLIC LIMITED COMPANY

Web Site: https://www.wtw-healthandbenefits.co.u
Insurance Related Services
N.A.I.C.S.: 524298

PT Towers Watson Purbajaga (1)
Chase Plaza 10th Floor Jl Jend Sudirman Kav 21, Mega Kuningan Area, Jakarta, 12920, Selatan, Indonesia
Tel.: (62) 2130447900
Risk Management & Human Resource Consulting Services
N.A.I.C.S.: 541618

PT. Towers Watson Indonesia (1)
Menara DEA 2nd Floor Jl Mega Kuningan Barat Kav E 4 3, No 1-2 Mega Kuningan Area, Jakarta, 12950, Indonesia
Tel.: (62) 21 3044 7900
Web Site: http://www.willistowerswatson.com
Human Capital & Financial Management Services
N.A.I.C.S.: 541611

Saville Assessment Limited (1)
Claygate House Littleworth Road, Esher, KT10 9FD, Surrey, United Kingdom
Tel.: (44) 2086199000
Web Site: http://www.savilleassessment.com
Insurance Agency Services
N.A.I.C.S.: 524210
Gabrielle Parry (CEO)

Towers Watson (Bermuda) Ltd. (1)
90 Pitts Bay Road Wellesley House Floor 2, Pembroke Parish, Hamilton, HM 08, Bermuda
Tel.: (441) 2796700
Risk Management & Human Resource Consulting Services
N.A.I.C.S.: 541618

Towers Watson (Malaysia) Sdn. Bhd. (1)
Menara Dion 26-01 27 Jalan Sultan Ismail, 50250, Kuala Lumpur, Malaysia
Tel.: (60) 327230500
Risk Management & Human Resource Consulting Services
N.A.I.C.S.: 541618

Towers Watson (Pty) Limited (1)
Tel.: (27) 216813700
Web Site: http://www.towerswatson.com
Risk Management & Human Resource Consulting Services
N.A.I.C.S.: 541612

Towers Watson (Thailand) Limited (1)
Floor 9 S-Metro Building 725 Sukhumvit Road, Khlong Tan Nuea Watthana, Bangkok, 10110, Thailand
Tel.: (66) 22399000
Human Capital & Financial Management Services
N.A.I.C.S.: 541611

Towers Watson AB (1)
Lastmakargatan 22 KV Boeken 35 Floor 1, 114 44, Stockholm, Sweden
Tel.: (46) 84638900
Human Capital & Financial Management Services
N.A.I.C.S.: 541611

Towers Watson AG (1)
Talstrasse 62, 8001, Zurich, Switzerland
Tel.: (41) 434884400
Human Capital & Financial Management Services
N.A.I.C.S.: 541611

Towers Watson Australia Pty. Ltd. (1)
Level 4 555 Bourke Street, Melbourne, 3000, VIC, Australia
Tel.: (61) 386819800
Web Site: https://www.wtwco.com
Human Capital & Financial Management Services
N.A.I.C.S.: 541611

Towers Watson Austria GmbH (1)
Thomas-Klestil-Platz 13 Orbi Tower, 1030, Vienna, Austria
Tel.: (43) 17159474
Risk Management & Human Resource Consulting Services
N.A.I.C.S.: 541618

Towers Watson Canada Inc. (1)
1800 McGill College Avenue Floor 22 Suite 2200, Montreal, H3A 3J6, QC, Canada
Tel.: (514) 982-9411
Risk Management & Human Resource Consulting Services
N.A.I.C.S.: 541612

Towers Watson Consulting (Shanghai) Limited (1)
11th Floor Kerry Center 1515 West Nanjing Road, Shanghai, 200040, China
Tel.: (86) 2150298088
Web Site: http://www.towerswatson.com
Human Capital & Financial Management Services
N.A.I.C.S.: 541611

Towers Watson Consultores Colombia S.A. (1)
Carrera 7 No 74-09, Ed Deloitte, Bogota, Colombia
Tel.: (57) 6014262000
Human Capital & Financial Management Services
N.A.I.C.S.: 541611

Towers Watson Consultoria Ltda. (1)
Condominio Parque da Cidade Av Das Nacoes Unidas, 14 40116 andar - Torre Sucupira Chacara Santo Antonio, Sao Paulo, 04794-000, Brazil
Tel.: (55) 1121616000
Risk Management & Human Resource Consulting Services
N.A.I.C.S.: 541618

Towers Watson Data Services, Inc. (1)
44 S Broadway, White Plains, NY 10601-4411
Tel.: (914) 289-3200
Web Site: http://www.twdataservices.com
Global Compensation, Benefits & Employment Practices Services
N.A.I.C.S.: 541612

Towers Watson Hong Kong Limited (1)
36/F & 27/F Sun Hung Kai Centre 30 Harbour Road, Wanchai, China (Hong Kong)
Tel.: (852) 2195 5500
Web Site: http://www.towerswatson.com
Human Capital & Financial Management Services
N.A.I.C.S.: 541611

Towers Watson India Private Limited (1)
Unitech Business Park Tower B 2nd Floor South City 1 Sector 41, Gurgaon, 122002, Haryana, India
Tel.: (91) 124 432 2800
Web Site: http://www.willistowerswatson.com
Human Capital & Financial Management Services
N.A.I.C.S.: 541611

Towers Watson Investment Management (Ireland) Limited (1)
Trinity Point 10-11 Leinster Street South, Dublin, Ireland
Tel.: (353) 16616448
Insurance Brokerage Services
N.A.I.C.S.: 551112

Towers Watson Italia S.r.l. (1)
Via Pola 9, 20124, Milan, Italy
Tel.: (39) 0263780101
Human Capital & Financial Management Services
N.A.I.C.S.: 541611

Towers Watson K.K. (1)
Hibiya Park Front 13F 2-1-6 Uchisaiwai-Cho, Chiyoda-ku Chiyoda-ku, Tokyo, 100-0011, Japan
Tel.: (81) 368334600
Web Site: http://www.towerswatson.com
Human Capital & Financial Management Services
N.A.I.C.S.: 541611

Towers Watson LLC (1)
11 Gogolevsky Boulevard Floor 8, 119019, Moscow, Russia
Tel.: (7) 495 956 3435
N.A.I.C.S.: 541618

Towers Watson Limited (1)
21 Tothill Street Westminster, London, SW1H 9LL, United Kingdom
Tel.: (44) 1737241144
Web Site: http://www.willistowerswatson.com
Human Capital & Financial Management Services
N.A.I.C.S.: 541611

Towers Watson Management Consulting (Shenzhen) Co., Ltd. (1)
Unit 801-802 Tower One Kerry Plaza No1 Zhong Xin Si Road, Fution District, Shenzhen, 518048, China
Tel.: (86) 75523373999
Risk Management & Human Resource Consulting Services
N.A.I.C.S.: 541618

Towers Watson Mexico, Agente de Seguros, S.A. de C.V. (1)
Edificio Cervantes 169 Blvd Miguel de Cervantes Saavedra Floor 8, col Ampliacion Granada, 11520, Mexico, Mexico
Tel.: (52) 5553506000
Human Capital & Financial Management Consultant Services
N.A.I.C.S.: 541611

Towers Watson Middle East FZ-LLC (1)
Gate Village 4 Floor 2 Unit 209 210 DIFC Unit 209, Near Dubai Internet City Metro Station, Dubai, United Arab Emirates
Tel.: (971) 44294700
Risk Management & Human Resource Consulting Services
N.A.I.C.S.: 541618

Towers Watson NV (1)
Serenitas Building A avenue Van Nieuwenhuyse 2 Van Nieuwenhuyselaan, Brussels, 1160, Belgium
Tel.: (32) 26781550
Web Site: http://www.willistowerswatson.com
Risk Management & Human Resource Consulting Services
N.A.I.C.S.: 541618

Towers Watson Netherlands B.V. (1)
Prof EM Meijerslaan 5, 1183 AV, Amstelveen, Netherlands
Tel.: (31) 885433000
Human Capital & Financial Management Services
N.A.I.C.S.: 541611

Towers Watson Pension Services BV (1)
Fascinatio Boulevard 238, 3065 WB, Rotterdam, Netherlands
Tel.: (31) 885433000
Insurance Brokerage Services
N.A.I.C.S.: 551112

Towers Watson SA (Proprietary) Limited (1)
Illovo Edge 1 Harries Road Floor 2, Illovo, Johannesburg, 2196, South Africa
Tel.: (27) 115355400
Risk Management & Human Resource Consulting Services
N.A.I.C.S.: 541618

Towers Watson Superannuation Pty Ltd (1)
Level 32 385 Bourke Street, Melbourne, 3000, VIC, Australia
Tel.: (61) 386819800
Risk Management & Human Resource Consulting Services
N.A.I.C.S.: 541618

Towers Watson Vietnam Company Limited (1)
Saigon Trade Center 37 Ton Duc Thang Street, Ben Nghe Ward Suite 708 District 1, Ho Chi Minh City, Vietnam
Tel.: (84) 2839100976
Risk Management & Human Resource Consulting Services
N.A.I.C.S.: 541618

Towers Watson de Espana, S.A. (1)
Calle Martinez Villergas 52-52 5a Planta, 28027, Madrid, Spain
Tel.: (34) 915903009
Human Capital & Financial Management Services
N.A.I.C.S.: 541611

Trade Credit Brokers Limited (1)
Elm Park Merrion Road, Dublin, Ireland
Tel.: (353) 16396480
Insurance Agency Services
N.A.I.C.S.: 524210
Peter Boucher (Head-Trade Credit & Political Risk)

Trustee Principles Limited (1)
Willis Towers Watson House Merrion Road, Elm Park, Dublin, D04 P231, Ireland
Tel.: (353) 12682994
Web Site: https://www.trusteeprinciples.ie
Trust Services
N.A.I.C.S.: 523991
Bruce Mullen (Mng Dir)

WTW Services Spolka Z Ograniczona Odpowiedzialnoscia (1)
ul Sienkiewicza 34 a/10, 50-335, Wroclaw, Poland
Tel.: (48) 717494700
Web Site: http://www.wtwservices.pl
Product Warranty Insurance Services
N.A.I.C.S.: 524128

Willis Affinity SL (1)
Paseo De La Castellana, Madrid, Spain
Tel.: (34) 914233554
Insurance Brokerage Services
N.A.I.C.S.: 551112

Willis Chile Limitada (1)
Av Andres Bello 2457 Piso 23 Providencia Torre Costanera Center, Santiago, Chile
Tel.: (56) 223864000
Web Site: http://www.willischile.cl
Insurance Agency Services
N.A.I.C.S.: 524210

Willis Faber Dumas & Roland Risk Services (Pvt) Ltd. (1)
Celestial Office Park West Wing Ground Floor Block 3 Borrowdale Road, PO Box 774, Borrowdale, Harare, Zimbabwe
Tel.: (263) 24 288 52052
Web Site: http://www.willistowerswatson.com
Financial Services
N.A.I.C.S.: 523999

Willis Galicia Correduria de Seguros S.A. (1)
Calle Menendez Y Pelayo 8 - Piso 5, A Coruna, Spain
Tel.: (34) 981126644
Insurance Brokerage Services
N.A.I.C.S.: 551112

Willis Group Limited (1)
The Willis Building 51 Lime Street, London, EC3M 7DQ, United Kingdom
Tel.: (44) 2031246000
Web Site: http://www.willistowerswatson.com
Emp.: 10,450
Holding Company; Insurance Brokerage Services
N.A.I.C.S.: 551112

Subsidiary (Non-US):

AF Willis Bahrain WLL (2)
Al Raya Building 2nd Floor Building No 1025 Office 41-42 Road 3621, PO Box 10264, Block 436 Seef District, Manama, Bahrain
Tel.: (973) 17171661
Risk Management & Insurance Services
N.A.I.C.S.: 524210

Asifina S.A. (2)
San Martin 344 Piso 25, Buenos Aires, C1004AAH, Argentina
Tel.: (54) 1152182100
Web Site: http://www.willistowerswatson.com
Insurance Brokerage Services
N.A.I.C.S.: 524210

CXG Willis Correduria de Seguros S.A. (2)

WILLIS TOWERS WATSON PUBLIC LIMITED COMPANY — INTERNATIONAL PUBLIC

Willis Towers Watson Public Limited Company—(Continued)

Menendez y Pelayo Street 8 5th 6th Plant, 15005, A Coruna, Spain
Tel.: (34) 981126644
Web Site: http://www.willistowerswatson.com
Insurance Brokerage Services
N.A.I.C.S.: 524210

Claim Management Administrator, S.L. (2)
Calle de Martinez Villergas 52 Edificio 1 3 Planta, 28027, Madrid, Spain
Tel.: (34) 7248383
Web Site: https://www.cma.es
General Insurance Services
N.A.I.C.S.: 524210

Gras Savoye & Cie SAS (2)
2-8 Rue Ancelle, PO Box 129, 92200, Neuilly-sur-Seine, France
Tel.: (33) 141435000
Web Site: http://www.grassavoye.com
Holding Company; Insurance Brokerage Services
N.A.I.C.S.: 551112

Subsidiary (Non-US):

Gras Savoye Algerie Services EURL (3)
5 Rue des Pins, Hydra, Algiers, 16000, Algeria
Tel.: (213) 21694350
Web Site: http://www.grassavoye.com
Insurance Management & Brokerage Services
N.A.I.C.S.: 524210

Gras Savoye Belgium S.A. (3)
Zuiderlaan 91 Bus 7, 1731, Zellik, Brussels, Belgium
Tel.: (32) 24811914
Web Site: http://www.grassavoye.com
Insurance Brokerage Services
N.A.I.C.S.: 524210

Division (Domestic):

Gras Savoye Belgium S.A. - Hasselt (4)
Gouverneur Roppesingel 15 Bus 0 1 Kantoorgebouw Singelbeek I, Kantoorunit Ground Floor K1, Hasselt, 3500, Belgium
Tel.: (32) 11 57 23 78
Web Site: http://www.grassavoye.com
Insurance Brokerage Services
N.A.I.C.S.: 524210

Gras Savoye Belgium S.A. - Liege (4)
Quai des Vennes 18-20, 4020, Liege, Belgium
Tel.: (32) 43446767
Web Site: http://www.grassavoye.com
Insurance Brokerage Services
N.A.I.C.S.: 524210

Subsidiary (Non-US):

Gras Savoye Benin SA (3)
Boulevard Marina Carre 01, BP 6901, Cotonou, Benin
Tel.: (229) 21303130
Insurance Management Services
N.A.I.C.S.: 524298

Gras Savoye Brokers and Consultants Limited (3)
Old Moka Road, PO Box 766, Bell Village, Soreze, Mauritius
Tel.: (230) 286 4449
Web Site: http://www.brokersandconsultants.com
Insurance Management & Brokerage Services
N.A.I.C.S.: 524210
Jean Michel de Robillard *(Mng Dir)*

Gras Savoye Burkina SA (3)
BICIA-B Commercial Area Sector 4, BP 1304, Ouagadougou, Kadiogo, Burkina Faso
Tel.: (226) 25305880
Web Site: http://www.grassavoye.com
Insurance Management & Brokerage Services
N.A.I.C.S.: 524210

Gras Savoye Cameroun SA (3)
Immeuble Wuitcheu 578 rue Christian Tobie Kuoh, BP 3014, Douala, Cameroon
Tel.: (237) 33 43 21 22
Web Site: http://www.grassavoye.com
Insurance Management & Brokerage Services
N.A.I.C.S.: 524210
Fayez Samb *(CEO & Gen Mgr)*

Gras Savoye Caraibes (3)
BP 2064, Jarry, 97192, Pointe-a-Pitre, Cedex, Leeward Islands, Guadeloupe
Tel.: (590) 32 65 56
Web Site: http://www.grassavoye.com
Insurance Management Services
N.A.I.C.S.: 524298

Gras Savoye Congo SA (3)
118 Avenue Fayette Tchitembo, BP 1901, Quartier Plateau Centre Ville, Pointe Noire, Congo, Republic of
Tel.: (242) 6 667 12 12
Web Site: http://www.grassavoye.com
Insurance Management & Brokerage Services
N.A.I.C.S.: 524210

Gras Savoye Cote D'Ivoire SA (3)
Immeuble The Green 01 Nogues Avenue Abidjan Plateau Floor 1, BP 5675, Abidjan, 01, Cote d'Ivoire
Tel.: (225) 20252510
Web Site: http://www.grassavoye.com
Insurance Management & Brokerage Services
N.A.I.C.S.: 524210

Gras Savoye Egypte SAE (3)
3 Al Mansur Mohamed St, Zamalek, Cairo, Egypt
Tel.: (20) 2 2737 34 11
Web Site: http://www.grassavoye.com
Financial Consulting Services
N.A.I.C.S.: 541618
Hamed Mabrouk *(Mng Dir)*

Gras Savoye Gabon SA (3)
Avenue Colonel Parant, BP 2148, Libreville, Gabon
Tel.: (241) 1743153
Insurance Management & Brokerage Services
N.A.I.C.S.: 524210

Gras Savoye Guinee SA (3)
5eme Avenue & 5eme Boulevard Quartier Manquepas, BP 6441, Conakry, Guinea
Tel.: (224) 67 45 58 43
Web Site: http://www.grassavoye.com
Insurance Management & Brokerage Services
N.A.I.C.S.: 524210

Gras Savoye Luxembourg SA (3)
145 Rue du Kiem, Strassen, 8030, Luxembourg, Luxembourg
Tel.: (352) 469601300
Web Site: http://www.grassavoye.com
Insurance Brokerage Services
N.A.I.C.S.: 524210

Gras Savoye Mali SA (3)
Avenue Moussa Travele Immeuble Sogefih Floor 3, BP E5691, Quatier du Fleuve, Bamako, Mali
Tel.: (223) 20226475
Insurance Management & Brokerage Services
N.A.I.C.S.: 524210

Gras Savoye Maroc (3)
40 Boulevard Moulay Youssef, 20300, Casablanca, Morocco
Tel.: (212) 522889595
Web Site: https://www.askgs.ma
Emp.: 320
Insurance Management & Brokerage Services
N.A.I.C.S.: 524210

Gras Savoye Mauritanie - Rema Broking SA (3)
Moctar Ould Daddah Rue n 26015 - Cite SMAR, BP 2713, Quartier Tevragh Zeina Avenue, Nouakchott, Mauritania
Tel.: (222) 45 29 19 29
Web Site: http://www.grassavoye.com
Insurance Management & Brokerage Services

Gras Savoye Niger SA (3)
8 Rue du Grand Hotel, BP 10661, Niamey, Niger
Tel.: (227) 20744023
Insurance Brokerage Services
N.A.I.C.S.: 524210

Gras Savoye Nouvelle Caledonie SA (3)
Immeuble Le Latino 67 rue de Sebastopol Quartier Latin, BP 829, 98845, Noumea, Cedex, New Caledonia
Tel.: (687) 24 25 50
Web Site: http://www.grassavoye.com
Insurance Management & Brokerage Services
N.A.I.C.S.: 524210

Gras Savoye Ocean Indien (3)
5 Rue Andre Lardy Business Center of the Mare Building B Level R1, 97438, Sainte-Marie, Reunion
Tel.: (262) 200656
Insurance Management & Brokerage Services
N.A.I.C.S.: 524210

Gras Savoye RDC SA (3)
10/13 avenue Mutombo Katshi Immeuble Kavali Center, BP 9980, Gombe, Kinshasa, Congo, Democratic Republic of
Tel.: (243) 810 838 870
Web Site: http://www.grassavoye.com
Insurance Management & Brokerage Services
N.A.I.C.S.: 524210

Gras Savoye Romania SRL (3)
Calea Floreasca nr 133-137 Sector 1, CP 014456, Bucharest, Romania
Tel.: (40) 21 231 91 69
Web Site: http://www.grassavoye.com
Insurance Brokerage Services
N.A.I.C.S.: 524210

Subsidiary (Domestic):

Gras Savoye SAS (3)
Immeuble Quai 33 33 quai de Dion Bouton, CS 70001, 92814, Puteaux, Cedex, France
Tel.: (33) 141435000
Web Site: http://www.grassavoye.fr
Risk Management & Insurance Brokerage Services
N.A.I.C.S.: 524210

Subsidiary (Non-US):

Gras Savoye Senegal SA (3)
Immeuble Isocele au Point E Rue de Diourbel x Rond-Point de l'Ellipse, BP 9, Dakar, Senegal
Tel.: (221) 33 859 40 51
Web Site: http://www.grassavoye.com
Insurance Management & Brokerage Services
N.A.I.C.S.: 524210

Gras Savoye Tahiti Nui Insurance SA (3)
Immeuble Budan Rue des Remparts, BP 40200, 98713, Papeete, French Polynesia
Tel.: (689) 544844
Insurance Management & Brokerage Services
N.A.I.C.S.: 524210

Gras Savoye Tchad SA (3)
Avenue Idriss Miskine, BP 5620, N'djamena, Chad
Tel.: (235) 22 52 00 72
Web Site: http://www.grassavoye.com
Insurance Management & Brokerage Services
N.A.I.C.S.: 524210

Gras Savoye Togo SA (3)
140 Boulevard du 13 Janvier, BP 2932, Lome, Togo
Tel.: (228) 22213538
Insurance Management & Brokerage Services
N.A.I.C.S.: 524210

Gras Savoye Tunisie (3)
Avenue du Japon Immeuble Ennouzha - Bloc Amira Appartements A3-1 A3-2, Montplaisir, 1073, Tunis, Tunisia
Tel.: (216) 71906767

Insurance Management & Brokerage Services
N.A.I.C.S.: 524210
Elyes Darghouth *(Mng Dir)*

Gras Savoye Ukraine LLC (3)
8 Illinka Street Block 1 Floor 3, 04070, Kiev, Ukraine
Tel.: (380) 442306984
Insurance Management & Brokerage Services
N.A.I.C.S.: 524210

Gras Savoye Willis SA (3)
Evripidou 2A Street Syngrou Ave Kallithea, Athens, 17674, Greece
Tel.: (30) 2109473700
Web Site: http://www.grassavoye.com
Insurance Brokerage Services
N.A.I.C.S.: 524210

Gras Savoye Willis Vietnam Co., Ltd. (3)
Saigon Trade Centre - Suite 708 37 Ton Duc Thang Street, District 1, Ho Chi Minh City, Vietnam
Tel.: (84) 2839100976
Web Site: http://www.willistowerswatson.com
Insurance Management & Brokerage Services
N.A.I.C.S.: 524210

Subsidiary (Domestic):

Sageris SARL (3)
Immeuble Quai 33 33 Quai de Dion Bouton, CS 70001, Puteaux, 92814, Paris, Cedex, France
Tel.: (33) 141435430
Web Site: http://www.grassavoye.com
Risk Managemeng Srvices
N.A.I.C.S.: 541611

Subsidiary (Non-US):

Kieffer & Asociados S.A. (2)
Av Roca y Coronado 3125 entre 3er y 4to anillo, Casilla 1387, Santa Cruz, Bolivia
Tel.: (591) 33331809
Web Site: https://www.kieffer-asociados.com.bo
Insurance Services
N.A.I.C.S.: 524210
Gonzalo Kieffer Guzman *(Pres, CEO & Coord-Intl Accounts)*

PT Willis Indonesia (2)
Chase Plaza 10th floor Jl Jend Sudirman, Kav 21, Jakarta, 12920, Selatan, Indonesia
Tel.: (62) 2130447900
Risk Management & Insurance Services
N.A.I.C.S.: 524210

Richard Oliver Underwriting Managers Pty Limited (2)
Level 4 555 Bourke Street, Melbourne, 3000, VIC, Australia
Tel.: (61) 386819909
Web Site: https://www.roum.com.au
Insurance Brokerage Services
N.A.I.C.S.: 524210
Michael Falzon *(Acct Mgr-Marine Insurance)*

Rontarca Willis, C.A. (2)
Calle 3B Edificio Murrieta, PO Box 75918, La Urbina, Caracas, 1070, Venezuela
Tel.: (58) 212 204 51 11
Web Site: http://www.rontarcaprimawillis.com
Insurance Services
N.A.I.C.S.: 524210
Juan Bautista Arismendi *(Chm)*

Trinity Square Insurance Limited (2)
Ste 827 Europort, PO Box 708, GX11 1AA, Gibraltar, Gibraltar
Tel.: (350) 20051801
Web Site: http://www.willistowerswatson.com
Insurance Brokerage Services
N.A.I.C.S.: 524210

Willis (Bermuda) 2 Limited (2)
90 Pitts Bay Road Wellesley House Floor 2, Pembroke Parish, Hamilton, HM 08, Bermuda
Tel.: (441) 2796700
Insurance Brokerage Services
N.A.I.C.S.: 524210

AND PRIVATE COMPANIES — WILLIS TOWERS WATSON PUBLIC LIMITED COMPANY

Willis (Bermuda) Limited (2)
90 Pitts Bay Road Wellesley House Floor 2, Hamilton, HM 08, Pembroke Parish, Bermuda
Tel.: (441) 2796700
Insurance Services
N.A.I.C.S.: 524210

Willis (Taiwan) Limited (2)
14F No 68 Sec 5 Zhongxiao East Road, Xinyi Dist, Taipei, 00110, Taiwan
Tel.: (886) 2 2176 9068
Web Site:
 http://www.willistowerswatson.com
Risk Management & Insurance Services
N.A.I.C.S.: 523910

Willis AB (2)
Lastmakargatan 22 KV Boeken 35 Floor 1, PO Box 7273, 114 44, Stockholm, Sweden
Tel.: (46) 84638900
Risk Management & Insurance Services
N.A.I.C.S.: 524210

Division (Domestic):

Willis AB (Gothenburg) (3)
Drakegatan 5, 412 50, Gothenburg, Sweden
Tel.: (46) 317787700
Web Site: http://www.willis.se
Risk Management & Insurance Services
N.A.I.C.S.: 524210

Subsidiary (Non-US):

Willis AG (2)
Seehofstr 6, 8008, Zurich, Switzerland
Tel.: (41) 434884400
Web Site:
 http://www.willistowerswatson.com
Insurance Brokerage Services
N.A.I.C.S.: 524210

Willis Australia Limited (2)
Level 16/ 123 Pitt Street, Sydney, 2000, NSW, Australia
Tel.: (61) 292854000
Web Site:
 http://www.willistowerswatson.com
Risk Management & Insurance Services
N.A.I.C.S.: 523910

Subsidiary (Domestic):

Willis Australia Group Services Pty Limited (3)
Level 4 555 Bourke Street, Melbourne, 3000, VIC, Australia
Tel.: (61) 386819800
Web Site: http://www.willis.com.au
Insurance Brokerage Services
N.A.I.C.S.: 524210

Willis Australia Holdings Limited (3)
Level 4 555 Bourke Street, Melbourne, 3000, VIC, Australia
Tel.: (61) 386819800
Web Site: http://www.willis.com.au
Insurance Brokerage Services
N.A.I.C.S.: 524210

Willis Reinsurance Australia Limited (3)
Level 16 123 Pitt Street, Sydney, 2000, NSW, Australia
Tel.: (61) 292337733
Web Site: http://www.willisre.com
Risk Management & Reinsurance Services
N.A.I.C.S.: 524130

Subsidiary (Non-US):

Willis B.V. (2)
De Ruyterkade 7, PO Box 1315, 1013 AA, Amsterdam, Netherlands
Tel.: (31) 205312525
Web Site:
 http://www.willistowerswatson.com
Risk Management & Insurance Services
N.A.I.C.S.: 524210

Willis CIS Insurance Broker LLC (2)
ul Ostozhenka 28, 119034, Moscow, Russia
Tel.: (7) 4959563435
Web Site:
 http://www.willistowerswatson.com
Risk Management & Insurance Services
N.A.I.C.S.: 524210

Willis Corredores de Reaseguro Limitada (2)
Avenida Apoquindo 3846 Piso 14, Las Condes, Chile
Tel.: (56) 2 2386 4000
Web Site:
 http://www.willistowerswatson.com
Insurance Brokerage Services
N.A.I.C.S.: 524210

Willis Corredores de Reaseguros S.A. (2)
Av Calle 26 No 59-41 Piso 6, Bogota, Colombia
Tel.: (57) 16067575
Web Site:
 http://www.willistowerswatson.com
Insurance Brokerage Services
N.A.I.C.S.: 524210

Willis Corredores de Seguros SA (2)
Av De La Floresta 497 Piso 6 - Oficina 604, Lima, Peru
Tel.: (51) 17000202
Web Site: http://www.willis.com.pe
Insurance Brokerage Services
N.A.I.C.S.: 524210

Willis Corretaje de Reaseguros S.A (2)
Edificia Murrieta Calle 3B de La Urbina Floor 2, Caracas, 1070-A, Miranda, Venezuela
Tel.: (58) 251 204 51 11
Web Site:
 http://www.willistowerswatson.com
Risk Management & Insurance Services
N.A.I.C.S.: 523910

Willis Corretores de Seguros Ltda (2)
Rua Alexandre Dumas 2100 Chacara Santo Antonio Zona Sul, Sao Paulo, 04717-004, Brazil
Tel.: (55) 1151819377
Web Site: http://www.willis.com
Risk Management & Insurance Services
N.A.I.C.S.: 524210

Willis Corretores de Seguros S.A (2)
Avenida Da Liberdade 49 Floor 3, Lisbon, 0125-139, Portugal
Tel.: (351) 213222800
Web Site: http://www.willis.com
Risk Management & Insurance Services
N.A.I.C.S.: 524210

Willis Global Markets B.V. (2)
Hoogoorddreef 60-Centerp I, Amsterdam, 1101 BE, Netherlands
Tel.: (31) 205312525
Web Site:
 http://www.willistowerswatson.com
Insurance Brokerage Services
N.A.I.C.S.: 524210

Willis GmbH (2)
Thomas-Klestil-Platz 13, Orbi Tower, 1030, Vienna, Austria
Tel.: (43) 17159474
Risk Management & Insurance Services
N.A.I.C.S.: 524210

Willis Holding AB (2)
Lastmakargatan 22 KV Boeken 35 Floor 1, 114 44, Stockholm, Sweden
Tel.: (46) 84638900
Investment Management Service
N.A.I.C.S.: 523999

Willis Hong Kong Limited (2)
Lee Garden Three 1 Sunning Road Floor 17, Causeway Bay, China (Hong Kong)
Tel.: (852) 21955500
Risk Management & Insurance Services
N.A.I.C.S.: 524210

Willis Insurance Brokers (B) Sdn Bhd (2)
3rd Floor Scouts Headquarters Building, Bandar Seri Begawan, Brunei Darussalam
Tel.: (673) 2427800
Web Site: http://www.willis.com
Risk Management & Insurance Services
N.A.I.C.S.: 524210

Willis Insurance Brokers LLC (2)
2A Konstantynovskaya Street Office 400, Kiev, 04071, Ukraine
Tel.: (380) 442306984

Web Site:
 http://www.willistowerswatson.com
Insurance Brokerage Services
N.A.I.C.S.: 524210

Willis Italia S.p.A. (2)
Via Pola 9, 20124, Milan, Italy
Tel.: (39) 0247787301
Risk Management & Insurance Services
N.A.I.C.S.: 524210

Willis Japan Holdings KK (2)
Toranomon Kotohira Tower 12F 2-8 Toranomon 1-chome, Minato-ku, Tokyo, 105-0001, Japan
Tel.: (81) 368334600
Web Site: http://www.willis.com
Investment Management Service
N.A.I.C.S.: 523999

Willis Japan Limited (2)
12th Fl Toranomon Kotohira Tower 2-8, Tokyo, 105-0001, Japan
Tel.: (81) 335002524
Web Site: http://www.willis.com
Risk Management & Insurance Services
N.A.I.C.S.: 524126

Subsidiary (Domestic):

Willis Japan Services KK (3)
Toranomon Kotohira Tower 12f 2-8 Toranomon 1-chome, Minato-ku, Tokyo, 105-0001, Japan
Tel.: (81) 368334600
Web Site:
 http://www.willistowerswatson.com
Insurance Brokerage Services
N.A.I.C.S.: 524210

Subsidiary (Domestic):

Willis Limited (2)
51 Lime Street, London, EC3M 7DQ, United Kingdom
Tel.: (44) 2031246000
Holding Company; Reinsurance Brokerage Services
N.A.I.C.S.: 551112
Nicolas Aubert (CEO)

Subsidiary (Domestic):

Willis Towers Watson Securities Europe Limited (3)
51 Lime Street, London, EC3M 7DQ, United Kingdom
Tel.: (44) 2031246000
Financial Advisory Services
N.A.I.C.S.: 523940

Subsidiary (Non-US):

Willis Management (Labuan) Limited (2)
Menara Komtar Johor Bahru City Centre Level 19, 80000, Johor Bahru, Malaysia
Tel.: (60) 321709888
Insurance Brokerage Services
N.A.I.C.S.: 524210

Willis Management (Stockholm) AB (2)
Lastmakargatan 22 KV Boeken 35 Floor 1, 114 44, Stockholm, Sweden
Tel.: (46) 84638900
Insurance Brokerage Services
N.A.I.C.S.: 524210

Willis Nederland B.V. (2)
Herikerbergweg 238 Luna Arena, PO Box 12733, Amsterdam, 1101 CM, Netherlands
Tel.: (31) 205755600
Web Site:
 http://www.willistowerswatson.com
General Insurance Services
N.A.I.C.S.: 524210

Willis Netherlands Holdings BV (2)
Web Site:
 http://www.willistowerswatson.com
Financial Management Services
N.A.I.C.S.: 523999

Willis New Zealand Limited (2)
Level 8 21 Queen Street, PO Box 369, Auckland, 1140, New Zealand
Tel.: (64) 93583319
Web Site:
 http://www.willistowerswatson.com
Risk Management & Insurance Services
N.A.I.C.S.: 523910

Subsidiary (US):

Willis North America, Inc. (2)
200 Liberty St Fl 6, New York, NY 10281
Tel.: (212) 915-8888
Risk Management & Insurance Services
N.A.I.C.S.: 524210

Subsidiary (Domestic):

Freberg Environmental, Inc. (3)
1743 Wazee St Ste 450, Denver, CO 80202
Tel.: (303) 534-1171
Web Site: https://www.feiinsurance.com
Insurance Program Administrative Services
N.A.I.C.S.: 524210
Stacy D. Brown (Prés & CEO)

Willis Administrative Services Corporation (3)
26 Century Blvd One Century Pl N Tower Fl 3, Columbus, OH 43220
Tel.: (615) 872-3000
Web Site:
 http://www.willistowerswatson.com
Business Management Consulting Services
N.A.I.C.S.: 541611

Division (Domestic):

Willis Construction Division (3)
26 Century Blvd Ste 101, Nashville, TN 37214
Tel.: (615) 872-3000
Web Site:
 http://www.willistowerswatson.com
Insurance Services
N.A.I.C.S.: 524298

Subsidiary (Domestic):

Willis Insurance Services of California, Inc. (3)
Ste 900 One Bush St, San Francisco, CA 94104
Tel.: (415) 955-0100
Web Site:
 http://www.willistowerswatson.com
Risk Management & Insurance Services
N.A.I.C.S.: 524210

Willis Insurance Services of Georgia, Inc. (3)
5 Concourse Pkwy Fl 1800, Atlanta, GA 30328
Tel.: (404) 224-5000
Web Site:
 http://www.willistowerswatson.com
Risk Management & Insurance Services
N.A.I.C.S.: 524210
Rob Allen (Pres, CEO & Head-Corp Risk & Broking)

Willis Personal Lines, LLC (3)
16220 N Scottsdale Rd Ste 600, Scottsdale, AZ 85254
Tel.: (602) 787-6000
Web Site: http://www.willispersonallines.com
Insurance Brokerage Services
N.A.I.C.S.: 524210
Tyler Banks (CEO)

Willis Programs of Connecticut, Inc. (3)
10 State House Sq Fl 11, Hartford, CT 06103
Tel.: (860) 278-1320
Insurance Program Administrative Services
N.A.I.C.S.: 923130

Willis Securities, Inc. (3)
One World Financial Ctr 200 Liberty St 3rd Fl, New York, NY 10281
Tel.: (212) 915-8888
Web Site:
 http://www.willistowerswatson.com
Securities Brokerage Services
N.A.I.C.S.: 523150

Willis Towers Watson Management (Vermont), Limited (3)
38 Eastwood Dr Ste 300 S, Burlington, VT 05403
Tel.: (802) 658-9466
Risk Management & Insurance Services
N.A.I.C.S.: 524210

Willis of Alabama, Inc. (3)
11 N Water St Fl 19 Ste 19290 Battle

WILLIS TOWERS WATSON PUBLIC LIMITED COMPANY

Willis Towers Watson Public Limited Company—(Continued)
House Tower, Mobile, AL 36602
Tel.: (251) 433-0441
Risk Management & Insurance Services
N.A.I.C.S.: 523910

Willis of Arizona, Inc. (3)
11201 N Tatum Blvd Ste 300, Phoenix, AZ 85028
Tel.: (602) 279-3600
Web Site: http://www.willistowerswatson.com
Risk Management & Insurance Services
N.A.I.C.S.: 524210

Willis of Colorado, Inc. (3)
2000 S Colorado Blvd Tower II Ste 900, Denver, CO 80222
Tel.: (303) 722-7776
Web Site: http://www.willistowerswatson.com
Insurance Brokerage Services
N.A.I.C.S.: 524210

Willis of Connecticut, LLC (3)
10 State House Sq Fl 11, Hartford, CT 06103
Tel.: (860) 278-1320
Web Site: http://www.willistowerswatson.com
Risk Management & Insurance Services
N.A.I.C.S.: 524210

Willis of Florida, Inc. (3)
3407 W Dr M L King Jr Blvd Lakeside Ste 200, Tampa, FL 33607
Tel.: (813) 323-9500
Risk Management & Insurance Services
N.A.I.C.S.: 524210

Willis of Illinois, Inc. (3)
233 S Wacker Dr Willis Twr Ste 1800, Chicago, IL 60606
Tel.: (312) 288-7700
Risk Management & Insurance Services
N.A.I.C.S.: 524210

Willis of Louisiana, Inc. (3)
909 Poydras St 1100, New Orleans, LA 70112
Tel.: (504) 581-6151
Web Site: http://www.willistowerswatson.com
Risk Management & Insurance Services
N.A.I.C.S.: 524210

Willis of Maryland, Inc. (3)
225 Schilling Cir Ste 150, Hunt Valley, MD 21031
Tel.: (410) 771-3838
Risk Management & Insurance Services
N.A.I.C.S.: 524210

Willis of Massachusetts, Inc. (3)
75 Arlington St Fl 2, Boston, MA 02116
Tel.: (617) 638-3700
Risk Management & Insurance Services
N.A.I.C.S.: 524210

Willis of Michigan, Inc. (3)
32255 Northwestern Hwy Ste 201, Farmington Hills, MI 48334
Tel.: (248) 539-6601
Web Site: http://www.willistowerswatson.com
Risk Management & Insurance Services
N.A.I.C.S.: 524210

Willis of Minnesota, Inc. (3)
8400 Normandale Lake Blvd Ste 1700, Minneapolis, MN 55437
Tel.: (952) 842-7000
Risk Management & Insurance Services
N.A.I.C.S.: 524210

Willis of New Hampshire, Inc. (3)
155 Fleet St, Portsmouth, NH 03801-4050
Tel.: (603) 334-3000
Risk Management & Insurance Services
N.A.I.C.S.: 524210

Willis of New Jersey, Inc. (3)
150 JFK Pkwy Ste 520, Short Hills, NJ 07078
Tel.: (973) 539-1923
Risk Management & Insurance Services
N.A.I.C.S.: 524210

Willis of New York, Inc. (3)
200 Liberty St Fl 6, New York, NY 10281
Tel.: (212) 915-8888
Risk Management & Insurance Services
N.A.I.C.S.: 524210

Willis of North Carolina, Inc. (3)
214 N Tryon St Ste 2500 Hearst Tower, Charlotte, NC 28202
Tel.: (704) 376-9161
Web Site: http://www.willis.com
Risk Management & Insurance Services
N.A.I.C.S.: 524210

Willis of Ohio, Inc. (3)
775 Yard St Fl 2 Ste 200, Columbus, OH 43212
Tel.: (614) 457-7000
Web Site: http://www.willistowerswatson.com
Insurance Brokerage Services
N.A.I.C.S.: 524210
Frank McKain (Pres & CEO)

Willis of Oklahoma, Inc. (3)
Two Leadership Sq 211 N Robinson Ave Ste S 700, Oklahoma City, OK 73102
Tel.: (405) 232-0651
Web Site: http://www.willistowerswatson.com
Insurance Brokerage Services
N.A.I.C.S.: 524210

Willis of Oregon, Inc. (3)
222 SW Columbia St Ste 600, Portland, OR 97201
Tel.: (503) 224-4155
Web Site: http://www.willistowerswatson.com
Risk Management & Insurance Services
N.A.I.C.S.: 524210

Willis of Pennsylvania, Inc. (3)
444 Liberty Ave Ste 505, Pittsburgh, PA 15222
Tel.: (412) 402-4500
Web Site: http://www.willistowerswatson.com
Risk Management & Insurance Services
N.A.I.C.S.: 524210

Willis of Seattle, Inc. (3)
600 University St Ste 3100, Seattle, WA 98101-1125
Tel.: (206) 625-1125
Risk Management & Insurance Services
N.A.I.C.S.: 524210

Willis of Tennessee, Inc. (3)
265 Brookview Ctr Way Brookview Promenade Fl 5 Ste 505, Knoxville, TN 37919
Tel.: (865) 588-8101
Risk Management & Insurance Services
N.A.I.C.S.: 524210

Willis of Texas, Inc. (3)
15305 N Dallas Pkwy Ste 1100, Addison, TX 75001
Tel.: (972) 385-9800
Web Site: http://www.willistowerswatson.com
Insurance Services
N.A.I.C.S.: 524210

Willis of Virginia, Inc. (3)
4951 Lake Brook Dr Ste 300, Glen Allen, VA 23060
Tel.: (804) 747-0200
Web Site: http://www.willistowerswatson.com
Insurance Brokerage Services
N.A.I.C.S.: 524210

Willis of Wisconsin, Inc. (3)
City Ctr E 122 E College Ave Unit 201, Appleton, WI 54911
Tel.: (920) 739-7711
Web Site: http://www.willistowerswatson.com
Insurance Services
N.A.I.C.S.: 524298

Willis of Wyoming, Inc. (3)
415 W 17th St 1E, Cheyenne, WY 82001
Tel.: (307) 634-5566
Insurance Brokerage Services
N.A.I.C.S.: 524210

Subsidiary (Non-US):

Willis Oy AB (2)
Hitsaajankatu 9 A, 00810, Helsinki, Finland
Tel.: (358) 96226870
Web Site:
Risk Management & Insurance Services
N.A.I.C.S.: 524210

Willis Processing Services (India) Private Limited
Godrej & Boyce Compound Plant No 6 L B S Marg, Vikhroli West, Mumbai, 400 079, India
Tel.: (91) 2225192000
Web Site: http://www.willistowerswatson.com
Insurance Brokerage Services
N.A.I.C.S.: 524210

Willis Re (Pty) Limited (2)
54 Wierda Rd West Wierda Valley, Sandton, 2196, South Africa
Tel.: (27) 11 341 9600
Web Site: http://www.willisre.com
Insurance Brokerage Services
N.A.I.C.S.: 524210

Willis Re Bermuda Limited (2)
Wessex House 45 Reid Street, Hamilton, HM 12, Bermuda
Tel.: (441) 2955278
Insurance Brokerage Services
N.A.I.C.S.: 524210

Willis Re Canada Inc. (2)
130 King Street West Exchange Tower Suite 1500, PO Box 424, Toronto, M5X 1E3, ON, Canada
Tel.: (416) 960-2700
Insurance Brokerage Services
N.A.I.C.S.: 524210

Willis Re GmbH (2)
Nymphenburger Strasse 5, Munich, 80335, Germany
Tel.: (49) 8954336187
Web Site: http://www.willistowerswatson.com
Insurance Brokerage Services
N.A.I.C.S.: 524210

Willis Re GmbH (2)
Nymphenburger Strasse 5, 80335, Munich, Germany
Tel.: (49) 8954336187
Web Site: http://www.willisre.com
Insurance Brokerage Services
N.A.I.C.S.: 524210

Willis Re Japan K.K. (2)
Toranomon Kotohira Tower 12F 2-8 Toranomon 1-chome, Minato-ku, Tokyo, 105-0001, Japan
Tel.: (81) 335002525
Web Site: http://www.willisre.com
Insurance Brokerage Services
N.A.I.C.S.: 524210

Willis Re Labuan Limited (2)
Suite 11 3 11th Floor Menara CIMB Jalan Stesen Sentral Dua, Letter Box No 56, Kuala Lumpur, 50470, Malaysia
Tel.: (60) 320821600
Web Site: http://www.willisre.com
Emp.: 5
Insurance Brokerage Services
N.A.I.C.S.: 524210

Willis Re Nordic Reinsurance Broking (Norway) AS (2)
Drammensveien 147B skoyen, PO Box 344, Lilleaker, 0213, Oslo, Norway
Tel.: (47) 24 12 63 40
Web Site: http://www.willisre.com
Insurance Brokerage Services
N.A.I.C.S.: 524210

Willis Risk Services (Ireland) Limited (2)
Willis Towers Watson House Elm Park Merrion Road, Dublin, Ireland
Tel.: (353) 16616211
Insurance Brokerage Services
N.A.I.C.S.: 524210

Subsidiary (Domestic):

Willis Trustsure Limited (3)
Willis Towers Watson House Elm Park Merrion Road, Dublin, D04 P231, Ireland
Tel.: (353) 1 661 6211
Web Site: http://www.willis.ie
Insurance Brokerage Services
N.A.I.C.S.: 524210

INTERNATIONAL PUBLIC

Subsidiary (Non-US):

Willis Risk Services Holdings (Ireland) Limited (2)
Willis Towers Watson House Elm Park Merrion Road, Dublin, Ireland
Tel.: (353) 1 661 6211
Web Site: http://www.willistowerswatson.com
Investment Management Service
N.A.I.C.S.: 523999

Willis S & C c Correduria de Seguros y Reaseguros SA (2)
Paseo Gracia 54-Primera Plt, Barcelona, 8007, Spain
Tel.: (34) 934 156 267
Web Site: http://www.willistowerswatson.com
Insurance Brokerage Services
N.A.I.C.S.: 524210

Willis Saudi Arabia Company Limited (2)
Adil Kashoggi Building Dhahran Street 20104, PO Box 20104, Al Khobar, 31952, Saudi Arabia
Tel.: (966) 138948400
Web Site: http://www.willistowerswatson.com
Insurance Brokerage Services
N.A.I.C.S.: 524210

Willis Slovakia o.z. (2)
Safarikovo nam 4, 811 02, Bratislava, Slovakia
Tel.: (421) 252 635 062
Web Site: http://www.willis.sk
Insurance Brokerage Services
N.A.I.C.S.: 524210

Willis South Africa (Pty) Limited (2)
1st Floor Eversheds Building 22 Fredman Drive Illovo, Sandton, 2196, South Africa
Tel.: (27) 115355400
Web Site: http://www.willistowerswatson.com
Insurance Brokerage Services
N.A.I.C.S.: 524210

Willis Towers Watson A/S (2)
Rundforbivej 303, Naerum, 2850, Copenhagen, Denmark (85%)
Tel.: (45) 88139600
Emp.: 450
Risk Management & Insurance Services
N.A.I.C.S.: 524210
Reiner Rudi Schwinger (Chm)

Subsidiary (Domestic):

Willis Towers Watson A/S (Aalborg) (3)
Ostre Havnevej 12, DK-9000, Aalborg, Denmark
Tel.: (45) 88139600
Web Site: http://www.willistowerswatson.com
Risk Management & Insurance Services
N.A.I.C.S.: 524210

Willis Towers Watson A/S (Aarhus) (3)
Tangen 17, 8200, Arhus, Denmark
Tel.: (45) 88139600
Risk Management & Insurance Services
N.A.I.C.S.: 524210

Subsidiary (Non-US):

Willis Towers Watson A/S (2)
Drammensveien 145, PO Box 344, Skoyen, 0277, Oslo, Norway
Tel.: (47) 23296000
Insurance Brokerage Services
N.A.I.C.S.: 524210

Willis Towers Watson Argentina S.A. (2)
San Martin 344 Floor 24 Ciudad Autonoma de, C1004AAH, Buenos Aires, Argentina
Tel.: (54) 1152182100
Insurance Brokerage Services
N.A.I.C.S.: 524210

Willis Towers Watson Colombia Corredores de Seguros S.A. (2)
Avenida Carrera 19 No 95-20 Torre Sigma Pisos 16 y 24, Bogota, Chapinero, Colombia

Tel.: (57) 16067575
Insurance Brokerage Services
N.A.I.C.S.: 524210

Willis Towers Watson Forsikringsservice I/S (2)
Rundforbivej 303, 2850, Naerum, Denmark
Tel.: (45) 88139600
Insurance Brokerage Services
N.A.I.C.S.: 524210

Willis Towers Watson I/S (2)
Rundforbivej 303, 2850, Naerum, Denmark
Tel.: (45) 88139600
Insurance Brokerage Services
N.A.I.C.S.: 524210

Willis Towers Watson Management (Bermuda) Limited (2)
90 Pitts Bay Road Wellesley House Floor 2, Pembroke Parish, Hamilton, HM 08, Bermuda
Tel.: (441) 2796700
Insurance Management Services
N.A.I.C.S.: 524210

Willis Towers Watson Management (Cayman) Limited (2)
62 Forum Lane Floor 3, Grand Cayman, Camana Bay, KY1-1203, Cayman Islands
Tel.: (345) 949 6039
Web Site:
 http://www.willistowerswatson.com
Risk Management & Insurance Services
N.A.I.C.S.: 524210

Willis Towers Watson Management (Dublin) Limited (2)
Willis Towers Watson House Elm Park Merrion Road, Dublin, DO4 P231, Ireland
Tel.: (353) 16616211
Captive Insurance Services
N.A.I.C.S.: 524298

Willis Towers Watson Management (Gibraltar) Limited (2)
Europort Suite 827, PO Box 708, GX11 1AA, Gibraltar, Gibraltar
Tel.: (350) 20043636
Captive Management Consultancy & Insurance Services
N.A.I.C.S.: 524298

Willis Towers Watson Management (Guernsey) Limited (2)
The Albany South Esplanade Floor 3 The Channel Islands, Saint Peter Port, GY1 4NF, Guernsey
Tel.: (44) 1481720049
Web Site:
 http://www.willistowerswatson.com
Risk Managemeng Srvices
N.A.I.C.S.: 523910

Willis Towers Watson Management (Isle of Man) Limited (2)
Tower House Loch Promenade, Douglas, IM1 2LZ, Isle of Man
Tel.: (44) 1624696100
Emp.: 16
Insurance Services
N.A.I.C.S.: 524210

Willis Towers Watson Management (Malta) Limited (2)
St Anne Street Development House Floor 3, Floriana, FRN 9010, Malta
Tel.: (356) 2132 2076
Web Site:
 http://www.willistowerswatson.com
Insurance Brokerage Services
N.A.I.C.S.: 524210

Willis Towers Watson Management (Singapore) Pte. Limited (2)
1 Raffles Quay 28-10 South Tower, Singapore, 048583, Singapore
Tel.: (65) 65918000
Insurance Brokerage Services
N.A.I.C.S.: 524210

Willis Towers Watson Versicherungsmakler GmbH (2)
Ulmenstrasse 30 Floor 4, 60325, Frankfurt, Germany
Tel.: (49) 69150550
Insurance Brokerage Services
N.A.I.C.S.: 524210

Willis s.r.o. (2)
Charles Square Center Karlovo Namesti 10, 120 00, Prague, Czech Republic
Tel.: (420) 296 214 551
Web Site: http://www.willis.cz
Financial Services
N.A.I.C.S.: 523910

Willis Insurance Agency I/S (1)
Brendstrupgardsvej 13, 8200, Arhus, Denmark
Tel.: (45) 88139600
Insurance Brokerage Services
N.A.I.C.S.: 551112

Willis Magyarorszag Biztositasi Alkusz es Tanacsado Kft (1)
Raday u 42-44, 1092, Budapest, Hungary
Tel.: (36) 18882970
Web Site: http://www.willis.hu
Insurance Agency Services
N.A.I.C.S.: 524210

Willis Re S.A. (1)
127 Avenue Charles de Gaulle Neuilly sur Seine, 92521, Paris, France
Tel.: (33) 170726970
Insurance Agency Services
N.A.I.C.S.: 524210
Myriam Hammouda *(Exec Dir)*

Willis Towers Watson (SL) Limited (1)
ASK Gras Savoye Sierra Leone 39 Liverpool Street Floor 1, Freetown, Sierra Leone
Tel.: (232) 8172379244
Insurance Agency Services
N.A.I.C.S.: 524210

Willis Towers Watson A/S (1)
Rundforbivej 303, 2850, Naerum, Denmark
Tel.: (45) 87410444
Insurance Brokerage Services
N.A.I.C.S.: 551112

Willis Towers Watson A/S (1)
Drammensveien 147 A Skoyan, PO Box 344, 0213, Oslo, Norway
Tel.: (47) 23296000
Web Site: http://www.willis.no
Insurance Agency Services
N.A.I.C.S.: 524210

Willis Towers Watson A/S (1)
Drammensveien 147 A Skoyan, PO Box 344, 0213, Oslo, Norway
Tel.: (47) 23296000
Web Site: http://www.willis.no
Insurance Agency Services
N.A.I.C.S.: 524210

Willis Towers Watson Agencia de Suscripcion, S.L. (1)
Paseo Castellana 36 - 38, Madrid, 28046, Spain
Tel.: (34) 914233400
Insurance Brokerage Services
N.A.I.C.S.: 551112

Willis Towers Watson Assekuranzdienste GmbH (1)
Herrlichkeit 1, 28199, Bremen, Germany
Tel.: (49) 421840000
Insurance Brokerage Services
N.A.I.C.S.: 551112

Willis Towers Watson Consulting (Singapore) Pte. Ltd. (1)
1 Raffles Quay 28-10 South Tower, Singapore, 048583, Singapore
Tel.: (65) 68805688
Human Capital & Financial Management Consulting Services
N.A.I.C.S.: 541611

Willis Towers Watson Consultores S.A. (1)
Boulevard Miguel De Cervantes Saavedra 169 Granada, 11520, Acuamanala de Miguel Hidalgo, Mexico
Tel.: (52) 5553506000
Insurance Brokerage Services
N.A.I.C.S.: 551112

Willis Towers Watson Consultores S.A. (1)
San Martin 344 P 20, C1004AAH, Buenos Aires, Argentina
Tel.: (54) 1152182100
Insurance Brokerage Services
N.A.I.C.S.: 551112

Willis Towers Watson Consultores S.A. (1)
Calle San Martin 344, C1004AAH, Buenos Aires, Argentina
Tel.: (54) 1152182100
Insurance Brokerage Services
N.A.I.C.S.: 551112

Willis Towers Watson Consultores S.A. (1)
Boulevard Miguel De Cervantes Saavedra 169 Granada, 11520, Acuamanala de Miguel Hidalgo, Mexico
Tel.: (52) 5553506000
Insurance Brokerage Services
N.A.I.C.S.: 551112

Willis Towers Watson Danypmanlyk Limited Pirketi (1)
Kempinski Residences Astoria A Block Floor 4, Esentepe, 34398, Istanbul, Turkiye
Tel.: (90) 2123292900
Risk Management & Human Resource Consulting Services
N.A.I.C.S.: 541618

Willis Towers Watson Global Business Services, Inc. (1)
Bonifacio One Technology Tower, 16th Floor Rizal Drive corner 31st Street Fort Bonifacio Global City, Taguig, 1634, Philippines
Tel.: (63) 282486000
Risk Management & Human Resource Consulting Services
N.A.I.C.S.: 541618

Willis Towers Watson GmbH (1)
Ulmenstrasse 30 Floor 4, 60325, Frankfurt am Main, Germany
Tel.: (49) 69150550
Human Capital & Financial Management Services
N.A.I.C.S.: 541611

Willis Towers Watson Greece Insurance Brokers S.A. (1)
32 Kifissias Avenue Atrina Center A, 15125, Maroussi, Greece
Tel.: (30) 2109473700
Insurance Brokerage Services
N.A.I.C.S.: 551112

Willis Towers Watson Lebanon SAL (1)
Sodeco Square Center Bloc B 14th Floor, PO Box 175707, Mar Mikhael, Beirut, Lebanon
Tel.: (961) 1428328
Insurance Agency Services
N.A.I.C.S.: 524210

Willis Towers Watson Management (Luxembourg) SA (1)
145 rue du Kiem, 8030, Strassen, Luxembourg
Tel.: (352) 469601300
Insurance Agency Services
N.A.I.C.S.: 524210
Nicolas Leonard *(Mng Dir)*

Willis Towers Watson Nigeria Limited (1)
Standard Chartered Building 142 Ahmadu Bello Way 10th Floor, Victoria Island, Lagos, Nigeria
Tel.: (234) 9069364408
Insurance Agency Services
N.A.I.C.S.: 524210

Willis Towers Watson Northeast, Inc. (1)
200 Liberty St Fl 6, New York, NY 10281
Tel.: (212) 915-8888
Insurance Services
N.A.I.C.S.: 524210

Willis Towers Watson Pensionsfonds AG (1)
Wettinerstrasse 3, 65189, Wiesbaden, Germany
Tel.: (49) 6117940
Insurance Brokerage Services
N.A.I.C.S.: 551112

Willis Towers Watson Philippines, Inc. (1)
23/F W City Centre 7th Ave corner 30th Street, Bonifacio Global City, Taguig, Philippines
Tel.: (63) 28775100
Human Capital & Financial Management Services
N.A.I.C.S.: 541611

Willis Towers Watson Polska Spolka Z Ograniczona Odpowiedzialnoscia (1)
Ul Domaniewska 34a Ambassador Building, 02-672, Warsaw, Poland
Tel.: (48) 223188100
Insurance Brokerage Services
N.A.I.C.S.: 524210

Willis Towers Watson Romania-Broker De Asigurare Reasigurare SRL (1)
bld Ion Mihalache no 15-17 floor 1 room 5 sector 1, 011171, Bucharest, Romania
Tel.: (40) 212319169
Web Site: https://www.wtwco.com
Insurance Agency Services
N.A.I.C.S.: 524210
Alexandra Loana Lonescu *(Head-Sls)*

Willis Towers Watson SARL (1)
Immeuble Quai 33 33-34 quai de Dion Bouton Floor 1, Puteaux, 92800, Paris, France
Tel.: (33) 141435000
Human Capital & Financial Management Services
N.A.I.C.S.: 541611

Willis Towers Watson Versicherungsmakler GmbH (1)
Ulmenstrasse 30, 60325, Frankfurt am Main, Germany
Tel.: (49) 69150550
Insurance Agency Services
N.A.I.C.S.: 524210

Willis Towers Watson d.d (1)
Avenija Veceslava Holjevca 40 Floor 1, 10000, Zagreb, Croatia
Tel.: (385) 14848510
Insurance Agency Services
N.A.I.C.S.: 524210

Willis of Greater Kansas, Inc. (1)
12980 Metcalf Ave 5th Fl, Overland Park, KS 66213
Tel.: (913) 339-0800
Insurance Brokerage Services
N.A.I.C.S.: 551112

WILLMOTT DIXON LIMITED
Suite 401 The Spirella Building
Bridge Road Letchworth Garden, Letchworth, SG6 4ET, Hertfordshire, United Kingdom
Tel.: (44) 1462671852
Web Site:
 http://www.willmottdixon.co.uk
Year Founded: 1852
Sales Range: $700-749.9 Million
Emp.: 3,000
Building Construction Services
N.A.I.C.S.: 236220
Colin Enticknap *(Chm)*

Subsidiaries:

Be:here Limited (1)
23 Hanover Square, London, W1S 1JB, United Kingdom
Tel.: (44) 8456004050
Web Site: http://www.be-here.co.uk
Property Rental Services
N.A.I.C.S.: 531110
Gregor Mitchell *(Dir-Land)*

Willmott Dixon Construction Limited (1)
Chantry House High Street, Coleshill, Birmingham, B46 3BP, United Kingdom
Tel.: (44) 1675467666
Building Construction Services
N.A.I.C.S.: 236220

Willmott Dixon Housing Limited (1)
44a Pentonville Road, London, N1 9HF, United Kingdom
Tel.: (44) 2083700200
Building Construction Services
N.A.I.C.S.: 236220

Willmott Dixon Interiors Limited (1)

WILLMOTT DIXON LIMITED

Willmott Dixon Limited—(Continued)
32 Farringdon Street, London, EC4A 4HJ, United Kingdom
Tel.: (44) 2076349600
Web Site: http://www.willmottdixoninteriors.co.uk
Interior Design Services
N.A.I.C.S.: 541410
Steve Donachy (Sr Mgr-Ops)

Willmott Dixon Partnerships Limited (1)
4 Portmill Lane, Hitchin, SG5 1DJ, Hertfordshire, United Kingdom
Tel.: (44) 1462446220
Building Construction Services
N.A.I.C.S.: 236220
Justine Fancy (Dir-Bus Solutions)

Willmott Dixon Regen Limited (1)
Suite 401 The Spirella Building Bridge Road, Letchworth, SG6 4ET, Hertfordshire, United Kingdom
Tel.: (44) 1462476610
Building Construction Services
N.A.I.C.S.: 236220
Mark Gregory (Head-Fin)

WILLOW BIOSCIENCES, INC.
202 1201 5th Street SW, Calgary, T2R 0Y6, AB, Canada
Tel.: (403) 910-5140   AB
Web Site: https://www.willowbio.com
CANSF—(OTCQB)
Rev.: $7,823
Assets: $17,103,770
Liabilities: $17,541,064
Net Worth: ($437,295)
Earnings: ($26,667,925)
Fiscal Year-end: 12/31/20
Research & Development in Biotechnology
N.A.I.C.S.: 541714
Travis Doupe (CFO)

WILLOWDALE NISSAN LTD.
7200 Yonge Street, Thornhill, L4J 1V8, ON, Canada
Tel.: (905) 881-3900
Web Site: http://willowdale.mynissandealer.ca
Rev.: $29,735,173
Emp.: 60
New & Used Car Dealers
N.A.I.C.S.: 441110
Jeff Lazarus (Mgr-Sls)

WILLOWGLEN MSC BERHAD
No 17 Jalan 2/149B Taman Sri Endah Bandar Baru Sri Petaling, 57000, Kuala Lumpur, Malaysia
Tel.: (60) 390571228   MY
Web Site: https://www.willowglen.com.my
WILLOW—(KLS)
Rev.: $40,746,032
Assets: $49,621,799
Liabilities: $7,789,206
Net Worth: $41,832,593
Earnings: $3,245,079
Emp.: 400
Fiscal Year-end: 12/31/22
Computer Control System Mfr
N.A.I.C.S.: 541512
Alfian Mohamed Basir (Chm)

Subsidiaries:

PT Willowglen Indonesia (1)
Jl Rempoa Raya No 11 Ciputat, Tangerang, 15412, Banten, Indonesia
Tel.: (62) 2173882525
Computer Control System Services
N.A.I.C.S.: 541512
Dwi Suprayogi (Engr-Project)

Willowglen (Malaysia) Sdn. Bhd. (1)
Kuala Lumpur Office No 17 Jalan 2/149B Taman Sri Endah, Bandar Baru Sri Petaling, 57000, Kuala Lumpur, Malaysia
Tel.: (60) 390571228
Computer Control System Services

N.A.I.C.S.: 541512
Chris Boey (Gen Mgr)

Willowglen Services Pte. Ltd. (1)
103 Defu Lane 10 05-01, Singapore, 539223, Singapore
Tel.: (65) 62800437
Web Site: https://www.willowglen.com.sg
Software Development Services
N.A.I.C.S.: 513210

Willowglen Systems Inc. (1)
9808 42 Avenue NW, Edmonton, T6E 5V5, AB, Canada
Tel.: (780) 465-1530
Web Site: https://www.willowglensystems.com
Software Development Services
N.A.I.C.S.: 513210

Willowglen Vietnam Co., Ltd. (1)
5th Floor 87B, Bui Thi Xuan District 1, Ho Chi Minh City, Vietnam
Tel.: (84) 839257389
Software Development Services
N.A.I.C.S.: 513210

WILLPLUS HOLDINGS CORPORATION
Shiba Mita Mori Building 8F 13-15 Shiba 5-chome, Minato-ku, Tokyo, Japan
Tel.: (81) 357300660
Web Site: https://www.willplus.co.jp
3538—(TKS)
Rev.: $296,973,900
Assets: $200,004,100
Liabilities: $131,098,940
Net Worth: $68,905,160
Earnings: $6,991,280
Emp.: 660
Fiscal Year-end: 06/30/24
Automotive Distr
N.A.I.C.S.: 423110
Takaaki Naruse (Pres)

WILLS TRANSFER LIMITED
146 Hwy 15, PO Box 340, Smiths Falls, K7A 4T2, ON, Canada
Tel.: (613) 283-0225
Web Site: http://www.willstransfer.com
Year Founded: 1945
Rev.: $15,650,091
Emp.: 200
Logistics & Warehousing Services
N.A.I.C.S.: 541614
Terry Wills (Pres)

WILLS, INC.
6th floor Toranomon 2-chome Tower 2-3-17 Toranomon, Minato-Ku, Tokyo, 105-0001, Japan
Tel.: (81) 364358151
Web Site: https://www.wills-net.co.jp
Year Founded: 2004
4482—(TKS)
Rev.: $31,763,200
Assets: $25,963,580
Liabilities: $12,825,810
Net Worth: $13,137,770
Earnings: $3,587,540
Emp.: 358
Fiscal Year-end: 12/31/23
Software Development Services
N.A.I.C.S.: 541511
Mitsuo Sugimoto (Founder, Chm, Pres & CEO)

WILLSON INTERNATIONAL
2345 Argentia Road Suite 201, Mississauga, L5N 8K4, ON, Canada
Tel.: (905) 363-1133
Web Site: http://www.willsonintl.com
Year Founded: 1918
Rev.: $37,300,000
Emp.: 180
Brokerage & Logistics Services
N.A.I.C.S.: 541614
Peter Wilson (Chm & CEO)

Subsidiaries:

Willson International Inc. (1)
160 Wales Ave Ste 100, Tonawanda, NY 14150
Tel.: (716) 260-1580
Freight Transportation Services
N.A.I.C.S.: 488510

WILLTEC CO., LTD.
4F Gloria 240 Bldg 4-3-1 Higashimikuni, Yodogawa-ku, Osaka, 532-0002, Japan
Tel.: (81) 663999088
Web Site: https://www.willtec.jp
Year Founded: 1992
7087—(TKS)
Rev.: $235,950,560
Assets: $122,179,240
Liabilities: $71,374,780
Net Worth: $50,804,460
Earnings: $4,402,260
Emp.: 3,924
Fiscal Year-end: 03/31/24
Consignment Store Operator
N.A.I.C.S.: 459510
Chikara Miyagi (Pres)

Subsidiaries:

Devices Sales Technology Co., Ltd. (1)
2-9-18 Chidori, Ota-ku, Tokyo, 146-8540, Japan
Tel.: (81) 337581781
Web Site: https://www.dstec.co.jp
Emp.: 117
Power Supply Device Mfr & Distr
N.A.I.C.S.: 335999

Partner Co., Ltd. (1)
8F Ichikawa Building 5-13-3 Ginza, Chuo-ku, Tokyo, 104-0061, Japan
Tel.: (81) 335470300
Web Site: https://www.go-partner.jp
Emp.: 381
System Integration Design Services
N.A.I.C.S.: 541512

Thousandplan, Inc. (1)
Asahi New City Building 3F/9F 1-7-18 Okubo, Shinjuku-ku, Tokyo, 169-0072, Japan
Tel.: (81) 362056425
Web Site: https://www.thousandplan.com
Emp.: 43
Construction Engineering Services
N.A.I.C.S.: 541330

Wat Consulting Co., Ltd. (1)
FORECAST Kayabacho 3F 1-10-14 Shinkawa, Chuo-ku, Tokyo, 104-0033, Japan
Tel.: (81) 335378711
Web Site: https://www.jp-wat.com
Emp.: 852
Construction Engineering Services
N.A.I.C.S.: 541330

Willhearts Co., Ltd. (1)
4-3-1 Higashimikuni, Yodogawa-ku, Osaka, 532-0002, Japan
Tel.: (81) 663999500
Web Site: https://www.w-hearts.jp
Emp.: 49
Printing Business Card Mfr
N.A.I.C.S.: 323111

Willtec Myanmar Co., Ltd. (1)
No 169 Room No 6-B MTP Condo Insein Road, 9 Ward Hlaing Township, Yangon, Myanmar
Tel.: (95) 9443881177
Web Site: http://www.willtec-myanmar.com
Emp.: 7
Human Resources Consulting & Training Services
N.A.I.C.S.: 541612
Shinji Murakami (Mng Dir)

Willtec Vietnam Co., Ltd. (1)
Floor 12A CDC Bldg 25 Le Dai Hanh, Hai Ba Trung, Hanoi, Vietnam
Tel.: (84) 2436331533
Web Site: https://www.willtec-vietnam.com
Human Resources Consulting & Training Services

INTERNATIONAL PUBLIC

N.A.I.C.S.: 541612

WILMAR INTERNATIONAL LIMITED
28 Biopolis Road, Singapore, 138568, Singapore
Tel.: (65) 62160244   SG
Web Site: https://www.wilmar-international.com
Year Founded: 1991
F34—(SES)
Rev.: $67,155,262,000
Assets: $61,808,692,000
Liabilities: $39,056,875,000
Net Worth: $22,751,817,000
Earnings: $1,658,174,000
Emp.: 100,000
Fiscal Year-end: 12/31/23
Food Products Mfr
N.A.I.C.S.: 333241
Matthew John Morgenroth (Head-Grp Technical)

Subsidiaries:

Benso Oil Palm Plantation Limited (1)
Adum Banso Estate, PO Box 470, Takoradi, Ghana
Tel.: (233) 242109409
Web Site: https://bopplc.com
Rev.: $21,050,128
Assets: $20,250,741
Liabilities: $3,651,985
Net Worth: $16,598,756
Earnings: $4,198,737
Fiscal Year-end: 12/31/2020
Palm Oil Mfr
N.A.I.C.S.: 311224
Santosh Pillai (Mng Dir & Exec Dir)

Calofic Corporation (1)
Cai Lan Industrial Zone, Bai Chay Ward, Ha Long, Quang Ninh, Vietnam
Tel.: (84) 2033846993
Web Site: https://www.calofic.com.vn
Emp.: 1,000
Vegetable Oil Mfr
N.A.I.C.S.: 311225

Global Eco Chemicals Singapore Pte. Ltd. (1)
56 Neil Road, Singapore, 088830, Singapore (50%)
Tel.: (65) 62160244
Toilet Preparation Mfr
N.A.I.C.S.: 325620

Subsidiary (Non-US):

Global Eco Chemicals Malaysia Sdn. Bhd. (2)
Industrial Complex Plo 116 Jalan Rumbia 1 Kampung Tanjung Langsat, 81700, Pasir Gudang, Johor, Malaysia
Tel.: (60) 72551224
Toilet Preparation Mfr
N.A.I.C.S.: 325620

Goodman Fielder Limited (1)
Level 3 118 Talavera Road, Macquarie Park, 2113, NSW, Australia
Tel.: (61) 288997000
Web Site: https://goodmanfielder.com
Emp.: 1,600
Bread, Baked Goods & Food Products Mfr
N.A.I.C.S.: 311812
Emily Forsyth (Gen Counsel)

Subsidiary (Non-US):

Goodman Fielder New Zealand, Ltd. (2)
2/8 Nelson Street, Auckland, 1010, New Zealand
Tel.: (64) 9 301 6000
Web Site: https://goodmanfielder.com
Baked Goods & Food Product Mfr
N.A.I.C.S.: 311812

Subsidiary (Domestic):

Goodman Fielder Pty. Ltd. (2)
75 Talavera Rd, Macquarie Park, North Ryde, 2113, NSW, Australia (100%)
Tel.: (61) 288746500

AND PRIVATE COMPANIES

Web Site:
    http://www.goodmanfielder.com.au
Food Products Mfr & Distr
N.A.I.C.S.: 311812
Julie Coates *(Mng Dir)*

KOG-KTV Food Products (India) Private Limited (1)
48/310 Thambu Chetty Street, Parrys Corner, Chennai, 600 001, Tamil Nadu, India
Tel.: (91) 4425222962
Web Site: https://www.kogktv.com
Sales Range: $75-99.9 Million
Emp.: 200
Food Product Retailer
N.A.I.C.S.: 424420

Kaminsky Sdn Bhd (1)
Lot 964 Sublot 7 Taman Seaview Commercial Centre Jln Tanjung Batu, PO Box 730, Bintulu, 97008, Sarawak, Malaysia
Tel.: (60) 86315286
Palm Oil Mfr
N.A.I.C.S.: 311224

Kerry (New Zealand) Limited (1)
Wellesley St, PO Box 5990, Auckland, New Zealand
Tel.: (64) 95254585
Sales Range: $25-49.9 Million
Emp.: 10
Vegetable Oils Distr
N.A.I.C.S.: 311225
Paul Goodman-Jones *(Mgr-HR)*

Kerry Oils & Grains (Qingdao) Ltd (1)
No 99 Qian Wan Gang Rd ETDZ, Qingdao, 266555, Shandong, China
Tel.: (86) 53286827763
Web Site: http://www.yhkqd.com
Peanut & Soybean Oil Mfr
N.A.I.C.S.: 311224

PGEO Group Sdn. Bhd. (1)
Plo 338 Jalan Tembaga Dua Kawasan Perindustrian Pasir Gudang, 81707, Pasir Gudang, Johor, Malaysia **(100%)**
Tel.: (60) 7 278 8222
Web Site: https://www.pgeogroup.com.my
Edible Oil Mfr
N.A.I.C.S.: 311224

Subsidiary (Domestic):

Bintulu Edible Oils Sdn Bhd (2)
Km 18 Jalan Tanjung Kidurong, PO Box 256, 97007, Bintulu, Sarawak, Malaysia
Tel.: (60) 86251150
Sales Range: $25-49.9 Million
Emp.: 168
Edible Oils Refinery
N.A.I.C.S.: 311225
Lu Khai Ing *(Gen Mgr)*

Natural Oleochemicals Sdn. Bhd. (2)
PLO 428 Jalan Besi Satu Perindustrian Pasir Gudang, Jalan Besi Satu, 81700, Pasir Gudang, Johor, Malaysia
Tel.: (60) 72533888
Web Site: http://www.natoleo.com.my
Emp.: 300
Oleochemical Products Mfr
N.A.I.C.S.: 325199

PGEO Bioproducts Sdn Bhd (2)
PLO 338 Jalan Tembaga Dua Kawasan Perindustrian Pasir Gudang, 81707, Pasir Gudang, Johor, Malaysia
Tel.: (60) 7 268 8222
Web Site: https://www.pgeogroup.com.my
Sales Range: $100-124.9 Million
Emp.: 400
Chemical Products Mfr
N.A.I.C.S.: 325998

PGEO Edible Oils Sdn Bhd (2)
Plo 338 Jalan Tembaga Dua Kawasan Perindustrian Pasir Gudang, 81707, Pasir Gudang, Johor, Malaysia
Tel.: (60) 7 278 8222
Web Site: https://www.pgeogroup.com.my
Edible Oils Refinery
N.A.I.C.S.: 311225

Sandakan Edible Oils Sdn Bhd (2)
km 8 Jalan Batu Sapi Karamunting, PO Box 2605, 90729, Sandakan, Sabah, Malaysia
Tel.: (60) 8 961 1011
Web Site: http://www.wilmar-international.com.my

Sales Range: $25-49.9 Million
Emp.: 247
Edible Oils Refinery
N.A.I.C.S.: 311225
Joseph Keokyong *(Mgr)*

Wilmar Tank Terminals Sdn. Bhd. (2)
Lot 154 Lorong Sawit 2 Kawasan Zon Bebas, PO Box 95, 81707, Pasir Gudang, 81700, Johor, Malaysia
Tel.: (60) 72519703
Emp.: 17
Chemical Terminals Operation Services
N.A.I.C.S.: 424710
Ismail Batutty *(Mgr-Ops)*

Qinhuangdao Goldensea Foodstuff Industries Co., Ltd (1)
No 1 Jinhai Rd Economic and Technological Development Zone E Zone, Qinhuangdao, 066206, Hebei, China
Tel.: (86) 3355087521
Web Site: http://www.goldensea.21food.com
Sales Range: $450-499.9 Million
Emp.: 1,500
Oil Grains Mfr
N.A.I.C.S.: 327910

Raffles Ship Management Services Pte Ltd (1)
Tan Boon Liat Bldg, 315 Outram Rd 08-02, Singapore, 169074, Singapore
Tel.: (65) 62276456
Web Site: http://www.raffles-shipbrokers.com.sg
Sales Range: $25-49.9 Million
Emp.: 200
Shipping Agencies
N.A.I.C.S.: 488510

Raffles Shipping International Pte. Ltd. (1)
09-05 Tan Boon Liat Bldg 315 Outram Rd, Singapore, 169074, Singapore
Tel.: (65) 62277990
Web Site: http://www.raffles-shipping-corp.com.sg
Sales Range: $50-74.9 Million
Emp.: 600
Boat Charter Services
N.A.I.C.S.: 487210

Sea Ocean Shipping Agency Pte Ltd (1)
315 Outram Rd, 09 05 Tan Boon Liat Bldg, Singapore, 169074, Singapore
Tel.: (65) 65977606
Sales Range: $50-74.9 Million
Emp.: 180
Shipping Agencies
N.A.I.C.S.: 488510
Kenny Beh *(Mng Dir)*

Segarmas Plantations Sdn Bhd (1)
Lot 964 Sublot 7 Taman Seaview Commercial Centre Tanjong Batu Road, Bintulu, 9700, Sarawak, Malaysia
Tel.: (60) 86315286
Sales Range: $100-124.9 Million
Emp.: 400
Palm Oil Mfr
N.A.I.C.S.: 311224

Southseas Oils & Fats Industrial (Chiwan) Ltd (1)
15 Youpaotailu Chiwan Shekou, Shenzhen, 518068, Guangdong, China
Tel.: (86) 75526694322
Edible Oil Suppliers
N.A.I.C.S.: 424490

Sucrogen Ltd. (1)
Level 8 100 Pacific Highway, North Sydney, 2060, NSW, Australia
Tel.: (61) 1300997624
Web Site: http://www.sucrogen.com.au
Sugar Cane & Renewable Energy Processing
N.A.I.C.S.: 311314

Volac Ingredients Sdn Bhd (1)
Plot 679 Jalan Tembaga Kawasan Perindustrian Pasir Gudang, PO Box 80, Pasir Gudang, 81707, Johor, Malaysia
Tel.: (60) 72520097
Web Site: http://www.volac.com
Sales Range: $25-49.9 Million
Emp.: 25
Palm Oil Refinery Services

N.A.I.C.S.: 311224

Wilmar Europe Holdings B.V. (1)
Delftseplein 27G, 3013 AA, Rotterdam, Netherlands
Tel.: (31) 10 217 8800
Web Site: https://www.wilmareurope.nl
Sales Range: $50-74.9 Million
Emp.: 93
Holding Company; Regional Managing Office
N.A.I.C.S.: 551112

Subsidiary (Domestic):

Olenex Edible Oil B.V. (2)
Vondelingenplaat 540, Vondelingenplaat, 3196 KK, Rotterdam, Netherlands
Tel.: (31) 180457000
Web Site: http://www.wilmareurope.nl
Sales Range: $25-49.9 Million
Emp.: 100
Edible Oil Mfr
N.A.I.C.S.: 111120

Subsidiary (Non-US):

Wilmar Edible Oils GmbH (2)
Nordstr 40, 26919, Brake, Germany
Tel.: (49) 44018010
Web Site: http://www.wilmareurope.de
Edible Oil Mfr
N.A.I.C.S.: 311221

Wilmar Surfactants (2)
Route de Ponteau Lavera Sud, BP 111, 13693, Martigues, Cedex, France
Tel.: (33) 4 4213 1313
Sales Range: $10-24.9 Million
Surfactants Mfr
N.A.I.C.S.: 325998

Wilmar Marketing Sdn Bhd (1)
Lot 32 AB D 32nd Floor UBN Tower No 10 Jalan P Ramlee, 50250, Kuala Lumpur, Johor, Malaysia
Tel.: (60) 327768788
Web Site: http://www.pgeogroup.com.my
Sales Range: $25-49.9 Million
Emp.: 250
Palm Kernel Products Whslr
N.A.I.C.S.: 311224

Wilmar Oleochemicals (Shanghai) Co., Ltd (1)
No 118 Gaodong Road, Pudong New District, Shanghai, 200137, China
Tel.: (86) 2158487988
Web Site: http://www.wilmar-international.com
Processing of Oleochemical Products (Fatty Acid, Soap & Glycerine)
N.A.I.C.S.: 311225

Yihai (Lianyungang) Oleochemical Industries Co., Ltd (1)
Dagang Rd Xugou, Lianyungang, 222042, Jiangsu, China
Tel.: (86) 51882387248
Oil Refinery Services
N.A.I.C.S.: 237120

Yihai Kerry (1)
Floor 26 Huaneng Union Tower 958 LuJiaZui Ring Rd, Shanghai, 200120, Pudong, China
Tel.: (86) 21 3119 9999
Web Site: http://www.yihaikerry.com.cn
Agribusiness & Food Mfr
N.A.I.C.S.: 111419

WILMCOTE HOLDINGS PLC
11 Buckingham Street, London, WC2N 6DF, United Kingdom
Tel.: (44) 2072602700
Web Site:
    http://www.wilmcoteplc.com
Investment Services
N.A.I.C.S.: 523999
Adrian Whitfield *(CEO)*

WILMINGTON CAPITAL MANAGEMENT INC.
1420 205 5th Avenue SW, Calgary, T2P 2V7, AB, Canada
Tel.: (403) 705-8036   ON

WILMINGTON PLC

Web Site:
    https://www.wilmingtoncapital.ca
Year Founded: 1979
WCM.A—(TSX)
Rev.: $1,521,535
Assets: $50,082,348
Liabilities: $1,099,103
Net Worth: $48,983,244
Earnings: ($360,631)
Emp.: 4
Fiscal Year-end: 12/31/21
Investment Holding Company; Real Estate & Financial Services
N.A.I.C.S.: 551112
Ian G. Cockwell *(Chm)*

WILMINGTON PLC
51 5th Floor 10 Whitechapel High Street, London, E1 8QS, United Kingdom
Tel.: (44) 2074900049
Web Site:
    https://www.wilmingtonplc.com
WIL—(LSE)
Rev.: $124,271,992
Assets: $216,951,466
Liabilities: $71,204,499
Net Worth: $145,746,966
Earnings: $21,737,866
Emp.: 582
Fiscal Year-end: 06/30/24
Business Magazines, Directories & Database Publisher; Professional Training Services
N.A.I.C.S.: 513140
Martin Morgan *(Chm)*

Subsidiaries:

APM International SAS (1)
33 Avenue de la Republique, 75011, Paris, France
Tel.: (33) 14 806 5492
Web Site: https://www.apminternational.fr
Sales Range: $25-49.9 Million
Emp.: 30
Medicine & Health Care Information Services
N.A.I.C.S.: 519290
Loic Lebrun *(Dir-Publication & Mgr-Editorial)*

APM Media SARL (1)
33 Avenue De La Republique, 75011, Paris, France
Tel.: (33) 148065492
Healthcare News Information Services
N.A.I.C.S.: 519290
Loic Lebrun *(Gen Mgr)*

Adkins & Matchett (UK) Limited (1)
5th Floor Whitechapel Building 10 Whitechapel High Street, London, E1 8QS, United Kingdom
Tel.: (44) 207 324 2385
Web Site: https://www.amttraining.com
Professional Training Services
N.A.I.C.S.: 611430

Adkins, Matchett & Toy (Hong Kong) Limited (1)
Suites 01-03 16th Floor Kinwick Centre, 32 Hollywood Road, Central, China (Hong Kong)
Tel.: (852) 2987 9011
Sales Range: $10-24.9 Million
Emp.: 5
Professional Training Services
N.A.I.C.S.: 611430

Adkins, Matchett & Toy Limited (1)
31 W 34th St 8th Fl Ste 8080, New York, NY 10001
Tel.: (347) 325-0525
Professional Learning Services
N.A.I.C.S.: 611710

Ark Conferences Limited (1)
5th Floor Whitechapel Building 10 Whitechapel High Street, London, E1 8QS, United Kingdom
Tel.: (44) 2087852700
Web Site: http://www.ark-group.com
Sales Range: $25-49.9 Million
Emp.: 75
Periodical Publishers

8421

WILMINGTON PLC

Wilmington plc—(Continued)
N.A.I.C.S.: 513120

Ark Group Australia Pty Limited (1)
69 Carlton Crescent, Summer Hill, Summer Hill, 2130, NSW, Australia (85%)
Tel.: (61) 1300550662
Web Site: http://www.arkgroupaustralia.com.au
Sales Range: $25-49.9 Million
Emp.: 100
Periodical Publishers
N.A.I.C.S.: 513120
Steven Oesterreich (Pres)

Ark Group Limited (1)
5th Floor Whitechapel Building 10 Whitechapel High Street, London, E1 8QS, United Kingdom
Tel.: (44) 2073242385
Web Site: http://www.ark-group.com
Sales Range: $25-49.9 Million
Emp.: 25
Periodical Publishers
N.A.I.C.S.: 513120

Axco Insurance Information Services Limited (1)
Fifth Floor 10 Whitechapel High Street, London, E1 8QS, United Kingdom
Tel.: (44) 2073745252
Sales Range: $50-74.9 Million
Emp.: 50
Insurance Management & Consulting Services
N.A.I.C.S.: 524298

Bond Solon Training Limited (1)
5th Floor 10 Whitechapel High Street, London, E1 8QS, United Kingdom
Tel.: (44) 207 549 2549
Web Site: https://www.bondsolon.com
Sales Range: $10-24.9 Million
Emp.: 30
Professional & Management Development Training
N.A.I.C.S.: 611430
Mark Solon (Founder)

CLT International Limited (1)
6th Floor Fort Dunlop Fort Parkway, Sutton Coldfield, Birmingham, B24 9FD, United Kingdom
Tel.: (44) 121 362 7733
Web Site: https://www.cltint.com
Emp.: 15
Professional Training Services
N.A.I.C.S.: 611430

Central Law Group Limited (1)
Wrens Ct 52-54 Victoria Rd, Sutton Coldfield, Birmingham, B7 21FX, United Kingdom
Tel.: (44) 1213550900
Web Site: http://www.centlaw.com
Sales Range: $25-49.9 Million
Emp.: 150
Professional & Management Development Training
N.A.I.C.S.: 611430
Pedro Ross (Gen Mgr)

Central Law Training (Scotland) Limited (1)
Tontine House 8 Gordon Street, Glasgow, G1 3PL, United Kingdom (80%)
Tel.: (44) 141 225 6700
Web Site: https://clt.law.ac.uk
Sales Range: $10-24.9 Million
Emp.: 10
Professional & Management Development Training
N.A.I.C.S.: 611430
Lucy Morrison (Mng Dir)

Central Law Training Limited (1)
Wrens Court 52-54 Victoria Road, Sutton Coldfield, Birmingham, B72 1SX, United Kingdom
Tel.: (44) 1213550900
Web Site: http://www.clt.co.uk
Sales Range: $25-49.9 Million
Emp.: 200
Professional & Management Development Training
N.A.I.C.S.: 611430
Lucy Morrison (Mng Dir)

Subsidiary (Non-US):

La Touche Bond Solon Training Limited (2)
Suite 329 The Capel Building Mary's Abbey, Dublin, Ireland
Tel.: (353) 1 8788 255
Web Site: http://www.latouchetraining.ie
Sales Range: $10-24.9 Million
Emp.: 6
Professional Training Services
N.A.I.C.S.: 611430
Adrian Kiernan (Mng Dir)

Compliance Week (1)
129 Portland St Ste 600, Boston, MA 02114-2012
Tel.: (617) 570-8600
Web Site: http://www.complianceweek.com
Sales Range: $1-9.9 Million
Periodical Publishers
N.A.I.C.S.: 513120
Stephen Moylan (Mng Dir)

Financial Research Associates, LLC (1)
343 Soquel Ave Ste 334, Santa Cruz, CA 95062
Tel.: (831) 465-2281
Web Site: http://www.frallc.com
Sales Range: $1-9.9 Million
Emp.: 30
Business Support Services
N.A.I.C.S.: 561499
Lori Medlen (Pres & CEO)

ICA Risk Management Limited (1)
5th Floor 10 Whitechapel High Street, London, United Kingdom
Tel.: (44) 1213627534
Web Site: https://www.int-comp.org
Financial Services
N.A.I.C.S.: 921130

International Company Profile FZ LLC (1)
DMC Building 8 Business Centre Gr Floor EX-14, PO Box 500717, Dubai, United Arab Emirates
Tel.: (971) 45545809
Credit Report Information Services
N.A.I.C.S.: 561450

International Compliance Training Academy Pte Limited (1)
6 Shenton Way 17-08 Oue Downtown 2, Singapore, 068809, Singapore
Tel.: (65) 6 500 0010
Web Site: https://www.int-comp.com
Education Services
N.A.I.C.S.: 611710

International Compliance Training Limited (1)
Wrens Court 52-54 Victoria Road, Sutton Coldfield West Midlands, Birmingham, B72 1SX, United Kingdom
Tel.: (44) 121 362 7534
Web Site: https://www.int-comp.com
Sales Range: $10-24.9 Million
Emp.: 50
Professional Training Services
N.A.I.C.S.: 611430
William Howarth (CEO)

International Compliance Training Sdn. Bhd. (1)
MZ02 Penthouse 16-1 Level 16 Wisma UOA Damansara II, No 6 Changkat Semantan Bukit Damansara, 50490, Kuala Lumpur, Malaysia
Tel.: (60) 39 213 1438
Education Services
N.A.I.C.S.: 611710

John Matchett Limited (1)
1 Summerville Court Trinity Way, Adderbury, OX17 3NS, United Kingdom
Tel.: (44) 1295 256 161
Software Training Services
N.A.I.C.S.: 611420

Mercia Group Limited (1)
Grove Park 2 Thorpe Way, Enderby, LE19 1SU, Leicester, United Kingdom
Tel.: (44) 330 058 7141
Web Site: https://www.mercia-group.com
Sales Range: $10-24.9 Million
Emp.: 60
Accountancy Training Services
N.A.I.C.S.: 611430
Nicola Hurley (Mng Dir)

Subsidiary (Non-US):

Mercia Ireland Limited (2)
13 Upper Baggot Street 2nd Floor, Dublin, D04 W7K5, Ireland
Tel.: (353) 18090080
Web Site: https://www.mercia-group.com
Professional Training Services
N.A.I.C.S.: 611430

Subsidiary (Domestic):

Mercia NI Limited (2)
Wyncroft 30 Rathfriland Road, Newry, BT34 1JZ, Co Down, United Kingdom
Tel.: (44) 2830835588
Professional Training Services
N.A.I.C.S.: 611430

Pendragon Professional Information Limited (1)
8 Paulton House, Shepherdess Walk, N17AD, London, United Kingdom
Tel.: (44) 2076089000
Web Site: http://www.pendragon.co.uk
Sales Range: $50-74.9 Million
Emp.: 14
Health & Welfare Funds
N.A.I.C.S.: 525120
Simon Freeman (Mng Dir)

Practice Track Limited (1)
5th Floor 10 Whitechapel High Street, London, E1 8QS, United Kingdom
Tel.: (44) 800181343
Web Site: https://www.practicetrackonline.co.uk
Sales Range: $25-49.9 Million
Emp.: 9
Marketing Consulting Services
N.A.I.C.S.: 541613

Smee and Ford Limited (1)
5th Floor 10 Whitechapel High Street, London, E1 8QS, United Kingdom
Tel.: (44) 207 324 2349
Web Site: https://smeeandford.com
Sales Range: $10-24.9 Million
Emp.: 8
Professional Training Services
N.A.I.C.S.: 611430
Tanya Noronha (Publr)

The Matchett Group Limited (1)
Tel.: (44) 2075498620
Web Site: http://www.matchettgroup.com
Management Training Services
N.A.I.C.S.: 611430

Subsidiary (Non-US):

Adkins Matchett & Toy Limited (2)
Tel.: (44) 207 324 2385
Web Site: https://www.amttraining.com
Emp.: 25
Financial Training Services
N.A.I.C.S.: 611430

Wilmington Compliance Week Inc. (1)
129 Portland St Ste 600, Boston, MA 02114-2012
Tel.: (617) 570-8608
Web Site: https://www.complianceweek.com
Financial Services
N.A.I.C.S.: 921130

Wilmington FRA Inc. (1)
3420 Toringdon Way Ste 240, Charlotte, NC 28277
Tel.: (704) 341-2384
Professional & Development Training Services
N.A.I.C.S.: 611430
Ellen Wofford (Mng Dir)

Wilmington Healthcare Limited (1)
5th Floor 10 Whitechapel High Street, Southfields, London, E1 8QS, United Kingdom
Tel.: (44) 1268495600
Web Site: https://wilmingtonhealthcare.com
Sales Range: $25-49.9 Million
Emp.: 110
Women Healthcare Services
N.A.I.C.S.: 621610
Steve Harvey (Mng Dir)

Wilmington Healthcare Limited (1)
5th Floor 10 Whitechapel High Street, London, E1 8QS, United Kingdom
Tel.: (44) 126 849 5600
Web Site: https://www.wilmingtonhealthcare.com

INTERNATIONAL PUBLIC

Healtcare Services
N.A.I.C.S.: 621610
Gareth Thomas (Mng Dir)

Wilmington Inese SL (1)
Calle Maudes 51 2a Planta, 28003, Madrid, Spain
Tel.: (34) 91 375 5800
Web Site: https://www.inese.es
Insurance Services
N.A.I.C.S.: 524210

Wilmington Publishing & Information Limited (1)
6-14 Underwood Street, London, N1 7JQ, United Kingdom (100%)
Tel.: (44) 20 7549 2571
Web Site: http://www.wlrstore.com
Business Information Services
N.A.I.C.S.: 519290

WILMS GMBH
Frondenberger Strasse 27-29, 58706, Menden, Germany
Tel.: (49) 2373 9591 0
Web Site: http://www.wilms-galvanik.de
Year Founded: 1974
Sales Range: $1-9.9 Million
Metal Electroplating Services
N.A.I.C.S.: 332813
Johann Erich Wilms (Mng Dir)

WILSON BAYLY HOLMES-OVCON LIMITED
53 Andries Street, Wynberg, Johannesburg, 2090, South Africa
Tel.: (27) 113217200
Web Site: https://www.wbho.co.za
Year Founded: 1970
WBO—(JSE)
Rev.: $1,255,228,034
Assets: $773,477,804
Liabilities: $562,189,609
Net Worth: $211,288,195
Earnings: $49,319,648
Emp.: 172
Fiscal Year-end: 06/30/23
Construction & Engineering Services
N.A.I.C.S.: 237990
Elia Louw Nel (Chm)

Subsidiaries:

Byrne Group Limited (1)
53 Great Suffolk Street, London, SE1 0DB, United Kingdom
Tel.: (44) 2086143400
Web Site: https://www.byrnegroup.co.uk
Building Construction Services
N.A.I.C.S.: 236220

Kalcon (Pty) Ltd. (1)
Plot 20714 Western By-pass Broadhurst Ext 34 Industrial, Gaborone, Botswana
Tel.: (267) 3909202
Construction & Engineering Services
N.A.I.C.S.: 541330

Monaco Hickey Pty Ltd (1)
Level 10 580 St kilda Road, Melbourne, 3004, VIC, Australia
Tel.: (61) 39 693 1555
Web Site: https://www.monacohickey.com.au
Road Construction Services
N.A.I.C.S.: 237310
Eric Meyerowitz (Mng Dir)

Ovcon Holdings (Pty) Limited (1)
53 Andries St, Wynberg, 2090, Johannesburg, South Africa
Tel.: (27) 11 321 7200
Web Site: http://www.wbho.co.za
Sales Range: $150-199.9 Million
Emp.: 400
Holding Company: Construction & Property Management
N.A.I.C.S.: 551112

Probuild Constructions (Australia) Pty. Ltd. (1)
Level 10 580 St Kilda Road, Melbourne, 3004, VIC, Australia
Tel.: (61) 396938222

Web Site: http://www.probuild.com.au
Sales Range: $200-249.9 Million
Emp.: 75
Construction & Engineering Services
N.A.I.C.S.: 237990
Simon Gray *(Mng Dir)*

Roadspan Surfaces (Pty) Ltd. (1)
53 Andries Street North, Wynberg, Johannesburg, 2090, South Africa
Tel.: (27) 113218400
Web Site: https://www.roadspan.co.za
Heavy Vehicle Distr
N.A.I.C.S.: 423120

Tekfalt Binders (Pty) Ltd. (1)
24 Dolomiet Road Pendale Agricultural Holdings, Randvaal, Midvaal, Gauteng, South Africa
Tel.: (27) 163655641
Web Site: https://www.tekfalt.co.za
Road Construction Services
N.A.I.C.S.: 237310

WBHO Construction (Pty) Limited (1)
53 Andries Street, Wynberg, Johannesburg, 2090, South Africa
Tel.: (27) 113217200
Web Site: https://www.wbho.co.za
Sales Range: $200-249.9 Million
Emp.: 700
Construction & Engineering Services
N.A.I.C.S.: 237990

WBHO Construction Pvt. Ltd. (1)
Plot No 73 Second Close Trade Fair Site, PO Box 147, Airport Residential Area, Accra, Ghana
Tel.: (233) 30 276 2189
Construction & Engineering Services
N.A.I.C.S.: 541330

WBHO Infrastructure Pty Ltd (1)
Level 1 30 Delhi Street, PO Box 991, West Perth, 6005, WA, Australia
Tel.: (61) 86 229 3700
Web Site: https://www.wbho.com.au
Road Construction Services
N.A.I.C.S.: 237310
Will Grobler *(Exec Gen Mgr)*

iKusasa Rail (Pty) Ltd. (1)
WBHO Building 3 53 Andries Street, Wynberg, Cape Town, South Africa
Tel.: (27) 11 321 8400
Web Site: https://www.ikusasarail.co.za
Rail Track Construction Services
N.A.I.C.S.: 237990

WILSON EQUIPMENT LIMITED
66 Atlantic Central Drive, Truro, B6L 2A3, NS, Canada
Tel.: (902) 895-1611
Web Site:
http://www.wilsonequip.ns.ca
Year Founded: 1955
Rev.: $11,563,678
Emp.: 40
Industrial Heavy Duty Equipment Dealer & Services
N.A.I.C.S.: 336120
Mark Kozlowski *(VP-Sls & Gen Mgr)*

WILSON LEARNING WORLDWIDE INC.
Toranomon Twin Bldg East Tower 13Fl 2-10-1 Toranomon, Minato-Ku, Tokyo, 105-0001, Japan
Tel.: (81) 363810234
Web Site:
https://japan.wilsonlearning.com
Year Founded: 1981
9610—(TKS)
Rev.: $11,567,500
Assets: $11,666,650
Liabilities: $6,008,490
Net Worth: $5,658,160
Earnings: ($3,886,680)
Fiscal Year-end: 03/31/24
Educational Planning Services
N.A.I.C.S.: 611710
Shozo Mori *(Chm & CEO)*

Subsidiaries:

Siam Wilson Learning Co., Ltd. (1)
719 KPN Tower 14th Floor Rama 9 Road Bangkapi Huaykwang, Bangkok, 10320, Thailand
Tel.: (66) 27170696
Educational Support Services
N.A.I.C.S.: 611710

Soluciones Estrategicas De Transformacion, S.C. (1)
Wilson Learning Mexico Centro America y Caribe Avenida Revolucion, No 1314 Col, Guadalupe, 1020, Mexico
Tel.: (52) 5556608360
Educational Support Services
N.A.I.C.S.: 611710

Wilson Learning Andina y Rio de la Plata S.A. (1)
Carrera 23 114-11 Oficina 603, Bogota, Colombia
Tel.: (57) 17551921
Educational Support Services
N.A.I.C.S.: 611710

Wilson Learning Australia Pty Ltd (1)
Suite 13 01 Level 13 82 Elizabeth Street, Locomotive St Eveleigh, Sydney, 2000, NSW, Australia
Tel.: (61) 292324124
Educational Support Services
N.A.I.C.S.: 611710
Hazel Stewart *(Mng Dir)*

Wilson Learning China Limited (1)
4038B UDIT No 355 Hongqiao Rd, Xuhui District, Shanghai, 200030, China
Tel.: (86) 13761130953
Educational Support Services
N.A.I.C.S.: 611710
Daniel Kong *(Mng Dir)*

Wilson Learning Corporation (1)
8000 W 78th St Ste 200, Minneapolis, MN 55439
Tel.: (952) 944-2880
Educational Support Services
N.A.I.C.S.: 611710
Ed Emde *(Pres)*

Wilson Learning Europa Limited. (1)
G 15D St Mary's Court, Amersham, HP7 0UT, Buckinghamshire, United Kingdom
Tel.: (44) 1494678121
Web Site: http://www.wilsonlearning.com
Educational Support Services
N.A.I.C.S.: 611710
Richard Chappell *(Mng Dir)*

Wilson Learning FZ LLC (1)
Churchill Tower Office 1211 Business Bay, Dubai, United Arab Emirates
Tel.: (971) 44433494
Web Site: https://wl-uae.com
Educational Support Services
N.A.I.C.S.: 611710

Wilson Learning France SAS (1)
21 avenue Edouard Belin, 92566, Rueil-Malmaison, Cedex, France
Tel.: (33) 147517070
Web Site: https://www.wilsonlearning.com
Educational Support Services
N.A.I.C.S.: 611710
Caroline Hazemann *(Dir)*

Wilson Learning India Pvt Ltd. (1)
WeWork DLF Two Horizon Centre 5th Floor DLF Phase-5 Sector-43, Golf Course Road, Gurgaon, 122002, Haryana, India
Tel.: (91) 1244075097
Educational Support Services
N.A.I.C.S.: 611710
Vivek Chandramohan *(Mng Dir)*

Wilson Learning SEM Ltd. (1)
35 Costa Mishiaouli Street Kato Deftera, 2045, Nicosia, Cyprus
Tel.: (357) 22625222
Educational Support Services
N.A.I.C.S.: 611710

Wilson Learning Sa (Pty) Ltd (1)
Usher Place 1 George Street, Bryanston, Johannesburg, 2021, Gauteng, South Africa
Tel.: (27) 114634401
Web Site: http://www.wilsonlearning.co.za
Educational Support Services
N.A.I.C.S.: 611710

Wilson Learning Singapore Pte Ltd (1)
3 Temasek Ave 34-00 Centennial Tower, Singapore, 039190, Singapore
Tel.: (65) 62359766
Web Site: http://www.wilsonlearning.com.sg
Educational Support Services
N.A.I.C.S.: 611710

WILSON M. BECK INSURANCE SERVICE INC.
303 - 8678 Greenall Avenue, Burnaby, V5J 3M6, BC, Canada
Tel.: (604) 437-6200
Web Site: https://www.wmbeck.com
Year Founded: 1981
Rev.: $10,433,394
Emp.: 44
Insurance Agency Services
N.A.I.C.S.: 524298
Wilson M, Beck *(Chm & CEO)*

Subsidiaries:

Wilson M. Beck Insurance Services (Alberta) Inc (1)
2nd Floor 1311 - 9 Ave SW, Calgary, T3C 0H9, AB, Canada
Tel.: (403) 228-5888
Insurance Advisory Services
N.A.I.C.S.: 524298
Brent Williams *(Mng Partner)*

WILSON NIBLETT
10675 Yonge Street, Richmond Hill, L4C 3E1, ON, Canada
Tel.: (905) 884-0991
Web Site:
http://www.wilsonniblett.com
Year Founded: 1960
Rev.: $31,647,962
Emp.: 65
New & Used Car Dealers
N.A.I.C.S.: 441110

WILSON SONS LTD.
Clarendon House 2 Church Street, PO Box HM 666, Hamilton, HM CX, Bermuda
Tel.: (441) 2121264222
Web Site:
http://www.wilsonsons.com.br
Year Founded: 1837
WSON33—(BRAZ)
Rev.: $349,041,795
Assets: $1,038,401,848
Liabilities: $608,534,885
Net Worth: $429,866,963
Earnings: $22,653,010
Emp.: 3,674
Fiscal Year-end: 12/31/20
Transportation Related Services
N.A.I.C.S.: 488999
Augusto Cezar Tavares Baiao *(Chm)*

WILSONS FUEL COMPANY LIMITED
97 Pleasant St, Truro, B2N 5G1, NS, Canada
Tel.: (902) 895-4429
Web Site: http://www.wilsons.ca
Year Founded: 1909
Rev.: $208,451,484
Emp.: 500
Gasoline Distr
N.A.I.C.S.: 336310
Ian Wilson *(Pres)*

WILTON RESOURCES CORPORATION LIMITED
62 Ubi Road 1 09-14 Oxley Bizhub 2, Singapore, 408734, Singapore
Tel.: (65) 67324889 SG
Web Site: https://www.wilton.sg
Year Founded: 1998
5F7—(CAT)
Rev.: $346,423
Assets: $41,583,303
Liabilities: $31,816,429
Net Worth: $9,766,874
Earnings: ($9,947,212)
Fiscal Year-end: 12/31/22
Investment Holding Company
N.A.I.C.S.: 551112
Kok Liang Chew *(Sec)*

WILTON RESOURCES INC.
1900 520-3rd Ave SW, Calgary, T2P 0R3, AB, Canada
Tel.: (403) 619-6609 AB
Web Site:
http://www.wiltonresources.com
Year Founded: 2007
WIL—(TSXV)
Rev.: $10,229
Assets: $533,075
Liabilities: $852,627
Net Worth: ($319,551)
Earnings: ($1,373,571)
Fiscal Year-end: 12/31/19
Oil & Gas Exploration Services
N.A.I.C.S.: 211120
Richard G. Anderson *(Chm & CEO)*

WILTROM CO., LTD.
1F No 26 Sec 2 Shengyi Rd, Hsinchu County, Zhubei, 30261, Taiwan
Tel.: (886) 36107168
Web Site: https://www.wiltrom.com.tw
Year Founded: 2009
6767—(TPE)
Rev.: $6,467,936
Assets: $15,758,684
Liabilities: $4,210,424
Net Worth: $11,548,260
Earnings: ($530,907)
Emp.: 45
Fiscal Year-end: 12/31/22
Biomedical Research & Development Services
N.A.I.C.S.: 541715
Huang-Chien Liang *(Chm & CEO)*

WILUNA MINING CORPORATION LIMITED
Level 3 1 Altona Street, West Perth, 6005, WA, Australia
Tel.: (61) 893226418
Web Site:
http://www.blackhamresources.com
Year Founded: 2006
BLK—(ASX)
Rev.: $100,728,701
Assets: $267,891,438
Liabilities: $99,213,177
Net Worth: $168,678,261
Earnings: $15,633,341
Fiscal Year-end: 06/30/21
Minerals Exploration
N.A.I.C.S.: 213115
Jim Malone *(Gen Mgr-IR & Comm)*

WIM PLAST LTD.
Cello House Corporate Avenue B Wing 1st Floor Sonawala Road, Goregaon E, Mumbai, 400063, India
Tel.: (91) 2226863426
Web Site:
https://www.cellowimplast.com
Year Founded: 1988
526586—(BOM)
Rev.: $40,955,254
Assets: $58,316,660
Liabilities: $5,136,107
Net Worth: $53,180,553
Earnings: $4,998,393
Emp.: 440
Fiscal Year-end: 03/31/23
Plastic Furniture Mfr
N.A.I.C.S.: 337126
Pradeep Ghisulal Rathod *(Chm, CEO & Mng Dir)*

WIMEX AGRARPRODUKTE IMPORT UND EXPORT GMBH

WIMEX AGRARPRODUKTE IMPORT UND EXPORT GMBH

Wimex Agrarprodukte Import und Export GmbH—(Continued)
Peter Henlein Str1, Regensburg, 93128, BA, Germany
Tel.: (49) 940293070
Web Site: http://www.wimex-online.de
Year Founded: 1985
Rev.: $110,186,943
Emp.: 125
Poultry Product Mfr
N.A.I.C.S.: 311615
Gerhard Wagner (Gen Mgr)

WIMI HOLOGRAM CLOUD INC.

Room 816 8th Floor Building 6 Yard 49 Badachu Road, Shijingshan District, Beijing, 100020, China
Tel.: (86) 1053384913
Web Site: https://en.wimiar.com
Year Founded: 2018
WIMI—(NASDAQ)
Rev.: $104,534,107
Assets: $193,096,901
Liabilities: $17,002,726
Net Worth: $176,094,175
Earnings: ($54,807,981)
Emp.: 155
Fiscal Year-end: 12/31/22
Holding Company
N.A.I.C.S.: 551112
Fanhua Meng (CEO)

WIN CHANCE FOODS CO., LTD.

134 Moo 17 Theparak Rd, Bangsaothong District, Samut Prakan, 10540, Thailand
Tel.: (66) 2 705 6969
Web Site: http://www.wcf.co.th
Year Founded: 1987
Sales Range: $100-124.9 Million
Emp.: 20
Sauce & Condiment Mfr
N.A.I.C.S.: 311941
Metha Kornsantiwong (Founder)

WIN HANVERKY HOLDINGS LIMITED

6th Floor Phase 6 Hong Kong Spinners Ind Bldg 481 Castle Peak Road, Kowloon, China (Hong Kong)
Tel.: (852) 27860240
Web Site: http://www.winhanverky.com
3322—(HKG)
Rev.: $567,348,225
Assets: $441,810,960
Liabilities: $204,690,923
Net Worth: $237,120,038
Earnings: $3,012,953
Emp.: 19,000
Fiscal Year-end: 12/31/22
Sportswear Mfr & Retailer
N.A.I.C.S.: 424350

Subsidiaries:

Charmtech Industrial Limited (1)
6th Floor Phase 6 Hong Kong Spinners Ind Bldg 481 Castle Peak Road, Kowloon, China (Hong Kong)
Tel.: (852) 35122800
Web Site: http://www.charmtech.com.hk
Clothing & Furnishing Product Distr
N.A.I.C.S.: 424350

Sports Corner Limited (1)
Shop R15 3/F Choi Yuen Plaza, Sheung Shui, China (Hong Kong)
Tel.: (852) 22644889
Web Site: http://www.esportscorner.com
Clothing & Furnishing Product Distr
N.A.I.C.S.: 424350

WIN SEMICONDUCTORS CORP.

No 69 Keji 7th Road Hwaya Technology Park, Guishan District, Taoyuan, 33383, Taiwan
Tel.: (886) 33975999
Web Site: https://www.winfoundry.com
Year Founded: 1999
3105—(TPE)
Rev.: $573,252,540
Assets: $2,161,404,903
Liabilities: $1,061,147,141
Net Worth: $1,100,257,762
Earnings: $44,218,960
Emp.: 3,237
Fiscal Year-end: 12/31/22
Semiconductor Product Mfr
N.A.I.C.S.: 334413
Dennis Chen (Chm & Pres)

Subsidiaries:

Guzip Biomarkers Corporation (1)
4F No 66 Shengyi 5th Rd, Hsinchu, Zhubei, 302041, Taiwan
Tel.: (886) 3578116830108
Web Site: https://www.guzipbio.com
Endometrial Diagnostic Tool Mfr & Distr
N.A.I.C.S.: 325413

PhalanxBio, Inc. (1)
6150 Lusk Blvd Ste B100, San Diego, CA 92121
Microarray Mfr & Distr
N.A.I.C.S.: 334516

WIN-PARTNERS CO., LTD.

21st floor Kyobashi Edogrand 2-2-1 Kyobashi Chuoku, Tokyo, 104 0031, Japan
Tel.: (81) 335480790
Web Site: http://www.win-partners.co.jp
3183—(TKS)
Rev.: $509,393,040
Assets: $315,488,690
Liabilities: $160,913,840
Net Worth: $154,574,850
Earnings: $12,129,350
Emp.: 609
Fiscal Year-end: 03/31/24
Medical Instrument Sales
N.A.I.C.S.: 423450
Hideumi Akizawa (CEO)

Subsidiaries:

TOSAY Medical.Co., Ltd. (1)
3-14-26 Ueda, Morioka, 020-0066, Japan
Tel.: (81) 196260711.
Web Site: https://to-say.co.jp
Emp.: 37
Medical Equipment & Material Distr
N.A.I.C.S.: 423450

Trytech Co., Ltd. (1)
3F Magnifique Minamioi Building 1-20-17 Minamioi, Shinagawa-ku, Tokyo, 140-0013, Japan
Tel.: (81) 357679831
Web Site: https://www.trytech.co.jp
Medical Equipment Distr
N.A.I.C.S.: 423450

Win International Co., Ltd. (1)
21st floor Kyobashi Edgran 2-2-1 Kyobashi, Chuo-ku, Tokyo, 104-0031, Japan
Tel.: (81) 335480788
Web Site: https://www.win-int.co.jp
Medical Equipment Retailer
N.A.I.C.S.: 423450

WINALL HI-TECH SEED CO., LTD.

No 98 Innovation Avenue, High-tech Industrial Development Zone, Hefei, 230088, China
Tel.: (86) 55165316938
Web Site: https://www.winallseed.com
Year Founded: 2002
300087—(CHIN)
Rev.: $490,071,816
Assets: $712,966,644
Liabilities: $405,059,616
Net Worth: $307,907,028
Earnings: $32,760,936
Emp.: 60
Fiscal Year-end: 12/31/22
Seed Production, Research & Development Services
N.A.I.C.S.: 111191
Ying Minjie (Chm)

WINBO-DONGJIAN AUTOMOTIVE TECHNOLOGY CO., LTD.

B333 Lecong Avenue West, West Lecong Town Shunde, Foshan, 528313, Guangdong, China
Tel.: (86) 75728082476
Web Site: https://www.dongjian.cc
Year Founded: 2003
300978—(SSE)
Rev.: $248,111,665
Assets: $380,308,065
Liabilities: $160,586,768
Net Worth: $219,721,297
Earnings: $12,006,868
Emp.: 2,800
Fiscal Year-end: 12/31/22
Automotive Parts Mfr & Distr
N.A.I.C.S.: 336390
Yongtao Ma (Chm)

WINBOND ELECTRONICS CORPORATION

No 8 Keya 1st Rd Central Taiwan Science Park, Daya Dist, Taichung, 428303, Taiwan
Tel.: (886) 425218168
Web Site: https://www.winbond.com
Year Founded: 1987
2344—(TAI)
Rev.: $2,452,862,264
Assets: $6,239,181,687
Liabilities: $2,953,914,863
Net Worth: $3,285,266,824
Earnings: $1,126,557
Emp.: 7,950
Fiscal Year-end: 12/31/23
Integrated Circuits & Electronic Devices Mfr
N.A.I.C.S.: 334413
Arthur Yu-Cheng Chiao (Chm & CEO)

Subsidiaries:

Winbond Electronics (H.K.) Ltd. (1)
Unit 9 15 22 F Jos Tower Millennium City 2, 378 Kwun Tong Road, Kwun Tong, China (Hong Kong) (100%)
Tel.: (852) 27513100
Sales Range: $25-49.9 Million
Emp.: 10
N.A.I.C.S.: 334413

Winbond Electronics Corporation America (1)
2727 N 1st St, San Jose, CA 95134-2029
Tel.: (408) 943-6666
Web Site: https://www.winbond.com
Sales Range: $75-99.9 Million
Emp.: 200
Sales & Marketing of Electronics
N.A.I.C.S.: 423690

Winbond Electronics Corporation Japan (1)
No 2 Ueno Building 7-18 3-chome Shinyokohama, Kohoku-ku, Yokohama, 222 0033, Kanagawa, Japan
Tel.: (81) 454781881
Sales Range: $25-49.9 Million
Emp.: 40
Semiconductor Distr
N.A.I.C.S.: 334413
Tatsuo Okamato (Pres)

WINCHESTER ENERGY LIMITED

Level 4 105 St Georges Terrace, Perth, 6000, WA, Australia
Tel.: (61) 863242933

INTERNATIONAL PUBLIC

Web Site: https://www.winchesterenergyltd.com
Year Founded: 2014
WEL—(ASX)
Rev.: $2,771,959
Assets: $8,023,453
Liabilities: $1,406,560
Net Worth: $6,616,893
Earnings: ($2,564,925)
Fiscal Year-end: 12/31/23
Oil & Gas Exploration
N.A.I.C.S.: 211120
Neville McVicers Henry (Mng Dir)

Subsidiaries:

Winchester Energy USA Holding Inc. (1)
Two Riverway Ste 1700, Houston, TX 77056
Tel.: (713) 333-0610
Oil & Gas Exploration Services
N.A.I.C.S.: 213111

WIND PROSPECT GROUP LTD

7 Hill St, Clifton, Bristol, BS15PU, United Kingdom
Tel.: (44) 117 3017 151
Web Site: http://www.windprospect.com
Year Founded: 1997
Sales Range: $25-49.9 Million
Emp.: 200
Holding Company; Wind Power Development, Engineering & Advisory Services
N.A.I.C.S.: 551112
Bruce Allan (Dir-Construction & Ops)

Subsidiaries:

Wind Prospect (HK) Ltd (1)
2802 Admiralty Centre Tower 1 18 Harcourt Road, Hong Kong, China (Hong Kong) (85%)
Tel.: (852) 3748 3815
Web Site: http://www.windprospect.hk
Emp.: 1
Wind Power Development, Engineering & Advisory Services
N.A.I.C.S.: 221118
Alex Tancock (Gen Mgr)

Division (Non-US):

Wind Prosptect - China (2)
5F Building C Dragon Century Plaza, 1 Hangda Road, Hangzhou, 310007, Zhejiang, China
Tel.: (86) 571 2880 7871
Wind Power Development, Engineering & Advisory Services
N.A.I.C.S.: 221118

Wind Prospect Africa (Pty) Ltd (1)
20 Kloof Street 2nd Floor Rozenhof Office Court, Cape Town, 8001, South Africa
Tel.: (27) 21 180 4060
Engineeering Services
N.A.I.C.S.: 541330

Wind Prospect Asia Pacific (1)
14/F Net Cube Center 3rd Avenue corner 30th Street, Bonafacio Global City, Taguig, 1634, Philippines
Tel.: (63) 63 2 4795456
Engineeering Services
N.A.I.C.S.: 541330

Wind Prospect Enterprises Ltd (1)
7 hill street, Clifton, Bristol, BS1 5PU, United Kingdom (100%)
Tel.: (44) 117 3017 151
Web Site: http://www.windprospect.com
Wind Power Development Assets Management
N.A.I.C.S.: 541611

Wind Prospect Inc. (1)
1791 Barrington Street Suite 1030, Halifax, B3J 3LI, NS, Canada (90%)
Tel.: (902) 422-9663
Web Site: http://www.windprospect.ca
Wind Power Development, Engineering & Advisory Services
N.A.I.C.S.: 221118

AND PRIVATE COMPANIES

Division (Domestic):

Wind Prospect Inc. (2)
1540 W 2nd Avenue Suite 512, Vancouver, V6J 1H2, BC, Canada
Tel.: (604) 732-9322
Wind Power Development, Engineering & Advisory Services
N.A.I.C.S.: 221118

Wind Prospect Ltd (1)
7 Berkeley Square, Clifton, Bristol, BS8 1HG, United Kingdom (100%)
Tel.: (44) 117 3017 151
Web Site: http://www.windprospect.com
Wind Power Development, Engineering & Advisory Services
N.A.I.C.S.: 221118

Division (Domestic):

Wind Prospect Ltd (2)
Sutton House Dovenby Hall Estate, Dovenby, Cockermouth, CA13 0PN, Cumbria, United Kingdom
Tel.: (44) 1900 898 100
Web Site: http://www.windprospect.com
Emp.: 5
Wind Power Engineering Services
N.A.I.C.S.: 237990
Paula Little (Mng Dir)

Wind Prospect Ltd (2)
Bede House Belmont Business Park, Durham, DH1 1TW, United Kingdom
Tel.: (44) 191 300 1730
Web Site: http://www.windprospect.com
Emp.: 10
Wind Power Development & Engineering
N.A.I.C.S.: 221118
Euan Cameron (Mng Dir)

Subsidiary (Non-US):

Wind Prospect Ltd (2)
Level 6 75 High Street, Singapore, 179435, Singapore
Tel.: (65) 6595 6210
Wind Power Development, Engineering & Advisory Services
N.A.I.C.S.: 221118

Wind Prospect Ltd (2)
1st Floor ICR House 1 Main Road, Constantia, 7848, Cape Town, South Africa
Tel.: (27) 21 794 3415
Wind Power Development, Engineering & Advisory Services
N.A.I.C.S.: 221118

Wind Prospect Ltd (2)
Haluk Turksoy sok 12-3, Altunizade, Istanbul, 34662, Turkiye
Tel.: (90) 532 341 5040
Web Site: http://www.windprospect.com
Wind Power Development & Advisory Services
N.A.I.C.S.: 221118
Ferit Kalfaoglu (Gen Mgr)

Wind Prospect Polska Sp. z o.o (2)
Ul Mila 6, 00-180, Warsaw, Poland
Tel.: (48) 22 498 17 70
Web Site: http://www.windprospect.com
Wind Power Development, Engineering & Advisory Services
N.A.I.C.S.: 221115

Wind Prospect Operations Ltd (1)
The Hyde Building The Park Carrickmines, Malahide, Dublin, 18, Ireland (100%)
Tel.: (353) 1 845 5031
Web Site: http://www.windprospect.com
Wind Farm Asset Management
N.A.I.C.S.: 541611

Wind Prospect Pty Ltd (1)
11 Petra Gonia Walk, Aldinga Beach, Adelaide, 5173, SA, Australia (80%)
Tel.: (61) 8 8384 7755
Web Site: http://www.windprospect.com.au
Emp.: 10
Wind Power Development, Engineering & Advisory Services
N.A.I.C.S.: 221118
Michael Vawser (Mng Dir)

Division (Domestic):

Wind Prospect Pty Ltd (2)
Suite 10 19-35 Gertrude Street, Fitzroy, 3065, VIC, Australia
Tel.: (61) 3 9005 9075
Web Site: http://www.windprospect.com
Emp.: 3
Wind Power Development, Engineering & Advisory Services
N.A.I.C.S.: 221118

Wind Prospect Pty Ltd - Newcastle (2)
Level 6 Suite A T & G Building 41-45 Hunter Street, PO Box 1708, Newcastle, 2300, NSW, Australia
Tel.: (61) 2 4013 4640
Web Site: http://www.windprospect.com
Wind Power Development, Engineering & Advisory Services
N.A.I.C.S.: 221118
Ed Mounsey (COO)

Wind Prospect SAS (1)
22 rue de Palestro, Paris, 75002, France
Tel.: (33) 1 75 77 06 80
Web Site: http://www.windprospect.fr
Wind Power Development, Engineering & Advisory Services
N.A.I.C.S.: 221118
Barthelemy Rouer (Dir Gen & Gen Mgr)

Subsidiary (Non-US):

Wind Prospect GmbH (2)
Robert Bosch Strasse 7, 64283, Darmstadt, Germany
Tel.: (49) 6151 277310 1
Engineeering Services
N.A.I.C.S.: 541330

WIND PROSPECT IRELAND LTD
The Hyde Building The Park Carrickmines, Malahide, Dublin, 18, Ireland
Tel.: (353) 1 845 5031
Wind Power Engineering & Advisory Services
N.A.I.C.S.: 237990
Ken Doynea (Mng Dir)

WIND RIVER ENERGY CORP.
Suite 1010 609 Granville Street Pacific Centre, PO Box 10354, Vancouver, V7Y 1G5, BC, Canada
Tel.: (778) 786-1285
Web Site: http://windriverenergy.com
Sales Range: Less than $1 Million
Oil & Gas Exploration Service
N.A.I.C.S.: 213112
Alan C. O'Hare (Pres, CEO, Treas & Sec)

Subsidiaries:

Wind River Hydrocarbons, Inc. (1)
98 Inverness Dr E 350, Englewood, CO 80112-5319
Tel.: (303) 708-1900
Oil & Gas Exploration Services
N.A.I.C.S.: 213112

WIND TELECOM SP. O.O.
ul Feldmana 4/5, 31-130, Krakow, Poland
Tel.: (48) 12 397 76 59
Web Site: http://www.windtelecom.pl
Sales Range: $1-9.9 Million
Emp.: 50
Telecommunications Solutions
N.A.I.C.S.: 517810
Pawel Olech (Chm)

WIND WORKS POWER CORP.
7129 Mark Lane, Victoria, V9E2A1, BC, Canada
Tel.: (206) 925-3889 NV
Web Site: https://www.windworkspower.com
Year Founded: 2002
WWPW—(OTCIQ)
Sales Range: $50-74.9 Million
Wind Energy Services
N.A.I.C.S.: 221118
Ingo Stuckmann (CEO)

WINDAR PHOTONICS PLC
Helgeshoj Alle 16-18, DK-2630, Taastrup, Denmark
Tel.: (45) 20555599 DK
Web Site: https://www.windarphotonics.com
Year Founded: 2008
WPHO—(AIM)
Rev.: $1,972,470
Assets: $4,573,998
Liabilities: $4,211,490
Net Worth: $362,508
Earnings: ($1,151,496)
Emp.: 4
Fiscal Year-end: 12/31/22
Wind Power Product Mfr & Distr
N.A.I.C.S.: 333611
Jorgen Korsgaard Jensen (CEO)

WINDCHILL HOLDINGS LTD
191 Range Road, Whitehorse, Y1A 3E5, YT, Canada
Tel.: (867) 668-3399
Web Site: http://www.klondikemotors.ca
Rev.: $11,302,844
Emp.: 70
New & Used Vehicles
N.A.I.C.S.: 423120
John Brooks (Gen Mgr)

WINDELN.DE SE
Stefan-George-Ring 23, 81929, Munich, Germany
Tel.: (49) (89) 4161 7152 65
Web Site: http://corporate.windeln.de
WDL—(DEU)
Rev.: $93,428,532
Assets: $25,845,854
Liabilities: $13,314,122
Net Worth: $12,531,733
Earnings: ($16,885,844)
Emp.: 218
Fiscal Year-end: 12/31/20
Baby & Children's Products Online Retailer
N.A.I.C.S.: 424350
Xiaowei Wei (Member-Mgmt Bd)

WINDFALL GEOTEK INC.
7005 Taschereau Boulevard Suite 340, Brossard, J4Z 1A7, QC, Canada
Tel.: (450) 678-8882 QC
Web Site: https://www.windfallgeotek.com
Year Founded: 1996
L7C2—(DEU)
Rev.: $266,178
Assets: $771,735
Liabilities: $68,296
Net Worth: $703,438
Earnings: ($1,149,925)
Fiscal Year-end: 02/29/24
Precious Metals, Base Metals, Uranium & Diamonds Mining & Exploration Services
N.A.I.C.S.: 212290
Michel Fontaine (Pres)

WINDFIRE CAPITAL CORP.
1177 West Hastings Street Suite 2000, Vancouver, V6E 2K3, BC, Canada
Tel.: (604) 669-2191 AB
Web Site: http://www.windfirecapital.com
Year Founded: 2007
Sales Range: Less than $1 Million
Investment Services
N.A.I.C.S.: 523999

WINDHURST SAS
42 avenue Raymond Poincare, 75116, Paris, France
Tel.: (33) 1 4505 4000 FR
Web Site: http://www.windhurst.com
Privater Equity Firm
N.A.I.C.S.: 523999
Nathalie Williams (Gen Counsel)

WINDLAS BIOTECH LIMITED
40/1 Mohabewala Industrial Area, Dehradun, 248110, Uttarakhand, India
Tel.: (91) 1356608000
Web Site: https://www.windlas.com
Year Founded: 2001
543329—(BOM)
Rev.: $58,789,868
Assets: $40,420,790
Liabilities: $13,241,046
Net Worth: $27,179,744
Earnings: $2,125,305
Emp.: 954
Fiscal Year-end: 03/31/21
Pharmaceutical Preparation Mfr
N.A.I.C.S.: 325412
Vivek Dhariwal (Chm)

WINDMILL GROUP LIMITED
Unit 1603 16/F Tower 1 Enterprise Square 9 Sheung Yuet Road, Kowloon Bay, Kowloon, China (Hong Kong)
Tel.: (852) 28879208 Ky
Web Site: http://www.windmill.hk
Year Founded: 1985
1850—(HKG)
Rev.: $29,485,523
Assets: $24,815,198
Liabilities: $7,340,048
Net Worth: $17,475,150
Earnings: ($891,480)
Emp.: 56
Fiscal Year-end: 04/30/23
Fire Safety System Services
N.A.I.C.S.: 541990
Alexander Shing Kuen Li (Chm, CEO & Officer-Compliance)

Subsidiaries:

Windmill Engineering Company Limited (1)
Unit 1603 16/F Tower 1 Enterprise Square 9 Sheung Yuet Road, Kowloon Bay, Kowloon, China (Hong Kong)
Tel.: (852) 28879208
Web Site: https://www.windmill.hk
Fire System Installation Contractor Services
N.A.I.C.S.: 541990

WINDMOELLER & HOELSCHER KG
Muensterstrasse 50, 49525, Lengerich, Germany
Tel.: (49) 5481140 De
Web Site: http://www.wuh-lengerich.de
Year Founded: 1869
Sales Range: $650-699.9 Million
Emp.: 2,950
Mfr of Printing, Extrusion & Converting Equipment for the Packaging Industry
N.A.I.C.S.: 333243
Peter Steinbeck (Chief Sls & Svc Officer & Member-Mgmt Bd)

Subsidiaries:

BSW Machinery Handels-GmbH (1)
Triester Strasse 10/1/122, 2351, Wiener Neudorf, Austria
Tel.: (43) 1 997 50 50 0
Web Site: http://www.bswtex.com
Packaging Machinery Mfr
N.A.I.C.S.: 333993

Druckfarben Hellas A.E.B.E. (1)
Megaridos ave, Aspropyrgos, Greece
Tel.: (30) 2105519300
Packaging Machinery Mfr
N.A.I.C.S.: 333993
Jenny Kokkinogeni (Mgr-HR)

Garant Maschinenhandel Gmbh (1)
Munsterstr 91, 49525, Lengerich, Germany
Tel.: (49) 5481 809 0

WINDMOELLER & HOELSCHER KG

Windmoeller & Hoelscher KG—(Continued)
Web Site: http://www.garant-maschinen.de
Industrial Machinery & Equipment Mfr
N.A.I.C.S.: 333310
Dieter Schallenberg (Co-Mng Dir)

Impressum S.A. (1)
12 calle 1-25 Zona 10 Edificio Geminis 10 Torre Norte Office 1406, Guatemala, Guatemala
Tel.: (502) 23352747
Web Site: http://www.impressumsa.com
Printing Machinery & Equipment Mfr
N.A.I.C.S.: 333248

Incotecnica S.A. De C.V. (1)
Apartado 12-840, Mexico, Mexico
Tel.: (52) 5556871966
Packaging Machinery Mfr
N.A.I.C.S.: 333993

Krist Seven Ltd. (1)
28 Gbolade Adebanjo Street Off Coker Road, Ilupeju, Lagos, Nigeria
Tel.: (234) 8028025787
Web Site: http://www.kristseven.com
Pharmacy & Cosmetic Material Mfr
N.A.I.C.S.: 325412
V.J Mathew (Mng Dir)

Lapeyra & Taltavull Comercial S.L. (1)
Industria 127, Barcelona, Spain
Tel.: (34) 934558806
Packaging Machinery Mfr
N.A.I.C.S.: 333993

Roberto Delfino & Co. (1)
Apartado 1351, Caracas, Venezuela
Tel.: (58) 2122351073
Packaging Machinery Mfr
N.A.I.C.S.: 333993

WINDMOLLER & HOLSCHER America Latina
Marchant Pereira 221 Of 32, Providencia, Santiago, Chile
Tel.: (56) 2 7547773
Packaging Machinery Distr
N.A.I.C.S.: 423830

Webconvert Ltd. (1)
21 Goodrich Road Unit 11, Toronto, M8Z 6A3, ON, Canada
Tel.: (416) 252-4462
Packaging Machinery Mfr
N.A.I.C.S.: 333993

Windmoeller & Hoelscher AG (1)
Mariahilfer Strasse 123 3, 1060, Vienna, Austria (100%)
Tel.: (43) 0159999395
Mfr of Printing, Extrusion & Converting Equipment for the Packaging Industry
N.A.I.C.S.: 333243

Windmoeller & Hoelscher Asia (1)
Silvercord Twr 2 Rm 1201 3, 30 Canton Rd TST, Kowloon, China (Hong Kong) (100%)
Tel.: (852) 23022926
Web Site: http://www.wuh-lengerich.de
Sales Range: $50-74.9 Million
Emp.: 1
Mfr of Printing, Extrusion & Converting Equipment for the Packaging Industry
N.A.I.C.S.: 333243
Klaus Meyer (Gen Mgr)

Windmoeller & Hoelscher Asia (1)
1 Tsu Chiang St Tu Cheng Industrial Est, Taipei, 236, Taiwan (100%)
Tel.: (886) 222693782
N.A.I.C.S.: 333243

Windmoeller & Hoelscher Asia Co. (Taiwan) (1)
10 F 4 Mincyuan Rd, Taichung, 40041, Taiwan
Tel.: (886) 4 22256601
Packaging Machinery Distr
N.A.I.C.S.: 423830
Scott Lai (Pres)

Windmoeller & Hoelscher Asia Pacific Co., Ltd. (1)
Bangna, PO Box 16, 10260, Bangkok, Samutprakarn, Thailand
Tel.: (66) 2 3014040
Packaging Machinery Distr
N.A.I.C.S.: 423830

Windmoeller & Hoelscher Australasia Pty. Ltd. (1)
Unit 7/26 Howleys Road, Notting Hill, 3168, VIC, Australia
Tel.: (61) 3 95589558
Web Site: http://www.wuh-group.com
Emp.: 3
Packaging Machinery Distr
N.A.I.C.S.: 423830
Nigel Compton (Mng Dir)

Windmoeller & Hoelscher Benelux B.V. (1)
Willem de Zwijgerlaan 350 A/2, Postbus 74700, Amsterdam, 1055 RD, Netherlands
Tel.: (31) 203012600
Web Site: http://www.vuhgroupe.com
Emp.: 4
Mfr of Printing, Extrusion & Converting Equipment for the Packaging Industry
N.A.I.C.S.: 333243
Hugo Kruip (Mng Dir)

Windmoeller & Hoelscher Corp. (1)
23 New England Way, Lincoln, RI 02865-4252 (100%)
Tel.: (401) 333-2770
Web Site: http://www.whcorp.com
Sales Range: $25-49.9 Million
Emp.: 50
Mfr of Printing, Extrusion & Converting Equipment for the Packaging Industry
N.A.I.C.S.: 423830
Walter H. Kaehler (Controller)

Windmoeller & Hoelscher Dis Ticaret A.S. (1)
Kultur Mah Esra Sk No 23, Etiler, 34340, Istanbul, Turkiye (100%)
Tel.: (90) 2122630533
Web Site: http://www.wuh.com
Sales Range: Less than $1 Million
Emp.: 8
Mfr of Printing, Extrusion & Converting Equipment for the Packaging Industry
N.A.I.C.S.: 333243
Servar Bunut (Gen Mgr)

Windmoeller & Hoelscher India Pvt. Ltd. (1)
406 - 407 Hemkunt Tower 98 Nehru Place, New Delhi, 110019, India
Tel.: (91) 1151618274
Flexible Packaging Mfr
N.A.I.C.S.: 322220

Windmoeller & Hoelscher Italiana S.R.L. (1)
Via Saragat 9, PO Box 234, I 26900, Lodi, Italy (100%)
Tel.: (39) 037133799
Web Site: http://www.wuh.it
Mfr of Printing, Extrusion & Converting Equipment for the Packaging Industry
N.A.I.C.S.: 333243

Windmoeller & Hoelscher Machinery (Taicang) Co. Ltd. (1)
No 18 Suzhou Road Taicang Economic Development Zone, 215400, Taicang, Jiangsu, China
Tel.: (86) 512 5367 6800
Packaging Machinery Distr
N.A.I.C.S.: 423830

Windmoeller & Hoelscher Vietnam Company Limited (1)
Suite 33 Vietcom Bank Tower Level 21 No 5 Me Linh Square, Ben Nghe Ward Dist 1, Ho Chi Minh City, Vietnam
Tel.: (84) 2838271941
Packaging Machinery Mfr
N.A.I.C.S.: 333993

Windmoeller & Hoelscher do Brasil Ltda. (1)
Av Ibirapuera 2033, 13 Andar-conj 134, Sao Paulo, 04029 110, SP, Brazil (100%)
Tel.: (55) 1127686339
Web Site: http://www.wuhdobrasil.com.br
Sales Range: $25-49.9 Million
Emp.: 50
Mfr of Printing, Extrusion & Converting Equipment for the Packaging Industry
N.A.I.C.S.: 333243

Windmoller & Holscher Austria Cee Gmbh & Co. KG (1)
Karl-Popper-Strasse 8 Top 303, Vienna, Austria
Tel.: (43) 12927380
Packaging Machinery Mfr
N.A.I.C.S.: 333993
Helmut Gass (Sls Dir)

Windmoller & Holscher Dis. Ticaret A.s. (1)
Kultur Mah Ezra Sk No 23, Etiler Besiktas, 34340, Istanbul, Turkiye
Tel.: (90) 2122630533
Packaging Machinery Mfr
N.A.I.C.S.: 333993

Windmoller & Holscher GmbH (1)
Moskowska Str 46/2 App 117, 01015, Kiev, Ukraine
Tel.: (380) 44 2542231
Packaging Machinery Distr
N.A.I.C.S.: 423830

Windmoller & Holscher India Pvt. Ltd. (1)
3rd Floor 17 18 19 Kailash Enclave Opposite Metro Pillar No 76, New Delhi, India
Tel.: (91) 1143222777
Packaging Machinery Mfr
N.A.I.C.S.: 333993
Rakesh Shah (Mng Dir)

Windmoller & Holscher KG (1)
Munsterstrasse 50, Lengerich, Germany
Tel.: (49) 5481140
Packaging Machinery Mfr
N.A.I.C.S.: 333993
Bernd Richter (Gen Mgr-HR)

Windmoller & Holscher KG (Polen) (1)
Ul Okrezna 83A/8, 02-933, Warsaw, Poland
Tel.: (48) 22 6429060
Packaging Machinery Distr
N.A.I.C.S.: 423830

Windmoller & Holscher Machinery GmbH (1)
Triester Strasse 10/1/122, Wiener Neudorf, Austria
Tel.: (43) 22363742740
Packaging Machinery Mfr
N.A.I.C.S.: 333993

Windmoller & Holscher Machinery K.S. (1)
Grove 374, Kralice na Hane, 798 12, Prostejov, Czech Republic
Tel.: (420) 582311111
Packaging Machinery Mfr
N.A.I.C.S.: 333993
Vladimira Travnickova (Mgr-HR)

Windmoller & Holscher Polska Sp.z o.o (1)
Ul Okrezna 83A/8, Warsaw, Poland
Tel.: (48) 226429060
Packaging Machinery Mfr
N.A.I.C.S.: 333993

WINDON ENERGY GROUP AB
Humlegardsgatan 4, 114 46, Stockholm, Sweden
Tel.: (46) 729424892
Web Site: https://www.windonenergygroup.se
Year Founded: 2021
NW1—(DEU)
Renewable Energy Services
N.A.I.C.S.: 221210
Henrik Karstensen (CEO)

WINDRIDGE PROPERTIES LTD
11-7228 Progress Way, Delta, V4G 1H2, BC, Canada
Tel.: (604) 940-8470
Web Site: http://www.windridge.ca
Year Founded: 1991
Commercial Building Construction Services
N.A.I.C.S.: 236220
Richard Roberts (Pres)

WINDSOR GMBH
Am Ellerbrocks Hof 2 6, 33617, Bielefeld, Germany

INTERNATIONAL PUBLIC

Tel.: (49) 52114530
Web Site: http://www.windsor.de
Year Founded: 1889
Rev: $109,044,949
Emp.: 284
Women & Men Clothing Mfr
N.A.I.C.S.: 315250

WINDSOR MACHINES LTD
5403 Phase IV GIDC, Vatva, Ahmedabad, 382 445, Gujarat, India
Tel.: (91) 7935002700
Web Site: https://www.windsormachines.com
522029—(BOM)
Rev.: $46,052,791
Assets: $69,766,201
Liabilities: $34,844,913
Net Worth: $34,921,288
Earnings: $556,561
Emp.: 541
Fiscal Year-end: 03/31/23
Plastic Processing Machinery Mfr
N.A.I.C.S.: 333248
Priti Patel (Compliance Officer & Sec)

Subsidiaries:

Wintal Machines S.R.L. (1)
Viale Enrico Mattei 16, Mazzano, 25080, Brescia, Italy
Tel.: (39) 0302060400
Industrial Machinery Mfr
N.A.I.C.S.: 333248

WINDSUN SCIENCE & TECHNOLOGY CO., LTD.
Jincheng Road, Economic Development Zone Wenshang, Jining, 272500, Shandong, China
Tel.: (86) 15063706318
Web Site: https://www.fgi-energyrouter.com
Year Founded: 2004
688663—(SHG)
Rev.: $182,977,985
Assets: $339,768,997
Liabilities: $179,033,054
Net Worth: $160,735,943
Earnings: $18,067,571
Fiscal Year-end: 12/31/22
Power Supply Equipment Mfr & Distr
N.A.I.C.S.: 335312
Hongchen He (Chm)

WINDWARD ISLAND BANK LTD.
Clem Labega Square, Philipsburg, Saint Martin
Tel.: (721) 5422313
Web Site: http://www.wib-bank.net
Sales Range: $50-74.9 Million
Emp.: 210
Banking Services
N.A.I.C.S.: 522110
Jan J. Beaujon (Mng Dir)

WINDWARD LTD.
2 Hashlosha Street, Tel Aviv, 6706054, Israel
Tel.: (972) 36033956
Web Site: https://www.windward.ai
Year Founded: 2010
WNWD—(AIM)
Rev.: $21,643,000
Assets: $31,345,000
Liabilities: $19,010,000
Net Worth: $12,335,000
Earnings: ($19,199,000)
Emp.: 150
Fiscal Year-end: 12/31/22
Software Development Services
N.A.I.C.S.: 541511

WINE'S LINK INTERNATIONAL HOLDINGS LIMITED
26F AIA Financial Centre 712 Prince

AND PRIVATE COMPANIES

Edward Road East, San Po Kong,
Kowloon, China (Hong Kong)
Tel.: (852) 23171100   Ky
Web Site: https://www.wines-link.com
Year Founded: 2007
8509—(HKG)
Rev.: $18,835,193
Assets: $54,998,910
Liabilities: $21,427,650
Net Worth: $33,571,260
Earnings: $2,082,713
Emp.: 30
Fiscal Year-end: 03/31/23
Alcoholic Beverage Distr
N.A.I.C.S.: 424820
Shirley Chi Lou Wong *(Exec Dir)*

WINFAIR INVESTMENT COMPANY LIMITED
5th Floor Lee Kiu Building 51 Jordan Road, Kowloon, China (Hong Kong)
Tel.: (852) 23322343   HK
Web Site:
https://www.winfairinvestment.com
Year Founded: 1971
0287—(HKG)
Rev.: $2,453,068
Assets: $148,668,612
Liabilities: $2,930,725
Net Worth: $145,737,887
Earnings: ($4,618,988)
Emp.: 4
Fiscal Year-end: 03/31/23
Property Development Investor
N.A.I.C.S.: 525990
Mimoona Ma *(Sec)*

WINFARM SA
ZI de tres le Bois 80 Rue Arthur Enaud, 22600, Loudeac, France
Tel.: (33) 330296289751
Web Site: https://www.winfarm-group.com
Year Founded: 1990
ALWF—(EUR)
Emp.: 400
Agriculture Product Distr
N.A.I.C.S.: 424910

WINFRESH LIMITED
99 Chaussee Road, Castries, Saint Lucia
Tel.: (758) 457 8600   LC
Web Site: http://www.winfresh.net
Year Founded: 1994
Bananas Distr
N.A.I.C.S.: 111339

WINFULL GROUP HOLDINGS LIMITED
Unit A 6th Floor 9 Queens Road Central, Hong Kong, China (Hong Kong)
Tel.: (852) 3 183 0727   Ky
Web Site: http://www.winfullgroup.hk
Year Founded: 2002
183—(HKG)
Rev.: $6,534,127
Assets: $275,640,965
Liabilities: $37,999,314
Net Worth: $237,641,652
Earnings: $4,654,501
Emp.: 24
Fiscal Year-end: 06/30/21
Holding Company; Property Investment & Development
N.A.I.C.S.: 551112
Wing Yin Lee *(CEO, Officer-Compliance & Sec)*

WING CHI HOLDINGS LIMITED
Room 3010 Cable TV Tower 9 Hoi Shing Road Tsuen Wan New Territories, Hong Kong, China (Hong Kong)
Tel.: (852) 22780039   Ky
Web Site:
http://www.wingchiholdings.com
Year Founded: 2001
6080—(HKG)
Rev.: $68,505,623
Assets: $18,190,935
Liabilities: $1,982,370
Net Worth: $16,208,565
Earnings: $1,252,433
Emp.: 53
Fiscal Year-end: 03/31/23
Construction Work Services
N.A.I.C.S.: 238910
Cheuk Kam Li *(Chm & CEO)*

WING FUNG GROUP ASIA LTD.
Unit 13&14 9/F World-Wide Industrial Centre 43-47 Shan Mei Street, Fotan, New Territories, China (Hong Kong)
Tel.: (852) 26886373   Ky
Web Site:
http://www.wingfunggroup.com
8526—(HKG)
Rev.: $23,462,550
Assets: $23,746,110
Liabilities: $10,788,795
Net Worth: $12,957,315
Earnings: ($1,427,873)
Emp.: 230
Fiscal Year-end: 12/31/22
Residential Building Contract Services
N.A.I.C.S.: 236220
Chi Keung Chung *(Chm, CEO & Compliance Officer)*

WING LEE PROPERTY INVESTMENTS LIMITED
Office J 11/F King Palace Plaza 55 King Yip Street, Kwun Tong, Kowloon, China (Hong Kong)
Tel.: (852) 39983052   BM
Web Site:
http://www.wingleeproperties.com
0864—(HKG)
Rev.: $3,739,703
Assets: $135,769,140
Liabilities: $16,626,510
Net Worth: $119,142,630
Earnings: $2,234,693
Emp.: 7
Fiscal Year-end: 12/31/22
Property Investment Services
N.A.I.C.S.: 523999
Choi Fa Chau *(Chm)*

WING ON COMPANY INTERNATIONAL LIMITED
7th Floor Wing On Centre 211 Des Voeux Road, Central, China (Hong Kong)
Tel.: (852) 28521523
Web Site: http://www.wingonet.com
0289—(HKG)
Rev.: $132,731,070
Assets: $2,537,585,198
Liabilities: $167,963,783
Net Worth: $2,369,621,415
Earnings: ($38,455,658)
Emp.: 551
Fiscal Year-end: 12/31/22
Department Stores
N.A.I.C.S.: 455110
Kar Tim Sin *(Sec)*

Subsidiaries:

Woco Investment Corporation   (1)
5100 Westheimer Rd Ste 155, Houston, TX 77056
Tel.: (713) 629-5535
Emp.: 6
Property Investment Management Services
N.A.I.C.S.: 523940

WING REAL ESTATE DEVELOPER AND INVESTOR PRIVATE LIMITED COMPANY
Mariassy utca 7, Mariassy House, Budapest, 1095, Hungary
Tel.: (36) 1454289
Web Site: http://www.wing.hu
Holding Company
N.A.I.C.S.: 523999
Noah M Steinberg *(Chm & CEO)*

WING TAI HOLDINGS LIMITED
3 Killiney Road 10-01 Winsland House I, Singapore, 239519, Singapore
Tel.: (65) 62809111
Web Site: https://www.wingtaiasia.com
Year Founded: 1963
W05—(SES)
Rev.: $352,924,787
Assets: $3,076,637,273
Liabilities: $591,031,493
Net Worth: $2,485,605,780
Earnings: $8,407,558
Emp.: 692
Fiscal Year-end: 06/30/23
Investment Holding Company
N.A.I.C.S.: 551112
Edmund Wai Wing Cheng *(Deputy Chm & Deputy Mng Dir)*

Subsidiaries:

Brave Dragon Ltd   (1)
12F Kennedy Terrace 20 Kennedy Road, Wanchai, China (Hong Kong)
Tel.: (852) 23031100
Investment Management Service
N.A.I.C.S.: 523999

Fox Fashion Apparel (S) Pte Ltd   (1)
230 Victoria Street 01-20 Bugis Junction, Singapore, 188024, Singapore
Tel.: (65) 68359766
Web Site: http://www.foxfashion.sg
Fashion Apparels Mfr
N.A.I.C.S.: 315120

Wing Tai Clothing Pte Ltd   (1)
Raffles City Shopping Centre 02-04 252 North Bridge Road, Singapore, 179103, Singapore
Tel.: (65) 63381062
Fashion Apparels Retailer
N.A.I.C.S.: 458110

Wing Tai Investment & Development Pte Ltd   (1)
Winsland House I 10-01 3 Killiney Road, Singapore, 239519, Singapore
Tel.: (65) 62809111
Investment Management Service
N.A.I.C.S.: 523999

Wing Tai Investment Management Pte Ltd
3 Killiney Road 07-01 Winsland House 1, Singapore, 239519, Singapore
Tel.: (65) 63394031
Web Site: http://www.wingtaiasia.com.sg
Sales Range: $50-74.9 Million
Emp.: 25
Investment Management Service
N.A.I.C.S.: 523999
Jacquelin Aw *(Head-Mktg)*

Wing Tai Investment Pte Ltd   (1)
3 Killiney Road 10-01 Winsland House I, Singapore, 239519, Singapore
Tel.: (65) 62809111
Web Site: http://www.wingtaiasia.com.sg
Investment Property Development Services
N.A.I.C.S.: 236116

Wing Tai Land Pte Ltd   (1)
3 Killiney Road 10-01 Winsland House I, Singapore, 239519, Singapore
Tel.: (65) 62809111
Investment Management Service
N.A.I.C.S.: 523999

Wing Tai Malaysia Sdn. Bhd.   (1)
17 01 Menara Boustead Penang 39, Jalan Sultan Ahmad Shah, 10050, Penang, Malaysia   (96.75%)
Tel.: (60) 42993888
Web Site: http://www.wingtaiasia.com.my

WING TAI HOLDINGS LIMITED

Sales Range: $50-74.9 Million
Investment Holding Company; Textile Garment Manufacturing & Trading, Residential & Commercial Property Development & Commercial & Hotel Property Investment
N.A.I.C.S.: 551112
Kok Cheang Tan *(Sr Gen Mgr-DNP Land)*

Subsidiary (Domestic):

DNP Hartajaya Sdn Bhd   (2)
No 2 Jalan Bukit Minyak Utama Taman Bm Utama, 14000, Bukit Mertajam, Penang, Malaysia
Tel.: (60) 45308989
Web Site: http://www.dnplend.com.my
Sales Range: $50-74.9 Million
Emp.: 8
Property Development Services
N.A.I.C.S.: 531311

DNP Land Sdn Bhd   (2)
No 2338 Jalan Rozhan, Galeri Impian, 14000, Bukit Mertajam, Penang, Malaysia
Tel.: (60) 45387788
Web Site: https://www.dnpland.com.my
Sales Range: $25-49.9 Million
Emp.: 50
Property Development Services
N.A.I.C.S.: 531311

Subsidiary (Domestic):

DNP Property Management Sdn Bhd   (3)
1-1 Jalan SU 1E Persiaran Sering Ukay 1, Sering Ukay, Ampang, 68000, Selangor, Malaysia
Tel.: (60) 341083380
Property Development Services
N.A.I.C.S.: 531312

Subsidiary (Domestic):

Seniharta Sdn Bhd   (2)
No 1 Lanson Place Jln Ampang Hilir, Kuala Lumpur, 55000, Malaysia
Tel.: (60) 3 4253 2888
Web Site: http://www.34wlansonplace.com
Property Development Services
N.A.I.C.S.: 531312
Michael Chan *(Gen Mgr)*

Starpuri Development Sdn Bhd   (2)
1-1 Jalan Su1 East Persiaran Sering Ukay 1 Sering Ukay, Ampang, 68000, Selangor, Malaysia
Tel.: (60) 341083380
Web Site: http://www.wingtaiasia.com.my
Property Development Services
N.A.I.C.S.: 236220

Wing Tai Clothing Sdn. Bhd.   (2)
Lot1 05 Level 1 1 First Avenue, Bandar Utama, 47800, Petaling Jaya, Selangor, Malaysia
Tel.: (60) 377241988
Web Site: https://www.wtplus.com.my
Sales Range: $25-49.9 Million
Emp.: 40
Family Apparel Retailer
N.A.I.C.S.: 458110

Wing Tai Property Management Pte Ltd   (1)
Winsland House I 10-01 3 Killiney Rd, Singapore, 239519, Singapore
Tel.: (65) 62809111
Sales Range: $50-74.9 Million
Emp.: 100
Property Management Services
N.A.I.C.S.: 531312

Wing Tai Retail Management Pte. Ltd   (1)
107 Tampines Road Wing Tai Industrial Centre, Singapore, 535129, Singapore
Tel.: (65) 62809111
Property Management Services
N.A.I.C.S.: 531312

Wing Tai Retail Pte. Ltd   (1)
159 Kampong Ampat 03-02/03, Singapore, 368328, Singapore
Tel.: (65) 63091200
Web Site: http://www.wintaiasia.com.sg
Apparel Store Management Services
N.A.I.C.S.: 458110
Helen Khoo *(Exec Dir)*

Winnorth Investment Pte Ltd   (1)

WING TAI HOLDINGS LIMITED

Wing Tai Holdings Limited—(Continued)
Winsland House I 10-01 3 Killiney Rd, Singapore, 239519, Singapore
Tel.: (65) 63523800
Property Development Services
N.A.I.C.S.: 236210

Winrose Investment Pte Ltd (1)
Winsland House I 10-01 3 Killiney Rd, Singapore, 239519, Singapore
Tel.: (65) 62383800
Property Development Services
N.A.I.C.S.: 236210

Winshine Investment Pte Ltd (1)
3 Killiney Road 10-01 Winsland House, Singapore, 239519, Singapore
Tel.: (65) 62809111
Web Site: http://www.wingtaiasia.com.sg
Emp.: 400
Investment Management Service
N.A.I.C.S.: 523999

Winsland Investment Pte Ltd (1)
Winsland House I 07 01 3 Killiney Road, Singapore, 239519, Singapore
Tel.: (65) 67362622
Sales Range: $25-49.9 Million
Emp.: 20
Property Development Services
N.A.I.C.S.: 236210
Jacqueline A. W. (Head-Mktg & Leasing)

Wintrust Investment Pte Ltd (1)
Wing Tai Bldg 107 Tampines Rd, Singapore, 535129, Singapore
Tel.: (65) 62809111
Sales Range: $150-199.9 Million
Emp.: 500
Property Development Services
N.A.I.C.S.: 531312

Yoshinoya (S) Pte Ltd (1)
3 Killiney Rd 10th Floor 101 Winsland House 1, Singapore, 239519, Singapore
Tel.: (65) 6280 9111
Hospital Management Services
N.A.I.C.S.: 611519

WING TAI PROPERTIES LIMITED
27th Floor AIA Kowloon Tower Landmark East 100 How Ming Street, Kwun Tong, Kowloon, China (Hong Kong)
Tel.: (852) 27522338
Web Site: http://www.wingtaiproperties.com
0369—(HKG)
Rev.: $522,329,250
Assets: $4,526,148,000
Liabilities: $1,041,917,250
Net Worth: $3,484,230,750
Earnings: ($41,297,250)
Emp.: 360
Fiscal Year-end: 12/31/22
Real Estate Investment; Textile & Apparel Manufacturing
N.A.I.C.S.: 531190
Christopher Wai Chee Cheng (Chm)

WING YIP FOOD (CHINA) HOLDINGS GROUP LTD.
17F Winsan Tower 98 Thomson Road, Wanchai, China (Hong Kong)
Tel.: (852) 64595536
900340—(KRS)
Rev.: $112,210,443
Assets: $145,543,071
Liabilities: $27,415,779
Net Worth: $118,127,292
Earnings: $10,879,316
Emp.: 356
Fiscal Year-end: 12/31/22
Veal Product Mfr
N.A.I.C.S.: 311612
Xiantao Wang (CEO)

WING'S FOOT INC.
7F 58 Myeongdong-gil, Jung-gu, Seoul, Korea (South)
Tel.: (82) 7071243583
Web Site: https://www.wingsfoot.co.kr
Year Founded: 2007
335870—(KRS)
Footwear Distr
N.A.I.C.S.: 458210
Hwang Sung-Ung (CEO)

WINGARA AG LIMITED
Suite 11 13-25 Church St, Hawthorn, 3122, VIC, Australia
Tel.: (61) 398539631
Web Site: https://www.wingaraag.com.au
WNR—(ASX)
Rev.: $1,935,737
Assets: $3,309,822
Liabilities: $2,097,795
Net Worth: $1,212,027
Earnings: ($2,037,939)
Fiscal Year-end: 03/31/24
Agricultural Product Mfr & Distr
N.A.I.C.S.: 311213

Subsidiaries:

JC Tanloden Victoria Pty. Ltd. (1)
Suite 11 13-25 Church street, Hawthorn, 3122, VIC, Australia
Tel.: (61) 398539631
Web Site: http://www.jotanloden.com.au
Meat & Dairy Product Distr
N.A.I.C.S.: 424490

WINGENBACK INC.
Bay F 707 Barlow Trail SE, Calgary, T2E 8C2, AB, Canada
Tel.: (403) 221-8120   Ca
Web Site: https://www.wingenback.com
Year Founded: 1975
ATM Products Distr, Construction & Project Management, Installation & Security Services
N.A.I.C.S.: 561621
Bill Vander Doelen (VP-Sls & Mktg)

WINGTECH TECHNOLOGY CO LTD
4F-6F Building 4 of Juxin Yuan No 188 Pingfu Road, Xuhui District, Shanghai, 200231, China
Tel.: (86) 2153529900   CN
Web Site: https://www.wingtech.com
Year Founded: 2006
600745—(SHG)
Rev.: $8,154,249,255
Assets: $10,767,247,794
Liabilities: $5,626,652,696
Net Worth: $5,140,595,098
Earnings: $204,951,329
Fiscal Year-end: 12/31/22
Holding Company
N.A.I.C.S.: 551112

WINHITECH CO., LTD.
Eumseong High-tech Industrial Complex, 99 High-tech Industrial Complex Road Samseong-myeon, Eumseong, Chungcheongbuk-do, Korea (South)
Tel.: (82) 438830048
Web Site: https://www.winhitech.co.kr
192390—(KRS)
Rev.: $89,567,074
Assets: $111,964,057
Liabilities: $64,165,447
Net Worth: $47,798,610
Earnings: $4,825,861
Emp.: 150
Fiscal Year-end: 12/31/22
Steel Mfrs
N.A.I.C.S.: 331513
Cheon Seop Byeon (Pres & CEO)

WINHOLD LIMITED
884 Linton Jones Street Industries East, Germiston, South Africa
Tel.: (27) 113459800   ZA
Web Site: http://www.winhold.co.za
Year Founded: 1945
Investment Management Service
N.A.I.C.S.: 551114
Wietsche Fourie (CFO)

Subsidiaries:

Gundle Limited (1)
884 Linton Jones St, Germiston, 1401, Gauteng, South Africa
Tel.: (27) 113459800
Web Site: http://www.gundle.co.za
Emp.: 100
Polyethylene Mfr
N.A.I.C.S.: 325211
Ramon Scheepbouwer (Gen Mgr)

Subsidiary (Domestic):

Gundle Geo Synthetics (pty) Limited (2)
Corner Watt Road & Industry Road, Springs, 1559, Gauteng, South Africa
Tel.: (27) 118132180
Web Site: http://www.gundle.co.za
Packaging Material Mfr & Distr
N.A.I.C.S.: 326112

Gundle Plastic Group (pty) Limited (2)
884 Linton Jones Street, Industries East, Germiston, 1401, South Africa
Tel.: (27) 11 876 6400
Web Site: http://www.gundle.co.za
Plastic Sheet Mfr
N.A.I.C.S.: 326112

Inmins Limited (1)
884 Linton Jones Street Industries East, Germiston, South Africa
Tel.: (27) 11 345 9800
Web Site: http://www.inmins.co.za
Mining Supplies Distr
N.A.I.C.S.: 423840

Subsidiary (Domestic):

Inmins Trading (pty) Limited (2)
884 Linton Jones Street Industries East, Germiston, 1401, South Africa
Tel.: (27) 118766400
Web Site: http://www.inmins.co.za
Emp.: 8
Mining Supplies Distr
N.A.I.C.S.: 423840
Francois Marie (Mgr)

Winhold Management Company (pty) Limited (1)
884 Linton-Jones St, Germiston, 1401, Gauteng, South Africa
Tel.: (27) 113459800
Web Site: http://www.winhold.co.za
Mining Supplies Distr
N.A.I.C.S.: 423840

WINIA CO., LTD
110 Hanam Industrial Complex 9beon-ro, Gwangsan-gu, Gwangju, Korea (South)
Tel.: (82) 15889588
Web Site: https://winia.com
Year Founded: 1999
071460—(KRS)
Rev.: $599,855,679
Assets: $591,107,912
Liabilities: $491,356,355
Net Worth: $99,751,557
Earnings: ($55,320,112)
Emp.: 606
Fiscal Year-end: 12/31/22
Home Appliance Mfr & Distr
N.A.I.C.S.: 335220
Myung Heon Jeon (Gen Mgr)

WINKEL GMBH
Am Illinger Eck 7, 75428, Illingen, Germany
Tel.: (49) 704282500
Web Site: http://www.winkel.de
Rev.: $36,454,507
Emp.: 160
Linear & Handling System Mfr & Distr
N.A.I.C.S.: 333998
August Winkel (Co-CEO)

INTERNATIONAL PUBLIC

Subsidiaries:

WINKEL Srl. (1)
Via Pio X 2/G, 28021, Borgomanero, Italy
Tel.: (39) 0322831583
Web Site: http://www.winkel-srl.it
Industrial Machinery Whslr
N.A.I.C.S.: 423830

WINKWORTH MACHINERY LIMITED
Willow Tree Works, Swallowfield, Reading, RG7 1QX, Berks, United Kingdom
Tel.: (44) 118 988 3551   UK
Web Site: http://www.mixer.co.uk
Year Founded: 1924
Emp.: 45
Industrial Mixing Equipment Mfr & Distr
N.A.I.C.S.: 333248
Tim Simpson (Dir-Sls)

WINLAND OCEAN SHIPPING CORP.
Room 703 7th Floor Bonham Trade Center, 50 Bonham Strand, Sheung Wan, China (Hong Kong)
Tel.: (852) 2854 9088   TX
Web Site: http://www.winlandshipping.com
Year Founded: 2006
Sales Range: $50-74.9 Million
Emp.: 74
Shipping Services
N.A.I.C.S.: 541614
Ying Xue Sharry (Founder & CEO)

WINMAR RESOURCES LIMITED
Office 7 Level 10 418a Elizabeth Street, Surry Hills, Sydney, 2010, NSW, Australia
Tel.: (61) 28 384 0308
Web Site: http://www.winmarresources.com
Year Founded: 1999
WFE—(ASX)
Sales Range: Less than $1 Million
Mineral Exploration Services
N.A.I.C.S.: 212290
Nicola Betteridge (Sec)

WINMARK INVESTMENT HOLDINGS LIMITED
120 Lower Delta Road No 06-16 Cendex Centre, Singapore, 169208, Singapore
Tel.: (65) 62573384
Web Site: http://www.serrano.com.sg
Rev.: $3,742,977
Assets: $5,871,379
Liabilities: $5,335,540
Net Worth: $535,838
Earnings: ($2,327,230)
Fiscal Year-end: 12/31/19
Paneling, Interior Fit-Out Products, Furnishings & Furniture Mfr & Supplier
N.A.I.C.S.: 321999

WINMATE COMMUNICATION INC.
9F No 111-6 Shing-De Road, San-Chung Dist, New Taipei City, 241458, Taiwan
Tel.: (886) 285110288
Web Site: https://www.winmate.com.tw
3416—(TAI)
Rev.: $81,112,002
Assets: $125,949,078
Liabilities: $25,683,409
Net Worth: $100,265,669
Earnings: $16,545,733
Emp.: 430
Fiscal Year-end: 12/31/23

Industrial Displays, Touch Screens, Digital Signage, Embedded Panel PC, Rugged Tablets & Handheld Devices Mfr
N.A.I.C.S.: 334118
Ken Lu *(Bd of Dirs, Chm & Head-R&D)*

WINMEDIA GROUP
375 avenue du Mistral, 13600, La Ciotat, France
Tel.: (33) 49410210
Web Site: https://winmedia.org
Year Founded: 1995
Software Devolepment
N.A.I.C.S.: 513210

Subsidiaries:

Win-OMT Software Inc (1)
280 - 1630 Ness Avenue, Winnipeg, R3J 3X1, MB, Canada
Tel.: (204) 786-3994
Web Site: https://www.imediatouch.com
Broadcast Services
N.A.I.C.S.: 516210

WINNCOM TECHNOLOGIES HOLDING LIMITED
Suite 144 The Capel Building, Mary's Abbey Suite 5, Dublin, 7, Ireland
Tel.: (353) 1 436 6492   IE
Web Site: http://www.winncom.com
Year Founded: 2003
Sales Range: $50-74.9 Million
Holding Company
N.A.I.C.S.: 551112
Gregory E. Raskin *(Pres & CEO)*

Subsidiaries:

Winncom Technologies Corp. (1)
30700 Carter St Ste A, Solon, OH 44139
Tel.: (440) 498-9510
Web Site: http://www.winncom.com
Sales Range: $50-74.9 Million
Emp.: 200
Telcommunication Network Product Mfr
N.A.I.C.S.: 334220
Aleksander Postelnicu *(Reg Mgr-Sls)*

WINNER GROUP ENTERPRISE PUBLIC COMPANY LIMITED
43 Thai CC Tower 21st Floor 214-219 Room South Sathorn Road Yannawa, Sathorn, Bangkok, 10120, Thailand
Tel.: (66) 26756525
Web Site:
 http://www.winnergroup.co.th
WINNER—(THA)
Rev.: $60,479,030
Assets: $35,968,240
Liabilities: $17,977,379
Net Worth: $17,990,860
Earnings: $3,321,144
Emp.: 347
Fiscal Year-end: 12/31/23
Food Ingredients, Additives & Other Food Products Mfr & Distr
N.A.I.C.S.: 311999
Prakarn Tawisuwan *(Chm)*

Subsidiaries:

Aesthetic Zecret (AT-ZE) Company Limited (1)
43 Thai CC Tower 175-178 FL 17th South Sathorn Rd, Yanawa Sathorn, Bangkok, 10120, Thailand
Tel.: (66) 21164257
Web Site: https://www.at-z.co.th
Beauty & Healthcare Product Mfr
N.A.I.C.S.: 325620

WINNER HOLDING LIMITED
Winner Industrial Park Bulong Road, Longhua, Shenzhen, 518109, China
Tel.: (86) 755 2813 8888   Ky
Holding Company
N.A.I.C.S.: 551112

Jianquan Li *(Owner, Chm, Pres & CEO)*

Subsidiaries:

Winner Medical Co.Ltd (1)
42F, Building 2, Minzhi Subdistrict Huilong Business Ctr, Beizhan Cmnty, Longhua New District, 518109, Guangdong, China
Tel.: (86) 7552806685
Web Site: https://www.winnermedical.com
Hospitals & Health Care
N.A.I.C.S.: 621610

Subsidiary (US):

Global Resources International, Inc. (2)
4142 Industry Way, Flowery Branch, GA 30542 **(75.2%)**
Tel.: (678) 866-0550
Web Site: http://www.gri-usa.com
Emp.: 40
Healthcare Product Mfr & Distr
N.A.I.C.S.: 333248
Martin D. Paugh *(Sec)*

Winner Medical Group Inc. (1)
Winner Industrial Park Bulong Road, Longhua, Shenzhen, 518109, China **(100%)**
Tel.: (86) 75528138888
Web Site: http://www.winnermedical.com
Emp.: 4,581
Holding Company; Medical Dressings, Disposable Products & Other Supplies Mfr & Distr
N.A.I.C.S.: 551112

Subsidiary (Domestic):

Shanghai Winner Medical Apparatus Co., Ltd. (2)
98 Jie Chen Rd Shihudang Indust Park, Songjiang, Shanghai, China
Tel.: (86) 2157841010
Web Site: http://www.guardbandage.com
Sales Range: $25-49.9 Million
Emp.: 100
Flexible Bandage Mfr & Distr
N.A.I.C.S.: 339113

Winner Industries (Shenzhen) Co., Ltd (2)
Winner Indust Park Bulong Rd, Longhua, Shenzhen, 518109, Guangdong, China
Tel.: (86) 75528138888
Web Site: http://www.winnermedical.com
Surgical Medical Products Mfr
N.A.I.C.S.: 339112

Subsidiary (Non-US):

Winner Medical (Hong Kong) Limited (2)
13 F Epoch Industrial Building, 8 Cheung Ho Street, Tsing Yi, NT, China (Hong Kong)
Tel.: (852) 31707000
Web Site: http://www.winnermedical.com
Emp.: 18
Medical & Surgical Products Mfr
N.A.I.C.S.: 339112
Kevin Orr *(Gen Mgr)*

WINNING APPLIANCES PTY. LTD.
Level 2 20A Danks Street, Redfern, 2016, NSW, Australia
Tel.: (61) 296940000
Web Site:
 http://www.winningappliances.com
Year Founded: 1906
Kitchen Appliance Distr
N.A.I.C.S.: 423620
John Winning *(CEO)*

WINNING BRANDS CORPORATION
92 Caplan Avenue Suite 134, Barrie, L4N 9J2, ON, Canada
Tel.: (705) 737-4062
Web Site:
 https://www.winningbrandscorp.com
WNBD—(OTCIQ)
Rev.: $407,000
Assets: $900,000
Liabilities: $2,747,000

Net Worth: ($1,847,000)
Earnings: $66,000
Emp.: 3
Fiscal Year-end: 12/31/21
Soap & Detergent Mfr
N.A.I.C.S.: 325611
Eric Lehner *(CEO)*

WINNING HEALTH TECHNOLOGY GROUP CO., LTD.
Winning Health Building No 9 Lane 99 Shouyang Road, Jingan District, Shanghai, 200072, China
Tel.: (86) 2180331033
Web Site: http://www.winning.com.cn
Year Founded: 2004
300253—(CHIN)
Rev.: $445,568,383
Assets: $1,204,118,988
Liabilities: $403,911,108
Net Worth: $800,207,880
Earnings: $50,418,539
Fiscal Year-end: 12/31/21
Software Development Services
N.A.I.C.S.: 541511
Wei Zhou *(Chm)*

WINNING TOWER GROUP HOLDINGS LIMITED
Unit 803 Riley House 88 Lei Muk Road Kwai Chung N T, Hong Kong, China (Hong Kong)
Tel.: (852) 35211515   Ky
Web Site: http://www.wtgl.hk
Year Founded: 2004
8362—(HKG)
Rev.: $11,895,623
Assets: $16,848,360
Liabilities: $5,389,170
Net Worth: $11,459,190
Earnings: ($1,729,283)
Emp.: 90
Fiscal Year-end: 12/31/22
Food Products Distr
N.A.I.C.S.: 424420
King Wah Lai *(Chm)*

WINNOVA CO., LTD.
178 Cheongbuksandan-ro Cheongbuk-myeon, Pyeongtaek, Gyeonggi-do, Korea (South)
Tel.: (82) 3180944550
Web Site: http://www.winnova.co.kr
Year Founded: 1995
039790—(KRS)
Rev.: $5,310,981
Assets: $9,318,275
Liabilities: $5,462,992
Net Worth: $3,855,283
Earnings: ($2,068,520)
Emp.: 57
Fiscal Year-end: 12/31/22
Medical Equipment Mfr & Distr
N.A.I.C.S.: 339113
Yunwoo Koh *(CEO)*

WINOX HOLDINGS LIMITED
Units 2 & 3 1/F Sunray Industrial Centre 610 Cha Kwo Ling Road, Kowloon, China (Hong Kong)
Tel.: (852) 23493776   Ky
Web Site: https://www.winox.com
6838—(HKG)
Rev.: $146,594,655
Assets: $167,794,335
Liabilities: $38,774,025
Net Worth: $129,020,310
Earnings: $14,330,490
Emp.: 3,301
Fiscal Year-end: 12/31/22
Stainless Steel Watch Bracelets, Costume Jewelry & Accessories Mfr
N.A.I.C.S.: 339910
Hon Ming Yiu *(Founder & Chm)*

Subsidiaries:

Winox Holdings Limited - Dalang Factory (1)
60 Lian Ying Road, Xin Ma Lian Village Dalang Town, Dongguan, 523797, China
Tel.: (86) 76983103333
Stainless Steel Products Mfr
N.A.I.C.S.: 339910

Winox Holdings Limited - Huizhou Factory (1)
Dongfeng Village, Huzhen Town Boluo County, Huizhou, China
Tel.: (86) 7525899088
Stainless Steel Watch Bracelet Mfr
N.A.I.C.S.: 339910

WINPAC INC.
50 Gheongganggachang-ro, Baegammyeon Cheoin-gu, Yongin, 449-862, Gyeonggi-do, Korea (South)
Tel.: (82) 3180204400
Web Site: http://www.winpac.co.kr
Year Founded: 2002
097800—(KRS)
Rev.: $117,071,375
Assets: $136,942,258
Liabilities: $78,533,568
Net Worth: $58,408,689
Earnings: ($1,205,323)
Emp.: 563
Fiscal Year-end: 12/31/22
Semiconductor Packaging Mfr
N.A.I.C.S.: 334413
Byoungwoo Lee *(CFO)*

WINPAK LTD.
100 Saulteaux Crescent, Winnipeg, R3J 3T3, MB, Canada
Tel.: (204) 889-1015   MB
Web Site: https://www.winpak.com
Year Founded: 1977
WPK—(TSX)
Rev.: $1,001,994,000
Assets: $1,321,694,000
Liabilities: $205,955,000
Net Worth: $1,115,739,000
Earnings: $106,348,000
Emp.: 2,563
Fiscal Year-end: 12/26/21
Packaging Materials & Related Machinery Designer & Mfr
N.A.I.C.S.: 322220
Antti I. Aarnio-Wihuri *(Chm)*

Subsidiaries:

Embalajes Winpak de Mexico, S.A. de C.V. (1)
Av Jalpan de Serra 140 Ampliacion Parque Industrial, Santa Rosa Jauregui, 76220, Queretaro, Mexico
Tel.: (52) 442 256 1900
Packaging Material Mfr & Distr
N.A.I.C.S.: 333993

Winpak Control Group, Inc. (1)
500 Walnut St, Norwood, NJ 07648
Tel.: (201) 784-8721
Web Site: http://www.controlgroupusa.com
Commercial Gravure Printing Services
N.A.I.C.S.: 323111

Winpak Films Inc. (1)
100 Wihuri Pkwy, Senoia, GA 30276-9703 **(100%)**
Tel.: (770) 599-6656
Web Site: http://www.winpak.com
Sales Range: $50-74.9 Million
Emp.: 200
Unsupported Plastics Film & Sheet Mfr
N.A.I.C.S.: 326113

Winpak Heat Seal Corporation (1)
1821 Riverway Dr, Pekin, IL 61554
Tel.: (309) 477-6600
Packaging Material Mfr & Distr
N.A.I.C.S.: 333993

Winpak Heat Seal Packaging Inc. (1)
21919 Dumberry Road, Vaudreuil-Dorion, J7V 8P7, QC, Canada **(100%)**

WINPAK LTD.

Winpak Ltd.—(Continued)
Tel.: (450) 424-0191
Web Site: http://www.winpak.com
Sales Range: $75-99.9 Million
Emp.: 300
Packaging & Labeling Services
N.A.I.C.S.: 561910

Winpak Inc. (1)
PO Box 14748, Minneapolis, MN 55414
Tel.: (204) 889-1015
Packaging Material Mfr & Distr
N.A.I.C.S.: 333993

Winpak Lane Inc. (1)
998 S Sierra Way, San Bernardino, CA 92408 (100%)
Tel.: (909) 885-0715
Web Site: http://www.winpak.com
Emp.: 100
Packaging Machinery Mfr
N.A.I.C.S.: 333993

Winpak Portion Packaging Inc (1)
828A Newtown Yardley Rd Ste 101, Newtown, PA 18940-1785 (100%)
Tel.: (267) 685-8200
Web Site: http://www.winpak.com
Sales Range: $10-24.9 Million
Emp.: 45
Packaging & Labeling Services
N.A.I.C.S.: 561910

Winpak Portion Packaging Ltd. (1)
26 Tidemore Avenue, Toronto, M9W 7A7, ON, Canada
Tel.: (416) 741-6182
Packaging Material Mfr & Distr
N.A.I.C.S.: 333993

Wipak B.V. (1)
Nieuwstadterweg 17, 6136 KN, Sittard, Netherlands
Tel.: (31) 46 420 2999
Packaging Material Mfr & Distr
N.A.I.C.S.: 333993

Wipak Gryspeert S.A.S. (1)
Zone des Bois, CS 20006, 59558, Bousbecque, Cedex, France
Tel.: (33) 32 011 5656
Packaging Material Mfr & Distr
N.A.I.C.S.: 333993

Wipak Iberica S.L. (1)
C/Sant Celoni n 76 P I Can Prat, Llinars del Valles, 08450, Barcelona, Spain
Tel.: (34) 93 781 2020
Packaging Material Mfr & Distr
N.A.I.C.S.: 333993

Wipak Packaging (Changshu) Co. Ltd. (1)
No 88 Fuchunjiang Road, New and Hi-tech Industrial, Jiangsu, 215533, China
Tel.: (86) 5128 236 5958
Packaging Material Mfr & Distr
N.A.I.C.S.: 333993

Wipak UK Ltd. (1)
Buttington Business Park Unit 3, Powys, Welshpool, SY21 8SL, United Kingdom
Tel.: (44) 193 855 5255
Packaging Material Mfr & Distr
N.A.I.C.S.: 333993

Wipak Walsrode GmbH & Co. KG (1)
Bahnhofstrasse 13, 29699, Bomlitz, Germany
Tel.: (49) 51 614 8800
Packaging Material Mfr & Distr
N.A.I.C.S.: 333993

WINPAR HOLDINGS LIMITED
Level 2 16-18 Grosvenor Street, Sydney, 2000, NSW, Australia
Tel.: (61) 287055486
Web Site:
https://www.winparholdings.com.au
Year Founded: 1985
WPH—(NSXA)
Rev.: $100,559
Assets: $3,631,038
Liabilities: $58,047
Net Worth: $3,572,991
Earnings: ($8,798)
Fiscal Year-end: 06/30/20
Investment Services
N.A.I.C.S.: 523999
Gordon Bradley Elkington (Sec)

WINPRO INDUSTRIES LTD.
Office No 212 2nd Floor Trade Centre G Block Opp MTNL, Bandra Kurla Complex Bandra East, Mumbai, 400051, Maharashtra, India
Tel.: (91) 8108106033
Web Site:
http://www.jumpnetworks.in
Year Founded: 1992
531337—(BOM)
Rev.: $20,694,001
Assets: $7,940,778
Liabilities: $5,050,555
Net Worth: $2,890,224
Earnings: $291,305
Emp.: 3
Fiscal Year-end: 03/31/21
Television Broadcasting Services
N.A.I.C.S.: 516120
Atul Kumar (Mng Dir)

WINRO COMMERCIAL (INDIA) LIMITED
209-210 Arcadia Building 2nd Floor 195, Nariman Point, Mumbai, 400021, India
Tel.: (91) 2240198600
Web Site:
https://www.winrocommercial.com
Year Founded: 1983
512022—(BOM)
Rev.: $13,163
Assets: $394,844
Liabilities: $487
Net Worth: $394,357
Earnings: ($1,307,204)
Fiscal Year-end: 03/31/20
Investment Management Service
N.A.I.C.S.: 523999
Ritesh V. Zaveri (CFO)

WINS CO., LTD.
WINS Building 4F 15 Pangyo-ro 228beon-gil, Bundang-gu, Seongnam, 463-400, Gyeonggi-do, Korea (South)
Tel.: (82) 316228600
Web Site: https://www.wins21.com
Year Founded: 1996
136540—(KRS)
Rev.: $77,792,141
Assets: $157,703,257
Liabilities: $22,358,596
Net Worth: $135,344,662
Earnings: $14,755,955
Emp.: 476
Fiscal Year-end: 12/31/22
Integration Design Services
N.A.I.C.S.: 541512
Dae-yeon Kim (CEO)

WINSAN CHENGDU MEDICAL SCIENCE AND TECHNOLOGY CO LTD.
No 12 Building, Shanghai, 201201, China
Tel.: (86) 21 50720888
Web Site: http://www.winsan.cn
600767—(SHG)
Rev.: $7,456,731
Assets: $51,182,865
Liabilities: $16,201,958
Net Worth: $34,980,907
Earnings: $1,476,944
Fiscal Year-end: 12/31/20
Investment Services
N.A.I.C.S.: 523999
Hai Le (Chm)

WINSHEAR GOLD CORP.
Suite 960-789 West Pender Street, Vancouver, V6C 1H2, BC, Canada
Tel.: (604) 200-7874
Web Site: https://www.winshear.ca
Year Founded: 1998
HELOF—(OTCIQ)
Rev.: $105,375
Assets: $2,522,489
Liabilities: $195,536
Net Worth: $2,326,952
Earnings: $17,642,558
Fiscal Year-end: 03/31/24
Mineral Exploration Services
N.A.I.C.S.: 213114
Richard D. Williams (CEO)

WINSHINE SCIENCE COMPANY LIMITED
Rooms 2202-2203 22/F Harbor Centre, 25 Harbour Road, Wanchai, China (Hong Kong)
Tel.: (852) 22752333
Web Site: http://www.winshine.com
0209—(HKG)
Rev.: $108,259,740
Assets: $43,470,615
Liabilities: $54,900,735
Net Worth: ($11,430,120)
Earnings: $1,030,073
Emp.: 1,696
Fiscal Year-end: 12/31/22
Toy Mfr; Beverage Products; Securities Investments
N.A.I.C.S.: 339930
Deyong Zhao (Chm)

Subsidiaries:

Sewco Toys & Novelty Limited (1)
Room 1301 13 Floor Telford House No 16 Wang Hoi Road, Kowloon, China (Hong Kong)
Tel.: (852) 27705033
Web Site: https://www.sewco.com.hk
Toy Mfr & Distr
N.A.I.C.S.: 339930

WINSLOW CONSTRUCTORS PTY LTD
50 Barry Road, Campbellfield, 3061, VIC, Australia
Tel.: (61) 393587700
Web Site: http://www.winslow.com.au
Year Founded: 1985
Sales Range: $75-99.9 Million
Emp.: 146
Civil Construction Services
N.A.I.C.S.: 237990
Trevor Lockwood (CEO)

Subsidiaries:

Winslow Infrastructure Pty Ltd (1)
9/75 Lorimer Street, Docklands, Melbourne, 3008, VIC, Australia
Tel.: (61) 3 9279 4600
Civil Construction Services
N.A.I.C.S.: 237990

WINSOME BREWERIES LTD.
Village Sarehkurd, Tehsil Tijara, Alwar, 301411, Rajasthan, India
Tel.: (91) 1126811299
Web Site:
https://www.winsomeindia.in
Year Founded: 1992
526471—(BOM)
Rev.: $339,740
Assets: $6,233,163
Liabilities: $2,220,358
Net Worth: $4,012,805
Earnings: ($97,128)
Emp.: 37
Fiscal Year-end: 03/31/23
Beer Mfr
N.A.I.C.S.: 312120
Rajendra Kumar Bagrodia (Chm & Mng Dir)

WINSOME DIAMONDS & JEWELLERY LTD.
Kesharba Market 2 Gotalawadi Katargam, Surat, 395 004, Surat, India
Tel.: (91) 2243470944
Web Site:
http://www.winsomejewellery.com
Year Founded: 1985
Sales Range: Less than $1 Million
Cut & Polished Diamonds & Jewelry Mfr
N.A.I.C.S.: 423940

Subsidiaries:

Su-Raj Diamonds N.V. (1)
Rm 821 Hoveniersstraat 2, Bus 118, 2018, Antwerp, Belgium
Tel.: (32) 32265454
Sales Range: $50-74.9 Million
Emp.: 3
Diamond & Jewelry Whslr
N.A.I.C.S.: 423940
Shah Paras (Mng Dir)

Su-Raj Diamonds and Jewellery DMCC (1)
Emirates Towers Level No 41, Sheikh Zayed Rd, 114176, Dubai, United Arab Emirates
Tel.: (971) 42250553
Web Site: http://www.su-raj.com
Sales Range: $25-49.9 Million
Emp.: 15
Diamond & Jewelry Whslr
N.A.I.C.S.: 423940

Su-Raj Diamonds and Jewelry USA, Inc. (1)
36 W 44 S Ste 1018, New York, NY 10036
Tel.: (212) 719-2333
Sales Range: $50-74.9 Million
Emp.: 3
Diamond & Jewelry Whslr
N.A.I.C.S.: 423940

WINSOME RESOURCES LIMITED
Level 1 16 Ord Street, West Perth, 6005, WA, Australia
Tel.: (61) 419853904
Web Site:
https://www.winsomeresources.com
Year Founded: 2021
WR1—(ASX)
Rev.: $1,857
Assets: $19,217,231
Liabilities: $288,643
Net Worth: $18,928,588
Earnings: ($2,481,189)
Fiscal Year-end: 06/30/22
Exploration & Mining Services
N.A.I.C.S.: 213115
Chris Evans (Mng Dir)

WINSOME TEXTILE INDUSTRIES LTD.
1 Industrial Area, Solan, Baddi, 173205, Himachal Pradesh, India
Tel.: (91) 1795244045
Web Site:
https://www.winsometextile.com
Year Founded: 1980
514470—(BOM)
Rev.: $105,258,833
Assets: $91,074,408
Liabilities: $60,353,564
Net Worth: $30,720,844
Earnings: $2,939,620
Emp.: 2,376
Fiscal Year-end: 03/31/23
Textile Products Mfr
N.A.I.C.S.: 314999
Videshwar Sharma (Compliance Officer, Sec & Head-Legal)

WINSOME YARNS LIMITED
SCO 13-14-15 Sector 34 A, Chandigarh, 160 022, India
Tel.: (91) 1724612000
Web Site:
https://www.winsomeyarns.com
Rev.: $52,106,737
Assets: $72,327,859

Liabilities: $101,005,033
Net Worth: ($28,677,173)
Earnings: ($2,800,784)
Emp.: 1,347
Fiscal Year-end: 03/31/18
Textile Products Mfr
N.A.I.C.S.: 313110
Manish Bagrodia *(Chm & Mng Dir)*

WINSON HOLDINGS HONG KONG LIMITED
Suite 2702 27th Floor Tower 2 Nina Tower No 8 Yeung Uk Road, Tsuen Wan, New Territories, China (Hong Kong)
Tel.: (852) 21563388   Ky
Web Site:
http://www.winsongrouphk.com
Year Founded: 1983
6812—(HKG)
Rev.: $58,930,118
Assets: $35,064,158
Liabilities: $8,125,320
Net Worth: $26,938,838
Earnings: $3,154,988
Emp.: 1,647
Fiscal Year-end: 03/31/23
Pest Control Services
N.A.I.C.S.: 561710
Sing Mui Ng *(Founder & Chm)*

WINSON MACHINERY CO., LTD.
No 23 Lugong S 6th Rd, Lugang Town Changhua County, Hsien, 505, Taiwan
Tel.: (886) 47813033
Web Site: https://www.wsmc.com.tw
Year Founded: 1980
4538—(TPE)
Rev.: $18,998,593
Assets: $31,399,744
Liabilities: $7,858,581
Net Worth: $23,541,162
Earnings: $2,506,832
Emp.: 145
Fiscal Year-end: 12/31/22
Machine Tool Casting Mfr
N.A.I.C.S.: 333517
Spencer Hsieh *(Pres & CEO)*

WINSTECH PRECISION HOLDING CO., LTD.
No 180 Tianxin Road, Tangxia Town, Dongguan, 523710, Guangdong, China
Tel.: (86) 76938899778
Web Site:
https://www.winstechfield.com
Year Founded: 2003
001319—(SSE)
Rev.: $121,560,693
Assets: $222,843,580
Liabilities: $50,962,849
Net Worth: $171,880,731
Earnings: $13,959,573
Fiscal Year-end: 12/31/23
Holding Company
N.A.I.C.S.: 551112

WINSTON GOLD CORP.
919 Notre Dame Avenue Suite 201, Winnipeg, R3E 0M8, MB, Canada
Tel.: (204) 989-2434
Web Site:
https://www.winstongoldmining.com
Year Founded: 2013
WGMCF—(OTCQB)
Assets: $805,529
Liabilities: $2,103,881
Net Worth: ($1,298,352)
Earnings: ($2,726,229)
Fiscal Year-end: 12/31/19
Mineral Exploration Services
N.A.I.C.S.: 213114
Murray Nye *(CEO)*

WINTAO COMMUNICATIONS CO., LTD.
10F South Tower High-tech Talent Building No 567 Dongrong Street, North District Xinshi District Urumqi High-tech Industrial Dev Zone, Xinjiang, 830013, China
Tel.: (86) 31167365929
Web Site:
https://www.wintaotel.com.cn
Year Founded: 2008
301139—(CHIN)
Rev.: $246,355,851
Assets: $393,784,836
Liabilities: $130,184,177
Net Worth: $263,600,659
Earnings: $9,592,476
Fiscal Year-end: 12/31/23
Telecommunications Equipment Mfr
N.A.I.C.S.: 334290
Jin Li *(Chm)*

WINTEK CORPORATION
10 Jianguo Rd, Tanzi Dist, Taichung, 42760, Taiwan
Tel.: (886) 425318899
Web Site: http://www.wintek.com.tw
Year Founded: 1990
Sales Range: $1-4.9 Billion
Emp.: 40,100
Electronic Products Mfr
N.A.I.C.S.: 334419
Hyley H. Huang *(Chm & Pres)*

Subsidiaries:

Mactech Co., Ltd.   (1)
No 89 Lane 36 Section 2 Tanshin Road Tantzu Shiang, Taichung, 427, Taiwan
Tel.: (886) 425378884
Web Site: http://www.mactech.com.tw
Sales Range: $100-124.9 Million
Emp.: 300
Laminating Machines Mfr
N.A.I.C.S.: 333243

Wintek Central Europe GmbH   (1)
Richard Strauss Strasse 48, 81677, Munich, Germany
Tel.: (49) 894142420
Web Site: http://www.wintek.com.tw
Sales Range: $25-49.9 Million
Emp.: 3
Electronic Components Mfr
N.A.I.C.S.: 334419

Wintek Electro-Optics Corporation   (1)
1665 Highland Dr Ste E, Ann Arbor, MI 48108-2297
Tel.: (734) 477-5480
Web Site: http://www.wintek.com.tw
Sales Range: $25-49.9 Million
Emp.: 20
Electronic Components
N.A.I.C.S.: 334419

WINTER VALLEY TOURISM INVESTMENT COMPANY PLC
Wasfi Al-Tal Street Ghadaf Building 2 5th floor, Box 940372, AL-Rabieh, Amman, 11194, Jordan
Tel.: (962) 65563999
Web Site: https://www.winter-valley.com
Year Founded: 2005
WIVA—(AMM)
Rev.: $1,464,482
Assets: $13,928,398
Liabilities: $5,692,746
Net Worth: $8,235,652
Earnings: ($2,116,331)
Emp.: 3
Fiscal Year-end: 12/31/20
Investment Management Service
N.A.I.C.S.: 523999

WINTERHILL ASSET LIMITED
6 Anchor Ct, Commercial Rd, Blackburn, BB3 0DB, United Kingdom
Tel.: (44) 1254763183
Web Site:
http://www.winterhillassetltd.co.uk
Year Founded: 2008
Sales Range: $10-24.9 Million
Emp.: 100
Corporate Recovery & Management Consulting Services
N.A.I.C.S.: 561499
Andrew Duckworth *(CEO)*

WINTEST CORP.
1-2-24 Hiranuma, Nishi-ku, Yokohama, 220-0023, Kanagawa, Japan
Tel.: (81) 453177888
Web Site: https://www.wintest.co.jp
Year Founded: 1993
6721—(TKS)
Rev.: $2,885,630
Assets: $13,988,570
Liabilities: $2,183,720
Net Worth: $11,804,850
Earnings: ($3,927,860)
Emp.: 96
Fiscal Year-end: 12/31/23
Testing Equipment Mfr & Whslr
N.A.I.C.S.: 334515

WINTIME ENERGY CO., LTD.
20th 26th and 27th Floor Shuangxi Plaza No 9 Qinxian North Street, Xiaodian District, Taiyuan, 030006, Shanxi, China
Tel.: (86) 3518366507
Web Site: https://www.wtecl.com
Year Founded: 1992
600157—(SHG)
Rev.: $4,992,013,260
Assets: $14,582,096,966
Liabilities: $7,901,398,683
Net Worth: $6,680,698,282
Earnings: $268,058,630
Fiscal Year-end: 12/31/22
Coal Mining Services
N.A.I.C.S.: 212115
Wang Guangxi *(Chm)*

WINTLE HEATING & PLUMBING LTD
Mansion Close Moulton Park, Northampton, NN3 6RU, United Kingdom
Tel.: (44) 1604790800
Web Site: http://www.wintle.co.uk
Year Founded: 1966
Rev.: $18,549,977
Emp.: 104
Plumbing & Heating Installation Services
N.A.I.C.S.: 238220
R. D. Wintle *(Founder)*

WINTO GROUP (HOLDINGS) LIMITED
Suites 2101-05 21/F Sun Hung Kai Centre 30 Harbour Road, Wanchai, Hong Kong, China (Hong Kong)
Tel.: (852) 37285788   Ky
Web Site: http://www.wintogroup.hk
8238—(HKG)
Sales Range: $1-9.9 Million
Magazine Distr
N.A.I.C.S.: 424920
Patrick Siu Hung Wong *(Exec Dir)*

Subsidiaries:

Ocean Media (Hong Kong) Limited   (1)
Rm 4 7/F Nan Fung Commercial Centre 19 Lam Lok Street Kowloon Bay, Kowloon, China (Hong Kong)
Tel.: (852) 36430795
Web Site: http://oceanmediahk.com
Magazine Publishing Services
N.A.I.C.S.: 513120

WINTON LAND LIMITED
Level 4 10 Viaduct Harbour Ave, Auckland, 1010, New Zealand
Tel.: (64) 93777003   NZ
Web Site: https://www.winton.nz
Year Founded: 2017
WIN—(NZX)
Rev.: $126,447,967
Assets: $353,238,038
Liabilities: $47,966,507
Net Worth: $305,271,531
Earnings: $38,659,091
Emp.: 65
Fiscal Year-end: 06/30/23
Property Management Services
N.A.I.C.S.: 531311
Chris Meehan *(Chm)*

Subsidiaries:

Northbrook Wynyard Limited   (1)
136 Beaumont Street, Wynyard Quarter, Auckland, 1010, New Zealand
Tel.: (64) 800189891
Home Management Services
N.A.I.C.S.: 721110

WINTONI GROUP BHD
Mayang Pasir 3, Bayan Baru, 11950, Malaysia
Tel.: (60) 46452828
Rev.: $466,906
Assets: $314,307
Liabilities: $1,187,437
Net Worth: ($873,130)
Earnings: ($100,911)
Fiscal Year-end: 12/31/19
Investment Holding Company Services
N.A.I.C.S.: 551112
Encik Raja Kamarudin Bin Raja Adnan *(Exec Dir)*

WINY COMMERCIAL & FISCAL SERVICES LIMITED
3 Kapalitala Lane, Kolkata, 700 012, West Bengal, India
Tel.: (91) 3340074761
Web Site: http://www.winycomm.co.in
Rev.: $44,614
Assets: $1,314,798
Liabilities: $5,887
Net Worth: $1,308,911
Earnings: $1,446
Fiscal Year-end: 03/31/18
Financial Support Services
N.A.I.C.S.: 523999
Amit Kumar Bajoria *(Mng Dir)*

WIPAM, INC.
8F Samheon Building 8-4 Hwangsaeul-ro 319, Bundang-Gu, Seongnam, 13590, Gyeonggi-do, Korea (South)
Tel.: (82) 317818564
Web Site: https://www.wipam.co.kr
Year Founded: 2006
332570—(KRS)
Rev.: $39,414,982
Assets: $90,990,485
Liabilities: $43,453,550
Net Worth: $47,536,935
Earnings: ($7,968,850)
Emp.: 37
Fiscal Year-end: 12/31/22
Power Amplifier Mfr & Distr
N.A.I.C.S.: 334220
Dae-Kyu Yu *(CEO)*

WIPRO LIMITED
Doddakannelli Sarjapur Road, Bengaluru, 560035, Karnataka, India
Tel.: (91) 8046827999   In
Web Site: https://www.wipro.com
Year Founded: 1946
WIT—(NYSE)
Rev.: $10,761,980,697
Assets: $13,817,624,843
Liabilities: $4,810,694,802

WIPRO LIMITED

Wipro Limited—(Continued)

Net Worth: $9,006,930,040
Earnings: $1,332,306,217
Emp.: 234,000
Fiscal Year-end: 03/31/24
Holding Company; Information Technology Services
N.A.I.C.S.: 551112
Rishad Azim Premji *(Chm)*

Subsidiaries:

Appirio Inc. (1)
201 S Capitol Ave Ste 1100, Indianapolis, IN 46225 **(100%)**
Tel.: (317) 378-7300
Web Site: http://www.appirio.com
Cloud Technology Consulting Services
N.A.I.C.S.: 541690
Matt Passey *(VP-Digital & CRM Strategy)*

Subsidiary (Domestic):

TopCoder, Inc. (2)
201 S Capitol Ave Ste 1100, Indianapolis, IN 46225
Tel.: (650) 268-9911
Web Site: https://www.topcoder.com
Emp.: 200
Computer Programming & Software Services
N.A.I.C.S.: 541519
Adam Morehead *(VP-Community)*

Capco Austria GmbH (1)
Kohlmarkt 8/10, 1010, Vienna, Austria
Tel.: (43) 6997609000
Digital Financial Transaction Services
N.A.I.C.S.: 522320

Capco Consultancy (Malaysia) Sdn. Bhd. (1)
Suite 25 01 Level 25 The Gardens North Tower Mid Valley City, Lingkaran Syed Putra Wilayah Persekutuan, 59200, Kuala Lumpur, Malaysia
Tel.: (60) 327062500
Digital Financial Transaction Services
N.A.I.C.S.: 522320

Capco Consultancy (Thailand) Ltd. (1)
No 999/9 Level 29 The Offices at Central World Suite 2962 Rama I Road, Kwaeng Pathumwan Khet Pathumwan, Bangkok, Thailand
Tel.: (66) 22072645
Digital Financial Transaction Services
N.A.I.C.S.: 522320

Capco Consulting Services, LLC (1)
717 Texas Ave Ste 1600, Houston, TX 77002
Tel.: (713) 350-1000
Digital Financial Transaction Services
N.A.I.C.S.: 522320

Capco Poland Sp. z.o.o. (1)
Prime Corporate Center Ul Grzybowska 78, 00-844, Warsaw, Poland
Tel.: (48) 222453870
Digital Financial Transaction Services
N.A.I.C.S.: 522320

Capco RISC Consulting, LLC (1)
77 Water St 10th Fl, New York, NY 10005
Tel.: (212) 284-8600
Digital Financial Transaction Services
N.A.I.C.S.: 522320

Convergence Acceleration Solutions, LLC (1)
3700 Mansell Rd Ste 140, Alpharetta, GA 30022
Tel.: (770) 225-6326
Web Site: http://www.casgroup.com
Sales Range: $10-24.9 Million
Emp.: 55
Information Technology Consulting Services
N.A.I.C.S.: 541511
Tom McAllister *(COO)*

Designit Denmark A/S (1)
Mejlgade 47b, Aarhus, 8000, Denmark
Tel.: (45) 7 027 7700
Graphic Design Services
N.A.I.C.S.: 541430
Michael Sylva *(Head-Finance)*

Designit Germany GmbH (1)
Gabrielenstrasse 9, 80636, Munich, Germany
Tel.: (49) 894 161 7200
Graphic Design Services
N.A.I.C.S.: 541430
Danusch Mahmoudi *(Mng Dir)*

Designit Oslo A/S (1)
Akersbakken 12, 0172, Oslo, Norway
Tel.: (47) 4 551 3441
Graphic Design Services
N.A.I.C.S.: 541430
Niklas Mortensen *(Mng Dir)*

Designit Spain Digital, S.L. (1)
Joaquin Maria Lopez 8 bis, 28015, Madrid, Spain
Tel.: (34) 91 308 0890
Graphic Design Services
N.A.I.C.S.: 541430
Paula Otero *(Mng Dir)*

Designit Sweden AB (1)
Birger Jarlsgatan 57 C, 113 56, Stockholm, Sweden
Tel.: (46) 81 214 0800
Graphic Design Services
N.A.I.C.S.: 541430
Mark Weedon *(Dir)*

Designit TLV Ltd. (1)
18 Raoul Wallenberg Street Building C 4th Floor, Tel Aviv, Israel
Tel.: (972) 77 365 2380
Graphic Design Services
N.A.I.C.S.: 541430
Tzachi Toledo *(Mng Dir)*

Designit Tokyo Ltd. (1)
The Park Rex Koamicho Building 8F 11-8 Koamicho Nihonbashi, Chuo-ku, Tokyo, 103-0016, Japan
Tel.: (81) 36 231 1535
Graphic Design Services
N.A.I.C.S.: 541430
Hector Noval *(Head-Global)*

Dongguan Unza Consumer Products Ltd (1)
Shilong Road Sangyuan Dongguan Science Park, Dongguan, 523119, Guangdong, China
Tel.: (86) 7692253905
Cosmetics Products Mfr
N.A.I.C.S.: 325620

Edgile, LLC (1)
7000 N Mopac Expy Ste 200, Austin, TX 78757
Tel.: (408) 236-7338
Web Site: http://www.edgile.com
Rev.: $4,256,000
Emp.: 7
Data Processing, Hosting & Related Services
N.A.I.C.S.: 518210
Dean Fantham *(CTO)*

Formapac Sdn Bhd (1)
Kidomai Ind Park Lot 5755-1 Bkt Angkat Sg Chua, Kajang, 43000, Selangor, Malaysia
Tel.: (60) 387399391
Cosmetic Products Mfr & Distr
N.A.I.C.S.: 424210

Gervas (B) Sdn Bhd (1)
No 8 Jalan Subang 2 Taman Perindustrian Subang, 47610, Subang Jaya, Selangor, Malaysia
Tel.: (60) 380234511
Cosmetic Product Distr
N.A.I.C.S.: 424210

HealthPlan Services, Inc. (1)
3501 East Frontage Rd, Tampa, FL 33607-1742
Tel.: (813) 289-1000
Web Site: http://www.healthplan.com
Emp.: 1,500
Insurance & Managed Care Industry Business Process Outsourcing & Employee Benefit Services
N.A.I.C.S.: 524292

ITI Proficiency Ltd. (1)
11 Moshe Levi Street Suite 717, PO Box 17179, Rishon Lezion, Tel Aviv, 75071, Israel
Tel.: (972) 3 716 0773
Information Technology Services
N.A.I.C.S.: 541519

Infocrossing, Inc. (1)
2 Christie Heights St, Leonia, NJ 07605
Tel.: (201) 840-4700
Sales Range: $200-249.9 Million
Emp.: 882
Information Technology Services, Data Center Outsourcing, Infrastructure Management Consulting & Internet Data Center & Colocation Services
N.A.I.C.S.: 518210

International TechneGroup Inc. (1)
5303 Dupont Cir, Milford, OH 45150
Tel.: (513) 576-3900
Web Site: http://www.iti-oh.com
Prepackaged Software
N.A.I.C.S.: 513210
Andy Chinn *(Head-C3 Global Sls)*

Unit (Domestic):

ITI TranscenData (2)
5303 DuPont Cir, Milford, OH 45150
Tel.: (513) 576-3900
Sales Range: $10-24.9 Million
Data Interoperability Solutions Services
N.A.I.C.S.: 541511

Subsidiary (Domestic):

Manta Corporation (2)
1000 Ford Cir Ste A, Milford, OH 45150
Tel.: (513) 248-5200
Web Site: http://www.manta-corp.com
Rev.: $1,700,000
Emp.: 3
Consulting Engineer
N.A.I.C.S.: 541330

International TechneGroup Ltd. (1)
4 Carisbrooke Court Anderson Road, Buckingway Business Park Swavesey, Cambridge, CB24 4UQ, United Kingdom
Tel.: (44) 195 423 4300
Web Site: https://www.iti-global.com
Information Technology Services
N.A.I.C.S.: 541519
Andy Chinn *(Head & Gen Mgr)*

LeanSwift AB (1)
Nors-Mon 225, S-66050, Valberg, Sweden
Tel.: (46) 722034999
Information Technology Services
N.A.I.C.S.: 541519

LeanSwift Solutions, Inc. (1)
1980 N Atlantic Ave Ste 1024, Cocoa Beach, FL 32931
Web Site: https://www.leanswift.com
Emp.: 100
Ecommerce & Mobile Software Services
N.A.I.C.S.: 812990

MechWorks S.R.L. (1)
Via Vallescura 8/2, 40136, Bologna, Italy
Tel.: (39) 05 158 2294
Web Site: https://www.mechworks.it
Software Development Services
N.A.I.C.S.: 541511
Ciro Ettorre *(Co-Founder)*

PT Unza Vitalis (1)
Komp Industri Pergudangan Semanan Megah Jl Daan Mogot Km 18, Jakarta, 11850, Indonesia
Tel.: (62) 215439788
Web Site: https://unzavitalis.com
Personal Care Products Mfr & Distr
N.A.I.C.S.: 316990

PT. WT Indonesia (1)
Regus Menara BCA Menara BCA 50th Floor Jl MH Thamrin No 1, Jakarta, 10310, Indonesia
Tel.: (62) 212 358 4691
Information Technology Services
N.A.I.C.S.: 541519

Rational Interaction, Inc. (1)
1201 3rd Ave Ste 5200, Seattle, WA 98101
Tel.: (206) 623-1873
Web Site: http://www.rationalcx.com
Sales Range: $1-9.9 Million
Emp.: 80
General Marketing & Advertising Services
N.A.I.C.S.: 541613
Kahly Berg *(CEO)*

Rizing Lanka (Pvt.) Ltd. (1)
Level 9 No 19 Dudley Senanayake Mawatha, 08, Colombo, Sri Lanka
Tel.: (94) 114761500
Systems Application & Product Consulting Services
N.A.I.C.S.: 541618

Rizing Philippines Inc. (1)
10F The Curve 32nd St and 3rd Ave, Bonifacio, Taguig, Philippines
Tel.: (63) 284055123
Human Capital Management Services
N.A.I.C.S.: 541612

Rizing SDN. BHD. (1)
Level 28 Unit 2 Menara LGB Jalan Wan Kadir, Taman Tun Dr Ismail, 60000, Kuala Lumpur, Malaysia
Tel.: (60) 327790503
Human Capital Management Services
N.A.I.C.S.: 541612

Rizing, LLC (1)
300 1st Stamford Pl, Stamford, CT 06902
Tel.: (203) 517-0400
Web Site: http://rizing.com
Emp.: 1,250
SAP Functional & Technical Services
N.A.I.C.S.: 541990
Mike R. Maiolo *(CEO)*

Subsidiary (Domestic):

Rizing Geospatial, LLC (2)
2970 University Pkwy Ste 201, Sarasota, FL 34243-2401
Tel.: (941) 359-9697
Custom Computer Programming Services
N.A.I.C.S.: 541511
Connie Gurchiek *(Pres)*

Shubido Pacific Sdn Bhd (1)
7 Persiaran Subang Permai Taman Perindustrian Subang, Subang Jaya, 47610, Selangor, Malaysia
Tel.: (60) 356315588
Cosmetic Products Mfr & Distr
N.A.I.C.S.: 424210

Unza Cathay Limited (1)
18/F Centre Point 181 - 185 Gloucester Road, Wanchai, China (Hong Kong)
Tel.: (852) 25291191
Cosmetic Product Distr
N.A.I.C.S.: 424210

Unza China Limited (1)
10 Floor Cenrtepoint 181-185 Gloucester Road, Wanchai, China (Hong Kong)
Tel.: (852) 25291191
Web Site: http://www.wipro-unza.com
Emp.: 100
Cosmetic Product Distr
N.A.I.C.S.: 424210

Unza Company Pte Ltd (1)
163 Penang Road 04-01 Winsland House II, Singapore, 238463, Singapore
Tel.: (65) 67325611
Personal Care Products Mfr & Distr
N.A.I.C.S.: 424210

Unza Holdings Pte Ltd. (1)
163 Penang Road 04-01 Winsland House II, Singapore, 238463, Singapore
Tel.: (65) 67325611
Web Site: https://www.wipro-unza.com
Sales Range: $50-74.9 Million
Emp.: 15
Personal Care Products Mfr & Distr
N.A.I.C.S.: 424210

Unza Holdings Sdn Bhd (1)
No 7 Persiaran Subang Permai Taman Perindustrian Subang, 47610, Subang Jaya, Selangor, Malaysia
Tel.: (60) 356315588
Cosmetic Products Mfr & Distr
N.A.I.C.S.: 325620
Kumar Chandan *(Mng Dir)*

WIPRO UNZA Singapore Pte Ltd (1)
163 Penang Road #04-01 Winsland House II, Singapore, 238463, Singapore
Tel.: (65) 67325611
Web Site: http://www.wipro-unza.com
Personal Care Products Mfr & Distr
N.A.I.C.S.: 456199
Chan Woei Shyong *(Sr Gen Mgr)*

Wipro (Dalian) Limited (1)
D-7 Spring Field Park, Ganjingzi District,

AND PRIVATE COMPANIES — WIPRO LIMITED

Dalian, 116039, China
Tel.: (86) 4113 952 6000
Information Technology Services
N.A.I.C.S.: 541519

Wipro (Shanghai) Limited (1)
Room 156 Changxing Building No 888 Bibo Road, Pudong New Area, Shanghai, 201203, China **(100%)**
Tel.: (86) 2120592612
Microelectronics Mfr
N.A.I.C.S.: 334419

Wipro (Thailand) Co. Limited (1)
No 1 Empire Tower Room No 2605 Floor 26 South Sathorn Road, Yannawa Sathorn, Bangkok, 10120, Thailand
Tel.: (66) 2 670 0754
Web Site: https://www.wipro-unza.com
Personal Care Product Mfr & Distr
N.A.I.C.S.: 325620

Wipro 4C Consulting France SAS (1)
35 Rue des Mathurins, 75008, Paris, France
Tel.: (33) 18 283 2884
Web Site: https://www.weare4c.com
Strategic Design Services
N.A.I.C.S.: 541430

Wipro 4C Danmark ApS (1)
Niels Bohrs Alle 2A, 2860, Soborg, Denmark
Tel.: (45) 7 262 7999
Web Site: https://www.weare4c.com
Cloud Marketing Services
N.A.I.C.S.: 541613

Wipro Arabia Limited (1) **(100%)**
Tel.: (966) 38984015
Web Site: http://www.wipro.com
Infotechnology Solutions
N.A.I.C.S.: 541690

Wipro Arabia Limited-Riyadh (1)
Ground Floor Building 22 Student housing Street, PO Box 250 767, Princess Noura University 3633 - King Khalid International Airport, Riyadh, 13415 - 7264, Saudi Arabia **(100%)**
Tel.: (966) 112192122
Infotechnology & Outsourcing Services
N.A.I.C.S.: 541618

Wipro Chengdu Limited (1)
D2 building Tianfu Software Park 599 South Century City Tianfu Ave, Chengdu, 610041, Sichuan, China
Tel.: (86) 2865542001
Information Technology Consulting Services
N.A.I.C.S.: 541512

Wipro Consumer Care Limited (1)
B16-17 Subhash Nagar Shopping Ctr Shastri Nagar, Jaipur, 302023, Rajasthan, India
Tel.: (91) 1412280289
Web Site: http://www.wcclg.com
Telephonic Consumer Care Services
N.A.I.C.S.: 561421

Wipro Cyprus Private Limited (1)
Alphamega Akropolis Building 10 Diomidous Street 3rd Floor Office 401, Nicosia, 2024, Cyprus
Tel.: (357) 22361600
Information Technology Consulting Services
N.A.I.C.S.: 541512

Wipro Enterprises (P) Limited (1)
Wipro House No 8 7th Main 80 Feet Road Koramangala 1st Block, Bengaluru, 560034, Karnataka, India
Tel.: (91) 8061990100
Web Site: https://www.wiproenterprises.com
Personal Care Product Mfr
N.A.I.C.S.: 325620
Azim Premji *(Chm)*

Subsidiary (Non-US):

Splash Corporation (2)
5F W Office Bldg 11th Avenue cor 28th Street, Bonifacio Global City, Taguig, 1634, Philippines
Tel.: (63) 24917707
Web Site: http://www.splash.com.ph
Sales Range: $75-99.9 Million
Personal Care Product Mfr
N.A.I.C.S.: 325620

Veneranda M. Tomas *(Pres & COO)*

Wipro Fluid Power Ltd. (1)
Wipro House 3rd Floor No 8 7th Main 80 Feet Road, Koramangala 1st Block, Bengaluru, 560034, Karnataka, India **(100%)**
Tel.: (91) 8061990100
Web Site: https://www.wiproinfra.com
Sales Range: $25-49.9 Million
Emp.: 500
Mfr of Hydraulic Cylinders
N.A.I.C.S.: 333995

Wipro France SAS (1)
Immeuble Madelaine D 76 Route de la Demi-Lune, Paris, 92057, France
Tel.: (33) 146939595
Web Site: http://www.wipro.com
Sales Range: $25-49.9 Million
Emp.: 30
Information Technology Consulting Services
N.A.I.C.S.: 541512

Wipro Gallagher Solutions (1)
810 Crescent Centre Dr Ste 400, Franklin, TN 37067
Tel.: (615) 221-7300
Sales Range: $25-49.9 Million
Emp.: 2
Mortgage Banking Origination & Solutions Software
N.A.I.C.S.: 541511
Joey McDuffee *(Head-Sls & Mktg)*

Wipro Gulf LLC (1)
Office No 0400Z209-Zone2 KOM 4 Ground Floor Knowledge Oasis, PO Box 137, 102, Muscat, Oman
Tel.: (968) 2 417 0801
Information Technology Services
N.A.I.C.S.: 541519

Wipro Holding Austria GmbH (1)
Millenium Park 6, 6890, Lustenau, Vorarlberg, Austria
Tel.: (43) 55 77 995 0
Web Site: http://www.wipro.com
Emp.: 20
Investment Management Service
N.A.I.C.S.: 523999

Wipro IT Services Austria GmbH (1)
Lassallestr 7b, 1020, Vienna, Austria
Tel.: (43) 153278030
Information Technology Consulting Services
N.A.I.C.S.: 541512

Wipro IT Services UK Societas (1)
Kings Court 185 Kings Road, Reading, RG1 4EX, Berks, United Kingdom
Tel.: (44) 1182291300
Web Site: https://www.wipro.com
Holding Company
N.A.I.C.S.: 551112

Subsidiary (Non-US):

Wipro Doha LLC (2)
1st Floor Bldg D The Business Park Bldg No 58 St No 310, PO Box 31887, Zone 26 Airport Rd, Doha, Qatar **(100%)**
Tel.: (974) 40297585
Information Technology Services
N.A.I.C.S.: 541519

Wipro Information Technology (Egypt) SAE (1)
B-124 Smart Village Cairo-Alex Desert Road, Giza, Egypt **(100%)**
Tel.: (20) 111122111
Web Site: http://www.wipro.com
Information Technology Services
N.A.I.C.S.: 519290

Wipro Information Technology Netherlands BV (1)
Claude Debussylaan 24, Amsterdam, 1082 MD, Netherlands
Tel.: (31) 205222555
Information Technology Consulting Services
N.A.I.C.S.: 541512

Wipro Infrastructure Engineering AB (1)
Maskinvagen 13, PO Box 295, 931 37, Skelleftea, Sweden
Tel.: (46) 91084800
Hydraulic Cylinder Mfr
N.A.I.C.S.: 333995

Wipro Infrastructure Engineering Oy (1)

Torpanmaentie 3, 25500, Pernio, Varsinais-Suomi, Finland
Tel.: (358) 290552849
Web Site: https://nummi.fi
Hydraulic Cylinder Mfr & Distr
N.A.I.C.S.: 333995
Fransisca Lindgren *(Mgr-Orderdesk-2 Act Cylinders)*

Wipro Japan KK (1)
Yokohama Landmark Tower 26F 2-2-1-1 Minato-Mirai, Nishi-Ku, Yokohama, 220-8126, Kanagawa, Japan
Tel.: (81) 456503950
Software Development Services
N.A.I.C.S.: 541511

Wipro Networks Pte Limited (1)
1300 Hub Synergy Point 70 Anson Road, Singapore, Singapore
Tel.: (65) 64962035
Information Technology Consulting Services
N.A.I.C.S.: 541512

Wipro Newlogic (1)
Millennium Park 6, 6890, Lustenau, Austria
Tel.: (43) 5577 111
Web Site: http://www.wipro.com
Sales Range: $25-49.9 Million
Emp.: 25
Wireless Application Software & Consulting Services
N.A.I.C.S.: 513210

Wipro Outsourcing Services (Ireland) Limited (1)
Dromore House East Industrial Park, County Clare, Shannon, Ireland
Tel.: (353) 6 147 7000
Information Technology Services
N.A.I.C.S.: 541519

Wipro Portugal S.A. (1)
Rua Eng Frederico Ulrich 2650, Moreira, 4470-605, Maia, Portugal
Tel.: (351) 22 607 7500
Information Technology Services
N.A.I.C.S.: 541519

Wipro Retail (1)
Rua Eng Frederico Ulrich, 2650 Edificio Wipro, 4470-605, Maia, Moreira, Portugal **(100%)**
Tel.: (351) 223271609
Sales Range: $100-124.9 Million
Emp.: 300
Retail of Information Technology Products
N.A.I.C.S.: 449210

Wipro Solutions Canada Limited (1)
10040 104 Street NW Suite 100, Edmonton, T5J 0Z2, AB, Canada
Tel.: (780) 420-7875
Web Site: http://www.wipro.com
Online Billing & Payment Processing Services
N.A.I.C.S.: 522320

Wipro Technologies Argentina SA (1)
Carlos Pellegrini 581 Piso 7, Capital Federal, 1009, Buenos Aires, Argentina
Tel.: (54) 4130282507
Information Technology Consulting Services
N.A.I.C.S.: 541512

Wipro Technologies Australia Pty Ltd (1)
Level 5 12-14 The Esplanade, Perth, 6000, WA, Australia
Tel.: (61) 86 213 7000
Software Services
N.A.I.C.S.: 541511
David Taylor *(Mng Dir-Australia & New Zealand)*

Wipro Technologies BPO (1)
Joao Marchesii St 139 5-6th Flr, Curitiba, 80215 432, Prado Velho, Brazil **(100%)**
Tel.: (55) 4130282500
Web Site: http://www.wipro.com
Emp.: 600
Outsourcing Service Center for Local Businesses
N.A.I.C.S.: 561311

Wipro Technologies Nigeria Limited (1)
7th Floor Mulliner Towers 39 Alfred Rewane Road Kingsway Road, Ikoyi, Lagos, Nigeria

Tel.: (234) 1 271 9133
Software Services
N.A.I.C.S.: 541519

Wipro Technologies S.A. de C.V. (1)
Suite 38-27 Av E Garza Sada 427, Altavista, Monterrey, 64849, Mexico **(100%)**
Tel.: (52) 8182188188
Web Site: http://www.wipro.com
Sales Range: $25-49.9 Million
Emp.: 150
Global Development Center
N.A.I.C.S.: 541715

Wipro Technologies S.R.L. (1)
319C Spl Independentei St Sector 6, 60044, Bucharest, Romania **(100%)**
Tel.: (40) 213118110
Web Site: http://www.wipro.com
Sales Range: $100-124.9 Million
Emp.: 350
Information Technology, Outsourcing & Consulting Services
N.A.I.C.S.: 513199

Wipro Technologies Sdn. Bhd. (1)
Suite 25 01 Level 25 The Gardens North Tower, Mid Valley City Lingkaran Syed Putra Wilayah Persekutuan, 59200, Kuala Lumpur, Malaysia
Tel.: (60) 32 706 2500
Software Services
N.A.I.C.S.: 541511

Wipro Technologies South Africa (Proprietary) Limited (1)
2 Maude Street The Forum 10th Floor, Johannesburg, Sandton, RSA, South Africa
Tel.: (27) 110616500
Information Technology & Consulting Services
N.A.I.C.S.: 541519

Wipro Technologies/Wipro BPO (1)
475 A Old Mahabalipuram Road, Chennai, 600 119, Schollinganallur, India **(100%)**
Tel.: (91) 4424500200
Web Site: http://www.wipro.com
Information Technology & Outsourcing Services
N.A.I.C.S.: 519290

Wipro Technologies/Wipro BPO (1)
Plot No 2 MIDC Pune Infotech Park, Pune, 411 057, Hinjewadi, India **(100%)**
Tel.: (91) 2022933700
Web Site: http://www.wipro.com
Sales Range: $1-4.9 Billion
Emp.: 8,000
Information Technology & Outsourcing Services
N.A.I.C.S.: 519290

Wipro UK Limited (1)
Hemel One First Floor Building 1, Boundary Way, Hemel Hempstead, HP2 7YU, United Kingdom
Tel.: (44) 1442 227700
Web Site: http://www.wipro.com
Sales Range: $10-24.9 Million
Emp.: 28
Engineeering Services
N.A.I.C.S.: 541330

Wipro Weare4C UK Limited (1)
19th Floor 100 Bishopsgate, London, EC2M 1GT, United Kingdom
Tel.: (44) 207 432 8500
Web Site: https://www.weare4c.com
Automobile Mfr
N.A.I.C.S.: 336110

Wipro do Brasil Technologia Ltda (1)
Rua Joao Marchesini 139 - 5th and 6th floor, Curitiba, 80215-432, Brazil
Tel.: (55) 4130282500
Emp.: 400
Information Technology Consulting Services
N.A.I.C.S.: 541512

Women's Business Park Technologies Limited (1)
Ground Floor Building 22 Student Housing Street, Princess Noura University 7264 3633 King Khalid International Airport, Riyadh, 13415, Saudi Arabia **(55%)**
Tel.: (966) 11 510 7322
Web Site: https://www.wipro.com
Software Services
N.A.I.C.S.: 541511

WIPRO LIMITED

Wipro Limited—(Continued)

Haya Albassam *(Mgr-Business Development)*

WIRA FAHRZEUG- UND MASCHINENTEILE GMBH
Alte Papiermuhle Hammern 8, 51688, Wipperfurth, Germany
Tel.: (49) 226788240
Web Site: http://www.wira-gmbh.de
Year Founded: 1976
Rev.: $11,035,200
Emp.: 50
Vehicle & Machine Parts Mfr
N.A.I.C.S.: 336390
Max Kurt Meier *(Mng Dir)*

WIRECARD AG
Einsteinring 35, 85609, Aschheim, Germany
Tel.: (49) 8944241400 De
Web Site: https://www.wirecard.com
WDI—(OTCIQ)
Rev.: $2,306,109,398
Assets: $6,696,776,071
Liabilities: $4,497,611,038
Net Worth: $2,199,165,033
Earnings: $397,352,646
Emp.: 5,154
Fiscal Year-end: 12/31/18
E-Commerce Business Solutions
N.A.I.C.S.: 513210
Alfons W. Henseler *(Deputy Chm-Supervisory Bd)*

Subsidiaries:

GI Technology Pte. Ltd. (1)
Unit No 301 & 302 3rd Floor Campus 3B RMZ Millenia Business Park II, 143 MGR Main Road Kandanchavadi Perungudi, Chennai, 600096, India
Tel.: (91) 4466816000
Web Site: http://www.gitechnology.in
Online Payment & Processing Services
N.A.I.C.S.: 522320

Hermes I Tickets Pte. Ltd. (1)
RMZ Millenia Business Park - Phase 2 Campus 3B Unit No 301 and 302, 3rd Floor 143 MGR Main Road Kandanchavadi Perungudi, 600096, Chennai, India
Tel.: (91) 4466816000
Web Site: http://www.hermesnetwork.in
Online Payment & Processing Services
N.A.I.C.S.: 522320
Balan Prabhakar *(Assoc VP)*

Subsidiary (Non-US):

GI Philippines Corp. (2)
Mezzanine Floor Roxas Strip Building Boulevard, 1300, Pasay, Philippines
Tel.: (63) 9175291443
Online Payment & Processing Services
N.A.I.C.S.: 522320

PT Prima Vista Solusi (1)
Graha Pratama Level 19 Jl MT Haryono Kav 15, Jakarta, 12810, Indonesia
Tel.: (62) 2183709520
Online Payment & Processing Services
N.A.I.C.S.: 522320

PT Wipro Wirecard Technologies Indonesia (1)
Wisma Barito Pacific Tower A Lantai M Jl Letjen S Parman Kav 62-63, Jakarta, 11410, Indonesia
Tel.: (62) 2153665115
Online Payment & Processing Services
N.A.I.C.S.: 522320

Provus srl (1)
Vasile Milea 2H sector 6, 061344, Bucharest, Romania
Tel.: (40) 212026900
Web Site: http://www.provus.ro
Financial Management Services
N.A.I.C.S.: 522320

Systems@Work Pte. Ltd. (1)
8 Marina View 40-01 Asia Square Tower 1, Singapore, 018960, Singapore
Tel.: (65) 6690 6690

Web Site: http://www.wirecard.com
Emp.: 120
Financial Transaction Processing Services
N.A.I.C.S.: 522320

Wirecard (Gibraltar) Ltd. (1)
Suite 3a ICOM House, Gibraltar, Gibraltar
Tel.: (350) 200 70 321
Software Development Services
N.A.I.C.S.: 541511

Wirecard Africa Holding Proprietary Ltd. (1)
Block C Grosvenor Square Century Way, Century City, Cape Town, 7441, South Africa
Tel.: (27) 215553260
Web Site: http://www.wirecard.co.za
Online Payment & Processing Services
N.A.I.C.S.: 522320

Wirecard Asia Holding Pte. Ltd. (1)
80 Pasir Panjang Rd 14-81 Mapletree Business City, Singapore, 117372, Singapore
Tel.: (65) 66906690
Web Site: http://www.wirecard.asia
Online Payment & Processing Services
N.A.I.C.S.: 522320

Wirecard Australia A&I Pte. Ltd. (1)
Level 8 360 Collins Street, Melbourne, 3000, VIC, Australia
Tel.: (61) 1300599980
Online Payment & Processing Services
N.A.I.C.S.: 522320

Wirecard Australia Pty. Ltd. (1)
Level 8 360 Collins Street, Melbourne, 3000, VIC, Australia
Tel.: (61) 396618200
Online Payment & Processing Services
N.A.I.C.S.: 522320

Wirecard Bank AG (1)
Einsteinring 35, 85609, Aschheim, Germany
Tel.: (49) 8944242000
Web Site: http://www.wirecardbank.com
Online Payment & Processing Services
N.A.I.C.S.: 522320
Wulf Matthias *(Chm)*

Wirecard Brazil S.A. (1)
Av Brigadeiro Faria Lima 3064 12th Floor, Itaim Bibi, 01451-001, Sao Paulo, Brazil
Tel.: (55) 1131818180
Web Site: http://www.wirecard.com.br
Online Payment & Processing Services
N.A.I.C.S.: 522320

Wirecard Communication Services GmbH (1)
Bauhofstrasse 3, 04103, Leipzig, Germany
Tel.: (49) 341 94 034 0
Web Site: http://www.wirecard-communication.de
Business Process Outsourcing Services
N.A.I.C.S.: 561422
Marcel Bielefeldt *(Mgr-Sls)*

Wirecard E-Money Philippines Inc. (1)
11th Flr M1 Tower 141 H V Dela Costa St Brgy Bel-Air, Metro Manila, 1209, Makati, Philippines
Tel.: (63) 22492999
Online Payment & Processing Services
N.A.I.C.S.: 522320

Wirecard Forex India Pte. Ltd. (1)
Cunningham Classic 22 Cunningham Road, Bengaluru, 560 052, India
Tel.: (91) 8041502666
Online Payment & Processing Services
N.A.I.C.S.: 522320
S. K. Nandeesha *(Acct Mgr)*

Wirecard Hong Kong Ltd. (1)
Suite 2106-07 21/F Prudential Tower Harbour City, Kowloon, China (Hong Kong)
Tel.: (852) 82288366
Online Payment & Processing Services
N.A.I.C.S.: 522320

Wirecard Malaysia Sdn. Bhd. (1)
W501 West Wing Metropolitan Square, Petaling Jaya, 47820, Malaysia
Tel.: (60) 377257552
Emp.: 8
Financial Transaction Processing Services
N.A.I.C.S.: 522320
Christopher Eddie *(Gen Mgr)*

Wirecard Myanmar Ltd. (1)
Unit No 10C-2 10th Floor Centrepoint Towers, Yangon, Myanmar
Tel.: (95) 9254381973
Online Payment & Processing Services
N.A.I.C.S.: 522320
Win Pa Pa Phyo *(Deputy Mgr-Fin & Admin)*

Wirecard Odeme ve Elektronik Para Hizmetleri A.S. (1)
Gayrettepe Mh Yildiz Posta Cd D Plaza No 52 K 6, Besiktas, Istanbul, Türkiye
Tel.: (90) 2122862718
Web Site: http://www.wirecard.com.tr
Online Payment & Processing Services
N.A.I.C.S.: 522320

Wirecard UK & Ireland Ltd. (1)
1st Floor Ulysses House Foley Street, Dublin, Ireland
Tel.: (353) 18765800
Web Site: http://www.wirecard.co.uk
Online Payment & Processing Services
N.A.I.C.S.: 522320
Matthew Lynch *(Mgr-Fraud & Compliance)*

WIRELESSGATE, INC.
5F Tennozu Ocean Square 2-2-20 Higashishinagawa, Shinagawa-ku, Tokyo, 140-0002, Japan
Tel.: (81) 364332045
Web Site: https://www.wirelessgate.co.jp
9419—(TKS)
Rev.: $60,144,470
Assets: $21,043,120
Liabilities: $13,846,770
Net Worth: $7,196,350
Earnings: $1,708,690
Emp.: 10
Fiscal Year-end: 12/31/23
Wireless Broadband Services
N.A.I.C.S.: 517112
Nobuhiro Hama *(Pres)*

WIRES & FABRIKS (S.A.) LIMITED
63 Industrial Area, Jhotwara, Jaipur, 302012, India
Tel.: (91) 2341722
Web Site: https://www.wirefabrik.com
Year Founded: 1963
507817—(BOM)
Rev.: $12,370,465
Assets: $13,761,301
Liabilities: $7,594,228
Net Worth: $6,167,072
Earnings: $63,868
Fiscal Year-end: 03/31/21
Paper Machine Clothing Mfr & Whslr
N.A.I.C.S.: 313220
Mahendra Kumar Khaitan *(Mng Dir)*

WIREX LIMITED
9th Floor 107 Cheapside, London, United Kingdom
Tel.: (44) 2039346602
Web Site: https://wirexapp.com
Digital Payment Platforms
N.A.I.C.S.: 522320
Dmitry Lazarichev *(Founder & CEO)*

WIRTEK A/S
Niels Jernes Vej 10, 9220, Aalborg, Denmark
Tel.: (45) 72146660
Web Site: https://www.wirtek.com
Year Founded: 2001
Software Development Services
N.A.I.C.S.: 541511
Michael Aaen *(Mng Dir)*

WIRTUALNA POLSKA HOLDING S.A.
Zwirki i Wigury 16, 02-092, Warsaw, Poland
Tel.: (48) 225767900 PL
Web Site: https://www.holding.wp.pl

WPL—(WAR)
Rev.: $270,743,104
Assets: $505,159,021
Liabilities: $273,317,339
Net Worth: $231,841,682
Earnings: $44,798,272
Emp.: 1,553
Fiscal Year-end: 12/31/22
Holding Company; Online Media Publisher
N.A.I.C.S.: 551112
Jacek Swiderski *(CEO & Member-Mgmt Bd)*

Subsidiaries:

Businessclick Sp. z o.o. (1)
Ul Zwirki i Wigury 16, 02-092, Warsaw, Poland
Tel.: (48) 225767416
Web Site: https://www.businessclick.com
Advertising Agency Services
N.A.I.C.S.: 541810

Extradom.pl Sp. z o.o. (1)
Ul Jaworska 13, 53-612, Wroclaw, Poland
Tel.: (48) 717152060
Web Site: https://www.extradom.pl
Internet Services
N.A.I.C.S.: 513199

Grupa Wirtualna Polska S.A. (1)
ul Jutrzenki 137 A, 02-231, Warsaw, Poland (100%)
Tel.: (48) 225763900
Web Site: http://www.onas.wp.pl
Online Media Publisher
N.A.I.C.S.: 513199
Malgorzata Pogorzelska *(Mgr-Product Adv)*

Nocowanie.pl Sp. z o.o. (1)
Ul Naleczowska 14, 20-701, Lublin, Poland
Tel.: (48) 801000781
Web Site: https://www.nocowanie.pl
Online Accommodation Services
N.A.I.C.S.: 721199

Parklot Sp. z o.o. (1)
Ul Swieradowska 47, District Court, 02-662, Warsaw, Poland
Tel.: (48) 226999126
Web Site: https://www.parklot.pl
Airport Parking Services
N.A.I.C.S.: 488119

Superauto24.com Sp. z o.o. (1)
Ul Stalowa 16, 41-506, Chorzow, Poland
Tel.: (48) 881979410
Web Site: https://www.superauto.pl
Car Lending Services
N.A.I.C.S.: 532112

Wakacje.pl S.A. (1)
Al Grunwaldzka 413, 80-309, Gdansk, Poland
Tel.: (48) 587706001
Web Site: https://www.wakacje.pl
Tour Services
N.A.I.C.S.: 561520

WIS KUNSTSTOFFE GMBH
Lange Somme 25, 98597, Breitungen, Germany
Tel.: (49) 368488680
Web Site: http://www.wiskunststoffe.de
Sales Range: $10-24.9 Million
Emp.: 22
Plastic Product Distr
N.A.I.C.S.: 326199
Siegmar Romhild *(CEO & Mng Dir)*

WISAP GESELLSCHAFT FUR WISSENSCHAFTLICHEN APPARATEBAU MBH
Rudolf Diesel Ring 20 Sauerlach, Munich, 82054, Germany
Tel.: (49) 810489080
Web Site: http://www.wisap.com
Year Founded: 1975
Sales Range: $10-24.9 Million
Emp.: 40
Mfr of Endoscopic Equipment & Instruments
N.A.I.C.S.: 334510

Isolde Semm (Mng Dir)

Subsidiaries:

WISAP WIEN Handelsgesellschaft mbH (1)
Neumayrgasse 21, A 1160, Vienna, Austria (100%)
Tel.: (43) 14952799
Mfr & Sales of Endoscopic Equipment & Instruments
N.A.I.C.S.: 334510

WISBET INTERNATIONAL CO., LTD.

No 1300 Chenggong Road 6th Neighborhood Poluow Village, Hukoku Township, Hsin-chu, Taiwan
Tel.: (886) 3 5996720
Web Site:
http://www.candmark.com.tw
Rev.: $4,174,928
Assets: $24,046,317
Liabilities: $23,063,349
Net Worth: $982,968
Earnings: ($2,837,011)
Emp.: 300
Fiscal Year-end: 12/31/18
Lenses & Glass Products for Electronic Devices
N.A.I.C.S.: 333310
Huang Pi-Cheng (Chm & Pres)

WISCOM CO., LTD

Kangchon-ro 237, Danwon-gu, Ansan, Gyunggi-do, Korea (South)
Tel.: (82) 314951181
Web Site: https://www.wiscom.co.kr
Year Founded: 1978
024070—(KRS)
Rev.: $96,398,334
Assets: $98,562,005
Liabilities: $12,215,915
Net Worth: $86,346,091
Earnings: ($5,695,145)
Emp.: 237
Fiscal Year-end: 12/31/22
Plastics Product Mfr
N.A.I.C.S.: 335929
Young-il Koo (Pres & CEO)

Subsidiaries:

WISCOM Co., Ltd - Ansan 2 Factory (1)
352 Haebong-ro, Danwon-gu, Ansan, Gyeonggi-do, Korea (South)
Tel.: (82) 31 495 2206
Web Site: http://www.wiscom.co.kr
Chemical Products Mfr
N.A.I.C.S.: 325998

WISCOM Co., Ltd - Ansung Factory (1)
267-3 Gyereuk-ri Iyang-myun, Ansan, Gyeonggi-do, Korea (South)
Tel.: (82) 31 677 7081
Chemical Products Mfr
N.A.I.C.S.: 325998

WISCOM Co., Ltd - Sihwa Factory (1)
1 Third 502 Sihwa industrial complex, Ansan, Gyeonggi-do, Korea (South)
Tel.: (82) 31 432 3321
Chemical Products Mfr
N.A.I.C.S.: 325998

WISCOM Co., Ltd - Yeosu Factory (1)
1449 Jugnheung-dong, Yeosu, Junnam, Korea (South)
Tel.: (82) 61 686 8855
Chemical Products Mfr
N.A.I.C.S.: 325998

Wiscom Engineering Plastics (Wuxi) Co., Ltd. (1)
No 79 Xinmei Road Xinwu Zone, Wuxi, 214028, Jiangsu, China
Tel.: (86) 51085322080
Polyvinyl Chloride Compounds Mfr
N.A.I.C.S.: 325211

WISCOM SYSTEM CO., LTD.

100 General Avenue Economic and Technological Development Zone, Jiangning, Nanjing, China
Tel.: (86) 2552762828
Web Site: http://www.wiscom.com.cn
Year Founded: 1995
002090—(SSE)
Rev.: $214,499,133
Assets: $366,261,789
Liabilities: $189,237,354
Net Worth: $177,024,435
Earnings: $4,214,822
Fiscal Year-end: 12/31/22
Electrical Power Automation Services
N.A.I.C.S.: 335313
Bing Xu (Chm)

WISDEK CORP.

180 Brodie Dr Unit 105, Richmond Hill, L4B 3K8, ON, Canada
Tel.: (416) 514-5194
Web Site: http://www.wisdek-seo.com
Year Founded: 1998
Sales Range: $75-99.9 Million
Emp.: 400
Sear Engine Optimization Software & Marketing Services
N.A.I.C.S.: 513210
Eran Hurvitz (Owner)

WISDOM EDUCATION INTERNATIONAL HOLDINGS COMPANY LIMITED

Rm 3302 33-F Lee Garden One 33 Hysan Avenue, Causeway Bay, Hong Kong, China (Hong Kong)
Tel.: (852) 3 899 3588   Ky
Web Site:
http://www.wisdomeducationintl.com
Year Founded: 2002
6068—(HKG)
Rev.: $291,978,088
Assets: $181,283,583
Liabilities: $106,649,564
Net Worth: $74,634,019
Earnings: ($293,889,443)
Emp.: 6,800
Fiscal Year-end: 08/31/21
Education Services
N.A.I.C.S.: 611310
Xuebin Liu (Co-Founder)

WISDOM MARINE LINES CO., LTD.

2nd FL No 237 Fu-Hsing S Rd Sec 2, Taipei, 10667, Taiwan
Tel.: (886) 227552637
Web Site:
https://www.wisdomlines.com.tw
Year Founded: 1999
WML—(LSE)
Rev.: $545,530,289
Assets: $2,859,446,133
Liabilities: $1,394,023,663
Net Worth: $1,465,422,470
Earnings: $104,966,718
Emp.: 2,700
Fiscal Year-end: 12/31/23
Bulk Ship & Marine Transportation Services
N.A.I.C.S.: 483111
James Chun-Sheng Lan (Chm)

Subsidiaries:

Well Shipmanagement and Maritime Consultant Co., Ltd. (1)
2f 237 Fu Hsing South Road Section 2, Taipei, 10656, Taiwan
Tel.: (886) 227001158
Web Site: http://www.wisdomlines.com.tw
Ship Management Services
N.A.I.C.S.: 561110

Wisdom Marine International Inc. (1)
7F 11 237 Fu Hsing South Road Section 2, Taipei, 10667, Taiwan

Tel.: (886) 227556911
Ship Management Services
N.A.I.C.S.: 561110

WISDOM SPORTS GROUP

7/F Block 1 No 16 Xinyuanli, Chaoyang District, Beijing, China
Tel.: (86) 1084865300
Web Site:
http://www.wisdomsports.com.cn
1661—(HKG)
Rev.: $698,630
Assets: $70,081,362
Liabilities: $5,389,114
Net Worth: $64,692,248
Earnings: ($10,601,183)
Emp.: 14
Fiscal Year-end: 12/31/22
Holding Company; Media Investment Management Services; Television Program Producer & Distr; Sports Competitions Organizer
N.A.I.C.S.: 551112

WISDOM TOOTHBRUSHES LTD.

The Silk Mill, Haverhill, CB9 8DT, Suffolk, United Kingdom
Tel.: (44) 1440714800
Web Site: http://www.wisdom-toothbrushes.com
Sales Range: $25-49.9 Million
Emp.: 28
Broom Brush & Mop Mfr
N.A.I.C.S.: 339994
Julian Edge-Partington (Dir-Fin)

WISDOM WEALTH RESOURCES INVESTMENT HOLDING GROUP LIMITED

Unit 10-12 19/F China Merchants Tower, Shun Tak Centre 168-200 Connaught Road Central, Sheung Wan, China (Hong Kong)
Tel.: (852) 25877007
Web Site:
http://www.hoifuenergy.com
0007—(HKG)
Rev.: $65,220,968
Assets: $713,654,603
Liabilities: $185,128,215
Net Worth: $528,526,388
Earnings: $30,545,813
Emp.: 72
Fiscal Year-end: 12/31/22
Oil & Gas Exploration Services; Financial & Investment Services
N.A.I.C.S.: 523999
Kwok Lun Nam (Exec Dir)

Subsidiaries:

Karl Thomson Finance Limited (1)
27/F Fortis Bank Tower 117-119 Jaffe Road, Wanchai, China (Hong Kong)
Tel.: (852) 28779266
Security Trading Services
N.A.I.C.S.: 523150

Karl Thomson Investment Consultants Limited (1)
Rm 606-610 6/F Tai Yau Building 181 Johnston Road, Wanchai, China (Hong Kong)
Tel.: (852) 31102338
Web Site: http://ktic.ktg.hk
Financial Advisory Services
N.A.I.C.S.: 523940

WISDOMCOME GROUP HOLDINGS LIMITED

Unit 02 11/F The Eastmark 21 Sheung Yuet Road, Kowloon, China (Hong Kong)
Tel.: (852) 28927859   BM
Web Site: http://www.ecrepay.com
8079—(HKG)
Rev.: $12,674,994
Assets: $29,037,654
Liabilities: $2,806,992

Net Worth: $26,230,663
Earnings: ($8,296,510)
Emp.: 90
Fiscal Year-end: 03/31/22
Holding Company
N.A.I.C.S.: 551112
Chi To (Sec)

Subsidiaries:

Cool Cool Frozen Food Limited (1)
FlatB 16/F Roxy Industrial Centre 58 - 66 Tai Lin Pai Road, Kwai Chung, New Territories, China (Hong Kong)
Tel.: (852) 21560660
Web Site: https://www.coolcool.com.hk
Frozen Food Whslr
N.A.I.C.S.: 424420

WISE ALLY INTERNATIONAL HOLDINGS LIMITED

Units 3203-3207 Tower 1 Enterprise Square Five 38 Wang Chiu Road, Kowloon Bay, China (Hong Kong)
Tel.: (852) 28962212   Ky
Web Site: http://www.wiseally.com.hk
Year Founded: 1978
9918—(HKG)
Rev.: $170,282,498
Assets: $124,633,290
Liabilities: $104,738,828
Net Worth: $19,894,463
Earnings: $1,929,585
Emp.: 1,700
Fiscal Year-end: 12/31/22
Holding Company
N.A.I.C.S.: 551112
Raymond Wai Hang Chu (Founder & Chm)

Subsidiaries:

Dongguan Wise Ally Industrial Co., Ltd. (1)
No 3 Zhen An Middle Road, Wu Sha Community Changan Town, Dongguan, Guangdong, China
Tel.: (86) 76981588228
Electronic Product Mfr & Distr
N.A.I.C.S.: 334419

WISE EQUITY SGR S.P.A.

Foro Buonaparte 76, 20121, Milan, Italy
Tel.: (39) 028545691   IT
Web Site: http://www.wisesgr.com
Year Founded: 2000
Privater Equity Firm
N.A.I.C.S.: 523999
Paolo Gambarini (Co-Founder & Partner)

Subsidiaries:

Special Flanges SpA (1)
Via Giovanni De Medici 7, 20811, Cesano Maderno, Italy
Tel.: (39) 0362552247
Web Site: https://www.special-flanges.it
Forged Special Flanges & Fittings Mfr
N.A.I.C.S.: 332919

Subsidiary (Non-US):

Hertecant Flanges N.V. (2)
Lossing 22, B 2260, Westerlo, Belgium
Tel.: (32) 15224910
Web Site: http://www.hertecant.com
Sales Range: $25-49.9 Million
Emp.: 30
Stainless Steel Flanges Mfr
N.A.I.C.S.: 331221
Ron Deckers (CFO)

Tapi S.p.A. (1)
Via Cornara Est 2/F, 35010, Massanzago, Padova, Italy
Tel.: (39) 049 5797 300
Web Site: http://www.tapigroup.com
Alcoholic Beverage, Condiment & Cosmetic Closures Mfr
N.A.I.C.S.: 332119
Robert Casini (CEO)

Wanho Manufacturing LLC (1)

WISE EQUITY SGR S.P.A.

Wise Equity SGR S.p.A.—(Continued)
137 Mattatuck Hts Rd, Waterbury, CT 06705
Tel.: (203) 759-3744
Web Site: http://www.wanho.com
Durable Goods Merchant Wholesalers
N.A.I.C.S.: 423990
Johanna Mendoza *(Supvr-Production)*

WISE GROUP AB
Linnegatan 87, 115 23, Stockholm, Sweden
Tel.: (46) 855529000
Web Site: https://www.wisegroup.se
Year Founded: 1991
WISE—(OMX)
Rev.: $85,275,413
Assets: $38,390,139
Liabilities: $25,964,952
Net Worth: $12,425,188
Earnings: $1,792,689
Emp.: 600
Fiscal Year-end: 12/31/22
Human Resouce Services
N.A.I.C.S.: 541612
Nathalie Berthelius *(Chief People & Culture Officer)*

Subsidiaries:

Talentum HR AB (1)
Andra Hotorgshuset, Sveavägen 13 12 tr, 104 22, Stockholm, Sweden
Tel.: (46) 8 505 129 00
Web Site: http://www.talentumhr.se
Sales Range: $25-49.9 Million
Emp.: 150
Human Resource & Consulting Services
N.A.I.C.S.: 541612

WISE ITECH CO., LTD.
11 13F Gwacheon pentaone G-dong 117 Gwacheon-daero 12-gil, Bundang-gu, Gwacheon, 13824, Gyeonggi-do, Korea (South)
Tel.: (82) 62461400
Web Site: https://www.wise.co.kr
Year Founded: 1990
065370—(KRS)
Rev.: $29,063,214
Assets: $37,602,953
Liabilities: $16,137,058
Net Worth: $21,465,895
Earnings: $2,968,470
Emp.: 158
Fiscal Year-end: 12/31/22
Software Development Services
N.A.I.C.S.: 541511
Jong-Hyun Kim *(CEO)*

WISE PLC
TEA Building 56 Shoreditch High Street, London, E16JJ, United Kingdom UK
Web Site: https://www.wise.com
Year Founded: 2010
WISE—(LSE)
Rev.: $1,068,038,374
Assets: $15,026,760,919
Liabilities: $14,298,535,723
Net Worth: $728,225,196
Earnings: $143,903,055
Emp.: 5,157
Fiscal Year-end: 03/31/23
Information Technology Services
N.A.I.C.S.: 541512
David Wells *(Chm)*

Subsidiaries:

TINV Ltd. (1)
17th Floor 88 Wood Street, London, EC2V 7DA, United Kingdom
Tel.: (44) 2031467040
Web Site: https://tinv.com
Financial Investment Services
N.A.I.C.S.: 551112

Wise Brasil Corretora de Cambio Ltda. (1)
Avenida Paulista 2537 Andar 10 Conj 102 Bela Vista, Sao Paulo, 01311-300, SP, Brazil
Tel.: (55) 8008782802
International Money Transfer Services
N.A.I.C.S.: 522320

WISEC GLOBAL LIMITED
NH II 2nd Floor C Block Community Centre Naraina Vihar, New Delhi, 110028, India
Tel.: (91) 2577719293
Web Site: https://www.wisecglobal.com
Year Founded: 1991
Rev.: $249
Assets: $650,035
Liabilities: $167,503
Net Worth: $482,531
Earnings: ($17,225)
Fiscal Year-end: 03/31/18
Biotechnology Product Whslr
N.A.I.C.S.: 424210

WISECHIP SEMICONDUCTOR INC.
8 Kebei Rd 2 Science Park, Chunan, 35053, Taiwan
Tel.: (886) 37587168
Web Site: https://www.wisechip.com.tw
Year Founded: 2005
5245—(TPE)
Rev.: $44,416,471
Assets: $60,310,134
Liabilities: $22,312,010
Net Worth: $37,998,124
Earnings: $5,520,839
Fiscal Year-end: 12/31/22
Semiconductor Device Mfr & Distr
N.A.I.C.S.: 334413
Jakie Wang *(Chm)*

WISEKEY INTERNATIONAL HOLDING LTD
General-Guisan Strasse 6, Postfach 3467, 6303, Zug, Switzerland
Tel.: (41) 225943000 CH
Web Site: https://www.wisekey.com
WIHN—(SWX)
Rev.: $30,918,000
Assets: $47,801,000
Liabilities: $26,717,000
Net Worth: $21,084,000
Earnings: ($15,449,000)
Emp.: 102
Fiscal Year-end: 12/31/23
Holding Company
N.A.I.C.S.: 551112
Peter Ward *(Co-CFO)*

Subsidiaries:

QV (Holdings) Ltd. (1)
Washington Mall 3rd Floor 7 Reid Street, Hamilton, HM 11, Bermuda (100%)
Tel.: (441) 2782800
Web Site: http://www.quovadisglobal.com
Data Security & Privacy Services
N.A.I.C.S.: 561621
Roman Brunner *(CEO)*

WISe.Art AG (1)
Av Louis-Casaï 58, 1216, Geneva, Switzerland
Tel.: (41) 225943000
Web Site: https://platform.wise.art
Cyber Security Services
N.A.I.C.S.: 561621

WISeCoin AG (1)
World Trade Center II Rte de Pre-Bois 29, PO Box 853, 1215, Geneva, Switzerland
Tel.: (41) 22 594 3000
Web Site: https://www.wisecoin.com
Software Services
N.A.I.C.S.: 541511
Carlos Moreira *(CEO)*

WISeKey India Private Ltd. (1)
311 3rd Floor Qutab Plaza DLF Phase-1, Gurgaon, Haryana, India
Tel.: (91) 1244789266

Cyber Security Services
N.A.I.C.S.: 561621

WISeKey Semiconductors SAS (1)
Arteparc Bachasson Bat A Rue de la Carriere de Bachasson, 13590, Meyreuil, France
Tel.: (33) 44 237 0370
Cyber Security Services
N.A.I.C.S.: 561621

WISeKey IoT Japan KK (1)
5th floor 2-25 Kandasuda-cho, Chiyoda-ku, Tokyo, Japan
Tel.: (81) 368597310
Cyber Security Services
N.A.I.C.S.: 561621

WISELINK CO., LTD.
7/F 196 Chou-Tzu Street, Neihu District, Taipei, Taiwan
Tel.: (886) 226271828
Web Site: https://wiselink.tw
8932—(TPE)
Rev.: $24,980,771
Assets: $47,252,009
Liabilities: $24,164,525
Net Worth: $23,087,484
Earnings: ($907,545)
Fiscal Year-end: 12/31/22
Textile Products Mfr
N.A.I.C.S.: 314999
P. C. Hung *(Pres)*

WISEMAN GLOBAL LIMITED
Building 2 Duoli Hi Tech Industrial Park No 9 Jinlong 1st Road, Baolong Street Longgang District, Shenzhen, 518116, Guangdong, China
Tel.: (86) 75584899169 NV
Web Site: http://wisemanglobal.cn
Year Founded: 2018
WISM—(OTCIQ)
Rev.: $552,778
Assets: $1,643,161
Liabilities: $651,316
Net Worth: $991,845
Earnings: ($590,785)
Emp.: 15
Fiscal Year-end: 12/31/20
Household Appliance Distr
N.A.I.C.S.: 423440
Lai Jinpeng *(Founder)*

WISEPOWER CO., LTD.
5F Ace Techno Tower Mullaedong 3ga, Youngdeongpo-gu, Seoul, Korea (South)
Tel.: (82) 2 2637 7550 KR
Web Site: http://eng.wisepower.co.kr
Year Founded: 1998
Mobile Device Battery Mfr
N.A.I.C.S.: 335910
Ki-Ho Park *(CEO)*

Subsidiaries:

Unidym, Inc. (1)
1244 Reamwood Ave, Sunnyvale, CA 94089
Tel.: (408) 636-7500
Web Site: http://www.unidym.com
Carbon Nanotube Based Ink & Conductive Film Products Mfr
N.A.I.C.S.: 334419

WISESOFT CO., LTD.
No 7 Wuke East 1st Road, Wuhou District, Chengdu, 610045, Sichuan, China
Tel.: (86) 2868727819
Web Site: https://www.wisesoft.com.cn
Year Founded: 2000
002253—(SSE)
Rev.: $34,521,945
Assets: $245,865,883
Liabilities: $45,092,886
Net Worth: $200,772,997
Earnings: ($8,134,467)
Emp.: 360

Fiscal Year-end: 12/31/22
Air Traffic Control Software Products
N.A.I.C.S.: 513210
Zhi Sheng You *(Chm)*

INTERNATIONAL PUBLIC

WISETECH GLOBAL LIMITED
74 O Riordan Street, PO Box 6390, Alexandria, 2015, NSW, Australia
Tel.: (61) 280012200 AU
Web Site: https://www.wisetechglobal.com
Year Founded: 1994
WTC—(ASX)
Rev.: $554,198,800
Assets: $1,803,860,100
Liabilities: $518,374,000
Net Worth: $1,285,486,100
Earnings: $143,977,700
Emp.: 2,895
Fiscal Year-end: 06/30/23
Holding Company; Logistics Industry Cloud-Based Software & Services
N.A.I.C.S.: 551112
Andrew Harrison *(Chm)*

Subsidiaries:

A.C.O. Informatica S.r.l. (1)
Via Copernico 38, 20125, Milan, MI, Italy
Tel.: (39) 02264271
Web Site: https://www.acoinformatica.it
Software Development Services
N.A.I.C.S.: 541511

ABM Data Systems Ltd. (1)
S2U3 Shanowen Business Centre Shanowen Road, Santry, Dublin, Ireland
Tel.: (353) 18527794
Software Solutions Services
N.A.I.C.S.: 541511

CMS Transport Systems Pty Ltd (1)
Level 7 5 Queens Rd, Melbourne, 3004, VIC, Australia
Tel.: (61) 39 699 7988
Web Site: https://transportsystems.com.au
Freight Logistics Services
N.A.I.C.S.: 488510
Robert Mullins *(Founder)*

Cargo Community Network Pty Ltd (1)
Unit 3a 72 O'Riordan Street, Alexandria, 2015, NSW, Australia
Tel.: (61) 29 025 1195
Air Freight Services
N.A.I.C.S.: 481112

Cargo Community Systems Ltd. (1)
Grand Canal House 1 Grand Canal Street Upper, Swords, Dublin, D04 Y7R5, Ireland
Tel.: (353) 18428255
Web Site: https://www.customsmatters.com
Software Services
N.A.I.C.S.: 541511

CargoIT i Skandinavien AB (1)
Vasagatan 28, 111 20, Stockholm, Sweden
Tel.: (46) 859480630
Web Site: https://www.cargoit.se
Logistic Services
N.A.I.C.S.: 541614
Joel Winninge *(Mng Dir)*

Cargoguide International B.V. (1)
Daalsplein 100 Level 5, 3511 SX, Utrecht, Netherlands
Tel.: (31) 308993673
Web Site: https://cargoguide.com
Logistic Services
N.A.I.C.S.: 541614

Container Chain Pty Ltd (1)
74 O'Riordan Street, Alexandria, 2015, NSW, Australia
Tel.: (61) 396733083
Web Site: https://www.containerchain.com
Logistic Services
N.A.I.C.S.: 541614
Tony Paldano *(CEO)*

Containerchain (Singapore) Pte Ltd (1)
3 Anson Road 24-03 Springleaf Tower, Singapore, 079909, Singapore
Tel.: (65) 65133171
Logistic Services

AND PRIVATE COMPANIES

N.A.I.C.S.: 541614

Containerchain Australia Pty Ltd (1)
477 Collins Street, Melbourne, 3000, VIC, Australia
Tel.: (61) 386868600
Logistic Services
N.A.I.C.S.: 541614

EXA-System Co., Ltd. (1)
6F Kinshicho Sunrise Building 2-14-7 Kotobashi, Sumida-ku, Tokyo, Japan
Tel.: (81) 356256090
Web Site: https://www.j-exa.co.jp
Emp.: 110
Information Technology Consulting Services
N.A.I.C.S.: 541512

EasyLog SAS (1)
27 rue d'Alsace, Franconville, 95130, Paris, France
Tel.: (33) 134138741
Web Site: https://www.easy-log.fr
Logistic Services
N.A.I.C.S.: 541614

Inobiz AB (1)
Vasagatan 28, SE-111 20, Stockholm, Sweden
Tel.: (46) 854545420
Web Site: https://www.inobiz.se
Data Mapping Tool Development Services
N.A.I.C.S.: 541519

Intris N.V. (1)
Wapenstilstandlaan 47, 2600, Berchem, Belgium
Tel.: (32) 33265075
Web Site: https://www.intris.be
Software Services
N.A.I.C.S.: 541511

LSP Solutions B.V. (1)
Neonstraat 16, 6718 WV, Ede, Netherlands
Tel.: (31) 882020300
Software Solutions Services
N.A.I.C.S.: 541511

Pierbridge Inc. (1)
67 Forest St Ste 288, Marlborough, MA 01752-3199
Tel.: (508) 630-1220
Web Site: https://pierbridge.com
Information Technology Services
N.A.I.C.S.: 541519
Mark Picarello *(Mng Dir)*

Ready Korea Co., Ltd. (1)
811 8F Gangnam N-Tower 129 Teheran-ro, Gangnam-gu, Seoul, 06133, Korea (South)
Tel.: (82) 234665000
Web Site: https://www.readykorea.co.kr
Information Technology Services
N.A.I.C.S.: 541519
Jitae Kim *(Mng Dir)*

Sisa Studio Informatica SA (1)
Gewerbestrasse 7, 4147, Aesch, Switzerland
Tel.: (41) 617169444
Web Site: https://www.sisa.ch
Emp.: 40
Logistic Services
N.A.I.C.S.: 541614
Roland Schumacher *(Mng Dir)*

Systema AS (1)
Epicenter Edvard Storms gate 2, 0166, Oslo, Norway
Tel.: (47) 22660660
Web Site: https://www.systema.no
Emp.: 10
Logistic Services
N.A.I.C.S.: 541614
Birgit Vegheim *(Mng Dir)*

Taric S.A.U. (1)
Boix y Morer 6-6, 28003, Madrid, Spain
Tel.: (34) 915541006
Web Site: https://www.taric.es
Emp.: 80
Logistic Services
N.A.I.C.S.: 541614

Taric Trans S.L. (1)
Antoni Bell 2, Sant Cugat del Valles, 08174, Barcelona, Spain
Tel.: (34) 931740020
Web Site: https://www.tarictrans.com
Logistic Services
N.A.I.C.S.: 541614

Ulukom Bilgisayar Yazilim Donanim Danismanlik ve Ticaret A.S. (1)
Fatih Sultan Mehmet Mah Poligon Cad Buyaka 2 sitesi 3 Blok No 8C, Ic kapi No 1 Umraniye, 34805, Istanbul, Turkiye
Tel.: (90) 2166803535
Web Site: https://www.ulukom.com.tr
Software Development Services
N.A.I.C.S.: 541511

WiseTech Academy Pty Ltd (1)
PO Box 6390, Alexandria, 2015, NSW, Australia
Tel.: (61) 280012332
Web Site: https://wisetechacademy.com
Software Development Services
N.A.I.C.S.: 541511

WiseTech Global (Australia) Pty. Ltd. (1)
74 O'Riordan Street, PO Box 6390, Alexandria, 2015, NSW, Australia **(100%)**
Tel.: (61) 280012200
Web Site: http://www.wisetechglobal.com
Logistics Industry Cloud-Based Software & Services
N.A.I.C.S.: 541511

WiseTech Global (HK) Ltd. (1)
21st Floor Edinburgh Tower The Landmark 15 Queens Road, Central, China (Hong Kong)
Tel.: (852) 22518667
Software Development Services
N.A.I.C.S.: 541511

WiseTech Global (Japan) K.K. (1)
Fukken Kaikan Building 5-1-21 Kitanagasadori 502 503, Chuo-ku, Kobe, 650-0012, Japan
Tel.: (81) 783411560
Logistic Services
N.A.I.C.S.: 541614

WiseTech Global (NZ) Ltd. (1)
PO Box 76029, Manukau, Auckland, 2241, New Zealand
Tel.: (64) 92716993
Software Solutions Services
N.A.I.C.S.: 541511

WiseTech Global (Pty) Ltd. (1)
3rd Floor Allendale Building Magwa Crescent West, Waterfall City Midrand, Johannesburg, 2090, South Africa **(100%)**
Tel.: (27) 105918179
Web Site: https://www.wisetechglobal.com
Logistics Industry Cloud-Based Software & Services
N.A.I.C.S.: 518210
Jessica Schneiderman *(Mgr-Delivery)*

WiseTech Global (SG) Pte Ltd (1)
The Great Room One George Street, Singapore, 049145, Singapore
Tel.: (65) 68174790
Software Solutions Services
N.A.I.C.S.: 541511

WiseTech Global (Taiwan) Ltd. (1)
10F No 221 Section 4 ZhongXiao E Road, Taipei, 106, Taiwan
Tel.: (886) 223323113
Web Site: https://wisetechglobal.co
Information Technology Services
N.A.I.C.S.: 541519

WiseTech Global (US) Inc. (1)
1051 E Woodfield Rd, Schaumburg, IL 60173 **(100%)**
Tel.: (847) 364-5600
Web Site: https://www.wisetechglobal.com
Logistics Industry Cloud-Based Software & Services
N.A.I.C.S.: 541511

WiseTech Global FZ-LLC (1)
EO-08 DIC Business Centre Ground Floor Building 01, Dubai Internet City, Dubai, United Arab Emirates
Tel.: (971) 45808159
Software Development Services
N.A.I.C.S.: 541511

X Ware Aktiebolag (1)
Vasagatan 28, 111 20, Stockholm, Sweden
Tel.: (46) 854542000
Web Site: https://www.xware.se
Software Development Services
N.A.I.C.S.: 541511

Jonas Ericsson *(CEO & CTO)*

znet group GmbH (1)
Hagenauer Strasse 47, 65203, Wiesbaden, Germany
Tel.: (49) 6114485760
Web Site: https://www.znet-group.com
Software Services
N.A.I.C.S.: 541511
Werner Tholl *(Mng Dir)*

WISEWAY LOGISTICS PTY. LTD.
39-43 Warren Avenue, Bankstown, 2200, NSW, Australia
Tel.: (61) 297907888 AU
Web Site: http://www.wiseway.com.au
Rev.: $12,294,293
Assets: $13,957,804
Liabilities: $12,578,974
Net Worth: $1,378,830
Earnings: $907,110
Fiscal Year-end: 06/30/18
Logistics Management Services
N.A.I.C.S.: 541614

Subsidiaries:

Four Seasons Pty. Ltd. (1)
9-11 Platinum Street, Crestmead, 4132, QLD, Australia
Tel.: (61) 738033755
Web Site: http://www.fourseasonco.com.au
Animal Nutrition Product Distr
N.A.I.C.S.: 424590
Tania Seery *(Mgr)*

WISHBONE GOLD PLC
Suite 16 Watergardens 5 Waterport Wharf, GX11 1AA, Gibraltar, Gibraltar
Tel.: (350) 714168167
Web Site: https://www.wishbonegold.com
WSBN—(AIM)
Assets: $9,108,276
Liabilities: $1,155,948
Net Worth: $7,952,328
Earnings: ($1,616,756)
Fiscal Year-end: 12/31/23
Gold Exploration Services
N.A.I.C.S.: 212220
Richard O'Dell Poulden *(Chm & CEO)*

WISHER INDUSTRIAL CO., LTD.
6F No 62-5 Xining North Rd, Taipei, 103, Taiwan
Tel.: (886) 225522174
Web Site: https://www.wisher.com.tw
Year Founded: 1972
1465—(TAI)
Rev.: $19,044,605
Assets: $63,653,126
Liabilities: $9,586,121
Net Worth: $54,067,005
Earnings: $1,886,262
Fiscal Year-end: 12/31/23
Polyester Woven Fabrics Mfr & Distr
N.A.I.C.S.: 332999
Chian-Chun Chen *(Chm, Pres & Gen Mgr)*

WISHPOND TECHNOLOGIES LTD.
422 Richards St Suite 170, PO Box 111, Vancouver, V6B 2Z4, BC, Canada
Tel.: (416) 865-7878
Year Founded: 2018
WISH—(OTCIQ)
Rev.: $6,165,945
Assets: $7,110,596
Liabilities: $3,935,472
Net Worth: $3,175,124
Earnings: ($1,733,136)
Emp.: 130
Fiscal Year-end: 12/31/20

WISR FINANCE PTY LTD

Asset Management Services
N.A.I.C.S.: 523940
Jordan Gutierrez *(COO)*

WISOL CO., LTD
531-7 Gajang-ro, Osan, 18103, Gyeonggi-do, Korea (South)
Tel.: (82) 7078372730
Web Site: https://www.wisol.co.kr
Year Founded: 2008
122990—(KRS)
Rev.: $265,294,125
Assets: $307,862,890
Liabilities: $45,176,286
Net Worth: $262,686,603
Earnings: ($11,333,518)
Emp.: 491
Fiscal Year-end: 12/31/22
Electronic Components Mfr
N.A.I.C.S.: 334419

WISON ENGINEERING SERVICES CO., LTD.
Room 5408 54th Floor Central Plaza 18 Harbour Road, Wanchai, China (Hong Kong)
Tel.: (852) 21164313
Web Site: http://www.wison-engineering.com
Year Founded: 2004
2236—(HKG)
Rev.: $654,092,712
Assets: $1,255,673,718
Liabilities: $894,059,338
Net Worth: $361,614,380
Earnings: ($168,112,994)
Emp.: 1,370
Fiscal Year-end: 12/31/22
Chemicals Mfr
N.A.I.C.S.: 325998
Zhiyong Li *(CFO)*

Subsidiaries:

Wison (Yangzhou) Chemical Machinery Co., Ltd. (1)
Zhaojiahe Road Hanjiang Industry Park, Yangzhou, 225127, Jiangsu, China
Tel.: (86) 51487845000
Construction Management Services
N.A.I.C.S.: 541330

Wison Engineering Limited (1)
No 699 Zhongke Road Zhangjiang Pudong, Shanghai, 201210, China
Tel.: (86) 2120306000
Construction Management Services
N.A.I.C.S.: 541330
Qu Song *(CEO)*

Wison Petrochemicals (NA), LLC (1)
2925 Briarpark Dr Ste 675, Houston, TX 77042
Tel.: (832) 925-8818
Engineeering Services
N.A.I.C.S.: 541330

WISR FINANCE PTY LTD
Level 4 55 Harrington Street, Sydney, 2000, NSW, Australia
Tel.: (61) 1300992007
Web Site: https://www.wisr.com.au
Year Founded: 2006
WZR—(ASX)
Rev.: $21,127,822
Assets: $361,207,229
Liabilities: $305,845,175
Net Worth: $55,362,054
Earnings: ($13,515,073)
Fiscal Year-end: 06/30/21
Renting Services
N.A.I.C.S.: 522310
John Nantes *(Chm)*

Subsidiaries:

Undacar Parts (QLD) Pty Ltd. (1)
24 Container St, Brisbane, 4173, QLD, Australia
Tel.: (61) 738903900

WISR FINANCE PTY LTD

Wisr Finance Pty Ltd—(Continued)
Sales Range: $25-49.9 Million
Emp.: 4
Automotive Part Whslr
N.A.I.C.S.: 441330

Undacar Parts (TAS) Pty Ltd. (1)
107 Grove Rd, Glenorchy, 7010, TAS, Australia
Tel.: (61) 362731033
Sales Range: $50-74.9 Million
Emp.: 3
Automotive Part Whslr
N.A.I.C.S.: 423120

Undacar Parts (WA) Pty Ltd. (1)
62 Division St, Welshpool, 6106, WA, Australia
Tel.: (61) 894516511
Sales Range: $25-49.9 Million
Emp.: 4
Automotive Part Whslr
N.A.I.C.S.: 441330

WISTIL S.A.
Ul Majkowska 13, 62-800, Kalisz, Poland
Tel.: (48) 62 768 61 00
Web Site: http://www.wistil.pl
Fabric & Knitwear Mfr
N.A.I.C.S.: 313240
Mieczyslaw Kedzierski (Chm-Mgmt Bd & CEO)

WISTRON CORPORATION
158 Singshan Rd, Neihu, Taipei, Taiwan
Tel.: (886) 266169999   TW
Year Founded: 2001
3231—(TAI)
Rev.: $27,109,933,621
Assets: $14,144,726,136
Liabilities: $10,118,738,205
Net Worth: $4,025,987,931
Earnings: $571,093,550
Emp.: 50,538
Fiscal Year-end: 12/31/23
Computer Equipment Mfr
N.A.I.C.S.: 334118
Simon Hsien-Ming Lin (Chm, Chm, Chief Strategy Officer & Chief Strategy Officer)

Subsidiaries:

AOpen International (Shanghai) Co., Ltd (1)
Room 506 Qilai Building No 889 Yishan Road, Shanghai, China
Tel.: (86) 2162258622
Web Site: http://www.aopen.com.cn
Computer Hardware Mfr
N.A.I.C.S.: 332510

ICT Service Management Solutions (India) Private Limited (1)
No 93 Digital Park Rd Goraguntepalya, Yeshwanthpur, Bengaluru, 560 022, India
Tel.: (91) 8066506788
Web Site: https://www.ictsms.in
Information Technology Services
N.A.I.C.S.: 541519

International Standards Laboratory Corp. (1)
No 120 Lane 180 Hsin Ho Rd, Iung-Tan Dist, Taoyuan, 325, Taiwan
Tel.: (886) 32638888
Web Site: https://www.isl.com.tw
Automotive Component Mfr & Distr
N.A.I.C.S.: 336390

Kaohsiung Opto-Electronics Inc. (1)
2 East 13th St Kaohsiung Cianjhen Technology Industrial Park, Kaohsiung, 806, Taiwan
Tel.: (886) 7 821 7000
Web Site: https://www.koe.j-display.com
LCD Display Mfr
N.A.I.C.S.: 334419
Hideki Matsuoka (Pres & CEO)

Subsidiary (Non-US):

KOE Asia Pte Ltd. (2)
7 Tampines Grande Unit 02-03 Hitachi Square, Singapore, 528736, Singapore
Tel.: (65) 6636 2374
Web Site: http://www.koe.j-display.com
LCD Display Mfr
N.A.I.C.S.: 334419

KOE Europe Ltd. (2)
Cavendish House Bourne End Business Park, Bourne End, SL8 5AS, United Kingdom
Tel.: (44) 1628 523222
Web Site: http://www.koe-europe.com
LCD Display Distr
N.A.I.C.S.: 423690
Raymond Sun (Mng Dir)

SMS (Kunshan) Co., Ltd. (1)
No 278 Xiongying Rd, Kunshan, 215300, Jiangsu, China
Tel.: (86) 51257033999
Personal Computer Mfr
N.A.I.C.S.: 334111

SMS InfoComm (Czech) s.r.o. (1)
Vlastimila Pecha 1269/10, Cernovice, 627 00, Brno, Czech Republic
Tel.: (420) 77 735 4470
Web Site: https://smsinfocomm.jobs.cz
Emp.: 370
Electrical Repair Shop Services
N.A.I.C.S.: 811114

SMS InfoComm (Singapore) Pte. Ltd (1)
37A Tampines St 92 03-00, Singapore, 528886, Singapore
Tel.: (65) 67831588
Sales Range: $25-49.9 Million
Emp.: 40
Computer Hardware Mfr
N.A.I.C.S.: 332510

SMS InfoComm Corporation (1)
4051 N TX-121, Grapevine, TX 76051
Tel.: (972) 906-7800
Web Site: https://www.smsinfocomm.com
Communication Devices Mfr
N.A.I.C.S.: 334290
Jerry Wang (Gen Mgr)

Wistron Europe Holding Cooperatie U.A. (1)
Siriusstraat 45, 5015 BT, Tilburg, Netherlands
Tel.: (31) 13 4647500
Circuit Board Assembly Mfr
N.A.I.C.S.: 334418

Wistron InfoComm (Philippines) Corp. (1)
4 Rizal Highway Corner Aim High Ave Subic Bay Ind Park II, Subic, 2200, Philippines   (100%)
Tel.: (63) 472527740
Sales Range: $125-149.9 Million
Emp.: 500
Software & Computers Mfr
N.A.I.C.S.: 513210

Wistron InfoComm (Shanghai) Corporation (1)
5th Floor Building 39, No 333 Qin Jiang Road, Shanghai, 200233, China   (100%)
Tel.: (86) 2164952080
Software Research & Development, Design & Consultation
N.A.I.C.S.: 513210

Wistron InfoComm (Zhongshan) Co., Ltd (1)
Wistron Infocomm In And Out Affairs No 38, Technology Ave Zh Zone, Zhongshan, 528400, Guangdong, China
Tel.: (86) 76023082382
Circuit Board & Electronic Component Mfr
N.A.I.C.S.: 334418

Wistron InfoComm Technology (America) Corporation (1)
1394 Eberhardt Rd, Grapevine, TX 76504   (100%)
Tel.: (254) 298-4856
Computer Mfr
N.A.I.C.S.: 334111

Wistron Information Technology & Services Corporation (1)
Rm 1501 15F No 136 Section 3 Jen-Ai Road, Taipei, 10657, Taiwan   (52.67%)
Tel.: (886) 227079899
Web Site: http://www.wistronits.com
Sales Range: $150-199.9 Million
Emp.: 300
Information Technology & Software Development Services
N.A.I.C.S.: 513210

Wistron K.K. (1)
2-6-2 Akanehama, Narashino-shi, Chiba, 275-0024, Japan
Tel.: (81) 474552071
Circuit Board Mfr
N.A.I.C.S.: 334418

Wistron Mexico S.A. de C.V. (1)
Calle Baudelio Perez Mucharras Number 420 Oriente, Col Zaragoza, 32570, Ciudad Juarez, Chihuahua, Mexico   (100%)
Tel.: (52) 6566494400
Software & Computers Mfr
N.A.I.C.S.: 513210

Wistron NeWeb Corporation (1)
20 Park Avenue II Hsinchu Science Park, Hsin-chu, 308, Taiwan
Tel.: (886) 36667799
Web Site: http://www.wnc.com.tw
Rev.: $3,097,772,307
Assets: $2,142,350,836
Liabilities: $1,480,367,505
Net Worth: $661,983,331
Earnings: $101,518,334
Emp.: 12,279
Fiscal Year-end: 12/31/2022
Wireless Communications Components Mfr
N.A.I.C.S.: 334290
Haydn Hsieh (Chm & Chief Strategy Officer)

WISYNCO GROUP LTD.
Lakes Pen St, Catherine, Kingston, Jamaica
Tel.: (876) 6659000
Web Site: https://www.wisynco.com
Year Founded: 1965
WISYNCO—(JAM)
Rev.: $220,806,024
Assets: $155,219,027
Liabilities: $50,742,136
Net Worth: $104,476,891
Earnings: $21,321,762
Fiscal Year-end: 06/30/21
Footwear Mfr
N.A.I.C.S.: 316210
William Mahfood (Chm)

WITAN INVESTMENT TRUST PLC
14 Queen Annes Gate, London, SW1H 9AA, United Kingdom
Tel.: (44) 1268448646
Web Site: https://www.witan.com
WTAN—(LSE)
Rev.: $123,879,731
Assets: $3,000,641,305
Liabilities: $386,747,900
Net Worth: $2,613,893,406
Earnings: $62,304,413
Emp.: 7
Fiscal Year-end: 12/31/20
Investment Management Service
N.A.I.C.S.: 523940
Andrew L. C. Bell (CEO)

WITBE SA
Les Collines de l'Arche Immeuble Opera E La Defense, 92057, Paris, France
Tel.: (33) 147677777
Web Site: http://www.witbe.net
Year Founded: 2000
ALWIT—(EUR)
Sales Range: $10-24.9 Million
Business Monitoring Services
N.A.I.C.S.: 541840
Yoann Hinard (COO)

WITEG LABORTECHNIK GMBH

INTERNATIONAL PUBLIC

Am Bildacker 16, Wertheim, 97877, Germany
Tel.: (49) 934293010
Web Site: http://www.witeg.de
Rev.: $12,867,802
Emp.: 70
Laboratory Equipment Mfr
N.A.I.C.S.: 334516
Elmar Swiegot (Co-Mng Dir)

WITHSECURE CORPORATION
Tammasaarenkatu 7, PO Box 24, 00181, Helsinki, Finland
Tel.: (358) 925200700
Web Site: https://www.f-secure.com
Year Founded: 1988
FSECURE—(HEL)
Rev.: $243,388,133
Assets: $256,857,809
Liabilities: $171,571,511
Net Worth: $85,286,298
Earnings: $3,768,329
Emp.: 1,696
Fiscal Year-end: 12/31/19
Software Encryption & Security Services
N.A.I.C.S.: 541511
Risto Siilasmaa (Founder & Chm)

Subsidiaries:

F-Secure (UK) Ltd (1)
Cavendish House Bourne End Business Park, Wooburn Green, Bourne End, SL8 5AS, Bucks, United Kingdom
Tel.: (44) 8458903300
Web Site: http://www.f-secure.co.uk
Sales Range: $25-49.9 Million
Emp.: 15
Software Encryption & Security Services
N.A.I.C.S.: 541511

F-Secure AB (1)
Gardsvagen 18, 169 70, Solna, Sweden
Tel.: (46) 850744000
Web Site: http://www.f-secure.se
Sales Range: $25-49.9 Million
Emp.: 20
Software Encryption & Security Services
N.A.I.C.S.: 541511

F-Secure BV BA (1)
Interleuvenlaan 62 Zone 2 Bus 56, Heverlee, 3001, Leuven, Belgium
Tel.: (32) 16394735
Software Development Services
N.A.I.C.S.: 541511

F-Secure Belgie (1)
Luchthavenlaan 27 / 48 - bus 48, 1800, Vilvoorde, Belgium
Tel.: (32) 16394735
Web Site: http://www.f-secure.com
Emp.: 2
Security Software Development Services
N.A.I.C.S.: 541511

F-Secure Danmark A/S (1)
Rued Langgaards Vej 8 2nd Floor, 2300, Copenhagen, Denmark
Tel.: (45) 70261595
Web Site: http://www.f-secure.com
Sales Range: $25-49.9 Million
Emp.: 4
Software Development Services
N.A.I.C.S.: 541511

F-Secure GmbH (1)
Kistlerhofstr 172c, 81379, Munich, Germany
Tel.: (49) 897874670
Web Site: http://www.f-secure.com
Sales Range: $25-49.9 Million
Emp.: 15
Software Encryption & Security Services
N.A.I.C.S.: 541511

F-Secure Inc. (1)
470 Ramona St, Palo Alto, CA 94301
Tel.: (408) 938-6700
Web Site: http://www.f-secure.com
Sales Range: $25-49.9 Million
Emp.: 25
Software Encryption & Security Services
N.A.I.C.S.: 541511

F-Secure India Pvt Ltd (1)
Office No 117 6-3-1192/1/1 Block 2 212 2nd

AND PRIVATE COMPANIES

Fl White House Kundanbagh, Begumpe,
Hyderabad, 500016, India
Tel.: (91) 4040133503
Web Site: http://www.f-secure.co.in
Security Software Development Services
N.A.I.C.S.: 541511
Rahul Kumar *(Mgr-India & SAARC)*

F-Secure KK (1)
KDX Shinbashi Building 2nd Floor 2-2-9
Shinbashi, Minato-ku, Tokyo, 105-0004,
Japan
Tel.: (81) 34 578 7700
Cyber Security Services
N.A.I.C.S.: 541519

F-Secure Malaysia (M) Sdn Bhd (1)
Unit 17 01 Level 17 Mercu 3 No 3 Jalan
Bangsar, KL Eco City, 59200, Kuala Lumpur, Malaysia
Tel.: (60) 322980999
Web Site: http://www.f-secure.com
Emp.: 200
Security Software Development Services
N.A.I.C.S.: 541511

F-Secure Norge (1)
Strandveien 15, 1366, Lysaker, Norway
Tel.: (47) 21 38 75 20
Web Site: http://www.f-secure.com
Software Development Services
N.A.I.C.S.: 541511

F-Secure Pte Ltd (1)
21 Science Park Road 02-01 The Aquarius,
Singapore, 117628, Singapore
Tel.: (65) 81184552
Security Software Development Consulting
Services
N.A.I.C.S.: 541690

F-Secure Pty Ltd (1)
Suite 1 Level 12 309 Kent Street, North
Sydney, 2000, Australia
Tel.: (61) 299472986
Web Site: http://www.f-secure.com
Security Software Development Services
N.A.I.C.S.: 541511

F-Secure Pvt Ltd (1)
1st Floor Southern Park D-2 District Centre,
Saket, New Delhi, 110017, India
Tel.: (91) 116 639 4490
Software Development Services
N.A.I.C.S.: 541511

F-Secure SARL (1)
Immeuble Seine Way Batiment G 12-14
Rue Louis Bleriot, Espace Media - Le Technoparc, 92500, Rueil-Malmaison, Cedex,
France
Tel.: (33) 141292323
Web Site: http://www.f-secure.de
Sales Range: $25-49.9 Million
Emp.: 10
Software Encryption & Security Services
N.A.I.C.S.: 541511

F-Secure SDC SAS (1)
9 Rue Raymond Manaud, 33520, Bruges,
France
Tel.: (33) 557924720
Sales Range: $25-49.9 Million
Emp.: 80
Security Software Development Services
N.A.I.C.S.: 541511

F-Secure Sp.z.o.o. (1)
Skylight/17 pietro Ul Zlota 59, 00-120, Warsaw, Poland
Tel.: (48) 225702021
Web Site: http://www.f-secure.com
Sales Range: $25-49.9 Million
Emp.: 6
Security Software Development Services
N.A.I.C.S.: 541511

F-Secure eStore GmbH (1)
Kistlerhofstr 172c, 81379, Munich, Germany
Tel.: (49) 89 787 4670
Cyber Security Services
N.A.I.C.S.: 541519

WITHTECH INC.
300 Techno 2-Ro, Yuseong-Gu, Daejeon, Korea (South)
Tel.: (82) 429367117
Web Site: https://www.withtech.co.kr
Year Founded: 2003

348350—(KRS)
Rev.: $55,688,761
Assets: $113,185,567
Liabilities: $29,153,984
Net Worth: $84,031,583
Earnings: $9,392,184
Emp.: 226
Fiscal Year-end: 12/31/22
Semiconductor Testing Equipment
Mfr
N.A.I.C.S.: 334515
Seoungkyo Yoo *(CEO)*

WITHUS CORP.
KF Center Building 4F 3-6-2 Bingocho, Chuo-ku, Osaka, 541-0051, Japan
Tel.: (81) 662644200
Web Site: https://www.with-us.co.jp
Year Founded: 1976
9696—(TKS)
Rev.: $170,706,800
Assets: $181,722,640
Liabilities: $124,726,800
Net Worth: $56,995,840
Earnings: $12,429,120
Emp.: 672
Fiscal Year-end: 03/31/22
Education Services
N.A.I.C.S.: 611710

WITHUS PHARMACEUTICAL CO., LTD.
3rd 4th 5th floor Withers Building 9
Dongsan-ro 12-gi, Seocho-Gu, Seoul,
Korea (South)
Tel.: (82) 234867474
Web Site: https://www.withuspharm.com
Year Founded: 2004
330350—(KRS)
Rev.: $49,609,848
Assets: $91,575,809
Liabilities: $27,887,079
Net Worth: $63,688,730
Earnings: $1,901,519
Emp.: 196
Fiscal Year-end: 12/31/22
Medical & Dental Instrument Mfr
N.A.I.C.S.: 339112
Kwangyoung Kwon *(CFO)*

WITHUS TECHNOLOGY CORP.
1004 Girin-daero, Deokjin-gu, Jeonju,
561330, Jeollabuk-do, Korea (South)
Tel.: (82) 6322862014
Web Site: http://www.withusco.kr
Year Founded: 1999
Ball Bearing Mfr
N.A.I.C.S.: 332991

WITTCHEN SA
Palmiry Gdanska 60 Street, 05-152,
Czosnow, Poland
Tel.: (48) 222668800
Web Site: https://www.wittchen.com
Year Founded: 1990
WTN—(WAR)
Rev.: $118,674,542
Assets: $85,862,805
Liabilities: $30,815,041
Net Worth: $55,047,764
Earnings: $15,571,138
Fiscal Year-end: 12/31/23
Clothing Apparel & Accessory Distr
N.A.I.C.S.: 458110
Jedrzej Wittchen *(Founder)*

WITTMANN KUNSTSTOFFGERATE GMBH
Lichtblaustrasse 10, 1220, Vienna,
Austria
Tel.: (43) 431250390
Web Site: http://www.wittmann-group.com
Year Founded: 1976

Plastics Manufacturing Machinery Mfr
N.A.I.C.S.: 333248
Michael Wittmann *(Mng Dir & CEO)*

Subsidiaries:

BATTENFELD Schweiz AG (1)
Javastrasse 13, 8604, Volketswil, Switzerland
Tel.: (41) 44 908 65 65
Web Site: http://www.battenfeld.ch
Industrial Machinery Distr
N.A.I.C.S.: 423830

BATTENFELD Sverige AB (1)
Skallebackavagen 29, 302 41, Halmstad,
Sweden
Tel.: (46) 35 15 59 50
Web Site: http://www.battenfeld.se
Industrial Machinery Distr
N.A.I.C.S.: 423830
Hakan Tjellander *(Mgr-Svc)*

Battenfeld Polska Injection Moulding
Technology Sp. z o.o. (1)
ul Radziejowicka 108 Adamowizna 151, 05-
825, Grodzisk Mazowiecki, Poland
Tel.: (48) 22 724 38 07
Web Site: http://www.battenfeld.pl
Industrial Machinery Distr
N.A.I.C.S.: 423830

OOO WITTMANN BATTENFELD (1)
Altufyevskoye shosse house 48 block 1 office 19, 127566, Moscow, Russia
Tel.: (7) 4959830245
Web Site: http://www.battenfeld.ru
Industrial Machinery Distr
N.A.I.C.S.: 423830
Nikolay Merkulov *(Project Mgr)*

WITTMANN BATTENFELD (Malaysia) Sdn Bhd (1)
No 16 Jalan Bandar Limabelas Pusat Bandar, Puchong, 47100, Selangor, Malaysia
Tel.: (60) 3 5882 6028
Web Site: http://www.wittmann-group.com
Emp.: 6
Industrial Machinery Distr
N.A.I.C.S.: 423830
David Tan *(Mgr)*

WITTMANN BATTENFELD (Shanghai) Co., Ltd. (1)
1908-1909 Building 915 Oasis Middlering
Business Centre, No 915 Zhenbei Road,
Shanghai, 200333, China
Tel.: (86) 21 5489 2121
Web Site: http://www.wittmann-group.cn
Industrial Machinery Mfr
N.A.I.C.S.: 333248
Terry Liu *(Deputy Gen Mgr)*

WITTMANN BATTENFELD (Singapore) Pte. Ltd. (1)
No 48 Toh Guan Road East 03-123 Enterprise Hub, Singapore, 608586, Singapore
Tel.: (65) 6795 8829
Industrial Machinery Distr
N.A.I.C.S.: 423830

WITTMANN BATTENFELD (Taiwan)
Co. Ltd. (1)
No 16 Gongyequ 36th Rd, Xitun Dist, Taichung, 40768, Taiwan
Tel.: (886) 423595158
Web Site: http://www.wittmann-group.com
Industrial Machinery Distr
N.A.I.C.S.: 423830

WITTMANN BATTENFELD (Thailand)
Co. Ltd. (1)
294/2 Soi RK Office Park Romklao Rd,
Klong Sam Prawet Lad Krabang, Bangkok,
10520, Thailand
Tel.: (66) 2 184 9653
Web Site: http://www.wittmann-group.com
Emp.: 8
Industrial Machinery Distr
N.A.I.C.S.: 423830
Pitthaya Tubkuanchum *(Gen Mgr)*

WITTMANN BATTENFELD Australia
Pty Ltd (1)
Unit 9 42 Garden Boulevard, Dingley, 3172,
VIC, Australia
Tel.: (61) 3 9551 4200
Web Site: http://www.wittmann-group.com.au

WITTMANN KUNSTSTOFFGERATE GMBH

Emp.: 8
Industrial Machinery Mfr
N.A.I.C.S.: 333248
Peter Lucas *(Mng Dir)*

WITTMANN BATTENFELD Benelux
NV (1)
Nieuwlandlaan 1A Industriepark B190,
3200, Aarschot, Belgium
Tel.: (32) 16 551180
Web Site: http://www.wittmann-group.be
Industrial Machinery Distr
N.A.I.C.S.: 423830
Vander Motten *(Gen Mgr)*

WITTMANN BATTENFELD Bulgarien
EOOD (1)
Hr Smirnenski Str 24, 4147, Kalekovets,
Bulgaria
Tel.: (359) 3124 2284
Industrial Machinery Distr
N.A.I.C.S.: 423830

WITTMANN BATTENFELD CZ spol.
S.r.o. (1)
Male Nepodrice 67, 397 01, Pisek, Czech
Republic
Tel.: (420) 382 272 995
Web Site: http://www.wittmann-group.cz
Industrial Machinery Mfr
N.A.I.C.S.: 333248

WITTMANN BATTENFELD France
SAS (1)
Centr'Alp 365 Rue de Corporat, 38430,
Moirans, France
Tel.: (33) 4 76 310 880
Web Site: http://www.wittmann-group.fr
Industrial Machinery Mfr
N.A.I.C.S.: 333248

WITTMANN BATTENFELD India pvt
Ltd. (1)
1 & 2 Arumugam Nagar, Chinna Porur,
Chennai, 600 116, India
Tel.: (91) 44 42077009
Web Site: http://www.wittmann-group.in
Industrial Machinery Distr
N.A.I.C.S.: 423830
Aravindh Deva *(Engr-Sls)*

WITTMANN BATTENFELD Italia
Srl (1)
Via Donizetti 9, Solaro, 20020, Milan, Italy
Tel.: (39) 02 969810 1
Web Site: http://www.wittmann-group.it
Industrial Machinery Mfr
N.A.I.C.S.: 333248

WITTMANN BATTENFELD Maquilas,
Inc. (1)
11601 Pellicano Dr C7, El Paso, TX 79936
Tel.: (915) 594-7400
Emp.: 8
Industrial Machinery Distr
N.A.I.C.S.: 423830
Hector Gandara *(Gen Mgr)*

WITTMANN BATTENFELD Mexico
S.A. de C.V. (1)
Av Rafael Sesma Huerta No 21 Parque Industrial Finsa, 76246, El Marques, Queretaro, Mexico
Tel.: (52) 4421017100
Web Site: http://www.wittmann-group.com
Industrial Machinery Mfr
N.A.I.C.S.: 333248

WITTMANN BATTENFELD Plastik
Makineleri Ltd. Sti. (1)
Kucukyali is merkezi Girne Mahallesi Irmak
Sokak F Blok No 20, Maltepe, 34852, Istanbul, Turkiye
Tel.: (90) 216 550 93 14
Web Site: http://www.wittmann.com.tr
Industrial Machinery Distr
N.A.I.C.S.: 423830

WITTMANN BATTENFELD
S.R.L. (1)
B-dul Iuliu Maniu Nr 7 Corp T Et 2 Sector 6,
Bucharest, 61072, Romania
Tel.: (40) 720 227 255
Web Site: http://www.wittmann-group.ro
Emp.: 20
Industrial Machinery Mfr
N.A.I.C.S.: 333248
Bogdan Nestor *(Mng Dir)*

WITTMANN BATTENFELD SPAIN
S.L. (1)

WITTMANN KUNSTSTOFFGERATE GMBH

Wittmann Kunststoffgerate GmbH—(Continued)

Pol Ind Plans d arau C/Thomas Alva Edison Nr 1, La Pobla de Claramunt, 08787, Barcelona, Spain
Tel.: (34) 93 808 7860
Industrial Machinery Distr
N.A.I.C.S.: 423830

WITTMANN BATTENFELD UK Ltd (1)
Sanders Road Finedon Road Industrial Estate, Wellingborough, NN8 4NL, Northants, United Kingdom
Tel.: (44) 1933 27 57 77
Web Site: http://www.wittmann-group.co.uk
Emp.: 21
Industrial Machinery Mfr
N.A.I.C.S.: 333248
Barry Hill *(Mng Dir)*

WITTMANN BATTENFELD do Brasil Ltda. (1)
Av Francisco de Angelis 152/166 -Jd Okita, Campinas, Sao Paulo, 13043-030, Brazil
Tel.: (55) 19 2511 8150
Web Site: http://www.wittmann-group.com.br
Industrial Machinery Mfr
N.A.I.C.S.: 333248

WITTMANN Canada Inc. (1)
35 Leek Crescent, Richmond Hill, L4B 4C2, ON, Canada
Tel.: (905) 887-5355
Web Site: http://www.wittmann-group.ca
Industrial Machinery Distr
N.A.I.C.S.: 423830
Amir-Peiman Babolmorad *(Coord-Project)*

WITTMANN Kunststofftechnik AG (1)
Uznacherstrasse 18, 8722, Kaltbrunn, Switzerland
Tel.: (41) 55293 40 93
Web Site: http://www.wittmann-group.ch
Industrial Machinery Distr
N.A.I.C.S.: 423830

WITTMANN Robot (Kunshan) Co., Ltd. (1)
No 1 Wittmann Rd, Dianshanhu, Kunshan, 215345, Jiangsu, China
Tel.: (86) 512 5748 3388
Industrial Machinery Distr
N.A.I.C.S.: 423830

WITTMANN Robot Systeme GmbH (1)
Lagerstrasse 49, 64807, Dieburg, Germany
Tel.: (49) 9128 7099 800
Industrial Machinery Distr
N.A.I.C.S.: 423830

WITTMANN Robottechnikai Kft. (1)
Eke u 6 Kozpont es gyarto uzem, 9200, Mosonmagyarovar, Hungary
Tel.: (36) 96 577470
Industrial Machinery Distr
N.A.I.C.S.: 423830

Wittmann Battenfeld GmbH (1)
Wiener Neustadter Strasse 81, Kottingbrunn, 2542, Austria
Tel.: (43) 22524040
Web Site: http://www.battenfeld-imt.com
Sales Range: $75-99.9 Million
Emp.: 440
Injection Molding Machine Mfr
N.A.I.C.S.: 333248
Rainer Weingraber *(CEO & Mng Dir)*

Subsidiary (Non-US):

Wittmann Battenfeld GmbH & Co. KG (2)
Am Tower 2, 90475, Nuremberg, Germany
Tel.: (49) 912870990
Web Site: http://www.wittmann-group.com
Sales Range: $25-49.9 Million
Emp.: 100
Injection Molding Machine Mfr
N.A.I.C.S.: 333248
Klaus Ehlig *(Mng Dir)*

Wittmann Inc. (1)
1 Technology Pk Dr, Torrington, CT 06790
Tel.: (860) 496-9603
Web Site: http://www.wittmann-ct.com
Sales Range: $25-49.9 Million
Emp.: 80
Plastics Manufacturing Machinery Mfr

N.A.I.C.S.: 333248
David Preusse *(Pres)*

WITZ CORPORATION
12F Meiji Yasuda Life Nagoya Building 1-1 Shin-Sakae-cho, Naka-Ku, Nagoya, 460-0004, Japan
Tel.: (81) 522201218
Web Site: https://www.witz-inc.co.jp
Year Founded: 1997
4440—(TKS)
Rev.: $21,626,940
Assets: $22,161,860
Liabilities: $6,742,480
Net Worth: $15,419,380
Earnings: $1,710,500
Fiscal Year-end: 08/31/24
Information Technology Services
N.A.I.C.S.: 541512
Hiroyuki Hattori *(Founder, Chm & Pres)*

WIWORLD CO., LTD.
32-4 Techno 7-ro, Yuseong-gu, Daejeon, Korea (South)
Tel.: (82) 426300600
Web Site: https://www.wiworld.co.kr
Year Founded: 2000
Satellite Antenna Systems Mfr
N.A.I.C.S.: 334220
Chan-Goo Park *(CEO)*

WIWYNN CORP.
8F 90 Sec 1 Xintai 5th Rd, Xizhi, New Taipei City, 221-02, Taiwan
Tel.: (886) 266158888
Web Site: https://www.wiwynn.com
Year Founded: 2012
6669—(TAI)
Rev.: $7,910,689,684
Assets: $2,905,438,165
Liabilities: $1,524,292,594
Net Worth: $1,381,145,571
Earnings: $393,853,774
Emp.: 7,999
Fiscal Year-end: 12/31/23
Data Processing Services
N.A.I.C.S.: 518210
Emily Hong *(Pres & CEO)*

WIX.COM LTD.
5 Yunitsman St, Tel Aviv, 6350671, Israel
Tel.: (972) 35454900
Web Site: https://www.wix.com
Year Founded: 2006
WIX—(NASDAQ)
Rev.: $1,561,665,000
Assets: $1,804,136,000
Liabilities: $1,858,621,000
Net Worth: ($54,485,000)
Earnings: $33,137,000
Emp.: 4,414
Fiscal Year-end: 12/31/23
Global Web Development Platform
N.A.I.C.S.: 513210
Avishai Abrahami *(Co-Founder & CEO)*

Subsidiaries:

DeviantArt, Inc. (1)
7111 Santa Monica Blvd Ste B, Hollywood, CA 90046
Tel.: (323) 645-6000
Web Site: https://www.deviantart.com
Online Social Network for Artists
N.A.I.C.S.: 516210

WIZ CORP, INC.
8F 429 Bongeunsa-ro, Gangnam-gu, Seoul, 06097, Korea (South)
Tel.: (82) 220070300
Web Site: https://www.wizcorp.co.kr
Year Founded: 1995
038620—(KRS)
Rev.: $31,611,093
Assets: $67,123,811

Liabilities: $7,018,000
Net Worth: $60,105,811
Earnings: $1,994,938
Emp.: 66
Fiscal Year-end: 12/31/22
Gasoline Operators
N.A.I.C.S.: 457110
Seung-Hwan Jeong *(CEO)*

WIZ SOLUCOES E CORRETAGEM DE SEGUROS S.A.
SHN Qd 01 block E 1st floor, Ed Caixa Seguradora Building, Brasilia, 70701-050, DF, Brazil
Tel.: (55) 6134269500 BR
Web Site: http://www.wizsolucoes.com.br
Year Founded: 1973
WIZC3—(BRAZ)
Rev.: $231,113,858
Assets: $524,237,814
Liabilities: $286,096,857
Net Worth: $238,140,958
Earnings: $48,614,735
Emp.: 1,700
Fiscal Year-end: 12/31/23
Insurance Related Services
N.A.I.C.S.: 524298

WIZIBOAT SA
1503 Dolines road, 6560, Valbonne, France
Tel.: (33) 422462451
Web Site: https://www.wiziboat.com
Year Founded: 2017
MLWIZ—(EUR)
Online Booking Services
N.A.I.C.S.: 561599
Pierre-Olivier Bidault-Sire *(CEO)*

WIZIT CO., LTD.
58B-5L Industrial complex 626-4 Kojandong, Namdonggu, Incheon, Korea (South)
Tel.: (82) 318209900
Web Site: https://www.wizit.co.kr
Year Founded: 1992
036090—(KRS)
Rev.: $27,012,695
Assets: $122,472,781
Liabilities: $16,308,883
Net Worth: $106,163,899
Earnings: $10,492,455
Emp.: 146
Fiscal Year-end: 12/31/22
Liquid Crystal Display & Semiconductor Component Mfr
N.A.I.C.S.: 334419
Lee Hyun *(Mng Dir)*

WIZZ AIR HOLDINGS PLC
Laurus Offices Koer street 2/A Building B, H-1103, Budapest, Hungary
Tel.: (36) 17779324
Web Site: https://wizzair.com
Year Founded: 2003
WIZZ—(LSE)
Rev.: $4,204,295,273
Assets: $7,591,625,297
Liabilities: $7,977,876,106
Net Worth: ($386,250,809)
Earnings: ($577,487,589)
Emp.: 7,389
Fiscal Year-end: 03/31/23
Holding Company
N.A.I.C.S.: 551112
William A. Franke *(Chm)*

Subsidiaries:

Wizz Air UK Limited (1)
Main Terminal Building London Luton Airport, Luton, LU2 9LY, United Kingdom
Tel.: (44) 3309770444
Air Transport Services
N.A.I.C.S.: 488190

WKT-LETSCH PRODUKTIONS-

INTERNATIONAL PUBLIC

UND HANDELS GMBH
Lise Meitner Str 26, 63457, Hanau, Germany
Tel.: (49) 618150090 De
Web Site: http://www.wkt-produktion.de
Year Founded: 1981
Sales Range: $10-24.9 Million
Insulating System Supplier
N.A.I.C.S.: 221330
Michael Tetzlaff *(Gen Mgr)*

WLM PARTICIPACOES E COMERCIO DE MAQUINAS E VEICULOS S.A.
Tel.: (55) 2139746550
Web Site: https://www.wlm.com.br
Year Founded: 1946
Automobile Whslr
N.A.I.C.S.: 423110
Leandro Cardoso Massa *(Dir-Investor Relations)*

WLS HOLDINGS LIMITED
Room 1001 - 1006 10/F Tower A Southmark 11 Yip Hing Street, Wong Chuk Hang, Hong Kong, China (Hong Kong)
Tel.: (852) 28655622 Ky
Web Site: http://www.wls.com.hk
8021—(HKG)
Rev.: $18,609,900
Assets: $73,389,638
Liabilities: $22,885,995
Net Worth: $50,503,643
Earnings: ($13,424,603)
Emp.: 50
Fiscal Year-end: 04/30/23
Holding Company
N.A.I.C.S.: 551112
Francis Yu Shing So *(Chm)*

Subsidiaries:

Mass Fidelity Asset Management Limited (1)
Room 410 Harcourt House 39 Gloucester Road, Wan Chai, Hong Kong, China (Hong Kong)
Tel.: (852) 38990428
Web Site: http://www.massfidelityhk.com
Financial Services
N.A.I.C.S.: 523999

WLT DISTRIBUTORS INC.
75 Henlow Bay, Winnipeg, R3Y 1G4, MB, Canada
Tel.: (204) 487-6336
Web Site: http://www.wltdistributors.com
Rev.: $18,164,892
Emp.: 10
Livestock Products Distr
N.A.I.C.S.: 424520

WM CAPITAL S.P.A.
Via Cusani 10, 20121, Milan, Italy
Tel.: (39) 02 467781
Web Site: http://www.wmcapital.it
WMC—(ITA)
Sales Range: $1-9.9 Million
Franchising Business Development Services
N.A.I.C.S.: 523999
Fabio Pasquali *(Founder & CEO)*

WM LAWRENCE LIMITED
Grane Road Mill, Haslingden, Rossendale, BB4 5ET, Lancashire, United Kingdom
Tel.: (44) 1706215351
Year Founded: 1892
Sales Range: $25-49.9 Million
Emp.: 70
Textile Weaver
N.A.I.C.S.: 314999

WM PARTNERS CO., LTD.

AND PRIVATE COMPANIES

Kojimachi-Tsuruyahachiman Bldg 9F
2-4 Kojimachi, Chiyoda-ku, Tokyo,
102-0083, Japan
Tel.: (81) 3 6261 4601 JP
Web Site: http://www.wmpartners.jp
Year Founded: 2014
Emp.: 10
Privater Equity Firm
N.A.I.C.S.: 523999
Moriyoshi Matsumoto *(Chm & Mng Partner)*

WM SE
Pagenstecherstrasse 121, 49090,
Osnabruck, Germany
Tel.: (49) 541 9989 0 De
Web Site: http://www.wm.de
Automobile Parts Distr
N.A.I.C.S.: 423120
Frank Schroder *(Chm-Mgmt Bd & CEO)*

Subsidiaries:

SSF Imported Auto Parts LLC (1)
466 Forbes Blvd, South San Francisco, CA 94080-2015
Tel.: (650) 742-7050
Web Site: http://www.ssfautoparts.com
Sales Range: $50-74.9 Million
Provider of Auto Parts
N.A.I.C.S.: 423120
Michael Toliver *(Dir-Acctg & Fin)*

WM. SCHMIDT MECHANICAL CONTRACTORS, LTD.
4603D 13th Street NE, Calgary, T2E 6M3, AB, Canada
Tel.: (403) 250-1157
Web Site: https://www.wmschmidt.com
Year Founded: 1956
Rev.: $14,345,917
Emp.: 100
Mechanical Contracting, Furner Repair & Oil Burner Supplier & Services
N.A.I.C.S.: 238220
Manfred Schmidt *(VP)*

WMCH GLOBAL INVESTMENT LIMITED
31/F 148 Electric Road North Point, Hong Kong, China (Hong Kong) Ky
Web Site: https://www.tw-asia.com
Year Founded: 2005
8208—(HKG)
Rev.: $7,716,548
Assets: $4,716,298
Liabilities: $1,780,219
Net Worth: $2,936,078
Earnings: ($1,306,098)
Emp.: 153
Fiscal Year-end: 12/31/22
Investment Management Service
N.A.I.C.S.: 523999
Kim Sun Chan *(Sec)*

Subsidiaries:

TW-Asia Consultants Pte. Ltd. (1)
28 Sin Ming Lane 04-136, Midview City, Singapore, 573972, Singapore
Tel.: (65) 62916292
Engineering Consulting Services
N.A.I.C.S.: 541330

WMG AS
Raatuse 20, 51009, Tartu, Estonia
Tel.: (372) 7309399
Web Site: http://www.webmedia.ee
Year Founded: 2000
Sales Range: $10-24.9 Million
Emp.: 300
IT Software & Solutions
N.A.I.C.S.: 513210
Priit Alamae *(Chm & CEO)*

WMG HOLDINGS BERHAD
Lot 1 & 2 Jalan Indah Jaya Taman Indah Jaya Jalan Lintas Selatan, Sabah, 90000, Sandakan, Malaysia
Tel.: (60) 89212133 MY
Web Site: https://www.wmghb.com.my
Year Founded: 1995
WMG—(KLS)
Rev.: $16,515,069
Assets: $93,432,853
Liabilities: $57,536,017
Net Worth: $35,896,836
Earnings: ($671,554)
Fiscal Year-end: 12/31/22
Holding Company
N.A.I.C.S.: 551112
Eric Usip Juin *(Chm)*

Subsidiaries:

Wah Mie Trading Sdn. Bhd. (1)
Lot 2 Jalan Kolombong off mile 5 5 Jalan Tuaran, 88450, Kota Kinabalu, Sabah, Malaysia
Tel.: (60) 88428391
Building Material Whslr & Retailer
N.A.I.C.S.: 423390

WMHW HOLDINGS LIMITED
Unit 2202 22/FCauseway Bay Plaza, 489 Hennessy Road Causeway Bay, Hong Kong, China (Hong Kong)
Tel.: (852) 235948400 Ky
Web Site: http://www.luenwong.hk
8217—(HKG)
Rev.: $11,963,411
Assets: $18,617,876
Liabilities: $10,812,909
Net Worth: $7,804,967
Earnings: ($2,598,560)
Emp.: 43
Fiscal Year-end: 03/31/22
Civil Engineering Services
N.A.I.C.S.: 541330
Kwok Hung So *(Chm & & Officer-Compliance)*

WNS (HOLDINGS) LIMITED
Plant No 10/11 Gate No 4 Godrej & Boyce Complex Pirojshanagar, Vikhroli West, Mumbai, 400 079, India
Tel.: (91) 2240952100 JE
Web Site: https://www.wnscareers.com
Year Founded: 2002
WNS—(NYSE)
Rev.: $1,109,800,000
Assets: $1,164,492,000
Liabilities: $410,489,000
Net Worth: $754,003,000
Earnings: $132,101,000
Emp.: 52,081
Fiscal Year-end: 03/31/22
Holding Company; Business Process Outsourcing Services
N.A.I.C.S.: 551112
Sanjay Jain *(Chief Bus Transformation Officer)*

Subsidiaries:

Denali Group, Inc. (1)
221 N Hogan St, Jacksonville, FL 32034
Tel.: (904) 432-7001
Web Site: http://www.denaliusa.com
Procurement Transformation, Strategic Sourcing, Logistics Optimization, Supply Market Intelligence, Workforce Services & On-Demand Sourcing Execution for International Clients
N.A.I.C.S.: 561499

WNS Global Services (Romania) S.R.L. (1)
WestGate Park H5 Building 2nd 3rd rd Floor Preciziei Blvd no 24, Sector 6, 062204, Bucharest, Romania
Tel.: (40) 372303000
Business Process Outsourcing Services
N.A.I.C.S.: 561499

WNS Global Services (UK) Ltd. (1)
HPH3 Hyde Park Hayes Millington Road, Hayes, UB3 4AZ, Middlesex, United Kingdom
Tel.: (44) 2087548289
Web Site: http://www.wns.com
Sales Range: $10-24.9 Million
Emp.: 40
Offshore Business Process Outsourcing Services
N.A.I.C.S.: 561499

Subsidiary (Domestic):

Accidents Happen Assistance Limited (2)
Assistance House Hercules Office Park Bird Hall Lane, Cheadle, SK3 0UX, United Kingdom
Tel.: (44) 8000832890
Web Site: http://www.accidentshappen.co.uk
Accident Claims Handling Services
N.A.I.C.S.: 524291

WNS Workflow Technologies Limited (2)
WNS Assistance 16 Museum Street, Ipswich, IP1 1HT, Suffolk, United Kingdom
Tel.: (44) 3448540660
Software Development Services
N.A.I.C.S.: 541511

WNS Global Services Private Limited (1)
Plant No 10/11 Gate No 4 Godrej Boyce Complex Pirojshanagar, Vikhroli West, Mumbai, 400 079, India
Tel.: (91) 2268262100
Business Process Outsourcing Services
N.A.I.C.S.: 561499

WNS North America, Inc. (1)
15 Exchange Place, Jersey City, NJ 07302
Tel.: (201) 942-6254
Web Site: http://www.wns.com
Sales Range: $10-24.9 Million
Emp.: 35
Offshore Business Process Outsourcing Services
N.A.I.C.S.: 561499

Subsidiary (Non-US):

WNS Business Consulting Services Private Limited (2)
3rd to 5th Floor Wing A B Tower 1 Cyber City, Magarpatta City Hadapsar, Pune, 411 013, India
Tel.: (91) 2041454000
Business Process Outsourcing Services
N.A.I.C.S.: 561499

WOANS SARL
18 Rue Henri Becquerel, 93270, Sevran, 93270, Seine Saint Denis, France
Tel.: (33) 14385888
Clothing: Womens, Childrens & Infants
N.A.I.C.S.: 424350

WOB AG
Werner-Heisenberg-Strasse 6a-10, 68519, Viernheim, Germany
Tel.: (49) 62049700
Web Site: http://www.wob.ag
Year Founded: 1973
Sales Range: $100-124.9 Million
Advertising Services
N.A.I.C.S.: 541810
Gudmund Semb *(Partner)*

WOBURN ENERGY PLC
5th Floor 16 Upper Woburn Place, London, WC1H 0AF, United Kingdom
Tel.: (44) 207 380 4609
Web Site: http://www.woburnenergy.com
Emp.: 6
Investment Services
N.A.I.C.S.: 523999
Antony Brian Baldry *(Deputy Chm)*

WOCKHARDT LIMITED
Wockhardt Towers Bandra Kurla Complex Bandra East, Mumbai, 400 051, Maharashtra, India
Tel.: (91) 2226534444 In
Web Site: http://www.wockhardt.com
Year Founded: 1999
WOCKPHARMA—(NSE)
Rev.: $332,474,072
Assets: $921,167,796
Liabilities: $482,105,389
Net Worth: $439,062,406
Earnings: ($74,455,968)
Emp.: 2,740
Fiscal Year-end: 03/31/23
Pharmaceuticals & Biotechnologies Developer & Mfr
N.A.I.C.S.: 325412
Habil Khorakiwala *(Founder & Chm)*

Subsidiaries:

Laboratoire Negma S.A.S. (1)
10 Rue Paul Dautier, Velizy Villacoublay, Paris, 78141, Cedex, France
Tel.: (33) 139258080
Sales Range: $150-199.9 Million
Emp.: 100
Pharmaceuticals Developer & Mfr
N.A.I.C.S.: 325412

Morton Grove Pharmaceuticals, Inc. (1)
6451 W Main St, Morton Grove, IL 60053-2633
Tel.: (847) 967-5600
Web Site: http://www.wockhardtusa.com
Sales Range: $50-74.9 Million
Emp.: 200
Producer of Pharmaceutical Preparations
N.A.I.C.S.: 325412

Pinewood Healthcare Limited (1)
Ballymacarbry, Clonmel, Tipperary, Ireland
Tel.: (353) 526186000
Web Site: https://pinewood.ie
Pharmaceutical Product Mfr & Distr
N.A.I.C.S.: 325412
Jeffrey Walsh *(Head)*

Pinewood Laboratories Ltd. (1)
(100%)
Tel.: (353) 526186000
Web Site: http://www.pinewood.ie
Sales Range: $10-24.9 Million
Emp.: 360
Pharmaceuticals Product Mfr
N.A.I.C.S.: 325412

Wockhardt Bio AG (1)
Grafenauweg 6, 6300, Zug, Switzerland
Tel.: (41) 417275220
Pharmaceutical Product Mfr & Distr
N.A.I.C.S.: 325412

Wockhardt UK Limited (1)
Ash Road North, Wrexham Industrial Estate, Wrexham, LL13 9UF, United Kingdom (100%)
Tel.: (44) 1978661261
Web Site: https://www.wockhardt.co.uk
Sales Range: $10-24.9 Million
Emp.: 350
Pharmaceuticals Developer & Mfr
N.A.I.C.S.: 325412

WOCO INDUSTRIETECHNIK GMBH
Hanauer Landstrasse 16, 63628, Bad Soden-Salmunster, Germany
Tel.: (49) 6056780
Web Site: http://www.wocogroup.com
Year Founded: 1956
Sales Range: $400-449.9 Million
Emp.: 2,600
Automotive Acoustic, Comfort & Safety Equipment Mfr
N.A.I.C.S.: 336390
Hans Jurgen Kracht *(Co-CEO)*

Subsidiaries:

EFFBE France S.A.S. (1)
153 rue du General de Gaulle, Habsheim, 68440, Mulhouse, France
Tel.: (33) 389443868
Web Site: http://www.effbe-diaphragm.com

WOCO INDUSTRIETECHNIK GMBH

Woco Industrietechnik GmbH—(Continued)
Fabricated Metal & Hardware Product Mfr
N.A.I.C.S.: 332999

EFFBE-CZ s.r.o. (1)
Hrabuvky 641, 760 01, Zlin, Czech Republic
Tel.: (420) 577008800
Web Site: http://www.effbe.cz
Rubber & Rubber Textile Membrane Mfr
N.A.I.C.S.: 326299

PTE Compounding de Mexico S.A. de C.V. (1)
Avenida Santa Maria 1050, Parque Industrial Colinas de Lagos, 47480, Lagos de Moreno, Jalisco, Mexico
Tel.: (52) 34916590
Chemical Plant Mfr
N.A.I.C.S.: 325199

Polymer-Technik Elbe GmbH (1)
Heuweg 5, 06886, Lutherstadt Wittenberg, Germany
Tel.: (49) 3491659154
Web Site: http://www.polymertechnik.com
Synthetic Rubber Mfr
N.A.I.C.S.: 325212
Matthias Klaue *(CFO)*

Woco Eisenacher Kunststofftechnik GmbH (1)
Eichrodter Weg 133, 99817, Eisenach, Germany
Tel.: (49) 369179320
Plastics Product Mfr
N.A.I.C.S.: 326199

Woco Ipartechnika Magyarorszag Kft. (1)
Ujhegyi ut 25-31, 1108, Budapest, Hungary
Tel.: (36) 14 31 05 80
Plastics Product Mfr
N.A.I.C.S.: 326199

Woco Kronacher Kunststoffwerk GmbH (1)
Industriestrasse 7, 96317, Kronach, Germany
Tel.: (49) 92 61 5 05 0
Plastics Product Mfr
N.A.I.C.S.: 326199

Woco Motor Acoustic Systems, Inc. (1)
23031 Sherwood Ave, Warren, MI 48091
Tel.: (586) 427-3838
Sales Range: $25-49.9 Million
Emp.: 47
Automotive Acoustic, Comfort & Safety Equipment Mfr
N.A.I.C.S.: 336390

Woco STV, s.r.o. (1)
Prumyslovy areal Jasenice, 75501, Vsetin, Czech Republic
Tel.: (420) 571 48 95 13
Rubber Products Mfr
N.A.I.C.S.: 326299

Woco Tech Elastomere Noida Ltd. (1)
Plot No 27I and 27J Sector-31 Ecotech-1 Site-IV Kasna, Distt G B Nagar, 201301, Noida, Uttar Pradesh, India
Tel.: (91) 1204505400
Automotive Rubber Component Mfr
N.A.I.C.S.: 326291
Pankaj Gupta *(Asst Mgr-IT)*

Woco Tech Kandla Ltd. (1)
Plot no-341-344 Sector-4, Kandla Special Economic Zone, 370230, Gandhidham, Gujarat, India
Tel.: (91) 2836253368
Electro Pneumatic Pressure Transducer Mfr
N.A.I.C.S.: 334519
Hiren Patel *(Sr Engr-Electrical Maintenance)*

Woco Tech Ltd. (1)
Shed No B3 5 to 8 SAIF Zone, PO Box 8327, Sharjah, United Arab Emirates
Tel.: (971) 65571345
Automotive Rubber Component Mfr.
N.A.I.C.S.: 326291

Woco Tech USA Inc. (1)
28970 Cabot Dr Ste 300, Novi, MI 48377
Tel.: (248) 385-2854
Web Site: http://www.wocogroup.com

Emp.: 15
Automobile Parts Distr
N.A.I.C.S.: 423120
Petr Tomecek *(VP-Sls & Bus Dev)*

Woco Tecnica, S. A. (1)
Avda Letxunborro 104, 20303, Irun, Spain
Tel.: (34) 943 66 71 00
Rubber Products Mfr
N.A.I.C.S.: 326299

Wuxi Elbe Polymer Technology Co., Ltd. (1)
98 Ximei Road, Wuxi, 214028, China
Tel.: (86) 510 88 55 60 02
Rubber Products Mfr
N.A.I.C.S.: 326299

Wuxi Woco Motor Acoustic System Co., Ltd. (1)
No 100 Xi Mei Road, New District, 214112, Wuxi, Jiangsu, China
Tel.: (86) 51080189688
Plastics Product Mfr
N.A.I.C.S.: 326199

Zhonglan Woco (Ma Anshan) Rubber & Plastic Products Co., Ltd. (1)
No 1 Yongxin Road, Yushan District, Ma'anshan, 243000, Anhui, China
Tel.: (86) 5555210866
Rubber & Plastic Product Mfr
N.A.I.C.S.: 326299

WODEN VENTURE CAPITAL CORPORATION
3030 boul Le Carrefour Blvd Suite 1002, Laval, H7T 2P5, QC, Canada
Tel.: (450) 681-7744 Ca
Year Founded: 2010
Assets: $35,329
Liabilities: $15,373
Net Worth: $19,957
Earnings: ($47,454)
Fiscal Year-end: 01/31/19
Investment Services
N.A.I.C.S.: 523999
Andre O. Bergeron *(Pres & CEO)*

WOGEN GROUP
4 The Sanctuary Westminster, London, SW1P 3JS, United Kingdom
Tel.: (44) 20 7222 2171
Web Site: http://www.wogen.com
Year Founded: 1972
Sales Range: $450-499.9 Million
Emp.: 63
Metal Product Whslr
N.A.I.C.S.: 423510
John Craig *(CEO)*

Subsidiaries:

Wogen Metal Commercial (Shanghai) Ltd (1)
Room 987 HK-Macau Centre 2 Chaoyangmen Bei Dajie, Dongcheng District, Beijing, 100027, China
Tel.: (86) 1065542311
Metal Product Distr
N.A.I.C.S.: 423510

Wogen Metals LLC (1)
Butirskaya ulitsa 77, Business Center Diagonal House Office 304, Moscow, 127015, Russia
Tel.: (7) 4959673154
Metal Product Distr
N.A.I.C.S.: 423510

Wogen Pacific Ltd (1)
Room 2808 China Resources Building 26 Harbour Road, Wanchai, China (Hong Kong)
Tel.: (852) 28271727
Metal Product Distr
N.A.I.C.S.: 423510
Ross Sabberton *(Mng Dir)*

Wogen Resources South Africa (Pty) Ltd (1)
First Floor Block C Office 101 St Andrews Office Park Meadowbrook Lane, Epsom Downs Bryanston, 2191, Johannesburg, South Africa
Tel.: (27) 100033432

Metal Product Distr
N.A.I.C.S.: 423510

WOHLER TECHNIK GMBH
Wohler-Platz 1, 33181, Bad Wunnenberg, Germany
Tel.: (49) 2953 73 100
Web Site: http://www.woehler.de
Year Founded: 1932
Testing & Measuring Products
N.A.I.C.S.: 334515
Martin Zomers *(Mgr-Comml)*

Subsidiaries:

Retrotec, Inc. (1)
1060 East Pole Road, Everson, WA 98247
Tel.: (360) 738-9835
Web Site: http://www.retrotec.com
Blower Door & Door Fan Test Equipment Mfr
N.A.I.C.S.: 333413
Colin Genge *(Co-Founder, Pres & Co-CEO)*

WOJAS S.A.
Ul Szewska 8, 34-400, Nowy Targ, Poland
Tel.: (48) 182649210
Web Site: https://wojas.pl
Year Founded: 1990
WOJ—(WAR)
Rev.: $103,676,321
Assets: $72,097,561
Liabilities: $36,035,569
Net Worth: $36,061,992
Earnings: $5,926,067
Emp.: 500
Fiscal Year-end: 12/31/23
Leather Footwear Mfr
N.A.I.C.S.: 316210
Kazimierz Adam Ostatek *(Vice Chm-Mgmt Bd)*

WOKSAL A.D.
Milosa Obrenovica 2, 31000, Uzice, Serbia
Tel.: (381) 31563469
Web Site: https://www.woksal.com
Year Founded: 1965
WKSL—(BEL)
Rev.: $1,389,641
Assets: $3,249,128
Liabilities: $1,340,188
Net Worth: $1,908,939
Earnings: $61,653
Emp.: 47
Fiscal Year-end: 12/31/22
Nonferrous Metal Casting Services
N.A.I.C.S.: 331523
Ljubisa Stevanovic *(Mng Dir)*

WOLF MINERALS LIMITED
Level 3 Suite 25 22 Railway Road, Subiaco, 6008, WA, Australia
Tel.: (61) 861432070
Web Site: http://www.wolfminerals.com.au
Rev.: $18,647,021
Assets: $227,095,966
Liabilities: $144,537,513
Net Worth: $82,558,454
Earnings: ($56,270,692)
Emp.: 110
Fiscal Year-end: 06/30/17
Minerals Exploration
N.A.I.C.S.: 213115

WOLFDEN RESOURCES CORPORATION
1100 Russell Street Unit 5, Thunder Bay, P7B 5N2, ON, Canada
Tel.: (807) 624-1130 ON
Web Site: https://www.wolfdenresources.com
Year Founded: 2009
WLF—(TSXV)
Rev.: $2,472,783
Assets: $783,057

Liabilities: $356,592
Net Worth: $426,465
Earnings: ($488,287)
Emp.: 2
Fiscal Year-end: 12/31/20
Metal Mining
N.A.I.C.S.: 212290
Ronald N. Little *(Pres & CEO)*

WOLFFKRAN GMBH
Austrasse 72, 74076, Heilbronn, Germany
Tel.: (49) 713198150
Web Site: http://www.wolffkran.de
Year Founded: 1969
Emp.: 860
Crane Mfr
N.A.I.C.S.: 333923
Peter Schiefer *(CEO)*

WOLFGANG STEUBING AG
Goethestrasse 29, D-60313, Frankfurt, Germany
Tel.: (49) 69297160
Web Site: http://www.steubing.com
Year Founded: 1987
Rev.: $14,662,945
Assets: $29,554,416
Liabilities: $6,803,344
Net Worth: $22,751,071
Earnings: $1,293,495
Emp.: 51
Fiscal Year-end: 06/30/19
Direct Order Execution & Block Trading Financial Services
N.A.I.C.S.: 523999
Wolfgang Steubing *(Founder)*

WOLFTANK-ADISA HOLDING AG
Grabenweg 58, A-6020, Innsbruck, Austria
Tel.: (43) 512341819
Web Site: https://wolftank.at
WAH—(BER)
Rev.: $95,801,373
Assets: $121,348,204
Liabilities: $94,175,784
Net Worth: $27,172,420
Earnings: $494,599
Emp.: 400
Fiscal Year-end: 12/31/23
Environmental Protection Services
N.A.I.C.S.: 541620
Peter Werth *(CEO)*

WOLFVISION HOLDING AG
Oberes Ried 14, A 6833, Klaus, Austria
Tel.: (43) 5523 52250 0
Web Site: http://www.wolfvision.com
Emp.: 100
Holding Company
N.A.I.C.S.: 551112
Michael Lisch *(Mng Dir)*

Subsidiaries:

WolfVision GmbH (1)
Oberes Ried 14, 6833, Klaus, Austria
Tel.: (43) 552352250
Web Site: http://www.wolfvision.com
Emp.: 75
Opto-Electronic Devices (Document Cameras) Mfr & Sales
N.A.I.C.S.: 334419
Michael Lisch *(Mng Dir)*

Subsidiary (Non-US):

WolfVision Canada, Inc. (2)
500-1101 Polyteck Street, Ottawa, K1J 0B3, ON, Canada
Tel.: (613) 741-9898
Web Site: http://www.wolfvision.com
Visualizers Distr
N.A.I.C.S.: 423690

WolfVision Co. Ltd. (2)
Advance Bldg 2F 8-1-16 Nishi Shinjuku,

AND PRIVATE COMPANIES

Shinjuku, Tokyo, 160 0023, Japan
Tel.: (81) 3 3360 3231
Web Site: http://www.wolfvision.com
Visualizers Distr
N.A.I.C.S.: 423690
Norihisa Nishihama *(Mng Dir)*

Subsidiary (US):

WolfVision Inc. (2)
2055 Sugarloaf Cir Ste 125, Duluth, GA 30097
Tel.: (770) 931-6802
Web Site: http://www.wolfvision.us
Emp.: 10
Visualizers Distr
N.A.I.C.S.: 423690
Arthur Jenni *(VP & Gen Mgr)*

Branch (Domestic):

WolfVision Inc. (3)
1601 Bayshore Hwy Ste 168, Burlingame, CA 94010
Tel.: (650) 648-0002
Web Site: http://www.wolfvision.us
Emp.: 3
Visualizers Distr
N.A.I.C.S.: 423690
Andrea Mayer *(Asst VP & Mgr-Sls-West)*

Subsidiary (Non-US):

WolfVision Pte Ltd (2)
81 Ubi Avenue 4 #06-27, UB One, Singapore, 408830, Singapore
Tel.: (65) 6636 1268
Web Site: http://www.wolfvision.com
Visualizers Distr
N.A.I.C.S.: 423690
Martin Low *(Mng Dir)*

WolfVision UK Ltd. (2)
Trident One Styal Road, Manchester, M22 5XB, United Kingdom
Tel.: (44) 161 435 6081
Web Site: http://www.wolfvision.us
Visualizers Distr
N.A.I.C.S.: 423690
Julien Bussell *(Mgr-Sls-South)*

Wolfvision Middle East UAE (1)
Suite 401 Jumeirah Terrace Jumeirah, Dubai, United Arab Emirates
Tel.: (971) 43542233
Electronic Components Distr
N.A.I.C.S.: 423690
Hazem Mahdy *(Mgr-Sls)*

WOLKOFF ET ARNODIN
8 rue de la Vrilliere, 75001, Paris, France
Tel.: (33) 1 42 97 49 65
Web Site: http://www.wolkoff-arnodin.com
Year Founded: 1987
Rev.: $11,000,000
Emp.: 9
N.A.I.C.S.: 541810
Antoine Arnodin *(Mng Dir)*

WOLONG ELECTRIC GROUP CO., LTD.
No 1801 West Renmin Road, Shangyu, 312300, Zhejiang, China
Tel.: (86) 57582176629
Web Site: http://www.wolong.com.cn
Year Founded: 1998
600580—(SHG)
Rev.: $2,105,725,757
Assets: $3,291,767,168
Liabilities: $1,867,953,092
Net Worth: $1,423,814,076
Earnings: $112,258,561
Emp.: 18,000
Fiscal Year-end: 12/31/22
Electric Motor Mfr & Whslr
N.A.I.C.S.: 335312
Pang Xinyuan *(Chm)*

Subsidiaries:

ATB Motors (Wuhan) Co., Ltd. (1)
No 1 Canglongdao Science Park, Jiangxia District, Wuhan, 430205, China
Tel.: (86) 278 799 3001
Web Site: http://www.atb-motors.com
Electric Motor Mfr
N.A.I.C.S.: 335312

Shanghai Wolong Electric Bicycle Co., Ltd. (1)
No 1801 Zhejiang Shangyu Renminxilu, Shangyu, 201505, Zhejiang, China
Tel.: (86) 575 82176619
Web Site: http://www.wolong-ebike.com
Automobile Mfr
N.A.I.C.S.: 336110

Wolong Americas LLC (1)
26410 Oakridge Dr Ste 101, Spring, TX 77380
Tel.: (346) 616-0102
Motor & Generator Mfr
N.A.I.C.S.: 335312

Wolong EMEA (Germany) GmbH (1)
Breite Str 131, 41238, Monchengladbach, Germany
Tel.: (49) 7182141
Electric Motor Distr
N.A.I.C.S.: 423610

Wolong Electric Private Limited (1)
C 30 Renaisanace Park -I Behind World Trade Ccentre, Bengaluru, 560055, Karnataka, India
Tel.: (91) 9900254767
Power Transmission Equipment Mfr
N.A.I.C.S.: 333612

Wolong International (Malaysia) Sdn Bhd (1)
K3-3-13A UOA Business Park Jalan Pengatacarara U1/51A, Temasya Industrial Area, 40150, Shah Alam, Selangor, Malaysia
Tel.: (60) 350391774
Power Transmission Equipment Mfr
N.A.I.C.S.: 333612

Wolong International Business Co., Ltd. (1)
No 1801 Renmin West Road, Shangyu, Zhejiang, China
Tel.: (86) 2133282771
Motor & Generator Mfr
N.A.I.C.S.: 335312

Wolong International Korea Co.,Ltd. (1)
B-1609 Mapo-daero 53 Mapo Tra Palace, Mapo-gu, Seoul, Korea (South)
Tel.: (82) 1098897247
Web Site: https://wolong.co.kr
Power Transmission Equipment Mfr
N.A.I.C.S.: 333612

Zhejiang Wolong New Energy Co., Ltd. (1)
No 58 Qiuyi Road, Binjiang District, Hangzhou, Zhengjiang, China
Tel.: (86) 571 56693891
Web Site: http://www.wolong-solar.com
Electric Equipment Mfr
N.A.I.C.S.: 334419

WOLONG HOLDING GROUP CO., LTD.
1801 West Remin Road, Shangyu, 312300, Zhejiang, China
Tel.: (86) 575 8211 1888 CN
Web Site: http://www.wolong.com
Year Founded: 1984
Sales Range: $1-4.9 Billion
Emp.: 6,000
Holding Company
N.A.I.C.S.: 551112
Jian-chen Chen *(Chm)*

Subsidiaries:

ATB Austria Antriebstechnik AG (1)
Donau-City-Strasse 6/15a, 1220, Vienna, Austria (100%)
Tel.: (43) 1902500
Web Site: http://www.atb-motors.com
Sales Range: $350-399.9 Million
Emp.: 3,708
Industrial Motors & Electrical Drive Systems Mfr
N.A.I.C.S.: 334419
Andreas Schindler *(Chm-Mgmt Bd & CEO)*

Subsidiary (Non-US):

ATB Antriebstechnik GmbH (2)
Silcherstrasse 74, 73642, Welzheim, Germany
Tel.: (49) 7182 141
Electronic Components Mfr
N.A.I.C.S.: 334419

ATB FOD Bor d.o.o. (2)
Dorda Vajferta 16, 19210, Bor, Serbia
Tel.: (381) 30 423 147
Electronic Components Mfr
N.A.I.C.S.: 334419

ATB Laurence Scott Ltd. (2)
Hardy Road, Norwich, NR1 1JD, Norfolk, United Kingdom
Tel.: (44) 160 362 8333
Electronic Components Mfr
N.A.I.C.S.: 334419

ATB Morley Ltd. (2)
Bradford Road, Leeds, LS28 6QA, W Yorkshire, United Kingdom
Tel.: (44) 113 257 1734
Web Site: http://www.atbgroup.co.uk
Emp.: 140
Electronic Components Mfr
N.A.I.C.S.: 334419
Ian Lomax *(Dir)*

ATB Motorentechnik GmbH (2)
Helgolander Damm 75, 26954, Nordenham, Germany
Tel.: (49) 4731 3650
Electronic Components Mfr
N.A.I.C.S.: 334419

Subsidiary (Domestic):

ATB Motorenwerke GmbH (2)
G-Bauknecht-Strasse 1, 8724, Spielberg, Austria
Tel.: (43) 3577 7570
Electronic Components Mfr
N.A.I.C.S.: 334419

Subsidiary (Non-US):

ATB Motors B.V. (2)
Tasveld 14, 8271 RW, IJsselmuiden, Netherlands
Tel.: (31) 384432110
Web Site: https://www.atb-motors.nl
Electronic Components Mfr
N.A.I.C.S.: 334419

ATB Sever d.o.o. (2)
Magnetna polja 6, 24000, Subotica, Serbia
Tel.: (381) 24665100
Web Site: https://sever.rs
Electronic Components Mfr
N.A.I.C.S.: 334419

Brook Crompton Holdings Ltd. (2)
19 Keppel Road, 08-01 Jit Poh Building, Singapore, 089058, Singapore (66.03%)
Tel.: (65) 62270308
Web Site: https://www.brookcromptonholdings.com
Rev.: $54,389,154
Assets: $50,146,179
Liabilities: $17,565,705
Net Worth: $32,580,474
Earnings: $4,216,466
Emp.: 75
Fiscal Year-end: 12/31/2023
Holding Company; Electric Motors & Components Mfr & Distr
N.A.I.C.S.: 551112
Richard Eason *(CEO)*

Subsidiary (Non-US):

Brook Crompton UK Limited (3)
St Thomas Rd, Huddersfield, HD13LJ, United Kingdom
Tel.: (44) 1484557200
Web Site: https://www.brookcrompton.com
Sales Range: $25-49.9 Million
Emp.: 30
Relays & Industrial Controls
N.A.I.C.S.: 335314
Godrich Eason *(Mng Dir)*

Subsidiary (Non-US):

Brook Crompton Ltd. (4)
264 Attwell Drive, Toronto, M9W 5B2, ON, Canada
Tel.: (416) 675-3844
Web Site: https://www.brookcromptonna.com
Sales Range: $25-49.9 Million
Emp.: 25
Electrical Apparatus Mfr
N.A.I.C.S.: 423610
Ramzi Mallouk *(VP-Sls)*

Subsidiary (US):

Brook Crompton Motors Inc (4)
7615 Detour Ave, Cleveland, OH 44103
Tel.: (216) 938-5840
Web Site: http://www.brookcromptonna.com
Sales Range: $25-49.9 Million
Emp.: 3
Electric Motor Mfr
N.A.I.C.S.: 335312
Earl Clagett Jr. *(Mgr-Warehouse)*

Subsidiary (Non-US):

Brook Motors Ltd (2)
Saint Thomas Road, Huddersfield, HD1 3LT, United Kingdom
Tel.: (44) 14 8455 7200
Electric Motor Mfr
N.A.I.C.S.: 335312

Fabryka Silnikow Elektrycznych Tamel SA (2)
Ul Elektryczna 6, 33-100, Tarnow, Poland
Tel.: (48) 14 632 1133
Electronic Components Mfr
N.A.I.C.S.: 334419

Schorch Beteiligungs GmbH (2)
Breite Str 131, Monchengladbach, 41238, Germany
Tel.: (49) 21669250
Web Site: http://www.schorch.de
Emp.: 510
Electric Motor Mfr
N.A.I.C.S.: 335312
Harald Lutz *(Gen Mgr)*

Schorch Elektrische Maschinen und Antriebe GmbH (2)
Breite Strasse 131, 41238, Monchengladbach, Germany
Tel.: (49) 21669250
Web Site: http://www.schorch.de
Emp.: 520
Electronic Components Mfr
N.A.I.C.S.: 334419
Micheal Gruener *(Gen Mgr)*

Wolong Resources Group Co., Ltd. (1)
No 1801 Renmin West Road Economic Development Zone, Shangyu District, Shaoxing, 312300, Zhejiang, China
Tel.: (86) 57589289213
Web Site: https://www.wolong-re.com
Rev.: $735,418,233
Assets: $910,907,997
Liabilities: $391,373,213
Net Worth: $519,534,784
Earnings: $42,288,424
Fiscal Year-end: 12/31/2022
Property Development Services
N.A.I.C.S.: 531390
Wang Xiquan *(Chm)*

WOLTERS KLUWER N.V.
Zuidpoolsingel 2, PO Box 1030, 2400 BA, Alphen aan den Rijn, Netherlands
Tel.: (31) 172641400 NI
Web Site: https://www.wolterskluwer.com
Year Founded: 1987
WKL—(EUR)
Rev.: $5,859,933,040
Assets: $11,088,550,720
Liabilities: $8,119,894,640
Net Worth: $2,968,656,080
Earnings: $894,158,720
Fiscal Year-end: 12/31/21
Book, Periodical & Internet Publishing Services
N.A.I.C.S.: 513130
Karen Abramson *(CEO-Corp Performance & ESG)*

WOLTERS KLUWER N.V.

Wolters Kluwer n.v.—(Continued)

Subsidiaries:

CCH Prosystems India Private Limited (1)
56 Sai Arcade Outer Ring Road Devarabeesanahalli, Bengaluru, 560 103, India
Tel.: (91) 80 4225 5555
Web Site: http://www.cchprosystem.in
Sales Range: $25-49.9 Million
Emp.: 100
Account Management Services
N.A.I.C.S.: 541219

Invistics Corporation (1)
5445 Triangle Pkwy, Norcross, GA 30092
Tel.: (770) 559-6386
Web Site: http://invistics.com
Rev.: $2,200,000
Emp.: 25
Data Processing, Hosting & Related Services
N.A.I.C.S.: 518210
Tom Knight (Pres)

Kluwer b.v. (1)
Staverenstraat 15, PO Box 23, Deventer, 7400GA, Netherlands (100%)
Tel.: (31) 570647111
Web Site: http://www.wolterskluwer.nl
Sales Range: $200-249.9 Million
Emp.: 800
Publishes Information for Specialists in Law, Taxation & Social-Labor Law Fields
N.A.I.C.S.: 513120
Christof Abrahamse (Dir-Fin)

Subsidiary (Domestic):

Kluwer Law International b.v. (2)
Zuidpoolsingel 2, 2408 ZE, Alphen aan den Rijn, Netherlands
Tel.: (31) 172641400
Web Site: http://www.kluwerlaw.com
Sales Range: $25-49.9 Million
Law Book Publisher
N.A.I.C.S.: 513130

La Ley (1)
Collado Mediano 9, Las Rozas, 28230, Madrid, Spain
Tel.: (34) 916020000
Web Site: http://www.laley.net
Publishes Information in the Legal & Taxation Market & for Industry
N.A.I.C.S.: 513120
Vicente Sanchez (CEO)

LicenseLogix, LLC (1)
140 Grand St Ste 300, White Plains, NY 10601
Tel.: (800) 292-0909
Web Site: http://www.licenselogix.com
Sales Range: $1-9.9 Million
License Issuing Services
N.A.I.C.S.: 561990
Donna Caruso (Dir-Sls)

Norstedts Juridik AB (1)
Warfvinges vag 39, 112 51, Stockholm, Sweden
Tel.: (46) 859819100
Web Site: https://www.nj.se
Sales Range: $50-74.9 Million
Educational, Legal, Business & Trade Publishing for Specific Target Groups in Selected Markets & Professional Training
N.A.I.C.S.: 513120

Wolters Kluwer Deutschland GmbH (1)
Wolters-Kluwer-Strasse 1, 50354, Hurth, Germany (100%)
Tel.: (49) 223337607000
Web Site: https://www.wolterskluwer.de
Publisher of Law, Business Economics, Social Sciences & Education Information
N.A.I.C.S.: 513120
Nick Schlattmann (Mng Dir)

Subsidiary (Domestic):

Wolters Kluwer Deutschland Information Services GmbH (2)
Feldstiege 100, D-48161, Munster, Germany (100%)
Tel.: (49) 253393000
Web Site: http://www.wkdis.de

Sales Range: $75-99.9 Million
Emp.: 250
Legal, Tax, Regulatory, Risk Management & Business Data Publisher & Information Services
N.A.I.C.S.: 513199

Wolters Kluwer ELM Solutions, Inc. (1)
3009 Post Oak Blvd Ste 1100, Houston, TX 77056
Tel.: (713) 572-3282
Software Publisher
N.A.I.C.S.: 513210

Wolters Kluwer Financial Services, Inc. (1)
100 S 5th St Ste 700, Minneapolis, MN 55402-1466
Tel.: (612) 656-7700
Web Site: https://www.wolterskluwerfs.com
Financial Publishing
N.A.I.C.S.: 519290
Brian Longe (CEO)

Unit (Domestic):

BizFilings (2)
8020 Excelsior Dr Ste 200, Madison, WI 53717
Tel.: (608) 827-5300
Web Site: http://www.bizfilings.com
Sales Range: $10-24.9 Million
Emp.: 50
Incorporation Services
N.A.I.C.S.: 561499

Subsidiary (Domestic):

Emmi Solutions, LLC (2)
300 W Adams St Ste 1100, Chicago, IL 60606
Tel.: (312) 236-3650
Web Site: https://www.emmisolutions.com
Computer Software Development Services
N.A.I.C.S.: 513210
David Sobel (Co-Founder & Chief Medical Officer)

Unit (Domestic):

Wolters Kluwer Financial Services (2)
111 Eighth Ave 13th Fl, New York, NY 10011
Tel.: (212) 894-8917
Web Site: http://www.wolterskluwerfs.com
Rev.: $627,043,200
Legal Representation, Search & Filing Information Services; Financial Compliance, Content & Technology Information Services
N.A.I.C.S.: 519290
Paul Kuhn (CFO)

Wolters Kluwer Financial Services/CCH (2)
2700 Lake Cook Rd, Riverwoods, IL 60015
Tel.: (847) 267-7000
Web Site: http://www.cch.com
Publisher
N.A.I.C.S.: 513199

Wolters Kluwer France SA (1)
14 rue Fructidor, 75 814, Paris, Cedex, France (100%)
Tel.: (33) 185583000
Web Site: http://www.wolterskluwer.fr
Sales Range: $200-249.9 Million
Law/Taxation, Business & Medical Publishing
N.A.I.C.S.: 513120

Subsidiary (Domestic):

Editions Lamy (2)
1 Rue Eugene Et Armand Peugeot, 92856, Rueil-Malmaison, France
Tel.: (33) 176733000
Web Site: http://www.wkf.fr
Sales Range: $100-124.9 Million
Emp.: 300
Legal & Business Publishing
N.A.I.C.S.: 513120

Wolters Kluwer Health (1)
2001 Market St, Philadelphia, PA 19103
Tel.: (215) 521-8300
Web Site: https://www.wolterskluwerhealth.com
Rev.: $829,315,200
Emp.: 2,600

Electronic & Print Publisher of Medical Information, Drug Reference Tools & Textbooks
N.A.I.C.S.: 513140
Diana Nole (CEO)

Subsidiary (Domestic):

Health Language, Inc. (2)
4600 S Syracuse St Ste 1200, Denver, CO 80237
Tel.: (720) 940-2900
Web Site: https://www.healthlanguage.com
Sales Range: $10-24.9 Million
Emp.: 150
Healthcare Software Developer
N.A.I.C.S.: 513210
George T. Schwend (Pres & CEO)

Unit (Domestic):

IFI Claims Patent Services (2)
398 Carl St, Wilmington, NC 28403-0516
Tel.: (910) 392-0068
Web Site: http://www.ificlaims.com
Sales Range: $25-49.9 Million
Emp.: 20
Patent Database Publisher
N.A.I.C.S.: 513140

Subsidiary (Domestic):

Lexi-Comp, Inc. (2)
1100 Terex Rd, Hudson, OH 44236
Tel.: (330) 650-6506
Web Site: http://www.wolterskluwercdi.com
Sales Range: $50-74.9 Million
Emp.: 150
Health Care Information Services
N.A.I.C.S.: 519290
Michael Hofherr (VP)

Lippincott Williams & Wilkins, Inc. (2)
2001 Market St, Philadelphia, PA 19103
Tel.: (215) 521-8300
Web Site: http://www.lww.com
Rev.: $19,757,032
Emp.: 350
Medical Books Publisher
N.A.I.C.S.: 513130
Susan Driscoll (Exec VP & Gen Mgr)

Unit (Domestic):

Facts & Comparisons (3)
77 Westport Plz Ste 450, Saint Louis, MO 63146 (100%)
Tel.: (314) 216-2100
Web Site: http://www.factsandcomparisons.com
Sales Range: $25-49.9 Million
Emp.: 70
Book Publishing of Medical Information
N.A.I.C.S.: 513130

Subsidiary (Non-US):

Lippincott Williams & Wilkins Asia Ltd. (3)
15/F W Square 314-324 Hennessy Road, Wanchai, China (Hong Kong)
Tel.: (852) 26107000
Web Site: http://www.lww.com
Sales Range: $25-49.9 Million
Emp.: 5
Health Care Publisher
N.A.I.C.S.: 513199

Lippincott Williams & Wilkins Pty. Ltd. (3)
55 Mountain St Ste 303, Broadway, 2007, NSW, Australia
Tel.: (61) 292125955
Web Site: http://www.lww.com
Sales Range: $25-49.9 Million
Emp.: 20
Publisher
N.A.I.C.S.: 513199

Unit (Domestic):

Nursing2014 (3)
2 Commerce Sq 2001 Market St, Philadelphia, PA 19103
Tel.: (215) 521-8300
Web Site: http://journals.lww.com
Sales Range: $25-49.9 Million
Emp.: 80
Nursing Journal
N.A.I.C.S.: 513120

INTERNATIONAL PUBLIC

Jennifer E. Brogan (VP-Society Svcs)

Unit (Domestic):

Medi-Span (2)
8425 Woodfield Crossing Blvd Ste 490, Indianapolis, IN 46240
Tel.: (317) 735-5300
Web Site: http://www.medi-span.com
Health Care Publishing
N.A.I.C.S.: 513130

Subsidiary (Domestic):

Ovid Technologies, Inc. (2)
333 7th Ave 20th Fl, New York, NY 10001-5004
Tel.: (646) 674-6300
Web Site: https://www.ovid.com
Sales Range: $25-49.9 Million
Emp.: 75
Information Retrieval Services & Knowledge Management Solutions
N.A.I.C.S.: 517810
Karen Abramsom (Pres & CEO)

Branch (Domestic):

Ovid Technologies (3)
100 River Ridge Dr, Norwood, MA 02062-5030
Tel.: (781) 769-2599
Web Site: http://www.ovid.com
Sales Range: $25-49.9 Million
Information Retrieval Services
N.A.I.C.S.: 517810
Karen Abramson (Pres & CEO)

Subsidiary (Non-US):

Ovid Technologies Sarl (3)
51 rue Le Peletier, 75009, Paris, France
Tel.: (33) 149964262
Web Site: http://www.ovid.com
Sales Range: $25-49.9 Million
Emp.: 64
Health Care Publisher
N.A.I.C.S.: 513199

Subsidiary (Domestic):

Pharmacy OneSource, Inc. (2)
3535 Factoria Blvd SE Ste 440, Bellevue, WA 98006
Tel.: (425) 451-4063
Web Site: http://www.pharmacyonesource.com
Sales Range: $25-49.9 Million
Emp.: 40
Software Programming Applications
N.A.I.C.S.: 541511
Kaj Pedersen (CTO)

Unit (Domestic):

UCC Direct (2)
2727 Allen Pkwy, Houston, TX 77019
Tel.: (713) 942-8172
Book Publishers
N.A.I.C.S.: 513130

Subsidiary (Non-US):

Wolters Kluwer Health Mexico, S.A. de C.V (2)
Cerro de tuera 27 Colonia Barrio Oxtopulco University, Mexico, 04318, DF, Mexico
Tel.: (52) 5555244948
Web Site: http://www.wkhealth.com
Sales Range: $25-49.9 Million
Emp.: 15
Publishing
N.A.I.C.S.: 513199

Wolters Kluwer Holdings (UK) PLC (1)
145 London Road, Kingston upon Thames, KT2 6SR, Surrey, United Kingdom
Tel.: (44) 2082471100
Sales Range: $150-199.9 Million
Emp.: 300
Holding Company; Business & Educational Publishing & Information Services
N.A.I.C.S.: 551112
Claudio Salinardi (Exec VP/Gen Mgr-Fin, Risk & Reporting Bus-Global)

Subsidiary (Domestic):

Wolters Kluwer (UK) Ltd. (2)
145 London Road, Kingston upon Thames,

AND PRIVATE COMPANIES

WOLTERS KLUWER N.V.

KT2 6SR, Surrey, United Kingdom
Tel.: (44) 2082471100
Business & Educational Publishing & Information Services
N.A.I.C.S.: 513130

Wolters Kluwer Financial Services UK Ltd. (2)
250 Waterloo Road, London, SE1 8RD, United Kingdom
Tel.: (44) 800 840 1160
Financial Compliance, Content & Technology Information Services
N.A.I.C.S.: 519290
Dean Curtis *(Mng Dir)*

Wolters Kluwer India (1)
Building No 10 Tower B 3rd Floor Cyber City, DLF Phase-2 Sector 24, Gurgaon, 122002, Haryana, India
Tel.: (91) 1244960999
Web Site: https://www.wolterskluwer.com
Online Publishing Services
N.A.I.C.S.: 513130
Shireesh Sahai *(CEO)*

Wolters Kluwer Italia S.r.l. (1)
Tel.: (39) 0282476261
Web Site: https://www.wolterskluwer.com
Sales Range: $100-124.9 Million
Emp.: 450
Book Publishers
N.A.I.C.S.: 513130
Giulietta Lemmi *(Mng Dir)*

Subsidiary (Domestic):

Ipsoa Editore srl (2)
Centro Direzionale Milanofiori Strada 1 Palazzo F 6, Milan, 20090, Assago, Italy **(100%)**
Tel.: (39) 0282476100
Web Site: http://www.ipsoa.it
Sales Range: $100-124.9 Million
Emp.: 400
Legal, Taxation & Business Publishing
N.A.I.C.S.: 513120

OSRA SpA (2)
Corso Lombardia 69, 10099, San Mauro Torinese, Torino, Italy **(100%)**
Tel.: (39) 011273661
Web Site: http://www.osra.it
Sales Range: $25-49.9 Million
Emp.: 100
Provider of Tax Compliance & HR Software
N.A.I.C.S.: 541511

Wolters Kluwer Legal & Regulatory Europe (1)
Zuidpoolsimgel 2, 2400 MH, Alphen aan den Rijn, Netherlands
Tel.: (31) 206070400
Web Site: http://www.wolterskluwer.com
Sales Range: $50-74.9 Million
Emp.: 100
Online & Print Publisher of Legal, Tax & Regulatory Information
N.A.I.C.S.: 513199
Gregory Samios *(Pres-Clinical Effectiveness & CEO-Clinical Effectiveness)*

Wolters Kluwer Limited (1)
90 Sheppard Ave E Suite 300, Toronto, M2N 6X1, ON, Canada
Tel.: (416) 224-2224
Web Site: http://www.wolterskluwer.com
Sales Range: $50-74.9 Million
Publisher of Topical Law Reports
N.A.I.C.S.: 513120
Doug Finley *(Pres)*

Wolters Kluwer Polska Sp. z o.o. (1)
ul Przyokopowa 33, 01-208, Warsaw, Poland
Tel.: (48) 225358800
Web Site: https://www.wolterskluwer.com
Sales Range: $50-74.9 Million
Emp.: 200
Book Publishers
N.A.I.C.S.: 513130
Wlodek Albin *(CEO)*

Branch (Domestic):

Wolters Kluwer Polska - Sopot (2)
Redakcja LEX, ul Rzemieslnicza 7, 80-266, Sopot, Poland
Tel.: (48) 587676000
Web Site: http://www.wolterskluwer.pl

Software Publisher
N.A.I.C.S.: 513210
Joanna Jeziorowska *(Dir-Mgmt)*

Wolters Kluwer SRL (1)
Tudor Vladimirescu Nr 22 Sector 5 Greengate Building 6th Floor, Bucharest, 50881, Romania
Tel.: (40) 312244100
Web Site: http://www.wolterskluwer.com
Online Publishing Services
N.A.I.C.S.: 513130
Dan Stoici *(Pres)*

Wolters Kluwer Tax & Accounting (1)
2700 Lake Cook Rd, Riverwoods, IL 60015
Tel.: (847) 267-7000
Web Site: http://www.cchgroup.com
Rev.: $390,637,792
Emp.: 500
Tax Law, Medical & Allied Health Care & Business Law Information Services
N.A.I.C.S.: 513130
Jason Marx *(CEO)*

Subsidiary (Domestic):

Aspen Publishers, Inc. (2)
76 9th Ave 7th Fl, New York, NY 10011
Tel.: (212) 771-0600
Web Site: http://www.wolterskluwer.com
Sales Range: $50-74.9 Million
Emp.: 170
Publisher of Legal, Business, Tax & Education Books & Periodicals
N.A.I.C.S.: 513120
Stacey Caywood *(Pres & CEO)*

CCH Inc. (2)
2700 Lake Cook Rd, Riverwoods, IL 60015-3867
Tel.: (847) 267-7000
Web Site: https://www.cch.com
Sales Range: $200-249.9 Million
Tax, Legal, Securities, Human Resources, Health Care & Small Business Information & Software
N.A.I.C.S.: 513120
Teresa Mackintosh *(Exec VP & Gen Mgr-Tax)*

Unit (Domestic):

CCH (3)
2700 Lake Cook Rd, Riverwoods, IL 60015
Tel.: (847) 267-2145
Web Site: http://www.cch.com
Sales Range: $100-124.9 Million
Emp.: 300
Publishing
N.A.I.C.S.: 513199

Subsidiary (Non-US):

CCH Australia Limited (3)
101 Waterloo Road, North Ryde, 2113, NSW, Australia **(100%)**
Tel.: (61) 298571300
Web Site: http://www.cch.com.au
Sales Range: $50-74.9 Million
Emp.: 120
Book Publishers
N.A.I.C.S.: 513130
Rusell Evins *(CEO)*

Subsidiary (Non-US):

CCH Asia Limited (4)
8 Chang Charn Rd 03-00 Link Bldg, Singapore, 159637, Singapore **(100%)**
Tel.: (65) 62252555
Web Site: http://www.cch.com.sg
Sales Range: $25-49.9 Million
Emp.: 30
Law Publishing, News Reports
N.A.I.C.S.: 513120
Sandy Cheung *(Gen Mgr)*

Subsidiary (Non-US):

CCH (M) Sdn Bhd (5)
Suite 9-1 & 9-2 Level 9 Menara Weld 76 Jalan Raja Chulan, 50200, Kuala Lumpur, Malaysia
Tel.: (60) 320248600
Web Site: http://www.cch.com.my
Financial Management Services
N.A.I.C.S.: 523999

CCH Hong Kong Limited (5)
Room 1608 16/F Harcourt House 39 Gloucester Road, Wanchai, China (Hong Kong)
Tel.: (852) 3718 9100
Web Site: http://www.cch.com.hk
Accounting Software Development Services
N.A.I.C.S.: 541511

Subsidiary (Non-US):

CCH New Zealand Limited (4)
41 Centorian Dr Windsor Park, Auckland, 632, New Zealand
Tel.: (64) 94882760
Web Site: http://www.cch.co.nz
Sales Range: $10-24.9 Million
Emp.: 35
Publishing of Legal Information
N.A.I.C.S.: 513120
Julie Benton *(Gen Mgr)*

Subsidiary (Non-US):

CCH Japan Limited (3)
5th Fl 3 6 2 Misakicho Chiyoda Ku, Tokyo, 101-0061, Japan **(100%)**
Tel.: (81) 332651161
Web Site: http://www.cch-japan.jp
Sales Range: $25-49.9 Million
Emp.: 4
Publisher of Legal Information
N.A.I.C.S.: 513120

Unit (Domestic):

CCH Small Firm Services (3)
225 Chastain Meadows Ct Nw Ste 200, Kennesaw, GA 30144-5938
Tel.: (770) 857-5000
Web Site: http://www.cchsfs.com
Sales Range: $150-199.9 Million
Emp.: 600
Tax Preparation & Electronic Filing Services
N.A.I.C.S.: 541213
Rusty Tillman *(VP-Sls)*

Subsidiary (Domestic):

CCH Tax Compliance (3)
20101 Hamilton Ave, Torrance, CA 90502 **(100%)**
Tel.: (310) 800-9800
Web Site: http://www.prosystemfx.com
Sales Range: $100-124.9 Million
Emp.: 300
Computerized Tax Return Processing
N.A.I.C.S.: 541511
Nancy McKinstry *(CEO)*

Wolters Kluwer Corporate Legal Services (3)
111 8th Ave Fl 13, New York, NY 10011-5213 **(100%)**
Tel.: (212) 894-8940
Web Site: http://www.cch-lis.com
Sales Range: $150-199.9 Million
Emp.: 600
Legal Information Services
N.A.I.C.S.: 541110
Sandeep Sacheti *(VP-Customer Insights & Operational Excellence)*

Subsidiary (Domestic):

CCH Washington Service Bureau, Inc. (4)
1015 15th St NW 10th Fl, Washington, DC 20005 **(100%)**
Tel.: (202) 312-6600
Web Site: http://www.wsb.com
Sales Range: $10-24.9 Million
Loose Leaf Publication & Information Retrieval
N.A.I.C.S.: 811210
Paula Swain *(Co-Founder)*

CCH-LIS Research Corporation (4)
111 8th Ave Fl 13, New York, NY 10011 **(100%)**
Tel.: (212) 894-8940
Web Site: http://ux-ctadmin.ctadvantage.com
Sales Range: $1-9.9 Million
Trademark Search
N.A.I.C.S.: 533110
Richard Flynn *(Pres)*

CT Corporation System (4)
111 8th Ave Fl 13, New York, NY 10011 **(100%)**
Tel.: (212) 894-8940
Web Site: http://www.ctadvantage.com

Sales Range: $150-199.9 Million
Emp.: 600
Corporate Business Services
N.A.I.C.S.: 541110
Nancy McKintry *(Pres)*

Subsidiary (Non-US):

IQS Avantiq Luxembourg SARL (4)
2 rue Sangenberg, 5080, Howald, Luxembourg
Tel.: (352) 31 17 501
Web Site: http://www.avantiq.com
Trademark Search Services
N.A.I.C.S.: 541720
Catherine McGirr *(COO)*

Subsidiary (Non-US):

Avantiq AG (5)
98 Baarerstrasse, 6302, Zug, Switzerland
Tel.: (41) 417617676
Trademark & Domain Research Services
N.A.I.C.S.: 541720
Brigitta Best *(CEO)*

Avantiq Oceania Pty Ltd (5)
PO Box 1244, Blackwood, Adelaide, 5051, SA, Australia
Tel.: (61) 88374 2453
Trademark, Domain & Company Name Search Services
N.A.I.C.S.: 541720

Subsidiary (Domestic):

National Registered Agents, Inc. (4)
100 Canal Pointe Blvd Ste 10, Princeton Junction, NJ 08550
Tel.: (609) 716-0300
Web Site: https://www.nrai.com
Sales Range: $10-24.9 Million
Emp.: 42
Business Compliance Services
N.A.I.C.S.: 541618

Subsidiary (Domestic):

Novem Professional Services LLC (5)
1720 Windward Concourse Ste 390, Alpharetta, GA 30005 **(100%)**
Tel.: (877) 805-6723
Web Site: http://www.triadpros.com
Professional, Scientific & Technical Services
N.A.I.C.S.: 541990

Subsidiary (Domestic):

esalestax.com, inc. (3)
6766 S Revere Pkwy Ste 120, Englewood, CO 80112-6782
Tel.: (303) 302-3829
Web Site: http://www.cch.com
Sales Range: $25-49.9 Million
Emp.: 18
Online Financial Applications
N.A.I.C.S.: 541512

Subsidiary (Domestic):

CPE Link (2)
4320 Stevens Creek Blvd Ste 160, San Jose, CA 95129
Tel.: (408) 400-0000
Web Site: http://www.cpelink.com
Professional Education Services
N.A.I.C.S.: 923110
Janaye Fletcher *(Acct Mgr)*

CT Corsearch (2)
111 Eighth Ave 13th Fl, New York, NY 10011
Tel.: (917) 408-5000
Web Site: http://www.corsearch.com
Sales Range: $25-49.9 Million
Emp.: 115
Provider of Research Services
N.A.I.C.S.: 541910

Vanguard Software Corp. (2)
1100 Cresc Green Dr, Cary, NC 27518
Tel.: (919) 859-4101
Web Site: http://www.vanguardsw.com
Rev.: $1,600,000
Emp.: 14
Mail-Order Houses
N.A.I.C.S.: 513210
Katherine Suggs *(Sec)*

eOriginal, Inc (1)

WOLTERS KLUWER N.V.

Wolters Kluwer n.v.—(Continued)
250 W Pratt St Ste 1400, Baltimore, MD 21201
Tel.: (410) 659-9796
Web Site: http://www.eoriginals.com
Sales Range: $1-9.9 Million
Custom Computer Programming Services
N.A.I.C.S.: 541511

WOLUWE SHOPPING CENTER
Rue St Lambert 200, 1200, Brussels, Belgium
Tel.: (32) 27712045
Web Site:
 http://www.thewshopping.be
WOLS—(EUR)
Sales Range: Less than $1 Million
Shopping Centre Services
N.A.I.C.S.: 812990

WOLVERINE ENERGY & INFRASTRUCTURE, INC.
450-1010 8th Ave, Calgary, T2P 1J2, AB, Canada
Tel.: (780) 435-3451
Web Site: https://wnrgi.com
WEII—(TSXV)
Rev.: $91,391,839
Assets: $180,655,568
Liabilities: $133,749,562
Net Worth: $46,906,006
Earnings: ($16,899,010)
Fiscal Year-end: 03/31/21
Construction Services
N.A.I.C.S.: 236220
Shannon Ostapovich (Pres)

WOLVERINE RESOURCES CORP.
Ste 55 11020 Williams Rd, Richmond, V7A 1X8, BC, Canada
Tel.: (778) 297-4409 NV
Web Site:
 https://wolverineresourcescorp.com
Year Founded: 2006
WOLV—(OTCIQ)
Assets: $22,732
Liabilities: $87,542
Net Worth: ($64,810)
Earnings: ($458,653)
Fiscal Year-end: 05/31/24
Investment Services
N.A.I.C.S.: 523999
Luke Rich (Executives)

WOMANCART LIMITED
F-14/57 2nd floor Model Town-II, New Delhi, 110009, India
Tel.: (91) 9311866860
Web Site: https://www.womancart.in
Year Founded: 2018
WOMANCART—(NSE)
Rev.: $1,060,437
Assets: $622,365
Liabilities: $247,342
Net Worth: $375,023
Earnings: $54,912
Emp.: 27
Fiscal Year-end: 03/31/23
Online Shopping Services
N.A.I.C.S.: 425120

WOMEN'S NEXT LOUNGERIES LTD
101-105 Indian Complex Building No 28 1st Floor, Dapode Village Bhiwandi, Thane, 421329, Maharastra, India
Tel.: (91) 2225610990
Web Site: http://www.womensnext.in
Rev.: $6,031,550
Assets: $10,308,006
Liabilities: $5,679,808
Net Worth: $4,628,198
Earnings: $282,644
Emp.: 26

Fiscal Year-end: 03/31/18
Women's Lingerie Mfr
N.A.I.C.S.: 315250
Bhavesh Tulsidas Bhanushali (Chm & Mng Dir)

WON TECH CO., LTD.
64 Techno 8-ro Yuseong-gu, Daejeon, 305-500, Korea (South)
Tel.: (82) 70 7836 6966
Web Site: http://www.wtlaser.com
Medical Equipment Mfr
N.A.I.C.S.: 339112
Jong Won Kim (Co-CEO)

WONBIOGEN CO., LTD.
56 1Gongdan-Ro 5-Gil, Gumi, Gyeongsangbuk-do, Korea (South)
Tel.: (82) 544627965
Web Site:
 https://www.wonbiogen.co.kr
Year Founded: 2018
307280—(KRS)
Rev.: $20,515,503
Assets: $29,861,286
Liabilities: $9,286,064
Net Worth: $20,575,222
Earnings: $2,510,004
Emp.: 63
Fiscal Year-end: 12/31/22
Medical & Dental Instrument Mfr & Distr
N.A.I.C.S.: 339112
Won-Il Kim (CEO)

WONDER AUTO TECHNOLOGY, INC.
16 Yulu Street, Taihe District, Jinzhou, 121013, Liaoning, China
Tel.: (86) 4162661186 NV
Sales Range: $200-249.9 Million
Emp.: 3,766
Automotive Electrical Parts Including Alternators & Starters Mfr
N.A.I.C.S.: 336320

Subsidiaries:

Jinzhou Dong Woo Precision Co., Ltd. (1)
4-15 Gohai Street Jetdz, Jinzhou, 121007, Liaoning, China
Tel.: (86) 4162930039
Web Site: http://www.jzdwp.com
Sales Range: $50-74.9 Million
Emp.: 140
Automobile Component Parts Mfr
N.A.I.C.S.: 336390
Ling Wing (Pres)

WONDER ELECTRICALS LIMITED
45 Okhla Industrial Estate Phase-Iii, New Delhi, 110020, India
Tel.: (91) 1166058952
Web Site:
 https://www.wonderelectricals.com
Year Founded: 2014
WFL—(NSE)
Rev.: $41,745,259
Assets: $26,834,800
Liabilities: $20,407,394
Net Worth: $6,427,406
Earnings: $579,433
Emp.: 101
Fiscal Year-end: 03/12/21
Household Appliances Mfr
N.A.I.C.S.: 335220
Harsh Kumar Anand (Mng Dir)

WONDERFI TECHNOLOGIES INC.
110 Cumberland St 341, PO Box 10068, Toronto, M5R 3V5, ON, Canada
Tel.: (778) 331-8508
Web Site: https://www.wonder.fi

WRC—(DEU)
Rev.: $22,722,681
Assets: $857,217,192
Liabilities: $778,248,006
Net Worth: $78,969,186
Earnings: ($12,605,353)
Emp.: 94
Fiscal Year-end: 12/31/23
Mineral Exploration & Mining Services
N.A.I.C.S.: 212390
Scott Edwin Ackerman (Pres, CEO, CFO & Sec)

WONDERFUL HI-TECH CO., LTD.
72 WuGong 6th Rd, WuGu Dist New Taipei Industrial Park, New Taipei City, 24891, Taiwan
Tel.: (886) 222988033
Web Site: https://www.wontex.com
Year Founded: 1978
6190—(TPE)
Rev.: $282,283,870
Assets: $197,212,863
Liabilities: $102,340,431
Net Worth: $94,872,432
Earnings: $16,823,625
Emp.: 1,071
Fiscal Year-end: 12/31/22
Electronic Wire & Cable Mfr
N.A.I.C.S.: 335929
Chien-Chung Chen (Pres)

Subsidiaries:

Aba Industry Inc. (1)
639 EWalnut St, Carson, CA 90746
Tel.: (310) 327-7670
Web Site: https://www.aba-cable.com
Wire & Cable Mfr
N.A.I.C.S.: 335929

Shanghai Elitech Technology Co., Ltd. (1)
Room 201 Building 2 No 268 Taihong Road, Minhang District, Shanghai, China
Tel.: (86) 2133676880
Electronic Parts Distr
N.A.I.C.S.: 423690

Thai Wonderful Wire Cable Co., Ltd. (1)
52-52/1 M5 Tambol Nongkakha Amphur, Phanthong, Chon Buri, 20160, Thailand
Tel.: (66) 38451432
Web Site: http://www.thaiwonderful.com
Wire & Cable Mfr
N.A.I.C.S.: 335929

Wonderful (vietnam) Wire & Cable Co., Ltd (1)
Lot XN21 Km 51 Highway No 5, Dai An Industrial Zone, Hai Duong, Vietnam
Tel.: (84) 2203555588
Web Site: http://www.vwt-wonderful.com
Wire & Cable Mfr
N.A.I.C.S.: 335929

Wonderful Cabling Systems Corp. (1)
1F No 72 Wugong 6th Rd, New Taipei Industrial park Wugu, New Taipei City, Taiwan
Tel.: (886) 222901338
Wire & Cable Mfr
N.A.I.C.S.: 335929

Wonderful Photoelectricity (Dong Guan) Co., Ltd. (1)
Longyan Industrial Area, Humen, Dongguan, Guangdong, China
Tel.: (86) 76988620666
Web Site: http://www.wonderful-wire.com.cn
Wire & Cable Mfr
N.A.I.C.S.: 335929

WONDERFUL SKY FINANCIAL GROUP HOLDINGS LIMITED
9/F The Center 99 Queens Road Central, Central, China (Hong Kong)
Tel.: (852) 39702111
Web Site: http://www.wsfg.hk

INTERNATIONAL PUBLIC

1260—(HKG)
Rev.: $35,190,893
Assets: $205,546,193
Liabilities: $17,480,250
Net Worth: $188,065,943
Earnings: $3,470,805
Emp.: 270
Fiscal Year-end: 03/31/23
Holding Company; Financial Public Relations Consulting
N.A.I.C.S.: 551112
Tianni Liu (Chm & CEO)

Subsidiaries:

Alpha Financial Press Limited (1)
9/F The Center 99 Queen's Road Central, Central, China (Hong Kong)
Tel.: (852) 39771888
Web Site: http://www.alphafp.hk
Financial Services
N.A.I.C.S.: 525990

Wonderful Sky Financial Group (1)
9/F The Center 99 Queens Road, Central, China (Hong Kong)
Tel.: (852) 39702111
Financial Services
N.A.I.C.S.: 523940

WONDERFUL TIMES GROUP AB
Ostra Storgatan 3, 553 21, Jonkoping, Sweden
Tel.: (46) 3669000
Web Site:
 https://www.wonderfultimes.se
Toy Mfr
N.A.I.C.S.: 339930
Sofia Ljungdahl (CEO)

WONDERLA HOLIDAYS LTD.
28th Km Mysore Road, Bengaluru, 562109, Karnataka, India
Tel.: (91) 8022010333
Web Site: https://www.wonderla.com
538268—(BOM)
Rev.: $6,102,710
Assets: $124,366,815
Liabilities: $13,868,591
Net Worth: $110,498,224
Earnings: ($6,815,854)
Emp.: 587
Fiscal Year-end: 03/31/21
Amusement Park
N.A.I.C.S.: 713110
George Joseph (Mng Dir)

Subsidiaries:

Wonderla Holidays Ltd (1)
Kakkanad Pallikara Road Kumarapuram Post Office, Pallikara, Cochin, 683565, India
Tel.: (91) 484 268 4001
Web Site: https://www.wonderla.com
Sales Range: $150-199.9 Million
Emp.: 500
Amusement Park
N.A.I.C.S.: 713110
Priya Sarah Cheeran Joseph (Exec Dir)

WONDERS INFORMATION CO., LTD.
No 1518 Lianhang Road, Minhang District, Shanghai, 201112, China
Tel.: (86) 2124178888
Web Site:
 https://www.wondersgroup.com
300168—(CHIN)
Rev.: $452,585,016
Assets: $963,365,832
Liabilities: $790,861,968
Net Worth: $172,503,864
Earnings: ($40,701,960)
Fiscal Year-end: 12/31/22
Software Applications & IT Services
N.A.I.C.S.: 513210
Hongwei Hu (Vice Chm & Pres)

WONDERSHARE TECHNOLOGY CO., LTD.

10F Block D Building 5 Software Industry Base Haitian 2nd Road, Yuehai Subdistrict Nanshan District, Shenzhen, 518057, Guangdong, China
Tel.: (86) 75586665000
Web Site: http://www.wondershare.com
Year Founded: 2003
300624—(CHIN)
Rev: $208,589,836
Assets: $236,454,712
Liabilities: $40,120,587
Net Worth: $196,334,125
Earnings: $12,142,073
Fiscal Year-end: 12/31/23
Software Product Development Services
N.A.I.C.S.: 541511
Tobee Wu *(Founder & CEO)*

WONG ENGINEERING CORPORATION BERHAD
Lot 24 Jalan Hi-Tech 4 Kulim Hi-Tech Park Phase 1, 09000, Kulim, Kedah, Malaysia
Tel.: (60) 44271788   MY
Web Site: https://www.wec.com.my
Year Founded: 1982
WONG—(KLS)
Rev.: $11,470,457
Assets: $27,196,669
Liabilities: $10,646,185
Net Worth: $16,550,484
Earnings: ($1,650,871)
Emp.: 400
Fiscal Year-end: 10/31/23
Oil Mfr
N.A.I.C.S.: 211120
Joo Huat Chang *(Exec Dir)*

Subsidiaries:

WEC Marketing Sdn. Bhd. (1)
Lot 24 Jalan Hi-tech 4 Kulim Hi-tech Park Phase 1, 09000, Kulim, Kedah, Malaysia
Tel.: (60) 44271788
Web Site: http://www.wec.com.my
Emp.: 300
Healthcare Product Distr
N.A.I.C.S.: 423450

Wong Engineering Electronics Sdn. Bhd. (1)
Lot 24 Jalan Hi Tech 4 Kulim Hi Tech Park, Kulim, 09000, Kedah, Malaysia
Tel.: (60) 44271788
Web Site: http://www.wec.com.my
Sales Range: $50-74.9 Million
Emp.: 200
High Precision Metal Components Mfr
N.A.I.C.S.: 332999

Wong Engineering Industries Sdn. Bhd. (1)
Lot 24 Jalan Hi-Tech 4 Kulim Hi-Tech Park Phase 1, 09000, Kulim, Kedah, Malaysia
Tel.: (60) 44271788
Sales Range: $100-124.9 Million
Emp.: 300
High Precision Metal Stampings Mfr
N.A.I.C.S.: 332119
Freddy Kem Woh Wong *(Mng Dir)*

WONG FONG INDUSTRIES LIMITED
79 Joo Koon Circle, Singapore, 629107, Singapore
Tel.: (65) 68616555   SG
Web Site: https://www.wongfongindustries.com
Year Founded: 1964
1A1—(CAT)
Rev.: $59,045,671
Assets: $61,973,794
Liabilities: $20,952,056
Net Worth: $41,021,737
Earnings: $3,172,006
Emp.: 386
Fiscal Year-end: 12/31/23
Investment Holding Services
N.A.I.C.S.: 551112
Ah Kuie Liew *(Founder & CEO)*

Subsidiaries:

1Summit Global Pte Ltd (1)
79 Joo Koon Circle, Singapore, 629107, Singapore
Tel.: (65) 6 863 3686
Web Site: https://www.1sg.sg
Human Capital Development Services
N.A.I.C.S.: 541612
James Liew *(Chm)*

Ce Asia Heavy Machinery Sdn Bhd (1)
No 21 Jalan Kempas Utama 3, Kempas Utama Industrial Park, 81200, Johor Bahru, Johor, Malaysia
Tel.: (60) 75590188
Web Site: https://www.ceasia.my
Mechanical Engineering Services
N.A.I.C.S.: 541330

Smatra Training Hub Pte. Ltd. (1)
1 Kaki Bukit Road 1 01-14 Enterprise One, Singapore, 415934, Singapore
Tel.: (65) 68633686
Web Site: http://www.sth.sg
Training Academy Services
N.A.I.C.S.: 611519

Wfric Shenzhen Co., Ltd. (1)
Qiaoxiang Gongguan Block 6 Unit A 2002 Qiaoxiang Road No 3028 Futian, Shenzhen, Guangdong, China
Tel.: (86) 75529193270
Web Site: http://www.wfricworld.com
Construction Equipment Distr
N.A.I.C.S.: 423810

Wong Fong Myanmar Company Limited (1)
No 1107/1108 Thit Taw Street 2, Ward 13 East Dagon Township, Yangon, Myanmar
Tel.: (95) 33445566
Construction Equipment Distr
N.A.I.C.S.: 423810

WONG'S KONG KING INTERNATIONAL (HOLDINGS) LIMITED
17/F Octa Tower No 8 Lam Chak Street, Kowloon Bay, Hong Kong, China (Hong Kong)
Tel.: (852) 23578888   BM
Web Site: http://www.wkkintl.com
Year Founded: 1975
0532—(HKG)
Rev.: $587,648,393
Assets: $473,719,748
Liabilities: $237,443,505
Net Worth: $236,276,243
Earnings: $14,372,055
Emp.: 3,779
Fiscal Year-end: 12/31/22
Investment Management Service
N.A.I.C.S.: 523940
Senta Wong *(Founder & Chm)*

Subsidiaries:

Dongguan Nissin Plastic Products Co., Ltd. (1)
WKK Technology Park 38-8 Gangjian Road Tu Tang, Chang Ping Town, Dongguan, 523000, Guangdong, China
Tel.: (86) 76983391824
Plastics Product Mfr
N.A.I.C.S.: 326199

Dongguan Wong's Kong King Electronics Co., Limited (1)
33 Gangjian Avenue Wangshi, Tutang Changping Town, Dongguan, 523581, China
Tel.: (86) 76983903333
Electrical Equipment Mfr & Distr
N.A.I.C.S.: 335999

Grace Year Enterprises Limited (1)
4/F Block B Goodman Kwai Chung Logistics Centre Castle Peak Road, 585609, Kwai Chung, New Territories, China (Hong Kong)
Tel.: (852) 23578068
Plastic Product Distr
N.A.I.C.S.: 424610

TAIWAN WKK DISTRIBUTION CO., LTD. (1)
7F-3 No 99 Sec 1 Nankan Road, Luchu, Taoyuan, 33859, Taiwan
Tel.: (886) 32223303
Web Site: http://www.wkkintl.com
Emp.: 20
Electronic Equipment Distr
N.A.I.C.S.: 423690
Liu Chien Wei *(Gen Mgr)*

Taiwan Kong King Co., Limited (1)
5F-4 No 66 Sec 2 Nankan Road, Luzhu, Taoyuan, Taiwan
Tel.: (886) 33529333
Web Site: http://www.tkk.com
Electronic Component Mfr & Distr
N.A.I.C.S.: 334419

WKK (THAILAND) LTD. (1)
99/101 Moo 3 Chaeng Wattana Road, Talad Bangkhen Laksi, Bangkok, 10210, Thailand
Tel.: (66) 25525109
Web Site: http://www.wkkintl.com
Emp.: 16
Electronic Equipment Distr
N.A.I.C.S.: 423690
Suranart Ramjed *(Country Mgr)*

WKK America (Holdings) Inc. (1)
Ste 200 175 Bernal Rd, San Jose, CA 95119
Tel.: (408) 738-3131
Emp.: 6,500
Electronic Product Distr
N.A.I.C.S.: 423690

WKK DISTRIBUTION (MALAYSIA) SDN. BHD. (1)
Unit 2 Lower Level 4 Hotel Equatorial Penang 1 Jalan Bukit Jambul, 11900, Bayan Lepas, Penang, Malaysia
Tel.: (60) 46451670
Web Site: http://www.wkkdistribution.com
Emp.: 10
Electronic Equipment Distr
N.A.I.C.S.: 423690

WKK Distribution (Singapore) Pte Ltd (1)
63 Ubi Avenue 1 05-03 63 UBI, Singapore, 408937, Singapore
Tel.: (65) 67417322
Web Site: http://www.wkkintl.com
Emp.: 15
Electronic Components Distr
N.A.I.C.S.: 423690
Leung Man Hoy *(Gen Mgr)*

WKK Distribution Limited (1)
17/F Harbourside HQ No 8 Lam Chak Street, Kowloon, China (Hong Kong)
Tel.: (852) 23578888
Web Site: https://www.wkkdistribution.com
Electronic Component Mfr & Distr
N.A.I.C.S.: 334419

WKK EMS EQUIPMENT (BEIJING) LTD. (1)
Room 1801 Blk B Yicheng International Centre 10 Rong Hua Mid-Road, Beijing, 100176, China
Tel.: (86) 10 5778 0051
Electronic Equipment Distr
N.A.I.C.S.: 423690

WKK EMS EQUIPMENT (CHENGDU) LTD. (1)
Rm1205 Highland Centre Building 9 Jianshe Road, Chengdu, 610051, Sichuan, China
Tel.: (86) 28 8432 3383
Electronic Equipment Distr
N.A.I.C.S.: 423690

WKK EMS EQUIPMENT (CHONGQING) LTD. (1)
Room17-3 Yugaoweilai building No 6 Keyuan one road, Jiulongpo District, Chongqing, 400039, China
Tel.: (86) 23 6819 3303
Electronic Equipment Distr
N.A.I.C.S.: 423690

WKK ENGINEERING SERVICE LTD. (1)
1 Wang Yuen Street, Kowloon, China (Hong Kong)
Tel.: (852) 23578585
Web Site: https://www.wkkes.com
Engineeering Services
N.A.I.C.S.: 541330

WKK Electronic Equipment (Xi'an) Ltd. (1)
Rm 2206D Tower VanMetropolis No 1 Tangyan Rd, Xi'an, 710065, Shaanxi, China
Tel.: (86) 29 8928 1076
Electronic Equipment Distr
N.A.I.C.S.: 423690
Frank Lin Fu Chan *(Gen Mgr)*

WKK JAPAN LTD. (1)
6th floor Ikeda Building 1-7-15 Shibakoen, Minato-ku, Tokyo, 105-0011, Japan
Tel.: (81) 334357131
Web Site: https://www.wkkj.co.jp
Emp.: 7
Electronic Equipment Distr
N.A.I.C.S.: 423690

WKK TRADING (SHANGHAI) CO., LTD. (1)
Building 1 No 14 Block 172 Lane 1340 Jinshajiang Road, Shanghai, 200333, China
Tel.: (86) 2152833303
Electronic Equipment Distr
N.A.I.C.S.: 423690

WKK Technology Limited (1)
17/F Harbourside HQ No 8 Lam Chak Street, Kowloon, China (Hong Kong)
Tel.: (852) 23578888
Web Site: https://www.wkktechnology.com
Electronic Component Mfr & Distr
N.A.I.C.S.: 334419

WKK Travel Limited (1)
Room 1701 Harbourside HQ No 8 Lam Chak Street, Kowloon, China (Hong Kong)
Tel.: (852) 23450121
Web Site: https://www.wkktravel.com
Electronic Component Mfr & Distr
N.A.I.C.S.: 334419

WONGA.COM LTD.
88 Crawford Street, London, W1H 2EJ, United Kingdom
Tel.: (44) 8712 885704
Web Site: http://www.wonga.com
Year Founded: 2006
Sales Range: $100-124.9 Million
Emp.: 50
Online Money Lending Services
N.A.I.C.S.: 522291
Andy Haste *(Grp Chm)*

WONGS INTERNATIONAL (HOLDINGS) LTD
17/F C-Bons International Center No 108 Wai Yip Street, Kwun Tong, Kowloon, China (Hong Kong)
Tel.: (852) 23450111
Web Site: http://www.wih.com.hk
0099—(HKG)
Rev.: $420,052,906
Assets: $999,243,658
Liabilities: $421,601,956
Net Worth: $577,641,702
Earnings: $11,540,357
Emp.: 3,471
Fiscal Year-end: 12/31/21
Electric Equipment Mfr
N.A.I.C.S.: 238210
Ada Yin-Man Wong *(Exec Dir)*

Subsidiaries:

Altai Technologies Limited (1)
Unit 209 2/F Lakeside 2 10 Science Park West Avenue, HK Science Park, Sha Tin, China (Hong Kong)
Tel.: (852) 3 758 6000
Web Site: https://www.altaitechnologies.com
Wifi Product Mfr
N.A.I.C.S.: 334220
Raymond Leung *(Founder, Chm & CEO)*

Welco Technology (Suzhou) Limited (1)
198 Xinglong St Suzhou Indus Park, Suzhou, 215126, Jiangsu, China
Tel.: (86) 512 6283 8860

WONGS INTERNATIONAL (HOLDINGS) LTD

Wongs International (Holdings) Ltd.—(Continued)
Sales Range: $200-249.9 Million
Emp.: 530
Circuit Boards & Soldering Equipments Mfr
N.A.I.C.S.: 333992

Wong's Electronics Co., Limited (1)
Wongs Indus Ctr 180 Wai Yip St, Kwun Tong, Kowloon, China (Hong Kong)
Tel.: (852) 23450111
Web Site: http://www.wongswec.com
Communication Equipment Mfr
N.A.I.C.S.: 334220

Wong's International (Europe) Limited (1)
Mercury Hse 19-21 Chapel St, Marlow, SL7 3HN, Buckinghamshire, United Kingdom
Tel.: (44) 1342811768
Customer Relationship Management Services
N.A.I.C.S.: 541613

Wong's International (Japan), Inc. (1)
Shimbashi No 2 Naka Building 5 F 2-3-7 Shimbashi, Minato-ku, Tokyo, 105-0004, Japan
Tel.: (81) 335391980
Sales Range: $25-49.9 Million
Emp.: 8
Customer Relationship Management Services
N.A.I.C.S.: 541613
Yu Yang *(Gen Mgr)*

Wong's International USA Corporation (1)
2905 Stender Way Ste 52, Santa Clara, CA 95054
Tel.: (650) 967-1111
Electrical Equipment Whslr
N.A.I.C.S.: 423610

Wong's Technology (Shanghai) Limited (1)
Room 2003 Shenxin Building 200 East Ninghai Road, Huangpu District, Shanghai, 200021, China
Tel.: (86) 216 328 7872
Web Site: http://www.wongswec.com
Sales Range: $25-49.9 Million
Emp.: 3
Printed Circuit Board Mfr
N.A.I.C.S.: 334412

WONHE HIGH-TECH INTERNATIONAL, INC.
Room 1001 10th Fl Resource Hi-Tech Building South Tower, No. 1 Songpingshan Road North Central Avenue North High-Tech Zone, Shenzhen, 518057, Guangdong, China
Tel.: (86) 852 2815 0191   NV
Rev.: $49,201,963
Assets: $73,854,552
Liabilities: $2,567,145
Net Worth: $71,287,407
Earnings: $5,283,834
Emp.: 51
Fiscal Year-end: 12/31/16
Computer Services
N.A.I.C.S.: 541519
Nanfang Tong *(CEO)*

WONIK CORPORATION
20 Pangyo-ro 255 beon-gil, Bundang-gu, Seongnam, Gyeonggi-do, Korea (South)
Tel.: (82) 3180389018   KR
Web Site: https://www.wonik.com
Year Founded: 1981
Holding Company
N.A.I.C.S.: 551112
Soon-Hyung Kwon *(Mng Dir & CFO)*

Subsidiaries:

WONIK Corporation USA, Ltd. (1)
1164 Tower Ln, Bensenville, IL 60106
Tel.: (630) 694-8884
Web Site: https://www.wonikcorpusa.com
Rev.: $2,100,000
Emp.: 12
Wholesale Trade Broker & Product Distr
N.A.I.C.S.: 425120
Hyung S. Kim *(CFO)*

WONIK PNE Co., Ltd. (1)
185 Saneop-ro, Gwonseon-gu, Suwon, Gyeonggi-do, Korea (South)
Tel.: (82) 312990100
Web Site: http://www.wonikpne.com
Rev.: $221,543,083
Assets: $315,833,170
Liabilities: $227,910,218
Net Worth: $87,922,952
Earnings: $23,300
Emp.: 730
Fiscal Year-end: 12/31/2022
Industrial Machinery Mfr
N.A.I.C.S.: 333248

Subsidiary (Domestic):

PNE Systems Co., Ltd. (2)
185 Saneop-ro, Gwonseon-gu, Suwon, Gyeonggi-do, Korea (South)
Tel.: (82) 312789450
Energy Storage System Mfr
N.A.I.C.S.: 333248
Daetaek Chung *(CEO)*

WONIK QnC Corporation (1)
117 Okgye2gongdan-ro, Gumi, 730-400, Gyeongsangbuk-do, Korea (South)
Tel.: (82) 544799500
Web Site: https://www.wonikqnc.com
Rev.: $600,698,144
Assets: $977,378,587
Liabilities: $616,959,034
Net Worth: $360,419,553
Earnings: $41,291,446
Emp.: 1,164
Fiscal Year-end: 12/31/2022
Semiconductor Devices Mfr
N.A.I.C.S.: 334413
Hong-Joo Baek *(CEO)*

Joint Venture (US):

MPM Holdings Inc. (2)
260 Hudson River Rd, Waterford, NY 12188   (5%)
Tel.: (518) 237-3330
Web Site: http://www.momentive.com
Rev.: $2,705,000,000
Assets: $2,830,000,000
Liabilities: $2,234,000,000
Net Worth: $596,000,000
Earnings: $69,000,000
Emp.: 5,200
Fiscal Year-end: 12/31/2018
Holding Company
N.A.I.C.S.: 551112
Suraj Kunchala *(Controller)*

Subsidiary (Domestic):

Momentive Performance Materials Inc. (3)
260 Hudson River Rd, Waterford, NY 12188
Tel.: (518) 233-3330
Web Site: https://www.momentive.com
Sales Range: $1-4.9 Billion
Emp.: 5,199
Thermoplastics, Silicon-Based Products & Fused Quartz & Specialty Ceramics Mfr
N.A.I.C.S.: 325211
Suraj Kunchala *(Controller)*

Division (Domestic):

WONIK QnC Corporation - Ceramics & Cleaning Division (2)
63 Okgye 2gongdan-ro 3-gil, Gumi, Gyeongsangbuk-do, Korea (South)
Tel.: (82) 54 479 9800
Semiconductor Product Mfr
N.A.I.C.S.: 334413

Subsidiary (Non-US):

Wonik QnC Europe (2)
Borsigstr 1-7, 21502, Geesthacht, Germany
Tel.: (49) 4152 876 126
Web Site: http://www.wonik.de
Emp.: 60
Semiconductor Product Mfr
N.A.I.C.S.: 334413
Ludwig Pabst *(Mng Dir)*

Subsidiary (US):

Wonik QnC International

5601-B Ballon Fiesta Pkwy NE, Albuquerque, NM 87113
Tel.: (505) 797-7500
Emp.: 63
Semiconductor Product Mfr
N.A.I.C.S.: 334413
Ludwig Pabst *(Pres)*

Subsidiary (Non-US):

Wonik Quartz Europe GmbH (2)
Borsigstrasse 1-7, 21502, Geesthacht, Germany
Tel.: (49) 41528760
Web Site: https://www.wonik.de
Computer System Design Services
N.A.I.C.S.: 541512

Wonik Taiwan QnC co., ltd (2)
No23 Ruixing ST, Tong-Luo Township, Miao-li, Hsian, Taiwan
Tel.: (886) 37230005
Emp.: 114
Semiconductor Product Mfr
N.A.I.C.S.: 334413
Lee Jae-Heon *(Pres)*

Wonik Co., Ltd. (1)
7F of WONIK Building 20 Pangyo-ro 255beon-gil, Bundang-gu, Seongnam, Gyeonggi-do, Korea (South)
Tel.: (82) 3180389000
Web Site: http://www.wonik.co.kr
Rev.: $82,904,026
Assets: $289,165,765
Liabilities: $93,439,077
Net Worth: $195,726,688
Earnings: $29,383,284
Emp.: 99
Fiscal Year-end: 12/31/2022
Electical & Electronic Parts & Equipment Distr
N.A.I.C.S.: 423690

Subsidiary (Domestic):

Winix Co., Ltd. (2)
295 Gongdan1-daero, Gongdan 1-daero, Siheung, Gyeonggi-do, Korea (100%)
Tel.: (82) 314995085
Web Site: http://www.winixcorp.com
Rev.: $252,335,814
Assets: $315,299,254
Liabilities: $160,292,481
Net Worth: $155,006,774
Earnings: $1,671,732
Emp.: 359
Fiscal Year-end: 12/31/2022
Home Appliance Mfr
N.A.I.C.S.: 333415
Lee Kwang Ho *(Mgr)*

Subsidiary (US):

Winix Inc. (3)
220 N Fairway Dr, Vernon Hills, IL 60061
Tel.: (847) 551-9900
Web Site: http://www.winixamerica.com
Home Appliance Mfr
N.A.I.C.S.: 333415
Anthony Kircher *(Pres)*

Wonik Cube Corp. (1)
20 Pangyo-ro 255 beon-gil, Bundang-gu, Seongnam, 13486, Gyeonggi-do, Korea (South)
Tel.: (82) 3180389300
Web Site: https://www.wonikcube.com
Rev.: $188,666,592
Assets: $104,922,604
Liabilities: $28,615,967
Net Worth: $76,306,636
Earnings: $3,295,607
Emp.: 120
Fiscal Year-end: 12/31/2022
Chemicals, Construction Materials & Silicone Mfr
N.A.I.C.S.: 325199
Gyeong-Soo Moon *(CEO)*

Subsidiary (US):

Wonik Materials North America LLC (2)
N115W19392 Edison Dr, Germantown, WI 53022
Tel.: (262) 293-0251
Web Site: http://www.wimna.com
Precursor Chemical Mfr
N.A.I.C.S.: 325998

INTERNATIONAL PUBLIC

Moo C. Lee *(CFO)*

Wonik Holdings Co., Ltd. (1)
Masan12-ro 21, Jinwi-myeon, Pyeongtaek, Gyeonggi-do, Korea (South)
Tel.: (82) 312304600
Web Site: http://www.wonikholdings.kr
Rev.: $675,735,966
Assets: $1,392,508,429
Liabilities: $379,182,947
Net Worth: $1,013,325,482
Earnings: $98,758,092
Emp.: 416
Fiscal Year-end: 12/31/2022
Industrial Gas Processing Equipment Mfr & Whslr
N.A.I.C.S.: 334513

Subsidiary (Domestic):

CMS LAB Co., Ltd. (2)
X14th 15th floor 1 Gangnam-daero 51-gil, Seocho-gu, Seoul, Korea (South)
Tel.: (82) 234568800
Medical Cosmetic Lab Services
N.A.I.C.S.: 621511

TLI Co., Ltd. (2)
TLi Building 12 Yanghyeon-ro 405 beon-gil, Jungwon-gu, Seongnam, 13438, Gyeonggi-do, Korea (South) (62.51%)
Tel.: (82) 317846800
Web Site: https://www.tli.co.kr
Rev.: $16,116,867
Assets: $52,940,760
Liabilities: $4,538,445
Net Worth: $48,402,315
Earnings: ($4,563,098)
Emp.: 78
Fiscal Year-end: 12/31/2022
Semiconductor Devices Mfr
N.A.I.C.S.: 334413
Youngmu Byun *(Dir)*

Affiliate (Domestic):

Wonik IPS Co., Ltd. (2)
75 Jinwisandan-ro Jinwi-myeon, Pyeongtaek, 17709, Gyeonggi, Korea (South) (32.9%)
Tel.: (82) 3180477000
Web Site: http://www.ips.co.kr
Rev.: $799,073,136
Assets: $886,119,726
Liabilities: $199,035,155
Net Worth: $687,084,570
Earnings: $70,656,188
Emp.: 1,606
Fiscal Year-end: 12/31/2022
Semiconductor Equipment Mfr
N.A.I.C.S.: 334413
Hyun Deok Lee *(CEO)*

Subsidiary (Non-US):

Wonik IPS (Xian) Semiconductor Equipment Co., Ltd. (3)
Main Building 1107-1109 of Customs Clearance Service Center No 5, Tonghai Road, Xianning, Shaanxi, China
Tel.: (86) 2989525359
Semiconductor Machinery Mfr
N.A.I.C.S.: 333242

Wuxi Wonik IPS Semiconductor Equipment Technology Co., Ltd. (3)
Rm 815 IC SHEJI Bldg B XINDA Road 33-1, New District, Wuxi, Jiangsu, China
Tel.: (86) 51081813885
Semiconductor Machinery Mfr
N.A.I.C.S.: 333242

Subsidiary (Domestic):

Wonik Investment Partners Co., Ltd. (2)
5F 504 Teheran-ro, Gangnam-gu, Seoul, Korea (South)
Tel.: (82) 264467125
Web Site: https://www.wiipco.com
Financial & Investment Services
N.A.I.C.S.: 523999
Yong-Sung LEE *(CEO)*

Wonik L&D Co., Ltd. (2)
255 Yeomgok-gil Gangdong-myeon, Gangneung, Gangwon-do, Korea (South)
Tel.: (82) 336500000
Web Site: https://www.maplebeach.co.kr
Golf Course Services
N.A.I.C.S.: 713910

AND PRIVATE COMPANIES

Wonik Robotics Co., Ltd. (2)
5F Wonik Bldg Pangyo-ro 255-20, Bundang-gu, Seongnam, Gyunggi-do, Korea (South)
Tel.: (82) 3180389180
Web Site: http://www.simlab.co.kr
Software & Hardware Services
N.A.I.C.S.: 541512

Wonik Materials Co., Ltd. (1)
112 Gwahaksaneop 3-ro Ochang-eup, cheongwon-gu, Cheongju, chungcheongbuk-do, Korea (South)
Tel.: (82) 432104300
Web Site: https://www.wimco.co.kr
Rev.: $445,824,905
Assets: $447,174,949
Liabilities: $105,578,491
Net Worth: $341,596,458
Earnings: $44,280,316
Emp.: 426
Fiscal Year-end: 12/31/2022
Specialty Gases & Chemicals Mfr
N.A.I.C.S.: 325120
Oh Dong-Keun (CFO)

WONIL SPECIAL STEEL
Gongdan2daero 256-4 Jeongwang-dong, Siheung, 429-450, Gyeonggi-do, Korea (South)
Tel.: (82) 314341221
Web Site:
  https://www.wonilsteel.co.kr
Year Founded: 1977
012620—(KRS)
Rev.: $295,369,537
Assets: $209,664,130
Liabilities: $95,955,828
Net Worth: $113,708,302
Earnings: $8,134,004
Emp.: 147
Fiscal Year-end: 12/31/22
Steel Products Mfr
N.A.I.C.S.: 331221
Yong-Mun Shin (Pres & CEO)

WONLIM CORPORATION
2495 Nambusunhwan-ro, Seocho-gu, Seoul, 137-070, Korea (South)
Tel.: (82) 25239231
Web Site: https://www.wonlim.co.kr
Year Founded: 1968
005820—(KRS)
Rev.: $62,838,140
Assets: $130,337,711
Liabilities: $19,943,970
Net Worth: $110,393,741
Earnings: $7,071,142
Emp.: 95
Fiscal Year-end: 12/31/22
Plastic Bag Mfr & Whslr
N.A.I.C.S.: 326111

WONPOONG CORPORATION
Wonpoong Bldg 343 Gonghang-Daero, Gangseo-gu, Seoul, Korea (South)
Tel.: (82) 236618112
Web Site:
  https://www.wonpoong.co.kr
Year Founded: 1973
008370—(KRS)
Rev.: $68,639,278
Assets: $71,614,568
Liabilities: $5,857,519
Net Worth: $65,757,049
Earnings: $6,519,529
Emp.: 190
Fiscal Year-end: 12/31/22
Fabric Product Mfr
N.A.I.C.S.: 313320

Subsidiaries:

WONPOONG Corporation (M) Sdn.Bhd. (1)
Lot No 14/5/4 Jalan Perusahaan Tiga Kamunting Industrial Estate, Kamunting, 34600, Taiping, Perak Darul Ridzuan, Malaysia
Tel.: (60) 5 891 1709

Fabric Product Distr
N.A.I.C.S.: 424310

Wonpoong China (Zhejiang) Specialty Textiles Co., Ltd (1)
No 180 Golf Road Dong Zhou Street, Fuyang, Zhejiang, China
Tel.: (86) 571 2320 1805
Web Site: http://www.wonpoongchina.com
Fabric Product Mfr
N.A.I.C.S.: 314910

Wonpoong Corporation - Cheong-ju Factory (1)
5 Jikji-daero 474beon-gil, Heungdeok-gu, Cheongju, Chungcheongbuk-do, Korea (South)
Tel.: (82) 43 272 8388
Fabric Product Mfr
N.A.I.C.S.: 313320

WONPUNG MULSAN CO., LTD.
31 Gajwa-ro, Seo-gu, Incheon, Korea (South)
Tel.: (82) 25690433
Web Site: http://www.wonpung.com
Year Founded: 1972
008290—(KRS)
Rev.: $25,541,125
Assets: $25,378,723
Liabilities: $14,595,082
Net Worth: $10,783,641
Earnings: ($2,690,431)
Emp.: 41
Fiscal Year-end: 12/31/22
Menswear Mfr
N.A.I.C.S.: 315250
Yi Doo Sik (CEO)

Subsidiaries:

Kinloch Anderson Ltd. (1)
4 Dock Street, Leith, Edinburgh, EH6 6EY, United Kingdom
Tel.: (44) 1315551390
Web Site: https://www.kinlochanderson.com
Clothing Distr
N.A.I.C.S.: 458110
John Kinloch Anderson (CEO)

WOOD FRIENDS CO., LTD.
2F KDX Nagoya Sakae Building 5-3 Sakae 4-chome, Naka-ku, Nagoya, 460-0008, Japan
Tel.: (81) 522493503
Web Site:
  https://www.woodfriends.co.jp
Year Founded: 1982
88860—(TKS)
Rev.: $289,065,081
Assets: $252,520,648
Liabilities: $203,871,820
Net Worth: $48,648,827
Earnings: ($1,519,656)
Emp.: 196
Fiscal Year-end: 05/31/23
Real Estate Development Services
N.A.I.C.S.: 531390
Kazuhiko Maeda (CEO & Chm)

WOOD ONE CO., LTD.
1-1 Mokuzaiko-Minami, Hatsukaichi, 738-8502, Hiroshima, Japan
Tel.: (81) 829323333
Web Site: https://www.woodone.co.jp
Year Founded: 1935
7898—(TKS)
Rev.: $428,189,190
Assets: $672,593,940
Liabilities: $377,014,570
Net Worth: $295,579,370
Earnings: ($15,302,150)
Emp.: 1,211
Fiscal Year-end: 03/31/24
Interior Design Product Mfr
N.A.I.C.S.: 337212
Y. Nakamoto (Pres)

Subsidiaries:

Belkitchen Corporation (1)
Lot 1187 A Jalan Sungai Buaya Kampung Hilir Indah, Sungai Choh Selangor Darul Ehsan, 48000, Rawang, Malaysia
Tel.: (60) 125772906
Web Site: https://www.belkitchen.com
Aluminium Kitchen Customization & Design Services
N.A.I.C.S.: 541410

Forest One Co., Ltd. (1)
2-19-1 Maehara Nishi Tsudanuma Beat 4th & 5th Floors, Funabashi, 274-0825, Japan
Tel.: (81) 474748105
Web Site: https://www.forest-one.co.jp
Emp.: 56
Dental Material Mfr & Distr
N.A.I.C.S.: 339114

Juken Nissho Ltd. (1)
Level 3 AON Centre 29 Customs Street West, PO Box 1450, Auckland, 1010, New Zealand
Tel.: (64) 93733933
Web Site: https://www.jnl.co.nz
Wood Product Mfr & Distr
N.A.I.C.S.: 321999

P.T. Woodone Integra Indonesia (1)
Jl Raya Sidorejo No 111 Bareng Sidorejo Kec Krian, Sidoarjo, 61262, Indonesia
Tel.: (62) 3133101108
Web Site: https://woodoneintegra.com
Door & Kitchen Cabinet Mfr
N.A.I.C.S.: 321911

WOOD WHEATON CHEVROLET CADILLAC LTD
2879 Highway 16 West, Prince George, V2N 0A3, BC, Canada
Tel.: (250) 564-4466
Web Site:
  http://www.woodwheaton.com
Year Founded: 1993
Rev.: $34,256,310
Emp.: 70
New & Used Car Dealers
N.A.I.C.S.: 441110
Kelly Ireland (Mgr-Svc)

WOODALL CONSTRUCTION CO. LIMITED
620 North Service Road East, Windsor, N8X 3J3, ON, Canada
Tel.: (519) 966-3381
Web Site:
  http://www.woodallconstruction.ca
Year Founded: 1909
Rev.: $12,744,604
Emp.: 25
General & Design Construction Contractor
N.A.I.C.S.: 238190
Dave Woodall (Pres)

WOODBOIS LTD.
Dixcart House Sir William Place, PO Box 161, Saint Peter Port, GY1 1GX, Guernsey
Tel.: (44) 2070991940 UK
Web Site: https://www.woodbois.com
Year Founded: 2007
WBI—(AIM)
Rev.: $23,108,000
Assets: $225,273,000
Liabilities: $77,368,000
Net Worth: $147,905,000
Earnings: ($111,191,000)
Fiscal Year-end: 12/31/22
Investment Services
N.A.I.C.S.: 523999
Paul Dolan (Chm)

Subsidiaries:

Madeiras SL Limitada (1)
Av Ahmed S Toure 571 R/C, Bairro Polana, Maputo, Mozambique
Tel.: (258) 840230475
Wood Mfr
N.A.I.C.S.: 321113

WoodGroup ApS (1)
Ventrupparken 10, 2670, Greve, Denmark

Tel.: (45) 61276340
Web Site: https://www.woodgroup.dk
Wooden Construction Services
N.A.I.C.S.: 238350

Woodbois Gabon Ltd. (1)
12 rue de Georgelin Derriere l'hopital, PO Box 720, Libreville, Gabon
Tel.: (241) 66181301
Wood Mfr
N.A.I.C.S.: 321113

WOODBRIDGE FOAM CORPORATION
4240 Sherwoodtowne Boulevard, Mississauga, L4Z 2G6, ON, Canada
Tel.: (905) 896-3626
Web Site:
  https://www.woodbridgegroup.com
Year Founded: 1978
Urethane & Foam Products Mfr
N.A.I.C.S.: 326150
Charles Daly (Pres & CEO)

WOODBRIDGE VENTURES, INC.
6 - 6150 Highway 7 Suite # 491, Woodbridge, L4H 0R6, ON, Canada
Tel.: (416) 637-2240 Ca
Year Founded: 2018
WOOD.P—(TSXV)
Sales Range: Less than $1 Million
Business Consulting Services
N.A.I.C.S.: 522299

WOODFIELD SYSTEMS INTERNATIONAL PVT LTD.
302-A Nitco Biz Park Plot No C-19, Road No 16 Wagle Estate, Thane, 400604, Maharashtra, India
Tel.: (91) 2267040000 In
Web Site:
  https://www.woodfieldsystems.com
Industrial Machinery Mfr & Bulk Fluid Handling & Safety Access Solutions Services
N.A.I.C.S.: 333248
Kartik Gala (CEO)

Subsidiaries:

Woodfield Systems Limited (1)
Tyler Way Swalecliffe, Whitstable, CT5 2RS, Kent, United Kingdom
Tel.: (44) 1227793351
Web Site:
  http://www.woodfieldsystemsltd.com
Marine Loading Arms & Swivels Mfr & Designer
N.A.I.C.S.: 333613

WOODFORD INVESTMENT MANAGEMENT LLP
9400 Garsington Road, Oxford, OX4 2HN, United Kingdom
Tel.: (44) 870 870 8482 UK
Web Site:
  http://www.woodfordfunds.com
Investment Management Service
N.A.I.C.S.: 523940
Craig Newman (CEO)

WOODLANDOR HOLDINGS BERHAD
Lot 1339 Batu 22 1/2 Sg Lalang, 43500, Semenyih, Selangor Darul Ehsan, Malaysia
Tel.: (60) 387232233
Web Site:
  https://www.woodlandor.com.my
WOODLAN—(KLS)
Rev.: $1,815,912
Assets: $10,742,484
Liabilities: $2,057,933
Net Worth: $8,684,551
Earnings: $449,605
Fiscal Year-end: 06/30/22
Durable Wood Products Mfr
N.A.I.C.S.: 321992

WOODLANDOR HOLDINGS BERHAD

Woodlandor Holdings Berhad—(Continued)
Weng Sum Mun *(Chm)*

Subsidiaries:

Multec Enterprise Sdn. Bhd. (1)
9 Jalan 2/116D Kuchai Entrepreneurs Park Off Jalan Kuchai Lama, 58200, Kuala Lumpur, Wilayah Persekutuan, Malaysia
Tel.: (60) 379816762
Web Site: http://www.woodlandor.com.my
Sales Range: $25-49.9 Million
Emp.: 20
Wooden Furnitures & Doors Mfr
N.A.I.C.S.: 337211
Dany Mun Weng Sum *(Mng Dir)*

Woodlandor Buildmat Sdn. Bhd. (1)
No A-07-03 Cova Suites Jalan Teknologi
Kota Damansara PJU 5, 47810, Petaling Jaya, Selangor, Malaysia
Tel.: (60) 379810034
Door Accessories Mfr
N.A.I.C.S.: 339999
See Fun Mun *(CEO)*

Woodlandor Roof Systems Sdn. Bhd. (1)
Lot 442 Batu 22 1/2 Sg Lalang, 43500, Semenyih, Selangor, Malaysia
Tel.: (60) 387237742
Sales Range: $50-74.9 Million
Emp.: 150
Wooden Furniture & Doors Mfr
N.A.I.C.S.: 321911

Woodlandor Wood Products Sdn. Bhd. (1)
Lot 1339 Batu 22 1/2 Sungai Lalang, 43500, Semenyih, Selangor, Malaysia
Tel.: (60) 387237743
Sales Range: $25-49.9 Million
Emp.: 100
Wooden Furniture & Doors Mfr
N.A.I.C.S.: 337211
Mun See Fun *(CEO)*

WOODLORE INTERNATIONAL INC.
160 Delta Park Blvd, Brampton, L6T 5T6, ON, Canada
Tel.: (905) 791-9555
Web Site: http://www.woodlore.ca
Year Founded: 1981
Rev.: $18,867,054
Emp.: 200
Office Furniture Mfr
N.A.I.C.S.: 337211
William J. Phillips *(Pres)*

WOODPECKER.CO SA
Krakowska 29D, 50-424, Wroclaw, Poland
Tel.: (48) 500730530
Web Site: https://www.woodpecker.co
Year Founded: 2015
8FG—(DEU)
Software Development Services
N.A.I.C.S.: 541511
Mateusz Tarczynski *(CEO)*

WOODS BAGOT PTY. LTD.
498 Little Collins Street, Melbourne, 3000, VIC, Australia
Tel.: (61) 386466600
Web Site: http://www.woodsbagot.com
Architectural Design & Engineering Services
N.A.I.C.S.: 541310
Nik Karalis *(CEO)*

WOODSIDE ENERGY GROUP LTD
Mia Yellagonga 11 Mount Street, Perth, 6000, WA, Australia
Tel.: (61) 893484000 AU
Web Site: https://www.woodside.com
Year Founded: 1954
WDS—(NYSE)
Rev.: $13,994,000,000
Assets: $55,361,000,000
Liabilities: $20,191,000,000
Net Worth: $35,170,000,000
Earnings: $1,660,000,000
Emp.: 4,193
Fiscal Year-end: 12/31/23
Oil & Gas Distribution Services
N.A.I.C.S.: 211120
Richard Goyder *(Chm)*

Subsidiaries:

BHP Petroleum Pty. Ltd. (1)
180 Longsdale St, Melbourne, 3000, VIC, Australia
Tel.: (61) 396093333
Web Site: http://www.bhpbilliton.com
Sales Range: $125-149.9 Million
Emp.: 300
Hydrocarbons Exploration, Development & Production; Manufacturer of Petrochemicals
N.A.I.C.S.: 325110

Branch (Domestic):

BHP Petroleum Pty. Ltd. (2)
Level 46 152 158, St Georges Terrace, Perth, 6000, WA, Australia (100%)
Tel.: (61) 892784888
Web Site: http://www.bhpbilliton.com
N.A.I.C.S.: 212210

Tellurian Inc. (1)
1201 Louisiana St Ste 3100, Houston, TX 77002
Tel.: (832) 962-4000
Web Site: https://www.tellurianinc.com
Rev.: $391,926,000
Assets: $1,426,683,000
Liabilities: $754,140,000
Net Worth: $672,543,000
Earnings: ($49,810,000)
Emp.: 171
Fiscal Year-end: 12/31/2022
Holding Company; Petroleum & Natural Gas Exploration, Production & Distribution
N.A.I.C.S.: 551112
Charif Souki *(Chm)*

Subsidiary (Domestic):

Driftwood LNG LLC (2)
1201 Louisiana St Ste 3100, Houston, TX 77002
Tel.: (832) 962-4027
Web Site: https://www.driftwoodlng.com
Natural Gas Pipeline Transportation Services
N.A.I.C.S.: 486210

Tellurian Investments LLC (2)
1201 Louisiana St Ste 3100, Houston, TX 77002
Tel.: (832) 962-4000
Web Site: http://www.tellurianinc.com
Natural Gas Distr
N.A.I.C.S.: 221210
Antoine J. Lafargue *(CFO & Sr VP)*

Woodside Energy (UK) Limited (1)
4th Floor 7 Albemarle Street, London, WIS 4HQ, United Kingdom
Tel.: (44) 2075145560
Oil & Gas Exploration & Production Services
N.A.I.C.S.: 211120

Woodside Energy (USA), Inc. (1)
5151 San Felipe St Ste 980, Houston, TX 77056
Tel.: (713) 401-0000
Oil & Gas Exploration Services
N.A.I.C.S.: 213112
David Moon *(Mgr-Well Delivery)*

Woodside Energy Ltd. (1)
11 Mount Street, Perth, 6000, WA, Australia
Tel.: (61) 893484000
Web Site: http://www.woodside.com.au
Sales Range: $1-4.9 Billion
Oil & Gas Exploration Services
N.A.I.C.S.: 213112

Woodside Mauritania Pty. Ltd. (1)
Zone des Ambassades 031-121, Nouakchott, 2034, Mauritania
Tel.: (222) 5254510
Sales Range: $50-74.9 Million
Emp.: 100
Oil & Gas Exploration Services
N.A.I.C.S.: 211120

WOODSVILLA LIMITED
E-4 IInd Floor Defence Colony, New Delhi, 110024, India
Tel.: (91) 1141552060
Web Site: https://www.woodsvilla.in
526959—(BOM)
Rev.: $113,895
Assets: $556,642
Liabilities: $57,708
Net Worth: $498,934
Earnings: ($11,738)
Emp.: 9
Fiscal Year-end: 03/31/23
Home Management Services
N.A.I.C.S.: 721110
Meena Aggarwal *(CEO)*

WOOGENE B&G CO., LTD.
R No 1504 Acehitech City 1-dong
775 Gyeongin-ro, Yeongdeungpo-gu, Seoul, Korea (South)
Tel.: (82) 27952361
Web Site: https://www.woogenebng.com
Year Founded: 1977
018620—(KRS)
Rev.: $33,520,558
Assets: $70,197,739
Liabilities: $20,675,274
Net Worth: $49,522,465
Earnings: $651,616
Emp.: 103
Fiscal Year-end: 12/31/22
Veterinary Medicine Mfr
N.A.I.C.S.: 325412
Jae-Ku Kang *(CEO)*

Subsidiaries:

Woogene B&G Co., Ltd. - Hwaseong Factory (1)
230 Jeongmunsongsan-ro, Yanggam-myeon, Hwaseong, Gyeonggi-do, Korea (South)
Tel.: (82) 31 352 0185
Pharmaceuticals Product Mfr
N.A.I.C.S.: 325412

WOOJEON CO., LTD.
33-23 Gasan digital 1-ro, Geumcheon-gu, Seoul, Korea (South)
Tel.: (82) 221050600
Web Site: http://www.woojeon.co.kr
Year Founded: 1988
Sales Range: $50-74.9 Million
Telecommunications Equipment Mfr
N.A.I.C.S.: 517810
J. W. Lee *(CEO)*

Subsidiaries:

WOOJEON CORPORATION (1)
569-12 Kasan-dong, Kumcheon-ku, Seoul, 153-803, Korea (South)
Tel.: (82) 2 2105 0600
Sales Range: $100-124.9 Million
Emp.: 35
Industrial Mold Mfr
N.A.I.C.S.: 333511
Dong-Yun Shin *(Mgr-Sls)*

WOOJEON JAPAN CO., LTD. (1)
803 8/F Sinyokohama IK Bldg 12-12 Shinyokohama, Kohoku-ku, Yokohama, Japan
Tel.: (81) 45 478 5272
Industrial Mold Mfr
N.A.I.C.S.: 333511

WOOJIN I&S CO., LTD.
3F Hanseung Bldg 166 Bangbae-Ro 875-2 Bangbae-Dong, Seocho-Gu, Seoul, Korea (South)
Tel.: (82) 25357050
Web Site: https://www.woojini.com
Year Founded: 1975
010400—(KRS)
Rev.: $82,316,200
Assets: $105,483,871
Liabilities: $16,157,322
Net Worth: $89,326,549

INTERNATIONAL PUBLIC

Earnings: ($2,955,045)
Emp.: 145
Fiscal Year-end: 12/31/21
Construction Equipment Mfr
N.A.I.C.S.: 333120
Gyeong-Mo Hong *(CEO)*

WOOJIN INC.
24 Dongtanyeok-ro, Hwaseong, Gyeonggi-do, Korea (South)
Tel.: (82) 313793114
Web Site: https://www.woojininc.com
Year Founded: 1980
105840—(KRS)
Rev.: $95,151,457
Assets: $174,149,939
Liabilities: $38,721,186
Net Worth: $135,428,754
Earnings: $9,038,912
Emp.: 153
Fiscal Year-end: 12/31/22
Industrial Measuring Equipment Mfr & Distr
N.A.I.C.S.: 334513
Im Jimin *(Asst Mgr)*

WOOJIN INDUSTRY COMPANY LTD.
248 Sandan-ro, Danwon-gu, Ansan, Gyeonggi-do, Korea (South)
Tel.: (82) 314913636 KR
Web Site: http://www.ngkntk.co.kr
Year Founded: 1966
Air Heater Equipment Mfr
N.A.I.C.S.: 333415

WOOJIN PLAIMM CO., LTD.
Woojinplaimm-ro 100 Jangan-myeon, Chungcheongbuk-do, Boeun, 376-840, Korea (South)
Tel.: (82) 435409000
Web Site: https://www.woojinplaimm.com
Year Founded: 1985
049800—(KRS)
Rev.: $195,261,891
Assets: $218,782,952
Liabilities: $139,947,069
Net Worth: $78,835,883
Earnings: $16,758,907
Emp.: 560
Fiscal Year-end: 12/31/22
Plastic Injection Molding Machine Mfr
N.A.I.C.S.: 333248

Subsidiaries:

WOOJIN SELEX (AMERICA), INC (1)
615 N Berry St Ste E, Brea, CA 92821
Tel.: (714) 529-7890
Plastic Injection Molding Machine Mfr
N.A.I.C.S.: 333248

WOOJUNG BIO, INC.
593-8 Dongtan Giheung-ro, Yeongtong-gu Gyeonggi-do, Hwaseong, 18469, Gyeonggi-do, Korea (South)
Tel.: (82) 318889341
Web Site: http://www.woojungbsc.co.kr
Year Founded: 2015
215380—(KRS)
Rev.: $35,985,993
Assets: $72,860,225
Liabilities: $50,066,258
Net Worth: $22,793,967
Earnings: ($1,442,109)
Emp.: 133
Fiscal Year-end: 12/31/22
Financial Investment Management Services
N.A.I.C.S.: 523940
Nam Pyo *(Dir)*

AND PRIVATE COMPANIES

WOOLWORTHS GROUP LIMITED

WOOL INDUSTRY TRIA ALFA S.A.
Al Panagouli Str 64, 14234, Nea Ionia, Greece
Tel.: (30) 2102790028
Web Site: http://www.triaalfa.gr
Year Founded: 1927
AAAK—(ATH)
Sales Range: Less than $1 Million
Emp.: 7
Wool Weaving Services
N.A.I.C.S.: 313110
Minas Dimitrios Efraimoglou *(Chm & Mng Dir)*

WOOLTEX UK LTD.
Woodland Mill Dale Street, Huddersfield, HD3 4TG, West Yorkshire, United Kingdom
Tel.: (44) 1484 648 492
Web Site: http://wooltexuk.com
Year Founded: 1996
Sales Range: $25-49.9 Million
Textile Mfr
N.A.I.C.S.: 314999

WOOLWORTH PROPERTIES PLC
Tel.: (357) 22740000
Web Site: http://www.woolworthgroup.com.cy
Year Founded: 2003
FWW—(CYP)
Sales Range: Less than $1 Million
Real Estate Development Services
N.A.I.C.S.: 531390
Demetris Demetriou *(Chm)*

WOOLWORTHS GROUP LIMITED
1 Woolworths Way, Bella Vista, 2153, NSW, Australia
Tel.: (61) 288850000 AU
Web Site: https://www.woolworthsgroup.com
Year Founded: 1924
WOW—(ASX)
Rev.: $41,920,845,015
Assets: $21,939,101,519
Liabilities: $17,658,603,377
Net Worth: $4,280,498,142
Earnings: $1,062,137,315
Emp.: 210,067
Fiscal Year-end: 06/30/23
Department Store Retailer
N.A.I.C.S.: 551112
David Marr *(COO)*

Subsidiaries:

ALH Group Pty. Ltd. (1)
Level 2 10 Yarra Street, South Yarra, 3141, VIC, Australia (75%)
Tel.: (61) 398291000
Web Site: https://www.alhgroup.com.au
Sales Range: $1-4.9 Billion
Emp.: 14,000
Holding Company; Pubs, Hotels, Retail Liquor Stores, Gambling Machine Operations & Property Development
N.A.I.C.S.: 551112

Subsidiary (Domestic):

ALH Group Property Holdings Pty Ltd (2)
Level 2 10 Yarra Street, South Yarra, Melbourne, 3141, VIC, Australia
Tel.: (61) 398291000
Web Site: http://www.alhgroup.com.au
Emp.: 110
Commercial Property Management Services
N.A.I.C.S.: 531312
Bruce Mathieson Jr. *(CEO)*

Albion Charles Hotel (BMG) Pty Ltd (2)
2 Charles St, Northcote, 3070, VIC, Australia
Tel.: (61) 394825033
Web Site: https://www.albioncharles.com.au
Sales Range: $10-24.9 Million
Emp.: 15
Tavern Operators
N.A.I.C.S.: 722410

Balaclava Hotel (BMG) Pty Ltd (2)
423 Mulgrave Rd, Earlville, Cairns, 4870, QLD, Australia
Tel.: (61) 740543588
Web Site: https://www.balaclavahotel.com.au
Sales Range: $10-24.9 Million
Emp.: 30
Tavern Operators
N.A.I.C.S.: 722410

Chelsea Heights Hotel (BMG) Pty Ltd (2)
Cnr Springvale Rd and Wells Rd, Chelsea Heights, 3196, VIC, Australia
Tel.: (61) 397734453
Web Site: http://www.chelseaheightshotel.com.au
Tavern Operators
N.A.I.C.S.: 722410

Cherry Hill Tavern (BMG) Pty Ltd (2)
193-195 Reynolds Rd, Doncaster, 3109, VIC, Australia
Tel.: (61) 3 9841 8122
Web Site: http://www.cherryhilltavern.com.au
Sales Range: $10-24.9 Million
Emp.: 30
Home Management Services
N.A.I.C.S.: 721110

Club Management (BMG) Pty Ltd (2)
Ground Floor 16-20 Claremont Street, South Yarra, 3141, VIC, Australia
Tel.: (61) 398291000
Club Management Services
N.A.I.C.S.: 561499

Compass Hotel Group Ltd. (2)
493 Beach Road Duncraig Suite 1 Compass House, Perth, 6026, WA, Australia
Tel.: (61) 892477220
Hotel Owner & Operator
N.A.I.C.S.: 721110

Subsidiary (Domestic):

Albion Hotel (WA) Pty Ltd (3)
535 Stirling Highway, Cottesloe, 6011, WA, Australia
Tel.: (61) 893840021
Web Site: http://www.albioncottesloe.com.au
Sales Range: $10-24.9 Million
Emp.: 30
Tavern Operators
N.A.I.C.S.: 722410

Belmont Tavern (WA) Pty Ltd (3)
174 Wright St, Cloverdale, 6105, WA, Australia
Tel.: (61) 892772077
Web Site: http://www.belmonttavern.com.au
Tavern Operators
N.A.I.C.S.: 722410

Brighton Hotel (WA) Pty Ltd (3)
10-12 Mandurah Terrace, Mandurah, 6210, WA, Australia
Tel.: (61) 895348864
Web Site: http://www.brightonmandurah.com.au
Sales Range: $10-24.9 Million
Emp.: 16
Home Management Services
N.A.I.C.S.: 721110

Carine Glades Tavern (WA) Pty Ltd (3)
493 Beach Road, Duncraig, Perth, 6023, WA, Australia
Tel.: (61) 894477400
Web Site: http://www.thecarine.com.au
Hotel Business Services
N.A.I.C.S.: 721110

Greenwood Hotel (WA) Pty Ltd (3)
349 Warwick Rd, Greenwood, Perth, 6024, WA, Australia
Tel.: (61) 8 9246 9711
Web Site: http://www.greenwoodhotel.com.au
Home Management Services
N.A.I.C.S.: 721110

Herdsman Lake Tavern (WA) Pty Ltd (3)
33 Herdsman Pde, Wembley, Perth, 6014, WA, Australia
Tel.: (61) 893875555
Web Site: http://www.herdsmantavern.com.au
Tavern Operators
N.A.I.C.S.: 722410

Kalamunda Hotel (WA) Pty Ltd (3)
43 Railway Road, Kalamunda, Perth, 6076, WA, Australia
Tel.: (61) 892571084
Web Site: http://www.kalamundahotel.com.au
Home Management Services
N.A.I.C.S.: 721110

Lakers Tavern (WA) Pty Ltd (3)
119 Murdoch Road, Thornlie, Perth, 6108, WA, Australia
Tel.: (61) 894933522
Web Site: http://www.lakerstavern.com.au
Tavern Operators
N.A.I.C.S.: 722410

Peel Alehouse (WA) Pty Ltd (3)
8 Guava Way, Halls Head, Mandurah, 6210, WA, Australia
Tel.: (61) 895815400
Web Site: https://www.peelalehouse.com.au
Sales Range: $10-24.9 Million
Emp.: 30
Hotel Business Services
N.A.I.C.S.: 721110

Peninsula Tavern (WA) Pty Ltd (3)
223 Railway Parade, Maylands, Perth, 6051, WA, Australia
Tel.: (61) 8 9271 1147
Web Site: http://www.peninsulatavern.com.au
Emp.: 7
Home Management Services
N.A.I.C.S.: 721110

Subsidiary (Domestic):

Croxton Park Hotel (BMG) Pty Ltd (2)
607 High St, Thornbury, 3071, VIC, Australia
Tel.: (61) 394802233
Web Site: http://www.croxtonparkhotel.com.au
Emp.: 30
Tavern Operators
N.A.I.C.S.: 722410

Excelsior Hotel (BMG) Pty Ltd (2)
82 Mahoneys Rd, Thomastown, 3074, VIC, Australia
Tel.: (61) 394603666
Web Site: http://www.theexcelsiorhotel.com.au
Home Management Services
N.A.I.C.S.: 721110

Fabcot Pty Ltd (2)
Cnr Ranford Rd and Nicholson Rd, Canning Vale, 6155, WA, Australia
Tel.: (61) 894565155
Web Site: https://www.livingstonmarketplace.com.au
Home Management Services
N.A.I.C.S.: 721110
Grant O'Brian *(Mng Dir)*

First and Last Hotel (BMG) Pty Ltd (2)
1141 Sydney Rd, Hadfield, Melbourne, 3046, VIC, Australia
Tel.: (61) 393541791
Web Site: http://www.firstandlasthotel.com.au
Tavern Operators
N.A.I.C.S.: 722410

Glengala Hotel (BMG) Pty Ltd (2)
214 Glengala Rd, Sunshine, 3020, VIC, Australia
Tel.: (61) 393611007
Web Site: http://www.glengalahotel.com.au
Tavern Operators
N.A.I.C.S.: 722410

MGW Hotels Pty Ltd (2)
53 Station St, Nerang, Gold Coast, 4211, QLD, Australia
Tel.: (61) 755571699
Web Site: https://www.hinterlandhotel.com.au
Tavern Operators
N.A.I.C.S.: 722410

Subsidiary (Domestic):

Chatswood Hills Tavern Pty. Ltd (3)
Cnr Chatswood & Magellan Rd, Springwood, 4127, QLD, Australia
Tel.: (61) 732905633
Web Site: https://www.chatswoodhillstavern.com.au
Tavern Operators
N.A.I.C.S.: 722410

Subsidiary (Domestic):

Management (BMG) Pty Ltd (2)
Level 2 Claremont Street 16-20 South Yara, South Yarra, Melbourne, 3141, VIC, Australia
Tel.: (61) 398291000
Management Consulting Services
N.A.I.C.S.: 541618

Manningham Hotel (BMG) Pty Ltd (2)
1 Thompsons Rd, Bulleen, 3105, Australia
Tel.: (61) 398502777
Web Site: https://www.themanningham.com.au
Sales Range: $50-74.9 Million
Emp.: 60
Convention Centre Operators
N.A.I.C.S.: 531120

Milanos Hotel (BMG) Pty Ltd (2)
4 The Esplanade, Brighton, 3186, Australia
Tel.: (61) 395923555
Web Site: http://www.milanos.com.au
Tavern Operators
N.A.I.C.S.: 722410

Monash Hotel (BMG) Pty Ltd (2)
2077 Dandenong Rd, Clayton, 3168, VIC, Australia
Tel.: (61) 3 9544 8011
Web Site: http://www.monashhotel.com.au
Club Hotel Management Services
N.A.I.C.S.: 721110

Moreland Hotel (BMG) Pty Ltd (2)
Cnr Sydney Rd and Moreland Rd, Brunswick, 3056, VIC, Australia
Tel.: (61) 3 9386 3748
Web Site: http://www.morelandhotel.com.au
Restaurant Management Services
N.A.I.C.S.: 722511

Preston Hotel (BMG) Pty Ltd (2)
635 High St, Preston, 3072, VIC, Australia
Tel.: (61) 3 9471 4811
Web Site: http://www.prestonhotel.com.au
Tavern Operators
N.A.I.C.S.: 722410

Racecourse Hotel (BMG) Pty Ltd (2)
895 Dandenong Road, Malvern, 3145, VIC, Australia
Tel.: (61) 3 9571 2154
Web Site: http://www.racecoursehotel.com.au
Sales Range: $10-24.9 Million
Emp.: 50
Club & Hotel Management Services
N.A.I.C.S.: 721110

Shoppingtown Hotel (BMG) Pty Ltd (2)
19 Williamsons Rd, Doncaster, 3108, VIC, Australia
Tel.: (61) 398486811
Web Site: http://www.shoppingtownhotel.com.au
Club Hotel Management Services
N.A.I.C.S.: 721110

Cartology Pty Limited (1)
1 Woolworths Way, Bella Vista, 2153, NSW, Australia
Tel.: (61) 28 885 0000
Web Site: https://www.cartology.com.au
Marketing & Advertising Services
N.A.I.C.S.: 541810
Mike Tyquin *(Mng Dir)*

DSE (NZ) Limited (1)

WOOLWORTHS GROUP LIMITED

Woolworths Group Limited—(Continued)

Dick Smith Private Bag 94005, Manukau, 2241, Auckland, New Zealand
Tel.: (64) 92791300
Web Site: http://www.dicksmith.co.nz
Electronic Appliance Distr
N.A.I.C.S.: 423620

Danks Holdings Limited (1)
414 426 Lower Dandenong Rd, 3195, Braeside, Victoria, Australia
Tel.: (61) 392645000
Web Site: http://www.danks.com.au
Sales Range: $350-399.9 Million
Hardware & Garden Supplies Distr
N.A.I.C.S.: 423710
James Aylen (Gen Mgr)

Elizabeth Tavern Pty. Ltd. (1)
Elizabeth City Centre Elizabeth Way, Elizabeth, 5112, SA, Australia
Tel.: (61) 882523022
Web Site:
    https://www.elizabethtavern.com.au
Sales Range: $10-24.9 Million
Emp.: 20
Tavern Operators
N.A.I.C.S.: 722410

Fountain Jade Pty. Ltd. (1)
1124 Magid Dr, Narre Warren, 3805, VIC, Australia
Tel.: (61) 397047922
Emp.: 30
Home Management Services
N.A.I.C.S.: 721110

Grocery Wholesalers Pty Ltd (1)
1 Woolworths Way, Bella Vista, Sydney, 2153, NSW, Australia
Tel.: (61) 288850000
Grocery Store Operating Services
N.A.I.C.S.: 445110

Hudson Building Supplies Pty Limited (1)
Withers Rd, Rouse Hill, Sydney, 2155, NSW, Australia
Tel.: (61) 2 9629 0488
Building Materials Distr
N.A.I.C.S.: 423390

New Zealand Wine Cellars Limited (1)
L 11 92 Albert St, Auckland, 1010, New Zealand
Tel.: (64) 93598222
Web Site: https://www.vineonline.co.nz
Emp.: 90
Alcoholic Beverage Distr
N.A.I.C.S.: 424820

PFD Food Services Pty., Ltd. (1)
6 Henderson Road, Knoxfield, 3180, VIC, Australia (65%)
Tel.: (61) 3 9756 2000
Web Site: http://www.pfdfoods.com.au
Sales Range: $450-499.9 Million
Emp.: 3,000
Warehousing & Processed Food Distr
N.A.I.C.S.: 493110
Kerry Smith (CEO)

Philip Leong Stores Pty Limited (1)
Fox Rd, Acacia Ridge, 4110, QLD, Australia
Tel.: (61) 747712577
Alcoholic Beverage Distr
N.A.I.C.S.: 424820

Playford Tavern Pty Limited (1)
80 Peachey Rd, Davoren Park, Adelaide, 5113, SA, Australia
Tel.: (61) 882556533
Web Site:
    https://www.playfordtavern.com.au
Tavern Operators
N.A.I.C.S.: 722410

Statewide Independent Wholesalers Limited (1)
8 Translink Avenue, Launceston, 7212, TAS, Australia
Tel.: (61) 63910800
Web Site: https://www.siw.com.au
Emp.: 430
Grocery Product Distr
N.A.I.C.S.: 424490

The Common Link Pty Ltd (1)
346 Tapleys Hill Rd, Seaton, 5023, SA, Australia
Tel.: (61) 883563111
Web Site: http://www.linkshotels.com.au
Home Management Services
N.A.I.C.S.: 721110

V I Packaging Pty Ltd (1)
773 Stockwell Road, PO Box 345, Angaston, 5355, SA, Australia
Tel.: (61) 885610600
Web Site: https://www.vinpac.com.au
Sales Range: $75-99.9 Million
Emp.: 30
Wine Bottle Labeling & Mfr Services
N.A.I.C.S.: 561910
Lisa Ashby (Gen Mgr-Wine Svcs)

Waltzing Matilda Hotel (BMG) Pty Ltd (1)
856-868 Heatherton Rd, Springvale, 3171, VIC, Australia
Tel.: (61) 395461333
Web Site:
    http://www.waltzingmatildahotel.com.au
Tavern Operators
N.A.I.C.S.: 722410

Werribee Plaza Tavern Pty. Ltd. (1)
Cnr Heaths And Derrimut Rds Hoppers Crossing, Melbourne, 3029, VIC, Australia
Tel.: (61) 397496000
Web Site: http://www.voltnightclub.com.au
Tavern Operators
N.A.I.C.S.: 722410

Wheelers Hill Hotel (BMG) Pty Ltd (1)
Cnr Ferntree Gully & Jells Rd, Wheelers Hill, Melbourne, 3150, VIC, Australia
Tel.: (61) 3 9560 8922
Web Site:
    http://www.wheelershillhotel.com.au
Sales Range: $10-24.9 Million
Emp.: 50
Tavern Operators
N.A.I.C.S.: 722410

Winemarket Pty Ltd (1)
Siegersdorf Road, Tanunda, 5352, SA, Australia
Tel.: (61) 1300 289 946
Web Site: http://www.winemarket.com.au
Wine Mfr
N.A.I.C.S.: 325193

Woolies Liquor Stores Pty. Ltd. (1)
1 Woolworths Way, Bella Vista, 2153, NSW, Australia
Tel.: (61) 288850000
Beverage Products Retailer
N.A.I.C.S.: 445320

Woolworths (HK) Procurement Limited (1)
9 Cheung Yee St 5th Floor D2 Place, Lai Chi Kok, Cheung Sha Wan, China (Hong Kong)
Tel.: (852) 36041000
Sales Range: $25-49.9 Million
Emp.: 90
Supermarket Stores
N.A.I.C.S.: 445110

Woolworths (HK) Sales Limited (1)
5th Floor D2 Place One, 9 Cheung Yee Street, Cheung Sha Wan, China (Hong Kong)
Tel.: (852) 36041000
Supermarket Stores
N.A.I.C.S.: 445110

Woolworths (International) Pty Limited (1)
1 Woolworths Way, Bella Vista, 2153, NSW, Australia
Tel.: (61) 288850000
Web Site: http://www.woodworths.com.au
Supermarket Stores
N.A.I.C.S.: 445110
Brad Banducci (CEO)

Woolworths (Project Finance) Pty. Limited (1)
1 Woolworths Way, Bella Vista, 2153, NSW, Australia (100%)
Tel.: (61) 288850000
Web Site: http://www.woolworths.com.au
Financial Development Services
N.A.I.C.S.: 525990

Grant O'Brien (CEO)

Woolworths (Victoria) Pty Limited (1)
127 Shepperton Rd, Victoria Park, 6100, WA, Australia
Tel.: (61) 893621722
Web Site: http://www.woolworths.com.au
Sales Range: $50-74.9 Million
Emp.: 120
Supermarket Operations
N.A.I.C.S.: 445110

Woolworths Management Pty. Ltd. (1)
1 Woolworths Way, Bella Vista, 2153, NSW, Australia (100%)
Tel.: (61) 288850000
Web Site: http://www.woolworthsltd.com.au
Supermarket Management Services
N.A.I.C.S.: 561110

Woolworths New Zealand Group Limited (1)
80 Favona Rd, Private Bag 93306, Mangere, Manukau, 2024, New Zealand
Tel.: (64) 9 275 2788
Web Site: https://www.woolworthsnz.co.nz
Supermarket Services
N.A.I.C.S.: 445110
Spencer Sonn (Mng Dir)

Woolworths New Zealand Limited (1)
80 Favona Rd, Mangere, 2024, Manukau, New Zealand
Tel.: (64) 800404040
Web Site: https://www.countdown.co.nz
Sales Range: $1-4.9 Billion
Emp.: 18,000
Supermarkets Franchisor & Operator
N.A.I.C.S.: 445110
Richard Manaton (Gen Mgr-Strategic Plng)

Subsidiary (Domestic):

Countdown (2)
80 Favona Rd, Mangere, Manukau, 2024, New Zealand
Tel.: (64) 800404040
Web Site: https://www.countdown.co.nz
Supermarket Stores
N.A.I.C.S.: 445110
Brett Ashley (Gen Mgr-Ops & Supply Chain)

Subsidiary (Non-US):

Fresh Zone Limited (2)
18521 Stony Plain Rd NW, Edmonton, T5S 2V9, AB, Canada
Tel.: (780) 484-9913
Emp.: 14
Supermarket Operating Services
N.A.I.C.S.: 445110
Rechel Sabate (Mgr)

Subsidiary (Domestic):

General Distributors Limited (2)
80 Favona Rd, Manukau, 2024, New Zealand
Tel.: (64) 800404040
Web Site: https://www.countdown.co.nz
Supermarket Management Services
N.A.I.C.S.: 445110
Dave Chambers (Gen Mgr)

The Supplychain Limited (2)
80 Favona Rd, Auckland, 1701, New Zealand
Tel.: (64) 92752788
Supermarket Stores
N.A.I.C.S.: 445110

Woolworths (New Zealand) Ltd. (2)
80 Favona Rd, Mangere, 2024, New Zealand (100%)
Tel.: (64) 92752788
Web Site: http://www.woolworthsnz.co.nz
Sales Range: $200-249.9 Million
Emp.: 600
Supermarkets Franchisor & Operator
N.A.I.C.S.: 445110
Peter Smith (Mng Dir)

Woolworths Properties Pty. Ltd. (1)
1 Woolworths Way, Bella Vista, 2153, NSW, Australia (100%)
Tel.: (61) 288850000
Intellectual Property Holding Company
N.A.I.C.S.: 551112

INTERNATIONAL PUBLIC

WOOLWORTHS HOLDINGS LIMITED

Woolworths House 93 Longmarket Street, Cape Town, 8001, South Africa
Tel.: (27) 214079111 ZA
Web Site:
    https://www.woolworthsholdings.com
WLWHF——(OTCIQ)
Rev.: $3,838,654,823
Assets: $2,071,578,703
Liabilities: $1,436,749,438
Net Worth: $634,829,265
Earnings: $205,061,312
Emp.: 33,756
Fiscal Year-end: 06/25/23
General Merchandise Store Operator
N.A.I.C.S.: 455219
Zyda Rylands (CEO-Woolworths)

Subsidiaries:

Country Road Group Proprietary Limited (1)
Building 2 572 Swan Street, PO Box 5218, Burnley, 3121, VIC, Australia (100%)
Tel.: (61) 385094000
Web Site:
    https://www.countryroadgroup.com.au
Sales Range: $700-749.9 Million
Holding Company; Apparel Designer, Distr & Online Retailer
N.A.I.C.S.: 551112
Elle Roseby (Mng Dir-Country Road)

Subsidiary (Domestic):

Country Road Clothing (Proprietary) Limited (2)
658 Church Street, Richmond, 3121, VIC, Australia
Tel.: (61) 392671400
Web Site: http://www.countryroad.com.au
Emp.: 300
Apparel Retailer
N.A.I.C.S.: 458110
Matthew Keogh (CEO)

Subsidiary (Domestic):

Country Road Australia Limited (3)
Level 1 Bunda Street, Canberra Centre, Canberra, 2601, ACT, Australia
Tel.: (61) 482089338
Web Site: https://www.countryroad.com.au
Apparel Retailer
N.A.I.C.S.: 458110

Subsidiary (Non-US):

Country Road Clothing (NZ) Limited (3)
Westfield Shopping Centre Shop 265 219 Don McKinnon Drive, Albany, Auckland, 1001, New Zealand
Tel.: (64) 99095570
Web Site: http://www.countryroad.com.au
Apparel Retailer
N.A.I.C.S.: 458110

David Jones Limited (1)
86-108 Castlereagh Street, Sydney, 2000, NSW, Australia
Tel.: (61) 292665544
Web Site: http://www.davidjones.com.au
Sales Range: $1-4.9 Billion
Emp.: 9,000
Departmental Store Operator
N.A.I.C.S.: 455110

Subsidiary (Domestic):

David Jones (Adelaide) Pty Limited (2)
100 Rundle Mall, Adelaide, 5000, SA, Australia
Tel.: (61) 883053000
Web Site: http://www.davidjones.com.au
Store Retailers
N.A.I.C.S.: 459999

David Jones Employee Share Plan Pty Limited (2)
86-108 Castlereagh Street, Sydney, NSW, Australia
Tel.: (61) 292665544
Web Site: http://www.davidjones.com

Sales Range: $25-49.9 Million
Emp.: 40
Durable Goods Merchant Whslr
N.A.I.C.S.: 423990

David Jones Insurance Pty Limited (2)
86-108 Castlereagh Street, Sydney, 2000, NSW, Australia
Tel.: (61) 292665544
Insurance Brokerage Services
N.A.I.C.S.: 524210

David Jones Properties Pty Limited (2)
86-108 Castlereagh Street, 2000, Sydney, NSW, Australia
Tel.: (61) 292665544
Store Retailers
N.A.I.C.S.: 459999

Woolworths (Proprietary) Limited (1)
Woolworths House 93 Longmarket Street, Cape Town, 8001, South Africa (100%)
Tel.: (27) 860022002
Web Site: https://www.woolworths.co.za
Discount Grocery, Clothing, Health & Beauty Department Stores Franchisor & Operator
N.A.I.C.S.: 455110

WOOMERA MINING LIMITED
147 Pirie Street, Adelaide, 5000, SA, Australia
Tel.: (61) 882326201
Web Site: https://www.woomeramining.com.au
WML—(ASX)
Rev.: $47,732
Assets: $5,117,311
Liabilities: $160,094
Net Worth: $4,957,217
Earnings: ($2,769,709)
Fiscal Year-end: 06/30/24
Metal Mining Services
N.A.I.C.S.: 212290
Peter Neil Landau (Chm)

WOONGJIN CO., LTD.
9th K-square City 24 Cheonggyecheon-ro, Jung-gu, Seoul, 03130, Korea (South)
Tel.: (82) 220764701
Web Site: http://www.woongjin.com
Year Founded: 1980
016880—(KRS)
Rev.: $805,228,271
Assets: $839,418,443
Liabilities: $665,950,292
Net Worth: $173,468,151
Earnings: $6,207,139
Emp.: 854
Fiscal Year-end: 12/31/22
Holding Company: IT Consulting, IT Sourcing & Business Shared Services & System Integration
N.A.I.C.S.: 551112
Su Yeong Lee (CEO)

Subsidiaries:

Woongjin Energy Co., Ltd. (1)
Daedeok Techno Vally 1316 Beonji Kwanpyung-Dong, Yuseong-Gu, Daejeon, Korea (South)
Tel.: (82) 429398114
Web Site: http://www.woongjinenergy.com
Rev.: $149,254,111
Assets: $213,069,912
Liabilities: $175,989,132
Net Worth: $37,080,780
Earnings: ($100,585,055)
Emp.: 306
Fiscal Year-end: 12/31/2018
Solar Cell Ingots & Wafers Mfr
N.A.I.C.S.: 339999

WOONGJIN THINKBIG CO., LTD.
Hoidong-gil 20, P'aju, 10881, Gyeonggi, Korea (South)
Tel.: (82) 3195671111
Web Site: http://www.wjthinkbig.com
Year Founded: 2007
095720—(KRS)
Rev.: $715,829,285
Assets: $606,537,641
Liabilities: $326,637,000
Net Worth: $279,900,641
Earnings: $2,384,825
Emp.: 2,106
Fiscal Year-end: 12/31/22
Educational Books Publishing Services
N.A.I.C.S.: 513120
Jae-jin Lee (CEO)

WOOREE E&L CO., LTD.
79 Seonggok-ro Danwon-gu, Ansan, Kyunggy-do, Korea (South)
Tel.: (82) 315993126
Web Site: http://www.wooreeenl.co.kr
153490—(KRS)
Rev.: $104,436,325
Assets: $83,476,590
Liabilities: $25,617,179
Net Worth: $57,859,410
Earnings: $4,062,337
Emp.: 81
Fiscal Year-end: 12/31/22
LED Packaging & Applications
N.A.I.C.S.: 334413
Lee Hee (Gen Mgr & Dir)

Subsidiaries:

Wooree Enterprise Co., Ltd. (1)
79 Seonggok-ro, Danwon-gu, Ansan, Gyeonggi-do, Korea (South)
Tel.: (82) 315993240
Web Site: https://www.wooreeenterprise.co.kr
Rev.: $1,058,078,677
Assets: $500,453,142
Liabilities: $272,203,856
Net Worth: $228,249,285
Earnings: $5,443,781
Emp.: 55
Fiscal Year-end: 12/31/2022
Lighting Mfr
N.A.I.C.S.: 335132
Kwang-Jin Yoo (Gen Mgr)

Subsidiary (Domestic):

IMTECH CO., LTD. (2)
4F Sincere B / D 332-34, Gocheon-dong, Uiwang, Korea (South)
Tel.: (82) 31 4595197
Communication Equipment Mfr
N.A.I.C.S.: 334220

Subsidiary (Non-US):

NEW OPTICS LTD. (2)
Web Site: http://www.newoptics.net
Liquid Crystal Display Mfr
N.A.I.C.S.: 334419

WOOREE VINA CO., LTD. (2)
Street No 1 Of Nhon Trach Industrial Zone, Nhon Trach, Dong Nai, Vietnam
Tel.: (84) 61 3560859
Lighting Equipment Mfr & Distr
N.A.I.C.S.: 335139

Subsidiary (Domestic):

Wooree Bio Co., Ltd. (2)
79 Seonggok-ro, Danwon-gu, Ansan, Gyeonggi-do, Korea (South)
Tel.: (82) 315993100
Web Site: https://www.wooreebio.co.kr
Rev.: $1,039,328,322
Assets: $428,704,896
Liabilities: $254,803,966
Net Worth: $173,900,930
Earnings: $16,737,337
Emp.: 99
Fiscal Year-end: 12/31/2022
Electric Lamp & Parts Mfr
N.A.I.C.S.: 335132
Gi Hyeon Cha (CEO)

Subsidiary (US):

Wooree Litech Inc. (2)
207 s brdwy ste300, Los Angeles, CA 90012
Tel.: (213) 617-1813
Sales Range: $25-49.9 Million
Emp.: 5
Fluorescent Lighting Fixtures Mfr
N.A.I.C.S.: 335132
Jimmy Yun (Pres)

WOORI FINANCIAL GROUP INC.
51 Sogong-ro, Jung-gu, Seoul, 04632, Korea (South)
Tel.: (82) 221252000
Web Site: https://www.woorifg.com
Year Founded: 2019
WF—(NYSE)
Rev.: $15,321,136,232
Assets: $369,642,783,130
Liabilities: $344,853,588,765
Net Worth: $24,789,194,365
Earnings: $1,949,804,789
Emp.: 115
Fiscal Year-end: 12/31/23
Commercial Banking Services
N.A.I.C.S.: 551112
Kyong-Hoon Park (Deputy Pres-Fin Plng Unit)

Subsidiaries:

Woori Asset Management Corp. (1)
6F 7F Yeouido Finance Tower 32 International Finance-ro 2-gil, Yeongdeungpo-gu, Seoul, 07325, Korea (South) (73%)
Tel.: (82) 237701300
Web Site: http://www.wooriam.kr
Investment Banking & Wealth Management Services
N.A.I.C.S.: 523150

Woori Asset Trust Co., Ltd. (1)
13th Floor Samjeong Building 301 Teheran-ro, Gangnam-gu, Seoul, Korea (South)
Tel.: (82) 262023000
Web Site: https://www.wooriat.com
Real Estate Investment Advisory Services
N.A.I.C.S.: 531190

Woori Bank (1)
51 Sogong-ro, Jung-gu, Seoul, 04632, Korea (South)
Banking Services
N.A.I.C.S.: 522110

Subsidiary (US):

Woori America Bank (2)
330 5th Ave, New York, NY 10001 (100%)
Tel.: (212) 244-1500
Web Site: http://www.wooriamericabank.com
Commercial Banking Services
N.A.I.C.S.: 522110
Seok Young Chung (Pres)

Subsidiary (Non-US):

Woori Bank Vietnam Limited (2)
Keangnam Landmark 72 E6 Pham Hung, Nam Tu Liem, Hanoi, Vietnam
Tel.: (84) 18006003
Web Site: https://retail.woori.com.vn
Finance Services
N.A.I.C.S.: 921130

Woori Finance Myanmar Co., Ltd. (2)
115 A Pyay Road 10 Miles, Insein Township, Yangon, Myanmar
Tel.: (95) 19666206
Web Site: https://woorifinancemyanmar.com
Finance Services
N.A.I.C.S.: 921130

Woori Global Markets Asia Limited (2)
Rooms 1907-1909 19/FGloucester Tower The Landmark 15 Queen's Road, Central, China (Hong Kong)
Tel.: (852) 37630888
Finance Services
N.A.I.C.S.: 921130

Woori Card Co., Ltd. (1)
The K Twin Tower 50 Jongno 1-gil, Jongno-gu, Seoul, Korea (South)
Tel.: (82) 269589000
Web Site: https://pc.wooricard.com
Card Loan Financial Services
N.A.I.C.S.: 522291

Subsidiary (Non-US):

PT Woori Finance Indonesia Tbk (2)
Chase Plaza Floor 16 Jl Jend Sudirman Kav 21, Jakarta, 12920, Indonesia (82.03%)
Tel.: (62) 215200434
Web Site: https://woorifinance.co.id
Rev.: $23,591,236
Assets: $120,165,257
Liabilities: $51,425,444
Net Worth: $68,739,813
Earnings: $5,628,062
Emp.: 799
Fiscal Year-end: 12/31/2023
Financial Services
N.A.I.C.S.: 522320
Markus Dinarto Pranoto (Chm)

Woori Finance Research Institute Co., Ltd. (1)
7th Floor Woori Financial Digital Tower 48 Sogong-ro, Jung-gu, Seoul, Korea (South)
Tel.: (82) 221730500
Web Site: https://www.wfri.re.kr
Research & Management Consulting Services
N.A.I.C.S.: 541613

Woori Financial Capital Co., Ltd. (1)
Cheongnam Bld 351 Gangnam-daero, Seocho-Gu, Seoul, 100-714, Korea (South)
Tel.: (82) 15448600
Web Site: http://www.ajucapital.co.kr
Rev.: $1,185,486,254
Assets: $9,561,350,521
Liabilities: $8,313,446,220
Net Worth: $1,247,904,301
Earnings: $98,433,467
Fiscal Year-end: 12/31/2023
Financial Products & Services
N.A.I.C.S.: 523999

Woori Financial F&I Co., Ltd. (1)
9th Floor 41 Cheonggyecheon-ro, Jongno-gu, Seoul, Korea (South)
Tel.: (82) 27391389
Web Site: https://www.woorifni.co.kr
Investment Services
N.A.I.C.S.: 522310

Woori Fund Service Co., Ltd. (1)
2 3th Floor Woori Financial Sangam Center 17 World Cup buk-ro 60-gil, Mapo-gu, Seoul, Korea (South)
Tel.: (82) 231513500
Web Site: https://www.woorifs.co.kr
Accounting Services
N.A.I.C.S.: 525920

Woori Global Asset Management Co., Ltd. (1)
18F ABL Tower 147 Seongdang-daero, Yeongdeungpo-Gu, Seoul, 07332, Korea (South) (100%)
Tel.: (82) 220719900
Web Site: https://www.wooriam.kr
Investment & Financial Services
N.A.I.C.S.: 523999

Woori Investment Bank Co., Ltd. (1)
15th FL 48 Sogong-ro, Jung-gu, Seoul, 04631, Korea (South) (100%)
Tel.: (82) 220006690
Web Site: http://www.wooriib.com
Sales Range: Less than $1 Million
Emp.: 175
Investment Banking Services
N.A.I.C.S.: 523150
Ki-Hwa Jung (CEO & Gen Dir)

Woori Private Equity Asset Management Co., Ltd. (1)
28th Fl Parc 1 Tower 1 108 Yeoui-daero, Yeongdeungpo-gu, Seoul, 07335, Korea (South) (100%)
Tel.: (82) 269492801
Web Site: http://www.wooripe.com
Rev.: $1,852,000,000
Emp.: 29
Privater Equity Firm
N.A.I.C.S.: 523999
Shinkook Kang (CEO)

Joint Venture (Domestic):

Doosan Engineering & Construction Co., Ltd. (2)
726 Eonju-ro, Gangnam-gu, Seoul, 135-

WOORI FINANCIAL GROUP INC.

Woori Financial Group Inc.—(Continued)

714, Korea (South)
Tel.: (82) 25103114
Web Site: https://www.doosanenc.com
Rev.: $1,532,520,000
Assets: $2,003,800,000
Liabilities: $1,516,180,000
Net Worth: $487,620,000
Earnings: ($64,500,000)
Emp.: 1,328
Fiscal Year-end: 12/31/2019
Construction Industry
N.A.I.C.S.: 236116
Jeongwon Park (Chm & CEO-Doosan Grp)

Subsidiary (Non-US):

Doosan Cuvex Co., Ltd. (3)
Tel.: (82) 332601114
Golf Club & Resort Management Operator
N.A.I.C.S.: 721110

Plant (Non-US):

Doosan Engineering & Construction Co., Ltd. - Doosan Vina (CPE Plant) (3)
Dung Quat Econ Zone Binh Thuan, Binh Soon, Quang Ngai, Vietnam
Tel.: (84) 553618900
Chemical Process Equipment Mfr
N.A.I.C.S.: 333248

WOORI SPECIAL PURPOSE ACQUISITION 3 CO., LTD.
60 Yeoui-daero Yeongdeungpo-gu, Seoul, Korea (South)
Tel.: (82) 2 750 5644
198440—(KRS)
Investment Services
N.A.I.C.S.: 523999
Gang-Wook Nam (CEO)

WOORI TECHNOLOGY INC.
9 World Cup Buk-ro 46 gil, Mapo-gu, Seoul, Korea (South)
Tel.: (82) 221025100
Web Site: https://www.wooritg.com
Year Founded: 1993
032820—(KRS)
Rev.: $37,962,336
Assets: $124,264,889
Liabilities: $51,037,561
Net Worth: $73,227,328
Earnings: $2,584,954
Emp.: 119
Fiscal Year-end: 12/31/22
Electronic Components Mfr
N.A.I.C.S.: 334419
Rho Gab Seon (CEO)

Subsidiaries:

Woori Biome, Inc. (1)
9 World Cup Buk-ro 56-gil Samam-dong Woori Tech Building 13th Floor, Mapo-gu, Seoul, Korea (South)
Tel.: (82) 221025187
Web Site: http://www.wooribiome.com
Molecular Diagnostics Services
N.A.I.C.S.: 621511

WOORI TECHNOLOGY INVESTMENT CO., LTD.
528 Teheran-ro, Gangnam-gu, Seoul, Korea (South)
Tel.: (82) 220083100
Web Site: https://www.wooricapital.co.kr
Year Founded: 1996
041190—(KRS)
Rev.: $27,928,197
Assets: $380,506,140
Liabilities: $65,272,477
Net Worth: $315,233,662
Earnings: ($258,981,566)
Emp.: 15
Fiscal Year-end: 12/31/22
Investment Banking Services
N.A.I.C.S.: 523150
Man Hoe Jung (CEO)

WOORIDUL HUEBRAIN LTD.
Hyangnam Pharmaceutical Industries Complex, Sangsin-ri Hyangnam-eup, Hwaseong, Gyeonggi-do, Korea (South)
Tel.: (82) 21943535
Web Site: http://www.wooridulls.co.kr
Year Founded: 1992
118000—(KRS)
Rev.: $14,648,417
Assets: $145,620,571
Liabilities: $46,233,041
Net Worth: $99,387,530
Earnings: ($38,008,468)
Emp.: 31
Fiscal Year-end: 12/31/22
Medical Devices Mfr & Sales
N.A.I.C.S.: 339112

Subsidiaries:

GID GROUP INC. (1)
115-16 Cheongdam-dong, Gangnam-gu, Seoul, Korea (South)
Tel.: (82) 25186876
Web Site: http://www.gidgroup.co.kr
Real Estate Development Services
N.A.I.C.S.: 531390

WOORIM POWER TRAIN SOLUTION CO., LTD.
613 Nammyeon-ro, Seongsan-gu, Changwon, 51534, Gyeongnam, Korea (South)
Tel.: (82) 552600300
Web Site: https://www.woorimpts.com
Year Founded: 1976
101170—(KRS)
Rev.: $52,402,620
Assets: $73,031,582
Liabilities: $6,933,264
Net Worth: $66,098,318
Earnings: $3,907,361
Emp.: 118
Fiscal Year-end: 12/31/22
Industrial Reducer & Precision Gear Mfr
N.A.I.C.S.: 333998
Hyun Seok Han (CEO)

Subsidiaries:

Woorim Machinery Co., Ltd. - Factory 1 (1)
145 Seongsanpaechong-ro Oe-dong, Seongsan-gu, Changwon, Gyeongnam, Korea (South)
Tel.: (82) 55 260 0300
Industrial Machinery Mfr
N.A.I.C.S.: 333248

WOORINET, INC.
WooriNet Bldg 353 Simin-daero, Dongan-gu, Anyang, 14057, GyeongGi-Do, Korea (South)
Tel.: (82) 312765101
Web Site: https://www.woori-net.com
Year Founded: 2000
115440—(KRS)
Rev.: $47,758,002
Assets: $85,971,124
Liabilities: $40,235,382
Net Worth: $45,735,742
Earnings: $7,454,956)
Emp.: 168
Fiscal Year-end: 12/31/22
Fiber Optic Transmission System Mfr
N.A.I.C.S.: 335921
Jang Kook (Co-CEO)

WOORIRO CO., LTD.
102-22 Pyeongdongsandan 6beon-ro, Gwangsan-gu, Gwangju, 62453, Korea (South)
Tel.: (82) 626028100
Web Site: https://www.wooriro.com
Year Founded: 1998
046970—(KRS)
Rev.: $75,938,058
Assets: $46,767,849
Liabilities: $17,883,661
Net Worth: $28,884,188
Earnings: ($2,660,653)
Emp.: 130
Fiscal Year-end: 12/31/22
Telecommunication Optical Component Mfr
N.A.I.C.S.: 334290
Ho-Youn Hong (Pres)

WOORISON F&G CO., LTD.
73 Jangsong-gil, Bannam-myeon, Naju, 58298, Jeollanam-do, Korea (South)
Tel.: (82) 415631055
Web Site: https://www.woorisonfng.co.kr
Year Founded: 2001
073560—(KRS)
Rev.: $220,025,428
Assets: $366,019,979
Liabilities: $165,126,310
Net Worth: $200,893,670
Earnings: $20,330,820
Emp.: 123
Fiscal Year-end: 12/31/22
Processed Meat Mfr & Distr
N.A.I.C.S.: 311612
Taehyun Lee (Gen Mgr)

WOORY INDUSTRIAL CO., LTD.
89 Jisam-ro Jigok-dong, Giheung-gu, 17088, Yongin, 17088, Gyeonggi-do, Korea (South)
Tel.: (82) 312016500
Web Site: https://www.woory.com
Year Founded: 1989
215360—(KRS)
Rev.: $279,649,692
Assets: $182,723,268
Liabilities: $116,956,084
Net Worth: $65,767,184
Earnings: ($13,773,251)
Emp.: 344
Fiscal Year-end: 12/31/22
Motor Vehicle Parts Mfr & Distr
N.A.I.C.S.: 336390
Kim Joon (Chm & CEO)

WOORY INDUSTRIAL HOLDINGS CO., LTD.
89 Jisam-Ro, Giheung-Gu, Yongin, 17088, Gyeonggi-do, Korea (South)
Tel.: (82) 312016500
Web Site: https://www.woory.com
Year Founded: 1989
072470—(KRS)
Rev.: $380,065,662
Assets: $308,203,284
Liabilities: $165,818,968
Net Worth: $142,384,317
Earnings: ($14,040,885)
Emp.: 16
Fiscal Year-end: 12/31/22
Automotive Components Mfr
N.A.I.C.S.: 336320
Myung Joon Kim (Chm & CEO)

Subsidiaries:

Tianjin Woory Electronics Co Ltd (1)
South 4Wei Road Dong Li Economic Development Zone, Tianjin, China
Tel.: (86) 2224983272
Emp.: 423
Electronic Equipment Distr
N.A.I.C.S.: 423690
Jin Wook Yang (Mgr-Ops)

WOORY Slovakia s.r.o. (1)
ul L'udovita Stura 1030/74, 019 01, Ilava, Slovakia
Tel.: (421) 1914323080
Emp.: 53
Automobile Spare Parts Mfr

INTERNATIONAL PUBLIC

N.A.I.C.S.: 336110
Chunkyu Park (Mgr-Ops)

WR America, Inc. (1)
29120 Airport Dr Bldg 21, Romulus, MI 48174
Tel.: (734) 947-1433
Emp.: 10
Automobile Spare Parts Mfr
N.A.I.C.S.: 336110
Johnny Lee (Mgr-Ops)

Woory Automotive India Pvt Ltd (1)
Plot No-A1B M M D A Industrial Complex, Kilakaranai Village Maraiamalai Nagar Chengalpattu, Kanchipuram, 603209, Tamil Nadu, India
Tel.: (91) 4447404451
Emp.: 317
Automobile Spare Parts Mfr
N.A.I.C.S.: 336110
Sang Hoon Lee (Mgr-Ops)

Woory Industrial (Thailand) Co., Ltd. (1)
32/8 Moo, Pong District Banglamung, Chon Buri, 20150, Thailand
Tel.: (66) 38227106
Emp.: 73
Automobile Spare Parts Mfr
N.A.I.C.S.: 336110
Jae Hee Jung (Mgr-Ops)

Woory Platech Co., Ltd. (1)
111-3 Sindu-ri, Ipjang-myeon, Cheonan, Chungcheongnam-do, Korea (South)
Tel.: (82) 41 585 8523
Electronic Equipment Distr
N.A.I.C.S.: 423690
M. J. Kim (Pres & CEO)

WOOSHIN SYSTEMS CO., LTD.
333 Gongdan 1-daero, Siheung, Gyeonggi-do, Korea (South)
Tel.: (82) 314966114
Web Site: https://www.wooshinsys.co.kr
Year Founded: 1984
017370—(KRS)
Rev.: $195,231,001
Assets: $216,689,554
Liabilities: $147,622,343
Net Worth: $69,067,211
Earnings: $2,123,743
Emp.: 929
Fiscal Year-end: 12/31/22
Automotive Body Welding System Mfr
N.A.I.C.S.: 336390
Kang Sung-Woo (Head)

Subsidiaries:

WS Systems Mexico S.A.de C.V. (1)
Av USA282 Parque Industrial Tres Naciones, 78395, San Luis Potosi, Mexico
Tel.: (52) 4448802080
Automotive Body Mfr & Distr
N.A.I.C.S.: 336211

Wooshin Engineering Pvt. Ltd. (1)
Gat No 581/1 2&715 A/P Wadhu-Bk Off Koreagaon Bhima Nagar Road, Pune, 412216, Maharashtra, India
Tel.: (91) 2137241000
Web Site: https://www.wooshin.co
Automotive Body & Spare Parts Mfr
N.A.I.C.S.: 336110

Wooshin Systems Co., Ltd. - Dangjin Plant (1)
28-226 Bugokgondan 4-gil, Songak-eup, Dangjin, Chungcheongnam-do, Korea (South)
Tel.: (82) 41 359 3202
Automotive Body & Spare Parts Mfr
N.A.I.C.S.: 336110

Wooshin Systems Co., Ltd. - Hwaseong Plant (1)
295 Toseong-ro, Hyangnap-eup, Hwaseong, Gyeonggi-do, Korea (South)
Tel.: (82) 31 494 2181
Automotive Body & Spare Parts Mfr
N.A.I.C.S.: 336110

Wooshin Systems Co., Ltd. - Sihwa 2nd Plant (1)

Sihwa Gongdan 2C 601 45 Gunjacheon-ro 185-gil, Siheung, Gyeonggi-do, Korea (South)
Tel.: (82) 31 496 4924
Automotive Body & Spare Parts Mfr
N.A.I.C.S.: 336110

Wuhan Wooshin Machinery Co., Ltd. (1)
308 CheCheng East Road, Economic & Technological Development Zone, Wuhan, Hubei, China
Tel.: (86) 27 8423 7008
Automotive Body & Spare Parts Mfr
N.A.I.C.S.: 336110

Yantai Wooshin Science and Technology Co., Ltd. (1)
116 Taishan Road, Yantai Economic Technological Development Zone, Yantai, China
Tel.: (86) 5356397010
Web Site: https://www.wooshin.com.cn
Automotive Body & Spare Parts Mfr
N.A.I.C.S.: 336110

WOOSU AMS CO., LTD.
62 Wollim-ro Sinchon-dong, Seongsan-gu, Changwon, Gyeongsangnam, Korea (South)
Tel.: (82) 552745011
Web Site: https://www.woosu.co.kr
Year Founded: 1983
066590—(KRS)
Rev.: $273,742,813
Assets: $212,895,688
Liabilities: $156,973,593
Net Worth: $55,922,095
Earnings: ($13,436,038)
Emp.: 372
Fiscal Year-end: 12/31/22
Automobile Parts Mfr
N.A.I.C.S.: 336390
Kim Sun Woo (CEO)

Subsidiaries:

Woosu AMS Co., Ltd. - Ulsan Plant (1)
312 Jeoneupri, Duseomyeon Kyungnam, Ulsan, 641-833, Uljugun, Korea (South)
Tel.: (82) 55 264 8011
Automobile Spare Parts Mfr
N.A.I.C.S.: 336390

Woosu India Pvt. Ltd. (1)
130 Narasingapuram Village, Kanchipuram, Tamil Nadu, India
Tel.: (91) 7074901191
Automobile Parts Distr
N.A.I.C.S.: 423140

Woosu Precision Co., Ltd. (1)
Andong 162-12, Kyungnam, Gimhae, 641-833, Korea (South)
Tel.: (82) 55 333 2211
Automobile Parts Mfr
N.A.I.C.S.: 336390

WOOSUNG CO., LTD.
1027 Hanbat-daero, Daedeok-gu, Daejeon, Korea (South)
Tel.: (82) 426701724
Web Site:
https://www.woosungfeed.co.kr
Year Founded: 1968
006980—(KRS)
Rev.: $469,651,269
Assets: $308,310,432
Liabilities: $175,441,501
Net Worth: $132,868,931
Earnings: $96,689
Emp.: 64
Fiscal Year-end: 12/31/22
Animal Feed Mfr
N.A.I.C.S.: 311119
Han Jae-Gyu (CEO)

Subsidiaries:

Woosung Transportation Co., Ltd (1)
Sannaero 1267 Namwal Dong, Dong-gu, Daejeon, Korea (South)
Tel.: (82) 42 272 2111
Car Rental Services
N.A.I.C.S.: 532111

Woosung Vietnam Co., Ltd (1)
Pet Food Mfr
N.A.I.C.S.: 311111

Woosung Yanghang (1)
Ansimro 259-5, Eumjin myon, Nonsan, Choong Cheong Nam Do, Korea (South)
Tel.: (82) 41 741 7836
Pet Food Mfr & Distr
N.A.I.C.S.: 311111

WOOWON DEVELOPMENT CO., LTD.
8th Floor Backhyang Bldg Gangnam Daero Road, Seocho-gu, Seoul, Korea (South)
Tel.: (82) 25668890
Web Site:
https://www.woowonerd.com
Year Founded: 1998
046940—(KRS)
Rev: $150,556,004
Assets: $126,628,437
Liabilities: $46,983,149
Net Worth: $79,645,288
Earnings: $2,867,329
Emp.: 224
Fiscal Year-end: 12/31/22
Civil Engineering Construction Services
N.A.I.C.S.: 237990
Hwang Eui Joong (CEO)

WOOYANG CO., LTD.
14-5 Sindae-gil Ungok-myeon, Cheongyang, Chungcheongnam-do, Korea (South)
Tel.: (82) 419422911
Web Site: https://www.foodkorea.com
Year Founded: 1992
103840—(KRS)
Rev.: $125,337,715
Assets: $115,834,326
Liabilities: $85,101,509
Net Worth: $30,732,817
Earnings: ($2,300,078)
Emp.: 309
Fiscal Year-end: 12/31/22
Health Food Product Mfr & Distr
N.A.I.C.S.: 333241

WOQU.COM
4th Floor West Tower Skyworth Semiconductor Design Building, Gaoxin South 3rd Road Nanshan District, Shenzhen, 518057, Guangdong, China
Tel.: (86) 400 661 5757
Web Site: http://www.woqu.com
Customized Tours & Travel Packages
N.A.I.C.S.: 561520
Ivan Huang (Founder)

Subsidiaries:

Lulutrip Inc. (1)
2033 Gateway Place Ste 674, San Jose, CA 95110
Tel.: (408) 786-0688
Web Site: http://www.lulutrip.com
Online Tour & Hotel Booking & Travel Consulting
N.A.I.C.S.: 561520

WORK SERVICE S.A.
ul Sienna 75, 00-833, warsaw, Poland
Tel.: (48) 508000773
Web Site: https://pl.gigroup.com
Year Founded: 1999
WSE—(WAR)
Rev.: $244,415,209
Assets: $113,187,647
Liabilities: $112,781,711
Net Worth: $405,936
Earnings: ($3,052,725)
Emp.: 154
Fiscal Year-end: 12/31/20
Employment Placement
N.A.I.C.S.: 561311
Maciej Witucki (Pres-Mgmt Bd)

Subsidiaries:

Finance Care Sp. z o.o. (1)
Ruska 51, Wroclaw, Poland
Tel.: (48) 71 371 09 76
Web Site: http://www.financecare.pl
Financial Management Services
N.A.I.C.S.: 523999

Stermedia Sp. z o.o. (1)
13 Ostrowskiego Street, 53-238, Wroclaw, Poland
Tel.: (48) 717000277
Web Site: http://stermedia.ai
Emp.: 30
Software Development Services
N.A.I.C.S.: 541511

Work Service Czech s.r.o. (1)
Hornopolni 3308, 702 00, Ostrava, Czech Republic
Tel.: (420) 595 221 500
Web Site: http://www.workservice.cz
Employment Placement Agency
N.A.I.C.S.: 561320

Work Service International Sp. z o.o. (1)
Ruska 51, 50-079, Wroclaw, Poland
Tel.: (48) 71 758 28 47
General Management Consulting Services
N.A.I.C.S.: 541611

WORKFORCE HOLDINGS LTD.
11 Wellington Road Parktown, PO Box 11137, Johannesburg, 2193, South Africa
Tel.: (27) 115320000   ZA
Web Site:
https://www.workforce.co.za
WKF—(JSE)
Rev.: $245,321,333
Assets: $86,423,282
Liabilities: $38,239,960
Net Worth: $48,183,322
Earnings: ($1,457,132)
Emp.: 1,269
Fiscal Year-end: 12/31/23
Temporary Employment Services
N.A.I.C.S.: 561320
Ronny S. Katz (Founder & CEO)

Subsidiaries:

Africa Upskill Proprietary Limited (1)
11 Wellington Road, Parktown, 2193, South Africa
Tel.: (27) 115320000
Web Site: https://africaupskill.co.za
Digital Training Courses Services
N.A.I.C.S.: 518210

Albrecht Nursing Agency (Proprietary) Limited (1)
240 Main Road, Tokai, Cape Town, 7945, Western Cape, South Africa
Tel.: (27) 21 713 0720
Medical Staff Recruitment Services
N.A.I.C.S.: 561311

Allmed Healthcare Professionals Proprietary Limited (1)
215 Main Road, Claremont, Cape Town, 7708, South Africa
Tel.: (27) 861000466
Web Site: https://www.allmed.co.za
Healtcare Services
N.A.I.C.S.: 621999

Day-Click Limited (1)
Centre Commercial La Source 1er etage, Centre de Flacq, Mauritius
Tel.: (230) 413 8080
Web Site: https://dayclick.mu
Human Resouce Services
N.A.I.C.S.: 541612

Dyna Training Proprietary Limited (1)
D7 Collingwood Building, Blackriver Park Observatory, Cape Town, South Africa
Tel.: (27) 21 447 6547
Web Site: https://dyna-training.co.za

Professional Training & Coaching Services
N.A.I.C.S.: 611430

Essential Employee Benefits Proprietary Limited (1)
15 Wellington Road, Parktown, Johannesburg, 2193, South Africa
Tel.: (27) 105937158
Web Site: https://www.eeb.co.za
Financial Services
N.A.I.C.S.: 521110

GetSavvi Health Proprietary Limited (1)
Suite 401 Tygervalley Chambers 5 27 Willie van Schoor Ave Tygervalley, Bellville, 7530, South Africa
Tel.: (27) 861189202
Web Site: https://www.getsavvi.co.za
Medical Research & Development Services
N.A.I.C.S.: 524114

KBC Health & Safety Proprietary Limited (1)
Cresta Junction Cnr Judges and Beyers Naude, Randburg, 2194, Gauteng, South Africa
Tel.: (27) 876505577
Professional Training & Coaching Services
N.A.I.C.S.: 611430
Graham Emmett (Chm)

Nursing Emergencies Proprietary Limited (1)
13 Wellington Road, Parktown, Johannesburg, 2193, Gauteng, South Africa
Tel.: (27) 860009894
Web Site: https://nursingemergencies.co.za
Healtcare Services
N.A.I.C.S.: 621999

Only The Best (Pte) Ltd. (1)
3rd Floor 13 Wellington Road, Parktown, Johannesburg, 2193, Gauteng, South Africa
Tel.: (27) 117898282
Web Site: https://www.onlythebest.co.za
Emp.: 40
Temporary Employment Services
N.A.I.C.S.: 561320

OpenSource Intelligent Solutions Proprietary Limited (1)
1328 Eikendal Rd, Stellenbosch, 7600, South Africa
Tel.: (27) 218554907
Web Site: https://osourceint.com
Information Technology Professionals Recruitment Services
N.A.I.C.S.: 561311

Oxyon Peoples Solutions Proprietary Limited (1)
74 Hennie Alberts Brackenhurst, Alberton, 1448, South Africa
Tel.: (27) 871358033
Web Site: https://www.oxyon.co.za
Human Resource Consulting Services
N.A.I.C.S.: 541612

Prisma Training Solutions Proprietary Limited (1)
11 Maury Avenue, Potchefstroom, 2520, South Africa
Tel.: (27) 871357020
Web Site: https://www.prisma.co.za
Education Management Services
N.A.I.C.S.: 611710

Programmed Process Outsourcing Proprietary Limited (1)
11 Wellington Road, Parktown, Johannesburg, South Africa
Tel.: (27) 871359090
Web Site: https://www.pposa.co.za
Healtcare Services
N.A.I.C.S.: 621999

Quyn Payroll & HR Services Proprietary Limited (1)
11 Wellington Road, Parktown, Johannesburg, 2193, South Africa
Tel.: (27) 108223333
Web Site: https://quyn.co.za
Staffing & Recruitment Services
N.A.I.C.S.: 541612

RecruitCo Proprietary Limited (1)
888 Port Road, Woodville South, Adelaide, 5011, SA, Australia
Tel.: (61) 883543122

WORKFORCE HOLDINGS LTD.

Workforce Holdings Ltd.—(Continued)
Web Site: https://www.recruitco.com.au
Human Resource Management Services
N.A.I.C.S.: 541612
Lindsay Davie *(Exec Dir)*

Sikekela Skills Academy Proprietary Limited (1)
13 Wellington Road, Parktown, Johannesburg, South Africa
Tel.: (27) 10 025 3304
Web Site: https://www.sikelelaskills.co.za
Courses Training Services
N.A.I.C.S.: 611430

Sikekela Skills Academy Proprietary Limited (1)
Office 104 Cnr Gertrude St & Voortrekker Rd Goodwood Mall, Goodwood, South Africa
Tel.: (27) 219512750
Web Site: https://sikelelaskills.co.za
Software Development Services
N.A.I.C.S.: 541519

TWG Mauritius Ltd. (1)
Le Moulin, Pereybere, Grand Baie, Mauritius
Tel.: (230) 2682163
Web Site: https://workforcegroup.mu
Employee Placement Services
N.A.I.C.S.: 561311

Teleresources (Pty) Ltd. (1)
284 Oak Ave, Ferndale Randburg, Johannesburg, 2118, South Africa
Tel.: (27) 117898282
Web Site: http://www.telesouces.co.za
Sales Range: $25-49.9 Million
Emp.: 50
Temporary Employment Services
N.A.I.C.S.: 561320
Gillian Jhonson *(Mng Dir)*

The Cyber Academy Proprietary Limited (1)
13 Wellington Road, Parktown, Johannesburg, South Africa
Tel.: (27) 878089849
Web Site: https://thecyberacademy.co.za
Cyber Academy Services
N.A.I.C.S.: 611699

The Workforce Group (Proprietary) Limited (1)
11 Wellington Rd, Pk Town, Johannesburg, 2193, Gauteng, South Africa
Tel.: (27) 115320000
Web Site: http://www.workforce.co.za
Sales Range: $75-99.9 Million
Emp.: 400
Employment Services
N.A.I.C.S.: 561311

Division (Domestic):

Workforce Worldwide Staffing (Proprietary) Limited (2)
11 Wellington Rd, Parktown, Johannesburg, 2000, Gauteng, South Africa
Tel.: (27) 115320000
Web Site: http://www.workforceworldwide.com
Sales Range: $25-49.9 Million
Emp.: 17
Employment Services
N.A.I.C.S.: 561311

The Workforce Group Mauritius Limited (1)
Le Moulin Pereybere, Grand Baie, Mauritius
Tel.: (230) 268 2163
Web Site: https://workforcegroup.mu
Employment Solutions Services
N.A.I.C.S.: 561311

Training Force (Proprietary) Limited (1)
13 Wellington Road, Parktown, Johannesburg, 2193, Gauteng, South Africa
Tel.: (27) 119746633
Web Site: https://www.trainingforce.co.za
Sales Range: $10-24.9 Million
Emp.: 24
Professional Management Training Services
N.A.I.C.S.: 611430

Workforce Healthcare (Proprietary) Limited (1)
11 Wellington Road, Parktown, Johannesburg, 2193, Gauteng, South Africa
Tel.: (27) 115320020
Web Site: http://www.workforcehealthcare.co.za
Emp.: 50
Employee Healthcare Services
N.A.I.C.S.: 621999
Richard B. Malkin *(Mng Dir)*

Workforce Software (Proprietary) Limited (1)
Durban Road Palm Street Victoria Tower Building 1st Floor, Tyger Valley, Cape Town, Western Cape, South Africa
Tel.: (27) 219190548
Sales Range: $25-49.9 Million
Emp.: 60
Workforce Management Software Development Services
N.A.I.C.S.: 541511
Sean Monderg *(Reg Dir)*

WORKING WORD PUBLIC RELATIONS LTD.
15 Neptune Court Ocean Way, Cardiff, CF24 5PJ, United Kingdom
Tel.: (44) 2920 455 182 UK
Web Site: http://www.workingwordpr.com
Year Founded: 1999
Sales Range: $1-9.9 Million
Emp.: 17
Public Relations Agency
N.A.I.C.S.: 541820
Eoghan Mortell *(Assoc Dir)*

WORKMAN CO., LTD.
1732 Shiba-machi, Isesaki, 372-0824, Gunma, Japan
Tel.: (81) 338477730
Web Site: https://www.workman.co.jp
Year Founded: 1979
7564—(TKS)
Rev.: $846,455,190
Assets: $894,276,740
Liabilities: $183,574,230
Net Worth: $710,702,510
Earnings: $122,593,730
Fiscal Year-end: 03/31/20
Franchise Store Operator
N.A.I.C.S.: 458110
Hideyuki Kohama *(Pres & CEO)*

WORKPOINT ENTERTAINMENT PUBLIC COMPANY LIMITED
99 Moo 2 Bangpoon, Muang Pathum Thani, Pathumthani, 12000, Thailand
Tel.: (66) 28332000
Web Site: https://www.workpoint.co.th
WORK—(THA)
Rev.: $72,846,226
Assets: $149,495,873
Liabilities: $20,286,960
Net Worth: $129,208,914
Earnings: $393,508
Fiscal Year-end: 12/31/23
Entertainment Services
N.A.I.C.S.: 711130
Phanya Nirunkul *(Chm)*

WORKSPACE GROUP PLC
Canterbury Court Kennington Park 1-3 Brixton Road, London, SW9 6DE, United Kingdom
Tel.: (44) 2071383300 UK
Web Site: https://www.workspace.co.uk
Year Founded: 1987
WKP—(LSE)
Rev.: $180,440,988
Assets: $3,410,456,868
Liabilities: $967,103,956
Net Worth: $2,443,352,912
Earnings: $168,221,508
Emp.: 246
Fiscal Year-end: 03/31/22
Business Real Estate
N.A.I.C.S.: 531210
Graham Clemett *(CFO)*

Subsidiaries:

McKay Securities PLC (1)
20 Greyfriars Road, Reading, RG1 1NL, Berkshire, United Kingdom
Tel.: (44) 1189502333
Web Site: http://www.mckaysecurities.plc.uk
Rev.: $224,024
Assets: $606,927,994
Liabilities: $213,322,251
Net Worth: $393,605,743
Earnings: ($22,334,494)
Emp.: 18
Fiscal Year-end: 03/31/2021
Commercial Property Investment
N.A.I.C.S.: 531120
Joanne S. McKeown *(Sec)*

Subsidiary (Domestic):

Baldwin House Limited (2)
20 Greyfriars Rd, Reading, RG1 1NL, Berkshire, United Kingdom
Tel.: (44) 1189502333
Web Site: http://www.mckaysecurities.plc.uk
Property Development & Investment Services
N.A.I.C.S.: 531312
Simon Perkins *(Mng Dir)*

McKay Securities Overseas Limited (2)
20 Greyfriars Rd, Reading, RG1 1NL, Berkshire, United Kingdom
Tel.: (44) 1189502333
Web Site: http://www.mckaysecurities.plc.uk
Property Development & Investment Services
N.A.I.C.S.: 531312

Workspace 15 Ltd. (1)
chester house kennington prk 1-3 brixton london, London, SW9 6DE, United Kingdom
Tel.: (44) 2072477614
Web Site: http://www.workspace.co.uk
Emp.: 80
Real Estate Property Investment Services
N.A.I.C.S.: 525990
Jamie Hopkins *(CEO)*

Workspace Holdings, Ltd. (1)
Chester House Kennington Park 1-3, Brickston Rd, London, SW9 6DE, United Kingdom
Tel.: (44) 2073771154
Web Site: http://www.workspacegroup.co.uk
Sales Range: $75-99.9 Million
Real Estate Agency
N.A.I.C.S.: 531210
Harry Plant *(CEO)*

Subsidiary (Non-US):

Workspace Management, Ltd. (2)
Chesteo House 113, Whitechapel Road, SW9 6DA, London, United Kingdom - England
Tel.: (44) 2072477614
Web Site: http://www.workspace.co.uk
Sales Range: $75-99.9 Million
Emp.: 200
Real Estate Agency
N.A.I.C.S.: 531210
Jamie Hopkins *(CEO)*

WORKSPACE TECHNOLOGY LTD.
Technology House 5 Emmanuel Court, Reddicroft, Sutton Coldfield, B72 1TJ, United Kingdom
Tel.: (44) 121 354 4894
Web Site: http://www.workspace-technology.com
Year Founded: 2004
Sales Range: $10-24.9 Million
Emp.: 40
Data Center Design & Construction Services
N.A.I.C.S.: 236220
Roy Griffiths *(Mng Dir & Dir-Technical)*

WORKSPORT, LTD.
3120-414 Rutherford Rd, Vaughan, L4K 0B1, ON, Canada NV
Web Site: https://www.worksport.com
Year Founded: 1997
WKSP—(NASDAQ)
Rev.: $116,502
Assets: $32,764,130
Liabilities: $8,645,876
Net Worth: $24,118,254
Earnings: ($12,534,414)
Emp.: 21
Fiscal Year-end: 12/31/22
Diversified Franchising Services
N.A.I.C.S.: 561499
Steven Rossi *(Chm, Pres, CEO & Sec)*

Subsidiaries:

Truxmart, Inc. (1)
1895 Clements Road Unit 155, Pickering, M1P 4Y9, ON, Canada
Tel.: (888) 554-9789
Web Site: http://www.truxmart.ca
Aftermarket Motor Vehicle Parts Distr
N.A.I.C.S.: 423120

WORLD CO., LTD.
6-8-1 Minatojima-Nakamachi, Chuo-ku, Kobe, 650-8585, Japan
Tel.: (81) 783023111 JP
Web Site: https://corp.world.co.jp
Year Founded: 1959
3612—(TKS)
Rev.: $1,434,604,780
Assets: $1,699,366,650
Liabilities: $1,072,483,030
Net Worth: $626,883,620
Earnings: $47,956,760
Emp.: 7,183
Fiscal Year-end: 02/29/24
Clothing Whslr & Retailer
N.A.I.C.S.: 458110

Subsidiaries:

Asplund Co., Ltd. (1)
5F Mita 43 MT Building 3-13-16 Mita, Minato-ku, Tokyo, 108-0073, Japan
Tel.: (81) 337690637
Web Site: http://www.asplund.co.jp
Emp.: 124
Interior Lifestyle Product Whslr
N.A.I.C.S.: 424450

Fashion-Co-Lab. Co., Ltd. (1)
2-4-12 Jingumae DT Gaien 3F, Shibuya-ku, Tokyo, 150-0001, Japan
Tel.: (81) 364472490
Web Site: http://fashion-co-lab.jp
Fashion Accessories Whslr
N.A.I.C.S.: 424450

Fastech & Solutions Co., Ltd. (1)
3-5-10 Kita-Aoyama, Minato-ku, Tokyo, 107-8526, Japan
Tel.: (81) 364474124
Web Site: http://fastech-solutions.jp
Fashion Related Consulting Services
N.A.I.C.S.: 541618

Intercube Co., Ltd. (1)
5-11-2 Minami Aoyama Sanwa Minami Aoyama Building 8F, Minato-ku, Tokyo, 107-0062, Japan
Tel.: (81) 357783557
Web Site: http://www.inter-cube.co.jp
Shop Window Mfr
N.A.I.C.S.: 321911
Fumihisa Maruyama *(Pres & CEO)*

KaysWay Co., Ltd. (1)
18 34 Hiroshibacho, Suita, 564-0052, Osaka Prefecture, Japan
Tel.: (81) 663687111
Web Site: http://www.kays-way.co.jp
Clothing Distr
N.A.I.C.S.: 424350

Kobe Leather Cloth Co., Ltd. (1)
2-5-12 Nishishiriike- cho, Nagata-ku, Kobe, 653-0031, Hyogo, Japan
Tel.: (81) 786111505
Web Site: http://www.kobe-leather.co.jp
Women Shoe Mfr & Whslr
N.A.I.C.S.: 316210

La Mode Co., Ltd. (1)
640 1 Naka, Yamagata, Kumamoto Prefecture, Japan
Tel.: (81) 968442231
Clothing Mfr
N.A.I.C.S.: 315250

Laxus Technologies Inc. (1)
Roppongi Hills Mori Tower 19F 6 10 1, Roppongi Minato-ku, Tokyo, 106-6119, Japan
Tel.: (81) 341300303
Web Site: http://corp.laxus.co
Emp.: 71
Luxury Bag Whslr
N.A.I.C.S.: 458110
Shoji Kodama *(Founder & CEO)*

Narumiya International Co., Ltd. (1)
9th floor Tower B Shiba Park Building 2-4-1 Shibakoen, Minato-Ku, Tokyo, Japan (58%)
Tel.: (81) 364309100
Web Site: https://www.narumiya-net.co.jp
Rev.: $265,761,560
Assets: $100,394,400
Liabilities: $57,797,680
Net Worth: $42,596,720
Earnings: $8,621,440
Emp.: 1,584
Fiscal Year-end: 02/29/2024
Children Clothing Product Mfr & Distr
N.A.I.C.S.: 315250
Hirotaka Kunikyo *(Pres & CEO)*

ThinkAgent Corporation (1)
World Kita Aoyama Building 3 5 10 Kita Aoyama, Minato-ku, Tokyo, 107-0061, Japan
Tel.: (81) 364275636
Web Site: http://think-agent.co.jp
Technology Services
N.A.I.C.S.: 541519

Tin Pan Alley Co., Ltd. (1)
7 22 17 Nishigotanda TOC Building 4th Floor, Shinagawa-ku, Tokyo, Japan
Tel.: (81) 357194550
Web Site: http://www.tinpanalley.co.jp
Clothing Whslr
N.A.I.C.S.: 424350

World Franchise Systems Co., Ltd. (1)
6-8-1 Minatojima Nakamachi, Chuo-ku, Kobe, 650-8585, Japan
Tel.: (81) 368871302
Web Site: http://world-fs.co.jp
Clothing Distr
N.A.I.C.S.: 424350

World Saha Fashion Co., Ltd. (1)
129/1 Chongnonthri Road Chongnonthri, Yannawa, Bangkok, 10120, Thailand
Tel.: (66) 22942250
Web Site: https://www.takeokikuchith.com
Lifestyle Accessories Whslr
N.A.I.C.S.: 424450
Varakul Yansombut *(Mgr-Brand)*

World Space Solutions Co., Ltd. (1)
1 8 10 Harumi Harumi Island Triton Square Office Tower X Building, Chuo-ku, Tokyo, 104-8545, Japan
Tel.: (81) 120977917
Web Site: http://platform.world.co.jp
Clothing Mfr
N.A.I.C.S.: 315250

World Store Partners Co., Ltd. (1)
World Kita-Aoyama Building 3 5 10 Kita-Aoyama, Minato-ku, Tokyo, 107-8526, Japan
Tel.: (81) 120977917
Web Site: http://www.world-sp.co.jp
Emp.: 8,937
Clothing Whslr
N.A.I.C.S.: 424350

World Taiwan Fashion Co., Ltd. (1)
10th Fl No 138 Section 3 Min Sheng East Rd, Taipei, Taiwan
Tel.: (886) 2 2778 8363
Web Site: http://www.worldtaiwan.com.tw
Women's & Men's Clothing Retailer
N.A.I.C.S.: 313150

WORLD COPPER LTD.
2710-200 Granville Street, Vancouver, V6C 1S4, BC, Canada
Tel.: (604) 638-3287
Web Site: https://www.worldcopperltd.com
WCU—(TSXV)
Assets: $3,774,446
Liabilities: $1,363,538
Net Worth: $2,410,909
Earnings: ($1,540,906)
Fiscal Year-end: 12/31/20
Asset Investment Services
N.A.I.C.S.: 523999
Nolan Peterson *(CEO)*

Subsidiaries:

Cardero Resource Corp. (1)
2300-1177 West Hastings Street, Vancouver, V6E 2K3, BC, Canada
Tel.: (604) 408-7488
Web Site: http://www.cardero.com
Rev.: $15,517
Assets: $5,573,855
Liabilities: $3,365,857
Net Worth: $2,207,998
Earnings: ($853,431)
Fiscal Year-end: 10/31/2020
Metal Exploration Services
N.A.I.C.S.: 213114
Stuart R. Ross *(Pres & CEO)*

WORLD CORPORATION PUBLIC COMPANY LIMITED
4 Moo 11 Hathairat Road Ladsawai, Lamlukka, Pathumthani, 12150, Thailand
Tel.: (66) 25634056
Web Site: https://www.worldcorp.co.th
Year Founded: 1988
WORLD—(THA)
Rev.: $43,301,796
Assets: $77,445,312
Liabilities: $7,892,444
Net Worth: $69,552,868
Earnings: $1,242,932
Fiscal Year-end: 12/31/21
Holding Company
N.A.I.C.S.: 551112
Chirasak Chiyachantana *(Chm & CEO)*

WORLD EXCELLENT PRODUCT SA
2 Kapetan Agra St, PO Box 1025, Kalochori, 57009, Thessaloniki, Greece
Tel.: (30) 2310751379
Web Site: http://www.fiveoliveoil.com
Year Founded: 2011
Rev.: $15,879,959
Assets: $76,920,472
Liabilities: $24,837,076
Net Worth: $52,083,396
Earnings: ($19,673,378)
Fiscal Year-end: 12/31/19
Food Products Mfr
N.A.I.C.S.: 311999
Ioannis Sompolos *(CEO)*

WORLD FINANCIAL SPLIT CORP.
121 King Street West Suite 2600, PO Box 113, Toronto, M5H 3T9, ON, Canada
Tel.: (416) 681-3966
Web Site: https://www.strathbridge.com
Year Founded: 2003
WFS—(TSX)
Rev.: $1,519,933
Assets: $11,626,327
Liabilities: $8,633,852
Net Worth: $2,992,474
Earnings: $1,144,739
Fiscal Year-end: 12/31/19
Financial Investment Services
N.A.I.C.S.: 523999
John P. Mulvihill *(Chm & CEO)*

WORLD GAS (THAILAND) CO., LTD.
East Tower 15th Floor 1 Soi Vibhavadi-Rangsit Rd 5, Chatuchak, Bangkok, 10900, Thailand
Tel.: (66) 22723322 TH
Web Site: http://www.worldgas.co.th
Sales Range: $50-74.9 Million
Emp.: 110
Energy Consultant Services
N.A.I.C.S.: 457210

WORLD HOLDINGS CO., LTD.
11-2 Otemachi, Kokurakita-ku, Kitakyushu, 803-0814, Fukuoka, Japan
Tel.: (81) 935810101
Web Site: https://www.witc.co.jp
Year Founded: 1993
2429—(TKS)
Rev.: $1,515,430,780
Assets: $1,128,756,360
Liabilities: $824,411,020
Net Worth: $304,345,340
Earnings: $43,986,360
Emp.: 52,521
Fiscal Year-end: 12/31/23
Human Resource Consulting Services
N.A.I.C.S.: 541612
Eikichi Iida *(Chm & Pres)*

Subsidiaries:

Dimples' Co., Ltd. (1)
22nd floor Osaka Ekimae 4th Building 1-11-4 Umeda, Kita-ku, Osaka, 530-0001, Japan (90%)
Tel.: (81) 6 6344 0312
Web Site: http://www.dimples.co.jp
Temporary Staffing Services
N.A.I.C.S.: 561320

JW Solution Co., Ltd. (1)
NBF Commodio Shiodome 2F 2-14-1 Higashi-Shinbashi, Minato-ku, Tokyo, 105-0021, Japan
Tel.: (81) 366956580
Web Site: https://www.jwsol.co.jp
Human Resource Consulting Services
N.A.I.C.S.: 541612

World Retech Co., Ltd. (1)
2-10-2 Minamihorie, Nishi-ku, Osaka, 550-0015, Japan
Tel.: (81) 665380506
Web Site: https://www.wrtc.co.jp
Digital Equipment Distr
N.A.I.C.S.: 423690

World Staffing Co., Ltd. (1)
6F Fukuoka Asahi Building 2-1-1 Hakata Ekimae, Hakata-ku, Fukuoka, 812-0011, Fukuoka, Japan
Tel.: (81) 922608393
Web Site: https://www.wsff.co.jp
Human Resources & Logistics Services
N.A.I.C.S.: 541612

WORLD HOUSEWARE (HOLDINGS) LIMITED
18/F Bold Win Industrial Building 16-18 Wah Sing Street, Kwai Chung, NT, China (Hong Kong)
Tel.: (852) 37565100
Web Site: http://www.worldhse.com
0713—(HKG)
Rev.: $80,155,680
Assets: $408,499,673
Liabilities: $199,032,473
Net Worth: $209,467,200
Earnings: ($27,215,130)
Emp.: 570
Fiscal Year-end: 12/31/22
PVC Manufacturing & Marketing Services
N.A.I.C.S.: 326122
Belinda Fung Mei Lee *(Sr Mgr-Sls)*

Subsidiaries:

South China Reborn Resources (Zhongshan) Company Limited (1)
18th Floor Bold Win Industrial Building 16-18 Wah Sing Street, Kwai Chung, China (Hong Kong)
Tel.: (852) 37565100
Web Site: https://www.southchinazs.com
Food Waste Recovery Services
N.A.I.C.S.: 562212

World Home Linen Manufacturing Company Limited (1)
Flat A 19 f Bold Win Indl Bldg 16-18 Wah Sing St, Kwai Chung, New Territories, China (Hong Kong)
Tel.: (852) 24238247
Household Appliances Mfr
N.A.I.C.S.: 321999

World Houseware Producing Company Limited (1)
18/F Bold Win Industrial Building 16-18 Wah Sing Street, Kwai Chung, New Territories, China (Hong Kong)
Tel.: (852) 37565100
Web Site: https://www.worldproducing.com.hk
Emp.: 50
Household Appliances Mfr
N.A.I.C.S.: 314120

WORLD MOTO, INC.
Sukhumvit 13 No 19/125 Sukhumvit Suite 13 Floor Saengjan, Sukhumvit Rd Klongtoey Nue Wattana, Bangkok, 10110, Thailand
Tel.: (66) 23981892 NV
Web Site: http://www.worldmoto.com
Year Founded: 2008
FARE—(OTCBB)
Sales Range: Less than $1 Million
Emp.: 2
Metering Device Mfr
N.A.I.C.S.: 334514
Paul Giles *(Pres & CEO)*

WORLD OUTFITTERS CORPORATION SAFARI NORDIK
639 boulevard Cure-Labelle, Blainville, J7C 3H8, QC, Canada
Tel.: (450) 971-1800 QC
Web Site: http://www.safarinordik.com
Year Founded: 1988
Sales Range: $1-9.9 Million
Emp.: 65
Sport Hunting & Fishing
N.A.I.C.S.: 114210
Nicolas Laurin *(Chm & CEO)*

WORLD PRECISION MACHINERY LIMITED
9 Straits View 06-07 Marina One West Tower, Singapore, 68913, Singapore
Tel.: (65) 62320919 SG
Web Site: https://www.wpmlimited.com
Year Founded: 1999
B49—(SES)
Rev.: $151,871,126
Assets: $305,057,323
Liabilities: $157,725,915
Net Worth: $147,331,408
Earnings: $847,606
Emp.: 1,883
Fiscal Year-end: 12/31/23
Stamping Tool Mfr
N.A.I.C.S.: 333517
Jianjun Shao *(Chm)*

WORLD QUANTUM GROWTH ACQUISITION CORP.
Ugland House, PO Box 309, Georgetown, KY1-1104, Grand Cayman, Cayman Islands
Tel.: (345) 949 8066 Ky
Year Founded: 2021
WQGA.U—(NYSE)
Investment Services
N.A.I.C.S.: 523999
Xavier Rolet *(Chm & CEO)*

WORLD SCAN PROJECT, INC.

World Scan Project, Inc.—(Continued)

WORLD SCAN PROJECT, INC.
2-18-23 Nishiwaseda, Shinjuku-Ku, Tokyo, 162-0051, Japan
Tel.: (81) 366701692   DE
Web Site: https://www.world-scan-project.com
Year Founded: 2019
WDSP—(OTCIQ)
Rev.: $30,986,882
Assets: $14,039,776
Liabilities: $5,324,089
Net Worth: $8,715,687
Earnings: ($3,416,587)
Emp.: 14
Fiscal Year-end: 10/31/23
Industrial Automation Equipments Mfr
N.A.I.C.S.: 333998
Ryohei Uetaki *(Pres, CEO, CFO, Treas & Sec)*

WORLD SUPER HOLDINGS LIMITED
Unit 3403 34/F AIA Tower 183 Electric Road North Point, Hong Kong, China (Hong Kong)
Tel.: (852) 27107732   Ky
Web Site: https://www.worldsuperhk.com
Year Founded: 2016
8612—(HKG)
Rev.: $2,107,783
Assets: $13,168,726
Liabilities: $3,312,107
Net Worth: $9,856,619
Earnings: ($4,322,821)
Emp.: 13
Fiscal Year-end: 12/31/22
Holding Company
N.A.I.C.S.: 551112
Peng Kan AlbertSou *(Chm)*

Subsidiaries:

World Super Limited   (1)
Unit 3403 34/F AIA Tower 183 Electric Road North Point, Hong Kong, China (Hong Kong)
Tel.: (852) 27107732
Web Site: https://www.worldsuperhk.com
Construction Machinery Distr
N.A.I.C.S.: 423810

WORLD TELEVISION GROUP PLC
3rd Floor Astley House 33 Notting Hill Gate, London, W11 3JQ, United Kingdom
Tel.: (44) 2072437350   UK
Web Site: http://www.world-television.com
Year Founded: 1991
Sales Range: $10-24.9 Million
Emp.: 97
Internet Broadcasting Services
N.A.I.C.S.: 516210
Evelyn Kimber *(CFO & Sec)*

WORLD TRADE ORGANIZATION
Center William Rappard rue de Lausanne 154, 1211, Geneva, Switzerland
Tel.: (41) 227395111
Web Site: http://www.wto.org
Sales Range: $150-199.9 Million
Emp.: 800
International Trade Organization
N.A.I.C.S.: 926110
K. Rockwell *(Dir-Info & External Rels Div)*

WORLD TRADE SYSTEMS PLC
Lexham House 14 Hill Avenue 1st Floor, Amersham, HP6 5BW, United Kingdom
Tel.: (44) 1494590515
Web Site: http://www.worldtradesystems.com
Year Founded: 1988
Health Food Product Mfr & Distr
N.A.I.C.S.: 325411
Shao Chen *(Vice Chm)*

WORLD TRAVEL MEDIA LTD.
PO Box 4386, West Kensington, London, W14 0YE, United Kingdom
Tel.: (44) 2077511689
Magazine Publisher
N.A.I.C.S.: 513120
Ray Carmen *(Chm)*

Subsidiaries:

Caribbean World Magazine   (1)
PO Box 4386, West Kensington, London, W14 0YE, United Kingdom
Tel.: (44) 2077511689
Web Site: http://www.caribbeanworld-magazine.com
Magazine
N.A.I.C.S.: 513120

WORLD WEB PUBLISHING-.COM CORP.
13071 Vanier Place Suite 280, Richmond, V6V 2J1, BC, Canada
Tel.: (604) 249-5010   NV
Year Founded: 2000
Sales Range: Less than $1 Million
Ecommerce Services
N.A.I.C.S.: 513120
Jordan S. Wangh *(Pres & CEO)*

WORLD-LINK LOGISTICS (ASIA) HOLDING LIMITED
3/F Allied Cargo Centre 150-164 Texaco Road, Tsuen Wan, New Territories, China (Hong Kong)
Tel.: (852) 24080618   Ky
Web Site: https://www.world-linkasia.com
Year Founded: 1990
6083—(HKG)
Rev.: $41,774,865
Assets: $27,352,193
Liabilities: $13,421,415
Net Worth: $13,930,778
Earnings: $2,733,983
Emp.: 196
Fiscal Year-end: 12/31/22
General Warehousing Services
N.A.I.C.S.: 493110
Kwong Fat Yeung *(Co-Founder, Chm & CEO)*

Subsidiaries:

Skya Link Limited   (1)
Room 701 Kam Hon Ind Bldg 8 Wang Kwun Road, Kowloon Bay, China (Hong Kong)
Tel.: (852) 36982770
Web Site: https://www.skyalink.com
Light Equipment Whslr
N.A.I.C.S.: 423610

WORLD.NET SERVICES LIMITED
Level 14 Lumley House 309 Kent Street, Sydney, 2000, NSW, Australia
Tel.: (61) 2 9261 8255
Web Site: http://www.world.net
Year Founded: 2000
Rev.: $290,557
Assets: $28,343
Liabilities: $2,489,638
Net Worth: ($2,461,296)
Earnings: ($164,871)
Fiscal Year-end: 06/30/18
Information Technology Products & Services
N.A.I.C.S.: 541512
Gregory Star *(Sec)*

Subsidiaries:

World Net Services Sdn. Bhd.   (1)
E-5-1 Level 5 Block E South Gate Commercial Centre No 2, Kuala Lumpur, 55200, Malaysia
Tel.: (60) 327309985
Sales Range: $25-49.9 Million
Software Technology Solution Service
N.A.I.C.S.: 541511

WORLDCALL TELECOM LIMITED
Plot No 112-113 Block S Quaid-e-Azam Industrial Estate Kot Lakhpat, Lahore, Pakistan
Tel.: (92) 4235400609
Web Site: https://www.worldcall.com.pk
Year Founded: 1995
WTL—(LAH)
Rev.: $24,999,075
Assets: $99,608,246
Liabilities: $80,038,085
Net Worth: $19,570,162
Earnings: $465,599
Emp.: 631
Fiscal Year-end: 12/31/19
Telecommunication Servicesb
N.A.I.C.S.: 517810
Babar Ali *(CEO)*

WORLDEX INDUSTRY & TRADING CO., LTD.
360 Hanggok-ri, Goa-eub, Gumi, Gyeongsagbuk, Korea (South)
Tel.: (82) 5 4456 9980
Web Site: http://www.worldexint.com
Electrode Mfr
N.A.I.C.S.: 334419
Jhong-Sik Bae *(CEO)*

Subsidiaries:

West Coast Quartz Corporation   (1)
1000 Corporate Way, Fremont, CA 94539-6105
Tel.: (510) 249-2160
Web Site: http://www.westcoastquartz.com
Sales Range: $25-49.9 Million
Emp.: 169
Pressed & Blown Glass
N.A.I.C.S.: 327212
Michele Graff *(Controller)*

WORLDGATE GLOBAL LOGISTICS LTD
No 42 Jalan Puteri 2/2, 47100, Puchong, Selangor, Malaysia
Tel.: (60) 380603433   Ky
Web Site: http://www.worldgate.com.my
8292—(HKG)
Rev.: $25,326,731
Assets: $12,728,559
Liabilities: $4,790,161
Net Worth: $7,938,398
Earnings: ($4,520,026)
Emp.: 380
Fiscal Year-end: 12/31/23
Logistics Consulting Servies
N.A.I.C.S.: 541614
Li Ngut Lee *(Sr VP-Fin)*

Subsidiaries:

My Forwarder International Sdn. Bhd.   (1)
No 69B Jalan Bayu Tinggi 6/KS6 Taman Bayu Tinggi, 41200, Klang, Selangor, Malaysia
Tel.: (60) 333239330
Web Site: http://www.mfikul.com.my
Emp.: 15
Freight Forwarding Services
N.A.I.C.S.: 488510
Ronald Lee *(Mng Dir)*

WORLDLINE SA
Tour Voltaire 1 place des degres, CS 81162, Paris la Defense, 92059, Paris, Cedex, France
Tel.: (33) 173260000   FR
Web Site: http://www.worldline.com
Year Founded: 1973
WLN—(EUR)
Rev.: $4,709,799,266
Assets: $23,590,006,475
Liabilities: $12,217,137,924
Net Worth: $11,372,868,552
Earnings: $322,900,928
Emp.: 18,054
Fiscal Year-end: 12/31/22
Electronic Transaction Processing Platform Development & Operating Services
N.A.I.C.S.: 541519
Christophe Duquenne *(Chief Tech & Ops Officer)*

Subsidiaries:

SIX Payment Services Ltd   (1)
Hardturmstrasse 201, CH 8021, Zurich, Switzerland   (27%)
Tel.: (41) 583999111
Web Site: http://www.six-payment-services.com
Card-Based Payment Systems & Services
N.A.I.C.S.: 522320
Marc Schluep *(Head-Org Dev)*

Subsidiary (Non-US):

SIX Payment Services (Europe) SA   (2)
10 rue Gabriel Lippmann, 5365, Munsbach, Luxembourg
Tel.: (352) 355 66 1
Web Site: http://www.six-payment-services.com
Electronic Financial Payment Services
N.A.I.C.S.: 522320

SIX Payment Services (Germany) GmbH   (2)
Langenhorner Chaussee 92 - 94, 22415, Hamburg, Germany
Tel.: (49) 40 325 967 0
Web Site: http://www.six-payment-services.com
Electronic Financial Payment Services
N.A.I.C.S.: 522320
Sascha Breite *(Mng Dir)*

SIX Payment Services (Sweden) AB   (2)
Veterinargrand 6, 121 63, Stockholm, Sweden
Tel.: (46) 8 545 135 45
Electronic Financial Payment Services
N.A.I.C.S.: 522320

SIX Payment Services (UK) Ltd   (2)
70 London Road, Regal House, Twickenham, TW1 3QS, United Kingdom
Tel.: (44) 208 892 2573
Financial Data Processing Services
N.A.I.C.S.: 522320

Worldline B.V.   (1)
Wolweverstraat 18, 2984 CD, Ridderkerk, Netherlands
Tel.: (31) 180 442 442
Web Site: http://nl.worldline.com
Payment & Transactional Services
N.A.I.C.S.: 522320

equensWorldline SE   (1)
Lyonerstrasse 15, 60528, Frankfurt am Main, Germany   (100%)
Tel.: (49) 69665710
Web Site: https://equensworldline.com
Payment Processing Services
N.A.I.C.S.: 522320

WORLDLINK GROUP PLC
Alma House Suite 4A Alma Road, Reigate, RH2 0AX, United Kingdom
Tel.: (44) 1737221078
Financial Services
N.A.I.C.S.: 523999
Neil Riches *(Mng Dir)*

WORLDMARK INTERNATIONAL LTD.

4 Redwood Crescentpeel Park Campus, East Kilbride, G74 5PA, United Kingdom
Tel.: (44) 1355 249191
Web Site: http://www.worldmark.com
Year Founded: 1999
Sales Range: $25-49.9 Million
Emp.: 1,705
Electrical & Electronic Component Mfr
N.A.I.C.S.: 335999
Bill Graham *(CEO)*

Subsidiaries:

Worldmark (Shenzhen) Co., Ltd. (1)
1st floor 20 building Changxing High New Tech Industry Zone, Wan An Road ShaJing, Shenzhen, China
Tel.: (86) 755 29545097
Electronic Component Mfr & Distr
N.A.I.C.S.: 334419
David Zhang *(Mgr-HR)*

Worldmark (Suzhou) Co., Ltd. (1)
China-Singapore Suzhou Industrial Park No 13 Bai He Street, Suzhou, 215021, Jiangsu, China
Tel.: (86) 512 6715 6128
Electronic Component Mfr & Distr
N.A.I.C.S.: 334419

Worldmark (Tianjin) Co. Ltd. (1)
2-C Zhong Xiao Yuan Weiliu Road Microelectronic Industrial Park, Tianjin, 300385, China
Tel.: (86) 222 3886100
Label Mfr & Distr
N.A.I.C.S.: 323111

WORLDREMIT LTD.
Kensington Centre 66 Hammersmith Rd, London, W14 8UD, United Kingdom
Tel.: (44) 207 148 5800
Web Site: http://www.worldremit.com
Year Founded: 2009
Emp.: 50
Online Money Transfer Services
N.A.I.C.S.: 522320
Ismail Ahmed *(Co-Founder & Chm)*

Subsidiaries:

WorldRemit Corporation (1)
600 17th St Ste 200S, Denver, CO 80202
Tel.: (888) 961-4869
Online Money Transfer Services
N.A.I.C.S.: 522320

WorldRemit Inc. (1)
2 Bloor St W Suite 700, Toronto, M4W 3E2, ON, Canada
Online Money Transfer Services
N.A.I.C.S.: 522320
Richard Meseko *(Country Dir)*

WorldRemit Pty, Ltd. (1)
Level 1 7 Beissel Street, Belconnen, ACT 2617, Australia
Tel.: (61) 2 6145 2161
Online Money Transfer Services
N.A.I.C.S.: 522320
Lee Towle *(Country Dir)*

WORLDSEC LIMITED
Unit 607 6th Floor FWD Financial Centre 308 Des Voeux Road Street, Sheung Wan, Hong Kong, China (Hong Kong)
Tel.: (852) 2079720880 BM
Web Site: https://www.worldsec.com
Year Founded: 1991
WSL—(LSE)
Rev.: $193,000
Assets: $5,657,000
Liabilities: $215,000
Net Worth: $5,442,000
Earnings: ($843,000)
Fiscal Year-end: 12/31/22
Investment Brokerage Services
N.A.I.C.S.: 523150
Henry Ying Chew Cheong *(Deputy Chm)*

WORLDSENSING SL
Viriat 47 10th floor, 08014, Barcelona, Spain
Tel.: (34) 934180585
Web Site: https://www.worldsensing.com
Year Founded: 2008
Wireless Services
N.A.I.C.S.: 541511

WORLDUNION GROUP INCORPORATED
12/F Golden Business Centre 2028 Shennan Road East, Shenzhen, 518001, China
Tel.: (86) 75522162800
Web Site: https://www.worldunion.com.cn
Year Founded: 1992
002285—(SSE)
Rev.: $558,712,000
Assets: $947,200,892
Liabilities: $464,437,444
Net Worth: $482,763,448
Earnings: ($48,190,222)
Emp.: 2,800
Fiscal Year-end: 12/31/22
Real Estate Consulting Service
N.A.I.C.S.: 531390
Jinsong Chen *(Founder & Chm)*

WORLDWIDE ALUMINIUM LTD.
602 Rohit House 3 Tolstoy Marg, Connaught place, New Delhi, 110001, India
Tel.: (91) 1149446667
Web Site: https://www.wwal.in
526525—(BOM)
Rev.: $47,775
Assets: $847,501
Liabilities: $9,050
Net Worth: $838,451
Earnings: $996
Emp.: 10
Fiscal Year-end: 03/31/21
Leather Footwear Whslr
N.A.I.C.S.: 424340
Mahesh Agarwal *(Chm)*

WORLDWIDE HEALTHCARE TRUST PLC
Frostrow Capital LLP 25 Southampton Buildings, London, WC2A 1AL, United Kingdom
Tel.: (44) 2030084910
Web Site: https://www.worldwidewh.com
WWH—(LSE)
Rev.: $27,010,856
Assets: $2,768,502,907
Liabilities: $142,376,925
Net Worth: $2,626,125,982
Earnings: $253,928,301
Fiscal Year-end: 03/31/24
Other Financial Vehicles
N.A.I.C.S.: 525990
Martin Smith *(Chm)*

WORLDWIDE MARIJUANA INC.
14th Floor 1040 West Georgia Street, PO Box 27, Vancouver, V6E 4H8, BC, Canada
Tel.: (250) 388-0281 BC
Year Founded: 2011
Investment Services
N.A.I.C.S.: 523999
Bruce Clark *(CEO)*

WORLDWIDE NATURAL RESOURCES PLC
7 St John's Road, Harrow, HA1 2EY, Middlesex, United Kingdom
Tel.: (44) 2034116777
Web Site: http://www.wnrplc.com

Coal Mining Services
N.A.I.C.S.: 212115
Alexander Johnson *(CEO)*

WORLDWIDE NFT INC.
9 NOF Commercial Centre Industrial Park, Old Mallow Rd, Cork, Ireland
Tel.: (353) 871547690 NV
Web Site: http://www.goff-corp.com
Year Founded: 2010
GOFF—(OTCIQ)
Web-Based Employment Placement Services
N.A.I.C.S.: 561311
David Lazar *(Chm, Pres, CEO, CFO & Sec)*

WORLDWIDE REINSURANCE LTD.
99 Saddle Road, Maraval, Port of Spain, Trinidad & Tobago
Tel.: (868) 6289748
Web Site: http://www.worldwidereinsure.com
Insurance Services
N.A.I.C.S.: 524210
Patrick E. Taylor *(Mng Dir-Underwriting & Treaties)*

WORLDWIDE RESOURCES CORP.
7382 Black Walnut Trail, Mississauga, L5N 7L8, ON, Canada
Tel.: (647) 534-5929
Web Site: https://worldwideresourcesinc.ca
WR.H—(TSXV)
Assets: $155
Liabilities: $1,931,186
Net Worth: ($1,931,031)
Earnings: ($133,490)
Fiscal Year-end: 12/31/23
Metal Exploration Services
N.A.I.C.S.: 213114

WORLEY LIMITED
Level 17 141 Walker Street, North Sydney, 2060, NSW, Australia
Tel.: (61) 289236866 AU
Web Site: https://www.worley.com
WYGPF—(OTCIQ)
Rev.: $7,435,873,950
Assets: $7,965,311,240
Liabilities: $3,611,053,470
Net Worth: $4,354,257,770
Earnings: $135,615,630
Emp.: 51,000
Fiscal Year-end: 06/30/22
Engineeering Services
N.A.I.C.S.: 541330
Chris Ashton *(CEO & Mng Dir)*

Subsidiaries:

Rosenberg Worley AS (1)
Bangarvagsgata 15, 4077, Hundvag, Norway
Tel.: (47) 5 193 1000
Construction Engineering Services
N.A.I.C.S.: 541330

Rosenberg WorleyParsons AS (1)
Bangarvagsgata 15, 4077, Hundvag, Norway
Tel.: (47) 5193 1000
Offshore Oil & Gas Engineering & Construction Services
N.A.I.C.S.: 237990

Worley Equipment Incorporated (1)
226 E Hwy 54, Weaubleau, MO 65774-9577
Tel.: (417) 428-3100
Web Site: https://worleyequipment.com
Farm & Lawn Equipment Whslr
N.A.I.C.S.: 423820

WorleyParsons Corporation (1)
575 N Dairy Ashford Rd Energy Center II Ste 100, Houston, TX 77079
Tel.: (713) 892-0999

Web Site: http://www.worleyparsons.com
Sales Range: $1-4.9 Billion
Emp.: 6,000
Engineering Services; Oil & Gas Production, Transportation & Storage Facilities; Refining; Chemicals & Petrochemicals; Power
N.A.I.C.S.: 541330
Chris Parker *(Mng Dir)*

WorleyParsons RSA (Pty) Ltd. (1)
31 Allen Drive, Loevenstein, Cape Town, 7530, South Africa (70%)
Tel.: (27) 21 912 3000
Engineering, Procurement & Construction Management Services
N.A.I.C.S.: 541330

Subsidiary (Domestic):

WorleyParsonsTWP (2)
39 Melrose Boulevard, Melrose Arch, Johannesburg, 2076, South Africa
Tel.: (27) 11 218 3000
Web Site: http://www.twp.co.za
Sales Range: $100-124.9 Million
Underground Mine Planning & Engineering Services, Mineral Processing & Project Management Solutions
N.A.I.C.S.: 541330
Steve Dewsbery *(CFO)*

Subsidiary (Domestic):

TWP Limpopo Engineering (Pty) Limited (3)
2nd Fl 91 Schoeman St, Polokwane, 0700, Limpopo, South Africa
Tel.: (27) 152972605
Sales Range: $25-49.9 Million
Emp.: 20
Construction Engineering Services
N.A.I.C.S.: 237990

Joint Venture (Non-US):

TWSP Pty. Ltd. (3)
Level 2 503 Murray Street, Perth, 6000, WA, Australia (50%)
Tel.: (61) 8 9426 4900
Web Site: http://www.twsp.com.au
Mining Engineering Services
N.A.I.C.S.: 541330

WORSLEY INVESTORS LIMITED
1 Royal Plaza Royal Avenue, Saint Peter Port, GY1 2HL, Guernsey
Tel.: (44) 1481745604 GY
Web Site: https://www.worsleyinvestors.com
Year Founded: 2005
WINV—(LSE)
Rev.: $1,038,879
Assets: $19,045,696
Liabilities: $539,005
Net Worth: $18,506,690
Earnings: $37,869
Fiscal Year-end: 03/31/24
Investment Management Service
N.A.I.C.S.: 523999
William Scott *(Chm)*

WORTH INVESTMENT & TRADING COMPANY LIMITED
497/501 Village Biloshi Taluka Wada, Thane, 421303, Maharashtra, India
Tel.: (91) 2262872900
Web Site: https://www.worthinvt.com
Year Founded: 1980
538451—(BOM)
Rev.: $437,051
Assets: $5,396,462
Liabilities: $3,992,489
Net Worth: $1,403,973
Earnings: $107,791
Fiscal Year-end: 03/31/23
Security Brokerage Services
N.A.I.C.S.: 523150
Mihir Rajesh Ghatalia *(Exec Dir)*

WORTH PERIPHERALS LIMITED

WORTH PERIPHERALS LIMITED

Worth Peripherals Limited—(Continued)
102 Sanskriti Apartments 44 Saket Nagar, Pithampur District Dhar, Indore, 452018, Madhya Pradesh, India
Tel.: (91) 7312560267
Web Site:
https://www.worthindia.com
WORTH—(NSE)
Rev.: $35,918,710
Assets: $21,932,750
Liabilities: $3,082,597
Net Worth: $18,850,153
Earnings: $2,477,190
Emp.: 114
Fiscal Year-end: 03/31/23
Corrugated Box Mfr
N.A.I.C.S.: 322211
Raminder Singh Chadha (Chm & Mng Dir)

WOT CO., LTD.
53-15 Dongtan Industrial Complex 10-gil, Hwaseong, Gyeonggi-do, Korea (South)
Tel.: (82) 3180478600
Web Site: https://www.wot.co.kr
Year Founded: 2004
396470—(KRS)
Electronic Products Mfr
N.A.I.C.S.: 334419
Seungbae Park (CEO)

WOTSO PROPERTY
Level 1 50 Yeo Street, PO Box 612, Neutral Bay, 2089, NSW, Australia
Tel.: (61) 291574069   AU
Web Site: https://wotso.com
Year Founded: 2014
WOT—(ASX)
Rev.: $33,201,368
Assets: $261,796,148
Liabilities: $101,373,616
Net Worth: $160,422,532
Earnings: $584,940
Emp.: 113
Fiscal Year-end: 06/30/24
Real Estate Investment Services
N.A.I.C.S.: 525990
Jessica Glew (CEO, Co-Mng Dir & COO)
Subsidiaries:
WOTSO Chermside Pty. Ltd. (1)
Level 2 Westfield, Chermside, 4032, QLD, Australia
Tel.: (61) 731235353
Meeting Rooms & Event Spaces Operator
N.A.I.C.S.: 721110

WOTSO at RFW Manly Pty. Ltd. (1)
44 & 46 The Barracks Precinct North Head Sanctuary, Manly, 2095, NSW, Australia
Tel.: (61) 280352250
Meeting Rooms & Event Spaces Operator
N.A.I.C.S.: 721110

WOW WORLD GROUP INC.
KDX Nishi-Gotanda Building 4F 7-20-9, Nishi-Gotanda Shinagawa-ku, Tokyo, 141-0031, Japan
Tel.: (81) 363870080
Web Site: https://www.wow-world-group.co.jp
Year Founded: 2022
5128—(TKS)
Rev.: $27,430,865
Assets: $29,792,968
Liabilities: $15,736,408
Net Worth: $14,056,560
Earnings: $2,066,022
Fiscal Year-end: 03/31/22
Software Development Services
N.A.I.C.S.: 541511

WOW WORLD INC
9F Daigo TOC Bldg 7-21-1 Nishi Gotanda, Shinagawa-ku, Tokyo, 141-0031, Japan
Tel.: (81) 366726788
Web Site: http://www.azia.jp
Year Founded: 1995
2352—(TKS)
Rev.: $27,430,865
Assets: $29,792,968
Liabilities: $14,325,306
Net Worth: $15,467,662
Earnings: $2,066,022
Fiscal Year-end: 03/31/22
Application Software Development Services
N.A.I.C.S.: 541511

WOWJOINT HOLDINGS LIMITED
1108 A Block Tiancheng Mansion 2 Xinfeng Road Deshemengwai Street, Xicheng District, Beijing, 100088, China
Tel.: (86) 1089579330   Ky
Web Site: http://www.wowjoint.com
Year Founded: 1996
BWOWF—(OTCEM)
Sales Range: $10-24.9 Million
Emp.: 186
Lifting & Carrying Machinery Mfr
N.A.I.C.S.: 333248
Yabin Liu (Chm & CEO)
Subsidiaries:
BWI Tech S.r.l. (1)
Via S Antonio 87/B1, 35019, Tombolo, Padova, Italy
Tel.: (39) 0423371995
Heavy Lifting & Carrying Machinery Distr
N.A.I.C.S.: 423830

WOWOW, INC.
21F Akasaka Park Building 5-2-20 Akasaka, Minato-ku, Tokyo, 107-6121, Japan
Tel.: (81) 343308111
Web Site: https://www.wowow.co.jp
Year Founded: 1984
4839—(TKS)
Rev.: $494,884,090
Assets: $589,255,060
Liabilities: $138,287,810
Net Worth: $450,967,250
Earnings: $7,218,120
Emp.: 312
Fiscal Year-end: 03/31/24
Satellite Television Services
N.A.I.C.S.: 517111
Akira Tanaka (Chm, Pres, Pres & CEO)
Subsidiaries:
AcTVila Corporation (1)
5F 8-34 Akasaka 5th floor Toda Building Aoyama, Minato-ku, Tokyo, 107-0052, Japan   (70%)
Tel.: (81) 570091017
Web Site: http://www.actvila.jp
Online Movie Streaming Services
N.A.I.C.S.: 518210
Hajimoto Hashi (Pres & CEO)

Wowow Communications Inc (1)
YOKOHAMA i-MARK PLACE 3F 4-4-5 Minatomirai, Nishi-ku, Yokohama, 220-8080, Kanagawa, Japan
Tel.: (81) 456833660
Web Site: https://www.wowcom.co.jp
Sales Range: $300-349.9 Million
Emp.: 1,500
Telemarketing Services
N.A.I.C.S.: 561422

WOWPRIME CORP.
29F No 218 Sec 2 Taiwan Boulevard, West District, Taichung, 403, Taiwan
Tel.: (886) 423221868
Web Site: https://www.wowprime.com
Year Founded: 1993
2727—(TAI)
Rev.: $729,837,672
Assets: $520,680,676
Liabilities: $364,341,430
Net Worth: $156,339,247
Earnings: $45,137,184
Emp.: 9,268
Fiscal Year-end: 12/31/23
Catering Services
N.A.I.C.S.: 722320
Cheng-Hui Chen (Chm & Pres)

WOWWEE HOLDINGS INC.
3700 St Patrick Suite 206, Montreal, H4E 1A2, QC, Canada
Tel.: (514) 738-8885   Ca
Web Site: http://www.wowwee.com
Year Founded: 1984
Sales Range: $25-49.9 Million
Emp.: 135
Consumer Electronics & Toy Mfr
N.A.I.C.S.: 339930
Neil S. Wechsler (Principal)

WP ENERGY PCL
1 East Water Building 15th Floor, Vipavadeerangsit Soi 5 Vipavadeerangsit Road Jomphol Jatujak, Bangkok, 10900, Thailand
Tel.: (66) 22723322
Web Site: https://www.wp-energy.co.th
Year Founded: 2014
WP—(THA)
Rev.: $523,502,084
Assets: $209,548,384
Liabilities: $170,975,950
Net Worth: $38,572,434
Earnings: $3,569,083
Emp.: 363
Fiscal Year-end: 12/31/23
Liquefied Petroleum Gas Distr
N.A.I.C.S.: 457210
Chulchit Bunyaketu (Chm)
Subsidiaries:
Eagle Intertrans Company Limited (1)
Pongsupee Building 7th Floor No 19 Soi Tobacco 1, Vibhavadi Rangsit Road Chomphon Sub-district Chatuchak District, Bangkok, 10900, Thailand
Tel.: (66) 26199135
Web Site: https://www.eagle-intertrans.com
Petroleum Gas Distr
N.A.I.C.S.: 424720

Thai Gas Corporation Company Limited (1)
909 Ample Tower 10th Floor Debaratana Road, Bangna Nua Bangna, Bangkok, 10260, Thailand
Tel.: (66) 27443290
Web Site: http://www.thaigas.co.th
Petroleum Gas Distr
N.A.I.C.S.: 424720

WPD PHARMACEUTICALS INC.
750 West Pender Street Suite 401, Vancouver, V6C 2T7, BC, Canada
Tel.: (604) 428-7050   BC
Web Site:
https://www.wpdpharmaceutical.com
Year Founded: 2006
WBIO—(CNSX)
Rev.: $1,374,677
Assets: $55,659
Liabilities: $406,996
Net Worth: $(351,338)
Earnings: $2,830,596
Emp.: 16
Fiscal Year-end: 12/31/22
Mineral Exploration Services
N.A.I.C.S.: 212290
Mariusz Olejniczak (CEO)

WPG HOLDINGS LIMITED

INTERNATIONAL PUBLIC

22F No 189 Jingmao 2nd Rd, Nangang Dist, Taipei, 11568, Taiwan
Tel.: (886) 221910068
Web Site:
https://www.wpgholdings.com
Year Founded: 2005
3702—(TAI)
Rev.: $21,007,664,415
Assets: $9,829,303,286
Liabilities: $7,182,773,442
Net Worth: $2,646,529,844
Earnings: $256,315,449
Emp.: 5,000
Fiscal Year-end: 12/31/23
Holding Company
N.A.I.C.S.: 551112
Simon Huang (Chm)
Subsidiaries:
AIT Japan Inc. (1)
7F Shinagawa-Gotenyama Bldg 3-6-6 Kita-Shinagawa, Shinagawa-ku, Tokyo, 140-0001, Japan
Tel.: (81) 364795997
Computer Component Distr
N.A.I.C.S.: 423430

Aeco Technology Co., Ltd. (1)
Minsheng West Road Taipei 292 No 10 10F No 292 Chang'an West Rd, Taipei, 103, Datong, Taiwan
Tel.: (886) 225559676
Web Site: http://www.aecotech.com.tw
Sales Range: $125-149.9 Million
Emp.: 400
Optoelectronic Components Mfr & Distr
N.A.I.C.S.: 334413

Asian Information Technology Inc. (1)
13F No 189 Jingmao 2nd Rd, Nangang Dist, Taipei, Taiwan
Tel.: (886) 221910098
Web Site: http://www.aitgroup.com.tw
Sales Range: $800-899.9 Million
Emp.: 536
Electronics Component Design & Distribution Services
N.A.I.C.S.: 334419

Subsidiary (Domestic):
Adivic Technology Co., Ltd. (2)
6F No 345 Xinhu 2nd Rd, Neihu Dist, Taipei, 114, Taiwan
Tel.: (886) 227911718
Web Site: http://www.adivic.com
Emp.: 60
Electronic Components Distr
N.A.I.C.S.: 423690

Frontek Technology Corporation, Ltd. (2)
7F 435 Rueiguang Road, Neihu District, Taipei, 114, Taiwan
Tel.: (886) 287971158
Web Site: http://www.frontek.com.tw
Sales Range: $200-249.9 Million
Emp.: 199
Semiconductors & Electronic Component Distr
N.A.I.C.S.: 334413

Subsidiary (Domestic):
Frontek Electronics Co., Ltd. (3)
7F No 435 Ruei-Guang Road, Neihu, Taipei, 114, R.O.C., Taiwan
Tel.: (886) 2 8797 1158
Sales Range: $50-74.9 Million
Emp.: 132
Telecommunications Equipment
N.A.I.C.S.: 517810

Dstar Electronic Company Limited (1)
Units C&G 15/F CDW Building 388 Castle Peak Road Tsuen Wan, Hong Kong, 230, NT, China (Hong Kong)
Tel.: (852) 27504402
Electronic Components Distr
N.A.I.C.S.: 423690

Genuine C&C Inc. (1)
No 36 Lane 66 Rueiguang Road, Neihu District, Taipei, 114, Taiwan
Tel.: (886) 227956677

AND PRIVATE COMPANIES

Web Site: http://www.gcnc-group.com
Information Technology Products Distr
N.A.I.C.S.: 423690
Lee Rain *(Mgr-Product)*

Long-Think International (Hong Kong) LTD. (1)
Unit 07-11 15/FCDB Building 388 Castle Peak Road Tsuen Wan, Hong Kong, 230, New Territories, China (Hong Kong)
Tel.: (852) 23654860
Web Site: http://www.wpgholdings.com
Electronic Components Distr
N.A.I.C.S.: 423690

Pernas Electronics Co., Ltd. (1)
11F No 258 Liancheng Rd, Zhonghe Dist, New Taipei City, 23553, Taiwan
Tel.: (886) 282271188
Web Site: http://www.pernas.com.tw
Electronic Components Distr
N.A.I.C.S.: 423690

Subsidiary (Domestic):

Everwiner Enterprise Co., Ltd. (2)
11F No 268 Liancheng Rd, Zhonghe Dist, New Taipei City, 235-53, Taiwan
Tel.: (886) 282280899
Web Site: http://www.wpgholdings.com
Electronic Components Distr
N.A.I.C.S.: 423690

Richpower Electronic Devices Co., Ltd. (1)
14F No 189 Jingmao 2nd Rd, Nangang, Taipei, 115, Taiwan
Tel.: (886) 223162688
Web Site: http://www.rich-power.com.tw
Semiconductor Distr
N.A.I.C.S.: 423690

SAC Components (South Asia) Pte. Ltd. (1)
10 Upper Aljunied Link 06-07, Singapore, 367904, Singapore
Tel.: (65) 62825188
Computer Component Distr
N.A.I.C.S.: 423430

Silicon Application Corporation (1)
18F No 189 Jingmao 2nd Rd, Nangang Dist, New Taipei City, 11568, Taiwan
Tel.: (886) 221910070
Web Site: http://www.sacg.com.tw
Emp.: 680
Semiconductor Distr
N.A.I.C.S.: 423690

WPG (Thailand) Co., Ltd. (1)
9/303-4 U M Tower 30th Floor Ramkamheang Road, Suanluang, Bangkok, 10250, Thailand
Tel.: (66) 27172137
Electronic Components Distr
N.A.I.C.S.: 423690
Anon Ittipong *(Acct Mgr)*

WPG Americas Inc. (1)
Tel.: (408) 392-8100
Web Site: http://www.wpgamericas.com
Electronics Mfr
N.A.I.C.S.: 334419

WPG C&C (Malaysia) SDN BHD. (1)
THE CEO Unit No 31-15-1 31-15-2 31-15-3 Lebuh Nipah 5, Bayan Lepas, 11950, Penang, Malaysia
Tel.: (60) 46429500
Electronic Components Distr
N.A.I.C.S.: 423690

WPG C&C Computers And Peripheral (India) Private Limited (1)
1st Flr City Point 3 Ram Mohan Rai Marg, Lucknow, 226001, India
Tel.: (91) 8400255280
Electronic Components Distr
N.A.I.C.S.: 423690

WPG China (SZ) Inc. (1)
Room 3009 JiDa HaiBin NanLu No 47, XiangZhou Distric, Zhuhai, 519000, Guangdong, China
Tel.: (86) 7568123571
Computer Component Distr
N.A.I.C.S.: 423430

WPG China Inc. (1)
No 37 1555 Lane West Jingshajiang Road, Jiading District, Shanghai, 201803, China
Tel.: (86) 2123099388
Electronic Components Distr
N.A.I.C.S.: 423690

WPG Cloud Service Limited (1)
11F Block2 Kai Da Er Building No 168 TongSha Road, XiLi Town Nanshan, Shenzhen, China
Tel.: (86) 755 23992258
Web Site: http://www.wpgcloud.com
Semiconductor Distr
N.A.I.C.S.: 423690

WPG Electronics (Hong Kong) Limited (1)
Units 07-11 15/F CDW Building 388 Castle Peak Road, Tsuen Wan, 230, New Territories, China (Hong Kong)
Tel.: (852) 27654999
Computer Component Distr
N.A.I.C.S.: 423430

WPG Electronics (Philippines) Inc. (1)
Unit 501 Richville Corporate Centre 1314 Commerce Avenue Extension, Madrigal Business Park Metro Manila Alabang, Muntinlupa, 1770, Philippines
Tel.: (63) 28503129
Electronic Components Distr
N.A.I.C.S.: 423690

WPG Electronics Limited (1)
No 238 Sec 2 Zhongyi Rd, Guishan Dist, Taoyuan, 33378, Taiwan
Tel.: (886) 32114319
Electronic Component Mfr & Distr
N.A.I.C.S.: 334419

WPG India Electronics Pvt Ltd (1)
1M-504 Hennur Main Road H R B R Layout 3rd Block, Next to State Bank Of Mysore, Bengaluru, 560043, India
Tel.: (91) 80 71444450
Web Site: http://www.wpgholdings.com
Emp.: 35
Electronic Components Distr
N.A.I.C.S.: 423690
Animesh Unde *(Sr Dir-Mktg)*

WPG Korea Co., Ltd. (1)
Pangyo Innovalley B-301 253 Pangyo-ro, Bundang-gu, Seongnam, 463-400, Gyeonggi-do, Korea (South)
Tel.: (82) 24252800
Web Site: https://www.wpgkorea.com
Emp.: 50
Electronic Components Distr
N.A.I.C.S.: 423690

Subsidiary (Non-US):

Apache Communication Inc. (2)
7F No 431 Ruei-Guang Road, Neihu, Taipei, 114, Taiwan
Tel.: (886) 226563868
Web Site: http://www.wpgholdings.com
Electronic Components Distr
N.A.I.C.S.: 423690

Subsidiary (Non-US):

Apache Korea Corp. (3)
7f Newai Bldg 981-3, Gwanyang-dong, Dongan, Korea (South)
Tel.: (82) 31 442 1818
Electronic Components Distr
N.A.I.C.S.: 423690

WPG Malaysia Sdn. Bhd (1)
25-4 27-4 Block D1 Dataran Prima Jalan PJU 1/41, 47301, Petaling Jaya, Selangor, Malaysia
Tel.: (60) 378808309
Electronic Components Distr
N.A.I.C.S.: 423690

WPG Vietnam Co., Ltd. (1)
126 Toong 2nd & 3rd Floor Itaxa Building Nguyen Thi Minh Khai, Vo Thi Sau Ward District 3, Ho Chi Minh City, Vietnam
Tel.: (84) 344145429
Semiconductor Mfr & Distr
N.A.I.C.S.: 334413

WPI International (Hong Kong) Limited (1)
Units 07-11 15/F CDW Building 388 Castle Peak Road, Tsuen Wan, 230, New Territories, China (Hong Kong)
Tel.: (852) 23654860
Computer Component Distr
N.A.I.C.S.: 423430

Subsidiary (Domestic):

AIO Components Company Limited (2)
Units 07-11 15/F CDW Building 388 Castle Peak Road, Tsuen Wan, China (Hong Kong)
Tel.: (852) 27869813
Computer Component Distr
N.A.I.C.S.: 423430

World Peace Industrial Co., Ltd. (1)
1F No 76 Sec 1 Chenggong Rd, NanGang, Taipei, 00115, Taiwan
Tel.: (886) 2 27885200
Web Site: http://www.wpgholdings.com
Electronic Components Distr
N.A.I.C.S.: 423690

Subsidiary (Domestic):

Longview Technology Inc. (2)
No 76 Sec 1 ChengGong Rd, NanGang, Taipei, 115, Taiwan
Tel.: (886) 227893077
Computer Component Distr
N.A.I.C.S.: 423430

World Peace International (India) Pvt., Ltd. (1)
Building No 26 2nd Floor Okhla Phase III, New Delhi, 110020, India
Tel.: (91) 1140619000
Semiconductor Mfr & Distr
N.A.I.C.S.: 334413

World Peace International Pte. Ltd. (1)
10 Upper Aljunied Link 06-07, Singapore, 367904, Singapore
Tel.: (65) 62825188
Web Site: http://www.sa.wpi-group.com
Electronic Component Distr423690

Subsidiary (Non-US):

WPG SCM Limited (2)
18 F Shenfubao Bldg No 8 Ronghua Road Futian Free Trade Zone, Shenzhen, 518038, China
Tel.: (86) 5583580555
Electronic Components Distr
N.A.I.C.S.: 423690

Subsidiary (Domestic):

World Peace International (South Asia) Pte. Ltd. (2)
10 Upper Aljunied Link 06-07, Singapore, 367904, Singapore
Tel.: (65) 67833133
Web Site: http://www.genuineasia.com
Computer Component Distr
N.A.I.C.S.: 423430

Subsidiary (Non-US):

WPG C&C (Thailand) Co., Ltd. (3)
9/304 U M Tower 30th Floor Ramkamheang Road, Suanluang, Bangkok, 10250, Thailand
Tel.: (66) 27174511
Computer Component Distr
N.A.I.C.S.: 423430

Wpg Emea B.V. (1)
Unit 5 Eghams Court Boston Drive, Bourne End, SL8 5YS, Buckinghamshire, United Kingdom
Tel.: (44) 1628958460
Web Site: https://www.wpgemea.com
Semiconductor Component Distr
N.A.I.C.S.: 423690

Yosun Industrial Corporation (1)
Web Site: http://www.yosun.com.tw
Sales Range: $1-4.9 Billion
Emp.: 1,320
Electronic Components Mfr & Whslr
N.A.I.C.S.: 334419

Subsidiary (Domestic):

Mec Technology Co., Ltd. (2)
5F NO 489 Sec 2 Tiding Blvd, Neihu Dist, Taipei, 00114, Taiwan
Tel.: (886) 2 5579 0688
Web Site: http://www.mect.com.tw
Electronic Components Distr
N.A.I.C.S.: 423690

Sertek Inc. (2)
15F No 189 Jingmao 2nd Rd, Nangang, Taipei, 11568, Taiwan
Tel.: (886) 223162168
Web Site: http://www.sertek.com.tw
Sales Range: $25-49.9 Million
Emp.: 100
Electronic Components Marketing Services
N.A.I.C.S.: 423620

Subsidiary (Non-US):

Yosun Hong Kong Corp. Ltd. (2)
Units 07-11 15/F CDW Building 388 Castle Peak Road, Tsuen Wan, New Territories, China (Hong Kong)
Tel.: (852) 23654860
Web Site: http://www.yosungroup.com
Sales Range: $350-399.9 Million
Emp.: 80
Electronic Components Distr
N.A.I.C.S.: 423690

Yosun Japan Corp. (2)
2-14-4 Shin-Yokohama 6th Floor Silver Building, Kohoku-ku, Yokohama, 222 0033, Kanagawa, Japan
Tel.: (81) 454742240
Web Site: http://www.yosun-jp.com
Sales Range: $50-74.9 Million
Emp.: 7
Technical Support for Electronic Components Manufacturing Plants; Electronic Components Distr
N.A.I.C.S.: 423690

Yosun Shanghai Corp. Ltd. (2)
15 Fl Nextage Business Center No 1111 Pudong South Road, Pudong New District, Shanghai, 200120, China
Tel.: (86) 2158365838
Web Site: http://www.yosungroup.com
Sales Range: $75-99.9 Million
Emp.: 233
Electronic Components Sales & Services
N.A.I.C.S.: 423690

Yosun Singapore Pte. Ltd. (2)
10 Upper Aljunied Link 06-07, Singapore, 367904, Singapore
Tel.: (65) 65524811
Web Site: http://www.yosun.com.sg
Sales Range: $125-149.9 Million
Emp.: 85
Electronic Components Distr
N.A.I.C.S.: 423620

Yosun South China Corp. Ltd. (2)
17 F No 1016 Fuzhongyi Rd Shenzhen Metro Bldg, Futian District, Shenzhen, 51826, China
Tel.: (86) 75523992268
Web Site: http://www.yosungroup.com
Sales Range: $10-24.9 Million
Emp.: 350
Semiconductors & Passive Products Distr
N.A.I.C.S.: 813910

WPG RESOURCES LTD

Level 9 Kyle House 27 31 Macquarie Place, Sydney, 2000, NSW, Australia
Tel.: (61) 29 251 9251
Web Site:
http://www.westernplains.com.au
Year Founded: 2005
WPG—(ASX)
Sales Range: $50-74.9 Million
Coal Exploration Services
N.A.I.C.S.: 212115
Larissa Brown *(Sec)*

Subsidiaries:

WPG Ore Marketing Pty Ltd (1)
Level 9 27-31 Macquarie Pl, Sydney, 2000, NSW, Australia
Tel.: (61) 2 9251 1044
Web Site: http://www.wpg.com.au
Sales Range: $50-74.9 Million
Emp.: 10
Iron Ores Whslr
N.A.I.C.S.: 423520
Myles Fang *(Mgr-Bus Dev)*

WPG SHANGHAI SMART WATER PCL

WPG Resources Ltd—(Continued)

WPG SHANGHAI SMART WATER PCL
No 1 Hengding Road, Waigang Town Jiading District, Shanghai, 201800, China
Tel.: (86) 2169080888
Web Site: https://www.shwpg.com
Year Founded: 2011
603956—(SHG)
Rev.: $148,385,194
Assets: $486,603,122
Liabilities: $189,762,239
Net Worth: $296,840,883
Earnings: $(20,265,673)
Fiscal Year-end: 12/31/22
Water Equipment Mfr
N.A.I.C.S.: 333310
Jixi Li *(Chm)*

WPIL LIMITED
Trinity Plaza 3rd Floor 84 1A Topsia Road South, Kolkata, 700046, India
Tel.: (91) 3340556800
Web Site: https://www.wpil.co.in
Year Founded: 1952
505872—(BOM)
Rev.: $137,889,707
Assets: $207,042,340
Liabilities: $126,521,782
Net Worth: $80,520,558
Earnings: $13,471,049
Emp.: 248
Fiscal Year-end: 03/31/21
Pump & Pumping System Design, Mfr & Servicing
N.A.I.C.S.: 333914

Subsidiaries:

Gruppo Aturia S.p.A. **(1)**
Tel.: (39) 0295423200
Web Site: https://www.gruppoaturia.com
Magnetic Drive Sealless Pumps Mfr
N.A.I.C.S.: 333914

Mathers Foundry Limited **(1)**
Park Works Grimshaw Lane, Newton Heath, Manchester, M40 2BA, United Kingdom
Tel.: (44) 1619544347
Web Site: https://www.mathersfoundry.co.uk
Steel Casting Mfr
N.A.I.C.S.: 331512

Mody Industries (F.C) Private Limited **(1)**
Plot No C-41 Road No 34, Wagle Industrial Estate, Thane, 400604, India
Tel.: (91) 2225811644
Web Site: http://www.modyindustries.com
Pumps Mfr
N.A.I.C.S.: 333914
Vikas Garge *(Gen Mgr)*

PSV Services (Pty) Limited **(1)**
16 Impangela Road, Edenvale, 1610, Gauteng, South Africa **(100%)**
Tel.: (27) 114525524
Pumping Equipment Mfr
N.A.I.C.S.: 333914

Subsidiary (Domestic):

APE Pumps (Pty) Limited **(2)**
26 Nagington Rd Wadeville, Germiston, 1400, Gauteng, South Africa **(100%)**
Tel.: (27) 118244810
Web Site: http://www.apepumps.com
Pumping Equipment Mfr
N.A.I.C.S.: 333914
Peter Robinson *(Mng Dir)*

Mather + Platt (Pty) Limited **(2)**
26 Nagington Rd, Wadeville, Germiston, 1400, Johannesburg, South Africa **(100%)**
Tel.: (27) 118244810
Web Site: https://www.matherandplatt.com
Emp.: 120
Pumping Equipment Mfr
N.A.I.C.S.: 333914

Subsidiary (Non-US):

PSV Zambia Limited **(2)**

Plot 4065 Mulilakwenda Road Industrial Area Chibote Metals, Kitwe, 10101, Zambia **(100%)**
Tel.: (260) 212214137
Web Site: http://www.psvholdings.com
Emp.: 13
Industrial Equipment Distr
N.A.I.C.S.: 423840
John Clark *(Dir)*

Sterling Pumps Pty Limited **(1)**
14 Sharnet Circuit, Pakenham, 3810, VIC, Australia
Tel.: (61) 359413400
Web Site: https://www.sterlingpumps.com.au
Pumps Mfr
N.A.I.C.S.: 333914

UCP Australia Pty Limited **(1)**
31 Western Avenue, Sunshine, 3020, VIC, Australia
Tel.: (61) 394649500
Web Site: https://www.unitedpumps.com.au
Fluid Power Pump & Motor Mfr
N.A.I.C.S.: 333996

WPP PLC
Sea Containers 18 Upper Ground, London, SE1 9GL, United Kingdom
Tel.: (44) 2072824600 JE
Web Site: https://www.wpp.com
Year Founded: 1985
WPP—(NYSE)
Rev.: $18,738,702,348
Assets: $16,004,544,307
Liabilities: $11,166,498,359
Net Worth: $4,838,045,948
Earnings: $248,927,039
Emp.: 114,173
Fiscal Year-end: 12/31/23
Advertising Agencies Services
N.A.I.C.S.: 551112
Wendy Lund *(Chief Client Officer-Health & Wellness & Exec VP)*

Subsidiaries:

Addison Corporate Marketing Ltd. **(1)**
2 Cathedral St, London, SE1 9DE, United Kingdom
Tel.: (44) 2074037444
Web Site: http://www.addison.co.uk
Sales Range: $25-49.9 Million
Emp.: 45
Brand Development, Communications, Corporate Identity, Investor Relations, New Product Development, Outdoor
N.A.I.C.S.: 541810
Tom Robinson *(Head-Offer-Global)*

Buchanan Communications Ltd. **(1)**
107 Cheapside, London, EC2V 6DN, United Kingdom
Tel.: (44) 2074665000
Web Site: https://www.buchanancomms.co.uk
Sales Range: $25-49.9 Million
Emp.: 45
Public Relations Agency
N.A.I.C.S.: 541820
Bobby Morse *(Sr Partner)*

Cavendish Square Holding BV **(1)**
Laan Op Zuid 167, 3072 DB, Rotterdam, Netherlands **(100%)**
Tel.: (31) 104 841 600
Investment Services
N.A.I.C.S.: 523999

Subsidiary (Non-US):

WPP AUNZ Ltd. **(2)**
1 Kent Street, Millers Point, 2000, NSW, Australia **(100%)**
Tel.: (61) 293736488
Web Site: http://www.wppaunz.com
Sales Range: $800-899.9 Million
Holding Company; Communications & Other Marketing Services
N.A.I.C.S.: 541613
Rob Currie *(Dir-Bus)*

Subsidiary (Domestic):

AMR Interactive Group Pty Limited **(3)**

1 Kent Street, Millers Point, 2000, NSW, Australia
Tel.: (61) 290206700
Web Site: http://www.amr-australia.com
Marketing Consulting Services
N.A.I.C.S.: 541613
Dorothy Dudley *(Dir-Qualitative)*

Ethnic Communications Pty. Limited **(3)**
Level 3 72 Christie Street, Saint Leonards, 2065, NSW, Australia
Tel.: (61) 295688309
Web Site: http://www.etcom.com.au
Advertising Agency
N.A.I.C.S.: 541810
Melissa Chaw *(Mng Partner)*

Subsidiary (Non-US):

Haines NZ Limited **(3)**
Level 1 15 Allen Street, Te Aro, Wellington, 6011, New Zealand
Tel.: (64) 800170019
Web Site: https://www.hainesattract.co.nz
Recruitment Advertising Services
N.A.I.C.S.: 541890
Grace Fox *(Ops Mgr)*

Subsidiary (Domestic):

Hawker Britton Group Pty Limited **(3)**
GPO Box 4572, Sydney, 2001, NSW, Australia
Tel.: (61) 261112191
Web Site: https://www.hawkerbritton.com
Government Lobbying Services
N.A.I.C.S.: 541820
Simon Banks *(Mng Dir)*

Haylix Pty Limited **(3)**
Level 17 / 31 Queens St, Melbourne, 3000, VIC, Australia
Tel.: (61) 1300362671
Web Site: https://www.haylix.com
Web Hosting Services
N.A.I.C.S.: 518210
Thomas Ludbrook *(CEO)*

Subsidiary (Non-US):

Hoed Mystery Shopping New Zealand Ltd. **(3)**
195 Main Highway Building 3 Ellerslie, Auckland, 1051, New Zealand **(100%)**
Tel.: (64) 95790731
Web Site: https://hoed.co.nz
Mystery Shopping Services
N.A.I.C.S.: 561499
Richard Potton *(Mng Dir)*

Subsidiary (Domestic):

Hoed Research Pty Ltd **(3)**
North Tower Level 10 1-5 Railway Street, 1-5 Railway St, Chatswood, 2067, NSW, Australia
Tel.: (61) 1800025121
Web Site: https://www.hoedresearch.com.au
Mystery Shopping Services
N.A.I.C.S.: 561499
Peter Farnie *(Mng Dir)*

IM Advertising Pty Limited **(3)**
Level 2 Suite 222 4 Hyde Parade, Campbelltown, 2560, NSW, Australia
Tel.: (61) 246278011
Web Site: https://www.imab2b.com
Advertising Agency Services
N.A.I.C.S.: 541810
Karl Boothroyd *(CEO)*

IM Promos Pty Ltd **(3)**
Level 3 1 Kent St, Millers Point, 2000, NSW, Australia
Tel.: (61) 292771240
Web Site: http://www.impromos.com.au
Promotional Agency
N.A.I.C.S.: 541810
Karl Boothroyd *(CEO)*

Ikon Communications (Melbourne) Pty Limited **(3)**
L25 2 Southbank Boulevard, Southbank, 3006, VIC, Australia **(100%)**
Tel.: (61) 396337200
Marketing Communication Services
N.A.I.C.S.: 541613
Melissa Roberts *(Mng Partner)*

INTERNATIONAL PUBLIC

OgilvyOne Pty Limited **(3)**
72 Christie St, Saint Leonards, 2065, NSW, Australia
Tel.: (61) 293736333
Sales Range: $75-99.9 Million
Emp.: 400
Marketing Communication Services
N.A.I.C.S.: 541613
Ben Frost *(Gen Mgr)*

Oxygen Learning Pty Limited **(3)**
Sydney The Bond 30 Hickson Road, Millers Point, 2000, NSW, Australia
Tel.: (61) 280145000
Web Site: http://www.phuel.com.au
Marketing Communication Services
N.A.I.C.S.: 541613
Dean Gale *(Mng Dir)*

Singleton Ogilvy & Mather (Holdings) Pty Limited **(3)**
Cost Corporate Centre, Australia
L 6 72 Christie St, Saint Leonards, 2065, NSW, Australia **(66.6%)**
Tel.: (61) 293736488
Investment Management Service
N.A.I.C.S.: 523999

Subsidiary (Domestic):

Singleton Ogilvy & Mather (Sydney) Pty Limited **(4)**
72 Christie Street, Saint Leonards, 2065, NSW, Australia **(100%)**
Tel.: (61) 2 9268 1650
Sales Range: $25-49.9 Million
Emp.: 150
Advertising Services
N.A.I.C.S.: 541810

Subsidiary (Domestic):

The Punch Agency **(3)**
72 Christie Street, Saint Leonards, 2065, NSW, Australia
Tel.: (61) 246051650
Web Site: http://www.thepunchagency.com.au
Advertising Agency
N.A.I.C.S.: 541810
Andrew Bex *(Creative Dir & Dir-Acct)*

WPP AUNZ Analytics Pty. Ltd. **(3)**
L 6 72 Christie St, Saint Leonards, 2065, NSW, Australia
Tel.: (61) 293736488
Emp.: 100
Marketing Consulting Services
N.A.I.C.S.: 541613

Y&R ANZ **(3)**
Level 15 35 Clarence St, Sydney, 2000, NSW, Australia
Tel.: (61) 297787100
Web Site: http://www.yranz.com
Emp.: 304
Advertising Services
N.A.I.C.S.: 541810

Branch (Domestic):

Y&R ANZ - Sydney **(4)**
Level 15 35 Clarence St, Sydney, 2000, NSW, Australia
Tel.: (61) 2 9778 7100
Web Site: http://www.yranz.com
Advetising Agency
N.A.I.C.S.: 541810

Coley Porter Bell **(1)**
18 Upper Ground, London, SE1 9RQ, United Kingdom
Tel.: (44) 2031932600
Web Site: https://www.coleyporterbell.com
Sales Range: $25-49.9 Million
Emp.: 45
Consulting, Graphic Design
N.A.I.C.S.: 541810
Vicky Bullen *(CEO)*

Commarco GmbH **(1)**
Tel.: (49) 40 8221 95 900
Web Site: http://www.commarco.com
Emp.: 20
Holding Company; Communication & Marketing Services Agencies
N.A.I.C.S.: 551112

Subsidiary (Non-US):

Scholz & Friends Group GmbH **(2)**
Tel.: (49) 30700186300

AND PRIVATE COMPANIES

Web Site: https://www.s-f.family
Sales Range: $150-199.9 Million
Holding Company; Advertising Agencies
N.A.I.C.S.: 551112

United Visions GmbH (2)
Tel.: (49) 30 240 86 0
Marketing Film Production & Motion Graphics Services
N.A.I.C.S.: 512199

deepblue networks AG (2)
(100%)
Tel.: (49) 402840880
Web Site: https://www.db-n.com
Sales Range: $10-24.9 Million
Emp.: 120
Advetising Agency
N.A.I.C.S.: 541810

gkk DialogGroup GmbH (2)
Tel.: (49) 69754475
Web Site: https://www.gkk.de
Advertising & Public Relations Agency
N.A.I.C.S.: 541810

DesignWorks (NZ) Limited (1)
Level 1 36 Lorne St, Auckland, 1010, New Zealand
Tel.: (64) 93583033
Web Site: https://www.designworks.co.nz
Sales Range: $10-24.9 Million
Emp.: 47
N.A.I.C.S.: 541810
Vic Smith *(Mng Dir-Wellington)*

Dialogue (1)
77 Hatton Garden, London, EC1N 8JS, United Kingdom
Tel.: (44) 2074705800
Web Site: http://www.dialoguelondon.com
Advertising Agencies
N.A.I.C.S.: 541810

Essence Global Limited (1)
Digital Advertising Services
N.A.I.C.S.: 541890
Andrew Shebbeare *(Founder)*

EssenceMediacom Holdings Limited (1)
124 Theobalds Road, London, United Kingdom
Tel.: (44) 2071585500
Web Site: https://www.essencemediacom.com
Marketing Consulting Services
N.A.I.C.S.: 541613

Fitch Worldwide Limited (1)
121-141 Westbourne Terrace, London, W2 6JR, United Kingdom
Tel.: (44) 2074790900
Sales Range: $25-49.9 Million
Emp.: 80
Advetising Agency
N.A.I.C.S.: 541810
Matt Michaluk *(Exec Creative Dir)*

Unit (Non-US):

Code Computerlove Ltd. (2)
Tel.: (44) 1612762080
Web Site: http://www.codecomputerlove.com
Digital Marketing & Communications Services
N.A.I.C.S.: 541810
Tony Foggett *(Co-Founder & CEO)*

Subsidiary (Non-US):

Fitch Design Pvt. Ltd. (2)
30 Maxwell Road, Singapore, 062822, Singapore
Tel.: (65) 65382988
Sales Range: $10-24.9 Million
Emp.: 30
Advetising Agency
N.A.I.C.S.: 541810
Andrew Crombie *(CEO-South East & North Asia)*

Fitch Dubai (2)
33rd Floor Tiffany Tower, PO Box 62615, Jumeirah Lakes Towers, Dubai, United Arab Emirates
Tel.: (971) 44234700
Sales Range: $10-24.9 Million
Emp.: 30
Advetising Agency

Subsidiary (US):

Fitch Inc. (2)
585 S Front St Ste 300, Columbus, OH 43215
Tel.: (614) 885-3453
Sales Range: $25-49.9 Million
Emp.: 55
Advetising Agency
N.A.I.C.S.: 541810

Branch (Domestic):

Fitch Inc. - Phoenix (3)
16435 N Scottsdale Rd Ste 195, Scottsdale, AZ 85254-1649
Tel.: (480) 998-4200
Sales Range: $10-24.9 Million
Emp.: 50
Advetising Agency
N.A.I.C.S.: 541810

Fitch Inc. - Seattle (3)
414 Olive Way Ste 500, Seattle, WA 98101-3275
Tel.: (206) 624-0551
Web Site: http://www.fitch.com
Sales Range: $25-49.9 Million
Emp.: 20
Advetising Agency
N.A.I.C.S.: 541810

Unit (Domestic):

Fitch London (2)
121-141 Westbourne Terrace, London, W2 6JR, United Kingdom
Tel.: (44) 207 479 0900
Emp.: 20
Advetising Agency
N.A.I.C.S.: 541810
Gavin Clark *(Chief Dev Officer)*

Subsidiary (Non-US):

Fitch: Qatar Limited (2)
Villa 7 Qatar Foundation,, PO Box 24453, Doha, Qatar
Tel.: (974) 492 7268
Sales Range: $25-49.9 Million
Emp.: 30
Advetising Agency
N.A.I.C.S.: 541810

Geometry Global Limited (1)
121-141 Westbourne Terrace, London, W2 6JR, United Kingdom
Tel.: (44) 2075336000
Web Site: http://www.geometry.com
Sales Range: $25-49.9 Million
Emp.: 8
Advertising Services
N.A.I.C.S.: 541810

Subsidiary (US):

Geometry Global LLC (2)
The Chocolate Factory 636 11th Ave, New York, NY 10036
Tel.: (212) 537-3700
Web Site: http://www.geometry.com
Emp.: 4,000
Advertising Agencies
N.A.I.C.S.: 541810
Mike Forster *(CEO-Korea)*

Branch (Non-US):

G2 Direct & Digital (3)
Grey House 28 Dr E Borges Rd Opp Dr Shirodkar High School, Parel, Mumbai, 400 012, India
Tel.: (91) 22 4036 6363
Web Site: http://www.g2.com
Emp.: 250
Direct Marketing
N.A.I.C.S.: 541810

G2 Direct Interactive Kuala Lumpur (3)
15th Floor Wisma Genting Jalan Sultan Ismail, 50250, Kuala Lumpur, Malaysia
Tel.: (60) 2178 0055
Web Site: http://www.g2.com
Emp.: 32
Direct Marketing
N.A.I.C.S.: 541810

G2 Istanbul (3)
Buyukdere Cad. Ucyol Mevkii, 80670, Istanbul, Turkiye
Tel.: (90) 212 328 3144
Web Site: http://www.g2.com
N.A.I.C.S.: 541810

G2 Kuala Lumpur (3)
15th Floor, Wisma Genting, Jln Sultan Ismail, Kuala Lumpur, 50250, Malaysia
Tel.: (60) 3 2178 0055
Web Site: http://www.g2.com
Emp.: 1
Advertising Services
N.A.I.C.S.: 541810

G2 Moscow (3)
5 Str. Yamoskogo Polya 7, Building 2, 125040, Moscow, Russia
Tel.: (7) 495 792 3874
Web Site: http://www.g2.com
Sales Range: $10-24.9 Million
Emp.: 100
N.A.I.C.S.: 541810

G2 Stockholm (3)
Drottninggatan 94, SE-103 99, Stockholm, Sweden
Tel.: (46) 8458 2800
Web Site: http://www.g2.com
N.A.I.C.S.: 541810

G2 Tokyo (3)
Ebisu Square 1-23-23 Ebisu, Shibuya-Ku, Tokyo, 150-0013, Japan
Tel.: (81) 3 5423 1727
Web Site: http://www.g2.com
Emp.: 100
N.A.I.C.S.: 541810

Geometry Global - Amsterdam (3)
Pilotenstraat 41, 1059 CH, Amsterdam, Netherlands
Tel.: (31) 20 79 63 400
Web Site: http://www.geometry.com
Sales Range: $50-74.9 Million
Emp.: 21
Advertising Services
N.A.I.C.S.: 541810

Geometry Global - Beijing (3)
Suite 901 Tower W3 Oriental Plaza 1 East Chang An Avenue, Beijing, 100738, China
Tel.: (86) 10 83306666
Advertising Services
N.A.I.C.S.: 541810

Geometry Global - Berlin (3)
Rosenthaler Strabe 51, 10178, Berlin, Germany
Tel.: (49) 30 2888 41 501
Web Site: http://www.geometry.com
Emp.: 80
Full Service
N.A.I.C.S.: 541810

Geometry Global - Bogota (3)
Calle 100 7A 81 Floor 1 & 2, 110221, Bogota, Colombia
Tel.: (57) 1 7462727
Web Site: http://www.geometry.com
Emp.: 100
Advertising Services
N.A.I.C.S.: 541810

Geometry Global - Brazil (3)
Av Major Sylvio de Magalhaes Padilha 5200, Edificio Dallas 2 Andar Morumbi, Sao Paulo, Brazil
Tel.: (55) 11 4085 2622
Web Site: http://www.geometry.com
Emp.: 60
Advertising Services
N.A.I.C.S.: 541810

Branch (Domestic):

Geometry Global - Rio de Janeiro (4)
Praia de Botafogo 228 salas 706/707/709 Bloco B, Rio de Janeiro, 22250-040, Brazil
Tel.: (55) 21 2141 2500
Sales Range: $50-74.9 Million
Emp.: 35
Advertising Services
N.A.I.C.S.: 541810
Adrian Anthony Finch *(Reg Dir)*

Branch (Non-US):

Geometry Global - Budapest (3)
Andrassy U 9, 1061, Budapest, Hungary
Tel.: (36) 1 214 6750

WPP PLC

Web Site: http://www.geometry.com
Emp.: 60
Advertising Agencies
N.A.I.C.S.: 541810
Reka Salyi *(Mng Dir)*

Geometry Global - Buenos Aires (3)
Arevalo 1880, C1414CQL, Buenos Aires, Argentina
Tel.: (54) 11 4779 4300
Advertising Services
N.A.I.C.S.: 541810
Gonzalo Vidal Meyrelles *(Mng Dir)*

Geometry Global - Cape Town (3)
41 Sir Lowry Road, Woodstock, 7925, Cape Town, South Africa
Emp.: 21
Advertising Agencies
N.A.I.C.S.: 541810
Grant Rightford *(Mng Dir-Western Cape)*

Geometry Global - Caracas (3)
Centro Banaven Torre D Piso 3 Calle La Estancia, Municipio Chacao, Caracas, 1080, Venezuela
Tel.: (58) 2129023199
Emp.: 11
Advertising Services
N.A.I.C.S.: 541810
Roberto Coimbra *(Pres & Exec Dir-Creative)*

Geometry Global - Copenhagen (3)
Toldbodgade 55B, DK-1253, Copenhagen, O, Denmark
Tel.: (45) 33 13 79 14
Advertising Services
N.A.I.C.S.: 541810

Geometry Global - Dubai (3)
Al Attar Business Tower 24th Floor Sheikh Zayed Road, PO Box 74170, Dubai, United Arab Emirates
Tel.: (971) 4 3050300
Web Site: http://www.memacogilvy.com
Advertising Services
N.A.I.C.S.: 541810
Philippe Berthelot *(Mng Dir)*

Geometry Global - Dusseldorf (3)
Platz Der Ideen 2, 40476, Dusseldorf, Germany
Tel.: (49) 211 31 133 0
Web Site: http://www.geometry.com
N.A.I.C.S.: 541810
Stefan Kniess *(CEO)*

Geometry Global - Jakarta (3)
Jl Asia Afrika No 8 Sentral Senayan III 11th Floor Gelora, 10270, Jakarta, Indonesia
Tel.: (62) 21 2924 3000
Sales Range: $50-74.9 Million
Emp.: 20
Advertising Services
N.A.I.C.S.: 541810

Geometry Global - Johannesburg (3)
The Brand Bldg 15 Sloane St Bryanston, 2021, Johannesburg, South Africa
Tel.: (27) 117096720
Advertising Services
N.A.I.C.S.: 541810

Geometry Global - Kiev (3)
Verkhnii Val St 4A 1st Floor, 04071, Kiev, Ukraine
Tel.: (380) 44 590 5111
Advertising Services
N.A.I.C.S.: 541810
Julie Mazour *(Gen Mgr)*

Geometry Global - Lima (3)
Avenida Arequipa No 4080, Miraflores, Lima, 18, Peru
Tel.: (51) 1 221 8803
Emp.: 75
Advertising Agencies
N.A.I.C.S.: 541810

Geometry Global - Madrid (3)
Calle de Maria de Molina 39, 28006, Madrid, Spain
Tel.: (34) 91 4512000
Advertising Services
N.A.I.C.S.: 541810
Alfonso Alvarez *(Mng Dir & CEO)*

Geometry Global - Mexico (3)
Montes Urales 505 Planta Baja Col Lomas

WPP PLC

INTERNATIONAL PUBLIC

WPP plc—(Continued)
de Chapultepec Piso 1, 11000, Mexico, DF, Mexico
Tel.: (52) 55 5350 1800
Advertising Services
N.A.I.C.S.: 541810
Katya Rueda *(VP-Client Svcs-Ogilvy & Mather)*

Geometry Global - Milan (3)
Viale Vincenzo Lancetti 29, 20158, Milan, Italy
Tel.: (39) 02607891
Advertising Services
N.A.I.C.S.: 541810
Pietro Leone *(CEO-EMEA)*

Geometry Global - Mumbai (3)
#11-14 Commerz International Business Park Oberoi Garden City Off, Western Express Highway Goreag, Mumbai, 400063, India
Tel.: (91) 22 4436 0360
Advertising Services
N.A.I.C.S.: 541810
Aaradhee Mehta *(VP-Shopper Mktg-Geometry Global Encompass Network)*

Geometry Global - New Zealand (3)
22 Stanley Street Parnell, Auckland, 1140, New Zealand
Tel.: (64) 93588236
Web Site: http://www.g2.com
Advetising Agency
N.A.I.C.S.: 541810

Geometry Global - Paris (3)
Rue Marbeuf 32/34, 75008, Paris, France
Tel.: (33) 1 53 23 73 00
Sales Range: $50-74.9 Million
Emp.: 55
Advertising Services
N.A.I.C.S.: 541810
Georges-Eric Armand *(CEO)*

Geometry Global - Prague (3)
Privozni 2A, 170 00, Prague, Czech Republic
Tel.: (420) 221998111
Web Site: http://www.geometry.com
Emp.: 20
Advertising Services
N.A.I.C.S.: 541810

Geometry Global - Santiago (3)
Av Del Parque 4161 of 602, Huechuraba, Santiago, Chile
Tel.: (56) 2 431 0050
Advertising Services
N.A.I.C.S.: 541810

Geometry Global - Seoul (3)
JS Tower 11th Floor, Gangnam-gu, 135-877, Seoul, Korea (South)
Tel.: (82) 2 513 1400
Advertising Services
N.A.I.C.S.: 541810
Michael Lee *(Dir-Bus Dev)*

Geometry Global - Shanghai (3)
10th Floor WPP Campus 399 Hengfeng Rd, 200070, Shanghai, China
Tel.: (86) 21 2405 1888
Web Site: http://www.geometry.com
Advertising Services
N.A.I.C.S.: 541810

Geometry Global - Singapore (3)
71 Robinson Rd 07-01, Singapore, 068895, Singapore
Tel.: (65) 6213 7899
Advertising Services
N.A.I.C.S.: 541810
Jane Perry *(Mng Dir)*

Geometry Global - Taipei (3)
3F 89 Song Ren Road, Taipei, 110, Taiwan
Tel.: (886) 2 7745 1688
Sales Range: $50-74.9 Million
Emp.: 50
Advertising Services
N.A.I.C.S.: 541810
Harry Bailey *(Mng Dir)*

Grey Direct Canada (3)
46 Spadina Ave Suite 500, Toronto, M5V 2H8, ON, Canada
Tel.: (416) 486-0700
Web Site: http://www.grey.com
Direct Marketing

N.A.I.C.S.: 541810

Grey Group (3)
404 Vo Van Tan St, Ward 5, District 3, Ho Chi Minh City, Vietnam
Tel.: (84) 4 3719 1458
Web Site: http://www.grey.com
N.A.I.C.S.: 541810
Graham Drew *(Chief Creative Officer-Malaysia)*

Jotabequ Integrato G2 San Jose (3)
APDO Postal: 60-2050 Calle 23 Ave 1 43 B, La California, San Jose, Costa Rica
Tel.: (506) 2284 9800
Web Site: http://www.jotabequ.com
Emp.: 200
N.A.I.C.S.: 541810

Unit (Domestic):

Local Marketing Corp. (3)
312 Elm St, Cincinnati, OH 45202
Tel.: (513) 852-2480
Emp.: 25
N.A.I.C.S.: 541810

OgilvyAction (3)
636 W 11th Ave, New York, NY 10036
Tel.: (212) 297-8000
Advertising Services
N.A.I.C.S.: 541810

Branch (Non-US):

Geometry Global - Tokyo (4)
Yebisu Garden Palace Tower 25 Fl 4-20-3 Ebisu, Shibuya-ku, Tokyo, 150-6026, Japan
Tel.: (81) 3 5793 5170
Web Site: http://www.ogilvy.com
Sales Range: $200-249.9 Million
Emp.: 300
Advertising Services
N.A.I.C.S.: 541810
Ichiro Ota *(CEO)*

OgilvyAction (4)
10 Imathias St, Gerakas, 15344, Athens, Greece
Tel.: (30) 210 6660 300
Web Site: http://www.ogilvy.com
Advertising Services
N.A.I.C.S.: 541810

OgilvyAction (4)
3 Umaru Abass Close By 75 Oduduwa Crescent, GRA Ikeja, Lagos, 2341, Nigeria
Tel.: (234) 1 791 1214
Web Site: http://www.ogilvyaction.com
Emp.: 100
Advertising Services
N.A.I.C.S.: 541810

OgilvyAction (4)
ul Angorska 13a, 03-913, Warsaw, Poland
Tel.: (48) 226720606
Advertising Services
N.A.I.C.S.: 541810

OgilvyAction (4)
Jakobsgatan 6, Humlegardsgatan 6, 114 80, Stockholm, Sweden
Tel.: (46) 841098100
Advertising Services
N.A.I.C.S.: 541810

OgilvyAction (4)
Avenida la Reforma 6-39 zona 10 Centro Corporativo Guayacan, Nivel 9, Guatemala, Guatemala
Tel.: (502) 24208300
Web Site: http://ogilvyaction.com
Advetising Agency
N.A.I.C.S.: 541810

OgilvyAction (4)
Calle Magua 3 Los Rios, Distrito Nacional, Santo Domingo, Dominican Republic
Tel.: (809) 4725050
Advetising Agency
N.A.I.C.S.: 541810

OgilvyAction (4)
Ave. La Capilla 550, Col. San Benito, San Salvador, El Salvador
Tel.: (503) 2275 3777
Web Site: http://www.ogilvy.com
Advetising Agency
N.A.I.C.S.: 541810

OgilvyAction (4)
Rotonda El Gueguense 1 c arriba, 1 c lago 25 vrs, Managua, Nicaragua
Tel.: (505) 268 0606
Web Site: http://www.ogilvyaction.com
Advetising Agency
N.A.I.C.S.: 541810

OgilvyAction (4)
139/140 Marshalls Road, Lakshmipathy Salai Egmore, Chennai, 600 008, India
Tel.: (91) 044 44360360
Web Site: http://www.ogilvy.com
Advertising Services
N.A.I.C.S.: 541810

OgilvyAction (4)
Motijug House 1 Auckland Place, Kolkata, 700 017, India
Tel.: (91) 33 22831684
Web Site: http://www.ogilvy.com
Advetising Agency
N.A.I.C.S.: 541810
Parthaa Ghosh *(Mng Dir)*

OgilvyAction (4)
Level 6 5th Fl 6/2 Bagmani Tech Park, C V Raman Nagar Byrasandra, Bengaluru, 560 093, India
Tel.: (91) 080 44360360
Web Site: http://www.ogilvy.com
Advetising Agency
N.A.I.C.S.: 541810

OgilvyAction (4)
3rd Fl 66 Norodom Blvd, Phnom Penh, Cambodia
Tel.: (855) 23 211 529
Web Site: http://www.ogilvy.com
Sales Range: $50-74.9 Million
Emp.: 64
Advertising Services
N.A.I.C.S.: 541810

OgilvyAction (4)
27th Floor Ayala Life FGU Center 6811 Ayala Avenue, Makati, Philippines
Tel.: (63) 2 812 1141
Web Site: http://www.ogilvyaction.com
Advertising Services
N.A.I.C.S.: 541810

OgilvyAction (4)
Edificio Atrium Saldanha, Praca Duque de Saldanha no1 no4, 1050 094, Lisbon, Portugal
Tel.: (351) 21 321 2000
Web Site: http://www.ogilvy.com
Advertising Services
N.A.I.C.S.: 541810

OgilvyAction (4)
53 Rosmead Place, Colombo, 7, Sri Lanka
Tel.: (94) 11 471 3671
Web Site: http://www.ogilvyaction.com
Sales Range: $50-74.9 Million
Emp.: 85
Advertising Services
N.A.I.C.S.: 541810

Branch (Domestic):

OgilvyAction (4)
350 W Mart Center Dr Ste 1100, Chicago, IL 60654-1866
Tel.: (312) 527-3900
Web Site: http://www.ogilvyaction.com
Emp.: 125
Advertising Services
N.A.I.C.S.: 541810

OgilvyAction (4)
1010 Washington Blvd Ste 64, Stamford, CT 06901
Tel.: (203) 969-1311
Web Site: http://www.ogilvyaction.com
Sales Range: $50-74.9 Million
Emp.: 37
Advertising Services
N.A.I.C.S.: 541810

Branch (Non-US):

OgilvyAction (4)
Am Handelshasen 2-4, 40221, Dusseldorf, Germany
Tel.: (49) 49 211 49 70 00
Web Site: http://www.ogilvy.com
Sales Range: $50-74.9 Million
Emp.: 45
Advertising Services
N.A.I.C.S.: 541810

Branch (Domestic):

OgilvyAction (4)
55 Park Square Ct Ste 205, Roswell, GA 30075-4449
Tel.: (678) 323-3144
Web Site: http://www.ogilvy.com
Sales Range: $10-24.9 Million
Emp.: 40
Advertising Services
N.A.I.C.S.: 541810

Branch (Non-US):

OgilvyAction (4)
2nd Zvenigorodskaya 13 Building 41, 123022, Moscow, Russia
Tel.: (7) 495 661 2521
Advertising Services
N.A.I.C.S.: 541810

OgilvyAction (4)
C Bolivia 68-70, 08018, Barcelona, Spain
Tel.: (34) 934955555
Advertising Services
N.A.I.C.S.: 541810

OgilvyAction (4)
Co-Labs Starling Mall Damansara Utama Petaling Jaya, Kuala Lumpur, Malaysia
Tel.: (60) 7669 1366
Web Site: http://www.ogilvy.com
Advertising Services
N.A.I.C.S.: 541810
Anand Badami *(Reg Dir-Bus)*

OgilvyAction (4)
86 Grigore Alexandrescu Street, 010627, Bucharest, Romania
Tel.: (40) 212010100
Web Site: http://www.ogilvy.com
Advertising Services
N.A.I.C.S.: 541810

OgilvyAction (4)
The Offices at Centralworld 999/9 Rama 1 Road, Pathumwan, Bangkok, 10330, Thailand
Tel.: (66) 22056000
Advertising Services
N.A.I.C.S.: 541810

OgilvyAction Vietnam (4)
Center Tower 12th Floor 72-74 Nguyen Thi Minh Khai Street, District 3, Ho Chi Minh City, Vietnam
Tel.: (84) 2838219529
Sales Range: $50-74.9 Million.
Emp.: 75
Advertising Services
N.A.I.C.S.: 541810

Grey Shopper GmbH (1)
Volklinger Strasse 33, 40221, Dusseldorf, Germany
Tel.: (49) 21154595007
Web Site: https://edition.grey.de
Shopper Marketing Agency
N.A.I.C.S.: 541810

Group United (1)
121-141 Westbourne Terr, London, W2 6JR, United Kingdom
Tel.: (44) 2071503300
Web Site: http://www.theunitednetwork.net
Sales Range: $25-49.9 Million
Emp.: 7
Advertising Agencies
N.A.I.C.S.: 541810
Leurence Mellaman *(CEO)*

Subsidiary (Non-US):

Bates France (2)
11 rue Galvani, 75017, Paris, France
Tel.: (33) 144095959
Advetising Agency
N.A.I.C.S.: 541810

Norgard Mikkelsen Reklamebureau A/S (2)
Englandsgade 24, 5000, Odense, Denmark
Tel.: (45) 70202065
Web Site: https://www.nmic.dk
Emp.: 70
N.A.I.C.S.: 541810

Taivas Ogilvy (2)
Valkas iela 1a, LV-1010, Riga, Latvia
Tel.: (371) 7 322 366
Web Site: http://www.ogilvy.lv

AND PRIVATE COMPANIES — WPP PLC

Sales Range: $25-49.9 Million
N.A.I.C.S.: 541810

IMRB International Ltd. (1)
3rd Floor The ORB JW Marriott IA Project Road, Andheri E, Mumbai, 400099, India
Tel.: (91) 2224323500
Emp.: 200
Marketing Research Service
N.A.I.C.S.: 541910

Interactive Television Private Limited (1)
211 Ground Floor Okhla Industrial Estate Phase-3, Delhi, 110 020, India
Tel.: (91) 11 46 49 2200
Web Site: http://www.wpp.com
Communication Service
N.A.I.C.S.: 517810

Isobar Commerce (1)
10 Triton Street, London, NW1 3BF, United Kingdom
Tel.: (44) 2079838795
Web Site: http://www.isobar.com
Retail Software Development Services
N.A.I.C.S.: 541511
Patrick Deloy *(Mng Dir-Asia Pacific)*

John St. Inc. (1)
172 John St, Toronto, M5T 1X5, ON, Canada
Tel.: (416) 348-0048
Web Site: https://www.johnst.com
Sales Range: $10-24.9 Million
Emp.: 110
Advertising Services
N.A.I.C.S.: 541810
Ally Ballantyne *(Pres)*

Joule (1)
121-141 Westbourne Terrace, London, W2 6JR, United Kingdom
Tel.: (44) 2075444600
Mobile Advertising Services
N.A.I.C.S.: 561422
Tom Einar Jensen *(Exec VP & Head-Corp Dev)*

Lambie-Nairn & Company Limited (1)
6 Brewhouse Yard, London, EC1V4DJ, United Kingdom
Tel.: (44) 2078025800
Advetising Agency
N.A.I.C.S.: 541810

Les Ouvriers Du Paradis (1)
47 rue de Babylone, 75007, Paris, France
Tel.: (33) 1 53 59 53 79
Web Site: http://www.lesouvriers.fr
Sales Range: $25-49.9 Million
Emp.: 56
Advertising Agencies
N.A.I.C.S.: 541810

MQI Brno, spol. s r.o. (1)
Lipova 549/17, 602 00, Brno, Czech Republic
Tel.: (420) 541420211
Web Site: https://www.mqibrno.cz
Sales Range: $25-49.9 Million
Emp.: 7
Media Buying Services
N.A.I.C.S.: 541830
Miroslav Prima *(CEO)*

Mando Brand Assurance Limited (1)
The Corner Bldg, Aylesbury, HP19 8TY, Buckinghamshire, United Kingdom
Tel.: (44) 1296 717 900
Web Site: http://www.mando.co.uk
Sales Range: $25-49.9 Million
Emp.: 35
Advertising Services
N.A.I.C.S.: 541810

Mando Corporation Limited (1)
Tel.: (44) 1296717900
Sales Range: $50-74.9 Million
Emp.: 25
Risk Management & Logistics Services
N.A.I.C.S.: 523940
Becky Munday *(CEO)*

Media Basics BV (1)
Karperstraat 10, 1075 KZ, Amsterdam, Netherlands
Tel.: (31) 20 5757752
Media Representative Services
N.A.I.C.S.: 541840

MediaCom Holdings Ltd. (1)
124 Theobalds Road, London, WC1X 8RX, United Kingdom
Tel.: (44) 2071585500
Web Site: https://www.essencemediacom.com
Sales Range: $300-349.9 Million
Emp.: 800
Holding Company; Advertising Agencies
N.A.I.C.S.: 551112
Matthew Mee *(Chief Strategy Officer-Global)*

Co-Headquarters (US):

MediaCom Worldwide Inc. (2)
498 7th Ave, New York, NY 10018
Tel.: (212) 912-4200
Web Site: http://www.mediacom.com
Holding Company; Corporate Headquarters; Advertising Agencies
N.A.I.C.S.: 551112

Subsidiary (Non-US):

El Taller Creativo (3)
Avenida Los Proceres 37, Arroyo Hondo, Santo Domingo, Dominican Republic
Tel.: (809) 683 6940
Sales Range: $10-24.9 Million
Emp.: 40
N.A.I.C.S.: 541810

MC MediaCompany Budapest (3)
2nd Floor C Building Alkotas Str 53, 1123, Budapest, Hungary
Tel.: (36) 1 346 7020
Web Site: http://www.mcmedia.hu
Sales Range: $10-24.9 Million
Emp.: 32
N.A.I.C.S.: 541810

Media Compete (3)
Narva Mnt 7, 10117, Tallinn, Estonia
Tel.: (372) 6 109 374
Web Site: http://www.mediacom.ee
Sales Range: $25-49.9 Million
Emp.: 5
N.A.I.C.S.: 541810

MediaCom (3)
Level 3 W Wing Methodist Central Bldg, Colombo, 3, Sri Lanka
Tel.: (94) 11 2577101
Media Buying Services
N.A.I.C.S.: 541890

MediaCom (3)
5F No 31 Lane 11, GuangFu N Rd, 10560, Taipei, Taiwan
Tel.: (886) 2 7710 6199
Web Site: http://www.mediacom.com
Sales Range: $10-24.9 Million
Emp.: 28
Media Buying Services
N.A.I.C.S.: 541890

MediaCom (3)
1 High Street, Dublin, D08 R990, Ireland
Tel.: (353) 871344450
Sales Range: $10-24.9 Million
Advertising Agency Services
N.A.I.C.S.: 541810
Ed Ling *(COO & Chief Growth Officer)*

MediaCom (3)
98 Yigal Alon Street 24th Floor, Tel Aviv, 67891, Israel
Tel.: (972) 3 608 8888
Sales Range: $25-49.9 Million
Emp.: 13
N.A.I.C.S.: 541810
Galit Dohanhachan *(Co-Mng Dir)*

MediaCom (3)
2nd Floor Trade World 'C' Wing Kamala City Senapati Bapat Marg, Lower Parel, Mumbai, 400 013, India
Tel.: (91) 22 4095 9100
Sales Range: $25-49.9 Million
Emp.: 60
N.A.I.C.S.: 541810
Hariharan Vishwanathan *(Head-South)*

MediaCom (3)
bcg2 Level 2 1 Cross St, PO Box 3396, Auckland, 1010, New Zealand
Tel.: (64) 99144940
Web Site: http://www.greygroup.co.nz
Sales Range: $10-24.9 Million
Emp.: 35
N.A.I.C.S.: 541810

Matthew Vogts *(Chief Growth Officer)*

MediaCom AS (3)
Kongens gate 6, PB 8904, Youngstorget, 0153, Oslo, Norway
Tel.: (47) 22911000
Sales Range: $25-49.9 Million
Emp.: 64
N.A.I.C.S.: 541810

MediaCom Agentur fur Media-Beratung GmbH (3)
Derendorfer Alle, Dusseldorf, 40476, Germany
Tel.: (49) 211171620
Web Site: http://www.mediacom.de
Rev.: $3,513,640,000
Emp.: 394
Media Buying Services
N.A.I.C.S.: 541830
Claus Brockers *(Mng Dir)*

MediaCom Amsterdam (3)
Amsteldijk 166, 1079 LH, Amsterdam, Netherlands
Tel.: (31) 205757700
Sales Range: $25-49.9 Million
Emp.: 70
N.A.I.C.S.: 541810
Maiko Valentijn *(CEO)*

MediaCom Argentina (3)
Ricardo Rojas 401 Piso 12, C1001 AEA, Buenos Aires, Argentina
Tel.: (54) 11 5555 0600
Sales Range: $10-24.9 Million
Emp.: 31
N.A.I.C.S.: 541810

MediaCom Athens (3)
294 Syngrou Avenue, 176 73 Kalithea, Athens, Greece
Tel.: (30) 210 957 8000
Sales Range: $25-49.9 Million
Emp.: 5
N.A.I.C.S.: 541810

MediaCom Australia Pty. Ltd. (3)
Freshwater Place Level 25 2 Southbank Boulevard, Melbourne, 3006, VIC, Australia
Tel.: (61) 399407000
Sales Range: $10-24.9 Million
Emp.: 50
Media Buying Services
N.A.I.C.S.: 541810
Carl Colman *(Mng Dir)*

MediaCom Beijing (3)
12F Jin Bao Building Jing Bao Street, Dong Cheng District, Beijing, 100005, China
Tel.: (86) 10 85181988
N.A.I.C.S.: 541810
Michael Zhang *(Pres-China)*

MediaCom Belgium SA (3)
WPP Victoria Building Square Victoria Regina 1, 1210, Brussels, Belgium
Tel.: (32) 22079705
Advertising Services
N.A.I.C.S.: 541810
Marianne Gyselinck *(Dir-Client Svc)*

MediaCom Bucuresti (3)
39 Frumoasa Str Sector 1, Bucharest, Romania
Tel.: (40) 21 310 65 06
Sales Range: $25-49.9 Million
Emp.: 16
N.A.I.C.S.: 541810

MediaCom Company Ltd. (3)
23rd Floor Ploenchit Center, Sukhumvit Road Klongtoey, Bangkok, 10110, Thailand
Tel.: (66) 2 692 6300
Sales Range: $25-49.9 Million
Emp.: 8
N.A.I.C.S.: 541810
Suporn Aroonpakmongkol *(Mng Dir)*

MediaCom Denmark (3)
Holmbladsgade 133, 2300, Copenhagen, Denmark
Tel.: (45) 33760000
Sales Range: $10-24.9 Million
Emp.: 90
N.A.I.C.S.: 541810
Charlotte Hviid *(COO)*

MediaCom Dhaka (3)
4th Fl Farhen Tower House 1A Rd 23, Gulshan 1, Dhaka, 1212, Bangladesh

Tel.: (880) 2 988 1689
N.A.I.C.S.: 541810

MediaCom Edinburgh (3)
6 Dock Pl, Leith, Edinburgh, EH6 6LU, United Kingdom
Tel.: (44) 1315551500
Web Site: http://www.mediacomedinburgh.com
Sales Range: $25-49.9 Million
Emp.: 42
N.A.I.C.S.: 541810
David Shearer *(Mng Dir)*

MediaCom Finland (3)
Ruoholahdenkatu 21, 00180, Helsinki, Finland
Tel.: (358) 207199211
Sales Range: $10-24.9 Million
Emp.: 30
N.A.I.C.S.: 541810

MediaCom Ghana (3)
10 Labone, Box CT 5864, 10, Accra, Ghana
Tel.: (233) 21 784 852
N.A.I.C.S.: 541810

MediaCom Guangzhou (3)
8/F, Development Center 3 Lin Jiang Road, Pearl River New City, Guangzhou, China
Tel.: (86) 20 2881 8266
N.A.I.C.S.: 541810

MediaCom Hong Kong (3)
36 Floor PCCW Tower 979 Kings Road Taikoo Place, Quarry Bay, China (Hong Kong)
Tel.: (852) 2510 6729
Web Site: http://www.mediacom.com
Sales Range: $25-49.9 Million
Emp.: 10
Media Buying Services
N.A.I.C.S.: 541810
Alice Chow *(Mng Dir)*

MediaCom Iberia (3)
Edificio 5C 4o Lagoas Park, 2470-298, Porto Salvo, Portugal
Tel.: (351) 211208750
Web Site: http://www.mediacom.pt
Sales Range: $10-24.9 Million
Emp.: 32
N.A.I.C.S.: 541810

MediaCom Iberia (3)
Lasnordias 92 2nd Fl, 28221, Madrid, Spain
Tel.: (34) 91 598 35 55
Web Site: http://www.mediacom.com
Sales Range: $10-24.9 Million
Emp.: 50
N.A.I.C.S.: 541810

MediaCom Indonesia (3)
Tempo Scan Tower 23rd Floor Jalan H R Rasuna Said Kav 3-4, Jakarta, 12950, Indonesia
Tel.: (62) 2129036737
Advetising Agency
N.A.I.C.S.: 541810
Partha Kabi *(Mng Dir)*

MediaCom Istanbul (3)
Esentepe Mah Buyukdere Cad Astoria AVM No 127 Kat 2, 34394, Istanbul, Turkiye
Tel.: (90) 2123247272
Sales Range: $10-24.9 Million
Emp.: 36
N.A.I.C.S.: 541810
Burc Doken *(Grp Acct Dir)*

MediaCom Italy (3)
Via Morimondo 26, 20143, Milan, Italy
Tel.: (39) 02336441
Sales Range: $25-49.9 Million
Emp.: 90
N.A.I.C.S.: 541810

MediaCom Japan (3)
Yebisu Garden Place Tower 30F 4 Chome-20 Ebisu, Shibuya City, Tokyo, 150-0013, Japan
Tel.: (81) 357914660
N.A.I.C.S.: 541810
Linda Lee *(Mng Dir)*

MediaCom Korea (3)
37 Nonhyun-1 Dong, Kangnam-Ku, Seoul, 318, Korea (South)
Tel.: (82) 2 3015 5800
Web Site: http://www.greyworldwide.co.kr
Sales Range: $25-49.9 Million
Emp.: 7
N.A.I.C.S.: 541810

WPP PLC

WPP plc—(Continued)
Yonghyun Cho (Assoc Dir-Media Plng)

Subsidiary (Domestic):

MediaCom LLC (3)
498 7th Ave, New York, NY 10018
Tel.: (212) 912-4200
Web Site: http://www.mediacomusa.com
Rev.: $7,400,000,000
Emp.: 1,000
N.A.I.C.S.: 541810
Sasha Savic (CEO)

Branch (Domestic):

MediaCom Los Angeles (4)
3500 W Olive Ave Ste 800, Burbank, CA 91505
Tel.: (818) 525-3000
Sales Range: $10-24.9 Million
Emp.: 60
N.A.I.C.S.: 541810

Division (Domestic):

MediaCom Outdoor (4)
10 E 40th St, New York, NY 10016-0200
Tel.: (212) 584-3561
N.A.I.C.S.: 541810

Subsidiary (Non-US):

MediaCom MENA (3)
41st Floor Tower B Business Central Towers Dubai Media City, PO Box 34780, Dubai, United Arab Emirates
Tel.: (971) 44494700
Advertising Services
N.A.I.C.S.: 541810
Yves Massaad (Mng Dir-Client)

MediaCom Mexico (3)
Jaime Balmes No 8-101 Col Los Morales Polanco, Piso 1, 11510, Mexico, DF, Mexico
Tel.: (52) 55 5351 4700
N.A.I.C.S.:

MediaCom Paris (3)
32 Rue Guersant, Paris, 75017, France
Tel.: (33) 173002100
Web Site: http://www.mediacomparis.fr
Sales Range: $25-49.9 Million
Emp.: 85
N.A.I.C.S.: 541810

MediaCom Praha (3)
Bubenska 1477/1, 17000, Prague, Czech Republic
Tel.: (420) 226522201
Sales Range: $10-24.9 Million
Emp.: 45
N.A.I.C.S.: 541810

MediaCom Santiago (3)
Bacuma Sequentes 2209 Providencia, 7510451, Santiago, Chile
Tel.: (56) 2 584 9900
Sales Range: $25-49.9 Million
Emp.: 3
N.A.I.C.S.: 541810

MediaCom Shanghai (3)
Ste 3709 Westgate Mall 1038 Nanjing Xi Road, Shanghai, 200041, China
Tel.: (86) 21 6287 8660
N.A.I.C.S.: 541810
Shane Crombie (Head-Interaction)

MediaCom South Africa (3)
2 Harris Road Corner Katherine Street, Sandton, 2146, South Africa
Tel.: (27) 11 293 6300
N.A.I.C.S.: 541810
Ashish Williams (CEO)

MediaCom Sverige AB (3)
Birger Jarlsgatan 52 3tr, 103 77, Stockholm, Sweden
Tel.: (46) 850757200
Web Site: http://www.mediacom.se
Sales Range: $25-49.9 Million
Emp.: 60
N.A.I.C.S.: 541810
Marie Melin (Chief Culture & Growth Officer)

MediaCom Switzerland (3)
Manessestrasse 85, Zurich, Switzerland
Tel.: (41) 445674747

Sales Range: $25-49.9 Million
Emp.: 19
N.A.I.C.S.: 541810
Gabriela Boecker-Flamm (Chief HR & Talent Officer)

MediaCom Sydney (3)
Level 17, 65 Berry St, Sydney, 2060, NSW, Australia
Tel.: (61) 2 9463 7000
Web Site: http://www.mediacom.com
Sales Range: $25-49.9 Million
Emp.: 150
N.A.I.C.S.: 541810

MediaCom Vancouver (3)
1500 W Georgia St Ste 1600, Vancouver, V6G 2Z6, BC, Canada
Tel.: (604) 687-1611
Web Site: http://mediacom.com
Sales Range: $25-49.9 Million
Emp.: 6
N.A.I.C.S.: 541830

MediaCom Vienna (3)
Vordere Zollamtstrasse 13/5 OG, 1030, Vienna, Austria
Tel.: (43) 160555
Sales Range: $75-99.9 Million
Emp.: 100
N.A.I.C.S.: 541810
Andrea Kainz (Chief Investment Officer)

MediaCom Warszawa (3)
ul Plac Konesera 11, 03-736, Warsaw, Poland
Tel.: (48) 221133200
Sales Range: $25-49.9 Million
Emp.: 95
N.A.I.C.S.: 541810
Daniel Marciniak (Dir-New Bus)

Subsidiary (Domestic):

MediaCom de Puerto Rico, Inc. (3)
270 Ave Munoz Rivera 3rd Fl, San Juan, PR 00918-1901
Tel.: (787) 999-9950
Web Site: http://mediacom.com
Sales Range: $10-24.9 Million
Emp.: 35
N.A.I.C.S.: 541810

Subsidiary (Non-US):

MediaCompete Malaysia (3)
Unit 12 1 12th Floor Menara Surian 1 Jalan PJU 7/3, Mutiara Damansara, Kuala Lumpur, Malaysia
Tel.: (60) 327111863
Sales Range: $25-49.9 Million
Emp.: 44
N.A.I.C.S.: 541810
Rana Himanshu (Dir-Corp Portfolio & Ops)

MediaCompete Singapore (3)
1 Shenton Way 01-02, Singapore, 068803, Singapore
Tel.: (65) 6511 7602
Sales Range: $10-24.9 Million
Emp.: 38
N.A.I.C.S.: 541810

Mediacom Colombia (3)
Calle 71 No 5-97 Of 201, Bogota, 11001000, Colombia
Tel.: (57) 1 317 5030
Emp.: 400
Advertising Services
N.A.I.C.S.: 541810
Paulina Perra (CEO)

Mediacom London (3)
124 Theobalds Road, London, WC1X 8RX, United Kingdom
Tel.: (44) 2071585500
Web Site: http://www.mediacomuk.com
Rev.: $1,407,527,800
Emp.: 800
N.A.I.C.S.: 541810
Tom Curtis (Exec Creative Dir)

Millward Brown UK Ltd. (3)
Olympus Avenue Tachbrook Park, Warwick, CV34 6RJ, United Kingdom
Tel.: (44) 1926452233
Sales Range: $50-74.9 Million
Emp.: 400
Marketing & Advertising
N.A.I.C.S.: 541810

Pak MediaCom (Pvt.) Ltd. (3)
6 7 Floor Khayaban-e-Iqbal Clifton Block 9, Karachi, 75530, Pakistan
Tel.: (92) 21536126185
Sales Range: Less than $1 Million
Emp.: 36
N.A.I.C.S.: 541810

Promedia A/S (3)
Holmbladsgade 133, 2300, Copenhagen, Denmark
Tel.: (45) 33760000
Sales Range: $25-49.9 Million
Emp.: 15
N.A.I.C.S.: 541810

The Media Company (3)
1 Dundas Street W Suite 2800, Toronto, M5G 1Z3, ON, Canada
Tel.: (416) 961-1255
Sales Range: $25-49.9 Million
Emp.: 200
N.A.I.C.S.: 541810

Metro Broadcast Ltd. (1)
Camberwell New Road, London, SE5 0TA, United Kingdom
Tel.: (44) 20 7202 2000
Web Site: http://www.metrobroadcast.com
Sales Range: $25-49.9 Million
Emp.: 50
Event Management Services
N.A.I.C.S.: 711310
Mary Metcalfe (Mng Dir)

Ohal Limited (1)
Greater London House Hampstead Rd, Blackheath, London, NW1 7QP, United Kingdom
Tel.: (44) 2083187321
Web Site: https://gaintheory.com
Sales Range: $25-49.9 Million
Emp.: 5
Research & Insight Consulting Services
N.A.I.C.S.: 541611
Manjiry Tamhane (Global Mng Dir)

Quisma GmbH (1)
Rosenheimer Strasse 145d, 81671, Munich, Germany
Tel.: (49) 894423820
Sales Range: $25-49.9 Million
Emp.: 15
Online Marketing Services
N.A.I.C.S.: 541613

RLM Finsbury Limited (1)
1-11 John Adam Street, London, WC2N 6HT, United Kingdom
Tel.: (44) 2072513801
Sales Range: $25-49.9 Million
Emp.: 50
Public Relations Agency
N.A.I.C.S.: 541820
Roland Rudd (Founder & Chm)

Santo Buenos Aires (1)
Darwin 1212, Buenos Aires, 1414, Argentina
Tel.: (54) 114 777 7757
Web Site: http://www.santobuenosaires.net
Sales Range: $25-49.9 Million
Emp.: 35
Advertising Services
N.A.I.C.S.: 541810

Smollan Headcount (1)
Kestrel Court Pound Road, Chertsey, KT16 8ER, Surrey, United Kingdom
Tel.: (44) 1932560650
Web Site: http://www.smollan.co.uk
Sales Range: $25-49.9 Million
Emp.: 50
Marketing Services
N.A.I.C.S.: 541613

Spafax Airline Network Limited (1)
The Pumphouse 13-16 Jacob's Well Mews, London, W1U 3DY, United Kingdom
Tel.: (44) 2079062001
Sales Range: $25-49.9 Million
Emp.: 65
Advetising Agency
N.A.I.C.S.: 541830
Niall McBain (CEO)

Subsidiary (Non-US):

Spafax Canada (2)
2 Bloor St Ste 1020, Toronto, M4W 1A8, ON, Canada

Tel.: (416) 350-2425
Web Site: http://www.spafax.com
Sales Range: $25-49.9 Million
Emp.: 14
Audio/Visual, Print, Transportation
N.A.I.C.S.: 541810

Spafax Montreal (2)
4200 Boulevard St-Laurent, Saint Laurent Suite 707, Montreal, H2W 2R2, QC, Canada
Tel.: (514) 844-2001
Web Site: http://www.spafax.com
Sales Range: $10-24.9 Million
Emp.: 33
Audio/Visual, Aviation, Media Buying Services, Print
N.A.I.C.S.: 541830

Subsidiary (US):

Spafax Networks Inc. (2)
1507 W Yale Ave, Orange, CA 92867
Tel.: (714) 363-4900
Web Site: http://www.spafax.com
Sales Range: $10-24.9 Million
Emp.: 35
N.A.I.C.S.: 541810

Subsidiary (Non-US):

Spafax Singapore (2)
50 Scotts Road 04-01, Singapore, 228242, Singapore
Tel.: (65) 65312682
Sales Range: $25-49.9 Million
Emp.: 5
Advetising Services
N.A.I.C.S.: 541810

Superunion Limited (1)
6 Brewhouse Yard, London, EC1V 4DG, United Kingdom
Tel.: (44) 2075597000
Web Site: https://www.designbridge.com
Brand Development
N.A.I.C.S.: 541810
Jim Prior (CEO-Global)

Subsidiary (US):

The Brand Union Company, Inc. (2)
3 Columbus Cir, New York, NY 10019
Tel.: (212) 755-4200
Web Site: http://www.thebrandunion.com
Advetising Agency
N.A.I.C.S.: 541810
Wally Krantz (Dir-Worldwide Creative-Corp Branding)

The Brand Union AB (1)
Jakobsgatan 6, 114 80, Stockholm, Sweden
Tel.: (46) 841098100
Web Site: https://www.brandunionstockholm.com
Advertising Services
N.A.I.C.S.: 541810

The Farm Group (1)
13 Soho Square, London, W1D 3QF, United Kingdom
Tel.: (44) 20 7437 6677
Web Site: http://www.farmgroup.tv
Sales Range: $50-74.9 Million
Emp.: 23
Television Broadcasting Services
N.A.I.C.S.: 516120
Nicky Sargent (Co-Founder)

The Jeffrey Group, LLC (1)
201 S Biscayne Blvd Ste 1400, Miami, FL 33131
Tel.: (305) 860-1000
Web Site: http://www.jeffreygroup.com
Sales Range: $1-9.9 Million
Emp.: 32
Public Relations Agency
N.A.I.C.S.: 541820
Jeffrey R. Sharlach (Founder & Chm)

Branch (Non-US):

The Jeffrey Group Argentina (2)
San Martin 674 3 A, C1004AAN, Buenos Aires, Argentina
Tel.: (54) 11 4328 3354
Web Site: http://www.thejeffreygroup.com
Emp.: 8
Public Relations Agency
N.A.I.C.S.: 541820
Maria Eugenia Vargas (Mng Dir)

AND PRIVATE COMPANIES — WPP PLC

The Jeffrey Group Brazil (2)
Rua Claudio Soares 72 cj. 1501 Pinheiros,
05422-030, Sao Paulo, SP, Brazil
Tel.: (55) 11 3185 0800
Web Site: http://www.thejeffreygroup.com
Emp.: 30
Public Relations Agency
N.A.I.C.S.: 541820
Cristina Iglecio (Mng Dir)

The Jeffrey Group Mexico (2)
Homero 1343 No 402, Col Los Morales Polanco, Mexico, 11540, CP, Mexico
Tel.: (52) 55 5281 1121
Web Site: http://www.thejeffreygroup.com
Public Relations Agency
N.A.I.C.S.: 541820
Rodrigo Gonzales (Dir-Creative)

Branch (Domestic):

The Jeffrey Group New York (2)
1 Grand Central Pl 60 E 42nd St Ste 5310,
New York, NY 10165
Tel.: (212) 620-4100
Web Site: http://www.thejeffreygroup.com
Emp.: 30
Public Relations Agency
N.A.I.C.S.: 541820
Jeffrey Sharlach (Chm)

The Partners (1)
Albion Courtyard Greenhills Rents, Smithfield, London, EC1M 6PQ, United Kingdom
Tel.: (44) 2076080051
Sales Range: $25-49.9 Million
Emp.: 45
Advertising Agencies
N.A.I.C.S.: 541810
Jim Prior (CEO-Global)

The United Network (1)
121-141 Westbourne Terrace, London, W2 6JR, United Kingdom
Tel.: (44) 20 7150 3300
Advertising Agencies
N.A.I.C.S.: 541810

Subsidiary (Non-US):

Bates United (2)
Holbergs Gate 21, PO Box 7094, Saint Olavs plass, N 0130, Oslo, Norway
Tel.: (47) 22879700
Web Site: http://www.bates.no
Emp.: 60
Advertising Agencies
N.A.I.C.S.: 541810

Subsidiary (US):

Berlin Cameron United (2)
175 Greenwich St 28th Fl, New York, NY 10007
Tel.: (212) 824-2000
Web Site: https://berlincameron.com
Emp.: 83
Advertising Agencies
N.A.I.C.S.: 541810
Ewen Cameron (Founder)

Cole & Weber United (2)
221 Yale Ave N Ste 600, Seattle, WA 98109
Tel.: (206) 447-9595
Web Site: http://www.coleweber.com
Emp.: 65
Advertising Agencies
N.A.I.C.S.: 541810
Mike Doherty (Pres)

Subsidiary (Non-US):

LDV United (2)
Rijnkaai 100 busA15 / De Hangar, Hangar 26, 2000, Antwerp, Belgium
Tel.: (32) 32292929
Web Site: https://www.ldv.be
Rev.: $5,000,000
Emp.: 40
Advertising Agencies
N.A.I.C.S.: 541810
Harry Demey (CEO)

Les Ouvriers Duparadis (2)
47 rue de Bourgogne, 75007, Paris, France
Tel.: (33) 153595370
Web Site: http://www.lesouvriers.fr
Emp.: 50
Advertising Agencies
N.A.I.C.S.: 541810

Sra. Rushmore (2)
Gran Via 27 Fl 9, 28013, Madrid, Spain
Tel.: (34) 912090333
Web Site: https://www.srarushmore.com
Emp.: 100
Advertising Agencies
N.A.I.C.S.: 541810
Clemente Manzano (Gen Mgr)

WPP Group USA Inc. (1)
100 Park Ave, New York, NY 10017-5529   (100%)
Tel.: (212) 632-2200
Web Site: http://www.wpp.com
Marketing & Advertising
N.A.I.C.S.: 541820
Michael Houston (Pres)

Subsidiary (Domestic):

AKQA, Inc. (2)
360 3rd St, San Francisco, CA 94107
Tel.: (415) 944-2000
Web Site: https://www.akqa.com
Sales Range: $150-199.9 Million
Emp.: 1,300
Advetising Agency
N.A.I.C.S.: 541810
Ajaz Ahmed (Founder & CEO)

Subsidiary (Non-US):

AKQA (Shanghai) Co., Ltd. (3)
3rd Floor Building 11 No 207 Meng Zi Road, Shanghai, 200023, China
Tel.: (86) 2123122572
Advertising Agencies
N.A.I.C.S.: 541810
Sam Sterling (Chief Strategy Officer-APAC)

AKQA B.V. (3)
Nieuwe Herengracht 95, 1011 RX, Amsterdam, Netherlands
Tel.: (31) 207082572
Emp.: 30
Advertising Agency
N.A.I.C.S.: 541810

AKQA Limited (3)
1 St John's Lane, Clerkenwell, London, EC1M 4BL, United Kingdom
Tel.: (44) 2077804786
Sales Range: $75-99.9 Million
Emp.: 300
Advetising Agency
N.A.I.C.S.: 541810
Aivory Gaw (Dir-Bus Dev)

Branch (Domestic):

AKQA, Inc. - New York (3)
114 5th Ave, New York, NY 10014
Tel.: (212) 989-2572
Web Site: http://www.akqa.com
Sales Range: $25-49.9 Million
Emp.: 150
Advertising Agency
N.A.I.C.S.: 541810
Resh Sidhu (Creative Dir-Grp)

AKQA, Inc. - Washington, DC (3)
3299 K St NW 5th Fl, Washington, DC 20007
Tel.: (202) 337-2572
Web Site: http://www.akqa.com
Emp.: 100
Advertising Agency
N.A.I.C.S.: 541810
Erik Rogstad (Mng Partner)

Subsidiary (Domestic):

B to D Group (2)
Klamath House 1001 Front St, San Francisco, CA 94111
Tel.: (415) 365-1700
Web Site: http://www.wpp.com
Marketing Communication Services
N.A.I.C.S.: 517810

Blast Radius (2)
3 Colmbus Cir, New York, NY 10019
Tel.: (212) 925-4900
Web Site: http://www.blastradius.com
Advertising Agency
N.A.I.C.S.: 541810

Subsidiary (Non-US):

Blast Radius Hamburg (3)
Chilehaus Fischertwiete 1, 20095, Hamburg, Germany
Tel.: (49) 40 3910 5825
N.A.I.C.S.: 541810

Blast Radius Toronto (3)
60 Bloor St W 9th FL, Toronto, M4W 1J2, ON, Canada
Tel.: (416) 214-4220
Web Site: http://www.blastradius.com
Advertising Services
N.A.I.C.S.: 541810

Blast Radius Vancouver (3)
1146 Homer St, Vancouver, V6B 2X6, BC, Canada
Tel.: (604) 647-6500
Advertising Services
N.A.I.C.S.: 541810

Subsidiary (Domestic):

Blue State Digital (2)
406 7th St NW 3rd Fl, Washington, DC 20004-2261
Tel.: (202) 449-5600
Web Site: http://bluestatedigital.com
N.A.I.C.S.: 541810

Burson Cohn & Wolfe (2)
3 World Trade Ctr 175 Greenwich St, New York, NY 10007
Tel.: (212) 601-3000
Brand Marketing & Digital Communication Agency
N.A.I.C.S.: 541820
Jerry Lombardo (CFO)

Subsidiary (Domestic):

Burson-Marsteller, LLC (3)
230 Park Ave S, New York, NY 10003-1566
Tel.: (212) 614-4000
Web Site: http://www.bcw-global.com
Public Relations
N.A.I.C.S.: 541820

Subsidiary (Non-US):

ASDA'A BCW (4)
4th Floor Block A The Gateway Building, Dubai Media City, Dubai, United Arab Emirates
Tel.: (971) 44507600
Web Site: https://asdaa-bcw.com
Public Relations
N.A.I.C.S.: 541820
Sunil John (Founder & Pres-Middle East)

Burson Cohn & Wolfe AG (4)
Hardturmstrasse 133, Postfach 8037, 8037, Zurich, Switzerland
Tel.: (41) 444558400
Advertising Agencies
N.A.I.C.S.: 541810
Nick Stravs (CEO)

Branch (Domestic):

Burson Cohn & Wolfe AG- Zweigniederlassung Bern (5)
Aarbergergasse 29, 3011, Bern, Switzerland
Tel.: (41) 31 356 7300
Web Site: http://www.bcw-global.com
Advertising Agencies
N.A.I.C.S.: 541810

Burson-Marsteller AG - Geneva (5)
18 bd des Philosophes, CH-1205, Geneva, Switzerland
Tel.: (41) 225936920
Web Site: http://www.b-m.ch
Public Relations
N.A.I.C.S.: 541820

Branch (Non-US):

Burson-Marsteller (4)
Suite 602 Tower W1 Oriental Plaza 1 East Chang An Avenue, Dong Cheng District, Beijing, 100738, China
Tel.: (86) 10 5816 2525
Advertising Agencies
N.A.I.C.S.: 541810
Daisy King (Pres)

Burson-Marsteller (4)
Room 303-304 K Wah Centre, 1010 Huahai Middle Road, Shanghai, 200031, China
Tel.: (86) 21 5403 2121
Emp.: 15
Advertising Agencies
N.A.I.C.S.: 541810

Burson-Marsteller (4)
Carrera 11 A 93 B - 30 Piso 3, Bogota, Colombia
Tel.: (57) 1 622 6500
Emp.: 18
Public Relations
N.A.I.C.S.: 541870

Branch (Domestic):

Burson-Marsteller (4)
4025 Camino Del Rio S Ste 300, San Diego, CA 92108-4107
Tel.: (619) 542-7812
Emp.: 11
Public Relations
N.A.I.C.S.: 541810

Burson-Marsteller (4)
303 2nd St Ste 350 N Twr, San Francisco, CA 94107
Tel.: (415) 591-4000
Web Site: http://www.bm.com
Emp.: 19
Public Relations
N.A.I.C.S.: 541820
Jennifer Graham (Chm-Global Tech Practice)

Burson-Marsteller (4)
1845 Woodall Rodgers Hwy, Dallas, TX 75201-2287
Tel.: (214) 224-8400
Emp.: 37
Advertising Agencies
N.A.I.C.S.: 541810

Branch (Non-US):

Burson-Marsteller (4)
Wisma BNI 46 Kota BNI Suite 16-07, Jln Jend Sudirman Kav 1, Jakarta, 10220, Indonesia
Tel.: (62) 21 251 5060
Advertising Agencies
N.A.I.C.S.: 541810

Burson-Marsteller (4)
Av Jorge Basadre 145 piso 7, San Isidro, Lima, Peru
Tel.: (51) 12001500
Web Site: http://latam.bm.com
Public Relations Agency
N.A.I.C.S.: 541820

Branch (Domestic):

Burson-Marsteller (4)
2425 Olympic Blvd Ste 200E, Santa Monica, CA 90404-4047
Tel.: (310) 309-6600
Web Site: http://www.bm.com
Sales Range: $10-24.9 Million
Emp.: 34
Public Relations
N.A.I.C.S.: 541810
Lynda Herrera (Mng Dir)

Burson-Marsteller (4)
Courvoisier Ctr II 601 Brickell Key Dr Ste 900, Miami, FL 33133
Tel.: (305) 347-4300
Emp.: 30
Public Relations
N.A.I.C.S.: 541810
Claudia Adriasola (COO-Latin America)

Burson-Marsteller (4)
4 Gateway Ctr 444 Liberty Ave Ste 310, Pittsburgh, PA 15222-1220
Tel.: (412) 471-9600
Emp.: 20
Public Relations
N.A.I.C.S.: 541810
Tom Dowling (Mng Dir)

Burson-Marsteller (4)
Munet Ct 9 Pueblo Viejo, Guaynabo, PR 00968-1412
Tel.: (787) 622-6555
Public Relations
N.A.I.C.S.: 541820

Branch (Non-US):

Burson-Marsteller (4)
Oestergade 26B, DK-1100, Copenhagen, K, Denmark
Tel.: (45) 33327878

WPP PLC — INTERNATIONAL PUBLIC

WPP plc—(Continued)
Sales Range: $10-24.9 Million
Emp.: 20
Advertising Agencies
N.A.I.C.S.: 541810

Burson-Marsteller (4)
6 rue Escudier, CEDEX, 92772, Boulogne-Billancourt, France
Tel.: (33) 141867676
Emp.: 50
Public Relations
N.A.I.C.S.: 541820
Philippe Pailliart *(Chm)*

Burson-Marsteller (4)
Kojimachi Diamond Building 5th Floor 1 Kojimachi 4-chome, Chiyoda-ku, Tokyo, 102-0083, Japan
Tel.: (81) 332646701
Web Site: http://www.b-m.co.jp
Advertising Agencies
N.A.I.C.S.: 541810

Subsidiary (Non-US):

Burson-Marsteller (Hong Kong) Limited (4)
12F K11 ATELIER Kings Road 728 Kings Road, Quarry Bay, China (Hong Kong)
Tel.: (852) 28800229
Public Relations
N.A.I.C.S.: 541820
Matt Stafford *(Pres-Asia Pacific)*

Burson-Marsteller (SEA) Pte. Ltd. (4)
50 Scotts Road 01-01, Singapore, 228242, Singapore
Tel.: (65) 63366266
Advanced Marketing Solutions & Advertising Services
N.A.I.C.S.: 541810

Branch (Domestic):

Burson-Marsteller - Chicago (4)
333 N Green St 17th Fl, Chicago, IL 60607
Tel.: (312) 596-3400
Web Site: http://www.bcw-global.com
Public Relations Agency
N.A.I.C.S.: 541820
David M. Coronna *(Exec VP & Mng Dir)*

Burson-Marsteller - Washington (4)
1801 K St 9th Fl, Washington, DC 20036
Tel.: (202) 530-0400
Web Site: http://www.bcw-global.com
Public Relations
N.A.I.C.S.: 541810
Michael Fleischer *(Pres & Exec VP)*

Subsidiary (Non-US):

Burson-Marsteller A/S (4)
Kongens Gate 6, 0278, Oslo, Norway
Tel.: (47) 23164500
Web Site: http://www.bcw-global.com
Public Relations
N.A.I.C.S.: 541820
Kristian Sarastuen *(CEO)*

Burson-Marsteller AB (4)
Master Samuelsgatan 56 6th floor, 10120, Stockholm, Sweden
Tel.: (46) 84401200
Web Site: http://www.burson-marsteller.se
Emp.: 15
Advertising Agencies
N.A.I.C.S.: 541810
Anders Bylund *(Chm & Head-Crisis Practice-Europe)*

Burson-Marsteller GmbH (4)
Darmstadter Landstrasse 112, 60598, Frankfurt am Main, Germany
Tel.: (49) 692380942
Public Relations
N.A.I.C.S.: 541820

Branch (Domestic):

Burson-Marsteller GmbH - Berlin (5)
Lennestrasse 1, D-10785, Berlin, Germany
Tel.: (30) 30408194550
Web Site: http://www.burson-marsteller.de
Advetising Agency
N.A.I.C.S.: 541810

Branch (Domestic):

Burson-Marsteller LLC (4)
206 East 9th St Ste 1650, Austin, TX 78701
Tel.: (512) 472-4122
Web Site: http://www.bcw-global.com
Public Relations Services
N.A.I.C.S.: 541820
Callie Jernigan *(Exec VP)*

Subsidiary (Non-US):

Burson-Marsteller Ltd. (4)
Lynton House 7-12 Tavistock Square, London, WC1H 9LT, United Kingdom
Tel.: (44) 2073315300
Web Site: http://www.bcw-global.com
Advertising Services
N.A.I.C.S.: 541810
Rebecca Grant *(CEO-UK)*

Burson-Marsteller Mexico, S.A. de C.V. (4)
Edificio Punto Polanco Lago Alberto 319, Piso 16 Colonia Granada Miguel Hidalgo, 11520, Mexico, DF, Mexico
Tel.: (52) 5553516500
Advertising Services
N.A.I.C.S.: 541810

Burson-Marsteller Pty. Ltd. (4)
Lev 4 30 Hickson Rd, Millers Point, Sydney, 2000, NSW, Australia
Tel.: (61) 299281500
Advanced Marketing Solutions & Advertising Services
N.A.I.C.S.: 541810
Pamela Klioufis *(CEO & Mng Dir)*

Branch (Domestic):

Burson-Marsteller Pty. Ltd. - Melbourne (5)
Level 25 2 Southbank Boulevard, Southbank, Melbourne, 3006, VIC, Australia
Tel.: (61) 394261300
Web Site: http://www.bcw-global.com
Advertising & Marketing Services
N.A.I.C.S.: 541810
Pamela Klioufis *(Mng Dir)*

Subsidiary (Non-US):

Burson-Marsteller S.A./N.V. (4)
37 Square de Meeus, 1000, Brussels, Belgium
Tel.: (32) 27436611
Public Relations & Marketing Consulting Agency
N.A.I.C.S.: 541820
Andrew Cecil *(CEO)*

Burson-Marsteller S.r.l. (4)
Via Morimondo 26, 20143, Milan, Italy
Tel.: (39) 02721431
Emp.: 50
Advertising Agencies
N.A.I.C.S.: 541810
Fabio Caporizzi *(Mng Dir)*

Branch (Domestic):

Burson-Marsteller S.r.l. (5)
Via Gregoriana 54, 00187, Rome, Italy
Tel.: (39) 066889631
Emp.: 12
Advertising Agencies
N.A.I.C.S.: 541810

Division (Domestic):

Marsteller (5)
Via Tortona 37, 20144, Milan, Italy
Tel.: (39) 0272143577
Emp.: 60
Public Relations
N.A.I.C.S.: 541820

Subsidiary (Non-US):

Burson-Marsteller, Ltda. (4)
Rua Fidencio Ramos 308 Torre A 11o andar, CJ 113/114 Vila Olimpia, Sao Paulo, 04551-010, SP, Brazil
Tel.: (55) 1130942240
Web Site: http://www.bcw-global.com
Advance Marketing Solutions & Other Advertising Services
N.A.I.C.S.: 541810
Elaine Rodrigues *(Sr VP)*

Burson-Marsteller, S.A. (4)
La Matriz c/ Rios Rosas 26, 28003, Madrid, Spain
Tel.: (34) 913846700
Emp.: 35
Public Relations
N.A.I.C.S.: 541820

Burson-Marsteller, S.A. (4)
Santalo 10, 08029, Barcelona, Spain
Tel.: (34) 932011028
Web Site: http://www.bursonmarsteller.es
Emp.: 13
Public Relations
N.A.I.C.S.: 541820

Communique PR (4)
24-28 Bloomsbury Way, London, WC1A 2PX, United Kingdom
Tel.: (44) 2073006300
Web Site: http://www.communiquepr.co.uk
Sales Range: Less than $1 Million
Emp.: 8
Public Relations
N.A.I.C.S.: 541820
Colleen Moffitt *(Partner)*

Compass Public Relations (4)
10-C/Fl 167 Tun-Hwa North Road, Taipei, 105, Taiwan
Tel.: (886) 225466086
Emp.: 30
Public Relations
N.A.I.C.S.: 541820
Pauline Leung *(Chm)*

Donath Burson-Marsteller s.r.o. (4)
Chynska 12, 160 00, Prague, 6, Czech Republic
Tel.: (420) 602222128
Web Site: https://www.dbm.cz
Emp.: 9
Public Relations
N.A.I.C.S.: 541820
Michal Donath *(Mng Dir)*

Genesis Burson-Marsteller (4)
Level 7 Tower-B DLF Cyber Park Phase III Udyog Vihar Sector 20, Gurgaon, 122 016, Haryana, India
Tel.: (91) 1244417500
Emp.: 200
Public Relations
N.A.I.C.S.: 541820
Prema Sagar *(Founder & Chm)*

Branch (Domestic):

Genesis Burson-Marsteller (5)
No 7 Eden Gardens Road No 10 Opposite Taj Krishna, Banjara Hills, Hyderabad, 500 034, India
Tel.: (91) 40 6682 8123
Web Site: http://www.genesisbm.in
Emp.: 5
Public Relations
N.A.I.C.S.: 541820

Genesis Burson-Marsteller (5)
Flat No 5G Everest Building 46C, Chowringhee Road, Kolkata, 700 071, India
Tel.: (91) 33 2288 2399
Public Relations
N.A.I.C.S.: 541820

Genesis Public Relations Pvt Ltd (5)
36 Crown Pt Lavelle Rd, Bengaluru, 560 001, India
Tel.: (91) 80 2558 9122 3 4
Public Relations
N.A.I.C.S.: 541820

Genesis Public Relations Pvt Ltd (5)
Elegant House Raguvanshi Mill Compound, SB Marg Lower Parel, Mumbai, 400 013, India
Tel.: (91) 22 249 61593
Public Relations
N.A.I.C.S.: 541820

Subsidiary (Non-US):

Heneghan PR (4)
54 Pembroke Road, Dublin, 4, Ireland
Tel.: (353) 16607395
Web Site: https://heneghan.ie
Emp.: 13
Public Relations
N.A.I.C.S.: 541820
Nigel Heneghan *(Mng Dir)*

Unit (Domestic):

Marsteller Advertising (4)
444 Liberty Ave Ste 310, Pittsburgh, PA 15222-1433
Tel.: (412) 471-9600
Advertising Agencies
N.A.I.C.S.: 541810
Thomas Dowling *(Mng Dir)*

Prime Policy Group (4)
1110 Vermont Ave NW Ste 1200, Washington, DC 20005-3554
Tel.: (202) 530-0500
Emp.: 30
Advertising Agencies
N.A.I.C.S.: 541810
Rich Meade *(Co-Chm)*

Subsidiary (Non-US):

Prime Policy Group (4)
37 Square de Meeus, 1000, Brussels, Belgium
Tel.: (32) 27436611
Public Relations
N.A.I.C.S.: 541820

TSE Consulting SA (4)
Rue du Petit-Chene 38, 1001, Lausanne, Switzerland
Tel.: (41) 213132300
Web Site: http://www.tseconsulting.com
International Management Consulting Services
N.A.I.C.S.: 541611

Subsidiary (Non-US):

TSE Consulting Turkiye (5)
Olimpiyatevi 4 Kisim Sonu, 34158, Istanbul, Turkiye
Tel.: (90) 212 560 46 56
Web Site: http://www.tseconsulting.com
General Management Consulting Services
N.A.I.C.S.: 541611

Subsidiary (US):

TSE North America (5)
201 S Capitol Ste 555, Indianapolis, IN 46225
Tel.: (317) 714-3667
Web Site: http://www.tseconsulting.com
General Management Consulting Services
N.A.I.C.S.: 541611

Subsidiary (Non-US):

TSE Scandinavia (5)
Kronprinsessegade 54, 1306, Copenhagen, K, Denmark
Tel.: (45) 38343511
Web Site: http://www.tseconsulting.com
General Management Consulting Services
N.A.I.C.S.: 541611

Unit (Domestic):

The Direct Impact Company (4)
99 Canal Center Plz Ste 450, Alexandria, VA 22314-1588
Tel.: (703) 684-1245
Web Site: http://www.directimpact.com
Emp.: 50
Advertising Agencies
N.A.I.C.S.: 541810
Amy Cloessner *(Exec VP)*

Subsidiary (Non-US):

The Willard Group (4)
26 Presnensky Val Str, 123557, Moscow, Russia
Tel.: (7) 4957754795
Emp.: 20
Public Relations
N.A.I.C.S.: 541820

The Willard Group Advertising (4)
3/4 Malozemelnaya, Kiev, 02132, Ukraine
Tel.: (380) 044 353 1518
Emp.: 60
Public Relations
N.A.I.C.S.: 541820
Michael Willard *(Chm)*

Subsidiary (Domestic):

Cohn & Wolfe (3)
200 Fifth Ave, New York, NY 10010
Tel.: (212) 798-9700

AND PRIVATE COMPANIES — WPP PLC

Communications & Public Relations Services
N.A.I.C.S.: 541820

Branch (Non-US):

AxiCom Cohn & Wolfe (4)
AxiCom Court 67 Barnes High Street, London, SW13 9LE, United Kingdom
Tel.: (44) 20 8392 4050
Web Site: http://www.axicom.com
Rev.: $14,973,700
Emp.: 40
Public Relations Services
N.A.I.C.S.: 541820
Kate Stevens (Pres-Europe)

Branch (Non-US):

AxiCom (5)
37 rue de Bellefond, 75 009, Paris, France
Tel.: (33) 1 41 06 18 25
Web Site: http://www.axicom.com
Sales Range: $25-49.9 Million
Emp.: 6
Public Relations Services
N.A.I.C.S.: 541820
Francois Gobillot (Mgr)

AxiCom (5)
Lilienthalstr 5, Puchheim, 82178, Germany
Tel.: (49) 89 800 908 11
Web Site: http://www.axicom.com
Sales Range: $10-24.9 Million
Emp.: 15
Public Relations Services
N.A.I.C.S.: 541820
Martina Brembeck (Founder & Country Mgr)

AxiCom (5)
Herengracht 138-140, 1015 BW, Amsterdam, Netherlands
Tel.: (31) 31206264092
Web Site: http://www.axicom.com
Sales Range: $25-49.9 Million
Emp.: 4
Public Relations Services
N.A.I.C.S.: 541820

AxiCom (5)
Drottninggatan 94, Stockholm, 11183, Sweden
Tel.: (46) 854513150
Web Site: http://www.axicom.com
Sales Range: $25-49.9 Million
Emp.: 5
Public Relations Services
N.A.I.C.S.: 541820
Mattias Kallman (Mgr-Sweden)

AxiCom Srl (5)
Via M Melloni 34, 20129, Milan, Italy
Tel.: (39) 02 752611 21
Web Site: http://www.axicom.com
Sales Range: $25-49.9 Million
Emp.: 5
Public Relations Services
N.A.I.C.S.: 541820
Chiara Possenti (Mng Dir)

Branch (Non-US):

Blackie McDonald - Melbourne (4)
Level 8 65 Berry St, Sydney, 2060, NSW, Australia
Tel.: (61) 2 8907 4900
Web Site: http://www.bmcd.com.au
Sales Range: $25-49.9 Million
Emp.: 25
Public Relations Services
N.A.I.C.S.: 541820

Cohn & Wolfe (4)
Speitherstrasse 59, Torhaus Westhafen, 60327, Frankfurt, Germany
Tel.: (49) 69 7506 1510
Sales Range: $25-49.9 Million
Emp.: 15
Public Relations Services
N.A.I.C.S.: 541820

Cohn & Wolfe (4)
25 Rue Eugene Marziano Building 43 Acacias, Geneva, 1227, Switzerland
Tel.: (41) 22 908 40 70
Sales Range: $25-49.9 Million
Emp.: 10
Public Relations Services
N.A.I.C.S.: 541820

Cohn & Wolfe (4)
C/ Fuencarral 6, 28006, Madrid, Spain
Tel.: (34) 91 531 42 67
Sales Range: $25-49.9 Million
Emp.: 15
Public Relations Services
N.A.I.C.S.: 541820

Branch (Domestic):

Cohn & Wolfe (4)
233 N Michigan Ave 16th Fl Two Illinois Ctr, Chicago, IL 60610
Tel.: (312) 596-3330
Public Relations Services
N.A.I.C.S.: 541820

Branch (Non-US):

Cohn & Wolfe (4)
via Benedetto Marcello 63, 20124, Milan, Italy
Tel.: (39) 02 202 391
Sales Range: $10-24.9 Million
Emp.: 30
Public Relations Services
N.A.I.C.S.: 541820

Cohn & Wolfe (4)
294 Syngrou Avenue, Kalithea, 17673, Athens, Greece
Tel.: (30) 2 1 0957 8000
Web Site: http://www.wolfe.com
Sales Range: $10-24.9 Million
Emp.: 35
Public Relations Services
N.A.I.C.S.: 541820

Branch (Domestic):

Cohn & Wolfe (4)
8730 W Sunset Blvd 5th Fl, Los Angeles, CA 90069-2210
Tel.: (310) 967-2900
Sales Range: $10-24.9 Million
Emp.: 26
Public Relations Services
N.A.I.C.S.: 541820

Cohn & Wolfe (4)
1001 Front St, San Francisco, CA 94111-1424
Tel.: (415) 365-8520
Public Relations Services
N.A.I.C.S.: 541820

Branch (Non-US):

Cohn & Wolfe Benelux (4)
Dan Zigerkade 53, Amsterdam, 1013 AP, Netherlands
Tel.: (31) 206768666
Web Site: http://www.cohnwolfe.nl
Sales Range: $25-49.9 Million
Emp.: 9
Public Relations Services
N.A.I.C.S.: 541820

Cohn & Wolfe Limited (4)
7-12 Tavistock Square Lynton House, London, WC1H 9LT, United Kingdom
Tel.: (44) 207 331 5300
Public Relations Services
N.A.I.C.S.: 541820
Rebecca Grant (Mng Dir & Head-Consumer Mktg-EMEA)

Branch (Domestic):

Cohn & Wolfe Read-Poland (4)
206 E 9th St Ste 1650, Austin, TX 78701-3656
Tel.: (512) 472-4122
Sales Range: $25-49.9 Million
Emp.: 20
Communications & Public Relations Services
N.A.I.C.S.: 541810
Brooke Hovey (Head-Digital)

Branch (Non-US):

Consultores del Plata S.A. (4)
1731 SantaFe Avenue, 1060, Buenos Aires, Capital Federal, Argentina
Tel.: (54) 11 43 27 76 00
Web Site: http://www.cdelplata.com
Rev.: $500,000
Emp.: 20
Public Relations Services
N.A.I.C.S.: 541820

Grey Group Budapest (4)
Nagymezo Utca 44, 1065, Budapest, Hungary
Tel.: (36) 1 214 6750
Sales Range: $25-49.9 Million
Emp.: 3
Public Relations Services
N.A.I.C.S.: 541820

Grey Two PR (4)
15th Fl Wisma Genting, Jalan Sultan Ismail, Kuala Lumpur, 50250, Malaysia
Tel.: (60) 3 2178 0060
Web Site: http://www.grey.com
Sales Range: $25-49.9 Million
Emp.: 25
Public Relations Services
N.A.I.C.S.: 541820
Irene Wong (CEO)

Grey Worldwide Warsaw (4)
Ul Jasna 24, 00-054, Warsaw, Poland
Tel.: (48) 22 332 93 00
Web Site: http://www.grey.pl
Public Relations Services
N.A.I.C.S.: 541820
Adam Smilowski (Chief Growth Officer)

Hering Schuppener Consulting (4)
Berliner Allee 44, Dusseldorf, 40212, Germany
Tel.: (49) 211 430 79 0
Web Site: http://www.heringschuppener.com
Sales Range: $50-74.9 Million
Emp.: 65
Public Relations Services
N.A.I.C.S.: 541820
Tina Mentner (Mng Partner)

Hering Schuppener-Frankfort AmMain (4)
Mainzer Land Street 41, 60329, Frankfurt, AmMain, Germany
Tel.: (49) 69 921 874 0
Web Site: http://www.heringschuppener.com
Sales Range: $10-24.9 Million
Emp.: 50
Public Relations Services
N.A.I.C.S.: 541820

Media In PR (4)
Revova 7, Bratislava, 81102, Slovakia
Tel.: (421) 2 32 15 12 21
Web Site: http://www.cohnwolfe.sk
Sales Range: $25-49.9 Million
Emp.: 9
Public Relations Services
N.A.I.C.S.: 541820

Subsidiary (Domestic):

Hirzu, Inc. (3)
10101 Molecular Dr Ste 300, Rockville, MD 20850
Tel.: (301) 294-6302
Web Site: https://www.hzdg.com
Advertising Services
N.A.I.C.S.: 541810
Glenn Watts (CIO)

Subsidiary (Domestic):

DeepLocal, Inc. (2)
1601 Marys Ave Ste 3G, Pittsburgh, PA 15215
Tel.: (412) 362-0201
Web Site: https://www.deeplocal.com
Emp.: 54
Digital Marketing & Engineering Services
N.A.I.C.S.: 541890
Zach Olshenske (VP-Engrg)

Dewey Square Group (2)
100 Cambridge St Ste 1301, Boston, MA 02114
Tel.: (617) 367-9929
Web Site: http://www.deweysquare.com
Public Affairs Services
N.A.I.C.S.: 541820
Joseph A. Ricca (Principal-Boston)

Fabric Worldwide (2)
1218 3rd Ave Ste 600, Seattle, WA 98101
Tel.: (206) 224-4588
Web Site: http://www.fabricww.com
Sales Range: $25-49.9 Million
Emp.: 15
Fabric Shop & Stationery Product Distr
N.A.I.C.S.: 459130

GCI Health (2)
3 World Trade Ctr 175 Greenwich St, New York, NY 10007
Tel.: (212) 798-9950
Web Site: http://www.gcihealth.com
Health Care Srvices
N.A.I.C.S.: 621999
David Chadwick (Chief Content Officer)

GTB Agency, LLC (2)
550 Town Center Dr, Dearborn, MI 48126
Tel.: (313) 615-2000
Web Site: https://www.gtb.com
Advertising Agencies
N.A.I.C.S.: 541810
Robert Guay (CEO-Global)

Subsidiary (Domestic):

Zubi Advertising Services, Inc. (3)
2990 Ponce de Leon Blvd Ste 600, Coral Gables, FL 33134-5006
Tel.: (305) 448-9824
Web Site: http://www.zubiad.com
Emp.: 130
Advetising Agency
N.A.I.C.S.: 541810
Tere A. Zubizarreta (Founder)

Subsidiary (Domestic):

Grey Group (2)
200 5th Ave, New York, NY 10010
Tel.: (212) 546-2020
Web Site: https://www.grey.com
Sales Range: $1-4.9 Billion
Emp.: 10,500
Advertising Services
N.A.I.C.S.: 541810
Arun Raman (Natl Dir-Plng-India)

Subsidiary (Non-US):

Adler, Chomski Grey (3)
98 Tigal Alon Street, Tel Aviv, 67891, Israel
Tel.: (972) 36088888
Sales Range: $50-74.9 Million
Emp.: 300
Advertising Services
N.A.I.C.S.: 541810
Rami Yehudiha (Mng Dir)

Advize Grey (3)
PO Box 841041, Amman, 841041, Jordan
Tel.: (962) 6 462 2212
Sales Range: $10-24.9 Million
Emp.: 28
Advertising Services
N.A.I.C.S.: 541810

Subsidiary (Domestic):

ArcTouch LLC (3)
360 3rd St, San Francisco, CA 94107-1836
Tel.: (415) 944-2000
Web Site: https://www.arctouch.com
Emp.: 250
Customer Experience & Marketing Application Platform Developer
N.A.I.C.S.: 541511
Eric Shapiro (Co-Founder & CEO)

Subsidiary (Non-US):

Batey Group (3)
1 Magazine Road 03 07 Central Mall, Singapore, 59567, Singapore
Tel.: (65) 6511 7600
Web Site: http://www.batey.com.sg
Emp.: 100
Advertising Services
N.A.I.C.S.: 541810
Subbaraju Alluri (CEO-Grey Grp-Singapore)

Blu Grey (3)
Qurtoba Ste 5, PO Box 3054, Safat, Kuwait, 13031, Kuwait
Tel.: (965) 2535 8724
Web Site: http://www.blu-grey.com
Sales Range: $10-24.9 Million
Emp.: 18
Advertising Services
N.A.I.C.S.: 541810

Campaigns & Grey (3)
8th Floor BDO Equitable Tower, 8747 Paseo de Roxas, Makati, 1226, Philippines
Tel.: (63) 288847300
Web Site: http://www.grey.com
Advertising Services
N.A.I.C.S.: 541890

WPP PLC

INTERNATIONAL PUBLIC

WPP plc—(Continued)

Contact Advertising (3)
Medcon Tower 46 Them Dervis St 5th Fl,
PO Box 24000, 1687, Nicosia, Cyprus
Tel.: (357) 22 452 045
Sales Range: $25-49.9 Million
Emp.: 12
Advertising Services
N.A.I.C.S.: 541810
Mikis Chrisodoulou (Mng Dir)

Unit (Domestic):

Ericsson Fina (3)
570 Lexington Ave, New York, NY 10022
Tel.: (212) 546-1600
Web Site: http://www.ericssonfina.com
Sales Range: $10-24.9 Million
Emp.: 12
Healthcare Advertising Services
N.A.I.C.S.: 541810

Subsidiary (Domestic):

G2 Interactive (3)
200 5th Ave, New York, NY 10010
Tel.: (212) 537-3700
Web Site: http://www.g2.com
Sales Range: $25-49.9 Million
Emp.: 105
Advertising Services
N.A.I.C.S.: 541810

Branch (Domestic):

G2 Interactive (4)
1140 Welsh Rd Ste 110, North Wales, PA 19454
Tel.: (215) 647-9200
Advertising Services
N.A.I.C.S.: 541810

Branch (Non-US):

Grey Interactive Argentina AR (4)
Ramirez de Velasco 845, C1414, Buenos Aires, Argentina
Tel.: (54) 1155551800
Sales Range: $10-24.9 Million
Emp.: 15
Advertising Services
N.A.I.C.S.: 541810

Grey Interactive India (4)
Grey House 280 Dr E Borges Road Parel, Mumbai, 400 012, India
Tel.: (91) 22 4036 6363
Web Site: http://www.grey.com
Emp.: 200
Advertising Services
N.A.I.C.S.: 541810

Grey Interactive Italy (4)
Via Cirillo,6, 20154, Milan, Italy
Tel.: (39) 02 3616 7650
Sales Range: $10-24.9 Million
Emp.: 10
Advertising Services
N.A.I.C.S.: 541810

Grey Interactive Portugal (4)
Rue do Alecrem 73, 1200-015, Lisbon, Portugal
Tel.: (351) 214 111 000
Web Site: http://www.grey.pt
Sales Range: $10-24.9 Million
Emp.: 35
Advertising Services
N.A.I.C.S.: 541810

Grey Interactive-Hong Kong (4)
31 Convoy 169 Electric Rd North Point, Hong Kong, China (Hong Kong)
Tel.: (852) 2510 6888
Web Site: http://www.grey.com
Advertising Services
N.A.I.C.S.: 541810
Owen Smith (Head-Strategy)

Grey Interactive/Toronto (4)
1881 Yonge Street Ste 800, Toronto, M4S 3C4, ON, Canada
Tel.: (416) 486-0700
Web Site: http://www.grey.com
Sales Range: $10-24.9 Million
Emp.: 57
Advertising Services
N.A.I.C.S.: 541810

Subsidiary (Non-US):

GForce (3)
Abdullinikh St 31, 050010, Almaty, Kazakhstan
Tel.: (7) 3272 501 011
Sales Range: $10-24.9 Million
Emp.: 38
Advertising Services
N.A.I.C.S.: 541810

Subsidiary (Domestic):

GHG GreyHealth Group LLC (3)
200 5th Ave, New York, NY 10010-5604
Tel.: (212) 886-3000
Sales Range: $100-124.9 Million
Emp.: 300
Advertising Services
N.A.I.C.S.: 541810

Branch (Domestic):

GHG GreyHealth Group LLC - Kansas City (4)
1656 Washington Ste 300, Kansas City, MO 64108
Tel.: (816) 842-8656
Sales Range: $10-24.9 Million
Emp.: 48
Advertising Services
N.A.I.C.S.: 541810
Bryan Archambault (VP-Acct Svcs)

Branch (Non-US):

Grey Healthcare (4)
19th Floor Devon House, Taikoo Place 979 Kings Road, Quarry Bay, 200041, China (Hong Kong)
Tel.: (852) 212 886 3217
Healthcare Advertising Services
N.A.I.C.S.: 541810

Grey Healthcare (4)
Maynds Tower 7F 2-1-1 Yoyogi, Shibuya-ku, Tokyo, 151-0053, Japan
Tel.: (81) 3 5423 7800
Healthcare Advertising Services
N.A.I.C.S.: 541810

Grey Healthcare Paris (4)
63 bis rue de Sevres, 92100, Boulogne-Billancourt, France
Tel.: (33) 1 46 84 85 72
Sales Range: $10-24.9 Million
Emp.: 12
Advertising Services
N.A.I.C.S.: 541810

Unit (Domestic):

OnCall (4)
8044 Montgomery Rd Ste 700, Cincinnati, OH 45236-2941
Tel.: (513) 381-4320
Web Site: https://www.oncall-llc.com
Sales Range: $50-74.9 Million
Emp.: 200
Advertising Services
N.A.I.C.S.: 541611
Michelle Parker (Dir-Client Fin)

Phase Five Communications (4)
466 Lexington Ave, New York, NY 10017
Tel.: (212) 210-7000
Web Site: https://www.phase-five.com
Sales Range: $10-24.9 Million
Emp.: 80
Public Relations Services
N.A.I.C.S.: 541820

Subsidiary (Non-US):

Grey (3)
In the Zeisehof Friedensallee 11, 22765, Frankfurt, Germany
Tel.: (49) 40210913214
Sales Range: $25-49.9 Million
Emp.: 20
Advertising Services
N.A.I.C.S.: 541810

Grey (India) Pvt. Ltd. (3)
Bay99 2nd Floor The ORB - Wing A Next to J W Marriott Hotel, Village Marol Andheri East, Mumbai, 400099, India
Tel.: (91) 2250466601
Sales Range: $50-74.9 Million
Emp.: 290
Advertising Services
N.A.I.C.S.: 541810
Ketan Desai (Grp COO)

Grey (India) Pvt. Ltd. (Ahmedabad) (3)
M-1 Suryarath Bldg Opp White House Panchwati Ellis Bridge, Ahmedabad, 380 006, India
Tel.: (91) 79 2642 4561
Web Site: http://www.greyindia.com
Sales Range: Less than $1 Million
Emp.: 20
Advertising Services
N.A.I.C.S.: 541810

Grey (India) Pvt. Ltd. (Calcutta) (3)
Bay99 2nd Floor The ORB-Wing A Next to J W Marriott Hotel, Village Marol Andheri East, Mumbai, 400099, India
Tel.: (91) 3322271900
Advertising Services
N.A.I.C.S.: 541810

Grey (India) Pvt. Pty. Ltd. (Delhi) (3)
Sheldon 3rdFloor Plot 91 Sector 44, Opp 32nd Milestone, Gurgaon, 122 003, India
Tel.: (91) 124 497 3200
Web Site: http://www.greyindia.com
Sales Range: Less than $1 Million
Advertising Services
N.A.I.C.S.: 541810
Ketan Desai (Pres & COO)

Grey Amsterdam (3)
Amsteldijk 166, 1079 LH, Amsterdam, Netherlands
Tel.: (31) 205775111
Advertising Services
N.A.I.C.S.: 541810

Grey Argentina (3)
Ramirez de Velasco 845, C1414AQQ, Buenos Aires, Argentina
Tel.: (54) 1155551800
Sales Range: $10-24.9 Million
Advertising Services
N.A.I.C.S.: 541810
Diego Medvedocky (Pres & Chief Creative Officer-Latam)

Branch (Domestic):

Grey Atlanta (3)
191 Peachtree St NE Ste 4025, Atlanta, GA 30309
Tel.: (404) 261-2360
Web Site: http://www.grey.com
Sales Range: $10-24.9 Million
Emp.: 22
Advertising Services
N.A.I.C.S.: 541810

Subsidiary (Non-US):

Grey Bangladesh Ltd. (3)
Floor 5 House 6 Road 137 Block SE D, Gulshan 1, Dhaka, 1212, Bangladesh
Tel.: (880) 255044825
Sales Range: $25-49.9 Million
Emp.: 21
Advertising Services
N.A.I.C.S.: 541810
Gousul Alam Shaon (Mng Partner & Head-Country)

Grey Beijing (3)
607 Tower W3 Oriental Plaza 1 East Chang An Avenue, Dong Cheng District, Beijing, 100 738, China
Tel.: (86) 1085181988
Web Site: http://www.grey.com
Sales Range: $25-49.9 Million
Emp.: 84
Advertising Services
N.A.I.C.S.: 541810
Hongbin Zhang (Dir-Fin)

Grey Canada (3)
46 Spadina Ave Suite 500, Toronto, M5V 2H8, ON, Canada
Tel.: (416) 486-0700
Sales Range: $10-24.9 Million
Emp.: 70
Advertising Services
N.A.I.C.S.: 541810
Nicole Lupke (Co-Mng Dir & Sr VP)

Branch (Domestic):

Grey Vancouver (4)
1600 - 1500 W Georgia St, Vancouver, V6G 2Z6, BC, Canada
Tel.: (604) 687-1001
Web Site: http://www.greyvancouver.com
Advertising Services
N.A.I.C.S.: 541810

Subsidiary (Non-US):

Grey Chile (3)
Eleodoro Yanez 2376, Providencia Las Condes, 7510451, Santiago, Chile
Tel.: (56) 25849900
Web Site: http://www.grey.cl
Sales Range: $10-24.9 Million
Emp.: 75
Advertising Services
N.A.I.C.S.: 541810
Daniel Perez Pallares (Pres & Chm-Creative)

Grey Direct Argentina (3)
Ramirez de Velasco 845, C1414AQQ, Buenos Aires, Argentina
Tel.: (54) 1155551800
Advertising Services
N.A.I.C.S.: 541810
Pablo Sanchez Rubio (CEO)

Grey Direct Greece (3)
280 Kifissias Av Chalandri, PO Box 176 73, 15232, Athens, Greece
Tel.: (30) 2130117700
Sales Range: $25-49.9 Million
Emp.: 30
Advertising Services
N.A.I.C.S.: 541860

Grey Direct Singapore (3)
50 Scotts Road 03-01, Singapore, 228242, Singapore
Tel.: (65) 65117600
Advertising Services
N.A.I.C.S.: 541810

Grey First Serve Advertising (3)
NO11 Keppetipola Mawatha, Colombo, 5, Sri Lanka
Tel.: (94) 11 255 3352
Sales Range: $10-24.9 Million
Emp.: 28
Advertising Services
N.A.I.C.S.: 541810

Grey Group Asia Pacific (3)
No 1 Magazine Road #03-07 Central Mall, Singapore, 059567, Singapore
Tel.: (65) 65117600
Web Site: http://www.grey.com
Advertising Services
N.A.I.C.S.: 541810
Nirvik Singh (Chm/CEO-Asia Pacific, Middle East & Africa & COO-Global)

Grey Group Belgium (3)
Sq Victoria Regina 1 Saint-Josse-ten-Noode, 1210, Brussels, Belgium
Tel.: (32) 24113545
Sales Range: $10-24.9 Million
Emp.: 6
Advertising Services
N.A.I.C.S.: 541810
Peter Ampe (Exec Creative Dir)

Grey Group Bulgaria (3)
14 Yanko Sakazov Blvd, Sofia, 1504, Bulgaria
Tel.: (359) 2 401 5070
Advertising Services
N.A.I.C.S.: 541810

Grey Group Croatia (3)
Nova Ves 17, 10000, Zagreb, Croatia
Tel.: (385) 16064000
Sales Range: $25-49.9 Million
Emp.: 24
Advertising Services
N.A.I.C.S.: 541810

Grey Group Denmark (3)
Ny Ostergade 14-20, 1101, Copenhagen, Denmark
Tel.: (45) 33300100
Sales Range: $25-49.9 Million
Emp.: 2
Advertising Services
N.A.I.C.S.: 541810

Grey Group Germany (3)
Platz der Ideen 1, PO Box 101051, 40476, Dusseldorf, Germany
Tel.: (49) 21138070
Web Site: http://www.grey.de

AND PRIVATE COMPANIES — WPP PLC

Sales Range: $50-74.9 Million
Emp.: 500
Advertising Services
N.A.I.C.S.: 541810
Jan-Philipp Jahn *(CEO)*

Branch (Domestic):

Market Horizons (4)
Corneilustr 12236, 40215, Dusseldorf, Germany
Tel.: (49) 211 380 7243
Sales Range: $50-74.9 Million
Emp.: 10
Advertising Services
N.A.I.C.S.: 541810

Subsidiary (Non-US):

Grey Group Greece (3)
280 Kifissias Av, Chalandri, 15232, Athens, Greece
Tel.: (30) 2130117700
Sales Range: $10-24.9 Million
Emp.: 40
Advertising Services
N.A.I.C.S.: 541810
Nadine Lianou *(Dir-Acct-PR)*

Grey Group Hungary (3)
Andrassy ut 9 6th District, PO Box 1538, Budapest, 466, Hungary
Tel.: (36) 12146750
Web Site: http://www.geometry.com
Sales Range: $10-24.9 Million
Emp.: 75
Advertising Services
N.A.I.C.S.: 541810

Grey Group Indonesia (3)
5th Fl Tetra Pak Building, Jl Buncit Raya Kav 100, Jakarta, 12510, Indonesia
Tel.: (62) 2179192129
Web Site: http://www.grey.com
Sales Range: $25-49.9 Million
Emp.: 120
Advertising Services
N.A.I.C.S.: 541810
Subbaraju Alluri *(CEO)*

Grey Group Japan (3)
Hiroo MTR Building B1F 2-36-13 Ebisu, Shibuya-ku, Tokyo, 150-0013, Japan
Tel.: (81) 354231711
Rev.: $81,101
Emp.: 120
Advertising Services
N.A.I.C.S.: 541810
Yukiko Ochiai *(Pres & CEO)*

Grey Group Korea (3)
3-5F ICON Building 12 Eonju-ro 152-gil, Gangnam-gu, Seoul, 06021, Korea (South)
Tel.: (82) 230155800
Sales Range: $10-24.9 Million
Emp.: 100
Advertising Services
N.A.I.C.S.: 541810
Jinwan Oh *(CEO)*

Grey Group Latvia (3)
Antonijas 9, LV 1010, Riga, Latvia
Tel.: (371) 3 89 2 3 29 88 20
Web Site: http://www.grey.com
Sales Range: $25-49.9 Million
Emp.: 12
Advertising Services
N.A.I.C.S.: 541810

Grey Group Luxembourg (3)
Rue de la Gare 19, Grand Duchy of Luxembourg, L-3237, Bettembourg, Luxembourg
Tel.: (352) 2651 771
Sales Range: $25-49.9 Million
Emp.: 5
Advertising Services
N.A.I.C.S.: 541810

Grey Group Macedonia (3)
Nikola Trimpare 26, 1000, Skopje, North Macedonia
Tel.: (389) 2 329 8820
Web Site: http://www.grey.com
Sales Range: $10-24.9 Million
Emp.: 43
Advertising Services
N.A.I.C.S.: 541810

Grey Group Malaysia (3)
14th Floor Wisma Genting, Jalan Sultan Ismail, Kuala Lumpur, 50250, Malaysia
Tel.: (60) 321780000
Web Site: http://www.grey.com
Sales Range: $25-49.9 Million
Emp.: 90
Advertising Services
N.A.I.C.S.: 541810
Alicia Tang *(Dir-HR)*

Grey Group Middle East Network (3)
Concord Tower 25th Floor Media City, PO Box 60416, Dubai, United Arab Emirates
Tel.: (971) 43310331
Sales Range: $25-49.9 Million
Emp.: 83
Advertising Services
N.A.I.C.S.: 541810
Shagorika Heryani *(Head-Strategy)*

Grey Group Poland (3)
Plac Konesera 11, 00-054, Warsaw, Poland
Tel.: (48) 222500900
Sales Range: $25-49.9 Million
Emp.: 80
Advertising Services
N.A.I.C.S.: 541810
Jakub Korolczuk *(CEO & Chm-Creative)*

Grey Group Romania (3)
Frumoasa St 39, Sector 1, Bucharest, Romania
Tel.: (40) 213106506
Sales Range: $10-24.9 Million
Emp.: 100
Advertising Services
N.A.I.C.S.: 541810

Grey Group South Africa (3)
Innesfree View 2 Harris Rd Corner Katherine St, Sandton, 2146, South Africa
Tel.: (27) 112936200
Web Site: http://www.wpp.com
Sales Range: $10-24.9 Million
Emp.: 65
Advertising Services
N.A.I.C.S.: 541810
Fran Luckin *(Chief Creative Officer)*

Grey Group Taiwan (3)
12F No 180 Nanking East Road, Section 4, Taipei, Taiwan
Tel.: (886) 225783888
Sales Range: $25-49.9 Million
Emp.: 90
Advertising Services
N.A.I.C.S.: 541810

Grey Group Ukraine (3)
4A Verhnii Val St, 04071, Kiev, Ukraine
Tel.: (380) 444990166
Sales Range: $25-49.9 Million
Advertising Services
N.A.I.C.S.: 541810

Grey Group Uzbekistan (3)
Ivlieva St 44, 100070, Tashkent, Uzbekistan
Tel.: (998) 71 361 3041
Web Site: http://www.grey.com
Sales Range: $25-49.9 Million
Emp.: 20
Advertising Services
N.A.I.C.S.: 541810

Grey Guangzhou (3)
Room 601 Dongshan Plaza 69 Xian Lie Rd Central, Guangzhou, 510095, China
Tel.: (86) 20 8732 1828
Web Site: http://www.grey.com
Sales Range: $10-24.9 Million
Emp.: 50
Advertising Services
N.A.I.C.S.: 541810

Grey Hong Kong (3)
31/F Convoy 169 Electric Rd, 979 King's Road, North Point, China (Hong Kong)
Tel.: (852) 2510 6888
Web Site: http://www.grey.com
Emp.: 100
Advertising Services
N.A.I.C.S.: 541810
Adam O'Conor *(CEO)*

Grey Istanbul (3)
Beybi Giz Plaza Dereboyu Caddesi, Meydan Sok No 28 Kat 5 Maslak, 80670, Istanbul, Turkiye
Tel.: (90) 2122902810
Web Site: http://www.grey.com.tr
Sales Range: $10-24.9 Million
Emp.: 100
Advertising Services

N.A.I.C.S.: 541810
Alemsah Ozturk *(CEO & COO)*

Grey Italia S.p.A (3)
Via Morimondo 26, 20143, Milan, Italy
Tel.: (39) 0236167500
Sales Range: $25-49.9 Million
Emp.: 82
Advertising Services
N.A.I.C.S.: 541810
Marta Di Girolamo *(CEO)*

Branch (Domestic):

Grey Italia - Rome (4)
Via Rasella 155, 00187, Rome, Italy
Tel.: (39) 06 420 3191
Web Site: http://www.grey.com
Sales Range: $10-24.9 Million
Emp.: 5
Advertising Services
N.A.I.C.S.: 541810

Subsidiary (Non-US):

Grey Ljubljana d.o.o. (3)
Bravnicarjeva ulica 13, Ljubljana, 1000, Slovenia
Tel.: (386) 1 5132 600
Web Site: http://www.grey.si
Sales Range: $25-49.9 Million
Emp.: 20
Advertising Services
N.A.I.C.S.: 541810
Petra Krulc *(Exec Creative Dir)*

Grey London (3)
The Johnson Building 77 Hatton Garden, London, EC1N 8JS, United Kingdom
Tel.: (44) 2030373000
Web Site: http://www.grey.co.uk
Sales Range: $75-99.9 Million
Emp.: 260
Advertising Services
N.A.I.C.S.: 541810
Laura Jordan Bambach *(Chief Creative Officer)*

Branch (Domestic):

Grey Los Angeles (3)
3500 W Olive Ave Ste 700, Burbank, CA 91505
Tel.: (818) 531-0800
Web Site: http://www.grey.com
Sales Range: $10-24.9 Million
Emp.: 100
Advertising Services
N.A.I.C.S.: 541810

Subsidiary (Non-US):

Grey Madrid (3)
C/ Gran Via 27, 28013, Madrid, Spain
Tel.: (34) 915555000
Sales Range: $25-49.9 Million
Emp.: 100
Advertising Services
N.A.I.C.S.: 541810

Unit (Domestic):

Grey & Trace (4)
C Santalo 10, 08021, Barcelona, Spain
Tel.: (34) 933650200
Web Site: http://www.grey.com
Advertising Services
N.A.I.C.S.: 541810
Maximo Lorenzo *(CEO)*

Grey & Trace (4)
Paseo Castellana 91 11th Floor, 28046, Madrid, Spain
Tel.: (34) 915971750
Web Site: http://www.greytrace.com
Advertising Services
N.A.I.C.S.: 541810

Branch (Domestic):

Grey Barcelona (4)
Santalo 10, Barcelona, 8021, Spain
Tel.: (34) 93 365 0200
Web Site: http://www.grey.com
Advertising Services
N.A.I.C.S.: 541810
Anna Domenech *(Dir-Bus Dev)*

Subsidiary (Non-US):

Grey Mexico, S.A. de C.V (3)
Punto Polanco Lago Alberto 319 Piso 16, Granada Miguel Hidalgo, 11520, Mexico, CDMX, Mexico
Tel.: (52) 5553503700
Sales Range: $25-49.9 Million
Emp.: 150
Advertising Services
N.A.I.C.S.: 541810
Coral Arnedo *(Gen Mgr)*

Grey Middle East Network (3)
24 Abdallah Al Kateb Street, Doki, Cairo, Egypt
Tel.: (20) 23 338 2184
Web Site: http://www.grey.com
Sales Range: $10-24.9 Million
Emp.: 35
Advertising Services
N.A.I.C.S.: 541810

Branch (Domestic):

Grey New York (3)
200 5th Ave, New York, NY 10010-3302
Tel.: (212) 546-2000
Web Site: http://www.grey.com
Sales Range: $150-199.9 Million
Emp.: 700
Advertising Services
N.A.I.C.S.: 541810
Ben Tauber *(Mng Dir)*

Subsidiary (Non-US):

Grey New Zealand Limited (3)
Level 2 1 Cross St, Newton, Auckland, 1010, New Zealand
Tel.: (64) 99144739
Web Site: http://www.bcg2.com
Sales Range: $25-49.9 Million
Emp.: 20
Advertising Services
N.A.I.C.S.: 541810

Grey Peru (3)
Lima Piso 4 Miraflores, 15074, Lima, Peru
Tel.: (51) 144212288
Advertising Services
N.A.I.C.S.: 541810

Grey Pty. Ltd. (3)
Level 2 16 Palmer Parade, Cremorne, 3121, VIC, Australia
Tel.: (61) 392081800
Web Site: http://www.grey.com.au
Sales Range: $10-24.9 Million
Emp.: 80
Advertising Services
N.A.I.C.S.: 541810

Branch (Domestic):

Grey Puerto Rico (3)
304 Ponce de Leon Ave 8th Fl Hato Rey, San Juan, PR 00918
Tel.: (787) 999-9000
Web Site: http://www.greypr.com
Sales Range: $25-49.9 Million
Emp.: 75
Advertising Services
N.A.I.C.S.: 541810
Mariana Gallardo Garcia *(Dir-Digital)*

Grey San Francisco (3)
303 2nd St Ste 300 N Tower, San Francisco, CA 94107
Tel.: (415) 403-8000
Web Site: http://www.grey.com
Sales Range: $25-49.9 Million
Emp.: 45
Advertising Services
N.A.I.C.S.: 541810

Subsidiary (Non-US):

Grey Shanghai (3)
Tel.: (86) 2123202288
Web Site: http://www.grey.com
Sales Range: $25-49.9 Million
Emp.: 120
Advertising Services
N.A.I.C.S.: 541810
Cherry Chuai *(CFO)*

Grey Singapore (3)
50 Scotts Road 03-01, 03-07 Central Mall, Singapore, 228242, Singapore
Tel.: (65) 65117600
Advertising Services
N.A.I.C.S.: 541810
Konstantin Popovic *(CEO)*

WPP PLC

WPP plc—(Continued)

Grey Stockholm (3)
Jakobsgatan 6, Box 7852, 114 80, Stockholm, Sweden
Tel.: (46) 8841098100
Sales Range: $10-24.9 Million
Advertising Services
N.A.I.C.S.: 541810

Grey Thailand (3)
1028/5 Phongamon Building Floors 1-2
Rama 4 Road, Khwaeng Thungmahamek
Khet Sathorn, Bangkok, 10120, Thailand
Tel.: (66) 21190200
Sales Range: $25-49.9 Million
Emp.: 20
Advertising Services
N.A.I.C.S.: 541810
Jureeporn Thaidumrong *(Chm-Creative)*

Grey Vilnius (3)
Konstitucijos pr 12-305, 09308, Vilnius, Lithuania
Tel.: (370) 52754686
Web Site: https://www.grey.lt
Sales Range: $25-49.9 Million
Emp.: 3
Advertising Services
N.A.I.C.S.: 541810

Grey d.o.o. Belgrade (3)
Bade Pivljanina 39, Belgrade, 11000, Serbia
Tel.: (381) 111 367 5765
Sales Range: $25-49.9 Million
Emp.: 70
Advertising Services
N.A.I.C.S.: 541810

Imagen Publicidad S.A. (3)
Bolonia Embajada Alemana 250 Mts Al Oeste, Managua, Nicaragua
Tel.: (505) 2687253
Advertising Services
N.A.I.C.S.: 541810

Inorek & Grey (3)
Narva mnt 7, Tallinn, 10117, Estonia
Tel.: (372) 6109370
Web Site: http://www.grey.com.ee
Sales Range: $25-49.9 Million
Emp.: 10
Advertising Services
N.A.I.C.S.: 541810

Insight Communications (3)
37/39 Oduduwa Street GRA Ikeja, PMB 21236, Ikeja, Lagos, Nigeria
Tel.: (234) 1497971015
Sales Range: $10-24.9 Million
Emp.: 50
Advertising Services
N.A.I.C.S.: 541810
Chuka Obi *(Exec Creative Dir)*

Insight Media Advertising Ltd. (3)
19 Ring Road East Osu, PO Box 5504, Accra, North, Ghana
Tel.: (233) 21 784 855
Sales Range: $10-24.9 Million
Emp.: 25
Advertising Services
N.A.I.C.S.: 541810
Kwamena Ackommensah *(Mng Dir)*

Jotabequ El Salvador (3)
Calle El Mirador 5253, San Salvador, El Salvador
Tel.: (503) 264 1220
Web Site: http://www.grey.com
Advertising Services
N.A.I.C.S.: 541810

La Fabrica Jotabequ (3)
15 Avenida 5-50 zone 15 Vista Hermosa 3 Spazio Business Center, Office 805A, Guatemala, Guatemala
Tel.: (502) 22512097
Web Site: https://www.lafabricayjbq.com
Advertising Services
N.A.I.C.S.: 541810

Matos Grey (3)
Avenida Major Sylvio de Magalnaes Padiha Edificio Philadelphia 1st Fl, 5200 Condominio America Bus Pk, CEP 05693-000, Sao Paulo, Brazil
Tel.: (55) 11 3755 8200
Web Site: http://www.grey.com.br
Sales Range: $25-49.9 Million
Emp.: 180
Advertising Services

N.A.I.C.S.: 541810

Subsidiary (Domestic):

Mediacom Interaction (3)
498 7th Ave, New York, NY 10018
Tel.: (212) 912-5200
Sales Range: $25-49.9 Million
Emp.: 200
Advertising Services
N.A.I.C.S.: 541830
Michael Turcotte *(Media Supvr)*

Branch (Non-US):

Mediacom Interaction (4)
36/F PCCW Tower 979 Kings Road, Taikoo Place, Quarry Bay, China (Hong Kong)
Tel.: (852) 2280 3480
Web Site: http://www.beyondinteractive.com
Advertising Services
N.A.I.C.S.: 541810

Branch (Domestic):

Mediacom Interaction (4)
2301 Platt Rd Ste 400, Ann Arbor, MI 48104
Tel.: (734) 677-8000
Advertising Services
N.A.I.C.S.: 541810
Sarah Hammel *(CFO & COO)*

Subsidiary (Non-US):

Orange Communications (3)
6th Floor TN Tower, St Georges Street, Port Louis, Mauritius
Tel.: (230) 211 5782
Sales Range: Less than $1 Million
Emp.: 12
Advertising Services
N.A.I.C.S.: 541810

Prestige Communications Pvt. Ltd. (3)
9 Karachi Chambers Hasrat Mohani Road, Karachi, 74000, Pakistan
Tel.: (92) 21 241 2505
Sales Range: $25-49.9 Million
Emp.: 55
Advertising Services
N.A.I.C.S.: 541810

Publicidad Interamericana, S.A. (3)
Apartado 08434 Calle 64 N0 2 San Francisco, Zona 7, Panama, Panama
Tel.: (507) 2266077
Sales Range: $10-24.9 Million
Emp.: 30
Advertising Services
N.A.I.C.S.: 541810

Rep GREY Colombia (3)
Calle 94 #16-57, Bogota, Colombia
Tel.: (57) 15303131
Web Site: http://grey.com
Sales Range: $25-49.9 Million
Emp.: 80
Advertising Services
N.A.I.C.S.: 541810
Jorge Serrano *(Pres)*

SEK & Grey (3)
John Stenbergin ranta 2, 00530, Helsinki, Finland
Tel.: (358) 969571
Web Site: https://sek.fi
Rev.: $17,568,200
Emp.: 122
Advertising Services
N.A.I.C.S.: 541810

Talento Grey Publicidad (3)
Colonia La Modern 22 Avenida, 7a Calle Casa no 720, San Pedro Sula, Honduras
Tel.: (504) 557 6426
Web Site: http://www.greyny.com
Advertising Services
N.A.I.C.S.: 541810

Uncle Grey A/S (3)
Studsgade 35, Arhus, 8000, Denmark
Tel.: (45) 70271100
Web Site: http://www.unclegrey.dk
Sales Range: $10-24.9 Million
Emp.: 25
Advertising Services
N.A.I.C.S.: 541810
Bente Soe Larsen *(Controller)*

Uncle Grey Oslo (3)
Sorkedalsveien 6, 0365, Oslo, Norway
Tel.: (47) 21603400
Web Site: http://www.uncle.no
Sales Range: $10-24.9 Million
Emp.: 30
Advertising Services
N.A.I.C.S.: 541810
Rune Skalstad *(Mng Dir)*

Valdez & Torry Advertising Limited (3)
46 Murray Street, Woodbrook, Port of Spain, Trinidad & Tobago
Tel.: (868) 6227103
Web Site: https://www.vtinternational.net
Sales Range: $10-24.9 Million
Emp.: 45
Advertising Services
N.A.I.C.S.: 541810
Steven Valdez *(Co-Pres)*

WMC/Grey (3)
Plynarni 1617/10, 170 00, Prague, 7, Czech Republic
Tel.: (420) 724666649
Web Site: https://www.wmcgrey.cz
Sales Range: $10-24.9 Million
Emp.: 35
Advertising Services
N.A.I.C.S.: 541810
Tomas Vondracek *(CEO-Grp)*

excentricGrey (3)
Garage Avenida 24 de Julho n 62, 1200-869, Lisbon, Portugal
Tel.: (351) 211223000
Web Site: https://www.excentricgrey.com
Sales Range: $10-24.9 Million
Emp.: 20
Advertising Services
N.A.I.C.S.: 541810

jotabequ Advertising (3)
Barrio La California, 10101, San Jose, Costa Rica
Tel.: (506) 22849800
Web Site: https://www.jotabequ.com
Sales Range: $25-49.9 Million
Emp.: 150
Advertising Services
N.A.I.C.S.: 541810

Subsidiary (Domestic):

wing (3)
200 5th Ave 4th Fl, New York, NY 10010
Tel.: (212) 500-9400
Rev.: $70,000,000
Emp.: 50
Advertising Services
N.A.I.C.S.: 541810
Jose Aguilar *(Chief Creative Officer)*

Branch (Domestic):

wing-Miami (4)
800 S Douglas Rd Ste 355, Coral Gables, FL 33134
Tel.: (305) 586-3354
Sales Range: $10-24.9 Million
Emp.: 7
Advertising Services
N.A.I.C.S.: 541810

Subsidiary (Domestic):

Group M Worldwide, Inc. (2)
3 World Trade Ctr 175 Greenwich St, New York, NY 10007
Tel.: (212) 297-8181
Web Site: https://www.groupm.com
Holding Company; Media Buying Agencies
N.A.I.C.S.: 551112
Elizabeth McCune *(Chief Growth Officer)*

Subsidiary (Non-US):

Bikini (3)
Rua Ruiz Soriano 67-1, 1200-246, Lisbon, Portugal
Tel.: (351) 21 322 0350
Television Broadcasting Services
N.A.I.C.S.: 516120

CLS AUDIOVISUAIS LD (3)
Travessa Da Fonte De Cima 2 Asseiceira Grande, 2665-618, Venda do Pinheiro, Portugal
Tel.: (351) 218 310 680

INTERNATIONAL PUBLIC

Sales Range: $25-49.9 Million
Emp.: 10
Audio Visual Production Services
N.A.I.C.S.: 512110
Francisco De la Fuente *(Mng Dir)*

Eumovil (3)
Pol Ind Lama Antonio Alonso Martin s/n, Paracuellos de Jarama, 28860, Madrid, Spain
Tel.: (34) 91 658 28 84
Web Site: http://www.eumovil.es
Sales Range: $25-49.9 Million
Emp.: 1
Audio Visual Production Services
N.A.I.C.S.: 512110

GroupM APAC HQ (3)
GroupM House Level 11 65 Berry Street, Sydney, 2060, NSW, Australia
Tel.: (61) 289131033
N.A.I.C.S.: 541830
Mark Lollback *(CEO-Australia & New Zealand)*

GroupM China (3)
20F WPP Campus 399 Hengfeng Road, Shanghai, 200070, China
Tel.: (86) 21 2307 7700
Advertising Services
N.A.I.C.S.: 541810
Patrick Xu *(CEO-China)*

GroupM EMEA HQ (3)
Sea Containers House 18 Upper Ground, London, WC2N 4DB, United Kingdom
Tel.: (44) 2078964700
N.A.I.C.S.: 541830
Dominic Grainger *(CEO)*

Subsidiary (Non-US):

Magic Poster GmbH (4)
Derendorf Allee 10, 40476, Dusseldorf, Germany
Tel.: (49) 2118767050
Sales Range: $10-24.9 Million
Emp.: 60
Out-of-Home Media, Outdoor
N.A.I.C.S.: 541810

Branch (Domestic):

Magic Poster GmbH - Munich Office (5)
Rosenheimerstrasse 145D, 80339, Munich, Germany
Tel.: (49) 895458210
Web Site: http://www.kineticww.com
N.A.I.C.S.: 541870

Subsidiary (Domestic):

Mediaedge:cia Worldwide Ltd. (4)
See Container 18 Upper Ground, London, SE1 9ET, United Kingdom
Tel.: (44) 2078032000
Holding Company; Media Planning & Buying Agencies
N.A.I.C.S.: 551112

Subsidiary (Non-US):

GroupM Asia Pacific Holdings Pte. Ltd. (5)
18 Cross Street, Cross Street Exchange #04-01, Singapore, 048423, Singapore
Tel.: (65) 62251262
Web Site: http://www.groupm.com
Media Planning & Buying Services
N.A.I.C.S.: 541830
Prasanth Kumar *(CEO-South Asia)*

Unit (Domestic):

GroupM Singapore Pte. Ltd. (6)
18 Cross Street China Square Central 04-01/03, Singapore, 048423, Singapore
Tel.: (65) 62251262
N.A.I.C.S.: 541830

Subsidiary (Domestic):

Wavemaker Global Limited (5)
Sea Containers, 18 Upper Ground, London, SE19ET, United Kingdom
Tel.: (44) 2078032000
Web Site: https://wavemakerglobal.com
Sales Range: $350-399.9 Million
Emp.: 300
Media Buying Agency

AND PRIVATE COMPANIES — WPP PLC

N.A.I.C.S.: 541830
James Northway *(Head-Data-Global)*

Unit (Non-US):

KR Wavemaker (6)
145 - 149 rue Anatole France, Levallois-Perret, 92300, Paris, France
Tel.: (33) 762804111
Media Buying Services
N.A.I.C.S.: 541830
Marie Costeux *(Mng Dir)*

MEC (6)
Pohjoinen Makasiinikatu 3-5, 00130, Helsinki, Finland
Tel.: (358) 207 199 211
Media Buying Agency
N.A.I.C.S.: 541830
Marika Virtanan *(Acct Dir)*

MEC (6)
Birger Jarlsgatan 52, PO Box 5514, Stockholm, 114 29, Sweden
Tel.: (46) 84631500
Media Buying Services
N.A.I.C.S.: 541830

MEC (6)
Rosenheimer Str 145d, 81671, Munich, Germany
Tel.: (49) 896388900
Emp.: 20
N.A.I.C.S.: 541830

MEC (6)
Tegetthoffstrasse 7/5Anif, 1010, Vienna, Austria
Tel.: (43) 1 532 2721
Sales Range: $10-24.9 Million
Emp.: 47
Media Buying Services
N.A.I.C.S.: 541830
Sibylle Bluemel *(Mng Dir)*

MEC (6)
Rosstrasse 92, 40476, Dusseldorf, Germany
Tel.: (49) 21155880
N.A.I.C.S.: 541830

MEC (6)
Kristen Bernikows Gade 1 4th Fl, Copenhagen, 1105, Denmark
Tel.: (45) 87 30 18 00
Emp.: 150
N.A.I.C.S.: 541830
Jonas Hemmingsen *(Dir-Fin)*

MEC (6)
Sodra Larmgatan 13A, PO Box 3183, SE-400 10, Gothenburg, Sweden
Tel.: (46) 31 10 55 00
Media Buying Services
N.A.I.C.S.: 541830

MEC (6)
Baltzarsgatan 30,, PO Box 4027, 114 85, Malmo, Sweden
Tel.: (46) 40 660 7550
Media Buying Services
N.A.I.C.S.: 541830

MEC (6)
Calle Las Norias 92, Madrid, 28221, Spain
Tel.: (34) 91 709 25 00
Emp.: 50
N.A.I.C.S.: 541830
Hugo Llebres *(Mng Dir)*

Wavemaker - Greece (6)
262 Kifissias Avenue, 14561, Athens, Greece
Tel.: (30) 2106289600
Media Buying Agency
N.A.I.C.S.: 541830

Wavemaker - Morocco (6)
9 Angle Ibnou Sinaa et Abou Rayan El Falaki, PO Box 20100, Casablanca, Morocco
Tel.: (212) 522361333
Media Buying Agency
N.A.I.C.S.: 541830

Wavemaker - Romania (6)
The Podium Bucharest A WPP CAMPUS 84-98 Calea Grivitei Street, 3rd floor 1st District, 010735, Bucharest, Romania
Tel.: (40) 730712386
Media Buying Agency
N.A.I.C.S.: 541830

Wavemaker - Slovakia (6)
CBC I Karadzicova 8, 821 08, Bratislava, Slovakia
Tel.: (421) 257880410
Media Buying Agency
N.A.I.C.S.: 541830

Wavemaker A/S (6)
Holmbladsgade 133, 2300, Copenhagen, Denmark
Tel.: (45) 33381800
Media Buying Services
N.A.I.C.S.: 541830
Kristian Bae-Mikkelsen *(CEO)*

Wavemaker AG (6)
Rue Bellefontaine 2, 1003, Lausanne, Switzerland
Tel.: (41) 216328240
Media Buying Services
N.A.I.C.S.: 541830
Henning Gronki *(CEO)*

Wavemaker AS (6)
Kongens gate 6, 0153, Oslo, Norway
Tel.: (47) 22472600
Magazines, Media Buying Services, Newspaper, Outdoor, Planning & Consultation, Print, Sales Promotion, Strategic Planning/Research, T.V.
N.A.I.C.S.: 541830
Cathrine Hagen *(CEO)*

Wavemaker B.V. (6)
Amsteldijk 166, PO Box 9432, 1079 LH, Amsterdam, Netherlands
Tel.: (31) 20 355 0000
Web Site: http://www.wavemakerglobal.com
Media Buying Services, Strategic Planning/Research
N.A.I.C.S.: 541830
Isabelle Dacz *(CEO)*

Wavemaker Czech s.r.o. (6)
Bubenska 1477/1, 170 00, Prague, 7, Czech Republic
Tel.: (420) 234299100
Media Buying Services
N.A.I.C.S.: 541830
Ondrej Simunek *(CEO)*

Wavemaker Egypt (6)
Infinity Tower 20th Floor 11B El-Hegaz Square, PO Box 6063, Mohandessin Al Orman Giz, Cairo, Egypt
Tel.: (20) 225871976
Communications, Media Buying Services, Planning & Consultation
N.A.I.C.S.: 541830
Rasha Mamdouh *(Acct Dir)*

Wavemaker GmbH (6)
Volklinger Strasse 33, 40221, Dusseldorf, Germany
Tel.: (49) 21155880
Web Site: https://www.wavemakerglobal.com
Advertising Services
N.A.I.C.S.: 541810
Jana Tasche *(Head-Mktg-Global)*

Wavemaker GmbH (6)
Derendorfer Allee 4, 40476, Dusseldorf, Germany
Tel.: (49) 21155880
Web Site: http://www.wavemakerglobal.com
Marketing & Advertising
N.A.I.C.S.: 541830
Jana Tasche *(Grp Head-Mktg)*

Wavemaker Hungary Kft. (6)
Alkotas st 53 MOM Park - B tower 3rd floor, 1123, Budapest, Hungary
Tel.: (36) 18018111
Media Buying Services
N.A.I.C.S.: 541830
Janos Gulyas *(CEO)*

Wavemaker Ireland (6)
1 High St Merchants Quay, Dublin, D08 R990, Ireland
Tel.: (353) 14150300
Web Site: https://wavemakerglobal.com
Marketing & Advertising
N.A.I.C.S.: 541830
David Hayes *(Mng Dir)*

Wavemaker Italy (6)
Via Morimondo 26, 20143, Milan, Italy
Tel.: (39) 02467671
Marketing & Advertising
N.A.I.C.S.: 541830

Francesco Riccadonna *(Gen Mgr)*

Wavemaker Lebanon (6)
Damascus Road Sodeco Square Bloc B 3rd Floor, Dynagraph Building, Beirut, Lebanon
Tel.: (961) 1423678
Media Buying Services
N.A.I.C.S.: 541830

Subsidiary (Domestic):

Wavemaker Limited (6)
Sea Containers 18 Upper Ground, London, SE1 9ET, United Kingdom
Tel.: (44) 2078032390
Advertising Services
N.A.I.C.S.: 541810

Branch (Non-US):

MEC Interaction (7)
700 Beach Rd #04-01, Singapore, 199598, Singapore
Tel.: (65) 6225 1262
Advertising Services
N.A.I.C.S.: 541810

MEC Interaction (7)
Yebisu Garden Place Tower 29F, 4-20-3 Ebisu Shibuya-ku, Tokyo, 150-6029, Japan
Tel.: (81) 3 5791 4378
Advertising Services
N.A.I.C.S.: 541810

MEC Interaction (7)
Kristen Bernikows Gade 1 4 Sal, Copenhagen, 1105, Denmark
Tel.: (45) 33 38 1800
Emp.: 15
Advertising Services
N.A.I.C.S.: 541810

Branch (Domestic):

MEC Interaction (7)
Eastgate 2 Castle St, Castlefield, Manchester, M3 4LZ, United Kingdom
Tel.: (44) 161 930 9000
Web Site: http://www.mecmanchester.co.uk
Advertising Services
N.A.I.C.S.: 541810

Branch (Non-US):

MEC Interaction (7)
Via Carducci 14, 20123, Milan, Italy
Tel.: (39) 02 467 671
Sales Range: $10-24.9 Million
Advertising Services
N.A.I.C.S.: 541810

MEC Interaction (7)
Birger Jarlsgatan 50, Stockholm, 10377, Sweden
Tel.: (46) 8 463 15 00
Emp.: 13
Advertising Services
N.A.I.C.S.: 541810

Unit (Non-US):

Wavemaker Middle East (6)
4th Floor Al Suhaili Plaza Al Andalus Street, PO Box 234, Jeddah, 21411-KSA, Saudi Arabia
Tel.: (966) 2 6511996
Web Site: http://www.wavemakerglobal.com
Media Buying Services
N.A.I.C.S.: 541830

Wavemaker Netherlands (6)
Amsteldijk 166, 1079 LH, Amsterdam, Netherlands
Tel.: (31) 203550000
Web Site: https://wavemakerglobal.com
Marketing & Advertising Services
N.A.I.C.S.: 541830
Ruud Verheijen *(Dir-Bus Dev)*

Wavemaker Poland (6)
Plac Konesera 11, 03-736, Warsaw, Poland
Tel.: (48) 221133200
Media Buying Services, Newspaper, Outdoor, Planning & Consultation, Print, Strategic Planning/Research, T.V.
N.A.I.C.S.: 541830

Wavemaker Portugal (6)
Av 24 de Julho 62-64, 1200-869, Lisbon, Portugal
Tel.: (351) 213592200
Marketing & Advertising

N.A.I.C.S.: 541830
Maria Joao Oliveira *(Mng Dir)*

Wavemaker Publicidad Spain SL (6)
LA Matriz Calle Rios Rosas 26, 28003, Madrid, Spain
Tel.: (34) 917092500
Web Site: https://wavemakerglobal.com
Media Buying Services
N.A.I.C.S.: 541830
Hugo Llebres *(CEO)*

Branch (Domestic):

Wavemaker Publicidad Spain SL -Barcelona (7)
Calle Bolivia 68, 08018, Barcelona, Spain
Tel.: (34) 93 365 23 00
Web Site: http://www.wavemakerglobal.com
Media Buying Services
N.A.I.C.S.: 541830
Penelope Garcia Jimenez *(Head-Mktg & Comm)*

Unit (Non-US):

Wavemaker Russia (6)
2 Tsvetnoy Boulevard, Moscow, 127051, Russia
Tel.: (7) 495 641 23 14
Web Site: http://www.wavemakerglobal.com
Media Buying Agency
N.A.I.C.S.: 541830

Wavemaker South Africa (6)
The Base 3012A William Nicol Road, Braynston, Johannesburg, 2193, South Africa
Tel.: (27) 100360200
Media Buying Services
N.A.I.C.S.: 541830
Lwandile Qokweni *(CEO)*

Wavemaker Switzerland (6)
Manessestrasse 85, 8038, Zurich, Switzerland
Tel.: (41) 2883842
Web Site: http://www.wavemakerglobal.com
Media Buying Services
N.A.I.C.S.: 541830

Wavemaker Turkey (6)
Astoria AVM Esentepe Buyukdere Caddesi No 127 Floor 2, 34394, Istanbul, Sisli, Turkiye
Tel.: (90) 2122271700
Web Site: https://wavemakerglobal.com
Media Buying Services
N.A.I.C.S.: 541830
Serdar Aytok *(CEO)*

Wavemaker-Belgium (6)
Jules Cockxstraat 8-10, 1160, Brussels, Belgium
Tel.: (32) 23330900
Media Buying Services
N.A.I.C.S.: 541830
Thierry Brynaert *(CEO)*

Subsidiary (US):

Wavemaker Global, LLC (5)
175 Greenwich St 3 World Trade Ctr, New York, NY 10007
Tel.: (212) 474-0374
Communications, Co-op Advertising, Direct Marketing, Event Marketing, Internet/Web Design, Media Buying Services, Planning & Consultation, Retail, Strategic Planning, T.V.
N.A.I.C.S.: 541830
Amanda Richman *(CEO)*

Group (Domestic):

MEC - Latin American HQ (6)
601 Brickell Key Dr Ste 804, Miami, FL 33131
Tel.: (786) 264-7600
Media Planning & Buying Services
N.A.I.C.S.: 541830

Unit (Non-US):

MEC (7)
Cra14 No 94-65 Piso 3 Edificio Plazuela 94, Bogota, DC, Colombia
Tel.: (57) 1 638 2593
N.A.I.C.S.: 541830

Unit (Domestic):

MEC (7)

WPP PLC

WPP plc—(Continued)

270 Ave Munoz Rivera 3rd Fl, San Juan, PR 00918
Tel.: (787) 474-8800
Emp.: 14
Media Buying Agency
N.A.I.C.S.: 541830

Unit (Non-US):

MEC (7)
Av Alfredo Leon 135, Miraflores, Lima, Peru
Tel.: (51) 1 243 2121
N.A.I.C.S.: 541830

MEC/Y&R Media (7)
Avenida Amazonas y Naciones Unidas, Edificio La Previsora,, Torre A, Piso 8, Quito, Ecuador
Tel.: (593) 2 2555410
N.A.I.C.S.: 541830

Wavemaker - Medellin (7)
Carrera 25 1 Sur - 155 Ed Platinum Superior Of 840, Edificio platino Superior, Medellin, Colombia
Tel.: (57) 3186961690
Media Buying Agency
N.A.I.C.S.: 541830
Camilo Salah (Mng Partner)

Wavemaker - Venezuela (7)
GroupM Venezuela Av La Estancia Centro Banaven Torre C Piso 2, Chuao, Caracas, Venezuela
Tel.: (58) 2129910179
Media Buying Agency
N.A.I.C.S.: 541830

Wavemaker Dubai (7)
Business Central Towers Block B 43rd floor, Dubai Media City, Dubai, United Arab Emirates
Tel.: (971) 4450 7300
Web Site: http://www.wavemakerglobal.com
Media Buying Services
N.A.I.C.S.: 541830
Marc Ghosn (Mng Dir)

Y&R Media (7)
Iglesia San Francisco Guadalupe, 50 Mts Sur Edificio Asesores, Apartado 6947-1000, San Jose, Costa Rica
Tel.: (506) 2257 6727
N.A.I.C.S.: 541830

Y&R Media (7)
Avenida Gustavo Mejia Ricart Torre Solazar Piso 10, Naco Distrito Nacional, Santo Domingo, Dominican Republic
Tel.: (809) 562 2441
Media Buyer
N.A.I.C.S.: 541830

Y&R Media (7)
Blvd Orden de Maltan No 5 Urbanization Santa Elena Antiguo Cuscatlan, La Libertad, San Salvador, El Salvador
Tel.: (503) 233 5000
N.A.I.C.S.: 541830

Y&R Media (7)
Calles 50 y 64 Este Edificio Interfinanzas, Piso 8 Apartado 7188, Panama, 5, Panama
Tel.: (507) 300 58 11
Emp.: 15
N.A.I.C.S.: 541830

Y&R Media (7)
Rua General Furtado do Nascimento 9, CEP: 05465-070, Sao Paulo, Brazil
Tel.: (55) 11 3026 4626
Web Site: http://www.yrbrasil.com.br
Sales Range: $10-24.9 Million
Emp.: 400
N.A.I.C.S.: 541830

Unit (Non-US):

MEC Japan (6)
YGP Tower 30F 4-20-3 Ebisu, Shibuya-ku, Tokyo, 150 6029, Japan
Tel.: (81) 3 5791 3838
Emp.: 5
N.A.I.C.S.: 541830

Wavemaker - Bangalore (7)
29 5th Floor Mahalakshmi Chambers M G Road, Karnataka, Bengaluru, 560 001, India
Tel.: (91) 2242398999
Media Buying Agency

N.A.I.C.S.: 541830

Wavemaker - Gurgaon (6)
6th Floor Omega Building No 9A Cyber City, DLF Phase III, Gurgaon, 122 022, India
Tel.: (91) 22 4239 8999
Web Site: http://wavemakerglobal.com
Media Buying Agency
N.A.I.C.S.: 541830

Group (Domestic):

Wavemaker Global LLC (6)
175 Greenwich St 3 World Trade Ctr, New York, NY 10007
Tel.: (212) 474-0000
Web Site: http://www.wavemakerglobal.com
Media Buying Services
N.A.I.C.S.: 541830
Amanda Richman (CEO)

Unit (Domestic):

MEC (7)
3340 Peachtree Rd NE Ste 300, Atlanta, GA 30326
Tel.: (404) 806-1950
Media Buying Services
N.A.I.C.S.: 541830

MEC (7)
601 Brickell Key Dr Ste 804, Miami, FL 33131
Tel.: (786) 264-7600
Sales Range: $10-24.9 Million
Emp.: 15
Media Buying Services
N.A.I.C.S.: 541830

MEC (7)
6300 Wilshire Blvd Ste 1900, Los Angeles, CA 90048
Tel.: (323) 761-1400
Emp.: 50
N.A.I.C.S.: 541830

Unit (Non-US):

Wavemaker Canada (7)
155 Queens Quay East, Toronto, M5A 1B6, ON, Canada
Tel.: (647) 457-6906
Web Site: http://www.wavemakerglobal.com
Media Buying Services
N.A.I.C.S.: 541830
Ryan Webber (CEO)

Unit (Domestic):

Wavemaker San Francisco (7)
360 3rd St 5th Fl, San Francisco, CA 94107
Tel.: (415) 764-1300
Media Buying Services
N.A.I.C.S.: 541830
Amanda Richman (CEO)

Unit (Non-US):

Wavemaker New Zealand Limited (6)
22 Fanshawe Street Level 12, GroupM House, Auckland, 1010, New Zealand
Tel.: (64) 93799007
Media Buying Services
N.A.I.C.S.: 541830
Anderson Grant (Mng Dir)

Branch (Domestic):

Wavemaker Manchester (5)
Bass Warehouse 1st Floor 4 Castle Street, Castlefield, Manchester, M3 4LZ, United Kingdom
Tel.: (44) 161 930 9000
Web Site: http://www.wavemakerglobal.com
Marketing & Advertising
N.A.I.C.S.: 541830
Mick Style (CEO-Manchester)

Subsidiary (Non-US):

GroupM LATAM HQ (3)
Avenida Lago Alberto 319 Piso 3 Colonia Granada Del Miguel Hidalgo, 11529, Mexico, Mexico
Tel.: (52) 5585038390
N.A.I.C.S.: 541830
Cesar Recalde (CEO)

GroupM Malaysia (3)
Level 10 Menara Milenium No 8 Jalan Damanlela, Bukit Damansara, KL 50490, Kuala Lumpur, Malaysia
Tel.: (60) 3 2718 8689
N.A.I.C.S.: 541830
Edmund Wong (Head-Tech)

GroupM Singapore (3)
700 Beach Rd 07-01, Singapore, 199598, Singapore
Tel.: (65) 62251262
N.A.I.C.S.: 541830

GroupM Thailand (3)
Ploanchit Center 23rd Floor, 2 Sukhumvit Road Khlong Toey, Bangkok, Thailand
Tel.: (66) 2629 6256
N.A.I.C.S.: 541810
Kevin Clarke (CEO-Thailand & Myanmar)

Subsidiary (Domestic):

IEG LLC (3)
123 N Wacker Dr Ste 880, Chicago, IL 60606
Tel.: (312) 500-8960
Web Site: https://www.sponsorship.com
Sales Range: $10-24.9 Million
Emp.: 30
Sponsorship Consulting Services
N.A.I.C.S.: 541618
Lesa Laren Ukman (Founder)

Subsidiary (Non-US):

IMASBLUE (3)
Alcala 226, 28027, Madrid, Spain
Tel.: (34) 91 725 94 07
Web Site: http://www.imasblue.es
Audio Visual Production Services
N.A.I.C.S.: 512110

Imagina International Sales, S.L.U. (3)
Carretera Fuencarral Alcobendas Km 12 450, Planta Baja, Madrid, 28149, Spain
Tel.: (34) 91 728 57 38
Web Site: http://www.imaginasales.tv
Sales Range: $25-49.9 Million
Emp.: 11
Television Broadcasting Services
N.A.I.C.S.: 516120
Maria Jose Camacho (Coord-Sls & Database)

K 2000, s.a.u. (3)
Errekalde s/n, 48960, Galdakao, Bizkaia, Spain
Tel.: (34) 944570000
Web Site: https://www.k2000.com
Audio Visual Production Services
N.A.I.C.S.: 512110

Kinetic
Tel.: (212) 624-4200
Web Site: http://www.kineticww.com
Sales Range: $25-49.9 Million
Emp.: 130
Advetising Agency
N.A.I.C.S.: 541810

Unit (Domestic):

Alcance (4)
1680 Michigan Ave Ste 700, Miami Beach, FL 33139
Tel.: (305) 777-2213
Sales Range: $10-24.9 Million
Emp.: 6
N.A.I.C.S.: 541830

Destination Media Group (4)
10 E 40th St 26th Fl, New York, NY 10016
Tel.: (212) 792-5572
Alternative Advertising, Media Buying Services
N.A.I.C.S.: 541830

Hi Resolution Production (4)
10 E 46th St, New York, NY 10016
Tel.: (212) 792-8262
N.A.I.C.S.: 541810

Joule (4)
10 E 40th St 37th Fl, New York, NY 10016
Tel.: (212) 796-8382
N.A.I.C.S.: 541830

Subsidiary (Non-US):

Kinetic (4)
The Inspire Hornbeam Park, Cornwall Rd, Harrogate, HG2 8PA, Yorkshire, United Kingdom
Tel.: (44) 1423514404
Web Site: https://www.kineticwm.com
N.A.I.C.S.: 541830
Jackie Blease (Sec & Mgr-HR)

Kinetic (4)
Springfield House, Water Lane, Wilmslow, SK9 5BG, Chesire, United Kingdom
Tel.: (44) 1625524499
N.A.I.C.S.: 541830

Kinetic (4)
Kissbojtar St 3, H-1037, Budapest, Hungary
Tel.: (36) 1 454 33 33
Web Site: http://www.kinetic.hu
Sales Range: $10-24.9 Million
Emp.: 3
N.A.I.C.S.: 541830

Kinetic (4)
2 Ploenchit Ctr 18th Fl Sukhumvit Rd, Klongtoey, Bangkok, 10110, Thailand
Tel.: (66) 2 656 8611
Web Site: http://www.kinetic.com
N.A.I.C.S.: 541830

Kinetic (4)
11-B Country Space 1 Building HV dela Costa St, Salcedo Village, Makati, Philippines
Tel.: (63) 894 3365
N.A.I.C.S.: 541830

Kinetic (4)
Darmstadter Landstrasse 112, 60598, Frankfurt, Germany
Tel.: (49) 6966777610
Sales Range: $10-24.9 Million
Emp.: 20
N.A.I.C.S.: 541810
Ralf Stoffel (Deputy Mng Dir)

Kinetic (4)
Princesa 25 3o, 28002, Madrid, Spain
Tel.: (34) 91 540 0978
N.A.I.C.S.: 541810

Kinetic (4)
Rue Jules Cockxstraat 8-10, Uccle, 1160, Brussels, Belgium
Tel.: (32) 23338177
N.A.I.C.S.: 541810

Kinetic (4)
Amsteldijk 166, 1079 LH, Amsterdam, Netherlands
Tel.: (31) 205757790
Advetising Agency
N.A.I.C.S.: 541810

Kinetic (4)
31 Ballsbridge Terr, Dublin, 4, Ireland
Tel.: (353) 1668 1822
Web Site: http://www.kinetic.ie
Sales Range: $10-24.9 Million
Emp.: 20
N.A.I.C.S.: 541810

Unit (Domestic):

Kinetic (4)
12180 Millennium Dr Playa Vista, Los Angeles, CA 90094
Tel.: (310) 309-8583
N.A.I.C.S.: 541810

Kinetic (4)
333 N Green St, Chicago, IL 60607
Tel.: (312) 205-0054
Web Site: https://www.kineticwm.com
Emp.: 13
N.A.I.C.S.: 541810

Subsidiary (Non-US):

Kinetic (4)
1009 Level 10 Block A, Phileo Damansara, 46350, Petaling Jaya, Malaysia
Tel.: (60) 3 7956 5359
N.A.I.C.S.: 541810
Manjiri Kamat (Mng Dir-Malaysia & Singapore)

Kinetic (4)
Commerz 9th Floor International Business Park Oberoi Garden City, Off Western Expres Highway, Goregaon East, Mumbai, 400063, India
Tel.: (91) 22 4239 9309
Web Site: http://www.kineticww.com

AND PRIVATE COMPANIES

WPP PLC

N.A.I.C.S.: 541810

Kinetic Design & Advertising Pvt. Ltd. (4)
2 Leng Kee Rd 04-03A, Thye Hong Ctr, Singapore, 48543, Singapore
Tel.: (65) 64759377
Web Site: http://www.kineticww.com
Emp.: 30
N.A.I.C.S.: 541850

Kinetic Italia
Kinetic - WPP Campus Via Morimondo 26, Milanofiori Nord Assago, 20143, Milan, Italy
Tel.: (39) 024335951
Advetising Agency
N.A.I.C.S.: 541810
Leonardo Freddi *(Fin Dir)*

Unit (Domestic):

Target:Health (4)
261 Madison Ave, New York, NY 10016
Tel.: (212) 681-2100
Web Site: http://www.targethealth.com
Sales Range: $10-24.9 Million
Emp.: 75
N.A.I.C.S.: 541810
Jules T. Mitchel *(CEO)*

Subsidiary (Non-US):

Liquid Media S.L. (3)
Edificio Mediapro Virgilio 2, Pozuelo de Alarcon, 28223, Madrid, Spain
Tel.: (34) 91 838 77 50
Web Site: http://www.liquidmedia.es
Television Broadcasting Services
N.A.I.C.S.: 516120

Subsidiary (Domestic):

M80 (3)
2894 Rowena Ave, Los Angeles, CA 90039
Tel.: (323) 644-7800
Sales Range: $10-24.9 Million
Emp.: 35
Advertising Agencies
N.A.I.C.S.: 541810

Maxus Global (3)
498 7th Ave, New York, NY 10018
Tel.: (212) 297-8300
Web Site: http://www.maxusglobal.com
Customer Relationship Management, Media Buying Services, Media Planning, Media Relations
N.A.I.C.S.: 541830

Unit (Non-US):

Maxus (4)
700 Beach Rd 07 01, Singapore, 199598, Singapore
Tel.: (65) 63950755
Web Site: http://www.maxusglobal.com
N.A.I.C.S.: 541830
Desh Balakrishnan *(Mng Dir)*

Maxus (4)
2 Ploenchit Center 14th Floor, Sukhumvit Rd Klongtoey, Bangkok, 10110, Thailand
Tel.: (66) 2 629 6000
N.A.I.C.S.: 541830
Dujduan Sornmani *(Mng Dir)*

Maxus (4)
Rm 503 5/F Jin Bao Building 89 Jin Bao St, Dong Cheng District, Beijing, 100005, China
Tel.: (86) 10 8523 3569
Web Site: http://www.maxusglobal.com
Emp.: 70
N.A.I.C.S.: 541830
Annie Hsiao *(Pres-Shanghai)*

Maxus (4)
6/F Saigon Centre 65 Le Loi Blvd, District 1, Ho Chi Minh City, Vietnam
Tel.: (84) 8 821 2233
N.A.I.C.S.: 541830
Kishan Kumar *(Mng Dir)*

Maxus (4)
36/F PCCW Tower Taikoo Pl 979 Kings Rd, Quarry Bay, China (Hong Kong)
Tel.: (852) 2280 3488
Sales Range: $10-24.9 Million
Emp.: 70
N.A.I.C.S.: 541830
Mark Edward *(Gen Mgr)*

Maxus (4)
6th Fl Bldg No 9A Cyber City DLF Phase III, Gurgaon, 122002, Haryana, India
Tel.: (91) 124 409 2300
Sales Range: $50-74.9 Million
Emp.: 300
N.A.I.C.S.: 541830

Maxus (4)
Ground Fl Orbit Plz, New Prabhadevi Rd, Mumbai, 400025, India
Tel.: (91) 22 566 3888
N.A.I.C.S.: 541830
Ajit Varghese *(CEO-Asia Pacific)*

Maxus (4)
5th Fl Mahalaxmi Chambers, 29 MG Rd, Bengaluru, 560 001, India
Tel.: (91) 80 419 3101
N.A.I.C.S.: 541830
Kishankumar Shyamalan *(Gen Mgr)*

Maxus (4)
Wisma Indomobil Jl Letjen M T Haryono No Kav 8 Bidara Cina, Kecamatan Jatinegara Kota Jakarta Timur Daerah Khusus Timur, Jakarta, 13330, Ibukota, Indonesia
Tel.: (62) 2152916360
Web Site: https://maxus.id
Sales Range: $10-24.9 Million
Emp.: 24
N.A.I.C.S.: 541830

Maxus (4)
30/F Yebisu Garden Pl Tower 4-20-3 Yebisu, Shibuya-ku, Tokyo, 150, Japan
Tel.: (81) 3 5791 2780
N.A.I.C.S.: 541830
Takashi Komura *(Mng Dir)*

Maxus (4)
Level 10 Menara Milenium 8 Jalan Damanlela, Bukit Damansara, 50490, Kuala Lumpur, Malaysia
Tel.: (60) 3 2718 8128
N.A.I.C.S.: 541830

Maxus (4)
Level 11 65 Berry St, Sydney, 2060, NSW, Australia
Tel.: (61) 2 9287 8400
Sales Range: $10-24.9 Million
Emp.: 130
Media Buying Services
N.A.I.C.S.: 541810
David Gaines *(CEO)*

Maxus (4)
Stortorvet 10, N-0155, Oslo, Norway
Tel.: (47) 22 47 26 90
Sales Range: $10-24.9 Million
Emp.: 12
N.A.I.C.S.: 541830

Maxus (4)
25 F Philamlife Tower, 8767 Paseo de Roxas St, Makati City, Manila, 1200, Philippines
Tel.: (63) 2 885 7001
Rev: $12,000,000
Emp.: 15
N.A.I.C.S.: 541830

Maxus (4)
Changle Rd 989 30Fl, Nanjing Road, Shanghai, 200031, China
Tel.: (86) 21 2307 7777
Web Site: http://www.maxusglobal.com
N.A.I.C.S.: 541830

Maxus (4)
5 F No 31 Ln 11 GuangFu N Rd, Taipei, 10560, Taiwan
Tel.: (886) 2 7710 6099
Web Site: http://www.mindshareworld.com
Sales Range: $10-24.9 Million
Emp.: 80
N.A.I.C.S.: 541810
Rob Guenette *(CEO-TAXI)*

Maxus (4)
Via Carducci 14, Milan, 20123, Italy
Tel.: (39) 0258151076
Sales Range: $10-24.9 Million
Emp.: 13
N.A.I.C.S.: 541810

Maxus Communications (UK) Limited
Sea Containers 18 Upper Ground, London, SE1 9ET, United Kingdom
Tel.: (44) 2078032000

Advertising Services
N.A.I.C.S.: 541810

Subsidiary (Non-US):

Media 3.14 (3)
Edifici Imagina Centre Audiovisual, Barcelona, 48418, Spain
Tel.: (34) 93 476 15 51
Web Site: http://www.media314.cat
Emp.: 30
Television Broadcasting Services
N.A.I.C.S.: 516120
Joan Ubeda *(Gen Mgr)*

Media Base Sport SL (3)
Edifici Imagina Centre Audiovisual Avinguda Diagonal 177, 8018, Barcelona, Spain
Tel.: (34) 93 476 15 51
Athletes Sport Agencies Services
N.A.I.C.S.: 611620

Media Travel & Logistics (3)
Praca D Afonso V 55 D, 4150-024, Porto, Portugal
Tel.: (351) 226100610
Web Site: https://www.mediatravel.com.pt
Sales Range: $25-49.9 Million
Emp.: 12
Transportation & Logistics Services
N.A.I.C.S.: 488999
Teresa Ferreira *(Gen Dir)*

Subsidiary (Domestic):

Mindshare Group LLC (3)
3 World Trade Ctr 175 Greenwich St, New York, NY 10007
Tel.: (212) 297-7000
Emp.: 2,000
Media Buying Services
N.A.I.C.S.: 541830
Dawn Dickie *(CFO-Global)*

Unit (Non-US):

HappiMindshare (4)
Ruoholahdenkatu 21, 00180, Helsinki, Finland
Tel.: (358) 207199211
Sales Range: $10-24.9 Million
Emp.: 18
Media Buying Services
N.A.I.C.S.: 541830

Unit (Domestic):

Mindshare (4)
1845 Woodall Rodgers Fwy Ste 1100, Dallas, TX 75201
Tel.: (214) 740-1200
Web Site: http://www.mindshareworld.com
Sales Range: $10-24.9 Million
Emp.: 25
Media Buying Services
N.A.I.C.S.: 541830

Unit (Non-US):

Mindshare (4)
155 Queens Quay E, Toronto, M5A 1B6, ON, Canada
Tel.: (416) 987-5100
Web Site: https://www.mindshareworld.com
Sales Range: $10-24.9 Million
Emp.: 200
Media Buying Services
N.A.I.C.S.: 541830
Sandra Bonnick *(Head-Ops)*

Mindshare (4)
Lago Alberto 319 Piso 4 Colonia Granada Miguel Hidalgo, Col Veronica Anzures, 11529, Mexico, DF, Mexico
Tel.: (52) 5585038300
Media Buying Services
N.A.I.C.S.: 541830
Carlos Suarez *(CEO)*

Mindshare (4)
30/F Yebisu Garden Place Tower 4-20-3 Ebisu, Shibuya-Ku, Tokyo, 150-6030, Japan
Tel.: (81) 357912780
Sales Range: $10-24.9 Million
Emp.: 40
N.A.I.C.S.: 541810
Kevin Rooney *(CEO)*

Mindshare (4)
16/F K11 Atelier King's Road 728 King's Road, Quarry Bay, China (Hong Kong)

Tel.: (852) 22803160
N.A.I.C.S.: 541810

Mindshare (4)
Level 13 65 Berry Street, Sydney, 2060, NSW, Australia
Tel.: (61) 292878400
Sales Range: $10-24.9 Million
Emp.: 70
N.A.I.C.S.: 541810
Kerry Field *(Mng Dir-Melbourne)*

Mindshare (4)
Millennium Castle House 47 Road 27 Block A, Banani, Dhaka, 1213, Bangladesh
Tel.: (880) 28832419
N.A.I.C.S.: 541810
Morshed Alam *(Mng Dir)*

Mindshare (4)
17F WPP Campus 399 Hengfeng Road, Shanghai, 200070, China
Tel.: (86) 2124051188
N.A.I.C.S.: 541810
Vincent Chan *(Chief Comml Officer)*

Mindshare (4)
17F Jin Bao Building 89 JinBao Street, Dongcheng District, Beijing, 100005, China
Tel.: (86) 1085233679
N.A.I.C.S.: 541810
Amrita Randhawa *(Chm-Greater China & CEO-APAC)*

Mindshare (4)
21F Tower A M Plaza 109 Pazhou Avenue, Haizhu District, Guangzhou, 510335, China
Tel.: (86) 13521642957
N.A.I.C.S.: 541810

Mindshare (4)
Room 208 2nd Floor The Forum G-20 Block 9, Clifton, Karachi, Pakistan
Tel.: (92) 21111476876
N.A.I.C.S.: 541810

Mindshare (4)
17th/F Philamlife Tower 8767 Paseo de Roxas, Makati, 1200, Philippines
Tel.: (63) 2 885 7001
Web Site: http://www.mindshareworld.com
Media Buying Services
N.A.I.C.S.: 541830

Mindshare (4)
718 Cross Street 04-01 03 Cross Street Exchange, Singapore, 048423, Singapore
Tel.: (65) 63950776
N.A.I.C.S.: 541810
Ashutosh Srivastava *(CEO-APAC)*

Mindshare (4)
5F No 31 Ln 11 Guangfu N Road, Songshan District, Taipei, 10560, Taiwan
Tel.: (886) 277106099
Media Buying Services
N.A.I.C.S.: 541830
Joanna Chang *(Gen Mgr)*

Mindshare (4)
RDTX Place Floor 40 Jalan Professor Doktor Satrio No 17, Jakarta, 12930, Selatan, Indonesia
Tel.: (62) 2152916300
Sales Range: $25-49.9 Million
Emp.: 200
N.A.I.C.S.: 541810

Mindshare (4)
Level 20 WPP Campus Tower H 8 Jalan PJU 8/1, Damansara Perdana Petaling Jaya, 47820, Kuala Lumpur, Selangor, Malaysia
Tel.: (60) 376690873
Sales Range: $25-49.9 Million
Emp.: 200
Media Buying Services
N.A.I.C.S.: 541830
Dheeraj Raina *(Mng Dir)*

Mindshare (4)
Via Dei Magazzini Generali 38, 00154, Rome, Italy
Tel.: (39) 06518391
Sales Range: $10-24.9 Million
Emp.: 16
Media Buying Services
N.A.I.C.S.: 541830
Roberto Binaghi *(Chm & CEO)*

Mindshare (4)

WPP PLC

WPP plc—(Continued)

139/140 Rukmani Lakshmipathy Salai 3rd Floor, Egmore, Chennai, 600 008, India
Tel.: (91) 4442891000
Emp.: 50
N.A.I.C.S.: 541810
Parthasarathy Mandayam A. *(CEO-South Asia)*

Mindshare (4)
2nd Floor Mahalakshmi Chambers 29 MG Road, Bengaluru, 560 001, India
Tel.: (91) 8041193100
N.A.I.C.S.: 541810

Mindshare (4)
Via Morimondo n 26, Milan, Italy
Tel.: (39) 02480541
Sales Range: $25-49.9 Million
Emp.: 140
Media Buying Services
N.A.I.C.S.: 541830

Mindshare (4)
Floor 6 405-B Tower B Sector-20 Udyog Vihar Phase-III, DLF Cyber Park, Gurgaon, 122 016, India
Tel.: (91) 1244512300
Sales Range: $10-24.9 Million
Emp.: 60
N.A.I.C.S.: 541810

Mindshare (4)
Charcas 5051, Capital Federal, 1425, Buenos Aires, Argentina
Tel.: (54) 1143400500
Sales Range: $10-24.9 Million
Emp.: 50
Media Buying Services
N.A.I.C.S.: 541830
Pablo Iesulauro *(Chm)*

Mindshare (4)
Providencia 111 129 Piso 31 Providencia, 2201 Providencia, 7500775, Santiago, Chile
Tel.: (56) 974954215
Sales Range: $10-24.9 Million
Emp.: 50
N.A.I.C.S.: 541810
Tita Fuentes *(Mng Dir & Gen Mgr)*

Mindshare (4)
Av Jose Pardo No 1051, Miraflores, 18, Lima, Peru
Tel.: (51) 12131515
Sales Range: $10-24.9 Million
Emp.: 70
Media Buying Services
N.A.I.C.S.: 541830
Fidel La Riva *(CEO & Gen Mgr)*

Mindshare (4)
Centro Benaven Torre A Piso 5 Ave, La Estancia Chuao, Caracas, Venezuela
Tel.: (58) 2129925024
Media Buying Services
N.A.I.C.S.: 541830
Jhon DaSilva *(CEO)*

Mindshare (4)
Damascus Road Sodeco square Bloc B 3rd floor, Saifi Downtown, Beirut, Lebanon
Tel.: (961) 1423678
Sales Range: $10-24.9 Million
Emp.: 15
N.A.I.C.S.: 541810
Hana Khatib *(Mng Dir)*

Mindshare (4)
Business Central Towers Level 45 Tower B Sheikh Zayed Road, PO Box 35661, Dubai Internet City, Dubai, United Arab Emirates
Tel.: (971) 44547444
Sales Range: $10-24.9 Million
Emp.: 80
N.A.I.C.S.: 541810
Zahi Lawand *(Deputy Mng Dir)*

Unit (Domestic):

Mindshare (4)
555 17th St Ste 300, Denver, CO 80202-3908
Tel.: (303) 296-7668
Web Site: http://www.mindshareworld.com
Sales Range: Less than $1 Million
Emp.: 5
Media Buying Services
N.A.I.C.S.: 541830

David Lang *(Chief Content Officer-New York)*

Mindshare (4)
601 Brickell Key Dr Ste 800, Miami, FL 33131
Tel.: (305) 341-8111
Sales Range: $10-24.9 Million
Emp.: 53
Media Buying Services
N.A.I.C.S.: 541830

Mindshare (4)
303 2nd St S Tower 9th Fl, San Francisco, CA 94107
Tel.: (415) 856-5260
Web Site: http://www.mindshareworld.com
Sales Range: $10-24.9 Million
Emp.: 15
N.A.I.C.S.: 541810

Unit (Non-US):

Mindshare (4)
Gigergasse 8/6 OG, 1030, Vienna, Austria
Tel.: (43) 66488110420
Sales Range: $10-24.9 Million
Emp.: 50
Media Buying Services
N.A.I.C.S.: 541830

Mindshare (4)
6 Baba Nedelja Street, 1463, Sofia, Bulgaria
Tel.: (359) 29506725
Media Buying Services
N.A.I.C.S.: 541830

Mindshare (4)
Strojarska 22, 10000, Zagreb, Croatia
Tel.: (385) 14646764
Sales Range: $10-24.9 Million
Emp.: 7
Media Buying Services
N.A.I.C.S.: 541830

Mindshare (4)
WPP Campus Bubenska 1, 170 00, Prague, 2, Czech Republic
Tel.: (420) 234299200
Sales Range: $10-24.9 Million
Emp.: 30
Media Buying Services
N.A.I.C.S.: 541830
Martin Hanzal *(CEO)*

Mindshare (4)
Hovedkontor Mindshare Lighthouse Holmbladsgade 133, 2300, Copenhagen, Denmark
Tel.: (45) 70227525
Sales Range: $10-24.9 Million
Emp.: 35
Media Buying Services
N.A.I.C.S.: 541830
Martin Ove Rasmussen *(CEO-Denmark & Nordics)*

Mindshare (4)
145-149 rue Anatole France, Levallois-Perret, 92300, Paris, France
Tel.: (33) 630103376
Sales Range: $10-24.9 Million
Emp.: 90
Media Buying Services
N.A.I.C.S.: 541830
Olivier Baconnet *(COO)*

Mindshare (4)
Alkotas utca 53/B, 1123, Budapest, Hungary
Tel.: (36) 14369810
Sales Range: $10-24.9 Million
Emp.: 40
Media Buying Services
N.A.I.C.S.: 541830
Zsolt Somloi *(Mng Dir)*

Mindshare (4)
3 Christchurch Square, Dublin, D08 V0VE, Ireland
Tel.: (353) 14150300
Sales Range: $10-24.9 Million
Emp.: 60
Media Buying Services
N.A.I.C.S.: 541830
Bill Kinlay *(CEO)*

Mindshare (4)
Kongens Gate 6, 0153, Oslo, Norway
Tel.: (47) 98683859

Sales Range: $10-24.9 Million
Emp.: 40
Media Buying Services
N.A.I.C.S.: 541830
Petter Skippervold *(CEO)*

Mindshare (4)
Plac Konesera 11, 03-736, Warsaw, Poland
Tel.: (48) 510096373
Media Buying Services
N.A.I.C.S.: 541830
Adrian Kawecki *(CEO)*

Mindshare (4)
Edificio Garagem Av 24 de Julho 62 5, 1200-869, Lisbon, Portugal
Tel.: (351) 217228000
Sales Range: $10-24.9 Million
Emp.: 45
Media Buying Services
N.A.I.C.S.: 541830
Tomas Gonzalez-Quijano *(CEO)*

Mindshare (4)
Office Building The Podium 3rd Floor 84-98, Calea Grivitei, 010735, Bucharest, Romania
Tel.: (40) 372359300
Sales Range: $25-49.9 Million
Emp.: 200
Media Buying Services
N.A.I.C.S.: 541830
Clara Berindean *(CEO)*

Mindshare (4)
Kozhevnichesky proezd 4 bldn 1, Moscow, 115114, Russia
Tel.: (7) 495 787 2270
Rev.: $230,000,000
Emp.: 106
Media Buying Services
N.A.I.C.S.: 541830
Alexey Kulakov *(CEO)*

Mindshare (4)
Carrer de Bolivia 68-70, 08018, Barcelona, Spain
Tel.: (34) 933273000
Sales Range: $10-24.9 Million
Emp.: 27
Media Buying Services
N.A.I.C.S.: 541830
Beatriz Delgado *(CEO)*

Mindshare (4)
Matrix Rios Rosa 26, 28003, Madrid, Spain
Tel.: (34) 917403500
Sales Range: $50-74.9 Million
Emp.: 120
Media Buying Services
N.A.I.C.S.: 541830
Beatriz Delgado *(CEO)*

Mindshare (4)
Manessestrasse 85, 8045, Zurich, Switzerland
Tel.: (41) 443551515
Sales Range: $10-24.9 Million
Emp.: 35
Media Buying Services
N.A.I.C.S.: 541830
Xavier Reynaud *(CEO)*

Mindshare (4)
Buyukdere Cd Astoria AVM No 127 K 2, Esentepe, 34394, Istanbul, Turkiye
Tel.: (90) 2122833565
Sales Range: $10-24.9 Million
Emp.: 80
Media Buying Services
N.A.I.C.S.: 541830
Esra Koca *(Chief Client Officer)*

Mindshare (4)
3rd Fl 66 Norodom Blvd, PO Box 808, Phnom Penh, Cambodia
Tel.: (855) 23218057
Web Site: http://www.mindshareworld.com
N.A.I.C.S.: 541810

Mindshare (4)
Level 42 Bitexco Financial Tower 02 Hai Trieu Street, District 1, Ho Chi Minh City, Vietnam
Tel.: (84) 2862883325
N.A.I.C.S.: 541810

Mindshare (4)
2 Ploenchit Center 22nd Floor Sukhumvit Road, Klongtoey, Bangkok, 10110, Thailand
Tel.: (66) 26296000
N.A.I.C.S.: 541810

Panduranga Mattu *(Mng Partner)*

Mindshare (4)
Rm 22 13 Fl Shenzhen Kerry Ctr 2008 Renmin S Rd, Shenzhen, 518001, China
Tel.: (86) 75582364855
Web Site: http://www.mindshareworld.com
N.A.I.C.S.: 541810

Mindshare (4)
Tulcan 1017 Y LUQUE, Edificio Contemporaneo Piso 1, Guayaquil, Ecuador
Tel.: (593) 43729610
Sales Range: $10-24.9 Million
Emp.: 17
N.A.I.C.S.: 541810

Mindshare (4)
Avenida Ejercito Nacional 216 Piso 2, Colonia Veronica Anzures, Mexico, 11590, Mexico
Tel.: (52) 33 3818 4367
Sales Range: $25-49.9 Million
Emp.: 150
N.A.I.C.S.: 541810

Mindshare (4)
Luis Alberto de Herrera 1248 Office 301, World Trade Center Torre A, Montevideo, Uruguay
Tel.: (598) 2 623 2260
Sales Range: $10-24.9 Million
Emp.: 6
N.A.I.C.S.: 541810

Mindshare (4)
Lavrska Street 16, 12 N Amosova Street, 01015, Kiev, Ukraine
Tel.: (380) 445863072
Sales Range: $10-24.9 Million
Emp.: 35
N.A.I.C.S.: 541810

Mindshare (4)
14/14A Vajira Road, 4, Colombo, Sri Lanka
Tel.: (94) 112174600
Sales Range: $10-24.9 Million
Emp.: 35
N.A.I.C.S.: 541810

Mindshare (4)
Tel.: (49) 69609050
Web Site: http://www.mindshareworld.com
Sales Range: $25-49.9 Million
Emp.: 180
Media Buying Services
N.A.I.C.S.: 541830

Unit (Domestic):

Mindshare (4)
12180 Millennium Dr Ste 320, Playa Vista, CA 90094
Tel.: (310) 309-8500
Sales Range: $50-74.9 Million
Emp.: 60
Media Buying Services, Media Planning
N.A.I.C.S.: 541830
Autumn Nazarian *(Sr VP-Sponsorship & Partnerships)*

Mindshare (4)
505 N Angier Ave NE Ste 5000, Atlanta, GA 30308
Tel.: (404) 704-1800
Sales Range: $10-24.9 Million
Emp.: 50
Media Buying Services
N.A.I.C.S.: 541830
Matt Chamberlin *(Mng Dir)*

Unit (Non-US):

Mindshare (4)
Carrera 19 No 89-21 Level 7, Bogota, Colombia
Tel.: (57) 16444144
Sales Range: $10-24.9 Million
Emp.: 30
Media Buying Services
N.A.I.C.S.: 541830
Maria Victoria Torres *(CEO)*

Mindshare (4)
Mindshare London Rose Court 2 Southwark Bridge Rd, London, SE1 9HS, United Kingdom
Tel.: (44) 2079694040
Sales Range: $50-74.9 Million
Emp.: 500
Media Buying Services

AND PRIVATE COMPANIES — WPP PLC

N.A.I.C.S.: 541830
Sidharth Parashar (*Chief Investment Officer-Asia-Pacific*)

Mindshare (4)
Amsteldijk 166, 1079 LH, Amsterdam, Netherlands
Tel.: (31) 205171611
Sales Range: $10-24.9 Million
Emp.: 120
Media Buying Services
N.A.I.C.S.: 541830
Atvan van Zanten (*Mng Dir*)

Unit (Domestic):

Mindshare (4)
333 N Green St, Chicago, IL 60607
Tel.: (312) 242-1100
Media Buying Services
N.A.I.C.S.: 541830
Dan Reaume (*Chief Dev Officer-New York*)

Unit (Non-US):

Mindshare (4)
Sodra Hamngatan 35, 411 14, Gothenburg, Sweden
Tel.: (46) 317552070
Sales Range: $10-24.9 Million
Emp.: 50
Media Buying Services
N.A.I.C.S.: 541830
Charlotte Berg (*VP-Media & Comm*)

Mindshare (4)
Level 25 2 Southbank Boulevard Southbank, Saint Kilda, Melbourne, 3006, VIC, Australia
Tel.: (61) 399165300
Media Buying Services
N.A.I.C.S.: 541810
Tanya Koppe (*Head-Digital-Natl*)

Mindshare (4)
350 Kifisias Avenue 2 Christou Lada, Chalandri, 15233, Athens, Greece
Tel.: (30) 2108114600
Sales Range: $10-24.9 Million
Emp.: 100
Media Buying Services
N.A.I.C.S.: 541830
Maria Velivassaki (*Mng Dir*)

Mindshare (4)
Rue Jules Cockxstaat 8-10, 1160, Brussels, Belgium (100%)
Tel.: (32) 26635686
Sales Range: $10-24.9 Million
Emp.: 60
Media Buying Services
N.A.I.C.S.: 541830
Gerda Walravens (*Partner-Client Leadership*)

Unit (Domestic):

Mindshare Team Detroit (4)
500 Town Ctr Dr 2nd Fl, Dearborn, MI 48126
Tel.: (313) 615-2900
Web Site: http://www.teamdetroit.com
Sales Range: $10-24.9 Million
Emp.: 25
Media Buying Services
N.A.I.C.S.: 541830

Subsidiary (Domestic):

Outrider (3)
111 W Port Plz Ste 350, Saint Louis, MO 63146
Tel.: (212) 474-0000
Web Site: http://www.outrider.com
Sales Range: $100-124.9 Million
Emp.: 80
Internet Services
N.A.I.C.S.: 517121
Frank Burgess (*Founder*)

Subsidiary (Non-US):

Overon S.L (3)
Edificio Overon Virgilio 2, Pozuelo de Alarcon, Madrid, 28223, Spain
Tel.: (34) 915121700
Web Site: http://www.mediapro.es
Emp.: 30
Television Broadcasting Services
N.A.I.C.S.: 516120

Ovideo (3)
Avenida Diagonal 177 Planta 14, 8035, Barcelona, Spain
Tel.: (34) 932530320
Web Site: http://www.ovideo.com
Sales Range: $25-49.9 Million
Emp.: 2
Advertising Services
N.A.I.C.S.: 541890

Park Media (3)
Bullidor s/n, Sant Just Desvern, 8960, Barcelona, Spain
Tel.: (34) 934806100
Emp.: 14
Video Production Services
N.A.I.C.S.: 512110
Jaume Ferrus Guash (*Gen Mgr*)

Reddion B.V. (3)
Van Nellewg 1, 3044BC, Rotterdam, Netherlands
Tel.: (31) 102061000
Sales Range: $10-24.9 Million
Emp.: 45
N.A.I.C.S.: 541810

T & Media (3)
Rua Comandante Joao Belo 64 Maputo, Maputo, Mozambique
Tel.: (258) 84 49 70 200
Audio Visual Production Services
N.A.I.C.S.: 512110

Umedia Sports Advertising S.L. (3)
Avda Diagonal 177 14a Planta, Barcelona, 08018, Spain
Tel.: (34) 93 476 15 51
Advertising Agencies
N.A.I.C.S.: 541810
Albert Ramon (*Dir-Mktg*)

Unitecnic Media Solutions (3)
Edificio IMAGINA Avinguda Diagonal 177, 08018, Barcelona, Spain
Tel.: (34) 934175490
Web Site: https://www.unitecnic.com
Emp.: 50
Television Broadcasting Services
N.A.I.C.S.: 516120

Zeligstudio (3)
Passatge Mendez Vigo 3, 08009, Barcelona, Spain
Tel.: (34) 93 467 22 37
Audio & Video Production Services
N.A.I.C.S.: 512110

Subsidiary (Domestic):

Hill & Knowlton, Inc. (2)
3 World Trade Ctr 175 Greenwich St 29th Fl, New York, NY 10007
Tel.: (212) 885-0300
Web Site: https://hillandknowlton.com
Sales Range: $25-49.9 Million
Emp.: 120
Public Relations Services
N.A.I.C.S.: 541820
AnnaMaria DeSalva (*CEO & Chm-Global*)

Branch (Non-US):

B.I.G. Prague (3)
Opletalova 55, 110 00, Prague, 1, Czech Republic
Tel.: (420) 2216024557
Rev: $1,599,379
Emp.: 30
Public Relations Services
N.A.I.C.S.: 541820

Branch (Domestic):

Blanc & Otus Public Relations (3)
60 Green St, San Francisco, CA 94111
Tel.: (415) 856-5100
Web Site: http://www.blancandotus.com
Emp.: 30
Public Relations Services
N.A.I.C.S.: 541820
Tony Hynes (*CEO*)

Branch (Domestic):

Blanc & Otus Public Relations (4)
20 Park Plz Ste 1120, Boston, MA 02116-4308
Tel.: (617) 451-6070
Web Site: http://www.bando.com

Sales Range: $10-24.9 Million
Emp.: 10
Public Relations Services
N.A.I.C.S.: 541820

Blanc & Otus Public Relations (4)
206 E 9th St Ste 1850, Austin, TX 78701
Tel.: (512) 691-0650
Web Site: http://www.blancandotus.com
Sales Range: $10-24.9 Million
Emp.: 10
Public Relations Services
N.A.I.C.S.: 541820

Branch (Non-US):

Feedback/Hill & Knowlton (3)
ul. Raclawicka 95, 02-634, Warsaw, Poland
Tel.: (48) 22 646 22 02
Sales Range: $10-24.9 Million
Emp.: 39
Public Relations Services
N.A.I.C.S.: 541820

Gambit Hill & Knowlton (3)
Fridtjof Nansens Plass 4, Oslo, 0160, Norway
Tel.: (47) 22 04 82 00
Web Site: http://www.gambit.no
Sales Range: $10-24.9 Million
Emp.: 80
Public Relations Services
N.A.I.C.S.: 541820

Gulf Hill & Knowlton (3)
Prince Mamdouh bin Abdulaziz Street, PO Box 251, Office 2108 Al-Rajhi Building, Riyadh, 11411, Saudi Arabia
Tel.: (966) 1 472 5555
Web Site: http://www.hillandknowlton.com
Public Relations Services
N.A.I.C.S.: 541820

Gulf Hill & Knowlton (3)
312 Al Safeena building Near Lamcy Plaza Karama, Dubai, United Arab Emirates
Tel.: (971) 4 33 44 930
Web Site: http://www.hillandknowlton.com
Public Relations
N.A.I.C.S.: 541820
Melanie Faithful Kent (*Sr VP-Europe*)

Gulf Hill & Knowlton (3)
1 Government Ave Bldg 4th Fl Ofc 402, PO Box 1596, Manama, Bahrain
Tel.: (973) 17 533532
Web Site: http://www.hkstrategies.com
Sales Range: $25-49.9 Million
Emp.: 10
Public Relations
N.A.I.C.S.: 541820

HKDP Communications & Public Affairs (3)
500 Rue Saint Jacques Ouest Suite 1530, Montreal, H2Y 1S1, QC, Canada
Tel.: (514) 395-0375
Web Site: https://hkstrategies.ca
Sales Range: $25-49.9 Million
Emp.: 15
Public Relations Services
N.A.I.C.S.: 541820
Daniel Matte (*VP & Gen Mgr*)

HKDP Communications & Public Affairs (3)
500 Grande Allee Est Bureau 250, Quebec, G1R 2J7, QC, Canada
Tel.: (418) 523-3352
Web Site: https://www.hkstrategies.ca
Sales Range: $25-49.9 Million
Emp.: 25
Public Relations Services
N.A.I.C.S.: 541820
Josiane Hebert (*VP & Asst Gen Mgr*)

Branch (Domestic):

Hill & Knowlton (3)
PO Box 2125, San Juan, PR 00922-2126
Tel.: (787) 474-2525
Web Site: http://www.hillandknowlton.com
Sales Range: $25-49.9 Million
Emp.: 3
Public Relations
N.A.I.C.S.: 541820

Branch (Non-US):

Hill & Knowlton (Canada) Limited (3)
50 O'Connor Street Suite 1115, Ottawa,
K1P 6L2, ON, Canada
Tel.: (613) 238-4371
Web Site: http://www.hillandknowlton.ca
Sales Range: $10-24.9 Million
Emp.: 45
Public Relations
N.A.I.C.S.: 541820

Hill & Knowlton (China) Public Relations Co. Ltd (3)
Scitech Tower Suite 1901 22 Jianguomenwai Avenue, Beijing, 100004, China
Tel.: (86) 10 6512 8811
Sales Range: $25-49.9 Million
Public Relations
N.A.I.C.S.: 541820

Hill & Knowlton (China) Public Relations Co. Ltd. (3)
37th Floor The Center 989 Chang Le Road, Shanghai, 200031, China
Tel.: (86) 21 5109 7070
Web Site: http://www.hkstrategies.com
Sales Range: $25-49.9 Million
Emp.: 60
Public Relations Services
N.A.I.C.S.: 541820

Hill & Knowlton (SEA) Pvt. Ltd. (3)
50 Scotts Road 04-01, Singapore, 228242, Singapore
Tel.: (65) 6338 2881
Web Site: http://www.hillandknowlton.com
Sales Range: $10-24.9 Million
Emp.: 50
Public Relations
N.A.I.C.S.: 541820

Hill & Knowlton (SEA) Sdn. Bhd. (3)
7th floor Wisma Genting, Jalan Sultan Ismail, Kuala Lumpur, 50250, Malaysia
Tel.: (60) 3 2026 0899
Web Site: http://www.hillandknowlton.com
Public Relations Services
N.A.I.C.S.: 541820
Justin Then (*Mng Dir*)

Hill & Knowlton (UK) Ltd. (3)
49 Clerkenwell Green, London, EC1R 0EB, United Kingdom
Tel.: (44) 20 7413 3000
Web Site: http://www.hillandknowlton.co.uk
Sales Range: $75-99.9 Million
Public Relations Services
N.A.I.C.S.: 541820
Simon Whitehead (*CEO*)

Hill & Knowlton Australia Pty. Ltd. (3)
Level 7 235 Pyrmont Street, Pyrmont, 2009, NSW, Australia
Tel.: (61) 2 9268 0242
Web Site: http://www.hillandknowlton.com.au
Sales Range: $25-49.9 Million
Emp.: 30
Public Relations Services
N.A.I.C.S.: 541820

Hill & Knowlton Brazil (3)
Rua Andre Ampère 34 8 andar, Sao Paulo, 04562-080, SP, Brazil
Tel.: (55) 11 5503 2860
Web Site: http://www.hkbrasil.com
Sales Range: $25-49.9 Million
Emp.: 25
Public Relations Services
N.A.I.C.S.: 541820
Daniel Medina (*Gen Mgr*)

Hill & Knowlton Captiva (3)
Alcantara 271 Piso 4th Fl, Las Condes, Santiago, Chile
Tel.: (56) 2 372 0420
Web Site: http://www.hkcaptiva.cl
Sales Range: $10-24.9 Million
Emp.: 30
Public Relations Services
N.A.I.C.S.: 541820

Hill & Knowlton Eesti AS (3)
Bremeni Krik 1, 10123, Tallinn, Estonia
Tel.: (372) 6 800 480
Web Site: http://www.hillandknowlton.ee
Sales Range: $25-49.9 Million
Emp.: 13
Public Relations Services
N.A.I.C.S.: 541820

Hill & Knowlton Espana, S.A. (3)

WPP PLC

WPP plc—(Continued)

Corsega Street 329 6th Floor, 08037, Barcelona, Spain
Tel.: (34) 93 410 82 63
Sales Range: $25-49.9 Million
Emp.: 15
Public Relations
N.A.I.C.S.: 541820

Hill & Knowlton Espana, S.A. (3)
Oquendo 23, 28006, Madrid, Spain
Tel.: (34) 91 435 11 22
Web Site: http://www.hkstrategies.es
Sales Range: $25-49.9 Million
Emp.: 20
Public Relations
N.A.I.C.S.: 541820

Hill & Knowlton Frankfurt (3)
Darmstadter Landstrasse 112, Frankfurt am Main, 60598, Germany
Tel.: (49) 69 97 362 0
Web Site: http://www.hillandknowlton.de
Public Relations
N.A.I.C.S.: 541820
Udo Becker (Mng Dir)

Hill & Knowlton Hong Kong Ltd. (3)
36/F PCCW Tower Taikoo Place 979 Kings Road, Quarry Bay, China (Hong Kong)
Tel.: (852) 2894 6321
Web Site: http://www.hillandknowlton.com
Public Relations
N.A.I.C.S.: 541820

Hill & Knowlton International Belgium S.A./N.V. (3)
Rue Montoyer 51, PO Box 7, Brussels, 1000, Belgium
Tel.: (32) 2 737 95 00
Web Site: http://www.hkstrategies.be
Sales Range: $10-24.9 Million
Emp.: 35
Public Relations
N.A.I.C.S.: 541820
Thomas Tindemans (Chm)

Hill & Knowlton Italy (3)
Via Paolo Lomazzo 19, 20154, Milan, Italy
Tel.: (39) 02 31914 1
Web Site: http://www.hillandknowlton.com
Sales Range: $10-24.9 Million
Emp.: 40
Public Relations
N.A.I.C.S.: 541820

Hill & Knowlton Japan, Ltd. (3)
3-5-27 Roppongi Minato-Ku, Yamada Roppongi Building 8F, Tokyo, 106-0032, Japan
Tel.: (81) 3 4520 5800
Web Site: http://www.hillandknowlton.co.jp
Sales Range: $10-24.9 Million
Emp.: 30
Public Relations Services
N.A.I.C.S.: 541820

Hill & Knowlton Latvia (3)
Brivibas iela 40 36, Riga, LV 1050, Latvia
Tel.: (371) 67 24 0571
Web Site: http://www.hillandknowlton.lv
Sales Range: $25-49.9 Million
Emp.: 14
Public Relations Services
N.A.I.C.S.: 541820
Marika Kukuce (Office Mgr & Jr Acct Exec)

Hill & Knowlton Mexico (3)
Prol Paseo de la Reforma No 490 1st Fl, 01210, Mexico, DF, Mexico
Tel.: (52) 55 5729 4010
Web Site: http://www.hillandknowlton.com
Sales Range: $25-49.9 Million
Emp.: 25
Public Relations
N.A.I.C.S.: 541820
Daniel Karam (Mng Dir)

Hill & Knowlton Nederland B.V. (3)
Weerdestein 20, 1083 GA, Amsterdam, Netherlands
Tel.: (31) 20 404 47 07
Web Site: http://www.hillandknowlton.nl
Sales Range: $25-49.9 Million
Emp.: 25
Public Relations
N.A.I.C.S.: 541820
Jack de Vries (CEO, Mng Dir & Dir-Strategy)

Hill & Knowlton Result, Inc. (3)
324-8th Ave SW Ste 1165, Calgary, T2P 2Z2, AB, Canada
Tel.: (403) 299-9380
Web Site: http://www.hkstrategies.ca
Public Relations Services
N.A.I.C.S.: 541820

Hill & Knowlton Strategies GmbH (3)
Friedrichstrasse 148, 10117, Berlin, Germany
Tel.: (49) 30 28875859
Web Site: http://www.hkstrategies.de
Public Relations Services
N.A.I.C.S.: 541820
Susanne Marell (CEO)

Hill & Knowlton Strategies GmbH-Frankfurt (3)
Darmstadter Landstrasse 112, 60598, Frankfurt, Germany
Tel.: (49) 69 97362 10
Web Site: http://www.hkstrategies.de
Public Relations Services
N.A.I.C.S.: 541820

Hill & Knowlton Sweden AB (3)
Vasagatan 11, S-111 20, Stockholm, Sweden
Tel.: (46) 8 402 89 00
Web Site: http://www.hillandknowlton.se
Sales Range: $10-24.9 Million
Emp.: 40
Public Relations Services
N.A.I.C.S.: 541820
Oscar Thorbjornsen (CEO)

Hill & Knowlton Thailand (3)
Unit 14C 14th Fl Q House Ploenjit Bldg 598 Ploenchit Rd, Lumpini Pathumwan, Bangkok, 10330, Thailand
Tel.: (66) 2 627 3501
Web Site: http://www.hkstrategies.com
Sales Range: $10-24.9 Million
Emp.: 40
Public Relations Services
N.A.I.C.S.: 541820
Kanpirom Ungpakorn (Mng Dir)

Hill & Knowlton de Argentina (3)
Lavalle 1675 Piso 7 Oficina 8, Ciudad Autonoma de, 1654, Buenos Aires, Argentina
Tel.: (54) 11 4737 2300
Web Site: http://www.hillandknowlton.com
Sales Range: $25-49.9 Million
Emp.: 10
Public Relations Services
N.A.I.C.S.: 541820

Hill & Knowlton de Guatemala (3)
Centro Corporativo Guayacan Avenida Reforma 6-39 Zona 10 Nivel 9, Guatemala, Guatemala
Tel.: (502) 2420 8390
Web Site: http://www.hillandknowlton.com
Public Relations Services
N.A.I.C.S.: 541820
Fernando Bolanos (Mng Dir)

Branch (Domestic):

Hill & Knowlton, Inc (3)
106 East College Ave Ste 730, Tallahassee, FL 32301
Tel.: (850) 222-0075
Advetising Agency
N.A.I.C.S.: 541810

Hill & Knowlton, Inc. (3)
10 Corporate Park Ste 200, Irvine, CA 92606
Tel.: (949) 223-2300
Web Site: http://www.hillandknowlton.com
Sales Range: $25-49.9 Million
Emp.: 20
Public Relations Services
N.A.I.C.S.: 541820

Hill & Knowlton, Inc. (3)
607 14th St NW Ste 300, Washington, DC 20005-2000
Tel.: (202) 333-7400
Web Site: http://www.hkstrategies.com
Sales Range: $25-49.9 Million
Emp.: 60
Public Relations
N.A.I.C.S.: 541820

Hill & Knowlton, Inc. (3)
201 E Kennedy Blvd Ste 1611, Tampa, FL 33602
Tel.: (813) 221-0030

Web Site: http://www.hkstrategies.com
Sales Range: $25-49.9 Million
Emp.: 20
Public Relations Services
N.A.I.C.S.: 541820
James Fuller (Exec VP)

Hill & Knowlton, Inc. (3)
825 3rd Ave, New York, NY 10022-4731
Tel.: (212) 885-0300
Web Site: http://www.hillplusknowltonstrategies.com
Sales Range: $25-49.9 Million
Public Relations Services
N.A.I.C.S.: 541820
Avra Lorrimer (Exec VP)

Hill & Knowlton, Inc. (3)
222 Merchandise Mart Plz Ste 275, Chicago, IL 60654
Tel.: (312) 255-1200
Web Site: http://www.hillandknowlton.com
Sales Range: $10-24.9 Million
Emp.: 45
Public Relations Services
N.A.I.C.S.: 541820
Liz Torrez (Exec VP)

Hill & Knowlton, Inc. (3)
1001 Fannin St Ste 500, Houston, TX 77002
Tel.: (713) 752-1900
Sales Range: $25-49.9 Million
Emp.: 12
Public Relations Services
N.A.I.C.S.: 541820
Marvin Singleton (Exec VP)

Hill & Knowlton, Inc. (3)
6300 Wilshire Blvd 10th Fl, Los Angeles, CA 90048
Tel.: (310) 633-9400
Web Site: http://www.hillandknowlton.com
Sales Range: $10-24.9 Million
Emp.: 40
Public Relations
N.A.I.C.S.: 541820

Hill & Knowlton, Inc. (3)
60 Green St, San Francisco, CA 94111
Tel.: (415) 281-7120
Web Site: http://www.hillandknowlton.com
Sales Range: $10-24.9 Million
Emp.: 35
Public Relations
N.A.I.C.S.: 541820
Chip Scarinzi (Sr VP-Tech-US)

Branch (Non-US):

Hill + Knowlton Strategies Italy S.R.L. (3)
Via dei Magazzini Generali, 00154, Rome, Italy
Tel.: (39) 06 977991
Web Site: http://www.hkstrategies.it
Public Relations Services
N.A.I.C.S.: 541820
Sandro Pello (VP)

PubliCom/Hill & Knowlton (3)
Charilaou Trikoupi & Xenias 5 Street, Amarousiou, Athens, 14562, Greece
Tel.: (30) 21 0 628 1800
Web Site: http://www.hkstrategies.com
Sales Range: $25-49.9 Million
Emp.: 15
Public Relations Services
N.A.I.C.S.: 541820

Branch (Domestic):

Rockey Hill & Knowlton (3)
1218 Third Ave Ste 700, Seattle, WA 98101
Tel.: (206) 728-1100
Web Site: http://www.hillandknowlton.com
Sales Range: $25-49.9 Million
Emp.: 12
Public Relations Services
N.A.I.C.S.: 541820

Branch (Domestic):

Hill & Knowlton (4)
1218 3rd Ave Ste 700, Seattle, WA 98101-3063
Tel.: (503) 248-9468
Sales Range: $10-24.9 Million
Emp.: 5
Public Relations Services
N.A.I.C.S.: 541820

INTERNATIONAL PUBLIC

Rockey Hill & Knowlton (4)
421 W Riverside Ave Ste 450, Spokane, WA 99201-0415
Tel.: (509) 744-3350
Web Site: http://www.hillandknowlton.com
Sales Range: $10-24.9 Million
Emp.: 6
Public Relations Services
N.A.I.C.S.: 541820
Jennifer P. West (COO)

Subsidiary (Domestic):

J. Walter Thompson Company (2)
175 Greenwich St Fl 16, New York, NY 10007
Tel.: (212) 210-7000
Web Site: http://www.jwt.com
Sales Range: $50-74.9 Million
Emp.: 110
Marketing & Advertising
N.A.I.C.S.: 541810
Maureen Tan (CEO-Bangkok)

Subsidiary (Non-US):

AIMS Polska sp. z o.o. (3)
ul Flory 9/10, 00-586, Warsaw, Poland
Tel.: (48) 22 331 66 67
Web Site: http://www.aims.pl
Sales Range: $25-49.9 Million
Emp.: 2
N.A.I.C.S.: 541810

Unit (Non-US):

Action Line (3)
Aribenos 2740, Buenos Aires, 1428, Argentina
Tel.: (54) 11 4784 0043
Web Site: http://www.actionline.com
Consumer Marketing, Telemarketing
N.A.I.C.S.: 541810

Action Line Telemarketing Brazil (3)
Av Paulista 1 009 9 floor, Sao Paulo, 01311-100, Brazil
Tel.: (55) 1132542400
Web Site: https://actionline.com.br
Direct Marketing, Telemarketing
N.A.I.C.S.: 541810

Subsidiary (Non-US):

Adam 360 Ltd. (3)
House No 5 2nd Soula Loop, North Labone, Accra, Ghana
Tel.: (233) 302784685
Web Site: https://www.adamsghana.com
Advertising Services
N.A.I.C.S.: 541810

Altai Communications (3)
House 733-124 St 4 Qala-e-Fatullah, Kabul, Afghanistan
Tel.: (93) 79 888 000
N.A.I.C.S.: 541810

Unit (Non-US):

Burrows Shenfield (3)
The Burrows Building 5 Rayleigh Road, Shenfield, Brentwood, CM13 1AB, Essex, United Kingdom
Tel.: (44) 1277246666
Emp.: 150
Direct Marketing, Full Service, Sales Promotion
N.A.I.C.S.: 541810

Subsidiary (Non-US):

Cheetham Bell/JWT (3)
WPP Campus 1 New Quay Street, Manchester, M3 4BN, United Kingdom
Tel.: (44) 1618328884
Web Site: https://cheethambell.com
Sales Range: $25-49.9 Million
Emp.: 50
Marketing & Advertising
N.A.I.C.S.: 541810
David Bell (CEO)

Corporacion / JWT (3)
Convencion 1343 Piso 8, Montevideo, Uruguay
Tel.: (598) 2 902 3434
Sales Range: $10-24.9 Million
Emp.: 50
Full Service
N.A.I.C.S.: 541810

AND PRIVATE COMPANIES

WPP PLC

DDFH&B Advertising Ltd. (3)
3 Christ Church Square, Dublin, 8, Ireland
Tel.: (353) 141 066 66
Web Site: http://www.ddfhb.ie
Sales Range: Less than $1 Million
Emp.: 100
Advertising Services
N.A.I.C.S.: 541810

DDH&M Advertising Pty. Ltd. (3)
74 Glenara Ave, North Highlands, Harare, Zimbabwe
Tel.: (263) 4 746 981
Sales Range: $25-49.9 Million
Emp.: 13
N.A.I.C.S.: 541810
Praxie Ozangare *(Mng Dir)*

Unit (Domestic):

DesignKitchen (3)
1140 W Fulton Market, Chicago, IL 60607-1219
Tel.: (312) 455-0388
Advertising Services
N.A.I.C.S.: 541810

Subsidiary (Non-US):

Enterprise/JWT (3)
630 Sherbrooke W Suite 710, Montreal, H3A 1E4, QC, Canada
Tel.: (514) 287-3597
Web Site: http://www.jwtcanada.ca
Sales Range: $25-49.9 Million
Emp.: 20
N.A.I.C.S.: 541810

Subsidiary (Domestic):

Gorilla, LLC (3)
71 S Wacker Dr Ste 3550, Chicago, IL 60606
Tel.: (312) 243-8777
Web & Software Design & Development Services
N.A.I.C.S.: 541511
Todd Shall *(Mgr-Program)*

Subsidiary (Non-US):

Huts/JWT (3)
Iztok District 14 B Charles Darwin Street, 1113, Sofia, Bulgaria
Tel.: (359) 2 971 7182
Web Site: http://www.hutsjwt.com
N.A.I.C.S.: 541810
Yiannis Manakos *(Mng Dir)*

Imagem Global Maputo (3)
R Kwame Nkrumah 385, Maputo, Mozambique
Tel.: (258) 21 495 723
Web Site: http://www.teledata.mz
N.A.I.C.S.: 541810

J. Walter Thompson Argentina SRL (3)
Adolfo Alsina 465, Buenos Aires, C1087 AAE, Argentina
Tel.: (54) 11 4339 6100
Web Site: http://www.jwt.com
Marketing & Advertising
N.A.I.C.S.: 541810

J. Walter Thompson Canada Ltd. (3)
160 Bloor St E, Toronto, M4W 3P7, ON, Canada
Tel.: (416) 926-7300
Web Site: http://www.jwt.com
Sales Range: $25-49.9 Million
Marketing & Advertising
N.A.I.C.S.: 541810
Ari Elkouby *(Exec Creative Dir)*

Branch (Non-US):

J. Walter Thompson Caracas (3)
Ave La Estancia Chuao, Caracas, 1060, Venezuela
Tel.: (58) 212 902 3191
Web Site: http://www.jwt.com
Advetising Agency
N.A.I.C.S.: 541810

Subsidiary (Non-US):

J. Walter Thompson Chile Ltda. (3)
Avenida Ricardo Lyon 1262 Providencia, Santiago, 7510566, Chile
Tel.: (56) 2 230 9000
Web Site: http://www.jwt.com
Sales Range: $10-24.9 Million
Emp.: 50
Consumer Marketing
N.A.I.C.S.: 541810

J. Walter Thompson Colombia Ltda. (3)
Carrera 11B #96-59 piso 7, Bogota, Colombia
Tel.: (57) 1 744 1620
Web Site: http://www.jwt.com
Sales Range: $25-49.9 Million
Advetising Agency
N.A.I.C.S.: 541810

J. Walter Thompson El Salvador (3)
Calle Loma Linda No 251, Colonia San Benito, San Salvador, 503, El Salvador
Tel.: (503) 2511 9700
Sales Range: $10-24.9 Million
Emp.: 29
Marketing & Advertising
N.A.I.C.S.: 541810
Reynaldo Pino *(Dir-Creative)*

J. Walter Thompson Espana S.A. (3)
Castellana 130 8th Floor, Madrid, 28046, Spain
Tel.: (34) 91 592 3300
Sales Range: $25-49.9 Million
Emp.: 16
Communications
N.A.I.C.S.: 541810
Facundo Goldaracena *(Dir-Creative)*

Branch (Domestic):

J. Walter Thompson Espana S.A. - Barcelona (4)
Calatrava 71, 08017, Barcelona, Spain
Tel.: (34) 93 413 1414
Web Site: http://www.jwt.com
Sales Range: $10-24.9 Million
Marketing & Advertising
N.A.I.C.S.: 541810

Subsidiary (Non-US):

J. Walter Thompson GmbH (3)
Hanauer Landstrasse 147, Frankfurt, 60314, Germany
Tel.: (49) 69 405 76 0
Sales Range: $25-49.9 Million
Emp.: 100
Marketing & Advertising
N.A.I.C.S.: 541810

J. Walter Thompson Italia - S.p.A. (3)
Via Lomazzo 19, 20154, Milan, 20154, Italy
Tel.: (39) 02 33634 1
Web Site: http://www.jwtitalia.it
Sales Range: $25-49.9 Million
Emp.: 100
N.A.I.C.S.: 541810
Daniela Radice *(Exec Dir-Creative)*

J. Walter Thompson Lda. (3)
Avenida Escazu Edificio 202 Suite 201, 10101, San Jose, Costa Rica
Tel.: (506) 22890606
Sales Range: $25-49.9 Million
Emp.: 15
Marketing & Advertising
Rene Zuleta *(Mng Dir)*

J. Walter Thompson Poland Sp. z o.o. (3)
Ul Zurawia 45, 00-680, Warsaw, Poland
Tel.: (48) 22 440 1200
Web Site: http://www.jwt.com.pl
Sales Range: $10-24.9 Million
Emp.: 50
Marketing & Advertising
N.A.I.C.S.: 541810

J. Walter Thompson Portugal (3)
Avenida 24 de Julho 62-64, Rua Bartolomeu Dias, 1200-869, Lisbon, Portugal
Tel.: (351) 210960500
Sales Range: $25-49.9 Million
Emp.: 18
Marketing & Advertising
N.A.I.C.S.: 541810
Nuno Santos *(CEO)*

Subsidiary (Domestic):

J. Walter Thompson Puerto Rico, Inc. (3)
Calle C 60 Urb Industrial Mario Julia, San Juan, PR 00920
Tel.: (787) 474-2501
Web Site: http://www.jwt.com
Sales Range: $10-24.9 Million
Emp.: 100
Marketing & Advertising
N.A.I.C.S.: 541810
Carlos Laureano *(CEO)*

Subsidiary (Non-US):

J. Walter Thompson Roma S.r.l. (3)
Via dei Magazzini Generali 38, 00154, Rome, Italy
Tel.: (39) 06571081
Sales Range: $10-24.9 Million
Emp.: 50
Marketing & Advertising
N.A.I.C.S.: 541810

J. Walter Thompson S.A./N.V. (3)
Victoria Reginaplantsoen 1 Sint-Joost-ten-Node, 1210, Brussels, Belgium
Tel.: (32) 25809090
Sales Range: $25-49.9 Million
Emp.: 25
Marketing & Advertising
N.A.I.C.S.: 541810
Jean-Jacques Luycx *(CEO)*

Unit (Domestic):

JWT Dialogue (4)
86 Avenue Franklin Roosevelt, 1050, Brussels, Belgium
Tel.: (32) 2 890 90 00
Web Site: http://www.jwtbrussels.com
Sales Range: $10-24.9 Million
Emp.: 25
Corporate Communications, Web (Banner Ads, Pop-ups, etc.)
N.A.I.C.S.: 541810

Subsidiary (Non-US):

J. Walter Thompson SAS (3)
51 Avenue Andre Morizet, 92513, Boulogne, France
Tel.: (33) 141058000
Web Site: http://www.jwt.com
Sales Range: $25-49.9 Million
Emp.: 100
Communications, Direct Marketing, Publicity/Promotions
N.A.I.C.S.: 541810
Alain Lauent *(Mng Dir)*

Unit (Domestic):

Hill & Knowlton/Thompson Corp. (4)
88 Avenue Charles de Gaulle, CEDEX, 922522, Neuilly-sur-Seine, France
Tel.: (33) 141054400
Web Site: http://www.hillandknowlton.com
Sales Range: $10-24.9 Million
Emp.: 40
Financial, Government/Political/Public Affairs, Investor Relations, Public Relations
N.A.I.C.S.: 541820

RPCA (4)
65 rue Chardon Lagache, 75016, Paris, France
Tel.: (33) 1 42 30 81 00
Web Site: http://www.rpca.fr
Consumer Marketing, Public Relations Agency
N.A.I.C.S.: 541820

Subsidiary (Non-US):

J. Walter Thompson South Africa (Pty) Ltd. (3)
2929 William Nicol Drive Building 2 1st Floor Bryanston Office Park, Bryanston, 2128, Johannesburg, South Africa
Tel.: (27) 11 806 8000
Web Site: http://www.jwt.com
Sales Range: $25-49.9 Million
Emp.: 70
Full Service
N.A.I.C.S.: 541810
Qingqile Mdlulwa *(Chief Creative Officer-Grp)*

Subsidiary (Domestic):

J. Walter Thompson Cape Town (Pty) Ltd. (4)
2nd Floor Cape Quarter Square 27 Somerset Road Green Point, Cape Town, 8001, South Africa
Tel.: (27) 214262880
Web Site: http://www.jwt.com
Sales Range: $10-24.9 Million
Emp.: 45
N.A.I.C.S.: 541810
Jim Faulds *(CEO)*

Subsidiary (Non-US):

J. Walter Thompson UK Limited (3)
Greater London House Hampstead Road, London, NW1 7QP, United Kingdom
Tel.: (44) 2076116333
Advetising Agency
N.A.I.C.S.: 541810
Pip Hulbert *(CEO)*

J. Walter Thompson de Mexico, S.A. de C.V. (3)
Av Lago Alberto 319 3rd floor Col Granada, 11520, Mexico, Mexico
Tel.: (52) 5557294000
Marketing & Advertising Services
N.A.I.C.S.: 541810
Agustin Rodriguez *(CEO)*

J. Walter Thompson do Brasil Ltda. (3)
Rua Mario Amaral 50, Paraiso, Sao Paulo, 04002-020, Brazil
Tel.: (55) 1138888000
Marketing & Advertising
N.A.I.C.S.: 541810
Ricardo John *(CEO & COO)*

JWT Amsterdam (3)
Amsteldijk 166, 1079 LH, Amsterdam, Netherlands
Tel.: (31) 203019696
Sales Range: $10-24.9 Million
Emp.: 75
Marketing & Advertising
N.A.I.C.S.: 541810

Group (Non-US):

JWT Asia Pacific (3)
50 Scotts Road #01-01, Singapore, 228242, Singapore
Tel.: (65) 68805088
Web Site: http://www.jwt.com
Regional Managing Office
N.A.I.C.S.: 551114
Matthew Parry *(Mng Dir-Hong Kong)*

Subsidiary (Non-US):

Asiatic Marketing Communications, Ltd. (4)
House 146 Road 13B Block E, Banani, Dhaka, 1213, Bangladesh
Tel.: (880) 248811521
Web Site: https://www.asiaticmcl.com
N.A.I.C.S.: 541810
Aly Zaker *(Chm)*

J. Walter Thompson (China) Co., Ltd. (4)
25/F No 989 Chang Le Road The Center, Shanghai, 200031, China
Tel.: (86) 21 2405 0000
Web Site: http://www.jwtchina.com
Marketing & Advertising
N.A.I.C.S.: 541810
Sheung Yan Lo *(Chief Creative Officer-APAC)*

Subsidiary (Domestic):

J. Walter Thompson (Beijing) Co., Ltd. (5)
RM 501 5/F JinBao Tower No 89 JinBao Street, Dongcheng District, Beijing, 100005, China
Tel.: (86) 10 8515 9599
Web Site: http://www.jwt.com
Emp.: 150
Marketing & Advertising
N.A.I.C.S.: 541810
Janet Dai *(Mng Dir)*

Subsidiary (Non-US):

J. Walter Thompson (M) Sdn. Bhd. (4)
Level 6 Wismean Anta Jalan Changtat Senantan, Damansara Heights, Kuala Lumpur, 50490, Malaysia

WPP PLC

WPP plc—(Continued)
Tel.: (60) 3 2718 6100
Sales Range: $10-24.9 Million
Emp.: 60
Full Service
N.A.I.C.S.: 541810
Edwin Leong *(Deputy Chm & Exec Dir-Creative)*

Subsidiary (Domestic):

J. Walter Thompson (Singapore) Pte. Ltd. (4)
50 Scotts Rd Unit 01-01, Singapore, 228242, Singapore
Tel.: (65) 6880 5088
Sales Range: $10-24.9 Million
Emp.: 90
Full Service
N.A.I.C.S.: 541810
Thomas Ong *(Dir-Bus Dev)*

Subsidiary (Non-US):

J. Walter Thompson (Taiwan) Limited (4)
2nd Floor 156 Jian Kang Rd, Taipei, 105, Taiwan
Tel.: (886) 2 3766 1000
Web Site: http://www.jwttpi.com.tw
Sales Range: $10-24.9 Million
Emp.: 100
Marketing & Advertising
N.A.I.C.S.: 541810

J. Walter Thompson (Thailand) Co., Ltd. (4)
19/F UBC II Bldg 591 Sukhumvit 33 Road, Klongton Nua Waltana, Bangkok, 10110, Thailand
Tel.: (66) 2 240 8000
Web Site: http://www.jwt.com
Marketing & Advertising
N.A.I.C.S.: 541810
Ratchanida Nakpresha *(CFO)*

J. Walter Thompson Australia Pty. Ltd. (4)
The Rosella Complex Building 18A 64 Balmain Street, Richmond, 3121, VIC, Australia
Tel.: (61) 398689111
Web Site: https://www.wundermanthompson.com
Sales Range: $10-24.9 Million
Emp.: 110
Marketing & Advertising
N.A.I.C.S.: 541810
Angela Morris *(Chief Strategy Officer)*

Branch (Domestic):

J. Walter Thompson Australia Pty. Ltd. - Sydney (5)
Level 7 235 Pyrmont Street, Pyrmont, 2009, NSW, Australia
Tel.: (61) 2 9947 2222
Web Site: http://www.jwt.com
Direct Marketing, Full Service, Sales Promotion
N.A.I.C.S.: 541810
Paul Everson *(Mng Dir)*

Subsidiary (Non-US):

J. Walter Thompson Co., Ltd. (4)
38/F PCCW Tower Taikoo Place 979 King's Road, Quarry Bay, China (Hong Kong)
Tel.: (852) 2280 3333
Emp.: 100
Advertising Specialties, Full Service
N.A.I.C.S.: 541810
Mark Webster *(Chm)*

J. Walter Thompson India Pvt. Ltd. (4)
3rd Floor Peninsula Chambers Ganpatrao Kadam Marg, Lower Parel West, Mumbai, 400 013, India
Tel.: (91) 22 4098 5555
Marketing & Advertising
N.A.I.C.S.: 541810
Senthil Kumar *(Chief Creative Officer)*

Subsidiary (Domestic):

Contract Advertising (India) Limited (5)
Vaswani Chambers 264 Dr Annie Bessant Road, Mumbai, 400 030, India
Tel.: (91) 22 40569696
Full Service
N.A.I.C.S.: 541810
Rohit Srivastava *(Chief Strategy Officer)*

Branch (Domestic):

Contract Advertising (India) Limited (6)
Chimes 61 Sector 44, Gurgaon, 122003, Haryana, India
Tel.: (91) 11 42300399
Marketing & Advertising
N.A.I.C.S.: 541810
V. Bhaskar Preenja *(Sr VP & Gen Mgr)*

Contract Advertising (India) Limited (6)
158 Lavelle Road, Bengaluru, 560 001, India
Tel.: (91) 80 401 382 00
Marketing & Advertising
N.A.I.C.S.: 541810
Jayanth Govindraj *(Sr VP-Strategic & Plng)*

Branch (Domestic):

JWT Bangalore (5)
9th Floor Embassy Heights 13 Magrath Road, Bengaluru, 560025, India
Tel.: (91) 80 4261 2100
Web Site: http://www.jwt.com
Sales Range: $50-74.9 Million
Emp.: 80
Marketing & Advertising
N.A.I.C.S.: 541810

JWT Chennai (5)
26 Ethiraj Salai, Egmore, Chennai, 600 008, India
Tel.: (91) 44 4292 9600
Web Site: http://www.jwt.com
Sales Range: $50-74.9 Million
Emp.: 52
Marketing & Advertising
N.A.I.C.S.: 541810

JWT Kolkata (5)
Bengal Intelligent Park Omega Bldg 18th Floor, Block EP&GP Salt Lake Sector V, Kolkata, 700091, India
Tel.: (91) 33 4407 5300
Web Site: http://www.jwt.com
Emp.: 100
Marketing & Advertising
N.A.I.C.S.: 541810

Subsidiary (Non-US):

J. Walter Thompson International (NZ) Ltd. (4)
Suite 2 1 Imperial Bldg 44 Queen Street, Auckland, 1010, New Zealand
Tel.: (64) 93799625
Web Site: http://www.jwt.com
Sales Range: $10-24.9 Million
Emp.: 45
Marketing & Advertising
N.A.I.C.S.: 541810
Megan Clark Cook *(Mng Partner)*

Branch (Non-US):

JWT Colombo (4)
26B Alwis Place, 00300, Colombo, Sri Lanka
Tel.: (94) 112 498 900
Web Site: http://www.jwt.com
N.A.I.C.S.: 541810
Alyna Omar *(CEO)*

JWT Jakarta (4)
Jalan Proklamasi No 46, Jakarta, 10320, Indonesia
Tel.: (62) 21 310 0367
Web Site: http://www.jwt.com
Full Service
N.A.I.C.S.: 541810
Vaishali Sarkar *(CEO)*

Subsidiary (Non-US):

JWT Japan Limited (4)
Yebisu Garden Place Tower 30F 4-20-3 Ebisu, Shibuya-ku, Tokyo, 150-6030, Japan
Tel.: (81) 3 3280 9500
Web Site: http://www.jwt.com
Marketing & Advertising
N.A.I.C.S.: 541810
Hironobu Kitajima *(CEO)*

JWT Korea, Ltd. (4)
8F JS Tower 144 20 Samsung-dong, Kangnam-gu, Seoul, 135-090, Korea (South)
Tel.: (82) 2 3148 3600
Sales Range: $10-24.9 Million
Emp.: 31
Full Service
N.A.I.C.S.: 541810
Gyoo Yang Oh *(COO)*

Branch (Non-US):

JWT Manila (4)
7th F Equitable Bank Tower 8751 Paseo de Roxas, Salcedo Village, Makati, 1227, Philippines
Tel.: (63) 2 864 8700
Web Site: http://www.jwt.com
Sales Range: $10-24.9 Million
Emp.: 55
Marketing & Advertising
N.A.I.C.S.: 541810

JWT Vietnam (4)
Suite 1601 The Metropolitan 235 Dong Khai Street, District 1, Ho Chi Minh City, Vietnam
Tel.: (84) 8 3822 9580
Web Site: http://www.jwt.com
N.A.I.C.S.: 541810
Trung Nguyen *(Fin Dir)*

Subsidiary (Non-US):

Thompson Nepal Private Limited (4)
5th Fl Saket Complex, Kathmandu, 44600, Tripureshwor, Nepal
Tel.: (977) 1 4 265 777
N.A.I.C.S.: 541810
Joydeb Chakravarty *(Mng Dir)*

Branch (Domestic):

JWT Atlanta (3)
10B Glenlake Pkwy Ste 400, Atlanta, GA 30328
Tel.: (404) 365-7300
Web Site: http://www.jwt.com
Sales Range: $10-24.9 Million
Emp.: 80
Advetising Agency
N.A.I.C.S.: 541810
Tahlisha Williams *(Chief Inclusion, Equity & Diversity Officer)*

Branch (Non-US):

JWT Bahrain (3)
502 Almoayyad Tower, Seef District, Manama, 18490, Bahrain
Tel.: (973) 1756 3700
Web Site: http://www.jwt.com
Emp.: 13
N.A.I.C.S.: 541810

JWT Beirut (3)
47 Patriarch Howeiyek Street Sabbagh Bld 3rd Floor, Bab Idriss, Beirut, 11/1/3093, Lebanon
Tel.: (961) 1 973 030
Web Site: http://www.jwt.com
Sales Range: $25-49.9 Million
Emp.: 80
Advertising Services
N.A.I.C.S.: 541810

JWT Cairo (3)
306 Corniche el Nile, Maadi, Cairo, 12411, Egypt
Tel.: (20) 2 2525 4740
Web Site: http://www.jwt.com
Advetising Agency
N.A.I.C.S.: 541810
Hany Shoukry *(CEO)*

JWT Casablanca (3)
3 Angle Rue Alfred de Musset & Abdelkader El Mazini, Casablanca, 20000, Morocco
Tel.: (212) 522 22 1660
Web Site: http://www.jwt.com
Sales Range: $25-49.9 Million
Emp.: 25
N.A.I.C.S.: 541810
Hazem Kaddour *(Mng Dir)*

JWT Damascus (3)
Shoshara Building Hilal Al Bizim Street, Malki, Damascus, 5566, Syria
Tel.: (963) 11 373 7703
Web Site: http://www.jwt.com
Emp.: 10

JWT Dubai (3)
Business Central Tower Block B 36 Rd 51 flr, PO Box 202032, Media City, Dubai, 282032, United Arab Emirates
Tel.: (971) 4 369 8400
Web Site: http://www.jwt.com
Sales Range: $25-49.9 Million
Advertising Services
N.A.I.C.S.: 541810

JWT Helsinki (3)
Pursimiehenkatu 26, Entrance-Albertinkatu 36, 00150, Helsinki, Finland
Tel.: (358) 9 8562 6200
Web Site: http://www.jwt.com
Emp.: 120
Marketing & Advertising
N.A.I.C.S.: 541810

JWT Jeddah (3)
Nojoud Ctr Block-A 2nd Fl Tahlia Rd, Jeddah, 21414, Saudi Arabia
Tel.: (966) 2 669 0888
Advertising Services
N.A.I.C.S.: 541810
Nagib Badreddine *(CEO)*

JWT Kuwait (3)
ali al salem street Al Jawhara Tower 21st Floor, Kuwait, Kuwait
Tel.: (965) 2226 6500
Emp.: 65
Advertising Services
N.A.I.C.S.: 541810

JWT Lima (3)
Paseo de la Republica 5883, Lima, 18, Peru
Tel.: (51) 1 610 6767
Web Site: http://www.jwt.com
Sales Range: $25-49.9 Million
Emp.: 60
Marketing & Advertising
N.A.I.C.S.: 541810

Subsidiary (Non-US):

JWT Lithuania San Vilnius (3)
Pylimo Street 30/2, Vilnius, 011413, Lithuania
Tel.: (370) 5 2333 520
Web Site: http://www.san.lt
Sales Range: $25-49.9 Million
Emp.: 8
N.A.I.C.S.: 541810

Branch (Non-US):

JWT Riyadh (3)
NCCI Bldg South Tower 7th Floor, King Fahd Road, Riyadh, 11445, Saudi Arabia
Tel.: (966) 1 218 0500
Web Site: http://www.jwt.com
N.A.I.C.S.: 541810

Subsidiary (Domestic):

JWT Specialized Communications, Inc. (3)
2425 Olympic Blvd, Santa Monica, CA 90404
Tel.: (310) 309-8282
Web Site: http://www.jwt.com
Emp.: 20
Advertising Agencies, Advertising Specialties, Business-To-Business, Consulting, Corporate Identity, Over-50 Market, Recruitment
N.A.I.C.S.: 541810

Branch (Domestic):

JWT Inside (4)
3630 Peachtree Rd Ne Ste 1200, Atlanta, GA 30326-1552
Tel.: (404) 817-0993
Sales Range: $50-74.9 Million
Emp.: 14
Communications, Recruitment
N.A.I.C.S.: 541810

JWT Inside (4)
607 14th St NW Ste 300, Washington, DC 20005
Tel.: (202) 628-2076
Marketing & Advertising
N.A.I.C.S.: 541810
Jhon Windlth *(Dir-Client Svcs)*

AND PRIVATE COMPANIES — WPP PLC

Branch (Non-US):

JWT Inside (4)
160 Bloor St E 8th Floor, Toronto, M4W 3P7, ON, Canada
Tel.: (416) 926-7304
N.A.I.C.S.: 541810

Branch (Domestic):

JWT Inside (4)
2425 Olympic Blvd, Santa Monica, CA 90404
Tel.: (310) 309-8282
Sales Range: $50-74.9 Million
Emp.: 15
N.A.I.C.S.: 541810
Bruce Carey *(Dir-Creative-Los Angels)*

JWT Specialized Communications (4)
303 2nd St N Twr Ste 300, San Francisco, CA 94107
Tel.: (415) 490-6479
Emp.: 2
Communications, Recruitment
N.A.I.C.S.: 541810

Branch (Non-US):

JWT Tunis (3)
91 Avenue Louis Braille, El Khadra, Tunis, 1003, Tunisia
Tel.: (216) 71 806 250
Web Site: http://www.jwt.com
N.A.I.C.S.: 541810

Branch (Domestic):

JWT U.S.A., Inc. (3)
591 Camino De La Reina Ste 314, San Diego, CA 92108-3105
Tel.: (619) 297-9334
N.A.I.C.S.: 541810

JWT U.S.A., Inc. (3)
3630 Peachtree Rd NE, Atlanta, GA 30326
Tel.: (404) 365-7300
Web Site: http://www.jwt.com
Sales Range: $10-24.9 Million
Emp.: 100
Marketing & Advertising
N.A.I.C.S.: 541810

JWT U.S.A., Inc. (3)
550 Town Ctr Dr, Dearborn, MI 48126
Tel.: (313) 615-3100
Web Site: http://www.teamdetroit.com
Sales Range: $250-299.9 Million
Emp.: 1,400
Marketing & Advertising
N.A.I.C.S.: 541810

JWT U.S.A., Inc. (3)
11540 N Community House Rd Ste 200, Charlotte, NC 28277-2155
Tel.: (704) 540-8797
Web Site: http://www.jwt.com
Sales Range: $10-24.9 Million
Emp.: 2
Marketing & Advertising
N.A.I.C.S.: 541810

JWT U.S.A., Inc. (3)
555 17th St Ste 300, Denver, CO 80202-1239
Tel.: (303) 296-7668
Web Site: http://www.jwt.com
Sales Range: $10-24.9 Million
Emp.: 13
Marketing & Advertising
N.A.I.C.S.: 541810

JWT U.S.A., Inc. (3)
1001 Fannin Ste 500, Houston, TX 77002
Tel.: (713) 659-6688
Web Site: http://www.jwt.com
Sales Range: $10-24.9 Million
Emp.: 25
Full Service
N.A.I.C.S.: 541810

JWT U.S.A., Inc. (3)
10401 N Meridian St Ste 216, Indianapolis, IN 46290-1090
Tel.: (317) 844-5181
Web Site: http://www.jwt.com
Sales Range: $10-24.9 Million
Emp.: 4
Marketing & Advertising
N.A.I.C.S.: 541810

JWT U.S.A., Inc. (3)
White Station Tower Bldg 5050 Poplar Ave Ste 1000, Memphis, TN 38157-0101
Tel.: (901) 682-9656
Web Site: http://www.jwt.com
Sales Range: $10-24.9 Million
Emp.: 3
Marketing & Advertising
N.A.I.C.S.: 541810

JWT U.S.A., Inc. (3)
6309 E 100 2nd St, Tulsa, OK 74145
Tel.: (918) 250-1884
Web Site: http://www.jwt.com
Sales Range: $10-24.9 Million
Emp.: 2
Marketing & Advertising
N.A.I.C.S.: 541810
Kyle McQuaid *(Sr VP)*

JWT U.S.A., Inc. (3)
340 Thomas More Pkwy Ste 200, Crestview Hills, KY 41017-5101
Tel.: (859) 341-6603
Web Site: http://www.jwt.com
Sales Range: Less than $1 Million
Emp.: 3
Marketing & Advertising
N.A.I.C.S.: 541810

JWT U.S.A., Inc. (3)
1660 Hwy 100 S Ste 432, Minneapolis, MN 55416-1534
Tel.: (952) 545-4733
Web Site: http://www.jwt.com
Sales Range: Less than $1 Million
Emp.: 5
Marketing & Advertising
N.A.I.C.S.: 541810

JWT U.S.A., Inc. (3)
16435 N Scottsdale Rd Ste 195, Scottsdale, AZ 85254
Tel.: (480) 991-0489
Web Site: http://www.jwt.com
Sales Range: $10-24.9 Million
Emp.: 3
Marketing & Advertising
N.A.I.C.S.: 541810

JWT U.S.A., Inc. (3)
175 W Ostend St Ste #A-2, Baltimore, MD 21230
Tel.: (410) 567-8910
Web Site: http://www.jwt.com
Sales Range: $10-24.9 Million
Emp.: 4
N.A.I.C.S.: 541810

JWT U.S.A., Inc. (3)
1 Dallas Ctr 350 N Saint Paul St Ste 2410, Dallas, TX 75201
Tel.: (214) 468-3460
Web Site: http://www.jwt.com
Sales Range: $10-24.9 Million
Emp.: 11
Full Service
N.A.I.C.S.: 541810

JWT U.S.A., Inc. (3)
2600 Douglas Ave Ste 610, Coral Gables, FL 33134
Tel.: (305) 476-7702
Web Site: http://www.jwt.com
Sales Range: $10-24.9 Million
Emp.: 11
Full Service
N.A.I.C.S.: 541810

JWT U.S.A., Inc. (3)
221 Yale Ave N Ste 520, Seattle, WA 98109
Tel.: (206) 516-3036
Web Site: http://www.jwt.com
Sales Range: $10-24.9 Million
Emp.: 8
Full Service
N.A.I.C.S.: 541810

Subsidiary (Non-US):

JWT Werbeagentur GmbH (3)
Fleischmarkt 10/6th Floor, A-1010, Vienna, Austria
Tel.: (43) 1 93 9990
Web Site: http://www.jwt.at
Sales Range: $25-49.9 Million
Emp.: 55
N.A.I.C.S.: 541810

Koenigsteiner Agentur GmbH (3)
Jurastr 8, 70565, Stuttgart, Germany
Tel.: (49) 711990070
Web Site: https://www.koenigsteiner-agentur.de
Sales Range: $25-49.9 Million
Emp.: 260
HR Marketing Agency
N.A.I.C.S.: 541810

Subsidiary (Domestic):

aws:pwu PersonalMarketing GmbH (4)
Hans-Henny-Jahnn-Weg 41-45, 22085, Hamburg, Germany
Tel.: (49) 402274210
Web Site: https://aws-personalmarketing.de
Sales Range: $50-74.9 Million
Advetising Agency
N.A.I.C.S.: 541810

Subsidiary (Non-US):

LTC Advertising Lagos (3)
2nd Fl Motorway Centre 1 Motorway Ave, PMB 21772 Ikeja, Lagos, Nigeria
Tel.: (234) 1 471 2056
Web Site: http://www.ltc-jwtlagos.net
N.A.I.C.S.: 541810

Manajans Thompson Istanbul (3)
Buyukdere Cad Harman Sokak No 4 Kat 7 Levent, 80498, Istanbul, Turkiye
Tel.: (90) 212 317 2000
Web Site: http://www.manajans-jwt.com
Emp.: 90
Full Service
N.A.I.C.S.: 541810

Mar.Te srl (3)
Via Aldo Moro 15, 01019, Vetralla, Italy
Tel.: (39) 0761466017
Web Site: https://www.martecostruzioni.it
Sales Range: $25-49.9 Million
Emp.: 3
N.A.I.C.S.: 541810

Master Publicidade S/A (3)
Avenue 7 de Setembro 4476, 80250-210, Curitiba, Brazil
Tel.: (55) 41 3025 1162
N.A.I.C.S.: 541810

Norlop JWT (3)
Tulcan 1017 y Luque, PO Box 0901, 5063, Guayaquil, Ecuador
Tel.: (593) 4 245 1811
Sales Range: $25-49.9 Million
Emp.: 100
Marketing & Advertising
N.A.I.C.S.: 541810

ORC Image & Strategies d'Employeur (3)
6 boulevard des Capucines, Paris, 75009, France
Tel.: (33) 147615800
Sales Range: $25-49.9 Million
Emp.: 80
N.A.I.C.S.: 541810

Branch (Domestic):

ORC Image & Strategies d'Employeur (4)
5-7 Rue Vert Bois, 59000, Lille, France
Tel.: (33) 3 20 31 50 00
Sales Range: $10-24.9 Million
Emp.: 4
N.A.I.C.S.: 541810

ORC Image & Strategies d'Employeur (4)
1 allee claude Debussy, 69130, Lyon, Cedex 03, France
Tel.: (33) 4 72 13 54 16
Sales Range: $10-24.9 Million
Emp.: 10
N.A.I.C.S.: 541810

ORC Image & Strategies d'Employeur (4)
La Fregate 98 bis quai de la Fosse CS 413, CEDEX, 44124, Nantes, France
Tel.: (33) 2 40 92 15 01
Sales Range: $10-24.9 Million
Emp.: 2
N.A.I.C.S.: 541810

ORC Image & Strategies d'Employeur (4)
14 Quai Roubert de L'isle, Strasbourg, 67000, France
Tel.: (33) 3 88 79 14 15
Sales Range: $10-24.9 Million
N.A.I.C.S.: 541810

ORC Image & Strategies d'Employeur (4)
805 Avenue De Bregasque, 13090, Aix-en-Provence, France
Tel.: (33) 4 42 91 57 44
Sales Range: $10-24.9 Million
Emp.: 2
N.A.I.C.S.: 541810

ORC Image & Strategies d'Employeur (4)
2 Allees Remi Raymond, 31840, Seilh, France
Tel.: (33) 5 61 59 22 55
Sales Range: $10-24.9 Million
Emp.: 4
N.A.I.C.S.: 541810
Olivier Rigaud *(Mgr-Agency)*

Subsidiary (Non-US):

Partners/JWT Budapest (3)
Alkotas Street 50, Budapest, 1138, Hungary
Tel.: (36) 1488 0500
Web Site: http://www.jwt.com
Emp.: 25
Marketing & Advertising
N.A.I.C.S.: 541810

Subsidiary (Domestic):

Pierry Inc. (3)
785 Broadway St, Redwood City, CA 94063
Web Site: https://www.pierryinc.com
Digital Marketing & Advertising Agency
N.A.I.C.S.: 541810
J. Brooke Hern *(Chief Legal Officer & Exec VP-New Bus & Ops)*

Unit (Non-US):

Rediffusion Wunderman (3)
Building No 9A 4th Floor DLF Cyber City, Phase III, Gurgaon Haryana, New Delhi, 122 002, India
Tel.: (91) 124 4609 000
Web Site: http://www.wundermanindia.com
Direct Marketing, Event Marketing, Interactive Agencies, Sales Promotion, Strategic Planning/Research
N.A.I.C.S.: 541810

Subsidiary (Non-US):

SAN Riga (3)
Tirgonu Str 8, LV-1050, Riga, Latvia
Tel.: (371) 7215221
Web Site: http://www.san.lv
N.A.I.C.S.: 541810

SAN Vilnius (3)
Dominiku g 5, Vilnius, LT-01131, Lithuania
Tel.: (370) 5 2333 520
Web Site: http://www.san.lt
N.A.I.C.S.: 541810

SM International d.o.o (3)
Podmilscakova ulica 25, 1000, Ljubljana, Slovenia
Tel.: (386) 15896810
Web Site: https://www.sm-studiomarketing.com
Advetising Agency
N.A.I.C.S.: 541810
Tina Bolcar Repovs *(Dir)*

Subsidiary (Non-US):

Studio Marketing Komunikacije d. o. o. Zagreb (4)
Petrinjska 31, 10000, Zagreb, Croatia
Tel.: (385) 98485622
Advetising Agency
N.A.I.C.S.: 541810

Subsidiary (Domestic):

Studio Marketing Ljubljana, d. o. o. (4)
Podmilscakova c 25, Ljubljana, 1000, Slovenia
Tel.: (386) 1 589 6810
Web Site: http://www.sm-studiomarketing.com
Advetising Agency

WPP PLC

INTERNATIONAL PUBLIC

WPP plc—(Continued)
N.A.I.C.S.: 541810
Tina Bolcar Repovs (Dir)

Subsidiary (Non-US):

Scala/JWT (3)
Str Trotusului Nr 39 Sector 1, 012141, Bucharest, Romania
Tel.: (40) 121 224 1460
N.A.I.C.S.: 541810

Unit (Domestic):

Shaw Wunderman (3)
285 Madison Ave 17th Fl, New York, NY 10016
Tel.: (212) 941-3000
Advetising Agency
N.A.I.C.S.: 541810

Subsidiary (Non-US):

Silikons Advertising Network (3)
Vene 20-5, 10141, Tallinn, Estonia
Tel.: (372) 631 4535
N.A.I.C.S.: 541810

Team Cosmo Zurich AG (3)
Giesshubelstrasse 62A, 8045, Zurich, Switzerland
Tel.: (41) 442777111
Web Site: http://www.teamcosmo.ch
Full Service
N.A.I.C.S.: 541810
Remy Fabrikant (CEO)

Thompson Kenya Ltd. (3)
5th Floor Chancery Building, PO Box 34537-00100, Valley Road, Nairobi, Kenya
Tel.: (254) 202710021
N.A.I.C.S.: 541810

Wunderman (3)
Avenida del Valle 961 Oficina 1707, Huechuraba, Santiago, Chile
Tel.: (56) 2 940 9910
Web Site: http://www.wunderman.com
Emp.: 37
N.A.I.C.S.: 541810

Wunderman (3)
Avenida La Estancia Centro Benaven Torre C Piso 5, Chuao, Caracas, 1060, Venezuela
Tel.: (58) 212 902 9200
Direct Marketing, Full Service, Sales Promotion
N.A.I.C.S.: 541810

Wunderman (3)
23 Avenida 31-53 Zona 12, 01012, Guatemala, Guatemala
Tel.: (502) 24770682
Direct Marketing, Full Service, Information Technology, Planning & Consultation, Publicity/Promotions, Sales Promotion
N.A.I.C.S.: 541810
Raul Martinez-Mont (Gen Mgr)

Branch (Domestic):

Wunderman (3)
233 N Michigan Ave Ste 1500, Chicago, IL 60601-5519
Tel.: (312) 596-2500
Sales Range: $100-124.9 Million
Emp.: 150
Advetising Agency
N.A.I.C.S.: 541810
Ian Sohn (Pres)

Subsidiary (Non-US):

Wunderman (3)
Nadrazni 32, 150 00, Prague, 5, Czech Republic
Tel.: (420) 2 21 420 130
Web Site: http://www.wunderman.cz
Direct Marketing, Full Service, Information Technology, Publicity/Promotions, Sales Promotion
N.A.I.C.S.: 541810

Wunderman (3)
137 Chrysostomou Smirnis St, Moshato, 18346, Athens, Greece
Tel.: (30) 210 480 5600
Web Site: http://www.wunderman.gr

Direct Marketing, Full Service, Information Technology, Planning & Consultation, Publicity/Promotions, Sales Promotion
N.A.I.C.S.: 541810

Wunderman (3)
Unit 2 Wintersells Road, Byfleet, KT14 7LF, Surrey, United Kingdom
Tel.: (44) 1932 335 000
Direct Marketing, Full Service, Information Technology, Planning & Consultation, Sales Promotion
N.A.I.C.S.: 541810
Ian Haworth (Exec Dir-Creative-UK & EMEA)

Wunderman (3)
ul Dobra 56/66, 00-312, Warsaw, Poland
Tel.: (48) 22 552 7000
N.A.I.C.S.: 541810

Wunderman (3)
Esentepe Buyukdere Cad Astoria AVM No 127, 34394, Istanbul, Turkiye
Tel.: (90) 2123172000
N.A.I.C.S.: 541810

Wunderman (3)
No 74 1st Floor Fagun Mansion Ethiraj Salai, Egmore, Chennai, 600 008, India
Tel.: (91) 4442929600
Emp.: 25
N.A.I.C.S.: 541810

Branch (Domestic):

Wunderman (3)
285 Madison Ave, New York, NY 10017
Tel.: (212) 941-3000
Advetising Agency
N.A.I.C.S.: 541810
Seth Solomons (CEO-North America)

Subsidiary (Non-US):

Wunderman (3)
L61 Solaris Mont Kiara No 2, Jalan Solaris, 50480, Kuala Lumpur, Malaysia
Tel.: (60) 3 6207 6800
Direct Marketing, Full Service, Information Technology, Planning & Consultation, Publicity/Promotions, Sales Promotion
N.A.I.C.S.: 541810

Wunderman (3)
Level 3 21-31 Goodwood St, Richmond, 3121, VIC, Australia
Tel.: (61) 3 9426 1222
N.A.I.C.S.: 541810

Wunderman (3)
18th Floor No 6 Hsin Yi Road, Sec 4 Da-An District, Taipei, 10683, Taiwan
Tel.: (886) 2 2326 7300
Web Site: http://www.wunderman.com
Advetising Agency
N.A.I.C.S.: 541810

Wunderman (3)
Room 605-606 Ocean Tower, 550 Yan An Road East, Shanghai, 200001, China
Tel.: (86) 21 6351 8588
Emp.: 57
N.A.I.C.S.: 541810
K2 Kung (Mng Dir-South China)

Wunderman (3)
Greater London House Hampstead Road, Hampstead Rd 3rd Fl, London, NW1 7QP, United Kingdom
Tel.: (44) 2076116333
Emp.: 250
Direct Marketing, Sales Promotion
N.A.I.C.S.: 541810
Mel Edwards (CEO-Global)

Wunderman (3)
35 Clarence St, Sydney, 2000, NSW, Australia
Tel.: (61) 297787700
Direct Marketing, Sales Promotion
N.A.I.C.S.: 541810
Hurol Inan (CEO)

Wunderman (3)
Rua Mario Amaral 50, Paraiso, Sao Paulo, 04002-020, Brazil
Tel.: (55) 1130265500
Emp.: 18
N.A.I.C.S.: 541810

Wunderman

La Matriz Rio Rosas 26, 28003, Madrid, Spain
Tel.: (34) 914563262
Advetising Agency
N.A.I.C.S.: 541810

Wunderman (3)
32/F 633 Kings Road, North Point, China (Hong Kong)
Tel.: (852) 28846668
Direct Marketing, Full Service, Information Technology, Planning & Consultation, Publicity/Promotions, Sales Promotion
N.A.I.C.S.: 541810

Wunderman (3)
Strandboulevarden 122 4, DK-2100, Copenhagen, Denmark
Tel.: (45) 32887777
Web Site: http://www.wunderman.dk
Emp.: 60
N.A.I.C.S.: 541810
Chandra Mostov (Partner)

Wunderman (3)
Avenidas Eng Duarte Pacheco Amoreiras Torre 1 9th Fl, 1070-101, Lisbon, Portugal
Tel.: (351) 217227500
Direct Marketing, Full Service, Information Technology, Planning & Consultation, Sales Promotion
N.A.I.C.S.: 541810

Branch (Domestic):

Wunderman (3)
303 2nd St 8th Fl S Tower, San Francisco, CA 94107
Tel.: (415) 371-6800
Emp.: 30
Advetising Agency
N.A.I.C.S.: 541810

Subsidiary (Non-US):

Wunderman (3)
Kleyerstrasse 19, 60326, Frankfurt am Main, Germany
Tel.: (49) 697502701
Web Site: http://www.wunderman.com
Emp.: 143
N.A.I.C.S.: 541810

Wunderman (3)
Via Morimondo 26, 20143, Milan, Italy
Tel.: (39) 02336341
N.A.I.C.S.: 541810

Branch (Domestic):

Wunderman (3)
2010 Main St Ste 800, Irvine, CA 92614-7214
Tel.: (949) 754-2000
Emp.: 20
Advetising Agency
N.A.I.C.S.: 541810

Subsidiary (Non-US):

Wunderman (3)
Hardturmstrasse 133, 8005, Stockholm, Sweden
Tel.: (46) 444483838
Emp.: 82
Addvanced Marketing Solutions
N.A.I.C.S.: 541810

Wunderman (3)
Hardturmstrasse 133, Postfach, 8005, Zurich, Switzerland
Tel.: (41) 444483838
Emp.: 82
Advertising Agencies, Communications
N.A.I.C.S.: 541810

Wunderman (3)
Level 4 Corner Augustus Terrace & Parnell Rise, Parnell, Auckland, New Zealand
Tel.: (64) 93085444
Web Site: http://www.wunderman.com
Direct Marketing, Full Service, Information Technology, Planning & Consultation, Publicity/Promotions, Sales Promotion
N.A.I.C.S.: 541810

Wunderman (3)
Via dei Magazzini Generali 38, 00154, Rome, Italy
Tel.: (39) 06571081
Emp.: 10

N.A.I.C.S.: 541810

Wunderman (3)
Pasaje Tupiza 3950 Capital, C1425AFB, Buenos Aires, Argentina
Tel.: (54) 1157778500
Emp.: 190
Direct Marketing, Full Service, Information Technology, Planning & Consultation, Publicity/Promotions, Sales Promotion
N.A.I.C.S.: 541810
Juan Pablo Jurado (Pres)

Branch (Domestic):

Wunderman (3)
Courvoisier Ctr II 601 Brickell Key Dr Ste 1100, Miami, FL 33131
Tel.: (305) 347-1900
Sales Range: $10-24.9 Million
Emp.: 30
Advetising Agency
N.A.I.C.S.: 541810

Subsidiary (Non-US):

Wunderman (3)
Avenida Diagonal 508-2 5f Edificio Beethoven, 08006, Barcelona, Spain
Tel.: (34) 932388818
Direct Marketing, Full Service, Sales Promotion
N.A.I.C.S.: 541810

Wunderman (3)
Manuel Avila Camacho # 176, 4th Fl, Colonia Reforma Social, Mexico, 11650, CP, Mexico
Tel.: (52) 5515000055
Direct Marketing, Full Service, Information Technology, Planning & Consultation, Publicity/Promotions, Sales Promotion
N.A.I.C.S.: 541810

Wunderman (3)
300 Beach Road The Concourse 33-00, Singapore, 199555, Singapore
Tel.: (65) 62950025
Emp.: 25
Direct Marketing, Full Service, Information Technology, Planning & Consultation, Publicity/Promotions, Sales Promotion
N.A.I.C.S.: 541810
Nimesh Desai (COO)

Wunderman (3)
989 Siam Tower 19th Fl Unit B1 Rama I Rd Kwaeng Pathumwam, Khet Patumwan, Bangkok, 10330, Thailand
Tel.: (66) 26580950
Web Site: http://www.wunderman.com
Direct Marketing, Full Service, Interactive Agencies, Planning & Consultation, Publicity/Promotions, Sales Promotion
N.A.I.C.S.: 541810

Wunderman Beijing (3)
#502 Building 17 Jianwal SOHO 39 East 3rd Ring Road, Chao Yang District, Beijing, 100022, China
Tel.: (86) 10 5869 4575
N.A.I.C.S.: 541810

Unit (Non-US):

Wunderman Direct (3)
102 Western Service Road, Gallo manor Ext 6, 2052, Johannesburg, South Africa
Tel.: (27) 11 797 9900
Emp.: 43
N.A.I.C.S.: 541810
Unati Moalusi (Chief People Officer)

Unit (Domestic):

Wunderman Interactive (3)
233 N Michigan Ave Ste 1500, Chicago, IL 60601-5519
Tel.: (312) 596-2500
Interactive Advertising Agency
N.A.I.C.S.: 541810

Subsidiary (Non-US):

Wunderman Korea (3)
9F Bosung Bldg 891-25, Daechi-dong Gangnam-gu, Seoul, 135-840, Korea (South)
Tel.: (82) 2 531 9600
Emp.: 25
N.A.I.C.S.: 541810

AND PRIVATE COMPANIES

WPP PLC

Unit (Non-US):

Wunderman Limited (3)
Greater London House Hampstead Road, London, NW1 7QP, United Kingdom
Tel.: (44) 2076116333
Interactive Agencies
N.A.I.C.S.: 541810
Julian Ormerod (Mng Dir)

Branch (Domestic):

Wunderman Seattle (3)
221 Yale Ave N Ste 500, Seattle, WA 98109
Tel.: (206) 505-7500
Emp.: 300
Advetising Agency
N.A.I.C.S.: 541810
Justin Marshall (Mng Dir)

Unit (Domestic):

Wunderman Team Detroit (3)
Corp Crossing at Fairlane 550 Town Ctr Dr Ste 300, Dearborn, MI 48126
Tel.: (313) 615-3400
Web Site: http://www.teamdetroit.com
Emp.: 1,100
Advetising Agency
N.A.I.C.S.: 541810

Subsidiary (Non-US):

Wunderman Thompson (3)
51 Avenue Andre Morizet, 92513, Boulogne-Billancourt, Cedex, France
Tel.: (33) 141058000
Web Site:
  http://www.wundermanthompson.com
Advertising Services
N.A.I.C.S.: 541810
Tom Murphy (Chief Creative Officer-North America)

Wunderman Thompson - Guangzhou (3)
Room 02-03 23/F Onelink Center 230-232 Tianhe Road, Guangzhou, 510630, China
Tel.: (86) 2028633339
Advertising Services
N.A.I.C.S.: 541810

facts & fiction GmbH (3)
Anna-Schneider-Steig 2, Rheinauhafen, 50678, Cologne, Germany
Tel.: (49) 2219515300
Emp.: 80
Consumer Marketing, Information Technology, Planning & Consultation
N.A.I.C.S.: 541810
Jorg Krauthauser (Mng Partner)

Subsidiary (Domestic):

iStrategyLabs LLC (3)
641 S St NW, Washington, DC 20001
Tel.: (202) 683-9980
Web Site: http://www.isl.co
Digital Marketing & Creative User Services
N.A.I.C.S.: 541613
Darien Jay Saul (CEO)

Subsidiary (Domestic):

Johannes Leonardo (2)
115 Broadway - 20th Fl, New York, NY 10006
Tel.: (212) 462-8111
Web Site:
  https://www.johannesleonardo.com
Digital Agency
N.A.I.C.S.: 541810
Jan Jacobs (Co-Founder & Co-Chief Creative Officer)

Landor Associates (2)
44 Montgomery St Fl 17, San Francisco, CA 94104
Tel.: (415) 365-1700
Web Site: http://www.landor.com
Emp.: 30
N.A.I.C.S.: 541810
Mary Zalla (Pres-Consumer Brands)

Branch (Non-US):

Landor Associates (3)
44 rue des Petites Ecuries, Paris, 75010, France
Tel.: (33) 1 53 34 31 00
Web Site: http://www.landor.com
N.A.I.C.S.: 541810
Luc Speisser (Chief Innovation Officer)

Landor Associates (3)
Complejo Triada Torre, Madrid, 28036, Spain
Tel.: (34) 91 766 6369
Web Site: http://www.landor.com
N.A.I.C.S.: 541810

Landor Associates (3)
1227 Les Acacias, 1201, Geneva, Switzerland
Tel.: (41) 229084066
Web Site: http://www.landor.com
N.A.I.C.S.: 541810

Landor Associates (3)
Via Tortona 37, Milan, I-20144, Italy
Tel.: (39) 02 7645 171
Web Site: http://www.landor.com
Emp.: 25
N.A.I.C.S.: 541810
Antonio Marazza (Gen Mgr)

Landor Associates (3)
Sjolyst Plass 4, 0278, Oslo, Norway
Tel.: (47) 9240 1087
Web Site: http://www.landor.com
N.A.I.C.S.: 541810

Landor Associates (3)
An der Alster 47, Hamburg, 20099, Germany
Tel.: (49) 40 378 5670
Web Site: http://www.landor.com
N.A.I.C.S.: 541810

Landor Associates (3)
Level 7 2 More London Riverside, London, SE1 2AP, United Kingdom
Tel.: (44) 207 880 8000
Web Site: http://www.landor.com
Emp.: 40
N.A.I.C.S.: 541810

Branch (Domestic):

Landor Associates (3)
233 N Michigan Ave Ste 1400, Chicago, IL 60601
Tel.: (312) 596-1444
Web Site: http://www.landor.com
N.A.I.C.S.: 541810

Landor Associates (3)
110 Shillito Pl, Cincinnati, OH 45202
Tel.: (513) 419-2300
Web Site: http://www.landor.com
Sales Range: $25-49.9 Million
Emp.: 180
N.A.I.C.S.: 541810

Landor Associates (3)
230 Park Ave S 6th Fl, New York, NY 10003
Tel.: (212) 614-5050
Web Site: http://www.landor.com
Sales Range: $25-49.9 Million
Emp.: 100
N.A.I.C.S.: 541810

Branch (Non-US):

Landor Associates (3)
Room 502 5/F JinBao Tower No 89 JinBao Street, Dongcheng District, 100005, Beijing, China
Tel.: (86) 10 6539 1107
Web Site: http://www.landor.com
N.A.I.C.S.: 541810

Subsidiary (Domestic):

Lightspeed Online Research, Inc. (2)
3 Mountain View Rd 3rd Fl, Warren, NJ 07059-6711
Tel.: (908) 605-4500
Web Site:
  http://www.lightspeedresearch.com
Emp.: 120
Online Marketing Software Development Services
N.A.I.C.S.: 541511
Jennifer Carrea (CEO-Health-Americas & Global)

Mediapro USA, Inc. (2)
7331 NW 74th St, Miami, FL 33166
Tel.: (305) 357-6000
Web Site: https://mediaprous.tv
Television Broadcasting Services
N.A.I.C.S.: 516120
Erika Lucas (Gen Counsel)

PACE Advertising (2)
1065 Ave of the Americas, New York, NY 10018
Tel.: (212) 818-0111
Web Site: http://www.paceadv.com
Sales Range: $25-49.9 Million
Emp.: 20
Advertising Services
N.A.I.C.S.: 541810
Cara Faske (CEO)

Division (Domestic):

Green Advertising (3)
902 Clint Moore Rd Ste 108, Boca Raton, FL 33487-2846
Tel.: (561) 756-2500
Web Site: http://www.greenad.com
Sales Range: $25-49.9 Million
Emp.: 19
Advertising Services
N.A.I.C.S.: 541810
Phyllis M. Green (Chm)

Subsidiary (Domestic):

Possible Worldwide, Inc. (2)
5780 W Jefferson Blvd, Los Angeles, CA 90016
Tel.: (310) 202-2900
Sales Range: $25-49.9 Million
Emp.: 100
Digital/Interactive
N.A.I.C.S.: 541810
Nick Worth (Pres)

Subsidiary (Non-US):

BLUE Interactive Marketing (3)
Unit 3103 Bldg No 18 JianWai SOHO 39 E 3rd Ring Rd, Chao Yang District, Beijing, China
Tel.: (86) 10 5166 3960
Web Site: http://www.blue-interactive.com
N.A.I.C.S.: 541810

BLUE Interactive Marketing Pte. Ltd. (3)
1 Maritime Square Harbour-Front Centre #13-02, Singapore, 099253, Singapore
Tel.: (65) 63333336
Web Site: http://www.bluesingapore.com
E-Commerce, Electronic Media, Interactive Agencies, Internet/Web Design
N.A.I.C.S.: 541810

Branch (Non-US):

Possible Singapore (3)
1 Maritime Square, HarbourFront Centre #13-02, Singapore, 099253, Singapore
Tel.: (65) 6333 3336
Web Site: http://www.possible.com
Advertising, Performance Marketing & Creative Design Services
N.A.I.C.S.: 541613

Possible Worldwide (3)
Centro Corporativo El Roble Edificio Las Terrazas A Piso 2, Guachipelin de Escazu, 2010, San Jose, Costa Rica
Tel.: (506) 22890606
Sales Range: $25-49.9 Million
Emp.: 62
N.A.I.C.S.: 541810

Subsidiary (Non-US):

Quasar Media (3)
136-A 2nd Floor Vishal House, Zamrudpur Kailash Colony, New Delhi, 110048, India
Tel.: (91) 1129240252
Digital
N.A.I.C.S.: 541810

Subsidiary (Domestic):

Public Strategies, Inc. (2)
98 San Jacinto Blvd Ste 1200, Austin, TX 78701
Tel.: (512) 474-8848
Web Site: http://www.pstrategies.com
Sales Range: $25-49.9 Million
Emp.: 200
Public Relations Services
N.A.I.C.S.: 541820

Catherine Boshart (Principal)

Subsidiary (Non-US):

De la Calle, Madrazo, Mancera, S.C. (3)
Governor Protasio Tagle 81 Col San Miguel Chapultepec, Juarez, 11850, Mexico, DF, Mexico
Tel.: (52) 5510844500
Web Site: https://www.cmmsc.com.mx
Sales Range: $25-49.9 Million
Emp.: 25
Public Relations Services
N.A.I.C.S.: 541820
Luis de la Calle (Partner)

Subsidiary (Domestic):

Rockfish Digital (2)
3100 Market St Ste 100, Rogers, AR 72758
Tel.: (474) 464-0622
Web Site: http://www.rockfishdigital.com
Advetising Agency
N.A.I.C.S.: 541810
Dawn Maire (Pres & Chief Strategy Officer)

The Food Group, Inc. (2)
285 Madison Ave Fl 24, New York, NY 10017-6401
Tel.: (212) 725-5766
Web Site: http://www.thefoodgroup.com
Sales Range: $25-49.9 Million
Emp.: 23
N.A.I.C.S.: 541810

Branch (Domestic):

The Food Group (Chicago) (3)
233 N Michigan Ave 16th Fl, Chicago, IL 60601
Tel.: (312) 596-3333
Web Site: http://www.thefoodgroup.com
Sales Range: $25-49.9 Million
Emp.: 19
N.A.I.C.S.: 541810

The Food Group (Los Angeles) (3)
9714 Variel Ave, Chatsworth, CA 91311
Tel.: (818) 993-0304
Web Site: http://www.thefoodgroup.com
Rev.: $30,000,000
Emp.: 10
N.A.I.C.S.: 541810

The Food Group (Tampa) (3)
202B, Tampa, FL 33624
Tel.: (813) 933-0683
Web Site: http://www.thefoodgroup.com
Sales Range: $25-49.9 Million
Emp.: 13
N.A.I.C.S.: 541810
Mark Cotter (CEO)

Subsidiary (Domestic):

The Ogilvy Group, Inc (2)
636 11th Ave, New York, NY 10036-2010
Tel.: (212) 237-4000
Marketing Consulting Services
N.A.I.C.S.: 541613
Michael Frohlich (Grp CEO-UK)

Subsidiary (Domestic):

B/W/R (3)
9100 Wilshire Blvd Ste 500, Beverly Hills, CA 90212
Tel.: (310) 550-7776
Sales Range: $10-24.9 Million
Emp.: 80
Public Relations
N.A.I.C.S.: 541820
Nancy Ryder (Pres)

B/W/R (3)
825 3rd Ave 22-Fl, New York, NY 10022
Tel.: (212) 901-3920
Sales Range: $25-49.9 Million
Emp.: 16
N.A.I.C.S.: 541820
Nanci Ryder (Pres)

Feinstein Kean Healthcare (3)
111 Sutter St 11th Fl, San Francisco, CA 94104
Tel.: (415) 677-2898
Web Site: http://www.fkhealth.com
Sales Range: $25-49.9 Million
Emp.: 20
N.A.I.C.S.: 541810

WPP PLC
INTERNATIONAL PUBLIC

WPP plc—(Continued)

Feinstein Kean Healthcare (3)
245 1st St 14th Fl, Cambridge, MA 02142-1292
Tel.: (617) 577-8110
Web Site: http://www.fkhealth.com
Sales Range: $50-74.9 Million
Emp.: 50
N.A.I.C.S.: 541810
Jennifer Gosenza *(Sr VP)*

Ogilvy & Mather (3)
636 11th Ave, New York, NY 10036
Tel.: (212) 237-4000
Web Site: http://www.ogilvy.com
Sales Range: $1-4.9 Billion
Emp.: 11,000
Advertising Services
N.A.I.C.S.: 541810
Carla C. Hendra *(Vice Chm)*

Branch (Domestic):

A. Eicoff & Co. (4)
401 N Michigan Ave 4th Fl, Chicago, IL 60611-4212
Tel.: (312) 527-7183
Web Site: http://www.eicoff.com
Sales Range: $25-49.9 Million
Emp.: 125
Direct Response Television Advertising Services
N.A.I.C.S.: 541810
Mike Powell *(Sr VP & Exec Creative Dir)*

Branch (Non-US):

Adell Taivas Ogilvy (4)
J Jasinskio Street 16A, 2001, Vilnius, Lithuania
Tel.: (370) 5 252 65 22
Web Site: http://www.ogilvy.lt
Sales Range: $10-24.9 Million
Emp.: 41
Advertising Services
N.A.I.C.S.: 541810

BADJAR Ogilvy (4)
Level 12 Royal Domain Centre, 380 St Kilda Road, Melbourne, 3004, VIC, Australia
Tel.: (61) 3 9690 1477
Web Site: http://www.stwgroup.com.au
Sales Range: $50-74.9 Million
Emp.: 300
Advertising Services
N.A.I.C.S.: 541810

BCD Pinpoint Direct Marketing Inc. (4)
4th Floor Bloomingdale Bldg 205 Salcedo St, Legaspi Village, Manila, 1227, Philippines
Tel.: (63) 2 849 6999
Web Site: http://www.bcdpinpoint.com
Sales Range: $10-24.9 Million
Emp.: 30
Advertising Services
N.A.I.C.S.: 541810

Barker McCormac, Ogilvy & Mather (4)
The Brand Building Glenroy Crescent Highlands, Harare, Zimbabwe (100%)
Tel.: (263) 4 498 561
Advertising Services
N.A.I.C.S.: 541810

Bold Ogilvy Greece (4)
10 Imathias Str, Gerakas, Athens, 15344, Greece
Tel.: (30) 210 6660000
Web Site: http://www.boldogilvy.gr
Sales Range: $25-49.9 Million
Emp.: 106
Advertising Services
N.A.I.C.S.: 541810

Boomerang Communication (4)
1 bd Abdellatif Ben Kaddour 3rd floor, angle Boulevard Zerktouni, corner bd Zerktouni, Casablanca, Morocco
Tel.: (212) 522942712
Web Site: https://www.boomerang.ma
Advertising Services
N.A.I.C.S.: 541810
Mehdi Sebti *(Gen Mgr)*

CD Ogilvy & Mather (4)
Misikova 10A, 811 06, Bratislava, Slovakia (100%)
Tel.: (421) 5441 9059
Advertising Services
N.A.I.C.S.: 541810

CM&A Pvt. Ltd. (4)
Block 2 Arundel Office Park, Norfolk Rd Mt Pleasant, Harare, Zimbabwe (100%)
Tel.: (263) 4 301 226
Advertising Services
N.A.I.C.S.: 541810

Cactus Advertising & Marketing Ethiopia (4)
PO Box 5790, Addis Ababa, Ethiopia
Tel.: (251) 544 901
Advertising Services
N.A.I.C.S.: 541810

Care Company (4)
Am Modenapark 10/24, A-1030, Vienna, Austria
Tel.: (43) 1513 18 26
Advertising Services
N.A.I.C.S.: 541810

Castillo Ogilvy & Mather (4)
Oficentro Norte Antiguo Sovipe Klm 4 1/2, Carretera Norte Ste B, Managua, Nicaragua (100%)
Tel.: (505) 249 8493
Advertising Services
N.A.I.C.S.: 541810

Fogel Levin 2/OgilvyOne (4)
Nemal Tel Aviv Street No 40 Floor 2, Tel Aviv, 63506, Israel (100%)
Tel.: (972) 3 544 4883
Advertising Services
N.A.I.C.S.: 541810

Go Advertising Pty. Ltd. (4)
The Brand Building 15 Sloane Street, Bryanston, Johannesburg, 2021, South Africa
Tel.: (27) 11 709 6600
Web Site: http://www.ogilvygo.co.za
Advertising Services
N.A.I.C.S.: 541810

Grendene Ogilvy & Mather AG (4)
Bergstrasse 50, 8032, Zurich, Switzerland
Tel.: (41) 44 268 6363
Web Site: http://www.ogilvy.ch
Sales Range: $10-24.9 Million
Emp.: 25
Advertising Services
N.A.I.C.S.: 541810

Horizon Ogilvy (4)
Millennium Office Park Unit 1 Plot 128 Kgale Court, Gaborone, Botswana
Tel.: (267) 392 2655
Web Site: http://www.horizon.ogilvy.co.bw
Advertising Services
N.A.I.C.S.: 541810

Inglefield/Ogilvy & Mather Caribbean Ltd. (4)
29 Cipriani Blvd, Port of Spain, Trinidad & Tobago (100%)
Tel.: (868) 625 7006
Web Site: http://www.iomcaribbean.com
Sales Range: $10-24.9 Million
Emp.: 35
Advertising Services
N.A.I.C.S.: 541810
Anthony Inglefield *(Dir)*

MEMAC Ogilvy (4)
4 Abdel Rahman El Rafei St Mohandessin, Cairo, Egypt
Tel.: (20) 2 748 0202
Advertising Services
N.A.I.C.S.: 541810

MEMAC Ogilvy (4)
Future Trade Zone Shuwaikh Al Argan Building Block A 1st Floor, Safat, Kuwait, Kuwait (100%)
Tel.: (965) 461 0371
Web Site: http://www.memacogilvy.com
Advertising Services
N.A.I.C.S.: 541810
Patou Nuytemans *(Chief Growth Officer-Growth & Global Innovation)*

MEMAC Ogilvy (4)
Suhaily Plz 9th Floor Al Andlus St, PO Box 7868, Jeddah, 21472, Saudi Arabia
Tel.: (966) 2 651 0704

Web Site: http://www.memacogilvy.com
Sales Range: $10-24.9 Million
Emp.: 30
Advertising Services
N.A.I.C.S.: 541810
Ziad Ghawi *(Deputy Mng Dir)*

MEMAC Ogilvy (4)
Al-Attar Business Tower 24th Fl Sheikh Zayed Rd, PO Box 74170, Dubai, United Arab Emirates (100%)
Tel.: (971) 4 3320 002
Web Site: http://www.memacogilvy.com
Rev.: $16,000,000
Emp.: 180
Advertising Services
N.A.I.C.S.: 541810
Mary McFarland *(Mng Dir)*

MEMAC Ogilvy (4)
Rizkallah & Boutrous Centre Futuroscope Roundabout 8th Floor, Sin-El-Fil, Beirut, 114584, Lebanon (100%)
Tel.: (961) 1 486 065
Web Site: http://www.memacogilvy.com
Sales Range: $10-24.9 Million
Emp.: 55
Advertising Services
N.A.I.C.S.: 541810
Samer Abboud *(Reg Mng Dir-Iraq)*

MEMAC Ogilvy & Mather W.L.L. (4)
Offices 3501 3502 3503 3504 Almoayyed Tower Building 2504, Road 2382 Al Seef District, Manama, 428, Bahrain (100%)
Tel.: (973) 17 561756
Web Site: http://www.memacogilvy.com
Sales Range: $10-24.9 Million
Emp.: 40
Advertising Services
N.A.I.C.S.: 541810
Ghassan Boujacli *(Mng Dir)*

Marketing Counselors Ltd. (4)
15A Lady Musgrave Road, Kingston, 5, Jamaica (100%)
Tel.: (876) 927 9583
Web Site: http://www.tmarkc.com
Advertising Services
N.A.I.C.S.: 541810

Mather Communications s.r.o. (4)
Prohunu 13, 170 00, Prague, 7, Czech Republic
Tel.: (420) 221 998 555
Advertising Services
N.A.I.C.S.: 541810

Maurice Publicite Ltd. (4)
5th Fl Cerne House Chaussee St, Port Louis, Mauritius (100%)
Tel.: (230) 212 0844
Web Site: http://www.maupub.com
Sales Range: $10-24.9 Million
Emp.: 32
Advertising Services
N.A.I.C.S.: 541810
Geraldine Neubert *(Mng Dir)*

Maxx Marketing (4)
Shibakoen-annex Bldg, 3-1-8 Shibakoen, Minato-Ku, Tokyo, 105-8567, Japan
Tel.: (81) 354721672
Emp.: 80
Advertising Services
N.A.I.C.S.: 541810
Ryu Kawa *(Mng Dir)*

Maxx Marketing (4)
6th Floor WPP Campus 399 Hengfeng Road, 500 Guang Dong Rd, Shanghai, 200070, China
Tel.: (86) 2124017181
Advertising Services
N.A.I.C.S.: 541810

Maxx Marketing (4)
Great Western Studios Studio 306 65 Alfred Road, London, W2 5EU, United Kingdom
Tel.: (44) 2079210380
Sales Range: Less than $1 Million
Emp.: 6
Advertising Services
N.A.I.C.S.: 541810

Branch (Domestic):

Maxx Marketing Inc. (4)
2425 Olympic Blvd Ste 2000 W, Santa Monica, CA 90404
Tel.: (310) 748-6886

Web Site: http://www.maxx-marketing.com
Emp.: 155
Advertising Services
N.A.I.C.S.: 541810

Branch (Non-US):

Maxx Marketing Ltd. (5)
Room 9K World Trade Tower 500 Guang Dong Road, Shanghai, 200001, China
Tel.: (86) 21 6362 0707
Web Site: http://www.maxx-marketing.com
Sales Range: Less than $1 Million
Emp.: 8
Advertising Services
N.A.I.C.S.: 541810

Branch (Non-US):

Maxx Marketing Ltd. (4)
7 Floor Manley Tower 828 Cheung Sha Wan Road, Kowloon, China (Hong Kong)
Tel.: (852) 2523 2093
Web Site: http://www.maxx-marketing.com
N.A.I.C.S.: 541810

Maxx Marketing Ltd. (4)
The Ogilvy Centre, 35 Robinson Rd. #03-01, Singapore, 06887, Singapore
Tel.: (65) 2 6213 9968
Web Site: http://www.maxx-marketing.com
Advertising Services
N.A.I.C.S.: 541810
Colin Yau *(Client Svcs)*

Molina Bianchi: Ogilvy & Mather (4)
550 Avenida La Capilla No, Col San Benito, San Salvador, El Salvador (100%)
Tel.: (503) 2525 3780
Web Site: http://www.ogilvy.com
Advertising Services
N.A.I.C.S.: 541810

Momentum, Ogilvy & Mather (4)
Avenida el Bosque 128, San Isidro, Lima, Peru
Tel.: (51) 12218803
Sales Range: $10-24.9 Million
Emp.: 27
Advertising Services
N.A.I.C.S.: 541810

Neo@Ogilvy (4)
7th Floor Huali Building, 58 Jinbao Street, Beijing, 100005, China
Tel.: (86) 1085130166
Advertising Services
N.A.I.C.S.: 541810
Jean Thomas *(Dir-Search-Hong Kong)*

Neo@Ogilvy (4)
11-14 Floor Commerz Oberoi Garden City Intl Business Park off Western, Express Highway, Goregaon (East), Mumbai, 400 063, India
Tel.: (91) 2244344365
Advertising Services
N.A.I.C.S.: 541810
Mary Keane-Dawson *(Mng Dir-UK)*

Northcote Ogilvy & Mather (4)
Avenida del Parque 4161 Office 602, Huechuraba, Santiago, Chile (100%)
Tel.: (56) 2 596 9100
Advertising Services
N.A.I.C.S.: 541810

Ocean Ogilvy & Mather (4)
Villa N 66 Ave C 16 Jean Mermoz-Cocody 01, BP 7759, Abidjan, 01, Cote d'Ivoire (100%)
Tel.: (225) 22 40 4170
Web Site: http://www.oceanogilvy.com
Sales Range: $10-24.9 Million
Emp.: 40
Advertising Services
N.A.I.C.S.: 541810
Martine Coffi Studer *(CEO)*

Ogilvy (4)
Tower A 6th to 8th Floor Global Business Park Mehrauli Gurgaon Road, Gurgaon Haryana, New Delhi, 122002, India
Tel.: (91) 124 4760760
Web Site: http://www.ogilvyindia.com
Advertising Services
N.A.I.C.S.: 541810
Amarinder Butalia *(Mng Partner)*

Branch (Domestic):

Ogilvy (4)

AND PRIVATE COMPANIES — WPP PLC

Meridian 115 N Duke St Ste 2A, Durham, NC 27701
Tel.: (919) 281-0600
Sales Range: $10-24.9 Million
Emp.: 30
Advertising Services
N.A.I.C.S.: 541810
Sukesh Nayak (Chief Creative Officer-West)

Branch (Non-US):

Ogilvy & Mather (4)
SCN Q 1 Bloco F Salas 811 a 880, 70711-905, Brasilia, DF, Brazil
Tel.: (55) 61 3327 8290
Web Site: http://www.ogilvy.com.br
Advertising Services
N.A.I.C.S.: 541810
Fernando Muso (CEO)

Ogilvy & Mather (4)
Carrera 13 No 94A-26, Bogota, 110221, Colombia
Tel.: (57) 1 651 6363
Web Site: http://www.ogilvy.com.co
Emp.: 200
Advertising Services
N.A.I.C.S.: 541810

Ogilvy & Mather (4)
Hybesova 18, 602 00, Brno, Czech Republic
Tel.: (420) 543 247 192
Web Site: http://www.ogilvymorava.cz
Sales Range: $10-24.9 Million
Emp.: 11
Advertising Services
N.A.I.C.S.: 541810
Roman Valla (Mng Dir)

Ogilvy & Mather (4)
2nd Zvenigorodskaya St 13 Bldg 41, 123022, Moscow, Russia
Tel.: (7) 495 661 2521
Advertising Services
N.A.I.C.S.: 541810

Ogilvy & Mather (4)
Av La Estancia Centro Banaven Torre D Piso 3, Chuao, Caracas, 1080, Venezuela
Tel.: (58) 2129590902
Sales Range: $10-24.9 Million
Emp.: 27
Advertising Services
N.A.I.C.S.: 541810

Branch (Domestic):

Ogilvy & Mather (4)
Douglas Entrance N Tower Ste 355 800 Douglas Rd, Coral Gables, FL 33134
Tel.: (305) 448-6002
Web Site: http://www.ogilvy.com
Sales Range: $10-24.9 Million
Emp.: 15
Advertising Services
N.A.I.C.S.: 541810

Branch (Non-US):

Ogilvy & Mather (4)
94 Jinnah Cooperative Housing Society, Block 7/8 Tipu Sultan Rd, Karachi, 75350, Pakistan
Tel.: (92) 214389054
Advertising Services
N.A.I.C.S.: 541810

Ogilvy & Mather (4)
74-B/11 Gulberg III, Lahore, Pakistan
Tel.: (92) 42111543200
Advertising Services
N.A.I.C.S.: 541810

Ogilvy & Mather (4)
Mahavir House 303-304 3rd Floor Basheer Bagh, Hyderabad, 500 029, India
Tel.: (91) 04023220067
Advetising Agency
N.A.I.C.S.: 541810

Ogilvy & Mather (4)
33 Yonge St, Toronto, M5E 1X6, ON, Canada
Tel.: (416) 367-3573
Web Site: http://www.ogilvy-canada.com
Sales Range: $25-49.9 Million
Emp.: 148
Advertising Services

Ogilvy & Mather (4)
6 Ely Place, Dublin, 2, Ireland (100%)
Tel.: (353) 1 669 0010
Web Site: http://www.ogilvy.ie
Advertising Services
N.A.I.C.S.: 541810
Jane Gregory (Mng Dir)

Ogilvy & Mather (4)
32-34 Rue Marbeuf, 75008, Paris, France
Tel.: (33) 153233000
Web Site: http://www.decouvrir.ogilvy.fr
Sales Range: $50-74.9 Million
Emp.: 280
Advertising Services
N.A.I.C.S.: 541810
Emmanuel Ferry (Co-Pres)

Ogilvy & Mather (4)
Am Handelshafen 2-4, Postfach 19 00 21, Dusseldorf, 40110, Germany (100%)
Tel.: (49) 211 497 00 0
Web Site: http://www.ogilvy-duesseldorf.de
Sales Range: $25-49.9 Million
Emp.: 200
Advertising Services
N.A.I.C.S.: 541810
Helmut Hechler (CFO)

Ogilvy & Mather (4)
Viale Lancetti 29, 20158, Milan, Italy
Tel.: (39) 02607891
Web Site: http://www.ogilvy.com
Advertising Services
N.A.I.C.S.: 541810

Ogilvy & Mather (4)
Tolgpodgade 55, DK-1253, Copenhagen, Denmark
Tel.: (45) 3917 8810
Web Site: http://www.ogilvy.dk
Sales Range: $10-24.9 Million
Emp.: 50
Advertising Services
N.A.I.C.S.: 541810
Camilla Ploug (Creative Dir)

Ogilvy & Mather (4)
Montes Urales 505 5th Fl Col Lomas de Chapultepec, 11000, Mexico, DF, Mexico
Tel.: (52) 55 5350 1800
Web Site: http://www.ogilvy.com.mx
Advertising Services
N.A.I.C.S.: 541810

Ogilvy & Mather (4)
Harmancy Giz Plaza Harman Sokak M1-2 Levant, 80640, Istanbul, Turkiye (100%)
Tel.: (90) 212 3398 360
Web Site: http://www.ogilvy.com
Advertising Services
N.A.I.C.S.: 541810

Ogilvy & Mather (4)
3rd Floor Campus D RMZ Centennial ITPL Road, Doddanekundi Village, Bengaluru, 560048, India
Tel.: (91) 8051344360
Advertising Services
N.A.I.C.S.: 541810
N. Ramamoorthi (Pres-South)

Ogilvy & Mather (4)
Calle 64 Norte 5BN 146 of 315, Centro Empresa, Cali, Valle del Cauca, Colombia
Tel.: (57) 26646694
Advertising Services
N.A.I.C.S.: 541810

Ogilvy & Mather (4)
Plaza Bapindo Bank Mandiri Tower 26 Fl, PO Box 2580, Sudirman Kav 54-55, Jakarta, 12190, Indonesia (100%)
Tel.: (62) 215266261
Advertising Services
N.A.I.C.S.: 541810
Din Sumedi (Chief Creative Officer)

Ogilvy & Mather (4)
Privozni 2A, Prague, 7, Czech Republic
Tel.: (420) 2 2199 8111
Web Site: http://www.ogilvy.cz
Sales Range: $125-149.9 Million
Emp.: 200
Advertising Services
N.A.I.C.S.: 541810
Kristyna Hlinakova (Mgr-PR)

Ogilvy & Mather (4)
Revesz utca 27, RiverLoft, 1138, Budapest, Hungary (100%)

Tel.: (36) 1 801 4500
Sales Range: $10-24.9 Million
Emp.: 60
Advertising Services
N.A.I.C.S.: 541810

Ogilvy & Mather (4)
V Pio Emanuelli 1, Rome, 00143, Italy (100%)
Tel.: (39) 06 51 8371
Web Site: http://www.ogilvy.it
Sales Range: $10-24.9 Million
Emp.: 23
Advertising Services
N.A.I.C.S.: 541810

Ogilvy & Mather (4)
86 Grigore Alexandrescu Street, Bucharest, 10627, Romania (100%)
Tel.: (40) 212010100
Emp.: 100
Advertising Services
N.A.I.C.S.: 541810
Manuela Necula (Mng Dir)

Ogilvy & Mather (4)
60-62 Dospat Street, 1463, Sofia, Bulgaria (100%)
Tel.: (359) 29523400
Web Site: http://www.ogilvy.bg
Sales Range: $10-24.9 Million
Emp.: 38
Advertising Services
N.A.I.C.S.: 541810

Ogilvy & Mather (4)
Praia do Botafogo 228 18th Floor, 22359-900, Rio de Janeiro, RJ, Brazil
Tel.: (55) 21 2141 2500
Web Site: http://www.ogilvy.com.br
Sales Range: $10-24.9 Million
Emp.: 50
Advertising Services
N.A.I.C.S.: 541810
Luiz Fernando Musa (CEO)

Ogilvy & Mather (4)
No 27 Chervonoarmiyska 5, 01004, Kiev, Ukraine
Tel.: (380) 442309520
Sales Range: $10-24.9 Million
Emp.: 75
Advertising Services
N.A.I.C.S.: 541810

Ogilvy & Mather (4)
Corner of Gen Murtala Mohammed Road, Windhoek, 47199, Namibia (100%)
Tel.: (264) 61 247 372
Web Site: http://www.ogilvy.com.na
Advertising Services
N.A.I.C.S.: 541810
Anny Mouton (Founder)

Ogilvy & Mather (4)
303-304 Mahavir House, Basheerbagh Crossroads, Hyderabad, 500 029, Andhra Pradesh, India
Tel.: (91) 40 322 7316
Web Site: http://www.ogilvyindia.com
Advertising Services
N.A.I.C.S.: 541810

Ogilvy & Mather (4)
27-8 Chamwon-Dong, Seocho-Ku, Seoul, 137-903, Korea (South)
Tel.: (82) 2 513 1400
Web Site: http://www.ogilvy.co.kr
Advertising Services
N.A.I.C.S.: 541810

Ogilvy & Mather (Amsterdam) B.V. (4)
Pilotenstraat 41, Amsterdam, 1059 CH, Netherlands
Tel.: (31) 20 7963300
Web Site: http://www.ogilvy.nl
Emp.: 80
Advertising Services
N.A.I.C.S.: 541810
Joost van Liemt (Dir-Strategy)

Ogilvy & Mather (China) Ltd. (4)
26 Fl The Center 989 Changle Road, Shanghai, 200031, China (100%)
Tel.: (86) 21 2405 1888
Web Site: http://www.ogilvy.cn
Emp.: 600
Advertising Services
N.A.I.C.S.: 541810

T. B. Song (Chm)

Ogilvy & Mather (Eastern Africa) Ltd. (4)
3rd Fl CVS Plaza Kasuku Road Lenana Road, PO Box 30280, Nairobi, 100, Kenya (100%)
Tel.: (254) 202717748
Advertising Services
N.A.I.C.S.: 541810
Irene Wahome (Mgr-Knowledge)

Ogilvy & Mather (Philippines) Inc. (4)
15th Floor Philamlife Tower 8767 Paseo de Roxas, Makati, Manila, 1200, Philippines (100%)
Tel.: (63) 2 885 0001
Advertising Services
N.A.I.C.S.: 541810

Ogilvy & Mather (Singapore) Pvt. Ltd. (4)
71 Robinson Rd No 07-01, Singapore, 68895, Singapore
Tel.: (65) 6213 7899
Web Site: http://www.ogilvy.com
Advertising Services
N.A.I.C.S.: 541820
Chris Riley (CEO)

Ogilvy & Mather (Vietnam) Ltd. (4)
Centec Tower 12th Floor 72-74 Nguyen Thi Minh Khai Street, District 3, Ho Chi Minh City, 700000, Vietnam (100%)
Tel.: (84) 838219529
Emp.: 100
Advertising Services
N.A.I.C.S.: 541810
Nguyen Trong Duc (Dir-Fin)

Ogilvy & Mather Advertising (4)
Level 11 Menara Milenium 8 Jalan Damanlela, Bukit Damansara, 50490, Kuala Lumpur, Malaysia (100%)
Tel.: (60) 3 2718 8888
Web Site: http://www.ogilvy.com.my
Sales Range: $200-249.9 Million
Emp.: 270
Advertising Services
N.A.I.C.S.: 541810

Ogilvy & Mather Advertising (4)
71 Robinson Road 07-01, Singapore, 068895, Singapore (100%)
Tel.: (65) 6213 7899
Sales Range: $50-74.9 Million
Emp.: 500
Advertising Services
N.A.I.C.S.: 541810

Branch (Domestic):

Ogilvy & Mather Advertising (4)
636 11th Ave, New York, NY 10036
Tel.: (212) 237-4000
Web Site: http://www.ogilvy.com
Advertising Services
N.A.I.C.S.: 541810

Branch (Non-US):

Ogilvy & Mather Advertising (4)
14th Flr The Offices at Centralworld 999/9 Rama 1 Rd, Patumwan, Bangkok, 10330, Thailand (100%)
Tel.: (66) 2 205 6000
Web Site: http://www.ogilvy.com
Emp.: 200
Advertising Services
N.A.I.C.S.: 541810

Ogilvy & Mather Advertising (4)
90 Song Ren Rd, 110, Taipei, Taiwan (100%)
Tel.: (886) 2 2758 8686
Web Site: http://www.ogilvy.com.tw
Advertising Services
N.A.I.C.S.: 541810

Ogilvy & Mather Advertising (4)
23rd Floor The Center 99 Queen's Road, Central, China (Hong Kong)
Tel.: (852) 2568 0161
Web Site: http://www.ogilvy.com.cn
Advertising Services
N.A.I.C.S.: 541810

Ogilvy & Mather Advertising Beijing (4)
9th Floor Huali Building 58 Jinbao Street,

WPP PLC

WPP plc—(Continued)
Beijing, 100005, China **(100%)**
Tel.: (86) 10 8520 6688
Web Site: http://www.ogilvy.com.cn
Advertising Services
N.A.I.C.S.: 541810

Ogilvy & Mather Africa (4)
The Brand Bldg 15 Sloane St, Bryanston,
Johannesburg, 2021, South Africa
Tel.: (27) 11 709 6600
Web Site: http://www.ogilvy.co.za
Sales Range: $10-24.9 Million
Emp.: 566
Advertising Services
N.A.I.C.S.: 541810

Ogilvy & Mather Argentina (4)
Sarmiento 700, Capital Federal, 1041 AAN,
Buenos Aires, Argentina **(100%)**
Tel.: (54) 1143237000
Advertising Services
N.A.I.C.S.: 541810

Ogilvy & Mather Asia/Pacific (4)
23rd Floor The Center 99 Queen's Road,
Central, China (Hong Kong)
Tel.: (852) 2568 0161
Web Site: http://www.ogilvy.com
Advertising Services
N.A.I.C.S.: 541810
Jerry Smith *(COO)*

Branch (Domestic):

Ogilvy & Mather Chicago (4)
350 W Mart Ctr Dr Ste 1100, Chicago, IL
60654-1866
Tel.: (312) 856-8200
Web Site: http://www.ogilvy.com
Advertising Services
N.A.I.C.S.: 541810

Branch (Non-US):

Ogilvy & Mather EMEA (4)
10 Cabot Square Canary Wharf, London,
E14 4QB, United Kingdom
Tel.: (44) 207 345 3000
Web Site: http://www.ogilvy.com
Emp.: 1,200
Advertising Services
N.A.I.C.S.: 541810
Ralph Clementson *(COO)*

Ogilvy & Mather Frankfurt (4)
Darmstadter Landstrasse 112, Frankfurt,
60599, Germany **(100%)**
Tel.: (49) 69 96225 1706
Web Site: http://www.ogilvy.de
Emp.: 250
Advertising Services
N.A.I.C.S.: 541810
Stephan Vogel *(Chm-Creative)*

Ogilvy & Mather Ges m.b.H. (4)
Franz-Klein-Gasse 5, Vienna, 1190, Austria
Tel.: (43) 1 90100 0
Web Site: http://www.ogilvy.at
Sales Range: $10-24.9 Million
Emp.: 40
Advertising Services
N.A.I.C.S.: 541810
Florian Krenkel *(CEO)*

Ogilvy & Mather India (4)
139/140 Rukmani Lakshmipathy Salia Marshalls Road, Egmore, Chennai, 600 008,
India **(100%)**
Tel.: (91) 44 4436 0360
Web Site: http://www.ogilvyindia.com
Advertising Services
N.A.I.C.S.: 541810

Ogilvy & Mather Japan K.K. (4)
Yebisu Garden Place Tower 25F 4-20-3
Ebisu, Shibuya-ku, Tokyo, 150-6025, Japan
Tel.: (81) 3 5791 8888
Web Site: http://www.ogilvy.co.jp
Sales Range: $50-74.9 Million
Emp.: 300
Advertising Services
N.A.I.C.S.: 541810
Ajab Samrai *(Chief Creative Officer-ASEAN)*

Branch (Domestic):

Ogilvy & Mather Los Angeles (4)
12180 Millennium Dr Ste 440, Playa Vista,
CA 90094
Tel.: (310) 280-2200
Web Site: http://www.ogilvy.com
Emp.: 75
Advertising & Public Relations Services
N.A.I.C.S.: 541810

Ogilvy & Mather N America & Corporate (4)
636 11th Ave, New York, NY 10036
Tel.: (212) 237-4000
Web Site: http://www.ogilvy.com
Emp.: 2,000
Advertising Services
N.A.I.C.S.: 541810
Horacio Genolet *(CEO-Latinamerica)*

Branch (Non-US):

Ogilvy & Mather Portugal (4)
Edificio Atrium Saldanha Praa Duque de
Saldanha Number 1-4E, Lisbon, 1050, Portugal
Tel.: (351) 21 321 8000
Web Site: http://www.ogilvy.pt
Sales Range: $50-74.9 Million
Advertising Services
N.A.I.C.S.: 541810

Ogilvy & Mather Publicidad Madrid, SA (4)
La Matriz WPP Campus Calle de Rios Rosas 26, 28003, Madrid, Spain
Tel.: (34) 91 451 20 00
Web Site: http://www.ogilvy.es
Advertising Services
N.A.I.C.S.: 541810

Ogilvy & Mather South Africa (Pty.) Ltd. (4)
The Brand Building 15 Sloane Street, Bryanston, Johannesburg, 2152, South Africa
Tel.: (27) 11 709 6600
Web Site: http://www.ogilvy.co.za
Sales Range: $50-74.9 Million
Emp.: 400
Advertising Services
N.A.I.C.S.: 541810
Tracey Edwards *(Mng Dir-Acting & Chief Delivery Officer)*

Ogilvy & Mather Sp. z o.o. (4)
Angorska 13a, 03-913, Warsaw, Poland
Tel.: (48) 226726006
Web Site: http://www.ogilvy.pl
Advertising Services
N.A.I.C.S.: 541810
Elzbieta Twardowska *(Dir-Strategic)*

Ogilvy & Mather Werbeagentur GmbH (4)
Darmstadter Landstrasse 112, Frankfurt,
60598, Germany
Tel.: (49) 69 96225 0
Web Site: http://www.ogilvy.de
Advertising Services
N.A.I.C.S.: 541810

Ogilvy & Mather, Ltd. (4)
10 Cabot Sq Canary Wharf, London, E14
4QB, United Kingdom **(100%)**
Tel.: (44) 207 345 3000
Web Site: http://www.ogilvy.com
Sales Range: $25-49.9 Million
Emp.: 400
Advertising Services
N.A.I.C.S.: 541810

Ogilvy AG (4)
Binzmuhlestrasse 170d, Postfach 6359,
8050, Zurich, Switzerland
Tel.: (41) 44 268 6363
Web Site: http://www.ogilvy.ch
Advertising Services
N.A.I.C.S.: 541860
Jonathan Schipper *(CEO)*

Ogilvy Activation (4)
Master Samuelsgatan 56, 114 80, Stockholm, Sweden
Tel.: (46) 8 562 58250
Advertising Services
N.A.I.C.S.: 541810

Ogilvy Advertising (4)
Master Samuelsgatan 56, 114 80, Stockholm, Sweden **(100%)**
Tel.: (46) 8 562 584 00
Advertising Services
N.A.I.C.S.: 541810

Ogilvy Asia Pacific (4)
The Offices at Centralworld 999/9 Rama 1
Road, Pathumwan, Bangkok, 10330, Thailand
Tel.: (66) 22056000
Advertising Services
N.A.I.C.S.: 541810
Punnee Chaiyakul *(Chm-Thailand)*

Ogilvy Brasil (4)
Av das Nacoes Unidas 5777 Alto de Pinheiros, 05477-900, Sao Paulo, SP, Brazil
Tel.: (55) 11 3024 9000
Web Site: http://www.ogilvy.com.br
Advertising Services
N.A.I.C.S.: 541810
Luiz Leite *(CFO & Exec VP)*

Ogilvy CID (4)
Privozni 2A, Prague, 170 00, Czech Republic
Tel.: (420) 221 998 111
Web Site: http://www.ogilvycid.com
Sales Range: $10-24.9 Million
Emp.: 10
Advertising Services
N.A.I.C.S.: 541810
Ondrej Obluk *(CEO)*

Ogilvy Cape Town (4)
41 Sir Lowry Road, Woodstock, Cape
Town, 8000, South Africa
Tel.: (27) 21 467 1000
Web Site: http://www.ogilvy.co.za
Sales Range: $25-49.9 Million
Emp.: 208
Advertising Services
N.A.I.C.S.: 541810
Vicki Buys *(Mng Dir)*

Ogilvy Durban (4)
76 Mahatma Gandhi Road, PO Box 2424,
Durban, 4001, South Africa
Tel.: (27) 31 334 5600
Web Site: http://www.ogilvy.co.za
Emp.: 20
Advertising Services
N.A.I.C.S.: 541810

Ogilvy Group Zrt. (4)
Nagymezo Street 44, H1065, Budapest,
Hungary
Tel.: (36) 1 801 4500
Web Site: http://www.ogilvy.com
Advertising Services
N.A.I.C.S.: 541810

Ogilvy Healthcare (4)
Master Samuelsgatan 56, 114 80, Stockholm, Sweden
Tel.: (46) 8 562 58483
Sales Range: $25-49.9 Million
Emp.: 185
Advertising Services
N.A.I.C.S.: 541810

Ogilvy Healthworld (4)
Harmanci Giz Plaza Haman Sokak M 1-2,
Istanbul, 34934, Turkiye
Tel.: (90) 212 339 8388
Web Site: http://www.ogilvy.com.tr
Advertising Services
N.A.I.C.S.: 541810

Ogilvy Healthworld (4)
The Brand Building 15 Sloane Street, Bryanston, Johannesburg, 2152, South Africa
Tel.: (27) 11 709 9600
Web Site: http://www.ogilvy.co.za
Sales Range: $10-24.9 Million
Emp.: 18
Advertising Services
N.A.I.C.S.: 541810
Nunu Ntshingila *(CEO)*

Ogilvy Healthworld Barcelona (4)
Bolivia 68-70, Barcelona, 8018,
Spain **(100%)**
Tel.: (34) 93 366 60 00
Emp.: 20
Advertising Services
N.A.I.C.S.: 541810

Ogilvy Healthworld Sao Paulo (4)
Av Nacoes Unidas 5777, Alto de Pinheiros,
05477-900, Sao Paulo, Brazil
Tel.: (55) 11 3024 9076
Advertising Services
N.A.I.C.S.: 541810

Ogilvy India (4)
14th Floor Commerz International Business
Park Oberoi Garden City, off Western Express Highway, Goregaon, Mumbai, 400
063, India
Tel.: (91) 22 4436 0360
Web Site: http://www.ogilvyindia.com
Sales Range: $125-149.9 Million
Emp.: 650
Advertising Services
N.A.I.C.S.: 541810
Piyush Pandey *(Chm)*

Ogilvy Johannesburg (Pty.) Ltd. (4)
The Brand Building 15 Sloane Street, Bryanston, Johannesburg, 2021, South Africa
Tel.: (27) 11 709 66 00
Web Site: http://www.ogilvy.co.za
Sales Range: $25-49.9 Million
Emp.: 500
Advertising Services
N.A.I.C.S.: 541810
Tracey Edwards *(Mng Dir)*

Ogilvy Montreal (4)
215 Rue Saint-Jacques Bureau 333, Montreal, H2Y 1M6, QC, Canada **(100%)**
Tel.: (514) 861-1811
Web Site: http://www.ogilvy-montreal.ca
Sales Range: $10-24.9 Million
Emp.: 60
Advertising Services
N.A.I.C.S.: 541810
David Aubert *(CEO)*

Ogilvy Mozambique (4)
17 Avenue Agostinho Neto, Maputo, 1103,
Mozambique
Tel.: (258) 843019250
Web Site: http://www.ogilvy.com
Advertising Services
N.A.I.C.S.: 541810

Ogilvy New Zealand (4)
22 Stanley St, PO Box 4567, Parnell, Auckland, 1140, New Zealand
Tel.: (64) 9 358 5752
Web Site: http://www.ogilvy.co.nz
Sales Range: $25-49.9 Million
Emp.: 200
Advertising Agencies
N.A.I.C.S.: 541810
Kelly-Ann Maxwell *(CEO)*

Ogilvy One Middle East Company (4)
Al Saqr Business Tower 24th Floor, PO Box
74170, Sheikh Zayed Road, Dubai, 74170,
United Arab Emirates
Tel.: (971) 4 305 0 200
Web Site: http://www.ogilvy.com
Advertising Services
N.A.I.C.S.: 541810

Ogilvy PR (4)
Level 11 Menara Milenium, 10th Floor Jalan
Damanlela, Bukit Damansara, 50490, Kuala
Lumpur, Malaysia
Tel.: (60) 3 2718 8266
Advertising Services
N.A.I.C.S.: 541810

Ogilvy Public Relations (4)
90 Song Ren Road, Hsin Yi Dist, Taipei,
110 ROC, Taiwan
Tel.: (886) 2 2758 8686
Web Site: http://www.ogilvy.com
Emp.: 80
Advertising Services
N.A.I.C.S.: 541810
Eric Huang *(Mng Dir)*

Ogilvy Public Relations (4)
The Brand Building 15 Sloane St, Bryanston, Johannesburg, 2021, South Africa
Tel.: (27) 11 709 9600
Web Site: http://www.ogilvy.co.za
Sales Range: $50-74.9 Million
Emp.: 460
Public Relations Services
N.A.I.C.S.: 541820

Ogilvy Public Relations Worldwide (4)
Building12 No1 Xia Shi Zhi Street, Fangcun
Avenue Liwan District, Guangzhou, 510370,
China **(100%)**
Tel.: (86) 20 3877 1888
Web Site: http://www.ogilvy.com.cn
Advertising Services
N.A.I.C.S.: 541810

AND PRIVATE COMPANIES — WPP PLC

Ella Chan *(Mng Dir-Shanghai)*

Ogilvy Public Relations Worldwide (4)
10 Cabot Square Canary Wharf, London, E14 4QB, United Kingdom
Tel.: (44) 20 7345 3000
Web Site: http://www.ogilvy.co.uk
Emp.: 1,000
Public Relations Services
N.A.I.C.S.: 541820
Rory Sutherland *(Vice Chm)*

Ogilvy Sydney (4)
72 Thristia Street, Saint Leonards, 2065, NSW, Australia
Tel.: (61) 2 9373 6333
Web Site: http://www.ogilvy.com.au
Advertising Services
N.A.I.C.S.: 541810
David Fox *(Chief Transformation Officer)*

OgilvyAction (4)
Bldg 12 No 1 X1a Shi Zhi St Fangcun Ave, Liwan District, Guangzhou, 510370, China
Tel.: (86) 20 8113 6288
Web Site: http://www.ogilvy.com.cn
Advertising Services
N.A.I.C.S.: 541810

OgilvyAction (4)
Josep Tarradellas 123 2nd floor, 08029, Barcelona, Spain
Tel.: (34) 93 495 94 25
Web Site: http://www.ogilvy.com
Advertising Services
N.A.I.C.S.: 541810

OgilvyAction (4)
C/ Mara de Molina 39, 28006, Madrid, Spain
Tel.: (34) 91 398 4600
Web Site: http://www.ogilvy.com
Sales Range: $50-74.9 Million
Emp.: 400
Advertising Services
N.A.I.C.S.: 541810

OgilvyHealthcare (4)
14 Fl Commerz International Business Pk, Oberoi Garden City Goregaon, Mumbai, 400 063, Maharashtra, India
Tel.: (91) 22 4434 4600
Sales Range: $125-149.9 Million
Emp.: 700
Advertising Services
N.A.I.C.S.: 541810

OgilvyHealthcare (4)
44 avenue George V, 75008, Paris, France (100%)
Tel.: (33) 1 53 53 12 30
Web Site: http://www.ogilvy.fr
Advertising Services
N.A.I.C.S.: 541810

OgilvyHealthcare (4)
Bergstrasse 50, Zurich, 6359, Switzerland
Tel.: (41) 44 268 63 23
Web Site: http://www.ogilvy.ch
Sales Range: $10-24.9 Million
Emp.: 20
Advertising Services
N.A.I.C.S.: 541810

Branch (Domestic):

OgilvyHealthcare (4)
636 11th Ave, New York, NY 10036
Tel.: (212) 237-4000
Web Site: http://www.ogilvy.com
Emp.: 1,000
Advertising Services
N.A.I.C.S.: 541810

Branch (Non-US):

OgilvyHealthworld (4)
Arvalo 1880, C1414CQL, Buenos Aires, Argentina
Tel.: (54) 1143237000
Advertising Services
N.A.I.C.S.: 541810
Sandra Alonso *(Gen Dir)*

OgilvyInteractive (4)
Avenida del Parque 4161 Office 601, Santiago, Chile
Tel.: (56) 2 596 9100
Web Site: http://www.ogilvychile.com
Sales Range: $10-24.9 Million
Emp.: 20
Advertising Services
N.A.I.C.S.: 541810

OgilvyInteractive (4)
Edificio Atrium Saldanha Praca Duque de Saldanha I 4 E, 1050-094, Lisbon, Portugal
Tel.: (351) 21 321 80 00
Web Site: http://www.ogilvy.pt
Sales Range: $10-24.9 Million
Emp.: 100
Advertising Services
N.A.I.C.S.: 541810

OgilvyInteractive (4)
Sea Containers 18 Upper Ground, London, SE1 9RQ, United Kingdom
Tel.: (44) 207 345 3000
Web Site: http://www.ogilvy.co.uk
Sales Range: Less than $1 Million
Emp.: 10
Advertising Services
N.A.I.C.S.: 541810
Paul O'Donnell *(CEO-EMEA)*

OgilvyInteractive (4)
JS Tower 6 Teheran Ro 79 Gil Gangnam-gu, Seoul, 135877, Korea (South)
Tel.: (82) 2 513 1400
Web Site: http://www.ogilvy.co.kr
Advertising Services
N.A.I.C.S.: 541810

OgilvyInteractive (4)
ul Angorska 13A, 03-913, Warsaw, Poland
Tel.: (48) 226163070
Sales Range: $25-49.9 Million
Emp.: 120
Advertising Services
N.A.I.C.S.: 541810
Tomasz Baluk *(Dir-Interactive)*

OgilvyInteractive (4)
Weberstrasse 21, 8036, Zurich, Switzerland (100%)
Tel.: (41) 1 295 9400
Advertising Services
N.A.I.C.S.: 541810

Branch (Domestic):

OgilvyInteractive (4)
636 11th Ave, New York, NY 10036
Tel.: (212) 237-4000
Web Site: http://www.ogilvy.com
Emp.: 1,000
Advertising Services
N.A.I.C.S.: 541810

Branch (Non-US):

OgilvyInteractive (4)
Bachofengasse 8, 1190, Vienna, Austria
Tel.: (43) 1 90 100 0
Web Site: http://www.ogilvy.at
Sales Range: $10-24.9 Million
Emp.: 70
Advertising Services
N.A.I.C.S.: 541810
Jorg Spreitzer *(Mng Dir)*

OgilvyInteractive (4)
Privozni 2A/1064, Prague, 17000, Czech Republic
Tel.: (420) 221 998 777
Web Site: http://www.ogilvy.cz
Emp.: 200
Advertising Services
N.A.I.C.S.: 541810

OgilvyInteractive (4)
136 avenue de Champs-Elysees, 75008, Paris, France
Tel.: (33) 140762424
Web Site: http://www.ogilvy.com
Emp.: 600
Advertising Services
N.A.I.C.S.: 541810

OgilvyInteractive (4)
Bapindo Plaza Bank Mandiri Tower 25th Floor Jalan Jendral, Sudirman Kav 54-55, Jakarta, 12190, Indonesia
Tel.: (62) 215266261
Sales Range: $25-49.9 Million
Emp.: 200
Advertising Services
N.A.I.C.S.: 541810
Alan Couldrey *(Country Head & Tech Advisor)*

OgilvyInteractive (4)
Montes Urales 505 5th Fl, Col Lomas de Chapultepec, 11000, Mexico, DF, Mexico
Tel.: (52) 55 5350 1800
Web Site: http://www.ogilvy.com.mx
Sales Range: Less than $1 Million
Emp.: 30
Advertising Services
N.A.I.C.S.: 541810

OgilvyInteractive (4)
Master Samuelsgatan 56, 114 80, Stockholm, Sweden
Tel.: (46) 8 562 58200
Sales Range: $10-24.9 Million
Emp.: 65
Advertising Services
N.A.I.C.S.: 541810

OgilvyInteractive (4)
14th Fl The Offices at Centralworld 999/9 Rama 1 Rd, Patumwan, Bangkok, 10330, Thailand
Tel.: (66) 22056000
Advertising Services
N.A.I.C.S.: 541810
Kanokporn Nitheranont *(Mng Dir)*

Branch (Domestic):

OgilvyInteractive (4)
350 W Mart Ctr Dr Ste 1100, Chicago, IL 60654
Tel.: (312) 856-8200
Web Site: http://www.ogilvy.com
Advertising Services
N.A.I.C.S.: 541810

Branch (Non-US):

OgilvyInteractive Asia Pacific (4)
Yebisu Garden Place Tower 25F 4-20-3 Ebisu, Shibuya-ku, Tokyo, 150-6025, Japan
Tel.: (81) 3 5791 8700
Web Site: http://www.ogilvy.co.jp
Sales Range: $50-74.9 Million
Emp.: 300
Advertising Services
N.A.I.C.S.: 541810

OgilvyOffice (4)
Pilotenstraat 41, Amsterdam, 1059 CH, Netherlands
Tel.: (31) 20 7963400
Web Site: http://www.ogilvy.com
Sales Range: $10-24.9 Million
Emp.: 100
Advertising Services
N.A.I.C.S.: 541810

OgilvyOne (4)
32-34 Rue Marbeuf, Paris, 75008, France
Tel.: (33) 1 40 76 24 24
Web Site: http://www.decouvrir.ogilvy.fr
Sales Range: $25-49.9 Million
Emp.: 600
Advertising Services
N.A.I.C.S.: 541810
Matthieu Elkaim *(Chief Creative Officer)*

OgilvyOne (4)
26F The Center 989 Changle Road, Shanghai, 200031, China
Tel.: (86) 21 2405 1888
Web Site: http://www.ogilvy.com.cn
Sales Range: $50-74.9 Million
Emp.: 600
Advertising Services
N.A.I.C.S.: 541810

Branch (Domestic):

OgilvyOne (4)
1001 front st 2nd fl, San Francisco, CA 94124
Tel.: (415) 782-4700
Sales Range: $10-24.9 Million
Emp.: 85
Advertising Services
N.A.I.C.S.: 541810

Branch (Non-US):

OgilvyOne Dogrudan Pazarlama A.S. (4)
Harmanci Giz Plaza Harman Sokak M 1-2, Levent, 34394, Istanbul, Turkiye
Tel.: (90) 212 33 98 360
Web Site: http://www.ogilvy.com.tr
Advertising Services
N.A.I.C.S.: 541810

OgilvyOne El Salvador (4)
Avenida el Almendro 111, Colonia Maquilishuat SS, San Salvador, El Salvador
Tel.: (503) 2275 3777
Advertising Services
N.A.I.C.S.: 541810

OgilvyOne Worldwide (4)
9th Floor Huali Building 58 Jinbao Street, Beijing, 100005, China
Tel.: (86) 10 8520 6688
Web Site: http://www.ogilvy.com.cn
Advertising Services
N.A.I.C.S.: 541810

OgilvyOne Worldwide (4)
27-8 Chamwon-dong, Seocho-Ku, Seoul, 135-903, Korea (South)
Tel.: (82) 2 513 1400
Web Site: http://www.ogilvy.co.kr
Advertising Services
N.A.I.C.S.: 541810

OgilvyOne Worldwide (4)
Yebisu Garden Place Tower 25F 4-20-3 Ebisu, Shibuya-ku, Tokyo, 150-6025, Japan
Tel.: (81) 3 5791 8700
Web Site: http://www.ogilvy.co.jp
Sales Range: $50-74.9 Million
Emp.: 300
Advertising Services
N.A.I.C.S.: 541810

OgilvyOne Worldwide (4)
33 Yonge St, Toronto, M5E 1X6, ON, Canada (100%)
Tel.: (416) 363-9514
Web Site: http://www.ogilvy.com
Sales Range: $10-24.9 Million
Emp.: 200
Advertising Services
N.A.I.C.S.: 541810

OgilvyOne Worldwide (4)
RDTX Place 36th Floor Jalan Prof DR Satrio Kav 3, Karet Kuningan Setiabudi, Jakarta, 12940, Indonesia (100%)
Tel.: (62) 2129243000
Web Site: http://www.ogilvy.com
Advertising Services
N.A.I.C.S.: 541810

OgilvyOne Worldwide (4)
6 Ely Place, Dublin, 2, Ireland (100%)
Tel.: (353) 1 669 0020
Web Site: http://www.ogilvy.ie
Sales Range: $10-24.9 Million
Emp.: 90
Advertising Services
N.A.I.C.S.: 541810
Jane Gregory *(Mng Dir)*

OgilvyOne Worldwide (4)
15th Floor Philamlife Tower 8767 Paseo de Roxas, Makati City Metro, Manila, 1200, Philippines (100%)
Tel.: (63) 27290101
Advertising Services
N.A.I.C.S.: 541810

OgilvyOne Worldwide (4)
12 Floor Commerz International Business Park Oberoi Garden City, Off Western Express Highway, Goregaon (East), Mumbai, 400 063, India (100%)
Tel.: (91) 22 5034 4600
Web Site: http://www.ogilvyindia.com
Advertising Services
N.A.I.C.S.: 541810
Vikram Menon *(Pres)*

OgilvyOne Worldwide (4)
ul Angorska 13A, 03-913, Warsaw, Poland (100%)
Tel.: (48) 22 616 30 70
Sales Range: $10-24.9 Million
Emp.: 90
Advertising Services
N.A.I.C.S.: 541810

Branch (Domestic):

OgilvyOne Worldwide (4)
636 11th Ave, New York, NY 10036
Tel.: (212) 237-4000
Web Site: http://www.ogilvy.com
Advertising Services
N.A.I.C.S.: 541810
Mat Zucker *(Chief Creative Officer)*

OgilvyOne Worldwide (4)

WPP PLC

WPP plc—(Continued)
350 W Mart Ctr Dr Ste 1100, Chicago, IL
60654-1866 **(100%)**
Tel.: (312) 856-8200
Web Site: http://www.ogilvy.com
Sales Range: $25-49.9 Million
Emp.: 150
Advertising Services
N.A.I.C.S.: 541810
Jack Rooney *(Pres)*

Branch (Non-US):

OgilvyOne Worldwide (4)
Via le V Lancetti 29, 20158, Milan,
Italy **(100%)**
Tel.: (39) 02607891
Sales Range: $10-24.9 Million
Emp.: 100
Advertising Services
N.A.I.C.S.: 541810

OgilvyOne Worldwide (4)
23rd Floor The Center, 99 Queen's Road,
Central, China (Hong Kong)
Tel.: (852) 2568 1177
Web Site: http://www.ogilvyone.com
Emp.: 40
Advertising Services
N.A.I.C.S.: 541810

OgilvyOne Worldwide (4)
Montes Urales 505 5th Fl, Col Lomas de
Chapultepec, 11000, Mexico, Districto Federal, Mexico
Tel.: (52) 55 5350 1800
Web Site: http://www.ogilvy.com
Sales Range: $10-24.9 Million
Advertising Services
N.A.I.C.S.: 541810

OgilvyOne Worldwide (4)
14th Fl The Offices at Centralworld 999/9
Rama 1 Rd, Patumwan, Bangkok, 10330,
Thailand **(100%)**
Tel.: (66) 22056000
Advertising Services
N.A.I.C.S.: 541810

OgilvyOne Worldwide (4)
Edificio Atrium Saldanha Praca Duque de
Saldanha I 4 E, 1050-094, Lisbon,
Portugal **(100%)**
Tel.: (351) 21 321 80 00
Web Site: http://www.ogilvy.pt
Sales Range: $10-24.9 Million
Emp.: 50
Advertising Services
N.A.I.C.S.: 541810
Jose Bomtempo *(Co-Chief Creative Officer)*

OgilvyOne Worldwide (4)
90 Song Ren Road, Taipei, 110 ROC,
Taiwan **(100%)**
Tel.: (886) 227588686
Advertising Services
N.A.I.C.S.: 541810
Daniel Lee *(CEO)*

OgilvyOne Worldwide (4)
Privozni 2A Grounds, Prague, 17000,
Czech Republic
Tel.: (420) 221 998 777
Web Site: http://www.ogilvy.cz
Advertising Services
N.A.I.C.S.: 541810
Ondrej Obluk *(CEO)*

OgilvyOne Worldwide (4)
Level 11 Menara Milenium 8 Jalan Damanlela, Bukit Damansara, Kuala Lumpur,
50490, Malaysia
Tel.: (60) 3 2718 8811
Web Site: http://www.wpp.com
Emp.: 180
Advertising Services
N.A.I.C.S.: 541810

OgilvyOne Worldwide (4)
Av La Estancia Centro Banaven, Torre D
Piso 3, Chuao, Caracas, 1080, Venezuela
Tel.: (58) 2129590902
Advertising Services
N.A.I.C.S.: 541810

OgilvyOne Worldwide (4)
Gospodar Jevremova 52, 111000, Belgrade,
Serbia
Tel.: (381) 111 324 6006
Advertising Services

N.A.I.C.S.: 541810

Branch (Domestic):

OgilvyOne Worldwide (4)
N Tower Ste 355 800 Douglas Rd, Coral
Gables, FL 33134
Tel.: (305) 448-6002
Web Site: http://www.ogilvy.com
Sales Range: $10-24.9 Million
Emp.: 20
Advertising Services
N.A.I.C.S.: 541810

Branch (Non-US):

OgilvyOne Worldwide (4)
Orinoco 90 Piso 6, Santiago, Chile
Tel.: (56) 27268500
Advertising Services
N.A.I.C.S.: 541810

OgilvyOne Worldwide Athens (4)
10 Imathias Street, 15 344, Athens, Greece
Tel.: (30) 210 6660 300
Web Site: http://www.ogilvyone.gr
Advertising Services
N.A.I.C.S.: 541810

OgilvyOne Worldwide GmbH (4)
Bachofengasse 8, A-1190, Vienna, Austria
Tel.: (43) 1 90 100 0
Web Site: http://www.ogilvy.com
Sales Range: $10-24.9 Million
Emp.: 60
Advertising Services
N.A.I.C.S.: 541810
Florian Krenkel *(CEO & Mng Dir)*

OgilvyOne Worldwide Ltd. (4)
10 Cabot Square Canary Wharf, London,
E14 4QB, United Kingdom **(100%)**
Tel.: (44) 20 7566 7000
Web Site: http://www.ogilvy.com
Emp.: 500
Advertising Services
N.A.I.C.S.: 541810
John Cornwell *(COO & Dir-Comml)*

OgilvyOne Worldwide SA (4)
Maria de Molina 39, 28006, Madrid, Spain
Tel.: (34) 915673320
Advertising Services
N.A.I.C.S.: 541810

**OgilvyOne Worldwide-Cape
Town** (4)
41 Sir Lowry Road, Woodstock, Cape
Town, 8000, South Africa
Tel.: (27) 21 467 1000
Web Site: http://www.ogilvy.co.za
Sales Range: $10-24.9 Million
Emp.: 209
Advertising Services
N.A.I.C.S.: 541810
Vicki Buys *(Mng Dir)*

OgilvyOne teleservices (4)
Oberai Commerce Intl Buisness Park off
western Express Highway 14th Fl, Goregaon East, Mumbai, 400 063, India
Tel.: (91) 22 4434 4335
Web Site: http://www.ogilvyindia.com
Advertising Services
N.A.I.C.S.: 541810

OgilvyStreamline/Design Direct (4)
Pilotenstraat 41, Amsterdam, 1059 CH,
Netherlands
Tel.: (31) 20 7963600
Web Site: http://www.ogilvy.nl
Sales Range: $10-24.9 Million
Emp.: 100
Advertising Services
N.A.I.C.S.: 541810
Heleen Heijt *(CFO)*

Pandora/Ogilvy & Mather (4)
Kennedy Business Center 12-14 Kennedy
Ave 1st Fl Ofc 101, Nicosia, 1087,
Cyprus **(100%)**
Tel.: (357) 22 767374
Web Site: http://www.ogilvy.com.cy
Sales Range: $50-74.9 Million
Emp.: 22
Advertising Services
N.A.I.C.S.: 541810
Andreas Mishellis *(Mng Dir)*

Partners Ogilvy & Mather (4)
Calle Magua No 3 Esquina Avenida Los
Proceres Los Rios, Santo Domingo, Dominican Republic **(100%)**
Tel.: (809) 472 5050
Advertising Services
N.A.I.C.S.: 541810
Noriora Elmudesi de Martinez *(CEO)*

Partners OgilvyInteractive (4)
Calle Magua #3 Esquina Avenida Los Proceres Los Rios, Distrito Nacional, Santo
Domingo, Dominican Republic
Tel.: (809) 472 5050
Advertising Services
N.A.I.C.S.: 541810

Partners OgilvyOne (4)
Calle Magua #3 Esquina Avenida los Proceres los Rios, Santo Domingo, Dominican
Republic
Tel.: (809) 472 5050
Advertising Services
N.A.I.C.S.: 541810

Phoenix O&M (Pvt.) Ltd. (4)
No 16 Barnes Pl, Colombo, 00700, Sri
Lanka **(100%)**
Tel.: (94) 112699166
Advertising Services
N.A.I.C.S.: 541810
Irwin Weerakkody *(Chm & Mng Dir)*

Poster One (4)
St Korolenko d 3A, Moscow, 107076, Russia
Tel.: (7) 495 787 9779
Web Site: http://www.posterone.ru
Sales Range: $10-24.9 Million
Emp.: 50
Advertising Services
N.A.I.C.S.: 541810

Prima Garnet Comm Ltd. (4)
Ivory Music House IPM Avenue, Alausa
Ikeja, Lagos, 2341, Nigeria **(100%)**
Tel.: (234) 17911214
Advertising Services
N.A.I.C.S.: 541810
Lolu Akinwunmi *(Grp CEO)*

Punto Ogilvy & Mather (4)
Plaza Independencia, Montevideo, 11100,
Uruguay
Tel.: (598) 29006070
Web Site: http://www.puntoogilvy.com.uy
Sales Range: $10-24.9 Million
Emp.: 25
Advertising Services
N.A.I.C.S.: 541810
Elbio Acuna *(Founder)*

Raynet Ogilvy (4)
981 Harwei Building, Guanghua Road, Beijing, China
Tel.: (86) 10 6561 8288
Web Site: http://www.raynet-ogilvy.com
Advertising Services
N.A.I.C.S.: 541810

Red & Yellow School (4)
97 Durham Ave Salt River, Cape Town,
7925, South Africa **(100%)**
Tel.: (27) 21 462 1946
Web Site: http://www.redandyellow.co.za
Sales Range: $10-24.9 Million
Emp.: 12
Marketing & Advertising Career Development Services
N.A.I.C.S.: 611430

Red Works (4)
Level 11 Menara Milenium 8 Jalan Damanlela, Bukit Damansara, 50490, Kuala Lumpur, Malaysia
Tel.: (60) 3 2718 8888
Advertising Services
N.A.I.C.S.: 541810

Branch (Domestic):

Redworks (4)
3530 Hayden Ave, Culver City, CA 90232
Tel.: (310) 280-2200
Advertising Services
N.A.I.C.S.: 541810

Branch (Non-US):

SLM/Ogilvy (4)
Rua Cel Genuino 421 10 Andar, 90010-
350, Porto Alegre, RS, Brazil **(100%)**
Tel.: (55) 51 3228 4847

INTERNATIONAL PUBLIC

Advertising Services
N.A.I.C.S.: 541810

Saltiveri Ogilvy & Mather (4)
Avenida Francisco de Orellana Edificio
World Trade Center, Torre A Oficina 1105,
Guayaquil, Ecuador **(100%)**
Tel.: (593) 42630350
Sales Range: $10-24.9 Million
Emp.: 2
Advertising Services
N.A.I.C.S.: 541810

**Saltiveri Ogilvy & Ogilvy One
Projects** (4)
Av Amazonas y calle UN de Periodistas
Edificio Puerta del Sol, Torre Este Piso 7,
Quito, Ecuador
Tel.: (593) 2 226 1220
Advertising Services
N.A.I.C.S.: 541810

**Singleton Ogilvy & Mather Pty.
Ltd.** (4)
72 Christie St St Leonards, 201 Sussex
Street, Sydney, 2065, NSW, Australia
Tel.: (61) 2 9373 6333
Advertising Services
N.A.I.C.S.: 541810

Strike Media (Pty) Ltd. (4)
Block A 4th Floor The District 41 Sir Lowry
Road, Woodstock, Cape Town, 7925, South
Africa
Tel.: (27) 21 467 1330
Web Site: http://www2.strikemedia.co.za
Sales Range: $1-9.9 Million
Emp.: 20
Mobile Advertising Services
N.A.I.C.S.: 541810
Russel Stromin *(Founder)*

Taivas (4)
Unioninkatu 13, 00130, Helsinki, Finland
Tel.: (358) 9 618 420
Web Site: http://www.taivas.com
Sales Range: $10-24.9 Million
Emp.: 20
Advertising Services
N.A.I.C.S.: 541810
David Gamrasni *(CEO)*

Branch (Domestic):

The Lacek Group (4)
900 2nd Ave S Ste 1800, Minneapolis, MN
55402
Tel.: (612) 359-3700
Web Site: http://www.lacek.com
Sales Range: $200-249.9 Million
Emp.: 280
Direct Marketing Services
N.A.I.C.S.: 541810
William Baker *(CEO)*

Branch (Non-US):

The MC Group (4)
350 Talbot Street, London, N6A 2R6, ON,
Canada
Tel.: (519) 660-8460
Advertising Services
N.A.I.C.S.: 541810

Wurmser Ogilvy & Mather (4)
Avenida Reforma 6-39 Z 10, C Corporativo
Guayaon, Guatemala, 010010,
Guatemala **(100%)**
Tel.: (502) 2420 8300
Web Site: http://www.ogily.com
Advertising Services
N.A.I.C.S.: 541810
Ramiro Eduardo *(VP-Creativity)*

ZOOM Advertising (4)
2nd Floor 41 Sir Lowry Rd, Woodstock,
Cape Town, 8001, South Africa
Tel.: (27) 21 467 1400
Advertising Services
N.A.I.C.S.: 541810

Branch (Domestic):

de la Cruz Group (4)
Metro Office Park St I No 9 Ste 201, Guaynabo, PR 00968-1705
Tel.: (787) 792-4141
Web Site: http://www.delacruz.com
Sales Range: $10-24.9 Million
Emp.: 70
Advertising Services

AND PRIVATE COMPANIES — WPP PLC

N.A.I.C.S.: 541810

Branch (Domestic):

DLC Integrated Marketing Corp. (5)
2600 Douglas Rd Ste 611, Coral Gables, FL 33134
Tel.: (305) 374-9494
Advertising Services
N.A.I.C.S.: 541810

Subsidiary (Non-US):

Ogilvy & Mather S.p.A. (3)
Via Lancetti 29, 20158, Milan, Italy
Tel.: (39) 02607891
Sales Range: $25-49.9 Million
Emp.: 250
N.A.I.C.S.: 541810

Ogilvy CommonHealth Worldwide GmbH (3)
Am Handelshafen 2-4, D-40221, Frankfurt, Germany
Tel.: (49) 21149700510
Web Site: http://www.ochww.com
Sales Range: $25-49.9 Million
Emp.: 25
N.A.I.C.S.: 541810

Subsidiary (Domestic):

Ogilvy CommonHealth Worldwide LLC (3)
400 Interpace Pkwy Bldg B, Parsippany, NJ 07054
Tel.: (973) 352-1000
Web Site: http://www.ogilvychww.com
Advertising Services
N.A.I.C.S.: 541810
Ripal R. Patel (CFO)

Unit (Domestic):

Ogilvy CommonHealth Insights & Analytics (4)
400 Interpace Pkwy Bldg B, Parsippany, NJ 07054
Tel.: (973) 352-3800
Web Site: http://www.ogilvychww.com
Advertising Services
N.A.I.C.S.: 541810

Ogilvy CommonHealth Interactive Marketing (4)
400 Interpace Pkwy, Parsippany, NJ 07054
Tel.: (973) 352-1400
Web Site: http://www.ogilvychww.com
Advertising Services
N.A.I.C.S.: 541810

Ogilvy CommonHealth Medical Education (4)
400 Interpace Pkwy, Parsippany, NJ 07054
Tel.: (973) 352-2000
Web Site: http://www.ogilvychww.com
Advertising Services
N.A.I.C.S.: 541810

Ogilvy CommonHealth Medical Marketing (4)
400 Interpace Pkwy Bldg, Parsippany, NJ 07054
Tel.: (973) 352-3500
Web Site: http://www.ogilvychww.com
Emp.: 550
N.A.I.C.S.: 541810

Ogilvy CommonHealth Medical Media (4)
442 & 426 Interpace Pkwy, Parsippany, NJ 07054
Tel.: (973) 352-1700
Web Site: http://www.ogilvychww.com
Sales Range: $25-49.9 Million
Emp.: 25
Advertising Services
N.A.I.C.S.: 541810

Ogilvy CommonHealth Payer Marketing (4)
400 Interpace Parkway Building B, Parsippany, NJ 07054
Tel.: (973) 352-1800
Web Site: http://www.ochww.com
Sales Range: $10-24.9 Million
Emp.: 550
Advertising Services
N.A.I.C.S.: 541810
Michael Zilligen (Pres)

Ogilvy CommonHealth Scientific Communications (4)
432 Interpace Pkwy, Parsippany, NJ 07054
Tel.: (973) 352-2900
Web Site: http://www.ogilvychww.com
Sales Range: $25-49.9 Million
Emp.: 25
Advertising Services
N.A.I.C.S.: 541810

Ogilvy CommonHealth Specialty Marketing (4)
444 Interpace Pkwy Bld B, Parsippany, NJ 07054
Tel.: (973) 352-4100
Web Site: http://www.ogilvychww.com
Advertising Services
N.A.I.C.S.: 541810
Amy Graham (Pres)

Ogilvy Commonhealth Consumer Care (4)
424 Interpace Pkwy, Parsippany, NJ 07054
Tel.: (973) 352-2300
Web Site: http://www.ogilvychww.com
Advertising Services
N.A.I.C.S.: 541810

Subsidiary (Domestic):

Ogilvy Government Relations (3)
1111 19th St NW Ste 1100, Washington, DC 20036
Tel.: (202) 729-4200
Web Site: https://www.ogilvygr.com
Sales Range: $25-49.9 Million
Emp.: 14
Government Relation Services
N.A.I.C.S.: 541820
Moses C. Mercado (Principal)

Ogilvy Healthworld, LLC (3)
The Chocolate Factory 636 11th Ave, New York, NY 10036
Tel.: (212) 625-4000
Sales Range: $25-49.9 Million
Emp.: 66
Advertising Services
N.A.I.C.S.: 541810

Branch (Non-US):

Healthworld (Schweiz) AG (4)
Sennweidstr 46, 6312, Steinhausen, Switzerland
Tel.: (41) 748 76 00
Web Site: http://www.healthworld.ch
Rev.: $13,000,000
Emp.: 40
Advertising Services
N.A.I.C.S.: 541810

Healthworld Communications Group (Netherlands) BV (4)
Amsteldijk 166, 1079LH, Amsterdam, Netherlands
Tel.: (31) 334343350
Advertising Services
N.A.I.C.S.: 541810

Healthworld Pan Gulf/Dubai (4)
Level 6 MAF Tower, PO Box 3294, Deira City Ctr, Dubai, United Arab Emirates
Tel.: (971) 4 295 3456
Advertising Services
N.A.I.C.S.: 541810

Medica Healthworld/Brno (4)
Bidlaky 20 Brno, 639 00, Brno, Czech Republic
Tel.: (420) 533 337 311
Web Site: http://www.mhw.cz
Emp.: 30
Advertising Services
N.A.I.C.S.: 541810
Miroslav Lekes (Mng Dir)

Ogilvy 4D Oxford (4)
Godstow Court 5 West Way, Oxford, OX2 0JB, United Kingdom
Tel.: (44) 1865 320 200
Web Site: http://www.ogilvychww.com
Sales Range: $10-24.9 Million
Emp.: 30
Advertising Services
N.A.I.C.S.: 541810
Caroline Howe (CEO)

Ogilvy Healthworld (4)
215 Rue Saint Jacques Ste 333, Montreal, H2Y 1M6, QC, Canada
Tel.: (514) 861-1811
Web Site: http://www.ogilvy-montreal.ca
Sales Range: $10-24.9 Million
Emp.: 65
Advertising Services
N.A.I.C.S.: 541810

Ogilvy Healthworld (4)
Montes Urales 505-5, Lomas de Chapultepec, Mexico, 11000, DF, Mexico
Tel.: (52) 55 5350 1800
Web Site: http://www.ogilvy.com.mx
Sales Range: $10-24.9 Million
Emp.: 20
Advertising Services
N.A.I.C.S.: 541810

Ogilvy Healthworld (4)
15th Floor Philamlife Tower, 8767 Paseo de Roxas, Makati, 1200, Philippines
Tel.: (63) 2 885 0001
Advertising Services
N.A.I.C.S.: 541810

Ogilvy Healthworld (4)
The Ogilvy Ctr, 35 Robinson Rd, Singapore, 068 876, Singapore
Tel.: (65) 9955 9500
Web Site: http://www.ogilvy.com
Sales Range: $10-24.9 Million
Emp.: 6
Advertising Services
N.A.I.C.S.: 541810
Dan Blomfield (Mng Dir)

Ogilvy Healthworld (4)
72 Christie St, St Leonards, Sydney, 2065, NSW, Australia
Tel.: (61) 2 995500
Advertising Services
N.A.I.C.S.: 541810

Ogilvy Healthworld (4)
Ul Angorska 13a, Warsaw, 03-913, Poland
Tel.: (48) 22 672 6006
Advertising Services
N.A.I.C.S.: 541810

Ogilvy Healthworld EAME (4)
121-141 Westbourne Terrace, London, W2 6JR, United Kingdom
Tel.: (44) 20 7108 6500
Web Site: http://www.ogilvy.com
Advertising Services
N.A.I.C.S.: 541810
Matt De Gruchy (CEO)

Ogilvy Healthworld India (4)
Trade World 2nd Floor C Wing, Senapati Bapat Marg, Mumbai, 400013, India
Tel.: (91) 22 4434 4600
Advertising Services
N.A.I.C.S.: 541810

Ogilvy Healthworld London (4)
121-141 Westbourne Terrace, London, W2 6JR, United Kingdom
Tel.: (44) 2072622141
Web Site: http://www.healthworld.com
Advertising Services
N.A.I.C.S.: 541810
Matt de Gruchy (CEO)

Ogilvy Healthworld Madrid (4)
Maria de Molina 39, 28006, Madrid, Spain
Tel.: (34) 91 451 2000
Sales Range: $10-24.9 Million
Emp.: 40
Advertising Services
N.A.I.C.S.: 541810

Branch (Domestic):

Ogilvy Healthworld Payer Marketing (4)
400 Interpace Pkwy Bldg B, Parsippany, NJ 07054
Tel.: (973) 352-2400
Web Site: http://www.ogilvychww.com
Advertising Services
N.A.I.C.S.: 541810
Michael Zilligen (Pres)

Branch (Non-US):

Ogilvy Healthworld Taivas (4)
Unioninkatu 15, 00130, Helsinki, Finland
Tel.: (358) 9618 420
Web Site: http://www.taivas.fi
Sales Range: $25-49.9 Million
Emp.: 30
Advertising Services
N.A.I.C.S.: 541810
David Gamrasni (CEO)

Branch (Domestic):

Ogilvy Healthworld USA (4)
The Chocolate Factory 636 11 Ave, New York, NY 10036
Tel.: (212) 237-4000
Sales Range: $25-49.9 Million
Advertising Services
N.A.I.C.S.: 541810

Branch (Non-US):

Ogilvy Healthworld-Toronto (4)
33 Yonge St, Toronto, M5E 1X6, ON, Canada
Tel.: (416) 945-2127
Web Site: http://www.ochww.com
Sales Range: $10-24.9 Million
Emp.: 20
Advertising Services
N.A.I.C.S.: 541810
Terry Cully (Mng Dir)

Ogilvy Healthworld/Copenhagen (4)
Toltbodsgade 55, Copenhagen, 1253, Denmark
Tel.: (45) 3 917 8812
Sales Range: $10-24.9 Million
Emp.: 60
Advertising Services
N.A.I.C.S.: 541810
Morten Frederiksen (Mng Dir)

Ogilvy ZZAD/Beijing (4)
9th Fl Huali Bldg, No 58 Jinbao St, Beijing, 100005, China
Tel.: (86) 10 62078 333 8003
Advertising Services
N.A.I.C.S.: 541810

OgilvyHealthcare (4)
V le V Lancetti 29, 20158, Milan, Italy
Tel.: (39) 02 60789 1
Rev.: $3,700,000
Emp.: 15
Advertising Services
N.A.I.C.S.: 541810
Giorgio Pasqual (Mng Dir)

Subsidiary (Domestic):

Ogilvy Interactive Worldwide (3)
636 11th Ave 5th Fl, New York, NY 10036
Tel.: (212) 237-6000
Online Marketing Services
N.A.I.C.S.: 541613

Subsidiary (Non-US):

Ogilvy Noor (3)
Al Saqr Business Tower 24th Floor Sheikh Zayed Road, PO Box 74170, 74170, Dubai, United Arab Emirates
Tel.: (971) 43050200
Sales Range: $25-49.9 Million
Emp.: 106
Advertising Agencies
N.A.I.C.S.: 541810

Subsidiary (Domestic):

Ogilvy Public Relations Worldwide, Inc. (3)
3 World Trade Ctr 175 Greenwich St, New York, NY 10007
Tel.: (212) 237-4000
Public Relations Agency
N.A.I.C.S.: 541820

Subsidiary (Non-US):

Bassat, Ogilvy & Mather Comunicacion (4)
Enrique Larreta 2, 28036, Madrid, Spain
Tel.: (34) 91 398 4710
Sales Range: $10-24.9 Million
Emp.: 100
N.A.I.C.S.: 541820

Bassat, Ogilvy & Mather Comunicacion (4)
C/ Bolivia 68-70, 08029, Barcelona, Spain
Tel.: (34) 934959444
Web Site: http://www.ogilvy.
Emp.: 180

WPP PLC

INTERNATIONAL PUBLIC

WPP plc—(Continued)
Communications, Publicity/Promotions
N.A.I.C.S.: 541820

Bassat, Ogilvy & Mather Comunicacion (4)
C/ Astronomia 1 torre 5 planta 6 modulo 14
Torneo Parque Empresarial, Seville, 41015, Spain
Tel.: (34) 95 492 4526
Web Site: http://www.ogilvy.com
Sales Range: $10-24.9 Million
Emp.: 5
N.A.I.C.S.: 541820

Beijing/H-Line Ogilvy Communications Co. Ltd. (4)
418 East Wing Capital Times Sq, No 88 East Chang'an Ave, Beijing, 100031, China
Tel.: (86) 10 8391 3200
N.A.I.C.S.: 541810

Era Ogilvy Public Relations Co. Ltd. (4)
7F 126 Nan Jing East Road Sec 4, Taipei, 105, Taiwan
Tel.: (886) 2 2577 2100
Web Site: http://www.eraogilvy.com
Sales Range: $10-24.9 Million
Emp.: 70
Public Relations Agency
N.A.I.C.S.: 541820

H-Line Ogilvy Communications Co Ltd (4)
Room 704 Guangzhou Metro Plaza 183 Tian He Bei Road, Guangzhou, 510613, China
Tel.: (86) 20 8113 6288
N.A.I.C.S.: 541810

H-Line Ogilvy Communications Co Ltd (4)
17D Boai Tower, 758 Nanjing Xilu, Shanghai, 200041, China
Tel.: (86) 21 6272 8896
Web Site: http://www.h-line.com
Sales Range: $10-24.9 Million
Emp.: 20

Memac Ogilvy PR (4)
Al Saqr Business Tower 24th Floor Sheikh Zayed Road, PO Box 74170, Shiekh Zayed Rd, Dubai, United Arab Emirates
Tel.: (971) 43050200
N.A.I.C.S.: 541820

Ogilvy (4)
Hardturmstrasse 133, 8005, Zurich, Switzerland
Tel.: (41) 442686363
Sales Range: $10-24.9 Million
Emp.: 4
N.A.I.C.S.: 541820

Ogilvy Communicacao & Imagem (4)
Edificio Atrium Saldanha Praca Duque de Saldanha 1 - 4 Fl E Codigo, Lisbon, 1050-094, Portugal
Tel.: (351) 21 321 80 41
Web Site: http://www.ogilvy.pt
N.A.I.C.S.: 541810

Branch (Domestic):

Ogilvy PR (4)
350 W Mart Ctr Dr 11th Fl, Chicago, IL 60654
Tel.: (312) 397-6000
Sales Range: $10-24.9 Million
Emp.: 35
Marketing & Advertising
N.A.I.C.S.: 541820
Mike Hatcliffe (Mng Dir)

Ogilvy PR (4)
5700 Wilshire Blvd Ste 550, Los Angeles, CA 90036
Tel.: (310) 248-6179
Rev.: $30,000,000
Emp.: 18
Public Relations
N.A.I.C.S.: 541820

Subsidiary (Non-US):

Ogilvy PR (4)
Privozni 2a, Prague, 7 1 7000, Czech Republic
Tel.: (420) 2 199 8111
Sales Range: $10-24.9 Million
Emp.: 33
Public Relations
N.A.I.C.S.: 541820

Ogilvy PR (4)
Vordere Zollamtsstrasse 13/7, 1030, Vienna, Austria
Tel.: (43) 190100
Sales Range: $10-24.9 Million
Emp.: 70
N.A.I.C.S.: 541820
Florian Kremkel (CEO)

Branch (Domestic):

Ogilvy PR (4)
111 Sutter St 11th Fl, San Francisco, CA 94104-4541
Tel.: (415) 677-2700
Sales Range: $25-49.9 Million
Emp.: 25
Public Relations
N.A.I.C.S.: 541820
Aleena Abrahamian (Exec VP-Digital Content & Social)

Subsidiary (Non-US):

Ogilvy PR (4)
139/140 Marshalls Road 3rd Floor Egmore, Chennai, 600 008, India
Tel.: (91) 4444344700
Emp.: 1
N.A.I.C.S.: 541820
Kavita Baskaran (Pres)

Ogilvy PR Worldwide (4)
Room 1901-1904 19th Floor Jinbao Tower, No 89 Jinbao Street, Beijing, 10005, China
Tel.: (86) 10 8520 6688
N.A.I.C.S.: 541810
Chris Reitermann (CEO-Asia & Greater China)

Ogilvy PR Worldwide (4)
11th Floor Oberoi Commerz International Business Park, Off Western Express Highway, Mumbai, 400 063, India
Tel.: (91) 22 4434 4700
N.A.I.C.S.: 541810

Ogilvy PR Worldwide (4)
RDTX Place 36th Floor Jalan Prof DR Satrio Kav 3 Karet Kuningan, Setiabudi, Jakarta, 12940, Indonesia
Tel.: (62) 2129243000
Sales Range: $25-49.9 Million
Emp.: 180
N.A.I.C.S.: 541810

Ogilvy PR Worldwide (4)
15th Floor Philamlife Tower 8767 Paseo de Roxas, Makati, 1200, Metro Manila, Philippines
Tel.: (63) 28850001
Sales Range: $10-24.9 Million
Emp.: 16
N.A.I.C.S.: 541810

Ogilvy PR Worldwide (4)
26th Floor The Center, 989 Changle Road, Shanghai, 200031, China
Tel.: (86) 21 2405 1888
Sales Range: $25-49.9 Million
Emp.: 250
N.A.I.C.S.: 541810

Ogilvy PR Worldwide (4)
Level - 06 Fifth Floor Bagmane Laurel 65/2 Bagmane Teck Park, CV Raman Nagar Byrasandra, Bengaluru, 560 093, India
Tel.: (91) 44 4434 4700
N.A.I.C.S.: 541820

Ogilvy PR Worldwide (4)
A/20F M Plaza 109 Pazhou Avenue, Haizhu District, Guangzhou, 510335, China
Tel.: (86) 2081137388
N.A.I.C.S.: 541810

Ogilvy PR Worldwide (4)
27-8 Chamwon-Dong, Seocho-Gu, Seoul, 137-903, Korea (South)
Tel.: (82) 25131400
N.A.I.C.S.: 541810

Ogilvy PR Worldwide (4)
7 Granikou Street, Maroussi, 15125, Athens, Greece
Tel.: (30) 210 6199 286
Advertising Agencies
N.A.I.C.S.: 541820

Ogilvy PR Worldwide (4)
10 Cabot Square, Canary Wharf, London, E14 4QB, United Kingdom
Tel.: (44) 2073091000
Sales Range: $10-24.9 Million
Emp.: 900
Marketing & Advertising
N.A.I.C.S.: 541820

Ogilvy PR Worldwide (4)
86 Grigore Alexandrescu Street, 010627, Bucharest, Romania
Tel.: (40) 21 2010 100
Sales Range: $25-49.9 Million
Emp.: 150
N.A.I.C.S.: 541820

Branch (Domestic):

Ogilvy PR Worldwide (4)
555 17th St 3rd Fl, Denver, CO 80202
Tel.: (303) 615-5070
Sales Range: $10-24.9 Million
Emp.: 13
N.A.I.C.S.: 541820

Subsidiary (Non-US):

Ogilvy PR Worldwide (4)
Level 11 Menara Milenium 8 Jalan Damanlela, Bukit Damansara, Kuala Lumpur, 50490, Malaysia
Tel.: (60) 3 2718 8288
N.A.I.C.S.: 541810

Ogilvy PR Worldwide (4)
No 16 Barnes Pl, Colombo, Sri Lanka
Tel.: (94) 11 2675 016
N.A.I.C.S.: 541810
Manilka Philips (CEO & Head)

Ogilvy PR Worldwide (4)
Level 2 72 Christie Street, Saint Leonards, 2065, NSW, Australia
Tel.: (61) 282813292
Sales Range: $10-24.9 Million
Emp.: 20
N.A.I.C.S.: 541810
Leon Beswick (Mng Dir-Grp)

Branch (Domestic):

Ogilvy PR Worldwide (4)
1414 K St Ste 300, Sacramento, CA 95814
Tel.: (916) 231-7700
Web Site: http://www.ogilvy.com
Sales Range: $10-24.9 Million
Emp.: 25
Public Relations
N.A.I.C.S.: 541820

Subsidiary (Non-US):

Ogilvy PR Worldwide (4)
CVS Plaza 3rd Floor Lenara Rd, PO Box 30280, Nairobi, 00100, Kenya
Tel.: (254) 20 271 7750
Emp.: 20
N.A.I.C.S.: 541810

Ogilvy PR Worldwide, Mumbai (4)
11th Floor Oberoi Commerz International Business Park Oberoi Garden, City Off Western Express Hwy, Gurgaon (East), Mumbai, 400 063, India
Tel.: (91) 2244360360
N.A.I.C.S.: 541810
Deepali Girdhar (Partner)

Branch (Domestic):

Ogilvy PR/Atlanta (4)
3340 Peachtree Rd NE Ste 300, Atlanta, GA 30326
Tel.: (404) 881-2300
Sales Range: $10-24.9 Million
Emp.: 20
Public Relations
N.A.I.C.S.: 541820

Subsidiary (Non-US):

Ogilvy Public Relations (4)
32-34 Rue Marbeuf, 75008, Paris, France
Tel.: (33) 153671250

Sales Range: $10-24.9 Million
Emp.: 24
Public Relations
N.A.I.C.S.: 541820

Ogilvy Public Relations AB (4)
Humlegardsgatan 6, 114 80, Stockholm, Sweden
Tel.: (46) 856258280
Sales Range: $10-24.9 Million
Emp.: 10
N.A.I.C.S.: 541820

Branch (Domestic):

Ogilvy Public Relations Worldwide (4)
1111 19th St 3rd Fl, Washington, DC 20036
Tel.: (202) 729-4000
Sales Range: $25-49.9 Million
Emp.: 200
Marketing & Advertising
N.A.I.C.S.: 541820
Natalie Adler (Sr VP)

Subsidiary (Non-US):

Ogilvy Public Relations Worldwide (4)
23rd Floor The Center 99 Queens Road, Central, China (Hong Kong)
Tel.: (852) 2567 4461
Sales Range: $25-49.9 Million
Emp.: 40
Business-To-Business, Communications, Consumer Marketing, Government/Political/Public Affairs
N.A.I.C.S.: 541820

Ogilvy Public Relations Worldwide (4)
Ogilvy Center No 89 Song Ren Rd, Taipei, 110, Taiwan
Tel.: (886) 2 2758 8686
Web Site: http://www.ogilvy.com
Sales Range: $10-24.9 Million
Emp.: 50
Public Relations
N.A.I.C.S.: 541820

Ogilvy Public Relations Worldwide (4)
999/9 The Offices at Centralworld, 15th Floor Rama I Road, Patumwan, Bangkok, 10330, Thailand
Tel.: (66) 2 205 6000
Web Site: http://www.ogilvy.com
Sales Range: $10-24.9 Million
Emp.: 35
Marketing & Advertising
N.A.I.C.S.: 541820
Chutharat Thanapaisarnkit (Mng Dir)

Publicitaria Nasta (4)
Bernardino Caballero 219, Asuncion, Paraguay
Tel.: (595) 21444978
Web Site: https://www.nasta.com.py
Sales Range: $10-24.9 Million
Emp.: 30
N.A.I.C.S.: 541810

Wilson Hartnell Public Relations (4)
6 Ely Pl, Dublin, 2, Ireland
Tel.: (353) 1 669 0030
Web Site: http://www.wilsinhartnell.ie
Sales Range: $10-24.9 Million
Emp.: 35
Public Relations
N.A.I.C.S.: 541820
Roddy Guiney (Chm)

Subsidiary (Non-US):

Ogilvy Recruitment Advertising (3)
6 Ely Place, Dublin, 2, Ireland
Tel.: (353) 1 669 0216
Web Site: http://www.ogilvy.ie
Sales Range: $25-49.9 Million
Emp.: 100
N.A.I.C.S.: 541810

Subsidiary (Domestic):

VML, Inc. (2)
250 Richards Rd, Kansas City, MO 64116-4279
Tel.: (816) 283-0700
Web Site: http://www.vml.com

AND PRIVATE COMPANIES — WPP PLC

Sales Range: $75-99.9 Million
Emp.: 425
Advertising Services
N.A.I.C.S.: 541810
Craig Braasch *(COO)*

Subsidiary (Domestic):

VML, Inc. - Kalamazoo (3)
261 E Kalamazoo Ave Ste 300, Kalamazoo, MI 49007-3841
Tel.: (269) 349-7711
Web Site: http://www.vml.com
Sales Range: $50-74.9 Million
Emp.: 125
Advetising Agency
N.A.I.C.S.: 541810

Branch (Domestic):

VML-New York (3)
285 Madison Ave, New York, NY 10019
Tel.: (212) 210-3653
Web Site: http://www.vml.com
Sales Range: $10-24.9 Million
Emp.: 30
Advertising Services
N.A.I.C.S.: 541810
Brian Yamada *(Chief Innovation Officer)*

VML-White Salmon (3)
131B NE Estes Ave, White Salmon, WA 98672-0558
Tel.: (816) 283-0700
Web Site: http://www.vml.com
Sales Range: $25-49.9 Million
Emp.: 4
Advertising Services
N.A.I.C.S.: 541810

Subsidiary (Domestic):

Wexler & Walker Public Policy Associates (2)
1317 F St NW Ste 800, Washington, DC 20004-1105
Tel.: (202) 638-2121
Web Site: http://www.wexlerwalker.com
Sales Range: $25-49.9 Million
Emp.: 53
Government/Political/Public Affairs, Public Relations
N.A.I.C.S.: 541820

Xaxis, LLC (2)
3 World Trade Ctr 175 Greenwich St, New York, NY 10007
Tel.: (646) 259-4200
Web Site: https://www.xaxis.com
Sales Range: $25-49.9 Million
Emp.: 300
Advetising Agency
N.A.I.C.S.: 541810
Arshan Saha *(CEO-Asia Pacific)*

Branch (Domestic):

24/7 Real Media (3)
580 Virginia Dr Ste 200, Fort Washington, PA 19034-2715
Tel.: (215) 793-4900
Web Site: http://www.247realmedia.com
Sales Range: $25-49.9 Million
Emp.: 20
Electronic Media, Media Buying Services
N.A.I.C.S.: 541830

24/7 Real Media (3)
303 2nd St N Tower Ste 300, San Francisco, CA 94108
Tel.: (415) 403-8156
Web Site: http://www.247realmedia.com
Sales Range: $25-49.9 Million
Emp.: 3
Electronic Media, Media Buying Services
N.A.I.C.S.: 541830

24/7 Real Media (3)
2425 Olympic Blvd Ste 2000-W, Santa Monica, CA 90404
Tel.: (310) 309-8120
Sales Range: $25-49.9 Million
Emp.: 3
N.A.I.C.S.: 541830
Michael Tarter *(VP-West Coast Sls)*

24/7 Real Media (3)
15455 N Dallas Plwy Ste 600, Addison, TX 75001
Tel.: (972) 964-5200
N.A.I.C.S.: 541810

Subsidiary (Non-US):

24/7 Real Media (3)
Via Paleocapa 7, 20121, Milan, Italy
Tel.: (39) 02 30417 535
N.A.I.C.S.: 541810

Branch (Domestic):

24/7 Real Media (3)
222 Merchandise Mart Plz Ste 250, Chicago, IL 60654
Tel.: (847) 283-9911
Web Site: http://www.247realmedia.com
Sales Range: $25-49.9 Million
Emp.: 4
N.A.I.C.S.: 541830

Subsidiary (Non-US):

24/7 Real Media France SARL (3)
39 Rue Etienne Marcel, 75001, Paris, France
Tel.: (33) 156596990
Web Site: http://www.247media.fr
Electronic Media, Media Buying Services
N.A.I.C.S.: 541830
Nicolle Pangis *(Pres)*

24/7 Real Media South Korea (3)
58 Baeklim B/D 9F Nonhyeonro 85gil, Gangnam, Seoul, 135-933, Korea (South)
Tel.: (82) 25688431
Sales Range: $25-49.9 Million
Emp.: 60
N.A.I.C.S.: 541830

24/7 Real Media UK Ltd. (3)
121-141 Westbourne Terrace, Paddington, London, W2 6JR, United Kingdom
Tel.: (44) 2075633800
Web Site: http://www.247realmedia.co.uk
Sales Range: $25-49.9 Million
Emp.: 25
Electronic Media, Media Buying Services
N.A.I.C.S.: 541830

24/7 Real Media, Inc. (3)
4200 Saint-Laurent Blvd Ste 707, Montreal, H2W 2R2, QC, Canada
Tel.: (514) 848-0247
Sales Range: $25-49.9 Million
Emp.: 5
Electronic Media, Media Buying Services
N.A.I.C.S.: 541830

DA Search & Link Inc. (3)
11 Toyokaiji Bldg 5th Fl 1-5-11 Nishi-Shinbashi, Minato-ku, Tokyo, 105 0003, Japan
Tel.: (81) 3 5157 3971
Web Site: http://www.dasl.co.jp
Sales Range: $25-49.9 Million
Emp.: 150
N.A.I.C.S.: 541830

Real Media Scandinavia (3)
Vasagatan 11, 114 87, Stockholm, Sweden
Tel.: (46) 86606616
Web Site: http://www.247realmedia.com
Sales Range: $25-49.9 Million
Emp.: 3
Electronic Media, Media Buying Services
N.A.I.C.S.: 541830

Real Media Spain S.A. (3)
Paseo de la Castellana, 53 - 3a, 28046, Madrid, Spain
Tel.: (34) 91 555 00 00
Sales Range: $25-49.9 Million
Emp.: 25
Electronic Media, Media Buying Services
N.A.I.C.S.: 541830

Subsidiary (Domestic):

Young & Rubicam Inc. (2)
3 World Trade Ctr 28th Fl 175 Greenwich St, New York, NY 10007
Tel.: (212) 210-3017
Web Site: http://www.yr.com
Sales Range: $900-999.9 Million
Emp.: 11,500
Advertising Services
N.A.I.C.S.: 541810
Belle Frank *(Exec VP & Dir-Strategy & Res-Global)*

Subsidiary (Non-US):

Advantage Y&R (3)
84 Frans Indongo str, Windhoek, Namibia
Tel.: (264) 61 225 665
Web Site: http://www.advantageyr.com
Sales Range: $25-49.9 Million
Emp.: 25
Advertising Services
N.A.I.C.S.: 541810
Truda Meaden *(Mng Dir)*

Armstrong Y&R (3)
Wing F 2nd Floor Comesa Centre Ben bella Rd, Lusaka, Zambia
Tel.: (260) 1228490
Web Site: http://www.yr.com
Sales Range: $25-49.9 Million
Emp.: 23
Advertising Services
N.A.I.C.S.: 541810

Asesores/Y&R S.A. (3)
Edificio Asesores Apartado 6947-1000, Iglesia San Francisco de, Guadalupe, 50 Mts Sur, San Jose, Costa Rica
Tel.: (506) 257 6727
Web Site: http://actividadesasesores.blogspot.com
Sales Range: $25-49.9 Million
Emp.: 51
Advertising Services
N.A.I.C.S.: 541810

Baader Hermes/Y&R (3)
Nymphenburger Strasse 86, Munich, 80636, Germany
Tel.: (49) 892102270
Web Site: http://www.bbh-digital.de
Sales Range: $10-24.9 Million
Emp.: 28
Advertising Services
N.A.I.C.S.: 541810

Subsidiary (Domestic):

BrandBuzz (3)
285 Madison Ave 22nd Fl, New York, NY 10017
Tel.: (212) 210-3879
Advertising Services
N.A.I.C.S.: 541810

Subsidiary (Non-US):

CS Reklam Hizmetleri Sanayi Ve Ticaret A.S. (3)
Istiklal Cad Kallavi Sok No 1 Kat 1, Beyoglu, Istanbul, 34430, Turkiye
Tel.: (90) 212 251 08 60 61
Web Site: http://www.csdlab.com
Sales Range: $1-9.9 Million
Emp.: 40
Digital Advertising Services
N.A.I.C.S.: 541810

Cerebro Y&R (3)
Calles 50 y 64 Este San Francisco Edificio San George piso 8, Apartado, 7188 Zona 5, Panama, Panama
Tel.: (507) 270 7355
Sales Range: $10-24.9 Million
Emp.: 29
Advertising Services
N.A.I.C.S.: 541810

ECO/Y&R, S.A (3)
8 Calle 2-38 Zona 9, Guatemala City, Guatemala, 01009, Guatemala
Tel.: (502) 3347314
Web Site: http://www.yr.com
Sales Range: $25-49.9 Million
Emp.: 56
Advertising Services
N.A.I.C.S.: 541810

Energia/Y&R (3)
Carrera 13 #93-40, Bogota, Colombia
Tel.: (57) 16001010
Web Site: http://www.yr.com
Sales Range: $25-49.9 Million
Emp.: 100
Advertising Services
N.A.I.C.S.: 541810

Energia/Y&R (3)
Avenida Victor Andres Belaunde 147, Oficina 601 San Isidro, Lima, Peru
Tel.: (51) 1 441 6368
Web Site: http://www.yr.com
Advertising Services
N.A.I.C.S.: 541810

Everest Brand Solutions Pvt. Ltd. (3)
G/1801 Lotus Corporate Park, Goregaon East, Mumbai, 400063, India
Tel.: (91) 2261952000
Advertising Services
N.A.I.C.S.: 541810
Veerendra Prabhu *(Sr Mgr-Comml)*

HS Ad, Inc. (3)
155 Mapo-daero LG Mapo Building, Mapogu, Seoul, 121-721, Korea (South)
Tel.: (82) 27052600
Web Site: https://www.hsad.co.kr
Advertising Services
N.A.I.C.S.: 541810

Branch (US):

HS Ad, Inc. (4)
920 Sylvan Ave, Englewood Cliffs, NJ 07632-3302
Tel.: (201) 816-3090
Web Site: http://www.g2rgroup.com
Sales Range: Less than $1 Million
Emp.: 10
Advertising Services
N.A.I.C.S.: 541810

Branch (Non-US):

HS Ad, Inc. (4)
17floorwest Twins Tower No:12, Jian Guo Men Wai RoadChao Yan, Beijing, 10022, China
Tel.: (86) 13260312852
Web Site: http://www.hsad.co.kr
Advertising Services
N.A.I.C.S.: 541810

Subsidiary (Non-US):

Ideaworks (3)
65 Berry Street, GPO Pox 3 557, Sydney, 2060, NSW, Australia
Tel.: (61) 299094411
Sales Range: $50-74.9 Million
Emp.: 80
Advertising Agencies
N.A.I.C.S.: 541810

Subsidiary (Domestic):

KBM Group (3)
2050 N Greenville Ave, Richardson, TX 75082
Tel.: (972) 664-3600
Web Site: http://www.kbmg.com
Sales Range: $25-49.9 Million
Emp.: 100
Marketing Solutions
N.A.I.C.S.: 541810
Bret Harper *(COO)*

Subsidiary (Domestic):

I-Behavior, Inc. (4)
2051 Dogwood St Ste 220, Louisville, CO 80027
Tel.: (303) 228-5000
Web Site: http://www.i-behavior.com
Sales Range: $10-24.9 Million
Emp.: 40
Marketing Services
N.A.I.C.S.: 541890
Joe Bank *(Gen Mgr-Merchant Svcs)*

Branch (Domestic):

I-Behavior, Inc. - Harrison (5)
2051 Dogwood St, Louisville, CO 80027
Tel.: (914) 777-3777
Web Site: http://www.i-behavior.com
Sales Range: $1-9.9 Million
Emp.: 40
Marketing Services
N.A.I.C.S.: 541890

Subsidiary (Non-US):

Lemusimun/Y&R (3)
Blvd Orden de Malta No 5 Urbanizacion Santa Elena, Antiguo Cuscatlan La Libertad, San Salvador, El Salvador
Tel.: (503) 2 233 5000
Web Site: http://www.yr.com
Sales Range: $25-49.9 Million
Emp.: 51
Advertising Services
N.A.I.C.S.: 541810

Matari Advertising (3)
Puri Matari Jalan HR Rasuna Said Kav H

WPP PLC

WPP plc—(Continued)
1-2, Jakarta, 12920, Indonesia
Tel.: (62) 21 525 5160
Web Site: http://www.matari-ad.com
Advertising Agency
N.A.I.C.S.: 541810
Aswan Soendojo *(Pres)*

Paragon Communications Sdn. Bhd. (3)
8th Floor Wisma E&C No 2 Dungun Kiri, Damansara Heights, 50490, Kuala Lumpur, Malaysia
Tel.: (60) 3 2095 2600
Web Site: http://www.yr.com
Sales Range: $10-24.9 Million
Emp.: 35
Advertising Services
N.A.I.C.S.: 541810

Rainey Kelly Campbell Roalfe/Y&R (3)
Greater London House Hampstead Road, London, NW1 7QP, United Kingdom
Tel.: (44) 2076116569
Web Site: http://www.rkcr.com
Sales Range: $125-149.9 Million
Emp.: 100
Advertising Services
N.A.I.C.S.: 541810
Mark Roalfe *(Chm)*

Rediffusion DY&R (3)
4th Fl Premier House 514 Yhimbirigasyaya Road, Colombo, 00500, Sri Lanka
Tel.: (94) 11 535 3678
Web Site: http://www.yr.com
Advertising Services
N.A.I.C.S.: 541810

Rediffusion Y&R Pvt. Ltd. (3)
Terminal 9 5th Floor Nehru Road, Vile Parle East, Mumbai, 400 99, India
Tel.: (91) 2226138800
Web Site: http://www.rediffusionyr.com
Sales Range: $50-74.9 Million
Emp.: 500
Advetising Agency
N.A.I.C.S.: 541810
Diwan Arun Nanda *(Chm)*

Branch (Domestic):

Rediffusion Y&R Pvt. Ltd. (4)
Uniworth Plaza 2nd Floor 20 Sanky Road, Palace Guttahalle, Bengaluru, 560 020, India
Tel.: (91) 80 2336 1567
Web Site: http://www.rediffusionyr.com
Sales Range: $10-24.9 Million
Emp.: 60
Advertising Services
N.A.I.C.S.: 541810

Rediffusion Y&R Pvt. Ltd. (4)
Jindal Tower 21 / 1A/3 Darga Road, 1st Floor Block B, Kolkata, 700 017, India
Tel.: (91) 33 2247 5432
Web Site: http://www.rediffusionyr.com
Advertising Services
N.A.I.C.S.: 541810

Rediffusion Y&R Pvt. Ltd. (4)
Shakti Towers 2nd Floor Anna Salai, Chennai, 600 062, India
Tel.: (91) 44 2858 5406
Web Site: http://www.rediffusionyr.com
Advertising Services
N.A.I.C.S.: 541810

Rediffusion Y&R Pvt. Ltd. (4)
Plot No 184 Platinum Towers 3rd Floor Udyog Vihar Phase I, Building No 9B, Gurgaon, 122016, Haryana, India
Tel.: (91) 124 433 8000
Web Site: http://www.rediffusionyr.com
Emp.: 50
Advertising Services
N.A.I.C.S.: 541810

Rediffusion Y&R Pvt. Ltd.-Corporate Office (4)
Terminal Line 5th Floor Nehru Rd, Vileparie E, Mumbai, 400 099, India
Tel.: (91) 22 2613 8800
Web Site: http://www.rediffusionyr.com
Sales Range: $10-24.9 Million
Advertising Services
N.A.I.C.S.: 541810

Dhunji S. Wadia *(Pres)*

Subsidiary (Domestic):

Sudler & Hennessey New York/Worldwide Headquarters (3)
230 Park Ave S, New York, NY 10003
Tel.: (212) 614-4100
Advertising Services
N.A.I.C.S.: 541810
Louisa Holland *(CEO)*

Branch (Non-US):

Broca & Wernicke Integrated Healthcare Communications (4)
Amsterdamsestraatweg 24, Abcoude, Utrecht, 1391 AB, Netherlands
Tel.: (31) 294 299 220
Web Site: http://www.broca-wernicke.nl
Sales Range: Less than $1 Million
Emp.: 2
Advertising Services
N.A.I.C.S.: 541810

Creative Healthcare Advertising Paris (4)
46 rue Escudier, 92100, Boulogne-Billancourt, France
Tel.: (33) 1 4186 7777
Public Relations Services
N.A.I.C.S.: 541820

Joint Venture (Non-US):

Dentsu, Sudler & Hennessey Inc. (4)
Tsukiji Eto Bldg 1-12-6 Tsukiji, Chuo-ku, Tokyo, 104-8427, Japan
Tel.: (81) 335460463
Web Site: http://www.dsh.co.jp
Rev.: $98,000,000
Emp.: 77
Marketing Communication in General Healthcare
N.A.I.C.S.: 541613

Branch (Non-US):

ENE Publicidad SA Barcelona (4)
Calle Brol 216, 08026, Barcelona, Spain
Tel.: (34) 934391848
Web Site: http://www.ene.es
Sales Range: $10-24.9 Million
Emp.: 3
Advertising Services
N.A.I.C.S.: 541810

ENE Publicidad, S.A. Madrid (4)
C/Julian Camarillo 29 Edif Diapason D-2 1A Planta, 28037, Madrid, Spain
Tel.: (34) 913043443
Web Site: http://www.ene.es
Sales Range: $10-24.9 Million
Emp.: 30
Advertising Services
N.A.I.C.S.: 541810

Unit (Domestic):

HealthAnswers Education LLC (4)
1140 Welsh Rd 150, North Wales, PA 19454
Tel.: (215) 412-3900
Web Site: http://www.labruell.com
Producer of Interactive Training Healthcare Website for Consumers & Professionals
N.A.I.C.S.: 517810
Michael Tague *(Mng Dir)*

Branch (Non-US):

IntraMed Communications Milan (4)
Via Bertieri 4, I-20146, Milan, Italy
Tel.: (39) 02345451
Sales Range: $10-24.9 Million
Emp.: 20
Advertising Services
N.A.I.C.S.: 541810

Unit (Domestic):

IntraMed West Educational Group (4)
1001 Front St, San Francisco, CA 94111
Tel.: (415) 365-6801
Sales Range: $10-24.9 Million
Emp.: 10
Advertising Services
N.A.I.C.S.: 541810

Branch (Non-US):

IntraMedic GmbH (4)
Dorn Hofster 44-46, Neu-Isenburg, 63263, Germany
Tel.: (49) 6102 7993 300
Web Site: http://www.intramedic.de
Sales Range: $10-24.9 Million
Emp.: 25
Advertising Services
N.A.I.C.S.: 541820
Roger Stenz *(Gen Mgr)*

IntraMedical Health Services Paris (4)
46 rue Escudier, 92100, Paris, France
Tel.: (33) 1 4186 7777
Sales Range: $10-24.9 Million
Emp.: 11
Public Relations Services
N.A.I.C.S.: 541820

Intramed (4)
4700 Rue de la Savane, Montreal, H4P 1T7, QC, Canada
Tel.: (514) 737-9393
Sales Range: $10-24.9 Million
Emp.: 20
Advertising Services
N.A.I.C.S.: 541810

NextHealth Milan (4)
Piazzale Stefano Turr 5, I-20149, Milan, Italy
Tel.: (39) 0234538324
Sales Range: $10-24.9 Million
Emp.: 11
Advertising Services
N.A.I.C.S.: 541810

Unit (Domestic):

Precept Medical Communications (4)
4 Connell Dr Bldg IV Ste 601, Berkeley Heights, NJ 07922-2705
Tel.: (908) 288-0100
Advertising Services
N.A.I.C.S.: 541810

Branch (Non-US):

Sentrix Global Health Communications Milan (4)
Via Bertiere 4, 20146, Milan, Italy
Tel.: (39) 02349911
Sales Range: $25-49.9 Million
Emp.: 130
Advertising Services
N.A.I.C.S.: 541810

Sudler & Hennessey (4)
4700 De La Savane Ste 200, Montreal, H4P 1T7, QC, Canada
Tel.: (514) 733-0073
Sales Range: $10-24.9 Million
Emp.: 12
Advertising Services
N.A.I.C.S.: 541810

Sudler & Hennessey European Headquarters (4)
Via Bertiere, I-20146, Milan, Italy
Tel.: (39) 02 349 721
Sales Range: $25-49.9 Million
Emp.: 200
Advertising Services
N.A.I.C.S.: 541810

Sudler & Hennessey Frankfurt (4)
Dornhof Str 44 46, Neu-Isenburg, 63263, Germany
Tel.: (49) 61027993333
Web Site: http://www.sudler.de
Sales Range: $10-24.9 Million
Emp.: 25
Advertising Services
N.A.I.C.S.: 541810
Roger Stenz *(CEO)*

Sudler & Hennessey Ltd. - London (4)
4th Fl Middlesex House 34 Cleveland St, London, W1P 4JE, United Kingdom
Tel.: (44) 2073077800
Web Site: http://www.sudler-hennessey.co.uk
Sales Range: $10-24.9 Million
Emp.: 25
Advertising Services

INTERNATIONAL PUBLIC

N.A.I.C.S.: 541810
Tara Page *(Mng Dir)*

Sudler & Hennessey Milan (4)
Via Bertieri 4, I-20146, Milan, Italy
Tel.: (39) 02349721
Web Site: http://www.sudler.it
Rev.: $59,036,000
Emp.: 130
Advertising Services
N.A.I.C.S.: 541810
Maurizio Mioli *(CEO)*

Sudler & Hennessey Ontario (4)
2121 Argentia Rd Ste 401, Mississauga, L5N 2X4, ON, Canada
Tel.: (905) 858-9179
Sales Range: $10-24.9 Million
Emp.: 12
Advertising Services
N.A.I.C.S.: 541810

Sudler & Hennessey Paris (4)
6 rue Escudier, 92100, Boulogne-Billancourt, France
Tel.: (33) 141867777
Sales Range: $10-24.9 Million
Emp.: 45
Advertising Services
N.A.I.C.S.: 541810

Sudler & Hennessey Sydney (4)
The Denison Level 8 65 Berry St, North, Sydney, 2060, NSW, Australia
Tel.: (61) 299316111
Sales Range: $10-24.9 Million
Emp.: 35
Advertising Services
N.A.I.C.S.: 541810
Rob Rogers *(CEO-Americas)*

Transferase Consulting & Media Relations Milan (4)
Via Bertieri 4, 20146, Milan, Italy
Tel.: (39) 02 3497 2403
Advertising Services
N.A.I.C.S.: 541810

Subsidiary (Domestic):

Viscira LLC (4)
200 Vallejo St, San Francisco, CA 94111
Tel.: (415) 848-8010
Web Site: http://www.viscira.com
Sales Range: $10-24.9 Million
Emp.: 100
Develops Interactive, Digital Marketing Programs for Healthcare Industry
N.A.I.C.S.: 541511
Dave Gulezian *(Founder)*

Subsidiary (Non-US):

TAXI (3)
155 Queens Quay East Floor 10, Toronto, M5A 0W4, ON, Canada
Tel.: (416) 342-8294
Sales Range: $25-49.9 Million
Emp.: 120
Advertising Services
N.A.I.C.S.: 541810
Rob Guenette *(CEO)*

Branch (Domestic):

TAXI (4)
500 Rue Saint-Jacques Bureau 1410, Montreal, H2Y 1S1, QC, Canada
Tel.: (514) 842-8294
Sales Range: $10-24.9 Million
Emp.: 70
Advertising Services
N.A.I.C.S.: 541810

Branch (US):

TAXI New York (4)
3 Columbus Circle, New York, NY 10003
Tel.: (212) 414-8294
Web Site: http://www.taxi-nyc.com
Rev.: $10,000,000
Emp.: 20
Advertising Services
N.A.I.C.S.: 541810
Paul Lavoie *(Founder)*

Branch (Domestic):

TAXI Vancouver (4)
515 Richards St, Vancouver, V6B 2Z5, BC, Canada

AND PRIVATE COMPANIES • WPP PLC

Tel.: (604) 683-8294
Web Site: http://vancouver.taxi.ca
Sales Range: $10-24.9 Million
Emp.: 27
Advertising Services
N.A.I.C.S.: 541810

Taxi 2 (4)
49 Spadina Ave Ste 403, Toronto, M5V2J1, ON, Canada
Tel.: (416) 598-4750
Advertising Services
N.A.I.C.S.: 541810

Subsidiary (Non-US):

Team/Y&R Amman (3)
Al Abdali The Boulevard Al-Bonouk Street Building 12A Fourth Floor, PO Box 940138, Al Rabieh, Amman, 11194, Jordan
Tel.: (962) 65532285
Web Site: https://www.vmlyr-amman.com
Emp.: 60
Advertising Services
N.A.I.C.S.: 541810

Team/Y&R Jeddah (3)
1st Floor Peatro Mall Thalia Street, Jeddah, 21411, Saudi Arabia
Tel.: (966) 2 660 1999
Advertising Services
N.A.I.C.S.: 541810

Subsidiary (Domestic):

The Bravo Group HQ (3)
3 Columbus Cir, New York, NY 10019
Tel.: (212) 780-5800
Web Site: http://www.bbravo.com
Rev.: $275,000,000
Emp.: 144
Advertising Services
N.A.I.C.S.: 541810

Branch (Domestic):

The Bravo Group (4)
303 2nd St 3rd Fl S, San Francisco, CA 94107
Tel.: (415) 268-3380
Web Site: http://www.thebravogroup.com
Rev.: $50,000,000
Emp.: 20
Advertising Services
N.A.I.C.S.: 541810

The Bravo Group (4)
Courvoisier Ctr 601 Brickell Key Dr Ste 1100, Miami, FL 33131-4330
Tel.: (305) 503-8000
Sales Range: $10-24.9 Million
Emp.: 24
Advertising Services
N.A.I.C.S.: 541810

Subsidiary (Non-US):

Upstairs/Y & R Poland SP. z.o.o. (3)
ul Dobra 56/66, 00-312, Warsaw, Poland
Tel.: (48) 225527000
Web Site: http://www.yr.com
Sales Range: $25-49.9 Million
Emp.: 100
Advertising Services
N.A.I.C.S.: 541810

VMLY&R Dubai (3)
The Gateway Building, Dubai Media City, 14129, Dubai, United Arab Emirates
Tel.: (971) 44507500
Advertising Agencies
N.A.I.C.S.: 541810
Kalpesh Patankar (Chief Creative Officer)

VMLY&R Hungary (3)
Mom Park C Alkotas UT 53/C, 1123, Budapest, Hungary
Tel.: (36) 18017200
Advertising Services
N.A.I.C.S.: 541810
Laszlo Palicnsar (Grp CEO)

Vinizius/Y&R (3)
C/Numancia 164-168 8th Floor, 08029, Barcelona, Spain
Tel.: (34) 933666600
Web Site: http://www.yr.com
Sales Range: $25-49.9 Million
Emp.: 130
Advertising Services
N.A.I.C.S.: 541810

Y&R (3)
9 Upper Pembroke Street, Dublin, Ireland
Tel.: (353) 16760221
Web Site: http://www.yr.com
Sales Range: $25-49.9 Million
Emp.: 25
Advertising Services
N.A.I.C.S.: 541810

Branch (Domestic):

Y&R (3)
3 Columbus Cir, New York, NY 10019
Tel.: (212) 210-3000
Web Site: http://www.yr.com
Sales Range: $75-99.9 Million
Emp.: 400
Advertising Services
N.A.I.C.S.: 541810

Y&R (3)
303 2nd St 3th Fl N Tower, San Francisco, CA 94107
Tel.: (415) 882-0600
Web Site: http://www.yr.com
Sales Range: $25-49.9 Million
Emp.: 70
Advertising Services
N.A.I.C.S.: 541810
Mike Reese (Pres)

Subsidiary (Non-US):

Y&R Abu Dhabi (3)
Arwada Cmt Royal Business Centre 11th Floor Central Abu Dhabhi, PO Box 44281, Abu Dhabi, United Arab Emirates
Tel.: (971) 2 621 5050
Web Site: http://www.yr.com
Sales Range: $10-24.9 Million
Emp.: 45
Advertising Services
N.A.I.C.S.: 541810

Y&R Argentina S.A. (3)
French 3155, 1425, Buenos Aires, Argentina
Tel.: (54) 1157773660
Web Site: http://www.yr.com.ar
Sales Range: $25-49.9 Million
Emp.: 123
Advertising Services
N.A.I.C.S.: 541810

Subsidiary (Domestic):

Y&R Austin (3)
500 W 5th St Ste 1000, Austin, TX 78701
Tel.: (512) 343-0264
Advertising Services
N.A.I.C.S.: 541810
Jennifer Wilson (Mng Dir-Austin)

Subsidiary (Non-US):

Y&R Belgium S.A. (3)
Generaal Lemanstraat 47, 1180, Antwerp, Belgium
Tel.: (32) 23758012
Web Site: http://www.thesedaysyr.com
Sales Range: $10-24.9 Million
Emp.: 45
Advertising Services
N.A.I.C.S.: 541810
Erwin Jansen (Founder)

Y&R Budapest (3)
MOM Park Alkotasu 53C, Budapest, 1123, Hungary
Tel.: (36) 18017200
Web Site: http://www.yr.hu
Sales Range: $25-49.9 Million
Emp.: 70
Advertising Services
N.A.I.C.S.: 541810

Y&R Cape Town (3)
Ground & 1st Floor The Warehouse, 24 Alfred St, Cape Town, 8001, South Africa
Tel.: (27) 21 440 3700
Web Site: http://www.yr.com
Sales Range: $10-24.9 Million
Emp.: 52
Advertising Services
N.A.I.C.S.: 541810

Y&R GmbH (3)
Rotemturmstrasse 1618 6th Fl, A-1010, Vienna, Austria
Tel.: (43) 1531170
Web Site: http://www.yrvienna.at

Sales Range: $10-24.9 Million
Emp.: 20
Advertising Services
N.A.I.C.S.: 541810

Y&R Hong Kong (3)
32nd Fl 633 Kings Rd, North Point, China (Hong Kong)
Tel.: (852) 2884 6668
Web Site: http://www.yr.com
Emp.: 18
Advetising Agency
N.A.I.C.S.: 541810

Y&R Italia, srl (3)
Tortona 37, 20144, Milan, Italy
Tel.: (39) 0277321
Web Site: http://www.yr.com
Sales Range: $10-24.9 Million
Emp.: 300
Advertising Services
N.A.I.C.S.: 541810

Y&R Johannesburg (3)
Georgian Crescent East, 56 Lotus Rd, Bryanston, 2144, South Africa
Tel.: (27) 117976300
Web Site: http://www.yr.com
Sales Range: $25-49.9 Million
Emp.: 150
Advetising Agency
N.A.I.C.S.: 541810

Branch (Domestic):

Y&R Latin American Headquarters (3)
Courvoisier Ctr II 601 Brickell Key Dr Ste 1100, Miami, FL 33131
Tel.: (305) 347-1950
Web Site: http://www.yr.com
Sales Range: $25-49.9 Million
Emp.: 75
Advertising Services
N.A.I.C.S.: 541810

Y&R Miami (3)
601 Brickell Key Dr Ste 1100, Miami, FL 33131
Tel.: (305) 347-1950
Web Site: http://www.yr.com
Sales Range: $25-49.9 Million
Emp.: 80
Advertising Services
N.A.I.C.S.: 541810
Jesus Portillo (Chm)

Subsidiary (Non-US):

Y&R Paris (3)
67 Avenue Andre Morizet, BP 73, 92105, Boulogne, France
Tel.: (33) 146843333
Web Site: http://www.yr.com
Sales Range: $25-49.9 Million
Emp.: 10
Advertising Services
N.A.I.C.S.: 541810

Y&R Paris S.A. (3)
57 Avenue Andre Morizet, 92100, Boulogne-Billancourt, France
Tel.: (33) 146843364
Web Site: http://www.yrparis.fr
Sales Range: $75-99.9 Million
Emp.: 169
Advertising Services
N.A.I.C.S.: 541810

Y&R Peru (3)
Av Angamos Oeste 915, Miraflores, Lima, Peru
Tel.: (51) 14478282
Web Site: http://www.yr.com
Sales Range: $25-49.9 Million
Emp.: 100
Advetising Agency
N.A.I.C.S.: 541810

Y&R Portugal (3)
Av Eng Duarte Pacheco, Tower 1 9th Fl, 1070-101, Lisbon, Portugal
Tel.: (351) 213816300
Web Site: http://www.yrportugal.pt
Sales Range: $10-24.9 Million
Emp.: 30
Advertising Services
N.A.I.C.S.: 541810
Judite Mota (Chief Creative Officer & Gen Dir)

Y&R Praha, s.r.o. (3)
Nadrazni 762/32, 150 00, Prague, 5, Czech Republic
Tel.: (420) 221420121
Web Site: http://www.yr.cz
Sales Range: $25-49.9 Million
Emp.: 100
Advertising Services
N.A.I.C.S.: 541810

Branch (Domestic):

Y&R Puerto Rico, Inc. (3)
PO Box 366288, San Juan, PR 00936-6288
Tel.: (787) 622-6500
Web Site: http://www.yr.com
Sales Range: $25-49.9 Million
Emp.: 48
Advertising Services
N.A.I.C.S.: 541810
Ivan Santos (CEO)

Subsidiary (Non-US):

Y&R Sao Paulo (3)
Rua General Furtado do Nascimento 9, Sao Paulo, 1054220011, SP, Brazil
Tel.: (55) 1130264400
Web Site: http://www.yrbrasil.com.br
Sales Range: $25-49.9 Million
Emp.: 130
Advetising Agency
N.A.I.C.S.: 541810

Y&R Singapore (3)
300 Beach Rd 30th Floor The Concourse, 199555, Singapore, Singapore
Tel.: (65) 62950025
Web Site: http://www.yr.com
Sales Range: $25-49.9 Million
Emp.: 100
Advertising Services
N.A.I.C.S.: 541810

Y&R Turkey (3)
Bomonti Firin Sokak No 51, 80260, Istanbul, Turkiye
Tel.: (90) 2122249070
Web Site: http://www.reklamevi.com.tr
Sales Range: $75-99.9 Million
Emp.: 108
Advertising Services
N.A.I.C.S.: 541810

Y&R Uruguay (3)
Punta Carretas Tower-6 th Floor, 11300, Montevideo, Uruguay
Tel.: (598) 27160385
Web Site: https://www.vmlyr.com
Sales Range: $10-24.9 Million
Emp.: 40
Advertising Services
N.A.I.C.S.: 541810
Alvaro More (Founder)

Y&R West (3)
605 11th Avenue SW Suite 215, Calgary, T2R 0E1, AB, Canada
Tel.: (403) 262-6852
Web Site: http://www.yr.com
Sales Range: $25-49.9 Million
Emp.: 11
Advertising Services
N.A.I.C.S.: 541810

Y&R, Ltd. (3)
60 Bloor Street West, Toronto, M4W 1J2, ON, Canada
Tel.: (416) 961-5111
Sales Range: $25-49.9 Million
Emp.: 151
Advertising Services
N.A.I.C.S.: 541810
Israel Diaz (Chief Creative Officer & Exec VP)

Y&R-Atlantic (3)
200 Waterfront Drive Suite 210, Bedford, B4A 4J4, NS, Canada
Tel.: (902) 453-2401
Web Site: http://www.yr.com
Sales Range: $10-24.9 Million
Emp.: 33
Advertising Services
N.A.I.C.S.: 541810

Young & Rubicam Australia/New Zealand (3)
Level 15 35 Clarence Street, Sydney, 2000, NSW, Australia

WPP PLC

WPP plc—(Continued)
Tel.: (61) 297787100
Web Site: http://www.yr.com
Sales Range: $25-49.9 Million
Emp.: 110
Advertising Services
N.A.I.C.S.: 541810

Young & Rubicam Bogota (3)
Carrera 11 A Suite 93B 30, 5 Piso Santa Fe De, Bogota, 110221, Colombia
Tel.: (57) 16285999
Web Site: http://www.yr.com
Sales Range: $25-49.9 Million
Emp.: 120
Advetising Agency
N.A.I.C.S.: 541810
Vicente Arteaga (Pres)

Young & Rubicam Brands Africa (3)
2nd Fl Panesars Centre Mombasa Road, PO Box 41036, 00-100, Nairobi, Kenya
Tel.: (254) 20559729
Sales Range: $25-49.9 Million
Emp.: 60
Advertising Services
N.A.I.C.S.: 541810

Branch (Domestic):

Young & Rubicam Brands, San Francisco (3)
303 2nd north towr 3rd fl, San Francisco, CA 94107
Tel.: (415) 882-0600
Sales Range: $10-24.9 Million
Emp.: 80
Advertising Services
N.A.I.C.S.: 541810
Neil Nordstrom (Office Mgr)

Young & Rubicam Brands, Southern California (3)
2010 Main St Ste 400, Irvine, CA 92614
Tel.: (949) 754-2000
Web Site: http://www.wundermanwest.com
Sales Range: $25-49.9 Million
Emp.: 30
Advertising Services
N.A.I.C.S.: 541810
Jeff Browe (CEO)

Young & Rubicam Chicago (3)
233 N Michigan Ave 16th Fl, Chicago, IL 60601-5519
Tel.: (312) 596-3000
Web Site: http://www.yrchicago.com
Sales Range: $25-49.9 Million
Emp.: 110
Advertising Services
N.A.I.C.S.: 541810

Subsidiary (Non-US):

Young & Rubicam Guangzhou (3)
28th Fl 246 ZhongShanSi Road, Guangzhou, 510023, China
Tel.: (86) 20 8363 5990
Web Site: http://www.yr.com
Sales Range: $25-49.9 Million
Emp.: 64
Advertising Services
N.A.I.C.S.: 541810

Young & Rubicam Korea Co., Ltd. (3)
2nd Fl Chungho Bldg 97-7 Nonhyun-Dong, Kangnam, Seoul, 135-010, Korea (South)
Tel.: (82) 2 546 7310
Sales Range: $10-24.9 Million
Emp.: 24
Advertising Services
N.A.I.C.S.: 541810

Young & Rubicam Ltd. (3)
17th Floor Siam Tower 989 Rama 1 Rd, Pathumwan, Bangkok, 10330, Thailand
Tel.: (66) 2 658 0999
Web Site: http://www.yr.com
Sales Range: $25-49.9 Million
Emp.: 115
Advertising Services
N.A.I.C.S.: 541810
Yupin Muntzing (CEO)

Young & Rubicam Ltd. (3)
Greater London House Hampstead Road, London, NW1 7QP, United Kingdom
Tel.: (44) 2073879366

Sales Range: $25-49.9 Million
Emp.: 180
Advertising Services
N.A.I.C.S.: 541810
James Murphy (CEO)

Young & Rubicam NZ Ltd. (3)
Level 2 36 Lorne Street, Auckland, 1010, New Zealand
Tel.: (64) 21424103
Sales Range: $25-49.9 Million
Emp.: 60
Advertising Services
N.A.I.C.S.: 541810

Young & Rubicam S. de. R.L. de C.V. (3)
Blvd Manuel Avila Camacho No 176 Piso 7 Col Reforma, 11650, Mexico, DF, Mexico
Tel.: (52) 5515000000
Advertising Services
N.A.I.C.S.: 541810

Young & Rubicam S.A. Cali (3)
Avenida 5A Norte #20-83, Cali, Valle, Colombia
Tel.: (57) 2 667 2012
Web Site: http://www.yr.com
Sales Range: $10-24.9 Million
Emp.: 50
Advertising Services
N.A.I.C.S.: 541810

Young & Rubicam Sdn. Bhd. (3)
6th & 8th Floors Wisma E&C No 2 Lorong Dungan Kiri, Damansara Heights, 50490, Kuala Lumpur, Malaysia
Tel.: (60) 3 2095 2600
Web Site: http://www.yr.com
Sales Range: $10-24.9 Million
Emp.: 30
Advertising Services
N.A.I.C.S.: 541810

Young & Rubicam Shanghai (3)
399 Heng Feng Road, Shanghai, 200070, China
Tel.: (86) 2151759888
Sales Range: $10-24.9 Million
Advertising Services
N.A.I.C.S.: 541810

Young & Rubicam Taiwan Ltd. (3)
18-1 Floor No 6 Hsin Yi Road Section 4 Da-An District, Taipei, 10683, Taiwan
Tel.: (886) 2 2326 7300
Web Site: http://www.yr.com
Sales Range: $10-24.9 Million
Emp.: 40
Advetising Agency
N.A.I.C.S.: 541810

Young & Rubicam Vietnam (3)
16th Floor Me Linh Point Tower 2 Ngo Duc Ke Street, District 1, Ho Chi Minh City, Vietnam
Tel.: (84) 8 825 8351
Advertising Services
N.A.I.C.S.: 541810
Kittisak Poonnotok (Exec Creative Dir-Indochina)

Young & Rubicam Wellington (3)
Level 3 107 Custom House Quay, PO Box 3214, Wellington, 6011, New Zealand
Tel.: (64) 4384 6488
Web Site: http://www.yr.com
Sales Range: $25-49.9 Million
Emp.: 8
Advertising Services
N.A.I.C.S.: 541810

WPP Scangroup Limited (1)
The Chancery 5th Floor Valley Road, PO Box 34537, 00100, Nairobi, Kenya (50.1%)
Tel.: (254) 202799000
Web Site: http://www.wpp-scangroup.com
Sales Range: $75-99.9 Million
Multiple Platform Advertising & Marketing Agency
N.A.I.C.S.: 541810
Alec Graham (COO-Interim)

WREN EXTRA CARE GROUP PLC
Oaks House 12 22 W St, KT18 7RG, Epsom, Surrey, United Kingdom - England
Tel.: (44) 1372742244
Sales Range: $10-24.9 Million

Emp.: 6
Retirement Sector
N.A.I.C.S.: 623311
Paul A. Treadaway (CEO & Mng Dir)

WRG CREATIVE COMMUNICATION LTD.
The Tower Deva Ctr Trinity Way, London, M3 7BF, Manchester, United Kingdom
Tel.: (44) 845.313 0000
Emp.: 70
Communications, Digital/Interactive, Environmental, Event Planning & Marketing, Graphic Design, Logo & Package Design, Media Relations, Strategic Planning/Research
N.A.I.C.S.: 541810
Mark Wallace (Chm)

WRH WALTER REIST HOLDING AG
Industriestrasse 1, 8340, Hinwil, Switzerland
Tel.: (41) 449387000
Web Site: http://www.walter-reist-holding.com
Year Founded: 1957
Sales Range: $150-199.9 Million
Emp.: 750
Holding Company; Print Media
N.A.I.C.S.: 551112

Subsidiaries:

Ferag AG (1)
Zurichstrasse 74, Hinwil, 8340, Switzerland (100%)
Tel.: (41) 449386000
Web Site: http://www.ferag.ch
Sales Range: $200-249.9 Million
Systems & Equipment for Newspaper Mailrooms & Magazine Handling; Supplement Inserting Systems
N.A.I.C.S.: 333248

Ferag Americas LLC (1)
3150 Brunswick Pike Ste 220, Lawrenceville, NJ 08648 (100%)
Tel.: (856) 842-0600
Web Site: http://www.ferag-americas.com
Sales Range: $25-49.9 Million
Emp.: 15
Conveying & Processing Systems
N.A.I.C.S.: 333248
Cynthia Noda (Controller)

WRIGHT INDUSTRIES LTD.
1st Floor Gibraltar House Crown Square, London, DE14 2WE, United Kingdom
Tel.: (44) 2033974830
Web Site: https://www.wrightindustries.co.uk
Investment Services
N.A.I.C.S.: 523999
Craig Wright (Chm & CEO)

Subsidiaries:

Accura Group Limited (1)
Stringes Close Willenhall, West Midlands, Wolverhampton, WV13 1NS, United Kingdom
Tel.: (44) 1902606206
Web Site: http://www.accura.co.uk
Industrial Machinery & Equipment Mfr & Distr
N.A.I.C.S.: 333998
Denise Brinton (Bus Mgr)

WRIGHT MEDICAL GROUP N.V.
Prins Bernhardplein 200, 1097 JB, Amsterdam, Netherlands
Tel.: (31) 205214777 NI
Web Site: http://www.wright.com
Year Founded: 1940
WMGI—(NASDAQ)
Rev.: $920,900,000
Assets: $2,585,640,000

INTERNATIONAL PUBLIC

Liabilities: $1,693,847,000
Net Worth: $891,793,000
Earnings: ($114,225,000)
Emp.: 3,030
Fiscal Year-end: 12/29/19
Medical Device Mfr & Sales
N.A.I.C.S.: 339112
Jennifer S. Walker (Sr VP-Process Improvement)

Subsidiaries:

IMASCAP SAS (1)
65 place Nicolas Copernic, 29280, Plouzane, France
Tel.: (33) 290262170
Web Site: http://www.imascap.com
Software Development Services
N.A.I.C.S.: 513210

TORNIER Pty Ltd (1)
e2/15 Narabang Way, Belrose, 2085, NSW, Australia
Tel.: (61) 2 9450 1977
Medical & Surgical Device Mfr
N.A.I.C.S.: 339112
Lucile Ferrand (Product Mgr)

Tornier AG (1)
Alte Steinhauserstrasse 19, 6330, Cham, Switzerland
Tel.: (41) 41 760 26 12
Web Site: http://www.tornier.ch
Medical & Surgical Devices Mfr
N.A.I.C.S.: 339112

Tornier Belgium N.V. (1)
Quellinstraat 49, Antwerp, 2018, Belgium
Tel.: (32) 27193030
Medical Device Mfr
N.A.I.C.S.: 334510
Vick Breman (Gen Mgr)

Tornier Espana SA (1)
Carrer de Ganduxer, 08022, Barcelona, Spain
Tel.: (34) 902 36 04 60
Medical & Surgical Devices Mfr
N.A.I.C.S.: 339112

Tornier GmbH (1)
Industriestr 48, 51399, Burscheid, Germany
Tel.: (49) 217478880
Web Site: http://www.tornier.de
Medical & Surgical Device Mfr
N.A.I.C.S.: 339112

Tornier Orthopedics Ireland, Ltd. (1)
Hartnettss Cross Macroom, Cork, Ireland
Tel.: (353) 2621800
Medical Device Mfr
N.A.I.C.S.: 339112

Tornier Orthopedics, Inc. (1)
6295 Shawson Dr, Mississauga, L5T 1H4, ON, Canada
Tel.: (905) 795-3900
Medical Device Mfr
N.A.I.C.S.: 334510

Tornier SAS (1)
161 rue Lavoisier, Montbonnot, Saint Ismier, France
Tel.: (33) 4 76 61 35 00
Web Site: http://www.recrutement-tornier.com
Human Resource Consulting Services
N.A.I.C.S.: 541612

Tornier Scandinavia A/S (1)
Teglardsparken 26 Office 414, Middelfart, 5500, Denmark
Tel.: (45) 70 239 444
Medical & Surgical Device Mfr
N.A.I.C.S.: 339112

Tornier Srl (1)
Via Giuliani Padre Reginaldo 49, 20035, Lissone, Italy
Tel.: (39) 092454038
Web Site: http://www.tornier.it
Medical & Surgical Device Mfr
N.A.I.C.S.: 339112

Tornier UK, Ltd. (1)
18 Amor Way Letchworth Garden City, Hertford, SG6 1UG, United Kingdom
Tel.: (44) 1753 46 48 50
Web Site: http://www.tornier.co.uk
Emp.: 2

AND PRIVATE COMPANIES

Medical Device Mfr
N.A.I.C.S.: 339112

Tornier, Inc. (1)
7701 France Ave S Ste 600, Edina, MN 55435
Tel.: (952) 426-7600
Web Site: http://www.tornier-us.com
Emp.: 27
Medical & Surgical Device Mfr
N.A.I.C.S.: 339112

Wright Medical Group, Inc. (1)
1023 Cherry Rd, Memphis, TN 38117
Web Site: http://www.wmt.com
Sales Range: $250-299.9 Million
Emp.: 1,180
Holding Company; Orthopedic Medical Devices Designer, Mfr & Marketer
N.A.I.C.S.: 551112

Subsidiary (Non-US):

TriMed Hellas S.A (2)
Ave Sygrou 344 & Solonos Street 4, Kallithea, 17673, Athens, Greece
Tel.: (30) 2109484090
Web Site: http://www.wright.com
Medical Product Distr
N.A.I.C.S.: 424210

WG Healthcare UK Limited (2)
Unit 1 Campus Five 3rd Avenue, Letchworth, SG6 2JF, Hertfordshire, United Kingdom
Tel.: (44) 8458334435
Web Site: http://www.wrightmedical.co.uk
Medical Product Distr
N.A.I.C.S.: 424210

Wright Medical Australia Pty Ltd. (2)
Unit 5 & 6 15 Rodborough Road, PO Box 6043, French's Forest, 2086, NSW, Australia
Tel.: (61) 1800924420
Web Site: http://www.wright.com
Orthopedic Implants Mfr
N.A.I.C.S.: 339113
Kenneth Tang *(VP-Sls-Asia Pacific Reg)*

Wright Medical Brasil Ltda (2)
Rua Joaquim Floriano 466 sala 2111, 04534-002, Sao Paulo, Brazil
Tel.: (55) 11 3368 5250
Web Site: http://www.wright.com
Medical Product Distr
N.A.I.C.S.: 424210

Wright Medical Device (Shanghai) Co., Ltd (2)
Room 2G03-04 Apollo Building No 1440 Yan an Road M, Jing an District, Shanghai, 200050, China
Tel.: (86) 21 6103 1731
Web Site: http://www.wright.com
Medical Product Distr
N.A.I.C.S.: 424210

Wright Medical Italy Srl (2)
Via Liguria 18, Peschiera Borromeo, 20068, Milan, Italy
Tel.: (39) 02516991
Web Site: http://www.wright.com
Orthopedic Implants Mfr
N.A.I.C.S.: 339113

Wright Medical Japan, K.K. (2)
Akasaka Twin Tower Main Tower 16/Fl 2-17-22 Akasaka, Minato-ku, Tokyo, 107-0052, Japan
Tel.: (81) 362301451
Web Site: http://www.wright.com
Orthopaedic Product Mfr
N.A.I.C.S.: 339113

Wright Medical Netherlands, B.V. (2)
Hoogoorddreef 7, 1101 BA, Amsterdam, Netherlands
Tel.: (31) 20 56 59060
Web Site: http://www.wright.com
Orthopaedic Product Mfr
N.A.I.C.S.: 339113

Wright Medical Technology Canada Ltd. (2)
2891 Portland Drive, Oakville, L6H 5S4, ON, Canada
Tel.: (905) 829-6030
Web Site: http://www.wright.com
Emp.: 10
Orthopedic Implants & Instrument Mfr

N.A.I.C.S.: 339113
Will Throp *(VP-Sls-EMEAC Reg)*

Subsidiary (Domestic):

Wright Medical Technology, Inc. (2)
1023 Cherry Rd, Memphis, TN 38117
Web Site: http://www.wmt.com
Sales Range: $200-249.9 Million
Orthopedic Medical Devices Designer, Mfr & Marketer
N.A.I.C.S.: 339113

Subsidiary (Non-US):

Wright Medical UK Limited (2)
18 Amor Way, Letchworth, SG6 1UG, Hertfordshire, United Kingdom
Tel.: (44) 845 833 4435
Web Site: http://wrightmedical.co.uk
Emp.: 3
Orthopedic Implants Mfr
N.A.I.C.S.: 339113

WRITEUP CO., LTD.
32F Shibuya Cross Tower 2-15-1, Shibuya, Shibuya-Ku, Tokyo, 150-0002, Japan
Tel.: (81) 357840700
Web Site: https://www.writeup.jp
6580—(TKS)
Rev.: $18,349,360
Assets: $22,573,150
Liabilities: $4,719,540
Net Worth: $17,853,610
Earnings: $1,520,300
Emp.: 150
Fiscal Year-end: 03/31/24
Information Technology Services
N.A.I.C.S.: 541519
Takashi Shiraishi *(Founder, Chm & Pres)*

WRITTLE HOLDINGS LIMITED
30 Park Street, London, SE1 9EQ, United Kingdom
Tel.: (44) 20 7043 0250   UK
Web Site: http://www.writtle.com
Rev.: $90,001,436
Assets: $59,180,748
Liabilities: $18,871,596
Net Worth: $40,309,151
Earnings: $5,367,955
Emp.: 587
Fiscal Year-end: 12/31/18
Investment Holding Company; Advertising & Marketing Services
N.A.I.C.S.: 551112
Robert T. T. Essex *(Chm)*

Subsidiaries:

20.20 Limited (1)
20-23 Mandela Street, London, NW1 0DU, United Kingdom
Tel.: (44) 20 7383 7071
Web Site: http://20.20.co.uk
Emp.: 4
Strategic Design Consulting
N.A.I.C.S.: 541890

Arken POP International Limited (1)
Studlands Park Avenue, Newmarket, CB8 7EA, Suffolk, United Kingdom
Tel.: (44) 1638 565656
Web Site: http://www.arken-pop.com
Point-of-Purchase Display Mfr
N.A.I.C.S.: 339950

Beyond Communications Limited (1)
4a King Street Studios, London, W6 0QA, United Kingdom **(76.58%)**
Tel.: (44) 20 8846 3880
Web Site: http://www.beyond-communications.co.uk
Marketing Consulting Services
N.A.I.C.S.: 541613
Nigel D. Stern *(Founder & Mng Dir)*

Epoch Design Limited (1)
54 Queen Square, Bristol, BS1 4LH, United Kingdom
Tel.: (44) 117 314 7200
Web Site: http://www.epochdesign.co.uk
Emp.: 40

Graphic Design & Marketing Consulting Services
N.A.I.C.S.: 541430
Anthony W. Lucas *(CEO)*

Magnet Harlequin Holdings Limited (1)
Unit F Tomo Estate Packet Boat Lane, Uxbridge, UB8 2JP, United Kingdom
Tel.: (44) 1895 432 400
Web Site: http://www.magharl.co.uk
Emp.: 180
Holding Company; Advertising & Marketing Services
N.A.I.C.S.: 551112
Alan Wright *(Chm)*

Subsidiary (Domestic):

Identica Limited (2)
20-23 Mandela Street, London, NW1 0DU, United Kingdom
Tel.: (44) 20 3150 2900
Web Site: http://www.identica.co.uk
Advetising Agency
N.A.I.C.S.: 541810
Karen O'Neill *(Dir-Client Svcs)*

MagLabs (Holdings) Limited (2)
Tomo Estate Packet Boat Lane, Cowley, Uxbridge, UB8 2JP, United Kingdom
Tel.: (44) 870 314 1234
Web Site: http://www.maglabs.net
Holding Company; Marketing Consulting & Technology Services
N.A.I.C.S.: 551112

Subsidiary (Domestic):

MagLabs Limited (3)
Tomo Estate Packet Boat Lane, Cowley, UB8 2JP, Uxbridge, United Kingdom **(100%)**
Tel.: (44) 844 5555 500
Web Site: http://www.maglabs.net
Marketing Consulting & Technology Services
N.A.I.C.S.: 541613

Subsidiary (Domestic):

Magnet Harlequin Ltd. (2)
Unit F Tomo Estate Packet Boat Lane, Uxbridge, UB8 2JP, United Kingdom
Tel.: (44) 1895 432400
Web Site: http://www.magharl.co.uk
Emp.: 180
Advetising Agency
N.A.I.C.S.: 541810
Alan Wright *(Chm)*

Subsidiary (Domestic):

Technik Limited (3)
Unit 3-4 River Park Billet Lane, Berkhamsted, HP4 1HL, United Kingdom
Tel.: (44) 1442 871117
Web Site: http://www.technik.com
Graphic Design Services
N.A.I.C.S.: 541430

Seymourpowell Limited (1)
265 Merton Road, London, SW18 5JS, United Kingdom **(79.88%)**
Tel.: (44) 20 7381 6433
Web Site: http://www.seymourpowell.com
Sales Range: $25-49.9 Million
Emp.: 90
Product Design & Development, Transportation Design, Consumer Behavioral Research, Brand Strategy & Packaging Design
N.A.I.C.S.: 541430
Dick H. Powell *(Co-Founder & Chm)*

The Team Brand Communication Consultants Limited (1)
30 Park Street, London, SE1 9EQ, United Kingdom **(75.5%)**
Tel.: (44) 2070430240
Web Site: http://www.theteam.co.uk
Sales Range: $25-49.9 Million
Emp.: 100
Design Communications
N.A.I.C.S.: 541430
Kevin MacKenzie *(Mng Dir)*

Williams Murray Hamm Limited (1)
Unit 2 10 Dallington Street, London, EC1V 0DB, United Kingdom **(84.54%)**
Tel.: (44) 2032170000
Web Site: http://www.wmhagency.com

WSP GLOBAL, INC.

Advetising Agency
N.A.I.C.S.: 541810
Richard C. J. Williams *(Co-Founder & Partner)*

Subsidiary (Domestic):

Branded Limited (2)
10 Dallington Street, London, EC1V 0DB, United Kingdom
Tel.: (44) 7803194354
Web Site: http://www.branded.co.uk
Brand Strategy Consulting
N.A.I.C.S.: 541890

WRKR LTD
2 Southbank Blvd, GPO Box 1888, Southbank, 3006, NSW, Australia
Tel.: (61) 280901130
Web Site:
https://www.inpaytech.com.au
WRK—(ASX)
Rev.: $6,405,953
Assets: $36,827,551
Liabilities: $30,944,941
Net Worth: $5,882,609
Earnings: ($2,547,902)
Fiscal Year-end: 06/30/24
Payroll Advisory Services
N.A.I.C.S.: 523940
Donald Sharp *(Chm)*

WSM VENTURES CORP.
Suite 1430 800 West Pender Street, Vancouver, V6C 2V6, BC, Canada
Tel.: (604) 685-6747   BC
Web Site:
http://www.avalonblockchain.com
Year Founded: 1981
WSM—(CNSX)
Assets: $30,906
Liabilities: $11,412
Net Worth: $19,494
Earnings: ($66,790)
Fiscal Year-end: 12/31/22
Gambling Industry Operator
N.A.I.C.S.: 713290
David Ebert *(CFO)*

WSP GLOBAL, INC.
1600 Boulevard Rene-Levesque West 11th Floor, Montreal, H3H 1P9, QC, Canada
Tel.: (514) 340-0046   Ca
Web Site: https://www.wsp.com
Year Founded: 2014
WSP—(TSX)
Rev.: $16,018,724,960
Assets: $19,923,498,080
Liabilities: $11,856,882,240
Net Worth: $8,066,615,840
Earnings: $583,541,280
Emp.: 66,200
Fiscal Year-end: 12/31/22
Holding Company; Environment & Construction Management Consulting Services
N.A.I.C.S.: 551112
Christopher Cole *(Chm)*

Subsidiaries:

Consultores Regionales Asociados-CRA S.A.S. (1)
Autopista Norte No 102-10 Pisos 5 6 y 7, Bogota, Colombia
Tel.: (57) 1 756 29 89
Environment & Construction Management Services
N.A.I.C.S.: 541620

Ecology and Environment, Inc. (1)
368 Pleasant View Dr, Lancaster, NY 14086
Tel.: (716) 684-8060
Web Site: http://www.ene.com
Rev.: $88,510,000
Assets: $51,810,000
Liabilities: $18,035,000
Net Worth: $33,775,000
Earnings: ($554,000)
Emp.: 775

WSP GLOBAL, INC.

WSP Global, Inc.—(Continued)
Fiscal Year-end: 07/31/2019
Environmental, Scientific & Engineering Services
N.A.I.C.S.: 541330
Peter F. Sorci *(Acting CFO)*

Branch (Non-US):

Ecology & Environment Argentina (2)
Florida 9102 B, C1005AAR, Buenos Aires, Argentina
Tel.: (54) 1148941159
Web Site: http://www.ene.com
Ecological Services
N.A.I.C.S.: 813312

Subsidiary (Domestic):

Ecology & Environment Engineering, Inc. (2)
Buffalo Corporate Ctr 368 Pleasantview Dr, Lancaster, NY 14086 **(100%)**
Tel.: (716) 684-8060
Web Site: http://www.ene.com
Sales Range: $50-74.9 Million
Emp.: 225
Environmental Consulting
N.A.I.C.S.: 541330

Subsidiary (Non-US):

Ecology & Environment do Brasil Ltda. (2)
Av Presidente Wilson 231/1601 Centro, Rio de Janeiro, 20030-905, Brazil **(100%)**
Tel.: (55) 2121088700
Web Site: http://www.ene.com
Sales Range: $150-199.9 Million
Emp.: 200
Drilling Services
N.A.I.C.S.: 213111

Ecology and Environment of Saudi Arabia Co., Ltd. (2)
c/o Star Navigation Co, Ltd 2nd Floor, Prince Fahd Street, Jeddah, 21481, Saudi Arabia
Tel.: (966) 26474000
Web Site: http://www.ene.com
Sales Range: $25-49.9 Million
Emp.: 20
Ecology & Environmental Services for Oil Drilling
N.A.I.C.S.: 213111

Gestion Ambienal Consultores S.A. (2)
Padre Mariano 103, Oficina 307, Santiago, Chile **(100%)**
Tel.: (56) 236 0866
Web Site: http://www.gac.cl
Sales Range: $75-99.9 Million
Environmental Services
N.A.I.C.S.: 541620

Gestion Ambiental Consultores S.A. (2)
Padre Mariano 103 office 307, Providencia, Santiago, 7500499, Chile
Tel.: (56) 27195600
Web Site: http://www.gac.cl
Environmental Consulting Services
N.A.I.C.S.: 541620
Soledad Ubilla F. *(Project Mgr)*

Subsidiary (Domestic):

Walsh Environmental Scientists and Engineers, LLC (2)
4888 Pearl E Cir Ste 108, Boulder, CO 80301 **(60%)**
Tel.: (303) 443-3282
Web Site: http://www.walshenv.com
Sales Range: $75-99.9 Million
Emp.: 20
Environmental Services
N.A.I.C.S.: 541690

Subsidiary (Domestic):

Gustavson Associates LLC (3)
5665 Flatiron Pkwy Ste 250, Boulder, CO 80301-2871
Tel.: (303) 443-2209
Web Site: http://www.gustavson.com

Sales Range: $10-24.9 Million
Oil & Mineral Appraisers for Exploration, Development & Valuation
N.A.I.C.S.: 541620
Letha Lencioni *(VP & Chief Reservoir Engr)*

Lowham-Walsh Engineering & Environment Services, LLC (3)
205 S 3rd St, Lander, WY 82520-3114
Tel.: (307) 335-8466
Web Site: http://www.lowhamwalsh.com
Sales Range: $25-49.9 Million
Emp.: 12
Engineeering Services
N.A.I.C.S.: 541330
Andrew Strike *(Gen Mgr)*

Subsidiary (Non-US):

Servicios Ambientales Walsh, S.A. (3)
Miravalle N24-798 La Floresta, Quito, Ecuador
Tel.: (593) 22545220
Web Site: http://www.ene.com
Environmental Consulting Services
N.A.I.C.S.: 541620

Branch (Domestic):

Walsh Colorado Springs (3)
130 E Kiowa Ste 202, Colorado Springs, CO 80903
Tel.: (303) 443-3282
Web Site: http://www.walshenv.com
Sales Range: $75-99.9 Million
Emp.: 4
Environmental Services
N.A.I.C.S.: 541620

Subsidiary (Non-US):

Walsh Peru, S.A. (3)
Calle Alexander Fleming 187 Urb Higuereta, Santiago de Surco, Lima, Peru
Tel.: (51) 4480808
Web Site: https://www.walshp.com.pe
Sales Range: $75-99.9 Million
Environmental Services
N.A.I.C.S.: 541620
Gonzalo Morante *(Gen Mgr)*

Golder Associates Ltd. (1)
6925 Century Avenue Suite 100, Mississauga, L5N 7K2, ON, Canada
Tel.: (905) 567-4444
Web Site: http://www.golder.com
Comprehensive Civil Geotechnical & Environmental Consulting Services
N.A.I.C.S.: 541330
John Scholte *(Principal & Engr-Geotechnical)*

Subsidiary (Non-US):

GeoTesting Limited (2)
Unit C5 M7 Business Park, Naas, Ireland
Tel.: (353) 45888794
Sales Range: $25-49.9 Million
Emp.: 15
Testing Laboratories
N.A.I.C.S.: 541380

Golden Associated Portugal Ltd. (2)
Sez No 731 4150 Hisen, Oporto, 4150-331, Portugal
Tel.: (351) 226099184
Sales Range: $25-49.9 Million
Emp.: 11
Engineeering Services
N.A.I.C.S.: 541330
Beatriz Sequeira *(Mgr-Fin)*

Golder Associates (HK) Limited (2)
17 Fl No 88 Gloucester Road, Hong Kong, Wan Chai, China (Hong Kong)
Tel.: (852) 25623658
Web Site: http://www.golder.com
Sales Range: $25-49.9 Million
Emp.: 6
Engineeering Services
N.A.I.C.S.: 541330
Tom Henderson *(Mgr)*

Golder Associates (NZ) Limited (2)
Level 2, Nielsen Ctr 129 Hurstmere Rd, Takapuna, 0622, Auckland, New Zealand
Tel.: (64) 92713630
Sales Range: $50-74.9 Million
Emp.: 50
Oil & Gas Operations

N.A.I.C.S.: 213112
Paul Kennedy *(Office Mgr)*

Golder Associates (Philippines) Inc. (2)
108 Aguirre Street, 4th Floor CJV Building, 1229, Makati, Philippines
Tel.: (63) 28152326
Engineeering Services
N.A.I.C.S.: 541330

Golder Associates (Singapore) Pte Ltd. (2)
Hiap Hoe Building 10-50 18 Ah Hood Road, Singapore, 329983, Singapore
Tel.: (65) 62949390
Web Site: http://www.golder.com.sg
Sales Range: $25-49.9 Million
Emp.: 16
Environment Conservation & Wildlife Organizations
N.A.I.C.S.: 813312
Nick Shirlaw *(Mng Dir)*

Golder Associates (UK) Ltd. (2)
1st Floor Carnmoney House Edgewater Office Park, Edgewater, Belfast, BT3 9JQ, United Kingdom
Tel.: (44) 2890787777
Web Site: http://www.golder.com
Sales Range: $25-49.9 Million
Emp.: 50
Engineeering Services
N.A.I.C.S.: 541330

Golder Associates A/S (2)
No 6 Ist floor Nybrovej, 2800, Lyngby, Denmark
Tel.: (45) 70274757
Web Site: http://www.golderassociates.dk
Sales Range: $25-49.9 Million
Emp.: 11
Engineeering Services
N.A.I.C.S.: 541330
Hans Christian Krarup *(Mgr)*

Golder Associates AB (2)
Lilla Bommen 6, 41104, Gothenburg, Sweden
Tel.: (46) 317008230
Web Site: http://www.golder.se
Sales Range: $25-49.9 Million
Emp.: 140
Engineeering Services
N.A.I.C.S.: 541330
Anna-Lena Oberg-Hogsta *(Mng Dir)*

Golder Associates AS (2)
Vebjornver No 5 3400, 3300, Lier, Norway
Tel.: (47) 32850771
Sales Range: $25-49.9 Million
Emp.: 12
Architectural Services
N.A.I.C.S.: 541310

Golder Associates Africa (Pty) Ltd. (2)
Building 1 Magwa Crescent West Maxwell Office Park, Matuka Close Gauteng Midrand, Midrand, 1685, South Africa
Tel.: (27) 112544800
Sales Range: $25-49.9 Million
Emp.: 200
Engineeering Services
N.A.I.C.S.: 541330

Golder Associates Argentina S.A. (2)
Caseros 34 Norte, San Juan, J5400ERB, Argentina
Tel.: (54) 2644265844
Sales Range: $25-49.9 Million
Emp.: 30
Freight Transportation Arrangement
N.A.I.C.S.: 488510

Golder Associates Brasil Consultoria e Projetos Ltda. (2)
Rua Inconfidentes 1011 10 andar, Bairro Funcionarios, Belo Horizonte, 30140 120, Brazil
Tel.: (55) 3121219800
Web Site: http://www.golder.com.br
Sales Range: $25-49.9 Million
Emp.: 100
Engineeering Services
N.A.I.C.S.: 541330

Golder Associates GmbH (2)
Vorbruch 3, Celle, 29227, Germany
Tel.: (49) 514198960

INTERNATIONAL PUBLIC

Web Site: http://www.golder.com
Sales Range: $25-49.9 Million
Emp.: 40
Engineeering Services
N.A.I.C.S.: 541330
MarK Gillgan *(Mng Dir)*

Golder Associates Ireland Limited (2)
Town Centre House, Dublin Road, Naas, Ireland
Tel.: (353) 45874411
Web Site: http://www.golder.com
Sales Range: $25-49.9 Million
Emp.: 20
Engineeering Services
N.A.I.C.S.: 541330

Golder Associates OY (2)
Ruosilankuja 3E, Helsinki, 390, Finland
Tel.: (358) 95617210
Web Site: http://www.golder.com
Sales Range: $25-49.9 Million
Emp.: 60
Engineeering Services
N.A.I.C.S.: 541330
Kim Brander *(Mng Dir-Finland)*

Division (Non-US):

Golder Associates Pty Ltd (2)
7 Botanical Copper park 570-588 Swan St, Richmond, 3121, VIC, Australia
Tel.: (61) 388623500
Web Site: http://www.golder.com.au
Sales Range: $75-99.9 Million
Engineeering Services
N.A.I.C.S.: 541330
Adam Kilsby *(Mng Dir)*

Subsidiary (Non-US):

Golder Associates S.r.l. (2)
Via Decembrio 28, 20137, Milan, Italy
Tel.: (39) 0239257495
Web Site: http://www.golder.com
Sales Range: $25-49.9 Million
Emp.: 30
Engineeering Services
N.A.I.C.S.: 541330

Golder Associates Sarl (2)
31 rue Gorge de Loup, 69009, Lyon, France
Tel.: (33) 472537310
Web Site: http://www.golder.com
Sales Range: $25-49.9 Million
Emp.: 30
Engineeering Services
N.A.I.C.S.: 541330
Perre Harnois *(Mgr)*

Golder Associates Turkey Ltd. (2)
Resit Galip Cad 132/2, 06700, Ankara, Turkiye
Tel.: (90) 3124476778
Sales Range: $25-49.9 Million
Emp.: 12
Engineeering Services
N.A.I.C.S.: 541330

Division (US):

Golder Associates, Inc. (2)
3730 Chamblee Tucker Rd, Atlanta, GA 30341-4414
Tel.: (770) 496-1893
Web Site: http://www.golder.com
Sales Range: $25-49.9 Million
Emp.: 110
International Group Providing Comprehensive Civil, Geotechnical & Environmental Consulting Services to A Wide Range of Industries
N.A.I.C.S.: 541330
Steve Thompson *(Mgr-Project)*

Subsidiary (Non-US):

Golder Paste Technology Ltd. (2)
Unit 6 Penstraze Business Centre, Plymouth, TR48HY, United Kingdom
Tel.: (44) 1326211470
Industrial Building Construction
N.A.I.C.S.: 236210

Greencap Limited (1)
Level 1/677 High Street, Kew East, Melbourne, 3102, VIC, Australia
Tel.: (61) 39 896 8600
Web Site: https://www.greencap.com.au

AND PRIVATE COMPANIES — WSP GLOBAL, INC.

Risk Managemeng Srvices
N.A.I.C.S.: 541611
Dean Comrie *(Gen Mgr)*

Subsidiary (Domestic):

AEC Environmental Pty. Ltd. (2)
12 Greenhill Road, Wayville, 5034, SA, Australia
Tel.: (61) 88 299 9955
Web Site: https://www.greencap.com.au
Sales Range: $25-49.9 Million
Emp.: 35
Environmental Consulting Services
N.A.I.C.S.: 541620
Chris Hearne *(Mng Dir)*

ENV Australia Pty. Ltd. (2)
Level 1 503 Murray Street, Perth, 6000, WA, Australia
Tel.: (61) 892898360
Sales Range: $25-49.9 Million
Emp.: 40
Environmental Consulting Services
N.A.I.C.S.: 541620

Noel Arnold & Associates Pty. Ltd. (2)
Level 1 / 677 High Street, Kew, 3102, VIC, Australia
Tel.: (61) 398908811
Web Site: http://www.noel-arnold.com.au
Sales Range: $25-49.9 Million
Emp.: 80
Risk Managemeng Srvices
N.A.I.C.S.: 541618
Earl Edding *(Gen Mgr)*

Subsidiary (Domestic):

MC2 Pacific Pty. Ltd. (3)
68 Alfred St, Milsons Point, 2061, New South Wales, Australia
Tel.: (61) 294602290
Web Site: http://www.mc2pacific.com.au
Business Management Services
N.A.I.C.S.: 541611

Trimevac Pty. Ltd. (3)
Ste 2 Level 3 11 17 Khartoum Rd, North Ryde, 2113, NSW, Australia
Tel.: (61) 291114555
Web Site: http://www.trimevac.com.au
Sales Range: $10-24.9 Million
Emp.: 20
Emergency Management Services
N.A.I.C.S.: 624230
Gaurav Bhalla *(Gen Mgr)*

Leggette, Brashears & Graham, Inc. (1)
4 Research Dr Ste 301, Shelton, CT 06484
Tel.: (201) 818-0505
Web Site: http://www.lbgweb.com
Emp.: 150
Environmental & Civil Engineering Consulting Services
N.A.I.C.S.: 541330
John Naso *(Pres)*

Magnate Communication Corp. (1)
19425 Langley Bypass, Surrey, V3S 6K1, BC, Canada
Tel.: (604) 539-1411
Environment & Construction Management Services
N.A.I.C.S.: 541620

Orbicon A/S (1)
Ringstedvej 20, Roskilde, 4000, Denmark (100%)
Tel.: (45) 46300310
Web Site: http://www.orbicon.com
Sales Range: $75-99.9 Million
Emp.: 400
Environmental Engineering & Consulting Services
N.A.I.C.S.: 541620
Per Christensen *(CEO)*

POWER Engineers, Inc. (1)
3940 Glenbrook Dr, Hailey, ID 83333
Tel.: (208) 788-3456
Web Site: http://www.powereng.com
Engineering & Technical Services
N.A.I.C.S.: 541330
Tim Ostermeier *(Exec VP)*

Subsidiary (Domestic):

Zephyr Environmental Corporation (2)
2600 Via Fortuna Terrace Bldg One Ste 450, Austin, TX 78746
Tel.: (512) 329-5544
Web Site: http://www.powereng.com
Full-Service Environmental, Health & Safety Consulting, Training & Data Systems Solutions
N.A.I.C.S.: 541620

Parsons Brinckerhoff Group Inc. (1)
1 Penn Plz 4th fl 250 W 34th St, New York, NY 10119-0002
Tel.: (212) 465-5000
Web Site: http://www.wsp-pb.com
Sales Range: $1-4.9 Billion
Emp.: 7,700
Engineeering Services
N.A.I.C.S.: 541330
Alexandre L'Heureux *(Pres)*

Subsidiary (Domestic):

Halvorson & Partners, Inc. (2)
600 W Chicago Ste 650, Chicago, IL 60654
Tel.: (312) 274-2400
Web Site: http://hpse.com
Sales Range: $1-9.9 Million
Emp.: 40
Engineering & Architectural Design Services
N.A.I.C.S.: 541330
Viral Shah *(VP)*

Subsidiary (Non-US):

WSP Parsons Brinckerhoff (2)
Westbrook Mills, Godalming, GU7 2AZ, Surrey, United Kingdom (100%)
Tel.: (44) 1483528400
Web Site: http://www.wsp-pb.com
Sales Range: $75-99.9 Million
Emp.: 5,150
Engineeering Services
N.A.I.C.S.: 541330

WSP Parsons Brinckerhoff (Asia) Limited (2)
7/F One Kowloon 1 Wang Yuen Street, Kowloon Bay, Kowloon, China (Hong Kong)
Tel.: (852) 25798899
Web Site: http://www.wsp-pb.com
Sales Range: $25-49.9 Million
Emp.: 500
Engineering Consulting Services
N.A.I.C.S.: 541330

Technip TPS SAS (1)
80 Ave des Terroirs de France, 75012, Paris, France (100%)
Tel.: (33) 144085400
Web Site: http://www.techniptps.com
Sales Range: $25-49.9 Million
Emp.: 40
Architectural, Construction & Infrastructure Engineering
N.A.I.C.S.: 541310

Subsidiary (Domestic):

Technip TPS Lyon (2)
Immeuble le Quadrille 30 rue Edouard Niepour, 69008, Lyon, France (70%)
Tel.: (33) 478765858
Web Site: http://www.techniptps.com
Sales Range: $25-49.9 Million
Emp.: 25
Architectural, Construction & Infrastructure Engineering Services
N.A.I.C.S.: 541310
Guyot Jean Jacques *(Mgr)*

Technip TPS Toulouse (2)
3 rue des Charrons - Espace Hadrien Batiment B, 31700, Blagnac, France (100%)
Tel.: (33) 534368830
Web Site: http://www.techniptps.com
Architectural, Construction & Infrastructure Engineering Services
N.A.I.C.S.: 541310
Denis Ovis *(Dir)*

Tecnoambiental S.A.S. (1)
Transversal 27 No 39 E 24, Barrio El Emporio Meta, Villavicencio, Colombia
Tel.: (57) 6641235
Web Site: http://www.tecnoambientalsas.com
Environmental Management Services
N.A.I.C.S.: 541620

WSP Asia Limited (1)
29/F AIA Kowloon Tower Landmark East 100 How Ming Street, Kwun Tong, Kowloon, China (Hong Kong)
Tel.: (852) 2217 2000
Web Site: http://www.wspgroup.com
Emp.: 400
Holding Company; Regional Managing Office; Environment & Construction Management Consulting Services
N.A.I.C.S.: 551112

Subsidiary (Non-US):

Shanghai WSP Consulting Limited (2)
Unit 1507 Shanghai Oriental Center 31 Wujiang Rd, Shanghai, 200041, China
Tel.: (86) 21 5117 8300
Web Site: http://www.wspgroup.com
Environmental & Construction Management Consulting Services
N.A.I.C.S.: 541330

Subsidiary (Domestic):

WSP Hong Kong Limited (2)
29/F AIA Kowloon Tower Landmark East 100 How Ming Street, Kwun Tong, Kowloon, China (Hong Kong)
Tel.: (852) 2217 2000
Emp.: 350
Environment & Construction Management Consulting Services
N.A.I.C.S.: 541330
Don Pan *(Mng Dir)*

WSP Asia Pacific Pty. Ltd. (1)
Level 1 41 McLaren Street, PO Box 6245, North Sydney, 2060, NSW, Australia
Tel.: (61) 2 8907 0900
Web Site: http://www.wspgroup.com
Emp.: 150
Holding Company; Regional Managing Office; Environment & Construction Management Consulting Services
N.A.I.C.S.: 551112

Joint Venture (Domestic):

TWSP Pty. Ltd. (2)
Level 2 503 Murray Street, Perth, 6000, WA, Australia (50%)
Tel.: (61) 8 9426 4900
Web Site: http://www.twsp.com.au
Mining Engineering Services
N.A.I.C.S.: 541330

Subsidiary (Domestic):

WSP Buildings Pty. Ltd. (2)
Level 1 41 McLaren Street, North Sydney, 2060, NSW, Australia
Tel.: (61) 2 8907 0900
Web Site: http://www.wspgroup.com.au
Emp.: 150
Engineering Consultancy Services
N.A.I.C.S.: 541330

WSP Australia Pty Ltd (1)
Level 27 Ernst and Young Centre 680 George Street, Sydney, 2000, NSW, Australia
Tel.: (61) 292725100
Web Site: https://www.wsp.com
Construction Engineering Services
N.A.I.C.S.: 541330
Greg Kane *(COO)*

WSP Consultants India Limited (1)
FC-24 2nd Floor Sector 16A, Filmcity, Noida, 201301, India
Tel.: (91) 120 480 8400
Web Site: http://www.wspgroup.com
Environment & Construction Management Consulting Services
N.A.I.C.S.: 541330

WSP Deutschland AG (1)
Georg-Muche-Strasse 1, 80807, Munich, Germany
Tel.: (49) 89 28633 0
Web Site: http://www.wspgroup.com
Sales Range: $25-49.9 Million
Engineering Consultancy Services
N.A.I.C.S.: 541330

WSP Finland Oy (1)
Heikkilantie 7, 00210, Helsinki, Finland
Tel.: (358) 2078 6411
Web Site: http://www.wspgroup.com
Sales Range: $25-49.9 Million
Emp.: 350

Environment & Construction Management Consulting Services
N.A.I.C.S.: 541330
Kirsi Hautala *(Mng Dir)*

WSP France SAS (1)
7 Rue Pasquier 4th Floor, 75008, Paris, France
Tel.: (33) 1 5334 9770
Web Site: http://www.wspgroup.com
Emp.: 20
Engineering Consultancy Services
N.A.I.C.S.: 541330

WSP Group Africa Pty. Ltd. (1)
WSP House Bryanston Place 199 Bryanston Drive, Bryanston, 2191, Johannesburg, South Africa
Tel.: (27) 11 361 1300
Sales Range: $300-349.9 Million
Emp.: 1,300
Environment & Construction Management Consulting Services
N.A.I.C.S.: 541330
Mathieu du Plooy *(Mng Dir)*

WSP Middle East Limited (1)
Boulevard Downtown Dubai, PO Box 7497, Dubai, United Arab Emirates
Tel.: (971) 4 329 2399
Web Site: http://www.wspgroup.com
Sales Range: $75-99.9 Million
Emp.: 400
Environment & Construction Management Consulting Services
N.A.I.C.S.: 541330
Dean McGrail *(Head-HR)*

WSP New Zealand Limited (1)
Level 9 Majestic Centre 100 Willis Street, PO Box 12343, Wellington, 6011, New Zealand
Tel.: (64) 44991000
Web Site: https://www.wsp.com
Asset Development & Asset Management Services
N.A.I.C.S.: 531390
Guy Templeton *(Pres & CEO-Asia Pacific)*

WSP Polska Sp. z o.o. (1)
ul Rakowiecka 30, 02-528, Warsaw, Poland
Tel.: (48) 224808080
Web Site: http://www.wspgroup.com
Emp.: 80
Environmental & Construction Management Consulting Services
N.A.I.C.S.: 541330
Hugues Millet *(Mng Dir)*

WSP Sverige AB (1)
Tel.: (46) 107225000
Sales Range: $150-199.9 Million
Emp.: 2,500
Environment & Construction Management Consulting Services
N.A.I.C.S.: 541330

WSP UK Limited (1)
WSP House 70 Chancery Lane, London, WC2A 1AF, United Kingdom
Tel.: (44) 2073145000
Web Site: https://www.wspgroup.com
Sales Range: $150-199.9 Million
Environment & Construction Management Consulting Services
N.A.I.C.S.: 541330

Subsidiary (Domestic):

WSP Environmental Limited (2)
WSP House 70 Chancery Lane, London, WC2A 1AF, United Kingdom
Tel.: (44) 20 7314 5000
Web Site: http://www.wspgroup.com
Sales Range: $75-99.9 Million
Environmental & Energy Infrastructure Consulting Services
N.A.I.C.S.: 541620

Subsidiary (Domestic):

WSP Remediation Limited (3)
WSP House 70 Chancery Lane, London, WC2A 1AF, United Kingdom
Tel.: (44) 20 7314 5000
Environmental Remediation Consulting Services
N.A.I.C.S.: 541620

Subsidiary (Domestic):

WSP Management Services Limited (2)

WSP GLOBAL, INC.

WSP Global, Inc.—(Continued)
WSP House 70 Chancery Lane, London, WC2A 1AF, United Kingdom
Tel.: (44) 20 7314 5000
Web Site: http://www.wspgroup.com
Engineering Projects Management Consulting Services
N.A.I.C.S.: 541690

WSP USA Corp. (1)
1 penn plaza, New York, NY 10018
Tel.: (212) 532-9600
Web Site: http://www.wspgroup.com
Sales Range: $10-24.9 Million
Emp.: 1,000
Environment & Construction Management Consulting Services
N.A.I.C.S.: 541330
Lewis P. Cornell (Pres & CEO)

Subsidiary (Domestic):

Smith Carter (USA) LLC (2)
1123 Zonolite Rd NE Ste 25, Atlanta, GA 30306
Tel.: (404) 815-2053
Web Site: http://www.wspgroup.com
Emp.: 35
Construction Engineering Services
N.A.I.C.S.: 541330

WSP Environment & Energy LLC (2)
13530 Dulles Technology Dr, Herndon, VA 20171
Tel.: (703) 709-6500
Web Site: http://www.wspgroup.com
Sales Range: $10-24.9 Million
Emp.: 30
Environmental Consulting Services
N.A.I.C.S.: 541620
Dane Pehrman (Dir-Environmental Assessment, Plng, and Permitting Practice-Americas)

WSP HOLDINGS LIMITED
38 Zhujiang Road, Xinqu, Wuxi, Jiangsu, China
Tel.: (86) 51085360632 Ky
Web Site: http://www.wsphl.com
Sales Range: $550-599.9 Million
Emp.: 3,552
Seamless Casing, Tubing & Drill Pipes Mfr
N.A.I.C.S.: 322219

Subsidiaries:

Houston OCTG Group, Inc (1)
13500 Industrial Rd, Houston, TX 77015
Tel.: (713) 451-5008
Pipes Mfr
N.A.I.C.S.: 331210

WSP Pipe Company Limited (1)
7/296 Moo 6 Amata Industrial Estates, Pluak Daeng, 21140, Thailand
Tel.: (66) 38036293
Web Site: http://www.wspp.co.th
Industrial Pipe Mfr & Distr
N.A.I.C.S.: 326112

WT FINANCIAL GROUP LIMITED
Square Plaza Building Level 5 95 Pitt Street, Sydney, 2000, NSW, Australia
Tel.: (61) 292480422
Web Site: https://www.wtfglimited.com
WTL—(ASX)
Rev.: $124,200,677
Assets: $36,253,863
Liabilities: $16,601,450
Net Worth: $19,652,413
Earnings: $2,573,536
Fiscal Year-end: 06/30/24
Financial Services
N.A.I.C.S.: 525990
Chris Kelesis (Exec Dir)

Subsidiaries:

Wealth Today Pty. Ltd. (1)
Level 5 95 Pitt Street, Sydney, 2000, NSW, Australia
Tel.: (61) 29 248 0422
Web Site: https://www.wealthtoday.com.au
Financial Services
N.A.I.C.S.: 523999

WT GROUP HOLDINGS LIMITED
Flat A 6/F Evernew Commercial Centre 33 Pine Street Tai Kok Tsui, Kowloon, China (Hong Kong)
Tel.: (852) 2 390 3877 Ky
Web Site: http://www.wtgholdings.com
Year Founded: 2002
8422—(HKG)
Rev.: $4,362,877
Assets: $8,447,545
Liabilities: $1,038,289
Net Worth: $7,409,256
Earnings: ($953,936)
Emp.: 21
Fiscal Year-end: 06/30/21
Civil Engineering Services
N.A.I.C.S.: 238910
Kin Bun Kam (Chm & Compliance Officer)

WT MICROELECTRONICS CO., LTD.
14F No 738 Chung Cheng Road, Chung Ho District, New Taipei City, 235603, Taiwan
Tel.: (886) 282269088
Web Site: http://www.wtmec.com
Year Founded: 1993
3036—(TAI)
Rev.: $18,588,588,094
Assets: $8,291,435,200
Liabilities: $6,041,938,530
Net Worth: $2,249,496,670
Earnings: $124,404,652
Emp.: 2,655
Fiscal Year-end: 12/31/23
Integrated Circuits Mfr
N.A.I.C.S.: 334413
Jack Yang (CMO)

Subsidiaries:

BSI Semiconductor Korea Co., Ltd. (1)
6F Hanwon Building 19 Hwangsaeul-Ro Beon-Gil, Bundang, Seongnam, Gyeonggi, Korea (South)
Tel.: (82) 31 783 0500
Web Site: http://www.wtmec.com
Emp.: 170
Semiconductor Mfr
N.A.I.C.S.: 334413

Excelpoint Technology Ltd (1)
15 Changi Business Park Central 1 06-00, Singapore, 486057, Singapore
Tel.: (65) 67418966
Web Site: http://www.excelpoint.com
Rev.: $1,108,638,000
Assets: $405,415,000
Liabilities: $318,100,000
Net Worth: $87,315,000
Earnings: $10,339,000
Emp.: 650
Fiscal Year-end: 12/31/2020
Electronic Components Mfr
N.A.I.C.S.: 327110
Yoen Har Wong (Co-Sec)

Subsidiary (Non-US):

Excelpoint Systems (H.K.) Limited (2)
3108 31/F Skyline Tower 39 Wang Kwong Road, Kowloon Bay, New Territories, China (Hong Kong)
Tel.: (852) 2 503 2212
Web Site: https://www.excelpoint.com
Electric Component Whslr
N.A.I.C.S.: 423690

Subsidiary (Non-US):

Excelpoint International Trading (Shanghai) Co., Ltd. (3)
20/F Block B Central Towers No 567 Langao Road, Putuo District, Shanghai, 200333, China
Tel.: (86) 212 220 3188
Web Site: http://www.excelpoint.com
Electric Component Whslr
N.A.I.C.S.: 423690

Excelpoint International Trading (Shenzhen) Co., Ltd. (3)
9/F China Energy Storage Tower 3099 Keyuan South Road, Nanshan District, Shenzhen, 518057, Guangdong, China
Tel.: (86) 75583640166
Web Site: http://www.excelpoint.com.cn
Emp.: 100
Electric Component Whslr
N.A.I.C.S.: 423690

Subsidiary (Non-US):

Excelpoint Systems (India) Private Limited (2)
No 304-306 2nd Floor Oxford Towers Old Airport Road, Bengaluru, 560008, India
Tel.: (91) 8049424311
Electronic Components Mfr
N.A.I.C.S.: 327110

Subsidiary (Domestic):

Excelpoint Systems (Pte) Ltd (2)
15 Changi Business Park Central 1 06-00, Singapore, 486057, Singapore
Tel.: (65) 6 741 8966
Web Site: https://www.excelpoint.com
Sales Range: $75-99.9 Million
Emp.: 150
Electronic Components Distr
N.A.I.C.S.: 423690
Albert Yong Hen Phuay (Founder, Chm & Grp CEO)

Subsidiary (Non-US):

Excelpoint Systems Sdn. Bhd. (3)
Level 3A Elit Avenue Business Park 1-3A-5 Jalan Mayang Pasir 3, Bandar Damansara Perdana, 11950, Bayan Baru, Penang, Malaysia
Tel.: (60) 4 637 4219
Web Site: https://www.excelpoint.com
Sales Range: $25-49.9 Million
Emp.: 3
Electric Component Whslr
N.A.I.C.S.: 423690

Subsidiary (US):

Excelpoint Systems (USA) Inc. (2)
5230 Carroll Canyon Rd Ste 216, San Diego, CA 92121
Tel.: (858) 352-6938
Electronic Components Mfr
N.A.I.C.S.: 327110

Subsidiary (Domestic):

PlanetSpark Pte. Ltd. (2)
15 Changi Business Park Central 1 05-06/07, Singapore, 486057, Singapore
Tel.: (65) 63035718
Web Site: http://www.planetspark.com.sg
Investment Holding Services
N.A.I.C.S.: 551112

Maxtek International (HK) Limited (1)
Units B on 22nd Floor Nos 66-82 Chai Wan Kok Street New Territories, Golden Bear Industrial Centre, Tsuen Wan, China (Hong Kong)
Tel.: (852) 27630732
Electronic Components Distr
N.A.I.C.S.: 423690

Maxtek Technology Co., Ltd. (1)
6F No 738 Chung Cheng Road, Chung Ho District, New Taipei City, 23511, Taiwan
Tel.: (886) 282269180
Web Site: http://www.maxtek-icrep.com.tw
Electronic Components Mfr
N.A.I.C.S.: 334419
Hsien Liu (Gen Mgr)

Subsidiary (Domestic):

HongTech Electronics CO.,LTD. (2)
8F No 738 Chung Cheng Road, Chung Ho District, New Taipei City, 23511, Taiwan
Tel.: (886) 28 226 9170
Web Site: https://www.maxtek-icrep.com.tw
Semiconductor Devices Mfr

INTERNATIONAL PUBLIC

N.A.I.C.S.: 334413
Adah Wu (Gen Mgr)

Subsidiary (Non-US):

Sun International Industrial Ltd. (2)
Unit B1 B3 21 F Block B Kong Nam Industrial Building, 603 609 Castle Peak Road, Tsuen Wan, New Territories, China (Hong Kong)
Tel.: (852) 26909898
Integrated Circuit Components Mfr
N.A.I.C.S.: 334413

Morrihan International Corp. (1)
8F No 738 Chung Cheng Rd, Chung Ho District, New Taipei City, 235, Taiwan
Tel.: (886) 28 226 9938
Web Site: https://www.morrihan.com
Emp.: 90
Electronic Components Distr
N.A.I.C.S.: 423690
Allegro Rockworks (Mgr-Product)

WT Microelectronics (HK) Ltd. (1)
Room 2001E Nan Fung Centre 264-298 Castle Peak Road, Tsuen Wan, New Territories, China (Hong Kong)
Tel.: (852) 2 950 0820
Web Site: http://www.wtmec.com
Semiconductor Products Mfr & Distr
N.A.I.C.S.: 334413

WT Microelectronics (Shanghai) Co., Ltd. (1)
6F No 61 Lane 91 Eshan Road Software Park Building 10, Pudong New District, Shanghai, 200127, China
Tel.: (86) 2158750858
Integrated Circuits Mfr
N.A.I.C.S.: 334418

WT Microelectronics (Shenzhen) Co., Ltd. (1)
East of B Section 2/F Tower 1 Changcheng Computer Building, No 3 Kefa Road Science Industry Park Nanshan District, Shenzhen, 518057, Guangdong, China
Tel.: (86) 75526743880
Electronic Components Mfr
N.A.I.C.S.: 334419

WT Microelectronics (Thailand) Co., Ltd. (1)
Le Concorde Tower Unit 2003 Floor 10th 202 Ratchadapisek Rd, Huaykwang, Bangkok, 10310, Thailand
Tel.: (66) 2 694 1727
Web Site: http://www.wtmec.com
Sales Range: $50-74.9 Million
Emp.: 6
Electronic Components Distr
N.A.I.C.S.: 423690

WT Microelectronics India Private Limited (1)
No 10 3rd Floor 100 Ft Rd Near Dalmia circle JP Nagar 4th Phase, Dollar Layout, Bengaluru, Karnataka, India
Tel.: (91) 8026582935
Electronic Components Distr
N.A.I.C.S.: 423690

WT Microelectronics Korea Co., Ltd. (1)
Hanwon Bldg 6-1 Sunae-Dong, Bundang-Gu 1603 Burim Dong Dongan-Gu, Seongnam, 463-825, Gyeonggi, Korea (South)
Tel.: (82) 31 385 5775
Web Site: http://www.wtmec.com
Sales Range: $25-49.9 Million
Emp.: 154
Semiconductor Parts Distr
N.A.I.C.S.: 423690
Hyung Jin Yoo (Gen Mgr)

WT Microelectronics Singapore Pte. Ltd. (1)
2 Serangoon North Avenue 5 05-01, Singapore, 554911, Singapore
Tel.: (65) 6 853 1788
Web Site: https://www.wtmec.com
Sales Range: $25-49.9 Million
Emp.: 55
Semiconductor Devices Mfr
N.A.I.C.S.: 334413

WT Microeletronics (Malaysia) Sdn., Bhd. (1)

1-3-28 Level 3 Krystal Point Corporate Park, Lebuh Bukit Kecil 6, 11900, Sungai Nibong, Penang, Malaysia
Tel.: (60) 4 646 3512
Web Site: http://www.wtmec.com
Sales Range: $50-74.9 Million
Emp.: 4
Semiconductor Device Distr
N.A.I.C.S.: 423690

Wonchang Semiconductor Co., Ltd. (1)
Rm 4410/4505 Na-Dong Chungang Circulation Complex 15, Gyeongin-ro 53-gil Guro-gu, Seoul, Korea (South)
Tel.: (82) 2 2619 1100
Semiconductor Mfr
N.A.I.C.S.: 334413

WT SA
26 rue Marie Magne, 31300, Toulouse, France
Tel.: (33) 5 62 57 69 70   FR
Web Site: http://www.wt-trader.com
Sales Range: $10-24.9 Million
Mobile Phone Whslr
N.A.I.C.S.: 423690
Christophe Lanlo (Chm & CEO)

WTP PLETTENBERG GMBH & CO. KG
Osterloh 48, 58840, Plettenberg, Germany
Tel.: (49) 2391918401
Web Site: http://www.wtp.com
Sales Range: $10-24.9 Million
Emp.: 50
Metal Forming
N.A.I.C.S.: 333517
Cornell Miller (Pres)

WTW-BETEILIGUNGSGESELLSCHAFT MBH
Elverdisser Strasse 313, 32052, Herford, Germany
Tel.: (49) 52219790   De
Holding Company
N.A.I.C.S.: 551112
Jan A. Ahlers (Owner)

Subsidiaries:

Ahlers AG (1)
Elverdisser Str 313, 32052, Herford, Germany   (75.6%)
Tel.: (49) 52216905212
Web Site: https://www.ahlersfashion.de
Rev.: $209,893,934
Assets: $178,684,355
Liabilities: $119,655,141
Net Worth: $59,029,214
Earnings: ($11,422,632)
Emp.: 1,700
Fiscal Year-end: 11/30/2022
Jean Apparel Mfr
N.A.I.C.S.: 315250
Stella A. Ahlers (Chm-Mgmt Bd)

Subsidiary (Domestic):

Baldessarini GmbH (2)
Wilhen Wagenfede 24, 80807, Munich, Germany
Tel.: (49) 8930668442
Web Site: http://www.baldessarini.com
Sales Range: $25-49.9 Million
Emp.: 20
Men's Clothing & Accessories Designer & Mfr
N.A.I.C.S.: 315250
Christina Jonski (CEO)

WUCHAN ZHONGDA GERON CO., LTD.
No 999 Guangzhou Road, Haimen Economic & Technological Development Zone, Haimen, 226009, Jiangsu, China
Tel.: (86) 51380776888
Web Site: https://www.geron-china.com
Year Founded: 2004
002722—(SSE)
Rev.: $398,121,694
Assets: $386,383,734
Liabilities: $93,018,482
Net Worth: $293,365,252
Earnings: $14,587,546
Fiscal Year-end: 12/31/22
Industrial Machinery Mfr & Distr
N.A.I.C.S.: 333248
Guangliang Zheng (Chm)

WUCHAN ZHONGDA GROUP CO., LTD.
no 56 Huancheng West Road, Hangzhou, 310003, Zhejiang, China
Tel.: (86) 57185777029
Web Site: https://www.zhongda.com
600704—(SHG)
Rev.: $80,947,435,009
Assets: $20,365,143,706
Liabilities: $13,909,378,888
Net Worth: $6,455,764,818
Earnings: $549,122,540
Fiscal Year-end: 12/31/22
Holding Company
N.A.I.C.S.: 551112
Tingge Wang (Chm)

WUENSCHE HANDELSGESELLSCHAFT INTERNATIONAL MBH & CO. KG
Domstrasse 19, 20095, Hamburg, Germany
Tel.: (49) 40 333 12 0
Web Site: http://www.wuensche.com
Holding Company; Consumer Goods Distr
N.A.I.C.S.: 551112
Andre Zuppa (Mng Dir)

Subsidiaries:

Jansen Textil GmbH (1)
Widdiger Strasse 1-9, 50389, Wesseling, Germany
Tel.: (49) 22 36 89 21 0
Web Site: http://www.jansen-textil.de
Textile Products Distr
N.A.I.C.S.: 424990

WUESTENROT & WUERTTEMBERGISCHE AG
W W-Platz 1, 70806, Kornwestheim, Germany
Tel.: (49) 7116620   De
Web Site: https://www.ww-ag.com
Year Founded: 1999
WUW—(DUS)
Rev.: $1,456,541,118
Assets: $74,121,251,889
Liabilities: $68,074,545,651
Net Worth: $6,046,706,238
Earnings: $149,640,622
Emp.: 6,437
Fiscal Year-end: 12/31/23
Private Equity Firm; Real Estate & Insurance Investment Services
N.A.I.C.S.: 531390
Bernd Hertweck (Member-Exec Bd, Head-Housing Div & Dir-HR)

Subsidiaries:

Adam Riese GmbH (1)
Presselstr 10, 70191, Stuttgart, Germany
Tel.: (49) 71167411111
Web Site: http://www.adam-riese.de
Insurance Services
N.A.I.C.S.: 524210
Maren Teufel (Mgr-Brand & Content Mktg)

Allgemeine Rentenanstalt Pensionskasse AG (1)
Gutenbergstrasse 30, 70176, Stuttgart, Germany
Tel.: (49) 7116620
Financial Consulting Services
N.A.I.C.S.: 541611

City Immobilien GmbH & Co. KG (1)
Eichstr 17-19, Cronenberg, 42349, Wuppertal, Germany
Tel.: (49) 20297974420
Web Site: http://city.immo
Real Estate Manangement Services
N.A.I.C.S.: 531390

GMA Gesellschaft fur Markt- und Absatzforschung mbH (1)
Hohenzollernstrasse 14, 71638, Ludwigsburg, Germany
Tel.: (49) 714193600
Web Site: https://gma.biz
Financial Consulting Services
N.A.I.C.S.: 541611

Gerber GmbH & Co. KG (1)
Markgrafenstrasse 111, 79211, Denzlingen, Germany
Tel.: (49) 7666944790
Web Site: https://www.gerber-bau.de
Construction Services
N.A.I.C.S.: 236220

Treefin GmbH (1)
Leopoldstrasse 252, 80807, Munich, Germany
Tel.: (49) 89809133349
Web Site: http://www.treefin.com
Financial Consulting Services
N.A.I.C.S.: 541611
Manuel Wanner-Behr (CEO)

W&W Informatik GmbH (1)
W W-Platz 1, 70806, Kornwestheim, Germany
Tel.: (49) 7141160
Innovative Digital Consulting Services
N.A.I.C.S.: 541613
Tom Riek (Project Mgr-IT)

W&W Investment Managers DAC (1)
5 Earlsfort Terrace, Dublin, DO2CK83, Ireland
Tel.: (353) 16768971
Web Site: https://www.ww-im.com
Investment Advisory Services
N.A.I.C.S.: 523940
Peter Walsh (Head-Trading)

W&W Service GmbH (1)
Elmar-Doch-Str 38-40, 71638, Ludwigsburg, Germany
Tel.: (49) 7116620
Innovative Digital Consulting Services
N.A.I.C.S.: 541613

W&W brandpool GmbH (1)
Gutenbergstrasse 30, 70176, Stuttgart, Germany
Tel.: (49) 711662724808
Web Site: http://www.ww-ag.com
Financial Consulting Services
N.A.I.C.S.: 541611
Daniel Welzer (CEO)

Wohnimmobilien GmbH & Co. KG (1)
Feldbrunnenstrasse 7, 20148, Hamburg, Germany
Tel.: (49) 406568990
Web Site: http://nord-boden.de
Construction Services
N.A.I.C.S.: 236220

Wuerttembergische Lebensversicherung AG (1)
Gutenbergstrasse 30, 70176, Stuttgart, Germany
Tel.: (49) 7116620
Web Site: http://www.wuerttembergische.de
Sales Range: $1-4.9 Billion
Emp.: 4,000
Individual Endowment, Term Assurance, Property & Health Insurance & Pension Scheme
N.A.I.C.S.: 524298

Wuestenrot Bank AG Pfandbriefbank (1)
Im Tambour 1, 71630, Ludwigsburg, Badin Wirttamberg, Germany
Tel.: (49) 7141161
Web Site: http://www.wuestenrot.de
Sales Range: $1-4.9 Billion
Emp.: 3,000
Loan & Banking Services to the Construction Industry
N.A.I.C.S.: 522110

Subsidiary (Non-US):

Wuestenrot International Management-Gesellschaft AG (2)
33 Parc dActivite Syrdall, L 5365, Munsbach, Luxembourg
Tel.: (352) 4434441
Web Site: http://www.wuestenrot.lu
Sales Range: $50-74.9 Million
Emp.: 8
Investment Fund Management
N.A.I.C.S.: 523940

Wuestenrot Bausparkasse AG (1)
Hohenzollernstrasse 46, 71630, Ludwigsburg, Badin Wirttamberg, Germany
Tel.: (49) 7141161
Web Site: http://www.wuestenrot.de
Sales Range: $700-749.9 Million
Emp.: 2,500
Building Society
N.A.I.C.S.: 522110
Bernd Hertweck (Head-Sls & Mktg)

Subsidiary (Domestic):

Wuestenrot Staedtebau und Entwicklungsgesellschaft mbH (2)
Hohenzollernstr 12 14, 71630, Ludwigsburg, Germany
Tel.: (49) 71411490
Web Site: http://www.wuestenrot.de
Sales Range: $25-49.9 Million
Emp.: 100
Real Estate Investment Services
N.A.I.C.S.: 925120

Subsidiary (Domestic):

Fuer Markt Und Absatzforschung GmbH (3)
Hohenzollernstrasse 14, 71638, Ludwigsburg, Germany
Tel.: (49) 714193600
Web Site: http://gma.biz
Sales Range: $10-24.9 Million
Emp.: 30
Market & Opinion Research
N.A.I.C.S.: 541910

Wuestenrot Grundstuecksverwertungs-GmbH (1)
Hohenzollernstr 46, 7168, Ludwigsburg, Badin Wirttamberg, Germany
Tel.: (49) 7141161
Web Site: http://www.wuestenrot.de
Sales Range: $1-4.9 Billion
Emp.: 9,500
Real Estate Investment Services
N.A.I.C.S.: 524128
Alexander Ertland (Mgr)

Wurttembergische Rechtsschutz Schaden-Service- GmbH (1)
Gutenbergstr 30, 70176, Stuttgart, Germany
Tel.: (49) 8008182100
Financial Consulting Services
N.A.I.C.S.: 541611

Wurttembergische Versicherung AG (1)
Gutenbergstrasse 30, 70176, Stuttgart, Germany
Tel.: (49) 7116620
Web Site: http://www.wuerttembergische.de
Insurance Providing Services
N.A.I.C.S.: 524126
Thomas Bischof (Chm)

Wurttembergische Vertriebspartner GmbH (1)
Gutenbergstrasse 30, 70176, Stuttgart, Germany
Tel.: (49) 7116620
Web Site: http://www.wuerttembergische-makler.de
Financial Brokerage Services
N.A.I.C.S.: 523999
Markus Riedel (Acct Mgr)

Wustenrot Haus- und Stadtebau GmbH (1)
Hohenzollernstrasse 12-14, 71638, Ludwigsburg, Germany
Tel.: (49) 714116757100
Web Site: https://www.whs-wuestenrot.de
Real Estate Manangement Services
N.A.I.C.S.: 531390
Andreas Mock (Acct Mgr)

WUESTENROT & WUERTTEMBERGISCHE AG

Wuestenrot & Wuerttembergische AG—(Continued)

Wustenrot Immobilien GmbH (1)
Hohenzollernstrasse 46, 71638, Ludwigsburg, Germany
Tel.: (49) 714116756200
Web Site: http://wuestenrot-immobilien.de
Real Estate Manamgenent Services
N.A.I.C.S.: 531390

WUHAN DDMC CULTURE & SPORTS CO., LTD.
7F China Railway Science and Technology Building No 45 Xudong Avenue, Hongshan District, Wuhan, 430063, Hubei, China
Tel.: (86) 2787115482
Web Site: http://www.whggfz.com
Year Founded: 1992
600136—(SHG)
Rev.: $92,160,919
Assets: $479,085,937
Liabilities: $1,169,703,274
Net Worth: ($690,617,337)
Earnings: ($725,374,494)
Fiscal Year-end: 12/31/22
Investment Services
N.A.I.C.S.: 523999
Ju Ling (Chm)

WUHAN DEPARTMENT STORE GROUP CO., LTD.
8th Floor Wuhan International Plaza No 690 Jiefang Avenue Hankou, Jianghan District, Wuhan, 430022, Hubei, China
Tel.: (86) 2785714165
Web Site: https://www.wushang.com.cn
Year Founded: 1959
000501—(SSE)
Rev.: $889,736,632
Assets: $4,316,406,312
Liabilities: $2,798,318,858
Net Worth: $1,518,087,453
Earnings: $42,780,568
Fiscal Year-end: 12/31/22
Departmental Store Operator
N.A.I.C.S.: 455110
Jun Chen (Chm)

WUHAN DR LASER TECHNOLOGY CO., LTD.
No 88 Jiulonghu Street, East-Lake High-Tech Development Zone, Wuhan, 430078, Hubei, China
Tel.: (86) 2787922082
Web Site: https://www.drlaser.com.cn
Year Founded: 2008
300776—(SSE)
Rev.: $185,933,278
Assets: $660,860,540
Liabilities: $284,701,028
Net Worth: $376,159,512
Earnings: $57,731,638
Fiscal Year-end: 12/31/22
Water Equipment Mfr
N.A.I.C.S.: 334510
Zhigang Li (Chm & Gen Mgr)

WUHAN EAST LAKE HIGH TECHNOLOGY GROUP CO., LTD.
Block A Building A8 Phase 1 1 Wuhan Software New City, No 9 Huacheng Avenue East Lake High-tech Development Zone, Wuhan, 430074, Hubei, China
Tel.: (86) 2787172020
Web Site: https://www.elht.com
Year Founded: 1993
600133—(SHG)
Rev.: $1,963,649,310
Assets: $4,909,810,099
Liabilities: $3,511,301,775
Net Worth: $1,398,508,324
Earnings: $81,240,214
Emp.: 3,000
Fiscal Year-end: 12/31/22
Industrial Park Construction Services
N.A.I.C.S.: 236210
Yang Tao (Chm)

WUHAN EASYDIAGNOSIS BIOMEDICINE CO., LTD.
No 388 Gaoxin 2nd Rd, East Lake Hi-Tech Development Zone, Wuhan, 430074, Hubei, China
Tel.: (86) 2765523649
Web Site: https://www.easydiagnosis.com.cn
002932—(SSE)
Rev.: $1,478,451,003
Assets: $1,290,409,155
Liabilities: $339,643,030
Net Worth: $950,766,125
Earnings: $590,863,965
Fiscal Year-end: 12/31/22
Diagnostic Equipment Mfr & Distr
N.A.I.C.S.: 325413
Chen Lili (Chm & Gen Mgr)

WUHAN FINGU ELECTRONIC TECHNOLOGY CO., LTD.
Fingu Electronic Industrial Park No 5 Jiufeng Street, Canglongdao Science Part Guanggu Avenue Jiangxia District, Wuhan, 430200, China
Tel.: (86) 2781383981
Web Site: https://www.fingu.com
Year Founded: 1989
002194—(SSE)
Rev.: $291,069,179
Assets: $484,210,874
Liabilities: $104,009,036
Net Worth: $380,201,838
Earnings: $38,786,974
Fiscal Year-end: 12/31/22
Electronic Components Mfr
N.A.I.C.S.: 334419
Fanbo Meng (Chm, Vice Chm & Pres)

WUHAN GENERAL GROUP (CHINA), INC.
Canglongdao Science Park of Wuhan East Lake Hi-Tech Development Zone, Wuhan, 430200, Hubei, China
Tel.: (86) 2759700069
Web Site: http://www.wuhangeneral.com
Year Founded: 1998
WUHN—(OTCIQ)
Sales Range: Less than $1 Million
Emp.: 3
Blower & Turbine Mfr
N.A.I.C.S.: 333611
Hyder A. Khoja (Chief Scientific Officer)

WUHAN GOLDEN LASER CO., LTD.
Golden Laser Industrial Park Tianxing Road Hengdian Street, Chuanlong Boulevard Huangpi District, Wuhan, 430015, Hubei, China
Tel.: (86) 15871714482
Web Site: https://www.goldenlaser.cc
Year Founded: 2005
300220—(CHIN)
Rev.: $36,936,432
Assets: $49,961,340
Liabilities: $35,504,352
Net Worth: $14,456,988
Earnings: $7,818,876
Emp.: 200
Fiscal Year-end: 12/31/22
Laser Cutting Machinery Mfr
N.A.I.C.S.: 333517
Nie Jinping (Chm-Supervisory Bd)

WUHAN GUIDE INFRARED CO., LTD.
No 6 Huanglong Hill South Road East Lake Development Zone, Wuhan, 430205, China
Tel.: (86) 2781298784
Year Founded: 1999
002414—(SSE)
Rev.: $355,014,626
Assets: $1,247,846,769
Liabilities: $247,725,354
Net Worth: $1,000,121,415
Earnings: $70,474,440
Fiscal Year-end: 12/31/22
Infrared Thermal Imagers Mfr
N.A.I.C.S.: 334513
Huang Li (Chm)

Subsidiaries:

Wuhan Global Sensor Technology Co., Ltd. (1)
No 6 Huanglongshan South Rd, Wuhan, 430205, China
Tel.: (86) 2781298493
Web Site: http://www.gsten.gst-ir.com
Infrared Product Mfr
N.A.I.C.S.: 334513
Lydia Zhou (Sls Dir)

Wuhan Guide Sensmart Tech Co., Ltd. (1)
No 6 Huanglong Hill South Road, East Lake Development Zone, Wuhan, 430205, China
Tel.: (86) 4008822866
Web Site: https://www.guideir.com
Optical Instrument Mfr
N.A.I.C.S.: 333310

Xuanyuan Idrive Technology (Shenzhen) Co., Ltd. (1)
12th Floor Building 1 Novel Park No 4078 Dongbin Road, Nanshan District, Shenzhen, Guangdong, China
Tel.: (86) 75526650808
Web Site: http://www.xy-idrive.com
Infrared Product Mfr
N.A.I.C.S.: 334513

WUHAN HITECK BIOLOGICAL PHARMA CO., LTD.
HITECK science and Technology Park Wuhan Economic Development Zone, Wuhan, 430056, Hubei, China
Tel.: (86) 2784891666
Web Site: https://www.hiteck.com.cn
Year Founded: 1992
300683—(CHIN)
Rev.: $84,831,744
Assets: $418,500,732
Liabilities: $67,006,627
Net Worth: $351,494,105
Earnings: ($17,017,891)
Emp.: 1,000
Fiscal Year-end: 12/31/23
Pharmaceutical Product Mfr & Distr
N.A.I.C.S.: 325412
Ya Chen (Chm & Gen Mgr)

WUHAN HUAKANG CENTURY MEDICAL CO., LTD.
Building 3 No 718 Gaoxin Avenue, East Lake New Technology Development Zone, Wuhan, 430000, Hubei, China
Tel.: (86) 2787267611
Year Founded: 2008
301235—(CHIN)
Rev.: $166,921,560
Assets: $332,746,596
Liabilities: $100,693,476
Net Worth: $232,053,120
Earnings: $14,389,596
Fiscal Year-end: 12/31/22
Medical Equipment Mfr & Distr
N.A.I.C.S.: 339112

WUHAN HUAZHONG NUMERICAL CONTROL CO., LTD.
HUST Park Miaoshan Region, East-Lake Development Zone, Wuhan, Hebei, China
Tel.: (86) 2787180025
Web Site: https://www.huazhongcnc.cnc.com
Year Founded: 1994
300161—(CHIN)
Rev.: $297,851,636
Assets: $622,650,144
Liabilities: $358,415,248
Net Worth: $264,234,896
Earnings: $3,815,725
Fiscal Year-end: 12/31/23
CNC Controllers, Drives & Motors Mfr
N.A.I.C.S.: 334513

WUHAN HVSEN BIOTECHNOLOGY CO., LTD.
No 208 Zhangbei Road, Dongxihu, Wuhan, 430042, China
Tel.: (86) 2788605516
Web Site: https://www.whhsyy.com
Year Founded: 2002
300871—(SSE)
Rev.: $143,615,272
Assets: $419,671,648
Liabilities: $203,254,567
Net Worth: $216,417,081
Earnings: $7,399,993
Fiscal Year-end: 12/31/22
Pharmaceutical Product Mfr & Distr
N.A.I.C.S.: 325412
Weiyuan Zhang (Chm & Gen Mgr)

WUHAN JINGCE ELECTRONIC GROUP CO., LTD.
No 22 Liufangyuan South Road East Lake New Technology Development Zone, Wuhan, China
Tel.: (86) 2787526915
Web Site: https://www.wuhanjingce.com
Year Founded: 2006
300567—(CHIN)
Rev.: $342,176,426
Assets: $1,298,825,021
Liabilities: $704,566,659
Net Worth: $594,258,362
Earnings: $21,141,923
Fiscal Year-end: 12/31/23
Flat Panel Display Mfr & Distr
N.A.I.C.S.: 334118

Subsidiaries:

Hirose Optrocnis Co., Ltd. (1)
7F-9 No 51 Section 4 Zhongyang Road Tucheng District, New Taipei City, Taiwan
Tel.: (886) 222673800
Electrical Testing Product Distr
N.A.I.C.S.: 423830

WUHAN KEQIAN BIOLOGY CO., LTD.
No 419 Gaoxin 2nd Road, East Lake New Technology Development Zone, Wuhan, 430073, Hubei, China
Tel.: (86) 2781322942
Web Site: https://www.kqbio.com
Year Founded: 2001
688526—(SHG)
Rev.: $140,577,985
Assets: $616,446,109
Liabilities: $125,184,515
Net Worth: $491,261,594
Earnings: $57,496,383
Fiscal Year-end: 12/31/22
Pharmaceutical Product Mfr & Distr
N.A.I.C.S.: 325412
Huanchun Chen (Chm & Deputy Gen Mgr)

WUHAN KOTEI INFORMATICS CO., LTD.
Gangbiantian Road 1 No 6, East Lake Hi-Tech Development Zone, Wuhan, 430205, Hubei, China
Tel.: (86) 2759598171
Web Site: https://www.kotei-info.com
Year Founded: 2011

AND PRIVATE COMPANIES — WUHAN YANGTZE COMMUNICATIONS INDUSTRY GROUP CO.

301221—(CHIN)
Rev.: $89,970,845
Assets: $320,949,464
Liabilities: $36,679,408
Net Worth: $284,270,055
Earnings: ($2,178,254)
Emp.: 1,800
Fiscal Year-end: 12/31/23
Software Development Services
N.A.I.C.S.: 541511
Dunyao Zhu *(Chm)*

Subsidiaries:

Denso Kotei Automotive Electronics (Wuhan) Co., Ltd. (1)
6F Gangbiantian Road 1 NO 6 East Lake Hi-Tech Development Zone, Wuhan, Hubei, China
Tel.: (86) 2759332818
Automotive Electronic Material Mfr & Distr
N.A.I.C.S.: 336320

Japan KOTEI Informatics Co., Ltd. (1)
4F Omori-prime building 6-21-12 Minami-ooi, Shinagawa-ku, Tokyo, Japan
Tel.: (81) 364231283
Software Development Services
N.A.I.C.S.: 541519

Shandong Kotei Informatics Co., Ltd. (1)
133 Beiguan Rd Penglaige Street, Penglai District, Yantai, Shandong, China
Tel.: (86) 5355775223
Web Site: https://www.sdkotei.com
Emp.: 120
Software Development Services
N.A.I.C.S.: 541519

Wuhan CLARION KOTEI Software Technology Co., Ltd. (1)
Gangbiantian Road 1 NO 6 East Lake Hi Tech Development Zone, Wuhan, Hubei, China
Tel.: (86) 2759906703
Automotive Electronic Material Mfr & Distr
N.A.I.C.S.: 336320

WUHAN LIGONG GUANGKE CO.,LTD.
Technology Park of Wuhan University of Technology, East Lake Development Zone, Wuhan, 430223, Hubei, China
Tel.: (86) 2787960139
Web Site: http://www.wutos.com
Year Founded: 2000
300557—(CHIN)
Rev.: $85,087,471
Assets: $236,979,125
Liabilities: $93,935,189
Net Worth: $143,043,936
Earnings: $3,550,462
Fiscal Year-end: 12/31/23
Optical Fiber Product Mfr & Distr
N.A.I.C.S.: 335921
Guoqing Lu *(Chm)*

WUHAN LINCONTROL AUTOMOTIVE ELECTRONICS CO., LTD.
No 8 Qingshui Road Jinyinhu lake, Dongxihu, Wuhan, 430048, Hubei, China
Tel.: (86) 2781821900
Web Site: https://www.whldqc.com
Year Founded: 2005
688667—(SHG)
Rev.: $99,964,968
Assets: $269,492,240
Liabilities: $56,300,934
Net Worth: $213,191,307
Earnings: $9,410,844
Fiscal Year-end: 12/31/22
Electronic Product Mfr & Distr
N.A.I.C.S.: 334419
Heping Wang *(Chm & Gen Mgr)*

WUHAN NUSUN LANDSCAPE CO., LTD.
Office 7-9 27F Building No S11 Lvdi Hankou Center, No 66 Jiankang Street Jiangan District, Wuhan, 430013, Hubei, China
Tel.: (86) 2785887559
Web Site: http://www.nusunlandscape.com
Year Founded: 2000
300536—(CHIN)
Rev.: $10,060,549
Assets: $140,938,905
Liabilities: $56,004,777
Net Worth: $84,934,128
Earnings: ($4,192,626)
Fiscal Year-end: 12/31/23
Landscaping Services
N.A.I.C.S.: 561730
Liang Wu *(Chm)*

WUHAN P&S INFORMATION TECHNOLOGY CO., LTD.
P&S Building Wudayuan 3 Road, Donghu High-Tech Develop District, Wuhan, China
Tel.: (86) 4008008051
Web Site: https://www.icbase.com
300184—(CHIN)
Rev.: $1,128,738,780
Assets: $751,222,836
Liabilities: $252,707,364
Net Worth: $498,515,472
Earnings: $31,634,928
Fiscal Year-end: 12/31/22
Integrated Circuits & Other Electronic Components Distr
N.A.I.C.S.: 423690

Subsidiaries:

Wuhan Xinyuan Semiconductor Co., Ltd. (1)
Liyuan Building No 5 Wudayuan 3rd Road Guanggu Avenue East Lake New, Technology Development Zone, Wuhan, China
Tel.: (86) 2781566668
Web Site: https://en.whxy.com
Semiconductor Product Mfr
N.A.I.C.S.: 334413

WUHAN RAYCUS FIBER LASER TECHNOLOGIES CO., LTD.
No 999 Gaoxin Avenue East Lake Hi-Tech Development Zone, Wuhan, 430075, Hubei, China
Tel.: (86) 2787001978
Web Site: https://www.raycuslaser.com
Year Founded: 2007
300747—(CHIN)
Rev.: $518,287,970
Assets: $822,678,145
Liabilities: $357,265,687
Net Worth: $465,412,458
Earnings: $30,624,396
Fiscal Year-end: 12/31/23
Pulse Electric Equipment Mfr & Distr
N.A.I.C.S.: 334515
Xiaofeng Wu *(Chm)*

Subsidiaries:

Innotech Laser GmbH (1)
Giesenheide 31, 40724, Hilden, Germany
Tel.: (49) 21033098900
Web Site: https://innotech-laser.de
Laser Component Mfr & Distr
N.A.I.C.S.: 335999

Red Optics Solutions (M) SDN. BHD. (1)
A12-07 Casa Subang Service apartment Jalan Subang1 USJ 1, 47600, Subang Jaya, Selangor Darul Ehsan, Malaysia
Tel.: (60) 122835892
Fibber Laser Mfr & Distr
N.A.I.C.S.: 335999

Veego Corporation (1)
No 192 Wenxin S 10th Rd, South Dist, Taichung, Taiwan
Tel.: (886) 422603233
Web Site: https://www.veego.com.tw
Laser Beam Product Mfr & Distr
N.A.I.C.S.: 335999

WUHAN SAILI SI MEDICAL TECHNOLOGY CO., LTD
No 1310 Jinshan Avenue Dongxi District, Wuhan, 430040, Hubei, China
Tel.: (86) 2783386378
Web Site: http://www.thalys.net.cn
603716—(SHG)
Rev.: $398,277,056
Assets: $657,817,860
Liabilities: $390,786,619
Net Worth: $267,031,241
Earnings: ($7,585,427)
Fiscal Year-end: 12/31/21
Diagnostic Product Mfr & Distr
N.A.I.C.S.: 334510
Wei Wen *(Chm)*

WUHAN SANTE CABLEWAYS GROUP CO., LTD.
Building D1 Guanggu Software Park Te No 1 Guanshan 1st Road, East Lake New Technology Development Zone, Wuhan, 430073, Hubei, China
Tel.: (86) 2787341812
Web Site: http://www.sante.com.cn
Year Founded: 1989
002159—(SSE)
Rev.: $35,968,725
Assets: $262,857,779
Liabilities: $99,952,361
Net Worth: $162,905,418
Earnings: ($10,812,681)
Fiscal Year-end: 12/31/22
Rope Car Services & Hotel Operator
N.A.I.C.S.: 487990

WUHAN SANZHEN INDUSTRY HOLDING CO., LTD.
No 263 Zhongbei Road Wuhan Holdings Building 16-17th Floor, Wuchang District, Wuhan, 430062, Hubei, China
Tel.: (86) 2785725739
Web Site: https://www.600168.com.cn
Year Founded: 1998
600168—(SHG)
Rev.: $406,299,488
Assets: $2,864,306,718
Liabilities: $2,118,296,330
Net Worth: $746,010,388
Earnings: $1,011,442
Emp.: 1,100
Fiscal Year-end: 12/31/22
Holding Company
N.A.I.C.S.: 551112
Wang Jing *(Chm)*

WUHAN TIANYU INFORMATION INDUSTRY CO., LTD.
Tianyu Building Huagong University Science Park, East Lake High-tech Development Zone, Wuhan, 430223, Hubei, China
Tel.: (86) 2787920301
Web Site: http://www.whty.com
Year Founded: 1999
300205—(CHIN)
Rev.: $251,565,912
Assets: $461,288,412
Liabilities: $251,038,008
Net Worth: $210,250,404
Earnings: $12,136,176
Emp.: 930
Fiscal Year-end: 12/31/22
Smartcard Mfr
N.A.I.C.S.: 334118
Yan Chunyu *(Chm)*

WUHAN TIANYUAN ENVIRONMENTAL PROTECTION CO., LTD.
No 400 Xingcheng Avenue Tianjiao Building, Tianyuan Tianjiao Building Hannan District, Wuhan, 430000, Hubei, China
Tel.: (86) 2782863611
Web Site: https://www.tianyuanhuanbao.com
Year Founded: 2009
301127—(CHIN)
Rev.: $269,594,608
Assets: $790,130,898
Liabilities: $424,462,049
Net Worth: $365,668,850
Earnings: $39,145,658
Emp.: 1,100
Fiscal Year-end: 12/31/23
Engineeering Services
N.A.I.C.S.: 541330
Kaiming Huang *(Chm)*

WUHAN XIANGLONG POWER INDUSTRY CO., LTD.
No 31 Huagong Road Zuoling Street, East Lake High-tech Zone, Wuhan, 430078, China
Tel.: (86) 2787602482
600769—(SHG)
Rev.: $7,184,100
Assets: $33,498,162
Liabilities: $22,548,072
Net Worth: $10,950,091
Earnings: $1,497,549
Emp.: 368
Fiscal Year-end: 12/31/22
Water Supply Services
N.A.I.C.S.: 221310
Wang Fengjuan *(Sec)*

WUHAN XINGTU XINKE ELECTRONICS CO., LTD.
8F Building A3 Software Industry Phase III No 1 Guanshan Avenue, East Lake Hi-tech Development Zone, Wuhan, 430223, Hubei, China
Tel.: (86) 2787179175
Web Site: http://www.xingtu.com
Year Founded: 2004
688081—(SHG)
Rev.: $20,148,832
Assets: $94,889,537
Liabilities: $11,303,155
Net Worth: $83,586,382
Earnings: ($11,106,314)
Emp.: 500
Fiscal Year-end: 12/31/22
Electronic Product Mfr & Distr
N.A.I.C.S.: 334419
Jiaming Cheng *(Chm & Gen Mgr)*

WUHAN YANGTZE COMMUNICATIONS INDUSTRY GROUP CO.
No 2 Wenhua Road Guandong Industrial Park East Lake Development Zone, Wuhan, 430074, Hubei, China
Tel.: (86) 2767840308
Web Site: http://www.ycig.com
Year Founded: 1996
600345—(SHG)
Rev.: $32,551,754
Assets: $348,767,935
Liabilities: $41,330,390
Net Worth: $307,437,544
Earnings: $26,060,795
Emp.: 183
Fiscal Year-end: 12/31/22
Communication Equipment Mfr
N.A.I.C.S.: 334220
CunHai Xia *(Chm)*

Subsidiaries:

Shenzhen Lianheng Technology Co., Ltd. (1)
12 Lingwu Industrial Zone Guanlan Bao an,

Wuhan Yangtze Communications Industry Group Co.—(Continued)
Shenzhen, China
Tel.: (86) 755 89803882
Web Site: http://www.sz-lianheng.com
Emp.: 1,200
Communication Equipment Mfr & Distr
N.A.I.C.S.: 334220
Dylan Xie *(Mgr-Intl Trade)*

Wuhan Yangtze LED Lighting Technology Co., Ltd. (1)
2nd Floor Hong Ye Building Wuhan University Science Park, East Lake Development Area, Wuhan, Hubei, China
Tel.: (86) 27 86698817
Ligting Product Mfr & Distr
N.A.I.C.S.: 335139

Yangtze Optical Fibre & Cable Joint Stock Limited Company (1)
No 9 Optics Valley Avenue, Wuhan, 430073, China
Tel.: (86) 2768789088
Web Site: http://www.yofc.com
Rev.: $1,259,622,143
Assets: $2,429,236,476
Liabilities: $991,280,957
Net Worth: $1,437,955,519
Earnings: $83,297,213
Emp.: 7,000
Fiscal Year-end: 12/31/2020
Fiber Optic Cable Mfr
N.A.I.C.S.: 335921
Frank Franciscus Dorjee *(Exec Dir)*

WUHAN ZHONGYUAN HUADIAN
No 6 The 6th Road Technology Park of Huazhong University, Science and Technology East Lake New Technology Development Zone, Wuhan, 430223, Hubei, China
Tel.: (86) 2787180718
Web Site: http://www.zyhd.com.cn
Year Founded: 2001
300018—(CHIN)
Rev.: $63,112,829
Assets: $202,638,726
Liabilities: $25,562,106
Net Worth: $177,076,620
Earnings: $8,466,958
Fiscal Year-end: 12/31/23
Electric Equipment Mfr
N.A.I.C.S.: 335999
Zhigang Deng *(Board of Directors, Chm & Gen Mgr)*

WUHU 37 INTERACTIVE ENTERTAINMENT NETWORK TECHNOLOGY GROUP CO., LTD.
7th Floor B1 Wanjiang Fortune Plaza No 88 Ruixiang Road, Jiujiang District, Wuhu, 241000, Anhui, China
Tel.: (86) 5537653737
Web Site: https://www.37entertainment.net
Year Founded: 1995
002555—(SSE)
Rev.: $2,303,407,202
Assets: $2,400,084,325
Liabilities: $671,489,339
Net Worth: $1,728,594,986
Earnings: $414,794,517
Fiscal Year-end: 12/31/22
Software Development Services
N.A.I.C.S.: 541511
Weiwei Li *(Chm & Gen Mgr)*

WUHU FUCHUN DYE & WEAVE CO., LTD.
No 3 Jiuhua North Road, Pilot Free Trade Zone, Wuhu, 241008, Anhui, China
Tel.: (86) 5535710228
Web Site: http://www.fc858.com
Year Founded: 2002
605189—(SHG)
Rev.: $309,945,650
Assets: $435,275,437
Liabilities: $193,162,994
Net Worth: $242,112,443
Earnings: $22,871,076
Fiscal Year-end: 12/31/22
Textile Product Mfr & Distr
N.A.I.C.S.: 313310
Peifu He *(Chm)*

WUHU TOKEN SCIENCES CO., LTD.
East of Qijing Second Road, Economic and Technological Development Zone, Wuhu, 241009, Anhui, China
Tel.: (86) 5532398888
Web Site: https://www.tokengroup.com
Year Founded: 2000
300088—(CHIN)
Rev.: $981,011,304
Assets: $1,834,300,728
Liabilities: $606,046,428
Net Worth: $1,228,254,300
Earnings: $95,424,264
Emp.: 20,000
Fiscal Year-end: 12/31/22
Vacuum Thin Film Materials & Indium Tin Oxide Conductive Glass Mfr
N.A.I.C.S.: 334413
Gao Qianwen *(Chm)*

Subsidiaries:

Chongqing Yongxin Technology Co., Ltd. (1)
28 Fenghuang 1st Road Fenghuanghu Industrial Park, Yongchuan, Chongqing, China
Tel.: (86) 2361130999
Photoelectric Material Mfr & Distr
N.A.I.C.S.: 334413

Dongguan DPT Electronics Co., Ltd. (1)
Jingqian 1st Road, Dalingshan, Dongguan, China
Tel.: (86) 76988961111
Web Site: https://www.dpt-e.com
Liquid Crystal Display Module Mfr
N.A.I.C.S.: 334419

Ganzhou Deput Technology Co., Ltd. (1)
Deput Technology Co Ltd West of Longling Industrial Park, Longling Nankang, Ganzhou, Jiangxi, China
Tel.: (86) 7976799028
Photoelectric Material Mfr & Distr
N.A.I.C.S.: 334413

Tianjin Mattel Vacuum Technology Co., Ltd. (1)
200 meters South, Jinzhuangzi Village Dafengdui Jinghai, Tianjin, China
Tel.: (86) 2268676758
Photoelectric Material Mfr & Distr
N.A.I.C.S.: 334413

Token sciences Japan co. Ltd. (1)
5F 1-14-11 Higashi Kanda, Chiyoda-ku, Tokyo, 101-0031, Japan
Tel.: (81) 358091799
Photoelectric Material Mfr & Distr
N.A.I.C.S.: 334413

WULF GAERTNER AUTOPARTS AG
Merkurring 111, 22143, Hamburg, Germany
Tel.: (49) 4067506510
Web Site: http://www.wulfgaertner.com
Year Founded: 1958
Rev.: $91,285,194
Emp.: 300
Automobile Spare Parts Mfr
N.A.I.C.S.: 336390
Karl J. Gaertner *(Chm)*

Subsidiaries:

MEYLE France S.A.R.L (1)
78 Allees Jean Jaures Pre Catelan Bat F, 31000, Toulouse, France
Tel.: (33) 5 61 63 31 52
Web Site: http://www.meyle.fr
Automobile Parts Distr
N.A.I.C.S.: 423120

MEYLE UK Ltd. (1)
47 Dolphin Road, Shoreham-by-Sea, BN43 6PB, Sussex, United Kingdom
Tel.: (44) 845 4506510
Web Site: http://www.meyle.co.uk
Emp.: 3
Automobile Parts Distr
N.A.I.C.S.: 423120
Ben Kelly *(Coord-Sls & Ops)*

MEYLE USA (1)
1357 Wagon Wheel Ct, Oakdale, CA 95361
Tel.: (925) 699-7199
Web Site: http://www.meyle.us
Automobile Parts Distr
N.A.I.C.S.: 423120

Meycar Automotive S.L. (1)
Calle Cobalto N 21 Poligono Industrial Sur, Colmenar Viejo, 28770, Madrid, Spain
Tel.: (34) 91 846 72 56
Web Site: http://www.meycar.es
Automobile Parts Distr
N.A.I.C.S.: 423120

Wulf Gaertner Autoparts (M) Sdn Bhd (1)
63 Jalan Segambut Pusat, 51200, Kuala Lumpur, Malaysia
Tel.: (60) 3 62 52 63 27
Web Site: http://www.wg-autoparts.my
Automobile Parts Distr
N.A.I.C.S.: 423120

Wulf Gaertner Autoparts (S) PTE LTD (1)
61 Kaki Bukit Ave 1 03-11 Shun Li Industrial Park, Singapore, 417943, Singapore
Tel.: (65) 6841 1163
Web Site: http://www.wg-autoparts.sg
Automobile Parts Mfr
N.A.I.C.S.: 336390

Wulf Gaertner Autoparts (Thailand) Ltd (1)
277 Soi Saeng U - Thai Sukhumvit 50, Phrakhanong Klongtoey, Bangkok, 10110, Thailand
Tel.: (66) 2 7414 381
Web Site: http://www.wg-autoparts.co.th
Automobile Parts Distr
N.A.I.C.S.: 423120

WULFF YHTIOT OYJ
Kilonkartanontie 3, 2610, Espoo, Finland
Tel.: (358) 300870410
Web Site: https://www.wulff.fi
Year Founded: 1890
WUF1V—(HEL)
Rev.: $110,264,408
Assets: $58,406,000
Liabilities: $35,401,468
Net Worth: $23,004,533
Earnings: $3,393,050
Emp.: 280
Fiscal Year-end: 12/31/22
Software Development Services
N.A.I.C.S.: 541511
Elina Pienimaki *(CEO)*

Subsidiaries:

Mavecom Palvelut Oy (1)
Kilonkartanontie 3, 02610, Espoo, Finland
Tel.: (358) 207589700
Web Site: https://www.mavecom.fi
Printer Services
N.A.I.C.S.: 811210

WULFF-GROUP PLC
Manttaalitie 12, 01530, Vantaa, Finland
Tel.: (358) 952590050
Web Site: http://www.wulff-group.com
Sales Range: $100-124.9 Million
Emp.: 326
Office Supplies Sales & Marketing
N.A.I.C.S.: 459410

Heikki Vienola *(Chm)*

Subsidiaries:

Active Office Finland Oy (1)
Manttaalitie 12, 01530, Vantaa, Finland (100%)
Tel.: (358) 207496290
Web Site: http://www.active-office-finland-oy.onverkossa.fi
Emp.: 300
Stationery & Office Supplies Whslr
N.A.I.C.S.: 424120

Everyman Oy (1)
Valuraudantie 12, 00700, Helsinki, Finland (100%)
Tel.: (358) 98256150
Web Site: http://www.everyman.fi
Emp.: 30
Stationery & Office Supplies Whslr
N.A.I.C.S.: 424120

Grande Leasing Oy (1)
Manttaalitie 12, 1530, Vantaa, Finland
Tel.: (358) 95259000
Automobile Leasing Services
N.A.I.C.S.: 532112

KB Eesti Ou (1)
Regati Pst 1-5P, 11911, Tallinn, Estonia
Tel.: (372) 639 8742
Web Site: http://www.kb.ee
Emp.: 12
Promotional Products Advertising Services
N.A.I.C.S.: 541810
Carl Los *(Gen Mgr)*

KB-tuote Oy (1)
Merimiehenkatu 36 D, 00150, Helsinki, Finland (100%)
Tel.: (358) 9478822
Web Site: http://www.kbtuote.fi
Emp.: 50
Stationery & Office Supplies Whslr
N.A.I.C.S.: 424120
Topi Ruuska *(CEO)*

Naxor Finland Oy (1)
Manttaalitie 12, Vantaa, 1530, Finland
Tel.: (358) 207496270
Web Site: http://www.wulffnaxor.fi
Emp.: 10
Office Equipment Distr
N.A.I.C.S.: 423420
Petri Kautonen *(Gen Mgr)*

Office Solutions Svenska AB (1)
Akerbarsvagen 26, SE-611 38, Nykoping, Sweden (75%)
Tel.: (46) 155205170
Web Site: http://www.eniro.se
Stationery & Office Supplies Whslr
N.A.I.C.S.: 424120

Office Solutions Why Not Oy (1)
Valuraudantie 12, 00700, Helsinki, Finland (85%)
Tel.: (358) 982561529
Web Site: http://www.whynot.fi
Emp.: 30
Office Supplies & Stationery Stores
N.A.I.C.S.: 459410

Officeman Oy (1)
Valuraudantie 12, 00700, Helsinki, Finland (70%)
Tel.: (358) 98256150
Emp.: 33
Office Furniture Mfr
N.A.I.C.S.: 337214
Juhani Jaakkola *(CEO)*

Suomen Rader Oy (1)
Manttaalitie 12, 01530, Vantaa, Finland (100%)
Tel.: (358) 207496250
Web Site: http://www.suomenrader.com
Emp.: 50
Stationery & Office Supplies Whslr
N.A.I.C.S.: 424120

Torkkelin Paperi Oy (1)
Kauppakeskus Maili Ajokatu 55, 15500, Lahti, Finland
Tel.: (358) 300870410
Web Site: http://www.wulfftorkkeli.fi
Emp.: 15
Office Supplies & Stationery Stores
N.A.I.C.S.: 459410
Juha Broman *(Gen Mgr)*

AND PRIVATE COMPANIES

WURTH VERWALTUNGSGESELLSCHAFT MBH

Vinstock Oy (1)
Manttaalitie 12, Vantaa, 1530, Finland (100%)
Tel.: (358) 95259000
Web Site: http://www.wulff.fi
Emp.: 300
Stationery & Office Supplies Whslr
N.A.I.C.S.: 424120
Jarkko Vehvilainen *(Dir-Sls)*

Wulff Beltton (1)
Manttaalitie 12, 1530, Vantaa, Finland
Tel.: (358) 9 525 9000
Emp.: 100
Office Equipment Distr
N.A.I.C.S.: 423420
Popi Ruuska *(Mng Dir)*

Wulff Beltton AB (1)
Akerbarsvagen 26, 611 38, Nykoping, Sweden
Tel.: (46) 155292600
Web Site: https://www.wulffbelttton.se
Emp.: 5
Healthcare Product Distr
N.A.I.C.S.: 424210
Veijo Agerfalk *(Mng Dir)*

Wulff Care (1)
Manttaalitie 12, Vantaa, 01530, Finland
Tel.: (358) 207 496 270
Web Site: http://www.wulff.fi
Emp.: 80
Stationery & Office Supplies Distr
N.A.I.C.S.: 424120
Heikki Vienola *(Chm)*

Wulff Direct AS (1)
I angnesveien 8, 9408, Harstad, Norway
Tel.: (47) 77 01 98 00
Web Site: http://www.wulffdirect.no
Computer Accessories & Office Supplies Distr
N.A.I.C.S.: 423430

Wulff Entre Oy (1)
Ruoholahdenkatu 21 B, 180, Helsinki, Finland
Tel.: (358) 10 6335 500
Web Site: http://www.entre.fi
Emp.: 30
Event & Trade Fair Organizing Services
N.A.I.C.S.: 561920
Ninni Arion *(VP & Project Dir)*

Wulff Oy AB (1)
Manttaalitie 12, 01530, Vantaa, Finland
Tel.: (358) 300870411
Web Site: https://www.wulff1890.fi
Emp.: 100
Sales of Office & Computer Distr
N.A.I.C.S.: 449210
Topi Ruusaa *(Mng Dir)*

Wulff Supplies A/S (1)
Kirkebjerg Parkvej 12, Brondby, 2605, Denmark
Tel.: (45) 70104444
Web Site: https://www.wulffsupplies.dk
Stationery & Office Supplies Distr
N.A.I.C.S.: 424120
Mattias Ortenblad *(Mng Dir)*

Wulff Visual Globe Oy (1)
Manttaalitie 12, 01530, Vantaa, Finland (100%)
Tel.: (358) 207 496 280
Web Site: http://www.visualglobe.fi
Emp.: 50
Stationery & Office Supplies Whslr
N.A.I.C.S.: 424120

WULIANGYE YIBIN CO., LTD.
No 150 Minjiang West Road, Yibin, Sichuan, China
Tel.: (86) 8313567000 HK
Web Site: https://www.wuliangye.com.cn
000858—(SSE)
Rev.: $10,385,197,154
Assets: $21,441,147,797
Liabilities: $5,058,687,577
Net Worth: $16,382,460,220
Earnings: $3,747,368,861
Emp.: 16,000
Fiscal Year-end: 12/31/22
Liquor & Related Products Mfr
N.A.I.C.S.: 312140

Congqin Zeng *(Chm)*

WULING MOTORS HOLDINGS LIMITED
Unit 1901 19/F Beautiful Group Tower 77 Connaught Road, Central, China (Hong Kong)
Tel.: (852) 25911288 BM
Web Site: http://www.wuling.com.hk
0305—(HKG)
Rev.: $1,768,423,223
Assets: $2,182,576,406
Liabilities: $1,778,241,114
Net Worth: $404,335,292
Earnings: $5,621,335
Emp.: 8,700
Fiscal Year-end: 12/31/22
Automotive Components Mfr
N.A.I.C.S.: 336110
Shing Lee *(Vice Chm & CEO)*

Subsidiaries:

Dragon Hill Financial Services Limited (1)
Unit 1302 13/F Henan Building 90-92 Jaffe Road, Wanchai, China (Hong Kong)
Tel.: (852) 2918 1668
Financial Management Services
N.A.I.C.S.: 523999

WUNONG ASIA PACIFIC COMPANY LIMITED
3 KeZhen Industrial Street Wuchun District, Hohhot, China
Tel.: (86) 52 3875 3362 NV
Year Founded: 2011
AITA—(OTCIQ)
Sales Range: $1-9.9 Million
Emp.: 3
Investment Services
N.A.I.C.S.: 523999
Peijiang Chen *(Chm)*

WUNSCHENDORFER DOLOMITWERK GMBH
Geraer Strasse 34, 07570, Wunschendorf, Germany
Tel.: (49) 36603810
Web Site: http://www.dolomitwerk-wuenschendorf.de
Year Founded: 1922
Rev.: $13,794,000
Emp.: 70
Dolomite Rock Mfr
N.A.I.C.S.: 327410
Olaf Ortlepp *(Co-Mng Dir)*

WUPPERMANN AG
Ottostrasse 5, D-51381, Leverkusen, Germany
Tel.: (49) 21715000800
Web Site: http://www.wuppermann.com
Year Founded: 1872
Sales Range: $600-649.9 Million
Emp.: 1,300
Holding Company; Steel Products Mfr
N.A.I.C.S.: 551112
Carl Ludwig Thoedore Wuppermann *(Member-Mgmt Bd)*

Subsidiaries:

H&B Fertigungstechnik GmbH (1)
Industriestrasse 6, 5303, Thalgau, Austria
Tel.: (43) 6235 20200 0
Steel Pipe Distr
N.A.I.C.S.: 423510

KLB Intralogistik GmbH (1)
Allmendstrasse 4, 79336, Herbolzheim, Germany
Tel.: (49) 7643 9102 0
Web Site: http://www.wuppermann.com
Industrial Equipment Mfr
N.A.I.C.S.: 334513
Graven Chirstian *(Mgr)*

Wuppermann Austria GmbH (1)
Gussstahlwerkstrasse 23, 8750, Judenburg, Austria
Tel.: (43) 50 910 400
Steel Pipe Distr
N.A.I.C.S.: 423510

Subsidiary (Domestic):

Wuppermann Bandstahl GmbH (2)
Voestalpine-Strasse 3, 4020, Linz, Austria
Tel.: (43) 50 910 300
Steel Pole Mfr
N.A.I.C.S.: 331210

Wuppermann Business Services GmbH (1)
Grossalmstrasse 1, 4813, Altmunster, Austria
Tel.: (43) 50 910 500
Engineering Consulting Services
N.A.I.C.S.: 541330

Wuppermann France S.A.S. (1)
11 Cite Malesherbes, 75009, Paris, France
Tel.: (33) 153 2019 00
Web Site: http://www.wuppermann.de
Steel Pipe Distr
N.A.I.C.S.: 423510

Wuppermann KLB AG (1)
Kantonsstrasse 7, 4416, Bubendorf, Switzerland
Tel.: (41) 61 935 96 00
Web Site: http://www.klbag.ch
Steel Pipe Distr
N.A.I.C.S.: 423510

Wuppermann Kovotechnika s.r.o. (1)
MUDr Slejmara 609, 34562, Holysov, Czech Republic
Tel.: (420) 379 415 611
Steel Pole Mfr
N.A.I.C.S.: 331210

Wuppermann Otel Romania S.R.L. (1)
Str Frumoasa Nr 41 Attic office 2 Sector 1, 010986, Bucharest, Romania
Tel.: (40) 31 620 08 66
Steel Pole Mfr
N.A.I.C.S.: 331210
Aurora Cartofeanu *(Dir-Sls)*

Wuppermann Polska sp. z o.o. (1)
Ul Fabryczna 3, 67-320, Malomice, Poland
Tel.: (48) 68 3780 101
Web Site: http://www.wuppermann.de
Steel Pipe Distr
N.A.I.C.S.: 423510

Wuppermann Rohrtechnik GmbH (1)
Rothenburger Strasse 42, 91593, Burgbernheim, Germany
Tel.: (49) 9843 9822 600
Web Site: http://www.wuppermann.com
Emp.: 120
Steel Pole Mfr
N.A.I.C.S.: 331210
Rainer Bodendorfer *(Mgr)*

Wuppermann Technologies C.V. (1)
Vlasweg 15, 4782 PW, Moerdijk, Netherlands
Tel.: (31) 168 357 130
Steel Pipe Distr
N.A.I.C.S.: 423510

Wuppermann Tube & Steel AB (1)
Stora Avagen 21, Askim, 436 34, Gothenburg, Sweden
Tel.: (46) 31 60 72 70
Steel Pipe Distr
N.A.I.C.S.: 423510

WURTH VERWALTUNGSGESELLSCHAFT MBH
Reinhold-Wurth-Strasse 12-17, 74653, Kunzelsau, Germany
Tel.: (49) 7940150 De
Web Site: http://www.wuerth.com
Year Founded: 1945
Holding Company
N.A.I.C.S.: 551112

Subsidiaries:

Wurth Management AG (1)
Churehstrasse 10, 9400, Rorschach, Switzerland
Tel.: (41) 712251000
Web Site: http://www.wuerth-haus-rorschach.ch
Emp.: 100
Holding Company
N.A.I.C.S.: 551112
Juerg Michel *(Mng Dir)*

Group (Non-US):

Adolf Wurth GmbH & Co. KG (2)
Reinhold-Wurth-Strasse 12-17, 74653, Kunzelsau, Germany (100%)
Tel.: (49) 7940150
Web Site: http://www.wuerth.de
Holding Company; Assembly Materials & Fastening Hardware Mfr & Distr
N.A.I.C.S.: 551112
Bernd Herrmann *(Member-Mgmt Bd)*

Subsidiary (Non-US):

AG Wurth Eurasien (3)
ul Sibirskij Trakt 12 Litera P office 301, Sverdlovskaya oblast, 620100, Yekaterinburg, Russia
Tel.: (7) 3433565505
Web Site: http://www.wurth.ur.ru
Hardware Whslr
N.A.I.C.S.: 423710

Subsidiary (Domestic):

AHD Auto-Hifi & -Design GmbH (3)
Eichendorffstrasse 15, D-74653, Ingelfingen, Germany
Tel.: (49) 794098200
Web Site: http://www.ahd-gmbh.de
Car Audio Systems Distr
N.A.I.C.S.: 423620

Subsidiary (Non-US):

AO Wurth-Rus (3)
Ul Admirala Kornilova vlad 3 str 1, 108803, Moscow, Russia
Tel.: (7) 4955057007
Web Site: http://www.wurth.ru
Fastener Products Whslr
N.A.I.C.S.: 423710

AP Winner (Changzhou) Chemical Technology Co., Ltd. (3)
Pno 6 Xingtang Road, Yangtze Riverside Economic Development Zone, Changzhou, 213127, Jiangsu, China
Tel.: (86) 51989889180
Automobile Mfr
N.A.I.C.S.: 336110

AP Winner Industria e Comercio de Produtos Quimi-cos Ltd. a. (3)
Rua Jumbo 86 Cara-Cara, Ponta Grossa, Parana, 84043-300, Brazil
Tel.: (55) 4232193200
Web Site: http://www.apwinner.com.br
Automotive Chemical Product Distr
N.A.I.C.S.: 424690

Action Bolt (Pty.) Ltd. (3)
11 Aloefield Crescent Springfield Park, Durban, 4091, South Africa
Tel.: (27) 315793161
Web Site: http://www.actionbolt.co.za
Information Technology Services
N.A.I.C.S.: 541511
Praven Veera *(Mgr-IT & QA)*

Subsidiary (Domestic):

Adolf Menschel Verbindungstechnik GmbH & Co. KG (3)
Posensche Strasse 17-23, 58840, Plettenberg, Germany
Tel.: (49) 239160090
Web Site: http://www.menschel.de
Assembly Materials & Fastening Hardware Mfr & Distr
N.A.I.C.S.: 332510

Subsidiary (Non-US):

Airproduct AG (3)
Bremgartenstrasse 21, Oberwil-Lieli, 8966, Bremgarten, Switzerland
Tel.: (41) 566339633
Web Site: http://www.airproduct.ch
Ventilation Component Mfr
N.A.I.C.S.: 333415

WURTH VERWALTUNGSGESELLSCHAFT MBH

Wurth Verwaltungsgesellschaft mbH—(Continued)

Subsidiary (Domestic):

Arnold Umformtechnik GmbH & Co. KG (3)
Ernsbach plant Carl-ARNOLD-Strasse 25, 74670, Forchtenberg, Germany
Tel.: (49) 79478210
Web Site: http://www.arnold-fastening.com
Assembly Materials & Fastening Hardware Mfr & Distr
N.A.I.C.S.: 332510
Gert-Thomas Hohn *(Mng Dir)*

Subsidiary (Domestic):

Arnold & Shinjo GmbH & Co. KG (4)
Max-Planck-Strasse 19, 74677, Dorzbach, Germany
Tel.: (49) 793780310
Web Site: http://www.arnold-shinjo.de
Assembly Materials & Fastening Hardware Mfr & Distr
N.A.I.C.S.: 332510

Subsidiary (Non-US):

Arnold Fasteners (Shenyang) Co., Ltd. (4)
No 119-2 Jianshe Road, Dadong District, Shenyang, 110122, China
Tel.: (86) 24 8879 0633
Web Site: http://www.arnold-fastening.com
Emp.: 200
Fastener Mfr
N.A.I.C.S.: 332722

Arnold Technique France (4)
4 Rue Saint Didier, F-26140, Anneyron, France
Tel.: (33) 4 7531 3260
Web Site: http://www.arnold-france.com
Hardware Mfr & Distr
N.A.I.C.S.: 332722

Subsidiary (Non-US):

Arvid Nilsson Logistics & Trade (Shanghai) Co., Ltd. (3)
Block A No 10 Jin Wen Road, Pudong, Shanghai, 201323, China
Tel.: (86) 2168139998
Industrial Equipment Mfr
N.A.I.C.S.: 333248
Chu Tony *(Dir-Sls)*

Arvid Nilsson Sverige AB (3)
Bultgatan 27, PO Box 583, 442 16, Kungalv, Sweden
Tel.: (46) 30362600
Web Site: http://www.arvidnilsson.no
Fastener Mfr
N.A.I.C.S.: 332722
Annika Folkesson *(CEO)*

Autocom Diagnostic Partner AB (3)
Grafitvagen 23 B, 461 38, Trollhattan, Sweden
Tel.: (46) 520470700
Web Site: http://www.autocom.se
Automotive Services
N.A.I.C.S.: 811111
Per Aalto *(Mgr-Export Area)*

Subsidiary (Domestic):

BB-Stanz- und Umformtechnik GmbH (3)
Nordhauser Strasse 44, Berga, 06536, Greiz, Germany
Tel.: (49) 3465129880
Web Site: http://www.bb-berga.de
Metal & Plastic Product Mfr
N.A.I.C.S.: 332999

Subsidiary (Non-US):

Baier & Michels S.r.l. (3)
Via Eugenio Montale 6, 35030, Selvazzano Dentro, PD, Italy
Tel.: (39) 0498536600
Web Site: http://www.baier-michels.it
Fastening Product Mfr & Distr
N.A.I.C.S.: 332722

Blumel Srl (3)
Via L Zuegg 22, 39012, Merano, South Tyrol, Italy
Tel.: (39) 0473449549
Web Site: http://www.blumel.com

Switch Mfr
N.A.I.C.S.: 335313

Subsidiary (Domestic):

Conmetall GmbH & Co. KG (3)
Hafenstrasse 26, 29223, Celle, Germany
Tel.: (49) 5141180
Web Site: http://www.conmetallmeister.de
Tools, Hardware & Sanitaryware Distr
N.A.I.C.S.: 423710
Hans-Peter Heffels *(Mng Dir)*

Subsidiary (Non-US):

Conmetall N.V. (4)
Oudestraat 53, Saint-Katelijne-Waver, 2860, Belgium
Tel.: (32) 15293949
Web Site: http://www.conmetall.de
Emp.: 6
Assembly Materials & Fastening Hardware Distr
N.A.I.C.S.: 423710
Jean-Paul Standaert *(Mgr)*

Subsidiary (Domestic):

Conpac GmbH & Co. KG (4)
Hafenstrasse 31, 29223, Celle, Germany (100%)
Tel.: (49) 5141180
Web Site: http://www.conmetall.de
Emp.: 500
Hardware Packaging Services
N.A.I.C.S.: 561910
Michel Hunke *(Gen Mgr)*

Subsidiary (Non-US):

Conmetall spol. s.r.o. (3)
Partyzanska 18, 747 05, Opava, Czech Republic
Tel.: (420) 553662403
Web Site: http://www.conmetall.cz
Industrial Tools Distr
N.A.I.C.S.: 423830

DIY Products Asia Ltd. (3)
16/F Rykadan Capital Tower 135 Hoi Bun Road, Kwun Tong, Kowloon, China (Hong Kong)
Tel.: (852) 23457555
Hand Tools Distr
N.A.I.C.S.: 423710

Subsidiary (Domestic):

Deko-Light Elektronik-Vertriebs GmbH (3)
Auf der Hub 2, 76307, Karlsbad, Germany
Tel.: (49) 72489271500
Web Site: http://www.deko-light.com
Electrical & Electronic Mfr
N.A.I.C.S.: 336320
Werner Spiess *(CEO)*

Subsidiary (Non-US):

Diffutherm B.V. (3)
Emerald Road 50, 5527 LB, Hapert, Netherlands
Tel.: (31) 497749000
Web Site: http://www.diffutherm.nl
Adhesive & Sealant Mfr
N.A.I.C.S.: 325520

Subsidiary (Domestic):

Dinol GmbH (3)
Pyrmonter Strasse 76, 32676, Lugde, Germany
Tel.: (49) 5281982980
Web Site: http://www.dinol.com
Chemical Products Distr
N.A.I.C.S.: 424690
Mark Feldmann *(CEO)*

Subsidiary (Non-US):

Dokka Fasteners A/S (3)
Hojmarksvej 11, 7330, Brande, Denmark
Tel.: (45) 73207310
Fastener Product Mfr
N.A.I.C.S.: 332722
Henrik Dybdal Rasmussen *(Acct Mgr)*

Dokka Fasteners AS (3)
Rosteinvegen 7, Vinjarmoen Dokka, 2870, Oppland, Norway
Tel.: (47) 61113030
Web Site: http://www.dokkafasteners.com

Fastener Mfr
N.A.I.C.S.: 332722
Andre Klaseie *(Co-CEO & CFO)*

Subsidiary (Domestic):

Dringenberg GmbH Betriebseinrichtungen (3)
In den Muhlwiesen 15-19, Sulzbach, 74182, Obersulm, Germany
Tel.: (49) 71345030
Web Site: http://www.dringenberg.com
Emp.: 120
Metal Desk Workbench Cabinet & Shelf Furniture Mfr
N.A.I.C.S.: 337126
Gerhard Schulz *(Mng Dir)*

Subsidiary (Non-US):

Dringenberg Polska Sp. z o.o. (3)
ul Reinholda Wurtha 1, Zagan, 68-100, Zary, Poland
Tel.: (48) 684592302
Web Site: http://www.dringenberg.pl
Metalware Mfr
N.A.I.C.S.: 332312

Duvimex Belgium BvbA (3)
Prins Boudewijnlaan 41 Bus 2, 2650, Edegem, Belgium
Tel.: (32) 34481933
Web Site: http://www.eurofastgroup.nl
Fastening Product Mfr & Distr
N.A.I.C.S.: 332722

EDL Fasteners Ltd. (3)
15 Business Parade North, East Tamaki, Auckland, 2013, New Zealand
Tel.: (64) 92575959
Web Site: http://www.edlfast.co.nz
Industrial Equipment Retailer
N.A.I.C.S.: 423840
Peter Thomsen *(Mng Dir)*

Elfetex spol. s r.o. (3)
Hrbitovni 31a, 312 16, Plzen, Czech Republic
Tel.: (420) 377432375
Web Site: http://www.elfetex.cz
Electrical Installation Materials Whslr
N.A.I.C.S.: 423610
Vaclav Planeta *(Mgr-HR)*

Subsidiary (Domestic):

Emil Nickisch GmbH (3)
Erlenweg 2, 51399, Burscheid, Germany
Tel.: (49) 217478340
Web Site: http://www.nickisch.eu
Emp.: 30
Automobile Parts Mfr
N.A.I.C.S.: 336370

Subsidiary (Non-US):

Enexon Polska Sp. z o.o. (3)
Ul Jana Czochralskiego 11, 61-248, Poznan, Poland
Tel.: (48) 616464300
Web Site: http://www.enexon.pl
Electrical Equipment Whslr
N.A.I.C.S.: 423610

Subsidiary (Domestic):

Erwin Biichele GmbH & Co. KG (3)
Hauptstrasse 6, 73730, Esslingen am Neckar, Germany
Tel.: (49) 7119308000
Emp.: 40
Rod Core Chokes & Bent Wire Parts Mfr
N.A.I.C.S.: 332618

Subsidiary (Non-US):

FE WuerthBel (3)
st Rosa Luxemburg 95 4th floor, 220036, Minsk, Belarus
Tel.: (375) 291803336
Web Site: http://www.wuerth.by
Emp.: 122
Assembly Materials & Fastening Hardware Distr
N.A.I.C.S.: 423710

Subsidiary (Domestic):

FEGA & Schmitt Elektrogrosshandel GmbH (3)
Rettstrasse 5, 91522, Ansbach, Germany

INTERNATIONAL PUBLIC

Tel.: (49) 98189030
Web Site: http://www.fega-schmitt.de
Sales Range: $250-299.9 Million
Emp.: 100
Electrical Apparatus, Wiring & Components Whslr
N.A.I.C.S.: 423610
Uwe Schaffitzel *(Mng Dir)*

Subsidiary (Non-US):

TIM S.A. (4)
ul Jaworska 13, 53-612, Wroclaw, Poland (97.31%)
Tel.: (48) 717328600
Web Site: https://www.timsa.pl
Sales Range: Less than $1 Million
Electro-Technical Product Mfr
N.A.I.C.S.: 335313
Krzysztof Wieczorkowski *(Chm-Supervisory Bd)*

Subsidiary (Domestic):

FELO-Werkzeugfabrik Holland-Letz GmbH (3)
Emil-Rossler-Str 59, 35279, Neustadt, Germany
Tel.: (49) 6692880
Web Site: http://www.felo.com
Emp.: 220
Tool Mfr
N.A.I.C.S.: 333517
Andreas Siewert *(Mng Dir)*

Subsidiary (Non-US):

FIME S.r.l. (3)
Largo Leonardo da Vinci 8, 37050, Belfiore, VR, Italy
Tel.: (39) 045 613 4211
Web Site: http://www.fimesrl.it
Hardware Whslr
N.A.I.C.S.: 423710

Fega Poland Sp. z o.o. (3)
ul Ryzowa 88, 02-495, Warsaw, Poland
Tel.: (48) 887680051
Web Site: http://www.fega.pl
Electrical Equipment Whslr
N.A.I.C.S.: 423610

Ferrometal Baltic OU (3)
Laki 14A, 10621, Tallinn, Estonia
Tel.: (372) 6990470
Fastener Distr
N.A.I.C.S.: 423120

Subsidiary (Domestic):

Flugplatz Schwabisch Hall GmbH (3)
Adolf Wurth Airport GAT, 74523, Schwabisch Hall, Germany
Tel.: (49) 791499790
Web Site: http://www.edty.de
Airport Operator
N.A.I.C.S.: 488190
Peter Wohlleben *(Mng Dir)*

Subsidiary (Non-US):

Gaudre UAB (3)
Ateities Str 10, 08303, Vilnius, Lithuania
Tel.: (370) 852796162
Web Site: http://www.gaudre.lt
Lighting Product Mfr
N.A.I.C.S.: 335131
Vytautas Rinkevicius *(Project Mgr)*

Subsidiary (Domestic):

Glessdox GmbH & Co. KG (3)
Ohringer Strasse 50, D-74632, Neuenstein, Germany
Tel.: (49) 7942947570
Web Site: http://www.glessdox.de
Emp.: 30
Commercial, Industrial & Institutional Hygiene Product Distr
N.A.I.C.S.: 424210

Subsidiary (Non-US):

Grass GmbH (3)
Grass Platz 1, 6973, Hochst, Austria
Tel.: (43) 55787010
Web Site: http://www.grass.at
Emp.: 500
Furniture Fittings Mfr & Distr
N.A.I.C.S.: 332510

AND PRIVATE COMPANIES

WURTH VERWALTUNGSGESELLSCHAFT MBH

Thomas Muller *(Member-Mgmt Bd)*

Subsidiary (Non-US):

Grass (Shanghai) International Trading Co., Ltd. (4)
No 1387 Capital of Leaders Building 9 Zhangdong Road, Shanghai, 201203, China
Tel.: (86) 2150297625
Web Site: http://www.grass.net.cn
Emp.: 50
Furniture Fittings Distr
N.A.I.C.S.: 423710

Subsidiary (US):

Grass America, Inc. (4)
1202 NC Highway 66 S, Kernersville, NC 27284-1019
Tel.: (336) 996-4041
Web Site: http://www.grassusa.com
Emp.: 215
Furniture Fittings Mfr & Distr
N.A.I.C.S.: 332510
Tom Kipp *(Pres)*

Subsidiary (Non-US):

Grass Australia/New Zealand Pty Ltd. (4)
Amsterdam Street 4-12, Richmond, Melbourne, 3121, VIC, Australia
Tel.: (61) 92737491
Furniture Accessory Mfr & Distr
N.A.I.C.S.: 337127

Grass Canada Inc. (4)
3135 Markham Rd, Toronto, M1X 0B5, ON, Canada
Tel.: (416) 335-7132
Web Site: http://www.grasscanada.com
Furniture Hardware Whslr
N.A.I.C.S.: 423710

Grass Czech s.r.o. (4)
Domoradice Tovarni 175, 38101, Cesky Krumlov, Czech Republic
Tel.: (420) 380 700 311
Web Site: http://www.grass.at
Furniture Hardware Mfr & Whslr
N.A.I.C.S.: 332722

Grass GmbH & Co. KG (4)
Egerlander Strasse 2, 64354, Reinheim, Germany
Tel.: (49) 61628020
Web Site: http://www.grass.at
Emp.: 250
Furniture Fittings Mfr & Distr
N.A.I.C.S.: 332510
Helmut Kainrad *(Gen Mgr)*

Grass Iberia, S.A. (4)
Pl Tabernabarri 7B, 48215, Iurreta, Bizkaia, Spain
Tel.: (34) 943788240
Web Site: http://www.grass-iberia.com
Metalware Mfr
N.A.I.C.S.: 332312
Daniel Martinez *(Mgr-Sls)*

Grass Italia SRL (4)
via Interpor Centro Ingrosso 76, 33170, Pordenone, Italy
Tel.: (39) 0434573589
Mechanical Parts Mfr
N.A.I.C.S.: 333517
Tommaso Belloni *(Area Mgr)*

Grass Movement Systems Ltd. (4)
Doranda Way, West Midlands, West Bromwich, B71 4LU, United Kingdom
Tel.: (44) 1215005824
Fastener Mfr
N.A.I.C.S.: 332722
David Shoebridge *(Mng Dir)*

Grass Nordiska AB (4)
St Goransvagen 29, 554 54, Jonkoping, Sweden
Tel.: (46) 36312900
Metalware Mfr
N.A.I.C.S.: 332312

Grass Sp. z o.o. (4)
ul Gnieznienska 26-28, Janikowo k Poznania, 62-006, Kobylnica, Poland
Tel.: (48) 61 662 4336
Web Site: http://www.grass-polska.pl
Cabinet Components & Hardware Distr
N.A.I.C.S.: 423710

Grass TR Mobilya Aksesuarlari Ticaret Limited Sirketi (4)
FSM Mah Poligon Cad No 8 Buyaka 2 Site Block No 3 D 65, Umraniye, 34771, Istanbul, Turkiye
Tel.: (90) 2162900632
Web Site: http://www.grass-turkey.com
Fastener Mfr
N.A.I.C.S.: 332722

Grass ZA (Pty.) Ltd. (4)
3 Graph Avenue, Montague Gardens, Cape Town, 7441, South Africa
Tel.: (27) 215 298 040
Web Site: http://www.grass.at
Hardware Whslr
N.A.I.C.S.: 423710

Subsidiary (Non-US):

Grupo Electro Stocks, S.L.U. (3)
Camino ca N ametller 16-P 4, 08195, Sant Cugat del Valles, Spain
Tel.: (34) 936036688
Web Site: http://www.grupoelectrostocks.com
Electrical Equipment Whslr
N.A.I.C.S.: 423610
Ricard Vilella Bonet *(CEO)*

Subsidiary (Domestic):

H. Sartorius Nachf. GmbH & Co. KG (3)
Harkortstrasse 54, 40880, Ratingen, Germany
Tel.: (49) 210244000
Web Site: http://www.sartorius-werkzeuge.de
Sales Range: $50-74.9 Million
Emp.: 160
Metal Processing Industry Tools & Equipment Distr
N.A.I.C.S.: 423830

Subsidiary (Non-US):

HAGARD: HAL, spol. s r.o. (3)
Prazska 9, 949 11, Nitra, Slovakia
Tel.: (421) 945430420
Web Site: http://www.hagard.sk
Electrical Installation Services
N.A.I.C.S.: 238210

HSR Belgium S.A./N.V. (3)
Wilmingtonstraat 1, 2030, Antwerp, Belgium
Tel.: (32) 35423453
Electrical & Electronic Mfr
N.A.I.C.S.: 335999

Subsidiary (Domestic):

HSR GmbH Hochdruck Schlauch + RohrVerbindungen (3)
Oderstrasse 3, 47506, Neukirchen-Vluyn, Germany
Tel.: (49) 28452950170
Web Site: http://www.hsr-hydraulics.com
Industrial Machinery Mfr
N.A.I.C.S.: 333248

Subsidiary (Non-US):

HSR Italia S.r.l. (3)
Via la Rizza 10, 37135, Verona, Italy
Tel.: (39) 045500652
Mechanical Parts Mfr.
N.A.I.C.S.: 333517
Matteo Rosamilia *(Mgr-Div)*

Subsidiary (Domestic):

Hahn + Kolb Werkzeuge GmbH (3)
Borsigstrasse 50, D-70469, Stuttgart, Germany
Tel.: (49) 71198130
Web Site: http://www.hahn-kolb.de
Sales Range: $150-199.9 Million
Emp.: 680
Tools & Machinery Distr
N.A.I.C.S.: 423710
Katrin Hummel *(Mng Dir)*

Subsidiary (Non-US):

HAHN + KOLB POLSKA Sp. z o.o. (4)
Wichrowa 4, 60-449, Poznan, Poland
Tel.: (48) 618498700
Web Site: http://www.hahn-kolb.pl
Electronic Tool Retailer
N.A.I.C.S.: 444140
Andrzej Samul *(Reg Sls Mgr)*

HAHN + KOLB ROMANIA SRL (4)
Drumul Garii Street Otopeni No 25-35, Ilfov, Bucharest, Romania
Tel.: (40) 213000757
Web Site: http://www.hahn-kolb.ro
Electronic Tool Retailer
N.A.I.C.S.: 444140
George Marin *(Mgr-Sls)*

HAHN+KOLB Mexico, S. de R.L de CV. (4)
Calle Alejandra No 7B Col Alvaro Obregon, Santiago Momoxpan San Pedro Cholula, 72760, Puebla, Mexico
Tel.: (52) 2222249310
Web Site: http://www.hahn-kolb.mx
Electronic Tool Retailer
N.A.I.C.S.: 444140

HAHN+KOLB Tools Pvt. Ltd. (4)
Plot T - 134 General Block M I D C, Bhosari, Pune, 411 026, Maharashtra, India
Tel.: (91) 2027120631
Web Site: http://www.hahn-kolb.in
Mechanical Parts Mfr
N.A.I.C.S.: 333517
Katrin Hummel *(Mng Dir)*

Hahn + Kolb (Guangzhou) Tools Co., Ltd. (4)
Room 515 No 12 Keyan Road, Guangzhou Science City, Guangzhou, 5106653, China
Tel.: (86) 2032290300
Web Site: http://www.hahn-kolb.cn
Tools & Machinery Distr
N.A.I.C.S.: 423710

Hahn + Kolb (Tianjin) International Trade Co., Ltd. (4)
No 391 Zhonghuanxi Road, Airport Economic Area, Tianjin, 300308, China
Tel.: (86) 2258631700
Web Site: http://www.hahn-kolb.cn
Emp.: 80
Tools & Machinery Distr
N.A.I.C.S.: 423710

Hahn + Kolb Hungaria Kft. (4)
Budafoki ut 60 A1-es lepcsohaz, 1117, Budapest, Hungary
Tel.: (36) 13712900
Web Site: http://www.hahn-kolb.hu
Emp.: 15
Tools & Machinery Distr
N.A.I.C.S.: 423710

Hahn + Kolb Soveco S.A.R.L. (4)
CA la Vigne aux Loups - Bat A 1 route de Longjumeau, 91385, Chilly-Mazarin, Cedex, France
Tel.: (33) 169194390
Web Site: http://www.hahn-kolb.fr
Tools & Machinery Distr
N.A.I.C.S.: 423710

Hahn + Kolb d.o.o. (4)
Pancevacki put 36v, Krnjaca, 11210, Belgrade, Serbia
Tel.: (381) 116557783
Web Site: http://www.hahn-kolb.rs
Tool & Machinery Distr
N.A.I.C.S.: 423710

Hahn Kolb Endustri Urunleri Tic. Ltd. Sti (4)
Muratcesme Mahallesi Eski Silivri Caddesi No 46 Mimarsinan, Buyukcekmece, Istanbul, Turkiye
Tel.: (90) 2128615585
Web Site: http://www.hahn-kolb.com.tr
Machining Tool Mfr
N.A.I.C.S.: 333517

Hahn i Kolb Instrumenti EOOD (4)
Okolovrasten pat 255, 1186, Sofia, Bulgaria
Tel.: (359) 24899050
Automotive Services
N.A.I.C.S.: 811111

OOO Hahn + Kolb (4)
Business-Park Rumyantsevo korpus A podyezd 8 office 612A, Rumyantsevo, 142784, Moscow, Russia
Tel.: (7) 4955181410
Web Site: http://www.hahn-kolb.ru
Tools Whslr
N.A.I.C.S.: 423710

Subsidiary (Domestic):

Hommel Hercules-Werkzeughandel GmbH & Co. KG (3)
Heidelberger Strasse 52, 68519, Viernheim, Germany
Tel.: (49) 62047390
Web Site: http://www.hommel-hercules.com
Emp.: 200
Tools, Machinery, Workshop Equipment & Safety Products Distr
N.A.I.C.S.: 423710
Dirk Adamczyk *(Mng Dir)*

Subsidiary (Non-US):

HHW Hommel Hercules PL Sp. z o.o. (4)
Ul Rozdzienskiego 188a, 40-203, Katowice, Poland
Tel.: (48) 322054110
Web Site: http://www.hhw.pl
Electronic Tool Retailer
N.A.I.C.S.: 444140

HHW-Hommel Hercules Werkzeughandel CZ/SK s.r.o. (4)
Novodvorska 803/82, 142 00, Prague, Czech Republic
Tel.: (420) 261711011
Web Site: http://www.hhw.cz
Electronic Tool Retailer
N.A.I.C.S.: 444140

Hommel & Seitz GmbH (4)
Eduard Kittenbergergasse 56 Obj 8, 1230, Vienna, Austria
Tel.: (43) 186548280
Web Site: http://www.hommel-seitz.at
Electrical & Electronic Mfr
N.A.I.C.S.: 335999

Hommel Hercules France, s.r.o. (4)
Pribylinska 2, 831 04, Bratislava, Slovakia
Tel.: (421) 24 488 4881
Web Site: http://www.hommel.sk
Hardware Whslr
N.A.I.C.S.: 423710

Subsidiary (Domestic):

IMS-Verbindungstechnik GmbH & Co. KG (3)
Robert-Bosch-Strasse 5, 74632, Neuenstein, Germany
Tel.: (49) 794291310
Web Site: http://www.ims-verbindungstechnik.com
Emp.: 40
Metal & Plastic Fasteners Distr
N.A.I.C.S.: 423710
Oliver Ganssler *(Gen Mgr)*

Subsidiary (Non-US):

IQD Frequency Products Limited (3)
Station Road, Crewkerne, Somerset, TA18 8AR, United Kingdom
Tel.: (44) 1460270200
Web Site: http://www.iqdfrequencyproducts.com
Frequency Product Mfr
N.A.I.C.S.: 334419

IQD Group Limited (3)
Station Road, Crewkerne, TA18 8AR, Somerset, United Kingdom
Tel.: (44) 1460270200
Electrical & Electronic Mfr
N.A.I.C.S.: 335999

IQD Holdings Limited (3)
Station Road, Crewkerne, Somerset, TA18 8AR, United Kingdom
Tel.: (44) 1460270200
Frequency Product Mfr
N.A.I.C.S.: 334515

Subsidiary (Domestic):

IVT Installations- und Verbindungstechnik GmbH & Co. KG (3)
Gewerbering Nord 5, 91189, Rohr, Germany
Tel.: (49) 9876978697
Web Site: http://www.ivt-group.com
Emp.: 100
Plumbing & Heating Products Mfr & Distr
N.A.I.C.S.: 326122

WURTH VERWALTUNGSGESELLSCHAFT MBH

Wurth Verwaltungsgesellschaft mbH—(Continued)

Indunorm Hydraulik GmbH (3)
Keniastrasse 12, Duisburg, 47269, Germany
Tel.: (49) 20373830
Web Site: http://www.indunorm.de
Emp.: 200
High-Pressure Equipment & Components Distr & Maintenance Services
N.A.I.C.S.: 423830
Klaus Ochel (Mng Dir)

Division (Domestic):

HSR GmbH (4)
Paul-Rucker-Strasse 20-22, 47059, Duisburg, Germany
Tel.: (49) 2037135111
Web Site: http://www.hsr-hydraulics.com
High-Pressure Hoses & Fittings Whslr
N.A.I.C.S.: 423830
Klaus Ochel (Mng Dir)

Subsidiary (Non-US):

Inox Ege Metal Urunleri Dis Ticaret Limited Sirketi (3)
6 Cadde No 4, Mermerciler Sanayi Sitesi Beylikduzu, 34520, Istanbul, Turkiye
Tel.: (90) 2122220919
Web Site: http://www.inoxege.com.tr
Assembly & Fastener Product Mfr
N.A.I.C.S.: 332722

Inox Mare S.r.l. (3)
Via Pomposa 51/l, 47924, Rimini, Italy
Tel.: (39) 0541794444
Web Site: http://www.inoxmare.com
Emp.: 80
Hardware Whslr
N.A.I.C.S.: 423710

Inox Tirrenica S.r.l. (3)
via Monte Solarolo 115 Fiumicino Isola Sacra, 00054, Fiumicino, RM, Italy
Tel.: (39) 0665191201
Web Site: http://www.inoxtirrenica.it
Stainless Steel Distr
N.A.I.C.S.: 423510

Subsidiary (Domestic):

Internationales Bankhaus Bodensee AG (3)
Otto-Lilienthal-Str 8, 88046, Friedrichshafen, Germany
Tel.: (49) 75413040
Web Site: http://www.ibb-ag.com
Financial Banking Services
N.A.I.C.S.: 522110
Nina Schmid (Acct Mgr)

Subsidiary (Non-US):

KBlue s.r.l. (3)
via Pra Bordoni 12, Zane, 36010, Vicenza, Italy
Tel.: (39) 0445315055
Web Site: http://www.kblue.eu
Electrical & Electronic Mfr
N.A.I.C.S.: 336320
Carlo Foletto (Area Mgr)

KMT Kunststoff- und Metallteile AG (3)
Zurichstrasse 70, 8340, Hinwil, Switzerland
Tel.: (41) 449385959
Web Site: http://www.kmt.ch
Metalware Mfr
N.A.I.C.S.: 332312

Kisling AG (3)
Motorenstrasse 102, 8620, Wetzikon, Switzerland
Tel.: (41) 582720101
Web Site: http://www.kisling.ch
Adhesive & Sealant Mfr & Distr
N.A.I.C.S.: 325520
Thomas Plantenberg (Mng Dir)

Subsidiary (Non-US):

Kisling Deutschland GmbH (4)
Burgermeister-Seidl-Strasse 2, 82515, Wolfratshausen, Germany
Tel.: (49) 81719998230
Web Site: http://www.kisling.com
Emp.: 6
Adhesive & Sealant Distr
N.A.I.C.S.: 424690

Heiko Haupt (CEO)

Subsidiary (Non-US):

Lagerhaus Landquart AG (3)
Muhlestrasse 9, 7302, Landquart, Switzerland
Tel.: (41) 813006131
Web Site: http://www.lagerhaus-landquart.ch
Logistics Warehouse Services
N.A.I.C.S.: 541614

Subsidiary (Domestic):

Licht Zentrale Lichtgrosshandel GmbH (3)
Rettistrasse 5, 91522, Ansbach, Germany
Tel.: (49) 9818903333
Web Site: http://www.lichtzentrale.de
Emp.: 220
Lighting Equipment & Supplies Whslr
N.A.I.C.S.: 423610

Liqui - Moly Gesellschaft mit beschrdnkter Haftung (3)
Jerg-Wieland-Str 4, 89081, Ulm, Germany
Tel.: (49) 73114200
Web Site: http://www.liqui-moly.com
Emp.: 800
Chemical Products Distr
N.A.I.C.S.: 424690

Subsidiary (Non-US):

Liqui Moly South Africa (Pty) Ltd. (3)
Unit 3 86 Tsessebe Crescent, Corporate Park South Old Pretoria Main Midrand, Johannesburg, 1685, South Africa
Tel.: (27) 110265515
Web Site: http://www.liqui-moly.co.za
Automotive Chemical Distr
N.A.I.C.S.: 424690
Theuns Labuschagne (Mgr-Warhouse)

Liqui-Moly Iberia, Unipessoal, Lda (3)
Sintra Business Park Building 01-1 P, 2710-089, Sintra, Portugal
Tel.: (351) 219250732
Lubricant Oil Mfr
N.A.I.C.S.: 324191

MEF S.R.L. (3)
Via Panciatichi 68, 50127, Florence, Italy
Tel.: (39) 055436210
Web Site: http://www.mefsrl.com
Mechanical Parts Mfr
N.A.I.C.S.: 333517
Louie Del Bianco (Mgr-IT & Fin)

Subsidiary (Domestic):

MKT Metall-Kunststoff-Technik GmbH & Co KG (3)
Auf dem Immel 2, 67685, Weilerbach, Germany
Tel.: (49) 637491160
Web Site: http://www.mkt.de
Anchor System Mfr
N.A.I.C.S.: 332722
Timothy Stevens (Project Mgr-ERP)

Marbet Marion & Bettina Wurth GmbH & Co. KG (3)
Karl-Kurz-Strasse 44, 74523, Schwabisch Hall, Germany
Tel.: (49) 79149380100
Web Site: http://www.marbet.com
Event & Travel Services
N.A.I.C.S.: 561920
Rodny Klaiss (Dir-Bus Dev)

Subsidiary (Non-US):

Masidef S.r.l. (3)
Via Guglielmo Oberdan 125, 21042, Caronno Pertusella, VA, Italy
Tel.: (39) 029651011
Web Site: http://www.masidef.com
Fastening Product Mfr & Distr
N.A.I.C.S.: 332722

Subsidiary (Domestic):

Meguin GmbH & Co. KG Mineraloelwerke (3)
Rodener Str 25, 66740, Saarlouis, Germany
Tel.: (49) 683189090
Web Site: http://www.meguin.de
Oil Product Distr
N.A.I.C.S.: 424720

Subsidiary (Non-US):

Meister Tools Trading (Shanghai) Co., Ltd. (3)
Room 202 Yuwell Building No 683 Shenhong Road, Minghang District, Shanghai, 201106, China
Tel.: (86) 2158965322
Industrial Tools Distr
N.A.I.C.S.: 423830

Subsidiary (Domestic):

Meister Werkzeuge GmbH (3)
Oberkamper Strasse 37-39, D-42349, Wuppertal, Germany
Tel.: (49) 202247500
Web Site: http://www.meister-werkzeuge.de
Emp.: 400
Power-Driven Handtools Mfr & Distr
N.A.I.C.S.: 333991

Subsidiary (Non-US):

Meister France S.A.S. (4)
Rue de la Durance 3, 67100, Strasbourg, France
Tel.: (33) 390404790
Web Site: http://www.meister-france.fr
Sales Range: $10-24.9 Million
Emp.: 2
Hand-Held Power Tools Mfr & Distr
N.A.I.C.S.: 333991

Subsidiary (Domestic):

Metzler GmbH (3)
Im Besterwasen 34, 72768, Reutlingen, Germany
Tel.: (49) 71213179114
Web Site: http://www.metzlergmbh.de
Doorbell Mfr
N.A.I.C.S.: 332812

Subsidiary (Non-US):

Metzler GmbH & Co. KG (3)
Interpark Focus 40, Rothis, 6832, Feldkirch, Austria
Tel.: (43) 552390909
Web Site: http://www.metzler.at
Electronic Tool Retailer
N.A.I.C.S.: 444140

Subsidiary (Domestic):

Momper Auto-Chemie GmbH (3)
Wiesentalstrasse 4, 89269, Vohringen, Germany
Tel.: (49) 800 443 3003
Web Site: https://www.momper-auto-chemie.de
Automobile Parts Distr
N.A.I.C.S.: 441330

Subsidiary (Non-US):

Optima Versicherungsbroker AG (3)
Ratusstrasse 22, Postfach 423, 7007, Chur, Switzerland
Tel.: (41) 812587000
Web Site: http://www.optima.swiss
Insurance Services
N.A.I.C.S.: 524210

PT. Tunap Indonesia (3)
Building 3rd Floor Suite 3B Jl Raden Saleh No 13-17, Jakarta Pusat, Indonesia
Tel.: (62) 2129578181
Automobile Mfr
N.A.I.C.S.: 336110
Ekawiyanti Widjaja (Mgr-Fin & GA)

Subsidiary (Domestic):

Panorama Hotel- und Service GmbH (3)
Hauptstrasse 86, 74638, Waldenburg, Germany
Tel.: (49) 794291000
Web Site: http://www.panoramahotel-waldenburg.de
Holding Company; Hotel & Restaurant Operator; Caterer
N.A.I.C.S.: 551112

Unit (Domestic):

Altes Amtshaus (4)
Am Marktplatz 1, Lindlar, 51789, Cologne, Germany

INTERNATIONAL PUBLIC

Tel.: (49) 2266464646
Web Site: http://www.amtshauslindlar.de
Emp.: 16
Hotel & Restaurant Operator
N.A.I.C.S.: 721110

Panorama Catering (4)
Kur 29, 74653, Kunzelsau, Germany
Tel.: (49) 79409307820
Web Site: http://www.panorama-catering.de
Emp.: 170
Catering Services
N.A.I.C.S.: 722320

Panoramahotel Waldenburg (4)
Hauptstrasse 84, 74638, Waldenburg, Germany
Tel.: (49) 794291000
Web Site: http://www.panoramahotel-waldenburg.de
Emp.: 40
Hotel & Restaurant Operator
N.A.I.C.S.: 721110

Sudhaus an der Kunsthalle Wurth (4)
Lange Strasse 35-1, 74523, Schwabisch Hall, Germany
Tel.: (49) 7919467270
Web Site: http://www.sudhaus-sha.de
Emp.: 26
Hotel & Restaurant Operator
N.A.I.C.S.: 721110

Wald & SchlossHotel Friedrichsruhe (4)
Karcherstrasse 11, Zweiflingen-Friedrichsruhe, 74639, Berlin, Germany
Tel.: (49) 794160870
Web Site: http://www.schlosshotel-friedrichsruhe.de
Hotel, Spa & Resort
N.A.I.C.S.: 721110

Subsidiary (Domestic):

RECA Verwaltungsgesellschaft GmbH (3)
Am Wasserturm 4, 74635, Kupferzell, Germany
Tel.: (49) 7944610
Web Site: http://www.recanorm.de
Sales Range: $550-599.9 Million
Emp.: 3,400
Holding Company; Craft, Automotive, Cargo & Specialist Product Distribution Services
N.A.I.C.S.: 551111
Ulrich Hafele (Gen Mgr)

Subsidiary (Domestic):

Baier & Michels GmbH & Co. KG (4)
Carl-Schneider-Strasse 1, 64372, Ober-Ramstadt, Germany
Tel.: (49) 615469600
Web Site: http://www.baier-michels.com
Industrial & Automotive Fasteners Distr
N.A.I.C.S.: 423710

CODESI GmbH (4)
Im Lipperfeld 9, 46047, Oberhausen, Germany
Tel.: (49) 2086070203
Corporate Logo Design & Marketing Services
N.A.I.C.S.: 541430

Normfest GmbH (4)
Siemensstrasse 23, 42551, Velbert, Germany
Tel.: (49) 20512750
Web Site: http://www.normfest.de
Sales Range: $75-99.9 Million
Emp.: 500
Automotive Repair Industry Tools & Supplies Distr
N.A.I.C.S.: 423840
Enver Zolj (Mng Dir-Sls)

Unit (Domestic):

Normfest GmbH - Dress & Safe (5)
Im Lipperfeld 9, 46047, Oberhausen, Germany
Tel.: (49) 20860700
Web Site: http://www.dress-safe.de
Automotive Repair Industry Safety Apparel & Gear Distr
N.A.I.C.S.: 424350

AND PRIVATE COMPANIES — WURTH VERWALTUNGSGESELLSCHAFT MBH

Subsidiary (Non-US):

Normfest Polska Sp. z o.o. **(5)**
ul Wichrowa 4/10, 60-449, Poznan, Poland
Tel.: (48) 618439140
Web Site: http://www.normfest.pl
Automobile Product Distr
N.A.I.C.S.: 423120

Normfest, s.r.o. **(5)**
Pekarska 12, 155 00, Prague, Czech Republic
Tel.: (420) 257013280
Automotive Services
N.A.I.C.S.: 811111

Group (Domestic):

RECA NORM GmbH & Co. KG **(4)**
Am Wasserturm 4, 74635, Kupferzell, Germany
Tel.: (49) 7944610
Web Site: http://www.recanorm.de
Sales Range: $150-199.9 Million
Emp.: 730
Craft Industry Tools, Hardware, Equipment & Supplies Distr
N.A.I.C.S.: 423710
Thomas Hausele (Mng Dir)

Subsidiary (Non-US):

Kellner & Kunz AG **(5)**
Boschstrasse 37, 4600, Wels, Austria
Tel.: (43) 72424840
Web Site: http://www.reca.co.at
Sales Range: $125-149.9 Million
Emp.: 1,340
Craft Industry Tools, Hardware, Equipment & Supplies Distr
N.A.I.C.S.: 423710
Ernst Wiesinger (Mng Dir)

Subsidiary (Non-US):

reca Bulgaria E.O.O.D. **(6)**
Dobri Voinikov Str 4, Gemeinde Losenetz, Sofia, 1164, Bulgaria
Tel.: (359) 29632295
Web Site: http://www.reca.bg
Emp.: 9
Craft Industry Tools, Hardware, Equipment & Supplies Distr
N.A.I.C.S.: 423710

reca Kft. **(6)**
Kondorfa u 10, 1116, Budapest, Hungary
Tel.: (36) 14330380
Web Site: http://www.reca.hu
Emp.: 50
Craft Industry Tools, Hardware, Equipment & Supplies Distr
N.A.I.C.S.: 423710
Bogar Akos (Mgr)

reca Polska Spolka z o.o. **(6)**
ul Warszawska 67, 32-086, Krakow, Poland
Tel.: (48) 126563073
Web Site: http://www.reca.pl
Craft Industry Tools, Hardware, Equipment & Supplies Distr
N.A.I.C.S.: 423710

reca Slovensko s.r.o. **(6)**
Vajnorska 134/B, 831 04, Bratislava, Slovakia
Tel.: (421) 244455916
Web Site: http://www.reca.sk
Emp.: 60
Craft Industry Tools, Hardware, Equipment & Supplies Distr
N.A.I.C.S.: 423710

reca d.o.o. **(6)**
Kucanska 23, 42000, Varazdin, Croatia
Tel.: (385) 42350813
Web Site: http://www.reca.hr
Craft Industry Tools, Hardware, Equipment & Supplies Distr
N.A.I.C.S.: 423710

reca d.o.o. **(6)**
Kralsevica Marka Ulica 5, 2000, Maribor, Slovenia
Tel.: (386) 22501145
Web Site: http://www.reca.si
Emp.: 10
Craft Industry Tools, Hardware, Equipment & Supplies Distr
N.A.I.C.S.: 423710

reca d.o.o., Beograd **(6)**
Bulevar Mihajla Pupina 10z br 15, Novi Beograd, 11070, Serbia
Tel.: (381) 113114426
Web Site: http://www.reca.rs
Emp.: 30
Craft Industry Tools, Hardware, Equipment & Supplies Distr
N.A.I.C.S.: 423710
Vladimir Ilic (Dir)

reca d.o.o., Sarajevo **(6)**
Hifzi Bjelevca 11A, Ilidza, 71210, Sarajevo, Bosnia & Herzegovina
Tel.: (387) 33777720
Web Site: http://www.reca.ba
Emp.: 10
Craft Industry Tools, Hardware, Equipment & Supplies Distr
N.A.I.C.S.: 423710

Subsidiary (Non-US):

Reca Bucuresti S.R.L. **(5)**
Str Costache Sibiceanu nr 15 et 2 sect 1, 011511, Bucharest, Romania
Tel.: (40) 212242275
Web Site: http://www.reca.ro
Fastening Material Mfr
N.A.I.C.S.: 332722

Reca France SAS **(5)**
5 rue Edouard Branly, 67116, Reichstett, France
Tel.: (33) 390203550
Web Site: http://www.fr.reca.com
Consumer Products Distr
N.A.I.C.S.: 423990

Reca-UK Ltd. **(5)**
Doranda Way, West Bromwich, B71 4LU, W Midlands, United Kingdom
Tel.: (44) 121 525 0525
Web Site: http://www.reca-uk.com
Fastener Whslr
N.A.I.C.S.: 423710

Subsidiary (Domestic):

Siller & Laar Schrauben- Werkzeug- und Beschlage- Handel GmbH & Co. KG
Alter Postweg 96, 86159, Augsburg, Germany
Tel.: (49) 821257900
Web Site: http://www.sillerundlaar.de
General Hardware Product Distr
N.A.I.C.S.: 423710

Subsidiary (Non-US):

reca (Shanghai) International Trading Co., Ltd. **(5)**
Bldg No 10 555 Yin Du Road, Min Hang District, Shanghai, 201108, China
Tel.: (86) 2154407566
Web Site: http://www.reca.com.cn
Craft Industry Tools, Hardware, Equipment & Supplies Distr
N.A.I.C.S.: 423710

reca AG **(5)**
Stationsstrasse 48d, Samstagern, 8833, Horgen, Switzerland
Tel.: (41) 447457575
Web Site: http://www.ch.reca.com
Craft Industry Tools, Hardware, Equipment & Supplies Distr
N.A.I.C.S.: 423710

reca Belux S.A./N.V. **(5)**
Assesteenweg 117 - 3, 1740, Ternat, Belgium
Tel.: (32) 23630780
Web Site: http://www.be.reca.com
Sales Range: $1-9.9 Million
Emp.: 40
Craft Industry Tools, Hardware, Equipment & Supplies Distr
N.A.I.C.S.: 423710

reca Hispania, S.A.U. **(5)**
Avda Ovidi Montllor No 7, Aldaya, 46960, Valencia, Spain
Tel.: (34) 961519460
Web Site: http://www.recahispania.es
Craft Industry Tools, Hardware, Equipment & Supplies Distr
N.A.I.C.S.: 423710

reca Union France Sarl **(5)**
5 rue Edouard Branly, 67116, Reichstett, France
Tel.: (33) 3 9020 3550
Web Site: http://fr.reca.com
Craft Industry Tools, Hardware, Equipment & Supplies Distr
N.A.I.C.S.: 423710

reca spol. s r.o. **(5)**
Olomoucka 36, 618 00, Brno, Czech Republic
Tel.: (420) 548210881
Web Site: http://www.reca.cz
Automotive Services
N.A.I.C.S.: 811111
Jiri Hurtik (Reg Mgr)

Subsidiary (Non-US):

REISSER Csavar Kft **(3)**
Railway Station Hrsz 018, Szar, 2066, Zirc, Hungary
Tel.: (36) 22591220
Web Site: http://www.reisser.hu
Fastening Product Mfr
N.A.I.C.S.: 332722

Subsidiary (Domestic):

REISSER Schraubentechnik GmbH **(3)**
Fritz-Muller-Strasse 10, 74653, Ingelfingen, Germany
Tel.: (49) 79401270
Web Site: http://www.reisser-screws.com
Emp.: 342
Metal Screw Mfr & Whslr
N.A.I.C.S.: 332510
Michael Dartsch (Mng Dir)

Division (Domestic):

KERONA GmbH **(4)**
Zeilbaumweg 15, 74613, Ohringen, Germany
Tel.: (49) 794192054080
Web Site: http://www.kerona.de
Emp.: 6
Protective Surface Coating Mfr
N.A.I.C.S.: 325510

Subsidiary (Non-US):

Reinhold Handels AG **(3)**
Aspermontstrasse 1, 7000, Chur, Switzerland
Tel.: (41) 815580900
Web Site: http://www.reinhold-handelsag.com
Clothing & Protective Equipment Mfr
N.A.I.C.S.: 339113
Pius Giger (Mng Dir)

Subsidiary (Domestic):

Reinhold Wurth Musikstiftung gemeinnijtzige GmbH **(3)**
Reinhold-Wurth-Strasse 12-17, 74653, Kunzelsau, Germany
Tel.: (49) 7940153806
Web Site: http://www.wuerth-philharmoniker.de
Event Organizing Services
N.A.I.C.S.: 561920

Subsidiary (Non-US):

Reisser Tehnic S.R.L. **(3)**
Calea Baciului Nr 1, Cluj-Napoca, Romania
Tel.: (40) 264406890
Web Site: http://www.reisser.ro
Tool Product Mfr
N.A.I.C.S.: 333515

S.C. Wurth Industrie S.r.l. **(3)**
Str Costache Sibiceanu 15, 011511, Bucharest, Romania
Tel.: (40) 743010507
Industrial Equipment Mfr
N.A.I.C.S.: 333248

SCAR S.r.l. **(3)**
Via Caduti Sul Lavoro 25, 37012, Bussolengo, VR, Italy
Tel.: (39) 0456768311
Web Site: http://www.scar.it
Consumer Products Distr
N.A.I.C.S.: 423990
Silvano Brignone (Dir-Sls)

Subsidiary (Domestic):

SCREXS GmbH **(3)**
Am Bahnhof 50, 74638, Waldenburg, Germany
Tel.: (49) 7942100933
Web Site: http://www.screxs.de
Fastener Mfr
N.A.I.C.S.: 332722

Subsidiary (Non-US):

SIA Baltjas Elektro Sabiedriba **(3)**
Krustpils iela 38a, Riga, LV-1057, Latvia
Tel.: (371) 67100125
Web Site: http://www.baltikelektro.lv
Automobile Parts Distr
N.A.I.C.S.: 423120
Kaspars Pridans (Mgr-Corp Client)

SIA Wurth **(3)**
Lubanas iela 143, Riga, LV-1021, Latvia
Tel.: (371) 67788996
Web Site: http://wurth.lv
Fastener Product Mfr
N.A.I.C.S.: 332722
Kristaps Gribusts (Dir-Sls)

Subsidiary (Domestic):

SVH Handels-GmbH **(3)**
Unterste-Wilms-Str 53, 44143, Dortmund, Germany
Tel.: (49) 23133681000
Web Site: http://www.svh24.de
Internet Services
N.A.I.C.S.: 517810

Subsidiary (Non-US):

SWG France SARL **(3)**
1 Avenue Saint-Remy Espace Pierrard, 57600, Forbach, France
Tel.: (33) 387133516
Fastening Product Mfr & Distr
N.A.I.C.S.: 332722

SWG SCREWS Iberia S.L.U. **(3)**
Avda de Sant Julia 1, 08400, Granollers, Barcelona, Spain
Tel.: (34) 9354714677110
Tool Product Mfr
N.A.I.C.S.: 333515

Subsidiary (Domestic):

SWG Schraubenwerk Gaisbach GmbH **(3)**
Am Bahnhof 50, 74638, Waldenburg, Germany
Tel.: (49) 79421000
Web Site: http://www.swg.de
Emp.: 400
Fastening Product Mfr & Distr
N.A.I.C.S.: 332722

Subsidiary (Non-US):

Schmid Schrauben Hainfeld GmbH **(3)**
Landstal 10, Hainfeld, 3170, Saint Polten, Austria
Tel.: (43) 27642652
Web Site: http://www.schmid-screw.com
Screw Mfr
N.A.I.C.S.: 332722
Alois Kargl (Mgr-Sls-Eastern Austria, Switzerland & Italy)

Subsidiary (Domestic):

Schossmetall GmbH & Co. KG **(3)**
Pommernstrasse 14, D-83395, Freilassing, Germany
Tel.: (49) 865463010
Web Site: http://www.schoessmetall.de
Emp.: 30
Door & Window Fittings, Railing Systems & Other Decorative Hardware Whslr
N.A.I.C.S.: 423710

Sonderschrauben Guldner GmbH & Co. KG **(3)**
Hohe Buche 13, 97996, Niederstetten, Germany
Tel.: (49) 793291550
Web Site: http://www.gueldner.com
Sales Range: $10-24.9 Million
Emp.: 55
Bolts, Screws & Fasteners Mfr & Whslr
N.A.I.C.S.: 332722

WURTH VERWALTUNGSGESELLSCHAFT MBH

Wurth Verwaltungsgesellschaft mbH—(Continued)

Markus Beckert *(Mng Dir)*

Sonderschrauben Hamburg GmbH Eiben & Co. (3)
Hohe Buche 13, 97996, Niederstetten, Germany
Tel.: (49) 793291550
Web Site: http://www.gueldner.com
Screw Mfr
N.A.I.C.S.: 332722

Subsidiary (Non-US):

Steenkist RECA Nederland B.V. (3)
Hurksestraat 1a, 5652 AH, Eindhoven, Netherlands
Tel.: (31) 402507373
Web Site: http://www.steenkist.nl
Fastening Material Mfr
N.A.I.C.S.: 332722

Subsidiary (Domestic):

Swiridoff Verlag GmbH & Co. KG (3)
Goethestrasse 14, 74653, Kunzelsau, Germany
Tel.: (49) 7940151762
Web Site: http://www.swiridoff-verlag.de
Emp.: 3
Book & Catalog Publisher
N.A.I.C.S.: 513130

TOGE Dübel GmbH & Co. KG (3)
Illesheimer Strasse 10, 90431, Nuremberg, Germany
Tel.: (49) 911659680
Web Site: http://www.toge.de
Industrial Equipment Mfr
N.A.I.C.S.: 333248

Subsidiary (Non-US):

TUNAP AG (3)
Weinfelder Strasse 19, Marstetten, Weinfelden, Switzerland
Tel.: (41) 716590404
Automotive Chemical Whslr
N.A.I.C.S.: 424690

Subsidiary (Domestic):

TUNAP GmbH & Co. KG (3)
Burgermeister-Seidl-Strasse 2, 82515, Wolfratshausen, Germany
Tel.: (49) 81711600704
Chemical Products Distr
N.A.I.C.S.: 424690

Subsidiary (Non-US):

TUNAP Polska Sp. z o.o. (3)
Ul Jozefa Poniatowskiego 51, 05-220, Zielonka, Poland
Tel.: (48) 228125034
Web Site: http://www.sklep.tunap.pl
Aerosol Mfr
N.A.I.C.S.: 325998

TUNAP Russia OOO (3)
Gorbunova St 12 Bldg 2 Office A315 MKAD 56 km, 121596, Moscow, Russia
Tel.: (7) 4995583238
Web Site: http://www.tunap.ru
Chemical Products Mfr
N.A.I.C.S.: 325998

Subsidiary (Domestic):

TUNAP Sports GmbH (3)
Burgermeister-Seidl-Strasse 2, 82515, Wolfratshausen, Germany
Tel.: (49) 817116008600
Chemical Products Distr
N.A.I.C.S.: 424690
Carolin Kemper Schorsten *(Mgr-Sls)*

Subsidiary (Non-US):

TUNAP do Brasil Comercio de Produtos Quimicos Ltda. (3)
Rua Verbo Divino 714, Chacara Santo Antonio, Sao Paulo, 04719-001, Brazil
Tel.: (55) 1151814343
Web Site: http://www.tunap.com.br
Automobile Mfr
N.A.I.C.S.: 336110

Subsidiary (Domestic):

Teudeloff GmbH & Co. KG (3)
Rodbachstrasse 37, 74397, Pfaffenhofen, Germany
Tel.: (49) 7046880840
Web Site: http://www.teudeloff.de
Tool Mfr & Distr
N.A.I.C.S.: 333517

Subsidiary (Non-US):

Tooling International Ltd. (3)
Unit 3 Focus Park, Ashbourne Way West Midlands, Solihull, B90 4QU, United Kingdom
Tel.: (44) 1217015900
Web Site: http://www.tooling-international.com
Fastener Mfr
N.A.I.C.S.: 332722
Amy Inman *(Office Mgr-Sls)*

Tunap (Shanghai) International Trading Co., Ltd. (3)
Building 5 No 51 Lane 1159 East Kangqiao Road, Pudong District, Shanghai, 201315, China
Tel.: (86) 2150297146
Automotive Chemical Product Distr
N.A.I.C.S.: 424690

Tunap (UK) Limited (3)
Unit L4 Deacon Trading Estate Morley Road, Tonbridge, TN9 1RA, Kent, United Kingdom
Tel.: (44) 1732365163
Web Site: http://www.tunap.co.uk
Emp.: 800
Automotive Services
N.A.I.C.S.: 811111
David Bradbury *(Mgr-Reg Sls)*

Tunap Benelux NV (3)
Oeverstraat 23, 9160, Lokeren, Belgium
Tel.: (32) 93267600
Web Site: http://www.tunap.nl
Automotive Chemical Product Distr
N.A.I.C.S.: 424690
Barbara Van Hamme *(Mgr-HR)*

Tunap Cosmetics GmbH (3)
Bahnhofstrasse 47, 6175, Kematen in Tirol, Austria
Tel.: (43) 523231310
Emp.: 75
Cosmetic Product Mfr & Distr
N.A.I.C.S.: 325620

Tunap France SAS (3)
1 rue Georges Guynemer, 67120, Altorf, France
Tel.: (33) 388686494
Web Site: http://www.tunap.fr
Automobile Parts Distr
N.A.I.C.S.: 423120

Tunap Italia S.r.l. (3)
via Enzenberg 12, Terlano, 39018, Bolzano, BZ, Italy
Tel.: (39) 0471566444
Web Site: http://www.tunap.it
Automobile Parts Mfr
N.A.I.C.S.: 336390
Davide Bigi *(Head-Market Dev)*

Tunap Kimyasal Urunler Pazarlama Ltd. Sti. (3)
Marshal Fevzi Cakmak Caddesi No 24, 34522, Istanbul, Turkiye
Tel.: (90) 2126592532
Automotive Chemical Whslr
N.A.I.C.S.: 424690
Aynur Karaca Sumer *(Mgr-Acctg & Fin)*

Tunap Norge AS (3)
Mastev 2, 1481, Hagan, Norway
Tel.: (47) 67073600
Web Site: http://www.tunap.no
Aerosol Mfr
N.A.I.C.S.: 325998

Tunap Productos Quimicos SA. (3)
P I El Coll de la Manya Cami de Can Ferran 10, 08403, Granollers, Spain
Tel.: (34) 938404825
Automotive Chemical Whslr
N.A.I.C.S.: 424690
Jesus Salazar *(CEO)*

Tunap Sverige AB (3)
Hammerbacken 10, 191 49, Sollentuna, Sweden
Tel.: (46) 8356040

Automotive Chemical Whslr
N.A.I.C.S.: 424690
Isabelle Andersson *(Mgr-Reg Sls & Mktg)*

Tunap chemisch-technische Produkte Produktions-und Handelsgesellschaft m.b.H. (3)
Kolpingstrasse 19, 1230, Vienna, Austria
Tel.: (43) 158642240
Web Site: http://www.tunap.es
Automotive Chemical Product Distr
N.A.I.C.S.: 424690

UAB Elektrobalt (3)
Liepkalnio g 85A, 02120, Vilnius, Lithuania
Tel.: (370) 52660091
Web Site: http://www.elektrobalt.lt
Electrical Equipment Whslr
N.A.I.C.S.: 423610
Zilvinas Cesna *(Head-Sls)*

Subsidiary (Domestic):

UNI ELEKTRO Fachgrosshandel GmbH & Co. KG (3)
Ludwig-Erhard-Strasse 21-39, 65760, Eschborn, Germany
Tel.: (49) 61964770
Web Site: http://www.unielektro.de
Electrical Components Whslr
N.A.I.C.S.: 423610

Subsidiary (Non-US):

Unifix SWG S.r.l. (3)
Via Enzenberg 2, Terlano, 39018, Bolzano, Italy
Tel.: (39) 0471545200
Web Site: http://www.unifix.it
Fastening Product Mfr & Distr
N.A.I.C.S.: 332722

Van Roij Fasteners Europe B.V. (3)
Jan Tooropstraat 16, 5753 DK, Deurne, Netherlands
Tel.: (31) 493315885
Web Site: http://www.eurofast.nl
Fastening Product Mfr & Distr
N.A.I.C.S.: 332722

Van Roij Fasteners Hungary Kft. (3)
Jedlik Anyos Ut 18/C, Industrial Area, 2330, Dunaharaszti, Hungary
Tel.: (36) 24531000
Fastening Product Mfr & Distr
N.A.I.C.S.: 332722

Vu Viet Co. Ltd. (3)
236/31 Dien Bien Phu Str, 12 Ward Binh Thanh District, Ho Chi Minh City, Vietnam
Tel.: (84) 88409291
Assembly Materials & Fastening Hardware Distr
N.A.I.C.S.: 423710

W.EG Eesti OU (3)
Foundry 5, Tallinn, 11415, Estonia
Tel.: (372) 6711900
Web Site: http://www.weg.ee
Automobile Parts Distr
N.A.I.C.S.: 423120
Timo Raimla *(CEO)*

W.EG Italia S.r.l. (3)
Via Panciatichi 68, 50127, Florence, Italy
Tel.: (39) 055 436 2275
Information Technology Support Services
N.A.I.C.S.: 541519

W.EG Polska Sp. z o.o. (3)
Ul Jana Czochralskiego 11, 61-248, Poznan, Poland
Tel.: (48) 616464400
Web Site: http://www.wegpolska.pl
Electrical Equipment Whslr
N.A.I.C.S.: 423610
Joanna Rucinska-Paulik *(Mgr-HR)*

WASI d.o.o. (3)
Beogradska 27, 11272, Belgrade, Serbia
Tel.: (381) 1112078281
Web Site: http://www.wasi.rs
Assembly & Fastener Product Mfr
N.A.I.C.S.: 332722
Sasa Marinkovic *(Mng Dir)*

WASI d.o.o. (3)
Franje Lucica 32, 10000, Zagreb, Croatia
Tel.: (385) 13455945
Web Site: http://www.wasi.hr
Nautical Product Distr

N.A.I.C.S.: 423860
Alen Pulic *(Mgr-Pur)*

Subsidiary (Domestic):

WLC Wurth-Logistik GmbH & Co. KG (3)
Lachenstrasse 37, 74740, Adelsheim, Germany
Tel.: (49) 629162260
Web Site: http://www.wlc-online.com
Freight Warehousing Transportation & Logistics Services
N.A.I.C.S.: 493110
Klaus Groninger *(Mng Dir)*

WOW! Wurth Online World GmbH (3)
Schliffenstrasse 22, 74653, Kunzelsau, Germany
Tel.: (49) 7940981880
Web Site: http://www.wow-portal.com
Automotive Diagnostic & Test Systems Mfr & Whslr
N.A.I.C.S.: 334519

WUCATO Marketplace GmbH (3)
Feuerseeplatz 14, 70176, Stuttgart, Germany
Tel.: (49) 71145997690
Web Site: http://www.wucato.de
Emp.: 30
Hardware Products Distr
N.A.I.C.S.: 423710
Goran Stanar *(Sr Mgr-Category)*

Wagener & Simon WASI GmbH & Co. KG (3)
Emil-Wagener-Strasse, 42289, Wuppertal, Germany
Tel.: (49) 20226320
Web Site: http://www.wasi.de
Stainless Steel Hardware Mfr & Distr
N.A.I.C.S.: 332510
Werner Rau *(Mng Dir)*

Subsidiary (Non-US):

WASI Bulgarien E.O.O.D. (4)
Drujba 1 Amsterdam 4, 1592, Sofia, Bulgaria
Tel.: (359) 29742028
Web Site: http://www.wasi.bg
Emp.: 10
Assembly Materials & Fastening Hardware Distr
N.A.I.C.S.: 423710

WASI Inox Denmark Aps (4)
Montagevej 6, 6000, Kolding, Denmark
Tel.: (45) 82281000
Web Site: http://www.wasi.dk
Assembly Materials & Fastening Hardware Distr
N.A.I.C.S.: 423710
Jakob Tonspert *(Gen Mgr)*

WASI Tianjin Fastener Co., Ltd. (4)
No 1 Fengze Third Avenue Balitai Industry Park, Jin Nan District, Tianjin, 300350, China
Tel.: (86) 2288829200
Web Site: http://www.wasi.com.cn
Assembly Materials & Fastening Hardware Distr
N.A.I.C.S.: 423710

Subsidiary (Domestic):

Waldenburger Versicherung AG (3)
Alfred Leikam Strasse 25, D-74523, Schwabisch Hall, Germany
Tel.: (49) 7919566990
Web Site: http://www.waldenburger.com
Property & Casualty Insurance Products & Services
N.A.I.C.S.: 524126

Walter Kluxen GmbH (3)
Helbingstrasse 64, 22047, Hamburg, Germany
Tel.: (49) 40237010
Web Site: http://www.kluxen.de
Emp.: 100
Electrical Apparatus Wiring & Supply Distr
N.A.I.C.S.: 423610

Subsidiary (Non-US):

Walter Martinez S. A. (3)
C/Turiaso 29 Plataforma Logistica Pla-za,

AND PRIVATE COMPANIES

WURTH VERWALTUNGSGESELLSCHAFT MBH

50197, Zaragoza, Spain
Tel.: (34) 976392270
Web Site: http://www.waltermartinezsa.es
Fastening Product Mfr & Distr
N.A.I.C.S.: 332722

Subsidiary (Domestic):

Werkzeugtechnik Niederstetten GmbH & Co. KG (3)
Hohe Buche 15, 97996, Niederstetten, Germany
Tel.: (49) 793291200
Web Site: http://www.wtn.de
High-Precision Steel & Carbide Tools & Components Mfr
N.A.I.C.S.: 333515
Dieter Prummer *(Acct Mgr-Technical)*

Subsidiary (Non-US):

Wuerth (Malaysia) Sdn. Bhd. (3)
Lot 806 Jalan Subang 5, Taman Perindustrian Subang, 47600, Subang Jaya, Selangor, Malaysia
Tel.: (60) 380210200
Web Site: http://www.wuerth.my
Fastener Product Distr
N.A.I.C.S.: 423710
Chamara Perera *(Mgr-Fin & HR)*

Wuerth Elektronik India Pvt. Ltd. (3)
Plot No 27 III Phase Koorgalli Indl Area Ilawala Hobli, Mysore, 570 018, India
Tel.: (91) 821240800605
Electrical & Electronic Mfr
N.A.I.C.S.: 335999
Avinash Sg *(Mgr-HR & Admin)*

Wuerth India Pvt. Ltd. (3)
703/704 Sahar Windfall Sahar Plaza Complex Andheri-Kurla Road, J B Nagar Andheri East, Mumbai, 400059, Maharashtra, India
Tel.: (91) 2267377600
Web Site: http://eshop.wuerth.in
Mechanical Parts Mfr
N.A.I.C.S.: 333517

Wuerth Kazakhstan Ltd. (3)
Raiymbek ave 169, 050050, Almaty, Kazakhstan
Tel.: (7) 7272939386
Web Site: http://www.wurth.kz
Installation & Maintenance Equipment Distr
N.A.I.C.S.: 423850
Timur Karabajak *(CEO)*

Wuerth Kenya Ltd. (3)
Mombasa Rd-Alpha Center Unit 26, PO Box 18446, 00500, Nairobi, Kenya
Tel.: (254) 724257046
Web Site: http://www.wurth.co.ke
Fastening Material Mfr
N.A.I.C.S.: 332722
John Machagua *(Mgr)*

Wuerth Philippines, Inc. (3)
Building B Panorama Compound 1 Lot 1 Block 3 Technology Ave, Laguna Technopark, Binan, Laguna, Philippines
Tel.: (63) 285844619
Web Site: http://www.wuerth.com.ph
Emp.: 100
Electronic Tool Retailer
N.A.I.C.S.: 449210
Norman Santos *(Area Mgr)*

Wurth (China) Co., Ltd. (3)
Building 5 No 51 Lane 1159 East Kangqiao Road, Pudong District, Shanghai, 201315, China
Tel.: (86) 2150297666
Web Site: http://www.wuerth.cn
Emp.: 800
Automobile Parts Distr
N.A.I.C.S.: 423120

Wurth (China) Holding Co., Ltd. (3)
Building 5 No 51 Lane 1159 East Kangqiao Road, Pudong, Shanghai, 201315, China
Tel.: (86) 2150297666
Web Site: http://www.wuerth.cn
Assembly & Fastener Product Mfr
N.A.I.C.S.: 332722
Johannes Mirecki *(Mng Dir)*

Wurth (Chongqing) Hardware & Tools Co., Ltd.
No 5 B2 floor Building 4 Yinghua tianyuan Tongyuanju Road, Nan'an District, Chongqing, China
Tel.: (86) 2368198210
Automobile Parts Distr
N.A.I.C.S.: 423120

Wurth (Guangzhou) International Trading Co., Ltd. (3)
No 3 Guangpu Xilu Guangzhou Science Park, Dongpu Tianhe District, Guangzhou, 510663, China
Tel.: (86) 2082346399
Assembly Materials & Fastening Hardware Trade Agency
N.A.I.C.S.: 425120

Wurth (Portugal) Tecnica de Montagem Lda.
Estrada Nacional 249-4 Abrunheira, 2710-089, Sintra, Portugal
Tel.: (351) 219157200
Web Site: http://www.wurth.pt
Industrial Equipment Mfr
N.A.I.C.S.: 333248

Wurth (Shanghai) Hardware & Tools Co., Ltd. (3)
No 1758 Wenchuan Road, Baoshan District, Shanghai, 201901, China
Tel.: (86) 2156808800
Web Site: http://www.wuerth.sh.cn
Emp.: 200
Assembly Materials & Fastening Hardware Distr
N.A.I.C.S.: 423710

Wurth (Shenyang) Hardware & Tool Co., Ltd. (3)
No 119-2 Jianshe Road, Dadong District, Shenyang, 110122, China
Tel.: (86) 2488790750
Industrial Equipment Mfr
N.A.I.C.S.: 333248

Wurth (Thailand) Company, Limited (3)
123/2 Ladkrabang Chalongkrung Road, Lumplatiew Ladkrabang Industrial Estate, Bangkok, 10520, Thailand
Tel.: (66) 21705000
Automobile Parts Distr
N.A.I.C.S.: 423120
Wanai Piyakulchaidej *(Mgr-Bus Dev)*

Wurth (Tianjin) International Trade Co., Ltd. (3)
No 391 West Central Road, Tianjin Airport Economic Area, Tianjin, 300309, China
Tel.: (86) 2258211328
Hardware Products Distr
N.A.I.C.S.: 423710

Wurth (Tianjin) International Trading Co., Ltd. (3)
No 391 West Central Road, Tianjin Airport Economic Area, Tianjin, 300309, China
Tel.: (86) 2258211328
Web Site: http://www.wuerth.com.cn
Assembly Materials & Fastening Hardware Trade Agency
N.A.I.C.S.: 425120

Wurth - Jordan Co., Ltd. (3)
Ibn Atabeh Al Hathali, PO Box 951, Wadi Al Seer Industrial Zone, 11592, Amman, Jordan
Tel.: (962) 65853835
Industrial Equipment Mfr
N.A.I.C.S.: 333248

Wurth AG (3)
Dornwydenweg 11, 4144, Arlesheim, Switzerland
Tel.: (41) 617059111
Web Site: http://www.wuerth-ag.ch
Emp.: 500
Holding Company; Assembly Materials & Fastening Hardware Distr
N.A.I.C.S.: 551112

Wurth AS (3)
Vana-Tartu MNT 85, Rae Vald, 75301, Harjumaa, Estonia
Tel.: (372) 6511200
Web Site: http://www.wurth.ee
Emp.: 150
Assembly Materials & Fastening Hardware Distr
N.A.I.C.S.: 423710

Subsidiary (Domestic):

Talger-Elektrotehnika Osauhing (4)
Betooni 14, EE-11415, Tallinn, Estonia
Tel.: (372) 6838800
Electrical Equipment Whslr
N.A.I.C.S.: 423610

Subsidiary (Non-US):

Wurth Albania Ltd. (3)
Rr Asim Vokshi, Pall 49/1 Ap 9, Tirana, Albania
Tel.: (355) 4247773
Assembly Materials & Fastening Hardware Distr
N.A.I.C.S.: 423710

Wurth Argentina S.A. (3)
Highway Provincial Route 6 Km101 5 Industrial Park Canuelas I, CP 1814, Buenos Aires, Canuelas, Argentina
Tel.: (54) 1152637053
Web Site: http://www.wurth.com.ar
Emp.: 250
Assembly Materials & Fastening Hardware Distr
N.A.I.C.S.: 423710

Wurth Australia Pty. Ltd. (3)
Building 5 43-63 Princes Highway, Dandenong South, 3175, VIC, Australia
Tel.: (61) 1300657765
Web Site: http://www.wurth.com.au
Holding Company; Assembly Materials & Fastening Hardware Distr
N.A.I.C.S.: 551112
Serge Oppedisano *(CEO & Mng Dir)*

Subsidiary (Domestic):

James Glen Pty. Ltd. (4)
Unit F2 Lidcombe Business Park 3-29 Birnie Avenue, Lidcombe, 2141, NSW, Australia
Tel.: (61) 297375299
Web Site: http://www.jamesglen.com.au
Fastening Hardware Distr
N.A.I.C.S.: 423710

Thomas Warburton Pty. Ltd. (4)
481 Frankston Dandenong Road, Dandenong South, 3175, VIC, Australia
Tel.: (61) 395743400
Web Site: http://www.warburtons.com.au
Emp.: 60
Assembly Material & Fastening Hardware Distr
N.A.I.C.S.: 423710

Branch (Domestic):

Wurth North Pty. Ltd. (4)
37 Motorway Circuit, Ormeau, 4208, QLD, Australia
Tel.: (61) 755499500
Assembly Materials & Fastening Hardware Distr
N.A.I.C.S.: 423710

Wurth South Pty. Ltd. (4)
2-1 Healey Rd, Dandenong, 3175, VIC, Australia
Tel.: (61) 387881152
Web Site: http://www.wurth.com.au
Emp.: 150
Assembly Materials & Fastening Hardware Distr
N.A.I.C.S.: 423710
Serge Oppedisano *(Gen Mgr)*

Wurth West Pty. Ltd. (4)
28 Mumford Place, Balcatta, 6021, WA, Australia
Tel.: (61) 892409500
Web Site: http://www.wurth.com.au
Emp.: 10
Assembly Materials & Fastening Hardware Distr
N.A.I.C.S.: 423710
Alan Baldwin *(Gen Mgr)*

Subsidiary (Domestic):

Wurth Aviation GmbH (3)
Reinhold Wurth Str 12-17, 74650, Kunzelsau, Germany
Tel.: (49) 79409815012
Airport Operator
N.A.I.C.S.: 488190

Subsidiary (Non-US):

Wurth Azerbaijan LLC (3)
U Vezirov-Str 1996, Narimanov District, 370134 , Baku, Azerbaijan
Tel.: (994) 124472524
Assembly Materials & Fastening Hardware Distr
N.A.I.C.S.: 423710

Wurth BH d.o.o. (3)
Bottles no 8, Hadzici, 71240, Sarajevo, Bosnia & Herzegovina
Tel.: (387) 33775000
Web Site: http://www.wurth.ba
Emp.: 150
Assembly Materials & Fastening Hardware Distr
N.A.I.C.S.: 423710

Wurth Baier & Michels (Shanghai) Automotive Fastener Co., Ltd. (3)
No 1969 Xizha Rd, Nanqiao Fengxian District, Shanghai, 201401, China
Tel.: (86) 2167156028
Fastening Product Mfr
N.A.I.C.S.: 332722

Wurth Baier & Michels Espana, S.A. (3)
Calle Formentera 12, Poligono Industrial Can Canals Sant Quirze del Valles, 08192, Barcelona, Spain
Tel.: (34) 61546960236
Industrial Equipment Mfr
N.A.I.C.S.: 333248

Wurth Baier & Michels Mexico SA. de C.V. (3)
Cerrada Bicentenario No 3 Bodega 4, Fraccionamiento Parque Industrial El Marques, 76246, Queretaro, Mexico
Tel.: (52) 14424469047
Automobile Parts Distr
N.A.I.C.S.: 423120

Wurth Baier Michels Otomotiv Ltd. Sti. (3)
Minarelicavus Mahallesi Celik Cad No 11/1, Nilufer, 16140, Bursa, Turkiye
Tel.: (90) 2242420424
Tool Product Mfr
N.A.I.C.S.: 333515
Umut Incir *(Mgr-Technical)*

Wurth Belgie N.V. (3)
Everdongenlaan 29, 2300, Turnhout, Belgium
Tel.: (32) 14445566
Web Site: http://www.wurth.be
Emp.: 372
Assembly Materials & Fastening Hardware Distr
N.A.I.C.S.: 423710
Serge Vranken *(CEO)*

Subsidiary (Domestic):

Wurth Industry Belux S.A. (4)
Liege Airport - Liege Logistics 8 rue de l'Aeropostale, 4460, Grace-Hollogne, Belgium
Tel.: (32) 42479611
Web Site: http://www.wurth-industry.be
Emp.: 20
Assembly Materials & Fastening Hardware Distr
N.A.I.C.S.: 423710
Cloes Jeanyves *(CEO & Mng Dir)*

Subsidiary (Non-US):

Wurth Bulgarien E.O.O.D. (3)
53 Manastirska Vodenitsa Str, German, 1186, Sofia, Bulgaria
Tel.: (359) 29659955
Web Site: http://www.wuerth.bg
Holding Company; Assembly Materials & Fastening Hardware Distr
N.A.I.C.S.: 551112

Wurth Cambodia Ltd. (3)
No 164 St 598 Phnom Penh Thmei, Sen Sok, Phnom Penh, 12101, Cambodia
Tel.: (855) 23885171
Web Site: http://www.wuerth.com.kh
Assembly Materials & Fastening Hardware Distr
N.A.I.C.S.: 423710

Wurth Canarias, S.L. (3)
C / Las Casuarinas 117 Pol In Arinaga,

WURTH VERWALTUNGSGESELLSCHAFT MBH

Wurth Verwaltungsgesellschaft mbH—(Continued)

Aguimes Gran Canaria, 35118, Las Palmas, Spain
Tel.: (34) 928188925
Web Site: http://www.wurthcanarias.es
Fastening Product Mfr & Distr
N.A.I.C.S.: 332722
Bernat Bennasar Mora *(Mng Dir)*

Wurth Caraibes Sarl (3)
ZI Cocotte Canal, 97224, Ducos, FWI, Martinique
Tel.: (596) 596560701
Web Site: http://www.wurth-caraibes.com
Emp.: 19
Assembly Materials & Fastening Hardware Distr
N.A.I.C.S.: 423710
Patrick Abel *(Dir-Publ)*

Wurth Centroamerica S.A. (3)
Costa del Este Parque Industrial, Calle 2a, Panama, Panama
Tel.: (507) 3002026
Web Site: http://www.wurth.com.pa
Emp.: 80
Assembly Materials & Fastening Hardware Distr
N.A.I.C.S.: 423710

Wurth Chile Ltda. (3)
Coronel Santiago Bueras 1345 Comuna de Padre Hurtado, Santiago, Chile
Tel.: (56) 225772100
Web Site: http://www.wurth.cl
Assembly Materials & Fastening Hardware Distr
N.A.I.C.S.: 423710

Wurth Co. Ltd.
20/2 Ashtarak Highway, Yerevan, 0088, Armenia
Tel.: (374) 10349347
Web Site: http://www.wurth.am
Assembly Material & Fastening Hardware Distr
N.A.I.C.S.: 423710
Samvel Mooradian *(CEO)*

Wurth Colombia S.A. (3)
Trv 93 No 53-48 Bodega 26 Alamos Sur, Parque Industrial El Dorado, Bogota, Colombia
Tel.: (57) 1 224 1910
Assembly Materials & Fastening Hardware Distr
N.A.I.C.S.: 423710

Wurth Construction Tools Commercial (Beijing) Co., Ltd. (3)
Room 6B12 Bldg No 2 Dacheng International Ctr No 78 Middle Rd of E 4th, Ring Chaoyang District, Beijing, 100022, China
Tel.: (86) 1059624849
Construction Tools Distr
N.A.I.C.S.: 423810

Wurth Costa Rica, S.A. (3)
Barrio Cuba Calle 24 Av 26 y 28, 10103, San Jose, Costa Rica
Tel.: (506) 44045000
Automobile Parts Distr
N.A.I.C.S.: 423120

Wurth Danmark A/S (3)
Montagevej 6 Industri N2, 6000, Kolding, Denmark
Tel.: (45) 79323232
Web Site: http://www.wuerth.dk
Holding Company; Assembly Materials & Fastening Hardware Distr
N.A.I.C.S.: 551112

Wurth Dominicana S.A. (3)
Avenida San Martin No 222-B, Ensanche Kennedy, Santo Domingo, Dominican Republic
Tel.: (809) 5627777
Web Site: http://www.wurth.com.do
Assembly Materials & Fastening Hardware Distr
N.A.I.C.S.: 423710

Division (Domestic):

Wurth Elektronik GmbH & Co. KG (3)
Salzstrasse 21, 74676, Niedernhall, Germany
Tel.: (49) 79409460
Web Site: http://www.we-online.com
Sales Range: $500-549.9 Million
Emp.: 7,300
Holding Company; Electronic Components Mfr & Distr
N.A.I.C.S.: 551112
Daniel Klein *(Mng Dir)*

Subsidiary (Non-US):

Wuerth Electronic Tianjin Co., Ltd. (4)
No 7 Haitai Development 6th Road, Huayuan Hi-Tech Industry Park, Tianjin, 300384, China
Tel.: (86) 222388666
Web Site: http://www.we-online.com
Emp.: 100
Electronic Components Distr
N.A.I.C.S.: 423690

Wurth Electronics (HK) Limited (4)
Unit 08 12/F New Tech Plaza 34 Tai Yau Street, San Po Kong, Kowloon, China (Hong Kong)
Tel.: (852) 23278488
Web Site: http://www.we-online.com
Emp.: 30
Electronic Components Distr
N.A.I.C.S.: 423690

Wurth Electronics (Shenyang) Co., Ltd. (4)
No 119-3 Jianshe Road, Shenyang-European Economic Development Zone, Shenyang, China
Tel.: (86) 2429877700
Electronic & Electromechanical Component Mfr
N.A.I.C.S.: 334419

Wurth Electronics Australia Pty. Ltd. (4)
Suite 2 and 2A 8-18 Whitehall Street, Footscray, Melbourne, 3011, VIC, Australia
Tel.: (61) 386094900
Electronic & Electromechanical Component Mfr
N.A.I.C.S.: 334419

Wurth Electronics Co., Ltd. (4)
4th Floor No 18-1 Section 6 Mincyuan East Road, Neihu District, Taipei, 114, Taiwan
Tel.: (886) 227918625
Electronic & Electromechanical Component Mfr
N.A.I.C.S.: 334419

Wurth Electronics Japan Co., Ltd. (4)
401 Plus Tarla Bldg 3-1-4 Shin-Yokohama, Kohoku-ku, Yokohama, 222-0033, Kanagawa, Japan
Tel.: (81) 454718070
Electronic & Electromechanical Component Distr
N.A.I.C.S.: 423690

Subsidiary (US):

Wurth Electronics Midcom Inc. (4)
121 Airport Dr, Watertown, SD 57201-6330
Tel.: (605) 886-4385
Web Site: http://www.we-online.com
Emp.: 80
Telecommuncations Transformers Mfr
N.A.I.C.S.: 335311

Subsidiary (Non-US):

Wurth Electronics Services India Private Limited (4)
Prestige Sterling Square No 3 Madras Bank Road Next to Airlines Hotel, Bengaluru, 560001, Karnataka, India
Tel.: (91) 8040627411
Electrical & Electronic Mfr
N.A.I.C.S.: 335999
Deepak Chadha *(Mng Dir)*

Wurth Electronics Singapore Pte. Ltd. (4)
25 Tai Seng Avenue 05-01/02 Scorpio East Building, Orion Industrial Building, Singapore, 534104, Singapore
Tel.: (65) 67421567
Emp.: 30
Electronic Components Distr
N.A.I.C.S.: 423690
Sebastin Tan *(Country Mgr)*

Wurth Electronics UK Limited (4)
8th Floor 8 Building Exchange Quay, Salford, M5 3EJ, Manchester, United Kingdom
Tel.: (44) 1618486030
Emp.: 50
Electronic Components Distr
N.A.I.C.S.: 423690
Robert Sperring *(Gen Mgr)*

Wurth Elektronik (Schweiz) AG (4)
Industriestrasse 18, 8604, Volketswil, Switzerland
Tel.: (41) 442696161
Electronic & Electromechanical Component Mfr
N.A.I.C.S.: 334419

Wurth Elektronik Belgie (4)
Everdongenlaan 29, 2300, Turnhout, Belgium
Tel.: (32) 14151560
Electronic & Electromechanical Component Mfr
N.A.I.C.S.: 334419

Wurth Elektronik España, S.L. (4)
C/Balmes 4 5 Planta, 08007, Barcelona, Spain
Tel.: (34) 935471410
Electronic & Electromechanical Component Mfr
N.A.I.C.S.: 334419

Wurth Elektronik France SARL (4)
1861 Avenue Henri Schneider C S 70029, 69881, Meyzieu, Cedex, France
Tel.: (33) 427861100
Web Site: http://www.we-online.com
Emp.: 40
Electronic Components Distr
N.A.I.C.S.: 423690

Division (Domestic):

Wurth Elektronik GmbH & Co. KG - Circuit Board Technology (4)
Salzstrasse 21, 74676, Niedernhall, Germany
Tel.: (49) 79409460
Emp.: 50
Electronic Circuit Board Distr
N.A.I.C.S.: 423690

Subsidiary (Non-US):

Wurth Elektronik CBT India Private Limited (5)
Ground Floor No 27 III rd Phase, Koorgally Industrial Area Ilawala Hobli, Mysore, 570018, India
Tel.: (91) 8212305554
Printed Circuit Board Mfr
N.A.I.C.S.: 334412

Subsidiary (Domestic):

Wurth Elektronik Rot am See GmbH & Co. KG (5)
Rudolf-Diesel-Strasse 10, 74585, Rot am See, Germany
Tel.: (49) 79553888070
Web Site: http://www.wurth-elektronik.com
Electronic Circuit Board Mfr
N.A.I.C.S.: 334412

Wurth Elektronik Schopfheim GmbH & Co. KG (5)
Salzstrase 21, 79650, Niedernhall, Germany
Tel.: (49) 76223970
Electronic Circuit Board Mfr & Distr
N.A.I.C.S.: 334412
Andreas Gimmer *(Mng Dir)*

Subsidiary (Non-US):

Wurth Elektronik Hungary Kft. (4)
Nepfurdo u 22 A tower 5th Floor, Budapest, Hungary
Tel.: (36) 18773000
Electrical & Electronic Mfr
N.A.I.C.S.: 336320
Attila Levachich *(Gen Mgr)*

Division (Domestic):

Wurth Elektronik ICS GmbH & Co. KG (4)
Zeilbaumweg 15, D-74613, Ohringen, Germany

INTERNATIONAL PUBLIC

Tel.: (49) 794192050
Web Site: http://www.we-online.com
Emp.: 200
Electronic Circuit Board Connecting Systems Mfr & Distr
N.A.I.C.S.: 334417

Subsidiary (Non-US):

Wurth Elektronik Israel Ltd. (4)
20 Alon Hatavor St, Southern Industrial Park, 3079820, Caesarea, Israel
Tel.: (972) 777744222
Electrical & Electronic Mfr
N.A.I.C.S.: 335999

Wurth Elektronik Italia s.r.l. (4)
Via Trento 26, 20871, Vimercate, MB, Italy
Tel.: (39) 0396872710
Electrical & Electronic Mfr
N.A.I.C.S.: 335999

Wurth Elektronik Ithalat Ihracat ve Ticaret Ltd. Sti. (4)
Serifali Mah Cetin Cad Kule Sok No 25/A, Umraniye, 34775, Istanbul, Turkiye
Tel.: (90) 2164664130
Electronic & Electromechanical Component Mfr
N.A.I.C.S.: 334419

Wurth Elektronik Mexico S.A. de C.V. (4)
Calle Rio Duero 1122, Parque Tecnoindustrial Castro del Rio, 36814, Irapuato, Guanajuato, Mexico
Tel.: (52) 4621671900
Electrical & Electronic Distr
N.A.I.C.S.: 423690
Fabian Gutierrez Gasca *(Mgr-Supply Chain)*

Wurth Elektronik Nederland B.V. (4)
Het Sterrenbeeld 35, 5215 MK, 's-Hertogenbosch, Netherlands
Tel.: (31) 736291570
Electrical & Electronic Distr
N.A.I.C.S.: 423690

Wurth Elektronik Osterreich GmbH (4)
Hauptplatz 20-Top 13, 2320, Schwechat, Austria
Tel.: (43) 170701010
Electronic & Electromechanical Component Mfr
N.A.I.C.S.: 334419

Wurth Elektronik Oy (4)
Karhutie 4, 01900, Nurmijarvi, Finland
Tel.: (358) 1030812
Web Site: http://www.wurthelektronik.fi
Electronic Components Distr
N.A.I.C.S.: 423690

Wurth Elektronik Polska sp. z o.o. (4)
ul Wagonowa 2, 53-609, Wroclaw, Poland
Tel.: (48) 717497600
Electrical & Electronic Distr
N.A.I.C.S.: 423690

Wurth Elektronik RUS OOO (4)
Leninskyi prospekt 119A Floor 4, 119571, Moscow, Russia
Tel.: (7) 4957300216
Electronic & Electromechanical Component Mfr
N.A.I.C.S.: 334419

Wurth Elektronik Stelvio Kontek S.p.A. (4)
Via al Mognago 49, 23848, Oggiono, LC, Italy
Tel.: (39) 0341265411
Web Site: http://www.stelvio-kontek.com
Mechanical Parts Mfr
N.A.I.C.S.: 333517
Flavio Genova *(Gen Mgr)*

Wurth Elektronik Sweden AB (4)
Annelundsgatan 17C, 749 40, Enkoping, Sweden
Tel.: (46) 171428400
Electronic & Electromechanical Component Mfr
N.A.I.C.S.: 334419

Subsidiary (Domestic):

Wurth Elektronik eiSos GmbH & Co. KG (4)

AND PRIVATE COMPANIES — WURTH VERWALTUNGSGESELLSCHAFT MBH

Max-Eyth-Strasse 1, 74638, Waldenburg, Germany
Tel.: (49) 79429450
Web Site: http://www.we-online.com
Emp.: 500
Inductors, Transformers & Other Electronic Components Mfr & Distr
N.A.I.C.S.: 334416
Thomas Schrott (Mng Dir)

Subsidiary (Domestic):

AMBER wireless GmbH (5)
Rudi-Schillings-Strasse 31, 54296, Trier, Germany
Tel.: (49) 651 993 550
Web Site: http://www.amber-wireless.de
Short Range Radio Module Mfr, Design & Marketing
N.A.I.C.S.: 334220
Oliver Konz (Mng Dir)

Subsidiary (Non-US):

Wurth Elektronik eiSos Czech s.r.o. (5)
Prikop 4, 602 00, Brno, Czech Republic
Tel.: (420) 539010749
Electronic & Electromechanical Component Mfr
N.A.I.C.S.: 334419

Wurth Elektronik eiSos, izdelava in prodaja elek-tronskih ter elektromehanskih komponent d.o.o. (5)
Trg Franca Fakina 6, 1420, Trbovlje, Slovenia
Tel.: (386) 35653400
Electronic & Electromechanical Component Mfr
N.A.I.C.S.: 334419

Subsidiary (Domestic):

Wurth Elektronik iBE GmbH (4)
Gewerbepark 8, 94136, Thyrnau, Germany
Tel.: (49) 85019001100
Web Site: http://www.we-online.de
Emp.: 155
Automotive Electronic Coil & Other Components Mfr & Distr
N.A.I.C.S.: 334416
Rainer Schaetzl (Mng Dir)

Subsidiary (Non-US):

Wurth Elektronik iBE BG EOOD (5)
Zona B-5 bl 16, 1303, Sofia, Bulgaria
Tel.: (359) 887870540
Electronic & Electromechanical Component Distr
N.A.I.C.S.: 423690

Subsidiary (Non-US):

Wurth Espana, S.A. (3)
C/Joiers 21, Palau-solita i Plegamans, 08184, Barcelona, Spain
Tel.: (34) 938629500
Web Site: http://www.wurth.es
Industrial Equipment Distr
N.A.I.C.S.: 423830
Daniel Guisado (CIO)

Wurth Finance International B.V. (3)
Het Sterrenbeeld 35, 5215 MK, 's-Hertogenbosch, Netherlands
Tel.: (31) 736814900
Web Site: http://www.wurthfinance.net
Financial Banking Services
N.A.I.C.S.: 522110

Wurth Financial Services AG (3)
Churerstrasse 10, 9400, Rorschach, Switzerland
Tel.: (41) 714217400
Web Site: http://www.wuerth-fs.com
Emp.: 60
Insurance Brokerage Services
N.A.I.C.S.: 524210
Adrian Parpan (Mng Dir)

Wurth Foreign Swiss Company Ltd. (3)
Erkindik Boulevard Building 3, Bishkek, Kyrgyzstan
Tel.: (996) 312301980
Web Site: http://www.wurth.kg
Fastening Product Mfr & Distr
N.A.I.C.S.: 332722

Wurth France S.A. (3)
ZI Ouest Rue Georges Besse, BP 40013, 67158, Erstein, Cedex, France
Tel.: (33) 388881212
Web Site: http://www.wurth.fr
Sales Range: $500-549.9 Million
Emp.: 4,000
Holding Company; Hardware & Hand Tools Mfr & Distr
N.A.I.C.S.: 551112
Thierry Gonzalez (Dir-IT)

Subsidiary (Domestic):

Inter-Inox S.a.r.l. (4)
7 avenue Marechal de Lattre de Tassigny, 69330, Meyzieu, Cedex, France
Tel.: (33) 4 7245 2870
Web Site: http://www.interinox.fr
Stainless Steel Screws Mfr & Distr
N.A.I.C.S.: 332722

Wurth Industrie France S.A.S. (4)
1 Rue de Rome ZA Krafft, BP10115, 67152, Erstein, Cedex, France
Tel.: (33) 3 90 406 310
Web Site: http://www.wurth-industrie.fr
Sales Range: $25-49.9 Million
Emp.: 109
Fasteners & Safety Equipment Mfr & Distr
N.A.I.C.S.: 332722

Subsidiary (Non-US):

Wurth Georgia Ltd. (3)
1 Sq M Building 2a Digomi, Tbilisi, Georgia
Tel.: (995) 322530610
Web Site: http://www.wurth.com.ge
Fastener Product Mfr
N.A.I.C.S.: 332722

Group (US):

Wurth Group of North America, Inc. (3)
93 Grant St, Ramsey, NJ 07446-1105
Tel.: (201) 818-8877
Emp.: 10
Holding Company; Regional Managing Office
N.A.I.C.S.: 551112
Craig McCutcheon (Controller)

Subsidiary (Non-US):

Wurth Canada Ltd., Ltee (4)
345 Hanlon Creek Boulevard, Guelph, N1C 0A1, ON, Canada
Tel.: (905) 564-6225
Web Site: http://www.wurth.ca
Assembly Materials & Fastening Hardware Distr
N.A.I.C.S.: 423710
Ali Moghaddam (CEO)

Division (Domestic):

Wurth Industry North America LLC (4)
9485 Winnetka Ave, Brooklyn Park, MN 55445
Tel.: (763) 424-3374
Web Site: https://www.wuerth.com
Fastener Mfr
N.A.I.C.S.: 339993
Heather Stewart (VP-Strategic Procurement, Quality & Profitability)

Subsidiary (Domestic):

Atlantic Fasteners, Inc. (5)
106 Longale Rd, Greensboro, NC 27409
Tel.: (336) 852-0700
Web Site: http://www.afast.com
Rev: $6,184,230
Emp.: 21
Iron & Steel Pipe & Tube Mfr & Distr
N.A.I.C.S.: 331210
William C. Davis (CEO)

Northern Safety Co., Inc. (5)
232 Industrial Park Dr, Frankfort, NY 13340
Tel.: (315) 793-4900
Web Site: http://www.northernsafety.com
Sales Range: $25-49.9 Million
Emp.: 350
Industrial Supplies, Uniform & Safety Equipment Whslr
N.A.I.C.S.: 423840
Salvatore Longo (CEO)

Subsidiary (Domestic):

ORR Safety Corporation (6)
11601 Interchange Dr, Louisville, KY 40229
Tel.: (502) 774-5791
Web Site: http://www.orrsafety.com
Whslr of Industry Safety Equipment
N.A.I.C.S.: 423830
Linn Hason (Mgr-Mktg Svcs)

Division (Domestic):

Wurth USA Inc. (4)
93 Grant St, Ramsey, NJ 07446
Tel.: (201) 825-2710
Web Site: http://www.wurthusa.com
Automotive Parts, Assembly Materials & Fastening Hardware Distr
N.A.I.C.S.: 423120
Marc Weber (VP-Ops)

Subsidiary (Domestic):

Arnold Fastening Systems, Inc. (5)
1873 Rochester Industrial Ct, Rochester Hills, MI 48309-3336
Tel.: (248) 997-2000
Automobile Mfr
N.A.I.C.S.: 336110
Genevieve Dantzler (Dir-Fin)

Baier & Michels USA Inc. (5)
65 Brookfield Oaks Dr, Greenville, SC 29607
Tel.: (864) 968-1999
Fastening Product Mfr & Distr
N.A.I.C.S.: 332722

Dakota Premium Hardwoods LLC (5)
6301 E Stassney Ln 600, Austin, TX 78744
Tel.: (512) 389-9773
Web Site: http://www.dakotahardwoods.com
Lumber Distr
N.A.I.C.S.: 423310

Dinol U.S. Inc. (5)
8520 Cotter St, Lewis Center, OH 43035
Tel.: (740) 548-1656
Adhesive & Sealant Mfr
N.A.I.C.S.: 325520
Joe Renzi (CEO)

House of Threads Inc. (5)
144 Industrial Blvd, Birmingham, AL 35211-4466
Tel.: (205) 916-2512
Web Site: http://www.houseofthreads.com
Sales Range: $25-49.9 Million
Emp.: 100
Fastener Distr
N.A.I.C.S.: 423710
Foster Yeilding (Pres)

IQD Frequency Products Inc. (5)
777 E Tahquitz Canyon Way Ste 200-200, Palm Springs, CA 92262
Tel.: (408) 250-1435
Frequency Product Mfr
N.A.I.C.S.: 334419

Marine Fasteners, Inc. (5)
2152 Martin Luther King Jr Blvd Ste 1080, Sanford, FL 32771
Tel.: (407) 321-2994
Web Site: http://www.marfas.com
Stainless Steel Fasteners Distr
N.A.I.C.S.: 423710
Keith Brantley (CEO & Mng Dir)

Wurth Adams Nut & Bolt Co. (5)
10100 85th Ave N, Osseo, MN 55369
Tel.: (763) 424-3374
Web Site: http://www.wurthadams.com
Emp.: 100
Assembly Materials & Fastening Hardware Distr
N.A.I.C.S.: 423710

Wurth Adams Nut & Bolt Company (5)
9485 Winnetka Ave, Brooklyn Park, MN 55445
Tel.: (763) 424-3374
Fastening Product Mfr & Distr
N.A.I.C.S.: 332722

Wurth Baer Supply Co. (5)
909 Forest Edge Dr, Vernon Hills, IL 60061
Web Site: http://www.baersupply.com
Emp.: 400

Industrial Equipment Mfr
N.A.I.C.S.: 333248
Jeff Jacobson (Dir-Mktg)

Wurth Des Moines Bolt Inc. (5)
2300 Delaware Ave, Des Moines, IA 50317
Tel.: (515) 265-7581
Fastening Product Mfr & Distr
N.A.I.C.S.: 332722

Wurth Electronics ICS, Inc. (5)
1982 Byers Rd, Miamisburg, OH 45342
Intelligent Power & Control System Mfr
N.A.I.C.S.: 335314

Wurth International Trading America, Inc. (5)
91 Grant St, Ramsey, NJ 07446
Tel.: (201) 995-1111
Fastener Mfr
N.A.I.C.S.: 332722
Johannes Hoenig (Head-Supply Chain)

Wurth Logistics USA Inc. (5)
598 Chaney Ave, Greenwood, IN 46143
Tel.: (317) 704-8544
Logistic Services
N.A.I.C.S.: 541614
Ryan McGrath (Supvr-Team)

Wurth Louis & Company (5)
895 Columbia St, Brea, CA 92821
Web Site: http://www.wurthlac.com
Industrial Equipment Mfr
N.A.I.C.S.: 333248
Thomas Stolmeier (Pres & CEO)

Wurth McAllen Bolt & Screw Co. (5)
4403 W. Military Hwy Ste 500A, McAllen, TX 78503
Tel.: (956) 687-8596
Web Site: http://www.wurthmcallen.com
Assembly Materials & Fastening Hardware Distr
N.A.I.C.S.: 423710

Wurth Revcar Fasteners, Inc. (5)
3845 Thirlane Rd NW, Roanoke, VA 24019
Tel.: (540) 561-6565
Web Site: http://www.wurthrevcar.com
Assembly Materials & Fastening Hardware Distr
N.A.I.C.S.: 423710

Wurth Service Supply Inc. (5)
598 Chaney Ave, Greenwood, IN 46143
Tel.: (317) 704-1000
Web Site: http://www.wurthindustry.com
Distr of Fasteners, Nuts, Bolts, Screws
N.A.I.C.S.: 423710

Wurth Snider Bolt & Screw, Inc. (5)
11503 Champions Way, Louisville, KY 40299
Tel.: (502) 968-2250
Web Site: http://www.wurthsnider.com
Distr of Fasteners & Assembly Components
N.A.I.C.S.: 339993

Wurth Wood Group Inc. (5)
4250 Golf Acres Dr, Charlotte, NC 28208
Web Site: http://www.wurthwoodgroup.com
Lumber Distr
N.A.I.C.S.: 423310

Subsidiary (Non-US):

Wurth Gulf FZE (3)
PO Box 17036, Jebel Ali Freezone South 6, Dubai, United Arab Emirates
Tel.: (971) 48809991
Web Site: http://www.wurth.ae
Emp.: 208
Assembly Materials & Fastening Hardware Distr
N.A.I.C.S.: 423710

Wurth Handelsgesellschaft m.b.H. (3)
Wurth Strasse 1, 3071, Boheimkirchen, Austria
Tel.: (43) 5082420
Web Site: http://eshop.wuerth.at
Fastening Material Mfr
N.A.I.C.S.: 332722

Wurth Hellas S.A. (3)
23rd km E O, Athens-Lamia Krioneri, 14568, Athens, Greece
Tel.: (30) 210 6290 800
Web Site: http://www.wurth.gr

WURTH VERWALTUNGSGESELLSCHAFT MBH — INTERNATIONAL PUBLIC

Wurth Verwaltungsgesellschaft mbH—(Continued)

Holding Company; Hardware Distr
N.A.I.C.S.: 551112

Subsidiary (Domestic):

Inox Mare Hellas SA (4)
Stadiou 4, Kalohori, 57009, Thessaloniki, Greece
Tel.: (30) 231 075 3384
Web Site: http://www.inoxmare.gr
Emp.: 6
Stainless Steel Hardware Distr
N.A.I.C.S.: 423710

Subsidiary (Non-US):

Wurth Hong Kong Co., Ltd. (3)
Unit 01 1/F Prosperity Centre 982 Canton Road, Mongkok, Kowloon, China (Hong Kong)
Tel.: (852) 27508118
Web Site: http://www.wurth.com.hk
Emp.: 25
Assembly Materials & Fastening Hardware Distr
N.A.I.C.S.: 423710

Subsidiary (Domestic):

Wurth IT GmbH (3)
Industriepark Wurth Drillberg 6, 97980, Bad Mergentheim, Germany
Tel.: (49) 7940 930 0
Web Site: http://www.wuerth-it.com
Emp.: 500
Information Technology Consulting Services
N.A.I.C.S.: 541690
Christian Berndt (Mng Dir & Member-Mgmt Bd)

Subsidiary (Non-US):

Comgroup (Schweiz) AG (4)
Zurichstrasse 23c, 2504, Biel/Bienne, Switzerland
Tel.: (41) 323444052
Web Site: http://www.comgroup-ag.biz
Information Technology Consulting Services
N.A.I.C.S.: 541690

Comgroup Information Technology (Shanghai) Co., Ltd. (4)
Room 906-908 Jiahe International Bldg No 1, Lane 66 Huayuan Road, Shanghai, 200083, China
Tel.: (86) 2151506800
Web Site: http://www.comgroup.cn
Information Technology Consulting Services
N.A.I.C.S.: 541690

Subsidiary (Non-US):

Wurth ITensis AG (3)
Aspermontstrasse 1, 7000, Chur, Switzerland
Tel.: (41) 815580600
Web Site: http://www.wuerth-itensis.com
Information Technology Services
N.A.I.C.S.: 541511
Phil Merz (Sr Mgr-Bus & Product Dev)

Wurth Indonesia P.T. (3)
Jalan Daan Mogot KM 21 Pergudangan Era Prima Unit 18-19, Batu Ceper, Tangerang, 15122, Indonesia
Tel.: (62) 2155727327
Mechanical Parts Mfr
N.A.I.C.S.: 333517
Deddy Irawan (Project Mgr)

Wurth Industri Danmark A/S (3)
Merkurvej 5, 6000, Kolding, Denmark
Tel.: (45) 73207320
Web Site: http://www.wurthindustri.dk
Fastening Product Mfr & Distr
N.A.I.C.S.: 332722
Line Sand (Coord-Fin & Mktg)

Wurth Industri Norge AS (3)
Rosteinvegen 7, Dokka, 2870, Oslo, Norway
Tel.: (47) 61114900
Web Site: http://www.wurthindustri.no
Automobile Parts Distr
N.A.I.C.S.: 423120
Jordi Somers (Mng Dir)

Wurth Industria Espana, S.A. (3)
Carrer dels Joiers 21, Palau-solita i Plegamans, 08184, Barcelona, Spain
Tel.: (34) 938602110
Web Site: http://www.wurth-industria.es
Automobile Parts Distr
N.A.I.C.S.: 423120

Wurth Industrial Services India Pvt. Ltd. (3)
711 7th Floor Tower 2 World Trade Center EON Free Zone, Kharadi, Pune, 411014, Maharashtra, India
Tel.: (91) 8484997697
Web Site: http://www.wuerth-industry.in
Emp.: 80
Fastening Product Mfr
N.A.I.C.S.: 332722
Norman Dentel (CEO)

Wurth Industrial Services Malaysia Sdn. Bhd. (3)
Lot 806 Jalan Subang 5, Taman Perindustrian Subang, 47600, Subang Jaya, Selangor, Malaysia
Tel.: (60) 380210200
Web Site: http://www.wuerth.my
Automobile Parts Distr
N.A.I.C.S.: 423120

Wurth Industrie Service Endustriyel Hizmetler Pazarlama Limited Sirketi (3)
Alipasa Mahallesi Ulugbey, Caddesi No 1 Silivri, 34570, Istanbul, Turkiye
Tel.: (90) 2127165200
Web Site: http://www.wurth-industrie.com.tr
Automobile Parts Distr
N.A.I.C.S.: 423120

Subsidiary (Domestic):

Wurth Industrie Service GmbH & Co. KG. (3)
Industrial Park Wurth Drillberg, 97980, Bad Mergentheim, Germany
Tel.: (49) 7931910
Web Site: http://www.wuerth-industrie.com
Emp.: 1,700
Logistic Services
N.A.I.C.S.: 541614
Mike Breuninger (Mgr-Sls-Intl)

Subsidiary (Non-US):

Wurth Industry Belgium N.V. (3)
Zoomstraat 2A, 9160, Lokeren, Belgium
Tel.: (32) 93377300
Web Site: http://www.wurth-industry.be
Fastening Material Mfr
N.A.I.C.S.: 332722

Wurth Industry de Mexico S de RL de CV (3)
Carretera Mexico-Queretaro Km 188 5 B Col Calamanda, El Marques, 76247, Queretaro, Mexico
Tel.: (52) 81110314411
Automobile Parts Distr
N.A.I.C.S.: 423120

Wurth Industry of Canada Ltd. (3)
10 Abbott Court Building B Unit 203, Brantford, N3S 0E7, ON, Canada
Tel.: (519) 756-9700
Web Site: http://www.wurthindustry.ca
Fastening Material Mfr
N.A.I.C.S.: 332722
Tino Schablow (Mng Dir)

Wurth Information Technology (Shanghai) Co., Ltd. (3)
Capital of Leaders - Building 9 Zhangdong Road No 1387, Shanghai, 201203, China
Tel.: (86) 33836081
Web Site: http://www.wuerth-it.cn
Information Technology Services
N.A.I.C.S.: 541511

Wurth Information Technology India Private Limited (3)
10th Floor IT-9 Building Plot No 2 Blue Ridge Township, SEZ Rajiv Gandhi Infitech Park Phark Phase I Hinjawadi, Pune, 411057, India
Tel.: (91) 2067701300
Web Site: http://www.wurth-it.in
Information Technology Services
N.A.I.C.S.: 541511
Abhishek Bhate (Mng Dir)

Wurth International AG
Aspermontstrasse 1, 7004, Chur, Switzerland
Tel.: (41) 815580000
Web Site: http://www.wurth-international.com
Assembly & Fastener Product Mfr
N.A.I.C.S.: 332722
Nicole Ochsner (Mgr-HR)

Wurth International Trading (Shanghai) Co., Ltd. (3)
Capital of Leaders - Building 9 Zhangdong Road No 1387, Shanghai, 201203, China
Tel.: (86) 2138499566
Web Site: http://www.wurth-international.com.cn
Emp.: 390
Trading Services
N.A.I.C.S.: 522299

Wurth International Trading (Singapore) Pte. Ltd. (3)
30 Pioneer Road, Singapore, 628502, Singapore
Tel.: (65) 62541125
Motor Vehicle Whslr
N.A.I.C.S.: 423120

Wurth International Trading s.r.o. (3)
Rybnicna 40/A, 831 07, Bratislava, Slovakia
Tel.: (421) 249211111
Web Site: http://www.wurth-int.com
Logistic Services
N.A.I.C.S.: 541614
Lucia Kraskova (Partner-HR Bus)

Wurth Ireland Ltd. (3)
Monaclinie Industrial Estate Ballysimon Road, Limerick, V94 AK71, Ireland
Tel.: (353) 61 430 200
Web Site: http://www.wurth.ie
Hardware Whslr
N.A.I.C.S.: 423710

Wurth Israel Ltd. (3)
Hahita 6, PO Box 3585, Industrial Park, 38900, Caesarea, Israel
Tel.: (972) 46328800
Electrical & Electronic Mfr
N.A.I.C.S.: 335999
Daniel Miller (Mgr-IT)

Wurth Japan Co., Ltd. (3)
33 Sanmaicho, Kanagawa Ward, Yokohama, 221-0862, Kanagawa, Japan
Tel.: (81) 454884186
Web Site: http://www.eshop.wuerth.co.jp
Automobile Parts Distr
N.A.I.C.S.: 423120

Wurth Korea Co., Ltd. (3)
BoegaeWonsam-ro Bogae-Myeon 1759, Anseong, 456-871, Gyeonggi-Do, Korea (South)
Tel.: (82) 316757311
Industrial Equipment Mfr
N.A.I.C.S.: 333248
Tai Yoen Dan Choi (Mng Dir)

Wurth Lanka (Private) Limited (3)
375 B Highlevel Rd, Makumbura Pannipitiya, 10230, Colombo, Sri Lanka
Tel.: (94) 112894930
Web Site: http://www.wurth.lk
Automotive Products Mfr
N.A.I.C.S.: 336110
Rohan Amirthiah (Mng Dir)

Wurth Leasing AG (3)
Riedstrasse 14, 8953, Dietikon, Switzerland
Tel.: (41) 449139595
Web Site: http://www.wuertheasing.ch
Leasing Services
N.A.I.C.S.: 532490

Wurth Leasing Danmark A/S (3)
Birkemosevej 7, 6000, Kolding, Denmark
Tel.: (45) 79324245
Web Site: http://www.wuerth-leasing.dk
Financial Banking Services
N.A.I.C.S.: 522110
Christian Vangkilde (CFO)

Wurth Leasing GmbH (3)
Wienerbergstrasse 11, 1100, Vienna, Austria
Tel.: (43) 120555150
Financial Banking Services
N.A.I.C.S.: 522110
Drazen Gasic (Acct Mgr)

Subsidiary (Domestic):

Wurth Leasing GmbH & Co. KG (3)
Breitensteinstrasse 2, 73095, Albershausen, Germany
Tel.: (49) 7161951360
Web Site: http://www.wuerth-leasing.de
Emp.: 90
Equipment Leasing Services
N.A.I.C.S.: 532420
Axel Ziemann (Mng Dir & Member-Mgmt Bd)

Subsidiary (Non-US):

Wurth Lebanon SAL (3)
Sarieddine Bld Shwayfat Main Road 14-5540, Beirut, Lebanon
Tel.: (961) 5433828
Fastening Material Mfr
N.A.I.C.S.: 332722

Wurth Lietuva UAB (3)
Jacioniu k 1B Pivonijos sen, 20101, Ukmerge, Lithuania
Tel.: (370) 52356160
Web Site: http://www.wurth.lt
Fastening Material Mfr
N.A.I.C.S.: 332722
Tomas Zvinakis (Mgr-Pur)

Wurth Limited (3)
Mdina Road, Zebbug, ZBG 9016, Malta
Tel.: (356) 21494604
Web Site: http://www.wuerth.com.mt
Fastening Product Mfr & Distr
N.A.I.C.S.: 332722
Arthur Calleja (Mng Dir)

Wurth Logistics AG (3)
Churerstrasse 10, 9400, Rorschach, Switzerland
Tel.: (41) 714217200
Web Site: http://www.wurth-logistics.com
Logistic Services
N.A.I.C.S.: 541614
Thomas Knorr (Head-Global Sls)

Wurth Logistics Asia-pacific Sdn. Bhd. (3)
Lot 806 Jalan Subang 5 Taman Perindustrian Subang, 47600, Subang Jaya, Selangor, Malaysia
Tel.: (60) 380210175
Logistic Services
N.A.I.C.S.: 541614
Andreas Sprint (Mgr-Logistics APAC)

Subsidiary (Domestic):

Wurth Logistics Deutschland GmbH (3)
Konsul-Smidt-Strasse 76, 28217, Bremen, Germany
Tel.: (49) 42138020779
Logistic Services
N.A.I.C.S.: 541614

Subsidiary (Non-US):

Wurth MODYF AS (3)
Brennaveien 6, 1481, Hagan, Norway
Tel.: (47) 23177500
Web Site: http://www.modyf.no
Safety Wear Mfr & Distr
N.A.I.C.S.: 315990

Wurth Makedonija DOOEL (3)
Ul 20 br 39 Brazda, Cucer Sandevo, 1011, Skopje, North Macedonia
Tel.: (389) 22728080
Fastening Material Mfr
N.A.I.C.S.: 332722
Vasilka Anchevski (Chief Ops Officer)

Wurth Mexico S.A. de C.V. (3)
Carr Temixco-Emiliano Zapata Lot 17 Warehouse 1 Col Palo Escrito, Industrial Development Emiliano Zapata DIEZ, 62760, Morelos, Mexico
Tel.: (52) 7774621628
Web Site: http://www.tiendawurth.com.mx
Automotive Product Mfr & Distr
N.A.I.C.S.: 336110

Subsidiary (Domestic):

Wurth Modyf GmbH & Co. KG (3)
Benzstrasse 7, 74653, Kunzelsau, Germany
Tel.: (49) 79405480479
Web Site: http://www.modyf.de

AND PRIVATE COMPANIES — WURTH VERWALTUNGSGESELLSCHAFT MBH

Emp.: 100
Work & Leisure Apparel Online Retailer
N.A.I.C.S.: 458110

Subsidiary (Non-US):

Modyf S.r.l. (4)
via stazione 18, Termeno, 39040, Bolzano, Italy
Tel.: (39) 0690779910
Web Site: http://www.modyf.it
Textile Products Mfr
N.A.I.C.S.: 314999

Wurth Modyf Danmark A/S (4)
Montagevej 6 Industri N2, 6000, Kolding, Denmark
Tel.: (45) 79323232
Web Site: http://www.wuerth.dk
Work & Leisure Apparel Online Retailer
N.A.I.C.S.: 458110

Wurth Modyf France S.a.r.l. (4)
4 rue de l'expansion, 67150, Erstein, France
Tel.: (33) 3 88 988 380
Web Site: http://www.modyf.fr
Work & Leisure Apparel Online Retailer
N.A.I.C.S.: 458110
Jerome Nussbaumer (Dir-Publication)

Wurth Modyf Lda. (4)
Estrada Nacional 249-4 Abrunheira, 2710-089, Sintra, Portugal
Tel.: (351) 219157389
Industrial Equipment Mfr
N.A.I.C.S.: 333248

Wurth Modyf S.A. (4)
Calle de Tramuntana 4-6 P I Llevant, 08213, Barcelona, Spain
Tel.: (34) 902 401 511
Web Site: http://www.modyf.es
Work & Leisure Apparel Online Retailer
N.A.I.C.S.: 315990

Wurth-Modyf N.V. (4)
Parklaan 20-A, 2300, Turnhout, Belgium
Tel.: (32) 14438919
Work & Leisure Apparel Online Retailer
N.A.I.C.S.: 458110

Subsidiary (Non-US):

Wurth Mongolia LLC (3)
KH Building 6b Suite 2 Stadium Orgil-1 Chinggis Avenue 15th khoroo, Khan-Uul District, Ulaanbaatar, 17010, Mongolia
Tel.: (976) 76117940
Web Site: http://www.wuerthmongolia.com
Chemical Part Distr
N.A.I.C.S.: 424690
Binderya Oidov (Mgr-Sls)

Wurth Namibia (Pty) Ltd. (3)
5 Diesel Street, Southern Industrial, Windhoek, Namibia
Tel.: (264) 61251888
Automobile Parts Distr
N.A.I.C.S.: 423120

Wurth Nederland B.V. (3)
Het Sterrenbeeld 35, 5215 MK, 's-Hertogenbosch, Netherlands
Tel.: (31) 736291911
Web Site: http://www.wurth.nl
Automobile Parts Distr
N.A.I.C.S.: 423120

Wurth New Zealand Ltd. (3)
99 McLaughlins Road, Wiri, 2104, Auckland, New Zealand
Tel.: (64) 92623040
Web Site: http://www.wurth.co.nz
Emp.: 190
Industrial Equipment Distr
N.A.I.C.S.: 423830
Philip Cryer (CEO)

Wurth Norge AS (3)
Gjellerasen Naeringspark Morteveien 12, 1481, Hagan, Norway
Tel.: (47) 46401500
Web Site: http://www.wurth.no
Automobile Parts Distr
N.A.I.C.S.: 423120
Hoff Arild (Mgr-IT)

Wurth North-West JSC (3)
Shushary Lenina 25, 196626, Saint Petersburg, Russia
Tel.: (7) 8123201111
Web Site: http://www.wuerth.spb.ru
Fastening Product Mfr & Distr
N.A.I.C.S.: 332722

Wurth Oy (3)
Wurthintie 1, 11710, Riihimaki, Finland
Tel.: (358) 197701
Web Site: http://www.eshop.wurth.fi
Sales Range: $300-349.9 Million
Emp.: 1,000
Hardware Mfr & Distr
N.A.I.C.S.: 332722
Mika Rantanen (Mng Dir)

Subsidiary (Domestic):

Ferrometal Oy (4)
Karhutie 9, 01900, Nurmijarvi, Finland
Tel.: (358) 10 308 11
Web Site: http://www.ferrometal.fi
Emp.: 85
Fastener & Other Hardware Distr
N.A.I.C.S.: 423710

Subsidiary (Non-US):

Wurth Peru S.A.C. (3)
Av Los Ingenieros 142 Urb Santa Raquel Ate, Lima, Peru
Tel.: (51) 3482727
Web Site: http://www.eshop.wurth.pe
Industrial Equipment Retailer
N.A.I.C.S.: 423840

Wurth Phoenix S.r.l. (3)
Johann Kravogl Str 4, 39100, Bolzano, Italy
Tel.: (39) 0471564111
Web Site: http://www.wuerth-phoenix.com
Emp.: 100
Business Software, IT Management & Process Consulting Services
N.A.I.C.S.: 541690

Subsidiary (Non-US):

Wurth Phoenix GmbH (4)
WITI - Wurth IT International Drillberg 6, D-97980, Bad Mergentheim, Germany
Tel.: (49) 7931916831
Business Software, IT Management & Process Consulting Services
N.A.I.C.S.: 541690

Wurth Phoenix Kft. (4)
Gyar u 2/d, HU-2040, Budaors, Hungary
Tel.: (36) 23501350
Web Site: http://www.wuerth-phoenix.com
Emp.: 10
Business Software, IT Management & Process Consulting Services
N.A.I.C.S.: 541690
Hubert Kofler (CEO)

Subsidiary (Non-US):

Wurth Polska Sp. z o.o. (3)
ul Posag 7 Panien 1, 02-495, Warsaw, Poland
Tel.: (48) 225102000
Web Site: http://www.wurth.pl
Assembly Material & Fastening Hardware Distr
N.A.I.C.S.: 423710

Wurth Reinsurance Company, S.A. (3)
Siege social 74 rue de Merl, 2146, Luxembourg, Luxembourg
Tel.: (352) 494177
Financial Banking Services
N.A.I.C.S.: 522110

Wurth Romania S.R.L. (3)
Str Drumul Garii-Otopeni 25-35 jud, Otopeni, 075100, Romania
Tel.: (40) 213007800
Web Site: http://www.wuerth.ro
Industrial Equipment Mfr
N.A.I.C.S.: 333248

Wurth S.R.L. (3)
Codrilor 16 DEPO Office 4, Chisinau, MD2071, Moldova
Tel.: (373) 60398784
Web Site: http://www.wurth.md
Fastening Material Mfr
N.A.I.C.S.: 332722

Wurth S.r.l. (3)
Via Stazione 51, Egna Neumarkt, 39044, Bolzano, BZ, Italy
Tel.: (39) 0471828000
Web Site: http://www.wuerth.it
Hardware Whslr
N.A.I.C.S.: 423710
Damiano Faccennini (Mgr-Retail Mktg)

Wurth SW Industry Pecas de Fixacao Ltda. (3)
Rua Carlos Ayres 542 G1 Jardim Vera Cruz, Sao Bernardo do Campo, 09860-065, Sao Paulo, Brazil
Tel.: (55) 1138836300
Web Site: http://www.wurthindustry.com.br
Logistics & Supply Management Services
N.A.I.C.S.: 541614
Pedro Ramos (CEO)

Wurth Sanayi Urunleri Tic. Ltd. Sti. (3)
Eski Silivri Cad No 46 Mimarsinan, Buyukcekmece, 34535, Istanbul, Turkiye
Tel.: (90) 2128666200
Web Site: http://www.wurth.com.tr
Industrial Equipment Mfr
N.A.I.C.S.: 333248

Wurth Saudi Arabia LLC (3)
Al Malaz, Riyadh, 12629, Saudi Arabia
Tel.: (966) 114733077
Web Site: http://www.wurthsaudi.com
Fastening Product Mfr & Distr
N.A.I.C.S.: 332722

Wurth South Africa (Pty.) Ltd. (3)
Plumbago Business Park Spier Road Glen Erasmia Ext 17, Kempton Park, Johannesburg, 1619, South Africa
Tel.: (27) 112811000
Web Site: http://www.co.za
Fastening Product Mfr & Distr
N.A.I.C.S.: 332722
John Anderson (Mng Dir)

Wurth Svenska AB (3)
Berglundavagen 38, 702 36, Orebro, Sweden
Tel.: (46) 19351030
Web Site: http://www.wurth.se
Automotive Products Mfr
N.A.I.C.S.: 336110

Wurth Szerelestechnika KFT (3)
Gyar u 2, 2040, Budaors, Hungary
Tel.: (36) 623418130
Web Site: http://www.wuerth.hu
Automobile Parts Distr
N.A.I.C.S.: 423120

Wurth Taiwan Co., Ltd. (3)
No 205-33 Guosheng Rd, Houlong Town Miaoli County, Hsinchu, 35651, Taiwan
Tel.: (886) 37721100
Web Site: http://www.wurth.com.tw
Automobile Parts Distr
N.A.I.C.S.: 423120

Subsidiary (Domestic):

Wurth TeleServices GmbH & Co. KG (3)
Schliffenstrasse 22, 74653, Kunzelsau, Germany
Tel.: (49) 794054840
Web Site: http://www.wuerth-teleservices.de
Call Center Services
N.A.I.C.S.: 561421

Wurth Truck Lease GmbH (3)
Frankfurter Strasse 151 C, 63303, Dreieich, Germany
Tel.: (49) 6925627950
Web Site: http://www.wuerth-truck-lease.de
Financial Banking Services
N.A.I.C.S.: 522110

Subsidiary (Non-US):

Wurth U.K. Ltd. (3)
1 Centurion Way, Erith, DA18 4AE, Kent, United Kingdom
Tel.: (44) 3300555444
Web Site: http://eshop.wurth.co.uk
Automobile Parts Distr
N.A.I.C.S.: 423120

Wurth Ukraine Ltd. (3)
Zroshuvalna Street 11, Kiev, 02099, Ukraine
Tel.: (380) 445859893
Automobile Parts Distr
N.A.I.C.S.: 423120
Kalenskyi Andrii (CEO)

Subsidiary (Domestic):

Wurth Versicherungsdienst GmbH (3)
Zeppelinstrasse 14, 74653, Kunzelsau, Germany
Tel.: (49) 794092860
Web Site: http://www.wuerthversicherungsdienst.de
Insurance Services
N.A.I.C.S.: 524210

Subsidiary (Non-US):

Wurth Vietnam Company Limited (3)
324-326-328 Le Van Sy Street, Ward 2 Tan Binh District, Ho Chi Minh City, Vietnam
Tel.: (84) 2838446901
Web Site: http://www.wurth.com.vn
Industrial Equipment Mfr
N.A.I.C.S.: 333248
Nguyen Giang (Mgr-Sls)

Wurth a Islandi ehf. (3)
Norolingabraut 8, 110, Reykjavik, Iceland
Tel.: (354) 5302000
Web Site: http://www.wurth.is
Emp.: 35
Assembly Materials & Fastening Hardware Distr
N.A.I.C.S.: 423710
Haraldur Leifsson (Mng Dir)

Wurth d.o.o. (3)
Ludvika Kube 6, 81000, Podgorica, Montenegro
Tel.: (382) 20209000
Automobile Parts Distr
N.A.I.C.S.: 423120
Veselin Scepanovic (CEO)

Wurth d.o.o. (3)
Brodisce 25 IOC, 1236, Trzin, Slovenia
Tel.: (386) 15305780
Web Site: http://www.wuerth.si
Fastening Product Mfr & Distr
N.A.I.C.S.: 332722

Wurth d.o.o. (3)
Svetog Save 60v, Surcin, 11271, Belgrade, Serbia
Tel.: (381) 112078200
Web Site: http://www.wurth.rs
Emp.: 150
Holding Company; Assembly Materials & Fastening Hardware Distr
N.A.I.C.S.: 551112

Wurth del Uruguay S.A. (3)
Ruta 101 Km 27 700, Barros Blancos, 91001, Canelones, Uruguay
Tel.: (598) 222880000
Web Site: http://www.wurth.com.uy
Emp.: 130
Assembly Materials & Fastening Hardware Distr
N.A.I.C.S.: 423710

Wurth do Brasil Pecas de Fixacao Ltda. (3)
557 Adolf Wurth Street Jd Sao Vicente, Cotia, 06713-250, Brazil
Tel.: (55) 1146131900
Web Site: http://www.wurth.com.br
Assembly Materials & Fastening Hardware Distr
N.A.I.C.S.: 423710

Subsidiary (Domestic):

SW Pecas de Fixacao Ltda. (4)
Rua Carlos Ayres 542, Galpao 01, Jardim Vera Cruz, CEP 09860-065, Sao Bernardo do Campo, SP, Brazil
Tel.: (55) 1169463488
Web Site: http://www.swindustry.com.br
Assembly Materials & Fastening Hardware Distr
N.A.I.C.S.: 423710

Subsidiary (Non-US):

Wurth spol. s r.o. (3)
Pribylinska 2, 832 55, Bratislava, Slovakia
Tel.: (421) 249 201 211
Web Site: http://www.wurth.sk
Fastening Product Mfr & Distr
N.A.I.C.S.: 332722

WURTH VERWALTUNGSGESELLSCHAFT MBH

Wurth Verwaltungsgesellschaft mbH—(Continued)

Miroslava Vankova *(Mgr-Logistics)*

Wurth, spol. s r.o. (3)
No 137, CP 137, Neprevazka, 293 01,
Mlada Boleslav, Czech Republic
Tel.: (420) 326345111
Web Site: http://www.wuerth.cz
Fastening Material Mfr
N.A.I.C.S.: 332722

Wurth-Kosova Sh.p.k. (3)
Magj Prishtina-Ferizaj Km 7 Fsh, Llapnaselle Gracanice, 10500, Pristina, Kosovo
Tel.: (383) 38600308
Web Site: http://www.wurth-kosova.com
Fastener Product Mfr
N.A.I.C.S.: 332722
Petrit Blakaj *(Mgr-Fin)*

baier & michels Kft. (3)
Vasarter Utca 4, 2351, Alsonemedi, Hungary
Tel.: (36) 704217205
Fastening Product Mfr
N.A.I.C.S.: 332722

marbet Viajes Espana S.A. (3)
Poligono Industrial Riera de Caldes C/Joiers 21, 08184, Palau de Plegamans, Spain
Tel.: (34) 902602300
Web Site: http://www.marbet.es
Event & Travel Services
N.A.I.C.S.: 561920

WUS PRINTED CIRCUIT (KUNSHAN) CO., LTD.

No 1 Donglong Road, Kunshan, 215301, Jiangsu, China
Tel.: (86) 51257356423
Web Site: https://wustec.com
Year Founded: 1992
002463—(SSE)
Rev.: $1,170,378,640
Assets: $1,755,185,679
Liabilities: $594,513,130
Net Worth: $1,160,672,549
Earnings: $191,165,130
Emp.: 9,840
Fiscal Year-end: 12/31/22
Printed Circuit Board Mfr
N.A.I.C.S.: 334412

WUS PRINTED CIRCUIT CO., LTD.

No 37 Kaifa Rd, Nanzih Dist, Kaohsiung, Taiwan
Tel.: (886) 73612116
Web Site: http://www.wus.com.tw
2316—(TAI)
Rev.: $114,978,870
Assets: $468,111,202
Liabilities: $177,553,281
Net Worth: $290,557,921
Earnings: $27,326,138
Emp.: 1,413
Fiscal Year-end: 12/31/23
Printed Circuit Board Mfr
N.A.I.C.S.: 334412
Hsu Huan-Chung *(Chm)*

WUTONG HOLDING GROUP CO., LTD.

No 2596 Taidong Road, Caohu Subdistrict, Suzhou, 215143, China
Tel.: (86) 51283952295
Web Site: https://www.cnwutong.com
Year Founded: 1999
300292—(CHIN)
Rev.: $518,768,072
Assets: $349,660,688
Liabilities: $168,967,449
Net Worth: $180,693,240
Earnings: $3,557,209
Emp.: 1,011
Fiscal Year-end: 12/31/23
Wireless Communication Radio Frequency Connecting Systems Mfr
N.A.I.C.S.: 334220

Weifang Wan *(Chm)*

Subsidiaries:

Adin Media(Shanghai) Co., Ltd. (1)
Floor 7 Block D Shengyin Building No 666 of Shengxia Road, Pudong New District, Shanghai, 200135, China
Tel.: (86) 2168810966
Communication Equipment Mfr
N.A.I.C.S.: 334290

Beijing Guodu Interconnection Technology Co., Ltd. (1)
2nd Floor Jiayou International Building No 25 Landianchang South Road, Haidian District, Beijing, 100142, China
Tel.: (86) 4001104488
Web Site: https://www.guodulink.net
Mobile Information Services
N.A.I.C.S.: 517112

Jiangsu Wutong Interconnect Technology Co., Ltd. (1)
No 2596 of Taidong Road Caohu Street, Xiangcheng District, Suzhou, 215143, China
Tel.: (86) 51283952295
Communication Equipment Mfr
N.A.I.C.S.: 334290

Mobile Center(Beijing) Technology Co., Ltd. (1)
2 Jiayou International Building No 25 Lanchang South Road, Haidian District, Beijing, 100142, China
Tel.: (86) 1062781880
Web Site: https://www.mocentre.cn
Mobile Information Services
N.A.I.C.S.: 517112

Shanghai Broadmobi Communication Technology Co., Ltd. (1)
Room1501 Building 9 No 1515 Gumei Rd, Xuhui District, Shanghai, China
Tel.: (86) 2160913308
Web Site: https://www.broadmobi.com
Communication Equipment Mfr
N.A.I.C.S.: 334290

Suzhou Wutong Intelligent Electronics Co., Ltd. (1)
No 2596 of Taidong Road Caohu Street, Xiangcheng District, Suzhou, 215143, China
Tel.: (86) 51280667007
Communication Equipment Mfr
N.A.I.C.S.: 334290

WUXI ACRYL TECHNOLOGY CO., LTD.

New Material Industrial, Xishan Donggang, Wuxi, 214101, China
Tel.: (86) 51088263255
Web Site: https://www.chinaacryl.com
Year Founded: 1999
603722—(SHG)
Rev.: $100,118,482
Assets: $133,018,638
Liabilities: $25,997,938
Net Worth: $107,020,700
Earnings: $16,873,019
Emp.: 100
Fiscal Year-end: 12/31/22
Chemical Products Mfr
N.A.I.C.S.: 325211
Xuejun Zhu *(Chm & Pres)*

WUXI AUTOWELL TECHNOLOGY CO., LTD.

No 3 Xinhua Road, New District, Wuxi, 214028, Jiangsu, China
Tel.: (86) 51081816658
Web Site: https://www.wxautowell.com
Year Founded: 2010
688516—(SHG)
Rev.: $496,966,481
Assets: $1,194,585,397
Liabilities: $831,082,089
Net Worth: $363,503,308
Earnings: $100,065,846
Emp.: 4,000
Fiscal Year-end: 12/31/22

Photovoltaic Product Mfr
N.A.I.C.S.: 334413
Zhiyong Ge *(Chm & Gen Mgr)*

WUXI BEST PRECISION MACHINERY CO., LTD.

Plot 16 Xituo District Hu Tai Industrial Park, Wuxi, China
Tel.: (86) 510 8223 8655
Web Site: http://www.wuxibest.com
Year Founded: 1997
Sales Range: $25-49.9 Million
Emp.: 70
Mfr & Distr of Precision Components & Toolings to Various Industries
N.A.I.C.S.: 336330
He Liangliang *(Sls Mgr-Overseas)*

WUXI BIOLOGICS (CAYMAN) INC.

No 108 Meiliang Road Mashan, Wuxi, China
Tel.: (86) 51081831205
Web Site: https://www.wuxibiologics.com
Year Founded: 2010
2269—(HKG)
Rev.: $2,358,531,098
Assets: $7,833,369,240
Liabilities: $1,738,735,600
Net Worth: $6,094,633,640
Earnings: $494,381,923
Emp.: 12,740
Fiscal Year-end: 12/31/23
Pharmaceutical Product Mfr & Distr
N.A.I.C.S.: 325412
Eileen Wang *(Sr Dir-IR)*

Subsidiaries:

WuXi Apptec (Suzhou) Testing Technology Co., Ltd. (1)
288 Fute Zhong Road Waigaoqiao Free Trade Zone, Shanghai, 200131, Jiangsu, China
Tel.: (86) 2150461111
Web Site: https://www.wuxiapptec.com
Rev.: $5,585,512,710
Assets: $10,200,120,320
Liabilities: $2,513,278,689
Net Worth: $7,686,841,632
Earnings: $1,495,053,029
Emp.: 41,116
Fiscal Year-end: 12/31/2023
Pharmaceuticals Product Mfr
N.A.I.C.S.: 325412
Ge Li *(Chm & Co-CEO)*

WUXI BOTON TECHNOLOGY LTD.

No 19 Zhang Highway, Xinwu District, Wuxi, 214112, Jiangsu, China
Tel.: (86) 51083709871
Web Site: http://www.botontech.cn
Year Founded: 2000
300031—(CHIN)
Rev.: $514,863,541
Assets: $817,404,932
Liabilities: $284,813,053
Net Worth: $532,591,880
Earnings: $14,939,086
Fiscal Year-end: 12/31/23
Rubber Conveyor Belt Mfr & Distr
N.A.I.C.S.: 326220
Zhifang Bao *(Chm)*

WUXI CHEMICAL EQUIPMENT CO., LTD.

36 Huayi Road, Binhu, Wuxi, 214131, Jiangsu, China
Tel.: (86) 51085633999
Web Site: https://www.wce.cn
Year Founded: 1984
001332—(SSE)
Rev.: $164,206,294
Assets: $413,309,969
Liabilities: $115,178,502
Net Worth: $298,131,467
Earnings: $32,362,270

INTERNATIONAL PUBLIC

Fiscal Year-end: 12/31/22
Industrial Machinery Mfr & Distr
N.A.I.C.S.: 333248
Honghai Cao *(Chm)*

WUXI CHIPOWN MICROELECTRONICS LTD.

Chipown Building No 16 Changjiang Road, Xinwu, Wuxi, 214028, Jiangsu, China
Tel.: (86) 51085217718
Web Site: https://www.chipown.com.cn
Year Founded: 2005
688508—(SHG)
Rev.: $101,030,633
Assets: $241,507,684
Liabilities: $35,067,371
Net Worth: $206,440,313
Earnings: $12,614,154
Fiscal Year-end: 12/31/22
Electronic Product Mfr & Distr
N.A.I.C.S.: 334419
Lixing Zhang *(Chm)*

WUXI COMMERCIAL MANSION GRAND ORIENT CO., LTD.

No 343 Zhongshan Road, Liangxi District, Wuxi, 214000, Jiangsu, China
Tel.: (86) 51082766978
Web Site: https://www.eastall.com
Year Founded: 1999
600327—(SHG)
Rev.: $439,392,835
Assets: $771,208,411
Liabilities: $293,632,813
Net Worth: $477,575,598
Earnings: $24,466,652
Fiscal Year-end: 12/31/22
Automotive Distr
N.A.I.C.S.: 423110
Lin Naiji *(Chm)*

WUXI DELINHAI ENVIRONMENTAL TECHNOLOGY CO., LTD.

No 9 Kangle Road, Binhu, Wuxi, 214092, Jiangsu, China
Tel.: (86) 51085505177
Web Site: https://www.wxdlh.com
Year Founded: 2009
688069—(SHG)
Rev.: $63,014,384
Assets: $250,466,594
Liabilities: $42,791,266
Net Worth: $207,675,328
Earnings: $7,922,547
Fiscal Year-end: 12/31/22
Pollution Control Equipment Mfr & Distr
N.A.I.C.S.: 333248
Hu Mingming *(Chm & Gen Mgr)*

WUXI DOUBLE ELEPHANT MICRO FIBRE MATERIAL CO., LTD.

No 156 Houzhai Middle Road Hongshan Street, Hongshan Town New District, Wuxi, Jiangsu, China
Tel.: (86) 51088993888
Web Site: https://www.sxcxgf.com
002395—(SSE)
Rev.: $195,571,612
Assets: $286,039,630
Liabilities: $165,386,497
Net Worth: $120,653,133
Earnings: ($6,381,601)
Emp.: 1,000
Fiscal Year-end: 12/31/22
Leather Mfr
N.A.I.C.S.: 316990

WUXI HODGEN TECHNOLOGY CO., LTD.

No 177 Changjiang East Road, New

AND PRIVATE COMPANIES / WUXI SUNLIT SCIENCE AND TECHNOLOGY COMPANY LIMITED

District, Wuxi, 214145, Jiangsu, China
Tel.: (86) 51085259761
Web Site: http://www.hodgen-china.com
Year Founded: 1998
300279—(CHIN)
Rev.: $282,367,967
Assets: $322,272,307
Liabilities: $193,014,417
Net Worth: $129,257,890
Earnings: $6,306,897
Fiscal Year-end: 12/31/23
Industrial Control Equipment Mfr
N.A.I.C.S.: 335314

WUXI HONGHUI NEW MATERIALS TECHNOLOGY CO., LTD
No 1 Minxiang Road New Materials Industrial Park, Donggang Town Xishan District, Wuxi, 214196, Jiangsu, China
Tel.: (86) 51088790970
Web Site: https://www.wuxihonghui.com
Year Founded: 2001
002802—(SSE)
Rev.: $72,515,800
Assets: $104,975,578
Liabilities: $8,063,411
Net Worth: $96,912,167
Earnings: $11,870,918
Fiscal Year-end: 12/31/22
Vinyl Chloride Copolymer Mfr & Distr
N.A.I.C.S.: 325211
Hongwei Xiang (Chm & Gen Mgr)

WUXI HUADONG HEAVY MACHINERY CO., LTD.
24th Floor Block B Huafa Sensing Building No 508 Gaolang East Road, Binhu District, Wuxi, 214131, Jiangsu, China
Tel.: (86) 51085628888
Web Site: https://www.hdhm.com
Year Founded: 1989
002685—(SSE)
Rev.: $207,204,440
Assets: $474,173,580
Liabilities: $159,698,429
Net Worth: $314,475,151
Earnings: ($25,073,362)
Emp.: 230
Fiscal Year-end: 12/31/22
Container Handling Equipment Mfr
N.A.I.C.S.: 333248
Yaogen Weng (Chm)

WUXI HUAGUANG ENVIRONMENT & ENERGY GROUP CO., LTD.
No 131 Meiyu Road, Wuxi, 214028, Jiangsu, China
Tel.: (86) 51085215556 CN
Web Site: https://www.wxboiler.com
Year Founded: 1958
600475—(SHG)
Rev.: $1,241,037,537
Assets: $2,966,061,534
Liabilities: $1,690,322,100
Net Worth: $1,275,739,433
Earnings: $102,376,437
Emp.: 3,807
Fiscal Year-end: 12/31/22
Power Plant Boilers & Water Treatment Equipment Mfr
N.A.I.C.S.: 332410
Zhijian Jiang (Chm)

WUXI HYATECH CO., LTD.
No 35 Xindongan Road, Xinwu District, Wuxi, 214142, Jiangsu, China
Tel.: (86) 51081893698
Web Site: https://www.hyatech.cn
Year Founded: 2013

688510—(SHG)
Rev.: $50,896,923
Assets: $202,513,437
Liabilities: $61,949,787
Net Worth: $140,563,650
Earnings: $2,816,733
Fiscal Year-end: 12/31/22
Aircraft Parts Mfr & Distr
N.A.I.C.S.: 336413
Qi Yan (Chm)

WUXI LEAD INTELLIGENT EQUIPMENT CO.,LTD.
No 18 Xinzhou Road, Xinwu District, Wuxi, Jiangsu, China
Tel.: (86) 51081163688
Web Site: https://www.leadintelligent.com
300450—(CHIN)
Rev.: $1,956,101,940
Assets: $4,620,079,620
Liabilities: $3,058,358,472
Net Worth: $1,561,721,148
Earnings: $325,388,232
Emp.: 21,000
Fiscal Year-end: 12/31/22
Automation Equipment Mfr
N.A.I.C.S.: 334519

WUXI LIHU CORPORATION LIMITED
No 2 Tianzhu Road Hudai Town, Binhu District, Wuxi, 214161, Jiangsu, China
Tel.: (86) 51085618806
Web Site: http://www.chinalihu.com
Year Founded: 1994
300694—(CHIN)
Rev.: $225,514,329
Assets: $303,386,998
Liabilities: $115,517,367
Net Worth: $187,869,632
Earnings: $9,525,587
Emp.: 480
Fiscal Year-end: 12/31/23
Turbo Charger Component Mfr & Distr
N.A.I.C.S.: 333611
Zhang Jiabin (Chm)

WUXI LONGSHENG TECHNOLOGY CO., LTD.
No 99 Zhujiang Road, Wuxi National High-tech District, Wuxi, 214028, China
Tel.: (86) 51068758688
Web Site: https://www.china-lsh.com
Year Founded: 2004
300680—(CHIN)
Rev.: $257,336,415
Assets: $494,497,180
Liabilities: $244,634,055
Net Worth: $249,863,125
Earnings: $20,680,259
Fiscal Year-end: 12/31/23
Valve Product Mfr & Distr
N.A.I.C.S.: 332911
Ni Ming (Chm & Gen Mgr)

WUXI NCE POWER CO., LTD.
No 6 Dianteng Road, Xinwu District, Wuxi, 214029, China
Tel.: (86) 51085629718
Web Site: https://www.ncepower.com
Year Founded: 2013
605111—(SHG)
Rev.: $254,256,931
Assets: $560,125,323
Liabilities: $75,481,286
Net Worth: $484,644,036
Earnings: $61,099,412
Fiscal Year-end: 12/31/22
Semiconductor Product Mfr & Distr
N.A.I.C.S.: 334413
Yuanzheng Zhu (Chm & Gen Mgr)

WUXI NEW HONGTAI ELECTRICAL TECH CO LTD
No 18 Yanqiao Yanxin Road, Huishan District, Wuxi, 214174, Jiangsu, China
Tel.: (86) 51083572670
Web Site: https://www.newhongtai.com
Year Founded: 2008
603016—(SHG)
Rev.: $86,284,505
Assets: $145,124,362
Liabilities: $26,768,832
Net Worth: $118,355,529
Earnings: $9,421,008
Fiscal Year-end: 12/31/22
Circuit Breaker Mfr & Distr
N.A.I.C.S.: 335313
Ding Kui (Chm)

WUXI ONLINE OFFLINE COMMUNICATION INFORMATION TECHNOLOGY CO., LTD.
12F Building C1 No 999 Gaolang East Road Economic Development Zone, Wuxi, 214131, Jiangsu, China
Tel.: (86) 51068869309
Web Site: https://www.wxxsxx.com
Year Founded: 2012
300959—(SSE)
Rev.: $271,942,880
Assets: $187,756,681
Liabilities: $24,081,057
Net Worth: $163,675,624
Earnings: $7,036,680
Fiscal Year-end: 12/31/22
Information Technology Services
N.A.I.C.S.: 541512
Kun Wang (Chm & Gen Mgr)

WUXI PAIKE NEW MATERIALS TECHNOLOGY CO., LTD.
30 Lianhe Rd Hudai Industrial Park, BinhuDist, Wuxi, 214161, Jiangsu, China
Tel.: (86) 51085585888
Web Site: https://www.wuxipaike.com
Year Founded: 2006
605123—(SHG)
Rev.: $390,590,441
Assets: $841,223,546
Liabilities: $298,995,517
Net Worth: $542,228,029
Earnings: $68,180,486
Emp.: 450
Fiscal Year-end: 12/31/22
Forging Product Mfr & Distr
N.A.I.C.S.: 332111
Yufeng Shi (Chm & Gen Mgr)

WUXI PHARMATECH (CAYMAN) INC.
288 Fute Zhong Road China Shanghai Pilot Free Trade Zone, Shanghai, 200131, China
Tel.: (86) 21 5046 1111 Ky
Web Site: http://www.wuxiapptec.com
Year Founded: 2000
Holding Company; Pharmaceutical & Biotechnological Research & Development Services
N.A.I.C.S.: 551112
Steve Yang (Chief Business Officer & Exec VP)

Subsidiaries:

Ambrx, Inc. (1)
10975 N Torrey Pines Rd, La Jolla, CA 92037
Tel.: (858) 875-2400
Web Site: http://www.ambrx.com
Biopharmaceutical Developer
N.A.I.C.S.: 325412
Feng Tian (Chm, Pres & CEO)

Cycle Solutions, Inc. (1)
5301 SW Pkwy Ste 100, Austin, TX 78735

Tel.: (512) 343-1092
Web Site: http://www.researchpoint.com
Emp.: 450
Research & Development in the Physical, Engineering & Life Sciences
N.A.I.C.S.: 541715
John V. Farinacci (Pres & CEO)

WuXi AppTec, Inc. (1)
2540 Executive Dr, Saint Paul, MN 55120
Tel.: (651) 675-2000
Web Site: http://www.wuxiapptec.com
Sales Range: $50-74.9 Million
Emp.: 125
Pharmaceutical Testing & Manufacturing Services
N.A.I.C.S.: 325412
Minzhang Chen (Co-CEO)

XenoBiotic Laboratories, Inc. (1)
107 Morgan Ln, Plainsboro, NJ 08536
Tel.: (609) 799-2295
Web Site: http://www.xbl.com
Emp.: 150
Bio-Analytical, Drug Metabolism & Pharmacokinetic Services
N.A.I.C.S.: 325412
Jinn Wu (CEO)

WUXI PUBLIC UTILITIES INDUSTRIAL GROUP CO., LTD.
No 800 Jiefang East Road, Wuxi, Jiangsu, China
Tel.: (86) 510 8282 6690
Web Site: http://www.wxszjt.com
Year Founded: 2003
Engineering & Construction Services
N.A.I.C.S.: 541330

WUXI RURAL COMMERCIAL BANK CO., LTD
No 9 Financial 2nd Street, Wuxi, 214125, Jiangsu, China
Tel.: (86) 51082830815
Web Site: http://www.wrcb.com.cn
Year Founded: 2005
600908—(SHG)
Rev.: $629,035,103
Assets: $29,709,117,500
Liabilities: $26,968,494,197
Net Worth: $2,740,623,304
Earnings: $280,958,512
Fiscal Year-end: 12/31/22
Commercial Bank Services
N.A.I.C.S.: 522110
Tao Chang (Chm & Sec-Party)

WUXI SANWA PLASTICS CO., LTD.
No 1 Quanfeng Road Huanghong Xiang, Wuxi, 214046, China
Tel.: (86) 510 8310 7184
Web Site: http://www.sanwa.cc
Year Founded: 1994
Plastics Product Mfr
N.A.I.C.S.: 326199

WUXI SMART AUTO-CONTROL ENGINEERING CO., LTD.
No 258 Xida Road, Wuxi New District, Wuxi, 214112, Jiangsu, China
Tel.: (86) 51088551877
Web Site: http://www.wuxismart.com
Year Founded: 2001
002877—(SSE)
Rev.: $121,095,225
Assets: $298,352,274
Liabilities: $171,982,124
Net Worth: $126,370,151
Earnings: $11,741,624
Fiscal Year-end: 12/31/22
Valve Product Mfr & Distr
N.A.I.C.S.: 332912
Shen Jianbiao (Chm & Gen Mgr)

WUXI SUNLIT SCIENCE AND TECHNOLOGY COMPANY LIMITED

WUXI SUNLIT SCIENCE AND TECHNOLOGY COMPANY LIMITED

Wuxi Sunlit Science and Technology Company Limited—(Continued)
No1 Yan Xin East Road Huishan Economic Development Zone, Wuxi, 214174, Jiangsu, China
Tel.: (86) 51083620059
Web Site: https://www.wxsunlit.com
Year Founded: 2006
1289—(HKG)
Rev.: $29,209,939
Assets: $132,780,773
Liabilities: $40,872,827
Net Worth: $91,907,946
Earnings: $3,173,602
Emp.: 192
Fiscal Year-end: 12/31/22
Steel Pole Mfr
N.A.I.C.S.: 331222
Degang Zhang *(Founder, Chm & Gen Mgr)*

WUXI TAIJI INDUSTRY CO., LTD.
21F No 401 Xingyuan North Road, Liangxi District, Wuxi, 214000, Jiangsu, China
Tel.: (86) 51085419120
Web Site: http://www.wxtj.com
Year Founded: 1990
600667—(SHG)
Rev.: $4,941,343,813
Assets: $4,061,642,720
Liabilities: $2,955,688,501
Net Worth: $1,105,954,219
Earnings: ($104,280,907)
Emp.: 2,800
Fiscal Year-end: 12/31/22
Industrial Yarn Mfr
N.A.I.C.S.: 313110
Sun Hongwei *(Chm)*

Subsidiaries:

Hitech Semiconductor (Wuxi) Co., Ltd. (1)
Export processing zone K5/K6 East Gaolang Road, Wuxi New District, 214028, China
Tel.: (86) 510 81158888
Web Site: http://www.hitechsemi.com
Semiconductor Devices Mfr
N.A.I.C.S.: 334413

Jiangsu Taiji Industry New Materials Co., Ltd. (1)
No 28 Yingchun Road Guangling Industrial Park, Yangzhou, 225006, Jiangsu, China
Tel.: (86) 51487922102
Web Site: http://www.jstjsy.com
Rubber Material Mfr
N.A.I.C.S.: 326299

Taiji Semiconductor (Suzhou) Co., Ltd. (1)
Plant 1 Genway Factory No 158 Qiming Road, Integrated Free Trade Zone East Suzhou Industrial Park, Suzhou, 215126, China
Tel.: (86) 512 62622600
Web Site: http://www.taijisemi.com
Semiconductor Devices Mfr
N.A.I.C.S.: 334413

WUXI WEIFU HIGH-TECHNOLOGY CO., LTD.
No 5th Huashan Road, Xinwu District, Wuxi, 214028, Jiangsu, China
Tel.: (86) 51080505555
Web Site: https://www.weifu.com.cn
Year Founded: 1958
000581—(SSE)
Rev.: $1,787,240,740
Assets: $4,005,459,399
Liabilities: $1,417,226,565
Net Worth: $2,588,232,835
Earnings: $16,682,300
Emp.: 8,000
Fiscal Year-end: 12/31/22
Automotive Components Mfr
N.A.I.C.S.: 336310

Yin Zhenyuan *(Chm)*

Subsidiaries:

Chongqing WEIFU Lida Automobile Components Co., Ltd. (1)
No10 Jiangshui Road, Tongliang District, Chongqing, China
Tel.: (86) 2345211655
Automotive Components Mfr
N.A.I.C.S.: 334419

Nanchang WEIFU Lida Automobile Components Co., Ltd. (1)
No 358 Jinsha Road Xiaolan Economic Technological Development Zone, Jiangxiang, China
Tel.: (86) 79182311075
Automotive Components Mfr
N.A.I.C.S.: 334419

Nanjing WEIFU Jinning Co., Ltd. (1)
No 12 Liuzhou North Road, Pukou District, Nanjing, China
Tel.: (86) 2558498022
Automotive Components Mfr
N.A.I.C.S.: 334419

Ningbo WEIFU Tianli Supercharging Technique Co., Ltd. (1)
No 268 Changyang Road, Jiangbei District, Ningbo, China
Tel.: (86) 57427861792
Automotive Components Mfr
N.A.I.C.S.: 334419

Wuhan WEIFU Lida Catalytic Converter Co., Ltd. (1)
Donghe Center Economic Development Zone, Wuhan, China
Tel.: (86) 2784296872
Automotive Components Mfr
N.A.I.C.S.: 334419

Wuxi WEIFU Changan Co., Ltd. (1)
88 Huichang Road Huishan Economic & Technological Development Zone, HuiShan District, Wuxi, China
Tel.: (86) 51083761184
Automotive Components Mfr
N.A.I.C.S.: 334419

Wuxi WEIFU Electric Drive Technology Co., Ltd. (1)
No 6 Huashan Road, Xinwu District, Wuxi, China
Tel.: (86) 51080505084
Automotive Components Mfr
N.A.I.C.S.: 334419

Wuxi WEIFU Lida Catalytic Converter Co., Ltd. (1)
No 559 Xinhui Road, Huishan District, Wuxi, China
Tel.: (86) 51081136535
Automotive Components Mfr
N.A.I.C.S.: 334419

Wuxi WEIFU Mashan Fuel Injection Equipment Co., Ltd. (1)
No 5 Yinghui Road No 7 Bridge MaShan, Binhu District, Wuxi, China
Tel.: (86) 51085996359
Automotive Components Mfr
N.A.I.C.S.: 334419

Wuxi WEIFU Schmidt Power System Co., Ltd. (1)
No 139 Xixie Road, Xinwu District, Wuxi, China
Tel.: (86) 51066616699
Automotive Components Mfr
N.A.I.C.S.: 334419

WUXI XINJE ELECTRIC CO., LTD
No 816 Jianshe West Road, Binhu District, Wuxi, 214072, JiangSu, China
Tel.: (86) 51085134136
Web Site: https://www.xinje.com
Year Founded: 2008
603416—(SHG)
Rev.: $187,447,872
Assets: $378,204,143
Liabilities: $102,532,548
Net Worth: $275,671,595

Earnings: $31,174,935
Emp.: 500
Fiscal Year-end: 12/31/22
Controller Component Mfr & Distr
N.A.I.C.S.: 334513
Li Xin *(Chm & Gen Mgr)*

WUXI XUELANG ENVIRONMENTAL TECHNOLOGY CO., LTD.
2020 Lihu Avenue, Binhu District, Wuxi, 214125, Jiangsu, China
Tel.: (86) 51068567222
Web Site: https://www.cecm.com.cn
300385—(CHIN)
Rev.: $252,722,808
Assets: $447,237,180
Liabilities: $329,751,864
Net Worth: $117,485,316
Earnings: ($16,369,236)
Emp.: 370
Fiscal Year-end: 12/31/22
Air Purification Equipment Mfr
N.A.I.C.S.: 333413
Jianping Yang *(Chm & Gen Mgr)*

WUXI ZHENHUA AUTO PARTS CO., LTD.
No 188 Luoou East Road, Hudai Town Binhu District, Wuxi, 214161, Jiangsu, China
Tel.: (86) 51085592554
Web Site: http://www.wxzhenhua.com.cn
Year Founded: 2006
605319—(SHG)
Rev.: $245,231,949
Assets: $469,248,095
Liabilities: $215,071,038
Net Worth: $254,177,057
Earnings: $11,360,298
Fiscal Year-end: 12/31/22
Automotive Parts Mfr & Distr
N.A.I.C.S.: 336390
Jinxiang Qian *(Chm)*

WUXIN TECHNOLOGY HOLDINGS, INC.
Tefa Information and Technology Plaza Floor 15 No 2 Qiongyu Road, Nanshan District, Shenzhen, 518052, China
Tel.: (86) 75586379339
Year Founded: 2021
Rev.: $46,977,350
Assets: $35,859,182
Liabilities: $16,339,498
Net Worth: $19,519,684
Earnings: $5,961,239
Emp.: 340
Fiscal Year-end: 06/30/21
Holding Company
N.A.I.C.S.: 551112
Lianqi Liu *(CEO & Chm)*

WUYANG PARKING
Zhujiang Road North Yinshan Road East, Tongshan New District, Xuzhou, 221116, Jiangsu, China
Tel.: (86) 51683501768
Web Site: http://www.wuyangkeji.com
Year Founded: 2001
300420—(CHIN)
Rev.: $204,689,160
Assets: $499,666,752
Liabilities: $146,105,856
Net Worth: $353,560,896
Earnings: $7,675,668
Fiscal Year-end: 12/31/22
Bulk Material Handling Equipment Mfr
N.A.I.C.S.: 333248
Youfu Hou *(Chm & Gen Mgr)*

WUZHOU INTERNATIONAL HOLDINGS LIMITED

INTERNATIONAL PUBLIC

19th Fl Wuzhou International Columbus Plaza Tower B 287 Guangyi Road, Wuxi, China
Tel.: (86) 510 83250999
Web Site: http://www.wz-china.com
Sales Range: $500-549.9 Million
Commercial Property Developer
N.A.I.C.S.: 237210
Xiaowei Shen *(Exec Dir)*

WUZHOU SPECIAL PAPER GROUP CO., LTD.
No 1 Tongbo North Road, Qujiang, Quzhou, 324022, Zhejiang, China
Tel.: (86) 5708566059
Web Site: http://www.wztzzy.com
Year Founded: 2008
605007—(SHG)
Rev.: $837,075,414
Assets: $921,995,357
Liabilities: $612,644,021
Net Worth: $309,351,337
Earnings: $28,809,561
Fiscal Year-end: 12/31/22
Paper Products Mfr
N.A.I.C.S.: 322299
Lei Zhao *(Chm & Gen Mgr)*

Subsidiaries:

Jaingxi Five Star Paper Co., Ltd. (1)
1 Donggang 4th Road, Quzhou, China
Tel.: (86) 570 856 6059
Web Site: https://jxwxzy.com
Paper Products Mfr
N.A.I.C.S.: 322299

WVI GMBH
Nordstrasse 11, 38106, Braunschweig, Germany
Tel.: (49) 531387370
Web Site: http://www.wvigmbh.de
Engineering Consulting Services
N.A.I.C.S.: 541330

WW HOLDING INC
3F-7 No 1 Wuquan 1st Rd, Xinzhuang Dist, New Taipei City, 242, Taiwan
Tel.: (886) 222982927
Web Site: http://www.ww-holding.com.tw
Year Founded: 2009
8442—(TAI)
Rev.: $259,039,364
Assets: $201,778,043
Liabilities: $97,616,138
Net Worth: $104,161,905
Earnings: $20,163,052
Fiscal Year-end: 12/31/23
Sports Good Mfr & Distr
N.A.I.C.S.: 339920
Yong-Yu Hong *(Chm)*

Subsidiaries:

Dongguan Wei Bao Sports Equipment Co., Ltd. (1)
Quantang Industrial Zone, Liaobu Town, Dongguan, Guangdong, China
Tel.: (86) 76938921688
Sports Protective Equipment Retailer
N.A.I.C.S.: 423910

Jiangsu Hongsheng Leather Co., Ltd. (1)
No 2-1 Hongsheng Road, Economic Development Zone, Huai'an, Jiangsu, China
Tel.: (86) 51783329666
Sports Protective Equipment Retailer
N.A.I.C.S.: 423910

Na Sheng Leather (Huai'an) Co., Ltd. (1)
No 2 Hongsheng Road, Economic Development Zone, Huai'an, Jiangsu, China
Tel.: (86) 51786282888
Sports Protective Equipment Retailer
N.A.I.C.S.: 423910

Nice-Bag International Industries Co., Ltd. (1)

AND PRIVATE COMPANIES — X FINANCIAL

No 2 Wilson Road Economic Develop Area, Huai'an, Jiangsu, China
Tel.: (86) 51786282888
Fashion Bag Mfr
N.A.I.C.S.: 316990

TWT Manufacturing Co., Ltd. (1)
700/156 MOO 1 T bankao A panthong, Chon Buri, 20160, Thailand
Tel.: (66) 38465032
Sports Protective Equipment Retailer
N.A.I.C.S.: 423910

Wellpower Commerce Holding Co., Limited (1)
Room 505 5/F Baolong Centre 11 Wang Chiu Road, Kowloon Bay, China (Hong Kong)
Tel.: (852) 27513932
Sports Protective Equipment Retailer
N.A.I.C.S.: 423910

Wellpower Sporting Goods (HK) Co., Limited (1)
Unit5 5/F Block A Po Lung Centre No 11 Wang Chiu Road Kowloon Bay, Kowloon, China (Hong Kong)
Tel.: (852) 2795 9713
Sports Equipment Mfr
N.A.I.C.S.: 339920

Subsidiary (Non-US):

Wellpower Sporting Goods Co., Ltd. (2)
Quan Tang Industrial Zone, Liao Bu Town, Dongguan, 523425, Guangdong, China
Tel.: (86) 76987813606
Sports Equipment Mfr
N.A.I.C.S.: 339920

Wilson Group Holdings (Samoa) Limited (1)
Offshore Chambers, PO Box 217, Apia, Samoa (Western)
Tel.: (685) 769 2265 2170
Fashion Bag Mfr
N.A.I.C.S.: 316990

Wilson Group Holdings Limited. (1)
Unit5 5/F Block A Po Lung Centre No 11 Wang Chiu Road Kowloon Bay, Kowloon, 114, China (Hong Kong)
Tel.: (852) 2795 9713
Fashion Bag Mfr
N.A.I.C.S.: 316990

Subsidiary (Non-US):

Hong Sheng Leather Ind. Co., Ltd. (2)
Wen Tang industry Section Dong Cheng District, Dongguan, Guangdong, China
Tel.: (86) 76922652170
Fashion Bag Mfr
N.A.I.C.S.: 316990

Wilson International Ind. Co., Ltd. (1)
No 2-1 Wilson Road Economic Develop Area, Huai'an, Jiangsu, China
Tel.: (86) 51783329666
Fashion Bag Mfr
N.A.I.C.S.: 316990

WWF INTERNATIONAL
Av du Mont-Blanc 27, Gland, 1196, Switzerland
Tel.: (41) 223649111
Web Site: http://wwf.panda.org
Year Founded: 1961
Sales Range: $550-599.9 Million
Emp.: 6,400
Wildlife Conservation Organization
N.A.I.C.S.: 813312
Andre S. Hoffmann (VP)

Subsidiaries:

World Wildlife Fund Canada (1)
410 Adelaide St West Suite 400, Toronto, M5V 1S8, ON, Canada
Tel.: (416) 489-8800
Web Site: http://www.wwf.ca
Sales Range: $10-24.9 Million
Emp.: 70
Wildlife Conservation Organization
N.A.I.C.S.: 813312

Patricia Koval (Chm)

World Wildlife Fund, Inc. (1)
1250 24th St NW, Washington, DC 20037
Tel.: (202) 293-4800
Web Site: http://www.worldwildlife.org
Emp.: 300
Wildlife Conservation Organization
N.A.I.C.S.: 813312
Pamela Matson (Vice Chm)

WWPKG HOLDINGS COMPANY LIMITED
Room 703 7/F Lippo Sun Plaza 28 Canton Road, Tsim Tsa Tsui, China (Hong Kong)
Tel.: (852) 34430883   Ky
Web Site: http://www.wwpkg.com.hk
Year Founded: 1979
8069—(HKG)
Rev.: $32,733,635
Assets: $7,585,436
Liabilities: $2,304,317
Net Worth: $5,281,118
Earnings: ($3,351,244)
Emp.: 121
Fiscal Year-end: 03/31/20
Tour Operator
N.A.I.C.S.: 561520

WYELANDS BANK PLC
No 7 Hertford Street, London, W1J 7RH, United Kingdom
Tel.: (44) 203 889 0880   UK
Web Site: http://www.wyelandsbank.co.uk
Rev.: $37,964,002
Assets: $1,086,334,419
Liabilities: $931,870,573
Net Worth: $154,463,845
Earnings: $15,228
Emp.: 36
Fiscal Year-end: 04/30/19
Commercial Banking Services
N.A.I.C.S.: 522110
Iain Hunter (CEO)

WYLLIE GROUP PTY LTD
19th Floor St Georges Square, 225 St Georges Terrace, Perth, 6000, WA, Australia
Tel.: (61) 893226699
Web Site: http://www.wylliegroup.com
Sales Range: $50-74.9 Million
Emp.: 26
Property Management & Investment Services
N.A.I.C.S.: 541611
Rhonda N. Wyllie (Exec Dir)

WYNCOAST INDUSTRIAL PARK PUBLIC COMPANY LIMITED
105 Moo 3 Bangna-trad Rd K M 52, Bang Pakong, Chachoengsao, 24130, Thailand
Tel.: (66) 38573162
Web Site: http://www.wyncoast.com
Year Founded: 1985
WIN—(THA)
Rev.: $3,008,094
Assets: $22,717,222
Liabilities: $10,229,434
Net Worth: $12,487,788
Earnings: $338,122
Emp.: 44
Fiscal Year-end: 12/31/23
Logistic Services
N.A.I.C.S.: 541614
Jak Chamikorn (Chm & CEO)

WYNNSTAY GROUP PLC
Eagle House, Powys, SY22 6AQ, United Kingdom
Tel.: (44) 1691223110
Web Site:
https://www.wynnstay.co.uk

WYN—(AIM)
Rev.: $968,100,522
Assets: $348,357,009
Liabilities: $170,901,647
Net Worth: $177,455,362
Earnings: $23,274,036
Emp.: 900
Fiscal Year-end: 10/31/22
Animal, Farm & Garden Store Operator
N.A.I.C.S.: 424910
Bryan Paul Roberts (Fin Dir)

Subsidiaries:

Bibby Agriculture Limited (1)
Network House, Oxon Business Park, Shrewsbury, SY3 5AB, United Kingdom
Tel.: (44) 1743237890
Web Site: https://bibbyagri.com
Sales Range: $25-49.9 Million
Emp.: 70
Other Animal Food Mfr
N.A.I.C.S.: 311119

Glasson Fertilizers Limited (1)
Pk Ln Winmarleigh, Lancashire, PR3 0JU, Preston, United Kingdom - England (100%)
Tel.: (44) 1524799920
Web Site: http://www.glassongrain.co.uk
Emp.: 60
Nitrogenous Fertilizer Mfr
N.A.I.C.S.: 325311

Glasson Grain Limited (1)
West Quay Glasson Dock, Lancaster, LA2 0DB, United Kingdom
Tel.: (44) 1524752200
Web Site: http://www.glassongrain.co.uk
Emp.: 80
Animal Food Distr
N.A.I.C.S.: 424910

Glasson Group (Lancaster) Limited (1)
West Quay Glasson Dock, Lancaster, LA2 0DB, Lancs, United Kingdom (100%)
Tel.: (44) 1524752200
Web Site: http://www.glassongrain.co.uk
Emp.: 50
Animal Feed Mfr
N.A.I.C.S.: 311119

Glasson Shipping Services Limited (1)
West Quay Glasson Dock, Lancaster, LA2 0DB, Lancashire, United Kingdom (100%)
Tel.: (44) 1524751674
Web Site: http://www.glassongrain.co.uk
Emp.: 2
Navigational Services to Shipping
N.A.I.C.S.: 488330

Welsh Feed Producers Limited (1)
Eagle House, Llansantffraid Ym Mechain, Powys, SY22 6AQ, United Kingdom (100%)
Tel.: (44) 1267231341
Emp.: 40
Animal Feed Mfr
N.A.I.C.S.: 311119
Kenneth Greetham (Mng Dir)

Woodheads Seeds Limited (1)
Pease Farm Little Airmyn, Selby, YO8 8PT, North Yorkshire, United Kingdom
Tel.: (44) 1757617000
Web Site: http://www.woodheadsseeds.co.uk
Emp.: 15
Seeds & Fertilizer Distr
N.A.I.C.S.: 424910

Wynnstay (1)
Dovefields, Uttoxeter, ST14 8AE, Staffordshire, United Kingdom (100%)
Tel.: (44) 188 956 4844
Web Site: http://www.wynnstay.co.uk
Emp.: 7
Farm Supplies Whslr
N.A.I.C.S.: 424910

Wynnstay & Clwyd Farmers Limited (1)
Eagle House, Llansantffraid Ym Mechain, Powys, SY22 6AQ, United Kingdom (100%)
Tel.: (44) 1691828512

Emp.: 100
Pesticide & Agricultural Chemical Mfr
N.A.I.C.S.: 325320
Ken Greetham (CEO)

Wynnstay (Agricultural Supplies) Limited (1)
Eagle House, Llansantffraid, Powys, SY22 6AQ, United Kingdom
Tel.: (44) 1691223110
Feed & Nutrition Product Distr
N.A.I.C.S.: 424490

Wynnstay Arable (1)
Astley Park Astley, Shrewsbury, SY4 4RT, Shropshire, United Kingdom (100%)
Tel.: (44) 193 921 0555
Web Site: http://www.wynnstaygroup.co.uk
Emp.: 700
Agricultural Services
N.A.I.C.S.: 424510

Youngs Animal Feeds Limited (1)
Standon Mill, Standon, ST21 6RP, Staffordshire, United Kingdom
Tel.: (44) 1782 791209
Web Site:
http://www.youngsanimalfeeds.co.uk
Animal Feeds Mfr & Distr
N.A.I.C.S.: 311119

WYNNSTAY PROPERTIES PLC
Hamilton House Mabledon Place, London, WC1H 9BB, United Kingdom
Tel.: (44) 7469042389   UK
Web Site:
https://www.wynnstayproperties.com
Year Founded: 1886
WSP—(AIM)
Rev.: $3,309,982
Assets: $56,944,421
Liabilities: $17,950,287
Net Worth: $38,994,134
Earnings: $1,731,375
Fiscal Year-end: 03/25/24
Real Estate Manangement Services
N.A.I.C.S.: 531390
Philip G. H. Collins (Chm)

WYSADA
Sweifieh, Amman, 11814, Jordan
Tel.: (962) 6 5820347
Web Site: http://www.wysada.com
Year Founded: 2012
Emp.: 75
Online Home Furnishings Retailer
N.A.I.C.S.: 449129
Fadi Alsabbagh (Co-Founder & Chief Product Officer)

WYSIWYG STUDIOS CO., LTD.
9th floor 128 Dosandaero, Gangnam-gu, Seoul, Korea (South)
Tel.: (82) 27490507
Web Site:
https://www.wswgstudios.com
Year Founded: 2016
299900—(KRS)
Rev.: $142,926,338
Assets: $296,484,324
Liabilities: $108,107,475
Net Worth: $188,376,848
Earnings: ($9,430,877)
Emp.: 108
Fiscal Year-end: 12/31/22
Video Production Services
N.A.I.C.S.: 512110
Kwan-Woo Park (CEO)

X FINANCIAL
7-8F Block A Aerospace Science and Technology Plaza No 168, Third Avenue Nanshan District, Shenzhen, 518067, China
Tel.: (86) 75586282977   Ky
Web Site:
https://ir.xiaoyinggroup.com
Year Founded: 2014
XYF—(NYSE)
Rev.: $545,879,587

X Financial—(Continued)

Assets: $1,354,018,417
Liabilities: $625,772,266
Net Worth: $728,246,151
Earnings: $124,405,974
Emp.: 461
Fiscal Year-end: 12/31/22
Financial Management Services
N.A.I.C.S.: 541611
Yue Tang (Co-Founder, Chm & CEO)

X-FAB SILICON FOUNDRIES GMBH
Transportstraat 1, B-3980, Tessenderlo, Belgium
Tel.: (32) 3614276489
Web Site: https://www.xfab.com
Holding Company; Semiconductor Foundries
N.A.I.C.S.: 551112
Rudi de Winter (CEO)

Subsidiaries:

X-FAB Semiconductor Foundries GmbH (1)
Haarbergstrasse 67, 99097, Erfurt, Germany (100%)
Tel.: (49) 361 427 6000
Web Site: http://www.xfab.com
Semiconductor Foundries
N.A.I.C.S.: 334413
Charles Hage (VP-Sls)

Subsidiary (Domestic):

X-FAB Dresden GmbH & Co. KG (2)
Grenzstrasse 28, 01109, Dresden, Germany
Tel.: (49) 351 40756 0
Web Site: http://www.xfab.com
Semiconductor Devices Mfr
N.A.I.C.S.: 334413

Subsidiary (Non-US):

X-FAB France SAS (2)
224 Boulevard John Kennedy, 91105, Corbeil-Essonnes, Cedex, France (100%)
Tel.: (33) 1 60 88 51 51
Web Site: http://www.xfab.com
Semiconductor Applications & Foundry Services
N.A.I.C.S.: 334413
Dirk Drescher (CEO)

Subsidiary (Domestic):

X-FAB MEMS Foundry Itzehoe GmbH (2)
Fraunhoferstrasse 1, 25524, Itzehoe, Germany
Tel.: (49) 4821 17 4228
Web Site: http://www.xfab.com
Semiconductor Devices Mfr
N.A.I.C.S.: 334413
Volker Herbig (VP)

Subsidiary (Non-US):

X-FAB Sarawak Sdn. Bhd. (2)
1 Silicon Drive Sama Jaya Free Industrial Zone, Kuching, 93350, Sarawak, Malaysia
Tel.: (60) 82 354 888
Web Site: http://www.xfab.com
Semiconductor Devices Mfr
N.A.I.C.S.: 334413

Subsidiary (US):

X-FAB Texas, Inc. (2)
2301 N University Ave, Lubbock, TX 79415
Tel.: (806) 747-2400
Web Site: http://www.xfab.com
Emp.: 259
Semiconductor Devices Mfr
N.A.I.C.S.: 334413
Pamela Riley (Mgr-Acctg)

X-LEGEND ENTERTAINMENT CO., LTD.
110 7th Floor No 288 Section 6 Citizen Avenue, Xinyi District, Taipei, 110, Taiwan
Tel.: (886) 277186898
Web Site: https://www.x-legend.tw
Year Founded: 2002
4994—(TAI)
Rev.: $53,096,862
Assets: $54,232,805
Liabilities: $15,935,511
Net Worth: $38,297,294
Earnings: $5,104,189
Emp.: 316
Fiscal Year-end: 12/31/23
Online Gaming Software Publisher
N.A.I.C.S.: 513210
Feng-Chi Chang (Chm)

X-TENTION INFORMATION-STECHNOLOGIE GMBH
Romerstrasse 80A, 4600, Wels, Austria
Tel.: (43) 7242 2155   AT
Web Site: https://x-tention.com
Year Founded: 2001
Emp.: 600
Wolfgang Pramendorfer (Mng Dir)

Subsidiaries:

InterComponentWare GmbH (1)
Altrottstrasse 31, 69190, Walldorf, Germany
Tel.: (49) 62273850
Web Site: http://icw-global.com
Sales Range: $50-74.9 Million
Emp.: 250
Holding Company; Healthcare Industry Software Publisher
N.A.I.C.S.: 551112
Ralf Brandner (Member-Exec Bd)

Subsidiary (US):

InterComponentWare Inc. (2)
150 Monument Rd Ste 207, Bala Cynwyd, PA 19004
Tel.: (484) 278-6571
Web Site: http://us.icw-global.com
Healthcare Software Development Services
N.A.I.C.S.: 541511

X-TERRA RESOURCES INC.
C P 491 Rouyn-Noranda, Quebec, J9X 5C4, QC, Canada
Tel.: (819) 762-4101
Web Site: http://www.xterraresources.com
Year Founded: 1987
CLIC—(TSXV)
Rev.: $47,298
Assets: $5,648,554
Liabilities: $762,321
Net Worth: $4,886,233
Earnings: $2,615,483
Fiscal Year-end: 12/31/23
Mining Exploration Services
N.A.I.C.S.: 213114
Sylvain Champagne (CFO)

X1 ESPORTS & ENTERTAINMENT LTD.
615-800 West Pender St, Vancouver, V6C 2V6, BC, Canada
Tel.: (604) 229-9445
Web Site: https://www.x1esports.com
Year Founded: 2020
XONE—(CNSX)
Entertainment Broadcasting Services
N.A.I.C.S.: 516120
Mark Elfenbein (CEO)

X20 JOINT STOCK COMPANY
35 Phan Dinh Giot-Phuong Lie, Thanh Xuan, Hanoi, Vietnam
Tel.: (84) 2438645077
Web Site: https://www.gatexco20.com.vn
Year Founded: 1957
X20—(HNX)
Rev.: $103,439,500
Assets: $58,976,400
Liabilities: $33,055,700
Net Worth: $25,920,700
Earnings: $2,038,000
Fiscal Year-end: 12/31/23
Industrial Machinery Mfr
N.A.I.C.S.: 333248

X2M CONNECT LIMITED
Suite 1 01b Building B18-24 Ricketts Road, Mount Waverley, 3149, VIC, Australia
Tel.: (61) 1800926926   AU
Web Site: https://www.x2mconnect.com
Year Founded: 2019
X2M—(ASX)
Rev.: $11,000,656
Assets: $9,242,664
Liabilities: $8,978,436
Net Worth: $264,228
Earnings: ($4,247,297)
Emp.: 58
Fiscal Year-end: 06/30/23
Information Technology Services
N.A.I.C.S.: 541512
Keith Jelley (COO)

Subsidiaries:

Freestyle Technology Co., Ltd. (1)
Room 809 55 Digital-ro 34-gil, Guro-gu, Seoul, 08378, Korea (South)
Tel.: (82) 260125466
Network Technology Services
N.A.I.C.S.: 541519

Freestyle Technology Japan KK Ltd. (1)
Level 9 Tower B Ariake Frontier Building 3-7-26, Koto-ku, Tokyo, 135-0063, Japan
Tel.: (81) 355308876
Software Development Services
N.A.I.C.S.: 541511

Freestyle Technology Taiwan Limited (1)
Room 411 4F No19-13 Sanchong Rd, Nangang District, Taipei, 115, Taiwan
Tel.: (886) 223759880
Information Technology Services
N.A.I.C.S.: 541511

X3 HOLDINGS CO., LTD.
Suite 412 Tower A Tai Seng Exchange, One Tai Seng Avenue, Singapore, 536464, Singapore
Tel.: (86) 7563395666   Ky
Web Site: https://www.x3holdings.com
Year Founded: 1997
XTKG—(NASDAQ)
Rev.: $10,482,809
Assets: $130,588,110
Liabilities: $28,037,968
Net Worth: $102,550,142
Earnings: $21,505,598)
Emp.: 177
Fiscal Year-end: 12/31/22
Software Development Services
N.A.I.C.S.: 541511
Ban Lor (Co-Founder, Co-Chm & Co-CEO)

X3 TELECOMUNICACOES E EQUIPAMENTOS LTDA.
Avenida Paulista 575 An 12 Conj 1201, Bela Vista, 01311-000, Sao Paulo, Brazil
Tel.: (55) 1131712788   BR
Web Site: http://www.x3technology.com.br
Sales Range: $1-9.9 Million
Emp.: 41
Telecommunications Equipment Mfr
N.A.I.C.S.: 334290

X5 RETAIL GROUP N.V.
Koroviy Val street 5 building 1, Moscow, 119049, Russia
Tel.: (7) 4956628888
Web Site: https://www.x5.ru
FIVE—(LSE)
Rev.: $34,023,447,597
Assets: $17,121,407,288
Liabilities: $14,857,329,808
Net Worth: $2,264,077,481
Earnings: $850,007,841
Emp.: 372,200
Fiscal Year-end: 12/31/23
Food Products Distr
N.A.I.C.S.: 424420
Frank Lhoest (Member-Mgmt Bd & Sec)

Subsidiaries:

Torgovyi Dom Kopeyka OAO (1)
ul Konenkova 5, 127560, Moscow, Russia
Tel.: (7) 495 662 8888
Web Site: http://www.kopeyka.ru
Discount Grocery & General Merchandise Stores
N.A.I.C.S.: 445110
Sergey Evgenevich Solodov (CEO & Gen Dir)

XAAR PLC
3950 Cambridge Research Park, Waterbeach, Cambridge, CB25 9PE, Cambridgeshire, United Kingdom
Tel.: (44) 1223423663
Web Site: https://www.xaar.com
XAR—(LSE)
Rev.: $80,450,341
Assets: $141,121,417
Liabilities: $47,707,565
Net Worth: $93,413,851
Earnings: $19,317,640
Emp.: 407
Fiscal Year-end: 12/31/21
Commercial Printing (except Screen & Books)
N.A.I.C.S.: 323111
John Mills (CEO)

Subsidiaries:

FUJIFILM Electronic Imaging Limited (1)
The Cube Maylands Avenue, Hemel Hempstead, HP2 7DF, United Kingdom
Tel.: (44) 144 221 3440
Web Site: https://www.ffei.co.uk
Sales Range: $25-49.9 Million
Emp.: 100
Electronic Pre-Press Equipment Designer, Mfr & Supplier
N.A.I.C.S.: 333310

Honaz FZco. (1)
St No 831 Warehouse RA08NC06, PO Box 18344, Jebel Ali Free Zone, Dubai, 18344, United Arab Emirates
Tel.: (971) 48830244
Web Site: http://www.honazfz.com
Emp.: 10
Inkjet Cartridges Mfr
N.A.I.C.S.: 325910

Xaar Americas Inc. (1)
Tel.: (972) 606-2520
Inkjet Cartridges Mfr
N.A.I.C.S.: 325910

Xaar Asia-Pacific (1)
Cypress Hotel Bldg No 8, 2419 Hongqiao Rd, Shanghai, 200335, China
Tel.: (86) 2162686633
Web Site: http://www.xaar.co.cn
Emp.: 30
Inkjet Cartridges Mfr
N.A.I.C.S.: 325910

Xaar Korea (1)
Unit 2814 Daelim Acrotel, Dogok2-dong Gangnam-gu, Seoul, 135-971, Korea (South)
Tel.: (82) 70 7625 7703
Inkjet Heads Mfr
N.A.I.C.S.: 325910

Xaar Technology Limited (1)
Tel.: (44) 1223423663
Emp.: 175
Business Research & Development Services
N.A.I.C.S.: 561499

XaarJet (Overseas) Limited (1)

AND PRIVATE COMPANIES

Tel.: (44) 1223423663
Emp.: 400
Inkjet Cartridges Whslr
N.A.I.C.S.: 325910

XaarJet Limited (1)
Tel.: (44) 1223423663
Emp.: 200
Business Research & Development Company
N.A.I.C.S.: 561499

XAC AUTOMATION CORP.
4F No 30 industry E Road IX,
Science-Based Industrial Park, Hsinchu, 300096, Taiwan
Tel.: (886) 35772738
Web Site: https://www.xac.com.tw
Year Founded: 1993
5490—(TPE)
Rev.: $43,911,641
Assets: $63,792,296
Liabilities: $21,555,076
Net Worth: $42,237,220
Earnings: ($5,173,811)
Emp.: 87
Fiscal Year-end: 12/31/22
Transaction Device Mfr
N.A.I.C.S.: 334118
Edmund Chang (Chm)

XAIT AS
Kanalsletta 4, Stavanger, 4033, Norway
Tel.: (47) 51 95 02 00
Web Site: http://www.privia.com
Software Publisher
N.A.I.C.S.: 513210
Kris Saether (Chief Comml Officer)

Subsidiaries:

Privia LLC (1)
555 Herndon Pkwy Ste 250, Herndon, VA 20170-5248
Web Site: http://www.privia.com
Data Processing, Hosting & Related Services
N.A.I.C.S.: 518210
Danai Torrence (Dir-Pro Svcs)

XALI GOLD CORP.
Suite 801 - 1112 West Pender Street,
Vancouver, V6E 2S1, BC, Canada
Tel.: (604) 689-1957
Web Site: https://www.xaligold.com
XGC—(TSXV)
Assets: $631,689
Liabilities: $3,074,243
Net Worth: ($2,442,554)
Earnings: ($1,295,019)
Emp.: 1
Fiscal Year-end: 03/31/22
Gold Mining Services
N.A.I.C.S.: 212220
Joanne C. Freeze (Pres & CEO)

XAMBLE GROUP LIMITED
600 North Bridge Road 23-01
Parkview Square, Singapore, 188778, Singapore
Tel.: (65) 326948828
Web Site:
https://www.netccentric.com
XGL—(ASX)
Rev.: $7,092,338
Assets: $4,478,790
Liabilities: $1,407,052
Net Worth: $3,071,738
Earnings: ($1,274,450)
Fiscal Year-end: 12/31/23
Holding Company; Internet Solutions
N.A.I.C.S.: 551112
Ming Shen Cheo (Co-Founder)

Subsidiaries:

Nuffnang Live Commerce Sdn. Bhd. (1)
Level 9 Menara HLX No 3 Jalan Kia Peng, 50450, Kuala Lumpur, Malaysia
Tel.: (60) 189070889
Web Site: https://www.nuffnang.live
Live Commerce Technology Services
N.A.I.C.S.: 541512

Plata & Punta Sdn Bhd (1)
L5-02 Wisma BU8 No 11 Lebuh Bandar Utama, 47800, Petaling Jaya, Selangor, Malaysia
Tel.: (60) 123938805
Web Site: https://www.platapunta.com
Digital Marketing Services
N.A.I.C.S.: 541810

XANADU MINES LIMITED
L12 680 George Street, Sydney, 2000, NSW, Australia
Tel.: (61) 282807497
Web Site:
https://www.xanadumines.com
XAM—(ASX)
Rev.: $766
Assets: $41,858,492
Liabilities: $378,498
Net Worth: $41,479,994
Earnings: ($6,986,120)
Fiscal Year-end: 12/31/21
Underground Coal Mining
N.A.I.C.S.: 212115
Ganbayar Lkhagvasuren (Founder & Country Mgr)

Subsidiaries:

Xanadu Mines Mongolia LLC (1)
Suite 23 Building 9B Olympic Street Khoroo 1, Sukhbaatar District, Ulaanbaatar, 14240, Mongolia
Tel.: (976) 70120211
Emp.: 30
Gold Mining Services
N.A.I.C.S.: 212220

XANDER RESOURCES INC.
Suite 3302-939 Homer Street, Vancouver, V6B 2W6, BC, Canada
Tel.: (604) 647-2291 BC
Year Founded: 2010
1XI—(DEU)
Rev.: $81,286
Assets: $917,488
Liabilities: $315,925
Net Worth: $601,563
Earnings: ($2,422,936)
Fiscal Year-end: 03/31/23
Metal Mining
N.A.I.C.S.: 212290
Bryce Clark (CFO)

XANO INDUSTRI AB
Industrigatan 14 B, 553 02, Jonkoping, 553 02, Sweden
Tel.: (46) 36312200
Web Site: https://www.xano.se
Year Founded: 1937
XANO.B—(OMX)
Rev.: $273,389,614
Assets: $303,539,712
Liabilities: $175,237,294
Net Worth: $128,302,418
Earnings: $23,821,470
Emp.: 1,215
Fiscal Year-end: 12/31/20
Precision Component & Molding Mfr
N.A.I.C.S.: 332721
Fredrik Rapp (Chm)

Subsidiaries:

AB LK Precision Parts (1)
Frasarvagen 22, 142 50, Skogas, Sweden
Tel.: (46) 84483270
Web Site: http://www.lkprecision.com
Industrial Precision Component Mfr
N.A.I.C.S.: 332721

Ackurat Industriplast AB (1)
Varnamovagen 42, SE 363 44, Lammhult, Sweden
Tel.: (46) 472269300
Web Site: https://www.ackurat.com
Thermosetting Plastic Product Mfr

N.A.I.C.S.: 325211

CIM Industrial Systems A/S (1)
Skanderborgvej 277d 2, 8260, Viby, Denmark
Tel.: (45) 96840500
Web Site: https://cim.as
Software Solutions Services
N.A.I.C.S.: 541511

Canline Systems B.V. (1)
Meerheide 216, 5521 DW, Eersel, Netherlands
Tel.: (31) 497531100
Web Site: https://canline.com
Conveying & Handling Equipment Mfr
N.A.I.C.S.: 333922
Tom Brouwer (Reg Sls Mgr)

Canline USA Corporation (1)
4570 Avery LN SE Ste C, Lacey, WA 98503
Tel.: (360) 888-6002
Conveying & Handling Equipment Mfr
N.A.I.C.S.: 333922

Case Packing Systems B.V. (1)
Industrieweg 24, 6039 AP, Stramproy, Netherlands
Tel.: (31) 495566600
Web Site: https://www.casepacker.nl
Case Packing System Mfr & Distr
N.A.I.C.S.: 333993

Cipax AB (1)
Stinsvagen 11, Skebobruk, SE-763 93, Norrtalje, Sweden
Tel.: (46) 17525200
Web Site: https://cipax.com
Molded Plastic Product Mfr
N.A.I.C.S.: 326199

Cipax AS (1)
Holtermoen 12, 1940, Bjorkelangen, Norway
Tel.: (47) 63853000
Molded Plastic Product Mfr
N.A.I.C.S.: 326199

Cipax Eesti AS (1)
Nurme 5, EE-908 01, Taebla, Estonia
Tel.: (372) 4724430
Molded Plastic Product Mfr
N.A.I.C.S.: 326199

Cipax Nederland B.V. (1)
Jutestraat 22, 7461 TR, Rijssen, Netherlands
Tel.: (31) 548515172
Plastic Moulding Mfr & Distr
N.A.I.C.S.: 326199

Cipax Norge AS (1)
Holtermoen 12, 1940, Bjorkelangen, Norway
Tel.: (47) 63853000
Plastic Moulding Mfr & Distr
N.A.I.C.S.: 326199

Cipax Oy (1)
Bultvagen 18, FI-00880, Helsinki, Finland
Tel.: (358) 97276006
Molded Plastic Product Mfr
N.A.I.C.S.: 326199

Fredriksons Verkstads AB (1)
Kronangsgatan 4, SE-592 30, Vadstena, Sweden
Tel.: (46) 14329600
Web Site: https://www.fredriksons.se
Conveyor System Mfr
N.A.I.C.S.: 333922

Jorgensen Engineering A/S (1)
M P Allerups Vej 20, DK-5220, Odense, Denmark
Tel.: (45) 63132211
Web Site: https://www.jorgensen.dk
Industrial Product & Automation Equipment Mfr
N.A.I.C.S.: 333998
Kenneth Bo Madsen (CEO)

Jorgensen Engineering USA Inc. (1)
Williams Tower 2800 Post Oak Blvd Ste 1910, Houston, TX 77056
Tel.: (713) 622-9018
Web Site: https://jorgensen.dk
Industrial Machinery Mfr
N.A.I.C.S.: 333248

Kungsors Mekaniska Verkstad AB (1)
Malmbergavagen 21, 736 32, Kungsor, Sweden
Tel.: (46) 227616500
Web Site: http://www.kmv.se
Industrial Product & Automation Equipment Mfr
N.A.I.C.S.: 333998

Mikroverktyg AB (1)
Box 281, SE-151 23, Sodertalje, Sweden
Tel.: (46) 855026800
Web Site: https://mikroverktyg.se
Transmission Component Mfr
N.A.I.C.S.: 333613

Modellteknik i Eskilstuna AB (1)
Froslundavagen 5, Eskilstuna, Sweden
Tel.: (46) 16107670
Web Site: https://modellteknik.se
Shaping Tool Mfr & Distr
N.A.I.C.S.: 333515

NPB Automation AB (1)
Industrigatan 14B, SE-553 02, Jonkoping, Sweden
Tel.: (46) 362907600
Web Site: https://npb.se
Automation Equipment Mfr
N.A.I.C.S.: 334512

Pioner Boat AS (1)
Holtermoen 12, 1940, Bjorkelangen, Norway
Tel.: (47) 63853000
Web Site: https://pionerboat.no
Boat Mfr & Distr
N.A.I.C.S.: 336612

Polyketting B.V. (1)
Ambachtsweg 18, 7021 BT, Zelhem, Netherlands
Tel.: (31) 314622141
Web Site: https://www.polyketting.nl
Industrial Product & Automation Equipment Mfr
N.A.I.C.S.: 333998

Resinit AB (1)
Polymergatan 7, SE-593 50, Vastervik, Sweden
Tel.: (46) 49082320
Web Site: https://www.resinit.se
Plastic Mfr
N.A.I.C.S.: 325211

XAU RESOURCES, INC.
66 Wellington Street West Suite 4100
TD Bank Tower, Toronto, M5J 2W4, ON, Canada
Tel.: (647) 370-9736
Web Site:
https://www.xauresources.com
GIG—(TSXV)
Assets: $205,558
Liabilities: $18,747
Net Worth: $186,811
Earnings: ($241,815)
Fiscal Year-end: 10/31/23
Asset Management Services
N.A.I.C.S.: 523940
Andrey Maruta (CFO)

XAVER FASSIN GMBH
Dechant-Sprunken-Strasse 53-57,
D-46446, Emmerich am Rhein, Germany
Tel.: (49) 2822 601 0
Investment Holding Company
N.A.I.C.S.: 551112
Tobias Bachmuller (Mng Partner)

Subsidiaries:

Katjes Fassin GmbH & Co. KG (1)
Dechant-Sprunken-Strasse 53-57, 46446, Emmerich am Rhein, Germany
Tel.: (49) 2822 601 0
Web Site: http://www.katjes.com
Emp.: 50
Non-Chocolate Confectionery Mfr & Whslr
N.A.I.C.S.: 311340

Subsidiary (Domestic):

Katjesgreenfood GmbH & Co. KG (2)
Kaistrabe 16, Dusseldorf, 40221, Germany

XAVER FASSIN GMBH

Xaver Fassin GmbH—(Continued)
Tel.: (49) 302 576 217
Web Site: https://katjesgreenfood.de
Sustainable Food Brand Mfr
N.A.I.C.S.: 311919
Tobias Bachmuller (Mng Partner)

Subsidiary (Non-US):

Genius Foods Limited (3)
22 Northumberland Street South West
Lane, Edinburgh, EH3 6JD, United Kingdom
Tel.: (44) 8000192736
Web Site: http://www.geniusglutenfree.com
Gluten-Free Foods Mfr & Distr
N.A.I.C.S.: 311999
Lucinda Bruce-Gardyne (Founder)

Subsidiary (Domestic):

Livwell Ltd. (4)
1 Main Street, Hull, HU2 0YX, United Kingdom
Tel.: (44) 8451200038
Web Site: http://www.livwellfoods.co.uk
Sales Range: $25-49.9 Million
Emp.: 50
Gluten-Free Bakery Products Mfr
N.A.I.C.S.: 311812

United Central Bakeries Ltd. (4)
Unit 43 Whitehill Industrial Estate, Bathgate, EH48 2EP, W Lothian, United Kingdom
Tel.: (44) 1506633622
Sales Range: $50-74.9 Million
Emp.: 200
Gluten-Free Frozen Cakes, Pies & Pastries Mfr
N.A.I.C.S.: 311813

Katjes International GmbH & Co. KG (1)
Dechant-Sprunken-Strasse 53-57, D-46446, Emmerich am Rhein, Germany
Tel.: (49) 2822 601 700
Web Site: http://www.katjes-international.de
Holding Company; Non-Chocolate Confectionery Mfr & Whslr
N.A.I.C.S.: 551112

Subsidiary (Non-US):

Lamy Lutti S.A.S. (2)
Avenue Albert Calmette 262, BP 90100, F-59588, Bondues, Cedex, France (100%)
Tel.: (33) 320113100
Web Site: http://www.lamylutti.com
Sales Range: $125-149.9 Million
Emp.: 500
Confectionery Mfr & Whslr
N.A.I.C.S.: 311340

Subsidiary (Domestic):

Piasten GmbH (2)
Piastenstrasse 1, 91301, Forchheim, Bavaria, Germany
Tel.: (49) 91916110
Web Site: http://www.piasten.com
Candy & Chocolate Mfr
N.A.I.C.S.: 311352
Bertram Strothmann (Exec Dir)

XAVIS CO., LTD.

Room 177 619 sagimakgol-ro, Jungwon-gu, Seongnam, Gyeonggi-do, Korea (South)
Tel.: (82) 317403800
Web Site: https://www.xavisxray.com
Year Founded: 2002
254120—(KRS)
Rev.: $17,635,021
Assets: $22,392,511
Liabilities: $14,411,179
Net Worth: $7,981,332
Earnings: $207,105
Emp.: 119
Fiscal Year-end: 12/31/22
X-ray Machine Mfr & Distr
N.A.I.C.S.: 334517
Hyeong Cheol Kim (CEO)

XBRANE BIOPHARMA AB

Retzius vag 8, 171 65, Solna, Sweden
Tel.: (46) 855905600
Web Site: https://www.xbrane.com
Year Founded: 2008
XBRANE—(OMX)
Rev.: $5,396,611
Assets: $64,674,946
Liabilities: $24,879,129
Net Worth: $39,795,817
Earnings: ($16,157,895)
Emp.: 79
Fiscal Year-end: 12/31/22
Biopharmaceutical Product Mfr
N.A.I.C.S.: 325412
Paolo Sarmientos (Co-CEO & Head-Long, -Acting, and Injectables)

XCELERA INC.

c/o Maples & Calder Ltd. Uganda House South Church Stree, PO Box 309, Georgetown, Grand Cayman, Cayman Islands
Tel.: (345) 949 8066
Web Site: http://www.xcelera.com
Year Founded: 1989
Emp.: 200
Investment Services
N.A.I.C.S.: 523999
Gustav Vik (Treas, Sec & Exec VP)

Subsidiaries:

Ineo USA, Inc. (1)
1300 Crescent Green Ste 135, Cary, NC 27511
Tel.: (919) 468-5900
Web Site: http://www.ineousa.com
Telecommunications Network Security Solutions
N.A.I.C.S.: 517810

Mirror Image Internet, Inc. (1)
2 Highwood Dr, Tewksbury, MA 01876-1100
Tel.: (781) 376-1100
Web Site: http://www.mirror-image.com
Emp.: 77
Content Delivery Software
N.A.I.C.S.: 513210
Gustav Vik (Pres & CEO)

Subsidiary (Non-US):

Mirror Image Internet (UK) Ltd. (2)
90 Long Acre, Covent Garden, London, WC2E 9RZ, United Kingdom
Tel.: (44) 207 849 3253
Content Delivery Software
N.A.I.C.S.: 513210

Protegrity Corporation (1)
5 High Rdg Ste 2e, Stamford, CT 06905-1326
Tel.: (203) 326-7200
Web Site: http://www.protegrity.com
Security Software Mfr
N.A.I.C.S.: 513210
Gustav Vik (Chm)

XCLINICAL GMBH

Arnulfstrasse 19, Munich, 80335, Germany
Tel.: (49) 89 4522775888
Web Site: http://www.xclinical.com
Year Founded: 2002
Computer Software Services
N.A.I.C.S.: 541512
Franciscus Pijpers (CEO)

Subsidiaries:

Fortress Medical Systems, Inc. (1)
32 10th Ave S Ste 205, Hopkins, MN 55343-9481
Tel.: (952) 238-9010
Web Site: http://www.fortressmedical.com
Software Publisher
N.A.I.C.S.: 513210
Mark Jones (Pres)

XCURE CORP, LTD.

6F Gwachoen Pentaone 117 Gwachen-daero 12-gil, Guro-gu, Gwacheon, 152-790, Gyeonggi-do, Korea (South)
Tel.: (82) 316893119
Web Site: https://www.xcure.co.kr
Year Founded: 2000
070300—(KRS)
Rev.: $7,881,417
Assets: $19,957,420
Liabilities: $1,140,604
Net Worth: $18,816,816
Earnings: $683,071
Emp.: 42
Fiscal Year-end: 12/31/22
Smart Card Solution Services
N.A.I.C.S.: 334413
Sang Jin Park (CEO)

XD INC.

A1 700 Wanrong Rd, Shanghai, China
Web Site: https://www.xd.com
Year Founded: 2011
2400—(HKG)
Rev.: $469,254,541
Assets: $610,523,095
Liabilities: $351,779,325
Net Worth: $258,743,769
Earnings: ($9,049,900)
Emp.: 1,452
Fiscal Year-end: 12/31/23
Software Development Services
N.A.I.C.S.: 541511
Rui Gong (CFO)

XDC INDUSTRIES (SHENZHEN) LTD.

Rm 2401 Block B Shenzhen International Innovation Valley Bldg 7 Bldg 9, Vanke Cloud City Dashi Rd Xili Community Xili St Nanshan District, Shenzhen, 518055, China
Tel.: (86) 75586363066
Web Site: https://www.xdc-industries.com
Year Founded: 2005
300615—(CHIN)
Rev.: $86,782,277
Assets: $98,310,539
Liabilities: $22,201,693
Net Worth: $76,108,847
Earnings: $8,498,551
Fiscal Year-end: 12/31/23
Radio Frequency Component Mfr & Distr
N.A.I.C.S.: 334515
Shi Weiping (Chm & Gen Mgr)

XEBEC ADSORPTION INC.

730 Industriel Blvd, Blainville, J7C 3V4, QC, Canada
Tel.: (450) 979-8700
Web Site: https://ivysads.com
Year Founded: 1996
XEBEQ—(OTCEM)
Rev.: $98,489,834
Assets: $388,470,078
Liabilities: $142,200,512
Net Worth: $246,269,567
Earnings: ($18,344,466)
Emp.: 600
Fiscal Year-end: 12/31/21
Gas & Compressed Air Purification, Separation, Dehydration & Filtration Equipment Mfr
N.A.I.C.S.: 333912
Kurt Sorschak (Founder, Chm, Pres & CEO)

Subsidiaries:

Applied Compression Systems Ltd. (1)
400 Industrial Rd A, Cranbrook, V1C 4Z3, BC, Canada
Tel.: (250) 417-2396
Web Site: https://www.appliedcompression.com
Air & Gas Compressor Mfr
N.A.I.C.S.: 333912

Compressed Air International Inc. (1)
60 Haist Ave Unit 1, Woodbridge, L4L 5V4, ON, Canada
Tel.: (905) 850-9888
Web Site: https://ca-intl.com
Air Compressor Mfr & Distr
N.A.I.C.S.: 333912

HyGear B.V. (1)
Westervoortsedijk 73 HG, 6827 AV, Arnhem, Netherlands
Tel.: (31) 889494300
Web Site: https://www.inmatec.de
Industrial Gas Distr
N.A.I.C.S.: 424720
Niels Lanser (Mng Dir)

Inmatec Gase Technologie GmbH & Co. KG (1)
Gewerbestrasse 72, 82211, Herrsching am Ammersee, Germany
Tel.: (49) 815290970
Web Site: https://www.inmatec.de
Generator Mfr & Distr
N.A.I.C.S.: 335312

Tiger Filtration Limited (1)
Unit 3 Rivergreen Industry Centre, Pallion, Sunderland, SR4 6AD, United Kingdom
Tel.: (44) 1915655348
Web Site: https://www.tigerfiltration.com
Air Compressor Distr
N.A.I.C.S.: 423830
Bob Thompson (Chm)

Xebec Adsorption (Shanghai) Co. Ltd. (1)
Block 5 No 5 Jiang Tian Dong Road Songjiang Industriel Zone, Shanghai, 201613, China
Tel.: (86) 2133528700
Web Site:
Gas Field Machinery Whslr
N.A.I.C.S.: 423720
Peter Cheng (Gen Mgr)

Xebec Adsorption Asia Pte Ltd. (1)
133 Cecil Street 09-01B Keck Seng Tower, Singapore, 069535, Singapore
Tel.: (65) 69093062
Air Purification Equipment Mfr & Distr
N.A.I.C.S.: 333413

Xebec Adsorption Europe SRL. (1)
Via Senigallia 14/2 - Torre A, 20161, Milan, Italy
Tel.: (39) 02 6467 2619
Gas Field Machinery Whslr
N.A.I.C.S.: 423720
Francesco Massari (Gen Mgr)

Xebec Adsorption USA, Inc. (1)
14090 Southwest Fwy Ste 300, Sugar Land, TX 77478
Tel.: (832) 532-8741
Gas Field Machinery Whslr
N.A.I.C.S.: 423720

XEBIO HOLDINGS CO., LTD.

3-7-35 Asahi, Koriyama, 963-8024, Fukushima, Japan
Tel.: (81) 249241266
Web Site: https://www.xebio.co.jp
Year Founded: 1973
8281—(TKS)
Rev.: $1,602,482,130
Assets: $1,384,993,300
Liabilities: $559,979,370
Net Worth: $825,013,930
Earnings: $17,133,120
Emp.: 2,560
Fiscal Year-end: 03/31/24
Sporting Goods & Apparel Distr
N.A.I.C.S.: 423910
Yuuichi Hoshikawa (Auditor)

Subsidiaries:

GOLF Partner Co., Ltd. (1)
13F Nishikicho Trad Square 3-20 Kanda Nishikicho, Chiyoda-ku, Tokyo, 101-0054, Japan
Tel.: (81) 352179700
Web Site: https://www.golfpartner.co.jp
Emp.: 388
Golf Goods Distr
N.A.I.C.S.: 423910

Transview Lifestyle Pte. Ltd. (1)
No 4 Chang Charn Road, Singapore, 159633, Singapore

Tel.: (65) 64760955
Sales Range: $50-74.9 Million
Emp.: 10
Lifestyle Sporting Goods Whslr
N.A.I.C.S.: 423910
Derrick Lim *(Mgr)*

Xross Sports Marketing Co., Ltd. (1)
14th Floor Nishikicho Trad Square 3-20
Kanda Nishikicho, Chiyoda-ku, Tokyo, 101-0054, Japan
Tel.: (81) 352827655
Web Site: https://www.xsmktg.com
Emp.: 60
Spectator Sports Services
N.A.I.C.S.: 711219

XEBRA BRANDS LTD.
1090 Hamilton Street, Vancouver, V6B 2R9, BC, Canada   BC
Web Site:
   https://www.xebrabrands.com
Year Founded: 2019
XBRAF—(OTCQB)
Rev.: $118,576
Assets: $987,512
Liabilities: $576,035
Net Worth: $411,476
Earnings: ($3,076,725)
Emp.: 3
Fiscal Year-end: 02/28/23
Beverage Product Mfr
N.A.I.C.S.: 312111
Jay Garnett *(CEO)*

XELPMOC DESIGN & TECH LTD.
17 4th Floor Agies Building 1st A Cross 5th Block Koramangala, Bengaluru, 560 034, India
Tel.: (91) 8043708360
Web Site: https://www.xelpmoc.in
542367—(BOM)
Rev.: $2,073,099
Assets: $9,526,121
Liabilities: $1,450,735
Net Worth: $8,075,386
Earnings: $556,749
Emp.: 64
Fiscal Year-end: 03/31/21
Software Development Services
N.A.I.C.S.: 541511
Sandipan Chattopadhyay *(CEO & Mng Dir)*

Subsidiaries:

Signal Analytics Private Limited (1)
My Home Twitza M Hotel Hitech City Main Rd Lumbini Avenue, Diamond Hills Hitec City, Hyderabad, 500081, Telangana, India
Tel.: (91) 8374411904
Web Site: https//signalz.ai
Information Technology Services
N.A.I.C.S.: 541519

XEMPLAR ENERGY CORP.
605-815 Hornby St, Vancouver, V5N 4E8, BC, Canada
Tel.: (604) 687-4191   BC
Web Site: http://www.xemplar.ca
Year Founded: 1979
Sales Range: Less than $1 Million
Uranium Ore Exploration Services
N.A.I.C.S.: 213114
Ryan E. S. K. Cheung *(CEO)*

Subsidiaries:

Namura Mineral Resources (Pty.) Ltd. (1)
24 Copper St, Prosperita, Windhoek, Namibia
Tel.: (264) 61305496
Emp.: 126
Mineral Mining Services
N.A.I.C.S.: 212323

XENEL INDUSTRIES LTD.
Al-Matt haf Ln Al-Balad, PO Box 2824, Jeddah, 22236, Saudi Arabia
Tel.: (966) 126048000
Web Site:
   http://www.xenel.business.site
Year Founded: 1973
Emp.: 8,000
Holding Company Medical Industrial Petrochemicals Oils & Gas Electricity Services
N.A.I.C.S.: 551112
Khalid Ahmed Yousuf Xenel Alireza *(Vice Chm)*

Subsidiaries:

AMI Saudi Arabia Ltd. (1)
PO Box 2824, Jeddah, Saudi Arabia
Tel.: (966) 26448480
Web Site: http://www.xenel.com
Emp.: 1,800
Hospital Operator
N.A.I.C.S.: 622110
Mutasim AliReza *(Mng Dir)*

Arabian Bulk Trade Ltd. (1)
PO Box 2194, Al Khobar, 31952, Saudi Arabia
Tel.: (966) 3 859 3030
Emp.: 300
Bulk Materials Importer, Exporter, Handler & Distr
N.A.I.C.S.: 561499

Subsidiary (Non-US):

Arabian Bulk Trade Pte. Ltd. (2)
10 Anson Road #34-14, International Plaza, Singapore, 079903, Singapore
Tel.: (65) 6278 9898
Bulk Materials Handler & Distr
N.A.I.C.S.: 561499

Subsidiary (Domestic):

BINEX International Company for Building Materials Ltd. (2)
PO Box 2194, Al Khobar, 31952, Saudi Arabia
Tel.: (966) 38823030
Web Site: http://www.binexinternational.com
Emp.: 100
Bulk Materials Handler & Distr
N.A.I.C.S.: 561499

Imdad Medical Business Company Ltd. (1)
PO Box 3886, Riyadh, 11481, Saudi Arabia
Tel.: (966) 14652340
Emp.: 80
Medical Equipment Distr
N.A.I.C.S.: 423450

Saudi Cable Company (1)
PO Box 4403, Jeddah, 21491, Saudi Arabia
Tel.: (966) 26380080
Web Site: http://www.saudicable.com
Emp.: 1,700
Power & Telecommunication Cable Mfr
N.A.I.C.S.: 335921
Abdulhadi A. Abulkhair *(Pres)*

Subsidiary (Domestic):

Alujain Corporation (2)
PO Box 50575, Jeddah, 21533, Saudi Arabia
Tel.: (966) 2 669 5140
Power & Telecommunication Cables Mfr
N.A.I.C.S.: 335921
Muhammad Saleh Hassan Alkhalil *(Chm)*

Hidada Ltd. (2)
Phase 2 Jeddah Industrial City, PO Box 11809, Jeddah, 21463, Saudi Arabia
Tel.: (966) 26374450
Web Site: http://www.hidada.com
Emp.: 1,036
Power & Telecommunication Cables Mfr
N.A.I.C.S.: 335921

Safra Company Ltd. (2)
Abdul Aziz Street, PO Box 2824, Jeddah, 21641, Saudi Arabia
Tel.: (966) 26444090
Web Site: http://www.safra.com
Power & Telecommunication Cables Mfr
N.A.I.C.S.: 335921

Saudi Services and Operations Company Ltd. (1)
PO Box 753 Dhahran International Airport, Dhahran, 31932, Saudi Arabia
Tel.: (966) 3 864 2009
Emp.: 450
Operations & Maintenance Services
N.A.I.C.S.: 811310

XENEMETRIX LTD.
Ramat Gabriel Industrial Zone 6 Hatikshoret St, Migdal Ha'Emeq, 2307049, Israel
Tel.: (972) 4 9891313
Web Site: http://www.xenemetrix.com
Spectrometer Designer, Marketer & Mfr
N.A.I.C.S.: 334519
Yoav Allon *(CEO)*

XENER SYSTEMS INC.
3 5 Fl Hyundai Intelex Bldg 261, Nonhyeon Dong Gangnam Gu, 135010, Seoul, Korea (South)
Tel.: (82) 2 3438 5000
Sales Range: $25-49.9 Million
Information Technology Services & Solutions
N.A.I.C.S.: 541512
Hyung Il Jeon *(Gen Dir-Korean Bus)*

XENIA HOTELLERIE SOLUTION S.P.A.
Via Falzarego 1, Baranzate, 20021, Milan, Italy
Tel.: (39) 0289030
Web Site: https://en.xeniahs.com
Year Founded: 1992
XHS—(ITA)
Management Consulting Services
N.A.I.C.S.: 541613

XENIA VENTURE CAPITAL LTD.
Igal Alon 76, Tel Aviv, Israel
Tel.: (972) 99575259
Web Site: http://www.xenia.co.il
XENA—(TAE)
Rev.: $19,244,347
Assets: $34,959,872
Liabilities: $2,693,997
Net Worth: $32,265,875
Earnings: $16,855,105
Fiscal Year-end: 12/31/20
Investment Management Service
N.A.I.C.S.: 523999
Eli Sorzon *(CEO & CFO)*

XENICS N.V.
Ambachtenzone Haasrode 3227 Ambachtenlaan 44, 3001, Leuven, Belgium
Tel.: (32) 16 38 99 00
Web Site: http://www.xenics.com
Year Founded: 2000
Emp.: 70
Infrared Detection & Imaging Equipment Mfr & Distr
N.A.I.C.S.: 333310
Bob Grietens *(Founder)*

Subsidiaries:

sInfraRed Pte Ltd (1)
Blk 28 Sin Ming Lane 06-143, Midview City, Singapore, 573972, Singapore
Tel.: (65) 64766648
Web Site: http://www.sinfrared.com
Photographic Equipment Mfr
N.A.I.C.S.: 333310
Bob Grietens *(CEO)*

XENON PHARMACEUTICALS INC.
200-3650 Gilmore Way, Burnaby, V5G 4W8, BC, Canada
Tel.: (604) 484-3300   Ca
Web Site: https://www.xenon-pharma.com
XENE—(NASDAQ)
Rev.: $9,434,000
Assets: $754,146,000
Liabilities: $32,649,000
Net Worth: $721,497,000
Earnings: ($124,936,000)
Emp.: 213
Fiscal Year-end: 12/31/22
Biopharmaceutical Mfr
N.A.I.C.S.: 325412
Simon N. Pimstone *(Co-Founder)*

XENOUS HOLDINGS, INC.
Suite 20 03 Plaza 138 Jalan Ampang, 50450, Kuala Lumpur, Malaysia
Tel.: (60) 321810150   NV
Year Founded: 1980
XITO—(OTCIQ)
Liabilities: $839,166
Net Worth: ($839,166)
Earnings: ($63,746)
Fiscal Year-end: 03/31/24
Real Estate Asset Management Services
N.A.I.C.S.: 531390
Tang Wai Kee *(Chm)*

XERO LIMITED
19-23 Taranaki Street, Te Aro, Wellington, 6011, New Zealand
Tel.: (64) 48194800   NZ
Web Site: https://www.xero.com
Year Founded: 2006
XRO—(ASX)
Rev.: $788,612,861
Assets: $1,684,861,460
Liabilities: $941,470,823
Net Worth: $743,390,637
Earnings: ($6,552,966)
Emp.: 4,784
Fiscal Year-end: 03/31/22
Online Accounting System Design & Services
N.A.I.C.S.: 423420
Gary Turner *(Mng Dir-United Kingdom & EMEA)*

Subsidiaries:

Waddle Loans Pty. Ltd. (1)
Level 7 1-3 Smail Street, Ultimo, 2007, NSW, Australia
Tel.: (61) 1300649322
Web Site: https://www.waddle.com.au
Emp.: 30
Financial Consulting Services
N.A.I.C.S.: 541511

Xero Pty Limited (1)
235 Burnley Street, Richmond, 3121, VIC, Australia
Tel.: (61) 394290109
Emp.: 10
Online Accounting Software Development Services
N.A.I.C.S.: 541511
James Solomons *(Head-Acctg)*

XEROS TECHNOLOGY GROUP PLC
Unit 2 Evolution Advanced Manufacturing Park Whittle Way, Catcliffe, Rotherham, S60 5BL, South Yorkshire, United Kingdom
Tel.: (44) 1142699656   UK
Web Site: https://xerostech.com
XSG—(AIM)
Rev.: $643,559
Assets: $11,429,287
Liabilities: $1,841,068
Net Worth: $9,588,219
Earnings: ($8,741,001)
Emp.: 46
Fiscal Year-end: 12/31/21
Polymer Bead Cleaning Systems
N.A.I.C.S.: 812320
Klaas de Boer *(Chm)*

XFONE 018 LTD.

Xfone 018 Ltd.—(Continued)
1 Haodem St, Petah Tiqwa, 49170, Israel
Tel.: (972) 39254446
Web Site: http://www.018.co.il
Year Founded: 2004
Sales Range: $10-24.9 Million
Emp.: 50
Wireless Telecommunication Services
N.A.I.C.S.: 517112
Hezi Bezalel (Mng Dir)

XGAINS4KEEPS INC.
14 Rosenthal Road, London, SE6 2BY, United Kingdom
Tel.: (44) 7455212970
Web Site:
   http://www.xgains4keeps.com
Year Founded: 2009
Rev.: $60,067
Assets: $1,513,499,350
Liabilities: $511,160
Net Worth: $1,512,988,190
Earnings: ($650)
Fiscal Year-end: 06/30/20
Internet Publisher
N.A.I.C.S.: 516210
Ugochukwu Unamka (Founder & Chm)

XGD INC.
8th Floor Jialian Payment Building, Science and Technology South 12th Road No 20 Nanshan District, Shenzhen, Guangdong, China
Tel.: (86) 75526067135
Web Site:
   https://www.nexgoglobal.com
Year Founded: 2001
300130—(CHIN)
Rev.: $535,408,161
Assets: $770,287,325
Liabilities: $163,848,129
Net Worth: $606,439,196
Earnings: $106,347,821
Emp.: 3,000
Fiscal Year-end: 12/31/23
Point of Sale Terminal Software & Hardware Products Mfr
N.A.I.C.S.: 513210
Liu Xiang (Chm & Pres)

XI'AN CATERING CO., LTD.
7F Xiying Building No 508 Xiying Road, Qujiang New District, Xi'an, 710054, Shaanxi, China
Tel.: (86) 2982065865
Web Site: http://www.xcsg.com
Year Founded: 1996
000721—(SSE)
Rev.: $68,060,416
Assets: $225,978,335
Liabilities: $149,805,312
Net Worth: $76,173,023
Earnings: ($31,092,675)
Fiscal Year-end: 12/31/22
Restaurant Operators
N.A.I.C.S.: 722511
Jin Wenping (Chm)

XI'AN GLOBAL PRINTING CO.,LTD.
No 32 Keji 1st Road Hi-tech Zone, Xi'an, 710075, Shaanxi, China
Tel.: (86) 2968682020
Web Site:
   http://www.globalprinting.cn
Year Founded: 2001
002799—(SSE)
Rev.: $416,518,559
Assets: $365,673,850
Liabilities: $129,123,606
Net Worth: $236,550,244
Earnings: $12,660,809
Fiscal Year-end: 12/31/22
Packaging Services
N.A.I.C.S.: 561910
Yiling Li (Chm)
Subsidiaries:
Tianjin Binhai Global Printing Co., Ltd. (1)
Medical Instrument Industrial Park, Tianjin, 300400, China
Tel.: (86) 2286882020
Pharmaceutical Packaging Services
N.A.I.C.S.: 561910

Xi'an Thiebaut Pharmaceutical Packaging Co., Ltd. (1)
No 12 Fenghui South Road, High-tech Zone, Xi'an, 710075, Shaanxi, China
Tel.: (86) 298 831 7879
Web Site: https://www.thiebaut-tube.com
Collapsible Aluminum Tube Mfr
N.A.I.C.S.: 332439

XI'AN HAITIAN ANTENNA TECHNOLOGIES CO., LTD.
No 25 Master Road, Xian High-tech Zone, Xi'an, Shaanxi, China
Tel.: (86) 2963362328
Web Site: https://www.xaht.com
Year Founded: 1999
8227—(HKG)
Rev.: $2,882,424
Assets: $12,951,081
Liabilities: $11,266,942
Net Worth: $1,684,139
Earnings: ($4,250,315)
Emp.: 113
Fiscal Year-end: 12/31/22
Antenna Mfr & Whslr
N.A.I.C.S.: 334220
Xiao Bing (Chm)

XI'AN INTERNATIONAL MEDICAL INVESTMENT COMPANY LIMITED
No 777 Xitai Road Xian High-tech Zone, Xi'an, 710075, Shaanxi, China
Tel.: (86) 2987217854
Web Site: https://www.000516.cn
000516—(SSE)
Sales Range: $250-299.9 Million
Departmental Store Operator
N.A.I.C.S.: 455110
Cao Jianan (Chm-Supervisory Bd)

XI'AN MANARECO NEW MATERIALS CO., LTD.
No 71 Jinye 2nd Road Xian Hightech Industries Development Zone, High-tech Zone, Xi'an, 710077, Shaanxi, China
Tel.: (86) 2968669089
Web Site: https://www.xarlm.com
Year Founded: 1999
688550—(SHG)
Rev.: $207,845,268
Assets: $469,000,107
Liabilities: $54,047,429
Net Worth: $414,952,677
Earnings: $34,614,005
Emp.: 1,700
Fiscal Year-end: 12/31/22
Chemical Product Mfr & Distr
N.A.I.C.S.: 325520
Xiaochun Liu (Chm)

XI'AN PERI POWER SEMICONDUCTOR CONVERTING TECHNOLOGY CO., LTD.
No 13 Jinye 2nd Road, High-tech Zone, Xi'an, 710077, Shaanxi, China
Tel.: (86) 2981168036
Web Site:
   https://www.chinaxaperi.com
Year Founded: 2010
300831—(SSE)
Rev.: $24,681,028
Assets: $133,015,465
Liabilities: $13,280,955
Net Worth: $119,734,510
Earnings: $7,718,855
Fiscal Year-end: 12/31/22
Semiconductor Product Mfr & Distr
N.A.I.C.S.: 334413
Jianqiu Lu (Chm & Gen Mgr)

XI'AN QUJIANG CULTURAL TOURISM CO., LTD.
7-8th Floor Qujiang Cultural Building Yanta South Road, Qujiang New District, Xi'an, 710061, Shaanxi, China
Tel.: (86) 2988668899
Web Site: http://www.qjtourism.com
Year Founded: 1992
600706—(SHG)
Rev.: $125,088,215
Assets: $512,468,115
Liabilities: $371,218,162
Net Worth: $141,249,954
Earnings: ($34,922,282)
Fiscal Year-end: 12/31/22
Tourism Services
N.A.I.C.S.: 561520
Geng Lin (Chm)

XI'AN SHAANGU POWER CO., LTD.
No 8 Fenghui South Road Hi-tech Zone, Xi'an, 710075, Shaanxi, China
Tel.: (86) 2988225341
Web Site: http://www.shaan-gu.com
Year Founded: 1999
601369—(SHG)
Rev.: $1,511,552,999
Assets: $3,862,695,513
Liabilities: $2,646,950,544
Net Worth: $1,215,744,969
Earnings: $135,958,081
Fiscal Year-end: 12/31/22
Turbine & Generator Mfr & Distr
N.A.I.C.S.: 333611
Li Hongan (Chm)

XI'AN SINOFUSE ELECTRIC CO., LTD.
Sinofuse Electric Industrial Base No 97 Jinye Second Road Hi-tech Zone, Pioneering Research & Development Park No 69 Jinye Road High-tech Zone, Xi'an, 710000, Shaanxi, China
Tel.: (86) 2968590678
Web Site: https://www.sinofuse.com
Year Founded: 2007
301031—(CHIN)
Rev.: $105,945,840
Assets: $191,686,716
Liabilities: $74,118,564
Net Worth: $117,568,152
Earnings: $21,593,520
Fiscal Year-end: 12/31/22
Electrical Component Mfr & Distr
N.A.I.C.S.: 335210
Guangwen Fang (Chm & Gen Mgr)

XI'AN TECH FULL SIMO MOTOR CO., LTD.
No 159 Ming Guang Road Economy and Technology Developing Zone, Xi'an, 710021, China
Tel.: (86) 29 8617 1285
Web Site: http://www.simo.com.cn
Industrial Rotary Motors Mfr
N.A.I.C.S.: 335312

XI'AN TIANHE DEFENSE TECHNOLOGY CO., LTD.
No158 West Avenue high tech Zone, Xi'an, 710119, Shaanxi, China
Tel.: (86) 2988452688
Web Site: https://www.thtw.com.cn
Year Founded: 2004
300397—(CHIN)
Rev.: $70,456,932
Assets: $359,186,724
Liabilities: $102,035,700
Net Worth: $257,151,024
Earnings: ($21,236,904)
Fiscal Year-end: 12/31/22
Reconnaissance Product Mfr
N.A.I.C.S.: 334511
Zenglin He (Chm & Gen Mgr)

XI'AN TOURISM CO., LTD.
3rd Floor Xiying Building No 508 Xiying Road, Qujiang New District, Xi'an, 710054, Shaanxi, China
Tel.: (86) 2982065555
Web Site: http://www.xatourism.com
Year Founded: 1994
000610—(SSE)
Rev.: $55,597,670
Assets: $285,097,237
Liabilities: $194,334,155
Net Worth: $90,763,082
Earnings: ($23,512,226)
Fiscal Year-end: 12/31/22
Hotel Operator
N.A.I.C.S.: 722511
Wang Wei (Chm)

XI'AN TRIANGLE DEFENSE CO., LTD.
No 8 Lantian 2nd Road Aviation Base, Xi'an, 710089, Shaanxi, China
Tel.: (86) 2981662206
Web Site: http://www.400mn.com
Year Founded: 2002
300775—(SSE)
Rev.: $263,459,336
Assets: $978,683,514
Liabilities: $318,623,311
Net Worth: $660,060,203
Earnings: $87,704,426
Emp.: 300
Fiscal Year-end: 12/31/22
Aerospace Parts Mfr
N.A.I.C.S.: 334511
Jianya Yan (Chm)

XI'AN TYPICAL INDUSTRIES CO., LTD.
No 335 South Taibai Road, Xi'an, 710068, China
Tel.: (86) 2988279092
Web Site:
   https://www.typicalinternational.com
Year Founded: 1999
600302—(SHG)
Rev.: $147,529,498
Assets: $216,783,806
Liabilities: $66,476,339
Net Worth: $150,307,466
Earnings: $15,937,576
Fiscal Year-end: 12/31/22
Sewing machines Mfr
N.A.I.C.S.: 333248
Chang Hong (Chm)
Subsidiaries:
Typical International Corporation (1)
No 335 South Taibai Road, Xi'an, 710068, China
Tel.: (86) 2988279092
Web Site:
   https://www.typicalinternational.com
Sewing Equipment Mfr
N.A.I.C.S.: 333248

Vetron Typical Europe GmbH (1)
Clara-Immerwahr-Str 6, 67661, Kaiserslautern, Germany
Tel.: (49) 6301320750
Web Site: https://www.vetrontypical-europe.com
Sewing Machine Mfr & Distr
N.A.I.C.S.: 333248
Shouqi Yu (Co-CEO)

XIABUXIABU CATERING MANAGEMENT (CHINA) HOLDINGS CO., LTD.
Suncun Industrial Development Zone

Huangcun Town, Daxing District, Beijing, China
Tel.: (86) 1060265888
Web Site: http://www.xiabu.com
0520—(HKG)
Rev: $663,366,694
Assets: $605,143,375
Liabilities: $391,535,867
Net Worth: $213,607,508
Earnings: ($46,498,795)
Emp.: 27,059
Fiscal Year-end: 12/31/22
Restaurant Owner
N.A.I.C.S.: 722511
Kuang-Chi Ho *(Chm)*

XIAMEN AMOYTOP BIOTECH CO., LTD.
No 330 Wengjiao Road, Haicang, Xiamen, 361028, Fujian, China
Tel.: (86) 5926889106
Web Site: https://www.amoytop.com
Year Founded: 1996
688278—(SHG)
Rev.: $214,377,476
Assets: $248,305,768
Liabilities: $50,678,686
Net Worth: $197,627,082
Earnings: $40,297,594
Fiscal Year-end: 12/31/22
Medical Product Mfr & Distr
N.A.I.C.S.: 339112
Li Sun *(Chm & Gen Mgr)*

XIAMEN ANNE CORPORATION LIMITED
No 99 South Jinyuan Road, Jimei District, Xiamen, 361002, Fujian, China
Tel.: (86) 5923152188
Web Site: https://www.anne.com.cn
Year Founded: 2007
002235—(SSE)
Rev.: $50,713,603
Assets: $178,018,144
Liabilities: $36,636,004
Net Worth: $141,382,140
Earnings: ($19,306,867)
Fiscal Year-end: 12/31/22
Paper Products Mfr
N.A.I.C.S.: 322120
Zhang Jie *(Chm & Gen Mgr)*

Subsidiaries:

Beijing Lianyi Hetong Science and Technology Co., Ltd. (1)
Room 412 3/10 Wanghai Road Phase II Software Park, Xiamen, Fujian, China
Tel.: (86) 5925158758
Web Site: https://www.zhongdj.com
Lottery Marketing Services
N.A.I.C.S.: 713290

Beijing Zhimei Digital Anti-counterfeiting Printing Co., Ltd (1)
No 16 Centre Road North Printing Industrial Base Beiwu Town, Shunyi district, Beijing, China
Tel.: (86) 1064450852
Business Information Paper Distr
N.A.I.C.S.: 424120

Shanghai Super Labels Co., Ltd. (1)
No 251 Taogan Road Sheshan Industrial Park Songjiang District, Shanghai, China
Tel.: (86) 2157793322
Business Information Paper Distr
N.A.I.C.S.: 424120

Shenzhen Micro-dream Network Technology Co., Ltd. (1)
7 401 Chi Heng Strategic Emerging Industrial park Road No 2, Nantouguankou Nanshan district, Shenzhen, China
Tel.: (86) 75588302719
Web Site: http://www.yesweibo.com
Digital Marketing Services
N.A.I.C.S.: 541910

XIAMEN C&D INC.
29/F C D International Building No1699 Huandao East Road, Xiamen, 361008, Fujian, China
Tel.: (86) 5922132319
Web Site: https://www.chinacnd.com
Year Founded: 1980
600153—(SHG)
Rev.: $116,926,805,909
Assets: $93,331,521,832
Liabilities: $70,117,235,155
Net Worth: $23,214,286,677
Earnings: $881,930,982
Fiscal Year-end: 12/31/22
Real Estate Development Services
N.A.I.C.S.: 531390

Subsidiaries:

C&D (Canada) Import & Export Inc. (1)
5250 Satellite Drive Unit 25, Mississauga, L4W 5G5, ON, Canada
Tel.: (905) 361-1850
Real Estate Development Services
N.A.I.C.S.: 531390

C&D (Shanghai) Co., Ltd. (1)
15/F Shanghai C & D International Building No 288 Yangshupu Road, Yangpu District, Shanghai, 200080, China
Tel.: (86) 2161635000
Supply Chain Real Estate Development Services
N.A.I.C.S.: 531320

C&D (Singapore) Business Pte, Ltd. (1)
7 Temasek Boulevard 21-03 Suntec Tower One, Singapore, 038987, Singapore
Tel.: (65) 69310008
Real Estate Development Services
N.A.I.C.S.: 531390

C&D International Investment Group Limited (1)
Office No 3517 35th Floor Wu Chung House 213 Queen s Road East, Wanchai, China (Hong Kong)
Tel.: (852) 25257922
Web Site: https://www.cndintl.com
Rev.: $13,988,824,340
Assets: $55,242,228,647
Liabilities: $44,091,592,132
Net Worth: $11,150,636,515
Earnings: $780,891,181
Emp.: 19,594
Fiscal Year-end: 12/31/2022
Building Property Developer
N.A.I.C.S.: 236210
Yuekai Zhuang *(Chm)*

C&D Japan Corporation (1)
33/F Kasumigaseki Common Gate West Wing 2-1 Kasumigaseki 3-Chome, Chiyoda-ku, Tokyo, 100-0013, Japan
Tel.: (81) 362057870
Supply Chain Real Estate Development Services
N.A.I.C.S.: 531320

C&D Metals Korea Co.,Ltd. (1)
Room 1224 800 Gukhoe-Daero, Yeongdeungpo-Gu, Seoul, Korea (South)
Tel.: (82) 27859118
Supply Chain Real Estate Development Services
N.A.I.C.S.: 531320

CDMA Australia Pty. Ltd. (1)
Suite 1303 370 Pitt Street, Sydney, 2000, NSW, Australia
Tel.: (61) 280045205
Web Site: https://www.cdmaaustralia.com.au
Real Estate Investment Services
N.A.I.C.S.: 531390

Cheongfuli (Hongkong) Company Limited (1)
Room 2306B & 2307 23/F West Tower Shun Tak Centre 168-200, Connaught Road Central, Hong Kong, China (Hong Kong)
Tel.: (852) 25712223
Real Estate Development Services
N.A.I.C.S.: 531390

Cheongfuli (Malaysia) Sdn. Bhd. (1)
Level 1 No 11 Jalan Pju 1A/41B Nzx Commercial Centre Ara Jaya, 47301, Petaling Jaya, Selangor, Malaysia
Tel.: (60) 1159601170
Supply Chain Real Estate Development Services
N.A.I.C.S.: 531320

Fujian Shipbuilding Industry Trading Co., Ltd. (1)
12F/Shipbuilding Bldg No 166 Jiangbin Dong Avenue, Fuzhou, 350015, China
Tel.: (86) 13950171971
Web Site: https://www.fujianshipbuilding.com
Shipbuilding & Repairing Services
N.A.I.C.S.: 541990

Getop (Thailand) Co., Ltd. (1)
184/69 - 70 Forum Tower Floor 16 Ratchadaphisek Road, Huai Khwang Sub-District Huai Khwang District, Bangkok, 10310, Thailand
Tel.: (66) 957497098
Supply Chain Real Estate Development Services
N.A.I.C.S.: 531320

Hang Yue Tong Company Limited (1)
Room 2306B & 2307 23/F West Tower Shun Tak Centre, 168-200 Connaught Road Central, Hong Kong, 999077, China (Hong Kong)
Tel.: (852) 29698991
Supply Chain Real Estate Development Services
N.A.I.C.S.: 531320

LFMA Australia Pty. Ltd. (1)
Suite 21 Level 2 8 Hill Street, Surry Hills, 2010, NSW, Australia
Tel.: (61) 293283322
Web Site: https://www.logicalfinancial.com.au
Active Portfolio Management & Investment Services
N.A.I.C.S.: 525110

Vietnam Natural Resources Trading Company Limited (1)
Unit 2 37th Floor Bitexco Financial Tower, District 1, Ho Chi Minh City, Vietnam
Tel.: (84) 283915003
Supply Chain Real Estate Development Services
N.A.I.C.S.: 531320

Xiamen C&D Automobile Co., Ltd. (1)
Floor 38-39 Block B Portman Fortune Center No 83 Zhanhong Road, Siming District, Xiamen, Fujian, China
Tel.: (86) 5922263688
Web Site: https://www.autocnd.com
Passenger Car Brand Distr
N.A.I.C.S.: 423110

Xiamen C&D Hitek Co.,Ltd. (1)
29 / F C & D International Building No 1699 Huandao East Road, Xiamen, 361008, China
Tel.: (86) 5922263333
Real Estate Investment Services
N.A.I.C.S.: 531390

Xiamen C&D Ship Trading Co., Ltd. (1)
23F/C & D International Building No 1699 Huandao East Road, Xiamen, 361008, China
Tel.: (86) 13950171971
Web Site: https://www.xiamenshipbuilding.com
Shipbuilding & Repairing Services
N.A.I.C.S.: 541990

Xiamen Conference & Exhibition Group Inc. (1)
No 198 Exhibition Road, Siming District, Xiamen, China
Tel.: (86) 5925959898
Web Site: http://www.xicec.com
Real Estate Services
N.A.I.C.S.: 531390

XIAMEN CHANGELIGHT CO., LTD.
259-269 Xiangtian Road, Xiamen Xiang An Industry Park, Xiamen, 300102, China
Tel.: (86) 5927615555
Web Site: https://www.changelight.com.cn
Year Founded: 2006
300102—(CHIN)
Rev.: $238,358,484
Assets: $984,941,100
Liabilities: $411,310,224
Net Worth: $573,630,876
Earnings: ($7,069,140)
Emp.: 250
Fiscal Year-end: 12/31/22
LED Wafer Mfr
N.A.I.C.S.: 334413
Jin Zhangyu *(Chm)*

Subsidiaries:

Jiangxi Changelight Co., Ltd. (1)
No 19 Huangxi Avenue, Wangcheng New District, Nanchang, Jiangxi, China
Tel.: (86) 19979130620
Semiconductor Device Mfr & Distr
N.A.I.C.S.: 334413

Xiamen Changelight Lighting Co., Ltd. (1)
259-269 Xiangtian Road, Xiang An Industry Park, Xiamen, China
Tel.: (86) 5927615555
Semiconductor Device Mfr & Distr
N.A.I.C.S.: 334413

Yangzhou Changelight Co., Ltd. (1)
NO 8 West Road Dongfeng River, Yangzhou Economic and Technological Development Zone, Yangzhou, Jiangsu, China
Tel.: (86) 51485068200
Light Emitting Diode Wafer Mfr
N.A.I.C.S.: 334413

XIAMEN COMFORT SCIENCE & TECHNOLOGY GROUP CO. LTD.
8F No 31-37 Anling 2nd Road, Huli District, Xiamen, 361000, Fujian, China
Tel.: (86) 5925569658
Year Founded: 1996
002614—(SSE)
Biotechnology Research & Development Services
N.A.I.C.S.: 541714
Jianhan Zou *(Chm & Pres)*

XIAMEN EAST ASIA MACHINERY INDUSTRIAL CO., LTD.
No 611 Xike Street, Xike Town Tongan District, Xiamen, 361100, Fujian, China
Tel.: (86) 5927113080
Web Site: https://www.jaguar-compressor.com
Year Founded: 1991
301028—(CHIN)
Rev.: $135,013,084
Assets: $266,138,154
Liabilities: $82,526,507
Net Worth: $183,611,647
Earnings: $22,964,070
Fiscal Year-end: 12/31/23
Industrial Machinery Mfr & Distr
N.A.I.C.S.: 333248
Yinghuan Han *(Chm)*

XIAMEN FARATRONIC CO., LTD.
99 Xinyuan Road, Haicang District, Xiamen, 361028, Fujian, China
Tel.: (86) 5926208778
Web Site: https://www.faratronic.com
Year Founded: 1955
600563—(SHG)
Rev.: $538,604,769
Assets: $796,136,206
Liabilities: $214,627,851
Net Worth: $581,508,355
Earnings: $141,351,589

XIAMEN FARATRONIC CO., LTD.

Xiamen Faratronic Co., Ltd.—(Continued)

Fiscal Year-end: 12/31/22
Capacitor Mfr & Distr
N.A.I.C.S.: 334416
Lu Huixiong (Chm)

Subsidiaries:

Faratronic (Hong Kong) Company
Limited (1)
Unit 1605 Block B Kailey Industrial Centre
12 Fung Yip Street, Chai Wan, China (Hong Kong)
Tel.: (852) 28989168
Film Capacitor Mfr
N.A.I.C.S.: 423690

XIAMEN GUANGPU ELECTRONICS CO., LTD.

No 1800-1812 Minan Avenue, Industrial Zone Torch High-tech Zone Xiangan, Xiamen, 361101, Fujian, China
Tel.: (86) 5925625818
Web Site: http://www.goproled.cn
Year Founded: 1994
300632—(CHIN)
Rev.: $125,988,452
Assets: $366,023,613
Liabilities: $94,289,314
Net Worth: $271,734,299
Earnings: $12,576,835
Fiscal Year-end: 12/31/23
Electric Light Product Mfr & Distr
N.A.I.C.S.: 335139
Lin Guobiao (Chm)

XIAMEN HEXING PACKAGING PRINTING CO., LTD.

19th Floor Building No 2 Tongan Business Building, Wuyuanwan Huli District, Xiamen, 361016, Fujian, China
Tel.: (86) 5927896162
Web Site: http://www.hxpp.com.cn
Year Founded: 2007
002228—(SSE)
Rev.: $2,158,687,880
Assets: $1,239,950,266
Liabilities: $732,598,271
Net Worth: $507,351,995
Earnings: $18,560,501
Emp.: 11,000
Fiscal Year-end: 12/31/22
Corrugated Cases Mfr
N.A.I.C.S.: 322211

Subsidiaries:

Chengdu Hexing Packaging Printing Co., Ltd. (1)
No 80 Junyue Road Xindu Industrial East Area, Chengdu, Sichuan, China
Tel.: (86) 2883939098
Packaging Products Mfr
N.A.I.C.S.: 322211

Chongqing Hexin Packaging Printing Co., Ltd. (1)
Haier Industrial Park No 1 Gangcheng South Road Jiangbei District, Chongqing, China
Tel.: (86) 2386856679
Packaging Products Mfr
N.A.I.C.S.: 322211

Zunyi Hexin Packaging Co., Ltd. (1)
Donggongsi Industrial Park Huichuan District, Zunyi, Guizhou, China
Tel.: (86) 18985629151
Packaging Products Mfr
N.A.I.C.S.: 322211

XIAMEN HONGFA ELECTROACOUSTIC CO., LTD.

No 90-101 Sunban South Road, Jimei North Industrial District, Xiamen, 361021, China
Tel.: (86) 592 6196710
Web Site: http://www.hongfa.com
Year Founded: 1984
Sales Range: $650-699.9 Million

Relay Mfr & Distr
N.A.I.C.S.: 335314
Manjin Guo (Pres)

XIAMEN HONGXIN ELECTRON-TECH CO., LTD.

No 19 Xianghai Road, Xiangan District, Xiamen, 361101, Fujian, China
Tel.: (86) 13163907393
Web Site: https://www.fpc98.com
Year Founded: 2003
300657—(CHIN)
Rev.: $489,918,090
Assets: $800,473,523
Liabilities: $582,844,526
Net Worth: $217,628,997
Earnings: ($61,343,513)
Emp.: 800
Fiscal Year-end: 12/31/23
Printed Circuit Board Mfr & Distr
N.A.I.C.S.: 334412

XIAMEN INTERNATIONAL AIRPORT CO., LTD.

Office area on the east side of the first floor of Terminal T4, Xiamen Airport Huli District, Xiamen, 361006, China
Tel.: (86) 59296363
Web Site: https://www.xiamenairport.com.cn
Year Founded: 1996
600897—(SHG)
Rev.: $141,198,399
Assets: $690,570,345
Liabilities: $121,350,879
Net Worth: $569,219,466
Earnings: $3,945,100
Fiscal Year-end: 12/31/22
Airport Ground Services
N.A.I.C.S.: 488119
Zhu Zhao (Chm)

XIAMEN INTERNATIONAL BANK CO., LTD.

Building 8-10 LuJiang Road, Xiamen, 361001, Fujian, China
Tel.: (86) 5922078888
Web Site: http://www.xib.com.cn
Year Founded: 1985
Rev.: $5,213,326,699
Assets: $131,011,594,270
Liabilities: $122,136,050,611
Net Worth: $8,875,543,658
Earnings: $903,684,548
Emp.: 5,692
Fiscal Year-end: 12/31/19
Commericial Banking
N.A.I.C.S.: 522110

Subsidiaries:

Chiyu Banking Corporation Limited (1)
78 Des Voeux Road, Central, China (Hong Kong)
Tel.: (852) 28430111
Web Site: http://www.chiyubank.com
Rev.: $540,368,156
Assets: $19,242,852,428
Liabilities: $17,429,319,411
Net Worth: $1,813,533,017
Earnings: $162,126,357
Fiscal Year-end: 12/31/2019
Commericial Banking
N.A.I.C.S.: 522110

XIAMEN INTERNATIONAL PORT CO., LTD.

No 439 Gangnan Road, Haicang District, Xiamen, Fujian, China
Tel.: (86) 5925829478
Web Site: http://www.xipc.com.cn
Year Founded: 1998
3378—(HKG)
Rev.: $2,710,551,179
Assets: $3,676,513,724
Liabilities: $1,746,402,488

Net Worth: $1,930,111,236
Earnings: $94,466,069
Emp.: 7,082
Fiscal Year-end: 12/31/20
Cargo Handling Services
N.A.I.C.S.: 488320
Liqun Cai (Chm)

XIAMEN INTRETECH INC.

No 100 Dongfu West Road, Haicang District, Xiamen, 361027, Fujian, China
Tel.: (86) 5927702685
Web Site: http://www.intretech.com
Year Founded: 2011
002925—(SSE)
Rev.: $610,068,888
Assets: $1,089,119,894
Liabilities: $322,623,798
Net Worth: $766,496,096
Earnings: $97,347,590
Emp.: 6,000
Fiscal Year-end: 12/31/22
Electronic Product Mfr & Distr
N.A.I.C.S.: 334290
Lin Songhua (Chm)

XIAMEN ITG GROUP CORP., LTD.

Guomao Center Building A No 4688 Xianyue Road, Huli District, Xiamen, 361000, China
Tel.: (86) 5925161888
Web Site: https://www.itg.com.cn
Year Founded: 1980
600755—(SHG)
Rev.: $73,277,285,838
Assets: $15,850,676,631
Liabilities: $10,506,196,359
Net Worth: $5,344,480,272
Earnings: $503,894,421
Fiscal Year-end: 12/31/22
Logistics & Real Estate Development Services
N.A.I.C.S.: 541614

Subsidiaries:

Fujian Golden Strait Pawn Co., Ltd. (1)
8/F Guomao Building Hubin South Road, Xiamen, China
Tel.: (86) 592 5862525
Real Estate Management Services
N.A.I.C.S.: 531390

Fujian Keerun Catering Administration Corp., Ltd. (1)
14/F Guomao Building Hubin South Road, Xiamen, China
Tel.: (86) 592 5898988
Restaurant Operators
N.A.I.C.S.: 722511

Guangzhou Keerun Paper Co., Ltd. (1)
No 90 Dongpu Yi Heng Road Room 411 Block A Donglong Business Center, Tianhe District, Guangzhou, China
Tel.: (86) 20 32016790
Printing Paper Distr
N.A.I.C.S.: 424110

ITG Futures Co., Ltd. (1)
11/F Guomao Building Hubin South Road, Xiamen, 361004, China
Tel.: (86) 592 5898732
Web Site: http://www.itf.com.cn
Commodity Brokerage Services
N.A.I.C.S.: 523160

Longyan ITG Longfeng Motor Sales & Service Co., Ltd. (1)
No 332 Logistics Road, Longmen Town Xinluo District, Longyan, China
Tel.: (86) 597 2505333
New Car Dealers
N.A.I.C.S.: 441110

Ningde ITG Zhongbang Motor Sales & Service Co., Ltd. (1)
West Side of Southern Bus Station Wan'an West Road, Ningde, Fuzhou, China

INTERNATIONAL PUBLIC

Tel.: (86) 593 2990933
New Car Dealers
N.A.I.C.S.: 441110

Quanzhou ITG Motor Sales & Service Co., Ltd. (1)
Yingbin Road Qingmeng Economic Developing District, Quanzhou, China
Tel.: (86) 595 24671111
New Car Dealers
N.A.I.C.S.: 441110

Shanghai Volkswagen Fujian Fushen Motor Sales & Service Co., Ltd. (1)
Huaxia Motor World Junction of Huangshan High Speed, Cangshan District, Fuzhou, China
Tel.: (86) 591 83402943
New Car Dealers
N.A.I.C.S.: 441110

Xiamen CCRE Group CO., Ltd. (1)
23-28 F Block B Haiyi Building 668 Xiahe Road, Xiamen, 361000, China
Tel.: (86) 5925881194
Small Machinery Mfr
N.A.I.C.S.: 333132

Xiamen DBTS Automobile Trading Co., Ltd. (1)
No 2 Changhao Road, Huli District, Xiamen, China
Tel.: (86) 592 5626888
Web Site: http://www.dbts.audi-online.cn
New Car Dealers
N.A.I.C.S.: 441110

Xiamen ITG Chemical Fibre Co., Ltd. (1)
B Section 22/F Guomao Building No 388 Hubin South Road, Xiamen, China
Tel.: (86) 592 5166428
Chemical Products Mfr
N.A.I.C.S.: 325998

Xiamen ITG Dongfeng Honda Sales & Service Co., Ltd. (1)
No 697 Fangfu road, Xiamen, China
Tel.: (86) 592 3127777
New Car Dealers
N.A.I.C.S.: 441110

Xiamen ITG Financial Group Co., Ltd. (1)
26/27F BuildingB ITG Center No 4688 Xianyue Road, Huli District, Xiamen, 361016, China
Tel.: (86) 5925391661
Supply Chain Management Services
N.A.I.C.S.: 541614

Xiamen ITG Keerun Motor Sales & Service Co., Ltd. (1)
17 Binbei Motor World No 101 Hubin North Road, Xiamen, China
Tel.: (86) 592 5767666
New Car Dealers
N.A.I.C.S.: 441110

Xiamen ITG Real Estate Group Co., Ltd. (1)
19F Building A ITG Center No 4688 Xianyue Road, Huli District, Xiamen, 361016, China
Tel.: (86) 5925769980
Supply Chain Management Services
N.A.I.C.S.: 541614

Xiamen ITG Shipbuilding Imp. & Exp. Co., Ltd. (1)
24/F South Tower of Guomao Center No 4686-4688 Xianyue Road, Huli District, Xiamen, China
Tel.: (86) 591 87809330
Web Site: http://www.itg.com
Emp.: 15
Marine Machinery & Equipment Distr
N.A.I.C.S.: 423860

Xiamen ITG Terminals Ltd. (1)
Berth 20 Zhaishang West Road, Huli District, Xiamen, China
Tel.: (86) 592 2656688
Logistics Consulting Servies
N.A.I.C.S.: 541614

Xiamen Keerun Dongheng Motor Sales & Service Co., Ltd. (1)
B/12 Binbei Motor World No 101 Hubin North Road, Xiamen, China

AND PRIVATE COMPANIES

Tel.: (86) 592 5036767
Web Site: http://www.gacfiatauto.com
New Car Dealers
N.A.I.C.S.: 441110

Xiamen Keerun Infiniti Motor sales & service Co., Ltd. (1)
No 1213 Maqing Road Zhongcang Industria District, Haicang, Xiamen, China
Tel.: (86) 592 5377577
Web Site: http://www.infiniti-xmqr.com.cn
New Car Dealers
N.A.I.C.S.: 441110

Xiamen Zhongsheng Toyota Sales & Service Co., Ltd. (1)
Industrial Building Hubin North road, Xiamen, China
Tel.: (86) 592 5122088
New Car Dealers
N.A.I.C.S.: 441110

Zhejiang Keerun Catering Administration Corp., Ltd. (1)
Rm1001 10/F Liyuan Building No 88 Jiaogong Road, Hangzhou, China
Tel.: (86) 571 89932995
Restaurant Operators
N.A.I.C.S.: 722511

XIAMEN ITG HOLDING GROUP CO., LTD.
21-23F ITG Business Center No 669 Sishui Road, Xiamen, China
Tel.: (86) 592 5830991
Web Site:
    http://www.itgholding.com.cn
Year Founded: 2006
Sales Range: Less than $1 Million
Emp.: 18,454
Holding Company
N.A.I.C.S.: 551112
Xiaoxi Xu *(CEO)*

Subsidiaries:

Xiamen ITG Assets Operation Group Co., Ltd. (1)
14-17 19-20F ITG Business Center No 669 Sishui Road, Huli District, Xiamen, 361015, Fujian, China
Tel.: (86) 5925391661
Real Estate Development Services
N.A.I.C.S.: 531390

Xiamen ITG MICE Group Co., Ltd. (1)
20 F ITG Business Center No 669 Sishui Road, Huli District, Xiamen, 361015, China
Tel.: (86) 5925520005
Web Site: http://www.itgmicegroup.com.cn
Real Estate Development Services
N.A.I.C.S.: 531390

Zhonghong Pulin Group Co., Ltd. (1)
35 Songhe st, Luannan, Tangshan, 063500, Hebei, China
Tel.: (86) 3154167691
Web Site: http://en.zhonghongpulin.cn
Real Estate Development Services
N.A.I.C.S.: 531390

XIAMEN JIARONG TECHNOLOGY CO., LTD.
No 1670 Butang Middle Rd, Torch High-tech Zone Tongxiang Industrial Base, Xiamen, 361100, Fujian, China
Tel.: (86) 5925929683
Web Site: https://jiarong.com
Year Founded: 2005
301148—(CHIN)
Rev.: $106,162,056
Assets: $302,766,984
Liabilities: $56,492,748
Net Worth: $246,274,236
Earnings: $14,966,640
Emp.: 800
Fiscal Year-end: 12/31/22
Information Technology Services
N.A.I.C.S.: 541512
Linyu Jiang *(Chm)*

XIAMEN JIHONG TECHNOLOGY CO., LTD.
No 9 Putou Rd Dongfu Industry Park II, Haicang district, Xiamen, 361025, Fujian, China
Tel.: (86) 5926316330
Web Site: https://www.jihong.cc
Year Founded: 2003
002803—(SSE)
Rev.: $754,774,057
Assets: $455,230,896
Liabilities: $155,172,986
Net Worth: $300,057,910
Earnings: $25,830,778
Fiscal Year-end: 12/31/22
Packaging Services
N.A.I.C.S.: 561910
Yapeng Wang *(Chm)*

Subsidiaries:

Huhehaote Jihong Package Co., Ltd (1)
South Rd Jinshan Industry Park, Huhehaote, 010110, China
Tel.: (86) 4715293601
Packaging Products Mfr
N.A.I.C.S.: 322211

Xiamen Jihong Package & Technology Co., Ltd - Langfang Factory (1)
No 113 Huaxiang Rd Economic and Technology Industry Park, Langfang, 065001, China
Tel.: (86) 3616073766
Packaging Products Mfr
N.A.I.C.S.: 322211

XIAMEN KING LONG MOTOR GROUP CO., LTD.
No 9 Jinlong Road, Jimei District, Xiamen, 361023, China
Tel.: (86) 5923155658
Web Site: https://www.king-long.com
Year Founded: 1988
600686—(SHG)
Rev.: $2,560,953,424
Assets: $3,896,918,111
Liabilities: $3,268,238,571
Net Worth: $628,679,540
Earnings: ($54,319,426)
Fiscal Year-end: 12/31/22
Passenger Vehicles Mfr
N.A.I.C.S.: 336110

XIAMEN KINGDOMWAY GROUP COMPANY
No 299 Yangguang West Road, Haicang District, Xiamen, China
Tel.: (86) 5926511111
Web Site:
    https://www.kingdomway.com
Year Founded: 1997
002626—(SSE)
Rev.: $422,495,766
Assets: $752,287,882
Liabilities: $238,451,724
Net Worth: $513,836,159
Earnings: $36,058,244
Emp.: 1,500
Fiscal Year-end: 12/31/22
Food Nutrition & Feed Additives Mfr
N.A.I.C.S.: 311999

Subsidiaries:

Doctor's Best, Inc. (1)
18100 Von Karman Ave Ste 800, Irvine, CA 92612
Web Site: http://www.drbvitamins.com
Emp.: 30
Dietary Supplements Mfr
N.A.I.C.S.: 325412
Gale Bensussen *(CEO)*

Zipfizz Corporation (1)
14400 NE 145th St Ste 201, Woodinville, WA 98072-5003
Tel.: (425) 398-4240
Web Site: http://www.zipfizz.com
Energy & Sport Drink Powder Mfr
N.A.I.C.S.: 311999

Brian Winn *(Founder)*

XIAMEN LEADING OPTICS CO., LTD.
No 26 Xinmei Road, Haicang Xinyang Industry District, Xiamen, 361022, Fujian, China
Tel.: (86) 5923136623
Web Site:
    https://www.leadingoptics.com
Year Founded: 2002
605118—(SHG)
Rev.: $82,152,154
Assets: $214,580,747
Liabilities: $24,869,838
Net Worth: $189,710,909
Earnings: $21,926,142
Emp.: 1,000
Fiscal Year-end: 12/31/22
Optical Instrument Mfr & Distr
N.A.I.C.S.: 333310
Fubao Wu *(Chm & Gen Mgr)*

XIAMEN LUTONG INTERNATIONAL TRAVEL AGENCY CO. LTD.
20F Longhai Fortune Center 42 Ziwei Road Shima Town, Zhangzhou, 363199, Fujian, China
Tel.: (86) 5966565220 NV
Year Founded: 2007
LTGJ—(OTCIQ)
Liabilities: $403,209
Net Worth: ($403,209)
Earnings: ($66,212)
Fiscal Year-end: 06/30/20
Travel & Ticketing Services
N.A.I.C.S.: 561510

XIAMEN MEIYA PICO INFORMATION CO.,LTD.
Meiya Pico Building 12 Guanri Road 2nd Phase of Xiamen Software Park, Xiamen, 361008, Fujian, China
Tel.: (86) 5925300188
Web Site: https://www.meiyapico.com
Year Founded: 1999
300188—(CHIN)
Rev.: $320,068,476
Assets: $827,010,756
Liabilities: $222,174,576
Net Worth: $604,836,180
Earnings: $20,759,544
Emp.: 4,000
Fiscal Year-end: 12/31/22
Information Security Product Mfr
N.A.I.C.S.: 541511

XIAMEN OVERSEAS CHINESE ELECTRONIC CO., LTD.
No 22 Huli Road, Xiamen, 361005, Fujian, China
Tel.: (86) 592 551 0275
Web Site: http://www.cccme.org.cn
600870—(SHG)
Rev.: $1,303,817
Assets: $13,715,359
Liabilities: $11,996,343
Net Worth: $1,719,016
Earnings: $174,659
Fiscal Year-end: 12/31/20
Television Product Distr
N.A.I.C.S.: 423620

XIAMEN PORT DEVELOPMENT CO., LTD.
20-21F Ports Building No 31 Donggang North Road, Xiamen, 361013, Fujian, China
Tel.: (86) 5925826220
Web Site: http://www.xmgw.com.cn
Year Founded: 1999
000905—(SSE)
Rev.: $3,088,223,054
Assets: $1,681,400,972
Liabilities: $818,552,906

XIAMEN TUNGSTEN CO., LTD.

Net Worth: $862,848,067
Earnings: $34,567,379
Fiscal Year-end: 12/31/22
Portfolio Management Services
N.A.I.C.S.: 523940
Dong Ke *(Chm)*

XIAMEN SOLEX HIGH-TECH INDUSTRIES CO., LTD.
No 298 Yangguang West Road, Haicang District, Xiamen, 361022, Fujian, China
Tel.: (86) 5923502118
Web Site: http://www.solexgrp.com
Year Founded: 2004
603992—(SHG)
Rev.: $446,546,187
Assets: $620,155,814
Liabilities: $286,244,052
Net Worth: $333,911,762
Earnings: $36,664,393
Emp.: 3,700
Fiscal Year-end: 12/31/22
Household Appliances Mfr
N.A.I.C.S.: 335220
Huasong Zhou *(Chm & Gen Mgr)*

XIAMEN SUNRISE GROUP CO. LTD.
No 30 Xingbei Road Xinglin Street, Jimei District, Xiamen, 361022, Fujian, China
Tel.: (86) 05926666866
Web Site: http://www.cccme.org.cn
Year Founded: 1995
002593—(SSE)
Rev.: $474,273,966
Assets: $705,025,606
Liabilities: $374,192,185
Net Worth: $330,833,421
Earnings: $4,066,349
Fiscal Year-end: 12/31/22
Wheel Mfr
N.A.I.C.S.: 336390
Ziwen Wu *(Chm & Gen Mgr)*

XIAMEN TUNGSTEN CO., LTD.
21 22F Building A Tefang Boteman Wealth Center No 81 Zhanhong Road, Siming District, Xiamen, 361009, Fujian, China
Tel.: (86) 5925363856
Web Site: http://www.cxtc.com
Year Founded: 1997
600549—(SHG)
Rev.: $6,770,479,295
Assets: $5,587,747,322
Liabilities: $3,332,918,436
Net Worth: $2,254,828,886
Earnings: $203,044,613
Fiscal Year-end: 12/31/22
Non Ferrous Metal Product Smelting Services
N.A.I.C.S.: 331492
Changgeng Huang *(Chm)*

Subsidiaries:

Chengdu Hongbo Industrial Co., Ltd. (1)
No 198 Nanjing Road Longquanyi, Economic and Technological Development Zone, Chengdu, Sichuan, China
Tel.: (86) 2888432322
Web Site: https://www.cd-hb.com
Emp.: 668
Tungsten Product Mfr
N.A.I.C.S.: 331492

Jiujiang Golden Egret Hardmaterial Co., Ltd. (1)
No 18 of ChunJiang Road, City-West Port District Economic-Technological Development Area, Jiujiang, 332000, Jiangxi, China
Tel.: (86) 7926849299
Web Site: https://www.gehm.com.cn
Tungsten Product Mfr
N.A.I.C.S.: 331492

XIAMEN TUNGSTEN CO., LTD.

Xiamen Tungsten Co., Ltd.—(Continued)

Luoyang Golden Egret Geotools Co., Ltd. (1)
No 68 North Binhe Rd, National High New Tech Industry Zone, Luoyang, 471000, Henan, China
Tel.: (86) 37961101002
Web Site: https://en.xtcgtl.com
Tungsten Product Mfr
N.A.I.C.S.: 331492

Xiamen Golden Egret Special Alloy Co., Ltd. (1)
No 69 Xinglong Road, Huli District, Xiamen, China
Tel.: (86) 5927107392
Web Site: http://www.en.gesac.com.cn
Tungsten Product Mfr
N.A.I.C.S.: 331492
Sunny Xu (Engr-Sls)

Xiamen Honglu Tungsten & Molybdenum Industry Co., Ltd. (1)
No 339 Liansheng Road, Jimei North Industrial District, Xiamen, 361021, China
Tel.: (86) 5926298216
Web Site: https://www.xiamen-honglu.com
Tungsten Product Mfr
N.A.I.C.S.: 331492

XIAMEN VOKE MOLD & PLASTIC ENGINEERING CO., LTD.
1152-1158 Chunguang Rd, Xiangan, Xiamen, 361101, Fujian, China
Tel.: (86) 5927769619
Web Site: https://www.ctmold.com
Year Founded: 2005
301196—(CHIN)
Rev.: $188,883,704
Assets: $520,551,280
Liabilities: $79,898,648
Net Worth: $440,652,632
Earnings: $23,671,732
Fiscal Year-end: 12/31/23
Plastic Product Mfr & Distr
N.A.I.C.S.: 326199
Zhuang Huiyang (Chm & Gen Mgr)

Subsidiaries:

Quanzhou Gruenluft Molding Engineering Co.,Ltd. (1)
No 5088 Binhu East Road Dongyuan Town, Quanzhou Taiwanese Investment Zone, Quanzhou, China
Tel.: (86) 5927769688
Plastic Molding Machinery Distr
N.A.I.C.S.: 424610

Shanghai Cobi Mold & Plastic Engineering Co., Ltd. (1)
1888 Huangqing Rd, Qingpu, Shanghai, 201707, China
Tel.: (86) 2137775628
Web Site: https://www.cobi.cn
Modern Machine Mfr
N.A.I.C.S.: 333120

Tianjin Voke Mold & Plastic Technology Co., Ltd. (1)
45-2 Dongjiu Rd Dongli, Tianjin, China
Tel.: (86) 2258679366
Injection Moulded Parts Mfr
N.A.I.C.S.: 333248

VOK E Mexico S. de R.L. de C.V. (1)
Blvr Industrial De La Transformacion 3095, In Parque Industrial Saltillo, CP 25903, Ramos Arizpe, Mexico
Tel.: (52) 16018139151
Injection Moulded Parts Mfr & Whslr
N.A.I.C.S.: 325314

Voke Technology Germany GmbH (1)
Industriestrasse 3, OT Foritztal, 96524, Neuhaus-Schierschnitz, Germany
Tel.: (49) 3676480323
Automotive Electronic Product Mfr & Distr
N.A.I.C.S.: 336320

Vork Technologies (Malaysia) Sdn.Bhd. (1)
No 58&59 Jalan 1-park SAC7 Taman Perindustrian 1-Park Sac, 81400, Senai, Malaysia
Tel.: (60) 75706099
Web Site: https://www.vork.com.my
Plastic Engineering & Home Appliances Mfr
N.A.I.C.S.: 333511

Xiamen Gruenluft Molding Engineering Co., Ltd. (1)
No 5088 Binhu East Road Quanzhou Taiwanese Investment Zone, Dongyuan Town, Quanzhou, China
Tel.: (86) 5927769688
Injection Molded Plastic Product Mfr & Distr
N.A.I.C.S.: 326199

Xiamen Grunluft Technology Co., Ltd. (1)
16 Xianghong Rd, Xiang An, Xiamen, 361101, Fujian, China
Tel.: (86) 5927769688
Injection Moulded Parts Mfr
N.A.I.C.S.: 333248

Xiamen Vork Health Industry Co., Ltd. (1)
16 Xianghong-Road Torch Hi-tech Industrial Area, Xiang An, Xiamen, 361101, China
Tel.: (86) 5927687698
Web Site: https://www.vorktech.com
Home Electrical Appliance Mfr
N.A.I.C.S.: 335210

XIAMEN WANLI STONE STOCK CO., LTD.
8/f Fortune Bldg 201 North Hubin Rd, Xiamen, 361012, China
Tel.: (86) 5925081199
Web Site: https://en.wanlistone.com
Year Founded: 1996
002785—(SSE)
Rev.: $183,304,246
Assets: $191,191,006
Liabilities: $103,824,789
Net Worth: $87,366,217
Earnings: ($3,815,230)
Fiscal Year-end: 12/31/22
Construction Materials Distr
N.A.I.C.S.: 423390

XIAMEN XGMA MACHINERY CO., LTD.
No 668-8 Guankou South Road, Jimei District, Xiamen, 361023, China
Tel.: (86) 5922360090
Web Site: https://www.xiagong.com
Year Founded: 1951
600815—(SHG)
Rev.: $141,411,175
Assets: $386,791,793
Liabilities: $151,640,663
Net Worth: $235,151,130
Earnings: $36,251,378
Fiscal Year-end: 12/31/22
Construction Machinery Mfr
N.A.I.C.S.: 333120
Zhiyong Wang (Sec)

XIAMEN XIANGYU CO., LTD.
No 99 Xiangyu Road Modern Logistics Park, Unit 8 7F Building E Xiamen International Shipping Center, Xiamen, 361006, Fujian, China
Tel.: (86) 5926516003 CN
Web Site: https://www.xiangyu.cn
Year Founded: 1981
600057—(SHG)
Rev.: $75,555,988,200
Assets: $16,153,919,810
Liabilities: $11,044,535,154
Net Worth: $5,109,384,655
Earnings: $370,221,041
Emp.: 1,405
Fiscal Year-end: 12/31/22
Supply Chain & Logistics Services
N.A.I.C.S.: 561499
Qidong Deng (Pres)

Subsidiaries:

Fuzhou Singamas Container Co., Ltd. (1)
8-5 Fuzhou Bonded Zone, Mawei, Fuzhou, 350015, Fujian, China
Tel.: (86) 59183999758
Dry Freight Container Mfr
N.A.I.C.S.: 332439

Honesty Shipping Co., Limited (1)
7F No 4 Building AiJia International Mansion No 288 Wu Hua Road, Shanghai, 200086, China
Tel.: (86) 2155155333
Web Site: https://www.honesty-shipping.com
International Freight Transportation Services
N.A.I.C.S.: 424510

Xiamen Modern Terminal Co., Ltd. (1)
Berth One, Kwai Chung, Hong Kong, China (Hong Kong)
Tel.: (852) 21153838
Web Site: https://www.modernterminals.com
International Freight Transportation Services
N.A.I.C.S.: 424510

Xiamen Xiangyu Singamas Container Co., Ltd. (1)
Room 301 No 56 Gangxing 2nd Road Mordern Logistic Park, Xiamen, 361006, China
Tel.: (86) 5926032576
Dry Freight Container Mfr
N.A.I.C.S.: 332439

XIAMEN XINDE CO., LTD.
11th Floor Building A International Trade Center No 4688 Xianyue Road, Huli District, Xiamen, 361016, Fujian, China
Tel.: (86) 5926021666
Web Site: https://www.xindeco.com
Year Founded: 1984
000701—(SSE)
Rev.: $13,197,655,725
Assets: $2,249,458,768
Liabilities: $1,737,309,066
Net Worth: $512,149,702
Earnings: $7,138,119
Fiscal Year-end: 12/31/22
Automotive Distr
N.A.I.C.S.: 423110
Wang Mingcheng (Chm)

Subsidiaries:

Shenzhen Anni Digital Technology Co., Ltd. (1)
3rd Floor Hasee Building No 1 Banlan Road, Bantian Buji Town Longgang District, Shenzhen, 518129, China
Tel.: (86) 75589392688
Web Site: http://www.annigroup.com
Video Equipment Mfr
N.A.I.C.S.: 334310

XIAMEN YANJAN NEW MATERIAL CO., LTD.
No 666 Houdi Road Industrial Concentration Zone, Neicuo Town Xiangan District, Xiamen, 361199, Fujian, China
Tel.: (86) 5927268000
Web Site: https://www.yanjan.com
Year Founded: 2000
300658—(CHIN)
Rev.: $177,275,190
Assets: $380,561,685
Liabilities: $182,326,522
Net Worth: $198,235,163
Earnings: $2,939,793
Emp.: 1,000
Fiscal Year-end: 12/31/23
Hygiene Product Mfr & Distr
N.A.I.C.S.: 322291
Xie Jihua (Chm & Pres)

XIAMEN ZHONGCHUANG ENVIRONMENTAL TECHNOLOGY CO., LTD.
No 1178-1188 Chunguang Road Industrial Zone, Torch High-tech Zone Xiangan, Xiamen, 361101, China
Tel.: (86) 5927769777

INTERNATIONAL PUBLIC

Web Site: https://www.savings.com.cn
Year Founded: 2001
300056—(CHIN)
Rev: $141,401,052
Assets: $179,460,684
Liabilities: $108,821,232
Net Worth: $70,639,452
Earnings: ($11,644,776)
Emp.: 700
Fiscal Year-end: 12/31/22
Filtration Material & Filter Bags
N.A.I.C.S.: 322220
Zhang Hongliang (Chm)

Subsidiaries:

Beijing Zhongchuang Green City Environmental Service Co., Ltd. (1)
Room 907 Building 8 No 93 Jianguo Road, Chaoyang District, Beijing, China
Tel.: (86) 1058203220
Filter Bag Distr
N.A.I.C.S.: 424130

Henan Zhongchuang City Service Co., Ltd. (1)
1002 10th floor northeast corner of the intersection of Wenchang Ave, and Renhe Road Chuanhui District, Zhoukou, Henan, China
Tel.: (86) 1064802759
Filter Bag Distr
N.A.I.C.S.: 424130

Jiangxi Xiangsheng Environmental Protection Technology Co., Ltd. (1)
Industrial Park, West District Yongfeng County, Jian, Jiangxi, China
Tel.: (86) 7962219801
Filter Bag Distr
N.A.I.C.S.: 424130

Potent Mechanical & Industrial (Xiamen) Co., Ltd (1)
13 F No 168 East Tapu Road, Siming District, Xiamen, 361004, China
Tel.: (86) 5925853191
Web Site: https://en.potent.com.cn
Conveyance Equipment Mfr & Distr
N.A.I.C.S.: 333922

Xiamen Brv Environmental Technology Co., Ltd. (1)
No 5 Xiangming Road, Xiang An Industrial Zone, Xiamen, Fujian, China
Tel.: (86) 5927170118
Filter Bag Distr
N.A.I.C.S.: 424130

Zhongchuang Environmental Protection (Xinjiang) Technology Co., Ltd. (1)
No 32 Huihuang Avenue, Technology Industry Development Zone Changji National High-tech Zone, Xinjiang, Changji, China
Tel.: (86) 9942517578
Filter Bag Distr
N.A.I.C.S.: 424130

XIAN BRIGHT LASER TECHNOLOGIES CO., LTD.
No 1000 Shanglinyuan 7th Road, Hi-Tech Zone, Xi'an, 710000, Shaanxi, China
Tel.: (86) 2988485673
Web Site: https://www.xa-blt.com
Year Founded: 2011
688333—(SHG)
Rev.: $128,898,235
Assets: $425,631,866
Liabilities: $210,907,883
Net Worth: $214,723,983
Earnings: $11,161,632
Emp.: 1,100
Fiscal Year-end: 12/31/22
Printing Equipment Mfr
N.A.I.C.S.: 333248
Xue Lei (Chm & Gen Mgr)

XIAN CHENXI AVIATION TECHNOLOGY CORP LTD
No 11 Zone C Pioneer Park No 69

Jinye Road High-tech Zone, Xi'an, 710077, Shaanxi, China
Tel.: (86) 2981881858
300581—(CHIN)
Rev.: $32,867,404
Assets: $178,383,384
Liabilities: $32,860,699
Net Worth: $145,522,685
Earnings: $810,479
Fiscal Year-end: 12/31/23
Aviation Electrical Product Mfr & Distr
N.A.I.C.S.: 334511

XIAN LIJUN PHARMACEUTICAL CO., LTD.
No 151 Hancheng Road, Xi'an, 710077, Shaanxi, China
Tel.: (86) 2984264676
Web Site: http://www.lijun.com
Year Founded: 1938
Sales Range: $450-499.9 Million
Emp.: 2,000
Pharmaceuticals Mfr
N.A.I.C.S.: 325412
Qin Wu (Chm)

XIANA MINING INC.
507 - 837 West Hastings Street, Vancouver, V6C 3N6, BC, Canada
Tel.: (604) 685-1017   BC
Year Founded: 1981
XIA—(TSXV)
Sales Range: $25-49.9 Million
Mineral Exploration Services
N.A.I.C.S.: 213114
Anton J. Drescher (CFO)

XIANDAI INVESTMENT CO., LTD.
Modern Plaza No 128 Section 2 Furong South Road, Tianxin District, Changsha, 410004, Hunan, China
Tel.: (86) 73188749898
Web Site: http://www.xdtz.net
Year Founded: 1993
000900—(SSE)
Rev.: $2,298,879,189
Assets: $8,129,914,959
Liabilities: $6,198,503,047
Net Worth: $1,931,411,912
Earnings: $60,739,680
Fiscal Year-end: 12/31/22
Transportation Services
N.A.I.C.S.: 488490
Luo Weihua (Chm)

XIANGCAI CO., LTD.
No 7 Taihu North Road Yingbin Road, Central Area High-tech Industrial Development Zone Daoli District, Harbin, 150078, Heilongjiang, China
Tel.: (86) 45184348333
Web Site:
https://www.600095.com.cn
Year Founded: 1994
600095—(SHG)
Rev.: $493,669,426
Assets: $4,884,299,222
Liabilities: $3,215,905,285
Net Worth: $1,668,393,937
Earnings: ($45,811,228)
Fiscal Year-end: 12/31/22
Soybean Processing & Pharmaceutical Mfr
N.A.I.C.S.: 311224
Chen Jian (Chm)

XIANGPIAOPIAO FOOD CO., LTD.
No 888 Chuangye Avenue Economic and Technological Development Zone, Huzhou, 313000, China
Tel.: (86) 5722669999
Web Site: https://www.zjxpp.com
603711—(SHG)
Rev.: $439,145,872
Assets: $708,170,678
Liabilities: $269,514,985
Net Worth: $438,655,693
Earnings: $30,030,802
Fiscal Year-end: 12/31/22
Food Product Mfr & Distr
N.A.I.C.S.: 311999

XIANGTAN ELECTRIC MANUFACTURING GROUP CO., LTD.
No 302 Xiashesi Street, Xiangtan, 411101, Hunan, China
Tel.: (86) 73158595732
Web Site: http://www.xemc.com.cn
Year Founded: 1936
600416—(SHG)
Rev.: $625,004,935
Assets: $1,972,075,431
Liabilities: $1,001,240,866
Net Worth: $970,834,564
Earnings: $35,843,067
Fiscal Year-end: 12/31/22
Wind Power Generation Services
N.A.I.C.S.: 221115
Zhou Jianjun (Chm)

XIANGTAN ELECTROCHEMICAL SCIENTIFIC CO., LTD.
Minmetals Zuncheng Jiuhua, Yuhu District, Xiangtan, 411100, Hunan, China
Tel.: (86) 73155544098
Web Site: https://www.chinaemd.com
Year Founded: 2000
002125—(SSE)
Rev.: $294,882,527
Assets: $720,876,457
Liabilities: $380,109,553
Net Worth: $340,766,904
Earnings: $55,333,816
Emp.: 2,700
Fiscal Year-end: 12/31/22
Battery Mfr
N.A.I.C.S.: 335910
Xinqiao Tan (Chm)

XIANGXING INTERNATIONAL HOLDING LIMITED
No 233 Jiangang Road Pilot Free Trade Zone, Xiamen, Fujian, China
Tel.: (86) 5925750333   Ky
Web Site: http://www.xxlt.com.cn
1732—(HKG)
Rev.: $33,313,129
Assets: $27,006,642
Liabilities: $4,324,882
Net Worth: $22,681,760
Earnings: $1,415,794
Emp.: 929
Fiscal Year-end: 12/31/22
Logistics Management Services
N.A.I.C.S.: 541614
Youguo Cheng (Founder & Chm)

XIANGXUE PHARMACEUTICAL CO., LTD.
No 2 Jinfengyuan Road Science City, Guangzhou Economic and Technological Development Zone Luogang District, Guangzhou, 510663, Guangdong, China
Tel.: (86) 2022211007
Web Site: http://www.xphcn.com
Year Founded: 1986
300147—(CHIN)
Rev.: $307,064,628
Assets: $1,308,595,392
Liabilities: $912,375,360
Net Worth: $396,220,032
Earnings: ($74,855,664)
Emp.: 10,000
Fiscal Year-end: 12/31/22
Pharmaceuticals Mfr
N.A.I.C.S.: 325412
Wang Yonghui (Chm & Gen Mgr)

XIANGYANG AUTOMOBILE BEARING CO., LTD.
No 97 Dengcheng Avenue Hi-tech Zone, Xiangyang, 441004, Hubei, China
Tel.: (86) 7103855209
Web Site: http://www.zxy.com.cn
Year Founded: 1968
000678—(SSE)
Rev.: $158,732,098
Assets: $336,896,553
Liabilities: $201,187,949
Net Worth: $135,708,604
Earnings: ($17,490,864)
Emp.: 4,500
Fiscal Year-end: 12/31/22
Automobile Parts Mfr
N.A.I.C.S.: 336110
Shaobing Gao (Chm)

Subsidiaries:

Fabryka Lozysk Tocznych - Krasnik S.A.   (1)
Ul Fabryczna 6, 23-204, Krasnik, Poland
Tel.: (48) 818257101
Web Site: https://www.flt.krasnik.pl
Emp.: 200
Ball Bearing Mfr
N.A.I.C.S.: 332991
Grzegorz Jasinski (Pres)

XIANGYANG BOYA PRECISION INDUSTRIAL EQUIPMENTS CO., LTD.
No 3 Tianlai Avenue, High-tech Industrial Development Zone, Xiangyang, 441004, Hubei, China
Tel.: (86) 7103333670
Web Site: http://www.fboya.com
Year Founded: 1999
300971—(SSE)
Rev.: $58,209,054
Assets: $176,775,717
Liabilities: $42,189,652
Net Worth: $134,586,064
Earnings: $8,692,712
Fiscal Year-end: 12/31/22
Industrial Machinery Product Mfr & Distr
N.A.I.C.S.: 333248
Wenxi Li (Chm & Gen Mgr)

XIANGYANG CHANGYUAN DONGGU INDUSTRIAL CO., LTD.,
No 396 Diamond Avenue, Xiangzhou District, Xiangyang, 441100, Hubei, China
Tel.: (86) 7103062982
Web Site: https://www.cydgsy.com
Year Founded: 2001
603950—(SHG)
Rev.: $156,692,493
Assets: $539,115,474
Liabilities: $218,968,359
Net Worth: $320,147,114
Earnings: $14,048,129
Emp.: 1,360
Fiscal Year-end: 12/31/22
Engine Parts Mfr & Distr
N.A.I.C.S.: 333618
Zuoyuan Li (Chm)

Subsidiaries:

Beijing Changyuan Langhong Technology Co., Ltd.   (1)
No 1 Xingguang Second Street, Optical Mechatronics Industrial Base Tongzhou District, Beijing, China
Tel.: (86) 1050961476
Diesel Engine Parts Mfr & Distr
N.A.I.C.S.: 336310

Wuhan Changyuan Langhong Technology Co., Ltd.   (1)
No 38 East Section of Xingcheng Avenue, Xiantao, Hubei, China
Tel.: (86) 7283312500

Diesel Engine Parts Mfr & Distr
N.A.I.C.S.: 336310

Xiangyang Changyuan East Grain Stream Co., Ltd.   (1)
No 396 Diamond Avenue, Xiangzhou District, Xiangyang, China
Tel.: (86) 7103062981
Diesel Engine Parts Mfr & Distr
N.A.I.C.S.: 336310

Xiangyang Changyuan Langhong Technology Co., Ltd.   (1)
South of Huan 5 Road, West of Guanghua Avenue Economic Development Zone Laohekou, Xiangyang, Hubei, China
Tel.: (86) 7107172666
Diesel Engine Parts Mfr & Distr
N.A.I.C.S.: 336310

XIANGYU MEDICAL CO., LTD.
Middle Section of Diku Road, Neihuang County, Anyang, 456353, Henan, China
Tel.: (86) 3727775555
Web Site:
https://www.xiangyumedical.com
Year Founded: 2002
688626—(SHG)
Rev.: $68,589,528
Assets: $332,478,207
Liabilities: $60,122,046
Net Worth: $272,356,161
Earnings: $17,616,002
Emp.: 1,000
Fiscal Year-end: 12/31/22
Medical Product Mfr & Distr
N.A.I.C.S.: 339112
Yongzheng He (Chm & Gen Mgr)

Subsidiaries:

Anyang Xiangyu Medical Equipment Co., Ltd.   (1)
Diku Road, Neihuang County, Henan, China
Tel.: (86) 372 770 3111
Medical Equipment Mfr & Distr
N.A.I.C.S.: 339112

XIANHE CO., LTD.
No 12 North Bailing Rd, Qujiang District, Quzhou, 324022, Zhejiang, China
Tel.: (86) 5702833055
Web Site: https://xianhepaper.com
Year Founded: 1997
603733—(SHG)
Rev.: $1,086,458,513
Assets: $1,862,212,711
Liabilities: $891,794,994
Net Worth: $970,417,717
Earnings: $99,724,407
Emp.: 3,800
Fiscal Year-end: 12/31/22
Paper Product Mfr & Distr
N.A.I.C.S.: 322120
Wang Minliang (Chm, Pres & Gen Mgr)

XIAO-I CORPORATION
5F Building 2 No 2570 Hechuan Road, Shanghai, 201803, China
Tel.: (86) 2139512112   Ky
Web Site: https://ir.xiaoi.com
Year Founded: 2018
AIXI—(NASDAQ)
Rev.: $32,524,013
Assets: $47,190,411
Liabilities: $50,573,072
Net Worth: ($3,382,661)
Earnings: $3,677,813
Emp.: 443
Fiscal Year-end: 12/31/21
Software Development Services
N.A.I.C.S.: 541511
Hui Yuan (Chm)

XIAOMI CORPORATION
Xiaomi Campus Anningzhuang Road,

XIAOMI CORPORATION

Xiaomi Corporation—(Continued)
Haidian District, Beijing, China
Tel.: (86) 1060606666 Ky
Web Site: https://ir.mi.com
Year Founded: 2010
1810—(HKG)
Rev.: $38,164,808,477
Assets: $45,668,653,243
Liabilities: $22,533,193,031
Net Worth: $23,135,460,212
Earnings: $2,461,154,359
Emp.: 33,627
Fiscal Year-end: 12/31/23
Holding Company; Smartphone & Other Electronics Mfr & Whslr
N.A.I.C.S.: 551112
Jun Lei *(Chm & CEO)*

Subsidiaries:

Xiaomi Inc. (1)
Xiaomi Office Bldg 68 Qinghe Middle Street, Haidian District, Beijing, 100085, China **(100%)**
Tel.: (86) 1060606666
Web Site: https://www.mi.com
Mobile Phones & Consumer Electronics Mfr
N.A.I.C.S.: 334111
Jun Lei *(Co-Founder, Chm & CEO)*

XIAOTAI INTERNATIONAL INVESTMENT INC.
Room 301 Block 2 611 Jianghong Road Changhe Street, Binjiang District, Hangzhou, Zhejiang, China
Tel.: (86) 571 26890017 Ky
Year Founded: 2018
Sales Range: $25-49.9 Million
Emp.: 294
Financial Investment Services
N.A.I.C.S.: 523940
Baofeng Pan *(Chm)*

XICE TESTING TECHNOLOGY CO., LTD.
No 16 Zhangba 2nd Road High-tech Zone, Xi'an, 710065, Shaanxi, China
Tel.: (86) 2988607193
Web Site: https://www.xcet.com.cn
Year Founded: 2010
301306—(SSE)
Rev.: $42,702,744
Assets: $198,235,786
Liabilities: $23,097,864
Net Worth: $175,137,922
Earnings: $9,079,275
Fiscal Year-end: 12/31/22
Laboratory Testing Services
N.A.I.C.S.: 541380
Li Zexin *(Chm & Gen Mgr)*

XIDELANG (FUJIAN) SPORTS CO., LTD.
Hongpeng Building, Yangguang Road East, Jingjiang, 362211, Fujian, China
Tel.: (86) 59585129977
Emp.: 2,000
Shoes, Clothing & Other Apparel Mfr
N.A.I.C.S.: 316210
Ding Jia Xing *(CEO)*

XIDELANG HOLDINGS LTD
XiDeLang Industrial Park Neikeng Town, Jinjiang, Fujian, China
Tel.: (86) 59586776888 BM
Web Site:
http://www.xidelang.com.my
Year Founded: 1993
XDL—(KLS)
Rev.: $68,006,548
Assets: $232,446,382
Liabilities: $32,533,224
Net Worth: $199,913,158
Earnings: ($21,601,384)
Emp.: 2,000
Fiscal Year-end: 06/30/22
Athletic Shoe Mfr & Distr

N.A.I.C.S.: 316210
Lihong Ding *(Founder & Chm)*

XIEZHONG INTERNATIONAL HOLDINGS LIMITED
389 Kening Road Science Park, Jiangning District, Nanjing, 211100, China
Tel.: (86) 2552161888 Ky
Web Site:
http://www.xiezhonginternational.hk
Year Founded: 2011
Rev.: $282,405,274
Assets: $435,644,339
Liabilities: $363,537,680
Net Worth: $72,106,659
Earnings: ($41,151,553)
Emp.: 2,233
Fiscal Year-end: 12/31/19
Holding Company
N.A.I.C.S.: 551112
Cunyou Chen *(Chm & CEO)*

XIGEM TECHNOLOGIES CORPORATION
70 Great Gulf Drive 67, Vaughan, L4K 0K7, ON, Canada
Tel.: (647) 250-9824 ON
Web Site:
https://www.xigemtechnologies.com
Year Founded: 2017
XIGM—(CNSX)
Assets: $458,995
Liabilities: $242,053
Net Worth: $216,942
Earnings: ($4,645,775)
Fiscal Year-end: 12/31/22
Software Development Services
N.A.I.C.S.: 541511
Brian Kalish *(Founder)*

XILAM ANIMATION S.A.
57 Boulevard de la Villette, 75010, Paris, France
Tel.: (33) 140187200
Web Site: https://www.xilam.com
Year Founded: 1999
XIL—(EUR)
Rev.: $50,419,814
Assets: $166,996,547
Liabilities: $92,011,656
Net Worth: $74,984,891
Earnings: $1,583,207
Emp.: 201
Fiscal Year-end: 12/31/22
Motion Picture & Video Production Services
N.A.I.C.S.: 512191
Marc du Pontavice *(Founder & CEO)*

XILINMEN FURNITURE CO., LTD.
No 1 Erhuan North Road, Lingzhi Town Yuecheng District, Shaoxing, 312001, Zhejiang, China
Tel.: (86) 57585159531
Web Site: http://www.chinabed.com
Year Founded: 1996
603008—(SHG)
Rev.: $1,100,557,046
Assets: $1,269,545,814
Liabilities: $747,672,990
Net Worth: $521,872,823
Earnings: $33,351,571
Fiscal Year-end: 12/31/22
Mattress Mfr
N.A.I.C.S.: 337910
Ayu Chen *(Chm)*

XILONG SCIENTIFIC CO., LTD.
No 2 Xilong Middle Street Chaoshan Road, Shantou, 510663, Guangdong, China
Tel.: (86) 2062612188
Web Site: https://xilongchemical.str-cc.com

Year Founded: 1994
002584—(SSE)
Rev.: $868,122,516
Assets: $698,829,234
Liabilities: $373,614,930
Net Worth: $325,214,304
Earnings: $12,361,855
Emp.: 462
Fiscal Year-end: 12/31/22
Chemical Reagent Mfr
N.A.I.C.S.: 325998
Peter Chow *(Sls Dir)*

XIMALAYA INC.
Building 1-2 Phase III Guochuang Center No 799 Dangui Road, Pudong New District, Shanghai, China
Tel.: (86) 2150179079 Ky
Year Founded: 2013
Rev.: $620,503,717
Assets: $601,445,619
Liabilities: $1,689,613,975
Net Worth: ($1,088,168,356)
Earnings: ($91,088,707)
Emp.: 3,074
Fiscal Year-end: 12/31/20
Holding Company
N.A.I.C.S.: 551112
Yuxin Chen *(Co-Founder)*

XIMEI RESOURCES HOLDING LIMITED
Hongqiao Village, Qiaotou Yingde, Qingyuan, Guangdong, China
Tel.: (86) 2085820864 Ky
Web Site:
https://www.ximeigroup.com
Year Founded: 2006
9936—(HKG)
Rev.: $156,212,916
Assets: $260,316,353
Liabilities: $106,783,693
Net Worth: $153,532,660
Earnings: $16,465,019
Emp.: 550
Fiscal Year-end: 12/31/22
Holding Company
N.A.I.C.S.: 551112

XIMEN MINING CORP.
888 Dunsmiur Street Suite 888, Vancouver, V6C 3K4, BC, Canada
Tel.: (604) 488-3900
Web Site:
https://www.ximenminingcorp.com
Year Founded: 2006
XXMMF—(OTCIQ)
Assets: $2,086,049
Liabilities: $1,709,902
Net Worth: $376,147
Earnings: ($4,105,432)
Fiscal Year-end: 06/30/19
Mineral Exploration Services
N.A.I.C.S.: 212290
Christopher R. Anderson *(Pres & CEO)*

XIN HEE CO., LTD.
Hongzhan Building No 95 Huli Avenue, Huli District, Xiamen, 361006, Fujian, China
Tel.: (86) 5923107822
Web Site: http://www.xinhee.cn
Year Founded: 2006
003016—(SSE)
Rev.: $244,663,862
Assets: $511,694,708
Liabilities: $111,847,737
Net Worth: $399,846,971
Earnings: $18,129,178
Fiscal Year-end: 12/31/22
Clothing Apparel Distr
N.A.I.C.S.: 458110
Ruihong Sun *(Chm, Gen Mgr & Dir)*

XIN HWA HOLDINGS BERHAD

INTERNATIONAL PUBLIC

No 2 Jalan Permatang 2 Kempas Baru, 81200, Johor Bahru, Johor Darul Takzim, Malaysia
Tel.: (60) 72316999
Web Site:
https://www.xinhwa.com.my
XINHWA—(KLS)
Rev.: $25,033,123
Assets: $80,707,417
Liabilities: $39,592,794
Net Worth: $41,114,623
Earnings: ($3,324,736)
Emp.: 672
Fiscal Year-end: 03/31/23
Logistics, Transportation, Warehousing & Distribution Services
N.A.I.C.S.: 541614
Aik Chuan Ng *(Mng Dir)*

XIN JIANG READY HEALTH INDUSTRY CO., LTD.
No 130 Shanghai Road Economic and Technological Development Zone, Urumqi, 830026, Xinjiang, China
Tel.: (86) 991 368 7305
600090—(SHG)
Rev.: $136,942,162
Assets: $1,059,229,592
Liabilities: $434,734,907
Net Worth: $624,494,685
Earnings: ($346,519,653)
Emp.: 935
Fiscal Year-end: 12/31/20
Bio-Pharmaceutical Products Sales
N.A.I.C.S.: 424210
Meihua Zhang *(Chm & Sec-Interim)*

XIN POINT HOLDINGS LIMITED
Keen Point Industrial Park Xikeng, Zhongkai Distirct, Huizhou, Guangdong, China
Tel.: (86) 7522652600 Ky
Web Site: http://www.xinpoint.com
Year Founded: 2002
1571—(HKG)
Rev.: $404,754,386
Assets: $556,563,852
Liabilities: $146,764,192
Net Worth: $409,799,660
Earnings: $60,160,136
Emp.: 6,059
Fiscal Year-end: 12/31/22
Automotive Parts Mfr & Distr
N.A.I.C.S.: 332813
Xiaoming Ma *(Founder & Chm)*

Subsidiaries:

Bernd Lindecke Werkzeugbau GmbH (1)
Daimlerstrasse 11, 32108, Bad Salzuflen, Germany
Tel.: (49) 52 229 2600
Web Site: https://www.lindecke.de
Construction Tool & Mold Product Mfr
N.A.I.C.S.: 333511
Bernd Lindecke *(Mng Dir)*

Huizhou Keen Point Precision Plastic Co., Ltd. (1)
Keen Point Industrial Park Xikeng, Zhongkai Hi-Tech District, Huizhou, Guangdong, China
Tel.: (86) 7522652600
Web Site: https://en.xinpoint.com
Automobile Plastic Component Mfr & Distr
N.A.I.C.S.: 332813
Micky Lin *(Sls Mgr)*

Huizhou Keen Point Surface Decoration Co., Ltd. (1)
NO 406 Longxi Plating Base, Boluo, Huizhou, Guangdong, China
Tel.: (86) 7526872600
Automobile Plastic Component Mfr & Distr
N.A.I.C.S.: 332813

Huizhou Xin Point Surface Decoration Co., Ltd. (1)

AND PRIVATE COMPANIES

XINGQUAN INTERNATIONAL SPORTS HOLDINGS LIMITED

2-3/F No 306 Longxi Plating Base, Boluo, Huizhou, Guangdong, China
Tel.: (86) 7526677551
Automobile Plastic Component Mfr & Distr
N.A.I.C.S.: 332813

Huizhou Xinsheng Technology Co., Ltd. (1)
Huipengxing Industrial Park Xikeng, Zhongkai Distirct, Huizhou, Guangdong, China
Tel.: (86) 7523218155
Automobile Plastic Component Mfr & Distr
N.A.I.C.S.: 332813

Keen Point (Europe) GmbH. (1)
Mina-Rees-StraSSe 5a, 64295, Darmstadt, Germany
Tel.: (49) 61516084911
Automobile Plastic Component Distr
N.A.I.C.S.: 423120

Maksun Limited (1)
Unit 1503 15/F Midas Plaza 1 Tai Yau Street, San Po Kong, Kowloon, China (Hong Kong)
Tel.: (852) 22859585
Automobile Plastic Component Distr
N.A.I.C.S.: 423120

Tianjin Jinxin Precision Plastic Components Co., Ltd. (1)
Suyang Village North, Nancai Town Wuqing District, Tianjin, China
Tel.: (86) 2222252528
Automobile Plastic Component Mfr & Distr
N.A.I.C.S.: 332813

Wuxi Jinxin Surface Decoration Co., Ltd. (1)
3 Xingye Road Yangshi Surface Treatment Industrial Park, Huishan District, Wuxi, Jiangsu, China
Tel.: (86) 51083550732
Automobile Plastic Component Mfr & Distr
N.A.I.C.S.: 332813

Wuxi Keen Point Electronics Co., Ltd. (1)
9 Xingye Road Yangshi Surface Treatment Industrial Park, Huishan District, Wuxi, Jiangsu, China
Tel.: (86) 51068786690
Automobile Plastic Component Mfr & Distr
N.A.I.C.S.: 332813

Xin Point North America Inc. (1)
1400 Combermere Dr, Troy, MI 48083
Tel.: (248) 588-1804
Automobile Plastic Component Distr
N.A.I.C.S.: 423120
Tim Chamberlain *(Sr Mgr-Sls)*

XIN YUAN ENTERPRISES GROUP LIMITED
Room 02-05 40th Floor International Commerce Centre No 23, Changting Street Taijiang, Fuzhou, China
Tel.: (86) 59187573330   Ky
Web Site: https://www.xysgroup.com
Year Founded: 2010
1748—(HKG)
Rev.: $58,916,000
Assets: $187,723,000
Liabilities: $63,356,000
Net Worth: $124,367,000
Earnings: $8,497,000
Emp.: 41
Fiscal Year-end: 12/31/23
Investment Management Service
N.A.I.C.S.: 523999
Jiagan Chen *(Vice Chm)*

XINCHEN CHINA POWER HOLDINGS LIMITED
Suites 1602-05 Chater House 8 Connaught Road, Central, China (Hong Kong)
Tel.: (852) 25166918
Web Site:
   http://www.xinchenpower.com
1148—(HKG)
Rev.: $232,008,332
Assets: $583,520,792
Liabilities: $348,361,182
Net Worth: $235,159,610
Earnings: ($16,262,392)
Emp.: 998
Fiscal Year-end: 12/31/22
Automotive Engine Mfr
N.A.I.C.S.: 336310
Xiao An Wu *(Chm)*

Subsidiaries:

Mianyang Xinchen Engine Co., Ltd. (1)
No 69 Xingchang Rd High-tech Zone, Mianyang, 621000, Sichuan, China
Tel.: (86) 816 237 7315
Web Site: https://en.xce.com.cn
Engine Mfr
N.A.I.C.S.: 333618
Wu Xiao An *(Chm & Exec Dir)*

Xinchen Engine (Shenyang) Co., Limited (1)
No 19 of 13 Rd Economic-Technological Development Area, Shenyang, Liaoning, China
Tel.: (86) 2431086583
Crankshaft Machine Mfr
N.A.I.C.S.: 333517

XINDA INVESTMENT HOLDINGS LIMITED
4209 42nd Floor Building A 19 East Third Ring North Road, Chaoyang District, Beijing, China
Tel.: (86) 1088088815   Ky
Web Site: http://www.ljth.hk
1281—(HKG)
Rev.: $27,407,344
Assets: $165,643,639
Liabilities: $44,015,400
Net Worth: $121,628,239
Earnings: ($42,983,179)
Emp.: 62
Fiscal Year-end: 12/31/22
Investment Services
N.A.I.C.S.: 523999
Shaojun Wei *(Chm)*

Subsidiaries:

Tianjin Lion Window & Door Co., Ltd. (1)
Bingying Bridge Inter-junction of Kuaisu Road & Manjiang Road, Hedong District, Tianjin, 300250, China
Tel.: (86) 22 86862688
Web Site: http://www.lion-tjmc.cn
Sales Range: $25-49.9 Million
Emp.: 10
Metal Window & Door Mfr
N.A.I.C.S.: 332321

XINFENGMING GROUP CO., LTD.
No 888 Desheng Road, Zhouquan Industrial Park, Tongxiang, 314513, Zhejiang, China
Tel.: (86) 57388519583
Web Site:
   https://www.xinfengming.com
Year Founded: 2000
603225—(SHG)
Rev.: $7,130,541,216
Assets: $5,799,089,982
Liabilities: $3,594,806,037
Net Worth: $2,204,283,945
Earnings: ($28,790,270)
Emp.: 10,000
Fiscal Year-end: 12/31/22
Yarn Product Mfr & Distr
N.A.I.C.S.: 325220
Zhuang Yaozhong *(Chm & Pres)*

Subsidiaries:

Tongxiang Zhongcen Chemical Fibre Co., Ltd. (1)
Zhouquan Industrial Park, Tongxiang, 314513, Zhejiang, China
Tel.: (86) 57388519777
Polyester Filament Mfr
N.A.I.C.S.: 325220

Tongxiang Zhongchi Chemical Fiber Co., Ltd. (1)
Zhouquan Industrial Park, Tongxiang, 314513, Zhejiang, China
Tel.: (86) 57388518672
Polyester Filament Mfr
N.A.I.C.S.: 325220

Tongxiang Zhongwei Chemical Fibre Co., Ltd. (1)
Zhouquan Industrial Park, Tongxiang, 314513, Zhejiang, China
Tel.: (86) 57388533118
Polyester Filament Mfr
N.A.I.C.S.: 325220

Tongxiang Zhongxin Chemical Fibre Co., Ltd. (1)
Zhouquan Industrial Park, Tongxiang, 314513, Zhejiang, China
Tel.: (86) 57388519593
Polyester Filament Mfr
N.A.I.C.S.: 325220

Zhejiang Xin Feng Ming Chemical Fiber Co., Ltd. (1)
200 Jinji Road, Zhouquan, Tongxiang, 314513, Zhejiang, China
Tel.: (86) 57388512460
Polyester Filament Mfr
N.A.I.C.S.: 325220

Zhejiang Xin Feng Ming Import & Export Co., Ltd. (1)
Room 2206 Longhill Hotel No 3788 Jiangnan Avenue, Binjiang, Hangzhou, 310053, Zhejiang, China
Tel.: (86) 57186699909
Polyester Filament Mfr
N.A.I.C.S.: 325220

XINGDA INTERNATIONAL HOLDINGS LTD
6th Floor No 599 Yunling East Road, Putuo District, Shanghai, 200062, China
Tel.: (86) 2132500808   Ky
Web Site: http://www.xingda.com.cn
XNGIF—(OTCIQ)
Rev.: $1,497,013,181
Assets: $2,909,002,271
Liabilities: $1,811,890,092
Net Worth: $1,097,112,179
Earnings: $77,288,990
Emp.: 7,400
Fiscal Year-end: 12/31/22
Steel Pole Mfr
N.A.I.C.S.: 331110
Jinlan Liu *(Chm)*

Subsidiaries:

Jiangsu Xingda Steel Cord Co., Ltd. (1)
88 Renmin West Road, Dainan Township Xinghua City, Taizhou, 225721, China
Tel.: (86) 52380956874
Steel Products Mfr
N.A.I.C.S.: 331222

XINGFA ALUMINUM HOLDINGS LIMITED
Unit No 5 6th Floor Wing On Plaza No 62 Mody Road, Kowloon, China (Hong Kong)
Tel.: (852) 21755388   Ky
Web Site: http://www.xingfa.com
0098—(HKG)
Rev.: $2,377,402,186
Assets: $1,698,274,328
Liabilities: $1,044,647,183
Net Worth: $653,627,146
Earnings: $64,767,784
Emp.: 9,366
Fiscal Year-end: 12/31/22
Holding Company; Aluminum Mfr & Sales
N.A.I.C.S.: 551112
Yuqing Liao *(CEO)*

Subsidiaries:

Guangdong Xingfa Aluminium (Jiangxi) Co., Ltd. (1)
North of Jingfa Avenue Yichun Economic Development zone, Yichun, Jiangxi, China
Tel.: (86) 7953557888
Aluminum Mfr & Distr
N.A.I.C.S.: 331313

Guangdong Xingfa Aluminium Co., Ltd. (1)
No 5 Section D, Leping Central Science and Technology Industrial Zone, Foshan, 528061, Guangdong, China
Tel.: (86) 75766880192
Web Site:
   https://www.aluminiumsupplier.com.cn
Emp.: 5,000
Aluminium Profiles Mfr
N.A.I.C.S.: 332439

Xingfa Aluminium (Chengdu) Co., Ltd (1)
South West Airport Economic Development Zone, Shuangliu, Chengdu, 610200, Sichuan, China
Tel.: (86) 2885877679
Aluminum Mfr & Distr
N.A.I.C.S.: 331313

Xingfa Aluminium (Hong Kong) Limited (1)
Room 605 6/f Wing On Plaza No 62 Mody Road, Tsim Eaat, Kowloon, China (Hong Kong)
Tel.: (852) 2780 3680
Aluminum Distr
N.A.I.C.S.: 423510

XINGHUA PORT HOLDINGS LTD.
No 1 Xinghua Port Area Yi Lu, Changshu, 215513, Jiangsu, China
Tel.: (86) 51252695858   SG
Web Site:
   http://www.xinghuaport.com
Year Founded: 1994
1990—(HKG)
Rev.: $56,824,438
Assets: $242,595,427
Liabilities: $108,213,651
Net Worth: $134,381,776
Earnings: $11,987,773
Emp.: 460
Fiscal Year-end: 12/31/19
Maritime Commercial Facility Services
N.A.I.C.S.: 541614
Patrick Bee Soon Ng *(Chm)*

Subsidiaries:

Changshu Xinghua Port Co., Ltd. (1)
No 1 Xinghua Port Area Yi Lu, Changshu, 215513, Jiangsu, China
Tel.: (86) 51252695858
Logistic Services
N.A.I.C.S.: 541614

XINGMIN INTELLIGENT TRANSPORTATION SYSTEMS (GROUP) CO., LTD.
Longkou Economic Development Zone, Longkou, 265716, Shandong, China
Tel.: (86) 5358880188
Web Site: https://www.xingmin.com
Year Founded: 1999
002355—(SSE)
Rev.: $115,158,130
Assets: $362,328,132
Liabilities: $168,801,713
Net Worth: $193,526,419
Earnings: ($73,191,727)
Fiscal Year-end: 12/31/22
Steel Wheels & Other Automotive Parts Mfr
N.A.I.C.S.: 336390
Gao Henan *(Chm & Gen Mgr)*

XINGQUAN INTERNATIONAL SPORTS HOLDINGS LIMITED
Houyang Industrial Zone, Chendai, Jinjiang, 362100, Fujian, China
Tel.: (86) 5958 516 6555   BM

XINGQUAN INTERNATIONAL SPORTS HOLDINGS LIMITED

Xingquan International Sports Holdings Limited—(Continued)
Web Site: http://www.xingquan-international.com
Year Founded: 1995
XINQUAN—(KLS)
Sales Range: $100-124.9 Million
Shoe & Sports Apparel Mfr
N.A.I.C.S.: 316210
Qingquan Wu *(Chm & CEO)*

XINGYE ALLOY MATERIALS GROUP LTD.
Flat 11 11th Floor Hung Tai Industrial Building 37-39 Hung To Road, Kwun Tong, Kowloon, 315336, China (Hong Kong)
Tel.: (852) 57463073286 Ky
0505—(HKG)
Rev.: $875,885,962
Assets: $585,676,494
Liabilities: $334,988,082
Net Worth: $250,688,412
Earnings: $30,442,370
Emp.: 1,457
Fiscal Year-end: 12/31/22
Copper Plates & Strips Mfr
N.A.I.C.S.: 331420
Hu Changyuan *(Chm)*

XINGYE LEATHER TECHNOLOGY CO., LTD.
No 1 Xingye Road Anhai No 2 Industrial Park, Jinjiang, 362261, Fujian, China
Tel.: (86) 59568580889
Web Site: https://www.xingyeleather.com
Year Founded: 1992
002674—(SSE)
Rev.: $279,074,821
Assets: $531,697,285
Liabilities: $183,724,127
Net Worth: $347,973,159
Earnings: $21,139,607
Emp.: 2,000
Fiscal Year-end: 12/31/22
Leather Product Mfr
N.A.I.C.S.: 316990
Wu Huachun *(Chm)*

XINGYE WULIAN SERVICE GROUP CO., LTD.
Room 105 1st Floor No 1 Gangwan Road, Guancheng Hui District, Zhengzhou, Henan, China Ky
Web Site: https://www.xingyewulian.com
Year Founded: 1999
9916—(HKG)
Rev.: $49,698,577
Assets: $96,789,710
Liabilities: $33,787,107
Net Worth: $63,002,603
Earnings: $5,563,386
Emp.: 632
Fiscal Year-end: 12/31/23
Property Management Services
N.A.I.C.S.: 531311
Jackson Eric Chang *(Sec)*

XINGYUAN ENVIRONMENT TECHNOLOGY CO., LTD.
No 1588 Wangmei Road, Yuhang, Hangzhou, 311100, Zhejiang, China
Tel.: (86) 57188778808
Web Site: https://www.xingyuan.com
Year Founded: 1988
300266—(CHIN)
Rev.: $103,073,129
Assets: $1,440,852,977
Liabilities: $1,299,812,717
Net Worth: $141,040,260
Earnings: ($139,405,034)
Emp.: 935
Fiscal Year-end: 12/31/23

Filters & Water Treatment Products Mfr
N.A.I.C.S.: 333248

XINHUA NEWS MEDIA HOLDINGS LIMITED
Unit 508B 5/F New East Ocean Centre 9 Science Museum Road, Tsim Sha Tsui, Hong Kong, China (Hong Kong)
Tel.: (852) 36110571 Ky
Web Site: https://www.xhnmedia.com
0309—(HKG)
Rev.: $35,653,425
Assets: $24,630,666
Liabilities: $9,938,425
Net Worth: $14,692,241
Earnings: ($2,212,523)
Emp.: 1,071
Fiscal Year-end: 03/31/22
Information Broadcasting Services
N.A.I.C.S.: 516120
Kou Hong Lo *(Co-Chm, Chm & Exec Dir)*

Subsidiaries:

Lo's Cleaning Services Limited (1)
15/F Harbour East 218 Electric Road, North Point, China (Hong Kong)
Tel.: (852) 2 838 3822
Web Site: https://en.loscleaningservices.com
Buildings & Dwellings Services
N.A.I.C.S.: 561790

XINHUA SPORTS & ENTERTAINMENT LTD.
18th Floor Tower A Winterless Centre, No 1 West Da Wang Road, Chaoyang District, Beijing, 100026, China
Tel.: (86) 10 8567 6000 Ky
Year Founded: 2005
Sales Range: $75-99.9 Million
Emp.: 817
Sports & Entertainment Multi-Media Products & Services
N.A.I.C.S.: 541890
Shan Zhu *(COO)*

XINHUA WINSHARE PUBLISHING AND MEDIA CO., LTD.
No 238 Sanse Road, JinJiang District, Chengdu, 610081, Sichuan, China
Tel.: (86) 2886361111 CN
Web Site: https://www.winshare.com.cn
Year Founded: 2005
0811—(HKG)
Rev.: $1,380,124,345
Assets: $2,599,795,365
Liabilities: $1,063,382,501
Net Worth: $1,536,412,864
Earnings: $190,439,256
Emp.: 7,633
Fiscal Year-end: 12/31/20
Books Publishing Services
N.A.I.C.S.: 513130
Qiang Li *(Gen Mgr)*

Subsidiaries:

China Wenxuan Movie & TV Culture Co., Ltd. (1)
Floor 9 Xinhua Winshare Building No 3 Zone 3 Fangqunyuan Fangzhuang, Fengtai District, Beijing, China
Tel.: (86) 1064820781
Film Production Services
N.A.I.C.S.: 512110

Sichuan Children's Publishing House Co., Ltd. (1)
No 2 Huaishu Street, Qingyang District, Chengdu, China
Tel.: (86) 288 625 9192
Online Book Publisher
N.A.I.C.S.: 513130

Sichuan Lexicographical Press Co., Ltd. (1)
21/F Sichuan Publishing Tower No 2 Huaishu Street, Chengdu, China
Tel.: (86) 288 773 4326
Online Book Publisher
N.A.I.C.S.: 513130

Sichuan Printing Material Co., Ltd. (1)
No 6 Western First Road of North Railway Station, Chengdu, China
Tel.: (86) 288 317 3817
Printing Material Mfr
N.A.I.C.S.: 333248

Sichuan Publishing & Printing Co., Ltd. (1)
No 2 Huaishu Street, Chengdu, China
Tel.: (86) 288 625 9554
Printing Products Mfr
N.A.I.C.S.: 323111

Sichuan Wenchuan Logistics Co., Ltd. (1)
Tongxiang Logistics Park 227 Zhongji Avenue Xindu District, Chengdu, China
Tel.: (86) 2883628969
Logistics Transportation Services
N.A.I.C.S.: 541614

Sichuan Xinhua Culture Transmission Co., Ltd. (1)
5F 55 East of Yulong Street, Jinjiang District, Chengdu, China
Tel.: (86) 288 651 9651
Web Site: http://www.xhcbmedia.com
Advertising Services
N.A.I.C.S.: 541810

Winshare Education Co., Ltd. (1)
11th Floor Block B Yinhaixin Tower Sanse Road, Jinjiang District, Chengdu, Sichuan, China
Tel.: (86) 288 531 5875
Web Site: https://www.winshare-edu.com
Educational Support Services
N.A.I.C.S.: 611710

Winshare Internatioinal Cultural Media Co., Ltd. (1)
W5 Global Center No 1700 North Section of Tianfu Avenue High-tech Zone, Chengdu, 712004, Sichuan, China
Tel.: (86) 286 527 8997
Web Site: https://wicc.winshare.com.cn
Media Publishing Services
N.A.I.C.S.: 513199

Winshare Investment Co., Ltd. (1)
Room 1803-1804 Block 1 Unit 2 177 Jiaozi Avenue Hi-Tech Zone, Chengdu, China
Tel.: (86) 2885328939
Investment Management Service
N.A.I.C.S.: 523940

Winshare Music & Culture Media Co., Ltd. (1)
15-17 Block B Shiwaitaoyuan Plaza 65 North Kehua Road, Chengdu, China
Tel.: (86) 2861508812
Musical Event Services
N.A.I.C.S.: 711130

Winshare Musicand Culture Media Co., Ltd. (1)
15-17 Block B Shiwaitaoyuan Plaza 65 North Kehua Road, Chengdu, China
Tel.: (86) 286 150 8812
Online Music Distribution Services
N.A.I.C.S.: 512250

XINHUANET CO., LTD.
4-8th Floor Jinyu Building No 129 Xuanwumen West Street, Xicheng District, Beijing, 100031, China
Tel.: (86) 1088050888
603888—(SHG)
Rev.: $272,456,660
Assets: $727,425,794
Liabilities: $266,734,728
Net Worth: $460,691,066
Earnings: $34,000,064
Fiscal Year-end: 12/31/22
Online News Publishing Services
N.A.I.C.S.: 513110
Yang Qingbing *(Sec)*

INTERNATIONAL PUBLIC

XINING SPECIAL STEEL CO., LTD.
52 Qaidam Road, Chengbei District, Xining, 810005, Qinghai, China
Tel.: (86) 9715299673
Web Site: https://www.xntg.com
Year Founded: 1997
600117—(SHG)
Rev.: $1,089,115,485
Assets: $2,356,680,578
Liabilities: $2,277,693,967
Net Worth: $78,986,611
Earnings: ($161,555,149)
Fiscal Year-end: 12/31/22
Steel Processing Services
N.A.I.C.S.: 331513
Wang Shifeng *(Chm)*

XINJI SHAXI GROUP CO., LTD.
Xinjicheng Club No 250 Nanda Road, Panyu District, Guangzhou, Guangdong, China Ky
Web Site: https://www.xjsx.net.cn
Year Founded: 2002
3603—(HKG)
Rev.: $37,850,576
Assets: $406,274,922
Liabilities: $221,331,413
Net Worth: $184,943,509
Earnings: ($11,113,619)
Emp.: 272
Fiscal Year-end: 12/31/23
Online Shopping Services
N.A.I.C.S.: 459999
Hon Chuen Cheung *(CEO)*

XINJIANG BAIHUACUN CO., LTD.
No 141 Zhongshan Road, Urumqi, 830002, Xinjiang, China
Tel.: (86) 9912356615
Web Site: http://www.xjbhc.net
600721—(SHG)
Rev.: $49,123,798
Assets: $140,586,676
Liabilities: $46,936,576
Net Worth: $93,650,099
Earnings: ($4,879,602)
Fiscal Year-end: 12/31/22
Coal Mining Services
N.A.I.C.S.: 212115
Ziyun Cai *(CFO)*

XINJIANG BEIKEN ENERGY ENGINEERING LIMITED
2500-1 Pingan Ave, Baijiantan District Uygur Autonomous Region, Karamay, 834009, Xinjiang, China
Tel.: (86) 1053673296
Web Site: https://www.beiken.com
Year Founded: 2009
002828—(SSE)
Rev.: $93,946,568
Assets: $284,053,082
Liabilities: $197,336,258
Net Worth: $86,716,824
Earnings: ($44,746,322)
Emp.: 1,000
Fiscal Year-end: 12/31/22
Petroleum Engineering Services
N.A.I.C.S.: 541330
Pinggui Chen *(Chm & Pres)*

XINJIANG BEIXIN ROAD & BRIDGE GROUP CO., LTD.
16-17F Tower A Yingke Square No 217 Gaoxin Street, Hi-tech Zone Urumqi, Xinjiang, 830000, China
Tel.: (86) 9916557799
Web Site: http://www.xjbxlq.com
Year Founded: 2001
002307—(SSE)
Rev.: $1,636,792,845
Assets: $7,182,304,281
Liabilities: $6,403,553,961
Net Worth: $778,750,320

XINJIANG COMMUNICATIONS CONSTRUCTION GROUP CO., LTD.

Earnings: $6,503,047
Fiscal Year-end: 12/31/22
Road & Bridge Construction Services
N.A.I.C.S.: 237310
Zhang Bin *(Chm)*

XINJIANG COMMUNICATIONS CONSTRUCTION GROUP CO., LTD.

No 840 Auxiliary Road Wuchang Road, Xinshi District High-tech Industrial Development Zone, Urumqi, 830016, Xinjiang, China
Tel.: (86) 9916272850
Web Site: http://www.xjjtjt.com
Year Founded: 1999
002941—(SSE)
Rev.: $1,109,857,535
Assets: $2,613,441,219
Liabilities: $1,987,129,877
Net Worth: $626,311,343
Earnings: $49,361,972
Fiscal Year-end: 12/31/22
Construction Services
N.A.I.C.S.: 237310
Wang Tong *(Chm)*

XINJIANG EAST UNIVERSE (GROUP) GAS CO., LTD.

24F No 198 Yanan North Road, Changji, 831100, Xinjiang, China
Tel.: (86) 9942266212
Web Site: http://www.dfhyrq.com
Year Founded: 2001
603706—(SHG)
Rev.: $151,423,571
Assets: $394,768,547
Liabilities: $130,222,372
Net Worth: $264,546,175
Earnings: $23,871,650
Fiscal Year-end: 12/31/21
Industrial Gas Product Distr
N.A.I.C.S.: 424690
Tian Rongjiang *(Vice Chm, Pres & Gen Mgr)*

XINJIANG GOLDWIND SCIENCE & TECHNOLOGY CO., LTD.

No 8 Boxing 1st Road, Economic Technological Development District, Beijing, 100176, Xinjiang, China
Tel.: (86) 1067511888
Web Site: https://www.goldwind.com
Year Founded: 1998
002202—(SSE)
Rev.: $6,986,208,061
Assets: $19,867,993,977
Liabilities: $14,297,973,845
Net Worth: $5,570,020,132
Earnings: $184,287,494
Emp.: 10,000
Fiscal Year-end: 12/31/23
Renewable Energy Services
N.A.I.C.S.: 221210
Gang Wu *(Chm)*

Subsidiaries:

Jiangsu Goldwind Science & Technology Co., Ltd. (1)
No 99 Jinhai Road, Dafeng Economic Development Zone, Jiangsu, 224100, China
Tel.: (86) 5158 362 6886
Wind Energy Conservation Services
N.A.I.C.S.: 221115

Vensys Energy AG (1)
Im Langental 6, 66539, Neunkirchen, Germany
Tel.: (49) 6821 9517 0
Web Site: http://www.vensys.de
Emp.: 133
Wind Turbine Mfr
N.A.I.C.S.: 333611
Helmut Lange *(Head-Sls-Natl & Int)*

XINJIANG GUANGHUI INDUSTRY INVESTMENT GROUP CO., LTD.

Zhongtian Plaza No 165 Xinhua North Road, Urumqi, 830002, Xinjiang, China
Tel.: (86) 99 1236 5093 CN
Web Site: http://www.guanghui.com
Year Founded: 1989
Investment Holding Company
N.A.I.C.S.: 551112
Jiqiang Shang *(Pres)*

Subsidiaries:

China Grand Automotive Services Group Co., Ltd. (1)
No 3998 Hongxin Road, Hongqiao Town Minhang District, Shanghai, 201103, China
Tel.: (86) 2124032888
Web Site: https://www.chinagrandauto.com
Rev.: $18,749,560,668
Assets: $17,731,118,696
Liabilities: $11,543,094,473
Net Worth: $6,188,024,223
Earnings: ($374,711,229)
Emp.: 37,600
Fiscal Year-end: 12/31/2022
Car Dealership Operator
N.A.I.C.S.: 441110

Grand Baoxin Auto Group Limited (1)
No.3998 Hongxin Road Minhang District, Shanghai, China
Tel.: (86) 31506788
Web Site: http://www.klbaoxin.com
Rev.: $4,450,495,655
Assets: $3,534,571,685
Liabilities: $2,457,125,377
Net Worth: $1,077,446,308
Earnings: ($98,347,392)
Emp.: 6,785
Fiscal Year-end: 12/31/2022
Motor Vehicle Sales & Services
N.A.I.C.S.: 423110
Xing Xu *(Co-Sec & VP)*

Guanghui Energy Co., Ltd. (1)
27F Zhongtian Plaza No 165 Xinhua North Road, Urumqi, 830002, Xinjiang, China
Web Site: http://www.xjguanghui.com
Rev.: $8,511,731,724
Assets: $8,108,591,839
Liabilities: $4,180,392,044
Net Worth: $3,928,199,795
Earnings: $716,285,141
Fiscal Year-end: 12/31/2023
Natural Gas Extraction & Distribution Services
N.A.I.C.S.: 211130

XINJIANG GUANNONG FRUIT AND VELVET CO., LTD.

Community No 48 Tuanjie South Road, Korla, 841000, Xinjiang, China
Tel.: (86) 9962113386
Web Site: http://www.gngf.cn
Year Founded: 1999
600251—(SHG)
Rev.: $338,783,164
Assets: $977,413,666
Liabilities: $512,415,325
Net Worth: $464,998,342
Earnings: $66,681,464
Fiscal Year-end: 12/31/22
Sugar Product Mfr & Distr
N.A.I.C.S.: 311999
Zhonghai Liu *(Chm)*

Subsidiaries:

Tianjin Sanhe Fruits & Vegetables Co., Ltd. (1)
South of Sanwei Road Panzhuang Industrial Park, Ninghe County, Tianjin, China
Tel.: (86) 2269480120
Web Site: http://www.johnz-canned.com
Canned Fruit & Vegetable Mfr
N.A.I.C.S.: 311421

XINJIANG GUOTONG PIPELINE CO., LTD.

The Industry Development Zone of Miquan, Urumqi, 831407, Xinjiang, China
Tel.: (86) 9916913982
Web Site: https://www.xjgt.com
Year Founded: 2001
002205—(SSE)
Rev.: $87,046,456
Assets: $598,988,632
Liabilities: $467,999,518
Net Worth: $130,989,114
Earnings: ($14,406,205)
Emp.: 600
Fiscal Year-end: 12/31/22
Pipe & Tube Mfr
N.A.I.C.S.: 331210
Jiang Shaobo *(Chm)*

Subsidiaries:

Taiwan Kuotoong International Co., Ltd. (1)
8F-5 91 Ta Shun 1st Rd, Kaohsiung, 81357, Taiwan
Tel.: (886) 75573755
Web Site: http://www.kti.com.tw
Construction Services
N.A.I.C.S.: 236220

XINJIANG HAOYUAN GAS CO., LTD.

No 2 Ying awati Road, Aksu, 843000, Xinjiang, China
Tel.: (86) 9972530396
Web Site: http://www.hytrq.com
Year Founded: 2006
002700—(SSE)
Rev.: $64,199,586
Assets: $166,462,665
Liabilities: $30,479,597
Net Worth: $135,983,068
Earnings: ($30,818,192)
Emp.: 280
Fiscal Year-end: 12/31/20
Natural Gas Distr & Pipeline Transportation
N.A.I.C.S.: 221210
Kang Ying *(Chm)*

XINJIANG HONGTONG NATURAL GAS CO., LTD.

No 151 Nanyuan Road, Korla Economic and Technological Development Zone, Korla, 841000, China
Tel.: (86) 9962159777
Web Site: https://www.xjhtrq.com
Year Founded: 2000
605169—(SHG)
Rev.: $201,496,099
Assets: $338,308,739
Liabilities: $86,951,503
Net Worth: $251,357,235
Earnings: $22,562,505
Fiscal Year-end: 12/31/22
Oil & Gas Distribution Services
N.A.I.C.S.: 221210
Hongbing Liu *(Chm & Gen Mgr)*

XINJIANG INTERNATIONAL INDUSTRY CO., LTD.

9F Dacheng International No 358 Beijing South Road, Hi-tech Industrial Development Zone, Urumqi, 830002, Xinjiang, China
Tel.: (86) 9915854232
Web Site: http://www.xjgjsy.com
Year Founded: 1999
000159—(SSE)
Rev.: $226,242,554
Assets: $432,086,139
Liabilities: $65,404,301
Net Worth: $366,681,838
Earnings: $41,824,360
Fiscal Year-end: 12/31/22
Real Estate Development Services
N.A.I.C.S.: 531390
Feng Jianfang *(Chm)*

XINJIANG JOINWORLD CO., LTD.

No 18 Kashi East Road High-tech Zone Uygur Autonomous Region, Urumqi, 830013, Xinjiang, China
Tel.: (86) 9916689800
Web Site: http://www.joinworld.com
Year Founded: 1996
600888—(SHG)
Rev.: $1,086,053,642
Assets: $2,013,543,778
Liabilities: $824,331,601
Net Worth: $1,189,212,177
Earnings: $217,317,438
Emp.: 2,600
Fiscal Year-end: 12/31/22
Electronic Material & Aluminum Product Mfr
N.A.I.C.S.: 334419
Sun Jian *(Chm, Pres & Gen Mgr)*

XINJIANG KORLA PEAR CO., LTD.

St. fruit St. Fruit gardens Xinjiang Korla City Road, Korla, 841000, Xinjiang, China
Tel.: (86) 9962115936
Web Site: http://www.xjxlgf.com.cn
600506—(SHG)
Rev.: $282,288,128
Assets: $352,572,508
Liabilities: $289,320,834
Net Worth: $63,251,674
Earnings: $11,824,825
Fiscal Year-end: 12/31/22
Fruit Product Mfr
N.A.I.C.S.: 312111

XINJIANG LIXIN ENERGY CO., LTD.

5th Floor Western Green Valley Building No 752 Kashi West Road, Urumqi Economic & Technological Development Zone, Xinjiang, 830000, China
Tel.: (86) 9913720088
Year Founded: 2013
001258—(SSE)
Rev.: $136,194,822
Assets: $1,325,422,740
Liabilities: $919,714,694
Net Worth: $405,708,046
Earnings: $18,606,127
Fiscal Year-end: 12/31/23
Electricity Distribution Services
N.A.I.C.S.: 221114

XINJIANG MACHINERY RESEARCH INSTITUTE CO., LTD.

No 661 Ronghe South Road Economic and Technological Development Zone, Urumqi, 830026, Xinjiang, China
Tel.: (86) 9913718201
Web Site: http://www.xjjxy.com.cn
Year Founded: 2009
300159—(CHIN)
Rev.: $167,708,898
Assets: $417,900,189
Liabilities: $414,402,659
Net Worth: $3,497,531
Earnings: ($18,762,023)
Fiscal Year-end: 12/31/23
Agricultural Machinery Mfr & Distr
N.A.I.C.S.: 333111
Desong Fang *(Chm)*

XINJIANG QINGSONG CHEMICALS (GROUP) CO., LTD.

No 237 Henglian Lane Midong South Road, Midong District, Urumqi, 830029, Xinjiang, China
Tel.: (86) 9916670581
600425—(SHG)
Rev.: $525,244,122
Assets: $1,246,293,917

XINJIANG QINGSONG CHEMICALS (GROUP) CO., LTD.

Xinjiang Qingsong Chemicals (Group) Co., Ltd.—(Continued)
Liabilities: $475,998,682
Net Worth: $770,295,235
Earnings: $58,334,726
Fiscal Year-end: 12/31/22
Cement Mfr
N.A.I.C.S.: 327310
Jiang Junkai *(Sec)*

XINJIANG SAILING INFORMATION TECHNOLOGY CO., LTD.
10F Dacheng Intentional Building No 358 Beijing South Road, Hi-tech Park New District, Urumqi, 830000, Xinjiang, China
Tel.: (86) 9915573585
Web Site: http://www.sit.com.cn
Year Founded: 1999
300588—(CHIN)
Rev.: $22,397,685
Assets: $106,483,192
Liabilities: $52,334,465
Net Worth: $54,148,726
Earnings: ($5,655,691)
Emp.: 1,450
Fiscal Year-end: 12/31/23
Software Development Services
N.A.I.C.S.: 513210
He Yue *(Chm)*

XINJIANG SAYRAM MODERN AGRICULTURE CO., LTD.
No 17 Yingbin Road Jingchu Industrial Park Shuanghe Diwushi, Uygur Autonomous Region, Bozhou, 833408, Xinjiang, China
Tel.: (86) 9092268189
Web Site: http://www.xinsai.com.cn
Year Founded: 1999
600540—(SHG)
Rev.: $185,922,271
Assets: $370,213,417
Liabilities: $264,441,336
Net Worth: $105,772,081
Earnings: ($39,061,779)
Fiscal Year-end: 12/31/22
Agricultural Product Mfr
N.A.I.C.S.: 111920
Yunfeng Shen *(Chm)*

XINJIANG TALIMU AGRICULTURE DEVELOPMENT CO., LTD.
11-12F Leading Business Office Building Junken Avenue, Aksu, 843300, Xinjiang, China
Tel.: (86) 9976378598
Web Site: http://www.xnkf.com
Year Founded: 1999
600359—(SHG)
Rev.: $90,905,911
Assets: $266,067,000
Liabilities: $183,484,927
Net Worth: $82,582,073
Earnings: $9,001,269
Fiscal Year-end: 12/31/22
Agriculture & Livestock Product Mfr
N.A.I.C.S.: 311119
Tang Jianguo *(Chm)*

Subsidiaries:

Xinjiang alar Xinnong licorice industry limited liability company (1)
No 388 Xin Yue Rd Small-Medium Enterprise Park, Economic & Technological Zone Alar, Xinjiang, 843300, China
Tel.: (86) 9976370388
Web Site: http://www.xngc.cn
Licorice Product Mfr
N.A.I.C.S.: 311340
Yi Bao Xiang *(Deputy Mgr-Sls)*

XINJIANG TIANFU ENERGY CO., LTD.
No 2 Beiyi East Road Xinjiang Uygur Autonomous Region, Shihezi, 832000, Xinjiang, China
Tel.: (86) 9932902860
Web Site: http://www.tfny.com
Year Founded: 1999
600509—(SHG)
Rev.: $1,143,226,965
Assets: $3,062,053,547
Liabilities: $2,194,118,241
Net Worth: $867,935,306
Earnings: ($27,878,751)
Fiscal Year-end: 12/31/22
Electric Power Generation & Distribution Services
N.A.I.C.S.: 221118
Liu Wei *(Chm & Pres)*

XINJIANG TIANRUN DAIRY CO., LTD.
No 2702 Wuchang Road Economic and Technological Development Zone, Toutunhe District Urumqi, Xinjiang, 830088, China
Tel.: (86) 9913960621
Web Site: https://www.xjtrry.com
Year Founded: 2002
600419—(SHG)
Rev.: $338,333,772
Assets: $552,260,409
Liabilities: $195,829,906
Net Worth: $356,430,504
Earnings: $27,597,164
Fiscal Year-end: 12/31/22
Dairy Product Mfr & Distr
N.A.I.C.S.: 311511
Feng Yubo *(Sec)*

XINJIANG TIANSHAN ANIMAL HUSBANDRY BIO-ENGINEERING CO., LTD.
No 1 Guangming South Road High-tech Zone, Changji, 831100, Xinjiang, China
Tel.: (86) 9946536922
Web Site: https://www.xjtssw.com
Year Founded: 2003
300313—(SSE)
Rev.: $10,719,540
Assets: $44,391,672
Liabilities: $31,758,480
Net Worth: $12,633,192
Earnings: ($4,471,740)
Emp.: 170
Fiscal Year-end: 12/31/22
Oxen Freeze-Drying Sperm Products
N.A.I.C.S.: 112990

XINJIANG TIANSHUN SUPPLY CHAIN CO LTD
No 52 Dalian Street Yingbin Road Economic Development Zone, Urumqi, 830026, Xinjiang, China
Tel.: (86) 9913792620
Web Site: https://www.xjtsscm.com
Year Founded: 2008
002800—(SSE)
Rev.: $174,268,650
Assets: $155,641,220
Liabilities: $74,874,084
Net Worth: $80,767,136
Earnings: $490,122
Emp.: 200
Fiscal Year-end: 12/31/22
Logistic Services
N.A.I.C.S.: 541614
Puyu Wang *(Board of Directors & Chm)*

XINJIANG TIANYE CO., LTD.
No 36 Beisan East Road Economic and Technological Development Zone, Shihezi, 832000, Xinjiang, China
Tel.: (86) 9932623118
Web Site: http://www.xj-tianye.com
Year Founded: 1997
600075—(SHG)
Rev.: $1,635,136,575
Assets: $2,815,208,964
Liabilities: $1,281,115,967
Net Worth: $1,534,092,997
Earnings: $119,791,498
Emp.: 4,560
Fiscal Year-end: 12/31/22
Chemicals & Plastic Products Mfr
N.A.I.C.S.: 325998
Zhang Qiang *(Chm)*

Subsidiaries:

Xinjiang Tianye Water Saving Irrigation System Company Limited (1)
36 Bei San Dong Road Shihezi Econ and Tech Dev Zone, Xinjiang, Shihezi, China
Tel.: (86) 9932623165
Web Site: http://www.tianyejiashui.com.cn
Rev.: $202,661,115
Assets: $144,529,188
Liabilities: $81,798,857
Net Worth: $62,730,331
Earnings: ($11,429,975)
Emp.: 384
Fiscal Year-end: 12/31/2022
Irrigation Equipment Mfr & Distr
N.A.I.C.S.: 333111

XINJIANG TORCH GAS CO., LTD.
Torch Building North Side of Shidai Avenue, Kashgar Kashgar District, Xinjiang, 844000, China
Tel.: (86) 9982836777
Web Site: http://www.xjhjrq.com
Year Founded: 2003
603080—(SHG)
Rev.: $119,092,377
Assets: $260,854,144
Liabilities: $75,495,621
Net Worth: $185,358,523
Earnings: $13,487,133
Fiscal Year-end: 12/31/22
Natural Gas Transmission Services
N.A.I.C.S.: 221210
Chen Zhilong *(Chm & Gen Mgr)*

XINJIANG WESTERN ANIMAL HUSBANDRY CO., LTD.
No 28 Beiyidong Road Development Zone, Shihezi, 832000, Xinjiang, China
Tel.: (86) 9932011608
Web Site: https://www.xjxbmy.com
Year Founded: 2003
300106—(CHIN)
Rev.: $158,160,902
Assets: $169,464,283
Liabilities: $74,117,171
Net Worth: $95,347,112
Earnings: ($9,049,007)
Emp.: 600
Fiscal Year-end: 12/31/23
Animal Husbandry Services
N.A.I.C.S.: 115210
Wenshou Wu *(Vice Chm)*

XINJIANG WINKA TIMES DEPARTMENT STORE CO
23F Block 1 No 5 Zuanshi City Beijing South Road, Hi-tech Industrial Development Zone, Urumqi, 830002, Xinjiang, China
Tel.: (86) 9912806989
Web Site: http://www.wuikatimes.com
Year Founded: 2008
603101—(SHG)
Rev.: $267,810,866
Assets: $595,873,451
Liabilities: $414,352,973
Net Worth: $181,520,478
Earnings: ($21,900,505)
Fiscal Year-end: 12/31/22
Grocery Distr
N.A.I.C.S.: 445110
Pan Dingrui *(Chm)*

INTERNATIONAL PUBLIC

XINJIANG XINTAI NATURAL GAS CO., LTD.
No 61 Midong North Road, Midong District, Urumqi, 831400, Xinjiang, China
Tel.: (86) 9913358922
Web Site: https://www.xjxtrq.com
Year Founded: 2002
603393—(SHG)
Rev.: $479,640,054
Assets: $1,773,813,361
Liabilities: $532,724,704
Net Worth: $1,241,088,657
Earnings: $129,626,322
Fiscal Year-end: 12/31/22
Natural Gas Distr
N.A.I.C.S.: 423690
Zaiyuan Ming *(Chm)*

Subsidiaries:

AAG Energy Holdings Ltd. (1)
Unit 2109 10 21st Floor Merchants Tower Shun Tak Centre No 200, Connaught Road Central, Hong Kong, China (Hong Kong) (51.65%)
Tel.: (852) 28030898
Web Site: http://www.aagenergy.com
Energy Exploration Services
N.A.I.C.S.: 213112
Ming Zaiyuvan *(Chm)*

XINJIANG XINXIN MINING INDUSTRY CO., LTD.
No 501 Fusion South Road Cooperation Zone, Economic & Technological Development Zone, Urumqi, 830000, China
Tel.: (86) 9914852773
Web Site: http://kunlun.wsfg.hk
3833—(HKG)
Rev.: $402,066,963
Assets: $1,099,256,205
Liabilities: $300,427,121
Net Worth: $798,829,083
Earnings: $104,350,397
Emp.: 1,977
Fiscal Year-end: 12/31/22
Mining Services
N.A.I.C.S.: 212230
Cheuk Fai Lam *(Co-Sec)*

XINJIANG XUEFENG SCI-TECH GROUP CO., LTD.
No 500 Alishan Street Economic and Technological Development Zone, Toutunhe District, Urumqi, 830026, Xinjiang, China
Tel.: (86) 9918801120
Web Site: http://www.xjxfkj.com
Year Founded: 1984
603227—(SHG)
Rev.: $969,113,204
Assets: $1,171,360,780
Liabilities: $530,340,544
Net Worth: $641,020,236
Earnings: $93,478,166
Fiscal Year-end: 12/31/22
Industrial Explosive Mfr & Distr
N.A.I.C.S.: 325920
Jian Kang *(Chm)*

XINJIANG YILITE INDUSTRY CO., LTD.
No 619 Tianshan North Road, Kekedala, Xinjiang, 835811, China
Tel.: (86) 9913667490
Web Site: http://www.xjyilite.com
Year Founded: 1999
600197—(SHG)
Rev.: $227,888,140
Assets: $657,882,880
Liabilities: $131,026,587
Net Worth: $526,856,293
Earnings: $23,227,102
Fiscal Year-end: 12/31/22
Liquor Product Distr
N.A.I.C.S.: 424820

AND PRIVATE COMPANIES

Chen Zhi *(Chm)*

XINJIANG YILU WANYUAN INDUSTRIAL INVESTMENT HOLDING CO., LTD.
No 4 19F 9 Building, Guiyang, 550002, Guizhou, China
Tel.: (86) 851 5833922
Web Site: http://www.swell.com.cn
600145—(SHG)
Sales Range: $1-9.9 Million
Holding Company
N.A.I.C.S.: 551112
Jingfei Huang *(Chm)*

XINJIANG YOUHAO (GROUP) CO., LTD.
No 668 Youhao South Road, Urumqi, 830000, Xinjiang, China
Tel.: (86) 9914553700
Web Site: http://www.xjyh.com
Year Founded: 1997
600778—(SHG)
Rev.: $202,205,428
Assets: $597,379,775
Liabilities: $548,474,215
Net Worth: $48,905,560
Earnings: ($30,655,231)
Emp.: 10,000
Fiscal Year-end: 12/31/22
Merchandise Store Operator
N.A.I.C.S.: 455219
Weishun Lv *(Chm)*

XINJIANG ZHONGTAI CHEMICAL CO., LTD.
No 39 Yanghcenghu road E&T development zone, Urumqi, 830054, Xinjiang, China
Tel.: (86) 9918751690
Web Site: https://www.zthx.com
Year Founded: 2001
002092—(SSE)
Rev.: $7,849,840,504
Assets: $11,285,613,692
Liabilities: $6,660,378,134
Net Worth: $4,625,235,557
Earnings: $100,245,474
Emp.: 22,700
Fiscal Year-end: 12/31/22
Chemical Products Mfr
N.A.I.C.S.: 325199
Chen Chen *(Chm)*

XINJIANG ZHUNDONG PETROLEUM TECHNOLOGY CO., LTD.
Floor 5 Building A Scientific Research and Production Office Building, No 278 Baoshi Road Karamay District, Karamay, 834000, Xinjiang, China
Tel.: (86) 9913830616
Web Site: http://www.zygf.com.cn
Year Founded: 2001
002207—(SSE)
Rev.: $27,619,460
Assets: $43,103,390
Liabilities: $28,096,988
Net Worth: $15,006,401
Earnings: ($1,362,947)
Emp.: 531
Fiscal Year-end: 12/31/22
Petroleum & Natural Gas Extraction Services
N.A.I.C.S.: 211120
Lin Jun *(Chm)*

XINLEI COMPRESSOR CO., LTD.
No 8 Chaoping Street, Eastern New District Wenling City, Taizhou, 317500, Zhejiang, China
Tel.: (86) 576899666666
Web Site: https://www.xinlei.com
Year Founded: 2006
301317—(CHIN)
Rev.: $100,025,284
Assets: $104,680,204
Liabilities: $47,835,333
Net Worth: $56,844,871
Earnings: $10,800,761
Fiscal Year-end: 12/31/22
Air Compressor Mfr & Distr
N.A.I.C.S.: 333912
Zhong Renzhi *(Chm)*

XINLING ELECTRICAL CO., LTD.
Che Zhan Road 175, LiuShi, Wenzhou, China
Tel.: (86) 57762779963
Web Site: https://www.xinling.com
Year Founded: 1990
301388—(CHIN)
Rev.: $60,237,636
Assets: $176,035,958
Liabilities: $35,871,469
Net Worth: $140,164,488
Earnings: $5,927,669
Fiscal Year-end: 12/31/23
Relay & Industrial Control Mfr
N.A.I.C.S.: 335314
Zhixing Hu *(Chm)*

XINLIWANG INTERNATIONAL HOLDINGS COMPANY LTD.
Level 9B Chulan Tower No 3 Jalan Conlay 50450, 50450, Kuala Lumpur, Malaysia
Tel.: (60) 3321432888
XLWH—(OTCIQ)
Sales Range: Less than $1 Million
Motion Picture & Video Production Services
N.A.I.C.S.: 512110

XINLONG HOLDING (GROUP) COMPANY LTD.
23rd Floor Block B Internet Finance Building No 3 Guoxing Avenue, Meilan District, Haikou, 570203, Hainan, China
Tel.: (86) 89868581055
Web Site: http://www.xinlong-holding.com
Year Founded: 1993
000955—(SSE)
Rev.: $117,585,351
Assets: $148,528,725
Liabilities: $39,775,503
Net Worth: $108,753,222
Earnings: ($16,909,874)
Emp.: 12,100
Fiscal Year-end: 12/31/22
Holding Company
N.A.I.C.S.: 551112
Bao Yue *(Chm)*

XINLUN NEW MATERIALS CO., LTD.
Floor 5 Building 5 Next Park, No 136 Zhongkang Road Futian District, Shenzhen, 518052, China
Tel.: (86) 75526993699
Web Site: https://www.szselen.com
Year Founded: 2002
002341—(SSE)
Rev.: $137,419,842
Assets: $674,208,199
Liabilities: $511,890,481
Net Worth: $162,317,718
Earnings: ($173,099,806)
Fiscal Year-end: 12/31/22
Electro-Static Discharge & Cleanroom System Solutions
N.A.I.C.S.: 333248

Subsidiaries:

Shenzhen Selen Science & Technology Co., Ltd. - Dongguan Dalingshan Factory (1)
Floor 3 Fulin Industrial Park K Building Weixi Road No.8, Taigongling Village Dalingshan County, Dongguan, China
Tel.: (86) 76923360581
Industrial Machinery Mfr
N.A.I.C.S.: 333248

XINMING CHINA HOLDINGS LTD.
Block i 5/F Hengli Building No 5 Huanglong Road, Hangzhou, 310007, Zhejiang, China
Tel.: (86) 57187633333
Web Site: http://www.xinm.com.cn
Year Founded: 2014
2699—(HKG)
Rev.: $14,297,353
Assets: $733,403,830
Liabilities: $730,214,082
Net Worth: $3,189,748
Earnings: ($116,687,282)
Emp.: 58
Fiscal Year-end: 12/31/21
Holding Company
N.A.I.C.S.: 551112
Chengshou Chen *(Chm & Co-CEO)*

Subsidiaries:

Xinming Group Holding Limited (1)
Block I 5/F Hengli Building No 5 Huanglong Road, Hangzhou, 310007, Zhejiang, China
Tel.: (86) 57187633333
Integrated Residential & Commercial Property Services
N.A.I.C.S.: 236118
Chen Chengshou *(Chm & CEO)*

XINREN ALUMINUM HOLDINGS LIMITED
250 North Bridge Road 15-01 Raffles City Tower, Singapore, 179101, Singapore
Tel.: (65) 6336 8850
Web Site: http://www.xinren-aluminum.com
Sales Range: $1-4.9 Billion
Aluminium Products Mfr
N.A.I.C.S.: 331318
Chaoyi Zeng *(Gen Mgr-Ops)*

Subsidiaries:

Jiangyin Xinren Technology Co., Ltd. (1)
Huangtang Industrial Park Xiake Town, Jiangyin, 214407, Jiangsu, China
Tel.: (86) 510 86530212
Web Site: http://www.xinren.alu.com.cn
Emp.: 250
Aluminium Products Mfr
N.A.I.C.S.: 331315
Batty Qian *(Mgr-Sls)*

XINTELA AB
Scheeletorget 1, Medicon Village, 223 81, Lund, Sweden
Tel.: (46) 462756500
Web Site: https://www.xintela.se
Year Founded: 2009
1XT—(NASDAQ)
Rev.: $4,287
Assets: $1,831,535
Liabilities: $832,711
Net Worth: $998,824
Earnings: ($5,251,330)
Emp.: 15
Fiscal Year-end: 12/31/19
Pharmaceuticals Product Mfr
N.A.I.C.S.: 325412
Gregory Batcheller *(Chm)*

XINXIANG CHEMICAL FIBER CO., LTD.
Xinchang Road South Side, Economic And Technological Development Zone, Xinxiang, 453000, Henan, China
Tel.: (86) 3733978861
Web Site: http://www.bailu.com
Year Founded: 1993
000949—(SSE)
Rev.: $1,021,329,368
Assets: $1,570,448,931
Liabilities: $796,811,488
Net Worth: $773,637,443
Earnings: ($61,019,581)
Fiscal Year-end: 12/31/22
Chemical Fiber Textile Raw Material Mfr
N.A.I.C.S.: 313110
Shao Changjin *(Chm)*

XINXIANG RICHFUL LUBE ADDITIVE CO., LTD.
Dazhaoying Township North of Xinhuo Rd, Xinxiang, 453700, Henan, China
Tel.: (86) 3735466880
Web Site: https://www.richful.com
Year Founded: 1996
300910—(SSE)
Rev.: $427,691,787
Assets: $476,854,434
Liabilities: $90,371,858
Net Worth: $386,482,576
Earnings: $82,573,578
Fiscal Year-end: 12/31/22
Chemical Product Mfr & Distr
N.A.I.C.S.: 325520
Chunxuan Guo *(Chm & Gen Mgr)*

Subsidiaries:

Shenyang Haorunda Additive Co., Ltd. (1)
Ruibao Oriental Building Sanyi Street, Hunnan District, Shenyang, China
Tel.: (86) 2431215756
Lubricant Product Mfr & Distr
N.A.I.C.S.: 324191

Xuanrun (Shanghai) Chemical Technology Co., Ltd. (1)
Room 1902 Sinopec Tower Pudong Avenue No 1525, Pudong District, Shanghai, China
Tel.: (86) 2158999571
Lubricant Product Mfr & Distr
N.A.I.C.S.: 324191

XINXIANG TIANLI ENERGY CO., LTD.
No 1618 Xinqi Street, Muye District, Xinxiang, 453002, Henan, China
Tel.: (86) 3737075928
Web Site: https://www.xxtlln.com
Year Founded: 2009
301152—(CHIN)
Rev.: $344,130,605
Assets: $447,041,590
Liabilities: $168,538,929
Net Worth: $278,502,661
Earnings: ($70,655,183)
Fiscal Year-end: 12/31/23
Battery Product Mfr
N.A.I.C.S.: 335910
Ruiqing Wang *(Chm & Gen Mgr)*

XINXING CATHAY INTERNATIONAL GROUP CO., LTD.
27 F Office Tower Beijing Fortune Plaza No 7Dongsanhuan Zhong Road, Chaoyang District, Beijing, 100020, China
Tel.: (86) 10 5929 0000
Web Site: http://www.xxcig.com
Year Founded: 1911
Sales Range: $25-49.9 Billion
Emp.: 80,000
Investment Management Service
N.A.I.C.S.: 523940
Sha Ming *(Gen Mgr)*

Subsidiaries:

China New United Import & Export Corp (1)
Building 6 Area 15 188 Nansihuan West Road, Fengtai, Beijing, 100000, China

XINXING CATHAY INTERNATIONAL GROUP CO., LTD.

Xinxing Cathay International Group Co., Ltd.—(Continued)
Tel.: (86) 1063706126
Web Site: http://www.cnuiec.com
Investment Management Service
N.A.I.C.S.: 523940

XINXING DUCTILE IRON PIPES CO., LTD.
2672 Industrial Zone, Chaoyang District, Wuhan, 056300, Hebei, China
Tel.: (86) 3105793205
Web Site: https://www.xinxing-pipes.com
Year Founded: 1971
000778—(SSE)
Rev.: $6,705,512,185
Assets: $7,850,729,826
Liabilities: $3,977,032,260
Net Worth: $3,873,697,565
Earnings: $235,300,193
Fiscal Year-end: 12/31/22
Iron Product Mfr
N.A.I.C.S.: 331210
Chengzhang Li *(Chm)*

XINYA ELECTRONIC CO., LTD.
No 1 Panzhuyan Road Laizhai Intelligent Industrial Park, Beibaixiang Town, Yueqing, 325603, Zhejiang, China
Tel.: (86) 57762866852
Web Site: http://www.xinya-cn.com
Year Founded: 1987
605277—(SHG)
Rev.: $236,714,302
Assets: $385,416,350
Liabilities: $217,480,527
Net Worth: $167,935,824
Earnings: $20,175,438
Emp.: 700
Fiscal Year-end: 12/31/22
Electronic Product Mfr & Distr
N.A.I.C.S.: 334419
Zhanbing Zhao *(Chm & Gen Mgr)*

XINYANGFENG AGRICULTURAL TECHNOLOGY CO., LTD.
Building 17 Area 16 No 188 South 4th Ring Road, Fengtai District, Beijing, 100070, China
Tel.: (86) 1056961605
Web Site: https://en.yonfer.com
000902—(SSE)
Rev.: $2,240,465,699
Assets: $2,364,223,497
Liabilities: $1,098,566,034
Net Worth: $1,265,657,464
Earnings: $183,833,203
Emp.: 5,266
Fiscal Year-end: 12/31/22
Textile Products Mfr
N.A.I.C.S.: 314999
Caixue Yang *(Chm)*

XINYAQIANG SILICON CHEMISTRY CO., LTD.
No 2 Yangzi Road Eco-chemical Industrial Park, Suqian Ecological Chemical Technology Industrial Park, Suqian, 223800, Jiangsu, China
Tel.: (86) 52788262133
Web Site: https://www.newasiaman.com
Year Founded: 2009
603155—(SHG)
Rev.: $159,157,257
Assets: $379,804,998
Liabilities: $46,142,530
Net Worth: $333,662,467
Earnings: $42,361,067
Fiscal Year-end: 12/31/22
Chemical Product Mfr & Distr
N.A.I.C.S.: 325520
Yajun Chu *(Chm & Gen Mgr)*

XINYI ELECTRIC STORAGE HOLDINGS LIMITED
Unit 2116-2117 21st Floor Rykadan Capital Tower No 135 Hoi Bun Road, Kwun Tong, Kowloon, China (Hong Kong)
Tel.: (852) 39192888
Web Site: http://www.xyglass.com.hk
8328—(HKG)
Rev.: $135,946,493
Assets: $293,759,490
Liabilities: $147,072,015
Net Worth: $146,687,475
Earnings: $7,003,575
Emp.: 518
Fiscal Year-end: 12/31/22
Vehicle Glass Replacement Services
N.A.I.C.S.: 811122
Pik Li *(COO)*

Subsidiaries:
Xinyi Energy Storage Micro-grid Research Institute (Dongguan) Company Limited
Xinyi Glass Industrial Park Ludong, Humen Town, Dongguan, Guangdong, China
Tel.: (86) 76985267768
Web Site: http://www.xinyies.com
Storage Battery Mfr
N.A.I.C.S.: 335910

XINYI GLASS HOLDINGS LIMITED
21/F Rykadan Capital Tower No 135 Hoi Bun Road Kwun Tong, Kowloon, China (Hong Kong)
Tel.: (852) 39192888
Web Site: http://www.xinyiglass.com
0868—(OTCIQ)
Rev.: $3,290,348,512
Assets: $6,675,244,930
Liabilities: $2,574,433,013
Net Worth: $4,100,811,916
Earnings: $657,431,467
Emp.: 15,068
Fiscal Year-end: 12/31/22
Glass Products Mfr
N.A.I.C.S.: 327212
Shing Kan Lee *(Exec Dir)*

Subsidiaries:
Dongguan Benson Automobile Glass Company Limited (1)
Xinyi Glass Industrial Zone, Humen Town, Dongguan, Guangdong, China
Tel.: (86) 76985266666
Automotive Glass Mfr
N.A.I.C.S.: 327215

Shenzhen Benson Automobile Glass Company Limited (1)
Ludong Village, Humen Town, Dongguan, 523935, Guangdong, China
Tel.: (86) 76985260396
Web Site: https://www.bensonautomobileglass.com
Emp.: 600
Automotive Glass Mfr
N.A.I.C.S.: 327215

Xinyi Auto Glass (North America) Corporation (1)
Suite 702-704 3601 Highway 7 East, Markham, L3R 0M3, ON, Canada
Tel.: (905) 947-8801
Web Site: http://www.xinyiglass.ca
Emp.: 22
Glass Distr
N.A.I.C.S.: 423390

Xinyi Automobile Glass (Shenzhen) Company Limited (1)
No 25 Xinyi Rd 228 Indus Zone Henggang, Henggang Town, Shenzhen, 518115, Guangdong, China
Tel.: (86) 75528631182
Automotive Glass Mfr
N.A.I.C.S.: 327215

Xinyi Automobile Parts (Wuhu) Company Limited (1)
The North Road of Fengming Lake Economy Technology Development Zone, Wuhu, Anhui, China
Tel.: (86) 5535895300
Automotive Glass Mfr
N.A.I.C.S.: 327215

Xinyi Electronic Glass (Wuhu) Company limited (1)
Xinyi Glass Industrial Park No 2 Xinyi Road ETDZ, Wuhu, Anhui, China
Tel.: (86) 5535895678
Automotive Glass Mfr
N.A.I.C.S.: 327215

Xinyi Energy Smart (Wuhu) Company Limited (1)
Xinyi Glass Industrial Park No 2 Xinyi Road, Economic & Technical Development Zone, Wuhu, Anhui, China
Tel.: (86) 13925830098
Automotive Glass Mfr
N.A.I.C.S.: 327215

Xinyi Energy-Saving Glass (Sichuan) Co., Ltd. (1)
Minshan South Road Deyang Economic & Technical, Sichuan, China
Tel.: (86) 18227187260
Automotive Glass Mfr
N.A.I.C.S.: 327215

Xinyi Environment-friendly Special Glass (Jiangmen) Co., Ltd. (1)
Xinyi Glass Industrial Park No 1 Xinyi Road High-Tech, Industrial Development Zone, Jiangmen, Guangdong, China
Tel.: (86) 7503872666
Automotive Glass Mfr
N.A.I.C.S.: 327215

Xinyi Glas Deutschland GmbH (1)
Gueterbahnhofstrasse 11, 69151, Neckargemund, Baden-Wurttemberg, Germany
Tel.: (49) 6223973824
Web Site: http://www.xinyiglass.de
Glass Distr
N.A.I.C.S.: 423390
Wolfgang Willnat *(Mgr)*

Xinyi Glass (Hong Kong) Co., Ltd (1)
3F Harbour View 2 No 16 Science Park East Ave Hong Kong Science Park, Pak Shek Kok, Tai Po, NT, China (Hong Kong)
Tel.: (852) 39192888
Web Site: http://www.xinyiglass.com.hk
Automobile Glass Mfr & Distr
N.A.I.C.S.: 811122
Dong Shiqing *(Pres)*

Xinyi Glass (India) Co., Ltd. (1)
Unit No 25-30 1st Floor Idea Cosmic Plaza C2 Block Palam Vihar, Gurgaon, 122017, Haryana, India
Tel.: (91) 8800407868
Automotive Glass Mfr
N.A.I.C.S.: 327215

Xinyi Glass (Philippines) Co., Ltd. (1)
20 Juno St, Bel-Air Village, Makati, 1209, Philippines
Tel.: (63) 9953331157
Automotive Glass Mfr
N.A.I.C.S.: 327215

Xinyi Glass (Poland) Co., Ltd. (1)
Ul Rzeznicka 9A, 82-300, Elblag, Poland
Tel.: (48) 501169598
Automotive Glass Mfr
N.A.I.C.S.: 327215

Xinyi Glass (Taiwan) Co., Ltd. (1)
RM 705 7F No 908 Jingguo Rd, Luzhu District, Taoyuan, Taiwan
Tel.: (886) 936110555
Automotive Glass Mfr
N.A.I.C.S.: 327215

Xinyi Glass (Tianjin) Company Limited (1)
No 2 Xinchuang Rd Wuqing Development Area, Tianjin, China
Tel.: (86) 2282159888
Automotive Glass Mfr
N.A.I.C.S.: 327215

Xinyi Glass (Yingkou) Company Limited (1)
Xinyi Glass Industrial Park Binhai Industrial Park, Yingkou, Liaoning, China
Tel.: (86) 18702271008
Automotive Glass Mfr
N.A.I.C.S.: 327215

Xinyi Glass Engineering (Dongguan) Company Limited (1)
No 168 Binhai Avenue, Humen Town, Dongguan, Guangdong, China
Tel.: (86) 76985266666
Automotive Glass Mfr
N.A.I.C.S.: 327215
Doris Dong *(Mgr-Sls)*

Xinyi Glass Japan Company Limited (1)
Blue Heights 202 2-17-3 Nihonbashi-Kayabacho, Chuo-Ku, Tokyo, 103-0025, Japan
Tel.: (81) 356149188
Web Site: https://www.xinyiglass.co.jp
Glass Distr
N.A.I.C.S.: 423390

Xinyi Group (Glass) Company Limited (1)
1F Harbour View 2 No 16 Sci Park E Ave Phase II, Sha Tin, New Territories, China (Hong Kong)
Tel.: (852) 26733122
Web Site: https://www.xinyiglass.com.hk
Emp.: 10
Glass Distr
N.A.I.C.S.: 423390
Lau Kason *(Mgr-Fin)*

Xinyi Ultra-thin Glass (Dongguan) Company Limited (1)
Xinyi Glass Industrial Park, Ludong Humen, Dongguan, Guangdong, China
Tel.: (86) 5532660608
Flat Glass Mfr
N.A.I.C.S.: 327211

XINYI SOLAR HOLDINGS LIMITED
No 2 Xinyi Road, Wuhu Economic and Technology Development Zone, Wuhu, 241007, Anhui, China
Tel.: (86) 5535899999
Web Site: https://www.xinyisolar.com
Year Founded: 2007
0968—(HKG)
Rev.: $3,403,166,103
Assets: $7,723,362,429
Liabilities: $2,885,041,855
Net Worth: $4,838,320,575
Earnings: $600,731,785
Emp.: 11,063
Fiscal Year-end: 12/31/23
Holding Company
N.A.I.C.S.: 551112
Yin Yee Lee *(Chm)*

Subsidiaries:
Polaron Solartech Corporation (1)
3761 Victoria Park Ave Unit 9, Scarborough, M1W 3S2, ON, Canada
Tel.: (647) 557-1207
Web Site: https://www.polaronsolar.com
Solar Electric Power Generation Services
N.A.I.C.S.: 221114

Xinyi Energy Holdings Limited (1)
23 Wuyishan Road, Wuhu Economic and Technological Development Zone, Wuhu, 241006, Anhui, China
Tel.: (86) 5532618888
Web Site: https://www.xinyienergy.com
Solar Glass Mfr
N.A.I.C.S.: 327215

Xinyi Solar (Malaysia) Sdn Bhd (1)
Plot 23A B Elkay Industrial Park, Lipat Kajang Jasin, 77000, Melaka, Malaysia
Tel.: (60) 65306888
Solar Glass Mfr
N.A.I.C.S.: 327215

XINYU IRON & STEEL CO., LTD.
No 1 Yejin Road, Yushui District, Xinyu, 338001, jiangxi, China

Tel.: (86) 7906292246
Web Site:
https://www.xinsteel.com.cn
600782—(SHG)
Rev.: $13,899,785,370
Assets: $7,477,027,342
Liabilities: $3,682,922,607
Net Worth: $3,794,104,735
Earnings: $146,910,039
Fiscal Year-end: 12/31/22
Iron & Steel Product Mfr
N.A.I.C.S.: 331110

XINYUAN REAL ESTATE CO., LTD.
27/F China Central Place Tower II 79 Jianguo Road, Chaoyang District, Beijing, 100025, China
Tel.: (86) 1085889200 Ky
Web Site: https://ir.xyre.com
XIN—(NYSE)
Rev.: $804,974,475
Assets: $5,333,393,231
Liabilities: $5,225,980,849
Net Worth: $107,412,382
Earnings: $30,531,711
Emp.: 1,069
Fiscal Year-end: 12/31/23
Residential & Commercial Real Estate Developer
N.A.I.C.S.: 236116
Yong Zhang *(Co-Founder, Chm & CEO)*

Subsidiaries:

Xinyuan China Real Estate Ltd. (1)
27F China Central Place Tower II, 79 Jianguo Road, Chaoyang District, Beijing, 100025, China
Tel.: (86) 1085889390
Web Site: http://www.xyre.com
Residential & Commercial Real Estate Developer
N.A.I.C.S.: 236116

XINZHI GROUP CO., LTD.
28 Xinzhi Road, Qiansuo Town Jiaojiang District, Taizhou, 318016, Zhejiang, China
Tel.: (86) 57688928188 CN
Web Site:
https://www.chinaxinzhi.com
Year Founded: 1990
002664—(SSE)
Rev.: $521,883,648
Assets: $1,146,990,780
Liabilities: $696,018,960
Net Worth: $450,971,820
Earnings: $29,607,552
Fiscal Year-end: 12/31/22
Motors & Related Parts Mfr
N.A.I.C.S.: 335312
Jiang Hu *(Sls Dir & Mktg Dir)*

Subsidiaries:

Zhejiang Daxing Technology Co., Ltd. (1)
No 28 Xindu Road Qiansuo Street, Jiaojiang District, Taizhou, 318016, Zhejiang, China
Tel.: (86) 57689085139
Web Site: https://daxingkj.com
Engine Parts Mfr & Distr
N.A.I.C.S.: 336310

XIO (UK) LLP
The Shard Suite 1502 32 London Bridge Street, London, SE1 9SG, United Kingdom
Tel.: (44) 84 4499 7111
Web Site: http://www.xiogroup.com
Privater Equity Firm
N.A.I.C.S.: 523999
Athene Li *(Chm & Partner)*

XIONG'AN NEW POWER TECHNOLOGY CO., LTD.
Pilot Free Trade Zone Xiongan Area, Baoding Xiongan Citizen Service Center Corporate Office Bldg A W Area, Hebei, 071000, China
Tel.: (86) 1088332810
Web Site: https://www.kre.cn
Year Founded: 2003
300152—(CHIN)
Rev.: $26,226,720
Assets: $116,856,324
Liabilities: $61,149,816
Net Worth: $55,706,508
Earnings: ($12,186,720)
Fiscal Year-end: 12/31/22
Pollution Control Equipment Mfr
N.A.I.C.S.: 334519
Fangfang Cheng *(Chm)*

XIOR STUDENT HOUSING NV
Mechelsesteenweg 34 bus 108, 2018, Antwerp, Belgium
Tel.: (32) 32570489
Web Site: https://www.xior.be
Year Founded: 2007
XIOR—(EUR)
Rev.: $160,957,059
Assets: $3,749,711,889
Liabilities: $2,074,397,837
Net Worth: $1,675,314,053
Earnings: ($10,381,941)
Emp.: 232
Fiscal Year-end: 12/31/23
Residential Building Rental Services
N.A.I.C.S.: 531110
Leen Van den Neste *(Chm)*

XISHUI STRONG YEAR CO., LTD.
No 4-21 Shijingyuan, West Binhe District Haibo Bay, Wuhai, 016000, China
Tel.: (86) 473 695 3126
600291—(SHG)
Rev.: $3,231,106,974
Assets: $434,036,270
Liabilities: $145,259,933
Net Worth: $288,776,336
Earnings: ($1,339,645,259)
Fiscal Year-end: 12/31/20
Cement & Clinker Mfr
N.A.I.C.S.: 327310
Shaohua Li *(Vice Chm)*

XIWANG FOODSTUFFS CO., LTD.
Xiwang Industrial Park Zouping County, Binzhou, 256209, Shandong, China
Tel.: (86) 5434866888
Web Site:
http://www.xiwangshipin.com.cn
000639—(SSE)
Rev.: $852,342,524
Assets: $993,438,571
Liabilities: $443,416,826
Net Worth: $550,021,746
Earnings: ($86,863,879)
Emp.: 2,100
Fiscal Year-end: 12/31/22
Corn Oil Mfr
N.A.I.C.S.: 311221

XIWANG PROPERTY HOLDINGS CO. LTD.
Xiwang Industrial Park, Zouping, 256209, Shandong, China
Tel.: (86) 5434619688 BM
Web Site:
http://www.xiwangproperty.com
Year Founded: 2001
2088—(HKG)
Rev.: $6,803,082
Assets: $102,088,210
Liabilities: $22,372,459
Net Worth: $79,715,750
Earnings: ($1,029,413)
Emp.: 23
Fiscal Year-end: 12/31/22
Holding Company
N.A.I.C.S.: 551112
Jin Wang *(CEO)*

XIWANG SPECIAL STEEL COMPANY LIMITED
Xiwang Industrial Area, Zouping, Shandong, China
Tel.: (86) 5438138066
Web Site:
https://www.xiwangsteel.com
1266—(HKG)
Rev.: $2,030,222,048
Assets: $2,115,851,587
Liabilities: $1,489,398,581
Net Worth: $626,453,006
Earnings: ($186,562,397)
Emp.: 3,202
Fiscal Year-end: 12/31/22
Steel Furnace & Other Steel Products Mfr
N.A.I.C.S.: 333994
Xinhu Sun *(Exec Dir)*

Subsidiaries:

Win Cheoung International Industries Limited (1)
Unit 2110 21st Floor Harbour Centre 25 Harbour Road, Wanchai, China (Hong Kong)
Tel.: (852) 31884518
Steel Mfrs
N.A.I.C.S.: 331110

XIZI CLEAN ENERGY EQUIPMENT MANUFACTURING CO., LTD.
No 1216 Danonggang Road, Jianggan District, Hangzhou, 310021, Zhejiang, China
Tel.: (86) 57185387519
Web Site:
http://www.chinaboilers.com
Year Founded: 1955
002534—(SSE)
Rev.: $1,031,047,912
Assets: $2,239,824,015
Liabilities: $1,661,573,347
Net Worth: $578,250,668
Earnings: $28,621,200
Emp.: 2,000
Fiscal Year-end: 12/31/22
Boiler Mfr
N.A.I.C.S.: 332410
Wang Shuifu *(Chm)*

Subsidiaries:

Hangzhou Boiler Group Engineering Trading Co., Ltd. (1)
No 245 Dongxin Road, Xiacheng District, Hangzhou, 310004, Zhejiang, China
Tel.: (86) 571 85361219
Web Site: http://www.chinaboilers.com
Boiler Products Mfr
N.A.I.C.S.: 332410
Zhou Yinbao *(Gen Mgr)*

Hangzhou Boiler Group General Equipment Co., Ltd. (1)
No 885 Gongkang Road Chongxian Street, Linping District, Hangzhou, 311108, China
Tel.: (86) 57185387608
Boiler Auxiliary Equipment Mfr & Distr
N.A.I.C.S.: 332410

Hangzhou Boiler Group Industrial Boiler Co., Ltd. (1)
No 123 Liangyun Street Liangzhu Street, Yuhang District, Hangzhou, 311112, China
Tel.: (86) 57185387498
Boiler Auxiliary Equipment Mfr & Distr
N.A.I.C.S.: 332410

Hangzhou Hangguo Electric Technology Co., Ltd. (1)
1216 Danonggang Road, Jianggan District, Hangzhou, 310021, China
Tel.: (86) 57185387469

Web Site: http://www.chinaboilers.com
Power Boiler Mfr
N.A.I.C.S.: 332410
Weixiao He *(Chm & Pres)*

Hangzhou Hangguo Testing Technology Co., Ltd. (1)
245 Dongxin Road, Hangzhou, 310004, Zhejiang, China
Tel.: (86) 57185387295
Web Site: http://www.chinaboilers.com
Detecting Equipment Sales
N.A.I.C.S.: 423690

Hangzhou New Century Energy Environmental Protection Engineering Co., Ltd. (1)
8th Floor Building 13 Xizi Smart Industrial Park No 1279 Tongxie Road, Shangcheng District, Hangzhou, 310021, Zhejiang, China (55.5%)
Tel.: (86) 57188212091
Web Site: https://www.chinance.com.cn
Sales Range: $25-49.9 Million
Emp.: 32
Boiler Mfr
N.A.I.C.S.: 332410

Zhejiang Xizi United Engineering Co., Ltd. (1)
Building 2 No 1216 Danongang Road, Jianggan District, Hangzhou, 310019, Zhejiang, China
Tel.: (86) 57128001518
Web Site: https://www.xiziuec.cn
Sales Range: $25-49.9 Million
Emp.: 500
Engineeering Services
N.A.I.C.S.: 541330

XJ ELECTRIC CO., LTD.
No 1298 Xuji Ave, Xuchang, 461000, Henan, China
Tel.: (86) 3743212348
Web Site: https://xjec.com
Year Founded: 1993
000400—(SSE)
Rev.: $2,094,409,896
Assets: $2,661,449,076
Liabilities: $1,130,219,944
Net Worth: $1,531,229,132
Earnings: $106,594,095
Emp.: 1,450
Fiscal Year-end: 12/31/22
Electrical Machinery Mfr
N.A.I.C.S.: 335999
Li Juntao *(Chm)*

XL ENERGY LTD.
H No 19-66/11 D-4 Laxmipuram Colony, Opp A S Rao Nagar ECILKapra Medchal Malkajgiri, Hyderabad, 500062, Telangana, India
Tel.: (91) 40 2714 5317
Web Site: http://www.xlenergy.co
Rev.: $31,935
Assets: $66,951,438
Liabilities: $117,268,146
Net Worth: ($50,316,708)
Earnings: ($14,365,769)
Emp.: 2
Fiscal Year-end: 03/31/19
Solar Photovoltaic Module Mfr
N.A.I.C.S.: 335929
Aneesh Mittal *(Exec Dir)*

Subsidiaries:

Digrun Grun SL (1)
Cr De Fuencarral, 28108, Alcobendas, Spain
Tel.: (34) 91 334 6000
Eletric Power Generation Services
N.A.I.C.S.: 221118

Saptashva Solar S.A. (1)
Arbea Campus Empresarial Edificio 2 2 Planta, 28108, Alcobendas, Madrid, Spain
Tel.: (34) 696980363
Web Site: http://www.saptashvasolar.com
Energy Power Generation Services
N.A.I.C.S.: 221118

XL HOLDINGS BERHAD

XL HOLDINGS BERHAD

XL Holdings Berhad—(Continued)
B-09-09 Gateway Corporate Suites
Gateway Kiaramas, Jalan Desa Kiara
Mont Kiara, 50480, Kuala Lumpur,
Kuala Lumpur, Malaysia
Tel.: (60) 364136155
Web Site: https://xlhb.com.my
Year Founded: 1998
XL—(KLS)
Rev.: $14,927,589
Assets: $40,077,725
Liabilities: $1,584,044
Net Worth: $38,493,682
Earnings: $1,480,910
Emp.: 106
Fiscal Year-end: 04/30/24
Ornamental Fish Breeding & Trading Services
N.A.I.C.S.: 112511
Kai Seng Kuan (CEO)

Subsidiaries:

Xian Leng Aquatic Merchant Sdn. Bhd. (1)
No 1 Jalan Zahir Taman Jenang, 83000, Batu Pahat, Johor, Malaysia
Tel.: (60) 74345109
Web Site: http://www.xianleng.com.my
Tropical Fish Whslr
N.A.I.C.S.: 424460

XL-ID SOLUTIONS INC.
1550 Beaulac Street, Montreal, H4R 1W8, QC, Canada
Tel.: (514) 360-4550   Ca
Web Site: http://www.xl-id.com
Year Founded: 2009
Sales Range: $1-9.9 Million
Emp.: 10
Biometric Security & Identification Solutions Programming & Data Services
N.A.I.C.S.: 541511
Sylvain Lemieux (Pres & CEO)

XLENT AB
Regeringsgatan 67, Stockholm, 11156, Sweden
Tel.: (46) 8 519 510 00
Web Site: http://www.xlent.se
Engineeering Services
N.A.I.C.S.: 541330

XLIFE SCIENCES AG
Talacker 35, 8001, Zurich, Switzerland
Tel.: (41) 443858460
Web Site: https://www.xlifesciences.ch
XLS—(SWX)
Rev.: $1,174,750
Assets: $608,502,015
Liabilities: $174,657,354
Net Worth: $433,844,661
Earnings: $11,021,192
Emp.: 20
Fiscal Year-end: 12/31/23
Biotechnology Research & Development Services
N.A.I.C.S.: 541714
Oliver R. Baumann (CEO)

XLMEDIA PLC
12 Castle Street, Saint Helier, JE2 3RT, Jersey
Tel.: (44) 2045701831
Web Site: https://www.xlmedia.com
Year Founded: 2008
XLM—(AIM)
Rev.: $71,805,000
Assets: $131,081,000
Liabilities: $30,818,000
Net Worth: $100,263,000
Earnings: ($9,439,000)
Emp.: 193
Fiscal Year-end: 12/31/22
Digital Publishing & Marketing Services
N.A.I.C.S.: 541910
Ory Weihs (Founder)

Subsidiaries:

Blueclaw Media Ltd. (1)
46 The Calls, Leeds, LS2 7EY, Westyorkshire, United Kingdom
Tel.: (44) 1132343300
Web Site: https://www.blueclaw.co.uk
Marketing Research Service
N.A.I.C.S.: 541910

Marmar Media Ltd. (1)
19 HaBarzel st, Tel Aviv, Israel
Tel.: (972) 723660030
Web Site: http://www.marmarmedia.com
Online Advertising Services
N.A.I.C.S.: 541810

XLN TELECOM LTD.
69 Bondway, London, SW8 1SQ, United Kingdom
Tel.: (44) 844 880 7777
Web Site: http://www.xlntelecom.co.uk
Year Founded: 2002
Sales Range: $10-24.9 Million
Emp.: 312
Telecommunication Servicesb
N.A.I.C.S.: 517112
Christian Nellemann (Founder & CEO)

XMH HOLDINGS LTD.
55 Tuas Crescent Suite 07-01, Singapore, 638743, Singapore
Tel.: (65) 63680188
Web Site: https://www.xmh.com.sg
Year Founded: 1955
BQF—(SES)
Rev.: $92,013,338
Assets: $108,241,571
Liabilities: $65,119,674
Net Worth: $43,121,897
Earnings: $9,292,330
Emp.: 197
Fiscal Year-end: 04/30/24
Diesel Engine, Propulsion & Power Generating Equipment Mfr
N.A.I.C.S.: 336310
Tin Yeow Tan (Chm & Mng Dir)

Subsidiaries:

Mech-Power Generator Pte. Ltd. (1)
55 Tuas Crescent 07-01, Singapore, 638743, Singapore
Tel.: (65) 67466228
Web Site: https://www.mechpower.com.sg
Electrical Equipment Mfr & Whslr
N.A.I.C.S.: 335311
Alvin Lim (Mng Dir)

Xin Ming Hua Pte Ltd (1)
55 Tuas Crescent 07-01, Singapore, 638743, Singapore
Tel.: (65) 63680188
Industrial Diesel Engine Distr
N.A.I.C.S.: 423840

Z-Power Automation Pte. Ltd. (1)
No 55 Tuas Crescent 02-01 XMH Building, Singapore, 638743, Singapore
Tel.: (65) 6 465 1925
Web Site: https://www.z-power.com
System Integration Services
N.A.I.C.S.: 541512
Denis Wong (Gen Mgr-Marine & Offshore)

XMOS LTD.
33-35 Queen Square, Bristol, BS1 4LU, United Kingdom
Tel.: (44) 117 927 6004
Web Site: http://www.xmos.com
Voice & Music Processing Services
N.A.I.C.S.: 459140
Mark Lippett (Pres & CEO)

Subsidiaries:

XMOS, Inc. (1)
1 Merrill Industrial Dr Ste 6, Hampton, NH 03842
Tel.: (617) 500-0353
Web Site: http://www.xmos.com
Software Publisher
N.A.I.C.S.: 513210

XMREALITY AB
Granden Duvan 3, 582 22, Linkoping, Sweden
Tel.: (46) 13211110
Web Site: https://www.xmreality.com
Year Founded: 2007
XMR—(OMX)
Rev.: $2,922,776
Assets: $4,970,534
Liabilities: $2,051,214
Net Worth: $2,919,320
Earnings: ($3,442,197)
Emp.: 30
Fiscal Year-end: 12/31/22
Information Technology Services
N.A.I.C.S.: 541519
Johan Castevall (CEO)

XOGRAPH HEALTHCARE LTD.
Xograph House Ebley Road, Stonehouse, GL10 2LU, Gloucestershire, United Kingdom
Tel.: (44) 1453820320   UK
Web Site: http://www.xograph.com
Year Founded: 1967
Medical Equipment Distr
N.A.I.C.S.: 423450

XOGRAPH HEALTHCARE LTD.
Suite 1250 26 Upper Pembroke Street, Dublin, D02 X361, Ireland
Tel.: (353) 16499023   IE
Medical Equipment Distr
N.A.I.C.S.: 423450

XORTX THERAPEUTICS, INC.
3710 33rd Street NW, Calgary, T2L 2M1, AB, Canada
Tel.: (403) 455-7727   BC
Web Site: https://www.xortx.com
Year Founded: 2011
XRTX—(NASDAQ)
Rev.: $107,622
Assets: $13,105,481
Liabilities: $5,700,082
Net Worth: $7,405,399
Earnings: ($7,420,168)
Emp.: 3
Fiscal Year-end: 12/31/22
Nonmetallic Mineral Mining Services
N.A.I.C.S.: 213115
Allen W. Davidoff (Founder & CEO)

XOX BHD
Lot 17 1 Level 17 Menara Lien Hoe, No 8 Persiaran Tropicana, 47410, Petaling Jaya, Malaysia
Tel.: (60) 328567333
Web Site: https://xox.com.my
XOX—(KLS)
Rev.: $57,916,355
Assets: $76,611,039
Liabilities: $43,326,378
Net Worth: $33,284,660
Earnings: ($14,652,268)
Fiscal Year-end: 09/30/23
Mobile Services
N.A.I.C.S.: 517112
Kok Heng Ng (CEO)

Subsidiaries:

One XOX Sdn. Bhd. (1)
Lot 5 2 5th Floor Menara Lien Hoe No 8 Persiaran Tropicana, Tropicana Golf and Country Resort, 47410, Petaling Jaya, Selangor, Malaysia
Tel.: (60) 378000033
Web Site: https://www.onexox.my
Telecommunication Network Services
N.A.I.C.S.: 517810

INTERNATIONAL PUBLIC

XOX Com Sdn. Bhd. (1)
Lot 17 1 Level 17 Menara Lien Hoe No 8 Persiaran Tropicana, Tropicana Golf and Country Resort, 47410, Petaling Jaya, Selangor Darul Ehsan, Malaysia
Tel.: (60) 378000033
Mobile Virtual Network Operator
N.A.I.C.S.: 517121
Ng Kok Heng (CEO)

XOX Mobile Sdn Bhd (1)
Lot 8 1 8th Floor Menara Lien Hoe No 8 Persiaran Tropicana, Tropicana Golf Country Resort, 47410, Petaling Jaya, Selangor Darul Ehsan, Malaysia
Tel.: (60) 379551388
Mobile Network Operating Services
N.A.I.C.S.: 517112

XOX NETWORKS BERHAD
7th Floor Menara Lien Hoe 8 Persiaran Tropicana, Tropicana Golf & Country Resort, 47410, Petaling Jaya, Malaysia
Tel.: (60) 1158816040   MY
Web Site: https://www.xoxnetworks.com
XOXNET—(KLS)
Rev.: $5,870,851
Assets: $11,516,713
Liabilities: $842,517
Net Worth: $10,674,195
Earnings: ($2,608,918)
Fiscal Year-end: 06/30/23
Information Technology Services
N.A.I.C.S.: 541512
Sean Ng Chee Heng (Exec Dir)

Subsidiaries:

Macpie Pro Sdn Bhd (1)
V03-05-15 and 17 Designer Office Lingkaran SV Sunway Velocity, 55100, Kuala Lumpur, Malaysia
Tel.: (60) 113 112 1222
Web Site: https://www.macpiepro.com
Music Event Organization Services
N.A.I.C.S.: 561920

Trumpet International Sdn. Bhd. (1)
7th Floor Menara Lien Hoe 8 Persiaran Tropicana, Tropicana Golf and Country Resort, 47410, Petaling Jaya, Selangor, Malaysia
Tel.: (60) 103098998
Web Site: https://www.trumpet.com.my
Event & Ticket Management Services
N.A.I.C.S.: 512131

XOX TECHNOLOGY BHD
Lot 17 1 17th Floor Menara Lien Hoe No 8 Persiaran Tropicana, Tropicana Golf and Country Resort, 47410, Petaling Jaya, Selangor Darul Ehsan, Malaysia
Tel.: (60) 376126242   MY
Web Site: https://www.xoxtech.com.my
Year Founded: 1999
XOXTECH—(KLS)
Rev.: $18,541,255
Assets: $10,897,266
Liabilities: $5,929,193
Net Worth: $4,968,074
Earnings: $553,835
Fiscal Year-end: 03/31/23
Mobile Value Added Services
N.A.I.C.S.: 517112
Mark Shin Yong Chew (Chm)

Subsidiaries:

M3 Technologies (Thailand) Co., Ltd. (1)
10/71 4th Floor room 403 The Trendy Office Building, Sukhumvit Soi13 Klongtoey-Nua Wattana, Bangkok, 10110, Thailand
Tel.: (66) 21686168
Web Site: http://www.m3tech.co.th
Investment Holding Services
N.A.I.C.S.: 551112

M3 Technologies Pakistan (Private) Limited (1)

614 6th Floor Continental Trade Centre Block 8 Clifton, Karachi, Pakistan
Tel.: (92) 213530298388
Web Site: https://www.m3tech.com.pk
Mobile Application Development Services
N.A.I.C.S.: 541511
Muhammad Imran Afzal (CFO)

Subsidiary (Non-US):

M3 Technologies Middle East FZE (2)
Office No 19 1st Floor High Bay Building Dubai Silicon Oasis, PO Box 341364, Dubai, United Arab Emirates
Tel.: (971) 43339112
Mobile Application Development Services
N.A.I.C.S.: 541511

Messaging Technologies Hong Kong Ltd. (1)
6/F Malahon Centre 8-12 Stanley Street, Central, China (Hong Kong)
Tel.: (852) 21358100
Mobile Application Development Services
N.A.I.C.S.: 541511

Subsidiary (Non-US):

M3 Technologies (Shenzhen) Company Limited (2)
Futian District Xinghe Century Mansion No 3069 Caitian Road, 2112-2113 Room 21/F Block A, Shenzhen, China
Tel.: (86) 75582793836
Electronic Goods Distr
N.A.I.C.S.: 425120

M3 Technologies (Xiamen) Co., Ltd (2)
Suite 506 Hai De Building 28-30 Ban Wei Road, Xiamen, China
Tel.: (86) 5925898368
Mobile Application Development Services
N.A.I.C.S.: 541511

PT Surya Genta Perkasa (1)
Ruko Puri Meruya No 8-GJI H Sa'aba / Jl Murni Huk, Joglo Kec Kembangan, Jakarta, 11650, Indonesia
Tel.: (62) 2158905117
Web Site: https://en.ptsuryagentaperkasa.web.com
Emp.: 25
Mobile Application Development Services
N.A.I.C.S.: 541511

XP CHEMISTRIES AB
Storgatan 73F, 852 33, Sundsvall, Sweden
Tel.: (46) 737490933
Web Site: https://www.xpchemistries.com
Year Founded: 2021
86Q—(DEU)
Biotechnology Research & Development Services
N.A.I.C.S.: 541714
Anders Frejdh (CFO)

XP FACTORY PLC
70-88 Oxford Street Ground Floor, London, W1D 1BS, United Kingdom
Tel.: (44) 2078463322 UK
Web Site: https://www.escapehunt.com
Year Founded: 2016
XPF—(AIM)
Rev.: $9,482,316
Assets: $66,486,191
Liabilities: $36,864,813
Net Worth: $29,621,377
Earnings: ($1,186,647)
Emp.: 222
Fiscal Year-end: 12/31/21
Entertainment Facility Services
N.A.I.C.S.: 722310
Richard Harpham (CEO)

Subsidiaries:

Boom Battle Bar Cardiff Limited (1)
Brewery Quarter, Cardiff, CF10 1FG, United Kingdom
Tel.: (44) 2922801555
Web Site: https://boombattlebar.com
Bar Operator
N.A.I.C.S.: 722410

Escape Hunt Group Limited (1)
3 Pear Place, London, SE1 8BT, United Kingdom
Tel.: (44) 2078463322
Gambling Services
N.A.I.C.S.: 713120

XP INC.
Av Chedid Jafet 75 Torre Sul 30th floor, Vila Olimpia, Sao Paulo, 04551-065, Brazil
Tel.: (55) 1130750429 Ky
Web Site: http://www.xpinc.com
Year Founded: 2019
XP—(NASDAQ)
Rev.: $2,963,425,267
Assets: $49,664,109,682
Liabilities: $45,785,189,750
Net Worth: $3,878,919,932
Earnings: $777,623,093
Emp.: 6,669
Fiscal Year-end: 12/31/23
Investment Management Service
N.A.I.C.S.: 523940
Guilherme Dias Fernandes Benchimol (Founder, Chm & CEO)

Subsidiaries:

Banco Modal S.A. (1)
Praia de Botafogo 501 6 andar Torre Pao de Acucar, Rio de Janeiro, 22250-040, Brazil
Tel.: (55) 1135256600
Banking Services
N.A.I.C.S.: 522110

Subsidiary (Domestic):

MODAL DTVM (2)
Av Pres Juscelino Kubitschek 1455 7 andar, Sao Paulo, 04543-011, Brazil
Tel.: (55) 1121066897
Web Site: http://www.modaldtvm.com.br
Investment Management Service
N.A.I.C.S.: 523940

Modal Administradora de Recursos S.A. (2)
Praia de Botafogo 501 6 andar Torre Pao de Acucar, Rio de Janeiro, 22250-040, Brazil
Tel.: (55) 21 3223 7700
Privater Equity Firm
N.A.I.C.S.: 523999
John Michael Streithorst (PArtner & Mng Dir)

XP Investments US, LLC (1)
55 W 46th St 30th Fl, New York, NY 10036
Tel.: (646) 664-0505
Web Site: https://www.xpi.us
Investment Services
N.A.I.C.S.: 523999

XP POWER LIMITED
19 Tai Seng Avenue 07-01, Singapore, 534054, Singapore
Tel.: (65) 64116900 SG
Web Site: https://www.xppower.com
Year Founded: 1988
XPP—(LSE)
Rev.: $402,800,765
Assets: $568,173,140
Liabilities: $370,464,674
Net Worth: $197,708,467
Earnings: ($11,457,670)
Emp.: 2,669
Fiscal Year-end: 12/31/23
Power Supply Solutions to the Electronics Industry
N.A.I.C.S.: 335311
James R. Peters (Chm)

Subsidiaries:

Comdel, Inc. (1)
11 Kondelin Rd, Gloucester, MA 01930
Tel.: (978) 282-0620
Web Site: http://www.comdel.com
RF & DC Power Supplies Mfr
N.A.I.C.S.: 334220
Glenn Chapman (Mgr-RF Engrg)

EMCO High Voltage Corp. (1)
1 EMCO Ct, Sutter Creek, CA 95685
Tel.: (209) 267-1630
Web Site: http://www.emcohighvoltage.com
Sales Range: $1-9.9 Million
Emp.: 47
Electronic Components Mfr
N.A.I.C.S.: 335311
Mike Doherty (Pres & CEO)

Glassman High Voltage, Inc. (1)
124 W Main St, High Bridge, NJ 08829
Tel.: (908) 638-3800
Electronic Components Mfr
N.A.I.C.S.: 335311

Guth High Voltage GmbH (1)
Spitzenbergstrasse 6, 73084, Salach, Germany
Tel.: (49) 7162948930
Electrical & Electronic Equipment Mfr & Distr
N.A.I.C.S.: 335999

Powersolve Electronics Limited (1)
Unit 8A Arnhem Road, Newbury, RG14 5RU, Berkshire, United Kingdom
Tel.: (44) 1635521858
Web Site: https://www.powersolve.co.uk
Emp.: 20
Power Converter Mfr
N.A.I.C.S.: 335999

XP PLC (1)
Horseshoe Park, Pangbourne, Reading, RG8 7JW, Berkshire, United Kingdom
Tel.: (44) 1189845515
Emp.: 100
Power Converter Mfr
N.A.I.C.S.: 335999

XP Power (1)
1 Stiles Rd Ste 106, Salem, NH 03079 (100%)
Tel.: (978) 287-7200
Web Site: http://www.xppower.com
Emp.: 14
Supplier of Power Conversion Products
N.A.I.C.S.: 423840

Subsidiary (Domestic):

XPiQ-SSI (2)
1590 S Sinclair St, Anaheim, CA 92806-5933 (100%)
Tel.: (714) 712-4500
Switching Power Supplies Mfr
N.A.I.C.S.: 334419

XP Power (S) Pte Limited (1)
401 Commonwealth Drive Haw Par Technocentre, Singapore, 149598, Singapore
Tel.: (65) 64116900
Web Site: http://www.xppower.com
Emp.: 30
Power Supplies Distr
N.A.I.C.S.: 423610

XP Power (Shanghai) Co., Limited (1)
2899 Xie Tu Road Lobby B 507 Guang Qi Culture Plaza, Shanghai, 200030, China
Tel.: (86) 2164867817
Web Site: https://www.xppower.com
Electric Power Distr
N.A.I.C.S.: 221122

XP Power AG (1)
Dorfstrasse 69, Postfach 96, 5210, Windisch, Aargau, Switzerland
Tel.: (41) 564489080
Power Converter Mfr
N.A.I.C.S.: 335999

XP Power ApS (1)
Naverland 2, 2600, Glostrup, Denmark
Tel.: (45) 43423833
Emp.: 2
Power Inverters Mfr
N.A.I.C.S.: 423840

XP Power GmbH (1)
Auf der Hohe 2, 28357, Bremen, Germany
Tel.: (49) 421639330
Emp.: 12
Power Supplies Mfr
N.A.I.C.S.: 335999

XP Power LLC (1)
990 Benecia Ave, Sunnyvale, CA 94085
Tel.: (408) 732-7777
Emp.: 100
Electronic Equipment Whslr
N.A.I.C.S.: 423690

XP Power Norway AS (1)
Industrivegen 23, NO-2069, Jessheim, Norway
Tel.: (47) 63946018
Electronic Products Mfr
N.A.I.C.S.: 334111

XP Power SA (1)
16 Rue du Seminaire, 94516, Rungis, Cedex, France
Tel.: (33) 145123115
Power Converter Distr
N.A.I.C.S.: 423840

XP Power Singapore Holdings Pte Limited (1)
19 Tai Seng Avenue 07-01, Lobby B, Singapore, 534054, Singapore
Tel.: (65) 64116900
Emp.: 45
Power Converter Mfr
N.A.I.C.S.: 335999
Duncan Penny (CEO)

XP Power Srl (1)
Via Volturno 37, Brugherio, 20047, Monza and Brianza, Italy (100%)
Tel.: (39) 0392876027
Emp.: 4
Power Converter Mfr
N.A.I.C.S.: 335999

XP Power Sweden AB (1)
Sodertalje Science Park Kvarnbergagatan 12, 151 36, Sodertalje, Sweden
Tel.: (46) 855536700
Electronic Products Mfr
N.A.I.C.S.: 334111
Mikael Nilsson (Country Mgr)

XPD SOCCER GEAR GROUP LIMITED
Level 1 Exchange Tower 530 Little Collins Street, Melbourne, 3000, VIC, Australia
Tel.: (61) 3 9909 7412
XPD—(ASX)
Soccer Footwear Mfr & Sales
N.A.I.C.S.: 316210
Andrew Smith (Chm)

XPENG INC.
No 8 Songgang Road Changxing Street Cencun, Tianhe District, Guangzhou, 510640, Guangdong, China
Tel.: (86) 2066806680 Ky
Web Site: https://www.xiaopeng.com
Year Founded: 2018
XPEV—(NYSE)
Rev.: $4,114,472,782
Assets: $10,953,137,029
Liabilities: $5,298,054,045
Net Worth: $5,655,082,985
Earnings: ($1,400,181,900)
Emp.: 15,829
Fiscal Year-end: 12/31/22
Holding Company
N.A.I.C.S.: 551112
Xiaopeng He (Co-Founder, Chm, CEO & Exec Dir)

XPLORA TECHNOLOGIES AS
Nedre Slottsgate 8, 0157, Oslo, Norway
Tel.: (47) 96613400
Year Founded: 2016
XPLRA—(EUR)
Rev.: $50,338,340
Assets: $67,298,267
Liabilities: $20,489,832
Net Worth: $46,808,436
Earnings: ($1,578,039)
Emp.: 90
Fiscal Year-end: 12/31/21
Watch Product Distr

XPLORA TECHNOLOGIES AS

Xplora Technologies AS—(Continued)
N.A.I.C.S.: 423690
Sten Kirkbak (CEO)

Subsidiaries:

Xplora Mobile AB (1)
Sjoangsvagen 17, 192 71, Sollentuna, Sweden
Tel.: (46) 188008119
Web Site: https://xplora.se
Smart Watch Mfr & Distr
N.A.I.C.S.: 334519

Xplora Mobile AS (1)
Nedre Slottsgate 8 7 Etasje, 0157, Oslo, Norway
Tel.: (47) 46282182
Web Site: https://www.xploramobil.no
Smart Watch Mfr & Distr
N.A.I.C.S.: 334519

Xplora Mobile Denmark ApS (1)
Emil Holms Kanal 14, 2300, Copenhagen, Denmark
Tel.: (45) 70715075
Web Site: https://xplora.dk
Smart Watch Mfr & Distr
N.A.I.C.S.: 334519

Xplora Mobile Oy (1)
Piispanportti 11, 02240, Espoo, Finland
Tel.: (358) 922970908
Web Site: https://www.xplora.fi
Smart Watch Mfr & Distr
N.A.I.C.S.: 334519

XPLORE WEALTH LIMITED

Level 4 8-10 Loftus Street, Sydney, 2000, NSW, Australia
Tel.: (61) 1800 446 971
Web Site:
 http://www.managedaccounts.com
Year Founded: 2004
MGP—(ASX)
Investment Administration & Financial Software
N.A.I.C.S.: 525990
Don Sharp (Acting Grp CFO)

Subsidiaries:

DIY Master Pty. Ltd. (1)
Suite 4G 109 Upton Street, Bundall, 4217, QLD, Australia
Tel.: (61) 755555656
Web Site: http://www.diymaster.com.au
Financial Planning Services
N.A.I.C.S.: 541611

XPLUS, INC.

308 Sinbanpo-ro, Seocho-gu, Seoul, Korea (South)
Tel.: (82) 234467421
Web Site: https://www.haainc.co.kr
Year Founded: 2005
373200—(KRS)
Mobile Device Accessory Mfr
N.A.I.C.S.: 334413
Gil Sangpil (CEO)

XPON TECHNOLOGIES GROUP LIMITED

64 York Street, Newstead, Sydney, 2000, NSW, Australia
Tel.: (61) 1300473052
Web Site: https://www.xpon.ai
Year Founded: 2019
XPN—(ASX)
Rev.: $9,826,013
Assets: $9,533,483
Liabilities: $6,871,449
Net Worth: $2,662,034
Earnings: ($5,610,306)
Emp.: 90
Fiscal Year-end: 06/30/23
Software Development Services
N.A.I.C.S.: 541511
Matt Forman (Founder)

XPRO INDIA LIMITED

ECE House 2nd Floor 28A Kasturba Gandhi Marg, New Delhi, 110 001, India
Tel.: (91) 1123765301
Web Site: https://www.xproindia.com
Year Founded: 1998
590013—(BOM)
Rev.: $61,726,012
Assets: $40,782,555
Liabilities: $12,779,785
Net Worth: $28,002,770
Earnings: $5,439,014
Emp.: 203
Fiscal Year-end: 03/31/23
Polymers Mfr
N.A.I.C.S.: 325211
Sidharth Birla (Chm)

Subsidiaries:

Xpro Global Limited (1)
9/1 2nd Floor Birla Building R N Mukherjee Road, Kolkata, 700 001, West Bengal, India
Tel.: (91) 3322131680
Plastic Film & Sheet Mfr
N.A.I.C.S.: 322220

Xpro India Limited - Barjora Unit (1)
Barjora-Mejia Road P O Ghutgoria, Barjora, Bankura, 722 202, West Bengal, India
Tel.: (91) 9775301701
Web Site: http://www.xproindia.com
Plastic Film & Sheet Mfr
N.A.I.C.S.: 322220
H. Bakshi (Pres & COO)

Xpro India Limited - Ranjangaon Unit (1)
Plot No E-90/1, MIDC Industrial Area Ranjangaon, Pune, 412 220, India
Tel.: (91) 2138 611100
Web Site: http://www.xproindia.com
Emp.: 125
Plastic Film & Sheet Mfr
N.A.I.C.S.: 322220

XPS PENSIONS GROUP

Phoenix House 1 Station Hill, Reading, RG1 1NB, United Kingdom
Tel.: (44) 1189185000
Web Site: https://www.xpsgroup.com
Year Founded: 2012
XPS—(LSE)
Rev.: $251,744,509
Assets: $355,800,303
Liabilities: $121,195,405
Net Worth: $234,604,898
Earnings: $68,375,410
Emp.: 1,712
Fiscal Year-end: 03/31/24
Holding Company; Pension Actuarial, Consulting & Administration Services
N.A.I.C.S.: 551112
Ben Bramhall (Co-CEO)

Subsidiaries:

Punter Southall Group Limited (1)
11 Strand, London, WC2N 5HR, United Kingdom
Tel.: (44) 20 3327 5000
Web Site: http://www.puntersouthall.com
Investment Services
N.A.I.C.S.: 541611
Angus Samuels (Chm)

Xafinity Consulting Limited (1)
11 Strand, London, WC2N 5HR, United Kingdom
Tel.: (44) 2039673895
Web Site: http://www.xafinityconsulting.com
Pension Actuarial, Consulting & Administration Services
N.A.I.C.S.: 541611
Jonathan Bernstein (Head-Pensions)

XPV WATER PARTNERS

26 Wellington St E Suite 203, Toronto, M5E 1S2, ON, Canada
Tel.: (416) 864-0475
Web Site:
 https://xpvwaterpartners.com
Year Founded: 2006
Investment Services
N.A.I.C.S.: 523999

Subsidiaries:

Atlas-SSI, Inc. (1)
622 E McPherson Dr, Monticello, MS 39654
Tel.: (225) 452-2950
Web Site: https://www.atlas-ssi.com
Machine Mfg
N.A.I.C.S.: 333248

Subsidiary (Domestic):

Golden Harvest, Inc. (2)
11944 Westar Ln, Burlington, WA 98233
Tel.: (360) 757-4334
Web Site: http://www.goldenharvestinc.com
Sales Range: $10-24.9 Million
Hazardous Waste Treatment & Disposal
N.A.I.C.S.: 562211
Tom Cluin (Reg Mgr-Sls-Southern)

Axius Water (1)
53 Portside Dr, Pocasset, MA 02559
Tel.: (866) 642-7621
Web Site: https://www.axiuswater.com
Environmental Services
N.A.I.C.S.: 541620
Chris McIntire (CEO)

Subsidiary (Domestic):

Triplepoint Environmental, LLC (2)
6586 S Kenton St, Centennial, CO 80111
Tel.: (303) 578-2800
Web Site: http://www.triplepointwater.com
Sales Range: $1-9.9 Million
Emp.: 8
Environmental Services
N.A.I.C.S.: 541620
Erica Velasco (Ops Mgr)

XRAPPLIED TECHNOLOGIES INC.

Suite 908-510 Burrard Street, Vancouver, V6C 3A8, BC, Canada
Tel.: (604) 608-6314
Web Site:
 http://www.zadarventures.com
Year Founded: 2008
Rev.: $233
Assets: $354,760
Liabilities: $98,917
Net Worth: $255,843
Earnings: ($460,353)
Fiscal Year-end: 07/31/19
Uranium Mining
N.A.I.C.S.: 212290
Geoffrey R. Watson (CFO)

XREALITY GROUP LTD

2A / 106 Old Pittwater Rd, Brookvale, 2100, NSW, Australia
Tel.: (61) 247611880
Web Site:
 https://www.indoorskydive.com.au
Year Founded: 2011
XRG—(ASX)
Rev.: $6,836,663
Assets: $28,484,009
Liabilities: $22,186,106
Net Worth: $6,297,903
Earnings: ($2,745,553)
Fiscal Year-end: 06/30/24
Indoor Skydiving Facility Operating Services
N.A.I.C.S.: 611620
Wayne Peter Jones (CEO)

Subsidiaries:

Red Cartel Pty. Ltd. (1)
Suite 103 Level 1 24-26 Falcon Street, Crows Nest, NSW, Australia
Tel.: (61) 280021884
Web Site: https://www.redcartel.com
Online Gaming & Animation Entertainment Services
N.A.I.C.S.: 512110

upRAW Cafe & Juice Bar Pty Ltd (1)
Level 2 ifly Downunder Facility 123 Mulgoa Road, Penrith, 2750, NSW, Australia
Tel.: (61) 2 4761 1805
Web Site: http://www.uprawcafe.com.au
Restaurant Operators
N.A.I.C.S.: 722513

XREF LIMITED

L20 135 King Street, Sydney, 2000, NSW, Australia
Tel.: (61) 282443099
Web Site: https://www.xref.com
XF1—(ASX)
Rev.: $13,261,019
Assets: $13,593,041
Liabilities: $17,498,391
Net Worth: ($3,905,350)
Earnings: ($3,793,496)
Emp.: 99
Fiscal Year-end: 06/30/24
Investment Services
N.A.I.C.S.: 523999
Seymour Lee-Martin (CEO & Mng Dir)

XRF SCIENTIFIC LIMITED

86 Guthrie Street, Osborne Park, 6017, WA, Australia
Tel.: (61) 892440600
Web Site:
 https://www.xrfscientific.com
XRF—(ASX)
Rev.: $23,977,884
Assets: $37,063,047
Liabilities: $7,102,786
Net Worth: $29,960,261
Earnings: $3,930,903
Fiscal Year-end: 06/30/21
Mfr & Marketing Metal Products
N.A.I.C.S.: 339910
Vance Stazzonelli (Mng Dir & Co-Sec)

Subsidiaries:

XRF Chemicals Pty Ltd. (1)
88 Guthrie St, Osborne Park, Perth, 6017, WA, Australia
Tel.: (61) 892449600
Web Site: http://www.xrfscientific.com
Emp.: 7
Borate Fluxes Fusion Analysis Chemicals Mfr
N.A.I.C.S.: 325992
Jeff Brown (Gen Mgr)

XRF Labware (1)
107 Miller St, Epping, 3076, VIC, Australia
Tel.: (61) 394084811
Web Site: http://www.xrfscientific.com
Emp.: 10
Platinum Alloy Product Mfr & Distr
N.A.I.C.S.: 331492
Gino Manfredi (Gen Mgr)

XRF Scientific Americas Inc. (1)
620 Cathcart 259, Montreal, H3B 1M1, QC, Canada
Tel.: (514) 871-4997
Platinum Crucible Mfr
N.A.I.C.S.: 332999

XRF Scientific Europe GmbH (1)
Seligenstadter Str 100, 63791, Karlstein am Main, Germany
Tel.: (49) 61889542761
Platinum Crucible Mfr
N.A.I.C.S.: 332999

XRF Scientific Europe SPRL (1)
103 rue de la Consolation, 1030, Brussels, Belgium
Tel.: (32) 27627712
Platinum Crucible Mfr
N.A.I.C.S.: 332999

XRF Technology (VIC) Pty Ltd (1)
Factory 24 200 Canterbury Rd, Bayswater, 3153, VIC, Australia
Tel.: (61) 397206339
Web Site: http://www.xrfscientific.com
Emp.: 10
Automated Fusion Equipment Design, Manufacturing & Services
N.A.I.C.S.: 334516
Francis Linnane (Gen Mgr)

XRF Technology (WA) Pty Ltd. (1)
67 Boulder Rd, Midvale, Malaga, 6090, WA, Australia

AND PRIVATE COMPANIES — XTPL SA

Tel.: (61) 892747222
Web Site: http://www.srfscientific.com
Emp.: 20
Heat-Treatment Furnaces Designer & Mfr
N.A.I.C.S.: 333994
Robert McConnell (Gen Mgr)

XS FINANCIAL INC.
301 - 1665 Ellis Street, Kelowna, VIY 2B3, BC, Canada
Tel.: (310) 683-2336   BC
Web Site: http://xsfinancial.com
Year Founded: 2009
XSHLF—(OTCQB)
Rev.: $3,158,562
Assets: $52,306,515
Liabilities: $42,888,986
Net Worth: $9,417,529
Earnings: ($2,985,421)
Fiscal Year-end: 12/31/21
Investment Services
N.A.I.C.S.: 523999
David Kivitz (CEO)

XSOMO INTERNATIONAL LIMITED
29 Slipe Pen Road, Kingston, Jamaica
Tel.: (876) 9225857
Web Site: http://www.xsomo.com.jm
Sales Range: $50-74.9 Million
Emp.: 150
Commercial Printer Services
N.A.I.C.S.: 323111
Desmond K. Valentine (Chm & CEO)

XSPRAY PHARMA AB
Scheeles vag 2, 16967, Solna, Sweden
Tel.: (46) 87303700
Web Site: https://www.xspraypharma.com
Year Founded: 2003
XSPRAY—(OMX)
Assets: $75,968,691
Liabilities: $7,132,646
Net Worth: $68,836,045
Earnings: ($17,835,786)
Emp.: 26
Fiscal Year-end: 12/31/23
Pharmaceuticals Product Mfr
N.A.I.C.S.: 325412
Per Andersson (CEO)

XSPRING CAPITAL PUBLIC COMPANY LIMITED
No 59 Siri Campus Building D 2nd Floor Soi Rim Klong Prakanong, Prakanong Phrakanong Nuea Wattana, Bangkok, 10110, Thailand
Tel.: (66) 20303730
Web Site: https://www.xspringcapital.com
Year Founded: 1974
XPG—(THA)
Rev.: $18,148,907
Assets: $325,948,120
Liabilities: $11,727,384
Net Worth: $314,220,737
Earnings: $3,097,120
Emp.: 163
Fiscal Year-end: 12/31/23
Investment Banking & Securities Brokerage Services
N.A.I.C.S.: 523150
Chaipatr Srivisarvacha (Vice Chm & Co-CEO)

Subsidiaries:

Solaris Asset Managment Company Limited   (1)
8th Floor 287 Liberty Square Bldg Silom Road, Bangrak, Bangkok, 10500, Thailand   (100%)
Tel.: (66) 2624 6300
Web Site: http://www.seamicoasset.com

Sales Range: $50-74.9 Million
Emp.: 30
Mutual Fund Management Services
N.A.I.C.S.: 523940

XSTATE RESOURCES LIMITED
Level 1 31 Cliff Street, Fremantle, 6160, WA, Australia
XST—(ASX)
Rev.: $5,329,811
Assets: $8,673,809
Liabilities: $7,177,365
Net Worth: $1,496,444
Earnings: $954,135
Emp.: 1
Fiscal Year-end: 12/31/23
Uranium Mining & Exploration Services
N.A.I.C.S.: 212290
David Maxwell McArthur (Sec & Sec)

XT ENERGY GROUP, INC.
No 1 Fuqiao Village Henggouqiao Town, Xianning, 437012, Hubei, China
Tel.: (86) 4001037733   NV
Year Founded: 2008
XTNY—(OTCBB)
Rev.: $53,126,913
Assets: $64,376,788
Liabilities: $30,245,328
Net Worth: $34,131,460
Earnings: ($1,085,293)
Emp.: 418
Fiscal Year-end: 07/31/19
Holding Company
N.A.I.C.S.: 551112
Jianzheng Cao (CFO)

XTB SA
ul Prosta 67, 00-838, Warsaw, Poland
Tel.: (48) 222019570
XTB—(WAR)
Rev.: $403,533,027
Assets: $1,191,224,082
Liabilities: $750,506,858
Net Worth: $440,717,224
Earnings: $201,009,400
Fiscal Year-end: 12/31/23
Financial Management Services
N.A.I.C.S.: 522110
Omar Arnaout (Chm & Chm-Mgmt Bd)

XTC LITHIUM LIMITED
63 Sinclair Street, Sydney, 2065, NSW, Australia
Tel.: (61) 411403585   AU
Web Site: https://xantippe.com.au
XTC—(ASX)
Rev.: $17
Assets: $32,856,464
Liabilities: $6,126,281
Net Worth: $26,730,183
Earnings: ($3,839,067)
Fiscal Year-end: 06/30/23
Metal Mining Services
N.A.I.C.S.: 212290
Kevin Lynn (CEO & Sec)

XTECH CO., LTD.
1-9-9 5F xBridge-Tokyo Yaesu Tokyo Building Headquarters Building, Chuo-ku, 103-8285, Tokyo, Japan
Tel.: (81) 3 4405 3451
Web Site: http://www.xtech-corp.co.jp
Internet Service Industry
N.A.I.C.S.: 517410
Shiichi Saaijo (CEO)

Subsidiaries:

XTech HP Co., Ltd   (1)
1-9-9 chome 5th Floor Tokyo Building Headquarters Building, Chuo - ku, Tokyo, Japan
Tel.: (81) 3 4405 3451

Web Site: http://www.xtech-corp.co.jp
Internet Service Industry
N.A.I.C.S.: 517410

Subsidiary (Domestic):

Excite Japan Co., Ltd.   (2)
Daiwa Azabu Terrace 4F 3-20-1 Minami-azabu, Minato-ku, Tokyo, Japan   (95.1%)
Tel.: (81) 3 64502729
Web Site: http://corp.excite.co.jp
Rev.: $55,970,640
Assets: $53,910,480
Liabilities: $7,530,240
Net Worth: $46,380,240
Earnings: ($4,528,800)
Emp.: 262
Fiscal Year-end: 03/31/2018
Internet Information Services
N.A.I.C.S.: 519290
Tatsushi Iwasaki (Auditor)

Subsidiary (Non-US):

PT Creative Visions Indonesia   (3)
Wisma Nugra Santana Floor 11 Jl Jend Sudirman Kav 7-8, Jakarta Pusat, Indonesia
Tel.: (62) 215700300
Web Site: http://www.cv-indonesia.com
Internet Information Services
N.A.I.C.S.: 519290
Kenya Nakashige (Pres & CEO)

XTEK LIMITED
3 Faulding Street, PO Box 333, Fyshwick, 2609, ACT, Australia
Tel.: (61) 2 6163 5588
Web Site: http://www.xtek.net
XTE—(ASX)
Rev.: $21,708,048
Assets: $24,806,504
Liabilities: $8,403,340
Net Worth: $16,403,164
Earnings: ($3,045,565)
Emp.: 25
Fiscal Year-end: 06/30/21
Security Products
N.A.I.C.S.: 423610
Lawrence A. Gardiner (Sec & Head-Corp Svcs)

XTEP INTERNATIONAL HOLDINGS LIMITED
Unit A 27/F Tower A Billion Centre 1 Wang Kwong Road Kowloon Bay, Kowloon, China (Hong Kong)
Tel.: (852) 21520333
Web Site: http://www.xtep.com.hk
1368—(OTCIQ)
Rev.: $1,790,316,931
Assets: $2,283,661,525
Liabilities: $1,133,531,098
Net Worth: $1,150,130,428
Earnings: $126,312,168
Emp.: 9,800
Fiscal Year-end: 12/31/22
Sportswear Apparel, Footwear & Accessories Mfr & Marketer
N.A.I.C.S.: 315990
Shui Po Ding (Founder, Chm & CEO)

Subsidiaries:

Xtep (China) Co., Ltd.   (1)
Quanzhou Economic and Technological Development Zone, Quanzhou, 362000, China
Tel.: (86) 59522495555
Web Site: http://www.xtep.com.cn
Sports Wear Mfr & Distr
N.A.I.C.S.: 315250
Zhang Li Lin (VP)

XTGLOBAL INFOTECH LTD.
Plot Nos 31 and 32 Third Floor Tower A Ramky Selenium, Financial district Nanakramguda, Hyderabad, 500032, Telangana, India
Tel.: (91) 4066353456   In
Web Site: https://xtglobal.com
Year Founded: 1986
531225—(BOM)
Rev.: $24,814,867

Assets: $23,668,718
Liabilities: $13,196,929
Net Worth: $10,471,789
Earnings: $2,753,260
Emp.: 80
Fiscal Year-end: 03/31/21
Information Technology Consulting Services
N.A.I.C.S.: 541512
Ramarao Atchuta Mullapudi (Founder, Pres & CEO)

Subsidiaries:

Circulus LLC   (1)
2701 Dallas Pkwy Ste 550, Plano, TX 75093
Tel.: (972) 755-1800
Web Site: https://circulus.io
Information Technology Services
N.A.I.C.S.: 541511

XTIERRA INC.
55 University Avenue Suite 1805, Toronto, M5J 2H7, ON, Canada
Tel.: (416) 925-0090   BC
Web Site: http://www.xtierra.ca
Year Founded: 2007
XAG—(TSXV)
Assets: $227,127
Liabilities: $2,288,759
Net Worth: ($2,061,632)
Earnings: ($660,790)
Emp.: 5
Fiscal Year-end: 12/31/21
Silver Mining Services
N.A.I.C.S.: 212220
John F. Kearney (Chm)

XTL BIOPHARMACEUTICALS LTD.
5 Badner St, Ramat Gan, 4365603, Israel
Tel.: (972) 36116600   Il
Web Site: https://www.xtlbio.com
Year Founded: 1993
XTLB—(NASDAQ)
Rev.: $36,000
Assets: $4,186,000
Liabilities: $187,000
Net Worth: $3,999,000
Earnings: ($1,348,000)
Fiscal Year-end: 12/31/22
Pharmaceutical Development Services
N.A.I.C.S.: 325412
Doron Turgeman (Chm)

XTM, INC.
Unit 437-67 Mowat Avenue, Toronto, M6K 3E3, ON, Canada
Tel.: (416) 260-1641
Web Site: https://www.xtminc.com
XTMIF—(OTCQB)
Rev.: $762,729
Assets: $6,529,692
Liabilities: $5,870,041
Net Worth: $659,651
Earnings: ($2,814,187)
Fiscal Year-end: 12/31/20
Online Payment Services
N.A.I.C.S.: 522320
Marilyn Schaffer (CEO)

XTPL SA
Stablowicka 147, 54-066, Wroclaw, Poland
Tel.: (48) 717072204
Web Site: https://www.xtpl.com
XTP—(WAR)
Rev.: $3,219,866
Assets: $4,398,583
Liabilities: $3,399,990
Net Worth: $998,593
Earnings: ($536,854)
Emp.: 45
Fiscal Year-end: 12/31/22
Printing Electronic Product Mfr

XTPL SA—(Continued)
N.A.I.C.S.: 333248
Filip Granek *(Founder & Chm)*

XTRA-GOLD RESOURCES CORP.
Village Road Shopping Plaza Suite 2150, PO Box AP 59217, Nassau, Bahamas
Tel.: (242) 3633864   VG
Web Site: https://www.xtragold.com
Year Founded: 1998
XTGRF—(OTCQB)
Assets: $11,860,586
Liabilities: $1,519,103
Net Worth: $10,341,483
Earnings: $14,724
Fiscal Year-end: 12/31/23
Gold Mining Services
N.A.I.C.S.: 212220
Peter C. Minuk *(Treas & Sec)*

XTRACT ONE TECHNOLOGIES INC.
750-1095 West Pender Street, Vancouver, V6E 2M6, BC, Canada
Tel.: (888) 728-1832   BC
Web Site: http://www.patriot1tech.com
Year Founded: 2010
PAT—(OTCIQ)
Rev.: $659,647
Assets: $53,061,641
Liabilities: $1,476,993
Net Worth: $51,584,648
Earnings: ($13,339,638)
Fiscal Year-end: 07/31/19
Investment Services
N.A.I.C.S.: 523999
Jeff Tindale *(Sr VP-Capital Markets)*

XTRACT RESOURCES PLC
1st Floor 7/8 Kendrick Mews South Kensington, London, SW7 3HG, United Kingdom
Tel.: (44) 20 3416 6471   UK
Web Site: http://www.xtractresources.com
Year Founded: 2004
XTR—(AIM)
Rev.: $2,342,067
Assets: $17,746,758
Liabilities: $1,553,232
Net Worth: $16,193,526
Earnings: ($1,240,956)
Emp.: 27
Fiscal Year-end: 12/31/20
Metal Mining
N.A.I.C.S.: 212290
Joel Silberstein *(Dir-Fin)*

XTRIBE P.L.C.
Long Acre 37-38, London, WC2E 9JT, United Kingdom
Tel.: (44) 20 32140420   UK
Web Site: http://www.xtribeapp.com
Year Founded: 2011
Rev.: $29,087
Assets: $122,201
Liabilities: $2,298,989
Net Worth: ($2,176,788)
Earnings: ($1,492,058)
Emp.: 1
Fiscal Year-end: 12/31/18
Application Software Development Services
N.A.I.C.S.: 541511
Mattia Sistigu *(Co-Founder & COO)*

XTV NETWORKS LTD.
Suite 5 CPC 145 Stirling Hwy, Nedlands, 6009, WA, Australia
Tel.: (61) 8 9389 3170   AU
Web Site: http://www.xtv.net
XTV—(ASX)
Interactive Online TV Networks

N.A.I.C.S.: 516210
Joe Ward *(Mng Dir)*

XU YUAN PACKAGING TECHNOLOGY CO., LTD.
No 10 Lane 33 Lane 98 Xinlong Road 3rd Neighborhood Jupuli, Xinpu Township, Hsinchu, 305046, Taiwan
Tel.: (886) 35982727
Web Site: https://www.xuyuanpack.com
8421—(TPE)
Rev.: $39,704,312
Assets: $61,854,141
Liabilities: $31,010,349
Net Worth: $30,843,792
Earnings: $15,364,631
Fiscal Year-end: 12/31/22
Packaging Equipment Mfr
N.A.I.C.S.: 333993
Nan-Yuan Huang *(Chm & Pres)*

XUAN WU CLOUD TECHNOLOGY HOLDINGS LIMITED
Room 904 9/F 38 Haizhou Road, Haizhu District, Guangzhou, Guangdong, China   Ky
Web Site: https://www.cloud.wxchina.com
Year Founded: 2010
2392—(HKG)
Rev.: $177,403,079
Assets: $95,676,783
Liabilities: $48,736,708
Net Worth: $46,940,075
Earnings: ($9,937,140)
Emp.: 743
Fiscal Year-end: 12/31/23
Holding Company
N.A.I.C.S.: 551112
Hairong Li *(Sr VP)*

XUANCHENG VALIN PRECISION TECHNOLOGY CO., LTD.
Mei Zhu Zhen Lang Mei Lu, Langxi County, Xuancheng, 242115, Anhui, China
Tel.: (86) 5637799998
Web Site: https://www.xchualing.com
Year Founded: 2005
603356—(SHG)
Rev.: $246,101,025
Assets: $308,061,987
Liabilities: $172,069,986
Net Worth: $135,992,002
Earnings: ($1,330,458)
Emp.: 800
Fiscal Year-end: 12/31/22
Elevator Parts Mfr & Distr
N.A.I.C.S.: 332322

XUCHANG KETOP TESTING RESEARCH INSTITUTE CO., LTD.
Intersection between Weiwu Avenue & Shangde Road, Xuchang, 461000, Henan, China
Tel.: (86) 3743212185
Web Site: https://www.ketop.cn
Year Founded: 2005
003008—(SSE)
Rev.: $21,900,041
Assets: $159,999,672
Liabilities: $12,682,458
Net Worth: $147,317,213
Earnings: $9,688,892
Fiscal Year-end: 12/31/22
Testing Services
N.A.I.C.S.: 541380
Quanxi Li *(Deputy Gen Mgr)*

XUCHANG YUANDONG DRIVE SHAFT CO., LTD.
No 1699 North Section of Weiwu Avenue, Jian'an District, Xuchang, 461111, Henan, China

Tel.: (86) 3745654034
Web Site: https://www.yodonchina.com
Year Founded: 1954
002406—(SSE)
Rev.: $150,830,105
Assets: $639,370,705
Liabilities: $149,401,170
Net Worth: $489,969,535
Earnings: $10,224,405
Emp.: 800
Fiscal Year-end: 12/31/22
Drive Shaft Mfr
N.A.I.C.S.: 333612

Subsidiaries:

Xuchang Zhongxing Forging Co., Ltd.   (1)
Northern Suburbs, Shangji Town, Xuchang, 461111, Henan, China
Tel.: (86) 3748588266
Web Site: http://www.en.xczxdz.com
Automotive Products Mfr
N.A.I.C.S.: 336350

XUEDA (XIAMEN) EDUCATION TECHNOLOGY GROUP CO., LTD.
No 1 Changle Road Zhaishang, Huli District, Xiamen, 201103, Fujian, China
Tel.: (86) 2154222877
000526—(SSE)
Rev.: $252,385,062
Assets: $446,653,734
Liabilities: $387,227,735
Net Worth: $59,425,999
Earnings: $1,528,802
Fiscal Year-end: 12/31/22
Education Services
N.A.I.C.S.: 923110

Subsidiaries:

Xueda Education Group   (1)
A-4 Xibahe Beili, Chaoyang District, Beijing, 100028, China   (100%)
Tel.: (86) 1064278899
Web Site: http://www.xueda.com
Tutoring Services
N.A.I.C.S.: 611691
Xin Jin *(CEO)*

XUELONG GROUP CO., LTD.
No 211 Huangshan West Road, Beilun District, Ningbo, 315800, Zhejiang, China
Tel.: (86) 57486805201
Web Site: https://www.xuelong.net.cn
Year Founded: 2002
603949—(SHG)
Rev.: $40,860,458
Assets: $151,029,937
Liabilities: $9,659,323
Net Worth: $141,370,613
Earnings: $5,956,905
Fiscal Year-end: 12/31/22
Automobile Parts Mfr
N.A.I.C.S.: 336390
Cailin He *(Chm)*

XUNLEI LIMITED
Xunlei building No 3709 Baishi Road High tech Zone Community Yuehai St, Nanshan District, Shenzhen, 518057, China
Tel.: (86) 75586338443   Ky
Web Site: https://www.xunlei.com
Year Founded: 2003
XNET—(NASDAQ)
Rev.: $342,564,000
Assets: $463,323,000
Liabilities: $154,902,000
Net Worth: $308,421,000
Earnings: $21,463,000
Emp.: 1,097
Fiscal Year-end: 12/31/22
Digital Media Internet Services
N.A.I.C.S.: 516210

Sean Shenglong Zou *(Co-Founder)*

XURPAS INC.
Unit 804 Antel 2000 Corporate Center 121 Valero Street, Salcedo Village, Makati, 1227, Philippines
Tel.: (63) 288896467
Web Site: https://www.xurpasgroup.com
Year Founded: 2001
X—(PHI)
Rev.: $3,394,699
Assets: $9,614,741
Liabilities: $9,231,900
Net Worth: $382,842
Earnings: ($1,806,016)
Fiscal Year-end: 12/31/23
Mobile Applications
N.A.I.C.S.: 513210
Nico Jose S. Nolledo *(Chm)*

Subsidiaries:

Storm Technologies, Inc.   (1)
411 N Depot St, Albemarle, NC 28002
Tel.: (704) 983-2040
Web Site: http://www.stormeng.com
Industrial Boiler Mfr & Distr
N.A.I.C.S.: 332410
Richard Storm *(Founder)*

Xeleb Technologies, Inc.   (1)
7th floor Cambridge Center 108 Tordesillas St, Salcedo Village, Makati, 1227, Philippines
Tel.: (63) 28896467
Web Site: http://www.xeleb.com
Software Services
N.A.I.C.S.: 541511

Xurpas Enterprise Inc.   (1)
Unit 804 Antel 2000 Corporate Center Valero St, Salcedo Village, Makati, 1227, Philippines
Tel.: (63) 288896467
Web Site: http://www.xurpasenterprise.com
Software Services
N.A.I.C.S.: 541511

XUZHOU CONSTRUCTION MACHINERY GROUP CO., LTD.
NO 1 Tuolanshan Road Econominc Development Zone, Xuzhou, Jiangsu, China
Tel.: (86) 5187739782   CN
Web Site: https://www.xcmg.com
Year Founded: 1989
Sales Range: $5-14.9 Billion
Holding Company; Construction Machinery Mfr
N.A.I.C.S.: 551112
Min Wang *(Chm)*

Subsidiaries:

XCMG Construction Machinery Co., Ltd.   (1)
No 26 Tuolanshan Road, Economic & Technological Development Zone, Xuzhou, 221004, Jiangsu, China   (20.83%)
Tel.: (86) 51687739106
Web Site: https://www.xcmg.com
Rev.: $12,855,591,009
Assets: $22,429,470,481
Liabilities: $14,469,929,996
Net Worth: $7,959,540,485
Earnings: $737,493,119
Emp.: 13,000
Fiscal Year-end: 12/31/2023
Construction Machinery Mfr
N.A.I.C.S.: 333120

Affiliate (US):

Intensus Engineering, Inc. LLC   (2)
3691 Route 9, Cold Spring, NY 10516
Tel.: (845) 265-6000
Web Site: http://www.intensus.com
Sales Range: $1-9.9 Million
Emp.: 10
Construction & Mining Machinery Distr
N.A.I.C.S.: 423810
J. Carlos Salcedo *(Mng Dir)*

Subsidiary (Non-US):

Schwing GmbH (2)
Heerstrasse 9-27, PO Box 200362, 44653, Herne, Germany (52%)
Tel.: (49) 23259870
Web Site: http://www.schwing.de
Sales Range: $1-4.9 Billion
Emp.: 4,000
Mfr & Distr of Concrete Pumps, Sludge Pumps & Construction Equipment
N.A.I.C.S.: 333120
Gunther Abolins (Mng Dir)

Subsidiary (US):

Schwing America, Inc. (3)
5900 Centerville Rd, Saint Paul, MN 55127-6805 (100%)
Tel.: (651) 429-0999
Web Site: http://www.schwing.com
Emp.: 550
Truck & Trailer Mounted Concrete Pumps, Concrete Mixing Silos, Placing Booms & Slurry Pumps Mfr
N.A.I.C.S.: 333120
Tom O'Malley (VP-Mktg & Sls)

Subsidiary (Non-US):

Schwing Equipamentos Industriais Ltda. (3)
Rod Fernao Dias km 56, Terra Petra, Mairipora, 07600-970, SP, Brazil (100%)
Tel.: (55) 11 4486 8500
Web Site: http://www.schwingstetter.com.br
Emp.: 100
Mfr of Concrete Pumps, Sludge Pumps & Construction Equipment
N.A.I.C.S.: 333914
Ricardo Lessa (Pres)

Schwing GmbH (3)
Friedrich-Wilhelm-Schwing-Strasse 1, Saint Stefan, 9431, Austria (100%)
Tel.: (43) 52 28 12
Web Site: http://www.schwing-auftragsfertigung.at
Emp.: 100
Hydraulics & Machine Components Mfr
N.A.I.C.S.: 333914
Horst Berger (Gen Mgr)

Schwing Stetter India Pvt Ltd (3)
F71 & F72 SIPCOT Industrial Estate Irungattukottai, Sriperumpudur, Kanchipuram, 602 105, Tamil Nadu, India (100%)
Tel.: (91) 44 27156780
Web Site: http://www.schwingstetterindia.com
Concrete Pumping Equipment Mfr & Distr
N.A.I.C.S.: 333120
Anand Sundaresan (Vice Chm)

Schwing Stetter Ostrava s.r.o. (3)
Moravska 1215 / 6, Ostrava, 70300, Czech Republic
Tel.: (420) 596 746 780
Web Site: http://www.schwing.cz
Sales & Service of Concrete Pumps
N.A.I.C.S.: 423830
Peter Sedlak (Head-Svc Center)

Subsidiary (Domestic):

XCMG Xuzhou Truck-Mounted Crane Co., Ltd. (2)
No 55 Tuolanshan Road, Xuzhou, Jiangsu, China
Tel.: (86) 516 8789 2802
Truck-Mounted Cranes Mfr & Distr
N.A.I.C.S.: 333923

Xuzhou Heavy Machinery Co., Ltd. (2)
No 165 Tongshan Road, Yunlong District, Xuzhou, 221004, Jiangsu, China
Tel.: (86) 51683461361
Web Site: http://www.xzzx.com.cn
Mobile Cranes & Other Construction Machinery Mfr
N.A.I.C.S.: 333923
Yuchun Zhang (Gen Mgr)

Xuzhou Hirschmann Electronics Co., Ltd. (1)
No 11 Baoliansi Road, Xuzhou Economic Dev Zone, Xuzhou, 221001, Jiangsu, China (50%)
Tel.: (86) 516 8788 5799
Web Site: http://www.hirschmann-js.com
Emp.: 300
Electronic Components Mfr
N.A.I.C.S.: 334419

Xuzhou PAT Control Technology Co., Ltd. (1)
No 1 Industrial Zone Development Zone, Jinshan Bridge, Xuzhou, 221004, Jiangsu, China
Tel.: (86) 51687737991
Web Site: http://www.xzpat.com
Traffic Management Products Mfr
N.A.I.C.S.: 334290
Jong Zheng Shi (Mgr-Sls)

XUZHOU HANDLER SPECIAL VEHICLE CO., LTD.
19 Baoliansi Road Xuzhou Economic Development Zone, Xuzhou, 221004, Jiangsu, China
Tel.: (86) 51668782715
Web Site: https://www.handlergp.com
Year Founded: 2005
300201—(SSE)
Rev.: $143,794,872
Assets: $303,994,080
Liabilities: $112,713,120
Net Worth: $191,280,960
Earnings: $10,211,292
Fiscal Year-end: 12/31/22
Aerial Work Platform Mfr & Distr
N.A.I.C.S.: 333923
Ding Bo (Chm)

Subsidiaries:

Shanghai GrumMan International Fire Equipment Co., Ltd. (1)
No 32 Wazi Lane, Songjiang District, Shanghai, 201600, China
Tel.: (86) 2157833768
Web Site: https://www.xzhlz.com
Fire Equipment Mfr
N.A.I.C.S.: 333310

Shenzhen Giant Albert Technology Co., Ltd. (1)
5/F Block C Fengzheng Road, Wangdawang Industrial Area Shiyan Town, Shenzhen, 518108, China
Tel.: (86) 75527641207
Vehicle Platform Mfr
N.A.I.C.S.: 333923

XUZHOU KERONG ENVIRONMENTAL RESOURCES CO., LTD.
12 Yangshan Road, Economic Development Zone, Xuzhou, 221004, China
Tel.: (86) 516 8798 6553
Web Site: http://www.kre.cn
Sales Range: $150-199.9 Million
Emp.: 200
Environmental Services
N.A.I.C.S.: 541620
Fengli Mao (Chm & Pres)

XUZHOU METALFORMING MACHINE GROUP CO., LTD
Second Industrial Park Tongshan Economic Development Zone, Xuxhou, Jiangsu, China
Tel.: (86) 51683531000
Web Site: http://www.xuduan.com.cn
Year Founded: 1951
Metalforming Services
N.A.I.C.S.: 332999
Mao Chengfu (Gen Mgr-Export)

Subsidiaries:

ebu Umformtechnik GmbH (1)
Rathenaustrasse 47, 95444, Bayreuth, Germany
Tel.: (49) 921 5080 0
Web Site: http://www.ebu-umformtechnik.de
Punching Machine Mfr
N.A.I.C.S.: 333517

XVIVO PERFUSION AB
PO Box 53015, SE-400 14, Gothenburg, Sweden
Tel.: (46) 317882150 SE
Web Site: https://www.xvivoperfusion.com
Year Founded: 1998
XVIPF—(OTCIQ)
Rev.: $59,318,801
Assets: $217,961,268
Liabilities: $24,874,025
Net Worth: $193,087,243
Earnings: $9,115,095
Emp.: 150
Fiscal Year-end: 12/31/23
Medical Device Mfr
N.A.I.C.S.: 339112
Dag Andersson (CEO)

Subsidiaries:

STAR Teams Inc. (1)
2929 Arch St Ste 1910, Philadelphia, PA 19104
Web Site: https://www.starteams.com
Speciality Hospital Operator
N.A.I.C.S.: 622310

XVIVO Perfusion Lund AB (1)
Propellervagen 16, 224 78, Lund, Sweden
Tel.: (46) 317882150
Medical Devices
N.A.I.C.S.: 621610

XWINSYS TECHNOLOGY DEVELOPMENT LTD.
Ramat Gabriel Industrial Zone 6 Hatikshoret St, Migdal Ha'Emeq, 2307049, Israel
Tel.: (972) 4 9891313
Web Site: http://www.xwinsys.com
Year Founded: 2012
Semiconductor Mfr & Whslr
N.A.I.C.S.: 334413
Gilad David (Gen Mgr)

XXENTRIA TECHNOLOGY MATERIALS CO., LTD.
No 16 Ln 10 Zhongshan Rd, Rende District, Tainan City, Taiwan
Tel.: (886) 62703868
Web Site: https://www.xxentria-tech.com
Year Founded: 1994
8942—(TPE)
Rev.: $177,969,890
Assets: $523,532,470
Liabilities: $241,700,184
Net Worth: $281,832,286
Earnings: $37,044,148
Fiscal Year-end: 12/31/22
Plastics Product Mfr
N.A.I.C.S.: 326199
Hsien-Te Cheng (Chm & CEO)

Subsidiaries:

Alanod-Xxentria Technology Materials Company Limited (1)
No 168 Lane 256 Yi Lin Road, Rende Dist, Tainan City, 71752, Taiwan
Tel.: (886) 62496885
Web Site: http://www.alanod-xxentria.com
Coal Product Mfr
N.A.I.C.S.: 324199

Sunfly Solar Energy Solutions, Inc. (1)
No 168 Lane 256 Yi Lin Road, Rende Dist, Tainan City, 71752, Taiwan
Tel.: (886) 62490688
Web Site: http://www.sunfly-solar.com
Energy Saving Product Mfr
N.A.I.C.S.: 324199

Xxentria International (USA) Corp. (1)
3086 Route 27 Unit 4, Kendall Park, NJ 08824
Tel.: (732) 951-8900
Metal Products Mfr
N.A.I.C.S.: 324199

XXI CENTURY INVESTMENTS PUBLIC LIMITED
Naberezhne shosse 28, Kiev, Ukraine
Tel.: (380) 442000457
Web Site: http://www.21.com.ua
Year Founded: 1999
Sales Range: $1-9.9 Million
Emp.: 70
Real Estate Manangement Services
N.A.I.C.S.: 531390
Oleg Salmin (CEO)

XXL ASA
Stromsveien 245, NO-0668, Oslo, Norway
Tel.: (47) 24084000
Web Site: http://www.xxlasa.com
Year Founded: 2001
XXLLY—(OTCIQ)
Rev.: $778,311,472
Assets: $834,472,566
Liabilities: $551,265,472
Net Worth: $283,207,094
Earnings: ($48,217,255)
Emp.: 4,749
Fiscal Year-end: 12/31/22
Sporting Goods Retailer
N.A.I.C.S.: 459110
Espen Terland (Exec VP-IT)

Subsidiaries:

West System Norge AS (1)
Stromsveien 230, 0668, Oslo, Norway
Tel.: (47) 22233500
Web Site: https://www.westsystem.no
Boat Storage Equipment Mfr
N.A.I.C.S.: 336612

XXL Adventure AS (1)
Tel.: (47) 22329320
Web Site: http://www.xxladventure.travel
Fishing Whslr
N.A.I.C.S.: 424460

XXL Sport & Villmark AS (1)
Stromsveien 245, 0668, Oslo, Norway
Tel.: (47) 24084000
Web Site: http://www.xxl.no
Sports Product Distr
N.A.I.C.S.: 459110

XXL Sport og Vildmark AB (1)
Ulvsundavagen 185H, 168 67, Bromma, Sweden
Tel.: (46) 104513500
Web Site: http://www.xxl.se
Sports Product Distr
N.A.I.C.S.: 459110

XXL Sports & Outdoor Gmbh (1)
Donaustadtstr 1/4 Stock, 1220, Vienna, Austria
Tel.: (43) 577577
Sports Product Distr
N.A.I.C.S.: 459110

XXL Sports & Outdoor Oy (1)
Tel.: (358) 24084000
Web Site: http://www.xxx.fi
Sports Product Distr
N.A.I.C.S.: 459110

XXL ENERGY CORP.
RPO Box 60610, Granville Park, Vancouver, V6H 4B9, BC, Canada
Tel.: (604) 331-3396 BC
Web Site: https://xxlenergy.com
Year Founded: 1987
XL—(TSXV)
Rev.: $1,496,050
Assets: $4,541,422
Liabilities: $35,113,021
Net Worth: ($30,571,599)
Earnings: ($9,113,310)
Fiscal Year-end: 12/31/20
Oil & Gas Exploration Services
N.A.I.C.S.: 211120
John R. Hislop (CEO)

XXXLUTZ KG
Romerstrasse 39, 4600, Wels, Austria
Tel.: (43) 501111000 AT

XXXLutz KG—(Continued)

Web Site: http://www.xxxlgroup.com
Year Founded: 1945
Sales Range: $1-4.9 Billion
Emp.: 20,800
Furniture Retailer
N.A.I.C.S.: 449110
Gunther Gruber (Mng Dir)

Subsidiaries:

BUT SAS (1)
1 Avenue Spinoza, 77184, Emerainville-Malnoue, France (50%)
Tel.: (33) 164612626
Web Site: http://www.but.fr
Sales Range: $1-4.9 Billion
Emp.: 4,989
Home Appliances, Furniture & Decor Retailer
N.A.I.C.S.: 449210
Thierry Lernon (Dir-Internet)

Home24 SE (1)
OttoOstrowkIStr 3, 10405, Berlin, Germany
Tel.: (49) 30700149000
Web Site: https://www.home24.com
Rev.: $648,607,814
Assets: $572,846,967
Liabilities: $339,628,750
Net Worth: $233,218,217
Earnings: ($53,636,952)
Emp.: 1,871
Fiscal Year-end: 12/31/2022
Online Shopping Services
N.A.I.C.S.: 423210
Marc Appelhoff (CEO & Member-Mgmt Bd)

Subsidiary (Non-US):

Mobly Comercio Varejista Ltda (2)
Av Das Nacoes Unidas 16737 Varzea de Baixo, Sao Paulo, 04730-090, SP, Brazil
Tel.: (55) 1149611800
Web Site: http://www.mobly.com.br
Home Furnishing Product Distr
N.A.I.C.S.: 449129

Subsidiary (Domestic):

home24 Outlet GmbH (2)
Hermann-Blankenstein-Str 20, 10249, Berlin, Germany
Tel.: (49) 302016329478
Home Furnishing Product Distr
N.A.I.C.S.: 449129

XYLO TECHNOLOGIES LTD.

No 7A Omer Industrial Park, PO Box 3030, Omer, 8496500, Israel
Tel.: (972) 722602200
Web Site: https://medigus.com
Year Founded: 2000
XYLO—(NASDAQ)
Rev.: $91,724,000
Assets: $63,896,000
Liabilities: $31,461,000
Net Worth: $32,435,000
Earnings: ($21,732,000)
Emp.: 84
Fiscal Year-end: 12/31/23
Medical Device Mfr
N.A.I.C.S.: 334510
Eliyahu Yoresh (Chm)

XYLOTEK SOLUTIONS INC.

600 Jamieson Parkway Suite 3, Cambridge, N3C 0A6, ON, Canada
Tel.: (519) 584-2089
Web Site: http://www.xylotek.ca
Sales Range: $1-9.9 Million
Computer-Related Services & Distr
N.A.I.C.S.: 541512

XYMAX CORPORATION

1-1-1 Akasaka, Minato-ku, Tokyo, 107-0052, Japan
Tel.: (81) 3 5544 6600
Web Site: http://www.xymax.co.jp
Year Founded: 1990
Rev.: $642,840,000
Emp.: 3,666
Portfolio Management Services
N.A.I.C.S.: 523940
Masafumi Shimada (Chm, CEO & Mng Officer)

Subsidiaries:

AITEX Corporation (1)
2-3-7 Nishiki Aichi Addit Sakura-dori 2nd floor, Naka-ku, Nagoya, Japan
Tel.: (81) 522231033
Real Estate Development Services
N.A.I.C.S.: 531390

Abilitas Hospitality Co., Ltd. (1)
1-1-1 Akasaka, Minato-ku, Tokyo, 107-0052, Japan
Tel.: (81) 355445816
Web Site: http://www.abilitashospitality.com
Management Consulting Services
N.A.I.C.S.: 541618
Ryosuke Sato (Pres)

Karaksa Hotels Corporation (1)
1-1-1 Akasaka Zymax Akasaka 111 Building, Minato-ku, Tokyo, Japan
Tel.: (81) 355445813
Real Estate Development Services
N.A.I.C.S.: 531390

Karaksa Hotels Kansai Corporation (1)
1-5 Dojima Zymax Umeda Shindo Building, Kita-ku, Osaka, Japan
Tel.: (81) 676512332
Real Estate Development Services
N.A.I.C.S.: 531390

Karaksa Hotels Sapporo Corporation (1)
3-2 Kita 1 West Imon Sapporo Building 9th Floor, Chuo-ku, Sapporo, Hokkaido, Japan
Tel.: (81) 115226970
Real Estate Development Services
N.A.I.C.S.: 531390

Karaksa Hotels Tokyo Corporation (1)
1-1-1 Akasaka, Minato-ku, Tokyo, Japan
Tel.: (81) 355446810
Real Estate Development Services
N.A.I.C.S.: 531390

Max Security Service Corporation (1)
1-13-10 Tsukiji Shin-Hanwa Building, Chuo-ku, Tokyo, Japan
Tel.: (81) 368590404
Real Estate Development Services
N.A.I.C.S.: 531390

Max-Realty Inc. (1)
2-4-2 Nagatacho, Chiyoda-ku, Tokyo, 100-0014, Japan
Tel.: (81) 365509300
Web Site: http://www.maxrealty.co.jp
Real Estate Investment Services
N.A.I.C.S.: 531210

The Country Club Japan, Inc. (1)
905 Kayanonanamagari, Kisarazu, Chiba Prefecture, Japan
Tel.: (81) 438532111
Web Site: http://www.ccjapan.jp
Management Consulting Services
N.A.I.C.S.: 541618

XYMAX Geppetto Corporation (1)
4-13-4 Sengoku, Bunkyo-ku, Tokyo, Japan
Tel.: (81) 368590335
Real Estate Development Services
N.A.I.C.S.: 531390

XYMAX Travel Design Corporation (1)
1-5 Dojima Zymax Umeda Shindo Building, Kita-ku, Osaka, Japan
Tel.: (81) 676512250
Real Estate Development Services
N.A.I.C.S.: 531390

Xymax Alpha Corporation (1)
1-13-10 Tsukiji Shin-Hanwa Building, Chuo-ku, Tokyo, Japan
Tel.: (81) 368590400
Real Estate Development Services
N.A.I.C.S.: 531390

Xymax Asset Consulting Corporation (1)
2-4-2 Nagatacho Zymax Tameike Sanno Building, Chiyoda-ku, Tokyo, Japan
Tel.: (81) 335961458
Real Estate Development Services
N.A.I.C.S.: 531390

Xymax Bosai Technica Corporation (1)
1-13-10 Tsukiji Shin-Hanwa Building, Chuo-ku, Tokyo, Japan
Tel.: (81) 368590522
Real Estate Development Services
N.A.I.C.S.: 531390

Xymax Infonista Corporation (1)
1-1-1 Akasaka, Minato-ku, Tokyo, Japan
Tel.: (81) 355446555
Real Estate Development Services
N.A.I.C.S.: 531390

Xymax Kansai Corporation (1)
1-1-5 Dojima Umeda Shindo Building, Kita-ku, Osaka, Japan
Tel.: (81) 663412840
Real Estate Development Services
N.A.I.C.S.: 531390

Xymax Kyushu Corporation (1)
4-2-1 Hakata Ekimae Zymax Hakata Ekimae Building, Hakata-ku, Fukuoka, Fukuoka Prefecture, Japan
Tel.: (81) 926866700
Real Estate Development Services
N.A.I.C.S.: 531390

Xymax Real Estate Institute Corporation (1)
2-4-2 Nagatacho Zymax Tameike Sanno Building, Chiyoda-ku, Tokyo, Japan
Tel.: (81) 335961477
Real Estate Development Services
N.A.I.C.S.: 531390

Xymax Real Estate Investment Advisors Corporation (1)
1-1-1 Akasaka Zymax Akasaka 111 Building, Minato-ku, Tokyo, Japan
Tel.: (81) 355446860
Real Estate Development Services
N.A.I.C.S.: 531390

Xymax Sala Corporation (1)
1-13-10 Tsukiji Shin-Hanwa Building, Chuo-ku, Tokyo, Japan
Tel.: (81) 368590262
Real Estate Development Services
N.A.I.C.S.: 531390

Xymax With Corporation (1)
2-4-2 Nagatacho Zymax Tameike Sanno Building, Chiyoda-ku, Tokyo, Japan
Tel.: (81) 335961425
Real Estate Development Services
N.A.I.C.S.: 531390

XYMAX REIT INVESTMENT CORPORATION

1-1-1 Akasaka Minato-ku, Tokyo, 107-0052, Japan
Tel.: (81) 3 5544 6880
Web Site: http://www.xymaxreit.co.jp
3488—(TKS)
Rev.: $12,519,870
Assets: $364,318,668
Liabilities: $139,392,678
Net Worth: $224,925,990
Earnings: $6,295,252
Fiscal Year-end: 02/28/21
Real Estate Investment Services
N.A.I.C.S.: 531210
Shotaro Kanemitsu (Exec Dir)

XYNOMIC PHARMACEUTICALS HOLDINGS, INC.

Suite 3306 K Wah Centre 1010 Middle Huaihai Road, Shanghai, 200031, China
Tel.: (86) 2154180212 VG
Web Site: https://xynomicpharma.com
Year Founded: 2016
XYNO—(OTCIQ)
Rev.: $2,630
Assets: $937,517
Liabilities: $23,501,338
Net Worth: ($22,563,821)
Earnings: ($25,103,835)
Emp.: 27
Fiscal Year-end: 12/31/19
Biopharmaceutical Company
N.A.I.C.S.: 541714
Yinglin Mark Xu (Chm, Pres & CEO)

Subsidiaries:

Bison Finance Group Limited (1)
6th Floor China Taiping Finance Centre 18 King Wah Road, North Point, China (Hong Kong)
Tel.: (852) 21653000
Web Site: https://www.bison.com.hk
Rev.: $5,222,018
Assets: $26,492,460
Liabilities: $16,384,643
Net Worth: $10,107,818
Earnings: ($15,694,230)
Emp.: 31
Fiscal Year-end: 12/31/2022
Holding Company; Media Sales & Management
N.A.I.C.S.: 551112
Peixin Xu (Founder & Exec Dir)

Subsidiary (Domestic):

RoadShow Creations Limited (2)
No 9 Po Lun Street, KMB Building, Kowloon, China (Hong Kong)
Tel.: (852) 27465200
Web Site: http://www.roadshow.hk
Merchandising
N.A.I.C.S.: 455219

RoadShow Media Holdings Ltd. (2)
No9 Po Lun Street, KMB Building, Kowloon, China (Hong Kong)
Tel.: (852) 27465200
Web Site: http://www.roadshow.com.hk
Holding Company
N.A.I.C.S.: 551112

Subsidiary (Domestic):

Bus Focus Ltd. (3)
9 Po Lun Street 6F, Kowloon, Lai Chi Kok, China (Hong Kong)
Tel.: (852) 2746 8777
Web Site: http://www.roadshow.com.hk
Media Sales
N.A.I.C.S.: 541890

RoadShow Media Ltd. (3)
No9 Po Lun Street KMB Building 6th Fl, Kowloon, Lai Chi Kok, China (Hong Kong)
Tel.: (852) 27465200
Web Site: http://www.roadshow.com.hk
Sales Range: $25-49.9 Million
Emp.: 100
Media Sales
N.A.I.C.S.: 541890

Subsidiary (Domestic):

RoadVision Holdings (China) Limited (2)
6F 9 Po Lun Street, Lai Chi Kok, Kowloon, China (Hong Kong)
Tel.: (852) 2746 5200
Web Site: http://corp.roadshow.com.hk
Holding Company; Media Sales
N.A.I.C.S.: 551112

XYNYTH MANUFACTURING CORP.

122-3989 Henning Drive, Burnaby, V5C 6N5, BC, Canada
Tel.: (604) 473-9343
Web Site: http://www.xynyth.com
Year Founded: 1986
Rev.: $22,817,200
Emp.: 140
Icemelt & Absorbent Products Mfr
N.A.I.C.S.: 325998
Kevin Wice (Pres)

XYZ MACHINE TOOLS LIMITED

Woodlands Business Park, Burlescombe Nr Tiverton, Devon, EX16 7LL, United Kingdom
Tel.: (44) 1823 674 200 UK

AND PRIVATE COMPANIES

Web Site:
http://www.xyzmachinetools.com
Year Founded: 1984
Sales Range: $25-49.9 Million
Emp.: 40
Machine Tool Distr
N.A.I.C.S.: 423830
Nigel Atherton *(Mng Dir)*

Y VENTURES GROUP LTD.
60 Paya Lebar Road 04-54 Paya Lebar Square, Singapore, 409051, Singapore
Tel.: (65) 67499510
Web Site:
https://www.yventures.com.sg
1F1—(CAT)
Rev.: $22,626,872
Assets: $18,797,666
Liabilities: $17,291,566
Net Worth: $1,506,100
Earnings: ($406,708)
Emp.: 19
Fiscal Year-end: 12/31/23
Consumer Products Distr
N.A.I.C.S.: 425120
Adam Yik Sen Low *(Co-Founder & Mng Dir)*

Subsidiaries:

JustNile (SEA) Pte. Ltd. (1)
46 East Coast Road 09-06 Eastgate, Singapore, 482766, Singapore
Tel.: (65) 63440105
Web Site: https://www.shop.justnile.com.sg
Proprietary Data Analytics Publishing Services
N.A.I.C.S.: 513210

JustNile International Corp (1)
No 85 Wen-Wu 2nd St, QianJin Dist, Kaohsiung, 801, Taiwan
Tel.: (886) 72116051
Online Marketplace Services
N.A.I.C.S.: 445110

JustNile Pte. Ltd. (1)
46 East Coast Road 09-06 Eastgate Commercial Building, Singapore, 428766, Singapore
Tel.: (65) 67499510
Online Marketplace Services
N.A.I.C.S.: 445110

Skap Logistics Pte. Ltd. (1)
46 East Coast Road 09-06 East Gate, Singapore, 428766, Singapore
Tel.: (65) 67492306
Web Site: https://www.skaplogistics.com
Logistics Transportation Services
N.A.I.C.S.: 541614

Y&G CORPORATION BERHAD
Lot G-01 Ground Floor Tower B PJ City Development No 15A Jalan 219, Seksyen 51A, 46100, Petaling Jaya, Selangor Darul Ehsan, Malaysia
Tel.: (60) 378761188
Web Site:
https://www.ygcorp.com.my
Y&G—(KLS)
Rev.: $13,722,540
Assets: $81,705,820
Liabilities: $15,541,164
Net Worth: $66,164,656
Earnings: $2,057,566
Emp.: 42
Fiscal Year-end: 12/31/22
Construction Services
N.A.I.C.S.: 531312
Jun Jien Yap *(Exec Dir)*

Subsidiaries:

Kualiti Kinta Sdn. Bhd. (1)
Lot G 01 Ground Floor Tower B PJ City Development No 15 A Jalan 219, Seksyen 51A, 46100, Petaling Jaya, Selangor, Malaysia
Tel.: (60) 378761188
Web Site: https://www.alamaiahomes.com
Real Estate Services

Y'S TABLE CORPORATION
8-10-22 Akasaka, Minato-ku, Tokyo, 107-8460, Japan
Tel.: (81) 354120065
Web Site: https://www.ystable.co.jp
Year Founded: 1999
2798—(TKS)
Rev.: $80,003,560
Assets: $33,429,350
Liabilities: $30,472,820
Net Worth: $2,956,530
Earnings: $801,170
Fiscal Year-end: 02/29/24
Home Management Services
N.A.I.C.S.: 721110

Y-ENTEC CO., LTD.
1232 Yeosusandan-ro, Yeosu, 59614, Jeollanam-do, Korea (South)
Tel.: (82) 619204470
Web Site: http://www.y-entec.co.kr
Year Founded: 1990
067900—(KRS)
Rev.: $94,956,557
Assets: $215,595,271
Liabilities: $62,365,464
Net Worth: $153,229,807
Earnings: $18,894,237
Emp.: 135
Fiscal Year-end: 12/31/22
Waste Treatment Services
N.A.I.C.S.: 221320
Ji Yong Il *(Mng Dir)*

Y-OPTICS MANUFACTURE CO., LTD.
51 Saenggoksandan 1-ro 24beon-gil, Gangseo-gu, Busan, Korea (South)
Tel.: (82) 519727175
066430—(KRS)
Rev.: $28,694,511
Assets: $43,218,027
Liabilities: $14,341,738
Net Worth: $28,876,290
Earnings: $441,639
Emp.: 47
Fiscal Year-end: 12/31/22
Medicinal Product Mfr
N.A.I.C.S.: 339112
Jae Wuk Jeon *(Mng Dir)*

Y. T. REALTY GROUP LIMITED
Rooms 3301-07 China Resources Building 26 Harbour Road, Wanchai, China (Hong Kong)
Tel.: (852) 25005555   BM
Web Site:
http://www.ytrealtygroup.com.hk
0075—(HKG)
Rev.: $345,137,783
Assets: $2,337,223,538
Liabilities: $2,225,195,535
Net Worth: $112,028,003
Earnings: ($87,289,178)
Emp.: 83
Fiscal Year-end: 12/31/22
Property Investment Services
N.A.I.C.S.: 531390
Chung Kiu Cheung *(Mng Dir)*

Y.A.C. HOLDINGS CO., LTD.
3-11-10 Musashino, Akishima, Tokyo, 196-0021, Japan
Tel.: (81) 425461161   JP
Web Site: https://www.yac.co.jp
Year Founded: 1973
6298—(TKS)
Rev.: $177,207,490
Assets: $289,696,470
Liabilities: $177,399,180
Net Worth: $112,297,290
Earnings: $9,366,370
Fiscal Year-end: 03/31/24
Holding Company; Industrial Electronics Mfr
N.A.I.C.S.: 551112
Toshihiko Ito *(Deputy Gen Mgr-Bus Mgmt, Deputy Gen Mgr-Bus Mgmt, Sr Mng Operating Officer & Sr Mng Operating Officer)*

Subsidiaries:

HYAC Corporation (1)
46722 Fremont Blvd, Fremont, CA 94538-6573
Tel.: (510) 623-0700
Web Site: http://www.hyac.com
Automation System Mfr
N.A.I.C.S.: 334513

Y.A.C. CO. LTD. - FEL Division (1)
3-11-10 Musashino, Tokyo, 196-0021, Japan
Tel.: (81) 425462885
Electron Emitters Mfr
N.A.I.C.S.: 334413

Y.A.C. CO. LTD. - Memory Disk Division (1)
3-11-10 Musashino, Akishima, 196-0021, Tokyo, Japan
Tel.: (81) 425468481
Web Site: http://www.yac.co.jp
Emp.: 40
Semiconductor Systems Mfr
N.A.I.C.S.: 334413

Y.A.C. CO. LTD. - Plasma Etching & Ashing Manufacturing Unit (1)
Kushigata Kougyou Danchi, Shimo Ichinose, Minami-Alps, 400-0314, Yamanashi, Japan
Tel.: (81) 552838010
Web Site: http://www.yac.co.jp
Emp.: 10
Plasma Mfr
N.A.I.C.S.: 325998

Y.A.C. CO. LTD. - Semiconductor Division (1)
84 Ohzu Ohzu-machi, Kikuchi-Gun, Kumamoto, 869-1233, Japan
Tel.: (81) 962941700
Web Site: http://www.yac.co.jp
Emp.: 50
Semiconductor Devices Mfr
N.A.I.C.S.: 334413

YAC Niigata Seiki Co., Ltd. (1)
3-24 Nakagawa, Myoko-shi, Niigata, 944-0005, Japan
Tel.: (81) 255723151
Cleaning Product Mfr
N.A.I.C.S.: 334513

YAC Systems Singapore Pte Ltd. (1)
No 9 Kaki Bukit Rd 1 02-06 07 08 09 Eunos Technolink, Singapore, 415938, Singapore
Tel.: (65) 67488007
Emp.: 15
Machine Tools Mfr
N.A.I.C.S.: 333517
Masato Yamada *(Deputy Mng Dir)*

Y.C.C. PARTS MFG. CO., LTD.
No 8 Xingye Rd Lukang Town, Chung Hua, Hsien, 505, Taiwan
Tel.: (886) 47810781
Web Site: https://www.yccco.com.tw
Year Founded: 1986
1339—(TAI)
Rev.: $67,079,006
Assets: $177,203,303
Liabilities: $45,022,367
Net Worth: $132,180,936
Earnings: $14,142,516
Emp.: 280
Fiscal Year-end: 12/31/23
Automotive Plastic Parts Mfr
N.A.I.C.S.: 336390
Shi Yun Lin *(Pres)*

Y.H.DIMRI BUILDING & DEVELOPMENT LTD.
1 Jerusalem St, Netivot, Israel
Tel.: (972) 89939000
Web Site: https://www.dimri.co.il
Year Founded: 1989

Y.S.P. SOUTHEAST ASIA HOLDING BERHAD

DIMRI—(TAE)
Rev.: $384,998,373
Assets: $1,559,489,995
Liabilities: $1,066,326,392
Net Worth: $493,163,603
Earnings: $74,233,230
Emp.: 197
Fiscal Year-end: 12/31/22
Building Construction Services
N.A.I.C.S.: 236220
Yigal Dimri *(CEO)*

Y.H.O CO., LTD.
94/2 Inya Road Kamayut Township, Yangon, Myanmar
Tel.: (95) 1534473
Web Site:
http://www.myholdingmyanmar.com
Year Founded: 1990
Holding Company
N.A.I.C.S.: 551112
U. Ye Myint *(CEO)*

Subsidiaries:

M.Y Associates Co., Ltd. (1)
94/2 Inya Road Kamayut Township, Yangon, Myanmar
Tel.: (95) 1534473
Web Site:
http://www.myholdingmyanmar.com
Machinery Equipment & Parts Distr
N.A.I.C.S.: 425120
U. Ye Myint *(CEO)*

Y.S. FOOD CO., LTD.
552-8 Kanayama Kagamiyama Kawara-machi, Tagawa-gun, Fukuoka, 822-1402, Japan
Tel.: (81) 947327382
Web Site: https://www.ys-food.jp
Year Founded: 1994
3358—(TKS)
Sales Range: $10-24.9 Million
Restaurant Operators
N.A.I.C.S.: 722511
Masanori Ogata *(Board of Directors & Pres)*

Y.S.P. SOUTHEAST ASIA HOLDING BERHAD
Level 22 Menara LGB No 1 Jalan Wan Kadir, Taman Tun Dr Ismail, 60000, Kuala Lumpur, Malaysia
Tel.: (60) 377276390
Web Site: https://www.yspsah.com
YSPSAH—(KLS)
Rev.: $70,740,317
Assets: $100,326,984
Liabilities: $20,332,275
Net Worth: $79,994,709
Earnings: $7,359,365
Emp.: 1,138
Fiscal Year-end: 12/31/22
Pharmaceuticals Product Mfr
N.A.I.C.S.: 236210
Anis Ahmad *(Chm)*

Subsidiaries:

Alpha Active Industries Sdn. Bhd. (1)
No 3 Jalan PPU 2 Taman Perindustrian Puchong Utama, 47100, Puchong, Selangor Darul Ehsan, Malaysia
Tel.: (60) 380667763
Web Site: https://www.oem-aai.com
Food Products Distr
N.A.I.C.S.: 424490

PT Yung Shin Pharmaceutical Indonesia (1)
Foresta Business Loft 1 Unit No 31 BSD City Jalan BSD Raya Utama, Kecamatan Pagedangan Kabupaten, Tangerang, 15339, Banten, Indonesia
Tel.: (62) 2150556265
Web Site: https://id.yspsah.com
Industrial Building Construction Services
N.A.I.C.S.: 236210

Y.S.P. SOUTHEAST ASIA HOLDING BERHAD

Y.S.P. Southeast Asia Holding Berhad—(Continued)

Sun Ten (Singapore) Private Limited (1)
No 10 UBI Crescent 06-58 UBI Techpark, Singapore, 408564, Singapore
Tel.: (65) 67426616
Web Site: https://www.sunten.com.sg
Emp.: 8
Medicine & Health Products Whslr
N.A.I.C.S.: 424210

Y.S.P. (Cambodia) Pte. Ltd. (1)
19 St Mong Rithy Sangkat Phnom Penh Thmey, Khan Sen Sok, Phnom Penh, 120801, Cambodia
Tel.: (855) 12594318
Web Site: https://www.yspsah.com
Emp.: 3
Pharmaceutical Products Distr
N.A.I.C.S.: 424210

Y.S.P. Industries (M) Sdn. Bhd. (1)
Level 22 Menara LGB No 1 Jalan Wan Kadir Taman Tun Dr Ismail, 60000, Kuala Lumpur, Federal Territory, Malaysia
Tel.: (60) 377276390
Emp.: 120
Pharmaceutical Products Mfr & Distr
N.A.I.C.S.: 325412
Grace Yap (VP)

Plant (Domestic):

Y.S.P. Industries (M) Sdn. Bhd. - cGMP Factory (2)
Lot 5 & 7 Jalan P/7 Section 13 Kawasan Perindustrian, Bandar Baru Bangi, 43000, Kajang, Selangor, Malaysia
Tel.: (60) 389251215
Web Site: http://www.yspsah.com
Emp.: 500
Pharmaceuticals Product Mfr
N.A.I.C.S.: 325412

Y.S.P. Industries Vietnam Co., Ltd. (1)
82-84 Ha Huy Tap Phu My Hung, Tan Phong Ward Distric 7, Ho Chi Minh City, Vietnam
Tel.: (84) 2854122545
Web Site: https://www.vn.yspsah.com
Food Products Distr
N.A.I.C.S.: 424490

Yung Shin (Philippines), Inc. (1)
4th Floor Cacho-Gonzales Building 101 Aguirre Street, Legaspi Village, Makati, 1229, Philippines
Tel.: (63) 28928185
Emp.: 7
Pharmaceutical Products Mfr & Distr
N.A.I.C.S.: 325412

Yung Shin Pharm Ind (Kungshan) Co., Ltd. (1)
Lujia Jinyang West Road No 191, Kunshan, Jiangsu, China
Tel.: (86) 51257675190
Web Site: http://www.ysp.com.cn
Pharmaceutical & Medicine Mfr
N.A.I.C.S.: 325412

Yung Shin Pharmaceutical (Singapore) Pte. Ltd. (1)
10 Ubi Crescent 06 57/58 Ubi Techpark, Singapore, 408564, Singapore
Tel.: (65) 67412466
Web Site: https://www.yungshingroup.com
Emp.: 25
Pharmaceutical Products Distr
N.A.I.C.S.: 424210

Yung Zip Chemical Ind. Co., Ltd. (1)
59 61 You Shih Road, Youth Industrial District Dajia, Taichung, 43767, Taiwan
Tel.: (886) 426818866
Web Site: https://www.yungzip.com
Veterinary Drug Mfr
N.A.I.C.S.: 325412

Y.U.D YANGTZE RIVER INVESTMENT INDUSTRY CO., LTD.
4th Floor Building 6 No 89 Jiajie Road, Qingpu District, Shanghai, 201703, China
Tel.: (86) 2166601801
Web Site: https://www.cjtz.cn
Year Founded: 1997
600119—(SHG)
Rev.: $178,529,256
Assets: $108,620,418
Liabilities: $58,421,030
Net Worth: $50,199,388
Earnings: ($1,995,042)
Fiscal Year-end: 12/31/22
Logistics Management Services
N.A.I.C.S.: 541614
Lu Guofeng (Chm)

Y2 SOLUTION CO., LTD.
Room No 212 971 Sicheong-ro, Paltan-myeon, Hwaseong, Gyeonggi-do, Korea (South)
Tel.: (82) 313507400
Web Site: https://www.y2solution.com
Year Founded: 1976
011690—(KRS)
Rev.: $92,437,662
Assets: $97,107,562
Liabilities: $33,830,199
Net Worth: $63,277,364
Earnings: ($1,698,223)
Emp.: 115
Fiscal Year-end: 12/31/22
Chemical Engineering Services
N.A.I.C.S.: 541330
Choi Gwang (Sr Mgr-Display)

Subsidiaries:

Qingdao Yuyang Electronics Co., Ltd. (1)
No 93 Jiujiang Road Laixi Economic Development Zone, Qingdao, China
Tel.: (86) 53266893752
Electronic Products Mfr
N.A.I.C.S.: 334419

YA HORNG ELECTRONIC CO., LTD.
No 35 Shalun, Anding Dist, Tainan City, 745, Taiwan
Tel.: (886) 65932201
Web Site: https://www.yahorng.com
Year Founded: 1972
6201—(TAI)
Rev.: $111,392,782
Assets: $121,059,840
Liabilities: $30,929,068
Net Worth: $90,130,773
Earnings: $13,519,408
Emp.: 1,577
Fiscal Year-end: 12/31/23
Juice Extractor Mfr
N.A.I.C.S.: 333241
Cihuang Huang (Chm)

Subsidiaries:

Kunitakara Electric Co., Ltd. (1)
No 185 Industrial 11th Road, Dali, Taichung, 41279, Taiwan
Tel.: (886) 424912151
Web Site: http://www.kunitakara.com.tw
Emp.: 80
Household Appliances Mfr
N.A.I.C.S.: 333415

Subsidiary (Non-US):

Zhong Shan Kunitakara Electric Ltd. (2)
No 5 Sheng Ping North Road, Nantouzheng, Zhongshan, 528400, Guangdong, China
Tel.: (86) 760 23130270
Web Site: http://www.kunitakara.com.tw
Household Appliances Mfr
N.A.I.C.S.: 335220

Ya Horng (Dongguan) Electronic Co., Ltd. (1)
188 Industrial District Ping Shan Administrative District, Tang Shia Town, Dongguan, 511746, Guangdong, China
Tel.: (86) 769 8685 1766
Web Site: http://www.yahorng.com
Household Appliances Mfr
N.A.I.C.S.: 334310

Ya Horng (HK) Electronic Co., Ltd. (1)
Room 1608 16F Rightful Centre 11-12 Tak Hing Street, Kowloon, China (Hong Kong)
Tel.: (852) 23815378
Web Site: http://www.yahorng.com
Emp.: 164
Household Appliances Mfr
N.A.I.C.S.: 335210

YA ZHU SILK, INC.
Suite 1002 10/F Fang Da Building, Nanshan Science & Hi-Tech Park, Nanshan District, Shenzhen, 518057, China
Tel.: (86) 755 8668 1130 NV
Year Founded: 2008
Sales Range: $1-9.9 Million
Mobile Devices Mfr & Distr
N.A.I.C.S.: 334220

YA'ACOBI BROTHERS GROUP (YSB) LTD.
28 Moshe Sharet, Rishon le Zion, Israel
Tel.: (972) 39537111
Web Site: https://www.ysbgroup.com
Year Founded: 1974
YAAC—(TAE)
Rev.: $95,270,063
Assets: $138,034,257
Liabilities: $78,180,687
Net Worth: $59,853,570
Earnings: ($1,262,053)
Fiscal Year-end: 12/31/23
Commercial & Institutional Building Construction
N.A.I.C.S.: 236220

YA-MAN, LTD.
1-4-4 Furuishiba, Koto-ku, Tokyo, 135-0045, Japan
Tel.: (81) 336402166
Web Site: https://www.ya-man.com
Year Founded: 1978
6630—(TKS)
Rev.: $211,672,030
Assets: $192,284,900
Liabilities: $26,287,970
Net Worth: $165,996,930
Earnings: $2,630,780
Emp.: 432
Fiscal Year-end: 04/30/24
Household Electrical Devices & Beauty Products Mfr
N.A.I.C.S.: 335210
Kimiyo Yamazaki (CEO)

YAARI DIGITAL INTEGRATED SERVICES LIMITED
5th floor Plot No 108 IT Park Udyog Vihar Phase 1, Elphinstone Road, Mumbai, 400013, India
Tel.: (91) 2262498580 In
Web Site: https://yaari.com
Year Founded: 2007
YAARI—(NSE)
Rev.: $22,288,832
Assets: $4,506,924
Liabilities: $31,249,925
Net Worth: ($26,743,001)
Earnings: $11,372,220
Emp.: 3
Fiscal Year-end: 03/31/23
Investment Holding Company
N.A.I.C.S.: 551112
Mavinder Singh Walia (Exec Dir)

YABAO PHARMACEUTICAL GROUP CO., LTD.
No 1 Industrial Avenue Fenglingdu Economic Development Zone, Yuncheng, 044602, Shanxi, China
Tel.: (86) 3593388114
Web Site: https://www.yabao.com.cn
Year Founded: 1978

INTERNATIONAL PUBLIC

600351—(SHG)
Rev.: $381,626,126
Assets: $580,001,821
Liabilities: $157,869,284
Net Worth: $422,132,537
Earnings: 14,693,576
Emp.: 5,600
Fiscal Year-end: 12/31/22
Pharmaceutical Product Mfr & Whslr
N.A.I.C.S.: 325412
Wuxian Ren (Chm & Mgr)

YADEA GROUP HOLDINGS LTD
31/F Tower Two Times Square 1 Matheson Street, Causeway Bay, China (Hong Kong)
Tel.: (852) 51088100267 Ky
Web Site: http://www.yadea.com.cn
1585—(HKG)
Rev.: $4,360,745,797
Assets: $3,503,357,114
Liabilities: $2,570,736,917
Net Worth: $932,620,198
Earnings: $306,493,200
Emp.: 11,825
Fiscal Year-end: 12/31/22
Electric Vehicle Mfr & Distr
N.A.I.C.S.: 336320
Jinggui Dong (Co-Founder & Chm)

Subsidiaries:

Viet Nam Yadea Electric Motorcycle Co., Ltd. (1)
No 24/24bis Dong Du Street, Ben Nghe Ward District 1, Ho Chi Minh City, Vietnam
Tel.: (84) 18006959
Web Site: https://www.yadeavietnam.vn
Electric Motorcycle Part Mfr
N.A.I.C.S.: 336991

YADONG GROUP HOLDINGS LIMITED
No 381 Laodong East Road, Tianning, Changzhou, Jiangsu, China
Tel.: (86) 18206126618 Ky
Web Site: http://www.yadongtextile.com
Year Founded: 2011
1795—(HKG)
Holding Company
N.A.I.C.S.: 551112
Shidong Xue (Chm)

YADRAN-OIL GROUP
Privolnaya-2 str bld 33A, 420043, Kazan, Russia
Tel.: (7) 8435006000
Web Site: http://yadrangroup.com
Year Founded: 2008
Oil & Petroleum Products Wholesale Trade Agency
N.A.I.C.S.: 425120
Irek Salikhov (Chm)

Subsidiaries:

Astana Solar LLP (1)
Turan Avenue, Nur-Sultan, 010000, Kazakhstan
Tel.: (7) 7172 551400
Web Site: http://astanasolar.kz
Solar Module Mfr
N.A.I.C.S.: 334413

Kazakhstan Solar Silicon LLP (1)
st Sogrinskaya 223/6, Ust-Kamenogorsk, Oskemen, East Kazakhstan, Kazakhstan
Tel.: (7) 23 220 4150
Web Site: http://www.kazsolarsilicon.kz
Photovoltaic Silicon Cells Mfr
N.A.I.C.S.: 334413
Baizhumin Daniyar Anuarbekovich (Gen Dir)

MK KazSilicon LLP (1)
Komarova St 1, Karatal District, Bastobe, 041011, Almaty Region, Kazakhstan
Tel.: (7) 283440373
Web Site: http://www.kazsilicon.kz
Metallurgical & Polycrystalline Silicon Mfr & Whslr

AND PRIVATE COMPANIES — YAGUANG TECHNOLOGY GROUP COMPANY LIMITED

N.A.I.C.S.: 331110

YAGAMI, INC.
2-29 Marunouchi 3-chome, Naka-Ku,
Nagoya, 460-0002, Japan
Tel.: (81) 529519251
Web Site: https://www.yagami-inc.co.jp
7488—(NGO)
Rev.: $98,494,000
Assets: $159,371,520
Liabilities: $41,536,880
Net Worth: $117,834,640
Earnings: $10,076,880
Fiscal Year-end: 04/30/21
Scientific Equipment Distr
N.A.I.C.S.: 423490
Keisuke Kobayashi (Pres)

YAGEO CORPORATION
3F 233-1 Baoqiao Rd, Xindian Dist,
Taipei, 23145, Taiwan
Tel.: (886) 266299999
Web Site: https://www.yageo.com
Year Founded: 1977
YAGEA—(LUX)
Rev.: $3,519,059,876
Assets: $10,835,968,000
Liabilities: $6,368,243,718
Net Worth: $4,467,724,283
Earnings: $574,269,542
Emp.: 24,079
Fiscal Year-end: 12/31/23
Capacitors, Resistors, Inductors & Related Equipment Mfr
N.A.I.C.S.: 334416
Pierre T. M. Chen (Chm & Co-CEO)

Subsidiaries:

Chilisin Electronics Corp. (1)
No 29 Lane 301 Tehhsin Rd Hukou, Hsinchu, 303, Taiwan **(88.5%)**
Tel.: (886) 35992646
Web Site: http://www.chilisin.com
Rev.: $527,696,253
Assets: $1,337,893,284
Liabilities: $552,581,185
Net Worth: $785,312,099
Earnings: $38,147,891
Fiscal Year-end: 12/31/2019
Magnetic Materials & Inductors Mfr
N.A.I.C.S.: 334416

Subsidiary (Non-US):

ASJ Components (M) Sdn. Bhd. (2)
PTD 37440 Jalan Perindustrian Senai 3,
Kawansan Peridunstrian Senai Fasa 2,
81400, Senai, Johor, Malaysia
Tel.: (60) 7 597 7800
Electronic Resistor Mfr
N.A.I.C.S.: 334416

Chilisin Asia Investment Limited (2)
Dongyang Trebellepark 903ho 1598-1
Kwanyang-dong, Dongan-gu, Anyang, 430-010, Kyunggi-do, Korea (South)
Tel.: (82) 313848433
Electronic Components Distr
N.A.I.C.S.: 423690

Chilisin Electronics Singapore Pte. Ltd. (2)
19 Woodlands Industrial Park E1 03-07,
Singapore, Singapore
Tel.: (65) 68921191
Web Site: http://www.chilisin.com.sg
Electronic Components Mfr
N.A.I.C.S.: 334416

Chilisin International Ltd. (2)
Units 1-3 7-10 8F Prosperity Centre 25
Chong Yip Street, Kwun Tong, Kowloon,
China (Hong Kong)
Tel.: (852) 26871975
Web Site: http://www.chilisin.com.tw
Electronic Components Mfr
N.A.I.C.S.: 334416

Dongguan Chilisin Electronics Co., Ltd. (2)
Yuliangwei Administration Area, Qingzi Town, Dongguan, 523000, Guangdong, China
Tel.: (86) 76987730251
Inductors Mfr
N.A.I.C.S.: 334416

Subsidiary (US):

Mag Layers USA, Inc. (2)
5406 Bolsa Ave, Huntington Beach, CA 92649
Tel.: (714) 898-8377
Web Site: https://www.maglayersusa.com
Electronic Components Mfr
N.A.I.C.S.: 334419

Subsidiary (Domestic):

Magic Wireless Technology Co., Ltd. (2)
15F No 716 Chung Cheng Rd, Chung Ho District, New Taipei City, Taiwan
Tel.: (886) 28 227 3366
Web Site: https://www.magictec.com.tw
Electrical Equipment Component Mfr
N.A.I.C.S.: 335999

Ferroxcube International Holding B.V. (1)
Produktieweg 1C, 6045 JC, Roermond, Netherlands
Tel.: (31) 475385301
Web Site: http://www.ferroxcube.com
Emp.: 2
Holding Company; Ferrite Components Mfr & Sales
N.A.I.C.S.: 334419

Subsidiary (US):

Ferroxcube USA Inc. (2)
1200 Golden Key Cir Ste 233, El Paso, TX 79925-5820
Tel.: (915) 599-2328
Web Site: http://www.ferroxcube.com
Supplier of Ferrite Components & Accessories
N.A.I.C.S.: 423690

KEMET Corporation (1)
KEMET Tower 1 E Broward Blvd, Fort Lauderdale, FL 33301
Tel.: (954) 766-2800
Web Site: http://www.kemet.com
Rev.: $1,260,554,000
Assets: $1,393,097,000
Liabilities: $745,835,000
Net Worth: $647,262,000
Earnings: $41,381,000
Emp.: 12,450
Fiscal Year-end: 03/31/2020
Tantalum & Multilayer Ceramic Capacitors & Solid Aluminum Capacitors Mfr
N.A.I.C.S.: 334416
Frank G. Brandenberg (Chm)

Subsidiary (Domestic):

KEMET Electronics Corporation (2)
2835 Kemet Way, Simpsonville, SC 29681-6202 **(100%)**
Tel.: (864) 963-6300
Web Site: http://www.kemet.com
Sales Range: $100-124.9 Million
Mfr & Supplier of Solid Tantalum & Multilayered Ceramic Capacitors
N.A.I.C.S.: 334416

Subsidiary (Domestic):

KEMET Blue Powder Corporation (3)
16 Bruce Way, Mound House, NV 89706
Tel.: (775) 246-4480
Web Site: http://www.kemet.com
Emp.: 72
Tantalum Mfr
N.A.I.C.S.: 212290

Subsidiary (Non-US):

KEMET Electronics Asia Limited (3)
Flat 3007 34 Tower 2 Gateway, Kowloon, China (Hong Kong) **(100%)**
Tel.: (852) 23051168
Web Site: http://www.kemet.com
Sales Range: $25-49.9 Million
Emp.: 37
Sale of Capacitors
N.A.I.C.S.: 423690

KEMET Electronics Italia S.r.l. (3)
Via Sagittario 1/3, Sasso Marconi, 40037, Bologna, Italy
Tel.: (39) 051939111
Web Site: http://www.kemet.com
Electronic Capacitor Mfr
N.A.I.C.S.: 334416

KEMET Electronics Limited (3)
Units 16-20 Oxford Court Cambridge Road, Grandby Industrial Estate, Weymouth, DT4 9GH, Dorset, United Kingdom **(100%)**
Tel.: (44) 1305782871
Sales Range: $50-74.9 Million
Emp.: 150
Electronic Parts Sales
N.A.I.C.S.: 423690
Per Loose (CEO)

KEMET Electronics Oy (3)
Stella Business Park Lars Sonckin kaari 16, Espoo, 02600, Finland
Tel.: (358) 954065001
Web Site: http://www.kemet.com
Sales Range: $10-24.9 Million
Emp.: 6
Electronic Capacitor Mfr
N.A.I.C.S.: 334416

KEMET Electronics S.A. (3)
Chemen Des Menes 16b, PO Box 76, 1202, Geneva, Switzerland **(100%)**
Tel.: (41) 227150100
Sales Range: $10-24.9 Million
Emp.: 14
Sale of Capacitors
N.A.I.C.S.: 423690

NEC TOKIN Corporation (3)
Chiyoda First Bldg 8-1, Nishi-Kanda 3-chome Chiyoda-ku, Tokyo, 101-8362, Japan **(100%)**
Tel.: (81) 335159224
Web Site: http://www.nec-tokin.com
Emp.: 6,505
Electronic Computer Mfr
N.A.I.C.S.: 334111

Shanghai Arcotronics Components & Machineries Co., Ltd. (3)
No 55 Taifeng Road, Anting Town, Shanghai, 201814, Jiading, China
Tel.: (86) 2159501070
Sales Range: $25-49.9 Million
Emp.: 190
Electronic Capacitor Mfr
N.A.I.C.S.: 334416

Subsidiary (Non-US):

KEMET de Mexico, S.A. de C.V. (2)
Antiguo Camino al Mezquital #100 San Nicolas de los Garza, Nuevo Leon, 66490, Mexico **(100%)**
Tel.: (52) 81 83297900
Web Site: http://www.kemet.com
Sales Range: $10-24.9 Million
Emp.: 2,000
Mfr & Supplier of Solid Tantalum & Multilayered Ceramic Capacitors
N.A.I.C.S.: 334416

TOKIN Electronics (Vietnam) Co. Ltd. (2)
Lot A5-A6 Street 4th Long Binh Techno Park Loteco EPZ, Long Binh Ward, Bien Hoa, Dong Nai, Vietnam
Tel.: (84) 2513891970
Web Site: http://www.tokin.com.vn
Electronic Components Mfr
N.A.I.C.S.: 334416

TOKIN Hong Kong Ltd. (2)
Suite 1606 16/F Silvercord Tower 1 30 Canton Road, Tsim Tsa Tsui, Kowloon, China (Hong Kong)
Tel.: (852) 23051168
Electronic Components Mfr
N.A.I.C.S.: 334416

Subsidiary (Domestic):

The Forest Electric Company (2)
1301 W Armitage Ave Ste B, Melrose Park, IL 60160
Tel.: (708) 681-0180
Web Site: http://www.kemet.com
Electronic Transformer & Capacitor Mfr
N.A.I.C.S.: 334416

Yageo Europe B.V. (1)
Suskindstrasse 4, 81929, Munich, Germany
Tel.: (49) 8985 840 3700
Electronic Components Mfr
N.A.I.C.S.: 334419

Yageo Hong Kong Limited (1)
Room 7 1F South Seas Centre Tower 2 No 75 Mody Road East, Tsim Sha Tsui, Kowloon, China (Hong Kong)
Tel.: (852) 2 342 6833
Electronic Components Mfr
N.A.I.C.S.: 334419

Yageo Hungary Kft. (1)
Vasarter u 2, 9700, Szombathely, Hungary
Tel.: (36) 9 451 7702
Electronic Components Mfr
N.A.I.C.S.: 334419

Yageo Italy S.R.L. (1)
Viale Brianza 20, 20092, Cinisello Balsamo, Milan, Italy
Tel.: (39) 026 129 1017
Electronic Components Mfr
N.A.I.C.S.: 334419

Yageo Suzhou Co., Ltd. (1)
No 158 Jinchang Rd Building 1, Nan Bing Industrial Zone Mu Du New District, Suzhou, 215101, China
Electronic Components Mfr
N.A.I.C.S.: 334419

YAGI & CO., LTD.
2-2-8 Kyutaromachi, Chuo-ku, Osaka, 540-8660, Japan
Tel.: (81) 662667300
Web Site: https://www.yaginet.co.jp
Year Founded: 1918
7460—(TKS)
Rev.: $547,612,060
Assets: $489,582,870
Liabilities: $224,918,470
Net Worth: $264,664,400
Earnings: $13,715,750
Emp.: 762
Fiscal Year-end: 03/31/24
Textile Whslr
N.A.I.C.S.: 314999
Tetsuya Hamada (Sr Exec Officer)

Subsidiaries:

Yagi Tsusho (1)
1450 Broadway 2010, New York, NY 10018
Tel.: (212) 354-6729
Web Site: http://www.yagitsu.co.jp
Emp.: 8
Textiles Exporter
N.A.I.C.S.: 313310
Yuzo Yagi (Chm, Pres & CEO)

YAGUANG TECHNOLOGY GROUP COMPANY LIMITED
Yaguang Technology Park No 1820 Yuelu West Avenue, Yuanjiang, Changsha, 413100, Hunan, China
Tel.: (86) 4008888355
Web Site: https://www.ygkjgroup.com
Year Founded: 2003
300123—(SSE)
Rev.: $236,776,176
Assets: $955,631,196
Liabilities: $548,221,284
Net Worth: $407,409,912
Earnings: ($168,679,368)
Fiscal Year-end: 12/31/22
Yacht Mfr
N.A.I.C.S.: 336612
Li Yuexian (Chm)

Subsidiaries:

Changsha Sunbird Yacht LLC (1)
Lugu High-tech Development Zone, Changsha, 410000, China
Tel.: (86) 73188818888
Yacht Mfr & Distr
N.A.I.C.S.: 336612

Raphael S.R.L. (1)
Via Principe Amedeo 41, 70121, Bari, Italy
Tel.: (39) 0805210631
Web Site: https://raphael1966.com
Apparel & Footwear Distr
N.A.I.C.S.: 424340

YAHAGI CONSTRUCTION CO., LTD.

YaGuang Technology Group Company Limited—(Continued)

YAHAGI CONSTRUCTION CO., LTD.
3-19-7 Aoi, Higashi-ku, Nagoya, 4610004, Aichi, Japan
Tel.: (81) 529352351
Web Site: https://www.yahagi.co.jp
1870—(TKS)
Rev: $792,036,640
Assets: $832,860,000
Liabilities: $393,043,820
Net Worth: $439,816,180
Earnings: $42,713,820
Emp.: 1,324
Fiscal Year-end: 03/31/24
Construction & Real Estate Services
N.A.I.C.S.: 236220
Eiji Hayashi *(Exec Officer)*

Subsidiaries:

NANSHIN TAKAMORI KAIHATSU CO.,LTD. (1)
6955-23 Yamabuki Takamori-cho, Shimoina-gun, Nagano, 399-3101, Japan
Tel.: (81) 265353355
Golf Course Management Services
N.A.I.C.S.: 713910

PITACOLUMN CO.,LTD. (1)
No 19 No 7 Center Aoi Higashi-ku Nagoya Aoi Third Street, Nagoya, 461-0004, Aichi, Japan
Tel.: (81) 52 935 2485
Web Site: http://www.pita.co.jp
Civil Engineering Services
N.A.I.C.S.: 541330

TECHNO SUPPORT CO., LTD. (1)
3-19-7 Aoi, Higashi-ku, Nagoya, 461-0004, Aichi, Japan
Tel.: (81) 529352485
Web Site: https://www.techno-sp.co.jp
Civil Engineering & Real Estate Services
N.A.I.C.S.: 531312

WOODPITA CO., LTD. (1)
Aoi 3-19-7 Aoi Center Building 1F, Higashi-ku, Nagoya, 461-0004, Aichi, Japan
Tel.: (81) 529393550
Civil Engineering & Construction Services
N.A.I.C.S.: 541330

YAHAGI AOI BUILDING CO.,LTD. (1)
3-22-5 Aoi, Higashi-ku, Nagoya, 461-0004, Aichi, Japan
Tel.: (81) 529362575
Web Site: http://www.yahagiaoi.co.jp
Civil Engineering & Real Estate Services
N.A.I.C.S.: 531312

YAHAGI GREEN CO.,LTD. (1)
Aoi Center Building 3-19-7 Aoi, Higashi-ku, Nagoya, 461-0004, Aichi, Japan
Tel.: (81) 529376551
Web Site: https://www.yahagi-green.co.jp
Civil Engineering & Real Estate Services
N.A.I.C.S.: 531312
Suzuki Nobuyoshi *(Pres)*

YAHAGI JISHO CO., LTD. (1)
3-19-7 Aoi, Higashi-ku, Nagoya, 461-0004, Aichi, Japan
Tel.: (81) 529377223
Emp.: 50
Civil Engineering & Real Estate Management Services
N.A.I.C.S.: 531312

YAHAGI ROAD CO.,LTD. (1)
1-5-10 Kozakahonmachi, Yahagi Toyota Building, Toyota, 471-0034, Aichi, Japan
Tel.: (81) 565361112
Web Site: https://www.yahagiroad.co.jp
Emp.: 90
Civil Engineering & Real Estate Services
N.A.I.C.S.: 531312

YAIZU SUISANKAGAKU INDUSTRY CO., LTD.
11-1 Surugaku-minamichou, Shizuoka, 422-8067, Japan
Tel.: (81) 35 718 7001
Web Site: http://www.yskf.jp
Year Founded: 1959
2812—(TKS)
Rev: $117,311,920
Assets: $212,747,040
Liabilities: $25,593,920
Net Worth: $187,153,120
Earnings: $7,327,760
Emp.: 184
Fiscal Year-end: 03/31/22
Food Product Mfr & Whslr
N.A.I.C.S.: 311423
Jun Yamada *(Pres)*

YAK & YETI HOTEL LTD.
Durbar Marg, GPO Box no 1016, Kathmandu, Nepal
Tel.: (977) 14248999   NP
Web Site: https://www.yakandyeti.com
Home Management Services
N.A.I.C.S.: 721110
Radheshyam Saraf *(Chm)*

YAKINIKU SAKAI HOLDINGS, INC.
2-46 Kurokawa Hondori, Kita-ku, Nagoya, 462-0841, Aichi, Japan
Tel.: (81) 529101729
Web Site: https://ys-holdings.co.jp
Year Founded: 1959
2694—(TKS)
Rev: $150,820,370
Assets: $106,196,260
Liabilities: $56,885,660
Net Worth: $49,310,600
Earnings: $1,553,350
Emp.: 4,648
Fiscal Year-end: 03/31/24
Food Processing Services
N.A.I.C.S.: 311999
Hideo Sugimoto *(Chm & Pres)*

YAKKYO S.P.A.
Via Marsala 29H, 00185, Rome, RM, Italy
Tel.: (39) 0802223904
Web Site: https://www.yakkyofy.com
Year Founded: 2016
YKY—(ITA)
Online Shopping Services
N.A.I.C.S.: 425120

YAKOVLEV CORPORATION
68 Leningradsky prospect, 125315, Moscow, 125315, Russia
Tel.: (7) 4957772101
Web Site: https://yakovlev.ru
Year Founded: 1932
IRKT—(MOEX)
Sales Range: $1-4.9 Billion
Emp.: 15,000
Aircraft Mfr
N.A.I.C.S.: 336411
Alexey I. Fedorov *(Chm)*

Subsidiaries:

ZAO Irkut AviaSTEP (1)
Bldg 1 Leningradsky Prospect, Moscow, 125315, Russia
Tel.: (7) 4957772101
Aircraft Hardware Mfr
N.A.I.C.S.: 336413

YAKULT HONSHA CO., LTD.
1-10-30 Kaigan, Minato-ku, Tokyo, 105-8660, Japan
Tel.: (81) 366258960   JP
Web Site: https://www.yakult.co.jp
Year Founded: 1935
YKH—(DEU)
Rev: $3,463,619,070
Assets: $5,373,334,230
Liabilities: $1,462,120,740
Net Worth: $3,911,213,490
Earnings: $363,095,970
Emp.: 29,880
Fiscal Year-end: 03/31/23
Fermented Lactic Drinks, Fruit Juices, Soft Drinks, Pharmaceuticals & Cosmetics Mfr
N.A.I.C.S.: 325412
Hiroshi Narita *(Pres)*

Subsidiaries:

Distribujdora Yakult Gadarajara, S.A.De C.V. (1)
Av Periferico Poniente Manuel Gomez Morin No 7425, Colonia Vallarta Parque Industrial, 45010, Zapopan, Jalisco, Mexico
Tel.: (52) 333 134 5300
Web Site: https://www.yakult.mx
Healthy Food Mfr
N.A.I.C.S.: 311999

Guangzhou Yakult Co., Ltd. (1)
3rd Floor Building A No 488 Dalingshan Road, Tianhe District, Guangzhou, 510663, China
Tel.: (86) 208 252 1198
Web Site: https://www.yakult-gz.com.cn
Healthy Food Mfr
N.A.I.C.S.: 311999

P.T. Yakult Indonesia Persad (1)
Gedung Antam Office Park Tower B Lt 16 Jl TB Simatupang No 1, Tanjung Barat, Jakarta Selatan, 12530, Indonesia
Tel.: (62) 212 963 3345
Web Site: https://www.yakult.co.id
Healthy Food Mfr
N.A.I.C.S.: 311999

Shanghai Yakult Co., Ltd. (1)
986 Yining Road, Jiading District, Shanghai, China
Tel.: (86) 216 916 6060
Healthy Food Mfr
N.A.I.C.S.: 311999

Tianjin Yakult Co,. Ltd. (1)
19 Haiyun Street, Tianjin Economic and Technological Development Zone, Tianjin, China
Tel.: (86) 225 988 6550
Healthy Food Mfr
N.A.I.C.S.: 311999

Wuxi Yakult Co., Ltd. (1)
No 3 Xiqin Road, New District, Wuxi, Jiangsu, China
Tel.: (86) 5108 542 8960
Healthy Food Mfr
N.A.I.C.S.: 311999

Yakult (China) Co., Ltd. (1)
Unit 01 16th Floor Taikang Insurance Building No 429, Nanquan North Road New Area Pudong, Shanghai, China
Tel.: (86) 215 010 8358
Web Site: https://www.yakult.com.cn
Healthy Food Mfr
N.A.I.C.S.: 311999

Yakult (Malaysia) Sdn. Bhd. (1)
Lot No 7 Jalan Jururancang U1/21 Seksyen U1, Hicom Glenmarie Industrial Park, 40150, Shah Alam, Selangor, Malaysia
Tel.: (60) 35 569 8960
Web Site: https://yakult.com.my
Healthy Food Mfr
N.A.I.C.S.: 311999

Yakult (Singapore) Pte. Ltd. (1)
7 Senoko Avenue, Singapore, 758300, Singapore
Tel.: (65) 6 756 1033
Web Site: https://www.yakult.com.sg
Healthy Food Mfr
N.A.I.C.S.: 311999

Yakult Australia Pty. Ltd. (1)
10 Monterey Road, Dandenong, 3175, VIC, Australia
Tel.: (61) 39 238 4700
Web Site: https://www.yakult.com.au
Healthy Food Mfr
N.A.I.C.S.: 311999

Yakult Danone India Private Limited (1)
212 Ground Floor Okhla Near Titan Corporate Office, Industrial Estate Phase-III, New Delhi, 110020, India
Tel.: (91) 114 062 6262
Web Site: https://www.yakult.co.in
Healthy Food Mfr

INTERNATIONAL PUBLIC

N.A.I.C.S.: 311999

Yakult Deutschland GmbH (1)
Forumstrasse 2, 41468, Neuss, Germany
Tel.: (49) 213 134 1600
Web Site: https://www.yakult.de
Healthy Food Mfr
N.A.I.C.S.: 311999

Yakult Europe B.V. (1)
Schutsluisweg 1, 1332 EN, Almere, Netherlands
Tel.: (31) 36 521 1300
Web Site: https://yakulteurope.com
Healthy Food Mfr
N.A.I.C.S.: 311999

Yakult Fukuoka Plant Co., Ltd. (1)
1-1 Oaza Zokumyoin, Chikushino, 818-0067, Fukuoka, Japan
Tel.: (81) 92 925 8960
Healthcare Product Distr
N.A.I.C.S.: 423450

Yakult Middle East FZCO (1)
Block 4EA 111, Dubai, United Arab Emirates
Tel.: (971) 4 204 5855
Web Site: https://yakultme.com
Healthy Food Mfr
N.A.I.C.S.: 311999

Yakult Myanmar Co., Ltd. (1)
Lot No A-18 Thilawa SEZ Zone A, Yangon, Myanmar
Tel.: (95) 942 584 4493
Web Site: https://www.yakultmm.com
Healthy Food Mfr
N.A.I.C.S.: 311999

Yakult Oesterreich GmbH (1)
Albertgasse 35, 1080, Vienna, Austria
Tel.: (43) 1 212 2649
Web Site: https://www.yakult.at
Healthy Food Mfr
N.A.I.C.S.: 311999

Yakult Pharmaceutical Industry Co., Ltd. (1)
5-11 Izumi, Kunitachi, Tokyo, 186-8650, Japan
Tel.: (81) 42 573 1682
Web Site: https://www.yakult.co.jp
Pharmaceutical Product Mfr & Distr
N.A.I.C.S.: 325412
Yoshihiro Goto *(Pres & CEO)*

Yakult Swallows Baseball Club (1)
5F Shinbashi MCV Building, 5-13-5 Shinbashi, Minato-ku, Tokyo, 105-0004, Japan
Tel.: (81) 354708915
Web Site: http://www.yakult-swallows.co.jp
Emp.: 150
Professional Basketball Team
N.A.I.C.S.: 711211

Yakult UK Ltd. (1)
Anteros Odyssey Business Park West End Road, Ruislip, HA4 6QQ, South Middlesex, United Kingdom
Tel.: (44) 208 842 7600
Web Site: https://www.yakult.co.uk
Healthy Food Mfr
N.A.I.C.S.: 311999

Yakult Vietnam Co., Ltd. (1)
No 5 Tu Do Boulevard, VSIP Industrial Park Thuan An District, Thuan An, Binh Duong, Vietnam
Tel.: (84) 650 376 9246
Web Site: https://www.yakult.vn
Healthy Food Mfr
N.A.I.C.S.: 311999

YAKUODO CO., LTD.
426 Hirohiro Miyazawa Yanoh-cho, Shiwa-gun, Iwate, 028-3621, Japan
Tel.: (81) 019 697 2615   JP
Web Site: http://www.yakuodo.co.jp
Year Founded: 1978
Emp.: 703
Pharmaceutical Product Store
N.A.I.C.S.: 456110

YAKUODO HOLDING CO., LTD.
6F Marios 2-9-1 Morioka Station Nishidori, Shiwa-Gun, Morioka, 020-0045, Iwate, Japan

Tel.: (81) 196972615
Web Site: https://yakuodo-hd.co.jp
Year Founded: 2019
7679—(TKS)
Rev.: $1,008,488,690
Assets: $501,858,560
Liabilities: $265,662,300
Net Worth: $236,196,260
Earnings: $27,119,250
Emp.: 978
Fiscal Year-end: 02/29/24
Holding Company
N.A.I.C.S.: 551112
Tatsuhiro Saigo *(Founder & Pres)*

YAKUTSK FUEL AND ENERGY COMPANY JSC
Peter Alekseev street 76, Yakutsk, 677015, Russia
Tel.: (7) 4112401401   RU
Web Site: https://www.yatec.ru
Year Founded: 1963
YAKG—(MOEX)
Sales Range: Less than $1 Million
Oil & Gas Related Services
N.A.I.C.S.: 213112
Andrey Korobov *(Gen Dir)*

YAKUTSKENERGO PJSC
Ul Fedora Popova 14, Yakutsk, 677009, Russia
Tel.: (7) 4112 49 73 99
Web Site: http://www.yakutskenergo.ru
YKEN—(RUS)
Sales Range: Less than $1 Million
Electric Power Distribution Services
N.A.I.C.S.: 221122
Sloik Alexander Stepanovich *(Chm-Mgmt Bd & Gen Dir)*

YALCO - SOCRATES D. CONSTANTINOU & SON S.A.
9th Andrea Metaxa St, PO Box 51284, 14564, Kifissia, 14564, Greece
Tel.: (30) 2106299999   GR
Web Site: https://www.yalco.gr
Year Founded: 1920
Sales Range: $10-24.9 Million
Emp.: 140
Tableware, Houseware & Electrical Appliances Distr
N.A.I.C.S.: 423620
Georgios Vasilakis *(Plant Mgr)*

Subsidiaries:

EXCEL S.A.   (1)
9 A Metaxa str, Kifissia, 14564, Athens, Greece
Tel.: (30) 2106299999
Web Site: http://www.yalco.gr
Emp.: 150
Air Conditioners Import & Distr
N.A.I.C.S.: 423620
Socrates Constantinou *(Mng Dir)*

OMNISHOP S.A.   (1)
Andrea Metaxa 9, Kato Kifisia, 145 64, Athens, Greece
Tel.: (30) 2106251930
Web Site: http://www.omnishop.gr
Houseware Stores Operation Services
N.A.I.C.S.: 449129

ROTA LOGISTICS CENTER S.A   (1)
5th km Motorway Thessaloniki-Athens, PO Box 10071, 541 10, Thessaloniki, Greece
Tel.: (30) 2310 573373
Web Site: http://www.rotalogistics.gr
Emp.: 6
Logistics & Bonded Warehousing Services
N.A.I.C.S.: 493110

S.C.YALCO ROMANIA SRL   (1)
Str Neagoe Voda 58, Sector 1, Bucharest, 013964, Romania
Tel.: (40) 212323137
Web Site: http://www.yalco.ro
Emp.: 29
Kitchen Appliances Import & Distr
N.A.I.C.S.: 423620

YALIAN STEEL CORPORATION
Suite 1010 1055 West Hastings Street, Vancouver, V6E 2E9, BC, Canada
Tel.: (604) 696-6388   BC
Web Site: http://www.yaliansteel.com
Year Founded: 2007
Sales Range: $1-9.9 Million
Emp.: 27
Investment Services
N.A.I.C.S.: 523999
Xia Xu *(Acting CEO & VP-Ops)*

YALLA GROUP LIMITED
238 Building 16 Dubai Internet City, Dubai, United Arab Emirates
Tel.: (971) 45877388   Ky
Web Site: https://www.yallatech.ae
Year Founded: 2018
YALA—(NYSE)
Rev.: $303,603,522
Assets: $506,338,256
Liabilities: $66,473,782
Net Worth: $439,864,474
Earnings: $79,756,797
Emp.: 829
Fiscal Year-end: 12/31/22
Holding Company
N.A.I.C.S.: 551112
Tao Yang *(Founder, Chm & CEO)*

YAMABIKO CORPORATION
1-7-2 Suehirocho Ome City, Tokyo, 198-8760, Japan
Tel.: (81) 428326111
Web Site: https://www.yamabiko-corp.co.jp
6250—(TKS)
Rev.: $1,073,426,000
Assets: $954,044,580
Liabilities: $332,343,750
Net Worth: $621,700,830
Earnings: $64,497,730
Fiscal Year-end: 12/31/23
Agricultural Machinery & Equipment Mfr & Marketer
N.A.I.C.S.: 333111
Yasuharu Sato *(Mng Officer & Officer-Agri-Machinery Dev)*

Subsidiaries:

Echo Industry Corporation   (1)
1-7-2 Suehirocho, Ohme, Tokyo, 198-0025, Japan
Tel.: (81) 428326131
Industrial Machinery Mfr & Distr
N.A.I.C.S.: 333248

Kioritz Corporation   (1)
1-7-2 Suehiro-cho, Tokyo, 198-8711, Japan
Tel.: (81) 428 326111
Web Site: http://www.kioritz.co.jp
Sales Range: $550-599.9 Million
Emp.: 3,000
Agricultural & Forest Products
N.A.I.C.S.: 339999
Yoshiaki Nagao *(Pres & CEO)*

Subsidiary (US):

Echo Incorporated   (2)
400 Oakwood Rd, Lake Zurich, IL 60047-1564
Tel.: (847) 540-8400
Web Site: http://www.echo-usa.com
Emp.: 675
Outdoor Power Equipment Distr
N.A.I.C.S.: 333112

Subsidiary (Domestic):

Crary Industries   (3)
237 12th St NW, West Fargo, ND 58078-0849
Tel.: (701) 282-5520
Web Site: https://craryindustries.com
Emp.: 185
Holding Company; Agricultural & Outdoor Power Equipment
N.A.I.C.S.: 333111
Daniel Birrenkott *(Pres)*

Division (Domestic):

Lockwood Manufacturing, Inc.   (4)
237 12th St NW, West Fargo, ND 58078
Tel.: (701) 282-5520
Web Site: http://www.lockwoodmfg.com
Specialized Farm Equipment
N.A.I.C.S.: 339999

Newtech Co., Ltd.   (1)
1136-18 Wakaho Watanai, Nagano, 381-0101, Japan
Tel.: (81) 262827231
Web Site: https://www.newtech-plast-cast.com
Emp.: 40
Injection Molded Plastic Products Mfr
N.A.I.C.S.: 326199
Kodama Takechi *(Dir)*

Oppama Industry Co., Ltd.   (1)
14-2 Natsushima-cho, Yokosuka, 237-0061, Kanagawa, Japan
Tel.: (81) 468662139
Web Site: https://www.oppama.co.jp
Emp.: 105
Digital Meters Mfr
N.A.I.C.S.: 334515
Iwata Masao *(Pres)*

YAMABIKO CHUBU CO., Ltd.   (1)
1-39 Miyamae Nishi-biwajimacho, Kiyosu, 452-0031, Aichi, Japan
Tel.: (81) 525024111
Web Site: http://www.yamabiko-corp.co.jp
Agricultural & Industrial Machinery Sales
N.A.I.C.S.: 423820

YAMABIKO ENGINEERING CO., Ltd.   (1)
1489-45 Yoshida Yoshida-cho, Akitakata, 731-0601, Hiroshima, Japan
Tel.: (81) 826 42 3031
Web Site: http://www.yamabiko-corp.co.jp
Sheet Metal Parts Mfr
N.A.I.C.S.: 332999

YAMABIKO HOKKAIDO CO., Ltd.   (1)
1-2-20 Higashi Oyachi, Atsubetsu-Ku, Sapporo, 004-0041, Hokkaido, Japan
Tel.: (81) 118912374
Agricultural & Industrial Machinery Sales
N.A.I.C.S.: 423820

YAMABIKO SEIBU CO., Ltd   (1)
566-159 Fujita, Minami-Ku, Okayama, 701-0221, Japan
Tel.: (81) 862965911
Agricultural & Industrial Machinery Sales
N.A.I.C.S.: 423820

YAMABIKO TOHOKU CO., Ltd.   (1)
5-1-50 Oroshimachi-higashi, Wakabayashi-Ku, Sendai, 984-0002, Miyagi, Japan
Tel.: (81) 222880511
Web Site: http://www.yamabiko-corp.co.jp
Agricultural & Industrial Machinery Sales
N.A.I.C.S.: 423820

Yamabiko Corporation - HIROSHIMA PLANT   (1)
35 Shinujigami Kitahiroshimacho, Yamagata, 731-1597, Hiroshima, Japan
Tel.: (81) 826 72 5700
Web Site: http://www.yamabiko-corp.co.jp
Industrial Machinery Mfr
N.A.I.C.S.: 333248

Yamabiko Corporation - MORIOKA PLANT   (1)
10-2 Sugo Takizawa-aza, Iwate, 020-0173, Japan
Tel.: (81) 196416111
Agricultural & Industrial Machinery Mfr
N.A.I.C.S.: 333111

Yamabiko Corporation - YOKOSUKA PLANT   (1)
14 Natsushimacho, Yokosuka, 237-0061, Kanagawa, Japan
Tel.: (81) 468658333
Web Site: http://www.yamabiko-corp.co.jp
Chainsaws & Lawn Mowers Mfr
N.A.I.C.S.: 333112

Yamabiko Logistics Co., Ltd.   (1)
10-2 Azasugo Takizawa Takizawamura, Iwate, 020-0173, Japan
Tel.: (81) 196416115
Web Site: http://www.yamabiko-corp.co.jp
Agricultural & Forestry Machinery Packaging Services
N.A.I.C.S.: 561910

YAMADA BEE COMPANY, INC.
omada-gun, Kagamino-cho, Ichiba 194, 708-0393, Okayama, Japan
Tel.: (81) 868 54 1971
Web Site: http://www.3838.com
Year Founded: 1948
Royal Jelly & Honey Mfr
N.A.I.C.S.: 112910
Hideo Yamada *(Pres)*

YAMADA CONSULTING GROUP CO., LTD.
10th floor Marunouchi Trust Tower North 1-8-1 Marunouchi, Chiyoda-Ku, Tokyo, 100-0005, Japan
Tel.: (81) 362122510
Web Site: https://www.yamada-cg.co.jp
Year Founded: 1989
4792—(TKS)
Rev.: $146,593,427
Assets: $137,210,829
Liabilities: $24,449,075
Net Worth: $112,761,755
Earnings: $19,128,586
Emp.: 1,071
Fiscal Year-end: 03/31/24
Management Consulting Services
N.A.I.C.S.: 541618
Keisaku Masuda *(Pres)*

Subsidiaries:

PT Spire Indonesia   (1)
Wisma 46 Kota BNI 25th Floor Unit 07 - 09 Jalan Jendral Sudirman Kav 1, Jakarta, 10220, Indonesia
Tel.: (62) 2157945800
Management Consulting Services
N.A.I.C.S.: 541618

Takenaka Partners, LLC   (1)
660 S Figueroa St # 1600, Los Angeles, CA 90017
Tel.: (213) 891-0060
Web Site: http://www.takenakapartners.com
Sales Range: $1-9.9 Million
Emp.: 50
Investment Banking & Securities Dealing
N.A.I.C.S.: 523150
Joseph Kim *(VP)*

YAMADA Consulting Group (Shanghai) Co., Ltd.   (1)
1204 12th floor Tower 1 Jing An Kerry Centre 1515 West Nanjing Road, Jingan District, Shanghai, 200040, China
Tel.: (86) 2158660573
Management Consulting Services
N.A.I.C.S.: 541618

Yamada Consulting & Spire (Thailand) Co., Ltd.   (1)
Level 16 689 Bhiraj Tower at EmQuartier Unit 1608-1610 Sukhumvit Road, Soi35 Klongton Nuea Vadhana, Bangkok, 10110, Thailand
Tel.: (66) 22613395
Web Site: https://www.yamada-cg-th.com
Management Consulting Services
N.A.I.C.S.: 541618

Yamada Consulting & Spire Vietnam Co., Ltd.   (1)
19F Sun Wah Tower 115 Nguyen Hue, Ben Nghe Ward District 1, Ho Chi Minh City, Vietnam
Tel.: (84) 2838277780
Web Site: https://www.yamada-cg-vn.com
Management Consulting Services
N.A.I.C.S.: 541618
Brandon Copperfield *(Founder & CEO)*

YAMADA CORPORATION
1-1-3 Minamimagome, Ota-ku, Tokyo, 143-8504, Japan
Tel.: (81) 337775101

YAMADA CORPORATION

Web Site:
https://www.yamadacorp.co.jp
Year Founded: 1939
6392—(TKS)
Rev.: $97,517,330
Assets: $125,841,180
Liabilities: $21,356,910
Net Worth: $104,484,270
Earnings: $12,677,980
Emp.: 350
Fiscal Year-end: 03/31/24
Fluid Handling Equipment Mfr & Distr
N.A.I.C.S.: 333310
Shotaro Yamada (Pres & CEO)

Subsidiaries:

Yamada America, Inc. (1)
955 E Algonquin Rd, Arlington Heights, IL 60005
Tel.: (847) 631-9200
Web Site: http://www.yamadapump.com
Pump Mfr & Distr
N.A.I.C.S.: 333914
David Pressler (Reg Mgr-Southern US)

Yamada Shanghai Co., Ltd. (1)
Building No 12 No 1500 Zuchongzhi Road Pudong New District, Shanghai, 201203, China
Tel.: (86) 2138953699
Pump Distr
N.A.I.C.S.: 423830

Yamada Thailand Co., Ltd. (1)
No 41/79 Moo 6 Bangna-Trad Road Km 16 5 Bangcha-long, Bang Phli, 10540, Samutprakarn, Thailand
Tel.: (66) 21300990
Pump Distr
N.A.I.C.S.: 423830
Kei Nakajima (VP-Sls)

YAMADA GREEN RESOURCES LIMITED

No 2 Dongling Road Economic and Technological Development Zone, Ganzhe Street Minhou County, Fuzhou, 350100, Fujian, China
Tel.: (86) 59122626265
Web Site: https://www.yamada-green.com
Year Founded: 2010
Rev.: $9,371,856
Assets: $51,869,246
Liabilities: $8,897,977
Net Worth: $42,971,268
Earnings: ($3,108,324)
Fiscal Year-end: 06/30/21
Natural & Healthy Food Product Mfr
N.A.I.C.S.: 311999
Chen Qiuhai (CEO)

YAMADA HOLDINGS CO., LTD.

1-1 Sakae-cho, Takasaki, 370-0841, Gunma, Japan
Web Site: https://yamada-holdings.jp
Year Founded: 1973
9831—(TKS)
Rev.: $10,523,179,490
Assets: $8,520,250,340
Liabilities: $4,394,460,200
Net Worth: $4,125,790,140
Earnings: $159,003,550
Emp.: 25,284
Fiscal Year-end: 03/31/24
Holding Company
N.A.I.C.S.: 551112
Tsuneo Mishima (Pres)

Subsidiaries:

Best Denki Malaysia Sdn. Bhd. (1)
Lot LG29D-LG29i Lower Ground Floor Subang Parade No 5 Jalan SS16/1, Darul Ehsan, 47500, Subang Jaya, Selangor, Malaysia
Tel.: (60) 356123726
Web Site: https://bestdenki.com.my
Home Appliance Retailer
N.A.I.C.S.: 423620

Cosmos Berry's Co., Ltd. (1)
1-503 Inokoishi, Meito-ku, Nagoya, 465-0021, Aichi, Japan (100%)
Tel.: (81) 529771122
Web Site: https://www.berrys.co.jp
Emp.: 64
Home Electrical Appliances & Personal Computers Retailer
N.A.I.C.S.: 449210
Ikko Miura (Founder)

Hinokiya Group Co., Ltd. (1)
Marunouchi Trust Tower Main Bldg 7th Floor Marunouchi 1-8-3, Chiyoda-ku, Tokyo, 100-0005, Japan
Tel.: (81) 3 5224 5121
Web Site: http://www.hinokiya-group.jp
Rev.: $1,107,053,200
Assets: $715,158,400
Liabilities: $467,553,680
Net Worth: $247,604,720
Earnings: $36,784,000
Emp.: 3,058
Fiscal Year-end: 12/31/2020
Holding Company
N.A.I.C.S.: 551112
Akiro Kondo (Pres)

Housetec Inc. (1)
1-1 Sakaemachi, Takasaki, 370-0841, Gunma Prefecture, Japan
Tel.: (81) 273950410
Web Site: https://www.housetec.co.jp
Emp.: 1,692
Household Equipment Mfr
N.A.I.C.S.: 335220

Inversenet Co Ltd (1)
8F Techno Wave 100 Building 1-1-25 Shinurashima-cho, Kanagawa-ku, Yokohama, 221-0031, Kanagawa, Japan
Tel.: (81) 454512411
Web Site: https://www.inversenet.co.jp
Electronic Equipment Mfr & Distr
N.A.I.C.S.: 423830
Sekido Mitsuo (Chm)

Kouziro Co Ltd (1)
Yanai, Yamaguchi, 742 0021, Yamaguchi, Japan
Tel.: (81) 358462188
Computer & Peripherals Whslr
N.A.I.C.S.: 423430

Minami-Kyushu Yamada Denki Co., Ltd. (1)
13-8 Shineicho, Kagoshima, 890-0072, Japan (60%)
Tel.: (81) 992861220
Home Electrical Appliances, Personal Computers & IT Equipment Retailer
N.A.I.C.S.: 449210
Tadao Ichimiya (COO-Ops Div)

Nikka Maintenance Co., Ltd. (1)
2-5-12 Higashi-Kanda, Chiyoda-ku, Tokyo, Japan
Tel.: (81) 358392526
Web Site: https://www.nikka-mente.co.jp
Emp.: 300
Sewage Treatment Facilities Maintenance Services
N.A.I.C.S.: 562998

OTSUKA KAGU, LTD. (1)
Tokyo Fashion Town Bldg East Wing 3-6-11 Ariake, Koto-Ku, Tokyo, 135-8071, Japan (51.83%)
Tel.: (81) 3 55304321
Web Site: http://www.idc-otsuka.jp
Sales Range: Less than $1 Million
Furniture Retail Store Operator
N.A.I.C.S.: 449110

Okinawa Yamada Denki Co., Ltd. (1)
4-40-11 Hiyoshicho, Maebashi, 371-0017, Gunma, Japan
Tel.: (81) 272335522
Web Site: http://www.yamada-denki.jp
Home Electrical Appliances & Personal Computers Retailer
N.A.I.C.S.: 449210

Puinpul Co., Ltd. (1)
1-1 12F Sakae-cho, Takasaki, 370-0841, Gunma, Japan
Tel.: (81) 120114174
Web Site: http://www.puinpul.co.jp
Emp.: 10

Cosmetics Retailer
N.A.I.C.S.: 456120

Sato Musen Co., Ltd. (1)
2-10-1 Nishishinagawa, Shinagawa-ku, Tokyo, 141-0033, Japan
Tel.: (81) 334922632
Retail Store Properties Leasing Services
N.A.I.C.S.: 531120

Seidensha Co., Ltd. (1)
2-4-3 Tonyamachi, Takasaki, 370-0006, Gunma, Japan
Tel.: (81) 273625111
Web Site: http://www.sdnsha.co.jp
Emp.: 94
Industrial Machinery & Components Distr
N.A.I.C.S.: 423830
Eiichi Takizawa (Chm)

Y-Just Co., Ltd. (1)
1-1 Sakae-cho, Takasaki, 370-0841, Gunma, Japan
Tel.: (81) 273458870
Web Site: https://yjust.jp
Emp.: 45
Construction Engineering Services
N.A.I.C.S.: 541330

Yamada Auto Japan Co., Ltd. (1)
1-1 Sakaecho, Takasaki, 370-0841, Gunma, Japan
Tel.: (81) 273458181
Used Automobiles Retailer
N.A.I.C.S.: 441120

Yamada Eco Solution Co Ltd (1)
Hie cho 2 24, Hakata ku, Fukuoka, 812 0014, Japan
Tel.: (81) 92 434 5588
Household Appliance Installation Services
N.A.I.C.S.: 449210

Yamada Financial Co., Ltd. (1)
1-1 Sakae-cho, Takasaki, 370-0841, Gunma, Japan
Tel.: (81) 273458850
Web Site: https://www.labicard.com
Credit Card Processing Services
N.A.I.C.S.: 522320

Yamada Homes Co., Ltd. (1)
1-1 Sakaemachi, Takasaki, Gunma, Japan
Tel.: (81) 273102244
Web Site: https://www.yamadahomes.jp
Sales Range: $400-449.9 Million
Emp.: 2,296
Construction Engineering Services
N.A.I.C.S.: 541330

YAMADA SERVICER SYNTHETIC OFFICE CO., LTD.

18F Yokohama ST Bldg 1-11-15 Kita Saiwai, Nishi-ku, Yokohama, 220-0004, Kanagawa, Japan
Tel.: (81) 453253933
Web Site: https://www.yamada-servicer.co.jp
Year Founded: 1981
4351—(TKS)
Rev.: $17,604,470
Assets: $49,963,230
Liabilities: $26,793,110
Net Worth: $23,170,120
Earnings: $850,800
Fiscal Year-end: 12/31/23
Consulting Services
N.A.I.C.S.: 541618
Akihisa Yamada (Founder & Pres)

YAMADAI CORPORATION

2-3 Shiomicho, Ishinomaki, 986-0842, Miyagi, Japan
Tel.: (81) 225931111
Web Site: https://www.yamadai.com
Year Founded: 1964
7426—(TKS)
Sales Range: Less than $1 Million
Building Materials Whslr
N.A.I.C.S.: 423300
Sadao Takahashi (Chm)

YAMAE HISANO CO., LTD.

2-13-34 Hakataekihigashi, Hakata-ku, Fukuoka, Japan

INTERNATIONAL PUBLIC

Tel.: (81) 924740711
Web Site: http://www.yamaehisano.com
8108—(FKA)
Rev.: $4,787,675,340
Assets: $1,611,838,410
Liabilities: $1,097,254,690
Net Worth: $514,583,720
Earnings: $19,761,350
Fiscal Year-end: 03/31/20
Food Products Distr
N.A.I.C.S.: 424490
Hideto Ouda (Chm & CEO)

YAMAGUCHI FINANCIAL GROUP INC.

4-2-36 Takezakicho, Shimonoseki, 750-8603, Yamaguchi, Japan
Tel.: (81) 832235511
Web Site: https://www.ymfg.co.jp
Year Founded: 2006
8418—(TKS)
Rev.: $1,221,217,330
Assets: $82,945,842,790
Liabilities: $78,611,427,830
Net Worth: $4,334,414,960
Earnings: $145,420
Fiscal Year-end: 03/31/24
Bank Holding Company
N.A.I.C.S.: 551111
Keisuke Mukunashi (Chm, Pres & CEO)

Subsidiaries:

Hoken Hiroba, Ltd. (1)
1-38 Satsukicho, Shunan, 745-0811, Japan
Tel.: (81) 834348550
Web Site: https://www.hoken-hiroba.com
Insurance Services
N.A.I.C.S.: 524298

Izutsuya With Card Co., Ltd. (1)
1-1 Senbamachi, Kokurakita-ku, Kitakyushu, 802-8511, Fukuoka, Japan (100%)
Tel.: (81) 935223550
Web Site: https://www.withcard.co.jp
Credit Card Processing Services
N.A.I.C.S.: 522320

Momiji Bank, Ltd. (1)
1 24 Ebisu Cho, Naka Ku, Hiroshima, 730 8678, Japan
Tel.: (81) 822413131
Web Site: http://www.momijibank.co.jp
Banking Services
N.A.I.C.S.: 522110
Toshio Kato (Sr Mng Dir)

Subsidiary (Domestic):

Momiji Jisho Co., Ltd. (2)
1-24 Ebisu-cho, Naka-ku, Hiroshima, 730-0021, Japan
Tel.: (81) 822467007
Commercial Banking Services
N.A.I.C.S.: 522110

YM Lease Co., Ltd. (1)
19-7 Nanbu-cho Meiji Yasuda Seimei Shimonoseki Building 7F, Shimonoseki, 750-0006, Japan
Tel.: (81) 832326250
Web Site: https://www.ym-lease.co.jp
Financial Lending Services
N.A.I.C.S.: 522220

YM Securities Co., Ltd. (1)
3-3-1 Buzenda-cho Kaikyo Messe Shimonoseki 2nd floor, Shimonoseki, 750-0018, Yamaguchi, Japan
Tel.: (81) 832230186
Web Site: http://www.ymsec.co.jp
Emp.: 27
Financial Management Services
N.A.I.C.S.: 523999

YMFG Zone Planning Co., Ltd. (1)
4-2-36 Takezakicho, Shimonoseki, 750-8603, Japan
Tel.: (81) 832234202
Web Site: https://www.ym-zop.co.jp
Business Consulting Services
N.A.I.C.S.: 541611

Yamagin Card Co., Ltd. (1)

AND PRIVATE COMPANIES

2-2-1 Hosoecho, Shimonoseki, 750-0016, Yamaguchi, Japan
Tel.: (81) 832312055
Web Site: https://www.yamagincard.co.jp
Credit Card Processing Services
N.A.I.C.S.: 522320

Yamagin Credit Guarantee Co., Ltd. (1)
6-1 Tanakamachi, Shimonoseki, 750-0008, Yamaguchi, Japan
Tel.: (81) 832291218
Housing Credit Guarantee Services
N.A.I.C.S.: 561450

Yamaguchi Bank, Ltd. (1)
4-2-36 Takezakicho, Shimonoseki, 750-8603, Japan
Tel.: (81) 832233411
Web Site: https://www.yamaguchibank.co.jp
Sales Range: $750-799.9 Million
Emp.: 2,928
Banking Services
N.A.I.C.S.: 522110

YAMAHA CORPORATION

10-1 Nakazawa-cho, Chuo-ku, Hamamatsu, 430-8650, Shizuoka, Japan
Tel.: (81) 534601111   JP
Web Site: https://www.yamaha.com
Year Founded: 1887
YAMCF—(OTCIQ)
Rev.: $3,059,544,260
Assets: $4,407,792,570
Liabilities: $1,024,728,470
Net Worth: $3,383,064,100
Earnings: $195,933,620
Emp.: 19,644
Fiscal Year-end: 03/31/24
Musical Instruments, Professional Audio Equipment & Home Audio & Video System Mfr & Distr
N.A.I.C.S.: 339992
Takuya Nakata *(Pres & Exec Officer)*

Subsidiaries:

D.S. Corporation (1)
2152-5 Shimoyamanashi, Fukuroi, 437-0123, Shizuoka, Japan
Tel.: (81) 538486181
Audio Equipment Mfr
N.A.I.C.S.: 334310

Design Studio London (1)
37 Stukeley Street, London, WC2B 5LT, United Kingdom
Tel.: (44) 2074046900
Web Site: http://www.global.yamaha.com
Emp.: 2
Product Design
N.A.I.C.S.: 541490

Epicurus Corporation (1)
3-19-10 Takada Shoueitakadababa Bldg 3f, Toshima-Ku, Tokyo, 171-0033, Japan
Tel.: (81) 368940290
Web Site: http://www.epicurus.co.jp
Music Production Services
N.A.I.C.S.: 711130

Guangzhou Yamaha-Pearl River Piano Inc. (1)
5 Cang Lian 1 Rd E Zone GETDD, Guangzhou, China   **(100%)**
Tel.: (86) 2082269478
Mfr of Pianos
N.A.I.C.S.: 339992

Hangzhou Yamaha Musical Instruments Co., Ltd. (1)
Shatiantou Village Guali Town, Xiaoshan, Hangzhou, 311241, Zhejiang, China
Tel.: (86) 571 8250 5000
Emp.: 2,000
Piano & Guitar Mfr
N.A.I.C.S.: 339992

Katsuragi Co., Ltd. (1)
1-17-7 Nagisanishi, Hirakata, 573-1178, Osaka, Japan
Tel.: (81) 728484111
Web Site: http://www.katsuragi-4111.co.jp
Audio Equipment Mfr
N.A.I.C.S.: 334310

Kitami Mokuzai Co., Ltd. (1)
41 Maruseppumotomachi Engarucho, Mombetsu, 099-0207, Hokkaido, Japan
Tel.: (81) 158472336
Musical Instrument Distr
N.A.I.C.S.: 423990

L. Bosendorfer Klavierfabrik GmbH (1)
Bosendorferstrasse 12, 1010, Vienna, Austria
Tel.: (43) 50466510
Web Site: http://www.bosendorfer.com
Emp.: 180
Piano Mfr
N.A.I.C.S.: 339992

Matsukiya Co., Ltd. (1)
5-16-21 Hinode, Fukui, 910-0859, Japan
Tel.: (81) 776 53 9242
Web Site: http://www.katsurock.com
Musical Instrument Retailer
N.A.I.C.S.: 459140

Nexo S.A. (1)
Parc d'Activite du Pre de la Dame Jeanne, BP 5, 60128, Plailly, France
Tel.: (33) 344990070
Web Site: http://www.nexo-sa.com
Emp.: 94
Acoustic Speaker Systems Mfr
N.A.I.C.S.: 334310

P.T. Yamaha Indonesia (1)
Jl Jend Gatot Subroto Kav 4, Kawasan Industri Pulogadung, Jakarta, 12930, Indonesia   **(100%)**
Tel.: (62) 21520257778
Web Site: http://www.yamaha.com
Emp.: 800
Mfr of Pianos
N.A.I.C.S.: 339992

P.T. Yamaha Music Indonesia (Distributor) (1)
Yamaha Music Center Bldg, Jl Jend Gatot Subroto Kav 4, Jakarta, 12930, Indonesia
Tel.: (62) 215202577
Web Site: http://www.yamahaproaudio.com
Emp.: 100
Import & Sales of Musical Instruments & PA Equipment
N.A.I.C.S.: 423990

P.T. Yamaha Music Manufacturing Asia (1)
MM2100 Industrial Town, Block EE 3 Cibitung, Bekasi, 17849, Indonesia   **(100%)**
Tel.: (62) 218981380
Emp.: 2,000
Mfr of Electronic Instruments
N.A.I.C.S.: 339992
Masahiko Hakamata *(Gen Mgr)*

P.T. Yamaha Music Manufacturing Indonesia (1)
JL Pulo Buaran Raya No 1, Kawasan Industri Pulogadung, Jakarta, 13930, Timur, Indonesia   **(100%)**
Tel.: (62) 214613234
Emp.: 100
Musical Instrument Mfr
N.A.I.C.S.: 339992

P.T. Yamaha Musical Products Indonesia (1)
Jl Rembang Industri I 36 Kawasan Industri PIER, Kawasan Berikat, Pasuruan, Jawa Timur, Indonesia   **(100%)**
Tel.: (62) 343744234
Mfr of Wind Instruments Parts & Cases
N.A.I.C.S.: 339992

PT Yamaha Musik Indonesia Distributor (1)
Yamaha Music Center Building Jl Jend Gatot Subroto Kav 4, Jakarta, 12930, Indonesia
Tel.: (62) 21 520 2577
Web Site: https://id.yamaha.com
Musical Instrument Mfr
N.A.I.C.S.: 339992

Sakuraba Mokuzai Co., Ltd. (1)
44-3 Donoshita Komata, Kitaakita, 018-4513, Akita, Japan
Tel.: (81) 186752031
Musical Instrument Mfr
N.A.I.C.S.: 339992

Siam Music Yamaha Co., Ltd. (1)
No 891/1 Siam Motors Building Floor 3 4 15 and 16 Rama 1 Road, Wangmai Pathumwan, Bangkok, 10330, Thailand
Tel.: (66) 215262639
Web Site: http://www.th.yamaha.com
Import & Sales of Musical Instruments, PA Equipment & Audiovisual Equipment
N.A.I.C.S.: 459140

Steinberg Media Technologies GmbH (1)
Srankenhtr 18b 20097, 22143, Hamburg, Germany
Tel.: (49) 040210350
Web Site: http://www.wwsteinberg.de
Emp.: 250
Music & Media Production Products Mfr
N.A.I.C.S.: 334310
Kaz Kobayashi *(Mng Dir)*

Taiwan Yamaha Musical Instrument Manufacturing Co., Ltd. (1)
465 Chung Fong Rd, Lung Tan Hsiang, Taoyuan, 325, Hsien, Taiwan   **(100%)**
Tel.: (886) 3 479 3131
Pianos & Piano Parts Mfr
N.A.I.C.S.: 339992

Tianjin Yamaha Electronic Musical Instruments, Inc. (1)
130 Dongting Road TEDA, Tianjin, China
Tel.: (86) 2225329379
Mfr & Sales of Electronic Instruments
N.A.I.C.S.: 339992

Xiaoshan Yamaha Musical Instrument Co., Ltd. (1)
777 No 6 Hongtai Rd Xiaoshan Economic & Technical Development Zone, Hangzhou, 311232, Zhejiang, China   **(100%)**
Tel.: (86) 57182833011
Emp.: 500
Mfr & Assembly of Wind Instruments
N.A.I.C.S.: 339992
Funato Minoru *(Gen Mgr)*

Yamaha A&R, Inc. (1)
2-34-17 Jingumae Sumitomofudosanharajuku Bldg 4f, Shibuya-Ku, Tokyo, 150-0001, Japan
Tel.: (81) 368940222
Web Site: http://www.yamaha-ar.co.jp
Music Production Services
N.A.I.C.S.: 512110

Yamaha Ai Works Co., Ltd. (1)
10-1 Nakazawacho, Naka-Ku, Hamamatsu, 430-0904, Shizuoka, Japan
Tel.: (81) 534601665
Musical Instrument Mfr & Whslr
N.A.I.C.S.: 339992

Yamaha Atelier fur Blasinstrumente (1)
Freiherr Vom Stein Str 20 R, D 63263, Neu-Isenburg, Germany   **(100%)**
Tel.: (49) 610233054
Web Site: http://www.yamaha.com
Emp.: 6
Technical Support for Wind Instruments
N.A.I.C.S.: 339992
Thomas Lubitz *(Mng Dir)*

Yamaha Business Support Corporation (1)
111-2 Itayamachi Hamamatsu Act Tower 11f, Naka-Ku, Hamamatsu, 430-0928, Shizuoka, Japan
Tel.: (81) 534586161
Web Site: http://www.yamaha-bs.co.jp
Emp.: 149
Business Support Services
N.A.I.C.S.: 561499

Yamaha Canada Music Ltd. (1)
135 Milner Ave, Scarborough, M1S 3R1, ON, Canada   **(100%)**
Tel.: (416) 298-1311
Web Site: http://www.ca.yamaha.com
Emp.: 75
Import & Sales of Musical Instruments, PA Equipment, Audiovisual Equipment & Compact Disc Recorders
N.A.I.C.S.: 423990
Kenichi Matsushiro *(CEO)*

Yamaha Corporation (1)
10 1 Nakazawa, Hamamatsu, 430 8650, Shizuoka, Japan   **(100%)**
Tel.: (81) 534601510

YAMAHA CORPORATION

Emp.: 1,000
Management of Recreational Complexes
N.A.I.C.S.: 713990

Yamaha Corporation of America (1)
6600 Orangethorpe Ave, Buena Park, CA 90620
Tel.: (714) 522-9011
Web Site: http://www.yamaha.com
Emp.: 450
Musical Instrument Mfr
N.A.I.C.S.: 339992
Lisa Steele-MacDonald *(Dir-Mktg-Band & Orchestral)*

Subsidiary (Domestic):

Line 6, Inc. (2)
26580 Agoura Rd, Calabasas, CA 91302-1921
Tel.: (818) 575-3600
Web Site: http://www.line6.com
Sales Range: $50-74.9 Million
Emp.: 150
Digital Audio Processing Equipment Developer, Mfr & Whslr
N.A.I.C.S.: 334310
Joe Bentivegna *(Pres)*

Skeeter Products, Inc. (2)
1 Skeeter Rd, Kilgore, TX 75662   **(100%)**
Tel.: (903) 984-0541
Web Site: http://www.skeeterboats.com
Emp.: 150
Mfr & Sales of Bass Fishing Boats
N.A.I.C.S.: 336612

Yamaha Artist Services Incorporated (2)
689 5th Ave Fl 3, New York, NY 10022
Tel.: (212) 339-9995
Web Site: http://www.yamaha.com
Emp.: 4
N.A.I.C.S.: 339992

Yamaha Commercial Audio Systems, Inc. (2)
6600 Orangethorpe Ave, Buena Park, CA 90620
Tel.: (714) 522-9011
Web Site: http://www.yamahaaudiosystems.com
Musical Instrument Mfr
N.A.I.C.S.: 339992
Eileen Nepomuceno *(Coord-Dealer)*

Yamaha Electronics Corporation USA (2)
6660 Orangethorpe Ave, Buena Park, CA 90620   **(100%)**
Tel.: (714) 522-9105
Web Site: http://www.yamaha.com
Emp.: 50
Mfr of Stereo Components & Systems
N.A.I.C.S.: 423620
Nick Emoto *(Mgr-Mktg)*

Subsidiary (Non-US):

Yamaha Motor Europe N.V. (3)
Koolhovenlaan 101, Schiphol, NL-1117 ZN, Netherlands
Tel.: (31) 206546000
Web Site: http://www.yamaha-motor.nl
Yamaha Products Distr
N.A.I.C.S.: 541614

Subsidiary (Domestic):

Yamaha Exporting, Inc. (2)
6600 Orangethorpe Ave, Buena Park, CA 90620-1396
Tel.: (714) 522-9011
Emp.: 5
Musical Instrument Mfr
N.A.I.C.S.: 339992

Yamaha Musical Products, Inc. (2)
6827 High Grove Blvd, Burr Ridge, IL 60527-7579   **(100%)**
Tel.: (630) 413-4366
Web Site: http://www.yamaha.com
Mfr & Servicing of Wind Instruments
N.A.I.C.S.: 339992

Subsidiary (Domestic):

Yamaha Music InterActive, Inc. (3)
689 5th Ave 11th Fl, New York, NY 10022
Tel.: (212) 223-6260
Web Site: http://www.yamahamusicsoft.com

YAMAHA CORPORATION

Yamaha Corporation—(Continued)
Musical Instrument Mfr & Whslr
N.A.I.C.S.: 339992

Subsidiary (Domestic):

Yamaha Unified Communications, Inc. (2)
144 N Rd Ste 3250, Sudbury, MA 01776
Tel.: (978) 610-4040
Web Site: https://uc.yamaha.com
Sales Range: $25-49.9 Million
Emp.: 70
Wireless Audio Solutions
N.A.I.C.S.: 334310
Russell Harpham *(Dir-EMEA)*

Yamaha Credit Corporation (1)
10-1 Nakazawacho, Naka-Ku, Hamamatsu, 430-0904, Shizuoka, Japan
Tel.: (81) 534601552
Credit Card Processing Services
N.A.I.C.S.: 522320

Yamaha Electronics (China) Ltd. (1)
Unit B 18/F Chinaweal Centre 414-424 Jaffe Road, Wanchai, China (Hong Kong)
Tel.: (852) 28046889
Web Site: http://www.yamaha.com
Import & Sales of Audiovisual Equipment
N.A.I.C.S.: 532490

Yamaha Electronics (Suzhou) Co., Ltd. (1)
18 Lushan Road, Suzhou New District, Suzhou, 215129, Jiangsu, China
Tel.: (86) 512 6661 8800
Web Site: http://www.yamaha.com
Emp.: 1,026
Audio & Video Products Mfr
N.A.I.C.S.: 334310

Yamaha Electronics (U.K.) Ltd. (1)
Yamaha House, 200 Rickmansworth Rd, Watford, WD18 7GQ, Herts, United Kingdom (100%)
Tel.: (44) 01923233166
Web Site: http://www.yamaha-uk.com
Emp.: 15
Import & Sales of Audiovisual Equipment
N.A.I.C.S.: 512110

Yamaha Electronics Manufacturing (M) Sdn. Bhd. (1)
Plot 7 Kinta FTZ Jl Kuala Kangsar, Chemor, Perak, 31200, Dauul Ridzuan, Malaysia (100%)
Tel.: (60) 52912111
Web Site: http://www.yamaha.com
Emp.: 1,260
Manufacture of Audiovisual Equipment
N.A.I.C.S.: 512110
Yew Hong Wan *(Gen Mgr)*

Yamaha Fine Technologies Co., Ltd. (1)
283 Aoya-Cho, Minami-Ku, Hamamatsu, 435-8568, Shizuoka, Japan
Tel.: (81) 534673600
Web Site: http://www.yamaha.co.jp
Rev.: $193,392,000
Emp.: 378
Factory Automation Machine Mfr & Distr
N.A.I.C.S.: 332216
Tatsumi Ohara *(CEO)*

Division (Domestic):

Yamaha Fine Technologies Co., Ltd. - Automotive Component Division (2)
283 Aoya Cho Shizuoka, Minami Ku, Hamamatsu, 4358568, Japan
Tel.: (81) 53 461 6115
Web Site: http://www.yamaha.co.jp
Automotive Interior Component Mfr
N.A.I.C.S.: 423120
Tatsumi Ohara *(CEO)*

Yamaha Fine Technologies Co., Ltd. - Factory Automation Division (2)
283 Aoya-Cho, Minami-Ku, Hamamatsu, 435-8568, Shizuoka, Japan
Tel.: (81) 53 467 3601
Emp.: 300
Precision Machinery Mfr
N.A.I.C.S.: 332216
Yasuhiro Nakada *(CEO)*

Yamaha Hi-Tech Design Corporation (1)

203 Matsunokijima, Iwata, 438-0192, Shizuoka, Japan
Tel.: (81) 53 962 5997
Web Site: https://www.yhd.co.jp
Emp.: 43
Musical Instrument Mfr
N.A.I.C.S.: 339992

Yamaha KHS Music Co. Ltd. (1)
3F 6 Sec 2 Nan Jing E Rd, Taipei, 104, Taiwan (100%)
Tel.: (886) 225118688
Web Site: http://www.yamahakhs.com
Sales Range: $1-9.9 Million
Emp.: 75
Import & Sales of Musical Instruments, PA Equipment & Compact Disc Recorders
N.A.I.C.S.: 423990

Yamaha Motor Co., Ltd. (1)
2500 Shingai, Iwata, 438-8501, Shizuoka, Japan (23.62%)
Tel.: (81) 5383370134
Web Site: https://global.yamaha-motor.com
Rev.: $15,954,800,132
Assets: $16,993,472,085
Liabilities: $9,179,332,673
Net Worth: $7,814,139,412
Earnings: $1,084,367,360
Emp.: 53,701
Fiscal Year-end: 12/31/2023
Motorcycles, Boats, Outboard Motors, Snowmobiles, Portable Generators, Watercraft, Unmanned Helicopters & Car Engines Mfr
N.A.I.C.S.: 336991
Yoshihiro Hidaka *(Pres & CEO)*

Subsidiary (Non-US):

Inha Works Ltd. (2)
Hahdenniementie 2, FI-21120, Raisio, Finland (100%)
Tel.: (358) 40 843 6988
Web Site: http://www.buster.fi
Consumer Products & Aluminum Boats Mfr
N.A.I.C.S.: 333923
Artturi Niittynen *(Mgr-Mktg & After Sls)*

Torqeedo GmbH (2)
Friedrichshafener Strasse 4a, 82205, Gilching, Germany
Tel.: (49) 8153 921 5100
Web Site: https://www.torqeedo.com
Electric Boat Motor Mfr & Distr
N.A.I.C.S.: 336611
Christoph Ballin *(Founder & CEO)*

Subsidiary (US):

Torqeedo Inc. (3)
171 Erick St Unit D-2, Crystal Lake, IL 60014
Tel.: (815) 444-8806
Motor Engine Mfr
N.A.I.C.S.: 336310
Mary Jo Reinhart *(Mgr-Inside Sls)*

Subsidiary (Non-US):

Yamaha Motor Canada Ltd. (2)
480 Gordon Baker Road, Toronto, M2H 3B4, ON, Canada
Tel.: (416) 498-1911
Web Site: https://www.yamaha-motor.ca
Emp.: 170
Distr of Motorcycles, Snowmobiles, All-Terrain Vehicles, Power Products, Outboard Motors, Parts & Accessories, Golf Carts
N.A.I.C.S.: 441227
John Bayliss *(Mgr-Motorcycle Brand)*

Subsidiary (US):

Yamaha Motor Corporation USA (2)
6555 Katella Ave, Cypress, CA 90630
Tel.: (714) 761-7300
Web Site: http://www.yamaha-motor.com
Emp.: 375
Yamaha Motorized Products Distr
N.A.I.C.S.: 423860
Bob Starr *(Mgr-Corp Comm)*

Subsidiary (Domestic):

Bennett Marine, Inc. (3)
550 Jim Moran Blvd, Deerfield Beach, FL 33442
Tel.: (954) 427-1400
Web Site: http://www.bennetttrimtabs.com

Sales Range: $1-9.9 Million
Emp.: 100
Marine Trim Tab, Hydraulic & Electric Services Mfr
N.A.I.C.S.: 336612

Kracor, Inc. (3)
5625 W Clinton Ave, Milwaukee, WI 53223
Tel.: (414) 355-6335
Web Site: http://www.kracor.com
Sales Range: $1-9.9 Million
Emp.: 40
Rotationally Molded Plastics Product Mfr
N.A.I.C.S.: 326199

Subsidiary (US):

Yamaha Motor Manufacturing Corporation (2)
1000 Hwy 34 E, Newnan, GA 30265-1320
Tel.: (770) 254-4000
Web Site: http://www.yamaha-motor-mfg.com
Emp.: 1,000
Recreational Vehicles
N.A.I.C.S.: 336350

Subsidiary (Domestic):

Yamaha Motor Robotics Holdings, Co., Ltd. (2)
21st Floor New Pier Takeshiba South Tower 1-16-1 Kaigan, Minato-ku, Tokyo, 105-0022, Japan (100%)
Tel.: (81) 359376401
Web Site: http://www.ymrh.co.jp
Rev.: $101,653,200
Assets: $220,592,880
Liabilities: $58,255,800
Net Worth: $162,337,080
Earnings: ($28,828,920)
Emp.: 755
Fiscal Year-end: 03/31/2019
Semiconductors & Electronic Devices Mfr
N.A.I.C.S.: 334413

Subsidiary (Domestic):

APIC Yamada Corporation (3)
90 Kamitokuma, Chikuma, 389-0898, Nagano, Japan
Tel.: (81) 262767806
Web Site: http://www.apicyamada.co.jp
Rev.: $112,465,200
Assets: $98,115,120
Liabilities: $64,184,640
Net Worth: $33,930,480
Earnings: $408,480
Emp.: 405
Fiscal Year-end: 03/31/2018
Automated Equipment & Dies Mfr
N.A.I.C.S.: 333514
Taketoshi Gojo *(Pres)*

Subsidiary (Non-US):

APIC YAMADA (THAILAND) COMPANY LIMITED (4)
1/52 Moo 5 Rojana Industrial Park T Kanharm A U-Tai Pranakorn, 13210, Ayutthaya, Sriayutthaya, Thailand
Tel.: (66) 35226328
Web Site: http://www.ayt.th.com
Sales Range: $100-124.9 Million
Emp.: 260
Nonferrous Metal (except Copper & Aluminum) Rolling, Drawing & Extruding
N.A.I.C.S.: 331491

Plant (US):

APIC YAMADA CORPORATION - Apic Yamada America Plant (4)
Southgate Business Park 104 S 54th St, Chandler, AZ 85226
Tel.: (480) 820-0078
Web Site: http://www.apicyamada.co.jp
Semiconductor Mfr
N.A.I.C.S.: 334413

Subsidiary (Non-US):

APIC YAMADA SINGAPORE PTE. LTD. (4)
5 Kallang Sector No 04-02, Kolam Ayer Industrial Park, Singapore, 349279, Singapore
Tel.: (65) 67489300
Web Site: http://www.apicyamada.com.sg

INTERNATIONAL PUBLIC

Sales Range: $25-49.9 Million
Emp.: 30
Construction Machinery Mfr
N.A.I.C.S.: 333120
William Ho *(Mng Dir)*

Plant (Domestic):

Apic Yamada Singapore Pte. Ltd - Factory (5)
5 Kallang Sector 04-02 Kolam Ayer Industrial Park, Singapore, 349279, Singapore
Tel.: (65) 67489300
Web Site: http://www.apicyamada.com.sg
Sales Range: $25-49.9 Million
Precision Machining Tools Mfr
N.A.I.C.S.: 332721

Subsidiary (Non-US):

APIC YAMADA TECHNOLOGY (SHANGHAI) CO., LTD. (4)
2/F Building 1 No 14 Block 172 Lane 1340 Jinshajiang Road, Shanghai, 200333, PR, China (100%)
Tel.: (86) 2152833303
Web Site: http://www.apicyamada.co.jp
Sales Range: $25-49.9 Million
Emp.: 86
Printing Machinery & Equipment Mfr
N.A.I.C.S.: 333248

Plant (Domestic):

APIC Yamada Corporation - Yoshino Plant (4)
80 Haneo, Chikuma, 389-0812, Nagano, Japan
Tel.: (81) 262768177
Web Site: http://www.apicyamada.co.jp
Sales Range: $100-124.9 Million
Semiconductor Devices Mfr
N.A.I.C.S.: 334413

Subsidiary (Domestic):

APIC Yamada Distributors Inc. (4)
90 Kamitokuma, Chikuma, 389-0898, Nagano, Japan (100%)
Tel.: (81) 262768110
Web Site: http://www.apicyamada.co.jp
Sales Range: $25-49.9 Million
Emp.: 36
Sales & Distribution of Semiconductor Assemblies
N.A.I.C.S.: 333242

Apic Assist Corporation (4)
90 Kamitokuma, Chikuma, 389-0899, Nagano, Japan (100%)
Tel.: (81) 262768110
Web Site: http://www.apicyamada.co.jp
Sales Range: $25-49.9 Million
Emp.: 2
All Other Legal Services
N.A.I.C.S.: 541199

Subsidiary (Non-US):

Shanghai Apic Yamada Co., Ltd. (4)
Unit 502 XinHongQiao Building No 55, Lou Shan Guan Road, Shanghai, 201707, China (100%)
Tel.: (86) 2163293882
Sales Range: $50-74.9 Million
Emp.: 60
Industrial Machinery & Equipment Wholesalers
N.A.I.C.S.: 423830
Xu Yuzhen *(Mgr)*

Subsidiary (Domestic):

Pioneer Fa Corporation (3)
6-1-1 Fujimi Tsurugasima-shi, 350-2288, Saitama, Japan
Tel.: (81) 492791520
Web Site: http://www.pioneerfa.co.jp
Instrument Manufacturing for Measuring & Testing Electricity & Electrical Signals
N.A.I.C.S.: 333993
Hiroshi Kobayashi *(Pres)*

Subsidiary (Non-US):

Shinkawa (Malaysia) Sdn. Bhd. (3)
Ste B613 6F E Wing Wisma Consplant 2 No 7 Jalan SS 16 1, 47500, Subang Jaya, 47500, Selangor Darul Ehsan, Malaysia
Tel.: (60) 3 5637 5620
Web Site: http://www.shinkawa.com

AND PRIVATE COMPANIES

YAMAHA CORPORATION

Electronic Design Services
N.A.I.C.S.: 238210

Shinkawa (Shanghai) Co., Ltd. (3)
Rm 2105 Sunplus Bldg No 1077 Zuchongzhi Rd, Zhangjiang High Tech Park Pudong New Area, Shanghai, 201203, China
Tel.: (86) 2163917373
Web Site: http://www.shinkawa-tech.com
Sales Range: $25-49.9 Million
Emp.: 50
Electronic Components Mfr
N.A.I.C.S.: 334416

Shinkawa (Thailand) Co., Ltd. (3)
99 349 Na-Nakorn Bldg 5F Cheangwattana Rd, Tungsonghong Laksi, Bangkok, 10210, Thailand
Tel.: (66) 2 576 1458
Web Site: http://www.shinkawa.com
Sales Range: $25-49.9 Million
Emp.: 8
Electronic Components Mfr
N.A.I.C.S.: 334416

Shinkawa Korea Co., Ltd. (3)
No 501 Sunil Technopia 440 Sangdaewon-dong, Jungwon-gu, Seongnam, 462326, Kyungki-do, Korea (South)
Tel.: (82) 317773434
Sales Range: $25-49.9 Million
Emp.: 25
Electronic Components Mfr
N.A.I.C.S.: 334416
Hoseong Lee *(Gen Mgr)*

Shinkawa Singapore Pte. Ltd. (3)
31 Kaki Bukit Rd 3-02-03A Techlink, Singapore, 417818, Singapore
Tel.: (65) 62270072
Web Site: http://www.shinkawa.com
Sales Range: $25-49.9 Million
Emp.: 20
Electronic Components Mfr
N.A.I.C.S.: 334416

Subsidiary (Domestic):

Shinkawa Technologies Ltd.
2-51-1 Inadaira, Musashimurayama-shi, Tokyo, 208-0023, Japan
Tel.: (81) 425600988
Web Site: http://www.shinkawa.com
Electronic Components Mfr
N.A.I.C.S.: 334413

Subsidiary (US):

Shinkawa U.S.A., Inc. (3)
1177 South Porter Ct, Gilbert, AZ 85296
Tel.: (480) 831-7988
Web Site: http://www.shinkawa.com
Electronic Components Mfr
N.A.I.C.S.: 334416

Subsidiary (Non-US):

Yamaha Motor do Brasil Ltda. (2)
Rodovia Presidente Dutra Km 214, CEP 07178-580, Guarulhos, SP, Brazil
Tel.: (55) 11 2431 6500
Web Site: http://www.yamaha-motor.com.br
Emp.: 600
Mfr & Distr of Motorcycles & Automobiles
N.A.I.C.S.: 336110

Yamaha Music & Electronics (China) Co., Ltd. (1)
1-3/F Yunhedasha 1818 Xinzha-lu Jinganqu, Jingan-qu, Shanghai, 200042, China
Tel.: (86) 84498268
Web Site: http://www.yamaha.com.cn
Musical Instrument Whslr
N.A.I.C.S.: 423990

Yamaha Music (Asia) Pte., Ltd. (1)
202 Hougang Street 21, Singapore, 530202, Singapore
Tel.: (65) 67409200
Web Site: http://www.yamaha.com.sg
Emp.: 130
Import & Sales of Musical Instruments, PA Equipment & Audiovisual Equipment
N.A.I.C.S.: 423990

Yamaha Music (Malaysia) Sdn. Bhd. (1)
No 8 Jalan Perbandaran Kelana Jaya, 47301, Petaling Jaya, Selangor, Malaysia **(100%)**
Tel.: (60) 378030900
Web Site: http://www.my.yamaha.com
Emp.: 100
Import & Sales of Musical Instruments
N.A.I.C.S.: 423990

Yamaha Music (Russia) LLC. (1)
Room 37 7 Kievskaya Street, 121059, Moscow, Russia
Tel.: (7) 4956265005
Web Site: http://ru.yamaha.com
Musical Instrument Distr
N.A.I.C.S.: 423990

Yamaha Music Artist, Inc. (1)
2-34-17 Jingumae Sumitomofudosanharajuku Bldg 4f, Shibuya-Ku, Tokyo, 150-0001, Japan
Tel.: (81) 368940185
Web Site: http://www.yamaha-ma.co.jp
Music Production & Event Management Services
N.A.I.C.S.: 711130
Yoichi Okamoto *(Product Mgr)*

Yamaha Music Australia Pty., Ltd. (1)
Level 1 99 Queensbridge St, Southbank, 3006, VIC, Australia
Tel.: (61) 396935111
Web Site: http://www.yamaha.com.au
Emp.: 90
Import & Sales of Musical Instruments, PA Equipment, Audiovisual Equipment & Compact Disk Recorders
N.A.I.C.S.: 423990

Yamaha Music Central Europe GmbH (1)
Siemensstr 22 234, 25462, Rellingen, Germany **(100%)**
Tel.: (49) 41013030
Web Site: http://www.yamaha-europe.com
Emp.: 200
N.A.I.C.S.: 339992

Yamaha Music Communications Co., Ltd. (1)
2-34-17 Jingumae Sumitomofudosanharajuku Bldg 5f, Shibuya-Ku, Tokyo, 150-0001, Japan
Tel.: (81) 368940195
Web Site: http://www.yamahamusic.co.jp
Emp.: 25
Music Publishers
N.A.I.C.S.: 512230
Tsuyoshi Yoshikawa *(Mgr-Mktg)*

Yamaha Music Craft Corporation (1)
28 Iidacho, Minami-Ku, Hamamatsu, 435-0028, Shizuoka, Japan
Tel.: (81) 534619597
Web Site: http://www.yamaha.co.jp
Classical Guitar Mfr
N.A.I.C.S.: 339992

Yamaha Music Entertainment Holdings, Inc. (1)
2-34-17 Jingumae Sumitomofudosanharajuku Bldg 4f, Shibuya-Ku, Tokyo, 150-0001, Japan
Tel.: (81) 3 6894 0181
Web Site: http://www.yamaha-meh.co.jp
Musical & Video Software Publisher
N.A.I.C.S.: 513210

Yamaha Music Europe GmbH (1)
Siemensstrasse 22-34, 25462, Rellingen, Germany
Tel.: (49) 4101 303 0
Web Site: http://europe.yamaha.com
Musical Instrument Whslr
N.A.I.C.S.: 459140

Yamaha Music Europe GmbH (UK) (1)
Sherbourne Dr, Tilbrook, Milton Keynes, MK7 8BL, United Kingdom
Tel.: (44) 8704445575
Web Site: http://uk.yamaha.com
Emp.: 129
Musical Instruments & Audio-Visual Products Distr
N.A.I.C.S.: 459140
Mark Rolfe *(Mng Dir)*

Yamaha Music Europe Sp. z o.o. (1)
ul Wielicka 52, 02-657, Warsaw, Poland
Tel.: (48) 22 880 0888
Web Site: https://pl.yamaha.com

Musical Instrument Mfr
N.A.I.C.S.: 339992

Yamaha Music Gulf FZE (1)
LOB 16-513, PO Box 17328, Jebel Ali, Dubai, 17328, United Arab Emirates
Tel.: (971) 4 881 5868
Web Site: http://www.ae.yamaha.com
Emp.: 35
Consumer Audio & Video Product Whslr
N.A.I.C.S.: 423990
Toshiro Yamamoto *(Gen Mgr)*

Yamaha Music Hokkaido Co., Ltd (1)
1-1-50 Minami10jonishi Yamaha Center, Chuo-Ku, Sapporo, 064-0810, Hokkaido, Japan
Tel.: (81) 115126111
Web Site: http://www.yamahamusic.jp
Musical Instruments Sales & Maintenance Services
N.A.I.C.S.: 423990

Yamaha Music India Pvt. Ltd. (1)
P-401 JMD Megapolis Sector 48 Sohna Road, Gurgaon, 122018, Haryana, India
Tel.: (91) 1244853300
Web Site: http://www.in.yamaha.com
Emp.: 40
Musical Instrument Whslr
N.A.I.C.S.: 423990

Yamaha Music Japan Co., Ltd. (1)
7-9-14 Ginza, Chuo-Ku, Tokyo, 104-0061, Japan **(100%)**
Tel.: (81) 335723139
Web Site: http://www.yamaha.co.jp
Music Management
N.A.I.C.S.: 541611

Yamaha Music Kanto Co., Ltd. (1)
130 Bandai Niigata Kotsu Silver Ball Bldg 2f, Chuo-Ku, Niigata, 950-0082, Japan
Tel.: (81) 252434311
Web Site: http://www.ymn.co.jp
Musical Instrument Whslr
N.A.I.C.S.: 423990

Yamaha Music Korea Ltd. (1)
8F 9F Dongsung Bldg 158-9 Samsung-Dong, Kangnam-Gu, Seoul, 135-880, Korea (South)
Tel.: (82) 234673300
Web Site: http://www.yamaha-music.co.kr
Musical Instrument Whslr
N.A.I.C.S.: 423990

Yamaha Music Kyushu Co., Ltd. (1)
2-11-4 Hakataekimae, Hakata-Ku, Fukuoka, 812-0011, Japan
Tel.: (81) 924721415
Music School Management Services
N.A.I.C.S.: 611610

Yamaha Music LLC (1)
St Kievskaya 7 room 37, 121059, Moscow, Russia
Tel.: (7) 4956265005
Web Site: https://ru.yamaha.com
Musical Instrument Mfr
N.A.I.C.S.: 339992

Yamaha Music Latin America S.A. Sucursal Argentina (1)
Olga cossettini 1553 Piso 4 Norte Madero Este, C1107CEK, Buenos Aires, Argentina
Tel.: (54) 1141197000
Emp.: 15
Import & Sales of Musical Instruments, PA Equipment & Audiovisual Equipment
N.A.I.C.S.: 423990

Yamaha Music Latin America, S.A. (1)
Edif Torre Banco General Piso 7 Urbanizacion Marbella Calle 47, Panama, Panama **(100%)**
Tel.: (507) 2695311
Web Site: http://www.yamaha.com
Emp.: 23
Import & Sales of Musical Instruments, PA Equipment & Audiovisual Equipment
N.A.I.C.S.: 423990

Yamaha Music Lease Corporation (1)
10-1 Nakazawacho, Naka-Ku, Hamamatsu, 430-0904, Shizuoka, Japan
Tel.: (81) 53 460 1560

Web Site: http://www.yamaha-yml.co.jp
Musical Instrument Leasing & Rental Services
N.A.I.C.S.: 532289

Yamaha Music Media Corporation (1)
3-19-10 Takada Shoueitakadababa Bldg 1f, Toshima-Ku, Tokyo, Japan
Tel.: (81) 368940250
Web Site: http://www.ymm.co.jp
Musical Instrument Mfr
N.A.I.C.S.: 339992

Yamaha Music Osaka Co., Ltd. (1)
1-5-2 Shinsenrihigashimachi Serushi Bldg 5f, Toyonaka, 560-0082, Osaka, Japan
Tel.: (81) 676701770
Web Site: http://www.yamahamusic.jp
Emp.: 3,000
Music School Management Services
N.A.I.C.S.: 611610
Kaduo Hayama *(Gen Mgr)*

Yamaha Music Publishing, Inc. (1)
2-34-17 Jingumae Sumitomofudosanharajuku Bldg 4f, Shibuya-Ku, Tokyo, 150-0001, Japan
Tel.: (81) 3 6894 0200
Web Site: http://www.yamaha-mp.co.jp
Music Publishers
N.A.I.C.S.: 512230
Naoji Suda *(Pres)*

Yamaha Music Technical (Shanghai) Co., Ltd. (1)
1-3/F Yunhedasha 1818 Xinzha-lu Jinganqu, Shanghai, China
Tel.: (86) 84498268
Web Site: http://www.yamaha.com
Music School Management Services
N.A.I.C.S.: 611610

Yamaha Music Tokai Co., Ltd. (1)
1-18-28 Nishiki, Naka-Ku, Nagoya, 460-0003, Aichi, Japan
Tel.: (81) 522014353
Music School Management Services
N.A.I.C.S.: 611610

Yamaha Music Tokyo Co., Ltd. (1)
7-9-14 Ginza, Chuo-Ku, Tokyo, 104-0061, Japan
Tel.: (81) 335723171
Music School Management Services
N.A.I.C.S.: 611610

Yamaha Music Trading Corporation (1)
Hulic Kakigara-cho Building 7F 28-5 1-chome Nihonbashikigara-cho, Chuo-Ku, Tokyo, 103-0014, Japan
Tel.: (81) 3 5641 1081
Web Site: http://www.y-m-t.co.jp
Rev.: $57,528,000
Emp.: 90
Musical Instrument Mfr & Whslr
N.A.I.C.S.: 339992

Division (Domestic):

Yamaha Music Trading Corporation - LM Division (2)
1-28-5 Nohombashikakigara, Chuo-Ku, Tokyo, Japan
Tel.: (81) 3 5641 1031
Musical Instrument Mfr
N.A.I.C.S.: 339992

Yamaha Music Trading Corporation - Musician Support Goods Division (2)
1-28-5 Nihonbashi Kakigara-cho, Chuo-ku, Tokyo, 103-0014, Japan
Tel.: (81) 3 5641 1051
Musical Instrument Mfr
N.A.I.C.S.: 339992

Yamaha Music Trading Corporation - Percussion Division (2)
Hulic Kakigara-cho Building 7F 28-5 1-chome Nihonbashikigara-cho, Chuo-ku, Tokyo, 030-0014, Japan
Tel.: (81) 3 5641 1085
Musical Instrument Mfr
N.A.I.C.S.: 339992

Yamaha Music Trading Corporation - VISCOUNT & Wenger Division (2)
Hulic Kakigara-cho Building 7F 28-5 1-chome Nihonbashikigara-cho, Chuo-ku,

YAMAHA CORPORATION

Yamaha Corporation—(Continued)
Tokyo, 103-0014, Japan
Tel.: (81) 3 5641 1086
Musical Instrument Mfr
N.A.I.C.S.: 339992

Yamaha Music Trading Corporation - Wind & Educational Instruments Division (2)
1-28-5 Nihonbashi Kakigara-Cho, Tokyo, 103-0014, Japan
Tel.: (81) 3 5641 1083
Musical Instrument Mfr
N.A.I.C.S.: 339992

Yamaha Music Winds Corporation (1)
1465 Matsunokijima, Iwata, 438-0125, Shizuoka, Japan
Tel.: (81) 539625511
Emp.: 150
Wind Instrument Parts Processing & Assembling Services
N.A.I.C.S.: 561499

Yamaha Music and Visuals, Inc. (1)
8-27 Sakuragaokacho, Shibuya-Ku, Tokyo, 150-0031, Japan
Tel.: (81) 3 6892 6210
Web Site: http://www.yamaha-mv.co.jp
Emp.: 2
Music Video Production & Distribution Services
N.A.I.C.S.: 512110
Sotaro Nishida (Gen Mgr)

Yamaha Musica Italia S.p.A. (1)
Viale Italia 88, 20020, Lainate, Milan, Italy
Tel.: (39) 02935771
Web Site:
http://www.yamahacommercialaudio.com
Emp.: 54
Import & Sales of Musical Instruments, PA Equipment & Compact Disc Recorders
N.A.I.C.S.: 423990

Yamaha Musical do Brasil Ltda. (1)
Av Rebouças 2636 Pinheiros, CEP 05402 400, Sao Paulo, Brazil (100%)
Tel.: (55) 1130851377
Web Site:
http://www.yamahamusical.com.br
Emp.: 30
Import & Sales of Musical Instruments & PA Equipment
N.A.I.C.S.: 423990

Yamaha Office Link Co., Ltd. (1)
10-1 Nakazawacho, Naka-Ku, Hamamatsu, 430-0904, Shizuoka, Japan
Tel.: (81) 534626644
Business Support Services
N.A.I.C.S.: 561499

Yamaha Piano Artistes Services Europe (1)
5 Rue Scribe, 9 Arondissmant, 75116, Paris, France
Tel.: (33) 147233352
Web Site: http://www.yamahaproaudio.com
Emp.: 4
Technical Services for Pianos
N.A.I.C.S.: 459140

Yamaha Piano Service Co., Ltd. (1)
10-1 Nakazawacho, Naka-Ku, Hamamatsu, 430-0904, Shizuoka, Japan
Tel.: (81) 534601631
Piano Sales & Repair Services
N.A.I.C.S.: 459140

Yamaha R&D Centre London (1)
Unit 6 The Piazza 3 Devonhurst Pl, Heathfield Ter Chiswick, London, W4 4JD, United Kingdom (100%)
Tel.: (44) 2089879595
Emp.: 35
Research & Development of Digital Musical Instrument & PA Equipment
N.A.I.C.S.: 339992

Yamaha Resort Inc. (1)
2000 Tamari, Kakegawa, 436-0011, Shizuoka, Japan
Tel.: (81) 537241111
Resort Operating Services
N.A.I.C.S.: 721110

Yamaha Sound Systems Inc. (1)
41-12 Nihombashihakozakicho Nihombashi-daini Bldg, Chuo-ku, Tokyo, 103-0015, Japan
Tel.: (81) 356523600
Emp.: 140
Audio Equipment Mfr & Installation Services
N.A.I.C.S.: 334310
Shinjiro Takeda (Pres)

Yamaha Trading (Shanghai) Co., Ltd. (1)
1-3/F Yunhe Building 1818 Xinzha Road, Shanghai, China
Tel.: (86) 4000517700
Web Site: http://www.yamaha.com.cn
Emp.: 200
Import & Sales of Musical Instruments & PA Products
N.A.I.C.S.: 423990

Yamaha Travel Service Co., Ltd. (1)
10-1 Nakazawacho Yamaha K K Nai, Naka-Ku, Hamamatsu, 430-0904, Shizuoka, Japan
Tel.: (81) 53 460 2561
Web Site: http://www.yamaha-travel.co.jp
Travel Agency Services
N.A.I.C.S.: 561510

Yamaha de Mexico, S.A. de C.V. (1)
Javier Rojo Gomez 1149 Col Guadalupe Del Moral, 09300, Mexico, Mexico (100%)
Tel.: (52) 5558040600
Import & Sales of Musical Instruments, PA Equipment & Audiovisual Equipment
N.A.I.C.S.: 459140

Yamaha-Hazen Electronica Musical S.A. (1)
Ctra De La Coruna Km 17200, 28230, Madrid, Spain
Tel.: (34) 916398888
Emp.: 55
Import & Sales of Musical Instruments, Audiovisual Equipment, PA Equipment & Compact Disc Recorders
N.A.I.C.S.: 423990

Yamanashi Kogei Co., Ltd. (1)
1480 Ryoke, Kakegawa, 436-0038, Shizuoka, Japan
Tel.: (81) 537247013
Piano Wooden Parts Mfr
N.A.I.C.S.: 339992

YAMAICHI ELECTRONICS CO LTD

Technoport Taiju Seimei Bldg 2-16-2 Minamikamata, Ota-ku, Tokyo, 144-8581, Japan
Tel.: (81) 337340110
Web Site: https://www.yamaichi.co.jp
Year Founded: 1956
6941—(TKS)
Rev: $240,756,030
Assets: $337,519,820
Liabilities: $84,594,780
Net Worth: $252,925,040
Earnings: $13,616,600
Emp.: 2,123
Fiscal Year-end: 03/31/24
Electronic Components Mfr
N.A.I.C.S.: 334416
Yoshitaka Ota (Chm)

Subsidiaries:

Asia Yamaichi Electronics Inc. (1)
A-604 Woolim Lions Vally 168 Gasan Digital 1-Ro, Geumcheon-gu, Seoul, 08507, Korea (South)
Tel.: (82) 25570522
Web Site: http://www.yamaichi.co.kr
Emp.: 50
Semiconductor Devices Mfr
N.A.I.C.S.: 334413

Plant (Domestic):

Asia Yamaichi Electronics Inc. - Umsong Plant (2)
958 Geumil-ro Samseong-myeon, Eumseong, 27649, Chungcheongbuk-do, Korea (South)
Tel.: (82) 438773561
Web Site: http://yamaichi.co.kr
Emp.: 50
Semiconductor Devices Mfr
N.A.I.C.S.: 334413
Hong Se (Mgr-Pur)

High Enpla Co., Ltd. (1)
248 Yokomakura, Uozu, 937-0044, Toyama, Japan
Tel.: (81) 765224110
Emp.: 6
Electronic Components Mfr
N.A.I.C.S.: 334416

Koshin Kogaku Co., Ltd. (1)
69-3 Bodai, Hadano, 259-1302, Kanagawa, Japan
Tel.: (81) 463753331
Web Site: https://www.koshin-kogaku.com
Emp.: 73
Optical Device Mfr
N.A.I.C.S.: 333310
Fumihiko Narukawa (Exec VP)

Plant (Domestic):

Koshin Kogaku Co., Ltd.- Togawa Plant (2)
315-2 Togawa, Hadano, 259-1306, Kanagawa, Japan
Tel.: (81) 463742311
Web Site: http://www.koshin-kogaku.co.jp
Optical Filter Mfr
N.A.I.C.S.: 333310

Matty Co., Ltd. (1)
3000-1 Kosaka-nishi Kamogata-cho, Okayama, 719-0231, Japan
Tel.: (81) 865449270
Emp.: 202
Electronic Components Mfr
N.A.I.C.S.: 334416

Test Solution Services, Inc. (1)
No 5 Circuit St, Light Industry & Science Park I Barrio Diezmo, Cabuyao, 4025, Laguna, Philippines
Tel.: (63) 495391222
Web Site: https://www.tss-ph.com
Emp.: 500
Semiconductor Components Testing & Sales
N.A.I.C.S.: 423690
Shigeru Takeuchi (Dir-Sls & Mktg)

Yamaichi Electronics Co., Ltd. - Sakura Factory (1)
1-4-1 Osaku, Sakura, 285-0802, Chiba, Japan
Tel.: (81) 434987000
Web Site: http://www.yamaichi.co.jp
Emp.: 100
Electronic Components Mfr
N.A.I.C.S.: 334416
Yoshitaka Ota (Pres)

Yamaichi Electronics Deutschland GmbH (1)
Bahnhofstr 20, Concor Park Dornach, 85609, Aschheim, Germany
Tel.: (49) 89451090
Web Site: https://www.yamaichi.de
Emp.: 100
Electric Component Whslr
N.A.I.C.S.: 423690
Helge Puhlmann (Pres & Member-Mgmt Bd)

Yamaichi Electronics Deutschland Manufacturing GmbH (1)
Nicolaus-August-Otto-Strasse 3, 15236, Frankfurt, Germany
Tel.: (49) 89451090
Web Site: http://www.yamaichi.de
Electric Device Mfr
N.A.I.C.S.: 334419

Yamaichi Electronics Great Britain Ltd. (1)
6 The Clockhouse Stratton Park, Micheldever, Winchester, SO21 3DP, Hampshire, United Kingdom
Tel.: (44) 1962774902
Web Site: http://www.yamaichi.eu
Emp.: 2
Electronic Components Distr
N.A.I.C.S.: 423690

Yamaichi Electronics Hong Kong Ltd. (1)
Room 815-16 8/F Tower 1 Grand Central Plaza, 138 Shatin Rural Committee Road, Sha Tin, New Territories, China (Hong Kong)
Tel.: (852) 26871968
Web Site: https://www.yamaichi.com.cn
Electric Component Whslr
N.A.I.C.S.: 423690

Yamaichi Electronics Italia S.R.L. (1)
Centro Direzionale Colleoni Via Colleoni 1 Palazzo Taurus Ing 1, 20864, Agrate Brianza, Italy
Tel.: (39) 0396881185
Web Site: http://www.yamaichi.eu
Emp.: 3
Electric Component Whslr
N.A.I.C.S.: 423690
Carlo Cremonesi (Dir-Sls)

Yamaichi Electronics Shenzhen Ltd. (1)
No 6 Long Shan Ind, Nanling Nanwan Long Gang, Shenzhen, 518123, Guangdong, China
Tel.: (86) 75528727373
Web Site: http://www.yamaichi.com.cn
Electronic Connectors Whslr
N.A.I.C.S.: 423690

Yamaichi Electronics Singapore Pte. Ltd. (1)
19 Tai Seng Avenue 05-05, Singapore, 534054, Singapore
Tel.: (65) 62978312
Web Site: https://www.yamaichi.com.sg
Emp.: 18
Electronic Devices Sales
N.A.I.C.S.: 423690

Yamaichi Electronics Taiwan Co., Ltd. (1)
4F 3 No 9 Sanmin Rd, East Dist, Hsinchu, 30043, Taiwan
Tel.: (886) 353231887
Web Site: http://www.yamaichi.com.tw
Emp.: 1
Semiconductor Devices Mfr
N.A.I.C.S.: 334413

Yamaichi Electronics U.S.A. Inc. (1)
475 Holger Way, San Jose, CA 95134
Tel.: (408) 715-9100
Electronic Device Distr
N.A.I.C.S.: 423690
Alfred Muranaga (CEO & Chm)

Unit (Domestic):

Yamaichi Electronics U.S.A. Inc. - Arizona Unit (2)
7240 W Erie St 4, Chandler, AZ 85226
Tel.: (480) 940-9000
Emp.: 15
Electric Device Mfr
N.A.I.C.S.: 334515

YAMAMA SAUDI CEMENT COMPANY

PO Box 293, Riyadh, 11411, Saudi Arabia
Tel.: (966) 114085600
Web Site:
https://www.yamamacement.com
Year Founded: 1961
3020—(SAU)
Rev: $272,674,088
Assets: $1,693,324,445
Liabilities: $453,152,587
Net Worth: $1,240,171,858
Earnings: $94,866,964
Emp.: 1,000
Fiscal Year-end: 12/31/22
Cement Mfr & Distribution
N.A.I.C.S.: 327310
Mohamad Al-Amoudi (CFO)

YAMAMI COMPANY

73-5 Sodekake Obara Numata-nishimachi, Mihara, 729-0473, Hiroshima, Japan
Tel.: (81) 120047803
Web Site: https://www.yamami.co.jp
Year Founded: 1975
2820—(TKS)
Sales Range: Less than $1 Million
Consumer Product Mfr & Distr

N.A.I.C.S.: 311991
Kiyoshi Yamana *(Chm, Pres & Co-CEO)*

YAMANO HOLDINGS CORPORATION
Yamano 24 Building 1-30-7 Yoyogi, Shibuya-ku, Tokyo, 151-0053, Japan
Tel.: (81) 333767878
Web Site: https://www.yamano-hd.com
Year Founded: 1987
7571—(TKS)
Rev.: $91,462,570
Assets: $57,156,670
Liabilities: $49,072,640
Net Worth: $8,084,030
Earnings: ($185,080)
Emp.: 575
Fiscal Year-end: 03/31/24
Retail Business Service
N.A.I.C.S.: 459999
Yoshitomo Yamano *(Pres & CEO)*

Subsidiaries:

HM Retailings Co., Ltd. (1)
1-30-7 Yoyogi, Shibuya-ku, Tokyo, 151-0053, Japan
Tel.: (81) 3 3378 2984
Web Site: http://www.kimono-net.com
Apparel Retailer
N.A.I.C.S.: 458110

MARUFUKU SHOJI Co., Ltd. (1)
359 Gotokuishi-cho, Shimogyo-ku, Kyoto, 600-8429, Japan
Tel.: (81) 753618411
Web Site: https://www.marufuku-shoji.co.jp
Emp.: 20
Apparel Retailer
N.A.I.C.S.: 458110

My Style Co., Ltd. (1)
1-30-7 Yamano 24 Building 4F Yoyogi, Shibuya-ku, Tokyo, 151-0053, Japan **(72.9%)**
Tel.: (81) 120438220
Web Site: http://www.my-style.co.jp
Beauty Salon Operator
N.A.I.C.S.: 812112
Yoshitomo Yamano *(Pres)*

Yamano Holdings Corporation - Jewelry Business Division (1)
1-26-2-5F Higashi Ueno, Taito-ku, Tokyo, 110-0015, Japan
Tel.: (81) 3 5846 1622
Jewelry Retailer
N.A.I.C.S.: 458310

YAMASA CORPORATION
2-10-1 Araoicho, Choshi, 288-0056, Chiba, Japan
Tel.: (81) 479 22 0095
Web Site: http://www.yamasa.com
Year Founded: 1645
Sales Range: $550-599.9 Million
Emp.: 808
Soy Sauce Mfr
N.A.I.C.S.: 311941
Michio Hamaguchi *(Chm)*

Subsidiaries:

YAMASA (THAILAND) CO., LTD. (1)
208 Moo 6 Tambol Taibau, Amphur Muang, Samut Prakan, 10280, Samutprakarn, Thailand
Tel.: (66) 27035360
Food Products Distr
N.A.I.C.S.: 424490

YAMASA CORPORATION - Biochemicals Division (1)
23-8 Nihonbashi Kakigaracho 1-chome, Chuo-ku, Tokyo, 103-0014, Japan
Tel.: (81) 336688558
Food Products Mfr
N.A.I.C.S.: 311421

YAMASA CORPORATION - Diagnostics Division (1)
1-23-8 Nihonbashi Kakigaracho, Chuo-ku, Tokyo, 103-0014, Japan
Tel.: (81) 336680311
Food Products Mfr
N.A.I.C.S.: 311421

YAMASA Corporation (1)
3500 Fairview Industrial Dr SE, Salem, OR 97302
Tel.: (503) 363-8550
Web Site: http://www.yamasausa.com
Food Products Mfr
N.A.I.C.S.: 311421

YAMASHIN-FILTER CORP.
16th Floor Nisseki-Yokohama Bldg 1-1-8 Sakuragi-cho, Naka-ku, Yokohama, 231-0062, Japan
Tel.: (81) 456801671
Web Site: https://www.yamashin-filter.co.jp
6240—(TKS)
Rev.: $119,138,640
Assets: $171,483,230
Liabilities: $30,696,840
Net Worth: $140,786,390
Earnings: $5,195,460
Emp.: 775
Fiscal Year-end: 03/31/24
Filter Product Mfr
N.A.I.C.S.: 333248
Atsuhiko Yamazaki *(Pres)*

Subsidiaries:

AQC Corporation (1)
1-2-29 Nankoukita, Osaka Suminoe-ku, Osaka, 559-0034, Japan
Tel.: (81) 666127700
Blown Glass Mfr
N.A.I.C.S.: 327212

YAMASHIN AMERICA INC. (1)
1892 S Elmhurst Rd, Mount Prospect, IL 60056
Tel.: (847) 640-9331
Filter Product Mfr
N.A.I.C.S.: 333998
Yutaka Kagami *(Sec)*

YAMASHIN CEBU FILTER MFG. CORP. (1)
Mactan Economic Zone 2-Special Economic Zone Basak, Lapu-Lapu, 6015, Mactan Cebu, Philippines
Tel.: (63) 323400392
Filter Product Mfr
N.A.I.C.S.: 333998

YAMASHIN EUROPE BRUSSELS BVBA (1)
Rue Colonel Bourg 105, Brussels, 1030, Belgium
Tel.: (32) 27937820
Filter Product Distr
N.A.I.C.S.: 423120

YAMASHIN FILTER (SIP) TECHNOLOGY INC. (1)
G Unit SIP Science Industrial Square Phase II No 1 Ke Zhi Road, Suzhou, 215121, China
Tel.: (86) 51281878198
Filter Product Mfr
N.A.I.C.S.: 333998

YAMASHIN THAI LIMITED (1)
388 Exchange Tower 21st floor unit 2101 - 2 Sukhumvit Road, Klongtoey Subdistrict Klongtoey District, Bangkok, 10110, Thailand
Tel.: (66) 26634287
Filter Product Distr
N.A.I.C.S.: 423120

YAMASHIN VIETNAM CO., Ltd. (1)
Plot No B14-15 Thang Long Industrial Park, Thien Ke Commune, 15810, Binh Xuyen, Vinh Phuc, Vietnam
Tel.: (84) 2113888955
Air Filter Product Mfr & Distr
N.A.I.C.S.: 333415

Yamashin Cebu Filter Manufacturing Corp. (1)
Mactan Economic Zone 2-Special Economic Zone Basak Mactan, Lapu-Lapu City, Cebu, 6015, Philippines
Tel.: (63) 323400392
Air Filter Product Mfr & Distr
N.A.I.C.S.: 333415

YAMASHINA CORPORATION
16 Higashinokitsuneyabu-cho, Yamashina-ku, Kyoto, 607-8155, Japan
Tel.: (81) 755912131
Web Site: http://www.yamashina.ne.jp
Year Founded: 1917
5955—(TKS)
Rev.: $80,331,330
Assets: $119,621,170
Liabilities: $39,719,490
Net Worth: $79,901,680
Earnings: $1,619,450
Emp.: 97
Fiscal Year-end: 03/31/24
Metal Product Mfr & Distr
N.A.I.C.S.: 332722

YAMASHITA CORPORATION
18-1 Minami-cho Suruga-ku South Pot Shizuoka 7F, Shizuoka, 422 8067, Japan
Tel.: (81) 54 202 3333   JP
Web Site: http://www.yco.co.jp
Year Founded: 1963
Sales Range: $150-199.9 Million
Emp.: 1,200
Health & Medical Equipment Rental & Leasing; Linen Supply Services
N.A.I.C.S.: 423450

Subsidiaries:

Nissho Linen Supply Co., Ltd. (1)
777 Yamakawa-cho, Ashikaga, 326-0021, Tochigi, Japan
Tel.: (81) 284416481
Web Site: http://www.nissho-linen.co.jp
Emp.: 239
Linen Supply Services
N.A.I.C.S.: 812331
Kazuhiro Yamashita *(Pres & CEO)*

YAMASHITA HEALTH CARE HOLDINGS, INC.
Hakata Ward Shimokawabata-cho 2-1 Hakataza Nishigin Building 10th fl, Fukuoka, 812-0027, Japan
Tel.: (81) 924022922
Web Site: https://www.yhchd.co.jp
9265—(TKS)
Rev.: $406,878,550
Assets: $175,541,770
Liabilities: $118,986,610
Net Worth: $56,555,160
Earnings: $3,833,800
Fiscal Year-end: 05/31/24
Medical Equipment Whslr
N.A.I.C.S.: 423450
Naoto Yamashita *(Pres & CEO)*

Subsidiaries:

TOMS Co., Ltd (1)
3-2-2 Shonanmachi, Hakata-ku, Fukuoka, 812-0876, Japan
Tel.: (81) 92 592 3318
Web Site: https://www.toms-md.co.jp
Medical Equipment Distr
N.A.I.C.S.: 423450

YAMASHITA MEDICAL INSTRUMENTS CO., LTD.
6F NOF Tenjin Minami Bldg 3-6-15 Watanabe-Dori, Chuo-ku, Fukuoka, 810 0004, Japan
Tel.: (81) 92 726 8202   JP
Web Site: http://www.yamashitaika.co.jp
Year Founded: 1926
3022—(TKS)
Sales Range: $450-499.9 Million
Emp.: 521
Medical Equipment Mfr
N.A.I.C.S.: 423450
Hidenori Ito *(Gen Mgr-Mgmt)*

YAMATANE CORPORATION
1-2-21 Etchujima, Koto-ku, Tokyo, 135-8501, Japan
Tel.: (81) 338201111
Web Site: http://www.yamatane.co.jp
Year Founded: 1937
9305—(TKS)
Rev.: $426,424,320
Assets: $1,030,538,660
Liabilities: $660,041,550
Net Worth: $370,497,110
Earnings: $16,141,620
Fiscal Year-end: 03/31/24
Warehousing Services
N.A.I.C.S.: 493110
Iwao Kawarada *(Pres & CEO)*

Subsidiaries:

Active Co., Ltd. (1)
7-55 Fujizuka, Nisshin, 470-0117, Aichi, Japan
Tel.: (81) 561727011
Web Site: https://www.acv.co.jp
Motorcycle Product Mfr & Distr
N.A.I.C.S.: 336991

Air Sea Worldwide (China) Ltd. (1)
16/F Resource Plaza No 268 Zhong Shan Road South, Shanghai, 200010, China
Tel.: (86) 2163326700
Freight Forwarding Services
N.A.I.C.S.: 488510

Asian Tigers K.C.Dat (China) Ltd. (1)
8F Asionics Technology Building 6 Lane 1279 Zhong Shan W Road, Shanghai, 200051, China
Tel.: (86) 2132095561
Freight Forwarding Services
N.A.I.C.S.: 488510

Asian Tigers Transpo International (Vietnam) Ltd. (1)
Freight Forwarding Services
N.A.I.C.S.: 488510

Asian Tigers Transpo International Ltd. (1)
3388/74-77 Sirinrat Building 21st Floor Rama IV Road Klongton, Klongtoey, Bangkok, 10110, Thailand
Tel.: (66) 26877940
Freight Forwarding Services
N.A.I.C.S.: 488510

Chuo Logistics Co., Ltd. (1)
1-1-1 Etchujima Koto-Ku, Tokyo, Japan
Tel.: (81) 336439222
Freight Forwarding Services
N.A.I.C.S.: 488510

Harpers Sea Freight Co., Ltd. (1)
Freight Forwarding Services
N.A.I.C.S.: 488510

Solution Labo Tokyo Co., Ltd. (1)
8-1 Nihonbashi Hakozakicho, Chuo-ku, Tokyo, Japan
Tel.: (81) 332495681
Web Site: http://www.sltokyo.co.jp
Information System Support Services
N.A.I.C.S.: 541512

YS LOGISTICS PTE. LTD. (1)
21 Pandan Avenue 05-01 Senkee Logistics Hub, Singapore, 609388, Singapore
Tel.: (65) 64666882
Freight Forwarding Services
N.A.I.C.S.: 488510
Yasuhide Sakamoto *(Mng Dir)*

YAMATO HOLDINGS CO., LTD.
16-10 Ginza 2-chome, Chuo-ku, Tokyo, 104-8125, Japan
Tel.: (81) 335414141   JP
Web Site: https://www.yamato-hd.co.jp
Year Founded: 1919
9064—(TKS)
Rev.: $11,624,517,860
Assets: $7,508,265,950
Liabilities: $3,595,278,150
Net Worth: $3,912,987,800
Earnings: $248,707,860

YAMATO HOLDINGS CO., LTD.

Yamato Holdings Co. Ltd.—(Continued)

Emp.: 220,000
Fiscal Year-end: 03/31/24
Holding Company
N.A.I.C.S.: 551112
Masaki Yamauchi *(Chm)*

Subsidiaries:

Express Network Co., Ltd. (1)
2F Hamamatsucho Building 2-12-9 Shiba-daimon, Minato-ku, Tokyo, 105-0012, Japan
Tel.: (81) 354085790
Web Site: https://www.expressnetwork.co.jp
Air Freight Transport Services
N.A.I.C.S.: 481212

Fine Credit Co., Ltd. (1)
3-15-10 Takada, Toshima-ku, Tokyo, 171-0033, Japan
Tel.: (81) 359567711
Web Site: https://www.yamato-credit-finance.co.jp
Emp.: 248
Financial Support Services
N.A.I.C.S.: 522291

Guangxi Overland Total Logistics Co., Ltd. (1)
Shenzhen Bao'an International Airport T3 Office Tower Block D, Unit 305A Baoan District, Shenzhen, 518128, Guangdong, China
Tel.: (86) 75523453482
Domestic Trucking Services
N.A.I.C.S.: 484121

Kobe Yamato Transport Co., Ltd. (1)
1-2-12 Minatojima Nakamachi, Chuo-ku, Kobe, 650-0046, Hyogo, Japan
Tel.: (81) 783037008
Web Site: http://www.kobe-ytc.co.jp
Emp.: 114
Warehousing & Freight Forwarding Services
N.A.I.C.S.: 488510

Konan Industry Co., Ltd. (1)
3 Ozawatari-cho, Minami-ku, Hamamatsu, 432-8063, Shizuoka, Japan
Tel.: (81) 534453700
Web Site: https://www.y-logi.com
Emp.: 480
Vehicles Transportation Services
N.A.I.C.S.: 484220

OTL Asia Sdn. Bhd. (1)
No 2288 Mukim 14, Permatang Tinggi, 14000, Bukit Mertajam, Penang, Malaysia
Tel.: (60) 45682925
Marketing & Business Development Services
N.A.I.C.S.: 541613

Okinawa Yamato Transport Co., Ltd. (1)
4-21-3 Nishizaki-cho, Itoman, 901-0306, Okinawa, Japan
Tel.: (81) 988403580
Web Site: https://www.okinawayamato.co.jp
Emp.: 1,516
Courier Service
N.A.I.C.S.: 492110
Shinich Akamine *(Pres)*

Overland Total Logistic Services (M) Sdn. Bhd. (1)
No 2288 Mukim 14, Permatang Tinggi, 14000, Bukit Mertajam, Penang, Malaysia
Tel.: (60) 45682925
Web Site: https://www.otlsb.com
Freight Forwarding Services
N.A.I.C.S.: 488510
Lucas Lai *(Asst Mgr-Customer Svcs)*

Overland Total Logistics (Thailand) Co., Ltd. (1)
294/33 Leabmotorway-Romklao Road, Klongsamprawet Ladkrabang, Bangkok, 10520, Thailand
Tel.: (66) 27379801
Domestic Trucking Services
N.A.I.C.S.: 484121

Overland Total Logistics Services Vietnam Joint Stock Company (1)
14th Floor Handico Tower Me Tri Ha New Urban City Pham Hung Road, Nam Tu Liem District, 129400, Hanoi, Vietnam
Tel.: (84) 2473052525
Domestic Trucking Services
N.A.I.C.S.: 484121

PT. Yamato Indonesia (1)
Wisma Keiai 12A Floor Jl Jend Sudirman Kav-3, Jakarta Pusat, 10220, Indonesia
Tel.: (62) 215723251
Logistics Consulting Servies
N.A.I.C.S.: 541614

PT. Yamato Indonesia Forwarding (1)
Kompleks Pergudangan Soewarna Unit E6 Soewarna Business Park, Block B Lot7-8, Tangerang, 15126, Indonesia
Tel.: (62) 2155911222
Web Site: http://www.yamatoindonesia.com
Freight Forwarding Services
N.A.I.C.S.: 488510

Shanghai Wai Gao Qiao Bonded Logistics Zone Yamato Warehouse Co., Ltd. (1)
E1-1A No 160 Shen-ya Road Waigaoqiao Bonded Logistics Zone, Shanghai, 200441, China
Tel.: (86) 2138750116
Web Site: http://www.yamato-hd.co.jp
Logistics Consulting Servies
N.A.I.C.S.: 541614

Shenzhen Overland Supply Chain Management Co., Ltd. (1)
Shenzhen Bao'an International Airport T3 Office Tower Block D, Unit 305B Baoan District, Shenzhen, 518128, Guangdong, China
Tel.: (86) 75523453368
Freight Logistics Services
N.A.I.C.S.: 488510

Shenzhen Shun Zhi Tong International Logistics Co., Ltd. (1)
Shenzhen Bao'an International Airport T3 Office Tower Block D Unit 303, Baoan District, Shenzhen, 518128, Guangdong, China
Tel.: (86) 7552345348
Custom Clearance Services
N.A.I.C.S.: 488510

Swan Co., Ltd. (1)
2-16-10 Ginza, Chuo-ku, Tokyo, 104-0061, Japan
Tel.: (81) 335431067
Web Site: https://www.swanbakery.co.jp
Emp.: 80
Baked Goods Mfr & Retailer
N.A.I.C.S.: 311813

YAMATO INTERNATIONAL LOGISTICS (HK) LTD.
23F AIA Financial Center 712 Prince Edward Road East, Kowloon, China (Hong Kong)
Tel.: (852) 22620666
Web Site: http://www.yamatohk.com.hk
Emp.: 200
Logistics & Warehousing Services
N.A.I.C.S.: 493110

Yamato (China) Transport Co., Ltd. (1)
Room 1901 Building 1 Lane 66 Huayuan Road, Hongkou District, Shanghai, 200083, China
Tel.: (86) 2156067872
Door-to-Door Delivery Services
N.A.I.C.S.: 492210

Yamato 365 Express Company Limited (1)
13 Nguyen Quang Bich St, Ward 13 Tan Binh District, Ho Chi Minh City, Vietnam
Tel.: (84) 2838497999
Web Site: http://www.yamato365express.com
Emp.: 200
Parcel Delivery Services
N.A.I.C.S.: 492110

Yamato Asia Pte. Ltd. (1)
223 Mountbatten Road 03-10, Singapore, 398008, Singapore
Tel.: (65) 6632 7400
Web Site: http://www.yamato-asia.com
Freight Forwarding Services
N.A.I.C.S.: 488510
Richard Chua *(Mng Dir)*

Yamato Autoworks Co., Ltd. (1)
1-18-8 Shintomi, Chuo-ku, Tokyo, 104-0041, Japan
Tel.: (81) 351178900
Web Site: https://www.yaw.co.jp
Emp.: 2,147
Automotive Repair & Maintenance Services
N.A.I.C.S.: 811111

Yamato Autoworks Hokushinetsu Co., Ltd. (1)
123-3 Teraji, Nishi-ku, Niigata, 950-1104, Japan
Tel.: (81) 253771212
Automobile Maintenance & Repair Services
N.A.I.C.S.: 811111

Yamato Autoworks Iwate Co., Ltd. (1)
17-3 Distribution Center, Kitakami, 024-0014, Iwate, Japan
Tel.: (81) 197682774
Automotive Repair & Maintenance Services
N.A.I.C.S.: 811310

Yamato Autoworks Okinawa Co., Ltd. (1)
4-21-3 Nishizaki-cho, Itoman, 901-0305, Okinawa, Japan
Tel.: (81) 988408880
Web Site: http://www.yamato-hd.co.jp
Automotive Repair & Maintenance Services
N.A.I.C.S.: 811198

Yamato Autoworks Shikoku Co., Ltd. (1)
31 Nishiminato-machi Tadotsu-cho, Nakatado-gun, Kagawa, 764-0017, Japan
Tel.: (81) 877566932
Web Site: http://www.yamato-hd.co.jp
Automotive Repair & Maintenance Services
N.A.I.C.S.: 811111
Tetsuya Egashira *(Pres)*

Yamato Box Charter Co., Ltd. (1)
6-26 Akashicho, Chuo - ku, Tokyo, 104-0044, Japan
Tel.: (81) 335162223
Web Site: https://www.yamatobc.com
Emp.: 1,495
Freight Transportation Services
N.A.I.C.S.: 484220

Yamato Career Service Co., Ltd. (1)
2-27-14 Yoyogi, Shibuya-ku, Tokyo, 151-0053, Japan
Tel.: (81) 353516911
Web Site: http://www.yamato-career.com
Temporary Staffing Services
N.A.I.C.S.: 561320

Yamato Contact Service Co., Ltd. (1)
3-33-1 Minami-Otsuka JR Otsuka South Exit Building 8F, Toshima-ku, Tokyo, 170-0005, Japan
Tel.: (81) 367569625
Web Site: https://www.y-cs.co.jp
Telemarketing Services
N.A.I.C.S.: 561422
Yasuki Hirouchi *(Pres)*

Yamato Dialog & Media Co., Ltd. (1)
4-3-6 Nihonbashi Honmachi PMO Shin-Nihonbashi 4F, Chuo-ku, Tokyo, 103-0023, Japan
Tel.: (81) 364780001
Web Site: https://www.yamato-dm.co.jp
Emp.: 17
Direct Marketing Services
N.A.I.C.S.: 541613

Yamato Financial Co., Ltd. (1)
10-12F Yamato Ginza Building 2-12-18 Ginza, Chuo-ku, Tokyo, 104-0061, Japan
Tel.: (81) 366718080
Web Site: http://www.yamatofinancial.jp
Emp.: 456
Viatical Settlement Services
N.A.I.C.S.: 561990
Toshizo Kurisu *(Pres)*

Yamato Global Express Co., Ltd. (1)
2-6-2 Hamamatsucho Hamamatsucho 262 Building 6F, Minato-ku, Tokyo, 105-0013, Japan
Tel.: (81) 368608100
Web Site: http://www.yamato-ygx.co.jp
Emp.: 2,533
Freight Transportation Services
N.A.I.C.S.: 481212

Yamato Global Logistics Japan Co., Ltd. (1)

INTERNATIONAL PUBLIC

5F Tsukiji First Nagaoka Bldg 2-3-4 Tsukiji, Chuo-ku, Tokyo, 104-0045, Japan (70%)
Tel.: (81) 367578500
Web Site: http://www.y-logi.com
Emp.: 1,191
Courier Service
N.A.I.C.S.: 492110
Hiroyoshi Kanai *(Pres)*

Yamato Global Logistics Myanmar Co., Ltd. (1)
MGW Centre Suite 809 No170/176 Bo Aung Kyaw St, Botataung Township, 11161, Yangon, Myanmar
Tel.: (95) 1256568
Freight Forwarding Services
N.A.I.C.S.: 488510

Yamato Home Convenience Co., Ltd. (1)
TIE Hamacyo Building 2F 2-61-9 Hamacyo, Nihonbashi Chuo-ku, Tokyo, 103-0007, Japan
Tel.: (81) 366719452
Web Site: https://www.008008.jp
Emp.: 2,811
Household Goods Delivery & Moving Services
N.A.I.C.S.: 492210

Yamato International Logistics Co., Ltd. (1)
Tel.: (86) 2038824338
Emp.: 200
Logistics Consulting Servies
N.A.I.C.S.: 541614
Shinya Tamura *(Mng Dir)*

Yamato Investment (Hong Kong) Limited (1)
25/F Port 33 33 Tseuk Luk Street, San Po Kong, Kowloon, China (Hong Kong)
Tel.: (852) 22620674
Transportation Services
N.A.I.C.S.: 488510

Yamato Lease Co., Ltd. (1)
3-15-10 Takada, Toshima-ku, Tokyo, 171-0033, Japan
Tel.: (81) 359535160
Web Site: https://www.yamatolease.co.jp
Automobile Leasing Services
N.A.I.C.S.: 532112

Yamato Logistics (Hong Kong) Limited (1)
25/F Port 33 33 Tseuk Luk Street, San Po Kong, Kowloon, China (Hong Kong)
Tel.: (852) 22620666
Air Freight Services
N.A.I.C.S.: 488510

Yamato Logistics Co., Ltd. (1)
5F Yamato Ginza Building 2-12-18 Ginza, Chuo-ku, Tokyo, 104-0061, Japan (100%)
Tel.: (81) 366718700
Web Site: http://www.y-logi.com
Emp.: 4,641
International Freight Forwarding & Logistical Services
N.A.I.C.S.: 541614
Takashi Ikeda *(Mng Exec Officer)*

Yamato Logistics India Pvt. Ltd. (1)
1302 Tower A Signature Tower Sector 29, Gurgaon, 122001, Haryana, India
Emp.: 12
Logistics Support Services
N.A.I.C.S.: 541614
Yasuyoshi Iwasaki *(Pres)*

Yamato Logistics Vietnam Company Limited (1)
14th Floor Handico Tower Pham Hung Street, Me Tri Ward Nam Tu Liem District, Hanoi, Vietnam
Tel.: (84) 2437959824
Web Site: http://www.yamato.com.vn
Freight Forwarding Services
N.A.I.C.S.: 488510

Yamato Management Service Co., Ltd. (1)
2-16-7 Ginza Kozen third building 3F, Chuo-ku, Tokyo, 104-0061, Japan
Tel.: (81) 335448600
Web Site: http://www.yamato-ms.co.jp
Emp.: 100
Accounting & Payroll Processing Services
N.A.I.C.S.: 541214

AND PRIVATE COMPANIES

Yamato Multi Charter Co., Ltd. (1)
5-1 Takamiyasakae-machi, Neyagawa, 572-0846, Osaka, Japan
Tel.: (81) 72 820 3111
Arterial Transport Services
N.A.I.C.S.: 541614

Yamato Multi-Maintenance Solutions Co., Ltd. (1)
4-2-3 Ariake, Koto-ku, Tokyo, 135-0063, Japan
Tel.: (81) 335278237
Web Site: http://www.y-logi.com
Emp.: 300
Faulty Product Maintenance Services
N.A.I.C.S.: 811310

Yamato Packing Service Co., Ltd. (1)
8-4 Seaside, Koto-ku, Tokyo, 135-0012, Japan
Tel.: (81) 356065523
Web Site: http://www.y-logi.com
Emp.: 416
Packing & Cargo Transportation Services
N.A.I.C.S.: 488510

Yamato Packing Technology Institute Co., Ltd. (1)
Haneda Chronogate 11-1 Hanedaasahi-cho, Koto-ku, Tokyo, 144-0042, Japan
Tel.: (81) 367567200
Web Site: http://www.yamato-pti.co.jp
Packaging Materials Mfr
N.A.I.C.S.: 321920

Yamato Staff Supply Co., Ltd. (1)
KPP Akashicho Building 3F 6-26 Akashicho, Chuo-ku, Tokyo, 104-0044, Japan
Tel.: (81) 366718780
Web Site: https://www.y-staff-supply.co.jp
Temporary Staffing Services
N.A.I.C.S.: 561320

Yamato System Development Co., Ltd. (1)
2-5-15 Minamisuna, Koto-ku, Tokyo, 136-8675, Japan
Tel.: (81) 363330100
Web Site: https://www.nekonet.co.jp
Emp.: 2,696
Computer Software Consulting Services
N.A.I.C.S.: 541512
Nobuaki Kurimaru *(Pres & Exec Officer)*

Yamato Transport (M) Sdn. Bhd. (1)
Block A No 16 Jalan PPU 3 Taman Perindustrian Puchong Utama, 47100, Puchong, Selangor, Malaysia
Tel.: (60) 380226579
Web Site: http://my.ta-q-bin.com
Emp.: 70
Logistics Support Services
N.A.I.C.S.: 541614

Yamato Transport (S) Pte Ltd.-Seafreight (1)
2 Bukit Merah Central, Singapore, 159835, Singapore **(100%)**
Tel.: (65) 65951854
Web Site: http://www.yamatosingapore.com
Emp.: 80
Freight & Cargo Forwarding Services
N.A.I.C.S.: 488320

Yamato Transport Co., Ltd. (1)
2-16-10 Ginza, Chuo-ku, Tokyo, 104-8125, Japan
Tel.: (81) 335413411
Web Site: http://www.kuronekoyamato.co.jp
Emp.: 183,249
Courier Service
N.A.I.C.S.: 492110
Toshiyuki Nishide *(Mng Exec Officer)*

Subsidiary (Non-US):

Taiwan Yamato International Logistics Inc. (2)
Tel.: (886) 227541966
Web Site: http://www.yamato.com.tw
Emp.: 113
Freight Forwarding Services
N.A.I.C.S.: 488510

Yamato Transport Europe B.V. (1)
Capronilaan 22, 1119 NS, Schiphol-Rijk, Netherlands
Tel.: (31) 203166866
Web Site: http://www.yamatoeurope.com
Emp.: 10
Logistics Consulting Servies
N.A.I.C.S.: 541614

Yamato Transport Mexico S.A.de C.V. (1)
Petrarca 133 Room 303 Col Polanco V Secc en la, 11560, Mexico, Mexico
Tel.: (52) 5552509377
Freight Logistics Services
N.A.I.C.S.: 488510

Yamato Transport U.S.A., Inc. (1)
20 Murray Hill Pkwy Ste 160, East Rutherford, NJ 07073 **(100%)**
Tel.: (201) 583-9696
Web Site: http://www.yamatoamerica.com
Emp.: 50
International Air & Marine Freight Forwarding, Moving Services, Customs Clearances, Travel & Warehousing Services
N.A.I.C.S.: 488510
Hiroyuki Mizushima *(Pres)*

Yamato Unyu (Thailand) Co., Ltd. (1)
1617 Pattanakarn Road Kwang Suanluang, Khet Suanluang, Bangkok, 10250, Thailand **(100%)**
Tel.: (66) 20266828
Web Site: https://www.yamatothai.com
Emp.: 100
Customs Clearance & Freight Forwarding Services
N.A.I.C.S.: 483111

Yamato Web Solutions Co., Ltd. (1)
1-8-11 Harumi Island Triton Square Office Tower Y Building 33F Harumi, Chuo-ku, Tokyo, 104-6133, Japan
Tel.: (81) 342328010
Web Site: http://www.yamato-websolutions.co.jp
Software Development Services
N.A.I.C.S.: 541511

YAMATO INDUSTRY CO., LTD.
4274 Furuyakami, Kawagoe, 350-0001, Saitama, Japan
Tel.: (81) 492351234
Web Site: https://www.yamato-in.co.jp
Year Founded: 1955
7886—(TKS)
Rev.: $101,556,040
Assets: $56,713,800
Liabilities: $46,329,490
Net Worth: $10,384,310
Earnings: ($984,890)
Fiscal Year-end: 03/31/24
Synthetic Resin Moldings, Logistics Equipment Mfr & Distr
N.A.I.C.S.: 325211

Subsidiaries:

YMT International Mexicana S.A. de C.V. (1)
Paseo de los industriales 198-1 Parque Central Guanajuato, 36541, Irapuato, Gto, Mexico
Tel.: (52) 4626075200
Web Site: https://yamatomexico.mx
Automobile Application Mfr & Distr
N.A.I.C.S.: 334419

YAMATO INTERNATIONAL INC.
1-3-1Morikawachi Nishi, Higashiosaka, 577-0061, Osaka, Japan
Tel.: (81) 667479500
Web Site: https://www.yamatointr.co.jp
Year Founded: 1947
8127—(TKS)
Rev.: $131,484,580
Assets: $149,323,540
Liabilities: $41,418,980
Net Worth: $107,904,560
Earnings: $2,189,440
Emp.: 165
Fiscal Year-end: 08/31/24
Textile Product Mfr & Distr
N.A.I.C.S.: 315990

Tomoki Hannya *(Pres & CEO)*

YAMATO KOGYO CO. LTD.
380 Kibi, Otsu-ku, Himeji, 671-1192, Hyogo, Japan
Tel.: (81) 792731061
Web Site: https://www.yamatokogyo.co.jp
Year Founded: 1944
5444—(TKS)
Rev.: $1,080,596,190
Assets: $4,024,055,630
Liabilities: $355,895,620
Net Worth: $3,668,160,010
Earnings: $462,818,980
Emp.: 3,800
Fiscal Year-end: 03/31/24
Steel Production & Resource Development
N.A.I.C.S.: 331210
Hiroyuki Inoue *(Chm)*

Subsidiaries:

Hokuto Tsushin Co., Ltd. (1)
1-20 Hokuju 2-chome, Shiroishi-ku, Sapporo, 003-0832, Japan
Tel.: (81) 118752320
Web Site: https://www.hokuto-tsushin.co.jp
Emp.: 7
Communication Equipment Mfr
N.A.I.C.S.: 334290

Mastubara Techno Co., Ltd. (1)
27 Niijima, Harima-cho Kako-gun, Hyogo, 675-0155, Japan
Tel.: (81) 794370333
Web Site: http://www.mbrtechno.co.jp
Emp.: 48
Storage Tank Mfr
N.A.I.C.S.: 332420
Hidehiko Kinoshita *(Pres)*

Nucor-Yamato Steel Company (1)
PO Box 1228, Blytheville, AR 72316
Tel.: (870) 762-5500
Web Site: https://www.nucoryamato.com
Sales Range: $350-399.9 Million
Emp.: 800
Structural Steel Products Mfr; Owned by Nucor Corporation & Yamato Kogyo Co. Ltd.
N.A.I.C.S.: 331110
Keith Prevost *(Controller)*

Siam Yamato Steel Co., Ltd. (1)
Head Quarter Building 2 7th Floor 1 Siam Cement Road, Bangsue, Bangkok, 10800, Thailand
Tel.: (66) 25867777
Web Site: https://www.syssteel.com
Emp.: 450
Mfr of Structural Steel Beams & Channels
N.A.I.C.S.: 238120

Yamato Steel Company Limited (1)
380 Kibi, PO Box 8, Otsu-ku, Himeji, 671-1133, Hyogo, Japan
Tel.: (81) 792731010
Web Site: https://www.yamatokogyo.co.jp
Sales Range: $200-249.9 Million
Steel & Heavy-Duty Processing Goods Mfr
N.A.I.C.S.: 238120

Yamato Trackwork System Co., Ltd (1)
380 Yoshimi, Otsu-ku, Himeji, 671-1133, Hyogo, Japan
Tel.: (81) 792730721
Web Site: http://www.yamatokogyo.co.jp
Sales Range: $25-49.9 Million
Emp.: 130
Railroad Track Mfr
N.A.I.C.S.: 336510

YAMATO MANUFACTURING COMPANY, LTD.
37-4 Hamabancho, Ayautagun Utazucho, Kagawa, 769-0203, Japan
Tel.: (81) 877 85 6168
Web Site: http://www.yamatomfg.com
Year Founded: 1975
Sales Range: $10-24.9 Million
Emp.: 50
Noodle Making Machinery Mfr

YAMAU HOLDINGS CO., LTD.

N.A.I.C.S.: 333241
Kaoru Fujii *(Pres)*

YAMATO, INC.
118 Furuichicho, Maebashi, 371-0844, Japan
Tel.: (81) 272901800
Web Site: https://www.yamato-se.co.jp
1967—(TKS)
Rev.: $441,175,680
Assets: $443,256,880
Liabilities: $120,244,960
Net Worth: $323,011,920
Earnings: $26,687,760
Fiscal Year-end: 03/31/22
Facility Management Services
N.A.I.C.S.: 236220

YAMAU HOLDINGS CO., LTD.
5-15-7 Higashi-Irube, Sawara-ku, Fukuoka, 811-1102, Fukuoka, Japan
Tel.: (81) 928723301
Web Site: https://www.yamau.co.jp
Year Founded: 1968
5284—(TKS)
Rev.: $130,514,450
Assets: $157,271,730
Liabilities: $86,604,220
Net Worth: $70,667,510
Earnings: $11,481,570
Emp.: 455
Fiscal Year-end: 03/31/24
Concrete Product Mfr & Distr
N.A.I.C.S.: 327390
Keizo Komine *(Chm)*

Subsidiaries:

DAIEI KAIHATSU Co., Ltd. (1)
2690 Hiucho, Sasebo, 857-1151, Nagasaki, Japan
Tel.: (81) 956319358
Web Site: https://daieikaihatsu.co.jp
Civil Engineering Services
N.A.I.C.S.: 541330

KOYO SYSTEM KIKI Co., Ltd. (1)
1-67 Sori, Kasugai, Fukuoka, Japan
Tel.: (81) 925965600
Web Site: http://www.koyo-system.jp
Computer Peripheral Equipment Mfr & Distr
N.A.I.C.S.: 334118

MIYAZAKI PRECON Co., Ltd. (1)
600 Hanamikawahara Takaoka-cho, Miyazaki, Miyazaki, Japan
Tel.: (81) 985309101
Concrete Product Mfr & Distr
N.A.I.C.S.: 327390

YAMAU CO., LTD. - Fukuoka Factory (1)
5- chome Higashiiribe, Sawara-ku, Fukuoka, 811-1102, Japan
Tel.: (81) 928042357
Concrete Products Mfr
N.A.I.C.S.: 327390

YAMAU CO., LTD. - Kagoshima Factory (1)
666-17 Sumiyoshi, Hayato-cho, Kirishima, 899-5101, Kagoshima, Japan
Tel.: (81) 995434002
Concrete Products Mfr
N.A.I.C.S.: 327390

YAMAU CO., LTD. - Kawaminami Factory (1)
20555 Kawaminami, Koyu, 889-1301, Miyazaki, Japan
Tel.: (81) 983271181
Concrete Products Mfr
N.A.I.C.S.: 327390

YAMAU CO., LTD. - Kitakyushu Factory (1)
1673-8 Oaza Mitoku, Otake-cho, Kurate, 820-1101, Fukuoka, Japan
Tel.: (81) 949627100
Concrete Products Mfr
N.A.I.C.S.: 327390

YAMAU CO., LTD. - Oita Factory (1)
1180-6 Yoshida, Nozu-cho, Usuki, 875-

YAMAU HOLDINGS CO., LTD.

Yamau Holdings Co., Ltd.—(Continued)
0222, Oita, Japan
Tel.: (81) 974327711
Concrete Products Mfr
N.A.I.C.S.: 327390

YAMAU CO., LTD. - REC Factory (1)
21732-2 Toyohara, Kawaminami-cho, Koyu, 889-1301, Miyazaki, Japan
Tel.: (81) 983271134
Concrete Products Mfr
N.A.I.C.S.: 327390

YAMAU CO., LTD. - Saga Factory (1)
2974 Fujiwara, Mise Village, Saga, 842-0302, Japan
Tel.: (81) 952562331
Concrete Products Mfr
N.A.I.C.S.: 327390

YAMAU CO., LTD. - Takasaki Factory (1)
3706-7 Nawaze, Takazaki-cho, Miyakonojo, 889-4503, Miyazaki, Japan
Tel.: (81) 986623400
Concrete Products Mfr
N.A.I.C.S.: 327390

YAMAUCHI CORP., LTD.
2-7 Shodai Tajika, Hirakata, 573-1132, Osaka, Japan
Tel.: (81) 72 856 1130   JP
Web Site: http://www.yamauchi.co.jp
Year Founded: 1918
Emp.: 1,600
Industrial Rubber & Plastic Products Mfr
N.A.I.C.S.: 326220
Ichiro Yamauchi *(Pres & CEO)*

Subsidiaries:

MirrorMax Oy (1)
Pajatie 69, 48600, Kotka, Finland
Tel.: (358) 11 233061
Sales Range: $200-249.9 Million
Paper & Paperboard Production Machinery Mfr
N.A.I.C.S.: 333243

YAMAUCHI (SEOUL OFFICE) CORPORATION (1)
2108 Ho Hyundai 41 Tower Mok1-Dong, Yangcheon-Gu, Seoul, Korea (South)
Tel.: (82) 2 2061 7047
Electronic Parts Distr
N.A.I.C.S.: 423690

Yamauchi (U.S.A.) Corporation (1)
1 Woodfield Pl STE 320 1701 E Woodfield Rd, Schaumburg, IL 60173
Tel.: (847) 807-2880
Web Site: http://www.yamauchi.co.jp
Emp.: 2
Industrial Machinery Components Distr
N.A.I.C.S.: 423840
Kaoru Michihara *(Pres)*

Yamauchi Corp. N.V. (1)
Diepenbekerweg 1, 3500, Hasselt, Belgium
Tel.: (32) 11 233061
Web Site: http://www.yamauchi.co.jp
Molded Resin Parts Mfr & Distr
N.A.I.C.S.: 326199

Yamauchi Corp., Ltd. - Kanuma Factory (1)
11-2 Satsuki-cho, Kanuma, 322-0014, Tochigi, Japan
Tel.: (81) 289 76 2101
Industrial Rubber Product Mfr
N.A.I.C.S.: 326299

Yamauchi Corp., Ltd. - Kyoto Osadano Factory (1)
2-62-1 Osadano-cho, Fukuchiyama, 620-0853, Kyoto, Japan
Tel.: (81) 773 27 5141
Industrial Rubber Product Mfr
N.A.I.C.S.: 326299

Yamauchi Hong Kong Ltd. (1)
RM 1404 Nanfung Commercial Centre 19 Lamlok St, Kowloon Bay, Kowloon, China (Hong Kong)
Tel.: (852) 2795 8278
Electronic Parts Distr
N.A.I.C.S.: 423690

Yamauchi Malaysia Sdn. Bhd. (1)
PLO 138 Senai Industrial Area Phase III, 81400, Senai, Johor Darul Takzim, Malaysia
Tel.: (60) 7 599 3335
Web Site: http://www.yamauchi.co.jp
Rubber & Plastic Belt Mfr
N.A.I.C.S.: 326220

Yamauchi Precision Shanghai Co., Ltd. (1)
789-1 Shengfu Road, Xinzhuang Industrial Park, Shanghai, 201108, China
Tel.: (86) 2154 429 108
Web Site: http://www.yamauchi.co.jp
Rubber & Plastic Office Equipment Drive Components Mfr & Distr
N.A.I.C.S.: 326220

Yamauchi Precision Shenzhen Ltd. (1)
1&2/F No 1 Building Xinwei Industrial Zone, Dalan Baoan, Shenzhen, China
Tel.: (86) 755 8372 6626
Web Site: http://www.yamauchi.co.jp
Rubber & Plastic Industrial Components Mfr & Distr
N.A.I.C.S.: 326220

Yamauchi Singapore Pte. Ltd. (1)
514 Chai Chee Lane #02-13, Singapore, 469029, Singapore
Tel.: (65) 6449 4366
Web Site: http://www.yamauchi.co.jp
Precision Molded Resin Parts Mfr & Distr
N.A.I.C.S.: 326199
Takao Yamauthi *(Mng Dir)*

YAMAURA CORPORATION
22-1 Kitamachi, Komagane, 399-4195, Nagano, Japan
Tel.: (81) 265816010
Web Site: https://www.yamaura.co.jp
Year Founded: 1960
1780—(TKS)
Rev.: $248,179,060
Assets: $211,394,410
Liabilities: $76,041,440
Net Worth: $135,352,970
Earnings: $19,671,360
Emp.: 416
Fiscal Year-end: 03/31/24
Construction & Civil Engineering Services
N.A.I.C.S.: 236116
Yasutami Yamaura *(Chm)*

YAMAX CORP.
3-9-5 Suizenji, Chuo-ku, Kumamoto, 862-0950, Japan
Tel.: (81) 963816411
Web Site: https://www.yamax.co.jp
Year Founded: 1963
5285—(TKS)
Rev.: $137,534,270
Assets: $123,078,200
Liabilities: $76,867,690
Net Worth: $46,210,510
Earnings: $8,573,170
Emp.: 519
Fiscal Year-end: 03/31/24
Concrete Product Mfr & Distr
N.A.I.C.S.: 327390
Kiyoshi Shigemori *(Chm)*

YAMAYA CORPORATION
Tsutsumioka 3-4-1 Azalea Hills 19F, Miyagino-ku, Sendai, 9830852, Miyagi, Japan
Tel.: (81) 120545883
Web Site: https://www.yamaya.jp
Year Founded: 1953
9994—(TKS)
Rev.: $1,059,814,350
Assets: $412,582,980
Liabilities: $190,890,190
Net Worth: $221,692,790
Earnings: $23,908,370
Emp.: 5,532
Fiscal Year-end: 03/31/24
Wine & Liquor, Non-Alcoholic Beverages & International Food Retailer & Importer
N.A.I.C.S.: 445320

Subsidiaries:

Chimney Co., Ltd. (1)
6F 7F 8F Raiden Building 3-22-6 Ryogoku, Sumida-ku, Tokyo, 130-0026, Japan
Tel.: (81) 358392600
Web Site: https://www.chimney.co.jp
Rev.: $170,042,250
Assets: $118,272,730
Liabilities: $84,812,910
Net Worth: $33,459,820
Earnings: $6,200,180
Emp.: 630
Fiscal Year-end: 03/31/2024
Restaurant Owner & Operator
N.A.I.C.S.: 722511
Hideharu Yamauchi *(Chm)*

YAMAZAKI BAKING CO., LTD.
3-10-1 Iwamotocho, Chiyoda Ku, Tokyo, 101-8585, Japan
Tel.: (81) 338643111
Web Site: https://www.yamazakipan.co.jp
Year Founded: 1948
2212—(TKS)
Rev.: $8,334,734,580
Assets: $5,686,428,150
Liabilities: $2,523,352,270
Net Worth: $3,163,075,880
Earnings: $213,891,120
Emp.: 19,446
Fiscal Year-end: 12/31/23
Bread & Baked Goods
N.A.I.C.S.: 311812
Nobuhiro Iijima *(Pres)*

Subsidiaries:

Akita Inafuku Confectionery Co., Ltd (1)
170 Azaokawabata Kawashirimachi, Akita, 010-0941, Japan
Tel.: (81) 188631729
Web Site: http://www.yamazakipan.co.jp
Confectionery Food Mfr & Distr
N.A.I.C.S.: 311999

Bakewise Brands, Inc. (1)
1668 N Wayneport Rd, Macedon, NY 14502-8765   **(100%)**
Tel.: (315) 986-9999
Web Site: http://www.bakewisebrands.com
Frozen & Refrigerated Bagels Mfr & Whslr
N.A.I.C.S.: 311812
Karidee Perry *(Mgr-HR)*

Daitoku K.K. (1)
3-1-4 Sakuragikita, Wakaba-ku, Chiba, 264-0029, Japan
Tel.: (81) 432333341
Web Site: https://www.kk-daitoku.co.jp
Industrial Machine & Office Equipment Distr
N.A.I.C.S.: 423420

Four Leaves Pte.Ltd (1)
37 Chin Bee Crescent, Singapore, 619903, Singapore
Tel.: (65) 6 268 6516
Web Site: https://www.fourleaves.com.sg
Emp.: 300
Bakery Products Mfr & Distr
N.A.I.C.S.: 311812

Hong Kong Yamazaki Baking Co., Ltd. (1)
500 S Hennessy Rd, Causeway Bay, China (Hong Kong)   **(100%)**
Tel.: (852) 2 576 6056
N.A.I.C.S.: 445298

Ikeda Bakery Co., Ltd (1)
5000 Hiramatsu, Aira, 899-5652, Kagoshima, Japan
Tel.: (81) 995658611
Confectionery Food Mfr & Distr
N.A.I.C.S.: 311919

Kanazawa German Bakery Co., Ltd (1)
3F Murakami Building 1-3-24 Katamachi, Kanazawa, 920-0981, Ishikawa, Japan

INTERNATIONAL PUBLIC

Tel.: (81) 762643521
Web Site: https://www.german.co.jp
Baked Goods Mfr & Sales
N.A.I.C.S.: 311813

Morioka Delica Co., Ltd (1)
26-4 Chiwarihaba 15 Dai Takata Yahabacho, Shiwa-gun, Iwata, 028-3601, Japan
Tel.: (81) 196970810
Prepared Rice Mfr & Sales
N.A.I.C.S.: 311412

Nichinoh Seiken Co., Ltd (1)
5285-3 Nagayoshi Osakicho, Soo-Gun, Kagoshima, 899-7306, Japan
Tel.: (81) 994764000
Sweeteners Mfr & Distr
N.A.I.C.S.: 311999

PT Yamazaki Indonesia (1)
Kawasan Industri Greenland Batavia Blok AH No 6 7 8 & BA No 1, Kota Deltamas Desa Sukamahi Kabupaten Bekasi Kecamatan Cikarang Pusat, Bekasi, 17530, Jawa Barat, Indonesia
Tel.: (62) 2189970826
Web Site: http://www.yzki.co.id
Emp.: 270
Food Products Mfr
N.A.I.C.S.: 311999

Sapporo Paris Co., Ltd (1)
4-3-37 3 Jo Kikusui, Shiroishi-Ku, Sapporo, 003-0803, Hokkaido, Japan
Tel.: (81) 118234101
Processed Confectionery Food Mfr
N.A.I.C.S.: 311999

Shanghai Yamazaki Baking Co.,Ltd (1)
Room 316 Shanghai Airport City Terminal Building 1600, Nanjing Road West, Shanghai, 200040, China
Tel.: (86) 2162498996
Web Site: https://www.yamazakipan.co.jp
Baked Goods Mfr & Distr
N.A.I.C.S.: 311999

Suehiro Confectionery Co., Ltd (1)
779 Nishinagashima, Nishikan-ku, Niigata, 953-0193, Japan   **(100%)**
Tel.: (81) 25 682 4131
Web Site: https://www.suehiroseika.co.jp
Processed Confectionery Foods Mfr & Distr
N.A.I.C.S.: 311999

Sun Logistics Co., Ltd (1)
18-1 Hiyoshicho Arai 181 Building, Tokorozawa, 359-1123, Saitama, Japan
Tel.: (81) 429037600
General Truck Transport & Consigned Freight Forwarding
N.A.I.C.S.: 484122

Sun-Delica Co., Ltd. (1)
3-10-1 Iwamotocho Yamazaki Iwamotocho Building 6th floor, Chiyoda-ku, Tokyo, 101-0032, Japan
Tel.: (81) 33 864 3248
Web Site: https://www.sundelica.co.jp
Food Product Mfr & Distr
N.A.I.C.S.: 311812

Sun-Kimuraya Co., Ltd (1)
1065-1 Nishishimojo-cho, Kofu, 400-0054, Yamanashi, Japan
Tel.: (81) 552414155
Web Site: https://www.sunkimuraya.jp
Emp.: 325
Confectionery Products Mfr & Distr
N.A.I.C.S.: 424450

Super Yamazaki Co., Ltd. (1)
1-7-3 Jushicho Muragi Building 2F, Fuchu, 183-0056, Tokyo, Japan
Tel.: (81) 423602511
Web Site: http://www.super-yamazaki.co.jp
Supermarket Operator
N.A.I.C.S.: 445110

Thai Yamazaki Co., Ltd. (1)
1126/2 Vanit Building 2 15 Floor room no 1503 1504, New Phetchaburi Road Makkasan Ratchathewi, Bangkok, 10400, Thailand
Tel.: (66) 225585104
Web Site: http://www.thaiyamazaki.com
Bakery Products Mfr
N.A.I.C.S.: 311812

Three S Foods Co., Ltd (1)

AND PRIVATE COMPANIES

280 Sayama Shinkaichi Kumiyama-cho, Kuse-gun, Kyoto, 613-0034, Japan
Tel.: (81) 774435933
Web Site: https://www.3sfoods.co.jp
Emp.: 240
Bread Mfr & Sales
N.A.I.C.S.: 311811

Tohato Inc. (1)
JRE Minamiikebukuro Building 3F 1-13-23 Minamiikebukuro, Toshima-ku, Tokyo, 171-0022, Japan (100%)
Tel.: (81) 120510810
Web Site: https://www.tohato.jp
Sales Range: $200-249.9 Million
Emp.: 678
Confectionary Product Mfr
N.A.I.C.S.: 311919
Nobuhiro Iijima (Chm)

Tom Cat Bakery, Inc. (1)
4305 10th St, Long Island City, NY 11101
Tel.: (718) 786-7659
Web Site: https://www.tomcatbakery.com
Bakery Food Product Mfr & Distr
N.A.I.C.S.: 311812
James Rath (VP & Gen Mgr)

VDF Sun-Royal Co., Ltd (1)
9-10 Minamieicho, Kasukabe, 344-0057, Saitama, Japan
Tel.: (81) 487612431
Web Site: https://www.vdfsunroyal.co.jp
Emp.: 494
Management, Manufacturing Sales & Bakery Shop for Frozen Bread Dough & Baked Products
N.A.I.C.S.: 311813
Toki Fuminori (Pres)

Vie de France Co., Ltd (1)
3-10-1 Iwamotocho, Chiyoda-Ku, Tokyo, 101-0032, Japan
Tel.: (81) 356798411
Web Site: https://www.viedefrance.co.jp
Sales Range: $250-299.9 Million
Emp.: 450
Baked Goods Distr & Retail Bakery-Cafe
N.A.I.C.S.: 424490

Vie de France Yamazaki, Inc. (1)
2070 Chain Bridge Rd Ste 500, Vienna, VA 22182-2588 (100%)
Tel.: (703) 442-9205
Web Site: https://www.viedefrance.com
Emp.: 1,000
Mfr of Bakery Products
N.A.I.C.S.: 311812

YK Baking Company Co., Ltd. (1)
2-16-14 Toyoshin, Higashiyodogawa-ku, Osaka, 533-0014, Japan
Tel.: (81) 120470184
Web Site: https://www.ykbaking.co.jp
Emp.: 1,391
Chemical Product Mfr & Distr
N.A.I.C.S.: 325998

Yamazaki Biscuits Co., Ltd. (1)
shinjuku Nomura Building 40F 1-26-2 Nishi-Shinjuku, Shinjuku-ku, Tokyo, 163-0540, Japan
Tel.: (81) 333446211
Web Site: https://www.yamazaki-biscuits.co.jp
Emp.: 1,000
Food Products Mfr
N.A.I.C.S.: 311999

Yamazaki California Inc. (1)
123 Japanese Village Pl, Los Angeles, CA 90013-1820 (100%)
Tel.: (213) 624-2773
Web Site: http://www.yamazakipan.co.jp
Rev.: $700,000
Emp.: 11
Baked Goods Distr
N.A.I.C.S.: 445298
Tatsuya Nakamura (Gen Mgr)

Yamazaki Clean Service Co., Ltd. (1)
122-1 Togamihigashicho, Fujinomiya, 418-0007, Shizuoka, Japan
Tel.: (81) 544591717
Cleaning & Disinfecting Agents Mfr & Distr
N.A.I.C.S.: 325998

Yamazaki Delica Co., Ltd (1)
No 23 Higashinaebogojo 3-chome 558 Higashi-ku, Hokkaido, 007-0805, Sapporo, Japan
Tel.: (81) 11 783 0251
Web Site: http://www.sundelica.co.jp
Cooked Rice Products & Bakery Stores
N.A.I.C.S.: 722310
Kato Shingo (Pres)

Yamazaki Engineering Co., Ltd. (1)
3-8-16 Iwamotocho Kanda Iwamotocho Tosei Building 8f, Chiyoda-Ku, Tokyo, 101-0032, Japan
Tel.: (81) 338643054
Food Processing Machinery Mfr
N.A.I.C.S.: 333241

Yamazaki France S.A. (1)
6 Chaussee de la Muette, 75016, Paris, France (100%)
Tel.: (33) 140501919
Web Site: http://www.yamazaki.fr
Emp.: 25
Cake Shop Operator
N.A.I.C.S.: 445298
Hiroaki Kakeno (Office Mgr)

Yamazaki Logistics Co., Ltd (1)
1-255-3 Asahigaoka, Kiyose, 204-0002, Tokyo, Japan
Tel.: (81) 424947771
Emp.: 50
General Freight Trucking Services
N.A.I.C.S.: 484110

Yamazaki Nabisco Co., Ltd (1)
1-26-2 Shinjuku Nomura Building 40F Nishi-Shinjuku, Tokyo, 163-0540, Japan
Tel.: (81) 333446211
Web Site: http://www.yamazaki-nabisco.co.jp
Snack Foods Mfr & Sales
N.A.I.C.S.: 311919

YAMAZAKI CO., LTD.

489-23 Aritama Kita-cho, Higashi-ku, Hamamatsu, 431-3121, Shizuoka, Japan
Tel.: (81) 534343011
Web Site: https://www.yamazaki-iron.co.jp
Year Founded: 1946
6147—(TKS)
Rev.: $16,498,560
Assets: $24,675,130
Liabilities: $15,764,850
Net Worth: $8,910,280
Earnings: ($218,130)
Emp.: 498
Fiscal Year-end: 03/31/24
Automated Equipment Mfr & Distr
N.A.I.C.S.: 339999
Yoshikazu Yamazaki (Pres)

YAMAZAKI MAZAK CORPORATION

1-131 Takeda Oguchi-cho, Niwa-gun, Nagoya, Japan
Tel.: (81) 587951131
Web Site: http://www.mazak.com
Year Founded: 1919
Emp.: 8,398
Machine Tools Mfr
N.A.I.C.S.: 333517
Tomohisa Yamazaki (Pres)

Subsidiaries:

Mazak (Thailand) Co., Ltd. (1)
892/1 Rama 9 Rd, Suanluang, Bangkok, 10250, Thailand
Tel.: (66) 2402 0650
Web Site: http://www.mazakthai.com
Emp.: 28
Machine Tool Distr
N.A.I.C.S.: 423830
Ryoma Oshima (Mgr)

Mazak Corporation (1)
8025 Production Dr, Florence, KY 41042
Tel.: (859) 342-1700
Web Site: http://www.mazakusa.com
Machine Tool Mfr & Distr
N.A.I.C.S.: 333517
Greg Papke (Gen Mgr)

Mazak Mexico S.A. de C.V. (1)
AV Spectrum No 100 Parque Industrial Finsa, Apodaca, Mexico
Tel.: (52) 81 8221 0910
Machine Tool Distr
N.A.I.C.S.: 423830

Mazak Optonics Corporation (1)
2725 Galvin Ct, Elgin, IL 60124
Tel.: (847) 252-4500
Web Site: http://www.mazaklaser.com
Emp.: 60
Laser Cutting Machine Distr
N.A.I.C.S.: 423830
Bob Miner (Mgr-Facility)

Mazak Sulamericana Ltda (1)
Rua Vasco da Gama 100 Chacara do Trevo, Vinhedo, Sao Paulo, 13280-000, Brazil
Tel.: (55) 19 3464 9100
Machine Tool Distr
N.A.I.C.S.: 423830

Ningxia Little Giant Machine Tool Co., Ltd. (1)
No 65 Ningan Street High-tech Industrial Park, Yinchuan, 750002, Ningxia, China
Tel.: (86) 951 5672333
Web Site: http://www.ltmazak.com
Emp.: 800
Machine Tools Mfr
N.A.I.C.S.: 333517
Tong Qing_Fu (Gen Mgr)

Yamazaki Mazak Central Europe Sp. z o.o. (1)
ul Trasa Rencow 33, 40-865, Katowice, Poland
Tel.: (48) 32 35 004 60
Machine Tool Distr
N.A.I.C.S.: 423830

Yamazaki Mazak Central Europe s.r.o. (1)
Zdebradska 96, Ricany-Jazlovice, 251 01, Prague, Czech Republic
Tel.: (420) 226 211 131
Web Site: http://www.mazakeu.cz
Machine Tool Distr
N.A.I.C.S.: 423830
Jiri Mytina (Sls Mgr-Machine Tools & Engr-Sls)

Yamazaki Mazak Central Europe s.r.o. Magyarorszagi Fioktelepe (1)
Soskuti Ipari Park, 2038, Soskut, Hungary
Tel.: (36) 23 501 480
Web Site: http://www.mazak.hu
Machine Tool Distr
N.A.I.C.S.: 423830

Yamazaki Mazak Danmark A/S (1)
Odinsvej 7, 4100, Ringsted, Denmark
Tel.: (45) 44227700
Web Site: http://www.mazak.dk
Emp.: 45
Machine Tool Distr
N.A.I.C.S.: 423830
Neil Hobbins (CEO)

Yamazaki Mazak Deutschland GmbH (1)
Theodorstrasse 176, 40472, Dusseldorf, Germany
Tel.: (49) 211171660
Web Site: http://www.mazak.de
Machine Tool Distr
N.A.I.C.S.: 423830

Yamazaki Mazak Europe N.V. (1)
Grauwmeer 7 Research Park, 3001, Leuven, Belgium
Tel.: (32) 16 39 16 11
Machine Tool Distr
N.A.I.C.S.: 423830

Yamazaki Mazak France S.A.S. (1)
10 avenue Lionel Terray ZA de Courtaboeuf, 91140, Villejust, France
Tel.: (33) 1 69 31 81 00
Web Site: http://www.mazak.fr
Machine Tool Distr
N.A.I.C.S.: 423830

Yamazaki Mazak India Pvt. Ltd. (1)
115 Pune Nagar Road, Sanaswadi, Pune, 412 208, India
Tel.: (91) 2137 668800
Web Site: http://www.mazakindia.in
Machine Tool Distr

YAMAZAKI MAZAK CORPORATION

N.A.I.C.S.: 423830
Pradeep Patil (Gen Mgr)

Yamazaki Mazak Indonesia, PT (1)
komplek Ruko Graha Bulevar Blok C no 6 Jl Boulevard Raya, Kelapa Gading Timur, Jakarta, 14240, Indonesia
Tel.: (62) 21 2937 5280
Emp.: 20
Machine Tool Distr
N.A.I.C.S.: 423830
Munetoshi Watanabe (Gen Mgr)

Yamazaki Mazak Italia S.R.L. (1)
Via J F Kennedy 16, Cerro Maggiore, 20023, Milan, Italy
Tel.: (39) 0331 575800
Machine Tool Distr
N.A.I.C.S.: 423830
Vittorio Pronesti (Gen Mgr)

Yamazaki Mazak Korea Co., Ltd. (1)
90-18 Dongtangiheung-ro Dongtan-Myeon, Hwaseong, 445-812, Gyeonggi-do, Korea (South)
Tel.: (82) 31 376 6052
Web Site: http://www.mazak.co.kr
Machine Tool Distr
N.A.I.C.S.: 423830

Yamazaki Mazak LLC (1)
Bld I Dom17 Varshavskoe shosse, 117105, Moscow, Russia
Tel.: (7) 4952108989
Web Site: http://www.mazak.ru
Machine Tool Distr
N.A.I.C.S.: 423830

Yamazaki Mazak Machine Tool (Dalian) Co., Ltd. (1)
No 8 Haihui Jie Free Trade Zone, Dalian, China
Tel.: (86) 411 8758 8299
Machine Tool Distr
N.A.I.C.S.: 423830

Yamazaki Mazak Machine Tool (Guangzhou) Co., Ltd. (1)
No 18 East Baoying Road Bonded Area Development Area, Guangzhou, China
Tel.: (86) 20 8221 0188
Machine Tool Distr
N.A.I.C.S.: 423830

Yamazaki Mazak Machine Tool (Liaoning) Co, Ltd. (1)
No 1 Tieshan East Road Economic & Technology Development Zone, Dalian, 116600, Liaoning, China
Tel.: (86) 411 87963555
Machine Tools Mfr
N.A.I.C.S.: 333517

Yamazaki Mazak Machine Tool (Shanghai) Co., Ltd. (1)
No 5131 Jindu Road, Minhang District, Shanghai, 201108, China
Tel.: (86) 21 5483 2688
Machine Tool Distr
N.A.I.C.S.: 423830

Yamazaki Mazak Minokamo Corporation (1)
333 Yamazaki Naka-Hachiya, Hachiya-cho, Minokamo, 505-0005, Gifu, Japan
Tel.: (81) 505 0005
Web Site: http://www.madisonbound.com
Machine Tools Mfr
N.A.I.C.S.: 333517

Plant (Domestic):

Yamazaki Mazak Minokamo Corporation - Minokamo Plant 2 (2)
1-2 Yata, Hachiya-cho, Minokamo, 505-0009, Gifu, Japan
Tel.: (81) 574 24 1121
Machine Tools Mfr
N.A.I.C.S.: 333517

Yamazaki Mazak Nederland B.V. (1)
Peppelkade 54, 3992 AK, Houten, Netherlands
Tel.: (31) 30 634 4030
Web Site: http://www.mazak.com
Emp.: 16
Machine Tool Distr
N.A.I.C.S.: 423830
Frits Giasbers (Gen Mgr)

YAMAZAKI MAZAK CORPORATION

Yamazaki Mazak Corporation—(Continued)

Yamazaki Mazak Seiko Corporation (1)
413 Rengeji, Kuwana, 511-0854, Mie, Japan
Tel.: (81) 594 22 3111
Machine Tools Mfr
N.A.I.C.S.: 333517

Yamazaki Mazak Singapore Pte Ltd. (1)
21 Joo Koon Circle, Singapore, 629053, Singapore
Tel.: (65) 6862 1131
Web Site: http://www.mazak.com.sg
Machine Tool Mfr & Distr
N.A.I.C.S.: 333517
Thomas Lee *(Deputy Gen Mgr)*

Yamazaki Mazak Taiwan Corp. (1)
No 175 Kung Yeh Dist 38th Rd, Shi Tun Dist, Taichung, ROC407, Taiwan
Tel.: (886) 4 2350 9811
Web Site: http://www.mazak.com.tw
Emp.: 30
Machine Tool Distr
N.A.I.C.S.: 423830

Yamazaki Mazak Technology (Shanghai) Co., Ltd. (1)
The Ground Floor of No 186 Hedan Road Waigaoqiao Free Trade Zone, Shanghai, China
Tel.: (86) 21 5866 8318
Machine Tool Distr
N.A.I.C.S.: 423830

Yamazaki Mazak Turkey Makina Ltd. Sti. (1)
Kartal Soganlik Mevkii E-5 Yan yol Uzeri Kanuni Sokak No 2 B Blok, Kartal, 81140, Istanbul, Turkiye
Tel.: (90) 216 309 21 00
Web Site: http://www.mazak.com.tr
Emp.: 23
Machine Tool Distr
N.A.I.C.S.: 423830
Sirket Varlik *(Gen Mgr)*

Yamazaki Mazak UK Ltd (1)
Badgeworth Drive, Worcester, WR4 9NF, United Kingdom
Tel.: (44) 1905 755 755
Emp.: 500
Machine Tools Mfr
N.A.I.C.S.: 333517
Richard Smith *(Mng Dir)*

Yamazaki Mazak Vietnam Company Limited (1)
164 Le Van Viet Street, Tang Nhon Phu B Ward District 9, Ho Chi Minh City, Vietnam
Tel.: (84) 837361838
Web Site: http://www.mazak.com
Emp.: 20
Water Transportation Services
N.A.I.C.S.: 488390
Ricky San *(Dir-Gen)*

YAMAZAWA CO., LTD.
3-8-9 Akoyacho, Yamagata, Japan
Tel.: (81) 236312211
Web Site: https://www.yamazawa.co.jp
Year Founded: 1962
9993—(TKS)
Rev.: $722,407,190
Assets: $412,538,740
Liabilities: $207,928,430
Net Worth: $204,610,310
Earnings: $3,197,590
Emp.: 1,012
Fiscal Year-end: 02/29/24
Supermarket Store Operator
N.A.I.C.S.: 445110
Toshiaki Furuyama *(Pres)*

YAMAZEN CORPORATION
Tatemichibori 2-3-16, Nishi-ku, Osaka, 550-8660, Japan
Tel.: (81) 665343021
Web Site: https://www.yamazen.co.jp
8051—(TKS)
Rev.: $3,350,384,260
Assets: $1,949,771,530
Liabilities: $1,073,173,160
Net Worth: $876,598,370
Earnings: $42,885,680
Emp.: 3,276
Fiscal Year-end: 03/31/24
Die Cast Machines Sales
N.A.I.C.S.: 423420
Yuji Nagao *(Pres)*

Subsidiaries:

Ishihara-Giken Co., Ltd. (1)
2500-4 Moro, Kanuma, 322-0026, Tochigi, Japan
Tel.: (81) 28 964 7103
Web Site: https://www.ishihara-giken.co.jp
Industrial Automation Equipments Mfr
N.A.I.C.S.: 333248

Nihon Butsuryu Shinbun Co., Ltd. (1)
2-3-16 Tachiuribori, Nishi-ku, Osaka, 550-8660, Japan
Tel.: (81) 665418048
Web Site: http://www.nb-shinbun.co.jp
Emp.: 15
Corporate Magazine Publisher
N.A.I.C.S.: 513120

Ogaki Machine & Tools Co., Ltd. (1)
1-25 Kanda-cho, Ogaki, 503-0917, Gifu, Japan
Tel.: (81) 58 474 3131
Industrial Equipment Distr
N.A.I.C.S.: 423830

P.T. Yamazen Indonesia (1)
Komplek Gading Bukit Indah Blok J-16 Jl Bukit Gading Raya, Kelapa Gading, Jakarta Utara, 14240, Indonesia
Tel.: (62) 214513345
Web Site: http://www.yamazen.co.id
Emp.: 50
Cutting Machine Mfr
N.A.I.C.S.: 333517
Kazuhiko Uda *(Pres)*

PROCUEbyNET CORPORATION (1)
2-3-16 Tateuribori, Nishi-ku, Osaka, 550-0012, Japan
Tel.: (81) 665343403
Web Site: https://www.procuebynet.com
Emp.: 15
Internet Portal Services
N.A.I.C.S.: 519290

Plustech Inc. (1)
111 Northwest Point Blvd, Elk Grove Village, IL 60007
Tel.: (847) 490-8130
Injection Molding Machine Mfr
N.A.I.C.S.: 333511

Souzhen Trading (Shenzhen) Co., Ltd. (1)
Room 302 3/F Topchain XT Space 6099 Baoan Rd, Qiaotou Community Fuhai Subdistrict Baoan District, Shenzhen, 518001, China
Tel.: (86) 7558 280 5018
Industrial Machines & Equipment Distr
N.A.I.C.S.: 423830

Toho Industrial Co., Ltd. (1)
6861-9 Morijo Oaza Imuro, Asa-cho Asakita-ku, Hiroshima, 731-1142, Japan
Tel.: (81) 82 810 2232
Web Site: https://www.toho-industrial.co.jp
Industrial Equipment Design & Mfr
N.A.I.C.S.: 333248

Travel Topia Inc. (1)
Nikken building F7 2-1-9 Itachibori, Nishi-ku, Osaka, 550-0012, Kanagawa, Japan
Tel.: (81) 448720421
Emp.: 10
Travel & Tour Operating Agencies
N.A.I.C.S.: 561520

Yamazen (Malaysia) Sdn. Bhd. (1)
Level 1 Wismal Samudra NO 1 Jalan Kontractor U1/14 Section U1, Hicom Glenmarie Industrial Park, 40150, Shah Alam, Selangor Darul Ehsan, Malaysia
Tel.: (60) 355695099
Web Site: http://www.yamazen.co.jp
Emp.: 15

Cutting Machine Mfr
N.A.I.C.S.: 333517
Kazunori Watashige *(Pres)*

Yamazen (Shanghai) Trading Co., Ltd. (1)
Block B west 1st Floor Building 1 No 1388 Yishan Road, Xuhui District, Shanghai, 201103, China
Tel.: (86) 2154452266
Web Site: http://www.yamazensh.com
Emp.: 300
Machine Tool Distr
N.A.I.C.S.: 423830
Kazuyuki Kozawa *(Pres)*

Yamazen (Shenzhen) Trading Co., Ltd. (1)
A601 A602 Sunhope E Metro 7018 Caitian Road, Lianhua 1 Village Community Huafu Street Futian District, Shenzhen, 518100, Guangdong, China
Tel.: (86) 75582805000
Web Site: http://www.yamazen.com
Emp.: 100
Cutting Machine Mfr
N.A.I.C.S.: 333517
Keizo Asaoka *(Pres)*

Yamazen (Singapore) Pte. Ltd. (1)
BLK 215 Henderson Rd 01-10, Singapore, 159554, Singapore
Tel.: (65) 62769488
Web Site: http://www.yamazen.com
Emp.: 30
Drilling Machines Mfr
N.A.I.C.S.: 333517
Kazunori Watashige *(Pres)*

Yamazen (Thailand) Co., Ltd. (1)
1230 and 1230/1 Rama 9 Road Kwang Pattanakarn, Khet Suanluang, Bangkok, 10250, Thailand
Tel.: (66) 23745522
Web Site: http://www.yamazen.co.th
Emp.: 127
Cutting Tool Mfr
N.A.I.C.S.: 333515
Masashi Hagihara *(Mng Dir)*

Yamazen Co., Ltd. (1)
16th Floor No 11 Section 1 Zhongshan North Road, Zhongshan District, Taipei, 104, Taiwan
Tel.: (886) 225212632
Web Site: https://www.yamazen.com.tw
Industrial Machinery Mfr
N.A.I.C.S.: 333248
Shiro Nagatomi *(Pres)*

Yamazen Create Co., Ltd. (1)
2-3-16 Itachibori, Nishi-ku, Osaka, 550-8660, Japan
Tel.: (81) 66 534 3191
Web Site: https://www.yamazen-create.co.jp
Management Consulting Services
N.A.I.C.S.: 541618

Yamazen Europe GmbH (1)
Hedelfinger Strasse 61, 70327, Stuttgart, Germany
Tel.: (49) 711901150
Web Site: http://www.yamazen.co.jp
Emp.: 10
Electrical Engineering Services
N.A.I.C.S.: 541330
Ryuji Dozono *(Pres)*

Yamazen Hong Kong Ltd. (1)
Unit 1013A-1015 Level 10 Landmark North 39 Lung Sum Avenue, Sheung Shui, New Territories, China (Hong Kong)
Tel.: (852) 25117790
Web Site: http://www.yamazen.com.cn
Cutting Machine Mfr
N.A.I.C.S.: 333517

Yamazen Inc. (1)
111 Northwest Point Blvd, Elk Grove Village, IL 60007
Tel.: (847) 882-8800
Machine Tool Distr
N.A.I.C.S.: 423830

Yamazen Korea Ltd. (1)
905 Hoseo University Venturetower 70 Gasan Digital 1-Ro, Geumcheon-gu, Seoul, 08590, Korea (South)
Tel.: (82) 286417557
Web Site: https://www.yamazenkorea.co.kr

INTERNATIONAL PUBLIC

Emp.: 13
Cutting Machine Mfr
N.A.I.C.S.: 333517

Yamazen Logistics Co., Ltd. (1)
2-3-16 Itachibori, Nishi-ku, Osaka, 550-8660, Japan
Tel.: (81) 66 534 3152
Web Site: https://yamazen-logistics.co.jp
Logistic Services
N.A.I.C.S.: 541614

Yamazen Machinery & Tools India Private Ltd. (1)
Flat 8A 8th Fl Hansalaya 15 Barakhamba Rd, New Delhi, 110 001, India
Tel.: (91) 1123706046
Web Site: http://www.yamazen.co.in
Emp.: 30
Plastic Injection Molding Machine Mfr
N.A.I.C.S.: 333248

Yamazen Machinery & Tools Philippines Inc. (1)
124 North Science Avenue Sepz-Laguna Technopark, Binan, 4024, Laguna, Philippines
Tel.: (63) 49 543 1958
Industrial Machines & Equipment Distr
N.A.I.C.S.: 423830

Yamazen Mexicana, S.A. de C.V. (1)
Av Mina de Guadalupe 950-I Puerto Interior, Parque Industrial Santa Fe IV, 36275, Silao, Guanajuato, Mexico
Tel.: (52) 472 748 6400
Web Site: https://www.yamazen.com.mx
Industrial Machines & Equipment Distr
N.A.I.C.S.: 423830

Yamazen Thai Engineering Co., Ltd. (1)
1230 Rama 9 Rd Kwang Suanluang, Khet Suanluang, Bangkok, 10250, Thailand
Tel.: (66) 23745522
Web Site: http://www.yamazen.co.th
Emp.: 25
Measuring Equipment Suppliers
N.A.I.C.S.: 423830

Yamazen Viet Nam Co., Ltd. (1)
Ground Floor Thien Son Plaza 800 Nguyen Van Linh, Tan Phu Ward Dist 7, Ho Chi Minh City, Vietnam
Tel.: (84) 285 417 9229
Web Site: https://yamazenvn.com
Emp.: 49
Industrial Machinery Mfr
N.A.I.C.S.: 333248
Satoshi Ota *(Gen Dir)*

YAMAZEN HOMES CO., LTD.
900 Shimonoshiro Tado-cho, Kuwana, 511-0117, Mie, Japan
Tel.: (81) 594485224
Web Site: http://www.yamazen-k.co.jp
1440—(TKS)
Sales Range: Less than $1 Million
Building Construction Services
N.A.I.C.S.: 236115
Kazuma Maeno *(Chm, Pres & CEO)*

YAMBOLEN AD
ul Yambolen 35, Yambol, 8603, Bulgaria
Tel.: (359) 46661366
Web Site: http://www.jambolen.com
YAMB—(BUL)
Sales Range: Less than $1 Million
Polyester Fibre & Silk Mfr
N.A.I.C.S.: 313110

YAMEN MEDICAL CO., LTD
2-2-1 Yaesu Sumitomo Seimei Yaesu, Tokyo, Chuo-ku, Japan
Tel.: (81) 352013995
Web Site: http://www.ymmd.co.jp
Year Founded: 2002
Rev.: $55,455,600
Assets: $38,095,200
Liabilities: $27,634,560
Net Worth: $10,460,640
Earnings: ($2,592,960)

AND PRIVATE COMPANIES

Emp.: 1,096
Fiscal Year-end: 03/31/18
Nursing Home & Daycare Facilities Owner & Operator
N.A.I.C.S.: 623110

YAMINI INVESTMENTS COMPANY LIMITED
B-614 Crystal Plaza Opp Infinity Mall New Link Road Andheri W, Mumbai, 400053, Maharashtra, India
Tel.: (91) 2240164455
Web Site:
https://www.yaminiinvestments.com
Year Founded: 1983
511012—(BOM)
Rev.: $766,511
Assets: $8,416,463
Liabilities: $338,899
Net Worth: $8,077,564
Earnings: $25,252
Emp.: 5
Fiscal Year-end: 03/31/23
Financial Management Services
N.A.I.C.S.: 523999
Alkesh Patidar (Sec)

YAN TAT GROUP HOLDINGS LIMITED
81 Lijing South Road 8 Enda Road Nan Bu Village, Pinshan, Shenzhen, China
Tel.: (86) 75589666774
Web Site: http://www.yantat.com
1480—(HKG)
Rev.: $94,810,530
Assets: $134,943,578
Liabilities: $47,810,333
Net Worth: $87,133,245
Earnings: $12,018,660
Emp.: 696
Fiscal Year-end: 12/31/22
Printed Circuit Board Mfr
N.A.I.C.S.: 334412
Wing Yin Chan (Founder, Chm & CEO)

Subsidiaries:

Yan Tat (HK) Industrial Limited (1)
Rm 809-810 Kwong Sang Hong Centre 151- 153 Hoi Bun Rd, Kwun Tong, China (Hong Kong)
Tel.: (852) 27908790
Printed Circuit Board Distr
N.A.I.C.S.: 423690

YANAN BICON PHARMACEUTICAL LISTED COMPANY
39F Yongli International Financial Center No 6 Jinye 1st Road, Yanta District, Xi'an, 710065, Jiangsu, China
Tel.: (86) 75586951472
002411—(SSE)
Rev.: $1,065,331,946
Assets: $2,974,417,408
Liabilities: $1,598,159,556
Net Worth: $1,376,257,852
Earnings: $164,058,800)
Emp.: 5,266
Fiscal Year-end: 12/31/20
Pharmaceuticals Mfr
N.A.I.C.S.: 325412

YANBU CEMENT COMPANY
PO Box 5330, Jeddah, 21422, Saudi Arabia
Tel.: (966) 126531555
Web Site:
https://www.yanbucement.com
Year Founded: 1976
3060—(SAU)
Rev.: $261,610,037
Assets: $893,024,051
Liabilities: $154,805,120
Net Worth: $738,218,932
Earnings: $57,434,336

Emp.: 910
Fiscal Year-end: 12/31/22
Producer of Cement & Cement Products
N.A.I.C.S.: 327310
Ahmed Abduh Zugail (CEO)

Subsidiaries:

Yanbu Cement Company - Yanbu Plant (1)
PO Box 467, Yanbu, Saudi Arabia
Tel.: (966) 143225222
Cement Mfr
N.A.I.C.S.: 327320

Yanbu Saudi Kuwaiti for Paper Products Company (1)
PO Box 1896, Jeddah, 21441, Saudi Arabia
Tel.: (966) 26144646
Web Site: https://ysp.sa
Cement Mfr
N.A.I.C.S.: 327320

YANBU NATIONAL PETROCHEMICAL COMPANY
PO Box 31396, Yanbu, 51000, Saudi Arabia
Tel.: (966) 143259000
Web Site:
https://www.yansab.com.sa
2290—(SAU)
Rev.: $1,872,830,289
Assets: $4,447,297,960
Liabilities: $700,903,346
Net Worth: $3,746,394,614
Earnings: $110,423,943
Emp.: 985
Fiscal Year-end: 12/31/22
Petrochemical Products Mfr
N.A.I.C.S.: 324110
Majed A. Nouraddin (Vice Chm)

YANCHANG PETROLEUM INTERNATIONAL LIMITED
Room 3403 34th Floor Lee Garden One 33 Hysan Avenue Causeway Bay, Hong Kong, China (Hong Kong)
Tel.: (852) 35285228   BM
Web Site:
http://www.yanchangpetroleum.com
00346—(HKG)
Rev.: $3,553,875,270
Assets: $471,695,067
Liabilities: $299,102,856
Net Worth: $172,592,211
Earnings: $74,268,499
Emp.: 207
Fiscal Year-end: 12/31/23
Investment Holding Company; Oil & Gas Exploration & Distribution
N.A.I.C.S.: 551112
Yi Li (Chm)

Subsidiaries:

Novus Energy Inc. (1)
1700 700 4 Ave SW, Calgary, T2P 3J4, AB, Canada
Tel.: (403) 263-4310
Web Site: https://www.novusenergy.ca
Sales Range: $75-99.9 Million
Emp.: 25
Petroleum & Natural Gas Exploration Services
N.A.I.C.S.: 213112

YANCOAL SCN LIMITED
Level 26 363 George Street, Sydney, 2000, NSW, Australia
Tel.: (61) 282435300
Coal Mining Services
N.A.I.C.S.: 213113
Ling Zhang (Sec)

YANDAL RESOURCES LIMITED
Level 1 Unit 5/62 Ord Street, West Perth, 6005, WA, Australia
Tel.: (61) 893899021

Web Site:
https://www.yandalresources.com
YRL—(ASX)
Rev.: $116,483
Assets: $4,204,301
Liabilities: $794,852
Net Worth: $3,409,450
Earnings: ($3,503,710)
Fiscal Year-end: 06/30/24
Gold Mining Services
N.A.I.C.S.: 212220
David Lorry Hughes (Mng Dir)

YANDEX N.V.
Schiphol Boulevard 165, Schiphol P7, 1118 BG, Schiphol, Netherlands
Tel.: (31) 202066970   NI
Web Site: https://www.yandex.com
YNDX—(NYSE)
Rev.: $8,653,601,769
Assets: $8,507,627,499
Liabilities: $5,303,136,981
Net Worth: $3,204,490,518
Earnings: $235,503,426
Emp.: 26,361
Fiscal Year-end: 12/31/23
Holding Company; Internet Search Engine & Website Services
N.A.I.C.S.: 551112

Subsidiaries:

OOO Auto.ru (1)
ul Pokryshkina 8 Building 2, Moscow, 495, Russia
Tel.: (7) 4997308730
Web Site: http://www.auto.ru
Emp.: 200
Online Automotive Trading Platform Developer & Operator
N.A.I.C.S.: 441120

Yandex DC LLC (1)
16 Leo Tolstoy St, 119021, Moscow, Russia
Tel.: (7) 495 739 70 00
Online Information Services
N.A.I.C.S.: 519290

Yandex Europe AG (1)
Werftestrasse 4, 6005, Lucerne, Switzerland
Tel.: (41) 412480860
Online Information Services
N.A.I.C.S.: 519290

Yandex LLC (1)
16 Leo Tolstoy St, 119021, Moscow, Russia
Tel.: (7) 4957397000
Web Site: http://yandex.ru
Internet Search Engine Operator
N.A.I.C.S.: 519290

Subsidiary (Domestic):

PS Yandex.Money LLC (2)
16 Lva Tolstogo str, Moscow, 119021, Russia
Tel.: (7) 4957 39 23 25
Electronic Payment Services
N.A.I.C.S.: 522320

SPB Software (2)
Vasi Alekseeva Str 6, 198188, Saint Petersburg, Russia
Tel.: (7) 8123356993
Web Site: http://www.spb.com
Emp.: 75
Mobile Software Developer & Publisher
N.A.I.C.S.: 513210
Sebastian-Justus Schmidt (CEO)

Subsidiary (Non-US):

Spb Software Limited (2)
6/F Luk Kwok Centre 72 Gloucester Road, Wanchai, China (Hong Kong)
Tel.: (852) 2918 8759
Web Site:
http://www.spbsoftwarehouse.com
Emp.: 5
Mobile Software Development Services
N.A.I.C.S.: 541511

Subsidiary (US):

Yandex Inc. (2)

YANG MING MARINE TRANSPORT CORPORATION

299 S California Ave Ste 200, Palo Alto, CA 94306-1935
Tel.: (650) 838-0880
Emp.: 15
Software Development Services
N.A.I.C.S.: 541511
Maxim Kiselev (Dir-Bus Dev)

Subsidiary (Domestic):

Yandex.Probki LLC (2)
Leotolstoy 16, Moscow, Russia
Tel.: (7) 495 9743555
Software Development Services
N.A.I.C.S.: 541511

Yandex Zurich AG (1)
Odeonhaus Limmatquai 2, Zurich, 8001, Switzerland
Tel.: (41) 442525000
Online Information Services
N.A.I.C.S.: 519290

Yandex.Ukraine LLC (1)
Polsky Spusk 11 Morskoi Business Center 8th floor, Odessa, 65026, Ukraine
Tel.: (380) 487 37 44 10
Web Site: http://www.yandex.ua
Online Information Services
N.A.I.C.S.: 519290

YANG GUANG CO., LTD.
11F Yangguang Mansion 112 Xizhimen Wai Avenue, Xicheng District, Beijing, 100044, China
Tel.: (86) 1068361088
Web Site:
http://www.yangguangxinye.com
000608—(SSE)
Rev.: $53,519,722
Assets: $680,035,080
Liabilities: $232,886,141
Net Worth: $447,148,939
Earnings: ($53,939,574)
Fiscal Year-end: 12/31/22
Real Estate Development Services
N.A.I.C.S.: 531390
Guoping Li (VP)

YANG KEE LOGISTICS PTE LTD.
8 Jurong Pier Road, Singapore, 619160, Singapore
Tel.: (65) 64304388
Web Site: http://www.yangkee.com
Year Founded: 1990
Freight Transportation, Logistics & Warehousing Services
N.A.I.C.S.: 541614
Ken Koh (Grp CEO)

Subsidiaries:

Fliway Group Limited (1)
66 Westney Road, Mangere, Manukau, 2022, New Zealand
Tel.: (64) 9 255 4600
Web Site: http://www.fliway.co.nz
Logistic Services
N.A.I.C.S.: 488510
Sandra Fairchild (CEO)

Subsidiary (Domestic):

Fliway International Limited (2)
66 Westney Road, Mangere, Auckland, 2022, New Zealand
Tel.: (64) 092554600
Web Site: http://www.fliway.co.nz
Freight Forwarding Services
N.A.I.C.S.: 488510
Jon Gundy (Gen Mgr)

Fliway Transport Limited (2)
66 Westney Road, Mangere, Auckland, 2022, New Zealand
Tel.: (64) 092554600
Web Site: http://www.fliway.com
Freight Transportation Services
N.A.I.C.S.: 488510

YANG MING MARINE TRANSPORT CORPORATION
271 Ming De 1st Road, Cidu District, Keelung, 20646, Taiwan

YANG MING MARINE TRANSPORT CORPORATION

Yang Ming Marine Transport Corporation—(Continued)
Tel.: (886) 224559988
Web Site: http://www.yangming.com
2609—(TAI)
Rev.: $4,396,826,846
Assets: $12,275,601,194
Liabilities: $3,592,825,689
Net Worth: $8,682,775,506
Earnings: $158,760,091
Emp.: 5,968
Fiscal Year-end: 12/31/23
Marine Transportation & Logistics Services
N.A.I.C.S.: 483111
Cheng Cheng-Mount *(Chm & CEO)*

Subsidiaries:

Hong Ming Terminal & Stevedoring Corp. (1)
999 Shin San Road, Hsiao-Kang, Kaohsiung, 812002, Taiwan
Tel.: (886) 78129200
Web Site: https://www.hmterminal.com
Terminal & Stevedoring Services
N.A.I.C.S.: 488320

Huan Ming (Shanghai) International Shipping Agency Co., Ltd. (1)
Floor 23 Harbour Ring Plaza No 18 Xi Zang Middle Road, Huangpu, Shanghai, China
Tel.: (86) 2161206166
Marine Transportation Services
N.A.I.C.S.: 488390

Kuang Ming Shipping Corp (1)
4F No 243 Sec 2 Chongqing N Rd, Datong, Taipei, 10359, Taiwan (93.07%)
Tel.: (886) 225520818
Web Site: http://www.kms.com.tw
Emp.: 40
Shipping Services
N.A.I.C.S.: 488510

PT. YES Logistics Indonesia (1)
Cowell Tower 9th Floor 9 1003A Senen Raya No 135, Jakarta Pusat, 10410, Indonesia
Tel.: (62) 213455866
Web Site: https://idyeslogistics.com
Marine Transportation & Logistics Services
N.A.I.C.S.: 483111

Yang Ming (America) Co. (1)
13131 Dairy Ashford Rd Ste 300, Sugar Land, TX 77478
Tel.: (281) 295-8600
Marine Transportation & Logistics Services
N.A.I.C.S.: 483111
Winston Yeh *(VP)*

Yang Ming (America) Corp. (1)
Tel.: (201) 222-8899
Emp.: 100
Logistics Management Services
N.A.I.C.S.: 541614
Leo Chiang *(Mgr-Mktg & Pricing)*

Yang Ming (Belgium) N.V. (1)
Molenbergstraat 10, 2000, Antwerp, Belgium
Tel.: (32) 33049400
Marine Transportation & Logistics Services
N.A.I.C.S.: 483111
Wen-Hao Chen *(Mng Dir)*

Yang Ming (France) S.A.S. (1)
156 Rue Victor Hugo, 76600, Le Havre, France
Tel.: (33) 235197340
Marine Transport Services
N.A.I.C.S.: 488320

Yang Ming (Korea) Co., Ltd. (1)
6th FL Trade Center bldg 11 ChungJang-Daero, Jung-Gu, Pusan, 48939, Korea (South)
Tel.: (82) 516376500
Marine Transportation & Logistics Services
N.A.I.C.S.: 483111
J. S. Cho *(Gen Mgr-Export Bus)*

Yang Ming (Latin America) Corp. (1)
P H Torre Global Building 50th Street Floor 33 Office 3301, Panama, Panama
Tel.: (507) 3868692
Marine Transportation & Logistics Services

N.A.I.C.S.: 483111

Yang Ming (MEDITERRANEAN) Marine Services Single-Member Limited Liablity Company (1)
2nd Floor No 1-3 Filellinon, Piraeus, Greece
Tel.: (30) 2103002190
Marine Transportation & Logistics Services
N.A.I.C.S.: 483111

Yang Ming (Netherlands) B.V. (1)
Albert Plesmanweg 61D, 3088 GB, Rotterdam, Netherlands
Tel.: (31) 883088100
Marine Transportation & Logistics Services
N.A.I.C.S.: 483111
Jelle Van Dijk *(Deputy Mgr-Customer Svcs Export & Import)*

Yang Ming (Russia) LLC. (1)
Office 505 lit A block 2 D 22 BC MegaPark Zastavskaya Str, 196006, Saint Petersburg, Russia
Tel.: (7) 8124493390
Marine Transportation & Logistics Services
N.A.I.C.S.: 483111
Tim Tseng *(Mng Dir)*

Yang Ming (Singapore) Pte. Ltd. (1)
171 Chin Swee Road 08-01 Ces Centre, Singapore, 169877, Singapore
Tel.: (65) 63724648
Shipping Agency Services
N.A.I.C.S.: 424510

Yang Ming (Spain), S.L. (1)
Muelle Principe de Espana s/n Edificio Mestre 1 Plta, 08039, Barcelona, Spain
Tel.: (34) 934124550
Marine Transportation & Logistics Services
N.A.I.C.S.: 483111
Carlos Mestre *(Chm)*

Yang Ming (Vietnam) Corporation (1)
200 Dien Bien Phu St, District 3, Ho Chi Minh City, Vietnam
Tel.: (84) 839321858
Logistics Management Services
N.A.I.C.S.: 541614

Yang Ming Line (Hong Kong) Co., Ltd. (1)
22 Fl Ever Gain Plaza Tower 1, 88 Container Port Rd, Kwai Chung, China (Hong Kong)
Tel.: (852) 31893888
Web Site: http://www.hk.yangming.com
Emp.: 120
Shipping Services
N.A.I.C.S.: 488510

Yang Ming Line (Hong Kong) Ltd. (1)
22 Floor Ever Gain Plaza Tower 1 88 Container Port Road, Kwai Chung, NT, China (Hong Kong)
Tel.: (852) 31893888
Marine Transportation & Logistics Services
N.A.I.C.S.: 483111
Stephen Wang *(Mng Dir)*

Yang Ming Line (India) Pvt Ltd. (1)
13Th Floor Centre No 1 World Trade Centre, Cuffe Parade, Mumbai, 400 005, Maharastra, India
Tel.: (91) 2266221111
Web Site: http://www.yml.in
Emp.: 7
Logistics Management Services
N.A.I.C.S.: 541614

Yang Ming Line (M) Sdn Bhd (1)
Tel.: (60) 330518888
Web Site: http://www.yangming.com.my
Emp.: 50
Logistics Management Services
N.A.I.C.S.: 541614

Yang Ming Line Holding Co. (1)
525 Washington Blvd, Jersey City, NJ 07310
Tel.: (201) 420-5804
Web Site: http://www.yml.com.tw
Marine Cargo Handling Services
N.A.I.C.S.: 488320

Yang Ming Shipping (Canada) Ltd. (1)
1130 West Pender Street Suite 380, Vancouver, V6E 4A4, BC, Canada
Tel.: (604) 681-9999
Marine Transportation & Logistics Services
N.A.I.C.S.: 483111
Ralph Baladjay *(Mgr)*

Yang Ming Shipping (Vietnam) Co., Ltd. (1)
Ree Tower 19th Floor No 9 Doan Van Bo Street, Ward 13 District 4, Ho Chi Minh City, Vietnam
Tel.: (84) 2838254589
Marine Transportation & Logistics Services
N.A.I.C.S.: 483111
Vincent Lin *(Mng Dir)*

Yang Ming Shipping Europe GmbH (1)
Obernstrasse 62-66 Eingang Pieperstrasse 4, 28195, Bremen, Germany
Tel.: (49) 421160620
Web Site: http://www.yml.com.pw
Emp.: 6
Logistics Management Services
N.A.I.C.S.: 541614
C H Yeh *(Mng Dir)*

Yang Ming Shipping Philippines, Inc. (1)
5th Floor Double Dragon Center West 8 Meridian Avenue DD Meridian Park, Macapagal Avenue corner EDSA Extension Bay Area, Pasay, Metro Manila, Philippines
Tel.: (63) 288830288
Marine Transportation & Logistics Services
N.A.I.C.S.: 483111
Eddie Yi *(Pres)*

Yangming (Japan) Co., Ltd. (1)
8F Honmachi Allgo Bldg 4-25 Honmachi 4-Chome, Chuo-Ku, Osaka, 541-0053, Japan
Tel.: (81) 662449531
Marine Transportation & Logistics Services
N.A.I.C.S.: 483111

Yangming (UK) Ltd. (1)
2nd Floor 210 South Street, Romford, RM1 1TR, Essex, United Kingdom
Tel.: (44) 1708776900
Web Site: http://www.yangming.co.uk
Marine Transportation & Logistics Services
N.A.I.C.S.: 483111

Yangming Shipping (Singapore) Pte Ltd. (1)
79 Robinson Rd, 27-00 CPF Bldg, Singapore, 68897, Singapore
Tel.: (65) 63724648
Web Site: http://www.yml.com.sg
Emp.: 75
Logistics Management Services
N.A.I.C.S.: 541614
James Yang *(Mng Dir)*

Yes Logistics (Shanghai) Corp. (1)
Room 2305 Harbour Ring Plaza 18 Xi Zang Middle Road, HuangPu Area, Shanghai, 200001, China
Tel.: (86) 2160730566
Marine Transportation & Logistics Services
N.A.I.C.S.: 483111
Nelson Yen *(Pres)*

Yes Logistics Benelux B.V. (1)
Schillingweg 50, 2153 PL, Nieuw-Vennep, Netherlands
Tel.: (31) 203080112
Marine Transportation & Logistics Services
N.A.I.C.S.: 483111

Yes Logistics Company, Ltd. (1)
22/F Ever Gain Plaza Tower I 88 Container Port Rd, Kwai Chung, NT, China (Hong Kong)
Tel.: (852) 21161533
Marine Transportation & Logistics Services
N.A.I.C.S.: 483111

Yes Logistics Corp. (1)
5F No 243 Sec 2 Chongqing N Rd, Datong, Taipei, 10359, Taiwan
Tel.: (886) 225575666
Web Site: http://www.yeslogistics.com
Emp.: 60
Freight Forwarding Services
N.A.I.C.S.: 488510

Subsidiary (Non-US):

Yes Logistics Europe GmbH (2)
Kleine Reichenstrasse 7, 20457, Hamburg, Germany
Tel.: (49) 40180240100
Marine Transportation & Logistics Services
N.A.I.C.S.: 483111

Subsidiary (Domestic):

Yes MLC GmbH (3)
Georg-Beatzel-Strasse 15, 55252, Mainz-Kastel, Germany
Tel.: (49) 69153225200
Marine Transportation & Logistics Services
N.A.I.C.S.: 483111

YANGAROO INC.

360 Dufferin Street, Suite 203, Toronto, M6K 1Z8, ON, Canada
Tel.: (416) 534-0607
Web Site: https://www.yangaroo.com
Year Founded: 1999
76T—(DEU)
Rev.: $7,734,844
Assets: $9,138,288
Liabilities: $4,506,897
Net Worth: $4,631,391
Earnings: $1,570,289
Fiscal Year-end: 12/31/22
Digital Media Distribution Services
N.A.I.C.S.: 512290
Gary Moss *(Pres & CEO)*

Subsidiaries:

Millenia 3 Communications, Inc. (1)
1281 Kennestone Cir, Marietta, GA 30066
Tel.: (678) 391-9600
Web Site: http://www.millenia3.com
Rev.: $1,300,000
Emp.: 20
Other Motion Picture & Video Industries
N.A.I.C.S.: 512199
Robert Owen *(Pres & CEO)*

YANGARRA RESOURCES LTD.

1530 715 - 5 Ave SW, Calgary, T2P 2X6, AB, Canada
Tel.: (403) 262-9558
Web Site: https://www.yangarra.ca
Year Founded: 2005
YGR—(TSX)
Rev.: $67,040,614
Assets: $477,182,195
Liabilities: $232,907,442
Net Worth: $244,274,753
Earnings: $3,791,711
Emp.: 65
Fiscal Year-end: 12/31/20
Oil & Natural Gas Exploration Services
N.A.I.C.S.: 211120
James G. Evaskevich *(Pres & CEO)*

Subsidiaries:

Yangarra Holding Corp. (1)

Yangarra Production Partnership (1)

YANGJISA CO., LTD.

131 Hwanggeum 1-ro, Yangchon-Eup, Gimpo, Gyeonggi-do, Korea (South)
Tel.: (82) 319960041
Web Site: https://www.yangjisa.com
Year Founded: 1976
030960—(KRS)
Rev.: $41,305,994
Assets: $178,898,484
Liabilities: $9,208,442
Net Worth: $169,690,042
Earnings: ($3,760,953)
Emp.: 254
Fiscal Year-end: 06/30/22
Stationery Product Mfr
N.A.I.C.S.: 322230
Bae-Goo Lee *(Founder, Chm & CEO)*

YANGLIN SOYBEAN, INC.

No 99 Fanrong Street Shuang Ya Shan City, Jixian, 155900, Heilongjiang, China

AND PRIVATE COMPANIES

YANKERSHOP FOOD CO LTD

Tel.: (86) 4694693000 NV
Year Founded: 1921
Sales Range: $50-74.9 Million
Emp.: 472
Soybean Processing Services
N.A.I.C.S.: 311224
Shulin Liu *(Founder, Chm & CEO)*

YANGLING METRON NEW MATERIAL CO., LTD.
Fuhai Industrial Park East Section of Weihui Road, Demonstration Zone, Yangling, 712100, Shaanxi, China
Tel.: (86) 2987038269
Web Site: https://www.ylmetron.com
Year Founded: 2015
300861—(CHIN)
Rev.: $513,618,300
Assets: $978,266,484
Liabilities: $209,073,852
Net Worth: $769,192,632
Earnings: $206,796,564
Fiscal Year-end: 12/31/22
Diamond Wire Mfr
N.A.I.C.S.: 332618
Ying Wu *(Chm)*

YANGMEI CHEMICAL CO., LTD.
Lu'an Daisi Hotel No 72 Shuangta West Street, Yingze District, Taiyuan, 030006, Shanxi, China
Tel.: (86) 3517255821
Web Site: http://www.ymhg.com.cn
Year Founded: 1988
600691—(SHG)
Rev.: $2,391,806,425
Assets: $3,471,650,063
Liabilities: $2,521,726,787
Net Worth: $949,923,276
Earnings: $9,821,977
Fiscal Year-end: 12/31/22
Chemical Product Mfr & Distr
N.A.I.C.S.: 325180
Ma Junxiang *(Chm)*

YANGO FINANCIAL HOLDING INVESTMENT GROUP CO., LTD.
Floor 47 Fuzhou International Finance Center No 1 Wanglong 2 Road, Taijiang District, Fuzhou, Fujian, China
Tel.: (86) 591 86276998
Web Site: http://www.yangofinance.com
Year Founded: 1995
Sales Range: Less than $1 Million
Emp.: 10,234
Holding Company
N.A.I.C.S.: 551112
Lin Tengjiao *(Founder, Chm & CEO)*

YANGO GROUP CO., LTD.
No 99 Jinxin Road, Pudong New District, Shanghai, 200137, China
Tel.: (86) 2180325918 CN
Web Site: https://www.yangoholdings.com
Year Founded: 1995
000671—(SSE)
Rev.: $12,589,455,680
Assets: $53,976,166,439
Liabilities: $44,897,361,634
Net Worth: $9,078,804,805
Earnings: $799,800,631
Fiscal Year-end: 12/31/20
Real Estate Development Services
N.A.I.C.S.: 531311
Rongbin Zhu *(Chm & Pres)*

YANGTZEKIANG GARMENT LIMITED
22 Tai Yau Street San Po Kong, Kowloon, China (Hong Kong)
Tel.: (852) 23275111

Web Site: https://www.ygm.com.hk
0294—(HKG)
Rev.: $50,359,725
Assets: $167,328,076
Liabilities: $16,422,250
Net Worth: $150,905,826
Earnings: $3,904,741
Emp.: 1,700
Fiscal Year-end: 03/31/22
Department Stores
N.A.I.C.S.: 455110
Peter Wing Fui Chan *(Chm)*

Subsidiaries:

Easeley Knitwear Limited (1)
Yangtzekiang Garment Bldg 22 Tai Yau St, San Po Kong, Kowloon, China (Hong Kong)
Tel.: (852) 27266333
Apparels Mfr
N.A.I.C.S.: 315120

Exquisite Knitters (Guangzhou) Limited (1)
Shi Gang Dong Shi Ji Town Pan Yu, Guangzhou, Guangdong, China
Tel.: (86) 2084628881
Knitwear Mfr
N.A.I.C.S.: 313240

Hong Kong Knitters Limited (1)
22 Tai Yau Street, San Po Kong, Kowloon, China (Hong Kong)
Tel.: (852) 23275111
Web Site: http://www.hkknitters.com.hk
Emp.: 100
Garments Mfr & Whslr
N.A.I.C.S.: 315210
Peter Chan Wing Fui *(Mng Dir)*

Whampoa Garment Manufacturing (Guangzhou) Co., Ltd. (1)
No 1 Plant No 4-5 Zhiye No 2 Rd Zhushan Village, Shiji Town, Guangzhou, 511450, Guangdong, China
Tel.: (86) 2084642200
Garments Mfr
N.A.I.C.S.: 315210

YANGTZEKIANG INDUSTRIES SDN. BHD.
12 Jalan TPP 1/19, Puchong, 47100, Selangor, Malaysia
Tel.: (60) 389644418 MY
Men's Fashion Apparel Whslr & Retailer
N.A.I.C.S.: 424350

YANGUFANG INTERNATIONAL GROUP CO., LTD.
3/F Building 3 33 Suhong Road, Minhang District, Shanghai, 201100, China
Tel.: (86) 215 296 6658 Ky
Web Site: https://mx.yangufang.com
Year Founded: 2020
YGF—(NASDAQ)
Rev.: $29,837,029
Assets: $47,579,183
Liabilities: $34,727,026
Net Worth: $12,852,157
Earnings: $10,543,554
Emp.: 231
Fiscal Year-end: 06/30/21
Biotechnology Research & Development Services
N.A.I.C.S.: 541714
Junguo He *(CEO & Chm)*

YANGWOO ENGINEERING & CONSTRUCTION CO., LTD.
GSquare 23 180 Simin-daero, Dongan-gu, Anyang, Gyeonggi-do, Korea (South)
Tel.: (82) 2 2021 0400 KR
Web Site: http://www.tecconst.com
Year Founded: 1958
Construction & Engineering Services
N.A.I.C.S.: 541330

YANGZHOU ASIASTAR BUS CO., LTD.
No 2 Weichai Avenue Hanjiang Automobile Industrial Park, Yangzhou, 225116, Jiangsu, China
Tel.: (86) 51482989118
Web Site: http://www.asiastarbus.com
Year Founded: 1996
600213—(SHG)
Rev.: $149,925,178
Assets: $489,856,801
Liabilities: $476,095,479
Net Worth: $13,761,322
Earnings: $289,567
Fiscal Year-end: 12/31/21
Passenger Bus Mfr & Distr
N.A.I.C.S.: 336110
Hu Haihua *(Chm)*

YANGZHOU CHENHUA NEW MATERIAL CO.,LTD.
No 231 Zhenzhong Road, Caodian Town Baoying County, Yangzhou, 225800, Jiangsu, China
Tel.: (86) 51482659030
Web Site: http://www.chenhua.cc
Year Founded: 1995
300610—(CHIN)
Rev.: $151,409,312
Assets: $189,838,855
Liabilities: $31,624,721
Net Worth: $158,214,135
Earnings: $16,744,034
Fiscal Year-end: 12/31/22
Chemical Product Mfr & Distr
N.A.I.C.S.: 325998
Yu Zizhou *(Chm)*

Subsidiaries:

Shanghai Chenhua International Trade Co., Ltd. (1)
No 738 Shangcheng Road Pudong New Area, Shanghai, China
Tel.: (86) 2150598997
Synthetic Rubber Mfr & Distr
N.A.I.C.S.: 325212

YANGZHOU GUANGLING DISTRICT TAIHE RURAL MICRO-FINANCE COMPANY LIMITED
No 1 Hongqi Avenue Jiangwang Town, Hanjiang District, Yangzhou, China
Tel.: (86) 51487948990 CN
Web Site: https://www.gltaihe.com
Year Founded: 2008
1915—(HKG)
Rev.: $7,288,044
Assets: $126,052,336
Liabilities: $2,473,542
Net Worth: $123,578,794
Earnings: $(1,373,814)
Emp.: 23
Fiscal Year-end: 12/31/22
Finance Management Services
N.A.I.C.S.: 522299
Wanlin Bo *(Chm & Exec Dir)*

YANGZHOU SEASHINE NEW MATERIALS CO., LTD.
No 90 of Heye West Road Jiangyang Industrial Park, Hanjiang District, Yangzhou, 225008, Jiangsu, China
Tel.: (86) 51485823222
Web Site: https://www.seashinepm.com
Year Founded: 2001
300885—(SSE)
Rev.: $30,897,309
Assets: $117,908,833
Liabilities: $7,105,700
Net Worth: $110,803,132
Earnings: $8,031,063
Fiscal Year-end: 12/31/22
Machinery Parts Mfr & Distr

N.A.I.C.S.: 333612
Guangrong Zhou *(Chm)*

YANGZHOU YANGJIE ELECTRONIC TECHNOLOGY CO., LTD.
6 Heye West Road, Hanjiang District, Yangzhou, 225008, China
Tel.: (86) 51480889866
Web Site: https://www.21yangjie.com
Year Founded: 2000
300373—(SSE)
Rev.: $758,655,612
Assets: $1,331,446,896
Liabilities: $441,594,504
Net Worth: $889,852,392
Earnings: $148,845,060
Emp.: 4,500
Fiscal Year-end: 12/31/22
Semiconductor Components Mfr
N.A.I.C.S.: 334413
Liang Qin *(Chm)*

YANGZIJIANG FINANCIAL HOLDING LTD.
Raffles Place 5401 Republic Plaza, Singapore, 48581, Singapore
Tel.: (65) 62232835
Web Site: https://www.yzjfin.com
Year Founded: 2021
YF8—(SES)
Rev.: $263,905,173
Assets: $3,162,913,730
Liabilities: $198,785,124
Net Worth: $2,964,128,606
Earnings: $153,518,897
Emp.: 76
Fiscal Year-end: 12/31/23
Holding Company
N.A.I.C.S.: 551112

YANGZIJIANG SHIPBUILDING (HOLDINGS) LTD
1 Iianyi Road Jiangyin-Jingjiang Industry Zone, Jingjiang, 214532, Jiangsu, China
Tel.: (86) 52384660022
Web Site: https://www.yzjship.com
BS6—(SES)
Rev.: $2,569,010,878
Assets: $7,907,514,967
Liabilities: $2,382,522,594
Net Worth: $5,524,992,374
Earnings: $571,027,306
Emp.: 6,000
Fiscal Year-end: 12/31/21
Ship Building Services
N.A.I.C.S.: 336611
Yuanlin Ren *(Founder & Chm)*

Subsidiaries:

Jiangsu New Yangzi Shipbuilding Co., Ltd (1)
1 Iianyi Road Jiangyin-Jingjiang Industry Zone, Jingjiang, 214532, Jiangsu, China
Tel.: (86) 52384660022
Web Site: http://www.yzjship.com
Emp.: 2,330
Ship Building Services
N.A.I.C.S.: 336611

Jiangsu Yangzi-Mitsui Shipbuilding Co., Ltd. (1)
East to Taihai Ferry Port, Huangjing Town, Taicang, 215428, Jiangsu, China (56%)
Tel.: (86) 51253838321
Marine Engineering Services
N.A.I.C.S.: 541330

Odfjell Terminals (Jiangyin) Co Ltd. (1)
1314 West Binjiang Road, Shizhuang, 214446, Jiangyin, Jiangsu, China (55%)
Tel.: (86) 51086669111
Freight Transportation Arrangement
N.A.I.C.S.: 488510

YANKERSHOP FOOD CO LTD

YANKERSHOP FOOD CO LTD

Yankershop Food Co Ltd—(Continued)
32F Tower A Office Building Yunda Central Plaza Changsha Avenue, Yuhua District, Changsha, 410005, Hunan, China
Tel.: (86) 73185482847
Web Site: http://www.yanjinpuzi.com
Year Founded: 2005
002847—(SSE)
Rev.: $406,250,278
Assets: $344,646,535
Liabilities: $183,459,852
Net Worth: $161,186,683
Earnings: $42,329,603
Emp.: 2,471
Fiscal Year-end: 12/31/22
Snack Food Mfr & Distr
N.A.I.C.S.: 311911
Xuewu Zhang (Chm & Gen Mgr)

YANKUANG GROUP CO., LIMITED
No 298 Fushan South Road, Zoucheng, Shandong, China
Tel.: (86) 5375383493   CN
Web Site: http://www.yankuanggroup.com.cn
Year Founded: 1976
Holding Company
N.A.I.C.S.: 551112
Li Wei (Gen Mgr)

Subsidiaries:

Yankuang Energy Group Company Limited   (1)
No 949 Fushan South Road, Zoucheng, 273500, Shandong, China   (52.86%)
Tel.: (86) 5375382319
Web Site: https://www.yanzhoucoal.com.cn
Rev.: $16,398,187,583
Assets: $57,365,644,246
Liabilities: $34,279,805,328
Net Worth: $23,085,838,918
Earnings: $3,178,741,416
Emp.: 79,242
Fiscal Year-end: 12/31/2023
Coal Mining Services
N.A.I.C.S.: 212114
Xiyong Li (Chm)

Subsidiary (Non-US):

Monash Coal Holdings Pty Ltd   (2)
67 Bulwer Street, Maitland, 2320, NSW, Australia
Tel.: (61) 2 4934 2888
Holding Company
N.A.I.C.S.: 551112

SMT Scharf AG   (2)
Romerstrasse 104, 59075, Hamm, Germany   (52.66%)
Tel.: (49) 238196001
Web Site: https://www.smtscharf.com
Rev.: $105,469,015
Assets: $148,970,397
Liabilities: $60,905,837
Net Worth: $88,064,560
Earnings: $15,453,261
Emp.: 422
Fiscal Year-end: 12/31/2021
Mining Equipment Mfr
N.A.I.C.S.: 333131
Hans Joachim Theiss (CEO)

Subsidiary (Domestic):

Nowilan GmbH   (3)
Stollenstrasse 1, 46537, Dinslaken, Germany
Tel.: (49) 20644234949
Web Site: http://www.nowilan.de
Mining Tunnel Transportation Services
N.A.I.C.S.: 213114

Subsidiary (Non-US):

OOO SMT Scharf   (3)
Kurako av 53/1, Novokuznetsk, 654027, Russia
Tel.: (7) 3843200333
Mining Equipment Mfr
N.A.I.C.S.: 333131

RDH Mining Equipment Ltd   (3)
904 Hwy 64 Alban, Sudbury, P0M 1A0, ON, Canada
Tel.: (705) 857-2154
Web Site: http://www.rdhscharf.com
Mining & Tunneling Equipment Mfr & Whslr
N.A.I.C.S.: 333131
Shaun Amos (CEO)

SMT Scharf Africa (Pty.) Ltd.   (3)
5 Viking Way Airport Park Ext 2, Germiston, 1462, Gauteng, South Africa
Tel.: (27) 11 708 0515
Web Site: http://www.smtscharf.com
Transportation Equipment Whslr
N.A.I.C.S.: 423860

Subsidiary (Domestic):

SMT Scharf GmbH   (3)
Romerstrasse 104, 59075, Hamm, Germany
Tel.: (49) 238196001
Sales Range: $50-74.9 Million
Emp.: 170
Mfr of Rail Bounded Transportation Systems
N.A.I.C.S.: 336510

Subsidiary (Non-US):

Scharf Mining Machinery (Beijing) Co. Ltd.   (4)
Rm 1805 Huateng Mansion Jinsong Sanqu Jia Building 302, Chaoyang, Beijing, 100021, China
Tel.: (86) 1087730130
Mining Equipment Mfr
N.A.I.C.S.: 333131

Subsidiary (Non-US):

SMT Scharf Polska Sp. z o.o.   (3)
ul Przemyslowa 55, 43-100, Tychy, Poland
Tel.: (48) 327314500
Transportation Equipment Whslr
N.A.I.C.S.: 423860
Andrzej Lisowski (Mng Dir)

Subsidiary (Domestic):

SMT Scharf Saar GmbH   (3)
Friedrichsthaler Strasse 29, 66540, Neunkirchen, Germany
Tel.: (49) 6821 794 0
Emp.: 13
Transport System Mfr & Distr
N.A.I.C.S.: 333131

Subsidiary (Non-US):

SMT Scharf Sudamerica SpA   (3)
Isidora Goyenechea 3000 Of 2233, 7550653, Las Condes, Santiago, Chile
Tel.: (56) 223464265
Mining Transportation Services
N.A.I.C.S.: 213114

Sareco Engineering (Pty.) Ltd.   (3)
158 / 160 Queen Avenue, Brakpan, South Africa
Tel.: (27) 11 740 2937
Web Site: http://www.sareco.co.za
Mining Transport Equipment Mfr
N.A.I.C.S.: 333131

Scharf Mining Machinery (Xuzhou) Ltd.   (3)
Plant 5 District C Xuzhou Economic and Technical Development Zone, Xuzhou, 221000, China
Tel.: (86) 51687339791
Mining Transportation Services
N.A.I.C.S.: 213114
Chen Xixi (Supvr-Quality)

TOW SMT Scharf Ukrainia   (3)
Kuibyshev street 143, 83060, Donetsk, Ukraine
Tel.: (380) 62 388 80 25
Mining Equipment Mfr
N.A.I.C.S.: 333131

Subsidiary (Domestic):

ser Elektronik GmbH   (3)
Zeissweg 6, 59519, Mohnesee, Germany
Tel.: (49) 292497170
Web Site: https://www.ser-elektronik.de
Printed Circuit Board & Assembly Mfr
N.A.I.C.S.: 334418

Subsidiary (Non-US):

Yancoal Australia Limited   (2)
Level 18 Darling Park Tower 2 201 Sussex Street, Sydney, 2000, NSW, Australia   (62.26%)
Tel.: (61) 285835300
Web Site: https://www.yancoal.com.au
Rev.: $5,298,004,223
Assets: $7,665,690,348
Liabilities: $1,915,400,858
Net Worth: $5,750,289,489
Earnings: $1,239,016,416
Emp.: 3,400
Fiscal Year-end: 12/31/2023
Offices of Other Holding Companies
N.A.I.C.S.: 551112
Laura Ling Zhang (Chief Legal , Compliance & Corp Affairs Officer, Chief Legal , Compliance & Corp Affairs Officer, Sec & Sec)

Subsidiary (Domestic):

Ashton Coal Operations Pty Limited   (3)
Glennies Creek Road, Camberwell, 2330, NSW, Australia
Tel.: (61) 2 6576 1111
Web Site: http://www.ashtoncoal.com.au
Coal Mining Services
N.A.I.C.S.: 212115

Austar Coal Mine Pty Limited   (3)
Middle Road, Locked Bag 806, Paxton, Cessnock, 2325, NSW, Australia
Tel.: (61) 2 4993 7200
Coal Mining Services
N.A.I.C.S.: 212115
Brian Wesley (Mgr-Ops)

Moolarben Coal Operations Pty Ltd   (3)
Locked Bag 2003, Mudgeeraba, 2850, NSW, Australia   (95%)
Tel.: (61) 2 6376 1500
Web Site: http://www.moolarbencoal.com.au
Coal Mining Services
N.A.I.C.S.: 212115

Premier Coal Limited   (3)
Premier Rd, PO Box 21, Collie, 6225, WA, Australia
Tel.: (61) 897802222
Web Site: http://www.premiercoal.com.au
Emp.: 310
Coal Mining
N.A.I.C.S.: 212115

YANLORD LAND GROUP LIMITED
9 Temasek Boulevard 3602 Suntec Tower Two, Singapore, 038989, Singapore
Tel.: (65) 63362922
Web Site: https://www.yanlordland.com
Z25—(SES)
Rev.: $6,112,031,108
Assets: $21,793,576,836
Liabilities: $15,633,136,855
Net Worth: $6,160,439,982
Earnings: ($101,745,493)
Emp.: 10,509
Fiscal Year-end: 12/31/23
Property Development & Management Services
N.A.I.C.S.: 237210
Yiu Ling Chan (Exec Dir)

Subsidiaries:

Cambion Electronics Limited   (1)
Mill Lane, Castleton, Hope Valley, S33 8WR, United Kingdom
Tel.: (44) 1433621555
Web Site: http://www.cambion.com
Electrical & Electronic Component Mfr
N.A.I.C.S.: 336320
Paul Karlsons (Mgr-Engrg)

Nanjing Daji Real Estate Development Co., Ltd.   (1)
Tang Quan Street, Pukou District, Nanjing, 211802, Jiangsu, China
Tel.: (86) 2558166993
Real Estate Services

INTERNATIONAL PUBLIC

N.A.I.C.S.: 531390

O'Connor's Engineering Sdn. Bhd.   (1)
Bangunan O'Connor 13 Jalan 223, 46100, Petaling Jaya, Selangor, Malaysia
Tel.: (60) 379538400
Web Site: https://www.oconnors.com.my
Electronic Communication Equipment Distr
N.A.I.C.S.: 423690

O'Connor's Singapore Pte. Ltd.   (1)
801 Lorong 7 Toa Payoh WBL Building O'Connor's Annex Block, Singapore, 319319, Singapore
Tel.: (65) 64702000
Web Site: https://www.oconnors.co
Communication & Security Surveillance Services
N.A.I.C.S.: 561621
Y. Stanley (Gen Mgr)

UE Park Avenue International Pte. Ltd.   (1)
2 Changi Business Park Avenue 1, Singapore, 486015, Singapore
Tel.: (65) 68097300
Web Site: http://www.parkavenueintl.com
Real Estate Services
N.A.I.C.S.: 531390
Muhammad Rezzal (Mgr-Duty)

United Engineers Limited   (1)
12 Ang Mo Kio Street 64 01-01 UE BizHub CENTRAL, Singapore, 569088, Singapore   (33.4%)
Tel.: (65) 68188383
Web Site: http://www.uel.com.sg
Rev.: $274,185,948
Assets: $2,648,672,869
Liabilities: $1,031,763,502
Net Worth: $1,616,909,367
Earnings: $38,759,557
Fiscal Year-end: 12/31/2018
Property Development Services
N.A.I.C.S.: 531312
Roy Chee Keong Tan (Mng Dir)

Subsidiary (Non-US):

APG Geo-Systems Sdn Bhd   (2)
No 20 Lorong Rahim Kajai 14 Taman Tun Dr Ismail, 60000, Kuala Lumpur, Malaysia
Tel.: (60) 377288912
Sales Range: $25-49.9 Million
Emp.: 38
Industrial Building Contractors
N.A.I.C.S.: 236210
Tham Kok Wah (CEO)

APG Systems (EM) Sdn Bhd   (2)
Lot 16 Damai Point 3rd Floor Block B, Kota Kinabalu, 88300, Sabah, Malaysia
Tel.: (60) 88257961
Industrial Building Construction Services
N.A.I.C.S.: 236210
David Liew (Mng Dir-Integrated Property Svcs Div)

Applied Construction & Engineering (M) Sdn Bhd   (2)
No 22 Lorong Rahim Kajai 14 Taman Tun Dr Ismail, 60000, Kuala Lumpur, Malaysia
Tel.: (60) 3 7728 7919
Web Site: http://www.ues.com.sg
Construction Engineering Services
N.A.I.C.S.: 541330

McAlister Engineering Sdn Bhd   (2)
Lot 454 Zone 10 Jalan Keluli Pasir Gudang Industrial Estate, Pasir Gudang, 81700, Johor Bahru, Johor, Malaysia
Tel.: (60) 72518408
Web Site: http://www.mcalister-eng.com.my
Sales Range: $25-49.9 Million
Emp.: 42
Industrial Tank Mfr
N.A.I.C.S.: 237120

ServiceMaster Hong Kong Limited   (2)
Harbour City 5 Canton Rd Ste 1216 Ocean Ctr, Tsim Tsa Tsui, Kowloon, China (Hong Kong)
Tel.: (852) 24280222
Facility Management Services
N.A.I.C.S.: 531312

UE China (Shanghai) Co Ltd   (2)

AND PRIVATE COMPANIES

Hong Wei Cun Xi Chang No 18 Jidi Road
Hong Nan Road HuaCao Town, Minhang
District, Shanghai, 201107, China
Tel.: (86) 2162966992
Web Site: http://www.uesctw.com
Facility Management Services
N.A.I.C.S.: 531312

UE Envirotech Pte Ltd (2)
Henderson Ctr Office Tower 2 18 Jian Guo
Men Nei Ave, Beijing, 100005, China
Tel.: (86) 1065188613
Medical Waste Treatment Services
N.A.I.C.S.: 562211

UE Managed Solutions Taiwan Ltd (2)
5Floor Unit 7-10 No 2 Fu Hsing North
Road, Taipei, 104, Taiwan
Tel.: (886) 227766188
Web Site: http://www.uesctw.com
Facility Management Services
N.A.I.C.S.: 531312

UE ServiceCorp (Taiwan) Limited (2)
Unit 5-8 No 2 Fushing North Road, Taipei, Taiwan
Tel.: (886) 227766188
Emp.: 200
Facility Management Services
N.A.I.C.S.: 531312
Lin Bryan *(Mgr)*

Subsidiary (Domestic):

UE Support Services Pte Ltd (2)
83 Clemenceau Ave Suite 05-18 UE
Square, Singapore, 239918, Singapore
Tel.: (65) 67328200
Construction Engineering Services
N.A.I.C.S.: 541330

UE Trade Corporation Pte Ltd (2)
257 Jalan Ahmad Ibrahim, Singapore,
629147, Singapore
Tel.: (65) 6268 0988
Commodity Trading Services
N.A.I.C.S.: 423990

UMC ServiceMaster Pte Ltd (2)
12 Ang Mo Kio Street 64 03A-11 UE BizHub Central, Singapore, 569088, Singapore
Tel.: (65) 6818 8500
Web Site: http://www.servicemaster.com.sg
Quality Support Services
N.A.I.C.S.: 541330

Subsidiary (Non-US):

UMC ServiceMaster Taiwan Limited (2)
5F 7 No 2 Fushing North Road, Taipei, Taiwan
Tel.: (886) 227766188
Web Site: http://www.uefztw.com
Sales Range: $650-699.9 Million
Emp.: 2,000
Facility Management Services
N.A.I.C.S.: 531312
K. L. Wang *(Gen Mgr)*

United Engineers (B) Sdn Bhd (2)
Unit No 2 & 3 1st Floor Kompleks Haji Tahir 2 Lot 3005 Sungai Gadong, Kampong Menglait, BE3919, Gadong, Brunei Darussalam
Tel.: (673) 2445366
Web Site: http://www.uel.com.sg
Industrial Building Contractors
N.A.I.C.S.: 236210
John Seng Poh Lee *(Mgr)*

Subsidiary (Domestic):

United Engineers Developments Pte Ltd (2)
12 Ang Mo Kio Street 64 03A-13 Ue BizHub Central, Singapore, 569088, Singapore
Tel.: (65) 6 818 8000
Web Site: http://www.uel.com.sg
Facilities Management Services
N.A.I.C.S.: 531312

Subsidiary (Non-US):

United Engineers Managed Solutions Malaysia Sdn. Bhd.
Global Business Park No 8 Jalan 19/1 2nd Floor Block A Section 19, Petaling Jaya, 46300, Selangor Darul Ehsan, Malaysia

Tel.: (60) 379683320
Web Site: http://www.uemsgroup.com.my
Sales Range: $50-74.9 Million
Emp.: 70
Integrated Facility Management Services to Various Business Sectors
N.A.I.C.S.: 561210
John Bong *(VP-Fin)*

Subsidiary (Domestic):

United Tech Park Pte Ltd (2)
10 Pandan Crescent, Singapore, 128466, Singapore
Tel.: (65) 6776 2032
Real Estate Management Services
N.A.I.C.S.: 531210

WBL (USA) Inc. (1)
101 Hudson St 33rd Fl, Jersey City, NJ 07302
Web Site: http://www.wbl.com
Business Loan Services
N.A.I.C.S.: 522310
Doug Naidus *(Founder & CEO)*

WBL Engineering & Distribution Pte. Ltd. (1)
801 Lorong 7 Toa Payoh 05-00 WBL Building, Singapore, 319319, Singapore
Tel.: (65) 6 262 0928
Web Site: https://www.welmate.com.sg
Construction Services
N.A.I.C.S.: 236220
John Yuen *(Product Mgr)*

Yanlord (China) Investment Group Co., Ltd. (1)
7-8F No 30 Lane 1399 Dingxiang Road, Pudong, Shanghai, 200135, China
Tel.: (86) 2150585333
Real Estate Services
N.A.I.C.S.: 531390

YANMAR CO., LTD.
Yanmar Flying-Y Building 1-32
Chayamachi Kita-ku, Kita-ku, Osaka, 530-8311, Japan
Tel.: (81) 663766211
Web Site: http://www.yanmar.com
Year Founded: 1912
Emp.: 3,618
Agricultural Machinery & Industrial Engines Mfr & Distr
N.A.I.C.S.: 333924
Takehito Yamaoka *(Chm & Pres)*

Subsidiaries:

ASV Holdings, Inc. (1)
840 Lily Ln, Grand Rapids, MN 55744
Tel.: (218) 327-3434
Web Site: http://www.asvi.com
Rev.: $127,580,000
Assets: $87,631,000
Liabilities: $53,600,000
Net Worth: $34,031,000
Earnings: ($32,130,000)
Emp.: 179
Fiscal Year-end: 12/31/2018
Track & Steer Loader Mfr
N.A.I.C.S.: 333120
Melissa K. How *(CFO & Sec)*

HARBIN YANMAR AGRICULTURAL EQUIPMENT CO., LTD.
Northwest side of No 7 Avenue SongHua-Nan Road Hanan industrial city, Harbin, Heilongjiang, China
Tel.: (86) 451 5185 9188
Farm Machinery & Equipment Distr
N.A.I.C.S.: 423820

KANZAKI KOKYUKOKI MFG.CO., LTD. (1)
18-1 2-chome Inadera Amagasaki, Hyogo, Japan
Tel.: (81) 6 6491 1111
Web Site: http://www.kanzaki-kokyukoki.jp
Farm Machinery & Equipment Mfr
N.A.I.C.S.: 333111

Subsidiary (US):

Tuff Torq Corporation (2)
5943 Commerce Blvd, Morristown, TN 37814-1051
Tel.: (423) 585-2000

Web Site: http://www.tufftorq.com
Farm Machinery & Equipment Mfr
N.A.I.C.S.: 333111

KYORITSU IRRIGATE CO., LTD. (1)
Osaka Togami Bldg 5F 12-5 Enoki-cho Suita, Osaka, 564-0053, Japan
Tel.: (81) 6 6310 9211
Web Site: http://www.kyoritsu-jic.co.jp
Farm Machinery & Equipment Mfr
N.A.I.C.S.: 333111

New Delta Industrial Co., Ltd. (1)
767 Umena Mishima, Shizuoka, Japan
Tel.: (81) 559 77 1727
Web Site: http://www.newdelta.co.jp
Emp.: 126
Farm Machinery & Equipment Mfr
N.A.I.C.S.: 333111
Daisuke Takada *(Pres)*

P.T. YKT GEAR INDONESIA (1)
Jl Raya Setu Kp Rawa Banteng RT 024 RW 11 Cibuntu Cibitung, Bekasi, 17520, Indonesia
Tel.: (62) 21 825 2266
Web Site: http://www.id.yanmar.com
Farm Machinery & Equipment Mfr
N.A.I.C.S.: 333111

P.T.YANMAR AGRICULTURAL MACHINERY MANUFACTURING INDONESIA (1)
Desa Sumberejo Kec Pandaan Kab Pasuruan, Pasuruan, 67156, Jawa Timur, Indonesia
Tel.: (62) 343 631361
Farm Machinery & Equipment Distr
N.A.I.C.S.: 423820

P.T.YANMAR DIESEL INDONESIA (1)
Jl Raya Jakarta-Bogor Km 34 8 Cilodong, Depok, 16415, Jawa Barat, Indonesia
Tel.: (62) 21 874 1558
Farm Machinery & Equipment Distr
N.A.I.C.S.: 423820

PT. YANMAR INDONESIA (1)
EJIP Industrial Park Plot IA-1 Cikarang Selatan, Bekasi, Bekasi, Indonesia
Tel.: (62) 21 897 0701
Farm Machinery & Equipment Distr
N.A.I.C.S.: 423820
Gamci Panty *(Gen Mgr)*

YANMAR AGRICULTURAL EQUIPMENT (CHINA) CO., LTD. (1)
No 8 Huangshan Road, New District, Wuxi, 214028, Jiangsu, China
Tel.: (86) 510 8521 6877
Web Site: http://www.cn.yanmar.com
Farm Machinery & Equipment Mfr
N.A.I.C.S.: 333111

YANMAR AGRICULTURAL MACHINERY (KOREA) CO., LTD. (1)
1372 Gwangam-ri Wanggung-myeon, Iksan, 570 941, Jeollabuk-do, Korea (South)
Tel.: (82) 63 838 8899
Web Site: http://www.yanmar.co.kr
Farm Machinery & Equipment Mfr
N.A.I.C.S.: 333111

YANMAR ASIA (SINGAPORE) CORPORATION PTE. LTD. (1)
4 Tuas Lane, Singapore, 638613, Singapore
Tel.: (65) 6595 4200
Web Site: http://www.yanmar.com
Emp.: 70
Farm Machinery & Equipment Distr
N.A.I.C.S.: 423820
Jackson Hock Koon Tan *(Mng Dir)*

YANMAR CAPITAL (THAILAND) CO., LTD. (1)
No 1858/113 115 116 TCIF Tower 26th Floor Bangna-Trad Road, Bangna, Bangkok, 10260, Thailand
Tel.: (66) 2 751 4750
Farm Machinery & Equipment Distr
N.A.I.C.S.: 423820

YANMAR CONSTRUCTION EQUIPMENT CO., LTD. (1)
1717-1 Oaza Kumano Chikugo, Fukuoka, Japan
Tel.: (81) 942 53 5111

942 53 5111
N.A.I.C.S.: 333111

YANMAR CONSTRUCTION EQUIPMENT EUROPE S.A.S. (1)
25 Rue de la Tambourine, 52100, Saint Dizier, France
Tel.: (33) 325 56 39 75
Web Site: http://www.yanmarconstruction.eu
325 56 39 75
N.A.I.C.S.: 327910

YANMAR ENERGY SYSTEM CO., LTD. (1)
5-12-39 Oyodonaka, Kita-ku, Osaka, Japan
Tel.: (81) 6 6451 7838
Farm Machinery & Equipment Mfr
N.A.I.C.S.: 333111

YANMAR ENERGY SYSTEM MFG.CO., LTD. (1)
383-2 Saidaijishinchi, Higashi-ku, Okayama, Okayama, Japan
Tel.: (81) 86 942 0143
Web Site: http://www.yanmar.com
Farm Machinery & Equipment Mfr
N.A.I.C.S.: 333111

YANMAR ENGINE (SHANDONG) CO., LTD. (1)
No 278 Shaohai Road Hetao, Hongdao Economic Zone, Qingdao, 266113, Shandong, China
Tel.: (86) 532 8965 4999
Farm Machinery & Equipment Distr
N.A.I.C.S.: 423820

YANMAR ENGINE (SHANGHAI) CO., LTD. (1)
10F E-Block Poly Plaza No 18 Dongfang Road, Pudong, Shanghai, 200120, China
Tel.: (86) 21 6880 5090
Web Site: http://www.yanmar.com
Farm Machinery & Equipment Dis
N.A.I.C.S.: 423820

YANMAR ENGINEERING CO., LTD. (1)
1-1 Nagasu Higasi-dori 1-chome, Amagasaki, 6608585, Hyogo, Japan
Tel.: (81) 6 6489 8045
Web Site: http://www.yanmar-e.co.jp
Emp.: 70
Farm Machinery & Equipment Mfr
N.A.I.C.S.: 333111
Kentaro Tsudaka *(Pres)*

Subsidiary (Non-US):

Yanmar Engineering (HK) Co., Ltd. (2)
Unit J 23/F King Palace Plaza 55 King Yip Street Kwun Tong, Kowloon, China (Hong Kong)
Tel.: (852) 2833 9032
Farm Machinery & Equipment Distr
N.A.I.C.S.: 423820

YANMAR INDIA PRIVATE LIMITED (1)
K-4 Ocean Height 5th Floor Sector 18, Noida, 201 301, Uttar Pradesh, India
Tel.: (91) 120 4313724
Farm Machinery & Equipment Distr
N.A.I.C.S.: 423820

YANMAR INTERNATIONAL SINGAPORE PTE. LTD. (1)
30 Raffles Place Suite 15-02 Chevron House, Singapore, 048622, Singapore
Tel.: (65) 6715 4820
Farm Machinery & Equipment Distr
N.A.I.C.S.: 423820

YANMAR ITALY S.p.A. (1)
Via Carabelli 7/9, 21012, Cassano Magnago, Italy
Tel.: (39) 0331 208409
Web Site: http://www.yanmaritaly.it
Emp.: 170
Farm Machinery & Equipment Mfr
N.A.I.C.S.: 333111
Beodete Carlo *(Mgr-Sls)*

YANMAR KOTA KINABALU R&D CENTER SDN. BHD. (1)
Lot 11&12 IZ4 Jalan KKIP 1G KKIP Selatan, Industrial Park, 88450, Kota Kinabalu, Sabah, Malaysia
Tel.: (60) 88 496777

YANMAR CO., LTD.

Yanmar Co., Ltd.—(Continued)
Farm Machinery & Equipment Distr
N.A.I.C.S.: 423820

YANMAR MARINE SYSTEM CO., LTD. (1)
3-1-17 Chuo Itami, Hyogo, 6640851, Japan
Tel.: (81) 72 773 5860
Farm Machinery & Equipment Mfr
N.A.I.C.S.: 333111

YANMAR NORGE A.S. (1)
Hvamstubben 8, 2026, Skjetten, Norway
Tel.: (47) 64 83 4350
Web Site: http://www.yanmar.no
Farm Machinery & Equipment Mfr
N.A.I.C.S.: 333111

YANMAR OKINAWA CO., LTD. (1)
7-11-12 Oyama Ginowan, Okinawa, Japan
Tel.: (81) 98 898 3111
Farm Machinery & Equipment Mfr
N.A.I.C.S.: 333111

YANMAR R&D EUROPE S.R.L. (1)
Viale Galileo 3/A, 50125, Florence, Italy
Tel.: (39) 055 512 1694
Emp.: 14
Farm Machinery & Equipment Distr
N.A.I.C.S.: 423820
Shiozaki Shuji *(Pres)*

YANMAR RUS LLC (1)
Office 303 Roshchinskiy proezd 8, 115419, Moscow, Russia
Tel.: (7) 4952322135
Web Site: http://www.yanmarrus.ru
Farm Machinery & Equipment Mfr
N.A.I.C.S.: 333111

YANMAR S.P. CO., LTD. (1)
Lad Krabang Industrial Estate 109 Moo 9 Chalong Krung Road, Lab Krabang, Bangkok, 10520, Thailand
Tel.: (66) 2 326 0700
Web Site: http://www.th.yanmar.com
Farm Machinery & Equipment Mfr
N.A.I.C.S.: 333111

YANMAR SHIPBUILDING & ENGINEERING CO., LTD. (1)
3286-3 Itoharu Musashimachi Kunisaki, Oita, Japan
Tel.: (81) 978 68 0824
Farm Machinery & Equipment Mfr
N.A.I.C.S.: 333111

YANMAR SOUTH AMERICA INDUSTRIA DE MAQUINAS LTDA. (1)
Av Presidente Vargas 1400, Indaiatuba, 19 3801 9200, Sao Paulo, Brazil
Tel.: (55) 19 3801 9200
Web Site: http://www.yanmar.com.br
Farm Machinery & Equipment Mfr
N.A.I.C.S.: 333111

YANMAR SVERIGE A.B. (1)
Backvagen 17 Edsberg, 19254, Sollentuna, Sweden
Tel.: (46) 8 444 5280
Web Site: http://www.yanmar.se
Farm Machinery & Equipment Mfr
N.A.I.C.S.: 333111

YANMAR TECHNICAL SERVICE CO., LTD. (1)
1-2-6 Shioe, Amagasaki, Hyogo, Japan
Tel.: (81) 6 4960 8532
Farm Machinery & Equipment Mfr
N.A.I.C.S.: 333111

Yanmar Agri Japan Co., Ltd. (1)
10-6 Koei-cho, Ebetsu, 067-0051, Hokkaido, Japan
Tel.: (81) 11 381 2300
Web Site: http://www.yanmar.co.jp
Farm Machinery & Equipment Mfr
N.A.I.C.S.: 333111

Yanmar Agricultural Machinery Manufacturing Co., Ltd. (1)
931 Noishiki Maibara, Shiga, Japan
Tel.: (81) 749 55 1111
Farm Machinery & Equipment Mfr
N.A.I.C.S.: 333111

Plant (Domestic):

Yanmar Agricultural Machinery Manufacturing Co., Ltd. - Kouchi Plant (2)

263 Hachioji Tosayamada-cho, Kami, Kochi, Japan
Tel.: (81) 887 57 0111
Farm Machinery & Equipment Mfr
N.A.I.C.S.: 333111

Yanmar America Corporation (1)
101 International Pkwy, Adairsville, GA 30103
Tel.: (770) 877-9894
Web Site: http://www.yanmar.com
Sales Range: $25-49.9 Million
Emp.: 150
Mfr of Marine & Industrial Diesel Engines
N.A.I.C.S.: 423820
Doug Englert *(Dir-Parts)*

Subsidiary (Domestic):

Mastry Engine Center LLC (2)
2801 Anvil St N, Saint Petersburg, FL 33710
Tel.: (727) 522-9471
Web Site: http://www.mastry.com
Sales Range: $25-49.9 Million
Emp.: 48
Industrial Machinery & Equipment Merchant Whslr
N.A.I.C.S.: 423830
Adib Mastry *(COO)*

Yanmar Benelux B.V. (1)
Brugplein 11, 1332 BS, Almere, Netherlands
Tel.: (31) 36 5493200
Web Site: http://www.yanmarbenelux.nl
Farm Machinery & Equipment Mfr
N.A.I.C.S.: 333111
Peter Vandervorst *(Mgr)*

Yanmar Casting Technology Co., Ltd. (1)
960 Yahata-cho, Matsue, 6990025, Shimane, Japan
Tel.: (81) 852 37 1355
Emp.: 230
Farm Machinery & Equipment Mfr
N.A.I.C.S.: 333111
Tokio Fujii *(Pres)*

Yanmar Co., Ltd. - AMAGASAKI PLANT (1)
1-1-1 Nagasu Higashidori, Amagasaki, 660-8585, Hyogo, Japan
Tel.: (81) 6 6489 8002
Farm Machinery & Equipment Mfr
N.A.I.C.S.: 333111

Yanmar Co., Ltd. - BIWA PLANT (1)
1009-2 Kawamichicho, Nagahama, Shiga, Japan
Tel.: (81) 749 72 5157
Farm Machinery & Equipment Mfr
N.A.I.C.S.: 333111

Yanmar Co., Ltd. - KINOMOTO PLANT (1)
650 Kuroda Kinomoto-ch Ika-gun, Shiga, Japan
Tel.: (81) 749 82 3322
Farm Machinery & Equipment Mfr
N.A.I.C.S.: 333111

Yanmar Co., Ltd. - NAGAHARA PLANT (1)
18 Sho Nishi-azai-cho Ika-gun, Shiga, Japan
Tel.: (81) 749 89 1151
Farm Machinery & Equipment Mfr
N.A.I.C.S.: 333111

Yanmar Co., Ltd. - OMORI PLANT (1)
354 Shigenori Takatsuki-cho, Ika-gun, Shiga, 5290275, Japan
Tel.: (81) 749 85 3000
Web Site: http://www.yanmar.co.jp
Farm Machinery & Equipment Mfr
N.A.I.C.S.: 333111

Yanmar Co., Ltd. - YAMAMOTO PLANT (1)
3198 Yamamoto Kohoku-ch Higashi, Azai-gun, Shiga, Japan
Tel.: (81) 749 79 0305
Farm Machinery & Equipment Mfr
N.A.I.C.S.: 333111

Yanmar Equipment Iberica SL
Calle Tallers 30-32 Poligono Industrial El Foix, L'Arboc, 43720, Tarragona, Spain

Tel.: (34) 902 733 737
Web Site: http://www.yanmar.es
Farm Machinery & Equipment Mfr
N.A.I.C.S.: 333111

Yanmar Information System Service Co., Ltd (1)
4-1-14 Miyahara Sumitomo Seimei Shin Osaka Kita Building 12F, Yodogawa-ku, Osaka, 532-0003, Japan
Tel.: (81) 6 6395 1603
Web Site: http://www.yanmar.com
Sales Range: $25-49.9 Million
Emp.: 193
Information Systems Management & Consulting Services
N.A.I.C.S.: 541511
Takao Kanaiwa *(Pres)*

YANPAI FILTRATION TECHNOLOGY CO., LTD.
NO 1 Yongxing Road Shifeng Street, Tiantai, Taizhou, 317200, Zhejiang, China
Tel.: (86) 4008266678
Web Site: https://www.yanpai.com
Year Founded: 2014
301081—(SSE)
Rev.: $105,855,984
Assets: $215,526,636
Liabilities: $79,741,584
Net Worth: $135,785,052
Earnings: $8,942,076
Emp.: 900
Fiscal Year-end: 12/31/22
Filter Product Mfr
N.A.I.C.S.: 334419
Sun Shangze *(Chm)*

Subsidiaries:

Mid Atlantic Industrial Textile Inc. (1)
7854 Browning Rd, Pennsauken, NJ 08109
Tel.: (609) 261-4886
Web Site: https://www.midatlantictextilesinc.com
Woven Fabric Filter Mfr & Distr
N.A.I.C.S.: 313230

Mid-Atlantic Industrial Textiles Co., Ltd. (1)
7854 Browning Rd, Pennsauken, NJ 08109
Tel.: (609) 261-4886
Filtration Device Mfr
N.A.I.C.S.: 333998

Shanghai Yanpai Filter Cloth Co., Ltd. (1)
Room 2516 Building 3 Baoshan Wanda No 4995 Gonghe New Road, Baoshan District, Shanghai, China
Tel.: (86) 2163931577
Filtration Device Mfr
N.A.I.C.S.: 333998

Zhejiang Yanli New Materials Co., Ltd. (1)
No 18 Industrial Park, Tongyuan Haiyan, Jiaxing, Zhejiang, China
Tel.: (86) 57387889625
Web Site: https://www.inssfoil.com
Industrial Product Mfr & Distr
N.A.I.C.S.: 334513

YANTAI CHANGYU PIONEER WINE COMPANY LTD.
No 56 Dama Road, Zhifu District, Yantai, 264000, Shandong, China
Tel.: (86) 5356633656
Web Site: http://www.changyu.com.cn
Year Founded: 1892
200869—(SSE)
Rev.: $550,219,344
Assets: $1,849,279,499
Liabilities: $329,368,024
Net Worth: $1,519,911,474
Earnings: $60,186,869
Fiscal Year-end: 12/31/22
Alcoholic Beverages Mfr
N.A.I.C.S.: 312130
Hongjiang Zhou *(Chm)*

INTERNATIONAL PUBLIC

YANTAI CHINA PET FOODS CO., LTD.
No 88 Feilong Road Laishan Zone, Yantai, 264003, Shandong, China
Tel.: (86) 5356729569
Web Site: https://www.wanpy.com.cn
Year Founded: 1998
002891—(SSE)
Rev.: $456,017,670
Assets: $539,182,880
Liabilities: $227,404,616
Net Worth: $311,778,263
Earnings: $14,872,137
Fiscal Year-end: 12/31/22
Pet Food Product Mfr & Distr
N.A.I.C.S.: 311111

YANTAI DONGCHENG PHARMACEUTICAL GROUP CO., LTD.
No 7 ChangBaiShan Road Yantai Development Zone, Yantai, 264006, Shandong, China
Tel.: (86) 5356391521
Web Site: https://www.dcb-group.com
Year Founded: 1998
002675—(SSE)
Rev.: $599,365,181
Assets: $1,173,018,659
Liabilities: $403,326,857
Net Worth: $769,691,802
Earnings: $23,220,508
Emp.: 2,000
Fiscal Year-end: 12/31/21
Pharmaceuticals & Pharmaceutical Ingredients Mfr
N.A.I.C.S.: 325412
Shouyi You *(Chm)*

Subsidiaries:

Yantai Dayang Pharmaceutical Co., Ltd (1)
No 22-1 Tianjin North Road, Economic and Technological Development Zone, Yantai, 264006, Shandong, China
Tel.: (86) 5358019721
Web Site: http://www.ytdayang.com
Pharmaceuticals Product Mfr.
N.A.I.C.S.: 325412

YANTAI EDDIE PRECISION MACHINERY CO., LTD.
No 356 Changjianglu Road, Yantai Economic And Technological Development Zone, Yantai, 264006, Shandong, China
Tel.: (86) 5356392926
Web Site: https://www.cceddie.net
Year Founded: 2003
603638—(SHG)
Rev.: $284,309,045
Assets: $778,878,196
Liabilities: $339,356,179
Net Worth: $439,522,017
Earnings: $35,002,843
Emp.: 2,500
Fiscal Year-end: 12/31/22
Hydraulic Product Mfr & Distr
N.A.I.C.S.: 333998
Fei Song *(Chm & Pres)*

Subsidiaries:

Yantai Eddie Hydraulic Technology Co., Ltd (1)
No 75 Fuxin Road, Fushan District, Yantai, 265500, China
Tel.: (86) 5356311098
Web Site: http://www.fceddie.com
Hydraulic Pump Mfr & Distr
N.A.I.C.S.: 333996

YANTAI ISHIKAWA SEALING TECHNOLOGY CO., LTD.
No 5 Binglun Road APEC Technological Industrial Park, Zhifu, Yantai, 264002, Shandong, China
Tel.: (86) 15763807215

AND PRIVATE COMPANIES

Web Site:
https://www.ishikawaseal.com
Year Founded: 1991
301020—(CHIN)
Rev.: $72,152,549
Assets: $164,405,957
Liabilities: $37,046,225
Net Worth: $127,359,732
Earnings: $10,191,662
Emp.: 500
Fiscal Year-end: 12/31/23
Gasket Mfr & Distr
N.A.I.C.S.: 339991
Jiangbo Lou *(Chm)*

YANTAI JEREH OILFIELD SERVICES GROUP CO., LTD.
No 5 Jierui Road, Laishan District, Yantai, 264003, Shandong, China
Tel.: (86) 5356723532
Web Site: http://www.jereh.com
Year Founded: 1999
002353—(SSE)
Rev.: $1,601,825,299
Assets: $4,103,306,448
Liabilities: $1,559,012,439
Net Worth: $2,544,294,009
Earnings: $315,190,924
Emp.: 7,000
Fiscal Year-end: 12/31/22
Oil Field Equipment & Services
N.A.I.C.S.: 333132
Li Zhiyong *(Pres)*

Subsidiaries:

American Jereh International Corporation (1)
7501 Miller Rd 2, Houston, TX 77049
Tel.: (281) 860-0488
Web Site: www.americanjereh.com
Mining Machinery & Equipment Mfr
N.A.I.C.S.: 333131

Dezhou United Petroleum Technology Corp. (1)
The South Section of Jinghua road, Economic Development Zone, Dezhou, 253034, Shandong, China
Tel.: (86) 5342237999
Web Site: https://www.dupm.cn
Down Hole Motor Mfr
N.A.I.C.S.: 333132

Jereh C-Create Technology Co., Ltd. (1)
Building 6 Shenzhen Bay Science and Technology Ecological Park, Nanshan District, Shenzhen, China
Tel.: (86) 535 676 8317
Web Site: https://www.jereh-hc.com
Electrostatic Spraying Machine Distr
N.A.I.C.S.: 423830

Jereh Energy Equipment & Technologies Corporation (1)
7501 Miller Rd 2, Houston, TX 77049
Tel.: (281) 860-0488
Web Site: https://www.jereh-eet.com
Turbine Mfr
N.A.I.C.S.: 333611

Jereh Energy Services Corporation (1)
No 7 Aucma Street, Laishan District, Yantai, 264003, Shandong, China
Tel.: (86) 5356766750
Web Site: https://www.jereh-services.com
Oil & Gas Exploration Services
N.A.I.C.S.: 213112

Jereh Environmental Protection Technology Co., Ltd. (1)
No 9 Jerry Road, Laishan District, Yantai, Shandong, China
Tel.: (86) 5356768052
Web Site: https://www.jereh-env.com
Protection Equipment Mfr
N.A.I.C.S.: 334290

Jereh Global Development LLC (1)
No 9 Jereh Road, Laishan District, Yantai, 264003, China
Tel.: (86) 535 676 5628
Web Site: https://www.jereh-oilfield.com

Drilling Tool Mfr
N.A.I.C.S.: 333131

Jereh Oil & Gas Engineering Corporation (1)
No 5 Jereh Road, Laishan District, Yantai, China
Tel.: (86) 4009977567
Web Site: https://www.jereh-gas.com
Natural Gas Distr
N.A.I.C.S.: 221210

Sichuan Jereh Hengri Natural Gas Engineering Co., Ltd. (1)
T2-42th Floor Xiangnian Square No 88 of 5th Jitai road, Gaoxin Zone, Chengdu, China
Tel.: (86) 2866266745
Web Site: https://www.jereh-hengri.com
Natural Gas Distribution Services
N.A.I.C.S.: 221210

Yantai Jereh Compression Equipment Co., Ltd. (1)
No 9 Jereh Road, Laishan District, Yantai, 264003, Shandong, China
Tel.: (86) 5356723505
Web Site: http://www.jereh-ce.com
Natural Gas Compressors Mfr & Sales
N.A.I.C.S.: 333912

Yantai Jereh Funaike Heat Exchanger Equipment Co., Ltd. (1)
No 966 Fushan Road, Shandong, China
Tel.: (86) 535 731 7668
Web Site: https://en.chinafnk.com
Environmental Protection Equipment Mfr & Distr
N.A.I.C.S.: 334512

Yantai Jereh Machinery Equipment Co., Ltd. (1)
No 7 Aucma Street, Leishan Dist, Yantai, 264003, Shandong, China
Tel.: (86) 5356728521
Industrial Transmission Supplies Distr
N.A.I.C.S.: 423840

Yantai Jereh Oilfield Services Co., Ltd (1)
No 7 Aucma St, Laishan District, Yantai, Shandong, China
Tel.: (86) 5356723166
Web Site: http://www.jereh-services.net
Oilfield Support Services
N.A.I.C.S.: 213112

Yantai Jereh Petroleum Equipment & Technologies Co., Ltd. (1)
No 27 Jereh Road, Laishan District, Yantai, 264003, Shandong, China
Tel.: (86) 4008162161
Web Site: https://www.jereh-pe.com
Oil Field Equipments Mfr & Sales
N.A.I.C.S.: 333132

Yantai Jereh Power-Tech Co., Ltd. (1)
No 9 Jerry Road, Laishan District, Yantai, 264003, Shandong, China
Tel.: (86) 535 676 5379
Web Site: https://www.jereh-powertech.com
Engine Parts Mfr
N.A.I.C.S.: 336310

YANTAI LONGYUAN POWER TECHNOLOGY CO., LTD.
No 2 Baiyunshan Road Yantai Development Zone Pilot Free Trade Zone, Yantai, 264003, Shandong, China
Tel.: (86) 5353417182
Web Site: http://www.lypower.com
Year Founded: 1998
300105—(SSE)
Rev.: $102,875,292
Assets: $361,642,320
Liabilities: $94,546,764
Net Worth: $267,095,556
Earnings: $12,429,612
Fiscal Year-end: 12/31/22
Automation & Industiral Power Products Mfr
N.A.I.C.S.: 334513
Yang Huailiang *(Chm)*

YANTAI NORTH ANDRE JUICE CO., LTD.

No 889 Park Avenue, Muping District, Yantai, 264100, Shandong, China
Tel.: (86) 5354218988
Web Site: https://www.andre.com.cn
Year Founded: 1996
2218—(HKG)
Rev.: $149,586,275
Assets: $366,417,796
Liabilities: $33,752,657
Net Worth: $332,665,138
Earnings: $27,286,576
Emp.: 922
Fiscal Year-end: 12/31/22
Fruit Juices Mfr
N.A.I.C.S.: 311411
An Wang *(Chm)*

Subsidiaries:

North Andre Juice (USA) Inc. (1)
64 Copper Leaf, Irvine, CA 92602
Tel.: (714) 389-9060
Fresh Juice Distr
N.A.I.C.S.: 424490

Yantai Longkou Andre Juice Co., Ltd. (1)
Longkou Huangcheng Industrial Park, Yantai, 265718, Shandong, China
Tel.: (86) 5358955989
Web Site: http://www.andre.com.cn
Fresh Juice Mfr & Distr
N.A.I.C.S.: 311411

YANTAI ORIENTAL PROTEIN TECH CO., LTD.
668 Jincheng Road, 265400, Zhaoyuan, Shandong, China
Tel.: (86) 535 8072166
Web Site: http://www.dongfang-protein.cn
Year Founded: 2008
Emp.: 150
R&D, Production & Operation of Pea Proteins in Abstracting & Isolating of Starches, Proteins & Dietary Fibers
N.A.I.C.S.: 111130
Albert Co *(Mgr-Mktg)*

YANTAI RAYTRON TECHNOLOGY CO., LTD.
No 6 Nanchang Street YEDA China Shandong Pilot Free Trade Zone, Yantai Economic & Technological Development Area Yeda, Yantai, 264006, Shandong, China
Tel.: (86) 5353410615
Web Site: https://www.raytrontek.com
Year Founded: 2009
688002—(SHG)
Rev.: $371,482,647
Assets: $888,120,741
Liabilities: $278,878,429
Net Worth: $609,242,311
Earnings: $43,997,569
Emp.: 2,000
Fiscal Year-end: 12/31/22
Electric Equipment Mfr
N.A.I.C.S.: 335999
Hong Ma *(Chm & Gen Mgr)*

YANTAI SHUANGTA FOOD CO., LTD.
Jinling Town, Zhaoyuan, Shandong, China
Tel.: (86) 4001899988
Web Site: https://www.shuangtafood.com
002481—(SSE)
Rev.: $334,338,423
Assets: $550,914,619
Liabilities: $217,790,951
Net Worth: $333,123,668
Earnings: $(43,662,434)
Fiscal Year-end: 12/31/22
Vermicelli Products & Mushrooms Producer & Distr
N.A.I.C.S.: 311824

YANTAI ZHENGHAI MAGNETIC MATERIAL CO., LTD.

YANTAI T. FULL BIOTECH CO., LTD.
T. Full Industrial Park, Zhaoyuan Dingfeng Zhangxing Town, Yantai, Shandong, China
Tel.: (86) 5358930268
Web Site: http://www.tfull.com
Sales Range: $10-24.9 Million
Pea Product Manufacturing
N.A.I.C.S.: 311999
Shengu Luo *(Gen Mgr)*

YANTAI TAYHO ADVANCED MATERIALS CO., LTD.
No 10 Heilongjiang Road, Economic and Technical Development Area, Yantai, 264006, China
Tel.: (86) 5356939635
Web Site: https://en.tayho.com.cn
Year Founded: 1986
002254—(SSE)
Rev.: $526,517,831
Assets: $1,408,652,056
Liabilities: $762,395,461
Net Worth: $646,256,595
Earnings: $61,198,521
Emp.: 1,200
Fiscal Year-end: 12/31/22
Chemical Fiber Mfr
N.A.I.C.S.: 325220
Chi Haiping *(Pres)*

Subsidiaries:

Yantai Yuxiang Fine chemicals Co., Ltd (1)
South First of Zhejiang Road, Zhongqiao Economic & Technical Development Area Qixia, Yantai, China
Tel.: (86) 5355573597
Timber Product Mfr
N.A.I.C.S.: 313110

YANTAI YUANCHENG GOLD CO., LTD.
No 261 South Avenue, Zhifu District, Yantai, 264000, Shandong, China
Tel.: (86) 5356636299
Web Site: http://www.ytycgf.com
600766—(SHG)
Rev.: $13,240,001
Assets: $63,103,384
Liabilities: $55,082,444
Net Worth: $8,020,940
Earnings: $(170,754)
Fiscal Year-end: 12/31/22
Gold & Silver Product Whslr
N.A.I.C.S.: 423940

YANTAI ZHENGHAI BIO-TECH CO., LTD.
No 7 Nanjing Street Yantai Economic & Technological Development Area, Yantai, 264006, China
Tel.: (86) 4006886808
Web Site: https://www.zhbio.com
Year Founded: 2003
300653—(CHIN)
Rev.: $60,824,748
Assets: $138,561,434
Liabilities: $17,100,299
Net Worth: $121,461,135
Earnings: $26,035,327
Fiscal Year-end: 12/31/22
Pharmaceutical Product Mfr & Distr
N.A.I.C.S.: 325412
Guo Huanxiang *(Chm)*

YANTAI ZHENGHAI MAGNETIC MATERIAL CO., LTD.
9 Shantou Street Yeda, Yantai, China
Tel.: (86) 5356397197
Web Site: https://www.zhmag.com
Year Founded: 2000
300224—(SSE)
Rev.: $887,190,408
Assets: $1,246,686,012

YANTAI ZHENGHAI MAGNETIC MATERIAL CO., LTD.

Yantai Zhenghai Magnetic Material Co., Ltd.—(Continued)
Liabilities: $731,201,796
Net Worth: $515,484,216
Earnings: $56,737,044
Emp.: 720
Fiscal Year-end: 12/31/22
Neodymium-Iron-Boron Permanent Magnets Mfr
N.A.I.C.S.: 332999
Wang Qingkai *(Chm)*

Subsidiaries:

Zhenghai Magnetics Europe GmbH (1)
Besucheranschrift Stockstr 2, 73312, Geislingen, Germany
Tel.: (49) 17660173003
Industrial Equipment Mfr
N.A.I.C.S.: 333248

Zhenghai Magnetics Korea Co., Ltd. (1)
C-1105 60 Haan-ro, Geumcheon-gu, Gwangmyeong, 14322, Gyeonggi-do, Korea (South)
Tel.: (82) 269540190
Industrial Equipment Mfr
N.A.I.C.S.: 333248

Zhenghai Magnetics North America LLC (1)
40600 Ann Arbor Rd E Ste 201, Plymouth, MI 48170
Tel.: (765) 418-0061
Industrial Equipment Mfr
N.A.I.C.S.: 333248

YANTRA NATURAL RESOURCES LIMITED

House No 1-2-29/45/A4 First Floor Nandamuri Nagar Lane Nizampet Road, Hydernagar Kukutpally Municipality, Hyderabad, 500072, Andhra Pradesh, India
Tel.: (91) 40 40119926
Web Site:
 http://www.yantranaturalltd.com
Year Founded: 1988
Sales Range: $1-9.9 Million
Mining Services
N.A.I.C.S.: 212290
Rajinder Paul Singla *(Exec Dir)*

YAO I FABRIC CO., LTD.

No 334 Sec 6 Zhangmei Rd, Hemei Township, Chang-Hua, 508, Taiwan
Tel.: (886) 47556111
Web Site: https://www.yaoi.com.tw
Year Founded: 1973
4430—(TPE)
Rev.: $64,773,255
Assets: $120,678,204
Liabilities: $57,062,564
Net Worth: $63,615,640
Earnings: $295,157
Fiscal Year-end: 12/31/22
Fishing Net Mfr & Distr
N.A.I.C.S.: 339920
Chao-Jen Wang *(Chm)*

YAO SHENG ELECTRONICS CO., LTD.

No 309-28 Daying Rd, Daxi District, Taoyuan, 335, Taiwan
Tel.: (886) 33893755
Web Site: https://www.top-nation.com
Year Founded: 1992
3207—(TPE)
Rev.: $38,409,124
Assets: $52,593,190
Liabilities: $21,683,394
Net Worth: $30,909,796
Earnings: $6,634,056
Fiscal Year-end: 12/31/22
Transformer & Coil Mfr
N.A.I.C.S.: 334416
Su Haoxi *(Chm)*

Subsidiaries:

Dong Guan Top Nation Electronic Limited (1)
No 2 Shatian Road Second Industrial Zone, Second Village Shijie, Dongguan, China
Tel.: (86) 76986632772
Transformer & Inductor Mfr
N.A.I.C.S.: 334416

Top Nation Electronic (Suzhou) Co., Ltd. (1)
2888 Linhu Avenue, Foho Economic Development Zone, Wujiang, China
Tel.: (86) 51263271988
Electronic Products Mfr
N.A.I.C.S.: 334419

Wenshan Top Nation Electronic Limited (1)
Denggao Area Sanqi Industrial Park, Gumu, Wenshan, Yunnan, China
Tel.: (86) 8763051662
Transformer & Inductor Mfr
N.A.I.C.S.: 334416

YAOKO CO., LTD.

1-10-1 Arajukumachi, Kawagoe, 350-1124, Saitama, Japan
Tel.: (81) 492467000 JP
Web Site: https://www.yaoko-net.com
Year Founded: 1957
8279—(TKS)
Rev.: $4,095,470,070
Assets: $2,263,323,490
Liabilities: $1,153,491,270
Net Worth: $1,109,832,220
Earnings: $120,586,230
Emp.: 4,347
Fiscal Year-end: 03/31/24
Supermarket Store Operator
N.A.I.C.S.: 445110
Sumito Kawano *(Pres)*

YAPI KREDI FAKTORING A.S.

Levent Mah Comert Sok No 1A/30, Besiktas, 34330, Istanbul, Turkiye
Tel.: (90) 212 371 99 99
Web Site:
 http://www.yapikredifaktoring.com
Year Founded: 1999
YKFKT—(IST)
Sales Range: Less than $1 Million
Export-Import Services
N.A.I.C.S.: 522299
Bozkurt Coteli *(Gen Mgr)*

YAPI KREDI KORAY GAYRIMENKUL YATIRIM ORTAKLIGI A.S

Mesrutiyet Mah 19 Mayis Cad Ismet Ozturk Sk No 3 Elit Residence Kat 17, Daire 42 Sisli, Istanbul, Turkiye
Tel.: (90) 2123801680
Web Site:
 http://www.yapikredikoray.com
Year Founded: 1996
KGYO—(IST)
Rev.: $7,286,967
Assets: $125,678,305
Liabilities: $95,437,749
Net Worth: $30,240,556
Earnings: $21,798,809
Fiscal Year-end: 12/31/23
Real Estate Investment Services
N.A.I.C.S.: 523999
Faik Acikalin *(Chm)*

YAPI MERKEZI HOLDING A.S.

Haci Resit Pasa Sok 13, Istanbul, 34676, Turkiye
Tel.: (90) 2163219000
Web Site: http://www.yapi-merkezi.com
Sales Range: $200-249.9 Million
Emp.: 1,000
Construction Projects
N.A.I.C.S.: 212321
Koksal Anadol *(Founder & Vice Chm)*

Subsidiaries:

Freysas-Freyssinet Structural Systems Inc. (1)
Poyraz Sokak TuncLudemir Is Merkezi No 5 Kat 2 D 5-6, Hasanpasa KadiKoy, 34722, Istanbul, Turkiye
Tel.: (90) 216 349 87 74
Civil Engineering Construction Services
N.A.I.C.S.: 237990

Subor Boru Sanayi ve Ticaret A.S. (1)
Acibadem Mahallesi Sokullu Sokak No 12, Kadikoy, 34718, Istanbul, Turkiye
Tel.: (90) 2164741900
Web Site: http://www.subor.com.tr
Sales Range: $25-49.9 Million
Mfr of Plastic Products; Joint Venture of The Saudi Arabian Amiantit Group (50%) & Yapi Merkezi (50%)
N.A.I.C.S.: 325211

Yapi Merkezi Construction & Industry Inc. (1)
Haci Resit Pasa Sok No 4, Camlica, 34676, Istanbul, Turkiye
Tel.: (90) 216 321 90 00
Web Site: http://www.ym.com.tr
Civil Engineering Construction Services
N.A.I.C.S.: 237990
Nihat Demirok *(CFO)*

Yapi Merkezi Prefabrikasyon A.S. (1)
Mimar Sinan mh Baraj Yolu cd No 40 Sultanbeyli, Istanbul, 34935, Turkiye
Tel.: (90) 216 592 17 00
Civil Engineering Construction Services
N.A.I.C.S.: 237990

Plant (Domestic):

Yapi Merkezi Prefabrikasyon A.S. - LULEBURGAZ PLANT (2)
Kucukkaristiran mahallesi Merkez Sokak No 220, Buyukkaristiran, Luleburgaz, Kirklareli, Turkiye
Tel.: (90) 288 446 32 49
Web Site: http://www.ymprefab.com
Civil Engineering Construction Services
N.A.I.C.S.: 237990

Yapiray Insaat Sistemleri Sanayi ve Ticaret A.S. (1)
Kisikli Mah Alemdag Cad Masaldan is Merkezi No 60 E Blok No 5, uskudar, Istanbul, Turkiye
Tel.: (90) 216 521 30 00
Civil Engineering Construction Services
N.A.I.C.S.: 237990

Plant (Domestic):

Yapiray Insaat Sistemleri Sanayi ve Ticaret A.S. - Afyon Rayton Factory (2)
Zafer Mah Ahmet Ozyurt Cad No 160, Ihsaniye, Afyonkarahisar, Turkiye
Tel.: (90) 272 271 50 18
Civil Engineering Construction Services
N.A.I.C.S.: 237990

Yapiray Insaat Sistemleri Sanayi ve Ticaret A.S. - Karabuk Rayton Factory (2)
Karabuk Merkez ilcesi Zobran Koyu Hamzalar Mah Ada No 113 Parsel No 2, Karabuk, Turkiye
Tel.: (90) 370 442 20 22
Civil Engineering Construction Services
N.A.I.C.S.: 237990

YAPP AUTOMOTIVE SYSTEMS CO., LTD.

No 508 Yangzijiang South Road, Yangzhou, 225009, Jiangsu, China
Tel.: (86) 51487846666
Web Site: https://www.yapp.com
Year Founded: 1998
603013—(SHG)
Rev.: $1,185,457,418
Assets: $847,919,714
Liabilities: $299,489,655
Net Worth: $548,430,059
Earnings: $70,337,971

Fiscal Year-end: 12/31/22
Automobile Parts Mfr
N.A.I.C.S.: 336310
Lin Jiang *(Chm)*

YAPPLI, INC.

41F Sumitomo Fudosan Roppongi Grand Tower, 3 Chome-2-1 Roppongi Minato City, Tokyo, 106-6241, Japan
Tel.: (81) 368665730
Web Site: https://www.yappli.co.jp
Year Founded: 2013
4168—(TKS)
Application Development Services
N.A.I.C.S.: 541511
Yasubumi Ihara *(Co-Founder & CEO)*

YAPRAK SUT VE BESI CIFTLIKLERI SANAYI VE TICARET A.S.

Burcu Yolu Kume Evleri Mevkii No 12, Burhaniye, Balikesir, 10700, Turkiye
Tel.: (90) 2664222777
Web Site:
 http://www.yaprakciftligi.com.tr
Year Founded: 1994
YAPRK—(IST)
Rev.: $7,825,545
Assets: $16,211,581
Liabilities: $3,833,029
Net Worth: $12,378,552
Earnings: $4,616,871
Fiscal Year-end: 12/31/23
Milk Production Services
N.A.I.C.S.: 112120

YAQARA GROUP LIMITED

32 High St Toorak, Suva, Fiji
Tel.: (679) 3309517
Emp.: 4
Economic Development & Promotional Services
N.A.I.C.S.: 926110
Lyndon Driscoll *(Mng Dir)*

YARA INTERNATIONAL ASA

Drammensveien 131, 0277, Oslo, Norway
Tel.: (47) 24157000 NO
Web Site: https://www.yara.com
Year Founded: 1905
YARIY—(OTCIQ)
Rev.: $15,547,000,000
Assets: $16,027,000,000
Liabilities: $8,457,000,000
Net Worth: $7,570,000,000
Earnings: $54,000,000
Emp.: 18,000
Fiscal Year-end: 12/31/23
Chemical Product Mfr & Distr
N.A.I.C.S.: 325311
Trond Berger *(Co-Chm)*

Subsidiaries:

PT Yara Indonesia (1)
Wisma 46 Kota BNI 47th Floor Jln Jend Sudirman Kav 1, Jakarta, 10220, Indonesia
Tel.: (62) 21 572 2024
Web Site: http://www.yara.com
Fertilizer Mfr
N.A.I.C.S.: 325311

SynAgri LP (1)
5175 boulevard Laurier Est, Saint-Hyacinthe, J2R 2B4, QC, Canada
Tel.: (450) 799-3226
Web Site: https://www.synagri.ca
Sales Range: $1-9.9 Million
Emp.: 100
Crop Harvesting Services
N.A.I.C.S.: 115113

Division (Domestic):

SynAgri (2)
5175 boulevard Laurier Est, Saint-Hyacinthe, J2R 2B4, QC, Canada
Tel.: (450) 799-3226
Web Site: https://www.synagri.ca

AND PRIVATE COMPANIES — YARA INTERNATIONAL ASA

Emp.: 20
Farm Supplies
N.A.I.C.S.: 444240
Sylvain Lavoie *(Gen Mgr)*

Yara (Thailand) Ltd. (1)
Bhiraj Tower at EmQuartier 689 Unit 2709-2713 27th Floor, Sukhumvit Road, Bangkok, 10110, Thailand
Tel.: (66) 2 261 3242
Web Site: http://www.yara.com
Emp.: 58
Fertilizer Mfr
N.A.I.C.S.: 325311

Yara AB (1)
PO Box 4505, 203 20, Malmo, Sweden **(100%)**
Tel.: (46) 101396000
Web Site: http://www.yara.com
Emp.: 70
Mfr of Fertilizers
N.A.I.C.S.: 325311

Yara Agri Czech Republic s.r.o. (1)
Dusni 907/10, 110 00, Prague, Czech Republic
Tel.: (420) 22 018 3050
Web Site: https://www.yaraagri.cz
Emp.: 10
Fertilizer Mfr
N.A.I.C.S.: 325311
Tomas Mayer *(Mgr-Bus)*

Yara Argentina S.A. (1)
Avenida del Libertador 498 P-16, C1001ABR, Buenos Aires, Argentina
Tel.: (54) 1151696400
Fertilizer Mfr
N.A.I.C.S.: 325311

Yara Asia Pte. Ltd. (1)
10-10-01 238B Thomson Road, Novena Square Tower B, Singapore, 307685, Singapore
Tel.: (65) 63095600
Emp.: 30
Fertilizer Mfr
N.A.I.C.S.: 325311

Yara Australia Pty. Ltd. (1)
Level 1 6 Holt Street, McMahons Point, 2060, NSW, Australia
Tel.: (61) 29 959 4266
Web Site: http://www.yara.com
Emp.: 14
Fertilizer Mfr
N.A.I.C.S.: 325311

Subsidiary (Domestic):

Yara Pilbara Holdings Ltd. (2)
Level 5 182 Street Georges Terrace, Perth, 6000, WA, Australia **(100%)**
Tel.: (61) 893278100
Sales Range: $200-249.9 Million
Fertilizer Mfr; Liquid Ammonia Production & Shipping Services
N.A.I.C.S.: 325312

Yara Belgium S.A. (1)
Da Vincilaan 1, B-1930, Zaventem, Belgium
Tel.: (32) 27735211
Web Site: http://www.yara.be
Emp.: 150
Aluminium Extraction & Refining
N.A.I.C.S.: 331313
Yves Bonta *(Gen Mgr)*

Yara Belle Plaine Inc. (1)
1 km N Kalium Rd off Hwy 1, Belle Plaine, S0G 0G0, SK, Canada
Tel.: (306) 525-7600
Mineral Fertilizer Mfr
N.A.I.C.S.: 325311
Jaime Rozdeba *(Sls Mgr-Saskatchewan)*

Yara Benelux B.V. (1)
Zevenmanshaven 107, NL-3133 CA, Vlaardingen, Netherlands
Tel.: (31) 104453166
Web Site: http://www.yara.nl
Emp.: 40
Fertilizer Mfr
N.A.I.C.S.: 325311

Yara Brasil Fertilizantes S.A (1)
Rio Grande Unit 1 Av Admiral Maximiano Fonseca 2001, Rio Grande, 96204-040, Rio Grande do Sul, Brazil
Tel.: (55) 5332934300

Web Site: https://www.yarabrasil.com.br
Emp.: 150
Fertilizer Mfr
N.A.I.C.S.: 325311

Yara Canada Inc. (1)
1800 - 1874 Scarth Street, Regina, S4P 4B3, SK, Canada
Tel.: (514) 849-9222
Web Site: http://www.yara.com
Sales Range: $50-74.9 Million
Emp.: 6
Fertilizer Mfr
N.A.I.C.S.: 325311

Yara Chile Fertilizantes Ltda. (1)
Av Pedro de Valdivia 1215 Of 309, Providencia, Santiago, Chile
Tel.: (56) 225814993
Web Site: https://www.yara.cl
Emp.: 17,000
Fertilizer Mfr & Distr
N.A.I.C.S.: 325311

Yara China Limited (1)
Unit 2612 26th Floor China Merchants Tower 168 Connaught Road, Central, China (Hong Kong) **(100%)**
Tel.: (852) 2511 8000
Web Site: http://www.yara.com.cn
Sales Range: $50-74.9 Million
Emp.: 150
Mineral Fertilizers & Industrial Chemicals
N.A.I.C.S.: 325311

Yara Colombia Ltda. (1)
Centro Industrial Metroparque Interseccion Circunvalar/Cordialidad, Bodega MC11, Barranquilla, 52967, Colombia
Tel.: (57) 56931200
Web Site: http://www.yara.com
Fertilizer Mfr
N.A.I.C.S.: 325311

Yara Danmark A/S (1)
Vesterballevej 27, 7000, Fredericia, Denmark
Tel.: (45) 79223366
Mineral Fertilizer Mfr
N.A.I.C.S.: 325311
Jens Jakob Larsen *(Mktg Mgr)*

Yara East Africa Ltd. (1)
12th Floor Crowne Plaza Hotel Annexe Longonot Road, Upper Hill, Nairobi, Kenya
Tel.: (254) 72 425 5370
Web Site: https://www.yara.co.ke
Agricultural Research Services
N.A.I.C.S.: 541714

Yara Fertilisers India Pvt. Ltd. (1)
502 Global Business Square Institutional Area Sector 44, Gurgaon, 122003, Haryana, India
Tel.: (91) 124 460 3170
Web Site: https://www.yara.in
Fertilizer Mfr & Distr
N.A.I.C.S.: 325314
R. Mukundan *(Mng Dir)*

Plant (Domestic):

Yara Fertilisers India Pvt. Ltd. - Babrala Plant (2)
Indira Dham, Bhimnagar, Babrala, 202 521, Uttar Pradesh, India
Tel.: (91) 5836 664 990
Urea Mfr
N.A.I.C.S.: 325311

Yara Fertilizers Philippines, Inc. (1)
1605 One Global Place 5th Avenue Corner 25th Street, Bonifacio Global City, Taguig, 1634, Philippines
Tel.: (63) 2 845 3801
Web Site: http://www.yara.com
Emp.: 31
Fertilizer Mfr
N.A.I.C.S.: 325311

Yara France S.A. (1)
Tour Opus 77 Esplanade du General de Gaulle, CS 90047, 92800, Puteaux, France
Tel.: (33) 15 569 9600
Web Site: https://www.yara.fr
Emp.: 120
Mfr of Fertilizers
N.A.I.C.S.: 325311

Yara Ghana Ltd. (1)
No 2 Borstal Avenue Roman Ridge, Accra, Ghana
Tel.: (233) 54 010 1712
Web Site: https://www.yara.com.gh
Agricultural Research & Development Services
N.A.I.C.S.: 541715

Yara GmbH & Co. KG (1)
Hanninghof 35, 48249, Dulmen, Germany
Tel.: (49) 2 594 7980
Web Site: https://www.yara.de
Emp.: 150
Mfr of Fertilizers
N.A.I.C.S.: 325311

Yara Guatemala S.A. (1)
Calzada Roosevelt 33-86 Zona 7 Edificio Ilumina Nivel 11 Oficina 1102, Nivel 11 Oficina 1102, Guatemala, Guatemala
Tel.: (502) 2 421 2600
Web Site: https://www.yara.com.gt
Emp.: 30
Fertilizer Mfr
N.A.I.C.S.: 325311

Yara Hellas S.A. (1)
143 Syngrou Avenue, Nea Smyrni, Athens, 171 21, Greece
Tel.: (30) 2109370355
Emp.: 12
Fertilizer Mfr
N.A.I.C.S.: 325311

Yara Hungaria Kft. (1)
Szabadsag ter 4, 8200, Veszprem, Hungary
Tel.: (36) 8 857 7940
Web Site: https://www.yara.hu
Fertilizer Mfr
N.A.I.C.S.: 325311

Yara Iberian S.A. (1)
Infanta Mercedes 31, 28020, Madrid, Spain
Tel.: (34) 91 426 3500
Web Site: https://yara.es
Emp.: 30
Fertilizer Mfr
N.A.I.C.S.: 325311

Yara Industrial B.V. (1)
Zevenmanshaven Oost 67, 3133 AB, Vlaardingen, Netherlands
Tel.: (31) 10 445 3000
Web Site: https://www.yara.nl
Emp.: 27
Chemicals Mfr
N.A.I.C.S.: 325199

Yara Industrial GmbH (1)
Strudelstrasse 3, 53577, Bad Honningen, Germany **(100%)**
Tel.: (49) 26359610
Web Site: http://www.yara.de
Emp.: 40
Aluminum Extraction & Refining
N.A.I.C.S.: 331313
Jakob Hornvarger *(Mng Dir)*

Yara International (M) Sdn Bhd (1)
Lot 3 02 Level 3 1 First Avenue, Bandar Utama, 47800, Petaling Jaya, Selangor Darul Ehsan, Malaysia
Tel.: (60) 37 726 4181
Web Site: https://www.yara.my
Emp.: 20
Fertilizer Mfr
N.A.I.C.S.: 325311

Yara Italia SpA (1)
Via Benigno Crespi 57, 20159, Milan, Italy
Tel.: (39) 0275 4161
Web Site: https://www.yara.it
Fertilizer Mfr
N.A.I.C.S.: 325311

Yara Korea Limited (1)
968-5 IL Dong Bldg 6th FL, Daechi 3 Dong, Kangnam Gu, Seoul, 135-736, Korea (South)
Tel.: (82) 2 538 1495
Fertilizer Mfr
N.A.I.C.S.: 325311

Yara Latin America (1)
Edificio Brascan Century Corporate, Rua Joaquim Floriano 466 cj403, Sao Paulo, Brazil
Tel.: (55) 1121658388
Emp.: 1,300
Fertilizer Mfr
N.A.I.C.S.: 325311

Yara Lietuva, UAB (1)
Park Town East Hill Lvivo g 101, 08104, Vilnius, Lithuania
Tel.: (370) 52440044
Web Site: https://www.yara.lt
Crop Fertilizer Mfr & Distr
N.A.I.C.S.: 325311

Yara Marine Technologies AS (1)
Tel.: (47) 4 806 8590
Web Site: https://www.yaramarine.com
Marine Terminal Operator
N.A.I.C.S.: 488310
Thomas Koniordos *(CEO)*

Yara Mexico S.A. de C.V (1)
Av Americas No 1545 Piso 24, Col Providencia, 44630, Guadalajara, Jalisco, Mexico
Tel.: (52) 3330033350
Web Site: https://www.yara.com.mx
Emp.: 45
Fertilizer Mfr
N.A.I.C.S.: 325311

Yara Norge AS (1)
Drammensveien 131, Oslo, 0277, Norway
Tel.: (47) 24 15 70 00
Emp.: 200
Fertilizer Mfr
N.A.I.C.S.: 325314
Svein Tore Holsether *(Gen Mgr)*

Yara North America, Inc. (1)
100 N Tampa St Ste 3200, Tampa, FL 33602
Tel.: (813) 222-5700
Web Site: https://www.yara.us
Emp.: 60
Mineral Fertilizer, Gas & Chemicals Mfr
N.A.I.C.S.: 424910
Wes Johnson *(Reg Mgr-Sls)*

Yara North America, Inc. (1)
312 W Luce St, Stockton, CA 95203-4903
Tel.: (925) 467-0100
Web Site: http://www.yara.us
Emp.: 5
Provider of Mineral Fertilizer, Gas & Chemicals
N.A.I.C.S.: 424910

Yara Peru S.R.L. (1)
Jiron Monterrey 355 Dpto 501 Chacarilla del Estanque, Santiago de Surco, Lima, Peru
Tel.: (51) 1 627 0500
Web Site: https://www.yara.com.pe
Agricultural Research & Development Services
N.A.I.C.S.: 541715

Yara Poland Sp.z.o.o. (1)
ul Jacka Malczewskiego 26, 71612, Szczecin, Poland
Tel.: (48) 91 433 0035
Web Site: https://www.yara.pl
Emp.: 32
Fertilizer Mfr
N.A.I.C.S.: 325311
Krzysztof Michalski *(Dir-Comml)*

Yara S.A (1)
Da Vincilaan 1, 1200, Zaventem, Belgium **(100%)**
Tel.: (32) 27735500
Web Site: http://www.yara.com
Emp.: 150
Fertilizer Mfr
N.A.I.C.S.: 212390

Yara Servicios Logisticos, S.A. (1)
Hoyo Bolero 3, La Mojonera, 04745, Almeria, Spain
Tel.: (34) 950331588
Emp.: 2
Chemicals Mfr
N.A.I.C.S.: 325199

Yara Sluiskil B.V. (1)
Industrieweg 10, 4541 HJ, Sluiskil, Netherlands
Tel.: (31) 115474444
Mineral Fertilizer Mfr
N.A.I.C.S.: 325311
Gijsbrecht Gunter *(Mgr-External Rels & Comm)*

Yara Suomi OY Mechelininkatu (1)
Bertel Jung Square 9, PO Box 900, 02600, Espoo, Finland

YARA INTERNATIONAL ASA

Yara International ASA—(Continued)
Tel.: (358) 10215111
Web Site: https://www.yara.fi
Sales Range: $1-4.9 Billion
Emp.: 2,500
Fertilizer Mfr
N.A.I.C.S.: 325311

Subsidiary (Non-US):

Yara Danmark Godning A/S (2)
Vesterballevej 27, 7000, Fredericia, Denmark
Tel.: (45) 7 922 3366
Web Site: https://www.yara.dk
Mineral Fertilizers, Gas & Chemicals Mfr & Distr
N.A.I.C.S.: 325314

Yara Suomi Oy (1)
Bertel Jungin Aukio 9, 02600, Espoo, Finland
Tel.: (358) 1 021 5111
Web Site: https://www.yara.fi
Fertilizer Mfr
N.A.I.C.S.: 325311

Yara Switzerland (1)
Route de Florissant 13, Chene-Bougeries, 1206, Geneva, Switzerland
Tel.: (41) 228608100
Web Site: http://www.yara.com
Emp.: 40
Fertilizer Mfr
N.A.I.C.S.: 325311

Yara Tanzania Ltd. (1)
Plot no 2005 block 1 Kurasini, Dar es Salaam, Tanzania
Tel.: (255) 22 211 2955
Web Site: https://www.yara.co.tz
Mineral Fertilizer Mfr
N.A.I.C.S.: 325311

Yara Trinidad Ltd. (1)
Light Pole 887 Southern Main Road, Savonetta, Trinidad & Tobago
Tel.: (868) 636 2020
Web Site: http://www.yara.com
Emp.: 300
Fertilizer Mfr
N.A.I.C.S.: 325311

Yara UK Ltd. (1)
Harvest House Europarc, Grimsby, DN37 9TZ, Lincolnshire, United Kingdom
Tel.: (44) 148 450 9725
Web Site: https://www.yara.co.uk
Emp.: 100
Mineral Fertilizers & Gas & Industrial Chemicals
N.A.I.C.S.: 325311
Roger Brogden (Mgr-Bus-Solid & Foliar)

Plant (Domestic):

Yara UK Ltd. (2)
Manor Place Wellington Road, The Industrial Estate Pocklington, York, YO42 1DN, United Kingdom
Tel.: (44) 175 930 2545
Web Site: https://www.yara.co.uk
Emp.: 25
Fertilizer Mfr
N.A.I.C.S.: 325311

Yara Ukraine (1)
Lobanovskyi Avenue 6A office 142, 03037, Kiev, Ukraine
Tel.: (380) 44 220 0096
Emp.: 10
Fertilizer Mfr
N.A.I.C.S.: 325311

Yara Vietnam Ltd. (1)
Empress Tower 14th Flr Unit 1402-1403 138-142, Hai Ba Trung Str District 1st Ward Da Kao, Ho Chi Minh City, Vietnam
Tel.: (84) 83 829 6869
Web Site: http://www.yara.com
Emp.: 100
Fertilizer Mfr
N.A.I.C.S.: 325311

Yara Vlaardingen B.V. (1)
Zevenmanshaven Oost 67, 3133 CA, Vlaardingen, Netherlands
Tel.: (31) 10 445 2000
Web Site: https://www.yara.nl
Mineral Fertilizer Mfr

N.A.I.C.S.: 325311
Peter Van Noort (Mgr-Technical Product)

Yarecuador Cia Ltda. (1)
Samborondon Business Center Torre A ofc 213, Guayaquil, Ecuador
Tel.: (593) 45015326
Emp.: 5
Fertilizer Mfr
N.A.I.C.S.: 325311

Yarwil AS (1)
Stranveien 20, Lysaker, 3466, Norway (50%)
Tel.: (47) 6758 6900
Web Site: http://www.yarwil.com
Ship Exhaust Gas Emissions Control Services
N.A.I.C.S.: 541990
Kai Latun (Mng Dir)

YARI MINERALS LIMITED
Tel.: (61) 864006222
Web Site:
  https://www.consolidatedzinc.com
YAR—(ASX)
Assets: $2,433,432
Liabilities: $192,562
Net Worth: $2,240,869
Earnings: ($3,026,606)
Fiscal Year-end: 12/31/23
Mineral Exploration Services
N.A.I.C.S.: 212230
Bradley Marwood (Mng Dir)

YARN SYNDICATE LTD.
86/2/4 S N Banerjee Road 1st Floor Flat No 2, Kolkata, 700014, West Bengal, India
Tel.: (91) 3322652163
Web Site:
  https://www.yarnsyndicate.in
514378—(BOM)
Rev.: $3,525
Assets: $21,641,388
Liabilities: $72,153,948
Net Worth: ($50,512,559)
Earnings: ($19,267)
Emp.: 3
Fiscal Year-end: 03/31/23
Cotton Yarn Distr
N.A.I.C.S.: 313110
Sheela Patodia (Chm & Mng Dir)

YARNAPUND PUBLIC COMPANY LIMITED
70 Moo 1 Bangna-Trad Rd, T Rachathewa A Bangplee, Samut Prakan, 10540, Thailand
Tel.: (66) 23168010
Web Site: http://www.yarnapund.com
Year Founded: 1952
Rev.: $161,018,332
Assets: $141,307,932
Liabilities: $248,697,477
Net Worth: ($107,389,545)
Earnings: ($7,868,421)
Fiscal Year-end: 12/31/17
Automobile Parts Mfr
N.A.I.C.S.: 423140
Samphan Phanpanit (Pres)

YAS CO., LTD.
69 Hansan-Ro Tanhyeon-Myeon, Paju, Gyeonggi-do, Korea (South)
Tel.: (82) 7086208100
Web Site: http://www.yasoled.com
Year Founded: 2002
255440—(KRS)
Rev.: $42,041,030
Assets: $166,240,212
Liabilities: $43,776,563
Net Worth: $122,463,649
Earnings: ($966,818)
Emp.: 245
Fiscal Year-end: 12/31/22
Light Equipment Mfr
N.A.I.C.S.: 334419
Bosung Kwon (Head-Ops)

YASH CHEMEX LIMITED
411 Sigma Icon-1 132 Ft Ring Road Opp Medilink Hospital Satellite, Ahmedabad, 380015, Gujarat, India
Tel.: (91) 7926730257
Web Site:
  http://www.yashchemex.com
Year Founded: 1990
539939—(BOM)
Rev.: $10,960,866
Assets: $8,108,902
Liabilities: $3,730,724
Net Worth: $4,378,179
Earnings: $457,515
Emp.: 8
Fiscal Year-end: 03/31/23
Chemical Product Mfr & Distr
N.A.I.C.S.: 325130
Pritesh Y. Shah (Mng Dir)

Subsidiaries:

Yasons Chemex Care Limited (1)
412 Sigma Icon-1 Satellite, Ahmedabad, 380015, India
Tel.: (91) 9537200079
Web Site:
  http://www.yasonschemexcare.com
Dye & Pigment Mfr
N.A.I.C.S.: 325130

YASH INNOVENTURE LTD.
1st Floor Corporate House No 3 Parshwanath Business Park, B/H Prahladnagar Garden SG Highway, Ahmedabad, 380014, Gujarat, India
Tel.: (91) 7926584080
Web Site:
  https://www.yashinnoventures.com
Year Founded: 1992
523650—(BOM)
Rev.: $44,050
Assets: $3,409,748
Liabilities: $1,823,368
Net Worth: $1,586,380
Earnings: ($95,402)
Emp.: 12
Fiscal Year-end: 03/31/23
Fire Extinguisher Mfr
N.A.I.C.S.: 339999
Gnanesh Rajendrabhai Bhagat (Mng Dir & CFO)

YASH MANAGEMENT & SATELLITE LTD.
Office No 303 Morya Landmark- I Opp Infinity Mall Off New Link Road, Andheri West, Mumbai, 400053, India
Tel.: (91) 2267425443
Web Site:
  https://www.yashmanagement.in
Year Founded: 1993
511601—(BOM)
Rev.: $4,083,477
Assets: $4,955,780
Liabilities: $1,855,413
Net Worth: $3,100,367
Earnings: ($212,110)
Emp.: 7
Fiscal Year-end: 03/31/23
Investment & Financial Service
N.A.I.C.S.: 523999
Anurag Hargovind Gupta (Chm & Mng Dir)

Subsidiaries:

Sudarshan Polyfab Private Ltd. (1)
Plot 14 Divine Industrial Park Survey No 655, Village Lakshmanpura Kadi Dist Mehsana, Gujarat, 382165, India
Tel.: (91) 7506719066
Web Site:
  https://www.sudarshanpolyfab.com
Plastic Container Mfr
N.A.I.C.S.: 326160

YASH PAKKA LIMITED
Yash Nagar, Lucknow, 224135, Uttar Pradesh, India

INTERNATIONAL PUBLIC

Tel.: (91) 7800008275
Web Site: https://pakka.com
516030—(BOM)
Rev.: $26,614,715
Assets: $35,818,829
Liabilities: $18,066,567
Net Worth: $17,752,262
Earnings: $2,282,430
Emp.: 456
Fiscal Year-end: 03/31/21
Paper Mills
N.A.I.C.S.: 322120
Ved Krishna (Vice Chm & Head-Strategy)

Subsidiaries:

Pakka Impact Limited (1)
Ring Rd Phase 3, Yeshwanthpur Suburb II Stage Yesvanpur Surburb Peenya, Bengaluru, 560058, Karnataka, India
Tel.: (91) 8882894579
Web Site: https://pakkaimpact.com
Food Packaging Services
N.A.I.C.S.: 561910

YASH TRADING & FINANCE LTD.
Bagri Niwas 53/55 Nath Madhav Path, Mumbai, 400002, India
Tel.: (91) 2222720000
Web Site:
  https://www.yashtradingfinance.com
Year Founded: 1985
512345—(BOM)
Assets: $54,077
Liabilities: $140,269
Net Worth: ($86,191)
Earnings: ($21,898)
Fiscal Year-end: 03/31/23
Financial Consulting Services
N.A.I.C.S.: 541611

YASHIMA DENKI CO., LTD.
3-1-1 Shinbashi, Minato-ku, Tokyo, 105-8686, Japan
Tel.: (81) 335073711
Web Site:
  https://www.yashimadenki.co.jp
3153—(TKS)
Rev.: $428,737,820
Assets: $399,442,300
Liabilities: $217,680,520
Net Worth: $181,761,780
Earnings: $17,562,770
Emp.: 985
Fiscal Year-end: 03/31/24
Electronics & Appliances Whslr
N.A.I.C.S.: 423620
Akio Ohta (Pres & Chm)

Subsidiaries:

Chugoku Power Systems Co., Ltd. (1)
10-6 Hashimotocho 3rd floor Hiroshima NS Building, Naka-ku, Hiroshima, 730-0015, Japan
Tel.: (81) 822211637
Web Site: https://www.cps-yh.co.jp
Emp.: 20
Industrial Machinery Mfr
N.A.I.C.S.: 333248

Techno Eight Co., Ltd. (1)
1-1 Shimbashi 3-Chome, Minato-ku, Tokyo, 105-8686, Japan
Tel.: (81) 335073680
Industrial Machinery Mfr
N.A.I.C.S.: 333248

Yashima Control Systems Co., Ltd. (1)
8-2-37 Fukawa, Asakita-ku, Hiroshima, 739-1751, Japan
Tel.: (81) 828433131
Web Site: https://yashima-cs.co.jp
Emp.: 169
Electrical Equipment Mfr & Distr
N.A.I.C.S.: 335313

AND PRIVATE COMPANIES / YASKAWA ELECTRIC CORPORATION

Plant (Domestic):

Yashima Control Systems Co., Ltd. - Anjo Plant (2)
2-1-38 Imaike- cho, Anjo, 446-0071, Aichi, Japan
Tel.: (81) 566984321
Electric Equipment Mfr
N.A.I.C.S.: 335313

Yashima Control Systems Co., Ltd. - Ogawara Plant (2)
515-2 Hotokedou Ogawara-cho, Asakita-ku, Hiroshima, 739-1754, Japan
Tel.: (81) 828401161
Electric Equipment Mfr
N.A.I.C.S.: 335313

Yashima Eco Systems Co., Ltd. (1)
3-11-17 Higashi-Nippori, Asakita-ku, Tokyo, 116-0014, Japan
Tel.: (81) 342431100
Web Site: http://www.yashima-eco-s.co.jp
Air Conditioner Repair & Maintenance Services
N.A.I.C.S.: 811412

Yashima Electronic Solutions Co., Ltd. (1)
4-18-32 Shibaura, Minato-ku, Tokyo, 108-0023, Japan
Tel.: (81) 366991870
Web Site: https://tachibana-denshi-solutions.co.jp
Emp.: 70
Electronic Product Distr
N.A.I.C.S.: 423610

Yashima Industrial Equipment System, Ltd. (1)
3-1-1 Shimbashi, Minato-ku, Tokyo, 105-8686, Japan
Tel.: (81) 335073100
Web Site: https://www.yashimadenki.co.jp
Emp.: 55
Industrial Equipment Distr
N.A.I.C.S.: 423830

YASHO INDUSTRIES LTD.
Office No 101 102 Peninsula HeightsC D Barfiwala Marg Andheri West, Mumbai, 400058, India
Tel.: (91) 62510100
Web Site: https://www.yashoindustries.com
Year Founded: 1985
541167—(BOM)
Rev.: $50,439,548
Assets: $41,655,200
Liabilities: $30,881,146
Net Worth: $10,774,054
Earnings: $2,940,538
Emp.: 467
Fiscal Year-end: 03/31/21
Chemical Products Mfr
N.A.I.C.S.: 325998
Parag Jhaveri (CEO & Mng Dir)

YASHRAJ CONTAINEURS LTD.
Madhav Niwas CHSL Flat No B-1A 1st Floor Natakwala Lane, Opp SV Road Borivali West, Mumbai, 400 092, India
Tel.: (91) 2228993092
Web Site: https://www.barrelpeople.com
Year Founded: 1993
530063—(BOM)
Rev.: $894,515
Assets: $820,766
Liabilities: $10,286,290
Net Worth: ($9,465,524)
Earnings: ($706,085)
Emp.: 92
Fiscal Year-end: 03/31/23
Metal Barrels Mfr
N.A.I.C.S.: 332439
Jayesh Vinodrai Valia (Mng Dir & Compliance Officer)

YASKAWA ELECTRIC CORPORATION
2-1 Kurosakishiroishi, Yahatanishi-ku, Kitakyushu, 806-0004, Japan
Tel.: (81) 936458801 JP
Web Site: https://www.yaskawa.co.jp
Year Founded: 1915
6506—(TKS)
Rev.: $4,081,415,220
Assets: $4,979,555,150
Liabilities: $2,086,707,530
Net Worth: $2,892,847,620
Earnings: $359,370,830
Emp.: 13,010
Fiscal Year-end: 02/29/24
Motion Control, Robotics & Systems Engineering Products Mfr
N.A.I.C.S.: 541330
Junji Tsuda (Chm)

Subsidiaries:

AI Cube Inc. (1)
Horidome TH Building 8F 2-3-14, Nihonbashi Chuo-ku, Tokyo, 103-0012, Japan
Tel.: (81) 335273171
Web Site: https://www.ai3cube.co.jp
Information Technology Services
N.A.I.C.S.: 541511

Bestact Solutions Inc. (1)
2-13-1 Nishinomiya City Yaskawa Electric Corporation Yukuhashi Office, Yukuhashi, 824-8511, Fukuoka, Japan
Tel.: (81) 930588200
Web Site: https://www.bestact.co.jp
Switch Mfr & Distr
N.A.I.C.S.: 334419

Doei Corporation (1)
2-1 Kurosaki-shiroishi, Yahatanishi-ku, Kitakyushu, 806-0004, Fukuoka, Japan
Tel.: (81) 936458885
Insurance & Travel Tour Operating Agencies
N.A.I.C.S.: 524113

FUKUOKA KASEI Industries Co., Ltd. (1)
598-4 Katsuyama Kuroda Kyoto-cho, Miyako-gun, Fukuoka, 824-0822, Japan
Tel.: (81) 930322780
Web Site: http://www.yaskawa-control.co.jp
Emp.: 80
Automotive Plastic Product Mfr
N.A.I.C.S.: 336110

Plant (Domestic):

FUKUOKA KASEI Industries Co., Ltd. - Yukuhashi Plant (2)
170-1 Otani, Yukuhashi, 824-0045, Fukuoka, Japan
Tel.: (81) 930267501
Web Site: http://www.yaskawa-control.co.jp
Electronic Components Mfr
N.A.I.C.S.: 335999

Oji Electric Co., Ltd. (1)
3-2-5 Sama, Kawaguchi, 333-0816, Saitama, Japan
Tel.: (81) 482912860
Web Site: https://www.ojielectric.co.jp
Emp.: 45
Industrial Machinery Mfr
N.A.I.C.S.: 333248

PT. Yaskawa Electric Indonesia (1)
Secure Building Gedung B Lantai Dasar and Lantai 1 Jl, Raya Protokol Halim Perdanakusuma, Jakarta, Indonesia
Tel.: (62) 2129826470
Web Site: https://yaskawa.co.id
Automotive Parts Mfr & Distr
N.A.I.C.S.: 336390

Shanghai Yaskawa Drive Co., Ltd. (1)
No 915 Jiaxin Road, Cangchang Village Town of Malu Jiading District, Shanghai, 201818, China
Tel.: (86) 2159903067
Web Site: http://www.yaskawa.co.jp
Electrical Components Mfr & Whslr
N.A.I.C.S.: 335312

Suematsu Kyuki Co., Ltd. (1)
2-1-29 Minoshima, Hakata-ku, Fukuoka, 812-0017, Japan
Tel.: (81) 924411515
Web Site: https://www.suematsu.co.jp
Automotive Parts Mfr & Distr
N.A.I.C.S.: 336390

The Switch Engineering Oy (1)
Elimaenkatu 5, 00510, Helsinki, Finland
Tel.: (358) 207838200
Web Site: https://theswitch.com
Turbine Mfr & Distr
N.A.I.C.S.: 333611

Y-E Data Inc. (1)
182 Shinko, Iruma, 358-0055, Saitama, Japan
Tel.: (81) 4 2932 9850
Web Site: http://www.yedata.com
Sales Range: $25-49.9 Million
Emp.: 117
Electronic Components Mfr
N.A.I.C.S.: 334419
Nobuyuki Ido (Pres)

YASKAWA Europe GmbH (1)
Hauptstrasse 185, 65760, Eschborn, Germany
Tel.: (49) 6196569300
Web Site: http://www.yaskawa.eu.com
Industrial Drive & Motion Equipment Mfr
N.A.I.C.S.: 335312
Bruno J. Schnekenburger (Pres, CEO & Mng Dir)

Subsidiary (Non-US):

MOTOMAN Robotics Europe AB (2)
Lunavej 1C, 8723, Horsens, Denmark
Tel.: (45) 70222477
Web Site: http://www.motoman.dk
Industrial Robots Whslr
N.A.I.C.S.: 423830

Subsidiary (Non-US):

MOTOMAN Robotec d.o.o. (3)
Lepovce 23, 1310, Ribnica, Slovenia
Tel.: (386) 18372410
Web Site: http://www.motoman.si
Industrial Robots Whslr
N.A.I.C.S.: 423830

MOTOMAN Robotics Finland OY (3)
Messinkikatu 2, 20380, Turku, 20380, Finland
Tel.: (358) 403000600
Web Site: http://www.motoman.fi
Emp.: 30
Industrial Robots Whslr
N.A.I.C.S.: 423830
Nina Lehtinen (Gen Mgr)

MOTOMAN robotec GmbH (3)
Kammerfeldstrasse, Allershausen, 85391, Germany
Tel.: (49) 81669000
Web Site: http://www.yaskawa.eu.com
Emp.: 100
Electronic Robots Distr
N.A.I.C.S.: 423690
Koichi Takamiya (CEO & Chm)

YASKAWA France S.A. (3)
Forest business park 5 Chemin des Fontenelles, 44140, Le Bignon, France
Tel.: (33) 240131919
Web Site: https://www.yaskawa.fr
Industrial Robots Whslr
N.A.I.C.S.: 423830

YASKAWA Iberica S.L. (3)
Av del Segle XXI 69, Viladecans, 08840, Barcelona, Spain
Tel.: (34) 936303478
Web Site: http://www.yaskawa.es
Industrial Robots Whslr
N.A.I.C.S.: 423830

Yaskawa Benelux B.V. (3)
Brainport Industries Campus BIC 1, 5657 BX, Eindhoven, Netherlands
Tel.: (31) 402895500
Web Site: https://www.yaskawa.nl
Industrial Robots Whslr
N.A.I.C.S.: 423830
Eddie Mennen (Mng Dir)

Subsidiary (Domestic):

VIPA GmbH (2)
Ohmstr 4, D-91074, Herzogenaurach, Germany (100%)
Tel.: (49) 91327440
Web Site: http://www.vipa.de
Sales Range: $50-74.9 Million
Industrial Automation Equipments Mfr
N.A.I.C.S.: 333248
Norbert Gaub (Mng Dir)

Subsidiary (US):

VIPA USA, Inc. (3)
980 Birmingham Rd Ste 721, Alpharetta, GA 30004
Tel.: (678) 880-6910
Web Site: http://www.vipa-usa.com
Industrial Machinery Mfr
N.A.I.C.S.: 333248

Subsidiary (Non-US):

Yaskawa Electric UK Ltd. (2)
1 Hunt Hill Cumbernauld, Glasgow, G68 9LF, Oxon, United Kingdom
Tel.: (44) 1236806000
Web Site: http://www.yaskawa.co.uk
Adjustable Speed Drives Mfr
N.A.I.C.S.: 333612

Yaskawa Europe Technology Ltd. (2)
13 Hamelacha St, Afek Industrial Park, Rosh Ha'Ayin, 48091, Israel
Tel.: (972) 732400800
Web Site: https://www.yaskawa.co.il
Servomotors & Controllers Mfr
N.A.I.C.S.: 334513

Yaskawa Italia S.R.L. (2)
Via della Resistenza 123, 20090, Buccinasco, MI, Italy
Tel.: (39) 0249693699
Web Site: http://www.yaskawa.it
Industrial Robots Whslr
N.A.I.C.S.: 423830
Paolo Poletti (Mng Dir)

Yaskawa Nordic AB (2)
Verkstadsgatan 2, PO Box 504, 385 25, Torsas, Smaland, Sweden
Tel.: (46) 480 417800
Web Site: http://www.yaskawa.se
Industrial Robot Sales & Maintenance Services
N.A.I.C.S.: 423830
Par Tornemo (CEO)

YD Mechatro Solutions Inc. (1)
New Haratetsu Building 6F 4-1-13 Kudankita, Chiyoda-ku, Tokyo, 102-0073, Japan
Tel.: (81) 352263090
Web Site: http://www.mechasol.co.jp
Automated Process Equipments Mfr
N.A.I.C.S.: 333519
Kaneyuki Hamada (Pres)

Plant (Domestic):

YD Mechatro Solutions Inc. - Niigata Plant (2)
2-4 Shinko-chyo, Mitsuke, 954-0076, Niigata, Japan
Tel.: (81) 258615519
Web Site: http://www.mechasol.co.jp
Emp.: 28
Spray Coating Machinery Mfr
N.A.I.C.S.: 333912
Ikuo Nagamatsu (Pres)

YE DIGITAL Corporation (1)
AP Eltage Yonemachi Building 2-1-21 Yonemachi, Kokurakita-Ku, Kitakyushu, 802-0003, Fukuoka, Japan
Tel.: (81) 935221010
Web Site: https://www.ye-digital.com
Rev.: $138,283,360
Assets: $87,377,160
Liabilities: $43,603,500
Net Worth: $43,773,660
Earnings: $7,742,280
Emp.: 613
Fiscal Year-end: 02/29/2024
Information Processing Services
N.A.I.C.S.: 541512

Yaskawa America, Inc. (1)
2121 Norman Dr S, Waukegan, IL 60085
Tel.: (847) 887-7457
Web Site: http://www.yaskawa.com
Industrial Control Mfr
N.A.I.C.S.: 335314
Tom Kutcher (Mgr-Mktg Comm)

YASKAWA ELECTRIC CORPORATION

Yaskawa Electric Corporation—(Continued)

Division (Domestic):

Yaskawa America, Inc. - Cypress Division (2)
5626 Corporate Ave, Cypress, CA 90630-4728
Tel.: (714) 503-4700
Spindle Drives & Motors Mfr
N.A.I.C.S.: 333248

Yaskawa America, Inc. - Engineered Systems Group (2)
8628 Industrial Pkwy Unit A, Plain City, OH 43064
Tel.: (614) 733-3200
Emp.: 22
Industrial Machinery Mfr
N.A.I.C.S.: 333248
Dave Cecil *(Mng Dir)*

Yaskawa America, Inc. - Motoman Robotics Division (2)
100 Automation Way, Miamisburg, OH 45342
Tel.: (937) 847-6200
Web Site: http://www.motoman.com
Controllers & Industrial Robots Distr
N.A.I.C.S.: 423920

Unit (Domestic):

Yaskawa America, Inc. - Motoman Robotics Division - Irvine (3)
1701 Kaiser Ave, Irvine, CA 92614
Tel.: (949) 263-2640
Web Site: http://www.motoman.com
Robotic Machinery Mfr
N.A.I.C.S.: 333248

Yaskawa Automation & Drives Corp. (1)
2-13-1 Nishimiyaichi, Yukuhashi, 824-8511, Fukuoka, Japan
Tel.: (81) 930254361
Web Site: https://www.yaskawa-ad.co.jp
Automotive Parts Mfr & Distr
N.A.I.C.S.: 336390

Yaskawa Controls Co., Ltd. (1)
2-13-1 Nishinomiya City, Yukuhashi, 824-8511, Fukuoka, Japan
Tel.: (81) 930244601
Web Site: https://www.yaskawa-control.co.jp
Emp.: 341
Industrial Controls Mfr & Whslr
N.A.I.C.S.: 335314

Subsidiary (Domestic):

YASCO Co., Ltd. (2)
4-12-5 Minamiohashi, Yukuhashi, 824-0032, Fukuoka, Japan
Tel.: (81) 930258507
Web Site: http://www.yasco.co.jp
Emp.: 180
Cables & Control Devices Mfr
N.A.I.C.S.: 334220

Plant (Domestic):

YASCO Co., Ltd. - Takarayama Plant (3)
892-1 Takarayama, Yukuhashi, 824-0048, Fukuoka, Japan
Tel.: (81) 930266810
Emp.: 16
Fiber Optic Cable Mfr
N.A.I.C.S.: 335921

Yaskawa Czech S.R.O (1)
West Business center Chrastany Za Trati 206, 25219, Prague, Czech Republic
Tel.: (420) 257941718
Web Site: https://www.cz.yaskawa.eu.com
Automotive Parts Mfr & Distr
N.A.I.C.S.: 336390

Yaskawa Electric (Shenyang) Co., Ltd. (1)
No 5 34A City Development Road, Economic and Technological Development Area, Shenyang, 110141, China
Tel.: (86) 2425185555
Servo Motor Mfr
N.A.I.C.S.: 335312

Yaskawa Electric (Singapore) Pte Ltd (1)
30A Kallang Place 06-01, Singapore, 339213, Singapore
Tel.: (65) 62823003
Web Site: https://www.yaskawa.com.sg
Electric Equipments Mfr

Yaskawa Electric (Thailand) Co., Ltd. (1)
59 1st - 5th Floor Flourish Building Soi Ratchadapisek 18, Ratchadapisek Road Huaykwang, Bangkok, Thailand
Tel.: (66) 20170099
Web Site: https://www.yaskawa.co.th
Automotive Parts Mfr & Distr
N.A.I.C.S.: 336390

Yaskawa Electric Corporation - Nakama Plant (1)
319-4 Kamisokoino, Nakama, 809-0003, Fukuoka, Japan
Tel.: (81) 932457820
Semiconductor Making Machinery Mfr
N.A.I.C.S.: 333242

Yaskawa Electric Corporation - Tokyo Plant (1)
New Pier Takeshiba South Tower 16-1 Kaigan 1 Chome, Minato-ku, Tokyo, 105-6891, Japan
Tel.: (81) 354024511
Web Site: http://www.yaskawa.co.jp
Industrial Robots Mfr
N.A.I.C.S.: 334513

Yaskawa Electric Corporation - Yahata-higashi Plant (1)
2-3 Maedakitakukioka, Yahatahigashi-ku, Kitakyushu, 805-0058, Fukuoka, Japan
Tel.: (81) 932884440
Motor Mfr
N.A.I.C.S.: 333618

Yaskawa Electric Corporation - Yahata-nishi Plant (1)
2-1 Kurosaki Joseki, Yahatanishi-ku, Kitakyushu, 806-0004, Fukuoka, Japan
Tel.: (81) 936458801
Web Site: http://www.yaskawa.co.jp
Emp.: 13,094
Industrial Robots Mfr
N.A.I.C.S.: 334513

Yaskawa Electric Corporation - Yukuhashi Plant (1)
2-13-1 Nishimiyaichi, Yukuhashi, 824-8511, Fukuoka, Japan
Tel.: (81) 930231401
Web Site: http://www.yaskawa.co.jp
Emp.: 13,094
Adjustable Speed Drives Mfr
N.A.I.C.S.: 333612

Yaskawa Electric Engineering Corporation (1)
1-2-26 Yonemachi, Kokurakita-ku, Kitakyushu, 802-0003, Fukuoka, Japan
Tel.: (81) 935214301
Web Site: http://www.yaskawa-eng.co.jp
Electric Machines & Facilities Maintenance Services
N.A.I.C.S.: 561210
Hideki Takasaki *(Pres)*

Yaskawa Electric Korea Corporation (1)
35th floor Three IFC 10 Gukjeokhwa-ro, Yeongdeungpo-gu, Seoul, 07326, Korea (South)
Tel.: (82) 27847844
Web Site: http://www.yaskawa.co.kr
Electrical Equipment Mfr & Distr
N.A.I.C.S.: 334513

Yaskawa Electric Taiwan Corporation (1)
12th Floor No 207 Section 3 Beixin Road, Xindian District 12th Floor No 207-5, New Taipei City, 104, Taiwan
Tel.: (886) 289131333
Web Site: https://www.yaskawa.com.tw
Electric Equipments Mfr
N.A.I.C.S.: 333618

Yaskawa Electric Vietnam Co., Ltd. (1)
Room 1904A 19th Floor Centec Tower 72-74 Nguyen Thi Minh Khai, Vo Thi Sau Ward District 3, Ho Chi Minh City, Vietnam
Tel.: (84) 2838228680
Web Site: https://www.yaskawavn.com
Automatic Control Product Mfr
N.A.I.C.S.: 334512

Yaskawa Eletrico do Brasil Ltda. (1)
Av Piraporinha 777 - Vila Nogueira, Diadema, 09950-000, SP, Brazil
Tel.: (55) 1135851100
Web Site: https://www.yaskawa.com.br
Electric Equipment Mfr
N.A.I.C.S.: 335999
Anderson Sato *(Mgr-Sls Engrg)*

Yaskawa Eshed Technology Ltd. (1)
13 Hamelacha St, Afeq Industrial Estate, Rosh Ha'Ayin, 48091, Israel
Tel.: (972) 39004114
Web Site: http://www.yetmotion.com
Sales Range: $25-49.9 Million
Emp.: 35
Devloper of Advanced Motion Control Technology
N.A.I.C.S.: 334513

Yaskawa Finland Oy (1)
Messinkikatu 2, 20380, Turku, Finland
Tel.: (358) 403000600
Web Site: https://www.yaskawa.fi
Automotive Parts Mfr & Distr
N.A.I.C.S.: 336390

Yaskawa India Private Limited (1)
17/A 2nd Main Electronic City Phase - I Hosur Road, Bengaluru, 560 100, India
Tel.: (91) 8042441900
Web Site: https://yaskawaindia.in
Automotive Parts Mfr & Distr
N.A.I.C.S.: 336390

Yaskawa Logistec Corporation (1)
Web Site: http://www.ylnet.co.jp
Logistics Solutions
N.A.I.C.S.: 541614

Yaskawa Manufacturing Corporation (1)
3-2-8 Kurosaki, Yahatanishi-Ku, Kitakyushu, 806-0021, Fukuoka, Japan
Tel.: (81) 936455890
Web Site: http://www.yproduct.com
Contract Manufacturing Services
N.A.I.C.S.: 813910

Yaskawa Mechatrec Corporation (1)
7F New Pier Takeshiba South Tower 1-16-1 Kaigan, Minato-ku, Tokyo, 105-0022, Japan
Tel.: (81) 354023010
Web Site: https://www.ym-c.co.jp
Emp.: 229
Electric Machining Components Mfr
N.A.I.C.S.: 334514

Yaskawa Motoman Canada Ltd. (1)
3530 Laird Road Unit 3, Mississauga, L5L 5Z7, ON, Canada
Tel.: (905) 569-6686
Web Site: http://www.motoman.com
Electrical Equipments Mfr & Distr
N.A.I.C.S.: 333611

Yaskawa Motoman Mexico, S.A. de C.V. (1)
Circuito Aguascalientes Oriente 132 Parque Industrial, Valle de Ags, 20358, Aguascalientes, Mexico
Tel.: (52) 4499731170
Web Site: http://www.motoman.com
Industrial Robots Sales & Maintenance Services
N.A.I.C.S.: 423830

Yaskawa Motor Corporation (1)
2-3 Maeda, Yahatahigashi-ku, Kitakyushu, 805-0069, Fukuoka, Japan
Tel.: (81) 93 288 4440
Web Site: http://www.yaskawa.co.jp
Motors & Generators Mfr & Distr
N.A.I.C.S.: 333618

Yaskawa Obvious Communications Inc. (1)
3F 12-1 Otemachi, Kokurakita-ku, Kitakyushu, 803-8530, Fukuoka, Japan
Tel.: (81) 354024533
Web Site: https://www.y-obvious.com
Emp.: 62
Advertising & Marketing Communication Services
N.A.I.C.S.: 541613

INTERNATIONAL PUBLIC

Yaskawa Polska Sp. z o.o. (1)
Danish 11, 54-427, Wroclaw, Poland
Tel.: (48) 717928670
Web Site: https://www.yaskawa.pl
Automotive Parts Mfr & Distr
N.A.I.C.S.: 336390

Yaskawa Ristro d.o.o. (1)
Lepovce 23, Ribnica, Slovenia
Tel.: (386) 18372410
Industrial Robot Distr
N.A.I.C.S.: 423830

Yaskawa Shougang Robot Co., Ltd. (1)
No 7 Yongchang-North Road, Beijing Economic and Technological Development Area, Beijing, 100176, China
Tel.: (86) 1067882858
Industrial Robot Distr
N.A.I.C.S.: 423830

Yaskawa Slovenija d.o.o. (1)
Lepovce 23, Ribnica, Slovenia
Tel.: (386) 18372410
Web Site: https://www.yaskawa.si
Automotive Parts Mfr & Distr
N.A.I.C.S.: 336390

Yaskawa Southern Africa (Pty) Ltd. (1)
4 Friesland Drive Longmeadow Business Estate-South Modderfontein, Johannesburg, 1610, South Africa
Tel.: (27) 116083182
Web Site: https://www.yaskawa.za.com
Automotive Parts Mfr & Distr
N.A.I.C.S.: 336390

Yaskawa Techno Plate Corporation (1)
2-13-1 Nishimiyaichi, Yukuhashi, 824-0031, Fukuoka, Japan
Tel.: (81) 930231425
Electric Motor Mfr
N.A.I.C.S.: 333618

Yaskawa Turkey Elektrik Ticaret Ltd. Sti. (1)
Serifali Mah Barbaros Cad No 24, Umraniye, Istanbul, Turkiye
Tel.: (90) 2165273450
Web Site: https://www.yaskawa.com.tr
Automotive Parts Mfr & Distr
N.A.I.C.S.: 336390

Yaskawa UK Ltd. (1)
Walworth Road, Durham, Newton Aycliffe, DL5 6XF, United Kingdom
Tel.: (44) 3306781990
Web Site: https://www.yaskawa.co.uk
Automotive Parts Mfr & Distr
N.A.I.C.S.: 336390

YASUDA LOGISTICS CORPORATION

3-1-1 Shibaura, Minato-ku, Tokyo, 108-8435, Japan
Tel.: (81) 334527311
Web Site: https://www.yasuda-soko.co.jp
Year Founded: 1919
9324—(TKS)
Rev: $445,408,240
Assets: $1,399,251,070
Liabilities: $779,325,610
Net Worth: $619,925,460
Earnings: $15,216,220
Fiscal Year-end: 03/31/24
Warehousing & Logistics Services
N.A.I.C.S.: 493110
Nobuyuki Fujii *(Chm, Pres & CEO)*

Subsidiaries:

Japan Business Logistics Co., Ltd. (1)
3-23-19 Kaigan, Minato-ku, Tokyo, 108-0022, Japan
Tel.: (81) 3 6400 1111
Web Site: http://www.jbl.co.jp
Logistics Consulting Servies
N.A.I.C.S.: 541614
Sadayoshi Chiba *(Pres)*

Takagi Kogyo Transport Co., Ltd. (1)
Logistics Consulting Servies

N.A.I.C.S.: 541614

The Hokkai Yasuda Logistics Co., Ltd. (1)
4-4-16 Ryutsu Center, Shiroishi-ku, Sapporo, 003-0030, Hokkaido, Japan
Logistics Consulting Servies
N.A.I.C.S.: 541614

The Yasuda Building Co., Ltd. (1)
Yasuda Bldg No 5 2-20-3 Tsuruyacho, Yokohama, 221-0835, Kanagawa, Japan
Tel.: (81) 45 312 7696
Construction Engineering Services
N.A.I.C.S.: 541330

Yasuda Logistics (Shanghai) Ltd. (1)
Room 505 Pinzun International Center B No 567 Langu Road, Putuo District, Shanghai, 200080, China
Tel.: (86) 2168419300
Logistics Consulting Servies
N.A.I.C.S.: 541330

Yasuda Logistics (Vietnam) Co., Ltd. (1)
4F Grand Building No 30-32 Hoa Ma St, Hai Ba Trung, Hanoi, Vietnam
Tel.: (84) 2462528998
Logistics Consulting Servies
N.A.I.C.S.: 541330

Yasuda Medical Logistics Co., Ltd. (1)
3-3-8 Kaigan, Minato-Ku, Tokyo, 108-8435, Japan
Logistics Consulting Servies
N.A.I.C.S.: 541614
Kiyoshi Fujita *(Pres)*

Yasuda Transportation Co., Ltd. (1)
3-9-30 Moriyacho, Kanagawa-ku, Yokohama, 221-0022, Japan
Tel.: (81) 45 453 1547
Web Site: http://www.ytsc.co.jp
Logistics Consulting Servies
N.A.I.C.S.: 541614

Yasuda Works Co., Ltd. (1)
Tel.: (81) 354407671
Logistics Consulting Servies
N.A.I.C.S.: 541614

YASUHARA CHEMICAL CO., LTD.
1071 Takagi-cho, Fuchu, 726-0013, Hiroshima, Japan
Tel.: (81) 847453530
Web Site: https://www.yschem.co.jp
Year Founded: 1947
4957—(TKS)
Rev.: $111,956,530
Assets: $236,916,120
Liabilities: $67,096,890
Net Worth: $169,819,230
Emp.: 246
Fiscal Year-end: 03/31/20
Chemicals Mfr
N.A.I.C.S.: 325211
Kenji Shikita *(Gen Mgr-Mgmt Plng Dept)*

YASUNAGA CORPORATION
3860 Midorigaoka Nakamachi, Iga, 518-0834, Mie, Japan
Tel.: (81) 595242161
Web Site: https://www.fine-yasunaga.co.jp
Year Founded: 1923
7271—(TKS)
Rev.: $211,163,060
Assets: $232,083,710
Liabilities: $159,922,340
Net Worth: $72,161,370
Earnings: $4,012,270
Emp.: 1,714
Fiscal Year-end: 03/31/24
Engine Parts Mfr & Whslr
N.A.I.C.S.: 336310
Akitoshi Yasunaga *(Pres & CEO)*

Subsidiaries:

YASUNAGA AIR PUMP INC. (1)
3-4-1 Kamezawa, Sumida-ku, Tokyo, 130-0014, Japan
Tel.: (81) 336213317
Web Site: https://www.fine-yasunaga.co.jp
Emp.: 60
Engine Parts Mfr
N.A.I.C.S.: 336310

YASUNAGA CORPORATION - Casting Plant (1)
2260 Saimyoji, Iga, 518-0809, Mie, Japan
Tel.: (81) 595212116
Engine Parts Mfr
N.A.I.C.S.: 336310

YASUNAGA CORPORATION - Nabari Plant (1)
920 Minowa-nakamura, Nabari, 518-0444, Mie, Japan
Tel.: (81) 595632631
Engine Parts Mfr
N.A.I.C.S.: 336310

YASUNAGA CORPORATION - Saimyoji Plant (1)
2782-1 Saimyoji, Iga, 518-0809, Mie, Japan
Tel.: (81) 595242155
Engine Parts Mfr
N.A.I.C.S.: 336310

YASUNAGA CORPORATION - Yumeporisu Plant (1)
7-3-3 Yumegaoka, Iga, 518-0131, Mie, Japan
Tel.: (81) 595262455
Web Site: http://www.sine-yasunaga.co.jp
Engine Parts Mfr
N.A.I.C.S.: 336310

YASUNAGA TRANSPORT CO., LTD. (1)
2284-17 Saimyoji, Iga, 518-0809, Mie, Japan
Tel.: (81) 595212913
Engine Parts Mfr
N.A.I.C.S.: 336310

YATAI INDUSTRIAL DEVELOPENT CO., LTD.
Office Building No A1 Yatai Industrial Technology Headquarters Base, Lanzhou New Area, Lanzhou, 510610, Gansu, China
Tel.: (86) 2083628691
Web Site: http://www.ytsy000691.com
Year Founded: 1988
000691—(SSE)
Rev.: $76,967,280
Assets: $98,886,528
Liabilities: $54,646,488
Net Worth: $44,240,040
Earnings: $195,156
Fiscal Year-end: 12/31/22
Real Estate Development Services
N.A.I.C.S.: 531390
Chen Zhijian *(Chm)*

YATAS YATAK VE YORGAN SANAYI TICARET A.S.
Yali Mahallesi Kadir Sokak No 14/1, Kartal, 34876, Istanbul, 34876, Turkiye
Tel.: (90) 8508500987
Web Site: https://www.yatasbedding.com.tr
Year Founded: 1976
YATAS—(IST)
Rev.: $208,093,428
Assets: $132,238,231
Liabilities: $88,869,281
Net Worth: $43,368,950
Earnings: $15,881,008
Fiscal Year-end: 12/31/22
Household Furniture Mfr & Whslr
N.A.I.C.S.: 337121

YATIRIM FINANSMAN MENKUL DEGERLER A.S.
Meclis-i Mebusan Cad 81 Findikli, 34427, Istanbul, Turkiye
Tel.: (90) 2123176900
Web Site: http://www.yf.com.tr
Year Founded: 1976
YFMEN—(IST)
Rev.: $101,496,734
Assets: $114,469,993
Liabilities: $103,775,846
Net Worth: $10,694,147
Earnings: $3,555,836
Fiscal Year-end: 12/31/22
Securities Brokerage Services
N.A.I.C.S.: 523150
Ece Boru *(Chm)*

YATIRIM VARLIK KIRALAMA A.S.
Meclisi Mebusan Cad No 81, Findikli Beyoglu, Istanbul, Turkiye
Tel.: (90) 2123345092
Web Site: http://www.yatirimvks.com.tr
YATVK—(IST)
Financial Investment Services
N.A.I.C.S.: 523999
Meral Murathan *(Chm)*

YATRA ONLINE LIMITED
B2/101 Marathon Innova Marathon Nextgen Complex B Wing G 1st Floor, Kadam Marg Opp Peninsula Corp Park Lower Parel, Mumbai, 400013, Maharashtra, India
Tel.: (91) 2244357700
Year Founded: 2006
543992—(BOM)
Emp.: 990
Travel Agency Services
N.A.I.C.S.: 561510
Murlidhara Kadaba *(Chm)*

YATRA ONLINE, INC.
Gulf Adiba Plot No 272 4th Floor Udyog Vihar Phase-II Sector-20, Gurgaon, 122008, Haryana, India
Tel.: (91) 1244591700
Web Site: https://www.yatra.com
YTRA—(NASDAQ)
Rev.: $50,235,566
Assets: $149,748,411
Liabilities: $56,705,155
Net Worth: $93,043,256
Earnings: ($4,394,281)
Emp.: 1,268
Fiscal Year-end: 03/31/24
Telecommunication Servicesb
N.A.I.C.S.: 517112
Dhruv Shringi *(Co-Founder & CEO)*

Subsidiaries:

Air Travel Bureau Private Limited (1)
Gulf Adiba 5th Floor Plot No 272 Phase II Udyog Vihar Sector 20, Gurgaon, 122008, Haryana, India
Tel.: (91) 1244827700
Web Site: https://www.atbyatra.com
Travel Arrangement Services
N.A.I.C.S.: 561599
Naren Nautiyal *(Deputy Mng Dir)*

Asia Consolidated DMC Pte. Ltd. (1)
75 Bukit Timah Road 05-12 Boon Siew Building, Singapore, 229833, Singapore
Tel.: (65) 62938887
Web Site: https://www.asiandmc.com
Destination Management Services
N.A.I.C.S.: 561920

YATSEN HOLDING LIMITED
Building 35-36 Gongmeigang Digital innovation center No 2519, Xingang East Road Haizhu District, Guangzhou, 510330, China
Tel.: (86) 2038373543
Web Site: https://www.yatsenglobal.com
Year Founded: 2016
YSG—(NYSE)
Rev.: $567,814,952
Assets: $898,217,526
Liabilities: $174,667,673
Net Worth: $723,549,852
Earnings: ($124,922,991)
Emp.: 1,837
Fiscal Year-end: 12/31/22
Holding Company
N.A.I.C.S.: 551112
Jianhua Lyu *(Co-Founder & Chief Sls Officer)*

YAU LEE HOLDINGS LIMITED
10/F Tower 1 Enterprise Square 9 Sheung Yuet Road, Kowloon Bay, China (Hong Kong)
Tel.: (852) 2 753 4388
Web Site: http://www.yaulee.com
0406—(HKG)
Rev.: $868,415,117
Assets: $611,037,333
Liabilities: $412,233,107
Net Worth: $198,804,226
Earnings: $8,513,067
Emp.: 3,200
Fiscal Year-end: 03/31/22
Building Construction & Maintenance, Building Materials Sales & Mfr
N.A.I.C.S.: 236210
Ip Kuen Wong *(Chm)*

Subsidiaries:

Global Virtual Design & Construction (Singapore) Pte. Ltd. (1)
100 Pasir Panjang 07-05 100 Pasir Panjang Road, Singapore, 118518, Singapore
Tel.: (65) 6 499 1268
Design Construction Services
N.A.I.C.S.: 541310

Global Virtual Design & Construction Limited (1)
Rm 301-312 Metro Centre 1 32 Lam Hing St, Kowloon Bay, China (Hong Kong)
Tel.: (852) 3 199 0388
Design Construction Services
N.A.I.C.S.: 541310

Global Virtual Design & Construction Sdn. Bhd. (1)
1 Suite 2 1st Floor 2J-1 Jalan Giam Taman Majidee, 80250, Johor Bahru, Johor, Malaysia
Tel.: (60) 6 499 1268
Design Construction Services
N.A.I.C.S.: 541310

InnoVision Architects & Engineers Limited (1)
7/F Tower 1 Enterprise Square 9 Sheung Yuet Road, Kowloon, China (Hong Kong)
Tel.: (852) 3473 3780
Property Management Services
N.A.I.C.S.: 531311

Leena Theme Painting Limited (1)
10/F Tower 1 Enterprise Square 9 Sheung Yuet Road, Kowloon, China (Hong Kong)
Tel.: (852) 2753 4325
Web Site: http://www.leenapainting.com
Emp.: 5
Painting Services
N.A.I.C.S.: 238160

Lever Construction Materials (Shenzhen) Company Limited (1)
6/F Block 120 The First Campus Luohu High Technology, Guowei Road Liantang Luohu, Shenzhen, 518002, China (100%)
Tel.: (86) 755 25638212
Web Site: http://www.yaulee.com
Building Materials Mfr & Distr
N.A.I.C.S.: 327331

Million Wealth Enterprises Limited (1)
10/F Enterprise Square Tower One 9 Sheung Yuet Road, Kowloon, China (Hong Kong)
Tel.: (852) 27534388
Construction Engineering Services
N.A.I.C.S.: 237990

Ming Hop Company Limited (1)
23-25 Eggs Building Room 1A cheong lok street, Changle Street, Kowloon, China (Hong Kong) (100%)
Tel.: (852) 27830903

YAU LEE HOLDINGS LIMITED

Yau Lee Holdings Limited—(Continued)
Web Site: http://www.minghop.com
Emp.: 11
Plumbing Heating & Air-Conditioning Contractors
N.A.I.C.S.: 238220
Lai Ying Wong (Asst Gen Mgr)

REC Engineering Company Limited (1)
Units A-D 15/F Goodman Kwai Chung Logistics Centre, 585-609 Castle Peak Road, Kwai Chung, China (Hong Kong)
Tel.: (852) 26198888
Web Site: http://www.rec-eng.com
Emp.: 500
Electrical & Mechanical Engineering Services
N.A.I.C.S.: 541330

REC Engineering Contracting Company Limited (1)
11/F Success Center 26-38 Ta Chuen Ping Street, Kwai Chung, China (Hong Kong)
Tel.: (852) 26198888
Web Site: http://www.rec-eng.com
Construction Engineering Services
N.A.I.C.S.: 541330

REC Green Energy Solutions Company Limited (1)
Unit A-D15/F Goodman Kwai Chung Logistics Centre 585-609, Castle Peak Road, Kwai Chung, China (Hong Kong)
Tel.: (852) 2 619 8817
Web Site: https://www.rec-gt.com
Green Building Development Services
N.A.I.C.S.: 237310

Tin Sing Chemical Engineers Limited (1)
Units A-D 15/F Goodman Kwai Chung Logistics Centre, 585-609 Castle Peak Road, Kwai Chung, New Territories, China (Hong Kong)
Tel.: (852) 26198288
Web Site: http://www.rec-tsc.com
Emp.: 20
Property Development Services
N.A.I.C.S.: 531390

VHSoft Technologies Company Limited (1)
Room 301-312 3/F Metro Centre 32 Lam Hing Street, Kowloon Bay, Kowloon, China (Hong Kong) (100%)
Tel.: (852) 28360099
Web Site: https://www.vhsoft.com
Emp.: 50
Computer Related Services
N.A.I.C.S.: 541519
Hubert Yiu Kau Mak (COO)

Subsidiary (Non-US):

VHSoft Technologies (SZ) Company Limited (2)
11/F A1 Wen Jin Plaza 23 Tian Bei Road 1, Shenzhen, China
Tel.: (86) 755 25636330
Software Development Services
N.A.I.C.S.: 541511

Yau Lee Building Construction and Decoration Company Limited (1)
10/F Enterprise Square Tower 1 9 Sheung Yuet Road, Kowloon, China (Hong Kong)
Tel.: (852) 27534388
Building Materials Distr
N.A.I.C.S.: 423390

Yau Lee Building Materials Trading Company Limited (1)
10/F Tower I Enterprise Square Sheung Yuet Road, Kowloon Bay, Kowloon, China (Hong Kong)
Tel.: (852) 27534325
Web Site: http://www.yauleetrade.com
Construction Materials Distr
N.A.I.C.S.: 423390

Yau Lee Construction (Singapore) Pte. Ltd (1)
10 Raeburn Pk 02-12, Singapore, 088702, Singapore
Tel.: (65) 64991268
Web Site: http://www.yaulee.com
Emp.: 50

Building Materials Distr
N.A.I.C.S.: 423390

Yau Lee Construction (UAE) Company Limited (1)
10/F Enterprise Square Tower 1 9 Sheung Yuet Road, Kowloon, China (Hong Kong)
Tel.: (852) 27534393
Building Materials Distr
N.A.I.C.S.: 423390

Yau Lee Construction Company Limited (1)
10/F Tower 1 Enterprise Square 9 Sheung Yuet Road, Kowloon Bay, China (Hong Kong) (100%)
Tel.: (852) 27534388
Web Site: http://www.yaulee.com
Residential Property Managers
N.A.I.C.S.: 531311

Yau Lee Construction Materials & Technology (B.V.I.) Ltd. (1)
10th Fl Enterprise Sq Twr 1, 9 Sheung Yuet Road, Kowloon, China (Hong Kong) (100%)
Tel.: (852) 27534388
Web Site: http://www.yaulee.com
Lumber Plywood Millwork & Wood Panel Whslr
N.A.I.C.S.: 423310

Yau Lee Construction Materials & Technology Limited (1)
10/F Enterprise Square Tower 1 9 Sheung Yuet Road, Kowloon, China (Hong Kong)
Tel.: (852) 27534388
Web Site: http://www.yaulee.com
Emp.: 80
Building Materials Distr
N.A.I.C.S.: 423390

Yau Lee Curtain Wall and Steel Works Limited (1)
10/fF Enterprise Square Twr 1 9 Sheung Yuet Rd, Kowloon, China (Hong Kong)
Tel.: (852) 34733750
Curtain Wall Installation Services
N.A.I.C.S.: 238150

Yau Lee Development (Singapore) Pte. Ltd (1)
02-12 10 Raeburn Park, Singapore, 088702, Singapore
Tel.: (65) 64991268
Property Development Services
N.A.I.C.S.: 531311

Yau Lee Wah Concrete Precast Products Company Limited (1)
10th Floor Tower I Enterprise Square, Sheung Yuet Road, Kowloon, China (Hong Kong) (100%)
Tel.: (852) 27534388
Web Site: http://www.yaulee.com
Emp.: 80
Concrete Product Manufacturing
N.A.I.C.S.: 327390
Tin Cheung Wong (Mng Dir)

Subsidiary (Non-US):

Yau Lee Wah Concrete Precast Products (Shenzhen) Company Limited (2)
Qinghu Gong Ye Qu Heping Dong Lu, Longhau Zhen Baoan Qu, Shenzhen, 518109, Guangdong, China
Tel.: (86) 755 28122130
Web Site: http://www.yauleewah.com
Precast Concrete Products Mfr
N.A.I.C.S.: 327390

YAVOR PLC
No 117 Republika avenue, Varna, 9020, Bulgaria
Tel.: (359) 52 500 317
Web Site: http://www.yavorad.com
Year Founded: 1945
Construction Services
N.A.I.C.S.: 236210

YAWAL S.A.
ul Lubliniecka 36, 42-284, Herby, Poland
Tel.: (48) 34 352 88 00
Web Site: http://www.yawal.com
Year Founded: 1993
Aluminium Construction Material Mfr
N.A.I.C.S.: 331315
Tomasz Sek (Chm-Mgmt Bd)

YAXING MOTOR PERU S.A.C.
Av 9 de Octubre No 459 Tres Compuertas SJL, Lima, Peru
Tel.: (51) 4587973
Transportation Services
N.A.I.C.S.: 485999

YAYLA ENERJI URETIM TURIZM VE INSAAT TICARET A.S.
Turan Gunes Bulvari Ilkbahar Mah 606 Sok No 12, Yildiz Cankaya, 06550, Ankara, Turkiye
Tel.: (90) 3124917475
Web Site: https://www.yayla.tc
YAYLA—(IST)
Construction Services
N.A.I.C.S.: 236220
Huseyin Yayla (Owner)

YAZAKI CORPORATION
17 F Mita Kokusai Bldg 4 28 Mita 1 Chome, Minato Ku, Tokyo, 108 8333, Japan
Tel.: (81) 344558811
Web Site: http://www.yazaki-group.com
Year Founded: 1941
Sales Range: $1-4.9 Billion
Emp.: 3,278
Wholesale Automotive Parts & Equipment
N.A.I.C.S.: 441330

Subsidiaries:

Australian Arrow Pty. Ltd. (1)
46 Lathams Road, Carrum Downs, 3201, VIC, Australia
Tel.: (61) 8 9775 1566
Web Site: http://www.australianarrow.com.au
Sales Range: $150-199.9 Million
Emp.: 552
Automotive Component Mfr & Distr
N.A.I.C.S.: 336390
Isaia Crombie (Engr-Quality Reliability)

Auto Circuitos de Obregon, S.A. de C.V. (1)
Circuito del Parque 948 Sur Obregon, Sonora, 85065, Mexico
Tel.: (52) 644 410 5240
Automobile Component Distr
N.A.I.C.S.: 423120

Auto Conectores de Chihuahua ELCOM S. de R.L. de C.V. (1)
Ishikawa No 1400, Chihuahua, 31304, Mexico
Tel.: (52) 6141584800
Automobile Component Distr
N.A.I.C.S.: 423120

Circuit Controls Corporation (1)
2277 M-119 Hwy, Petoskey, MI 49770
Tel.: (231) 347-0760
Web Site: http://www.circuitcontrols.com
Emp.: 180
Automotive Components Mfr
N.A.I.C.S.: 336390
Maurice Davison (Engr-Mfg)

EDS Manufacturing, Incorporated (1)
Anabu II Imus, Cavite, Philippines
Tel.: (63) 2 711 9911
Automotive Wire Harness Distr
N.A.I.C.S.: 423120

ELCOM Inc. (1)
20 Butterfield Trl Blvd, El Paso, TX 79906
Tel.: (915) 298-2000
Automotive Wiring Harness Mfr
N.A.I.C.S.: 336320
Dave Kaufman (Plant Mgr & Dir-Ops)

Manufactura Avanzada de Colima S.A. de C.V. (1)
Blvd Marcelino Garcia Barragan No 1,

INTERNATIONAL PUBLIC

28000, Colima, Mexico
Tel.: (52) 312 316 3000
Automotive Wiring Harness Distr
N.A.I.C.S.: 423120

PT. Autocomp Systems Indonesia (1)
Jl Cempaka F16 No 3&5, Tangerang, 15119, Bataan, Indonesia
Tel.: (62) 2129288502
Automotive Wiring Harness Distr
N.A.I.C.S.: 423120

PT. EDS Manufacturing Indonesia (1)
Jl Raya Serang KM 24 Kec Balaraja, Tangerang, 15610, Indonesia
Tel.: (62) 21 595 1535
Automotive Wiring Harness Distr
N.A.I.C.S.: 423120

PT. Semarang Autocomp Manufacturing Indonesia (1)
Ktr Pusat Jl Walisongo Km 9 8 Jrakah Tugu, 50151, Semarang, Indonesia
Tel.: (62) 24 8665744
Automotive Wiring Harness Mfr
N.A.I.C.S.: 423120

Shantou Special Economic Zone Yazaki Auto Parts Co., Ltd. (1)
F5 F4 Longhu Industrial Zone, Longhu District, Shantou, 515041, Guangdong, China
Tel.: (86) 754 826 5924
Automotive Wiring Harness Mfr
N.A.I.C.S.: 336320

Taiwan Yazaki Corporation (1)
No 4 Szuwei Rd Loyang, Yenpu, 90744, Pingtung Pref, Taiwan
Tel.: (886) 8 703 2311
Emp.: 1,000
Automotive Wiring Harness Distr
N.A.I.C.S.: 423120

Tecnologia Autoelectronica de Durango, S. de R.L. de C.V. (1)
Oro No 107 Lote 5a, 34208, Durango, Mexico
Tel.: (52) 618 150-0500
Automotive Wiring Harness Distr
N.A.I.C.S.: 423120

Thai Metal Processing Co., Ltd. (1)
25th Floor 2 Pacific Place Building 142 Sukhumvit Road, Klongtoey District, Bangkok, 10110, Thailand
Tel.: (66) 26532550
Web Site: http://www.thaiyazaki.com
Emp.: 74
Copper Wire Production
N.A.I.C.S.: 331410

Tianjin Yazaki Automotive Parts Co., Ltd. (1)
138 Dongting Road, Economic & Technological Zone, Tianjin, 300457, China
Tel.: (86) 22 2532 3538
Automotive Wiring Harness Mfr
N.A.I.C.S.: 316990

UAB Yazaki Wiring Technologies Lietuva (1)
Vilniaus pl 10, 91003, Klaipeda, Lithuania
Tel.: (370) 46 496500
Emp.: 600
Automotive Wiring Harness Mfr
N.A.I.C.S.: 336320
Roma Budriane (Mgr)

YAZAKI Wiring Technologies Turkiye Elektrik Sistemleri Sanayi ve Tic. Ltd. Sti. (1)
Omer Bey Mahallesi Bursa Asfalti No 53, Mudanya, 16941, Bursa, Turkiye
Tel.: (90) 224 294 7000
Web Site: http://www.yazaki.com.tr
Electric Equipment Mfr
N.A.I.C.S.: 335999

YIC Asia Pacific Corporation Limited (1)
18th Floor Exchange Tower 388 Sukhumvit Road, Klongtoey, Bangkok, 10110, Thailand
Tel.: (66) 2663 7781
Web Site: http://www.yicap.com
Automobile Parts Mfr
N.A.I.C.S.: 336390
David Marderosian (Dir-Sls)

AND PRIVATE COMPANIES

YTC America Inc. (1)
3401 Calle Tecate, Camarillo, CA 93012
Tel.: (805) 388-9920
Web Site: http://www.ytca.com
Emp.: 350
Automobile Research & Development Services
N.A.I.C.S.: 541715
S. Ray Chaudhuri *(Pres & CEO)*

Yantai Yazaki Automotive Parts Co., Ltd. (1)
Western Head of Yongda Street Fushan New & High Tech Industry Park, Yantai, Shandong, China
Tel.: (86) 535 632 9901
Automotive Wiring Harness Distr
N.A.I.C.S.: 423120

Yazaki Argentina S.R.L. (1)
Ruta 9 Panamericana Km 55 5 Escobar Prov, Buenos Aires, Argentina
Tel.: (54) 3488 428833
Automotive Wiring Harness Distr
N.A.I.C.S.: 423120
Masahito Hirasawa *(Dir-HR & Legal)*

Yazaki Automotive Products Do Brasil Sistemas Eletricos Ltda (1)
Rodovia MG 424 Km 25 Distrito Industrial, Matozinhos, Minas Gerais, Brazil
Tel.: (55) 31 37129903
Automotive Wiring Harness Distr
N.A.I.C.S.: 423120
Rejane Avelar Silva *(Accountant)*

Yazaki Automotive Products Poland Sp. z o. o. (1)
Spolka z ograniczona odpowiedzialnoscia Wyzwolenia Str 27, 43-190, Mikolow, Poland
Tel.: (48) 32 2180530
Automotive Wiring Harness Distr
N.A.I.C.S.: 423120

Yazaki Automotive Products Tunisia S.A.R.L (1)
Z I Menzel Jemil, BP 124, Menzel Jemil, 7080, Bizerte, Tunisia
Tel.: (216) 72 593 150
Automotive Wiring Harness Distr
N.A.I.C.S.: 423120
Hatem Lazzem *(Mgr-IT)*

Yazaki Ciemel Ftz Ltda (1)
Autopista Norte Km 21, Bogota, Colombia
Tel.: (57) 1 6683000
Web Site: http://www.yazaki.com.co
Automotive Wiring Harness Mfr
N.A.I.C.S.: 336320

Yazaki Ciemel S.A. (1)
Km 21 Autopista Norte, Chia, Cundinamarca, Colombia
Tel.: (57) 1 668 3000
Automotive Wiring Harness Distr
N.A.I.C.S.: 423120
Consuelo Rojas *(Mgr-Product Dev)*

Yazaki EDS Vietnam, Ltd. (1)
Di An Commune, Di An, Binh Duong, Vietnam
Tel.: (84) 650 75 2590
Automotive Wiring Harness Distr
N.A.I.C.S.: 423120

Yazaki Energy Systems, Inc. (YESI) (1)
701 E Plano Parkway Ste305, Plano, TX 75074
Tel.: (469) 229-5443
Web Site: http://www.yazaki-na.com
Automotive Electrical Harnesses, Engine Controls, Intermittent Wiper Modules
N.A.I.C.S.: 336320
Joe Wiche *(Mgr-Product Support)*

Yazaki Europe Ltd. (1)
1-3 Zodiac Boundary Way, Hemel Hempstead, HP2 7SJ, Hertfordshire, United Kingdom
Tel.: (44) 1442 292 400
Web Site: http://www.yazaki-europe.com
Automotive Wiring Harness Mfr
N.A.I.C.S.: 316990
Masaaki Yoshizawa *(Chm)*

Subsidiary (Non-US):

YAZAKI A.S. (2)
Bursa Serbest Bolgesi Hisar Mevkii Liman Yolu, 16600, Gemlik, Bursa, Turkiye
Tel.: (90) 224 270 10 00
Automotive Wiring Harness Mfr
N.A.I.C.S.: 336320
Buket Sezgin *(Project Engr)*

YAZAKI Component Technology S.R.L. (2)
Zona Industriala Vest Strada III No 4-4a, 310491, Arad, Romania
Tel.: (40) 372577002
Automotive Wiring Harness Mfr
N.A.I.C.S.: 336320

YAZAKI Morocco S.A. (2)
ILOT 101 ZONE Franche Aeroport, 90000, Tangiers, Morocco
Tel.: (212) 53 9399000
Automotive Wiring Harness Mfr
N.A.I.C.S.: 336320
Khaledi El Mostafa *(Mgr-HR & Gen Affairs)*

YAZAKI Otomotiv Yan Sanayi ve Ticaret A.S (2)
Topcu Sirti Mahallesi Yazakisa Caddesi, Kuzuluk, 54440, Akyazi, Turkiye
Tel.: (90) 264 437 8248
Automotive Wiring Harness Mfr
N.A.I.C.S.: 336320
Yigit Taner *(Mgr-Acctg & Fin)*

YAZAKI Romania S.R.L. (2)
Parcul Industrial Ploiesti Drumul DN 72 Sos Ploiesti Tirgoviste km 8, Prahova, Ploiesti, Romania
Tel.: (40) 372 449 100
Automotive Wiring Harness Mfr
N.A.I.C.S.: 336320
Dan Culda *(Mgr-MP&L)*

YAZAKI Slovakia Spol. S.R.O. (2)
Lehotska cesta 2, 971 80, Prievidza, Slovakia
Tel.: (421) 46 5150111
Automotive Wiring Harness Mfr
N.A.I.C.S.: 336320

YAZAKI Ukraine LLC (2)
7 i Turyanytsi Street Minay Vil, 89424, Uzhgorod, Ukraine
Tel.: (380) 312 669 000
Automobile Parts Mfr
N.A.I.C.S.: 336390

Yazaki Bulgaria EOOD (2)
43 Evropa Blvd, 8600, Yambol, Bulgaria
Tel.: (359) 46 901 400
Web Site: http://www.yazaki-bulgaria.com
Emp.: 5,000
Automotive Wiring Harness Mfr
N.A.I.C.S.: 336320
Rosica Ganeva *(Deputy Mgr-HR)*

Yazaki Europe Limited ITALIA S.r.l (2)
Via della Liberta 30, 10095, Grugliasco, Italy
Tel.: (39) 011 4096 103
Automotive Wiring Harness Distr
N.A.I.C.S.: 423120
Mariateresa Bazzotti *(Mgr-Fin)*

Yazaki Tunisia SARL (2)
Zone Industrielle Al-Aguila, Gafsa, Tunisia
Tel.: (216) 76 10 01 00
Automobile Parts Mfr
N.A.I.C.S.: 336390

Yazaki India Limited (1)
GAT 93 Survey 166 High Cliff Industrial Estate Wagholi-Rahu Road, Kesnand, 412 207, Pune, Maharashtra, India
Tel.: (91) 20 7050 133
Automotive Wiring Harness Distr
N.A.I.C.S.: 423120
Yogesh Hedaoo *(Deputy Mgr-QA)*

Yazaki North America, Inc. (1)
6801 N Haggerty Rd, Canton, MI 48187-3538 **(100%)**
Tel.: (734) 983-1000
Web Site: http://www.yazaki-na.com
Emp.: 1,500
Distr of Automotive Products
N.A.I.C.S.: 423120
Lynn Weaver *(VP-HR)*

Yazaki Parts Co., Ltd. (1)
Kawashimada 25, Shizuoka-ken, Gotemba, 412-8510, Japan
Tel.: (81) 550 83 8550
Automotive Wiring Harness Distr
N.A.I.C.S.: 423120
Yoshinori Endo *(Project Mgr)*

Yazaki Sabanci Otomotiv Kablo Donanimi San. Ve Tic. A.S. (1)
Topcu Sirti Mah Yazakisa Cad, Kuzuluk Akyazi, 544440, Sakarya, Turkiye
Tel.: (90) 2644378250
Sales Range: $200-249.9 Million
Emp.: 850
Motor Vehicle Wire Harnesses Mfr; Owned 75% by Yazaki Corporation & 25% by Haci Omer Sabanci Holding A.S.
N.A.I.C.S.: 336340

Yazaki Saltano de Ovar Productos Electricos, LDA. (1)
Avenida D Manuel 1 Zona Industrial de Ovar, 3880-109, Ovar, Portugal
Tel.: (351) 256 580 300
Automotive Wiring Harness Mfr
N.A.I.C.S.: 336320
Teresa Portela *(Mgr-HR)*

Yazaki Service S. de R.L. de C.V. (1)
Antiguo Camino Real Apodaca 710 Col Tacuba San Nicolas de Los Garza, 66470, Nuevo Leon, Mexico
Tel.: (52) 81 8134 4800
Automotive Wiring Harness Distr
N.A.I.C.S.: 423120
David Conrad *(VP)*

Yazaki Wiring Technologies Czech s.r.o. (1)
U Nove Hospody 2/1122, 301 00, Plzen, Czech Republic
Tel.: (420) 37 8213 106
Web Site: http://www.yazaki-czech.cz
Electric Equipment Mfr
N.A.I.C.S.: 335999
Ivega Sustrova *(Gen Mgr)*

Yazaki Wiring Technologies India Private Limited (1)
D-7 Industrial Estate Maraimalainagar, Kanchipuram, Tamilnadu, India
Tel.: (91) 44 3029 6600
Electric Equipment Mfr
N.A.I.C.S.: 335999

Yazaki do Brasil Ltda. (1)
Al Santos 700 Cj 62 Cerqueira Cesar, Sao Paulo, 01418-100, Brazil
Tel.: (55) 11 2122 7877
Automotive Wiring Harness Distr
N.A.I.C.S.: 423120
Gustavo Melfi *(Mgr-Controllership)*

Yazaki-Torres Manufacturing Incorporated (1)
Brgy Makiling, Calamba, 4027, Laguna, Philippines
Tel.: (63) 49 502 1530
Electric Equipment Mfr
N.A.I.C.S.: 335999

Zhangzhou Yazaki Auto Parts Co., Ltd. (1)
North of HengQi Road Lantian Economic Development Zone, Zhangzhou, 363007, Fujian, China
Tel.: (86) 596 2101 353
Electric Equipment Mfr
N.A.I.C.S.: 335999

YAZDBAF FACTORY

No 723 Enghelab Ave college crossing, Tehran, Iran
Tel.: (98) 21 66 46 33 95
Web Site: http://www.yazdbaf.com
Year Founded: 1956
Textile Product Production & Sales
N.A.I.C.S.: 314999
M. Zarrabieh *(Mng Dir)*

YB COMMUNICATIONS LIMITED

Phoenix House The Old Church Elland Road, Churwell, LS27 7TB, United Kingdom
Tel.: (44) 3458050555
Web Site:
  https://northerntelecom.co.uk
Year Founded: 2013
Telecommunication Servicesb
N.A.I.C.S.: 517810
Simon Rogers *(Dir-Ops)*

YB VENTURES BERHAD

Lot 7020 Batu 23 Jalan Air Hitam, 81000, Kulai, Johor Darul Takzim, Malaysia
Tel.: (60) 76522652
Web Site:
  https://www.ybventures.com
YILAI—(KLS)
Rev.: $14,138,342
Assets: $78,898,158
Liabilities: $9,315,121
Net Worth: $69,583,037
Earnings: ($4,075,850)
Emp.: 682
Fiscal Year-end: 06/30/23
Tiles Mfr
N.A.I.C.S.: 327120
Aaron Jian Hong Tan *(Exec Dir)*

Subsidiaries:

Alpha Tiles Trading Sdn. Bhd. (1)
Lot 8 Jalan 51A 241 Section 51A, 46100, Petaling Jaya, Selangor, Malaysia
Tel.: (60) 378754388
Emp.: 20
Ceramic Tiles Distr
N.A.I.C.S.: 423320
Lim Onn Kok *(Mng Dir)*

Yi-Lai Industry Berhad (1)
Lot 7020 Batu 23 Jalan Air Hitam, 81000, Kulai, Malaysia
Tel.: (60) 76522652
Web Site: http://www.alpha-tiles.org
Emp.: 800
Ceramic & Homogeneous Tiles Mfr & Sales
N.A.I.C.S.: 327120

Yi-Lai Marketing Sdn. Bhd. (1)
No 8 Jalan 51A/241 Seksyen 51A, 46100, Petaling Jaya, Selangor, Malaysia
Tel.: (60) 378754388
Tiles Mfr
N.A.I.C.S.: 327120

Yi-Lai Trading Pte. Ltd. (1)
82 Lorong 23 Geylang 01-06 Atrix, Singapore, 388409, Singapore
Tel.: (65) 68420163
Tiles Mfr
N.A.I.C.S.: 327120

YBM NET, INC.

98 Jong-ro, Jongno-gu, Seoul, Korea (South)
Tel.: (82) 220085200
Web Site: http://www.ybm.co.kr
Year Founded: 2000
057030—(KRS)
Rev.: $47,985,460
Assets: $67,540,216
Liabilities: $29,810,160
Net Worth: $37,730,056
Earnings: $5,854,753
Emp.: 432
Fiscal Year-end: 12/31/22
Online Education Services
N.A.I.C.S.: 611710
SunShik Min *(Chm & CEO)*

YBOX REAL ESTATE LTD.

Comfort 7 St Florentine Neighborhood Near Neve Tzedek, Tel Aviv, Israel
Tel.: (972) 36285300
Web Site: https://www.ybox.co.il
YBOX—(TAE)
Rev.: $35,749,959
Assets: $324,826,474
Liabilities: $215,428,664
Net Worth: $109,397,809
Earnings: $9,506,263
Fiscal Year-end: 09/30/23
Real Estate Services

YBOX REAL ESTATE LTD.

Ybox Real Estate Ltd.—(Continued)
N.A.I.C.S.: 531390
Yehuda Gorsd (Chm)

YBS INTERNATIONAL BERHAD
No 978 Lorong Perindustrian Bukit Minyak 20, Taman Perindustrian Bukit Minyak, 14100, Pulau Penang, Simpang Ampat, Malaysia
Tel.: (60) 45088623 MY
Web Site: https://www.ybsinternational.com
Year Founded: 2002
YBS—(KLS)
Rev.: $20,855,999
Assets: $34,365,402
Liabilities: $18,783,476
Net Worth: $15,581,926
Earnings: ($1,668,528)
Emp.: 800
Fiscal Year-end: 03/31/24
Investment Holding Services
N.A.I.C.S.: 551112
Chan Cheah Yong (Mng Dir)

Subsidiaries:

Bumblebee Eco Solutions Sdn. Bhd. (1)
Web Site: http://www.bessboard.com
Paperboard Distr
N.A.I.C.S.: 423840

Edaran Precision India Private Limited (1)
Plot SDF 16A Ground Floor Csez Ernakulam, Kakkanad, 682 037, Kerala, India
Tel.: (91) 4842413015
Press Tool & Mould Mfr
N.A.I.C.S.: 333514

Edaran Precision Industries Sdn. Bhd. (1)
K27 Jalan Perindustrian Kawasan Perindustrian Tanjung Agas, 84000, Muar, Johor, Malaysia
Tel.: (60) 69536088
Mold & Die Mfr
N.A.I.C.S.: 333511

Edaran Resources Pte. Ltd. (1)
1002 Jalan Bukit Merah 05-12, Singapore, 159456, Singapore
Tel.: (65) 62702518
Web Site: http://edrres.com
Fabricated Metal Mfr
N.A.I.C.S.: 332312

Subsidiary (US):

Orifast Connector Solutions LLC (2)
615 St George Sq Ct Ste 300, Winston Salem, NC 27103
Tel.: (336) 778-3401
Web Site: http://orifastcs.com
High Precision Metal Mfr
N.A.I.C.S.: 332215

Oriental Fastech Manufacturing Sdn. Bhd. (1)
Plot 171 Mukim 13 Jalan Perindustrian Bukit Minyak, 14000, Bukit Mertajam, Penang, Malaysia
Tel.: (60) 45018623
Web Site: https://www.orientalfastech.com
High Precision Metal Component Mfr & Distr
N.A.I.C.S.: 333514

Subsidiary (Non-US):

Oriental Fastech Manufacturing (Vietnam) Co., Ltd. (2)
LTD 26 Dai Lo Doc Lap, Vietnam Singapore Industrial Park 1, Thuan An, Binh Duong, Vietnam
Tel.: (84) 2743766761
High Precision Metal Component Mfr
N.A.I.C.S.: 333514

YC INOX CO., LTD.
No 270 Sec 4 Jungshan Road, Shijou Shiang, 52441, Chang-Hua, 52441, Taiwan
Tel.: (886) 48899666
Web Site: https://www.ycinox.com
2034—(TAI)
Rev.: $498,125,394
Assets: $598,920,446
Liabilities: $306,230,408
Net Worth: $292,690,038
Earnings: ($5,553,321)
Emp.: 807
Fiscal Year-end: 12/31/23
Stainless Steel Wire Mfr
N.A.I.C.S.: 331110
Dominic Liao (Dir)

Subsidiaries:

YC Inox TR Celik Sanayi ve Ticaret A.S.
Yc Inox Tr Boru Fabrikasi Organize Sanayi Bolgesi Mah 4 Cad, Yc Inox Tr Celik Blok No 10 /3 Ic Kapi No 3 Dilovasi, Kocaeli, Turkiye
Tel.: (90) 2626768866
Web Site: http://www.ycinox.com.tr
Steel Tube Mfr & Distr
N.A.I.C.S.: 331210

YC Inox TR Company
Mah 4th St YC Inox TR Steel Block No 10/3 Interior Door No 3, Organized Industrial Zone Dilovasi, Kocaeli, Turkiye
Tel.: (90) 2626768866
Stainless Steel Welded Pipe Mfr & Distr
N.A.I.C.S.: 331210

Yeun Chyang Industrial Co., Ltd - Douliu Mill (1)
No 29 Ke-Jia Road, Douliu, 640, Yunlin, Taiwan
Tel.: (886) 55511100
Web Site: http://www.yeunchyang.com.tw
Stainless Steel Mfr
N.A.I.C.S.: 331110

Yeun Chyang Industrial Co., Ltd. - Puoshing Mill (1)
No 33 Section 4 Yuanlu Rd, Puoshing, Chang-Hua, Taiwan
Tel.: (886) 48292226
Web Site: http://www.yeunchyang.com.tw
Stainless Steel Products Mfr
N.A.I.C.S.: 331513

YCH GROUP PTE. LTD.
8 Bulim Avenue, YCH DistriPark, Singapore, 648166, Singapore
Tel.: (65) 67677777
Web Site: http://www.ych.com
Year Founded: 1955
Sales Range: $100-124.9 Million
Emp.: 500
Integrated End-To-End Supply Chain Management & Logistics Services
N.A.I.C.S.: 541611
Robert Yap (Chm)

Subsidiaries:

Igloo Supply Chain Philippines, Inc. (1)
Manggahan Light Industrial Park, A Rodriguez Ave, Pasig, 1610, Philippines (100%)
Tel.: (63) 26472794
Web Site: http://www.igloosupplychain.com
Emp.: 150
Warehouse Clubs & Superstores
N.A.I.C.S.: 455211
Albert Ladores (Pres)

YCH DistriPark Pte Ltd (1)
30 Tuas Road, YCH DistriPark, Singapore, 638492, Singapore
Tel.: (65) 67677777
Emp.: 400
Integrated End-To-End Supply Chain Management & Logistics Services
N.A.I.C.S.: 541611
Robert Yap (CEO)

YCH Districentre Pte Ltd (1)
No 28 Tuas Ave 13, Singapore, 638994, Singapore
Tel.: (65) 6861 1350
Integrated End-To-End Supply Chain Management & Logistics Services
N.A.I.C.S.: 541611

YCH Global Logistics Pte Ltd (1)
30 Tuas Rd, Singapore, 638492, Singapore
Tel.: (65) 67677777
Web Site: http://www.ych.com
Integrated End-To-End Supply Chain Management & Logistics Services
N.A.I.C.S.: 541611
Robert Yap (Mng Dir)

YCH Logistics Australia Pty Ltd (1)
Door K Building 7 14-54 Dennistoun Ave, Yennora, 2161, NSW, Australia
Tel.: (61) 2 8071 4867
Business Management Consulting Services
N.A.I.C.S.: 541611
Chan Yoke Ping (Sr Mgr)

YCIH GREEN HIGH-PERFORMANCE CONCRETE COMPANY LIMITED
5/F and 9/F YCIH Development Building 188 Linxi Road, Information Industrial Base Economic & Technological Development Zone, Kunming, Yunnan, China
Tel.: (86) 87163187896 CN
Web Site: http://www.ynhnt.com
Year Founded: 1996
1847—(HKG)
Rev.: $235,968,314
Assets: $678,249,515
Liabilities: $485,956,973
Net Worth: $192,292,542
Earnings: $4,194,731
Emp.: 1,087
Fiscal Year-end: 12/31/22
Construction Management Services
N.A.I.C.S.: 236116
Minchao Ma (Exec Dir)

YCO GROUP PLC
Brigade House 8 Parsons Green, London, SW6 4TN, United Kingdom
Tel.: (44) 2075841801
Web Site: http://www.ycogroup.com
Sales Range: $25-49.9 Million
Emp.: 70
Yacht Manufacturer
N.A.I.C.S.: 713930
Charles Nicholas Keith Birkett (Co-Founder & CEO)

Subsidiaries:

YCO Group plc - YCO crew (1)
9 Ave President J.F.Kennedy, 98000, Monaco, France
Tel.: (33) 492909290
Web Site: http://www.ycocrew.com
Emp.: 2
Marine Crew Search & Placement Services
N.A.I.C.S.: 561311

YCO S.A.M. (1)
9 Av President J F Kennedy, Monte Carlo, 98000, Monaco
Tel.: (377) 93501212
Web Site: http://www.ycoyacht.com
Emp.: 50
Yacht Management & Consulting Services
N.A.I.C.S.: 541618
Yves Damette (Dir-Yacht Mgmt)

Subsidiary (Non-US):

YCO Ltd. (2)
18 Coulson St, Chelsea, London, SW3 3NB, United Kingdom
Tel.: (44) 2075841801
Web Site: http://www.ycoyacht.com
Emp.: 7
Yacht Brokerage Services
N.A.I.C.S.: 488510
Charles Birkett (Mng Dir)

YCO Yacht Limited (2)
18 Coulson St, Chelsea, London, SW3 3NB, United Kingdom
Tel.: (44) 2075841801
Web Site: http://www.ycoyacht.com
Emp.: 9
Yacht Management & Consulting Services
N.A.I.C.S.: 561110
Gary Wright (Mng Dir)

INTERNATIONAL PUBLIC

YPI CREW SARL (2)
6 Avenue de la Liberation, 06600, Antibes, 06600, France
Tel.: (33) 4 92 90 46 10
Web Site: http://ypicrew.com
Yacht Management & Consulting Services
N.A.I.C.S.: 561110
Laurence Lewis (Dir)

YCP HOLDINGS (GLOBAL) LIMITED
20 Collyer Quay Level 1206, Singapore, 189352, Singapore
Tel.: (65) 69102604
Web Site: https://www.ycp.com
Year Founded: 2011
92570—(TKS)
Rev.: $122,454,671
Assets: $141,555,643
Liabilities: $64,137,859
Net Worth: $77,417,785
Earnings: $5,509,078
Emp.: 500
Fiscal Year-end: 12/31/23
Offices of Other Holding Companies
N.A.I.C.S.: 551112

Subsidiaries:

SOLIA Corporation (1)
10th floor Shin-Aoyama Building East Building 1-1-1 Minami-Aoyama, Minato-ku, Tokyo, 107-0062, Japan
Tel.: (81) 357721063
Web Site: https://www.solia.co.jp
Cosmetic Appliance Mfr & Distr
N.A.I.C.S.: 325620

YCQH AGRICULTURAL TECHNOLOGY CO., LTD.
No 1104 Ren Min Nan Road No 45, Wuhou District, Chengdu, 610000, Sichuan, China
Tel.: (86) 13981161812 NV
Web Site: https://www.ycqhgroup.com
Year Founded: 2019
YCQH—(OTCIQ)
Rev.: $118,396
Assets: $391,291
Liabilities: $614,409
Net Worth: ($223,118)
Earnings: ($74,450)
Emp.: 6
Fiscal Year-end: 12/31/22
Information Technology Services
N.A.I.C.S.: 541512
Wang Min (Pres)

YD YNVISIBLE, S.A.
Rua Mouzinho de Albuquerque 7, Cartaxo, 2070-104, Santarem, Portugal
Tel.: (351) 24 310 3174
Web Site: http://www.ynvisible.com
Year Founded: 2010
Interactive Electrochromic Displays
N.A.I.C.S.: 334419
Antonio Camara (Chm)

YDA INSAAT SANAYI VE TICARET A.S.
Bayraktar Mahallesi Vedat Dalokay Caddesi No 112 G O P, Cankaya, Ankara, Turkiye
Tel.: (90) 31245944
YDATH—(IST)
Rev.: $1,991,473,334
Assets: $6,077,850,156
Liabilities: $4,001,047,147
Net Worth: $2,076,803,009
Earnings: $733,638,899
Fiscal Year-end: 12/31/21
Civil Engineering & Construction Services
N.A.I.C.S.: 541330
Huseyin Arslan (Chm)

AND PRIVATE COMPANIES

YDUQS PARTICIPACOES SA
Av das Americas Barra da Tijuca, Rio de Janeiro, 22.640-102, Brazil
Tel.: (55) 2133118926
Web Site:
http://www.estacioparticipacoes.com
YDUQ3—(BRAZ)
Rev.: $920,176,947,705
Assets: $1,660,248,431,937
Liabilities: $1,113,764,651,037
Net Worth: $546,483,780,900
Earnings: $27,645,375,644
Fiscal Year-end: 12/31/23
Secondary Educational Services
N.A.I.C.S.: 611310

YDX INNOVATION CORP.
Suite 2820 - 200 Granville Street, Vancouver, V6C 1S4, BC, Canada
Tel.: (604) 704-6466   BC
Web Site: https://www.sedarplus.ca
Year Founded: 2007
YDX—(OTCIQ)
Rev.: $1,864,051
Assets: $858,152
Liabilities: $2,104,011
Net Worth: ($1,245,860)
Earnings: ($1,978,823)
Fiscal Year-end: 12/31/19
Technology Services
N.A.I.C.S.: 541511
Daniel Cavalcanti Japiassu (CEO)

YE XING GROUP HOLDINGS LIMITED
Room 108 No 45 Xinrong North Street Xihongmen, Daxing District, Beijing, China   Ky
Web Site:
https://www.hongkunwuye.com
Year Founded: 2003
1941—(HKG)
Rev.: $47,270,298
Assets: $60,850,133
Liabilities: $28,191,460
Net Worth: $32,658,673
Earnings: ($1,903,245)
Emp.: 846
Fiscal Year-end: 12/31/23
Holding Company
N.A.I.C.S.: 551112
Chunying Zhang (CFO)

YEA SHIN INTERNATIONAL DEVELOPMENT CO., LTD.
12/F 25 Dunhua South Road, Taipei, Taiwan
Tel.: (886) 225789393
Web Site: http://www.yeashin.com
5213—(TPE)
Rev.: $91,732,514
Assets: $1,576,120,533
Liabilities: $1,267,606,979
Net Worth: $308,513,554
Earnings: $7,019,854
Emp.: 100
Fiscal Year-end: 12/31/22
Electric Equipment Mfr
N.A.I.C.S.: 334419
Lien-Ti Yao (Chm & Pres)

YEAH YEAH GROUP HOLDINGS LIMITED
17/F Fun Tower 35 Hung To Road, Kwun Tong, Kowloon, China (Hong Kong)
Tel.: (852) 29778082   Ky
Web Site: http://www.sig.hk
Year Founded: 2001
8082—(HKG)
Rev.: $4,559,145
Assets: $18,319,710
Liabilities: $10,665,503
Net Worth: $7,654,208
Earnings: ($7,980,480)
Emp.: 83

Fiscal Year-end: 12/31/22
Funeral Services
N.A.I.C.S.: 812210
Ki Chi Jip (CFO & Sec)
Subsidiaries:

Sage Funeral Services Limited   (1)
Shop N Cheong Lok Mansion 10 Malacca Street, Hung Hom, Kowloon, China (Hong Kong)
Tel.: (852) 24268082
Web Site: http://www.sagefuneral.com
Funeral Services
N.A.I.C.S.: 812210

YEAHKA LIMITED
6/F Block C3 Kexing Science Park, Nanshan District, Shenzhen, China   Ky
Web Site: https://www.yeahka.com
Year Founded: 2011
9923—(HKG)
Rev.: $546,990,613
Assets: $1,165,867,440
Liabilities: $803,466,992
Net Worth: $362,400,449
Earnings: $1,400,227
Emp.: 1,103
Fiscal Year-end: 12/31/23
Payment Services
N.A.I.C.S.: 522320
Cherie Po Man Mak (Sec)

YEAL ELECTRIC CO., LTD.
Tel.: (86) 43181709358
Web Site: http://www.yeal.cc
Year Founded: 1986
300923—(SSE)
Rev.: $59,337,856
Assets: $191,440,160
Liabilities: $30,964,630
Net Worth: $160,475,529
Earnings: $7,008,768
Fiscal Year-end: 12/31/22
Electrical Equipment Mfr & Distr
N.A.I.C.S.: 335999
Biao Li (Chm & Gen Mgr)

YEALINK NETWORK TECHNOLOGY CO.,LTD.
No 666 Hu'an Road High Tech Park, Huli District, Xiamen, 361009, China
Tel.: (86) 5925702000
Web Site: https://www.yealink.com
Year Founded: 2001
300628—(CHIN)
Rev.: $612,421,040
Assets: $1,251,483,955
Liabilities: $106,974,786
Net Worth: $1,144,509,169
Earnings: $283,140,121
Fiscal Year-end: 12/31/23
Video Conferencing Services
N.A.I.C.S.: 561499

YEARIMDANG PUBLISHING CO., LTD.
3F 153 Achasan-ro Seongsu-dong 2ga, Seongdong-gu, Seoul, 133-832, Korea (South)
Tel.: (82) 234048459
Year Founded: 1989
036000—(KRS)
Rev.: $20,227,713
Assets: $162,518,292
Liabilities: $19,047,979
Net Worth: $143,470,313
Earnings: ($6,827,833)
Emp.: 56
Fiscal Year-end: 12/31/22
Publisher Services
N.A.I.C.S.: 513199
Chun Ho Nah (Chm & CEO)

YEBOYETHU LTD.
Vodacom Corporate Park 082 Vodacom, Midrand, 1685, South Africa

Tel.: (27) 822410001
Web Site:
https://www.yeboyethu.co.za
Financial Management Services
N.A.I.C.S.: 522110
Zarina Bassa (Chm)

YECHIU METAL RECYCLING CHINA LTD.
No 388 Hutaixin Road, Taicang, 215434, Jiangsu, China
Tel.: (86) 51253703988
Web Site: http://www.yechiu.com
Year Founded: 2001
601388—(SHG)
Rev.: $1,075,437,829
Assets: $791,583,975
Liabilities: $197,969,490
Net Worth: $593,614,485
Earnings: $53,549,557
Fiscal Year-end: 12/31/22
Metal Product Recycling Services
N.A.I.C.S.: 331314
Chung Sheng Huang (Founder & Chm)
Subsidiaries:

America Metal Export, Inc.   (1)
1525 S Garfield Ave, Alhambra, CA 91801
Tel.: (626) 281-3000
Aluminum Material Mfr
N.A.I.C.S.: 331315

YeChiu Metal Smelting Sdn. Bhd.   (1)
Plo 37 472 and 474 Jalan Keluli, Kawasan Perindustrian Pasir Gudang, 81700, Pasir Gudang, Johor, Malaysia
Tel.: (60) 72518763
Aluminum Material Mfr
N.A.I.C.S.: 331315

YeChiu Non-Ferrous Metal (M) Sdn. Bhd.   (1)
Plo 28 Jalan Nibong 3, Kompleks Perindustrian Tanjung Langsat, 81700, Pasir Gudang, Johor, Malaysia
Tel.: (60) 72518763
Aluminum Material Mfr
N.A.I.C.S.: 331315

YEDITEPE FAKTORING A.S.
Buyukdere Cad Oyal Is Merkezi No 108/1 Kat 5-6 Esentepe, Sisli, Istanbul, Turkiye
Tel.: (90) 2122673333
Web Site:
http://www.yeditepefaktoring.com
Financial Management Services
N.A.I.C.S.: 551112

YEE HOP HOLDINGS LTD.
Unit 1104-06 Nan Fung Commercial Centre 19 Lam Lok Street, Kowloon Bay, China (Hong Kong)
Tel.: (852) 2 686 8713   Ky
Web Site: http://www.yee-hop.com.hk
1662—(HKG)
Rev.: $94,929,667
Assets: $113,227,802
Liabilities: $52,068,323
Net Worth: $61,159,478
Earnings: $5,096,258
Emp.: 398
Fiscal Year-end: 03/31/22
Holding Company
N.A.I.C.S.: 551112
Jackin Yin Kwan Jim (Co-Founder & Chm)
Subsidiaries:

Yee Hop Engineering Company Limited   (1)
Unit 1104-06 Nan Fung Commercial Centre 19 Lam Lok Street, Kowloon Bay, China (Hong Kong)
Tel.: (852) 26868713
Engineering Services
N.A.I.C.S.: 541330

YEEBO (INTERNATIONAL HOLDINGS) LIMITED

YEE LEE CORPORATION BHD.
Lot 85 Jalan Portland Tasek Industrial Estate, 31400, Ipoh, Perak Darul Ridzuan, Malaysia
Tel.: (60) 5 291 1055
Web Site: http://www.yeelee.com.my
Rev.: $270,001,690
Assets: $235,259,771
Liabilities: $83,435,423
Net Worth: $151,824,348
Earnings: $9,017,021
Fiscal Year-end: 12/31/18
Food Mfr
N.A.I.C.S.: 327213
Yin Fatt Chok (Exec Dir)
Subsidiaries:

Canpac Sdn Bhd   (1)
Lot 119 Taman Perindustrian Integrasi Jalan Bt Arang, Rawang, Selangor, Malaysia
Tel.: (60) 360929929
Web Site: http://www.canpac.com.my
Automobile Product Can Mfr
N.A.I.C.S.: 336110

Subsidiary (Non-US):

Canpac Vietnam Pte Ltd   (2)
Lot No 6 2a Street, Bien Hoa Industrial Zone 2, Bien Hoa, Dong nai, Vietnam
Tel.: (84) 61994216
Automobile Product Can Mfr
N.A.I.C.S.: 336110

Desa Tea Sdn Bhd   (1)
Locked Bag No 2, Ranau, 89309, Beranang, Sabah, Malaysia
Tel.: (60) 88879223
Tea Product Mfr & Distr
N.A.I.C.S.: 311920

Sabah Tea Resort Sdn Bhd   (1)
Lot 83 Block 1-6 Lorong Kilang D Jalan Kiang Kolombong, Sedoo Industrial Estate, Kota Kinabalu, Sabah, Malaysia
Tel.: (60) 88440882
Web Site: http://www.sabahtea.com.my
Tea Product Mfr & Distr
N.A.I.C.S.: 311920

South East Asia Paper Products Sdn Bhd   (1)
Lot 70428 Jalan Lahat Darul Ridzuan, 31500, Ipoh, Perak, Malaysia
Tel.: (60) 53224993
Fibreboard Mfr
N.A.I.C.S.: 321219
Remus Shai (Asst Gen Mgr)

Yee Lee Palm Oil Industries Sdn Bhd   (1)
Lot 9399 Bidor Darul Ridzuan, Bidor Industrial Estate, 35500, Ipoh, Perak, Malaysia
Tel.: (60) 54341481
Oil Product Distr
N.A.I.C.S.: 424720

Subsidiary (Domestic):

Sementra Plantations Sdn Bhd   (2)
Lot 9399 Bidor Darul Ridzuan, Bidor Industrial Estate, 35500, Ipoh, Perak, Malaysia
Tel.: (60) 54342888
Oil Product Distr
N.A.I.C.S.: 424720

Yee Lee Trading Co Sdn Bhd   (1)
Lot 85 Jalan Portland Darul Ridzuan, Tasek Industrial Estate, 31400, Ipoh, Perak, Malaysia
Tel.: (60) 52911055
Oil Product Distr
N.A.I.C.S.: 424720

YEEBO (INTERNATIONAL HOLDINGS) LIMITED
7th Floor On Tat Industrial Building 26 Wah Sing Street, Kwai Chung, New Territories, China (Hong Kong)
Tel.: (852) 29456800
Web Site: https://www.yeebo.com.hk
0259—(HKG)
Rev.: $163,371,356
Assets: $384,129,784
Liabilities: $62,716,267
Net Worth: $321,413,517
Earnings: $36,417,890

YEEBO (INTERNATIONAL HOLDINGS) LIMITED

Yeebo (International Holdings) Limited—(Continued)
Emp.: 14
Fiscal Year-end: 03/31/22
LCD Module Mfr
N.A.I.C.S.: 334419
Siu Keung Tsui *(VP-Product Dev, Sls & Mktg-Global Market)*

Subsidiaries:

Jiangmen Yeebo Electronic Technology Co., Ltd. (1)
Building No 308 Nanshan Road, Jiangmen, Guangdong, China
Tel.: (86) 7503866733
Electronic Components Distr
N.A.I.C.S.: 423690

Jiangmen Yeebo Semiconductor Co., Ltd. (1)
Building No 16 Gaosha Road, Bei Jin Industrial Development District, Jiangmen, 529030, Guangdong, China
Tel.: (86) 7503365188
Electronic Components Distr
N.A.I.C.S.: 423690

Shenzhen Yeebo Electronics Technology Co., Ltd. (1)
1-4/F No F Building the 3rd Industrial Area, Xin Wei Village Da Lang North Road Longhua New District, Shenzhen, Guangdong, China
Tel.: (86) 75521638783
Electronic Components Distr
N.A.I.C.S.: 423690

YEEDEX ELECTRONIC CORPORATION
4F No 170 Sec 2 Min Sheng E Rd, Taipei, Taiwan
Tel.: (886) 225063000
Web Site: https://www.yeedex.com.tw
Year Founded: 1999
7556—(TPE)
Rev.: $16,923,459
Assets: $30,675,515
Liabilities: $5,083,326
Net Worth: $25,592,190
Earnings: $4,075,603
Fiscal Year-end: 12/31/22
Electronic Components Distr
N.A.I.C.S.: 423690
James Chueh *(Pres)*

YEH-CHIANG TECHNOLOGY CORP.
7F Building E No 19-13 San-Chung Rd, Nan-gan District, Taipei, Taiwan
Tel.: (886) 226551166
Web Site: https://eng.yctc.com.tw
Year Founded: 1994
6124—(TPE)
Rev.: $65,424,976
Assets: $161,608,480
Liabilities: $48,901,354
Net Worth: $112,707,126
Earnings: $2,635,181
Emp.: 3,500
Fiscal Year-end: 12/31/22
Information Technology Services
N.A.I.C.S.: 541512
Tai-Kuang Wang *(Chm)*

Subsidiaries:

So Bright Electronics Co. ,Ltd. (1)
No 13 Shih 2nd Rd Youth Industrial Park, Yangmei Dist, Taoyuan, 32657, Taiwan
Tel.: (886) 34643215
Web Site: https://www.sobright-led.com.tw
LED Traffic Light Mfr
N.A.I.C.S.: 334413

YELLOW BALLOON TOUR CO., LTD.
Yellow Balloon Bldg 31 Supyo-Ro, Jung-Gu, Seoul, Korea (South)
Tel.: (82) 215442288
Web Site: http://www.ybtour.co.kr
Year Founded: 2001

104620—(KRS)
Rev.: $16,877,562
Assets: $71,330,617
Liabilities: $46,263,320
Net Worth: $25,067,297
Earnings: ($18,468,432)
Emp.: 367
Fiscal Year-end: 12/31/22
Travel Agency Services
N.A.I.C.S.: 561510
Bae Jiyoung *(Asst Mgr)*

YELLOW BRICK ROAD HOLDINGS LTD.
Level 11 1 Chifley Square, Sydney, 2000, NSW, Australia
Tel.: (61) 282268200
Web Site: http://www.ybr.com.au
YBR—(ASX)
Rev.: $191,933
Assets: $294,353
Liabilities: $269,498
Net Worth: $24,855
Earnings: ($52)
Fiscal Year-end: 06/30/24
Financial & Investment Services
N.A.I.C.S.: 525990
Mark Leigh Bouris *(Chm)*

Subsidiaries:

Loan Avenue Holding Pty. Ltd. (1)
Level 11 1 Chifley Square, Sydney, 2000, NSW, Australia
Tel.: (61) 1300562628
Web Site: https://www.loanave.com.au
Home Mortgage Loan Services
N.A.I.C.S.: 522310

Money Management Pty. Ltd. (1)
Level 11 4 Martin Place, Sydney, 2000, NSW, Australia
Tel.: (61) 299923300
Web Site: https://www.moneymanagement.com.au
Financial Management Services
N.A.I.C.S.: 523940

Vow Financial Pty. Ltd. (1)
Level 11 1 Chifley Square, Sydney, 2000, NSW, Australia
Tel.: (61) 1300730050
Web Site: https://www.vow.com.au
Home Mortgage Loan Services
N.A.I.C.S.: 522310

YELLOW CAKE PLC
3rd Floor Gaspe House 6672 The Esplanade, Saint Helier, JE1 1BL, Jersey
Tel.: (44) 1534885200
Web Site: https://www.yellowcakeplc.com
Year Founded: 2018
YLLXF—(OTCQX)
Assets: $1,037,260,000
Liabilities: $1,930,000
Net Worth: $1,035,330,000
Earnings: ($102,940,000)
Fiscal Year-end: 03/31/23
Uranium Mining Services
N.A.I.C.S.: 212290
Andre Liebenberg *(CEO)*

YELLOW HAT LTD.
1-7-4 Iwamotocho Yellow Hat Headquarters Building, Chuo-ku, Tokyo, 101-0032, Japan
Tel.: (81) 368661680
Web Site: https://www.yellowhat.jp
Year Founded: 1949
9882—(TKS)
Rev.: $969,297,010
Assets: $952,038,300
Liabilities: $181,827,880
Net Worth: $770,210,420
Earnings: $67,811,990
Emp.: 3,784
Fiscal Year-end: 03/31/24
Automobile Product Mfr & Distr

N.A.I.C.S.: 336360

YELLOW PAGES LIMITED
1751 Rue Richardson Suite 8300, Montreal, H3K 1G6, QC, Canada
Tel.: (514) 934-2611   Ca
Web Site: https://www.corporate.yp.ca
Y—(TSX)
Rev.: $260,920,107
Assets: $287,810,982
Liabilities: $264,889,395
Net Worth: $22,921,586
Earnings: $47,169,919
Emp.: 686
Fiscal Year-end: 12/31/20
Holding Company; Media Publishing, Marketing & Advertising Services
N.A.I.C.S.: 551112
Susan Kudzman *(Chm)*

Subsidiaries:

Canpages Inc. (1)
1 Innovation Place, 2700 Production Way Suite 500, Burnaby, V5A 0C2, BC, Canada
Tel.: (604) 421-8202
Web Site: http://www.canpages.ca
Emp.: 700
Print & Online Directories Publisher
N.A.I.C.S.: 513140

DataNational, Inc. (1)
4465 Brookfield Corporate Dr Ste 200, Chantilly, VA 20151-2107
Tel.: (703) 818-0120
Emp.: 80
Community & University Classified Directories Publishing
N.A.I.C.S.: 513140

Enquiro Search Solutions, Inc. (1)
1620 Dickson Ave Ste 410, Kelowna, V1Y 9Y2, BC, Canada
Tel.: (250) 861-5252
Web Site: http://www.enquiro.com
Sales Range: $10-24.9 Million
Emp.: 35
Search Engine Optimization
N.A.I.C.S.: 541890

Totem (1)
37 Front St E, Toronto, M5E 1B3, ON, Canada
Tel.: (416) 360-7339
Web Site: http://www.totem.tc
Sales Range: $10-24.9 Million
Emp.: 100
Publishing, Editorial, Research & Strategic Services
N.A.I.C.S.: 541820
James McNab *(Gen Mgr)*

Yellow Pages Digital & Media Solutions Limited (1)
1751 Rue Richardson Suite 8 300, Montreal, H3K 1G6, QC, Canada
Tel.: (514) 934-2611
Web Site: https://www.corporate.yp.ca
Media Streaming Distribution Services
N.A.I.C.S.: 541840

Yellow Pages Group Co. (1)
16 Place du Commerce, Verdun, H3E 2A5, QC, Canada
Tel.: (514) 934-2611
Web Site: http://www.ypg.com
Emp.: 2,000
Directory Publisher
N.A.I.C.S.: 513140

Division (Domestic):

Mediative (2)
14 Place du Commerce 5th Floor, Montreal, H3E 1T5, QC, Canada
Tel.: (800) 544-8614
Web Site: http://www.mediative.com
Emp.: 150
Digital Media Advertising
N.A.I.C.S.: 541890
Sarah Alvi *(Head-Fin)*

Yellow Pages Group, LLC (1)
1 Sentry Pkwy, Blue Bell, PA 19422
Tel.: (610) 825-7720
Web Site: http://www.yellowpagesgroup.com
Emp.: 50

INTERNATIONAL PUBLIC

Directory Publishing Services
N.A.I.C.S.: 513140

YELLOW POINT EQUITY PARTNERS
Suite 900 – 1285 West Pender Street, Vancouver, V6E 4B1, BC, Canada
Tel.: (604) 659-1874
Web Site: https://www.ypoint.ca
Investment Services
N.A.I.C.S.: 523999

Subsidiaries:

CIMS LP (1)
1610 Industrial Avenue, Port Coquitlam, V3C 6N8, BC, Canada
Tel.: (604) 472-4300
Web Site: https://cimsltd.com
Industrial Construction & Maintenance
N.A.I.C.S.: 236220

YELLOWHEAD INVESTMENTS CORPORATION
10220 - 184 Street, Edmonton, T5S 0B9, AB, Canada
Tel.: (780) 483-4024
Web Site: http://www.pointewesthonda.com
Year Founded: 1981
Rev.: $35,212,705
New & Used Car Dealers
N.A.I.C.S.: 441110
Denise Cyre *(Mgr-Cafe)*

YELLOWHEAD PETROLEUM PRODUCTS LTD
9023 24 St, Edmonton, T6P 1K9, AB, Canada
Tel.: (780) 449-1171
Rev.: $50,844,999
Emp.: 12
Oil & Gas Distr
N.A.I.C.S.: 424710
Bryan Bradley *(Owner)*

YELLOWKNIFE MOTORS LTD
4808 49th Avenue, Yellowknife, X1A 2N5, NT, Canada
Tel.: (867) 766-5000
Web Site: http://www.yellowknifemotors.com
Sales Range: $10-24.9 Million
Emp.: 26
Car Dealer
N.A.I.C.S.: 441110
Mark Winter *(Mgr-Parts)*

YELO BANK OJSC
30 Pushkin Str, Baku, AZ1010, Azerbaijan
Tel.: (994) 12981
Web Site: http://www.yelo.az
NKYBN—(BAK)
Rev.: $47,170,522
Assets: $473,220,908
Liabilities: $430,786,391
Net Worth: $42,434,516
Earnings: $3,310,377
Fiscal Year-end: 12/31/22
Commercial Banking Services
N.A.I.C.S.: 522110
Nikoloz Shurgaia *(Chm-Mgmt Bd)*

YEM CHIO CO., LTD.
No 397 Xingshan Road, Neihu Dist, Taipei, 114, Taiwan
Tel.: (886) 281706199
Web Site: https://www.ycgroup.tw
Year Founded: 1978
4306—(TAI)
Rev.: $432,444,995
Assets: $1,018,369,987
Liabilities: $602,812,692
Net Worth: $415,557,295
Earnings: $27,977,958
Emp.: 1,308

Fiscal Year-end: 12/31/23
Packaging Materials Mfr
N.A.I.C.S.: 326112
Johnny Chih Hsien Lee *(Chm & CEO)*

Subsidiaries:

ACHEM Opto-Electronic Corporation (1)
No 397 Xingshan Rd, Neihu Dist, Taipei, 114, Taiwan
Tel.: (886) 281706199
Web Site: https://www.achem.com.tw
Packaging Tape Mfr & Distr
N.A.I.C.S.: 322220

Achem Technology (Chengdu) Co., Ltd. (1)
No 139 South Road Shen Xian Shu High-Tech Zone, Chengdu, 610041, Sichuan, China
Tel.: (86) 2885625190
Plastic Material Mfr & Distr
N.A.I.C.S.: 325211

Achem Technology (Dongguan) Adhesive Product Co., Ltd. (1)
157 XinMing Road, JinXia Villiage ChangAn Town, Dongguan, 523852, Guangdong, China
Tel.: (86) 76985322701
Web Site: https://www.achemwonder.com
Plastic Material Mfr & Distr
N.A.I.C.S.: 325211

Achem Technology (M) Sdn. Bhd. (1)
44/46/48 Jalan Jasa Merdeka 1 Taman Datuk Tamby Chik Karim, Batu Berendam, Melaka, 75350, Malaysia
Tel.: (60) 63172611
Plastic Material Mfr & Distr
N.A.I.C.S.: 325211

Achem Technology (Ningbo) Co., Ltd. (1)
No 201 Huangshan West Road, Beilun, Ningbo, 315800, Zhejiang, China
Tel.: (86) 57486802588
Pressure Sensitive Adhesive Tape Mfr & Distr
N.A.I.C.S.: 322230

Achem Technology (Shanghai) Co., Ltd. (1)
1688 Fu Hai Rd, Jiading Industrial District, Shanghai, 201821, Guangdong, China
Tel.: (86) 2159163999
Plastic Material Mfr & Distr
N.A.I.C.S.: 325211

Achem Technology (Viet Nam) Co., Ltd. (1)
No 01 Vsip II A Street 15, Viet Nam Singapore Industrial Park II A Tan Uyen District, Ho Chi Minh City, Binh Duong, Vietnam
Tel.: (84) 2742220766
Plastic Material Mfr & Distr
N.A.I.C.S.: 325211

Foshan Inder Adhesive Product Co., Ltd. (1)
Wufeng 4th Road, Weidajiang Industrial Zone, Foshan, Guangdong, China
Tel.: (86) 75782210082
Web Site: https://www.inder.com.cn
Plastic Material Mfr & Distr
N.A.I.C.S.: 325211

Ningbo Yem Chio Co., Ltd. (1)
201 Huangshan West Road, Beilun, Ningbo, Zhejiang, China
Tel.: (86) 57486802588
Plastic Material Mfr & Distr
N.A.I.C.S.: 325211

Shaanxi Heyangder Adhesive Product Co., Ltd. (1)
17 Xinxi Street, Heyang, Weinan, 715321, Shanxi, China
Tel.: (86) 2982300706
Plastic Material Mfr & Distr
N.A.I.C.S.: 325211

Wanchio Adhesive Product (Jiangsu) Co., Ltd. (1)
No 1 Wanchio Road, Libao Town Haian County, Nantong, 226600, Jiangsu, China
Tel.: (86) 51380675999
Plastic Material Mfr & Distr
N.A.I.C.S.: 325211

Winda Opto-Electronic Co., Ltd. (1)
Shinan Road, Foshan Plastic Group Industrial zone Sanshui District, Foshan, 528136, Guangdong, China
Tel.: (86) 75787320000
Web Site: http://www.jinsucn.com
Plastic Plate & Sheet Mfr
N.A.I.C.S.: 326130

Wong Chio Land Development Co., Ltd. (1)
7th Floor No 397 Xingshan Road, Neihu District, Taipei, Taiwan
Tel.: (886) 281706199
Web Site: http://www.wongchio.com
Plastic Material Mfr & Distr
N.A.I.C.S.: 325211

Yem Chio Distribution Co., Ltd. (1)
6F No 397 Xingshan Rd, Neihu Dist, Taipei, 114, Taiwan
Tel.: (886) 281706199
Plastic Material Mfr & Distr
N.A.I.C.S.: 325211

YEMEN GULF BANK
Shawkani St, PO Box 100, Sana'a, Yemen
Tel.: (967) 1260823
Web Site: http://www.yg-bank.com
Emp.: 125
Banking Services
N.A.I.C.S.: 522110
Abdulqader Baker *(Head-Trade Fin)*

YEN BAI JOINT STOCK FOREST AGRICULTURAL PRODUCTS & FOODSTUFF COMPANY
No 279 Nguyen Phuc Street, Nguyen Phuc Ward, Yen Bai, Vietnam
Tel.: (84) 2163862278
Web Site: https://www.yfatuf.com.vn
CAP—(HNX)
Rev.: $61,138,800
Assets: $29,217,400
Liabilities: $2,716,300
Net Worth: $26,501,100
Earnings: $11,440,900
Fiscal Year-end: 09/30/23
Forest Product Processing Services
N.A.I.C.S.: 113210
Tran Cong Binh *(Member-Mgmt Bd)*

YEN SUN TECHNOLOGY CORP.
No 1002 Chengguan Rd, Renwu Dist, Kaohsiung, 814017, Taiwan
Tel.: (886) 73713588
Web Site: https://www.ystech.com.tw
Year Founded: 1987
6275—(TPE)
Rev.: $113,861,082
Assets: $93,052,903
Liabilities: $53,147,547
Net Worth: $39,905,356
Earnings: $6,078,886
Emp.: 1,000
Fiscal Year-end: 12/31/22
Electronic Cooling Product Mfr
N.A.I.C.S.: 333415
C. J. Chen *(Chm)*

Subsidiaries:

R.D.S Reprotech LTD. (1)
Efraim Katzir 12, Rehovot, Israel
Tel.: (972) 772041181
Web Site: https://www.reprotech.co.il
Electrical Equipment & Component Distr
N.A.I.C.S.: 423610

Y.S. Tech USA Inc. (1)
12691 Monarch St, Garden Grove, CA 92841
Web Site: http://www.ystechusa.com
Electrical Home Appliance Mfr
N.A.I.C.S.: 335210

YENBAI CEMENT & MINERALS JSC
Yen Binh Town, Hanoi, Yen Bai, Vietnam
Tel.: (84) 29 388 5154
Sales Range: $10-24.9 Million
Emp.: 506
Cement Mfr & Whslr
N.A.I.C.S.: 327310
Pham Quang Phu *(Chm)*

YENI GIMAT GAYRIMENKUL YATIRIM ORTAKLIGI A.S.
Mevlana Boulevard No 2/A Floor 3 No 1, Akkopru, Ankara, Turkiye
Tel.: (90) 3125411471
Web Site:
    https://www.yenigimatgyo.com.tr
Year Founded: 1993
YGGYO—(IST)
Rev.: $48,849,243
Assets: $451,640,455
Liabilities: $5,390,797
Net Worth: $446,249,658
Earnings: $254,538,584
Fiscal Year-end: 12/31/23
Real Estate Investment Services
N.A.I.C.S.: 523999
Okyay Kepenek *(Vice Chm, VP & Deputy Gen Mgr)*

YEONG GUAN ENERGY TECHNOLOGY GROUP CO., LTD.
4F No 93 Xinhu 1st Rd, Neihu Dist, Taipei, 114757, Taiwan
Tel.: (886) 227917198
Web Site: http://www.ygget.com
1589—(TAI)
Rev.: $283,560,897
Assets: $820,056,413
Liabilities: $534,652,454
Net Worth: $285,403,959
Earnings: ($9,036,953)
Emp.: 2,399
Fiscal Year-end: 12/31/23
Iron Casting Products & Injection Molding
N.A.I.C.S.: 331511
Chang Chun-Chi *(Gen Mgr)*

Subsidiaries:

Dong Guan Yeong Guan Mould Factory Co., Ltd. (1)
Yinquan Industrial District, Qingxi Town, Dongguan, Guan Dong, China
Tel.: (86) 57486229582
Wind Electric Power Generation Services
N.A.I.C.S.: 221115

Dongguan Yeong Guan Foundry Co., Ltd. (1)
Luomayinquan Industrial Park Qingxi Town, Dongguan, Guangdong, China
Tel.: (86) 76987739480
Graphite Product Mfr & Distr
N.A.I.C.S.: 327992

Jiang Su Bright Steel Fine Machinery Co., Ltd. (1)
No 9 Yue-Peng Rd, Tian Mu Hu Industry Zone, Liyang, Jiangsu, China
Tel.: (86) 57486229582
Wind Electric Power Generation Services
N.A.I.C.S.: 221115

Jiangsu Gangrui Precision Machinery Co., Ltd. (1)
9th Yuen Po Road Tianmuhu Industrial Park, Liyang, Jiangsu, China
Tel.: (86) 51980895588
Industrial Precision Product Mfr & Distr
N.A.I.C.S.: 332721

Ningbo Lulin Machine Tool Foundry Co., Ltd. (1)
No 28 DingHai Road, Zhenhai District, Ningbo, Zhejiang, China
Tel.: (86) 57486229582
Wind Electric Power Generation Services
N.A.I.C.S.: 221115

Ningbo Lulin Machinery Casting Co., Ltd. (1)
No 28 Dinghai Road Zhenhai Economic Development Zone, Ningbo, China
Tel.: (86) 57486275777
Graphite Product Mfr & Distr
N.A.I.C.S.: 327992

Ningbo Yeong Shang Casting Iron Co., Ltd. (1)
No 95 Huang Hai Rd, Beilun District, Ningbo, Zhejiang, China
Tel.: (86) 57486228866
Wind Electric Power Generation Services
N.A.I.C.S.: 221115

Ningbo Yeongxiang Casting Co., Ltd. (1)
No 1 Gangkou Road Xiaogang Beilun District, Ningbo, China
Tel.: (86) 57486229800
Graphite Product Mfr & Distr
N.A.I.C.S.: 327992

Ningbo Yonghexing Machinery Industry Co., Ltd. (1)
No 95 Huanghai Rd, Beilun District, Ningbo, China
Tel.: (86) 57486228866
Web Site: http://www.ygget.com
Emp.: 700
Industrial Precision Product Mfr & Distr
N.A.I.C.S.: 332721

Ningbo Yutian Renewable Resources Co., Ltd. (1)
No 373 DaTong Road Houhaitang Zhenhai Economic Development Zone, Ningbo, China
Tel.: (86) 57486264111
Chemical Product Mfr & Distr
N.A.I.C.S.: 325180

Shanghai No1 Machine Tool Foundry (Suzhou) Co., Ltd. (1)
No 999 Laixiu Rd, FOHO New and Hi-Tech Industrial Development Zone, Suzhou, Jiangsu, China
Tel.: (86) 57486229582
Wind Electric Power Generation Services
N.A.I.C.S.: 221115

Yeong Chen Asia Pacific Co., Ltd. (1)
No 502 Sec 1 Chenggong Rd, Guanyin Dist, Taoyuan, 328, Taiwan
Tel.: (886) 57486228866
Wind Electric Power Generation Services
N.A.I.C.S.: 221115

Yeongcheng Asia-Pacific Limited (1)
No 502 1st Sestion of Chenggong Road Guanyin Industrial Zone, Taoyuan, Taiwan
Tel.: (886) 34839216
Turbine Machinery Mfr & Distr
N.A.I.C.S.: 333611

YEONG HWA METAL CO., LTD.
363-6 Namyang-dong Namui-ro 57, Jinhae-gu, Changwon, Gyeongnam, Korea (South)
Tel.: (82) 555517500
Web Site: http://www.yeonghwa.co.kr
Year Founded: 1977
012280—(KRS)
Rev.: $218,480,596
Assets: $169,306,764
Liabilities: $121,215,057
Net Worth: $48,091,708
Earnings: $360,042
Emp.: 375
Fiscal Year-end: 12/31/22
Industrial Machinery & Automotive Parts Mfr
N.A.I.C.S.: 333248
Dong Yeoun Choi *(Pres & CEO)*

Subsidiaries:

Yeong Hwa Metal Co., Ltd. - Plant 2 (1)
382-2 Namyang-dong 15 Namyeong-ro 552 Gil, Jinhae-gu, Changwon, Gyeongsangnam-do, Korea (South)
Tel.: (82) 55 547 8110
Automotive Casting Mfr

YEONG HWA METAL CO., LTD.

Yeong Hwa Metal Co., Ltd.—(Continued)
N.A.I.C.S.: 331511

YEOU YIH STEEL CO., LTD.
No 2 Yong Gong 10th Road, Yong An District, Kaohsiung, 82841, Taiwan
Tel.: (886) 76225616
Web Site:
https://www.yeouyih.com.tw
Year Founded: 1996
9962—(TPE)
Rev.: $110,396,398
Assets: $46,733,327
Liabilities: $9,124,285
Net Worth: $37,609,042
Earnings: $6,661,383
Emp.: 100
Fiscal Year-end: 12/31/22
Metal Products Mfr
N.A.I.C.S.: 331110
Sen-Tong Liu (Chm)

YEREVAN FACTORY OF CHAMPAGNE WINES OJSC
20 Tbilisyan Highway, Yerevan, 0052, Armenia
Tel.: (374) 10285476
Web Site:
http://www.armchampagne.am
Year Founded: 1939
ESHG—(ARM)
Sales Range: Less than $1 Million
Wine Product Mfr
N.A.I.C.S.: 312130

YEREVAN JEWELLERY FACTORY - 1 GNOMON OJSC
12 Arshakunyats Ave, Yerevan, 0023, Armenia
Tel.: (374) 10525321
Web Site: http://www.yerjewel.com
Year Founded: 1950
EVG1—(ARM)
Sales Range: Less than $1 Million
Jewelry Product Mfr
N.A.I.C.S.: 339910
Emil Grigoryan (Gen Dir)

YES BANK LTD.
Final Plot No 61A of TPS V CTS 34 Yes Bank House, Prabhat Nagar Off Western Express Highway Santacruz - East, Mumbai, 400055, Maharashtra, India
Web Site: http://www.yesbank.in
532648—(BOM)
Rev.: $3,216,445,345
Assets: $42,587,870,523
Liabilities: $37,705,887,932
Net Worth: $4,881,982,591
Earnings: $88,222,361
Emp.: 27,517
Fiscal Year-end: 03/31/22
Commercial Banking Services
N.A.I.C.S.: 522110
Shivanand R. Shettigar (Pres-Grp, Compliance Officer & Sec)

Subsidiaries:

YES Asset Management (India) Limited (1)
602 B 6th Floor One International Center 1 and 2, Senapati Bapat Marg Elphinstone West, Mumbai, 400013, India
Tel.: (91) 180030003060
Web Site: http://www.yesamc.in
Financial Investment Services
N.A.I.C.S.: 523999
Kanwar Vivek (CEO)

Yes Securities (India) Limited (1)
Tel.: (91) 2265078127
Web Site: https://www.yesinvest.in
Financial Investment Services
N.A.I.C.S.: 523999

YES OPTOELECTRONICS CO., LTD.
No 288 Yueling Road, Lishan District, Anshan, 114044, Liaoning, China
Tel.: (86) 4125291245
Web Site: https://www.yes-lcd.com
Year Founded: 2012
002952—(SSE)
Rev.: $124,209,226
Assets: $176,525,327
Liabilities: $45,646,876
Net Worth: $130,878,451
Earnings: $17,064,048
Emp.: 1,700
Fiscal Year-end: 12/31/22
Electronic Components Mfr
N.A.I.C.S.: 334419
Jitao Jia (Chm & Pres)

YES24 CO., LTD.
ILSIN building F5-6 11 Eunhaeng-ro, Yeongdeungpo-Gu, Seoul, Korea (South)
Tel.: (82) 232159100 KR
Web Site: https://www.yes24.com
Year Founded: 1999
053280—(KRS)
Rev.: $509,112,600
Assets: $297,320,744
Liabilities: $156,474,790
Net Worth: $140,845,954
Earnings: $674,803
Emp.: 497
Fiscal Year-end: 12/31/22
Online Shopping
N.A.I.C.S.: 449210
Sang Il Cho (Dir)

YESASIA HOLDINGS LTD.
5/F KC100 100 Kwai Cheong Road Kwai Chung New Territories, Hong Kong, China (Hong Kong)
Tel.: (852) 27860817 HK
Web Site:
https://www.yesasiaholdings.com
Year Founded: 1997
2209—(HKG)
Rev.: $128,592,000
Assets: $63,722,000
Liabilities: $36,585,000
Net Worth: $27,137,000
Earnings: ($6,782,000)
Emp.: 489
Fiscal Year-end: 12/31/22
Holding Company
N.A.I.C.S.: 551112
Curtis Sai Cheong Ng (CFO)

Subsidiaries:

AsianBeautyWholesale (Hong Kong) Limited (1)
KC100 5/F 100 Kwai Cheong Rd, Kwai Chung, China (Hong Kong)
Tel.: (852) 27467062
Web Site:
https://www.asianbeautywholesale.com
Beauty Care Services
N.A.I.C.S.: 812112

YesStyle.com Limited (1)
KC100 5/F 100 Kwai Cheong Rd, Kwai Chung, China (Hong Kong)
Tel.: (852) 27860817
Web Site: https://www.yesstyle.com
Beauty Care Services
N.A.I.C.S.: 812112

YESCO HOLDINGS CO., LTD
LS Yongsan Tower 92 Hangangdaero, Yongsan-Gu, Seoul, 04386, Korea (South)
Tel.: (82) 233903010
Web Site: http://www.lsyesco.co.kr
Year Founded: 1980
015360—(KRS)
Rev.: $1,128,617,999
Assets: $1,143,899,045
Liabilities: $745,412,892

Net Worth: $398,486,153
Earnings: ($7,642,824)
Emp.: 39
Fiscal Year-end: 12/31/22
Natural Gas Distr
N.A.I.C.S.: 221210
Bon Hyeok Gu (CEO)

YESIL GAYRIMENKUL YATIRIM ORTAKLIGI AS
Yilanli Ayazma Yolu No 15 Yesil Plaza K 18 Cevizlibag, 34020, Istanbul, Turkiye
Tel.: (90) 2127093745
Web Site: https://www.yesilgyo.com.tr
Year Founded: 1997
YGYO—(IST)
Rev.: $16,830,918
Assets: $144,652,043
Liabilities: $99,533,193
Net Worth: $45,118,850
Earnings: $59,954,350
Fiscal Year-end: 12/31/22
Real Estate Investment Services
N.A.I.C.S.: 531390
Yasar Altiparmak (Chm)

YESIL YAPI ENDUSTRISI AS
Yilanli Ayazma Yolu No 15 Kat 12 Yesil Plaza Topkapi, Istanbul, Turkiye
Tel.: (90) 2124821110
Web Site: https://www.yyapi.com.tr
Year Founded: 1979
YYAPI—(IST)
Rev.: $292,754
Assets: $102,222,709
Liabilities: $39,030,185
Net Worth: $63,192,524
Earnings: $26,474,945
Fiscal Year-end: 12/31/23
Building Construction Services
N.A.I.C.S.: 236220
Kamil Engin Yesil (Chm)

YESIL YATIRIM HOLDING AS
Yilanli Ayazma Yolu No 17 Kat 14 Yesil Plaza Topkapi, Istanbul, Turkiye
Tel.: (90) 2124830107
Web Site:
https://www.yesilyatirimholding.com
YESIL—(IST)
Sales Range: Less than $1 Million
Holding Company
N.A.I.C.S.: 551112
Alaittin Silaydin (Chm)

YEST CO., LTD.
654 Samnam-ro Jinwi-myeon, Pyeongtaek, Gyeonggi-do, Korea (South)
Tel.: (82) 316123337
Web Site: http://www.yest.co.kr
122640—(KRS)
Rev.: $58,287,214
Assets: $145,530,834
Liabilities: $82,645,423
Net Worth: $62,885,411
Earnings: ($4,011,043)
Emp.: 254
Fiscal Year-end: 12/31/22
Semiconductor Equipment Mfr
N.A.I.C.S.: 334413
Dong-Bok Jang (CEO)

YESTAR HEALTHCARE HOLDINGS COMPANY LIMITED
F8 Block A Green Land Building No 58 Xin Jian E Rd, Minhang District, Shanghai, 201199, China
Tel.: (86) 2164890111
Web Site: http://www.yestarcorp.com
2393—(HKG)
Rev.: $602,875,073
Assets: $473,098,158
Liabilities: $521,095,162
Net Worth: ($47,997,004)
Earnings: ($143,291,398)

Emp.: 909
Fiscal Year-end: 12/31/22
Investment Services
N.A.I.C.S.: 523999
Hartono James (Chm & CEO)

Subsidiaries:

Guangzhou HongEn Medical Diagnostic Technologies Company limited (1)
Rm 4102 Fuli Center No 10 Huaxia Road, Tian He Area, Guangzhou, China
Tel.: (86) 862087358472
Medical Equipment Distr
N.A.I.C.S.: 423450

Guangzhou Sheng Shi Yuan Trading Company limited (1)
4F No 51 1850 Creative Park 200 Fangcundadao, Liwan Area, Guangzhou, China
Tel.: (86) 2037885567
Medical Equipment Distr
N.A.I.C.S.: 423450

Shenzhen De Run Li Jia Company limited (1)
M N 3F TongTai Tower 422 Baguasi Road, Shenzhen, China
Tel.: (86) 75582443765
Medical Equipment Distr
N.A.I.C.S.: 423450

Yestar Biotech (Jiangsu) Co., Ltd. (1)
7th Floor International Outsourcing AB Building Block 301, Hanzhong Gate Avenue, Nanjing, China
Tel.: (86) 2586981998
Medical Equipment Distr
N.A.I.C.S.: 423450

YEW SANG HONG LIMITED
13-14/F Hing Yip Centre 37 Beech Street, Tai Kok Tsui, Kowloon, China (Hong Kong)
Tel.: (852) 2407 3333
Year Founded: 1954
Emp.: 10
Electrical Engineering Contract Services
N.A.I.C.S.: 238210
Stephen Lai (Mgr)

Subsidiaries:

Yew Sang Hong Trading (China) Limited (1)
Unit B 64 Yipkwong Indust Bldg 39-41 Beech St, Tai Kok Tsui, Kowloon, China (Hong Kong)
Tel.: (852) 24083333
Emp.: 8
Electrical Materials Whslr
N.A.I.C.S.: 423830
Bonitus Kong (Mgr)

Yew Sang Hong Trading Limited (1)
Unit B 6th Fl Hip Twong Indus Bld 39-41 Beech St, Tai Kok Tsui, Kowloon, China (Hong Kong)
Tel.: (852) 24083333
Web Site: http://www.ysh.com.hk
Electrical Goods Distr
N.A.I.C.S.: 423610

YFC-BONEAGLE ELECTRIC CO., LTD.
12-9 130 Lane, Chungshan East Road Section 2, 32749, Taoyuan, Taiwan
Tel.: (886) 3 477 8846
Web Site: http://www.cables.com.tw
Year Founded: 1983
Silo Mfr
N.A.I.C.S.: 332618
Yeh Chun-Jung (Pres)

Subsidiaries:

Monoprice, Inc. (1)
1 Pointe Dr 4th Fl, Brea, CA 92821 (100%)
Tel.: (877) 271-2592
Web Site: http://www.monoprice.com

AND PRIVATE COMPANIES — YG-1 CO., LTD

Sales Range: $125-149.9 Million
Cables, Components & Accessories for Computers & Consumer Electronics Mfr
N.A.I.C.S.: 334118
Bernard W. Luthi *(CEO)*

YFG BERHAD
E-3-6 Block E Pacific Place Commercial Centre, Jalan PJU 1A/4 Ara Damansara, Petaling Jaya, 47301, Selangor Darul Ehsan, Malaysia
Tel.: (60) 37832 6393
Web Site: http://www.yfg.my
Rev.: $823,170
Assets: $11,344,673
Liabilities: $34,656,569
Net Worth: ($23,311,896)
Earnings: ($3,474,020)
Fiscal Year-end: 09/30/18
Engineering & Mechanical Services
N.A.I.C.S.: 541330
Joseph Ha Thien Sen Noel *(CEO & Exec Dir)*

Subsidiaries:

Ocean Electrical Co. Sdn. Bhd. (1)
41 Jalan Utara 4 Kawasan Perusahaan Mergong Jalan Tunku Abdul Rahman, 05050, Alor Setar, Kedah Darul Aman, Malaysia
Tel.: (60) 47313929
Web Site: http://www.oceanelect.com
Sales Range: $25-49.9 Million
Emp.: 100
Electrical & Mechanical Engineering Services
N.A.I.C.S.: 541330
Lim Eng Cheik *(Gen Mgr)*

P.J. Indah Sdn. Bhd. (1)
Wisma PJI No 17 & 19 Jalan Astaka U8/83 Sekyen U8, 40150, Shah Alam, Selangor, Malaysia
Tel.: (60) 378448888
Web Site: http://www.pjindah.com.my
Sales Range: $25-49.9 Million
Emp.: 56
Electrical & Mechanical Engineering Services
N.A.I.C.S.: 541330

YFM EQUITY PARTNERS LLP
5th Floor Valiant Building 14 South Parade, Leeds, LS1 5QS, United Kingdom
Tel.: (44) 113 244 1000   UK
Web Site: http://www.yfmep.com
Holding Company; Private Equity Investment Services
N.A.I.C.S.: 551112
Paul Cook *(Partner, COO & Officer-Compliance)*

Subsidiaries:

YFM Private Equity Limited (1)
5th Floor Valiant Building 14 South Parade, Leeds, LS1 5QS, United Kingdom
Tel.: (44) 113 244 1000
Web Site: http://www.yfmep.com
Private Equity Equity Firm
N.A.I.C.S.: 523999
David Hall *(Partner & Mng Dir)*

Joint Venture (Domestic):

Indigo Telecom Group Limited (2)
102 Wales One Business Park, Magor, NP26 3DG, Monmouthshire, United Kingdom
Tel.: (44) 1291435500
Web Site: http://www.indigotg.com
Management & Maintenance of Telecommunication Network
N.A.I.C.S.: 517810
Mark Orchart *(Dir-Grp Product & Bid)*

YFY, INC.
51 Sec 2 Chung Ching South Road, Taipei, Taiwan
Tel.: (886) 0223968020
Web Site: http://www.yfy.com
Year Founded: 1926
1907—(TAI)
Rev.: $2,415,624,161
Assets: $4,721,953,254
Liabilities: $2,299,663,277
Net Worth: $2,422,289,977
Earnings: $68,685,664
Emp.: 12,059
Fiscal Year-end: 12/31/23
Paper Mfr & Paper Processing Machinery Designer & Mfr
N.A.I.C.S.: 322220
Huey-Ching Yeh *(Chm)*

Subsidiaries:

Arizon RFID Technology Co., Ltd. (1)
No 88 Wuzhou East Road, Economic Development Zone, Yangzhou, 225101, Jiangsu, China
Tel.: (86) 51480972024
Web Site: https://www.arizonrfid.com
Laundry Tag & Washable Label Mfr
N.A.I.C.S.: 323111

Ensilience Co., Ltd. (1)
9th Floor No 51 Section 2 Chongqing South Road, Taipei, Taiwan
Tel.: (886) 223968020
Web Site: https://www.yfyesl.com.tw
Power Generation Services
N.A.I.C.S.: 562213

Guangdong Dingfung Pulp & Paper Co., Ltd. (1)
Nanjie Street, Guangning County, Zhaoqing, 526300, Guangdong, China
Tel.: (86) 7588659000
Web Site: https://www.gddfpaper.com
Wood Pulp Mfr
N.A.I.C.S.: 322110

YG ENTERTAINMENT INC.
7 Huiujeong-ro 1-gil, Mapo-gu, Seoul, Korea (South)
Tel.: (82) 231421104
Web Site: https://www.ygfamily.com
Year Founded: 1998
122870—(KRS)
Rev.: $300,030,851
Assets: $546,773,208
Liabilities: $143,110,270
Net Worth: $403,662,938
Earnings: $35,876,147
Emp.: 415
Fiscal Year-end: 12/31/22
Music Publisher; Artist Management Services
N.A.I.C.S.: 512230
Hwang Bo Kyung *(Chief Admin Officer)*

YG PLUS INC.
10 Gukjegeumyung-ro 19th Floor, Yeongdeungpo-gu, Seoul, 07326, Gyeonggi-do, Korea (South)
Tel.: (82) 231404600
Web Site: https://www.ygplus.com
Year Founded: 1996
037270—(KRS)
Rev.: $107,549,596
Assets: $185,132,243
Liabilities: $62,853,138
Net Worth: $122,279,105
Earnings: $12,803,046
Emp.: 113
Fiscal Year-end: 12/31/22
Advetising Agency
N.A.I.C.S.: 541810
Seok-Gyu Hong *(Chm)*

Subsidiaries:

C & Marketing Services Inc. (1)
25th Floor Glass Tower 946-1 Daechi-Dong, Gangnam-Gu, Seoul, 135-798, Korea (South)
Tel.: (82) 2 3404 2800
Web Site: http://www.cnms.co.kr
Marketing Consulting Services
N.A.I.C.S.: 541613

Greenworks Co., Ltd. (1)
Kuojian Rd 1-18 12F, Cheng-Chen Dist, Kaohsiung, 80672, Taiwan
Tel.: (886) 78413105
Web Site: https://www.green-works.com.tw
Waste Water Treatment Services
N.A.I.C.S.: 221320

YG Investment Inc. (1)
10 Gukjegeumyung-ro 19th Floor Yeouido-dong Three IFC, Yeongdeungpo-gu, 07326, Seoul, Korea (South)
Tel.: (82) 231404670
Web Site: https://www.yg-investment.com
Information Technology Solutions Services
N.A.I.C.S.: 541519
Han Sang Bong *(CEO)*

YG-1 CO., LTD
13-40 Songdogwahak-ro 16beon-gil, Yeonsu-gu, Incheon, 21984, Korea (South)
Tel.: (82) 325260909
Web Site: https://brand.yg1.solutions
Year Founded: 1982
019210—(KRS)
Rev.: $421,697,129
Assets: $721,645,043
Liabilities: $461,019,626
Net Worth: $260,625,417
Earnings: $25,640,040
Emp.: 1,642
Fiscal Year-end: 12/31/22
Cutting Tools Mfr & Sales
N.A.I.C.S.: 333515
Ho-Keun Song *(Founder, Chm & CEO)*

Subsidiaries:

Minicut International. Inc. (1)
8400 Boulevard du Golf Anjou, Montreal, H1J 3A1, QC, Canada
Tel.: (514) 352-6464
Web Site: https://www.minicut.com
Aircraft & Metalworking Mfr
N.A.I.C.S.: 336411

National Tool Hardening Inc. (1)
217 Boulevard Industriel, Chateauguay, J6J 4Z2, QC, Canada
Tel.: (514) 325-3300
Web Site: https://www.nthi.com
Tool Heating Treatment Services
N.A.I.C.S.: 332811

New Sankyo Tool Co., Ltd. (1)
4074 Sue Ayagawa-Cho, Ayauta Gun, Takamatsu, Kagawa-ken, Japan
Tel.: (81) 878761155
Web Site: https://www.newsankyo-tool.co.jp
Emp.: 26
Cutting Tool Mfr & Distr
N.A.I.C.S.: 333519

Qingdao New Century Tool Co., Ltd. (1)
No 3 New York Qingdao Free-trade zone, Qingdao, China   (100%)
Tel.: (86) 53286769779
Web Site: https://www.qnct.cn
Cutting Tool Mfr
N.A.I.C.S.: 333515
Shihan Song *(Pres)*

Qingdao Yg-1 Tool Co., Ltd. (1)
NO 2425 Chaoyangshan Road, Huangdao District, Qingdao, China
Tel.: (86) 53285197366
Cutting Tool Mfr & Distr
N.A.I.C.S.: 333519

REGAL CUTTING TOOLS. INC (1)
5330 E Rockton Rd, Roscoe, IL 61073
Web Site: http://www.regalcuttingtools.com
Emp.: 60
Metal Cutting Tool Mfr
N.A.I.C.S.: 333517

YG Cutting Tool Corp. (1)
Plot No 2C KIADB Industrial Area Phase III Doddaballapura, Obadenahalli, Bengaluru, 561203, Karnataka, India
Tel.: (91) 8022044611
Cutting Tool Mfr & Distr
N.A.I.C.S.: 333519
Y. G. Sameer *(Reg Mgr)*

YG-1 (Hong Kong) LIMITED (1)
Unit B 44 Golden Bear Industrial Centre 66-82 Chai Wan Kok Street, Tsuen Wan, New Territories, China (Hong Kong)
Tel.: (852) 24399018
Emp.: 8
Cutting Tool Mfr
N.A.I.C.S.: 333517
Tony To *(Gen Mgr)*

YG-1 (THAILAND) CO, LTD (1)
88 Nimitkul Building 5th Floor Soi Rama IX 57/1 Suanluang, Suanluang, Bangkok, 10250, Thailand
Tel.: (66) 23704945
Emp.: 7
Cutting Tool Distr
N.A.I.C.S.: 423830

YG-1 AUSTRALIA PTY. LTD (1)
Unit 11 42-44 Garden Boulevard, Dingley Village, Kingston, 3172, VIC, Australia
Tel.: (61) 3 9558 0177
Web Site: http://www.yg1.co.kr
Cutting Tool Distr
N.A.I.C.S.: 423830

YG-1 CANADA INC. (1)
3375 North Service Road Unit A8, Burlington, L7N 3G2, ON, Canada
Tel.: (905) 335-2500
Emp.: 5
Cutting Tool Supplier
N.A.I.C.S.: 423830

YG-1 CORPORATION TRADING SRL (1)
Bucharest str Serg Pantaru Ion nr 1 ap 2 sector 2, Bucharest, Romania
Tel.: (40) 212525501
Cutting Tool Distr
N.A.I.C.S.: 423830

YG-1 Co., Ltd - Ansan Plant (1)
201 Byeolm ang-ro, Danwon-gu, Ansan, Gyeonggi-do, Korea (South)
Tel.: (82) 31 499 9545
Web Site: http://www.yg1.co.kr
Machine Tools Mfr
N.A.I.C.S.: 333517

YG-1 Co., Ltd - Gwangju Plant (1)
621-4 Dochun-dong, Gwangsan-gu, Gwangju, Korea (South)
Tel.: (82) 62 951 9212
Web Site: http://www.yg1.co.kr
Machine Tools Mfr
N.A.I.C.S.: 333517

YG-1 Co., Ltd - Incheon Plant (1)
68 Cheongcheon-dong, Pupyoung-gu, Incheon, 403-030, Korea (South)
Tel.: (82) 32 526 0909
Emp.: 30
Machine Tools Mfr
N.A.I.C.S.: 333517
V. J. Lee *(Gen Mgr)*

YG-1 Co., Ltd. - Cheongcheon 2 Plant (1)
19 Pyeongcheon-ro 37beon-gil, Bupyeong-gu, Incheon, 21301, Korea (South)
Tel.: (82).327136700
Cutting Tool Mfr & Distr
N.A.I.C.S.: 333519

YG-1 Co., Ltd. - Chungju Plant (1)
68 Chungjusandan 3-ro, Chungju, 27325, Chungcheongbuk-do, Korea (South)
Tel.: (82) 437225900
Cutting Tool Mfr & Distr
N.A.I.C.S.: 333519

YG-1 DEUTSCHLAND GMBH (1)
Rudolf-Diese-Str12b, 20537, Eschborn, Germany
Tel.: (49) 617396670
Web Site: https://yg-1.de
Machine Cutting Tool Mfr
N.A.I.C.S.: 333517

YG-1 EUROPE SAS (1)
Parc de l'Esplanade BAT B1.1 Rue Enrico Fermi, 77400, Saint-Thibault-des-Vignes, France
Tel.: (33) 172844070
Emp.: 22
Cutting Tool Mfr
N.A.I.C.S.: 333515
Bon Koo *(Gen Mgr)*

YG-1 INDUSTRIES INDIA PVT. LTD (1)

YG-1 CO., LTD

YG-1 Co., Ltd—(Continued)
A-306 Road No 32 Wagle Industrial Estate, 400 604, Thane, India
Tel.: (91) 2225804059
Web Site: http://www.yg1.co.kr
Cutting Tool Mfr
N.A.I.C.S.: 333515

YG-1 JAPAN (1)
Shinosaka No 2 Doi Bldg 2-14-6 Nishinaka-jima, Yodogawa-Ku, Osaka, 532-0011, Japan
Tel.: (81) 663059897
Emp.: 6
Machine Tools Mfr
N.A.I.C.S.: 333517
Toyokazu Kitaoka *(Mgr)*

YG-1 POLAND SP. Z.O.O (1)
ul Gogolinska 29, 02-872, Warsaw, Poland
Tel.: (48) 226222587
Web Site: https://www.yg-1.pl
Emp.: 15
Industrial Cutting Tool Mfr
N.A.I.C.S.: 333515

YG-1 Rus LLC (1)
Nobel Str 1 Skolkovo Innovation Center, 143026, Moscow, Russia
Tel.: (7) 4991107106
Cutting Tool Mfr & Distr
N.A.I.C.S.: 333519

YG-1 TOOLS ASIA PTE. LTD (1)
Block 3007 Ubi Road 1 02-416, Singapore, 408701, Singapore
Tel.: (65) 6842 0468
Emp.: 4
Industrial Machine Tool Distr
N.A.I.C.S.: 423830

YGGDRAZIL GROUP PUBLIC COMPANY LIMITED
348 Soi Ladprao 94 Punjamitr, Phlap-phla Wangthonglang, Bangkok, 10310, Thailand
Tel.: (66) 29344364 TH
Web Site: https://www.ygg-cg.com
Year Founded: 2006
YGG—(THA)
Rev.: $9,194,887
Assets: $20,115,019
Liabilities: $1,942,142
Net Worth: $18,172,877
Earnings: $2,027,966
Emp.: 200
Fiscal Year-end: 12/31/23
Advertising Agency Services
N.A.I.C.S.: 541840
Tanat Juwiwat *(Co-Founder & CEO)*

YGL CONVERGENCE BERHAD
35 Scotland Road, 10450, Penang, Malaysia
Tel.: (60) 42290619 MY
Web Site: https://www.yglworld.com
Year Founded: 1993
YGL—(KLS)
Rev.: $2,502,058
Assets: $4,577,829
Liabilities: $1,313,524
Net Worth: $3,264,305
Earnings: $93,197
Fiscal Year-end: 03/31/24
Software Solutions Services
N.A.I.C.S.: 541511
Kong Chean Yeap *(CEO)*

Subsidiaries:

Ai Solar Sdn. Bhd. (1)
Wisma UOA II Jalan Pinang, 50450, Kuala Lumpur, Malaysia
Tel.: (60) 321665928
Web Site: https://www.aisolar.my
Solar Energy Distribution Services
N.A.I.C.S.: 221122

YGM TRADING LTD
22 Tai Yau Street San Po Kong, Kow-loon, China (Hong Kong)
Tel.: (852) 23511111
Web Site: https://www.ygmtrading.com
0375—(HKG)
Rev.: $27,883,025
Assets: $89,081,585
Liabilities: $16,991,051
Net Worth: $72,090,533
Earnings: ($1,506,744)
Emp.: 400
Fiscal Year-end: 03/31/21
Apparel & Accessories Mfr & Sales
N.A.I.C.S.: 424350
Samuel Wing Sun Chan *(Chm)*

Subsidiaries:

Hong Kong Security Printing Limited (1)
8/F 20 Tai Yau Street Security Printing House, San Po Kong, Kowloon, China (Hong Kong)
Tel.: (852) 27269288
Web Site: http://www.hksp.net
Security Printing Services
N.A.I.C.S.: 323111

Luk Hop Garments Limited (1)
22-24 Tai Yau St, San Po Kong, Kowloon, China (Hong Kong)
Tel.: (852) 23200251
Web Site: http://www.hkgbusiness.com
Garments Mfr
N.A.I.C.S.: 315120

Michel Rene Limited (1)
3 F 22 Tai Yau St, San Po Kong, Kowloon, China (Hong Kong)
Tel.: (852) 23511111
Web Site: http://www.michelrene.com.hk
Garments Whslr
N.A.I.C.S.: 458110

YGM Advertising (1)
3 F 22 Tai Yau St San Po Kong, Kowloon, China (Hong Kong)
Tel.: (852) 23200251
Advertising Services
N.A.I.C.S.: 541810

YGM Clothing Limited (1)
3/F 22 Tai Yau Street, San Po Kong, Kow-loon, China (Hong Kong) (100%)
Tel.: (852) 23543731
Web Site: http://www.ygmclothing.com
Emp.: 1,000
Garments Whslr
N.A.I.C.S.: 424350

YGM Fashion Limited (1)
3 F 22 Tai Yau St San Po Kong, Kowloon, China (Hong Kong)
Tel.: (852) 23511111
Apparel Whslr
N.A.I.C.S.: 458110
William Fu *(Mgr)*

YGM Marketing Limited (1)
No 22 Tai Yau Street, San Po Kong, Kow-loon, China (Hong Kong)
Tel.: (852) 23200251
Web Site: http://www.ygmtrading.com
Garments Whslr & Retailer
N.A.I.C.S.: 424350

YGSOFT INC.
Yuanguang Intelligent Industrial Park No 23 Keji 2nd Road, Zhuhai, 519085, Guangdong, China
Tel.: (86) 7566298628
Web Site: https://www.ygsoft.com
Year Founded: 2001
002063—(SSE)
Rev.: $298,317,483
Assets: $550,798,916
Liabilities: $84,266,690
Net Worth: $466,532,226
Earnings: $45,299,442
Fiscal Year-end: 12/31/22
Software Development Services
N.A.I.C.S.: 513210
Chen Li Hao *(Chm)*

YH ENTERTAINMENT GROUP
Room 150 Building 119 No 27 West Dawang Road, Chaoyang District, Beijing, China Ky
Web Site: https://www.yuehuamusic.com
Year Founded: 2009
2306—(HKG)
Rev.: $150,184,715
Assets: $202,585,140
Liabilities: $220,488,188
Net Worth: ($17,903,048)
Earnings: $264,315,594
Emp.: 200
Fiscal Year-end: 12/31/22
Artist Management Services
N.A.I.C.S.: 711410
Hua Du *(CEO)*

YHI INTERNATIONAL LIMITED
No 2 Pandan Road, Singapore, 609254, Singapore
Tel.: (65) 62642155
Web Site: https://yhi.com.sg
Year Founded: 1948
BPF—(SES)
Rev.: $285,495,721
Assets: $296,176,626
Liabilities: $81,981,368
Net Worth: $214,195,259
Earnings: $10,160,570
Emp.: 1,361
Fiscal Year-end: 12/31/23
Alloy Steel Mfr
N.A.I.C.S.: 331110
Tiang Guan Tay *(Exec Dir)*

Subsidiaries:

Advanti Racing USA, LLC (1)
88 Sunnyside Blvd Ste 204, Plainview, NY 11803
Tel.: (516) 822-5700
Automotive Product Mfr & Distr
N.A.I.C.S.: 336390
Joseph Schaefer *(Pres)*

Evo-Trend Corporation (Malaysia) Sdn. Bhd. (1)
Lot Pt 1754 Jalan Persiaran Kip Utama, Taman Perindustrian Kip Kepong, 52200, Kuala Lumpur, Malaysia
Tel.: (60) 362801333
Automotive Product Mfr & Distr
N.A.I.C.S.: 336390
Tham Kong Moo *(Gen Mgr)*

YHI (East Malaysia) Sdn. Bhd. (1)
Lot 30D Jalan Nountun Kolombong, 88450, Kota Kinabalu, Sabah, Malaysia
Tel.: (60) 88388383
Automotive Product Mfr & Distr
N.A.I.C.S.: 336390
Thomas Chang Hong Woei *(Gen Mgr)*

YHI (Hong Kong) Co., Limited (1)
Unit A and B 11/F Dynamic Cargo Centre 188 Yeung Uk Road, Tsuen Wan, New Territories, China (Hong Kong)
Tel.: (852) 27271883
Web Site: https://www.yhi.com.hk
Tire Distr
N.A.I.C.S.: 423130
Benny Kan *(Gen Mgr)*

YHI (Malaysia) Sdn. Bhd. (1)
No 7 and 9 Jalan Mutiara Emas 5/2 Taman Mount Austin, 81100, Johor Bahru, Johor, Malaysia
Tel.: (60) 192385366
Automotive Product Mfr & Distr
N.A.I.C.S.: 336390
Lee Teck Hock *(Gen Mgr)*

YHI (Philippines) Inc. (1)
Blk 2 Lot 3 Mt View Industrial Complex II Maguyam Road, Barrio Bancala, Carmona, 4116, Cavite, Philippines
Tel.: (63) 462351514
Web Site: https://www.yhiph.com
Automotive Product Mfr & Distr
N.A.I.C.S.: 336390
Jason G. Dellaso *(Gen Mgr)*

YHI Aung (Myanmar) Company Limited (1)
Tel.: (95) 13682085
Automotive Product Mfr & Distr
N.A.I.C.S.: 336390
U. Maung Maung Latt *(Mng Dir)*

YHI Corporation (Guangzhou) Co., Ltd. (1)
Room 601-602 Mogaohui No 19 Tang Fu Road, Tianhe District, Guangzhou, 510630, China
Tel.: (86) 2038997251
Tire Distr
N.A.I.C.S.: 423130
Wang Zhan Wei *(Deputy Gen Mgr)*

YHI Corporation (Singapore) Pte Ltd (1)
No 2 Pandan Road, Singapore, 609254, Singapore
Tel.: (65) 62642155
Tire Distr
N.A.I.C.S.: 423130

Subsidiary (Non-US):

PT YHI Indonesia (2)
Jl Danau Agung Barat Blok A-2 No 12 Sunter Agung Podomoro, Jakarta, 14350, Indonesia
Tel.: (62) 216518719
Web Site: https://www.yhi.co.id
Tire Distr
N.A.I.C.S.: 423130

YHI (Vietnam) Co., Ltd. (2)
135/17/77 Nguyen Huu Canh Street, Ward 22 Binh Thanh District, Ho Chi Minh City, Vietnam (90%)
Tel.: (84) 835106087
Web Site: https://www.yhi.com.vn
Tire Distr
N.A.I.C.S.: 423130
Tan Foong Siong *(Dir)*

YHI Corporation (B) Sdn Bhd (2)
Tel.: (673) 2771321
Web Site: https://www.yhi.com.bn
Tire Distr
N.A.I.C.S.: 423130

YHI Corporation (Beijing) Co., Ltd. (2)
Room 1005 B Block Technological Edifice No 4 Fufeng Road Science Park, Fengtai District, Beijing, 100070, China
Tel.: (86) 1063737377
Tire Distr
N.A.I.C.S.: 423130

YHI Corporation (Shanghai) Co., Ltd. (2)
No 611 Shen Fu Road Xinzhuang Industrial Zone, Shanghai, 201108, China
Tel.: (86) 2152272061
Tire Distr
N.A.I.C.S.: 423130

YHI Corporation (Thailand) Co., Ltd (1)
204 Romklao Rd Khwang Klongsampravet, Khet Ladkrabang, Bangkok, 10520, Thailand
Tel.: (66) 23608455
Automotive Product Mfr & Distr
N.A.I.C.S.: 336390
Raymond Tay *(Head-Company)*

YHI Distribution (Taiwan) Co., Ltd. (1)
Tel.: (886) 34963672
Automotive Product Mfr & Distr
N.A.I.C.S.: 336390
Kelvin Lee Chiew Liang *(Gen Mgr)*

YHI International (Taiwan) Co., Ltd. (1)
No 439-1 Zhongzheng Road, Luzhou District, New Taipei City, Taiwan
Tel.: (886) 282853736
Web Site: http://www.yhi.com.tw
Tire Distr
N.A.I.C.S.: 423130

YHI Manufacturing (Malaysia) Sdn. Bhd. (1)
3533 Jalan PBR 28 Kawasan Perindustrian Bukit Rambai, 75250, Melaka, Malaysia
Tel.: (60) 63518008
Automotive Product Mfr & Distr
N.A.I.C.S.: 336390

AND PRIVATE COMPANIES

YHI Manufacturing (Singapore) Pte Ltd (1)
No 2 Pandan Road, Singapore, 609254, Singapore
Tel.: (65) 62642155
Tire Distr
N.A.I.C.S.: 423130

Subsidiary (Non-US):

YHI Advanti Manufacturing (Suzhou) Co., Ltd. (2)
No 138 Hong Xi Road, Suzhou New District, Suzhou, 215151, China
Tel.: (86) 51266162288
Tire Distr
N.A.I.C.S.: 423130
Lin Chen Wei *(Gen Mgr)*

YHI Corporation Japan Co., Ltd. (2)
Yamada Building 1-12-10, Osaka, 550-0014, Japan
Tel.: (81) 643900771
Tire Distr
N.A.I.C.S.: 423130

YHI Manufacturing (Shanghai) Co., Ltd. (2)
No 611 Shen Fu Road Xinzhuang Industrial Zone, Shanghai, 201108, China
Tel.: (86) 2134074121
Tire Distr
N.A.I.C.S.: 423130

YHI Power (Malaysia) Sdn. Bhd. (1)
Lot PT 1754 Jalan Persiaran KIP Utama, Taman Perindustrian KIP Kepong, 52200, Kuala Lumpur, Malaysia
Tel.: (60) 129684117
Web Site: https://www.yhipower.com.my
Alloy Wheel Mfr & Distr
N.A.I.C.S.: 336390

YHI Power Pty Limited (1)
20-22 Venture Way, Braeside, 3195, VIC, Australia
Tel.: (61) 395881888
Web Site: https://www.yhipower.com.au
Tire Distr
N.A.I.C.S.: 423130

YI HUA HOLDINGS LIMITED
Yihua Century Square Zhongshan 3rd Road, Zhongshan, Guangdong, China
Tel.: (86) 760 88305688   Ky
Web Site: http://www.yihua.com.cn
Year Founded: 1994
Sales Range: $100-124.9 Million
Emp.: 2,176
Holding Company
N.A.I.C.S.: 551112
Jianren Chen *(Founder & Chm)*

Subsidiaries:

Zhongshan Lonwalk Mould Plastic Co., Ltd. (1)
6 Jing Ye Road Torch Industrial Development Zone, Zhongshan, 528437, Guangdong, China
Tel.: (86) 76085335988
Web Site: http://www.lonwalk.com
Plastics Product Mfr
N.A.I.C.S.: 326199

YI JINN INDUSTRIAL CO., LTD.
7F No 607 Ruiguang Rd, Neihu District, Taipei, 114, Taiwan
Tel.: (886) 226575859
Web Site: https://www.yijinn.com.tw
Year Founded: 1981
1457—(TAI)
Rev.: $103,334,670
Assets: $669,799,935
Liabilities: $355,954,269
Net Worth: $313,845,667
Earnings: $35,338,172
Fiscal Year-end: 12/31/23
Polyester Yarn Mfr
N.A.I.C.S.: 313110
Cheng-Tien Chan *(Chm)*

YI PO INTERNATIONAL HOLDINGS LIMITED
320-324 Building C4 No 5 Jinxiu Street, Yuhuatai District, Nanjing, Jiangsu, China
Tel.: (86) 400 828 0910   Ky
Web Site: https://www.akandacorp.com
Year Founded: 2020
Rev.: $2,786,853
Assets: $10,727,013
Liabilities: $9,862,815
Net Worth: $864,198
Earnings: $480,230
Emp.: 19
Fiscal Year-end: 12/31/20
Holding Company
N.A.I.C.S.: 551112
Weiming Jin *(CEO & Chm)*

YI XI XIN, INC.
28 Xibahe Xili Building B-30A, Chaoyang, Beijing, 100028, China
Tel.: (86) 010 6553206939   NV
Web Site: http://www.yxx918.com
Year Founded: 2016
Business Management Services
N.A.I.C.S.: 561110
Ping Zhou *(Pres & CEO)*

YI XIN FASHION GROUP CO., LTD.
Building 4 No 50 Lane 2700 South Lianhua Road, Minhang District, Shanghai, 200235, China
Tel.: (86) 2161955100   CN
Web Site: http://www.lachapelle.cn
Year Founded: 1998
6116—(HKG)
Rev.: $27,776,876
Assets: $162,329,216
Liabilities: $523,607,760
Net Worth: ($361,278,544)
Earnings: ($150,757,870)
Emp.: 421
Fiscal Year-end: 12/31/22
Women Apparel Mfr
N.A.I.C.S.: 315250
Xinzai Yin *(Pres)*

YIACO MEDICAL COMPANY K.S.C.C.
Salmia Block No 5 Amr Bin Al Aas Street Sama Tower, PO Box 435, Safat, 13005, Kuwait, Kuwait
Tel.: (965) 22230600
Web Site:
http://www.yiacokuwait.com
YIACO—(KUW)
Rev.: $48,313,969
Assets: $89,967,373
Liabilities: $94,440,027
Net Worth: ($4,472,654)
Earnings: ($5,167,211)
Emp.: 320
Fiscal Year-end: 12/31/22
Pharmaceutical, Medical & Healthcare Products
N.A.I.C.S.: 423450
Ahmad Salem Al Ali Al Sabah *(Vice Chm & CEO)*

YIBIN PAPER INDUSTRY CO., LTD.
Peishi Light Industrial Park, Nanxi District, Yibin, 644100, Sichuan, China
Tel.: (86) 8313309663
Web Site: https://www.yb-zy.com
Year Founded: 1996
600793—(SHG)
Rev.: $323,165,489
Assets: $400,742,316
Liabilities: $308,370,671
Net Worth: $92,371,645
Earnings: $4,154,787
Fiscal Year-end: 12/31/22

Paper Product Mfr & Whslr
N.A.I.C.S.: 322120
Chen Hong *(Chm)*

YIBIN TIANYUAN GROUP CO., LTD.
No 61 Gangyuan Road West Section, Lingang Economic and Technological Development Zone, Yibin, 644000, Sichuan, China
Tel.: (86) 8313607079
Web Site: http://www.ybty.com
Year Founded: 1994
002386—(SSE)
Rev.: $2,855,657,924
Assets: $2,166,990,055
Liabilities: $1,288,785,794
Net Worth: $878,204,260
Earnings: $77,297,080
Emp.: 6,500
Fiscal Year-end: 12/31/22
Chlor-Alkali Chemicals Mfr & Distr
N.A.I.C.S.: 325180
Deng Min *(Chm)*

YIBITAS YOZGAT ISCI BIRLIGI INSAAT MALZEMELERI TICARET VE SANAYI A.S.
Fatih Neighborhood Yibitas Boulevard No 29, Saray Town Yerkoy, 66920, Yozgat, Turkiye
Tel.: (90) 3545572150   TR
Web Site:
https://www.yibitasyozgat.com
Year Founded: 1973
YBTAS—(IST)
Sales Range: Less than $1 Million
Cement Mfr
N.A.I.C.S.: 327310
Hatim Ben Moussa *(Chm, Mng Dir & Gen Mgr)*

YIDU TECH INC.
Building E7 Guizhou Big Health Pharmaceutical Industry, Zhihui Yunjin Incubation Base Wudang, Guiyang, China
Tel.: (86) 1084867760   Ky
Web Site:
http://www.yiducloud.com.cn
Year Founded: 2014
2158—(HKG)
Health Care Srvices
N.A.I.C.S.: 621610
Gong Rujing *(Co-Founder, Chm & CEO)*

YIEH HSING ENTERPRISE CO., LTD.
No 369 Baomi Rd, Gangshan Dist, Kaohsiung, 82053, Taiwan
Tel.: (886) 76111111
Web Site: https://www.yheco.com.tw
Year Founded: 1978
2007—(TAI)
Rev.: $164,006,305
Assets: $399,664,820
Liabilties: $209,322,468
Net Worth: $190,342,352
Earnings: ($32,091,696)
Emp.: 421
Fiscal Year-end: 12/31/23
Stainless Steel Mfr & Distr
N.A.I.C.S.: 331110
Lin-Maw Wu *(Chm)*

YIEH PHUI ENTERPRISE CO., LTD.
No 369 Yuliao Road, Qiaotou, Kaohsiung, 825004, Taiwan
Tel.: (886) 76117181
Web Site:
https://www.yiehphui.com.tw
Year Founded: 1978
2023—(TAI)
Rev.: $2,396,918,579

YIELD MICROELECTRONICS CORP.

Assets: $3,000,946,615
Liabilities: $2,006,017,649
Net Worth: $994,928,966
Earnings: ($47,521,762)
Emp.: 1,420
Fiscal Year-end: 12/31/23
Steel Coils Mfr
N.A.I.C.S.: 335312
Young-Jeaq Lan *(VP-Production)*

Subsidiaries:

E-Da Development Corp. (1)
6 Yi Ta Road, Yenchao Hsiang, Kaohsiung, 82445, Taiwan
Tel.: (886) 76151111
Web Site: http://www.edd.e-united.com.tw
Commercial Property Development & Operation Services
N.A.I.C.S.: 531390

United Brightening Developing Corp. (1)
9f 6 Yi Ta Road, Yenchao Hsiang, Kaohsiung, 82445, Taiwan
Tel.: (886) 76151111
Steel Products Mfr
N.A.I.C.S.: 331210

Yieh Phui Enterprise Co., Ltd. - Pingtung Works (1)
No 6 Gongye 6th Road, Pingtung, Kaohsiung, 90049, Taiwan
Tel.: (886) 8 7550976
Web Site: http://www.yiehphui.com.tw
Structured Steel Products Mfr
N.A.I.C.S.: 332312

Yieh Phui Enterprise Co., Ltd. - Yanchao Plant (1)
No 600 Zhong-an Road, Yanchao District, Kaohsiung, 82446, Taiwan
Tel.: (886) 76163001
Web Site: http://www.yiehphui.com.tw
Crane Equipment Mfr & Installation Services
N.A.I.C.S.: 333120

Yieh Phui Enterprise Co., Ltd. - Yieh Phui (China) Changshu Works (1)
1 Yiehphui Road Riverside Industrial Park, Changshu, 215536, Jiangsu, China
Tel.: (86) 51252298888
Web Site: http://www.yiehphui.com.tw
Steel Products Mfr
N.A.I.C.S.: 331110

YIEH UNITED STEEL CORP.
No 600 Xinglong St Jiaxing Vil, Gangshan Dist, Kaohsiung, 82445, Taiwan
Tel.: (886) 76232255
Web Site: http://www.yieh.com
Year Founded: 1988
9957—(TAI)
Stain Steel Mfr
N.A.I.C.S.: 331513
Chung-Chi Kuo *(Vice Chm)*

YIELD GO HOLDINGS LTD.
Unit 8 39/F Cable TV Tower No 9 Hoi Shing Road, Tsuen Wan, China (Hong Kong)
Tel.: (852) 24130055   Ky
Web Site: http://www.yield-go.com
Year Founded: 1995
1796—(HKG)
Rev.: $26,248,680
Assets: $24,891,825
Liabilities: $10,461,120
Net Worth: $14,430,705
Earnings: ($2,379,533)
Emp.: 58
Fiscal Year-end: 03/31/23
Building Contractor Services
N.A.I.C.S.: 238130
Hoi Yuen Man *(Chm)*

YIELD MICROELECTRONICS CORP.
11F 2 No 12 Taiyuan 2nd St, Hsin-Chu County, Zhubei, 302082, Taiwan

YIELD MICROELECTRONICS CORP.

Yield Microelectronics Corp.—(Continued)
Tel.: (886) 35526035
Web Site: https://www.ymc.com.tw
Year Founded: 2001
6423—(TAI)
Emp.: 67
Semiconductor Mfr
N.A.I.C.S.: 334413
Wen-Chien Huang *(Chm & Pres)*

YIFAN PHARMACEUTICAL CO., LTD.
No 50 Qinshan, Jincheng Subdistrict Lin and aposan District, Hangzhou, 311300, Zhejiang, China
Tel.: (86) 57163759225
Web Site: http://www.en.yifanyy.com
Year Founded: 1994
002019—(SSE)
Rev.: $538,664,368
Assets: $1,761,107,877
Liabilities: $476,975,262
Net Worth: $1,284,132,615
Earnings: $26,855,347
Emp.: 5,000
Fiscal Year-end: 12/31/22
Pharmaceuticals Mfr
N.A.I.C.S.: 325412
Xianfeng Cheng *(Chm, Pres & Gen Mgr)*

Subsidiaries:

Huzhou Xinfu new Materials Co., Ltd (1)
New Streams Of Phoenix Bridge Town, Huzhou, 313018, China
Tel.: (86) 57161090637
Emp.: 200
Pipe Resin Mfr
N.A.I.C.S.: 325211
Hang Lin *(Gen Mgr)*

SciGen Ltd. (1)
152 Beach Road 26-07/08 Gateway East, Singapore, 189721, Singapore (90.54%)
Tel.: (65) 67796638
Web Site: http://www.scigenltd.com
Rev.: $40,395,000
Assets: $26,145,000
Liabilities: $79,430,000
Net Worth: ($53,285,000)
Earnings: $1,763,000
Emp.: 12
Fiscal Year-end: 12/31/2017
Biopharmaceutical Mfr
N.A.I.C.S.: 325412
Leng Wong Lai *(Co-Sec)*

Subsidiary (Non-US):

Marvel Life Sciences Pvt Ltd (2)
Ste 1 2nd Fl Congress House, Lyon Rd, Harrow, HA1 2EN, Middlesex, United Kingdom
Tel.: (44) 2084274377
Pharmaceuticals Product Mfr
N.A.I.C.S.: 325412

SciGen (Australia) Pty. Ltd. (2)
Suite 1 13B Narabang Way, Belrose, 2085, NSW, Australia
Tel.: (61) 294851800
Web Site: http://www.scigen.com.au
Emp.: 12
Biopharmaceutical Mfr
N.A.I.C.S.: 325412
Slawomir Ziegert *(CEO)*

YIFENG PHARMACY CHAIN CO., LTD.
Yifeng Pharmaceutical Park No 68 Jinzhou Avenue Lugu High-tech Zone, Changsha, 410000, Hunan, China
Tel.: (86) 73189953915
Web Site: https://www.yfdyf.cn
Year Founded: 2008
603939—(SHG)
Rev.: $2,792,049,970
Assets: $2,953,859,679
Liabilities: $1,673,205,712
Net Worth: $1,280,653,947
Earnings: $177,691,630
Fiscal Year-end: 12/31/22
Pharmaceutical Products Distr
N.A.I.C.S.: 424210
Yi Gao *(Chm & Pres)*

YIHAI INTERNATIONAL HOLDINGS LIMITED
No 6 Building 10 Heng Tsung Yuan District, Fengtai District, Beijing, 100075, China
Tel.: (86) 1057423508
Web Site: http://www.yihchina.com
Year Founded: 2013
1579—(HKG)
Rev.: $863,040,344
Assets: $779,401,537
Liabilities: $142,403,789
Net Worth: $636,997,748
Earnings: $114,564,434
Emp.: 2,720
Fiscal Year-end: 12/31/22
Compound Condiment Product Mfr & Distr
N.A.I.C.S.: 311942
Chunxiang Dang *(VP)*

YIHAI KERRY ARAWANA HOLDINGS CO., LTD.
Arawana Building No 1379 Bocheng Road, Pudong New District, Shanghai, 200126, China
Tel.: (86) 4006165757
Web Site: https://www.yihaikerry.net
Year Founded: 2005
300999—(SSE)
Rev.: $36,150,956,338
Assets: $32,003,226,544
Liabilities: $18,906,236,341
Net Worth: $13,096,990,203
Earnings: $422,764,477
Emp.: 30,000
Fiscal Year-end: 12/31/22
Holding Company
N.A.I.C.S.: 551112
Robert Kuok *(Co-Founder)*

YIHUA HEALTHCARE CO., LTD.
Wenguan Road, Chenghai District, Shantou, 515800, Guangdong, China
Tel.: (86) 7548 589 9788
Web Site: http://www.yihuahealth.com
000150—(SSE)
Rev.: $239,258,864
Assets: $780,344,493
Liabilities: $738,136,670
Net Worth: $42,207,823
Earnings: ($95,721,012)
Fiscal Year-end: 12/31/20
Real Estate Development Services
N.A.I.C.S.: 531390
Yimin Chen *(Chm)*

YIHUA LIFESTYLE TECHNOLOGY CO., LTD.
Huaidong Industrial Zone Lianxia, Chenghai District, Shantou, 515800, Guangdong, China
Tel.: (86) 75485741912
Web Site: http://www.yihuatimber.com
600978—(SHG)
Rev.: $750,455,037
Assets: $2,316,521,403
Liabilities: $1,203,778,665
Net Worth: $1,112,742,738
Earnings: ($26,519,292)
Fiscal Year-end: 12/31/19
Wood Furniture & Flooring Product Mfr
N.A.I.C.S.: 337122
Zhuangchao Liu *(Chm)*

Subsidiaries:

HTL International Holdings Pte Ltd. (1)
15 Scotts Road, Singapore, 228218, Singapore
Tel.: (65) 6904 0933
Web Site: http://www.htlinternational.com
Sales Range: $450-499.9 Million
Emp.: 8,000
Upholstered Furniture Mfr
N.A.I.C.S.: 337121
Yong Tat Phua *(Grp Mng Dir)*

Subsidiary (Non-US):

Domicil Moebel GmbH (2)
Luitpold Park Uferweg 11 D, 88131, Lindau, Bodensee, Germany
Tel.: (49) 83 82 96 20 20
Web Site: http://www.domicil.de
Household Furniture Mfr
N.A.I.C.S.: 449110
Yong Tat Phua *(Grp Mng Dir)*

Subsidiary (Domestic):

Domicil City GmbH (3)
Brienner Strasse 05, Munich, 80333, Bayern, Germany
Tel.: (49) 896066630
Household Furniture Retailer
N.A.I.C.S.: 449110

Subsidiary (Domestic):

Domicil Pte Ltd (2)
11 Gul Circle, Singapore, 629567, Singapore
Tel.: (65) 68644688
Web Site: http://www.htlinternational.com
Emp.: 180
Furnishings Whslr
N.A.I.C.S.: 423220

Subsidiary (US):

H.T.L. Furniture, Inc (2)
4361 Federal Dr Ste 180, Greensboro, NC 27410
Tel.: (336) 869-4573
Upholstered Furniture Distr
N.A.I.C.S.: 423210
Stefanie Lucas *(Pres)*

Subsidiary (Non-US):

HTL (UK) Limited (2)
Unit M Metro Business Park Clough Street, Hanley, Stoke-on-Trent, ST1 4AF, Staffordshire, United Kingdom
Tel.: (44) 870 755 9331
Web Site: http://www.htlinternational.com
Sales Range: $25-49.9 Million
Emp.: 14
Household Furniture Mfr
N.A.I.C.S.: 337121
Mark Flint *(Mng Dir)*

HTL Australia Pty Ltd (2)
Unit 1 88 Henderson Road, Rowville, 3178, Australia
Tel.: (61) 3 9763 2883
Web Site: http://www.htlinternational.com
Emp.: 23
Upholstered Furniture Distr
N.A.I.C.S.: 337214

HTL Furniture (Changshu) Co., Ltd. (2)
5 Jincang Road Unit A Changkun Industry Park Shajiabang Town, Shajiabang, Changshu, 215542, Jiangsu, China
Tel.: (86) 51252577059
Upholstered Furniture Mfr
N.A.I.C.S.: 337121

HTL Furniture (Huai An) Co., Ltd. (2)
No 17 Jixian Road, Economic Development Zone, Huai'an, 223005, Jiangsu, China
Tel.: (86) 51783797078
Leather Sofa Mfr
N.A.I.C.S.: 316990

HTL Furniture (Kunshan) Co., Ltd. (2)
Kunshan, Kunshan, 215345, Jiangsu, China
Tel.: (86) 51250351236
Upholstered Furniture Mfr

INTERNATIONAL PUBLIC

N.A.I.C.S.: 327910

HTL Furniture (Yangzhou) Co., Ltd. (2)
No 111 Jinshan East Road Development Zone, Yangzhou, 225131, Jiangsu, China
Tel.: (86) 51487522719
Leather Sofa Mfr
N.A.I.C.S.: 316990

HTL Home (Jiang Su) Co., Ltd. (2)
10 South Taihu Road Kunshan Development Zone Jiang, Jiangsu, 215344, China
Tel.: (86) 51255161818
Leather Sofa Mfr
N.A.I.C.S.: 316990

HTL International GmbH (2)
Germaniastrasse 12, 33189, Schlangen, Nordrhein-Westfalen, Germany
Tel.: (49) 5252 9777100
Web Site: http://www.htlinternational.com
Sales Range: $25-49.9 Million
Emp.: 10
Upholstered Furniture Mfr
N.A.I.C.S.: 337121

Subsidiary (Domestic):

HTL International Pte Ltd (2)
11 Gul Circle, Singapore, 629567, Singapore
Tel.: (65) 67475050
Web Site: http://www.htlinternational.com
Emp.: 180
Household Furniture Mfr
N.A.I.C.S.: 327991
Yong Tat Phua *(Mng Dir)*

Subsidiary (Non-US):

HTL Korea Co., Ltd. (2)
5th Floor 56-18 Daeeun BD Nonhyun-dong, Gangnam-gu, Seoul, 135-010, Korea (South)
Tel.: (82) 25430480
Web Site: http://www.htlinternational.com
Sales Range: $50-74.9 Million
Emp.: 3
Household Furniture Distr
N.A.I.C.S.: 423210

HTL Leather (China) Co., Ltd. (2)
No 58 Shengxi Road Economic Development Zone, Kunshan, 215334, Jiangsu, China
Tel.: (86) 51257638741
Leather Sofas Mfr
N.A.I.C.S.: 337121

Subsidiary (Domestic):

HTL Manufacturing Pte Ltd (2)
11 Gul Circle, Singapore, 629567, Singapore
Tel.: (65) 6747 5050
Residential Furniture Mfr
N.A.I.C.S.: 337122

Subsidiary (Non-US):

Hwa Tat Lee Japan Co., Ltd. (2)
1F Akebonobashi SHK Bldg 4-3 Katamachi, Shinjuku-ku, Tokyo, 160-0001, Japan
Tel.: (81) 353681935
Web Site: http://www.htlinternational.com
Sales Range: $25-49.9 Million
Emp.: 30
Upholstered Furniture Mfr
N.A.I.C.S.: 337121
Kazuteru Kinoshita *(Pres)*

Hwatalee G.M. (Taiwan) Co., Ltd. (2)
No 228-3 Zhongzheng Road Daya Shiang, Taichung, 428, Taiwan
Tel.: (886) 425678689
Sales Range: $25-49.9 Million
Emp.: 50
Household Furniture Distr
N.A.I.C.S.: 423210
Morry Ta Yu Lin *(Gen Mgr)*

Trends Leather (Yangzhou) Co., Ltd. (2)
111 Jinshan East Road Yangzhou City Development Zone, Yangzhou, 225131, Jiangsu, China
Tel.: (86) 51487526222
Leather Tanning & Finishing Services
N.A.I.C.S.: 316110

YIJIA GROUP CORP.
Unit 1623 Tianxia International Center B Taoyuan Road, Nanshan District, Shenzhen, Guangdong, China
Tel.: (86) 75533975792 NV
Web Site:
http://www.soldinogroup.com
Year Founded: 2017
YJGJ—(OTCIQ)
Rev.: $120,000
Assets: $23,103
Liabilities: $58,091
Net Worth: ($34,988)
Earnings: $139,682
Fiscal Year-end: 04/30/22
Workwear Sewing & Distribution Services
N.A.I.C.S.: 315210

YIJIAHE TECHNOLOGY CO., LTD.
Yijiahe Industrial Park No 5 Chuangsilu, Yuhuatai District, Nanjing, 210012, Jiangsu, China
Tel.: (86) 2583168166
Web Site: https://www.yijiahe.com
Year Founded: 1999
603666—(SHG)
Rev.: $93,886,814
Assets: $522,279,351
Liabilities: $184,450,402
Net Worth: $337,828,950
Earnings: ($13,752,306)
Fiscal Year-end: 12/31/22
Robot Machinery Mfr & Distr
N.A.I.C.S.: 333998
Zhu Fuyun *(Chm)*

YIK CORPORATION
7F 28 Pangyo-ro 255beon-gil, Bundang-gu, Seongnam, 13486, Gyeonggi-do, Korea (South)
Tel.: (82) 316399180
Web Site: https://www.yccorp.com
Year Founded: 1991
232140—(KRS)
Rev.: $218,800,372
Assets: $398,148,194
Liabilities: $126,147,216
Net Worth: $272,000,978
Earnings: $26,347,273
Emp.: 155
Fiscal Year-end: 12/31/22
Semiconductor Test Equipment Mfr & Distr
N.A.I.C.S.: 334515
Choi Myung-Bae *(CEO)*

YIK WO INTERNATIONAL HOLDINGS LIMITED
Wukeng Industrial Zone, Longhu Town, Jinjiang, Fujian, China
Tel.: (86) 59522280000 Ky
Web Site: http://www.yikwo.cn
Year Founded: 2011
8659—(HKG)
Holding Company
N.A.I.C.S.: 551112
Youjiang Xu *(Chm)*

YILDIRIM HOLDING INC.
Meydan Sokak No 1 Beybi Giz Plaza Kat 3 4, 34485, Istanbul, Türkiye
Tel.: (90) 212 290 30 80 TR
Web Site:
http://www.yildirimgroup.com
Year Founded: 1963
Emp.: 10,000
Holding Company
N.A.I.C.S.: 551112
Robert Yuksel Yildirim *(Pres & CEO)*

Subsidiaries:

Bear Metallurgical Company (1)
679 E Butler Rd, Butler, PA 16002-9127
Tel.: (724) 431-2800
Web Site: http://www.bearmet.com
High-Purity Alloys
N.A.I.C.S.: 331110
Christy Weigel *(Mgr-Sls & Mktg)*

YILDIZ HOLDING AS
Kisikli Mahallesi Ferah Caddesi No 1 Buyuk Camlica, Topkapi, 34692, Istanbul, Türkiye
Tel.: (90) 02165242900 TR
Web Site:
http://www.english.yildizholding.com
Year Founded: 1989
Holding Company
N.A.I.C.S.: 551112
Dmitry Ivanov *(Chief Comml Officer)*

Subsidiaries:

Aytac Gida Yatirim Sanayi ve Ticaret A.S. (1)
Alemdag Cad Masaldan Is Mrk No 60 E-Blok D 6 B Camlica, Istanbul, Türkiye
Tel.: (90) 216 521 23 50
Web Site: http://www.aytac.com.tr
Meat Product Mfr & Distr
N.A.I.C.S.: 311612

DeMet's Candy Company (1)
11 Main St, Mohnton, PA 19540
Tel.: (610) 775-4100
Web Site: http://www.demetscandy.com
Emp.: 500
Confectionery Product Distr
N.A.I.C.S.: 424450

Kerevitas Gida Sanayi ve Ticaret A.S. (1)
Kisikli Mah Ferah Cad Yildiz Holding Placid Blogu No 1/A, Uskudar, Istanbul, Türkiye
Tel.: (90) 8502091616
Web Site: https://www.kerevitas.com.tr
Rev.: $640,326,294
Assets: $546,051,545
Liabilities: $299,284,299
Net Worth: $246,767,246
Earnings: $14,789,737
Emp.: 1,500
Fiscal Year-end: 12/31/2023
Frozen Food Mfr & Whslr
N.A.I.C.S.: 311411
Mehmet Tutuncu *(Chm)*

Subsidiary (Domestic):

Besler Gida ve Kimya San. ve Tic. A.S. (2)
Mahmut Bayram Caddesi No 88 eyhli Ky, Pendik, Istanbul, 34906, Türkiye
Tel.: (90) 216 585 05 85
Emp.: 236
Margarine Mfr
N.A.I.C.S.: 311221

Ulker Biskuvi Sanayi A.S. (1)
Ferah Street Kisikli Neighborhood No 1, Buyuk Camlica-Uskudar, 34692, Istanbul, Türkiye
Tel.: (90) 2165242900
Web Site: https://www.ulkerbiskuvi.com.tr
Rev.: $870,931,630
Assets: $1,169,365,446
Liabilities: $932,072,061
Net Worth: $237,293,385
Earnings: $6,162,685
Emp.: 7,575
Fiscal Year-end: 12/31/2022
Food Mfr
N.A.I.C.S.: 311821
Murat Ulker *(Chm)*

Subsidiary (Domestic):

BirleSik Dis Ticaret A.S. (2)
Tuzla Deri Serbest Bolgesi Hakki Matras Caddesi No 6, Istanbul, Türkiye
Tel.: (90) 216 394 29 97
Confectionery Product Distr
N.A.I.C.S.: 424450

Biskot Biskuvi Gida Sanayi ve Ticaret A.S. (2)
Organize Sanayi Bolgesi Eregli Yolu No 18, Karaman, 70100, Türkiye
Tel.: (90) 338 226 10 00
Web Site: http://www.biskot.com.tr
Emp.: 2,700
Confectionery Product Distr
N.A.I.C.S.: 424450

Subsidiary (Non-US):

Godiva Belgium BVBA (2)
Wapenstilstandstraat 5 Rue de l'Armistice, 1081, Brussels, Belgium
Tel.: (32) 2 422 17 11
Web Site: http://www.godivachocolates.eu
Confectionery Product Mfr & Distr
N.A.I.C.S.: 311352
Peter-Jan Roose *(Mgr-Fin & Supply Chain)*

Subsidiary (US):

Godiva Chocolatier, Inc. (2)
3333 W 31 St, New York, NY 10001-6603
Tel.: (212) 984-5900
Web Site: http://www.godiva.com
Sales Range: $500-549.9 Million
Emp.: 100
Chocolate Mfr
N.A.I.C.S.: 311351
Nirmal Kumar Tripathy *(Owner)*

Subsidiary (Domestic):

Istanbul Gida Dis Ticaret A.S. (2)
1 Kisikli Mahallesi Ferah Caddesi, Istanbul, 34692, Türkiye
Tel.: (90) 216 524 27 00
Confectionery Product Distr
N.A.I.C.S.: 424450

Rekor Gida Pazarlama A.S. (2)
Kisikli Mahallesi Alemdag Caddesi Alemdag Yanyol sokak No 6 B Camlica, Uskudar, Istanbul, Türkiye
Tel.: (90) 216 524 88 50
Web Site: http://www.halk.com.tr
Confectionery Product Distr
N.A.I.C.S.: 424450

Ulker Cikolata Sanayi A.S. (2)
Maltepe Mh Davutpasa Caddesi 10 Topkapi, Istanbul, 34015, Türkiye
Tel.: (90) 212 567 1567
Confectionery Product Distr
N.A.I.C.S.: 424450

United Biscuits (Holdings) Limited (1)
Hayes Park Building Hayes End Road, Hayes, UB4 8EE, Mddx, United Kingdom
Tel.: (44) 2082345000
Web Site: http://www.unitedbiscuits.com
Emp.: 450
Biscuits, Savory Snacks & Frozen & Chilled Food Mfr
N.A.I.C.S.: 311821
Jim Zaza *(Chm)*

YILI CHUANNIG BIOTECHNOLOGY CO., LTD.
No 516 Yining Park, Horgos Economic Development Zone Ili, Xinjiang, 835000, China
Tel.: (86) 9998077777
Web Site: https://www.klcnsw.com
Year Founded: 2010
301301—(CHIN)
Rev.: $536,420,664
Assets: $1,458,812,160
Liabilities: $586,859,364
Net Worth: $871,952,796
Earnings: $57,777,408
Emp.: 2,800
Fiscal Year-end: 12/31/22
Biotechnology Research & Development Services
N.A.I.C.S.: 541714
Gexin Liu *(Chm)*

YIMIKANG TECHNOLOGY GROUP CO., LTD.
No 2 Keyuan South 2nd Road Hi-tech Zone, Gaoxin District, Chengdu, 610041, Sichuan, China
Tel.: (86) 2885185206
Web Site: http://www.ymk.com.cn
Year Founded: 2002
300249—(SSE)
Rev.: $123,408,792
Assets: $320,336,640
Liabilities: $215,925,372
Net Worth: $104,411,268
Earnings: ($4,544,748)
Fiscal Year-end: 12/31/22
Air Conditioners & Environmental Air Cleaning Products Mfr
N.A.I.C.S.: 333415
Zhang Wan *(Chm & Gen Mgr)*

YIN SHENG HOLDINGS LIMITED
Room 2418A Wing On Centre 111 Connaught Road, Central, China (Hong Kong)
Tel.: (852) 3106 2393 Ky
Web Site: http://www.yinhe.com.hk
Rev.: $32,726,947
Assets: $180,007,785
Liabilities: $18,229,152
Net Worth: $161,778,633
Earnings: $3,948,047
Fiscal Year-end: 03/31/19
Holding Company
N.A.I.C.S.: 551112
Victor Tin Duk Chang *(Founder)*

YINBANG CLAD MATERIAL CO., LTD.
No 99 Hongshan Road Houzhai, Hongshan Street Xinwu District, Wuxi, 214145, Jiangsu, China
Tel.: (86) 51068567000
Web Site: https://www.cn-yinbang.com
Year Founded: 1988
300337—(SSE)
Rev.: $553,779,720
Assets: $565,813,404
Liabilities: $346,196,916
Net Worth: $219,616,488
Earnings: $9,448,920
Emp.: 1,000
Fiscal Year-end: 12/31/22
Aluminum Alloy Products Mfr
N.A.I.C.S.: 331314
Shen Jiansheng *(Chm & Gen Mgr)*

Subsidiaries:

Falcontech Co., Ltd. (1)
Hongshan Street No 11 Road and Hongxin Road, Xinwu District, Wuxi, 214145, Jiangsu, China
Tel.: (86) 5106 878 8619
Web Site: https://www.falcontech.com.cn
Emp.: 100
Metal Additive Mfr
N.A.I.C.S.: 339999

YINCHENG INTERNATIONAL HOLDING CO., LTD.
19-21/ F 289 Jiangdong Avenue North, Nanjing, 210000, Jiangsu, China
Tel.: (86) 2586500111
Web Site: http://www.yincheng.hk
Year Founded: 2002
1902—(HKG)
Rev.: $1,220,745,146
Assets: $5,458,970,743
Liabilities: $4,879,098,806
Net Worth: $579,871,937
Earnings: ($108,402,278)
Emp.: 623
Fiscal Year-end: 12/31/22
Real Estate Investment Services
N.A.I.C.S.: 531390
Ma Baohua *(Pres)*

YINCHENG LIFE SERVICE CO., LTD.
19/F Block A Yincheng Plaza 289 Jiangdong Avenue North, Gulou, Nanjing, Jiangsu, China
Tel.: (86) 2583628721 Ky
Web Site: http://www.yinchenglife.hk
Year Founded: 1997
1922—(HKG)
Rev.: $240,495,934

YINCHENG LIFE SERVICE CO., LTD.

Yincheng Life Service Co., Ltd.—(Continued)
Assets: $174,765,568
Liabilities: $123,522,937
Net Worth: $51,242,630
Earnings: $15,809,461
Emp.: 9,166
Fiscal Year-end: 12/31/22
Property Management Services
N.A.I.C.S.: 531311
Chunling Li *(Pres)*

Subsidiaries:

Yincheng Real Estate Group Co., Ltd. (1)
No 289 Jiangdong North Road, Gulou District, Nanjing, China
Tel.: (86) 258 650 0111
Web Site: https://www.ycdc.com
Real Estate Development Services
N.A.I.C.S.: 531390

YINCHUAN XINHUA COMMERCIAL GROUP CO., LTD.
No 97 Xinhua East Street, Xingqing District, Yinchuan, 750001, Ningxia, China
Tel.: (86) 9516071161
Web Site: https://www.xhbh.com.cn
Year Founded: 1997
600785—(SHG)
Rev.: $825,986,903
Assets: $1,144,252,812
Liabilities: $885,779,290
Net Worth: $258,473,522
Earnings: $13,124,409
Fiscal Year-end: 12/31/22
Departmental Store Operator
N.A.I.C.S.: 455110

YINDU KITCHEN EQUIPMENT CO., LTD.
No 1 Xingxing Road Xingqiao, Yuhang District, Hangzhou, 311100, China
Tel.: (86) 57186260777
Web Site: https://www.yinduchina.com
Year Founded: 2003
603277—(SHG)
Rev.: $373,864,365
Assets: $483,212,981
Liabilities: $127,829,511
Net Worth: $355,383,471
Earnings: $63,034,742
Fiscal Year-end: 12/31/22
Kitchen Equipment Mfr & Distr
N.A.I.C.S.: 333415

YINFU GOLD CORPORATION
Room 2313 Dongfang Sci &Tech Blg, Nanshan District, Shenzhen, 518000, China
Tel.: (86) 75583160998 **WY**
Year Founded: 2005
ELRE—(OTCIQ)
Rev.: $17,416
Assets: $25,860
Liabilities: $2,656,537
Net Worth: ($2,630,677)
Earnings: ($65,461)
Emp.: 8
Fiscal Year-end: 03/31/24
Investment Holding Company
N.A.I.C.S.: 551112
Libin Jiang *(Chm, Pres, CEO, Interim CFO & Sec)*

YING HAI GROUP HOLDINGS COMPANY LIMITED
Alameda Dr Carlos D Assumpcao Fl 9 NOPQ Ed Centro Comercial, Cheng Feng, Macau, China (Macau)
Tel.: (853) 28855550 **Ky**
Web Site: http://www.yinghaiholding.com
Year Founded: 2014

8668—(HKG)
Rev.: $12,124,304
Assets: $7,521,347
Liabilities: $3,210,779
Net Worth: $4,310,568
Earnings: ($325,930)
Emp.: 88
Fiscal Year-end: 12/31/23
Holding Company
N.A.I.C.S.: 551112
Wai Chan Choi *(Chm)*

YING HAN TECHNOLOGY CO., LTD.
46 Hwan Gong Rd, Yung Kang Ind Dist, Tainan City, 710, Taiwan
Tel.: (886) 62335611
Web Site: https://www.hannsa.tw
Year Founded: 1990
4562—(TAI)
Rev.: $24,271,460
Assets: $74,721,113
Liabilities: $40,113,606
Net Worth: $34,607,507
Earnings: ($2,807,188)
Fiscal Year-end: 12/31/23
Machine Tools Mfr
N.A.I.C.S.: 333517
Hu Pin-Kun *(Chm)*

YING KEE TEA HOUSE GROUP LTD.
8th Floor Wah Shing Centre 5 Fung Yip Street, Siu Sai Wan, Hong Kong, China (Hong Kong)
Tel.: (852) 25420038 **HK**
Web Site: https://www.yingkeetea.com
8241—(HKG)
Rev.: $4,773,855
Assets: $14,102,648
Liabilities: $11,457,660
Net Worth: $2,644,988
Earnings: ($851,955)
Emp.: 51
Fiscal Year-end: 03/31/23
Tea Product Whslr
N.A.I.C.S.: 424490
Kun Yuen Chan *(Exec Dir)*

YING LI INTERNATIONAL REAL ESTATE LIMITED
6 Temasek Boulevard 21-01 Suntec Tower Four, Singapore, 038986, Singapore
Tel.: (65) 63349052 **SG**
Web Site: https://www.yingligj.com
Year Founded: 1993
5DM—(SES)
Rev.: $29,368,732
Assets: $853,483,941
Liabilities: $576,128,731
Net Worth: $277,355,210
Earnings: $2,590,986
Emp.: 122
Fiscal Year-end: 12/31/23
Real Estate Development Services
N.A.I.C.S.: 531390
Bing Hu *(CEO)*

YINGGAO HOLDINGS PLC
6th Floor 25 Farringdon Street, London, EC4A 4AB, United Kingdom
Tel.: (44) 2074135100 **UK**
Web Site: http://www.yinggaoholdings.com
Sales Range: $50-74.9 Million
Emp.: 537
Terminal Operations & Shipping Services
N.A.I.C.S.: 488320
Yue Ying Feng *(Dir-Fin)*

YINGKOU FENGGUANG ADVANCED MATERIAL CO., LTD.
No 519 Jiangjiafang, Lunan Town Laobian District, Yingkou, 115005, LiaoNing, China
Tel.: (86) 4173908499
Web Site: https://www.ln-fengguang.com
Year Founded: 2003
301100—(CHIN)
Rev.: $117,187,668
Assets: $343,588,284
Liabilities: $46,579,104
Net Worth: $297,009,180
Earnings: $13,360,464
Fiscal Year-end: 12/31/22
Chemical Products Mfr
N.A.I.C.S.: 327120
Lei Wang *(Chm)*

YINGKOU JINCHEN MACHINERY CO., LTD.
No 95 Xingang Avenue, Xishi district, Yingkou, 215000, Liaoning, China
Tel.: (86) 4176682375
Web Site: https://www.jinchencorp.com
Year Founded: 2004
603396—(SHG)
Rev.: $274,018,146
Assets: $538,460,985
Liabilities: $328,876,161
Net Worth: $209,584,824
Earnings: $9,053,834
Emp.: 1,500
Fiscal Year-end: 12/31/22
Solar Module Mfr & Distr
N.A.I.C.S.: 334413
Li Yisheng *(Chm)*

YINGKOU PORT LIABILITY CO., LTD.
Camp No 1 Harbour Road, Bayuquan District, Yingkou, 115007, Liaoning, China
Tel.: (86) 4176268506
Web Site: http://www.ykplc.com
600317—(SHG)
Rev.: $682,347,594
Assets: $2,178,027,377
Liabilities: $331,955,724
Net Worth: $1,846,071,653
Earnings: $150,010,013
Fiscal Year-end: 12/31/19
Cargo Handling Services
N.A.I.C.S.: 488119
Xianping Zou *(CFO)*

YINGTONG TELECOMMUNICATION CO., LTD.
No 36 Industrial Road, Changping Park Eastern Industrial Park, Dongguan, Guangdong, China
Tel.: (86) 76989928999
Web Site: https://www.yingtong-wire.com
Year Founded: 2010
002861—(SSE)
Rev.: $101,773,208
Assets: $222,520,859
Liabilities: $93,689,861
Net Worth: $128,830,998
Earnings: ($16,514,845)
Fiscal Year-end: 12/31/22
Telecommunication Cable Mfr & Distr
N.A.I.C.S.: 334220
Huang Hui *(Chm)*

Subsidiaries:

Dongguan Kailai Electronic Co., Ltd. (1)
No 36 Industrial Main Road, 2nd District Shahukou Eastern Industrial Park Changping Town, Dongguan, Guangdong, China
Tel.: (86) 76983330508
Electrical Products Mfr
N.A.I.C.S.: 335999

Dongguan Yingtong Wire Co., Ltd. (1)

Daditang Industrial Zone Sukeng, Changping Town, Dongguan, Guangdong, China
Tel.: (86) 76983552935
Electrical Products Mfr
N.A.I.C.S.: 335999

Hubei Yingtong Electronics Co., Ltd. (1)
Tiezhu Industrial Zone, Tongcheng County, Xianning, Hubei, China
Tel.: (86) 7154357999
Electrical Products Mfr
N.A.I.C.S.: 335999

YINHANG INTERNET TECHNOLOGIES DEVELOPMENT, INC.
RM 1312 Tower 2 Grand Century Place 193 Prince Edward West, Kowloon, China (Hong Kong)
Tel.: (852) 66110528
Year Founded: 2010
Prefabricated Wood Building Mfr
N.A.I.C.S.: 321992
Alexander Shiu Yin Mak *(Pres & CEO)*

YINJI ENTERTAINMENT AND MEDIA CO., LTD.
Tower A Level 25 26 Chaoyangmenwai Street, Beijing, 100020, China
Tel.: (86) 10 8565 3333
Web Site: http://www.d-m-g.com
Rev.: $335,906,504
Assets: $711,925,286
Liabilities: $235,007,695
Net Worth: $476,917,591
Earnings: $116,848,604
Fiscal Year-end: 12/31/17
Advertising Production Services
N.A.I.C.S.: 541810

YINLIPS TECHNOLOGY, INC.
Room 2929-31 NanGuang JieJia B No 3037 Shen south-Mid Road, FuTian District, Shenzhen, Guangdong, China
Tel.: (86) 75526018046 **DE**
Web Site: http://www.yinlips.com
Year Founded: 2006
Sales Range: $10-24.9 Million
Emp.: 200
Electronic Products Designer, Mfr & Marketer
N.A.I.C.S.: 334419
Zifeng Zhao *(Chm & CEO)*

YINSHENG DIGIFAVOR COMPANY LIMITED
5/F Building F5 TCL International E City No 1001 Zhongshan Yuan Road, Nanshan District, Shenzhen, China
Tel.: (86) 75588888007 **Ky**
Web Site: http://www.nnk.com.hk
3773—(HKG)
Rev.: $12,166,362
Assets: $71,126,500
Liabilities: $34,208,460
Net Worth: $36,918,040
Earnings: $3,828,006
Emp.: 134
Fiscal Year-end: 12/31/22
Mobile Top Up Services
N.A.I.C.S.: 517112
Junmou Huang *(Co-Founder & Chm)*

YINSON HOLDINGS BERHAD
BO2-A-18 Menara 3 No 3 Jalan Bangsar, KL Eco City, 59200, Kuala Lumpur, Malaysia
Tel.: (60) 322893888 **MY**
Web Site: http://www.yinson.com.my
YINSON—(KLS)
Rev.: $1,338,412,698
Assets: $4,075,978,836
Liabilities: $2,709,206,349
Net Worth: $1,366,772,487
Earnings: $124,444,444

AND PRIVATE COMPANIES

Emp.: 1,488
Fiscal Year-end: 01/31/23
Transport Services
N.A.I.C.S.: 926120
Chern Yuan Lim (CEO)

Subsidiaries:

Farosson Pte. Ltd. (1)
Unit 9-02 Samsung Hub 3 Church St, Singapore, 049483, Singapore
Tel.: (65) 69295399
Web Site: https://www.farosson.com
Advisory Investment Services
N.A.I.C.S.: 541690

Yinson Haulage Sdn. Bhd. (1)
PLO 729 Jalan Keluli Kawasan Perindustrian, 81700, Pasir Gudang, Johor Darul Takzim, Malaysia
Tel.: (60) 7 252 5754
Web Site: http://www.yinson.com.my
Container Trucking Services
N.A.I.C.S.: 484110

Yinson Marine Services Sdn. Bhd. (1)
No 25 Jalan Firma 2 Kawasan Perindustrian Tebrau IV, 81100, Johor Bahru, Johor Darul Takzim, Malaysia
Tel.: (60) 73552244
Emp.: 100
Chartered Vessel Leasing & Lubricant Trading Services
N.A.I.C.S.: 532411
Linhan Weng (Mng Dir)

Yinson Production (The Netherlands) B.V. (1)
Anna van Buerenplein 45 New Babylon Unit 8 2, 2595 DA, Hague, Netherlands
Tel.: (31) 702230100
Provision Intercompany Services
N.A.I.C.S.: 518210

Yinson Production AS (1)
Olav Vs gate 5, 0161, Oslo, Norway (100%)
Tel.: (47) 22340110
Holding Company; Oil & Gas Transportation Vessel Operator & Leasing Services
N.A.I.C.S.: 551112
Lars Eik (VP-Asset Mgmt & Bus Dev)

YINTAI GOLD CO., LTD.
30F CP Center 20 Jinhe East Road, Chaoyang District, Beijing, 100022, China
Tel.: (86) 1085171856
Web Site: https://en.sji-gold.com
Year Founded: 1999
000975—(SSE)
Rev.: $1,176,768,778
Assets: $2,269,818,664
Liabilities: $489,633,754
Net Worth: $1,780,184,910
Earnings: $157,873,636
Fiscal Year-end: 12/31/22
Metal Mining Services
N.A.I.C.S.: 213114
Haifei Yang (Chm)

YINTECH INVESTMENT HOLDINGS LIMITED
3rd Floor Lujiazui Investment Tower No 360 Pudian Road, Pudong District, Shanghai, 200125, China
Tel.: (86) 21 2028 9009
Web Site: http://www.yintech.net
Year Founded: 2015
Rev.: $242,097,296
Assets: $524,515,878
Liabilities: $127,921,955
Net Worth: $396,593,923
Earnings: $12,260,808
Emp.: 2,975
Fiscal Year-end: 12/31/19
Commodity Trading Services
N.A.I.C.S.: 523160
Wenbin Chen (Co-Founder, Chm & CEO)

YINYI CO., LTD.
6F Yinyi Waitan Mansion No 132 Renmin Road, Jiangbei District, Ningbo, 315020, China
Tel.: (86) 57487037581
Web Site: http://www.chinayinyi.cn
Year Founded: 1994
000981—(SSE)
Sales Range: $1-9.9 Million
Holding Company; Property Management Services
N.A.I.C.S.: 551112

Subsidiaries:

ARC Automotive, Inc. (1)
1729 Midpark Rd Ste 100, Knoxville, TN 37921 (100%)
Tel.: (865) 544-8426
Web Site: https://www.arcautomotive.com
Motor Vehicle Airbag Inflation Device Mfr & Distr
N.A.I.C.S.: 336390

YIOULA GLASSWORKS S.A.
5 Orizomilon Str, 12244, Aegaleo, Greece
Tel.: (30) 210 54 03 400
Web Site: http://www.yioula.gr
Year Founded: 1947
Sales Range: $250-299.9 Million
Glass Container Mfr
N.A.I.C.S.: 327213
Evangelos K. Voulgarakis (Chm & Mng Dir)

Subsidiaries:

BA Glass Romania, S.A. (1)
45 Theodor Pallady Bld Sector 3, 032258, Bucharest, Romania
Tel.: (40) 212018500
Web Site: http://www.bavidros.pt
Sales Range: $50-74.9 Million
Emp.: 3,000
Household Glassware Mfr
N.A.I.C.S.: 327215
Nikolaos Barlagiannis (Member-Exec Bd)

Biomedsklo PJSC (1)
26 Promyslova Str, 10025, Zhytomyr, Ukraine (98.53%)
Tel.: (380) 44 49 86500
Web Site: http://www.biomedsklo.com.ua
Glass Container Mfr
N.A.I.C.S.: 327213

Bucha Glassworks S.A. (1)
84 Kirov Str Kiev Region, 8294, Bucha, Ukraine (100%)
Tel.: (380) 44 49 86700
Glass Mfr
N.A.I.C.S.: 327213

New Glass S.A. (1)
36 Tzar Osvoboditel Str, 9900, Novi Pazar, Bulgaria
Tel.: (359) 54 858 300
Web Site: http://www.newglass.bg
Emp.: 50
Glass Mfr
N.A.I.C.S.: 327213
Filipos Tsagarakis (Gen Mgr)

YIP IN TSOI & CO., LTD.
523 Mahaprutharam Road, Bangrak, Bangkok, 10500, Thailand
Tel.: (66) 23538600   TH
Web Site: http://www.yipintsoi.com
Year Founded: 1926
Emp.: 650
IT Products & Services
N.A.I.C.S.: 541512
Supak Lailert (COO)

Subsidiaries:

Sissons Paints (Thailand) Limited (1)
91/2 Moo 3 Suwinthawong Road, Min Buri, Bangkok, 10510, Thailand
Tel.: (66) 29186760
Web Site: http://www.sissonsthai.com
Emp.: 35
Paints & Wallpaper Products
N.A.I.C.S.: 444120

Tangerine Company Limited (1)
25 Sathorn-Tai Road 20th Floor Bangkok Insurance Building, Tungmahamek, Sathorn, 10102, Bangkok, Thailand
Tel.: (66) 22855511
Web Site: http://www.tangerine.co.th
Emp.: 50
Information Retrieval Services
N.A.I.C.S.: 519290

Thailand Computer Center Limited (1)
523 Mahaprutharam Road, Bangrak, Bangkok, 10500, Thailand
Tel.: (66) 22369294
Web Site: http://www.yipintsoi.com
Computer Products Whslr
N.A.I.C.S.: 423430

Yip In Tsoi & Jacks Ltd. (1)
523 Mahaprutharam Road, Bangrak, Bangkok, 10500, Thailand
Tel.: (66) 26390200
Fertilizer & Agricultural Chemicals Mfr; Electronic Parts & Equipment Whslr; Construction Materials Whslr
N.A.I.C.S.: 325314

YipInTsoi Consulting Limited (1)
523 Mahaprutharam Road, Bangrak, Bangkok, 10500, Thailand
Tel.: (66) 23538600
Web Site: http://www.yitconsulting.co.th
Emp.: 25
IT & Business Consulting
N.A.I.C.S.: 541690

YIPINHONG PHARMACEUTICAL CO., LTD.
17/F Yunrun Building No 27 Huanyu 1st Road, Guangzhou International Biological Island Huangpu District, Guangzhou, 510623, Guangdong, China
Tel.: (86) 2028877623
Web Site: https://www.gdyph.com
Year Founded: 2002
300723—(CHIN)
Rev.: $320,139,883
Assets: $575,421,285
Liabilities: $271,342,881
Net Worth: $304,078,404
Earnings: $40,811,879
Emp.: 1,700
Fiscal Year-end: 12/31/22
Pharmaceutical Product Mfr & Distr
N.A.I.C.S.: 325412
Li Hanxiong (Chm)

YIPS CHEMICAL HOLDINGS LIMITED
27/F Fortis Tower No 77-79 Gloucester Road, Wanchai, China (Hong Kong)
Tel.: (852) 26752288
Web Site: http://www.yipschemical.com
0408—(HKG)
Rev.: $428,209,898
Assets: $1,021,400,715
Liabilities: $452,954,970
Net Worth: $568,445,745
Earnings: $165,228,525
Emp.: 2,642
Fiscal Year-end: 12/31/22
Petrochemical Products Mfr
N.A.I.C.S.: 324110
Stephen Tsz Hin Yip (Deputy Chm & CEO)

Subsidiaries:

Bauhinia Paints Manufacturing Limited (1)
Yips Chem Bldg 13 Yip Cheong St, On Lok Tsuen, Fanling, New Territories, China (Hong Kong)
Tel.: (852) 26752233
Web Site: http://www.bauhiniahk.com.hk
Paints & Coatings Mfr
N.A.I.C.S.: 325510

Best Lubricant Blending Limited (1)
5 F Yips Chem Bldg 13 Yip Cheong St, On Lok Tsuen, Fanling, New Territories, China (Hong Kong)
Tel.: (852) 26752222
Lubricant Oils Mfr & Sales
N.A.I.C.S.: 325998

EUCA Sanitizing Technology Company Limited (1)
27/F Fortis Tower Nos 77-79 Gloucester Road, Wanchai, China (Hong Kong)
Tel.: (852) 2 675 2288
Web Site: https://www.euca.com.hk
Sanitizer Product Mfr
N.A.I.C.S.: 325612

Handsome Chemical Development Limited (1)
5 F Yips Chem Bldg 13 Yip Cheong St, On Lok Tsuen, Fanling, New Territories, China (Hong Kong)
Tel.: (852) 26752299
Web Site: http://www.yipschemical.com
Ethyl & Butyl Acetates Mfr & Sales
N.A.I.C.S.: 325194

Handsome Chemical Services Limited (1)
Yips Hang Cheung Bldg 13 Yip Cheong St, On Lok Tsuen, Fanling, New Territories, China (Hong Kong)
Tel.: (852) 26752299
Lubricants Solvents & Coatings Whslr
N.A.I.C.S.: 424690

Hang Cheung Coatings (Zhejiang) Limited (1)
976 Guangming Rd, Wutong, Zhejiang, China
Tel.: (86) 57388260088
Coating Thinner & Paper Varnish Mfr
N.A.I.C.S.: 325510

Jiangmen Handsome Chemical Development Limited (1)
32nd Floor Building 1 Wanda Plaza Development Avenue, Pengjiang District, Jiangmen, Guangdong, China
Tel.: (86) 7503292951
Web Site: http://www.handsomechemical.com
Ethyl Acetate Solvent Mfr
N.A.I.C.S.: 325199

Pacific Oil & Chemical Company Limited (1)
44 Yips Chemical Bldg 13 Yip Cheong St, On Lok Tsuen, Fanling, New Territories, China (Hong Kong)
Tel.: (852) 23458316
Web Site: http://www.pacoil.com
Emp.: 20
Lubricant Oils Supplier
N.A.I.C.S.: 424720
Steman Man Wong (Mng Dir)

Totalle Procurement Logistics (Macao Commercial Offshore) Limited (1)
Rm D 7 F Edf Centro Comm Kong Fat, 174 Rua Pequim, Macau, China (Macau)
Tel.: (853) 28752308
Emp.: 3
Commercial Service Agents & Overseas Sales
N.A.I.C.S.: 425120

Yip's Camel (Hong Kong) Limited (1)
27/F Fortis Tower 77-79 Gloucester Road, Wanchai, China (Hong Kong)
Tel.: (852) 26752333
Web Site: https://www.camel.com.hk
Petrochemical Product Mfr & Whslr
N.A.I.C.S.: 325998
Yu Alex (Dir-Bus)

Yip's H.C. (Holding) Limited (1)
5 F Yips Chem Building 13 Yip Cheong Street, On Lok Tsuen, Fanling, New Territories, China (Hong Kong)
Tel.: (852) 26752288
Investment Holding Services
N.A.I.C.S.: 551112

Yip's Ink and Chemicals Company Limited (1)
4 F Yips Hang Cheung Building 13 Yip Cheong Street, On Lok Tsuen, Fanling, New Territories, China (Hong Kong)

Yips Chemical Holdings Limited—(Continued)
Tel.: (852) 26752288
Gravure & Laminate Inks Mfr
N.A.I.C.S.: 325910

Yip's Lubricant Limited (1)
Yip's Chemical Building 13 Yip Cheong Street, On Lok Tsuen Fanling, Hong Kong, New Territories, China (Hong Kong)
Tel.: (852) 26752288
Petrochemical Product Mfr & Whslr
N.A.I.C.S.: 325998

YIREN DIGITAL LTD.
23/F China Merchants Bureau Building 118 Jianguo Road, Chaoyang District, Beijing, 100022, China
Tel.: (86) 1050905315
Web Site: https://ir.yirendai.com
YRD—(NYSE)
Rev.: $677,840,192
Assets: $1,422,922,574
Liabilities: $303,412,578
Net Worth: $1,119,509,997
Earnings: $288,020,187
Emp.: 754
Fiscal Year-end: 12/31/23
Online Financial Services
N.A.I.C.S.: 522320
Ning Tang (CEO & Chm)

YIT CORPORATION
Panuntie 11, PO Box 36, 00621, Helsinki, Finland
Tel.: (358) 20433111 FI
Web Site: https://www.yitgroup.com
YIT—(HEL)
Rev.: $2,334,340,600
Assets: $3,056,334,988
Liabilities: $2,144,398,878
Net Worth: $911,936,111
Earnings: $3,237,643
Emp.: 4,302
Fiscal Year-end: 12/31/23
Facility Management, Construction & Industrial Services
N.A.I.C.S.: 561210
Antti Inkila (Pres-Interim & CEO)

Subsidiaries:

AB YIT Kausta (1)
Karaliaus Mindaugo Ave 35, Kaunas, 44307, Lithuania
Tel.: (370) 37452348
Web Site: http://www.yit.lt
Emp.: 400
Property Management Services
N.A.I.C.S.: 531311

AS YIT Ehitus (1)
Parnu Mnt 102 C, Tallinn, 11312, Estonia
Tel.: (372) 6652100
Web Site: http://www.yit.ee
Construction Engineering Services
N.A.I.C.S.: 541330

Almrins ROrservice AB (1)
Eldsunda Park Byggnad 21, 645 35, Strangnas, Sweden
Tel.: (46) 152 10500
Construction Engineering Services
N.A.I.C.S.: 541330

LLC YIT Service (1)
Primorsky Prospect house 54 building 1 lit, Saint Petersburg, Russia (100%)
Tel.: (7) 8126777006
Web Site: http://spb.yitservice.ru
Industrial Building Construction Services
N.A.I.C.S.: 236220

Lemminkainen Oyj (1)
Panuntie 11, PO Box 36, 620, Helsinki, Finland
Tel.: (358) 20433111
Web Site: http://www.lemminkainen.com
Sales Range: $1-4.9 Billion
Emp.: 4,244
Engineering & Construction Services
N.A.I.C.S.: 237990
Berndt Brunow (Chm)

Subsidiary (Domestic):

Byggnads Ab Forsstrom Rakennus Oy (2)
Tervahovintie 2, 67100, Kokkola, Finland
Tel.: (358) 207158700
Engineeering Services
N.A.I.C.S.: 541330

Instel AB OY (2)
Klas Ake Lund, Tanhuantie 28, 68630, Pietarsaari, Finland (70%)
Tel.: (358) 400867714
Sales Range: $25-49.9 Million
Emp.: 10
Electrical Contractor
N.A.I.C.S.: 238210

Subsidiary (Non-US):

Lemminkainen (China) Co., Ltd. (2)
Xin Zha Rd 831 Office 6C, 200041, Shanghai, China
Tel.: (86) 21 6267 1230
Web Site: http://www.lemminkainen.cn
Sales Range: $25-49.9 Million
Emp.: 2
Construction Engineering Services
N.A.I.C.S.: 541330
Teemu Lahti (Office Mgr)

Lemminkainen A/S (2)
Norreskov Bakke 1, Silkeborg, 8600, Denmark
Tel.: (45) 8722 1500
Web Site: http://www.lemminkainen.dk
Sales Range: $100-124.9 Million
Emp.: 320
Civil Engineering Construction Services
N.A.I.C.S.: 541330
Claus Terkildsen (Mng Dir)

Subsidiary (Domestic):

LMK VEJ A/S (3)
Norreskov Bakke 1, 8600, Silkeborg, Denmark
Tel.: (45) 87221500
Web Site: http://www.lmkvej.dk
Sales Range: $125-149.9 Million
Emp.: 300
Asphalt Paving Mixture & Block Mfr
N.A.I.C.S.: 324121

Subsidiary (Domestic):

Lemminkainen Betonituote Oy (2)
Sundholmsplatsen 2, PO Box 169, 00180, Helsinki, Finland (100%)
Tel.: (358) 207150100
Web Site: http://www.lemminkainenbetonituote.fi
Sales Range: $50-74.9 Million
Emp.: 200
Engineering & Construction Services
N.A.I.C.S.: 237990

Subsidiary (Non-US):

Lemminkainen Eesti AS (2)
Liivalaia 14, 10118, Tallinn, Estonia
Tel.: (372) 6461125
Engineering & Construction Services
N.A.I.C.S.: 237990

Subsidiary (Domestic):

Ou Lohketood (3)
Betooni 28, 11415, Tallinn, Estonia
Tel.: (372) 6709 000
Sales Range: $25-49.9 Million
Emp.: 12
Construction Engineering Services
N.A.I.C.S.: 541330

Tekmanni Eesti OU (3)
Mustamae tee 18, 10617, Tallinn, Estonia
Tel.: (372) 6567503
Building Equipment & Machinery Installation Contractors
N.A.I.C.S.: 238220

Subsidiary (Domestic):

Lemminkainen Infra Oy (2)
Salmisaarenaukio 2, PO Box 169, 00181, Helsinki, Finland
Tel.: (358) 207150006
Web Site: http://www.lemminkaineninfra.com

Sales Range: $350-399.9 Million
Emp.: 2,000
Construction Engineering Services
N.A.I.C.S.: 541330
Jouko Viitala (Dir-Engrg-Foundation)

Subsidiary (Non-US):

SIA Lemminkainen Latvija (3)
Bicites, Garkalne, 1024, Latvia
Tel.: (371) 67358048
Web Site: http://www.lemminkainen.lv
Sales Range: $25-49.9 Million
Emp.: 10
Road Construction Engineering Services
N.A.I.C.S.: 237310

Subsidiary (Domestic):

Lemminkainen Katto Oy (2)
Puusepantie 11, 04361, Tuusula, Finland (100%)
Tel.: (358) 207150100
Sales Range: $50-74.9 Million
Emp.: 200
Engineering & Construction Services
N.A.I.C.S.: 237990

Subsidiary (Non-US):

Lemminkainen Norge AS (2)
Fjellhamarveien 44 B, 1472, Fjellhamar, Norway (100%)
Tel.: (47) 67914800
Web Site: http://www.lemminkainen.no
Sales Range: $25-49.9 Million
Emp.: 60
Asphalt Paving Mixture & Block Mfr
N.A.I.C.S.: 324121

Subsidiary (Domestic):

Asfalt Remix AS (3)
Vadbakken 8, 1592, Valer, Norway
Tel.: (47) 69289901
Web Site: https://www.asfaltremix.no
Emp.: 55
Infrastructure Construction & Cold Mining Services
N.A.I.C.S.: 237990
Per Erik Brynildsen (CEO)

Lemminkainen Anlegg AS (3)
Grensevelen 92 Helsfyr 8 Etasje, Oslo, 0609, Norway
Tel.: (47) 67914800
Audiovisual Products Distr
N.A.I.C.S.: 423620

Lemminkainen Industri AS (3)
Grenseveien 92, 663, Oslo, Norway
Tel.: (47) 67 91 48 00
Construction Engineering Services
N.A.I.C.S.: 541330
Jan Oyri (Mgr)

Subsidiary (Domestic):

Lemminkainen PP Oy (2)
Itkonniemenkatu 29e 3 Kerros, 70500, Kuopio, Finland
Tel.: (358) 2071 5000
Web Site: http://www.lemminkainen.fi
Sales Range: $25-49.9 Million
Emp.: 100
Construction Engineering Services
N.A.I.C.S.: 541330
Pentti Holopainen (Project Mgr)

Subsidiary (Non-US):

Lemminkainen Polska Sp. z o.o. (2)
ul Marconich 11-3, 02954, Warsaw, Poland (100%)
Tel.: (48) 228589837
Web Site: http://www.lemminkainen.pl
Sales Range: $25-49.9 Million
Emp.: 20
Lumber Plywood Millwork & Wood Panel Whslr
N.A.I.C.S.: 423310

Lemminkainen Sverige AB (2)
Svetsarvagen 24, 171 41, Solna, Sweden
Tel.: (46) 854525380
Web Site: http://www.lemminkainen.com
Emp.: 90
Civil Engineering Construction Services
N.A.I.C.S.: 237990

Subsidiary (Domestic):

Lemminkainen Talo Oy (2)
Salmisaarenaukio 2, PO Box 169, 00180, Tampere, Helsinki, Finland
Tel.: (358) 2071 5000
Web Site: http://www.lemminkainen.fi
Construction & Engineering Services
N.A.I.C.S.: 541330
Janne Korja (Reg Dir)

Lemminkainen Talo Oy International (2)
Salmisaarenaukio 2, PO Box 169, 181, Helsinki, Finland
Tel.: (358) 2071 5001
Construction Engineering Services
N.A.I.C.S.: 541330
Timo Kohtamaki (Gen Mgr)

Lemminkainen Talo Oy Russia (2)
Salmisaarenaukio 2, 180, Helsinki, Finland
Tel.: (358) 2071500
Construction Engineering Services
N.A.I.C.S.: 541330

Omni-Sica Oy (2)
Puusepantie 11, 04360, Tuusula, Finland (100%)
Tel.: (358) 207150100
Web Site: http://www.omni-sica.fi
Sales Range: $50-74.9 Million
Emp.: 200
Engineering & Construction Services
N.A.I.C.S.: 237990

Oulun LVI-Ykkonen Oy (2)
Kempeleentie 5, 90400, Oulu, Finland (100%)
Tel.: (358) 108434800
Web Site: http://www.lemminkainentaloteknikka.fi
Sales Range: $25-49.9 Million
Emp.: 50
Plumbing Heating & Air-Conditioning Contractors
N.A.I.C.S.: 238220

Oy Alfred A. Palmberg AB (2)
Esterinportti 2, 00240, Helsinki, Finland (100%)
Tel.: (358) 207150300
Web Site: http://www.palmberg.fi
Engineering & Construction Services
N.A.I.C.S.: 237990

Oy Konte AB (2)
Olympiakatu 16, 65100, Vaasa, Finland (100%)
Tel.: (358) 207150700
Web Site: http://www.Lemminkainen.com
Engineering & Construction Services
N.A.I.C.S.: 237990

Palmberg-Rakennus Oy (2)
Valtatie 21, 90500, Oulu, Finland (100%)
Tel.: (358) 207158600
Web Site: http://www.lemminkainen.fi
Sales Range: $50-74.9 Million
Emp.: 200
Engineering & Construction Services
N.A.I.C.S.: 237990

Palmberg-Urakoitsijat Oy (2)
Uudenmaankatu 32-34, 05800, Hyvinkaa, Finland
Tel.: (358) 207158000
Web Site: http://www.lemminkainen.fi
Engineeering Services
N.A.I.C.S.: 541330

Rakennusliike A. Taskinen Oy (2)
Nurmeksentie 14, 80100, Joensuu, Finland (100%)
Tel.: (358) 207157590
Sales Range: $25-49.9 Million
Emp.: 100
Engineering & Construction Services
N.A.I.C.S.: 237990
Ari Laamanen (Mng Dir)

Rakennustoimisto Palmberg Oy (2)
Satakunnankatu 22 E, 33210, Tampere, Finland (100%)
Tel.: (358) 207157100
Web Site: http://www.palmberg-tampere.fi
Sales Range: $25-49.9 Million
Emp.: 200
Engineeering Services
N.A.I.C.S.: 541330

AND PRIVATE COMPANIES YKK CORPORATION

Jukka Terhonen *(Mng Dir)*

Tekmanni Oy (2)
Laturikuja 8, PO Box 500, 02650, Helsinki, Finland
Tel.: (358) 207153000
Web Site: http://www.tekmanni.fi
Sales Range: $50-74.9 Million
Emp.: 150
Electrical Contractor
N.A.I.C.S.: 238210

Tekmanni Pohjanmaa Oy (2)
Valakilanatu 7, Seinajoki, 60120, Finland
Tel.: (358) 207153060
Web Site: http://www.lemminkainentalotekniikka.fi
Sales Range: $50-74.9 Million
Emp.: 150
Electrical Contractor
N.A.I.C.S.: 238210

Tekmanni RusService Oy (2)
Laturinkuja 8, 02650, Espoo, Finland
Tel.: (358) 20 715003
Property Management Services
N.A.I.C.S.: 531312

Subsidiary (Non-US):

UAB Lemminkainen Lietuva (2)
Granito 4, 02241, Vilnius, Lithuania
Tel.: (370) 52640330
Web Site: http://www.lemminkainen.com
Sales Range: $50-74.9 Million
Emp.: 250
Highway & Street Construction
N.A.I.C.S.: 237310

ZAO Lemminkainen Rus (2)
36/40 Sredny Pr Vasily Island, 199004, Saint Petersburg, Russia
Tel.: (7) 812 740 5353
Sales Range: $25-49.9 Million
Emp.: 10
Construction Engineering Services
N.A.I.C.S.: 541330
Juha Vatto *(Gen Dir)*

Subsidiary (Domestic):

OOO Tekmen SPb (3)
Polevaya Sabirovskaya ul 44, 197183, Saint Petersburg, Russia
Tel.: (7) 8124304270
Web Site: http://www.tekmen.fi
Sales Range: $25-49.9 Million
Emp.: 250
Electrical Contractor
N.A.I.C.S.: 238210
Timo Kahkonen *(Gen Dir)*

ZAO Lemminkainen Dorstroi (3)
Prospekt Stachek 62, 198097, Saint Petersburg, Russia
Tel.: (7) 8123313922
Engineering & Construction Services
N.A.I.C.S.: 237990

YIT Austria GmbH (1)
Oberlaaer Strasse 331, 1230, Vienna, Austria
Tel.: (43) 506062100
Web Site: http://www.yit.at
Emp.: 700
Installation & Maintenance of Heating & Ventilation Systems & Pipework for the Chemical & Pharmaceutical Industries
N.A.I.C.S.: 238220

YIT Eesti AS (1)
Parnu Mnt 102B, 11312, Tallinn, Estonia
Tel.: (372) 6652100
Web Site: https://www.yit.ee
Emp.: 100
Construction Services
N.A.I.C.S.: 236220

YIT Invest Export Oy (1)
Panuntie 11, 620, Helsinki, Finland
Tel.: (358) 20433111
Web Site: http://www.yitgroup.com
Construction Engineering Services
N.A.I.C.S.: 541330

Subsidiary (Non-US):

ZAO YIT Moskovia (2)
ul Krasnaya 4 4-6 floors, Lyubertsy, Russia
Tel.: (7) 4952297576
Web Site: http://www.yitdom.ru
Emp.: 100

Industrial Building Construction Services
N.A.I.C.S.: 236220
Yuri Belomestnov *(Gen Dir)*

YIT Kalusto Oy (1)
Yhteiskoulntie 11, 31700, Urjala, Finland
Tel.: (358) 204335600
Web Site: http://www.yit.com
Construction Engineering Services
N.A.I.C.S.: 541330

YIT Latvija SIA (1)
Vienibas Gatve 109, Riga, 1058, Latvia
Tel.: (371) 67606900
Web Site: https://www.yit.lv
Construction Services
N.A.I.C.S.: 236220

YIT POLAND Sp. z o. o. (1)
Ul Pory 53, 02-757, Warsaw, Poland
Tel.: (48) 222026969
Web Site: http://www.yit.pl
Emp.: 90
N.A.I.C.S.: 334220

YIT Romania S.R.L. (1)
Str Sibiului 2 Selimbar, Sibiu, 557260, Romania
Tel.: (40) 369408917
Web Site: http://www.cbs-ee.ro
Emp.: 30
Construction Engineering Services
N.A.I.C.S.: 541330

YIT Stavo s.r.o (1)
General Spades 430/26, 160 00, Prague, Czech Republic
Tel.: (420) 800200666
Web Site: https://www.yit.cz
Construction Services
N.A.I.C.S.: 236220

ZAO YIT CityStroi (1)
Krylatskye Kholmy Str 30-9, 121614, Moscow, Russia
Tel.: (7) 4997266105
Industrial Building Construction Services
N.A.I.C.S.: 236220

ZAO YIT Uralstroi (1)
23 Krashnykh komandirov Street, Yekaterinburg, 620135, Russia
Tel.: (7) 3433677172
Web Site: http://www.ekb.yit.ru
Emp.: 60
Construction Engineering Services
N.A.I.C.S.: 541330
Elena Richter *(Asst Sec)*

ZAO YIT-Peter (1)
Primorsky pr 54/1 A, 197374, Saint Petersburg, Russia
Tel.: (7) 8123206201
Web Site: http://english.yit.ru
Industrial Building Construction Services
N.A.I.C.S.: 236220

YITOA MICRO TECHNOLOGY CORP
465 Osato-cho, Kofu, 400-0053, Yamanashi, Japan
Tel.: (81) 552418611
Web Site: http://www.pmtc.co.jp
Year Founded: 2003
Sales Range: $100-124.9 Million
Emp.: 331
Semiconductor Product Mfr
N.A.I.C.S.: 334413
Katsuhiko Terada *(Pres)*

YIWU HUADING NYLON CO., LTD.
No 751 Xuefeng West Peak, No 751 Xuefeng West Road, Yiwu, 322000, Zhejiang, China
Tel.: (86) 57985210658
Web Site: https://www.hdnylon.com
Year Founded: 2002
601113—(SHG)
Rev.: $919,400,751
Assets: $786,525,377
Liabilities: $232,212,671
Net Worth: $554,312,706
Earnings: $60,174,345
Fiscal Year-end: 12/31/22
Nylon Filament Mfr

N.A.I.C.S.: 325220
Ermin Ding *(Chm)*

YIXIN GROUP LTD.
Lujiazui Century Financial Pla 799 South Yanggao Rd 3 Bldg, Shanghai, 200120, China
Tel.: (86) 4000169169
2858—(HKG)
Rev.: $730,291,723
Assets: $4,515,880,637
Liabilities: $2,364,080,332
Net Worth: $2,151,800,305
Earnings: $52,062,286
Emp.: 4,106
Fiscal Year-end: 12/31/22
Online Automobile Finance Services
N.A.I.C.S.: 522220
Jiang Dong *(Pres)*

YIXINTANG PHARMACEUTICAL GROUP CO., LTD.
No 1 Hongxiang Road Economic and Technological Development Zone, Kunming, 650500, Yunnan, China
Tel.: (86) 87168185283
Web Site: http://www.hx8886.com
Year Founded: 2000
002727—(SSE)
Rev.: $2,447,398,830
Assets: $2,271,544,685
Liabilities: $1,214,672,088
Net Worth: $1,056,872,597
Earnings: $141,803,466
Emp.: 3,000
Fiscal Year-end: 12/31/22
Pharmaceutical & Medical Equipment Retailer & Distr
N.A.I.C.S.: 456110
Hongxian Ruan *(Chm, Pres & CEO)*

YIZUMI HOLDINGS CO., LTD.
No 22 Ke Yuan 3rd Road Shunde, Foshan, 528300, Guangdong, China
Tel.: (86) 75729262000
Web Site: https://www.yizumi.com
300415—(CHIN)
Rev.: $516,656,556
Assets: $763,350,588
Liabilities: $423,318,636
Net Worth: $340,031,952
Earnings: $56,926,584
Emp.: 3,700
Fiscal Year-end: 12/31/22
Injection Molding Machine Mfr
N.A.I.C.S.: 333248
Jingcai Chen *(Chm)*

Subsidiaries:

Yizumi Germany Company (1)
Konrad-Zuse-Str 41, 52477, Alsdorf, Germany
Tel.: (49) 2404967910
Web Site: https://www.yizumi-germany.de
Industrial Molding Equipment Mfr
N.A.I.C.S.: 333511
Wing Fai Richard Yam *(Mng Dir)*

Yizumi Indian Company (1)
No 4/42 1st Main Road Thillai Ganga Nagar, Nanganallur, Chennai, 600061, Tamilnadu, India
Tel.: (91) 7259118421
Industrial Molding Equipment Mfr
N.A.I.C.S.: 333511

YKGI HOLDINGS BERHAD
Suite 27-1 Setia Avenue No 2 Jalan Setia Prima S U13/S Seksyen U13, Setia Alam, 40170, Shah Alam, Selangor Darul Ehsan, Malaysia
Tel.: (60) 350376228
Web Site: https://asteelgroup.com
YKGI—(KLS)
Rev.: $60,312,284
Assets: $53,085,338
Liabilities: $32,806,464
Net Worth: $20,278,875

Earnings: $2,005,742
Emp.: 450
Fiscal Year-end: 12/31/21
Steel Mfrs
N.A.I.C.S.: 331110
Victor Lu Thian Hii *(Mng Dir)*

Subsidiaries:

ASTAR Steel Sdn. Bhd. (1)
PTD 102979 Jalan Seelong Jaya 15, Mukim Senai Kulai, 81400, Senai, Johor, Malaysia
Tel.: (60) 75992846
Steel Products Mfr
N.A.I.C.S.: 331110

ASTEEL Resources Sdn. Bhd. (1)
Lot 712 Block 7 Demak Laut Industrial Park, 93050, Kuching, Sarawak, Malaysia
Tel.: (60) 82433888
Iron & Steel Product Mfr
N.A.I.C.S.: 331110

Subsidiary (Domestic):

ASTEEL (Sabah) Sdn. Bhd. (2)
Lot 10 Package 1 General Industrial Zone, Kota Kinabalu Industrial Park KM26 Jalan Tuaran, 88460, Kota Kinabalu, Sabah, Malaysia
Tel.: (60) 88498866
Iron & Steel Product Mfr
N.A.I.C.S.: 331110

ASTEEL Ajiya Sdn. Bhd. (2)
Lot 1268 Block 8 Jalan Bako Demak Laut Industrial Estate Phase IV, 93050, Kuching, Sarawak, Malaysia
Tel.: (60) 82433403
Iron & Steel Product Mfr
N.A.I.C.S.: 331110

ASTEEL Sdn Bhd. (1)
Lot 712 Block 7 Demak Laut Industrial Park, 93050, Kuching, Sarawak, Malaysia
Tel.: (60) 82433888
Emp.: 10
Galvanized Steel & Roofing Sheets Distr
N.A.I.C.S.: 423330

Plant (Domestic):

YKGI Holdings Berhad - Klang (2)
Wisma YKGI Lot 6479 Lorong Sungai Puloh/KU6, Kawasan Perindustrian Sungai Puloh, 42100, Klang, Selango, Malaysia
Tel.: (60) 33 291 5189
Web Site: https://www.ykgigroup.com
Emp.: 500
Galvanized & Coated Steel Mfr
N.A.I.C.S.: 331110

ASTEEL Synergy Sdn. Bhd. (1)
No 2 Jalan Sungai Chandong 19A/KU6, Kawasan Industrial Klang Utama KM10 Jalan Kapar, 42100, Klang, Selangor, Malaysia
Tel.: (60) 132079812
Steel Products Mfr
N.A.I.C.S.: 331110

YKGI LIMITED
32 Woodlands Terrace, Singapore, 738452, Singapore
Tel.: (65) 65556992
Web Site: https://www.ykgi.com.sg
Year Founded: 2022
YK9—(CAT)
Rev.: $46,920,397
Assets: $35,990,305
Liabilities: $22,834,962
Net Worth: $13,155,343
Earnings: $1,116,413
Emp.: 593
Fiscal Year-end: 12/31/23
Food Court Management Services
N.A.I.C.S.: 722310

YKK CORPORATION
1 Kanda Izumi-cho, Chiyoda-ku, Tokyo, 101-8642, Japan
Tel.: (81) 338642000   JP
Web Site: http://www.ykk.com
Year Founded: 1934
Rev.: $6,937,975,860
Assets: $9,168,122,040

YKK CORPORATION

YKK Corporation—(Continued)

Liabilities: $3,087,095,340
Net Worth: $6,081,026,700
Earnings: $415,165,440
Emp.: 46,167
Fiscal Year-end: 03/31/19
Zippers, Aluminum Architectural Products, Nonferrous Metal Products, Cotton, Synthetic Yarn & Precision Machinery Mfr
N.A.I.C.S.: 339993
Masayuki Sarumaru *(Chm)*

Subsidiaries:

DALIAN YKK ZIPPER CO., LTD. (1)
50 Tieshan West Road Dalian Economic & Technical Development Zone, Dalian, China
Tel.: (86) 411 87621216
Fastener Product Mfr
N.A.I.C.S.: 339993

DYNAT VERSCHLUSSTECHNIK GMBH (1)
Siemensstrasse 8, 31177, Harsum, Germany
Tel.: (49) 5127 4093 0
Web Site: http://www.dynat.de
Fastener Product Mfr
N.A.I.C.S.: 339993

Golden Hill Tower Ltd. (1)
No 24-26 Kaba Aye Pagoda Road, Bahan Township, Yangon, 11201, Myanmar
Tel.: (95) 1 558556
Web Site: http://www.goldenhilltower.com
Building Construction Services
N.A.I.C.S.: 236116
Ryuti Shimokawa *(Mng Dir)*

OOO YKK (1)
Kulmar St 11 Of 11, 220100, Minsk, Belarus
Tel.: (375) 17 289 5557
Fastener Product Mfr
N.A.I.C.S.: 339993

P.T. YKK ZIPPER INDONESIA (1)
Jl R P Soeroso No 7, Jakarta, 10330, Indonesia
Tel.: (62) 21 31931708
Web Site: http://www.ykk.co.id
Fastener Product Mfr
N.A.I.C.S.: 339993

Plant (Domestic):

P.T. YKK ZIPPER INDONESIA - FACTORY I (2)
Jl Raya Jakarta Bogor Km 29 Cimanggis, 16951, Depok, Indonesia
Tel.: (62) 21 8710641
Fastener Product Mfr
N.A.I.C.S.: 339993

P.T. YKK ZIPPER INDONESIA - FACTORY II (2)
Kampung Meriuk Desa Gandasari Kec, Cikarang Barat, 17520, Bekasi, Indonesia
Tel.: (62) 21 88332211
Fastener Product Mfr
N.A.I.C.S.: 339993

PT. YKK AP Indonesia (1)
Galaxy Mall 2nd Floor No 231 JL Dharmahusada Indah Timur No 35 37, 60115, Surabaya, Indonesia
Tel.: (62) 31 5937224
Web Site: http://www.ykkap.co.id
Aluminum Door & Window Mfr
N.A.I.C.S.: 332321
Louis Pardinata *(Mgr-Sls Plng)*

PT. YKK Zipco Indonesia - FACTORY I (1)
Kp Meriuk Ds Ganda Mekar Kec, Cikarang Barat, Bekasi, Indonesia
Tel.: (62) 21 88320152
Fastener Product Mfr
N.A.I.C.S.: 339993

SHANGHAI YKK ZIPPER CO., LTD (1)
23th Floor Ka Wah Centre 1010 Huai Hai Road M, 200031, Shanghai, China
Tel.: (86) 21 54038181
Fastener Product Mfr
N.A.I.C.S.: 339993

THE NEW ZIPPER COMPANY LTD. (1)
Regus 268 Bath Road, Slough, SL1 4DX, Berkshire, United Kingdom
Tel.: (44) 1753 57 2222
Fastener Product Mfr
N.A.I.C.S.: 339993
Dawn Steadman *(Acct Manager)*

YKK (KOREA) CO., LTD. (1)
Sowol-Ro 10 Chung-Gu, Seoul, 100704, Korea (South)
Tel.: (82) 2 37057900
Web Site: http://www.ykkkorea.com
Emp.: 80
Fastener Product Mfr
N.A.I.C.S.: 339993
Noriyuki Ogawa *(CEO)*

Plant (Domestic):

YKK (KOREA) CO., LTD. - Pyongtaek Factory (2)
383 Sin Ri Jinwi Myeon, Pyeongtaek, 451865, Gyeonggi-do, Korea (South)
Tel.: (82) 31 662 3393
Web Site: http://www.ykkkorea.co.kr
Emp.: 300
Fastener Product Mfr
N.A.I.C.S.: 339993
Shima Oo *(CEO)*

YKK (MALAYSIA) SDN BHD (1)
No 19 Jalan Bakti Kawasan Perindustrian Larkin, 80350, Johor Bahru, Johor, Malaysia
Tel.: (60) 7 2374 389
Web Site: http://www.ykk.com.my
Fastener Product Mfr
N.A.I.C.S.: 339993

YKK (U.K.) LTD. (1)
Whitehouse Industrial Estate, Runcorn, WA7 3BW, Cheshire, United Kingdom
Tel.: (44) 1928 593 800
Web Site: http://www.ykkfastening.com
Emp.: 150
Fastener Product Mfr
N.A.I.C.S.: 339993
Graham Lewtas *(Mgr-IT)*

YKK (XIAMEN) TRADING CO, LTD. (1)
A4 2 Floor Xiangyu Bldg Xiangyu Free Trading Zone, Xiamen, Fujian, China
Tel.: (86) 592 562 6306
Fastener Product Mfr
N.A.I.C.S.: 339993

YKK AP Facade PTE. Ltd (1)
7 International Business Park 02 02 TechQuest Building, 609919, Singapore, Singapore
Tel.: (65) 6567 2980
Emp.: 130
Architectural Services
N.A.I.C.S.: 541310
Alex Chan *(Sr Mgr-HR)*

YKK AP, Inc. (1)
1 Kanda Izumi-cho, 101-8642, Tokyo, Chiyoda-ku, Japan
Tel.: (81) 338642200
Web Site: http://www.ykkap.co.jp
Sales Range: $75-99.9 Million
Emp.: 12,416
Architectural Services
N.A.I.C.S.: 541310

Subsidiary (US):

YKK AP, America Inc. (2)
7680 The Bluffs Ste 100, Austell, GA 30168-2653 **(100%)**
Tel.: (678) 838-6000
Web Site: http://www.ykkap.com
Emp.: 70
Architectural Products Mfr & Distr
N.A.I.C.S.: 516110
Max Mizota *(Chm)*

YKK AUSTRIA GMBH (1)
Industriestr 2, 7221, Marz, Austria
Tel.: (43) 2626 62405
Fastener Product Mfr
N.A.I.C.S.: 339993
Robert Werner *(Gen Mgr)*

YKK Argentina S.A. (1)
Av Triunvirato 2729, C1427AAA, Buenos Aires, Argentina
Tel.: (54) 1145543333
Fastener Product Mfr
N.A.I.C.S.: 339993

YKK BANGLADESH PTE. LTD (1)
Bay's Edge Water 5th Fl 12 North Avenue Dhaka, 1213, Dhaka, Bangladesh
Tel.: (880) 2 882 2227
Fastener Product Mfr
N.A.I.C.S.: 339993
Ziaul Islam Mamun *(Asst Mgr-HR & Gen Affairs)*

YKK Business Support Inc. (1)
1 Kanda Izumi-cho, Chiyoda-ku, Tokyo, 101-8642, Japan
Tel.: (81) 338642000
Web Site: http://www.ykk.com
Sales Range: Less than $1 Million
Emp.: 182
Business Management Services
N.A.I.C.S.: 541618

YKK CZECH SPOL S.R.O. (1)
Masarykova 118, 66442, Modrice, Czech Republic
Tel.: (420) 531 015400
Web Site: http://www.ykk.cz
Fastener Product Mfr
N.A.I.C.S.: 339993

YKK Canada, Inc. (1)
3939 Boul Thimens, Saint Laurent, H4R 1X3, QC, Canada **(100%)**
Tel.: (514) 332-3350
Web Site: http://www.ykk.ca
Emp.: 40
Buttons, Zippers, Hook & Loop Fasteners Mfr
N.A.I.C.S.: 339993

YKK Corporation of America (1)
1 Parkway Ctr 1850 Pkwy Pl SE Ste 300, Marietta, GA 30067-8258 **(100%)**
Tel.: (770) 261-6120
Web Site: http://www.ykkamerica.com
Emp.: 28
Zippers, Buttons, Hook & Loop Fasteners Mfr
N.A.I.C.S.: 339993
Alex Gregory *(Pres & CEO)*

Subsidiary (Domestic):

Tape Craft Corporation (2)
200 Tape Craft Dr, Oxford, AL 36203 **(100%)**
Tel.: (256) 236-2535
Web Site: http://www.tapecraft.com
Fastener Mfr
N.A.I.C.S.: 313220

YKK (U.S.A.) Inc. (2)
1300 Cobb Industrial Dr, Marietta, GA 30066
Tel.: (770) 427-5521
Web Site: http://www.ykk-usa.com
Fastener Product Mfr
N.A.I.C.S.: 339993
John Smith *(Pres)*

Division (Domestic):

YKK Corporation of America - Rutherford (2)
301 Route 17 N, Rutherford, NJ 07070-3509 **(100%)**
Tel.: (201) 935-4200
Web Site: http://www.ykkamerica.com
Emp.: 5
Fastening Products Distr
N.A.I.C.S.: 339993

Subsidiary (Non-US):

YKK HONDURAS S.A. (2)
2da Calle N E Suite 1226 Colonia San Fernando, Salida a La Lima, San Pedro Sula, Honduras
Tel.: (504) 553 3164
Fastener Product Mfr
N.A.I.C.S.: 339993

Subsidiary (Domestic):

YKK Snap Fasteners America Inc. (2)
1090 industry Rd, Lawrenceburg, KY 40342
Tel.: (502) 839-6971
Web Site: http://www.ykksnap-america.com

INTERNATIONAL PUBLIC

Metal Buttons, Snap Fasteners, Rivets, Hooks & Eyes, Loops, Slides, Attaching Machines Mfr
N.A.I.C.S.: 339993
Steve Furuki *(Pres)*

Subsidiary (Non-US):

YKK Snap Fasteners Mexico S.A. de C.V. (3)
Calzada Agroindustrias Ste 300 Colonia Jumbo Plz, 27278, Torreon, Coahuila, Mexico **(100%)**
Tel.: (52) 8717335038
Web Site: http://www.ykk-ufi.com
Emp.: 26
Buttons, Hooks & Fasteners Mfr
N.A.I.C.S.: 339993
Jesus Llamas *(Mgr-Sls)*

YKK Costa Rica Ltda. (1)
Facing South Side of College Assn of Costa Rica Zapote Radial Parallel, Sts PO Box 6892-1000, Adj to Distribuidora La Natl, Barrio Cordoba, San Jose, Costa Rica **(100%)**
Tel.: (506) 2286 2265
Web Site: http://www.ykk-usa.com
Emp.: 55
Buttons, Needles, Pins, Hooks & Fasteners Mfr
N.A.I.C.S.: 339993

YKK DANMARK A/S (1)
Neptunvej 5A, 7430, Ikast, Denmark
Tel.: (45) 97 155 388
Web Site: http://www.ykk.dk
Fastener Product Mfr
N.A.I.C.S.: 339993

YKK DEUTSCHLAND GMBH (1)
Ostring 33, 63533, Mainhausen, Germany
Tel.: (49) 6182 8050
Web Site: http://www.ykk.de
Emp.: 63
Fastener Product Mfr
N.A.I.C.S.: 339993
Hiroyasu Ishizaki *(Mng Dir)*

YKK EGYPT S.A.E. (1)
Florida Tower 1229 El Sheikh Aly Gad El Hak St Sheraton Area, Cairo, 11341, Egypt
Tel.: (20) 2 2268 7895
Web Site: http://www.ykkfastening.com
Emp.: 35
Fastener Product Mfr
N.A.I.C.S.: 339993
Simon Fares *(Mgr-Sls-Snap & Buttons Div)*

YKK ESPANA SA (1)
Travessera de Les Corts 49-59, Barcelona, 08028, Spain
Tel.: (34) 934 479 700
Web Site: http://www.ykk.es
Fastener Product Mfr
N.A.I.C.S.: 339993

YKK Europe Limited (1)
14-20 Chiswell Street, London, EC1Y 4TW, United Kingdom **(100%)**
Tel.: (44) 2074481333
Web Site: http://www.ykkeurope.com
Emp.: 28
Buttons, Needles, Pins, Hooks & Fasteners Mfr
N.A.I.C.S.: 339993

YKK FRANCE SARL (1)
1 Bis Rue Collange, 92300, Levallois-Perret, France
Tel.: (33) 1 40 89 62 00
Web Site: http://www.ykk.fr
Fastener Product Mfr
N.A.I.C.S.: 339993

YKK Fastening Products Sales Inc. (1)
1-28-2 Taito Taito-ku, Tokyo, Japan
Tel.: (81) 358167200
Web Site: http://www.ykkfastening.com
Fasteners Distr & Mfr
N.A.I.C.S.: 339993
Masaru Kawakami *(Pres)*

YKK Fudosan Co., Ltd. (1)
1-19 Kanda Izumi-cho Chiyoda-ku, 101-8642, Tokyo, Japan
Tel.: (81) 338642080
Web Site: http://www.ykk.com.jp
Sales Range: $150-199.9 Million
Emp.: 6
Fastener Mfr

AND PRIVATE COMPANIES   YKT CORPORATION

N.A.I.C.S.: 339993

YKK HONG KONG LTD. (1)
14th Floor Tower 2 Silvercord 30 Canton Road, Tsimshatsui, Kowloon, China (Hong Kong)
Tel.: (852) 2378 8300
Web Site: http://www.ykk.com.hk
Fastener Product Mfr
N.A.I.C.S.: 339993

Plant (Domestic):

YKK HONG KONG LTD. - Tuen Mun Factory (2)
14th Floor Phase 2 YKK Building 2 SAN LIK Street, Tuen Mun, China (Hong Kong)
Tel.: (852) 2461 0900
Web Site: http://www.ykk.com.hk
Fastener Product Mfr
N.A.I.C.S.: 339993

YKK Hellas A.E.B.E (1)
6 Km Thessalonikis-Oraiokastrou A'Block 564 29 Efkarpia, Thessaloniki, Greece
Tel.: (30) 2310 327830
Web Site: http://www.ykk.gr
Emp.: 7
Fastener Product Mfr
N.A.I.C.S.: 339993
Chrispos Logaras *(Gen Mgr)*

YKK Holding Asia Pte Ltd. (1)
152 Beach Road 08-02 Gateway East, Singapore, 189721, Singapore
Tel.: (65) 6296 3035
Web Site: http://www.ykkasia.com
Emp.: 40
Fastener Product Mfr
N.A.I.C.S.: 339993
Ken Nakano *(Pres)*

Subsidiary (Non-US):

Bhoruka Extrusions Pvt Ltd (2)
Suite 1 KRS Road, Metagalli, Mysore, 570016, Karnataka, India
Tel.: (91) 821 4286100
Web Site: http://www.bhorukaextrusions.com
Aluminum Extrusions Mfr
N.A.I.C.S.: 331318
A. Srinivas *(Mgr-Powder Coating)*

YKK INDIA PVT. LTD. (1)
Global Business Park 3rd Floor Tower-A Mehrauli-Gurgaon Road, Gurgaon, 122 002, Haryana, India
Tel.: (91) 124 3924800
Web Site: http://www.ykkindia.com
Emp.: 60
Fastener Product Mfr
N.A.I.C.S.: 339993
Akihiko Taniguchi *(Gen Mgr)*

YKK ITALIA SPA (1)
Via Pitagora 1, Pero, 20016, Milan, Italy
Tel.: (39) 02 3394051
Web Site: http://www.ykk.it
Fastener Product Mfr
N.A.I.C.S.: 339993
Takashi Miyata *(Gen Mgr)*

Plant (Domestic):

YKK ITALIA SPA - CARPI PLANT (2)
Via dei Barrocciai 11, 41012, Carpi, Italy
Tel.: (39) 059 682804
Fastener Product Mfr
N.A.I.C.S.: 339993

YKK ITALIA SPA - VERCELLI PLANT (2)
S S N 31 del Monferrato-km 5, Prarolo, 13012, Vercelli, Italy
Tel.: (39) 0161 3001
Fastener Product Mfr
N.A.I.C.S.: 339993

YKK KENYA EPZ LTD. (1)
PO Box 16455-80100, Mombasa, Kenya
Tel.: (254) 41 432 101
Fastener Product Mfr
N.A.I.C.S.: 339993

YKK LANKA (PRIVATE) LTD. (1)
Suite 5 A Landmark Building No 385 Galle Road, Colombo, Sri Lanka
Tel.: (94) 11 5579200
Fastener Product Mfr

N.A.I.C.S.: 339993

YKK MACAU LTD. (1)
Avenida de venceslau de Morais 9 Andar L-M Centro Industrial Keck Seng, Macau, China (Macau)
Tel.: (853) 28481211
Fastener Product Mfr
N.A.I.C.S.: 339993

YKK MAROC S.A.R.L. (1)
Route Secondaire 110 Lotissement Badr No 6 Zone Industrielle, Ain Sebaa, 20250, Casablanca, Morocco
Tel.: (212) 5 22 34 29 15
Fastener Product Mfr
N.A.I.C.S.: 339993

YKK MEDITERRANEO SPA (1)
Zona Industriale Campolungo, 63100, Ascoli Piceno, Italy
Tel.: (39) 0736 32 0311
Fastener Product Mfr
N.A.I.C.S.: 339993

YKK METAL ve PLASTIK URUNLERI SANAYI ve TICARET A.S. (1)
Kaptanpasa Mahallesi Piyalepasa Bulvari No 73, Sisli, 34384, Istanbul, Turkiye
Tel.: (90) 212 314 79 00
Web Site: http://www.ykk.com.tr
Fastener Product Mfr
N.A.I.C.S.: 339993

YKK MIDDLE EAST SAL (1)
1100-2160 Yassouieh Garden Geitawi St, PO Box 16-6862, Ashrafieh, Beirut, Lebanon
Tel.: (961) 1 586 687
Fastener Product Mfr
N.A.I.C.S.: 339993

YKK Mexicana S.A. de C.V. (1)
Carretera Queretaro Leon, Parq Ind Textil Las Malvas, 36547, Irapuato, Guanajuapo, Mexico (100%)
Tel.: (52) 4626238100
Web Site: http://www.ykkamerica.com
Sales Range: Less than $1 Million
Emp.: 300
Zippers Mfr & Distr
N.A.I.C.S.: 339993

YKK NEDERLAND BV (1)
Einsteinstraat 5, 8606 JR, Sneek, Netherlands
Tel.: (31) 515 429729
Web Site: http://www.ykk.nl
Emp.: 20
Fastener Product Mfr
N.A.I.C.S.: 339993
Jan Cees van Baaren *(Acct Mgr)*

YKK NORGE FILIAL AV (UK) Ltd (1)
Kr Augustsgate 13, 0164, Oslo, Norway
Tel.: (47) 66 85 5850
Web Site: http://www.ykk.no
Emp.: 3
Fastener Product Mfr
N.A.I.C.S.: 339993
Pete Hovland *(Gen Mgr)*

YKK OCEANIA LTD (1)
49 Holmes Rd, Manurewa, Auckland, 2102, New Zealand
Tel.: (64) 9 267 0400
Emp.: 17
Fastener Product Mfr
N.A.I.C.S.: 339993
Keith Marshall *(Mng Dir)*

YKK PHILIPPINES INC. (1)
17 Flr Richville Corporate Tower 1107 Alabang Zapote Road Madrigal Bus, Muntinlupa, Philippines
Tel.: (63) 2 807 8875
Web Site: http://www.ykk.com.ph
Fastener Product Mfr
N.A.I.C.S.: 339993

Plant (Domestic):

YKK Philippines, Inc. - Batangas Plant (2)
Phil-Japan Friendship Highway Sto Tomas, Batangas, Philippines
Tel.: (63) 43 778 1210
Emp.: 130
Fastener Product Mfr
N.A.I.C.S.: 339993

YKK POLAND SP. Z.O.O. (1)
Ul Tarczynska 119, Pogorzalki, 96-320, Mszczonow, Poland
Tel.: (48) 46 857 07 00
Web Site: http://www.ykk.pl
Fastener Product Mfr
N.A.I.C.S.: 339993

YKK PORTUGAL LDA. (1)
Estrada Nacional N 1 Km 33 3 Carambancha, 2580-491, Carregado, Portugal
Tel.: (351) 263 850 150
Web Site: http://www.ykk.pt
Fastener Product Mfr
N.A.I.C.S.: 339993

YKK ROMANIA SRL (1)
Str Tamasi Nr 20, Buftea, 070000, Ilfov, Romania
Tel.: (40) 21 408 71 60
Web Site: http://www.ykk.ro
Emp.: 20
Fastener Product Mfr
N.A.I.C.S.: 339993
Raul Porutiu *(Gen Mgr)*

YKK Rokko Corp. (1)
1 Kanda Izumi-cho, Chiyoda-ku, Tokyo, 101-8642, Japan
Tel.: (81) 338642000
Web Site: http://www.ykk.com
Emp.: 17,826
Special-Purpose Printing Services
N.A.I.C.S.: 323111

YKK SNAP FASTERNERS ASIA LTD. (1)
4/F Tower 2 Silvercord 30 Canton Road, Lai Chi Kok, Kowloon, China (Hong Kong)
Tel.: (852) 2785 2222
Fastener Product Mfr
N.A.I.C.S.: 339993

YKK SOUTHERN AFRICA (PTY) LTD. (1)
30 Randworth Close, PO Box 201675, Redhill, Durban, 4016, South Africa
Tel.: (27) 31 569 4500
Web Site: http://www.ykk.com
Fastener Product Mfr
N.A.I.C.S.: 339993

YKK Stocko Fasteners GmbH (1)
Kirchhofstrasse 52, 42327, Wuppertal, Germany
Tel.: (49) 20274930
Web Site: http://www.stocko-ykk.de
Emp.: 200
Snap Fasteners, Small Metal Stampings & Connectors Mfr
N.A.I.C.S.: 339993
Keisei Takashima *(Mng Dir)*

YKK TAIWAN CO., LTD. (1)
7th Fl No 40 Sec 2 Min-Chuan East Road, Taipei, Taiwan
Tel.: (886) 2 2511 5157
Web Site: http://www.ykktaiwan.com.tw
Fastener Product Mfr
N.A.I.C.S.: 339993

Division (Domestic):

YKK TAIWAN CO., LTD. - Architectural Products Division (2)
1 Fl No 40 Sec 2 Min-Chuan East Road, Taipei, Taiwan
Tel.: (886) 2 25115156
Fastener Product Mfr
N.A.I.C.S.: 339993

YKK THAILAND CO., LTD. (1)
9th Floor Manoonpol Building 2 2884/1 New Petchburi Rd, Bangkapi Huaykwang, Bangkok, 10310, Thailand
Tel.: (66) 2 718 0590
Web Site: http://www.ykk.co.th
Fastener Product Mfr
N.A.I.C.S.: 339993

YKK TRADING TUNISIA S.A. (1)
Zone Industrial Sidi Abdelhamid Street No 7, Sidi Abdelhamid, 4061, Sousse, Tunisia
Tel.: (216) 73 321 180
Fastener Product Mfr
N.A.I.C.S.: 339993

YKK Tourist Co., Ltd. (1)
1-banchi Kanda-Izumi-cho, Chiyoda-ku, Tokyo, 101-8642, Tokyo, Japan

Tel.: (81) 338642146
Travel Services
N.A.I.C.S.: 561599

YKK VIETNAM CO., LTD. (1)
4th Floor AB Tower 76 Le Lai St Ben Thanh Ward Dist 1, District 1, Ho Chi Minh City, 7000, Vietnam
Tel.: (84) 8 3823 3793
Web Site: http://www.ykk.com.vn
Emp.: 80
Fastener Product Mfr
N.A.I.C.S.: 339993

YKK ZIPPER (SHENZHEN) CO., LTD. (1)
Rm 01 34F China Shine Plaza No 3-15 Linhexi Road, Tianhe District, Guangzhou, China
Tel.: (86) 20 3847 7968
Web Site: http://www.ykksz.com
Fastener Product Mfr
N.A.I.C.S.: 339993

Plant (Domestic):

YKK ZIPPER (SHENZHEN) CO., LTD. - Fu Yong Factory (2)
Tangwei Industry Park Fuyong Tower, Baoan District, Shenzhen, Guangdong, China
Tel.: (86) 755 27377448
Fastener Product Mfr
N.A.I.C.S.: 339993

YKK ZIPPER (SHENZHEN) CO., LTD. - Gong Ming Factory (2)
Apparel Industry Concentration Base Industrial Park Gongming Road, Baoan District, Shenzhen, Guangdong, China
Tel.: (86) 755 27121168
Fastener Product Mfr
N.A.I.C.S.: 339993

YKK do Brazil Ltda. (1)
100 Rua Tenente Negrao, Itaim Bibi, CEP 04530-911, Sao Paulo, Brazil (100%)
Tel.: (55) 11 3066 1111
Web Site: http://www.ykk.com.br
Emp.: 100
Zipper Aluminum Architectural Product Nonferrous Metal Product Cotton Synthetic Yarn & Precision Machinery Mfr
N.A.I.C.S.: 339993
Anna Carolina *(Mgr-Sls)*

YKT CORPORATION
YKT Bldg 7-5 Yoyogi 5-chome, Shibuya-ku, Tokyo, 151-8567, Japan
Tel.: (81) 334671252
Web Site: https://www.ykt.co.jp
Year Founded: 1924
2693—(TKS)
Rev.: $91,333,380
Assets: $88,171,240
Liabilities: $30,770,600
Net Worth: $57,400,640
Earnings: $2,155,360
Emp.: 135
Fiscal Year-end: 12/31/23
Electronic Equipment Whslr
N.A.I.C.S.: 423690
Hidehiro Imoto *(Pres)*

Subsidiaries:

Sun Instruments, Inc. (1)
Itsuwa Plaza Bldg 2-26-9 Nishi-gotanda, Shinagawa-ku, Tokyo, 141-0031, Japan
Tel.: (81) 354369361
Web Site: https://www.sun-ins.com
Optical Equipment Distr
N.A.I.C.S.: 423460
Toru Ichioka *(Pres)*

YKT (Shanghai) International Trading Co., Ltd. (1)
7th Fl-J Huamin Empire Plaza 726 Yan An West Road, Shanghai, 200050, China
Tel.: (86) 2162259911
Electronic Equipment Distr
N.A.I.C.S.: 423690

YKT (TAIWAN) CORPORATION (1)
6th Fl -3 Nanjing World Trade IC Building 343 Nanjing E Rd Sec 5, Taipei, 10569, Taiwan

YKT CORPORATION

YKT CORPORATION—(Continued)
Tel.: (886) 227455430
Electronic Equipment Distr
N.A.I.C.S.: 423690

YKT (Thailand) Co., Ltd. (1)
1 MD Tower 11th Floor Room no C3 Soi Bangna-Trad 25 Bangna-Trad Rd, Bangna nua Bangna, Bangkok, 10260, Thailand
Tel.: (66) 217358689
Web Site: https://www.ykt-thailand.co.th
Emp.: 8
Electronic Equipment Distr
N.A.I.C.S.: 423690
Hidehiro Imoto (Pres)

YKT Europe GmbH (1)
Rudolf-Diesel-Str 4, 71397, Leutenbach, Germany
Tel.: (49) 71957042618
Web Site: http://www.ykt-europe.de
Electronic Equipment Distr
N.A.I.C.S.: 423690
Hidehiro Imoto (Pres & Mng Dir)

YLI HOLDINGS BERHAD
45 Lorong Rahim Kajai, 13 Taman Tun Dr Ismail, 60000, Kuala Lumpur, Malaysia
Tel.: (60) 377222296
Web Site: https://www.yli.com.my
YLI—(KLS)
Rev.: $20,752,628
Assets: $46,140,435
Liabilities: $20,464,290
Net Worth: $25,676,145
Earnings: ($1,658,498)
Emp.: 259
Fiscal Year-end: 03/31/22
Ductile Iron Pipes Mfr
N.A.I.C.S.: 331511
Heng Chin Seah (Mng Dir-Grp)

Subsidiaries:

Laksana Wibawa Sdn.Bhd. (1)
Lot PT 7157 Batu 22 1/2 Mukim, 48200, Serendah, Selangor, Malaysia
Tel.: (60) 360813622
Web Site: http://www.laksanawibawa.my
Emp.: 70
Steel Pipes & Fittings Distr
N.A.I.C.S.: 423510
Ali Ahmad (CEO)

MRPI Pipes Sdn. Bhd. (1)
Lot 5 Jalan Perusahaan 2, Kawasan Perindustrian Bukit Raja, 41050, Klang, Selangor Darul Ehsan, Malaysia
Tel.: (60) 333430470
Web Site: https://www.mrpi.com.my
Pipes Mfr
N.A.I.C.S.: 332996
Anuar Shukry Ismail (Mktg Mgr)

Yew Lean Foundry & Co. Sdn, Bhd. (1)
2432 Tingkat Perusahaan Enam, Prai Industrial Estate, 13600, Prai, Penang, Malaysia
Tel.: (60) 43991819
Web Site: http://www.jaring.po.my
Emp.: 135
Ductile Iron Pipes Mfr
N.A.I.C.S.: 327332

Yew Li Foundry & Co. Sdn. Bhd. (1)
51 Jalan Layang-Layang 3 Bandar Puchong Jaya, Puchong, 47100, Selangor Darul Ehsan, Malaysia
Tel.: (60) 358821942
Web Site: http://www.yli.com.my
Emp.: 13
Pipe Fitting Mfr
N.A.I.C.S.: 332996
Lim Leong Hin (Mng Dir)

YLZ INFORMATION TECHNOLOGY CO., LTD
Room 502 No 18 Guanri Road 2nd Phase Software Park, Xiamen, 361008, Fujian, China
Tel.: (86) 5922517033
Web Site: https://www.ylzinfo.com

300096—(CHIN)
Rev.: $112,316,973
Assets: $154,554,973
Liabilities: $95,882,863
Net Worth: $58,672,110
Earnings: $5,218,422
Fiscal Year-end: 12/31/23
Software Development Services
N.A.I.C.S.: 541511

YM CO., LTD.
118 Poseung Industrial Complex-ro 118beongil, Poseung-eup, Pyeongtaek, 17960, Gyeonggi-do, Korea (South)
Tel.: (82) 316808600
Web Site: https://www.ysmic.com
Year Founded: 1967
007530—(KRS)
Rev.: $112,230,764
Assets: $109,794,479
Liabilities: $77,175,635
Net Worth: $32,618,845
Earnings: $1,907,432
Emp.: 333
Fiscal Year-end: 12/31/22
Fastener Mfr & Distr
N.A.I.C.S.: 332722
Ji-young Sun (CEO)

Subsidiaries:

Youngsin Metal (Thailand) Co., Ltd. (1)
300/145 Moo 1 T Tasit A, Pluakdaeng, Rayong, 21140, Thailand
Tel.: (66) 38338062
Automotive Metal & Steel Mfr
N.A.I.C.S.: 332312

YM TECH CO., LTD.
38 Gwahaksaneop3-Ro Oksan-Myeon, Heungdeok-Gu, Chilgok, Chungcheongbuk-do, Korea (South)
Tel.: (82) 432126651
Web Site: https://www.ymtech.en.ec21.com
Year Founded: 1998
273640—(KRS)
Electric Equipment Mfr
N.A.I.C.S.: 335311
Nam-Kook Son (Pres)

Subsidiaries:

Shanghai Sky International Trading Co., Ltd. (1)
Room F202 No 783 Shenglong Road, Shanghai, 201615, China
Tel.: (86) 213 355 2102
Relay Product Mfr & Distr
N.A.I.C.S.: 335314

YMAGIS S.A.S.
85 Avenue Jean Jaures, 92120, Paris, France
Tel.: (33) 1 75448888
Web Site: http://www.ymagis.com
Year Founded: 2007
MAGIS—(EUR)
Sales Range: $150-199.9 Million
Emp.: 772
Projection Equipment Migration & Film Digitizing Services
N.A.I.C.S.: 333310
Jean Mizrahi (Founder & CEO)

Subsidiaries:

Ymagis Deutschland Gmbh (1)
Reuchlinstr 10-11, 10553, Berlin, Germany
Tel.: (49) 3021018431
Web Site: http://www.ymagis.com
Digital Media Services
N.A.I.C.S.: 512131
Michael H. Krauth (CEO)

Ymagis Engineering Services SAS (1)
85-87 Avenue Baise Moi Jean Jaures, 92120, Montrouge, France
Tel.: (33) 179 977 840

Engineering Consulting Services
N.A.I.C.S.: 541330

Ymagis Spain SLU (1)
Pallars 99 office 43, 08018, Barcelona, Spain
Tel.: (34) 931 845 060
Web Site: http://www.ymagis.com
Emp.: 15
Digital Media Services
N.A.I.C.S.: 512131
Angel Martin (Gen Mgr)

YMOBILE CORP.
Shiodome Sumitomo Building 1-9-2 Higashi-shimbashi, Minato-ku, Tokyo, 105-0021, Japan
Tel.: (81) 3 35887200
Web Site: http://www.ymobile.jp
Year Founded: 1999
Sales Range: $1-4.9 Billion
Emp.: 1,250
Internet Access Services
N.A.I.C.S.: 517810
Sachio Semmoto (Chm)

YMT CO., LTD.
30 Namdongdong-Ro 153 Beon-Gil, Namdong-Gu Gojan-Dong, Incheon, Korea (South)
Tel.: (82) 328218277
Web Site: https://www.ymtechnology.com
Year Founded: 1999
251370—(KRS)
Rev.: $100,145,026
Assets: $190,148,857
Liabilities: $74,051,370
Net Worth: $116,097,486
Earnings: $1,991,935
Emp.: 191
Fiscal Year-end: 12/31/22
Basic Chemicals Mfr
N.A.I.C.S.: 325998
Sung-Wook Chun (Pres & Co-CEO)

Subsidiaries:

Beyond Solution Co., Ltd. (1)
76 Dongsan-ro, Danwon-gu, Ansan, Gyeonggi-do, Korea (South)
Tel.: (82) 313808487
Emp.: 11
Semiconductor Equipment Mfr
N.A.I.C.S.: 333242
Hogyeong Seon (CEO)

Chimielab Co., Ltd. (1)
A-604 1 Jeongjail-ro, Bundang-gu, Seongnam, Gyeonggi-do, Korea (South)
Tel.: (82) 314937522
Emp.: 10
Antibacterial Mask Material Mfr
N.A.I.C.S.: 339113
Hyejung Park (CEO)

YNFINITI GLOBAL ENERGY SERVICES, S.L.U.
Maria Tubau 5 3B, 28050, Madrid, Spain
Tel.: (34) 91 372 92 87   ES
Web Site: http://www.ynfinitienergy.com
Year Founded: 2005
Wind Electric Power Generation Services
N.A.I.C.S.: 221118
Gianluca Tabarrini (Gen Dir)

YNH PROPERTY BHD
188 Jalan PPMP 3/3 Pusat Perniagaan Manjung Point 3, 32040, Seri Manjung, Perak, Malaysia
Tel.: (60) 56881128
Web Site: https://www.ynhb.com.my
YNHPROP—(KLS)
Rev.: $65,082,962
Assets: $525,283,046
Liabilities: $272,756,258
Net Worth: $252,526,788
Earnings: $779,306

INTERNATIONAL PUBLIC

Fiscal Year-end: 06/30/23
Property Development Services
N.A.I.C.S.: 531311
Kuan Chon Yu (Chm)

Subsidiaries:

Hotel Sfera Sdn. Bhd. (1)
2479 Taman Samudera Jalan Dato' Yu Neh Huat, 32040, Seri Manjung, Perak, Malaysia
Tel.: (60) 5 688 1000
Web Site: https://www.hotelsfera.com.my
Home Management Services
N.A.I.C.S.: 721110

Kar Sin Berhad (1)
No 38 Jalan PPMP 7 Pusat Perniagaan Manjung Point 1, 32040, Seri Manjung, Perak, Malaysia
Tel.: (60) 568811288
Emp.: 50
Property Development Services
N.A.I.C.S.: 531390

Lead View Sdn Bhd (1)
The Lead View Hotel 2479 Jln Dato Yu Neh Huat Taman Samudera, Seri Manjung, 32040, Perak, Malaysia
Tel.: (60) 56881000
Web Site: http://www.leadviewhotel.com
Emp.: 40
Home Management Services
N.A.I.C.S.: 721110
Kuan Huat Yu (Mng Dir)

YNH Construction Sdn Bhd (1)
G-01 633 Residency 2A Jalan Tebing Off Jalan Tun Sambanthan, 50470, Kuala Lumpur, Malaysia
Tel.: (60) 322746721
Web Site: http://www.ynhb.com
Emp.: 76
Construction Services
N.A.I.C.S.: 236115

YNH Engineering Sdn. Bhd. (1)
55 Medan Ipoh 1A Medan Ipoh Bistari, 31400, Ipoh, Perak, Malaysia
Tel.: (60) 32 274 6721
Web Site: https://www.ynhe.com.my
Emp.: 55
Civil & Engineering Work Services
N.A.I.C.S.: 541330
Leonard Tan (Dir-Project)

YNVISIBLE INTERACTIVE INC.
1100 Melville Street Suite 830, PO Box 43, Vancouver, V6E 4A6, BC, Canada
Tel.: (778) 683-4324   BC
Web Site: https://www.ynvisible.com
Year Founded: 1983
YNV—(OTCIQ)
Rev.: $303,456
Assets: $4,720,421
Liabilities: $1,927,323
Net Worth: $2,793,099
Earnings: ($2,968,534)
Emp.: 26
Fiscal Year-end: 12/31/20
Minerals Exploration
N.A.I.C.S.: 212290
Carlos Pinheiro (CTO)

Subsidiaries:

Ynvisible, S.A (1)
Rua Quinta do Bom Retiro 12C, Charneca da Caparica, 2820-690, Almada, Portugal
Tel.: (351) 211308817
Electronic Products Mfr
N.A.I.C.S.: 334419

YO ELEVEN GAMING, INC.
Suite 303 - 570 Granville Street, Vancouver, V6C 3P1, BC, Canada
Tel.: (604) 681-0204   BC
Year Founded: 2021
Sports Betting & Online Gaming Company
N.A.I.C.S.: 713290
Jake Kalpakian (Pres & CEO)

YOANTION INDUSTRIAL INC., LTD.

Chengtan Industrial Zone, Xinchang County, Shaoxing, 312530, Zhejiang, China
Tel.: (86) 57586059777
Web Site: https://www.yoantion.com
Year Founded: 2010
301053—(CHIN)
Rev: $68,730,591
Assets: $146,899,422
Liabilities: $61,858,310
Net Worth: $85,041,112
Earnings: $2,578,944
Fiscal Year-end: 12/31/23
Industrial Machinery Mfr & Distr
N.A.I.C.S.: 333248
Shaojun Chen (Chm & Gen Mgr)

YOC AG
Greifswalder Str 212, 10405, Berlin, Germany
Tel.: (49) 307261620
Web Site: https://www.yoc.com
YOC—(MUN)
Rev: $33,811,538
Assets: $19,394,996
Liabilities: $14,339,271
Net Worth: $5,055,725
Earnings: $3,200,935,994
Emp.: 96
Fiscal Year-end: 12/31/23
Mobile & E-mail Marketing Services
N.A.I.C.S.: 541613
Dirk Kraus (Founder & Member-Mgmt Bd)
Subsidiaries:

Brutus Media GmbH (1)
Bischof von Henle Str 2, 93051, Regensburg, Germany
Tel.: (49) 941630950
Web Site: http://www.brutusmedia.de
Emp.: 30
Advertising Agencies
N.A.I.C.S.: 541810

Moustik GmbH (1)
Karl Liebknecht St 1, 10178, Berlin, Germany
Tel.: (49) 30531485830
Web Site: http://www.moustik.de
Emp.: 6
Mobile Software Development Services
N.A.I.C.S.: 513210

Moustik Sprl. (1)
Chaussee d, Alsembergse Steenweg 596, 1180, Brussels, Belgium
Tel.: (32) 23474442
GSM Mobile Services
N.A.I.C.S.: 517112

Sevenval GmbH (1)
Bahnhofsvorplatz 1, 50667, Cologne, Germany
Tel.: (49) 221650070
Web Site: http://www.sevenval.com
Mobile Software Development Services
N.A.I.C.S.: 513210

YOC Central Eastern Europe GmbH (1)
Dambockgasse 4 C/5/T 1, 1060, Vienna, Austria
Tel.: (43) 152250060
Internet Marketing Services
N.A.I.C.S.: 541613
Matthias Ragyoczy (Head-Sls)

YOC Germany GmbH (1)
Greifswalder Str 212, 10405, Berlin, Germany
Tel.: (49) 307261620
Digital Advertising Services
N.A.I.C.S.: 541850

YOC Ltd (1)
Ashbrook House 3-5 Rathbone Pl, W1T 1HJ, London, United Kingdom - England
Tel.: (44) 2071990127
Marketing Research Agency
N.A.I.C.S.: 541910

YOC Spain, S.L. (1)
Calle de Orense n 20 1st Floor Office 4, 28020, Madrid, Spain
Tel.: (34) 913924187
Internet Marketing Services
N.A.I.C.S.: 541613
Pablo Palencia (Mgr)

YOC Switzerland AG (1)
Eichstrasse 23, 8045, Zurich, Switzerland
Tel.: (41) 445852370
Digital Advertising Services
N.A.I.C.S.: 541850

YODOGAWA STEEL WORKS, LTD.
4-1-1 Minami-honmachi, Chuo-ku, Osaka, 541-0054, Japan
Tel.: (81) 662451111
Web Site: https://www.yodoko.co.jp
Year Founded: 1935
5451—(TKS)
Rev: $1,348,155,770
Assets: $1,757,354,430
Liabilities: $343,924,910
Net Worth: $1,413,429,520
Earnings: $29,454,160
Emp.: 2,405
Fiscal Year-end: 03/31/24
Steel Products Mfr
N.A.I.C.S.: 331110
Takaaki Kawamoto (Chm)
Subsidiaries:

Sadoshima Corporation (1)
1-16-19 Shimanouchi, Chuo-ku, Osaka, 542-0082, Japan
Tel.: (81) 662510855
Web Site: https://www.sadoshima.com
Emp.: 211
Metal Product Mfr & Distr
N.A.I.C.S.: 332999

Sheng Yu Steel Co., Ltd. (1)
No 11 Zhonglin Rd, Siaogang District, Kaohsiung, 81260, Taiwan (52.13%)
Tel.: (886) 78719000
Web Site: https://www.shengyusteel.com
Rev: $405,152,377
Assets: $356,773,949
Liabilities: $29,208,541
Net Worth: $327,565,408
Earnings: $20,625,919
Emp.: 210
Fiscal Year-end: 12/31/2023
Steel Mfrs
N.A.I.C.S.: 331110
Koichi Tarumiya (Chm)

YOGEN FRUZ
210 Shields Court, Markham, L3R 8V2, ON, Canada
Tel.: (905) 479-8762
Web Site: https://www.yogenfruz.com
Emp.: 60
Frozen Yogurt Retailer
N.A.I.C.S.: 722515
Aaron Serruya (Pres & CEO)
Subsidiaries:

Kayla Foods Int'l (Barbados) Inc. (1)
27 Pine Rd 2nd Floor Bellvile, BB11113, Saint Michael, Barbados
Tel.: (246) 2289505
Web Site: http://www.kaylafoodintl.com
Emp.: 5
N.A.I.C.S.: 311520
David Murray (Controller-Fin)

Yogen Fruz USA Inc. (1)
9311 E Via De Ventura, Scottsdale, AZ 85258
Tel.: (480) 362-4861
Yogurt Distr
N.A.I.C.S.: 424430

YOGI INFRA PROJECTS LIMITED
18A Rabindra Sarani Road Room No 308, 3rd Floor Gate No 1, Kolkata, 700001, West Bengal, India
Tel.: (91) 2226358290
Web Site: https://www.yogiinfraprojects.co.in
Year Founded: 1989
522209—(BOM)
Rev: $112,211
Assets: $46,671,794
Liabilities: $41,258,390
Net Worth: $5,413,404
Earnings: ($58,546)
Fiscal Year-end: 03/31/22
Corporate Building Construction
N.A.I.C.S.: 236220
Sanjay Basudeo Agarwal (Mng Dir)

YOGI LTD.
B/404 The Capital G-Block Bandra Kurla Complex Behind ICICI Bank, Bandra East, Mumbai, 400051, India
Tel.: (91) 9930268888
Web Site: https://yogiltd.com
Year Founded: 1992
511702—(BOM)
Rev: $21,593
Assets: $4,182,483
Liabilities: $2,106,385
Net Worth: $2,076,099
Earnings: ($36,221)
Emp.: 3
Fiscal Year-end: 03/31/23
Financial Investment Services
N.A.I.C.S.: 523999
Devendra Kumar Goyal (Chm)

YOHJI YAMAMOTO INC.
T33 2-2-43 Higashi-Shinagawa, Shinagawa-ku, Tokyo, 140-0002, Japan
Tel.: (81) 354631537
Web Site: http://www.yohjiyamamoto.co.jp
Year Founded: 2009
Sales Range: $100-124.9 Million
Emp.: 280
Women Clothing Distr
N.A.I.C.S.: 458110
Yohji Yamamoto (Pres)
Subsidiaries:

Y's GB Ltd (1)
15 Conduit St, London, W1S 2XJ, United Kingdom
Tel.: (44) 20 7491 4129
Emp.: 6
Women's Clothing Retailer
N.A.I.C.S.: 458110
Isabelle Pigeaud (Gen Mgr)

YOHO GROUP HOLDINGS LIMITED
2/F Eastcore 398 Kwun Tong Road, Kwun Tong, Kowloon, China (Hong Kong)
Web Site: https://www.yohohongkong.com
Year Founded: 2013
2347—(HKG)
Rev: $109,279,078
Assets: $44,338,441
Liabilities: $10,489,092
Net Worth: $33,849,349
Earnings: $805,526
Emp.: 105
Fiscal Year-end: 03/31/23
Holding Company
N.A.I.C.S.: 551112
Ka Wing Tsui (COO)

YOJEE LIMITED
Level 3 88 William Street, Perth, 6000, WA, Australia
Tel.: (61) 894632463
Web Site: http://www.yojee.com
Year Founded: 2010
YOJ—(ASX)
Rev: $656,132
Assets: $3,147,579
Liabilities: $464,083
Net Worth: $2,683,497
Earnings: ($5,672,307)
Fiscal Year-end: 06/30/24
Investment Services
N.A.I.C.S.: 523999
Mark Connell (CEO & Exec VP)
Subsidiaries:

Yojee Pte Ltd (1)
144 Robinson Road 15-01 Robinson Square, Singapore, 068908, Singapore
Tel.: (65) 31389076
Software Services
N.A.I.C.S.: 541511
Ed Clarke (Mng Dir)

YOKOGAWA BRIDGE HOLDINGS CORP.
4-4-44 Shibaura, Minato-ku, Tokyo, 108-0023, Japan
Tel.: (81) 334534111
Web Site: https://www.ybhd.co.jp
Year Founded: 2007
5911—(TKS)
Rev: $1,084,542,360
Assets: $1,393,692,060
Liabilities: $547,460,030
Net Worth: $846,232,030
Earnings: $78,354,940
Emp.: 1,996
Fiscal Year-end: 03/31/24
Holding Company
N.A.I.C.S.: 551112
Kazuhiko Takata (Pres)
Subsidiaries:

Narasaki Seisakusyo Co., Ltd. (1)
385 Sakimori-cho, Muroran, 050-8570, Hokkaido, Japan
Tel.: (81) 143593611
Web Site: https://www.narasaki-ss.co.jp
Emp.: 140
Bridge Construction Services
N.A.I.C.S.: 237310

YCE Corp. (1)
47-1 Yamano-cho, Funabashi, 273-0026, Chiba, Japan
Tel.: (81) 474356535
Web Site: https://www.yceng.co.jp
Emp.: 18
Construction Consulting Services
N.A.I.C.S.: 541330

Yokogawa Bridge Corp. (1)
27 Yamano-cho, Funabashi, 273-0026, Chiba, Japan
Tel.: (81) 474378000
Web Site: https://www.yokogawa-bridge.co.jp
Emp.: 620
Bridge Construction Services
N.A.I.C.S.: 237310

Yokogawa NS Engineering Corp. (1)
16-5 Sunayama, Kamisu, 314-0255, Ibaraki, Japan
Tel.: (81) 479466688
Web Site: http://www.ynse.co.jp
Emp.: 200
Engineeering Services
N.A.I.C.S.: 541330

Yokogawa New Life Corp. (1)
Yokogawa Building 4-4-44 Shibaura, Minato-ku, Tokyo, 108-0023, Japan
Tel.: (81) 334534113
Web Site: https://www.ynl.jp
Real Estate Services
N.A.I.C.S.: 531390

Yokogawa Sumikin Bridge Corp. (1)
16-5 Sunayama, Kamisu, 314-0255, Ibaraki, Japan
Tel.: (81) 479466688
Web Site: http://www.ysbc.co.jp
Emp.: 200
Bridge Construction Services
N.A.I.C.S.: 237310

Yokogawa System Buildings Corp. (1)
Yokogawa West Building 47-1, Yamano-cho, Funabashi, 273-0026, Chiba, Japan
Tel.: (81) 474103215
Web Site: https://www.yokogawa-yess.co.jp
Engineeering Services
N.A.I.C.S.: 541330

YOKOGAWA BRIDGE HOLDINGS CORP.

Yokogawa Bridge Holdings Corp.—(Continued)

Yokogawa Techno Philippines Inc. (1)
Unit 14C 14/F Marco Polo Ortigas Manila Sapphire Road Ortigas Center, Pasig, 1600, Philippines
Tel.: (63) 9171088483
Web Site: https://www.ytphil.com
Emp.: 156
Engineeering Services
N.A.I.C.S.: 541330

Yokogawa Techno-Information Service Inc. (1)
Yokogawa Building 4-4-44 Shibaura, Minato-ku, Tokyo, 108-0023, Japan
Tel.: (81) 354421701
Web Site: https://www.yti.co.jp
Emp.: 67
Software Development Services
N.A.I.C.S.: 541511
Shunichi Kaneko (Pres & CEO)

YOKOGAWA ELECTRIC CORPORATION

2-9-32 Nakamachi, Musashino-shi, Tokyo, 180-8750, Japan
Tel.: (81) 422520439   JP
Web Site: https://www.yokogawa.com
Year Founded: 1915
YKE—(DEU)
Rev.: $3,272,954,430
Assets: $4,435,612,950
Liabilities: $1,662,077,700
Net Worth: $2,773,535,250
Earnings: $279,056,400
Emp.: 17,084
Fiscal Year-end: 03/31/23
Industrial Automation Systems & Instruments, Measuring Instruments & Information Processing Equipment Mfr
N.A.I.C.S.: 334513
Hitoshi Nara (Pres & CEO)

Subsidiaries:

Amnimo Inc. (1)
2-9-32 Nakacho, Musashino, Tokyo, 180-8750, Japan
Tel.: (81) 5031600300
Web Site: https://amnimo.com
Emp.: 67
Information Technology Consulting Services
N.A.I.C.S.: 541512

Colbyco d.o.o. (1)
Cesta 24 junija 23, Ljubljana, 1231, Slovenia
Tel.: (386) 1 563 1113
Web Site: https://www.colbyco.si
Measurement Equipment Mfr
N.A.I.C.S.: 334515

DM Optics Ltd. (1)
The Hive 6 Beaufighter Road, North Somerset, Weston-super-Mare, BS24 8EE, United Kingdom
Tel.: (44) 193 475 0655
Web Site: https://www.dmoptics.co.uk
Water Equipment Mfr
N.A.I.C.S.: 334510

Emitec AG (1)
Birkenstrasse 47, 6343, Rotkreuz, Switzerland
Tel.: (41) 41 748 6010
Web Site: https://www.emitec.ch
Measurement Equipment Mfr
N.A.I.C.S.: 334515
Armin Diethelm (CEO)

Fast Laser Group Ltd. (1)
Shalom Aleichem 1 St, Hod Hasharon, 4521456, Israel
Tel.: (972) 9 744 4112
Web Site: https://www.fastlaser.co.il
Photonic Equipment Distr
N.A.I.C.S.: 423410

Fluid Imaging Technologies, Inc. (1)
65 Forest Falls Dr Second Fl, Yarmouth, ME 04096
Tel.: (207) 846-6100
Web Site: http://www.fluidimaging.com
Totalizing Fluid Meter & Counting Device Mfr
N.A.I.C.S.: 334514
Kent Peterson (CEO)

Grazper Technologies ApS (1)
Frederiksgade 7 1st floor, DK-1265, Copenhagen, Denmark
Tel.: (45) 42424342
Web Site: https://grazper.com
Software Development Services
N.A.I.C.S.: 541511

Interlab Sp. z o.o (1)
Ul Kosiarzy 37 Pawilon 20, 02-953, Warsaw, Poland
Tel.: (48) 22 840 8180
Web Site: https://www.interlab.pl
Measurement Equipment Distr
N.A.I.C.S.: 423830

KBC Advanced Technologies Limited (1)
42-50 Hersham Road, Walton-on-Thames, KT12 1RZ, Surrey, United Kingdom
Tel.: (44) 1932242424
Web Site: http://www.kbcat.com
Oil Refinery Process Engineering & Software Services
N.A.I.C.S.: 213112
Andrew Howell (CEO)

Subsidiary (Non-US):

KBC Advanced Technologies (Beijing) Co., Ltd (2)
6F Tower A Gemdale Plaza No 91 Jianguo Road, Chaoyang District, Beijing, 100022, China
Tel.: (86) 106 701 2889
Web Site: http://www.kbcat.com
Marine Software Development Services
N.A.I.C.S.: 541511

KBC Advanced Technologies Canada Limited (2)
Bay 4 11133 40th Street SE, Calgary, T2C 2Z4, AB, Canada
Tel.: (281) 293-8200
Web Site: https://www.kbc.global
Software Consulting Services
N.A.I.C.S.: 541690

Subsidiary (US):

KBC Advanced Technologies, Inc. (2)
15021 Katy Fwy Ste 600, Houston, TX 77094 (100%)
Tel.: (281) 293-8200
Web Site: https://www.kbc.global
Oil Refinery Process Engineering Services
N.A.I.C.S.: 541512
Carol Priddy (Mgr-HR)

Subsidiary (Non-US):

KBC Advanced Technology Pte. Ltd. (2)
5 Bedok South Road, Suntec Tower Three, Singapore, 469270, Singapore (100%)
Tel.: (65) 6 735 5488
Web Site: https://www.kbc.global
Oil Refinery Process Engineering Services
N.A.I.C.S.: 237120

Subsidiary (Domestic):

KBC Process Technology Ltd. (2)
42-50 Hersham Road, Walton-on-Thames, KT12 1RZ, Surrey, United Kingdom (100%)
Tel.: (44) 1932242424
Web Site: http://www.kbcat.com
Oil Refinery Process Engineering Services
N.A.I.C.S.: 213112

Subsidiary (Non-US):

KBC Process Technology Ltd. - Japan (2)
Nishi-Shimbashi YS Building 5F 2-19-2, Minato-ku Nishi-Shimbashi, Tokyo, 105-0003, Japan (100%)
Tel.: (81) 34 510 9300
Web Site: https://www.kbc.global
Oil Refinery Process Engineering Services
N.A.I.C.S.: 324110

KBC Process Technology Ltd. - Netherlands (2)
Willemstraat 26, 4811 AL, Breda, Netherlands (100%)
Tel.: (31) 76 531 6131
Web Site: http://www.kbcat.com
Oil Refinery Process Engineering Services
N.A.I.C.S.: 541330

MB Electronique S.A. (1)
106 Rue des Freres Farman ZI, BP 31, 78533, Buc, France
Tel.: (33) 13 967 6767
Web Site: https://www.mbelectronique.fr
Electrical Equipment Distr
N.A.I.C.S.: 423610

MDS Automatika d.o.o. (1)
Svetog Save bb, 74450, Brod, Bosnia & Herzegovina
Tel.: (387) 6 521 7260
Web Site: https://www.mdsautomatika.com
Oil & Gas Mfr
N.A.I.C.S.: 333132

Mesomatic Messtechnik AG (1)
Birkenstrasse 47, 6343, Rotkreuz, Switzerland
Tel.: (41) 41 748 6022
Web Site: https://www.mesomatic.ch
Fiber Optic Product Mfr
N.A.I.C.S.: 335921
Manuela Kalin (Head)

Mikro Kontrol d.o.o. (1)
Vase Pelagica 30, 11000, Belgrade, Serbia
Tel.: (381) 11 369 9080
Web Site: https://www.mikrokontrol.rs
Industrial Automation Mfr
N.A.I.C.S.: 333998

NBN Elektronik s.r.o. (1)
On the Battlefield 257, 375 01, Tyn nad Vltavou, Czech Republic
Tel.: (420) 38 512 4308
Web Site: https://www.nbn.cz
Measurement Product Mfr
N.A.I.C.S.: 334513

Netscope Solutions S.A. (1)
Lachana 4, Nea Filadelfeia, 143 42, Athens, Greece
Tel.: (30) 210 272 4107
Web Site: https://www.nsmarket.gr
Electric Equipment Mfr
N.A.I.C.S.: 335999

Omega Simulation Co., Ltd. (1)
Kosugi Building Nishiwaseda 2F 2-20-9 Nishi-Waseda, Shinjuku-ku, Tokyo, 169-0051, Japan
Tel.: (81) 332084921
Web Site: https://www.omegasim.co.jp
Emp.: 40
Environmental Engineering Services
N.A.I.C.S.: 541330

PT Yokogawa Indonesia (1)
Plaza Oleos 3rd Floor Suite A-H JI TB Simatupang Kav 53, Jakarta, 12520, Indonesia
Tel.: (62) 2129712600
Web Site: http://www.yokogawa.com
Emp.: 180
Industrial Automation Systems & Instruments, Measuring Instruments & Information Processing Equipment Mfr
N.A.I.C.S.: 334513
Ichsan Gaffar (Mgr)

PT Yokogawa Manufacturing Batam (1)
Lot 339-340 Jalan Beringin Mukakuning, Batamindo Industrial Park, Batam, 29433, Indonesia
Tel.: (62) 770 612424
Web Site: http://www.yokogawa.com
Industrial Automation Systems & Instruments, Measuring Instruments & Information Processing Equipment Mfr
N.A.I.C.S.: 334513

Rota Yokogawa GmbH & Co.KG (1)
Rheinstr 8, 79664, Wehr, Germany
Tel.: (49) 77615670
Web Site: http://www.yokogawa.com
Emp.: 220
Industrial Automation Systems & Instruments, Measuring Instruments & Information Processing Equipment Mfr

INTERNATIONAL PUBLIC

N.A.I.C.S.: 334513
Katsuya Ikezawa (Mng Dir)

Suzhou Yokogawa Meter Company (1)
8 Sandhya Taishan Street New District, New District, Suzhou, 215011, Jiangsu, China
Tel.: (86) 512 6825 2329
Web Site: http://www.yokogawa-syc.com.cn
Emp.: 300
Industrial Metering Board Mfr
N.A.I.C.S.: 334515

SynCrest Inc. (1)
2-26-1 Muraokahigashi Shonan Health Innovation Park, Fujisawa, 251-0012, Kanagawa, Japan
Tel.: (81) 466286050
Web Site: https://www.syncrest.com
Molecular Drug Product Mfr & Distr
N.A.I.C.S.: 325998

TCB Avgidis Automation SA (1)
108 Kasomouli Str Neos Kosmos, 117 44, Athens, Greece
Tel.: (30) 210 948 0260
Web Site: https://www.tcb.gr
Electric Equipment Mfr
N.A.I.C.S.: 335999

Test ve Muhendislik A.S. (1)
Birlik Mahallesi 398 Cadde No 2/2, Cankaya, 06610, Ankara, Turkiye
Tel.: (90) 312 496 1600
Web Site: https://www.t-m.com.tr
Electronic Equipment Distr
N.A.I.C.S.: 423690

Testpower AB (1)
Oxelbarsgrand 17, Hasselby, 165 72, Vallingby, Sweden
Tel.: (46) 84771900
Web Site: https://www.testpower.se
Measurement Product Distr
N.A.I.C.S.: 423490

UAB Indeel LT (1)
Betygalos g 6, LT-47183, Kaunas, Lithuania
Tel.: (370) 3 729 5610
Web Site: https://www.indeel.lt
Industrial Equipment Mfr & Distr
N.A.I.C.S.: 333248

Yokogawa & Co., Ltd. (1)
2F Sumitomo Fudosan Nishigotanda Building 3-6-21 Nishigotanda, Shinagawa-ku, Tokyo, 141-0031, Japan
Tel.: (81) 334956635
Emp.: 350
Project Management Services
N.A.I.C.S.: 561110

Yokogawa (Thailand) Ltd (1)
799 Rama 9 Road, Bangkapi Huaykwang, Bangkok, 10310, Thailand
Tel.: (66) 27158600
Web Site: http://www.yokogawa.com
Emp.: 300
Industrial Automation Systems & Instruments, Measuring Instruments & Information Processing Equipment Mfr
N.A.I.C.S.: 334513

Yokogawa Africa Holding B.V. (1)
92 Avenue Charles de Gaulle, Pointe Noire, Congo, Republic of
Tel.: (242) 9736 675 9181
Engineering Services
N.A.I.C.S.: 541330

Yokogawa African Anglophone Region (Pty) Ltd. (1)
Cambridge Commercial Park 6 Trinity Close, Paulshof, Johannesburg, 2056, South Africa
Tel.: (27) 118316300
Measuring Equipment Mfr
N.A.I.C.S.: 334515

Yokogawa America do Sul Ltda. (1)
Alameda Xingu 850 - Alphaville, Barueri, Sao Paulo, 06455 - 030, Brazil
Tel.: (55) 1156812400
Industrial Automation Systems & Instruments, Measuring Instruments & Information Processing Equipment Mfr
N.A.I.C.S.: 334513

Yokogawa Analytical Solutions Sdn. Bhd. (1)

AND PRIVATE COMPANIES — YOKOGAWA ELECTRIC CORPORATION

No 15 & 16 Jalan Ipark 1/2 Kawasan Perindustrian Ipark, Kulai, Johor, Malaysia
Tel.: (60) 76607248
Industrial Automation Machinery Mfr & Distr
N.A.I.C.S.: 333248

Yokogawa Argentina (1)
Tel.: (54) 1151990299
Emp.: 13
Industrial Automation Systems & Instruments, Measuring Instruments & Information Processing Equipment Mfr
N.A.I.C.S.: 334513

Yokogawa Australia Pty. Ltd. (1)
Level 3 66 Waterloo Road, Macquarie Park, 2113, NSW, Australia
Tel.: (61) 1300558965
Web Site: http://www.yokogawa.com
Emp.: 200
Industrial Automation Systems & Instruments, Measuring Instruments & Information Processing Equipment Mfr
N.A.I.C.S.: 334513
Russell Palmer *(Mng Dir)*

Yokogawa Belgium N.V./S.A. (1)
Ikaroslaan 36, 1930, Zaventem, Belgium
Tel.: (32) 27195511
Web Site: http://www.yokogawa.com
Emp.: 32
Industrial Automation Systems & Instruments, Measuring Instruments & Information Processing Equipment Mfr
N.A.I.C.S.: 334513
Jef Vreysen *(Mgr)*

Yokogawa Bio Frontier Inc. (1)
2-9-32 Nakamachi, Musashino, Tokyo, 180-8750, Japan
Tel.: (81) 422529776
Biomass Material Mfr & Distr
N.A.I.C.S.: 325199

Yokogawa Canada, Inc. (1)
Bay 4 11133 40th Street SE, Calgary, T2C 2Z4, AB, Canada
Tel.: (403) 258-2681
Web Site: https://www.yokogawa.com
Emp.: 50
Industrial Automation Systems & Instruments, Measuring Instruments & Information Processing Equipment Mfr
N.A.I.C.S.: 334513

Yokogawa Chile (1)
Badajoz 130 16th Floor, Las Condes, 7560908, Santiago, Chile
Tel.: (56) 223556300
Web Site: https://www.yokogawa.cl
Emp.: 22
Industrial Automation Systems & Instruments, Measuring Instruments & Information Processing Equipment Mfr
N.A.I.C.S.: 334513

Yokogawa China Co., Ltd. (1)
3F TowerD Cartelo Crocodile Building No 568 West Tianshan Road, Shanghai, 200335, China
Tel.: (86) 2162396262
Web Site: http://www.yokogawa.com
Emp.: 150
Industrial Automation Systems & Instruments, Measuring Instruments & Information Processing Equipment Mfr
N.A.I.C.S.: 334513

Yokogawa Colombia (1)
Av Calle 80 No 69 - 70 Bodega 11 Conjunto Empresarial CL80, Bogota, Colombia
Tel.: (57) 17560075
Web Site: http://www.yokogawa.com.co
Industrial Automation Systems & Instruments, Measuring Instruments & Information Processing Equipment Mfr
N.A.I.C.S.: 334513

Yokogawa Corporation of America (1)
2 Dart Rd, Newnan, GA 30265 **(100%)**
Tel.: (770) 254-0400
Web Site: https://www.yokogawa.com
Emp.: 350
Precision Electrical Power & Power Factor Instrumentation
N.A.I.C.S.: 334515
Dave Johnson *(CEO)*

Division (Domestic):

Yokogawa Corporation of America (2)
12530 W Airport Blvd, Sugar Land, TX 77478
Tel.: (281) 340-3900
Web Site: http://www.yokogawa.com
Emp.: 300
Analysis Instruments Mfr
N.A.I.C.S.: 334513
Shuji Mori *(CEO)*

Yokogawa Denshikiki Co., Ltd. (1)
Minami Shinjuku Hoshino Bldg 5-23-13 Sendagaya, Shibuya-ku, Tokyo, 151-0051, Japan
Tel.: (81) 332255383
Web Site: http://www.yokogawadenshikiki.co.jp
Emp.: 300
Industrial Automation Systems & Instruments, Measuring Instruments & Information Processing Equipment Mfr
N.A.I.C.S.: 334513
Takashi Fuji *(CEO)*

Yokogawa Deutschland GmbH (1)
Broichhofstr 7-11, 40880, Ratingen, Germany
Tel.: (49) 210249830
Web Site: https://www.yokogawa.com
Emp.: 80
Industrial Automation Systems & Instruments, Measuring Instruments & Information Processing Equipment Mfr
N.A.I.C.S.: 334513

Yokogawa Electric (Malaysia) Sdn. Bhd. (1)
No 9 Jalan Industri PBP 3 Taman Industri Pusat Bandar, 47100, Puchong, Malaysia
Tel.: (60) 380649888
Emp.: 200
Industrial Automation Systems & Instruments, Measuring Instruments & Information Processing Equipment Mfr
N.A.I.C.S.: 334513
Chin Konsiong *(Gen Mgr)*

Yokogawa Electric Asia Pte. Ltd. (1)
5 Bedok South Road, Singapore, 469270, Singapore
Tel.: (65) 62419933
Web Site: http://www.yokogawa.com
Industrial Automation Systems & Instruments, Measuring Instruments & Information Processing Equipment Mfr
N.A.I.C.S.: 334513

Yokogawa Electric CIS Ltd. (1)
d 1 dog 4 Samarskaya st, Moscow, 129110, Russia
Tel.: (7) 4957377868
Web Site: https://www.yokogawa.ru
Emp.: 2,000
Industrial Automation Systems & Instruments, Measuring Instruments & Information Processing Equipment Mfr
N.A.I.C.S.: 334513
Vladimir Savelev *(Gen Mgr)*

Yokogawa Electric China Co., Ltd. (1)
No 365 Xing Long Street, Suzhou Industrial Park, Jiangsu, 215126, China
Tel.: (86) 512 62833666
Web Site: http://www.yokogawa.com
Industrial Automation Systems & Instruments, Measuring Instruments & Information Processing Equipment Mfr
N.A.I.C.S.: 334513

Yokogawa Electric International Pte. Ltd. (1)
5 Bedok South Road, Singapore, 469270, Singapore
Tel.: (65) 62419933
Web Site: http://www.yokogawa.com
Emp.: 1,000
Industrial Automation Systems & Instruments, Measuring Instruments & Information Processing Equipment Mfr
N.A.I.C.S.: 334513

Yokogawa Electric Kazakhstan Ltd. (1)
TURAR Business Center 7th Floor Room 708 502 Seifullin Avenue, 050012, Almaty, Kazakhstan
Tel.: (7) 7273397287
Measuring Equipment Mfr
N.A.I.C.S.: 334515

Yokogawa Electric Korea Co., Ltd. (1)
Yokogawa B/D Yangpyeong-dong 4-Ga 21 Seonyu-ro 45-gil, Yeongdeungpo-gu, Seoul, 07209, Youngdeungpo-Gu, Korea (South)
Tel.: (82) 226286000
Web Site: http://www.yokogawa.com
Industrial Automation Systems & Instruments, Measuring Instruments & Information Processing Equipment Mfr
N.A.I.C.S.: 334513

Yokogawa Electric Sakhalin Ltd. (1)
36 room 22 Anton Buyukly St, 693007, Yuzhno-Sakhalinsk, Russia
Tel.: (7) 4242498448
Web Site: http://www.yokogawa.com
Industrial Automation Systems & Instruments, Measuring Instruments & Information Processing Equipment Mfr
N.A.I.C.S.: 334513

Yokogawa Electric Ukraine Ltd. (1)
Gorkogo Street 172 Office 1114, 03150, Kiev, Ukraine
Tel.: (380) 445212140
Measuring Equipment Mfr
N.A.I.C.S.: 334515

Yokogawa Electronics Manufacturing Korea Co., Ltd. (1)
82 Bupyeong-daero 297beon-gil, Bupyeong-gu, Incheon, 21315, Korea (South)
Tel.: (82) 325103289
Web Site: http://www.yokogawa.com
Emp.: 200
Industrial Automation Systems & Instruments, Measuring Instruments & Information Processing Equipment Mfr
N.A.I.C.S.: 334513

Yokogawa Engineering Asia Pte. Ltd. (1)
5 Bedok South Road, Singapore, 469270, Singapore
Tel.: (65) 62419933
Web Site: https://www.yokogawa.com
Emp.: 1,000
Industrial Automation Systems & Instruments, Measuring Instruments & Information Processing Equipment Mfr
N.A.I.C.S.: 334513
John Hewitt *(Mng Dir)*

Yokogawa Engineering Bahrain W.L.L (1)
Unit A8 Building 1318 Road 1516 Block 115, PO Box 10070, Bahrain International Investment Park, Al-Hidd, Bahrain
Tel.: (973) 17707700
Industrial Automation Machinery Mfr & Distr
N.A.I.C.S.: 333248

Yokogawa Engineering Middle East & Africa FZE (1)
Jebel Ali Free Zone Bldg no LIU FZS1-BH03, PO Box 18112, Free South Zone, Dubai, United Arab Emirates
Tel.: (971) 48049100
Measuring Equipment Mfr
N.A.I.C.S.: 334515

Yokogawa Engineering Middle East FZE (1)
Jebel Ali Free Zone Bldg No LIU FZS1-AH07, PO Box 18112, Free South Zone, Dubai, United Arab Emirates
Tel.: (971) 4 8049100
Emp.: 25
Engineeering Services
N.A.I.C.S.: 541330
Norio Kimura *(Gen Mgr)*

Yokogawa Europe B.V. (1)
Tel.: (31) 884641000
Emp.: 500
Industrial Automation Systems & Instruments, Measuring Instruments & Information Processing Equipment Mfr
N.A.I.C.S.: 334513
Herr van der Berg *(Gen Mgr)*

Yokogawa Europe Branches B.V. (1)
Euroweg 2, Amersfoort, 3825 HD, Netherlands
Tel.: (31) 884641000
Web Site: http://www.yokogawa.com
Emp.: 50

Industrial Control Systems Distr
N.A.I.C.S.: 423830
Herman van den Berg *(Gen Mgr)*

Yokogawa Europe Solutions B.V. (1)
Euroweg 2, 3825 HD, Amersfoort, Netherlands
Tel.: (31) 884641000
Web Site: http://www.yokogawa.com
Emp.: 550
Industrial Automation Systems & Instruments, Measuring Instruments & Information Processing Equipment Mfr
N.A.I.C.S.: 334513

Yokogawa Field Engineering Service Corporation (1)
2-9-32 Nakacho, Musashino, 180-0006, Tokyo, Japan
Tel.: (81) 422520439
Web Site: http://www.yokogawa.com
Engineeering Services
N.A.I.C.S.: 541330

Yokogawa Fluence Analytics, Inc. (1)
12875 Capricorn St, Stafford, TX 77477
Tel.: (281) 801-4191
Web Site: https://www.fluenceanalytics.com
Polymer Laboratory Analytics Services
N.A.I.C.S.: 541715

Yokogawa Fluid Imaging Technologies Inc. (1)
200 Enterprise Dr, Scarborough, ME 04074
Tel.: (207) 289-3200
Web Site: https://www.fluidimaging.com
Flow Cam Product Mfr & Distr
N.A.I.C.S.: 332721

Yokogawa Foundry Corporation (1)
2-9-32 Nakamachi, Musashino, Tokyo, 180-8750, Japan
Tel.: (81) 422528127
Emp.: 35
Stationery Product Mfr & Distr
N.A.I.C.S.: 322230

Yokogawa France S.A.S. (1)
17 Rue Paul Dautier, BP 267, 78147, Velizy-Villacoublay, Cedex, France
Tel.: (33) 139261000
Web Site: https://www.yokogawa.com
Emp.: 150
Industrial Automation Systems & Instruments, Measuring Instruments & Information Processing Equipment Mfr
N.A.I.C.S.: 334513
Pierre Delaveau *(Gen Mgr)*

Yokogawa GesmbH (1)
Modecenterstrasse 14, PO Box 27, 1030, Vienna, Austria
Tel.: (43) 1206340
Web Site: http://www.yokogawa.com
Industrial Automation Systems & Instruments, Measuring Instruments & Information Processing Equipment Mfr
N.A.I.C.S.: 334513

Yokogawa Hungaria Kft. (1)
Bacsalmas u 1-3, 1119, Budapest, Hungary
Tel.: (36) 13553938
Web Site: http://www.yokogawa.com
Emp.: 20
Industrial Automation Systems & Instruments, Measuring Instruments & Information Processing Equipment Mfr
N.A.I.C.S.: 334513
John van der Geer *(Country Mgr)*

Yokogawa IA Technologies India Private Limited (1)
Umiya Business Bay Tower - I 6th Floor Cessna Business Park, Marathahalli - Sarjapura Outer Ring Road Kadubeesanahalli, Bengaluru, 560 037, India
Tel.: (91) 8067925100
Web Site: http://www.yokogawa.com
Industrial Automation Systems & Instruments, Measuring Instruments & Information Processing Equipment Mfr
N.A.I.C.S.: 334513

Yokogawa Iberia S.A. (1)
Rua Rei Ramiro 870-1G, 4400-281, Vila Nova de Gaia, Portugal
Tel.: (351) 223722650
Web Site: http://www.yokogawa.com

YOKOGAWA ELECTRIC CORPORATION — INTERNATIONAL PUBLIC

Yokogawa Electric Corporation—(Continued)
Industrial Automation Systems & Instruments, Measuring Instruments & Information Processing Equipment Mfr
N.A.I.C.S.: 334513

Yokogawa India Ltd. (1)
Plot No 96 Electronic City Complex Hosur Road, Bengaluru, 560 100, India
Tel.: (91) 8041586000
Web Site: https://www.yokogawa.com
Industrial Automation Systems & Instruments, Measuring Instruments & Information Processing Equipment Mfr
N.A.I.C.S.: 334513
Tsutomu Murata (Mng Dir)

Yokogawa Industrial Safety Systems Sdn. Bhd. (1)
No 9 Jalan Industri PBP 3 Taman Industri Pusat Bandar, 47100, Puchong, Selangor Darul Ehsan, Malaysia
Tel.: (60) 380649888
Web Site: http://www.yokogawa.com
Emp.: 300
Industrial Automation Systems & Instruments, Measuring Instruments & Information Processing Equipment Mfr
N.A.I.C.S.: 334513
Chin Kon Siong (Pres)

Yokogawa Information Systems (Dalian) Corporation (1)
Unit 03-01/03/05/06 No3 Huixianyuan High-Tech Industrial Zone, Dalian, Liaoning, China
Tel.: (86) 41184736688
Industrial Automation Machinery Mfr & Distr
N.A.I.C.S.: 333248

Yokogawa Innovation Switzerland GmbH (1)
Gewerbestrasse 24, Basel-Landschaft, 4123, Allschwil, Switzerland
Tel.: (41) 614616978
Web Site: https://www.yokogawa.com
Measuring Equipment Mfr
N.A.I.C.S.: 334515

Yokogawa Ireland (1)
Unit 411 Grants park Greenogue Business park, Rathcoole, Dublin, Ireland
Tel.: (353) 14577454
Web Site: http://www.yokogawa.com
Emp.: 4
Industrial Automation Systems & Instruments, Measuring Instruments & Information Processing Equipment Mfr
N.A.I.C.S.: 334513
Donal Bourke (Mgr-Sales)

Yokogawa Italia S.r.l. (1)
Via Assunta 61, 20834, Nova Milanese, MB, Italy
Tel.: (39) 03621802000
Web Site: http://www.yokogawa.com
Industrial Automation Systems & Instruments, Measuring Instruments & Information Processing Equipment Mfr
N.A.I.C.S.: 334513

Yokogawa Kontrol (Malaysia) Sdn. Bhd. (1)
No 9 Jalan Industri PBP 3 Taman Industri Pusat Bandar, 47100, Puchong, Selangor Darul Ehsan, Malaysia
Tel.: (60) 380649888
Web Site: https://www.yokogawa.com
Emp.: 310
Industrial Automation Systems & Instruments, Measuring Instruments & Information Processing Equipment Mfr
N.A.I.C.S.: 334513
Ham Dan (Gen Mgr)

Yokogawa Manufacturing Corporation (1)
2-9-32 Nakamachi, Musashino, Tokyo, 180-8750, Japan
Tel.: (81) 422525880
Emp.: 1,383
Electronic Equipment Mfr & Distr
N.A.I.C.S.: 334416

Yokogawa Marex Limited (1)
Marex House 34 Medina Road, Cowes, PO31 7DA, Isle of Wight, United Kingdom
Tel.: (44) 1983296011
Web Site: https://www.ymx.yokogawa.com
Emp.: 40
Industrial Automation Systems & Instruments, Measuring Instruments & Information Processing Equipment Mfr
N.A.I.C.S.: 334513
Nigel Bowden (Mng Dir)

Yokogawa Measurement Technologies AB (1)
Finlandsgatan 52 1st floor, -164 74, Stockholm, Kista, Sweden
Tel.: (46) 84771900
Web Site: http://www.yokogawa.se
Industrial Automation Systems & Instruments, Measuring Instruments & Information Processing Equipment Mfr
N.A.I.C.S.: 334513

Yokogawa Measurement Technologies Ltd. (1)
Stuart Road Manor Park, Runcorn, WA7 1TR, Chesire, United Kingdom
Tel.: (44) 1928597200
Web Site: http://www.yokogawa.com
Emp.: 60
Industrial Automation Systems & Instruments, Measuring Instruments & Information Processing Equipment Mfr
N.A.I.C.S.: 334513
Simon Rogers (Mng Dir)

Yokogawa Measuring Instruments Korea Corp. (1)
City Air Terminal Bldg 405-9 159-6, Samsung-dong, Seoul, 135-728, Kangnam-ku, Korea (South)
Tel.: (82) 25510660
Web Site: http://www.yokogawa.com
Industrial Automation Systems & Instruments, Measuring Instruments & Information Processing Equipment Mfr
N.A.I.C.S.: 334513

Yokogawa Meters & Instruments Corporation (1)
Tachihi Bldg No 2, 2-9-32 Naka-cho, Tokyo, 180-8750, Musashino-Shi, Japan
Tel.: (81) 425341413
Web Site: http://www.yokogawa.com
Emp.: 100
Industrial Automation Systems & Instruments, Measuring Instruments & Information Processing Equipment Mfr
N.A.I.C.S.: 334513
Masayuki Oooka (Mgr-Global Sls)

Yokogawa Middle East B.S.C.(c) (1)
Building 577 Road 2516 Busaiteen 225, PO Box 10070, Muharraq, Manama, Bahrain
Tel.: (973) 17358100
Web Site: http://www.yokogawa.com
Industrial Automation Systems & Instruments, Measuring Instruments & Information Processing Equipment Mfr
N.A.I.C.S.: 334513

Yokogawa New Zealand Ltd. (1)
Unit C 55 Richard Pearce Drive, PO Box 201188, Airport Oaks, 2150, Auckland, New Zealand
Tel.: (64) 92550496
Web Site: http://www.yokogawa.com
Emp.: 10
Industrial Automation Systems & Instruments, Measuring Instruments & Information Processing Equipment Mfr
N.A.I.C.S.: 334513
Steve Poole (Mgr-Sales)

Yokogawa Norge AS (1)
Prof Olav Hanssens vei 7 A, 4068, Stavanger, Norway
Tel.: (47) 90640662
Measuring Equipment Mfr
N.A.I.C.S.: 334515

Yokogawa Norway (1)
Professor Olav Hanssens vei 7A, 4068, Stavanger, Norway
Tel.: (47) 90640662
Web Site: http://www.yokogawa.com
Emp.: 2
Industrial Automation Systems & Instruments, Measuring Instruments & Information Processing Equipment Mfr
N.A.I.C.S.: 334513

Yokogawa Nuclear Solutions, LLC (1)
2 Dart Rd, Newnan, GA 30265-1040
Tel.: (770) 253-7000
Nuclear Electric Power Generation Services
N.A.I.C.S.: 221113

Yokogawa Oddzia w Polsce (1)
Ul Pruszkowska 17, 02-119, Warsaw, Poland
Tel.: (48) 226214017
Industrial Automation Systems & Instruments, Measuring Instruments & Information Processing Equipment Mfr
N.A.I.C.S.: 334513

Yokogawa Oman Limited L.L.C. (1)
Building 232 Plot No 785 Complex 252, PO Box 2667, Ghala Heights District, Muscat, Oman
Tel.: (968) 24230400
Measuring Equipment Mfr
N.A.I.C.S.: 334515

Yokogawa Peru (1)
Tel.: (51) 12779400
Web Site: http://www.yokogawa.com.pe
Emp.: 7
Industrial Automation Systems & Instruments, Measuring Instruments & Information Processing Equipment Mfr
N.A.I.C.S.: 334513

Yokogawa Philippines Inc. (1)
Topy Industries Building No 3 Economia Street, Bagumbayan Libis, Quezon City, Philippines
Tel.: (63) 272387777
Web Site: http://www.yokogawa.com
Industrial Automation Systems & Instruments, Measuring Instruments & Information Processing Equipment Mfr
N.A.I.C.S.: 334513

Yokogawa Pionics Co., Ltd. (1)
Nippon Life Musashino Building 1-16-10 Nakamachi, Musashino, Tokyo, 180-0006, Japan
Tel.: (81) 422525791
Emp.: 45
Real Estate Manangement Services
N.A.I.C.S.: 531210

Yokogawa Polska Sp. z o.o. (1)
Krakowiakow 44, 02-255, Warsaw, Poland
Tel.: (48) 228685905
Web Site: https://www.yokogawa.com
Measuring Equipment Mfr
N.A.I.C.S.: 334515

Yokogawa Process Analyzers Europe B.V. (1)
Euroweg 2, Amersfoort, Netherlands
Tel.: (31) 884641920
Industrial Automation Machinery Mfr & Distr
N.A.I.C.S.: 333248

Yokogawa Process Control (Shanghai) Co., Ltd. (1)
No 135 FuTe Xi Yi Lu WaiGaoQiao Free Trade Zone, Shanghai, 200131, China
Tel.: (86) 21 62396262
Electrical Control System Mfr
N.A.I.C.S.: 334513

Yokogawa Qatar QFZ LLC (1)
Business Innovation Park Building 3rd Floor Wing-3, PO Box 24281, Ras Bufontas FZ, Doha, Qatar
Tel.: (974) 44452444
Industrial Automation Machinery Mfr & Distr
N.A.I.C.S.: 333248

Yokogawa RAP Limited (1)
Urban Village 220 High Street, Swansea, SA1 1NW, United Kingdom
Tel.: (44) 179 234 1343
Web Site: https://www.yokogawa-rap.com
Computer Programming Services
N.A.I.C.S.: 541511

Yokogawa Rental & Lease Corporation (1)
Shinjuku First West 1-23-7 Nish, Shinjuku, Tokyo, 160-0023, Japan
Tel.: (81) 368676704
Web Site: https://www.yrl.com
Emp.: 822
Measuring Equipment Mfr & Distr
N.A.I.C.S.: 334519

Yokogawa Saudi Arabia Company LLC (1)
Ibn Rushd Street Dhahran Techno-Valley - Dhahran, PO Box 3368, Al Khobar, 31952, Saudi Arabia
Tel.: (966) 133319600
Industrial Automation Machinery Mfr & Distr
N.A.I.C.S.: 333248

Yokogawa Saudi Arabia Ltd. (1)
Ibn Rushd Street Dhahran Techno-Valley - Dhahran, PO Box 3368, Al Khobar, 31952, Saudi Arabia
Tel.: (966) 133319600
Web Site: http://www.yokogawa.com
Industrial Automation Systems & Instruments, Measuring Instruments & Information Processing Equipment Mfr
N.A.I.C.S.: 334513

Yokogawa Service Ltda. (1)
Ave Ceci 1500, Tambore, Sao Paulo, 06460-120, Brazil
Tel.: (55) 1135131300
Web Site: http://www.yokogawa.com.br
Emp.: 400
Industrial Automation Systems & Instruments, Measuring Instruments & Information Processing Equipment Mfr
N.A.I.C.S.: 334513

Yokogawa Services Saudi Arabia Ltd. (1)
Jubail Industrial City Industrial Support Area No 1 Road No 114, PO Box 10318, Jubail, 31961, Saudi Arabia
Tel.: (966) 133429600
Web Site: http://www.yokogawa.com
Industrial Automation Systems & Instruments, Measuring Instruments & Information Processing Equipment Mfr
N.A.I.C.S.: 334513

Yokogawa Shanghai Instrumentation Co., Ltd. (1)
No 157 Changji Road Anting Zhen, Jiading District, Shanghai, 201805, China
Tel.: (86) 2159573587
Web Site: http://www.ysi.com.cn
Industrial Automation Systems & Instruments, Measuring Instruments & Information Processing Equipment Mfr
N.A.I.C.S.: 334513
Akio Tsukahara (Gen Mgr)

Yokogawa Shanghai Trading Co., Ltd. (1)
4F TowerD Cartelo Crocodile Building No 568 West Tianshan Road, Shanghai, 200335, China
Tel.: (86) 21 62396363
Industrial Automation Systems & Instruments, Measuring Instruments & Information Processing Equipment Mfr
N.A.I.C.S.: 334513

Yokogawa Sichuan Instrument Co., Ltd. (1)
No 1 Tongchang Road, Beibei District, Chongqing, 400707, China
Tel.: (86) 2368220100
Web Site: http://www.cys.com.cn
Emp.: 381
Industrial Automation Systems & Instruments, Measuring Instruments & Information Processing Equipment Mfr
N.A.I.C.S.: 334513

Yokogawa Slovakia s.r.o. (1)
Stefanikova 8, 81105, Bratislava, Slovakia
Tel.: (421) 252621062
Industrial Automation Machinery Mfr & Distr
N.A.I.C.S.: 333248

Yokogawa Software Engineering (Wuxi) Co., Ltd. (1)
No 11 Xi Kun Road Wuxi-Singapore Industrial Park, Wuxi, 214028, Jiangsu, China
Tel.: (86) 51085280003
Measuring Equipment Mfr
N.A.I.C.S.: 334515

Yokogawa Solution Service Corporation (1)
2-9-32 Nakamachi, Musashino, Tokyo, 180-8750, Japan
Tel.: (81) 422520439
Emp.: 2,572
Measuring Equipment Distr
N.A.I.C.S.: 423830

Yokogawa Solutions Corporation (1)
3-25-3 Yoyogi Aioisompo Shinjuku Bldg 8f,

Shibuya, Tokyo, 151-0053, Japan
Tel.: (81) 353518300
Web Site: http://www.yokogawa.com
Software Development Services
N.A.I.C.S.: 541511

Yokogawa South Africa (Pty) Ltd. (1)
Block C Cresta Junction Cnr Beyers Naude Drive and Judges Avenue, Cresta, Randburg, 2194, South Africa
Tel.: (27) 118316300
Web Site: http://www.yokogawa.com
Emp.: 100
Industrial Automation Systems & Instruments, Measuring Instruments & Information Processing Equipment Mfr
N.A.I.C.S.: 334513
Herman Vanden Berg (Pres)

Yokogawa Switzerland S.A. (1)
Switzerland Innovation Park Basel Area Hegenheimermattweg 167A, CH 4123, Allschwil, Switzerland
Tel.: (41) 614616978
Project Management Services
N.A.I.C.S.: 561110

Yokogawa System Integration & Procurement (Wuxi) Co., Ltd. (1)
J3-3-B Free Trade Zone Gao Lang East Road, Wuxi New District, Wuxi, 214028, Jiangsu, China
Tel.: (86) 51085280003
Industrial Automation Machinery Mfr & Distr
N.A.I.C.S.: 333248

Yokogawa Taiwan Corporation (1)
12F No 243 Sec 2 Chongqing N Rd, Datong Dist, Taipei, 103, Taiwan
Tel.: (886) 225572686
Web Site: http://www.yokogawa.com
Industrial Automation Systems & Instruments, Measuring Instruments & Information Processing Equipment Mfr
N.A.I.C.S.: 334513

Yokogawa Techinvent AS (1)
Professor Olav Hanssens vei 7A, 4021, Stavanger, Norway
Tel.: (47) 93068941
Industrial Automation Machinery Mfr & Distr
N.A.I.C.S.: 333248

Yokogawa Technologies Solutions India Private Limited (1)
Umiya Business Bay Tower - I 6th Floor Cessna Business Park, Marathahalli-Sarjapura Outer Ring Road Kadubeesanahalli, Bengaluru, 560 037, India
Tel.: (91) 8067925100
Measuring Equipment Mfr
N.A.I.C.S.: 334515

Yokogawa Test & Measurement (Shanghai) Co., Ltd. (1)
Room 603 No 799 West Tianshan Road, Changning District, Shanghai, 200335, China
Tel.: (86) 2162396363
Measuring Equipment Mfr
N.A.I.C.S.: 334515

Yokogawa Test & Measurement Corporation (1)
4-9-8 Keio Hachioji Myojin-cho Building, Hachioji, 192-8566, Tokyo, Japan
Tel.: (81) 42 690 8800
Web Site: https://tmi.yokogawa.com
Measurement Product Mfr & Distr
N.A.I.C.S.: 334513

Yokogawa Test Solutions Corporation (1)
2-9-32 Nakacho Yokogawadenkikknai, Musashino, 180-0006, Tokyo, Japan
Tel.: (81) 422529770
Web Site: http://www.yokogawa.com
Emp.: 18
Semiconductor Testing Equipment Mfr
N.A.I.C.S.: 334515
Yasunori Kawata (VP-Quality Assurance)

Yokogawa Turkey Industrial Automation Solutions A.S. (1)
Anadolu Caddesi Megapol Tower No 41 Kat 15, Bayrakli, 35580, Izmir, Turkiye
Tel.: (90) 2324526426
Web Site: https://www.yokogawa.com
Measuring Equipment Mfr
N.A.I.C.S.: 334515

Yokogawa UAE Industry-S.P. LLC (1)
B46-24J5 ICAD-1, PO Box 112873, Musaffah, 31952, Abu Dhabi, United Arab Emirates
Tel.: (971) 25101888
Industrial Automation Machinery Mfr & Distr
N.A.I.C.S.: 333248

Yokogawa USA, Inc. (1)
2 Dart Rd, Newnan, GA 30265-1040
Tel.: (770) 253-7000
Web Site: http://www.yokogawa.com
Portable Test Equipment Mfr
N.A.I.C.S.: 334515

Yokogawa United Kingdom Ltd. (1)
Stuart Road Manor Park, Runcorn, WA7 1TR, Cheshire, United Kingdom
Tel.: (44) 1928597100
Web Site: http://www.yokogawa.com
Industrial Automation Systems & Instruments, Measuring Instruments & Information Processing Equipment Mfr
N.A.I.C.S.: 334513

Yokogawa Vietnam Company Ltd. (1)
Level 10 Hoa Binh Tower 106 Hoang Quoc Viet Street, Cau Giay District, Hanoi, Vietnam
Tel.: (84) 437635115
Web Site: http://www.yokogawa.com
Industrial Automation Systems & Instruments, Measuring Instruments & Information Processing Equipment Mfr
N.A.I.C.S.: 334513

Yokogawa de Mexico, S.A. de C.V. (1)
Urbina No 18 Parque Industrial Naucalpan, Naucalpan de Juarez, 53370, Mexico, Mexico
Tel.: (52) 5559557400
Web Site: https://www.yokogawa.com
Emp.: 20
Industrial Automation Systems & Instruments, Measuring Instruments & Information Processing Equipment Mfr
N.A.I.C.S.: 334513
Mareo Montero (Mgr-Reg Sls)

Yokoshin Software Engineering (WUXI) Co., Ltd. (1)
No 11 Xikun Rd Singapore Ind Park, Wuxi, 214028, China
Tel.: (86) 51085280011
Engineering Services
N.A.I.C.S.: 541330

Zimmerli Messtechnik AG (1)
Schlossgasse 10, 4125, Riehen, Switzerland
Tel.: (41) 61 645 9800
Web Site: https://www.zimmerliag.com
Pressure Measurement Mfr
N.A.I.C.S.: 334513

YOKOHAMA GYORUI CO., LTD.

1 Yamauchi-cho, Kanagawa-ku, Yokohama, 221-0054, Kanagawa, Japan
Tel.: (81) 454593800
Web Site: https://www.yokohamagyorui.co.jp
Year Founded: 1947
7443—(TKS)
Sales Range: $300-349.9 Million
Seafood Product Whslr
N.A.I.C.S.: 424460
Hidetoshi Matsuo (Pres & CEO)

YOKOHAMA INDUSTRIES BERHAD

Lot 1238 Bt 23 Jalan Kachau Semenyih-Sg Lalang, 43500, Semenyih, Selangor Darul Ehsan, Malaysia
Tel.: (60) 3 9723 3327   MY
Web Site: http://www.yokohama.my
Sales Range: $50-74.9 Million
Battery Mfr
N.A.I.C.S.: 335910
Leh Kiah Tan (Co-Sec)

YOKOHAMA MARUUO CO., LTD.

1 Yamanouchi-cho, Kanagawa-ku, Yokohama, 221-0054, Japan
Tel.: (81) 454592921
Web Site: https://www.yokohama-maruuo.co.jp
Year Founded: 1947
8045—(TKS)
Rev.: $255,238,540
Assets: $151,891,190
Liabilities: $48,272,830
Net Worth: $103,618,360
Earnings: $2,703,490
Fiscal Year-end: 03/31/24
Marine Product Whslr
N.A.I.C.S.: 441222

Subsidiaries:

Hansui Co., Ltd. (1)
9308-18 Shimoto-cho, Seya-ku, Yokohama, 246-0001, Kanagawa, Japan
Tel.: (81) 459230604
Web Site: https://www.hansui.jp
Food Product Whslr
N.A.I.C.S.: 424490

Kawasaki Maruuo Co., Ltd. (1)
3-126-1Minamisaiwai-cho, Saiwai-ku, Kawasaki, 212-0016, Japan
Tel.: (81) 445486203
Marine Product Retailer
N.A.I.C.S.: 423860

Yokohama Uoichiba Unsou Co., Ltd. (1)
1 Yamanouchi-cho, Kanagawa-ku, Yokohama, 221-0054, Japan
Tel.: (81) 454592940
Marine Transportation Services
N.A.I.C.S.: 488510

YOKOREI CO., LTD.

Yokohama Connect Square 10F 333, Minato Mirai Nishi-ku, Yokohama, 220-0012, Japan
Tel.: (81) 452100011
Web Site: https://www.yokorei.co.jp
2874—(TKS)
Rev.: $949,081,580
Assets: $1,401,657,550
Liabilities: $782,459,490
Net Worth: $619,198,060
Earnings: $20,071,790
Emp.: 1,658
Fiscal Year-end: 09/30/23
Food Products Mfr
N.A.I.C.S.: 311999
Toshio Yoshikawa (Chm)

Subsidiaries:

Alliance Seafoods Inc. (1)
PO Box 8050, Dieppe, E1A 9J0, NB, Canada
Tel.: (506) 854-5800
Web Site: https://www.allianceseafood.ca
Seafood Distr
N.A.I.C.S.: 424460
Neil Veldhoven (VP-Sls)

Clover Trading Co., Ltd. (1)
35-26 Shibatani, Takatsuki, 569-1025, Osaka, Japan
Tel.: (81) 726899608
Web Site: https://www.clovertrading.jp
Transportation Services
N.A.I.C.S.: 485999
Kenji Nishii (Pres)

Thai Yokorei Co., Ltd. (1)
18th Floor Sindhorn Tower 3 130-132 Wireless Road, Lumpini Pathumwan, Bangkok, 10330, Thailand
Tel.: (66) 26514515
Web Site: https://www.thaiyokorei.co.th
Emp.: 324
Cold Storage Services
N.A.I.C.S.: 493120

YOKOTA MANUFACTURING CO., LTD.

1-3-6 Minami Yoshijima, Naka-ku, Hiroshima, 730-0826, Japan
Tel.: (81) 822418672
Web Site: https://www.aquadevice.com
Year Founded: 1953
6248—(TKS)
Sales Range: $10-24.9 Million
Emp.: 100
Fluid & Industrial Pumps & Valves Mfr
N.A.I.C.S.: 333996
Hiroshi Yokota (Chm)

YOKOWO CO., LTD.

5-11 Takinogawa 7-Chome, Kita-ku, Tokyo, 114-8515, Japan
Tel.: (81) 339163111
Web Site: https://www.yokowo.co.jp
Year Founded: 1922
6800—(TKS)
Rev.: $508,275,950
Assets: $505,056,880
Liabilities: $172,018,640
Net Worth: $333,038,240
Earnings: $9,987,710
Emp.: 9,244
Fiscal Year-end: 03/31/24
Electric Equipment Mfr
N.A.I.C.S.: 335312
Takayuki Tokuma (Pres & Exec Officer)

Subsidiaries:

DONGGUAN YOKOWO CAR COMPONENTS CO., LTD. (1)
Fu Zhu Shan Liao Bu, Dongguan, 523406, Guangdong, China
Tel.: (86) 76983326172
Web Site: http://www.yokowo.co.jp
Emp.: 2,000
Car Components Mfr
N.A.I.C.S.: 336390

Dongguan Yokowo Communication Components Co., Ltd. (1)
Rm 102 No 9 Liaobu Fuxing Rd, Liaobu Town, Dongguan, 523406, Guangdong, China
Tel.: (86) 7692 298 2285
Electric Equipment Mfr
N.A.I.C.S.: 335312

Dongguan Yokowo Electronics Co., Ltd. (1)
Fu Zhu Shan Liao Bu Dong Guan, Dongguan, 523406, Guangdong, China
Tel.: (86) 76983326171
Web Site: http://www.yokowo.co.jp
Electric Equipment Mfr
N.A.I.C.S.: 334515
Gao Yong Gie (Mgr)

LTCC Materials Co., Ltd. (1)
1299 Nanokaichi, Tomioka, 370-2343, Gunma, Japan
Tel.: (81) 27 489 1666
Electric Equipment Mfr
N.A.I.C.S.: 335312

YOKOWO (HONG KONG) LTD. (1)
Unit 1202 Millennium Trade Centre 56 Kwai Cheong Road, Kwai Chung, New Territories, China (Hong Kong)
Tel.: (852) 23167003
Web Site: http://www.yokowo.co.jp
Emp.: 20
Electric Equipment Mfr
N.A.I.C.S.: 334515

YOKOWO COMMUNICATION EQUIPMENT CO., LTD. (1)
1112 Kanohara, Tomioka, 370-2455, Gunma, Japan
Tel.: (81) 274627150
Web Site: http://www.yokowo.co.jp
Communication Equipment Mfr
N.A.I.C.S.: 334220

YOKOWO Co., Ltd. - Tomioka Plant (1)
1112 Kanohara, Tomioka, 370-2495, Gunma, Japan
Tel.: (81) 274622121

YOKOWO CO., LTD.

YOKOWO Co., Ltd.—(Continued)
Web Site: http://www.yokowo.co.jp
Emp.: 350
Electric Equipment Mfr
N.A.I.C.S.: 335999

YOKOWO DELIVERY CENTER CO., LTD. (1)
1112 Kanohara, Tomioka, 370-2455, Gunma, Japan
Tel.: (81) 274622118
Web Site: http://www.yokowo.co.jp
Emp.: 21
Packing & Crating Services
N.A.I.C.S.: 488991
Sotaro Matsumoto *(Gen Mgr)*

YOKOWO KOREA CO., LTD. (1)
A-1201 Woolim Lions Valley 149 Yangpyeong-Ro, Yeongdeungpo-Gu, Seoul, 150-714, Korea (South)
Tel.: (82) 27154504
Web Site: http://www.yokowo.co.jp
Emp.: 5
Electric Equipment Mfr
N.A.I.C.S.: 334515
Jaho Song *(Mng Dir)*

YOUR CONSULTING CO., LTD. (1)
5-11 Takinogawa 7-Chome, Kita-ku, Tokyo, 114-0023, Japan
Tel.: (81) 335766194
Web Site: http://www.yokowa.co.jp
Emp.: 500
Help Supply Services
N.A.I.C.S.: 561320

Yokowo (Singapore) Pte. Ltd. (1)
114 Lavender Street 08-79 CT Hub 2, Singapore, 338729, Singapore
Tel.: (65) 69082166
Web Site: http://www.yokowods.co.jp
Emp.: 8
Communication Devices Mfr
N.A.I.C.S.: 334290

Yokowo (Thailand) Co., Ltd. (1)
1858/105 Interlink Tower 24th Floor Debaratana Road, Bangna, Bangkok, 10260, Samut Prakan, Thailand
Tel.: (66) 23162311
Web Site: http://www.yokowo.co.jp
Emp.: 4
Communication Devices Mfr
N.A.I.C.S.: 334290
Junichi Tokuma *(Pres)*

Yokowo America Corporation (1)
3701 Algonquin Rd Ste 560, Rolling Meadows, IL 60008
Tel.: (847) 870-1660
Web Site: http://www.yokowo.com
Emp.: 5
Device Connectors & Medical Devices Distr
N.A.I.C.S.: 423450

Yokowo Communication Components & Systems Co., Ltd. (1)
1112 Kanohara, Tomioka, 370-2455, Gunma, Japan
Tel.: (81) 27 462 7150
Web Site: http://www.yokowo.co.jp
Emp.: 1,658
Electric Equipment Mfr
N.A.I.C.S.: 335312

Yokowo Corp. (H.K.) Ltd. (1)
Unit 1202 Millennium Trade Centre 56 Kwai Cheong Road, Kwai Chung, New Territories, China (Hong Kong)
Tel.: (852) 23684870
Web Site: http://www.yokowo.co.jp
Emp.: 10
Communication Equipment Mfr
N.A.I.C.S.: 334290

Yokowo Electronics (M) Sdn. Bhd. (1)
Plot69 Kulim Industrial Estate, Kulim, 09000, Kedah, Malaysia
Tel.: (60) 44891209
Web Site: http://www.yokowo.co.jp
Emp.: 400
Communication Devices Mfr
N.A.I.C.S.: 334290

Yokowo Europe GmbH (1)
Regus Moosacher Strasse 82a, 80809, Munich, Germany
Tel.: (49) 8925 552 0160
Web Site: http://www.yokowo.co.jp
Electric Equipment Mfr

Yokowo Fine Mechanics Co., Ltd. (1)
1112 Kanohara, Tomioka, 370-2455, Gunma, Japan
Tel.: (81) 274627132
Measuring Equipment Mfr
N.A.I.C.S.: 334515
Takayuki Tokuma *(Pres)*

Yokowo Manufacturing of America LLC (1)
4081 Leap Rd, Hilliard, OH. 43026
Tel.: (614) 921-2700
Web Site: http://www.yokowo.com
Emp.: 52
Antenna Mfr
N.A.I.C.S.: 334515
Robert Shield *(Pres)*

Yokowo Micro Tech Co., Ltd. (1)
7F-1 No104 Minquan West Road, Datong District, Taipei, 103045, Taiwan
Tel.: (886) 22 550 1522
Electric Equipment Mfr
N.A.I.C.S.: 335312

Yokowo Precision Co., Ltd. (1)
1112 Kanohara, Tomioka, 370-2455, Gunma, Japan
Tel.: (81) 274641019
Web Site: http://www.yokowo.co.jp
Connector Pins Mfr
N.A.I.C.S.: 334417

Yokowo Vietnam Co., Ltd. (1)
Dong Van II Industrial Zone, Duy Minh Ward Duy Tien Town, Ha Nam, Vietnam
Tel.: (84) 226 625 8888
Electric Equipment Mfr
N.A.I.C.S.: 335312

YOLO GROUP S.P.A.
Blend Tower Piazza Quattro Novembre 7, 20124, Milan, Italy
Tel.: (39) 0282900021
Web Site: https://www.yolo-insurance.com
YOLO—(ITA)
Software Development Services
N.A.I.C.S.: 541511

YOMA STRATEGIC HOLDINGS LTD.
63 Mohamed Sultan Road 02-14 Sultan-Link, Singapore, 239002, Singapore
Tel.: (65) 62232262
Web Site: https://yomastrategic.com
Year Founded: 1962
YMAIF—(OTCIQ)
Rev.: $220,834,000
Assets: $1,157,424,000
Liabilities: $480,986,000
Net Worth: $676,438,000
Earnings: $21,201,000
Emp.: 4,745
Fiscal Year-end: 03/31/24
Property Development & Management Services
N.A.I.C.S.: 531311
Serge Pun *(Chm)*

Subsidiaries:

Yoma Fleet Limited (1)
1 Rain Tree Drive Pun Hlaing Golf Estate, Hlaing Tharyar Township, 11401, Yangon, Myanmar **(80%)**
Tel.: (95) 996 623 5338
Web Site: http://www.yomafleet.com
Car Rental Services
N.A.I.C.S.: 532111
San Ohn *(Head-Ops)*

YOMEISHU SEIZO CO., LTD.
16-25 Nanpeidaicho, Shibuya-ku, Tokyo, 150-8563, Japan
Tel.: (81) 334628111
Web Site: https://www.yomeishu.co.jp
Year Founded: 1923
2540—(TKS)
Rev.: $100,513,209

Assets: $463,381,464
Liabilities: $61,037,008
Net Worth: $402,344,457
Earnings: $7,817,171
Emp.: 291
Fiscal Year-end: 03/31/21
Pharmaceuticals Product Mfr
N.A.I.C.S.: 325412
Shohei Kawamura *(Chm)*

YONDASHI HOLDINGS INC.
2-19-10 Kami-Osaki, Shinagawa-ku, Tokyo, 141-0021, Japan
Tel.: (81) 357193429
Web Site: https://www.yondoshi.co.jp
Year Founded: 1950
8008—(TKS)
Rev.: $279,750,130
Assets: $359,058,870
Liabilities: $85,413,230
Net Worth: $273,645,640
Earnings: $9,217,000
Emp.: 1,003
Fiscal Year-end: 02/29/24
Apparel & Accessories Mfr & Sales
N.A.I.C.S.: 315990
Masahiko Nishimura *(Exec Officer)*

Subsidiaries:

AS'TY Inc. (1)
2-15-1 Shoko Center, Nishi-ku, Hiroshima, 733-8641, Japan
Tel.: (81) 822781111
Web Site: http://www.asty.co.jp
Sales Range: $75-99.9 Million
Emp.: 105
Apparels Mfr
N.A.I.C.S.: 315990
Junji Yaguchi *(Exec Officer)*

F.D.C. Products Inc. (1)
2-19-10 Kami-Osaki Shinagawa-ku, Tokyo, 141-8544, Japan
Tel.: (81) 357194300
Web Site: http://www.fdcp.co.jp
Sales Range: $200-249.9 Million
Emp.: 257
Jewelry Mfr
N.A.I.C.S.: 339910
Hidenori Suzuki *(Pres)*

YONEX CO., LTD.
3-23-13 Yushima, Bunkyo-ku, Tokyo, 113-8543, Japan
Tel.: (81) 338361201 **JP**
Web Site: https://www.yonex.co.jp
Year Founded: 1946
7906—(TKS)
Rev.: $769,681,620
Assets: $603,003,860
Liabilities: $200,448,250
Net Worth: $402,555,610
Earnings: $58,557,990
Emp.: 2,633
Fiscal Year-end: 03/31/24
Golf, Tennis & Badminton Equipment Mfr
N.A.I.C.S.: 339920
Wataru Hirokawa *(Exec Officer & Exec Gen Mgr-Intl Sls)*

Subsidiaries:

YONEX CANADA Ltd. (1)
38 10221-15 Street NE, Calgary, T3J 0T1, AB, Canada
Tel.: (403) 243-0930
Sports Equipment Mfr
N.A.I.C.S.: 339920

YONEX GmbH (1)
Hanns-Martin-Schleyer-Str 11, 47877, Willich, Germany
Tel.: (49) 215491860
Web Site: https://www.yonex.de
Sporting Goods Distr
N.A.I.C.S.: 423910

YONEX TAIWAN CO.,Ltd. (1)
No 15 24 Road, Taichung Industrial Park, Taichung, 407, Taiwan
Tel.: (886) 423591301

INTERNATIONAL PUBLIC

Web Site: http://www.yonex.com.tw
Sports Equipment Mfr
N.A.I.C.S.: 339920

YONEX UK Ltd. (1)
Yonex House 74 Wood Lane, White City, London, W12 7RH, United Kingdom
Tel.: (44) 2087429777
Web Site: https://www.yonex.co.uk
Emp.: 16
Sporting Goods Distr
N.A.I.C.S.: 423910

Yonex Corporation (1)
20140 S Western Ave, Torrance, CA 90501
Tel.: (424) 201-4800
Web Site: https://www.yonex.com
Emp.: 22
Tennis Racquets, Golf Clubs, Badminton Racquets & Accessories
N.A.I.C.S.: 423910

Yonex Sports (China) Co., Ltd. (1)
27F Capital Square No 268 Hengtong Road, Jingan District, Shanghai, 200070, China
Tel.: (86) 2152985611
Web Site: http://www.yonex-china.com
Emp.: 13
Golf Equipment & Supplies Distr
N.A.I.C.S.: 423910
Takahiro Mochizuki *(Gen Mgr)*

YONG PYONG RESORT CORP
715 Olympic-ro, Daegwanryeongmyeon, Pyeongchang, 232-950, Gangwon-do, Korea (South)
Tel.: (82) 333355757
Web Site:
https://www.yongpyong.co.kr
Year Founded: 1975
070960—(KRS)
Rev.: $109,922,572
Assets: $665,975,258
Liabilities: $376,273,623
Net Worth: $289,701,635
Earnings: ($9,297,167)
Emp.: 340
Fiscal Year-end: 12/31/22
Hotel & Resort Operator
N.A.I.C.S.: 721120
Dal-Soon Shin *(Pres)*

YONG SHUN CHEMICAL CO., LTD.
11F No 168 Sung Chiang Road, Taipei, Taiwan
Tel.: (886) 225620950
Web Site:
https://www.yongshunchemical.com
Year Founded: 1965
4711—(TPE)
Rev.: $35,463,653
Assets: $39,730,232
Liabilities: $6,463,215
Net Worth: $33,267,017
Earnings: ($600,038)
Emp.: 141
Fiscal Year-end: 12/31/22
Polyester Resin Mfr & Distr
N.A.I.C.S.: 325211
Cheng-Fung Tsai *(Chm)*

YONG TAI BERHAD
B-25-2 Block B Jaya One No 72A Jalan Diaraja Ungku Aziz, 46200, Petaling Jaya, Malaysia
Tel.: (60) 379550955 **MY**
Web Site:
https://www.yongtai.com.my
YONGTAI—(KLS)
Rev.: $17,765,568
Assets: $200,655,467
Liabilities: $131,183,749
Net Worth: $69,471,718
Earnings: ($86,744,864)
Emp.: 117
Fiscal Year-end: 06/30/22
Textile Mfr
N.A.I.C.S.: 313310
Kuang Loon Boo *(CEO)*

AND PRIVATE COMPANIES

Subsidiaries:

PTS Impression Sdn. Bhd. (1)
No 3 Jalan KSB-Impression 8 Impression City at Kota Syahbandar, 75200, Melaka, Malaysia
Tel.: (60) 62707799
Web Site: https://www.encore-melaka.com
Entertainment Services
N.A.I.C.S.: 711130
Datuk Wira Boo Kuang Loon *(CEO)*

YONG THAI PUBLIC COMPANY LIMITED
633/14 Sathupradit Road, Yannawa, Bangkok, 10120, Thailand
Tel.: (66) 2 294 3364
Web Site: http://www.yci.co.th
Year Founded: 1964
Rev.: $378,627
Assets: $3,426,869
Liabilities: $1,561,023
Net Worth: $1,865,846
Earnings: ($1,432,538)
Emp.: 29
Fiscal Year-end: 12/31/19
Chemical Products Mfr
N.A.I.C.S.: 325199
Wirot Lophanitchakun *(Vice Chm)*

YONGA MOBILYA SANAYI VE TICARET A.S.
Kale Mahallesi Ataturk Bulvari No 196, Denizli, Turkiye
Tel.: (90) 2582671515
Web Site:
  https://www.yongamobilya.com
Year Founded: 1974
YONGA—(IST)
Rev.: $9,312,989
Assets: $8,613,989
Liabilities: $5,210,763
Net Worth: $3,403,226
Earnings: $1,213,372
Emp.: 328
Fiscal Year-end: 12/31/23
Furniture Mfr
N.A.I.C.S.: 337211

YONGHE MEDICAL GROUP CO., LTD.
11th Floor China Nuclear Construction Building No 20 Ganluyuan South, Chaoyang District, Beijing, 100020, China
Tel.: (86) 4008886667   Ky
Web Site:
  https://www.yonghegroup.cn
Year Founded: 2005
2279—(HKG)
Rev.: $246,075,820
Assets: $338,469,345
Liabilities: $208,007,034
Net Worth: $130,462,312
Earnings: ($75,692,844)
Emp.: 3,889
Fiscal Year-end: 12/31/23
Health Care Srvices
N.A.I.C.S.: 621610
Jian Ren *(Chief Growth Officer)*

YONGHUI SUPERSTORES CO., LTD.
No 436 West Second Ring Road, Fuzhou, Fujian, China
Tel.: (86) 4000601933   CN
Web Site:
  https://www.yonghui.com.cn
Year Founded: 2001
601933—(SHG)
Rev.: $12,648,751,044
Assets: $8,724,907,540
Liabilities: $7,649,878,794
Net Worth: $1,075,028,746
Earnings: ($387,948,520)
Fiscal Year-end: 12/31/22

Superstores & Supermarkets Operator
N.A.I.C.S.: 455211
Xuansong Zhang *(Chm)*

YONGJI PRINTING CO LTD
No 198 Guanshan East Road, Yunyan District, Guiyang, 550004, Guizhou, China
Tel.: (86) 85186607332
Web Site: http://www.gz-yongji.com
Year Founded: 1997
603058—(SHG)
Rev.: $91,729,343
Assets: $247,103,958
Liabilities: $81,156,002
Net Worth: $165,947,956
Earnings: $5,304,003
Emp.: 400
Fiscal Year-end: 12/31/22
Printing Product Mfr & Distr
N.A.I.C.S.: 323111
Chen Wang *(CFO)*

YONGMAO HOLDINGS LIMITED
81 Ubi Avenue 4 09-01 UB One, Singapore, 408830, Singapore
Tel.: (65) 66363456
Web Site:
  https://www.yongmaoholdings.com
Year Founded: 1992
BKX—(SES)
Rev.: $126,788,325
Assets: $281,651,529
Liabilities: $144,832,189
Net Worth: $136,819,340
Earnings: $8,173,599
Emp.: 1,100
Fiscal Year-end: 03/31/23
Tower Cranes Mfr
N.A.I.C.S.: 333120
Xiao Ming Liu *(Mgr-Production & Quality Control)*

YONGNAM HOLDINGS LIMITED
51 Tuas South Street 5, Singapore, 637644, Singapore
Tel.: (65) 67581511   SG
Web Site:
  http://www.yongnamgroup.com
Year Founded: 1994
AXB—(SES)
Rev.: $104,699,800
Assets: $230,191,260
Liabilities: $186,293,719
Net Worth: $43,897,542
Earnings: ($26,488,605)
Fiscal Year-end: 12/31/22
Civil Engineering Contract Services
N.A.I.C.S.: 541330
Pan Mi Keay *(Sec)*

Subsidiaries:

Global Maritime & Port Services Pte Ltd (1)
240 Macpherson Road 07-01, Pines Industrial Building, Singapore, 348574, Singapore
Tel.: (65) 67488895
Web Site: http://www.gmaritime.com
Marine Services
N.A.I.C.S.: 488390
Goon Kok Loon *(Chm)*

Yongnam Engineering & Construction (Private) Limited (1)
51 Tuas South Street 5, Singapore, 637644, Singapore
Tel.: (65) 6 758 1511
Web Site: http://www.yongnamgroup.com
Emp.: 1,700
Construction Engineering Services
N.A.I.C.S.: 237990

Subsidiary (Domestic):

YNE Project Engineering Pte. Ltd. (2)

51 Tuas South Street 5, Singapore, 637644, Singapore
Tel.: (65) 6 758 1511
Web Site: http://www.yongnam.com.sg
Emp.: 1,000
Construction Engineering Services
N.A.I.C.S.: 541330

Yongnam Engineering (HK) Limited (1)
Room 1811 18/F Beverley Commercial Centre 87-105 Chatham Road, Tsim Tsa Tsui, Kowloon, China (Hong Kong)
Tel.: (852) 29578082
Web Site: http://www.yongnam.com.sg
Construction Engineering Services
N.A.I.C.S.: 541330

Yongnam Engineering Sdn. Bhd. (1)
PLO 3 Kawasan Perindustrian Pontian Batu 34 1/4 Jalan Johor, Pontian, 82000, Johor, Malaysia
Tel.: (60) 76879555
Chemical Injection Mfr
N.A.I.C.S.: 333248

YONGSAN CHEMICALS, INC.
10th Floor Yongsan Building Hangangdaero 273, Yongsan-gu, Seoul, Korea (South)
Tel.: (82) 232749100
Web Site: http://www.yci.co.kr
Year Founded: 1973
Emp.: 130
Chemical Resins Mfr
N.A.I.C.S.: 325211
Kee-Joon Kim *(Chm & CEO)*

Subsidiaries:

Yongsan Chemicals, Inc. - Ulsan Plant (1)
489-3 Yongyeon-Dong, Nam-ku, Ulsan, Korea (South)
Tel.: (82) 52 228 7700
Chemical Products Mfr
N.A.I.C.S.: 327910

Yongsan Mitsui Chemicals, Inc. (1)
9F Yongsan B/D 273 Hangang-daero 04321, Yongsan-gu, Seoul, 140-150, Korea (South)
Tel.: (82) 232749191
Web Site: https://yongsan-mitsui.com
Sales Range: $25-49.9 Million
Emp.: 6
Acrylamide Mfr & Sales; Owned 50% by Yongson Chemicals, Inc. & 50% by Mitsui Chemicals, Inc.
N.A.I.C.S.: 325998

YONGSHENG ADVANCED MATERIALS COMPANY LIMITED
Unit C2 29/F Tower 1 Admiralty Centre No 18 Harcourt Road Admiralty, Hong Kong, China (Hong Kong)
Tel.: (852) 27765228   Ky
Web Site:
  http://www.chinaysgroup.com
Year Founded: 1997
3608—(HKG)
Rev.: $30,328,366
Assets: $203,644,584
Liabilities: $48,566,887
Net Worth: $155,077,697
Earnings: ($8,137,865)
Emp.: 282
Fiscal Year-end: 12/31/22
Textile Product Whslr
N.A.I.C.S.: 424310
Cheng Li *(Chm)*

Subsidiaries:

Hangzhou Huvis Yongsheng Dyeing & Finishing Company Limited (1)
Xiaoshan Jingjiang Town Industrial Park, Hangzhou, 311223, Zhejiang, China
Tel.: (86) 57182999788
Dyeing Product Distr
N.A.I.C.S.: 424690

Nantong Yongsheng Fiber New Materials Co., Ltd (1)
No 29 Tongfu South Road, Nantong,

226009, China
Tel.: (86) 51368225166
Web Site: https://www.ntyongsheng.com
Fiber Product Mfr & Distr
N.A.I.C.S.: 313110

Nantong Yongsheng Huvis Fiber Advanced Materials Co., Ltd. (1)
No 29 Tongfu South Road, Nantong, 226009, China
Tel.: (86) 51368225166
Chemical Dyeing & Finishing Mfr & Whslr
N.A.I.C.S.: 313310

YONGSHENG CAPITAL INC.
Room 1905 Cheung Kong Centre, 2 Queens Road, Hong Kong, China (Hong Kong)
Tel.: (852) 75525839921   BC
Rev.: $1,353
Assets: $140,891
Liabilities: $11,270
Net Worth: $129,621
Earnings: ($19,076)
Fiscal Year-end: 11/30/18
Investment Services
N.A.I.C.S.: 523999
Hilda Sung *(CEO & CFO)*

YONGTAIYUN CHEMICAL LOGISTICS CO., LTD.
5th to 6th floor Shengyangtai Building No 299 Heqing North Road, Yinzhou District, Ningbo, 315151, Zhejiang, China
Tel.: (86) 57427729933
Web Site:
  https://www.yongtaiyun.com
Year Founded: 2002
001228—(SSE)
Rev.: $422,871,125
Assets: $307,294,758
Liabilities: $62,775,058
Net Worth: $244,519,699
Earnings: $41,294,181
Fiscal Year-end: 12/31/22
Transportation Services
N.A.I.C.S.: 483211
Chen Yongfu *(Chm)*

Subsidiaries:

CWT Warehousing Transportation (Shanghai) Development Co., Ltd. (1)
No 288 Gongchuang Road, Caojing Town Jinshan District, Shanghai, China
Tel.: (86) 57486725520
Logistics & Warehousing Services
N.A.I.C.S.: 541614

DG-NVO Logistics.Co., Ltd. (1)
Room 904 Building B Dibiao No 55 North Haiyan Road, Yinzhou District, Ningbo, Zhejiang, China
Tel.: (86) 57428803208
Logistics & Warehousing Services
N.A.I.C.S.: 541614

General Tank Containers (Shanghai) Co., Ltd. (1)
Room 1503-1506 No 1063 Siping Road Transit Building, Yangpu District, Shanghai, 200092, China
Tel.: (86) 2125105022
Chemical & Foodstuff Distr
N.A.I.C.S.: 424690

General Tank Containers Co., Ltd. (1)
Room 1503-1506 No 1063 Siping Road Transit Building, Yangpu District, Shanghai, 200092, China
Tel.: (86) 2125105022
International Freight Forwarding Services
N.A.I.C.S.: 541614

Jiaxing Haitai Chemical logistics Comprehensive Service Co., Ltd. (1)
Building 1 No 318 Washan Road, Gang District, Jiaxing, China
Tel.: (86) 15355135977
Logistics & Warehousing Services
N.A.I.C.S.: 541614

YONGTAIYUN CHEMICAL LOGISTICS CO., LTD.

Yongtaiyun Chemical Logistics Co., Ltd.—(Continued)

Ningbo Kaimike Logistics Co., Ltd. (1)
Room 201 No 1 Building 2 No 17 Baifeng Haifa Road, Beilun District, Ningbo, China
Tel.: (86) 15355135977
Logistics & Warehousing Services
N.A.I.C.S.: 541614

Qingdao YongTai Ally International Logistics Co., Ltd. (1)
24AC Yuheng Building No 170 North Xuzhou Road, Shibei District, Qingdao, China
Tel.: (86) 53281111828
International Freight Forwarding Services
N.A.I.C.S.: 541614

Shaoxing Haitai Chemical logistics Service Co., Ltd. (1)
No 6 Kangyang Avenue Shangyu Economic, Technological Development Zone Hangzhou Bay Shangyu District, Shaoxing, China
Tel.: (86) 15888357296
Freight Forwarding Services
N.A.I.C.S.: 541614

Shipchem Logistics Co., Ltd. (1)
Room 1503-1506 Zhongtian Building No 1063 Siping Road, Yangpu District, Shanghai, China
Tel.: (86) 2125105000
International Freight Forwarding Services
N.A.I.C.S.: 541614

YongTaiYun (Ningbo) Cross-border E-commerce Logistics Co., Ltd. (1)
Room 306 No 1 Building 2 No 17 Baifeng Haifa Road, Beilun District, Ningbo, China
Tel.: (86) 13957808176
Logistics & Warehousing Services
N.A.I.C.S.: 541614

YongTaiYun (Zhejiang) Supply Chain Co., Ltd. (1)
5/F Baiguan Square No 588 North Jiangdong Road, Baiguan Sub-district Shangyu District, Shaoxing, China
Tel.: (86) 57589800539
Freight Forwarding Services
N.A.I.C.S.: 541614

YongTaiYun Chemical Logistics (Taicang) Co., Ltd. (1)
No 707 Building 2 Jinghu Dianjin No 101 Shuyuan Road, Taicang, China
Tel.: (86) 51253956089
Logistics & Warehousing Services
N.A.I.C.S.: 541614

YongTaiYun Chemical Logistics (Yiwu) Co., Ltd. (1)
Room 1501 Building A Yiwu Port No 266 Chengxin Avenue Futian Street, Yiwu, China
Tel.: (86) 57985660099
Logistics & Warehousing Services
N.A.I.C.S.: 541614

YONGXING SPECIAL MATERIALS TECHNOLOGY CO., LTD.
Yangjiabu, Huzhou, 313005, Zhejiang, China
Tel.: (86) 5722352506
Web Site: http://www.yongxingbxg.com
Year Founded: 2000
002756—(SSE)
Rev.: $2,187,253,931
Assets: $2,165,441,920
Liabilities: $400,259,003
Net Worth: $1,765,182,917
Earnings: $887,292,114
Emp.: 840
Fiscal Year-end: 12/31/22
Stainless Steel Rods & Wires Mfr
N.A.I.C.S.: 332999
Gao Xingjiang *(Chm)*

YONGYUE SCIENCE & TECHNOLOGY CO., LTD.
Quanhui Petrochemical Park Nanxing Village Wangchuan Town Huian, Quanzhou, 362000, China
Tel.: (86) 4006603879
Web Site: https://www.fjyykj.com
603879—(SHG)
Rev.: $41,604,507
Assets: $77,456,279
Liabilities: $5,982,374
Net Worth: $71,473,905
Earnings: ($5,574,371)
Fiscal Year-end: 12/31/22
Resin Product Mfr & Distr
N.A.I.C.S.: 325211

YONYOU NETWORK TECHNOLOGY CO., LTD.
No 68 Beiqing Road, Haidian District, Beijing, 100094, China
Tel.: (86) 1062436637
Web Site: http://www.yonyou.com
Year Founded: 1999
600588—(SHG)
Rev.: $1,300,348,872
Assets: $3,307,135,759
Liabilities: $1,549,605,807
Net Worth: $1,757,529,952
Earnings: $30,771,735
Fiscal Year-end: 12/31/22
Software Development Services
N.A.I.C.S.: 541511
Wenjing Wang *(Chm)*

Subsidiaries:

Yonyou (Hong Kong) Co., Ltd. (1)
9/F COFCO Tower 262 Gloucester Road, Causeway Bay, China (Hong Kong)
Tel.: (852) 21229886
Web Site: http://www.yonyou.com.hk
Enterprise Management Software Development Services
N.A.I.C.S.: 541511

Yonyou (Singapore) Pte Ltd. (1)
8 Temasek Boulevard Suntec Tower 3 10-03, Singapore, 38988, Singapore
Tel.: (65) 65150800
Web Site: http://www.yonyou.com.sg
Enterprise Management Software Development Services
N.A.I.C.S.: 541511

Yonyou (macau) Co., Ltd. (1)
Av Xian Xing Hai FL7 Flat A/B/N Ed Golden Dragon Centre, Macau, China (Macau)
Tel.: (853) 28787375
Web Site: https://www.yonyou.com.mo
Enterprise Management Software Development Services
N.A.I.C.S.: 541511
Joakim Liu Yu Jie *(Mng Dir & Gen Mgr)*

yonyou (Malaysia) Sdn Bhd. (1)
901 Level 9 Menara Binjai Jalan Binjai, 50450, Kuala Lumpur, Malaysia
Tel.: (60) 321818128
Web Site: http://www.yonyou.com.my
Enterprise Management Software Development Services
N.A.I.C.S.: 541511

YONYU PLASTICS CO., LTD.
No 88 Sheng Li Road, Rende Dist, T'ainan, 717, Taiwan
Tel.: (886) 62793711
Web Site: https://www.yonyu.com.tw
Year Founded: 1964
1323—(TAI)
Rev.: $108,207,426
Assets: $177,720,651
Liabilities: $82,737,856
Net Worth: $94,982,795
Earnings: $5,863,305
Emp.: 1,365
Fiscal Year-end: 12/31/23
Plastic Container Mfr
N.A.I.C.S.: 326160
Wei-Cheng Wang *(Chm & Gen Mgr)*

Subsidiaries:

YY Cable Accessories Co., Ltd. (1)
209 Anxin 2nd Rd, Annan Dist, T'ainan, Taiwan
Tel.: (886) 62705577
Web Site: http://www.yy-yonyu.com.tw
Cable Accessories Mfr & Distr
N.A.I.C.S.: 334417

Yonyu Applied Technology Material Co., Ltd. (1)
88 Sheng Li Rd Jen-Teh Hsiang, Tianan, Hsien, 71758, Taiwan
Tel.: (886) 62793711
Web Site: http://www.yatm.com.tw
Emp.: 500
Injection Molding Product Development
N.A.I.C.S.: 333248
T. H. Wang *(Chm)*

YOONG ONN CORPORATION BERHAD
LOT No PT 16690 to 16692 Jalan Permata 2, Arab-Malaysian Industrial Park, 71800, Nilai, Negeri Sembilan, Malaysia
Tel.: (60) 67996012 MY
Web Site: http://www.yoongonn.com
Year Founded: 1966
YOCB—(KLS)
Rev.: $55,554,709
Assets: $71,047,831
Liabilities: $6,500,106
Net Worth: $64,547,725
Earnings: $8,057,354
Emp.: 1,000
Fiscal Year-end: 06/30/23
Management Services
N.A.I.C.S.: 551114
Roland Hon Foong Chew *(Co-Founder, CEO-Grp & Mng Dir)*

Subsidiaries:

Monsieur (M) Sdn. Bhd. (1)
A-09-03 EkoCheras Office Tower No 693 Batu 5 Jalan Cheras, 56000, Kuala Lumpur, Malaysia
Tel.: (60) 391725012
Web Site: https://homes-harmony.com
Home Linen Retailer
N.A.I.C.S.: 423220

YOOSHIN ENGINEERING CORPORATION
Yushin Building 8 Yeoksam-ro 4-gil, Gangnam-gu, Seoul, 135-936, Korea (South)
Tel.: (82) 262020114
Web Site: https://www.yooshin.com
Year Founded: 1966
054930—(KRS)
Rev.: $233,138,318
Assets: $167,432,271
Liabilities: $83,263,542
Net Worth: $84,168,730
Earnings: $14,054,141
Emp.: 1,522
Fiscal Year-end: 12/31/22
Construction Engineering Services
N.A.I.C.S.: 237990

YOOSUNG ENTERPRISE CO., LTD.
22 Asan valley dong-ro, Asan, Chungcheongnam-Do, Korea (South)
Tel.: (82) 25642351
Web Site: http://www.ypr.co.kr
Year Founded: 1959
002920—(KRS)
Rev.: $227,612,124
Assets: $327,544,284
Liabilities: $76,555,775
Net Worth: $250,988,508
Earnings: $14,582,966
Emp.: 598
Fiscal Year-end: 12/31/22
Automobile Parts Mfr & Distr
N.A.I.C.S.: 336310
ShiYoung Ryu *(Pres)*

YOOSUNG T&S CO., LTD.

INTERNATIONAL PUBLIC

9Fm 2583 Nambusunhwan-ro, Seocho-gu, Seoul, Korea (South)
Tel.: (82) 234166000
Web Site: https://www.yoosungtns.co.kr
Year Founded: 1983
024800—(KRS)
Rev.: $212,283,338
Assets: $424,431,797
Liabilities: $132,159,958
Net Worth: $292,271,839
Earnings: $42,558,318
Emp.: 173
Fiscal Year-end: 12/31/22
Steel Mfr; Logistics Services
N.A.I.C.S.: 331110
Lee Bong-Kwan *(Chm & CEO)*

YORBEAU RESOURCES INC.
50 Boulevard Cremazie West Suite 403, Montreal, H2P 2T1, QC, Canada
Tel.: (514) 384-2202 QC
Web Site: https://www.yorbeauresources.com
Year Founded: 1984
YRB—(TSX)
Rev.: $702,372
Assets: $22,149,035
Liabilities: $671,785
Net Worth: $21,477,250
Earnings: ($757,720)
Emp.: 7
Fiscal Year-end: 12/31/21
Precious Metal Ores Exploration & Development
N.A.I.C.S.: 213114
Terry J. Kocisko *(CEO)*

YORHE FLUID INTELLIGENT CONTROL CO., LTD.
Qinggang Industrial Zone, Yuhuan, 317606, Zhejiang, China
Tel.: (86) 57687120271
Web Site: https://www.yhvalve.com
Year Founded: 2003
002795—(SSE)
Rev.: $138,959,019
Assets: $217,441,116
Liabilities: $101,891,579
Net Worth: $115,549,537
Earnings: ($3,749,143)
Fiscal Year-end: 12/31/22
Fluid Control Equipment Mfr & Distr
N.A.I.C.S.: 332911
Wei Pu *(Chm)*

YORK EXPORTS LTD.
D-6 Diwan Shree Apartments 30 Ferozeshah Road, New Delhi, 110001, India
Tel.: (91) 1141525005
Web Site: https://www.yorkexports.in
530675—(BOM)
Rev.: $4,131,566
Assets: $3,982,049
Liabilities: $2,146,791
Net Worth: $1,835,258
Earnings: $113,737
Fiscal Year-end: 03/31/23
Textile Products Mfr
N.A.I.C.S.: 314999
Gian Chand Dhawan *(Chm & Mng Dir)*

YORK HARBOUR METALS INC.
1518 - 800 West Pender Street, Vancouver, V6C 2V6, BC, Canada
Tel.: (778) 302-2257 BC
Web Site: https://yorkharbourmetals.com
Year Founded: 2011
YORKF—(OTCIQ)
Rev.: $428
Assets: $5,320,766
Liabilities: $638,523

AND PRIVATE COMPANIES

Net Worth: $4,682,243
Earnings: ($2,009,075)
Fiscal Year-end: 01/31/22
Investment Services
N.A.I.C.S.: 523999
Sean Choi (CFO)

YORK MAILING LIMITED
Brinkworth Rush Airfield Business Park Elvington, Elvington, York, YO41 4AU, United Kingdom
Tel.: (44) 1904 608050
Web Site: http://www.yorkmailing.co.uk
Year Founded: 1998
Sales Range: $75-99.9 Million
Emp.: 385
Writing Paper Whslr
N.A.I.C.S.: 322120
Chris Ingram (CEO)

Subsidiaries:

Pindar Scarborough Limited (1)
Pindar House Thornburgh Road Eastfield, Scarborough, YO11 3UY, North Yorkshire, United Kingdom
Tel.: (44) 1723581581
Web Site: http://www.pindar.com
Printing Services
N.A.I.C.S.: 323111
David Stephenson (Mgr-Comml)

YORK TIMBER HOLDINGS LIMITED
3 Main Road Sabie, PO Box 1191, 1260, Mpumalanga, 1260, South Africa
Tel.: (27) 137649200 ZA
Web Site: https://www.york.co.za
Year Founded: 1916
YRK—(JSE)
Rev.: $125,462,006
Assets: $318,321,197
Liabilities: $109,852,415
Net Worth: $208,468,782
Earnings: $1,987,403
Emp.: 5,253
Fiscal Year-end: 06/30/22
Forestry & Forest Products
N.A.I.C.S.: 115310
Pieter P. van Zyl (CEO)

YORKEY OPTICAL INTERNATIONAL (CAYMAN) LTD
Workshops 1-2 6th Floor Block A Goldfield Industrial Centre, 1 Sui Wo Road, Sha Tin, New Territories, China (Hong Kong)
Tel.: (852) 27597529
Web Site: http://www.yorkey-optical.com
2788—(HKG)
Rev.: $48,932,000
Assets: $110,181,000
Liabilities: $22,921,000
Net Worth: $87,260,000
Earnings: ($1,835,000)
Emp.: 1,643
Fiscal Year-end: 12/31/20
Electronic & Optical Products Mfr
N.A.I.C.S.: 333310
I-Jen Lai (Chm)

Subsidiaries:

Dongguan Yorkey Optical Machinery Components Ltd. (1)
Xiao-Bian The Second Industry Zone, Chang-An, Dongguan, Guang Dong, China
Tel.: (86) 7695311347
Optical & Opto-Electronic Product Mfr
N.A.I.C.S.: 334413

Yorkey Optical Technology Limited (1)
2 F Continental Electric Bldg 17 Wang Chiu Rd, Kowloon Bay, Kowloon, China (Hong Kong)
Tel.: (852) 35506600

Emp.: 43
Camera Cases & Bags Whslr
N.A.I.C.S.: 424350
James Chim (Gen Mgr)

YORKSHINE HOLDINGS LIMITED
24 Raffles Place 10-05 Clifford Centre, Singapore, 048621, Singapore
Tel.: (65) 6323 2213 SG
Web Site: http://www.yorkshinegroup.com
Year Founded: 2005
Steel Product Distr
N.A.I.C.S.: 423510
Jianqiao Wang (Exec Dir)

YORKSHIRE BUILDING SOCIETY
Yorkshire House Yorkshire Drive, Bradford, BD5 8LJ, West Yorkshire, United Kingdom
Tel.: (44) 3451200100 UK
Web Site: http://www.ybs.co.uk
Year Founded: 1864
Rev.: $1,316,321,760
Assets: $58,074,893,640
Liabilities: $54,577,118,760
Net Worth: $3,497,774,880
Earnings: $169,065,240
Emp.: 2,558
Fiscal Year-end: 12/31/19
Insurance & Financial Services
N.A.I.C.S.: 524128
Richard Wells (Chief Risk Officer)

Subsidiaries:

Chelsea Building Society (1)
Yorkshire House Yorkshire Drive, Bradford, BD5 8LJ, Gloucestershire, United Kingdom
Tel.: (44) 3451669300
Web Site: http://www.thechelsea.co.uk
Sales Range: $150-199.9 Million
Emp.: 943
Mortgage & Insurance Services
N.A.I.C.S.: 522310

Subsidiary (Domestic):

Chelsea Mortgage Services Limited (2)
Phirlestaine Hall Phirlestaine Road, Cheltenham, GL53 7AL, Gloucestershire, United Kingdom (100%)
Tel.: (44) 1242271271
All Other Miscellaneous Mfr
N.A.I.C.S.: 339999

Norwich & Peterborough Building Society (1)
Peterborough Business Park Lynch Wood, Peterborough, PE2 6WZ, United Kingdom
Tel.: (44) 1733372372
Web Site: http://www.nandp.co.uk
Sales Range: $250-299.9 Million
Emp.: 900
Insurance & Financial Services
N.A.I.C.S.: 524128
Anne Gunther (CEO)

Subsidiary (Non-US):

Norwich and Peterborough Estate Agents Ltd (2)
The Old Bank 17/21 Cannon Lane, Gibraltar, Gibraltar
Tel.: (350) 20048532
Real Estate Management Services
N.A.I.C.S.: 531390

Subsidiary (Domestic):

Norwich and Peterborough Insurance Brokers Limited (2)
45-53 Mill Road, Cambridge, CB1 2AP, United Kingdom
Tel.: (44) 1223273100
Web Site: http://www.npib.co.uk
Emp.: 13
Insurance Agents
N.A.I.C.S.: 524210
Charles Green (Mng Dir)

YORKSHIRE PURCHASING ORGANISATION
41 Industrial Park, Wakefield, WF2 0XE, Yorkshire, United Kingdom
Tel.: (44) 01924834926
Web Site: http://www.ypo.co
Supplies Procurement
N.A.I.C.S.: 611710
Simon Hill (Mng Dir)

YORKTON VENTURES INC.
Suite 1680 - 200 Burrard St, Vancouver, V6C 3L6, BC, Canada
Tel.: (306) 539-6300 BC
Web Site: https://www.lithiumonemetals.com
Year Founded: 2006
LONE—(TSXV)
Rev.: $214,027
Assets: $9,348,546
Liabilities: $2,150,714
Net Worth: $7,197,832
Earnings: ($2,795,850)
Fiscal Year-end: 06/30/24
Investment Services
N.A.I.C.S.: 523999

YORKWEST PLUMBING SUPPLY INC.
571 Chrislea Road Unit 3, Woodbridge, L4L 8A2, ON, Canada
Tel.: (905) 856-9466
Web Site: http://www.yorkwestplumbing.com
Year Founded: 1990
Rev.: $12,060,520
Emp.: 59
Plumbing & Heating Industrial Services
N.A.I.C.S.: 423720
Carlo Perfetto (Owner)

YORO NO TAKI CO. LTD.
19-3 Nishigotanda 2-chome, Shinagawa-ku, Tokyo, 141-0031, Japan
Tel.: (81) 334927811
Web Site: http://www.yoronotaki.co.jp
Emp.: 800
Operator of Bars & Restaurants
N.A.I.C.S.: 722410

YOROZU CORPORATION
3-7-60 Tarumachi, Kohoku-ku, Yokohama, 222-8560, Kanagawa, Japan
Tel.: (81) 455436800
Web Site: https://www.yorozu-corp.co.jp
Year Founded: 1948
7294—(TKS)
Rev.: $1,199,503,480
Assets: $940,318,770
Liabilities: $441,310,040
Net Worth: $499,008,730
Earnings: ($25,950,860)
Emp.: 5,726
Fiscal Year-end: 03/31/24
Automotive Components Including Suspension Parts & Agricultural Machinery Mfr
N.A.I.C.S.: 336390
Akihiko Shido (Chm & CEO)

Subsidiaries:

Guangzhou Yorozu Bao Mit Automotive Co., Ltd. (1)
No 28 Dong Feng Road Automotive City, Huadu, Guangzhou, 510800, China
Tel.: (86) 2086733222
Auto Part Mfr & Distr
N.A.I.C.S.: 336211

PT. Yorozu Automotive Indonesia (1)
Kawasan Industri Mitra Karawang Jl Mitra Barat III Blok L6 7 8, Desa Parungmulya - Kecamatan Ciampel Kabupaten, Karawang, 41361, Jawa Barat, Indonesia
Tel.: (62) 2678637974

YOROZU CORPORATION

Auto Parts Mfr & Distr
N.A.I.C.S.: 336390

Shonai Yorozu Corporation (1)
3-7-30 Takarada, Tsuruoka, 997-0011, Yamagata, Japan
Tel.: (81) 235241111
Web Site: http://www.yorozu-corp.co.jp
Emp.: 200
Automobile Parts Mfr
N.A.I.C.S.: 336330

Wuhan Yorozu Bao Mit Automotive Co., Ltd. (1)
No 9 Quanli 2nd Road Wuhan Economic Technological Development Zone, Wuhan, 430056, Hubei, China
Tel.: (86) 2784212400
Auto Parts Mfr & Distr
N.A.I.C.S.: 336390

Y-Ogura Automotive (Thailand) Co., Ltd. (1)
999/3 Moo 2 Tambol Tasit, WHA Eastern Seaboard Industrial Estate1, Pluak Daeng, 21140, Rayong, Thailand
Tel.: (66) 33010953
Auto Parts Mfr & Distr
N.A.I.C.S.: 336390

YOROZU Automotive Alabama, Inc. (1)
3680 Whitehouse Rd, Jasper, AL 35501
Tel.: (205) 717-3200
Auto Parts Mfr & Distr
N.A.I.C.S.: 336390

YOROZU Automotive Guanajuato de Mexico, S.A. de C.V. (1)
Av Amistad 102, Parques Industriales Amistad Bajio Apaseo el Grande, 38160, Guanajuato, Mexico
Tel.: (52) 4131586400
Auto Parts Mfr & Distr
N.A.I.C.S.: 336390

YOROZU Automotive North America, Inc. (1)
166 McQuiston Dr, Battle Creek, MI 49015
Tel.: (269) 969-3788
Auto Parts Mfr & Distr
N.A.I.C.S.: 336390

Yorozu (Thailand) Co., Ltd. (1)
58 Moo 4, Eastern Seaboard Industrial Estate Rayong T Pluak Daeng A Pluak Daeng, Rayong, 21140, Thailand
Tel.: (66) 38954040
Emp.: 800
Automobile Parts Mfr
N.A.I.C.S.: 336330

Yorozu Aichi Corporation (1)
1-1304 Tochi, Minato-ku, Nagoya, 455-0804, Aichi, Japan
Tel.: (81) 523819156
Web Site: http://www.yorozu-corp.co.jp
Emp.: 122
Automotive & Agricultural Machine Parts Mfr
N.A.I.C.S.: 333111

Yorozu America Corporation (1)
395 Mountain View Industrial Dr, Morrison, TN 37357
Tel.: (931) 668-7700
Web Site: http://www.yorozuamerica.com
Emp.: 800
Automobile Parts Distr
N.A.I.C.S.: 423120

Yorozu Automotive Tennessee, Inc. (1)
395 Mountain View Industrial Dr, Morrison, TN 37357 (85.01%)
Tel.: (931) 668-7700
Web Site: http://www.yorozu-corp.co.jp
Emp.: 1,800
Automobile Parts Mfr
N.A.I.C.S.: 336370

Yorozu Bao Mit Automotive Co., Ltd. (1)
No 28 Dong Feng Road Automotive City, Huadu, Guangzhou, 510800, Guangdong, China
Tel.: (86) 2086733222
Web Site: http://www.yorozu-corp.co.jp
Automobile Parts Mfr
N.A.I.C.S.: 336330

YOROZU CORPORATION

Yorozu Corporation—(Continued)

Yorozu Engineering Corporation (1)
207-1 Aza Togawara Aoyama Ooaza Mikawa-machi, Higashi-tagawa, Yamagata, 997-1311, Japan
Tel.: (81) 235664800
Emp.: 160
Automotive Tooling Parts Mfr
N.A.I.C.S.: 336310

Yorozu Engineering Systems (Thailand) Co., Ltd. (1)
58 Moo 4, Eastern Seaboard Industrial Estate Rayong T Pluak Daeng A Pluak Daeng, Rayong, 21140, Thailand
Tel.: (66) 38954041
Web Site: http://www.yorozu-eng.co.th
Emp.: 50
Automotive Tooling Parts Mfr
N.A.I.C.S.: 332216

Yorozu JBM Automotive Tamil Nadu Pvt. Ltd. (1)
Plot No B5 B6 Phase-II, SIPCOT Industrial Park Vengadu Sriperumbudur Taluk, Kanchipuram, 602105, Tamil Nadu, India
Tel.: (91) 4471158115
Auto Parts Mfr & Distr
N.A.I.C.S.: 336390

Yorozu Mexicana S.A. de C.V. (1)
Carr Aguascalientes-Zacatecas KM 18 8, San Francisco de los Romo, 20300, Aguascalientes, Mexico
Tel.: (52) 4499101200
Web Site: http://www.yorozumex.com
Emp.: 100
Automobile Parts Mfr
N.A.I.C.S.: 336330

Yorozu Oita Corporation (1)
255 Oaza Tajiri, Nakatsu, 879-0123, Oita, Japan
Tel.: (81) 979326411
Web Site: http://www.yorozu-corp.co.jp
Emp.: 360
Automobile Parts Mfr
N.A.I.C.S.: 336330

Yorozu Service Corporation (1)
3-7-60 Tarumachi, Kohoku-ku, Yokohama, 222-8560, Kanagawa, Japan
Tel.: (81) 455436806
Business Support Services
N.A.I.C.S.: 525190
Akihiko Shido (Chm)

Yorozu Tochigi Corporation (1)
443 Yokokura Shinden, Oyama, 323-0819, Tochigi, Japan
Tel.: (81) 285273212
Web Site: http://www.yorozu-corp.co.jp
Automotive & Agricultural Machine Parts Mfr
N.A.I.C.S.: 333111
Ruji Oikawa (Pres)

YOSHICON CO., LTD.
6F 1-4-12 Tokiwacho, Aoi-ku, Shizuoka, 420-0034, Japan
Tel.: (81) 542056363
Web Site: https://www.yoshicon.co.jp
Year Founded: 1969
5280—(TKS)
Rev.: $158,064,930
Assets: $251,847,610
Liabilities: $83,623,110
Net Worth: $168,224,500
Earnings: $13,894,220
Fiscal Year-end: 03/31/24
Construction Material Mfr & Distr
N.A.I.C.S.: 327331
Tatsushi Yoshida (Chm)

YOSHIKAWA INC.
Kurashiki Creative Park 20-26 Mutsue, Kurashiki, 710-0034, Okayama, Japan
Tel.: (81) 864201200
Web Site: http://www.yoshikawa-inc.co.jp
Year Founded: 1988
Rev.: $16,500,000
Emp.: 70
Clothes Accessories Mfr
N.A.I.C.S.: 313250

Subsidiaries:

Tokyo Yoshioka Co., Ltd (1)
5-10-2 Asakusabashi, Taito, Tokyo, 111-0053, Japan
Tel.: (81) 338652727
Web Site: http://www.tokyo-yoshioka.co.jp
Apparel Distr
N.A.I.C.S.: 424350

Yoshikawa Label (Kunshan) Co., Ltd (1)
No 32 Da Qiao North Road, Zhouzhuang, Kunshan, 215325, Jiang Su, China
Tel.: (86) 51257211096
Apparel Distr
N.A.I.C.S.: 424350

Yoshikawa Trading Inc Viet Nam Conpany Limited (1)
117 Phan Xich Long St Ward 7, Phu Nhuan, Ho Chi Minh City, Vietnam
Tel.: (84) 835178587
Apparel Distr
N.A.I.C.S.: 424350

Yoshioka Shanghai Co., Ltd (1)
Room C501A No 48 Xing Yi Road New Century Plaza, Shanghai, 200336, China
Tel.: (86) 2162084480
Apparel Distr
N.A.I.C.S.: 424350

YOSHIMURA FOOD HOLDINGS K.K.
18F Fukoku Seimei Bldg 2-2-2 Uchisaiwai-cho, Chiyoda-ku, Tokyo, 100-0011, Japan
Tel.: (81) 362061271
Web Site: https://www.y-food-h.com
2884—(TKS)
Rev.: $352,947,290
Assets: $371,196,950
Liabilities: $281,395,010
Net Worth: $89,801,940
Earnings: $7,288,520
Emp.: 1,792
Fiscal Year-end: 02/29/24
Food Product Mfr & Distr
N.A.I.C.S.: 311999
Motohisa Yoshimura (CEO)

Subsidiaries:

Daishow Co., Ltd. (1)
1-17-3 Kamezawa, Sumida-ku, Tokyo, 130-0014, Japan
Tel.: (81) 336269321
Web Site: https://www.daisho.co.jp
Packaging Food Product Mfr & Distr
N.A.I.C.S.: 311999

Hosokawa Foods Co., Ltd. (1)
712-8 Motoyama Otsu, Toyonaka Town, Mitoyo, 769-1505, Japan
Tel.: (81) 875625291
Web Site: http://www.hososyo.co.jp
Food Product Mfr & Distr
N.A.I.C.S.: 311991

Joy Dining Products K.K. (1)
1-2912-3 Minamikoshigaya, Koshigaya, 343-0845, Japan
Tel.: (81) 489904884
Web Site: https://www.joydining.co.jp
Packaging Food Product Mfr & Distr
N.A.I.C.S.: 311999

Junwa Food Corporation (1)
500 Saijo, Kumagaya, 360-0214, Japan
Tel.: (81) 485885890
Web Site: https://junwa.co.jp
Emp.: 31
Jelly Candy Mfr & Distr
N.A.I.C.S.: 311340

Kaorime Honpo Co., Ltd. (1)
908-1 Kuchidagi, Takicho, Izumo, 699-0904, Japan
Tel.: (81) 853862268
Web Site: https://kaorime.co.jp
Packaging Food Product Mfr & Distr
N.A.I.C.S.: 311999

Marukawa Shokuhin Co., Ltd. (1)
532-1 Hiramatsu, Iwata, 438-0123, Japan
Tel.: (81) 539626007

Web Site: https://www.marukawa-shokuhin.co.jp
Food Product Mfr & Distr
N.A.I.C.S.: 311991

Mori Yougyojou Co., Ltd. (1)
793 Sunomata, Sunomata, Ogaki, 503-0102, Japan
Tel.: (81) 584625637
Web Site: https://www.mori-yogyo.com
Fish Product Mfr & Distr
N.A.I.C.S.: 311999

Nkr Continental Pte. Ltd. (1)
17A Joo Yee Rd, Singapore, 619202, Singapore
Tel.: (65) 62619314
Web Site: https://www.continental-equipment.com
Refrigeration Machine Mfr
N.A.I.C.S.: 333415

ONESTORY Inc. (1)
5-27-8 Jingumae, Shibuya-ku, Tokyo, 150-0001, Japan
Tel.: (81) 354666501
Web Site: https://www.onestory-media.jp
Hotel & Restaurant Services
N.A.I.C.S.: 721110

Ohbun Co., Ltd. (1)
620-1 Nakamura, Doicho, Shikokuchuo, 799-0701, Ehime, Japan
Tel.: (81) 896743543
Web Site: https://www.ohbun.com
Food Product Mfr & Distr
N.A.I.C.S.: 311991

Omusubikororin Honpo Co., Ltd. (1)
1513-1 Akimori Misato, Azumino, 399-8101, Japan
Tel.: (81) 263772461
Web Site: https://omusbikororin.co.jp
Emp.: 50
Food Product Mfr & Distr
N.A.I.C.S.: 311991

YOSHINOYA HOLDINGS CO., LTD.
18F Daiwa Rivergate 36-2 Nihonbashihakozakicho, Chuo-ku, Tokyo, 103-0015, Japan
Tel.: (81) 356518800
Web Site: https://www.yoshinoya-holdings.com
Year Founded: 1958
9861—(TKS)
Rev.: $1,329,176,480
Assets: $800,716,240
Liabilities: $369,296,830
Net Worth: $431,419,410
Earnings: $39,732,360
Fiscal Year-end: 02/29/24
Fast Food Restaurants Owner & Operator
N.A.I.C.S.: 722513
Yasutaka Kawamura (Pres)

Subsidiaries:

Asia Yoshinoya International Sdn. Bhd. (1)
Level 13A-6 Menara Milenium Jalan Damaniela, Pusat Bandar Damansara, 50490, Kuala Lumpur, Selangor, Malaysia
Tel.: (60) 356115501
Hotel Operator
N.A.I.C.S.: 721110

Don Co., Ltd. (1)
2-3-5 Kamiochiai, Chuo-ku, Saitama, 338 0001, Japan
Tel.: (81) 492714711
Web Site: https://www.arcmeal.co.jp
Emp.: 526
Steakhouse Restaurant
N.A.I.C.S.: 722511

Green's Planet Co., Ltd. (1)
3-25-29 The Site Room07, Takanawa Minato- ku, Tokyo, 108-0074, Japan (100%)
Tel.: (81) 362774422
Web Site: https://www.greensplanet.co.jp
Fast Food Restaurants
N.A.I.C.S.: 722513
Mikio Kurihara (Pres)

INTERNATIONAL PUBLIC

Hanamaru, Inc. (1)
20F Daiwa Rivergate 36-2 Nihonbashihakozakicho, Chuo-ku, Tokyo, 103-0015, Japan
Tel.: (81) 356518701
Web Site: http://www.hanamaruudon.com
Emp.: 482
Self-Service Udon Restaurants
N.A.I.C.S.: 722513

Kyotaru Co., Ltd. (1)
2nd floor 2-3-8 Nihonbashi Ningyocho, Chuo-ku, Tokyo, 103-0013, Japan
Tel.: (81) 335272860
Web Site: https://www.kyotaru.co.jp
Sales Range: $250-299.9 Million
Emp.: 468
Restaurant & Takeout Chain Operations
N.A.I.C.S.: 722513

Mr. Service Co., Ltd. (1)
3100-36 Odai, Shibayama-cho Sanbu-gun, Chiba, 289-1605, Japan
Tel.: (81) 479773641
Web Site: https://www.mrservice.co.jp
Emp.: 17
Planning, Design & Construction of Stores; Store Maintenance & Management Services
N.A.I.C.S.: 561499

Senkichi Co., Ltd. (1)
36-2 Nihonbashi Hakozakicho, Chuo-ku, Tokyo, 103-0015, Japan
Tel.: (81) 356518731
Web Site: http://senkichi.co.jp
Emp.: 15
Restaurant
N.A.I.C.S.: 722511

Withlink Co.,Ltd. (1)
1-5-30-2 Tomominami, Asaminami-ku, Hiroshima, 731-3168, Japan
Tel.: (81) 828496667
Web Site: https://www.with-link.co.jp
Restaurant Services
N.A.I.C.S.: 721110

YOSHINOYA AMERICA, INC (1)
991 W Knox St, Torrance, CA 90502
Tel.: (310) 527-6060
Web Site: http://www.yoshinoyaamerica.com
Restaurant Operating Services
N.A.I.C.S.: 722511
Jonathon Gilliam (CEO)

YOSHINOYA NEW YORK, INC (1)
255 W 43rd St, New York, NY 10036-3917
Tel.: (212) 703-9940
Restaurant Operating Services
N.A.I.C.S.: 722511

Yoshinoya China Holdings Co., Ltd. (1)
Room 1003-1 10th Floor Tengfei Yuanchuang Building No686 Jiujiang Road, Huangpu District, Shanghai, China
Tel.: (86) 2163617700
Web Site: https://www.yoshinoya-holdings.com
Hotel Operator
N.A.I.C.S.: 721110

Yoshinoya Co., Ltd. (1)
Daiwa River Gate 18F 36-2 Nihonbashi, Hakozaki-cho Chuo-ku, Tokyo, 103-0015, Japan
Tel.: (81) 356518601
Web Site: https://www.yoshinoya.com
Restaurant
N.A.I.C.S.: 722513

Subsidiary (Domestic):

Okinawa Yoshinoya Co., Ltd. (2)
4-17-20 Jitchaku, Urasoe, 901-2122, Okinawa, Japan
Tel.: (81) 988779303
Restaurant Operating Services
N.A.I.C.S.: 722511

Sankosha Laundry Center Co., Ltd. (2)
2-3-1 Minato, Izumisano, 598-0063, Osaka, Japan
Tel.: (81) 724624177
Restaurant Operating Services
N.A.I.C.S.: 722511

Shikoku Yoshinoya Co., Ltd. (2)
10-12 Tenjimmae, Takamatsu, 760-0018, Kagawa, Japan
Tel.: (81) 878636922

AND PRIVATE COMPANIES

Restaurant Operating Services
N.A.I.C.S.: 722511

YOSHITAKE INC.
2-27-1 Gokiso-tori, Showa-ku, Nagoya, 466-0015, Japan
Tel.: (81) 5035085838
Web Site: https://www.yoshitake-inc.com
Year Founded: 1944
6488—(TKS)
Rev.: $59,172,720
Assets: $127,837,400
Liabilities: $23,478,720
Net Worth: $104,358,680
Earnings: $7,489,130
Emp.: 466
Fiscal Year-end: 03/31/24
Machinery Mfr
N.A.I.C.S.: 333248
Tetsu Yamada (Pres)

Subsidiaries:

KAWAKI MEASURING INSTRUMENT Co., LTD. (1)
5-6-28 Kisaki, Akashi, 673-0037, Hyogo, Japan
Tel.: (81) 789455679
Mfr & Sales of Flow Rate Measurement Gauges
N.A.I.C.S.: 333248
Tetsu Yamada (Pres)

Koyosuntech Co., Ltd. (1)
7-3 Futano-cho Mizuho-ku, 467-0861, Nagoya, Japan
Tel.: (81) 52 871 7160
Web Site: http://www.koyo-suntech.jp
Sales of GEMU Valve Products
N.A.I.C.S.: 332911
Tetsu Yamada (Pres)

Yoshitake Works (Thailand) Ltd. (1)
222 M 3 T Banbueng A Banbueng, Ban Bueng, 20170, Chonburi, Thailand
Tel.: (66) 38110003009
Industrial Valve Mfr & Sales
N.A.I.C.S.: 332911
Tetsu Yamada (Pres)

Yoshitake-Armstrong, Ltd. (1)
7-3 Ninomachi, Mizuho-ku, Nagoya, 467-0861, Japan
Tel.: (81) 52 881 7146
Web Site: http://www.yoshitake-armstrong.jp
Mfr & Sales of Fluid Control Valves & Fluid Control Engineering & Energy Services
N.A.I.C.S.: 332912
Tetsu Yamada (Pres)

Joint Venture (US):

Armstrong-Yoshitake, Inc. (2)
816 Maple St, Three Rivers, MI 49093
Tel.: (269) 273-1415
Web Site: http://www.yoshitake.jp
Industrial Water Heaters & Valves Mfr
N.A.I.C.S.: 332410
Patrick B. Armstrong (Pres & Dir)

YOSHITSU CO., LTD.
Harumi Building 2-5-9 Kotobashi, Sumida-ku, Tokyo, 130-0022, Japan
Tel.: (81) 356250668   JP
Web Site: https://www.ystbek.co.jp
Year Founded: 2006
TKLF—(NASDAQ)
Rev.: $195,681,315
Assets: $141,997,159
Liabilities: $105,954,375
Net Worth: $36,042,784
Earnings: $7,478,936
Emp.: 140
Fiscal Year-end: 03/31/24
Beauty & Health Product Distr
N.A.I.C.S.: 456120
Mei Kanayama (Pres & CEO)

YOSSIX HOLDINGS CO., LTD.
Yoshisix Building 1-9-30 Tokugawa, Higashi-ku, Nagoya, 461-0025, Aichi, Japan
Tel.: (81) 529328431
Web Site: https://yossix.co.jp
Year Founded: 1985
3221—(TKS)
Rev.: $139,583,370
Assets: $96,320,920
Liabilities: $30,868,700
Net Worth: $65,452,220
Earnings: $11,957,490
Emp.: 4,040
Fiscal Year-end: 03/31/24
Restaurant Operators
N.A.I.C.S.: 722511
Masanari Yoshioka (Chm, Pres & CEO)

YOTAI REFRACTORIES CO., LTD.
8-1 Nishinkinaka-machi, Kaizuka, 597-0093, Osaka, Japan
Tel.: (81) 724302100
Web Site: https://www.yotai.co.jp
Year Founded: 1936
5357—(TKS)
Rev.: $192,536,080
Assets: $281,129,910
Liabilities: $66,100,000
Net Worth: $215,029,910
Earnings: $25,633,580
Emp.: 531
Fiscal Year-end: 03/31/24
Refractory Product Mfr & Distr
N.A.I.C.S.: 327120
Mitsuo Taguchi (Pres)

Subsidiaries:

Yingkou New Yotai Refractories Co., Ltd. (1)
Nan lou economy development area, Qian jia village, Dashiqiao, Liaoning, China
Tel.: (86) 4175887299
Refractory Product Mfr & Distr
N.A.I.C.S.: 327120

YOTRIO GROUP CO., LTD.
No 1 Qianjiang South Road, Linhai, 317004, Zhejiang, China
Tel.: (86) 57685956868
Web Site: http://www.yotrio.com
Year Founded: 1992
002489—(SSE)
Rev.: $1,153,963,128
Assets: $1,172,063,145
Liabilities: $671,908,995
Net Worth: $500,154,151
Earnings: $30,442,834
Fiscal Year-end: 12/31/22
Outdoor Furniture Mfr
N.A.I.C.S.: 337121
Xie Jianyong (Chm)

Subsidiaries:

MWH GmbH. (1)
Blindeisenweg 23, 41468, Neuss, Germany
Tel.: (49) 2131718060
Web Site: http://mwh-dasoriginal.com
Furniture Mfr
N.A.I.C.S.: 337121

YOUBISHENG GREEN PAPER AG
Geschaftsanschrift Ziegelhauser Landstrasse 3, 69120, Heidelberg, Germany
Tel.: (49) 6221 649240
Web Site: http://www.youbisheng-greenpaper.de
Linerboard Mfr
N.A.I.C.S.: 322211

YOUCARE PHARMACEUTICAL GROUP CO., LTD.
No 6 Hongda Middle Road, Beijing Economic & Technical Development Zone, Beijing, 100176, China
Tel.: (86) 1067806688
Web Site: https://www.youcareyk.com
Year Founded: 2001
688658—(SHG)
Rev.: $637,689,134
Assets: $843,587,208
Liabilities: $282,399,240
Net Worth: $561,187,968
Earnings: $47,036,064
Fiscal Year-end: 12/31/22
Pharmaceutical Product Mfr & Distr
N.A.I.C.S.: 325412
Weishi Yu (Chm)

Subsidiaries:

America Youcare Pharma, Inc. (1)
132 Business Center Dr, Corona, CA 92880
Tel.: (951) 339-5600
Pharmaceutical Product Mfr & Distr
N.A.I.C.S.: 325412

YOUCEL INC
265 Iksan-daero 78-gil Hamyeol-eup, Iksan, Korea (South)
Tel.: (82) 638346877
Web Site: http://www.youcel.co.kr
Bio Cellulose Research & Development Services
N.A.I.C.S.: 541714
Cha Jae-Young (CEO)

YOUDAO, INC.
No 399 Wangshang Road, Binjiang District, Hangzhou, 310051, China
Tel.: (86) 57189852163   Ky
Web Site: https://www.youdao.com
Year Founded: 2006
DAO—(NYSE)
Rev.: $768,069,614
Assets: $348,729,861
Liabilities: $575,063,010
Net Worth: ($226,333,150)
Earnings: ($111,388,573)
Emp.: 5,068
Fiscal Year-end: 12/31/22
Holding Company
N.A.I.C.S.: 551112
Feng Zhou (CEO)

YOUGOV PLC
50 Featherstone Street, London, EC1Y 8RT, United Kingdom
Tel.: (44) 2070126000
Web Site: https://www.yougov.co.uk
YOU—(AIM)
Rev.: $423,785,670
Assets: $770,599,830
Liabilities: $539,053,350
Net Worth: $231,546,480
Earnings: $2,654,190
Fiscal Year-end: 07/31/24
Research & Consulting Services
N.A.I.C.S.: 541613
Stephan Shakespeare (Founder & CEO)

Subsidiaries:

GPW Deutschland GmbH. (1)
Hardefuststrasse 7, 50677, Cologne, Germany
Tel.: (49) 22 193 3350
Web Site: https://www.greatplacetowork.de
Emp.: 80
Marketing Research Service
N.A.I.C.S.: 541910
Frank Hauser (CEO)

Great Workplace Research & Consulting GmbH. (1)
Nibelungengasse 1-3 Top 50, 1010, Vienna, Austria
Tel.: (43) 17 985 9280
Web Site: https://www.greatplacetowork.at
Emp.: 5
Marketing Research Service
N.A.I.C.S.: 541910

YouGov Deutschland AG (1)
Tunisstrasse 19-23, 50667, Cologne, Germany
Tel.: (49) 221420610
Web Site: https://www.yougov.de
Emp.: 120
Market Research Services
N.A.I.C.S.: 541910

YouGov Finance Limited (1)
50 Featherstone Street, London, United Kingdom
Tel.: (44) 3333050899
Web Site: https://www.yougov.finance
Financial Services
N.A.I.C.S.: 921130

YouGov Nordic & Baltic A/S. (1)
Klosterstraede 9, 1157, Copenhagen, Denmark
Tel.: (45) 70272224
Web Site: http://www.yougov.dk
Emp.: 75
Internet Based Marketing Research Services
N.A.I.C.S.: 541910

YouGov Norway AS. (1)
Mollergata 13, 0179, Oslo, Norway
Tel.: (47) 22423200
Web Site: http://www.yougov.no
Emp.: 6
Market Research Services
N.A.I.C.S.: 541910

YouGov Sweden AB. (1)
Vasagatan 28, 111 20, Stockholm, Sweden
Tel.: (46) 841005810
Web Site: http://yougov.se
Emp.: 25
Internet Marketing Research Services
N.A.I.C.S.: 541910

YouGovM.E. FZ LLC. (1)
Suite 302 Cayan Business Centre, PO Box 500592, Barsha Heights, Dubai, United Arab Emirates
Tel.: (971) 43670340
Web Site: http://mena.yougov.com
Emp.: 50
Online Marketing Research Services
N.A.I.C.S.: 541910

YOUIL ENERGY TECH CO., LTD.
31-10 Jinwi2Sandan-Ro Jinwi-Myeon, Pyeongtaek, 17708, Gyeonggi-do, Korea (South)
Tel.: (82) 316117227
Year Founded: 2012
340930—(KRS)
Rev.: $36,408,399
Assets: $119,654,476
Liabilities: $74,028,047
Net Worth: $45,626,429
Earnings: $11,104,446
Emp.: 118
Fiscal Year-end: 12/31/22
General Purpose Machinery Mfr
N.A.I.C.S.: 333998
Chung-Won Park (CFO)

YOUJI CORPORATION
5F HI Gotanda Bldg 2-11-17 Nishi-Gotanda, Shinagawa-Ku, Tokyo, 141-0031, Japan
Tel.: (81) 334940262
Web Site: https://www.youji.co.jp
Year Founded: 1972
2152—(TKS)
Sales Range: Less than $1 Million
Physical Education Support Services
N.A.I.C.S.: 611710
Koichi Yamashita (Pres)

YOUKESHU TECHNOLOGY CO., LTD.
16th Floor Block B Wanda Plaza No 290 Section 1 Xiangjiang Middle Road, Kaifu District, Changsha, 410008, Hunan, China
Tel.: (86) 75584826159
Web Site: http://www.tiza.com.cn
Year Founded: 2000
300209—(CHIN)
Rev.: $65,412,881
Assets: $49,348,755
Liabilities: $107,177,441

YOUKESHU TECHNOLOGY CO., LTD.

Youkeshu Technology Co., Ltd.—(Continued)

Net Worth: ($57,828,686)
Earnings: ($68,242,572)
Emp.: 260
Fiscal Year-end: 12/31/23
Vehicle Management Information Software & Hardware
N.A.I.C.S.: 334511
Jin Chen *(Chm)*

YOUKOSHA CO., LTD.

1-10-14 Itabashi, Itabashi-Ku, Tokyo, 173-0004, Japan
Tel.: (81) 359442680
6576.—(TKS)
Rev.: $18,798,840
Assets: $13,233,220
Liabilities: $9,339,930
Net Worth: $3,893,290
Earnings: $304,060
Fiscal Year-end: 03/31/24
Health Care Srvices
N.A.I.C.S.: 621610
Susumu Ito *(Founder & Pres)*

YOULCHON CHEMICAL LTD.

15F Doyeongwan 112 Yeouidaebang-ro, Dongjak-gu, Seoul, Korea (South)
Tel.: (82) 28220022
Web Site: https://www.youlchon.com
Year Founded: 1973
008730—(KRS)
Rev.: $390,360,117
Assets: $500,955,429
Liabilities: $244,921,813
Net Worth: $256,033,616
Earnings: ($3,182,334)
Emp.: 777
Fiscal Year-end: 12/31/22
Plastic Packaging Products Mfr
N.A.I.C.S.: 326199
An Kwanghee *(Mng Dir)*

Subsidiaries:

YoulChon Chemical Ltd. - 1st Film Factory (1)
97 Wonsi-ro, Danwon-gu, Ansan, 425-100, Gyeonggi-do, Korea (South)
Tel.: (82) 31 492 7400
Plastic Packaging Products Mfr
N.A.I.C.S.: 326199

YoulChon Chemical Ltd. - 1st Flexible Packaging Factory (1)
78 Beomjigi-ro, Danwon-gu, Ansan, 425-851, Gyeonggi-do, Korea (South)
Tel.: (82) 31 489 7000
Plastic Packaging Products Mfr
N.A.I.C.S.: 326199

YoulChon Chemical Ltd. - 2nd Flexible Packaging Factory (1)
143 Wonsi-ro, Danwon-gu, Ansan, 425-851, Gyeonggi-do, Korea (South)
Tel.: (82) 31 492 7200
Plastic Packaging Products Mfr
N.A.I.C.S.: 326199

YOUNG & CO.'S BREWERY PLC

Copper House 5 Garratt Lane, Wandsworth, London, SW18 4AQ, United Kingdom
Tel.: (44) 2088757000
Web Site: https://www.youngs.co.uk
YNGN—(AIM)
Rev.: $426,324,080
Assets: $1,441,762,868
Liabilities: $491,766,184
Net Worth: $949,996,684
Earnings: $46,705,568
Emp.: 5,275
Fiscal Year-end: 03/28/22
Brewery & Pub Operator
N.A.I.C.S.: 312120
Patrick Dardis *(CEO)*

Subsidiaries:

Geronimo Inns Limited (1)
Riverside House 26 Osias Road 112, Wandsworth, London, SW18 1NH, United Kingdom
Tel.: (44) 2088778820
Web Site: http://www.geronimo-inns.co.uk
Emp.: 100
Tavern Operations Services
N.A.I.C.S.: 722410

YOUNG AN HAT CO., LTD.

215 Ojung-ro, Bucheon, Gyeonggi-do, Korea (South)
Tel.: (82) 326717111
Web Site: http://www.youngan.co.kr
Emp.: 5,000
Hats & Caps Bus Bodies Forklift Mfr
N.A.I.C.S.: 315250
Sung Hak Balk *(Gen Mgr)*

Subsidiaries:

A.J.M. International Sports Promotions Ltd. (1)
350 McCaffrey, Saint Laurent, H4T 1N1, QC, Canada
Tel.: (514) 344-6767
Web Site: http://www.ajmintl.com
Hat Distr
N.A.I.C.S.: 424350
Craig Lockhart *(Mgr-Product & Key Accounts)*

CLARK Material Handling International Inc. (1)
202-1 Ojung-Dong, Ojung-Ku, Bucheon, 421-170, Kyunggi-Do, Korea (South)
Tel.: (82) 326 806300
Web Site: http://www.clarkmhc.co.kr
Forklift Mfr
N.A.I.C.S.: 333924
Constantine Nawalaniec *(Exec VP)*

Subsidiary (Non-US):

CLARK MATERIAL HANDLING BRAZIL S.A. (2)
Rua Pedro Alves Pego 1210 Chacara Sao Bento, 13278-070, Valinhos, SP, Brazil
Tel.: (55) 193 8564421
Forklift Distr
N.A.I.C.S.: 423830

CLARK MATERIAL HANDLING CHILE S.A. (2)
Manquehue Sur 520 Of 305, Las Condes, Chile
Tel.: (56) 224 53317
Forklift Distr
N.A.I.C.S.: 423830

CLARK MATERIAL HANDLING EUROPE GMBH (2)
Neckarstrasse 37, 45478, Mulheim an der Ruhr, Germany
Tel.: (49) 208 3773360
Forklift Distr
N.A.I.C.S.: 423830

Subsidiary (Domestic):

CLARK Material Handling Asia Inc. (2)
40-1 Ungnam-dong Changwon, Kyungnam, Changwon, 641-290, Korea (South)
Tel.: (82) 260 9001
Forklift Distr
N.A.I.C.S.: 423830
Jeon Jong Yeol *(Engr-Electric Electronic & Control)*

Subsidiary (US):

Clark Material Handling Company (2)
700 Enterprise Dr, Lexington, KY 40510
Tel.: (859) 422-6400
Web Site: http://www.clarkmhc.com
Sales Range: $350-399.9 Million
Emp.: 80
Material Handling Equipment Mfr
N.A.I.C.S.: 333998
Michael J. Grossman *(Gen Counsel, Exec VP & Asst Sec)*

Subsidiary (Non-US):

QINGDACLARK MATERIAL HANDLING CO., LTD (2)
No 18 Huai hedong Road Huangdao Economic & Technical Development Area, Qingdao, 266500, Shandong, China
Tel.: (86) 532 86907990
Web Site: http://www.clarkmat.co.kr
Forklift Distr
N.A.I.C.S.: 423830

DAEWOO BUS(SHANGHAI) GLOBAL TRADING CO., LTD. (1)
No 999 Shuhai Road, Songjiang District, Shanghai, China
Tel.: (86) 216 7602041
Bus Mfr
N.A.I.C.S.: 336510

DAEWOO PAK MOTORS (PVT.) LTD. (1)
Plot No 145/147 Razzaqabad Main National Highway, Karachi, Pakistan
Tel.: (92) 214 102736
Bus Mfr
N.A.I.C.S.: 336510
Faisal Meraj *(Mgr-Mktg)*

Daewoo Bus Global Corporation - DONG-RAE PLANT (1)
75-11 Keumsa-Dong Keum, Gung-Gu, Busan, 609-809, Korea (South)
Tel.: (82) 326 806622
Bus Mfr
N.A.I.C.S.: 336510

Daewoo Bus Global Corporation - Factory No.1 (1)
188-9 Jeonpo-dong, Pusanjin, Pusan, Korea (South)
Tel.: (82) 518 032611
Bus Mfr
N.A.I.C.S.: 336510

Daewoo Bus Global Corporation - Factory No.2 (1)
75-11 Gumsa-dong, Gumjeong-gu, Pusan, Korea (South)
Tel.: (82) 515 205114
Bus Mfr
N.A.I.C.S.: 336510

Daewoo Bus Global Corporation - Factory No.3 (1)
1085-1 Banyeo-1-dong, Haeundae-gu, Pusan, Korea (South)
Tel.: (82) 515 285914
Bus Mfr
N.A.I.C.S.: 336510

Daewoo Bus Global Corporation - ULSAN PLANT (1)
1-26 Gilcheon-Ri Sangbuk-Myeon Ulju-Gun, Ulsan, Korea (South)
Tel.: (82) 326 806622
Bus Mfr
N.A.I.C.S.: 336510

HatFash Limited (1)
Unit A 14/F Capri Building 130 Austin Road Tsim Sha Tsui, Kowloon, China (Hong Kong)
Tel.: (852) 272 38789
Web Site: http://www.hatfashltd.com
Hat Distr
N.A.I.C.S.: 424350

Master Transportation Bus Manufacturing Ltd. (1)
No 385 Ma-Tso Rd Shinyuan Shiang 932 Roc, P'ingtung, Taiwan
Tel.: (886) 225 788978
Bus Mfr
N.A.I.C.S.: 336510

Pileum Import & Manufacturing Co., Ltd. (1)
Saltholmsgatan 1, PO Box 5030, 426 76, Vastra Frolunda, Sweden
Tel.: (46) 316 98225
Hat Distr
N.A.I.C.S.: 424350

SHANGHAI WANXIANG AUTOMOBILE CO., LTD (1)
No 999 Shuhai Road, Shanghai, China
Tel.: (86) 216 7600657
Bus Mfr

INTERNATIONAL PUBLIC

N.A.I.C.S.: 336510

VIETNAM DAEWOO BUS CO., LTD (1)
Lot CN9 Khai Quang Industrial Park, Vinh Yen, Vihn Phuc, Vietnam
Tel.: (84) 211 3726365
Web Site: http://www.daewoobus.com.vn
Bus Mfr
N.A.I.C.S.: 336510

Young An Hat (BD) S.A - Factory No. 1 (1)
Chittagong Export Processing Zone, Chittagong, Bangladesh
Tel.: (880) 317 41079
Hat Mfr
N.A.I.C.S.: 315250

Young An Hat, S.A. (1)
2 5 Kms Al Oeste Del Centro Comercial Santa Ana 2000 Apartado, 12143-1000, San Jose, Costa Rica
Tel.: (506) 282 9322
Hat Distr
N.A.I.C.S.: 424350

Young An Lanka (PVT) Ltd. (1)
Export Processing Zone, Biyagama, Sri Lanka
Tel.: (94) 112 465390
Hat Distr
N.A.I.C.S.: 424350

YOUNG AUSTRALIAN MINES LTD.

Level 11 100 Edward Street, Brisbane, 4000, QLD, Australia
Tel.: (61) 7 3210 0113   AU
Web Site: http://www.yamines.com.au
Year Founded: 2003
Rev.: $1,109,681
Assets: $40,480,859
Liabilities: $14,010,252
Net Worth: $26,470,607
Earnings: ($4,009,760)
Fiscal Year-end: 12/31/18
Metals Exploration & Mining Services
N.A.I.C.S.: 212290
Nelson Chen *(Chm)*

YOUNG CHANG AKKI CO. LTD.

178-55 Gajwa-Dong, Incheon, 404714, Seo Ku, Korea (South)
Tel.: (82) 325701000
Web Site: http://www.ycpiano.co.kr
Year Founded: 1956
Sales Range: $50-74.9 Million
Emp.: 405
Musical Instruments
N.A.I.C.S.: 339992

Subsidiaries:

A N D Music Corp. (1)
19060 S Dominguez Hill Dr, Rancho Dominguez, CA 90220
Tel.: (310) 637-2000
Web Site: http://www.youngchang.com
Sales Range: $50-74.9 Million
Emp.: 35
Piano Mfr
N.A.I.C.S.: 339992

Tianjin Young Chang Musical Instrument Co Ltd (1)
East Side Cuijiamatou Village, Dongli District, Tianjin, China
Tel.: (86) 22 2495 6661
Musical Instrument Distr
N.A.I.C.S.: 459140

YOUNG CHANG NORTH AMERICA, Inc. (1)
6000 Phyllis Dr, Cypress, CA 90630
Tel.: (657) 200-3470
Musical Instrument Distr
N.A.I.C.S.: 459140

Young Chang Akki Co. Ltd. - YOUNG CHANG CANADA DIVISION (1)
9350 Yonge Street, PO Box 61515, Richmond Hill, L4C 3N0, ON, Canada

YOUNG FAST OPTOELECTRONICS CO., LTD.
No 31 Jing Jiann 1st Rd Kuanyin Industrial Estate, Taoyuan, Taiwan
Tel.: (886) 34833665
Web Site: https://www.yfo.com.tw
Year Founded: 1999
3622—(TAI)
Rev: $53,598,186
Assets: $242,325,410
Liabilities: $25,265,802
Net Worth: $217,059,608
Earnings: $19,933,745
Emp.: 630
Fiscal Year-end: 12/31/23
Touch Screens, Power & Cable Apparatus Designer, Mfr & Sales
N.A.I.C.S.: 334419

YOUNG HWA TECH CO., LTD.
132 Asan valley-ro, Dunpo-myeon, Asan, Chungcheongnam-do, Korea (South)
Tel.: (82) 415852685
Web Site: https://yhtec.com
Year Founded: 1986
265560—(KRS)
Rev: $36,773,512
Assets: $62,361,099
Liabilities: $18,691,554
Net Worth: $43,669,544
Earnings: $3,701,044
Emp.: 147
Fiscal Year-end: 12/31/22
Automobile Parts Mfr
N.A.I.C.S.: 336390
Seung-Kwon Yoo (VP)

YOUNG JIN CHEMICAL INDUSTRIES CO., LTD.
350-90 Galsan-dong, Dalseo-gu, Taegu, 35890, Korea (South)
Tel.: (82) 535828000 KR
Web Site: http://www.yjchemical.co.kr
Sales Range: $50-74.9 Million
Emp.: 42
Adhesives & Surface Finishing Chemicals Mfr & Distr
N.A.I.C.S.: 325520
Chang Wook Seo (VP)

YOUNG OPTICS INC.
No 7 Hsin-Ann Rd Hsinchu Science Park, Hsin-chu, 30076, Taiwan
Tel.: (886) 36206789
Web Site: https://www.youngoptics.com
Year Founded: 2002
3504—(TAI)
Rev: $98,445,629
Assets: $154,244,934
Liabilities: $56,266,521
Net Worth: $97,978,413
Earnings: ($9,409,954)
Emp.: 946
Fiscal Year-end: 12/31/23
Optical Components & Optical Engines Mfr
N.A.I.C.S.: 333310
Claude Hsu (Pres & CEO)

Subsidiaries:
Young Optics (BD) Ltd. (1)
Plot 104 105 124 and 125 DEPZ Extension Area Savar, Ashulia, Dhaka, Bangladesh
Tel.: (880) 27790168
Optical Equipment Mfr
N.A.I.C.S.: 333310

Young Optics (Kunshan) Co., Ltd. (1)
No 20 3rd Ave Kunshan Free Trade Zone, Jiangsu, China
Tel.: (86) 51257353850
Optical Equipment Mfr
N.A.I.C.S.: 333310

Young Optics (Suzhou) Co., Ltd. (1)
Optical Equipment Mfr
N.A.I.C.S.: 333310

YOUNG POONG PAPER MFG CO., LTD.
9 Seotan-ro Jinwi-myeon, Pyeongtaek, 17706, Gyeonggi-do, Korea (South)
Tel.: (82) 316608200
Web Site: http://www.yp21.co.kr
Year Founded: 1970
006740—(KRS)
Rev: $80,879,413
Assets: $156,215,181
Liabilities: $51,496,285
Net Worth: $104,718,896
Earnings: $6,073,481
Emp.: 1,000
Fiscal Year-end: 12/31/22
Paperboard Mfr
N.A.I.C.S.: 322130
Kwan-hyung Lee (CEO)

YOUNG POONG PRECISION CORPORATION
542 Gangnam-daero, Gangnam-gu, Seoul, Korea (South)
Tel.: (82) 25193504
Web Site: https://www.yppc.co.kr
Year Founded: 1983
036560—(KRS)
Rev: $68,313,665
Assets: $316,163,136
Liabilities: $54,960,698
Net Worth: $261,202,438
Earnings: $11,895,859
Emp.: 215
Fiscal Year-end: 12/31/22
Pump & Valve Mfr
N.A.I.C.S.: 332911
Jongho Kim (Mgr)

Subsidiaries:
Young Poong Book Store Co., Ltd. (1)
Tel.: (82) 15449020
Book Distr
N.A.I.C.S.: 424920

Young Poong Electronics Co., Ltd. (1)
39 Beomjigi-ro 141beon-gil, Danwon-gu, Ansan, Gyeonggi, Korea (South)
Tel.: (82) 314907399
Electronic Products Mfr
N.A.I.C.S.: 334412
Jungho Seo (CEO)

Young Poong Precision Corporation - FRP Plant (1)
505 Daejung-Ri Onsan-Up, Uljoo-Gun, Ulsan, Korea (South)
Tel.: (82) 52 239 9961
Pump & Valve Mfr
N.A.I.C.S.: 332911

Young Poong Precision Corporation - Valve Plant (1)
491-3 Moknae-Dong, Ansan, Gyeonggi-Do, Korea (South)
Tel.: (82) 31 491 5581 4
Pump & Valve Mfr
N.A.I.C.S.: 332911

YOUNG POONG, CORP.
Young Poong Building 542 Gangnam-daero, Gangnamgu, Seoul, 06110, Korea (South)
Tel.: (82) 25193314
Web Site: http://www.ypzinc.co.kr
Year Founded: 1949
000670—(KRS)
Rev: $3,397,417,424
Assets: $4,503,773,111
Liabilities: $1,126,375,569
Net Worth: $3,377,397,543
Earnings: $281,617,686
Emp.: 687
Fiscal Year-end: 12/31/22
Zinc Product Mfr & Distr
N.A.I.C.S.: 331410
Park Young Min (CEO)

YOUNG'S EQUIPMENT INC.
Highway 1 East North Service Road, PO Box 3117, Regina, S4P 3G7, SK, Canada
Tel.: (306) 565-2405
Web Site: http://www.youngsequipment.com
Year Founded: 1988
Sales Range: $25-49.9 Million
Emp.: 200
Agricultural Equipment Products Distr
N.A.I.C.S.: 423820
Tim Young (Partner)

YOUNGHYUN TRADING CO.,LTD
242 Digital-ro Guro-gu, Seoul, Korea (South)
Tel.: (82) 28511827
Web Site: http://www.younghyun.co.kr
Year Founded: 2000
Garment Mfr & Distr
N.A.I.C.S.: 314999
Gwan-Muk Lee (CEO)

Subsidiaries:
C&C Vina Co., Ltd (1)
Moi Hamlet Ngoc Hoi Thanh Tri, Hanoi, Vietnam
Tel.: (84) 436866036
Emp.: 248
Garments Mfr
N.A.I.C.S.: 315250

Nan Jing H&H Garment Co., Ltd. (1)
Nanjing Lishui Tuo Tang Industrial Zone, Nanjing, China
Tel.: (86) 2161267350
Emp.: 476
Garments Mfr
N.A.I.C.S.: 315250

Shaoxing Weile Garment & Ornament Co., Ltd (1)
Renjjafan Lanting Industrial District, Shaoxing, Zhejiang, China
Tel.: (86) 13587337162
Emp.: 500
Garments Mfr
N.A.I.C.S.: 315250

Young Hyun Vina Company Limited (1)
Dai Phuc Dao Duc Community, Binh Xuyen, Vinch Phuc, Vietnam
Tel.: (84) 2113582266
Emp.: 150
Padding & Quilting Services
N.A.I.C.S.: 314999

YOUNGLIMWON SOFTLAB CO., LTD.
23rd floor Building A Woorim Blue 9 583 Yangcheonro, Gangseo-Gu, Seoul, Korea (South)
Tel.: (82) 16881155
Web Site: https://www.ksystem.co.kr
Year Founded: 1993
060850—(KRS)
Rev: $44,124,691
Assets: $47,069,266
Liabilities: $13,524,002
Net Worth: $33,545,264
Earnings: $5,483,503
Emp.: 344
Fiscal Year-end: 12/31/22
Software Development Services
N.A.I.C.S.: 541511
Young-Bum Kwon (CEO)

YOUNGONE HOLDINGS CO., LTD.
159 Mallijae-ro, Jung-gu, Seoul, 04500, Korea (South)
Tel.: (82) 23906114
Web Site: https://youngonecorporation.com
Year Founded: 1974
009970—(KRS)
Rev: $3,477,485,351
Assets: $4,210,998,518
Liabilities: $1,153,227,692
Net Worth: $3,057,770,827
Earnings: $338,126,662
Emp.: 52
Fiscal Year-end: 12/31/22
Holding Company
N.A.I.C.S.: 551112
Hyung Bae Bang (Deputy Gen Mgr)

Subsidiaries:
Youngone Corporation (1)
159 Manrijaero, Jung-Gu, Seoul, 100372, Korea (South)
Tel.: (82) 23906114
Web Site: https://www.youngone.co.kr
Rev: $2,999,707,013
Assets: $3,461,949,440
Liabilities: $1,073,278,164
Net Worth: $2,388,671,276
Earnings: $517,355,915
Emp.: 245
Fiscal Year-end: 12/31/2022
Sporting Goods Mfr & Distr
N.A.I.C.S.: 339920
Ki-Hak Sung (Founder & Chm)

YOUNGOR GROUP CO. LTD.
No 2 West Section of Jixian Avenue, Haishu District, Ningbo, Zhejiang, China
Tel.: (86) 57488265571 CN
Web Site: https://www.youngor.com
Year Founded: 1979
600177—(SHG)
Rev: $2,080,896,873
Assets: $10,919,901,147
Liabilities: $5,569,186,835
Net Worth: $5,350,714,312
Earnings: $711,479,962
Emp.: 23,920
Fiscal Year-end: 12/31/22
Clothing Mfr
N.A.I.C.S.: 315250

Subsidiaries:
Ningbo Youngor Dresses Co., Ltd (1)
No 2 West Section Yinxian Road, Ningbo, 315153, China
Tel.: (86) 574 88265571
Web Site: http://www.youngor.com.cn
Knitwear Mfr
N.A.I.C.S.: 315120

Ningbo Youngor Knitting D&F Co. Ltd. (1)
1 West Section Yinxian Rd, Ningbo, China
Tel.: (86) 57488261100
Men's & Women's Shirt Mfr
N.A.I.C.S.: 315120

Ningbo Youngor Pants Co., Ltd (1)
No 1 West Section Yinxian Road, Ningbo, 315153, China
Tel.: (86) 574 87425727
Web Site: http://www.pants.youngor.com
Emp.: 1,000
Knitwear Mfr
N.A.I.C.S.: 315250

Ningbo Youngor Shirts Co Ltd (1)
No 2 West of Yinxian Road, Ningbo, 315153, China
Tel.: (86) 574 87425741
Web Site: http://www.shirt.youngor.com
Emp.: 5,000
Knitwear Mfr
N.A.I.C.S.: 315120
Alley Fang (Mgr)

Ningbo Youngor Sunrise Textile Dyeing & Finishing Co., Ltd. (1)
1 W Section Yinxian Rd, Ningbo, China
Tel.: (86) 57488258956

YOUNGOR GROUP CO. LTD.

Youngor Group Co. Ltd.—(Continued)
Clothing & Textile Dyeing & Finishing
N.A.I.C.S.: 313310

Ningbo Youngor Yingcheng Uniform Co., Ltd. (1)
2 West Section Yinxian Road, Ningbo, 315153, China
Tel.: (86) 57487425768
Web Site: http://suit.youngor.com
Uniform & Work Attire Mfr
N.A.I.C.S.: 424350

Smart Shirts Ltd. (1)
23rd-25th Fl 2 Landmark E 100 Howmaing St, Kwun Tong, Kowloon, China (Hong Kong)
Tel.: (852) 27975111
Emp.: 150
Mfr of Men's & Women's Shirts
N.A.I.C.S.: 315250
Lei Su (Chm)

Youngor Fashion Co., Ltd. (1)
2 West Section Yinxian Road, Ningbo, China
Tel.: (86) 57488444032
Men's & Women's Clothing Mfr
N.A.I.C.S.: 424350

Youngor Shirts Co., Ltd. (1)
2 West Section Yinxian Rd, Ningbo, China
Tel.: (86) 574 88265326
Men's & Women's Shirt Mfr
N.A.I.C.S.: 315250

YOUNGTEK ELECTRONICS CORP.
No 13 Aly 17 Ln 99 Puding Rd, East Dist, Hsinchu, Taiwan
Tel.: (886) 35711509
Web Site: https://www.ytec.com.tw
Year Founded: 1991
6261—(TPE)
Rev.: $143,827,721
Assets: $271,393,115
Liabilities: $51,367,977
Net Worth: $220,025,138
Earnings: $27,828,565
Fiscal Year-end: 12/31/22
Semiconductor Components Mfr
N.A.I.C.S.: 334413
Cheng-Kuang Chang (Vice Chm)

Subsidiaries:

Suzhou YoungTek Micro-Electronics Co., Ltd. (1)
Changfang No 1 Yuankejiyuan Jingji Technology Development Area, Wujiang, China
Tel.: (86) 51263027861
Automated Test Equipment Distr
N.A.I.C.S.: 423830

YoungTek Micro Electronics (Shenzhen) Ltd. (1)
Building A 303 ABC No 168 Cen Under Road, Fuyong Phoenix Street Community Baoan, Shenzhen, China
Tel.: (86) 75529747768
Automated Test Equipment Distr
N.A.I.C.S.: 423830

YOUNGTIMERS AG
Gerbergasse 48, CH-4001, Basel, Switzerland
Tel.: (41) 615631072   CH
Web Site: https://ir.youngtimers.com
Year Founded: 1998
YTME—(SWX)
Rev.: $2,373,812
Assets: $12,812,422
Liabilities: $479,226
Net Worth: $12,333,196
Earnings: ($813,617)
Fiscal Year-end: 12/31/23
Investment Management Service
N.A.I.C.S.: 523940
Patrick Girod (Chm)

YOUNGWIRE CO. LTD.
50 Gwanchanggongdan-gil Jugyo-myeon, Boryeong, Chungcheongnam-do, Korea (South)
Tel.: (82) 419393900
Web Site: http://www.youngwire.co.kr
Year Founded: 1977
012160—(KRS)
Rev.: $404,491,822
Assets: $410,870,008
Liabilities: $258,884,129
Net Worth: $151,985,879
Earnings: ($2,191,031)
Emp.: 432
Fiscal Year-end: 12/31/22
Steel Wire Products Mfr & Sales
N.A.I.C.S.: 331110
Sang Don Jang (Chm)

Subsidiaries:

Daeheung Industrial Co., Ltd. (1)
607 Chongchon-Ri Chinrye-Myon, Kimhae, 621-880, Korea (South)
Tel.: (82) 56163252
Automobile Parts Mfr
N.A.I.C.S.: 336390

Sammok Kang Up Co., Ltd. (1)
3 654 Choji-dong, Danwon-gu, Ansan, Gyonggi-do, Korea (South)   (100%)
Tel.: (82) 31 494 3981
Web Site: http://www.sammokspring.co.kr
Sales Range: $50-74.9 Million
Emp.: 170
Automotive Springs Mfr
N.A.I.C.S.: 332613

Young Wire Vina Co., Ltd. (1)
Lot 11 Street N2, Nhon Trach 5 Industrial Zone, Nhon Trach, Dong Nai, Vietnam
Tel.: (84) 613569681
Port & Harbor Operations Services
N.A.I.C.S.: 488310

Youngheung Taicang Kangsasung (1)
Port Development Zone Liujia Gang, Taicang, 215433, Jiangsu, China
Tel.: (86) 512 5364 6561
Automobile Parts Mfr
N.A.I.C.S.: 336390
Roh Kyoung Taeg (Gen Mgr)

YOUNGWOO DSP CO., LTD.
164 Saetegil Seonggeo-eup, Seobuk-gu, Cheonan, Chungcheongnam-do, Korea (South)
Tel.: (82) 414184871
Web Site: https://www.ywdsp.com
143540—(KRS)
Rev.: $37,991,352
Assets: $62,979,203
Liabilities: $32,112,049
Net Worth: $30,867,154
Earnings: ($19,718,232)
Emp.: 179
Fiscal Year-end: 12/31/22
Display Equipment Distr
N.A.I.C.S.: 423690

YOUNGY CO., LTD.
Room 04-05 45th Floor Guangzhou International Finance Center No 5, Zhujiang West Road, Guangzhou, 510623, Guangdong, China
Tel.: (86) 2038289770
Web Site: https://youngergy.cn
002192—(SSE)
Rev.: $420,132,441
Assets: $542,008,458
Liabilities: $91,126,845
Net Worth: $450,881,613
Earnings: $342,567,478
Fiscal Year-end: 12/31/22
Asphalt Mfr
N.A.I.C.S.: 324121
Xiangyang Lu (Chm)

YOUNGY HEALTH CO., LTD.
No 34 Hehuan Road, High-Tech Development Zone, Hefei, 230088, Anhui, China
Tel.: (86) 55162355467
Web Site: https://www.chinasauna.com
Year Founded: 1995
300247—(CHIN)
Rev.: $65,049,988
Assets: $166,627,225
Liabilities: $22,187,454
Net Worth: $144,439,771
Earnings: $17,733,854
Emp.: 1,263
Fiscal Year-end: 12/31/22
Saunas & Related Products Mfr
N.A.I.C.S.: 335210
Xing Fenling (Chm)

YOUON TECHNOLOGY CO., LTD.
No 400 Hanjiang Road, Xinbei District, Changzhou, 213022, Jiangsu, China
Tel.: (86) 51981282003
Web Site: http://www.ibike668.com
Year Founded: 2010
603776—(SHG)
Rev.: $95,139,828
Assets: $662,284,561
Liabilities: $193,630,680
Net Worth: $468,653,880
Earnings: ($9,522,574)
Fiscal Year-end: 12/31/22
Bicycle Transportation Services
N.A.I.C.S.: 532284
Jisheng Sun (Chm, Pres & Gen Mgr)

YOUR DOLLAR STORE WITH MORE INC.
Suite 200 - 160 Dougall Road South, Kelowna, V1X 3J4, BC, Canada
Tel.: (250) 860-4225
Web Site: http://www.dollarstore.ca
Year Founded: 1998
Dollar Stores Operator & Franchisor
N.A.I.C.S.: 455219
Russell Meszaros (Pres)

YOUR FAMILY ENTERTAINMENT AG
Turkenstrasse 87, 80801, Munich, Germany
Tel.: (49) 899972710
Web Site: https://www.yfe.tv
RTV—(MUN)
Rev.: $3,112,913
Assets: $23,280,618
Liabilities: $2,836,946
Net Worth: $20,443,672
Earnings: $1,964,889
Emp.: 10
Fiscal Year-end: 12/31/23
Television Program Production & Sales
N.A.I.C.S.: 516120
Michael Huber (CFO)

YOURWAY CANNABIS BRANDS INC.
885 W Georgia St Suite 2200, Vancouver, V6C 3E8, BC, Canada
Tel.: (602) 675-4317
Web Site: https://www.yourwaycannabis.com
YOURF—(OTCEM)
Rev.: $30,576,267
Assets: $14,828,015
Liabilities: $9,757,263
Net Worth: $5,070,752
Earnings: ($3,571,809)
Emp.: 10
Fiscal Year-end: 12/31/20
Cannabis Product Mfr & Distr
N.A.I.C.S.: 325412
Carl Saling (CEO)

YOUSUF WEAVING MILLS LTD.
7/1 E-3 Main Boulevard Gulberg III, Lahore, Pakistan
Tel.: (92) 42357175109
Web Site: https://www.yousafweavingmills.com
Year Founded: 1988
YOUW—(PSX)
Rev.: $3,096,823
Assets: $5,459,974
Liabilities: $4,500,834
Net Worth: $959,140
Earnings: ($239,115)
Emp.: 354
Fiscal Year-end: 06/30/23
Textile Products Mfr
N.A.I.C.S.: 314999

Subsidiaries:

Kohinoor Spinning Mills Ltd. (1)
7/1 E-3 Main Boulevard Gulberg III, Lahore, Pakistan
Tel.: (92) 42357175109
Web Site: https://www.kohinoorspinningmills.com
Textile Products Mfr
N.A.I.C.S.: 314999

YOUYOU FOODS CO., LTD.
Baohuan 1st Road, Yubei District, Chongqing, 402760, China
Tel.: (86) 2341779525
Web Site: https://www.youyoufood.com
Year Founded: 2007
603697—(SHG)
Rev.: $143,928,470
Assets: $287,486,578
Liabilities: $26,412,357
Net Worth: $261,074,221
Earnings: $21,565,510
Fiscal Year-end: 12/31/22
Food Product Mfr & Distr
N.A.I.C.S.: 311421
Youzhong Lu (Chm & Gen Mgr)

Subsidiaries:

Chongqing You You Foods Sales Co., Ltd. (1)
22nd floor Century Emperor North Tower, Jiangbei District, Chongqing, China
Tel.: (86) 2367868549
Food Product Mfr & Distr
N.A.I.C.S.: 311999

Sichuan You You Foods Development Co., Ltd. (1)
Yong'an Road ande Sichuan Cuisine Park, Pidu District, Chengdu, Sichuan, China
Tel.: (86) 2887868136
Food Product Mfr & Distr
N.A.I.C.S.: 311999

YouYou Foods Chongqing Manufacturing Co., Ltd. (1)
Jianshan Road Biquan Street, Bishan District, Chongqing, China
Tel.: (86) 2341779525
Food Product Mfr & Distr
N.A.I.C.S.: 311999

YOUZU INTERACTIVE CO., LTD.
Building 2 Huaxin Business Center 711 Yishan Road, Xuhui District, Shanghai, 200333, China
Tel.: (86) 2133676512
Web Site: https://global.yoozoo.com
Year Founded: 2009
002174—(SSE)
Rev.: $278,069,487
Assets: $881,530,028
Liabilities: $244,110,110
Net Worth: $637,419,917
Earnings: ($89,129,964)
Fiscal Year-end: 12/31/22
Application Development Services
N.A.I.C.S.: 513210
Qi Lin (Founder, Chm & CEO)

AND PRIVATE COMPANIES

Subsidiaries:

Bigpoint GmbH (1)
Sachsenstrasse 20, 20097, Hamburg, Germany
Tel.: (49) 408814130
Web Site: https://www.bigpoint.net
Online Gaming Website Operator
N.A.I.C.S.: 541511
Jeff Lu *(Mng Dir)*

Mjoy Games Co. Ltd (1)
15A Building 1 1388 YiShan Rd, Shanghai, 201103, China
Tel.: (86) 2134681920
Web Site: http://www.mjoygames.com
Game Application Development Services
N.A.I.C.S.: 541511
Weisong Zhu *(Pres)*

YOWIE GROUP LTD.
Level 4 216 St Georges Terrace, Perth, 6000, WA, Australia
Tel.: (61) 862682640
Web Site:
http://www.yowiegroup.com
Year Founded: 1979
YWGRF—(OTCIQ)
Rev.: $8,239,604
Assets: $12,354,693
Liabilities: $2,089,709
Net Worth: $10,264,985
Earnings: ($6,231,121)
Fiscal Year-end: 06/30/20
Educational Toy Mfr & Distr
N.A.I.C.S.: 339930

YPB GROUP LTD.
Level 5 126 Phillip Street, Sydney, 2000, NSW, Australia
Tel.: (61) 282634000 AU
Web Site:
https://www.ypbsystems.com
YPB—(ASX)
Rev.: $371,146
Assets: $4,923,660
Liabilities: $2,039,437
Net Worth: $2,884,224
Earnings: ($2,204,150)
Fiscal Year-end: 12/31/22
Protection & Security Systems
N.A.I.C.S.: 561621
John Houston *(Chm & CEO)*

Subsidiaries:

YPB Print Solutions Inc. (1)
30012 Ivy Glenn Dr Ste 100, Laguna Niguel, CA 92677
Tel.: (800) 376-1176
Web Site:
http://www.continuousformscontrol.com
Sales Range: $1-9.9 Million
Emp.: 16
Printing Services
N.A.I.C.S.: 323111
Ralph Davis *(Pres)*

YPF GAS, S.A.
Av Roque Saenz Penna 777, 1035, Buenos Aires, Argentina
Tel.: (54) 1143292000 Ar
Web Site: http://www.repsol.com
Sales Range: $75-99.9 Million
Emp.: 100
Natural Gas Distr
N.A.I.C.S.: 221210
Gustavo Ramos *(Dir-Comml)*

YPF S.A.
Macacha Guemes 515, C1106BKK, Buenos Aires, Argentina
Tel.: (54) 1154413664
Web Site: http://www.ypf.com
Year Founded: 1922
YPF—(NYSE)
Rev.: $18,757,000,000
Assets: $25,912,000,000
Liabilities: $15,360,000,000
Net Worth: $10,552,000,000
Earnings: $2,234,000,000
Emp.: 20,224
Fiscal Year-end: 12/31/22
Oil & Natural Gas Drilling, Exploration, Production, Refining & Marketing
N.A.I.C.S.: 211120
Santiago Martinez Tanoira *(VP-Gas & Energy)*

Subsidiaries:

A-Evangelista S.A. (1)
Barreiro 2871 Ruta Provincial 52 Km 32 5, Canning Ezeiza, B1804EYA, Buenos Aires, Argentina
Tel.: (54) 11 5441 6000
Web Site: http://www.aesa.com.ar
Oil & Gas Pipeline Construction Engineering Services
N.A.I.C.S.: 237120

Apache Argentina Corp. (1)
Ing Enrique Butty 240 Piso 18, C1001AFB, Buenos Aires, Argentina
Tel.: (54) 1152185066
Sales Range: $150-199.9 Million
Oil & Gas Exploration & Production Services
N.A.I.C.S.: 211120
David Chi *(Interim VP)*

Subsidiary (Domestic):

Petrolera LF Company S.R.L. (2)
Tucuman 1 Piso 12, Buenos Aires, 1049, Argentina
Tel.: (54) 1143355200
Web Site: http://www.apachecorp.com
Sales Range: $100-124.9 Million
Emp.: 200
Crude Petroleum Natural Gas Extraction
N.A.I.C.S.: 211120

Operadora de Estaciones de Servicio, S.A. (1)
Av Roque Saenz Pena 777, CP 1364, Buenos Aires, Argentina (99%)
Tel.: (54) 11 4329 2000
Web Site: http://www.ypf.com
Marketing Management
N.A.I.C.S.: 541613

Petroken Petroquimica Ensenada SA (1)
Avda Eduardo Madero 1020 14/F, C1106ACX, Buenos Aires, Argentina
Tel.: (54) 1157765555
Web Site: http://www.petroken-pesa.com.ar
Polypropylene Mfr
N.A.I.C.S.: 325211

Profertil S.A. (1)
Manuela Saenz 323 Piso 8 - Of 803, Puerto Madero, 1107, Buenos Aires, Argentina (50%)
Tel.: (54) 91141212000
Web Site: https://www.profertil.com.ar
Fertilizer Production & Whslr
N.A.I.C.S.: 325311

YPF Brasil Comercio Derivado de Petroleo Ltda. (1)
Av Fabio Eduardo Ramos Esquivel 2746 Canhema, Diadema, Brazil
Tel.: (55) 1131450300
Web Site: https://ypf.com.br
Hydrocarbon Exploration & Production Services
N.A.I.C.S.: 211130

YPF Energia Electrica S.A. (1)
Macacha Guemes 515 Floor 3, Buenos Aires, Argentina
Tel.: (54) 1154415400
Web Site: https://www.ypfluz.com
Eletric Power Generation Services
N.A.I.C.S.: 221114

YPF Holdings Inc. (1)
1330 Lk Robbins Dr Ste 300, Spring, TX 77380
Tel.: (281) 681-7200
Oil & Gas Exploration Services
N.A.I.C.S.: 213112

YPF Inversora Energetica, S.A. (1)
Macacha Guemes 515 Ciudad de 1106, Buenos Aires, Argentina
Tel.: (54) 1154410000
Investment Management Service
N.A.I.C.S.: 523999

YPO CAMP MURET CAMPINGS-CARS
Lieu Dit Le Petit Joffrery Z I 14 Boulevard De Joffrery, Muret, 31600, Toulouse, France
Tel.: (33) 561516179
Rev.: $26,600,000
Emp.: 26
Sporting Goods & Bicycle Shops
N.A.I.C.S.: 459110
Guy Beauvois *(Mgr)*

YPSOMED HOLDING AG
Brunnmattstrasse 6, 3401, Burgdorf, Switzerland
Tel.: (41) 344244111 CH
Web Site: https://www.ypsomed.com
YPSN—(SWX)
Rev.: $551,507,761
Assets: $955,519,956
Liabilities: $332,090,909
Net Worth: $623,429,047
Earnings: $56,845,898
Emp.: 1,978
Fiscal Year-end: 03/31/23
Medical Delivery Systems Mfr
N.A.I.C.S.: 339112
Willy Michel *(Chm)*

Subsidiaries:

DiaExpert GmbH (1)
Hochster Strasse 82, 65835, Liederbach, Germany
Tel.: (49) 69 310 1950
Web Site: https://www.diaexpert.de
Diabetes Equipment Distr
N.A.I.C.S.: 423450

Ypsomed AB (1)
Etelainen Salmitie 1, 02430, Kirkkonummi, Finland
Tel.: (358) 8 008 9998
Web Site: https://www.ypsomed.com
Diabetes Care Products Mfr
N.A.I.C.S.: 339112

Ypsomed AB (1)
Elektrogatan 10, 171 54, Solna, Sweden
Tel.: (46) 8 601 2550
Web Site: https://www.ypsomed.com
Diabetes Care Products Mfr
N.A.I.C.S.: 339112

Ypsomed AS (1)
Papirbredden Gronland 58, 3045, Drammen, Norway
Tel.: (47) 22209300
Web Site: https://www.ypsomed.com
Medical Device Mfr
N.A.I.C.S.: 339112

Ypsomed ApS (1)
Smedeland 7, 2600, Glostrup, Denmark
Tel.: (45) 4 824 0045
Medical Device Mfr
N.A.I.C.S.: 339112

Ypsomed Australia Pty. Ltd. (1)
602/20 Bungan St, Mona Vale, 2103, NSW, Australia
Tel.: (61) 28 039 3554
Web Site: https://www.mylife-diabetescare.com
Diabetes Equipment Distr
N.A.I.C.S.: 423450

Ypsomed BV (1)
Tel.: (31) 30 888 5819
Web Site: https://www.ypsomed.com
Emp.: 1,800
Diabetes Care Products Mfr
N.A.I.C.S.: 339112

Ypsomed Diabetes, S.L. (1)
Avda Madrid 95 5 1, 08028, Barcelona, Spain
Tel.: (34) 937077003
Web Site: https://www.ypsomed.com
Medical Device Mfr
N.A.I.C.S.: 339112

Ypsomed GmbH (1)
Am Euro Platz 2, 1120, Vienna, Austria
Tel.: (43) 8005 500 0000
Web Site: https://www.ypsomed.com
Diabetes Care Products Mfr
N.A.I.C.S.: 339112

Ypsomed GmbH (1)
Hochster Strasse 70, 65835, Liederbach, Germany
Tel.: (49) 69 310 1970
Web Site: https://www.ypsomed.com
Diabetes Care Products Mfr
N.A.I.C.S.: 339112

Ypsomed India Private Ltd. (1)
10/61/1-F Kirti Nagar Industrial Area, New Delhi, 110 015, India
Tel.: (91) 114 305 5255
Web Site: https://www.mylife-diabetescare.com
Emp.: 20
Diabetes Care Products Mfr
N.A.I.C.S.: 339112
Sanjay Rajpal *(Country Mgr)*

Ypsomed Italia S.r.l. (1)
Via Santa Croce 7, 21100, Varese, Italy
Tel.: (39) 0332 189 0607
Diabetes Care Products Mfr
N.A.I.C.S.: 339112

Ypsomed Ltd. (1)
1 Park Court Riccall Road, Escrick, York, YO19 6ED, United Kingdom
Tel.: (44) 344 856 7820
Web Site: https://www.mylife-diabetescare.com
Diabetes Care Products Mfr
N.A.I.C.S.: 339112

Ypsomed Medical Devices Co., Ltd. (1)
Office 1201 Landmark Tower 2 8 North Dongsanhuan Road, Chaoyang District, Beijing, 100004, China
Tel.: (86) 1064618830
Pharmaceuticals Product Mfr
N.A.I.C.S.: 325412

Ypsomed S.A.S. (1)
44 rue Lafayette, 75009, Paris, France
Tel.: (33) 15 870 2001
Web Site: https://www.ypsomed.com
Diabetes Care Products Mfr
N.A.I.C.S.: 339112

Ypsomed S.r.l. (1)
Via Santa Croce 7, 21100, Varese, Italy
Tel.: (39) 0332 189 0607
Web Site: https://www.mylife-diabetescare.com
Blood Glucose Monitoring Systems Mfr
N.A.I.C.S.: 339112

Ypsotec AG (1)
Adolf Furrer-Strasse 7, 2540, Grenchen, Switzerland (100%)
Tel.: (41) 32 654 9711
Web Site: https://www.ypsotec.com
Precision Component Mfr
N.A.I.C.S.: 332721
Iris Rotzel-Schwunk *(Member-Mgmt Bd & Head-Quality)*

Ypsotec s.r.o. (1)
Vozicka 3149, 39002, Tabor, Czech Republic
Tel.: (420) 38 150 1010
Web Site: https://www.ypsotec.com
Precision Turned Mfr
N.A.I.C.S.: 332721
Daniele Marco Galatioto *(CEO)*

YRGLM INC.
8F Herbis ENT Office Tower 2-2-22 Umeda, Kita-ku, Osaka, 530-0001, Japan
Tel.: (81) 647957500
Web Site: https://www.yrglm.co.jp
Year Founded: 2001
3690—(TKS)
Rev.: $25,708,340
Assets: $22,432,760
Liabilities: $8,373,290
Net Worth: $14,059,470
Earnings: $1,396,730
Emp.: 371
Fiscal Year-end: 09/30/23
Marketing Automation Platform
N.A.I.C.S.: 541511
Hiroki Akazawa *(CFO, COO & Sr Exec Officer)*

YRGLM INC.

YRGLM Inc.—(Continued)

Subsidiaries:

LOCKON Vietnam Co., Ltd. (1)
12th Floor - Robot Building 308-308C Dien Bien Phu, Ward 4 District 3, Ho Chi Minh City, Vietnam
Tel.: (84) 2839296800
Web Site: https://yrglm.com.vn
Emp.: 22
Software Development Services
N.A.I.C.S.: 541511
Keizo Uno *(Gen Dir)*

YSS CORP.

800 138-4th Ave SE, Calgary, T2G 4Z6, AB, Canada
Tel.: (403) 455-7656
Web Site: http://www.ysscorp.ca
YSS—(TSXV)
Rev.: $8,541
Assets: $44,003
Liabilities: $14,078
Net Worth: $29,925
Earnings: ($2,702)
Fiscal Year-end: 12/31/19
Cannabis Product Mfr
N.A.I.C.S.: 325411
Theo Zunich *(Pres & CEO)*

YTL CORPORATION BERHAD

33rd Floor Menara YTL 205 Jalan Bukit Bintang, 55100, Kuala Lumpur, Malaysia
Tel.: (60) 320380888
Web Site: https://www.ytl.com
1773—(TKS)
Rev.: $6,267,954,497
Assets: $17,240,289,735
Liabilities: $12,983,520,847
Net Worth: $4,256,768,889
Earnings: $449,173,333
Emp.: 12,627
Fiscal Year-end: 06/30/23
Construction Services
N.A.I.C.S.: 236210
Francis Sock Ping Yeoh *(Mng Dir)*

Subsidiaries:

Autodome Sdn. Bhd. (1)
YTL Land Sdn Bhd Level 6 Annex Block Lot 10 Shopping Center, Jalan Sultan Ismail, 50250, Kuala Lumpur, Malaysia
Tel.: (60) 327823500
Food & Beverage Outlets
N.A.I.C.S.: 312111
Eric Sin *(Officer)*

Cameron Highlands Resort Sdn. Bhd. (1)
By The Golf Course, Tanah Rata Cameron Highlands, 39000, Pahang, Malaysia
Tel.: (60) 327831000
Web Site:
https://www.cameronhighlandsresort.com
Hotel & Resort Operating Services
N.A.I.C.S.: 721120

Dynamic Marketing Sdn. Bhd. (1)
4th Fl Plz Yeoh Tiong Lay, Jln Bukit Bintang, Kuala Lumpur, 55100, Malaysia
Tel.: (60) 321423300
Web Site: http://www.ytlcommunity.com.my
Emp.: 7,000
Building & Construction Materials Trading Services
N.A.I.C.S.: 444180
Tansri Dato Francis Yeoh Sock Ping *(Mng Dir)*

YTL Cement Berhad (1)
11th Fl Yeoh Tiong Lay Plz 55 Jalan Bukit Bintang, 55100, Kuala Lumpur, Malaysia **(97.49%)**
Tel.: (60) 321426633
Web Site: http://www.ytlcement.com
Cement & Ready Mixed Concrete Mfr
N.A.I.C.S.: 327310

Subsidiary (Domestic):

Malayan Cement Berhad (2)
33rd Floor Menara YTL 205 Jalan Bukit Bintang, 55100, Kuala Lumpur, Malaysia **(77%)**
Tel.: (60) 320380888
Web Site: https://ytlcement.com
Sales Range: $50-74.9 Million
Cement, Aggregates & Concrete Materials Mfr
N.A.I.C.S.: 327310

Subsidiary (Domestic):

CMCM Perniagaan SDN BHD (3)
Level 12 Bangunan TH Uptown 3 No 3 Jalan SS21/39, 47400, Petaling Jaya, Selangor Darul Ehsan, Malaysia
Tel.: (60) 377238200
Web Site: http://www.lafarge.com.my
Building Materials Whslr
N.A.I.C.S.: 423320

Subsidiary (Non-US):

Lafarge Cement Singapore Pte. Ltd. (3)
3A International Business Park #07-01105 Icon@IBP, Singapore, 609935, Singapore **(51%)**
Tel.: (65) 68840122
Web Site: http://www.lafarge.com.my
Cement Mfr
N.A.I.C.S.: 327310

Subsidiary (Non-US):

NSL limited (2)
317 Outram Road 03-02, Singapore, 169075, Singapore **(91.02%)**
Tel.: (65) 65361000
Web Site: https://www.nsl.com.sg
Rev.: $274,113,271
Assets: $450,350,767
Liabilities: $109,952,586
Net Worth: $340,398,181
Earnings: $7,115,434
Emp.: 2,534
Fiscal Year-end: 12/31/2022
Investment Holding Services
N.A.I.C.S.: 551112
Tao Soon Cham *(Chm)*

Subsidiary (Domestic):

CNC Petroleum Pte. Ltd. (3)
1 Kaki Bukit Ave 3 08-06 Kb-1, Singapore, 416087, Singapore
Tel.: (65) 67487752
Web Site: http://www.cncpetroleum.com
Petroleum Product Distr
N.A.I.C.S.: 424720

Subsidiary (Non-US):

Eastern Pretech (Malaysia) Sdn. Bhd. (3)
10th Floor Pusat Perdagangan Mines Jalan Mines 2, The Mines Resort City, 43300, Seri Kembangan, Selangor, Malaysia
Tel.: (60) 389493333
Web Site: https://www.epmsb.com.my
Precast Concrete Product Mfr & Distr
N.A.I.C.S.: 327390

Plant (Domestic):

Eastern Pretech (Malaysia) Sdn. Bhd. - Beranang Factory (4)
Lot 2 Jalan Perusahaan 5 Kawasan Perindustrian, 43700, Beranang, Selangor, Malaysia
Tel.: (60) 387667941
Precast Concrete Products Mfr
N.A.I.C.S.: 327390

Eastern Pretech (Malaysia) Sdn. Bhd. - Seelong Factory (4)
PTD 103274 Jalan Seelong, 81400, Senai, Johor, Malaysia
Tel.: (60) 75998063
Precast Concrete Products Mfr
N.A.I.C.S.: 327390

Eastern Pretech (Malaysia) Sdn. Bhd. - Sungai Petani Factory (4)
Plot 72 Bakar Arang Industrial Estate, 08000, Sungai Petani, Kedah Darul Aman, Malaysia
Tel.: (60) 44200330
Precast Concrete Products Mfr
N.A.I.C.S.: 327390

Subsidiary (Domestic):

NSL Chemicals Ltd. (3)
26 Tanjong Kling Road, Singapore, 628051, Singapore
Tel.: (65) 65136900
Web Site: https://www.nslchemicals.com.sg
Refractory Product Mfr & Distr
N.A.I.C.S.: 327120

NSL OilChem Waste Management Pte. Ltd. (3)
23 Tanjong Kling Road, Singapore, 628049, Singapore
Tel.: (65) 68635270
Web Site: https://www.nsloilchem.com.sg
Waste Treatment Services
N.A.I.C.S.: 562211
Jeffrey Fung *(CEO)*

Subsidiary (Non-US):

Parmarine Ltd (3)
Tel.: (358) 37777400
Web Site: https://www.parmarine.fi
Emp.: 270
Bathroom Fixture Mfr & Distr
N.A.I.C.S.: 332999
Jussi Raunio *(CEO)*

Subsidiary (Domestic):

Raffles Marina Ltd (3)
10 Tuas West Drive, Singapore, 638404, Singapore
Tel.: (65) 68618000
Web Site: https://www.rafflesmarina.com.sg
Marina Operation
N.A.I.C.S.: 713930
Sky Chong *(CFO)*

Subsidiary (Domestic):

YTL Technologies Sdn Bhd (2)
Lot 3792 Jalan Bukit Rimau Off Jalan Bukit Kemuning, Section 32, Shah Alam, 42450, Selangor, Malaysia
Tel.: (60) 351213377
Web Site: http://www.ytlcement.com
Emp.: 30
Maintenance Services of Fleet Vehicles & Plant Sites
N.A.I.C.S.: 811198

YTL Land & Development Berhad (1)
Level 36 Menara YTL 205 Jalan Bukit Bintang, 55100, Kuala Lumpur, Malaysia
Tel.: (60) 321433000
Web Site: https://www.ytlland.com
Rev.: $80,982,162
Assets: $883,056,786
Liabilities: $686,409,105
Net Worth: $196,647,681
Earnings: ($18,315,808)
Fiscal Year-end: 06/30/2018
Property Development Services
N.A.I.C.S.: 531311
Hamidah Maktar *(Exec Dir)*

YTL Power International Berhad (1)
33rd Floor Menara YTL 205 Jalan Bukit Bintang, 55100, Kuala Lumpur, Malaysia
Tel.: (60) 320380888
Web Site:
https://www.ytlpowerinternational.com
Rev.: $4,632,901,376
Assets: $12,514,710,265
Liabilities: $9,043,626,455
Net Worth: $3,471,083,810
Earnings: $430,177,143
Emp.: 4,782
Fiscal Year-end: 06/30/2023
Property Development Services
N.A.I.C.S.: 531312
Say Keng Ho *(Sec)*

Subsidiary (Domestic):

Ranhill Utilities Berhad (2)
Bangunan Ranhill SAJ Jalan Garuda, Larkin, 80350, Johor Bahru, Malaysia **(53.19%)**
Tel.: (60) 72255300
Web Site: https://www.ranhill.com.my
Rev.: $365,363,175
Assets: $690,311,958
Liabilities: $488,176,931
Net Worth: $202,135,026
Earnings: $30,098,836

Emp.: 3,015
Fiscal Year-end: 12/31/2022
Electric Power Distribution Services
N.A.I.C.S.: 221310
Mohamed Azman Yahya *(Chm)*

Subsidiary (Non-US):

Ranhill Water Technologies (Thai) Ltd. (3)
No 54 BB Building 9th Floor Room No 3922 Sukhumvit 21 Asoke Road, Klongtoey-Nua Wattana, Bangkok, 10110, Thailand
Tel.: (66) 21174907
Waste Water Treatment Services
N.A.I.C.S.: 221320
alan Petcharopas *(Engr-Ops)*

YTL HOSPITALITY REIT

33rd Floor Menara YTL 205 Jalan Bukit Bintang, 55100, Kuala Lumpur, Malaysia
Tel.: (60) 320380888
Web Site:
https://www.ytlhospitalityreit.com
Year Founded: 2005
YTLREIT—(KLS)
Rev.: $103,032,804
Assets: $1,085,138,201
Liabilities: $469,814,815
Net Worth: $615,323,386
Earnings: $29,888,042
Emp.: 9
Fiscal Year-end: 06/30/23
Real Estate Investment Management Services
N.A.I.C.S.: 525990
Francis Sock Ping Yeoh *(Chm)*

YTN CO., LTD.

76 Sangamsan-ro, Mapo-gu, Seoul, Korea (South)
Tel.: (82) 23988000
Web Site: https://www.ytn.co.kr
Year Founded: 1993
040300—(KRS)
Rev.: $116,730,724
Assets: $276,220,866
Liabilities: $80,408,116
Net Worth: $195,812,750
Earnings: $4,229,463
Emp.: 621
Fiscal Year-end: 12/31/22
Television Broadcasting Services
N.A.I.C.S.: 516120
Kim Do-Won *(Mgr)*

YTO EXPRESS GROUP CO., LTD.

No 28 Lane 3029 Huaxu Highway, Huaxin Town Qingpu District, Shanghai, 201705, China
Tel.: (86) 4006095554
Web Site: https://www.yto.net.cn
Year Founded: 2000
600233—(SHG)
Rev.: $7,986,867,191
Assets: $6,004,519,260
Liabilities: $1,941,201,858
Net Worth: $4,063,317,401
Earnings: $515,416,247
Emp.: 22,731
Fiscal Year-end: 12/31/23
Courier Service
N.A.I.C.S.: 492110
Dongmei Hu *(Vice Chm)*

Subsidiaries:

YTO International Express and Supply Chain Technology Limited (1)
Flat 18 1st Floor Sino Industrial Plaza 9 Kai Cheung Road, Kowloon Bay, Hong Kong, China (Hong Kong) **(61.87%)**
Tel.: (852) 23458351
Web Site: https://www.ytoglobal.com
Rev.: $855,072,375
Assets: $283,722,180
Liabilities: $129,394,778
Net Worth: $154,327,403
Earnings: $17,825,648
Emp.: 867

Fiscal Year-end: 12/31/2022
Freight & Logistics Services
N.A.I.C.S.: 488510
Spencer Chun Chin Lam *(Founder & CEO)*

YU GROUP PLC
Cpk House Mellors Way 2 Horizon Place Nottingham Business Park, Nottingham, NG8 6PY, United Kingdom
Tel.: (44) 1159758258   UK
Web Site:
https://www.yugroupplc.com
Year Founded: 2016
YU—(AIM)
Rev.: $335,561,655
Assets: $107,043,915
Liabilities: $89,217,315
Net Worth: $17,826,600
Earnings: $37,170,870
Fiscal Year-end: 12/31/22
Electric Power Distribution
N.A.I.C.S.: 221122
Bobby Kalar *(CEO)*

Subsidiaries:

Yu-Smart Limited   (1)
Cpk House 2 Horizon Place Mellors Way, Nottingham Business Park, Nottingham, Nottinghamshire, United Kingdom
Tel.: (44) 1204874363
Web Site: https://yusmart.co.uk
Electrical Meter Installation Services
N.A.I.C.S.: 238210

YU TAK INTERNATIONAL HOLDINGS LIMITED
7/F Nam Fung Tower 88 Connaught Road Central, Hong Kong, China (Hong Kong)
Tel.: (852) 21862800   BM
Year Founded: 1988
8048—(HKG)
Rev.: $3,670,088
Assets: $15,679,823
Liabilities: $2,665,005
Net Worth: $13,014,818
Earnings: ($930,113)
Emp.: 55
Fiscal Year-end: 12/31/22
Investment Holding Company
N.A.I.C.S.: 551112
Yu Ping Chong *(Chm)*

Subsidiaries:

Excel Technology International (Hong Kong) Limited   (1)
5th Floor 663 King's Road, North Point, China (Hong Kong)
Tel.: (852) 21862800
Web Site: https://www.excel.com.hk
Information Technology Services
N.A.I.C.S.: 513210

Subsidiary (Non-US):

Excel Consulting and Solutions Sdn. Bhd.   (2)
Unit 19-8-5 Level 8 UOA Centre No 19, Jalan Pinang, 50450, Kuala Lumpur, Malaysia
Tel.: (60) 321616860
Information Technology Services
N.A.I.C.S.: 513210

Excel Global IT Services (Hangzhou) Limited   (2)
Room 306 Guangfulianhe center 9 Ningyi Road, Xiaoshan District, Hangzhou, 311200, Zhejiang, China
Tel.: (86) 57185057079
Web Site: http://www.excel-gits.com
Emp.: 60
Information Technology Services
N.A.I.C.S.: 513210

Excel Software (Shenzhen) Co., Ltd.   (2)
401 Block A No 1079 Nanhai Avenue, Nanshan District, Shenzhen, 518067, China
Tel.: (86) 75526839002
Information Technology Services
N.A.I.C.S.: 513210

Excel Solution Technology Limited   (2)
5th Floor South Shekou Technology Bldg Annex 7 Industrial Road, Shekou Industrial District, Shenzhen, 518067, China
Tel.: (86) 755 2683 9001
Web Site: http://www.excelsolution.cn
Information Technology Services
N.A.I.C.S.: 513210

Excel Technology (Shanghai) Co., Ltd.   (2)
Unit 08 Floor 30 LL Land 580 West Nanjing Road, Jingan District, Shanghai, 200041, China
Tel.: (86) 2162792488
Web Site: http://www.excel-sh.com.cn
Information Technology Services
N.A.I.C.S.: 513210

Excelink Technology Pte Limited   (2)
20 Upper Circular Road B1-19 The Riverwals, Singapore, 58416, Singapore
Tel.: (65) 6236 9838
Information Technology Services
N.A.I.C.S.: 513210

New River Information Technology & Services Co.   (2)
7F No 268 Sec 2 Fuxing S Rd, Taipei, 106, Taiwan
Tel.: (886) 227367568
Web Site: http://www.excel-gits.com
Information Technology Services
N.A.I.C.S.: 513210

YUAN CHENG CABLE CO., LTD.
No 8 Yuancheng Road, Guanlin Town, Yixing, 214251, Jiangsu, China
Tel.: (86) 51080777896
Web Site: http://www.yccable.cn
Year Founded: 2001
002692—(SSE)
Rev.: $423,754,620
Assets: $344,720,849
Liabilities: $197,423,909
Net Worth: $147,296,939
Earnings: $9,541,163
Emp.: 1,394
Fiscal Year-end: 12/31/22
Wire & Cable Mfr & Distr
N.A.I.C.S.: 335931
Guoping Yu *(Chm)*

YUAN HENG GAS HOLDINGS LIMITED
Room 4102 Far East Finance Centre 16 Harcourt Road, Hong Kong, China (Hong Kong)
Tel.: (852) 35831120   HK
Web Site:
https://www.yuanhenggas.com
Year Founded: 1976
0332—(HKG)
Rev.: $363,781,671
Assets: $526,208,172
Liabilities: $293,719,657
Net Worth: $232,488,515
Earnings: $14,662,963
Emp.: 390
Fiscal Year-end: 03/31/22
Oil & Gas Production & Distr
N.A.I.C.S.: 213112
Jianqing Wang *(Chm & CEO)*

Subsidiaries:

Ngai Sing Holdings Limited   (1)
Rm 29-32 8F Block B Focal Industrial Centre, 21 Man Lok Street, Hung Hom, China (Hong Kong)   (100%)
Tel.: (852) 2303 9668
Web Site: http://www.ngai-sing.com
Consumer Electronics Products International Sales
N.A.I.C.S.: 551112
Shing Ngai Lam *(CEO)*

Subsidiary (Domestic):

Ngai Lik Electronics Enterprises Limited   (2)
Rm 29-32 8th Floor Block B Focal Industrial Centre, 21 Man Lok Street, Hung Hom, China (Hong Kong)   (100%)
Tel.: (852) 23039668
Web Site: http://www.ngai-sing.com
Emp.: 10
Sales of Consumer Electronic Products
N.A.I.C.S.: 532210

YUAN HIGH-TECH DEVELOPMENT CO., LTD.
18F NO 88 Sec 2 Chung Hsiao E Rd, Taipei, Taiwan
Tel.: (886) 223921233
Web Site: https://www.yuan.com.tw
Year Founded: 1990
5474—(TPE)
Rev.: $42,921,959
Assets: $66,117,844
Liabilities: $11,089,079
Net Worth: $55,028,765
Earnings: $9,827,221
Emp.: 142
Fiscal Year-end: 12/31/22
Software Development Services
N.A.I.C.S.: 541511
Li-Min Chen *(Chm)*

YUAN JEN ENTERPRISES CO., LTD.
3-3Fl No 54 Sec 4 Min Sheng East Road, Taipei, Taiwan
Tel.: (886) 227172222
Web Site: http://www.yuanjen.com
Year Founded: 1977
1725—(TAI)
Rev.: $245,191,789
Assets: $239,665,382
Liabilities: $89,694,329
Net Worth: $149,971,053
Earnings: $6,555,773
Emp.: 109
Fiscal Year-end: 12/31/23
Industrial Chemical Distr
N.A.I.C.S.: 424690
Hsu Yuan-Jen *(Chm)*

YUAN LONG PING HIGH-TECH AGRICULTURE CO., LTD.
No 638 Heping Road, Furong District, Changsha, 410125, Hunan, China
Tel.: (86) 73182183111
Web Site: https://www.lpht.com.cn
Year Founded: 1999
000998—(SSE)
Rev.: $517,908,320
Assets: $2,050,501,382
Liabilities: $1,242,590,951
Net Worth: $807,910,431
Earnings: ($123,055,840)
Fiscal Year-end: 12/31/22
Agricultural Product Mfr
N.A.I.C.S.: 325320
Liu Zhiyong *(Chm)*

YUANCHENG ENVIRONMENT CO., LTD.
15F Hangzhou Jintou Financial Building No 2-6 Qingchun East Road, Hangzhou, 310016, Zhejiang, China
Tel.: (86) 57181025756
Web Site: http://www.ycgf.cn
Year Founded: 1999
603388—(SHG)
Rev.: $45,898,431
Assets: $484,292,994
Liabilities: $254,419,065
Net Worth: $229,873,929
Earnings: ($7,410,747)
Fiscal Year-end: 12/31/22
Landscape Architectural Services
N.A.I.C.S.: 561730
Changren Zhu *(Chm & Gen Mgr)*

YUANDA CHINA HOLDINGS LIMITED
No 20 13th Street, Shenyang Economic and Technological Development District, Shenyang, 110027, China
Tel.: (86) 2425271602   Ky
Web Site: http://www.yuandacn.com
2789—(HKG)
Rev.: $458,209,580
Assets: $828,223,952
Liabilities: $686,214,547
Net Worth: $142,009,405
Earnings: $10,126,912
Emp.: 2,511
Fiscal Year-end: 12/31/22
Curtain Wall Installlation Services
N.A.I.C.S.: 812320
Bao Hua Kang *(Chm)*

Subsidiaries:

Shanghai Yuanda Aluminium Industry Engineering Co., Ltd.   (1)
No 2605 Jiahang Rd Tanghang Town, Jiading, Shanghai, 201816, China
Tel.: (86) 21 5995 3888
Curtain Wall Installation Services
N.A.I.C.S.: 238190

Yuanda (UK) Co., Ltd.   (1)
South Quay Building 10th Floor 77 Marsh Wall, London, E14 9SH, United Kingdom
Tel.: (44) 2075627766
Curtain Wall Installation Services
N.A.I.C.S.: 238190

Yuanda Aluminium Industry Engineering (Germany) GmbH   (1)
Lyoner Strasse 14, 60528, Frankfurt am Main, Germany
Tel.: (49) 696 655 4325
Web Site: http://www.yuanda-europe.com
Curtain Wall Installation Services
N.A.I.C.S.: 238190

Yuanda Aluminium Industry Engineering (Singapore) Pte Ltd.   (1)
Lavender Street 114, Singapore, 338729, Singapore
Tel.: (65) 62757818
Curtain Wall Installation Services
N.A.I.C.S.: 238190

Yuanda Australia Pty Ltd.   (1)
Unit 503/447 Kent Street, Sydney, 2000, NSW, Australia
Tel.: (61) 292850333
Web Site: https://www.yuanda.com.au
Emp.: 25
Curtain Wall Installation Services
N.A.I.C.S.: 238190

Yuanda Curtain Wall (Singapore) Pte. Ltd.   (1)
114 Lavender Street 06-72 City Hub 2, Singapore, 338729, Singapore
Tel.: (65) 62757818
Emp.: 5
Curtain Wall Installation Services
N.A.I.C.S.: 238190

Yuanda Europe Ltd.   (1)
Uferstrasse 90, 4057, Basel, Switzerland
Tel.: (41) 61 555 2300
Web Site: https://www.yuanda-europe.com
Emp.: 60
Construction Engineering Services
N.A.I.C.S.: 541330
Dominik Baumeler *(CFO)*

Yuanda International Aluminium Engineering India Private Limited   (1)
C-409 & C-410 Crystal Plz 4th Floor New Link Rd, Andheri West, Mumbai, 400053, India
Tel.: (91) 22 61270200
Curtain Wall Installation Services
N.A.I.C.S.: 238190

Yuanda Italy S.R.L.   (1)
Via San Giuseppe no 38/G, 31015, Conegliano, Italy
Tel.: (39) 0438373111
Web Site: https://www.yuanda-italy.com
Emp.: 12
Curtain Wall Installation Services
N.A.I.C.S.: 238190

Yuanda WA Pty Ltd.   (1)

YUANDA CHINA HOLDINGS LIMITED

Yuanda China Holdings Limited—(Continued)
U10 17 Foley St, Balcatta, 6914, WA, Australia
Tel.: (61) 292850333
Curtain Wall Installation Services
N.A.I.C.S.: 288190

YUANLI CHEMICAL GROUP CO., LTD.
No 277 National Highway 309 Zhuliu Street Industrial Park, Changle County, Weifang, 262404, Shandong, China
Tel.: (86) 13605368863
Web Site: https://www.yuanlichem.com.cn
Year Founded: 2003
603217—(SHG)
Rev.: $376,690,645
Assets: $498,412,868
Liabilities: $77,149,744
Net Worth: $421,263,124
Earnings: $65,893,230
Fiscal Year-end: 12/31/22
Chemical Product Mfr & Distr
N.A.I.C.S.: 325520
Xiuhua Liu (Chm & Gen Mgr)

Subsidiaries:

Chongqing Yuanli Technology Co., Ltd. (1)
No 58 Wuling Avenue, Baitao Chemical Industrial Park Fuling District, Chongqing, China
Tel.: (86) 2387806666
Chemical Products Distr
N.A.I.C.S.: 424690

Shandong Yuanli Science & Technology Co., Ltd. (1)
No 277 National Highway 309, Zhuliu Street Industrial Park Changle County, Weifang, 262402, Shandong, China
Tel.: (86) 5366776858
Chemical Products Mfr
N.A.I.C.S.: 325998

YUANSHENGTAI DAIRY FARM LIMITED
Qingxiang Street, Kedong County, Qiqihar, Heilongjiang, China
Tel.: (86) 15910319121 BM
1431—(HKG)
Web Site: http://www.ystdfarm.com
Rev.: $293,484,157
Assets: $1,114,959,924
Liabilities: $400,585,349
Net Worth: $714,374,575
Earnings: $3,206,876
Emp.: 2,241
Fiscal Year-end: 12/31/22
Dairy Farming Services
N.A.I.C.S.: 112120
Gang Liu (Exec Dir)

YUANTA FINANCIAL HOLDING CO., LTD.
6F 10F 12F-13F No 66 Sec 1 Dun Hua S Road, Taipei, 105, Taiwan
Tel.: (886) 227811999 TW
Web Site: http://www.yuanta.com
Year Founded: 2002
2885—(TAI)
Rev.: $1,949,632,086
Assets: $103,137,911,390
Liabilities: $93,496,034,581
Net Worth: $9,641,876,810
Earnings: $891,981,021
Emp.: 14,913
Fiscal Year-end: 12/31/23
Holding Company
N.A.I.C.S.: 551112
Ming Lang Liu (Chief Operational Support Officer)

Subsidiaries:

P.T. Yuanta Sekuritas Indonesia (1)
Equity Tower 10th Floor Unit Efgh Scbd Lot 9, Jl Jendral Sudirman Kav 52-53, Jakarta, 12190, Indonesia
Tel.: (62) 215153608
Web Site: https://www.yuanta.co.id
Investment Banking Services
N.A.I.C.S.: 523999

PT Yuanta Asset Management (1)
Equity Tower 10th Floor Unit B SCBD Lot 9 Jl Jend Sudirman Kav 52-53, Jakarta, 12190, Indonesia
Tel.: (62) 215153077
Web Site: http://www.yuanta-am.co.id
Investment Management Service
N.A.I.C.S.: 523940
Tay Ai Khim (Co-Pres)

Polaris Securities Co., Ltd. (1)
3 Fl No 270 Sec 4 Jhongsiao E Rd, 110, Taipei, Taiwan (100%)
Tel.: (886) 227925889
Web Site: http://www.polaris.com.tw
Sales Range: $125-149.9 Million
Internet Trading & Investment Services
N.A.I.C.S.: 523150
Ming-Chung Wei (Vice Chm)

Subsidiary (Non-US):

Polaris Capital (Asia) Ltd. (2)
Units 6503-06 The Center 99 Queens Road, Central, China (Hong Kong)
Tel.: (852) 21568222
Web Site: http://www.polariscapital.net
Investment Banking Services
N.A.I.C.S.: 523150

Ta Chong Bank, Ltd. (1)
No 112 Guangfu North Road, Songshan District, Taipei, Taiwan (100%)
Tel.: (886) 225771015
Web Site: http://www.tcbank.com.tw
Commercial Banking Services
N.A.I.C.S.: 522110
Jianping Chen (Chm)

Yuanta Commercial Bank Company Limited (1)
1F-10F No 66 & 1F 2F 2F-1 7F 9F No 68 Sec 1 Dunhua S Rd, Songshan District, Taipei, 10557, Taiwan
Tel.: (886) 2 21738888
Web Site: http://www.yuantabank.com.tw
Commercial Banking Services
N.A.I.C.S.: 522110
Tony Chich-Chiang Fan (Chm)

Yuanta Futures (Hong Kong) Limited (1)
23/F Tower 1 Admiralty Centre 18 Harcourt Road Admiralty, Hong Kong, China (Hong Kong)
Tel.: (852) 22939688
Web Site: https://www.yuantafutures.com.hk
Asset Management Services
N.A.I.C.S.: 531390

Yuanta Investment Consulting (Beijing) Co., Ltd. (1)
Rm 0706 7F No113 Zhichun Str, Haidian District, Beijing, 100080, China
Tel.: (86) 1065101266
Investment Banking Services
N.A.I.C.S.: 523150

Yuanta Leasing Co., Ltd. (1)
11F No 66 Section 1 Dunhua South Road, Songshan District, Taipei, 10557, Taiwan
Tel.: (886) 2 2173 6699
Emp.: 2,000
Real Estate Lending Services
N.A.I.C.S.: 531110

Yuanta Life Insurance Co., Ltd. (1)
17F No 156 Sec 3 Minsheng E Rd, Songshan Dist, Taipei, 105, Taiwan
Tel.: (886) 227517578
Web Site: http://www.yuantalife.com.tw
Emp.: 1,000
Fire Insurance Services
N.A.I.C.S.: 524113

Yuanta Savings Bank (Korea) Inc. (1)
542 Gangnam-daero, Gangnam-gu, Seoul, Korea (South)
Tel.: (82) 260223700
Investment Banking Services
N.A.I.C.S.: 523150

Yuanta Savings Bank (Philippines) Inc. (1)
Ground Floor Chatham House 116 Valero cor V A Rufino Streets, Salcedo Village, Makati, Metro Manila, Philippines
Tel.: (63) 288453838
Web Site: https://yuanta.com.ph
Investment Banking Services
N.A.I.C.S.: 523150

Yuanta Securities (Cambodia) Plc (1)
4th Floor Emerald Building No 64 corner St 178 Preah Norodom Blvd, Sangkat Chey Chumneah Khan Daun Penh, Phnom Penh, Cambodia
Tel.: (855) 23860800
Web Site: https://www.yuantacambodia.com.kh
Investment Banking Services
N.A.I.C.S.: 523150
Young Chul Choi (Head-Ops)

Yuanta Securities Co., Ltd. (1)
13 14F No 225 Sec 3 Nanjing E Rd, Taipei, 104, Taiwan (100%)
Tel.: (886) 227181234
Web Site: http://www.yuanta.com.tw
Securities Brokerage Services
N.A.I.C.S.: 523150
Bobby Hwang (Pres)

Subsidiary (Non-US):

Yuanta Securities (Hong Kong) Company Limited (2)
23/F Tower 1 Admiralty Centre 18 Harcourt Road, Admiralty, Hong Kong, China (Hong Kong) (100%)
Tel.: (852) 35557888
Web Site: https://www.yuanta.com.hk
Securities Brokerage Services
N.A.I.C.S.: 523150

Subsidiary (Non-US):

PT Yuanta Securities Indonesia Co., Ltd. (3)
10th Floor Unit EFGH SCBD Lot 9 Jl Jendral Sudirman Kav 52-53, Jakarta, 12190, Indonesia (99%)
Tel.: (62) 215153608
Web Site: http://www.yuanta.co.id
Securities Brokerage Services
N.A.I.C.S.: 523150

Subsidiary (Domestic):

Yuanta Securities Finance Co., Ltd. (2)
12F No 66 Section 1 Dunhua South Road, Songshan District, Taipei, 10557, Taiwan
Tel.: (886) 221736833
Web Site: https://www.yuantafinance.com.tw
Securities Lending Services
N.A.I.C.S.: 523150

Yuanta Securities Investment Consulting Co., Ltd. (2)
4F No 225 Nanjing E Rd Sec 3, Taipei, 104, Taiwan
Tel.: (886) 235187958
Web Site: http://www.yuanta-consulting.com.tw
Financial Management Consulting Services
N.A.I.C.S.: 541611

Yuanta Securities Investment Trust Co., Ltd. (2)
6F No 225 Nanking East Road Section 3, Taipei, Taiwan
Tel.: (886) 227175555
Web Site: http://www.yuanta.com
Securities Brokerage Services
N.A.I.C.S.: 523150

Yuanta Securities Thailand Co., Ltd. (1)
127 Gaysorn Tower Building 14th-16th Floor Ratchadamri Road, Lumpini Subdistrict Pathumwan District, Bangkok, 10330, Thailand
Tel.: (66) 20098888
Web Site: https://www.yuanta.co.th
Investment Banking Services
N.A.I.C.S.: 523150

Yuanta Securities Vietnam Joint Stock Co., Ltd. (1)
Level 4 Saigon Centre Tower 1 65 Le Loi Boulevard, Ben Nghe Ward District 1, Ho Chi Minh City, Vietnam
Tel.: (84) 2836226868

INTERNATIONAL PUBLIC

Investment Banking Services
N.A.I.C.S.: 523150

Yuanta Securities Vietnam Limited Company (1)
4th Floor - Tower 1 Saigon Centre 65 Le Loi, District 1, Ho Chi Minh City, Vietnam
Tel.: (84) 2836226868
Web Site: https://yuanta.com.vn
Financial Services
N.A.I.C.S.: 523999

Yuanta Venture Capital Corp. (1)
10F No 66 Sec 1 Dunhua S Rd, Songshan District, Taipei, 10557, Taiwan
Tel.: (886) 221736633
Web Site: http://www.yuanta.com
Emp.: 13
Financial Management Consulting Services
N.A.I.C.S.: 541611

Yuantal Futures Co., Ltd. (1)
3F No 77 Sec 2 Nanjing E Rd, Zhongshan Dist, Taipei, 10457, Taiwan
Tel.: (886) 227176000
Web Site: https://www.yuantafutures.com.tw
Emp.: 300
Futures Brokerage Services
N.A.I.C.S.: 523150

YUASA BATTERY (THAILAND) PUBLIC COMPANY LIMITED
164 Moo 5 Soi Thedsaban 55 Sukhumvit Road Tambol Taibanmai, Amphur Muangsamutprakan, Samut Prakan, 10280, Thailand
Tel.: (66) 27697300
Web Site: http://www.yuasathai.com
Year Founded: 1963
YUASA—(THA)
Rev.: $77,712,038
Assets: $46,697,876
Liabilities: $14,511,825
Net Worth: $32,186,051
Earnings: $3,591,369
Emp.: 636
Fiscal Year-end: 12/31/23
Automobile & Motorcycle Battery Mfr
N.A.I.C.S.: 335910
Sukthae Ruangwattanachot (COO)

Subsidiaries:

Yuasa Sales & Distribution Co., Ltd. (1)
164 Moo 5 Soi Thedsaban 55 Sukhumvit Road, Tambol Taibanmai, Amphur Muang, 10280, Samut Prakan, Thailand
Tel.: (66) 27697300
Automobile & Motorcycle Battery Distr
N.A.I.C.S.: 441330

YUASA FUNASHOKU CO., LTD.
4186 Miyamoto, Funabashi, Chiba, Japan
Tel.: (81) 474331211
Web Site: https://www.yuasa-funashoku.com
Year Founded: 1937
8006—(TKS)
Rev.: $790,423,800
Assets: $425,730,270
Liabilities: $173,505,890
Net Worth: $252,224,380
Earnings: $17,893,270
Emp.: 225
Fiscal Year-end: 03/31/24
Food Product Whslr
N.A.I.C.S.: 424690

YUASA TRADING CO., LTD.
7 Kanda-Mitoshirocho, Chiyoda-ku, Tokyo, 101-8580, Japan
Tel.: (81) 363691111
Web Site: https://www.yuasa.co.jp
Year Founded: 1666
8074—(TKS)
Rev.: $3,480,621,090
Assets: $1,923,437,290
Liabilities: $1,246,513,800
Net Worth: $676,923,490

AND PRIVATE COMPANIES

Earnings: $78,077,320
Emp.: 2,621
Fiscal Year-end: 03/31/24
Industrial Machinery & Equipment Whslr
N.A.I.C.S.: 423830
Etsuro Sato *(Chm)*

Subsidiaries:

CAC Knowledge Co., Ltd. (1)
4-1 Nihombashiyokoyamacho Nisshinyokoyamacho Building 4f, Chuo-ku, Tokyo, 103-0003, Japan (51%)
Tel.: (81) 358477561
Business Process Outsourcing Services
N.A.I.C.S.: 561499

CHUBU IBI CO., LTD. (1)
5-139-1 Horinouchi, Komaki, 485-0046, Aichi, Japan
Tel.: (81) 568746778
Construction Materials Distr
N.A.I.C.S.: 423320

FUSHIMAN SHOJI CO., LTD. (1)
5-1 Kita 8-jo Nishi, Kita-ku, Sapporo, 060-0808, Hokkaido, Japan
Tel.: (81) 117167101
Web Site: https://fs-net.co.jp
Emp.: 24
Industrial Machine Tool Distr
N.A.I.C.S.: 423830

Fuji Quality House Co., Ltd. (1)
1 Nishidamachi, Isesaki, 372-0058, Gunma, Japan
Tel.: (81) 27 026 5121
Web Site: https://www.fhc-house.co.jp
Container House Mfr & Distr
N.A.I.C.S.: 321991

HANAZONO TOOLS MFG. CO., LTD. (1)
5-12-38 Kano, Higashiosaka, 578-0901, Japan
Tel.: (81) 72 871 9901
Web Site: http://www.hanazonotool.co.jp
Emp.: 40
Industrial Machine Tool Mfr & Distr
N.A.I.C.S.: 333515
Saitou Akira *(Pres)*

KOKKO (HONG KONG) CO., LTD. (1)
RM1412 14F SHE KOU Building Shekou Xinjie, Shekou Nanshan Zone, Shenzhen, China
Tel.: (86) 755 2683 4987
Industrial Machine Tool Distr
N.A.I.C.S.: 423830

KOKKO (SHENZHEN) TRADING CO., LTD. (1)
RM1411 14F SHE KOU Building Shekou Xinjie, Shekou Nanshan Zone, Shenzhen, China
Tel.: (86) 755 2689 3008
Industrial Machine Tool Distr
N.A.I.C.S.: 423830

KOKKO CO., LTD. (1)
4600 Nakasu, Suwa, 392-8505, Nagano, Japan
Tel.: (81) 266522457
Emp.: 188
Industrial Machine Tool Distr
N.A.I.C.S.: 423830

MARUBOSHI CO., LTD. (1)
2-3-20 Tachiuribori, Nishi-ku, Osaka, 550-0012, Japan
Tel.: (81) 665321614
Emp.: 46
Industrial Valve Distr
N.A.I.C.S.: 423830

Maruken Service Co., Ltd. (1)
7-14 Taiheitori, Nakagawa-Ku, Nagoya, 454-0838, Aichi, Japan
Tel.: (81) 52 354 3151
Web Site: https://www.maruken-gr.co.jp
Industrial Machinery & Equipment Whslr
N.A.I.C.S.: 423830

Nakagawa Kinzoku Co., Ltd. (1)
1-32 Kanda Sudacho, Chiyoda-ku, Tokyo, 101-0041, Japan
Tel.: (81) 33 785 7001
Web Site: https://www.nakagawametal.co.jp

Machine Tool Distr
N.A.I.C.S.: 423830

PT. YUASA SHOJI INDONESIA (1)
Ruko Robson Square Blok A No 19-20 JL MH Thamrin-Lippo Cikarang Cibatu, Cikarang Selatan, Bekasi, 17530, Indonesia
Tel.: (62) 2189904007
Web Site: http://www.yuasatrading.co.id
Industrial Machine Tool Distr
N.A.I.C.S.: 423830

SANEI CO., LTD. (1)
4th floor Miyake Building 549-2 Shinanomachi, Totsuka-ku, Yokohama, 244-0801, Kanagawa, Japan
Tel.: (81) 458283601
Web Site: https://kk-sanei.com
Emp.: 35
Industrial Machine Tool Distr
N.A.I.C.S.: 423830

Y.S. ENGINEERING LTD. (1)
3-5-28 Kurumao, MianmiSenba Chou-ku, Yonago, 683-0006, Tottori, Japan
Tel.: (81) 859224030
Web Site: https://ysyonago.co.jp
Building Construction Services
N.A.I.C.S.: 236220

YOUR TECHNICA CO., LTD (1)
7 Kanda-Mitoshirocho, Chiyoda-ku, Tokyo, 101-8580, Japan
Tel.: (81) 363691633
Industrial Machine Tool Distr
N.A.I.C.S.: 423830

YUASA MACROS CO., LTD. (1)
1047 Kamazuka, Konosu, 369-0112, Saitama, Japan
Tel.: (81) 485988712
Web Site: https://yuasamacros.co.jp
Building Construction Services
N.A.I.C.S.: 236220

YUASA MECHATRONICS (M) SDN. BHD. (1)
No 31 Jalan Kartunis U1/47, Temasya Industrial Park Section U1 Glenmarie, 40150, Shah Alam, Selangor Darul Ehsan, Malaysia
Tel.: (60) 376280899
Web Site: https://www.yuasa.com.my
Emp.: 13
Industrial Machine Tool Distr
N.A.I.C.S.: 423830

YUASA NENRYO CO., LTD (1)
2-171 Takayashiro, Meito-ku, Nagoya, 465-8503, Aichi, Japan
Tel.: (81) 527798460
Automotive Repair Services
N.A.I.C.S.: 811114

YUASA PRIMUS CO., LTD. (1)
9-8 Nihonbashi Tomizawa-cho Tomizawacho Green Building 2F, Chuo-ku, Tokyo, 103-0006, Japan
Tel.: (81) 356951501
Web Site: https://www.yuasa-p.co.jp
Industrial Machine Tool Distr
N.A.I.C.S.: 423830

YUASA TRADING (SHANGHAI) CO., LTD. (1)
No 211 Fute North Road, Free Trade Pilot Zone, Shanghai, 200131, China
Tel.: (86) 2162375477
Web Site: https://www.yuasa.cn
Industrial Machine Tool Distr
N.A.I.C.S.: 423830

YUASA TRADING (TAIWAN) CO., LTD. (1)
Room 1103 11F No 18 Sec 1 Chang' An E Rd, Zhongshan Dist, Taipei, 10442, Taiwan
Tel.: (886) 225622680
Industrial Machine Tool Distr
N.A.I.C.S.: 423830

YUASA TRADING (THAILAND) CO., LTD. (1)
No 33/71-72 33/76 Wall Street Tower Building 15th Floor, Surawongse Road Kwaeng Suriyawongse Khet Bangrak, Bangkok, 10500, Thailand
Tel.: (66) 22670727
Web Site: https://www.yuasa.co.th
Industrial Machine Tool Distr
N.A.I.C.S.: 423830

YUASA TRADING DEUTSCHLAND GmbH (1)
Im Neugrund 14, 64521, Gross-Gerau, Germany
Tel.: (49) 615297780
Web Site: https://www.morookaeurope.com
Industrial Machine Tool Distr
N.A.I.C.S.: 423830

YUASA TRADING INDIA PRIVATE LIMITED (1)
Time Tower Unit 403 Mehrauli-Gurgaon Road, Gurgaon, 122002, Haryana, India
Tel.: (91) 1244265460
Industrial Machine Tool Distr
N.A.I.C.S.: 423830

YUASA TRADING VIETNAM CO., LTD. (1)
No 60 Street B4 Sala Urban Area, An Loi Dong Ward District 2, Ho Chi Minh City, Vietnam
Tel.: (84) 2839251237
Industrial Machine Tool Distr
N.A.I.C.S.: 423830

YUASA-YI, INC. (1)
1320 Landmeier Rd, Elk Grove Village, IL 60007
Tel.: (847) 981-0737
Industrial Machinery & Equipment Mfr
N.A.I.C.S.: 333998

Yuasa Business Support Co., Ltd. (1)
7 Kanda-Mitoshirocho, Chiyoda-ku, Tokyo, 101-8580, Japan
Tel.: (81) 36 369 1688
Industrial Machinery & Equipment Whslr
N.A.I.C.S.: 423830

Yuasa Construction Equipment Sdn. Bhd. (1)
No 31 Jalan Kartunis U1/47 Temasya Industrial Park, Section U1 Glenmarie, 40150, Shah Alam, Selangor, Malaysia
Tel.: (60) 35 567 0343
Industrial Machinery & Equipment Whslr
N.A.I.C.S.: 423830

Yuasa Engineering Solution (Thailand) Co., Ltd. (1)
23/14 Sorachai Bldg 12Th Floor Sukhumvit 63 Road Klongton-Nua, Wattana, Bangkok, 10110, Thailand
Industrial Machinery & Equipment Whslr
N.A.I.C.S.: 423830

Yuasa Lumber Co., Ltd. (1)
Op Building 3Rd Floor 1-8, Kanda-Nishiki-Cho Chiyoda-ku, Tokyo, 101-0054, Japan
Tel.: (81) 36 369 1391
Industrial Machinery & Equipment Whslr
N.A.I.C.S.: 423830

Yuasa Quobis Co., Ltd. (1)
1-8 Kanda Nishikicho OP Building 2F, Chiyoda-ku, Tokyo, 101-0054, Japan
Tel.: (81) 36 369 1403
Web Site: https://www.yuasaquobis.co.jp
Building Materials Distr
N.A.I.C.S.: 444180

Yuasa Shoji Mexico S.A. De C.V. (1)
Avenida De Los Industriales 522 Local 3 Industrial Julian De Obregon, 37290, Leon, Guanajuato, Mexico
Tel.: (52) 4777618918
Industrial Machine Tool Distr
N.A.I.C.S.: 423830

Yuasa System Solutions Co., Ltd. (1)
24-1-1 Nihonbashi Hakozakicho Nihonbashi Hakozaki Building 7F, Chuo-ku, Tokyo, 103-0015, Japan
Tel.: (81) 35 847 7561
Web Site: https://www.yuasa-sol.co.jp
Building Materials Distr
N.A.I.C.S.: 444180

Yuasa Technical Engineering Co., Ltd. (1)
MD-Kanda Building 5th Floor 9-1, Kanda-Mitoshiro-Cho Chiyoda-ku, Tokyo, 101-0053, Japan
Tel.: (81) 363691740
Web Site: http://www.yuasa-techno.com
Emp.: 57
Industrial Machinery & Equipment Distr

N.A.I.C.S.: 423830

Yuasa Trading (Philippines) Inc. (1)
11th Floor 6788 Ayala Ave Oledan Square, Makati, 1226, Philippines
Tel.: (63) 28845203637
Emp.: 13
Industrial Machine Tool Distr
N.A.I.C.S.: 423830
Masayuki Sanjo *(Pres)*

YUBICO AB

Kungsgatan 44, 111 35, Stockholm, Sweden
Tel.: (46) 84113000 SE
Web Site: https://www.yubico.com
Year Founded: 2007
YUBICO—(OMX)
Rev.: $1,349,460
Assets: $315,938,880
Liabilities: $238,680
Net Worth: $315,700,200
Earnings: ($73,440)
Fiscal Year-end: 12/31/22
Cybersecurity Company
N.A.I.C.S.: 516210
Caroline Af Ugglas *(Deputy Chm)*

YUCHENG TECHNOLOGIES LIMITED

Beijing Global Trade Center Tower D Floor 9 36 North Third Ring Road E, Dongcheng, Beijing, 100013, China
Tel.: (86) 10 5913 7700
Web Site:
    http://www.yuchengtech.com
Year Founded: 2005
Sales Range: $75-99.9 Million
Emp.: 2,646
Software Solutions & Services
N.A.I.C.S.: 541511
Weidong Hong *(Chm & CEO)*

YUCHENGCO GROUP OF COMPANIES

3/F Y Tower II Leviste Cor Gallardo Sts, Salcedo Village, Makati, Philippines
Tel.: (63) 856145758
Web Site: http://ygc.com
Year Founded: 1930
Holding Company
N.A.I.C.S.: 551112
Alfonso T. Yuchengco *(Chm)*

Subsidiaries:

House of Investments Inc. (1)
9F Grepalife Building 221 Sen Gil J Puyat Avenue, Makati, 1200, Philippines
Tel.: (63) 28159636
Web Site: https://www.hoi.com.ph
Rev.: $200,310,761
Assets: $2,888,226,612
Liabilities: $1,981,580,057
Net Worth: $906,646,555
Earnings: $18,812,170
Emp.: 4,322
Fiscal Year-end: 12/31/2023
Holding Company; Investment Services
N.A.I.C.S.: 551112
Helen Yuchengco Dee *(Chm)*

Subsidiary (Domestic):

Ipeople Inc. (2)
3rd Floor Grepalife Building, 219 Sen Gil Puyat Ave, Makati, Philippines
Tel.: (63) 82533637
Web Site: https://www.ipeople.com.ph
Rev.: $81,094,628
Assets: $360,464,148
Liabilities: $88,106,508
Net Worth: $272,357,639
Earnings: $11,952,893
Emp.: 1,848
Fiscal Year-end: 12/31/2023
Education Services
N.A.I.C.S.: 611710
Renato C. Valencia *(Chm)*

Malayan Insurance Company, Inc. (1)

YUCHENGCO GROUP OF COMPANIES

Yuchengco Group of Companies—(Continued)
4th Floor Y Tower I 484 Quintin Paredes St,
Binondo, Manila, Philippines
Tel.: (63) 22431033
Web Site: http://www.malayan.com
Non-Life Insurance Products & Services
N.A.I.C.S.: 524126
Alfonso T. Yuchengco *(Owner)*

RCBC Bankard Services Corporation (1)
30/F Robinson-Equitable Tower cor ADB
Ave and Poveda St, Ortigas Center, Pasig,
Philippines
Tel.: (63) 2 688 1888
Web Site: http://www.rcbcbankard.com
Credit Card Issuing Services
N.A.I.C.S.: 522210
Angela C. Mirasol *(Head-Mktg)*

Rizal Commercial Banking Corporation (1)
Yuchengco Tower RCBC Plaza, 6819 Ayala
Avenue, Makati, 0727, Philippines
Tel.: (63) 28949000
Web Site: http://www.rcbc.com
Sales Range: $200-249.9 Million
Emp.: 3,301
Bank Holding Company
N.A.I.C.S.: 551111
Helen Yuchengco Dee *(Chm)*

Subsidiary (Domestic):

Merchants Savings & Loan Association, Inc. (2)
117 Tordesillas Street Salcedo Village,
Makati, Philippines
Tel.: (63) 817 1657
Commercial Banking Services
N.A.I.C.S.: 522110

RCBC Forex Brokers Corporation (2)
8th Fl Yuchengco Twr Rcbc Plz, 6819 Ayala
Ave, Makati, 727, Philippines (100%)
Tel.: (63) 28949012
Emp.: 15
Foreign Exchange Currencies Dealing Services
N.A.I.C.S.: 523160
Samuel V. Torres *(Sec)*

RCBC Leasing and Finance Corporation (2)
2/F Grepalife Bldg 221 Sen Gil Puyat Ave,
Makati, Philippines
Tel.: (63) 2 810 9660
Financial Lending Services
N.A.I.C.S.: 533110

Subsidiary (US):

RCBC North America, Inc. (2)
39 Saint Francis Sq, Daly City, CA
94015 (100%)
Tel.: (650) 757-0500
Web Site: http://www.rcbcremit.com
Emp.: 2
Commericial Banking
N.A.I.C.S.: 522110

Subsidiary (Domestic):

RCBC Savings Bank, Inc. (2)
26th & 25th Streets, Bonifacio Global City,
Taguig, 1634, Philippines
Tel.: (63) 2 555 8700
Web Site: http://www.rcbcsavings.com
Commercial Banking Services
N.A.I.C.S.: 522110
Helen Y. Dee *(Chm)*

RCBC Securities, Inc. (2)
7th Fl Yuchengco Twr Rcbc Plz 6819 Ayala
Ave, Makati, Philippines (100%)
Tel.: (63) 28949000
Web Site: http://www.rcbc.com
Emp.: 25
Investment Banking & Securities Dealing Services
N.A.I.C.S.: 523150

Subsidiary (Non-US):

RCBC Telemoney Europe, SpA (2)
Via Principe Amedeo 7/b-c, 00187, Rome,
Italy (100%)
Tel.: (39) 064823616

Web Site: http://www.rcbc.com
Emp.: 6
Commericial Banking
N.A.I.C.S.: 522110

Subsidiary (Domestic):

RCBC-JPL Holding Company, Inc. (2)
2/F Pres Laurel Building Laurel Highway,
Tanauan, 4232, Batangas, Philippines
Tel.: (63) 43 778 4444
Holding Company
N.A.I.C.S.: 551111
Alfredo S. Del Rosario Jr. *(Exec VP)*

Sun Life Grepa Financial, Inc. (1)
21 Sen Gil Puyat Avenue, Makati, Philippines
Tel.: (63) 28161726
Web Site: http://www.sunlifegrepa.com
Sales Range: $25-49.9 Million
Life Insurance & Other Insurance Products & Services
N.A.I.C.S.: 524113

Subsidiary (Domestic):

Great Life Financial Assurance Corporation (2)
21/F Tower 2 RCBC Plz, 6819 Ayala Ave,
Makati, 1200, Philippines (80%)
Tel.: (63) 27532151
Web Site: http://grepalife.node27.com
Emp.: 200
Life, Health, Property & Casualty Insurance Products & Services
N.A.I.C.S.: 524113

Grepalife Asset Management Corporation (2)
6/F GREPALIFE Bldg 221 Sen Gil Puyat
Avenue, Makati, Philippines (100%)
Tel.: (63) 28456408
Web Site: http://www.grepafunds.com
Emp.: 8
Asset & Fund Management Services
N.A.I.C.S.: 523940

YUDIZ SOLUTIONS LIMITED
13th Floor Bsquare 2 Iscon-Ambli
Road, Ahmedabad, 380054, Gujarat,
India
Tel.: (91) 7433977525
Web Site: https://www.yudiz.com
Year Founded: 2011
YUDIZ—(NSE)
Rev.: $2,287,977
Assets: $1,165,633
Liabilities: $352,081
Net Worth: $813,553
Earnings: $90,081
Emp.: 430
Fiscal Year-end: 03/31/22
Pharmaceuticals Product Mfr
N.A.I.C.S.: 325412
Bharat Patel *(Chm)*

YUE DA INTERNATIONAL HOLDINGS LIMITED
Room 3321-3325 33rd Floor China
Merchants Tower Shun Tak Centre,
200 Connaught Road Central,
Sheung Wan, China (Hong Kong)
Tel.: (852) 28389903
Web Site: http://www.yueda.com.hk
0629—(HKG)
Rev.: $14,407,567
Assets: $127,079,129
Liabilities: $67,352,688
Net Worth: $59,726,441
Earnings: $4,288,237
Emp.: 23
Fiscal Year-end: 12/31/22
Mineral Mining Services
N.A.I.C.S.: 213115
Lian Chun Wang *(Chm)*

YUE KAN HOLDINGS LIMITED
Room 2901-2902 29/F Saxon Tower
7 Cheung Shun Street, Cheung Sha
Wan, Kowloon, China (Hong Kong)
Tel.: (852) 29888451

Web Site:
http://www.yuekanholdings.com
Year Founded: 2010
2110—(HKG)
Holding Company
N.A.I.C.S.: 551112
Che Kan Heung *(Chm)*

YUE XIU ENTERPRISES (HOLDINGS) LIMITED
160-174 Lockhart Road, Wanchai
26th Floor, Hong Kong, China (Hong Kong)
Tel.: (852) 25116671
Web Site: http://www.yuexiu.com
Sales Range: $15-24.9 Billion
Investment Holding Company
N.A.I.C.S.: 551112
Zhaoxing Zhang *(Chm)*

Subsidiaries:

Chong Hing Bank Limited (1)
Chong Hing Bank Centre Ground Floor, 24
Des Voeux Road, Central, China (Hong Kong) (74.97%)
Tel.: (852) 37681111
Web Site: http://www.chbank.com
Rev.: $944,106,900
Assets: $35,797,749,788
Liabilities: $31,215,063,825
Net Worth: $4,582,685,963
Earnings: $145,756,725
Emp.: 1,700
Fiscal Year-end: 12/31/2022
Banking Services
N.A.I.C.S.: 522110
Wai Man Lau *(Deputy CEO)*

Subsidiary (Domestic):

Chong Hing Information Technology Limited (2)
1/F Fung Yip Bldg 347 Des Voeux Rd W,
Sai Ying Pun, Hong Kong, China (Hong Kong) (100%)
Tel.: (852) 37688300
Sales Range: $50-74.9 Million
Emp.: 30
Electronic Data Processing Services
N.A.I.C.S.: 518210
Jimmy Lai *(Head-Dept)*

Chong Hing Securities Limited (2)
3/F Chong Hing Bank Centre 24 Des Voeux
Road, Central, China (Hong Kong) (100%)
Tel.: (852) 37689888
Securities Brokerage Services
N.A.I.C.S.: 523150

Chong Hing Commodities & Futures Limited (1)
2/F Chong Hing Bank Center 24 Des Voeux
Rd, Central, China (Hong Kong)
Tel.: (852) 37689988
Web Site: http://www.chcf.com.hk
Financial Management Services
N.A.I.C.S.: 551112

Chong Hing Insurance Company Limited (1)
5th Floor Chong Hing Bank Centre 24 Des
Voeux Road, Central, China (Hong Kong)
Tel.: (852) 37689200
Financial Management Services
N.A.I.C.S.: 551112

Gallbraith Limited (1)
Room 1612 Zhongrong Plaza 1088 Pudong
Nan Road, Shanghai, 200122, China
Tel.: (86) 2168880845
Web Site: http://www.galbraiths.co.uk
Financial Management Services
N.A.I.C.S.: 551112

Greater Lucky (H.K.) Co., Ltd. (1)
Shing Mun Tunnels Administration Building,
Tsuen Wan, New Territories, China (Hong Kong)
Tel.: (852) 27728629
Financial Management Services
N.A.I.C.S.: 551112

Yue Xiu Securities Company Limited (1)
24/F Siu On Centre 188 Lockhart Road,
Wanchai, China (Hong Kong)

INTERNATIONAL PUBLIC

Tel.: (852) 39259928
Web Site: http://www.yxsh.hk
Financial Management Services
N.A.I.C.S.: 551112

Yuexiu Financial Holdings Limited (1)
28/F Yue Xiu Bldg, Wanchai, China (Hong Kong)
Tel.: (852) 25116671
Web Site: http://www.yuexiu.com
Financial Management Services
N.A.I.C.S.: 551112

YUE YUEN INDUSTRIAL HOLDINGS LIMITED
22/F C-Bons International Center 108
Wai Yip Street, Kwun Tong, Kowloon,
China (Hong Kong)
Tel.: (852) 23705111
Web Site: http://www.yueyuen.com
0551—(HKG)
Rev.: $8,970,228,000
Assets: $7,935,421,000
Liabilities: $3,293,096,000
Net Worth: $4,642,325,000
Earnings: $293,201,000
Emp.: 310,000
Fiscal Year-end: 12/31/22
Athletic & Casual Footwear Mfr
N.A.I.C.S.: 339920
Chin Lu *(Chm)*

Subsidiaries:

Prime Asia Leather Corporation (1)
19F-8 No 213 Chaofu Rd, Xitun Dist, Taichung, 407, Taiwan
Tel.: (886) 42 252 8568
Web Site: https://www.primeasialeather.com
Leather Product Mfr
N.A.I.C.S.: 316990

Solar Link International Inc (1)
4602 E Brickell St, Ontario, CA 91761
Tel.: (909) 605-7789
Leather Shoes Mfr
N.A.I.C.S.: 316990

Yue Yuen Industrial Limited (1)
22/F C-BONS International Center 108 Wai
Yip Street, Kwun Tong, Kowloon, China
(Hong Kong)
Tel.: (852) 23705111
Web Site: https://www.yueyuen.com
Emp.: 70
Leather Product Mfr
N.A.I.C.S.: 316990

YUEN CHANG STAINLESS STEEL CO., LTD.
13F No 235 Zhongzheng 4th Rd
Qianjin Dist, Kaohsiung, Taiwan
Tel.: (886) 79695858
Web Site:
https://www.yuenchang.com.tw
Year Founded: 1987
2069—(TAI)
Rev.: $387,123,567
Assets: $283,830,167
Liabilities: $160,284,895
Net Worth: $123,545,272
Earnings: ($4,877,497)
Fiscal Year-end: 12/31/23
Stainless Steel Products Mfr
N.A.I.C.S.: 331513
Te-Ho Yen *(Chm)*

Subsidiaries:

Ningbo Qiyi Precision Metals Co., Ltd. (1)
182 Xinmei Road, Ningbo National Hi-Tech
Industrial Development Zone, Ningbo, Zhejiang, China
Tel.: (86) 57488365168
Web Site: http://www.qiyi.com.cn
Stainless Steel Mfr
N.A.I.C.S.: 331110

YUES INTERNATIONAL HOLDINGS GROUP LIMITED
1301-1302 unit 13/F Citic Plaza No

233 North Tianhe Road, Guangzhou, China
Tel.: (86) 4001880380 Ky
Web Site: http://www.goalrise-china.com
Year Founded: 1996
1529—(HKG)
Rev.: $25,199,413
Assets: $25,160,663
Liabilities: $4,941,940
Net Worth: $20,218,723
Earnings: ($23,868)
Emp.: 678
Fiscal Year-end: 12/31/22
Logistics Management Services
N.A.I.C.S.: 541614
Jianxin Li *(Chm)*

YUEXIU PROPERTY COMPANY LIMITED

26/F Yue Xiu Building 160 Lockhart Road, Wanchai, China (Hong Kong)
Tel.: (852) 25932326
Web Site:
   http://www.yuexiuproperty.com
0123—(HKG)
Rev.: $10,252,407,249
Assets: $51,270,812,683
Liabilities: $38,208,486,971
Net Worth: $13,062,325,712
Earnings: $584,693,215
Emp.: 19,300
Fiscal Year-end: 12/31/23
Financial Investment Services
N.A.I.C.S.: 523999
Feng Li *(Chief Capital Officer-Guangzhou)*

Subsidiaries:

Yue Xiu APT Parking Limited (1)
27/F Seabright Plaza 9-23 Shell Street, North Point, China (Hong Kong)
Tel.: (852) 25129611
Web Site:
   http://www.yuexiuaptparking.com.hk
Car Park Management Services
N.A.I.C.S.: 812930

YUEXIU REAL ESTATE INVESTMENT TRUST

24/F Yue Xiu Building 160 Lockhart Rd, Wanchai, China (Hong Kong)
Tel.: (852) 85228283692
0405—(HKG)
Rev.: $262,949,544
Assets: $6,158,847,053
Liabilities: $5,987,946,276
Net Worth: $170,900,777
Earnings: $80,857,062
Emp.: 672
Fiscal Year-end: 12/31/22
Real Estate Investment Trust Services
N.A.I.C.S.: 531190
Deliang Lin *(CEO)*

YUEXIU SERVICES GROUP LIMITED

26/F Yue Xiu Building 160 Lockhart Road, Wanchai, China (Hong Kong)
Tel.: (852) 4008300123 HK
Web Site: https://www.yuexiu.com
Year Founded: 1992
6626—(HKG)
Rev.: $380,911,468
Assets: $911,269,486
Liabilities: $391,699,750
Net Worth: $519,569,735
Earnings: $65,025,082
Emp.: 12,558
Fiscal Year-end: 12/31/22
Property Management Services
N.A.I.C.S.: 531311
Dongpeng Chen *(CFO)*

YUEXIU TRANSPORT INFRASTRUCTURE LIMITED

17A Yue Xiu Building 160 Lockhart Road, Wanchai, China (Hong Kong)
Tel.: (852) 28652205
Web Site:
   https://www.yuexiutransport.com
1052—(HKG)
Rev.: $461,764,789
Assets: $5,101,772,364
Liabilities: $3,103,181,874
Net Worth: $1,998,590,490
Earnings: $103,588,664
Emp.: 2,164
Fiscal Year-end: 12/31/22
Expressways & Bridges Management Services
N.A.I.C.S.: 237310
Baiqing He *(Deputy Chm & Gen Mgr)*

YUEYANG FOREST & PAPER CO., LTD.

Guangming Road Chenglingji, Yueyanglou District, Yueyang, 414028, Hunan, China
Tel.: (86) 7308590683
Web Site: http://www.yypaper.com
Year Founded: 2000
600963—(SHG)
Rev.: $1,373,321,659
Assets: $2,333,548,807
Liabilities: $1,036,118,543
Net Worth: $1,297,430,265
Earnings: $86,424,708
Fiscal Year-end: 12/31/22
Paper Pulp & Paper Product Mfr & Whslr
N.A.I.C.S.: 322110
Ye Meng *(Chm)*

YUEYANG XINGCHANG PETRO-CHEMICAL CO., LTD.

Yueyang Xingchang Building Yueyang Avenue, Yueyang, 414000, Hunan, China
Tel.: (86) 7308829751
Web Site: https://www.yyxc0819.com
Year Founded: 1990
000819—(SSE)
Rev.: $452,357,652
Assets: $194,698,324
Liabilities: $43,174,895
Net Worth: $151,523,429
Earnings: $11,228,125
Emp.: 684
Fiscal Year-end: 12/31/22
Petroleum Product Mfr
N.A.I.C.S.: 325110
Wang Miaoyun *(Chm)*

YUFO ELECTRONICS CO., LTD.

24F No 101 Xinpu 6th Street, Taoyuan Dist, Taoyuan, 330, Taiwan
Tel.: (886) 33460289
Web Site: https://www.yufo.com.tw
Year Founded: 1983
6194—(TPE)
Rev.: $38,092,893
Assets: $63,356,502
Liabilities: $10,575,181
Net Worth: $52,781,321
Earnings: $214,489
Fiscal Year-end: 12/31/22
Electronic Components Mfr
N.A.I.C.S.: 334419
Yung-Kan Liu *(Chm & Pres)*

YUG DECOR LIMITED

709-714 Sakar-V B/h Old Natraj Cinema Ashram Road, Ahmedabad, 380 009, Gujarat, India
Tel.: (91) 7926580920
Web Site: https://www.yugdecor.com
Year Founded: 2003
540550—(BOM)
Rev.: $2,178,425
Assets: $1,802,514

Liabilities: $955,722
Net Worth: $846,792
Earnings: $16,261
Emp.: 64
Fiscal Year-end: 03/31/21
Chemical Product Mfr & Distr
N.A.I.C.S.: 325520
Chandresh Santosh Kumar Saraswat *(Chm & Mng Dir)*

YUGOSLAVIA COMMERCE A.D.

ul Sarajevska broj 25-31, Belgrade, Serbia
Tel.: (381) 11 2688 986
Web Site:
   http://www.yugoslaviacommerce.rs
Year Founded: 1952
Sales Range: Less than $1 Million
Emp.: 5
Apparel & Footwear Whslr
N.A.I.C.S.: 424310

YUHAN CORPORATION

74 Noryangjin-ro, Dongjak-gu, Seoul, Korea (South)
Tel.: (82) 28280181
Web Site: https://www.yuhan.co.kr
Year Founded: 1926
000100—(KRS)
Rev.: $1,362,074,605
Assets: $1,896,582,431
Liabilities: $356,594,946
Net Worth: $1,539,987,485
Earnings: $69,484,468
Emp.: 1,934
Fiscal Year-end: 12/31/22
Biological Product Mfr
N.A.I.C.S.: 325412

Subsidiaries:

AddPharma Inc. (1)
25 Tapsil-ro 35beon-gil, Giheung-gu, Yongin, Gyeonggi, Korea (South)
Tel.: (82) 318915000
Web Site: https://www.addpharma.co.kr
Pharmaceutical Preparation Mfr
N.A.I.C.S.: 325412
Yongtaek Lee *(CEO)*

Yuhan ANZ Pty Ltd. (1)
Level 7 33 King William St, Adelaide, 5000, SA, Australia
Tel.: (61) 883100021
Web Site: https://yuhan-anz.com
Pharmaceutical Preparation Mfr
N.A.I.C.S.: 325412

Yuhan Chemical, Inc. (1)
45 Jiwon-ro, Danwon-gu, Ansan, 15619, Gyeonggi-do, Korea (South)
Tel.: (82) 314885800
Web Site: https://eng.yuhanchem.co.kr
Emp.: 320
Pharmaceuticals Product Mfr
N.A.I.C.S.: 325412
Sang-Hun Seo *(Pres & CEO)*

Yuhan Corporation - Synthetic Plant (1)
45 Jiwon-ro, Danwon-gu, Ansan, Gyeonggi-do, Korea (South)
Tel.: (82) 31 488 5800
Pharmaceuticals Product Mfr
N.A.I.C.S.: 325412

Yuhan Medica Corporation (1)
807-1 Yangcheong-Ri, Ochang-Myeon, Cheongwon, Chungcheong, Korea (South)
Tel.: (82) 43 215 9435
Web Site: http://www.yuhanmedica.co.kr
Pharmaceuticals Product Mfr
N.A.I.C.S.: 325412

Yuhan USA Corporation (1)
9171 Towne Centre Dr Ste 215, San Diego, CA 92122
Tel.: (619) 354-1628
Web Site: https://www.yuhan-usa.com
Pharmaceutical Preparation Mfr
N.A.I.C.S.: 325412

YUHE INTERNATIONAL, INC.

301 Hailong Street, Hanting District, Weifang, Shandong, China
Tel.: (86) 5367363688 NV
Web Site: http://www.yuhepoultry.com
Sales Range: $50-74.9 Million
Emp.: 1,279
Chicken Processor & Supplier
N.A.I.C.S.: 112320
Serena Wu *(Mgr-Internal IR)*

YUHUAN CNC MACHINE TOOL CO., LTD.

No 9 Yongyang Road Liuyang Manufacturing Industrial Base, Changsha, 410323, Hunan, China
Tel.: (86) 73183201588
Web Site: https://www.yh-cn.com
Year Founded: 2004
002903—(SSE)
Rev.: $50,237,816
Assets: $139,907,800
Liabilities: $31,677,736
Net Worth: $108,230,064
Earnings: $7,780,673
Fiscal Year-end: 12/31/22
Automation Equipment Mfr & Distr
N.A.I.C.S.: 333517
Xu Shixiong *(Chm)*

YUHWA SECURITIES CO., LTD.

Yu Hwa Securities Bldg 36 Gukjegeumyung-ro 2-gil, Yeongdeungpo-gu, Seoul, Korea (South)
Tel.: (82) 237700100
Web Site: https://www.yhs.co.kr
Year Founded: 1962
003460—(KRS)
Rev.: $9,586,351
Assets: $544,574,784
Liabilities: $150,856,547
Net Worth: $393,718,237
Earnings: $3,315,351
Fiscal Year-end: 12/31/22
Security Brokerage Services
N.A.I.C.S.: 523150
Dongsun Woo *(Mgr)*

YUIL ROBOTICS CO., LTD.

37-45 Namdongseo-ro 362beon-gil, Namdong-gu, Incheon, Korea (South)
Tel.: (82) 328639810
Web Site:
   https://www.yuilrobotics.com
Year Founded: 2010
388720—(KRS)
Rev.: $29,487,350
Assets: $41,880,961
Liabilities: $11,286,800
Net Worth: $30,594,161
Earnings: ($1,773,562)
Emp.: 89
Fiscal Year-end: 12/31/22
Industrial Machinery Mfr
N.A.I.C.S.: 333310

YUJIN CO., LTD.

235-1 Chungjin-dong, Jongno-gu, Seoul, Korea (South)
Tel.: (82) 2 3704 5445
Web Site: http://www.eugenes.co.kr
Year Founded: 1969
Cement & Construction Material Mfr
N.A.I.C.S.: 327310
Dae-Ki Kim *(Vice Chm)*

Subsidiaries:

Donghwa Corporation (1)
11th Fl Korea Bldg 2-3 Sinan-dong, Buk-gu, Kwangju, Korea (South)
Tel.: (82) 62 519 1459
Cement Mfr
N.A.I.C.S.: 327310

YUJIN ROBOT CO., LTD.

YUJIN ROBOT CO., LTD.

Yujin Robot Co., Ltd.—(Continued)
33 Harmony-ro 187 beon-gil, Yeonsu-gu, Incheon, Korea (South)
Tel.: (82) 325502300
Web Site: https://www.yujinrobot.com
Year Founded: 1988
056080—(KRS)
Rev: $38,065,339
Assets: $46,920,674
Liabilities: $13,117,814
Net Worth: $33,802,860
Earnings: $3,740,726
Emp.: 143
Fiscal Year-end: 12/31/22
Robot Mfr
N.A.I.C.S.: 333998
Soon Park (Mgr)

YUK WING GROUP HOLDINGS LIMITED

Unit B 13/F Eton Building 288 Des Voeux Road, Central, China (Hong Kong)
Web Site: http://www.yukwing.com
Year Founded: 1997
1536—(HKG)
Rev.: $18,282,657
Assets: $30,026,028
Liabilities: $5,996,409
Net Worth: $24,029,619
Earnings: ($190,246)
Emp.: 80
Fiscal Year-end: 03/31/22
Industrial Equipment Mfr & Distr
N.A.I.C.S.: 333120
Yee Man Choi (Sec)

Subsidiaries:

MAXA RockDrills Limited (1)
Flat 1502 Honour Industrial Center 6 Sun Yip St, Chai Wan, China (Hong Kong)
Tel.: (852) 28894884
Web Site: http://dthmaxa.com
Construction Machinery Mfr
N.A.I.C.S.: 333120

YUKEN INDIA LTD.

16C Doddanekundi Industrial Area, Mahadevapura, Bengaluru, 560 048, India
Tel.: (91) 8041163217
Web Site: https://www.yukenindia.com
Year Founded: 1976
522108—(BOM)
Rev.: $30,503,669
Assets: $61,455,931
Liabilities: $37,154,304
Net Worth: $24,301,627
Earnings: $707,903
Emp.: 317
Fiscal Year-end: 03/31/21
Oil Hydraulic Equipment Mfr
N.A.I.C.S.: 333132
Rangachar Padmanabhan Cattan Coletore (Mng Dir)

Subsidiaries:

Kolben Hydraulics Limited (1)
P B No 5 Koppathimanahalli Village, H Hoskote Gram Panchayat Lakkur Hobli Malur Taluk Kolar District, Karnataka, 563130, India
Tel.: (91) 8029724222
Web Site: https://www.kolbenhydraulics.com
Hydraulic Equipment Mfr & Distr
N.A.I.C.S.: 333996

Prism Hydraulics Pvt Ltd (1)
B-23 Angol Industrial Estate Udyambag, Belgaum, 590 008, Karnataka, India
Tel.: (91) 831 244 3448
Web Site: https://www.prismhydraulics.com
Hydraulic Equipment Mfr & Whslr
N.A.I.C.S.: 333996
R.K. Patil (Mng Dir)

Yuflow Engineering Pvt Ltd (1)
No1 IInd Cross Street Poonlamman Nagar Road Ayanambakkam, Maduravoyal Post, Chennai, 600 095, Tamil Nadu, India
Tel.: (91) 4426532496
Web Site: http://www.yuflow.com
Emp.: 50
Hydraulic Cylinder Mfr
N.A.I.C.S.: 333995
C. P. Rangachar (Chm)

YUKEN KOGYO CO., LTD.

4434 Kamitsuchidananaka, Ayase, 252-1113, Kanagawa, Japan
Tel.: (81) 467772111
Web Site: https://www.yuken.co.jp
Year Founded: 1929
6393—(TKS)
Rev.: $195,067,710
Assets: $285,889,110
Liabilities: $115,126,370
Net Worth: $170,762,740
Earnings: $5,188,850
Emp.: 1,252
Fiscal Year-end: 03/31/24
Hydraulic Equipment Mfr & Distr
N.A.I.C.S.: 333996
Hideharu Nagahisa (Pres)

Subsidiaries:

Hokuriku Yuken Co., Ltd. (1)
117 Shimenocho Nishi, Kanazawa, 920-0059, Ishikawa, Japan
Tel.: (81) 762689779
Web Site: https://www.h-yuken.jp
Emp.: 19
Industrial Machinery Mfr
N.A.I.C.S.: 423830

Toyo Hydro Elevator Co., Ltd. (1)
786-1 Kawamukai-cho, Tsuzuki-ku, Yokohama, 224-0044, Kanagawa, Japan
Tel.: (81) 454732600
Web Site: https://www.ev-the.com
Emp.: 42
Hydraulic Equipment Mfr
N.A.I.C.S.: 333996

YUKEN CR s.r.o. (1)
SKNeumanna 2476, 269 01, Rakovnik, Czech Republic
Tel.: (420) 313515167
Web Site: https://www.yuken.cz
Industrial Machinery Mfr
N.A.I.C.S.: 423830

YUKEN KOGYO (H.K.) CO., LTD. (1)
Flat20 7F Block B Focal Industrial Centre 21 Man Lok Street, Hung Hom, Kowloon, China (Hong Kong)
Tel.: (852) 23622355
Industrial Machinery Distr
N.A.I.C.S.: 423830

YUKEN SEA Co., Ltd. (1)
1 Vasu 1 Building 9th Floor Unit 903 Soi Sukhumvit 25 Sukhumvit Road, Khlongtoei-nue Wattana, Bangkok, 10110, Thailand
Tel.: (66) 22592802
Web Site: https://www.yuken-sea.com
Industrial Machinery Distr
N.A.I.C.S.: 423830

Yuken Europe Ltd. (1)
51 Spindus Road, Liverpool, L24 1YA, Merseyside, United Kingdom
Tel.: (44) 1512681891
Web Site: http://yukeneurope.com
Industrial Machinery Distr
N.A.I.C.S.: 423830
Barry Evans (Sec)

Yuken Hydraulics (T.W.) Co., Ltd. (1)
No 12 Gongyequ 7th Rd, Xitun Dist, Taichung, 407, Taiwan
Tel.: (886) 423593077
Web Site: https://www.yuken.com.tw
Hydraulic Equipment Mfr & Distr
N.A.I.C.S.: 333996
Shiro Hattori (Pres)

Yuken Hydraulics (Zhangjiagang) Co., Ltd. (1)
No 9 Xinjingxi Rd Zhangjiagang Economic Development Zone, Jiangsu, 215618, Zhangjiagang, China
Tel.: (86) 51256992111
Hydraulic Equipment Mfr
N.A.I.C.S.: 333996

Yuken Kogyo (Foshan) Co., Ltd. (1)
Unit 101 NO 1 Keying International Industrial Zone NO 7 Xingkai Road, Shunde Industrial Zone Wusha Daliang Shunde, Foshan, Guangdong, China
Tel.: (86) 75722805066
Industrial Machinery Distr
N.A.I.C.S.: 423830

Yuken Kogyo (Ningbo) Hydraulic Technology Co., Ltd. (1)
1st Floor Block No 5 No 58 Ke Chuang South Road, WangChun Industrial Zone, Ningbo, 315176, Zhejiang, China
Tel.: (86) 57487928836
Industrial Machinery Distr
N.A.I.C.S.: 423830

Yuken Kogyo (Shanghai) Co., Ltd. (1)
Room916 Bldg B Far East International Plaza No 317 Xian Xia Road, Shanghai, China
Tel.: (86) 2162351313
Industrial Machinery Distr
N.A.I.C.S.: 423830

Yuken Kogyo Co., Ltd. - Fukuroda Factory (1)
65 Kitatage, Daigo-machi Kuji-gun, Ibaraki, 319-3521, Japan
Tel.: (81) 295720425
Hydraulic Equipment Mfr
N.A.I.C.S.: 333996

Yuken Korea Co., Ltd. (1)
Rm 210 ASIA BLD 590 Gyeongin-Ro, Guro-Gu, Seoul, 08213, Korea (South)
Tel.: (82) 226752110
Web Site: http://www.yuken.co.kr
Industrial Machinery Distr
N.A.I.C.S.: 423830

YUKES CO., LTD.

Portus Center Building 5F 4-45-1 Ebisujima-cho, Sakai-ku, Sakai, 590-0985, Osaka, Japan
Tel.: (81) 722245155
Web Site: https://www.yukes.co.jp
Year Founded: 1993
4334—(TKS)
Rev: $28,976,830
Assets: $23,063,770
Liabilities: $5,806,710
Net Worth: $17,257,060
Earnings: ($9,564,410)
Emp.: 209
Fiscal Year-end: 01/31/24
Game Software Publishing Services
N.A.I.C.S.: 339930
Yukinori Taniguchi (Pres & CEO)

YUKI GOSEI KOGYO CO., LTD.

10-4 Nihonbashi-Ningyocho 3-Chome, Chuo-Ku, Tokyo, 103-0013, Japan
Tel.: (81) 336643980
Web Site: https://www.yuki-gosei.co.jp
Year Founded: 1947
4531—(TKS)
Sales Range: $75-99.9 Million
Emp.: 303
Pharmaceuticals & Food Additive Mfr
N.A.I.C.S.: 325412
Yasuhiko Yamato (Sr Mng Exec Officer-Bus Admin Sector)

Subsidiaries:

Yuki Gosei Kogyo Co.Ltd. - Joban Factory (1)
Joban'nishigo cho Ochiai 788, Iwaki, 972-8316, Fukushima, Japan
Tel.: (81) 246424221
Web Site: http://www.yuki-gosei.co.jp
Emp.: 230
Chemicals Mfr
N.A.I.C.S.: 325998

YUKIGUNI MAITAKE CO., LTD.

INTERNATIONAL PUBLIC

89, Minami-Uonuma, 949-6695, Niigata, Japan
Tel.: (81) 257 780111
Web Site: http://www.maitake.co.jp
Year Founded: 1982
Mushroom Mfr & Whslr
N.A.I.C.S.: 111411
Ashikaga Seki (Pres)

YUKOTERRE RESOURCES, INC.

200 Consumers Road Suite 702, Toronto, M2J 4R4, ON, Canada
Tel.: (541) 900-5871
Web Site: https://www.silowellness.com
SILO—(CNSX)
Rev.: $335,811
Assets: $64,182
Liabilities: $5,368,273
Net Worth: ($5,304,091)
Earnings: ($5,812,400)
Fiscal Year-end: 10/31/22
Mineral Exploration Services
N.A.I.C.S.: 213115
Winfield Ding (CFO)

YUKSELEN CELIK A.S.

Osmangazi Mahallesi 2647 Sokak No 40/1 Kirac, Esenyurt, 34522, Istanbul, Turkiye
Tel.: (90) 2128861500
Web Site: https://www.invest.yukselen.com
Year Founded: 1989
YKSLN—(IST)
Rev.: $47,865,585
Assets: $54,590,703
Liabilities: $32,578,494
Net Worth: $22,012,209
Earnings: ($4,996,811)
Emp.: 68
Fiscal Year-end: 12/31/23
Iron & Steel Product Distr
N.A.I.C.S.: 423390
Yuksel Gokturk (Chm)

YULHO CO., LTD.

13th Floor 6 Seocho-daero, Seocho-gu, Seoul, Korea (South)
Tel.: (82) 220822800
Web Site: https://www.yulho.net
Year Founded: 1998
072770—(KRS)
Rev.: $85,922,113
Assets: $94,497,478
Liabilities: $50,159,957
Net Worth: $44,337,521
Earnings: ($71,553)
Emp.: 40
Fiscal Year-end: 12/31/22
Wireless Internet Services
N.A.I.C.S.: 517112
Siwoog Nho (Mgr)

YULON FINANCE CORPORATION

15F 2 Sec 2 Dunhua S Rd, Daan Dist, Taipei, 10683, Taiwan
Tel.: (886) 227025055
Web Site: https://www.tac.com.tw
Year Founded: 1990
9941—(TAI)
Rev.: $1,356,792,879
Assets: $9,805,920,359
Liabilities: $8,516,083,919
Net Worth: $1,289,836,440
Earnings: $209,406,709
Emp.: 4,107
Fiscal Year-end: 12/31/23
Financial Services
N.A.I.C.S.: 523999
Kuo-Rong Chen (Vice Chm)

Subsidiaries:

Car-plus Auto Leasing Corporation (1)

5F No 309 Binjiang St, Zhongshan Dist,
Taipei, 104, Bangkok, Taiwan
Tel.: (886) 225183060
Web Site: http://www.car-plus.com.tw
Car Lending Services
N.A.I.C.S.: 532112

Ching-Tong Motor Co., Ltd. (1)
No 315 Zhongzheng South Road, Yongkang District, Tainan City, Taiwan
Tel.: (886) 62427767
Web Site: https://www.yulon-gm.com.tw
Automotive Repair & Maintenance Services
N.A.I.C.S.: 811111

Shinshin Credit Corporation (1)
Floor 14 No 2 Section 2 Dunhua South Road, Da'an District, Taipei, Taiwan
Tel.: (886) 227025055
Web Site: https://www.shincredit.com.tw
Consumer Finance Services
N.A.I.C.S.: 541611

Yulon Finance Philippines
Corporation (1)
17th floor The Curve building 32nd Street corner 3rd Avenue, Bonifacio Global City, Taguig, Philippines
Tel.: (63) 283969891
Web Site: https://www.yulon-finance.com.ph
Used Car Financing Services
N.A.I.C.S.: 522220

YULON NISSAN MOTOR CO., LTD.
39-2 Bogongkeng, Xihu Village Sanyi Township Miaoli County, Taipei, 367, Taiwan
Tel.: (886) 37875881
Web Site: https://www.nissan.com.tw
Year Founded: 2003
2227—(TAI)
Rev.: $854,710,619
Assets: $739,252,040
Liabilities: $159,381,890
Net Worth: $579,870,150
Earnings: $37,968,049
Emp.: 376
Fiscal Year-end: 12/31/23
Automotive Parts & Vehicle Mfr
N.A.I.C.S.: 336211
Leman C. C. Lee *(Pres)*

YULONG ECO-MATERIALS LIMITED
Eastern End of Xiwuzhuang Village, Jiaodian Town Xinhua Area, Pingdingshan, Henan, China
Tel.: (86) 375 8888988   Ky
Year Founded: 2011
YECOF—(OTCIQ)
Sales Range: $1-9.9 Million
Emp.: 103
Brick, Concrete & Gypsum Mfr
N.A.I.C.S.: 327331
Yulong Zhu *(CEO)*

YUMA RESOURCES INC.
64 Gainsborough Avenue, Saint Albert, T8N 0W5, AB, Canada
Tel.: (780) 458-2778   NV
Year Founded: 2012
Copper & Other Metal Mining
N.A.I.C.S.: 212230
Thomas Wielobob *(Pres, CEO, CFO, Treas & Sec)*

YUMBA RECORDS STORAGE, INC.
H No FF-2 First Floor Rosemina Arcade, Malbhat Margao, Goa, 403601, India
Tel.: (91) 8975161268   NV
Year Founded: 2017
Rev.: $3,002
Assets: $25,242
Liabilities: $15,656
Net Worth: $9,586
Earnings: ($23,528)
Fiscal Year-end: 08/31/20

Data Storage Services
N.A.I.C.S.: 518210
Chasma Mulla *(Chm, Pres, CEO, CFO, Treas & Sec)*

YUMCO A.D.
Radnicka 5, 17500, Vranje, Serbia
Tel.: (381) 17 422 041
Web Site: http://www.yumco.co.rs
Year Founded: 1960
YUMC—(BEL)
Sales Range: $1-9.9 Million
Yarn Mfr
N.A.I.C.S.: 313110
Zoran Stosic *(Gen Mgr)*

YUMEMITSUKETAI CO., LTD.
Freesia Group Honsha Bldg 17 Kanda Higashimatsushita-cho, Chiyoda-Ku, Tokyo, 101-0042, Japan
Tel.: (81) 366351791
Web Site: http://www.steilar.com
Year Founded: 1980
2673—(TKS)
Rev.: $3,576,010
Assets: $22,097,230
Liabilities: $5,744,090
Net Worth: $16,353,140
Earnings: $925,400
Fiscal Year-end: 03/31/24
Mail Order Retailing Services
N.A.I.C.S.: 541990
Kazuhiko Shimizu *(Exec Dir)*

YUMESHIN HOLDINGS CO., LTD.
22F Marunouchi Yongle Bldg 1-4-1 Marunouchi, Chiyoda-ku, Tokyo, 100-0005, Japan
Tel.: (81) 3 32101200
Web Site: http://www.yumeshin.co.jp
Year Founded: 1976
Rev.: $481,470,850
Assets: $264,673,710
Liabilities: $155,367,310
Net Worth: $109,306,400
Earnings: $22,961,680
Emp.: 8,187
Fiscal Year-end: 09/30/19
Holding Company
N.A.I.C.S.: 551112
Shingo Sato *(Chm)*

Subsidiaries:

Arrow Information Co., Ltd. (1)
300 Sumitomo Realty & Development Akihabara Ekimae Building 6th Floor, Kanda Neribeicho Chiyoda-ku, Tokyo, 101-0022, Japan
Tel.: (81) 36 859 5752
Web Site: https://www.arrow-i.co.jp
Software Technology Services
N.A.I.C.S.: 541511

Garenet Co., Ltd. (1)
2-2 Kanda Jinbocho 8th Floor, Kanda Jimbocho Chiyoda-ku, Tokyo, 101-0051, Japan
Tel.: (81) 35 213 4660
Web Site: https://www.garenet.com
Information Technology Engineering Services
N.A.I.C.S.: 541330

Information Port Co., Ltd. (1)
Sumitomo Realty and Development Akihabara Ekimae Building 6F, 300 Kanda Neribeicho Chiyoda-ku, Tokyo, 101-0022, Japan
Tel.: (81) 36 859 5745
Web Site: https://www.information-port.com
Information Technology Engineering Services
N.A.I.C.S.: 541330

Neplus Co., Ltd. (1)
5F and 6F 300, Kandaneribeicho Chiyoda-ku, Tokyo, 101-0022, Japan
Tel.: (81) 36 205 7236
Web Site: https://www.neplus.jp
Construction Engineering Services
N.A.I.C.S.: 541330

Yume Proeng Co., Ltd. (1)
Sumitomo Realty and Development Akihabara Ekimae Building 5F, 300 Kanda Neribeicho Chiyoda-ku, Tokyo, 101-0022, Japan
Tel.: (81) 36 859 4880
Web Site: https://yume-proeng.co.jp
Construction Engineering Services
N.A.I.C.S.: 541330

Yume Technology Co., Ltd. (1)
Shin Osaki Kangyou Building 4f 1-6-4 Osaki, Shinagawa-ku, Tokyo, 100-0005, Japan
Tel.: (81) 364203828
Web Site: http://www.yume-tec.co.jp
Emp.: 684
Human Resouce Services
N.A.I.C.S.: 561320

Yumeshin Co., Ltd. (1)
1-4-1 Marunouchi Eiraku Building 22F, Marunouchi Chiyoda-ku, Tokyo, 100-0005, Japan
Tel.: (81) 33 210 1210
Web Site: https://www.yumeshin.co.jp
Construction Engineering Services
N.A.I.C.S.: 541330

YUMMIES, INC.
6F No 516 Sec 1 Neihu Road, Neihu District, Taipei, 114, Taiwan
Tel.: (886) 287511886   NV
Year Founded: 1998
YUMM—(OTCIQ)
Liabilities: $13,000
Net Worth: ($13,000)
Earnings: ($63,000)
Fiscal Year-end: 09/30/23
Management Consulting Services
N.A.I.C.S.: 541611
Wei-Hsien Lin *(Chm, Pres, CEO, Treas & Sec)*

YUMMY MARKET INC.
4400 Dufferin Street, North York, M3H 6A8, ON, Canada
Tel.: (416) 665-0040
Web Site:
    https://www.yummymarket.com
Year Founded: 2002
Grocery Stores
N.A.I.C.S.: 445110
Alexei Tsetkov *(CEO)*

YUN LEE MARINE GROUP HOLDINGS LTD.
Flat D 31/F Billion Plaza II 10 Cheung Yue Street, Kowloon, China (Hong Kong)
Tel.: (852) 2 771 1825
Web Site: http://www.yunlee.com.hk
2682—(HKG)
Rev.: $46,949,365
Assets: $43,957,287
Liabilities: $9,057,105
Net Worth: $34,900,182
Earnings: $5,927,921
Emp.: 193
Fiscal Year-end: 03/31/22
Holding Company
N.A.I.C.S.: 551112
Wai Ming Chow *(Sr Mgr)*

YUNDA HOLDING CO., LTD.
No 6679 Yinggang East Road, Qingpu District, Shanghai, 201700, China
Tel.: (86) 2139296789
Web Site:
    http://www.xinhaigroup.com
Year Founded: 1993
002120—(SSE)
Rev.: $6,659,696,464
Assets: $5,345,380,643
Liabilities: $2,946,855,558
Net Worth: $2,398,525,085
Earnings: $208,224,320
Fiscal Year-end: 12/31/22
Holding Company

N.A.I.C.S.: 551112
Tengyun Nie *(Chm & Pres)*

Subsidiaries:

Ningbo Huakun Medical Equipment
Co., Ltd (1)
NO 465 Chongshou east road Changshou Cixi, Ningbo, 315334, Zhejiang, China
Tel.: (86) 57463905558
Web Site: http://www.chinahuakun.cn
Medical Product Mfr & Distr
N.A.I.C.S.: 339113

Unimed Medical Supplies Inc. (1)
No 8 Building Nangang 3rd Industrial Park Tangtou Shiyan, Shenzhen, 518108, China
Tel.: (86) 75526695137
Web Site: http://www.unimed.cn
Medical Product Mfr & Distr
N.A.I.C.S.: 339113
Liming Xue *(Gen Mgr)*

YUNDING TECHNOLOGY CO., LTD.
Room 1910 19th Floor J3 Office Building No 57-1 Gongye South Road, Gaoxin Wanda, Jinan, 250014, Shandong, China
Tel.: (86) 53188550409
Web Site: https://www.yundingkeji.cn
000409—(SSE)
Rev.: $153,187,098
Assets: $347,983,057
Liabilities: $118,194,392
Net Worth: $229,788,665
Earnings: $3,522,706
Fiscal Year-end: 12/31/22
Ferrous Metal Product Mfr
N.A.I.C.S.: 212210

YUNFENG CAPITAL
Suites 2201-03 50 Connaught Road, Central, China (Hong Kong)
Tel.: (852) 2516 6363
Web Site: http://www.yfc.cn
Year Founded: 2010
Emp.: 10
Privater Equity Firm
N.A.I.C.S.: 523999
David Feng Yu *(Co-Founder & Chm)*

YUNFENG FINANCIAL GROUP LIMITED
Room 1803-1806 18/F YF Life Insurance Centre 38 Gloucester Road, Central, China (Hong Kong)
Tel.: (852) 28431488   HK
Web Site: https://www.yff.com
0376—(HKG)
Rev.: $1,202,130,180
Assets: $13,115,998,058
Liabilities: $11,229,755,280
Net Worth: $1,886,242,778
Earnings: ($14,133,120)
Emp.: 603
Fiscal Year-end: 12/31/22
Investment Management Service
N.A.I.C.S.: 523999
Olivia Ou Hai *(CEO-Interim)*

Subsidiaries:

Beijing Youyu Technologies
Limited (1)
Suite 3203-3206 Block B Wangjing SOHO Tower 3 No 1 Futong East Street, Chaoyang District, Beijing, China
Tel.: (86) 1087412901
Brokerage & Investment Research Services
N.A.I.C.S.: 523999

REORIENT Financial Markets (USA)
LLC (1)
400 Madison Ave Ste 8 B, New York, NY 10017
Tel.: (212) 223-6601
Securities Brokerage Services
N.A.I.C.S.: 523150

Shenzhen Youyu Smart Technologies
Limited (1)

YUNFENG FINANCIAL GROUP LIMITED

Yunfeng Financial Group Limited—(Continued)
802 8/F Block B United Financial Mansion Shihua Road, Shenzhen-Hongkong Innovation Cooperation Zone Futian District, Shenzhen, Guangdong, China
Tel.: (86) 4008439666
Brokerage & Investment Research Services
N.A.I.C.S.: 523999

Youyu Smart Technologies Limited (1)
Rooms 1803-1806 18th Floor YF Life Centre 38 Gloucester Road, Wanchai, China (Hong Kong)
Tel.: (852) 28431488
Brokerage & Investment Research Services
N.A.I.C.S.: 523999

YUNG CHI PAINT & VARNISH MFG CO., LTD.
No 26 and 28 Haihai 3rd Road, Xiaogang District, Kaohsiung, 81264, Taiwan
Tel.: (886) 78713181
Web Site: https://www.rainbowpaint.com.tw
1726—(TAI)
Rev.: $305,908,619
Assets: $377,981,738
Liabilities: $57,892,277
Net Worth: $320,089,461
Earnings: $27,183,295
Emp.: 728
Fiscal Year-end: 12/31/23
Paints Mfr
N.A.I.C.S.: 339940
Hung-Wei Chen *(Gen Mgr)*

Subsidiaries:

Yung Chi Paint & Varnish Mfg. (Kunshan) Co., Ltd. (1)
No 1 Yongji Road, Zhangpu Town, Kunshan, 215321, Jiangsu, China
Tel.: (86) 51257442298
Paints Mfr
N.A.I.C.S.: 325510

Yung Chi Paint & Varnish Mfg., (Malaysia) Co., Ltd. (1)
Lot 5 6 Tangga Batu Kawasan Perindustrian Tanjung Kling, Tanjung Kling, 76400, Malacca, Malaysia
Tel.: (60) 4 890 57
Paints Mfr
N.A.I.C.S.: 325510

Yung Chi Paint & Varnish Mfg., (Vietnam) Co., Ltd. (1)
lot 219 Long Binh Industrial Zone Amata, Long Binh Ward, Bien Hoa, Dong Nai, Vietnam
Tel.: (84) 2513936740
Web Site: http://www.rainbowpaints.com.vn
Emp.: 113
Paints Mfr & Distr
N.A.I.C.S.: 325510

YUNGSHIN CONSTRUCTION & DEVELOPMENT CO., LTD.
5th Floor No 183 Liuhe Road, Xinxing District, Kaohsiung, 800, Taiwan
Tel.: (886) 72229460
Web Site: https://www.ys-construction.com.tw
5508—(TPE)
Rev.: $129,218,522
Assets: $542,759,372
Liabilities: $361,785,667
Net Worth: $180,973,705
Earnings: $47,925,210
Fiscal Year-end: 12/31/22
Building Construction Services
N.A.I.C.S.: 236210
Jung-Ming Chen *(Chm)*

YUNGSHIN GLOBAL HOLDING CORPORATION
11F No 181 Section 3 Minchuan East Road, Taipei, 10541, Taiwan
Tel.: (886) 225450185
Web Site: https://www.yungshingroup.com
3705—(TAI)
Rev.: $229,828,861
Assets: $376,481,689
Liabilities: $117,645,144
Net Worth: $258,836,545
Earnings: $28,489,191
Emp.: 1,343
Fiscal Year-end: 12/31/23
Pharmaceutical Product Mfr & Distr
N.A.I.C.S.: 325412
Tian De Li *(Founder)*

Subsidiaries:

AnTec Biotech Co., Ltd. (1)
No 1191 Sec 1 Zhongshan Rd Tachia, Taichung, 437, Taiwan
Tel.: (886) 426764628
Drug Product Mfr
N.A.I.C.S.: 325411

Angel Associates (Taiwan) Inc. (1)
Tel.: (886) 225471599
Medicine Mfr
N.A.I.C.S.: 325411

Carlsbad Technology Inc. (1)
5922 Farnsworth Ct Ste 101, Carlsbad, CA 92008
Tel.: (760) 431-8284
Emp.: 94
Pharmaceutical Product Mfr & Distr
N.A.I.C.S.: 325411
Andy Cheng *(CEO)*

Chemix Inc. (1)
2-15-10 Shinyokohama, Kohoku-ku, Yokohama, Japan
Tel.: (81) 454769031
Pharmaceutical Products Distr
N.A.I.C.S.: 424210

Farmtec Research Co, Ltd. (1)
191 Jin Yang West Road Lujia Town, Kunshan, 215331, Jiangsu, China
Tel.: (86) 51257870665
Biotechnology Research & Development Services
N.A.I.C.S.: 541714

Globecare Trading (Shanghai) Co., Ltd (1)
157 North Road, Kunshan, Jiangsu, China
Tel.: (86) 51255237262
Pharmaceutical Products Distr
N.A.I.C.S.: 424210

Myanmar YungShin Pharm. Ltd. (1)
Bldg No 7/B First Floor Aung Thapaya Street Mingalar Taung Nyunt Tsp, Yangon, Myanmar
Tel.: (95) 95004641
Pharmaceutical Products Distr
N.A.I.C.S.: 424210

Shanghai Yung Zip Pharm. Trading Co., Ltd. (1)
Room 1528 1524 Tomson International Trade Building No 1 JiLong Road, WaiGaoQiao Free Trade Zone, Shanghai, 200137, China
Tel.: (86) 51257675190
Pharmaceutical Products Distr
N.A.I.C.S.: 424210

Vetnostrum Animal Health Co., Ltd. (1)
12F No 181 Sec 3 Min Chuan East Road, Taipei, 10541, Taiwan
Tel.: (886) 227186200
Medicine Mfr & Distr
N.A.I.C.S.: 325412

Yung Shin Company Limited (1)
Unit 3 5 6 11/F Tower One Ever Gain Plaza No 88 Container Port Road, Kwai Chung, New Territories, China (Hong Kong)
Tel.: (852) 26375131
Medical Product Distr
N.A.I.C.S.: 424210

Yung Shin Pharmaceutical Ind (Kunshan) Co., Ltd. (1)
Jinyang West Road No 191, Lujia, Kunshan, Jiangsu, China
Tel.: (86) 5125 767 5190
Web Site: https://www.ysp.com.cn
Pharmaceutical Product Mfr & Distr
N.A.I.C.S.: 325412
TienTe Lee *(Founder)*

Yung Shin Pharmaceutical Industrial Co. (1)
1191 Sec 1 Chung Shan Rd Taichia, Taichung, 43744, Taiwan
Tel.: (886) 426875100
Pharmaceutical Products Distr
N.A.I.C.S.: 424210

Yung Zip Chemical Co., Ltd. (1)
59 You Shih Road Industrial District Dajia, Taichung, 43767, Taiwan
Tel.: (886) 426811344
Chemical Product Mfr & Distr
N.A.I.C.S.: 325199

YungShin Co (Hong Kong) Ltd. (1)
Unit 3 5 6 11/F Tower One Ever Gain Plaza No 88 Container Port Road, Kwai Chung, Hongkong, China (Hong Kong)
Tel.: (852) 26375131
Emp.: 16
Pharmaceutical Products Distr
N.A.I.C.S.: 424210
Paul Tang *(Mgr)*

YungShin Pharm. Ind. (KS) Co., Ltd. (1)
No 191 JinYang West Road Lujia Town, Kunshan, Jiangsu, China
Tel.: (86) 51257675190
Pharmaceutical Product Mfr & Distr
N.A.I.C.S.: 325411

YungShin Pharm. Indonesia, PT (1)
Komplex Tekstil Block C 6/17 Mangga Dua Raya Ancol Pademangan, Jakarta, 14430, Indonesia
Tel.: (62) 2156972793
Pharmaceutical Products Distr
N.A.I.C.S.: 424210

isRed Pharma and Biotech Research Co., Ltd. (1)
5th Floor No 32 Keya Road, Taichung, 428, Taiwan
Tel.: (886) 425653536
Biotechnology Research & Development Services
N.A.I.C.S.: 541714

YUNHONG GUIXIN GROUP HOLDINGS LIMITED
66 South Oujiang Road, Haimen, Jiangsu, China
Tel.: (86) 51382187301   Ky
8349—(HKG)
Rev.: $11,038,810
Assets: $15,525,292
Liabilities: $5,943,553
Net Worth: $9,581,738
Earnings: ($286,837)
Emp.: 107
Fiscal Year-end: 12/31/21
Fiber Glass Mfr & Distr
N.A.I.C.S.: 326191

YUNHONG INTERNATIONAL
4-19/F 126 Zhong Bei, Wuchang District, Wuhan, 430061, China
Tel.: (86) 13145555555   Ky
Year Founded: 2019
ZGYH—(NASDAQ)
Rev.: $20,736
Assets: $70,438,969
Liabilities: $76,806,397
Net Worth: ($6,367,428)
Earnings: ($2,054,921)
Emp.: 2
Fiscal Year-end: 06/30/21
Holding Company
N.A.I.C.S.: 551112
Yubao Li *(Chm)*

YUNJI INC.
17th Floor Building F HIPARK, Xiaoshan District, Hangzhou, 310000, Zhejiang, China
Tel.: (86) 57181688920   Ky

INTERNATIONAL PUBLIC

Web Site: https://www.yunjiglobal.com
Year Founded: 2015
YJ—(NASDAQ)
Rev.: $176,821,806
Assets: $289,936,289
Liabilities: $82,198,850
Net Worth: $207,737,439
Earnings: ($21,169,485)
Emp.: 493
Fiscal Year-end: 12/31/22
Holding Company
N.A.I.C.S.: 551112
Shanglue Xiao *(Founder, Chm & CEO)*

YUNKANG GROUP LIMITED
No 9 Yayingshi Road, Science City Huangpu District, Guangzhou, China
Tel.: (86) 2032106666   Ky
Web Site: https://en.yunkanghealth.com
Year Founded: 2008
2325—(HKG)
Rev.: $575,487,555
Assets: $751,797,946
Liabilities: $362,709,048
Net Worth: $389,088,899
Earnings: $57,292,726
Emp.: 2,605
Fiscal Year-end: 12/31/22
Medical Laboratory Services
N.A.I.C.S.: 621511
Shanghua Hu *(VP)*

YUNNAN ALUMINIUM CO., LTD.
Qidian Subdistrict, Chenggong District, Kunming, 650502, Yunnan, China
Tel.: (86) 87167455268
Web Site: http://www.ylgf.com
Year Founded: 1998
000807—(SSE)
Rev.: $6,804,208,696
Assets: $5,483,950,051
Liabilities: $1,935,128,005
Net Worth: $3,548,822,046
Earnings: $641,437,744
Fiscal Year-end: 12/31/22
Aluminium Products Mfr
N.A.I.C.S.: 331314
Shujun Ji *(Chm)*

YUNNAN BAIYAO GROUP CO., LTD.
No 3686 Yunnan Baiyao Street Chenggong District, Kunming, 650500, Yunnan, China
Tel.: (86) 87166324159
Web Site: http://www.yunnanbaiyao.com.cn
000538—(SSE)
Rev.: $5,415,276,390
Assets: $7,446,872,674
Liabilities: $1,921,651,086
Net Worth: $5,525,221,588
Earnings: $56,680,896
Fiscal Year-end: 12/31/23
Pharmaceuticals Product Mfr
N.A.I.C.S.: 325412
Minghui Wang *(Chm & CEO-Interim)*

YUNNAN BOTANEE BIO-TECHNOLOGY GROUP CO., LTD.
Tel.: (86) 87168281899
Web Site: http://www.botanee.com.cn
Year Founded: 2010
300957—(SSE)
Rev.: $703,947,867
Assets: $943,307,853
Liabilities: $156,818,544
Net Worth: $786,489,308
Earnings: $147,592,524
Fiscal Year-end: 12/31/22

AND PRIVATE COMPANIES

Cosmetics Products Mfr
N.A.I.C.S.: 325620
Zhenyu Guo *(Chm & Gen Mgr)*

YUNNAN BOWIN TECHNOLOGY & INDUSTRY CO., LTD.
Room 806 Donghang Investment Building No 219 Chuncheng Road, Guandu District, Kunming, 650041, Yunnan, China
Tel.: (86) 87167197370
Web Site: https://www.ynbowin.com
Year Founded: 1990
600883—(SHG)
Rev.: $1,649,630
Assets: $122,702,664
Liabilities: $6,742,949
Net Worth: $115,959,716
Earnings: $11,310,792
Fiscal Year-end: 12/31/22
Cement Mfr & Whslr
N.A.I.C.S.: 327310
Zhibo Liu *(Chm)*

YUNNAN CHIHONG ZINC & GERMANIUM CO., LTD.
Intersection of Cuifeng West Road and Xuefu Road, Qujing Economic and Technological Development Zone, Qujing, 655011, Yunnan, China
Tel.: (86) 8748966688
Web Site: https://chxz.chinalco.com.cn
Year Founded: 2000
600497—(SHG)
Rev.: $3,074,794,412
Assets: $3,734,571,808
Liabilities: $1,316,799,512
Net Worth: $2,417,772,296
Earnings: $94,011,559
Emp.: 10,014
Fiscal Year-end: 12/31/22
Nonferrous Metal Mfr & Whslr
N.A.I.C.S.: 331410
Chen Qing *(Chm & Sec-Party)*

YUNNAN CHUN WU ZHI FLORAL CO.,LTD.
17th Floor Building A Xin Tuo Mansion Nanping Street, Kunming, 650032, Yun Nan, China
Tel.: (86) 871 63130732
Web Site: http://www.cwzflower.com
Year Founded: 2008
Sales Range: $10-24.9 Million
Flower Planting, Dried Flower Processing, Delivery & E-Commerce
N.A.I.C.S.: 111421

YUNNAN COAL & ENERGY CO., LTD.
Jinfang Street, Anning, Kunming, 650309, Yunnan, China
Tel.: (86) 87168758679
Web Site: http://www.ymnygf.com
Year Founded: 1997
600792—(SHG)
Rev.: $1,058,753,381
Assets: $1,319,990,916
Liabilities: $863,694,103
Net Worth: $456,296,813
Earnings: ($25,417,777)
Fiscal Year-end: 12/31/22
Chemical Product Mfr & Distr
N.A.I.C.S.: 325998
Li Shuxiong *(Chm)*

YUNNAN COPPER CO., LTD.
M2-3 National High-tech Industrial Development Zone, Kunming, 650224, Yunnan, China
Tel.: (86) 87163106739
Web Site: http://www.yunnan-copper.com
Year Founded: 1998
000878—(SSE)
Rev.: $20,351,206,483
Assets: $5,452,532,538
Liabilities: $3,077,105,616
Net Worth: $2,375,426,922
Earnings: $218,623,629
Fiscal Year-end: 12/31/23
Metal Smelting Services
N.A.I.C.S.: 331410
Tian Yongzhong *(Chm)*

YUNNAN ENERGY INTERNATIONAL CO. LTD.
Room 2008 20/F China Resources Building 26 Harbour Road, Wanchai, China (Hong Kong)
Tel.: (852) 39550625 BM
Web Site: http://www.yeigi.com
Year Founded: 1988
1298—(HKG)
Rev.: $36,731,348
Assets: $28,285,238
Liabilities: $6,433,905
Net Worth: $21,851,333
Earnings: ($1,131,818)
Emp.: 21
Fiscal Year-end: 12/31/22
Analytical Instruments, Life Science Equipment & Laboratory Instruments Designer, Developer, Mfr & Distr
N.A.I.C.S.: 339112
Jincan Zhang *(Chm)*

Subsidiaries:

Shanghai Sanco Instrument Co., Ltd. (1)
No 50 Ln 2897 Xie Tu Rd, Shanghai, 201612, China
Tel.: (86) 2164873364
Web Site: http://www.sanco.com.cn
Scientific Instrument Mfr
N.A.I.C.S.: 423490

Shanghai Techcomp Bio-equipment Limited (1)
Bldg 16 No 201 Minyi Rd, Songjiang Dist, 201612, Shanghai, China
Tel.: (86) 2167687200
Web Site: http://www.techcomp.com.cn
Emp.: 200
Scientific Instrument Mfr
N.A.I.C.S.: 423490
Feng Bao *(Gen Mgr)*

Shanghai Techcomp Instrument Ltd. (1)
Block 16 No 201 Minyi Road, Songjiang District, Shanghai, 201612, China
Tel.: (86) 2167687200
Web Site: http://www.techcomp.cn
Sales Range: $25-49.9 Million
Emp.: 50
Scientific Instrument Mfr
N.A.I.C.S.: 423490

Techcomp (China) Limited (1)
2606 26/F Tower 1 Ever Gain Plaza 88 Container Port Road, Kwai Chung, New Territories, China (Hong Kong)
Tel.: (852) 2 751 9488
Web Site: https://www.techcomp.com.hk
Emp.: 100
Scientific Instrument Mfr
N.A.I.C.S.: 423490

Techcomp (Macao Commercial Offshore) Limited (1)
Rua de Beijing No 202nd S 246, Financial Ctr D7, Macau, China (Macau)
Tel.: (853) 28705075
Web Site: http://www.techcomp.com.sg
Scientific Instrument Mfr
N.A.I.C.S.: 423490

Techcomp (Singapore) Pte. Ltd. (1)
2 International Bus Park 09-06 Tower 1 The Strategy, Singapore, 609930, Singapore
Tel.: (65) 6 267 8921
Web Site: https://www.techcomp.com.sg
Sales Range: $50-74.9 Million
Emp.: 14
Scientific Instrument Mfr
N.A.I.C.S.: 423490

Techcomp (Tianjin) Ltd. (1)
Rm 1008 BoLian Bldg No 155 Weijin Rd, Heping Dist, Tianjin, 300070, China
Tel.: (86) 2223352643
Scientific Instrument Mfr
N.A.I.C.S.: 423490

YUNNAN ENERGY INVESTMENT CO., LTD.
No 276 Chuncheng Road, Guandu District, Kunming, 650200, Yunnan, China
Tel.: (86) 87163127429
Web Site: https://www.ynyh.com
Year Founded: 2002
002053—(SSE)
Rev.: $366,734,839
Assets: $1,876,201,592
Liabilities: $790,334,977
Net Worth: $1,085,866,615
Earnings: $40,942,030
Fiscal Year-end: 12/31/22
Investment Services
N.A.I.C.S.: 523999
Zhou Manfu *(Chm)*

YUNNAN ENERGY NEW MATERIAL CO., LTD.
No 125 Fuxian Road High-Tech Area, Yuxi, 653100, Yunnan, China
Tel.: (86) 8778888661
Web Site: http://www.cxxcl.cn
Year Founded: 2006
002812—(SSE)
Rev.: $1,767,765,940
Assets: $5,422,631,503
Liabilities: $2,775,470,471
Net Worth: $2,647,161,031
Earnings: $561,664,865
Fiscal Year-end: 12/31/22
Packing Product Mfr & Distr
N.A.I.C.S.: 322220
Paul Xiaoming Li *(Chm)*

Subsidiaries:

Shanghai Energy New Material Technology Co., Ltd. (1)
155 Nanlu Highway, Pudong New District, Shanghai, China
Tel.: (86) 2120977221
Web Site: https://en.semcorpglobal.com
Storage Battery Mfr & Distr
N.A.I.C.S.: 335910

YUNNAN JIANZHIJIA HEALTH-CHAIN CO., LTD.
Plot 5 Complex Building Intersection of Lianhe Road & Wanhong Road, Wanhong Jiayuan Fengyuan Panlong District, Kunming, 650224, Yunnan, China
Tel.: (86) 87165711920
Web Site: http://www.jzj.cn
Year Founded: 2004
605266—(SHG)
Rev.: $1,055,027,966
Assets: $1,317,691,248
Liabilities: $958,381,520
Net Worth: $359,309,728
Earnings: $51,014,635
Emp.: 10,000
Fiscal Year-end: 12/31/22
Pharmaceutical Product Mfr & Distr
N.A.I.C.S.: 325412
Bo Lan *(Chm & Gen Mgr)*

YUNNAN JINGGU FORESTRY CO., LTD.
No 201 Linzhi Road, Jinggu Dai and Yi Autonomous County, Pu'er, 650000, Yunnan, China
Tel.: (86) 87163822528
Web Site: http://www.jgly.cn
Year Founded: 1999
600265—(SHG)
Rev.: $15,892,761
Assets: $65,319,177
Liabilities: $43,811,483
Net Worth: $21,507,693
Earnings: ($3,128,463)
Fiscal Year-end: 12/31/22
Forest Chemical Product Mfr & Distr
N.A.I.C.S.: 325194
Chen Kai *(Chm)*

YUNNAN LINCANG XINYUAN GERMANIUM INDUSTRIAL CO., LTD.
No 666 Kuixing Street Power Equipment Park Majinpu, Chenggong New District, Kunming, 650503, Yunnan, China
Tel.: (86) 87165955312
Web Site: http://www.sino-ge.com
Year Founded: 2002
002428—(SSE)
Rev.: $75,338,317
Assets: $338,782,673
Liabilities: $129,799,449
Net Worth: $208,983,224
Earnings: ($8,761,367)
Emp.: 460
Fiscal Year-end: 12/31/22
Chemical Products Mfr
N.A.I.C.S.: 325998
Wendong Bao *(Chm, Pres & Gen Mgr)*

Subsidiaries:

Beijing Zhongke Jiaying Semiconductor Co., Ltd. (1)
OPTO-Mechatronics Industrial Park OIP Tongzhou District, Beijing, 101100, China
Tel.: (86) 1081501511
Semiconductor Material Mfr
N.A.I.C.S.: 334413

Kunming Yunzhe High Technology Co., Ltd. (1)
B5-5 Land Parcel Electronic Equipment Park Majinpu, Chenggong District, Kunming, 650503, Yunnan, China
Tel.: (86) 87163630756
Web Site: https://www.yzoptics.com
Emp.: 150
Infrared Optic Product Mfr
N.A.I.C.S.: 333310
Guibing Lu *(Gen Mgr)*

Wuhan Yunjingfei Optical Fiber Materials Co., Ltd. (1)
9 Guanggu Avenue East Lake High-tech Zone, Wuhan, 430073, China
Tel.: (86) 87165936955
Germanium Product Mfr
N.A.I.C.S.: 334413

YUNNAN LONGRUN TEA GROUP COMPANY LIMITED
No 1299 Haiyuan North Road, Kunming High tech Industrial Development Zone, Kwai Chung, 650106, China (Hong Kong)
Tel.: (852) 400 690 2898 Ky
Web Site: http://www.longruntea.com
Tea Mfr
N.A.I.C.S.: 311920

YUNNAN LUOPING ZINC & ELECTRICITY CO., LTD.
Changqing Industrial Park Jiulong Street, Luoping County, Qujing, 655800, Yunnan, China
Tel.: (86) 8748256825
Web Site: https://www.lpxdgf.cn
Year Founded: 2000
002114—(SSE)
Rev.: $276,404,188
Assets: $350,251,373
Liabilities: $170,617,744
Net Worth: $179,633,629
Earnings: ($33,200,879)
Fiscal Year-end: 12/31/22
Non-ferrous Metal Mining Services
N.A.I.C.S.: 212230
Youli Li *(Chm)*

Yunnan Luoping Zinc & Electricity Co., Ltd.—(Continued)

YUNNAN METROPOLITAN REAL ESTATE DEVELOPMENT CO., LTD.
Building A4 Rongcheng Youjun No 34 Xiyuan South Road, Xishan District, Kunming, 650034, Yunnan, China
Tel.: (86) 87167199767
Web Site: http://www.ynctzy.com
Year Founded: 1993
600239—(SHG)
Rev.: $360,601,437
Assets: $1,899,271,390
Liabilities: $1,541,460,305
Net Worth: $357,811,085
Earnings: ($113,962,427)
Fiscal Year-end: 12/31/22
Real Estate Development Services
N.A.I.C.S.: 531390
Kong Weiran *(Chm)*

YUNNAN NANTIAN ELECTRONICS INFORMATION CO., LTD.
No 455 Huancheng East Road, Kunming, 650041, Yunnan, China
Tel.: (86) 87163366327
Web Site: http://www.nantian.com.cn
Year Founded: 1998
000948—(SSE)
Rev.: $1,202,811,363
Assets: $1,387,122,825
Liabilities: $1,038,185,076
Net Worth: $348,937,749
Earnings: $19,244,670
Fiscal Year-end: 12/31/22
Automatic Teller Machine Mfr
N.A.I.C.S.: 334118

Subsidiaries:

Beijing Ecostar Nantian Technology Co., Ltd. (1)
Nantian Science & Technology Park 10 Xinxi Road Shangdi, Haidian, Beijing, 100085, China
Tel.: (86) 1051515600
Information Technology Services
N.A.I.C.S.: 541512

Beijing Nantian Information Engineering Co., Ltd. (1)
2/F Nantian Building 10 Xinxi Road Shangdi, Haidian, Beijing, 100085, China
Tel.: (86) 1051515572
Information Technology Consulting & Software Development Services
N.A.I.C.S.: 541512

Beijing Nantian Software Co., Ltd. (1)
Nantian Science & Technology Park 10 Xinxi Road Shangdi, Haidian, Beijing, 100085, China
Tel.: (86) 1051515600
Information Technology Consulting & Software Development Services
N.A.I.C.S.: 541512

Beijing Nantian Zhilian Information Technology Co., Ltd. (1)
Nantian Science & Technology Park 10 Xinxi Road Shangdi, Haidian, Beijing, 100085, China
Tel.: (86) 1051515600
Information Technology Services
N.A.I.C.S.: 541512

Guangzhou Highjet Computer Technology Co., Ltd. (1)
Room 405 Lunaler International Building 36 Jianzhong Road, Tianhe, Guangzhou, China
Tel.: (86) 2085573087
Artificial Intelligence Technology Services
N.A.I.C.S.: 541519

Guangzhou Nantian Computer System Co., Ltd. (1)
5/F Nantian Building 1 Jiangong Road, Tianhe, Guangzhou, 510665, China
Tel.: (86) 2085535888

Software Development Services
N.A.I.C.S.: 541511

Kunming Nantian Computer System Co., Ltd. (1)
455 Huancheng East Road, Kunming, 650041, China
Tel.: (86) 87168279131
Software Development Services
N.A.I.C.S.: 541511

Shanghai Nantian Computer System Co., Ltd. (1)
5/F Nantian Information Building No 1 of Lane 767 Jinzhong Road, Changning, Shanghai, 200335, China
Tel.: (86) 2162393030
Software Development Services
N.A.I.C.S.: 541511

Shenzhen Nantian Donghua Technology Co., Ltd. (1)
B2 7/F Tianxiang Building Tian an Digital Mall Chegongmiao, Futian, Shenzhen, 518000, China
Tel.: (86) 75583562988
Banking Financial Services
N.A.I.C.S.: 522110

Wuhan Nantian Computer System Co., Ltd. (1)
Room 1578 Block B Yamao Plaza 628 Wuluo Road, Wuhan, 430070, China
Tel.: (86) 2759713978
Software Development Services
N.A.I.C.S.: 541511

Xi'an Nantian Computer System Co., Ltd. (1)
Room 11001 Gaoke Building 52, Gaoxin, Xi'an, 710075, China
Tel.: (86) 298958989
Software Development Services
N.A.I.C.S.: 541511

Yunnan Nantian Information Equipment Co., Ltd. (1)
243 Tuoxiang Road, Information Economic and Technological Development Zone, Kunming, China
Tel.: (86) 87165953707
Professional Financial Equipment Mfr & Distr
N.A.I.C.S.: 334118

YUNNAN SHENNONG AGRICULTURAL INDUSTRY GROUP CO., LTD.
39F Office Building Kunming Henglong Plaza No 23 Dongfeng East Road, Panlong District, Kunming, 650051, Yunnan, China
Tel.: (86) 87163193176
Web Site: http://www.ynsnjt.com
Year Founded: 1999
605296—(SHG)
Rev.: $463,949,610
Assets: $767,884,483
Liabilities: $111,030,637
Net Worth: $656,853,846
Earnings: $35,855,549
Fiscal Year-end: 12/31/22
Animal Production Services
N.A.I.C.S.: 112990
Zuxun He *(Chm & Gen Mgr)*

YUNNAN TIN CO., LTD.
No 471 Minhang Road, Guandu District, Kunming, 650200, Yunnan, China
Tel.: (86) 8733118328
Web Site: https://www.ytl.com.cn
Year Founded: 1998
000960—(SSE)
Rev.: $7,300,497,312
Assets: $5,148,498,593
Liabilities: $2,716,503,791
Net Worth: $2,431,994,802
Earnings: $189,014,342
Emp.: 14,680
Fiscal Year-end: 12/31/22
Non-ferrous Metal Mining Services
N.A.I.C.S.: 331492

Liu Luke *(Chm)*

Subsidiaries:

Yuntinic (Hong Kong) Resources Co., Ltd. (1)
Rm1201 12th Floor Tower Two Lippo Center 89 Queensway, Hong Kong, China (Hong Kong)
Tel.: (852) 26684200
Web Site: https://www.yuntinic.com.hk
Emp.: 78
Metal Products Mfr
N.A.I.C.S.: 332999

Yuntinic Resources, GmbH (1)
Rotterdamer Str 11a, 40474, Dusseldorf, Germany
Tel.: (49) 211 130 6780
Web Site: https://www.yuntinic.de
Metal Products Mfr
N.A.I.C.S.: 332999

Yuntinic Resources, Inc. (1)
2050 Pioneer Ct Ste 220, San Mateo, CA 94403
Tel.: (650) 312-9282
Web Site: https://www.yuntinic.com
Tin Metals Mfr
N.A.I.C.S.: 332431

YUNNAN TOURISM CO., LTD.
Floor 16 and 17 Unit 1 Building B Low Carbon Center Expo Eco-city, Panlong District, Kunming, 650224, Yunnan, China
Tel.: (86) 8714562345
Web Site: https://www.ynlygf.com
Year Founded: 2000
002059—(SSE)
Rev.: $75,610,384
Assets: $703,068,051
Liabilities: $417,147,466
Net Worth: $285,920,585
Earnings: ($39,767,907)
Fiscal Year-end: 12/31/22
Travel & Tour Operating Services
N.A.I.C.S.: 561520
Cheng Xuzhe *(Chm & Sec-Party Committee)*

YUNNAN WATER INVESTMENT CO., LIMITED
Yunnan Water 2089 Haiyuan Bei Road, Gaoxin District, Kunming, Yunnan, China
Tel.: (86) 87167209716 CN
Web Site: https://www.yunnanwater.com.cn
Year Founded: 2009
6839—(HKG)
Rev.: $532,020,809
Assets: $6,552,257,962
Liabilities: $5,922,098,395
Net Worth: $630,159,566
Earnings: ($162,632,200)
Emp.: 6,516
Fiscal Year-end: 12/31/22
Water Supply & Sewage Treatment Services
N.A.I.C.S.: 221310
Tao Yang *(Chm)*

Subsidiaries:

PJT Technology Co. Ltd. (1)
252/126 Muang Thai Phatra Complex Build 27th Fl Ratchadapisek Road, Huai Kwang, Bangkok, 10310, Thailand
Tel.: (66) 2765625
Web Site: http://www.pjt.co.th
Eletric Power Generation Services
N.A.I.C.S.: 221118

Plant (Domestic):

PJT Technology Co. Ltd. - PHUKET GREEN INCINERATOR PLANT (2)
115/23-24 Moo 1 Rattanakosin 200 Pee Road, T Vichait A Muangphuket, Phuket, 83000, Thailand
Tel.: (66) 76210314
Electric Power Generation Services
N.A.I.C.S.: 221118

Pan Asia Waterworks Co., Ltd. (1)
252/126 Muang Thai Phatra Complex Building 27 FL Ratchadapisek Road, Huai Kwang, Bangkok, 10310, Thailand
Tel.: (66) 2 276 5623
Water Supply Services
N.A.I.C.S.: 221310

YUNNAN WENSHAN ELECTRIC POWER CO., LTD.
No 29 Fenghuang Road, Wenshan, 663000, Yunnan, China
Tel.: (86) 87668177335
600995—(SHG)
Rev.: $1,159,829,433
Assets: $5,719,798,380
Liabilities: $2,441,737,383
Net Worth: $3,278,060,997
Earnings: $233,419,563
Fiscal Year-end: 12/31/22
Electric Power Generation & Distribution Services
N.A.I.C.S.: 221111
Luo Dong *(Pres)*

YUNNAN XIYI INDUSTRY CO., LTD.
Shanchong Haikou Town, Xishan District, Kunming, 650114, China
Tel.: (86) 87168598506
Web Site: http://www.ynxygf.com
002265—(SSE)
Rev.: $597,525,496
Assets: $999,268,555
Liabilities: $700,547,857
Net Worth: $298,720,698
Earnings: $32,099,764
Fiscal Year-end: 12/31/22
Automobile Mfr
N.A.I.C.S.: 336110
Xie Li *(Chm)*

YUNNAN YUNTIANHUA CO., LTD.
No 1417 Dianchi Road, Kunming, Yunnan, China
Tel.: (86) 87163146731
Web Site: http://www.yyth.com.cn
Year Founded: 1997
600096—(SHG)
Rev.: $9,561,947,912
Assets: $7,278,852,154
Liabilities: $4,231,321,957
Net Worth: $3,047,530,198
Earnings: $626,135,107
Emp.: 13,000
Fiscal Year-end: 12/31/23
Chemical Products Mfr
N.A.I.C.S.: 325199

YUNNAN YUNTOU ECOLOGY & ENVIRONMENT TECHNOLOGY CO., LTD.
No 6 Economic and Technological Development Zone Pu Road, Kunming, 650217, Yunnan, China
Tel.: (86) 87167355849
Web Site: http://www.yt-eco.com
002200—(SSE)
Rev.: $82,020,739
Assets: $391,426,130
Liabilities: $346,242,869
Net Worth: $45,183,261
Earnings: $1,498,714
Fiscal Year-end: 12/31/22
Farming Services
N.A.I.C.S.: 111421
Huaizhang Yang *(Chm)*

YUNNAN YUNWEI CO., LTD.
20F No 393 Rixin Middle Road, Qianwei Subdistrict Xishan District, Kunming, 650100, Yunnan, China
Tel.: (86) 87165652998
Web Site: http://www.ywgf.cn
Year Founded: 1996

AND PRIVATE COMPANIES

600725—(SHG)
Rev.: $162,711,849
Assets: $64,979,409
Liabilities: $15,117,528
Net Worth: $49,861,881
Earnings: $3,085,487
Fiscal Year-end: 12/31/22
Organic Chemical Mfr
N.A.I.C.S.: 325199
Cai Dawei *(Chm)*

YURATECH CO., LTD.
25 Araegipeunnae-gil Jeondong-myeon, Sejong, Korea (South)
Tel.: (82) 7078783500
Web Site: http://www.yuratech.co.kr
Year Founded: 1987
048430—(KRS)
Rev.: $145,785,246
Assets: $110,062,509
Liabilities: $19,267,911
Net Worth: $90,794,598
Earnings: $664,580
Emp.: 257
Fiscal Year-end: 12/31/22
Automobile Parts Mfr
N.A.I.C.S.: 336320
Dae-yeol Ohm *(CEO)*

Subsidiaries:

BEIJING YURA Corporation (1)
No 13 Keji Road Miyun Economic Development, Beijing, China
Tel.: (86) 1069076801
Automotive Spare Parts Distr
N.A.I.C.S.: 423120

Rongcheng Shiyuan electric equipment CO., LTD (1)
NO 8 HeYang east road, The Economic Development Zone, Rongcheng, Shandong, China
Tel.: (86) 6317586025
Electronic Equipment Distr
N.A.I.C.S.: 423690

SEWONECS VINA CO,. LTD (1)
Moc Ty Village, Trung Trac, Hung Yen, Vietnam
Tel.: (84) 321 997555
Automotive Spare Parts Distr
N.A.I.C.S.: 423120

WEIHAI YURA corporation (1)
NO 2 Huiyou Road, Wenquantang Wenquan Town Huancui Area, Weihai, Shandong, China
Tel.: (86) 6315375000
Automotive Spare Parts Distr
N.A.I.C.S.: 423120

YURA Corporation RUS (1)
ul Gagarina dom 54/A, Ivangorod, Leningrad, Russia
Tel.: (7) 8137557930
Automotive Spare Parts Distr
N.A.I.C.S.: 423120

YURA Corporation Slovakia, s.r.o (1)
Puchovska Cesta 413, Lednicke Rovne, Slovakia
Tel.: (421) 424307010
Automotive Spare Parts Distr
N.A.I.C.S.: 423120

YURA Corporation Tunisia sarl (1)
AFI industrial zone road of tunis, 3100, Kairouan, Tunisia
Tel.: (216) 77270207
Automotive Spare Parts Distr
N.A.I.C.S.: 423120

YURA Corporation d.o.o (1)
Kralja Petra I 9, 34210, Raca, Serbia
Tel.: (381) 346170016
Automotive Spare Parts Distr
N.A.I.C.S.: 423120

YURATECH Co., Ltd. - Gyoengju Plant (1)
71-4 Shinpyeong-ri, Geoncheon-eup, Gyeongju, Gyeongsangbuk-do, Korea (South)
Tel.: (82) 70 7878 3300
Automobile Spare Parts Mfr
N.A.I.C.S.: 336110

YURATECH Co., Ltd. - Pyeongtaek Plant (1)
88-1 Habuk-ri, Jinwi-myeon, Pyeongtaek, Gyeonggi-do, Korea (South)
Tel.: (82) 70 7878 2222
Automobile Spare Parts Mfr
N.A.I.C.S.: 336110

Yan Tai YURA corporation (1)
Qinshuigongyeyuan Muping Area, Yantai, Shandong, China
Tel.: (86) 535 465 7140
Automotive Spare Parts Distr
N.A.I.C.S.: 423120

Yura Corporation (1)
308 Pangyo-ro, Bundang-gu, Seongnam, Gyeonggi, Korea (South)
Tel.: (82) 7078781000
Web Site: https://www.yuracorp.co.kr
Automotive Electronic Component Mfr
N.A.I.C.S.: 336390
Ohm Dae-yeol *(CEO)*

Yura Harness Co., Ltd. (1)
854 Sicheong-ro, Paltan-myeon, Hwaseong, Gyeonggi-do, Korea (South)
Tel.: (82) 7078783000
Web Site: https://www.yuraharness.co.kr
Automobile Spare Parts Mfr
N.A.I.C.S.: 336110
Ohm Dae-Yeol *(CEO)*

YURI GAGARIN PLC
1 Rogoshko shosse St, 4003, Plovdiv, Bulgaria
Tel.: (359) 32907213
Web Site: https://www.gagarin.eu
Year Founded: 1964
YGAG—(BUL)
Sales Range: Less than $1 Million
Paper Printed Package Mfr
N.A.I.C.S.: 322299
Kiril Dimitrov Hristov *(Exec Dir)*

YURTEC CORPORATION
4-1-1 Tsutsujigaoka, Miyagino-ku, Sendai, 983-8622, Miyagi, Japan
Tel.: (81) 222962111
Web Site: https://www.yurtec.co.jp
Year Founded: 1944
1934—(TKS)
Rev.: $1,607,360,310
Assets: $1,530,076,190
Liabilities: $588,772,530
Net Worth: $941,303,660
Earnings: $49,641,100
Emp.: 3,796
Fiscal Year-end: 03/31/24
Construction Machinery Rental Services
N.A.I.C.S.: 532412
Toshinori Abe *(Chm)*

Subsidiaries:

Aqua Clara Tohoku Corporation (1)
47-14 Matsubara Aiko, Aoba-ku, Sendai, 989-3124, Miyagi, Japan
Tel.: (81) 570049432
Web Site: https://tohoku.aquaclara-web.jp
Water Delivering Services
N.A.I.C.S.: 488390

Yurtec Vietnam Co., Ltd. (1)
27B Nguyen Dinh Chieu Street, Da Kao Ward District1, Ho Chi Minh City, Vietnam
Tel.: (84) 2839115935
Construction Services
N.A.I.C.S.: 236220
Ngan Nguyen *(Asst Mgr)*

YUS INTERNATIONAL GROUP LIMITED
Room A Block B 21/F Billion Centre, 1 Wang Kwong Road, Kowloon, China (Hong Kong)
Tel.: (852) 3698 6699   NV
Web Site:
   http://www.yusgroup.com.hk
Year Founded: 2002
YUSG—(OTCIQ)
Sales Range: Less than $1 Million
Investment Services
N.A.I.C.S.: 523999
Kam Hang Ho *(CEO)*

YUSEI HOLDINGS LTD.
Room D6B 17 / F TML Plaza 3 Hoi Shing Road Tsuen Wan, Hong Kong, New Territories, China (Hong Kong)
Tel.: (852) 57183531181   Ky
Web Site: http://www.yusei.ch
0096—(HKG)
Rev.: $247,909,334
Assets: $326,008,379
Liabilities: $210,302,914
Net Worth: $115,705,465
Earnings: $7,899,606
Emp.: 2,950
Fiscal Year-end: 12/31/22
Precision Plastic Injection Molds & Plastic Component Mfr
N.A.I.C.S.: 333511
Katsutoshi Masuda *(Founder & Chm)*

Subsidiaries:

Zhejiang Yusei Plastics & Mould Co., Ltd. (1)
Guali Lingang Industrial Zone, Xiaoshan District, Hangzhou, 311241, Zhejiang, China
Tel.: (86) 57182836200
Automotive Part Whslr
N.A.I.C.S.: 441330

YUSHIN PRECISION EQUIPMENT CO. LTD.
555 Kuzetonoshiro-cho, Minami-ku, Kyoto, 601-8205, Japan
Tel.: (81) 759339555
Web Site: https://www.ype.co.jp
Year Founded: 1973
6482—(TKS)
Rev.: $156,095,150
Assets: $283,046,810
Liabilities: $55,543,830
Net Worth: $227,502,980
Earnings: $11,184,120
Emp.: 787
Fiscal Year-end: 03/31/24
Take-out Robots & Optical Disk Related Equipment Mfr
N.A.I.C.S.: 518210
Yasushi Kitagawa *(Exec Mng Dir, Exec Mng Dir, Gen Mgr-Mfg & Mfg & Gen Mgr-Mfg & Quality Assurance Dept)*

Subsidiaries:

Guangzhou Yushin Precision Equipment Co., Ltd. (1)
No 2 Chuangli Road XiangShan street, Zengcheng Economic& Technological Development District, Guangzhou, 511356, Guangdong, China
Tel.: (86) 2082690091
Web Site: http://www.ype.co.jp
Emp.: 30
Industrial Automation System Mfr
N.A.I.C.S.: 334513

WEMO Automation AB (1)
Bredastensvagen 12, 331 44, Varnamo, Sweden
Tel.: (86) 370658500
Web Site: https://www.wemogroup.com
Linear-Robot-Systems & Automation Cell Mfr
N.A.I.C.S.: 336612

Yushin America Inc. (1)
35 Kenney Dr, Cranston, RI 02920-4443
Tel.: (401) 463-1800
Industrial Automation System Mfr
N.A.I.C.S.: 334513
Christopher E. Parrillo *(Mgr-Natl Sls)*

Yushin Automation Ltd. (1)
Unit 15-17 Aston Road, Aston Fields Industrial Estate, Bromsgrove, B60 3EX, Worcestershire, United Kingdom
Tel.: (44) 1527558218
Web Site:
   https://www.yushinautomation.com

YUSHIRO CHEMICAL INDUSTRY CO. LTD.

Emp.: 12
Industrial Automation System Mfr
N.A.I.C.S.: 334513

Yushin Korea Co., Ltd. (1)
Tawon Techno-town F-101 98 Okuchundong-Ro, Okuchundong-Ro, Siheung, 15097, Gyeonggi-Do, Korea (South)
Tel.: (82) 314339655
Web Site: http://www.yushinkorea.com
Emp.: 22
Industrial Automation System Mfr
N.A.I.C.S.: 334513

Yushin Precision Equipment (India) Pvt. Ltd. (1)
Plot No 7 4th Floor Dr Kannan Tower Lakshmi Nagar Extension Arcot Road, Porur, Chennai, 600116, Tamil Nadu, India
Tel.: (91) 4442318005
Web Site: http://www.yushin.com
Emp.: 5
Industrial Automation System Mfr
N.A.I.C.S.: 334513

Yushin Precision Equipment (Taiwan) Co., Ltd. (1)
10F No 45 Sec 1 Minquan East Road, Zhongshan, Taipei, 10452, Taiwan
Tel.: (886) 225850507
Web Site: http://www.ype.co.jp
Industrial Automation System Mfr
N.A.I.C.S.: 334513

Yushin Precision Equipment (Thailand) Co., Ltd. (1)
179/346 Supalai Place 1st Floor Soi Sukhumvit 39 Sukhumvit Rd, Klongton Nua Wattana, Bangkok, 10110, Thailand
Tel.: (66) 26622580
Web Site: http://www.yushin.com
Emp.: 18
Industrial Automation System Mfr
N.A.I.C.S.: 334513

Yushin Precision Equipment Sdn. Bhd. (1)
Unit No C-03A-5 Setiawalk Persiaran Wawasan, Pusat Bandar, 47160, Puchong, Selangor, Malaysia
Tel.: (60) 358805445
Web Site: https://www.yushin.com.my
Emp.: 74
Injection Molding Machines Repair & Maintenance Services
N.A.I.C.S.: 811310

Yushin Precision Equipment Technical Center (1)
487 Kuzetsukiyama-cho, Minami-ku, Kyoto, 601-8203, Japan (100%)
Tel.: (81) 759339555
Production of Semiconductor-Related Equipment & Specialized Automation for Medical Applications
N.A.I.C.S.: 334413

YUSHIRO CHEMICAL INDUSTRY CO. LTD.
2-34-16 Chidori, Ota-ku, Tokyo, 146-8510, Japan
Tel.: (81) 337506761
Web Site: https://www.yushiro.co.jp
Year Founded: 1944
5013—(TKS)
Rev.: $350,230,850
Assets: $410,937,090
Liabilities: $129,132,960
Net Worth: $281,804,130
Earnings: $19,896,100
Emp.: 410
Fiscal Year-end: 03/31/24
Metalworking Fluids Mfr
N.A.I.C.S.: 325998
Masanori Arisaka *(Sr Mng Dir)*

Subsidiaries:

San-I Chemical Co., Ltd. (1)
7th Fl No 48 Ming Chuang W Rd, Zhongshan, Taipei, 10449, Taiwan
Tel.: (886) 225221313
Web Site: http://www.san-i.com.tw
Metalworking Fluids Mfr
N.A.I.C.S.: 325998

YUSHIRO CHEMICAL INDUSTRY CO. LTD.

Yushiro Chemical Industry Co. Ltd.—(Continued)

Shanghai Yushiro Chemical Industry Co., Ltd. (1)
No 881 Fulian Road, Baoshan District, Shanghai, 201906, China
Tel.: (86) 2136041188
Chemical Products Mfr
N.A.I.C.S.: 325998

Yushiro Manufacturing America Inc. (1)
783 W Mausoleum Rd, Shelbyville, IN 46176-9720
Tel.: (317) 398-9862
Web Site: http://www.yushirousa.com
Lubricating Oil Mfr
N.A.I.C.S.: 324191
Gayle Pay *(Mgr-HR)*

Subsidiary (Domestic):

QualiChem, Inc. (2)
2003 Salem Industrial Dr, Salem, VA 24153
Tel.: (540) 375-6700
Web Site: https://www.qualichem.com
Emp.: 52
Chemical Product & Preparation Mfr; Cooling & Boiler Products
N.A.I.C.S.: 325998
Doug Frassa *(Exec VP)*

YUSIN HOLDING CORP
5F No 381 Wufeng N Rd, East Dist, Chiayi, 600, Taiwan
Tel.: (886) 52788687
Web Site: https://yusin.com
Year Founded: 2011
4557—(TAI)
Rev.: $105,764,311
Assets: $132,761,792
Liabilities: $60,425,257
Net Worth: $72,336,535
Earnings: $12,742,960
Fiscal Year-end: 12/31/23
Automotive Parts Mfr & Distr
N.A.I.C.S.: 336390

Subsidiaries:

Xiamen Yong Yu Machinery Co., Ltd. (1)
No 5 Si Ming Dist, Tung Ann Industrial Area, Xiamen, 361100, China
Tel.: (86) 5925932999
Automobile Parts Mfr
N.A.I.C.S.: 332119

YUSYS TECHNOLOGIES CO., LTD.
Building A2 Electronic City R&D Center Courtyard 9, East Jiuxianqiao Road Chaoyang District, Beijing, China
Tel.: (86) 1059137700
Web Site: https://www.yusys.com.cn
300674—(CHIN)
Rev.: $732,941,469
Assets: $784,011,172
Liabilities: $201,307,693
Net Worth: $582,703,478
Earnings: $45,877,690
Emp.: 13,000
Fiscal Year-end: 12/31/23
Software Development Services
N.A.I.C.S.: 541511
Weidong Hong *(Chm & CEO)*

YUTAKA FOODS CORPORATION
34-1 Kawawaki Taketoyo-cho, Chita, 470-2395, Aichi, Japan
Tel.: (81) 569721231
Web Site:
 https://www.yutakafoods.co.jp
Year Founded: 1944
2806—(TKS)
Sales Range: $150-199.9 Million
Food Product Mfr & Distr
N.A.I.C.S.: 311942

YUTAKA TRUSTY SECURITIES CO., LTD.
Nihonbashi Kakigaracho 1-16-12 Yutaka Building, Chuo-Ku, Tokyo, 103-0014, Japan
Tel.: (81) 336675211
Web Site: http://www.yutaka-shoji.co.jp
Year Founded: 1957
8747—(TKS)
Rev.: $48,927,220
Assets: $657,536,360
Liabilities: $575,103,050
Net Worth: $82,433,310
Earnings: $9,452,300
Emp.: 383
Fiscal Year-end: 03/31/24
Commodity Brokerage Services
N.A.I.C.S.: 523160
Masafumi Yasunari *(Pres)*

YUTONG BUS CO., LTD.
66 Yuxing Road Zhengzhou Economic and Technological Development Zone, Henan, 450016, China
Tel.: (86) 37166718999
Web Site: https://www.yutong.com
Year Founded: 1963
600066—(SHG)
Rev.: $3,060,574,068
Assets: $4,211,661,959
Liabilities: $2,162,371,541
Net Worth: $2,049,290,418
Earnings: $106,583,635
Emp.: 4,000
Fiscal Year-end: 12/31/22
Bus Parts Manufacturing Industry
N.A.I.C.S.: 336120
YuXiang Tang *(Chm & Pres)*

YUUZOO CORPORATION LIMITED
20 Science Park Road Teletech Park 03-11/14, Singapore Science Park II, Singapore, Singapore
Tel.: (65) 6311 9359   BM
Web Site: http://www.yuucorp.com
AFC—(SES)
Sales Range: $50-74.9 Million
Investment Management Service
N.A.I.C.S.: 523940
Mohan Das *(CEO)*

YUVALIM GROUP INVESTMENTS LTD.
Rogovin tidhar building Menachem Begin 11, Ramat Gan, 5268104, Israel
Tel.: (972) 36124433   II
Web Site: https://www.en.yuvalim-group.co.il
Year Founded: 2000
YBKB—(TAE)
Rev.: $56,139,245
Assets: $285,049,035
Liabilities: $250,366,069
Net Worth: $34,682,967
Earnings: $6,531,565
Fiscal Year-end: 12/31/23
Investment Management Service
N.A.I.C.S.: 523999

YUVRAAJ HYGIENE PRODUCTS LIMITED
A 650 TTC M I D C Mahape, Navi Mumbai, 400 705, India
Tel.: (91) 22 27784491
Web Site: http://www.hic.in
Rev.: $1,858,037
Assets: $1,433,769
Liabilities: $1,607,418
Net Worth: $(173,649)
Earnings: $(300,791)
Emp.: 14
Fiscal Year-end: 03/31/19
Home Furnishing Whslr
N.A.I.C.S.: 423220
Ravindra Sharma *(CFO)*

YUWANG GROUP
No. 62, Jalan Emas 7, Bandar Sungai Emas, 42700, 42700, Selangor, Malaysia
Tel.: (60) 60331818333
Web Site:
 https://www.yuwang.com.my
Holding Company
N.A.I.C.S.: 551112

Subsidiaries:

Yuwang Plantation Sdn Bhd (1)
No. 62, Jalan Emas 7 Bandar Sungai Emas Banting, 42700, Selangor, Malaysia
Tel.: (60) 6033181533
Web Site: https://www.yuwang.com.my
Holding Company
N.A.I.C.S.: 551112

YUXING INFOTECH INVESTMENT HOLDINGS LIMITED
B-7Floor Tiancheng Technology Building No 2 XinFengStreet, DeShengMenWai XiCheng District, Beijing, China
Tel.: (86) 1062352535   BM
Web Site: http://www.yuxing.com.cn
Year Founded: 1991
8005—(HKG)
Rev.: $28,462,718
Assets: $287,519,513
Liabilities: $54,712,545
Net Worth: $232,806,968
Earnings: $(37,110,788)
Emp.: 130
Fiscal Year-end: 12/31/22
Holding Company
N.A.I.C.S.: 551112
Guangrong Shi *(Compliance Officer)*

YUYU PHARMA INC.
197 Dongho-ro, Jung-gu, Seoul, 04590, Korea (South)
Tel.: (82) 222536600
Web Site: https://www.yuyu.co.kr
Year Founded: 1941
000220—(KRS)
Rev.: $109,716,035
Assets: $154,212,008
Liabilities: $56,746,515
Net Worth: $97,465,493
Earnings: $(3,496,060)
Emp.: 259
Fiscal Year-end: 12/31/22
Pharmaceuticals Product Mfr
N.A.I.C.S.: 325412
Seungpil Yu *(Chm)*

YUZHOU GROUP HOLDINGS COMPANY LIMITED
Units 5801-02 58/F The Center 99 Queens Road, Central, China (Hong Kong)
Tel.: (852) 25081718   Ky
Web Site: http://ir.yuzhou-group.com
Year Founded: 1994
1628—(HKG)
Rev.: $3,753,908,496
Assets: $20,140,909,589
Liabilities: $16,620,329,466
Net Worth: $3,520,580,123
Earnings: $(1,862,994,276)
Emp.: 1,979
Fiscal Year-end: 12/31/22
Property Development Services
N.A.I.C.S.: 531390
Lung On Lam *(Founder & Chm)*

Subsidiaries:

Shanghai Yanhai Real Estate Development Co., Ltd. (1)
2/F No 333 Jingang Rd, Shanghai, 201206, China
Tel.: (86) 2151330001

INTERNATIONAL PUBLIC

Property Development Services
N.A.I.C.S.: 531390

YW CO., LTD.
744 Pangyo-ro C-dong 801, Bundang-Gu, Seongnam, 13510, Gyeonggi-Do, Korea (South)
Tel.: (82) 317037118
Web Site: https://www.ywtc.com
Year Founded: 1995
051390—(KRS)
Rev.: $15,557,515
Assets: $75,030,028
Liabilities: $16,279,062
Net Worth: $58,750,967
Earnings: $2,322,613
Emp.: 17
Fiscal Year-end: 12/31/22
Telecommunication Equipment Whslr
N.A.I.C.S.: 423690
Byung-Il Woo *(CEO)*

Subsidiaries:

Nagatomo Co., Ltd. (1)
67 Mizuguchi Bldg 14-6, Nihonbashi Kodemma-Cho, Chuo, 103-0001, Tokyo, Japan
Tel.: (81) 356517771
Electronic Equipment Distr
N.A.I.C.S.: 423690

YX ASSET RECOVERY LIMITED
Xincheng Science and Technology Park Building 7 West Yuelu Road No 588, Changsha, 410205, Hunan, China
Tel.: (86) 73181829999   Ky
Year Founded: 2018
Rev.: $110,174,797
Assets: $85,246,519
Liabilities: $36,731,766
Net Worth: $48,514,753
Earnings: $18,029,087
Emp.: 11,492
Fiscal Year-end: 12/31/18
Holding Company
N.A.I.C.S.: 551112
Man Tan *(Founder, Chm & CEO)*

YX PRECIOUS METALS BERHAD
23 25 & 27 Jalan 2/131A Project Jaya Industrial Estate Batu 6, Jalan Klang Lama, 58200, Kuala Lumpur, Malaysia
Tel.: (60) 377848136
Web Site:
 https://www.yxgroup.com.my
Year Founded: 1987
YXPM—(KLS)
Rev.: $52,198,085
Assets: $23,832,390
Liabilities: $897,257
Net Worth: $22,935,133
Earnings: $1,961,907
Fiscal Year-end: 12/31/23
Gold Product Mfr & Distr
N.A.I.C.S.: 332999
Sheau Chyn Ng *(Mng Dir)*

YY GROUP HOLDING LIMITED
60 Paya Lebar Road 09-13 to 17 Paya Lebar Square, Singapore, 409051, Singapore
Tel.: (65) 66046896   VG
Web Site:
 https://www.yygroupholding.com
Year Founded: 2010
YYGH—(NASDAQ)
Rev.: $31,772,286
Assets: $10,670,090
Liabilities: $6,528,577
Net Worth: $4,141,513
Earnings: $864,037
Emp.: 770
Fiscal Year-end: 12/31/23

Holding Company
N.A.I.C.S.: 551112

YZ QUEENCO LTD.
16 Bar-Kochva st Noa House 9 Flr,
Bnei Brak, 5126107, Israel
Tel.: (972) 37566555
Web Site: https://www.queenco.com
Year Founded: 1992
QNCO—(TAE)
Rev.: $34,641,525
Assets: $55,974,029
Liabilities: $22,995,165
Net Worth: $32,978,864
Earnings: $4,746,236
Emp.: 300
Fiscal Year-end: 12/31/23
Offices of Other Holding Companies
N.A.I.C.S.: 551112

Z-COM, INC.
5F No 8 Hsin-Ann Road Hsinchu Science Park, Hsinchu, 300, Taiwan
Tel.: (886) 35777364
Web Site: https://www.zcom.com.tw
Year Founded: 1995
8176—(TPE)
Rev.: $10,193,853
Assets: $24,214,333
Liabilities: $8,056,999
Net Worth: $16,157,334
Earnings: ($2,022,012)
Fiscal Year-end: 12/31/22
Communication Equipment Mfr
N.A.I.C.S.: 334290
Wu Chia-Fang (CEO)

ZACATECAS SILVER CORP.
488 -1090 West Georgia Street, Vancouver, V6E 3V7, BC, Canada
Tel.: (604) 802-4447
Web Site: https://zacatecassilver.com
Year Founded: 2020
ZAC—(TSXV)
Silver Mining
N.A.I.C.S.: 212220
Bryan Slusarchuk (CEO & Dir)

Subsidiaries:

Minas de Oro Nacional S.A. de
C.V. (1)
De Los Pimas Parque Industrial, 83299,
Hermosillo, Sonora, Mexico
Tel.: (52) 662 217 3707
Gold Ore Mining Services
N.A.I.C.S.: 212220
Brian Peer (Gen Mgr)

ZACD GROUP LTD.
300 Beach Road 34 05 The Concourse, Singapore, 199555, Singapore
Tel.: (65) 65001120   SG
Web Site:
  https://www.zacdgroup.com
Year Founded: 2005
8313—(HKG)
Rev.: $7,502,840
Assets: $23,930,925
Liabilities: $6,899,190
Net Worth: $17,031,735
Earnings: $1,315,610
Emp.: 29
Fiscal Year-end: 12/31/23
Real Estate Manangement Services
N.A.I.C.S.: 531390
Stanley Choon Yeo (Co-Founder & CEO)

ZACHERT PRIVATE EQUITY GMBH
Karl Marx Strasse 25, 15537, Brandenburg, Germany
Tel.: (49) 33625089890
Web Site: http://www.olaf-zachert.com
Privater Equity Firm
N.A.I.C.S.: 523999
Olaf Zachert (Mng Dir)

Subsidiaries:

Brands Within Reach, LLC (1)
141 Halstead Ave Second Fl, Mamaroneck, NY 10543
Tel.: (847) 720-9090
Web Site: http://www.bwrgroup.com
Soft Drink & Bottled Water Mfr
N.A.I.C.S.: 312111
Jennifer Monaco-Lofgre (Mgr-Bus Dev)

ZACROS CORPORATION
22nd Floor Bunkyo Garden Gate Tower 1-1-1 Koishikawa, Bunkyo-ku, Tokyo, 112-0002, Japan
Tel.: (81) 358044221
Web Site: https://www.zacros.co.jp
Year Founded: 1914
79170—(TKS)
Rev.: $976,698,200
Assets: $969,722,000
Liabilities: $295,650,450
Net Worth: $674,071,550
Earnings: $36,647,700
Emp.: 2,664
Fiscal Year-end: 03/31/23
Plastic Packaging Materials Mfr
N.A.I.C.S.: 326112
Akihiko Fujimori (Chm)

Subsidiaries:

Fujimori Sangyo Co., Ltd. (1)
10F Shinjuku First West 1-23-7 Nishi-Shinjuku, Shinjuku-ku, Tokyo, 160-0023, Japan
Tel.: (81) 353398527
Emp.: 249
Plastic Packaging Materials Mfr
N.A.I.C.S.: 326112
Yukihiko Fujimori (Chm & Pres)

Zacros America, Inc. (1)
1821 Walden Office Sq Ste 400, Schaumburg, IL 60173
Tel.: (847) 397-6191
Plastic Packaging Film Mfr
N.A.I.C.S.: 326112
Kazuhiko Maeda (Pres)

Division (Domestic):

Hedwin Division of Zacros
America (2)
1600 Roland Heights Ave, Baltimore, MD 21211-1213
Tel.: (410) 467-8209
Web Site: http://www.hedwin.com
Sales Range: $50-74.9 Million
Emp.: 300
Designer, Mfr & Marketer of Specialty Industrial Plastic Containers & Liner Products
N.A.I.C.S.: 326199
Tom Carpenter (Mgr-Sls-Natl)

Zacros Malaysia Sdn. Bhd. (1)
No 18 Jalan Tiang U8/93, Taman Perindustrian Bukit Jelutong Seksyen U8, 40150, Shah Alam, Selangor, Malaysia
Tel.: (60) 378473115
Web Site: http://www.zacros.com.my
Packaging Material Whslr
N.A.I.C.S.: 423840

Zacros Taiwan Co., Ltd. (1)
No 33 Beiling 6th Rd, Luzhu Dist, Kaohsiung, 821, Taiwan
Tel.: (886) 76955966
Emp.: 140
Industrial Equipment Mfr
N.A.I.C.S.: 333248
Kimihiko Shiomi (Chm)

ZAD HOLDING COMPANY S.A.Q.
PO Box 1444, Doha, Qatar
Tel.: (974) 44415000
Web Site: https://zad.qa
Year Founded: 1969
ZHCD—(QE)
Rev.: $352,131,037
Assets: $694,203,264
Liabilities: $279,756,538
Net Worth: $414,446,726
Earnings: $51,783,760
Emp.: 180
Fiscal Year-end: 12/31/21
Holding Company; Food Mfr & Marketer
N.A.I.C.S.: 551112
Nasser Mohammad Jabor Al-Thani (Chm)

Subsidiaries:

ALCAT Contracting Company (1)
Al-Fereej Building Office 102 C-Ring Road Najma Area, Doha, Qatar
Tel.: (974) 44434241
Web Site: https://www.alcatqatar.com
Road & Infrastructure Construction Services
N.A.I.C.S.: 237310
Hossam Banna (Gen Mgr)

Gulf United Real Estate Investments
Company (1)
PO Box 3805, Doha, Qatar
Tel.: (974) 44355501
Web Site: https://www.guc.qa
Real Estate Rental Services
N.A.I.C.S.: 531110
Afaque A Khan (Gen Mgr)

Qatar Flour Mills Company (1)
PO Box 1444, Doha, Qatar
Tel.: (974) 44415000
Web Site: https://www.qfm.qa
Wheat Flour Mfr & Distr
N.A.I.C.S.: 311211

Qatar Foods Industries (1)
Doha Port, Doha, Qatar
Tel.: (974) 44415000
Web Site: https://www.qfi.qa
Edible Oil Retailer
N.A.I.C.S.: 424490

Umm Said Bakery (1)
Meena Street Near Doha Port, PO Box 1444, Doha, Qatar
Tel.: (974) 44415000
Web Site: https://www.qbake.com.qa
Bakery Products Mfr
N.A.I.C.S.: 311813
Aarif Ibrahim (Gen Mgr)

ZAFIN LABS
1701 401 W Georgia Street, Vancouver, V6B 5A1, BC, Canada
Tel.: (604) 564-0313
Web Site: http://www.zafin.com
Year Founded: 2002
Emp.: 200
Product & Pricing Lifecycle Management Software Developer
N.A.I.C.S.: 513210
Nizar Jaffer Somji (Chm)

Subsidiaries:

Zafin Labs UK Limited (1)
50 Liverpool Street, London, EC2M 7PD, United Kingdom
Tel.: (44) 2030360840
Application Software Development Services
N.A.I.C.S.: 541511

ZAGGLE PREPAID OCEAN SERVICES LIMITED
Boomerang Building Ground Floor B-1004 Yadav Nagar, Chandivali Powai, Mumbai, 400072, India
Tel.: (91) 2248794879
Web Site: https://www.zaggle.in
Year Founded: 2011
543985—(BOM)
Emp.: 250
Asset Management Services
N.A.I.C.S.: 523999

ZAGREBACKA BURZA D.D.
Ivana Lucica 2a, 10000, Zagreb, Croatia
Tel.: (385) 14686800
Web Site: https://www.zse.hr
Year Founded: 1991
ZB—(ZAG)
Rev.: $2,688,154
Assets: $7,697,366
Liabilities: $1,437,589
Net Worth: $6,259,777
Earnings: $91,384
Emp.: 39
Fiscal Year-end: 12/31/22
Stock Exchange Services
N.A.I.C.S.: 523210
Ivana Gazic (Chm-Mgmt Bd)

Subsidiaries:

Ljubljanska borza, d.d. (1)
Slovenska Cesta 56, 1000, Ljubljana, Slovenia
Tel.: (386) 14710211
Web Site: http://www.ljse.si
Emp.: 11
Stock Exchange Services
N.A.I.C.S.: 523210
Alice Ipavec (Chm-Mgmt Bd)

Affiliate (Non-US):

Banjaluka berza hartija od vrijednosti
a.d. (2)
Petra Kocica bb, 78000, Banja Luka, Bosnia & Herzegovina
Tel.: (387) 51326041
Web Site: https://www.blberza.com
Emp.: 10
Stock Exchange Services
N.A.I.C.S.: 523210
Smilja Jokic (Member-Mgmt Bd)

Beogradska Berza a.d. (2)
Omladinskih brigada 1, 11070, Belgrade, Serbia
Tel.: (381) 113117297
Web Site: http://www.belex.rs
Stock Exchange Services
N.A.I.C.S.: 523210
Radojko Miladinovic (Dir-IT)

Macedonian Stock Exchange,
Inc. (2)
Orce Nikolov 75, 1000, Skopje, North Macedonia
Tel.: (389) 23122055
Web Site: http://www.mse.com.mk
Stock Exchange Services
N.A.I.C.S.: 523210
Ivan Steriev (CEO)

The Sarajevo Stock Exchange (2)
Doke Mazalica 4/I, 71000, Sarajevo, Bosnia & Herzegovina
Tel.: (387) 33251460
Web Site: https://www.sase.ba
Stock Exchange Services
N.A.I.C.S.: 523210
Almir Mirica (Exec Dir-Trading & Surveillance Dept)

ZAGREBACKE PEKARNE KLARA D.D.
Utinjska 48, 10020, Zagreb, Croatia
Tel.: (385) 13688400
Web Site: https://www.klara.hr
Year Founded: 1909
ZPKL—(ZAG)
Sales Range: Less than $1 Million
Frozen Baked Food Distr
N.A.I.C.S.: 424420
Petar Thur (Dir)

ZAGREBACKI HOLDING D.O.O.
Ul Grada Vukovara 41, 10000, Zagreb, Croatia
Tel.: (385) 16420000
Web Site: http://www.zgh.hr
3ZGH2—(ZAG)
Rev.: $652,807,153
Assets: $2,340,103,765
Liabilities: $1,630,799,205
Net Worth: $709,304,559
Earnings: $18,039,519
Emp.: 7,302
Fiscal Year-end: 12/31/23
Offices of Other Holding Companies
N.A.I.C.S.: 551112

ZAGREBACKI HOLDING D.O.O.

Zagrebacki holding d.o.o.—(Continued)
Zeljko Horvat (Dir-Ops)

Subsidiaries:

AGM d.o.o. (1)
Mihanoviceva 28, 10000, Zagreb, Croatia
Tel.: (385) 14856309
Web Site: http://www.agm.hr
Gas Distribution Services
N.A.I.C.S.: 221210

Centar d.o.o. (1)
Palmoticeva 22-2, 10000, Zagreb, Croatia
Tel.: (385) 16420000
Gas Distribution Services
N.A.I.C.S.: 221210

Gradska Plinara Bjelovar d.o.o. (1)
Blajburskih zrtava 18, 43000, Bjelovar, Croatia
Tel.: (385) 43611323
Web Site: http://www.gpb.hr
Gas Distribution Services
N.A.I.C.S.: 221210

Gradska ljekarna Zagreb d.o.o. (1)
Kralja Drzislava 6, 10000, Zagreb, Croatia
Tel.: (385) 14557102
Web Site: http://www.gljz.hr
Pharmacy Services
N.A.I.C.S.: 456110

Gradska plinara Zagreb Opskrba d.o.o. (1)
Radnicka cesta 1, 10000, Zagreb, Croatia
Tel.: (385) 16437320
Web Site: http://www.gpz-opskrba.hr
Emp.: 124
Gas Distribution Services
N.A.I.C.S.: 221210

Gradska plinara Zagreb d.o.o. (1)
Radnicka cesta 1, PO Box 132, 10001, Zagreb, Croatia
Tel.: (385) 16437777
Web Site: http://www.plinara-zagreb.hr
Gas Distribution Services
N.A.I.C.S.: 221210
Tomislav Mazal (Gen Mgr)

Gradsko Stambeno Komunalno Gospodarstvo d.o.o. (1)
Savska cesta 1, 10000, Zagreb, Croatia
Tel.: (385) 4565811
Web Site: http://www.gskg.hr
Gas Distribution Services
N.A.I.C.S.: 221210

Vodoopskrba i odvodnja d.o.o. (1)
Folnegoviceva 1, 10000, Zagreb, Croatia
Tel.: (385) 16163000
Web Site: http://www.vio.hr
Water Supply Services
N.A.I.C.S.: 221310

Zagreb plakat d.o.o. (1)
Hebrangova 32, 10000, Zagreb, Croatia
Tel.: (385) 16311200
Web Site: http://www.zagrebplakat.hr
Outdoor Advertising Services
N.A.I.C.S.: 541850

Zagrebacka Stanogradnja d.o.o. (1)
Jankomir 25, 10000, Zagreb, Croatia
Tel.: (385) 16420951
Construction Services
N.A.I.C.S.: 236220

ZAGRO ASIA LTD

Zagro Global Hub 5 Woodlands Terrace, 738430, Singapore
Tel.: (65) 67591811
Web Site: http://www.zagro.com
Year Founded: 1953
Sales Range: $100-124.9 Million
Nutrition, Protection & Agriculture Products Mfr & Distr
N.A.I.C.S.: 325414
Beng Swee Poh (Chm & CEO)

Subsidiaries:

Agsin Limited (1)
12th Floor Ploenchit Center 2 Sukhumvit Road Kwaeng Klongtoey, Khet Klongtoey, Bangkok, 10110, Thailand
Tel.: (66) 2 656 8710

Emp.: 100
Crop & Animal Healthcare Products Mfr
N.A.I.C.S.: 325320

P.T. Zagro Indonesia (1)
Karindra Building Lt 2 Suite No 10, Jl Palmerah Selatan No 30A, Jakarta, 11270, Indonesia (100%)
Tel.: (62) 2126710709
Crop Care & Animal Health Products Distr & Trader
N.A.I.C.S.: 115114

Vetsquare.com Pte Ltd (1)
5 Woodlands Terrace, PO Box 0102, Singapore, 738430, Singapore (100%)
Tel.: (65) 67539188
Web Site: http://www.vetsquare.com
Emp.: 80
Animal Health Products Distr
N.A.I.C.S.: 812910
Poh Beng Swee (Chm)

Zagro (Thailand) Ltd. (1)
6/6 Moo 4 rangsit-Nakornnayok Road Bueng Yitho, Thanyaburi Pathumthani, Bangkok, 12130, Thailand (100%)
Tel.: (66) 2 957 8360
Web Site: http://www.zagro.com
Sales Range: $1-9.9 Million
Emp.: 100
Agri-Health Products Mfr & Distr
N.A.I.C.S.: 325320
Somchai Theveethivarak (Gen Mgr)

Zagro Animal Health Pte Ltd (1)
Zagro Global Hub, 5 Woodlands Terrace, Singapore, 738430, Singapore (100%)
Tel.: (65) 67591811
Web Site: http://www.neocidol.com
Emp.: 80
Animal Health Products Distr & Trader
N.A.I.C.S.: 311119

Zagro Chemicals Sdn Bhd (1)
27 Jalan PJS 3/34 Taman Sri Manja, 46000, Petaling Jaya, Selangor, Malaysia
Tel.: (60) 377830766
Web Site: http://www.zagro.com
Emp.: 100
Chemical Products Mfr & Distr
N.A.I.C.S.: 325199

Zagro Corporation (1)
7th Floor Raha Sulayman Building 108 Benavidez Street, Legaspi Village, Makati, 12229, Philippines (100%)
Tel.: (63) 28101340
Emp.: 20
Agri-Health Product Distr
N.A.I.C.S.: 325320
Chin Vui Nam (Pres)

Zagro Europe GmbH (1)
Rheinstrasse 1, 79618, Rheinfelden, Germany (100%)
Tel.: (49) 7623794555
Web Site: http://www.zagro.com
Emp.: 1
Animal Health Products Distr & Trader
N.A.I.C.S.: 311119

Zagro Singapore Pte Ltd (1)
Zagro Global Hub, 5 Woodlands Terrace, Singapore, 738430, Singapore (100%)
Tel.: (65) 6567591811
Web Site: http://www.zagro.com
Sales Range: $1-9.9 Million
Animal Health Products Mfr & Distr; Crop Care, Healthcare & Specialty Chemical Products Distr
N.A.I.C.S.: 923130

Zagro Singapore Pte Ltd (1)
5 Woodlands Terrace, Zagro Global Hub, Singapore, 738430, Singapore (100%)
Tel.: (65) 6759 1811
Web Site: http://www.zagro.com
Emp.: 50
Agri-Health Products Investment Holding & Trading
N.A.I.C.S.: 551112

Zagro Taiwan International Ltd (1)
No 332 Gongye Road, Nant'ou, Taiwan
Tel.: (886) 492254727
Crop & Animal Healthcare Products Mfr
N.A.I.C.S.: 325320

Zagro Vietnam Company Ltd. (1)
No 9 Workshop 5 Street Long Thanh Industrial Zone, Long Thanh District, Long Thanh, Dong Nai, Vietnam
Tel.: (84) 61 3 514676
Web Site: http://www.zagro.com
Emp.: 18
Crop & Animal Healthcare Products Mfr
N.A.I.C.S.: 325320

ZAHA HADID HOLDINGS LTD.

10 Bowling Green Lane, London, EC1R 0BQ, United Kingdom
Tel.: (44) 20 7253 5147
Web Site: http://www.zaha-hadid.com
Sales Range: $50-74.9 Million
Emp.: 500
Architectural Services
N.A.I.C.S.: 541310
Patrick Schumacher (Partner)

ZAHEEN SPINNING LTD.

House 59/A Road 12/A 6th and 7th Floor Near Takwa Masjid, Dhanmondi, Dhaka, 1209, Bangladesh
Tel.: (880) 255000958
Web Site:
    https://www.zaheenspinningltd.com
Year Founded: 2007
ZAHEENSPIN—(CHT)
Rev.: $5,386,386
Assets: $9,575,684
Liabilities: $4,275,974
Net Worth: $5,299,709
Earnings: $140,066
Emp.: 441
Fiscal Year-end: 06/30/23
Cotton Yarn Mfr
N.A.I.C.S.: 313110
Farida Khanom (Co-Founder & Chm)

ZAHIDJEE TEXTILES MILLS LTD

2 H Gullberg II, Lahore, Pakistan
Tel.: (92) 4235777290
Web Site:
    https://www.zahidjee.com.pk
Year Founded: 1990
ZAHID—(PSX)
Rev.: $116,261,881
Assets: $96,496,069
Liabilities: $39,790,803
Net Worth: $56,705,266
Earnings: $4,365,120
Emp.: 1,502
Fiscal Year-end: 06/30/23
Textile Mfr
N.A.I.C.S.: 314999
Muhammad Sharif (Chm)

ZAHINTEX INDUSTRIES LTD

Vogra By Pass Mor Bashan Garipur City Corporation, Gazipur, 1704, Bangladesh
Tel.: (880) 2224423459
Web Site: https://zahintex.com
Year Founded: 2002
ZAHINTEX—(CHT)
Rev.: $3,646,469
Assets: $32,201,166
Liabilities: $24,727,940
Net Worth: $7,473,226
Earnings: ($1,924,801)
Emp.: 635
Fiscal Year-end: 06/30/23
Knit Garment Mfr
N.A.I.C.S.: 313240
Khatib Abdul Zahid Mukul (Mng Dir)

ZAHRAT AL WAHA FOR TRADING CO

Al Rabwa Al Ahsa Street, Unit No 1 Building 7449, Riyadh, 12814, Saudi Arabia
Tel.: (966) 920021203
Web Site: https://www.zaoasis.com
3007—(SAU)
Rev.: $152,659,936
Assets: $161,977,761

INTERNATIONAL PUBLIC

Liabilities: $77,687,901
Net Worth: $84,289,860
Earnings: $9,032,611
Emp.: 163
Fiscal Year-end: 12/31/23
Plastics Bottle Mfr
N.A.I.C.S.: 326160
George Abdulkarim George Mousa (CEO)

ZAHRAVI PHARMACEUTICAL COMPANY

Tel.: (98) 2144991893
Year Founded: 1986
DZAH—(THE)
Sales Range: Less than $1 Million
Emp.: 318
Pharmaceutical Preparation Mfr
N.A.I.C.S.: 325412
Farhad Kiafar (Mng Dir)

ZAHUR COTTON MILLS LIMITED

623-B Pcsir Phase-II, Lahore, 54000, Pakistan
Tel.: (92) 4235138880
Web Site: https://zahurcotton.com
Year Founded: 1990
Yarn Spinning Mill Operator
N.A.I.C.S.: 313110
Rabia Zahur (Sec)

ZAI LAB LIMITED

Building 1 4/F Jinchuang Plaza 4560 Jinke Road, Pudong, Shanghai, 201210, China
Tel.: (86) 2161632588
Web Site:
    https://www.zailaboratory.com
Year Founded: 2014
ZLAB—(NASDAQ)
Rev.: $215,040,000
Assets: $1,220,140,000
Liabilities: $174,545,000
Net Worth: $1,045,595,000
Earnings: ($443,286,000)
Emp.: 2,036
Fiscal Year-end: 12/31/22
Biopharmaceutical Research & Development Services
N.A.I.C.S.: 325412
Ning Xu (Exec VP & Head-Clinical Ops)

ZAIGLE CO. LTD.

1114 11th floor 217 Heojun-ro, Gangseo-gu, Seoul, Korea (South)
Tel.: (82) 236659192
Web Site: https://www.zaigle.com
Year Founded: 2008
234920—(KRS)
Rev.: $11,499,640
Assets: $46,820,848
Liabilities: $14,830,026
Net Worth: $31,990,822
Earnings: ($2,864,833)
Emp.: 44
Fiscal Year-end: 12/31/22
Cooking Apparatus Mfr & Distr
N.A.I.C.S.: 332215

ZAIM CREDIT SYSTEMS PLC

10 Orange Street, London, WC2H 7DQ, United Kingdom
Tel.: (44) 79257089816
Web Site:
    https://www.zaimcreditsystems.com
Year Founded: 2011
ZAIM—(LSE)
Rev.: $12,958,097
Assets: $7,254,336
Liabilities: $4,239,718
Net Worth: $3,014,618
Earnings: $926,848
Emp.: 152
Fiscal Year-end: 12/31/21

Financial Consulting Services
N.A.I.C.S.: 541611
Siro Donato Cicconi (CEO)

ZAIN PARTICIPACOES SA
Av Rio Branco 311 - Sala 523/parte, 20040903, Rio de Janeiro, Brazil
Tel.: (55) 21 2196 7200
Year Founded: 1998
Financial Investment Services
N.A.I.C.S.: 523999
Alberto Ribeiro Guth (Dir-IR)

ZAKLAD BUDOWY MASZYN ZREMB CHOJNICE S.A.
ul Przemyslowa 15, 89-600, Chojnice, Poland
Tel.: (48) 523965710
Web Site: https://zrembchojnice.pl
Year Founded: 1973
ZRE—(WAR)
Rev.: $9,411,077
Assets: $11,198,933
Liabilities: $6,211,128
Net Worth: $4,987,805
Earnings: $594,512
Fiscal Year-end: 12/31/23
Steel Container Mfr
N.A.I.C.S.: 332439
Wojtek Kolakowski (Chm-Supervisory Bd)

ZAKLADY AUTOMATYKI POLNA S.A.
Obozowa 23 Str, 37-700, Przemysl, Poland
Tel.: (48) 166786601
Web Site: http://www.polna.com.pl
Sales Range: $1-9.9 Million
Emp.: 216
Industrial & Heat Engineering Automatics Mfr
N.A.I.C.S.: 333517
Lukasz Hladu (Chm-Mgmt Bd)

ZAKLADY CHEMICZNE POLICE S.A.
ul Kuznicka 1, 72-010, Police, Poland
Tel.: (48) 913171717
Web Site:
  https://zchpolice.grupaazoty.com
Year Founded: 1969
PCE—(WAR)
Sales Range: $500-549.9 Million
Emp.: 3,700
Mineral Fertilizer Mfr
N.A.I.C.S.: 325311
Pawel Jarczewski (Chm-Supervisory Bd)

Subsidiaries:

Automatika Sp. z o.o. (1)
ul Kuznicka 1, 72-010, Police, Poland
Tel.: (48) 913174056
Web Site: http://www.automatika.com.pl
Emp.: 289
Chemicals & Fertilizers Mfr
N.A.I.C.S.: 325314

Koncept Sp. z o.o. (1)
ul Kuznicka 1, 72-010, Police, Poland
Tel.: (48) 91 317 33 53
Web Site: http://www.koncept-zchpolice.pl
Chemicals & Fertilizers Mfr
N.A.I.C.S.: 325314
Slawomir Korzeb (CEO)

Remech Sp. z o.o. (1)
Chorzow ul Piekarska 1-3, 41-506, Police, Poland
Tel.: (48) 32 3453695
Web Site: http://www.remech.pl
Emp.: 400
Industrial Machinery Repair & Maintenance Services
N.A.I.C.S.: 811310
Marek Janiak (Mgr-Production)

Supra Sp. z o.o. (1)
ul Rakus 18, 30-864, Krakow, Poland

Tel.: (48) 12 651 25 10
Web Site: http://www.supra.com.pl
Software Development Services
N.A.I.C.S.: 541511

Transtech Sp. z o.o. (1)
ul Zolnierska 68, 41-936, Bytom, Poland
Tel.: (48) 913174335
Web Site: http://www.transtech.pl
Transportation & Shipping Services
N.A.I.C.S.: 488510

Zarzad Morskiego Portu Police Sp. z o.o. (1)
ul Kuznicka 1, 72-010, Police, West Pomeranian, Poland
Tel.: (48) 913173101
Web Site: https://www.portpolice.pl
Cost Management Services
N.A.I.C.S.: 488330

ZAKLADY MAGNEZYTOWE ROPCZYCE S.A.
Postepu 15c Street, 02-676, Warsaw, Poland
Tel.: (48) 172229222
Web Site:
  https://www.ropczyce.com.pl
Year Founded: 1971
RPC—(WAR)
Rev.: $113,411,077
Assets: $173,679,624
Liabilities: $71,922,764
Net Worth: $101,756,859
Earnings: $3,989,837
Fiscal Year-end: 12/31/23
Construction Materials Mfr
N.A.I.C.S.: 333120
Jozef Siwiec (Chm/Pres-Mgmt Bd & Mng Dir)

ZAKLADY MIESNE HENRYK KANIA S.A.
Ul Korczaka 5, 43-200, Pszczyna, Poland
Tel.: (48) 32 210 32 47
Web Site: http://www.zmkania.pl
Food Products Mfr
N.A.I.C.S.: 311999
Grzegorz Minczanowski (Chm-Mgmt Bd)

ZAKLADY PRZEMYSLU CUKIERNICZEGO MIESZKO S.A.
ul Chrzanowskiego 8b, 04-392, Warsaw, Poland
Tel.: (48) 228102196
Sales Range: $150-199.9 Million
Emp.: 900
Confectionery Mfr
N.A.I.C.S.: 311351

ZAKLADY TLUSZCZOWE KRUSZWICA S.A.
ul Niepodleglosci 42, 88-150, Kruszwica, Poland
Tel.: (48) 523535202
Web Site: http://www.ztkruszwica.pl
KSW—(WAR)
Rev.: $765,348,108
Assets: $287,489,353
Liabilities: $77,937,801
Net Worth: $209,551,552
Earnings: $26,220,494
Emp.: 854
Fiscal Year-end: 12/31/19
Oil Seeds & Vegetable Fats Mfr
N.A.I.C.S.: 311225
Wojciech Jachimczyk (Chm-Mgmt Bd)

Subsidiaries:

Zaklady Tluszczowe Kruszwica S.A. - Brzeg Plant (1)
Ziemi Tarnowskiej 3, 49-300, Brzeg, Poland
Tel.: (48) 775415622
Oil Seed & Vegetable Fat Mfr
N.A.I.C.S.: 311224

ZAKLADY URZADZEN KOMPUTEROWYCH ELZAB S.A.
ul ELZAB 1, 41-813, Zabrze, Poland
Tel.: (48) 32 272 2021
Web Site: http://www.elzab.com.pl
ELZ—(WAR)
Rev.: $44,190,157
Assets: $41,367,880
Liabilities: $21,060,046
Net Worth: $20,307,834
Earnings: $128,604
Emp.: 236
Fiscal Year-end: 12/31/21
Cash Registers & Sales Accessories Mfr
N.A.I.C.S.: 333310
Jerzy Poplawski (Vice Chm-Mgmt Bd)

ZAKLADY URZADZEN KOTLOWYCH STAPORKOW S.A.
ul Gornicza 3, 26-220, Staporkow, Poland
Tel.: (48) 413741016
Web Site: http://www.zuk.com.pl
Sales Range: $10-24.9 Million
Emp.: 249
Power Engineering Equipment Mfr
N.A.I.C.S.: 332420
Grzegorz Pasturczak (Chm)

ZALANDO SE
Valeska-Gert-Strasse 5, 10243, Berlin, Germany
Tel.: (49) 3027594693
Web Site: https://en.zalando.de
Year Founded: 2008
ZAL—(DEU)
Rev.: $12,717,196,960
Assets: $8,471,171,280
Liabilities: $5,745,952,368
Net Worth: $2,725,218,912
Earnings: $288,022,280
Emp.: 17,043
Fiscal Year-end: 12/31/21
Clothing Accessories Retailer
N.A.I.C.S.: 458110
Robert Gentz (Co-Founder, Co-CEO & Member-Mgmt Bd)

Subsidiaries:

nugg.ad GmbH (1)
Rotherstr - 16, 10245, Berlin, Germany
Tel.: (49) 30293819990
Web Site: https://www.nugg.ad
Digital Media Advertising Services
N.A.I.C.S.: 541810
Martin Hubert (CEO)

ZALARIS ASA
Tel.: (47) 40003300
Web Site: https://www.zalaris.com
Year Founded: 2000
0QWF—(LSE)
Rev.: $82,462,867
Assets: $83,663,588
Liabilities: $68,552,097
Net Worth: $15,111,491
Earnings: ($3,576,667)
Emp.: 1,036
Fiscal Year-end: 12/31/22
HR & Payroll Services
N.A.I.C.S.: 561330
Hans-Petter Mellerud (Founder & CEO)

Subsidiaries:

LBU Personal Complete GmbH (1)
Schattbucher Str 12, Amtzell, 88279, Ravensburg, Germany
Tel.: (49) 75 209 2440
Software Development Services
N.A.I.C.S.: 541511
Peter Martin (Exec VP)

ROC Systems Consulting Ltd. (1)
Hersham Place Technology Park Molesey Road, Hersham, Walton-on-Thames, KT12 4RZ, Surrey, United Kingdom

Tel.: (44) 1932 213 250
Web Site: http://www.roc-group.com
Emp.: 170
Human Capital Management Support Services
N.A.I.C.S.: 541690
Jerry Chilvers (Mng Dir)

Subsidiary (Non-US):

ZALARIS Deutschland GmbH (2)
Mehlbeerenstrasse 2, 82024, Taufkirchen, Germany
Tel.: (49) 892000564
Web Site: http://zalaris.de
Human Resource Consulting Services
N.A.I.C.S.: 541690
Oliver Back (Mng Dir)

Zalaris Consulting Poland Sp. z o.o. (2)
ul Unruga 36/7, 81-188, Gdynia, Poland
Tel.: (48) 58 351 4440
Web Site: http://www.roc-group.pl
Software Publishing Services
N.A.I.C.S.: 513210

Zalaris Consulting Ltd. (1)
Room 601 Linen Hall 162-168 Regent Street, London, W1B 5TF, United Kingdom
Tel.: (44) 193 221 3250
Software Development Services
N.A.I.C.S.: 541511
Will Jackson (Mng Dir & Exec VP)

Zalaris HR Services Denmark A/S (1)
Hoje Taastrup Boulevard 33 1, DK 2630, Taastrup, Denmark
Tel.: (45) 70210530
Software Development Services
N.A.I.C.S.: 541511
Jan Hagedorn (Sls Dir & Country Mgr)

Zalaris HR Services Finland OY (1)
Esterinportti 2, 00240, Helsinki, Finland
Tel.: (358) 97771440
Emp.: 50
Software Development Services
N.A.I.C.S.: 541511
Sami Seikkula (Exec VP)

Zalaris HR Services India Pvt. Ltd. (1)
2nd Floor Block B Global Infocity 40 DR MGR Salai, Kandanchavadi Perunguđi, Chennai, 600 096, Tamil Nadu, India
Tel.: (91) 4446814300
Emp.: 150
Software Development Services
N.A.I.C.S.: 541511
Balakrishnan Narayanan (Exec VP)

Zalaris HR Services Latvia SIA (1)
Marijas 2A, Riga, LV-1050, Latvia
Tel.: (371) 27525742
Software Development Services
N.A.I.C.S.: 541511
Ingrida Stalberga (Head)

Zalaris HR Services Poland Sp z o.o. (1)
Ul Puck 5, 81-036, Gdynia, Poland
Tel.: (48) 58 351 4440
Web Site: https://www.zalaris.pl
Software Development Services
N.A.I.C.S.: 541511
Piotr Lawrynowicz (Sls Dir)

Zalaris HR Services Sverige AB (1)
Strandvag 3, SE-171 54, Solna, Sweden
Tel.: (46) 856488200
Software Development Services
N.A.I.C.S.: 541511
Ia-Pia Emanuelsson (Country Mgr)

ba.se. service & consulting GmbH (1)
Kabeler Strasse 4, 58099, Hagen, Germany
Tel.: (49) 23316908070
Web Site: https://www.base-service-hagen.de
Financial Accounting & Document Management Services
N.A.I.C.S.: 561499
Walter Backhaus (Mng Dir)

ZALEKTA PUBLIC COMPANY LIMITED

ZALEKTA PUBLIC COMPANY LIMITED

ZALEKTA Public Company Limited—(Continued)
29 Vanissa Building Tower B 15th Floor Unit B Soi Chidlom Ploenchit Rd, Lumpini Pathumwan, Bangkok, 10330, Thailand
Tel.: (66) 22545662
Web Site: http://www.mpictures.co.th
Year Founded: 2001
MPIC—(THA)
Rev.: $5,330,082
Assets: $22,727,462
Liabilities: $8,250,245
Net Worth: $14,477,216
Earnings: ($693,007)
Emp.: 46
Fiscal Year-end: 12/31/21
Television Broadcasting Services
N.A.I.C.S.: 516120
Kittisak Chanokmat *(Chm)*

ZALEMARK HOLDING COMPANY, INC.
440 Kingston Road, Richmond Hill, Pickering, L1V 1A4, ON, Canada
Tel.: (647) 836-0831   DE
Web Site: http://zmarkholding.com
ZMRK—(OTCIQ)
Sales Range: Less than $1 Million
Jewelry Designer & Marketer
N.A.I.C.S.: 339910
Xia Wu *(CEO)*

ZALL SMART COMMERCE GROUP LTD.
Zall Plaza No 1 Enterprise Community 1 Chutian Avenue, Panlongcheng Econ & Tech Dev Zone, Wuhan, 430000, Hubei, China
Tel.: (86) 2761906975   Ky
Web Site: http://www.zallcn.com
2098—(HKG)
Rev.: $17,347,485,462
Assets: $8,830,675,953
Liabilities: $6,863,644,910
Net Worth: $1,967,031,042
Earnings: $9,093,376
Emp.: 1,655
Fiscal Year-end: 12/31/23
Shopping Mall Development, Management & Leasing Services
N.A.I.C.S.: 236220
Jinfeng Cui *(Exec Dir)*

Subsidiaries:

Commodities Intelligence Centre Pte. Ltd. (1)
Suntec City Tower 2 29-02A 9 Temasek Blvd, Singapore, 038989, Singapore
Tel.: (65) 63038899
Web Site: https://www.cic-tp.com
Digital Marketing Services
N.A.I.C.S.: 541613

Zall Development (HK) Holding Company Limited (1)
Suite 1606 16/F Two Exchange Square, Central, China (Hong Kong)
Tel.: (852) 31535808
Holding Company
N.A.I.C.S.: 551112

ZALMAN TECH CO., LTD.
1007 Daeryung Techno Town III 448 Gasan-dong, Gumchun-gu, Seoul, Korea (South)
Tel.: (82) 2 2107 3232
Web Site: http://www.zalman.com
Year Founded: 1999
Emp.: 141
Computer Peripherals Mfr
N.A.I.C.S.: 334118
Min Suk Park *(CEO)*

Subsidiaries:

Zalman USA, Inc (1)
13825 Norton Ave Bldg Ste 12, Chino, CA 91710
Tel.: (714) 530-0700

Electronic Equipment Distr
N.A.I.C.S.: 423690
Manki Lee *(CEO)*

ZAM CO., LTD.
22 Yongdu 5-Gil Duseong-Ri Maedong-Myeon, Chilgok, 27739, Chungcheongbuk-do, Korea (South)
Tel.: (82) 317374877
Web Site: http://www.zamled.com
Year Founded: 2009
248020—(KRS)
Light Mfr
N.A.I.C.S.: 335139
Choon-Ha Park *(CEO)*

ZAMANCO MINERALS LIMITED
168 Stirling Highway, Nedlands, 6009, WA, Australia
Tel.: (61) 8 9287 7625
Web Site: http://www.zamancominerals.com
Sales Range: Less than $1 Million
Manganese & Gold Exploration Services
N.A.I.C.S.: 212220
Peter Reynold Ironside *(Sec)*

ZAMANO PLC
3rd Floor Hospitality House 16 20 Cumberland Street South, Dublin, 2, Ireland
Tel.: (353) 15547313
Web Site: http://www.zamano.com
Sales Range: $25-49.9 Million
Mobile Services
N.A.I.C.S.: 517112

Subsidiaries:

Red Circle Technologies Limited (1)
64 Mulgrave St, Dun Laoghaire, Dublin, Ireland
Tel.: (353) 1 231 1200
Mobile Technology Services
N.A.I.C.S.: 517112

Zamano Solutions Limited (1)
1st Fl 4 St Catherines Ln W, The Digital Hub, Dublin, 2, Ireland
Tel.: (353) 1 4885834
Mobile Technology Services
N.A.I.C.S.: 517112

ZAMAZ PLC
9th Floor 107 Cheapside, London, EC2V 6DN, United Kingdom
Tel.: (44) 2079338780   UK
Web Site: https://www.zamaz.tech
Year Founded: 2019
ZAMZ—(LSE)
Rev.: $2,279,754
Assets: $29,631,188
Liabilities: $5,039,801
Net Worth: $24,591,387
Earnings: ($1,799,303)
Fiscal Year-end: 08/31/22
Online Shopping Retailer
N.A.I.C.S.: 459999
Martin Groak *(Chm)*

ZAMBAL SPAIN SOCIMI SA
C/ Ortega y Gasset 11 1Drch, 28006, Madrid, Spain
Tel.: (34) 915457634
Web Site: https://www.zambalspain.com
Year Founded: 2013
YZBL—(MAD)
Real Estate Manangement Services
N.A.I.C.S.: 531390
Thierry Julienne *(Chm)*

ZAMBEEF PRODUCTS PLC
Plot 4970 Manda Road Industrial Area, Private Bag 17, Woodlands, Lusaka, Zambia
Tel.: (260) 211369000

Web Site: https://www.zambeefplc.com
Year Founded: 1994
ZMBF—(LUS)
Rev.: $249,720,493
Assets: $318,208,504
Liabilities: $125,032,209
Net Worth: $193,176,295
Earnings: $5,403,256
Emp.: 7,000
Fiscal Year-end: 09/30/23
Beef, Chicken, Pork, Eggs, Milk, Dairy Products, Edible Oils & Bread Processor, Distr & Retailer
N.A.I.C.S.: 112111
Danny Shaba Museteka *(Sec)*

Subsidiaries:

Zamleather Ltd (1)
Mungwi Road Heavy Ind Area, Lusaka, 10990, Zambia
Tel.: (260) 211241519
Leather Product Mfr
N.A.I.C.S.: 315250

ZAMBIA NATIONAL COMMERCIAL BANK PLC.
Cairo Road, PO Box 33611, Lusaka, Zambia
Tel.: (260) 211228979   ZM
Web Site: https://zanacoinvestor.com
Year Founded: 1969
ZNCO—(LUS)
Rev.: $183,765,692
Assets: $1,741,166,783
Liabilities: $1,575,425,034
Net Worth: $165,741,750
Earnings: $67,562,460
Emp.: 1,316
Fiscal Year-end: 12/31/23
Commercial Banking Services
N.A.I.C.S.: 522110
Chanda Lumpa *(Chm)*

ZAMBIA TELECOMMUNICATIONS COMPANY LIMITED
Provident House, PO Box 71660, Ndola, Zambia
Tel.: (260) 2611111
Web Site: http://www.zamtel.zm
Emp.: 3,000
Telecommunication Servicesb
N.A.I.C.S.: 517111
Sydney Mupeta *(CEO)*

ZAMBON COMPANY S.P.A.
Via Lillo del Duca 10, Bresso, 20091, Milan, Italy
Tel.: (39) 02665241   IT
Web Site: http://www.zamboncompany.com
Year Founded: 1906
Sales Range: $750-799.9 Million
Emp.: 2,500
Holding Company; Pharmaceutical & Fine Chemical Mfr
N.A.I.C.S.: 551112
Roberto Tascione *(CEO)*

Subsidiaries:

CareApt S.r.l. (1)
Via Lillo del Duca 10, 20091, Bresso, MI, Italy
Tel.: (39) 0266 5241
Web Site: https://www.careaptitude.com
Health Care Srvices
N.A.I.C.S.: 621610

Fondazione Zoe S.r.l. (1)
Corso Andrea Palladio 36, 36100, Vicenza, Italy
Tel.: (39) 044 432 5064
Web Site: https://www.fondazionezoe.it
Education Services
N.A.I.C.S.: 611710
Chiara Bisin *(Mgr)*

Hainan Zambon Pharmaceutical Co., Ltd (1)

INTERNATIONAL PUBLIC

Room 1606 Shanghai International Group Mansion No 511 Weihai Road, Jingan District, Shanghai, China
Tel.: (86) 2160310188
Web Site: http://www.zambon.com.cn
Pharmaceutical Product Mfr & Distr
N.A.I.C.S.: 325412
Kim Hang Pang *(Asst Mgr)*

ItaliAssistenza S.p.A. (1)
Viale IV Novembre 21, 42121, Reggio Emilia, Italy
Tel.: (39) 024 539 5460
Web Site: https://www.italiassistenza.it
Health Care Srvices
N.A.I.C.S.: 621610

OpenZone S.p.A. (1)
Via Antonio Meucci 3, 20091, Bresso, MI, Italy
Tel.: (39) 0266 5241
Web Site: https://www.openzone.it
Scientific Research Services
N.A.I.C.S.: 541715

P.T. Zambon Indonesia (1)
Jl Kemang Raya 128, Jakarta, 12730, Indonesia (100%)
Tel.: (62) 217194778
Web Site: http://www.zambonpharma.com
Pharmaceuticals Mfr
N.A.I.C.S.: 325412

Pharmazam S.A. (1)
Maresme 5 Poligono Urvasa, Santa Perpetua de Mogoda, 08130, Barcelona, Spain (100%)
Tel.: (34) 935446440
Web Site: http://www.zambonspa.com
Emp.: 18
Pharmaceuticals Mfr
N.A.I.C.S.: 325412

Privatassistenza S.A. (1)
Via Cantonale 90, Melano, 6818, Lugano, Switzerland
Tel.: (41) 91 960 1800
Web Site: https://www.privatassistenza.ch
Health Care Srvices
N.A.I.C.S.: 621610

Z-Cube S.r.l. (1)
Via Lillo de Duca 10, Bresso, 20091, Milan, Italy (100%)
Tel.: (39) 0266524 919
Web Site: http://www.z-cube.it
Pharmaceutical & Chemical Incubation Services
N.A.I.C.S.: 325412

ZaCh Company Corporation (1)
914 S 16th St, La Porte, TX 77057
Tel.: (281) 842-0200
Pharmaceutical Product Mfr & Distr
N.A.I.C.S.: 325412

Zach System S.p.A. (1)
Via Lillo del Duca 10, Bresso, 20091, Milan, Italy
Tel.: (39) 02665241
Web Site: http://www.zachsystem.com
Fine Chemicals Mfr
N.A.I.C.S.: 325998

Zambon (India) Pvt. Ltd. (1)
Maine Mehrauli Gurgaon Road Suite 301 3rd Floor, JMD Regent Square, 122001, Gurgaon, Haryana, India (100%)
Tel.: (91) 1242804021
Emp.: 3
Pharmaceuticals Mfr
N.A.I.C.S.: 325412
Sanjeev Khurana *(Mng Dir)*

Zambon Advance Luxembourg S.A. (1)
1 Rue Jean Piret, 2350, Luxembourg, Luxembourg
Tel.: (352) 458078
Pharmaceuticals Product Mfr
N.A.I.C.S.: 325412

Zambon Colombia S.A. (1)
Calle 124 No 45-15 Stories 3rd & 4th, Bogota, Colombia (100%)
Tel.: (57) 1 595 4500
Web Site: http://www.zambonpharmaceuticals.com
Emp.: 53
Pharmaceuticals Mfr
N.A.I.C.S.: 325412

AND PRIVATE COMPANIES

ZAMIL INDUSTRIAL INVESTMENT COMPANY

Zambon Corporation (1)
301 Route 17 2nd Fl Ste 205, Rutherford, NJ 07070
Tel.: (201) 939-4800
Pharmaceuticals Mfr
N.A.I.C.S.: 325412

Zambon France S.A. (1)
13 Rue Rene Jacques, 92130, Issy-les-Moulineaux, France (100%)
Tel.: (33) 158044141
Web Site: http://www.zambonpharma.com
Emp.: 200
Pharmaceuticals Mfr
N.A.I.C.S.: 325412
Pascal Brossard *(Mng Dir)*

Zambon G.m.b.H. (1)
Lietzenburger Strasse 99, 10707, Berlin, Germany
Tel.: (49) 30 120 2120
Web Site: https://www.zambonpharma.com
Pharmaceuticals Product Mfr
N.A.I.C.S.: 325412
Dirk Greshake *(Gen Mgr)*

Zambon Laboratorios Farmaceuticos Ltda. (1)
Rua Descampado 63, 04296-090, Sao Paulo, Brazil (100%)
Tel.: (55) 1169489300
Web Site: http://www.zambongroup.com.br
Emp.: 200
Pharmaceuticals Mfr
N.A.I.C.S.: 325412

Zambon Nederland B.V. (1)
Basicweg 14 b, 3821 Br, Amersfoort, Netherlands (100%)
Tel.: (31) 334504370
Emp.: 24
Pharmaceuticals Mfr
N.A.I.C.S.: 325412

Zambon Pharma Ltd. (1)
Glazowsky Pereulok Builging 7, 119002, Moscow, Russia
Tel.: (7) 495 933 3830
Web Site: https://www.zambon.com
Pharmaceuticals Product Mfr
N.A.I.C.S.: 325412

Zambon Produtos Farmaceuticos Lda. (1)
Rua Comandante Enrique Maya 1, 1500-192, Lisbon, Portugal (100%)
Tel.: (351) 217600952
Web Site: http://www.zambon.com
Emp.: 45
Pharmaceuticals Mfr
N.A.I.C.S.: 325412
Ilina Zavala *(Mng Dir)*

Zambon Russia (1)
Glazovsky per Building 7 Office 17, 119002, Moscow, Russia
Tel.: (7) 4959333830
Web Site: http://www.zambonpharma.com
Emp.: 30
Pharmaceutical Product Mfr & Distr
N.A.I.C.S.: 325412

Zambon S.A. (1)
Maresme 5 Poligono Urvasa, Santa Perpetua de Mogoda, 08130, Barcelona, Spain (100%)
Tel.: (34) 935446400
Web Site: http://www.zambon.es
Pharmaceuticals Mfr
N.A.I.C.S.: 325412

Zambon S.A./N.V. (1)
Av Etienne Demunter 1-9, 1090, Brussels, Belgium (100%)
Tel.: (32) 27770200
Web Site: http://www.zambon.com
Emp.: 25
Pharmaceuticals Mfr
N.A.I.C.S.: 325412

Zambon S.p.A. (1)
Via Lillo del Duca 10, Bresso, 20091, Milan, Italy (100%)
Tel.: (39) 02655241
Web Site: http://www.zambonspa.com
Pharmaceuticals Mfr
N.A.I.C.S.: 325412

Zambon Svizzera SA (1)
Via Industria 13, 6814, Cadempino, Switzerland

Tel.: (41) 91 960 4111
Web Site: https://www.zambonpharma.com
Pharmaceuticals Product Mfr
N.A.I.C.S.: 325412

Zambon Switzerland Ltd. (1)
Via Industria 13, 6814, Cadempino, Switzerland (100%)
Tel.: (41) 919604111
Web Site: http://www.zambon.com
Emp.: 250
Pharmaceuticals Mfr
N.A.I.C.S.: 325412

Zamfarma - Produtos Pharmaceuticals Lda. (1)
Rua comandante Enrique Maya 1, 1500-192, Lisbon, Portugal
Tel.: (351) 21 760 0952
Paramedical Product Mfr
N.A.I.C.S.: 325412

ZAMEE CORP.
Residencia Perla Marina Villa No 4, Sosua, 57000, Dominican Republic
Tel.: (809) 829 947 5984 NV
Web Site: http://www.zameecorp.com
Year Founded: 2017
Assets: $8,725
Liabilities: $6,575
Net Worth: $2,150
Earnings: ($1,041)
Emp.: 1
Fiscal Year-end: 11/30/18
Mobile Game Development Services
N.A.I.C.S.: 541511
Alina Tarasova *(Pres, Treas & Sec)*

ZAMET INDUSTRY S.A.
ul R Dmowskiego 38B, 97-300, Piotrkow Trybunalski, Poland
Tel.: (48) 446489181 PL
Web Site: https://www.zamet-industry.com.pl
Year Founded: 1956
ZMT—(WAR)
Rev.: $56,704,522
Assets: $49,145,071
Liabilities: $15,054,624
Net Worth: $34,090,447
Earnings: $3,596,291
Emp.: 250
Fiscal Year-end: 12/31/23
Industrial Steel Structures, Machinery & Casting Mfr
N.A.I.C.S.: 331110
Adrian Smeja *(Vice Chm-Mgmt Bd)*

Subsidiaries:

Mostostal Chojnice S.A. (1)
Przemyslowa 4, 89-600, Chojnice, Poland
Tel.: (48) 523966100
Web Site: http://www.mostostal.chojnice.pl
Steel Mfrs
N.A.I.C.S.: 331110
Artur Jeziorowski *(Pres)*

Zamet Budowa Maszyn S.A. (1)
ul Zagorska 83, 42-680, Tarnowskie Gory, Poland
Tel.: (48) 323928500
Web Site: http://www.zamet.com.pl
Machinery Products Mfr
N.A.I.C.S.: 333248
Jacek Miera *(VP)*

ZAMIA METALS LIMITED
Suite 60 Level 6 Tower Building, Chatswood Village 47-53 Neridah Street, Chatswood, 2067, NSW, Australia
Tel.: (61) 282233744
Web Site: http://www.zamia.com.au
Sales Range: Less than $1 Million
Metal Mining Services
N.A.I.C.S.: 212290
John Stone *(Sec)*

ZAMIL GROUP HOLDING COMPANY

PO Box 9, Al Khobar, 31952, Saudi Arabia
Tel.: (966) 138824888
Web Site: http://www.zamil.com
Sales Range: $1-4.9 Billion
Emp.: 21,000
Holding Company; Industrial & Commercial Products & Services
N.A.I.C.S.: 551112
Osama Al Zamil *(VP)*

Subsidiaries:

Al Tawfiq Plastic Co. for Plastic & Woven Sacks Industries Ltd. (1)
PO Box 32368, Jeddah, 21428, Saudi Arabia
Tel.: (966) 2 6081033
Web Site: http://www.apws.com.sa
Bag Mfr
N.A.I.C.S.: 322220

Gulf Stabilizers Industries Ltd. (1)
Box 35625, Al Jubayl, 31951, Saudi Arabia
Tel.: (966) 33417727
Chemical Products Mfr
N.A.I.C.S.: 325998

Technical Seal Company Ltd. (1)
PO Box 7480, Dammam, 31462, Saudi Arabia
Tel.: (966) 13 8472703
Building Materials Distr
N.A.I.C.S.: 423390

Zamil Architectural Co. Ltd (1)
Near Resident Twr Lulu Alfara, PO Box 36450, Kuwait, 24755, Kuwait
Tel.: (965) 22449540
Architectural Services
N.A.I.C.S.: 541310

Zamil Food Industries Ltd. (1)
PO Box 240, Al Jubayl, 31951, Saudi Arabia
Tel.: (966) 3 341 5235
Web Site: http://www.zamilfood.com
Food Products Distr
N.A.I.C.S.: 424490
Abdalla Ali Al-Yami *(Mgr-Ops)*

Zamil Group Commercial Division (1)
PO Box 13793, Dammam, 31414, Saudi Arabia
Tel.: (966) 3 847 3232
Web Site: http://www.zamilcd.com.sa
Commercial Equipment Distr
N.A.I.C.S.: 423440
Nurul Islam *(Supvr-Sls-Chemical Div)*

Zamil Industrial Coating (1)
PO Box 4672, Al Khobar, 31952, Saudi Arabia
Tel.: (966) 13 8473833
Coating Mfr
N.A.I.C.S.: 325510
Ghassan H. Al-Zamil *(Mgr-Mktg & Sls)*

Zamil Ladder Factory (1)
PO Box 3408, Dammam, 31471, Saudi Arabia
Tel.: (966) 3 847 3544
Web Site: http://www.zamilladders.com
Ladder Mfr
N.A.I.C.S.: 332999
Binu Cherian *(Mgr-Production)*

Zamil Operations & Maintenance Co. Ltd (1)
Al-Zamil Building, PO Box 1922, Al Khobar, 31952, Saudi Arabia
Tel.: (966) 3 8822494
Web Site: http://www.zamil-om.com
Ship Building & Maintenance Services
N.A.I.C.S.: 336611
Mohammed A. Al Zamil *(Chm)*

Zamil Partition Industries Company (1)
PO Box 1633, Dammam, 31441, Saudi Arabia
Tel.: (966) 3 847 3810
Web Site: http://www.zamilptn.com
Partition Wall Installation Services
N.A.I.C.S.: 238390

Zamil Plastic Industries (1)
Dammam Second Industrial City Street 23

Cross 68, PO Box 1748, Al Khobar, 31952, Saudi Arabia
Tel.: (966) 38121114
Web Site: http://www.zamilplastic.com
Plastics Product Mfr
N.A.I.C.S.: 326199
Adel Alghassab *(Mng Dir)*

Zamil Travel (1)
Zamil Building Prince Talal St, Al Khobar, Saudi Arabia
Tel.: (966) 3 898 3350
Web Site: http://www.zamiltravel.com
Travel Agency
N.A.I.C.S.: 561510
Mirza Baig *(Mgr-Sls)*

ZAMIL INDUSTRIAL INVESTMENT COMPANY
PO Box 14441, Dammam, 31424, Saudi Arabia
Tel.: (966) 138108111
Web Site: https://www.zamilindustrial.com
2240—(SAU)
Rev.: $1,046,843,354
Assets: $1,574,049,060
Liabilities: $1,321,320,624
Net Worth: $252,728,436
Earnings: $46,303,426
Emp.: 9,000
Fiscal Year-end: 12/31/22
Construction Products Engineering Services
N.A.I.C.S.: 541330
Ahmed Abdullah Hamed Al Zamil *(Co-CEO)*

Subsidiaries:

Clima Tech Airconditioners GmbH (1)
Am Neuschacht 1, Grunbach am Schneeberg, 2733, Linz, Austria (100%)
Tel.: (43) 263571130
Web Site: http://www.climatech.at
Emp.: 5
Refrigeration Equipment & Supplies Whslr
N.A.I.C.S.: 423740

Geoclima S.r.l. (1)
Via Dell Industria 12, 34077, Ronchi dei Legionari, GO, Italy (85%)
Tel.: (39) 0481774411
Web Site: http://www.geoclima.it
Emp.: 140
Air Conditioning & Heating Equipment Mfr
N.A.I.C.S.: 333414

Saudi Preinsulated Pipes Industries LLC (1)
Zone B Street 236, PO Box 1799, 2nd Industrial City, Riyadh, 11441, Saudi Arabia
Tel.: (966) 112651414
Web Site: https://www.sppi-llc.com.sa
Preinsulated Piping System Mfr
N.A.I.C.S.: 332996

Zamil Air Conditioners Holding Company Limited (1)
First Industrial City, PO Box 14440, Dammam, 31424, Saudi Arabia
Tel.: (966) 138473333
Web Site: https://www.zamilac.com
Emp.: 6,500
Air Conditioner Mfr
N.A.I.C.S.: 333415

Zamil Air Conditioners India Private Limited (1)
H-9 Block B-1 1st Floor Mathura Road, Mohan Cooperative Industrial Estate, New Delhi, 110044, India
Tel.: (91) 8010950668
Web Site: https://www.zamilacindia.com
Plumbing & Heating Services
N.A.I.C.S.: 238220
Prenab Chowdhury *(Head-Design & Engrg)*

Zamil Information Technology Global Private Limited (1)
Office 201 2nd Floor Almonte Software Park Plot 2 Survey 8, Kharadi, Pune, 411014, India
Tel.: (91) 2040753000
Web Site: https://www.zamilitg.com

ZAMIL INDUSTRIAL INVESTMENT COMPANY

Zamil Industrial Investment Company—(Continued)
IT Infrastructure Services
N.A.I.C.S.: 518210

Zamil Steel Buildings Co., Egypt (S.A.E.) (1)
Main Post Office 5th Industrial Zone 6th of October City, PO Box 11, Cairo, Egypt
Tel.: (20) 2 3828 3333
Industrial Steel Distr
N.A.I.C.S.: 423510

Zamil Steel Buildings India (P) Ltd. (1)
Almonte Software Park Office No 101 1st Floor, Kharadi Village Haveli, Pune, 411014, India
Tel.: (91) 20 3055 3000
Emp.: 170
Industrial Steel Products Distr
N.A.I.C.S.: 423510
Alakesh Roy *(Mng Dir)*

Zamil Steel Buildings Vietnam Co., Ltd. (1)
14th floor Keangnam Hanoi Landmark Tower Pham Hung Street, Tu Liem District, Hanoi, Vietnam (90%)
Tel.: (84) 2438378522
Web Site: https://www.zamilsteel.com.vn
Iron & Steel Mills
N.A.I.C.S.: 331110

Zamil Steel Engineering India Private Limited (1)
117 4th Wingnelson Towers, Chennai, 600029, India (100%)
Tel.: (91) 4423743313
Web Site: https://www.zamilsteel.com
Emp.: 95
Engineeering Services
N.A.I.C.S.: 331512

Zamil Steel Holding Company Limited (1)
Street 11/32, PO Box 877, Dammam 1st Industrial City, Dammam, 31421, Saudi Arabia
Tel.: (966) 138471840
Web Site: https://www.zamilsteel.com
Steel Building Construction Services
N.A.I.C.S.: 238120

Subsidiary (Domestic):

Building Component Solutions Company Limited (2)
2nd Industrial City, PO Box 14441, Dammam, 31424, Saudi Arabia
Tel.: (966) 138124571
Web Site: https://www.bcoms.com
Polyisocyanurate Panel Mfr
N.A.I.C.S.: 326140

Zamil Inspection & Maintenance of Industrial Projects Company Limited (2)
Dammam 2nd Industrial City, PO Box 877, Dammam, 31421, Saudi Arabia
Tel.: (966) 138123855
Web Site: https://www.zimipco.com
Pressure Vessel & Heat Exchanger Mfr
N.A.I.C.S.: 332410

Zamil Process Equipment Company Limited (2)
Dammam 2nd Industrial City, PO Box 877, Dammam, 31421, Saudi Arabia
Tel.: (966) 138123855
Web Site: https://zamilsteel.com
Oil & Gas Refinery Equipment Mfr
N.A.I.C.S.: 333132
Mohamed Farooque *(Gen Mgr-Sls)*

Zamil Steel Construction Company Limited (2)
Street 11/32, PO Box 877, Dammam 1st Industrial City, Dammam, 31421, Saudi Arabia
Tel.: (966) 138471840
Steel Building Construction Services
N.A.I.C.S.: 238120

Zamil Steel Pre-Engineered Buildings Company Limited (2)
Street 11/32, PO Box 877, Dammam 1st Industrial City, Dammam, 31421, Saudi Arabia
Tel.: (966) 138471840
Steel Building Construction Services
N.A.I.C.S.: 238120

Zamil Structural Steel Company Limited (2)
Dammam 2nd Industrial City, PO Box 877, Dammam, 31421, Saudi Arabia
Tel.: (966) 138121120
Steel Building Construction Services
N.A.I.C.S.: 238120

Zamil Towers & Galvanizing Company (2)
PO Box 877, Dammam 1st Industrial City, Dammam, 31421, Saudi Arabia
Tel.: (966) 138472011
Galvanized Steel Tower Mfr
N.A.I.C.S.: 332312
Annoni Giovanni *(Mgr-Sls & Construction)*

Zamil Steel Industries L.L.C (1)
PO Box 31753, Ras al Khaimah, United Arab Emirates
Tel.: (971) 72051555
Emp.: 500
Industrial Steel Mfr
N.A.I.C.S.: 331210
Eyad Masarweh *(Mgr-Ops)*

Zamil Steel Polska Sp. z o.o. (1)
Ul Pulawska 479 lok 1, 02-844, Warsaw, Poland (100%)
Tel.: (48) 228944166
Web Site: http://www.zamilsteel.pl
Emp.: 80
Steel Investment Foundries
N.A.I.C.S.: 331512

ZAMIR TELECOM LTD.
4 6 Davenant Street, London, E1 5NB, United Kingdom
Tel.: (44) 207 870 3480
Web Site: http://www.zamirtelecom.com
Year Founded: 2004
Sales Range: $10-24.9 Million
Emp.: 40
VoIP Telecommunications Services
N.A.I.C.S.: 517810
Naufal Zamir *(Founder)*

Subsidiaries:

Simplecall Business Ltd (1)
7th Floor 5 Greenwich View Place, Millharbour, London, E14 9NN, United Kingdom
Tel.: (44) 2034350033
Web Site: http://www.simplecallbusiness.com
Telecommunication Servicesb
N.A.I.C.S.: 517810
Nick J. Saunders *(Product Mgr)*

ZAMP SA
Alameda Rio Negro 161 14th Andar Parte Conjunto 14, Barueri, 06454-000, Sao Paulo, Brazil
Tel.: (55) 1141995345
Web Site: http://www.burgerking.com.br
ZAMP3—(BRAZ)
Rev.: $791,748,787
Assets: $848,524,676
Liabilities: $561,316,021
Net Worth: $287,208,655
Earnings: ($20,159,918)
Fiscal Year-end: 12/31/23
Restaurant Management Services
N.A.I.C.S.: 722511
Iuri De Araujo Miranda *(CEO)*

ZANAGA IRON ORE COMPANY LIMITED
2nd Floor Coastal Building Wickhams Cay II, PO Box 2221, Road Town, Tortola, VG1130, Carrot Bay, Virgin Islands (British) VG
Web Site: http://www.zanagairon.com
Year Founded: 2009
ZIOC—(AIM)
Assets: $86,426,000
Liabilities: $1,224,000
Net Worth: $85,202,000
Earnings: $8,098,000
Fiscal Year-end: 12/31/22
Holding Company; Iron Ore Mining Services
N.A.I.C.S.: 551112

ZANE HOLDINGS LTD
9525 127 Ave NW, Edmonton, T5E 6M7, AB, Canada
Tel.: (780) 701-0456
Web Site: http://www.albertahonda.com
Year Founded: 1985
Rev.: $40,668,895
Emp.: 100
New & Used Car Dealers
N.A.I.C.S.: 441110
Brian Caines *(Gen Mgr)*

ZANGAN ELECTRICAL EQUIPMENT COMPANY
No 1-Industrial Estate Dey Jonobi St, Zanjan, Iran
Tel.: (98) 241 2221045
Year Founded: 2000
Emp.: 26
Transformer Oil Mfr
N.A.I.C.S.: 325998
Babak Ijlal Nouberian *(Chm)*

ZANGGE MINING COMPANY LIMITED
No 15-02 Kunlun South Road, Middle Section of Tianfu Avenue High-tech Zone, Golmud, 816000, Qinghai, China
Tel.: (86) 9798962706
Web Site: https://www.zgmining.com
Year Founded: 1996
000408—(SSE)
Rev.: $1,150,425,455
Assets: $1,900,518,970
Liabilities: $198,350,914
Net Worth: $1,702,168,056
Earnings: $793,944,155
Fiscal Year-end: 12/31/22
Holding Company
N.A.I.C.S.: 551112
Xiao Ning *(Chm)*

ZANINI AUTO GRUP, S.A.
C/ Marineta 2 Poligon Industrial Llevant, Parets del Valles, 08150, Barcelona, Spain
Tel.: (34) 935738600
Web Site: http://www.zanini.com
Year Founded: 1965
Rev.: $118,979,120
Emp.: 1,400
Automotive Components Mfr
N.A.I.C.S.: 336340
Joan Miguel Torras *(CEO)*

Subsidiaries:

ZANINI PARETS S.L. (1)
C Tenes 5-9 Poligono Industrial Llevant, Parets del Valles, 08150, Barcelona, Spain
Tel.: (34) 93 573 77 80
Automobile Component Distr
N.A.I.C.S.: 423120

Zanini CZ, s.r.o (1)
Kralovsky Vrch 1987, 43201, Kadan, Czech Republic
Tel.: (420) 474 359 000
Automobile Component Distr
N.A.I.C.S.: 423120
Michal Drozdik *(Mgr-IT)*

Zanini Do Brasil, Ltda. (1)
Rua Sebastiana Santana Fraga 1982 Bairro Guatupe, 83060-500, Sao Jose dos Pinhais, Brazil
Tel.: (55) 41 3020 8351
Automobile Component Distr
N.A.I.C.S.: 423120

Zanini Epila, S.L. (1)
Avda Rodel 5 Apartado Correos 19 Poligono Industrial Valdemuel, Epila, 50290, Zaragoza, Spain
Tel.: (34) 976 60 39 03
Automobile Component Distr
N.A.I.C.S.: 423120

Zanini France S.L. (1)
15 Rue Ampere, 01100, Oyonnax, Rhone-Alpes, France
Tel.: (33) 474 81 71 71
Automobile Component Distr
N.A.I.C.S.: 423120

Zanini Mexico. S.A. de c.v (1)
Avda La Canada Lote 5 Parque Industrial Finsa, 76246, El Marques, Queretaro, Mexico
Tel.: (52) 442 22 16 014
Automobile Component Distr
N.A.I.C.S.: 423120

Zanini Tennessee, Inc. (1)
840 Industrial Park Dr, Winchester, TN 37398-1246
Tel.: (931) 967-8544
Web Site: http://www.zanini.com
Emp.: 100
Mfr of Plastic Products
N.A.I.C.S.: 325998

Zanini USA, Inc. (1)
26899 Northwestern Hwy Ste 110, Southfield, MI 48033
Tel.: (248) 263-2660
Automobile Parts Distr
N.A.I.C.S.: 423120

ZANLAKOL LTD.
Alon Tavor Industrial Park, Afula, 1812302, Israel
Tel.: (972) 46595555
Web Site: https://www.sanlakol.com
Year Founded: 1940
ZNKL—(TAE)
Rev.: $110,116,865
Assets: $122,244,783
Liabilities: $70,193,672
Net Worth: $52,051,111
Earnings: $18,689,874
Emp.: 161
Fiscal Year-end: 12/31/23
Fruit & Vegetable Canning
N.A.I.C.S.: 311421

ZANUS A.D.
Karadordeva Bb, 75448, Sekovici, Bosnia & Herzegovina
Tel.: (387) 56743218
Year Founded: 1984
ZNUS-R-A—(BANJ)
Rev.: $139,266
Assets: $196,622
Liabilities: $89,398
Net Worth: $107,224
Earnings: ($81,370)
Emp.: 16
Fiscal Year-end: 12/31/12
Metal Products Mfr
N.A.I.C.S.: 332312
Vujadin Starcevic *(Exec Dir)*

ZANYU TECHNOLOGY GROUP CO., LTD.
No 702 Gudun Road, Shangcheng District, Hangzhou, 310030, Zhejiang, China
Tel.: (86) 57182900658
Web Site: https://en.zanyu.com
Year Founded: 1965
002637—(SSE)
Sales Range: $600-649.9 Million
Daily Chemical Products & Surfactants Mfr
N.A.I.C.S.: 325998
Jingguo Zhang *(Chm)*

Subsidiaries:

Hangzhou Oleochemicals Co.,Ltd. (1)
1188 Jingbalu, Linjiang Industrial Park Xiaoshan, Hangzhou, Zhejiang, China
Tel.: (86) 57186617528

Web Site: https://www.hofcc.com
Chemical Mfr & Distr
N.A.I.C.S.: 325199

Jiaxing Zanyu Technology Development Co., Ltd. (1)
RM 1713 No 702 Gudun RD Xihu District, Hangzhou, 314201, Zhejiang, China
Tel.: (86) 57187826197
Web Site: http://www.1surfactant.com
Chemical Products Mfr
N.A.I.C.S.: 325199

Pt. Dua Kuda Indonesia (1)
Kawasan Berikat Nusantara JL Madiun Blok C 2 No 11-13 Unit, Usaha Kawasan Marunda, Jakarta Utara, 14120, Indonesia
Tel.: (62) 2144853559
Web Site: https://www.duakuda.com
Chemical Mfr & Distr
N.A.I.C.S.: 325199

ZANZIBAR GOLD, INC.
5623 145A Street, Surrey, V3S 8E3, BC, Canada
Tel.: (778) 370-1372
Mineral Exploration Services
N.A.I.C.S.: 213114
Souhail Abi-Farrage *(Pres, CEO & Sec)*

ZAO BECEMA
Ilyinskoye Shosse 2nd km, Krasnogorsk, 143405, Moscow, Russia
Tel.: (7) 4957770227 RU
Web Site: http://www.becema.ru
Year Founded: 1932
Emp.: 1,000
Construction Machinery & Truck Trailer Mfr
N.A.I.C.S.: 333120
V. Sergey Trifonov *(CEO)*

ZAO BESTROM
Ilyinskoe Shosse 15, PO Box 143405, Krasnogorsk, 143405, Moscow, Russia
Tel.: (7) 4955621383 RU
Web Site: http://www.bestrom.ru
Year Founded: 1989
Emp.: 100
Packaging Machinery Mfr
N.A.I.C.S.: 333993
Oleg Bogdanov *(Gen Dir)*

ZAO IFD KAPITAL
6 Krasnopresnenskaya Naberezhnaya, 123100, Moscow, Russia
Tel.: (7) 4957775680
Web Site: http://www.ifdk.com
Holding Company
N.A.I.C.S.: 551112
Leonid Fedun *(Chm)*

ZAO MAKIZ-PHARMA
Avtomobilniy Prd 6, 109029, Moscow, Russia
Tel.: (7) 495 974 00 77
Web Site: http://www.makispharma.ru
Sales Range: $125-149.9 Million
Emp.: 300
Pharmaceuticals Product Mfr
N.A.I.C.S.: 325412
Igor Belotelov *(Mng Dir)*

ZAOH COMPANY, LTD.
1-19-5 Mouri, Koto-Ku, Tokyo, 135-0001, Japan
Tel.: (81) 356000325
Web Site: https://www.zaohnet.co.jp
Year Founded: 1956
9986—(TKS)
Rev.: $68,486,000
Assets: $132,751,520
Liabilities: $18,208,080
Net Worth: $114,543,440
Earnings: $7,676,240
Emp.: 193
Fiscal Year-end: 03/31/21

Industrial Machinery Whslr
N.A.I.C.S.: 423830
Takanori Kutsuzawa *(Pres & Pres)*

ZAPI S.P.A
Via Parma 59, 42028, Poviglio, Italy
Tel.: (39) 0522960050 IT
Web Site: http://www.zapigroup.it
Year Founded: 1975
Speed Regulating Device Mfr
N.A.I.C.S.: 335999
Pietro Zambotto *(Chm)*

Subsidiaries:

Schabmuller GmbH (1)
Industriestrasse 8, Berching, 92334, Germany
Tel.: (49) 8462 204 0
Web Site: http://www.schabmueller.de
Sales Range: $75-99.9 Million
Emp.: 450
Mfr of Electrical Drives & Generators
N.A.I.C.S.: 335312

Zapi, Inc. (1)
267 Hein Dr, Garner, NC 27529
Tel.: (919) 789-4588
Web Site: http://www.zapiinc.com
Emp.: 10
Speed Regulating Device Mfr
N.A.I.C.S.: 335999
Thomas Godwin *(Engr-Sls & Applications)*

ZAPORIZHSTAL JSC
72 Yuzhnoye Shosse, 69008, Zaporizhzhya, Ukraine
Tel.: (380) 61 218 30 09
Web Site:
http://www.zaporizhstal.com
Year Founded: 1929
Steel Products Mfr
N.A.I.C.S.: 331221
Oleksandr Tretyakov *(Dir-Production)*

ZAPOROZHTRANSFORMATOR PJSC
Dnepropetrovskoe Shosse 3, 69600, Zaporizhzhya, Ukraine
Tel.: (380) 61 270 3033
Web Site: http://www.ztr.com.ua
Year Founded: 1947
Transformer & Electric Reactor Mfr
N.A.I.C.S.: 334416
Igor Kleyner *(CEO & Gen Dir)*

ZAPP ELECTRIC VEHICLES GROUP LIMITED
87/1 Wireless Road 26/F Capital Tower All Seasons Place, Lumpini Patumwan, Bangkok, 10330, Thailand
Tel.: (66) 26543550 Ky
Web Site: https://www.zappev.com
Year Founded: 2022
ZAPP—(NASDAQ)
Electrical Product Mfr & Distr
N.A.I.C.S.: 336320
David McIntyre *(Chief Comml Officer)*

ZAPPALLAS, INC.
PORTAL POINT HARAJUKU ANNEX 3F 3-51-7 Sendagaya, Shibuya-ku, Tokyo, 151-0051, Japan
Tel.: (81) 364341036 JP
Web Site: https://www.zappallas.com
Year Founded: 2000
3770—(TKS)
Rev.: $28,905,530
Assets: $40,995,220
Liabilities: $3,470,250
Net Worth: $37,524,970
Earnings: $1,070,820
Emp.: 98
Fiscal Year-end: 04/30/24
Services & Products Through Mobile & Other Networks
N.A.I.C.S.: 513210
Mari Tamaki *(CEO)*

Subsidiaries:

Ares & Mercury Co., Ltd. (1)
1-19-19 Ebisu Shibuya-Ku, Tokyo, 150-0013, Japan
Tel.: (81) 354757133
Mobile Advertisement Distribution Services
N.A.I.C.S.: 541890

ZAPTEC ASA
Professor Olav Hanssens vei 7A, 4021, Stavanger, Norway
Tel.: (47) 91903676
Web Site: https://www.zaptec.com
Year Founded: 2012
ZAP—(OSL)
Rev.: $69,961,020
Assets: $56,636,338
Liabilities: $24,113,892
Net Worth: $32,522,446
Earnings: ($3,411,694)
Emp.: 144
Fiscal Year-end: 12/31/22
Electric Vehicle Charging Services
N.A.I.C.S.: 238210

ZARA INVESTMENT HOLDING CO. LTD.
Hussien Bin Ali Street Astra Plaza Building No 137, PO Box 5315, Al-Sharif, Amman, 11183, Jordan
Tel.: (962) 64630260
Web Site:
https://www.zaraholding.com
Year Founded: 1994
ZARA—(AMM)
Rev.: $34,502,343
Assets: $268,767,129
Liabilities: $33,822,561
Net Worth: $234,944,568
Earnings: ($19,891,238)
Emp.: 27
Fiscal Year-end: 12/31/20
Holding Company
N.A.I.C.S.: 551112
Yassen Al-Talhouni *(Gen Mgr-Acting)*

ZARA INVESTMENT HOLDING COMPANY LTD.
Astra Building Hussein Bin Ali Street, PO Box 5315, Wadi Saqra, 11183, Amman, Jordan
Tel.: (962) 64630260
Web Site:
http://www.zaraholding.com
Year Founded: 1994
Sales Range: $25-49.9 Million
Emp.: 30
Tourism Investment Services
N.A.I.C.S.: 523999
Sabih Taher Darwish Masri *(Chm)*

Subsidiaries:

Jordan Hotels & Tourism P.L.C. (1)
Astra Plaza Building / Arar Street - Wadi Saqra, PO Box 35103, Amman, 11180, Jordan (51.64%)
Tel.: (962) 4619696
Rev.: $8,277,599
Assets: $41,079,020
Liabilities: $4,300,199
Net Worth: $36,778,821
Earnings: ($4,246,025)
Emp.: 488
Fiscal Year-end: 12/31/2020
Home Management Services
N.A.I.C.S.: 721110

ZARAM TECHNOLOGY, INC.
41 Seongnamdaero 925 beon-gil 2nd Floor Fineventure Building, Bundang-gu, Seongnam, 13496, Gyeonggi-do, Korea (South)
Tel.: (82) 317796700
Web Site: https://www.zaram.com
Year Founded: 2000
389020—(KRS)
Emp.: 46

Semiconductor Product Mfr
N.A.I.C.S.: 334413
Seo Inshik *(Pres)*

ZARCLEAR HOLDINGS LIMITED
9th floor Katherine Towers Bidvest Bank Building 1 Park Lane, Wierda Valley, Sandton, 2196, South Africa
Tel.: (27) 117227516
Web Site: http://www.zarclear.com
ZCL—(JSE)
Rev.: $20,177,590
Assets: $98,080,079
Liabilities: $5,790,339
Net Worth: $92,289,740
Earnings: $16,335,013
Fiscal Year-end: 06/30/22
Asset Management Services
N.A.I.C.S.: 523940
Warren Chapman *(CEO)*

Subsidiaries:

Peresec Technology Solutions Proprietary Limited (1)
Katherine Towers Bidvest Bank Building 1 Park Lane Entrance, opposite 38 Road West Wierda Valley, Sandton, South Africa
Tel.: (27) 117227330
Web Site: https://www.peresec.com
Financial Services
N.A.I.C.S.: 523999

Sandown Capital International Limited (1)
Ground Floor Cambridge House, Le Truchot, Saint Peter Port, GY1 1WD, Guernsey
Tel.: (44) 7912102909
Web Site: https://sandowncapital.com
Investment Services
N.A.I.C.S.: 523999

ZARGON OIL & GAS LTD.
Sun Life Plaza-East Tower 1100 112-4th Ave SW, Calgary, T2P 0H3, AB, Canada
Tel.: (403) 264-9992 AB
Web Site: http://www.zargon.ca
Year Founded: 2004
ZAR—(TSX)
Rev.: $25,702,881
Assets: $77,624,415
Liabilities: $57,265,970
Net Worth: $20,358,445
Earnings: $17,250,805
Emp.: 15
Fiscal Year-end: 12/31/19
Oil & Gas Exploration Services
N.A.I.C.S.: 211120
Craig H. Hansen *(Pres & CEO)*

Subsidiaries:

Masters Energy Inc. (1)
736 6th Avenue Southwest Suite 1150, Calgary, T2P 3T7, AB, Canada
Tel.: (403) 290-1785
Sales Range: $25-49.9 Million
Emp.: 10
Petroleum & Natural Gas Exploration & Development Services
N.A.I.C.S.: 211120

ZARNENI HRANI BULGARIA AD
2 Stefan Karadzha St, 1000, Sofia, Bulgaria
Tel.: (359) 9634461
Web Site:
https://www.zarnenihrani.com
ZHBG—(BUL)
Sales Range: Less than $1 Million
Grain & Oil Seed Distr
N.A.I.C.S.: 424510
Snezhina Vaselinova Mincheva *(Dir-IR)*

ZASTAVA AUTO PROMET A.D.
Temerinska 37, Novi Sad, Serbia
Tel.: (381) 21 442 360

ZASTAVA AUTO PROMET A.D.

Zastava auto promet a.d.—(Continued)

Year Founded: 2009
Sales Range: $1-9.9 Million
Emp.: 35
Car & Motor Vehicle Whslr
N.A.I.C.S.: 423110

ZASTAVA KOVACNICA A.D.

4 Trg Topolivaca Street, 34000, Kragujevac, Serbia
Tel.: (381) 34 323 545
Web Site: http://www.zastava-kovacnica.co.rs
Emp.: 557
Metal Forging
N.A.I.C.S.: 332111
Daniela Andjelkovic *(Exec Dir)*

ZASTAVA PROMET A.D.

Mije Kovacevica 6, 11000, Belgrade, Serbia
Tel.: (381) 113206545
Web Site: http://www.zpb.co.rs
Year Founded: 1999
ZPBG—(BEL)
Sales Range: Less than $1 Million
Emp.: 8
Automobile Whslr
N.A.I.C.S.: 423110
Krsta Sandic *(Gen Mgr & Dir)*

ZASTAVA TAPACIRNICA A.D.

Stojana Protica bb, 34000, Kragujevac, Serbia
Tel.: (381) 34 300 444
Web Site:
http://www.zastavatapacirnica.rs
Sewing Equipment Mfr
N.A.I.C.S.: 339999
Alojz Kovse *(Gen Mgr)*

ZAVARCO PLC

Suite A 6 Honduras Street, London, EC1Y 0TH, United Kingdom
Web Site: http://www.zavarco.com
Sales Range: $10-24.9 Million
Emp.: 113
Investment Holding Company
N.A.I.C.S.: 551112
Tunku Mazlina Aziz *(Exec Dir)*

Subsidiaries:

Kyowa Kanko Kaihatsu (M) Berhad (1)
PT852 Jln Rawang Kilometer 21, 48000, Rawang, Selangor, Malaysia
Tel.: (60) 3 6091 9617
Golf Club Operator
N.A.I.C.S.: 713910
Manibalan Kutty *(Gen Mgr)*

Vasseti Berhad (1)
Suite 2B-G-1 Ground Floor Block 2B Plaza Sentrall, Jalan Stesen Sentral 5, 50470, Kuala Lumpur, Malaysia
Tel.: (60) 3 2096 9800
Web Site: http://www.vasseti.com.my
Information Technology Development Services
N.A.I.C.S.: 541511

Subsidiary (Domestic):

HD Technology Sdn Bhd (2)
No 22-3 22-4 Block 3A Jalan Wangsa Delima 10 D'Wangsa Wangsa Maju, 53300, Kuala Lumpur, Malaysia (51%)
Tel.: (60) 3 4149 7977
Web Site: http://www.hdtech.com.my
Network Telecommunication Services
N.A.I.C.S.: 517810

Vasseti Datatech Berhad (1)
Suite 2B-G-1 Ground Floor Block 2B Plaza Sentral, Jalan Stesen Sentral 5, Kuala Lumpur, 50470, Malaysia
Tel.: (60) 2096 9800
Web Site: http://www.vtelecoms.com.my
Emp.: 5
Information Technology & Communication Services

N.A.I.C.S.: 541511

ZAVARIVAC A.D.

Radnicka 7, 17501, Vranje, Serbia
Tel.: (381) 17 424 049
Web Site: http://www.zavarivac.rs
Year Founded: 1970
Sales Range: $1-9.9 Million
Emp.: 64
Iron Product Mfr
N.A.I.C.S.: 331511

ZAVAROVALNICA TRIGLAV, D.D.

Miklosiceva cesta 19, 1000, Ljubljana, Slovenia
Tel.: (386) 80555555
Web Site: https://www.triglav.si
ZVTG—(LJU)
Rev.: $1,965,138,537
Assets: $4,524,813,998
Liabilities: $3,541,151,342
Net Worth: $983,662,656
Earnings: $17,954,520
Emp.: 5,318
Fiscal Year-end: 12/31/23
Insurance Services
N.A.I.C.S.: 524128
Tadej Coroli *(Member-Mgmt Bd)*

Subsidiaries:

GRADIS IPGI, industrijsko podjetje gradbenih izdelkov, d.d. (1)
Dunajska cesta 22, 1000, Ljubljana, Slovenia
Tel.: (386) 14744440
Web Site: https://www.triglav-upravljanje.si
Commercial Property Rental Services
N.A.I.C.S.: 531120

Golf Arboretum, d.o.o. (1)
Volcji Potok 43 G, 1235, Radomlje, Slovenia
Tel.: (386) 18318080
Web Site: http://www.golfarboretum.si
Emp.: 9
Golf Training Services
N.A.I.C.S.: 611620
Dejan Ljubenovic *(Mng Dir)*

Lovcen Auto d.o.o. (1)
Bulevar 13 Jula B B Niksic, 81400, Niksic, Montenegro
Tel.: (382) 40 252 660
Motor Vechicles Repair & Maintenance Services
N.A.I.C.S.: 811111

Lovcen Osiguranje a.d. (1)
Slobode 13A, 81000, Podgorica, Montenegro
Tel.: (382) 20404404
Web Site: https://www.lo.co.me
Insurance Services
N.A.I.C.S.: 524210

Lovcen Zivotna osiguranja a.d., (1)
Marka Miljanova 29/III, Podgorica, Montenegro
Tel.: (382) 2 023 1882
Web Site: https://www.lovcenzivot.me
Insurance Services
N.A.I.C.S.: 524210

Pozavarovalnica Triglav RE, d.d. (1)
Miklosiceva 19, SLO-1000, Ljubljana, Slovenia
Tel.: (386) 14747900
Web Site: http://www.triglavre.si
Sales Range: $25-49.9 Million
Emp.: 38
Reinsurance Services
N.A.I.C.S.: 524130
Gojoko Kavcic *(Chm)*

Sarajevostan d.o.o. (1)
Dzemala Bijedica br 147, 71000, Sarajevo, Bosnia & Herzegovina
Tel.: (387) 3 327 6690
Web Site: https://sarajevostan.com.ba
Real Estate Services
N.A.I.C.S.: 531210

Slovenijales d.d. (1)

Dunajska cesta 22, 1000, Ljubljana, Slovenia (76.1%)
Tel.: (386) 1 474 42 92
Web Site: http://www.slovenijales.si
Sales Range: $50-74.9 Million
Emp.: 310
Real Estate & Financial Investment Services
N.A.I.C.S.: 531390
Aleksandra Vukovic Kacar *(Chm-Supervisory Bd)*

Subsidiary (Domestic):

Slovenijales Trgovina d.o.o. (2)
Dunajska Cesta 22, 1511, Ljubljana, Slovenia
Tel.: (386) 14744480
Web Site: http://www.slovenijales-trgovina.si
Emp.: 35
Home Furnishings Services
N.A.I.C.S.: 449129

TRI-PRO d.o.o. (1)
Ljubljanska Cesta 86, 1230, Domzale, Slovenia
Tel.: (386) 17246650
Web Site: http://www.tri-pro.si
Emp.: 80
General Insurance Services
N.A.I.C.S.: 524210
Edvard Kranjcic *(Mng Dir)*

Tri -pro BH d.o.o. (1)
Topal Osman Pase 30, 71000, Sarajevo, Bosnia & Herzegovina
Tel.: (387) 33618106
Web Site: http://www.tri-probh.ba
Automobile Insurance Services
N.A.I.C.S.: 524126

Triglav Avtoservis d.o.o. (1)
Verovskova 60 B, 1000, Ljubljana, Slovenia
Tel.: (386) 15806872
Web Site: https://www.triglav-avtoservis.si
Emp.: 30
Motor Vehicles Repair & Maintenance Services
N.A.I.C.S.: 811111

Triglav Avtoservis d.o.o. (1)
Verovskova 60b, 1000, Ljubljana, Slovenia
Tel.: (386) 1 580 6872
Web Site: https://www.triglav-avtoservis.si
Automotive Repair Services
N.A.I.C.S.: 811111

Triglav Druzba za upravljanje, d.o.o. (1)
Slovenska 54, Ljubljana, 1000, Slovenia
Tel.: (386) 13007300
Web Site: http://www.triglavskladi.si
Emp.: 42
Financial Services
N.A.I.C.S.: 525990
Igor Kusar *(Chm & Pres)*

Subsidiary (Non-US):

PROF-IN d.o.o., (2)
Mehmed Pase Sokolovica 15, Sarajevo, 71000, Bosnia & Herzegovina
Tel.: (387) 33263300
Web Site: http://www.prof-in.ba
Emp.: 6
Investemnt Manangement Services
N.A.I.C.S.: 523940
Senada Smajic *(Exec Dir)*

Triglav INT, d.o.o. (1)
Dunajska cesta 22, 1000, Ljubljana, Slovenia
Tel.: (386) 14309534
Web Site: https://www.triglav-int.si
Insurance Services
N.A.I.C.S.: 524210

Triglav Krajina Kopaonik a.d. (1)
Trg srpskih junaka 4, 78000, Banja Luka, Bosnia & Herzegovina
Tel.: (387) 51215262
Web Site: http://www.triglavrs.ba
Property & Personal Insurance Services
N.A.I.C.S.: 524113

Triglav Nalozbe, financna druzba d.d. (1)
Slovenska 54, 1000, Ljubljana, Slovenia
Tel.: (386) 14345540
Web Site: http://www.triglav-fd.si
Emp.: 5

Financial Investment Advisory Services
N.A.I.C.S.: 523940

Triglav Netherlands b.v. (1)
Melisse 1, 1705 RC, Heerhugowaard, Noord-Holland, Netherlands
Tel.: (31) 617519657
General Insurance Services
N.A.I.C.S.: 524113

Triglav Osiguranje d.d. (1)
Antuna Heinza 4, 10000, Zagreb, Croatia
Tel.: (385) 800202080
Web Site: https://triglav.hr
General Insurance Services
N.A.I.C.S.: 524210
Ivan Buneta *(Head-Mktg & PR)*

Triglav Osiguranje, a.d.o., Beograd (1)
Milutina Milankovica 7a, 11070, Novi Beograd, Serbia
Tel.: (381) 113305100
Web Site: http://www.triglav.rs
General Insurance Services
N.A.I.C.S.: 524113

Triglav Osiguranje, d.d., Sarajevo (1)
Ul Dolina Br 8, 71000, Sarajevo, Bosnia & Herzegovina
Tel.: (387) 33252110
Web Site: https://www.triglav.ba
Emp.: 245
Insurance Services
N.A.I.C.S.: 524113

Subsidiary (Domestic):

Autocentar BH d.o.o. (2)
Vranducka 57, 72000, Zenica, Bosnia & Herzegovina
Tel.: (387) 32403530
New Car Dealers
N.A.I.C.S.: 441110

Triglav Osiguruvanje d.d. (1)
Bulevar 8-mi Septemvri br 16, Delovna Zgrada Hiiperium, 1000, Skopje, North Macedonia
Tel.: (389) 25102222
Web Site: https://www.triglav.mk
Insurance Services
N.A.I.C.S.: 524114

Triglav Osiguruvanje Zivot a.d. (1)
Bulevar 8-mi Septemvri br 16, 1000, Skopje, North Macedonia
Tel.: (389) 2 510 2201
Insurance Services
N.A.I.C.S.: 524210

Triglav Osiguruvanje a.d. (1)
bul September 8 No 16, 1000, Skopje, North Macedonia
Tel.: (389) 2 510 2222
Web Site: https://www.triglav.mk
Insurance Services
N.A.I.C.S.: 524210

Triglav Savjetovanje d.o.o. (1)
Dolina br 8, 71000, Sarajevo, Bosnia & Herzegovina
Tel.: (387) 3 361 8106
Web Site: https://www.triglav-savjetovanje.ba
Insurance Services
N.A.I.C.S.: 524210

Triglav Skladi d.o.o. (1)
Slovenska Cesta 54, 1000, Ljubljana, Slovenia
Tel.: (386) 1 300 7300
Web Site: https://www.triglavskladi.si
Pension Insurance Services
N.A.I.C.S.: 525110

Triglav Svetovanje, d.o.o. (1)
Ljubljanska Cesta 86, 1230, Domzale, Slovenia
Tel.: (386) 17246650
Web Site: https://www.triglav-svetovanje.si
Insurance Agency Operator
N.A.I.C.S.: 524210

Triglav penzijski fondovi a.d. (1)
Kralja Petra 45, 11000, Belgrade, Serbia
Tel.: (381) 11 303 63 56
Web Site: http://www.triglavpenzija.com
Fund Management Services
N.A.I.C.S.: 523940

AND PRIVATE COMPANIES

Triglav penzisko drustvo A.D. (1)
Bul 8-mi Septemvri br 18 Kat 2, 1000, Skopje, North Macedonia
Tel.: (389) 2 510 2190
Web Site: https://www.triglavpenzisko.mk
Pension Insurance Services
N.A.I.C.S.: 525110

Triglav pokokninska druzba dd. (1)
Dunajska 22, 1000, Ljubljana, Slovenia (71.87%)
Tel.: (386) 14700840
Web Site: https://www.triglavpokojnine.si
Banking Services
N.A.I.C.S.: 522110
Aljosa Ursic (Pres)

Triglav, Upravljanje nepremicnin d.o.o. (1)
Dunajska Cesta 22, 1000, Ljubljana, Slovenia
Tel.: (386) 1 474 4440
Real Estate Services
N.A.I.C.S.: 531210

Triglav, Zdravstvena zavarovalnica d.d. (1)
Pasteaneska 10, Koper, 6000, Slovenia
Tel.: (386) 56622000
Web Site: http://www.zdravstvena.com
Emp.: 60
Health Insurance Services
N.A.I.C.S.: 524114
Meta Berk Skok (Pres)

Subsidiary (Domestic):

Triglav, Zdravstvena dejavnost d.o.o. (2)
Ferrarska 10, 6000, Koper, Slovenia
Tel.: (386) 56622000
Web Site: http://www.zdravstvena.net
Emp.: 60
Health Insurance Services
N.A.I.C.S.: 524114
Meta Berk Skok (Pres)

Triglav, pokojninska druzba d.d. (1)
Dunajska cesta 22, 1000, Ljubljana, Slovenia
Tel.: (386) 8 055 5555
Web Site: https://www.triglavpokojnine.si
Pension Insurance Services
N.A.I.C.S.: 525110

Zenit nepremicnine, inzeniring in trzenje d.d. (1)
Legatova Ulica 2, 1000, Ljubljana, Slovenia
Tel.: (386) 12420690
Emp.: 6
Real Estate Manangement Services
N.A.I.C.S.: 531311

ZAVOD ZA EKONOMIKU I RAZVOJ A.D.
Mladena Stojanovica 4, 78000, Banja Luka, Bosnia & Herzegovina
Tel.: (387) 51 315 012
IZER—(BANJ)
Sales Range: Less than $1 Million
Emp.: 3
Marketing Research Service
N.A.I.C.S.: 541910
Drago Makic (Chm)

ZAVOD ZA GEOTEHNIKU A.D.
Segedinski put 86, Subotica, Serbia
Tel.: (381) 24 548 255
Web Site: http://zzgeotehnikasu.rs
Year Founded: 2001
Sales Range: Less than $1 Million
Emp.: 13
Drilling Services
N.A.I.C.S.: 213111

ZAVOD ZA SHLIFOVACHNI MASHINI AD
13 Kozanovska Str, 4230, Asenovgrad, 4230, Bulgaria
Tel.: (359) 33169031
Web Site: https://www.zshm-as.com
GPP—(BUL)
Sales Range: Less than $1 Million
Industrial Machinery Mfr

N.A.I.C.S.: 333248
Ivan Atanasov Markov (CEO)

ZAVOD ZA SUDSKA VESTACENJA A.D.
Sremska br 9, 21000, Novi Sad, Serbia
Tel.: (381) 21525860 RS
Web Site: https://www.zsv-novisad.com
Year Founded: 1973
ZZSV—(BEL)
Rev.: $106,190
Assets: $26,396
Liabilities: $13,409
Net Worth: $12,988
Earnings: $394
Fiscal Year-end: 12/31/21
Law firm
N.A.I.C.S.: 541199
Marinko Marjanovic (Pres, Exec Dir & Dir)

ZAVOD ZA VODOPRIVREDU D.D.
Paromlinska 53 E / I, 71000, Sarajevo, Bosnia & Herzegovina
Tel.: (387) 33728628
Web Site: http://www.vodoprivreda.ba
Year Founded: 1952
ZVDPR—(SARE)
Rev.: $1,156,802
Assets: $5,277,894
Liabilities: $823,052
Net Worth: $4,454,841
Earnings: $46,332
Emp.: 28
Fiscal Year-end: 12/31/20
Waste Water Management Services
N.A.I.C.S.: 562998

ZB FINANCIAL HOLDINGS LIMITED
21 Natal Road Avondale, Harare, Zimbabwe
Tel.: (263) 8677002001
Web Site: https://www.zb.co.zw
Year Founded: 1951
ZBFH—(ZIM)
Sales Range: $75-99.9 Million
Emp.: 655
Commercial & Merchant Banking Services
N.A.I.C.S.: 522110
Shepherd T. Fungura (Co-CEO)

Subsidiaries:

ZB Bank Limited - Consumer Banking Unit (1)
12th Floor ZB Centre Corner First Street Kwame Nkrumah Avenue, PO Box 3198, Harare, Zimbabwe
Tel.: (263) 4781236
Personal Banking Services
N.A.I.C.S.: 522180

ZB Bank Limited - Group Credit Services Bulawayo Unit (1)
Corner Fife Street 10th Avenue, PO Box 849, Bulawayo, Matabeleland North, Zimbabwe
Tel.: (263) 975031
Emp.: 20
Financial Investment Advisory Services
N.A.I.C.S.: 523940

ZB Bank Limited - Group Treasury Unit (1)
5th Floor ZB House 46 Speke Avenue, PO Box 3198, Harare, Zimbabwe
Tel.: (263) 4757543
Liquidity Risk Management Services
N.A.I.C.S.: 522320

ZB Bank Limited - Investment Banking Unit (1)
1st Floor ZB Centre Corner First Street Kwame Nkrumah Avenue, PO Box 2540, Harare, Zimbabwe
Tel.: (263) 4781274

Investment Banking Services
N.A.I.C.S.: 523150

ZB Reinsurance Limited (1)
2th Floor Finsure House Sam Nujoma St, Kwame Nkrumah Ave, Harare, Zimbabwe
Tel.: (263) 4759735
Web Site: http://www.zbre.co.zw
Reinsurance Services
N.A.I.C.S.: 524130
Ngonidzashe Chawota (Mgr-Fin)

ZBI ZENTRAL BODEN IMMOBILIEN AG
Henkestrasse 10, 91054, Erlangen, Germany
Tel.: (49) 9131480090
Web Site: http://www.zbi-ag.de
Year Founded: 1998
Rev.: $55,176,000
Emp.: 25
Real Estate Investment Services
N.A.I.C.S.: 531390
Bernd Ital (Member-Mgmt Bd)

ZBOM HOME COLLECTION CO., LTD.
No 19 Lianshui Road Luyang Industrial Zone, Hefei, 230041, Anhui, China
Tel.: (86) 55165201686 CN
Web Site: https://www.zbomhome.com
Year Founded: 1998
603801—(SHG)
Rev.: $756,584,670
Assets: $811,150,021
Liabilities: $406,993,107
Net Worth: $404,156,914
Earnings: $75,355,418
Fiscal Year-end: 12/31/22
Cabinetry Mfr
N.A.I.C.S.: 332510
Sun Zhiyong (Chm)

ZCCM INVESTMENTS HOLDINGS PLC.
ZCCM-IH Office Park Stand No 16806 Alick Nkhata Road, PO Box 30048, Mass Media Complex Area, Lusaka, 10101, Zambia
Tel.: (260) 211388000 ZM
Web Site: https://www.zccm-ih.com.zm
ZCCM—(LUS)
Rev.: $456,552,880
Assets: $1,495,106,258
Liabilities: $40,694,250
Net Worth: $1,454,412,008
Earnings: ($158,407,432)
Fiscal Year-end: 12/31/23
Investment Management Service
N.A.I.C.S.: 523999
Chabby Chabala (Chief Corp Svcs Officer & Sec)

Subsidiaries:

Investrust Bank Plc (1)
Ody's Building Great East Road Plot No 19028/29, PO Box 32344, opposite Arcades Shopping Mall, Lusaka, Zambia
Tel.: (260) 211294682
Web Site: http://www.investrustbank.co.zm
Banking Services
N.A.I.C.S.: 522110
Simangolwa Shakalima (Mng Dir)

Misenge Environmental & Technical Services Limited (1)
Investments House Plot 1591 Kantanta Street, PO Box 20172, Kitwe, Zambia
Tel.: (260) 212245822
Mineral Mining Services
N.A.I.C.S.: 213115

Ndola Lime Company Limited (1)
PO Box 70057, Ndola, Copperbelt, Zambia
Tel.: (260) 962755820
Web Site: http://www.ndolalime.co.zm
Limestone Product Mfr & Distr
N.A.I.C.S.: 327991

Moses Chilambe (CEO)

ZCHOCOLAT
5 rue Fabrot, 13100, Aix-en-Provence, France
Tel.: (33) 442914365
Web Site: http://www.zchocolat.com
Year Founded: 1999
Emp.: 200
Internet Sales of Handmade French Chocolates
N.A.I.C.S.: 311352
Marc Segard (CFO)

Subsidiaries:

zChocolat (1)
409 N Montgomery St, Ojai, CA 93023-2747 (100%)
Tel.: (800) 529-9512
Web Site: http://www.zchocolat.com
Internet Sales of Handmade French Chocolates
N.A.I.C.S.: 311351
Adria Higdon (Mgr-PR & Special Events & Head-Sls)

ZEABORN SHIP MANAGEMENT GMBH & CIE. KG

ZEABORN SHIP MANAGEMENT GMBH & CIE. KG
Ludwig Erhard Strasse 22, 20459, Hamburg, Germany
Tel.: (49) 40 50098 0 De
Web Site: http://www.zea-ship.com
Year Founded: 2018
Holding Company; Vessel Ownership & Freight Shipping Services
N.A.I.C.S.: 551112
Rob Grool (CEO)

Subsidiaries:

ZEABORN Chartering GmbH & Co. KG (1)
Marcusallee 35, 28359, Bremen, Germany
Tel.: (49) 421 989618 00
Freighter Chartering Services
N.A.I.C.S.: 483111
Ove Meyer (Mng Dir)

Subsidiary (Domestic):

Rickmers-Line GmbH & Co. KG (2)
Neumuhlen 19, 22763, Hamburg, Germany
Tel.: (49) 40389177200
Web Site: http://www.rickmerslinie.de
Worldwide Cargo Transportation
N.A.I.C.S.: 488390
Ulrich Ulrichs (CEO)

Subsidiary (Non-US):

Rickmers-Line (Belgium) N.V. (3)
Rijnkaai 37, 2000, Antwerp, Belgium
Tel.: (32) 3 544 94 01
Web Site: http://www.rickmers.net
Marine Cargo Handling Services
N.A.I.C.S.: 488320

Rickmers-Line (Japan) Inc. (3)
Cross Shibaura Bldg 5F 3-Chome 12-6, Shibaura Minato-ku, Tokyo, 108-0023, Japan
Tel.: (81) 3 5419 1166
Web Site: http://www.rickmers-line.com
Marine Cargo Handling Services
N.A.I.C.S.: 488320
Richard Stinchcombe (CEO)

Rickmers-Line (Korea) Inc. (3)
Rm 1603 16FL Seoul Center Building 116 SoGong Ro, Jung-Gu, 100-070, Seoul, Korea (South)
Tel.: (82) 2 319 0051
Web Site: http://www.rickmers-linie.com
Marine Cargo Handling Services
N.A.I.C.S.: 488320
Minsik Seo (Pres & CEO)

Rickmers-Line (Singapore) Pte. Ltd. (3)
200 Cantonment Road #13-06 Southpoint, 089763, Singapore, Singapore
Tel.: (65) 6225 3522
Web Site: http://www.rickmers-line.com
Marine Cargo Handling Services
N.A.I.C.S.: 488320
Wendy Kwoh (Mgr-Customer Rels)

ZEABORN SHIP MANAGEMENT GMBH & CIE. KG

ZEABORN Ship Management GmbH & Cie. KG—(Continued)

Subsidiary (US):

Rickmers-Linie (USA) Inc. (3)
2002 Timberloch Pl Ste 350, Houston, TX 77380
Tel.: (281) 453-7500
Web Site: http://www.rickmers-linie.com
Marine Cargo Handling Services
N.A.I.C.S.: 488320
Ron Sralla (Mgr-Bus Dev)

ZEAL AQUA LIMITED

Block No 347 Village Orma Taluka Olpad, Surat, 394 540, Gujarat, India
Tel.: (91) 2621220047
Web Site: https://www.zealaqua.com
539963—(BOM)
Rev.: $41,335,761
Assets: $36,281,462
Liabilities: $28,355,636
Net Worth: $7,925,826
Earnings: $580,070
Emp.: 102
Fiscal Year-end: 03/31/21
Aquaculture Farming Services
N.A.I.C.S.: 112512
Shantilal Ishwarbhai Patel (Chm & Mng Dir)

ZEAL NETWORK SE

Strassenbahnring 11, 20251, Hamburg, Germany
Tel.: (49) 40809036065
Web Site:
https://www.zealnetwork.de
TIMA—(MUN)
Rev.: $128,104,113
Assets: $435,642,295
Liabilities: $149,508,153
Net Worth: $286,134,143
Earnings: $14,184,729
Emp.: 172
Fiscal Year-end: 12/31/23
Lottery Services
N.A.I.C.S.: 713290
Peter Steiner (Chm-Supervisory Bd)

Subsidiaries:

Lotto24 AG (1)
Strassenbahnring 11, 20251, Hamburg, Germany (95.12%)
Tel.: (49) 40809036065
Web Site: https://www.lotto24-ag.de
Rev.: $410,418,611
Assets: $84,709,570
Liabilities: $42,952,230
Net Worth: $41,757,340
Earnings: $5,556,745
Emp.: 119
Fiscal Year-end: 12/31/2019
Gambling
N.A.I.C.S.: 713290
Jens Schumann (Chm-Supervisory Bd)

ZEALAND PHARMA A/S

Sydmarken 11, 2860, Copenhagen, Denmark
Tel.: (45) 88773600   DK
Web Site:
https://www.zealandpharma.com
Year Founded: 1997
ZEAL—(NASDAQ)
Rev.: $50,756,619
Assets: $293,177,564
Liabilities: $57,325,893
Net Worth: $235,851,671
Earnings: ($104,202,634)
Emp.: 253
Fiscal Year-end: 12/31/23
Biopharmaceutical Products Developer & Mfr
N.A.I.C.S.: 541714
Marino Garcia (Sr VP-Corp & Bus Dev)

ZEB NICKEL CORP.

4 King St West Suite 401, Toronto, M5H 1B6, ON, Canada
Tel.: (416) 628-3100
Web Site: https://zebnickel.com
Year Founded: 2019
ZBNI—(TSXV)
Assets: $246,537
Liabilities: $28,641
Net Worth: $217,896
Earnings: ($88,841)
Fiscal Year-end: 01/31/21
Investment Services
N.A.I.C.S.: 523940
Tom Panoulias (VP-Corporate Development)

ZECH GROUP SE

August-Bebel-Allee 1, D-28329, Bremen, Germany
Tel.: (49) 421 41007 0   De
Web Site: http://www.zech-group.com
Holding Company
N.A.I.C.S.: 551112
Kurt Zech (CEO)

Subsidiaries:

ATECS AG (1)
Baarerstrasse 69, 6300, Zug, Switzerland
Tel.: (41) 417108644
Web Site: http://www.atecsag.com
Audio & Video Equipment Mfr
N.A.I.C.S.: 334310
Bernard Kolodziej (CEO)

Amphenol Precision Optics GmbH (1)
Zur Dornheck 32-34, Fleisbach, 35764, Sinn, Germany
Tel.: (49) 2772575590
Web Site: http://www.amphenol-po.de
Sales Range: $25-49.9 Million
Emp.: 50
Fiber Optic Components Mfr
N.A.I.C.S.: 334417
Michael Maage (Mng Dir)

ELABO GmbH (1)
Rossfelder Strasse 56, 74564, Crailsheim, Baden-Wurttemberg, Germany
Tel.: (49) 79513070
Web Site: http://www.elabo.de
Sales Range: $25-49.9 Million
Emp.: 170
Education & Laboratory & Test Systems Development & Installation Services
N.A.I.C.S.: 541512
Thomas Hosle (CEO)

GZS Digital GmbH (1)
Dornhofstrasse 100, 63263, Neu-Isenburg, Germany
Tel.: (49) 6102823750
Web Site: http://www.gzs-digital.de
Information & Communication Technology Services
N.A.I.C.S.: 541519
Gerd Kroll (Mng Dir)

Subsidiary (Domestic):

Telent GmbH (2)
Gerber Strasse 34, Backnang, 71522, Germany
Tel.: (49) 71919000
Web Site: http://www.telent.de
Rev.: $885,820,000
Emp.: 300
Technology Products & Services
N.A.I.C.S.: 517112
Robert Blum (Gen Mgr)

Subsidiary (Domestic):

Koramis GmbH (3)
Europaallee 5, 66113, Saarbrucken, Germany
Tel.: (49) 6819681910
Web Site: http://www.koramis.de
Security Services
N.A.I.C.S.: 561621

Netzikon GmbH (3)
Gerberstrasse 34, 71522, Backnang, Germany
Tel.: (49) 71919047901
Web Site: http://www.netzikon.de

Telecommunication Services b
N.A.I.C.S.: 517810

Subsidiary (Non-US):

ZECH Technik Austria GmbH (2)
Gewerbestrasse 2, 5201, Seekirchen, Austria
Tel.: (43) 621230000
Web Site: http://www.zech-technik.at
Emp.: 50
Communication, Security & Internet-of-Things Services
N.A.I.C.S.: 541519
Willibald Wandaller (Mng Dir)

LWL-Sachsenkabel GmbH (1)
Auerbacher Strasse 24, Erzgebirge, 09390, Gornsdorf, Saxony, Germany
Tel.: (49) 372139880
Web Site: http://www.sachsenkabel.de
Sales Range: $25-49.9 Million
Emp.: 70
Fiber Optic Cable Mfr
N.A.I.C.S.: 335921
Silvia Duus (Co-Mng Dir)

Microsens GmbH & Co. KG (1)
Kueferstrasse 16, 59067, Hamm, Germany
Tel.: (49) 238194520
Web Site: http://www.microsens.com
Sales Range: $25-49.9 Million
Emp.: 75
Fiber Optic Conversion & Transmission Products Mfr
N.A.I.C.S.: 334417
Klaus Witt (Mng Dir)

Subsidiary (Non-US):

Microsens Sp. z o.o. (2)
Ul Wyscigowa 56G/2f, 53-012, Wroclaw, Poland
Tel.: (48) 713371671
Web Site: http://www.microsens.com
Fiber Optic Transmission System Mfr
N.A.I.C.S.: 335921
Tomasz Niewolik (CEO)

ProCom Professional Communication & Service GmbH (1)
Alfredstr 157, 45131, Essen, Germany
Tel.: (49) 2018606700
Web Site: http://www.procomgmbh.de
Professional Communication Services
N.A.I.C.S.: 517810
Roland Hunteler (Mng Dir)

Qubix S.p.A. (1)
Via Canada 22/A, 35127, Padova, PD, Italy
Tel.: (39) 0497801994
Web Site: http://www.qubix.it
Fiber Optic Transmission Cable Mfr
N.A.I.C.S.: 335921

Rud. Otto Meyer Technik Ltd. & Co. KG (1)
Motorstrasse 62, 70499, Stuttgart, Germany
Tel.: (49) 711 1393 00
Web Site: http://www.rom-technik.de
Emp.: 2,300
Engineeering Services
N.A.I.C.S.: 541330
Burkhard Schmidt (Mng Dir)

SKM Skyline GmbH (1)
Ammerthalstrasse 30, Kirchheim, 85551, Heimstetten, Germany
Tel.: (49) 89 431982 0
Web Site: http://www.skm-skyline.de
Sales Range: $25-49.9 Million
Emp.: 30
Data Communication & Networking Equipment Distr
N.A.I.C.S.: 423690
Filippo Gnocco (Mng Dir)

Secure Information Management GmbH (1)
Chemnitzer Strasse 2, 67433, Neustadt, Germany
Tel.: (49) 632191270
Web Site: http://www.sim-secure.de
Audio & Video Surveillance Equipment Mfr
N.A.I.C.S.: 334310

ZECH Building SE (1)
Niermannsweg 11, 40699, Erkrath, Germany
Tel.: (49) 421 41007 0
Web Site: https://www.zech-building.de

INTERNATIONAL PUBLIC

Commercial & Industrial Building Construction Services
N.A.I.C.S.: 236220

Subsidiary (Domestic):

Wayss & Freytag Ingenieurbau AG (2)
Eschborner Landstrasse 130-132, 60489, Frankfurt am Main, Germany
Tel.: (49) 697929260
Web Site: http://www.wf-ingbau.de
Sales Range: $50-74.9 Million
Emp.: 150
Provider of Industrial, Commercial & Public Building, Civil & Maritime Engineering & Property Development
N.A.I.C.S.: 236210
Michael Blaschko (CEO, COO & Member-Mgmt Bd)

ZECH Hochbau AG (1)
Monchhaldenstrasse 26, 70191, Stuttgart, Germany
Tel.: (49) 711250070
Web Site: http://www.bam-deutschland.de
Construction Services
N.A.I.C.S.: 236220
Daniel Haussermann (Mng Dir)

ZECH Sicherheitstechnik GmbH (1)
Siemensstrasse 6, 63263, Neu-Isenburg, Germany
Tel.: (49) 610282220
Web Site: http://www.zech-sicherheitstechnik.de
Emp.: 450
Communication Equipment Mfr
N.A.I.C.S.: 334290
Gerd Kroll (Mng Dir)

Zech Bau Holding GmbH (1)
August-Bebel-Allee 1, D-28329, Bremen, Germany
Tel.: (49) 421410070
Web Site: http://www.zech-group.com
Holding Company; Construction Services
N.A.I.C.S.: 551112

Subsidiary (Domestic):

BFP Betonfertigteile Pulheim GmbH (2)
Industriestrasse 1, 50259, Pulheim, Germany
Tel.: (49) 2238 80 11 65
Web Site: http://www.bfp-gmbh.biz
Construction Engineering Services
N.A.I.C.S.: 541330

BWE-Bau Fertigteilwerk GmbH (2)
Schwarzer Weg 3, 26215, Wiefelstede, Germany
Tel.: (49) 441 68 04 0
Web Site: http://bwe-bau.de
Construction Engineering Services
N.A.I.C.S.: 541330

Ecotec GmbH (2)
Wilhelm-Herbst-Str 7, 28359, Bremen, Germany
Tel.: (49) 421 2 01 12 10
Web Site: http://www.ecotec-bremen.de
Construction Engineering Services
N.A.I.C.S.: 541330

Subsidiary (Non-US):

HTB Engenharia e Constrcao S.A. (2)
Avenida Alfredo Egidio de Souza Aranha 145, CEP 04726-170, Sao Paulo, SP, Brazil (100%)
Tel.: (55) 1156430100
Web Site: http://www.htb.eng.br
Emp.: 1,600
Construction & Engineering Services
N.A.I.C.S.: 541330
Fatima Idogava (Coord-Comm)

Subsidiary (Domestic):

Construtora Tedesco Ltda. (3)
Avenue Plinio Brasil Milano 1023 Bairro Higienopolis, 90520-002, Porto Alegre, Brazil
Tel.: (55) 51 3327 0700
Web Site: http://www.tedesco.com.br
Construction Engineering Services
N.A.I.C.S.: 541330

AND PRIVATE COMPANIES

Unit (Domestic):

Construtora Tedesco Ltda. - GRAV-
ATAI UNIT (4)
Street Ernesto Gomes 715 Neighborhood
Passo das Pedras, 94035-780, Gravatai,
Brazil
Tel.: (55) 51 3042 5875
Construction Engineering Services
N.A.I.C.S.: 541330

Subsidiary (Domestic):

Heitkamp Ingenieur- und Kraftwerks-
bau GmbH (2)
Langekampstrasse 36, 44652, Herne,
Germany (100%)
Tel.: (49) 23 25 69 90 0
Web Site: http://www.heitkamp-ikb.com
Sales Range: $200-249.9 Million
Emp.: 200
Power Plant Construction & Civil Engineer-
ing Services
N.A.I.C.S.: 237990

InFaCon GmbH (2)
Industriestrasse 161 Gebaude 4b, 50999,
Cologne, Germany
Tel.: (49) 221 349 21 901
Web Site: http://www.infacon-koeln.de
Construction Engineering Services
N.A.I.C.S.: 541330
Manfred Hammer *(Mng Dir)*

Renke Gebaudetechnik GmbH (2)
Am Alten Sicherheitshafen 1, 28197,
Bremen, Germany
Tel.: (49) 421 388 88 10
Web Site: http://www.renke-bremen.de
Heating System Installation Services
N.A.I.C.S.: 238220

Zechbau GmbH (2)
August-Bebel-Allee 1, Bremen, 28329, Ger-
many
Tel.: (49) 421 41007 0
Web Site: http://www.zechbau.de
Emp.: 700
Commercial Building Construction Services
N.A.I.C.S.: 236220
Rolf Biermann *(Member-Mgmt Bd)*

Zech Hotel Holding GmbH (1)
Langenstrasse 6-8, Bremen, Germany
Tel.: (49) 421 410 07 0
Holding Company
N.A.I.C.S.: 551112

Subsidiary (Domestic):

Zech Hotels GmbH (2)
Hochdahler Markt 65, 40699, Erkrath, Ger-
many
Tel.: (49) 2104 2886 0
Web Site: http://www.zech-hotels.com
Hotel Operator
N.A.I.C.S.: 721110

Zech Umwelt GmbH (1)
Industriepark 6 a, 27777, Ganderkesee,
Germany
Tel.: (49) 42 22 790 990
Web Site: http://www.zech-umwelt.com
Plastic Recycling Services
N.A.I.C.S.: 325991

ZECON BERHAD
8th Floor Menara Zecon No 92 Lot
393 Section 5 KTLD Jalan Satok,
93400, Kuching, Sarawak, Malaysia
Tel.: (60) 82275555
Web Site: https://www.zecon.com.my
ZECON—(KLS)
Rev.: $17,610,146
Assets: $335,399,203
Liabilities: $248,963,741
Net Worth: $86,435,462
Earnings: $4,676,371
Emp.: 170
Fiscal Year-end: 12/31/22
Construction Services
N.A.I.C.S.: 236117
Saini Ali *(VP-Properties)*

ZECOTEK PHOTONICS INC.
Unit 2325 - 6900 Graybar Road,
Richmond, V6W 0A5, BC, Canada
Tel.: (604) 233-0056
Web Site: https://www.zecotek.com
Year Founded: 2004
ZMS—(OTCIQ)
Rev.: $87,032
Assets: $2,585,436
Liabilities: $5,897,216
Net Worth: ($3,311,780)
Earnings: ($3,726,622)
Fiscal Year-end: 07/31/19
Clinical Laboratory Instruments Mfr
N.A.I.C.S.: 333248
Faouzi Zerrouk *(Founder, Chm, Pres & CEO)*

Subsidiaries:

Zecotek Photonics Singapore Pte.
Ltd. (1)
21 Kallang Avenue 03-177, Singapore,
339412, Singapore
Tel.: (65) 6292 2040
Web Site: http://www.zecotek.com
Emp.: 10
Medical Imaging Equipment Mfr
N.A.I.C.S.: 334510

ZEDCOR INC.
300 151 Canada Olympic Road SW,
Calgary, T3B 6B7, AB, Canada
Tel.: (403) 930-5430 Ca
Web Site: https://zedcor.com
Year Founded: 2005
CRFQF—(OTCIQ)
Rev.: $20,424,486
Assets: $32,448,262
Liabilities: $23,299,983
Net Worth: $9,148,279
Earnings: $2,002,578
Emp.: 100
Fiscal Year-end: 12/31/23
Energy & Construction Equipment
Rental Services
N.A.I.C.S.: 532490
Todd Ziniuk *(Pres & CEO)*

Subsidiaries:

TRAC Energy Services Ltd. (1)
7009-45 Street, Leduc, T9E 7H1, AB,
Canada (100%)
Tel.: (780) 612-8644
Web Site:
http://www.tracenergyservices.com
Oil & Gas Equipment Rental Services
N.A.I.C.S.: 532412
Cam Miller *(Gen Mgr)*

The Smart-Way Disposal & Recycling
Company Ltd. (1)
8430 24 Street Northwest, Edmonton, T6P
1X8, AB, Canada
Tel.: (780) 465-4888
Web Site: http://www.smartwaydisposal.com
Sales Range: $25-49.9 Million
Emp.: 12
Waste Disposal & Recycling Services
N.A.I.C.S.: 562219

Zedcor Holdings (USA), Inc. (1)
Zedcor Security Solutions Corp. (1)
300 -151 Canada Olympic Road SW, Cal-
gary, T3B 6B7, AB, Canada
Tel.: (403) 930-5430
Web Site: https://zedcorsecurity.ca
Investigation & Security Services
N.A.I.C.S.: 561611
Todd Ziniuk *(Pres & CEO)*

ZEDER INVESTMENTS LIM-
ITED
1st Floor Ou Kollege 35 Kerk Street,
Cape Town, Stellenbosch, 7600,
South Africa
Tel.: (27) 218319559 ZA
Web Site: https://www.zeder.co.za
ZED—(JSE)
Rev.: $3,432,651
Assets: $216,573,897
Liabilities: $4,858,522
Net Worth: $211,715,375
Earnings: $1,214,630
Fiscal Year-end: 02/28/23
Investment Holding Company
N.A.I.C.S.: 551112
Johann H. le Roux *(CEO-Acting & Dir-Fin)*

Subsidiaries:

Capespan Group Limited (1)
Old Oak Office Park 1st Floor Oak Leaf Ter-
race 1 Edmar Street, Cnr Old Oak & Dur-
ban Road, Bellville, 7530, South
Africa (96.4%)
Tel.: (27) 219172600
Web Site: https://www.capespan.com
Emp.: 26
Holding Company; Fruit Distr, Logistics Ser-
vices & Farming
N.A.I.C.S.: 551112
Tonie Fuchs *(Mng Dir)*

Subsidiary (Non-US):

Capespan International Limited (2)
Maidstone Studios New Cut Road, Vinters
Park, Maidstone, ME14 5NZ, Kent, United
Kingdom
Tel.: (44) 1622782727
Web Site: http://www.capespan.com
Emp.: 3
Fresh Produce Distr
N.A.I.C.S.: 424480
Gail Weightman *(Head-HR)*

Zaad Holdings Proprietary
Limited (1)
37 Eagle Street, Brackenfell, South Africa
Tel.: (27) 219811212
Web Site: https://zaad.co.za
Agricultural Input Distr
N.A.I.C.S.: 424910

ZEDRA TRUST CO. LTD
Boulevard Georges-Favon 8, Ge-
neva, 1204, Geneva, Switzerland
Tel.: (41) 228880600 CH
Web Site: http://www.zedra.com
Year Founded: 2016
Trust Fund Services
N.A.I.C.S.: 523999
Ivo Hemelraad *(CEO)*

Subsidiaries:

Atlas Fund Services (USA) LLC (1)
22110 Jamaica Ave, Jamaica, NY 11428-
2037
Tel.: (704) 322-3510
Web Site: http://www.atlasfundservices.com
Real Estate Credit
N.A.I.C.S.: 522292
Eileen Samet *(Pres)*

ZEE LEARN LIMITED
135 Continental Building Dr Annie
Besant Road, Worli, Mumbai,
400018, India
Tel.: (91) 2271541895
Web Site: https://www.zeelearn.com
533287—(BOM)
Rev.: $42,785,625
Assets: $200,791,746
Liabilities: $116,932,479
Net Worth: $83,859,266
Earnings: ($2,887,030)
Emp.: 253
Fiscal Year-end: 03/31/21
Education Services
N.A.I.C.S.: 611710
Umesh Pradhan *(CFO)*

Subsidiaries:

Liberium Global Resources Private
Limited (1)
18th Floor A-Wing Marathon Futurex N M
Joshi Marg Lower Parel, Mumbai, 400 013,
India
Tel.: (91) 2271541827
Web Site: https://liberiumglobal.in
Educational Support Services
N.A.I.C.S.: 611710

ZEECOL INTERNATIONAL,
INC.
57a Nayland Street Sumner,
Christchurch, 8081, New Zealand
Tel.: (64) 3477096963
Year Founded: 2007
Sales Range: $1-9.9 Million
Emp.: 9
Farm Management Services
N.A.I.C.S.: 115116
William Mook *(CEO)*

ZEFIRO METHANE CORP
2630 - 1075 West Georgia Street,
Vancouver, BC, Canada
Tel.: (604) 355-2646 BC
Web Site:
https://www.zefiromethane.com
Year Founded: 2018
ZEFIF—(OTCQB)
Renewable Energy Semiconductor
Manufacturing
N.A.I.C.S.: 334413
Luke Plants *(Sr VP-Bus Dev)*

Subsidiaries:

Plants & Goodwin, Inc. (1)
1034 Route 44, Shinglehouse, PA
16748-3406 (100%)
Tel.: (814) 697-6330
Web Site: http://www.plantsgoodwin.com
Oil & Gas Operations
N.A.I.C.S.: 213112
Luke Plants *(CEO)*

ZEGONA COMMUNICATIONS
PLC
8 Sackville St, Mayfair, London, W1S
3DG, United Kingdom
Tel.: (44) 2079203150 UK
Web Site: https://www.zegona.com
ZEG—(LSE)
Assets: $11,664,228
Liabilities: $426,480
Net Worth: $11,237,748
Earnings: ($3,529,122)
Emp.: 10
Fiscal Year-end: 12/31/22
Portfolio Management & Investment
Advice
N.A.I.C.S.: 523940
Eamonn O'Hare *(Co-Founder, Chm & CEO)*

Subsidiaries:

Vodafone Holdings Europe S.L (1)
Avenida De America 115, 28042, Madrid,
Spain
Tel.: (34) 607133333
Web Site: http://www.vodafone.es
Sales Range: $200-249.9 Million
Emp.: 12
Holding Company
N.A.I.C.S.: 551112
Jose Miguel Garcia *(CEO)*

Subsidiary (Domestic):

Vodafone Espana S.A.U. (2)
Avda America 115, 28042, Madrid,
Spain (100%)
Tel.: (34) 607123000
Web Site: https://www.vodafone.es
Sales Range: $750-799.9 Million
Emp.: 4,000
Cellular Communications Network Operator
N.A.I.C.S.: 517112

ZEHNDER GROUP AG
Moortalstrasse 1, 5722, Granichen,
Switzerland
Tel.: (41) 628551521
Web Site:
https://www.zehndergroup.com
ZEH—(SWX)
Rev.: $876,861,645
Assets: $575,005,396
Liabilities: $207,209,152
Net Worth: $367,796,244
Earnings: $61,191,453
Emp.: 3,827
Fiscal Year-end: 12/31/22

ZEHNDER GROUP AG

Zehnder Group AG—(Continued)
Radiators & Comfort Ventilation Systems Mfr
N.A.I.C.S.: 333414
Thomas Benz *(Deputy Chm)*

Subsidiaries:

Core Energy Recovery Solutions GmbH (1)
August-Horch-Strasse 7, 08141, Reinsdorf, Germany
Tel.: (49) 3753035050
Web Site: https://core.life
Emp.: 400
Ventilating Equipment Mfr & Distr
N.A.I.C.S.: 333415

Core Energy Recovery Solutions Inc. (1)
1455 East Georgia Street, Vancouver, V5L 2A9, BC, Canada
Tel.: (604) 488-1132
Heat Exchanger Mfr & Distr
N.A.I.C.S.: 332410
Peter Tyszewicz *(Mng Dir)*

Enervent Zehnder OY (1)
Kipinatie 1, 06150, Porvoo, Finland
Tel.: (358) 207528800
Web Site: https://www.enervent.com
Ventilation & Heating System Mfr & Distr
N.A.I.C.S.: 333414

Exvent AS (1)
Ringeriksveien 195, 1339, Voyenenga, Norway
Tel.: (47) 67105500
Web Site: https://www.exvent.no
Ventilation & Heating System Mfr & Distr
N.A.I.C.S.: 423730

Filtech France S.A.R.L. (1)
Pole Industriel du Frejus, 73500, Modane, France
Tel.: (33) 479050633
Air Conditioning Equipment Mfr & Distr
N.A.I.C.S.: 333415

Filtech Nederland B.V. (1)
Brabantsehoek 10, 5071 NM, Udenhout, Netherlands
Tel.: (31) 135114055
Cleaning Product Mfr & Distr
N.A.I.C.S.: 325611

Filtech Swiss S.A. (1)
Via Pra Mag 9, Rancate, 6862, Mendrisio, Switzerland
Tel.: (41) 916300743
Air Conditioning Equipment Mfr & Distr
N.A.I.C.S.: 333415

Hydro-Air Components, Inc. (1)
100 Rittling Blvd, Buffalo, NY 14220-1885
Tel.: (716) 827-6510
Web Site: https://zehnder-rittling.com
Emp.: 180
Heating & Cooling Systems Mfr
N.A.I.C.S.: 333415

J.E. Stork Ventilatoren B.V. (1)
Lingenstraat 2, 8028 PM, Zwolle, Netherlands
Tel.: (31) 384296911
Web Site: http://www.jestorkair.nl
Emp.: 200
Ventilation Systems Mfr & Whslr
N.A.I.C.S.: 335210
Erik van Heuveln *(Mng Dir)*

Metis B.V. (1)
Driemanssteeweg 200, 3084 CB, Rotterdam, Netherlands
Tel.: (31) 850080240
Web Site: https://metisit.com
Software Development Services
N.A.I.C.S.: 541511

Paul Warmeruckgewinnung GmbH (1)
August-Horch-Strasse 7, 08141, Reinsdorf, Germany
Tel.: (49) 3753035050
Web Site: http://paul-lueftung.de
Emp.: 100
Heating & Ventilation Systems Mfr & Whslr
N.A.I.C.S.: 335210
Michael Pitsch *(Mng Dir)*

Paul dPoint Technologies GmbH (1)
August-Horch-Strasse 7, 08141, Reinsdorf, Germany
Tel.: (49) 37530350588
Heat Exchange Distr
N.A.I.C.S.: 423730
Bert Schinkel *(Mng Dir)*

Radiatec AG (1)
Moortalstrasse 3, 5722, Granichen, Aargau, Switzerland
Tel.: (41) 628551055
Emp.: 250
Heating Systems Whslr
N.A.I.C.S.: 423730

Recair B.V. (1)
Spuiweg 28, 5145 NE, Waalwijk, Netherlands
Tel.: (31) 416347110
Web Site: http://www.recair.com
Heat Exchanger Mfr & Distr
N.A.I.C.S.: 332410
Henk Reijneveld *(Mng Dir-Sls)*

Runtal Italia S.r.l. (1)
Via XXV Luglio 6, 41011, Campogalliano, MO, Italy
Tel.: (39) 0599786200
Web Site: http://www.runtalitalia.it
Emp.: 10
Heating & Cooling System Whslr
N.A.I.C.S.: 238220

Runtal North America, Inc. (1)
187 Neck Rd, Ward Hill, MA 01835-8027
Web Site: https://www.runtalnorthamerica.com
Household Radiators Mfr & Distr
N.A.I.C.S.: 335220

Runtal Radiadores S.A. (1)
Argenters 7 Parque Tecnologico, 8290, Cerdanyola del Valles, Barcelona, Spain
Tel.: (34) 902111309
Web Site: http://www.runtal.es
Emp.: 15
Radiator Distr
N.A.I.C.S.: 423120

Sanpan Isitma Sistemleri San Ve Tic A.S. (1)
M O S B 4 Kisim Kecilikoy Mah Yusuf Karaoglu Cad No 3, Yunusemre, 45030, Manisa, Turkiye
Tel.: (90) 2362333636
Web Site: https://www.sanpan.com.tr
Heating Systems Mfr & Sales
N.A.I.C.S.: 333415

Zehnder (China) Indoor Climate Co., Ltd. (1)
18th Floor Beijing One International Plaza No 1 No 59 Zhongshan Street, Tongzhou District, Beijing, 101149, China
Tel.: (86) 1061562288
Web Site: http://www.zehnder.com.cn
Radiator & Heating System Distr
N.A.I.C.S.: 423730

Zehnder America, Inc. (1)
8 Merrill Industrial Dr Ste 1, Hampton, NH 03842
Tel.: (603) 601-8544
Web Site: https://www.zehnderamerica.com
Emp.: 7
Heating & Ventilation System Installation Services
N.A.I.C.S.: 238220

Zehnder Baltics OU (1)
Rannamoisa tee 38d Tiskre Arimaja, 13516, Tallinn, Estonia
Tel.: (372) 6840937
Web Site: https://www.zehnder.ee
Radiator & Heating System Distr
N.A.I.C.S.: 423730
Karl Penu *(Mgr-Sls-Estonia)*

Zehnder Caladair International S.A.S. (1)
Rue Saint-Veran, 71000, Macon, France
Tel.: (33) 385368200
Web Site: http://www.caladair.com
Ventilating Equipment Mfr & Distr
N.A.I.C.S.: 423730

Zehnder Comfosystems Cesovent AG (1)
Zugerstrasse 162, Wadenswil, 8820, Zurich, Switzerland
Tel.: (41) 438332020
Web Site: http://www.zehnder-comfosystems.ch
Emp.: 70
Heat, Ventilation & Airconditioning System Installation Services
N.A.I.C.S.: 238220
Hans Juerg Schwendener *(Mng Dir)*

Zehnder GmbH (1)
Almweg 34, 77933, Lahr, Germany
Tel.: (49) 1805055860
Web Site: http://www.zehnder-online.de
Emp.: 500
Heating & Cooling Systems Mfr
N.A.I.C.S.: 334512

Zehnder Group Belgium N.V. (1)
Wayenborgstraat 21, 2800, Mechelen, Belgium
Tel.: (32) 15280510
Web Site: https://www.zehnder.be
Emp.: 100
Radiator Distr
N.A.I.C.S.: 423120

Zehnder Group Boleslawiec Sp. z o.o. (1)
Tel.: (48) 757340211
Emp.: 500
Heating System Mfr
N.A.I.C.S.: 333415

Zehnder Group Czech Republic s.r.o. (1)
Tel.: (420) 383136222
Web Site: https://www.zehnder.cz
Radiator & Heating System Distr
N.A.I.C.S.: 423730

Zehnder Group Deutschland GmbH (1)
Tel.: (49) 78215860
Web Site: https://www.zehnder-systems.de
Emp.: 500
Heating & Cooling Systems Mfr
N.A.I.C.S.: 334512

Zehnder Group Finance Ltd. (1)
3rd Fl Elizabeth House, Ruettes Brayes, Saint Peter Port, GY1 3LH, Guernsey
Tel.: (44) 1481 715973
Financial Support Services
N.A.I.C.S.: 541611

Zehnder Group France SAS (1)
3 Rue du Bois Briard, Courcouronnes, 91080, Evry, Cedex, France
Tel.: (33) 810007170
Web Site: https://www.zehnder.fr
Radiator & Heating System Distr
N.A.I.C.S.: 423730

Zehnder Group Iberica Indoor Climate, S.A. (1)
Tel.: (34) 900700110
Web Site: https://www.zehnder.es
Radiator & Heating System Distr
N.A.I.C.S.: 423730

Zehnder Group Ic Mekan Iklimlendirme Sanayi Ve Ticaret Limitet Sirketi (1)
M O S B 4 Kisim Kecilikoy mah Yusuf Karaoglu Cad No 3, Yunusemre, 45030, Manisa, Turkiye
Tel.: (90) 2362333636
Web Site: http://www.zehnder.com.tr
Radiator & Heating System Distr
N.A.I.C.S.: 423730

Zehnder Group Italia S.r.l. (1)
Via XXV Luglio 6, 41011, Campogalliano, MO, Italy
Tel.: (39) 0599786200
Web Site: https://www.zehnder.it
Emp.: 6
Radiators & Ventilation System Whslr
N.A.I.C.S.: 423730

Zehnder Group Nordic AB (1)
Medevivagen 55, 591 39, Motala, Sweden
Tel.: (46) 86309300
Web Site: https://www.zehnder-cleanairsolutions.com
Emp.: 25
Household Radiators Mfr
N.A.I.C.S.: 333414

INTERNATIONAL PUBLIC

Zehnder Group Produktion Granichen AG (1)
Burners Indus Oberfeld 2, 5722, Granichen, Aargau, Switzerland
Tel.: (41) 628551212
Web Site: http://www.zehndergroup.com
Emp.: 300
Heating & Cooling Systems Mfr
N.A.I.C.S.: 333415

Zehnder Group Schweiz AG (1)
Moortalstrasse 3, 5722, Granichen, Switzerland
Tel.: (41) 628551111
Web Site: https://www.zehnder-systems.ch
Radiator & Heating System Distr
N.A.I.C.S.: 423730

Zehnder Group UK Limited (1)
Concept House Watchmoor Point, Camberley, GU15 3AD, Surrey, United Kingdom
Tel.: (44) 1276605580
Web Site: http://www.zehnder.co.uk
Heating & Cooling Systems Mfr
N.A.I.C.S.: 333415

Division (Domestic):

Chatsworth Heating Products Ltd (2)
Unit B Watchmoor Point, Camberley, GU15 3EX, Surrey, United Kingdom
Tel.: (44) 1276605580
Web Site: http://www.chatsworth-heating.co.uk
Emp.: 70
Heating Systems Distr
N.A.I.C.S.: 423730

Zehnder Group UK Ltd - Bisque Division (2)
Concept House Watchmoor Point, Camberley, GU15 3AD, Surrey, United Kingdom
Tel.: (44) 1276605580
Web Site: http://www.bisque.co.uk
Heating Systems Retailer
N.A.I.C.S.: 423730

Zehnder Group Vaux Andigny SAS (1)
17 rue Des Parachutistes, Vaux-Andigny, 02110, Aisne, France
Tel.: (33) 323668800
Emp.: 250
Heating & Cooling Systems Mfr
N.A.I.C.S.: 334512
Thierry Baschet *(Gen Mgr)*

Zehnder Nederland B.V. (1)
Lingenstraat 2, 8028 PM, Zwolle, Netherlands
Tel.: (31) 384296911
Web Site: http://www.zehnder.nl
Emp.: 200
Household Radiators Mfr
N.A.I.C.S.: 333414

Zehnder Polska Sp. z o.o. (1)
o ul Irysowa 1, 55-040, Bielany Wroclawskie, Poland
Tel.: (48) 713676424
Web Site: https://www.zehnder.pl
Emp.: 27
Heating & Cooling Systems Mfr
N.A.I.C.S.: 334512

Zehnder Tecnosystems S.r.l. (1)
Viale Europa 73, Campogalliano, Modena, 41011, Italy
Tel.: (39) 0599786200
Web Site: http://www.comfosystems.it
Emp.: 10
Heating & Cooling System Whslr
N.A.I.C.S.: 423730

ZEIDLER
315 Queen Street West, Toronto, M5V 2X2, ON, Canada
Tel.: (416) 596-8300
Web Site: http://www.zeidlerpartnership.com
Year Founded: 1962
Rev.: $11,100,000
Emp.: 105
Building Design Construction & Services
N.A.I.C.S.: 236210
Andrea Richardson *(Partner)*

AND PRIVATE COMPANIES

ZEIDLER & WIMMEL VERWALTUNGS-GMBH
Konsul-Metzing-Strasse 7-9, 97268, Kirchheim, Germany
Tel.: (49) 936690690
Web Site: http://www.zeidler-wimmel.de
Year Founded: 1776
Sales Range: $25-49.9 Million
Emp.: 90
Industrial Recovery Processing & Sale of Natural Stone Services
N.A.I.C.S.: 236210
Herbert Kratzer (Mng Dir)

Subsidiaries:

Bober Sp.zo.o. (1)
ul Bolka 16B, 59-420, Bolkow, Poland
Tel.: (48) 601931074
Processing & Sale of Natural Stone
N.A.I.C.S.: 541310

Stone & Cladding International (SCI) (1)
Vendelier 51D, 3905 PC, Veenendaal, Netherlands
Tel.: (31) 8 54 49 43
Web Site: http://www.stone-cladding.nl
Processing & Sale of Natural Stone
N.A.I.C.S.: 541310

Zeidler & Wimmel-Buro Stuttgart (1)
Lina Hahnle Weg 22, 75417, Muhlacker, Germany (100%)
Tel.: (49) 7041941111
Web Site: http://www.zeidlerwimmel.de
Processing & Sale of Natural Stone
N.A.I.C.S.: 541310

Zeidler & Wimmel-Niederlassung Berlin (1)
Hohenzollerndamm 196, 10717, Berlin, Germany (100%)
Tel.: (49) 308730326
Web Site: http://www.zeidler-wimmel.de
Emp.: 2
Processing & Sale of Natural Stone
N.A.I.C.S.: 327910

Zeidler & Wimmel-Niederlassung Dresden (1)
Saalhausener Str 51A, 01159, Dresden, Germany
Tel.: (49) 3514117122
Web Site: http://www.zeidler-wimmel.info
Processing & Sale of Natural Stone
N.A.I.C.S.: 541310

Zeidler & Wimmel-Niederlassung Dusseldorf (1)
Nettelbeckstrasse 2, 40477, Dusseldorf, Germany (100%)
Tel.: (49) 2111697020
Web Site: http://www.zeidler-wimmel.info
Processing & Sale of Natural Stone
N.A.I.C.S.: 541310

Zeidler & Wimmel-Niederlassung Frankfurt (1)
Konsul-Metzing-Strasse 7-9, 97268, Kirchheim, Germany
Tel.: (49) 936690690
Web Site: http://www.zeidler-wimmel.de
Processing & Sale of Natural Stone Services
N.A.I.C.S.: 541310

Zeidler & Wimmel-Niederlassung Hannover (1)
Am Listholze 35, 30177, Hannover, Germany (100%)
Tel.: (49) 511397300
Web Site: http://www.zeidler-wimmel.de
Processing & Sale of Natural Stone
N.A.I.C.S.: 327910

Zeidler & Wimmel-Niederlassung Munich (1)
Konrad Celtis Str 33, 81369, Munich, Germany (100%)
Tel.: (49) 89781085
Web Site: http://www.zeidler-wimmel.info
Processing & Sale of Natural Stone
N.A.I.C.S.: 541310

Zeidler & Wimmel-Zweigstelle Hamburg (1)
Fesslerstrasse 1, 22083, Hamburg, Germany (100%)
Tel.: (49) 40291144
Web Site: http://www.zeidler-wimmel.info
Processing & Sale of Natural Stone
N.A.I.C.S.: 541310

ZELAN BERHAD
24th Floor Wisma Zelan No 1 Jalan Tasik Permaisuri 2, Bandar Tun Razak Cheras, 56000, Kuala Lumpur, Malaysia
Tel.: (60) 391739173
Web Site: http://www.zelan.com
ZELAN—(KLS)
Rev.: $11,063,280
Assets: $169,590,899
Liabilities: $151,475,556
Net Worth: $18,115,344
Earnings: ($1,190,053)
Emp.: 371
Fiscal Year-end: 12/31/22
Engineering & Construction Services
N.A.I.C.S.: 541330
Raniz Mat Nor (Co-Sec)

Subsidiaries:

Zelan Development Sdn. Bhd. (1)
23rd Floor Wisma Zelan No 1 Jalan Tasik Permaisuri 2 Bandar Tun Razak, Cheras, 56000, Kuala Lumpur, Federal Territory, Malaysia
Tel.: (60) 391739173
Web Site: http://www.zelan.com.my
Emp.: 12
Property Development Services
N.A.I.C.S.: 531311

ZELEZARNA RAVNE MONTER DRAVOGRAD D.D.
Otiski vrh 177, 2373, Sentjanz, Slovenia
Tel.: (386) 28787727
Web Site: http://www.zr-monter.si
Sales Range: $25-49.9 Million
Emp.: 260
Construction & General Purpose Machinery Mfr
N.A.I.C.S.: 333120
Bogdan Kadis (Gen Mgr)

ZELEZIARNE PODBREZOVA A.S.
Kolkaren 35, Podbrezova, 976 81, Slovakia
Tel.: (421) 486451111   Sk
Web Site: http://www.zelpo.sk
Year Founded: 1840
Sales Range: $150-199.9 Million
Emp.: 4,400
Producer of Hot-rolled & Cold-drawn Seamless Steel Tubes
N.A.I.C.S.: 331210
Vladimir Sotak (Chm & CEO)

Subsidiaries:

KBZ s.r.o. (1)
Karpatska 14, 040 01, Kosice, Slovakia
Tel.: (421) 2 645 364 49
Web Site: http://www.kbz.sk
Waste Treatment Services
N.A.I.C.S.: 562219

PIPEX Italia S.p.A. (1)
Via Paleocapa 10, 28041, Arona, NO, Italy (100%)
Tel.: (39) 0322235511
Web Site: http://www.pipex.it
Emp.: 16
Steel Distr
N.A.I.C.S.: 331210
Luigi Cuzzolin (Mng Dir)

Pipex Deutschland GmbH (1)
Freseniusstr 17, 81247, Munich, Germany
Tel.: (49) 89 81 10 07 1
Web Site: http://www.pipex-deutschland.de
Steel Product Distr
N.A.I.C.S.: 423510
Nomaden Demiryolu (Gen Mgr)

SLOVRUR Sp. z o.o. (1)
Ul Brandwicka 138, 37 464, Stalowa Wola, Poland (100%)
Tel.: (48) 158448045
Web Site: http://www.slovrur.pl
Emp.: 10
Steel Products Sales
N.A.I.C.S.: 331210

Tale, a.s. (1)
Tale 100 Horna Lehota, 977 01, Brezno, Slovakia (100%)
Tel.: (421) 486712201
Web Site: http://www.tale.sk
Emp.: 30
Tourism Services
N.A.I.C.S.: 561520
Lubos Durindak (Mng Dir)

Transformaciones Metalurgicas S.A. (1)
C Industria 10, 8330, Madrid, Spain
Tel.: (34) 93 754 92 01
Web Site: http://www.transmesa.com
Steel Product Mfr & Distr
N.A.I.C.S.: 331110

ZANINONI SLOVAKIA, s.r.o. (1)
Stiavnicka 12, 97681, Podbrezova, Slovakia, Slovakia (60%)
Tel.: (421) 486451670
Web Site: http://www.zelpo.sk
Emp.: 7
Transportation Services
N.A.I.C.S.: 488510
Anna Kovacova (Mng Dir)

ZIAROMAT a.s. (1)
Tovarenska 1, 985 01, Bratislava, Slovakia
Tel.: (421) 47 43 020 13
Web Site: http://www.ziaromat.sk
Steel Product Mfr & Distr
N.A.I.C.S.: 331110
Marian Kurcik (CHM)

ZP - Gastroservis, s.r.o. (1)
Mierova 39321, 97646, Valaska, Slovakia
Tel.: (421) 486451530
Web Site: http://www.zelpo.sk
Emp.: 90
Catering Services
N.A.I.C.S.: 722320

ZP BYTOS, s.r.o. (1)
Kolkaren 36, 976 81, Podbrezova, Slovakia
Tel.: (421) 911 467 593
Web Site: http://www.zpbytos.sk
Apartment Owner & Operator
N.A.I.C.S.: 531110
Vera Bulakova (Mng Dir)

ZP Sport, a.s. (1)
Kolkaren 58, 97681, Podbrezova, Brezno, Slovakia (100%)
Tel.: (421) 486451225
Web Site: http://www.zpsport.sk
Sports-Related Services
N.A.I.C.S.: 711211

ZP Tazirny trub Svinov, spol. s r.o. (1)
Bilovecka 226/1, 72100, Ostrava, Czech Republic (99%)
Tel.: (420) 596 974 111
Tube Mfr
N.A.I.C.S.: 322219

ZP-Invest s.r.o. (1)
Razusova 51, 97710, Brezno, Slovakia
Tel.: (421) 486112844
Residential & Office Building Owner & Operator
N.A.I.C.S.: 531110

ZELIRA THERAPEUTICS LIMITED
Level 3 101 St George's Terrace, Perth, 6000, WA, Australia
Tel.: (61) 865580886
Web Site: https://www.zeliratx.com
ZLDAF—(OTCQB)
Rev.: $196,336
Assets: $22,097,355
Liabilities: $1,420,690
Net Worth: $20,676,664
Earnings: ($4,087,326)
Fiscal Year-end: 06/30/23
Research & Development in Biotechnology (except Nanobiotechnology)
N.A.I.C.S.: 541714
Osagie Imasogie (Chm)

ZELJEZARA ILIJAS D.D.
Bosanski put 215, Ilijas, 71 380, Sarajevo, Bosnia & Herzegovina
Tel.: (387) 33849811
Web Site: http://www.zeljezarailijas.com
Year Founded: 1952
ZEILRK2—(SARE)
Rev: $10,940,935
Assets: $42,947,209
Liabilities: $42,947,209
Earnings: ($860,785)
Emp.: 104
Fiscal Year-end: 12/31/21
Iron & Steel Mfr
N.A.I.C.S.: 331110
Adnan Sabani (Gen Mgr)

ZELJEZNIACAR KONFEKCIJA A.D.
Kosovska 2-4, Subotica, Serbia
Tel.: (381) 24 571 444
Year Founded: 1991
ZLSU—(BEL)
Sales Range: Less than $1 Million
Emp.: 21
Apparels Mfr
N.A.I.C.S.: 315990
Vesna Santo (CEO)

ZELJEZNICE RS A.D.
Svetog Save 71, 74000, Doboj, Bosnia & Herzegovina
Tel.: (387) 53241368
Web Site: https://www.zrs-rs.com
Year Founded: 1992
ZERS-R-A—(BANJ)
Sales Range: Less than $1 Million
Railway Transportation Services
N.A.I.C.S.: 488210
Dijana Kalenic (Chm-Supervisory Bd)

ZELTIA, S.A.
Plaza del Descubridor Diego de Ordas 3 Planta 5, 28003, Madrid, Spain
Tel.: (34) 914444500
Web Site: http://www.zeltia.com
Year Founded: 1939
Sales Range: $150-199.9 Million
Emp.: 628
Pharmaceutical & Chemical Mfr & Researcher
N.A.I.C.S.: 325412
Jose Maria Fernandez Sousa-Faro (Chm)

Subsidiaries:

Genomica, S.A.U. (1)
Parque Empresarial Alvento Edificio B, Calle Via de los Poblados 1 - 1 Planta, 28033, Madrid, Spain
Tel.: (34) 916748990
Web Site: http://www.genomica.es
Emp.: 50
Pharmaceutical Medicines Mfr
N.A.I.C.S.: 325412
Rosario Cospedal (Mng Dir)

Noscira S.A. (1)
Avda de la Industria 52 Tres Cantos, 28760, Madrid, Spain
Tel.: (34) 918061130
Web Site: http://www.noscira.com
Emp.: 30
Drug Research & Development Services
N.A.I.C.S.: 541715

Pharma Mar S.A.U. (1)
Avda de los Reyes 1 Pol Ind La Mina Norte, Colmenar Viejo, Madrid, 28770, Spain
Tel.: (34) 918466000
Web Site: http://www.pharmamar.com
Emp.: 300
Pharmaceutical Medicines Mfr

Zeltia, S.A.—(Continued)
N.A.I.C.S.: 325412
Jose Maria Fernandez *(Pres)*

Sylentis, S.A. (1)
C/O Santiago Grisoluia 2 Parque Cientifico de, Madrid, 28760, Spain
Tel.: (34) 918047667
Web Site: http://www.sylentis.com
Emp.: 15
Drug Research & Development Services
N.A.I.C.S.: 541715
Ana Jimenez *(Mng Dir)*

Zelnova S.A. (1)
Aptdo 7 Poligono Industrial Torneiros S/N, Porrino, 36400, Spain
Tel.: (34) 986344051
Web Site: http://www.zelnova.com
Emp.: 100
Chemical Products Mfr
N.A.I.C.S.: 325998
Santiago Dominguez *(Mgr-Export)*

ZEMACH HAMMERMAN LTD.
Tel Aviv 98 Yigal Alon St, PO Box 225, Nesher, 3688847, Israel
Tel.: (972) 49049999
Web Site: https://www.zhg.co.il
Year Founded: 1997
Rev.: $155,343,002
Assets: $265,599,162
Liabilities: $211,812,082
Net Worth: $53,787,080
Earnings: $9,008,791
Emp.: 170
Fiscal Year-end: 12/31/17
Real Estate Development Services
N.A.I.C.S.: 531390

ZEMAITIJOS PIENAS AB
Sedos G 35, 87101, Telsiai, Lithuania
Tel.: (370) 44422201
Web Site: http://www.zpienas.lt
Year Founded: 1924
Milk Product Distr
N.A.I.C.S.: 424430
Robertas Pazemeckas *(Gen Mgr)*

ZEMENTWERK LEUBE GMBH
Gartenauerplatz 9, Saint Leonhard, 5083, Salzburg, Austria
Tel.: (43) 50 8108 0 **AT**
Web Site: http://www.leube.at
Year Founded: 1838
Sales Range: $100-124.9 Million
Emp.: 253
Cement Mfr
N.A.I.C.S.: 327310
Rudolf Zrost *(Mng Dir)*

Subsidiaries:

Quarzsande GmbH (1)
Unterrudling 18, A 4070, Eferding, Austria **(100%)**
Tel.: (43) 72 72 57 77
Web Site: http://www.quarzsande.at
Construction Sand & Other Aggregates Mining Services
N.A.I.C.S.: 212321
Heimo Berger *(Mng Dir)*

ZEN CORP GROUP PCL
662 Onnut 17, Suan luang Subdistrict Suan Luang District, Bangkok, 10250, Thailand
Tel.: (66) 20195000
Web Site: https://zengroup.co.th
Year Founded: 1991
ZEN—(THA)
Rev.: $115,173,269
Assets: $94,577,575
Liabilities: $51,406,563
Net Worth: $43,171,012
Earnings: $5,179,035
Emp.: 2,510
Fiscal Year-end: 12/31/23
Catering Services
N.A.I.C.S.: 722320

Boonyong Tansakul *(Board of Directors & CEO)*

Subsidiaries:

King Marine Foods Co., Ltd. (1)
24 Sukhaphiban Soi 5 Soi 5, Tha Raeng Subdistrict Bang Khen District, Bangkok, 10220, Thailand
Tel.: (66) 945826767
Web Site: https://kingmarinefoods.co.th
Salmon Fish Mfr
N.A.I.C.S.: 311710

ZEN TECH INTERNATIONAL BERHAD
Unit No 53-6 The Boulevard Mid Valley City, Lingkaran Syed Putra, 59200, Kuala Lumpur, Selangor Darul Ehsan, Malaysia
Tel.: (60) 322023330 **MY**
Web Site: https://www.inix.com.my
Year Founded: 2003
ZENTECH—(KLS)
Rev.: $6,553,781
Assets: $14,517,776
Liabilities: $6,619,700
Net Worth: $7,898,076
Earnings: ($1,219,165)
Fiscal Year-end: 06/30/22
Software Development Services
N.A.I.C.S.: 541511
Li Zhang *(Exec Dir)*

Subsidiaries:

Ansi Systems Sdn. Bhd. (1)
No 11 Jalan Tasik Selatan 3 Metro Centre Bandar Tasik Selatan, 57000, Kuala Lumpur, Malaysia
Tel.: (60) 390593800
Web Site: https://www.ansi.com.my
Information Technology Services
N.A.I.C.S.: 541512

ZEN TECHNOLOGIES LTD
B-42 Industrial Estate Sanath Nagar, Hyderabad, 500018, Telangana, India
Tel.: (91) 4023812894
Web Site: https://www.zentechnologies.com
ZENSARTECH—(NSE)
Rev.: $7,870,781
Assets: $30,482,962
Liabilities: $1,728,240
Net Worth: $28,754,721
Earnings: $378,610
Emp.: 209
Fiscal Year-end: 03/31/21
Defense Equipment Mfrr
N.A.I.C.S.: 336992
Midathala Ravi Kumar *(Exec Dir)*

Subsidiaries:

Unistring Tech Solutions Private Limited (1)
Plot No 2 & 3 SY No 6 Rank One Ektha Towers, Kondapur Rangareddy, Hyderabad, 500084, Telangana, India
Tel.: (91) 4029881817
Web Site: https://unistring.com
Electronic Warfare Mfr & Distr
N.A.I.C.S.: 334511

Zen Medical Technologies Private Limited (1)
B-42 Industrial Estate Sanath Nagar, Hyderabad, 500018, Telangana, India
Tel.: (91) 4023814894
Web Site: https://www.zenmeddevices.com
Medical Equipment Mfr & Distr
N.A.I.C.S.: 339112

Zen Technologies USA Inc. (1)
Tel.: (469) 443-8722
Combat Training Services
N.A.I.C.S.: 611519

ZEN VOCE CORPORATION
No 53 Jinggong Rd, Xinfeng Township Hsinchu County, Hsien, Taiwan
Tel.: (886) 35599999

Web Site: https://www.zenvoce.com 3581—(TPE)
Rev.: $39,348,248
Assets: $64,803,489
Liabilities: $34,242,066
Net Worth: $30,561,423
Earnings: $2,822,781
Fiscal Year-end: 12/31/22
Semiconductor Equipment Mfr
N.A.I.C.S.: 333242
Tu-Cheng Li *(Chm)*

Subsidiaries:

Scientek Corporation (1)
3F No 53 Jinggong Road, Xinfeng Township, Hsinchu, 30443, Taiwan
Tel.: (886) 35590909
Web Site: https://www.scientek-co.com
Semiconductor Equipment & Instrument Distr
N.A.I.C.S.: 423690

Scneitek Corporation (1)
3F No 53 Jinggong Road, Xinfeng Township, Hsinchu, 302, Taiwan
Tel.: (886) 35590909
Web Site: http://www.scientek-co.com
Wafer Splitting Machine Mfr
N.A.I.C.S.: 333517
Cai Zongzhe *(Co-Founder)*

Zen Voce (PG) Sdn Bhd (1)
1-3-15 Elit Avenue Jalan Mayang Pasir 3, Bayan Baru, 11950, Pulau Penang, Malaysia
Tel.: (60) 46371190
Fixture Mfr
N.A.I.C.S.: 335132

Zen Voce (Suzhou) Corporation (1)
Blk A 1F-14/15 No 5 Xing Han Street, Suzhou Industrial Park, Suzhou, 215021, China
Tel.: (86) 51262652955
Fixture Mfr
N.A.I.C.S.: 335132

ZENA MINING CORP.
3345 Huntleigh Court, North Vancouver, V7H 1C9, BC, Canada
Tel.: (604) 681-2868
Year Founded: 2000
ZCC—(TSXV)
Rev.: $22,125
Assets: $1,339,646
Liabilities: $263,582
Net Worth: $1,076,064
Earnings: ($157,534)
Fiscal Year-end: 12/31/19
Mineral Exploration Services
N.A.I.C.S.: 212290

ZENDER FORD
99 Golden Spike Rd, Spruce Grove, T7X 2Y3, AB, Canada
Tel.: (780) 962-3000
Web Site: https://www.zenderford.com
Year Founded: 1963
Rev.: $17,597,658
Emp.: 100
New & Used Vehicle Dealers
N.A.I.C.S.: 423120
Sandra Denington *(Dir-Fin)*

ZENERGY AB
Storgatan 82, Skillingaryd, 568 32, Jonkoping, Sweden
Tel.: (46) 36121340
Web Site: https://zenergy.se
Year Founded: 2009
8T4—(DEU)
Portable Building Product Mfr
N.A.I.C.S.: 332311
Pontus Eklind *(Pres)*

ZENGAME TECHNOLOGY HOLDING LIMITED
Room 1303-1306 Changhong Technology Building Science & Technology Park, Nanshan District, Shenzhen, 518057, China
Tel.: (86) 75533201331
Web Site: http://www.zen-game.com
Year Founded: 2010
2660—(HKG)
Rev.: $248,150,822
Assets: $287,912,102
Liabilities: $39,999,398
Net Worth: $247,912,704
Earnings: $95,507,942
Emp.: 524
Fiscal Year-end: 12/31/22
Mobile Game Development Services
N.A.I.C.S.: 541511
Liqing Zeng *(Founder)*

ZENICOR MEDICAL SYSTEMS AB
Saltmatargatan 8, 113 59, Stockholm, Sweden
Tel.: (46) 84426860
Web Site: https://www.zenicor.com
Year Founded: 2003
Medical Equipment Mfr
N.A.I.C.S.: 339112
Mats Palerius *(CEO)*

ZENIT INVESTMENT HOLDING AD
73 Todor Alexandrov Blvd, 1303, Sofia, Bulgaria
Tel.: (359) 29804825
Web Site: https://www.zenit-bg.com
ZNTH—(BUL)
Sales Range: Less than $1 Million
Commercial Banking Services
N.A.I.C.S.: 522110

ZENITEL N.V.
Z 1 Research Park Zellik 110, BE-1731, Zellik, Belgium
Tel.: (32) 23705311
Web Site: http://www.zenitel.com
Year Founded: 1901
ZENT—(EUR)
Rev.: $85,397,164
Assets: $66,199,404
Liabilities: $29,716,605
Net Worth: $36,482,799
Earnings: $3,384,217
Emp.: 303
Fiscal Year-end: 12/31/19
Communication Products, Communication Networks & System Integration Services
N.A.I.C.S.: 517810
Jo Van Gorp *(Chm)*

Subsidiaries:

Zenitel CSS France S.A. (1)
Parc d'activite du Petit Nanterre 6 rue des Marguerites, 92737, Nanterre, Cedex, France
Tel.: (33) 147885000
Web Site: http://www.zenitel.com
Marine Communication Equipment Distr
N.A.I.C.S.: 424990

Zenitel Denmark A/S (1)
Park Alle 350 A, 2605, Brondby, Copenhagen, Denmark
Tel.: (45) 43437411
Emp.: 45
Radio Communication Software Development Services
N.A.I.C.S.: 541511
Svein Ingar Damre *(Gen Mgr)*

Zenitel Italia Srl (1)
Viale Brianza 181, 20092, Cinisello Balsamo, Milan, Italy
Tel.: (39) 0238608237
Web Site: https://www.zenitelcss.it
Emp.: 4
Electronic Components Mfr
N.A.I.C.S.: 334419

Zenitel Marine Asia Pte. Ltd. (1)

69 Ubi Crescent 05-01, Singapore, 408561, Singapore
Tel.: (65) 63830200
Web Site: http://www.zenitel.com.sg
Marine Communication Equipment Distr
N.A.I.C.S.: 423690

Zenitel Marine Brazil (1)
Rua Florianopolis 1360 Bloco 1 Apt 207 Praca Seca, Centro, Rio de Janeiro, 21321-050, Brazil
Tel.: (55) 2184409665
Web Site: http://www.vingtor.com
Marine Communication Equipment Mfr
N.A.I.C.S.: 334290

Zenitel Marine Germany (1)
Langeoogstrasse 6, 26603, Aurich, Germany
Tel.: (49) 41 6976 720
Web Site: http://www.zenitel.com
Marine Communication Equipment Distr
N.A.I.C.S.: 423690

Zenitel Marine Med. (1)
Permani 28, Jurdani, 51213, Opatija, Croatia
Tel.: (385) 51 29 19 10
Web Site: http://webshop.stentofon.com
Marine Communication Equipment Mfr
N.A.I.C.S.: 334290

Zenitel Norway AS (1)
Sandakerveien 24C, N-0473, Oslo, Norway
Tel.: (47) 40002500
Emp.: 110
Communications & Security Systems Mfr
N.A.I.C.S.: 334290
Kenneth Dastol *(Gen Mgr)*

Zenitel USA Inc (1)
6119 Connecticut Ave, Kansas City, MO 64120
Tel.: (816) 231-7200
Web Site: http://www.zenitelusa.com
Communication Equipment Mfr
N.A.I.C.S.: 334290
Peter Sandin *(Dir-Sls & Distr-Northeast)*

ZENITH BIRLA INDIA LTD
Dalamal House 1st floor J B Marg, Nariman Point, Mumbai, 400 021, India
Tel.: (91) 2266168400
Web Site:
  https://www.zenithsteelpipes.com
Rev.: $28,308,250
Assets: $33,853,284
Liabilities: $68,524,909
Net Worth: ($34,671,625)
Earnings: ($17,232,177)
Emp.: 208
Fiscal Year-end: 03/31/19
Steel Pole Mfr
N.A.I.C.S.: 331110
Girvanesh Balasubramanan *(CFO)*

Subsidiaries:

Birla Lifestyle Pvt. Ltd (1)
104 Mehta Chambers Mumbai-Pune Road, Kasarwadi, Pune, 411034, India
Tel.: (91) 20 271 46868
Web Site: http://www.birla-lifestyle.com
Kitchen Accessories Mfr
N.A.I.C.S.: 332215

ZENITH CAPITALS LIMITED
143-145 3rd Floor Khaitan Chambers Modi Street Fort, Mumbai, 400 001, Maharashtra, India
Tel.: (91) 2222655793
Web Site:
  http://www.zenithcapital.co.in
Year Founded: 1983
Rev.: $16,045
Assets: $236,206
Liabilities: $18,983
Net Worth: $217,222
Earnings: ($6,722)
Fiscal Year-end: 03/31/17
Equipment Contract Services
N.A.I.C.S.: 532420

ZENITH COMPUTERS LIMITED
Zenith House 29 MIDC Central Road, Andheri E, Mumbai, 400 093, India
Tel.: (91) 2228377300
Web Site: http://www.zenithpc.com
Year Founded: 1980
Sales Range: $1-9.9 Million
Emp.: 800
Computer Mfr
N.A.I.C.S.: 334111
Raj Kumar Saraf *(Chm & Mng Dir)*

ZENITH ENERGY LTD.
Tel.: (587) 315-1279 BC
Web Site:
  https://www.zenithenergy.ca
Year Founded: 2007
ZCL—(DEU)
Rev.: $9,816,614
Assets: $196,131,606
Liabilities: $127,759,214
Net Worth: $68,372,392
Earnings: ($9,568,942)
Emp.: 38
Fiscal Year-end: 03/31/23
Petroleum & Natural Gas Exploration Services
N.A.I.C.S.: 211120
Andrea Cattaneo *(Pres & CEO)*

Subsidiaries:

Ecumed Petroleum Limited (1)
Rue du Lac Windermere, les Berges du Lac, 1053, Tunis, Tunisia
Tel.: (216) 71962611
Sales Range: $50-74.9 Million
Emp.: 20
Oil & Gas Explorer, Developer & Producer
N.A.I.C.S.: 211120

ZENITH EXPORTS LIMITED
11 Taverekere Main Road, Bengaluru, 560034, Karnataka, India
Tel.: (91) 8025536594
Web Site:
  https://www.zenithexportsltd.com
Year Founded: 1981
512553—(BOM)
Rev.: $8,005,228
Assets: $11,991,020
Liabilities: $2,431,881
Net Worth: $9,559,139
Earnings: $189,173
Emp.: 193
Fiscal Year-end: 03/31/23
Silk Fabrics, Leather Gloves & Yarn Mfr
N.A.I.C.S.: 313310
Sushil Kumar Kasera *(CFO)*

ZENITH FIBRES LTD.
103 SYNERGY HOUSE Subhanpura Road, Vadodara, 390023, India
Tel.: (91) 2652283744
Web Site:
  https://www.zenithfibres.com
Year Founded: 1989
514266—(BOM)
Rev.: $6,329,872
Assets: $6,957,736
Liabilities: $459,553
Net Worth: $6,498,184
Earnings: $340,291
Emp.: 71
Fiscal Year-end: 03/31/23
Polypropylene Staple Fibre Mfr
N.A.I.C.S.: 313110
Sanjeev Rungta *(Chm)*

ZENITH HEALTHCARE LIMITED
504 Iscon Elegance Nr shapath 5 S G Road, Ahmedabad, 380015, India
Tel.: (91) 7966168889
Web Site:
  https://www.zenithhealthcare.com
Year Founded: 1994
530665—(BOM)
Rev.: $1,619,243
Assets: $1,108,866
Liabilities: $241,760
Net Worth: $867,106
Earnings: $9,328
Emp.: 42
Fiscal Year-end: 03/31/23
Pharmaceutical Product Mfr & Distr
N.A.I.C.S.: 325412
Mahendra C. Raycha *(Chm & Mng Dir)*

ZENITH LIFE S.A.
Rue de la Coulouvreniere 40, 1204, Geneva, Switzerland
Tel.: (41) 217217000
Web Site: http://www.zenithlife.ch
Year Founded: 1987
Sales Range: $50-74.9 Million
Emp.: 10
Fire Insurance Services
N.A.I.C.S.: 524113
Johan Cuypers *(Dir Gen)*

ZENITH MINERALS LIMITED
2nd Floor 33 Ord Street, West Perth, 6005, WA, Australia
Tel.: (61) 892261110
Web Site:
  https://www.zenithminerals.com.au
ZNC—(ASX)
Rev.: $1,065,917
Assets: $9,663,803
Liabilities: $290,754
Net Worth: $9,373,049
Earnings: ($2,987,150)
Fiscal Year-end: 06/30/24
Zinc Exploration Services
N.A.I.C.S.: 212230
Michael J. Clifford *(Mng Dir)*

ZENITH PROPERTIES REIT
Knyaz Aleksandar I Batenberg 42, Plovdiv, 4000, Bulgaria
Tel.: (359) 32624909
Web Site: http://www.zenitimoti.com
ZENP—(BUL)
Sales Range: Less than $1 Million
Real Estate Investment Services
N.A.I.C.S.: 531210
Luciana Adriano *(Exec Dir)*

ZENITHOPTIMEDIA
24 Percy Street, London, W1T 2BS, United Kingdom
Tel.: (44) 2079611000 UK
Sales Range: $25-49.9 Million
Emp.: 400
N.A.I.C.S.: 541810

ZENITRON CORPORATION
No 8 Lane 250 Shinhu 2nd Rd, Neihu District, Taipei, Taiwan
Tel.: (886) 227928788
Web Site:
  https://www.zenitron.com.tw
3028—(TAI)
Rev.: $1,065,241,400
Assets: $689,246,418
Liabilities: $500,642,939
Net Worth: $188,603,479
Earnings: $14,911,344
Emp.: 750
Fiscal Year-end: 12/31/23
Integrated Circuits Mfr
N.A.I.C.S.: 334413
Gary Yeou-Yih Chou *(Chm)*

Subsidiaries:

Zenicom Corporation (1)
2F No 280 Shinhu 2nd Rd, Neihu District, Taipei, Taiwan
Tel.: (886) 227930968
Web Site: https://www.zenicom.com.hk
Semiconductor Mfr & Distr
N.A.I.C.S.: 334413

ZENKEN CORPORATION
Sumitomo Fudosan Shinjuku Central Park Tower 18F & 19F 6-18-1, Nishi-Shinjuku-skyscraper business Shinjuku-ku, Tokyo, 160-8361, Japan
Tel.: (81) 333490451
Web Site: https://www.zenken.co.jp
Year Founded: 1975
7371—(TKS)
Rev.: $46,633,631
Assets: $94,945,491
Liabilities: $13,320,119
Net Worth: $81,625,372
Earnings: $2,814,668
Emp.: 468
Fiscal Year-end: 06/30/23
Management Consulting Services
N.A.I.C.S.: 541618

Subsidiaries:

Zenken Care Co. (1)
Sumitomo Fudosan Shinjuku Central Park Tower 6-18-1 Nishi-Shinjuku, Shinjuku-ku, Tokyo, 160-0023, Japan
Tel.: (81) 480536924
Web Site: https://www.zenken-living.jp
Senior Care Services
N.A.I.C.S.: 621610

ZENKOKU HOSHO CO., LTD.
24F Otemachi Nomura Bldg 2-1-1 Otemachi, Chiyoda-ku, Tokyo, Japan
Tel.: (81) 332702300
Web Site: https://www.zenkoku.co.jp
7164—(TKS)
Sales Range: $250-299.9 Million
Emp.: 258
Credit Services
N.A.I.C.S.: 522390

ZENLABS ETHICA LTD.
Plot No 194 195 Industrial Area Phase II, Chandigarh, 160 002, India
Tel.: (91) 7307971103 In
Web Site:
  https://www.zenlabsethica.com
Year Founded: 1993
530697—(BOM)
Rev.: $7,748,318
Assets: $4,383,104
Liabilities: $3,233,906
Net Worth: $1,149,197
Earnings: $113,551
Emp.: 63
Fiscal Year-end: 03/31/21
Investment Services
N.A.I.C.S.: 523999

ZENNER METERING TECHNOLOGY (SHANGHAI) LTD.
No 800 Songda Road, Qingpu District, Shanghai, China
Tel.: (86) 2131166688
Web Site: https://www.zenner-metering.com
Year Founded: 2011
301303—(SSE)
Rev.: $167,227,379
Assets: $251,070,103
Liabilities: $113,236,615
Net Worth: $137,833,488
Earnings: $29,750,676
Fiscal Year-end: 12/31/22
Measuring Instruments Mfr
N.A.I.C.S.: 334515
Shihua Li *(Chm & Pres)*

ZENNOH CHICKEN FOODS CORP.
Shinagawa Cana Building 4/F 2-12-33 Konan, Minato-Ku, Tokyo, 108-0075, Japan
Tel.: (81) 3 6864 0200
Year Founded: 1972
Livestock & Processed Products Distr
N.A.I.C.S.: 424520
Takehiko Yamashita *(Pres)*

ZENOSENSE, INC.

Zennoh Chicken Foods Corp.—(Continued)

ZENOSENSE, INC.
Avda Cortes Valencianas 58 Planta 5, Valencia, Spain
Tel.: (34) 960 454 202　　　NV
ZENO—(OTCIQ)
Liabilities: $1,524,577
Net Worth: ($1,524,577)
Earnings: ($243,674)
Emp.: 1
Fiscal Year-end: 12/31/21
Medical Device Developer
N.A.I.C.S.: 339112
Carlos Jose Gil *(CEO, CFO & Chief Acctg Officer)*

ZENOVA GROUP PLC
172 Arlington Road, Essex, London, NW1 7HL, United Kingdom
Tel.: (44) 2030393977　　　UK
Web Site: https://www.zenovagroup.com
Year Founded: 2020
ZED—(AIM)
Rev.: $237,601
Assets: $4,886,434
Liabilities: $480,633
Net Worth: $4,405,801
Earnings: ($2,758,887)
Emp.: 4
Fiscal Year-end: 11/30/22
Paint & Coating Mfr
N.A.I.C.S.: 325510

ZENRIN CO., LTD.
3-1 Nakahara Shinmachi, Tobata-ku, Kitakyushu, 804-0003, Fukuoka, Japan
Tel.: (81) 938829050
Web Site: https://www.zenrin.co.jp
9474—(TKS)
Rev.: $405,424,350
Assets: $498,407,220
Liabilities: $172,395,410
Net Worth: $326,011,810
Earnings: $13,735,580
Emp.: 2,426
Fiscal Year-end: 03/31/24
Maps Production & Sales
N.A.I.C.S.: 323111
Junya Amita *(Exec VP)*

Subsidiaries:

Daikei Data Processing Co., Ltd.　(1)
3-3-9 Kawaguchi, Nishi-ku, Osaka, 550-0021, Japan
Tel.: (81) 665841234
Web Site: http://www.daikei.co.jp
Emp.: 28
Tele Data Processing Services
N.A.I.C.S.: 518210

GEO Technical Laboratory Co., Ltd.
Fukuoka Hakataekihigashi 3-chome No 1 No 26 Hakata Sta East Place, Hakata-ku, Fukuoka, 812-0013, Japan
Tel.: (81) 924520315
Web Site: http://www.geogiken.co.jp
Emp.: 66
Digital Mapping & 3D Data Surveying, Creating & Sales
N.A.I.C.S.: 541360
Kiyonari Kishikawa *(Pres & CEO)*

Knockinon, Inc.　(1)
3F Izak Higashi-Azabu Bldg 3-3-1 Higashi-Azabu, Minato-ku, Tokyo, 106-0044, Japan
Tel.: (81) 355492906
Web Site: http://www.knocking.co.jp
Emp.: 22
Mobile Advertising Services
N.A.I.C.S.: 541810

Zenrin Biznexus Co., Ltd.　(1)
Septeni Gaien Building 24 Daikyo-cho, Shinjuku-ku, Tokyo, 160-0015, Japan
Tel.: (81) 3 5363 7360
Web Site: http://www.zenrin-bn.co.jp

Sales Range: $25-49.9 Million
Direct Mailing Service
N.A.I.C.S.: 541860

Zenrin DataCom Co., Ltd.　(1)
3-1-1 Shibaura msb Tamachi Tamachi Station Tower N22F, Minato-ku, Tokyo, 108-0023, Japan
Tel.: (81) 368115050
Web Site: https://www.zenrin-datacom.net
Emp.: 393
Digital Mapping Services
N.A.I.C.S.: 541370
Tatsuhiko Shimizu *(Pres)*

Zenrin Europe GmbH　(1)
Mies-van-der-Rohe-Strasse 8, 80807, Munich, Germany
Tel.: (49) 89189174476
Web Site: https://www.zenrin-europe.com
Emp.: 14
Map Publisher
N.A.I.C.S.: 513199

Zenrin Printex Co., Ltd.　(1)
3-5-8 Matsubara, Moji-ku, Kitakyushu, 800-0064, Fukuoka Prefecture, Japan
Tel.: (81) 933723333
Web Site: http://www.zpx.co.jp
Emp.: 308
Printing Services
N.A.I.C.S.: 323111

Zenrin Promo Co., Ltd.　(1)
6F Horiuchi Bldg 2-6-1 Kaji-cho, Chiyoda-ku, Tokyo, 101-0044, Japan
Tel.: (81) 368595200
Web Site: http://www.zenrin-promo.net
Emp.: 40
Advertising & Event Management Services
N.A.I.C.S.: 541810

Zenrin USA, Inc.　(1)
1350 Bayshore Hwy Ste 580, Burlingame, CA 94010
Tel.: (650) 615-4200
Web Site: http://www.zenrin.com
Emp.: 19
Digital Maps Mfr & Sales
N.A.I.C.S.: 424920

ZENSHO HOLDINGS CO., LTD.
JR Shinagawa East Building 2-18-1 Konan, Minato-ku, Tokyo, 108-0075, Japan
Tel.: (81) 368331600　　　JP
Web Site: https://www.zensho.co.jp
Year Founded: 1982
7550—(TKS)
Rev.: $6,383,792,580
Assets: $4,944,650,160
Liabilities: $3,525,800,440
Net Worth: $1,418,849,720
Earnings: $202,880,730
Emp.: 16,806
Fiscal Year-end: 03/31/24
Holding Company; Food Service Chain Restaurants Owner & Operator; Food Processing Systems
N.A.I.C.S.: 551112
Masashi Imamura *(Mng Exec Officer)*

Subsidiaries:

Advanced Fresh Concepts Corp.　(1)
19700 Mariner Ave, Torrance, CA 90503
Tel.: (310) 604-3200
Web Site: https://afcsushi.com
Food Service
N.A.I.C.S.: 722310
Jeffery Seiler *(Pres)*

Big Boy Japan, Inc.　(1)
2-18-1 Konan JR Shinagawa East Building 6F-8F, Minato-ku, Tokyo, 108-0075, Japan
Tel.: (81) 368338001
Web Site: https://www.bigboyjapan.co.jp
Emp.: 281
Fast Food Restaurants
N.A.I.C.S.: 722511

Coco's Japan Co., Ltd.　(1)
JR Shinagawa East Building 2-18-1 Konan, Minato-ku, Tokyo, 108-0075, Japan　(54.47%)
Tel.: (81) 368338000
Web Site: https://www.cocos-jpn.co.jp

Sales Range: $350-399.9 Million
Emp.: 348
Family Restaurants
N.A.I.C.S.: 722511

Subsidiary (Domestic):

El Torito Japan Co., Ltd.　(2)
JR Shinagawa East Building 5F-7F 2-18-1 Konan, Tokyo, 108-0075, Minato-ku, Japan
Tel.: (81) 120222214
Web Site: https://www.eltorito.jp
Emp.: 100
Mexican Restaurant
N.A.I.C.S.: 722511

Takarajima Co., Ltd.　(2)
JR Shinagawa East Building 5F-7F 2-18-1 Konan, Tokyo, 108 0075, Minato-ku, Japan
Tel.: (81) 368334270
Web Site: http://www.takarajima.co.jp
Korean Barbecue Family Restaurants
N.A.I.C.S.: 722511

FUJITA CORPORATION Co., Ltd.　(97.1%)
5 3-5 Wakasakucho, Tomakomai, 053-0021, Hokkaido, Japan
Tel.: (81) 144341111
Web Site: https://www.fujitacorp.co.jp
Sales Range: Less than $1 Million
Restaurant Services
N.A.I.C.S.: 722511
Daisuke Endo *(Pres & CEO)*

GM Foods Co., Ltd.　(1)
JR Shinagawa East Bldg 2-18-1 Konan, Minato-ku, Tokyo, 108-0075, Japan
Tel.: (81) 368336670
Web Site: http://www.gmfoods.co.jp
Restaurant Operators
N.A.I.C.S.: 722511

Global Fresh Supply Co., Ltd.　(1)
JR Shinagawa East Building 2-18-1 Konan, Minato-ku, Tokyo, 108-0075, Japan
Tel.: (81) 368336660
Web Site: https://www.globalfresh-s.jp
Fresh Food Product Distr
N.A.I.C.S.: 424490

Global Seafood, Ltd.　(1)
3-11-3 Nagahama Fukuokashisengyokaikankai, Chuo-ku, Fukuoka, 810-0072, Japan
Tel.: (81) 927915113
Seafood Restaurant Operator
N.A.I.C.S.: 722511

Global Table Supply Co., Ltd.　(1)
2-18-1 Konan Jr Shinagawa East Bldg, Minato-ku, Tokyo, 108-0075, Japan
Tel.: (81) 357838870
Web Site: http://www.zensho.co.jp
Restaurant Tableware & Supplies Distr
N.A.I.C.S.: 424130

Gyuan Co., Ltd.　(1)
Tatsuo Shin-Osaka Building 8F 7-1-5 Nishinakajima, Yodogawa-ku, Osaka, 532 0011, Japan
Tel.: (81) 663082900
Web Site: http://www.gyuan.co.jp
Restaurant
N.A.I.C.S.: 722511

Hamazushi Co., Ltd.　(1)
Tennozu Ocean Square 2-2-20 Higashi-Shinagawa, Shinagawa-ku, Tokyo, 140-0002, Japan
Tel.: (81) 368338032
Web Site: https://www.hama-sushi.co.jp
Restaurant Operators
N.A.I.C.S.: 722511

IMedicare Co., Ltd.　(1)
14-1 Honcho Honcho Center Building 8F, Matsudo, 271-0091, Chiba, Japan
Tel.: (81) 47 361 7722
Web Site: https://www.imedicare.jp
Welfare Consulting Management Services
N.A.I.C.S.: 624190

Igarashi Suisan Co., Ltd.　(1)
37-4 Tatehara, Numazu, 410-0843, Shizuoka, Japan
Tel.: (81) 559512415
Web Site: https://igarashi-suisan.co.jp
Dried Horse Mackerel Mfr & Distr
N.A.I.C.S.: 311423

INTERNATIONAL PUBLIC

Jinzai Co., Ltd.　(1)
2-18-1 Konan, Minato-ku, Tokyo, Japan
Tel.: (81) 368339630
Web Site: https://www.jin-zai.co.jp
Food & Beverage Mfr
N.A.I.C.S.: 333241

Jolly-Pasta Co., Ltd.　(1)
JR Shinagawa East Building 2-18-1 Konan, Minato-ku, Tokyo, 108-0075, Japan
Tel.: (81) 368338833
Web Site: https://www.jolly-pasta.co.jp
Emp.: 254
Restaurant Operators
N.A.I.C.S.: 722511

Joy Mart Co., Ltd.　(1)
243 Kobuchi, Kasukabe, 344-8566, Saitama, Japan
Tel.: (81) 48 761 0808
Web Site: http://www.joymart.co.jp
Supermarket Services
N.A.I.C.S.: 445110

Kagayaki Co., Ltd.　(1)
65-1 Higashikujo Minamikawabecho Grace 11 1F, Minami-ku, Kyoto, 601-8034, Japan
Tel.: (81) 75 694 5019
Web Site: https://www.m-kagayaki.co.jp
Healthy Food Services
N.A.I.C.S.: 456191

Kyubeiya Co., Ltd.　(1)
8F JR Shinagawa East Building 2-18-1, Minato-ku, Konan, 108-0075, Tokyo, Japan
Tel.: (81) 12 007 0140
Web Site: https://www.zensho.co.jp
Restaurant Operators
N.A.I.C.S.: 722511

Nakau Co., Ltd.　(1)
2-18-1 Konan JR Shinagawa East Building 8F, Minato-ku, Tokyo, 108-0075, Japan
Tel.: (81) 120295770
Web Site: https://www.nakau.co.jp
Sales Range: $150-199.9 Million
Emp.: 276
Fast Food Restaurant Operator
N.A.I.C.S.: 722513

Nihon Wendies, Ltd.　(1)
JR Shinagawa East Building 5F-7F 2-18-1 Konan, Minato-ku, Tokyo, 108-0075, Japan
Tel.: (81) 368338002
Fast Food Restaurants
N.A.I.C.S.: 722513

Nyereg Co., Ltd.　(1)
2-6-5 Mori, Ama, 490-1107, Aichi, Japan
Tel.: (81) 52 462 6193
Web Site: https://www.nyereg.co.jp
Physical Therapist Services
N.A.I.C.S.: 621340

Royalhouse Ishioka Co., Ltd.　(1)
13446-10 Ishioka, Ishioka, 315-0001, Ibaraki, Japan
Tel.: (81) 29 922 3317
Web Site: https://www.royalhouse.co.jp
Restaurant Management Services
N.A.I.C.S.: 561110

Sanbishi Co., Ltd.　(1)
53 Wakamiya, Shinozuka-cho, Toyokawa, 441-0102, Aichi, Japan
Tel.: (81) 533723111
Web Site: https://www.sanbishi.co.jp
Emp.: 105
Soy Sauce Mfr & Distr
N.A.I.C.S.: 311941

Senior Support Co., Ltd.　(1)
2-5-24 Aoki, Kawaguchi, 332-0031, Saitama, Japan
Tel.: (81) 48 240 2151
Home Care Services
N.A.I.C.S.: 621610

Setoudon Co., Ltd.　(1)
8F JR Shinagawa East Building 2-18-1 Konan, Minato-ku, Tokyo, 108-0075, Japan
Tel.: (81) 12 007 0140
Web Site: https://www.seto-udon.jp
Restaurant Management Services
N.A.I.C.S.: 561110

TAG-1 Co., Ltd.　(1)
8F JR Shinagawa East Building 2-18-1 Konan, Minato-ku, Tokyo, 108-0075, Japan
Tel.: (81) 12 055 4676
Web Site: https://www.takarajima.co.jp

AND PRIVATE COMPANIES

Restaurant Management Services
N.A.I.C.S.: 561110
Hiroshi Tanaka *(COO)*

TCRS Restaurants Sdn. Bhd. (1)
Lot 3 and 3A Lorong Teknologi A, Taman Sains Selangor 1 Kota Damansara, 47810, Petaling Jaya, Selangor, Malaysia
Tel.: (60) 32 106 8880
Web Site:
    https://www.thechickenriceshop.com
Restaurant Management Services
N.A.I.C.S.: 561110

Techno Construction Co., Ltd. (1)
8th Floor JR Shinagawa East Building
2-18-1, Konan Minato-ku, Tokyo, 108-0075, Japan
Tel.: (81) 36 833 8029
Web Site: https://www.tec-const.com
Construction Materials Whslr
N.A.I.C.S.: 423390

Tolona Japan Co., Ltd. (1)
2-18-1 Konan, Minato-ku, Tokyo, 108-0075, Japan
Tel.: (81) 354617050
Web Site: http://www.tolona.co.jp
Emp.: 75
Pizza Mfr & Distr
N.A.I.C.S.: 311999
Toshiyuki Hara *(Pres)*

United Veggies Co., Ltd. (1)
Marinx Tower 3F 1-9-11, Kaigan Minato-ku, Tokyo, 105-0022, Japan
Tel.: (81) 35 425 2855
Web Site: https://www.uvc.jp
Specialty Store Management Services
N.A.I.C.S.: 561110

Zensho CooCa Co., Ltd. (1)
JR Shinagawa East Building 2-18-1 Konan, Minato-ku, Tokyo, 108-0075, Japan
Tel.: (81) 570094905
Web Site: https://www.coo-ca.jp
Electronic Payment Systems Mfr & Distr
N.A.I.C.S.: 334419

Zensho Foods Malaysia Sdn. Bhd. (1)
No 19 Jalan PJS 5/26 Taman Desaria, 46000, Petaling Jaya, Selangor, Malaysia
Tel.: (60) 37 785 8804
Web Site: https://www.sukiya.my
Restaurant Management Services
N.A.I.C.S.: 561110

Zensho Tradings Co., Ltd. (1)
2-18-1 Konan, Minato-Ku, Tokyo, 108-0075, Japan
Tel.: (81) 368336675
Web Site: http://www.zensho.co.jp
Emp.: 15
Food Products Distr
N.A.I.C.S.: 424420

ZENSUN ENTERPRISES LIMITED
24/F Wyndham Place 40-44 Wyndham Street, Central, China (Hong Kong)
Tel.: (852) 22586888
Web Site:
    https://www.zensunenterprises.com
0185—(HKG)
Rev.: $1,355,850,662
Assets: $8,640,763,420
Liabilities: $7,893,801,022
Net Worth: $746,962,398
Earnings: ($413,130,791)
Emp.: 620
Fiscal Year-end: 12/31/22
Property Investment Services
N.A.I.C.S.: 523940
Ping Man Yuen *(COO-Hong Kong & Sec)*

Subsidiaries:

SingHaiyi Group Pte. Ltd. (1)
6 Shenton Way 45-01 OUE Downtown 1, Singapore, 068809, Singapore **(62.22%)**
Tel.: (65) 65309023
Web Site: http://www.singhaiyi.com
Rev.: $43,160,880
Assets: $1,636,759,861
Liabilities: $1,175,310,117
Net Worth: $461,449,744
Earnings: ($19,244,185)
Emp.: 43
Fiscal Year-end: 03/31/2020
Holding Company; Real Estate Investment Services
N.A.I.C.S.: 551112
Catherine Soy Lee Chang *(Dir-Technical-Project Dev & Sls & Admin)*

Xpress Finance Limited (1)
24 Fl Wyndham Pl 44 Wyndham St, Central, China (Hong Kong)
Tel.: (852) 25833633
Web Site: http://www.xpressfinance.com.hk
Credit Card Processing Services
N.A.I.C.S.: 522320
Tickman Tickman *(Mgr-Customer Svc)*

ZENTEK LTD.
210-1205 Amber Drive, Thunder Bay, P7B 6M4, ON, Canada
Tel.: (705) 618-0900 ON
Web Site: https://www.zentek.com
ZTEK—(NASDAQ)
Rev.: $515,212
Assets: $16,684,033
Liabilities: $1,781,678
Net Worth: $14,902,354
Earnings: ($8,645,971)
Emp.: 24
Fiscal Year-end: 03/31/24
Copper & Nickel Mining Services
N.A.I.C.S.: 212230
Brian Bosse *(CFO)*

ZENTIS GMBH & CO. KG
Julicher Strasse 177, 52070, Aachen, Germany
Tel.: (49) 241 4760 0 De
Web Site: http://www.zentis.de
Year Founded: 1893
Sales Range: $75-99.9 Million
Emp.: 2,125
Sweet Bread Spread, Confectionery & Processed Fruit Mfr
N.A.I.C.S.: 311999
Karl-Heinz Johnen *(Mng Dir)*

Subsidiaries:

OOO Zentis Russia (1)
Siedlung Ramenskoj Agrohimstanzii 15, Business Park Khimki, 140126, Khimki, Russia
Tel.: (7) 4959357300
Web Site: http://www.zentis.ru
Emp.: 46
Fruit Product & Confectionery Whslr
N.A.I.C.S.: 424490
Johannes Peter Schonhuber *(Mng Dir)*

Zentis GmbH & Co. KG - (Aachen-Eilendorf) Plant II (1)
Debyestrasse 111, 52078, Aachen, Germany
Tel.: (49) 241 4760 0
Web Site: http://www.zentis.de
Emp.: 346
Fruit Confectionery Mfr
N.A.I.C.S.: 311340

Zentis Hungaria Bt. (1)
Fo ut 178, 2646, Dregelypalank, Hungary
Tel.: (36) 35 567 27
Web Site: http://www.zentis.hu
Emp.: 127
Fruit Product Mfr
N.A.I.C.S.: 311999

Zentis North America Operating, LLC (1)
2050 N Oak Dr, Plymouth, IN 46563
Tel.: (574) 941-1100
Web Site: http://www.zentis.de
Emp.: 473
Fruit Product & Confectionery Mfr
N.A.I.C.S.: 311999
Norbert Weichele *(Pres & CEO)*

Subsidiary (Domestic):

Zentis North America, LLC (2)
1741 Tomlinson Rd, Philadelphia, PA 19116
Tel.: (267) 623-8000
Web Site: http://www.zentis-usa.com
Sweetener Ingredient Developer & Mfr
N.A.I.C.S.: 311999
Brian Fox *(Pres & CEO)*

Zentis Polska Sp. z o.o. (1)
Ul Przemyslowa 8, Zelkow Kolonia, 08 110, Siedlce, Poland
Tel.: (48) 25 6402 100
Web Site: http://www.zentis.pl
Emp.: 253
Fruit Product Mfr
N.A.I.C.S.: 311999

ZENTRUM HOLDINGS, INC.
4-30-4F Yotsuya, Shinjuku-ku, Tokyo, 160-0004, Japan
Tel.: (81) 363693727 DE
Year Founded: 2019
Assets: $2,384
Liabilities: $576,987
Net Worth: ($574,603)
Earnings: ($253,188)
Emp.: 1
Fiscal Year-end: 12/31/22
Holding Company
N.A.I.C.S.: 551112
Koichi Ishizuka *(Pres, CEO, CFO, Treas & Sec)*

ZENVIA INC.
Avenida Paulista 2300 18th Floor Suites 182 and 184, Sao Paulo, 01310-300, Brazil
Tel.: (55) 11999045082 Ky
Year Founded: 2020
ZENV—(NASDAQ)
Rev.: $161,048,360
Assets: $341,322,963
Liabilities: $164,047,662
Net Worth: $177,275,302
Earnings: ($12,119,055)
Emp.: 1,076
Fiscal Year-end: 12/31/23
Holding Company
N.A.I.C.S.: 551112
Cassio Bobsin *(Founder, CEO & Sec)*

ZEON CORPORATION
Shin Marunouchi Center Building 14th Floor 1-6-2 Marunouchi, Chiyoda-ku, Tokyo, 100-8246, Japan
Tel.: (81) 352192171 JP
Web Site: https://www.zeon.co.jp
Year Founded: 1950
4205—(TKS)
Rev.: $2,526,864,190
Assets: $3,518,198,940
Liabilities: $1,113,950,250
Net Worth: $2,404,248,690
Earnings: $205,577,610
Emp.: 4,462
Fiscal Year-end: 03/31/24
Mfr of Synthetic Rubber, Synthetic Latices & Chemicals
N.A.I.C.S.: 325212
Kimiaki Tanaka *(Pres, Pres & CEO)*

Subsidiaries:

Asia Technical Support Laboratory Pte. Ltd. (1)
61 Science Park Road 05-09/10 The Galen Singapore Science Park 2, Singapore, 117525, Singapore
Tel.: (65) 62667631
Optimal Composition Testing Services
N.A.I.C.S.: 541380

Optes Inc. (1)
422-1 Futagamishin, Takaoka, 933-0981, Toyama, Japan
Tel.: (81) 76 632 1590
Web Site: http://www.optes.co.jp
Optical Film Mfr
N.A.I.C.S.: 333310

PT. Tokyo Zairyo Indonesia (1)
Gedung MidPlaza 2 Lantai 12, Jl Jend Sudirman Kav 10 -11, Jakarta, 10220, Indonesia
Tel.: (62) 21 574 6454

Synthetic Rubber Product Mfr & Distr
N.A.I.C.S.: 325212

River Xemex Co., Ltd. (1)
2-11-17 Osachigosho, Okaya, 394-0082, Nagano, Japan
Tel.: (81) 26 621 2131
Medical Device Mfr
N.A.I.C.S.: 339112

Shanghai Zeon Co., Ltd. (1)
No 380 Shennan Road, Xinzhuang Industrial Zone, Shanghai, 201108, China
Tel.: (86) 216 489 6160
Rubber Product Mfr & Distr
N.A.I.C.S.: 326291

TFC Co., Ltd. (1)
34-23-2 Azono, Tsuruga, 914-8501, Fukui, Japan **(85.5%)**
Tel.: (81) 770211711
Web Site: http://www.tomoegawa.co.jp
Optical Film Mfr
N.A.I.C.S.: 326112

Takehara Zeon (Shanghai) Co., Ltd. (1)
No 380 Shennan Road, Xinzhuang Industrial Zone Minhang District, Shanghai, 201108, China
Tel.: (86) 216 489 8597
Rubber Product Mfr & Distr
N.A.I.C.S.: 326291

Telene S.A.S. (1)
2 Rue Marie Curie, 59910, Bondues, France
Tel.: (33) 32 069 5710
Web Site: https://www.telene.com
Resin Product Mfr & Distr
N.A.I.C.S.: 325211

Tohpe Corporation (1)
1-5-11 Chikkoshinmachi, Nishi-ku, Sakai, 592-8331, Osaka, Japan
Tel.: (81) 72 243 6411
Web Site: https://www.tohpe.co.jp
Chemical Product Mfr & Distr
N.A.I.C.S.: 325211

Tokyo Zairyo (Guangzhou) Co., Ltd. (1)
Room 1208 Goldlion Digital Network Center 138 Tiyu Road East, Tianhe District, Guangzhou, 510620, Guangdong, China
Tel.: (86) 203 878 0671
Rubber Product Mfr & Distr
N.A.I.C.S.: 326291

Tokyo Zairyo (India) Pvt. Ltd. (1)
Time Tower Unit No 708 7th Floor Sector-28 M G Road, Gurgaon, 122002, Haryana, India
Tel.: (91) 124 424 9011
Synthetic Rubber Product Mfr & Distr
N.A.I.C.S.: 325212

Tokyo Zairyo (Shanghai) Co., Ltd. (1)
Room 4108 Grand Gateway 66 Tower 2 1 Hongqiao Road, Xuhui District, Shanghai, 200030, China
Tel.: (86) 216 119 9400
Rubber Product Mfr & Distr
N.A.I.C.S.: 326291

Tokyo Zairyo (Singapore) Pte. Ltd, (1)
331 North Bridge Road 20-01/02 Odeon Towers, Singapore, 188720, Singapore
Tel.: (65) 6 337 5053
Rubber Product Mfr & Distr
N.A.I.C.S.: 326291

Tokyo Zairyo (Thailand) Co., Ltd. (1)
29th Floor Room 2903 Empire Tower 1 South Sathorn Rd, Yannawa Sathorn, Bangkok, 10120, Thailand
Tel.: (66) 2 670 0285
Synthetic Rubber Product Mfr & Distr
N.A.I.C.S.: 325212

Tokyo Zairyo (Tianjin) Co., Ltd. (1)
Room 1805 The Exchange Tower 1 189 Nanjing Road, Heping District, Tianjin, 300051, China
Tel.: (86) 222 302 1268
Rubber Product Mfr & Distr
N.A.I.C.S.: 326291

Tokyo Zairyo (U.S.A.) Inc. (1)

ZEON CORPORATION

Zeon Corporation—(Continued)
750 Old Hickory Blvd Bldg 1 Ste 220, Brentwood, TN 37027
Tel.: (615) 922-4633
Synthetic Rubber Product Mfr & Distr
N.A.I.C.S.: 325212

Tokyo Zairyo (Vietnam) LLC (1)
4F 85 Nguyen Du Street, Nguyen Du Ward Hai Ba Trung Dist, Hanoi, Vietnam
Tel.: (84) 43 941 3825
Synthetic Rubber Product Mfr & Distr
N.A.I.C.S.: 325212

Tokyo Zairyo Czech, s.r.o. (1)
Pobrezni 620/3, 186 00, Prague, Czech Republic
Tel.: (420) 22 122 8406
Synthetic Rubber Product Mfr & Distr
N.A.I.C.S.: 325212

Tokyo Zairyo Mexico, S.A. de C.V. (1)
Boulevard Bernardo Quintana 7001, Torre II Suite 807 Colonia Centro Sur, 76090, Queretaro, Mexico
Tel.: (52) 442 229 3242
Synthetic Rubber Product Mfr & Distr
N.A.I.C.S.: 325212

ZEON Chemicals L.P. (1)
4111 Bells Ln, Louisville, KY 40211
Tel.: (502) 775-7777
Web Site: http://www.zeonchemicals.com
Emp.: 175
Synthetic Rubber Mfr
N.A.I.C.S.: 325212
Bob Barlow (Pres & CEO)

ZEON Europe GmbH (1)
Hansaallee 249, 40549, Dusseldorf, Germany
Tel.: (49) 21152670
Web Site: https://www.zeon.eu
Emp.: 25
Synthetic Rubber Products Mfr
N.A.I.C.S.: 325212

ZEON do Brasil Ltda (1)
Rua Arandu 57/cj 23, Sao Paulo, 04562-031, Brazil
Tel.: (55) 1155012120
Web Site: http://www.zeondobrasil.com.br
Emp.: 3
Synthetic Rubber Products Mfr
Claudia deSouza (Gen Mgr)

ZIS Information Technology Co., Ltd. (1)
1-6-2 Shin-Marunouchi Center Building, Marunouchi, Chiyoda-ku, Tokyo, 100-0005, Japan
Tel.: (81) 33 216 6500
Web Site: https://www.ziftec.co.jp
Computer System Design Services
N.A.I.C.S.: 541512

ZS Elastomers Co., Ltd. (1)
1-6-2 Marunouchi, Chiyoda-ku, Tokyo, 100-0005, Japan
Tel.: (81) 332160620
Web Site: https://www.zs-elastomers.com
Synthetic Rubber Products Mfr
N.A.I.C.S.: 325212
Kei Itoh (Pres & Pres)

Zeon (Shanghai) Co., Ltd. (1)
Room 4109 2 Grand Gateway No 3 Hongqiao Road, Xuhui District, Shanghai, 200030, China
Tel.: (86) 216 167 5776
Financial Management Services
N.A.I.C.S.: 541611

Zeon Advanced Polymix Co., Ltd. (1)
111/2 Soi Nikom 13 Moo 2 T Makhamkhoo, Nikompattana District, Rayong, 21180, Thailand
Tel.: (66) 88 203 0380
Web Site: https://www.zeon.co.th
Rubber Product Mfr & Distr
N.A.I.C.S.: 326291
Hiroshi Mihara (Mng Dir)

Zeon Asia Malaysia Sdn. Bhd. (1)
Unit 208 Block B Phileo Damansara II No 15 Jalan16/11, Off Jalan Damansara, 46350, Petaling Jaya, Selangor, Malaysia
Tel.: (60) 37 956 7069
Synthetic Rubber Product Mfr & Distr
N.A.I.C.S.: 325212

Zeon Asia Pte. Ltd. (1)
331 North Bridge Road 20-01/02 Odeon Towers, Singapore, 188720, Singapore
Tel.: (65) 6 332 2338
Synthetic Rubber Product Mfr & Distr
N.A.I.C.S.: 325212

Zeon CSC Corporation (1)
3F -2 No 266 Sec 1 Wenhua 2nd Rd, Linkou Dist, New Taipei City, 24448, Taiwan
Tel.: (886) 22 609 2156
Optical Product Distr
N.A.I.C.S.: 423460

Zeon Chemicals (Thailand) Co., Ltd. (1)
3 Soi G-14 Pakorn-Songkhrorad Road, Tambol Huaypong Amphur Muangrayong, Rayong, 21150, Thailand
Tel.: (66) 3 868 5973
Chemical Product Mfr & Distr
N.A.I.C.S.: 325211

Zeon Chemicals Asia Co., Ltd. (1)
16 Phangmuang Chapoh 3-1 Road, Huaypong Sub-district Muang Rayong District, Rayong, 21150, Thailand
Tel.: (66) 3 301 7781
Rubber Product Mfr & Distr
N.A.I.C.S.: 326291

Zeon Chemicals Singapore Pte. Ltd. (1)
100 Banyan Drive Jurong Island, Singapore, 627571, Singapore
Tel.: (65) 6 933 4400
Synthetic Rubber Product Mfr & Distr
N.A.I.C.S.: 325212

Zeon Chemicals Yonezawa Co., Ltd. (1)
3-446-13 Hachimanpara, Yonezawa, 992-1128, Yamagata, Japan
Tel.: (81) 23 829 0055
Web Site: https://www.zeon.co.jp
Chemical Product Mfr & Distr
N.A.I.C.S.: 325211

Zeon F&B Co., Ltd. (1)
Shin Marunouchi Center Building 1-6-2 Marunouchi, Chiyoda-ku, Tokyo, 100-0005, Japan
Tel.: (81) 33 216 1410
Life Insurance Loan Services
N.A.I.C.S.: 524210

Zeon India Private Limited (1)
Time Tower Unit No 708 7th Floor Sector 28 M G Road, Gurgaon, 122002, Haryana, India
Tel.: (91) 124 422 9461
Synthetic Rubber Product Mfr & Distr
N.A.I.C.S.: 325212

Zeon Kasei (Changshu) Co., Ltd. (1)
Building 9 Huangpujiang Road 208, Xinhang Science and Technology Industrial Park, Changshu, Jiangsu, China
Tel.: (86) 5125 235 7000
Chemical Product Mfr & Distr
N.A.I.C.S.: 325998

Zeon Kasei Co., Ltd. (1)
1-6-2 Shin-Marunouchi Center Building, Marunouchi Chiyoda-ku, Tokyo, 100-0005, Japan
Tel.: (81) 35 208 5111
Web Site: https://www.zeonkasei.co.jp
Emp.: 131
Resin Product Mfr & Distr
N.A.I.C.S.: 325211
Masayoshi Oshima (Chm)

Zeon Kasei Mexico S.A. de C.V. (1)
Avenida Santiago Sur 100, 78420, San Luis Potosi, Mexico
Tel.: (52) 44 478 5400
Chemical Product Mfr & Distr
N.A.I.C.S.: 325211

Zeon Korea Co., Ltd. (1)
Room 403 4F City Airport Tower 159-9 Samseong-dong, Gangnam-gu, Seoul, 135-973, Korea (South)
Tel.: (82) 2 539 8565
Web Site: https://hwww.zeonkr.com
Rubber Product Mfr & Distr
N.A.I.C.S.: 326291

Zeon Manufacturing Vietnam Co., Ltd.
No 109 Road No 10, VSIP Haiphong Township Tan Duong Ward Thuy Nguyen District, Haiphong, Vietnam
Tel.: (84) 225 379 7027
Packing Containers Product Mfr & Distr
N.A.I.C.S.: 327213

Zeon Medical (Guangzhou) Inc. (1)
Room 1706A Goldlion Digital Network Center, No 138 Ti Yu Dong Road Tianhe District, Guangzhou, 510620, Guangdong, China
Tel.: (86) 202 283 6788
Medical Equipment Distr
N.A.I.C.S.: 423450

Zeon Medical Inc. (1)
Shin-Marunouchi Center Building, 1-6-2 Marunouchi Chiyoda-ku, Tokyo, 100-0005, Japan
Tel.: (81) 33 216 1265
Web Site: https://www.zeonmedical.co.jp
Emp.: 216
Medical Equipment Mfr & Distr
N.A.I.C.S.: 339112
Noboru Yanagida (Co-Pres)

Zeon Nano Technology Co., Ltd. (1)
Shin Marunouchi Center Building, 1-6-2 Marunouchi, Tokyo, 100-0005, Japan
Tel.: (81) 33 216 1766
Web Site: https://www.zeonnanotech.jp
Carbon Nanotube Product Mfr
N.A.I.C.S.: 335991
Kohei Arakawa (Pres)

Zeon North Co., Ltd. (1)
351 Ejiri, Takaoka, 933-0062, Toyama, Japan
Tel.: (81) 76 625 1111
Industrial Material Product Distr
N.A.I.C.S.: 423830

Zeon Opto Bio Lab Co., Ltd. (1)
234-1 Konaka-cho, Sano, 327-0001, Tochigi, Japan
Tel.: (81) 28 323 7061
Web Site: https://www.zeonoptobiolab.co.jp
Emp.: 56
Mold Plastic Product Mfr
N.A.I.C.S.: 333511

Zeon Polymix (Guangzhou) Co., Ltd. (1)
No 1 1st Jingquan Road, Yonghe Economic Zone Minhang District, Guangzhou, 511356, China
Tel.: (86) 203 222 1171
Rubber Product Mfr & Distr
N.A.I.C.S.: 326291

Zeon Polymix Inc. (1)
1-11-1 Ishizue, Otsu, 520-2272, Shiga, Japan
Tel.: (81) 77 546 1223
Web Site: https://www.zeon.co.jp
Synthetic Rubber Products Mfr
N.A.I.C.S.: 325212

Zeon Research Vietnam Co., Ltd. (1)
6th Floor Building 85 Nguyen Du Str, Hai Ba Trung District, Hanoi, 100000, Vietnam
Optical Product Distr
N.A.I.C.S.: 423460

Zeon Shinhwa (Zeshin) Inc. (1)
No 502 CALT B/D City Airport 22, Teheran-ro 87-gil Gangnam-gu, Seoul, 06164, Korea (South)
Tel.: (82) 2 761 7030
Electronic Equipment Distr
N.A.I.C.S.: 423690

Zeon Specialty Materials Inc. (1)
25 Metro Dr Ste 238, San Jose, CA 95110
Tel.: (408) 641-7889
Web Site: https://www.zeonsmi.com
Electronic Equipment Distr
N.A.I.C.S.: 423690

Zeon Taiwan Co., Ltd. (1)
4F No 36 Nanjing W Rd, Datong Dist, Taipei, 103, Taiwan
Tel.: (886) 22 552 3620
Web Site: https://www.zeontaiwan.com.tw
Electronic Equipment Distr
N.A.I.C.S.: 423690

INTERNATIONAL PUBLIC

Zeon Trading (Shanghai) Co., Ltd. (1)
Room 4106-07 2 Grand Gateway No 3 Hongqiao Road, Xuhui District, Shanghai, 200230, China
Tel.: (86) 216 040 7255
Chemical Products Distr
N.A.I.C.S.: 424690

Zeon Yamaguchi Co., Ltd. (1)
2-1 Nachicho, Shunan, 745-0023, Yamaguchi, Japan
Tel.: (81) 83 421 8482
Web Site: https://www.zeonyamaguchi.co.jp
Construction Materials Whslr
N.A.I.C.S.: 423390

ZEOTECH LIMITED
Level 4 216 St Georges Tce, Perth, 6000, WA, Australia
Tel.: (61) 731815523
Web Site: https://www.metalsearch.com.au
ZEO—(ASX)
Rev.: $517,579
Assets: $8,571,509
Liabilities: $866,936
Net Worth: $7,704,572
Earnings: ($3,691,720)
Fiscal Year-end: 06/30/24
Gold & Base Metals Mining & Exploration Services
N.A.I.C.S.: 212220
Neville Bassett (Sec)

ZEPHYR ENERGY PLC
First Floor Newmarket House Market Street, Newbury, RG14 5DP, Berks, United Kingdom
Tel.: (44) 2072254590
Web Site: https://www.zephyrplc.com
ZPHR—(AIM)
Rev.: $25,230,000
Assets: $112,570,000
Liabilities: $47,870,000
Net Worth: $64,700,000
Earnings: ($3,500,000)
Fiscal Year-end: 12/31/23
Gold & Silver Mining & Petroleum Exploration
N.A.I.C.S.: 212220
Chris Eadie (CFO)

Subsidiaries:

VANE Minerals (UK) Limited (1)
First Floor 9 Savoy Street, London, WC2E 7ER, United Kingdom
Tel.: (44) 207 225 4590
Web Site: http://www.rosepetroleum.com
Mineral Exploration Services
N.A.I.C.S.: 213115
Matthew C. Idiens (Founder)

Subsidiary (Non-US):

Minerales VANE S.A. de C.V. (2)
Avenida Juarez Oriente 9, Acaponeta, Nayarit, Mexico
Tel.: (52) 325 252 2841
Mineral Exploration Services
N.A.I.C.S.: 213115

ZEPHYR MINERALS LTD.
1301-1959 Upper Water Street, Purdys Wharf Tower 1, Halifax, B3J 3N2, NS, Canada
Tel.: (902) 706-0222
Web Site: https://www.zephyrminerals.com
Year Founded: 2010
ZPHYF—(OTCIQ)
Assets: $3,898,002
Liabilities: $120,516
Net Worth: $3,777,485
Earnings: ($1,536,729)
Fiscal Year-end: 12/31/23
Investment Services
N.A.I.C.S.: 523999
John M. Clark (CFO)

AND PRIVATE COMPANIES

ZEPPELIN GMBH

ZEPHYR TEXTILES LIMITED
3 rd Floor IEP Building 97 B/D-1, Gulberg III, Lahore, Pakistan
Tel.: (92) 4235782905
Web Site: https://www.zephyr.com.pk
Year Founded: 1999
ZTL—(PSX)
Rev.: $28,513,600
Assets: $21,134,968
Liabilities: $12,033,313
Net Worth: $9,101,655
Earnings: $856,056
Emp.: 1,218
Fiscal Year-end: 06/30/23
Textile Mill Operator
N.A.I.C.S.: 314999
Mussaid Hanif *(CEO)*

ZEPP HEALTH CORPORATION
Building B2 Zhong'an Chuanggu Technology Park, No 900 Wangjiang West Road, Hefei, 230088, China
Tel.: (86) 1059403268
Web Site: http://www.zepp.com
Year Founded: 2013
ZEPP—(NYSE)
Rev.: $634,727,887
Assets: $807,055,584
Liabilities: $395,698,838
Net Worth: $411,356,746
Earnings: ($44,171,669)
Emp.: 987
Fiscal Year-end: 12/31/22
Business Management Software Development Services
N.A.I.C.S.: 541511
Wang Huang *(Co-Founder, Chm & CEO)*

ZEPPELIN GMBH
Graf-Zeppelin-Platz 1, 85748, Garching, Germany
Tel.: (49) 89 320 00 0
Web Site: http://www.zeppelin.com
Rev.: $3,492,269,972
Assets: $3,124,810,310
Liabilities: $2,178,045,950
Net Worth: $946,764,360
Earnings: $100,181,556
Emp.: 9,748
Fiscal Year-end: 12/31/19
Holding Company
N.A.I.C.S.: 551112
Peter Gerstmann *(Chm-Mgmt Bd)*

Subsidiaries:

BIS Inspection Service GmbH (1)
Hermann-Blohm-Strasse 5, 20457, Hamburg, Germany
Tel.: (49) 407560770
Web Site: http://www.bis-hh.de
Laboratory Testing Services
N.A.I.C.S.: 541380

Baltic Marine Contractors OU (1)
Peterburi tee 90F, 11415, Tallinn, Estonia
Tel.: (372) 6069381
Web Site: http://www.balticmarine.net
Navigational Equipment & Spare Part Distr
N.A.I.C.S.: 423860
Aleksei Povjakel *(Acct Mgr)*

Deutsche Zeppelin Reederei GmbH (1)
Messestrasse 132, 88046, Friedrichshafen, Germany
Tel.: (49) 754159000
Web Site: http://www.zeppelin-nt.de
Transportation Services
N.A.I.C.S.: 481211

Levotec s.r.o. (1)
Novoveska cesta 2848/40, Levoca, 054 01, Presov, Slovakia
Tel.: (421) 917653788
Web Site: http://www.levotec.sk
Steel & Metal Construction Product Mfr
N.A.I.C.S.: 332312
Ludmila Combova *(Mgr)*

Luther HL GmbH & Co. KG (1)
Flugplatzstrasse Building 9805, Hoppstadten-Weiersbach, 55768, Birkenfeld, Germany
Tel.: (49) 67829899430
Web Site: http://www.horstluther.de
Traffic Sign Related Product Mfr
N.A.I.C.S.: 339950
Horst Luther *(Mng Dir)*

MWB Marine Services GmbH (1)
Barkhausenstr 60, 27568, Bremerhaven, Germany
Tel.: (49) 47194500
Web Site: http://www.mwb-marine.com
Diesel Engine Repair Services
N.A.I.C.S.: 811111
Eva-Maria Graf *(CFO)*

Meton GmbH (1)
Flugplatzstrasse Gebaude 9805, Hoppstadten-Weiersbach, 55768, Birkenfeld, Germany
Tel.: (49) 67829899430
Web Site: http://www.meton.eu
Traffic Signal & Transportable Protective Device Mfr
N.A.I.C.S.: 334290
Jens Luther *(Mng Dir)*

Nuova Ciba S.p.A. (1)
Via G Fattori 6, 42122, Reggio Emilia, RE, Italy
Tel.: (39) 0522550215
Web Site: http://www.nuovaciba.com
Industrial Equipment Distr
N.A.I.C.S.: 423830
Luca Bonilauri *(Mgr-Sls & Technical)*

Smart Controls India Ltd. (1)
Smart House Telegraph Road Besides VIP Circuit House, Morar, Gwalior, 474006, Madhya Pradesh, India
Tel.: (91) 7512437700
Web Site: http://www.smartcontrols.in
Automation Information Technology Services
N.A.I.C.S.: 541512

Zeppelin Baumaschinen GmbH (1)
Graf-Zeppelin-Platz 1, 85748, Garching, Germany
Tel.: (49) 89320000
Web Site: http://www.zeppelin.com
Electronic Components Distr
N.A.I.C.S.: 423690

Subsidiary (Domestic):

SITECH Deutschland GmbH (2)
Zum Aquarium 6a, 46047, Oberhausen, Germany
Tel.: (49) 2083021370
Web Site: http://www.sitech.de
Construction Engineering Services
N.A.I.C.S.: 541330

Zeppelin CZ s.r.o. (1)
Lipova 72, Modletice, 251 70, Prague, Czech Republic
Tel.: (420) 266 015 111
Web Site: http://www.zeppelin.cz
Financial Lending Services
N.A.I.C.S.: 533110
Stanislav Chladek *(CEO)*

Subsidiary (Non-US):

Zeppelin Polska Sp. z o.o. (2)
ul Klonowa 10, Kajetany Nadarzyn, 05-830, Warsaw, Poland
Tel.: (48) 225664700
Web Site: http://www.zeppelinpl.com
Construction Machinery Distr
N.A.I.C.S.: 423830

Zeppelin SK s.r.o. (2)
Zvolenska cesta 14605/50, 974 05, Banska Bystrica, Slovakia
Tel.: (421) 484149901
Web Site: http://www.zeppelin.sk
Construction Machinery Distr
N.A.I.C.S.: 423830

Zeppelin Danmark A/S (1)
Park Alle 363, 2605, Brondby, Denmark
Tel.: (45) 70252211
Web Site: http://www.zeppelin-cat.dk
Construction Industrial Machinery & Equipment Mfr
N.A.I.C.S.: 333248

Zeppelin International AG (1)
Hinterbergstrasse 20, 6300, Steinhausen, Switzerland
Tel.: (41) 41 747 00 30
Electronic Components Distr
N.A.I.C.S.: 423690

Subsidiary (Non-US):

Zeppelin Armenien LLC (2)
2 Artadrakan district block 4, Kajaran, Armenia
Construction Equipment Distr
N.A.I.C.S.: 423810

Zeppelin Central Asia Mach. LLC (2)
st Navruz 9, Sergili district, 100149, Tashkent, Uzbekistan
Tel.: (998) 78509933
Web Site: http://www.zeppelin.uz
Electronic Components Distr
N.A.I.C.S.: 423690

Zeppelin Power Systems Russia LLC (2)
p / o Putilkovo 69 km MKAD TVK Greenwood p 31, Krasnogorsk district, 143441, Moscow, Russia
Tel.: (7) 4953246382
Web Site: http://www.zeppelinps.ru
Construction Equipment Distr
N.A.I.C.S.: 423810

Zeppelin Russland OOO (2)
69 km MKAD TVK Greenwood bld 31 to Putilkovo, Krasnogorsky district, 143441, Moscow, Russia
Tel.: (7) 4952213535
Construction Equipment Rental Services
N.A.I.C.S.: 532412

Zeppelin Tadschikistan OOO (2)
st Kakharova house 12, 734005, Dushanbe, Tajikistan
Tel.: (992) 446251122
Web Site: http://www.zeppelin.tj
Construction Equipment Distr
N.A.I.C.S.: 423810

Zeppelin Turkmenistan LLC (2)
Ave Bitarap Turkmenistan 608, Ashgabat, 744001, Turkmenistan
Tel.: (993) 12379090
Web Site: http://www.zeppelin.tm
Construction & Mining Equipment Distr
N.A.I.C.S.: 423810

Zeppelin Ukraine LLC (2)
Vasilkovskaya Str 34/3rd floor, 03022, Kiev, Ukraine
Construction Equipment Distr
N.A.I.C.S.: 423810

Zeppelin Weissrussland OOO (2)
Kolodischi-1 Highway Airport Minsk 2 ABK Building, 223051, Minsk, Belarus
Tel.: (375) 172667252
Construction & Mining Equipment Distr
N.A.I.C.S.: 423810

Zeppelin Oesterreich GmbH (1)
Zeppelinstr 2, 2401, Fischamend Dorf, Austria
Tel.: (43) 22327900
Web Site: http://www.zeppelin-cat.at
Construction Machinery Distr
N.A.I.C.S.: 423830

Zeppelin Power Systems GmbH & Co. KG (1)
Ruhrstrasse 158, 22761, Hamburg, Germany
Tel.: (49) 408531510
Web Site: http://www.zeppelin-powersystems.com
Construction Equipment Distr
N.A.I.C.S.: 423810
Eva-Maria Graf *(Member-Mgmt Bd)*

Subsidiary (Domestic):

Klickrent GmbH (2)
Elsenstrasse 106, 12435, Berlin, Germany
Tel.: (49) 5632892664
Web Site: http://www.klickrent.de
Construction Equipment Rental Services
N.A.I.C.S.: 532490
Marko Piatkowski *(CTO)*

Zeppelin Rental GmbH & Co. KG (1)
Graf-Zeppelin-Platz 1, 85748, Garching, Germany
Tel.: (49) 89 32 000 220
Web Site: http://www.zeppelin-rental.de
Construction Equipment Rental Services
N.A.I.C.S.: 532412

Zeppelin Rental Osterreich GmbH & Co. KG (1)
Ghegastrasse 3, 1030, Vienna, Austria
Tel.: (43) 17962115
Web Site: http://www.zeppelin-rental.at
Construction Equipment Rental Services
N.A.I.C.S.: 532412

Zeppelin Rental Russland OOO (1)
Vostochnaya Street 10, Odintsovo, 143000, Moscow, Russia
Tel.: (7) 4956453018
Web Site: http://www.zeppelin-rental.ru
Construction Equipment Rental Services
N.A.I.C.S.: 532412

Zeppelin Streif Baulogistik Osterreich GmbH (1)
Industriestrasse 31, 2325, Himberg, Austria
Tel.: (43) 22358825213
Logistics Consulting Servies
N.A.I.C.S.: 541614

Zeppelin Systems China (Shanghai) Co. Ltd. (1)
Room 1005 Chunshengjiang Mansion No 398 Middle Zhejiang Road, Shanghai, 200001, China
Tel.: (86) 2163518035
Web Site: http://www.zeppelin.com
Polymer Product Mfr
N.A.I.C.S.: 325212

Zeppelin Systems GmbH (1)
Graf-Zeppelin-Platz 1, 88045, Friedrichshafen, Germany
Tel.: (49) 7541 202 02
Web Site: http://www.zeppelin.com
Emp.: 1,300
Engineeering Services
N.A.I.C.S.: 541330
Rochus C. Hofmann *(Member-Mgmt Bd)*

Subsidiary (Non-US):

Zeppelin Systems Benelux N. V. (2)
Munsterenstraat 9, 3600, Genk, Belgium
Tel.: (32) 89629400
Plant & Equipment Rental Services
N.A.I.C.S.: 238910

Zeppelin Systems China (Beijing) Co. Ltd. (2)
Rm906 Golden Land Building No 32 Liangmaqiao Road, Beijing, 100016, China
Tel.: (86) 10 6432 4859
Polymer Compound Mfr
N.A.I.C.S.: 325991
Rochus C. Hofmann *(Mng Dir)*

Zeppelin Systems France SARL (2)
33 Av du Dr Georges Levy Bat 59 Parc Club du Moulina Vent, 69693, Venissieux, Cedex, France
Tel.: (33) 472893838
Web Site: http://www.zeppelin-systems.com
Emp.: 20
Plant Engineering Services
N.A.I.C.S.: 541330

Zeppelin Systems Gulf Co. Ltd. (2)
Dammam-Jubail Highway, PO Box 1495, Jubail, Saudi Arabia
Tel.: (966) 366126260
Plant Engineering Services
N.A.I.C.S.: 541330
Wolfgang Horn *(Mng Dir)*

Zeppelin Systems India Pvt. Ltd. (2)
Level 4 ADM Building Alembic Campus Alembic Road, Vadodara, 390003, India
Tel.: (91) 2652291710
Web Site: http://www.zeppelin-india.com
Plant Engineering Services
N.A.I.C.S.: 541330
Kerstin Kleemann *(Mng Dir)*

Zeppelin Systems Korea Corp. (2)
801 Dongbu Root Building 16-2 Sunaedong, Bundang-gu, Seongnam, 463-825, Gyeonggi-do, Korea (South)
Tel.: (82) 3171995312
Plant Engineering Services

ZEPPELIN GMBH

Zeppelin GmbH—(Continued)
N.A.I.C.S.: 541330

Zeppelin Systems Singapore Pte Ltd. (2)
31 Harrison Road 04-01 Food Empire Building, Singapore, 369649, Singapore
Tel.: (65) 68765676
Web Site: http://www.zeppelin.sg
Metal Building & Component Mfr
N.A.I.C.S.: 332311
Gu Xiao Fei *(Mng Dir)*

Zeppelin Systems UK Limited (2)
Little Oak Drive Sherwood Business Park, Annesley, Nottingham, NG15 0EB, United Kingdom
Tel.: (44) 1623753291
Web Site: http://www.zeppelin-uk.com
Plant Engineering Services
N.A.I.C.S.: 236220
Steve Castledine *(Mgr-Svc & Commissioning)*

Zeppelin Systems Italy Srl (1)
Via Rombon 11, 20134, Milan, Italy
Tel.: (39) 0292106905
Web Site: http://www.zeppelin-zi.com
Construction & Mining Equipment Distr
N.A.I.C.S.: 423810
Marco Orlandi *(Project Mgr)*

Zeppelin Systems Ltd. (1)
PO Box 591, Cleveland, 4163, QLD, Australia
Tel.: (61) 732869970
Metal Building & Component Mfr
N.A.I.C.S.: 332311

Zeppelin Systems USA Inc. (1)
11050 W Little York Rd Bldg D, Houston, TX 77041
Tel.: (713) 849-5666
Plant Engineering Services
N.A.I.C.S.: 236220
Rochus C. Hofmann *(Mng Dir)*

Subsidiary (Non-US):

Zeppelin Systems Latin America Equipamentos Industriais Ltda. (2)
Rua Joao XXIII 650 Bairro Cooperativa, Sao Bernardo do Campo, 09851-707, SP, Brazil
Tel.: (55) 1143939400
Web Site: http://www.zeppelin-la.com.br
Metal Building & Component Mfr
N.A.I.C.S.: 332311

Subsidiary (Domestic):

Zeppelin Systems USA, Inc. (2)
13330 Byrd Dr, Odessa, FL 33556
Tel.: (813) 920-7434
Web Site: http://www.zeppelin-systems.com
Sales Range: $10-24.9 Million
Emp.: 55
Packaging Machinery & Equipment
N.A.I.C.S.: 423830
Robert Anderson *(CEO, Mng Dir, Member-Mgmt Bd & Gen Mgr)*

Zeppelin-Koros Spedit Kft. (1)
Ezred u 18, 1044, Budapest, Hungary
Tel.: (36) 16881939
Web Site: http://www.zks.hu
Construction & Mining Equipment Distr
N.A.I.C.S.: 423810

ZERA GMBH

Hauptstrasse 392, 53639, Konigswinter, Germany
Tel.: (49) 22237040
Web Site: http://www.zera.de
Year Founded: 1920
Sales Range: $10-24.9 Million
Emp.: 83
Test Equipment Mfr
N.A.I.C.S.: 334515
Prosper Suwelack *(Co-Mng Dir)*

Subsidiaries:

ZERA India Pvt Ltd (1)
A-47 Sector 25 GIDC Electronic Estate, Gandhinagar, 382024, Gujarat, India
Tel.: (91) 7923287750
Electrical Testing Equipment Distr
N.A.I.C.S.: 423830
Kartikeya Sharma *(Mgr-Technical)*

ZERIA PHARMACEUTICAL CO., LTD.

10-11 Nihonbashi Kobuna-cho, Chuo-ku, Tokyo, 103-8351, Japan
Tel.: (81) 336632351
Web Site: https://www.zeria.co.jp
Year Founded: 1955
4559—(TKS)
Rev.: $661,949,637
Assets: $1,307,134,308
Liabilities: $671,345,036
Net Worth: $635,789,273
Earnings: $59,975,973
Emp.: 1,737
Fiscal Year-end: 03/31/24
Pharmaceutical Product Mfr & Whslr
N.A.I.C.S.: 325412
Sachiaki Ibe *(Chm & CEO)*

Subsidiaries:

IONA INTERNATIONAL CORPORATION (1)
9-17 Nihonbashi Kobuna-cho, Chuo, 1030024, Tokyo, Japan
Tel.: (81) 3 3661 3915
Web Site: http://www.iona-intl.com
Emp.: 25
Pharmaceutical Products Distr
N.A.I.C.S.: 424210
Ayako Asami *(Mgr)*

Tillotts Pharma AG (1)
Baslerstrasse 15, 4310, Rheinfelden, Switzerland
Tel.: (41) 619352626
Emp.: 300
Pharmaceutical Products Distr
N.A.I.C.S.: 424210
Thomas A. Toth von Kisker *(CEO)*

Subsidiary (Non-US):

Tillotts Pharma AB (2)
Gustavslundsvagen 135, 167 51, Bromma, Sweden
Tel.: (46) 87047740
Pharmaceutical Products Distr
N.A.I.C.S.: 424210
Jan Deresiewicz *(Mng Dir)*

Tillotts Pharma Czech s.r.o. (2)
Budejovicka 1550/15a, 140 00, Prague, 4, Czech Republic
Tel.: (420) 222531021
Web Site: https://tillotts.cz
Pharmaceutical Products Distr
N.A.I.C.S.: 424210

Tillotts Pharma GmbH (2)
Warmbacher Strasse 80, 79618, Rheinfelden, Germany
Tel.: (49) 30991948300
Pharmaceutical Products Distr
N.A.I.C.S.: 424210

Tillotts Pharma Ltd (2)
25 Sandyford Office Park, Dublin, Ireland
Tel.: (353) 12942015
Pharmaceutical Products Distr
N.A.I.C.S.: 424210

Tillotts Pharma Spain S.L.U. (2)
Gran Via de les Corts Catalanes 680 1 1, 08010, Barcelona, Spain
Tel.: (34) 931785949
Pharmaceutical Products Distr
N.A.I.C.S.: 424210

Tillotts Pharma UK Ltd (2)
The Larboune Suite 8 The Stables Wellingore Hall, Wellingore, Lincoln, LN5 0HX, Lincolnshire, United Kingdom
Tel.: (44) 1522813500
Web Site: https://www.tillotts.co.uk
Pharmaceutical Products Distr
N.A.I.C.S.: 424210

ZERIA USA, Inc. (1)
777 Westchester Ave Ste 101, White Plains, NY 10604
Tel.: (212) 557-2535
Web Site: http://www.zeriausa.com
Pharmaceutical Products Distr
N.A.I.C.S.: 424210

Elio Loo *(Pres)*

ZPD A/S (1)
H E Bluhmes Vej 63, 6700, Esbjerg, Denmark
Tel.: (45) 76106868
Web Site: https://zpd.dk
Pharmaceuticals Product Mfr
N.A.I.C.S.: 325412

Zeria Ecotech Co., Ltd. (1)
2-15-1 Konanchuo, Kumagaya, 360-0114, Saitama, Japan
Tel.: (81) 485393007
Pharmaceutical Products Distr
N.A.I.C.S.: 424210

Zeria Healthway Co., Ltd. (1)
10-6 Nihonbashi Kobuna-cho, Chuo-ku, Tokyo, 103-0024, Japan
Tel.: (81) 336637921
Pharmaceutical Products Distr
N.A.I.C.S.: 424210

Zeria Pharmaceutical Co., Ltd. - Saitama Plant (1)
1212 Aza Kappayama, Narisawa, Kumagaya, 360-0115, Saitama, Japan
Tel.: (81) 485364041
Pharmaceuticals Product Mfr
N.A.I.C.S.: 325412

Zeria Pharmaceutical Co., Ltd. - Tsukuba Plant (1)
2200-5 Katsura-cho, Ushiku, 300-1281, Ibaraki, Japan
Tel.: (81) 298750880
Pharmaceuticals Product Mfr
N.A.I.C.S.: 325412

Zeria Shoji Co., Ltd. (1)
9-7 Kobunecho, Nihonbashi Chuo-ku, Tokyo, 103-0024, Japan
Tel.: (81) 336693901
Web Site: https://www.zeriashoji.com
Pharmaceutical Products Distr
N.A.I.C.S.: 424210

Zeriap Co., Ltd. (1)
9-7 Nihonbashi Kobuna-cho, Chuo-ku, Tokyo, 103-0024, Japan
Tel.: (81) 336637833
Pharmaceutical Products Distr
N.A.I.C.S.: 424210

Zevice Co., Ltd. (1)
9-7 Nihonbashi Kobuna-cho, Chuo-ku, Tokyo, 103-0024, Japan
Tel.: (81) 336637924
Pharmaceutical Products Distr
N.A.I.C.S.: 424210

ZERNA INGENIEURE GMBH

Lise-Meitner-Allee 11, 44801, Bochum, Germany
Tel.: (49) 23492040
Web Site: http://www.zerna.eu
Rev.: $17,932,200
Emp.: 125
Engineeering Services
N.A.I.C.S.: 541330
Zerna Ingenieure *(Founder)*

ZERNIKE GROUP HOLDING B.V.

Paterswoldseweg 802, 9728 BM, Groningen, Netherlands
Tel.: (31) 50 3050 600   NI
Web Site: http://www.zernikegroup.com
Year Founded: 1992
Holding Company; Technology Transfer, Facility Management, Licensing, Engineering & Consultancy Services
N.A.I.C.S.: 551112
Lex de Lange *(Founder & CEO)*

ZERO CO., LTD.

Solid Square West Tower 6th floor 580 Horikawa-cho, Saiwai-ku, Kawasaki, 212-0013, Japan
Tel.: (81) 455200106
Web Site: https://www.zero-group.co.jp
Year Founded: 1961

INTERNATIONAL PUBLIC

9028—(TKS)
Rev.: $875,471,220
Assets: $439,959,260
Liabilities: $204,389,200
Net Worth: $235,570,060
Earnings: $25,813,000
Emp.: 2,585
Fiscal Year-end: 06/30/24
Vehicles Transportation Services
N.A.I.C.S.: 484230
Takeo Kitamura *(Pres & CEO)*

Subsidiaries:

Kyuso Company, Ltd. (1)
1-7-14 Shinmoji, Moji-ku Kitakyushu, Fukuoka, 800-0115, Japan
Tel.: (81) 926223232
Emp.: 122
Cargo Transportation Services
N.A.I.C.S.: 488320

World Windows Co., Ltd. (1)
2F Nanba Arena Bld 1-13-8 Nanba Naka, Naniwa-Ku, Osaka, 556-0011, Japan
Tel.: (81) 666307684
Web Site: http://www.worldwindows.co.jp
Emp.: 8
Used Car Distr
N.A.I.C.S.: 423110
Keiichi Anekawa *(Pres)*

Zero SCM Logistics (Beijing) Co., Ltd. (1)
Room 1002 Block C Ruipu Building No 15 Hongjunying South Road, Chaoyang District, Beijing, 100012, China
Tel.: (86) 106 482 8300
Web Site: https://www.zeroscm.com
Vehicles Transportation Services
N.A.I.C.S.: 488490

ZERO COMMISSION NZ LTD.

PO Box 93020, Auckland, 0640, New Zealand
Tel.: (64) 9 8270198
Web Site: http://www.zeronz.co.nz
Securities Brokerage Services
N.A.I.C.S.: 523150
Roy Jackson *(Mng Dir)*

ZERO ONE TECHNOLOGY CO., LTD.

10th Floor No 8 Lane 360 Section 1 Neihu Road, Taipei, 114, Taiwan
Tel.: (886) 26565656
Web Site: https://www.zerone.com.tw
Year Founded: 1980
3029—(TAI)
Rev.: $455,235,831
Assets: $260,939,720
Liabilities: $120,758,653
Net Worth: $140,181,067
Earnings: $22,922,331
Emp.: 100
Fiscal Year-end: 12/31/23
Network Equipment Distr
N.A.I.C.S.: 423430

ZERO TO SEVEN INC.

YTN Newsquare 18F 76 Sangamsan-ro, Mapo-gu, Seoul, 03926, Korea (South)
Tel.: (82) 27403188
Web Site: https://www.zerotoseven.co.kr
Year Founded: 2000
159580—(KRS)
Rev.: $69,330,243
Assets: $76,232,108
Liabilities: $15,210,845
Net Worth: $61,021,263
Earnings: $3,165,509
Emp.: 123
Fiscal Year-end: 12/31/22
Infants' Clothing, Bottles, Skin Care Products & Detergents Mfr & Distr
N.A.I.C.S.: 315250
Park Yeong-Wook *(CEO)*

AND PRIVATE COMPANIES — ZETLAND FINANCIAL GROUP LIMITED

Subsidiaries:

Maeil Co., Ltd. (1)
The Twin Towers K 50 Jong-ro 1-gil, Jongno-gu, Seoul, Korea (South)
Tel.: (82) 15881539
Web Site: https://www.maeil.com
Dairy Product Mfr & Distr
N.A.I.C.S.: 311514

ZERO2IPO HOLDINGS, INC.
Floor 18 Tower D1 No 19 East Dongfang Road, Liangmaqiao Diplomatic Office Building Chaoyang, Beijing, 100600, China
Tel.: (86) 1084535220 Ky
Web Site: http://www.zero2ipo.com.cn
Year Founded: 2001
1945—(HKG)
Holding Company
N.A.I.C.S.: 551112
Gavin Ni *(Founder & Chm)*

ZERTUS GMBH
In Astraturm Zirkusweg 2, 20359, Hamburg, Germany
Tel.: (49) 40441940 De
Web Site: http://www.zertus.de
Year Founded: 1826
Holding Company; Confectionery & Specialty Food Mfr & Distr
N.A.I.C.S.: 551112
Jorn Riemer *(CEO)*

Subsidiaries:

Dextro Energy GmbH & Co. KG (1)
Hafenstr 77, PO Box 9239, 47809, Krefeld, Germany
Tel.: (49) 215152270
Web Site: http://www.dextro-energy.de
Packaged Food Distr
N.A.I.C.S.: 424420
Stefan Harms *(Deputy Mng Dir)*

Helmut Loser GmbH & Co. KG Waffelfabrik (1)
Am Zugmantel, An der B 417, 65232, Taunusstein, Germany
Tel.: (49) 6128 743 0
Web Site: http://www.waffel-loeser.de
Wafer Mfr
N.A.I.C.S.: 311821
Daniel Schenk *(CEO)*

Humdinger Limited (1)
Gothenburg Way Sutton Fields Indus Estate, Kingston upon Hull, HU7 0YG, East Yorkshire, United Kingdom
Tel.: (44) 1482625790
Web Site: http://www.humdinger-foods.co.uk
Grocery Product Whslr
N.A.I.C.S.: 445110
Jamie L'Estrange *(Mgr-Sls)*

Importhaus Wilms/Impuls GmbH & Co. KG (1)
Am Klingenweg 6A, Walluf, 65396, Germany
Tel.: (49) 6123 9990 0
Web Site: http://www.importhaus-wilms.de
Emp.: 200
Specialty & Snack Food Wholesale Trade Distr
N.A.I.C.S.: 425120
Laura Jess *(Chief Compliance Officer)*

Kalfany Susse Werbung GmbH & Co. KG (1)
Renkenrunsstrasse 14, Mullheim, 79379, Germany
Tel.: (49) 7631 3679 0
Web Site: http://www.kalfany-suesse-werbung.de
Emp.: 100
Confectionery Mfr & Distr
N.A.I.C.S.: 311340
Fritz Haasen *(Mng Dir)*

Kinnerton (Confectionery) Australia Pty Limited (1)
F24 16 Mars Road, Lane Cove West, Sydney, 2066, NSW, Australia
Tel.: (61) 2 9413 3149
Web Site: http://www.kinnerton.com.au
Emp.: 2
Chocolate & Confectionery Mfr
N.A.I.C.S.: 311351

Kinnerton (Confectionery) Company Limited (1)
53-79 Highgate Rd, 1000 Highgate Studios, London, NW5 1TL, United Kingdom
Tel.: (44) 2072849500
Web Site: http://www.kinnerton.com
Emp.: 75
Chocolate & Confectionery Mfr
N.A.I.C.S.: 311351

ZESPOL ELEKTROCIEPLOWNI WROCLAWSKICH KOGENERACJA S.A.
ul Lowiecka 24, 50-220, Wroclaw, Poland
Tel.: (48) 713238111
Web Site: https://kogeneracja.com.pl
KGN—(WAR)
Rev.: $803,957,061
Assets: $1,199,324,946
Liabilities: $656,367,376
Net Worth: $542,957,570
Earnings: $65,223,323
Fiscal Year-end: 12/31/23
Hydroelectric Power Generation
N.A.I.C.S.: 221111
Adam Lewandowski *(Chm-Supervisory Bd)*

Subsidiaries:

EC Zielona Gora S.A. (1)
ul Zjednoczenia 103, 65-120, Zielona Gora, Poland
Tel.: (48) 684290444
Web Site: https://www.ec.zgora.pl
Equipment Mfr
N.A.I.C.S.: 333248

ZESPOL ELEKTROWNI PATNOW-ADAMOW-KONIN S.A.
ul Kazimierska 45, 62 510, Konin, Poland
Tel.: (48) 632473000
Web Site: https://www.zepak.com.pl
Year Founded: 1958
ZEP—(WAR)
Rev.: $1,055,176,355
Assets: $1,140,394,664
Liabilities: $835,290,157
Net Worth: $305,104,507
Earnings: $54,107,421
Emp.: 3,259
Fiscal Year-end: 12/31/22
Electricity Generation & Distribution Services
N.A.I.C.S.: 221112
Wieslaw Walendziak *(Vice Chm-Supervisory Bd)*

Subsidiaries:

EL PAK Sp. z o.o. (1)
ul Przemyslowa 158, 62-510, Konin, Poland
Tel.: (48) 63 247 15 00
Web Site: http://www.elpak.com.pl
Industrial Equipment Installation & Maintenance Services
N.A.I.C.S.: 238220

PAK Gornictwo Sp. z o.o. (1)
600-lecia 9, 62-540, Kleczew, Poland
Tel.: (48) 632476430
Web Site: https://www.pakgornictwo.com.pl
Remodeling Services
N.A.I.C.S.: 236118

PAK Kopalnia Wegla Brunatnego Konin S.A. (1)
ul 600-lecia 9, 62-540, Kleczew, Poland
Tel.: (48) 632476000
Web Site: https://www.kwbkonin.pl
Coal Mining Services
N.A.I.C.S.: 212115
Adam Klapszta *(Chm-Mgmt Bd)*

PAK-Volt S.A. (1)
Stanow Zjednoczonych avenue 61A, 04-028, Warsaw, Poland
Tel.: (48) 225163122
Web Site: https://www.pakvolt.pl
Electric Power Distribution Services
N.A.I.C.S.: 221122

Przedsiebiorstwo Remontowe PAK Serwis Sp. z o.o. (1)
ul Przemyslowa 158, 62-510, Konin, Poland
Tel.: (48) 632471600
Web Site: https://www.pakserwis.com.pl
Construction & Repair Services
N.A.I.C.S.: 811310
Ryszard Mycek *(Pres)*

Zespol Elektrowni Patnow-Adamow-Konin S.A. - Adamow Power Plant (1)
ul Przemyslowa 1, 62-700, Turek, Poland
Tel.: (48) 63 278 90 00
Eletric Power Generation Services
N.A.I.C.S.: 221116

ZEST S.P.A.
Via Marsala 29H, 00185, Rome, Italy
Tel.: (39) 0645473124 IT
Web Site: https://zestgroup.vc
Year Founded: 1953
ZEST—(ITA)
Rev.: $4,847,863
Assets: $36,623,660
Liabilities: $9,330,939
Net Worth: $27,292,721
Earnings: ($889,246)
Emp.: 32
Fiscal Year-end: 12/31/20
Private Equity & Venture Capital
N.A.I.C.S.: 523999
Marco Gabriel Gay *(Exec Chm & Partner)*

Subsidiaries:

Digital Magics S.p.A. (1)
Via B Quaranta 40, 20139, Milan, Italy
Tel.: (39) 02525051
Web Site: https://www.digitalmagics.com
Rev.: $2,886,881
Assets: $24,016,584
Liabilities: $1,596,557
Net Worth: $22,420,026
Earnings: ($3,082,091)
Fiscal Year-end: 12/31/2020
Investment Services
N.A.I.C.S.: 523999
Marco Gabriel Gay *(Co-CEO)*

ZEST ST
8 The Oaks Lords Wood, Kent, ME5 8LF, United Kingdom
Tel.: (44) 1634 671167 UK
Year Founded: 1981
Rev.: $40,000,000
Emp.: 25
Advertising Agencies, Business-To-Business, Direct Marketing, Event Marketing, Full Service, Graphic Design, Interactive Agencies, Internet/Web Design, Logo & Package Design, Public Relations
N.A.I.C.S.: 541810
Terry Hewitt *(Mng Dir)*

ZETA BRIDGE CORPORATION
Higashi Gotanda 2-20-4 MY Building 8F, Shingawa-ku, Tokyo, 141-0022, Japan
Tel.: (81) 357919161 JP
Web Site: http://www.zeta-bridge.com
Year Founded: 2001
Rev.: $300,000,000
Medical Software Publisher
N.A.I.C.S.: 513210
Ando Takashi *(CEO)*

ZETA PETROLEUM PLC
Ashley Park House 42-50 Hersham Road, England, Walton-on-Thames, KT12 1RZ, Surrey, United Kingdom
Tel.: (44) 20 3755 5063 UK
Web Site: http://www.zetapetroleum.com
Year Founded: 2005
Assets: $283,315
Liabilities: $36,426
Net Worth: $246,889
Earnings: ($635,436)
Emp.: 2
Fiscal Year-end: 12/31/17
Oil & Gas Exploration
N.A.I.C.S.: 211120
Stephen P. West *(Founder)*

Subsidiaries:

Zeta Petroleum (Romania) SRL (1)
5th Floor 4-6 Ion Bogdan Street, Bucharest, 010539, Romania
Tel.: (40) 21 319 2550
Oil & Gas Exploration Services
N.A.I.C.S.: 213112

ZETADISPLAY AB
Hojdrodergatan 21, 212 39, Malmo, Sweden
Tel.: (46) 40286830
Web Site: http://www.zetadisplay.com
Year Founded: 2003
ZETA—(OMX)
Rev.: $51,841,861
Assets: $77,007,409
Liabilities: $50,482,452
Net Worth: $26,524,956
Earnings: ($643,832)
Emp.: 200
Fiscal Year-end: 12/31/22
Media Advertising Services
N.A.I.C.S.: 541840
Per Mandorf *(Pres & CEO)*

Subsidiaries:

ProntoTV AS (1)
Grev Wedels Plass 9, 0151, Oslo, Norway
Tel.: (47) 22545060
Web Site: http://www.prontotv.no
Television Broadcasting Services
N.A.I.C.S.: 516120

ZetaDisplay BV (1)
Saffierborch 24, 5241 LN, Rosmalen, Netherlands
Tel.: (31) 856207200
Television Broadcasting Services
N.A.I.C.S.: 516120

ZETLAND CAPITAL PARTNERS LLP
3 St Jamess Square, London, SW1Y 4JU, United Kingdom
Tel.: (44) 20 8059 8660
Web Site: http://www.zetlandcapital.com
Privater Equity Firm
N.A.I.C.S.: 523999
Ahmed Hamdani *(Chief Investment Officer & Mng Partners)*

Subsidiaries:

Typhoo Tea Ltd. (1)
Pasture Road, Moreton, Wirral, CH46 8XF, United Kingdom
Tel.: (44) 1515224000
Tea Mfr & Distr
N.A.I.C.S.: 311920
Des Kingsley *(CEO)*

ZETLAND FINANCIAL GROUP LIMITED
6th Fl ING Tower, Des Voeux Rd, Central, 308, China (Hong Kong)
Tel.: (852) 25257718
Web Site: http://www.zetland.biz
Emp.: 75
Offshore Banking Services
N.A.I.C.S.: 522299
James Campbell Sutherland *(Chm)*

Subsidiaries:

Zetland Coporate Services Japan Limited (1)

ZETLAND FINANCIAL GROUP LIMITED

Zetland Financial Group Limited—(Continued)
8F Roppongi Mikawadai Building 4-8-7
Roppongi, Minato-ku, Tokyo, 106-0032,
Japan
Tel.: (81) 3 6890 1353
Web Site: http://www.zetland.jp
Financial Banking Services
N.A.I.C.S.: 523150
Michiko Kawano (Gen Mgr)

Zetland Corporate Services Belize Limited (1)
No 21 Regent Street 2/Floor Office A, PO Box 2020, Belize, Belize
Tel.: (501) 227 1036
Web Site: http://www.zetland.biz
Financial Services
N.A.I.C.S.: 523999
Anju Gidwani (Mng Dir)

Zetland Corporate Services Limited (1)
8th Floor On Hing Building 1 On Hing Terrace, GPO Box 7862, Central, China (Hong Kong)
Tel.: (852) 3552 9085
Web Site: http://www.zetland.biz
Emp.: 30
Financial Banking Services
N.A.I.C.S.: 523150
Veronica Tam (Gen Counsel)

Zetland Corporate Services Pte Limited (1)
137 Market Street Ste 04-01, Singapore, 048943, Singapore
Tel.: (65) 6557 2071
Financial Banking Services
N.A.I.C.S.: 523150
Su Lee Chan (Mng Dir)

Zetland Fiduciaries (New Zealand) Limited (1)
68 Grand Drive Remuera, Auckland, 1050, New Zealand
Tel.: (64) 9 522 5214
Financial Banking Services
N.A.I.C.S.: 523150

Zetland Services (UK) Limited (1)
6 Porter Street, London, W1U 6DD, United Kingdom
Tel.: (44) 20 7229 3717
Financial Banking Services
N.A.I.C.S.: 523150

ZETRO AEROSPACE CORPORATION SDN. BHD.
Jalan KLIA 2A, Selangor Darul Ehsan, 43900, Sepang, Malaysia
Tel.: (60) 3 8783 5016 MY
Web Site: http://www.zetro.com.my
Year Founded: 1994
Avionic Repair & Maintenance Services
N.A.I.C.S.: 334511
Mohd Zamri Muda (Mng Dir)

ZETT CORPORATION
1-2-16 Karasugatsuji, Tennoji-ku, Osaka, 543-8601, Japan
Tel.: (81) 667791171
Web Site: https://www.zett.jp
Year Founded: 1950
8135—(TKS)
Rev.: $343,435,770
Assets: $195,252,790
Liabilities: $107,306,740
Net Worth: $87,946,050
Earnings: $5,354,100
Emp.: 584
Fiscal Year-end: 03/31/24
Sports Product Mfr & Distr
N.A.I.C.S.: 339920
Hiroyuki Watanabe (Pres)

ZETTASPHERE LIMITED
29 High Way, Poole, BH18 9NB, United Kingdom
Tel.: (44) 20 3384 9785
Web Site: http://www.zettasphere.com
Email Marketing Consulting Services
N.A.I.C.S.: 541613
Tim Watson (Founder)

ZEU TECHNOLOGIES, INC.
1000 Rue Sherbrooke Ouest Suite 2700, Montreal, H3A 3G4, QC, Canada
Tel.: (514) 996-6342
Web Site: https://www.zeuniverse.com
ZEUCF—(OTCIQ)
Assets: $186,682
Liabilities: $5,201,878
Net Worth: ($5,015,195)
Earnings: ($386,291)
Fiscal Year-end: 03/31/23
Software Development Services
N.A.I.C.S.: 541511
Francois Dumas (Pres & CEO)

ZEUS CO., LTD
132 Annyeongnam-ro, Hwaseong, Gyeonggi-do, Korea (South)
Tel.: (82) 313779500
Web Site: https://www.globalzeus.com
Year Founded: 1970
079370—(KRS)
Rev.: $390,415,190
Assets: $469,601,367
Liabilities: $255,483,054
Net Worth: $214,118,313
Earnings: $27,007,115
Emp.: 673
Fiscal Year-end: 12/31/22
Semiconductor Product Mfr
N.A.I.C.S.: 334413
Dong Ak Lee (Founder & Chm)

Subsidiaries:

Global Zeus Inc. (1)
3740 Industrial Blvd, Orangeburg, SC 29118
Tel.: (803) 268-9500
Web Site: https://www.zeusinc.com
Plastics Product Mfr
N.A.I.C.S.: 326199

J.E.T. Semi-Con. International Taiwan Inc. (1)
3F-2 No 30 Taiyuan St, Hsinchu County, Jhubei, 302, Taiwan
Tel.: (886) 3 552 5666
Semiconductor Devices Mfr
N.A.I.C.S.: 334413

Oribright Shanghai Co., Ltd. (1)
Room 2501B Bld A Baodi Plaza No 688 Dalian Road, Yangpu Dist, Shanghai, 200082, China
Tel.: (86) 2160452760
Semiconductor Devices Mfr
N.A.I.C.S.: 334413

ZEUS CO., Ltd - Ansan Plant 1 (1)
66 Haeaan-ro, Danwon-gu, Ansan, Gyeonggi-do, Korea (South)
Tel.: (82) 31 495 2655
Semiconductor Product Mfr
N.A.I.C.S.: 334413

ZEUS CO., Ltd - Yongin Plant (1)
339 Hanteo-ro Yangji-myeon, Cheoin-gu, Yongin, Gyeonggi-do, Korea (South)
Tel.: (82) 31 322 6900
Semiconductor Product Mfr
N.A.I.C.S.: 334413

ZEUS China Co., Ltd. (1)
A-2601 Victory Plaza No 103 Tiyuxi Road, Tianhe, Guangzhou, 510620, China
Tel.: (86) 2038254906
Plastics Product Mfr
N.A.I.C.S.: 326199

ZEUS GROUP LIMITED
82 King St, Manchester, M2 4WQ, United Kingdom
Tel.: (44) 1618311512
Web Site: https://zeuscapital.co.uk
Year Founded: 2015
Financial & Investment Services
N.A.I.C.S.: 523999

Subsidiaries:

Arden Partners PLC (1)
125 Old Broad Street, London, EC2N 1AR, United Kingdom
Tel.: (44) 1214238900
Web Site: http://www.arden-partners.co.uk
Rev.: $8,049,922
Assets: $9,642,527
Liabilities: $3,348,138
Net Worth: $6,294,390
Earnings: ($1,843,784)
Emp.: 39
Fiscal Year-end: 10/31/2020
Securities Brokerage Services
N.A.I.C.S.: 523150
James Reed-Daunter (Exec Dir)

ZEUS HOLDINGS INC.
21/F Lepanto Building 8747 Paseo de Roxas, Makati, Philippines
Tel.: (63) 28159447
Web Site: http://www.zeusholdingsinc.com
Year Founded: 1981
Holding Company
N.A.I.C.S.: 551112
Felipe U. Yap (Chm)

ZEUS PACKAGING GROUP LTD.
Unit 50 Grants Row Greenogue Business Park, Rathcoole, Dublin, Ireland
Tel.: (353) 14018900
Web Site: http://www.zeuspackaging.com
Year Founded: 1998
Packaging & Containers Supplier
N.A.I.C.S.: 561910
Keith Ockenden (CEO)

Subsidiaries:

PETRUZALEK Ges.m.b.H. (1)
Gewerbepark Mitterfeld 8, A-2523, Tattendorf, Austria
Tel.: (43) 225381282
Packaging Machinery Distr
N.A.I.C.S.: 423830
Nicholas Ballini (Gen Mgr)

Subsidiary (Non-US):

Petruzalek Com S.r.l. (2)
Str Industriilor Nr 10, 077040, Chiajna, Judet Ilfov, Romania
Tel.: (40) 21 224 69 00
Web Site: http://www.petruzalek.com
Packaging Machinery Supplier
N.A.I.C.S.: 423830

Subsidiary (Non-US):

ICS Petruzalek Srl (3)
Str Padurii Nr 36, 2002, Chisinau, Moldova
Tel.: (373) 22 639 666
Packaging Machinery Distr
N.A.I.C.S.: 423830

Subsidiary (Non-US):

Petruzalek Kft (2)
Sorhaz Utca 3/b, 1222, Budapest, Hungary
Tel.: (36) 1 424 0540
Web Site: http://www.petruzalek.hu
Sales Range: $25-49.9 Million
Emp.: 5
Packaging Material Distr
N.A.I.C.S.: 423840
Peter Syrovatka (Gen Mgr)

Petruzalek S.r.o. (2)
Bratislavska 3228/50, 690 00, Breclav, Czech Republic
Tel.: (420) 519365111
Sales Range: $25-49.9 Million
Emp.: 2
Packaging Machinery Distr
N.A.I.C.S.: 423830

Petruzalek d.o.o. (2)
Trzaska Cesta 43, 2000, Maribor, Slovenia
Tel.: (386) 2 330 13 40

INTERNATIONAL PUBLIC

Sales Range: $50-74.9 Million
Emp.: 9
Packaging Machinery Whslr
N.A.I.C.S.: 423830
Juirij Krivce (Gen Mgr)

Petruzalek d.o.o. (2)
Gubasevo bb Industrijska Zona Jug, 49210, Zabok, Croatia
Tel.: (385) 49588040
Emp.: 16
Packaging Machinery Supplier
N.A.I.C.S.: 423830
Pascal Buzon (Gen Mgr)

Petruzalek e.o.o.d. (2)
46 st No 3 Traddeena, 2180, Etropole, Sofia, Bulgaria
Tel.: (359) 28412811
Web Site: http://www.petruzalek.com
Emp.: 1
Packaging Machinery Whslr
N.A.I.C.S.: 423830

Petruzalek o.o.o. (2)
Ul Lanzeronovskaja 9 16, 65026, Odessa, Ukraine
Tel.: (380) 48 786 01 00
Web Site: http://www.petruzalek.com.ua
Emp.: 55
Packaging Machinery Distr
N.A.I.C.S.: 423830

ZEUS RESOURCES LIMITED
Level 1 9 Bowman St, South Perth, 6151, WA, Australia
Tel.: (61) 412593363
Web Site: https://www.zeusresources.com
Year Founded: 2009
Rev.: $25,578
Assets: $1,607,334
Liabilities: $45,233
Net Worth: $1,562,101
Earnings: ($182,897)
Emp.: 4
Fiscal Year-end: 06/30/19
Uranium & Other Metal Ore Mining
N.A.I.C.S.: 212290
Jiangang Zhao (CEO-Acting)

ZF FRIEDRICHSHAFEN AG
Lowentaler Strasse 20, 88046, Friedrichshafen, Germany
Tel.: (49) 7541770 De
Web Site: http://www.zf.com
Year Founded: 1915
Rev.: $40,895,047,480
Assets: $36,227,471,000
Liabilities: $28,269,745,840
Net Worth: $7,957,725,160
Earnings: $447,944,000
Emp.: 147,797
Fiscal Year-end: 12/31/19
Automotive Gear Boxes & Steering Mechanisms, Chassis & Axle Systems Mfr
N.A.I.C.S.: 336330
Franz-Josef Paefgen (Chm-Supervisory Bd)

Subsidiaries:

2 Getthere B.V. (1)
Proostwetering 24J, 3543 AE, Utrecht, Netherlands
Tel.: (31) 302383570
Web Site: http://www.2getthere.eu
Automated Vehicle Transit System Mfr
N.A.I.C.S.: 336350
Carel Van Helsdingen (Founder & CEO)

Alfaro Brakes S.L.U. (1)
Alfaro Office Calle Azagra N 2, Poligono Industrial del Pilar, 26540, Alfaro, Spain
Tel.: (34) 941184596
Automotive Components Mfr
N.A.I.C.S.: 336390

Beespeed Technical Engineering Center S.R.L. (1)
Timisoara Office Boulevardul Republicii 9 1-4 Floor, 300159, Timisoara, Romania
Tel.: (40) 372564100
Automotive Components Mfr

AND PRIVATE COMPANIES — ZF FRIEDRICHSHAFEN AG

N.A.I.C.S.: 336390
Sever Scridon *(Mng Dir)*

Brake Force One GmbH (1)
Bismarckstrasse 134, 72072, Tubingen, Germany
Tel.: (49) 70715391110
Web Site: http://www.brakeforceone.de
Automotive Two Wheeler Part Mfr
N.A.I.C.S.: 336390

Dalphi Metal Espana, S.A. (1)
Vigo Plant Camino del Caramuxo 35, 36213, Vigo, Spain
Tel.: (34) 986293129
Automotive Parts & Accessory Mfr
N.A.I.C.S.: 336330

FTU Beteiligungsverwaltung GmbH (1)
Emmastrasse 220, 28213, Bremen, Germany
Tel.: (49) 421 2238520
Automobile Parts Mfr
N.A.I.C.S.: 336390

Subsidiary (Domestic):

Lemforder Electronic GmbH (2)
Von dem Bussche-Munch-Str 12, 32339, Espelkamp, Germany
Tel.: (49) 5772 567 2000
Web Site: http://www.lemfoerder-electronic.com
Emp.: 350
Automobile Parts Mfr
N.A.I.C.S.: 336390

GAT - Gesellschaft fur Antriebstechnik mbH (1)
Industriestrasse 11, 65366, Geisenheim, Germany
Tel.: (49) 6722937880
Web Site: http://www.gat-mbh.de
Emp.: 200
Electrical Products Mfr
N.A.I.C.S.: 335999

GAT Transmission Technology (Beijing) Co. Ltd. (1)
Room 211 Building B No 6 Futong East Street, Chaoyang, Beijing, 100102, China
Tel.: (86) 1084783655
Electrical Products Mfr
N.A.I.C.S.: 335999

LucasVarity Langzhong Brake Company Limited (1)
Langfang Plant 16 Xiangyun Road, Langfang Economic and Technical Development Zone, Langfang, 065001, China
Tel.: (86) 3166070526
Automotive Components Mfr
N.A.I.C.S.: 336390
Xin Liu *(Controller-Fin & Mgr)*

Midwest Lemforder Ltd. (1)
Heath Road, Darlaston, Wednesbury, WS10 8XL, United Kingdom
Tel.: (44) 12 1526 4441
Automobile Parts Distr
N.A.I.C.S.: 423120

Subsidiary (Domestic):

ZF Lemforder UK Ltd. (2)
Birmingham International Park Starley Way, Solihull, B37 7GN, West Midlands, United Kingdom
Tel.: (44) 121 526 4441
Automobile Parts Distr
N.A.I.C.S.: 423120
Philip Mauldridge *(Dir-Financial & Sec)*

OOO ZF Kama (1)
Avtozavodskiy Prospect 2, 423827, Naberezhnye Chelny, Russia
Tel.: (7) 8552 372136
Automobile Parts Distr
N.A.I.C.S.: 423120

OOO ZF Russia (1)
Bereshkovskaya Nab 16a Building 1, 121059, Moscow, Russia
Tel.: (7) 495 66236 35
Automobile Parts Distr
N.A.I.C.S.: 423120

Openmatics s.r.o. (1)
Podebradova 2842/1, 30100, Plzen, Czech Republic
Tel.: (420) 371150000
Software Development Services
N.A.I.C.S.: 541511
Thomas Rosch *(Mng Dir)*

PT. ZFAG Aftermarket Jakarta (1)
Warehouse Bogor Jl Raya Sirkuit Sentul 75 Derkei Warehouse, Bogor, 16810, Indonesia
Tel.: (62) 25187953954
Automotive Components Mfr
N.A.I.C.S.: 336390
Rizqi Zulqornain *(Mgr-Auto OE & Svc)*

Qingdao FMG Asia Pacific Co., Ltd. (1)
Qingdao Production 1 Jinye Road, Hi-Tech Industrial Development Zone, Qingdao, 266108, China
Tel.: (86) 53258895757
Automotive Components Mfr
N.A.I.C.S.: 336390

Sistemas De Chassis Iracemapolis Ltda. (1)
Iracemapolis Plant Rodovia Luis Ometo SP-306 km 44 Predio 140 Ala, Noroeste Bloco 1 Distrito Industrial, Iracemapolis, 13495-000, Brazil
Tel.: (55) 1540097166
Automotive Components Mfr
N.A.I.C.S.: 336390

TRW (Suzhou) Automotive Electronics Co., Ltd. (1)
Suzhou Plant 43 Suxu Road, Suzhou, 215008, China
Tel.: (86) 51266152510
Automotive Components Mfr
N.A.I.C.S.: 336390

TRW B.V. (1)
Amsterdam Office Kingsfordweg 151, 1043 GR, Amsterdam, Netherlands
Tel.: (31) 204919528
Automotive Components Mfr
N.A.I.C.S.: 336390

WABCO Holdings Inc. (1)
1220 Pacific Dr, Auburn Hills, MI 48326
Tel.: (248) 260-9032
Web Site: http://www.wabco-auto.com
Sales Range: $1-4.9 Billion
Emp.: 12,000
Holding Company; Braking, Stability, Suspension & Transmission Control Systems Mfr
N.A.I.C.S.: 551112
Nick Rens *(Pres-EMEA)*

Subsidiary (Non-US):

AssetTrackr Private Ltd. (2)
421 2nd Floor 27th Main HSR Layout Sector 1, Bengaluru, 560102, India
Tel.: (91) 9845070108
Web Site: http://www.assettrackr.com
Software Application Development Services
N.A.I.C.S.: 541511
Magesh Srinivasan *(VP-Fleet Mgmt Solutions)*

Laydon Composites Ltd. (2)
2109 Wyecroft Rd, Oakville, L6L 5L7, ON, Canada
Tel.: (905) 829-9200
Automobile Parts Distr
N.A.I.C.S.: 423120
Andy Acott *(Mgr-Sls-Natl)*

Partslife GmbH (2)
Martin-Behaim-Strasse 2, 63263, Neu-Isenburg, Germany
Tel.: (49) 6102812920
Web Site: http://www.partslife.com
Industrial Waste Collection & Recycling Services
N.A.I.C.S.: 562111
Alexander Granzin *(Project Mgr)*

WABCO Europe BVBA (2)
Chaussee de la Hulpe 166, 1170, Brussels, Belgium
Tel.: (32) 26639800
Web Site: http://www.wabco-auto.com
Sales Range: $50-74.9 Million
Mfr of Electronic Braking, Stability, Suspension & Transmission Control Systems for Commercial Vehicles
N.A.I.C.S.: 336340

Subsidiary (US):

MICO, Incorporated (3)
1911 Lee Blvd, North Mankato, MN 56003-2507
Tel.: (507) 625-6426
Web Site: http://www.mico.com
Emp.: 260
Hydraulic Brake Systems & Components Mfr
N.A.I.C.S.: 336340

Subsidiary (Non-US):

Australian Brake Controls (4)
103 Long Street, Smithfield, 2164, NSW, Australia
Tel.: (61) 296043388
Web Site: http://www.ausbrake.com.au
Motor Vehicle Parts Mfr
N.A.I.C.S.: 336340

Off Highway Brakes and Controls Ltd (4)
15 Goodwood Road, Pershore Worcestershire, Worcester, WR10 2RY, Worcs, United Kingdom (100%)
Tel.: (44) 01386555562
Web Site: http://www.ohbc-ltd.com
Motor Vehicle Parts Mfr
N.A.I.C.S.: 336340

Trans-Auto AB (4)
Forrandsvagen 6, Box 215, 151 48, Sodertalje, Sweden
Tel.: (46) 855424000
Web Site: http://www.transauto.se
Motor Vehicle Parts Mfr
N.A.I.C.S.: 336340
Soren Lovgren *(Head-Aftermarket & Supvr-After Market)*

Subsidiary (Domestic):

Transics International NV (3)
Ieper Business Park Zone K Ter Waarde 91, 8900, Ieper, Belgium (100%)
Tel.: (32) 80054208
Web Site: http://www.transics.com
Sales Range: $75-99.9 Million
Emp.: 320
Transport & Fleet Management Software Development Services
N.A.I.C.S.: 541511
Peter Bal *(VP-Digital Customer Svc Bus Unit)*

Subsidiary (Domestic):

Transics Belux BVBA (4)
Ieper Business Park Zone K Ter Waarde 91, 8900, Ieper, Belgium
Tel.: (32) 57346171
Fleet Management Software Development Services
N.A.I.C.S.: 541511

Transics Belux NV (4)
Ter Waarde 91, 8900, Ieper, Belgium
Tel.: (32) 57346171
Sales Range: $25-49.9 Million
Emp.: 150
Information Technology Consulting Services
N.A.I.C.S.: 541511
Walter Mastelinck *(Gen Mgr)*

Subsidiary (Non-US):

Transics Deutschland GmbH (4)
Kaiser-Wilhelm-Ring 27-29, 50672, Cologne, Germany
Tel.: (49) 2212005308
Sales Range: $25-49.9 Million
Emp.: 5
Fleet Management Software Retailer
N.A.I.C.S.: 449210
Heiko Janssen *(Gen Mgr)*

Transics France SARL (4)
3087 Rue de la Gare, 59299, Boeschepe, France
Tel.: (33) 805111478
Fleet Management Software Development Services
N.A.I.C.S.: 541511

Transics Ireland Limited (4)
132 Lower Baggot Street, Dublin, D02 AE12, Ireland
Tel.: (353) 16629403
Fleet Management Software Development Services
N.A.I.C.S.: 541511

Transics Italia S.R.L (4)
Via Senigallia 18/2 Torre A, 20161, Milan, Italy
Tel.: (39) 0236046644
Fleet Management Software Development Services
N.A.I.C.S.: 541511

Subsidiary (Domestic):

Transics NV (4)
Ieper Business Park Zone K Ter Waarde 91, 8900, Ieper, Belgium
Tel.: (32) 57346171
Web Site: http://www.transics.com
Emp.: 300
Fleet Management Software Development Services
N.A.I.C.S.: 541511

Subsidiary (Non-US):

Transics Nederland BV (4)
Rhijnspoor 263, 2901 LB, Capelle aan den IJssel, Netherlands
Tel.: (31) 183788306
Web Site: http://www.transics.com
Fleet Management Software Development Services
N.A.I.C.S.: 541511

Transics Telematica Espana S.L.U (4)
Av de Castilla 33 San Fernando de Henares, 28830, Madrid, Spain
Tel.: (34) 914148767
Fleet Management Software Development Services
N.A.I.C.S.: 541511

Subsidiary (Non-US):

WABCO (China) Co Ltd. (3)
No 917 Weihe Road Economic and Tech Dev Zone, Qingdao, 266510, China
Tel.: (86) 53286861000
Commercial Vehicle Electronic & Mechanical Products Mfr
N.A.I.C.S.: 336390

WABCO (Schweiz) AG (3)
Morgenstrasse 136, PO Box 29, 3018, Bern, Switzerland
Tel.: (41) 319974141
Web Site: http://www.wabco-auto.com
Sales Range: $10-24.9 Million
Emp.: 30
Automotive Products Mfr
N.A.I.C.S.: 336390

WABCO (Schweiz) GmbH (3)
Morgenstrasse 136, PO Box 810, 3018, Bern, Switzerland
Tel.: (41) 319974141
Automobile Parts Distr
N.A.I.C.S.: 423120

WABCO Arac Kontrol Sistemleri Destek ve Pazarlama Limited Sirketi (3)
K 5 N 2 Adivar H Edip Mh Citecevizler Creek Plaza Sisli Sok Akin, Istanbul, Turkiye
Tel.: (90) 2122843900
Power Transmission Equipment Mfr
N.A.I.C.S.: 333613

WABCO Australia Pty Ltd. (3)
Unit 3 8 Anzed Court, Mulgrave, 3170, VIC, Australia
Tel.: (61) 385417000
Sales Range: $10-24.9 Million
Emp.: 6
Transport Equipment Parts & Accessories Mfr
N.A.I.C.S.: 336390
Paul Lewin *(Gen Mgr)*

WABCO Austria GesmbH. (3)
Rappachgasse 42, 1110, Vienna, Austria
Tel.: (43) 1680700
Web Site: http://www.wabco-auto.com
Sales Range: $10-24.9 Million
Emp.: 20
Automobile Parts Mfr
N.A.I.C.S.: 336340

ZF FRIEDRICHSHAFEN AG

ZF Friedrichshafen AG—(Continued)

WABCO Automotive AB (3)
Olof Asklunds Gata 14, 412 30, Frolunda, Sweden
Tel.: (46) 31578800
Sales Range: $10-24.9 Million
Emp.: 30
Automobile Parts Mfr
N.A.I.C.S.: 336340

WABCO Automotive B.V. (3)
Rhijnspoor 263, Capelle aan den IJssel, 2901 LB, Rotterdam, Netherlands
Tel.: (31) 102888600
Automobile Parts Distr
N.A.I.C.S.: 423120

WABCO Automotive Italia S.r.l. (3)
Studio Tributario e Societario Galleria San Federico 54, 10121, Turin, Italy
Tel.: (39) 0114010411
Web Site: http://www.wabco-auto.com
Automotive Products Mfr
N.A.I.C.S.: 336340

WABCO Automotive South Africa (Pty) Ltd. (3)
10 Sunrock Close Sunnyrock Ext 2 Germison 1401, Edenvale, 1610, South Africa
Tel.: (27) 114502052
Motor Vehicle Parts Distr
N.A.I.C.S.: 423110

WABCO Automotive UK Ltd. (3)
Unit A1 Grange Valley Grange Valley Road, Batley, WF17 6GH, West Yorkshire, United Kingdom
Tel.: (44) 1924595400
Web Site: http://www.wabco-auto.com
Sales Range: $50-74.9 Million
Emp.: 50
Automotive Braking System Mfr
N.A.I.C.S.: 336340

Subsidiary (Domestic):

WABCO Belgium BVBA (3)
t Hofveld 6 B1-3, 1702, Groot-Bijgaarden, Belgium
Tel.: (32) 24810900
Web Site: http://www.wabco.com
Sales Range: $10-24.9 Million
Emp.: 7
Vehicle Control Systems
N.A.I.C.S.: 336340

Joint Venture (US):

WABCO Compressor Manufacturing Co. (3)
8225 Lincoln Patriot Blvd, North Charleston, SC 29418
Tel.: (843) 745-1158
Web Site: http://www.wabco-auto.com
Sales Range: $125-149.9 Million
Air Compressors
N.A.I.C.S.: 333912

Subsidiary (Non-US):

WABCO Espana, S.L.U. (3)
Av de Castilla 33, 28830, San Fernando de Henares, Madrid, Spain
Tel.: (34) 916751100
Web Site: http://www.wabco-auto.com
Sales Range: $25-49.9 Million
Emp.: 50
Automotive Products Mfr
N.A.I.C.S.: 336390

WABCO Fahrzeugsysteme GmbH (3)
Am Lindener Hafen 21, 30453, Hannover, Germany
Tel.: (49) 5119220
Web Site: http://www.wabco-auto.com
Pneumatic, Hydraulic & Electronic Braking Systems Mfr
N.A.I.C.S.: 336340

WABCO France SAS (3)
1 cours de la Gondoire, Jossigny, 77600, Seine-et-Marne, France
Tel.: (33) 160266206
Web Site: http://www.wabco-auto.com
Truck Braking Equipment Mfr
N.A.I.C.S.: 336340

WABCO Holding GmbH (3)
Am Lindener Hafen 21, 30453, Hannover, Germany
Tel.: (49) 5119220
Web Site: http://www.wabco-auto.com
Emp.: 600
Investment Management Service
N.A.I.C.S.: 551112

WABCO Japan Inc. (3)
Gate City Ohsaki W Tower 2F 1-11-1 Osaki, Shinagawa-ku, Tokyo, 141-0032, Japan
Tel.: (81) 354355711
Web Site: http://www.wabco-auto.com
Commercial Vehicle Control System Mfr
N.A.I.C.S.: 333613

WABCO Logistik GmbH (3)
Am Lindener Hafen 21, 30453, Hannover, Germany
Tel.: (49) 5119220
Web Site: http://www.wabco-auto.com
Sales Range: $10-24.9 Million
Emp.: 9
Motor Vehicle Brake System Mfr
N.A.I.C.S.: 336340

WABCO Polska Spolka z ograniczona odpowiedzialnoscia (3)
ul Ostrowskiego 34, 53-238, Wroclaw, Poland
Tel.: (48) 717821888
Web Site: http://www.wabco-auto.com
Sales Range: $300-349.9 Million
Emp.: 2,000
Transmission Control Systems Mfr
N.A.I.C.S.: 333613

WABCO Radbremsen GmbH (3)
Barlochweg 25, 68229, Mannheim, Germany
Tel.: (49) 62148310
Web Site: http://www.wabco-auto.com
Automotive Products Mfr
N.A.I.C.S.: 336390

WABCO Vertriebs GmbH & Co. KG (3)
Am Lindener Hafen 21, 30453, Hannover, Germany
Tel.: (49) 5119220
Motor Vehicle Parts Distr
N.A.I.C.S.: 423110

WABCO do Brasil Industria e Comercio de Freios Ltda (3)
Rodovia Anhanguera Km106, 13180-901, Sumare, Sao Paulo, Brazil
Tel.: (55) 1921174600
Transmission Control Systems Mfr
N.A.I.C.S.: 333613

WABCO-TVS (India) (3)
Plot No 3 SP III Main Road, Ambattur Industrial Estate, Chennai, 600 058, India
Tel.: (91) 4442242000
Web Site: http://www.wabco-auto.com
Sales Range: $550-599.9 Million
Emp.: 3,000
Conventional Braking Products Mfr
N.A.I.C.S.: 336340
P. Kaniappan (Mng Dir)

Subsidiary (Non-US):

WABCO Global GmbH (2)
Giacomettistrasse 1, 3006, Bern, Switzerland
Tel.: (41) 315813300
Automotive Vehicle Control System Distr
N.A.I.C.S.: 423690
Regina Bisset (Office Mgr)

WABCO GmbH (2)
Am Lindener Hafen 21, 30453, Hannover, Germany
Tel.: (49) 5119220
Automobile Parts Distr
N.A.I.C.S.: 423120

WABCO South Africa (PTY) Ltd. (2)
10 Sunrock Close Sunnyrock Ext 2 Germiston, Johannesburg, 1610, South Africa
Tel.: (27) 114502052
Emp.: 40
Automobile Parts Distr
N.A.I.C.S.: 423120
Karen Haviga (Controller-Shipping)

ZF Commercial Vehicle Control Systems India Limited (2)
Plot No 3 SP III Main Road Ambattur Indusrial Estate, Chennai, 600 058, India (75%)
Tel.: (91) 4442242000
Web Site: https://www.zf.com
Rev: $352,290,543
Assets: $359,906,411
Liabilities: $71,334,818
Net Worth: $288,571,592
Earnings: $19,393,156
Emp.: 1,960
Fiscal Year-end: 03/31/2022
Air Brake Mfr
N.A.I.C.S.: 336340
P. Kaniappan (Mng Dir)

ZF (China) Investment Co., Ltd. (1)
No 889 Jiujing Road, Jiuting Town Songjiang District, Shanghai, 201615, China
Tel.: (86) 21 37617000
Automobile Parts Distr
N.A.I.C.S.: 423120
Bin Zhang (Supvr-Network)

Subsidiary (Domestic):

Liuzhou ZF Machinery Co., Ltd. (2)
No 143 Heping Road, Liuzhou, 545007, Guangxi, China
Tel.: (86) 7723691519
Automobile Parts Distr
N.A.I.C.S.: 423120
Li Kelly (Mgr-Sourcing)

Sachs Automotive Components & Systems (Shanghai) Co., Ltd. (2)
4440 Yuanjiang Road, Minhang District, Shanghai, 201111, China
Tel.: (86) 21 2416 9544
Automobile Parts Distr
N.A.I.C.S.: 423120

Shanghai Sachs Huizhong Shock Absorber Co., Ltd. (2)
280 Shenwang Road Xinzhuang Industrial Zone, Shanghai, 201108, China
Tel.: (86) 21 5179 5188
Automobile Parts Distr
N.A.I.C.S.: 423120
April Ni (Engr-Supply Quality Mgmt)

ZF Beiben Drivetech (Chongqing) Co., Ltd. (2)
No 100 Qinye Road, Yubei District, Chongqing, 401120, China
Tel.: (86) 2388167858
Automobile Parts Distr
N.A.I.C.S.: 423120

ZF Chassistech Commercial Vehicles (Shanghai) Co., Ltd. (2)
No 1088 North Huancheng Road, Fengxian District, Shanghai, 201401, China
Tel.: (86) 21 6758 8600
Automobile Parts Distr
N.A.I.C.S.: 423120
Thomas Kan (Acct Mgr)

ZF Dongfeng Shock Absorber Shiyan Co., Ltd. (2)
No 49 Bailang East Road, Bailang Hi-Tech Development Zone, Shiyan, 442013, Hubei, China
Tel.: (86) 719 8257 006
Automobile Parts Distr
N.A.I.C.S.: 423120
Yao Feng (Mgr-HR)

ZF Drivetech (Hangzhou) Co., Ltd. (2)
18 Hi-Tech Ba Road Xiaoshan Economic & Technological Development Zone, Hangzhou, 311231, Zhejiang, China
Tel.: (86) 571 2289 2002
Automobile Parts Distr
N.A.I.C.S.: 423120
Wei Lou (Supvr-Admin)

ZF Drivetech (Suzhou) Co., Ltd. (2)
No 18 Baihe Street Suzhou Industrial Park, Suzhou, 215021, Jiangsu, China
Tel.: (86) 512 67166559
Automobile Parts Distr
N.A.I.C.S.: 423120
Yingdi Sha (Engr-Application)

ZF Electronics (Zhuhai) Co., Ltd. (2)
No 1 Lvyuan Road Nanping S&T Industrial Park Zhuhai Avenue E, Zhuhai, 519060, Guangdong, China

Tel.: (86) 7568910688
Automobile Parts Distr
N.A.I.C.S.: 423120

ZF FAWER Chassis Technology (Changchun) Co., Ltd. (2)
No 5000 East Nanhu Road, Changchun, 130033, China
Tel.: (86) 431 85800808
Automobile Parts Distr
N.A.I.C.S.: 423120
Zhongjie Ma (Gen Mgr)

ZF Lemforder Automotive Systems (Shenyang) Co., Ltd. (2)
No 8A-3 Kaifa Ave Shenyang Economic & Technological Development Zone, Shenyang, 110141, Liaoning, China
Tel.: (86) 24 2534 8116
Automobile Parts Distr
N.A.I.C.S.: 423120
Newton Wang (Sr Mgr-Logistics & Pur)

ZF Services (China) Co., Ltd. (2)
Building 1-A Kangsheng Industrial Park No 11 Kangding Street, Economic and Technological Development Zone, Beijing, 100176, China
Tel.: (86) 1067218855
Automobile Parts Distr
N.A.I.C.S.: 423120

ZF Transmissions Shanghai Co., Ltd. (2)
649 Huiwang Road, Jiading District, Shanghai, 201807, China
Tel.: (86) 21 6708 9888
Automobile Parts Distr
N.A.I.C.S.: 423120
Zhiwei Xu (Mgr-Pur & Logistics Dept)

ZF YTO (Luoyang) Axle Co., Ltd. (2)
16 Hangong Western Road, Luoyang, 471041, Henan, China
Tel.: (86) 37964961229
Automobile Parts Distr
N.A.I.C.S.: 423120

ZF Active Safety France SAS (1)
Bouzonville Plant 1 Avenue de la Gare, 57320, Bouzonville, France
Tel.: (33) 387782111
Automotive Components Mfr
N.A.I.C.S.: 336390

ZF Active Safety GmbH (1)
Carl-Spaeter-Strasse 8, 56070, Koblenz, Germany
Tel.: (49) 2618950
Automotive Components Mfr
N.A.I.C.S.: 336390

ZF Aftermarket Japan Co., Ltd. (1)
14-6 Nihonbashi-Kodenmacho, Chuo-ku, Tokyo, 103-0001, Japan
Tel.: (81) 356956191
Automotive Components Mfr
N.A.I.C.S.: 336390

ZF Aftermarket Malaysia Sdn. Bhd. (1)
Senai Industrial Estate PLO 17, 81400, Senai, Malaysia
Tel.: (60) 75968000
Automotive Components Mfr
N.A.I.C.S.: 336390

ZF Algerie S.a.r.l. (1)
Route nationale no 5, Postfach BP 143A, Rouiba, 16300, Algiers, Algeria
Tel.: (213) 21 323859130
Automobile Parts Distr
N.A.I.C.S.: 423120

ZF Argentina S.A. (1)
Av de la Universidad 51, 2400, San Justo, Cordoba, Argentina
Tel.: (54) 3564 438900
Automobile Parts Distr
N.A.I.C.S.: 423120

ZF Asia Pacific Group Co., Ltd. (1)
456 Hongcao Road Bldg No 9 6F, Xuhui District, Shanghai, 200233, China
Tel.: (86) 2161202266
Automotive Components Mfr
N.A.I.C.S.: 423120
Andy Chen (Treas)

ZF Asia Pacific Pte. Ltd. (1)

AND PRIVATE COMPANIES

ZF FRIEDRICHSHAFEN AG

11 Tuas Drive 1, Singapore, 638678, Singapore
Tel.: (65) 64248787
Web Site: http://www.zf.com
Emp.: 72
Driveline & Chassis Technology Services
N.A.I.C.S.: 333612
Markus Wittig (Pres)

Subsidiary (Non-US):

ZF Chassis Systems Sdn. Bhd. (2)
Lot 1453 Kawasan Perindustrian Padang Meha Mukim Padang, Padang Serai, 9400, Kedah, Malaysia
Tel.: (60) 4 4882100
Automobile Parts Distr
N.A.I.C.S.: 423120

ZF Faster Propulsion Systems Co., Ltd. (2)
17 Dayou 1st Street, Dafa Industrial District - Daliao District, Kaohsiung, Taiwan
Tel.: (886) 7 7871831
Automobile Parts Distr
N.A.I.C.S.: 423120

ZF Holdings Australia Pty. Ltd. (2)
uno 1 no 13 Bessemer street, Blacktown, 2148, NSW, Australia
Tel.: (61) 2 9679 5555
Web Site: http://www.zf.com
Emp.: 60
Automobile Parts Distr
N.A.I.C.S.: 423120
Chris Adcock (Gen Mgr)

Subsidiary (Domestic):

ZF Services Australia Pty. Ltd. (3)
2 Pavers Circle, Malaga, 6090, WA, Australia
Tel.: (61) 892481096
Automobile Parts Distr
N.A.I.C.S.: 423120

Subsidiary (Non-US):

ZF Japan Co., Ltd. (2)
Palazzo Astec 78F 2-8-1 Higashi-Shimbashi, Minato-ku, Tokyo, 105-0021, Japan
Tel.: (81) 3 4590 7700
Automobile Parts Distr
N.A.I.C.S.: 423120
Masashi Saito (Sr Mgr)

ZF Lemforder (Thailand) Co., Ltd. (2)
Eastern Seaboard Industrial Estate 300/84 Moo 1, Tasit Pluakdeang, 21140, Rayong, Thailand
Tel.: (66) 38 929200
Automobile Parts Distr
N.A.I.C.S.: 423120
Prasanna Shanker (Project Mgr)

ZF Philippines Inc. (2)
Km 23 Uding's Compound West Service Road Brgy Cupang, 1771, Muntinlupa, Philippines
Tel.: (63) 2 808 9740
Automobile Parts Distr
N.A.I.C.S.: 423120
Dhing Bondoc (Mgr-Sls)

ZF Sales & Service (Malaysia) Sdn. Bhd. (2)
No 2 & 3 Lorong Teknologi B Nouvelle Industrial Park, Kota Damansara, 47810, Petaling Jaya, Malaysia
Tel.: (60) 3 6140 6058
Automobile Parts Distr
N.A.I.C.S.: 423120

ZF Services Hong Kong Ltd. (2)
2/F Technology Plaza No 29-35 Sha Tsui Road, Tsuen Wan, New Territories, China (Hong Kong)
Tel.: (852) 2615 9353
Automobile Parts Distr
N.A.I.C.S.: 423120
Pauline Lau (Mgr-Fin)

ZF Thailand Ltd. (2)
159/33 Moo 3 Soi Vipavadee Rangsit 64 Vipavadee Rangsit Road, Talad Bangkhen Laksi, Bangkok, 10210, Thailand
Tel.: (66) 2 521 6520
Web Site: http://www.zf.com
Automobile Parts Distr

N.A.I.C.S.: 423120
Dysler Koh (Mng Dir)

ZF Automotive Canada Limited (1)
Woodstock Plant 155 Beard's Lane, Woodstock, N4S 7W3, ON, Canada
Tel.: (519) 537-2331
Automotive Components Mfr
N.A.I.C.S.: 336390

ZF Automotive Czech s.r.o. (1)
Jablonec Plant Na Roli 2405/26, 466 01, Jablonec nad Nisou, Czech Republic
Tel.: (420) 483354111
Automotive Components Mfr
N.A.I.C.S.: 336390

ZF Automotive Italia S.r.l (1)
Bricherasio Plant Strada Tirabrasse 6, Bricherasio, 10060, Turin, Italy
Tel.: (39) 0121348295
Automotive Components Mfr
N.A.I.C.S.: 336390

ZF Automotive Japan Co. Ltd. (1)
Kannai Office 209 Yamashita-cho Teisan Kannai Building, Naka-ku, Yokohama, 231-0023, Japan
Tel.: (81) 456706900
Automotive Components Mfr
N.A.I.C.S.: 336390

ZF Automotive Ltda. (1)
Limeira Plant Rodovia Anhanguera km 147, Limeira, 13486-915, Brazil
Tel.: (55) 1934041403
Automotive Components Mfr
N.A.I.C.S.: 336390

ZF Automotive Malaysia Sdn Bhd. (1)
Rawang Plant Jalan Jasmine 4 4 Kawasan Perindustrian Bukit Beruntung, Section BB10, 48300, Rawang, Malaysia
Tel.: (60) 360995999
Automotive Components Mfr
N.A.I.C.S.: 336390

ZF Automotive Technologies (Shanghai) Co., Ltd. (1)
TACS 188 Bai an Road, Anting Jiading District, Shanghai, 201814, China
Tel.: (86) 2159564100
Automotive Components Mfr
N.A.I.C.S.: 336390
Steven Guo (Engr-Customer Application)

ZF Automotive Technologies (Zhangjiagang) Co., Ltd. (1)
Shared Services Center 2 Wangxi Avenue, Zhangjiagang, 215600, China
Tel.: (86) 2137617815
Automotive Components Mfr
N.A.I.C.S.: 336390

ZF Axle Drives Marysville LLC (1)
2900 Busha Hwy, Marysville, MI 48040
Tel.: (810) 989-8700
Automobile Parts Distr
N.A.I.C.S.: 423120

ZF BAIC (Beijing) Chassis Systems Co., Ltd. (1)
No 1 Xinghai 1st Street Economic-Technological Development Area, Beijing, 100176, China
Tel.: (86) 1067518980
Automobile Parts Distr
N.A.I.C.S.: 423120
Uwe Wragge (Mgr-Ops)

ZF Boge Elastmetall GmbH (1)
Dr Juergen Ulderup Platz, 49401, Damme, Germany
Tel.: (49) 5474600
Web Site: http://www.zf.com
Sales Range: $650-699.9 Million
Emp.: 3,400
Rubber Metal Components for Vehicle Chassis & Powertrain Mfr
N.A.I.C.S.: 336211

Subsidiary (Domestic):

ZF Boge Elastmetall GmbH (2)
Friesdorfer Str 175, D 53175, Bonn, Germany (100%)
Tel.: (49) 22838250
Emp.: 350
N.A.I.C.S.: 334220

ZF Boutheon S.A. (1)
4 Bld Pierre Desgranges, 42166, Andrezieux-Boutheon, Cedex, France
Tel.: (33) 477363333
Automobile Parts Distr
N.A.I.C.S.: 423120

ZF Braking Systems Poland Sp. z o.o. (1)
ul Leonarda da Vinci 7, 44-121, Gliwice, Poland
Tel.: (48) 323382075
Automotive Components Mfr
N.A.I.C.S.: 336390
Tomasz Chajda (Project Mgr)

ZF Car eWallet GmbH (1)
Ernst-Reuter-Platz 2, 10587, Berlin, Germany
Tel.: (49) 3085608045
Web Site: http://www.iomoto.io
Information Technology Services
N.A.I.C.S.: 541511
Thorsten Weber (Mng Dir)

ZF Chassis Components LLC (1)
3300 John Conley Dr, Lapeer, MI 48446
Tel.: (810) 245-2000
Automobile Parts Distr
N.A.I.C.S.: 423120

ZF Chassis Components Toluca S.A. de C.V. (1)
Calle 7 Norte s/n Manzana J Lotes 2 y 3 Parque Industrial Toluca 2000, Toluca, 50200, Edo de Mexico, Mexico
Tel.: (52) 7222769800
Automobile Parts Distr
N.A.I.C.S.: 423120
Sergio Gomez Robledo (Mgr-Matls & Logistics)

ZF Chassis Systems Chicago LLC (1)
3400 E 126th St, Chicago, IL 60633
Tel.: (773) 371-4550
Automobile Parts Distr
N.A.I.C.S.: 423120
Greg Basden (Plant Mgr)

ZF Chassis Systems Duncan LLC (1)
191 Parkway W, Duncan, SC 29334
Tel.: (864) 486-3761
Automobile Parts Distr
N.A.I.C.S.: 423120
Annika Waesche (Controller-Plant)

ZF Chassis Systems Tuscaloosa LLC (1)
1200 Commerce Dr, Tuscaloosa, AL 35401
Tel.: (205) 333-5100
Automobile Parts Distr
N.A.I.C.S.: 423120
Brad Newman (Plant Mgr)

ZF Chassis Systems Zatec s.r.o. (1)
Zatec Plant Prumyslova Zona Triangle, Stankovice, 438 01, Zatec, Czech Republic
Tel.: (420) 737182404
Automotive Components Mfr
N.A.I.C.S.: 336390
Tomas Kinter (Mgr-Logistics)

ZF Chassis Technology S.A. de C.V. (1)
Toluca Plant Calle 7 Norte Manzana J Lotes 2 y 3, Parque Industrial Toluca 2000, 50200, Toluca, Mexico
Tel.: (52) 7222769800
Automotive Components Mfr
N.A.I.C.S.: 336390

ZF Electronic Systems Juarez S.A. de C.V. (1)
Parque Industrial Intermex Av Valle de Los Cedros 1650, Juarez, Chihuahua, 32690, Mexico
Tel.: (52) 6566920300
Automobile Parts Distr
N.A.I.C.S.: 423120
Jose Chairez (Mgr-Ops)

ZF Electronic Systems Pleasant Prairie, LLC (1)
8401 102 St Ste 400, Pleasant Prairie, WI 53158
Tel.: (262) 942-6500
Web Site: http://www.zf.com

Switches, Electronic Controls & Displays Mfr
N.A.I.C.S.: 335931

Subsidiary (Domestic):

Cherry Americas, LLC (2)
8401 102 St Ste 400, Pleasant Prairie, WI 53158
Tel.: (262) 942-6500
Switches, Electronic Controls & Displays, Sales of Keyboard Mfr
N.A.I.C.S.: 335931

Subsidiary (Non-US):

Cherry Australia Pty. Ltd. (3)
Unit 5 15/16 Nicole Close, Bayswater, 3153, VIC, Australia
Tel.: (61) 397617844
Web Site: http://www.cherrycorp.com
Sales Range: $1-9.9 Million
Emp.: 350
Sales Office
N.A.I.C.S.: 335931

Affiliate (Non-US):

TVS Cherry Limited (3)
Madurai-Melur Road, Vallaripatti, Madurai, 625 122, India
Tel.: (91) 452822476
Emp.: 300
Keyboard, Keyswitches, Electrical Switches, Electronic Controls, Automotive Controls & Automotive Mechatronics
N.A.I.C.S.: 335931

Subsidiary (Non-US):

ZF Electronics Asia Limited (3)
2/F Technology Plaza 29-35 Sha Tsuni Road Tsuen Wan, Kowloon, China (Hong Kong)
Tel.: (852) 25656678
Web Site: http://www.cherry.de
Emp.: 500
Keyboard, Keyswitches, Electrical Switches, Electronic Controls, Automotive Controls & Automotive Mechatronics
N.A.I.C.S.: 423610

ZF Electronics France S.A.R.L. (3)
1 Ave des Violettes, ZA des Petits Carreaux, 94384, Paris, Cedex, France
Tel.: (33) 143772951
Web Site: http://www.cherry.fr
Sales Range: $1-9.9 Million
Emp.: 13
Keyboard, Keyswitches, Electrical Switches, Electronic Controls, Automotive Controls & Automotive Mechatronics
N.A.I.C.S.: 335931

ZF Electronics GmbH (3)
Cherrystrasse, 91275, Auerbach, Germany
Tel.: (49) 9643180
Web Site: http://www.switches-sensors.zf.com
Sales Range: $350-399.9 Million
Emp.: 1,500
Electrical Switche Electronic Control & Sensor Mfr
N.A.I.C.S.: 335313

ZF Electronics Klasterec s.r.o. (3)
Osvobozena 780, 431 51, Klasterec nad Ohri, Czech Republic
Tel.: (420) 474359111
Web Site: http://www.zf.com
Emp.: 300
Keyboard, Keyswitches, Electrical Switches, Electronic Controls, Automotive Controls & Automotive Mechatronics
N.A.I.C.S.: 336320

ZF Electronics UK, Ltd (3)
Unit L Airport Executive Park, President Way, Luton, LU2 9NY, Bedfordshire, United Kingdom
Tel.: (44) 1582506140
Web Site: http://www.cherry.co.uk
Keyboard, Keyswitches, Electrical Switches, Electronic Controls, Automotive Controls & Automotive Mechatronics
N.A.I.C.S.: 335931

ZF Engineering Plzen s.r.o. (1)
Univerzitni 1159/53, Plzen, 30100, Czech Republic
Tel.: (420) 373736311

ZF FRIEDRICHSHAFEN AG — INTERNATIONAL PUBLIC

ZF Friedrichshafen AG—(Continued)
Automobile Parts Mfr
N.A.I.C.S.: 336390

ZF Fonderie Lorraine S.A.S. (1)
Postfach 41002, 57214, Sarreguemines, Cedex, France
Tel.: (33) 387273000
Automobile Parts Distr
N.A.I.C.S.: 423120

ZF Gainesville LLC (1)
Oakwood Industrial Park 5405 Rafe Banks Dr, Flowery Branch, GA 30542
Tel.: (770) 965-6500
Automobile Parts Distr
N.A.I.C.S.: 423120
Joel Hipp (Mgr-Pur)

ZF Group North American Operations Inc. (1)
15811 Centennial Dr, Northville, MI 48168 **(100%)**
Tel.: (734) 416-6200
Emp.: 360
Mfr of Automotive Parts
N.A.I.C.S.: 423120
Mark Cybulski (Head-Sourcing & Vendor Mgmt)

ZF Gusstechnologie GmbH (1)
Nopitschstrasse 71, 90441, Nuremberg, Germany
Tel.: (49) 91141500
Web Site: http://www.zf.com
Automobile Parts Mfr
N.A.I.C.S.: 336390

ZF Hero Chassis Systems Private Ltd. (1)
603 International Trade Tower, Nehru Place, 110019, New Delhi, India
Tel.: (91) 1140511600
Automobile Parts Distr
N.A.I.C.S.: 423120

ZF Hungaria Ipari es Kereskedelmi Korlatolt Felelossegu Tarsasag (1)
IT Center Hungary Torvenyhaz ut 4, 3300, Eger, Hungary
Tel.: (36) 36520100
Automotive Components Mfr
N.A.I.C.S.: 336390

ZF Hungaria Kft. (1)
Kistalyai ut 2, 3300, Eger, Hungary
Tel.: (36) 36520100
Automobile Parts Distr
N.A.I.C.S.: 423120
Tibor Masszi (Mgr-Plng & Production Sys)

ZF India Private Limited (1)
B-38 MIDC Chakan Industrial Area Phase II, Vasuli Tal Khed, 410501, Pune, India
Tel.: (91) 21 3562 4884
Automobile Parts Distr
N.A.I.C.S.: 423120

ZF Industrieantriebe Witten GmbH (1)
Mannesmannstrasse 29, 58455, Witten, Germany
Tel.: (49) 23028770
Automotive Components Mfr
N.A.I.C.S.: 336390
Christoph Kainzbauer (VP)

ZF Italia S.r.l. (1)
Via Donizetti 11, 20090, Assago, Milan, Italy
Tel.: (39) 02 488831
Automobile Parts Distr
N.A.I.C.S.: 423120

ZF Lemforder AKS Modulleri Sanayi ve Ticaret A.S. (1)
Ataturk Organize Sanayi Bolgesi 10003 Sokak No 13, Cigli, 35620, Izmir, Turkiye
Tel.: (90) 232 3981300
Automobile Parts Distr
N.A.I.C.S.: 423120

ZF Lemforder Achssysteme Ges.m.b.H (1)
Parkring 1, 8403, Leibnitz, Austria
Tel.: (43) 7252 580 0
Automobile Parts Distr
N.A.I.C.S.: 423120

ZF Lemforder Chassis Technology Korea Co., Ltd. (1)
23 B4L Gumi National Industrial Complex 4, Gupo-dong, 730-400, Gumi, Gyeongsangbuk-Do, Korea (South)
Tel.: (82) 544708600
Automobile Parts Distr
N.A.I.C.S.: 423120

ZF Lemforder Metal France S.A. (1)
1 rue Pascal, BP 10103, 57192, Florange, Cedex, France
Tel.: (33) 3 82591282
Automobile Parts Distr
N.A.I.C.S.: 423120

ZF Lemforder SA (Pty.) Ltd. (1)
PO Box 59832, 118, Karenpark, South Africa
Tel.: (27) 12 5217500
Web Site: http://www.zflemforder.com
Emp.: 200
Automobile Parts Distr
N.A.I.C.S.: 423120
Morne Lewis (Mgr-Fin & HR)

ZF Luftfahrttechnik GmbH (1)
Flugplatzstrasse, 34379, Calden, Germany
Tel.: (49) 5674 701 0
Sales Range: $50-74.9 Million
Emp.: 329
N.A.I.C.S.: 336390

ZF Marine Krimpen B.V. (1)
Zaag 27, PO Box 2020, 2931 LD, Krimpen aan de Lek, Netherlands
Tel.: (31) 180 331 000
Automobile Parts Distr
N.A.I.C.S.: 423120

ZF Marine Propulsion Systems Miramar LLC (1)
15351 SW 29th St Ste 300, Miramar, FL 33027
Tel.: (954) 441-4040
Automobile Parts Distr
N.A.I.C.S.: 423120
Drew Orvieto (Sr Mgr-Comml Fast Craft Engrg-North America)

ZF Middle East FZE (1)
ZF Services Dubai Oman-Hatta Road Ras Al Khor Indu Area 1, 60203, Dubai, United Arab Emirates
Tel.: (971) 43331530
Automotive Components Mfr
N.A.I.C.S.: 336390
Javed Siddiqui (Head-Technical Svcs)

ZF Osterreich Ges.m.b.H. (1)
Carlbergergasse 70, 1230, Vienna, Austria
Tel.: (43) 1 86545000
Automobile Parts Distr
N.A.I.C.S.: 423120

ZF Overseas Inc. (1)
12001 Tech Ctr Dr, Livonia, MI 48150
Tel.: (734) 855-2600
Automotive Components Mfr
N.A.I.C.S.: 336390

ZF Padova S.r.l. (1)
Via Penghe 48, CaselllediSelvazzano, 35030, Padua, Italy
Tel.: (39) 049 8299311
Web Site: http://www.zfpaduva.com
Automobile Parts Distr
N.A.I.C.S.: 423120
Alessandro Zabeo (Coord-Lean Process)

Subsidiary (Non-US):

ZF Marine Middle East LLC (2)
Ras Al Khor Industrial Area 2 Al Aweer, PO Box 60203, Dubai, 60203, United Arab Emirates
Tel.: (971) 6 5747 074
Emp.: 70
Automobile Parts Distr
N.A.I.C.S.: 423120
Khalid Alexander Sabbah (Mng Dir)

ZF Passive Safety Czech s.r.o. (1)
Stara Boleslav Plant Hlavenec 161, Hlavenec, 294 74, Prague, Czech Republic
Tel.: (420) 202810222
Automotive Components Mfr
N.A.I.C.S.: 336390
Michal Salac (Plant Mgr-Quality)

ZF Passive Safety Systems US Inc. (1)
Washington Engineering Ctr-PSS 4505 W 26 Mile Rd W Bldg, Washington, MI 48094
Tel.: (586) 232-7200
Automotive Components Mfr
N.A.I.C.S.: 336390

ZF Pegasus GmbH (1)
Bayernstrasse 10, 93128, Regenstauf, Germany
Tel.: (49) 9402503300
Web Site: http://www.pegasus-gmbh.de
Information Technology Services
N.A.I.C.S.: 541511
Robert Weininger (CEO)

ZF Powertrain Modules Shanghai Co., Ltd. (1)
No 1139 Huazhi Road, Qingpu District, Shanghai, 201708, China
Tel.: (86) 2167002410
Automobile Parts Distr
N.A.I.C.S.: 423120
Xiaoyun Zhang (Supvr-Logistics Plng)

ZF Powertrain Systems (Beijing) Co., Ltd. (1)
Beijing Plant 1 ZFPS 2 Tai He Yi Jie, Beijing Economic-Technological Development Area Daxing District, Beijing, 100176, China
Tel.: (86) 1087141441
Automotive Components Mfr
N.A.I.C.S.: 336390
Sossdorf Lothar (COO)

ZF Race Engineering GmbH (1)
Ernst-Sachs-Strasse 62, 97424, Schweinfurt, Germany
Tel.: (49) 9721984300
Emp.: 100
Automobile Parts Mfr
N.A.I.C.S.: 336390
Norbert Odendahl (Mng Dir)

ZF Sachs AG (1)
Ernst-Sachs-Strasse 62, 97424, Schweinfurt, Germany
Tel.: (49) 9721980
Automotive Components Mfr
N.A.I.C.S.: 336340

Subsidiary (Domestic):

Franken Guss GmbH & Co. KG (2)
An der Jungfernmuehle 1, 97318, Kitzingen, Germany **(100%)**
Tel.: (49) 93219320
Web Site: http://www.frankenguss.de
Sales Range: $125-149.9 Million
Emp.: 581
Cast Metal Automotive Components Mfr
N.A.I.C.S.: 336370
Josef Ramthun (Mng Dir)

Unterstuetzungskasse der Sachs Fahrzeug-und Motorentechnik GmbH (2)
Strawefnky Str 27, Nuremberg, 90455, Germany **(100%)**
Tel.: (49) 91142310
Web Site: http://www.sachs-bikes.de
Emp.: 34
Radio & Television Broadcasting
N.A.I.C.S.: 334220
Tao Wang (Gen Mgr)

ZF Sachs AG (2)
Windelsbleicher Strasse 80, 33647, Bielefeld, Germany **(100%)**
Tel.: (49) 5214170354
Web Site: http://www.zfsachs.de
Sales Range: $10-24.9 Million
Emp.: 250
Automobile Parts Mfr
N.A.I.C.S.: 336340

Subsidiary (Non-US):

ZF Sachs Automotive Mexico SA de CV (2)
Industria Metalurgica No 1010-2, PO Box 25900, Parque Industrial Ramos Arizpe, Ramos Arizpe, 25000, Mexico **(100%)**
Tel.: (52) 8444115700
Web Site: http://www.zf.com
Emp.: 500
Mfr of Automotive Parts
N.A.I.C.S.: 336340
Thomas Joos (Gen Mgr)

ZF Sachs Brasil Ltda (2)
Avenida Piraporinha 1000 Anexo Parte 1, Jordanopolis, Sao Bernardo do Campo, 09891-901, Brazil **(100%)**
Tel.: (55) 1133433000
Web Site: http://www.sachs.com.br
Emp.: 1,000
Mfr of Automotive Parts
N.A.I.C.S.: 336340

ZF Sachs Espana S.A (2)
Barrio Aretxalde 130, Lezama Bizkaia, 48196, Bilbao, Spain **(99.8%)**
Tel.: (34) 944555050
Web Site: http://www.sachs.com
Mfr of Automotive Components
N.A.I.C.S.: 336340

ZF Sachs Slovakia a.s. (2)
Trnava Plant Strojarenska 2, 917 02, Trnava, Slovakia **(100%)**
Tel.: (421) 335959111
Web Site: http://www.sachs.sk
Emp.: 900
Mfr & Reconditioning of Clutches & Torque Converters
N.A.I.C.S.: 811114
Peter Doll (Mng Dir)

ZF Sachs South Africa (Pty.) Ltd. (2)
Postfach 123908, 1451, Alrode, South Africa
Tel.: (27) 11 3894902
Automobile Parts Distr
N.A.I.C.S.: 423120

ZF Sachs Suspansiyon Sistemleri Sanayi ve Ticaret A.S. (2)
Gebze Organize Sanayi Bolgesi 400 Sokak, 41480, Gebze, Kocaeli, Turkiye
Tel.: (90) 262 6780500
Automobile Parts Distr
N.A.I.C.S.: 423120

ZF Sachs Korea Co., Ltd. (1)
173 Seong sanpaechong-ro, Seongsan-gu, 642-020, Changwon, Gyeongsangman-do, Korea (South)
Tel.: (82) 55 239 1600
Automobile Parts Distr
N.A.I.C.S.: 423120

ZF Sachs Micro Mobility GmbH (1)
Escher-Wyss-Str 25, 88212, Ravensburg, Germany
Tel.: (49) 61889169065
Web Site: http://www.sachsmicromobility.com
Automotive Components Mfr
Hannes Proschek (Dir-Engrg)

ZF Serbia d.o.o. (1)
Pancevo Plant 7 Nova 7, 26000, Pancevo, Serbia
Tel.: (381) 1113533580
Automotive Components Mfr
N.A.I.C.S.: 336390
Zoran Matovic (Head-Sls)

ZF Services (Shanghai) Co., Ltd. (1)
ZF Services Shanghai Branch 162 Luoxiu Road, Xuhui District, Shanghai, 200231, China
Tel.: (86) 2123500600
Automotive Components Mfr
N.A.I.C.S.: 336390
Hang Zhou (Sls Mgr)

ZF Services Belgium N.V. - S.A. (1)
Van Osslaan 1 b 26 Av Van Oss, 1120, Brussels, Belgium
Tel.: (32) 22620127
Automobile Parts Distr
N.A.I.C.S.: 423120
Tom Elsen (Mgr-Mobile Svc)

ZF Services Bogota SAS (1)
Calle 93 15-27 - Oficina 202, Bogota, Colombia
Tel.: (57) 13770469
Automobile Parts Distr
N.A.I.C.S.: 423120

ZF Services Espana S.A.U. (1)
C/ Sant Esteve 29, Sant Cugat del Valles, 8173, Barcelona, Spain
Tel.: (34) 93 6753434
Automobile Parts Distr
N.A.I.C.S.: 423120

Subsidiary (Domestic):

ZF Lemforder TVA S.A. (2)

AND PRIVATE COMPANIES

ZF FRIEDRICHSHAFEN AG

Postfach Apartado 7, 48260, Ermua, Bizkaia, Spain
Tel.: (34) 943 172150
Automobile Parts Distr
N.A.I.C.S.: 423120

Zf Ansa Lemforder S. L.U. (2)
C/ Alcalde Martin Cobos s/n, Burgos, 09007, Spain
Tel.: (34) 94 747 90 00
Automobile Parts Distr
N.A.I.C.S.: 423120

ZF Services France S.A.S. (1)
3-11 rue Henri Poincare, 92167, Antony, Cedex, France
Tel.: (33) 170747800
Automobile Parts Distr
N.A.I.C.S.: 423120
Michel Victor Fetiveau *(Pres)*

ZF Services Korea Co., Ltd. (1)
422-2 Chongchon-dong, Bupyong-gu, 403-030, Incheon, Korea (South)
Tel.: (82) 325051530
Automobile Parts Distr
N.A.I.C.S.: 423120

ZF Services LLC (1)
777 Hickory Hill Dr, Vernon Hills, IL 60061
Tel.: (847) 478-6868
Automobile Parts Distr
N.A.I.C.S.: 423120
Bill Labuda *(Mgr-Svc Network)*

ZF Services Middle East LLC (1)
Ras Al Khor Ind Area-2 Al Aweer Al Kharbash Building, PO Box 60203, Dubai, United Arab Emirates
Tel.: (971) 43331530
Automobile Parts Distr
N.A.I.C.S.: 423120
Mirela Smajovic *(Mgr-Mktg)*

ZF Services Nederland B.V. (1)
PO Box 557, 2600 AN, Delft, Netherlands
Tel.: (31) 152702350
Automobile Parts Distr
N.A.I.C.S.: 423120

ZF Services Portugal, Unipessoal, lda (1)
Quinta do Carmo Lote 55, Sacavem, 2685-129, Lisbon, Portugal
Tel.: (351) 219497410
Automobile Parts Distr
N.A.I.C.S.: 423120

ZF Services S.A. de C.V. (1)
ProLogis Park Carretera San Martin de las Flores 520 Edificio 3-A, Tlaquepaque, 45629, Jalisco, Mexico
Tel.: (52) 3332086000
Automobile Parts Distr
N.A.I.C.S.: 423120

ZF Services Schweiz AG (1)
Sandbuelstrasse 3, 8604, Volketswil, Switzerland
Tel.: (41) 449081616
Automobile Parts Distr
N.A.I.C.S.: 423120

ZF Services South Africa (Pty.) Ltd. (1)
29 Proton Crescent, Bellville, Cape Town, 7530, South Africa
Tel.: (27) 219506300
Web Site: http://www.zf.com
Emp.: 15
Automobile Parts Distr
N.A.I.C.S.: 423120

ZF Services Turk Sanayi ve Ticaret A.S. (1)
Adil Mahellesi Demokrasi Cad No 17, Sultanbeyli, 34935, Istanbul, Turkiye
Tel.: (90) 2165920750
Automobile Parts Distr
N.A.I.C.S.: 423120

ZF Services UK Ltd. (1)
Eldon Way Crick Industrial Estate, Crick, NN6 7SL, Northamptonshire, United Kingdom
Tel.: (44) 3332401123
Automobile Parts Distr
N.A.I.C.S.: 423120
Graham Truckel *(Mng Dir)*

ZF Slovakia a.s. (1)
Strojarenska 2, 91702, Trnava, Slovakia
Tel.: (421) 335959111
Automobile Parts Distr
N.A.I.C.S.: 423120
Sven Wilhelm *(Mgr-Controlling)*

ZF Stankov s.r.o. (1)
Ohucov 25, Stankov, 34561, Czech Republic
Tel.: (420) 379410811
Automobile Parts Distr
N.A.I.C.S.: 423120

ZF Steering Systems Poland Sp. z o.o. (1)
ul Juliusza Slowackiego 33, 43-502, Czechowice-Dziedzice, Poland
Tel.: (48) 322158245
Automotive Components Mfr
N.A.I.C.S.: 336390
Mateusz Walusza *(Mgr-Logistics)*

ZF Suspension Technology Guadalajara S.A. de C.V. (1)
Km 3 5 Carretera El Salto - La Capilla, El Salto, 45680, Jalisco, Mexico
Tel.: (52) 3332080000
Automobile Parts Distr
N.A.I.C.S.: 423120

ZF TRW Automotive Holdings Corp. (1)
12001 Tech Ctr Dr, Livonia, MI 48150
Tel.: (734) 855-2600
Web Site: http://www.zf.com
Emp.: 63,515
Automotive Components Mfr
N.A.I.C.S.: 336310
John Harju *(Sr VP-HR)*

Subsidiary (Non-US):

Autocruise S.A.S. (2)
ZAC Technopole Brest-Iroise Secteur de la Pointe du Diable, Avenue du Technopole, 29280, Plouzane, France
Tel.: (33) 298454368
Web Site: http://www.zf.com
Motor Vehicle Parts Mfr
N.A.I.C.S.: 336390

Brakes India Ltd. (2)
Tel.: (91) 4426258161
Web Site: https://brakesindia.com
Motor Vehicle Parts & Accessories Mfr
N.A.I.C.S.: 336340

Frenos y Mecanismos, S. de R.L. de C.V. (2)
Santa Rosa de Jauregui Plant 1 2 La Griega 101 Parque Industrial, Queretaro Santa Rosa Jauregui, 76220, Queretaro, Mexico
Tel.: (52) 4422113303
Web Site: http://www.zf.com
Motor Vehicle Parts Mfr
N.A.I.C.S.: 336390

HEMA-TRW Otomotiv Direksiyon Sistemleri A.S (2)
Organize Sanayi Bolgesi Gazi Osman Pasa Mah 4 Cadde No 5, Cerkezkoy, 59501, Tekirdag, Turkiye
Tel.: (90) 2827581040
Web Site: http://www.hematrw.com.tr
Automotive Steering & Suspension Components Mfr
N.A.I.C.S.: 336330
Mehmet Hattat *(Chm)*

Kelsey-Hayes Canada Limited (2)
155 Beards Ln, Woodstock, N4S 7X8, ON, Canada
Tel.: (519) 537-2331
Web Site: http://www.zf.com
Motor Vehicle Parts & Accessories Mfr
N.A.I.C.S.: 336390

Subsidiary (Domestic):

Kelsey-Hayes Company (2)
5676 Industrial Park Rd, Winona, MN 55987-0649
Tel.: (507) 457-3750
Web Site: http://www.zf.com
Automobile Spare Parts Mfr
N.A.I.C.S.: 423120

Subsidiary (Non-US):

Lucas Automotive SDN. BHD. (2)
PLO 17 Senai Industrial Estate KB 105, Senai, 81400, Johor, Malaysia
Tel.: (60) 7 596 8000
Web Site: http://www.zf.com
Automotive Electronic Product Mfr
N.A.I.C.S.: 336320

LucasVarity (M) SDN. BHD. (2)
Suite 7-11 Block E Phileo Damansara 1 Section 16/11, Jalan Damansara, 46350, Petaling Jaya, Selangor, Malaysia
Tel.: (60) 379578801
Web Site: http://www.trwaftermarket.com
Motor Vehicle Parts Mfr
N.A.I.C.S.: 336390

Revestimientos Especiales de Mexico S de RL de CV (2)
Avenida Texas 120 Parque Industrial Nacional, 65550, Cienega de Flores, Nuevo Leon, Mexico
Tel.: (52) 8150009900
Web Site: http://www.zf.com
Brake System Mfr
N.A.I.C.S.: 336340

Roadster Automotive BV (2)
Kingsfordweg 151, Amsterdam, 1043 GR, Netherlands
Tel.: (31) 204919151
Automobile Parts Mfr
N.A.I.C.S.: 336390

Safe-Life - Industria de Componentes de Seguranca Automovel S.A (2)
Ponte de Lima Safe-Life Rua da Barreira 1319, 4990-645, Ponte de Lima, Portugal
Tel.: (351) 258 900 450
Web Site: http://www.zf.com
Motor Vehicle Parts Mfr
N.A.I.C.S.: 336390

Safebag - Industria Componentes de Seguranca Automovel S.A. (2)
Casal dos Santos 67, 4990-620, Ponte de Lima, Portugal
Tel.: (351) 258900840
Web Site: http://www.zf.com
Automotive Safety System Mfr
N.A.I.C.S.: 336390

TRW Aftermarket Asia Pacific PTE Ltd (2)
210 Middle Road 05-01 Singapore Pools Building, Singapore, 188994, Singapore
Tel.: (65) 62971788
Web Site: http://www.zf.com
Automobile Parts Distr
N.A.I.C.S.: 423120

TRW Aftermarket Japan Co., Ltd. (2)
14-6 Kodenmacho Nihonbashi, Chuo-ku, Tokyo, 103-0001, Kanagawa, Japan
Tel.: (81) 356956191
Web Site: http://www.trwaftermarket.com
Motor Vehicle Parts Mfr
N.A.I.C.S.: 336390

TRW Asia Pacific Co Ltd (2)
9 Building No 456 Hongcao Road, Shanghai, 200233, China
Tel.: (86) 21 6120 1166
Web Site: http://www.trw.cc
Steering Wheel & Airbag Mfr
N.A.I.C.S.: 336330

Subsidiary (Domestic):

Shanghai TRW Automotive Safety Systems Co., Ltd. (3)
NO 1010 Kaixuan Road, Shanghai, 201805, China
Tel.: (86) 2162821010
Web Site: http://www.trw.cc
Automotive Airbag & Seat Belt Mfr
N.A.I.C.S.: 336360

TRW Automotive Components (Langfang) Co., Ltd. (3)
No 9 Yao Hua Road Langsen Automotive Industry Park, Langfang Economic & Technical Development Zone, Langfang, 65001, China
Tel.: (86) 316 6070 851
Web Site: http://www.zf.com
Motor Vehicle Parts Mfr
N.A.I.C.S.: 336390

TRW Automotive Components (Shanghai) Co., Ltd. (3)
No 169 North Quanli Road, Wuhan Economic & Technology Development Zone, Wuhan, 430058, China
Tel.: (86) 27 5936 5128
Web Site: http://www.zf.com
Automotive Electronic Parts Mfr
N.A.I.C.S.: 336320

TRW Automotive Components Technical Service Shanghai Co. Ltd. (3)
ZF Services Shanghai Branch 162 Luoxiu Road, Xuhui District, Shanghai, 200231, China
Tel.: (86) 21 6121 5300
Web Site: http://www.zf.com
Motor Vehicle Parts Mfr
N.A.I.C.S.: 336390

TRW Automotive Technologies (Shanghai) Co., Ltd. (3)
No 289 Zhongbai Road, Jiading District, Shanghai, 201814, China (100%)
Tel.: (86) 2167075725
Web Site: http://www.zf.com
Motor Vehicle Parts Mfr
N.A.I.C.S.: 336390

TRW Dongfang (Xian) Airbag Inflator Co., Ltd. (3)
3 North of Weihua Road Jingwei Xin Cheng, Xi an Economical and Technological Development Zone, Xi'an, 710201, China
Tel.: (86) 298263277
Web Site: http://www.zf.com
Automobile Parts Distr
N.A.I.C.S.: 423120

TRW FAWER Automobile Safety Systems (Changchun) Co., Ltd. (3)
4579 Guigu Street High and New Technology Development Zone, High & New Technological Development Zone, Changchun, 130012, China
Tel.: (86) 43185542609
Web Site: http://www.zf.com
Automobile Parts Distr
N.A.I.C.S.: 423120

TRW FAWER Commercial Vehicle Steering (Changchun) Co., Ltd. (3)
No 4789 East Nanhu Road, Economic & Technological Development Zone, Changchun, 130033, China
Tel.: (86) 431 8705 3500
Web Site: http://www.zf.com
Motor Vehicle Power Steering Products Mfr
N.A.I.C.S.: 336330

Subsidiary (Non-US):

TRW Asiatic (M) SDN BHD (2)
No 22 Jalan Astaka U8/84 Bukit Jelutong Industrial Park Section U8, Shah Alam, 40150, Selangor, Malaysia
Tel.: (60) 378458700
Web Site: http://www.zf.com
Automobile Parts Distr
N.A.I.C.S.: 423120
KahHeng Cheong *(Bus Mgr)*

TRW Asiatic Co., Ltd. (2)
98 Athakravi Building 2nd Floor Soi Sukhumvit 26 Sukhumvit Road, Klongton, Bangkok, 10110, Thailand
Tel.: (66) 266124445
Web Site: http://www.zf.com
Automobile Parts Distr
N.A.I.C.S.: 423120

TRW Autoelektronika s.r.o. (2)
Jana Nohy 2048, Benesov, 256 01, Mlada Boleslav, Czech Republic
Tel.: (420) 317 972 201
Web Site: http://www.zf.com
Motor Vehicle Parts Mfr
N.A.I.C.S.: 336390

TRW Automotive (Slovakia) s.r.o. (2)
Trencianska 2571/16, 915 01, Nove Mesto nad Vahom, Slovakia (100%)
Tel.: (421) 32 323 62 02
Web Site: http://www.zf.com
Motor Vehicle Parts Mfr
N.A.I.C.S.: 336390

TRW Automotive Bonneval S.A.S. (2)
Le Clos Aux Moines, Eure Et Loir, 28800, Bonneval, France
Tel.: (33) 237444864

ZF FRIEDRICHSHAFEN AG

ZF Friedrichshafen AG—(Continued)
Motor Vehicle Parts Mfr
N.A.I.C.S.: 336390

TRW Automotive Czech s.r.o (2)
Na Roli 26, 466 21, Jablonec nad Nisou,
Czech Republic
Tel.: (420) 483 354 100
Web Site: http://www.zf.com
Motor Vehicle Parts Mfr
N.A.I.C.S.: 336390

Subsidiary (Domestic):

TRW-Carr s.r.o. (3)
Hlavenec 12, Stara Boleslav, 250 02, Mlada
Boleslav, Czech Republic **(100%)**
Tel.: (420) 326 553 222
Web Site: http://www.zf.com
Motor Vehicle Parts Mfr
N.A.I.C.S.: 336390

Subsidiary (Non-US):

TRW Automotive Espana SL (2)
Calle D I1 Poligono de Landaben, 31012,
Pamplona, Spain
Tel.: (34) 948188141
Web Site: http://www.zf.com
Steering & Brake Systems Mfr
N.A.I.C.S.: 336340

Subsidiary (Domestic):

TRW Automotive Inc. (2)
12001 Tech Ctr Dr, Livonia, MI 48150
Tel.: (734) 855-2600
Web Site: http://www.zf.com
Holding Company; Automotive Products Mfr
N.A.I.C.S.: 551112
R. Bruce McDonald (Executives)

Plant (Domestic):

TRW Automotive U.S. LLC - Commercial Steering Systems, Lafayette Plant (3)
800 Heath St, Lafayette, IN 47904-1863
Tel.: (765) 423-5377
Web Site: http://www.zf.com
Motor Vehicle Parts & Accessories Mfr
N.A.I.C.S.: 336330
Brian Kipp (Plant Mgr)

TRW Automotive U.S. LLC - Commercial Steering Systems, Lebanon Plant (3)
1103 Baddour Pkwy, Lebanon, TN 37087-2571
Tel.: (615) 444-6110
Web Site: http://www.zf.com
Commercial Vehicle Steering Systems Mfr
N.A.I.C.S.: 336330

TRW Automotive U.S. LLC - Steering Systems, Washington Plant (3)
4505 W 26 Mile Rd E Bldg, Washington, MI 48094
Tel.: (586) 232-7200
Web Site: http://www.zf.com
Automotive Steering & Suspension Systems Mfr
N.A.I.C.S.: 336310

Subsidiary (Domestic):

TRW Vehicle Safety Systems, Inc. (3)
4505 W 26 Mile Rd, Washington, MI 48094
Tel.: (586) 232-7200
Web Site: http://www.zf.com
Occupant Restraints Systems, Electrical & Electronic Controls & Engineered Fastening Systems Mfr
N.A.I.C.S.: 336390

Plant (Domestic):

TRW Vehicle Safety Systems, Inc. - Mesa Plant (4)
11202 E Germann Rd, Mesa, AZ 85212
Tel.: (480) 722-4000
Web Site: http://www.zf.com
Automotive Air Bags Mfr
N.A.I.C.S.: 336390

Subsidiary (Non-US):

TRW Automotive Italia S.r.l. (2)
Via G di Vittorio 9, Moncalieri, 10024, Turin, Italy
Tel.: (39) 011 68171
Web Site: http://www.zf.com
Motor Vehicle Parts Mfr
N.A.I.C.S.: 336390

TRW Automotive Japan Co. Ltd. (2)
1-16-5 Shinyamashita, Naka-ku, Yokohama, 231-0801, Kanagawa, Japan **(100%)**
Tel.: (81) 45 628 5700
Web Site: http://www.zf.com
Automotive Parts Distr & Mfr
N.A.I.C.S.: 423140

TRW Automotive Ltda. (2)
Via Anhanguera Km 147, Caixa Postal 155, 13486-915, Limeira, Sao Paulo, Brazil **(100%)**
Tel.: (55) 1934041120
Braking Systems, Clutch Equipment & Air Actuation Equipment Mfr
N.A.I.C.S.: 336390

Branch (Domestic):

TRW Automotive Ltda. - Engenheiro Coelho (2)
Rodovia SP 332 Km 164, Caixa Postal 31, 13165-970, Engenheiro Coelho, SP, Brazil
Tel.: (55) 1938585030
Web Site: http://www.zf.com
Automobile Parts Distr
N.A.I.C.S.: 423140
Leonardo Czarniak (Program Mgr)

Subsidiary (Non-US):

TRW Automotive Portugal Lda (2)
Estrada Octavio Pato Centro Empresarial de, Talaide, 2785-723, Sao Domingos de Rana, Portugal **(100%)**
Tel.: (351) 214228300
Web Site: http://www.zf.com
Automobile Braking Systems Mfr
N.A.I.C.S.: 336340

TRW Canada Limited/TRW Canada Limitee (2)
101 Spruce St, Tillsonburg, N4G 4J1, ON, Canada **(100%)**
Tel.: (519) 688-4200
Web Site: http://www.zf.com
Automobile Steering & Suspension Systems Mfr
N.A.I.C.S.: 336330

TRW Controls & Fasteners Inc. (2)
52 Aenggogae-ro 556 beon-gil, Namdong-gu, Incheon, 405-821, Korea (South)
Tel.: (82) 328169181
Web Site: http://www.zf.com
Automobile Parts Mfr
N.A.I.C.S.: 336390

TRW Deutschland Holding GmbH (2)
Carl-Spaeter-Strasse 8, 56070, Koblenz, Germany **(100%)**
Tel.: (49) 2618950
Web Site: http://www.zf.com
Holding Company; Investment Management Services
N.A.I.C.S.: 551112

Subsidiary (Domestic):

Lucas Automotive GmbH (3)
Carl Spaeter Strasse 8, Postfach 56070, Koblenz, Germany **(100%)**
Tel.: (49) 261 895 0
Web Site: http://www.zf.com
Automotive Braking & Suspension Mfr
N.A.I.C.S.: 336340

TRW Airbag Systems GmbH (3)
Wernher-von-Braun-Strasse 1, am Inn, 84544, Aschau, Germany **(100%)**
Tel.: (49) 8638965144
Web Site: http://www.zf.com
Airbag Systems Mfr
N.A.I.C.S.: 336390

Plant (Domestic):

TRW Airbag Systems GmbH-Laage (4)
Daimler-Benz Allee 1, 18299, Laage, Germany **(100%)**
Tel.: (49) 38459 94 0
Web Site: http://www.zf.com

Automotive Safety System Mfr
N.A.I.C.S.: 336390

Subsidiary (Domestic):

TRW Automotive Electronics & Components GmbH (3)
Industriestrasse 2-8, 78315, Radolfzell, Germany **(100%)**
Tel.: (49) 7732 8090
Web Site: http://www.zf.com
Automotive Fasteners & Componets Mfr
N.A.I.C.S.: 336390

TRW Automotive Holding GmbH & Co. KG (3)
Industriestrasse 20, 73553, Alfdorf, Germany **(100%)**
Tel.: (49) 71723020
Web Site: http://www.zf.com
Holding Company
N.A.I.C.S.: 551112

TRW Automotive Safety Systems GmbH (3)
Spessartstrasse 60, 63743, Aschaffenburg, Germany **(100%)**
Tel.: (49) 60213140
Web Site: http://www.zf.com
Steering Wheel & Airbag Mfr
N.A.I.C.S.: 336330

TRW KFZ Ausrustung GmbH (3)
Rudolf-Diesel Strasse 7, 56566, Neuwied, Germany **(100%)**
Tel.: (49) 2631 912 0
Automotive Body Control Systems Mfr
N.A.I.C.S.: 336390

TRW Logistic Services GmbH (3)
Im Hasfeld 1, 66802, Uberherrn, Germany
Tel.: (49) 683696960
Freight Forwarding Services
N.A.I.C.S.: 488510

TRW Receivables Finance GmbH (3)
Frankfurter Strasse 21-25, 65760, Eschborn, Germany **(100%)**
Tel.: (49) 6196 50970
Web Site: http://www.zf.com
Financial Management Services
N.A.I.C.S.: 523999

Subsidiary (Non-US):

TRW Limited (2)
Stratford Rd Technical Centre, Shirley, Solihull, B90 4GW, West Midlands, United Kingdom
Tel.: (44) 121 627 4242
Web Site: http://www.zf.com
Automobile Parts Mfr
N.A.I.C.S.: 336390

TRW Occupant Restraints South Africa Inc. (2)
Cnr Charel Uys & Niel Hare Sts, Dassenberg, Atlantis, 7350, South Africa **(100%)**
Tel.: (27) 21 573 9420
Web Site: http://www.zf.com
Automobile Parts Mfr
N.A.I.C.S.: 336390

TRW Overseas Seoul Inc. (2)
Level 3 Trust Tower 60 MabangRo, Seocho-Gu, Seoul, 137-739, Korea (South)
Tel.: (82) 234882501
Web Site: http://www.zf.com
Automobile Parts Distr
N.A.I.C.S.: 423120

TRW Polska Sp. z o.o. (2)
ul Rolnicza 33, 42-200, Czestochowa, Poland **(100%)**
Tel.: (48) 34 343 10 03
Web Site: http://www.zf.com
Motor Vehicle Parts Mfr
N.A.I.C.S.: 336390

TRW Sistemas de Direcciones, S. de R.L. de C.V. (2)
Avenida de las Fuentes 29 Parque Industrial Bernardo Quintana, El Marques, 76246, Queretaro, Mexico **(100%)**
Tel.: (52) 442 211 0851
Web Site: http://www.zf.com
Automobile Parts Mfr
N.A.I.C.S.: 336390

TRW Steering & Suspension Co., Ltd. (2)
64/2 Moo 4 Eastern Seaboard Industrial Estate, Pluakdaeng, Rayong, 21140, Thailand **(100%)**
Tel.: (66) 38927800
Web Site: http://www.zf.com
Motor Vehicle Parts Mfr
N.A.I.C.S.: 336390

TRW Steering Co. Ltd. (2)
780-3 Wonsidong, Danwon-gu, Ansan, 425-852, Kyungki-do, Korea (South)
Tel.: (82) 3454919132
Web Site: http://www.zf.com
Motor Vehicle Parts Mfr
N.A.I.C.S.: 336390
Lake Lee (Pres & Gen Mgr)

TRW Systemes de Freinage SAS (2)
1 Avenue de la Gare, 57320, Bouzonville, France **(100%)**
Tel.: (33) 387782111
Web Site: http://www.zf.com
Braking Systems Mfr
N.A.I.C.S.: 336340

TRW Vehicle Safety Systems de Mexico, S. de R.L. de C.V. (2)
Reynosa Seatbelt Assembly Plant 1 Blvd Mike Allen 1370, 88780, Reynosa, Tamaulipas, Mexico **(100%)**
Tel.: (52) 8999092800
Web Site: http://www.zf.com
Motor Vehicle Parts Mfr
N.A.I.C.S.: 336390

Subsidiary (Domestic):

ZF Active Safety and Electronics US LLC (2)
12001 Tech Center Dr, Livonia, MI 48150
Tel.: (734) 855-2600
Web Site: https://www.zf.com
Motor Vehicle Parts Mfr
N.A.I.C.S.: 336390

ZF Chassis Systems LLC (2)
1570 E P St Ext, Newton, NC 28658
Tel.: (828) 468-3800
Web Site: http://www.zf.com
Automobile Parts Distr
N.A.I.C.S.: 423120

Joint Venture (Non-US):

ZF Rane Automotive India Private Limited (2)
45 TTK Road, Alwarpet, Chennai, 600 018, Tamil Nadu, India **(51%)**
Tel.: (91) 4424994390
Web Site: http://ranegroup.com
Automotive Parts Distr
N.A.I.C.S.: 423120

Subsidiary (Domestic):

TRW Sun Steering Wheels Pvt. Ltd. (3)
A-47 LGF Hauz Khas, New Delhi, 110 016, India
Tel.: (91) 124 455 8500
Web Site: http://www.zf.com
Automobile Parts Distr
N.A.I.C.S.: 423120

ZF Taiwan Limited (1)
No 131-20 Zhongxing N St, Sanchong Dist, 24158, New Taipei City, Taiwan
Tel.: (886) 285112900
Automobile Parts Distr
N.A.I.C.S.: 423120
Alvin Yao (Head-Sls-Parts Sls)

ZF Trading Gmbh (1)
Standort Schweinfurt, Obere Weiden 12, Schweinfurt, 97424, DEU, Germany **(100%)**
Tel.: (49) 972147560
Web Site: http://www.zf-world.com
Emp.: 1,000
Wholesale of Automotive Parts
N.A.I.C.S.: 336340
Christian Haedge (Mng Dir)

Subsidiary (Non-US):

ZF Trading Asia Pacific Pte. Ltd. (2)

11 Tuas Dr 1, 638678, Singapore, 638678, Singapore
Tel: (65) 68227088
Emp.: 35
Automotive Spare Parts Whslr
N.A.I.C.S.: 336340

ZF Trading UK Ltd (2)
Eldon Way, Crick Industrial Est, Crick, NN6 7SL, United Kingdom (100%)
Tel.: (44) 788822353
Emp.: 100
N.A.I.C.S.: 334220

ZF Transmissions Gray Court LLC (1)
2846 N Old Laurens Rd, Gray Court, SC 29645
Tel.: (864) 601-2500
Automobile Parts Distr
N.A.I.C.S.: 423120
Michael Morris (Dir-Ops)

ZF Wind Power (Tianjin) Co., Ltd. (1)
No 78 Gaoxin Avenue Beichen Hi-Tech Industrial Park, Tianjin, 300402, China
Tel.: (86) 2228207000
Power Generation Services
N.A.I.C.S.: 221115
Zhixiang Ren (Mgr-R&D & Quality)

ZF Wind Power Antwerpen NV (1)
Lommel Plant Gerard Mercatorstraat 40, 3920, Lommel, Belgium
Tel.: (32) 1 134 9700
Web Site: http://www.zf.com
Designer & Mfr of Gearboxes for Wind Turbines
N.A.I.C.S.: 333611

Subsidiary (Non-US):

Hansen Wind Energy Drives (China) Co. Ltd. (2)
Beichen Hi-Tech Industrial Park South, 78 Gaoxin Avenue, Tianjin, 300402, China
Tel.: (86) 22 28207000
Mfr of Gearboxes for Wind Turbines
N.A.I.C.S.: 333611

ZF Wind Power Coimbatore Ltd. (2)
Plot No 3 Hi Tech Engineering & Services Sector SEZ, Annur Road, Coimbatore, 641659, Tamil Nadu, India
Tel.: (91) 4254 306000
Emp.: 60
Mfr of Gearboxes for Wind Turbines
N.A.I.C.S.: 333611
Michael McClintock (Exec Dir)

ZF Wind Power Gainesville LLC (1)
1925 New Harvest Dr, Gainesville, GA 30507
Tel.: (770) 297-4031
Automobile Parts Distr
N.A.I.C.S.: 423120

ZF do Brasil Ltda. (1)
Rua Borg Warner 50 Bairro Jordanopolis, 09891-901, Sao Bernardo do Campo, Sao Paulo, Brazil
Tel.: (55) 1133433000
Automobile Parts Distr
N.A.I.C.S.: 423120

Zukunft Ventures GmbH (1)
Graf-von-Soden-Platz 1, 88046, Friedrichshafen, Germany
Tel.: (49) 7541770
Automotive Components Mfr
N.A.I.C.S.: 336390
Franz Christoph Lissner (Mgr-Cooperation)

ZGP DOBOJ A.D.
Cara Dusana Bb, 74101, Doboj, Bosnia & Herzegovina
Tel.: (387) 53242168
Year Founded: 2001
DZGP-R-A—(BANJ)
Rev.: $55,808
Assets: $8,379,315
Liabilities: $8,062,382
Net Worth: $316,933
Earnings: ($539,946)
Emp.: 41
Fiscal Year-end: 12/31/12

Building Construction & Civil Engineering Services
N.A.I.C.S.: 237990
Miodrag Rada (Chm-Mgmt Bd)

ZGP GP BEOGRAD A.D.
Vodovodska 160, 11147, Belgrade, Serbia
Tel.: (381) 11 2510 961
Year Founded: 1947
Sales Range: $1-9.9 Million
Bridge Construction Services
N.A.I.C.S.: 237310
Milanko Delic (Exec Dir)

ZHANG JIA JIE TOURISM GROUP CO., LTD.
3F Zhangjiajie International Hotel No 145 Sanjiaoping, Zhangjiajie, 427000, Hunan, China
Tel.: (86) 7448288630
Web Site: https://www.zjjlyjt.com
Year Founded: 1992
000430—(SSE)
Rev.: $18,598,507
Assets: $401,779,802
Liabilities: $246,162,885
Net Worth: $155,616,917
Earnings: ($36,510,458)
Emp.: 1,100
Fiscal Year-end: 12/31/22
Travel & Tour Operating Services
N.A.I.C.S.: 561520
Zhao Hui (Pres)

ZHANG XIAOQUAN INC.
No 8 Wuxing Road, Dongzhou Industrial Zone Fuyang District, Hangzhou, 311401, Zhejiang, China
Tel.: (86) 57188902531
Web Site: https://www.zhangxiaoquan.com
Year Founded: 2008
301055—(CHIN)
Rev.: $116,047,620
Assets: $137,239,596
Liabilities: $39,240,396
Net Worth: $97,999,200
Earnings: $5,825,196
Fiscal Year-end: 12/31/22
Household Appliance Mfr & Distr
N.A.I.C.S.: 335220
Zhangsheng Zhang (Chm)

ZHANGJIAGANG ELEGANT PLASTICS CO., LTD.
Hexing Civil Industrial Zone, Zhangjiagang, 215626, Jiangsu, China
Tel.: (86) 51258500399 CN
Web Site: http://www.eletile.com
Year Founded: 1992
Emp.: 1,000
PVC Plastic Floor Tiles
N.A.I.C.S.: 326199
Song Zhengxing (Pres)

ZHANGJIAGANG FREETRADE SCIENCE & TECHNOLOGY CO., LTD.
27-28F Petrochemical Trading Building, Zhangjiagang Free Trade Zone, Suzhou, 215634, Jiangsu, China
Tel.: (86) 51258320165
Web Site: http://www.zftc.net
600794—(SHG)
Rev.: $188,325,161
Assets: $523,382,755
Liabilities: $161,321,172
Net Worth: $362,061,582
Earnings: $22,939,675
Fiscal Year-end: 12/31/22
Warehousing Services
N.A.I.C.S.: 493110
Yong Tang (Chm & Pres)

ZHANGJIAGANG FURUI SPECIAL EQUIPMENT CO., LTD.
No 1419 Chenfeng Road, Yangshe Town, Zhangjiagang, 215637, Jiangsu, China
Tel.: (86) 51258982158
Web Site: https://www.furuigroup.com
Year Founded: 2003
300228—(SSE)
Rev.: $225,326,556
Assets: $532,189,008
Liabilities: $285,614,316
Net Worth: $246,574,692
Earnings: ($31,375,188)
Emp.: 2,000
Fiscal Year-end: 12/31/22
Heat Exchangers, Evaporators, Reactors, Cylinder Temperature Insulation Equipment, LNG Vehicle Bottles, Vacuum Pipes & Vaporization Equipment Mfr
N.A.I.C.S.: 333415

Subsidiaries:

LNGTOP (Jiangsu) Technology Co., Ltd (1)
Floor 5 Software industry park business center, Zhangjiagang Economic and Development Zone, Suzhou, China
Tel.: (86) 5125 830 9960
Web Site: http://www.lngtop.com
Industrial Information Management Services
N.A.I.C.S.: 518210

Zhangjiagang Furui Heavy Equipment Co., Ltd (1)
No 11 Chaodongweigang Road Yangtse Heavy Equipment Industrial Zone, Zhangjiagang, 215636, Jiangsu, China
Tel.: (86) 51280616554
Web Site: https://en.frhe.cn
High End Energy Equipment Mfr
N.A.I.C.S.: 333132

ZHANGJIAGANG GUANGDA SPECIAL MATERIAL CO., LTD.
Langanqiao Development Zone, Fenhuang Town, Zhangjiagang, 215614, Jiangsu, China
Tel.: (86) 51258591731
Web Site: https://www.zjggdtc.com
Year Founded: 2006
688186—(SHG)
Rev.: $472,768,260
Assets: $1,469,084,119
Liabilities: $940,018,786
Net Worth: $529,065,333
Earnings: $14,451,863
Fiscal Year-end: 12/31/22
Steel Product Mfr & Distr
N.A.I.C.S.: 331210
Weiming Xu (Chm & Gen Mgr)

ZHANGJIAGANG HAIGUO NEW ENERGY EQUIPMENT MANUFACTURING CO., LTD.
No 11 Jinfeng Road, Nanfeng Town, Zhangjiagang, 215628, Jiangsu, China
Tel.: (86) 51258903383
Web Site: https://www.zjghgxny.com
Year Founded: 2001
301063—(CHIN)
Rev.: $177,153,436
Assets: $312,300,562
Liabilities: $94,687,507
Net Worth: $217,613,056
Earnings: $7,860,718
Fiscal Year-end: 12/31/23
Natural Gas Distribution Services
N.A.I.C.S.: 221210
Xuehua Sheng (Chm)

ZHANGJIAGANG ZHONGHUAN HAILU HIGH-END EQUIPMENT CO., LTD.
No 158 Huashan Road, Hexing jinfeng Town, Zhangjiagang, 215626, Jiangsu, China
Tel.: (86) 51256913102
Web Site: https://www.hlduanjian.com
Year Founded: 2000
301040—(CHIN)
Rev.: $87,974,366
Assets: $236,829,182
Liabilities: $90,453,746
Net Worth: $146,375,436
Earnings: ($4,533,859)
Emp.: 150
Fiscal Year-end: 12/31/23
Forging Product Mfr & Distr
N.A.I.C.S.: 332111

ZHANGMEN EDUCATION INC.
No 82 Tongjia Road, Hongkou District, Shanghai, China
Tel.: (86) 2161421535 Ky
Web Site: http://www.zhangmenedu.com
Year Founded: 2017
ZMENY—(OTCIQ)
Rev.: $14,917,445
Assets: $23,978,131
Liabilities: $12,247,148
Net Worth: $11,730,983
Earnings: $111,069,590
Emp.: 62
Fiscal Year-end: 12/31/22
Educational Support Services
N.A.I.C.S.: 611710
Yi Zhang (Co-Founder, Chm & CEO)

ZHANGZHOU PIENTZEHUANG PHARMACEUTICAL CO., LTD.
Shang Street, Zhangzhou, 363000, Fujian, China
Tel.: (86) 5962301158
Web Site: http://www.zzpzh.com
600436—(SHG)
Rev.: $1,220,637,811
Assets: $2,050,379,768
Liabilities: $390,298,704
Net Worth: $1,660,081,064
Earnings: $347,117,196
Emp.: 2,100
Fiscal Year-end: 12/31/22
Pharmaceutical Product Mfr & Distr
N.A.I.C.S.: 325412
Jianshun Liu (Chm)

ZHANJIANG GUOLIAN AQUATIC PRODUCTS CO., LTD.
No 6 Industrial Avenue Huayu Industrial Transfer Industrial Park, Huangpo Town Wuchuan City, Zhanjiang, 300094, Guangdong, China
Tel.: (86) 7593153930
Web Site: http://www.guolian.cn
Year Founded: 2001
300094—(SSE)
Rev.: $718,036,488
Assets: $832,765,752
Liabilities: $384,945,912
Net Worth: $447,819,840
Earnings: ($1,064,232)
Emp.: 2,697
Fiscal Year-end: 12/31/22
Fresh & Frozen Seafood Processor & Distr
N.A.I.C.S.: 311710

Subsidiaries:

SSC, Inc. (1)
2910 Faber St, Union City, CA 94587
Tel.: (510) 477-0008
Web Site: http://www.sunnyvaleseafood.com
Emp.: 40
Fish & Seafood Markets
N.A.I.C.S.: 445250
Kevin Tang (VP-Sls & Bus Dev)

Zhanjiang Guolian Aquatic Products Co., Ltd.—(Continued)

ZHANLING INTERNATIONAL LIMITED
22/F Wanchai Central Building, 89 Lockhart Road, Wanchai, China (Hong Kong)
Tel.: (852) 90272707 NV
Web Site: http://www.odzacorp.com
Year Founded: 2009
ZLME—(OTCIQ)
Assets: $166
Liabilities: $8,540
Net Worth: ($8,374)
Earnings: ($10,463)
Emp.: 2
Fiscal Year-end: 05/31/24
Metal Mining & Exploration Services
N.A.I.C.S.: 212290
Liang Zhao (Pres, CEO & CFO)

ZHAOBANGJI LIFESTYLE HOLDINGS LIMITED
Unit 16-18 11/F China Merchants Tower Shun Tak Centre, 168-200 Connaught Road, Central, China (Hong Kong)
Tel.: (852) 31507742 Ky
Web Site:
http://www.szzhaobangji.com
1660—(HKG)
Rev.: $30,969,001
Assets: $73,535,367
Liabilities: $16,535,752
Net Worth: $56,999,615
Earnings: $11,376,294
Emp.: 225
Fiscal Year-end: 03/31/21
Construction Machinery Distr
N.A.I.C.S.: 423810

ZHAOJIN MINING INDUSTRY CO., LTD.
118 Wenquan Road, Zhaoyuan, 265400, Shandong, China
Tel.: (86) 5358266009 CN
Web Site: https://www.zhaojin.com.cn
Year Founded: 2004
1818—(HKG)
Rev.: $1,107,132,203
Assets: $6,442,604,298
Liabilities: $3,627,942,037
Net Worth: $2,814,662,261
Earnings: $78,650,114
Emp.: 6,760
Fiscal Year-end: 12/31/22
Mineral Exploration Services
N.A.I.C.S.: 213114
Wanhong Wang (VP)

ZHAYREMSKY GORNO-OBOGATITELNY KOMBINAT JSC
20 Gani Muratbayev st Zhayrem set-t, Karazhal, Karaganda, 100702, Kazakhstan
Tel.: (7) 71043 23290
JGOK—(KAZ)
Sales Range: Less than $1 Million
Nonferrous Metal Casting Services
N.A.I.C.S.: 331523
Sergey Bartosh (Chm-Mgmt Bd & CEO)

ZHE JIANG HEADMAN MACHINERY CO., LTD.
No 45 Changshun Road Bingang Industrial City, Shamen Town, Yuhuan, 317604, Zhejiang, China
Tel.: (86) 57687370758
Web Site: https://www.headman.cn
Year Founded: 1993
688577—(SHG)
Rev.: $88,592,400
Assets: $193,594,261
Liabilities: $72,206,330
Net Worth: $121,387,931
Earnings: $8,379,114
Fiscal Year-end: 12/31/22
Industrial Machinery Product Mfr & Distr
N.A.I.C.S.: 333248
Changquan Gao (Chm)

ZHE JIANG LI ZI YUAN FOOD CO., LTD.
Liziyuan Industrial Park, Caozhai Town Jindong District, Jinhua, 321000, Zhejiang, China
Tel.: (86) 57982881528
Web Site: http://www.liziyuan.com
Year Founded: 1994
605337—(SHG)
Rev.: $197,057,690
Assets: $333,707,339
Liabilities: $90,969,821
Net Worth: $242,737,518
Earnings: $31,032,795
Emp.: 40
Fiscal Year-end: 12/31/22
Food Product Mfr & Distr
N.A.I.C.S.: 311421
Guoping Li (Chm)

ZHE JIANG TAIHUA NEW MATERIAL CO., LTD.
No 627 Meibei Road Wangdian Town, Xiuzhou District, Jiaxing, 314011, Zhejiang, China
Web Site: http://www.textaihua.com
603055—(SHG)
Rev.: $562,802,386
Assets: $1,065,081,167
Liabilities: $491,762,780
Net Worth: $573,318,388
Earnings: $37,722,518
Fiscal Year-end: 12/31/22
Nylon Fabric Spinning Services
N.A.I.C.S.: 313110
Subsidiaries:

Fuhua Weaving Co., Ltd. (1)
No 2288 The 3rd Nanhuan Road, Shengze, Wujiang, 215228, Jiangsu, China
Tel.: (86) 51263599999
Web Site: http://www.texfuhua.cn
Textile Products Mfr
N.A.I.C.S.: 313310

Prutex Nylon Co., Ltd. (1)
NO 113 Meibei Road, WangdianTown Xiuzhou District, Jiaxing, Zhejiang, China
Tel.: (86) 15957347283
Web Site: http://www.prutex-nylonyarn.com
Civil Yarn Equipment Mfr
N.A.I.C.S.: 333248

ZHEFU HOLDING GROUP CO., LTD.
Zhefu Tower No 21 Lvting Road, Yuhang District, Hangzhou, 311121, Zhejiang, China
Tel.: (86) 57188238737
Web Site: https://www.zhefu.cn
Year Founded: 1970
002266—(SSE)
Rev.: $2,355,882,797
Assets: $3,456,779,344
Liabilities: $1,935,276,689
Net Worth: $1,521,502,655
Earnings: $205,915,371
Emp.: 6,000
Fiscal Year-end: 12/31/22
Hydraulic Generator Mfr
N.A.I.C.S.: 333611
Yi Sun (Chm)
Subsidiaries:

Zhejiang Linhai ZHEFU Electric Machinery Co., Ltd. (1)
24th floor Zhefu Tower No 177 Yingchun south RD, Tonglu, 311500, Zhejiang, China
Tel.: (86) 57689399778

Web Site: http://www.gb.zfemc.com
Hydropower Equipment Mfr & Distr
N.A.I.C.S.: 335999

ZHEJIANG AKCOME NEW ENERGY TECHNOLOGY CO.,LTD.
Room 901 Building 1 No 1818-2 Wenyi West Road Yuhang Street, Yuhang District, Hangzhou, Zhejiang, China
Tel.: (86) 51282557328 CN
Web Site: https://akcome.com
Year Founded: 2006
002610—(SSE)
Rev.: $939,353,220
Assets: $1,623,165,804
Liabilities: $1,172,893,176
Net Worth: $450,272,628
Earnings: ($117,051,480)
Emp.: 3,500
Fiscal Year-end: 12/31/22
Photovoltaic Solar Energy Accessories Mfr
N.A.I.C.S.: 334419
Subsidiaries:

Suzhou Akcome Photovoltaics System Co., Ltd. (1)
West Road Economic Development Zone, Zhangjiagang, Jiangsu, China
Tel.: (86) 512 35002626
Web Site: http://www.akcome.com
Photovoltaic Device Mfr
N.A.I.C.S.: 334413

ZHEJIANG ANGLIKANG PHARMACEUTICAL CO., LTD.
No 1000 North of Shengzhou Avenue, Shengzhou, 312400, Zhejiang, China
Tel.: (86) 57583123228
Web Site: https://www.alkpharm.com
Year Founded: 2001
002940—(SSE)
Rev.: $220,208,583
Assets: $364,490,095
Liabilities: $133,369,737
Net Worth: $231,120,359
Earnings: $17,872,401
Fiscal Year-end: 12/31/22
Pharmaceutical Product Mfr & Distr
N.A.I.C.S.: 325412
Subsidiaries:

Jiangsu Yuexin Pharmaceutical Co., Ltd. (1)
29 No South Road Economic Development Zone, Xinghua, Taizhou, 225700, China
Tel.: (86) 52380516888
Web Site: https://www.yuexingyy.com
Emp.: 226
Pharmaceuticals Product Mfr
N.A.I.C.S.: 325412

Zhejiang Anglikang Capsule Co., Ltd. (1)
No 1000 North Shengzhou Avenue, Shengzhou, 312400, Zhejiang, China
Tel.: (86) 57583185582
Web Site: http://www.iecworld.com
Pharmaceuticals Product Mfr
N.A.I.C.S.: 325412

ZHEJIANG ANT SMALL & MICRO FINANCIAL SERVICES GROUP CO., LTD.
Building B Huanglong Times Plaza, 18 Wantang Road, Hangzhou, China
Tel.: (86) 571 2688 8888 CN
Web Site: http://www.antgroup.com
Year Founded: 2014
Holding Company; Payment Processing, Wealth Management, Credit Scoring & Reporting, Private Banking & Cloud Computing Services
N.A.I.C.S.: 551112
Eric Jing (Chm)

INTERNATIONAL PUBLIC

Subsidiaries:

Alipay Co., Ltd. (1)
Building B Huanglong Times Plaza No 18 Wantang Road, Hangzhou, China
Tel.: (86) 571 2688 8888
Web Site: http://www.alipay.com
Payment Processing Application Developer & Data Services
N.A.I.C.S.: 541511
Cherry Huang (Gen Mgr-Cros Border Bus-South & Southeast Asia)

EyeVerify Inc. (1)
1712 Main St 5th Fl, Kansas City, MO 64108
Tel.: (913) 608-9257
Web Site: http://www.eyeverify.com
Software Publisher
N.A.I.C.S.: 513210
Jeremy Paben (VP-Engrg)

ZHEJIANG AOKANG SHOES CO., LTD.
Aokang Industrial Park Qianshi Industrial Zone, Oubei Town Yongjia County, Wenzhou, 325102, Zhejiang, China
Tel.: (86) 57767915188
Web Site: http://www.aokang.com
Year Founded: 1988
603001—(SHG)
Rev.: $386,680,666
Assets: $598,852,908
Liabilities: $185,404,448
Net Worth: $413,448,460
Earnings: ($51,917,393)
Fiscal Year-end: 12/31/22
Shoe Mfr & Whslr
N.A.I.C.S.: 316210
Zhentao Wang (Chm)
Subsidiaries:

Chengdu Kanghua Biological Products Co., Ltd. (1)
No 182 Beijing Road, Chengdu Economic & Technological Development Zone, Chengdu, 610100, Sichuan, China
Tel.: (86) 2884846555
Web Site: http://www.kangh.com
Rev.: $222,176,142
Assets: $592,875,440
Liabilities: $97,921,258
Net Worth: $494,954,182
Earnings: $71,723,074
Fiscal Year-end: 12/31/2023
Pharmaceutical Product Mfr & Distr
N.A.I.C.S.: 325412
Zhentao Wang (Chm)

ZHEJIANG ASIA-PACIFIC MECHANICAL AND ELECTRONIC CO., LTD.
No 1399 Yatai Road, Shushan Subdistrict Xiaoshan District, Hangzhou, 311203, Zhejiang, China
Tel.: (86) 57182765229
Web Site: http://www.chinaapg.com
Year Founded: 2000
002284—(SSE)
Rev.: $526,483,138
Assets: $913,843,439
Liabilities: $533,176,427
Net Worth: $380,667,011
Earnings: $9,536,305
Emp.: 1,700
Fiscal Year-end: 12/31/22
Automobile Braking Systems Mfr & Sales
N.A.I.C.S.: 336340
Huang Weizhong (Chm)

ZHEJIANG AUSUN PHARMACEUTICAL CO., LTD.
No 5 Donghai Fourth Lane Linhai Park Zhejiang Chemical API Base, Linhai, 317016, Zhejiang, China
Tel.: (86) 57685589335
Web Site:
https://en.ausunpharm.com

AND PRIVATE COMPANIES   **ZHEJIANG CHENFENG SCIENCE & TECHNOLOGY CO., LTD.**

Year Founded: 2010
603229—(SHG)
Rev.: $107,342,455
Assets: $325,072,360
Liabilities: $119,928,234
Net Worth: $205,144,126
Earnings: $33,046,762
Emp.: 1,000
Fiscal Year-end: 12/31/22
Pharmaceutical Intermediate Mfr & Distr
N.A.I.C.S.: 325412
Zheng Zhiguo *(Chm & Gen Mgr)*

ZHEJIANG BAIDA PRECISION MANUFACTURING CORP.
No 2399 Haicheng Road Taizhou Bay, New District, Taizhou, 318000, Zhejiang, China
Tel.: (86) 57688488867
Web Site: https://www.baidapm.com
Year Founded: 1995
603331—(SHG)
Rev.: $180,758,584
Assets: $296,618,349
Liabilities: $155,634,341
Net Worth: $140,984,008
Earnings: $9,453,595
Fiscal Year-end: 12/31/22
Compressor Parts Mfr
N.A.I.C.S.: 333415
Shi Xiaoyou *(Chm)*

ZHEJIANG BANGJIE HOLDING GROUP CO., LTD.
Bangjie Plaza No 21 Suhua Road, Suxi Town, Yiwu, 322009, Zhejiang, China
Tel.: (86) 7985922188
Web Site: https://www.bangjie.cn
Year Founded: 2008
002634—(SSE)
Rev.: $85,426,338
Assets: $181,325,322
Liabilities: $51,988,337
Net Worth: $129,336,985
Earnings: $10,231,257
Fiscal Year-end: 12/31/22
Textile Products Mfr
N.A.I.C.S.: 315250
Shiqing Tao *(VP, Deputy Gen Mgr & Dir)*

ZHEJIANG BENLI TECHNOLOGY CO., LTD.
No 15 Donghai Sixth Avenue, Linhai Toumen Port New District, Taizhou, 317016, Zhejiang, China
Tel.: (86) 57685580770
Web Site: https://www.benlitech.com
Year Founded: 2011
301065—(SHG)
Rev.: $106,527,096
Assets: $195,777,972
Liabilities: $20,711,808
Net Worth: $175,066,164
Earnings: $8,352,396
Fiscal Year-end: 12/31/22
Pharmaceutical Product Mfr & Distr
N.A.I.C.S.: 325412
Zhengjie Wu *(Chm & Gen Mgr)*

ZHEJIANG BOFAY ELECTRIC CO., LTD.
16 Hangping Road Economic Development Zone, Haining Economic Development Zone Haining, Haining, 314400, Zhejiang, China
Tel.: (86) 57389238610
Web Site: https://www.bofay.com.cn
Year Founded: 2007
001255—(SSE)
Rev.: $49,635,865
Assets: $140,395,114
Liabilities: $31,008,182
Net Worth: $109,386,932

Earnings: $9,730,099
Emp.: 300
Fiscal Year-end: 12/31/22
Insulation Material Mfr & Distr
N.A.I.C.S.: 326140
Yunfeng Lu *(Chm)*

ZHEJIANG BUSEN GARMENTS CO., LTD.
No 419 Busen Avenue, Fengqiao Town, Zhuji, 310000, Zhejiang, China
Tel.: (86) 57187837827
Web Site: http://www.busen.cn
Year Founded: 1984
002569—(SSE)
Rev.: $19,419,524
Assets: $41,504,093
Liabilities: $18,666,742
Net Worth: $22,837,352
Earnings: ($9,972,303)
Emp.: 1,992
Fiscal Year-end: 12/31/22
Men's Apparels Mfr & Marketing
N.A.I.C.S.: 315250
Chunjiang Wang *(Chm)*

ZHEJIANG CANAAN TECHNOLOGY CO., LTD.
188 Jiangnan Avenue Oubei Street, Yongjia, Wenzhou, 325102, Zhejiang, China
Tel.: (86) 57767378828
Web Site:
https://www.chinacanaan.com
Year Founded: 2000
300412—(SSE)
Rev.: $154,921,572
Assets: $351,004,212
Liabilities: $198,886,428
Net Worth: $152,117,784
Earnings: ($10,558,080)
Emp.: 450
Fiscal Year-end: 12/31/22
Laboratory Equipment Mfr
N.A.I.C.S.: 334516
Fang Zheng *(Chm & Pres)*

Subsidiaries:

Zhejiang Canaan Kaixinlong Technology Co., Ltd.   (1)
No 199 Road 2 Economic Development Zone, Ruian, Zhejiang, China
Tel.: (86) 5775 881 2028
Web Site: https://www.kaixinlong.com
Pharmaceutical Machinery Mfr & Retailer
N.A.I.C.S.: 333248

ZHEJIANG CANGNAN INSTRUMENT GROUP CO., LTD.
Industrial Demonstration Park, Ling Xi Town Cangnan County, Wenzhou, Zhejiang, China
Tel.: (86) 57764837701   CN
Web Site: http://www.zjcnyb.com
Year Founded: 1977
1743—(HKG)
Rev.: $62,767,379
Assets: $216,743,429
Liabilities: $50,607,255
Net Worth: $166,136,174
Earnings: $12,494,735
Emp.: 535
Fiscal Year-end: 12/31/20
Measuring Equipment Mfr & Distr
N.A.I.C.S.: 334513
Zuobin Hong *(Chm)*

ZHEJIANG CAYI VACUUM CONTAINER CO., LTD.
No 3 Jinniu Rd Baiyang Industrial Area, Wuyi, Jinhua, 321200, Zhejiang, China
Tel.: (86) 57987950768
Web Site: https://www.cayigroup.com
Year Founded: 2004

301004—(CHIN)
Rev.: $250,056,605
Assets: $231,465,422
Liabilities: $47,481,563
Net Worth: $183,983,859
Earnings: $66,463,507
Fiscal Year-end: 12/31/23
Vacuum Container Mfr & Distr
N.A.I.C.S.: 335314

ZHEJIANG CENTURY HUATONG GROUP CO., LTD.
No 22 Boyun Road Pudong New Area, Caoe Sub-district Shangyu District, Shaoxing, 312300, Zhejiang, China
Tel.: (86) 57582218511
Web Site: https://www.sjhuatong.com
002602—(SSE)
Rev.: $1,611,107,690
Assets: $4,676,966,555
Liabilities: $1,118,017,948
Net Worth: $3,558,948,607
Earnings: ($995,729,576)
Emp.: 5,000
Fiscal Year-end: 12/31/22
Automobile Parts Mfr
N.A.I.C.S.: 336390
Miaotong Wang *(Chm)*

ZHEJIANG CFMOTO POWER CO., LTD.
No 116 Wuzhou Road Yuhang Economic Development Zone, Hangzhou, 311100, Zhejiang, China
Tel.: (86) 57189195143
Web Site: https://www.cfmoto.com
Year Founded: 1989
603129—(SHG)
Rev.: $1,597,473,573
Assets: $1,341,403,797
Liabilities: $738,379,872
Net Worth: $603,023,925
Earnings: $98,471,829
Emp.: 5,500
Fiscal Year-end: 12/31/22
Terrain Vehicle Mfr & Distr
N.A.I.C.S.: 336991
Lai Guogui *(Chm)*

ZHEJIANG CHANGAN RENHENG TECHNOLOGY CO., LTD.
Laoyatang Si'an, Changxing, Zhejiang, China
Tel.: (86) 5726822488   CN
Web Site: http://www.renheng.com
Year Founded: 2000
8139—(HKG)
Rev.: $21,174,783
Assets: $39,052,605
Liabilities: $22,888,773
Net Worth: $16,163,832
Earnings: $199,397
Emp.: 158
Fiscal Year-end: 12/31/22
Bentonite Clay Product Mfr & Whslr
N.A.I.C.S.: 327120
Nan Li *(Co-Sec)*

ZHEJIANG CHANGHUA AUTO PARTS CO., LTD.
No 707 Beixiang, Zhoucheng, Cixi, Zhejiang, China
Tel.: (86) 57463323168
Web Site:
http://www.zjchanghua.com
Year Founded: 1993
605018—(SHG)
Rev.: $257,682,241
Assets: $478,310,761
Liabilities: $109,246,181
Net Worth: $369,064,580
Earnings: $15,375,471
Emp.: 2,000
Fiscal Year-end: 12/31/22

Automotive Parts Mfr & Distr
N.A.I.C.S.: 336390
Changtu Wang *(Chm)*

ZHEJIANG CHANGSHENG SLIDING BEARINGS CO., LTD.
No 6 Xinda Road Economic Development Zone, Jiashan, 314100, Zhejiang, China
Tel.: (86) 57384184307
Web Site: https://www.csb-bearings.com
Year Founded: 1995
300718—(CHIN)
Rev.: $155,703,323
Assets: $275,757,243
Liabilities: $46,816,892
Net Worth: $228,940,351
Earnings: $34,119,335
Emp.: 800
Fiscal Year-end: 12/31/23
Bearing Parts Mfr
N.A.I.C.S.: 332991
Sun Zhihua *(Chm)*

Subsidiaries:

CSB Americas Inc.   (1)
493 Mission St, Carol Stream, IL 60188
Tel.: (248) 630-9082
Web Site: https://www.csbamerica.com
Bearing Component Mfr
N.A.I.C.S.: 332991

CSB Bearings France Sarl   (1)
3 Bd Eugene Marie, B P 111, Brionne, 27800, Beaumont, France
Tel.: (33) 23 243 3276
Web Site: https://www.csb-bearings.fr
Emp.: 750
Metal Product Bearing Mfr & Distr
N.A.I.C.S.: 336350

CSB Gleitlager GmbH   (1)
Meierstrasse 36a, 32120, Hiddenhausen, Germany
Tel.: (49) 52239850690
Web Site: https://www.csb-gleitlager.de
Bearing Component Mfr
N.A.I.C.S.: 332991

CSB Sliding Bearing (India) Pvt. Ltd.   (1)
Akash Deep Building Suite 206 Second Floor 26-A Barakkhamba Road, New Delhi, 110001, India
Tel.: (91) 1166302220
Web Site:
https://www.csbslidingbearings.com
Bearing Component Mfr
N.A.I.C.S.: 332991

ZHEJIANG CHENFENG SCIENCE & TECHNOLOGY CO., LTD.
No 10 Fourth Road, Yanguan Town, Haining, Zhejiang, China
Tel.: (86) 57387618171
Web Site:
https://www.cnlampholder.com
Year Founded: 2001
603685—(SHG)
Rev.: $163,202,827
Assets: $308,323,581
Liabilities: $150,859,519
Net Worth: $157,464,062
Earnings: ($5,683,055)
Fiscal Year-end: 12/31/22
Lighting Fixture Product Mfr & Distr
N.A.I.C.S.: 335139

Subsidiaries:

Haining Mingyi Electronic Technology Co., Ltd.   (1)
Building 15-16 tiantong road 2 industrial park, Yanguan Town Haining City, Jiaxing, Zhejiang, China   (51%)
Tel.: (86) 5738 761 1565
Web Site: https://www.lampcover.cn
Emp.: 200
Lampshade Production & Injection Mold Mfr
N.A.I.C.S.: 333511

ZHEJIANG CHENGCHANG TECHNOLOGY CO., LTD.

Zhejiang Chenfeng Science & Technology Co., Ltd.—(Continued)

ZHEJIANG CHENGCHANG TECHNOLOGY CO., LTD.
No 428 Zhiqiang Road, Sandun Town Xihu District, Hangzhou, 310000, Zhejiang, China
Tel.: (86) 57181023628
Web Site: https://www.zjcckj.com
Year Founded: 2010
001270—(SSE)
Rev.: $39,540,683
Assets: $203,730,676
Liabilities: $9,960,797
Net Worth: $193,769,879
Earnings: $10,968,021
Fiscal Year-end: 12/31/23
Amplifier Chips Mfr & Distr
N.A.I.C.S.: 334310
Luo Shanshan *(Chm)*

ZHEJIANG CHENGYI PHARMACEUTICAL CO., LTD
No 118 Huagong Road, Dongtou District, Wenzhou, 201100, Zhejiang, China
Tel.: (86) 57763484842
Web Site: http://www.chengyipharma.com
Year Founded: 1966
603811—(SHG)
Rev.: $91,958,181
Assets: $241,360,727
Liabilities: $88,193,889
Net Worth: $153,166,839
Earnings: $22,686,281
Fiscal Year-end: 12/31/22
Pharmaceutical Product Mfr & Distr
N.A.I.C.S.: 325412
Yan Yiyi *(Chm)*

ZHEJIANG CHINA COMMODITIES CITY GROUP CO., LTD.
Ocean Business Building No 105 Futian Road, Yiwu, 322000, Zhejiang, China
Tel.: (86) 57985182700
Web Site: http://www.cccgroup.com.cn
Year Founded: 1993
600415—(SHG)
Rev.: $1,069,804,995
Assets: $4,508,385,004
Liabilities: $2,362,919,069
Net Worth: $2,145,465,935
Earnings: $155,102,562
Fiscal Year-end: 12/31/22
Construction Engineering & Commodity Trading Services
N.A.I.C.S.: 541330
Wang Dong *(Chm)*

ZHEJIANG CHINA LIGHT & TEXTILE INDUSTRIAL CITY GROUP CO., LTD.
Zhongqing Building No 1 Jianhu Road, Keqiao District, Shaoxing, 312030, Zhejiang, China
Tel.: (86) 57584116158
Web Site: http://www.qfcgroup.com
Year Founded: 1993
600790—(SHG)
Rev.: $115,154,283
Assets: $1,468,321,031
Liabilities: $575,644,844
Net Worth: $892,676,187
Earnings: $166,632,378
Fiscal Year-end: 12/31/22
Market Leasing Services
N.A.I.C.S.: 531120
Pan Jianhua *(Chm)*

ZHEJIANG CHINASTARS NEW MATERIALS GROUP CO., LTD.
No 98 Shimin Street, Jianggan District, Hangzhou, 310016, Zhejiang, China
Tel.: (86) 57187155512
Web Site: https://www.chinastars.com.cn
Year Founded: 2003
301077—(CHIN)
Rev.: $98,252,267
Assets: $250,275,520
Liabilities: $76,803,253
Net Worth: $173,472,267
Earnings: $13,728,225
Emp.: 800
Fiscal Year-end: 12/31/23
Reflective Material Mfr
N.A.I.C.S.: 334417
Shijie Wang *(Chm & Gen Mgr)*

ZHEJIANG CHUNHUI INTELLIGENT CONTROL CO., LTD.
No 288 Chunhui Industrial Avenue, Shangyu District, Shaoxing, 312300, Zhejiang, China
Tel.: (86) 57582157070
Web Site: http://www.chunhuizk.com
Year Founded: 1993
300943—(SSE)
Rev.: $69,165,828
Assets: $168,782,043
Liabilities: $38,758,206
Net Worth: $130,023,836
Earnings: $10,576,318
Fiscal Year-end: 12/31/22
Industrial Flow Control Equipment Mfr & Distr
N.A.I.C.S.: 332912
Guangyu Yang *(Chm)*

ZHEJIANG COMMUNICATIONS INVESTMENT GROUP CO., LTD.
199 Wuxing Road Sijiqing Sub district, Qianjiang District, Hangzhou, 310020, China
Tel.: (86) 57185304777
Web Site: http://www.cncico.com
Year Founded: 2001
Emp.: 40,000
Transportation Services
N.A.I.C.S.: 561599
Zhan Xiaozhang *(Gen Mgr)*

ZHEJIANG CONBA PHARMACEUTICAL CO., LTD.
No 568 Binkang Road, Binjiang Science Economic Park High-tech Development Zone, Hangzhou, 310052, Zhejiang, China
Tel.: (86) 57187774801
Web Site: http://en.conbagroup.com
Year Founded: 1969
600572—(SHG)
Rev.: $842,462,253
Assets: $1,534,567,072
Liabilities: $506,274,018
Net Worth: $1,028,293,054
Earnings: $50,277,226
Emp.: 8,000
Fiscal Year-end: 12/31/22
Pharmaceuticals Product Mfr
N.A.I.C.S.: 325412
Jiang Yi *(Chm)*

Subsidiaries:

Hangzhou Conba Pharmaceutical Co., Ltd. (1)
No 568 Binkang Road Changhe Street, Binjiang District, Hangzhou, Zhejiang, China
Tel.: (86) 57187774413
Web Site: http://hzconba.conbagroup.com
Pharmaceuticals Product Mfr
N.A.I.C.S.: 325412

Zhejiang Jinhua Conba Bio-Pharm. Co., Ltd. (1)
High-tech Development Zone Jiangnan Avenue 288 Conba Building, Binjiang, Hangzhou, 310051, China
Tel.: (86) 57128335663
Web Site: http://www.jhconba.com
Emp.: 1,000
Pharmaceuticals Product Mfr
N.A.I.C.S.: 325412

ZHEJIANG CONSTRUCTION INVESTMENT GROUP CO., LTD.
No 52 Wensan West Road, Xihu District, Hangzhou, 310012, Zhejiang, China
Tel.: (86) 57188057132
Web Site: https://www.cnzgc.com
Year Founded: 2006
002761—(SSE)
Rev.: $12,187,801,877
Assets: $13,295,680,240
Liabilities: $12,171,463,562
Net Worth: $1,124,216,678
Earnings: $164,711,475
Fiscal Year-end: 12/31/20
Household Textile Mfr
N.A.I.C.S.: 313210

ZHEJIANG CRYSTAL-OPTECH CO., LTD.
No 2198 Kaifa Avenue East Section, Jiaojiang District, Taizhou, 318014, Zhejiang, China
Tel.: (86) 57688677966
Web Site: https://www.crystal-optech.com
Year Founded: 2002
002273—(SSE)
Rev.: $614,322,123
Assets: $1,443,115,791
Liabilities: $247,332,445
Net Worth: $1,195,783,346
Earnings: $80,894,366
Fiscal Year-end: 12/31/22
Optoelectronic Component Mfr
N.A.I.C.S.: 334419
Min Lin *(Chm)*

Subsidiaries:

Jiangxi Crystal Optech Co., Ltd. (1)
No 7 Hexie Road Yingtan Hi-Tech Industrial Development Zone, Yingtan, 335000, Jiangxi, China
Tel.: (86) 7017071001
Optoelectronic Component Mfr
N.A.I.C.S.: 334419

ZheJiang Crystal Display Technology Co, Ltd. (1)
Room A3079M F3 Tower I North No 368 Liuhe Road Binjiang Road Hangzhou, Tower A16 Xingxing Electronic Industrial Zone Jiaojiang District, Taizhou, 318015, Zhejiang, China
Tel.: (86) 57688032566
Optoelectronic Component Mfr
N.A.I.C.S.: 334419

Zhejiang Fangyuan Yeshili Reflective Material Co., Ltd. (1)
No 292 Donghai Avenue Jiaojiang Economic Development Zone, Taizhou, 318000, Zhejiang, China
Tel.: (86) 57688201676
Optoelectronic Component Mfr
N.A.I.C.S.: 334419

Zhejiang T.Best Electronic Information Technology Co., Ltd (1)
Economic Development Zone Linhai Road, Taizhou, 317000, Zhejiang, China
Tel.: (86) 57689117854
Web Site: http://www.t-best.net
Optoelectronic Component Mfr
N.A.I.C.S.: 334419

ZHEJIANG DAFENG INDUSTRIAL CO., LTD.
No 737 Xinjian North Road, Yuyao, Zhejiang, China
Tel.: (86) 57462888812
Web Site: https://en.chinadafeng.com
Year Founded: 1991
603081—(SHG)
Rev.: $399,075,038
Assets: $1,075,322,336
Liabilities: $668,856,235
Net Worth: $406,466,101
Earnings: $40,272,996
Fiscal Year-end: 12/31/22
Stage Designing Services
N.A.I.C.S.: 541410
Hua Feng *(Chm & Pres)*

ZHEJIANG DAHUA TECHNOLOGY CO., LTD.
No 1199 Binan Road, Binjiang District, Hangzhou, 310053, China
Tel.: (86) 57187688883
Web Site: https://www.dahuasecurity.com
002236—(SSE)
Rev.: $4,291,377,948
Assets: $6,493,906,290
Liabilities: $2,812,846,889
Net Worth: $3,681,059,401
Earnings: $326,339,596
Emp.: 23,000
Fiscal Year-end: 12/31/22
Security System Mfr & Distr
N.A.I.C.S.: 334290

Subsidiaries:

Dahua Guvenlik Teknolojileri Sanayi ve Ticaret A.S. (1)
Barbaros mah Begonya sk No 3 Kat 21 / 181-182 Nidakule Kuzey, 34746, Istanbul, Turkiye
Tel.: (90) 2165108589
Electrical Apparatus & Equipment Whslr
N.A.I.C.S.: 423610

Dahua IBERIA S.L. (1)
Tel.: (34) 917649862
Electrical Apparatus & Equipment Whslr
N.A.I.C.S.: 423610
Gavin Zou *(Mgr-Technical & Project)*

Dahua Security Malaysia Sdn. bhd. (1)
Unit 1103 Level 11 Uptown 2 No 2 Jalan SS21/37 Damansara Uptown, 47400, Petaling Jaya, Selangor Darul Ehsan, Malaysia
Tel.: (60) 376620732
Web Site: https://www.dahuasecurity.com
Information Technology Consulting Services
N.A.I.C.S.: 518210

Dahua Technology Australia Pty. Ltd. (1)
Unit 8 39 Herbert Street, Artarmon, 2064, NSW, Australia
Tel.: (61) 299285200
Electrical Apparatus & Equipment Whslr
N.A.I.C.S.: 423610

Dahua Technology Chile SpA (1)
Oficina 302 Edificio Alto el Golf Avenida Vitacura 2969, Comuna de Las Condes, Santiago, Chile
Tel.: (56) 232705421
Electrical Apparatus & Equipment Whslr
N.A.I.C.S.: 423610
Gonzalo Corro Gomez *(Project Mgr)*

Dahua Technology Colombia S.A.S. (1)
Calle113-52 Oficina 1903 Torres Unida II, CRA9A, Bogota, Colombia
Tel.: (57) 7446110
Electrical Apparatus & Equipment Whslr
N.A.I.C.S.: 423610

Dahua Technology GmbH (1)
Tel.: (49) 21120544121
Electrical Apparatus & Equipment Whslr
N.A.I.C.S.: 423610

Dahua Technology Hungary Ltd. (1)
Tel.: (36) 17899852
Web Site: https://dahuatechnology.hu
Electrical Apparatus & Equipment Whslr
N.A.I.C.S.: 423610

Dahua Technology India Private Limited (1)
9th Floor Tower A DLF Cyber Greens DLF Cyber City Phase III, Institutional Area, Gur-

AND PRIVATE COMPANIES

gaon, 122002, Haryana, India
Tel.: (91) 1244569100
Electrical Apparatus & Equipment Whslr
N.A.I.C.S.: 423610

Dahua Technology Kazakhstan LLP (1)
13 Al-Farabi Avenue block 1B office 504
Nur-Sultan, BURO Haus Business Center
4th floor, Nurly-Tau Business Center 11/4
Kabanbay Batyr Avenue, 050000, Almaty,
Kazakhstan
Tel.: (7) 7273110838
Web Site: https://www.dahua-technology.kz
Electrical Apparatus & Equipment Whslr
N.A.I.C.S.: 423610

Dahua Technology Korea Company Limited (1)
807 E and C Venture Dream Tower 3 38-21
Digital-ro 31-gil, Guro-gu, Seoul, Korea (South)
Tel.: (82) 7081618889
Electrical Apparatus & Equipment Whslr
N.A.I.C.S.: 423610

Dahua Technology Mexico S.A. de C.V. (1)
Oficina 1502 Plaza Carso II Lago Zurich,
No 219 col Ampliacion Granada Miguel Hidalgo, CP11529, Mexico, Mexico
Tel.: (52) 5567231936
Electrical Apparatus & Equipment Whslr
N.A.I.C.S.: 423610

Dahua Technology Middle East FZE (1)
Tel.: (971) 43991806
Information Technology Consulting Services
N.A.I.C.S.: 518210

Dahua Technology Peru S.A.C (1)
Av Javier Prado Este No 488 Torre
Orquideas Oficina 202 San Isidro, Lima, Peru
Tel.: (51) 15008555
Electrical Apparatus & Equipment Whslr
N.A.I.C.S.: 423610

Dahua Technology Rus LLC (1)
Leninskaya Sloboda street 19 floor 5 room 5010, Moscow, Russia
Tel.: (7) 8007076766
Web Site: https://dahuastore.ru
Electrical Apparatus & Equipment Whslr
N.A.I.C.S.: 423610
Dmitry Luzin *(Dir-Commi)*

Dahua Technology Singapore Pte.Ltd. (1)
11 Irving Place 07-03 Tai Seng Point, Singapore, 369551, Singapore
Tel.: (65) 31298008
Electrical Apparatus & Equipment Whslr
N.A.I.C.S.: 423610

Dahua Technology UK Ltd. (1)
Queen Anne House 25-27 Broadway, Maidenhead, SL61LY, United Kingdom
Tel.: (44) 1628673667
Information Technology Consulting Services
N.A.I.C.S.: 518210

Dahua Technology USA Inc. (1)
15245 Alton Pkwy Ste 100, Irvine, CA 92618
Tel.: (949) 679-7777
Web Site: https://us.dahuasecurity.com
Electrical Apparatus & Equipment Whslr
N.A.I.C.S.: 423610

ZHEJIANG DAILY DIGITAL CULTURE GROUP CO., LTD.
Building A Zhejiang Daily Digital Culture Technology Park, No 15 Chuxin Road Gongshu District, Hangzhou, 310015, Zhejiang, China
Tel.: (86) 57185311338
Web Site: http://www.600633.cn
Year Founded: 1992
600633—(SHG)
Rev.: $728,165,702
Assets: $1,712,817,452
Liabilities: $289,295,239
Net Worth: $1,423,522,213
Earnings: $68,752,827
Fiscal Year-end: 12/31/22

Newspaper Publishing Services
N.A.I.C.S.: 513110
Tong Jie *(Chm)*

ZHEJIANG DALI TECHNOLOGY CO., LTD.
639 Binkang Road, Hangzhou, 310053, China
Tel.: (86) 57186695603
Web Site: https://www.dali-tech.us
Year Founded: 1984
002214—(SSE)
Rev.: $56,269,989
Assets: $389,307,536
Liabilities: $65,077,253
Net Worth: $324,230,283
Earnings: $(21,171,885)
Fiscal Year-end: 12/31/22
Digital Imaging Equipment Mfr & Distr
N.A.I.C.S.: 333310
Pang Huimin *(Chm & Gen Mgr)*

ZHEJIANG DAYANG BIOTECH GROUP CO., LTD.
No 22 Chaoyang Road, Dayang Town, Jiande, 311616, Zhejiang, China
Tel.: (86) 57164156812
Web Site: https://www.dyhg.com
Year Founded: 1976
003017—(SSE)
Rev.: $148,557,928
Assets: $211,719,536
Liabilities: $73,418,600
Net Worth: $138,300,936
Earnings: $11,334,057
Fiscal Year-end: 12/31/22
Chemical Product Mfr & Distr
N.A.I.C.S.: 325520
Yanggui Chen *(Chm)*

ZHEJIANG DAYUAN PUMPS INDUSTRY CO., LTD.
East of Xincheng Avenue South of Zhongxing Avenue Zeguo, Wenling, 317523, Zhejiang, China
Tel.: (86) 57686425284
Web Site: https://www.cnpumps.com
Year Founded: 1998
603757—(SHG)
Rev.: $235,592,815
Assets: $338,138,307
Liabilities: $121,755,259
Net Worth: $216,383,048
Earnings: $36,610,114
Emp.: 1,200
Fiscal Year-end: 12/31/22
Water Pump Mfr & Distr
N.A.I.C.S.: 333914
Pang Huimin *(Chm & Gen Mgr)*

ZHEJIANG DEHONG AUTOMOTIVE ELECTRONIC & ELECTRICAL CO.,LTD.
No 1888 Southern Tai-Lake Avenue, Huzhou, Zhejiang, China
Tel.: (86) 5722756126
Web Site: https://www.dehong.com.cn
Year Founded: 1978
603701—(SHG)
Rev.: $69,053,564
Assets: $142,558,482
Liabilities: $35,248,641
Net Worth: $107,309,840
Earnings: $1,555,084
Fiscal Year-end: 12/31/22
Automobile Alternator Mfr & Distr
N.A.I.C.S.: 336320
Qin Xunyang *(Chm)*

ZHEJIANG DIBAY ELECTRIC CO., LTD.
No 66 Dibei Road, Sanjiang Subdistrict, Shengzhou, 312400, Zhejiang, China

Tel.: (86) 57583368521
Web Site: http://www.dibei.com
Year Founded: 1993
603320—(SHG)
Rev.: $140,464,247
Assets: $176,749,546
Liabilities: $65,238,250
Net Worth: $111,511,296
Earnings: $4,801,357
Fiscal Year-end: 12/31/22
Motor Vehicle Product Mfr & Distr
N.A.I.C.S.: 336390
Wu Jianrong *(Chm)*

ZHEJIANG DINGLI MACHINERY CO., LTD.
188 Qihang Road, Leidian Town Deqing County, Huzhou, 313219, Zhejiang, China
Tel.: (86) 5728681688
Web Site: https://www.cndingli.com
Year Founded: 2005
603338—(SHG)
Rev.: $764,499,425
Assets: $1,656,973,913
Liabilities: $665,022,262
Net Worth: $991,951,651
Earnings: $176,516,496
Fiscal Year-end: 12/31/22
Aerial Work Machinery Mfr & Distr
N.A.I.C.S.: 333923
Shugen Xu *(Chm)*

ZHEJIANG DONGRI COMPANY LIMITED
12th Floor Hezhong Building No 168 Shifu Road, Lucheng District, Wenzhou, 325003, Zhejiang, China
Tel.: (86) 57788850088
Web Site: https://www.dongri.com
Year Founded: 1997
600113—(SHG)
Rev.: $128,910,310
Assets: $401,169,174
Liabilities: $86,015,204
Net Worth: $315,153,971
Earnings: $22,497,443
Emp.: 150
Fiscal Year-end: 12/31/22
Real Estate Services; Various Products Distr, Importer & Exporter
N.A.I.C.S.: 531390
Zuojun Yang *(Chm)*

ZHEJIANG DONGWANG TIMES TECHNOLOGY CO., LTD.
14F Building A Xizi International No 9 Jingtan Road, Shangcheng District, Hangzhou, 310020, Zhejiang, China
Tel.: (86) 57187974176
Web Site: https://www.dwsd.cn
Year Founded: 1993
600052—(SHG)
Rev.: $30,856,747
Assets: $496,703,680
Liabilities: $81,370,322
Net Worth: $415,333,358
Earnings: $(29,835,814)
Fiscal Year-end: 12/31/22
Real Estate Support Services
N.A.I.C.S.: 531390
Wu Kaijun *(Chm)*

ZHEJIANG DOUBLE ARROW RUBBER CO., LTD.
Zhou Quan Town Industrial Zone, Tongxiang, 314513, Zhejiang, China
Tel.: (86) 57388539122
Web Site: https://www.doublearrow.net
Year Founded: 1986
002381—(SSE)
Rev.: $327,852,154
Assets: $493,166,400
Liabilities: $216,077,088

ZHEJIANG EAST ASIA PHARMACEUTICAL CO., LTD.

Net Worth: $277,089,312
Earnings: $15,955,632
Emp.: 1,500
Fiscal Year-end: 12/31/22
Rubber Conveyor Belts Mfr
N.A.I.C.S.: 326220
Shen Gengliang *(Chm)*

Subsidiaries:

Double Arrow Australia Pty Ltd. (1)
56 Forbes Street, Carrington, 2294, NSW, Australia
Tel.: (61) 249612199
Rubber Conveyor Belt Mfr & Distr
N.A.I.C.S.: 326220

ZHEJIANG DUN'AN ARTIFICIAL ENVIRONMENT CO., LTD.
Dunan Development Building No 239 Taian Road, Binjiang District, Hangzhou, 310020, Zhejiang, China
Tel.: (86) 57187113776 CN
Web Site: http://www.dunan.net
Year Founded: 1998
002011—(SSE)
Rev.: $1,424,170,032
Assets: $1,144,849,891
Liabilities: $647,528,577
Net Worth: $497,321,314
Earnings: $117,797,215
Emp.: 10,000
Fiscal Year-end: 12/31/22
Holding Company; Refrigeration Equipment & Accessories Mfr & Distr
N.A.I.C.S.: 551112
Deng Xiaobo *(Chm)*

Subsidiaries:

DunAn Microstaq, Inc. (1)
4150 Freidrich Ln Ste A, Austin, TX 78744
Tel.: (512) 628-2890
Web Site: http://www.dunanmicrostaq.com
Sales Range: $10-24.9 Million
Emp.: 15
Electronic Valve Mfr
N.A.I.C.S.: 333242

DunAn Pricision, Inc. (1)
12840 hillcrest Rd Ste E 230, Dallas, TX 75230
Tel.: (972) 239-7540
Web Site: http://www.dunausa.com
Refrigeration Equipment Distr
N.A.I.C.S.: 423740

Zhejiang Dun'An Electro-Mechanical Technology Co., Ltd. (1)
No 196 Central Rd, Diankou Industrial Zone, Zhuji, 311835, Zhejiang, China
Tel.: (86) 57587655999
Web Site: http://www.dunanac.com
Emp.: 200
Industrial Refrigeration Equipment Mfr & Distr
N.A.I.C.S.: 333415

Zhejiang DunAn International Trading Co., Ltd (1)
10th Floor DunAn Development Building No 239 Ta An Road, Binjiang, Hangzhou, 310052, Zhejiang, China
Tel.: (86) 571 87113788
Refrigeration Equipment Mfr & Distr
N.A.I.C.S.: 333415
Qi Jeremy *(Deputy Gen Mgr)*

ZHEJIANG EAST ASIA PHARMACEUTICAL CO., LTD.
23 Floor Chamber of Commerce Building Laodong North Road, Huangyan District, Taizhou, 318020, Zhejiang, China
Tel.: (86) 57689185675
Web Site: https://www.eapharm.cn
Year Founded: 1998
605177—(SHG)
Rev.: $165,609,761
Assets: $346,978,453
Liabilities: $88,672,035
Net Worth: $258,306,418

Zhejiang East Asia Pharmaceutical Co., Ltd.—(Continued)
Earnings: $14,661,116
Emp.: 1,300
Fiscal Year-end: 12/31/22
Pharmaceutical Product Mfr & Distr
N.A.I.C.S.: 325412
Zhengming Chi *(Chm & Gen Mgr)*

ZHEJIANG EAST CRYSTAL ELECTRONIC CO., LTD.
No 555 Binhong West Road, Jinhua, 321017, Zhejiang, China
Tel.: (86) 57989186668
Web Site: http://www.ecec.com
Year Founded: 1994
002199—(SSE)
Rev.: $25,387,956
Assets: $77,492,222
Liabilities: $25,961,518
Net Worth: $51,530,703
Earnings: ($9,702,819)
Emp.: 800
Fiscal Year-end: 12/31/22
Electronic Components Mfr
N.A.I.C.S.: 334419
Wang Hao *(Chm & Gen Mgr)*

ZHEJIANG ENTIVE SMART KITCHEN APPLIANCE CO., LTD.
No 68 Zheduan Road Pukou Street, Shengzhou, Shaoxing, 312400, Zhejiang, China
Tel.: (86) 57583260370
Web Site: http://www.entive.com
Year Founded: 2003
300911—(SSE)
Rev.: $179,115,244
Assets: $257,791,908
Liabilities: $69,147,674
Net Worth: $188,644,234
Earnings: $29,444,674
Emp.: 1,200
Fiscal Year-end: 12/31/22
Household Appliance Mfr & Distr
N.A.I.C.S.: 335220
Weiyong Sun *(Chm)*

ZHEJIANG EXPRESSWAY CO., LTD.
No 199 Wuxing Road, Shangcheng District, Hangzhou, 310020, Zhejiang, China
Tel.: (86) 57187985588
Web Site: http://www.zjec.com.cn
Year Founded: 1977
0576—(HKG)
Rev.: $2,348,945,503
Assets: $28,762,433,817
Liabilities: $20,398,854,813
Net Worth: $8,363,579,004
Earnings: $916,915,430
Emp.: 10,653
Fiscal Year-end: 12/31/23
Toll Road Construction & Management Services
N.A.I.C.S.: 237310
Tony H. Zheng *(Sec & Deputy Gen Mgr)*

ZHEJIANG EXPRESSWAY CO., LTD.
Block A Dragon Century Plaza 12th Floor 1 Hangda Road, Hangzhou, China
Tel.: (86) 57187985588
Web Site: http://www.zjec.com.cn
Business Support Services
N.A.I.C.S.: 561499
Zhihong Yu *(Chm)*

ZHEJIANG FEIDA ENVIRONMENTAL SCIENCE & TECHNOLOGY CO., LTD.
No 88 Wangyun Road, Zhuji, 311800, Zhejiang, China
Tel.: (86) 57587212511
Web Site: https://www.feidaep.com
Year Founded: 1969
600526—(SHG)
Rev.: $601,451,080
Assets: $1,363,958,327
Liabilities: $798,181,694
Net Worth: $565,776,633
Earnings: $21,425,658
Emp.: 2,032
Fiscal Year-end: 12/31/22
Air Purification Equipment Mfr
N.A.I.C.S.: 333413
Wu Gang *(Chm)*

ZHEJIANG FENGLONG ELECTRIC CO., LTD.
No 5 of Nilu Road Lianghu Industrial Zone, Shangyu, Zhejiang, China
Tel.: (86) 57582436333
Web Site: https://www.fenglong.com
Year Founded: 2003
002931—(SSE)
Rev.: $82,461,104
Assets: $161,503,945
Liabilities: $62,202,858
Net Worth: $99,301,087
Earnings: $6,822,373
Emp.: 823
Fiscal Year-end: 12/31/22
Automotive Parts Mfr & Distr
N.A.I.C.S.: 331523

ZHEJIANG FORE INTELLIGENT TECHNOLOGY CO., LTD.
No 9 Gaoyang Road, Yuanqiao Town Huangyan District, Taizhou, 318025, Zhejiang, China
Tel.: (86) 57684875999
Web Site: https://www.cn-fore.com
Year Founded: 1995
301368—(CHIN)
Rev.: $60,467,732
Assets: $172,343,957
Liabilities: $35,680,732
Net Worth: $136,663,225
Earnings: $3,393,056
Emp.: 700
Fiscal Year-end: 12/31/23
Industrial Machinery Mfr & Distr
N.A.I.C.S.: 333248

ZHEJIANG FOUNDER MOTOR CO., LTD.
No 73 Shiniu Road Shuige Industrial Zone, Liandu District, Lishui, 323000, Zhejiang, China
Tel.: (86) 5782171041
Web Site: https://www.fdm.com.cn
Year Founded: 1995
002196—(SSE)
Rev.: $327,222,137
Assets: $533,994,454
Liabilities: $357,919,417
Net Worth: $176,075,036
Earnings: ($32,827,612)
Fiscal Year-end: 12/31/22
Micro Motor Mfr
N.A.I.C.S.: 335312
Weng Weiwen *(Chm & Gen Mgr)*

ZHEJIANG FUCHUNJIANG ENVIRONMENTAL THERMO-ELECTRIC CO., LTD.
188 Chunyong Road, Lingqiao Town, Fuyang, 311418, Hangzhou, China
Tel.: (86) 57163553779
Web Site: http://www.zhefuet.com
Year Founded: 2008
002479—(SSE)
Rev.: $672,669,654
Assets: $1,285,501,698
Liabilities: $665,742,360

Net Worth: $619,759,338
Earnings: $36,356,608
Emp.: 300
Fiscal Year-end: 12/31/22
Electric & Thermal Power Distribution & Generation Services
N.A.I.C.S.: 221122
Wan Jiao *(Chm)*

ZHEJIANG FULAI NEW MATERIAL CO., LTD.
No 17 Yinhe Road, Yaozhuang Town Jiashan County, Jiaxing, Zhejiang, China
Tel.: (86) 57389107317
Web Site: https://www.fulai.com.cn
Year Founded: 2009
605488—(SHG)
Rev.: $266,962,092
Assets: $261,368,668
Liabilities: $105,460,028
Net Worth: $155,908,640
Earnings: $10,593,559
Fiscal Year-end: 12/31/22
Chemical Product Mfr & Distr
N.A.I.C.S.: 325520
Houjun Xia *(Chm)*

ZHEJIANG FURUN DIGITAL TECHNOLOGY CO., LTD.
No 12 Taozhu South Road, Zhuji, 311800, Zhejiang, China
Tel.: (86) 5757017092
Web Site: http://www.furun.net
Year Founded: 1994
600070—(SHG)
Rev.: $27,333,283
Assets: $255,026,154
Liabilities: $83,855,781
Net Worth: $171,170,373
Earnings: ($82,280,072)
Fiscal Year-end: 12/31/22
Textile Products Mfr
N.A.I.C.S.: 313210
Linzhong Zhao *(Board of Directors & Chm)*

Subsidiaries:
Zhuji Furun Mechanical Spring Co., Ltd. (1)
No 22 Wanwang Road West Industrial Zone, Zhuji, 311800, Zhejiang, China
Tel.: (86) 57587185193
Web Site: http://www.frspring.com
Spring Product Mfr
N.A.I.C.S.: 332613

ZHEJIANG GARDEN BIO-PHARMACEUTICAL CO., LTD.
Huayuan Village, Nanma Town, Dongyang, 322121, Zhejiang, China
Tel.: (86) 57186571191
Web Site: https://www.hybiotech.com
Year Founded: 2000
300401—(CHIN)
Rev.: $199,018,404
Assets: $580,113,144
Liabilities: $218,980,476
Net Worth: $361,132,668
Earnings: $53,874,288
Fiscal Year-end: 12/31/22
Pharmaceuticals, Biochemicals & Animal Nutrition Products
N.A.I.C.S.: 325412
Junfang Shao *(Chm)*

ZHEJIANG GEELY HOLDING GROUP CO., LTD.
1760 Jiangling Road Bianjiang District, Hangzhou, 310051, China
Tel.: (86) 4008869888
Web Site: http://www.zgh.com
Year Founded: 1986
Sales Range: Less than $1 Million
Emp.: 120,000
Holding Company; Automobile Mfr
N.A.I.C.S.: 551112

INTERNATIONAL PUBLIC

Li Shufu *(Chm)*
Subsidiaries:
Geely Automobile Holdings Ltd. (1)
Room 2301 23/F Great Eagle Centre 23 Harbour Road, Wanchai, China (Hong Kong)
Tel.: (852) 25983333
Web Site: https://www.geelyauto.com.hk
Rev.: $20,774,236,439
Assets: $22,158,816,592
Liabilities: $11,460,924,166
Net Worth: $10,697,892,426
Earnings: $652,812,685
Emp.: 49,000
Fiscal Year-end: 12/31/2022
Automobile Mfr
N.A.I.C.S.: 336110
Shu Li *(Chm)*

Subsidiary (Non-US):
Geely International Corporation (2)
No 87 Qianyang Road, Shanghai, 200333, China
Tel.: (86) 2152695666
Web Site: http://www.geely-global.com
Emp.: 160
Automobile Import & Export Services
N.A.I.C.S.: 423110

Group Lotus Limited (2)
Potash Ln, Hethel, Norwich, NR14 8EZ, Norfolk, United Kingdom (51%)
Tel.: (44) 1953608547
Web Site: http://www.lotuscars.com
High Performance Cars Engineering, Consulting & Mfr
N.A.I.C.S.: 336110

Subsidiary (Domestic):
Lotus Body Engineering Limited (3)
Potash Lane, Norwich, NR14 8EZ, Norfolk, United Kingdom
Tel.: (44) 1953608000
Car Repair & Maintenace Services
N.A.I.C.S.: 811111

Division (Domestic):
Lotus Cars Limited (3)
Potash Lane Hethel, Norwich, NR14 8EZ, Norfolk, United Kingdom
Tel.: (44) 1953608000
Web Site: http://www.lotuscars.com
Sports Cars Mfr
N.A.I.C.S.: 336999
Phil Popham *(CEO)*

Subsidiary (Domestic):
Lotus Engineering Limited (3)
Potash Lane, Hethel, Norwich, NR14 8EZ, Norfolk, United Kingdom
Tel.: (44) 1953608000
Design Engineering Services
N.A.I.C.S.: 541330

Subsidiary (US):
Lotus Engineering, Inc. (4)
1254 N Main St, Ann Arbor, MI 48104
Tel.: (734) 995-2544
Automotive Industry Engineering
N.A.I.C.S.: 811198
Geraint Castleton-White *(Head-Powertrain)*

Subsidiary (US):
Terrafugia, Inc. (2)
23 Rainin Rd, Woburn, MA 01801
Tel.: (781) 491-0812
Web Site: http://www.terrafugia.com
Prototype Vehicle Mfr
N.A.I.C.S.: 336999
Carl Dietrich *(Co-Founder & CTO)*

Geely-Motors LLC (1)
Butyrskiy Val Str 68/70 1 office 54, Business CenterBaker Plaza, Moscow, 127055, Russia
Tel.: (7) 8 985 960 60 25
Web Site: http://www.geely-motors.com
Passenger Car Mfr
N.A.I.C.S.: 336110

PT GEELY MOBIL INDONESIA (1)
Jl RS Fatmawati 29, Jakarta, 12430, Indonesia
Tel.: (62) 21 65833054

AND PRIVATE COMPANIES   ZHEJIANG GEELY HOLDING GROUP CO., LTD.

Web Site: http://gmi.geely.com
Passenger Car Mfr
N.A.I.C.S.: 336110
Fitrie Yulianti *(Mgr-Fin & Acctg)*

Saxo Bank A/S (1)
Philip Heymans Alle 15, 2900, Hellerup,
Denmark (52%)
Tel.: (45) 39774000
Web Site: http://www.home.saxo
Rev.: $391,477,073
Assets: $11,232,816,264
Liabilities: $10,171,159,790
Net Worth: $1,061,656,474
Earnings: $5,947,829
Emp.: 2,224
Fiscal Year-end: 12/31/2019
Online Trading & Investment Services
N.A.I.C.S.: 523150
Kim Fournais *(Founder & CEO)*

Subsidiary (Non-US):

BinckBank N.V. (2)
Barbara Strozzilaan 310, 1083 HN, Amsterdam, Netherlands
Tel.: (31) 205220378
Web Site: http://www.binck.com
Rev.: $156,008,816
Assets: $5,675,627,418
Liabilities: $5,205,810,312
Net Worth: $469,817,106
Earnings: $18,083,499
Emp.: 548
Fiscal Year-end: 12/31/2019
Investment Banking Services
N.A.I.C.S.: 523150
Vincent Germyns *(Chm-Exec Bd)*

Saxo Bank (Dubai) Limited (2)
Currency House 1st Floor DIFC, PO Box 506830, Dubai, United Arab Emirates
Tel.: (971) 4 381 6000
Web Site: http://ae.saxobank.com
Investment Banking Services
N.A.I.C.S.: 523150
Jakob Beck Thomsen *(CEO)*

Saxo Bank (Schweiz) AG (2)
Beethovenstrasse 33, Postfach 509, 8002, Zurich, Switzerland
Tel.: (41) 58 317 95 00
Web Site: http://www.home.saxo
Emp.: 60
Investment Banking Services
N.A.I.C.S.: 523150
Antonio Ferrante *(CEO)*

Saxo Bank FX Securities K.K. (2)
kamiyacho Sankei Building 10F 1-7-2
Azabudai, Minato, Tokyo, 106-0041, Japan
Tel.: (81) 3 5545 6351
Web Site: http://www.jp.saxobank.com
Emp.: 10
Investment Banking Services
N.A.I.C.S.: 523150
Wataru Kojima *(Pres & Dir-Rep)*

Saxo Bank Nederland (2)
WTC Amsterdam B-Toren 15e verdieping
Strawinskylaan 1527, 1077 XX, Amsterdam, Netherlands
Tel.: (31) 20 770 0671
Web Site: http://nl.saxobank.com
Investment Banking Services
N.A.I.C.S.: 523150

Saxo Banque France SAS (2)
10 rue de la Paix, 75002, Paris, France
Tel.: (33) 1 78 94 56 40
Web Site: http://fr.saxobank.com
Investment Banking Services
N.A.I.C.S.: 523150
Fabrice Pelosi *(Mgr-Mktg)*

Saxo Capital Markets (Australia) Pty. Ltd. (2)
Level 25 2 Park St, Sydney, 2000, NSW, Australia
Tel.: (61) 2 8267 9000
Web Site: http://au.saxomarkets.com
Investment Banking Services
N.A.I.C.S.: 523150
Torben Jorgensen *(COO)*

Saxo Capital Markets CY Ltd. (2)
Agias Fylaxeos 1 1st Floor, 3025, Limassol, Cyprus
Tel.: (357) 250 21 121
Web Site: http://www.cy.saxobank.com
Investment Banking Services

Saxo Capital Markets HK Limited (2)
Units 1201-2 12/F Agricultural Bank of China Tower, No 50 Connaught Road, Central, China (Hong Kong)
Tel.: (852) 3760 1388
Web Site: http://www.hk.saxomarkets.com
Investment Banking Services
N.A.I.C.S.: 523150
Jessi Law *(Mng Dir)*

Saxo Capital Markets Menkul Degerler A. S. (2)
Dereboyu Cad Meydan Sokak No 1 Beybi Giz Plaza Kat 30, Maslak, Istanbul, 34398, Turkiye
Tel.: (90) 212 705 58 00
Web Site: http://tr.saxomarkets.com
Investment Banking Services
N.A.I.C.S.: 523150
Cagri Selim Vural *(Sr Mgr-Compliance & Internal Audit)*

Saxo Capital Markets Pte. Ltd. (2)
3 Church Street 30-00 Samsung Hub, Singapore, 049483, Singapore
Tel.: (65) 6303 7800
Web Site: http://www.sg.saxomarkets.com
Investment Banking Services
N.A.I.C.S.: 523150
Chew Lee-Sian *(Head-Legal)*

Saxo Capital Markets UK Ltd. (2)
26th Floor 40 Bank Street, Canary Wharf, London, E14 5DA, United Kingdom
Tel.: (44) 20 7151 2222
Web Site: http://uk.saxomarkets.com
Investment Banking Services
N.A.I.C.S.: 523150
Andrew Edwards *(CEO)*

Saxo Capital Markets, Agente de Valores S.A. (2)
Zonamerica Ruta 8 Km 17 500 ED 1 of 109, 91600, Montevideo, Uruguay
Tel.: (598) 2518 3111
Web Site: http://www.latin.saxomarkets.com
Emp.: 13
Investment Banking Services
N.A.I.C.S.: 523150
Luis Simoes Pereira *(Mng Dir)*

Saxo Financial Services Private Limited (2)
20th Floor Tower 10C Cyber City DLF Phase - II, Gurgaon, 122 002, Haryana, India
Tel.: (91) 124 484 6500
Web Site: http://in.saxobank.com
Investment Banking Services
N.A.I.C.S.: 523150
Nitesh Baranwal *(Mgr)*

Subsidiary (Domestic):

Saxo Payments A/S (2)
Philip Heymans Alle 15, 2900, Hellerup, Denmark (50.1%)
Tel.: (45) 3977 4000
Payment Services
N.A.I.C.S.: 522320

Volvo Car AB (1)
Gropegardsgatan 2, 417 15, Gothenburg, Sweden
Tel.: (46) 31660000
Web Site: https://www.volvocars.com
Rev.: $39,643,318,723
Assets: $35,376,536,829
Liabilities: $22,423,114,724
Net Worth: $12,953,422,105
Earnings: $1,396,350,809
Emp.: 40,497
Fiscal Year-end: 12/31/2023
Automobiles Mfr & Distr
N.A.I.C.S.: 336110
Shufu Li *(Chm)*

Subsidiary (Domestic):

Getrag All Wheel Drive (2)
Volo Gatan, PO Box 961, Koping, 73129, Sweden (40%)
Tel.: (46) 221762000
Web Site: http://www.getrag.se
Emp.: 1,100
N.A.I.C.S.: 336412
Lars Christianson *(Mng Dir)*

Subsidiary (Non-US):

Swedish Motor Assemblies Sdn Bhd (2)
Jalan Bicu 15/6 Section 15, Shah Alam, 4000, Selangor Darul Ehsan, Malaysia
Tel.: (60) 355192149
Web Site: http://www.volvocars.com
Emp.: 300
Automobile Mfr
N.A.I.C.S.: 336110
Mark Hallum *(Mng Dir)*

Volvo Auto India Pvt. Ltd (2)
Tower A Ground Floor Unitech Cyber Park Greenwood City Sector-39, Gurgaon, 122001, Haryana, India
Tel.: (91) 124 4392150
New Car Dealers
N.A.I.C.S.: 441110
Tom Von Bonsdorff *(Mng Dir)*

Volvo Auto Italia SpA (2)
Via Enrico Mattei 66, Bologna, 40138, Italy (100%)
Tel.: (39) 051537611
Web Site: http://www.volvocars.it
Emp.: 90
N.A.I.C.S.: 336412

Volvo Auto Oy AB (2)
Paidaltie 1, 01610, Vantaa, Finland (100%)
Tel.: (358) 9504451
Web Site: http://www.volvocars.com
Emp.: 75
N.A.I.C.S.: 336412

Volvo Auto de Mexico S.A de C.V (2)
Bosques De Radiatas No 26 Local A 4o Piso Bosques De Las Lomas, 05120, Mexico, Mexico
Tel.: (52) 55 9177 9930
Passenger Car Mfr
N.A.I.C.S.: 336110

Volvo Automobiles France SA (2)
34 Rue de la Croix de Fer, 78128, Saint Germain-en-Laye, France (100%)
Tel.: (33) 00161017171
Web Site: http://www.volvocar.com
Emp.: 150
N.A.I.C.S.: 336412

Volvo Car Austria GmbH (2)
Concorde Business Park 1/A/1, 2320, Vienna, Austria
Tel.: (43) 1 70128 0
New Car Dealers
N.A.I.C.S.: 441110
Herbert Michael Strasser *(Mgr-Sls-Used Car)*

Volvo Car Brasil Importacao e Comercia de Veiculos Ltda (2)
Rua Surubim 577 10 Andar, Cidade Moncoes, Sao Paulo, 04571-050, Brazil
Tel.: (55) 11 3054 3342
Passenger Car Mfr
N.A.I.C.S.: 336110

Subsidiary (Domestic):

Volvo Car Components Corporation (2)
Zn Industriweg, 405 31, Gothenburg, Sweden (100%)
Tel.: (46) 31590000
Rev.: $12,400,000,000
Emp.: 13,000
Automotive Components Mfr.
N.A.I.C.S.: 336390
Doug Spec *(Sls & Customer Svcs)*

Unit (Domestic):

Volvo Car Components Corp. - Engines (3)
Component Bajen No 2, Skovde, 541 87, Sweden
Tel.: (46) 500274000
Web Site: http://www.volvocars.com
Emp.: 15
N.A.I.C.S.: 336412
Oskar Falk *(Mng Dir)*

Subsidiary (Non-US):

Volvo Car Czech Republic s.r.o. (2)
V Oblouku 731, 252 43, Pruhonice, Czech Republic
Tel.: (420) 296 787 111
Web Site: http://www.volvocars.cz
Emp.: 20
New Car Dealers
N.A.I.C.S.: 441110
Sarka Fuchsova *(Mng Dir)*

Volvo Car Espana S.A. (2)
Calle Jose Lazaro Galdiano 6, 28036, Madrid, Spain
Tel.: (34) 915666237
Web Site: http://www.volvocars.es
Sales Range: $25-49.9 Million
Emp.: 60
Automobiles, Parts & Accessories Mfr & Sales
N.A.I.C.S.: 336110
Rosa Fuentes *(Gen Mgr)*

Subsidiary (Domestic):

Volvo Car Finance Holding AB (2)
Maskingatan 5, 405 08, Gothenburg, Sweden (100%)
Tel.: (46) 31 66 65 00
Web Site: http://www.volvo.com
Emp.: 80
N.A.I.C.S.: 336412

Subsidiary (US):

Volvo Car Financial Services US LLC (2)
PO Box 91300, Mobile, AL 36691-1300
Web Site: http://www.volvocarfinancialservices.com
Automobile Financing Services
N.A.I.C.S.: 522220

Subsidiary (Non-US):

Volvo Car France SAS (2)
Immeuble Nielle 131-151 rue du 1er mai, 92737, Nanterre, Cedex, France
Tel.: (33) 1 56 83 54 00
New Car Dealers
N.A.I.C.S.: 441110

Volvo Car Germany GmbH (2)
Siegburger Street, Cologne, 50679, Germany
Tel.: (49) 22193930
Web Site: http://www.volvocar.com
Sales Range: $25-49.9 Million
Emp.: 150
Motor Vehicle Mfr & Sales
N.A.I.C.S.: 423110
Tomas Bewich *(Mng Dir)*

Volvo Car Hellas SA (2)
Andrea Papandreou 19, Maroussi, 15124, Greece
Tel.: (30) 21 0579 4900
Web Site: http://www.volvo.gr
Passenger Car Mfr
N.A.I.C.S.: 336110

Volvo Car Ireland Ltd (2)
Killakee House The Square Industrial Complex Belgard Square E, Dublin, Ireland
Tel.: (353) 1 462 1122
Web Site: http://www.volvocars.com
Emp.: 15
Passenger Car Mfr
N.A.I.C.S.: 336110
Adrian Yeates *(Gen Mgr)*

Volvo Car Malaysia Sdn Bhd (2)
Suite 20 02 20th Floor Menara IGB No 1 The Boulevard Mid Valley City, Lingkaran Syed Putra, Kuala Lumpur, 59200, Malaysia
Tel.: (60) 320811333
Web Site: http://www.volvocars.com
Emp.: 30
Automobile Sales
N.A.I.C.S.: 423110
Nalin Jain *(Mng Dir)*

Volvo Car Nederland B.V. (2)
Stationsweg 2, 4153 RD, Beesd, Netherlands
Tel.: (31) 345 688888
New Car Dealers
N.A.I.C.S.: 441110

Volvo Car Poland Sp Z.o.o (2)
Ul Pulawska 558/560, 02-884, Warsaw, Poland

8653

ZHEJIANG GEELY HOLDING GROUP CO., LTD.

Zhejiang Geely Holding Group Co., Ltd.—(Continued)

Tel.: (48) 22 566 28 00
New Car Dealers
N.A.I.C.S.: 441110
Rafal Gorzynski (Mgr-Fin Svcs)

Volvo Car South Africa Pty Ltd (2)
71 Regency Drive Route 21 Corporate Park, Irene, 0157, South Africa
Tel.: (27) 12 450 4910
New Car Dealers
N.A.I.C.S.: 441110
Lensha Dlamini (Coord-CRM & Digital)

Volvo Car Turkey Otomobil Ltd Sirketi (2)
Icerenkoy Mah Engin Sk No 9, Kadikoy, 34752, Istanbul, Turkiye
Tel.: (90) 216 655 75 00
New Car Dealers
N.A.I.C.S.: 441110

Volvo Car UK Limited (2)
Scandinavia House Norreys Drive, Maidenhead, SL6 4FL, Berkshire, United Kingdom **(100%)**
Tel.: (44) 1628477977
Web Site: http://www.volvocars.co.uk
Emp.: 90
N.A.I.C.S.: 336412
Georjina Williams (Head-Mktg Comm)

Volvo Cars N.V. (2)
John Kennedylaan 25, Gent, 9000, Belgium **(100%)**
Tel.: (32) 92502111
Web Site: http://www.volvocarsgent.be
Emp.: 5,000
Produce S40, S60, V50, V70 & C30; Car Body Painting & Welding
N.A.I.C.S.: 336110
Derk Ventroos (Dir-Pur)

Volvo Cars UK Ltd. (2)
Scandinavia House Norreys Drive, Maidenhead, SL6 4FL, Berkshire, United Kingdom **(100%)**
Tel.: (44) 1628422200
Web Site: http://www.volvocars.com
Emp.: 90
Car Parts Mfr
N.A.I.C.S.: 336390
Nick Connor (Mng Dir)

Volvo Cars of Canada Ltd. (2)
9130 Leslie Street Suite 101, Toronto, L4B 0B9, ON, Canada **(100%)**
Tel.: (416) 493-3700
Web Site: http://www.volvoca.com
Emp.: 60
Automotive Sales
N.A.I.C.S.: 423120
Marc Engelen (Pres & CEO)

Subsidiary (US):

Volvo Cars of North America LLC (2)
1 Volvo Dr, Rockleigh, NJ 07647-2507 **(100%)**
Tel.: (201) 768-7300
Web Site: http://www.volvocars.com
Sales Range: $75-99.9 Million
Automobiles, Parts & Accessories Sales
N.A.I.C.S.: 423110

Subsidiary (Non-US):

Volvo Malaysia Sdn. Bhd. (2)
Jalan Bicu 15 6 Section 15, 40200, Shah Alam, Selangor Darul Ehsan, Malaysia **(100%)**
Tel.: (60) 355103300
Web Site: http://www.volvotrucks.com
Sales Range: $1-9.9 Million
Emp.: 200
N.A.I.C.S.: 336412
Mats Nilsson (Mng Dir)

Subsidiary (Domestic):

Volvo Personbilar Sverige AB (2)
Gropegarsg 17, 4531, Gothenburg, Sweden **(100%)**
Tel.: (46) 313250200
Web Site: http://www.volvocars.se
Emp.: 100
Aircraft Part Mfr
N.A.I.C.S.: 336413

Thomas Anderson (Mng Dir)

Subsidiary (Non-US):

Volvo Personbiler Norge A/S (2)
Lienga 2, PO Box 601, Kolbotn, 6011411, Norway **(100%)**
Tel.: (47) 66818500
Web Site: http://www.volvocars.no
Emp.: 60
Automobile Mfr
N.A.I.C.S.: 336412
Oystein Herland (Mng Dir)

Subsidiary (Domestic):

Volvo Personvagnar Holding AB (2)
Dept 5000, 405 31, Gothenburg, Sweden
Tel.: (46) 31590000
Web Site: http://www.volvocars.com
Sales Range: $300-349.9 Million
Holding Company
N.A.I.C.S.: 551112

Subsidiary (Domestic):

Volvo Personvagnar AB (3)
Dept 50000, SE 405 31, Gothenburg, Sweden
Tel.: (46) 31590000
Web Site: http://www.volvocars.com
Motor Vehicles Mfr
N.A.I.C.S.: 336110

Affiliate (Domestic):

Volvofinans Bank AB (4)
Bohusgatan 15, 401 23, Gothenburg, Sweden **(50%)**
Tel.: (46) 31838800
Web Site: http://www.volvofinans.se
Rev.: $819,588,841
Assets: $5,375,914,025
Liabilities: $5,309,200,846
Net Worth: $66,713,180
Earnings: $1,606,451
Fiscal Year-end: 12/31/2019
Sales Financing Services
N.A.I.C.S.: 522220
Conny Bergstrom (CEO)

Subsidiary (Non-US):

Volvo Personvogne Danmark A/S (2)
Lyska Lyskar 5, 2730, Herlev, Denmark **(100%)**
Tel.: (45) 70112700
Web Site: http://www.volvocars.com
Emp.: 20
N.A.I.C.S.: 336412
Henrik Lundgaard (Mng Dir)

Volvo Thailand Ltd. (2)
1527 Sukhumvit 71 Rd, Bangkok, 10250, Thailand **(100%)**
Tel.: (66) 23199828
Web Site: http://www.volvocars.co.th
Emp.: 50
Automobile & Other Motor Vehicle Merchant Wholesalers
N.A.I.C.S.: 423110

ZHEJIANG GIUSEPPE GARMENT CO., LTD.

No 588 Pingrui Highway, Kunyang Town Pingyang County, Wenzhou, 325400, Zhejiang, China
Tel.: (86) 57763727222
Web Site: http://www.giuseppe.cn
Year Founded: 2001
002687—(SSE)
Rev.: $179,610,687
Assets: $277,196,564
Liabilities: $77,464,942
Net Worth: $199,731,622
Earnings: $17,053,518
Emp.: 2,620
Fiscal Year-end: 12/31/22
Clothing Mfr
N.A.I.C.S.: 315250
Chi Ye (Chm)

ZHEJIANG GLASS COMPANY LIMITED

1301 Ruttonjee House Ruttonjee Ctr, 11 Duddell St, Hong Kong, China (Hong Kong)
Tel.: (852) 28681166
Sales Range: $400-449.9 Million
Emp.: 6,350
Glass & Soda Ash Products Mfr
N.A.I.C.S.: 327212
Haiping Tao (Sec)

ZHEJIANG GOLDEN EAGLE CO., LTD.

Xiaosha Town, Dinghai District, Zhoushan, 316051, Zhejiang, China
Tel.: (86) 58080021228
Web Site: https://www.cn-goldeneagle.com
Year Founded: 1966
600232—(SHG)
Rev.: $182,901,804
Assets: $234,535,589
Liabilities: $79,881,170
Net Worth: $154,654,419
Earnings: $6,949,589
Fiscal Year-end: 12/31/22
Textile Product & Textile Machinery Mfr & Whslr
N.A.I.C.S.: 313310
Guoding Fu (Chm)

ZHEJIANG GOLDENSEA HI-TECH CO., LTD.

Yingdian Street Industrial Zone, Zhuji, 311817, Zhejiang, China
Tel.: (86) 57587081996
Web Site: https://www.goldensea.cn
603011—(SHG)
Rev.: $110,822,339
Assets: $228,273,229
Liabilities: $56,459,979
Net Worth: $171,813,250
Earnings: $10,616,627
Fiscal Year-end: 12/31/22
Air Purification Equipment Mfr & Distr
N.A.I.C.S.: 333413
Hongguang Ding (Chm & Dir)

ZHEJIANG GONGDONG MEDICAL TECHNOLOGY CO., LTD.

No 10 Beiyuan Ave, Economic Development Zone Huangyan, Taizhou, 318020, Zhejiang, China
Tel.: (86) 57684115678
Web Site: https://www.chinagongdong.com
Year Founded: 2009
605369—(SHG)
Rev.: $206,203,304
Assets: $262,195,343
Liabilities: $38,651,937
Net Worth: $223,543,406
Earnings: $45,777,167
Fiscal Year-end: 12/31/22
Medical Product Mfr & Distr
N.A.I.C.S.: 339112
Huiyong Shi (Chm)

ZHEJIANG GRANDWALL ELECTRIC SCIENCE & TECHNOLOGY CO., LTD.

East No 1 Great Wall Avenue, Lianshi Town, Huzhou, 313013, Zhejiang, China
Tel.: (86) 5723956866
Web Site: https://www.grandwall.com.cn
603897—(SHG)
Rev.: $1,407,710,435
Assets: $790,154,282
Liabilities: $404,698,802
Net Worth: $385,455,480
Earnings: $19,119,602
Fiscal Year-end: 12/31/22
Electric Equipment Mfr
N.A.I.C.S.: 335999

ZHEJIANG GREAT SOUTH-

INTERNATIONAL PUBLIC

EAST COMPANY LIMITED

No 5 Qianxi Road, Taozhu Subdistrict, Zhuji, 311800, Zhejiang, China
Tel.: (86) 57587380698
Web Site: http://www.chinaddn.com
Year Founded: 2000
002263—(SSE)
Rev.: $222,423,126
Assets: $415,473,491
Liabilities: $34,139,706
Net Worth: $381,333,785
Earnings: $9,508,099
Fiscal Year-end: 12/31/22
Plastics Product Mfr
N.A.I.C.S.: 326199
Luo Ping (Chm & Gen Mgr)

ZHEJIANG GUANGHUA TECHNOLOGY CO., LTD.

No 3-1 East HuanYuan Road, Yanguan Town, Haining, 314412, Zhejiang, China
Tel.: (86) 57387771177
Web Site: https://www.khua.com
Year Founded: 2014
001333—(SSE)
Rev.: $190,711,470
Assets: $313,435,095
Liabilities: $97,320,914
Net Worth: $216,114,182
Earnings: $18,573,797
Emp.: 300
Fiscal Year-end: 12/31/22
Resin Product Mfr & Distr
N.A.I.C.S.: 325211
Jiefeng Sun (Chm)

ZHEJIANG GUYUELONGSHAN SHAOXING WINE CO., LTD.

Beihai Bridge, Shaoxing, 312000, Zhejiang, China
Tel.: (86) 57585176000
Web Site: https://www.shaoxingwine.com.cn
Year Founded: 1997
600059—(SHG)
Rev.: $227,442,918
Assets: $885,545,355
Liabilities: $109,207,950
Net Worth: $776,337,405
Earnings: $28,343,699
Emp.: 3,500
Fiscal Year-end: 12/31/22
Wine Producer & Distr
N.A.I.C.S.: 312130
Sun Aibao (Chm)

ZHEJIANG HAERS VACUUM CONTAINERS CO., LTD.

No 1 Haers Road Economic Development Zone, Yongkang, Zhejiang, China
Tel.: (86) 57186978641
Web Site: https://www.haers.com
Year Founded: 1996
002615—(SSE)
Rev.: $340,876,963
Assets: $330,310,024
Liabilities: $136,268,898
Net Worth: $194,041,126
Earnings: $28,909,287
Emp.: 1,500
Fiscal Year-end: 12/31/22
Food Containers Mfr
N.A.I.C.S.: 332439
Lv Qiang (Chm)

Subsidiaries:

SIGG Switzerland AG (1)
Freiestrasse 4-8, 8500, Frauenfeld, Switzerland
Tel.: (41) 527210422
Web Site: http://www.sigg.com
Aluminum Bottle Mfr
N.A.I.C.S.: 332439

ZHEJIANG HAILIANG CO., LTD.
Hailiang Building No 1508 Binsheng Road, Binjiang District, Hangzhou, 310051, Zhejiang, China
Tel.: (86) 57156051000 CN
Web Site: https://www.hailiang.com
Year Founded: 2001
002203—(SSE)
Rev: $10,389,661,734
Assets: $4,701,406,306
Liabilities: $2,823,291,947
Net Worth: $1,878,114,359
Earnings: $169,639,901
Emp.: 20,000
Fiscal Year-end: 12/31/22
Copper Pipe Mfr & Distr
N.A.I.C.S.: 332999

Subsidiaries:

Hailiang America Corporation (1)
1001 James Dr Ste B38, Leesport, PA 19533
Web Site: https://www.hailiangusa.com
Copper Product Mfr
N.A.I.C.S.: 331420

JMF Company (1)
2735 62nd St Ct, Bettendorf, IA 52722
Tel.: (563) 332-9200
Web Site: https://www.jmfcompany.com
Fitting & Valve Distr
N.A.I.C.S.: 423720

Zhejiang Hailiang International Trade Co., Ltd. (1)
the town of Jiefang Road No 386, Zhuji, Zhejiang, China
Tel.: (86) 57587069001
Electronic Products Mfr
N.A.I.C.S.: 334416

ZHEJIANG HAILIDE NEW MATERIAL CO., LTD.
Warp Knitting Scientific-technical Industrial Zone, Haining, Zhejiang, China
Tel.: (86) 57387762777
Web Site: https://www.halead.com
Year Founded: 2001
002206—(SSE)
Rev: $773,892,494
Assets: $1,050,932,835
Liabilities: $556,073,659
Net Worth: $494,859,175
Earnings: $46,625,268
Emp.: 2,800
Fiscal Year-end: 12/31/22
Industrial Fiber Mfr
N.A.I.C.S.: 325220
Gao Limin *(Chm)*

ZHEJIANG HAIYAN POWER SYSTEM RESOURCES ENVIRONMENTAL TECHNOLOGY CO., LTD.
No 585 North Chang An Rd, Wuyuan Subdistrict Haiyan County, Jiaxing, 314300, Zhejiang, China
Tel.: (86) 57386038717
Web Site: https://www.psr-china.com
Year Founded: 1999
688565—(SHG)
Rev: $28,522,808
Assets: $134,863,424
Liabilities: $53,297,834
Net Worth: $81,565,591
Earnings: ($5,099,581)
Fiscal Year-end: 12/31/22
Semiconductor Product Mfr & Distr
N.A.I.C.S.: 334413
Wanzhong Shen *(Chm & Gen Mgr)*

ZHEJIANG HANGKE TECHNOLOGY INCORPORATED COMPANY
No 77 Gaoxin 11th Road, Xiaoshan Economic and Technological Development Zone, Hangzhou, 311215, Zhejiang, China
Tel.: (86) 57186463544
Web Site: https://www.chr-group.net
Year Founded: 2011
688006—(SHG)
Rev: $484,960,287
Assets: $1,118,438,629
Liabilities: $648,444,266
Net Worth: $469,994,363
Earnings: $68,879,454
Fiscal Year-end: 12/31/22
Electrical Equipment Mfr & Distr
N.A.I.C.S.: 335999
Ji Cao *(Chm & Gen Mgr)*

ZHEJIANG HANGMIN CO., LTD.
Hangmin Village Guali Town, Xiao Shan District, Hangzhou, 311241, Zhejiang, China
Tel.: (86) 57182557359
Web Site: http://www.hmgf.com
Year Founded: 1998
600987—(SHG)
Rev: $1,343,670,527
Assets: $1,147,740,095
Liabilities: $240,472,431
Net Worth: $907,267,664
Earnings: $92,353,449
Emp.: 7,914
Fiscal Year-end: 12/31/22
Printing & Dyeing Services
N.A.I.C.S.: 323111
Chongqing Zhu *(Chm)*

Subsidiaries:

Hangzhou Hangmin Damei Dyeing & Finishing Co. Ltd. (1)
Rm12198a Block-A Wonder Plaza Keqiao, Shaoxing, Zhejiang, China
Tel.: (86) 571 82551588
Emp.: 2,000
Dyeing Machinery Mfr
N.A.I.C.S.: 333248

Hangzhou Hangmin Meishida Printing & Dyeing Co., Ltd. (1)
No 1 Renmin Road Kanshan Town, Xiaoshan, Hangzhou, 311243, Zhejiang, China
Tel.: (86) 571 82551588
Dyeing Machinery Mfr
N.A.I.C.S.: 333248

Hangzhou Hangmin Thermal Electricity Co., Ltd. (1)
Hangmin Village Guali Town, Xiaoshan, Hangzhou, 311241, Zhejiang, China
Tel.: (86) 571 82551588
Emp.: 170
Holding company; Electric Power Generation Services
N.A.I.C.S.: 551112

Hangzhou Qianjiang Printing & Dyeing Co., Ltd. (1)
Room 203 118 Tonghui Zhong Road, Xiaoshan, Hangzhou, 311200, China
Tel.: (86) 571 82181948
Emp.: 1,500
Dyeing Machinery Mfr
N.A.I.C.S.: 333248

Hangzhou Xiaoshan Hangmin Nonwoven Fabric Co., Ltd. (1)
Hangmin Industrial Park Guali Town, Xiaoshan District, Hangzhou, 311241, Zhejiang, China
Tel.: (86) 57182572358
Web Site: http://www.zj-hangmin.com
Emp.: 200
Nonwoven Fabric Mfr
N.A.I.C.S.: 313230

ZHEJIANG HAOTAI CHEMICAL CO., LTD.
No 6 Kangyang Avenue Hangzhou, Bay Economic and Technological Development Zone Shangyu District, Shaoxing, Zhejiang, China
Tel.: (86) 13305087363 CN
Year Founded: 2022
Freight Forwarding Services
N.A.I.C.S.: 541614

ZHEJIANG HENGWEI BATTERY CO., LTD.
No 77 Zhengyang West Road, Youchegang Xiuzhou District, Jiaxing, 314018, Zhejiang, China
Tel.: (86) 57382235810
Web Site: https://www.hwbattery.com
Year Founded: 1999
301222—(SSE)
Rev: $81,469,754
Assets: $186,934,780
Liabilities: $10,019,520
Net Worth: $176,915,260
Earnings: $17,231,685
Fiscal Year-end: 12/31/22
Battery Product Mfr
N.A.I.C.S.: 335910
Jianping Wang *(Chm & Gen Mgr)*

ZHEJIANG HISOAR PHARMACEUTICAL CO., LTD.
No 100 waisha Branch Road, Jiaojiang, Taizhou, 318000, Zhejiang, China
Tel.: (86) 57689088829
Web Site: https://www.hisoar.com
Year Founded: 1966
002099—(SSE)
Rev: $379,661,818
Assets: $1,178,391,212
Liabilities: $321,261,174
Net Worth: $857,130,038
Earnings: $12,357,123
Fiscal Year-end: 12/31/22
Pharmaceutical Product Mfr & Whslr
N.A.I.C.S.: 325412
Wang Yangchao *(Chm)*

ZHEJIANG HISUN PHARMACEUTICAL CO., LTD.
No 46 Waisha Road, Jiaojiang District, Taizhou, 318000, Zhejiang, China
Tel.: (86) 57688827809
Web Site: http://www.hisunpharm.com
Year Founded: 1998
600267—(SHG)
Rev: $1,689,951,290
Assets: $2,636,415,349
Liabilities: $1,466,856,420
Net Worth: $1,169,558,929
Earnings: $68,661,932
Emp.: 242
Fiscal Year-end: 12/31/22
Pharmaceutical Product Mfr & Distr
N.A.I.C.S.: 325412
Xiao Weihong *(Pres)*

ZHEJIANG HONGCHANG ELECTRICAL TECHNOLOGY CO., LTD.
No 788 Xinhong Road qiubin street, Wucheng District, Jinhua, 321017, Zhejiang, China
Tel.: (86) 57982271102
Web Site: https://www.hongchang.com.cn
Year Founded: 1996
301008—(CHIN)
Rev: $124,581,591
Assets: $284,716,210
Liabilities: $124,586,169
Net Worth: $160,130,042
Earnings: $12,100,338
Fiscal Year-end: 12/31/23
Electrical Component Mfr & Distr
N.A.I.C.S.: 335210
Baohong Lu *(Chm)*

ZHEJIANG HUACE FILM AND TV CO., LTD.
4th Floor Building A Huace Center No 466 Wuchanggang Road, Xihu District, Hangzhou, 310012, Zhejiang, China
Tel.: (86) 57187553075
Web Site: http://www.huacemedia.com
Year Founded: 2005
300133—(CHIN)
Rev: $347,484,384
Assets: $1,347,321,924
Liabilities: $365,183,208
Net Worth: $982,138,716
Earnings: $56,539,080
Fiscal Year-end: 12/31/22
Film & Television Production & Distribution Services
N.A.I.C.S.: 512110
Meicheng Fu *(Chm)*

ZHEJIANG HUADA NEW MATERIALS CO., LTD.
198 Daqiao South Road, Dayuan Town Fuyang District, Hangzhou, 311413, Zhejiang, China
Tel.: (86) 57158982959
Web Site: https://www.hdnew.cn
Year Founded: 2003
605158—(SHG)
Rev: $1,138,929,812
Assets: $722,300,141
Liabilities: $418,213,495
Net Worth: $304,086,646
Earnings: $28,400,477
Fiscal Year-end: 12/31/22
Steel Product Mfr & Distr
N.A.I.C.S.: 331210
Mingxiang Shao *(Chm)*

ZHEJIANG HUAHAI PHARMACEUTICAL CO., LTD.
Xunqiao, Linhai, 317024, Zhejiang, China
Tel.: (86) 57685991096
Web Site: https://en.huahaipharm.com
Year Founded: 1989
600521—(SHG)
Rev: $1,160,510,570
Assets: $2,548,503,945
Liabilities: $1,461,018,757
Net Worth: $1,087,485,188
Earnings: $163,953,321
Emp.: 7,000
Fiscal Year-end: 12/31/22
Pharmaceuticals Product Mfr
N.A.I.C.S.: 325412
Li Hong *(Chm)*

Subsidiaries:

Huahai Japan Pharm Co., Ltd. (1)
Quest Marunouchi Building 9F 3-4-30 Marunouchi, Naka-ku, Nagoya, 460-0002, Aichi Prefecture, Japan
Tel.: (81) 522125035
Pharmaceuticals Product Mfr
N.A.I.C.S.: 325412

Huahai Pharmaceutical Sales Co., Ltd. (1)
23-24/F Block B Zhonghai-huayu Business Center, No 626 Science and Technology Museum Street Binjiang District, Hangzhou, Zhejiang, China
Tel.: (86) 57187233666
Pharmaceuticals Product Mfr
N.A.I.C.S.: 325412

Huahai US Inc. (1)
2001 and 2002 Eastpark Blvd, Cranbury, NJ 08512
Tel.: (609) 664-2220
Web Site: http://www.huahaius.com
Pharmaceutical Product Mfr & Whslr
N.A.I.C.S.: 325412

Linhai Huanan Chemicals Co., Ltd. (1)
Zhejiang Provincial Chemical and Medical Material Base, 317026, Linhai, China

ZHEJIANG HUAHAI PHARMACEUTICAL CO., LTD.

Zhejiang Huahai Pharmaceutical Co., Ltd.—(Continued)
Tel.: (86) 576 5588251
Pharmaceutical Product Mfr & Whslr
N.A.I.C.S.: 424210

Zhejiang Huahai Cultural Development Co., Ltd. (1)
Floor 25 Ruifeng Mansion 258 Zhonghe Middle Road, Shangcheng District, Hangzhou, Zhejiang, China
Tel.: (86) 57187233669
Pharmaceuticals Product Mfr
N.A.I.C.S.: 325412

ZHEJIANG HUAKANG PHARMACEUTICAL CO., LTD.
No 18 Huagong Road, Huabu Town Kaihua County, Quzhou, 324302, Zhejiang, China
Tel.: (86) 5706035901
Web Site: http://www.huakangpharma.com
Year Founded: 2001
605077—(SHG)
Rev.: $308,883,243
Assets: $548,267,462
Liabilities: $175,391,639
Net Worth: $372,875,822
Earnings: $44,826,603
Fiscal Year-end: 12/31/22
Pharmaceutical Product Mfr & Distr
N.A.I.C.S.: 325412
Deshui Chen *(Chm & Gen Mgr)*

ZHEJIANG HUAMEI HOLDING CO., LTD.
No 218 Tiyuchang Road, Xiacheng District, Hangzhou, 311200, Zhejiang, China
Tel.: (86) 57185098807
Web Site: http://www.000607.cn
Year Founded: 1993
000607—(SSE)
Rev.: $253,704,780
Assets: $555,135,717
Liabilities: $298,356,458
Net Worth: $256,779,259
Earnings: $11,901,540
Fiscal Year-end: 12/31/22
Holding Company
N.A.I.C.S.: 551112
Lu Yuanfeng *(Chm)*

ZHEJIANG HUANGMA TECHNOLOGY CO., LTD.
Zhangzhen Industrial New Zone, Shangyu District, Shaoxing, 312363, Zhejiang, China
Tel.: (86) 57582097088
Web Site: https://www.huangma.com
Year Founded: 2003
603181—(SHG)
Rev.: $306,402,024
Assets: $464,109,076
Liabilities: $109,446,321
Net Worth: $354,662,755
Earnings: $66,990,990
Fiscal Year-end: 12/31/22
Chemical Products Mfr
N.A.I.C.S.: 325998
Wang Weisong *(Chm)*

ZHEJIANG HUASHENG TECHNOLOGY CO., LTD.
No 8 Hongqi Road Maiqao Street, Haining, Jiaxing, Zhejiang, China
Tel.: (86) 57387987519
Web Site: https://www.huashengflex.com
Year Founded: 2006
605180—(SHG)
Rev.: $38,855,181
Assets: $158,270,786
Liabilities: $3,419,737
Net Worth: $154,851,049
Earnings: $8,279,220
Fiscal Year-end: 12/31/22
Fabric Product Mfr
N.A.I.C.S.: 313320
Shenghua Jiang *(Chm & Gen Mgr)*

ZHEJIANG HUATIE EMERGENCY EQUIPMENT SCIENCE & TECHNOLOGY CO., LTD.
10F Building 1 Huatie Venture Building No 68 Shengkang Street, Jiangan District, Hangzhou, 310019, Zhejiang, China
Tel.: (86) 57186038116
Web Site: http://www.zjhuatie.cn
Year Founded: 2008
603300—(SHG)
Rev.: $460,259,041
Assets: $2,023,499,500
Liabilities: $1,366,389,718
Net Worth: $657,109,782
Earnings: $90,037,481
Fiscal Year-end: 12/31/22
Safety Equipment Rental Services
N.A.I.C.S.: 423450
Danfeng Hu *(Chm & Gen Mgr)*

ZHEJIANG HUATONG MEAT PRODUCTS CO LTD
Yiting Gutang Industrial Zone, Yiwu, 322005, Zhejiang, China
Tel.: (86) 57989908661
Web Site: https://www.huatongmeat.com
Year Founded: 2001
002840—(SSE)
Rev.: $1,327,083,910
Assets: $1,245,594,051
Liabilities: $775,859,512
Net Worth: $469,734,539
Earnings: $12,319,356
Fiscal Year-end: 12/31/22
Meat Processing Services
N.A.I.C.S.: 115210
Jianyong Zhu *(Board of Directors & Chm)*

ZHEJIANG HUILONG NEW MATERIALS CO., LTD.
No 777 Hanghai Road, Yuyue Town Deqing County, Huzhou, 313213, Zhejiang, China
Tel.: (86) 4008701778
Web Site: https://www.hljtchina.com
Year Founded: 2004
301057—(CHIN)
Rev.: $86,379,696
Assets: $106,873,884
Liabilities: $19,415,916
Net Worth: $87,457,968
Earnings: $5,697,432
Fiscal Year-end: 12/31/22
Textile Material Mfr & Distr
N.A.I.C.S.: 314999
Shunhua Shen *(Chm & Gen Mgr)*

ZHEJIANG IDC FLUID CONTROL CO., LTD.
Xingye Building 1st Floor, No 901 East Baizhang Road Jiangdong District, Ningbo, China
Tel.: (86) 574 2767 0666
Web Site: http://www.idcgroup.com.cn
2468—(SSE)
Sales Range: $200-249.9 Million
Emp.: 2,001
Plumbing Equipment Mfr & Distr
N.A.I.C.S.: 332913
Shaodong Wang *(Chm & Gen Mgr)*

ZHEJIANG INT'L GROUP CO., LTD.
No 96 Zhonghua Building Jiangnan Avenue, Binjiang District, Hangzhou, 310051, Zhejiang, China
Tel.: (86) 57185068752
Web Site: http://www.intmedic.com
Year Founded: 1992
000411—(SSE)
Rev.: $4,298,943,725
Assets: $1,848,201,409
Liabilities: $1,303,028,420
Net Worth: $545,172,989
Earnings: $29,796,952
Fiscal Year-end: 12/31/22
Medical Equipment Distr
N.A.I.C.S.: 423450
Jufang Jiang *(Chm)*

ZHEJIANG JASAN HOLDING GROUP CO., LTD.
No 111 Jinyi Road, Xiaoshan Economic and Technological Development Zone, Hangzhou, 311215, China
Tel.: (86) 57122897170
Web Site: https://www.jasangroup.com
603558—(SHG)
Rev.: $330,442,829
Assets: $546,150,903
Liabilities: $196,865,356
Net Worth: $349,285,548
Earnings: $36,745,516
Emp.: 10,000
Fiscal Year-end: 12/31/22
Socks Mfr & Distr
N.A.I.C.S.: 316210

Subsidiaries:

Jasan Vietnam Textile & Dyeing Co., Ltd. (1)
Pho Noi B Textile and Garment Industrial Park, Lieu Xa Commune Yen My District, Hung Yen, Vietnam
Tel.: (84) 2213766818
Web Site: http://www.jasan.vn
Textile Products Mfr
N.A.I.C.S.: 313310

ZHEJIANG JIAAO ENPROTECH STOCK CO., LTD.
No 1 Economic & Development, Tongxiang, 314000, Zhejiang, China
Tel.: (86) 57388623097
Web Site: https://www.jiaaoplasticizers.com
Year Founded: 2003
603822—(SHG)
Rev.: $450,888,436
Assets: $418,244,566
Liabilities: $266,431,632
Net Worth: $151,812,933
Earnings: ($4,554,590)
Fiscal Year-end: 12/31/22
Plasticizer Mfr & Distr
N.A.I.C.S.: 325199
Shen Jian *(Chm & Gen Mgr)*

ZHEJIANG JIAHUA ENERGY CHEMICAL INDUSTRY CO., LTD.
2288 Binhai Avenue, Zhapu Economic Development Park Jiaxing Harbor District, Jiaxing, 314201, Zhejiang, China
Tel.: (86) 57385585033
Web Site: https://www.jhec.com.cn
Year Founded: 2003
600273—(SHG)
Rev.: $1,614,975,584
Assets: $1,722,750,892
Liabilities: $347,885,886
Net Worth: $1,374,865,006
Earnings: $224,417,354
Emp.: 1,000
Fiscal Year-end: 12/31/22
Chemical Product Mfr & Distr
N.A.I.C.S.: 325998
Han Jianhong *(Chm)*

ZHEJIANG JIAHUAN ELECTRONIC CO., LTD.

INTERNATIONAL PUBLIC

188 Jiangjun Road, Jinhua, 321016, Zhejiang, China
Tel.: (86) 579 8230 3312
Web Site: http://www.jiahuan.com
Year Founded: 1969
Industrial Automatic Environmental Control Systems Developer & Mfr
N.A.I.C.S.: 334512
T.C. Leung *(Chm & CEO)*

ZHEJIANG JIANFENG GROUP CO., LTD.
No 88 Wujiang East Road, Jinhua, 321000, Zhejiang, China
Tel.: (86) 57982326868
Web Site: https://www.jianfenig.com.cn
Year Founded: 1958
600668—(SHG)
Rev.: $499,879,332
Assets: $1,027,812,717
Liabilities: $243,639,911
Net Worth: $784,172,807
Earnings: $40,395,944
Fiscal Year-end: 12/31/22
Cement & Pharmaceutical Mfr & Whslr
N.A.I.C.S.: 327310
Xiaomeng Jiang *(Chm & Sec-Party Committee)*

Subsidiaries:

Tianjin Jianfeng Natural Product R&D Co., Ltd. (1)
Huanghai Road W 12th Avenue S Teda, Tianjin, 300457, China
Tel.: (86) 2266237098
Web Site: http://www.jf-natural.com
Pharmaceuticals Product Mfr
N.A.I.C.S.: 325412

Zhejiang Jianfeng Health Tech. Co., Ltd. (1)
No 96 Xixi Street Linjiang Industrial Park, Jinhua, 321000, Zhejiang, China
Tel.: (86) 57982600687
Web Site: http://www.jfhealth.com
Pharmaceuticals Product Mfr
N.A.I.C.S.: 325412

ZHEJIANG JIANYE CHEMICAL CO., LTD.
No 8 yandongguan Road, Meicheng Town Jiande, Hangzhou, 311604, Zhejiang, China
Tel.: (86) 57164149273
Web Site: https://www.chinaorganicchem.com
Year Founded: 1991
603948—(SHG)
Rev.: $392,566,852
Assets: $375,027,326
Liabilities: $96,938,590
Net Worth: $278,088,736
Earnings: $54,789,598
Emp.: 600
Fiscal Year-end: 12/31/22
Chemical Product Mfr & Distr
N.A.I.C.S.: 325520
Lie Feng *(Chm & Gen Mgr)*

ZHEJIANG JIAXIN SILK CORP., LTD.
Jiaxin Silk Plaza No 588 Zhonghuan Road West, Nanhu District, Jiaxing, 314033, Zhejiang, China
Tel.: (86) 57382085227
Web Site: https://www.jxsilk.cn
Year Founded: 1999
002404—(SSE)
Rev.: $607,696,662
Assets: $485,701,403
Liabilities: $197,774,628
Net Worth: $287,926,774
Earnings: $32,342,123
Fiscal Year-end: 12/31/22
Silk Fabric & Garment Mfr
N.A.I.C.S.: 313210

Guojian Zhou (Chm)

ZHEJIANG JIECANG LINEAR MOTION TECHNOLOGY CO., LTD.
No 2 Laisheng Road Provincial High-tech industrial park, Xinchang county, Shaoxing, 312500, Zhejiang, China
Tel.: (86) 4006666358
Web Site: https://www.jiecang.com
Year Founded: 2000
603583—(SHG)
Rev.: $422,125,489
Assets: $963,243,347
Liabilities: $405,566,783
Net Worth: $557,676,564
Earnings: $46,016,339
Emp.: 3,000
Fiscal Year-end: 12/31/22
Linear Actuator Mfr & Distr
N.A.I.C.S.: 334514
Mingfeng Xu (Sec)

Subsidiaries:

J-Star Motion Corporation (1)
500 West St, Cedar Springs, MI 49319
Tel.: (616) 952-0630
Web Site: http://www.jstarmotion.com
Emp.: 600
Warehouse Equipment Mfr
N.A.I.C.S.: 333922

Jiecang Europe GmbH (1)
Emanuel-Leutze-Str 11, 40547, Dusseldorf, Germany
Tel.: (49) 21156677116
Linear Actuator Mfr
N.A.I.C.S.: 334514

ZHEJIANG JIEMEI ELECTRONIC & TECHNOLOGY CO., LTD.
Yangguang Industrial Park Area II Economic Development Zone, Anji County, Hangzhou, Zhejiang, China
Tel.: (86) 5725302126
Web Site: https://www.jmkj.com
Year Founded: 2001
002859—(SSE)
Rev.: $182,686,065
Assets: $675,173,983
Liabilities: $284,683,871
Net Worth: $390,490,111
Earnings: $23,288,120
Emp.: 2,500
Fiscal Year-end: 12/31/22
Electronic Component Mfr & Distr
N.A.I.C.S.: 334413
Fang Juanyun (Chm & Gen Mgr)

ZHEJIANG JIHUA GROUP CO., LTD.
No 1766 Xinshiji Avenue Linjiang Industrial Park, Xiaoshan District, Hangzhou, 311228, Zhejiang, China
Tel.: (86) 57122898090
Web Site: https://wn.jihuadyes.com
Year Founded: 1990
603980—(SHG)
Rev.: $271,209,824
Assets: $735,656,674
Liabilities: $146,267,456
Net Worth: $589,389,218
Earnings: $(29,438,581)
Emp.: 2,000
Fiscal Year-end: 12/31/22
Dyestuff Product Mfr & Distr
N.A.I.C.S.: 325130
Shao Hui (Chm)

Subsidiaries:

Jiangsu Kangbei De Pharmaceutical Co. (1)
No 709 Zhongxin Road Zhongshan Park, Jiangbei New District, Nanjing, China
Tel.: (86) 2557671111
Pharmaceutical Product Mfr & Distr
N.A.I.C.S.: 325412

ZHEJIANG JINDAO TECHNOLOGY CO., LTD.
No 689 Bujin Road, Keqiao District, Shaoxing, 312030, Zhejiang, China
Tel.: (86) 57588576188
Web Site: https://www.sxjindao.com
Year Founded: 2003
301279—(CHIN)
Rev.: $91,758,420
Assets: $237,737,916
Liabilities: $52,516,620
Net Worth: $185,221,296
Earnings: $11,462,256
Fiscal Year-end: 12/31/22
Transmission Product Mfr & Distr
N.A.I.C.S.: 333613
Yanrong Jin (Chm)

ZHEJIANG JINDUN FANS CO., LTD.
Zhangzhen Town Industrial Park, Shangyu District, Shaoxing, 312363, Zhejiang, China
Tel.: (86) 57582952012
Web Site: http://www.jindunfan.com
Year Founded: 2005
300411—(SSE)
Rev.: $59,887,620
Assets: $201,639,672
Liabilities: $70,657,704
Net Worth: $130,981,968
Earnings: $1,896,804
Emp.: 300
Fiscal Year-end: 12/31/22
Subway, Tunnel & Power Plant Ventilation Systems Mfr
N.A.I.C.S.: 333413
Wang Miaogen (Chm & Gen Mgr)

ZHEJIANG JINFEI KAIDA WHEEL CO., LTD.
No 1588 Xinhong Road, Wucheng District, Jinhua, 321000, Zhejiang, China
Tel.: (86) 57982523261
Web Site: https://www.jfkd.com.cn
Year Founded: 2005
002863—(SSE)
Rev.: $592,381,759
Assets: $905,548,438
Liabilities: $611,509,280
Net Worth: $294,039,158
Earnings: $15,848,773
Emp.: 1,800
Fiscal Year-end: 12/31/22
Automobile Parts Mfr & Distr
N.A.I.C.S.: 336390
Ge Bingzao (Chm)

ZHEJIANG JINGGONG SCIENCE & TECHNOLOGY CO., LTD.
No 1809 Jianhu Road, Shaoxing, 312030, Zhejiang, China
Tel.: (86) 57584881111
Web Site: https://www.jgtec.com.cn
Year Founded: 1968
002006—(SSE)
Rev.: $330,939,465
Assets: $363,294,660
Liabilities: $169,694,530
Net Worth: $193,600,129
Earnings: $41,181,131
Emp.: 1,000
Fiscal Year-end: 12/31/22
Electric Equipment Mfr
N.A.I.C.S.: 334413
Yueshun Jin (Chm)

Subsidiaries:

Zhejiang Huayu Electric Co., Ltd. (1)
Linjiang Road No 69 Zhejiang, Gao Bu Town, Shaoxing, 312035, China
Tel.: (86) 57588708508
Semiconductor & Related Device Mfr
N.A.I.C.S.: 334413

Zhejiang Jinggong New Materials Technology Co., Ltd. (1)
M20-15-1 Number, Economic and Technological Development Zone, Hangzhou, China
Tel.: (86) 57186932885
Textile Special Equipment Mfr & Distr
N.A.I.C.S.: 314999

Zhejiang Jinggong Precision Manufacturing Co., Ltd. (1)
No 2106 Jianhu Road Zhejiang, Keqiao District, Shaoxing, 312030, China
Tel.: (86) 57584883909
Semiconductor & Related Device Mfr
N.A.I.C.S.: 334413

Zhejiang Jinggong Robot Intelligent Equipment Co., Ltd. (1)
Jianhu Road 1809 Huashe Street, Keqiao District, Shaoxing, Zhejiang, China
Tel.: (86) 5758 110 0188
Web Site: https://www.jinggong-robotics.com
Measuring & Controlling Device Mfr
N.A.I.C.S.: 334519

Zhejiang Jingheng Data Management Co., Ltd. (1)
Jianhu Road, Keqiao District No 2106, Hangzhou, Shaoxing, China
Tel.: (86) 57581182175
Textile Special Equipment Mfr & Distr
N.A.I.C.S.: 314999

Zhejiang Jonggong Power Technology Co., Ltd. (1)
Ko Bridge No Road 1809, Shaoxing, 312030, Zhejiang, China
Tel.: (86) 57584886688
Semiconductor & Related Device Mfr
N.A.I.C.S.: 334413

ZHEJIANG JINGHUA LASER TECHNOLOGY CO., LTD.
No 89 Zhongshan Road, Yuecheng District, Shaoxing, 312000, Zhejiang, China
Tel.: (86) 57588122757
Web Site: http://www.sx-jhjg.com
Year Founded: 1992
603607—(SHG)
Rev.: $123,445,366
Assets: $197,372,284
Liabilities: $55,976,595
Net Worth: $141,395,689
Earnings: $17,645,289
Fiscal Year-end: 12/31/22
Thin Film Material Mfr & Distr
N.A.I.C.S.: 326112
Sun Jiancheng (Chm & Gen Mgr)

ZHEJIANG JINGSHENG MECHANICAL & ELECTRICAL CO., LTD.
No 218 West Tongjiang Road Economic Development Zone, Shangyu District, Shaoxing, 311199, Zhejiang, China
Tel.: (86) 57188317398
Web Site: https://www.jsjd.cc
Year Founded: 2006
300316—(SSE)
Rev.: $1,493,618,724
Assets: $4,055,687,064
Liabilities: $2,481,407,136
Net Worth: $1,574,279,928
Earnings: $410,480,460
Emp.: 2,400
Fiscal Year-end: 12/31/22
Semiconductor Equipment Mfr
N.A.I.C.S.: 334413
Cao Jianwei (Chm)

Subsidiaries:

Inner Mongolia Jinghuan Electronic Material Co., Ltd. (1)
Baolier Street Industrial Zone 2 Jinqiao Development Zone, Hohhot, 10070, China
Tel.: (86) 4712849873
Web Site: http://jinghuan-sapphire.com
Industrial Crystal Mfr

N.A.I.C.S.: 334419

Zhejiang Jinray Electronic Material Co., Ltd. (1)
Shunyuan Road East District Hangzhou Bay, Sahngyu Economic and Technological Development Area, Shaoxing, Zhejiang, China
Tel.: (86) 57582723280
Web Site: http://www.jinray.cn
Industrial Crystal Mfr & Distr
N.A.I.C.S.: 334419

ZHEJIANG JINGU CO., LTD.
No 1181 Park West Road, Fuchun Subdistrict, Fuyang, 311400, Zhejiang, China
Tel.: (86) 57163133920
Web Site: http://www.jgwheel.com
Year Founded: 1996
002488—(SSE)
Rev.: $423,881,752
Assets: $1,033,718,180
Liabilities: $476,184,361
Net Worth: $557,533,819
Earnings: $15,437,977
Emp.: 1,800
Fiscal Year-end: 12/31/22
Steel Wheel Mfr
N.A.I.C.S.: 332999
Sun Fengfeng (Chm & Gen Mgr)

Subsidiaries:

Asia Wheel Co., Ltd. (1)
7/253 Moo6 T Mabyangporn A Pluakdaeng, Rayong, 21140, Thailand
Tel.: (66) 38650666
Motor Vehicle Parts Distr
N.A.I.C.S.: 423120

Chengdu Jingu Wheel Co. Ltd. (1)
No 99 Auto City Avenue Economic Development Zone, Longquanyi District, Chengdu, Sichuan, China
Tel.: (86) 28846458030
Steel Rolling Wheel Mfr
N.A.I.C.S.: 331221

Pacific Wheel Inc. (1)
3806 Ranya Dr, Commerce Township, MI 48382
Tel.: (313) 320-4534
Motor Vehicle Parts Distr
N.A.I.C.S.: 423120

Shandong Jingu Auto Parts Company Limited (1)
No 333 Shixian Road High-Tech Zone, Jining, Shandong, China
Tel.: (86) 5377975116
Steel Rolling Wheel Mfr
N.A.I.C.S.: 331221

ZHEJIANG JINGXIN PHARMACEUTICAL CO., LTD.
No 800 Xinchang Avenue East Road Yulin Street, Xinchang County, Shaoxing, 312500, Zhejiang, China
Tel.: (86) 57586098209
Web Site: https://www.jingxinpharm.com
Year Founded: 1974
002020—(SSE)
Rev.: $530,690,421
Assets: $1,033,702,848
Liabilities: $307,558,232
Net Worth: $726,144,616
Earnings: $92,980,434
Emp.: 4,000
Fiscal Year-end: 12/31/22
Pharmaceuticals Product Mfr
N.A.I.C.S.: 325412
Lv Gang (Chm & Pres)

Subsidiaries:

Shangyu Jingxin Pharmaceutical Co., Ltd. (1)
No 31 Weisan Road Shangyu Industrial Park Zhejiang Hangzhou Ba, Shangyu, 312369, Zhejiang, China
Tel.: (86) 57582728326
Web Site: http://www.jingxinpharm.com

ZHEJIANG JINGXIN PHARMACEUTICAL CO., LTD.

Zhejiang Jingxin Pharmaceutical Co., Ltd.—(Continued)
Emp.: 400
Pharmaceuticals Product Mfr
N.A.I.C.S.: 325412
Zhu Vhibin (Gen Mgr)

ZHEJIANG JINGXING PAPER JOINT STOCK CO., LTD.
No 1 Jingxing 1st Road Caoqiao Street, Pinghu, 314214, Zhejiang, China
Tel.: (86) 57385961198
Web Site: https://www.zjjxjt.com
Year Founded: 1984
002067—(SSE)
Rev.: $874,301,477
Assets: $1,117,143,972
Liabilities: $340,084,462
Net Worth: $777,059,511
Earnings: $16,510,240
Fiscal Year-end: 12/31/22
Paper Products Mfr
N.A.I.C.S.: 322299
Zhu Zailong (Chm)

Subsidiaries:

Chongqing Jing Xing Packaging Co., Ltd. (1)
Yanjia Iiindustrial park of Qixin road 888 Changshou, Chongqing, 401221, China
Tel.: (86) 2340716089
Web Site: http://www.cqjb.cn
Paper Box Mfr & Distr
N.A.I.C.S.: 322299

Nanjing Jing Xing Paper the Limited Company (1)
Economic Development Zone Airport Road Lishui, Nanjing, 211200, China
Tel.: (86) 2557224948
Paper Box Mfr & Distr
N.A.I.C.S.: 322211

Pinghu city Jing Xing Packing material Limited company (1)
Caoqiao street Jing Xing industrial park, Pinghu, 314200, Zhejiang, China
Tel.: (86) 57385960684
Paper Box Mfr & Distr
N.A.I.C.S.: 322211

Shanghai Jing Xing Industrial Investment Co., Ltd. (1)
New Area Rich City Road 99th Zhendan International Building 601-602, Pudong, Shanghai, 200120, China
Tel.: (86) 2168591307
Paper Box Mfr & Distr
N.A.I.C.S.: 322299

Zhejiang Infrotronic Intelligent Machinery Technology Co.,Ltd. (1)
No 1699 Xingping 4th Road, Economic Development Zone, Pinghu, Zhejiang, China
Tel.: (86) 57385098830
Web Site: https://en.infrotronic.com
Mobile Network Services
N.A.I.C.S.: 517112
Shinohara Hitoshi (Dir)

ZHEJIANG JINKE CULTURE INDUSTRY CO., LTD.
No 5 Weijiu Road, Shangyu Industrial Area, Hangzhou, 312369, Zhejiang, China
Tel.: (86) 57582735559
Web Site: http://www.jinke-chem.com
Year Founded: 2007
300459—(SSE)
Rev.: $229,258,725
Assets: $876,340,787
Liabilities: $331,361,985
Net Worth: $544,978,802
Earnings: $61,772,658
Fiscal Year-end: 12/31/22
Inorganic Chemical Product Mfr
N.A.I.C.S.: 325998
Jian Wang (Chm & CFO)

ZHEJIANG JINKE TOM CULTURE INDUSTRY CO.,LTD.
Weijiu Road Shangyu Industrial Area, Hangzhou, 312369, Zhejiang, China
Tel.: (86) 57582735515
Web Site: http://www.jinke-chem.com
300459—(CHIN)
Rev.: $229,259,160
Assets: $876,340,296
Liabilities: $331,360,848
Net Worth: $544,979,448
Earnings: $61,773,192
Emp.: 570
Fiscal Year-end: 12/31/22
Chemicals Mfr
N.A.I.C.S.: 325998
Zhu Zhigang (Chm)

ZHEJIANG JINSHENG NEW MATERIALS CO., LTD.
No 9 Yuzhou Road, Lihai Town Binhai New Area, Shaoxing, 312000, Zhejiang, China
Tel.: (86) 57582781459
Web Site: https://www.zj-jinsheng.com
Year Founded: 1998
300849—(SSE)
Rev.: $34,085,442
Assets: $112,230,607
Liabilities: $21,633,773
Net Worth: $90,596,835
Earnings: ($3,160,334)
Emp.: 900
Fiscal Year-end: 12/31/22
Packaging Product Mfr & Distr
N.A.I.C.S.: 333993
Rongtao Ruan (Chm)

ZHEJIANG JIULI HI-TECH METALS CO., LTD.
No 1899 Zhongxing Road, wuxing district, Huzhou, 313028, Zhejiang, China
Tel.: (86) 5722539999
Web Site: https://www.jiuli.com
Year Founded: 1987
002318—(SSE)
Rev.: $917,840,051
Assets: $1,385,830,738
Liabilities: $483,218,036
Net Worth: $902,612,702
Earnings: $180,813,438
Fiscal Year-end: 12/31/22
Stainless Steel Products Mfr
N.A.I.C.S.: 331210
Zhijiang Zhou (Pres)

Subsidiaries:

Jiuli USA, inc (1)
12950 S Kirkwood Rd Ste 100, Houston, TX 77477
Tel.: (281) 970-5042
Stainless Steel Products Mfr
N.A.I.C.S.: 331210

ZHEJIANG JIUZHOU PHARMACEUTICAL CO., LTD.
99 Waisha Road, Jiaojiang District, Taizhou, 318000, Zhejiang, China
Tel.: (86) 57688820189
Web Site: https://www.jiuzhoupharma.com
Year Founded: 1973
603456—(SHG)
Rev.: $764,492,770
Assets: $1,111,023,922
Liabilities: $356,868,158
Net Worth: $754,155,764
Earnings: $129,297,477
Fiscal Year-end: 12/31/22
Pharmaceutical Product Mfr & Distr
N.A.I.C.S.: 325412
Hua Lirong (Chm)

Subsidiaries:

Zhejiang Raybow Pharmaceutical Co., Ltd. (1)
No 18 Nanyangsan Road, Linhai, Taizhou, 317036, Zhejiang, China
Tel.: (86) 135 860 70358
Web Site: http://www.raybow.com
Emp.: 1,250
Pharmaceuticals Product Mfr
N.A.I.C.S.: 325412
Bin Wang (CEO)

Subsidiary (US):

PharmAgra Holding Company, LLC (2)
158 McLean Rd, Brevard, NC 28712
Tel.: (828) 884-8656
Holding Company
N.A.I.C.S.: 551112
Peter Newsome (Mgr)

Subsidiary (Domestic):

Pharmagra Labs Inc. (3)
158 Mclean Rd, Brevard, NC 28712
Tel.: (828) 884-8656
Web Site: http://www.pharmagra.com
Rev.: $2,000,000
Emp.: 12
Pharmaceutical Preparation Mfr
N.A.I.C.S.: 325412
Peter Newsome (Co-Founder)

ZHEJIANG JOLLY PHARMACEUTICAL CO., LTD.
Zhiyuan Road Wukang Town, Deqing, Huzhou, 313200, Zhejiang, China
Tel.: (86) 5728281088
Web Site: https://www.en.zuoli.com
Year Founded: 2000
300181—(CHIN)
Rev.: $253,444,464
Assets: $510,932,448
Liabilities: $123,438,276
Net Worth: $387,494,172
Earnings: $38,330,604
Fiscal Year-end: 12/31/22
Pharmaceutical Developer, Researcher, Mfr & Distr
N.A.I.C.S.: 325412

ZHEJIANG JUHUA CO., LTD.
Kecheng Giant International Regional Marketing Center, Quzhou, 324004, China
Tel.: (86) 5703091758
Web Site: http://www.jhgf.com.cn
Year Founded: 1998
600160—(SHG)
Rev.: $3,017,073,066
Assets: $3,176,787,444
Liabilities: $960,652,700
Net Worth: $2,216,134,744
Earnings: $334,254,857
Fiscal Year-end: 12/31/22
Chemical Product Mfr & Distr
N.A.I.C.S.: 325998
Zhou Liyang (Chm)

Subsidiaries:

Ningbo Juhua Chemical Science & Technology Co., Ltd. (1)
No 501 Yuejintang Road Ningbo Petrochemical Economic, Technological Development Zone Zhenhai District, Ningbo, Zhejiang, China
Tel.: (86) 57486555791
Web Site: http://www.en.nbjhgs.com
Acid Mfr
N.A.I.C.S.: 325180

Zhejiang Kaisheng Fluorochemicals Co., Ltd. (1)
8 Nianhua Lu, Quzhou Hi-tech Industrial Park, Hangzhou, Zhejiang, China
Tel.: (86) 5703687677
Web Site: http://www.kaisn.com
Emp.: 200
Fluorspar Powder Mfr
N.A.I.C.S.: 332117

ZHEJIANG JULI CULTURE DEVELOPMENT CO., LTD.
No 1958 Huannan Road Linglong

INTERNATIONAL PUBLIC

Industrial Zone, Linan District, Hangzhou, Zhejiang, China
Tel.: (86) 57163717320
Web Site: https://www.dilong.cc
Year Founded: 2000
002247—(SSE)
Rev.: $131,254,119
Assets: $148,678,883
Liabilities: $44,653,729
Net Worth: $104,025,154
Earnings: $7,423,453
Emp.: 1,674
Fiscal Year-end: 12/31/22
Decorative Materials Mfr
N.A.I.C.S.: 337122

Subsidiaries:

Haining Dilong Yongfu New Material Co., Ltd. (1)
No 6 Huajin Road, Zhouwangmiao Town, Haining, Zhejiang, China
Tel.: (86) 57387932868
Web Site: http://dilongyf.com
Floor Material Mfr
N.A.I.C.S.: 327120

ZHEJIANG JW PRECISION MACHINERY CO., LTD.
No 1 Liushan 1st Road, Hangbu Town Kecheng District, Quzhou, 324000, Zhejiang, China
Tel.: (86) 5703376108
Web Site: https://www.qzjianwo.com
Year Founded: 2011
300984—(CHIN)
Rev.: $146,628,144
Assets: $174,920,148
Liabilities: $79,568,892
Net Worth: $95,351,256
Earnings: $6,357,312
Fiscal Year-end: 12/31/22
Industrial Machinery Mfr & Distr
N.A.I.C.S.: 333248
Wei Yang (Chm)

ZHEJIANG KAIER NEW MATERIALS CO., LTD.
No 333 Guangshun Streert Jinyi Urban Economic Development Zone, Jinhua, 321031, Zhejiang, China
Tel.: (86) 57982889808
Web Site: https://www.zjke.com
300234—(CHIN)
Rev.: $98,806,500
Assets: $205,690,212
Liabilities: $56,840,940
Net Worth: $148,849,272
Earnings: $10,249,200
Emp.: 480
Fiscal Year-end: 12/31/22
Enamel Materials Mfr
N.A.I.C.S.: 332999

Subsidiaries:

Zhejiang Kaier Industry Co., Ltd (1)
Caozhai Industrial Zone, Jinhua, 321031, Zhejiang, China
Tel.: (86) 57983118973
Emp.: 350
Enamel Coating Mfr
N.A.I.C.S.: 325510

ZHEJIANG KAN SPECIALITIES MATERIAL CO., LTD.
No 1008 Kan Road, Suichang County, Lishui, 323300, Zhejiang, China
Tel.: (86) 5788123563
Web Site: https://www.zjkan.com
Year Founded: 1940
002012—(SSE)
Rev.: $195,408,874
Assets: $323,046,865
Liabilities: $82,387,492
Net Worth: $240,659,373
Earnings: $7,501,109
Fiscal Year-end: 12/31/22

AND PRIVATE COMPANIES

Paper Products Mfr
N.A.I.C.S.: 322120
Xi Liu *(Chm & Gen Mgr)*

ZHEJIANG KANGLONGDA SPECIAL PROTECTION TECHNOLOGY CO., LTD.
No 7 Weiwu East Road Shangyu Economic & Technological Development Zone, Hangzhou Bay Shangyu District, Shaoxing, 312361, Zhejiang, China
Tel.: (86) 57582871168
Web Site:
https://www.kanglongda.com.cn
Year Founded: 2000
603665—(SHG)
Rev.: $192,925,128
Assets: $577,788,120
Liabilities: $347,346,006
Net Worth: $230,442,114
Earnings: $29,350,817
Fiscal Year-end: 12/31/22
Glove Mfr & Distr
N.A.I.C.S.: 313310
Zhang Jiadi *(Chm & Gen Mgr)*

ZHEJIANG KANGSHENG CO., LTD.
No 268 Kang Sheng Road, Qiandaohu Town Chunan County, Hangzhou, 311700, Zhejiang, China
Tel.: (86) 57165021818
Web Site: https://www.kasun.cn
Year Founded: 2002
002418—(SSE)
Rev.: $442,361,874
Assets: $446,483,948
Liabilities: $237,104,712
Net Worth: $209,379,236
Earnings: $2,515,055
Emp.: 10,000
Fiscal Year-end: 12/31/22
Steel Pole Mfr
N.A.I.C.S.: 331210
Wang Yajun *(Chm & Gen Mgr)*

Subsidiaries:

Zhongzhi New Energy Vehicle Company Limited (1)
5th floor B1-1 Industry Incubation Park No 1666 Chenglong AV, Longquanyi Dist, Chengdu, China
Tel.: (86) 2884601576
Web Site: http://www.zevauto.com
Electric Vehicle Mfr
N.A.I.C.S.: 336320

ZHEJIANG KINGLAND PIPELINE & TECHNOLOGIES CO., LTD.
No 388 Funan Road, Wuxing District, Huzhou, Zhejiang, China
Tel.: (86) 5722099999
Web Site:
https://www.chinakingland.com
Year Founded: 2002
002443—(SSE)
Rev.: $854,900,444
Assets: $664,792,245
Liabilities: $200,732,281
Net Worth: $464,059,964
Earnings: $33,050,483
Emp.: 1,600
Fiscal Year-end: 12/31/22
Steel Tubes & Pipes Mfr
N.A.I.C.S.: 331210
Li Xingchun *(Chm)*

Subsidiaries:

Zhangjiagang Sha Steel & Kingland Pipline Co., Ltd (1)
Plate Mill East Road Shagang Group Jinfeng Town, Zhangjiagang, 215625, Jiangsu, China
Tel.: (86) 51256758626
Web Site: http://www.sgkdpipe.com

Pipes Mfr
N.A.I.C.S.: 331110

ZHEJIANG LANGDI GROUP CO., LTD
No 188 Langma Road, Langxia Subdistrict, Yuyao, 315480, Zhejiang, China
Tel.: (86) 57462193001
Web Site: http://www.langdi.com
Year Founded: 1998
603726—(SHG)
Rev.: $236,601,982
Assets: $300,937,979
Liabilities: $136,720,776
Net Worth: $164,217,203
Earnings: $12,833,178
Emp.: 2,700
Fiscal Year-end: 12/31/22
Fan Product Mfr & Distr
N.A.I.C.S.: 335210
Gao Yankang *(Chm & Gen Mgr)*

ZHEJIANG LANTE OPTICS CO., LTD.
1108 Hongfu Road, Honghe Town Xiuzhou, Jiaxing, 314023, Zhejiang, China
Tel.: (86) 57383382809
Web Site: https://www.lante.com.cn
Year Founded: 2003
688127—(SHG)
Rev.: $53,403,400
Assets: $270,504,285
Liabilities: $58,907,754
Net Worth: $211,596,531
Earnings: $13,488,003
Emp.: 800
Fiscal Year-end: 12/31/22
Optical Instrument Mfr
N.A.I.C.S.: 333310
Yunming Xu *(Chm & Gen Mgr)*

ZHEJIANG LEAPMOTOR TECHNOLOGY CO., LTD.
1/F No 451 Wulianwang Street, Binjiang District, Hangzhou, Zhejiang, China
Tel.: (86) 57187235715
Web Site: https://en.leapmotor.com
Year Founded: 2015
9863—(HKG)
Rev.: $2,318,715,247
Assets: $3,939,606,917
Liabilities: $2,209,130,068
Net Worth: $1,730,476,850
Earnings: $(583,777,415)
Emp.: 9,314
Fiscal Year-end: 12/31/23
Information Technology Services
N.A.I.C.S.: 541512
Jiangming Zhu *(CEO)*

ZHEJIANG LINUO FLOW CONTROL TECHNOLOGY CO., LTD.
No 2899 Wanghai Road Shangwang Street, Gexiang, Ruian, 325200, Zhejiang, China
Tel.: (86) 57765099770
Web Site: https://www.zj-lenor.com
Year Founded: 2003
300838—(SSE)
Rev.: $142,201,164
Assets: $198,241,402
Liabilities: $69,191,675
Net Worth: $129,049,727
Earnings: $14,995,661
Fiscal Year-end: 12/31/22
Industrial Control Valve Mfr & Distr
N.A.I.C.S.: 332911
Chen Xiaoyu *(Chm & Gen Mgr)*

ZHEJIANG LONGSHENG GROUP CO., LTD.
Daoxu Town, Shangyu District, Shaoxing, 312368, Zhejiang, China
Tel.: (86) 57582517037
Web Site:
https://www.longsheng.com
Year Founded: 1970
600352—(SHG)
Rev.: $2,980,080,235
Assets: $9,148,708,226
Liabilities: $4,268,669,526
Net Worth: $4,880,038,700
Earnings: $421,639,845
Emp.: 9,000
Fiscal Year-end: 12/31/22
Chemical Product Mfr & Distr
N.A.I.C.S.: 325998
Ruan Weixiang *(Chm & Pres)*

Subsidiaries:

Hangzhou Longshan Chemical Industry Ltd. (1)
9899 Hongshiwu road, Linjiang Industrial Park Xiaoshan, Hangzhou, 311228, China
Tel.: (86) 57186617638
Web Site:
https://www.longshanchemical.com
Fertilizer Mfr
N.A.I.C.S.: 325314

Huangshan Longsheng Chemical Co., Ltd. (1)
NO 199 Yongjia Road, Huizhou District, Huangshan, 245900, Anhui Province, China
Tel.: (86) 559 3516028
Chemical Products Distr
N.A.I.C.S.: 424690

Kiri Dyes and Chemicals Ltd. (1)
Plot No 299/1/A and B Phase-II Nr Water Tank, GIDC Vatva, Ahmedabad, 382 445, Gujarat, India
Tel.: (91) 7925894477
Web Site: https://www.kiriindustries.com
Dye Mfr
N.A.I.C.S.: 325130

Lonsen Kiri Chemical Industries Ltd. (1)
7th Floor Hasubhai Chambers, Opp Town Hall Ellisbridge, Ahmedabad, 380 006, India
Tel.: (91) 7926574371
Web Site: https://www.lonsenkiri.com
Dye Mfr
N.A.I.C.S.: 325130

Senda International Capital Limited (1)
Room 2503 9 Chong Yip Street, Kwun Tong, Kowloon, China (Hong Kong)
Tel.: (852) 29553327
Chemical Products Distr
N.A.I.C.S.: 424690

Shanghai Longsheng Lianye Invest Co., Ltd. (1)
Room 4301 Building 2 Henglong Square No 1266 Nanjing Xi Road, Jing, Shanghai, 200040, China
Tel.: (86) 21 62889928
Chemical Products Mfr
N.A.I.C.S.: 325998

Shanghai Longsheng Real Estate Co., Ltd. (1)
3 Floor No 1363 Hutai Road, Zhabei Zone, Shanghai, 200436, China
Tel.: (86) 21 66316688
Real Estate Development Services
N.A.I.C.S.: 531390

Well Prospering Ltd. (1)
Room 2503 Ste 9 Chong Yip St Kwun Tong, Central, Hong Kong, China (Hong Kong)
Tel.: (852) 29553327
Emp.: 20
Chemical Products Distr
N.A.I.C.S.: 424690
Miki Lau *(Dir-HR)*

Zhejiang Amino-Chem Ltd. (1)
No15 Weisan Road, Shangyu, Zhejiang, China
Tel.: (86) 57589281961
Aromatic Amine Mfr
N.A.I.C.S.: 325199

Zhejiang Hongsheng Chemical Co., Ltd. (1)

ZHEJIANG MEDICINE CO. LTD.

No 15 Weisan Road, Hangzhou Bay Chemical Zone, Shangyu, 312369, Zhejiang, China
Tel.: (86) 575 82738363
Web Site: http://www.amino-chem.cn
Chemical Products Distr
N.A.I.C.S.: 424690

Zhejiang Jisheng Chemical Construction Material Co. Ltd. (1)
Zhejiang Hangzhou Harbor Shangyu Industry Park, Shangyu, 312369, China
Tel.: (86) 575 82729306
Web Site: http://www.jilong-chem.com
Cement Mixture Mfr & Distr
N.A.I.C.S.: 325998

Zhejiang Longhua Holding Group Co., Ltd. (1)
Room 1103 Unit 1 Building No 1 Jiangnanxingzuo Changhe Street, Binjiang District, Hangzhou, 310052, China
Tel.: (86) 571 86617638
Chemical Products Distr
N.A.I.C.S.: 424690

Zhejiang Longsheng Dyestuff Chemicals Co., Ltd. (1)
Shangyu Industry Park, Hangzhou, 312369, Zhejiang, China
Tel.: (86) 57582516261
Chemical Products Distr
N.A.I.C.S.: 424690

Zhejiang Zhongsheng Chemical Co., Ltd. (1)
No 21 Weisan Road Hangzhou Bay Chemical Zone, Shangyu, Zhejiang, China
Tel.: (86) 575 82738020
Chemical Products Mfr
N.A.I.C.S.: 424690

Zhongshan Longsheng Colva Auto Co., Ltd. (1)
Fuhuang Southern Road Floor 1-3, Sanjiao Town, Zhongshan, China
Tel.: (86) 760 22810166
Chemical Products Distr
N.A.I.C.S.: 424690

ZHEJIANG MATERIALS INDUSTRY GROUP CORPORATION
No 56 West Huancheng Road, Hangzhou, 310006, Zhejiang, China
Tel.: (86) 571 87054509
Web Site: http://www.zjmi.com
Sales Range: $25-49.9 Billion
Investment Management Service
N.A.I.C.S.: 523940
Jiangchao Hu *(Chm)*

Subsidiaries:

ZheJiang Materials Industry Civil Explosives Monopoly Co., Ltd. (1)
45 Tian Mu Shan Road, Hangzhou, Zhejiang, China
Tel.: (86) 57185214319
Investment Management Service
N.A.I.C.S.: 523940

Zhejiang Materials Industry Chemical Group Co., Ltd. (1)
Floor 27 Block A Zhongda Square Zhongshan North Road 336, Hangzhou, 310003, China
Tel.: (86) 57188278506
Web Site: http://www.zjmichem.com
Chemical Products Distr
N.A.I.C.S.: 423830

Zhejiang Materials Industry Senhua Group Co., Ltd. (1)
Rm 301 International Holiday Hotel, Hangzhou, 310003, China
Tel.: (86) 57186781511
Wood Product Distr
N.A.I.C.S.: 423310

ZHEJIANG MEDICINE CO. LTD.
168 Mid Zhiyuan Middle Avenue, Binhai New Area, Shaoxing, 312366, Zhejiang, China
Tel.: (86) 57585211979
Web Site: https://www.zmc.top

ZHEJIANG MEDICINE CO. LTD.

Zhejiang Medicine Co. Ltd.—(Continued)
Year Founded: 1997
600216—(SHG)
Rev.: $1,139,458,966
Assets: $1,745,539,314
Liabilities: $382,275,111
Net Worth: $1,363,264,204
Earnings: $75,755,642
Emp.: 6,800
Fiscal Year-end: 12/31/22
Drug Substances & Finished Formulations Research & Development, Production & Sales; Natural Drugs, Foods & Feed Additives Production & Sales
N.A.I.C.S.: 325412
Chunbo Li (Chm)

Subsidiaries:

Changhai Biological Company (1)
No 88 Shiji Avenue Binhai New Area, PO Box 312000, Shaoxing, 312366, Zhejiang, China
Tel.: (86) 57582539808
Medicine Mfr
N.A.I.C.S.: 325412

Xinchang Pharmaceutical
Factory (1)
59 East Huancheng Road, Xinchang County, Shaoxing, 312500, Zhejiang, China
Tel.: (86) 57586022860
Web Site: http://www.xcpharma.com
Assets: $140,000,000
Emp.: 2,600
Pharmaceuticals Mfr
N.A.I.C.S.: 325412

Zhejiang Changhai Biological Co. Ltd. (1)
Zhejiang Shaoxing Binhai Park Century Avenue No 95, 312000, Shaoxing, Zhejiang, China
Tel.: (86) 575 82539808
Pharmaceuticals Product Mfr
N.A.I.C.S.: 325411

Zhejiang Health Creation Biotechnology Co. Ltd. (1)
Zhejiang Shaoxing Shengzhou Economic Development Northern Zone, Luoxin Road No 69, 312400, Shengzhou, China
Tel.: (86) 57583116607
Pharmaceutical Product Mfr & Distr
N.A.I.C.S.: 325412

Zhejiang Health Creation Pharmaceutical Co., Ltd. (1)
268 Dengyun Road, Gongshu District, Hangzhou, 310011, Zhejiang, China
Tel.: (86) 57185060219
Pharmaceutical Products Distr
N.A.I.C.S.: 424210

Zhejiang Medicine Co. Ltd. - ZMC Vitamin Factory (1)
D-11 Paojiang Industrial Zone, North District, Shaoxing, 312071, Zhejiang, China
Tel.: (86) 57588030706
Web Site: http://www.china-zmc.com
Pharmaceuticals Product Mfr.
N.A.I.C.S.: 325412

ZHEJIANG MEIDA INDUSTRIAL CO., LTD.
Dongxi Avenue 60KM Haining No 81 Tanqiao, Yuanhua, Haining, 314416, Zhejiang, China
Tel.: (86) 57387813679
Web Site: http://www.meida.com
Year Founded: 2001
002677—(SSE)
Rev.: $257,483,604
Assets: $320,210,870
Liabilities: $44,110,746
Net Worth: $276,100,124
Earnings: $63,483,096
Fiscal Year-end: 12/31/22
Kitchen Cabinet Mfr
N.A.I.C.S.: 337110
Peifei Wang (Chm)

ZHEJIANG MEILI HIGH TECHNOLOGY CO.,LTD.
No 1 Wenhua Road, Xinchang, Shaoxing, 312500, Zhejiang, China
Tel.: (86) 57586086086
Web Site: https://www.china-springs.com
Year Founded: 1990
300611—(CHIN)
Rev.: $193,842,165
Assets: $297,448,467
Liabilities: $144,654,978
Net Worth: $152,793,488
Earnings: $5,732,271
Emp.: 1,000
Fiscal Year-end: 12/31/23
Precision Instrument Mfr & Distr
N.A.I.C.S.: 332613
Zhang Bihong (Chm)

Subsidiaries:

Changchun Meili Spring Co., Ltd. (1)
No 3777 Tongda Road, Changchun Automobile Economic and Technological Development Zone, Changchun, 130000, Jilin, China
Tel.: (86) 43185907357
Web Site: https://www.ccmlth.com
Elastic Component Mfr
N.A.I.C.S.: 315990

Shanghai Techengin Machinery & Electronics Co., Ltd. (1)
No 398 Kefu Road East End of Yunbei Road, Nanxiang Town Jiading District, Shanghai, 201802, China
Tel.: (86) 2139126931
Web Site: http://www.techengin.com
Injection Mould & Engineering Plastic Part Mfr
N.A.I.C.S.: 326199

ZHEJIANG MEILUN ELEVATOR CO., LTD.
No 888 Qitao Road Qixian Street, Shaoxing, 312065, Zhejiang, China
Tel.: (86) 57585660116   CN
Web Site: https://www.zjml.cc
Year Founded: 1979
603321—(SHG)
Rev.: $142,680,868
Assets: $277,833,208
Liabilities: $117,301,869
Net Worth: $160,531,338
Earnings: $6,544,142
Fiscal Year-end: 12/31/22
Elevator Equipment Mfr
N.A.I.C.S.: 333922
Xuelin Qian (Chm & Pres)

ZHEJIANG MEORIENT COMMERCE & EXHIBITION, INC.
Room 2104 21st Floor No 218 Hengfeng Road, Shanghai, 200070, Zhejiang, China
Tel.: (86) 2161331777
Web Site: https://www.meorient.com
Year Founded: 2010
300795—(SSE)
Rev.: $48,903,145
Assets: $83,605,968
Liabilities: $19,200,542
Net Worth: $64,405,425
Earnings: $7,074,054
Emp.: 700
Fiscal Year-end: 12/31/22
Digital Marketing Services
N.A.I.C.S.: 541870
Jianjun Pan (Chm)

ZHEJIANG MING JEWELRY CO., LTD.
Fuquan Industrial Zone, Keqiao Subdistrict Keqiao District, Shaoxing, 312030, Zhejiang, China
Tel.: (86) 57584025665
Web Site: http://www.mingr.com
Year Founded: 2002
002574—(SSE)
Rev.: $487,691,137
Assets: $619,815,596
Liabilities: $205,484,568
Net Worth: $414,331,028
Earnings: ($22,820,532)
Emp.: 3,000
Fiscal Year-end: 12/31/22
Jewelry Mfr & Retailer
N.A.I.C.S.: 339910
Yu Awu (Chm)

ZHEJIANG MTCN TECHNOLOGY CO., LTD.
No 59 Luhui Road Taihu Street, Changxing County, Huzhou, 313100, Zhejiang, China
Tel.: (86) 5726508787
Web Site: https://www.mtcn.net
Year Founded: 2010
003026—(SSE)
Rev.: $47,474,814
Assets: $197,025,974
Liabilities: $76,044,627
Net Worth: $120,981,346
Earnings: $2,724,490
Emp.: 1,000
Fiscal Year-end: 12/31/22
Silicone Products Mfr
N.A.I.C.S.: 334413
Yijun Xu (Chm & Gen Mgr)

ZHEJIANG MUSTANG BATTERY CO., LTD.
No 818 Rongji Road Luotuo Street, Zhenhai, Ningbo, 315202, Zhejiang, China
Tel.: (86) 57486593264
Web Site: http://www.mustangbattery.com
Year Founded: 1996
605378—(SHG)
Rev.: $143,221,886
Assets: $208,906,200
Liabilities: $41,846,725
Net Worth: $167,059,475
Earnings: $13,852,622
Fiscal Year-end: 12/31/22
Electrical Battery Mfr & Distr
N.A.I.C.S.: 335910
Yijun Chen (Chm)

ZHEJIANG NARADA POWER SOURCE CO., LTD.
Block C No 822 Wen er West Road, Hangzhou, 310030, Zhejiang, China
Tel.: (86) 57156975980
Web Site: https://www.naradapower.com
Year Founded: 1997
300068—(CHIN)
Rev.: $1,649,503,440
Assets: $2,248,084,800
Liabilities: $1,540,506,708
Net Worth: $707,578,092
Earnings: $46,520,136
Emp.: 6,000
Fiscal Year-end: 12/31/22
Batteries & Power Supply Products Mfr
N.A.I.C.S.: 335910
Haiguang Wang (Chm)

Subsidiaries:

Narada Asia Pacific Pte. Ltd. (1)
13 Kaki Bukit Road 1 03-05, Eunos Technolink Building, Singapore, 415928, Singapore
Tel.: (65) 68481191
Web Site: https://www.narada-ap.com
Battery Distr
N.A.I.C.S.: 423610

Narada Europe (UK) Limited (1)
Gladstone Place 36-38 Upper Marlborough Road, Redbourn, Saint Albans, AL1 3UU, Hertfordshire, United Kingdom
Tel.: (44) 8453717095
Battery Distr

INTERNATIONAL PUBLIC

N.A.I.C.S.: 423610

ZHEJIANG NATURAL OUTDOOR GOODS, INC.
Xiacao Street, Pingqiao Town Tiantai County, Taizhou, Zhejiang, China
Tel.: (86) 57683683839
Web Site: https://www.zjnature.com
Year Founded: 2000
605080—(SHG)
Rev.: $132,790,474
Assets: $279,447,330
Liabilities: $28,761,670
Net Worth: $250,685,660
Earnings: $29,901,283
Fiscal Year-end: 12/31/22
Outdoor Goods Mfr & Distr
N.A.I.C.S.: 314910
Yonghui Xia (Chm & Gen Mgr)

ZHEJIANG NETSUN CO., LTD.
29 Wangsheng Building No 788 Liye Road, Changhe Subdistrict Binjiang District, Hangzhou, 310012, Zhejiang, China
Tel.: (86) 57188228198
Web Site: http://corp.netsun.com
Year Founded: 2000
002095—(SSE)
Rev.: $60,912,919
Assets: $229,433,635
Liabilities: $61,759,433
Net Worth: $167,674,202
Earnings: $3,187,979
Fiscal Year-end: 12/31/22
Software Application Services
N.A.I.C.S.: 513210
Deliang Sun (Chm & Gen Mgr)

ZHEJIANG NEW CENTURY HOTEL MANAGEMENT CO., LTD.
808 Shixin Road, Xiaoshan District, Hangzhou, 311200, China
Tel.: (86) 57183873676
Web Site: http://www.kaiyuanhotels.com
Rev.: $275,893,938
Assets: $642,823,231
Liabilities: $415,288,077
Net Worth: $227,535,153
Earnings: $29,331,779
Emp.: 5,745
Fiscal Year-end: 12/31/19
Hotel & Resort Operator
N.A.I.C.S.: 721110
Miaoqiang Chen (Pres)

Subsidiaries:

Ninghai Jinhai Grand New Century Hotel Co., Ltd. (1)
No 399 Jinshui Road, Ninghai, China
Tel.: (86) 57425599999
Web Site: http://www.jinhai.newcenturyhotel.com
Hotel Operator
N.A.I.C.S.: 721110

Zhuji Yaojiang New Century Hotel Co., Ltd. (1)
No 207 East Huancheng Road, Zhuji, China
Tel.: (86) 57588798888
Web Site: http://www.yaojiang.newcenturyhotel.com
Hotel Operator
N.A.I.C.S.: 721110

ZHEJIANG NHU COMPANY LTD.
No 418 West Xinchang Avenue, Chengguan Town, Xinchang, Zhejiang, China
Tel.: (86) 57586127777
Web Site: https://www.cnhu.com
Year Founded: 1999
002001—(SSE)
Rev.: $2,237,131,410
Assets: $5,372,774,578

Liabilities: $2,050,608,830
Net Worth: $3,322,165,748
Earnings: $508,286,048
Emp.: 1,900
Fiscal Year-end: 12/31/22
Pharmaceutical Intermediates, Food & Feed Additives, Flavors & Fragrances Research, Manufacturing & Sales
N.A.I.C.S.: 325412
Subsidiaries:

NHU EUROPE GmbH (1)
Daimlerstrasse 14-16, 21357, Bardowick, Germany
Tel.: (49) 41315808800
Web Site: https://www.nhu-eu.com
Food & Cosmetic Distr
N.A.I.C.S.: 424490

ZHEJIANG ORIENT FINANCIAL HOLDINGS GROUP CO., LTD.
International Trade Financial Building No 39 Xiangzhang Street, Shangcheng District, Hangzhou, 310006, Zhejiang, China
Tel.: (86) 57187600666
Web Site: https://www.zjorient.com
Year Founded: 1988
600120—(SHG)
Sales Range: $15-24.9 Billion
Investment Management Service
N.A.I.C.S.: 523999
Zhaoping Jin (Chm, Vice Chm & Pres)

Subsidiaries:

Hangzhou SuperStrength New Materials Technology Co., Ltd. (1)
No 57 Yonghua Street, Xiacheng, Hangzhou, 310009, China
Tel.: (86) 571 88143682
Web Site: http://www.supers.cn
Steel Cable Mfr
N.A.I.C.S.: 331222
Zhu Jianjiang (Chm & Gen Mgr)

Sunny I/E Co., Ltd (1)
9th Floor No 12 West Lake Avenue, Hangzhou, 310009, China
Tel.: (86) 571 8760068
Footwear Whslr
N.A.I.C.S.: 424340
Lieming Xia (Pres & Mgr)

ZHEJIANG ORIENT C&E CO., LTD. (1)
12th Floor 12 West Lake Avenue, Hangzhou, 310009, Zhejiang, China
Tel.: (86) 571 87600216
Textile Products Distr
N.A.I.C.S.: 424310
Yan Wei Er (Pres)

ZHEJIANG ORIENT CREATION I/E CO., LTD. (1)
11F No 12 West Lake Avenue, Hangzhou, 310009, China
Tel.: (86) 571 87600019
Textile Products Distr
N.A.I.C.S.: 424310
David Wei (Mng Dir)

ZHEJIANG ORIENT MULTITEX CO., LTD. (1)
21st Floor New Orient Mansion No 12 Westlake Avenue, Hangzhou, 310009, China
Tel.: (86) 571 87600696
Web Site: http://www.multitex.cn
Textile Products Distr
N.A.I.C.S.: 424310

Zhejiang Orient Garmtex I/E Co., Ltd (1)
25th Floor No 12 West Lake Avenue, Hangzhou, 310009, China
Tel.: (86) 571 87600666
Web Site: http://www.garmtex.cn
Textile Products Distr
N.A.I.C.S.: 424310
Huiyu Gong (Chm & Gen Mgr)

Zhejiang Orient Holly Trading Co., Ltd (1)
26th Floor No 12 West Lake Avenue, Hangzhou, 310009, China
Tel.: (86) 571 87600801
Textile Machinery Distr
N.A.I.C.S.: 423830
Wei Er Yan (Pres & Mgr)

Zhejiang Orient Home Textiles I/E Co., Ltd. (1)
10F No 12 West Lake Avenue, Hangzhou, 310009, China
Tel.: (86) 571 87600133
Textile Products Distr
N.A.I.C.S.: 424990
Xuechun Hong (Pres)

Zhejiang Orient Huaye I/E Co., Ltd. (1)
23F & 24F No 12 Westlake Avenue, Hangzhou, 310009, Zhejiang, China
Tel.: (86) 571 87600839
Textile Products Distr
N.A.I.C.S.: 424310
Guohua Qian (Pres & Mgr)

Zhejiang Orient International Transport Co., Ltd (1)
15th Floor No 12 West Lake Avenue, Hangzhou, 310009, China
Tel.: (86) 571 87600046
Freight Forwarding Services
N.A.I.C.S.: 488510
Xu Xiongwei (Gen Mgr)

Zhejiang Orient Junye I/E Co., Ltd. (1)
19th Floor No 12 West Lake Avenue, Hangzhou, 310009, China
Tel.: (86) 571 87600351
Textile Products Distr
N.A.I.C.S.: 424310
Chen Liang (Pres & Mgr)

Zhejiang Orient Knitex I/E Co., Ltd. (1)
22F & 23F No 12 Westlake Avenue, Hangzhou, 310009, Zhejiang, China
Tel.: (86) 571 87600666
Textile Products Distr
N.A.I.C.S.: 424310
Wang Jinliang (Pres & Mgr)

Zhejiang Orient Knitwear I/E Co., Ltd. (1)
27th Floor No 12 West Lake Avenue, Hangzhou, 310009, China
Tel.: (86) 571 87600964
Textile Products Distr
N.A.I.C.S.: 424310
Zhao Zu Kui (Mgr)

Zhejiang Orient New Horizon Garments & Accessories I/E Co., Ltd (1)
20th Floor No 12 West Lake Avenue, Hangzhou, 310009, China
Tel.: (86) 571 87600628
Knitted Hat & Glove Distr
N.A.I.C.S.: 424990
Xu Chuan (Founder, Mgr & Mng Dir)

Zhejiang Orient Penglai Real Estate Co., Ltd. (1)
No 682 Huangcheng South Road, Huzhou, 313000, China
Tel.: (86) 572 2216633
Web Site: http://www.hzfypz.com
Real Estate Development Services
N.A.I.C.S.: 531390
Qiu Gaorao (Gen Mgr)

Zhejiang Xindi Real Estate Co., Ltd. (1)
Buiding 2 Hangban Mansion Hushu South Road, Hangzhou, 3100014, China
Tel.: (86) 571 88318856
Real Estate Development Services
N.A.I.C.S.: 531390
Lin Ping (Chm)

ZHEJIANG ORIENT GENE BIO-TECH CO., LTD.
3787 East Yangguang Avenue Dipu Street, Anji, Huzhou, Zhejiang, China
Tel.: (86) 5725303755

Web Site: https://www.orientgene.com
Year Founded: 2005
688298—(SHG)
Rev.: $1,231,018,509
Assets: $1,502,805,012
Liabilities: $334,256,612
Net Worth: $1,168,548,400
Earnings: $290,307,088
Fiscal Year-end: 12/31/22
Medical Product Mfr & Distr
N.A.I.C.S.: 339112
Jianqiu Fang (Chm)

Subsidiaries:

Hangzhou DanWei Biotechnology Co. Ltd. (1)
2ndFloor Building 4 No 2959 Yuhangtang Road, Hangzhou, 311121, Zhejiang, China
Tel.: (86) 57186173159
Web Site: https://danweibio.com
Vitro Diagnostic Reagent Mfr & Distr
N.A.I.C.S.: 325413

Hangzhou Danwei Biological Technology Co., Ltd. (1)
Room 902 9/F building 4 No 2959 yuhangtang Rd, Yuhang District, Hangzhou, 311121, China
Tel.: (86) 57186173159
Web Site: https://www.dwsw.youledi.cn
Biotechnology Research & Development Services
N.A.I.C.S.: 541714

Hangzhou Shinedo Technology Co.,Ltd. (1)
No 3 Zhenning Road Industrial Zone, Ningwei Xiaoshan, Hangzhou, China
Tel.: (86) 57182655680
Web Site: https://www.shinedolight.com
Sensor Light Mfr & Distr
N.A.I.C.S.: 334413

Healgen Scientific Limited Liability Company (1)
3818 Fuqua St, Houston, TX 77047
Tel.: (713) 733-8088
Web Site: https://www.healgen.com
Medical Device Mfr & Distr
N.A.I.C.S.: 339112

Healstone Biotech Inc. (1)
Unit 650-655 West Kent Avenue North, Vancouver, V6P 6T7, BC, Canada
Tel.: (604) 800-2434
Web Site: https://www.healstone.com
Biotechnology Product Distr
N.A.I.C.S.: 424210

Nanjing Healvity Biotech Co., Ltd. (1)
No 1198 Xinji East Road Longchi Street, Liuhe District, Nanjing, 210000, China
Tel.: (86) 2558867817
Vitro Diagnostic Instrument Mfr & Distr
N.A.I.C.S.: 325413

Qingdao Handsen Biotechnology Co., Ltd. (1)
No 16 Yuting Road, Chengyang district, Qingdao, Shandong, China
Tel.: (86) 53284670782
Web Site: https://www.qdhenderson.com
Laboratory Equipment Mfr
N.A.I.C.S.: 334516

Qingdao Hansen Biologic Science Co., Ltd. (1)
Building 1 National Communications Industry Park 78 Zhuzhou Road, Laoshan District, Qingdao, 266101, China
Tel.: (86) 53285760620
Web Site: https://www.qdhansen.com
Biological Pesticide & Biomimetic Pesticide Mfr
N.A.I.C.S.: 325320

Shanghai Douglas Medical Device Co., Ltd. (1)
Room 1404 No 2299 Yan'an West Road, Changning District, Shanghai, China
Tel.: (86) 2180197197
Web Site: https://www.douglasmed.com
Biotechnology Product Mfr & Distr
N.A.I.C.S.: 325413

ZHEJIANG PEOPLE CULTURE CO., LTD.
12F Baima Mansion No 1 Miduqiao Road, Hangzhou, 310005, Zhejiang, China
Tel.: (86) 57185866518
Web Site: http://www.cn-pg.cn
600576—(SHG)
Rev.: $50,581,150
Assets: $471,969,468
Liabilities: $91,907,300
Net Worth: $380,062,168
Earnings: $3,072,205
Fiscal Year-end: 12/31/22
Real Estate Property Development Services
N.A.I.C.S.: 531390

ZHEJIANG PROVINCIAL NEW ENERGY INVESTMENT GROUP CO., LTD.
No 8 Fengqi East Road Kaixuan Street, Shangcheng District, Hangzhou, 310020, Zhejiang, China
Tel.: (86) 57186664353
Year Founded: 2002
600032—(SHG)
Rev.: $645,568,888
Assets: $6,548,477,270
Liabilities: $4,541,375,213
Net Worth: $2,007,102,057
Earnings: $108,838,347
Fiscal Year-end: 12/31/22
Investment Management Service
N.A.I.C.S.: 523940
Zhang Li (Sec)

ZHEJIANG QIANJIANG BIOCHEMICAL CO., LTD.
Floor 19-21 Qianjiang Building No 178 Qianjiang West Road, Haizhou Street, Haining, 314400, Zhejiang, China
Tel.: (86) 57387038237
Web Site: https://www.qianjiangbioch.com
Year Founded: 1970
600796—(SHG)
Rev.: $282,044,576
Assets: $940,245,504
Liabilities: $462,593,795
Net Worth: $477,651,709
Earnings: $28,928,760
Fiscal Year-end: 12/31/22
Chemicals Mfr
N.A.I.C.S.: 325320
Sun Yuchao (Chm & Gen Mgr)

ZHEJIANG QIANJIQNG MOTORYCLE CO., LTD.
Economic and Technology Development Zone, Wenling City, Taizhou, 317500, Zhejiang, China
Tel.: (86) 57686192111
Web Site: http://www.qjmotor.com
000913—(SSE)
Rev.: $793,033,493
Assets: $945,524,207
Liabilities: $452,115,364
Net Worth: $493,408,843
Earnings: $58,641,556
Fiscal Year-end: 12/31/22
Motorcycle & Motorcycle Parts Mfr
N.A.I.C.S.: 336991
Zhihao Xu (Chm)

ZHEJIANG REALSUN CHEMICAL CO., LTD.
No 9 Donghai Third Avenue, Toumen Port New District, Linhai, 317016, China
Tel.: (86) 57688312589
Web Site: https://www.realsunchem.com
Year Founded: 2007

ZHEJIANG REALSUN CHEMICAL CO., LTD.

Zhejiang Realsun Chemical Co., Ltd.—(Continued)
301212—(CHIN)
Rev.: $93,241,648
Assets: $237,114,605
Liabilities: $43,261,169
Net Worth: $193,853,436
Earnings: $10,015,887
Fiscal Year-end: 12/31/23
Chemical Product Mfr & Distr
N.A.I.C.S.: 327120
Jianyu Mu (Chm)

ZHEJIANG RECLAIM CONSTRUCTION GROUP CO., LTD.
1009 Canton Road Xian Hi-tech Zone, Ningbo, 315040, Zhejiang, China
Tel.: (86) 574 87901130
Web Site: http://www.zjwh.com.cn
Sales Range: $250-299.9 Million
Emp.: 450
Hydraulic, Hydropower, Civil Public, Port, Waterway, Housing Construction, Bridge & Tunnel Engineering Services
N.A.I.C.S.: 237990
Zhangquan Wang (Vice Chm)

ZHEJIANG RED DRAGONFLY FOOTWEAR CO., LTD.
Red Dragonfly Building Wuxing Industrial Zone, Oubei Town Yongjia County, Wenzhou, 325105, Zhejiang, China
Tel.: (86) 57767998807
Web Site: http://www.cnhqt.com
Year Founded: 2007
603116—(SHG)
Rev.: $316,086,409
Assets: $662,278,299
Liabilities: $195,487,555
Net Worth: $466,790,744
Earnings: ($5,194,295)
Fiscal Year-end: 12/31/22
Footwear Mfr & Distr
N.A.I.C.S.: 316210
Jun Wang (CFO)

ZHEJIANG RENZHI CO., LTD.
Room 2404 24th Floor Zhongzhou Building No 3088 Jintian Road, Futian District, Shenzhen, 518000, Guangdong, China
Tel.: (86) 75582002629
Web Site: https://www.chinarenzhi.com
Year Founded: 2011
002629—(SSE)
Rev.: $19,302,928
Assets: $55,465,084
Liabilities: $54,417,128
Net Worth: $1,047,956
Earnings: ($4,046,276)
Emp.: 501
Fiscal Year-end: 12/31/21
Oilfield Technology Services
N.A.I.C.S.: 213112
Xi Chen (Pres)

ZHEJIANG RIFA DIGITAL PRECISION MACHINERY CO., LTD.
Rifa Science and Technology Park Qixing Street, Xinchang, 312500, Zhejiang, China
Tel.: (86) 57586337988
Web Site: https://www.rifapm.com
Year Founded: 1998
002520—(SSE)
Rev.: $300,338,022
Assets: $836,479,809
Liabilities: $526,133,626
Net Worth: $310,346,183
Earnings: ($214,743,990)
Emp.: 300
Fiscal Year-end: 12/31/22
Computer Numerical Control (CNC) Machine Tools Including Lathes & Grinding Machines
N.A.I.C.S.: 333517
Niu Lei (Chm)

Subsidiaries:

Airwork Holdings Limited (1)
Level 4 32-34 Mahuhu Crescent, PO Box 3271, Auckland, 1010, New Zealand
Tel.: (64) 93771663
Web Site: https://www.airwork.co.nz
Sales Range: $125-149.9 Million (100%)
Holding Company
N.A.I.C.S.: 551112
Chris Hart (CEO)

ZHEJIANG RISUN INTELLIGENT TECHNOLOGY CO., LTD.
Risun Building 215 Yuanfeng North Road Yuelin Street, Fenghua District, Ningbo, 315503, Zhejiang, China
Tel.: (86) 18375852311
Web Site: https://www.rsit-sunrise.com
Year Founded: 2009
688215—(SHG)
Rev.: $42,967,707
Assets: $100,758,551
Liabilities: $35,165,103
Net Worth: $65,593,448
Earnings: $1,347,068
Fiscal Year-end: 12/31/22
Software Development Services
N.A.I.C.S.: 541511
Feng Yuan (Chm & Gen Mgr)

ZHEJIANG RONGSHENG PAPER INDUSTRY HOLDING CO., LTD.
No 588 Nandong Road Economic Development Zone, Pinghu, 314213, Zhejiang, China
Tel.: (86) 57385986681
Web Site: http://www.rszy.com
Year Founded: 1980
603165—(SHG)
Rev.: $359,827,425
Assets: $373,257,233
Liabilities: $93,834,178
Net Worth: $279,423,055
Earnings: $23,605,438
Fiscal Year-end: 12/31/22
Holding Company
N.A.I.C.S.: 551114
Feng Ronghua (Chm & Pres)

ZHEJIANG RUIYUAN INTELLIGENT CONTROL TECHNOLOGY COMPANY LIMITED
Factory No 3 Laiyan Road West Economic Development Zone Yuyao, Ningbo, Zhejiang, China
Tel.: (86) 57462730077
Web Site: http://www.ruiyuanhk.com
8249—(HKG)
Rev.: $3,016,033
Assets: $1,823,909
Liabilities: $9,044,085
Net Worth: ($7,220,176)
Earnings: ($486,542)
Emp.: 11
Fiscal Year-end: 12/31/23
Controller System Mfr & Distr
N.A.I.C.S.: 334512
Weiqiang Chen (Exec Dir)

ZHEJIANG RUNTU CO., LTD.
Runtu Buding Fortune Plaza 1 Shimin Road 1009, Shangyu, 312300, Zhejiang, China
Tel.: (86) 57582676999
Web Site: https://www.runtuchem.com
Year Founded: 1998
002440—(SSE)
Rev.: $880,022,679
Assets: $1,776,103,763
Liabilities: $393,857,872
Net Worth: $1,382,245,890
Earnings: $85,154,467
Emp.: 3,500
Fiscal Year-end: 12/31/22
Dyes & Chemical Intermediates Mfr
N.A.I.C.S.: 325130

ZHEJIANG RUNYANG NEW MATERIAL TECHNOLOGY CO., LTD.
No 9 Changxing Avenue, Lijiaxiang Town Changxing County, Huzhou, 313102, Zhejiang, China
Tel.: (86) 5726810788
Web Site: https://www.zj-runyang.com
Year Founded: 2012
300920—(SSE)
Rev.: $54,714,512
Assets: $190,977,064
Liabilities: $31,773,039
Net Worth: $159,204,025
Earnings: $4,698,654
Emp.: 900
Fiscal Year-end: 12/31/22
Polymer Material Mfr
N.A.I.C.S.: 325211
Qingfeng Yang (Chm & Gen Mgr)

ZHEJIANG SANFER ELECTRIC CO., LTD.
No 100 Wuhe West Road, Shengzhou Economic Development Zone, Shaoxing, 312400, Zhejiang, China
Tel.: (86) 57583356233
Web Site: http://www.sanfer.com
Year Founded: 1998
605336—(SHG)
Rev.: $132,870,053
Assets: $320,139,027
Liabilities: $50,346,092
Net Worth: $269,792,935
Earnings: $30,094,277
Emp.: 500
Fiscal Year-end: 12/31/22
Electrical Equipment Mfr & Distr
N.A.I.C.S.: 335999
Ruoyun Shang (Chm)

ZHEJIANG SANHUA INTELLIGENT CONTROLS CO., LTD.
Office Building Sanhua Industrial Park No 219 Woxi Avenue, Xinchang, Shaoxing, 312532, Zhejiang, China
Tel.: (86) 57128020008
Web Site: http://www.zjshc.com
Year Founded: 2001
002050—(SSE)
Rev.: $2,997,195,978
Assets: $3,925,754,474
Liabilities: $2,083,804,726
Net Worth: $1,841,949,748
Earnings: $361,297,526
Fiscal Year-end: 12/31/22
Appliance Parts Mfr
N.A.I.C.S.: 334519
Yabo Zhang (Chm & CEO)

Subsidiaries:

Sanhua Aweco Appliance Systems GmbH (1)
Huttenseestrasse 40, 88099, Neukirch, Germany
Tel.: (49) 7528200
Tubular Heating Element Mfr
N.A.I.C.S.: 333414

Sanhua International Europe, S.L (1)
Jose Celestino Mutis 4 2I, San Sebastian de los Reyes, 28703, Madrid, Spain
Tel.: (34) 916543000

INTERNATIONAL PUBLIC

Web Site: http://www.sanhuaeurope.com
Pressure Sensor Mfr
N.A.I.C.S.: 334519
Zhang Yabo (Pres)

Sanhua International, Inc. (1)
252 Fallbrook Dr Bldg 2 Ste 400, Houston, TX 77038
Tel.: (769) 237-4303
Web Site: http://www.sanhuausa.com
Software Services
N.A.I.C.S.: 541511

ZHEJIANG SANMEI CHEMICAL INDUSTRY CO., LTD.
218 Qingnian Road, Huchu Industrial Zone Wuyi County, Jinhua, 321200, Zhejiang, China
Tel.: (86) 57987651287
Web Site: https://www.sanmeichem.com
Year Founded: 2001
603379—(SHG)
Rev.: $669,799,443
Assets: $902,740,368
Liabilities: $101,102,981
Net Worth: $801,637,387
Earnings: $68,174,477
Fiscal Year-end: 12/31/22
Chemical Product Mfr & Distr
N.A.I.C.S.: 325998
Qixiang Hu (Chm, Pres & Gen Mgr)

ZHEJIANG SANXING NEW MATERIALS CO., LTD
333 Hanghai Road Yuyue Town Deqing, Huzhou, 313213, Zhejiang, China
Tel.: (86) 5728370557
Web Site: http://www.sxslhg.com
Year Founded: 1999
603578—(SHG)
Rev.: $126,539,203
Assets: $192,986,380
Liabilities: $47,665,163
Net Worth: $145,321,217
Earnings: $15,091,185
Emp.: 420
Fiscal Year-end: 12/31/21
Glass Door Mfr & Distr
N.A.I.C.S.: 327215
Xiaofei Tong (Chm)

ZHEJIANG SEMIR GARMENT CO., LTD.
No 2689 Lianhua South Road, Wenzhou, 201109, Zhejiang, China
Tel.: (86) 2167288431
Web Site: https://www.semir.com
Year Founded: 2002
002563—(SSE)
Rev.: $1,871,701,042
Assets: $2,565,261,457
Liabilities: $1,035,788,673
Net Worth: $1,529,472,784
Earnings: $89,434,688
Emp.: 1,400
Fiscal Year-end: 12/31/22
Garment Mfr & Retailer
N.A.I.C.S.: 315210
Guanghe Qiu (Chm)

ZHEJIANG SHAPUAISI PHARMACEUTICAL COMPANY LIMITED
No 1588 Xinming Road Economic Development Zone, Pinghu, 314200, Zhejiang, China
Tel.: (86) 4008265538
Web Site: https://www.zjspas.com
Year Founded: 1978
603168—(SHG)
Rev.: $77,154,995
Assets: $274,858,033
Liabilities: $33,835,515
Net Worth: $241,022,518
Earnings: $6,449,569

Fiscal Year-end: 12/31/22
Pharmaceutical Product Mfr & Distr
N.A.I.C.S.: 325412
Lin Hongli *(Chm & Gen Mgr)*

ZHEJIANG SHENGDA BIOLOGICAL PHARMACEUTICAL CO., LTD.

No 789 Renmin East Road, Tiantai, Taizhou, 317200, Zhejiang, China
Tel.: (86) 57683881111
Web Site: https://www.sd-pharm.com
Year Founded: 1999
603079—(SHG)
Rev.: $103,617,882
Assets: $232,391,133
Liabilities: $43,771,371
Net Worth: $188,619,762
Earnings: $4,420,648
Fiscal Year-end: 12/31/22
Pharmaceutical Product Mfr & Whslr
N.A.I.C.S.: 325412

ZHEJIANG SHENGHUA HOLDINGS CO., LTD.

700 Wuyuan Street, Wukang Street, Deqing County, Huzhou, 313200, China
Tel.: (86) 572 8377000
Private Investment Firm
N.A.I.C.S.: 523999

Subsidiaries:

Shenghua Lande Scitech Limited (1)
11th Floor Building 1 Xitou Innocentre 239 Shuanglong Street, Xihu District, Hangzhou, Zhejiang, China
Tel.: (86) 57186698392
Web Site: https://www.landpage.com.cn
Rev.: $18,957,370
Assets: $17,454,247
Liabilities: $3,833,482
Net Worth: $13,620,766
Earnings: ($2,668,302)
Emp.: 140
Fiscal Year-end: 12/31/2022
Computer Software & Telecommunication Solutions
N.A.I.C.S.: 517121
Wang Feng *(Chm)*

ZHEJIANG SHENGYANG SCIENCE & TECHNOLOGY CO., LTD.

No 1416 Renmin East Road, Yuecheng District, Shaoxing, 312000, Zhejiang, China
Tel.: (86) 57588622076
Web Site: https://www.shengyang.com
Year Founded: 2003
603703—(SHG)
Rev.: $114,945,494
Assets: $270,042,763
Liabilities: $149,788,492
Net Worth: $120,254,271
Earnings: $2,163,129
Emp.: 1,500
Fiscal Year-end: 12/31/22
Radio Frequency Cable Mfr & Distr
N.A.I.C.S.: 334220
Liming Ye *(Chm & Gen Mgr)*

ZHEJIANG SHIBAO COMPANY LIMITED

6 17th Avenue HEDA, Hangzhou, 310018, China
Tel.: (86) 57128025690
Web Site: https://www.zjshibao.com
Year Founded: 1993
002703—(SSE)
Rev.: $194,649,942
Assets: $335,483,441
Liabilities: $142,700,482
Net Worth: $192,782,959
Earnings: $2,221,633
Emp.: 1,697
Fiscal Year-end: 12/31/22
Automotive Steering System Mfr
N.A.I.C.S.: 336330

Subsidiaries:

Beijing Autonics Technology Co., Ltd. (1)
No 8 Building No 98 West Lake, Mentougou District, Beijing, 102300, China
Tel.: (86) 1068948631
Web Site: https://www.autoeps.com.cn
Automobile & Steering Product Mfr
N.A.I.C.S.: 336330

Wuhu Sterling Steering System Co., Ltd. (1)
No 18 Longshan Road Anhui Pilot free Trade Zone, Wuhu, 241006, China
Tel.: (86) 5535952915
Web Site: https://www.whstl.cn
Sales Range: $100-124.9 Million
Automobile Parts Mfr
N.A.I.C.S.: 336390

ZHEJIANG SHOUXIANGU PHARMACEUTICAL CO., LTD.

No 12 Huanglong Third Road, Wuyi County, Jinhua, 321200, Zhejiang, China
Tel.: (86) 57987622285
Web Site: https://www.sxg1909.com
Year Founded: 1997
603896—(SHG)
Rev.: $116,401,653
Assets: $401,009,020
Liabilities: $133,473,689
Net Worth: $267,535,331
Earnings: $39,000,733
Fiscal Year-end: 12/31/22
Pharmaceuticals Product Mfr
N.A.I.C.S.: 325412
Mingyan Li *(Chm & Pres)*

ZHEJIANG SHUANGHUAN DRIVELINE CO., LTD.

No 1 Shengyuan Road, Mechanical and Electrical Industrial Function Zone, Yuhuan, 310023, Zhejiang, China
Tel.: (86) 57181671018
Web Site: http://www.gearsnet.com
Year Founded: 2005
002472—(SSE)
Rev.: $960,047,661
Assets: $1,810,469,218
Liabilities: $759,752,894
Net Worth: $1,050,716,324
Earnings: $81,724,734
Emp.: 7,000
Fiscal Year-end: 12/31/22
Transmission Gears & Gear Components Mfr
N.A.I.C.S.: 333612
Wu Changhong *(Chm)*

ZHEJIANG SONGYUAN AUTOMOTIVE SAFETY SYSTEMS CO., LTD.

No 1 Yunheyan Road, Moushan Town, Yuyao, 315456, Zhejiang, China
Tel.: (86) 57462499207
Web Site: https://www.songyuansafety.com
Year Founded: 2001
300893—(SSE)
Rev.: $139,258,225
Assets: $217,124,865
Liabilities: $94,485,844
Net Worth: $122,639,021
Earnings: $16,572,816
Fiscal Year-end: 12/31/22
Automotive Parts Mfr & Distr
N.A.I.C.S.: 336390
Chanming Hu *(Chm)*

ZHEJIANG SOUTHEAST SPACE FRAME CO., LTD.

Yaqian Town, Xiaoshan District, Hangzhou, 311209, Zhejiang, China
Tel.: (86) 57182783318
Web Site: https://www.dongnanwangjia.com
Year Founded: 2001
002135—(SSE)
Rev.: $1,693,846,618
Assets: $2,460,432,471
Liabilities: $1,585,047,864
Net Worth: $875,384,607
Earnings: $40,809,871
Fiscal Year-end: 12/31/22
Steel Products Mfr
N.A.I.C.S.: 331221
Mingming Guo *(Chm)*

ZHEJIANG STARRY PHARMACEUTICAL CO., LTD.

No 1 Sitaili Avenue Modern Industrial Cluster Zone, Xianju, Taizhou, 317300, Zhejiang, China
Tel.: (86) 57687718628
Web Site: https://www.starrypharm.com
Year Founded: 1997
603520—(SHG)
Rev.: $299,226,096
Assets: $744,426,086
Liabilities: $495,747,640
Net Worth: $248,678,446
Earnings: ($10,648,736)
Emp.: 1,800
Fiscal Year-end: 12/31/22
Medical Instrument Mfr & Distr
N.A.I.C.S.: 339112

Subsidiaries:

Imax Diagnostic Imaging Limited (1)
Phoenix House Room 137 Monahan Road, Cork, T12H1XY, Ireland
Tel.: (353) 214519990
Web Site: https://www.imaxdiagnostic.com
Pharmaceuticals Product Mfr
N.A.I.C.S.: 325412

ZHEJIANG SUNFLOWER GREAT HEALTH LIMITED LIABILITY COMPANY

Sanjiang Road Paojiang Industrial Zone, Shaoxing, 312071, Zhejiang, China
Tel.: (86) 57588919159
Web Site: http://www.sunowe.com
Year Founded: 2005
300111—(SSE)
Rev.: $47,154,744
Assets: $86,521,500
Liabilities: $28,277,964
Net Worth: $58,243,536
Earnings: ($160,056)
Fiscal Year-end: 12/31/22
Semiconductor Devices Mfr
N.A.I.C.S.: 334413
Cao Yang *(Chm)*

ZHEJIANG SUNOREN SOLAR TECHNOLOGY CO., LTD.

No 9 Pidu Road, Haining, 314400, Zhejiang, China
Tel.: (86) 57387393016
Web Site: https://www.sunorensolar.com
Year Founded: 2008
603105—(SHG)
Rev.: $91,242,590
Assets: $492,720,715
Liabilities: $244,882,788
Net Worth: $247,837,927
Earnings: $26,891,079
Fiscal Year-end: 12/31/22
Energy Distribution Services
N.A.I.C.S.: 221122
Lizhong Zhang *(Chm)*

ZHEJIANG SUPCON TECHNOLOGY CO., LTD.

No 309 Liuhe Road, Binjiang, Hangzhou, 310053, China
Tel.: (86) 866673629
Web Site: https://www.supcon.com
Year Founded: 1999
688777—(SHG)
Rev.: $929,989,453
Assets: $1,833,992,269
Liabilities: $1,087,609,667
Net Worth: $746,382,602
Earnings: $112,029,260
Fiscal Year-end: 12/31/22
Automation Control Product Mfr & Distr
N.A.I.C.S.: 334512
Shan Cui *(Chm & Pres)*

ZHEJIANG SUPOR CO., LTD.

5F Supor Building No 1772 Jianghui Road, Hangzhou High-tech Industrial Zone, Hangzhou, 310051, Zhejiang, China
Tel.: (86) 57186858778
Web Site: http://www.supor.com.cn
Year Founded: 1998
002032—(SSE)
Rev.: $2,831,942,061
Assets: $1,818,552,888
Liabilities: $825,547,184
Net Worth: $993,005,704
Earnings: $290,299,394
Emp.: 33,000
Fiscal Year-end: 12/31/22
Electric Appliances Mfr
N.A.I.C.S.: 335220
Thierry de La Tour d'Artaise *(Chm)*

ZHEJIANG TAIFU PUMP CO., LTD.

East Industry Center, Wenling, Taizhou, 317511, Zhejiang, China
Tel.: (86) 57686312869
Web Site: https://www.chinataifu.com
Year Founded: 1993
300992—(SSE)
Rev.: $77,733,232
Assets: $187,728,826
Liabilities: $76,618,793
Net Worth: $111,110,033
Earnings: $8,591,778
Emp.: 860
Fiscal Year-end: 12/31/22
Solar Pump Product Mfr
N.A.I.C.S.: 333914
Yiwen Chen *(Chm & Gen Mgr)*

ZHEJIANG TAILIN BIOENGINEERING CO., LTD.

No 2930 Nanhuan Road, Binjiang, Hangzhou, 310052, Zhejiang, China
Tel.: (86) 57186589087
Web Site: https://www.tailingood.com
Year Founded: 2002
300813—(SSE)
Rev.: $52,492,485
Assets: $129,541,464
Liabilities: $38,638,810
Net Worth: $90,902,654
Earnings: $11,187,942
Fiscal Year-end: 12/31/22
Pharmaceutical Equipment Mfr
N.A.I.C.S.: 325411
Dalin Ye *(Chm & Gen Mgr)*

ZHEJIANG TAITAN CO., LTD.

99 Taitan Road, Xinchang County, Shaoxing, 312500, Zhejiang, China
Tel.: (86) 57586288859
Web Site: https://www.chinataitan.com
Year Founded: 1998
003036—(SSE)
Rev.: $224,718,919
Assets: $340,674,675
Liabilities: $161,722,843

ZHEJIANG TAITAN CO., LTD.

Zhejiang Taitan Co., Ltd.—(Continued)
Net Worth: $178,951,832
Earnings: $18,275,503
Fiscal Year-end: 12/31/22
Textile Machinery Mfr
N.A.I.C.S.: 333248
Qixin Chen (Chm)

ZHEJIANG TALENT TELEVISION & FILM COMPANY LIMITED

16 Huayuan Road, Haidian District, Beijing, 311215, Zhejiang, China
Tel.: (86) 1082025868
Web Site: http://www.tangde.com.cn
Year Founded: 2006
300426—(CHIN)
Rev.: $30,504,111
Assets: $344,630,574
Liabilities: $335,871,558
Net Worth: $8,759,016
Earnings: ($12,086,737)
Emp.: 160
Fiscal Year-end: 12/31/20
Film Production & Distr; Artist Agency Services
N.A.I.C.S.: 512110
Hongliang Wu (Chm & Gen Mgr)

Subsidiaries:

Blink Productions Ltd. (1)
181 Wardour Street, London, W1F 8WZ, United Kingdom
Tel.: (44) 2074940747
Web Site: http://www.blinkprods.com
Video Production Services
N.A.I.C.S.: 512110
James Studholme (Chm)

ZHEJIANG TENGEN ELECTRICS CO., LTD.

Sulv Industrial Zone, Liushi Town, Yueqing, 325699, Zhejiang, China
Tel.: (86) 2131198727
Web Site: https://www.tengenglobal.com
Year Founded: 1999
605066—(SHG)
Rev.: $342,137,826
Assets: $428,955,724
Liabilities: $180,387,787
Net Worth: $248,567,937
Earnings: $6,335,690
Emp.: 4,000
Fiscal Year-end: 12/31/22
Electrical Equipment Mfr & Distr
N.A.I.C.S.: 335999
Tianle Gao (Chm & Gen Mgr)

ZHEJIANG TENGY ENVIRONMENTAL TECHNOLOGY CO., LTD

Tengy Industrial Park Paitou Town, Zhuji, Zhejiang, China
Web Site: http://www.tengy.com
Year Founded: 2009
1527—(HKG)
Rev.: $66,334,928
Assets: $215,615,930
Liabilities: $98,491,302
Net Worth: $117,124,628
Earnings: $7,526,142
Emp.: 446
Fiscal Year-end: 12/31/22
Environmental Protection Equipment Mfr & Distr
N.A.I.C.S.: 334512
Yu Bian (Chm & Gen Mgr)

ZHEJIANG TIANCHENG CONTROLS CO., LTD.

West Industrial Zone, Taizhou, 317200, Zhejiang, China
Tel.: (86) 57683906272
Web Site: https://www.china-tc.com
Year Founded: 1992
603085—(SHG)
Rev.: $200,050,990
Assets: $334,825,415
Liabilities: $206,653,721
Net Worth: $128,171,694
Earnings: ($38,363,289)
Emp.: 2,700
Fiscal Year-end: 12/31/22
Motor Vehicle Seat Mfr & Distr
N.A.I.C.S.: 336360

Subsidiaries:

Acro Aircraft Seating Limited (1)
Eldon Way Crick Industrial Estate Crick, Northampton, NN6 7SL, East Midlands, United Kingdom
Tel.: (44) 1788227600
Web Site: https://acro.aero
Aircraft Passenger Seat Mfr
N.A.I.C.S.: 336360

ZHEJIANG TIANTAI XIANGHE INDUSTRIAL CO., LTD.

No 799 Renmin East Road Chicheng Street, Taizhou, 317200, China
Tel.: (86) 57683966191
Web Site: https://www.ttxh.com.cn
Year Founded: 1986
603500—(SHG)
Rev.: $85,178,771
Assets: $162,103,186
Liabilities: $30,170,163
Net Worth: $131,933,024
Earnings: $9,342,076
Fiscal Year-end: 12/31/22
Transportation Equipment Mfr
N.A.I.C.S.: 334290

ZHEJIANG TIANTIE INDUSTRY CO LTD

No 928 Renmin East Road, Tiantai, Taizhou, 317200, Zhejiang, China
Tel.: (86) 57683171283
Web Site: https://www.tiantiegroup.com
Year Founded: 2003
300587—(CHIN)
Rev.: $212,302,585
Assets: $742,411,476
Liabilities: $401,396,246
Net Worth: $341,015,231
Earnings: ($92,060,673)
Emp.: 918
Fiscal Year-end: 12/31/23
Rubber Product Mfr & Distr
N.A.I.C.S.: 325998
Xu Kongbin (Chm)

ZHEJIANG TIANYU PHARMACEUTICAL CO., LTD.

Jiangkou Chemical Industrial Development Zone, Huangyan District, Taizhou, 318020, Zhejiang, China
Tel.: (86) 57689189669
Web Site: http://www.tianyupharm.com
Year Founded: 2003
300702—(CHIN)
Rev.: $355,965,994
Assets: $892,724,737
Liabilities: $401,472,136
Net Worth: $491,252,602
Earnings: $3,853,557
Emp.: 2,600
Fiscal Year-end: 12/31/23
Pharmaceutical Product Mfr & Distr
N.A.I.C.S.: 325411
Tu Yongjun (Chm & Gen Mgr)

ZHEJIANG TIANZHEN TECHNOLOGY CO., LTD.

No 398 Sunshine Avenue Health Industry Park, Anji County, Huzhou, 313300, Zhejiang, China
Tel.: (86) 5725302880
Web Site: https://www.tzbamboo.com
Year Founded: 2003
301356—(CHIN)
Rev.: $416,614,536
Assets: $573,435,720
Liabilities: $91,455,156
Net Worth: $481,980,564
Earnings: $53,232,660
Fiscal Year-end: 12/31/22
Flooring Product Mfr & Distr
N.A.I.C.S.: 321918
Qinghua Fang (Chm)

ZHEJIANG TIELIU CLUTCH CO., LTD.

398 Xingguo Road, Linping District, Hangzhou, 311103, Zhejiang, China
Tel.: (86) 57186183166
Web Site: https://www.chinaclutch.com
Year Founded: 1985
603926—(SHG)
Rev.: $294,293,549
Assets: $364,094,897
Liabilities: $137,402,390
Net Worth: $226,692,508
Earnings: $11,754,400
Fiscal Year-end: 12/31/22
Motor Vehicle Parts & Accessories Mfr
N.A.I.C.S.: 336390

Subsidiaries:

Geiger Fertigungstechnologie GmbH (1)
Espachweg 1, 91362, Pretzfeld, Germany
Tel.: (49) 919473970
Web Site: http://www.geiger-pretzfeld.de
Automobile Parts Mfr
N.A.I.C.S.: 336390

ZHEJIANG TONGLI TRANSMISSION TECHNOLOGY CO., LTD.

No 3801 Jiangnan Avenue, Ruian, 325207, Zhejiang, China
Tel.: (86) 57765599838
Web Site: https://www.zjtongli.com
Year Founded: 2008
301255—(CHIN)
Rev.: $65,909,958
Assets: $186,200,563
Liabilities: $39,446,408
Net Worth: $146,754,154
Earnings: $11,374,000
Fiscal Year-end: 12/31/23
Industrial Machinery Mfr & Distr
N.A.I.C.S.: 333248
Jianzhong Xiang (Chm)

ZHEJIANG TONY ELECTRONIC CO., LTD.

No 555 Liji East Road, Zhili Town Wuxing District, Huzhou, 313008, Zhejiang, China
Tel.: (86) 5723256668
Web Site: http://www.tony-tech.com
Year Founded: 2008
603595—(SHG)
Rev.: $265,158,022
Assets: $602,077,854
Liabilities: $319,620,642
Net Worth: $282,457,211
Earnings: $15,170,122
Fiscal Year-end: 12/31/22
Wire Product Mfr & Distr
N.A.I.C.S.: 331110
Shen Xinfang (Chm)

ZHEJIANG TRUELOVE VOGUE CO., LTD.

Xujiang Industrial Zone Jiangdong Street, Jiangdong, Yiwu, 322000, Zhejiang, China
Tel.: (86) 57989982888
Web Site: https://www.zamj.cn
Year Founded: 2010

INTERNATIONAL PUBLIC

003041—(SSE)
Rev.: $137,387,606
Assets: $265,603,876
Liabilities: $86,991,433
Net Worth: $178,612,443
Earnings: $21,764,401
Fiscal Year-end: 12/31/22
Carpet Product Mfr & Distr
N.A.I.C.S.: 314110
Qizhong Zheng (Chm & Gen Mgr)

ZHEJIANG TUNA ENVIRONMENTAL SCIENCE & TECHNOLOGY CO., LTD.

South to Sanjiang Road Paojiang New Area, Shaoxing, 312000, Zhejiang, China
Tel.: (86) 57588556039
Web Site: http://www.zj-tuna.com
Year Founded: 2005
603177—(SHG)
Rev.: $111,915,227
Assets: $209,827,196
Liabilities: $156,976,354
Net Worth: $52,850,842
Earnings: $1,312,206
Emp.: 1,000
Fiscal Year-end: 12/31/22
Flue Gas Purification Services
N.A.I.C.S.: 238220
Jin Meng (Chm)

Subsidiaries:

Nano-Tuna Engineering Co., Ltd. (1)
60 Magonggongdan-ro, Cheongni-myeon, Sangju, 37257, Gyeongsangbuk, Korea (South)
Tel.: (82) 57588556170
Flue Gas & Solid Waste Treatment Services
N.A.I.C.S.: 924110

Shanghai Tuna Marine Environment Technology Co., Ltd. (1)
Room 702 7th Floor Block D Luneng International Center, No 209 Guoyao Road Pudong New Area, Shanghai, China
Tel.: (86) 2160792516
Flue Gas & Solid Waste Treatment Services
N.A.I.C.S.: 924110

Tuna Envirotech Private Limited (1)
405 Forth Floor Global Foyer Golf Course Road Sector 43, Gurgaon, 122002, Haryana, India
Tel.: (91) 9811682227
Web Site: https://www.tuna-india.com
Flue Gas & Solid Waste Treatment Services
N.A.I.C.S.: 924110

ZHEJIANG UNIFULL INDUSTRIAL FIBER CO., LTD.

Industrial Park Area, Hefu Town, Huzhou, 313017, Zhejiang, China
Tel.: (86) 5723961786
Web Site: https://www.unifull.com
Year Founded: 2003
002427—(SSE)
Rev.: $343,572,980
Assets: $348,254,043
Liabilities: $200,975,777
Net Worth: $147,278,266
Earnings: $72,626,337
Emp.: 1,800
Fiscal Year-end: 12/31/22
Polyester Industrial Fibers Mfr
N.A.I.C.S.: 314999
Guo Hui (Chm)

Subsidiaries:

Zhejiang Unifull Hi-Techindustry Co., Ltd. (1)
No 213 Longyuan Road New Energy Industrial Park, Taizhou, Jiangsu, China
Tel.: (86) 52389602213
Polyester Fiber Mfr
N.A.I.C.S.: 325220

ZHEJIANG UNITED INVEST-

AND PRIVATE COMPANIES

MENT HOLDINGS GROUP LIMITED
Unit 1901 Far East Finance Centre
16 Harcourt Road Admiralty, Hong Kong, China (Hong Kong)
Tel.: (852) 2336 8878   Ky
Web Site: http://www.zjuv8366.com
Year Founded: 2015
Rev.: $20,226,224
Assets: $17,565,164
Liabilities: $9,514,054
Net Worth: $8,051,110
Earnings: ($1,727,135)
Emp.: 59
Fiscal Year-end: 04/30/19
Investment Holding Company
N.A.I.C.S.: 551112
Zhou Ying (Chm & Exec Dir)

ZHEJIANG VIE SCIENCE & TECHNOLOGY CO., LTD.
No 3 Junlian Road, Diankou Town, Zhuji, 311835, Zhejiang, China
Tel.: (86) 57587655857
Web Site: https://www.vie.com.cn
Year Founded: 1973
002590—(SSE)
Rev.: $472,314,038
Assets: $675,511,518
Liabilities: $389,126,813
Net Worth: $286,384,705
Earnings: $10,057,905
Emp.: 3,600
Fiscal Year-end: 12/31/22
Automotive Brake System Mfr
N.A.I.C.S.: 336340
Chen Feng (Chm & Gen Mgr)
Subsidiaries:
Zhejiang Henglong & VIE Pump Manufacturing Co., Ltd.   (1)
VIE Science & Technology Zone, Diankou Town, Zhuji, 311835, Zhejiang, China
Tel.: (86) 5757659180
Web Site: http://www.chl.com.cn
Emp.: 250
Designs, Manufactures & Markets Power Steering Pumps
N.A.I.C.S.: 336390

ZHEJIANG VIEWSHINE INTELLGNT MTR CO LTD
No 6 Building No 1418-41 Moganshan Road, Gongshu District, Hangzhou, 310015, Zhejiang, China
Tel.: (86) 57188179018
Web Site: https://www.viewshine.cn
Year Founded: 2005
002849—(SSE)
Rev.: $133,735,858
Assets: $303,475,456
Liabilities: $123,429,333
Net Worth: $180,046,124
Earnings: $8,345,039
Fiscal Year-end: 12/31/22
Metering Device Mfr & Distr
N.A.I.C.S.: 334514
Huang Wenqian (Chm)

ZHEJIANG WALRUS NEW MATERIAL CO., LTD.
No 380 Haifeng Road Economic Development Zone, Haining, 314400, Zhejiang, China
Tel.: (86) 57380776966
Web Site: https://www.haixiang.com.cn
Year Founded: 2013
003011—(SSE)
Rev.: $265,987,575
Assets: $348,823,912
Liabilities: $143,960,221
Net Worth: $204,863,691
Earnings: $29,882,989
Fiscal Year-end: 12/31/22
Flooring Product Mfr & Distr
N.A.I.C.S.: 332322
Zhoulin Wang (Chm & Gen Mgr)

ZHEJIANG WANDEKAI FLUID EQUIPMENT TECHNOLOGY CO., LTD.
Longxi Industrial Zone, Yuhuan, 317609, Zhejiang, China
Tel.: (86) 57687499999
Web Site: https://www.zjwdk.com
Year Founded: 2016
301309—(CHIN)
Rev.: $97,069,464
Assets: $235,953,929
Liabilities: $33,534,310
Net Worth: $202,419,619
Earnings: $14,633,394
Fiscal Year-end: 12/31/23
Plumbing Valve Mfr & Distr
N.A.I.C.S.: 332919
Xingfu Zhong (Chm)

ZHEJIANG WANLIYANG GROUP CO., LTD.
Wucheng Industrial Garden, Jinhua, 321025, Zhejiang, China
Tel.: (86) 57982217058
Web Site: http://www.zjwly.com
2434—(SSE)
Emp.: 1,100
Automotive Transmission Mfr
N.A.I.C.S.: 336350
Heqing Huang (CEO)

ZHEJIANG WANMA CABLE CO., LTD.
88 Nanhuan Road Lin'an Economy Developing Zone, Hangzhou, 311305, Zhejiang, China
Tel.: (86) 57163751732
Web Site: http://www.wanma-cable.com
Emp.: 1,350
Power Cable Mfr
N.A.I.C.S.: 335921
Shuimiao Pan (Chm)

ZHEJIANG WAZAM NEW MATERIALS GROUP CO., LTD.
Huazheng Technology park No 8 Shuyan road Yuhang street, Yuhang District, Hangzhou, 311121, Zhejiang, China
Tel.: (86) 57188650709
Web Site: https://www.wazam.com.cn
Year Founded: 2003
603186—(SHG)
Rev.: $461,284,846
Assets: $791,888,755
Liabilities: $553,640,892
Net Worth: $238,247,863
Earnings: $5,065,618
Emp.: 1,800
Fiscal Year-end: 12/31/22
Insulating Material Mfr & Distr
N.A.I.C.S.: 331420
Tao Liu (Chm)
Subsidiaries:
Hangzhou Holycore Composite Material Co., Ltd.   (1)
No 2 Huayi Road, Yuhang, Hangzhou, China
Tel.: (86) 57186203579
Web Site: http://www.holycore.cn
Performance Composite Material Mfr & Distr
N.A.I.C.S.: 325211
Hangzhou Liansheng Insulation Co., Ltd.   (1)
CenLing Industrial Park ZhongTai, Yuhang, 311121, Zhejiang, China
Tel.: (86) 57189052735
Web Site: http://www.lesonccl.com
Performance Composite Material Mfr & Distr
N.A.I.C.S.: 325211
Hangzhou Wazam New Materials Co., Ltd.   (1)
NO 2 Huayi Rd Yuhang St Wazam Sci-Tech Park, Yuhang, Hangzhou, Zhejiang, China
Tel.: (86) 57188652961
Web Site: http://www.wazam.com.cn
Performance Composite Material Mfr & Distr
N.A.I.C.S.: 325211

ZHEJIANG WECOME PHARMACEUTICAL COMPANY LIMITED
No 2 Suisong Road, Lishui Economic Development Zone, Lishui, 323000, Zhejiang, China
Tel.: (86) 5782950088
Web Site: http://www.zjwk.com
Year Founded: 2000
300878—(SSE)
Rev.: $74,593,355
Assets: $268,693,743
Liabilities: $70,516,504
Net Worth: $198,177,240
Earnings: $6,239,980
Fiscal Year-end: 12/31/22
Pharmaceutical Product Mfr & Distr
N.A.I.C.S.: 325412
Zhongliang Liu (Chm)

ZHEJIANG WEIGANG TECHNOLOGY CO., LTD.
Songqiao Industrial Zone, Pingyang County, Wenzhou, 325409, Zhejiang, China
Tel.: (86) 57763170123
Web Site: https://www.weigangmachinery.cn
Year Founded: 1996
001256—(SSE)
Rev.: $54,631,339
Assets: $160,961,327
Liabilities: $14,413,590
Net Worth: $146,547,737
Earnings: $11,366,854
Emp.: 300
Fiscal Year-end: 12/31/22
Printing Equipment Mfr & Distr
N.A.I.C.S.: 333248
Bingsong Zhou (Chm)

ZHEJIANG WEIMING ENVIRONMENT PROTECTION CO., LTD.
16F Tongren Hengjiu Building 525 Shifu Road, Wenzhou, 325088, Zhejiang, China
Tel.: (86) 57786056018
Web Site: https://www.cnweiming.com
Year Founded: 1998
603568—(SHG)
Rev.: $624,238,351
Assets: $2,839,418,263
Liabilities: $1,359,045,563
Net Worth: $1,480,372,700
Earnings: $232,108,241
Fiscal Year-end: 12/31/22
Solid Waste Disposal Services
N.A.I.C.S.: 562213
Xiang Guangming (Chm & Pres)

ZHEJIANG WEIXING INDUSTRIAL DEVELOPMENT CO., LTD.
No 8 South Qian Jiang road, Linhai City, Taizhou, 317000, Zhejiang, China
Tel.: (86) 57685979788
Web Site: https://www.sab-cn.com
Year Founded: 1976
002003—(SSE)
Rev.: $509,380,986
Assets: $670,152,675
Liabilities: $258,481,932
Net Worth: $411,670,743

Earnings: $68,639,496
Fiscal Year-end: 12/31/22
Garment Accessories Mfr
N.A.I.C.S.: 339993
Kapeng Zhang (Board of Directors & Chm)

ZHEJIANG WEIXING NEW BUILDING MATERIALS CO., LTD.
No 688 Jiangshi West Road, Linhai, 317000, Zhejiang, China
Tel.: (86) 8657685225086
Web Site: https://www.vasen.com
Year Founded: 1999
002372—(SSE)
Rev.: $976,291,154
Assets: $974,206,004
Liabilities: $208,969,745
Net Worth: $765,236,258
Earnings: $182,166,473
Emp.: 2,800
Fiscal Year-end: 12/31/22
Plastic Pipes Mfr & Sales
N.A.I.C.S.: 326122

ZHEJIANG WELLSUN INTELLIGENT TECHNOLOGY CO., LTD.
No 109 Yongchang Road, Shifeng Sub-district Tiantai County, Taizhou, 317200, Zhejiang, China
Tel.: (86) 57683999688
Web Site: https://www.wellsun.com
Year Founded: 1997
300882—(SSE)
Rev.: $118,517,396
Assets: $194,339,026
Liabilities: $60,219,315
Net Worth: $134,119,711
Earnings: $18,980,395
Fiscal Year-end: 12/31/22
Measuring Instruments Mfr
N.A.I.C.S.: 334513
Yongqiang Wu (Chm & Gen Mgr)

ZHEJIANG WHYIS TECHNOLOGY CO., LTD.
Huashi Technology Park No 16 Jiaqi Road Xianlin Street, Yuhang District, Hangzhou, 311122, ZheJiang, China
Tel.: (86) 57128000066
Web Site: https://www.zjwhyis.com
Year Founded: 1998
301218—(SSE)
Rev.: $66,331,053
Assets: $180,639,904
Liabilities: $50,498,946
Net Worth: $130,140,958
Earnings: $5,245,849
Fiscal Year-end: 12/31/22
Information Technology Services
N.A.I.C.S.: 541512
Yongfang Yu (Chm)

ZHEJIANG WINDEY CO., LTD.
18F Building A S & T No 391 Wener Road, The West Lake International Plaza, Hangzhou, 310012, Zhejiang, China
Tel.: (86) 57187397666
Web Site: https://www.windeyenergy.com
Year Founded: 2001
300772—(SSE)
Rev.: $2,440,698,058
Assets: $4,069,542,480
Liabilities: $3,373,035,293
Net Worth: $696,507,187
Earnings: $86,555,449
Emp.: 1,600
Fiscal Year-end: 12/31/22
Wind Turbine Mfr
N.A.I.C.S.: 333611
Ling Gao (Chm & Gen Mgr)

ZHEJIANG WINDEY CO., LTD.

Zhejiang Windey Co., Ltd.—(Continued)
Subsidiaries:

Ningxia Windey Co., Ltd. (1)
Jinji Industrial Park, Litong District, Wuzhong, 751100, Ningxia, China
Tel.: (86) 9532128921
Wind Turbine Mfr
N.A.I.C.S.: 333611

Zhangbei Winey Co., Ltd. (1)
Xincheng Region, Zhangbei County, Zhangjiakou, 076450, Hebei, China
Tel.: (86) 3135856635
Wind Turbine Mfr
N.A.I.C.S.: 333611

ZHEJIANG WOLWO BIO-PHARMACEUTICAL COMPANY LIMITED
No 636 Zhiyuan North Road, Wukang Town Deqing County, Huzhou, 313200, Zhejiang, China
Tel.: (86) 5728351800
Web Site:
  https://www.wolwobiotech.com
Year Founded: 2002
300357—(SSE)
Rev.: $125,801,208
Assets: $308,582,352
Liabilities: $23,974,704
Net Worth: $284,607,648
Earnings: $48,967,308
Emp.: 560
Fiscal Year-end: 12/31/22
Biopharmaceutical Mfr
N.A.I.C.S.: 325412
Niu Lei *(Chm)*

ZHEJIANG XCC GROUP CO.,LTD
No 199 TaiTan Road XinChang, Shaoxing, 312500, Zhejiang, China
Year Founded: 2002
603667—(SHG)
Rev.: $449,327,441
Assets: $618,753,246
Liabilities: $280,765,111
Net Worth: $337,988,135
Earnings: $20,745,953
Emp.: 4,000
Fiscal Year-end: 12/31/22
Bearing Mfr & Distr
N.A.I.C.S.: 336310
Zhang Feng *(Chm & Gen Mgr)*

ZHEJIANG XIANJU PHARMACEUTICAL CO., LTD.
15 West Fengxi Road, Modern Industry Cluster Zone, Xianju, 317306, Zhejiang, China
Tel.: (86) 57687731075
Web Site: https://www.xjpharma.com
Year Founded: 1972
002332—(SSE)
Rev.: $614,927,528
Assets: $946,039,531
Liabilities: $172,794,689
Net Worth: $773,244,843
Earnings: $105,216,294
Fiscal Year-end: 12/31/22
Pharmaceuticals Mfr
N.A.I.C.S.: 325412
Zhang Yusong *(Chm)*

ZHEJIANG XIANTONG RUBBER&PLASTIC CO LTD
Modern Industrial Cluster, Xianju County, Taizhou, 317306, Zhejiang, China
Tel.: (86) 57687684158
Web Site: http://www.zjxiantong.com
Year Founded: 1996
603239—(SHG)
Rev.: $131,476,766
Assets: $176,503,579
Liabilities: $35,271,892
Net Worth: $141,231,687
Earnings: $17,717,848
Emp.: 1,800
Fiscal Year-end: 12/31/22
Rubber Product Mfr & Distr
N.A.I.C.S.: 326291
Qifu Li *(Chm & Vice Chm)*

ZHEJIANG XIDAMEN NEW MATERIAL CO., LTD.
Fenshui Bridge, Ruangang Village Lanting Town Keqiao, Shaoxing, 312043, Zhejiang, China
Tel.: (86) 57584600929
Web Site: http://www.xidamen.com
Year Founded: 1997
605155—(SHG)
Rev.: $70,074,131
Assets: $171,160,461
Liabilities: $12,078,486
Net Worth: $159,081,975
Earnings: $11,519,076
Fiscal Year-end: 12/31/22
Fabric Product Mfr
N.A.I.C.S.: 313320
Qinghua Liu *(Chm & Gen Mgr)*

ZHEJIANG XINAN CHEMICAL INDUSTRIAL GROUP CO., LTD.
Xinan Building No 1 Jiangbin Middle Road Xinan Jiang Street, Jiande, 311600, Zhejiang, China
Tel.: (86) 57164715693
Web Site: https://www.wynca.com
Year Founded: 1965
600596—(SHG)
Rev.: $3,061,104,836
Assets: $2,702,037,817
Liabilities: $942,346,253
Net Worth: $1,759,691,564
Earnings: $414,823,397
Fiscal Year-end: 12/31/22
Agricultural Chemical Product Mfr & Distr
N.A.I.C.S.: 325320
Jian Hua Wu *(Chm)*

ZHEJIANG XINAO TEXTILES INC.
No 48 Zhenzhi Street, Chongfu Town, Tongxiang, 314511, Zhejiang, China
Tel.: (86) 57388455835
Web Site: https://www.xinaotex.com
Year Founded: 1991
603889—(SHG)
Rev.: $554,562,576
Assets: $652,304,521
Liabilities: $226,717,401
Net Worth: $425,587,121
Earnings: $54,717,418
Fiscal Year-end: 12/31/22
Yarn Mfr & Distr
N.A.I.C.S.: 313110
Jianhua Shen *(Chm)*

Subsidiaries:

Zhejiang New Chuwa Wool Co., Ltd. (1)
Chongfu Industrial Park, Tongxiang, 314511, Zhejiang, China
Tel.: (86) 5738 822 2001
Web Site: https://www.newchuwa.cn
Fiber & Yarn Product Mfr
N.A.I.C.S.: 313110

ZHEJIANG XINCHAI CO., LTD.
No 888 the West Road Xinchang Avenue, Xinchang, 312500, Zhejiang, China
Tel.: (86) 57586290401
Web Site:
  https://www.xinchaiengine.com
Year Founded: 1958
301032—(CHIN)
Rev.: $326,180,915
Assets: $373,397,097
Liabilities: $217,813,098
Net Worth: $155,584,000
Earnings: $4,501,254
Emp.: 1,300
Fiscal Year-end: 12/31/23
Industrial Machinery Mfr & Distr
N.A.I.C.S.: 333248
Hongfa Bai *(Chm)*

Subsidiaries:

Champs Industrial Pte. Ltd. (1)
R Geronimo Medeiros 218-Flor de Napolis, Sao Jose, 88106-010, SC, Brazil
Tel.: (55) 4833430003
Automotive Car Parts Mfr & Distr
N.A.I.C.S.: 336390

DEMO Makina Elektrik Elektronik Taah.San.ve Tic.Ltd. (1)
Istasyon Mah Koseköy Sanayi Sitesi E Blok No 210, Kartepe, Kocaeli, Türkiye
Tel.: (90) 2623110919
Web Site: https://www.demomakina.com.tr
Diesel Forklift Mfr & Distr
N.A.I.C.S.: 333924

Everun Europe GmbH (1)
Walkmuhlenweg 11, D-98617, Meiningen, Germany
Tel.: (49) 3693504050
Web Site: https://www.everun.de
Agricultural Vehicle Mfr & Distr
N.A.I.C.S.: 336120

ZHEJIANG XINGUANG PHARMACEUTICAL CO., LTD.
Tel.: (86) 57583292898
Web Site: http://www.xgpharma.com
Year Founded: 1970
300519—(CHIN)
Rev.: $38,085,812
Assets: $131,047,657
Liabilities: $12,153,242
Net Worth: $118,894,415
Earnings: $9,064,613
Fiscal Year-end: 12/31/23
Pharmaceutical Mfr & Distr
N.A.I.C.S.: 325412
Wang Yuejun *(Chm & Gen Mgr)*

ZHEJIANG XINHUA CHEMICAL CO., LTD.
No 909 Xinanjiang Road, Yangxi, Jiande, 311607, Zhejiang, China
Tel.: (86) 57164755918
Web Site: https://www.xhchem.com
Year Founded: 1997
603667—(SHG)
Rev.: $376,743,983
Assets: $524,075,685
Liabilities: $218,219,354
Net Worth: $305,856,332
Earnings: $46,223,513
Fiscal Year-end: 12/31/22
Chemical Product Mfr & Distr
N.A.I.C.S.: 325520
Jian Hu *(Chm)*

ZHEJIANG XINNONG CHEMICAL CO., LTD.
11F Poly Center No 277 Xintang Road, Jiangganl District, Hangzhou, 310021, Zhejiang, China
Tel.: (86) 57187799703
Web Site: https://www.xnchem.com
Year Founded: 1981
002942—(SSE)
Rev.: $175,242,675
Assets: $230,370,173
Liabilities: $65,923,978
Net Worth: $164,446,196
Earnings: $14,238,020
Emp.: 1,000
Fiscal Year-end: 12/31/22
Pesticide Product Mfr & Distr
N.A.I.C.S.: 325320
Xu Qunhui *(Chm, Pres & Gen Mgr)*

ZHEJIANG YANGFAN NEW

INTERNATIONAL PUBLIC

MATERIALS CO., LTD.
No 25 Weisan Road Hangzhou Gulf Shangyu Industrial Area, Shangyu District, Shaoxing, 310000, Zhejiang, China
Tel.: (86) 57188902507
Web Site: https://www.zjyfxc.com
Year Founded: 2002
300637—(CHIN)
Rev.: $97,371,732
Assets: $186,619,081
Liabilities: $89,001,467
Net Worth: $97,617,614
Earnings: ($12,357,052)
Fiscal Year-end: 12/31/23
Chemical Product Mfr & Distr
N.A.I.C.S.: 325180

ZHEJIANG YANKON GROUP CO., LTD.
No 568 Renmin Avenue West Section Caoe Street, Shangyu District, Shaoxing, 312300, Zhejiang, China
Tel.: (86) 57582027721
Web Site: http://www.yankon.com
Year Founded: 1997
600261—(SHG)
Rev.: $523,855,566
Assets: $781,919,541
Liabilities: $274,451,210
Net Worth: $507,468,331
Earnings: $25,815,867
Fiscal Year-end: 12/31/22
Lighting Product Mfr & Distr
N.A.I.C.S.: 335131
Wei Chen *(Chm)*

ZHEJIANG YASHA DECORATION CO., LTD.
Block A Yasha Center No 99 Shaxiu Road, West Lake District, Hangzhou, 310008, Zhejiang, China
Tel.: (86) 57128208786
Web Site:
  http://www.chinayasha.com
Year Founded: 2007
002375—(SSE)
Rev.: $1,701,116,235
Assets: $3,254,492,541
Liabilities: $2,137,352,640
Net Worth: $1,117,139,901
Earnings: $26,148,222
Emp.: 1,270
Fiscal Year-end: 12/31/22
Decoration Engineering Services
N.A.I.C.S.: 541330
Ding Zecheng *(Chm)*

Subsidiaries:

Ying Chuang (Winsun) Building Tech (Shanghai) Co., Ltd. (1)
No 789 Xinjin Road, Qingpu District, Shanghai, China
Tel.: (86) 18321577198
Web Site: http://www.winsun3d.com
Construction Engineering Services
N.A.I.C.S.: 541330

ZHEJIANG YATAI PHARMACEUTICAL CO., LTD.
No 36 Nanbin West Road Lihai Town, Binhai New Town, Shaoxing, 312366, Zhejiang, China
Tel.: (86) 57584815472
Web Site: https://www.ytyaoye.com
Year Founded: 1989
002370—(SSE)
Rev.: $52,431,032
Assets: $213,916,346
Liabilities: $171,625,016
Net Worth: $42,291,330
Earnings: ($18,633,958)
Emp.: 803
Fiscal Year-end: 12/31/22
Pharmaceuticals Mfr
N.A.I.C.S.: 325412
Yaogen Chen *(Chm & Gen Mgr)*

ZHEJIANG YAYI METAL TECHNOLOGY CO., LTD.
Industrial Functional Zone, Jiaodao Town Wuyi County, Hangzhou, 321200, Zhejiang, China
Tel.: (86) 57987603899
Web Site: https://www.china-yayi.com
Year Founded: 2000
301113—(SSE)
Rev.: $24,404,328
Assets: $105,493,752
Liabilities: $6,442,956
Net Worth: $99,050,796
Earnings: $6,883,812
Emp.: 600
Fiscal Year-end: 12/31/22
Fireplace Product Mfr & Distr
N.A.I.C.S.: 333414
Ye Yueting *(Chm)*

ZHEJIANG YILIDA VENTILATOR CO., LTD.
Yilida Road Hengjie, Luqiao District, Taizhou, 318056, Zhejiang, China
Tel.: (86) 4001135666
Web Site: https://www.yilida.com
Year Founded: 1994
002686—(SSE)
Rev.: $267,905,411
Assets: $418,445,254
Liabilities: $177,467,046
Net Worth: $240,978,208
Earnings: $5,372,940
Emp.: 1,400
Fiscal Year-end: 12/31/22
Air-Conditioning Fans Mfr
N.A.I.C.S.: 333413
Wu Xiaoming *(Chm)*

Subsidiaries:

Essentec Industries Co., Ltd. (1)
Unit 4A Yindong Mansion No 58 New Jinqiao Road, Pudong, Shanghai, China
Tel.: (86) 216100208819
Web Site: https://www.essentecool.com
Air Conditioner Mfr
N.A.I.C.S.: 333415

Qingdao Advanced Marine Material Technology Co., Ltd. (1)
No 100 South Industrial Road, Lixia, Jinan, 250014, China
Tel.: (86) 13864024831
Web Site:
 https://sdxinjihua.hongkongfls.com
Coating Product Mfr
N.A.I.C.S.: 325510

Yilida Industries Sdn. Bhd. (1)
23 Jalan Udang Galah/KS10 Kampung Nelayan Telok Gong, Pelabuhan Klang, 42000, Port Klang, Selangor, Malaysia
Tel.: (60) 331343227
Air Conditioning Fan Mfr
N.A.I.C.S.: 333413

ZHEJIANG YIMING FOOD CO., LTD.
Yiming Industrial Park, Pingyang County, Wenzhou, 325400, Zhejiang, China
Tel.: (86) 57788350180
Web Site: http://www.inm.cn
Year Founded: 2005
605179—(SHG)
Rev.: $341,530,231
Assets: $370,243,112
Liabilities: $219,095,183
Net Worth: $151,147,929
Earnings: ($18,142,895)
Fiscal Year-end: 12/31/22
Food Product Mfr & Distr
N.A.I.C.S.: 311421
Like Zhu *(Chm & Gen Mgr)*

ZHEJIANG YINGFENG TECHNOLOGY CO., LTD.
4888 Xingbin Road Binhai Industrial Zone, Keqiao District, Shaoxing, 312000, Zhejiang, China
Tel.: (86) 57589972229
Web Site: https://www.zj-yfkj.com
Year Founded: 2008
605055—(SHG)
Rev.: $192,375,771
Assets: $321,821,693
Liabilities: $164,996,648
Net Worth: $156,825,045
Earnings: ($6,666,683)
Emp.: 1,902
Fiscal Year-end: 12/31/22
Textile Products Mfr
N.A.I.C.S.: 313310
Shuangli Fu *(Chm & Gen Mgr)*

ZHEJIANG YINLUN MACHINERY CO., LTD.
No 8 Shifeng East Road Fuxi Street, Tiantai County, Taizhou, 317200, Zhejiang, China
Tel.: (86) 57683938330
Web Site: https://www.yinlun.cn
Year Founded: 1958
002126—(SSE)
Rev.: $1,190,541,161
Assets: $1,898,703,935
Liabilities: $1,164,041,686
Net Worth: $734,662,249
Earnings: $53,812,863
Fiscal Year-end: 12/31/22
Heat Exchanger Mfr
N.A.I.C.S.: 333413
Xiaohong Zhu *(CFO)*

Subsidiaries:

Thermal Dynamics, LLC. (1)
4850 E Airport Dr, Ontario, CA 91761
Tel.: (909) 390-3944
Web Site: http://www.thermaldynamics.com
Automotive Heat Exchangers Mfr
N.A.I.C.S.: 332410

ZHEJIANG YONGAN RONGTONG HOLDING SHARES CO., LTD.
No 135 Yangjiang Middle Road Yangxunqiao Town, Keqiao District, Shaoxing, 312028, Zhejiang Province, China
Tel.: (86) 57584570099 CN
Web Site: https://www.zj-yongan.com
Year Founded: 1998
8211—(HKG)
Rev.: $11,091,319
Assets: $34,523,096
Liabilities: $10,229,263
Net Worth: $24,293,833
Earnings: ($4,994,870)
Emp.: 241
Fiscal Year-end: 12/31/22
Fabric Mfr & Distr
N.A.I.C.S.: 313210

ZHEJIANG YONGGUI ELECTRIC EQUIPMENT CO., LTD.
No 5 Dongyuan Road West Industrial Zone, Baihe Town Tiantai, Taizhou, 317201, Zhejiang, China
Tel.: (86) 57683938635
Web Site: http://www.yonggui.com
Year Founded: 1990
300351—(SSE)
Rev.: $212,054,544
Assets: $426,759,840
Liabilities: $107,292,276
Net Worth: $319,467,564
Earnings: $21,721,284
Emp.: 330
Fiscal Year-end: 12/31/22
Rain Transit Connector Mfr
N.A.I.C.S.: 334417
Fan Jijun *(Chm)*

Subsidiaries:

Jiangsu Permanent Expensive New Energy Technology Co., Ltd. (1)
Economic And Technological Development Zone In A2, Building Three Layer Red Maple Park, Nanjing, Jiangsu, China
Tel.: (86) 2586673908
Web Site: http://www.yonggui-js.com
Electronic Connector Mfr
N.A.I.C.S.: 334417

Sichuan Yonggui Science & Technology Co., Ltd. (1)
No 68 Jinjialin upper St, Fucheng District, Mianyang, 621000, Sichuan, China
Tel.: (86) 8162300798
Web Site: http://en.yonggui-sc.com
Electronic Connector Mfr
N.A.I.C.S.: 334417

Yiteng Electronic Science & Technology (Kunshan) Co., Ltd. (1)
No 1575 Datong Road, Development Zone Kunshan, Jiangsu, China
Tel.: (86) 5125 510 1900
Web Site: https://www.jxt-china.com
Electronic Connector Mfr
N.A.I.C.S.: 334417

Subsidiary (Domestic):

Dongguan Jiexunteng Precision Electronic Science & Technology Co., Ltd. (2)
8090 No 100 Room 306 Block A Gaotianfang Wennan Road, Dongcheng District, Dongguan, Guangdong, China
Tel.: (86) 76923832827
Electronic Connector Mfr
N.A.I.C.S.: 334417

Shenzhen Jiexunteng Precision Electronic Science & Technology Co., Ltd. (2)
Room 603-605 Block 4 Anhua Industrial Park Chegongmiao, Futian District, Shenzhen, China
Tel.: (86) 75583865789
Electronic Connector Mfr
N.A.I.C.S.: 334417

ZHEJIANG YONGJIN METAL TECHNOLOGY CO., LTD.
No 999 Gengtoufan Lingdong Township, Economic Development Zone, Lanxi, 321100, Zhejiang, China
Tel.: (86) 57988988809
Web Site: http://www.zjyj.com.cn
Year Founded: 2003
603995—(SHG)
Rev.: $5,553,542,386
Assets: $1,481,466,149
Liabilities: $806,579,860
Net Worth: $674,886,289
Earnings: $68,321,504
Fiscal Year-end: 12/31/22
Steel Product Mfr & Distr
N.A.I.C.S.: 331210
Jiquan Yu *(Chm)*

ZHEJIANG YONGTAI TECHNOLOGY CO., LTD.
No1 5th Donghai Avenue Zhejiang Provincial Chemical and Medical, Raw Materials Base Linhai Zone, Linhai, 317016, Zhejiang, China
Tel.: (86) 57685588006
Web Site:
 https://www.yongtaitech.com
Year Founded: 1999
002326—(SSE)
Rev.: $889,605,190
Assets: $1,594,170,424
Liabilities: $1,068,261,747
Net Worth: $525,908,677
Earnings: $77,771,533
Emp.: 3,000
Fiscal Year-end: 12/31/22
Chemical Products Mfr
N.A.I.C.S.: 325180

Subsidiaries:

Shanghai E-Tong Chemical Co., Ltd. (1)
No 23 Lane 5398 Shenzhuan Road, Songjiang District, Shanghai, 201619, China
Tel.: (86) 2151698968
Web Site: https://www.etongchem.com
Farm Supply Whslr
N.A.I.C.S.: 424910
Victor Ye *(Sls Mgr)*

Youngtech Pharmaceutical Inc. (1)
One Duncan Dr, Cranbury, NJ 08512
Tel.: (609) 803-3131
Web Site: http://www.youngtechpharma.com
Pharmaceuticals Product Mfr
N.A.I.C.S.: 325412

ZHEJIANG YOUPON INTEGRATED CEILING COMPANY LIMITED
No 388 Baibu Avenue, Haiyan County Baibu Town, Jiaxing, 314312, Zhejiang, China
Tel.: (86) 57386790032
Web Site:
 http://www.chinayoubang.com
Year Founded: 2007
002718—(SSE)
Rev.: $133,562,422
Assets: $231,410,439
Liabilities: $82,144,797
Net Worth: $149,265,642
Earnings: $13,711,731
Emp.: 420
Fiscal Year-end: 12/31/22
Integrated Ceilings Mfr
N.A.I.C.S.: 327120
Wuliang Wang *(Vice Chm)*

ZHEJIANG YUEJIAN INTELLIGENT EQUIPMENT CO., LTD.
No 688 Huping Mountain Road Qixian Street, Keqiao, Shaoxing, 312065, Zhejiang, China
Tel.: (86) 57585181411
Web Site: https://www.yuejian.com.cn
Year Founded: 2000
603095—(SHG)
Rev.: $177,530,086
Assets: $450,682,442
Liabilities: $92,686,885
Net Worth: $357,995,556
Earnings: $63,194,419
Fiscal Year-end: 12/31/22
Textile Machinery Mfr
N.A.I.C.S.: 333248
Jianhua Sun *(Chm)*

ZHEJIANG YUELING COMPANY LIMITED
No 888 Zeguo Avenue, Zeguo Town, Wenling, 317523, Zhejiang, China
Tel.: (86) 57686402693
Web Site: http://www.yuering.com
Year Founded: 1998
002725—(SSE)
Rev.: $108,612,359
Assets: $178,643,753
Liabilities: $35,400,624
Net Worth: $143,243,128
Earnings: $365,265
Emp.: 1,400
Fiscal Year-end: 12/31/22
Aluminum Alloy Wheels Mfr
N.A.I.C.S.: 331313
Lin Xianming *(Chm)*

ZHEJIANG ZHAOFENG MECHANICAL & ELECTRONIC CO., LTD.
6 Zhaofeng Road Qiaonanqukuai, Xiaoshan Econ Tech Zone, Hangzhou, 311232, China
Tel.: (86) 57122803999
Web Site: http://www.hzfb.com
Emp.: 670
Automobile Parts Mfr
N.A.I.C.S.: 336390
Aixiang Kong *(Pres)*

ZHEJIANG ZHAOLONG INTERCONNECT TECHNOLOGY CO., LTD.

Zhejiang Zhaofeng Mechanical & Electronic Co., Ltd.—(Continued)

ZHEJIANG ZHAOLONG INTERCONNECT TECHNOLOGY CO., LTD.
Shilin Industrial Zone, Xinshi Town
Deqing, Huzhou, 313215, Zhejiang, China
Tel.: (86) 5728066838
Web Site:
https://www.zhaolongcable.com
Year Founded: 1995
300913—(SSE)
Rev.: $226,216,439
Assets: $168,266,494
Liabilities: $31,463,823
Net Worth: $136,802,671
Earnings: $18,315,938
Emp.: 900
Fiscal Year-end: 12/31/22
Wire & Cable Mfr
N.A.I.C.S.: 331491
Jinlong Yao (Chm & Gen Mgr)

ZHEJIANG ZHE KUANG HEAVY INDUSTRIES CO., LTD.
Heping Industrial Park, Changxing County, Huzhou, 313103, Zhejiang, China
Tel.: (86) 5726955888
Web Site: https://ormaise-group.com
Year Founded: 2003
300837—(SSE)
Rev.: $97,550,103
Assets: $224,518,737
Liabilities: $52,285,788
Net Worth: $172,232,948
Earnings: $26,191,746
Fiscal Year-end: 12/31/22
Mining Machinery Equipment Mfr & Distr
N.A.I.C.S.: 333131
Lihua Chen (Chm & Gen Mgr)

ZHEJIANG ZHEDA INSIGMA GROUP CO., LTD.
Gemini International Building 4 1785 Jianghan Road, Binjian District, Hangzhou, Zhejiang, China
Tel.: (86) 571 8775000
Web Site:
http://www.insigmagroup.com.cn
Year Founded: 2001
Investment Services; Other Information Technology, Infrastructure Construction & Energy Research Services
N.A.I.C.S.: 519290

Subsidiaries:

Insigma Technology Co., Ltd. (1)
No 18 Insigma Software Park Building A, West Park, Hangzhou, 310030, China
Tel.: (86) 57187950588
Web Site: http://www.insigma.com.cn
Rev.: $579,775,299
Assets: $879,828,422
Liabilities: $378,146,368
Net Worth: $501,682,054
Earnings: $17,584,903
Emp.: 4,800
Fiscal Year-end: 12/31/2022
Information Technology Services
N.A.I.C.S.: 541512
Lie Shi (Chm)

Subsidiary (US):

Insigma US, Inc. (2)
135 W 50th St 18th Fl, New York, NY 10020
Tel.: (646) 202-1540
Software Development Services
N.A.I.C.S.: 513210
Xishi Pan (Mgr-Dev)

ZHEJIANG ZHENENG ELECTRIC POWER CO., LTD.
14th Floor Building D World Trade Regency City, European & American Center No 18 Jiaogong Road, Hangzhou, 310007, Zhejiang, China
Tel.: (86) 57187210223
Web Site: https://www.zzepc.com.cn
600023—(SHG)
Rev.: $11,259,319,453
Assets: $16,987,271,128
Liabilities: $7,502,145,408
Net Worth: $9,485,125,720
Earnings: ($255,872,177)
Emp.: 10,465
Fiscal Year-end: 12/31/22
Eletric Power Generation Services
N.A.I.C.S.: 221112

ZHEJIANG ZHENGGUANG INDUSTRIAL CO., LTD.
Room 132 1 st Floor Building 3 No 96 Longchuanwu Road, Donghu Subdistrict Linping District, Hangzhou, 311100, Zhejiang, China
Tel.: (86) 57186372141
Web Site:
https://www.chinaresin.com
Year Founded: 1996
301092—(SSE)
Rev.: $94,916,016
Assets: $259,362,324
Liabilities: $18,961,020
Net Worth: $240,401,304
Earnings: $24,965,928
Fiscal Year-end: 12/31/22
Resin Product Mfr & Distr
N.A.I.C.S.: 325211
Jianhua Shen (Chm)

ZHEJIANG ZHENGTE CO., LTD.
No 811 Dongfang Avenue, Linhai, Taizhou, 317004, Zhejiang, China
Tel.: (86) 57685953660
Web Site:
https://www.zhengte.com.cn
Year Founded: 1996
001238—(SSE)
Rev.: $194,056,247
Assets: $195,118,275
Liabilities: $41,622,619
Net Worth: $153,495,656
Earnings: $8,309,939
Fiscal Year-end: 12/31/22
Furniture Product Mfr & Distr
N.A.I.C.S.: 337126
Nengsen Chen (Founder)

ZHEJIANG ZHENGYUAN ZHIHUI TECHNOLOGY CO., LTD.
Building A, Zhengyuan Zhihui Building No 359 Shuxin Road, Yuhang District, Hangzhou, Zhejiang, China
Tel.: (86) 57188994988
Web Site: http://www.hzsun.com
300645—(CHIN)
Rev.: $172,492,333
Assets: $395,565,718
Liabilities: $203,856,008
Net Worth: $191,709,710
Earnings: $5,894,756
Fiscal Year-end: 12/31/23
Software Product Services
N.A.I.C.S.: 541511

ZHEJIANG ZHENYUAN SHARE CO., LTD.
No 558 Yanan East Road, Shaoxing, 312000, Zhejiang, China
Tel.: (86) 57585144121
Web Site: https://www.zjzy.com
Year Founded: 1752
000705—(SSE)
Rev.: $582,025,294
Assets: $453,324,194
Liabilities: $180,115,818
Net Worth: $273,208,375
Earnings: $10,927,557
Emp.: 2,000
Fiscal Year-end: 12/31/22
Pharmaceuticals Mfr
N.A.I.C.S.: 325412
Wu Haiming (Chm)

ZHEJIANG ZHONGCHENG PACKING MATERIAL CO., LTD.
No 1 Taishan Road Huimin Street, Huimin Sub-district, Jiashan, 314100, Zhejiang, China
Tel.: (86) 57384188888
Web Site:
https://www.zjzhongda.com
Year Founded: 2001
002522—(SSE)
Rev.: $264,551,971
Assets: $514,767,390
Liabilities: $196,800,997
Net Worth: $317,966,393
Earnings: $21,540,744
Fiscal Year-end: 12/31/22
Polyolefin Shrink Film Mfr
N.A.I.C.S.: 326112
Yi Xianyun (Chm)

ZHEJIANG ZHONGJIAN TECHNOLOGY CO., LTD.
No 10 Mingyuan South Ave Economic Development Zone, Yongkang, 321300, Zhejiang, China
Tel.: (86) 57986878687
Web Site: http://www.topsunpower.cc
Year Founded: 1997
002779—(SSE)
Rev.: $71,945,453
Assets: $124,969,071
Liabilities: $33,013,080
Net Worth: $91,955,991
Earnings: $3,843,984
Emp.: 860
Fiscal Year-end: 12/31/22
Garden Machinery Mfr
N.A.I.C.S.: 333112
Wu Minggen (Chm & Gen Mgr)

ZHEJIANG ZHONGXIN FLUORIDE MATERIALS CO., LTD.
No 5 No 13 Shangyu Economic and Technological Development Zone, Hangzhou Bay, Shangyu, 312369, Zhejiang, China
Tel.: (86) 57582738098
Web Site:
https://www.zxchemgroup.com
Year Founded: 2000
002915—(SSE)
Rev.: $224,976,820
Assets: $422,229,722
Liabilities: $147,629,870
Net Worth: $274,599,852
Earnings: $25,960,494
Emp.: 980
Fiscal Year-end: 12/31/22
Chemical Product Mfr & Distr
N.A.I.C.S.: 325180
Xu Jianguo (Chm)

ZHEJIANG ZOENN DESIGN CO., LTD.
No 180 Fengye Road, Lucheng District, Wenzhou, 325000, Zhejiang, China
Tel.: (86) 57788823999
Web Site: https://www.zoenn.com
Year Founded: 2011
300901—(SSE)
Rev.: $80,298,804
Assets: $170,316,643
Liabilities: $23,723,304
Net Worth: $146,593,339
Earnings: $10,355,258
Fiscal Year-end: 12/31/22
Footwear Product Distr
N.A.I.C.S.: 424340

INTERNATIONAL PUBLIC

Xiuhua Ni (Chm & Gen Mgr)

ZHEJIANG ZOMAX TRANSMISSION CO., LTD.
No 1 Jingyi Road Shangma Industrial Zone, Shitang Town, Wenling, 317513, Zhejiang, China
Tel.: (86) 57686051896
Web Site: https://www.zomaxcd.com
Year Founded: 2005
603767—(SHG)
Rev.: $139,774,939
Assets: $260,388,353
Liabilities: $54,437,685
Net Worth: $205,950,668
Earnings: $5,931,128
Fiscal Year-end: 12/31/22
Automobile Parts Mfr & Distr
N.A.I.C.S.: 333612
Liang Xiaorui (Chm)

ZHEJIANG ZUCH TECHNOLOGY CO., LTD.
No 201 Road Wei 15, Yueqing Economic Development Zone, Yueqing, 325600, Zhejiang, China
Tel.: (86) 57762830888
Web Site: https://www.zuchtech.com
Year Founded: 2000
301280—(CHIN)
Rev.: $146,529,864
Assets: $291,704,868
Liabilities: $55,053,648
Net Worth: $236,651,220
Earnings: $15,456,636
Fiscal Year-end: 12/31/22
Electronic Component Mfr & Distr
N.A.I.C.S.: 334419
Zhang Jianchun (Chm & Gen Mgr)

ZHEN DING RESOURCES INC.
Suite 111 3900 Place De Java Second Floor, Brossard, J4Y 9C4, QC, Canada
Tel.: (438) 882-4148 DE
Web Site:
https://www.zhendingresources.com
RBTK—(OTCIQ)
Rev.: $42
Assets: $6,293
Liabilities: $10,609,296
Net Worth: ($10,603,003)
Earnings: $1,247,099
Fiscal Year-end: 12/31/23
Metal Mining
N.A.I.C.S.: 212290
Wen Mei Tu (Pres, CEO, Treas & Sec)

ZHEN DING TECHNOLOGY HOLDING LIMITED
No 6 Lane 28 Sanhe Road, Sanshi Village Dayuan District, Taoyuan, 33754, Taiwan
Tel.: (886) 33835678
Web Site: https://www.zdtco.com
Year Founded: 2006
4958—(TAI)
Rev.: $4,951,045,890
Assets: $7,939,293,496
Liabilities: $3,546,545,437
Net Worth: $4,392,748,060
Earnings: $308,442,155
Emp.: 25,901
Fiscal Year-end: 12/31/23
Printed Circuit Board Mfr
N.A.I.C.S.: 334412
Charles Shen (Chm & Pres)

Subsidiaries:

Avary Holding Investment (Shenzhen) Co., Ltd. (1)
Avary Park Songluo Road, Yanchuan Community Yanluo Subdistrict Bao an District, Shenzhen, Guangdong, China
Tel.: (86) 75533810388

Economic Information Consulting Services
N.A.I.C.S.: 926110

Avary Holdings (Shenzhen) Co., Ltd. (1)
Songluo Road Yanchuan Community Yanluo Street, Baoan District, Shenzhen, Guangdong, China
Tel.: (86) 75533810388
Web Site: https://www.avaryholding.com
Rev.: $5,084,020,385
Assets: $5,447,944,710
Liabilities: $1,525,619,717
Net Worth: $3,922,324,993
Earnings: $703,619,739
Fiscal Year-end: 12/31/2022
Printed Circuit Board Mfr & Distr
N.A.I.C.S.: 334412

Avary Japan Co., Ltd. (1)
Suite 614 1-chome-12-9 Shinbashi, Minato City, Tokyo, Japan
Tel.: (81) 8010801418
Investigation & Analysis Services
N.A.I.C.S.: 561611

Avary Logistics Services (Shenzhen) Co., Ltd. (1)
1F Building A Pengding Age Building No 2038 Haixiu Rd, Haibing Community Xin an Subdistrict Bao an District, Shenzhen, Guangdong, China
Tel.: (86) 75533234596
Property Management Services
N.A.I.C.S.: 921190

Avary Singapore Private Limited (1)
9 Raffles Place 26-01 Republic Plaza, Singapore, 48619, Singapore
Tel.: (65) 33835678
Printed Circuit Board Mfr & Distr
N.A.I.C.S.: 334412

Avary Technology (India) Private Limited (1)
No 28 Padur Road, Kuthambakkam Village Poonamalle Taluk Thiruvallur, Chennai, 600124, Tamil Nadu, India
Tel.: (91) 9176999602
Electronic Component Mfr & Distr
N.A.I.C.S.: 334419

BoardTek Electronics Corp. (1)
No 16 Jingjian 1st Road, Guanyin Industrial Park Guanyin District, Taoyuan, Taiwan
Tel.: (886) 34839611
Electronic Component Mfr & Distr
N.A.I.C.S.: 334419
Di-Guang Yang (Chm)

Fu Bo Industrial (Shenzhen) Co., Ltd. (1)
Avary Park Songluo Road, Yanchuan Community Yanluo Subdistrict Bao an District, Shenzhen, Guangdong, China
Tel.: (86) 75533810388
Printed Circuit Board Mfr & Distr
N.A.I.C.S.: 334412

Garuda International Limited (1)
Unit B 26/F CKK Commercial Centre 289 Hennessy Road, Wanchai, China (Hong Kong)
Tel.: (852) 33835678
Printed Circuit Board Distr
N.A.I.C.S.: 423690

Garuda Technology Co., Ltd. (1)
8F No 8 Baoqiang Road, Xindian District, New Taipei City, Taiwan
Tel.: (886) 229126999
Electronic Components Distr
N.A.I.C.S.: 423690

Hong Heng Sheng Electronical Technology (Huaian) Co., Ltd. (1)
No 168 Fushikang Road, Huaian Economic and Technological Development Site, Jiangsu, China
Tel.: (86) 51783516888
Printed Circuit Board Mfr & Distr
N.A.I.C.S.: 334412

Hong Qi Sheng Precision Electronics (Qinhuangdao) Co., Ltd. (1)
No 18 Tengfei Road Economic and Technological Development Zone, Qinhuangdao, Hebei, China
Tel.: (86) 3358578888
Printed Circuit Board Mfr & Distr

N.A.I.C.S.: 334412

Kui Sheng Technology (Shenzhen) Co., Ltd. (1)
Avary Park Songluo Road, Yanchuan Community Yanluo Subdistrict Bao an District, Shenzhen, Guangdong, China
Tel.: (86) 75533810388
Printed Circuit Board Mfr & Distr
N.A.I.C.S.: 334412

Leading Interconnect Semiconductor Technology Qinhuangdao Co., Ltd. (1)
No 18-2 Tengfei Road, Qinhuangdao Economic and Technological Development Zone, Hebei, China
Tel.: (86) 3357138888
Printed Circuit Board Mfr & Distr
N.A.I.C.S.: 334412

Li Ding Semiconductor Technology (Shenzhen) Co., Ltd. (1)
Zone B Suite 403 Building B Rongchao Binhai Mansion No 2021 Haixiu Rd, Zone 26 Haiwang Community Xinan Subdistrict Baoan District, Shenzhen, China
Tel.: (86) 7553 323 4596
Electronic Component Mfr & Distr
N.A.I.C.S.: 334419

Qiding Technology Qinhuangdao Co., Ltd. (1)
No 18 Tengfei Road, Qinhuangdao Economic and Technological Development Zone, Qinhuangdao, Hebei, China
Tel.: (86) 3357138888
Electronic Component Mfr & Distr
N.A.I.C.S.: 334419

Qing Ding Precision Electronics (Huaian) Co., Ltd. (1)
No 8 Pengding Road Huaian Economic & Technological Development Zone, Jiangsu, China
Tel.: (86) 51783516888
Printed Circuit Board Mfr & Distr
N.A.I.C.S.: 334412

Yu Ding Precision Electronics (Huaian) Co., Ltd. (1)
No 18 Pengding Road Huaian Economic & Technological Development Zone, Jiangsu, China
Tel.: (86) 51783516888
Printed Circuit Board Mfr & Distr
N.A.I.C.S.: 334412

Zhanyang Automation (Dongguan) Co., Ltd. (1)
Suites 201-204 No 1 Songshan Lake, Intelligent Valley Science Research Center No 6 Minfu Rd, Dongguan, Guangdong, China
Tel.: (86) 7698 608 5999
Automated Equipment Research & Development Services
N.A.I.C.S.: 541715
Zhang-Yao Chen (Chm)

Zhen Ding Developer India Private Limited (1)
Unit No 02 3rd Floor No 27 Kamaraj Colony 3rd Street, Kodambakkam, Chennai, 600024, Tamil Nadu, India
Tel.: (91) 9176999602
Plant Lease Services
N.A.I.C.S.: 532490

Zhen Ding Technology Co., Ltd. (1)
No 6 Lane 28 Sanho Road, Sanshi Village Dayuan District, Taoyuan, Taiwan
Tel.: (886) 33835678
Electronic Component Mfr & Distr
N.A.I.C.S.: 334419
Chang-Fang Shen (Chm)

Zhen Ding Technology India Private Limited (1)
Unit No 01 3rd Floor No 27 Kamaraj Colony 3rd Street, Kodambakkam, Chennai, 600024, Tamil Nadu, India
Tel.: (91) 9176999602
Electronic Component Mfr & Distr
N.A.I.C.S.: 334419

ZHENDE MEDICAL CO., LTD.
Gaobu Town, Shaoxing, 312035, Zhejiang, China
Tel.: (86) 57588770886
Web Site: https://www.zdmedicalproduct.com
Year Founded: 1993
603301—(SHG)
Rev.: $861,723,870
Assets: $1,108,729,520
Liabilities: $300,447,450
Net Worth: $808,282,070
Earnings: $95,631,017
Fiscal Year-end: 12/31/22
Medical Product Distr
N.A.I.C.S.: 456199
Jianguo Lu (Chm)

ZHENENG JINJIANG ENVIRONMENT HOLDING COMPANY LIMITED
1 Yinxiu Road Tower A Hangyue Commercial Center, Gongshu District, Hangzhou, 310011, Zhejiang, China
Tel.: (86) 57187699700
Web Site: https://en.jinjiang-env.com
Year Founded: 1998
BWM—(SES)
Rev.: $472,601,371
Assets: $2,722,033,656
Liabilities: $1,786,992,719
Net Worth: $935,040,936
Earnings: $50,634,220
Emp.: 2,391
Fiscal Year-end: 12/31/20
Power Generation Services
N.A.I.C.S.: 562213
Ruihong Wang (Deputy Gen Mgr)

Subsidiaries:

Ecogreen Energy Lucknow Private Limited
5/189 Vineet Khand Gomti Nagar, Lucknow, 226010, Uttar Pradesh, India
Tel.: (91) 522 423 6822
Waste Management Services
N.A.I.C.S.: 562998

Ecogreen Energy Private Limited (1)
603-607 IId Trade Centre Sec-47 Sohna Road, Gurgaon, 122001, Haryana, India
Tel.: (91) 124 4410700
Web Site: http://www.ecogreenenergy.co.in
Power Generation Services
N.A.I.C.S.: 562213
Rakesh Aggarwal (Co-Founder)

Waste Tec GmbH (1)
Spilburgstrasse 1, 35578, Wetzlar, Germany
Tel.: (49) 644 189 7280
Web Site: https://www.wastetec.com
Waste Management Services
N.A.I.C.S.: 562998
Andreas Puchelt (Mng Dir)

ZHENG HSING INDUSTRIAL CO., LTD.
No 78 Yongcheng Road, Taiping District, Taichung, 411, Taiwan
Tel.: (886) 422785177
Web Site: https://www.zenghsing.com.tw
Year Founded: 1968
1558—(TAI)
Rev.: $225,064,722
Assets: $392,545,446
Liabilities: $135,371,291
Net Worth: $257,174,155
Earnings: $19,547,728
Emp.: 3,230
Fiscal Year-end: 12/31/22
Household Sewing Machine, Vacuum Cleaner & Spare Parts Retailer
N.A.I.C.S.: 423620

Subsidiaries:

Shinco Technologies Limited (1)
Lo K6 Durong N1-D3 KCN Nam Tan Uyen TX Tinh, Tan Uyen, Binh Dong, Binh Duong Province, Vietnam
Tel.: (84) 2743652971
Web Site: https://www.shincotech.com

Automobile Parts Mfr
N.A.I.C.S.: 336390

ZHENGHE REAL ESTATE, INC.
Unity Road 9 Rich Gate Building 1-6 Floors, River District, Shenyang, 110013, Liaoning, China
Tel.: (86) 24 86 897566
Web Site: http://www.zhenghechina.com
Emp.: 24
Residential Real Estate Developer
N.A.I.C.S.: 236117
Gordon G.E. Wang (Chm & CEO)

ZHENGPING ROAD & BRIDGE CONSTRUCTION CO., LTD
14F Chuangxin Building No 128 Changjiang Road, Chengxi District, Xining, 810008, Qinghai, China
Tel.: (86) 9718588071
Web Site: http://www.zhengpingjituan.com
Year Founded: 1993
603843—(SHG)
Rev.: $312,022,503
Assets: $1,246,910,778
Liabilities: $979,941,049
Net Worth: $266,969,730
Earnings: ($29,983,866)
Fiscal Year-end: 12/31/22
Bridge Construction Services
N.A.I.C.S.: 237310
Peng Youhong (Chm & Pres)

ZHENGWEI GROUP HOLDINGS COMPANY LIMITED
487 Yuhu Road Xiaolan Economic Development Zone, Nanchang, China
Year Founded: 2002
2147—(HKG)
Rev.: $54,672,529
Assets: $57,727,843
Liabilities: $18,131,484
Net Worth: $39,596,358
Earnings: $7,154,447
Emp.: 640
Fiscal Year-end: 12/31/22
Holding Company
N.A.I.C.S.: 551112
Shengyao Yang (CEO)

ZHENGYE INTERNATIONAL HOLDINGS COMPANY LIMITED
Suite 1404 14/F Jubilee Centre 18 Fenwick Street, Wanchai, China (Hong Kong)
Tel.: (852) 28777721
Web Site: http://www.zhengye-cn.com
Year Founded: 1999
3363—(HKG)
Rev.: $423,159,563
Assets: $418,906,285
Liabilities: $221,987,423
Net Worth: $196,918,862
Earnings: $9,632,002
Emp.: 2,484
Fiscal Year-end: 12/31/22
Paper Packaging Product Mfr
N.A.I.C.S.: 322220
Zheng Hu (Co-Chm)

ZHENGZHOU COAL INDUSTRY & ELECTRIC POWER CO., LTD.
No 66 Zhongyuan West Road, Zhengzhou, 450007, Henan, China
Tel.: (86) 37187785121
Web Site: http://www.zzce.com.cn
Year Founded: 1997
600121—(SHG)
Rev.: $621,003,268
Assets: $1,954,571,243
Liabilities: $1,576,455,370

ZHENGZHOU COAL INDUSTRY & ELECTRIC POWER CO., LTD.

Zhengzhou Coal Industry & Electric Power Co., Ltd.—(Continued)
Net Worth: $378,115,873
Earnings: $9,549,432
Emp.: 12,400
Fiscal Year-end: 12/31/22
Coal & Electric Power Generation & Distribution Services
N.A.I.C.S.: 212115
Yu Lefeng (Chm)

ZHENGZHOU COAL MINING MACHINERY GROUP CO., LTD.
No 167 the 9th Avenue Economic and Technological Development Zone, Zhengzhou, 450016, Henan, China
Tel.: (86) 37167891199
Web Site: http://www.zzmj.com
Year Founded: 1958
601717—(SHG)
Rev.: $4,498,880,162
Assets: $6,219,885,054
Liabilities: $3,603,070,374
Net Worth: $2,616,814,680
Earnings: $356,368,180
Emp.: 17,000
Fiscal Year-end: 12/31/22
Mining Machinery Mfr
N.A.I.C.S.: 333131
Chengyao Jiao (Chm & CEO)

Subsidiaries:

ASIMCO International Casting (Shanxi) Co., Ltd. (1)
Erliban Village, Jiangxian, Yuncheng, 043605, Shanxi, China
Tel.: (86) 35 9656 3600
Motor Vehicle Parts Mfr
N.A.I.C.S.: 336390

ASIMCO Shuanghuan Piston Ring (Yizheng) Co., Ltd. (1)
No 5 Daqing South Road, Yizheng, 211400, Jiangsu, China
Tel.: (86) 51483450568
Web Site: https://www.cypr.com.cn
Engine Valve Ring Designer, Developer & Mfr
N.A.I.C.S.: 336310

ZHENGZHOU DEHENG HONGSHENG TECHNOLOGY CO., LTD.
No 88 Yugong Road Economic and Technological Development Zone, Zhengzhou, 451482, Henan, China
Tel.: (86) 37185334130
600817—(SHG)
Rev.: $575,539,493
Assets: $731,876,510
Liabilities: $368,581,893
Net Worth: $363,294,616
Earnings: $60,197,741
Emp.: 3,500
Fiscal Year-end: 12/31/21
Real Estate Leasing & Property Management Services
N.A.I.C.S.: 531120
Xinjian Chu (Pres)

ZHENGZHOU J & T HI-TECH CO., LTD.
No 56 Xuemei Street High-tech Zone, High-tech Industry Development Zone, Zhengzhou, 450000, Henan, China
Tel.: (86) 37186589303
Web Site: https://www.jantech.cn
Year Founded: 2002
300845—(SSE)
Rev.: $42,300,779
Assets: $139,281,995
Liabilities: $30,517,737
Net Worth: $108,764,258
Earnings: $6,285,568
Fiscal Year-end: 12/31/22
Software Development Services
N.A.I.C.S.: 541511
Leguang Zheng (Chm)

ZHENGZHOU SINO-CRYSTAL DIAMOND CO., LTD.
Building 30 No 20 Bitao Road High and New Technology Development Zone, Zhengzhou, 450001, Henan, China
Tel.: (86) 37163379595
Web Site: http://www.sinocrystal.com.cn
300064—(CHIN)
Rev.: $73,291,068
Assets: $977,113,628
Liabilities: $901,411,035
Net Worth: $75,702,593
Earnings: ($189,392,074)
Fiscal Year-end: 12/31/20
Diamond Tool Mfr
N.A.I.C.S.: 333514

Subsidiaries:

Henan Huamao New Material Technology Development Co., Ltd. (1)
Luo new industrial agglomeration area of Jing Jin Road No 1, Luoyang, China
Tel.: (86) 37963087601
Web Site: https://www.henanhuamao.com
Grinding Wheel Mfr
N.A.I.C.S.: 327910

Henan Yuxing Sino-Crystal Miro Co., Ltd. (1)
North Mid-section of Yunxiang Rd, Industrial Zone, Jiaozuo, 454350, Henan, China
Tel.: (86) 37155592008
Web Site: https://en.microndiamond.com
Diamond Powder Mfr & Distr
N.A.I.C.S.: 327910

Sino-Crystal Precision Manufacturing Co., Ltd. (1)
North of the 4th Rd N and West of the 10th Ave, Economical and Technological Development Area, Zhengzhou, China
Tel.: (86) 37155592017
Web Site: http://www.hjjmzz.com
Industrial Equipment Mfr & Distr
N.A.I.C.S.: 332216

Xin An Town Luoxin New Material Industrial Park Development Co., Ltd. (1)
Jingjin Road, Luoxin Industrial Cluster Xin'an County, Luoyang, China
Tel.: (86) 37963088016
Web Site: https://www.idacn.org
Diamond Distr
N.A.I.C.S.: 423940

ZHENGZHOU TIAMAES TECHNOLOGY CO., LTD.
Building 10 316 Lianhua Street, High-tech District, Zhengzhou, 450001, Henan, China
Tel.: (86) 4006001276
Web Site: https://www.tiamaes.com
Year Founded: 2004
300807—(SSE)
Rev.: $46,247,592
Assets: $109,135,644
Liabilities: $25,624,755
Net Worth: $83,510,889
Earnings: ($1,194,874)
Emp.: 600
Fiscal Year-end: 12/31/22
Software Development Services
N.A.I.C.S.: 541511
Jianguo Guo (Chm & Gen Mgr)

ZHENJIANG DONGFANG ELECTRIC HEATING TECHNOLOGY CO., LTD.
No 18 Wufeng shan road, Dagang town, Zhenjiang, 212132, Jiangsu, China
Tel.: (86) 51188980999
Web Site: https://www.dongfang-heater.com
Year Founded: 1992
Rev.: $319,697,850
Assets: $510,986,131
Liabilities: $211,703,371
Net Worth: $299,282,760
Earnings: ($16,639,224)
Emp.: 900
Fiscal Year-end: 12/31/19
Electric Heaters & Control Systems Mfr
N.A.I.C.S.: 333415
Tan Ke (Chm)

ZHENRO PROPERTIES GROUP LIMITED
Building No 7 Hongqiao Zhenro Center Lane 666 Shenhong Road, Hongqiao Business Core District Minhang District, Shanghai, China
Tel.: (86) 2161253299 Ky
Web Site: https://www.zhenrodc.com
Year Founded: 1998
6158—(HKG)
Rev.: $5,368,705,001
Assets: $21,210,072,691
Liabilities: $20,358,343,487
Net Worth: $851,729,204
Earnings: ($1,313,353,179)
Emp.: 515
Fiscal Year-end: 12/31/23
Real Estate Manangement Services
N.A.I.C.S.: 531390
Xianzhi Huang (Chm)

ZHENRO SERVICES GROUP LIMITED
Building No 7 Hongqiao Zhenro Center Lane 666 Shenhong Road, Hongqiao Business Core Minhang, Shanghai, China
Tel.: (86) 2161258655 Ky
Web Site: http://www.zhenrowy.com
Year Founded: 2000
6958—(HKG)
Property Management Services
N.A.I.C.S.: 531311
Liang Huang (Exec Dir)

ZHENSHI HOLDING GROUP CO., LTD.
No 288 Phoenix Lake Road, Zhejiang, Tongxiang, 3145000, China
Tel.: (86) 57388181085
Web Site: http://www.zhenshigroup.com
Financial Investment Company
N.A.I.C.S.: 523999
Zhang Yuqiang (Founder)

Subsidiaries:

China Hengshi Foundation Co. Ltd. (1)
No 1 Guangyun South Road, Economic Development Zone, Tongxiang, 314500, Zhejiang, China
Tel.: (86) 57388136701
Web Site: http://www.chinahengshi.com.cn
Rev.: $211,985,890
Assets: $330,068,013
Liabilities: $110,530,712
Net Worth: $219,537,301
Earnings: $36,747,904
Emp.: 1,264
Fiscal Year-end: 12/31/2018
Fiberglass Fabric Mfr & Distr
N.A.I.C.S.: 313210
Hang Yin (Co-Sec)

ZHESHANG DEVELOPMENT GROUP CO., LTD.
8-10 building communication building 303 Wenhui Road, Xiacheng District, Hangzhou, 310014, China
Tel.: (86) 57187852866
Web Site: https://en.zmd.com.cn
Year Founded: 1999

INTERNATIONAL PUBLIC

000906—(SSE)
Rev.: $27,182,107,658
Assets: $3,660,423,409
Liabilities: $2,570,046,444
Net Worth: $1,090,376,965
Earnings: $140,755,114
Fiscal Year-end: 12/31/22
Metal Product Distr
N.A.I.C.S.: 423510
Renjun Yuan (Chm)

ZHESHANG SECURITIES CO., LTD.
No 201 Wuxing Road, Jiangnggan District, Hangzhou, 310020, Zhejiang, China
Tel.: (86) 57187901964
Web Site: https://www.stocke.com.cn
Year Founded: 2002
601878—(SHG)
Rev.: $2,360,701,086
Assets: $19,229,374,172
Liabilities: $15,395,219,621
Net Worth: $3,834,154,551
Earnings: $232,248,023
Fiscal Year-end: 12/31/22
Securities Brokerage Services
N.A.I.C.S.: 523150
Chenggen Wu (Chm)

Subsidiaries:

Zheshang Asset Management Co., Ltd. (1)
Room 301 No 193 West Lake Avenue Company, Hangzhou, Zhejiang, China
Tel.: (86) 5718 977 3800
Web Site: https://www.zsamc.com
Investment Management Service
N.A.I.C.S.: 541611

ZHEWEN INTERACTIVE GROUP CO LTD
Bldg No F1 Yuanjun Shuyuan Phase II Dongyi Intl Media Industry Park, No 8 Gaojing Cultural Park Road Gaobeidian Village Chaoyang District, Beijing, 100123, Shandong, China
Tel.: (86) 1087835799
Web Site: http://www.keda-group.com
Year Founded: 1984
600986—(SHG)
Rev.: $2,189,951,566
Assets: $1,172,143,830
Liabilities: $552,905,780
Net Worth: $619,238,050
Earnings: $45,101,960
Fiscal Year-end: 12/31/21
Real Estate Leasing & Road Construction Services
N.A.I.C.S.: 531110
Tang Ying (Chm & CEO)

Subsidiaries:

Ally (Hangzhou) Investment Co., Ltd. (1)
Room 103 11 No 107 Miaoqian Dazifu, Shangcheng District, Hangzhou, Zhejiang, China
Tel.: (86) 57128178235
Industrial Building Construction Services
N.A.I.C.S.: 236210

Ally Data Technology (Beijing) Co., Ltd. (1)
1201 F12 No 1 Qinglong Alley, Dongcheng District, Beijing, China
Tel.: (86) 1057278246
Industrial Building Construction Services
N.A.I.C.S.: 236210

Beijing AiChuang TianJie Brand Management Consulting Co., Ltd. (1)
12144 Yongxin Road Yongledian, Tongzhou District, Beijing, China
Tel.: (86) 1052325288
Industrial Building Construction Services
N.A.I.C.S.: 236210

AND PRIVATE COMPANIES

Beijing Aspiration Advertising Co., Ltd. (1)
5th Floor Block A Yisha Wenxin Plaza No 1 Nanjia Sihui Bridge, Chaoyang District, Beijing, China
Tel.: (86) 1087835788
Web Site: https://www.aspiration-cn.com
Industrial Building Construction Services
N.A.I.C.S.: 236210

Beijing Data 100 Information Technology Co., Ltd. (1)
E56 F6 18 Zhongguancun Avenue, Haidian District, Beijing, China
Tel.: (86) 1082251502
Industrial Building Construction Services
N.A.I.C.S.: 236210

Beijing Huizutong Investment Consulting Co., Ltd. (1)
604 F6 3 No 17 South Avenue Zhongguancun, Haidian District, Beijing, China
Tel.: (86) 1088578733
Industrial Building Construction Services
N.A.I.C.S.: 236210

Beijing Iforce Interactive Co., Ltd. (1)
Room 1002 No 1093 Luyuan South Avenue, Tongzhou District, Beijing, China
Tel.: (86) 1084793966
Industrial Building Construction Services
N.A.I.C.S.: 236210

Beijing Zhiyue Network Technology Co., Ltd. (1)
Sihui Mansion 1008-B Huihe South Street, Banbidian Village Gaobeidian Chaoyang District, Beijing, China
Tel.: (86) 13661276540
Industrial Building Construction Services
N.A.I.C.S.: 236210

Dongying Daqiao Lvda Landscape Co., Ltd. (1)
Technological Enterprise Accelerator, Dongying District, Dongying, Shandong, China
Tel.: (86) 5468306208
Industrial Building Construction Services
N.A.I.C.S.: 236210

Dongying Kechuang Biochemical Engineering Co., Ltd. (1)
756 Tuanjie Road Guangrao Development Zone, Dongying, Shandong, China
Tel.: (86) 5467724488
Industrial Building Construction Services
N.A.I.C.S.: 236210

Dongying Keda Electric Engineering Co., Ltd. (1)
E2-4-402 Technological Enterprise Accelerator, Dongying District, Dongying, Shandong, China
Tel.: (86) 5468301980
Industrial Building Construction Services
N.A.I.C.S.: 236210

Dongying Keying Real Estate Co., Ltd. (1)
Dongcheng Economic and Technological Development Zone, Dongying, Shandong, China
Tel.: (86) 5468090137
Industrial Building Construction Services
N.A.I.C.S.: 236210

Dongying Yellow River Bridge Co., Ltd. (1)
308 Zhongxing Road, Kenli District, Dongying, Shandong, China
Tel.: (86) 5462885001
Industrial Building Construction Services
N.A.I.C.S.: 236210

Dongying Zhongke Low Carbon Technology Service Co., Ltd. (1)
E2-4-401 Enterprise Accelerator Dongying Development Zone, Dongying, Shandong, China
Tel.: (86) 5466070686
Industrial Building Construction Services
N.A.I.C.S.: 236210

Guangdong YLMF Computer Technology Co., Ltd. (1)
17 Songkeyuan Songshanhu Technology Industrial Park, Dongguan, Guangdong, China
Tel.: (86) 1059006162
Industrial Building Construction Services
N.A.I.C.S.: 236210

Guangrao Jinqiao Micro Credit Co., Ltd. (1)
No 1 Fengchun Road, Dawang Town Guangrao County, Dongying, Shandong, China
Tel.: (86) 5467722444
Industrial Building Construction Services
N.A.I.C.S.: 236210

Guangzhou Target-uni Digital Marketing Co., Ltd. (1)
F19 Chow Tai Fook Finance Center No 6 Zhujiang East Road, Tianhe District, Guangzhou, Guangdong, China
Tel.: (86) 38686413
Industrial Building Construction Services
N.A.I.C.S.: 236210

Hainan Longao Investment Co., Ltd. (1)
Room 1201 A Block Yazhuang Huayuan 82 Haixiu Middle Road, Haikou, Hainan, China
Tel.: (86) 13976669802
Industrial Building Construction Services
N.A.I.C.S.: 236210

Keda Group Materials Company (1)
West to Dawang Section of Dongwang Road, Dawang Town Guangrao County, Dongying, Shandong, China
Tel.: (86) 5468301836
Industrial Building Construction Services
N.A.I.C.S.: 236210

Keda Semiconductor Co., Ltd. (1)
65 Fuqian Avenue, Dongying, Shandong, China
Tel.: (86) 5468301856
Industrial Building Construction Services
N.A.I.C.S.: 236210

Keda Traffic Appliances Company (1)
Economic and Technological Development Zone, Dawang Town Guangrao County, Dongying, Shandong, China
Tel.: (86) 5466872735
Industrial Building Construction Services
N.A.I.C.S.: 236210

Qingdao Bonded Area Longhan International Trade Co., Ltd. (1)
5313 No 1 Office Building, Qingdao Bonded Area, Qingdao, Shandong, China
Tel.: (86) 53266888172
Industrial Building Construction Services
N.A.I.C.S.: 236210

Qingdao Keda Real Estate Co., Ltd. (1)
17 Xueyuan Road Lingshanwei, Huangdao District, Qingdao, Shandong, China
Tel.: (86) 53285180810
Industrial Building Construction Services
N.A.I.C.S.: 236210

Shandong Dongke Engineering Detection Co., Ltd. (1)
267-13 Daduhe Road, Dongying, Shandong, China
Tel.: (86) 5468018770
Industrial Building Construction Services
N.A.I.C.S.: 236210

Shandong Keda Infrastructure Co., Ltd. (1)
65 Fuqian Avenue, Dongying, Shandong, China
Tel.: (86) 5468301956
Industrial Building Construction Services
N.A.I.C.S.: 236210

Shandong Keda Property Service Co., Ltd. (1)
18 Shengli Avenue, Dongying, Shandong, China
Tel.: (86) 5468090086
Industrial Building Construction Services
N.A.I.C.S.: 236210

Shandong Zhongke Industrial Park Development Co., Ltd. (1)
65 Fuqian Avenue, Dongying, Shandong, China
Tel.: (86) 5467761777
Industrial Building Construction Services
N.A.I.C.S.: 236210

Shanghai Kexu International Trade Co., Ltd. (1)
Room 3013 1 No 146 Fute East 1st Road Pilot Free Trade Zone, Shanghai, China
Tel.: (86) 13611696045
Industrial Building Construction Services
N.A.I.C.S.: 236210

Shouxin Financial Leasing Co., Ltd. (1)
Block C Weibo Shidai Center No 17 South Avenue Zhongguancun, Haidian District, Beijing, China
Tel.: (86) 1088579233
Industrial Building Construction Services
N.A.I.C.S.: 236210

Yantai Keda Real Estate Co., Ltd. (1)
Fu 21 Shifu Street, Zhifu District, Yantai, Shandong, China
Tel.: (86) 5356218387
Industrial Building Construction Services
N.A.I.C.S.: 236210

ZHEWEN PICTURES GROUP CO., LTD.
19F Block B Yuanyang International Center, Gongshu District, Hangzhou, 310015, Zhejiang, China
Tel.: (86) 51258353258
Web Site: http://www.lugangwool.com
Year Founded: 1993
601599—(SHG)
Rev.: $375,686,241
Assets: $516,300,847
Liabilities: $329,792,186
Net Worth: $186,508,661
Earnings: $13,065,749
Emp.: 4,500
Fiscal Year-end: 12/31/21
Woolen Yarn Mfr
N.A.I.C.S.: 313110
Fu Liwen (Chm-Supervisory Bd)

ZHI SHENG GROUP HOLDINGS LIMITED
3/F 222 Tianren Road, Gaoxin District, Chengdu, Sichuan, China Ky
Web Site: https://www.qtbgjj.com
Year Founded: 2016
8370—(HKG)
Rev.: $26,430,410
Assets: $41,337,590
Liabilities: $21,738,814
Net Worth: $19,598,776
Earnings: ($11,297,399)
Emp.: 198
Fiscal Year-end: 06/30/22
Holding Company
N.A.I.C.S.: 551112
Cong Yi (CEO)

ZHIDAO INTERNATIONAL (HOLDINGS) LIMITED
Room 2606 26/F C C Wu Building, 302-308 Hennessy Road Wan Chai, Sheung Wan, China (Hong Kong)
Tel.: (852) 31027000 BM
Web Site: http://www.zdihl.com
Year Founded: 1997
Rev.: $2,669,677
Assets: $64,772,896
Liabilities: $6,536,838
Net Worth: $58,236,059
Earnings: $323,074
Emp.: 32
Fiscal Year-end: 03/31/18
Aluminium Product Whslr
N.A.I.C.S.: 423520
Kwok Kit Fung (Chm)

ZHIHU INC.
A5 Xueyuan Road, Haidian District, Beijing, 100083, China
Tel.: (86) 1082716605 Ky
Web Site: https://ir.zhihu.com
Year Founded: 2011
ZH—(NYSE)
Rev.: $552,309,640
Assets: $1,173,012,377
Liabilities: $300,593,577
Net Worth: $872,418,800
Earnings: ($242,249,064)
Emp.: 2,515
Fiscal Year-end: 12/31/22
Holding Company
N.A.I.C.S.: 551112
Dahai Li (CTO)

ZHIXIN GROUP HOLDING LIMITED
1 No 55 Guankou Avenue, Jimei District, Xiamen, Fujian, China Ky
Web Site: https://www.xiamenzhixin.com
Year Founded: 2018
2187—(HKG)
Rev.: $97,158,428
Assets: $212,211,018
Liabilities: $144,328,263
Net Worth: $67,882,755
Earnings: $191,972
Emp.: 508
Fiscal Year-end: 12/31/22
Holding Company
N.A.I.C.S.: 551112
Limiao Qiu (COO)

ZHIYANG INNOVATION TECHNOLOGY CO., LTD.
Building 10 Instrumentation Industrial Park, High-tech Zone, Zibo, 255086, Shandong, China
Tel.: (86) 5333586028
Web Site: https://www.zhiyang.com.cn
Year Founded: 2006
688191—(SHG)
Rev.: $94,241,155
Assets: $170,958,313
Liabilities: $54,252,596
Net Worth: $116,705,717
Earnings: $3,930,217
Emp.: 800
Fiscal Year-end: 12/31/22
Electrical Equipment Mfr & Distr
N.A.I.C.S.: 335999
Guoyong Liu (Chm)

ZHONG AN GROUP LIMITED
Room 4009 40th Floor China Resources Building 26 Harbour Road, Wanchai, China (Hong Kong)
Tel.: (852) 28776991
Web Site: http://www.zafc.com
0672—(HKG)
Rev.: $1,298,770,060
Assets: $8,297,198,021
Liabilities: $6,565,621,795
Net Worth: $1,731,576,226
Earnings: $3,007,087
Emp.: 5,506
Fiscal Year-end: 12/31/22
Real Estate Development Services
N.A.I.C.S.: 531210
Jiangang Zhang (CEO)

Subsidiaries:

Hangzhou Xiaoshan Zhong'an Holiday Inn Co., Ltd. (1)
26/F Suite A Henglong Plaza No 688 Shanyin Rd Xiaoshan Dis, Hangzhou, 311202, Zhejiang, China
Tel.: (86) 57182977777
Web Site: http://www.holidayinn.com
Home Management Services
N.A.I.C.S.: 721110
Aider Son (Gen Mgr)

ZHONG AO HOME GROUP LIMITED

ZHONG AO HOME GROUP LIMITED

Zhong Ao Home Group Limited—(Continued)
1601 Block 1 Pacific Dingwang Commercial Center 2 Baichen Lu, Chihua She Qu Chencun Town Shunde District, Foshan, Guangdong, China **Ky**
Web Site: https://www.gdzawy.com
Year Founded: 2005
1538—(HKG)
Rev.: $236,713,835
Assets: $286,227,847
Liabilities: $143,241,166
Net Worth: $142,986,680
Earnings: $11,626,606
Emp.: 8,521
Fiscal Year-end: 12/31/23
Property Management Services
N.A.I.C.S.: 531311
Bing Liang (VP)

ZHONG FU TONG GROUP CO., LTD

Floors 20 21 & 22 Building 4 Zone F Software Park, No 89 Software Avenue Tongpan Road Gulou District, Fuzhou, 350003, Fujian, China
Tel.: (86) 59183800952
Web Site: http://www.zftii.com
Year Founded: 2001
300560—(CHIN)
Rev.: $181,225,779
Assets: $383,455,829
Liabilities: $228,508,674
Net Worth: $154,947,155
Earnings: ($7,439,359)
Fiscal Year-end: 12/31/23
Communication Network Optimization Services
N.A.I.C.S.: 541430
Rongjie Chen (Chm & Gen Mgr)

ZHONG HUA INTERNATIONAL HOLDINGS LIMITED

Suite 2911 West Tower Shuntak Centre, 168-200 Connaught Road Central, Central, China (Hong Kong)
Tel.: (852) 25597200 **BM**
Web Site:
  http://www.zhonghuagroup.com
1064—(HKG)
Rev.: $3,861,083
Assets: $563,034,773
Liabilities: $177,790,590
Net Worth: $385,244,183
Earnings: $4,341,375
Emp.: 30
Fiscal Year-end: 12/31/22
Property Developer & Investor
N.A.I.C.S.: 523999
Kam Hung Ho (Mng Dir)

ZHONG JI LONGEVITY SCIENCE GROUP LTD.

Victoria Place 5th Floor 31 Victoria Street, Hamilton, HM 10, Bermuda
Tel.: (441) 25116851 **BM**
0767—(HKG)
Rev.: $8,319,657
Assets: $65,192,859
Liabilities: $10,086,283
Net Worth: $55,106,575
Earnings: $322,985
Emp.: 30
Fiscal Year-end: 12/31/23
Investment Holding Company
N.A.I.C.S.: 551112
Siu Yeung (Exec Dir)

ZHONG YANG TECHNOLOGY CO., LTD.

No 21 Gongyequ 22nd Rd, Nantun Dist, Taichung, 40850, Taiwan
Tel.: (886) 423597888
Web Site: http://www.jmo-corp.com
Year Founded: 2013

6668—(TAI)
Rev.: $30,904,345
Assets: $120,633,993
Liabilities: $58,068,051
Net Worth: $62,565,942
Earnings: ($9,001,602)
Fiscal Year-end: 12/31/23
Mold Mfr
N.A.I.C.S.: 333511
Jung-Chou Lee (Chm)

Subsidiaries:

Dongguan City JMO Optical Co., Ltd. (1)
2F B Building XinHe Industrial Zhenan East Road No 162, Xiaobian Village Changan Town, Dongguan, 523849, China
Tel.: (86) 76985673988
Customized Optical Lens Mfr & Distr
N.A.I.C.S.: 339115

Dongguan JMO Optical Co.,Ltd. (1)
1F A Building XinHe Industrial Zhenan East Road No 162, Xiaobian Village 2-3rd District Changan Town, Dongguan, 523849, China
Tel.: (86) 76981622985
Customized Optical Lens Mfr & Distr
N.A.I.C.S.: 339115

Eterge Opto-Electronics Co., LTD. (1)
No 21 Gongyequ 22nd Rd, Nantun Dist, Taichung, 40850, Taiwan
Tel.: (886) 423585022
Web Site: https://www.eterge.com
Customized Optical Lens Mfr & Distr
N.A.I.C.S.: 339115

ZHONG YUAN BIO-TECHNOLOGY HOLDINGS LIMITED

Suite 901 Tesbury Centre 28 Queens Road East, Wanchai, 00000, China (Hong Kong)
Tel.: (852) 29198916 **DE**
Year Founded: 2016
ZHYBF—(OTCQB)
Rev.: $2,278,246
Assets: $3,168,233
Liabilities: $3,387,027
Net Worth: ($218,794)
Earnings: $271,869
Emp.: 23
Fiscal Year-end: 03/31/24
Holding Company
N.A.I.C.S.: 551112
Fung Ming Pang (CFO & Exec Dir)

ZHONG ZHU HEALTHCARE HOLDING CO., LTD.

Te No 1 Zhanghua South Road, Qianjiang, 519020, Hubei, China
Tel.: (86) 7286402068
Web Site:
  http://www.zzkg600568.com
Year Founded: 1994
600568—(SHG)
Rev.: $71,038,385
Assets: $521,258,952
Liabilities: $108,946,483
Net Worth: $412,312,469
Earnings: ($112,210,699)
Emp.: 863
Fiscal Year-end: 12/31/22
Holding Company; Healthcare Services
N.A.I.C.S.: 551112
Jige Ye (Chm)

ZHONGAN ONLINE P & C INSURANCE CO., LTD.

4F-5F Associate Mission Building 169 Yuanmingyuan Road, Shanghai, China
Tel.: (86) 10109955 **CN**
Web Site: https://www.zhongan.com
Year Founded: 2013

6060—(HKG)
Rev.: $3,278,641,720
Assets: $7,659,857,275
Liabilities: $5,269,311,403
Net Worth: $2,390,545,872
Earnings: ($229,274,744)
Emp.: 3,969
Fiscal Year-end: 12/31/22
Risk Managemeng Srvices
N.A.I.C.S.: 524126
Yaping Ou (Board of Directors & Chm)

Subsidiaries:

ZA Life Limited (1)
Unit 1304-1305 Level 13 Core F Cyberport 3 100 Cyberport Road, Hong Kong, China (Hong Kong)
Tel.: (852) 36653636
Web Site: https://insure.za.group
Medical Insurance Services
N.A.I.C.S.: 524114

ZA Tech Global Limited (1)
Level 13 Core F Cyberport 3 100 Cyberport Road, Hong Kong, China (Hong Kong)
Tel.: (852) 31226500
Web Site: http://www.zatech.com
Medical Insurance Services
N.A.I.C.S.: 524114
Minxin Zhang (Bus Mgr)

ZHONGBAI HOLDINGS GROUP CO., LTD.

17F & 20F Tower A Guochuang Building No 32 Tangjiadun Road, Jianghan District, Wuhan, 430024, Hubei, China
Tel.: (86) 2782814019
Web Site: http://www.whzb.com
Year Founded: 1989
000759—(SSE)
Rev.: $1,712,515,845
Assets: $1,765,649,663
Liabilities: $1,370,211,813
Net Worth: $395,437,850
Earnings: ($44,905,283)
Fiscal Year-end: 12/31/22
Holding Company
N.A.I.C.S.: 551112
Wang Meifang (Chm)

ZHONGBAO INTERNATIONAL, INC.

7 Minsheng Road Yuzhong District, Chongqing, China
Tel.: (86) 23 8611 8735 **NV**
Year Founded: 2009
Sales Range: $25-49.9 Million
Emp.: 53
Real Estate Development Services
N.A.I.C.S.: 531390
Haoji Xia (Chm, Pres, CEO, CFO & Sec)

ZHONGCHANG BIG DATA CO., LTD.

7-8F A7 Fuhua Community Anning Road, Jiangcheng District, Yangjiang, 200011, Guangdong, China
Tel.: (86) 213 177 3723
Web Site:
  http://www.zhongchangdata.com
Year Founded: 1993
600242—(SHG)
Rev.: $73,076,574
Assets: $161,716,219
Liabilities: $154,699,201
Net Worth: $7,017,018
Earnings: ($72,328,909)
Fiscal Year-end: 12/31/21
Information Technology Services
N.A.I.C.S.: 541519
Li Qunnan (Chm & Gen Mgr)

ZHONGCHANG INTERNATIONAL HOLDINGS GROUP LIMITED

INTERNATIONAL PUBLIC

Suite 1711 Tower 2 Times Square 1 Matheson Street Causeway Bay, Hong Kong, China (Hong Kong)
Tel.: (852) 21170237 **HK**
Web Site:
  https://www.zhongchangintl.hk
Year Founded: 1999
0859—(HKG)
Rev.: $4,293,945
Assets: $236,097,998
Liabilities: $105,248,700
Net Worth: $130,849,298
Earnings: ($8,075,595)
Emp.: 8
Fiscal Year-end: 12/31/22
Property Development & Consulting Services
N.A.I.C.S.: 531311
Yilin Ma (Chm)

Subsidiaries:

Uni-Land Property Consultants Limited (1)
3 Saloi Spuly Rd Spa House Rm 1432, Tsimshatsui, Kowloon, China (Hong Kong)
Tel.: (852) 31130113
Web Site: http://www.uni-land.com.hk
Sales Range: $50-74.9 Million
Emp.: 6
Property Consulting Services
N.A.I.C.S.: 531312
Linus Chan (Mgr)

ZHONGCHAO INC.

841 Yan'An Middle Road Suite 218 Nanxi Creative Center, JingAn District, Shanghai, 200040, China
Tel.: (86) 2132205987 **Ky**
Web Site: http://www.izcmd.com
Year Founded: 2019
ZCMD—(NASDAQ)
Rev.: $16,296,770
Assets: $36,267,420
Liabilities: $3,700,998
Net Worth: $32,566,422
Earnings: $238,665
Emp.: 136
Fiscal Year-end: 12/31/21
Holding Company
N.A.I.C.S.: 551112
Weiguang Yang (Chm, Pres & CEO)

ZHONGDA INTERNATIONAL HOLDINGS LIMITED

Room 2203 22/F 88 Hing Fat Street, Causeway Bay, China (Hong Kong)
Tel.: (852) 82010909 **BM**
Year Founded: 2000
Holding Company
N.A.I.C.S.: 551112
Ming Fai Kwok (Exec Dir)

ZHONGDE WASTE TECHNOLOGY AG

Barckhausstrasse 1, 60325, Frankfurt, Germany
Tel.: (49) 692475689630
Web Site: https://www.zhongde-ag.com
ZEF—(DEU)
Sales Range: $25-49.9 Million
Emp.: 370
Waste Management Activity
N.A.I.C.S.: 221320
William Jiuhua Wang (CFO & Member-Mgmt Bd)

ZHONGFU INFORMATION, INC.

25th Floor Building A1-5, Hanyu Jingu Hi-tech Zone, Jinan, 250101, China
Tel.: (86) 53166590000
Web Site: https://www.zhongfu.net
Year Founded: 2002
300659—(CHIN)
Rev.: $129,382,556
Assets: $237,970,160

AND PRIVATE COMPANIES

Liabilities: $99,577,415
Net Worth: $138,392,745
Earnings: ($26,240,186)
Fiscal Year-end: 12/31/23
Security Product Mfr & Distr
N.A.I.C.S.: 334290

ZHONGFU STRAITS (PINGTAN) DEVELOPMENT CO., LTD.
23rd Floor World Jinlong Building No 159 Wusi Road, Fuzhou, 350003, Fujian, China
Tel.: (86) 59187871990
Web Site: https://www.000592.com
Year Founded: 1993
000592—(SSE)
Rev.: $164,970,744
Assets: $576,435,015
Liabilities: $255,769,193
Net Worth: $320,665,822
Earnings: ($32,220,859)
Emp.: 1,000
Fiscal Year-end: 12/31/22
Wood Products Whslr
N.A.I.C.S.: 423310
Wang Zoulu *(Chm-Supervisory Bd)*

ZHONGGUANCUN SCIENCE-TECH LEASING CO., LTD.
Floor 56 Building 7 No 2 West Third Ring Road North, Haidian District, Beijing, China
Tel.: (86) 4000108828   CN
Web Site: https://www.zgclease.com
Year Founded: 2012
1601—(HKG)
Rev.: $115,422,436
Assets: $1,718,940,103
Liabilities: $1,386,607,637
Net Worth: $332,332,466
Earnings: $35,981,807
Emp.: 141
Fiscal Year-end: 12/31/23
Information Technology Services
N.A.I.C.S.: 541512
Wei Gao *(Sec)*

ZHONGGUO PENGJIE FABRICS LIMITED
Economic Development Zone, Guangrao, Dongying, 257300, China
Tel.: (86) 5466927688
Year Founded: 2006
Sales Range: $75-99.9 Million
Emp.: 1,270
Cotton Yarns & Loom-State Fabrics Mfr
N.A.I.C.S.: 313110
Liu Dejie *(Chm & Pres)*

ZHONGHANG ELECTRONIC MEASURING INSTRUMENTS CO., LTD.
No 166 West Avenue High-tech Industrial Development Zone, Xi'an, 710119, Shaanxi, China
Tel.: (86) 2961807799
Web Site: https://www.zemic.com.cn
Year Founded: 1965
300114—(CHIN)
Rev.: $267,462,000
Assets: $512,935,956
Liabilities: $184,227,264
Net Worth: $328,708,692
Earnings: $27,078,948
Emp.: 800
Fiscal Year-end: 12/31/22
Electronic Measuring Products Mfr
N.A.I.C.S.: 334513
Xuejun Kang *(Chm)*

Subsidiaries:

LLC GC Zemik (1)
Student cheskaya Str 18A Office 21, 308023, Belgorod, Russia
Tel.: (7) 4722777119
Testing & Measuring Equipment Distr
N.A.I.C.S.: 423830

PT Interskala Mandiri Indonesia (1)
Green Sedayu Biz Park Jl Daan Mogot KM 18 DM 12 No 62, Kalideres, Jakarta Barat, 11840, Jakarta, Indonesia
Tel.: (62) 2156983105
Web Site: https://imi.interskala.com
Industrial Scale Mfr & Distr
N.A.I.C.S.: 333998

ZEMIC EUROPE B.V. (1)
Leerlooierstraat 8, 4871 EN, Etten-Leur, Netherlands
Tel.: (31) 765039480
Web Site: http://www.zemiceurope.nl
Emp.: 225
Load Cells Distr
N.A.I.C.S.: 423610
Erik van Wijk *(Gen Mgr)*

ZEMIC(USA) Inc (1)
9252 Hall Rd, Downey, CA 90241
Tel.: (562) 923-6431
Web Site: https://www.zemicusa.com
Electric Equipment Mfr
N.A.I.C.S.: 334519

ZHONGHE CO., LTD.
No 5-8 Xixu Industrial Zone, Xiuyu District, Putian, 351152, Fujian, China
Tel.: (86) 592 5054995
Web Site: http://www.zhonghe.com
Rev.: $115,773,180
Assets: $300,206,221
Liabilities: $372,977,521
Net Worth: ($72,771,300)
Earnings: ($159,684,641)
Fiscal Year-end: 12/31/17
Printing Apparel Mfr
N.A.I.C.S.: 314999
Wang Xin *(Sec & VP)*

ZHONGHONG HOLDING CO., LTD.
No 32 Bldg No 1 Yard Wuliqiao First Street, Chaoyang District, Beijing, 100024, China
Tel.: (86) 10 59279999
Web Site: http://www.zhonghongholdings.com
Rev.: $156,014,832
Assets: $6,937,629,951
Liabilities: $5,637,217,213
Net Worth: $1,300,412,737
Earnings: ($389,582,271)
Fiscal Year-end: 12/31/17
Holding Company
N.A.I.C.S.: 551112
Yonghong Zhang *(Pres)*

ZHONGHONG PULIN MEDICAL PRODUCTS CO., LTD.
Southwest of the Intersection of Zhongda Street & Jinxiu Road, Chengxi Park Luannan Economic Development Zone, Tangshan, 063500, Hebei, China
Tel.: (86) 1067890877
Web Site: https://www.zhonghongpulin.com
Year Founded: 2010
300981—(SSE)
Rev.: $220,788,617
Assets: $957,055,596
Liabilities: $96,041,168
Net Worth: $861,014,429
Earnings: $9,395,006
Fiscal Year-end: 12/31/22
Medical Product Mfr & Distr
N.A.I.C.S.: 339112
Shujun Sang *(Chm)*

ZHONGHUA GAS HOLDINGS LIMITED
23/F Chinachem Century Tower 178 Gloucester Road, Wanchai, China (Hong Kong)
Tel.: (852) 35472200   Ky
Web Site: https://www.8246hk.com
Year Founded: 2011
8246—(HKG)
Rev.: $28,154,272
Assets: $48,680,752
Liabilities: $28,610,150
Net Worth: $20,070,601
Earnings: ($524,956)
Emp.: 31
Fiscal Year-end: 12/31/22
Construction Engineering Services
N.A.I.C.S.: 541330
Yishi Hu *(Chm)*

ZHONGJI INNOLIGHT CO., LTD.
Zhuyouguan Town Industrial Park, Longkou, 265705, Shandong, China
Tel.: (86) 5358573361
Web Site: https://www.zj-innolight.com
Year Founded: 1987
300308—(CHIN)
Rev.: $1,353,707,316
Assets: $2,324,601,396
Liabilities: $630,113,796
Net Worth: $1,694,487,600
Earnings: $171,848,196
Fiscal Year-end: 12/31/22
Industrial Automation Electrical Component Mfr
N.A.I.C.S.: 335999
Wei Xiu Wang *(Chm)*

Subsidiaries:

Chengdu Tsuhan Science & Technology Co.,Ltd. (1)
No 8 Muke Road, Huangjia Town Shuangliu, Chengdu, 610299, Sichuan, China
Tel.: (86) 2861406095
Web Site: https://www.tsuhan.cn
Optical Component Mfr
N.A.I.C.S.: 333310

InnoLight Technology (Suzhou) Ltd. (1)
No 8 Xiasheng Road, Suzhou Industrial Park, Suzhou, 215126, Jiangsu, China
Tel.: (86) 5128 666 9288
Web Site: http://www.innolight.com
Emp.: 3,000
High Speed Optical Transceivers to Cloud Data Center Networks
N.A.I.C.S.: 334413
Sheng Liu *(CEO)*

ZHONGJIE (JIANGSU) TECHNOLOGY CO., LTD.
No 8 Donggang Road, Donggang Town Xishan District, Wuxi, 214199, Jiangsu, China
Tel.: (86) 51088351766
Web Site: https://www.jiangsuzhongjie.com
Year Founded: 1998
301072—(CHIN)
Rev.: $97,241,040
Assets: $160,211,844
Liabilities: $44,843,760
Net Worth: $115,368,084
Earnings: $5,024,916
Fiscal Year-end: 12/31/22
Automobile Parts Mfr & Distr
N.A.I.C.S.: 336211
Zhong Wei *(Chm)*

ZHONGJIN GOLD CORPORATION LIMITED
No 9 Anwai Street, Dongcheng District, Beijing, 100011, China
Tel.: (86) 1056353909
Web Site: http://www.zjgold.com
Year Founded: 2000
600489—(SHG)
Rev.: $8,023,993,563
Assets: $6,829,380,759
Liabilities: $2,897,733,038
Net Worth: $3,931,647,722
Earnings: $297,246,428
Emp.: 26,000
Fiscal Year-end: 12/31/22
Metal & Gold Mining
N.A.I.C.S.: 212220
Yueqing Li *(Deputy Gen Mgr)*

ZHONGJIN IRRADIATION INCORPORATED COMPANY
Floor 19 Block B Zhongshe Plaza No 1028 Buji Road Dongxiao Street, Luohu District, Shenzhen, 518019, Guangdong, China
Tel.: (86) 75525177228
Web Site: https://www.zjfzgroup.com
Year Founded: 2003
300962—(SSE)
Rev.: $47,333,010
Assets: $150,149,685
Liabilities: $21,381,783
Net Worth: $128,767,902
Earnings: $15,124,773
Fiscal Year-end: 12/31/22
Management Consulting Services
N.A.I.C.S.: 541613
Qiangguo Zheng *(Chm)*

ZHONGJING FOOD CO., LTD.
No 211 North Section of Industrial Avenue, Xixia County, Nanyang, 474500, Henan, China
Tel.: (86) 37769766006
Web Site: https://www.zhongjing.com.cn
Year Founded: 2002
300908—(SSE)
Rev.: $123,784,348
Assets: $255,503,795
Liabilities: $30,194,087
Net Worth: $225,309,708
Earnings: $17,692,885
Emp.: 1,000
Fiscal Year-end: 12/31/22
Food Product Mfr & Distr
N.A.I.C.S.: 311421
Yaozhi Sun *(Chm)*

ZHONGLIANG HOLDINGS GROUP COMPANY LIMITED
10th Floor Building 3 Transnational Procurement Center, No 235 Yunling East Road Putuo District, Shanghai, China
Tel.: (86) 2162581310   Ky
Web Site: http://www.zldcgroup.com
2772—(HKG)
Rev.: $8,513,435,659
Assets: $23,102,228,200
Liabilities: $19,728,426,010
Net Worth: $3,373,802,190
Earnings: ($373,022,097)
Emp.: 3,145
Fiscal Year-end: 12/31/23
Holding Company
N.A.I.C.S.: 551112

ZHONGLU (GROUP) CO., LTD.
No 818 Nanliu Highway Pudong New Area, Shanghai, 200436, China
Tel.: (86) 2152860258
Web Site: https://www.zhonglu.com.cn
Year Founded: 1998
600818—(SHG)
Rev.: $130,219,062
Assets: $129,184,188
Liabilities: $47,631,893
Net Worth: $81,552,295
Earnings: ($10,716,521)
Fiscal Year-end: 12/31/22
Bicycle Mfr & Whslr
N.A.I.C.S.: 333613
Chen Shan *(Chm & Gen Mgr)*

ZHONGMAN PETROLEUM &

ZHONGMAN PETROLEUM & —(CONTINUED)

ZHONGMAN PETROLEUM & NATURAL GAS GROUP CORP., LTD.
No 3998 Jiangshan Road Pudong New Area, Shanghai, 201306, China
Tel.: (86) 2161048060
Web Site: http://www.zpec.com
Year Founded: 2003
603619—(SHG)
Rev.: $430,347,846
Assets: $1,004,493,611
Liabilities: $681,880,343
Net Worth: $322,613,268
Earnings: $70,667,293
Fiscal Year-end: 12/31/22
Petroleum Drilling Equipment Mfr
N.A.I.C.S.: 333132
Li Chundi (Chm & Pres)

ZHONGMIN BAIHUI RETAIL GROUP LTD.
80 Marine Parade Road 13 07 Parkway Parade, Singapore, 449269, Singapore
Tel.: (65) 64405297
Web Site: https://www.zhongminbaihui.com.sg
Year Founded: 1997
5SR—(CAT)
Rev.: $133,967,204
Assets: $161,727,039
Liabilities: $136,908,721
Net Worth: $24,818,319
Earnings: $2,863,519
Emp.: 1,888
Fiscal Year-end: 06/30/23
Department Stores Operation Services
N.A.I.C.S.: 459999
Swee Keng Lee (Chm)

Subsidiaries:

Xiamen Shi Zhongmin Baihui Commercial Co., Ltd. (1)
Basement 1 and 1st to 3rd Floors No 929 Xiahe Road, Siming District, Xiamen, Fujian, China
Tel.: (86) 5925863888
Departmental Store Operator
N.A.I.C.S.: 455110

ZHONGMIN ENERGY CO., LTD.
22nd Floor International Building No 210 Wusi Road, Gulou District, Fuzhou, 350003, Fujian, China
Tel.: (86) 59187868796
Web Site: http://www.zhongminenergy.com
Year Founded: 1998
600163—(SHG)
Rev.: $251,446,516
Assets: $1,636,190,178
Liabilities: $803,300,636
Net Worth: $832,889,543
Earnings: $102,364,334
Fiscal Year-end: 12/31/22
Paper Making Services
N.A.I.C.S.: 322120
Guo Zheng (Chm & Gen Mgr)

ZHONGNAN RED CULTURAL GROUP CO., LTD.
Jinshan Road, High-Tech Development Park, Jiangyin, 214437, China
Tel.: (86) 51086996882
Web Site: https://www.znhi.com.cn
002445—(SSE)
Rev.: $92,117,240
Assets: $376,371,628
Liabilities: $102,888,012
Net Worth: $273,483,616
Earnings: $3,892,365
Emp.: 1,100
Fiscal Year-end: 12/31/22
Metal Pipe Fitting Mfr
N.A.I.C.S.: 332919

ZHONGNONGFA SEED INDUSTRY GROUP CO., LTD.
3rd Floor Zhongshui Building No 31 Xidan Minfeng Hutong, Xicheng District, Beijing, 100032, China
Tel.: (86) 1088067521
Web Site: https://znfzy.cnadc.com.cn
Year Founded: 1999
600313—(SHG)
Rev.: $736,856,125
Assets: $562,233,148
Liabilities: $199,677,006
Net Worth: $362,556,141
Earnings: $32,302,109
Fiscal Year-end: 12/31/22
Agricultural Product & Seed Whslr
N.A.I.C.S.: 424910
He Caiwen (Gen Mgr)

ZHONGPIN INC.
21 Changshe Road, Changge, Henan, China
Tel.: (86) 1084554188   DE
Sales Range: $1-4.9 Billion
Emp.: 7,814
Meat Processing
N.A.I.C.S.: 311612
Xianfu Zhu (Chm, Pres & CEO)

Subsidiaries:

Henan Zhongpin Import and Export Trading Company (1)
21 Changshe Rd, Changge Xuchang Henan, Changge, 461500, Henan, China
Tel.: (86) 13653841115
Web Site: http://www.zt.com.cn
Food Products Mfr
N.A.I.C.S.: 311999
Brady Ji (Mgr-Pur)

ZHONGRUN RESOURCES INVESTMENT CORPORATION
Tower 17 Zhongrun Century Plaza No 13777 Jingshi Road East, Jinan, 250014, Shandong, China
Tel.: (86) 53181665777
Web Site: https://www.sdzr.com
Year Founded: 1988
000506—(SSE)
Rev.: $38,911,748
Assets: $241,165,094
Liabilities: $146,796,371
Net Worth: $94,368,723
Earnings: $35,520,807
Emp.: 1,500
Fiscal Year-end: 12/31/22
Real Estate Developing Services
N.A.I.C.S.: 531390
Mingji Li (Pres)

ZHONGSHAN BROAD-OCEAN MOTOR CO., LTD.
No 1 Guangfeng Industrial Avenue, West District, Zhongshan, 528411, Guangdong, China
Tel.: (86) 76088555306   CN
Web Site: http://www.broad-ocean.com
Year Founded: 1994
002249—(SSE)
Rev.: $1,534,592,175
Assets: $2,128,683,726
Liabilities: $947,544,016
Net Worth: $1,181,139,710
Earnings: $59,963,759
Fiscal Year-end: 12/31/22
Electric Motor & Motorized Products Mfr & Whslr
N.A.I.C.S.: 335312
Lu Chuping (Chm)

Subsidiaries:

Prestolite Electric Incorporated (1)
30120 Hudson Dr, Novi, MI 48377
Tel.: (734) 582-7200
Web Site: http://www.prestolite.com
Motor Vehicle Alternators, Starters & Other Electrical Equipment Mfr
N.A.I.C.S.: 336320
Beverley Hounslow (Pres-Europe)

ZHONGSHAN PUBLIC UTILITIES GROUP CO., LTD.
North Tower Caixing Mansion No 18 Xingzhong Road, Zhongshan, 528403, Guangdong, China
Tel.: (86) 76088380011
Web Site: https://www.zpug.net
Year Founded: 1998
000685—(SSE)
Rev.: $508,139,892
Assets: $3,579,449,211
Liabilities: $1,338,878,661
Net Worth: $2,240,570,550
Earnings: $150,517,238
Fiscal Year-end: 12/31/22
Water Supply & Sewage Treatment Services
N.A.I.C.S.: 221310
Guo Jingyi (Chm)

ZHONGSHENG GROUP HOLDINGS LIMITED
room 1808 18 / f sun hung kai centre 30 harbour road, Wanchai, China (Hong Kong)
Tel.: (852) 28035676   Ky
Web Site: https://en.zs-group.com.cn
ZSHGY—(OTCIQ)
Rev.: $22,728,407,345
Assets: $10,495,041,121
Liabilities: $6,376,488,663
Net Worth: $4,118,552,458
Earnings: $855,038,811
Emp.: 31,460
Fiscal Year-end: 12/31/20
Motor Vehicle Services
N.A.I.C.S.: 441227
Yi Huang (Co-Founder & Chm)

Subsidiaries:

Beijing Zhongsheng Star Automobile Sales & Service Co., Ltd. (1)
No 333 Mafangsi Road Wangsiying, Chaoyang District, Beijing, 100023, China
Tel.: (86) 1087391111
Car Retailer
N.A.I.C.S.: 441110

Changchun Zhongsheng Star Automobile Sales & Services Co., Ltd. (1)
Intersection of Avenue of Excellence and Yiju Road High-tech Zone, Changchun, 130000, China
Tel.: (86) 43182938888
Car Retailer
N.A.I.C.S.: 441110

Foshan Shunde Yifu Vehicle Sales & Service Co., Ltd. (1)
East Side of Lunjiao Guangzhu Highway North of Shunde Overpass, Shunde District, Foshan, China
Tel.: (86) 75727727888
Car Retailer
N.A.I.C.S.: 441110

Foshan Zhongsheng Star Automobile Sales & Service Co., Ltd. (1)
No 30 Foping 4th Road Pingzhou Guicheng Street, Nanhai District, Foshan, 528251, China
Tel.: (86) 75781062666
Car Retailer
N.A.I.C.S.: 441110

Hainan Zhongsheng Star Automobile Sales & Service Co., Ltd. (1)
289-9 Qiongshan Avenue, Haikou, 571158, China
Tel.: (86) 89865725522
Car Retailer
N.A.I.C.S.: 441110

Hangzhou Zhongsheng Star Automobile Sales & Service Co., Ltd. (1)
1780 Jiangling Road Xixing Street, Binjiang

INTERNATIONAL PUBLIC

District, Hangzhou, 310051, China
Tel.: (86) 57128099999
Car Retailer
N.A.I.C.S.: 441110

Hangzhou Zhongsheng Xingqi Automobile Sales & Services Co., Ltd. (1)
Room 105 Building 4 No 88 Kangqiao Road, Gongshu District, Hangzhou, 310000, China
Tel.: (86) 57156097777
Car Retailer
N.A.I.C.S.: 441110

Heilongjiang Zhongsheng Star Automobile Sales & Service Co., Ltd. (1)
345 Daxin Street, Daowai District, Harbin, 150000, China
Tel.: (86) 45155183333
Car Retailer
N.A.I.C.S.: 441110

Shanghai Zhongsheng Fengxing Automobile Sales & Service Co., Ltd. (1)
1st Floor Building 3 No 5890 Hangnan Road, Fengxian District, Shanghai, 201499, China
Tel.: (86) 2131115858
Car Retailer
N.A.I.C.S.: 441110

Shanghai Zhongsheng Star Automobile Sales & Service Co., Ltd. (1)
Tel.: (86) 2131115858
Car Retailer
N.A.I.C.S.: 441110

Shanghai Zhongsheng Xinghong Automobile Sales & Service Co., Ltd. (1)
Building 1 2 Qingsong Road, Qingpu District, Shanghai, 201799, China
Tel.: (86) 2159229333
Car Retailer
N.A.I.C.S.: 441110

Shenzhen Zhongsheng Star Automobile Sales & Service Co., Ltd. (1)
No 40 Xinhe Avenue Shajing Street, Baoan District, Shenzhen, 518000, China
Tel.: (86) 75586658666
Car Retailer
N.A.I.C.S.: 441110

Suzhou Haixing Automobile Sales & Services Co., Ltd. (1)
No 159 Zhongshan East Road in Kaima Automobile Plaza, Wuzhong District, Suzhou, 215101, China
Tel.: (86) 51266879888
Car Retailer
N.A.I.C.S.: 441110

Taicang Zhongsheng Star Automobile Sales & Service Co., Ltd. (1)
No 18 Ningbo West Road Economic Development Zone, Taicang, 215400, China
Tel.: (86) 51253658888
Car Retailer
N.A.I.C.S.: 441110

Wuhan Zhongsheng Juxing Automobile Sales & Service Co., Ltd. (1)
No 167 Innovation Avenue Changqing Office, Dongxihu District, Wuhan, 430040, China
Tel.: (86) 2783395555
Car Retailer
N.A.I.C.S.: 441110

Wuxi Zhongsheng Xinghui Automobile Sales & Service Co., Ltd. (1)
No 321 Datong Road Taihu Street, Binhu District, Wuxi, 214124, China
Tel.: (86) 51088360777
Car Retailer
N.A.I.C.S.: 441110

Yueqing Zhongsheng Xinghui Automobile Sales & Service Co., Ltd. (1)
No 261 Ningkang West Road Chengnan Street, Yueqing, 325600, China
Tel.: (86) 57727857777
Car Retailer
N.A.I.C.S.: 441110

Yunnan Zhongsheng Star Automobile Sales & Service Co., Ltd. (1)

Caiyun North Road and Sankunkou Guikun Road, Guandu District, Kunming, 430073, China
Tel.: (86) 87168199996
Car Retailer
N.A.I.C.S.: 441110

Yunnan Zhongsheng Yuanan Kunxing Automobile Sales & Service Co., Ltd. (1)
No 17 Yuanbo Road Jinjin Road intersection, Beicheng District, Kunming, 650224, China
Tel.: (86) 4008086611
Car Retailer
N.A.I.C.S.: 441110

ZHONGSHI MINAN HOLDINGS LIMITED
160 Sin Ming Drive 06-03 Sin Ming Autocity, Singapore, 575722, Singapore
Tel.: (65) 64515333   Ky
Web Site:
http://www.zhengliholdings.com
8283—(HKG)
Rev.: $18,079,982
Assets: $16,008,483
Liabilities: $11,382,262
Net Worth: $4,626,221
Earnings: ($1,157,313)
Emp.: 139
Fiscal Year-end: 12/31/23
Car Repair & Maintenance Services
N.A.I.C.S.: 811111
Boon Hou Chua *(COO)*

Subsidiaries:

KBS Motorsports Pte. Ltd. (1)
160 Sin Ming Drive 06-03 Sin Ming Autocity, Singapore, 575722, Singapore
Tel.: (65) 62628888
Automobile Maintenance Services
N.A.I.C.S.: 811111

ZHONGTAI FUTURES COMPANY LIMITED
Floor 15/16 Securities Tower No 86 Jingqi Road, Shizhong District, Jinan, 250001, Shandong, China
Tel.: (86) 53181678629   CN
Web Site:
https://www.luzhengqh.com
Year Founded: 1995
1461—(HKG)
Security Brokerage Services
N.A.I.C.S.: 523150
Zhongwei Liang *(Exec Dir)*

ZHONGTAI SECURITIES CO., LTD.
No 86 Jingqi Road, Jinan, 250001, Shandong, China
Tel.: (86) 4001895538   CN
Web Site: http://www.95538.cn
Year Founded: 2001
600918—(SSE)
Rev.: $1,766,988,162
Assets: $27,090,535,944
Liabilities: $21,229,862,262
Net Worth: $5,860,673,682
Earnings: $249,196,472
Fiscal Year-end: 12/31/23
Financial Investment Services
N.A.I.C.S.: 523999
Wei Li *(Chm)*

Subsidiaries:

Zhongtai Financial International Limited (1)
19/F Li Po Chun Chambers 189 Des Voeux Road, Central, China (Hong Kong)
Tel.: (852) 3979 2890
Holding Company
N.A.I.C.S.: 551112

ZHONGTIAN CONSTRUCTION (HUNAN) GROUP LIMITED
No 1197 East Xinhua Road, Hetang District, Zhuzhou, Hunan, China   Ky
Web Site: https://www.ztcon.com
Year Founded: 2020
2433—(HKG)
Rev.: $289,668,019
Assets: $270,835,752
Liabilities: $215,721,365
Net Worth: $55,114,387
Earnings: $10,033,416
Emp.: 338
Fiscal Year-end: 12/31/22
Construction Engineering Services
N.A.I.C.S.: 541330
Xiaohong Liu *(CEO)*

ZHONGTIAN FINANCIAL GROUP COMPANY LIMITED
201 Center 3 Zhongtian Road, Guanshanhu District, Guiyang, 550081, Guizhou, China
Tel.: (86) 8518 698 8177
Web Site: http://www.ztcn.cn
000540—(SSE)
Rev.: $3,590,784,302
Assets: $21,212,086,903
Liabilities: $17,891,686,076
Net Worth: $3,320,400,826
Earnings: $87,617,735
Fiscal Year-end: 12/31/20
Investment Services
N.A.I.C.S.: 523999
Yuping Luo *(Chm)*

ZHONGTIAN SERVICE CO., LTD.
Room 410 No 18 Dongsheng Road Huimin Street, Jiashan County, Jiaxing, 314100, Zhejiang, China
Tel.: (86) 57384252627
Year Founded: 1992
002188—(SSE)
Sales Range: $10-24.9 Million
Emp.: 1,818
Electronic Products Mfr
N.A.I.C.S.: 334419

ZHONGTONG BUS & HOLDING CO., LTD.
No 261 Huanghe Road Economic Development Zone, Liaocheng, 252000, Shandong, China
Tel.: (86) 6358322765
Web Site:
https://www.zhongtongbuses.com
Year Founded: 1994
000957—(SSE)
Rev.: $740,776,079
Assets: $1,315,274,052
Liabilities: $941,440,041
Net Worth: $373,834,010
Earnings: $13,805,027
Emp.: 4,000
Fiscal Year-end: 12/31/22
Automobile Mfr
N.A.I.C.S.: 336110
Hu Haihua *(Chm)*

ZHONGTONGGUOMAI COMMUNICATION CO LTD
No 6399 NanHu Road, Changchun, 130012, Jilin, China
Tel.: (86) 43185954071
Web Site: https://www.ztgmcom.com
Year Founded: 1947
603559—(SHG)
Rev.: $58,138,011
Assets: $174,702,009
Liabilities: $123,845,829
Net Worth: $50,856,179
Earnings: $21,318,996)
Fiscal Year-end: 12/31/22
Communication Equipment Installation Services
N.A.I.C.S.: 238210
Li Xuegang *(Chm & Gen Mgr)*

ZHONGWANG FABRIC CO., LTD.
No 1 Shuihong Temple Chongxian Street, Yuhang District, Hangzhou, 311108, Zhejiang, China
Tel.: (86) 57186172333
Web Site: https://www.zw-fabric.com
Year Founded: 1994
605003—(SHG)
Rev.: $58,479,155
Assets: $176,046,535
Liabilities: $17,267,375
Net Worth: $158,779,160
Earnings: $12,749,710
Fiscal Year-end: 12/31/22
Textile Product Mfr & Distr
N.A.I.C.S.: 313310
Linshan Yang *(Chm & Gen Mgr)*

ZHONGXING SHENYANG COMMERCIAL BUILDING GROUP CO., LTD.
No 86 Taiyuan North Street, Heping District, Shenyang, 110001, Liaoning, China
Tel.: (86) 2423838888
Web Site:
https://www.zxbusiness.com
Year Founded: 1987
000715—(SSE)
Rev.: $97,339,418
Assets: $337,370,909
Liabilities: $93,568,597
Net Worth: $243,802,311
Earnings: $12,021,848
Fiscal Year-end: 12/31/22
Departmental Store Operator
N.A.I.C.S.: 455110
Zhu Min *(Pres)*

ZHONGXING TIANHENG ENERGY TECHNOLOGY (BEIJING) CO., LTD.
No 1881 Renmin Avenue, Changchun, 130061, Jilin, China
Tel.: (86) 4318 896 5414
600856—(SHG)
Rev.: $84,928,899
Assets: $1,662,714,589
Liabilities: $1,716,684,344
Net Worth: ($53,969,755)
Earnings: $159,801,094)
Fiscal Year-end: 12/31/20
Investment Services
N.A.I.C.S.: 523999

ZHONGYAN TECHNOLOGY CO., LTD.
12th Floor Tongjing Building No 2 Pingguoyuan Road, Shijingshan District, Beijing, 100041, China
Tel.: (86) 1057712508
Web Site: https://www.zydd.com
Year Founded: 2008
003001—(SSE)
Rev.: $125,897,958
Assets: $309,244,310
Liabilities: $139,698,140
Net Worth: $169,546,170
Earnings: ($20,216,575)
Fiscal Year-end: 12/31/22
Engineeering Services
N.A.I.C.S.: 541330
Lijian Wang *(Chm)*

ZHONGYEDA ELECTRIC COMPANY LIMITED
No 1 Zhujin Yiheng Street Zhujin Industrial Zone, Longhu District, Shantou, 515000, Guangdong, China
Tel.: (86) 75488738831
Web Site: http://www.zyd.cn
Year Founded: 2000
002441—(SSE)
Rev.: $1,702,789,003
Assets: $1,003,735,957
Liabilities: $366,468,430
Net Worth: $637,267,527
Earnings: $41,465,708
Emp.: 1,400
Fiscal Year-end: 12/31/22
Power & Transmission Electric Component Wholesale Distr
N.A.I.C.S.: 423610
Wu Kaixian *(Chm)*

ZHONGYIN BABI FOOD CO., LTD.
No 785 Rongjiang Road, Chedun Town Songjiang District, Shanghai, 201611, China
Tel.: (86) 2157797068
Web Site: http://www.babifood.com
Year Founded: 2010
605338—(SHG)
Rev.: $214,129,853
Assets: $375,711,032
Liabilities: $85,127,412
Net Worth: $290,583,620
Earnings: $31,210,064
Fiscal Year-end: 12/31/22
Food Product Mfr & Distr
N.A.I.C.S.: 311421
Huiping Liu *(Chm & Gen Mgr)*

ZHONGYU ENERGY HOLDINGS LIMITED
Units 04-06 28th Floor China Merchants Tower Shun Tak Centre, 168-200 Connaught Road, Hong Kong, China (Hong Kong)
Tel.: (852) 22951555
Web Site: http://en.zhongyugas.com
3633—(HKG)
Rev.: $1,657,158,555
Assets: $3,354,637,455
Liabilities: $2,189,894,100
Net Worth: $1,164,743,355
Earnings: $30,971,918
Emp.: 5,067
Fiscal Year-end: 12/31/22
Gas Exploration, Production & Distribution
N.A.I.C.S.: 211120
Wenliang Wang *(Chm)*

Subsidiaries:

Baishan Weiye Gas Co., Ltd. (1)
No 38 Minzhong Street, Hunjiang District, Jilin, China
Tel.: (86) 4393270607
Natural Gas Distribution Services
N.A.I.C.S.: 221210

Beijing Zhongyu Gas Co., Ltd. (1)
Xiwengzhuang Town, Miyun District, Beijing, China
Tel.: (86) 1069016976
Natural Gas Distribution Services
N.A.I.C.S.: 221210

Changli Zhongyu Gas Co., Ltd. (1)
No 62 Binhai International 4th District Chaoyang Film 3rd Street, Changli Town Changli County, Qinhuangdao, Hebei, China
Tel.: (86) 3352981229
Natural Gas Distribution Services
N.A.I.C.S.: 221210

Cheng An Zhongyu Gas Co., Ltd. (1)
Cheng An Road Dongpengliu Village, Cheng An County, Handan, Hebei, China
Tel.: (86) 3107217777
Natural Gas Distribution Services
N.A.I.C.S.: 221210

Dezhou Zhongyu Gas Co., Ltd. (1)
Shihua North Road De Cheng Tian Qu Industrial Park, Dezhou, Shandong, China
Tel.: (86) 5342186769
Natural Gas Distribution Services
N.A.I.C.S.: 221210

Guannan Zhongyu Gas Co., Ltd. (1)
No 139 Xindong South Road, Guannan County, Lianyungang, Jiangsu, China

ZHONGYU ENERGY HOLDINGS LIMITED

Zhongyu Energy Holdings Limited—(Continued)

Tel.: (86) 51883288187
Natural Gas Distribution Services
N.A.I.C.S.: 221210

Gucheng Zhongyu Gas Co., Ltd. (1)
Xinfu Community, Gucheng County, Hengshui, Hebei, China
Tel.: (86) 3185380090
Natural Gas Distribution Services
N.A.I.C.S.: 221210

Henan Zhongyu Gas Engineering Design Co., Ltd. (1)
17th Floor Minsheng Bank Tower No 1 Business Waihuan Road CBD, Zheng Dong New District, Zhengzhou, Henan, China
Tel.: (86) 37187518088
Natural Gas Distribution Services
N.A.I.C.S.: 221210

Hengshui Zhongyu Gas Co., Ltd. (1)
200 Meters North of Weiqian Canal Pingyuan Street, Zaoqiang County, Hengshui, Hebei, China
Tel.: (86) 3188232839
Natural Gas Distribution Services
N.A.I.C.S.: 221210

Jiaozuo Zhongyu Gas Co., Ltd. (1)
No 219 Jiefang Road, Shanyang District, Jiaozuo, Henan, China
Tel.: (86) 3913901111
Web Site: https://jiaozuo.zhongyuenergy.com
Natural Gas Distribution Services
N.A.I.C.S.: 221210

Jiaozuo Zhongyu Gas Engineering Installation Co., Ltd. (1)
No 219 Jiefang Road, Jiaozuo, Henan, China
Tel.: (86) 3913901208
Natural Gas Distribution Services
N.A.I.C.S.: 221210

Jiyuan Zhongyu Gas Co., Ltd. (1)
207 National Road East, Jiyuan, Henan, China
Tel.: (86) 3916663602
Natural Gas Distribution Services
N.A.I.C.S.: 221210

Jize Zhongyu Gas Co. Ltd. (1)
300 Meters to the East of Chengnan Ring Island, Jize County, Handan, Hebei, China
Tel.: (86) 3107559388
Natural Gas Distribution Services
N.A.I.C.S.: 221210

Lingbao Zhongyu Gas Co., Ltd. (1)
Intersection of Yin xi Road and Xinhua Road, Lingbao, Henan, China
Tel.: (86) 3982123737
Natural Gas Distribution Services
N.A.I.C.S.: 221210

Linyi Zhongyu Energy Co., Ltd. (1)
Volvo Road No 67, Hedong District, Linyi, Shandong, China
Tel.: (86) 5396011802
Natural Gas Distribution Services
N.A.I.C.S.: 221210

Linzhang Zhongyu Gas Co., Ltd. (1)
50 meters westbound from the intersection of Jianan West Road, Linzhang County, Handan, Hebei, China
Tel.: (86) 3107488365
Natural Gas Distribution Services
N.A.I.C.S.: 221210

Longyao Zhongyu Gas Co. Ltd. (1)
Nanzhongyu Gas Xinhua Market Xikou Road International Famous Residence, Longyao County, Xingtai, Hebei, China
Tel.: (86) 3196681661
Natural Gas Distribution Services
N.A.I.C.S.: 221210

Nangong Zhongyu Gas Co., Ltd. (1)
Ge Bo Zhuang Canal Nanhuan Road, Hebei, China
Tel.: (86) 3195267146
Natural Gas Distribution Services
N.A.I.C.S.: 221210

Nanjing Jingqiao Zhongyu Gas Co., Ltd. (1)
100 Meters ahead of the Intersection of 246 Provincial Road, Pu Du Road Xinqiao Village Jingqiao Town Lishui District, Nanjing, Jiangsu, China
Tel.: (86) 2557285782
Natural Gas Distribution Services
N.A.I.C.S.: 221210

Ningjin Zhongyu Gas Co., Ltd. (1)
No 14 the West Area of Jinfu Park Jinlong Street, Ningjin County, Xingtai, Hebei, China
Tel.: (86) 3195868900
Natural Gas Distribution Services
N.A.I.C.S.: 221210

Qinyang Zhongyu Gas Co., Ltd. (1)
No 424 Zhu Zaiyu Street Taihang Street, Qinyang City, Jiaozuo, Henan, China
Tel.: (86) 3915689061
Natural Gas Distribution Services
N.A.I.C.S.: 221210

QuJing Gas Group Co., Ltd. (1)
North of Changzheng Road Mahuang Industrial Park, Qilin District, Qujing, Yunnan, China
Tel.: (86) 8743108088
Natural Gas Distribution Services
N.A.I.C.S.: 221210

Sanmenxia Zhongyu Gas Co., Ltd. (1)
Southwest Corner Intersection Gantang South Road & Xuanyuan Road, Sanmenxia, Henan, China
Tel.: (86) 3982929977
Natural Gas Distribution Services
N.A.I.C.S.: 221210

Shijiazhuang Gaocheng Weiye Gas Co., Ltd. (1)
Gang Shang Village, Gaocheng District, Shijiazhuang, Hebei, China
Tel.: (86) 3118651859
Natural Gas Distribution Services
N.A.I.C.S.: 221210

Shijiazhuang Luquan District Chenguang Gas Co., Ltd. (1)
Intersection of Tong Lin Road and Wen Yuan Street, Copper Smelting Town Luquan District, Shijiazhuang, Hebei, China
Tel.: (86) 3183170995
Natural Gas Distribution Services
N.A.I.C.S.: 221210

Sihong Weiye Gas Co., Ltd. (1)
No 3 Hengshan North Road Sihong Economic Development Zone, Suqian, Jiangsu, China
Tel.: (86) 52786551717
Natural Gas Distribution Services
N.A.I.C.S.: 221210

Sixian Zhongyu Gas Co., Ltd. (1)
West Gate of Yulan Mansion, Dongguan County, Suzhou, Anhui, China
Tel.: (86) 5577092200
Natural Gas Distribution Services
N.A.I.C.S.: 221210

Tieli Zhongyu Gas Co., Ltd. (1)
No 394 Chengnan street, Tieli, Heilongjiang, China
Tel.: (86) 4588787179
Natural Gas Distribution Services
N.A.I.C.S.: 221210

Wuhe Zhongyu Gas Co., Ltd. (1)
Shop No 4 115 Xiangyuan Aiqinnan Community, Chengguan Town Wuhe County, Bengbu, Anhui, China
Tel.: (86) 5525042066
Natural Gas Distribution Services
N.A.I.C.S.: 221210

Wuqiao Zhongyu Gas Co., Ltd. (1)
East side of Daguanli West Hebei Shandong connecting line, Sangyuan Town Wuqiao County, Cangzhou, Hebei, China
Tel.: (86) 3178323826
Natural Gas Distribution Services
N.A.I.C.S.: 221210

Wuzhi Zhongyu Gas Co., Ltd. (1)
North side of the west section of Qinhe Road, Wuzhi County, Jiaozuo, Henan, China
Tel.: (86) 3917289500
Natural Gas Distribution Services
N.A.I.C.S.: 221210

Xingtang Zhongyu Gas Co., Ltd. (1)
East side of the family building of the Electric Power Bureau Nantou, Hong Kong Road Longzhou Town Xingtang County, Shijiazhuang, Hebei, China
Tel.: (86) 31182990020
Natural Gas Distribution Services
N.A.I.C.S.: 221210

Xinhe County Zhongyu Gas Co., Ltd. (1)
West of Yingbin Street North of Kaiyuan Road, Xinhe County, Xingtai, Hebei, China
Tel.: (86) 3194782100
Natural Gas Distribution Services
N.A.I.C.S.: 221210

Xinmi Zhongyu Gas Co., Ltd. (1)
No 868 north side of the west section of Qinshui Road, Xinmi, Henan, China
Tel.: (86) 37169850505
Natural Gas Distribution Services
N.A.I.C.S.: 221210

Xiuwu Zhongyu Gas Development Co., Ltd. (1)
Southwest Corner of Itersection Between Ningcheng Avenue, Zhulin Avenue in Xiu Wu County, Jiaozuo, Henan, China
Tel.: (86) 3917172777
Natural Gas Distribution Services
N.A.I.C.S.: 221210

Yanshi Zhongyu Gas Co., Ltd. (1)
No 64 Shouyang Road, Luoyang, Henan, China
Tel.: (86) 37967712193
Natural Gas Distribution Services
N.A.I.C.S.: 221210

Yongcheng Zhongyu Gas Co., Ltd. (1)
Western of Hua Gong Road, Yongcheng EDZ, Zhengzhou, Henan, China
Tel.: (86) 3705152888
Natural Gas Distribution Services
N.A.I.C.S.: 221210

Yueqing Zhongyu Gas Co., Ltd. (1)
Hongying Business Pioneer Park 1888 Feihong South Road, Hongqiao Town, Yueqing, Zhejiang, China
Tel.: (86) 57761220777
Natural Gas Distribution Services
N.A.I.C.S.: 221210

Yutian County Zhongyu Gas Co., Ltd. (1)
No 2 North Corner Prosperity Community, Yutian County, Tangshan, Hebei, China
Tel.: (86) 3156157777
Natural Gas Distribution Services
N.A.I.C.S.: 221210

Yuxian Zhongyu Gas Co., Ltd. (1)
No 45 Jianshe Street, Yuzhou Town Yuxian County, Zhangjiakou, Hebei, China
Tel.: (86) 3137011197
Natural Gas Distribution Services
N.A.I.C.S.: 221210

Zhangjiakou Xiahuayuan Zhongyu Gas Co., Ltd. (1)
No 10 Gaoxin West Street, Xiahuayuan District, Zhangjiakou, Hebei, China
Tel.: (86) 3135187718
Natural Gas Distribution Services
N.A.I.C.S.: 221210

Zhejiang Zhongyu Gas Co., Ltd. (1)
Second Floor, Suncity District 1 Gaoting Town Daishan County, Zhoushan, Zhejiang, China
Tel.: (86) 5804475787
Natural Gas Distribution Services
N.A.I.C.S.: 221210

Zhongyu (Henan) Energy Trading Co., Ltd. (1)
Western of Hua Gong Road, Yongcheng EDZ, Zhengzhou, Henan, China
Tel.: (86) 3705571777
Natural Gas Distribution Services
N.A.I.C.S.: 221210

Zhongyu City Energy Investment Holdings (Shenzhen) Co., Ltd. (1)
27 Floor B Building South Plaza Meilin Center Square, Futian District, Shenzhen, Guangdong, China
Tel.: (86) 75583633699
Natural Gas Distribution Services
N.A.I.C.S.: 221210

ZHONGYUAN BANK CO., LTD.

No 23 Shangwu Waihuan Road, Zhongke Golden Tower Zhengdong New District, Zhengzhou, Henan, China
Tel.: (86) 37185517898 CN
Web Site: https://www.zybank.com.cn
Year Founded: 2014
1216—(HKG)
Rev.: $7,020,527,664
Assets: $186,426,464,472
Liabilities: $173,011,509,471
Net Worth: $13,414,955,001
Earnings: $443,942,041
Emp.: 18,835
Fiscal Year-end: 12/31/23
Commercial Banking Services
N.A.I.C.S.: 522110
Rongxing Dou *(Chm)*

ZHONGYUAN UNION CELL & GENE ENGINEERING CORP., LTD.

No 12 Meiyuan Road Huayuan Industrial Park, Nankai District, Tianjin, 300384, China
Tel.: (86) 2258617160
Web Site: http://www.vcanbio.com
Year Founded: 1995
600645—(SHG)
Rev.: $218,306,121
Assets: $741,960,564
Liabilities: $228,987,486
Net Worth: $512,973,078
Earnings: $15,863,319
Fiscal Year-end: 12/31/22
Stem Cell Research & Experimental Development Services
N.A.I.C.S.: 541715
Gong Hongjia *(Chm)*

Subsidiaries:

Shanghai Zhicheng Biological Technology Co., Ltd. (1)
No 6 Lane 3399 Kangxin Highway, Pudong New District, Shanghai, China
Tel.: (86) 2150610052
Web Site: http://www.shzhicheng.com
Emp.: 160
Diagnosis Reagent Mfr & Distr
N.A.I.C.S.: 325412
Wang Hui *(Chm)*

ZHONGZAI RESOURCES AND ENVIRONMENT CO., LTD.

Global Information Center 8th Floor Block B, Xuanwu Men Street on the 1st, Beijing, 100052, China
Tel.: (86) 1059535601
Web Site: http://www.qinling.com
600217—(SHG)
Rev.: $438,499,091
Assets: $1,028,868,301
Liabilities: $670,769,761
Net Worth: $358,098,540
Earnings: $8,946,176
Fiscal Year-end: 12/31/22
Waste Electrical Products Processing Services
N.A.I.C.S.: 562219

ZHONGZHENG INTERNATIONAL COMPANY LIMITED

Suite 3008 Man Yee Building 68 Des Voeux Road Central, Central, China (Hong Kong)
Tel.: (852) 21658000 BM
Web Site: http://www.eforce.com.hk
0943—(HKG)
Rev.: $26,646,863
Assets: $525,564,435

Liabilities: $396,080,918
Net Worth: $129,483,518
Earnings: ($46,194,653)
Emp.: 20
Fiscal Year-end: 06/30/22
Health Care Products Mfr
N.A.I.C.S.: 325412
Franky Lup Wai Tam *(Deputy Chm)*

Subsidiaries:

Dongguan Weihang Electrical Product Company Limited (1)
No 1 Hongye Beiyi Road, Tang Xia Town, Dongguan, 523710, Guangdong, China
Tel.: (86) 76987727984
Electrical Products Mfr
N.A.I.C.S.: 335999

Fairform Manufacturing Company Limited (1)
68 Des Voeux Road Central Unit 8 30/F Man Yee Building, Central, China (Hong Kong)
Tel.: (852) 23546666
Healthcare Product Mfr & Distr
N.A.I.C.S.: 325412
Toshio Sughara *(Gen Mgr)*

ZHONGZHI PHARMACEUTICAL HOLDINGS LTD.
No 3 Kangtai Road South Torch Development Zone, Zhongshan, Guangdong, China
Tel.: (86) 76085331222 Ky
Web Site: http://www.zeus.cn
Year Founded: 1993
3737—(HKG)
Rev.: $256,361,274
Assets: $263,286,083
Liabilities: $122,050,843
Net Worth: $141,235,240
Earnings: $15,010,866
Emp.: 2,599
Fiscal Year-end: 12/31/22
Holding Company
N.A.I.C.S.: 551112
Zhi Tian Lai *(Founder, Chm & Gen Mgr)*

ZHOU HEI YA INTERNATIONAL HOLDINGS COMPANY LIMITED
No 8-1 Huitong Road Zoumaling, Dongxihu District, Wuhan, 430040, Hubei, China
Tel.: (86) 4001717917 Ky
Web Site: http://www.zhouheiya.cn
Year Founded: 2002
1458—(HKG)
Rev.: $329,006,761
Assets: $804,733,348
Liabilities: $230,734,764
Net Worth: $573,998,584
Earnings: $3,549,733
Emp.: 4,217
Fiscal Year-end: 12/31/22
Food Product Mfr & Distr
N.A.I.C.S.: 311615
Fuyu Zhou *(Chm)*

ZHUBO DESIGN CO., LTD.
8F Block B Tairan Building Tairan 8th Road, Futian District, Shenzhen, 518000, Guangdong, China
Tel.: (86) 8916868698
Web Site: https://www.zhubo.com
Year Founded: 1996
300564—(SSE)
Rev.: $123,035,145
Assets: $281,185,342
Liabilities: $89,306,460
Net Worth: $191,878,881
Earnings: $20,995,500
Fiscal Year-end: 12/31/22
Architectural Design Services
N.A.I.C.S.: 541310
Xianlin Xu *(Chm & Gen Mgr)*

ZHUDING INTERNATIONAL LTD.
20th Floor Block9 Thaihot Plaza Hengy 89702, Fuzhou, 89702, China
Tel.: (86) 59186295373
Year Founded: 2006
ZHUD—(OTCIQ)
Sales Range: Less than $1 Million
Metal Mining Services
N.A.I.C.S.: 213114

ZHUGUANG HOLDINGS GROUP COMPANY LIMITED
Room 5702-5703 57th Floor Two International Finance Centre, 8 Finance Street, Central, China (Hong Kong)
Tel.: (852) 25062322 BM
Web Site: http://www.zhuguang.com.hk
Year Founded: 1996
1176—(HKG)
Rev.: $361,952,483
Assets: $4,732,682,955
Liabilities: $3,795,364,410
Net Worth: $937,318,545
Earnings: ($130,274,273)
Emp.: 883
Fiscal Year-end: 12/31/22
Property Development & Investment Services
N.A.I.C.S.: 531311
Hing Tsung Chu *(Chm)*

ZHUHAI AEROSPACE MICROCHIPS SCIENCE AND TECHNOLOGY CO., LTD.
Orbita Science Park No 1 Baisha Road Tangjia Dongan, Zhuhai, 519080, Guangdong, China
Tel.: (86) 7563391979
Web Site: http://www.obtdata.com
Year Founded: 2000
300053—(CHIN)
Rev.: $49,672,626
Assets: $387,971,607
Liabilities: $96,601,465
Net Worth: $291,370,141
Earnings: ($59,909,674)
Emp.: 985
Fiscal Year-end: 12/31/23
Integrated Circuit, Hardware & Software Products
N.A.I.C.S.: 334418
Yan Jun *(Chm)*

ZHUHAI BOJAY ELECTRONICS CO., LTD.
No 10 Futian Rd, Xiangzhou District, Zhuhai, 519070, Guangdong, China
Tel.: (86) 4009959855
Web Site: https://www.zhbojay.com
Year Founded: 2005
002975—(SSE)
Rev.: $170,838,608
Assets: $365,116,209
Liabilities: $120,091,154
Net Worth: $245,025,055
Earnings: $28,363,285
Fiscal Year-end: 12/31/22
Electronic Product Mfr & Distr
N.A.I.C.S.: 334419
Zhaochun Wang *(Chm)*

Subsidiaries:

Bojay M&E (Suzhou) Co., Ltd. (1)
No 29 Mu Qiao Street, New District, Suzhou, China
Industrial Automation Equipment Mfr & Distr
N.A.I.C.S.: 333248

Bojay Technologies Inc. (1)
710 Lakeway Dr Ste 285, Sunnyvale, CA 94085
Industrial Automation Equipment Mfr & Distr
N.A.I.C.S.: 333248

Chengdu Bojay Automation Equipment Co., Ltd. (1)
No 839 Siwei Road Section, Chongzhou Economic Development District, Chengdu, China
Industrial Automation Equipment Mfr & Distr
N.A.I.C.S.: 333248

Shenzhen Bowjum Technology Co., Ltd. (1)
No 12 Longhuan Road Yucui Community Longhua Street, 101 B Build Huahaotai Industrial Park Longhua District, Shenzhen, China
Industrial Automation Equipment Mfr & Distr
N.A.I.C.S.: 333248

ZHUHAI ENPOWER ELECTRIC CO., LTD.
No 7 Keji 6th Road High-tech Zone, Tangjiawan Town, Zhuhai, 519085, Guangdong, China
Tel.: (86) 7566860880
Web Site: http://www.in-powercar.com
Year Founded: 2005
300681—(CHIN)
Rev.: $276,509,621
Assets: $581,598,017
Liabilities: $325,089,533
Net Worth: $256,508,485
Earnings: $11,600,617
Fiscal Year-end: 12/31/23
Electric Vehicle Parts Mfr & Distr
N.A.I.C.S.: 336320
Guibin Jiang *(Chm & Pres)*

ZHUHAI HOKAI MEDICAL INSTRUMENTS CO., LTD.
No 5 Baosheng Road, Xiangzhou District, Zhuhai, 519030, Guangdong, China
Tel.: (86) 7568686333
Web Site: http://www.hokai.com
300273—(CHIN)
Rev.: $142,522,070
Assets: $1,016,995,723
Liabilities: $589,118,496
Net Worth: $427,877,228
Earnings: $9,581,753
Fiscal Year-end: 12/31/20
Medical Instrument Mfr
N.A.I.C.S.: 339112
He Xiongtao *(CFO)*

ZHUHAI HOLDINGS INVESTMENT GROUP LIMITED
Units 3709-10 168-200 West Wing Shun Tak Centre Connaught Road, Sheung Wan, China (Hong Kong)
Tel.: (852) 28030866
Web Site: http://www.0908.hk
Rev.: $1,690,337,268
Assets: $1,918,562,450
Liabilities: $1,412,280,517
Net Worth: $506,281,933
Earnings: $40,114,937
Emp.: 2,258
Fiscal Year-end: 12/31/19
Investment Services
N.A.I.C.S.: 523999
Tao Jin *(Exec Dir)*

Subsidiaries:

Zhuhai Holiday Resort Hotel Co., Ltd. (1)
No 9 Shihua East Road, Jida, Zhuhai, 519015, Guangdong, China
Tel.: (86) 7563333838
Web Site: http://www.zhuhai-holitel.com
Home Management Services
N.A.I.C.S.: 541618

ZHUHAI HUAFA GROUP CO., LTD
No 155 ChangSheng Road, Zhuhai, Guangdong, China
Tel.: (86) 7568131749 CH
Web Site: https://www.cnhuafag.com
Year Founded: 1980

Holding Company
N.A.I.C.S.: 551112

Subsidiaries:

Huafa Industrial Co., Ltd. (1)
No 155 Changsheng Road, Zhuhai, 519030, Guangdong, China
Tel.: (86) 7568928959
Web Site: https://www.cnhuafas.com
Rev.: $9,989,049,333
Assets: $62,541,456,261
Liabilities: $44,306,581,829
Net Worth: $18,234,874,432
Earnings: $254,464,153
Fiscal Year-end: 12/31/2023
Property Development Services
N.A.I.C.S.: 531390
Chen Yin *(Vice Chm & Pres)*

ZHUHAI LIVZON DIAGNOSTICS INC.
No 266 Tongchang Road, Xiangzhou District, Zhuhai, 519060, Guangdong, China
Tel.: (86) 7568919777 CN
Web Site: http://www.livzondiagnostics.com
Year Founded: 1989
Vitro Diagnostic Product Mfr
N.A.I.C.S.: 325413

ZHUHAI PORT CO., LTD.
No 2001-2 Office No 16 Rongwan Road, Nanshui Town, Zhuhai, 519099, Guangdong, China
Tel.: (86) 7563292216
Web Site: http://www.0507.com.cn
Year Founded: 1989
000507—(SSE)
Rev.: $737,137,894
Assets: $2,935,888,142
Liabilities: $1,650,576,349
Net Worth: $1,285,311,793
Earnings: $43,041,108
Fiscal Year-end: 12/31/22
Logistic Services
N.A.I.C.S.: 541614
Huisheng Ou *(Chm)*

ZHUHAI RAYSHARP TECHNOLOGY CO., LTD.
No 100 Keji 6th Road, National High-tech Zone, Zhuhai, 519085, China
Tel.: (86) 7568598208
Web Site: https://www.raysharp.cn
Year Founded: 2007
301042—(CHIN)
Rev.: $111,595,536
Assets: $182,960,856
Liabilities: $19,458,036
Net Worth: $163,502,820
Earnings: $14,409,252
Emp.: 1,400
Fiscal Year-end: 12/31/22
Security Device Mfr
N.A.I.C.S.: 334290
Jin Xu *(Chm)*

ZHUHAI RUNDU PHARMACEUTICAL CO., LTD.
No 6 North Airport Road, Sanzao Town Jinwan District, Zhuhai, 519040, Guangdong, China
Tel.: (86) 7567630088
Web Site: https://www.rdpharma.cn
Year Founded: 1997
002923—(SSE)
Rev.: $192,661,640
Assets: $321,003,540
Liabilities: $153,087,358
Net Worth: $167,916,182
Earnings: $21,828,957
Emp.: 800
Fiscal Year-end: 12/31/22
Pharmaceutical Preparation Mfr & Distr
N.A.I.C.S.: 325411
Chen Xinmin *(Chm)*

ZHUHAI SAILONG PHARMACEUTICAL CO., LTD.

Zhuhai Rundu Pharmaceutical Co., Ltd.—(Continued)

ZHUHAI SAILONG PHARMACEUTICAL CO., LTD.
21F Unit 2 No 31 Nanwan North Road, Xiangzhou District, Zhuhai, 519060, Guangdong, China
Tel.: (86) 7563882955
Web Site: http://www.sailong.cn
Year Founded: 2002
002898—(SSE)
Rev.: $37,092,655
Assets: $119,057,950
Liabilities: $45,158,593
Net Worth: $73,899,357
Earnings: ($5,238,647)
Fiscal Year-end: 12/31/22
Pharmaceutical Product Mfr & Distr
N.A.I.C.S.: 325411
Cai Nangui (Chm)

ZHUHAI SEINE TECHNOLOGY CO., LTD.
No 3883 Zhuhai Avenue, Xiangzhou District, Zhuhai, 519075, Guangdong, China
Tel.: (86) 7566258888   CN
Web Site: http://www.seinetec.com
Year Founded: 2006
Emp.: 18,000
Laser Printer & Printer Consumable Mfr & Distr
N.A.I.C.S.: 333248
Jackson Wang (CEO)

Subsidiaries:

Ninestar Corporation (1)
No 3883 Zhuhai Avenue, Xiangzhou District, Zhuhai, 519075, Guangdong, China   (70%)
Tel.: (86) 75662258888
Web Site: https://www.ninestargroup.com
Rev.: $3,630,091,870
Assets: $6,462,421,042
Liabilities: $3,830,329,690
Net Worth: $2,632,091,352
Earnings: $261,549,770
Emp.: 23,000
Fiscal Year-end: 12/31/2022
Holding Company; Printer Cartridge Components Designer, Mfr & Distr
N.A.I.C.S.: 551112
Jeffrey Lawson (Co-Founder)

Joint Venture (US):

Lexmark International, Inc. (2)
1 Lexmark Centre Dr 740 W New Cir Rd, Lexington, KY 40550   (51%)
Tel.: (859) 232-2000
Web Site: http://www.lexmark.com
Laser, Inkjet & Dot Matrix Printers & Supplies Mfr, Developer & Retailer
N.A.I.C.S.: 333248
Sharon Votaw (Chief HR Officer & Sr VP)

Subsidiary (Non-US):

Lexmark Canada, Inc. (3)
125 Commerce Valley Drive West Suite 600, Markham, L3T 7W4, ON, Canada
Tel.: (905) 763-0560
Web Site: https://www.lexmark.ca
Printers, Inks & Toners Mfr & Marketer
N.A.I.C.S.: 339940

Subsidiary (Domestic):

Lexmark Government Solutions, LLC (3)
901 Newyork Ave Northwest ste 420, Washington, DC 20001
Tel.: (202) 378-9043
Web Site: http://www.lexmark.com
Printing Machinery & Equipment Mfr
N.A.I.C.S.: 333248

Subsidiary (Non-US):

Lexmark Handelsgesellschaft m.b.H. (3)
Kelsenstrasse 2Business park MARXIMUM Modecenterstrasse 17 Object 4 8, 1110, Vienna, Austria

Tel.: (43) 1797320
Web Site: http://www.lexmark.com
Printing Machinery & Equipment Mfr
N.A.I.C.S.: 333248

Lexmark Information Technologies Products Tic. Ltd. Sti. (3)
Barbaros Neighborhood Kardelen Street Palladium Tower No 2, Atasehir, Istanbul, 34746, Türkiye
Tel.: (90) 216 217 48 00
Web Site: http://www.lexmark.com
Printing Machinery & Equipment Mfr
N.A.I.C.S.: 333248

Lexmark International (Australia) Pty Ltd. (3)
Level 4 11 Talavera Road, North Ryde, 2113, NSW, Australia
Tel.: (61) 284013000
Web Site: http://www.lexmark.com
Marketer of Printers & Keyboards & Supplies
N.A.I.C.S.: 423420

Lexmark International (Singapore) Pte Ltd (3)
238A Thomson Rd, 13-01/05 Novena Square Tower A, Singapore, 307684, Singapore
Tel.: (65) 64679898
Web Site: http://www.lexmark.com
Printing Machinery & Equipment Mfr
N.A.I.C.S.: 333248

Lexmark International Africa Sarl (3)
210 Bvd Zerktouni 5th Floor, Casablanca, 20060, Morocco
Tel.: (212) 5 29 05 76 84
Web Site: http://www.lexmark.com
Printing Machinery & Equipment Mfr
N.A.I.C.S.: 333248
David Vionnet (Gen Mgr)

Lexmark International B.V. (3)
Gooimeer 12, 1411 DE, Naarden, Netherlands
Tel.: (31) 356994600
Web Site: http://www.lexmark.com
Printing Machinery & Equipment Mfr
N.A.I.C.S.: 333248

Lexmark International CRT d.o.o. (3)
Heinzelova 62a Emporion center, 10000, Zagreb, Croatia
Tel.: (385) 1 223 10 41
Web Site: http://www.lexmark.com
Printing Machinery & Equipment Mfr
N.A.I.C.S.: 333248
Mira Licina (Branch Mgr)

Lexmark International Czech s.r.o. (3)
City Tower Hvezdova 1716/2b, Prague, Czech Republic
Tel.: (420) 844444666
Web Site: http://www.lexmark.com
Printing Machinery & Equipment Mfr
N.A.I.C.S.: 333248

Lexmark International Limited (3)
Highfield House 8 Roxborough Way, Maidenhead, SL6 3UD, United Kingdom
Tel.: (44) 1628 518600
Web Site: http://www.lexmark.com
Printing & Imaging Equipment Distr
N.A.I.C.S.: 423430

Lexmark International Polska Sp.Z.o.o. (3)
o ul Woloska 5, 02-675, Warsaw, Poland
Tel.: (48) 22 874 37 09
Web Site: http://www.lexmark.com
Printing Machinery & Equipment Mfr
N.A.I.C.S.: 333248

Subsidiary (Domestic):

Lexmark International Puerto Rico (3)
Colgate Palmolive Bldg Lote 8 Ste 202, Guaynabo, PR 00968
Tel.: (787) 300-3388
Web Site: http://www.lexmark.com
Printing Machinery & Equipment Mfr
N.A.I.C.S.: 333248

Subsidiary (Non-US):

Lexmark International RS d.o.o. (3)

Makenzijeva 67/III, 11000, Belgrade, Serbia
Tel.: (381) 112445110
Web Site: http://www.lexmark.com
Printing Machinery & Equipment Mfr
N.A.I.C.S.: 333248
Ivan Stankovic (Mng Dir)

Lexmark International SASU (3)
18 rue Gustave Flourens, 92150, Suresnes, France
Tel.: (33) 146674000
Web Site: http://www.lexmark.com
Mfr of Ribbons, Toners & Laser Printer Cartridges; European Support Center
N.A.I.C.S.: 339940

Lexmark International Technology S.A. (3)
Rte de Pre-Bois 20, 1217, Meyrin, Switzerland
Tel.: (41) 227107050
Web Site: http://www.lexmark.com
Printing Machinery & Equipment Mfr
N.A.I.C.S.: 333248

Lexmark Magyarorszag Kft (3)
Odon Lechner 8th Avenue, 1095, Budapest, Hungary
Tel.: (36) 12880097
Web Site: http://www.lexmark.com
Printing Machinery & Equipment Mfr
N.A.I.C.S.: 333248
Dany Molhoek (VP-EMEA)

Lexmark Research & Development Corporation (3)
Lexmark Plaza 1 Samar Loop corner Panay Road Cebu Business Park, Cebu, 6000, Philippines
Tel.: (63) 32 234 8300
Web Site: http://www.lexmark.com
Enterprise Software & Managed Print Services
N.A.I.C.S.: 333248

Lexmark Schweiz AG (3)
Zurcherstrasse 59, CH-8800, Thalwil, Switzerland
Tel.: (41) 44 722 8811
Web Site: http://www.lexmark.com
Printing Machinery & Equipment Mfr
N.A.I.C.S.: 333248

Lexmark Spain SL (3)
Calle Rosario Pino 14-16 Planta 9, 28020, Madrid, Spain
Tel.: (34) 914360048
Web Site: http://www.lexmark.com
Printing Machinery & Equipment Mfr
N.A.I.C.S.: 333248

Subsidiary (US):

Static Control Components, Inc. (2)
3010 Lee Ave, Sanford, NC 27331
Tel.: (919) 774-3808
Web Site: http://www.scc-inc.com
Laser Toner Parts & Supplies Mfr & Distr
N.A.I.C.S.: 325992
Erwin Pijpers (Sr VP)

Ninestar Image Tech Limited (1)
No 3883 Zhuhai Avenue, Xiangzhou District, Zhuhai, 519060, Guangdong, China
Tel.: (86) 756 853 9188
Web Site: http://www.ggimage.com
Printer Consumable Supplies Mfr & Distr
N.A.I.C.S.: 339940
Jim Wu (Gen Mgr)

Subsidiary (US):

Ninestar Technology Co., Ltd. (2)
13875 Ramona Ave, Chino, CA 91710
Tel.: (626) 965-6662
Cartridge Distr
N.A.I.C.S.: 424120

Seine (Holland) B.V. (1)
Energieweg 113, 3641 RT, Mijdrecht, Netherlands
Tel.: (31) 297 789380
Cartridge Distr
N.A.I.C.S.: 424120

Zhuhai Wanlida Electrical Automation Co., Ltd. (1)
Wanlida Relay Protection Industrial Park No 1 Technology Road, S&T Innovation Coast High-Tech, Zhuhai, 519085, Guangdong, China
Tel.: (86) 756 339 5623

INTERNATIONAL PUBLIC

Web Site: http://www.zhwld.com
Industrial Power Distribution & Automation Equipment Mfr & Distr
N.A.I.C.S.: 333248

ZHUHAI WINBASE INTERNATIONAL CHEMICAL TANK TERMINAL CO., LTD.
Gaolan Port Economic Zone, Southern Gulf Petrochemical Storage Area Runoff, Zhuhai, 519050, Guangdong, China
Tel.: (86) 7563226493
Web Site: https://www.winbase-tank.com
002492—(SSE)
Rev.: $56,403,046
Assets: $273,870,895
Liabilities: $45,481,106
Net Worth: $228,389,789
Earnings: $17,688,083
Fiscal Year-end: 12/31/22
Petroleum & Petroleum Products Transportation & Storage Services
N.A.I.C.S.: 424710
Qingyun Wang (Chm)

ZHUHAI ZHONGFU ENTERPRISE CO., LTD.
Room 201 No 3 Plant No 1 Bonded Area, Zhuhai, 510620, Guangdong, China
Tel.: (86) 2088909032
Web Site: http://www.zhongfu.com.cn
Year Founded: 1988
000659—(SSE)
Rev.: $182,759,480
Assets: $299,399,799
Liabilities: $254,521,978
Net Worth: $44,877,821
Earnings: ($26,152,168)
Fiscal Year-end: 12/31/22
Beverage Bottle Mfr
N.A.I.C.S.: 312112
Xu Renshuo (Chm)

Subsidiaries:

Beijing Daxing Zhongfu Beverage Containers Co. Ltd (1)
No 13 Dabai Building Xihongmen Town Daxing District, Beijing, China
Tel.: (86) 1061286190
Pet Bottle Mfr
N.A.I.C.S.: 326160

Beijing Northern China Full Tin Beverage Co., Ltd (1)
No 9 East Road Yanqi Economic & Technological Development Zone, Huairou District, Beijing, 101407, China
Tel.: (86) 61666787
Mineral Water Mfr
N.A.I.C.S.: 312112

Beijing Zhongfu Beverage Container Co., Ltd. (1)
No 18 North Yongchang Road Economical & Technological Development Zone, Beijing, China
Tel.: (86) 1067881751
Pet Bottle Mfr
N.A.I.C.S.: 326160

Changsha Zhongfu Preform Co., Ltd. (1)
No 11 Xingsha Road, Changsha Economic & Technological Development Zone, Changsha, China
Tel.: (86) 73184070888
Pet Bottle Mfr
N.A.I.C.S.: 326160

Chongqing Jiafu Container Co., Ltd. (1)
109 Jinyu Avenue North Subzone Economic Technological Development Zone, Chongqing, China
Tel.: (86) 2367465122
Pet Bottle Mfr
N.A.I.C.S.: 326160

AND PRIVATE COMPANIES — ZHUZHOU KIBING GROUP CO., LTD.

Chongqing Zhongfu In-Line Container Co. Ltd. (1)
768 Baohuan Road Yubei District, Chongqing, China
Tel.: (86) 2368650905
Pet Bottle Mfr
N.A.I.C.S.: 326160

Foshan Zhongfu Container Co., Ltd (1)
Dienan Industry Zone Deihao Road, Foshan, 528253, China
Tel.: (86) 75786366891
Soya Sauce Bottle Mfr
N.A.I.C.S.: 327213

Fushan Qingquan Beverage Co., Ltd. (1)
Southbridge Management Area Wuguishan Town, Zhongshan, Guangdong, China
Tel.: (86) 76023378323
Mineral Water Mfr
N.A.I.C.S.: 312112

Haikou Zhongfu Container Co., Ltd. (1)
No 20 Hai Li Road Xiuying District, Haikou, China
Tel.: (86) 89868703399
Carbonate Bottle Mfr
N.A.I.C.S.: 326160

Hangzhou Zhongfu Container Co., Ltd. (1)
The 29th On The 10th Street, Hangzhou Economic & Technological Development Zone, Hangzhou, 310018, China
Tel.: (86) 57186910035
Pet Bottle Mfr
N.A.I.C.S.: 326160

Harbin Zhongfu In-Line Container Co., Ltd (1)
Harbin Development Zone Dalian Road No 1 Concentration Area, Harbin, 150060, China
Tel.: (86) 45186810138
Pet Bottle Mfr
N.A.I.C.S.: 326160

Hefei CR Container Co., Ltd. (1)
Economic & Technological Development Zone No 1370 Lianhua Road, Hefei, 230601, Anhui, China
Tel.: (86) 5513815141
Pet Bottle Mfr
N.A.I.C.S.: 326160

Henan Zhongfu Preform Co., Ltd. (1)
No 9 Guolu Street Zhengzhou High-Tech Industrial Development Zone, Zhengzhou, China
Tel.: (86) 37167986051
Pet Bottle Mfr
N.A.I.C.S.: 326160

Kunming Futian Food Co., Ltd. (1)
67 Keyi Road High-Tech Development Zone, Kunming, China
Tel.: (86) 8718311167
Health Beverage Mfr
N.A.I.C.S.: 311421

Lanzhou Zhongfu Container Co., Ltd. (1)
Nth of 601-1 Rd New Area Of Lanzhou High-Tech Development Zone, Lanzhou, Gansu, China
Tel.: (86) 9318556888
Pet Bottle Distr
N.A.I.C.S.: 423840

Qingdao Zhongfu In-Line Container Co., Ltd. (1)
Fenghuangling High-Tech Park, Qingdao, 266100, China
Tel.: (86) 53288702866
Pet Bottle Mfr
N.A.I.C.S.: 326160

Shenyang Zhongfu Preform Co., Ltd. (1)
8 A 2-3 Shenyang Economic & Technological Development Zone 8th Road, Shenyang, 110027, China
Tel.: (86) 2425810117
Bottled Water Mfr
N.A.I.C.S.: 312112

Taiyuan Zhongfu In-line Container Co., Ltd (1)
Coca-Cola Factory No 445 Changzhi Road Hi-Tech District, Taiyuan, Shanxi, China
Tel.: (86) 3517028792
Carbonate Bottle Mfr
N.A.I.C.S.: 326160

Tianjin Zhongfu In-line Container Co., Ltd (1)
No 139 Dongting Road, Tianjin Economic & Technological Development Zone, Tianjin, China
Tel.: (86) 2225325731
Pet Bottle Mfr
N.A.I.C.S.: 326160

Ulan Bator Zhongfu Co., Ltd (1)
Chingis Street Khan-Uul District, Ulaanbaatar, Mongolia
Tel.: (976) 70152068
Pet Bottle Distr
N.A.I.C.S.: 423840

Zhanjiang Zhongfu Container Co., Ltd. (1)
No 6 Yue Jin Road, Zhanjiang Economic & Technological Development Zone, Zhanjiang, Guangdong, China
Tel.: (86) 7593632333
Pet Bottle Mfr
N.A.I.C.S.: 326160

Zhengzhou Xingang Container Co., Ltd (1)
Taiwanese Investment Zone Of Zhengzhou Xinzheng Airport, Zhengzhou, China
Tel.: (86) 37162584896
Pet Bottle Mfr
N.A.I.C.S.: 326160

Zhuhai Hot-fill Container Co., Ltd (1)
The 1st Industry Area Of Zhongfu, Zhuhai, Wanzai, China
Tel.: (86) 7568931191
Hot Fill Bottle Mfr
N.A.I.C.S.: 326299

Zhuhai Zhongfu Enterprise Co., Ltd. - Meitu Label Factory (1)
The Second Industrial Area Wanzai Town, Zhuhai, Guangdong, China
Tel.: (86) 7568931417
Plastic Packaging Bag Mfr
N.A.I.C.S.: 326111

Zhuhai Zhongfu Hot-Fill Bottles Co. Ltd (1)
No 34 Coca-Cola Factory Zhongkai Area Development Zone, Huizhou, China
Tel.: (86) 7522651352
Carbonate Bottle Mfr
N.A.I.C.S.: 326160

ZHULIAN CORPORATION BERHAD
Plot 42 Bayan Lepas Industrial Estate, Phase IV, 11900, Penang, Malaysia
Tel.: (60) 46162020
Web Site: http://www.zhulian.com
ZHULIAN—(KLS)
Rev.: $28,813,235
Assets: $109,550,501
Liabilities: $8,986,069
Net Worth: $100,564,433
Earnings: $6,363,953
Emp.: 541
Fiscal Year-end: 11/30/23
Holding Company
N.A.I.C.S.: 551112
Meng Keat Teoh (CEO)

Subsidiaries:

Coffee Mark Products Sdn. Bhd. (1)
Plot 53 Phase IV, Bayan Lepas Industrial Estate, 11900, Bayan Lepas, Pulau Pinang, Malaysia
Tel.: (60) 46438998
Web Site: https://www.coffeemark.com.my
Coffee Mfr
N.A.I.C.S.: 311920

Zhulian (Thailand) Ltd. (1)
88 Moo 9 Bang Bua Thong-Suphanburi Road, Bang Bua Thong, Nonthaburi, 11110, Laharn, Thailand
Tel.: (66) 29833984
Web Site: https://www.zhulian.co.th
Health & Personal Care Product Distr
N.A.I.C.S.: 456199

Zhulian Industries Sdn. Bhd. (1)
Plot 3 Phase IV, Bayan Lepas Industrial Estate, 11900, Penang, Malaysia
Tel.: (60) 46162020
Web Site: https://www.zhulian.com
Beverage Product Mfr
N.A.I.C.S.: 312111

ZHUOXIN INTERNATIONAL HOLDINGS LIMITED
Suite 605 6F Sino Plaza 255 - 257 Gloucester Road Causeway Bay, Hong Kong, China (Hong Kong)
Tel.: (852) 3181 9100   Ky
Web Site: http://www.zhuoxinintl 8266—(HKG)
Rev.: $64,004,102
Assets: $35,682,971
Liabilities: $26,238,635
Net Worth: $9,444,335
Earnings: ($3,493,343)
Emp.: 38
Fiscal Year-end: 03/31/19
Investment Holding Company; Electronic Parts & Components Trading; Property Development & Investment Services
N.A.I.C.S.: 551112
Chao Ma (Chm)

ZHUZHOU CRRC TIMES ELECTRIC CO. LTD.
No 169 Times Road, Shifeng District, Zhuzhou, 412001, Hunan, China
Tel.: (86) 73128492157
Web Site: https://www.tec.crrczic.cc
3898—(HKG)
Rev.: $2,531,942,510
Assets: $6,810,741,492
Liabilities: $1,855,220,834
Net Worth: $4,955,520,658
Earnings: $363,912,985
Emp.: 7,994
Fiscal Year-end: 12/31/22
Mass Transit Electric Drive Converter & Control System Mfr
N.A.I.C.S.: 335999
Tong Gong (Deputy Gen Mgr)

Subsidiaries:

CRRC Times Electric USA, LLC (1)
801 Echelon Ct, City of Industry, CA 91744
Tel.: (626) 269-4171
Web Site: https://teusaweb.com
Railroad Rolling Stock Mfr
N.A.I.C.S.: 336510

Dynex Power Inc. (1)
Doddington Road, Lincoln, LN6 3LF, United Kingdom   (100%)
Tel.: (44) 1522500500
Web Site: http://www.dynexsemi.com
Sales Range: $25-49.9 Million
Emp.: 371
Holding Company; Semiconductor Mfr
N.A.I.C.S.: 551112
Mark Kempton (Dir-Semiconductor Bus Unit)

Subsidiary (Domestic):

Dynex Semiconductor Limited (2)
Doddington Road, Lincoln, LN6 3LF, United Kingdom   (100%)
Tel.: (44) 1522500500
Web Site: https://www.dynexsemi.com
Semiconductor Mfr
N.A.I.C.S.: 334413

ZHUZHOU FEILU HIGH-TECH MATERIALS CO., LTD.
No 98 Xiangxie Road Jinshan Industrial Park, Hetang District, Zhuzhou, 412003, Hunan, China
Tel.: (86) 73122778601
Web Site: https://www.zzfeilu.com
Year Founded: 1998
300665—(CHIN)
Rev.: $116,206,997
Assets: $257,016,911
Liabilities: $177,636,583
Net Worth: $79,380,328
Earnings: $2,911,355
Fiscal Year-end: 12/31/23
Coating Product Mfr & Distr
N.A.I.C.S.: 325998
Zhang Weiguo (Chm)

ZHUZHOU HONGDA ELECTRONICS CORP., LTD.
No 1297 Xinhua East Road, Hetang District, Zhuzhou, 412011, Hunan, China
Tel.: (86) 73128412872
Web Site: https://www.zzhddz.com
Year Founded: 1993
300726—(CHIN)
Rev.: $240,319,312
Assets: $812,055,224
Liabilities: $101,299,052
Net Worth: $710,756,171
Earnings: $66,444,607
Fiscal Year-end: 12/31/23
Electronic Components Mfr
N.A.I.C.S.: 334416

ZHUZHOU HUARUI PRECISION CUTTING TOOLS CO., LTD.
No 68 Chuangye 2nd Rd, Lusong, Zhuzhou, 412000, Hunan, China
Tel.: (86) 73122286602
Web Site: https://www.zzhrjm.com
Year Founded: 2007
688059—(SHG)
Rev.: $84,469,652
Assets: $265,801,040
Liabilities: $109,386,525
Net Worth: $156,414,515
Earnings: $23,295,617
Fiscal Year-end: 12/31/22
Cutting Tool Mfr
N.A.I.C.S.: 333515
Xukai Xiao (Chm & Gen Mgr)

ZHUZHOU KIBING GROUP CO., LTD.
11F Jingjia Technology Building No 19 Middle 2nd Road Science Park, Nanshan District, Shenzhen, 518073, Guangdong, China
Tel.: (86) 75586353588
Web Site: http://www.kibinggroup.com
Year Founded: 2005
601636—(SHG)
Rev.: $1,869,100,258
Assets: $3,430,543,442
Liabilities: $1,615,893,772
Net Worth: $1,814,649,670
Earnings: $184,869,777
Emp.: 11,000
Fiscal Year-end: 12/31/22
Glass Products Mfr
N.A.I.C.S.: 327215
Zhang Baizhong (Chm)

Subsidiaries:

CS ECO GLASS (M) Sdn. Bhd. (1)
Lot 635 660 Kawasan Perindustrian Tuanku Jaafar, Senawang, 71450, Sungai Gadut, Malaysia
Tel.: (60) 66759888
Emp.: 300
Industrial Raw Material Mfr & Distr
N.A.I.C.S.: 327992

Changxing Kibing Energy Saving Glass Co., Ltd. (1)
Shenwan, Village Lijiaxiang Town Changxing County, Huzhou, 313102, Zhejiang, China
Tel.: (86) 5726673686

ZHUZHOU KIBING GROUP CO., LTD.

Zhuzhou Kibing Group Co., Ltd.—(Continued)

Laminated Glass & Collared Glazing Glass Mfr
N.A.I.C.S.: 327215

Changxing Kibing Glass Co., Ltd. (1)
LiJiaxiang Town, Changxing County, Huzhou, 313100, Zhejiang, China
Tel.: (86) 5726291856
Glass Product Mfr & Distr
N.A.I.C.S.: 327215

Guangdong Kibing Energy Saving Glass Co. Ltd. (1)
Kibing Silicon Industrial Park Lankou Town, Dongyuan County, Heyuan, 517000, China
Tel.: (86) 7628807993
Ceramic Frit Glass Mfr & Distr
N.A.I.C.S.: 327212

Heyuan Kibing Silicon Industry Co. Limited (1)
lankou Town, Dongyuan County, Heyuan, 517564, China
Tel.: (86) 7628687557
Flat Glass Mfr
N.A.I.C.S.: 327211

Hunan Kibing Solar Technology Co., Ltd. (1)
No 9 Jianggao Road Ziwi Industrial Park Tangdong Street, Zixing, Chenzhou, 518055, Hunan, China
Tel.: (86) 7353396698
Web Site: https://www.kibingsolar.com
Emp.: 3,000
Solar Glass Mfr
N.A.I.C.S.: 327215

Kibing Group (M) Sdn. Bhd. (1)
Lot635 660 Kawasan Perindustrian Tuanku Jaafar, 71450, Sungai Gadut, Malaysia
Tel.: (60) 6823910
Industrial Product Mfr & Distr
N.A.I.C.S.: 327992

Kibing Group (Singapore) Pte. Ltd. (1)
16 Tannery Lane Crystal Time Building 08-00, Singapore, 347778, Singapore
Tel.: (65) 65474826
Web Site: http://www.kibinggroup.sg
Glass Products Mfr
N.A.I.C.S.: 327212

Kibing Minerals (M) Sdn. Bhd. (1)
Lot 20196 Kampung Ulu Lakai, Jelebu, 72400, Negeri Sembilan, Malaysia
Tel.: (60) 66380060
Industrial Raw Material Mfr
N.A.I.C.S.: 325180

Liling Kibing Silicon Co., Ltd. (1)
Laohupo Group, Xianshi Village Pukou Town Liling, Zhuzhou, 412200, Hunan, China
Tel.: (86) 73123251369
Quartz Sand Mfr & Distr
N.A.I.C.S.: 334419

Ningbo Kibing Photovoltaic Technology Co., Ltd. (1)
Ningbo South Binhai New Area Ningdong New Town 21-D Plot, Ninghai County, Ningbo, 315602, Zhejiang, China
Tel.: (86) 18957895501
Ceramic Frit Glass Mfr & Distr
N.A.I.C.S.: 327212

Pinghu Kibing Glass Co., Ltd. (1)
345 Xinggang Road, Dushangang Town, Pinghu, 314204, Zhejiang, China
Tel.: (86) 57385722017
Float Glass Mfr & Distr
N.A.I.C.S.: 327211

SBH Kibing Solar New Materials (M) Sdn. Bhd. (1)
Industrial Zone 7 Phase 2 Jalan 7 KKIP Timur, Kota Kinabalu Industrial Park KKIP, 88460, Kota Kinabalu, Sabah, Malaysia
Tel.: (60) 167898903
Industrial Material Mfr & Distr
N.A.I.C.S.: 327992

Shaoxing Kibing Glass Co., Ltd. (1)
Intersection Of Qianbin Line & Jiuqi Qiutang Road, Keqiao Binhai Industrial Zone, Shaoxing, 312000, Zhejiang, China
Tel.: (86) 57588739819
Float Glass Mfr & Distr
N.A.I.C.S.: 327211

Tianjin Kibing Energy Saving Glass Co. Ltd. (1)
Tianjin Binhai High-tech Zone Future Science & Technology City, Tianjin Demonstration Area, Beijing, 300384, China
Tel.: (86) 2258101889
Insulating Glass & Digital Printing Glass Mfr
N.A.I.C.S.: 327215

Yiliang Kibing Silicon Industry Co., Ltd. (1)
Songlin Village, Kuixiang Miao Nationality & Yi Nationality Township Yiliang County, Zhaotong, 657600, Yunnan, China
Tel.: (86) 8705127595
Glass Product Distr
N.A.I.C.S.: 423460

Zhangzhou Kibing Glass Co., Ltd. (1)
Shankou, Chencheng Town Dongshan County, Zhangzhou, 363401, Fujian, China
Tel.: (86) 5963910733
Collared Glass Mfr & Distr
N.A.I.C.S.: 327215

Zhangzhou Kibing Photovoltaic New Energy Technology Co., Ltd. (1)
Cheng An Lu Kang Mei Zhen, Dongshan County, Zhangzhou, 363401, Fujian, China
Tel.: (86) 5963910822
Ultra Clear Glass Mfr & Distr
N.A.I.C.S.: 327212

Zhaotong Kibing Photovoltaic Technology Co., Ltd. (1)
Jiupu Industrial Park, Zhaoyang District, Zhaotong, 657000, Yunnan, China
Tel.: (86) 15854349569
Ceramic Frit Glass Mfr & Distr
N.A.I.C.S.: 327212

Zixing Kibing Silicon Industry Co., Ltd. (1)
Zhoumensi Town, Zixing, Chenzhou, 423400, Hunan, China
Tel.: (86) 7358193079
Quartz Sand Mfr & Distr
N.A.I.C.S.: 334419

ZHUZHOU SMELTER GROUP CO., LTD.
No 12 Hengshan East Road, Tianyuan District, Zhuzhou, 412007, Hunan, China
Tel.: (86) 73128392172
Web Site: http://www.torchcn.com
Year Founded: 1993
600961—(SHG)
Rev.: $2,201,075,103
Assets: $771,647,329
Liabilities: $648,021,999
Net Worth: $123,625,331
Earnings: $7,891,996
Fiscal Year-end: 12/31/22
Nonferrous Metal Product & Chemical Product Mfr & Whslr
N.A.I.C.S.: 331410
Liu Langming (Chm)

ZHUZHOU STATE-OWNED ASSET INVESTMENT HOLDING GROUP CO., LTD.
Zhuzhou Guotou Building 268 Senlin Road, Tianyuan District, Zhuzhou, 412007, Hunan, China
Tel.: (86) 73128686500
Holding Company
N.A.I.C.S.: 551112

ZHUZHOU TIANQIAO CRANE CO., LTD.
Tianxin North Gate Power Valley, Shifeng District Tianyuan District, Zhuzhou, 412001, Hunan, China
Tel.: (86) 73122504022
Web Site: http://www.tqcc.cn
Year Founded: 2007
002523—(SSE)
Rev.: $222,722,361
Assets: $583,448,599
Liabilities: $241,068,752
Net Worth: $342,379,847
Earnings: $5,723,785
Emp.: 1,600
Fiscal Year-end: 12/31/22
Cranes & Crane Equipment Mfr
N.A.I.C.S.: 333923
Long Jiuwen (Chm)

Subsidiaries:

Hangzhou Huaxin Mechanical & Electrical Engineering Co., Ltd. (1)
No 315 Jinpeng Road Sandun, Hangzhou, Zhejiang, China
Tel.: (86) 57128257193
Web Site: http://www.huaxinhz.com
Industry Heavy Equipment Mfr
N.A.I.C.S.: 333120

Hunan Tianqiao JiaCheng Intelligent Technology Co., Ltd. (1)
No 407 Building C Power Valley Innovation Park, Tianyuan District, Zhuzhou, Hunan, China
Tel.: (86) 73128668819
Emp.: 45
High End Intelligent Equipment Mfr
N.A.I.C.S.: 333248

Hunan Tianqiao Liheng Parking Equipment Co., Ltd. (1)
No C-1 No 9 Zhongda Road, Tianyuan District, Zhuzhou, 412000, Hunan, China
Tel.: (86) 73122118801
Web Site: http://www.hntqlh.com
Parking Related Equipment Mfr
N.A.I.C.S.: 333310

Zhuzhou Eureka Nonferrous Equipment Co., Ltd. (1)
Unit 1 Building F22 Power Valley Innovation Park, Tianyuan District, Zhuzhou, Hunan, China
Tel.: (86) 73128516796
Web Site: http://www.ene-tqcc.com
Nonferrous Product Mfr
N.A.I.C.S.: 331529

Zhuzhou Tianqiao Crane Fittings Manufacturing Co. (1)
Tianxin Beimen, Shifeng District, Zhuzhou, Hunan, China
Tel.: (86) 73128436822
Crane Fitting Equipment Mfr
N.A.I.C.S.: 333923

Zhuzhou Tianqiao Olympjoy Ice Technology Co., Ltd. (1)
F22-202 Power Valley Innovation Park No 899 Xianyue Ring Road, Tianyuan District, Zhuzhou, Hunan, China
Tel.: (86) 73128815966
Ice & Snow Equipment Mfr
N.A.I.C.S.: 312113

Zhuzhou Tianqiao Shunchen Coal Preparation Machinery Co. (1)
Six Blocks in Zone A No 9 Zhongda Road, Liyu Industrial Park Tianyuan District, Zhuzhou, Hunan, China
Tel.: (86) 73128350217
Web Site: http://www.tqscxm.com
Coal Washing & Processing Equipment Mfr
N.A.I.C.S.: 333131

ZHUZHOU TIMES NEW MATERIAL TECHNOLOGY CO., LTD.
No 118 Fubo Road, Lukou, 412000, Zhuzhou, Hunan, China
Tel.: (86) 731 22 83 77 51
Web Site: http://www.trp.com.cn
Elastomeric NVH Component Services
N.A.I.C.S.: 423690
Jun Yang (Gen Mgr)

ZHYTOMYRSKY BUTTER PLANT, PJSC
4 Ivana Honty St, Zhytomyr, 10002, Ukraine
Tel.: (380) 412 42 29 28

INTERNATIONAL PUBLIC

Web Site: http://www.rud.ua
Year Founded: 1981
Dairy Products Mfr
N.A.I.C.S.: 311514
Petro Rud (Pres)

ZIBAO METALS RECYCLING HOLDINGS PLC
Flat D5 12/FHang Cheng Factory Building No 1 Wing Ming Street, Cheung Sha Wan, Kowloon, China (Hong Kong)
Tel.: (852) 27697662
Web Site: http://www.zibaometals.com
Rev.: $46,380,583
Assets: $6,258,981
Liabilities: $6,105,753
Net Worth: $153,228
Earnings: ($8,274,567)
Emp.: 29
Fiscal Year-end: 03/31/19
Metal Distr
N.A.I.C.S.: 423510
Wenjie Zhou (Chm)

ZIBO QIXIANG TENGDA CHEMICAL CO., LTD.
Rubber Factory Road on the 1st, Linzi District, Zibo, 255438, Shandong, China
Tel.: (86) 5337544231
Web Site: https://www.qxtdgf.com
Year Founded: 2002
002408—(SSE)
Rev.: $4,185,393,189
Assets: $4,071,396,546
Liabilities: $2,093,652,325
Net Worth: $1,977,744,221
Earnings: $88,985,015
Emp.: 2,000
Fiscal Year-end: 12/31/22
Chemicals Mfr
N.A.I.C.S.: 325998
Wang Suilian (Vice Governor)

Subsidiaries:

Shandong Qilu Keli Chemical Research Institute Co., Ltd. (1)
No 200 Huashan West Road, High-tech Zone, Zibo, 255086, China
Tel.: (86) 5336208675
Web Site: https://www.kelicc.com
Science & Technology Research Services
N.A.I.C.S.: 541715

ZIBUYU GROUP LIMITED
No 108 Xincheng Road Yongan Star Skirt Building Nanyuan street, Linping District, Hangzhou, Zhejiang, China
Tel.: (86) 57186166396 Ky
Web Site: https://www.zbycorp.com
Year Founded: 2011
2420—(HKG)
Rev.: $415,414,821
Assets: $123,699,324
Liabilities: $56,721,865
Net Worth: $66,977,459
Earnings: ($36,800,233)
Emp.: 1,063
Fiscal Year-end: 12/31/23
Footwear Product Distr
N.A.I.C.S.: 424340
Bingru Hua (Chm)

ZICCUM AB
Scheelevagen 22, 223 63, Lund, Sweden
Tel.: (46) 709615599
Web Site: https://www.ziccum.com
ZICC—(OMX)
Emp.: 10
Civil Engineering Services
N.A.I.C.S.: 541330
Goran Conradson (Mng Dir)

ZICO HOLDINGS INC.

AND PRIVATE COMPANIES

77 Robinson Road 06-03 Robinson 77, Singapore, 68896, Singapore
Tel.: (65) 64387929
Web Site:
https://www.zicoholdings.com
Year Founded: 1987
40W—(CAT)
Rev.: $12,758,381
Assets: $34,393,339
Liabilities: $13,582,717
Net Worth: $20,810,623
Earnings: ($5,351,110)
Emp.: 27
Fiscal Year-end: 12/31/23
Management & Advisory Services
N.A.I.C.S.: 541611
Paul Subramaniam *(Chief Risk Officer)*

Subsidiaries:

ASEAN Advisory Pte. Ltd. (1)
77 Robinson Road 06-03 Robinson 77, Singapore, 068896, Singapore
Tel.: (65) 64387929
Facility Support Services
N.A.I.C.S.: 561210

B.A.C.S. Private Limited (1)
77 Robinson Road 06-03 Robinson 77, Singapore, 068896, Singapore
Tel.: (65) 63270625
Facility Support Services
N.A.I.C.S.: 561210

ZICO AA Sdn. Bhd. (1)
Level 19-1 Menara Milenium Jalan Damanlela, Pusat Bandar Damansara, 50490, Kuala Lumpur, Malaysia
Tel.: (60) 320879699
Facility Support Services
N.A.I.C.S.: 561210

ZICO Capital Pte. Ltd. (1)
77 Robinson Road 06-03 Robinson 77, Singapore, 068896, Singapore
Tel.: (65) 66364201
Facility Support Services
N.A.I.C.S.: 561210
Alex Tan *(CEO)*

ZICO Corporate Services Pte. Ltd. (1)
77 Robinson Road 06-03 Robinson 77, Singapore, 068896, Singapore
Tel.: (65) 65380779
Facility Support Services
N.A.I.C.S.: 561210

ZICO Corporate Services Sdn. Bhd. (1)
Level 19-1 Menara Milenium Jalan Damanlela, Pusat Bandar Damansara, 50490, Kuala Lumpur, Malaysia
Tel.: (60) 320940999
Facility Support Services
N.A.I.C.S.: 561210

ZICO Shariah Advisory Services Sdn. Bhd. (1)
Level 7-6 Menara Milenium Jalan Damanlela, Pusat Bandar Damansara, 50490, Kuala Lumpur, Malaysia
Tel.: (60) 320933999
Facility Support Services
N.A.I.C.S.: 561210

ZICO Trust (S) Ltd. (1)
16 Collyer Quay 23-01 Collyer Quay Centre, Singapore, 049318, Singapore
Tel.: (65) 65369119
Web Site: https://www.zicotrust.com
Facility Support Services
N.A.I.C.S.: 561210
Jamil Mohamed *(Mng Dir)*

ZICO Trust Limited (1)
Unit Level 13 A Main Office Tower Financial Park Labuan Jalan Merdeka, 87000, Labuan, Malaysia
Tel.: (60) 87451688
Facility Support Services
N.A.I.C.S.: 561210

ZICOInsource Sdn. Bhd. (1)
Level 13A Menara Milenium Jalan Damanlela, Pusat Bandar Damansara, 50490, Kuala Lumpur, Malaysia

Tel.: (60) 392120977
Facility Support Services
N.A.I.C.S.: 561210

ZICOlaw (Laos) Sole Co., Ltd. (1)
1st Floor Vieng Vang Tower Bourichane Road, Unit 15 Dongpalane Thong VillageSisattanak District, Vientiane, Lao People's Democratic Republic
Tel.: (856) 21410033
Facility Support Services
N.A.I.C.S.: 561210

ZICOlaw Myanmar Limited (1)
Unit 1 Level 1 Uniteam Marine Office Building No 84 Pan Hlaing Street, Sanchaung Township, Yangon, Myanmar
Tel.: (95) 1538362
Facility Support Services
N.A.I.C.S.: 561210
Myat Thuzar *(Office Mgr)*

ZICOM ELECTRONIC SECURITY SYSTEMS LTD
501 Silver Metropolis Western Express Highway, Goregaon East, Mumbai, 400063, India
Tel.: (91) 2242904290
Web Site: https://www.zicom.com
Rev.: $12,653,616
Assets: $99,886,704
Liabilities: $143,285,280
Net Worth: ($43,398,576)
Earnings: ($38,216,100)
Emp.: 27
Fiscal Year-end: 03/31/19
Electric Equipment Mfr
N.A.I.C.S.: 238210
Pramoud Rao *(Mng Dir)*

Subsidiaries:

Zicom Retail Products Private Limited (1)
A Wing 6th Fl Andheri Kurla Rd, Andheri E, Pune, 400093, Maharastra, India
Tel.: (91) 2240003535
Web Site: http://www.zicom.com
Metal Detectors Mfr
N.A.I.C.S.: 327999

ZICOM GROUP LIMITED
38 Goodman Place, Murarrie, 4172, QLD, Australia
Tel.: (61) 739086088
Web Site:
https://www.zicomgroup.com
ZGL—(ASX)
Rev.: $70,610,820
Assets: $89,059,340
Liabilities: $53,683,858
Net Worth: $35,375,482
Earnings: ($6,477,002)
Fiscal Year-end: 06/30/23
Mfr Of Deck Machine
N.A.I.C.S.: 332322
Kok Hwee Sim *(Exec Dir)*

Subsidiaries:

Cesco Australia Ltd (1)
38 Goodman Place, Murarrie, 4172, QLD, Australia
Tel.: (61) 739086088
Web Site: https://www.cescoaustralia.com
Concrete Mixers Mfr
N.A.I.C.S.: 333120
Jim Vaughan *(Mng Dir)*

Deqing Cesco Machinery Co., Ltd. (1)
69 Ganshan Industrial Zone, Zongguan Town Deqing County, Huzhou, 313223, Zhejiang, China
Tel.: (86) 572 823 5896
Marine Deck Machinery Mfr
N.A.I.C.S.: 336611

Deqing Cesco Machinery Co.,Ltd (1)
69 Ganshan Industrial Zone, Zongguan Town, Huzhou, 313223, Zhejiang, China
Tel.: (86) 5728235896
Web Site: http://www.zicomgroup.com

Integrated Mfr of Marine Deck Machinery, Fluid Regulating & Metering Stations & Concrete Mixers
N.A.I.C.S.: 333120

FA Geotech Equipment Sdn Bhd (1)
Lot 4353A Sg Bakau Jalan Velox 2 Off Jalan Rawang, Batu Arang, 48000, Kuala Selangor, Selangor, Malaysia
Tel.: (60) 36 093 7663
Foundation Equipment Mfr
N.A.I.C.S.: 333120

FAE Thai Company Limited (1)
18/8 Moo 7, Bangchalong Sub-District, Bang Phli, 10540, Samut Prakan, Thailand
Tel.: (66) 92 331 8032
Foundation Equipment Mfr
N.A.I.C.S.: 333120

FAEQUIP Corporation (1)
Unit 205 2nd Floor MJM Building II 9516 Taguig Street, Barangay Valenzuela, Makati, 1208, Metro Manila, Philippines
Tel.: (63) 915 533 8088
Web Site: https://faequip-corporation.business.site
Construction Equipment Distr
N.A.I.C.S.: 423810

Foundation Associates Engineering Pte Ltd (1)
5 Tuas Avenue 1, Singapore, 639490, Singapore
Tel.: (65) 68631633
Web Site: https://www.fnapl.com
Construction & Piling Equipments Mfr & Sales
N.A.I.C.S.: 333120

IPTEC Pte. Ltd. (1)
Woodlands Spectrum I 03-10 2 Woodlands Sector 1, Singapore, 738068, Singapore
Tel.: (65) 6 510 6399
Web Site: https://www.iptec.com.sg
Medical Device Product Mfr
N.A.I.C.S.: 339112
Sim Giok Lak *(Chm)*

Link Vue Systems Pte. Ltd. (1)
29 Tuas Avenue 3, Singapore, 639420, Singapore
Tel.: (65) 6 742 2869
Web Site: https://www.linkvuesystems.net
Industrial Automation Product Distr
N.A.I.C.S.: 423830

Orion Systems Integration Pte. Ltd. (1)
2 Woodlands Spectrum 03-10 Woodlands Sector 1, Singapore, 738068, Singapore
Tel.: (65) 6 507 0353
Web Site: https://www.orionsi.com
Semiconductor Equipment Mfr
N.A.I.C.S.: 333242

PT Sys-Mac Indonesia (1)
B-08/09 Puri Industrial Park 2000 Batam Centre, Batam, Riau Islands, Indonesia
Tel.: (62) 778463713
Emp.: 200
Precision Machining Tools Mfr
N.A.I.C.S.: 332216

Sys-Mac Automation Engineering Pte. Ltd. (1)
Blk 2 Woodlands Spectrum 05-18 Woodlands Sector 1, Singapore, Singapore
Tel.: (65) 65106399
Web Site: https://www.sysmac.com.sg
Firmware & Software Development Services
N.A.I.C.S.: 541511

Zicom Cesco Engineering Company Limited (1)
700/895 Moo 2 Tambon Nongkakha Ampur, Phan Thong, 20160, Chon Buri, Thailand
Tel.: (66) 38 185 2769
Web Site: https://www.zicomthai.com
Hydraulic Transmission & Spare Parts Distr
N.A.I.C.S.: 423830

ZIDANE CAPITAL CORP.
2625 Lakewood Drive, Vancouver, V5N4V3, BC, Canada
Tel.: (604) 417-6375
Year Founded: 2010
ZZE.H—(TSXV)
Assets: $3,018

Liabilities: $33,565
Net Worth: ($30,547)
Earnings: ($19,897)
Fiscal Year-end: 01/31/23
Financial Management Services
N.A.I.C.S.: 523940
Casper K. Bych *(Pres, CEO & CFO)*

ZIEGELMUNDSTUCKBAU BRAUN GMBH
Markdorfer Strasse 1, Friedrichshafen, 88048, Germany
Tel.: (49) 754450980
Web Site: http://www.zmb-braun.de
Year Founded: 1926
Rev.: $17,500,000
Emp.: 100
Aluminium Casting Tools Mfr
N.A.I.C.S.: 331523
Gerhard Fischer *(Mng Dir)*

Subsidiaries:

OOO KFO Braun (1)
Office 408 Ul Lva Tolstogo 7, 197376, Saint Petersburg, Russia
Tel.: (7) 8127405476
Metal Product Distr
N.A.I.C.S.: 423510

ZIENGS SCHOENEN BV
Transportweg 14, 9405 PR, Assen, Netherlands
Tel.: (31) 592379388 NI
Web Site: http://www.ziengs.nl
Year Founded: 1946
Emp.: 500
Shoe Stores
N.A.I.C.S.: 458210
Linda Keijzer *(CEO)*

Subsidiaries:

Scapino Retail B.V. (1)
Industrieweg 28, Assen, 9403 AB, Netherlands
Tel.: (31) 592340042
Web Site: http://www.scapino.nl
Shoe Mfr & Distr
N.A.I.C.S.: 458210

ZIF FIMA SEE ACTIVIST A.D.
Bulevar Mihaila Pupina 10a/II-4, Belgrade, Serbia
Tel.: (381) 11 4141600
Web Site:
http://www.fimaseeactivist.com
Year Founded: 2008
Sales Range: Less than $1 Million
Investment Fund Management Services
N.A.I.C.S.: 523940

ZIG SHENG INDUSTRIAL CO., LTD.
2F No 70 Xining N Rd, Datong Dist, Taipei, 103601, Taiwan
Tel.: (886) 225557151
Web Site: https://www.zigsheng.com
Year Founded: 1969
1455—(TAI)
Rev.: $252,641,509
Assets: $337,110,684
Liabilities: $130,879,095
Net Worth: $206,231,589
Earnings: ($7,853,625)
Emp.: 1,274
Fiscal Year-end: 12/31/23
Yarn Mfr & Distr
N.A.I.C.S.: 313110
Barry Su *(Gen Mgr)*

ZIGA INNOVATION PCL
No 999/9 10 11 Village No 9, Nai Khlong Bang Pla Kot Subdistrict Phra Samut Chedi District, Samut Prakan, 10290, Thailand
Tel.: (66) 20965977
Web Site: https://www.ziga.co.th

ZIGA INNOVATION PCL

Ziga Innovation PCL—(Continued)
Year Founded: 1998
ZIGA—(THA)
Rev.: $23,422,469
Assets: $37,110,292
Liabilities: $14,274,873
Net Worth: $22,835,419
Earnings: $1,213,510
Fiscal Year-end: 12/31/23
Steel Product Mfr & Distr
N.A.I.C.S.: 331511
Sai Chatchai Rungruang (Chm)

ZIGEXN CO., LTD.

3-4-8 Toranomon, Minato-ku, Tokyo, 105-0001, Japan
Tel.: (81) 364320350
Web Site: https://zigexn.co.jp
3679—(TKS)
Rev.: $153,675,890
Assets: $228,276,350
Liabilities: $99,718,460
Net Worth: $128,557,890
Earnings: $25,118,000
Emp.: 927
Fiscal Year-end: 03/31/24
Computer Programming Services
N.A.I.C.S.: 541511
Jo Hirao (Pres)

Subsidiaries:

Awesome Agent Co., Ltd. (1)
Hirokoji YMD Building 3F 1-20-25 Nishiki, Naka-ku, Nagoya, 460-0003, Aichi, Japan
Tel.: (81) 529902292
Web Site: https://www.awesomegroup.co.jp
Emp.: 61
Advertising Agency Services
N.A.I.C.S.: 541810

BizMo Co., Ltd. (1)
Nagoya Panasonic Building 6F 1-23-30 Izumi, Higashi Ward, Nagoya, 461-0001, Aichi, Japan
Tel.: (81) 522383350
Web Site: https://biz-mo.co.jp
Job Vacancy Advertising Services
N.A.I.C.S.: 541850

MIRAxS Co., Ltd. (1)
1-18-2 Nishi-Ikebukuro Fujikyu Building West Building 1 7F, Toshima-ku, Tokyo, 171-0021, Japan
Tel.: (81) 366327707
Temporary Staffing Services
N.A.I.C.S.: 561320

Sanko Ad Co., Ltd. (1)
6th floor Nagoya Panasonic Building 1-23-30 Izumi, Higashi-ku, Nagoya, 461-0001, Japan
Tel.: (81) 522383357
Web Site: https://www.sanko-kyujin.co.jp
Employment Placement Agencies Services
N.A.I.C.S.: 561311

Struct Co., Ltd. (1)
3rd floor Aobadai Tower Annex 3-1-18 Aobadai, Meguro-ku, Tokyo, 153-0042, Japan
Tel.: (81) 368202877
Web Site: https://www.struct-inc.co.jp
Construction Recruitment Services
N.A.I.C.S.: 561311

ZIGExN VeNtura Co., Ltd. (1)
Floor 11 VINA BUILDING 131 Xo Viet Nghe Tinh, Ward 17 Binh Thanh District, Ho Chi Minh City, Vietnam
Tel.: (84) 838633399
Web Site: https://www.zigexn.vn
Information Technology Services
N.A.I.C.S.: 541519

ZIGNAGO VETRO S.P.A.

Via Ita Marzotto 8 Fossalta di Portogruaro, 30025, Venice, Italy
Tel.: (39) 0421246111
Web Site: https://www.zignagovetro.com
Year Founded: 1950
ZV—(ITA)
Rev.: $445,159,621
Assets: $846,808,840
Liabilities: $525,594,602
Net Worth: $321,214,238
Earnings: $73,943,733
Emp.: 2,652
Fiscal Year-end: 12/31/21
Glass Container Mfr
N.A.I.C.S.: 327213
Nicolo Marzotto (Deputy Chm)

Subsidiaries:

Huta Szkla Czechy S.A. (1)
Trabki ul Osadnicza 8, Garwolin, Pilawa, 08 440, Poland
Tel.: (48) 25 685 4823
Web Site: http://www.huta-czechy.com.pl
Glass Container Mfr
N.A.I.C.S.: 327213
Krzysztof Janczuk (CEO)

Italian Glass Moulds S.R.L. (1)
Via Enrico Mattei 13, 30026, Summaga di Portogruaro, VE, Italy
Tel.: (39) 0421276987
Web Site: https://www.iglassmoulds.com
Glass Products Mfr
N.A.I.C.S.: 333511

Julia Vitrum S.p.A. (1)
Via Gemona 5, 33078, San Vito al Tagliamento, PN, Italy
Tel.: (39) 03421207670
Glass Waste Collection Services
N.A.I.C.S.: 562111

Verreries Brosse SAS (1)
34 rue Theodule Gerin, Vieux-Rouen-sur-Bresle, Rouen, 76390, France
Tel.: (33) 2 35 93 45 02
Glass Container Mfr
N.A.I.C.S.: 327213

Subsidiary (US):

Brosse USA Inc. (2)
225 Millburn Ave Ste 301, Millburn, NJ 07041
Tel.: (973) 467-2800
Web Site: http://www.brosseusa.com
Glass Container Distr
N.A.I.C.S.: 423840

Vetreco S.R.L. (1)
Via Morolense km 5.500, 03019, Supino, FR, Italy
Tel.: (39) 0775226432
Web Site: https://vetreco.it
Glass Products Mfr
N.A.I.C.S.: 327211

Vetri Speciali S.p.A. (1)
Via Torre d'Augusto 34, 38122, Trento, TN, Italy
Tel.: (39) 0461270111
Web Site: https://www.vetrispeciali.com
Special Glass Container Mfr
N.A.I.C.S.: 327213

Vetro Revet Srl (1)
Via VIII Marzo 9, Terrafino, 50053, Florence, Italy
Tel.: (39) 0571944155
Web Site: https://www.vetrorevet.com
Recycling Services
N.A.I.C.S.: 562111

Zignago Glass USA Inc. (1)
12973 SW 112th St Unit Ste 385, Miami, FL 33186
Tel.: (305) 338-9052
Glass Container Mfr
N.A.I.C.S.: 327213

Zignago Vetro Brosse SAS (1)
16bis Rue Grange Dame Rose, 78140, Velizy-Villacoublay, France
Tel.: (33) 13 067 6480
Glass Container Mfr
N.A.I.C.S.: 327213

Zignago Vetro Polska S.A. (1)
Trabki ul Osadnicza 8, 08-440, Pilawa, Poland
Tel.: (48) 256854922
Glass Container Mfr
N.A.I.C.S.: 327213

ZIGNSEC AB

Gavlegatan 12 B, 113 30, Stockholm, Sweden
Tel.: (46) 841078500
Web Site: https://www.zignsec.com
Year Founded: 2015
ZIGN—(OMX)
Rev.: $8,387,983
Assets: $25,741,925
Liabilities: $6,125,213
Net Worth: $19,616,713
Earnings: ($12,812,595)
Emp.: 75
Fiscal Year-end: 12/31/22
Software Development Services
N.A.I.C.S.: 541511
Daniel Grech (CTO)

ZIGUP PLC

Northgate Centre Lingfield Way, Darlington, DL1 4PZ, United Kingdom
Tel.: (44) 1325467558
Web Site: https://www.zigup.com
ZIG—(LSE)
Rev.: $1,506,388,982
Assets: $2,328,746,409
Liabilities: $1,095,761,503
Net Worth: $1,232,984,906
Earnings: $89,020,270
Emp.: 6,000
Fiscal Year-end: 04/30/21
New Car Dealers
N.A.I.C.S.: 441110
Avril Palmer-Baunack (Chm)

Subsidiaries:

FMG Legal LLP (1)
Helmont House Churchill Way, Cardiff, CF10 2HE, United Kingdom
Tel.: (44) 333 321 6396
Web Site: https://www.fmg-legal.co.uk
Personal Injury Claim Services
N.A.I.C.S.: 524291

Fleet Technique Limited (1)
Suite 3 Mayflower House, 5th Ave Team Vly Trading Est, Gateshead, NE11 0HF, United Kingdom
Tel.: (44) 8712710777
Web Site: http://www.fleet-technique.co.uk
Sales Range: $50-74.9 Million
Emp.: 60
Truck Utility Trailer & RV Rental & Leasing
N.A.I.C.S.: 532120

Furgonetas de Alquiler SA (1)
Puerto De La Morcuera, Leganes, Spain
Tel.: (34) 915087027
Web Site: http://www.fulasa.com
Truck Utility Trailer & RV Rental & Leasing
N.A.I.C.S.: 532120

GPS Body Repairs Limited (1)
Unit 2 15 Lock Lane Off Millers Road, Warwick, CV34 5AG, Warwickshire, United Kingdom
Tel.: (44) 1926411255
Web Site: http://www.gpsrepairs.co.uk
Sales Range: $25-49.9 Million
Emp.: 30
Vehicle Repair & Maintenance Services
N.A.I.C.S.: 811111

NewLaw Legal Limited (1)
Helmont House Churchill Way, Cardiff, CF10 2HE, United Kingdom
Tel.: (44) 333 003 1909
Web Site: https://www.new-law.co.uk
Legal Advising Services
N.A.I.C.S.: 541110
Tim Lock (Mng Dir)

Northgate (Malta) Limited (1)
Suite 1 Level 2 Verdala Business Cnetre Tg Complex Brewery Street, Birkirkara, BKR 3000, Malta
Tel.: (356) 21320385
Sales Range: $25-49.9 Million
Emp.: 2
Transportation Services
N.A.I.C.S.: 488999

Northgate Vehicle Hire (1)
Northgate Centre Lingfield Way, Darlington, DL1 4PZ, Durham, United Kingdom
Tel.: (44) 3330430001

INTERNATIONAL PUBLIC

Web Site: http://www.northgatevehiclehire.co.uk
Sales Range: $50-74.9 Million
Emp.: 250
Commercial Vehicle Transportation & Hiring Services
N.A.I.C.S.: 488999

Northgate Vehicle Hire (Ireland) Limited (1)
Unit 200a Northwest Business Park, Dublin, D15 Y8VX, Ireland
Tel.: (353) 180 081 4139
Web Site: https://www.northgatevehiclehire.ie
Vehicle Rental Services
N.A.I.C.S.: 532111

Northgate Vehicle Hire Limited (1)
Northgate Centre Lingfield Way, Darlington, DL1 4PZ, Durham, United Kingdom
Tel.: (44) 330 012 5456
Web Site: https://www.northgatevehiclehire.co.uk
Vehicle Rental Services
N.A.I.C.S.: 532111

Principia Law Limited (1)
Bowland House Gadbrook Business Park, Rudheath, Northwich, CW9 7TN, United Kingdom
Tel.: (44) 344 600 0111
Web Site: https://www.principia-law.co.uk
Legal Advising Services
N.A.I.C.S.: 541110

Redde Ltd. (1)
Pinesgate Lower Bristol Road, Bath, BA2 3DP, United Kingdom
Tel.: (44) 3444721726
Web Site: http://www.redde.com
Rev.: $748,371,550
Assets: $492,509,200
Liabilities: $288,090,382
Net Worth: $204,418,818
Earnings: $43,788,804
Emp.: 2,220
Fiscal Year-end: 06/30/2019
Vehicle Replacement & Repair Management Services
N.A.I.C.S.: 532111
Nicholas Tilley (Sec)

Subsidiary (Domestic):

Albany Assistance Limited (2)
Redmond House Fern Court, SR82RR, Peterlee, United Kingdom (100%)
Tel.: (44) 1913503050
Sales Range: $200-249.9 Million
Emp.: 340
Insurance Related Activities
N.A.I.C.S.: 524298

Albany Vehicle Rentals Limited (2)
Hamilton Hse Birchwood Lane Moore, WA46XJ, Warrington, United Kingdom (100%)
Tel.: (44) 1925577777
Passenger Car Rental
N.A.I.C.S.: 532111

Cab Aid Limited (2)
29 East Street, Epsom, KT17 1BD, Surrey, United Kingdom
Tel.: (44) 8000283253
Web Site: http://www.cabaid.co.uk
Taxi Operators Services
N.A.I.C.S.: 485310

Helphire (UK) Limited (2)
13 Bottings Industrial Estate, Curdridge, Southampton, SO30 2DY, United Kingdom (100%)
Tel.: (44) 1489787690
Web Site: http://www.homeserve.com
Sales Range: $50-74.9 Million
Emp.: 20
Passenger Car Rental
N.A.I.C.S.: 532111

Helphire Legal Services Limited (2)
Pinesgate Lower Bristol Rd, BA23DP, Bath, United Kingdom (100%)
Tel.: (44) 1225321000
Management Consulting Services
N.A.I.C.S.: 541618

Swift Rent-A-Car Limited (2)
Chelford House Gadbrook Park, Rudheath,

Northwich, CW9 7TN, Cheshire, United Kingdom (100%)
Tel.: (44) 8454029967
Web Site: http://www.swiftprestigehire.com
Passenger Car Rental
N.A.I.C.S.: 532111

Total Accident Management Limited (2)
Lower Bristol Rd, Bath, BA2 3DP, United Kingdom (100%)
Tel.: (44) 8450784157
Web Site: http://www.totalaccman.co.uk
Sales Range: $50-74.9 Million
Emp.: 70
Insurance Agencies & Brokerages
N.A.I.C.S.: 524210
Penny Stoolman (Mng Dir)

ZIJIN MINING GROUP COMPANY LIMITED

Zijin Road Shanghang, Zijin Tower, Longyan, 364200, Fujian, China
Tel.: (86) 5922933586
Web Site:
  https://www.zijinmining.com
Year Founded: 1993
ZIJMF—(OTCIQ)
Rev.: $37,954,191,389
Assets: $42,968,597,186
Liabilities: $25,495,052,638
Net Worth: $17,473,544,548
Earnings: $2,813,903,258
Emp.: 36,578
Fiscal Year-end: 12/31/22
Gold, Copper, Zinc & Other Metal Mining Services
N.A.I.C.S.: 212220
Hongfu Lin (Exec VP)

Subsidiaries:

Bayannaoer Zijin Non-ferrous Metals Co., Ltd. (1)
Industrial Park Zone Dongshengmiao Town Wulate Houqi, Bayan Nur, 015543, Inner Mongolia, China
Tel.: (86) 4784666979
Zinc Refining Services
N.A.I.C.S.: 331410

Continental Gold Inc. (1)
155 Wellington Street West Suite 2920, Toronto, M5V 3H1, ON, Canada
Tel.: (416) 583-5610
Web Site: http://www.continentalgold.com
Rev.: $739,000
Assets: $717,023,000
Liabilities: $372,713,000
Net Worth: $344,310,000
Earnings: ($30,454,000)
Emp.: 936
Fiscal Year-end: 12/31/2018
Gold Mining Services
N.A.I.C.S.: 212220

Fujian Zijin Mining & Metallurgy Testing Technology Company Limited (1)
No 53 Qingang Road Nangang Industry Development Zone Shanghan, Longyan, 364200, Fujian, China
Tel.: (86) 5973992181
Metal Products Testing Services
N.A.I.C.S.: 541380

Fuyun Jinshan Mining and Metallurgy Company Limited (1)
Aletai Area, Kueerqisi, Fuyun, China
Tel.: (86) 9068729285
Gold Exploration Services
N.A.I.C.S.: 212220

Gold Mountains (H.K.) International Mining Company Limited (1)
3712 Tower 2 Times Square, Causeway Bay, China (Hong Kong)
Tel.: (852) 28032738
Web Site: http://www.zjky.cn
Emp.: 10
Gold Exploration Services
N.A.I.C.S.: 212220

Guyana Goldfields Inc. (1)
375 University Avenue Suite 802, Toronto, M5G 2J5, ON, Canada
Tel.: (416) 628-5916

Web Site: http://www.guygold.com
Mineral Development & Exploration Services
N.A.I.C.S.: 327999
Lisa Zangari (Chief Talent & Compliance Officer)

Jinyu (HK) International Mining Co Ltd (1)
Suites 3712-15 Tower Two Times Square, 1 Matheson St, Hong Kong, Causeway Bay, China (Hong Kong) (100%)
Tel.: (852) 2846 9888
Mining Services
N.A.I.C.S.: 212290

Subsidiary (Non-US):

Norton Gold Fields Limited (2)
Paddington Site Menzies Highway, Kalgoorlie, 6430, WA, Australia
Tel.: (61) 890806800
Web Site:
  https://www.nortongoldfields.com.au
Sales Range: $100-124.9 Million
Emp.: 450
Gold Production Services
N.A.I.C.S.: 212220
Peter Ruzicka (Gen Mgr-Geology & Exploration)

Subsidiary (Domestic):

Paddington Gold Pty. Ltd. (3)
Menzies Hwy, PO Box 1653, Kalgoorlie, 6430, WA, Australia
Tel.: (61) 890806800
Emp.: 340
Gold Mining Services
N.A.I.C.S.: 212220
Maoheng Zhang (Gen Mgr)

Minera Majaz SA (1)
Calle 9 Num 315 Urb Corpac, San Isidro, 27, Lima, Peru
Tel.: (51) 12263322
Mining Services
N.A.I.C.S.: 212290

Neo Lithium Corp. (1)
401 Bay Street Suite 2702, Toronto, M5H 2Y4, ON, Canada
Tel.: (416) 457-6529
Web Site: http://www.neolithium.ca
Assets: $54,539,703
Liabilities: $2,322,145
Net Worth: $52,217,558
Earnings: ($3,308,492)
Fiscal Year-end: 12/31/2020
Developing Lithium Batteries for Portable Applications & Electric Vehicles
N.A.I.C.S.: 213114
Constantine Karayannopoulos (Chm)

Nevsun Resources Ltd. (1)
1750 -1066 West Hastings Street, Vancouver, V6E 3X1, BC, Canada
Tel.: (604) 623-4700
Web Site: http://www.nevsun.com
Rev.: $289,397,000
Assets: $1,086,352,000
Liabilities: $133,211,000
Net Worth: $953,141,000
Earnings: ($99,601,000)
Emp.: 1,420
Fiscal Year-end: 12/31/2017
Gold & Other Precious Metal Exploration, Development & Mining Services
N.A.I.C.S.: 212220
Scott A. Trebilcock (Chief Dev Officer)

Serbia Zijin Copper Doo (1)
DorDa Vajferta 29, 19210, Bor, Serbia
Tel.: (381) 30427807
Web Site: https://zijinbor.com
Copper Mining Services
N.A.I.C.S.: 212230

Serbia Zijin Mining Doo (1)
Suvaja 185A, 12910, Bor, Serbia
Tel.: (381) 302155005
Web Site: https://www.zijinmining.rs
Mining Services
N.A.I.C.S.: 212230

Xiamen Zijin Engineering Design Company Limited. (1)
5 F Zijin Technological Building No 128 Xiangyun Sanlu, Xiamen, Fujian, China
Tel.: (86) 592 5769245

Web Site: http://www.zijinmining.com
Mining Engineering Services
N.A.I.C.S.: 212290

Xinjiang Ashele Copper Company Limited (1)
20F Building B Haifu Center 599 Sishuidao, Xiamen, 361016, Huli, China
Tel.: (86) 592 2933650
Copper Ore & Nickel Ore Mining Services
N.A.I.C.S.: 212230

Zijin Xiangyu (Longyan) Logistics Co., Ltd. (1)
4F No 36 Xiqiao 91st South Road Xicheng, Xinluo District, Longyan, 364000, Fujian, China
Tel.: (86) 597 2991088
Metal Minerals Mining & Sales
N.A.I.C.S.: 212390

ZIJING INTERNATIONAL FINANCIAL HOLDINGS LIMITED

Unit 2610 26/F The Center 99 Queen's Road, Central, China (Hong Kong)
Tel.: (852) 28654388
Web Site: http://www.vinco.com.hk
ZIJH—(HKG)
Rev.: $2,137,410
Assets: $4,100,018
Liabilities: $1,033,005
Net Worth: $3,067,013
Earnings: ($965,048)
Emp.: 17
Fiscal Year-end: 12/31/22
Financial Advisory Services
N.A.I.C.S.: 525990

Subsidiaries:

Grand Vinco Capital Limited (1)
Ste 4909-10 49 F, The Ctr 99 Queen, Central, China (Hong Kong)
Tel.: (852) 28654388
Web Site: http://www.vinco.com.hk
Sales Range: $50-74.9 Million
Emp.: 10
Financial Services
N.A.I.C.S.: 522320

ZIL LIMITED

Ground Floor Bahria Complex III M T Khan Road, Karachi, Pakistan
Tel.: (92) 2135630251
Web Site: https://www.zil.com.pk
ZIL—(KAR)
Rev.: $15,580,479
Assets: $7,833,416
Liabilities: $3,897,971
Net Worth: $3,935,445
Earnings: $423,378
Emp.: 171
Fiscal Year-end: 12/31/19
Soap Mfr
N.A.I.C.S.: 325611
Feriel Ali Mehdi (Chm)

ZILLTEK TECHNOLOGY CORP.

5F No 6-1 Duxing Road, Hsinchu Science Park, Hsinchu, 30078, Taiwan
Tel.: (886) 35777509
Web Site: https://www.zilltek.com
Year Founded: 2005
6679—(TPE)
Rev.: $67,087,984
Assets: $159,484,445
Liabilities: $8,044,899
Net Worth: $151,439,546
Earnings: $16,128,412
Emp.: 67
Fiscal Year-end: 12/31/22
Semiconductor Devices Mfr
N.A.I.C.S.: 334413

ZILOR ENERGIA E ALIMENTOS LTDA.

Rua 15 de Novembro 890, 18680-900, Lencois Paulista, Brazil
Tel.: (55) 14 3269 9000

Web Site: http://www.zilor.com.br
Sales Range: $600-649.9 Million
Processed Sugarcane Product Mfr; Biomass Electric Power Generation
N.A.I.C.S.: 325193
Antonio Jose Zillo (CEO)

Subsidiaries:

Acucareira Quata S.A (1)
Rua 15 de Novembro 865, 18680-900, Lencois Paulista, Brazil
Tel.: (55) 14 3269 9200
Web Site: http://www.biorigin.net
Food Ingredient Mfr
N.A.I.C.S.: 311999
Mario Steinmetz (CEO)

Biorigin Europe N.V. (1)
Vosseschijnstraat 59 Haven 182, 2030, Antwerp, Belgium
Tel.: (32) 35424377
Food Flavor Distr
N.A.I.C.S.: 424490

Biorigin USA, LLC (1)
8340 Cane Run Rd, Louisville, KY 40258
Tel.: (502) 719-0140
Web Site: http://www.zjky.cn
Food Flavor Distr
N.A.I.C.S.: 424490

Zilor Energia e Alimentos Ltda. - Quata Production Unit (1)
Fazenda quata, PO Box 21, Quata, Sao Paulo, 19780-000, Brazil
Tel.: (55) 1833669800
Sugar Mfr
N.A.I.C.S.: 311314

ZIM CORPORATION

234 Perley Court, Ottawa, K1M 2J2, ON, Canada
Tel.: (613) 727-1397   Ca
Web Site: https://www.zim.biz
Year Founded: 1996
ZIMCF—(OTCIQ)
Assets: $1,160,784
Liabilities: $24,651
Net Worth: $1,136,133
Earnings: ($76,568)
Fiscal Year-end: 03/31/21
Mobile Entertainment & Internet TV Services
N.A.I.C.S.: 517810
Michael C. J. Cowpland (Pres & CEO)

Subsidiaries:

Equispheres Inc. (1)
Suite 4100 500 Palladium Dr, Ottawa, K2V 1C2, ON, Canada
Tel.: (613) 903-5855
Web Site: https://equispheres.com
Metal Machine Tool Mfr
N.A.I.C.S.: 333517

Spiderwort Inc. (1)

ZIM D.D. ZENICA

Kanal 32, 72000, Zenica, Bosnia & Herzegovina
Tel.: (387) 3 245 7484
Web Site: http://www.zim.ba
ZIMZR—(SARE)
Rev.: $3,192,118
Assets: $4,695,531
Liabilities: $747,538
Net Worth: $3,947,993
Earnings: $217,886
Emp.: 75
Fiscal Year-end: 12/31/20
Dairy Products Mfr
N.A.I.C.S.: 112120

ZIM LABORATORIES LIMITED

Sadoday Gyan Ground Floor Opp N A D T Nelson Square, Nagpur, 440013, India
Tel.: (91) 7122588070
Web Site: https://www.zimlab.in
Year Founded: 1989

ZIM LABORATORIES LIMITED

ZIM Laboratories Limited—(Continued)
ZIMLAB—(NSE)
Rev.: $48,551,082
Assets: $40,954,211
Liabilities: $16,933,349
Net Worth: $24,020,862
Earnings: $2,929,621
Emp.: 536
Fiscal Year-end: 03/31/23
Pharmaceuticals Product Mfr
N.A.I.C.S.: 325412
Anwar S. Daud (Chm)

ZIMBABWE ELECTRICITY SUPPLY AUTHORITY
Electricity Centre 25 Samora Machel Avenue, PO Box 377, Harare, Zimbabwe
Tel.: (263) 4774508   ZW
Year Founded: 1986
Emp.: 6,036
State Sponsored Provider of Generation, Transmission & Distribution of Electricity
N.A.I.C.S.: 221122

Subsidiaries:
PowerTel Communications (Pvt) ltd   (1)
10th Floor Kopje Plaza 1 Jason Moyo Avenue, Harare, Zimbabwe
Tel.: (263) 4 773201
Web Site: http://www.powertel.co.zw
Emp.: 100
Communication Service
N.A.I.C.S.: 517112
Samuel Maminimini (Mng Dir)

ZIMBABWE NEWSPAPERS (1980) LIMITED
Herald House Cnr George Silundika & Sam Nujoma, Harare, Zimbabwe
Tel.: (263) 242795771
Web Site: https://www.zimpapers.co.zw
ZIMP—(ZIM)
Sales Range: Less than $1 Million
Newspaper Publishing & Commercial Printing Services
N.A.I.C.S.: 513110
Pikirayi Deketeke (CEO)

ZIMBABWE STOCK EXCHANGE
4th Fl 101 Union Ave, Harare, Zimbabwe
Tel.: (263) 4736861
Web Site: http://www.zse.co.zw
Emp.: 11
Stock Exchange Services
N.A.I.C.S.: 523210

ZIMI LIMITED
Level 4 216 st Georges terrace, Perth, 6000, WA, Australia
Tel.: (61) 862540200
Web Site: https://www.quantifytechnology.com
ZMM—(ASX)
Rev.: $2,158,031
Assets: $2,320,091
Liabilities: $1,409,775
Net Worth: $910,316
Earnings: ($2,247,087)
Fiscal Year-end: 06/30/24
Energy Development Services
N.A.I.C.S.: 211120

Subsidiaries:
Huron Gas LLC   (1)
7564 Pigeon Rd, Pigeon, MI 48755-9597
Tel.: (989) 453-2320
Petroleum & Petroleum Products Whslr
N.A.I.C.S.: 424720

ZIMMER MEDIZINSYSTEME GMBH
Junkersstrasse 9, 89231, Neu-Ulm, Germany
Tel.: (49) 7319761291   De
Web Site: http://www.zimmer.de
Sales Range: $10-24.9 Million
Physiotherapy Systems Mfr
N.A.I.C.S.: 339112
Armin Zimmer (Co-Pres)

ZIMMER WHEATON PONTAIC-BUICK-GMC LTD.
685 W Notre Dame Dr, Kamloops, V2C 6B7, BC, Canada
Tel.: (250) 374-1135
Web Site: http://www.zimmerwheatongm.com
Year Founded: 2001
Sales Range: $10-24.9 Million
Emp.: 55
New & Used Vehicle Dealers
N.A.I.C.S.: 423120
Allen Mulford (Mgr-Svcs)

ZIMMITE TAIWAN LTD.
5F-4 No 77 Sec 1 Xintai 5th Road, Xizhi Dist, New Taipei City, 221, Taiwan
Tel.: (886) 226988112
Web Site: https://www.zimmite.com
Year Founded: 1977
8435—(TPE)
Rev.: $24,038,239
Assets: $32,144,420
Liabilities: $8,070,100
Net Worth: $24,074,321
Earnings: $3,964,012
Fiscal Year-end: 12/31/22
Water Supply Services
N.A.I.C.S.: 221310
Min Shyue Ting (Chm)

ZIMPA A.D.
7 Jula 2, Ub, Serbia
Tel.: (381) 14411233
Web Site: http://www.zimpaub.com
Year Founded: 1948
ZIMP—(BEL)
Sales Range: $1-9.9 Million
Emp.: 38
Metal Products Mfr
N.A.I.C.S.: 332999

ZIMPLOW HOLDINGS LIMITED
36 Birmingham Road Southerton, PO Box HG 298 Highlands, Harare, Zimbabwe
Tel.: (263) 242754613
Web Site: http://www.zimplow.com
ZIMW—(ZIM)
Rev.: $7,315,592
Assets: $7,639,045
Liabilities: $1,919,094
Net Worth: $5,719,951
Earnings: $636,569
Emp.: 194
Fiscal Year-end: 12/31/20
Agricultural Equipment Mfr
N.A.I.C.S.: 333111
Vimbayi Nyakudya (CEO)

Subsidiaries:
Zimplow - C.T. Bolts Division   (1)
Cnr Falcon & Wanderer St, Belmont, Bulawayo, Zimbabwe
Tel.: (263) 292471591
Web Site: http://www.ctbolts.co.zw
Emp.: 50
Bolt & Fastener Distr
N.A.I.C.S.: 423710

Zimplow - Tassburg Division   (1)
13 Greenock Road, Workington, Harare, Zimbabwe
Tel.: (263) 4 621541
Screw Mfr
N.A.I.C.S.: 332722

ZIMRE HOLDINGS LIMITED
Block D 2nd Floor Smatsatsa Office Park Stand Number, PO Box 4839, Borrowdale, 10667, Harare, Zimbabwe
Tel.: (263) 242870771
Web Site: https://www.zhl.co.zw
Year Founded: 1983
ZIMR—(ZIM)
Rev.: $988,205,520
Assets: $3,261,034,510
Liabilities: $1,539,545,633
Net Worth: $1,721,488,877
Earnings: $842,628,766
Emp.: 330
Fiscal Year-end: 12/31/23
Holding Company
N.A.I.C.S.: 551112
Stanley Kudenga (CEO-Grp)

Subsidiaries:
Emeritus International Reinsurance Company Limited   (1)
Plot 115 Unit 6 Kgale Mews Gaborone International Finance Park, PO Box 404271, Broadhurst, Gaborone, Botswana
Tel.: (267) 3121041
Web Site: https://www.emeritusre.com
Reinsurance Services
N.A.I.C.S.: 524130
Leo Huvaya (Mng Dir)

Emeritus Reinsurance Company Limited   (1)
No 5 Sharpe Road Namiwawa, Private Bag 157, Blantyre, Malawi
Tel.: (265) 1823211
Reinsurance Services
N.A.I.C.S.: 524130

Emeritus Reinsurance Zambia Limited   (1)
Emeritus Reinsurance Plot 110a/24 Polonalio Miti Road, Villa Elizabetha, Lusaka, Zambia
Tel.: (260) 211232820
Reinsurance Services
N.A.I.C.S.: 524130

Emeritus Reseguros, SA   (1)
Av Da Marginal N 141/8 4 Andar Predio Zen Residence, 2382, Maputo, Mozambique
Tel.: (258) 21328807
Reinsurance Services
N.A.I.C.S.: 524130

Fidelity Life Assurance of Zimbabwe Limited   (1)
7th Floor Fidelity House 66 Julius Nyerere Way, Harare, Zimbabwe
Tel.: (263) 475092734
Web Site: https://www.fidelitylife.co.zw
Financial Services
N.A.I.C.S.: 921130
Reginald Chihota (Gen Mgr-Employee Benefits)

Zimre Property Investments Ltd.   (1)
6th Floor Fidelity Life Tower 5 Raleigh Street Luck Street, Harare, Zimbabwe
Tel.: (263) 242782259
Web Site: http://www.zimreproperties.co.zw
Asset Management Services
N.A.I.C.S.: 523940
Edson Muvingi (Mng Dir)

ZIMTU CAPITAL CORP.
Suite 1450 - 789 West Pender Street, Vancouver, V6C 1H2, BC, Canada
Tel.: (604) 681-1568
Web Site: https://www.zimtu.com
Year Founded: 2006
ZC—(DEU)
Sales Range: $1-9.9 Million
Investment Services
N.A.I.C.S.: 523999
David Hodge (Pres & CEO)

ZINC MEDIA GROUP PLC
17 Dominion Street, London, EC2M 2EF, United Kingdom
Tel.: (44) 2078782311

INTERNATIONAL PUBLIC

Web Site: https://www.zincmedia.com
Year Founded: 1999
ZIN—(AIM)
Rev.: $37,357,069
Assets: $29,936,073
Liabilities: $21,294,386
Net Worth: $8,641,686
Earnings: ($2,833,788)
Emp.: 224
Fiscal Year-end: 12/31/22
Factual Websites, Radio Programs & Television Shows Producer
N.A.I.C.S.: 513199
Will Sawyer (CFO)

Subsidiaries:
Below the Radar Limited   (1)
2nd Floor Calender 58-60 Upper Arthur Street, Belfast, BT1 4GJ, Northern Ireland, United Kingdom
Tel.: (44) 2890315522
Web Site: https://www.belowtheradar.tv
Television Production Services
N.A.I.C.S.: 512110
Sabina Cherek (CFO)

Blakeway Productions Limited   (1)
17 Dominion Street, Finsbury, London, EC2M 2EF, United Kingdom
Tel.: (44) 2074283100
Web Site: https://www.blakeway.co.uk
Sales Range: $25-49.9 Million
Emp.: 50
Independent Radio & Television Production Services
N.A.I.C.S.: 711510
Jago Lee (Creative Dir)

Brook Lapping Productions Limited   (1)
17 Dominion Street, Finsbury, London, EC2M 2EF, United Kingdom
Tel.: (44) 2074283100
Web Site: https://www.brooklapping.com
Emp.: 30
Independent Radio & Television Production Services
N.A.I.C.S.: 711510

DBDA Limited   (1)
Pin Point 1-2, Rosslyn Crescent, Harrow, HA1 2SU, Middlesex, United Kingdom
Tel.: (44) 8703337771
Web Site: http://www.dbda.co.uk
Sales Range: $25-49.9 Million
Emp.: 15
Communication Consulting Services
N.A.I.C.S.: 541618

Ten Alps TV Limited   (1)
13th Fl Portland House Bressenden Place, Kentish Town, London, SW1E 5BH, United Kingdom
Tel.: (44) 2074283100
Sales Range: $50-74.9 Million
Emp.: 70
Radio & Television Production Services
N.A.I.C.S.: 711510
Fiona Stourton (Dir-Creative)

The Edge Picture Co., Ltd.   (1)
17 Dominion Street, London, EC2M 2EF, United Kingdom
Tel.: (44) 2078782311
Web Site: https://www.edgepicture.com
Digital Film Mfr & Distr
N.A.I.C.S.: 333310

ZINC OF IRELAND NL
Suite B9 431 Roberts Road, Subiaco, 6008, WA, Australia
Tel.: (61) 892874600   AU
Web Site: https://www.zincofireland.com.au
ZMI—(ASX)
Rev.: $616
Assets: $5,955,698
Liabilities: $230,710
Net Worth: $5,724,988
Earnings: ($1,115,617)
Fiscal Year-end: 06/30/24
Mineral Exploration Services
N.A.I.C.S.: 212230
Greg Hope (Mgr-exploration)

ZINC ONE RESOURCES INC.
1040 West Georgia St Suite 410, Vancouver, V6E 4H1, BC, Canada
Tel.: (604) 683-0911   BC
Web Site: http://www.zincone.com
Year Founded: 2007
RH3—(DEU)
Assets: $35,972
Liabilities: $1,289,881
Net Worth: ($1,253,909)
Earnings: ($68,751)
Fiscal Year-end: 02/28/23
Zinc Exploration & Development
N.A.I.C.S.: 212230
Gunther Roehlig *(CEO-Interim)*

ZINCORE METALS INC.
5626 Larch Street Suite 202, Vancouver, V6M 4E1, BC, Canada
Tel.: (604) 669-6611   BC
Web Site:
  http://www.zincoremetals.com
Year Founded: 2005
ZNC.H—(TSXV)
Rev.: $13,810
Assets: $11,455
Liabilities: $1,364,469
Net Worth: ($1,353,014)
Earnings: ($73,091)
Emp.: 24
Fiscal Year-end: 12/31/21
Mineral Development & Exploration Services
N.A.I.C.S.: 327999
Jorge Benavides *(CEO)*

ZINCX RESOURCES CORP.
Suite 2050 - 1055 West Georgia Street, PO Box 11121, Royal Centre, Vancouver, V6E 3P3, BC, Canada
Tel.: (604) 684-2181   BC
Web Site:
  https://www.zincxresources.com
Year Founded: 1988
M9R—(DEU)
Rev.: $84,427
Assets: $18,635,725
Liabilities: $1,078,372
Net Worth: $17,557,353
Earnings: ($649,713)
Fiscal Year-end: 06/30/24
Zinc Mining Properties Exploration & Development
N.A.I.C.S.: 213114
Peeyush K. Varshney *(Chm, Pres & CEO)*

ZINDART MANUFACTURING LIMITED
Unit K 54 Veliant Industrail Ctr 2-12, Autuiwan St, Fotan, NT, China (Hong Kong)
Tel.: (852) 22566000   HK
Web Site: http://www.zindart.com
Year Founded: 1978
Sales Range: $25-49.9 Million
Die-Cast & Injection-Molded Plastic Collectible Products Mfr
N.A.I.C.S.: 339930
Christopher S. Franklin *(CEO)*

ZINEMA MEDIA & ENTERTAINMENT LTD.
Third Floor B Block Work EZ 147 Pathari Road Thousand Lights, Chennai, 600017, Tamil Nadu, India
Tel.: (91) 6380416423
Web Site: https://www.zinema.co.in
Year Founded: 1984
538579—(BOM)
Rev.: $19,607
Assets: $1,121,615
Liabilities: $107,255
Net Worth: $1,014,360
Earnings: ($14,143)
Emp.: 2

Fiscal Year-end: 03/31/23
Insecticide Repellent Mfr
N.A.I.C.S.: 325320

ZINITIX CO., LTD.
19th Floor Heungdeok IT Valley 13 Heungdeok 1-ro, Giheung-gu, Yongin, 446908, Gyeonggi, Korea (South)
Tel.: (82) 3180656000
Web Site: https://www.zinitix.com
Year Founded: 2000
303030—(KRS)
Rev.: $21,177,744
Assets: $23,725,478
Liabilities: $6,952,255
Net Worth: $16,773,222
Earnings: ($6,952,723)
Emp.: 82
Fiscal Year-end: 12/31/22
Investment Services
N.A.I.C.S.: 523999
Park Jong Hwan *(Deputy Gen Mgr)*

ZINKIA ENTERTAINMENT SA
C/Infantas 27 1, 28004, Madrid, Spain
Tel.: (34) 915240365
Web Site: https://www.zinkia.com
Year Founded: 2000
Video Production Services
N.A.I.C.S.: 512110
Inigo Pastor Gili *(Gen Dir)*

ZINNWALD LITHIUM PLC
29-31 Castle Street, High Wycombe, HP13 6RU, Buckinghamshire, United Kingdom
Tel.: (44) 2072361177   UK
Web Site: https://zinnwaldlithium.com
ZNWLF—(OTCIQ)
Rev.: $1,516
Assets: $30,248,532
Liabilities: $2,482,922
Net Worth: $27,765,611
Earnings: ($2,121,544)
Emp.: 8
Fiscal Year-end: 12/31/21
Gold Exploration Services
N.A.I.C.S.: 212220
Anton Du Plessis *(CEO)*

ZINWELL CORPORATION
7F 512 Yuanshan Rd, Zhonghe Dist, New Taipei City, 235, Taiwan
Tel.: (886) 222251929
Web Site: https://www.zinwell.com.tw
2485—(TAI)
Rev.: $190,223,185
Assets: $282,978,406
Liabilities: $77,387,551
Net Worth: $205,590,855
Earnings: ($9,395,827)
Emp.: 638
Fiscal Year-end: 12/31/23
Amplifiers & Wireless Equipment Mfr
N.A.I.C.S.: 334220

Subsidiaries:

ZINWELL Corporation - Chia-Yi Plant (1)
1-61 Niu Chou His, Fu Hsing Village Min Hsiung Hsiang, Chiayi, 621, Taiwan
Tel.: (886) 52132546
Web Site: http://www.zintech.com.tw
Satellite Television & Communication Equipment Mfr
N.A.I.C.S.: 334220

ZINWELL Corporation - Hsinchu Plant (1)
2 Wen Hua Road, HsinChu Industrial Park, Hsinchu, 303, Taiwan
Tel.: (886) 3 5979050
Web Site: http://www.zinwell.com.tw
Satellite Television & Communication Equipment Mfr
N.A.I.C.S.: 334220

ZINWELL Corporation - Shenzhen Plant (1)
2 Road Tong Fu Yu Industrial Zone Guangming Town Baoan, Center city, Shenzhen, 518103, Guangdong, China
Tel.: (86) 75588825990
Emp.: 3,000
Satellite Television & Digital Receiver Mfr
N.A.I.C.S.: 334220

ZINZINO AB
Hulda Mellgrens Gata 5, 421 32, Vastra Frolunda, Sweden
Tel.: (46) 317717168
Web Site: https://www.zinzino.com
Year Founded: 2005
ZZ.B—(OMX)
Rev.: $138,748,803
Assets: $59,012,251
Liabilities: $48,338,797
Net Worth: $10,673,454
Earnings: $7,871,718
Emp.: 215
Fiscal Year-end: 12/31/20
Coffee Machines Direct Sales
N.A.I.C.S.: 423620
Dag Bergheim Pettersen *(CEO)*

Subsidiaries:

BioActive Foods AS (1)
Hoslegata 3, Bekkestua, 1356, Baerum, Norway
Tel.: (47) 40004443
Web Site: https://www.1life63.com
Bioactive Product Mfr
N.A.I.C.S.: 325414

Zinzino B.V. (1)
Bezuidenhoutseweg 1, 2594 AB, Hague, Netherlands
Tel.: (31) 708080500
Web Site: https://www.zinzino.com
Nutritional Supplement & Skincare Product Mfr
N.A.I.C.S.: 325411

Zinzino Oy (1)
Makelakatu 58-60, 00510, Helsinki, Finland
Tel.: (358) 942451010
Nutritional Supplement & Skincare Product Mfr
N.A.I.C.S.: 325411

ZIP CO LIMITED
Level 5 126 Phillip Street, Sydney, 2000, NSW, Australia
Tel.: (61) 282942345   AU
Web Site: https://www.zip.co
Year Founded: 2013
ZIP—(ASX)
Rev.: $579,583,630
Assets: $2,124,922,292
Liabilities: $1,858,805,867
Net Worth: $266,116,425
Earnings: $3,778,073
Fiscal Year-end: 06/30/24
Online Credit Services
N.A.I.C.S.: 522299
Adam Ezra *(CEO)*

Subsidiaries:

Nikita Engine s.r.o. (1)
Turkova 2319/5b, Chodov, 149 00, Prague, Czech Republic
Tel.: (420) 774409616
Web Site: https://www.nikitaengine.com
Credit Risk Assessment Services
N.A.I.C.S.: 561450

Twisto Payments a.s. (1)
Sokolovska 47/73, 186 00, Prague, Czech Republic
Tel.: (420) 222703333
Web Site: https://www.twisto.cz
Emp.: 180
Digital Payment Solution Services
N.A.I.C.S.: 522320

Twisto Polska Sp. z o.o. (1)
Ul Smolna 40, 00-375, Warsaw, Poland
Tel.: (48) 222630210
Web Site: https://www.twisto.pl
Emp.: 150

Digital Payment Services
N.A.I.C.S.: 522320

Zip Business Australia Pty. Ltd. (1)
Level 7 180 George Street, Sydney, NSW, Australia
Tel.: (61) 1800107010
Digital Payment Services
N.A.I.C.S.: 522320

Zip Business New Zealand Pty. Ltd. (1)
Level 13 5 - 7 Byron Avenue, Takapuna, Auckland, New Zealand
Tel.: (64) 800444540
Digital Payment Solution Services
N.A.I.C.S.: 522320

Zip Co NZ Limited (1)
Level 3 33-45 Hurstmere Road, Takapuna, Auckland, New Zealand
Tel.: (64) 94898144
Web Site: https://zip.co
Digital Payment Services
N.A.I.C.S.: 522320

Zip Co Payments UK Limited (1)
82 St John Street, London, EC1M 4JN, United Kingdom
Tel.: (44) 2033196601
Digital Payment Services
N.A.I.C.S.: 522320

ZIPPE INDUSTRIEANLAGEN GMBH
Alfred-Zippe-Strasse 11, 97877, Wertheim, Germany
Tel.: (49) 93428040
Web Site: http://www.zippe.de
Year Founded: 1920
Rev.: $35,245,050
Emp.: 250
Plant Construction Service
N.A.I.C.S.: 237990
Bernd-Holger Zippe *(Chm)*

Subsidiaries:

ZIPPE Glass Industries India Pvt. Ltd. (1)
1022-B 10th Floor Spaze I Tech Park Sohna Road Sector 49, Gurgaon, Haryana, India
Tel.: (91) 8744001830
Web Site: http://www.zippe.in
Glass Plant Construction Services
N.A.I.C.S.: 237990
Ashutosh Joshi *(VP)*

ZIPPE Polska Sp. z o.o. (1)
Swieradowska 51/57, Wroclaw, Poland
Tel.: (48) 713459450
Glass Plant Construction Services
N.A.I.C.S.: 237990

Zippe Italia S.R.L. (1)
Borgo Santa Chiara D'assisi 12, Parma, 43121, Italy
Tel.: (39) 0521242823
Glass Plant Construction Services
N.A.I.C.S.: 237990

ZIPPY TECHNOLOGY CORP.
10F No 50 Minquan Rd, Xindian Dist, New Taipei City, 23141, Taiwan
Tel.: (886) 229188512
Web Site: https://www.zippy.com
Year Founded: 1983
2420—(TAI)
Rev.: $69,540,761
Assets: $175,942,895
Liabilities: $55,109,518
Net Worth: $120,833,378
Earnings: $17,609,928
Emp.: 903
Fiscal Year-end: 12/31/23
Switch Mfr
N.A.I.C.S.: 334419
Chinwen Chou *(Chm)*

Subsidiaries:

G-BRIM INTERNATIONAL CORP. (1)
2310 2311 Building G Hualian City Panorama, District 27 Dalang community Baoan

ZIPPY TECHNOLOGY CORP.

Zippy Technology Corp.—(Continued)
District, Shenzhen, 518101, China
Tel.: (86) 75529778708
Web Site: http://www.zippy.com
Electronic Components Distr
N.A.I.C.S.: 423690

ZIPPY (DongGuan) Electronics CO., LTD. (1)
Tel.: (86) 76983216200
Web Site: http://www.zippy.com.tw
Computer Peripheral Equipment Mfr
N.A.I.C.S.: 334118

ZIPPY USA INC. (1)
1 Morgan, Irvine, CA 92618
Tel.: (949) 366-9525
Web Site: http://www.zippy.com.pw
Emp.: 32
Computer Peripheral Equipment Distr
N.A.I.C.S.: 423430

ZIPPY(Suzhou) Electronics Co., Ltd. (1)
No 011 Room 25 Floor Zhongxiang Building No 666 Xiangchengbig Road, Xiangcheng Zone, Suzhou, 21513, Jiangsu, China
Tel.: (86) 51265863699
Micro Switch Mfr & Distr
N.A.I.C.S.: 335313

Zippy Technology Europe GmbH (1)
Giesenheide 23, 40724, Hilden, Germany
Tel.: (49) 21035760100
Web Site: http://www.zippy-europe.com
Emp.: 12
Power Supplies Distr
N.A.I.C.S.: 423690

ZIPTEL LIMITED
Suite 3 138 Main Street, Osborne Park, 6017, WA, Australia
Tel.: (61) 8 6380 2555
Web Site: http://www.ziptel.com.au
Rev.: $353,662
Assets: $1,303,272
Liabilities: $113,477
Net Worth: $1,189,795
Earnings: ($220,318)
Fiscal Year-end: 06/30/18
Telecommunication Servicesb
N.A.I.C.S.: 517810

ZIRAAT KATILIM VARLIK KIRALAMA A.S.
Hobyar Eminonu Mah Hayri Efendi Cad No 12 Bahcekapi, Fatih, 34112, Istanbul, Turkiye
Tel.: (90) 212404132422
Web Site: http://www.ziraatkatilimvks.com.tr
ZKBVK—(IST)
Sales Range: Less than $1 Million
Financial Management Services
N.A.I.C.S.: 551112
Osman Karakutuk (Chm)

ZIRAX LIMITED
68 Lombard Street, London, EC3V 9LJ, United Kingdom
Tel.: (44) 2078681694
Web Site: http://www.zirax.com
Sales Range: $25-49.9 Million
Emp.: 260
Specialty Chemicals Mfr
N.A.I.C.S.: 325998

Subsidiaries:

Zirax (UK) Limited (1)
68 Lombard St, London, United Kingdom
Tel.: (44) 2078681694
Emp.: 200
Chemicals Mfr & Distr
N.A.I.C.S.: 325998

Zirax LLC (1)
mkrn 4 bld 6, Svetly Yar, 404171, Volgograd, Russia
Tel.: (7) 8442494999
Web Site: http://zirax.ru
Chemicals Mfr & Distr
N.A.I.C.S.: 325998
Irina Rudova (Mgr-Customer Svc)

ZISUNG ECS CO LTD
50 Geungok-ro, Namyangju, Korea (South)
Tel.: (82) 25171148
Web Site: http://www.zisung.co.kr
Commercial Building Construction Services
N.A.I.C.S.: 236220
Yoon Nam-Sik (CEO)

ZITKO A.D.
Glavna 90, 24300, Backa Topola, Serbia
Tel.: (381) 24 715 213
Web Site: http://www.zitko.co.rs
Year Founded: 1948
Sales Range: Less than $1 Million
Grain Mill Product Mfr
N.A.I.C.S.: 111199

ZITO POLOG AD
Marshal Tito Str No 134, 1200, Tetovo, North Macedonia
Tel.: (389) 44335658
Web Site: https://www.zitopolog.com.mk
Year Founded: 1903
ZPOG—(MAC)
Rev.: $4,161,078
Assets: $9,685,809
Liabilities: $1,918,308
Net Worth: $7,767,501
Earnings: ($425,549)
Fiscal Year-end: 12/31/23
Bakery Products Mfr
N.A.I.C.S.: 311812
Katerina Damjanovska (Pres)

ZITO PRILEP AD
Bb Lenin Str, 7500, Prilep, North Macedonia
Tel.: (389) 48 426 490
Year Founded: 1959
Flour Milling Services
N.A.I.C.S.: 311211

ZITO SKOPJE AD
Ul Ankarska br 33, Skopje, North Macedonia
Tel.: (389) 2 3094 112
Year Founded: 1950
Sales Range: Less than $1 Million
Emp.: 99
Bread Product Mfr
N.A.I.C.S.: 311812
Stojan Ilic (Chm)

ZITO STRUMICA AD
54 Goce Delcev Str, 2400, Strumica, North Macedonia
Tel.: (389) 34 348 056
Year Founded: 1947
Flour Milling Services
N.A.I.C.S.: 311211

ZITOBANAT A.D.
2 Oktobar 94, 26300, Vrsac, Serbia
Tel.: (381) 13 833 390
Web Site: http://www.zitobanat.rs
Year Founded: 1960
Sales Range: $1-9.9 Million
Mill Product Mfr
N.A.I.C.S.: 311211
Dimitrije Jovanovic (Dir-Comml)

ZITOPEK A.D.
Dimitrija Tucovica 51, 18000, Nis, Serbia
Tel.: (381) 18507701
Web Site: https://www.zitopek.rs
Year Founded: 1947
ZTPK—(BEL)
Rev.: $12,801,969
Assets: $5,607,054
Liabilities: $3,645,075
Net Worth: $1,961,979
Earnings: $878,571
Emp.: 370
Fiscal Year-end: 12/31/23
Bakery Products Mfr
N.A.I.C.S.: 311812
Dejan Vasiljevic (Gen Mgr)

ZITOPROMET A.D.
Kraljevica Marka 2, Zajecar, Serbia
Tel.: (381) 19420711
Year Founded: 1947
ZTZA—(BEL)
Sales Range: $1-9.9 Million
Emp.: 198
Grain Grinding Services
N.A.I.C.S.: 115114
Dragan Nikolic (Gen Mgr)

ZITOPROMET A.D.
Dimitrija Tucovica 45, 76300, Bijeljina, Bosnia & Herzegovina
Tel.: (387) 5 525 0777
ZTPR—(BANJ)
Sales Range: $10-24.9 Million
Emp.: 231
Grain Product Mfr
N.A.I.C.S.: 311211
Slavo Pavlovic (Chm)

ZITOPROMET-MLIN AD
Arpadova 104, Senta, Serbia
Tel.: (381) 24 814 334
Web Site: http://www.zitopromet.rs
Year Founded: 1953
Sales Range: $25-49.9 Million
Grain Mill Product Mfr
N.A.I.C.S.: 311230

ZITOSREM A.D.
Vojvode Putnika 2, Indija, Serbia
Tel.: (381) 22557671
Web Site: http://www.zitosrem.rs
Year Founded: 1956
ZISR—(BEL)
Sales Range: $10-24.9 Million
Emp.: 173
Grain Mill Product Mfr
N.A.I.C.S.: 311230
Radoslav Basaric (Exec Dir)

ZIXIN GROUP HOLDINGS LIMITED
60 Paya Lebar Road 13-40 Paya Lebar Square, Singapore, 409051, Singapore
Tel.: (65) 69805600
Web Site: https://www.zixingroup.com.sg
Year Founded: 2007
Wood Furnishing Product Mfr
N.A.I.C.S.: 337211
Liang Chengwang (Chm & CEO)

ZIYUANYUAN HOLDINGS GROUP LTD.
Room A1001 Majialong Innovation Building, No 198 Daxin Road Nanshan District, Shenzhen, China
Tel.: (86) 75533011380
Web Site: http://www.ziyygroup.com
8223—(HKG)
Rev.: $45,573,559
Assets: $84,559,691
Liabilities: $40,920,984
Net Worth: $43,638,707
Earnings: $2,165,810
Emp.: 281
Fiscal Year-end: 12/31/22
Financial Lending Services
N.A.I.C.S.: 522220
Junshen Zhang (Chm & CEO)

ZJAMP GROUP CO., LTD.
Zhejiang Agricultural Science and Technology Innovation Park, No 768 Jianghong Road Binjiang District, Hangzhou, China

INTERNATIONAL PUBLIC

Tel.: (86) 57187661111
Web Site: https://www.znjtgf.com
Year Founded: 1999
002758—(SSE)
Rev.: $5,870,583,459
Assets: $2,738,422,786
Liabilities: $1,816,105,674
Net Worth: $922,317,112
Earnings: $85,615,162
Fiscal Year-end: 12/31/22
Pharmaceuticals Mfr
N.A.I.C.S.: 325412

ZJBC INFORMATION TECHNOLOGY CO., LTD.
26F Jinyuan International Business Building No 146 Hebei Avenue, Haigang District, Qinhuangdao, 066000, Hebei, China
Tel.: (86) 3353280602
Web Site: http://www.000889.cn
Year Founded: 1997
000889—(SSE)
Sales Range: $300-349.9 Million
Real Estate Development Services
N.A.I.C.S.: 531390
Wu Ying (Chm)

ZJLD GROUP INC.
Shizipu Beijiao, Huichuan, Zunyi, Guizhou, China
Tel.: (86) 4000998899
Web Site: https://www.zjld.com
Year Founded: 2021
6979—(HKG)
Spirit Product Mfr
N.A.I.C.S.: 312140
Lianbo Wang (VP)

Subsidiaries:

Jiangxi Lidu Wine Industry Co., Ltd. (1)
No 23 Lidu Avenue, Lidu Town Jinxian County, Nanchang, Jiangxi, China
Tel.: (86) 4008551308
Wine Beverage Mfr & Distr
N.A.I.C.S.: 312111

ZK INTERNATIONAL GROUP CO., LTD.
No 678 Dingxiang Road Binhai Industrial Park, Economic & Technology Development Zone, Wenzhou, 325020, Zhejiang, China
Tel.: (86) 57786852999
Web Site: https://www.zkinternationalgroup.com
Year Founded: 2015
ZKIN—(NASDAQ)
Rev.: $111,599,686
Assets: $58,668,977
Liabilities: $33,430,185
Net Worth: $25,238,792
Earnings: ($61,290,390)
Emp.: 282
Fiscal Year-end: 09/30/23
Piping system designing & Instalation Services
N.A.I.C.S.: 237110
Jiancong Huang (Co-Founder, Chm & CEO)

ZK PELAGONIJA JSC
Boris Kidric 3, Bitola, North Macedonia
Tel.: (389) 47243612
Web Site: https://www.zkpelagonija.mk
Year Founded: 1963
ZPKO—(MAC)
Rev.: $27,538,040
Assets: $111,018,915
Liabilities: $51,362,743
Net Worth: $59,656,171
Earnings: $1,319,210
Fiscal Year-end: 12/31/21
Farming Services

AND PRIVATE COMPANIES

N.A.I.C.S.: 111199
Tomislav Davkov (CEO)

ZKH GROUP LIMITED
7/F Tower 4 Libao Plaza No 36
Shenbin Road, Minhang District,
Shanghai, 201106, China
Tel.: (86) 2150809696   Ky
Web Site: https://www.zkh.com
Year Founded: 2021
ZKH—(NYSE)
Rev.: $1,207,517,584
Assets: $1,022,738,702
Liabilities: $578,091,632
Net Worth: $444,647,070
Earnings: ($42,215,884)
Emp.: 3,476
Fiscal Year-end: 12/31/23
Industrial Product Distr
N.A.I.C.S.: 423840

ZKTECO CO., LTD.
No 32 Pingshan Industrial Road,
Tangxia Town, Dongguan, 523710,
China
Tel.: (86) 76982109991
Web Site: https://www.zkteco.com
Year Founded: 2007
301330—(CHIN)
Rev.: $277,490,659
Assets: $552,662,073
Liabilities: $89,170,618
Net Worth: $463,491,455
Earnings: $27,724,508
Emp.: 4,106
Fiscal Year-end: 12/31/23
Software Development Services
N.A.I.C.S.: 541511
Quanhong Che (Chm)

Subsidiaries:

Armatura Co., Ltd. (1)
A1007-A1008 17 Gosan-ro 148beon-gil,
Gunpo, Gyeonggi-do, Korea (South)
Tel.: (82) 7050672550
Biometric Verification Services
N.A.I.C.S.: 541990

PT. ZKTeco Biometrics Indonesia (1)
Gold Coast Office Tower A Lt 19E Pantai
Indah Kapuk, Jakarta, 14470, Indonesia
Tel.: (62) 2129218949
Web Site: https://www.zkteco.co.id
Biometric Machine Mfr
N.A.I.C.S.: 334118

ZK Intelligent Solutions (Pty) Ltd. (1)
Eco Square Unit 08B298 Witch-Hazel
StreetHighveld X71, Centurion, Gauteng,
South Africa
Tel.: (27) 122591047
Biometric Recognition Techniques Mfr
N.A.I.C.S.: 334118

ZK Technology LLC (1)
200 Centennial Ave Ste 211, Piscataway,
NJ 08854
Tel.: (732) 412-6007
Biometric Verification Services
N.A.I.C.S.: 541990

ZKTech Chile SPA (1)
501 Suecia 0142, Providencia, Santiago,
Chile
Tel.: (56) 2232263261
Biometric Recognition Techniques Mfr
N.A.I.C.S.: 334118

ZKTeco Argentina S.A (1)
11 De Septiembre De 1888 2173,
C1428DFZ, Buenos Aires, Argentina
Tel.: (54) 91154943498
Web Site: https://www.zkteco.com.ar
Emp.: 3,600
Biometric Identification Development Services
N.A.I.C.S.: 561611

ZKTeco Biometric Limited (1)
Raden House 64 Adetokunbo Ademola
Street Victoria Island, Lagos, Nigeria
Tel.: (234) 8175555512
Biometric Verification Services
N.A.I.C.S.: 541990

ZKTeco Colombia SAS (1)
Centro Empresarial Arrecife Calle 26
69D-91 Torre 1 Oficina 404, Bogota, Colombia
Tel.: (57) 7460840
Web Site: https://zktecocolombia.com
Emp.: 3,800
Biometric Recognition Techniques Services
N.A.I.C.S.: 561611

ZKTeco Deutschland GmbH (1)
Berliner Str 175, 63067, Offenbach, Germany
Tel.: (49) 34916532891
Biometric Recognition Techniques Mfr
N.A.I.C.S.: 334118

ZKTeco Europe SL (1)
Carretera De Fuencarral 44 Edificio 1
Planta 2, Alcobendas, 28108, Madrid, Spain
Tel.: (34) 916532891
Web Site: https://zkteco.eu
Emp.: 3,800
Biometric Recognition Techniques Mfr
N.A.I.C.S.: 334118

ZKTeco Ireland Ltd. (1)
Dublin Airport Business Park 9, Santry,
Dublin, Ireland
Tel.: (353) 18427470
Biometric Recognition Techniques Mfr
N.A.I.C.S.: 334118

ZKTeco Italia Srl (1)
Via Roma 2, Castel San Pietro Terme,
40024, Bologna, Italy
Tel.: (39) 03442724277
Biometric Recognition Techniques Mfr
N.A.I.C.S.: 334118

ZKTeco Japan Co., Ltd. (1)
Higasi-Ueno 3-4-4 Fujino Building Room
201, Aido-ku, Tokyo, Japan
Tel.: (81) 8032481089
Biometric Verification Services
N.A.I.C.S.: 541990

ZKTeco Panama S.A. (1)
Juan Diaz Costa del Este Edificio Financial
Park Piso 32 Oficina Abcd, Panama,
Panama
Tel.: (507) 3733288
Biometric Recognition Techniques Mfr
N.A.I.C.S.: 334118

ZKTeco Peru S.A.C. (1)
Ca Gavilanes 261, San Isidro, 15047, Lima,
Peru
Tel.: (51) 16805235
Web Site: https://www.zkteco.com.pe
Biometric Recognition Techniques Services
N.A.I.C.S.: 561611

ZKTeco Philippines Inc. (1)
Sunnymede IT Center Quezon Ave, South
Triangle, Quezon City, 1103, Philippines
Tel.: (63) 26356366
Biometric Verification Services
N.A.I.C.S.: 541990

ZKTeco Security LLC (1)
Office No 502 & 503 Bay Square 1, PO Box
4323, Business Bay, Dubai, United Arab
Emirates
Tel.: (971) 43927649
Web Site: https://www.zkteco.me
Biometric Recognition Techniques Mfr
N.A.I.C.S.: 334118

ZKTeco Thai Co., Ltd. (1)
No 90 38th Floor Cw Tower Ratchadaphisek Road, Huai Khwang, Bangkok,
10310, Thailand
Tel.: (66) 20130088
Web Site: https://www.zkteco.co.th
Biometric Recognition Techniques Services
N.A.I.C.S.: 561611

ZKTeco Turkey Elektronik Sanayi Ve
Ticaret Limited Sirketi (1)
Kucuk Piyale Mh Piyalepasa Bulvari Agac
Kopru Sok, No 26 Kastel Is Merkezi B Blok
Kat 1 Beyoglu, 34400, Istanbul, Turkiye
Tel.: (90) 8508111114
Web Site: https://zkteco.com.tr
Biometric Recognition Techniques Mfr
N.A.I.C.S.: 334118

ZKTeco UK Ltd. (1)
17 Ace Business Park - Ground Floor Ace
Business Park Kitts Green, Birmingham,
B33 0LD, United Kingdom
Tel.: (44) 1217901600
Biometric Recognition Techniques Mfr
N.A.I.C.S.: 334118

ZKTeco USA LLC (1)
1600 Union Hill Rd, Alpharetta, GA 30005
Tel.: (862) 505-2101
Web Site: https://www.zktecousa.com
Emp.: 3,800
Biometric Recognition Techniques Mfr
N.A.I.C.S.: 334118

ZKTeco Vietnam Technology Company Limited (1)
3rd Floor Richy Tower Group 44 Mac Thai
To Street, Yen Hoa Ward Cau Giay District,
Hanoi, Vietnam
Tel.: (84) 2839296667
Biometric Verification Services
N.A.I.C.S.: 541990

ZKTeco do Brasil S.A. (1)
Rodovia Mg-010 Km 26 - Loteamento 12,
Bairro Angicos, Vespasiano, 33206-240,
Minas Gerais, Brazil
Tel.: (55) 3130553530
Web Site: https://www.zkteco.com.br
Emp.: 3,800
Biometric Recognition Techniques Mfr
N.A.I.C.S.: 334118

ZLATA MONETA II DD
Trg Leona Stuklja 12, 2000, Maribor,
Slovenia
Tel.: (386) 22520833
Sales Range: $1-9.9 Million
Emp.: 4
Financial Investment Services
N.A.I.C.S.: 523999
Petar Zoric (CEO)

ZLATAR A.D.
Svetog Save 9, Nova Varos, Serbia
Tel.: (381) 3361677
Year Founded: 1992
ZLTR—(BEL)
Rev.: $5,922
Assets: $351,666
Liabilities: $2,472,839
Net Worth: ($2,121,173)
Earnings: $22,726
Emp.: 2
Fiscal Year-end: 12/31/21
Home Management Services
N.A.I.C.S.: 721110
Slobodan Ducic (Exec Dir)

ZLATARPLAST A.D.
Bistrica bb, 31320, Nova Varos, Serbia
Tel.: (381) 3361370
Web Site: https://www.zlatarplast.rs
Year Founded: 1989
ZLTP—(BEL)
Rev.: $12,824,210
Assets: $14,418,781
Liabilities: $7,381,796
Net Worth: $7,036,985
Earnings: $357,496
Emp.: 199
Fiscal Year-end: 12/31/22
Plastics Product Mfr
N.A.I.C.S.: 325211
Mico Zoric (Exec Dir)

ZLATEN LEV HOLDING AD
Geo Milev Quarter 67B Constantov
St, 1111, Sofia, Bulgaria
Tel.: (359) 29654521
Web Site: https://www.zlatenlev.com
HLEV—(BUL)
Sales Range: Less than $1 Million
Investment Management Service
N.A.I.C.S.: 523940

ZLATIBOR GRADNJA A.D.
Pozeska 104a, 11030, Belgrade, Serbia
Tel.: (381) 112544351
Web Site: https://www.gpzlatibor.rs

Year Founded: 1963
ZLGB—(BEL)
Rev.: $4,843,185
Assets: $8,730,332
Liabilities: $1,930,283
Net Worth: $6,800,048
Earnings: $47,018
Emp.: 14
Fiscal Year-end: 12/31/22
Construction Engineering Services
N.A.I.C.S.: 236220
Ostojic Marko (Dir-Technical)

ZLATIBOR MERMER A.D.
Pekarska bb, Uzice, Serbia
Tel.: (381) 31563833
Year Founded: 1997
ZLMR—(BEL)
Sales Range: Less than $1 Million
Emp.: 23
Stone Work Services
N.A.I.C.S.: 327991
Dragan Milojevic (Gen Mgr)

ZLATIBOR STANDARD A.D.
Nemanjina 106, Uzice, Serbia
Tel.: (381) 31 211 494
Year Founded: 2003
Sales Range: Less than $1 Million
Emp.: 6
Canteen Operating Services
N.A.I.C.S.: 722515

ZLATICA A.D.
Glavna bb naselje Zlatica bb, Lazarevo, Serbia
Tel.: (381) 23 898 006
Year Founded: 1949
Sales Range: $1-9.9 Million
Cereal Crop Farming Services
N.A.I.C.S.: 111998

ZLATNI PYASATZI AD
k k Zlatni pyasatsi, 9007, Varna, Bulgaria
Tel.: (359) 52355184
ZLP—(BUL)
Sales Range: Less than $1 Million
Hotel & Restaurant Operator
N.A.I.C.S.: 721110
Lyubomira Rizova-Solbakke (Dir-Investor Relations)

ZLOMREX SA
ul Zielona 26, 42 360, Poraj, Poland
Tel.: (48) 343160125
Web Site: http://www.zlomrex.pl
Sales Range: $300-349.9 Million
Steel & Non-Ferrous Metal Scraps
Procurement & Processing
N.A.I.C.S.: 331110
Krzysztof Leszek Zola (Chm-Supervisory Bd)

Subsidiaries:

voestalpine Stahlhandel GmbH (1)
Lunzer Strasse 105, A 4021, Linz,
Austria   (75%)
Tel.: (43) 73269240
Web Site: http://www.voestalpine.com
Sales Range: $450-499.9 Million
Emp.: 600
Steel Trading Services
N.A.I.C.S.: 423510

ZMAJ A.D.
Dure strugara 16, 11300, Smederevo,
Serbia
Tel.: (381) 26 222 244
Web Site: http://www.zmaj.rs
Year Founded: 1954
Sales Range: Less than $1 Million
Welding Repair Services
N.A.I.C.S.: 811310

ZMAJ A.D.

ZMAJ A.D.

Zmaj a.d.—(Continued)
Autoput 18, Zemun, Belgrade, 11080, Serbia
Tel.: (381) 11 2606233
Web Site: http://www.zmaj.co.rs
Year Founded: 1946
ZMAJ—(BEL)
Sales Range: $1-9.9 Million
Emp.: 41
Agricultural Machinery & Equipment Mfr
N.A.I.C.S.: 333111
Radoslava Halupka (Gen Mgr)

ZMFY AUTOMOBILE GLASS SERVICES LIMITED
No 12 Fengbei Road, Fengtai District, Beijing, China
Tel.: (86) 1063868636 Ky
Web Site: http://www.zmfy.com.hk
Year Founded: 1999
8135—(HKG)
Rev.: $12,328,655
Assets: $30,460,140
Liabilities: $3,340,438
Net Worth: $27,119,702
Earnings: ($3,165,165)
Emp.: 214
Fiscal Year-end: 12/31/20
Automobile Maintenance Services
N.A.I.C.S.: 811122
Wen Bai (Mgr-Fin Dept)

ZNEXT MINING CORP.
1240 Roxas Blvd, Ermita, Manila, 1000, Philippines
Tel.: (63) 25675162
Metal Mining Services
N.A.I.C.S.: 212220
Jason Piamonte (CEO)

ZOBITO AB
Vastra Ansgarigatan 10, SE-216 12, Limhamn, Sweden
Web Site: http://www.zobito.com
Equity Investment Firm
N.A.I.C.S.: 523999
Magnus Lindhe (Mng Partner)

ZOBNATICA A.D.
Suboticki put bb, Backa Topola, Serbia
Tel.: (381) 24 715 842
Web Site: http://www.zobnatica.rs
Year Founded: 1946
Sales Range: $1-9.9 Million
Emp.: 109
Resort Management Services
N.A.I.C.S.: 721110
Andrija Raicevic (Exec Dir)

ZODIAC CAPITAL LIMITED
Level 1 275 George Street, Sydney, 2000, NSW, Australia
Tel.: (61) 2 9299 9270
Investment Services
N.A.I.C.S.: 523999
Robin Armstrong (Chm)

ZODIAC CLOTHING COMPANY LIMITED
Nyloc House 254 D-2 Dr Annie Besant Road, Worli, Mumbai, 400 030, India
Tel.: (91) 2266677000
Web Site: https://www.zodiaconline.com
ZODIACLOTH—(BOM)
Rev.: $17,404,433
Assets: $52,551,080
Liabilities: $17,589,895
Net Worth: $34,961,185
Earnings: ($4,010,616)
Emp.: 1,173
Fiscal Year-end: 03/31/21
Garments Mfr

N.A.I.C.S.: 339999
M. Y. Noorani (Founder & Chm)

ZODIAC ENERGY LIMITED
4-5-6 Upper Ground Floor Milestone Building Nr Drive-In, Theater Drive-In-Road, Ahmedabad, 380054, Gujarat, India
Tel.: (91) 7927471193
Web Site: https://www.zodiacenergy.com
Year Founded: 1992
ZODIAC—(NSE)
Rev.: $16,605,263
Assets: $11,356,022
Liabilities: $7,033,691
Net Worth: $4,322,331
Earnings: $143,001
Emp.: 90
Fiscal Year-end: 03/31/23
Renewable Energy Equipment Mfr
N.A.I.C.S.: 333611
Pranav Mehta (Co-Chm)

ZODIAC-JRD-MKJ LIMITED
506-513 Vardhaman Chambers 17/G Cawasji Patel Street Fort, Mumbai, 400 001, India
Tel.: (91) 2222831050
Web Site: https://zodiacjrdmkjltd.co.in
Year Founded: 1987
512587—(BOM)
Rev.: $1,226,108
Assets: $9,270,857
Liabilities: $98,805
Net Worth: $9,172,052
Earnings: $47,069
Emp.: 9
Fiscal Year-end: 03/31/21
Jewel & Diamond Whslr
N.A.I.C.S.: 423940
Jayantilal A. Jhaveri (Chm)

ZOJE RESOURCES INVESTMENT CO., LTD.
No 198 Xinggang East Road, Damaiyu Subdistrict Yuhuan, Taizhou, 317604, Zhejiang, China
Tel.: (86) 57687338207
Web Site: http://www.zoje.com
Year Founded: 1994
002021—(SSE)
Rev.: $122,586,385
Assets: $190,196,005
Liabilities: $231,287,280
Net Worth: ($41,091,275)
Earnings: ($57,485,952)
Fiscal Year-end: 12/31/22
Sewing machines Mfr
N.A.I.C.S.: 333248
Zhang Lishu (Chm & Gen Mgr)

ZOJIRUSHI CORPORATION
19-9 1-Chome Tenma, Kita-ku, Osaka, 530-0043, Japan
Tel.: (81) 663562382
Web Site: https://www.zojirushi-world.com
Year Founded: 1918
7965—(TKS)
Rev.: $591,972,460
Assets: $797,043,620
Liabilities: $192,273,710
Net Worth: $604,769,910
Earnings: $31,486,690
Fiscal Year-end: 11/30/23
Cooking Appliance Mfr & Distr
N.A.I.C.S.: 335220
Norio Ichikawa (Pres)

Subsidiaries:

Zojirushi America Corporation (1)
19310 Pacific Gateway Dr Ste 101, Torrance, CA 90502
Tel.: (310) 769-1900
Web Site: http://www.zojirushi.com
Emp.: 40

Household Product Mfr & Distr
N.A.I.C.S.: 332215

Zojirushi SE Asia Corporation Ltd. (1)
4th Floor Saha-Union Building 1828 Sukhumvit Road Phrakhanong-Tai, Phrakhanong, Bangkok, 10260, Thailand
Tel.: (66) 27414818
Web Site: http://www.zojirushi.co.th
Household Product Distr
N.A.I.C.S.: 423620

Zojirushi Shanghai Corporation (1)
Unit 1108 Henderson 688 square No 688 Nanjing Road West, Jing'an District, Shanghai, China
Tel.: (86) 216 190 7755
Web Site: https://www.zojirushi-china.com
Household Product Distr
N.A.I.C.S.: 423620

Zojirushi Simatelex Co., Ltd. (1)
Rm 6-7 6/f One Island South 2 Heung Yip Rd, Wong Chuk Hang, Hong Kong, China (Hong Kong)
Tel.: (852) 25573161
Web Site: http://www.simatelex.com.hk
Household Product Distr
N.A.I.C.S.: 423620

Zojirushi Taiwan Corporation (1)
9F No 100 SEC 2 Chang-An East Road, Zhongshan District, Taipei, Taiwan
Tel.: (886) 22 506 9009
Web Site: http://www.zojirushi.com.tw
Household Product Distr
N.A.I.C.S.: 423620

ZOLTAV RESOURCES INC.
44 Esplanade, Saint Helier, JE4 9WG, Jersey
Tel.: (44) 1534504402 Ky
Web Site: http://www.zoltav.com
ZOL—(AIM)
Rev.: $1,688,752,502
Assets: $6,143,571,667
Liabilities: $4,107,200,756
Net Worth: $2,036,370,911
Earnings: ($1,330,682,364)
Emp.: 263
Fiscal Year-end: 12/31/20
Oil & Gas Operations
N.A.I.C.S.: 211120
Tigran Tagvoryan (CEO)

Subsidiaries:

Royal Atlantic Energy (Cyprus) Limited (1)
2 Sofouli Street Chantecrair Building, Nicosia, 1096, Cyprus
Tel.: (357) 2 288 9999
Oil & Gas Production Services
N.A.I.C.S.: 211120

Subsidiary (Non-US):

Diall Alliance LLC, (2)
128 Ul Im Chelyuskintsev, Saratov, Russia
Tel.: (7) 8452265435
Oil & Gas Production Services
N.A.I.C.S.: 211120

ZOMATO MEDIA PVT LTD.
22nd Floor One Horizon Centre Golf Course Road, Gurgaon, Haryana, India
Tel.: (91) 1130806376
Web Site: http://www.zomato.com
Restaurant Locator Services
N.A.I.C.S.: 541511
Deepinder Goyal (Co-Founder & CEO)

ZONA FRANCA DE IQUIQUE SA
Edificio Convenciones S/N Recinto Amurallado Zofri, Iquique, Chile
Tel.: (56) 572515100
Web Site: https://www.zofri.cl
Year Founded: 1975
ZOFRI—(SGO)
Sales Range: Less than $1 Million

Real Estate Manangement Services
N.A.I.C.S.: 531311
Bernardo Collao Bolados (COO)

ZONE RESOURCES INC.
430 - 609 Granville Street, PO Box 10325, Vancouver, V7Y 1G5, BC, Canada
Tel.: (604) 683-5445 AB
Web Site: http://www.zone-resources.com
Year Founded: 1990
Sales Range: Less than $1 Million
Oil & Gas Exploration Services
N.A.I.C.S.: 213112

ZONE3, INC.
1055 Rene Levesque Blvd E 9th Fl, Montreal, H2L 4S5, QC, Canada
Tel.: (514) 284-5555
Web Site: http://www.zone3.ca
Sales Range: $25-49.9 Million
Emp.: 500
Television Production
N.A.I.C.S.: 512110
Brigitte Lemonde (Pres)

ZONECO GROUP CO., LTD.
8th Floor Guohe Center 151 Ganglong Road, Zhongshan District, Dalian, 116001, Liaoning, China
Tel.: (86) 4006559988
Web Site: https://www.zhangzidao.cn
Year Founded: 1958
002069—(SSE)
Rev.: $283,691,847
Assets: $341,851,115
Liabilities: $324,206,036
Net Worth: $17,645,079
Earnings: $552,474
Emp.: 3,000
Fiscal Year-end: 12/31/22
Aquatic Product Distr
N.A.I.C.S.: 112519
Yan Tang (CEO-Cold Chain Logistics & VP)

Subsidiaries:

Zhangzidao group (Rongcheng) Food Co. Ltd. (1)
No 592 Lidao Road Lidao Town, Rongcheng, 264317, Shandong, China
Tel.: (86) 6317667766
Emp.: 500
Frozen Sea Food Distr
N.A.I.C.S.: 424490

ZONETAIL, INC.
70 University Ave Suite 1460, Toronto, M5J 2M4, ON, Canada
Tel.: (416) 583-3773
Web Site: https://www.zonetail.com
Year Founded: 2014
ZONE—(TSX)
Rev.: $31,248
Assets: $190,604
Liabilities: $883,931
Net Worth: ($693,327)
Earnings: ($954,764)
Fiscal Year-end: 12/31/20
Software Development Services
N.A.I.C.S.: 541511
Paul Scott (Chm)

ZONGSHEN INDUSTRIAL GROUP CO., LTD.
Zongshen Industrial Park Chaoyouchang No128 Yu nan Avenue, Banan District, Chongqing, 400054, China
Tel.: (86) 40 0700 3088 CN
Web Site: http://en.zongshen.cn
Year Founded: 1992
Holding Company
N.A.I.C.S.: 551112
Zongshen Zuo (Chm & CEO)

AND PRIVATE COMPANIES

Subsidiaries:

Zongshen PEM Power Systems Inc. (1)
580 Hornby Street Suite 588, Vancouver, V6C 3B6, BC, Canada (100%)
Tel.: (604) 687-7908
Web Site: http://www.zongshenpem.com
Emp.: 2,225
Fuel Cell Research; Electric Motorcycles Mfr
N.A.I.C.S.: 221118
Zongshen Zuo (Chm & CEO)

Zongshen Power Machinery Co., Ltd. (1)
Chaoyouchang, Banan District, Chongqing, 400054, China
Tel.: (86) 2366372632
Web Site: http://www.zse.cc
Rev.: $1,144,401,804
Assets: $1,211,965,626
Liabilities: $494,465,817
Net Worth: $717,499,809
Earnings: $54,802,009
Fiscal Year-end: 12/31/2022
Holding Company; Motor Vehicle, Motorcycle & Boat Engine & Other Power Machinery Mfr
N.A.I.C.S.: 551112
Zuo Zongshen (Chm)

ZONGTAI REAL ESTATE DEVELOPMENT CO., LTD.
3F No 875 Fuxing Rd, Hsinchu County, Zhubei, 302, Taiwan
Tel.: (886) 423026018
Web Site: http://www.zongtai.com.tw
3056—(TAI)
Rev.: $49,780,534
Assets: $731,160,540
Liabilities: $505,674,104
Net Worth: $225,486,436
Earnings: $10,035,449
Fiscal Year-end: 12/31/23
Real Estate Services
N.A.I.C.S.: 531390
Yu-Ling Weng (Chm & Pres)

ZONQING ENVIRONMENTAL LIMITED
3/F Zhongqing Building No 5888 Fuzhi Road, Jingyue High-tech Industrial Development Zone, Changchun, Jilin, China   Ky
Year Founded: 2008
1855—(HKG)
Rev.: $326,137,710
Assets: $532,568,952
Liabilities: $426,029,713
Net Worth: $106,539,239
Earnings: $21,215,247
Emp.: 899
Fiscal Year-end: 12/31/23
Landscaping Services
N.A.I.C.S.: 561730
Haitao Liu (CEO)

ZONTE METALS INC.
20 Fielding Ave, Dartmouth, B3B 1E1, NS, Canada
Tel.: (902) 405-3520   BC
Web Site:
  https://www.zontemetals.com
Year Founded: 2009
31E—(DEU)
Rev.: $149,826
Assets: $4,252,852
Liabilities: $1,213,837
Net Worth: $3,039,015
Earnings: ($48,226)
Fiscal Year-end: 01/31/24
Gold Exploration Services
N.A.I.C.S.: 212220
Terry Christopher (Pres & CEO)

ZOO DIGITAL GROUP PLC
Castle House Angel Street, Sheffield, S3 8LN, United Kingdom
Tel.: (44) 1142413700
Web Site: https://www.zoodigital.com
ZOO—(AIM)
Assets: $49,110,000
Liabilities: $21,460,000
Net Worth: $27,650,000
Earnings: ($21,930,000)
Fiscal Year-end: 03/31/24
Media Delivery Software Developer
N.A.I.C.S.: 513210
Roger D. Jeynes (Chm)

Subsidiaries:

Scope Seven LLC (1)
2201 Park Pl Ste 100, El Segundo, CA 90245
Tel.: (310) 220-3939
Digital Video Content Production Services
N.A.I.C.S.: 512110

ZOO Digital Inc. (1)
2201 Park Pl, El Segundo, CA 90245
Tel.: (310) 220-3939
Web Site: https://www.zoodigital.com
Digital Media Licensing & Distr
N.A.I.C.S.: 449210
Helen P. Gilder (CFO)

ZOO Digital Limited (1)
Floor 2 Castle House Angel Street, Sheffield, S3 8LN, United Kingdom
Tel.: (44) 1142413700
Web Site: http://www.zoodigital.com
Emp.: 30
Software Development Services
N.A.I.C.S.: 541511
Stuart Green (CEO)

ZOO Digital Production LLC (1)
The Tower 2 Furnival Sq, Sheffield, S1 4QL, South Yorkshire, United Kingdom
Tel.: (44) 1142413700
Interactive Digital Video Discs Mfr
N.A.I.C.S.: 334610
Stuart Green (CEO)

ZOO Employee Share Trust Limited (1)
The Tower 2 Furnival Sq, Sheffield, S1 4QL, South Yorkshire, United Kingdom
Tel.: (44) 1142413700
Web Site: http://www.zoodigital.com
Emp.: 35
Employee Benefit Services
N.A.I.C.S.: 525120
Stuart Green (CEO)

ZOOLOGICAL PARKS AND GARDENS BOARD
Elliott Avenue, PO Box 74, Parkville, 3052, VIC, Australia
Tel.: (61) 392859300
Web Site: http://www.zoo.org.au
Year Founded: 1936
Rev.: $70,575,159
Assets: $280,963,816
Liabilities: $16,600,915
Net Worth: $264,362,901
Earnings: ($5,732,649)
Emp.: 850
Fiscal Year-end: 06/30/19
Zoo Operator
N.A.I.C.S.: 712130
Geoff Wescott (Deputy Chm)

Subsidiaries:

Melbourne Zoo (1)
Elliott Avenue, Parkville, 3052, VIC, Australia
Tel.: (61) 392859300
Web Site: http://www.zoo.org.au
Emp.: 200
Zoo Operations
N.A.I.C.S.: 712130
Scott Killeen (Mgr-Interpretation)

Sir Colin MacKenzie Zoological Park (1)
Badger Creek Road, PO Box 248, Victoria, Healesville, 3777, VIC, Australia
Tel.: (61) 359572800
Web Site: http://www.zoo.org.au
Emp.: 100
Zoo Operations
N.A.I.C.S.: 712130

Miranda Wills (Dir-Discovery)

Werribee Zoological Park (1)
K Road, Werribee, 3030, VIC, Australia
Tel.: (61) 397319600
Zoo Operations
N.A.I.C.S.: 712130

ZOOLOGISCHER GARTEN BERLIN AG
Hardenbergplatz 8, 10787, Berlin, Germany
Tel.: (49) 30254010
Web Site: https://www.zoo-berlin.de
Year Founded: 1844
ZOO—(BER)
Sales Range: Less than $1 Million
Zoo & Aquarium Operator
N.A.I.C.S.: 712130
Andreas Knierim (Member-Mgmt Bd)

ZOOM CORPORATION
4-4-3 Kanda-surugadai Chiyoda-ku, Tokyo, 101-0062, Japan
Tel.: (81) 352971040   JP
Web Site: http://www.zoom.co.jp
Year Founded: 1983
6694—(TKS)
Rev.: $126,918,090
Assets: $136,553,400
Liabilities: $80,379,330
Net Worth: $56,174,070
Earnings: $623,920
Emp.: 95
Fiscal Year-end: 12/31/23
Musical Instrument Mfr & Distr
N.A.I.C.S.: 339992
Akio Araki (Chief Production Officer)

Subsidiaries:

Mogar Music S.p.A. (1)
Via Bernini 8, 20045, Lainate, Milano, Italy
Tel.: (39) 02935961
Web Site: https://www.mogarmusic.it
Musical Instrument Distr
N.A.I.C.S.: 423990
Maria Cristin Bonetti (CFO)

Sound Service MSL Distribution Limited (1)
Wyvols Court Business Centre, Swallowfield, Reading, RG7 1WY, United Kingdom
Tel.: (44) 2071180133
Music Electronic Device Mfr & Distr
N.A.I.C.S.: 339992

Sound-Service Musikanlagen-Vertriebsgesellschaft GmbH (1)
Moriz-Seeler-Strasse 3, 12489, Berlin, Germany
Tel.: (49) 307071300
Web Site: https://www.sound-service.eu
Musical Equipment Distr
N.A.I.C.S.: 459140

Zoom North America LLC (1)
2040 Express Dr S Ste 500, Hauppauge, NY 11788
Tel.: (631) 542-5270
Web Site: http://www.zoom-na.com
Recording Device Mfr
N.A.I.C.S.: 334310

Zoom Uk Distribution Ltd. (1)
15 Weston Barns Hitchin Road, Weston, SG4 7AX, Hertfordshire, United Kingdom
Tel.: (44) 8432080999
Web Site: http://www.zoom-uk.com
Recording Device Distr
N.A.I.C.S.: 423410

ZOOM MEDIA GROUP INC.
3510 Saint Laurent Blvd Suite 200, Montreal, H2X 2V2, QC, Canada
Tel.: (514) 842-1155
Web Site:
  http://www.zoommedia.com
Advetising Agency
N.A.I.C.S.: 541810

ZOOMERMEDIA LIMITED

Subsidiaries:

Zoom Media Corp. (1)
112 Madison Ave 8th Fl, New York, NY 10016-7416
Tel.: (212) 685-7981
Web Site: http://www.zoommedia.com
Emp.: 30
Advertising Agencies
N.A.I.C.S.: 541810
Francois de Gaspe Beaubien (Chm & CEO)

ZOOM2U TECHNOLOGIES LIMITED
Level 4 Suite 4 11 55 Miller Street, Pyrmont, 2009, NSW, Australia
Tel.: (61) 1300326150   AU
Web Site:
  https://www.zoom2u.com.au
Year Founded: 2014
Z2U—(ASX)
Rev.: $3,020,363
Assets: $5,160,526
Liabilities: $3,001,259
Net Worth: $2,159,266
Earnings: ($3,624,208)
Emp.: 75
Fiscal Year-end: 06/30/23
Custom Computer Programming Services
N.A.I.C.S.: 541511

Subsidiaries:

Talcasoft Australia Pty. Ltd. (1)
Level 4 Suite 4 11 55 Miller St, Pyrmont, NSW, Australia
Tel.: (61) 1300345865
Web Site: https://www.talcasoft.com.au
Information Technology Consulting Services
N.A.I.C.S.: 541512

ZOOMCAR HOLDINGS, INC.
Anjaneya Techno Park, No.147, 1st Floor Kodihalli,, Bangalore, 560008, India
Tel.: (91) 8048821871   DE
Web Site: https://www.zoomcar.com
Year Founded: 2021
ZCAR—(NASDAQ)
Rev.: $3,383,943
Assets: $238,208,934
Liabilities: $257,017,206
Net Worth: ($18,808,272)
Earnings: ($4,625,808)
Emp.: 3
Fiscal Year-end: 12/31/22
Investment Services
N.A.I.C.S.: 523999
Mohan Ananda (CEO & Chm)

ZOOMD TECHNOLOGIES LTD.
333 Bay Street 3400, Toronto, M5H 2S7, ON, Canada
Tel.: (604) 638-8063   AB
Web Site: https://www.zoomd.com
Year Founded: 2013
3ZD—(DEU)
Rev.: $32,113
Assets: $18,644
Liabilities: $9,958
Net Worth: $8,686
Earnings: ($4,654)
Fiscal Year-end: 12/31/23
Investment Services
N.A.I.C.S.: 523999
David Wood (Pres, Co-CEO & Co-CFO)

ZOOMERMEDIA LIMITED
70 Jefferson Avenue, Toronto, M6K 1Y4, ON, Canada
Tel.: (416) 363-7063
Web Site:
  https://www.zoomermedia.ca
ZUMRF—(OTCIQ)
Rev.: $48,714,911
Assets: $77,438,211
Liabilities: $38,444,953

ZOOMERMEDIA LIMITED

ZoomerMedia Limited—(Continued)
Net Worth: $38,993,259
Earnings: ($264,109)
Fiscal Year-end: 08/31/23
Publishing & Printing Services
N.A.I.C.S.: 516210
Moses Znaimer *(Founder, Pres & CEO)*

ZOOMLION HEAVY INDUSTRY SCIENCE & TECHNOLOGY CO., LTD.
Zoomlion Science Park Yinpen South Road 361, Changsha, Hunan, China
Tel.: (86) 73188997340
Web Site: https://en.zoomlion.com
Year Founded: 1992
1157—(HKG)
Rev.: $5,764,150,421
Assets: $17,101,932,875
Liabilities: $9,218,265,397
Net Worth: $7,883,667,479
Earnings: $335,899,424
Emp.: 25,283
Fiscal Year-end: 12/31/22
Construction Machinery Mfr
N.A.I.C.S.: 333120
Chunxin Zhan *(Chm & CEO)*

Subsidiaries:

CIFA S.p.A (1)
Via Stati Uniti d'America 26, 20030, Senago, Milano, Italy
Tel.: (39) 0299 0131
Web Site: https://www.cifa.com
Construction Equipment & Machinery Distr
N.A.I.C.S.: 423810
Berardino Gurliaccio *(Mgr-Plant)*

Hunan Zoomlion International Trade Co., Ltd. (1)
No 307 Yinpeng'S Rd, Changsha, 410013, Hunan, China
Tel.: (86) 73189751863
Industrial Machinery Distr
N.A.I.C.S.: 423830

Shenzhen RoadRover Technology Co.,Ltd (1)
9F Block C No 5 Bld Software Industrial Base NO 11 Haitian First Road, Nanshan District, Shenzhen, 518000, China (53.82%)
Tel.: (86) 75589488626
Web Site: https://www.roadrover.cn
Rev.: $47,943,862
Assets: $77,402,239
Liabilities: $22,499,970
Net Worth: $54,902,269
Earnings: $461,762
Emp.: 1,400
Fiscal Year-end: 12/31/2022
Automotive Electronic Product Mfr & Distr
N.A.I.C.S.: 336390
Tang Hongbing *(Chm)*

Zoomlion Gulf FZE (1)
South 2 Jebel Ali Free Zone, PO Box 262120, Dubai, United Arab Emirates
Tel.: (971) 48809048
Construction Equipment & Machinery Distr
N.A.I.C.S.: 423810
Ophelia Li *(Mgr-HR)*

Zoomlion Heavy Industry (Thailand) Co., Ltd. (1)
No 23 25 Soi Udom-suk 39/1 Sukhumvit Rd Bangchak Phakhanong, Bangkok, 10260, Thailand
Tel.: (66) 23616612
Construction Equipment & Machinery Distr
N.A.I.C.S.: 423810

Zoomlion Heavy Machinery Co., Ltd. (1)
11th Floor Block A Guohai Plaza No 17 Fuxing Road, Haidian District, Beijing, China
Tel.: (86) 5535631723
Agricultural Machinery Mfr
N.A.I.C.S.: 333248

Zoomlion Pakistan (Pvt.) Ltd. (1)
Bungalow No 85/1 Street No 30 Khayaban-e-Seher D H A Phase-6, Karachi, Pakistan

Tel.: (92) 2135240008
Construction Equipment & Machinery Distr
N.A.I.C.S.: 423810
Jawad Jadoon *(Mgr-HR)*

Zoomlion Vietnam Company Limited (1)
10th Floor Center Building No 01 Nguyen Huy Tuong Street, Thanh Xuan Trung ward Thanh Xuan district, Hanoi, Vietnam
Tel.: (84) 2422400008
Construction Equipment & Machinery Distr
N.A.I.C.S.: 423810

m-tec Mathis technik GmbH (1)
Otto-Hahn-Strasse 6, 79395, Neuenburg, Germany
Tel.: (49) 7 631 7090
Web Site: https://www.m-tec.com
Emp.: 100
Dry Mortar Production Machinery Mfr
N.A.I.C.S.: 333248
Michael Meding *(Mng Dir)*

Subsidiary (Non-US):

m-tec CZ s.r.o. (2)
Trida 3 Kvetna 1273, Malenovice, 763 02, Zlin, Czech Republic
Tel.: (420) 577100411
Web Site: http://www.m-tec.com
Sales Range: $25-49.9 Million
Emp.: 100
Dry Mortar Production Machinery Sales
N.A.I.C.S.: 423830

ZOOMMED INC.
6300 Auteuil Suite 121, Brossard, J4Z 3P2, QC, Canada
Tel.: (450) 678-5457
Web Site: http://www.zoommed.com
Year Founded: 2005
Sales Range: $1-9.9 Million
Professional Equipment Whslr
N.A.I.C.S.: 423490
Yves Marmet *(Chm, Pres & CEO)*

Subsidiaries:

ZoomMed Inc. (1)
590 Madison Ave, New York, NY 10022
Clinical Information Services
N.A.I.C.S.: 621999

ZOOMPASS HOLDINGS, INC.
2075 Kennedy Rd Ste 404, Toronto, M1T 3V3, ON, Canada
Tel.: (416) 862-5257 NV
Web Site: http://www.zoompass.com
Year Founded: 2013
ZPAS—(OTCBB)
Rev.: $872,465
Assets: $601,661
Liabilities: $3,410,896
Net Worth: ($2,809,235)
Earnings: ($18,686,189)
Fiscal Year-end: 12/31/20
Electronic Shopping & Internet Catalog
N.A.I.C.S.: 459999
Steven Roberts *(Chm)*

ZOONO GROUP LIMITED
Level 12 225 George Street, Sydney, 2000, NSW, Australia
Tel.: (61) 280428481 AU
Web Site: https://www.zoono.com
Year Founded: 1930
ZNO—(ASX)
Rev.: $19,509,060
Assets: $22,793,494
Liabilities: $7,641,341
Net Worth: $15,152,153
Earnings: $3,331,297
Fiscal Year-end: 06/30/21
Gold & Other Minerals Exploration
N.A.I.C.S.: 213115
Elissa Hansen *(Sec)*

Subsidiaries:

Zoono Group Limited (1)
Unit 3 24 Bishop Dunn Place, Flatbush, Auckland, 2013, New Zealand

Tel.: (64) 21659977
Sanitizer Product Mfr
N.A.I.C.S.: 325611
Paul Hyslop *(CEO & Mng Dir-Global)*

ZOOPLUS AG
Sonnenstrasse 15, 80331, Munich, Germany
Tel.: (49) 8995006100
Web Site: https://www.zooplus.de
Year Founded: 1999
ZO1—(DEU)
Rev.: $1,706,325,741
Assets: $404,219,276
Liabilities: $291,369,221
Net Worth: $112,850,055
Earnings: ($13,513,831)
Emp.: 713
Fiscal Year-end: 12/31/19
Pet Food & Accessories Online Retailer
N.A.I.C.S.: 459910
Cornelius Patt *(CEO & Member-Mgmt Bd)*

Subsidiaries:

BITIBA GmbH (1)
Herzog-Wilhelm-Strasse 12, 80331, Munich, Germany
Tel.: (49) 1865951302
Web Site: http://www.bitiba.co.uk
Dog & Cat Food Retailer
N.A.I.C.S.: 459910
Cornelius Patt *(Mng Dir)*

ZORLU FAKTORING A.S.
Esentepe Mah Buyukdere Cad No 199 Kat 1 Levent, Sisli, Istanbul, 34394, Turkiye
Tel.: (90) 2123177300
Web Site: http://www.zorlufaktoring.com
ZORLF—(IST)
Sales Range: Less than $1 Million
Financial Management Services
N.A.I.C.S.: 551112
Fikret Ozdemir *(Gen Mgr)*

ZORLU HOLDING AS
Zorlu Plaza, Avcilar, Istanbul, 34310, Turkiye
Tel.: (90) 2124562000
Web Site: http://www.zorlu.com
Holding Company; Energy Production, Home Textiles, Real Estate & Electronic Goods
N.A.I.C.S.: 551112
Ahmet Zorlu *(Chm)*

Subsidiaries:

Zorlu Enerji Elektrik Uretim AS (1)
Levent 199 Buyukdere Caddesi No 199, Sisli, 34394, Istanbul, Turkiye
Tel.: (90) 2124562300
Web Site: https://www.zorluenerji.com.tr
Rev.: $928,708,375
Assets: $2,082,676,252
Liabilities: $1,538,788,497
Net Worth: $543,887,755
Earnings: $1,235,471
Emp.: 2,645
Fiscal Year-end: 12/31/2022
Hydroelectric Power Generation Services
N.A.I.C.S.: 221111
Bekir Agirdir *(Chm)*

ZOTA HEALTH CARE LTD.
2/896 Hira Modi Street Sagrampura, Surat, 395 002, India
Tel.: (91) 2612331601
Web Site: https://www.zotahealthcare.com
Year Founded: 2000
ZOTA—(NSE)
Rev.: $17,014,927
Assets: $18,957,137
Liabilities: $9,322,619
Net Worth: $9,634,518
Earnings: ($692,141)

Emp.: 338
Fiscal Year-end: 03/31/23
Digital Marketing Services
N.A.I.C.S.: 541840
Ketankumar Chandulal Zota *(Chm)*

ZOTEFOAMS PLC
675 Mitcham Road, Croydon, CR9 3AL, Surrey, United Kingdom
Tel.: (44) 2086641600
Web Site: https://www.zotefoams.com
ZTF—(LSE)
Rev.: $160,778,844
Assets: $215,045,443
Liabilities: $76,774,804
Net Worth: $138,270,639
Earnings: $12,630,649
Emp.: 534
Fiscal Year-end: 12/31/22
Foam Products Mfr
N.A.I.C.S.: 326150
David Stirling *(CEO-Grp & CEO-Grp)*

Subsidiaries:

MuCell Extrusion LLC (1)
212 W Cummings Park, Woburn, MA 01801-1757
Tel.: (781) 281-7976
Web Site: https://www.mucellextrusion.com
Emp.: 15
Industrial Machinery Equipment Mfr
N.A.I.C.S.: 333248

T-FIT Insulation Solutions India Private Limited (1)
810 Shapath V SG Highway, Ahmedabad, 380015, Gujarat, India
Tel.: (91) 9902742816
Plastics Product Mfr
N.A.I.C.S.: 326199

Zotefoams Far East (1)
3F No 2 Lane 49 Sec 3 Muzha Road, Wenshan District, Taipei, 11648, Taiwan
Tel.: (886) 286618894
Web Site: http://www.zotefoams.com
Polyolefin Foam Product Mfr
N.A.I.C.S.: 326140

Zotefoams Inc. (1)
55 Precision Dr, Walton, KY 41094 (100%)
Tel.: (859) 371-4025
Emp.: 22
Foam Products Mfr
N.A.I.C.S.: 326150

Zotefoams International Limited (1)
675 Mitcham Road, Croydon, CR9 3AL, Surrey, United Kingdom
Tel.: (44) 2086641600
Emp.: 220
Foam Products Mfr
N.A.I.C.S.: 326140
David Stirling *(CEO)*

Zotefoams T-FIT Material Technology (Kunshan) Limited (1)
181 Huanlou Road, Development Zone, Kunshan, 215333, Jiangsu, China
Tel.: (86) 51250126001
Plastics Product Mfr
N.A.I.C.S.: 326199

ZOTYE AUTOMOBILE CO., LTD
No 1 Beihu Road Economic Development Zone Yongkang, Xixian County, Jinhua, 321300, Zhejiang, China
Tel.: (86) 57989270888
Web Site: https://www.zotye.com
Year Founded: 1998
000980—(SSE)
Rev.: $109,957,447
Assets: $999,777,547
Liabilities: $656,934,619
Net Worth: $342,842,928
Earnings: ($127,606,752)
Fiscal Year-end: 12/31/22
Automobile Parts Mfr
N.A.I.C.S.: 336390
Hu Zeyu *(Chm)*

ZOUM ARMADA
145 Saint Pierre St Ste 203, Montreal, H2Y 2L6, QC, Canada
Tel.: (514) 843-9855 Ca
Year Founded: 1993
Rev.: $14,000,000
Emp.: 45
N.A.I.C.S.: 541810
Elizabeth Deschesnes *(Pres & CEO)*

ZOY HOME FURNISHING CO., LTD.
Tong Pu Industrial Park, Anji County, Huzhou, 313300, Zhejiang, China
Tel.: (86) 5725528888
Web Site: https://www.zoy-living.com
Year Founded: 2003
603709—(SHG)
Rev.: $101,374,599
Assets: $155,821,466
Liabilities: $75,991,907
Net Worth: $79,829,559
Earnings: ($5,880,500)
Emp.: 1,500
Fiscal Year-end: 12/31/22
Furniture Product Mfr & Distr
N.A.I.C.S.: 337121

ZPC OTMUCHOW S.A.
ul Nyska 21, 48-385, Otmuchow, Poland
Tel.: (48) 774017247
Web Site:
http://www.grupaotmuchow.pl
Year Founded: 2011
OTM—(WAR)
Rev.: $72,334,858
Assets: $57,019,563
Liabilities: $26,147,358
Net Worth: $30,872,205
Earnings: $5,183,943
Fiscal Year-end: 12/31/23
Snack Food Mfr
N.A.I.C.S.: 311919
Marek Piatkowski *(CEO)*

ZPUE S.A.
ul Jedrzejowska 79c, 29-100, Wloszczowa, Poland
Tel.: (48) 413881000
Web Site: http://www.zpue.pl
PUE—(WAR)
Sales Range: $125-149.9 Million
Emp.: 1,951
Electric Equipment Mfr
N.A.I.C.S.: 335313
Andrzej Grzybek *(Chm-Mgmt Bd & CEO)*

ZQ CAPITAL MANAGEMENT LIMITED
7/F St John's Building 33 Garden Road, Central, Hongkong, China (Hong Kong)
Tel.: (852) 38906566
Web Site: http://www.zqcap.com
Emp.: 100
Investment Services
N.A.I.C.S.: 523999
Simon Shen *(Founder & Mng Partner)*

Subsidiaries:
Allergy Therapeutics plc (1)
Dominion Way, Worthing, BN14 8SA, W Sussex, United Kingdom (65%)
Tel.: (44) 1903844700
Web Site:
https://www.allergytherapeutics.com
Rev.: $69,766,178
Assets: $81,935,035
Liabilities: $77,247,219
Net Worth: $4,687,816
Earnings: ($50,829,120)
Emp.: 622
Fiscal Year-end: 06/30/2024
Biological Product Mfr
N.A.I.C.S.: 325412

Manuel Llobet *(CEO)*

Subsidiary (Non-US):
Allergy Therapeutics Netherlands BV (2)
Sputnik 52, 3824 MG, Amersfoort, Netherlands
Tel.: (31) 88 255 3749
Web Site: https://allergytherapeutics.nl
Pharmaceutical Products Distr
N.A.I.C.S.: 456110

Bencard A.G. (2)
Tumigerstrasse 71, 8606, Greifensee, Switzerland
Tel.: (41) 44 942 0013
Web Site: https://bencard.ch
Pharmaceutical Products Distr
N.A.I.C.S.: 456110
Martin Graf *(Gen Mgr)*

Bencard Allergie GmbH (2)
Leopoldstrasse 175, 80804, Munich, Germany
Tel.: (49) 8 936 8110
Web Site: https://www.bencard.com
Emp.: 140
Pharmaceuticals Producut Sales
N.A.I.C.S.: 424210

Subsidiary (Non-US):
Bencard Allergie (Austria) GmbH (3)
Stiftgasse 18/5-6, 1070, Vienna, Austria
Tel.: (43) 1 606 1111
Web Site: http://www.bencard.com
Sales Range: $25-49.9 Million
Emp.: 9
Pharmaceutical Products Distr
N.A.I.C.S.: 424210
Bodo Steinert *(Gen Mgr)*

POPULAR Holdings Limited (1)
15 Serangoon North Avenue 5, Singapore, 554360, Singapore (100%)
Tel.: (65) 64629500
Web Site: http://www.popularworld.com
Sales Range: $400-449.9 Million
Emp.: 4,000
Book Publishers
N.A.I.C.S.: 513130
Ngoh Lim Lee *(CEO-Malaysia & Singapore)*

ZRAK D.D. SARAJEVO
Adema Buce br 148, 71000, Sarajevo, Bosnia & Herzegovina
Tel.: (387) 3 361 9807
Web Site: http://www.zrak.ba
Year Founded: 1948
ZRKSRK1—(SARE)
Rev.: $2,451,961
Assets: $21,198,156
Liabilities: $12,002,915
Net Worth: $9,195,241
Earnings: $79,059
Emp.: 113
Fiscal Year-end: 12/31/20
Electromechanical Device Mfr
N.A.I.C.S.: 334419

ZRAK-OPTOELEKTRONIKA A.D.
Vojvode Misica Bb, 74270, Teslic, Bosnia & Herzegovina
Tel.: (387) 53433847
ZRKV-R-A—(BANJ)
Rev.: $57,481
Assets: $765,319
Liabilities: $86,690
Net Worth: $678,629
Earnings: ($20,114)
Emp.: 1
Fiscal Year-end: 12/31/12
Optical Instrument Mfr
N.A.I.C.S.: 333310
Sasa Vajic *(Chm-Supervisory Bd)*

ZRP PRINTING GROUP CO., LTD.
28 Yanjiang East 3rd Road, Torch Development Zone, Zhongshan, 528436, Guangdong, China
Tel.: (86) 76085283388
Web Site: https://www.zrp.com.cn
Year Founded: 1990
301223—(CHIN)
Rev.: $365,143,041
Assets: $568,085,083
Liabilities: $165,587,577
Net Worth: $402,497,506
Earnings: $28,728,662
Emp.: 3,500
Fiscal Year-end: 12/31/23
Packaging Products Mfr
N.A.I.C.S.: 322220
Huanran Huang *(Chm)*

Subsidiaries:
Guangdong Fusion E-commerce Co., Ltd. (1)
28 Yanjiang East 3rd Road Torch Development Zone, Zhongshan, 528436, China
Tel.: (86) 76085283388
Packaging Products Mfr
N.A.I.C.S.: 326199

Tianjin Masterwork Green Packging Technology Co., Ltd. (1)
No 102 Yongxing Road, Tianjin Beichen Economic and Technological Development Zone Beichen, Tianjin, China
Tel.: (86) 18698008756
Web Site: https://www.gptech-eco.com
Moulded Pulp Packaging Products Mfr
N.A.I.C.S.: 322299

Tianjin ZRP Printing Technology Co., Ltd. (1)
No 19 Tong Sheng Road Wind Power IndustrialPark, Beichen District, Tianjin, 300400, China
Tel.: (86) 2258873388
Printing & Product Packaging Services
N.A.I.C.S.: 561910

ZRP Printing (Kunshan) Company Limited (1)
No 23 Beiyuan Road, Dianshanhu, Kunshan, 215245, China
Tel.: (86) 51255173388
Packaging Products Mfr
N.A.I.C.S.: 326199

ZRP Printing (Shenyang) Company Limited (1)
No 30 Puyue Street Shenbei New Area, Shenyang, 110000, China
Tel.: (86) 2431721688
Packaging Products Mfr
N.A.I.C.S.: 326199

ZRP Printing (Vietnam) Co., Ltd. (1)
No 26 VSIP II-A Road No 29 Vietnam - Singapore Industrial Park II-A, Vinh Tan Commune, Tan Uyen, Binh Duong, Vietnam
Tel.: (84) 347085022
Printing & Product Packaging Services
N.A.I.C.S.: 561910

ZSA LEGAL RECRUITMENT LTD.
200 University Avenue Suite 1000, Toronto, M5H 3C6, ON, Canada
Tel.: (163) 82051
Web Site: http://www.zsa.ca
Year Founded: 1997
Recruitment Services
N.A.I.C.S.: 561311
Christopher Sweeney *(CEO)*

ZSK-LOZOVO AD
Severnata promishlena zona, Burgas, 8000, Bulgaria
Tel.: (359) 56881070
ZSK—(BUL)
Sales Range: Less than $1 Million
Concrete Products Mfr
N.A.I.C.S.: 327390
Dimitrina Popova *(Dir-IR)*

ZST DIGITAL NETWORKS, INC.
206 Tongbo Street Boyaxicheng Second Floor, Zhengzhou, 450007, Henan, China
Tel.: (86) 37167660609 DE
Web Site: http://www.zstdigital.com
Year Founded: 2006
Sales Range: $125-149.9 Million
Emp.: 124
Digital & Optical Network Equipment Developer & Supplier
N.A.I.C.S.: 334290
Bo Zhong *(Chm & CEO)*

ZTC BANJA VRUCICA A.D. TESLIC
Nede Nedica 1, 74270, Teslic, Bosnia & Herzegovina
Tel.: (387) 53431270
Web Site: https://www.banja-vrucica.com
BVRU—(BANJ)
Sales Range: $1-9.9 Million
Emp.: 296
Medical Rehabilitation Services
N.A.I.C.S.: 621999

ZTE CORPORATION
ZTE Plaza Keji Road South, Hi-Tech Industrial Park Nanshan District, Shenzhen, 518057, Guangdong, China
Tel.: (86) 75526770000 CH
Web Site: https://www.zte.com.cn
Year Founded: 1997
000063—(SSE)
Rev.: $17,203,544,251
Assets: $27,824,312,971
Liabilities: $18,363,268,858
Net Worth: $9,461,044,113
Earnings: $1,291,226,324
Emp.: 72,093
Fiscal Year-end: 12/31/23
Telecommunication Servicesb
N.A.I.C.S.: 517810
Zixue Li *(Chm)*

Subsidiaries:
Anhui Wantong Posts & Telecommunication Company Limited (1)
Building B1 Huayi Science Park No 71, Tianda Road High-tech Zone, Hefei, Anhui, China
Tel.: (86) 551 661 0972
Web Site: https://www.ahwt.com.cn
Integrated Communication Services
N.A.I.C.S.: 541511

ZTE (Australia) Pty Ltd (1)
Level 6 128 Exhibition Street, Melbourne, 3000, VIC, Australia
Tel.: (61) 1300789475
Web Site: http://www.ztemobiles.com.au
Emp.: 50
Telecom Services
N.A.I.C.S.: 517121

ZTE (H.K) Limited (1)
Rm 1206-07 Berkshire House 25 Westlands Road, Hong Kong, China (Hong Kong)
Tel.: (852) 25198993
Telecommunication Servicesb
N.A.I.C.S.: 517810

ZTE (Malaysia) Corporation (1)
165 Jalan Ampang, Bhd Lvl 20-01, 50450, Kuala Lumpur, Malaysia
Tel.: (60) 321619023
Telecom Services
N.A.I.C.S.: 517121

ZTE (Thailand) Co., Ltd. (1)
20th Floor Unit 2005-7 Empire Tower 195 South Sathorn Road, Yannawa Sathorn, Bangkok, 10120, Thailand
Tel.: (66) 2 670 4071
Telecommunication Servicesb
N.A.I.C.S.: 517810

ZTE Canada Inc (1)
2550 Victoria Park Ave Suite 600, Toronto, M2J 5A9, ON, Canada
Tel.: (416) 753-8858
Web Site: http://www.ztecanada.com
Telecommunication Servicesb
N.A.I.C.S.: 517810

ZTE CORPORATION

ZTE Corporation—(Continued)

ZTE Corporation (1)
PO Box 5632, Kampala, Uganda
Tel.: (256) 41 255975
Telecom Services
N.A.I.C.S.: 517121

ZTE Corporation (1)
Jose Bardasano Baos No 9, 8th Fl Ofc C,
28016, Madrid, Spain
Tel.: (34) 913844246
Telecommunications Equipment Mfr
N.A.I.C.S.: 517112

ZTE Corporation Armenia (1)
403 Citadel Business Center, Terian 105 1,
Yerevan, Armenia
Tel.: (374) 10514345
Web Site: http://wwwen.zte.com.cn
Telecommunication Servicesb
N.A.I.C.S.: 517810

ZTE Corporation Istanbul Telekominikasyon. San. Ve Tic. Ltd. Sti. (1)
No 1 17 Partas Ctr, Icerenkoy, Istanbul,
Turkiye
Tel.: (90) 2164694710
Web Site: http://wwwen.zte.com.cn
Emp.: 50
Telecommunication Servicesb
N.A.I.C.S.: 517112

ZTE Deutschland GmbH (1)
Am Seestern 18, 40547, Dusseldorf, Germany
Tel.: (49) 2115638440
Web Site: http://www.zte-deutschland.de
Emp.: 150
Telecommunications Equipment Provider
N.A.I.C.S.: 517410

ZTE Korea Limited (1)
23 5 Yoido Dong Youngdeungpo Gu, Han-
wha Securities Bldg, Seoul, 150-717, Korea
(South)
Tel.: (82) 2 6290 6800
Telecom Services
N.A.I.C.S.: 517111

ZTEST ELECTRONICS INC.
523 McNicoll Avenue, North York,
M2H 2C9, ON, Canada
Tel.: (604) 837-3751 **ON**
Web Site: https://www.ztest.com
Year Founded: 1996
ZTSTF—(OTCIQ)
Rev.: $7,132,132
Assets: $5,122,912
Liabilities: $1,835,598
Net Worth: $3,287,315
Earnings: $1,281,723
Fiscal Year-end: 06/30/24
Electronics Designer & Mfr
N.A.I.C.S.: 334419
Steve Smith (Pres & CEO)

Subsidiaries:

Permatech Electronic
Corporation (1)
523 McNicoll Avenue, North York, M2H
2C9, ON, Canada
Tel.: (416) 297-5155
Emp.: 40
Contract Electronic Mfr
N.A.I.C.S.: 334419
John Perrault (Pres)

ZTO EXPRESS (CAYMAN) INC.
No 1685 Huazhi Road, Huaxin Town
Qingpu District, Shanghai, 201708,
China
Tel.: (86) 2159804508 **CH**
Web Site: https://en.zto.com
Year Founded: 2002
ZTO—(NYSE)
Rev.: $5,319,411,138
Assets: $12,248,729,093
Liabilities: $3,902,416,510
Net Worth: $8,346,312,583
Earnings: $1,212,125,748
Emp.: 23,554
Fiscal Year-end: 12/31/23
Express Delivery Services

N.A.I.C.S.: 492110
Jianfa Lai (VP-Operations)

ZTR ACQUISITION CORP.
918-1030 W Georgia St, Vancouver,
V6E 2Y3, BC, Canada
Tel.: (604) 288-8005
Web Site:
https://www.angoldresources.com
Year Founded: 2004
ZTH—(CNSX)
Assets: $106,345
Liabilities: $555,807
Net Worth: ($449,462)
Earnings: ($155,479)
Fiscal Year-end: 12/31/19
Oil & Gas Exploration Services
N.A.I.C.S.: 213112

ZTS INMART AS
T G Masaryka 1, 94048, Nove
Zamky, Slovakia
Tel.: (421) 356428085
Web Site: https://www.ztsinmart.sk
1ZIM01AE—(BRA)
Sales Range: Less than $1 Million
Securities Brokerage Services
N.A.I.C.S.: 523150
Frantisek Zvrskovec (Chm-Mgmt Bd)

ZTS SABINOV AS
Holleho 27, Sabinov, 083 30, Kosice,
Slovakia
Tel.: (421) 514561205
Web Site: https://www.ztssabinov.sk
Year Founded: 1957
1ZTS01NE—(BRA)
Sales Range: Less than $1 Million
Gear Mfr
N.A.I.C.S.: 333612
Alexej Beljajev (Chm, Chm-Mgmt Bd,
Dir Gen & Gen Mgr)

**ZTS VYSKUMNO-VYVOJOVY
USTAV KOSICE AS**
Juzna Trieda 95, 041 24, Kosice,
Slovakia
Tel.: (421) 556834216
Web Site: http://www.ztsvvu.eu
Year Founded: 1976
1SVV01AE—(BRA)
Sales Range: Less than $1 Million
Industrial Machinery Mfr
N.A.I.C.S.: 333248

**ZU JEDDELOH PFLANZEN-
HANDELS GMBH**
Wischenstrasse 7, 26188, Edewecht,
Germany
Tel.: (49) 440591800
Web Site: http://www.jeddeloh.de
Year Founded: 1932
Sales Range: $10-24.9 Million
Emp.: 55
Nursery Product Distr
N.A.I.C.S.: 424930
Rolf Watermann (Co-Mng Dir)

ZUBLER GERATEBAU GMBH
Buchbrunnenweg 26, 89081, Ulm,
Germany
Tel.: (49) 73114520
Web Site: http://www.zubler.de
Rev.: $10,000,000
Emp.: 50
Mechanical & Electronic Equipment
Mfr
N.A.I.C.S.: 334419
Kurt Zubler (Mng Dir)

**ZUBLIN IMMOBILIEN HOLD-
ING AG**
Hardturmstrasse 76, CH-8005, Zu-
rich, Switzerland
Tel.: (41) 442062939
Web Site: https://www.zueblin.ch

Year Founded: 1912
ZUBN—(SWX)
Rev.: $10,022,173
Assets: $254,319,290
Liabilities: $102,906,874
Net Worth: $151,412,417
Earnings: $1,483,370
Emp.: 4
Fiscal Year-end: 03/31/24
Real Estate Business Management
N.A.I.C.S.: 531210
Wolfgang Zurcher (Chm)

Subsidiaries:

Mingari BV (1)
Paasheuvelweg 26, Zuidoost, 1105 BJ, Am-
sterdam, Noord-Holland, Netherlands
Tel.: (31) 203420410
Emp.: 3
Property Management Services
N.A.I.C.S.: 531312

ZIAG Immobilien AG (1)
Rosstrase 96, 40476, Dusseldorf, Germany
Tel.: (49) 21141554700
Web Site: http://www.buerostandort-
fasanenhof.de
Emp.: 7
Commercial Property Management Services
N.A.I.C.S.: 531312
Matthias Ulrich (Head-Asset Mgmt)

Zublin Immobilien Management
AG (1)
Claridenstrasse 20, 8002, Zurich, Switzer-
land
Tel.: (41) 442062939
Property Management Services
N.A.I.C.S.: 531312

ZUCCHETTI GROUP S.P.A.
Via Solferino 1, 26900, Lodi, Italy
Tel.: (39) 03715942444
Web Site: http://www.zucchetti.com
Sales Range: $300-349.9 Million
Emp.: 1,900
IT Consulting Services
N.A.I.C.S.: 541690
Alessandro Zucchetti (CEO)

Subsidiaries:

PITECO S.p.A. (1)
Via Imbonati 18, 20159, Milan, Italy
Tel.: (39) 023660931
Web Site: http://www.pitecolab.it
Rev.: $20,439,664
Assets: $123,791,537
Liabilities: $67,071,786
Net Worth: $56,719,751
Earnings: $5,025,439
Emp.: 156
Fiscal Year-end: 12/31/2020
Financial Software Publisher
N.A.I.C.S.: 513210

Subsidiary (US):

Juniper Payments, LLC (2)
9440 E Boston, Wichita, KS 67207
Tel.: (316) 267-3200
Web Site: https://www.juniperpayments.com
Financial Services
N.A.I.C.S.: 523999

Subsidiary (Domestic):

Rad Informatica S.R.L. (2)
Via Imbonati 18, 20159, Milan, Italy
Tel.: (39) 02366093900
Web Site: https://www.radinformatica.it
Emp.: 2,170
Software Development Services
N.A.I.C.S.: 541511

Zucchetti AXESS S.p.A. (1)
Via G Rossini 1, 20020, Lainate, Milano,
Italy
Tel.: (39) 0284524600
Web Site: http://www.axessmc.com
Emp.: 200
Computer & Peripheral Equipment Mfr
N.A.I.C.S.: 334118
Alberto Alberto Pavesi (CEO)

Zucchetti Brasil Solucoes de Informatica Ltda (1)

INTERNATIONAL PUBLIC

Rua Pascoal Stabile 515 sala 01 Jardim
Brasilia, Mogi Mirim, 13801-035, Sao Paulo,
Brazil
Tel.: (55) 8007746090
Human Resource Consulting Services
N.A.I.C.S.: 541612

Zucchetti Centro Sistemi S.P.A. (1)
Via Lungarno 305/a, Terranuova Bracciolini,
52028, Arezzo, Italy
Tel.: (39) 05591971
Web Site: http://www.centrosistemi.it
Emp.: 200
Software Development Services
N.A.I.C.S.: 541511

Zucchetti GmbH (1)
Saarwiesenstrasse 5 Volklingen, Volklingen,
Saarbrucken, Saarland, Germany
Tel.: (49) 68985662400
Business Management Consulting Services
N.A.I.C.S.: 541611
Dirk Schwindling (CEO)

Zucchetti Romania SRL (1)
Soseaua Borsului nr 32 E Parc Industrial,
410605, Oradea, Bihor, Romania
Tel.: (40) 259414584
Human Resource Consulting Services
N.A.I.C.S.: 541612

Zucchetti USA LLC (1)
9 Bartlet St 385, Andover, MA 01810
Tel.: (978) 688-6401
Software Development Services
N.A.I.C.S.: 541511
Jay Huapaya (Gen Mgr)

Zucchetti s.p.a. (1)
Via Solferino 1, Lodi, 26900, Italy
Tel.: (39) 03715942444
Human Resource Consulting Services
N.A.I.C.S.: 541612

ZUE S.A.
ul K Czapinskiego 3, 30-048, Krakow,
Poland
Tel.: (48) 122663939
Web Site: https://www.grupazue.pl
ZUE—(WAR)
Rev.: $377,066,564
Assets: $237,642,530
Liabilities: $186,810,467
Net Worth: $50,832,063
Earnings: $5,367,632
Emp.: 907
Fiscal Year-end: 12/31/23
Other Heavy & Civil Engineering
Construction
N.A.I.C.S.: 237990
Ewa Bosak (Chief Acctg Officer)

Subsidiaries:

Biuro Projektow Komunikacyjnych w
Poznaniu Sp. z o.o. (1)
Ul Kosciuszki 68, 61-891, Poznan, Poland
Tel.: (48) 618588720
Web Site: http://www.bpk-poznan.com.pl
Engineeering Services
N.A.I.C.S.: 541330

Railway gft Polska Sp. z o.o. (1)
Ul K Czapinskiego 3, 30-048, Krakow, Po-
land
Tel.: (48) 126204130
Web Site: https://www.railwaygft.pl
Railway Construction Services
N.A.I.C.S.: 237990
Miroslaw Musyl (Pres & CEO)

ZUG ESTATES HOLDING AG
Baarerstrasse 18, 6300, Zug, Swit-
zerland
Tel.: (41) 417291010
Web Site: https://www.zugestates.ch
ZUGN—(SWX)
Rev.: $94,351,841
Assets: $2,010,474,016
Liabilities: $906,059,863
Net Worth: $1,104,414,153
Earnings: $26,921,108
Emp.: 134
Fiscal Year-end: 12/31/23
Real Estate Services

AND PRIVATE COMPANIES

N.A.I.C.S.: 531390
Beat Schwab (Chm)

Subsidiaries:

Hotelbusiness Zug AG (1)
Industriestrasse 14, 6302, Zug, Switzerland
Tel.: (41) 41 727 48 48
Web Site: http://www.hotelbusinesszug.ch
Home Management Services
N.A.I.C.S.: 721110

ZEW Immobilien AG (1)
Industriestrasse 8, 5036, Oberentfelden, Switzerland
Tel.: (41) 41 7291020
Real Estate Manangement Services
N.A.I.C.S.: 531390

Zug Estates AG (1)
Suurstoffi 12, 6343, Rotkreuz, Switzerland
Tel.: (41) 41 799 40 60
Real Estate Manangement Services
N.A.I.C.S.: 531390

ZUGER KANTONALBANK AG

Bahnhofstrasse 1, 6301, Zug, Switzerland
Tel.: (41) 417091111
Web Site: https://www.zugerkb.ch
Year Founded: 1892
ZUGER—(SWX)
Rev.: $387,728,787
Assets: $22,367,867,936
Liabilities: $20,593,043,826
Net Worth: $1,774,824,110
Earnings: $148,347,992
Emp.: 477
Fiscal Year-end: 12/31/23
Financial Services
N.A.I.C.S.: 523999
Hanspeter Rhyner (Chm-Mgmt Bd, Pres & CEO)

ZUIKO CO., LTD.

2-1-2 Saitohanada, Ibaraki, 567-0082, Osaka, Japan
Tel.: (81) 726482220
Web Site: https://www.zuiko.co.jp
Year Founded: 1946
6279—(TKS)
Rev.: $154,115,330
Assets: $349,331,390
Liabilities: $102,939,710
Net Worth: $246,391,680
Earnings: $9,770,020
Emp.: 617
Fiscal Year-end: 02/29/24
Paper Product Machine Mfr
N.A.I.C.S.: 333248
Toyoshi Umebayashi (Pres & CEO)

Subsidiaries:

Zuiko (Shanghai) Corporation (1)
No 328 Xingbang Road, Jiangding, Shanghai, 201815, China
Tel.: (86) 2169169492
Web Site: https://www.zuiko.co.jp
Sanitary Napkin Machine Mfr
N.A.I.C.S.: 333248

Zuiko Co., Ltd. - Torikai-Kami Factory (1)
4350 Torikai-Kami, Settsu, 566-0062, Osaka, Japan
Tel.: (81) 726532900
Sanitary Napkin Machine Mfr
N.A.I.C.S.: 333248

Zuiko Co., Ltd. - Torikai-Naka Factory (1)
2236 Torikai-Naka, Settsu, 566-0064, Osaka, Japan
Tel.: (81) 726533222
Sanitary Napkin Machine Mfr
N.A.I.C.S.: 333248

ZUIVELCOOPERATIE FRIESLANDCAMPINA U.A.

Stationsplein 4, 3818 LE, Amersfoort, Netherlands
Tel.: (31) 337133333   NI
Web Site: http://www.frieslandcampina.com
Sales Range: $5-14.9 Billion
Emp.: 23,816
Dairy Products Mfr
N.A.I.C.S.: 311511
Hein Schumacher (CEO)

Subsidiaries:

CMG Grundstucksverwaltungs- und Beteiligungs - GmbH (1)
Wimpfener Str 125, 74078, Heilbronn, Baden-Wurttemberg, Germany
Tel.: (49) 7131 4890
Dairy Products Distr
N.A.I.C.S.: 424430

Den Hollander Food B.V (1)
Hanzeweg 30, 7241 CS, Lochem, Netherlands
Tel.: (31) 573 29 89 29
Web Site: http://www.denhollanderfood.nl
Emp.: 150
Cheese Distr
N.A.I.C.S.: 424430
Annemarie Lina (Mgr-HRM)

Engro Foods Limited (51%)
5th Floor Harbor Front Building HC-3 Marine Drive Block 4, Clifton, Karachi, 75600, Pakistan
Tel.: (92) 21 3529 6000
Web Site: http://www.engrofoods.com
Rev.: $232,915,258
Assets: $163,477,586
Liabilities: $100,214,656
Net Worth: $63,262,930
Earnings: $457,962
Emp.: 1,423
Fiscal Year-end: 12/31/2018
Dairy Products Mfr
N.A.I.C.S.: 112120
Ali Ahmed Khan (Mng Dir)

France Creme S.A.S (1)
Z I Les Fraries, 42740, Saint-Paul-en-Jarez, France
Tel.: (33) 47 7737120
Dairy Products Distr
N.A.I.C.S.: 424430

Friesland Arabia Ltd. (1)
Industrial Area Al Majhar District Phase 1, Jeddah, Saudi Arabia
Tel.: (966) 26364007
Dairy Products Distr
N.A.I.C.S.: 424430
Irshad Mavad (Head-Acct & Fin)

FrieslandCampina (Hong Kong) Ltd. (1)
39/F Office Tower Langham Place 8 Argyle Street, Mongkok, Kowloon, China (Hong Kong)
Tel.: (852) 2547 6226
Web Site: http://www.friso.com.hk
Dairy Products Distr
N.A.I.C.S.: 424430
Arnoud van den Berg (Mng Dir)

FrieslandCampina (Singapore) Pte. Ltd. (1)
47 Scotts Road Goldbell Towers 03-01/02, Singapore, 228233, Singapore
Tel.: (65) 64 19 8488
Web Site: http://www.friso.com.sg
Dairy Products Distr
N.A.I.C.S.: 424430
Pohling Cheang (Head-Sls)

FrieslandCampina (Thailand) PCL (1)
Phaholyothin road 6th Floor S P Building 388, Samsen Nai Phayathai, 10400, Bangkok, Thailand
Tel.: (66) 2620 1900
Dairy Product Mfr & Distr
N.A.I.C.S.: 311511
Arpa Phusangmook (Dir-HR)

FrieslandCampina AMEA Pte Ltd (1)
3 Temasek Avenue 11-01 Centennial Tower, 039190, Singapore, Singapore
Tel.: (65) 65808100
Dairy Products Distr
N.A.I.C.S.: 424430
Philip Langerak (Mgr-Supply Chain)

FrieslandCampina Austria GmbH (1)
Bahnhofstrasse 134, 8950, Stainach, Austria
Tel.: (43) 36 82285413
Dairy Products Distr
N.A.I.C.S.: 424430

FrieslandCampina Belgium N.V (1)
Venecoolaan 17, 9880, Aalter, Belgium
Tel.: (32) 9 325 36 46
Web Site: http://www.frieslandcampina.be
Dairy Product Mfr & Distr
N.A.I.C.S.: 311511

FrieslandCampina Canarias S.A. (1)
Pol Ind Valle de Guimar 20, Guimar, 38500, Santa Cruz de Tenerife, Spain
Tel.: (34) 928716629
Dairy Products Distr
N.A.I.C.S.: 424430

FrieslandCampina Cheese & Butter B.V (1)
Noorderweg 27, Groningen, 9824 PA, Noordwijk, Netherlands
Tel.: (31) 594 677777
Web Site: http://www.frieslandcampina.com
Emp.: 60
Dairy Product Mfr & Distr
N.A.I.C.S.: 311511

FrieslandCampina Cheese France S.A.S. (1)
2820 RN 7 Est, BP 3, 13560, Senas, France
Tel.: (33) 490 572929
Dairy Products Distr
N.A.I.C.S.: 424430

FrieslandCampina Cheese Germany (1)
Hatzper Strasse 30, 45149, Essen, Germany
Tel.: (49) 201 8712746
Dairy Products Distr
N.A.I.C.S.: 424430

FrieslandCampina Consumer Products Europe B.V. (1)
Stationsplein 4, 3818 LE, Amersfoort, Netherlands
Tel.: (31) 33 713 25 11
Dairy Products Distr
N.A.I.C.S.: 424430

FrieslandCampina Consumer Products International B.V. (1)
P Stuyvesantweg 1, 8937 AC, Leeuwarden, Netherlands
Tel.: (31) 58 2999111
Dairy Products Distr
N.A.I.C.S.: 424430

FrieslandCampina Fresh (Thailand) Co., Ltd (1)
99/30 Moo2 Chaeng Watthana Road Tuongsonghong, Laksi, 10210, Bangkok, Thailand
Tel.: (66) 25760030
Dairy Products Distr
N.A.I.C.S.: 424430

FrieslandCampina Germany GmbH (1)
Wimpfener Strasse 125, 74078, Heilbronn, Germany
Tel.: (49) 7131 489 0
Web Site: http://www.campina.de
Dairy Products Distr
N.A.I.C.S.: 424430

FrieslandCampina Ghana (1)
Ridge Street No 10 Roman Ridge, Accra, Ghana
Tel.: (233) 30276 0433
Dairy Products Distr
N.A.I.C.S.: 424430

FrieslandCampina Hungaria Zrt (1)
Vaci ut 33, 1134, Budapest, Hungary
Tel.: (36) 1 802 7700
Dairy Product Mfr & Distr
N.A.I.C.S.: 311511
Ildiko Nemeth (Mgr-Sls-Modern Trade)

FrieslandCampina Indonesia (1)
Jalan Raya Bogor Km 26, 13740, Jakarta, Indonesia
Tel.: (62) 21 8710511
Dairy Product Mfr & Distr
N.A.I.C.S.: 311511

Heru Trimandias (Mgr-Sls & Ops Plng)

FrieslandCampina Ingredients Latin America Ltda (1)
Rua dos Canarios 65, Vinhedo, Sao Paulo, 13280 000, Brazil
Tel.: (55) 19 38866820
Dairy Products Distr
N.A.I.C.S.: 424430
Eliane Stefanow Ferreira Cabral (Mgr-Bus Dev)

FrieslandCampina Ingredients North America, Inc. (1)
61 S Paramus Rd Ste 422, Paramus, NJ 07652
Tel.: (201) 655-7786
Dairy Products Distr
N.A.I.C.S.: 424430

FrieslandCampina Italy SRL (1)
Palazzo Andromedia ingresso 2 Via Paracelso 18, 20041, Agrate Brianza, Italy
Tel.: (39) 039 6072533
Dairy Products Distr
N.A.I.C.S.: 424430

FrieslandCampina Kievit Gmbh (1)
Wiedenbruckerstrasse 80, 59555, Lippstadt, Germany
Tel.: (49) 2941 662 0
Dairy Products Distr
N.A.I.C.S.: 424430

FrieslandCampina Middle East JLT (1)
8th floor Palladium Tower Jumeirah Lake Towers, Dubai, United Arab Emirates
Tel.: (971) 4 4551800
Dairy Products Distr
N.A.I.C.S.: 424430
Maurits Klavert (Mng Dir)

FrieslandCampina Nederland Holding B.V. (1)
Kanaalstraat 4, Lochem, 7241 DA, Gelderland, Netherlands
Tel.: (31) 573288444
Emp.: 200
Holding Company
N.A.I.C.S.: 551112
Rein Dem (Gen Mgr)

FrieslandCampina Nutrifeed B.V. (1)
Lage Landstraat 7, 5462 GJ, Veghel, Netherlands
Tel.: (31) 413 372 600
Web Site: http://www.nutrifeed.nl
Cattle Feed Mfr
N.A.I.C.S.: 311119
Joost van de Rakt (Mng Dir)

FrieslandCampina Professional NV (1)
Grote Baan 34, 3560, Lummen, Belgium
Tel.: (32) 13 310 310
Web Site: http://www.frieslandcampinaprof.com
Dairy Product Mfr & Distr
N.A.I.C.S.: 311511
Liesbeth Buyle (Mgr-Compliance)

FrieslandCampina Romania S.A. (1)
Calea Baciului 2-4, 400230, Cluj-Napoca, Romania
Tel.: (40) 264 50 20 00
Dairy Products Distr
N.A.I.C.S.: 424430
Poturlu Gabriel (Mgr-ICT)

FrieslandCampina Russia (1)
Naberezhnaya Tower Presnenskaya naberezhnaya 10 Block B 12th floor, 123112, Moscow, Russia
Tel.: (7) 49593336463
Dairy Products Distr
N.A.I.C.S.: 424430

FrieslandCampina Spain (1)
Roger de Lluria 50 4o B, 8009, Barcelona, Spain
Tel.: (34) 932 722 664
Dairy Products Distr
N.A.I.C.S.: 424430
Cristina Tomas (Mgr-Mktg & Shopper Mktg)

FrieslandCampina Trading (Shanghai) Co. Ltd. (1)
28th Fl Shanghai Times Square Office Tower no 93 Huai Hai Zhong Road 9,

ZUIVELCOOPERATIE FRIESLANDCAMPINA U.A.

Zuivelcooperatie FrieslandCampina U.A.—(Continued)
200021, Shanghai, China
Tel.: (86) 21 63910066
Dairy Products Distr
N.A.I.C.S.: 424430

FrieslandCampina UK Ltd. (1)
Denne Rd 10, Horsham, RH12 1JF, West Sussex, United Kingdom
Tel.: (44) 1403273273
Dairy Products Distr
N.A.I.C.S.: 424430

FrieslandCampina Vietnam Co. Ltd. (1)
Binh Hoa Commune, Thuan An, Vietnam
Tel.: (84) 650 3754422
Dairy Product Mfr & Distr
N.A.I.C.S.: 311511
Hang Vo *(Mgr-Ops)*

FrieslandCampina WAMCO Nigeria Plc. (1)
Acme Road Plot 7B Ikeja Industrial Estate, Ogba, Ikeja, Lagos, Nigeria
Tel.: (234) 1 271 51 00
Dairy Products Distr
N.A.I.C.S.: 424430
Bamisaye Adebayo *(Mgr-Shift Production)*

FrieslandCampina Werknemers B.V. (1)
Frisaxstraat 4, Wolvega, 8471 ZW, Netherlands
Tel.: (31) 418 57 13 00
Dairy Products Distr
N.A.I.C.S.: 424430

Frieslandcampina Hellas S.A. (1)
18 Nik Zekakou, 15125, Maroussi, Greece
Tel.: (30) 2106166400
Web Site: http://www.nounou.gr
Dairy Products Distr
N.A.I.C.S.: 424430
Velia Kouveli *(Mgr-Logistics)*

Kaashandel Culemborg B.V. (1)
Broekveldselaan 9, Bodegraven, 2411 NL, Zuid-Holland, Netherlands
Tel.: (31) 172630100
Dairy Products Distr
N.A.I.C.S.: 424430

Koninklijke FrieslandCampina N.V. (1)
Stationsplein 4, 3818 LE, Amersfoort, Netherlands
Tel.: (31) 337133333
Web Site: http://www.frieslandcampina.com
Sales Range: $5-14.9 Billion
Emp.: 16,438
Nutritional Dairy Products, Fruit-Based Drinks & Ingredients Mfr
N.A.I.C.S.: 311514
Kees Gielen *(CFO)*

Subsidiary (Non-US):

Alaska Milk Corporation (2)
6/F Corinthian Plaza 121 Paseo de Roxas, Makati, Philippines
Tel.: (63) 2 840 4500
Web Site: http://www.alaskamilk.com.ph
Emp.: 700
Milk Products
N.A.I.C.S.: 424430
Wilfred Steven Uytengsu Jr. *(Pres & CEO)*

Dutch Lady Milk Industries Berhad (2)
Level 5 Quill 9 112 Jalan Prof Khoo Kay Kim, 46300, Petaling Jaya, Selangor Darul Ehsan, Malaysia
Tel.: (60) 379532600
Web Site: http://www.dutchlady.com.my
Rev.: $283,473,016
Assets: $178,661,164
Liabilities: $94,671,534
Net Worth: $83,989,630
Earnings: $9,792,804
Emp.: 600
Fiscal Year-end: 12/31/2022
Dairy Products Mfr
N.A.I.C.S.: 311514
Katrina Neo *(Dir-Sls)*

Subsidiary (Domestic):

FrieslandCampina DMV (2)
NCB-Laan 80, 5462 GE, Veghel, Netherlands
Tel.: (31) 413372222
Web Site: http://www.dmv-international.com
Sales Range: $600-649.9 Million
Emp.: 800
Develops, Produces & Markets Constituents for the Food & Pharmaceutical Industries Worldwide
N.A.I.C.S.: 325412

Subsidiary (Non-US):

N.V. Yoko Cheese S.A. (2)
Bosdel 51, 3600, Genk, Belgium
Tel.: (32) 89 36 33 88
Web Site: http://www.food.be
Sales Range: $100-124.9 Million
Emp.: 160
Cheese Prepacking Services; Cheese & Butter Distr
N.A.I.C.S.: 424530
Luc Lamberigts *(Mng Dir)*

PT Frisian Flag Indonesia (1)
Jalan Raya Bogor Km 5, 13760, Jakarta, Indonesia
Tel.: (62) 21 841 0 945
Dairy Products Mfr
N.A.I.C.S.: 311514

PT Kievit Indonesia (1)
Jl Merpati 1, Mangunsari, 50721, Salatiga, Indonesia
Tel.: (62) 298 324444
Dairy Products Mfr
N.A.I.C.S.: 311514
Felisia Veridiana *(Dir-Fin & Acctg)*

ZUJI PTE. LIMITED
238A Thomson Road Novena Square Office Tower A 12-06/07, Singapore, 307684, Singapore
Tel.: (65) 6215 9600   SG
Web Site: http://www.zuji.com.sg
Year Founded: 2002
Holding Company; Online Travel Arrangement Services
N.A.I.C.S.: 551112
Hui Wan Chua *(CEO-Singapore)*

Subsidiaries:

ZUJI Limited (1)
2801-03 28/F Chinachem Leighton Plaza 29 Leighton Road, Causeway Bay, China (Hong Kong)
Tel.: (852) 800 938 600
Web Site: http://www.zuji.com.hk
Online Travel Arrangement Services
N.A.I.C.S.: 561599
Charlie Wong *(CEO)*

ZUJI Travel Pte. Ltd. (1)
238A Thomson Road Novena Square Office Tower A 12-06/07, Singapore, 307684, Singapore
Tel.: (65) 6215 9600
Web Site: http://www.zuji.com.sg
Online Travel Arrangement Services
N.A.I.C.S.: 561599
Hui Wan Chua *(CEO)*

ZUKEN, INC.
2-25-1 Edahigashi, Tsuzuki-Ku, Yokohama, 224-8585, Kanagawa, Japan
Tel.: (81) 459421511   JP
Web Site: https://www.zuken.com
Year Founded: 1976
6947—(TKS)
Rev.: $254,260,260
Assets: $422,240,190
Liabilities: $151,117,820
Net Worth: $271,122,370
Earnings: $25,567,480
Fiscal Year-end: 03/31/24
Computer-Aided Design & Engineering Software
N.A.I.C.S.: 541330
Jinya Katsube *(Pres & COO)*

Subsidiaries:

Cadlab Inc. (1)
5F Zuken Center Minami Building 32-11 Chigasaki-Chuo, Tsuzuki-Ku, Yokohama, 224-8580, Kanagawa, Japan
Tel.: (81) 459485806
Web Site: http://www.cadlab.co.jp
Computer Aided Design Training & Consulting Services
N.A.I.C.S.: 541512

Inventure Inc. (1)
Zuken Shin-Yokohama Building 3-1-1 Shin-Yokohama, Kouhoku-ku, Yokohama, 222-8505, Kanagawa, Japan
Tel.: (81) 454773377
Web Site: http://www.inventure.co.jp
Network Systems Integration Design Services
N.A.I.C.S.: 541512

ZUKEN (SHANGHAI) TECHNICAL CENTER Co., Ltd. (1)
Room 301 Sanwu Commercial Building No 555 Nanjing West Road, Shanghai, 200041, China
Tel.: (86) 2132181784
Web Site: http://www.zuken.com.cm
Emp.: 12
Electronic Engineering Systems Integrated Design Services
N.A.I.C.S.: 541512
Hoshi Xing *(Gen Mgr)*

ZUKEN Group Ltd. (1)
Zuken Technology Center 1500 Aztec West, Almondsbury, Bristol, BS32 4RF, United Kingdom
Tel.: (44) 1454207800
Web Site: http://www.zuken.com
Emp.: 70
Industrial Automation Software Development Services
N.A.I.C.S.: 541511
Mark Sandham *(Controller-Finance)*

Zsas (Zuken Support and Service) Inc. (1)
4F YS Shin-Yokohama Building 2-15-10 Shin-Yokohama, Kouhoku-ku, Yokohama, 222-0033, Kanagawa, Japan
Tel.: (81) 454712334
Web Site: http://www.zsas.co.jp
Industrial Automation Software Development Services
N.A.I.C.S.: 541511

Zuken Alfatech Inc. (1)
5F Shin-Osaka 2nd Doi Building 2-14-6 Nishinakajima, Yodogawa-ku, Osaka, 532-0011, Japan
Tel.: (81) 663000306
Web Site: https://www.alfatech.jp
Emp.: 65
Electrical Product Mfr & Distr
N.A.I.C.S.: 334515

Zuken B.V. (1)
Kerkplein 1, 6075 HA, Herkenbosch, Netherlands
Tel.: (31) 475520998
Industrial Automation Software Development Services
N.A.I.C.S.: 541511

Zuken E3 GmbH (1)
Laemmerweg 55, 89079, Ulm, Germany
Tel.: (49) 730593090
Web Site: http://www.zuken.com
Industrial Automation Software Development Services
N.A.I.C.S.: 541511

Zuken E3 GmbH Sp. z o.o (1)
Ul prof Michala Zyczkowskiego 14, 31-864, Krakow, Poland
Tel.: (48) 668581370
Electronic Component Mfr & Distr
N.A.I.C.S.: 334416

Zuken Elmic, Inc. (1)
1-1 Shin-Yokohama 3-chome, Kouhoku-ku, Yokohama, 222-8505, Kanagawa, Japan (86.62%)
Tel.: (81) 456248111
Web Site: https://www.elwsc.co.jp
Sales Range: $10-24.9 Million
Emp.: 48
Information Technology Services
N.A.I.C.S.: 541512
Jinya Katsube *(Chm)*

Zuken Korea, Inc. (1)
DongNamYuHwa Bldg 3F 1001-10 Daechi-Dong, KangNam-ku, Seoul, 135-280, Korea (South)
Tel.: (82) 25648031
Web Site: https://www.zuken.com
Engineering Services
N.A.I.C.S.: 541330

Zuken Ltd. (1)
1500 Aztec West, Almondsbury, Bristol, BS32 4RF, United Kingdom (100%)
Tel.: (44) 1454207800
Web Site: http://www.zuken.com
Emp.: 70
Engineering Services
N.A.I.C.S.: 541330

Zuken Modelinx Inc. (1)
6F Shinbashi Enter Building 5-8-11 Shinbashi, Minato-ku, Tokyo, 105-0004, Japan
Tel.: (81) 364530045
Web Site: https://modelinx.co.jp
Technical Consulting Services
N.A.I.C.S.: 541330

Zuken NetWave Inc. (1)
3-1-1 Shin-Yokohama, Kohoku-ku, Yokohama, 222-8505, Kanagawa, Japan
Tel.: (81) 454736821
Web Site: https://www.znw.co.jp
Emp.: 50
Industrial Automation Software Development Services
N.A.I.C.S.: 541511
Ikuo Nakamura *(Pres & CEO)*

Zuken PreSight Inc. (1)
5F Zuken Center South Building 32-11, Chigasaki Chuo Tsuzuki-ku, Yokohama, 224-0032, Japan
Tel.: (81) 459422273
Web Site: https://www.presight.co.jp
Emp.: 46
Electrical Product Mfr & Distr
N.A.I.C.S.: 334515

Zuken S.A. (1)
3 avenue du Canada Batiment Theta 2, ZI de Courtaboeuf, 91940, Les Ulis, France
Tel.: (33) 169294800
Web Site: https://www.zuken.com
Emp.: 9
Industrial Automation Software Development Services
N.A.I.C.S.: 541511

Zuken S.r.l. (1)
Strada 2 Palazzo C4 Milanofiori Assago, 20090, Milan, Italy
Tel.: (39) 02575921
Web Site: https://www.zuken.com
Emp.: 6
Industrial Automation Software Development Services
N.A.I.C.S.: 541511

Zuken Singapore Pte., Ltd. (1)
152 Beach Road 22-05 Gateway East, Singapore, 189721, Singapore (100%)
Tel.: (65) 63925855
Web Site: https://www.zuken.com.sg
Emp.: 12
Engineering Services
N.A.I.C.S.: 541330

Zuken UK Ltd. (1)
1500 Aztec West, Almondsbury, BS32 4RF, Bristol, United Kingdom
Tel.: (44) 1454207801
Emp.: 80
Industrial Automation Software Development Services
N.A.I.C.S.: 541511
Stephanie Coombs *(Mgr)*

Zuken USA Inc. (1)
238 Littleton Rd Ste 100, Westford, MA 01886
Tel.: (978) 692-4900
Web Site: https://www.zuken.com
Emp.: 10
Industrial Software Development Services
N.A.I.C.S.: 541511
Humair Mandavia *(Chief Strategy Officer)*

Zuken Vitech Inc. (1)
2270 Kraft Dr Ste 1600, Blacksburg, VA 24060
Tel.: (540) 951-3322
Web Site: http://www.vitechcorp.com
Custom Computer Programming Services
N.A.I.C.S.: 541511

AND PRIVATE COMPANIES

Enrique Krajmalnik (Pres)

Zuken, GmbH (1)
Am Soeldnermoos 17, 85399, Hallbergmoos, Germany
Tel.: (49) 89710405900
Web Site: http://www.zuken.com
Industrial Automation Software Development Services
N.A.I.C.S.: 541511

ZULEIKA GOLD LIMITED
Ground Floor 8 Kings Park Road, West Perth, 6005, WA, Australia
Tel.: (61) 863706188
Web Site: https://zuleikagold.com.au
ZAG—(ASX)
Rev.: $711,810
Assets: $7,618,552
Liabilities: $128,460
Net Worth: $7,490,093
Earnings: $132,333
Emp.: 5
Fiscal Year-end: 06/30/24
Gold Mining Services
N.A.I.C.S.: 212220
Alexander Neuling (Sec)

ZUMBACH ELECTRONIC AG
Hauptstrasse 93, 2552, Orpund, Switzerland
Tel.: (41) 323560400
Web Site: http://www.zumbach.com
Year Founded: 1970
Emp.: 200
Process Control Instruments Mfr
N.A.I.C.S.: 334513
Rainer Zumbach (Chm)

Subsidiaries:

Metrocontrol AG (1)
Quellenstrasse 4, CH-8610, Uster, Switzerland (100%)
Tel.: (41) 19942194
Mfr of Process Control Instruments
N.A.I.C.S.: 334519

Zumbach Bureau France (1)
6 rue de l Avenir, FR-77760, Seine-et-Marne, La Chapelle la Reine, France
Tel.: (33) 164244631
Web Site: http://www.zumbach.com
Monitoring & Control Equipment Mfr
N.A.I.C.S.: 334513
Roland Moller (Gen Mgr)

Zumbach Electronic GmbH (1)
Kesselsgasse 2, Pulheim, 50259, Germany (100%)
Tel.: (49) 223880990
Web Site: http://www.zumbach.com
Emp.: 10
Mfr of Manufacturing Monitoring & Control Equipment
N.A.I.C.S.: 334513
Guenther Hentschel (Gen Mgr)

Zumbach Electronic India Pvt. Ltd. (1)
Premdeep 3rd Floor 12B Sind Hindu Society Manikchand Malabar Hills, Lullanagar, Pune, 411 040, India (100%)
Tel.: (91) 2026837949
Web Site: http://www.zumbach.com
Emp.: 3
Mfr of Manufacturing Monitoring & Control Equipment
N.A.I.C.S.: 334513

Zumbach Electronic P.R. China (1)
Bldg 18 No 481 Guiping Rd, Shanghai, 200233, China
Tel.: (86) 2154260443
Web Site: http://www.zumbach.com.cn
Mfr of Manufacturing Monitoring & Control Equipment
N.A.I.C.S.: 334513

Zumbach Electronic S.A. (1)
J P Ballingslaan 1, 1090, Brussels, Belgium (100%)
Tel.: (32) 24781688
Web Site: http://www.zumlux.com
Emp.: 2

Mfr of Manufacturing Monitoring & Control Equipment
N.A.I.C.S.: 334513

Zumbach Electronic Srl (1)
Via Adua 19, Schianno, 21045, Gazzada, Varese, Italy
Tel.: (39) 0332 870 102
Web Site: http://www.zumbach.com
Mfr of Manufacturing Monitoring & Control Equipment
N.A.I.C.S.: 334513

Zumbach Electronica Argentina S.R.L. (1)
Deheza 2570 Piso 1 Dto 9, 1429, Buenos Aires, Argentina (100%)
Tel.: (54) 11 4701 0774
Web Site: http://www.zumbach.com.ar
Emp.: 1
Mfr of Measuring, Monitoring & Control Equipment
N.A.I.C.S.: 334513

Zumbach Electronica S.L. (1)
Calle Jose Ricart 3, San Feliu De Llobregat, 8980, Barcelona, Spain
Tel.: (34) 936669361
Web Site: http://www.zumbach.com
Emp.: 12
Mfr of Manufacturing Monitoring & Control Equipment
N.A.I.C.S.: 334513
Guillermo Canales (Gen Mgr)

Zumbach Electronics Corp. (1)
140 Kisco Ave, Mount Kisco, NY 10549-1407
Tel.: (914) 241-7080
Web Site: http://www.zumbach.com
Emp.: 40
Mfr of Manufacturing Monitoring & Control Equipment
N.A.I.C.S.: 334513
Sigrid G. Fuchs (Controller)

Zumbach Electronics Far East (1)
4F No 262 Sec 6 Ming Chuan E Rd, Taipei, 114, Taiwan (100%)
Tel.: (886) 226305530
Web Site: http://www.zumbach.com
Emp.: 2
Mfr of Manufacturing Monitoring & Control Equipment
N.A.I.C.S.: 334513
Sebastian Haarring (Engr-Svc Control)

Zumbach Electronics Ltd. (1)
22 Cromwell Bus Ctr, Howard Way New Port Pagnell, Milton Keynes, MK1 69QS, United Kingdom (100%)
Tel.: (44) 8707743301
Web Site: http://www.zumbach.co.uk
Emp.: 3
Mfr of Manufacturing Monitoring & Control Equipment
N.A.I.C.S.: 334513
Bruno Zumbach (Mng Dir)

Zumbach do Brasil Ltda (1)
Rua Constantino Suriani 838 Vila Paraiso, Campinas, 13043-510, Brazil
Tel.: (55) 19 3829 6000
Electric Component Whslr
N.A.I.C.S.: 423610

Zumelec S.A.R.L. (1)
6 rue de l'Avenir, La Chapelle la Reine, 77760, Fontainebleau, France
Tel.: (33) 164244269
Web Site: http://www.zumbach.com
Emp.: 4
Mfr Monitoring & Control Equipment Service & Sales
N.A.I.C.S.: 334513

ZUMDIECK GMBH
Senefelder Strasse 21, Paderborn, 330100, Germany
Tel.: (49) 525150030
Web Site: http://www.zumdieck.de
Year Founded: 1967
Rev.: $119,531,820
Emp.: 60
Fruit & Vegetables Mfr
N.A.I.C.S.: 424480
Wolfgang Zumdieck (Mng Dir)

Subsidiaries:

Zumdieck Asia Ltd. (1)
Room 1001 10/Fl 173 Nan Fung Tower Des Voeux Rd Central, Central, China (Hong Kong)
Tel.: (852) 25450091
Frozen Food Product Distr
N.A.I.C.S.: 424420

ZUMEX GROUP, S.A.
Pol Ind Moncada III C/ Moli 2, 46113, Montcada, Spain
Tel.: (34) 961 301 251
Web Site: http://www.zumex.com
Emp.: 150
Fruit & Vegetable Juicer Mfr
N.A.I.C.S.: 335220
Victor Bertolin Munoz (CEO)

Subsidiaries:

ZUMEX France SARL (1)
45 rue de Villeneuve Rungis Cedex, 94573, Paris, France
Tel.: (33) 975187354
Web Site: http://www.zumex.com
Electronic Appliance Distr
N.A.I.C.S.: 423620
Esther Hernandez (Acct Mgr)

Zumex Mexico S.A. de CV (1)
Uxmal 616 Colonia Vertiz Narvarte, Delegacion Benito Juarez, 3600, Mexico, Mexico
Tel.: (52) 5552120619
Web Site: http://www.zumex.com
Electronic Appliance Distr
N.A.I.C.S.: 423620
Carlos Alberto Hernandez (Dir-Comml)

Zumex UK Ltd. (1)
3 More London Riverside, London, SE1 2RE, United Kingdom
Tel.: (44) 2035191292
Web Site: http://www.zumex.com
Electronic Appliance Distr
N.A.I.C.S.: 423620
Esther Hernandez (Acct Mgr)

ZUMING BEAN PRODUCTS CO., LTD.
No 77 Jiangling Road, Binjiang District, Hangzhou, 310051, Zhejiang, China
Tel.: (86) 57186687777
Web Site: https://www.chinazuming.cn
Year Founded: 2000
003030—(SSE)
Rev.: $208,837,559
Assets: $245,637,171
Liabilities: $100,065,411
Net Worth: $145,571,760
Earnings: $5,388,524
Fiscal Year-end: 12/31/22
Bean Product Mfr & Distr
N.A.I.C.S.: 311351
Zuming Cai (Chm & Gen Mgr)

ZUMINTERNET CORP.
Banpo-daero 3, Seocho-gu, Seoul, Korea (South)
Tel.: (82) 237741736
Web Site: https://estaid.ai
239340—(KRS)
Rev.: $306,752
Assets: $34,802,893
Liabilities: $10,480,599
Net Worth: $24,322,294
Earnings: $(1,894,828)
Emp.: 118
Fiscal Year-end: 12/31/22
Financial Investment Management Services
N.A.I.C.S.: 523940

ZUMTOBEL GROUP AG
Hochsterstrasse 8, 6850, Dornbirn, Austria
Tel.: (43) 55725090   AT
Web Site: https://z.lighting
Year Founded: 1977

ZAG—(VIE)
Rev.: $1,304,985,970
Assets: $1,081,788,258
Liabilities: $626,656,594
Net Worth: $455,131,664
Earnings: $64,720,483
Emp.: 5,192
Fiscal Year-end: 04/30/23
Lighting System & Component Designer & Mfr
N.A.I.C.S.: 335139
Emanuel Hagspiel (Sr Dir-Investor Relations & Head-Investor Relations)

Subsidiaries:

ACDC LED Limited (1)
Ground Floor Office Finance House 17 Kenyon Road, Lomeshaye Industrial Estate, Nelson, BB9 5SP, Lancashire, United Kingdom
Tel.: (44) 128 295 6000
Web Site: https://www.acdclighting.com
Lighting Equipment Mfr
N.A.I.C.S.: 335139

Thorn Lighting Group Plc (1)
3 King George Close, Eastern Ave W, Romford, RM7 7PP, Essex, United Kingdom
Tel.: (44) 1708766033
Web Site: https://www.thornlighting.com
Emp.: 50
Holding Company
N.A.I.C.S.: 551112

Thorn Lighting Ltd. (1)
Durhamgate, County Durham, Spennymoor, DL16 6HL, United Kingdom
Tel.: (44) 1913652222
Web Site: https://www.thornlighting.co.uk
Lighting Equipment Mfr
N.A.I.C.S.: 335139

Tridonic (ME) FZE (1)
Warehouse LB 4 Blue Shed Area JAFZA North, PO Box 17972, Jebel Ali, Dubai, United Arab Emirates
Tel.: (971) 48833664
Web Site: https://www.tridonic.ae
Lighting Equipment Mfr
N.A.I.C.S.: 335139
Alexander Stieger (CFO)

Tridonic (Malaysia) Sdn. Bhd. (1)
VO3-10-01 Designer Office Lingkaran SV Sunway Velocity, Cheras, 55100, Kuala Lumpur, Malaysia
Tel.: (60) 327336484
Lighting Equipment Mfr
N.A.I.C.S.: 335139

Tridonic (S.E.A.) Pte. Ltd. (1)
158 Kallang Way 06-02, Singapore, 349245, Singapore
Tel.: (65) 67499071
Lighting Equipment Mfr
N.A.I.C.S.: 335139

Tridonic (Shanghai) Co. Ltd. (1)
Room 602 Buliding B Zhongshan International Plaza No 789 Tianshan Road, Shanghai, 200335, China
Tel.: (86) 2152400599
Lighting Equipment Mfr
N.A.I.C.S.: 335139

Tridonic AG (1)
Obere Allmeind 2, 8755, Ennenda, Switzerland
Tel.: (41) 556454747
Web Site: https://www.tridonic.ch
Lighting Equipment Mfr
N.A.I.C.S.: 335139

Tridonic Australia Pty. Ltd. (1)
2/7 Millner Avenue, Horsley Park, 2175, NSW, Australia
Tel.: (61) 298326600
Lighting Equipment Mfr
N.A.I.C.S.: 335139

Tridonic Aydinlatma Ticaret Limited Sirketi (1)
Kemankes Mah Necatibey cad Akce Sok Akce Han No 10, Karakoy Beyoglu, 34420, Istanbul, Turkiye
Tel.: (90) 2122447805
Lighting Equipment Mfr
N.A.I.C.S.: 335139

ZUMTOBEL GROUP AG

Zumtobel Group AG—(Continued)

Tridonic Deutschland GmbH (1)
Edisonallee 1, 89231, Neu-Ulm, Germany
Tel.: (49) 7311766290
Lighting Equipment Mfr
N.A.I.C.S.: 335139

Tridonic France Sarl (1)
8 Rue de Bruxelles ZI Krafft, 67150, Erstein, France
Tel.: (33) 388596270
Lighting Equipment Mfr
N.A.I.C.S.: 335139

Tridonic GmbH & Co KG (1)
Farbergasse 15, 6851, Dornbirn, Austria
Tel.: (43) 55723950
Web Site: https://www.tridonic.com
Lighting Equipment Mfr
N.A.I.C.S.: 335139

Tridonic Iberia SL (1)
Paseo del Club Deportivo 1 Parque Empresarial La Finca Edificio 13, Pozuelo de Alarcon, 28223, Madrid, Spain
Tel.: (34) 916162095
Web Site: https://www.tridonic.es
Lighting Equipment Mfr
N.A.I.C.S.: 335139

Tridonic Italia SRL (1)
Via G Savelli 86, 35129, Padova, Italy
Tel.: (39) 0498945127
Web Site: https://www.tridonic.it
Lighting Equipment Mfr
N.A.I.C.S.: 335139

Tridonic Korea LLC (1)
Tel.: (82) 1099223878
Web Site: https://www.tridonic.kr
Lighting Equipment Distr
N.A.I.C.S.: 423610

Tridonic Portugal Unipessoa Lda (1)
Rotunda Engenheiro Edgar Cardoso 23 piso 8, 4400-676, Vila Nova de Gaia, Portugal
Tel.: (351) 938448467
Lighting Equipment Mfr
N.A.I.C.S.: 335139

Tridonic SA (Proprietary) Limited (1)
Office 5 Ground Floor The Estuaries Building 12 Oxbow Crescent, Oxbow Crescent Century City Cape Town, Milnerton, South Africa
Tel.: (27) 211105687
Lighting Equipment Mfr
N.A.I.C.S.: 335139

Tridonic UK Ltd. (1)
Unit 5 Cherrywood, Chineham Business Park Stag Oak Lane Chineham, Basingstoke, RG24 8WF, United Kingdom
Tel.: (44) 1256374300
Lighting Equipment Mfr
N.A.I.C.S.: 335139

ZG Lighting (N.Z.) Limited (1)
Tel.: (64) 98287155
Web Site: https://www.thornlighting.co.nz
Lighting Equipment Mfr
N.A.I.C.S.: 335139

ZG Lighting (UK) Limited (1)
Chiltern Park Chiltern Hill, Chalfont Saint Peter, SL9 9FG, Buckinghamshire, United Kingdom
Tel.: (44) 1388420042
Lighting Equipment Mfr
N.A.I.C.S.: 335139

ZG Lighting Australia Pty Ltd (1)
2/7 Millner Avenue, Horsley Park, 2175, NSW, Australia
Tel.: (61) 1300139965
Web Site: https://www.zumtobel.com
Lighting Equipment Distr
N.A.I.C.S.: 423610

ZG Lighting Austria GmbH (1)
Vertriebszentrum Wien Wagramer Strasse 19, 1220, Vienna, Austria
Tel.: (43) 125826010
Lighting Equipment Mfr
N.A.I.C.S.: 335139

ZG Lighting Benelux SA (1)
Rijksweg 47 Industriezone Puurs Nr 442, 2870, Puurs, Belgium
Tel.: (32) 38609393

Web Site: https://www.zumtobel.be
Lighting Equipment Mfr
N.A.I.C.S.: 335139

ZG Lighting Czech Republic, s r.o. (1)
Jankovcova 2, 170 00, Prague, 7, Czech Republic
Tel.: (420) 266782200
Web Site: https://www.zumtobel.com
Lighting Equipment Mfr
N.A.I.C.S.: 335139

ZG Lighting Denmark A/S (1)
Forbindelsesvej 12, 2100, Copenhagen, Denmark
Tel.: (45) 76963600
Web Site: https://www.zumtobel.com
Lighting Equipment Mfr
N.A.I.C.S.: 335139

ZG Lighting France SAS (1)
10 rue dUzs, CS 55466, 75002, Paris, Cedex, France
Tel.: (33) 149536262
Web Site: https://www.zumtobel.com
Lighting Equipment Mfr
N.A.I.C.S.: 335139

ZG Lighting Hungary Kft. (1)
Vaci ut 49, 1134, Budapest, Hungary
Tel.: (36) 14502490
Web Site: https://www.zumtobel.com
Lighting Equipment Mfr
N.A.I.C.S.: 335139

ZG Lighting Iberia S.L. (1)
Avenida manoteras 26 4-2, 28050, Madrid, Spain
Tel.: (34) 916593076
Lighting Equipment Mfr
N.A.I.C.S.: 335139

ZG Lighting Netherlands B.V. (1)
Radarweg 60, 1043 NT, Amsterdam, Netherlands
Tel.: (31) 20 235 2300
Web Site: https://www.zumtobel.nl
Lighting Equipment Mfr
N.A.I.C.S.: 335139

ZG Lighting Nordic AB (1)
Hyllie Boulevard 10b, 215 32, Malmo, Sweden
Tel.: (46) 406492000
Web Site: https://www.zumtobel.se
Lighting Equipment Mfr
N.A.I.C.S.: 335139

ZG Lighting Norway AS (1)
Radhusgata 9, 151, Oslo, Norway
Tel.: (47) 22547200
Web Site: https://www.thornlighting.no
Lighting Equipment Mfr
N.A.I.C.S.: 335139

ZG Lighting Polska Sp. z o.o. (1)
ul Antoni Slonimskiego 1, 50-304, Wroclaw, Poland
Tel.: (48) 713366026
Web Site: https://www.thornlighting.pl
Lighting Equipment Mfr
N.A.I.C.S.: 335139

ZG Lighting Singapore Pte Limited (1)
158 Kallang Way 06-01/02, Singapore, 349245, Singapore
Tel.: (65) 68445800
Web Site: https://www.thornlighting.ae
Lighting Equipment Mfr
N.A.I.C.S.: 335139

ZG Lighting Slovakia s.r.o. (1)
Tomasikova 64, 831 04, Bratislava, Slovakia
Tel.: (421) 220300044
Web Site: https://www.zumtobel.com
Lighting Equipment Mfr
N.A.I.C.S.: 335139

ZG Lighting d.o.o. (1)
Hrvatska Ulica Petra Hektorovica 2, 10000, Zagreb, Croatia
Tel.: (385) 16404080
Lighting Equipment Mfr
N.A.I.C.S.: 335139

ZG Lighting d.o.o. (1)
Stukljeva cesta 46, 1000, Ljubljana, Slovenia
Tel.: (386) 1 560 9820

Web Site: https://www.zumtobel.si
Lighting Equipment Mfr
N.A.I.C.S.: 335139

Zumtobel Group Deutschland GmbH (1)
Carl-Benz-Strasse 21, 60386, Frankfurt, Germany
Tel.: (49) 69 264 8890
Web Site: https://www.zumtobel.de
Lighting Equipment Mfr
N.A.I.C.S.: 335139

Zumtobel Holding GmbH (1)
Grevenmarschstr 74-78, 32657, Lemgo, Germany
Tel.: (49) 52612120
Lighting Equipment Mfr
N.A.I.C.S.: 335139

Zumtobel Lighting GmbH (1)
Schweizer Strasse 30, 6851, Dornbirn, Austria
Tel.: (43) 55723900
Web Site: https://www.zumtobel.com
Emp.: 1,500
Lighting Designer & Mfr
N.A.I.C.S.: 335139

Subsidiary (US):

Zumtobel Lighting Inc. (2)
3300 Route 9W, Highland, NY 12528
Tel.: (845) 691-6262
Web Site: https://www.zumtobel.us
Commercial Lighting Fixtures
N.A.I.C.S.: 335132
Kevin Maddy (CEO)

Zumtobel Lighting Romania SRL (1)
Radu Greceanu 2 Ground Floor, 012225, Bucharest, Romania
Tel.: (40) 312253801
Lighting Equipment Mfr
N.A.I.C.S.: 335139

ZUNGWON EN-SYS, INC.
Jeongwon Building 46 Dosan-daero 1-gil, Gangnam-gu, Seoul, Korea (South)
Tel.: (82) 25147007
Web Site: https://www.zungwon.co.kr
45510—(KRS)
Rev.: $123,410,966
Assets: $70,870,389
Liabilities: $40,196,783
Net Worth: $30,673,606
Earnings: $889,355
Emp.: 132
Fiscal Year-end: 12/31/22
Information Technology Services
N.A.I.C.S.: 541519
Duk-Hee Han (CEO)

ZUNGWON ENGINEERING & SYSTEM INC.
46 Dosan-daero 1-gil, Gangnam-gu, Seoul, 06027, Korea (South)
Tel.: (82) 25147007
Web Site: http://www.zungwon.co.kr
045510—(KRS)
Rev.: $127,526,527
Assets: $73,233,805
Liabilities: $41,537,283
Net Worth: $31,696,522
Earnings: $919,014
Emp.: 132
Fiscal Year-end: 12/31/22
System Integration Services
N.A.I.C.S.: 541512
Deok Hui Han (CEO)

ZUOAN FASHION LIMITED
Building 1 Lane 618 Dingyuan Road Songjiang, Shanghai, 201616, China
Tel.: (86) 21 56535557
Men's Clothing Mfr
N.A.I.C.S.: 315250
James Jinshan Hong (Chm, CEO & Acting CFO)

ZUOLI KECHUANG MICROFINANCE COMPANY LIMITED

INTERNATIONAL PUBLIC

No 399 Deqing Avenue Wukang Road, Deqing, Huzhou, 313200, Zhejiang, China
Tel.: (86) 5728219781 CN
Web Site: https://www.zlkcxd.com
Year Founded: 2011
6866—(HKG)
Rev.: $35,164,303
Assets: $391,384,375
Liabilities: $115,986,686
Net Worth: $275,397,689
Earnings: $13,576,118
Emp.: 94
Fiscal Year-end: 12/31/22
Credit-Based Financing Services
N.A.I.C.S.: 522220
Yin Yu (Co/Co-Founder, Chm, Chm & Exec Dir)

ZUPLJANKA A.D.
ul Krusevacka 18, 37230, Aleksandrovac, Serbia
Tel.: (381) 37 3 552 051
Web Site: http://www.zupljanka.com
Year Founded: 1960
Sales Range: Less than $1 Million
Textile Products Mfr
N.A.I.C.S.: 315120

ZUR ROSE GROUP AG
Walzmuhlestrasse 49, 8500, Frauenfeld, Switzerland
Tel.: (41) 527240020 CH
Web Site: https://www.zurrosegroup.com
Year Founded: 1993
ROSE—(SWX)
Rev.: $1,955,212,852
Assets: $1,437,346,779
Liabilities: $888,186,029
Net Worth: $549,160,750
Earnings: ($255,638,115)
Emp.: 2,131
Fiscal Year-end: 12/31/21
Medical Product Whslr
N.A.I.C.S.: 423450
Walter Oberhansli (CEO)

Subsidiaries:

Aerztemedika AG (1)
Hammerstrasse 35, 4410, Liestal, Switzerland
Tel.: (41) 619030714
Web Site: https://www.aerztemedika.ch
Medical Product Distr
N.A.I.C.S.: 423450

Bluecare AG (1)
Pflanzschulstrasse 3, 8400, Winterthur, Switzerland
Tel.: (41) 522351935
Web Site: http://www.bluecare.ch
Software & IT System Services
N.A.I.C.S.: 541511

Dia Plus Minus Handelsgesellschaft mbH (1)
Nordel 1, 49176, Hilter, Germany
Tel.: (49) 5424216436
Web Site: https://www.dia-plus-minus.de
Diabetes Medicine Distr
N.A.I.C.S.: 423450

DocMorris N.V. (1)
Avantisallee 152, 6422 RA, Heerlen, Netherlands
Tel.: (31) 4808000
Medical Product Distr
N.A.I.C.S.: 423450

Doctipharma SAS (1)
33 rue Lafayette, 75009, Paris, France
Tel.: (33) 186760892
Pharmaceutical Product Whslr
N.A.I.C.S.: 424210

Helena Abreu, Unipessoal, Lda. (1)
R das Vitoria 622, Vila Da Lixa, 4615-691, Porto, Portugal
Tel.: (351) 255311360
Web Site: https://helena-abreu.com
Real Estate Services
N.A.I.C.S.: 531210

AND PRIVATE COMPANIES

ZURICH INSURANCE GROUP LIMITED

Promofarma Ecom, S.L. (1)
Av Diagonal 534 6, 08006, Barcelona, Spain
Tel.: (34) 902930918
Pharmaceutical Product Whslr
N.A.I.C.S.: 424210

Zur Rose Pharma GmbH (1)
Thuringer Strasse 29, 06112, Halle, Germany
Tel.: (49) 34527994697
Logistic Services
N.A.I.C.S.: 541614

Subsidiary (Domestic):

eHealth-Tec GmbH (2)
Schonhauser Allee 122a, 10437, Berlin, Germany
Tel.: (49) 3040505600
Medical Product Distr
N.A.I.C.S.: 423450

ZUR SHAMIR HOLDINGS LTD.
35 Efal St, Petach Tikva, 4951132, Israel
Tel.: (972) 36251400
Web Site: https://www.zur-shamir.com
Year Founded: 1957
ZUR—(TAE)
Rev.: $1,207,345,471
Assets: $5,676,906,114
Liabilities: $4,948,734,278
Net Worth: $728,171,836
Earnings: $62,992,125
Fiscal Year-end: 12/31/23
Offices of Other Holding Companies
N.A.I.C.S.: 551112
Moshe Schneidman *(CEO)*

Subsidiaries:

Direct Insurance - Financial Investments Ltd. (1)
35 Efal St, Petach Tikva, 4951132, Israel
Tel.: (972) 36251400
Web Site: https://www.d-ifi.com
Financial Investment Services
N.A.I.C.S.: 523940
Moshe Schneidman *(Chm)*

ZURCHER KANTONALBANK
Bahnhofstrasse 9, 8010, Zurich, Switzerland
Tel.: (41) 844 843 823
Web Site: http://www.zkb.ch
Banking Services
N.A.I.C.S.: 522110
Heidi Kunz Fields *(Member-Exec Bd & Head-Corp Banking)*

Subsidiaries:

Swisscanto Holding SA (1)
Bahnhofstrasse 9, CH-8001, Zurich, Switzerland (100%)
Tel.: (41) 58 344 49 00
Web Site: http://www.swisscanto.ch
Investment & Pension Fund Management Services
N.A.I.C.S.: 524292
Chantal Guex *(Head-Customer Svc)*

Subsidiary (Non-US):

Swisscanto Asset Management International S.A. (2)
19 rue de Bitbourg, L-1273, Luxembourg, Luxembourg (100%)
Tel.: (352) 27 843 592
Web Site: http://www.swisscanto.ch
Pension Fund Management Services
N.A.I.C.S.: 524292

Subsidiary (Domestic):

Swisscanto Asset Management Ltd. (2)
Europaallee 39, CH-8021, Zurich, Switzerland
Tel.: (41) 58 344 49 00
Web Site: http://www.swisscanto.co.uk
Asset Management Services
N.A.I.C.S.: 523999

Swisscanto Pensions Ltd. (2)
Picassoplatz 8, CH-4052, Basel, Switzerland
Tel.: (41) 58 344 42 62
Web Site: http://www.swisscanto.co.uk
Pension Fund Management Services
N.A.I.C.S.: 524292
Othmar Simeon *(Mng Dir)*

ZURICH INSURANCE GROUP LIMITED
Mythenquai 2, 8002, Zurich, Switzerland
Tel.: (41) 446252525 CH
Web Site: https://www.zurich.com
Year Founded: 1872
ZFSVF—(OTCQX)
Rev.: $56,099,000,000
Assets: $361,382,000,000
Liabilities: $335,102,000,000
Net Worth: $26,280,000,000
Earnings: $4,717,000,000
Emp.: 56,228
Fiscal Year-end: 12/31/23
Investment Management Service
N.A.I.C.S.: 551112
Urban Angehrn *(Chief Investment Officer)*

Subsidiaries:

AAS Zurich Latvia Ltd. (1)
Valdemara St 21 Rm 609, LV 1010, Riga, Latvia (100%)
Tel.: (371) 7035254
Web Site: http://www.zurich.lv
Non-Life Insurance
N.A.I.C.S.: 524128

Allied Zurich plc (1)
Tri Centre One New Bridge Square, Sta Rd, Swindon, SN1 1HN, United Kingdom
Tel.: (44) 1793514514
Web Site: http://www.zurich.co.uk
Holding Company
N.A.I.C.S.: 551112

Centre Group Holdings Limited (1)
PO Box HM 1788, Hamilton, HM HX, Bermuda (100%)
Tel.: (441) 2958501
Emp.: 12
Reinsurance
N.A.I.C.S.: 524130

Centre Reinsurance Holdings Ltd. (1)
IFCS House Custom House Quay, 1, Dublin, Ireland
Tel.: (353) 018189800
Web Site: http://www.centre.com
Emp.: 10
Holding Company
N.A.I.C.S.: 551112

Subsidiary (Domestic):

Centre Insurance International Company (2)
Lincoln House Lincoln Place, Dublin, 02 VH29, Ireland
Tel.: (353) 15677000
Web Site: http://www.centresolutions.com
Insurance Services
N.A.I.C.S.: 524298

Centre Reinsurance International Company (2)
La Touche House 5th Fl IFSC, Dublin, 1, Ireland (100%)
Tel.: (353) 18189800
Web Site: http://www.centresolutions.com
Reinsurance
N.A.I.C.S.: 524130
Seamus Palmer *(Sr VP)*

Centre Reinsurance Ltd. (2)
La Touche House Custom House Q, Dublin, 1, Ireland
Tel.: (353) 18189800
Emp.: 12
Insurance Services
N.A.I.C.S.: 524298
Caroline Chew *(Head-Office)*

Chilena Consolidada Seguros Generales S.A. (1)

Av Apoquindo N, 5550, Santiago, Chile (80%)
Tel.: (56) 226339411
Web Site: http://www.chilena.cl
Emp.: 130
Non-Life Insurance
N.A.I.C.S.: 524128

Chilena Consolidada Seguros de Vida S.A. (1)
Avenida Apoquindo 5550 Piso 20, Santiago, 7560943, Chile (80%)
Tel.: (56) 22007000
Web Site: http://www.chilena.cl
Sales Range: $125-149.9 Million
Emp.: 60
Life Insurance
N.A.I.C.S.: 524113

Consisa (1)
Traungasse 14 16, A 1030, Vienna, Austria (100%)
Tel.: (43) 50232
Emp.: 61
Provider of Insurance Services
N.A.I.C.S.: 524298

Cover-More Group Limited (1)
Level 2 60 Miller Street, North Sydney, 2060, NSW, Australia
Tel.: (61) 28 907 5000
Web Site: https://www.covermore.com.au
Travel & Medical Insurance
N.A.I.C.S.: 524298
Hanno Mijer *(CEO)*

Subsidiary (US):

Travelex Insurance Services, Inc. (2)
810 N 96th St Ste 300, Omaha, NE 68114
Web Site: https://www.travelexinsurance.com
Insurance Brokerage Services
N.A.I.C.S.: 524128
Shannon Lofdahl *(Pres & CEO)*

Eagle Star Life Assurance Co. Ltd. (1)
UK Life Ctr Station Rd, Swindon, SN1 1EL, United Kingdom (100%)
Tel.: (44) 793511227
Web Site: http://www.zurich.co.in
Emp.: 2,000
Life Insurance
N.A.I.C.S.: 524113

Eagle Star Malta Ltd. (1)
4th Fl Kingsway Palace, Republic St, NIL, Valletta, Malta (100%)
Tel.: (356) 21245335
Non-Life Insurance
N.A.I.C.S.: 524128
Ivan Micallef *(Mng Dir)*

Farmers Reinsurance Company (1)
6301 Owensmouth Ave, Woodland Hills, CA 91367
Web Site: https://www.farmers.com
Insurance Services
N.A.I.C.S.: 524210

Genevoise Life Insurance Company Ltd. (1)
Ave Eugene Pittard 16, 1206, Geneva, Switzerland (100%)
Tel.: (41) 227042424
Web Site: http://www.zurich.ch
Emp.: 450
Life Insurance
N.A.I.C.S.: 524113

Orion Rechtsschutz Versicherungsgesellschaft AG (1)
Aeschenvorstadt 50, Postfach 4002, 4002, Basel, Switzerland (56%)
Tel.: (41) 61 285 2727
Web Site: https://www.orion.ch
Emp.: 80
Legal Protection Insurance
N.A.I.C.S.: 524128

P.T. Zurich Asuransi Indonesia Tbk (1)
Graha Zurich MT Haryono Kav 42, Jakarta Selatan, Indonesia
Tel.: (62) 1500456
Web Site: https://www.zurich.co.id
Insurance Services
N.A.I.C.S.: 524210

P.T. Zurich Insurance Indonesia (1)
Sudirman Plaza 8th Floor Indofood Tower, Jl Jend Sudirman, Kav 76-78, Jakarta, 12190, Indonesia (100%)
Tel.: (62) 2157936770
Web Site: http://www.zurich.co.id
Sales Range: $10-24.9 Million
Emp.: 180
Non-Life Insurance
N.A.I.C.S.: 524128

PT Asuransi Adira Dinamika (1)
Graha Adira MT Haryono Kav 42, Jl Menteng Raya No 21, 12780, Jakarta, Indonesia (80%)
Tel.: (62) 212 966 7373
Web Site: https://www.asuransiadira.co.id
Sales Range: $50-74.9 Million
Emp.: 100
Insurance Services
N.A.I.C.S.: 524298

Societa Italiana Assicurazioni e Reassicurazioni S.p.A. (1)
Via Benignocrespi 23, 20159, Milan, Italy (100%)
Tel.: (39) 0259661
Web Site: http://www.zurich.it
Reinsurance
N.A.I.C.S.: 524130

Standard Insurance Co., Inc. (1)
28/F Petron Megaplaza Building, Senator Gil Puyat Avenue, Makati, 1226, Metro Manila, Philippines
Tel.: (63) 2 988 6382
Web Site: https://www.standard-insurance.com
Non-Life Insurance
N.A.I.C.S.: 524128
Marichu M. Mabiog *(Branch Mgr)*

Thai Metropole Zurich Insurance Co. Ltd. (1)
126/2 Krungthonburi Road, Klongsarn, Bangkok, 10600, Thailand (100%)
Tel.: (66) 24394800
Web Site: http://www.zurich.com
Emp.: 600
Insurance Services
N.A.I.C.S.: 524128

Zurich Versicherungs-Aktiengesellschaft (1) (99.98%)
Tel.: (43) 800 080 8080
Web Site: https://www.zurich.at
Emp.: 1,000
Non-Life & Life Insurance
N.A.I.C.S.: 524128

Zurich AG (1)
Riehler Strasse 90, 50668, Cologne, Germany (100%)
Tel.: (49) 22177150
Web Site: http://www.zurich.de
Emp.: 1,200
Health Insurance
N.A.I.C.S.: 524113

Subsidiary (Domestic):

Zuerich Insurance AG (2)
Riehler Strasse 90, 50668, Cologne, 50668, Germany (100%)
Tel.: (49) 22177150
Web Site: http://www.zurich.de
Emp.: 1,200
Non-Life Insurance
N.A.I.C.S.: 524128
Carsten Schildknecht *(CEO)*

Zurich Deutscher Herold Lebensversicherung AG (2)
Poppelsdorfer Allee 25-33, 53115, Bonn, Germany (100%)
Tel.: (49) 22826801
Web Site: http://www.zurich.de
Emp.: 1,000
Life Insurance
N.A.I.C.S.: 524113
Hanno Mijer *(Chm)*

Zurich Insurance AG (2)
Riehler Strasse 90, Cologne, 50668, Germany (100%)
Tel.: (49) 22177150
Web Site: http://www.zurich.de
Non-Life Insurance
N.A.I.C.S.: 524128

ZURICH INSURANCE GROUP LIMITED INTERNATIONAL PUBLIC

Zurich Insurance Group Limited—(Continued)

Branch (Domestic):

Zurich Insurance AG (3)
Poppels A'lee 25-33, Bonn, 53115, Germany
Tel.: (49) 6971150
Web Site: http://www.zurich.de
Non-Life Insurance
N.A.I.C.S.: 524128

Zurich American Life Insurance Company (1)
2500 Westfield Dr, Elgin, IL 60123-7836
Web Site:
 https://www.zurichamericaninsurance.com
Fire Insurance Services
N.A.I.C.S.: 524210

Zurich Assurance Ltd. (1)
Unity Place 1 Carfax Close, Swindon, SN1 1AP, Wiltshire, United Kingdom **(100%)**
Tel.: (44) 179 351 1227
Web Site: https://www.zurich.co.uk
Financial Services
N.A.I.C.S.: 522320

Zurich Australia Limited (1)
118 Mount Street, North Sydney, Sydney, 2060, NSW, Australia **(100%)**
Tel.: (61) 180 039 4268
Web Site: https://www.zurich.com.au
Insurance Services
N.A.I.C.S.: 524210
Justin Delaney *(CEO)*

Zurich Australian Insurance Ltd. (1)
5 Blue Street, PO Box 677, North Sydney, 2059, NSW, Australia **(100%)**
Tel.: (61) 29 995 1111
Web Site: https://www.zurich.com.au
Emp.: 1,500
Insurance Services
N.A.I.C.S.: 524128
Tim Plant *(CEO-Gen Insurance-Australia & New Zealand)*

Zurich Beteiligungs-Aktiengesellschaft (1)
Unit 2 place, 60327, Frankfurt am Main, Germany
Tel.: (49) 697 1150
Web Site: https://www.zurich.de
Insurance Services
N.A.I.C.S.: 524210

Zurich Brasil Seguros S.A. (1)
Rua Dr Geraldo Campos, Moreira 240 5th Fl, 04571 020, Sao Paulo, SP, Brazil **(100%)**
Tel.: (55) 155048500
Emp.: 100
Non-Life & Life Insurance
N.A.I.C.S.: 524128
Ivanyra Correia *(CFO-Gen Insurance)*

Zurich Compagnie Marocaine Dassurances (1)
City Park Center, 106 Rue Abderrahmane Sehraoui, 2000, Casablanca, Morocco **(88.76%)**
Tel.: (212) 22279015
Web Site: http://www.zurich.com
Emp.: 140
Non-Life Insurance
N.A.I.C.S.: 524128

Zurich Companhia de Seguros S.A. (1)
Rua Barata Salgueiro 41, 1269-058, Lisbon, Portugal **(100%)**
Tel.: (351) 21 381 6780
Web Site: https://www.zurich.com.pt
Emp.: 500
Non-Life Insurance
N.A.I.C.S.: 524128

Zurich Compania de Seguros S.A. (1)
Manuel Avila Camacho No 126, Lomas De Chapultepec, CP 11000, Mexico, DF, Mexico **(90.86%)**
Tel.: (52) 5552841000
Web Site: http://www.zurich.com.mx
Emp.: 850
Non-Life Insurance
N.A.I.C.S.: 524128

Zurich Finance Company AG (1)
Bahnhofstr 52, 8001, Zurich, Switzerland
Tel.: (41) 44 214 6314
Web Site: https://finanzagzurich.com
Financial Services
N.A.I.C.S.: 523999
Hanspeter Rellstab *(CEO & Chm)*

Zurich Financial Services Australia Ltd. (1)
5 Blue Street North, Sydney, 2060, NSW, Australia **(100%)**
Tel.: (61) 299952078
Web Site: http://www.zurich.com.au
Emp.: 1,100
Financial & Insurance Services
N.A.I.C.S.: 524128
Tim Bailey *(Exec Dir)*

Zurich Financial Services Taiwan Ltd. (1)
No 56 Tun Hwa N Rd, Taipei, 105, Taiwan **(100%)**
Tel.: (886) 227316300
Web Site: https://www.zurich.com.tw
Emp.: 300
Non-Life Insurance
N.A.I.C.S.: 524128

Zurich GSG Ltd. (1)
Hawthorne Hall Hall Road, Wilmslow, SK9 5BZ, Cheshire, United Kingdom **(100%)**
Tel.: (44) 625527242
Emp.: 12
Non-Life Insurance
N.A.I.C.S.: 524128

Zurich Global Corporate UK Ltd. (1)
The Zurich Bldg 90 Fenchurch St, London, EC3M 4JX, United Kingdom **(100%)**
Tel.: (44) 2076174242
Web Site: http://www.zurich.co.uk
Emp.: 400
Non-Life Insurance
N.A.I.C.S.: 524128

Zurich Group Frankfurt (1)
Sonnsstrasse 27-37, Frankfurt, 60486, Frankfurt Am Main, Germany **(100%)**
Tel.: (49) 6971150
Web Site: http://www.zurich.de
Emp.: 1,000
Non-Life & Credit Insurances
N.A.I.C.S.: 524128
Brand Ralph *(Mng Dir)*

Subsidiary (Domestic):

Zurich International (Deutschland) Versicherungs AG (2)
Unit place 2, 60327, Frankfurt am Main, Germany **(100%)**
Tel.: (49) 697 1150
Web Site: https://www.zurich.de
Non-Life Insurance
N.A.I.C.S.: 524128

Zurich Group Holding AG (1)
25-26/F Hagenholzstrasse 60, 8050, Zurich, Switzerland **(100%)**
Tel.: (41) 44 628 9898
Web Site: http://www.zurich.com
Emp.: 50
Property & Casualty, Life Insurance; Reinsurance, Fund & Asset Management
N.A.I.C.S.: 524126

Zurich Holding Company of America, Inc. (1)
1299 Zurich way, Schaumburg, IL 60196-1056 **(100%)**
Tel.: (847) 605-6000
Web Site: http://www.zurichna.com
Emp.: 5,000
Holding Company; Commercial, Personal & Casualty Insurance Services
N.A.I.C.S.: 551112
Tom McDonald *(Mgr-Sls-Corp Life & Pensions-Global Life-North America)*

Subsidiary (Domestic):

American Guarantee and Liability Insurance Company (2)
1 Liberty Plz 165 Broadway 32nd Fl, New York, NY 10006 **(100%)**
Tel.: (212) 225-7000
Emp.: 500
Insurance Services
N.A.I.C.S.: 524128

American Zurich Insurance Company (2)
Zurich Towers 1400 American Ln, Schaumburg, IL 60196-0001 **(100%)**
Tel.: (847) 605-6000
Web Site: http://www.zurichna.com
Emp.: 750
Non-Life Insurance
N.A.I.C.S.: 524113
Dalynn Hoch *(CFO)*

Assurance Company of America (2)
4 WTC 54th Fl, New York, NY 10007 **(100%)**
Tel.: (212) 225-7000
Insurance Services
N.A.I.C.S.: 524113

Centre Group Holdings (U.S.) Limited (2)
105 E 17th St, New York, NY 10003
Tel.: (917) 534-4500
Web Site: http://www.centresolutions.com
Emp.: 200
Financial Services
N.A.I.C.S.: 561499

Colonial American Casualty and Surety Company (2)
600 Red Brook Blvd, Owings Mills, MD 21117 **(100%)**
Tel.: (410) 559-8400
Insurance Services
N.A.I.C.S.: 524126

Farmers Group, Inc. (2)
4680 Wilshire Blvd, Los Angeles, CA 90010-3807 **(100%)**
Tel.: (323) 932-3200
Web Site: http://www.farmersinsurance.com
Emp.: 20,000
Auto, Home & Life Insurance Carrier
N.A.I.C.S.: 524298
Jeff Dailey *(CEO)*

Subsidiary (Non-US):

21st Century Insurance Group (3)
Tel.: (302) 252-2000
Web Site: https://www.21st.com
Sales Range: $1-4.9 Billion
Emp.: 2,900
Holding Company; Auto, Home & Life Insurance Carrier
N.A.I.C.S.: 551112

Subsidiary (Domestic):

Bristol West Insurance Group (3)
1300 Concord Ter Ste 120, Sunrise, FL 33323
Tel.: (954) 316-5200
Web Site: https://www.bristolwest.com
Sales Range: $650-699.9 Million
Emp.: 1,154
Insurance Services
N.A.I.C.S.: 524126

Farmers Insurance Exchange (3)
4680 Wilshire Blvd, Los Angeles, CA 90010-3807
Tel.: (323) 932-3200
Web Site: http://www.farmers.com
Sales Range: Less than $1 Million
Emp.: 18,000
Auto, Fire, Marine & Casualty Insurance
N.A.I.C.S.: 524126

Subsidiary (Domestic):

Farmers Insurance of Columbus Inc. (4)
7400 Skyline Dr E 2545 Farmers Dr Ste 440, Columbus, OH 43235
Tel.: (614) 799-3200
Sales Range: Less than $1 Million
Emp.: 20
Auto, Fire, Marine & Casualty Insurance
N.A.I.C.S.: 524298

Fire Insurance Exchange (4)
6301 Owensmouth Ave, Woodland Hills, CA 91367
Tel.: (323) 932-3200
Web Site: https://www.farmers.com
Emp.: 17,000
Fire & Casualty Insurance Services
N.A.I.C.S.: 524298

Subsidiary (Domestic):

Farmers Insurance Hawaii (3)
500 Ala Moana Blvd Ste 4-400, Honolulu, HI 96813 **(100%)**
Tel.: (808) 533-2444
Web Site: https://www.farmershawaii.com
Emp.: 200
Auto Insurance
N.A.I.C.S.: 524126

Subsidiary (Domestic):

Hawaii Insurance Consultants, Ltd. (4)
6 Waterfront Plz 500 Ala Moana Blvd 5th Fl, Honolulu, HI 96813-4920 **(100%)**
Tel.: (808) 543-9789
Web Site:
 https://www.hawaiiinsuranceconsultant.com
Emp.: 50
Insurance Agents
N.A.I.C.S.: 524210
Raymond Joao *(Exec VP)*

Subsidiary (Domestic):

Farmers New World Life Insurance Co. (3)
3003 77th Ave SE, Mercer Island, WA 98040-2837 **(100%)**
Tel.: (206) 232-8400
Web Site:
 http://www.farmersnewworldlife.com
Life Insurance
N.A.I.C.S.: 524126
Roy Smith *(Head-Distr & Sls-Life)*

Fire Underwriters Association (3)
4680 Wilshire Blvd, Los Angeles, CA 90010-3807 **(100%)**
Tel.: (323) 932-3200
Insurance Management
N.A.I.C.S.: 541110

Foremost Insurance Company (3)
5600 Beech Tree Ln, Caledonia, MI 49316-9587
Tel.: (616) 942-3000
Web Site: https://www.foremost.com
Sales Range: $350-399.9 Million
Emp.: 1,525
Insurance Carrier
N.A.I.C.S.: 524126

Subsidiary (Domestic):

American Federation Insurance Company (4)
5600 Beech Tree Ln, Caledonia, MI 49316
Tel.: (616) 942-3000
Web Site: http://www.foremost.com
Insurers of Mobile Homes & Recreational Vehicles
N.A.I.C.S.: 524210
Steve Boshoven *(Pres)*

Foremost Property & Casualty Insurance Company (4)
5600 Beech Tree Ln, Caledonia, MI 49316
Tel.: (616) 942-3000
Web Site: https://www.foremost.com
Emp.: 1,500
Insurers of Mobile Homes & Recreational Vehicles
N.A.I.C.S.: 524126
Nancy Treul *(Sr VP-Midwest Svc Point)*

Foremost Signature Insurance Company (4)
5600 Beechtree Ln, Caledonia, MI 49316-2450
Tel.: (616) 942-3000
Web Site: http://www.signus.com
Mortgage & Automobile Insurance
N.A.I.C.S.: 524126
Steve Boshoven *(Pres)*

Southern Way Insurance Agency (4)
PO Box 3278, Grand Rapids, MI 49501
Web Site:
 http://www.southernwayinsurance.com
Rev.: $260,000
Emp.: 3
Insurance Agents Brokers & Services
N.A.I.C.S.: 524210

Subsidiary (Domestic):

Investors Brokerage Services Inc. (2)

AND PRIVATE COMPANIES

1600 Macano Pkwy, Schaumburg, IL
60196-0001
Tel.: (847) 874-7650
Rev.: $860,000
Emp.: 5
Security Dealers
N.A.I.C.S.: 523150
Dale Seligmueller *(Treas)*

Kemper Investors Life Insurance Company (2)
1 Kemper Dr, Long Grove, IL
60049-0001 (100%)
Sales Range: $350-399.9 Million
Emp.: 11
Life Insurance
N.A.I.C.S.: 524113

Maryland Casualty Company (2)
600 Red Brook Blvd, Owings Mills, MD 21117
Tel.: (410) 559-8400
Insurance Services
N.A.I.C.S.: 524126
Barry J. Gilway *(Pres & CEO)*

Northern Insurance Company of New York (2)
1 Liberty Plz 165 Broadway 32nd Fl, New York, NY 10006 (100%)
Tel.: (212) 225-7000
Emp.: 330
Insurance Services
N.A.I.C.S.: 524210

Rural Community Insurance Company (2)
3501 Thurston Ave, Anoka, MN 55303-1060
Tel.: (763) 427-0290
Web Site: https://www.rcis.com
Insurance Agents Brokers & Service
N.A.I.C.S.: 524210

Steadfast Insurance Company (2)
Zurich Towers 1400 American Ln, Schaumburg, IL 60196 (100%)
Tel.: (847) 605-6000
Web Site: http://www.zurichna.com
Emp.: 120
Insurance Services
N.A.I.C.S.: 524210

The Fidelity and Deposit Company of Maryland (2)
1299 Zurich Way Schaumburg, Schaumburg, MD 21117
Tel.: (410) 559-8400
Financial Services
N.A.I.C.S.: 522320
Thomas B. Bosley *(Pres & CEO)*

Universal Underwriters Insurance Company (2)
7045 College Blvd, Overland Park, KS 66211 (100%)
Tel.: (913) 339-1000
Web Site: http://www.uuic.com
Emp.: 600
Property & Casualty Insurance
N.A.I.C.S.: 524126
Vicki Evans *(Mgr-Onsite)*

Division (Domestic):

Universal Underwriters Life Insurance (3)
7045 College Blvd, Overland Park, KS 66211-1523
Tel.: (913) 339-1000
Web Site: http://www.zlifeusa.com
Sales Range: $75-99.9 Million
Emp.: 1,100
Life Insurance
N.A.I.C.S.: 524126
David Dietz *(Pres)*

Universal Underwriters of Texas Insurance Company (3)
6900 N Dallas Pkwy Ste 800, Plano, TX 75024
Tel.: (972) 423-1701
Sales Range: $1-9.9 Million
Emp.: 35
Insurance Services
N.A.I.C.S.: 524210

Subsidiary (Domestic):

Zurich American Insurance Co. (2)
1 Liberty Plz 165 Broadway 28th Fl, New York, NY 10006
Tel.: (212) 225-7000
Web Site: http://www.zurichna.com
Insurance Services
N.A.I.C.S.: 524298
Nadine Hunt-Robinson *(Head-Environmental Claims)*

Zurich American Insurance Company of Illinois (2)
1400 American Ln, Schaumburg, IL 60196-5452 (100%)
Tel.: (847) 605-6000
Insurance Services
N.A.I.C.S.: 524113

Subsidiary (Domestic):

Empire Fire & Marine Insurance Co. (3)
13810 FNB Pkwy, Omaha, NE 68154-5202 (100%)
Tel.: (402) 963-5000
Web Site: http://www.zurichna.com
Emp.: 400
Fire & Marine Insurance
N.A.I.C.S.: 524126

Subsidiary (Domestic):

Zurich Capital Markets (2)
105 E 17th St, New York, NY 10003 (100%)
Tel.: (917) 534-4900
Emp.: 175
Capital Markets-Based Solutions for Risk Management Problems
N.A.I.C.S.: 551112

Zurich Iguazu Compania de Seguros (Vidal) (1)
Cerrito 1010, C1010AAV, Buenos Aires, Argentina (100%)
Tel.: (54) 800 333 987424
Web Site: http://www.zurich.com.ar
Emp.: 5
Life Insurance
N.A.I.C.S.: 524113

Zurich Insurance Company (Poland) SA (1)
ul Postepu 15, 02 676, Warsaw, Poland (100%)
Tel.: (48) 225430543
Web Site: http://www.generale.pl
Emp.: 35
Non-Life Insurance
N.A.I.C.S.: 524128

Zurich Insurance Company (Russia) Ltd. (1)
26-28 Denisovskiy pereoulok, 105005, Moscow, Russia (99%)
Tel.: (7) 4959335141
Web Site: http://www.zurich.ru
Emp.: 600
Non-Life Insurance
N.A.I.C.S.: 524128

Zurich Insurance Company Ltd. (1)
Thurgauerstrasse 80, 8085, Zurich, Switzerland (100%)
Tel.: (41) 446283333
Web Site: http://www.zurich.ch
Emp.: 200
Insurance Services
N.A.I.C.S.: 524128
Juan Beer *(CEO)*

Zurich Insurance Group (Hong Kong) (1)
25-26/F One Island East 18 Westlands Road Island East, Island East, Hong Kong, China (Hong Kong) (60%)
Tel.: (852) 2 968 2288
Web Site: https://www.zurich.com.hk
Emp.: 450
Insurance Services
N.A.I.C.S.: 524128

Zurich Insurance plc (1)
Zurich House, Ballsbridge Park, Dublin, 4, Ireland (100%)
Tel.: (353) 16670666
Emp.: 410
Non-Life Insurance
N.A.I.C.S.: 524128
Markus Hongler *(CEO)*

Zurich International (Belgique) S.A. (1)
Ave Lloyd George 7, 1000, Brussels, Belgium (100%)
Tel.: (32) 26395511
Web Site: http://www.zurich.be
Emp.: 50
Non-Life Insurance
N.A.I.C.S.: 524128

Zurich International (Bermuda) Ltd. (1)
3rd Fl Wellesley House, 90 Pitts Bay Rd, Pembroke, HM 08, Bermuda (100%)
Tel.: (441) 2942400
Web Site: http://www.zurichbermuda.com
Emp.: 120
Non-Life Insurance
N.A.I.C.S.: 524128

Zurich International (Italia) S.p.A. (1)
Via Benigno Crespi 23, 20159, Milan, Italy (100%)
Tel.: (39) 0259661
Web Site: http://www.zurich.it
Non-Life Insurance
N.A.I.C.S.: 524128

Zurich International (Nederland) N.V. (1)
Muzenstraat 31, 2511 VW, Hague, Netherlands (100%)
Tel.: (31) 704184184
Emp.: 70
Non-Life Insurance
N.A.I.C.S.: 524128

Zurich International (UK) Limited (1)
3 Minster Court, Mincing Lane, London, EC3R 7DD, United Kingdom (100%)
Tel.: (44) 2076483200
Web Site: http://www.zurich.com
Emp.: 500
Non-Life Insurance
N.A.I.C.S.: 524128

Zurich International Services (Luxembourg) S.A. (1)
45 rue des Scillas, L 2529, Howald, Luxembourg (100%)
Tel.: (352) 2664 2610
Web Site: http://www.zurich.com
Emp.: 60
Insurance Services
N.A.I.C.S.: 524298

Zurich International de Venezuela C.A. de Corretaje de Reaseguros (1)
Edificio Centro Seguros Sud America Piso 7, Caracas, Venezuela (100%)
Tel.: (58) 2129530246
Emp.: 4
Non-Life Insurance
N.A.I.C.S.: 524128

Zurich Investment Management Ltd. (1)
5 Blue Street, PO Box 677, Sydney, 2060, NSW, Australia (100%)
Tel.: (61) 299951111
Web Site: http://www.zurich.com.au
Emp.: 400
Asset Management Services
N.A.I.C.S.: 531390

Zurich Investment Services Ltd. (1)
Wellesley House 90 Pitts Bay Rd, Pembroke, HM 08, Bermuda (100%)
Tel.: (441) 2942400
Emp.: 35
Investment Services
N.A.I.C.S.: 523940

Zurich Investments Life (1)
Piazza Carlo Erba 6, 20129, Milan, Italy (100%)
Tel.: (39) 0259661
Life Insurance
N.A.I.C.S.: 524113

Zurich Investments SGR (1)
Via Benigno Crespi 23, 20159, Milan, Italy (100%)
Tel.: (39) 0259661
Web Site: http://www.zurich.it
Asset Management & Investment Services
N.A.I.C.S.: 531390

Zurich Italy Bank S.p.A. (1)

ZVECEVO PREHRAMBENA INDUSTRIJA D.D

Via Benigno Crespi 23, 20159, Milan, Italy
Tel.: (39) 0259661
Web Site: https://www.zurichbank.it
Financial Services
N.A.I.C.S.: 523999

Zurich Life Assurance plc (1)
Zurich House Frascati Road, Blackrock, Dublin, Ireland (100%)
Tel.: (353) 1 799 2711
Web Site: https://www.zurich.ie
Emp.: 1,000
Life Insurance
N.A.I.C.S.: 524113

Zurich Life Insurance Malaysia Berhad (1)
Level 23A Mercu 3 No 3 Jalan Bangsar, KL Eco City, 59200, Kuala Lumpur, Malaysia
Tel.: (60) 321096000
Web Site: http://www.zurich.com.my
Rev.: $265,166,633
Assets: $1,920,302,483
Liabilities: $1,573,765,633
Net Worth: $346,536,850
Earnings: $18,177,219
Fiscal Year-end: 12/31/2019
Life & General Insurance
N.A.I.C.S.: 524113
Khoo Ai Lin *(CEO)*

Zurich Pacific Insurance Pty. Ltd. (1)
Cuthbertson House 5th Floor Cuthbertson Street, PO Box 707, Port Moresby, Papua New Guinea (100%)
Tel.: (675) 3212800
Non-Life Insurance
N.A.I.C.S.: 524128

Zurich Santander Seguros Mexico, S.A. (1)
Calle Juan Salvador Agraz Number 73 Floor 4, Colonia Santa Fe Mayor's Office Cuajimalpa de Morelos, 05348, Mexico, Mexico
Tel.: (52) 1555 169 4300
Web Site: https://www.zurichsantander.com.mx
Insurance Services
N.A.I.C.S.: 524210

Zurich Seguros S.A. (1)
Av Francisco De Miranda Piso 7 Y 8, Urb El Rosal, 1060, Caracas, Venezuela (100%)
Tel.: (58) 2129010799
Web Site: http://www.zurich.com.ve
Emp.: 150
Insurance Services
N.A.I.C.S.: 524128

Zurich Versicherungs-Aktiengesellschaft (1)
Schwarzenbergplatz 15, 1010, Vienna, Austria
Tel.: (43) 180 130 3190
Web Site: https://www.zurich.at
Insurance Services
N.A.I.C.S.: 524210

Zurich Vida Compania de Seguros S.A. (1)
Manuel Avila Camacho No 126, 11000, Mexico, Mexico (100%)
Tel.: (52) 5552841000
Emp.: 300
Life Insurance
N.A.I.C.S.: 524113

ZUU CO., LTD.

Tel.: (81) 344059086
Web Site: http://zuu.co.jp
4387—(TKS)
Rev.: $19,162,390
Assets: $61,664,690
Liabilities: $29,136,880
Net Worth: $32,527,810
Earnings: ($297,450)
Fiscal Year-end: 03/31/24
Financial Support Services
N.A.I.C.S.: 541611

ZVECEVO PREHRAMBENA INDUSTRIJA D.D

Kralja Zvonimir 1, 34000, Pozega, Hrvatska, Croatia
Tel.: (385) 34276200
HR

ZVECEVO PREHRAMBENA INDUSTRIJA D.D

Zvecevo prehrambena industrija d.d—(Continued)
Web Site: https://www.zvecevo.hr
Year Founded: 1921
ZVCV—(ZAG)
Sales Range: Less than $1 Million
Chocolate Product Mfr
N.A.I.C.S.: 311351
Hrvoje Alvir (CEO)

ZVECEVO-LASTA D.D.
Kneza Domagoja b b, 88300, Capljina, Bosnia & Herzegovina
Tel.: (387) 36 806 036
Web Site: http://www.en.zvecevo-lasta.ba
Year Founded: 1952
ZVLCR—(SARE)
Sales Range: $1-9.9 Million
Emp.: 154
Biscuits & Wafer Mfr
N.A.I.C.S.: 311919
Zdravko Alvira (Chm)

ZVEZDARA AVALA A.D.
Zivka Davidovica 64, Belgrade, Serbia
Tel.: (381) 112864058
Year Founded: 1973
ZVAV—(BEL)
Sales Range: Less than $1 Million
Emp.: 25
Textile Product Retailer
N.A.I.C.S.: 458110
Stojan Nikolic (Exec Dir)

ZVI SARFATI & SONS INVESTMENTS & CONSTRUCTIONS LTD.
The French 91 Herzl Street, Rishon le Zion, 7526201, Israel
Tel.: (972) 39673336
Web Site: http://www.zarfati-zvi.com
SRFT—(TAE)
Rev.: $82,074,871
Assets: $365,259,284
Liabilities: $226,726,616
Net Worth: $138,532,668
Earnings: $9,136,068
Emp.: 29
Fiscal Year-end: 12/31/23
Other Activities Related to Real Estate
N.A.I.C.S.: 531390
Zvi Zarfati (Chm)

ZVIJEZDA D.D.
Marijana Cavica 1, 10 000, Zagreb, Croatia
Tel.: (385) 1 2382 666
Web Site: http://www.zvijezda.com
Year Founded: 1916
Refined Oil Production & Distr
N.A.I.C.S.: 311225

ZVON DVA HOLDING D.D.
Slovenska ulica 17, 2000, Maribor, Slovenia
Tel.: (386) 59080532
ZV2R—(LJU)
Sales Range: $150-199.9 Million
Financial Investment Services
N.A.I.C.S.: 523999
Franc Jesovnik (CEO)

ZVON ENA HOLDING D.D.
Slovenska ulica 17, 2000, Maribor, Slovenia
Tel.: (386) 59080500
Sales Range: $150-199.9 Million
Emp.: 9
Financial Investment Services
N.A.I.C.S.: 523999
Simon Zdolsek (CEO)

ZVORNIKPUTEVI A.D.
Karakaj bb, 75400, Zvornik, Bosnia & Herzegovina
Tel.: (387) 56260215
Web Site: http://www.zvornikputevi.com
Year Founded: 1978
ZVPT—(BANJ)
Sales Range: $1-9.9 Million
Emp.: 183
Road Maintenance Services
N.A.I.C.S.: 237990
Dragan Toskovic (Chm-Mgmt Bd)

ZW DATA ACTION TECHNOLOGIES INC.
Room 1106 Xinghuo Keji Plaza No 2 Fengfu Road, Fengtai District, Beijing, China
Tel.: (86) 1060846616   NV
Web Site: https://www.zdat.com
Year Founded: 2003
CNET—(NASDAQ)
Rev.: $30,585,000
Assets: $11,233,000
Liabilities: $4,979,000
Net Worth: $6,254,000
Earnings: ($5,974,000)
Emp.: 50
Fiscal Year-end: 12/31/23
Holding Company; Full-Service Media Development & Advertising Services
N.A.I.C.S.: 551112
Handong Cheng (Chm, Pres, CEO, Interim CFO & Sec)

ZWACK UNICUM RT.
Soroksari ut 26, 1095, Budapest, 1095, Hungary
Tel.: (36) 14762300
Web Site: https://www.zwackunicum.hu
Year Founded: 1840
ZWACK—(BUD)
Rev.: $43,958,880
Assets: $43,874,880
Liabilities: $20,314,560
Net Worth: $23,560,320
Earnings: $4,824,960
Emp.: 244
Fiscal Year-end: 03/31/21
Alcoholic Beverage Producer & Distr
N.A.I.C.S.: 312140
Sandor Zwack (Chm)

ZWAHLEN & MAYR SA
ZI2 Route de l Industrie 18, 1860, Aigle, Switzerland
Tel.: (41) 244684646
Web Site: https://zwahlen.ch
Year Founded: 1881
ZWM—(SWX)
Sales Range: Less than $1 Million
Steel Pole Mfr
N.A.I.C.S.: 331210

ZWANENBERG FOOD GROUP B.V.
Twentepoort Oost 5, 7609 RG, Almelo, Netherlands
Tel.: (31) 88 054 6000   NI
Web Site: http://www.zwanenberg.nl
Year Founded: 1875
Sales Range: $400-449.9 Million
Emp.: 1,600
Meat Cheese Spreadable Topping & Snack Food Products Mfr & Whslr
N.A.I.C.S.: 311999

Subsidiaries:

Zwanenberg Food Group (USA) Inc.   (1)
3640 Muddy Creek Rd, Cincinnati, OH 45238
Tel.: (513) 682-6000
Web Site: http://www.zwanfood.com
Meat Products Mfr & Whslr
N.A.I.C.S.: 311999

Robert Russo (Pres & CEO)

Subsidiary (Domestic):

Vietti Foods Company, Inc.   (2)
636 Southgate Ave, Nashville, TN 37203
Tel.: (615) 244-7864
Web Site: https://www.viettifoods.com
Canned Chili, Soups, Baked Beans & Other Related Food Products Mfr & Whslr
N.A.I.C.S.: 311999
Robert Russo (CEO)

Zwanenberg Food Oss B.V.   (1)
Molenweg 80, 5349 TD, Oss, Netherlands
Tel.: (31) 412620111
Meat Food Products Mfr
N.A.I.C.S.: 311991

ZWICK GMBH & CO. KG
August Nagel Strasse 11, 89079, Ulm, Germany
Tel.: (49) 7305100   De
Web Site: http://www.zwickroell.com
Year Founded: 1935
Sales Range: $100-124.9 Million
Emp.: 1,000
Testing Machine for Plant & Equipment Mfr
N.A.I.C.S.: 334519
Jan Stefan Roell (Exec Dir)

Subsidiaries:

Zwick USA L.P.   (1)
2125 Barrett Park Dr Ste 107, Kennesaw, GA 30144   (100%)
Tel.: (770) 420-6555
Web Site: http://www.zwick.com
Emp.: 15
Materials Testing Specialists
N.A.I.C.S.: 423830

ZWIPE AS
Radhusgata 24, 0151, Oslo, 0151, Norway
Tel.: (47) 99166135
Web Site: https://www.zwipe.com
Year Founded: 2009
ZWIPE—(OMX)
Rev.: $362,923
Assets: $6,248,199
Liabilities: $1,201,644
Net Worth: $5,046,555
Earnings: ($9,678,552)
Emp.: 43
Fiscal Year-end: 12/31/22
Biometric Technology Development Services
N.A.I.C.S.: 541511
Patrice Meilland (Chief Comml Officer)

ZWSOFT GUANGZHOU CO., LTD.
Room 01-08 32/F No 15 Zhujiang West Road, Tianhe, Guangzhou, 510623, China
Tel.: (86) 2038289780
Web Site: https://www.zwsoft.com
Year Founded: 1998
688083—(SHG)
Rev.: $84,377,171
Assets: $440,234,435
Liabilities: $56,572,018
Net Worth: $383,662,417
Earnings: $884,773
Fiscal Year-end: 12/31/22
Software Development Services
N.A.I.C.S.: 541511
Yulin Du (Chm & Gen Mgr)

ZYDUS LIFESCIENCES LIMITED
Zydus Corporate Park Scheme No 63 Survey No 536, Khoraj Gandhinagar Near Vaishnodevi Circle Sarkhej Gandhinagar Highway, Ahmedabad, 382481, India
Tel.: (91) 7948040000

INTERNATIONAL PUBLIC

Web Site: https://www.zyduslife.com
Year Founded: 1952
ZYDUSLIFE—(NSE)
Rev.: $2,114,371,350
Assets: $3,794,072,100
Liabilities: $1,193,228,400
Net Worth: $2,600,843,700
Earnings: $630,397,950
Emp.: 23,743
Fiscal Year-end: 03/31/22
Pharmaceutical Company
N.A.I.C.S.: 325412
Sharvil P. Patel (Mng Dir)

Subsidiaries:

Dialforhealth India Ltd.   (1)
8th Fl N G Tower Satellite Cross Rd, Ahmedabad, 380 015, Gujarat, India
Tel.: (91) 7926868600
Web Site: http://www.dialforhealth.net
Sales Range: $50-74.9 Million
Emp.: 100
Health Information Resource Services
N.A.I.C.S.: 926150
Pankaj Patel (Mng Dir)

Etna Biotech S.R.L.   (1)
Via Vincenzo Lancia 57, Zona Industriale Blocco Palma 1, 95121, Catania, Italy
Tel.: (39) 0952500276
Web Site: https://www.etnabiotech.it
Vaccine Research Services
N.A.I.C.S.: 541714
Antonio Di Mauro (Mgr-Administration)

German Remedies Limited   (1)
Shivsagar Estate A-Block Dr Annie Besant Road, PB No 6570, Worli, Mumbai, 400018, Maharashtra, India
Tel.: (91) 22 2493 5529
Pharmaceutical Preparation Mfr
N.A.I.C.S.: 325412

Hercon Pharmaceuticals LLC   (1)
101 Sinking Springs Ln, Emigsville, PA 17318
Tel.: (717) 764-1191
Web Site: https://www.herconpharma.com
Generic Transversal Medication Mfr
N.A.I.C.S.: 325412

Laboratorios Combix S.L.   (1)
Calle Badajoz 2 - Edificio 2, Pozuelo de Alarcon, 28223, Madrid, Spain
Tel.: (34) 914904253
Web Site: https://combix.es
Pharmaceutical Product Mfr & Distr
N.A.I.C.S.: 325412

Sentynl Therapeutics Inc.   (1)
420 Stevens Ave Ste 200, Solana Beach, CA 92075
Tel.: (760)
Web Site: https://sentynl.com
Human Pharmaceutical Mfr
N.A.I.C.S.: 325412
Matt Heck (CEO & Founder)

Violio Healthcare Limited   (1)
1011 10th Floor Corporate Avenue Sonawala Lane, Goregaon- East, Mumbai, 400 063, India
Tel.: (91) 2264480509
Web Site: https://www.violahealth.com
Pharmaceutical Ingredient Mfr & Distr
N.A.I.C.S.: 325412

Viona Pharmaceuticals Inc.   (1)
20 Commerce Dr Ste 340, Cranford, NJ 07016
Web Site: https://vionausa.com
Pharmaceutical Product Mfr & Distr
N.A.I.C.S.: 325412

Zydus Animal Health Limited   (1)
Astron Tech Park 5th Floor Satellite Cross Roads, Ahmedabad, 380 015, Gujarat, India   (100%)
Tel.: (91) 79 26868681
Web Site: http://www.zydusahl.com
Sales Range: $50-74.9 Million
Emp.: 55
Animal Healthcare Products Mfr
N.A.I.C.S.: 325412
Arun Atrey (Mng Dir)

Zydus France SAS.   (1)
ZAC des hautes patures 25 rue des Peupliers, 92752, Nanterre, France

AND PRIVATE COMPANIES

Tel.: (33) 141191850
Web Site: https://www.zydusfrance.com
Sales Range: $25-49.9 Million
Emp.: 22
Pharmaceuticals Product Mfr
N.A.I.C.S.: 325412

Zydus Healthcare (USA) LLC. (1)
Tel.: (609) 631-9552
Pharmaceutical Preparations Mfr & Whslr
N.A.I.C.S.: 325412

Zydus Healthcare Brasil Ltda. (1)
Alameda Jau N 1905 - Cj 41 E 47 Jardim Paulista, Sao Paulo, 01420-002, Brazil
Tel.: (55) 1130864180
Web Site: http://www.zydusbrasil.com.br
Generic Drugs Supplier
N.A.I.C.S.: 424210

Zydus Healthcare Limited (1)
Zydus Tower CTS No 460/6, Village Pahadi Off I B Patel Road Goregaon East, Mumbai, 400063, India
Tel.: (91) 2262721700
Web Site: https://www.zydushealthcare.com
Emp.: 8,000
Medicinal Product Mfr
N.A.I.C.S.: 325412

Zydus Healthcare Philippines Inc. (1)
903 904 Eco Tower 9th Avenue Corner 32nd St, Taguig, Metro Manila, Philippines
Tel.: (63) 288151124
Web Site: https://zydusph.com
Pharmaceutical Product Mfr & Distr
N.A.I.C.S.: 325412

Zydus NIKKHO Farmaceutica Ltda. (1)
Rua Jaime Perdigao 431/445 Ilha Do Governador, Rio de Janeiro, CEP 21920-240, RJ, Brazil
Tel.: (55) 2133934266
Web Site: http://www.nikkho.com.br
Pharmaceutical Preparation Mfr
N.A.I.C.S.: 325412
Vaibhav Bakshi *(Head-HR)*

Zydus Nycomed Healthcare Private Ltd. (1)
C 4 MIDC Village Pawne, Thane-Belapur Road, Vashi, 400 705, Navi Mumbai, India
Tel.: (91) 2227682666
Web Site: http://www.zydusnycomed.com
Sales Range: $50-74.9 Million
Emp.: 240
Pharmaceuticals Mfr
N.A.I.C.S.: 325412
Ravi Chandran *(Mng Dir)*

Zydus Pharmaceuticals USA Inc. (1)
73 Route 31 N, Pennington, NJ 08534-3601
Tel.: (609) 730-1900
Web Site: https://zydususa.com
Sales Range: $25-49.9 Million
Emp.: 20
Pharmaceutical Products Mfr & Sales
N.A.I.C.S.: 325412

Subsidiary (Domestic):

Nesher Pharmaceuticals (USA) LLC (2)
13910 Saint Charles Rock Rd, Bridgeton, MO 63044
Tel.: (314) 209-4700
Web Site: https://www.nesher.com
Pharmaceuticals Mfr
N.A.I.C.S.: 325412
Kaiman Vince *(Pres)*

Zydus Wellness Limited (1)
Zydus Corporate Park Scheme No 63 Survey No 536 Khoraj Gandhinagar, Nr Vaishnodevi Circle, Ahmedabad, 382481, Gujarat, India
Tel.: (91) 7971800000
Web Site: https://www.zyduswellness.com
Rev.: $275,661,750
Assets: $776,982,570
Liabilities: $115,772,475
Net Worth: $661,210,095
Earnings: $42,160,755
Emp.: 1,075
Fiscal Year-end: 03/31/2022
Pharmaceuticals Product Mfr
N.A.I.C.S.: 325412
Tarun G. Arora *(CEO)*

Zydus Wellness Products Limited (1)
Tel.: (91) 7948040000
Web Site: https://www.zyduswellness.com
Cosmetic Product Mfr & Distr
N.A.I.C.S.: 325620

ZYF LOPSKING ALUMINUM CO., LTD.
31 Yangchenghuzhong Road, Xiangcheng District, Suzhou, 215131, Jiangsu, China
Tel.: (86) 51265768211
2333—(SSE)
Rev.: $191,018,387
Assets: $385,715,967
Liabilities: $141,748,602
Net Worth: $243,967,365
Earnings: ($6,819,644)
Fiscal Year-end: 12/31/22
Window & Door Mfr
N.A.I.C.S.: 332321

ZYF LOPSKING MATERIAL TECHNOLOGY CO LTD
No 2777 Taidong Road Panyang Industrial Park, Huangdai Town Xiangcheng District, Suzhou, 215143, Jiangsu, China
Tel.: (86) 51265768211
Web Site: http://www.lpsk.com.cn
Year Founded: 1993
002333—(SSE)
Rev.: $193,697,412
Assets: $391,125,618
Liabilities: $143,736,620
Net Worth: $247,388,998
Earnings: ($6,915,290)
Fiscal Year-end: 12/31/22
Aluminum Producer
N.A.I.C.S.: 331318
Gong Changyi *(Chm & Gen Mgr)*

Subsidiaries:

Suzhou Mingde Aluminium Co., Ltd. (1)
No 31 Middle Yangchenghu Road, Xiangcheng District, Suzhou, 215131, Jiangsu, China
Tel.: (86) 51266186723
Web Site: http://www.mindalu.com
Aluminum Extrusion Product Mfr
N.A.I.C.S.: 331318

ZYLOX-TONBRIDGE MEDICAL TECHNOLOGY CO., LTD.
ZyloxTonbridge Industrial Park No 270 Shuyun Road, Hangzhou, 311121, Zhejiang, China
Tel.: (86) 57188610082   CN
Web Site: https://www.zyloxtb.com
Year Founded: 2012
2190—(HKG)
Rev.: $51,185,929
Assets: $498,498,764
Liabilities: $24,443,583
Net Worth: $474,055,181
Earnings: ($17,397,762)
Emp.: 715
Fiscal Year-end: 12/31/22
Information Technology Services
N.A.I.C.S.: 541512
Quanwei Yuan *(CFO)*

ZYNP CORPORATION
No 69 Huaihe Road Mengzhou Industrial Zone, Jiaozuo, 454750, Henan, China
Tel.: (86) 3918190221
Web Site: https://www.hnzynp.com
Year Founded: 1958
002448—(SSE)
Rev.: $323,140,442
Assets: $720,652,645
Liabilities: $252,659,165
Net Worth: $467,993,481
Earnings: $23,472,058
Emp.: 2,000
Fiscal Year-end: 12/31/22
Internal Combustion Engine Cylinder Liner Mfr
N.A.I.C.S.: 333995
Xue Delong *(Chm)*

Subsidiaries:

ZYNP Europe GmbH (1)
Gottfried-Leibniz-strasse 6, 74172, Neckarsulm, Germany
Tel.: (49) 71323458777
Cylinder Liner Mfr & Distr
N.A.I.C.S.: 336310

ZYNP International Corp. (1)
2510 Ouellette Ave Ste 206, Windsor, ON, Canada
Tel.: (519) 966-8688
Web Site: http://www.hnzynp.com
Cylinder Liner Mfr
N.A.I.C.S.: 339999

ZYROFISHER
Roundhouse Road Faverdale Industrial Estate, Darlington, DL3 0UR, United Kingdom
Tel.: (44) 1325741296
Web Site: http://www.zyro.co.uk
Cycling Accessories Whslr & Distr
N.A.I.C.S.: 423910
James Browning *(Chm)*

ZYTRONIC PLC
Whiteley Road, Blaydon, NE21 5NJ, Tyne & Wear, United Kingdom
Tel.: (44) 1914145511
Web Site: https://www.zytronicplc.com
ZYT—(AIM)
Rev.: $15,862,243
Assets: $25,654,119
Liabilities: $2,891,944
Net Worth: $22,762,176
Earnings: $551,234
Emp.: 111
Fiscal Year-end: 09/30/21
Optical & Touch Sensing Product Mfr
N.A.I.C.S.: 333310
Mark Cambridge *(CEO)*

Subsidiaries:

Zytronic Displays Limited (1)
Whiteley Road, Blaydon, NE21 5NJ, Tyne and Wear, United Kingdom
Tel.: (44) 1914145511
Web Site: https://www.zytronic.co.uk
Emp.: 150
Touch Interactive Products Mfr
N.A.I.C.S.: 541850
Mark Cambridge *(CEO)*

ZZLL INFORMATION TECHNOLOGY, INC.
Unit 1504 15F Carnival Commercial Building, 18 Java Road, North Point, China (Hong Kong)
Tel.: (852) 37051571   NV
Web Site: http://www.zzlliti.com
Year Founded: 2005
ZZLL—(OTCEM)
Rev.: $78,485,299
Assets: $3,810,411
Liabilities: $4,880,426
Net Worth: ($1,070,015)
Earnings: $15,968
Emp.: 18
Fiscal Year-end: 12/31/21
Investment Services
N.A.I.C.S.: 523999
Yanfei Tang *(Pres, CEO, CFO & Sec)*

Subsidiaries:

Bao Shinn Express Co., Ltd. (1)
Flat E-F 8F No 8 Hart Avenue, Kowloon, Tsim Sha Tsui, China (Hong Kong)
Tel.: (852) 23668818
Web Site: http://www.roh.com.hk
Sales Range: $10-24.9 Million
Emp.: 50
Sales Agents for Thai Airways
N.A.I.C.S.: 561510

Bao Shinn Holidays Limited (1)
Room 208 Takshing House, 20 Des Voeux Road, Hong Kong, China (Hong Kong)
Tel.: (852) 21118868
Web Site: http://www.baoshinn.com.hk
Sales Range: $25-49.9 Million
Emp.: 20
Travel Services
N.A.I.C.S.: 561510

BaoShinn International Express Limited (BSIE) (1)
Flat A-B 8F No 8 Hart Avenue, Kowloon, China (Hong Kong)
Tel.: (852) 28151355
Web Site: http://www.baoshinn.com.hk
Bulk Ticketing & Travel Related Services
N.A.I.C.S.: 561599

Chung Tai Travel and Tour Co., Ltd. (1)
13F No 131 Song Jiang Road, Taipei, 104, Taiwan
Tel.: (886) 22509 1588
Web Site: http://www.baoshinn.com.hk
Travel & Tour Services
N.A.I.C.S.: 561599

Grand Power Express Tourism Co., Ltd. (1)
11 Andar B-C Macau Finance Centre, No 244-246 Rua de Pequim, Macau, China (Macau)
Tel.: (853) 701777
Web Site: http://www.grandpowerexpress.com
Travel Services
N.A.I.C.S.: 561510

Patterson Travel Service (1)
Flat F 8/F 8 Hart Ave, Tsim Sha Tsui, Hong Kong, China (Hong Kong)
Tel.: (852) 31022382
Web Site: http://www.pattersontravel.com.hk
Emp.: 30
Sales Agents for MAS Golden Holidays & Malaysia Airlines
N.A.I.C.S.: 561510

Patterson Travel Services (1)
No 8 Hart Ave Tsim Sha Tsui, Kowloon, China (Hong Kong)
Tel.: (852) 31022371
Web Site: http://www.pattersontravel.com.hk
Sales Range: $25-49.9 Million
Emp.: 20
Travel Services
N.A.I.C.S.: 561510